SUBJECT GUIDE TO

Children's Books In Print®

2008

SUBJECT GUIDE TO CHILDREN'S BOOKS IN PRINT 2008
was prepared by R.R. Bowker's Database Publishing Group in
collaboration with the Information Technology Department.

Annie Callanan, President and CEO
Gary Aiello, Chief Operating Officer
Belinda Tseo, Senior Vice President, Chief Financial Officer
Angela D'Agostino, Senior Vice President, Business Development and Marketing
Ian Singer, Vice President, Data Services
Mark Heinzelman, Chief Information Officer

International Standard Book Number/Standard Address Number Agency
Louise Timko, Associate Editor
Marina Dallendorfer, Leo Dos Reis, and Heidi Weber, Assistant Editors

Data Integration
Lisa Heft, Director
Adrene Allen, Manager Data Analyst Unit
Ila Joseph, Misty Poush, Laura Ferretti and John Litzenberger, Senior Analysts
Stacey Volanto, Anthony Giuffra, Chris Palomares, Vida Aning and Ryan Karwell, Analysts
Steve Zaffuto and Cheryl Patrick, Associate Analysts
Eleanor Schubauer, Manager Quality Control Unit
Mervaine Ricks, Senior Analyst
Jen Modoni and Natalie Ferry, Analysts
Lucia Fernandez, Jen Holland and Jenny Marie DeJesus, Associate Analysts

PAD Control
Roy Crego, Senior Director, Quality Oversight
Beverly Palacio, Senior Analyst
Rhonda McKendrick, Analyst
Marissa Hubbard, Associate Analyst

Syndetics
Kathleen Cunningham, Director
Lynda Williams, Fiction Profiler
Rosemary Walker, Non-Fiction Profiler
Ron Butkiewicz, Data Specialist

Publisher Relations
Pat Payton, Senior Director
Grace Cook, Data Submission Manager
Sandy Gurshman, Tricia McCraney, and Denielle Starr, Publisher Liaisons

Production & Manufacturing Services
Doreen Gravesande, Director
Ralph Coviello, Manager Manufacturing Services
Ashley Ludwig, Manager Quality Control/Production
Andy Haramasz, Gunther Stegmann II, Myriam Nunez and Lorena Soriano, Project Managers Production

Business Analyst Group
Andrew LaCroix
Stephanie Halpern, Kevin Mark, Evelyn Nicholas, Michael Olenick

Editorial Systems Group
Frank Morris, IT Director
Youliang Zhou, Senior Programmer Analyst

Computer Operations Group
John Nesselt, UNIX Administrator

SUBJECT GUIDE TO

Children's Books In Print® 2008

A Subject Index to Books
for Children and Young Adults

SUBJECT GUIDE
Subjects A-Z

Published by
R.R. Bowker LLC
630 Central Avenue
New Providence, NJ 07974 USA

Annie Callanan, President and CEO

Telephone: 908-219-1090, Toll-free: 1-888-BOWKER2 (1-888-269-5372); Fax: 908-219-0098
E-mail address: info@bowker.com
URL: http://www.bowker.com

Readers may send any corrections and/or updates to the information in this work to R.R. Bowker through the corrections option on the Bowker Web site at http://www.bowker.com or may send e-mail directly to the address: corrections@bowker.com. Publishers may also update their listings using the BowkerLink Publisher Access System at www.bowkerlink.com.

International Standard Book Number

ISBN 10 : 0-8352-4894-1
ISBN 13: 978-0-8352-4894-5

International Standard Serial Number
0000-0167

Library of Congress Control Number
74-643526

Printed and bound in the United States of America

CONTENTS

How to Use
SUBJECT GUIDE TO CHILDREN'S BOOKS IN PRINT 2008

The thirty-eighth edition of R.R. Bowker's *Subject Guide to Children's Books In Print* was produced from the Books In Print database. This volume only includes books published after 1999. Titles listed in *Children's Books In Print are included in Subject Guide*. There are approximately 365,500 listings under 9,580 subject categories. These titles are available from approximately 14,000 United States publishers. An index with full contact information for all of the publishers listed in the bibliographic entries is included in this volume, as well as in a separate index to wholesalers and distributors.

RELATED PRODUCTS

In addition to the printed version, the entire Books In Print database (more than 5 million records, including OP/OSI titles, audiobooks, and videos) can be searched by customers on Bowker's Web site, www.booksinprint.com. For further information about subscribing to this online service, please contact Bowker at 1-888-269-5372.

This Books In Print database is also available in an array of other formats such as Books In Print On Disc, and online access through Books In Print site licensing. Database vendors such as OCLC Online Computer Library Center, Inc., OVID Technologies, Inc., and SilverPlatter Information, Inc., make the Books In Print database available to their subscribers.

COMPILATION

In order to be useful to subscribers, the information contained in *Subject Guide to Books In Print* must be complete and accurate. Publishers are asked to review and correct their entries prior to each publication, providing current price, publication date, availability status, and ordering information, as well as recently published and forthcoming titles. Tens of thousands of entries are added or updated for each edition.

DATA ACQUISITION AND EDI

Bowker receives bibliographic information from publishers in many different formats: catalogs, Advance Book Information forms, checklists, phoned or faxed information, and most notably from Electronic Data Interchange. Publishers may also add to or update their listings using the BowkerLink Publisher Access System at www.bowkerlink.com.

Larger publishing houses are urged to use Electronic Data Interchange. EDI is a process by which participating publishers can submit their bibliographic information to the Books In Print database from their own databases. Bowker's EDI system accepts publisher data 24 hours a day, 7 days a week via FTP. The benefits to this method are: no paper intervention, reduced costs, increased timeliness, and less chance of human error that can occur when re-keying information.

To communicate new title information to Books In Print via EDI, the quality of the publisher's textual data must be up to—or extremely close to—reference book standards. Publishers interested in taking advantage of electronic data interchange are invited to access the Bowker Data Submission Guide at www.bowker.com or contact Data Acquisition at 908-219-0260 (email: edi@bowker.com).

Updated information or corrections to the listings in *Children's Books In Print* can now be submitted at any time via the Internet. Users may access the Bowker Web site at www.bowker.com and then follow our directions under the option "Make Corrections." This will enable them to contact our editors directly via e-mail. Publishers can submit updates and new titles to Books in Print by accessing the BowkerLink Publisher Access System at www.bowkerlink.com.

To ensure the accuracy, timeliness and comprehensiveness of data in *Children's Books In Print*, Bowker has initiated discussions with the major publishers. This outreach entails analyzing the quality of all publisher's submissions to *Children's Books In Print*, including EDI and paper-based sources, and working closely with each publisher to improve the content and timeliness of the information. This outreach also lays the groundwork for incorporating new valuable information into *Children's Books In Print*. We are now collecting cover art, descriptive jacket and catalog copy, tables of contents, contributor biographies, as well as awards won, bestseller listings, and review citations. Bowker will make this important additional information available to customers who receive *Books In Print* in specific electronic formats and through subscriptions to www.booksinprint.com.

HOW THE SUBJECT HEADINGS WERE ASSIGNED

R.R. Bowker's *Subject Guide to Children's Books In Print 2008* is based primarily on the Library of Congress Subject Headings. Many headings were consolidated where they seemed too cumbersome for the needs of this *Subject Guide*. Some books have been assigned to a single category, while other books have been assigned two, three, or more headings.

ALPHABETICAL ARRANGEMENT OF SUBJECT CATEGORIES

Headings are filed alphabetically with the following conditions and variations. First, punctuation is not considered:

ART, ANCIENT
ART—FICTION
ART, GREEK

Second, proper nouns precede improper nouns and names of people precede geographical names:

CLEVELAND, GROVER, 1837-1908
CLEVELAND (OHIO)
CLEVELAND BROWNS (FOOTBALL TEAM)

Third, when personal names appear as headings, those without surnames appear first and religious titles precede royal titles:

PETER, THE APOSTLE, SAINT
PETER I, EMPEROR OF RUSSIA, 1672-1725
PETER, SARAH (WORTHINGTON) KING, 1800-1877

ALPHABETICAL ARRANGEMENT OF TITLES WITHIN THE SUBJECT CATEGORIES

Under each subject heading entries are filed alphabetically by contributor's last name if available, and by title when no contributor exists. Please note the following exceptions:

Initial articles of titles in English, French, German, Italian, and Spanish are deleted from both author and title entries.

Nu merals, including year dates, are written out in most cases and are filed alphabetically.

U.S., UN, Dr., Mr., and St. are filed in strict alphabetical order unless the author/publisher requests that the title be filed as if it were spelled out.

Proper names beginning with "Mc" and "Mac" are filed in strict alphabetical order. For example, entries for contributor's names such as MacAdam, MacAvory, MacCarthy, MacDonald, and MacLean are located prior to the pages with entries for names such as McAdams, McCarthy, McCoy, and McDermott.

Entries beginning with initial letters (whether authors' given names, or titles) are filed first, e.g., Smith, H.C., comes before Smith, Harold A.; B is for Betsy comes before Babar, etc.

Compound names are listed under the first part of the name, and cross-references appear under the last part of the name.

INFORMATION INCLUDED IN ENTRIES

Entries include the following bibliographic information, when available: author, co-author, editor, co-editor, translator, co-translator, illustrator, co-illustrator, photographer, co-photographer, title, number of volumes, edition, series information, language if other than English, whether or not illustrated, grade range, year of publication, price, International Standard Book Number, publisher's order number, imprint, and publisher abbreviation. Entries new to this edition are indicated by an asterisk (*) before the bolded ISBN. (Information on the International Standard Book Numbering System is available from R.R. Bowker.)

The prices cited are those provided by the publishers and generally refer to either the trade edition or the Publisher's Library Bound edition. The abbreviation "lib. bdg." is used whenever the price cited is for a publisher's library bound edition.

ISBN AGENCY

Each title included in R.R. Bowker's *Subject Guide to Children's Books In Print* and other *Books In Print* products has been assigned an International Standard Book Number (ISBN) by the publisher. All ISBNs listed in this volume have been validated by using the check digit control, ensuring accuracy.

Note: The ISBN prefix 0-615 is for decentralized use by the U.S. ISBN Agency and has been assigned to numerous publishers. The prefix 0-615 is not unique to one exclusive publisher.

ISBNs allow order transmission and bibliographic information updating using the Book Industry Study Group's (BISG) standard format for data transmission. Publishers not currently participating in the ISBN system may request the assignment of an ISBN publisher prefix from the ISBN Agency by calling 877-310-7333, faxing 908-219-0188, or through the ISBN/SAN Web site at www.isbn.org.

PUBLISHER NAME INDEX

A key to the abbreviated publisher names (e.g., "Middle Atlantic Pr.") used in the bibliographic entries of *Subject Guide to Children's Books In Print* is found after the Subject Index. Entries in this index contain each publisher's abbreviated name, followed by its ISBN prefix(es), business affiliation, (e.g., "Div. of International Publishing") when available, ordering address(es), SAN (Standard Address Number), telephone, fax, and toll-free numbers. Editorial address(es) (and associated contact numbers) follow. Addresses without a specific label are for editorial offices rather than ordering purposes.

Abbreviations used to identify publishers' imprints are followed by the full name of the imprint. E-mail and Web site addresses are then supplied. A listing of distributors associated with the publisher concludes each entry; each distributor name is in bold type and may be found in the Wholesaler & Distributor Name Index (see below).

A dagger preceding an entry and the note "CIP" at the end of the entry both indicate that the publisher participates in the Cataloging in Publication Program of the Library of Congress.

Foreign publishers with U.S. distributors are listed, followed by their three-character ISO (International Standards Organization) country code ("GBR," "CAN," etc.), ISBN prefix(es), when available, and a cross-reference to their U.S. distributor, as shown below:

Atrium (GBR) *(0-9535353) Dist by* **Dufour**.

Publishers with like or similar names are referenced by a "Do not confuse with . . ." notation at the end of the entry. In addition, cross-references are provided from imprints and former company names to the new name.

WHOLESALER & DISTRIBUTOR NAME INDEX

Full information on distributors as well as wholesalers is provided in this index. Note that those publishers who also serve as distributors may be listed both here and in the Publisher Name Index.

SAMPLE ENTRY WHOLESALER & DISTRIBUTOR NAME INDEX

1 **New Leaf Distributing Co., Inc.,** 2 *(0-9627209),* 3 Div. of Al-Wali Corp.,
4 401 Thornton Rd., Lithia Springs, GA 30122-1557 5 (SAN 169-1449)
6 Tel: 770-948-7845; 7 Fax: 770-944-2313; 8 Toll Free Fax: 800-326-1066;
9 Toll Free: 800-326-2665
10 Email: NewLeaf-dist.com
11 Web site: http://www.NewLeaf-dist.com

KEY

1 Distributor name
2 ISBN prefix
3 Division of
4 Editorial address
5 SAN
6 Telephone
7 Fax
8 Toll free fax
9 Toll free
10 E-mail
11 Web site

SAMPLE ENTRY PUBLISHER NAME INDEX

1 † 2 **Mosby, Inc.,** 3 *(0-323; 0-7234; 0-8016; 0-8151; 0-88416; 0-941158; 1-55664; 1-56815),* 4 Div. of Harcourt, Inc., A Harcourt Health Sciences Co., 5 Orders Addr.: 6227 Sea Harbor Dr., Orlando, FL 32887 6 Toll Free Fax: 800-235-0256 7 Toll Free: 800-543-1918 8 Edit Addr.: 11830 Westline Industrial Dr., Saint Louis, MO 63146
9 (SAN 200-2280) 10 Toll Free: 800-325-4177
11 Web site: http://www.mosby.com/
12 Dist(s): ***PennWell Corp.*** 13 *CIP.*

KEY

1 CIP Identifier
2 Publisher Name
3 ISBN Prefixes
4 Division of
5 Orders Address
6 Orders Fax
7 Orders Telephone
8 Editorial Address
9 SAN
10 Toll-Free
11 Web site
12 Distributors
13 Cataloging in Publication

PUBLISHER COUNTRY CODES

Foreign publishers are listed in **Subject Guide to Children's Books In Print** with the three-letter International Standards Organization (ISO) code for their country of domicile. This is the complete list of ISO codes, though not all countries may be represented in **Subject Guide to Children's Books In Print**. The codes are mnemonic in most cases. The country names listed here may have been shortened to a more common usage form.

ABW	Aruba
AFG	Afghanistan
AGO	Angola
AIA	Anguilla
ALB	Albania
AND	Andorra
ANT	Netherlands Antilles
ARE	United Arab Emirates
ARG	Argentina
ARM	Armenia
ASM	American Samoa
ATA	Antarctica
ATF	French Southern Territories
ATG	Antigua & Barbuda
AUS	Australia
AUT	Austria
AZE	Azerbaijan
BDI	Burundi
BEL	Belgium
BEN	Benin
BFA	Burkina Faso
BGD	Bangladesh
BGR	Bulgaria
BHR	Bahrain
BHS	Bahamas
BIH	Bosnia & Herzegovina
BLR	Belarus
BLZ	Belize
BMU	Bermuda
BOL	Bolivia
BRA	Brazil
BRB	Barbados
BRN	Brunei Darussalam
BTN	Bhutan
BVT	Bouvet Island
BWA	Botswana
CAF	Central African Republic
CAN	Canada
CCK	Cocos (Keeling) Islands
CHE	Switzerland
CHL	Chile
CHN	China
CIV	Cote D'Ivoire
CMR	Cameroon
COD	Congo, Democratic Republic of
COG	Congo
COK	Cook Islands
COL	Colombia
COM	Comoros
CPV	Cape Verde
CRI	Costa Rica
CSK	Czechoslovakia
CUB	Cuba
CXR	Christmas Island
CYN	Cayman Islands
CYP	Cyprus
CZE	Czech Republic
DEU	Germany
DJI	Djibouti
DMA	Dominica
DNK	Denmark
DOM	Dominican Republic
DZA	Algeria
ECU	Ecuador
EGY	Egypt
ERI	Eritrea
ESH	Western Sahara
ESP	Spain
EST	Estonia
ETH	Ethiopia
FIN	Finland
FJI	Fiji
FLK	Falkland Islands
FRA	France
FRO	Faeroe Islands
FSM	Fed. States of Micronesia
GAB	Gabon
GBR	United Kingdom
GEO	Georgia
GHA	Ghana
GIB	Gibraltar
GIN	Guinea
GLP	Guadeloupe
GMB	Gambia
GNB	Guinea-Bissau
GNQ	Equatorial Guinea
GRC	Greece
GRD	Grenada
GRL	Greenland
GTM	Guatemala
GUF	French Guiana
GUM	Guam
GUY	Guyana
HKG	Hong Kong
HMD	Heard Island & McDonald Islands
HND	Honduras
HRV	Croatia
HTI	Haiti
HUN	Hungary
IDN	Indonesia
IND	India
IOT	British Indian Ocean Territory
IRL	Ireland
IRN	Iran
IRQ	Iraq
ISL	Iceland
ISR	Israel
ITA	Italy
JAM	Jamaica
JOR	Jordan
JPN	Japan
KAZ	Kazakstan
KEN	Kenya
KGZ	Kyrgyzstan
KHM	Cambodia
KIR	Kiribati
KNA	Saint Kitts & Nevis
KOR	Korea, Republic of
KWT	Kuwait
LAO	Laos
LBN	Lebanon
LBR	Liberia
LBY	Libya
LCA	St. Lucia
LIE	Liechtenstein
LKA	Sri Lanka
LSO	Lesotho
LTU	Lithuania
LUX	Luxembourg
LVA	Latvia
MAC	Macau
MAR	Morocco
MCO	Monaco
MDA	Moldova
MDG	Madagascar
MDV	Maldive Islands
MEX	Mexico
MHL	Marshall Islands
MKD	Macedonia
MLI	Mali
MLT	Malta
MMR	Myanmar
MNG	Mongolia
MNP	Northern Mariana Islands
MOZ	Mozambique
MRT	Mauritania
MSR	Monteserrat
MTQ	Martinique
MUS	Mauritius
MWI	Malawi
MYS	Malaysia
MYT	Mayotte
NAM	Namibia
NCL	New Caledonia
NER	Niger
NFK	Norfolk Island
NGA	Nigeria
NIC	Nicaragua
NIU	Niue
NLD	Netherlands
NOR	Norway
NPL	Nepal
NRU	Nauru
NZL	New Zealand
OMN	Oman
PAK	Pakistan
PAN	Panama
PCN	Pitcairn
PER	Peru
PHL	Philippines
PLW	Palau
PNG	Papua New Guinea
POL	Poland
PRI	Puerto Rico
PRK	Korea, Democratic People's Rep. of
PRT	Portugal
PRY	Paraguay
PSE	Occupied Palestinian Territory
PYF	French Polynesia
QAT	Qatar
REU	Reunion
ROM	Romania
RUS	Russia
RWA	Rwanda
SAU	Saudi Arabia
SDN	Sudan
SEN	Senegal
SGP	Singapore
SGS	South Georgia & Sandwich Islands
SHN	Saint Helena
SJM	Svalbard & Jan Mayen
SLB	Solomon Islands
SLE	Sierra Leone
SLV	El Salvador
SMR	San Marino

SOM	Somalia
SPM	Saint Pierre & Miquelon
STP	Sao Tome e Principe
SUN	U.S.S.R.
SUR	Suriname
SVK	Slovakia
SVN	Slovenia
SWE	Sweden
SWZ	Swaziland
SYC	Seychelles
SYR	Syrian Arab Republic
TCA	Turks & Caicos Islands
TCD	Chad
TGO	Togo
THA	Thailand
TJK	Tajikistan
TKL	Tokelau
TKM	Turkmenistan
TNP	East Timor
TON	Tonga
TTO	Trinidad & Tobago
TUN	Tunisia
TUR	Turkey
TUV	Tuvalu
TWN	Taiwan
TZA	Tanzania
UGA	Uganda
UKR	Ukraine
URY	Uruguay
USA	United States
UZB	Uzbekistan
VAT	Vatican City
VCT	St. Vincent & Grenadines
VEN	Venezuela
VGB	Virgin Islands, British
VIR	Virgin Islands, U.S.
VNM	Viet Nam
VUT	Vanuatu
WLF	Wallis & Futuna
WSM	Samoa
YEM	Yemen
YUG	Yugoslavia
ZAF	South Africa
ZAR	Zaire
ZMB	Zambia
ZWE	Zimbabwe

LANGUAGE CODES

ACE	Acholi
AFR	Afrikaans
AFA	Afro-Asiatic
AKK	Akkadian
ALB	Albanian
ALE	Aleut
ALG	Algonquin
AMH	Amharic
ANG	Anglo-Saxon
APA	Apache
ARA	Arabic
ARC	Aramaic
ARP	Arapaho
ARN	Araucanian
ARW	Arawak
ARM	Armenian
ASM	Assamese
AVA	Avar
AVE	Avesta
AYM	Aymara
AZE	Azerbaijani
BAT	Baltic
BAL	Baluchi
BAM	Bambara
BAK	Bashkir
BAQ	Basque
BEJ	Beja
BEL	Belorussian
BEM	Bemba
BEN	Bengali
BER	Berber Group
BIH	Bihari
BLA	Blackfoot
BRE	Breton
BUL	Bulgarian
BUR	Burmese
CAD	Caddo
CAM	Cambodian
CAR	Carib
CAT	Catalan
CAU	Caucasian
CEL	Celtic Group
CAI	Central American Indian
CHE	Chechen
CHR	Cherokee
CHY	Cheyenne
CHB	Chibcha
CHI	Chinese
CHN	Chinook
CHO	Choctaw
CHU	Church Slavic
CHV	Chuvash
COP	Coptic
COR	Cornish
CRE	Cree
CRP	Creoles and Pidgins
CRO	Croatian
CUS	Cushitic
CZE	Czech
DAK	Dakota
DAN	Danish
DEL	Delaware
DIN	Dinka
DOI	Dogri
DRA	Dravidian
DUA	Duala
DUT	Dutch
EFI	Efik
EGY	Egyptian
ELX	Elamite
ENG	English
ENM	English, Middle
ESK	Eskimo
ESP	Esperanto
EST	Estonian
ETH	Ethiopic
EWE	Ewe
FAN	Fang
FAR	Faroese
FIJ	Fijian
FIN	Finnish
FIU	Finno-Ugrian
FLE	Flemish
FON	Fon
FRE	French
FEM	French, Middle
FRO	French, Old
FRI	Frisian
GAA	Ga
GAE	Gaelic
GAL	Galla
GAG	Gallegan
GEO	Georgian
GER	German
GEH	German, Middle High
GOH	German, Old High
GEM	Germanic
GON	Gondi
GOT	Gothic
GRE	Greek
GEC	Greek, Classical
GUA	Guarani
GUJ	Gujarati
HAU	Hausa
HAW	Hawaiian
HEB	Hebrew
HER	Herero
HIL	Hiligaynon
HIN	Hindi
HUN	Hungarian
HUP	Hupa
IBA	Iban
ICE	Icelandic
IBO	Igbo
ILO	Ilocano
INC	Indic
INE	Indo-European
IND	Indonesian
INT	Interlingua
IKU	Inuktitut
IRA	Iranian
IRI	Irish
IRO	Iroquois
ITA	Italian
JPN	Japanese
JAV	Javanese
KAC	Kachin
KAM	Kamba
KAN	Kannada
KAU	Kanuri
KAA	Karakalpak
KAR	Karen
KAS	Kashmiri
KAZ	Kazakh
KHA	Khasi
KIK	Kikuyu
KIN	Kinyarwanda
KIR	Kirghiz
KON	Kongo
KOK	Konkani
KOR	Korean
KPE	Kpelle
KRO	Kru
KUR	Kurdish
KRU	Kurukh
KUA	Kwanyama
LAD	Ladino
LAH	Lahnda
LAM	Lamba
LAO	Laotian
LAP	Lapp
LAT	Latin
LAV	Latvian
LIN	Lingala
LIT	Lithuanian
LOL	Lolo
LUB	Luba
LUG	Luganda
LUI	Luiseno
MAC	Macedonian
MAI	Maithili
MLA	Malagasy
MAY	Malay
MAL	Malayalam
MAP	Malayo-Polynesian
MLT	Maltese
MAN	Mandingo
MNO	Manobo
MAO	Maori
MAR	Marathi
MAS	Masai
MYN	Mayan
MEN	Mende
MIC	Micmac
MIS	Miscellaneous
MOL	Moldavian
MON	Mongol
MOS	Mossi
MUL	Multiple languages
MUS	Muskogee
NAV	Navaho
NDE	Ndebele, Northern
NBL	Ndebele, Southern
NEP	Nepali
NEW	Newari
NIC	Niger-Congo
NAI	North American Indian
NOR	Norwegian
NUB	Nubian
NYM	Nyamwezi
NYA	Nyanja
NYO	Nyoro Group
OJI	Ojibwa
ORI	Oriya
OSA	Osage
OES	Ossetic
OTO	Otomi
PAH	Pahari
PAL	Pahlavi
PLI	Pali
PAN	Panjabi
PAA	Papuan-Australian
PER	Persian, Modern
PEO	Persian, Old
POL	Polish
POR	Portuguese
PRO	Provencal

LANGUAGE CODES

PUS	Pushto
QUE	Quechua
RAJ	Rajasthani
ROA	Romance
RUM	Romanian
ROH	Romansh
ROM	Romany
RUN	Rundi
RUS	Russian
SAM	Samaritan
SAO	Sampan
SAD	Sandawe
SAG	Sango
SAN	Sanskrit
SRD	Sardinian
SCO	Scots
SEL	Selkup
SEM	Semitic
SER	Serbian
SBC	Serbo-Croatian
SRR	Serer
SHN	Shan
SHO	Shona
SID	Sidamo
SND	Sindhi
SNH	Singhalese
SIT	Sino-Tibetan
SIO	Siouan languages
SLA	Slavic
SLO	Slovak
SLV	Slovenian
SOG	Sogdian
SOM	Somali
SON	Songhai
NSO	Sotho, Northern
SOT	Sotho, Southern
SAI	South American Indian
SPA	Spanish
SSA	Sub-Saharan African
SUK	Sukuma
SUX	Sumerian
SUN	Sundanese
SUS	Susu
SWA	Swahili
SWE	Swedish
SYR	Syriac
TAG	Tagalog
TAJ	Tajik
TAM	Tamil
TAR	Tatar
TEL	Telugu
TEM	Temne
TER	Tereno
THA	Thai
TIB	Tibetan
TIG	Tigre
TIR	Tigrinya
TOG	Tonga, Nyasa
TON	Tonga, Tonga Islands
TSI	Tsimshian
TSO	Tsonga
TSW	Tswana
TUR	Turkish
TUK	Turkmen
TUT	Turko-Tataric
TWI	Twi
UGA	Ugaritic
UIG	Uigur
UKR	Ukrainian
UMB	Umbundu
UND	Undetermined
URD	Urdu
UZB	Uzbek
VIE	Vietnamese
VOT	Votic
WAL	Walamo
WAS	Washo
WEL	Welsh
WEN	Wendic
WOL	Wolof
XHO	Xhosa
YAO	Yao
YID	Yiddish
YOR	Yoruba
ZAP	Zapotec
ZEN	Zenaga
ZUL	Zulu
ZUN	Zuni

LIST OF ABBREVIATIONS

abr.	abridged
adapt.	adapted
aft.	afterword
Amer.	American
anno.	annotated by
annot.	annotation(s)
ans.	answer(s)
app.	appendix
Apple II	Apple II disk
approx.	approximately
assn.	association
audio	analog audio cassette
auth.	author
bd.	bound
bdg.	binding
bds.	boards
bibl(s).	bibliography(ies)
bk(s).	book(s)
bklet(s)	booklet(s)
boxed	boxed set, slipcase, or caseboard
Bro.	Brother
C	college audience level
co.	company
comm.	commission, committee
comment.	commentaries
comp.	compiled
cond.	condensed
contrib.	contributed
corp.	corporation
dept.	department
des	designed
diag(s).	diagram(s)
digital audio	digital audio cassette
dir.	director
disk	software disk or diskette
dist.	distributed
Div.	Division
doz.	dozen
ea.	each
ed.	edited, edition, editor
eds.	editions, editors
educ.	education
elem.	elementary
ency.	encyclopedia
ENG	English
enl.	enlarged
epil.	epilogue
exp.	expurgated
expr.	experiments
fac.	facsimile
fasc.	fascicule
fict.	fiction
fig(s).	figure(s)
flmstrp.	filmstrip
footn.	footnotes
for.	foreign
frwd.	foreword
gen.	general
gr.	grade(s)
hdbk.	handbook
Illus.	illustrated, illustration(s), illustrator(s)
in prep.	in preparation
incl.	includes, including
info.	information
inst.	institute
intro.	introduction
ISBN	International Standard Book Number
ISO	International Standards Organization
ITA	Italian
i.t.a.	initial teaching alphabet
J	juvenile audience level
JPN	Japanese
Jr.	Junior
jt. auth.	joint author
jt. ed.	joint editor
k	kindergarten audience level
lab	laboratory
lang(s).	languages(s)
LC	Library of Congress
lea.	leather
lib.	library
lib. bdg.	library binding
lit.	literature, literary
lp	record, album, long playing
ltd. ed.	limited edition
mac hd	144M, Mac
mac ld	800K, Mac
mass mkt.	mass market paperbound
math.	mathematics
mic. film	microfilm
mic form	microform
mod.	modern
mor.	morocco
MS(S)	manuscript(s)
natl.	national
net	net price (see publisher for specific pricing policies)
no(s).	number(s)
o.p.	out of print
orig.	original text, not a reprint (paperback)
o.s.i.	out of stock indefinitely
p.	pages
pap.	paper
per.	perfect binding
photos	photographer, photographs
pop. ed.	popular edition
prep.	preparation
probs.	problems
prog. bk.	programmed books
ps	preschool audience level
pseud.	pseudonym
pt(s).	part(s)
pub.	published, publisher, publishing
pubn.	publication
ref(s).	reference(s)
reprod(s).	reproduction(s)
ret.	retold by
rev.	revised
rpm.	revolution per minute (phono records)
SAN	Standard Address Number
S&L	Signed and Limited
SER	Serbian
sec.	section
sel.	selected
ser.	series
Soc.	society
sols.	solutions
s.p.	school price
Sr.(after given name)	Senior
Sr.(before given name)	Sister
St.	Saint
subs.	subsidiary
subsc.	subscription
suppl.	supplement
tech.	technical
text ed.	text edition
tr.	translated, translation, translator
trans.	transparencies
univ.	university
vdisk	videodisc
VHS	video, VHS format
vol(s).	volume(s)
wkbk.	workbook
YA	young adult audience level
yrbk.	yearbook
3.5 hd	1.44M, 3.5 disk, DOS
3.5 ld	720, 3.5 Disk, DOS
5.25 hd	1.2M, 5.25 Disk, DOS
5.25 ld	360K, 5.25 Disk, DOS

SUBJECT GUIDE TO CHILDREN'S BOOKS IN PRINT 2008

A - Z

A

A B C BOOKS
see Alphabet Books

A. D. C.
see Child Welfare

AARDVARK—FICTION

Brown, Marc. Arthur & the 1,001 Dads. Brown, Marc, illus. 28th ed. 2003. (Arthur Chapter Bks. : Bk. 28). (Illus.). 64p. (J). (gr. 1-4). 14.95 (978-0-316-12516-1(4)); pap. 4.25 (978-0-316-12280-1(7)) Little, Brown Bks. for Young Readers.
—Arthur & the 1,001 Dads. 2003. (Arthur Chapter Bks.: Bk. 28). (Illus.). 57p. (J). (ps). lib. bdg. 12.10 (978-0-613-58311-4(6)) Tandem Library Bks.
—Arthur & the Babysitter. 2004. 32p. (J). 15.95 (978-0-316-12128-6(2)) Little Brown & Co.
—Arthur & the Bad-Luck Brain. 30th ed. 2003. (Arthur Chapter Bks.: Bk. 30). (Illus.). 64p. (J). (gr. 2-4). pap. 4.25 (978-0-316-12377-8(3)) Little Brown & Co.
—Arthur & the Bad-Luck Brain. 30th ed. 2003. (Arthur Chapter Bks. : Bk. 30). (Illus.). 64p. (J). (gr. 2-4). 14.95 (978-0-316-12650-2(0)) Little, Brown Bks. for Young Readers.
—Arthur & the Best Coach Ever. Brown, Marc, illus. 4th ed. 2001. (Arthur Good Sports Ser.: Bk. 4). (Illus.). 64p. (J). (gr. 2-4). 13.95 (978-0-316-11965-8(2)); pap. 4.25 (978-0-316-12117-0(7)) Little, Brown Bks. for Young Readers.
—Arthur & the Best Coach Ever. 2001. (Arthur Good Sports Ser.: Bk. 4). (gr. 3-6). lib. bdg. 11.80 (978-0-613-35627-5(6)); (Illus.). (J). 10.75 (978-0-606-21910-5(2)) Tandem Library Bks.
—Arthur & the Big Blow-Up. 2002. (Arthur Chapter Bks.: Bk. 20). (Illus.). (J). 11.45 (978-0-7587-0000-1(8)) Book Wholesalers, Inc.
—Arthur & the Big Blow-Up. 1999. (Arthur Chapter Bks. : Bk. 20). (J). (gr. 3-6). pap. 3.95 (978-0-316-12326-6(9)) Little, Brown Bks. for Young Readers.
—Arthur & the Big Blow-Up. Brown, Marc, illus. 20th ed. 2000. (Arthur Chapter Bks. : Bk. 20). (Illus.). 64p. (J). (gr. 2-4). pap. 4.25 (978-0-316-12203-0(3)) Little, Brown Bks. for Young Readers.
—Arthur & the Big Blow-Up. 2000. (Arthur Chapter Bks.: Bk. 20). (gr. k-3). lib. bdg. 11.80 (978-0-613-24244-8(0)); (Illus.). (J). (gr. 3-6). 10.75 (978-0-606-18251-5(9)) Tandem Library Bks.
—Arthur & the Cootie-Catcher. 1999. (Arthur Chapter Bks. : Bk. 15). (J). (gr. 3-6). pap. 3.95 (978-0-316-12085-2(5)) Little, Brown Bks. for Young Readers.
—Arthur & the Cootie-Catcher. Brown, Marc, illus. 15th ed. 1999. (Arthur Chapter Bks. : Bk. 15). (Illus.). 64p. (J). (gr. 2-4). pap. 4.25 (978-0-316-12266-5(1)) Little, Brown Bks. for Young Readers.
—Arthur & the Double Dare. 2002. (Arthur Chapter Bks.: Bk. 25). (Illus.). (J). 11.70 (978-0-7587-9423-9(1)) Book Wholesalers, Inc.
—Arthur & the Double Dare. Brown, Marc, illus. 2002. (Arthur Chapter Bks. : Bk. 25). (Illus.). 64p. (J). (gr. 2-4). 13.95 (978-0-316-12264-1(5)); pap. 4.25 (978-0-316-12087-6(1)) Little, Brown Bks. for Young Readers.
—Arthur & the Double Dare. 2002. (Arthur Chapter Bks.: Bk. 25). (gr. k-3). lib. bdg. 12.10 (978-0-613-50586-4(7)) Tandem Library Bks.
—Arthur & the Lost Diary. 1998. (Arthur Chapter Bks. : Bk. 9). (J). (gr. 3-6). pap. 3.95 (978-0-316-61004-9(6)); 9th ed. (Illus.). 64p. (gr. 2-4). pap. 4.25 (978-0-316-11537-7(1)) Little, Brown Bks. for Young Readers.
—Arthur & the Lost Diary. (Arthur Chapter Bks.: Bk. 9). 55p. (J). (gr. 3-6). pap. 3.95 (978-0-8072-1305-6(5) , Listening Library) Random Hse. Audio Publishing Group.
—Arthur & the Nerves of Steal. 2004. (Arthur Chapter Bks. : Bk. 32). (Illus.). 64p. (J). (gr. 2-4). 14.99 (978-0-316-12895-7(3)); pap. 4.25 (978-0-316-12618-2(7)) Little, Brown Bks. for Young Readers. (Tingley, Megan Bks.).
—Arthur & the New Kid. 2004. (Arthur Ser.). (Illus.). 24p. (J). (gr. k-3). pap. 3.99 (978-0-375-81381-8(0)); lib. bdg. 11.99 (978-0-375-91381-5(5)) Random Hse. Children's Bks. (Random Hse. Bks. for Young Readers).
—Arthur & the Pen-Pal Playoff. 2002. (Arthur Good Sports Ser.: Bk. 6). (Illus.). (J). 11.70 (978-0-7587-6863-6(X)) Book Wholesalers, Inc.
—Arthur & the Pen-Pal Playoff. Brown, Marc, illus. 6th ed. 2001. (Arthur Good Sports Ser.: Bk. 6). (Illus.). 64p. (J). (gr. 2-4). 14.95 (978-0-316-12054-8(5)); pap. 4.25 (978-0-316-12170-5(3)) Little, Brown Bks. for Young Readers.
—Arthur & the Pen-Pal Playoff. 2001. (Arthur Good Sports Ser.: Bk. 6). (ps-3). (Illus.). 55p. (J). lib. bdg. 12.10 (978-0-613-44165-0(6)); 11.05 (978-0-606-22556-4(0)) Tandem Library Bks.
—Arthur & the Perfect Brother. ed. 2000. (Arthur Chapter Bks. : Bk. 21). (J). pap. 3.95 (978-0-316-12108-8(8)) Little, Brown Bks. for Young Readers.
—Arthur & the Perfect Brother. Brown, Marc, illus. 21st ed. 2000. (Arthur Chapter Bks. : Bk. 21). (Illus.). 64p. (J). (gr. 2-4). pap. 4.25 (978-0-316-12226-9(2)) Little, Brown Bks. for Young Readers.
—Arthur & the Perfect Brother. 2000. (Illus.). (J). 54p. (ps-ps). lib. bdg. 11.80 (978-0-613-24245-5(9)); (Arthur Chapter Bks.: Bk. 21). (gr. 3-6). 10.75 (978-0-606-18252-2(7)) Tandem Library Bks.
—Arthur & the Poetry Contest. 1999. (Arthur Chapter Bks. : Bk. 18). (J). (gr. 3-6). pap. 3.95 (978-0-316-12153-8(3)) Little, Brown Bks. for Young Readers.
—Arthur & the Poetry Contest. Brown, Marc, illus. 18th ed. 1999. (Arthur Chapter Bks. : Bk. 18). (Illus.). 64p. (J). (gr. 2-4). pap. 4.25 (978-0-316-12295-5(5)) Little, Brown Bks. for Young Readers.
—Arthur & the Poetry Contest. 1999. (Arthur Chapter Bks.: Bk. 18). (gr. k-3). lib. bdg. 11.80 (978-0-613-21137-6(5)); (J). (gr. 3-6). 10.75 (978-0-606-17238-7(6)) Tandem Library Bks.
—Arthur & the Popularity Test. (Arthur Chapter Bks. : Bk. 12). (J). 1999. (gr. 3-6). pap. 3.95 (978-0-316-11999-3(7)); 12th ed. 1998. (Illus.). 64p. (gr. 2-4). pap. 4.25 (978-0-316-11545-2(2)) Little, Brown Bks. for Young Readers.
—Arthur & the Popularity Test. (Arthur Chapter Bks.: Bk. 12). 58p. (J). (gr. 3-6). pap. 3.95 (978-0-8072-1308-7(X)); 2004. (gr. 2-4). pap. 17.00 incl. audio (978-0-8072-0413-9(7) , FTR204SP) Random Hse. Audio Publishing Group. (Listening Library).
—Arthur & the Recess Rookie. 2001. (Arthur Good Sports Ser.: Bk. 3). (Illus.). 64p. (J). (gr. 2-4). 13.95 (978-0-316-11916-0(4)); 3rd ed. pap. 4.25 (978-0-316-12105-7(3)) Little, Brown Bks. for Young Readers.
—Arthur & the Recess Rookie. 2001. (Arthur Good Sports Ser.: Bk. 3). (gr. 3-6). lib. bdg. 11.80 (978-0-613-35629-9(2)); (Illus.). (J). 10.75 (978-0-606-21909-9(9)) Tandem Library Bks.
—Arthur & the School Pet. 2003. (Arthur Ser.). (Illus.). 24p. (J). (gr. k-2). pap. 3.99 (978-0-375-81001-5(3) , Random Hse. Bks. for Young Readers) Random Hse. Children's Bks.
—Arthur & the School Pet. 2003. (Arthur Ser.). (ps-2). lib. bdg. 11.80 (978-0-613-57492-1(3)) Tandem Library Bks.
—Arthur & the True Francine. 1998. (Arthur Adventure Ser.). (Illus.). 32p. (J). (ps-3). 9.95 (978-0-316-11946-7(6)) Little, Brown Bks. for Young Readers.
—Arthur & the True Francine. (Arthur Adventure Ser.). (J). (gr. k-3). 7.98 incl. audio NewSound, LLC.
—Arthur & the World Record. 33rd ed. 2005. (Arthur Chapter Bks. : Bk. 33). (Illus.). 64p. (J). (gr. 2-4). 14.99 (978-0-316-12949-7(6) , Tingley, Megan Bks.) Little, Brown Bks. for Young Readers.
—Arthur Babysits. Brown, Marc, illus. 2002. (Arthur Adventure Ser.). (Illus.). (J). 13.15 (978-0-7587-1971-3(X)) Book Wholesalers, Inc.
—Arthur Babysits. 1999. (Arthur Adventure Ser.). (Illus.). (J). (gr. k-3). lib. bdg. 14.10 (978-0-7857-5838-9(0)) Tandem Library Bks.
—Arthur Goes to Camp. Brown, Marc, illus. 2002. (Arthur Adventure Ser.). (Illus.). (J). 13.15 (978-0-7587-1972-0(8)) Book Wholesalers, Inc.
—Arthur Goes to Camp. Brown, Marc, illus. 1998. (Arthur Adventure Ser.). (Illus.). 32p. (J). (gr. k-3). pap. 5.95 (978-0-316-11529-2(0)) Little, Brown Bks. for Young Readers.
—Arthur in a Pickle. 1999. (Arthur Ser.). (Illus.). 24p. (J). (gr. k-3). lib. bdg. 11.99 (978-0-679-98469-6(0) , Random Hse. Bks. for Young Readers) Random Hse. Children's Bks.
—Arthur in a Pickle. 1999. (Arthur Ser.). lib. bdg. 11.80 (978-0-613-65119-6(7)) Tandem Library Bks.
—Arthur in New York. 2008. (J). ***(*978-0-375-82976-5(8)); (*978-0-375-92976-2(2))*** Random Hse., Inc.
—Arthur Loses a Friend. 2006. (Illus.). 24p. (J). (gr. 1-3). pap. 3.99 (978-0-375-82974-1(1)); lib. bdg. 11.99 (978-0-375-92974-8(6)) Random Hse. Children's Bks. (Random Hse. Bks. for Young Readers).
—Arthur Loses His Marbles. 2004. (Arthur Chapter Bks.: Bk. 31). (Illus.). 64p. (J). (gr. 2-4). 14.95 (978-0-316-12711-0(6)); pap. 4.25 (978-0-316-12557-4(1)) Little Brown & Co.
—Arthur Lost & Found. ed. 2004. (Arthur Adventure Ser.). (J). (gr. k-3). spiral bd. (978-0-616-11102-4(9)) Canadian National Institute for the Blind/Institut National Canadien pour les Aveugles.
—Arthur Lost & Found. Brown, Marc, illus. (Arthur Adventure Ser.). (Illus.). 32p. (J). (ps-3). 2000. pap. 6.99 (978-0-316-10824-9(3)); 1998. 15.95 (978-0-316-10912-3(6)) Little, Brown Bks. for Young Readers.
—Arthur Lost & Found. 2000. (Arthur Adventure Ser.). (J). (gr. k-3). 12.75 (978-0-606-19835-6(0)) Tandem Library Bks.
—Arthur Rocks with Binky. Brown, Marc, illus. 2002. (Arthur Chapter Bks.: Bk. 11). (Illus.). (J). 11.70 (978-0-7587-0439-9(9)) Book Wholesalers, Inc.
—Arthur Rocks with Binky. 11th ed. 1998. (Arthur Chapter Bks. : Bk. 11). (Illus.). 64p. (J). (gr. 2-4). pap. 4.25 (978-0-316-11543-8(6)) Little, Brown Bks. for Young Readers.
—Arthur Rocks with Binky. (Arthur Chapter Bks.: Bk. 11). 61p. (J). (gr. 3-6). pap. 3.95 (978-0-8072-1307-0(1) , Listening Library) Random Hse. Audio Publishing Group.
—Arthur Writes a Story. Brown, Marc, illus. 2002. (Arthur Adventure Ser.). (Illus.). (J). 13.15 (978-0-7587-1974-4(4)) Book Wholesalers, Inc.
—Arthur Writes a Story. ed. 2004. (Arthur Adventure Ser.). (J). (gr. k-3). spiral bd. (978-0-616-01604-6(2)); spiral bd. (978-0-616-01605-3(0)) Canadian National Institute for the Blind/Institut National Canadien pour les Aveugles.
—Arthur Writes a Story. 2003. (Arthur Adventure Ser.). (Illus.). 14.95 (978-1-59319-021-7(2)) LeapFrog Enterprises, Inc.
—Arthur Writes a Story. Brown, Marc, illus. (Arthur Adventure Ser.). (Illus.). 32p. (J). (ps-3). 1999. 9.95 (978-0-316-11976-4(8)); 1998. pap. 6.99 (978-0-316-11164-5(3)); 2007. pap. 10.99 incl. audio compact disk ***(*978-0-316-11865-1(6))*** Little, Brown Bks. for Young Readers.
—Arthur Writes a Story. 1998. (Arthur Adventure Ser.). (J). (gr. k-3). 12.75 (978-0-606-13153-7(1)) Tandem Library Bks.
—Arthur's Baby. 1998. (Arthur Adventure Ser.). (Illus.). 30p. (J). (ps-k). bds. 5.95 (978-0-316-11858-3(3)) Little, Brown Bks. for Young Readers.
—Arthur's Back-to-School Surprise. 2002. (Arthur Ser.). (Illus.). 24p. (J). (gr. k-3). pap. 3.99 (978-0-375-81000-8(5)); lib. bdg. 11.99 (978-0-375-91000-5(X)) Random Hse. Children's Bks. (Random Hse. Bks. for Young Readers).
—Arthur's Birthday. 1998. (Arthur Adventure Ser.). (Illus.). 30p. (J). (ps-3). bds. 5.95 (978-0-316-11857-6(5)) Little, Brown Bks. for Young Readers.
—Arthur's Birthday Activity Book. Brown, Marc, illus. 2001. (Arthur Ser.). (Illus.). 18p. (J). (ps-3). pap., act. bk. ed. 7.95 (978-0-316-11851-4(6)) Little Brown & Co.
—Arthur's Birthday Surprise. 2004. (Arthur's 8 x 8 Bks.). (Illus.). 24p. (J). (ps-1). pap. 3.99 (978-0-316-73379-3(2)) Little, Brown Bks. for Young Readers.
—Arthur's Chicken Pox. Brown, Marc, illus. 2002. (Arthur Adventure Ser.). (Illus.). (J). 13.15 (978-0-7587-1978-2(7)) Book Wholesalers, Inc.
—Arthur's Chicken Pox. Brown, Marc, illus. 1999. (Arthur Adventure Ser.). (Illus.). 30p. (J). (ps-k). bds. 5.95 (978-0-316-11953-5(9)) Little, Brown Bks. for Young Readers.
—Arthur's Chicken Pox. 1998. (Arthur Adventure Ser.). 32p. (J). (ps-3). 9.95 (978-0-316-11947-4(4)) Little, Brown Bks. for Young Readers.
—Arthur's Christmas. Brown, Marc, illus. 2002. (Arthur Adventure Ser.). (Illus.). (J). 13.15 (978-0-7587-1979-9(5)) Book Wholesalers, Inc.
—Arthur's Christmas. Brown, Marc, illus. 1999. (Arthur Adventure Ser.). 32p. (J). (ps-3). 9.95 (978-0-316-11964-1(4)) Little, Brown Bks. for Young Readers.
—Arthur's Classroom Fib. 2007. (Illus.). 24p. (J). (gr. 1-3). pap. 3.99 (978-0-375-82975-8(X)); lib. bdg. 11.99 (978-0-375-92975-5(4)) Random Hse. Children's Bks. (Random Hse. Bks. for Young Readers).
—Arthur's Family Vacation. Brown, Marc, illus. 2002. (Arthur Adventure Ser.). (Illus.). (J). 13.15 (978-0-7587-1981-2(7)) Book Wholesalers, Inc.
—Arthur's Family Vacation. ed. 2004. (Arthur Adventure Ser.). (J). (gr. k-3). spiral bd. (978-0-616-01601-5(8)); spiral bd. (978-0-616-01602-2(6)) Canadian National Institute for the Blind/Institut National Canadien pour les Aveugles.
—Arthur's Family Vacation. Brown, Marc, illus. 1998. (Arthur Adventure Ser.). (Illus.). (J). (gr. k-3). pap. 5.95 (978-0-316-11528-5(2)) Little, Brown Bks. for Young Readers.
—Arthur's First Kiss. Brown, Marc, illus. 2001. (Arthur Ser.). (Illus.). 24p. (J). (gr. k-3). pap. 3.99 (978-0-375-80602-5(4)); lib. bdg. 11.99 (978-0-375-90602-2(9)) Random Hse. Children's Bks. (Random Hse. Bks. for Young Readers).
—Arthur's First Sleepover. Brown, Marc, illus. 2002. (Arthur Adventure Ser.). (Illus.). (J). 13.15 (978-0-7587-1982-9(5)) Book Wholesalers, Inc.
—Arthur's First Sleepover. Brown, Marc, illus. 2005. (Arthur Adventure Ser.). 32p. (J). (ps-1). pap. 10.99 (978-0-316-05956-5(0)) Little Brown & Co.
—Arthur's First Sleepover. Brown, Marc, illus. 1999. (Arthur Adventure Ser.). (Illus.). 30p. (J). (ps-k). bds. 5.95 (978-0-316-10560-6(0)) Little, Brown Bks. for Young Readers.
—Arthur's First Sleepover. 1998. (Arthur Adventure Ser.). (J). (gr. k-3). pap. 5.95 (978-0-316-11974-0(1)); 32p. 9.95 (978-0-316-11948-1(2)) Little, Brown Bks. for Young Readers.
—Arthur's Halloween. Brown, Marc, illus. 2002. (Arthur Adventure Ser.). (Illus.). (J). 13.15 (978-0-7587-1983-6(3)) Book Wholesalers, Inc.
—Arthur's Hiccups. 2001. (Arthur Ser.). (Illus.). (J). (ps-3). lib. bdg. (978-0-375-90699-2(1) , Random Hse. Bks. for Young Readers) Random Hse. Children's Bks.

—Arthur's Hiccups. 2001. (Arthur Ser.). 10.79 (978-0-606-22767-4(9)) Tandem Library Bks.

—Arthur's Jelly Beans. 2004. (Arthur's 8 x 8 Bks.). (Illus.). 24p. (J). (ps-1). pap. 3.99 (978-0-316-73382-3(2)) Little Brown & Co.

—Arthur's Jelly Beans. 2004. (Arthur's 8 x 8 Bks.). (ps-2). lib. bdg. 11.80 (978-0-613-71774-8(0)) Tandem Library Bks.

—Arthur's Lost Puppy. 2001. (Arthur Ser.). (J). (ps-1). spiral bd. 14.99 (978-1-58605-223-2(3)) LeapFrog Enterprises, Inc.

—Arthur's New Puppy. Brown, Marc, illus. 2002. (Arthur Adventure Ser.). (Illus.). (J). 13.15 (978-0-7587-1984-3(1)) Book Wholesalers, Inc.

—Arthur's New Puppy. Brown, Marc, illus. 2005. (Arthur Adventure Ser.). 32p. (J). (ps-1). pap. 10.99 (978-0-316-05955-8(2)) Little Brown & Co.

—Arthur's New Puppy. 1998. (Arthur Adventure Ser.). (Illus.). 32p. (J). (ps-3). 9.95 (978-0-316-11949-8(0)) Little, Brown Bks. for Young Readers.

—Arthur's New Puppy. (Arthur Adventure Ser.). (J). (gr. k-3). 7.98 incl. audio NewSound, LLC.

—Arthur's Nose. Brown, Marc, illus. 25th rev. anniv. ed. 2005. (Arthur Adventure Ser.). (Illus.). 30p. (J). reprint ed. 16.00 (978-0-7567-9715-7(2)) DIANE Publishing Co.

—Arthur's Nose. Brown, Marc, illus. 25th ltd. anniv. ed. 2001. (Arthur Adventure Ser.). (Illus.). 40p. (J). (ps-3). pap. 15.95 (978-0-316-11884-2(2)) Little, Brown Bks. for Young Readers.

—Arthur's off to School. 2004. (Arthur's 8 x 8 Bks.). (Illus.). 24p. (J). (ps-1). pap. 3.99 (978-0-316-73378-6(4)) Little, Brown Bks. for Young Readers.

—Arthur's off to School. 2004. (Arthur's 8 x 8 Bks.). (ps-2). lib. bdg. 11.80 (978-0-613-71773-1(2)) Tandem Library Bks.

—Arthur's Pet Business. Brown, Marc, illus. rev. ed. 2007. (Arthur Adventure Ser.). (Illus.). 32p. (J). (ps-1). pap. 10.99 incl. audio compact disk ***(978-0-316-11863-7(X))** Little, Brown Bks. for Young Readers.

—Arthur's Science Fair Trouble. Brown, Marc, illus. 2003. (Arthur Ser.). (Illus.). 24p. (J). (gr. k-3). pap. 3.99 (978-0-375-81003-9(X)); lib. bdg. 11.99 (978-0-375-91003-6(4)) Random Hse. Children's Bks. (Random Hse. Bks. for Young Readers).

—Arthur's Science Fair Trouble. 2003. (Arthur Ser.). (gr. k-3). lib. bdg. 11.80 (978-0-613-70564-6(5)) Tandem Library Bks.

—Arthur's Teacher Moves In. Brown, Marc, illus. 2000. (Arthur Adventure Ser.). (Illus.). 32p. (J). (ps-3). 15.95 (978-0-316-11979-5(2)) Little, Brown Bks. for Young Readers.

—Arthur's Teacher Moves In. 2000. (Arthur Adventure Ser.). (J). (gr. k-3). 15.95 (978-0-316-11856-9(7)) Little, Brown Bks. for Young Readers.

—Arthur's Teacher Trouble. ed. 2004. (Arthur Adventure Ser.). (J). (gr. k-3). spiral bd. (978-0-616-00406-7(0)); spiral bd. (978-0-616-01603-9(4)) Canadian National Institute for the Blind/Institut National Canadien pour les Aveugles.

—Arthur's Tooth. Brown, Marc, illus. 2002. (Arthur Adventure Ser.). (Illus.). (J). 13.15 (978-0-7587-1989-8(2)) Book Wholesalers, Inc.

—Arthur's Tree House. 2007. (Arthur's 8 x 8 Bks.). (Illus.). (J). ***(978-1-4287-1970-5(9))** Little Brown & Co.

—Arthur's TV Trouble. Brown, Marc, illus. 2002. (Arthur Adventure Ser.). (Illus.). (J). 13.15 (978-0-7587-1990-4(6)) Book Wholesalers, Inc.

—Arthur's TV Trouble. Brown, Marc, illus. 1999. (Arthur Adventure Ser.). (Illus.). 32p. (J). (ps-3). 9.95 (978-0-316-11594-0(0)) Little, Brown Bks. for Young Readers.

—Arthur's Underwear. ed. 2004. (Arthur Adventure Ser.). (Illus.). (J). (gr. k-3). spiral bd. (978-0-616-14563-0(2)); spiral bd. (978-0-616-14564-7(0)) Canadian National Institute for the Blind/Institut National Canadien pour les Aveugles.

—Arthur's Underwear. Brown, Marc, illus. 2001. (Arthur Adventure Ser.). (Illus.). 32p. (J). (ps-3). pap. 6.99 (978-0-316-10619-1(4)) Little, Brown Bks. for Young Readers.

—Arthur's Underwear. 2001. (Arthur Adventure Ser.). 12.75 (978-0-606-22553-3(6)); lib. bdg. 14.10 (978-0-613-43675-5(X)) Tandem Library Bks.

—Arthur's Underwear: An Arthur Adventure. Brown, Marc, illus. 1999. (Arthur Adventure Ser.). (Illus.). 32p. (J). (ps-3). 15.95 (978-0-316-11012-9(4)) Little, Brown Bks. for Young Readers.

—Arthur's Valentine. Brown, Marc, illus. 2002. (Arthur Adventure Ser.). (Illus.). (J). 13.15 (978-0-7587-1991-1(4)) Book Wholesalers, Inc.

—Arthur's Valentine. Brown, Marc, illus. 2000. (Arthur Adventure Ser.). 32p. (J). (ps-3). 9.95 (978-0-316-11866-8(4)) Little, Brown Bks. for Young Readers.

—Arturo Tiene Varicela. Sarfatti, Esther, tr. from ENG. 2001. (SPA., Illus.). (J). (gr. k-2). pap. 6.95 (978-1-930332-00-3(9) , LC30182) Lectorum Pubns., Inc.

—Arturo Tiene Varicela. 2001. 13.75 (978-0-606-22646-2(X)); (SPA.). lib. bdg. 15.25 (978-0-613-64340-5(2)) Tandem Library Bks.

—Arturo Visita la Casa Blanca. Sarfatti, Esther, tr. from ENG. 2001. (SPA., Illus.). (J). (gr. k-2). pap. 6.95 (978-1-930332-11-9(4) , LC30189) Lectorum Pubns., Inc.

—Arturo Visita la Casa Blanca. 2001. (SPA.). lib. bdg. 15.25 (978-0-613-64341-2(0)) Tandem Library Bks.

—Arturo y los Terribles Gemelos. Sarfatti, Esther, tr. from ENG. 2000. (Arthur Adventure Ser.). (SPA., Illus.). (J). (gr. k-3). pap. 6.95 (978-1-880507-65-0(X) , LC2344) Lectorum Pubns., Inc.

—Arturo y los Terribles Gemelos. 2000. (Arthur Adventure Ser.). (J). (gr. k-3). 13.75 (978-0-606-17569-2(5)) Tandem Library Bks.

—Binky Rules. Brown, Marc, illus. 24th ed. 2000. (Arthur Chapter Bks.: Bk. 24). (Illus.). 64p. (J). (gr. 2-4). pap. 3.95 (978-0-316-12333-4(1)) Little Brown & Co.

—Binky Rules. Brown, Marc, illus. 24th ed. 2000. (Arthur Chapter Bks. : Bk. 24). (Illus.). 64p. (J). (gr. 2-4). 13.95 (978-0-316-12193-4(2)) Little, Brown Bks. for Young Readers.

—Binky Rules. 2000. (Arthur Chapter Bks.: Bk. 24). (gr. k-3). lib. bdg. 11.80 (978-0-613-30275-3(3)); (J). (gr. 3-6). 10.75 (978-0-606-19447-1(9)) Tandem Library Bks.

—Buster Baxter, Cat Saver. 2000. (Arthur Chapter Bks. : Bk. 19). (J). (gr. 3-6). pap. 3.95 (978-0-316-11817-0(6)) Little, Brown Bks. for Young Readers.

—Buster Baxter, Cat Saver. Brown, Marc, illus. 19th ed. 2000. (Arthur Chapter Bks. : Bk. 19). (Illus.). 64p. (J). (gr. 2-4). 13.95 (978-0-316-12111-8(8)); pap. 3.95 (978-0-316-12220-7(3)) Little, Brown Bks. for Young Readers.

—Buster Baxter, Cat Saver. (Arthur Chapter Bks.: Bk. 19). 2000. (gr. k-3). lib. bdg. 11.80 (978-0-613-21268-7(1)); 1999. (Illus.). (J). (gr. 3-6). 10.75 (978-0-606-18250-8(0)) Tandem Library Bks.

—Buster Makes the Grade. 1999. (Arthur Chapter Bks. : Bk 16). (J). (gr. 3-6). pap. 3.95 (978-0-316-12262-7(9)) Little, Brown Bks. for Young Readers.

—Buster Makes the Grade. Brown, Marc, illus. 16th ed. 1999. (Arthur Chapter Bks. : Bk. 16). (Illus.). 64p. (J). (gr. 2-4). pap. 4.25 (978-0-316-12277-1(7)) Little, Brown Bks. for Young Readers.

—Buster Makes the Grade. 1999. (Arthur Chapter Bks.: Bk. 16). (J). (gr. 3-6). 10.75 (978-0-606-17235-6(1)) Tandem Library Bks.

—Buster's Dino Dilemma. 7th ed. 1998. (Arthur Chapter Bks. : Bk. 7). (Illus.). 64p. (J). (gr. 2-4). pap. 4.25 (978-0-316-11560-5(6)); 13.95 (978-0-316-11559-9(2)) Little, Brown Bks. for Young Readers.

—Buster's Dino Dilemma. (Arthur Chapter Bks.: Bk. 7). 58p. (J). (gr. 3-6). pap. 3.95 (978-0-8072-1303-2(9) , Listening Library) Random Hse. Audio Publishing Group.

—Buster's New Friend. Brown, Marc, illus. 23rd ed. 2000. (Arthur Chapter Bks.: Bk. 23). (Illus.). 64p. (J). (gr. 2-4). pap. 4.25 (978-0-316-12307-5(2)) Little Brown & Co.

—Buster's New Friend. Brown, Marc, illus. 23rd ed. 2000. (Arthur Chapter Bks. : Bk. 23). (Illus.). 64p. (J). (gr. 2-4). 13.95 (978-0-316-12212-2(2)) Little, Brown Bks. for Young Readers.

—Buster's New Friend. 2000. (Arthur Chapter Bks.: Bk. 23). (gr. k-3). lib. bdg. 12.10 (978-0-613-30292-0(3)); (J). (gr. 3-6). 10.75 (978-0-606-19446-4(0)) Tandem Library Bks.

—Los Calzoncillos de Arturo. 2001. 13.75 (978-0-606-22643-1(5)) Tandem Library Bks.

—D. W. la Quisquillosa. Sarfatti, Esther, tr. from ENG. 2003. (SPA.). (J). (gr. k-2). pap. 6.95 (978-1-930332-42-3(4)) Lectorum Pubns., Inc.

—D. W. 's Guide to Perfect Manners. 2006. (D. W. Ser.). (Illus.). 32p. (J). (ps-3). 15.99 (978-0-316-12106-4(1)) Little Brown & Co.

—D. W. the Big Boss. 2005. (Arthur's 8 x 8 Bks.). (Illus.). 23p. (J). (ps-7). lib. bdg. 11.19 (978-0-606-34230-8(3)) Tandem Library Bks.

—D. W.'s Guide to Preschool. 2006. (D. W. Ser.). 32p. (J). (ps-1). reprint ed. pap. 5.99 (978-0-316-01315-4(3)) Little Brown & Co.

—D. W.'s Guide to Preschool. Brown, Marc, illus. 2003. (D. W. Ser.). (Illus.). 32p. (J). (ps-1). 15.95 (978-0-316-12069-2(3)) Little, Brown Bks. for Young Readers.

—D. W.'s Library Card. Brown, Marc, illus. 2002. (D. W. Ser.). (Illus.). (YA). 20.60 (978-0-7587-9783-4(4)) Book Wholesalers, Inc.

—D. W.'s Library Card. Brown, Marc, illus. (D. W. Ser.). (Illus.). 24p. (J). (ps-1). 2003. pap. 5.99 (978-0-316-73820-0(4)); 2001. 14.95 (978-0-316-11013-6(2)) Little, Brown Bks. for Young Readers.

—D. W.'s Lost Blankie. Brown, Marc, illus. 2002. (D. W. Ser.). (Illus.). (J). 13.15 (978-0-7587-2330-7(X)) Book Wholesalers, Inc.

—La Fiesta de Arturo. 1999. (Arthur Adventure Ser.). (SPA., Illus.). (J). (gr. k-3). pap. 6.95 (978-1-880507-64-3(1) , LC2343) Lectorum Pubns., Inc.

—Francine, Believe It or Not! ed. 1999. (Arthur Chapter Bks. : Bk. 14). (J). (gr. 3-6). pap. 3.95 (978-0-316-10463-0(9)) Little, Brown Bks. for Young Readers.

—Francine, Believe It or Not! Brown, Marc, illus. 14th ed. 1999. (Arthur Chapter Bks. : Bk. 14). (Illus.). 64p. (J). (gr. 2-4). pap. 4.25 (978-0-316-12258-0(0)) Little, Brown Bks. for Young Readers.

—King Arthur. 1999. (Arthur Chapter Bks. : Bk. 13). (J). (gr. 3-6). pap. 3.95 (978-0-316-10667-2(4)) Little, Brown Bks. for Young Readers.

—King Arthur. Brown, Marc, illus. 13th ed. 1999. (Arthur Chapter Bks. : Bk. 13). (Illus.). 64p. (J). (gr. 2-4). pap. 4.25 (978-0-316-12241-2(6)) Little, Brown Bks. for Young Readers.

—Marc Brown Arthur: King Arthur; Francine, Believe it or Not; Arthur & the Cootie-Catcher; (Arthur Chapter Bks.: No. 5). 58p. (J). (gr. 3-6). pap. 3.95 (978-0-8072-1299-8(7) , Listening Library) Random Hse. Audio Publishing Group.

—Marc Brown's Arthur: Arthur & the Crunch Cereal Contest; Arthur Accused!; Locked in the Library. (Arthur Chapter Bks.: No. 2). 58p. (J). (gr. 3-6). pap. 3.95 (978-0-8072-1296-7(2) , Listening Library) Random Hse. Audio Publishing Group.

—Marc Brown's Arthur: Arthur & the Scare-Your-Pants-off Club; Arthur Makes the Team. (Arthur Chapter Bks.: No. 1). 58p. (J). (gr. 3-6). pap. 3.95 (978-0-8072-1295-0(4) , Listening Library) Random Hse. Audio Publishing Group.

—Marc Brown's Arthur: Buster's Dino Dilemma; the Mystery of the Stolen Bike; Arthur & the Lost Diary. (Arthur Chapter Bks.: No. 3). 61p. (J). (gr. 3-6). pap. 3.95 (978-0-8072-1297-4(0)); pap. 3.95 (978-0-8072-1298-1(9)) Random Hse. Audio Publishing Group. (Listening Library).

—Muffy's Secret Admirer. 1999. (Arthur Chapter Bks. : Bk. 17). (J). (gr. 3-6). pap. 3.95 (978-0-316-12047-0(2)) Little, Brown Bks. for Young Readers.

—Muffy's Secret Admirer. Brown, Marc, illus. 17th ed. 1999. (Arthur Chapter Bks. : Bk. 17). (Illus.). 64p. (J). (gr. 2-4). 13.95 (978-0-316-12017-3(0)); pap. 3.95 (978-0-316-12230-6(0)) Little, Brown Bks. for Young Readers.

—Muffy's Secret Admirer. 1999. (Arthur Chapter Bks.: Bk. 17). (gr. k-3). lib. bdg. 11.80 (978-0-613-22040-8(4)); (J). (gr. 3-6). 10.75 (978-0-606-17237-0(8)) Tandem Library Bks.

—The Mystery of the Stolen Bike. 8th ed. 1998. (Arthur Chapter Bks. : Bk. 8). (Illus.). 64p. (J). (gr. 2-4). pap. 4.25 (978-0-316-11571-1(1)) Little, Brown Bks. for Young Readers.

—The Mystery of the Stolen Bike. (Arthur Chapter Bks.: Bk. 8). 59p. (J). (gr. 3-6). pap. 3.95 (978-0-8072-1304-9(7) , Listening Library) Random Hse. Audio Publishing Group.

—Vacaciones de Arturo. 1999. Tr. of Arthur's Family Vacation. (978-0-606-17376-6(5)); (SPA.). lib. bdg. 15.25 (978-0-613-18151-8(4)) Tandem Library Bks.

—La Visita del Señor Rataquemada. Sarfatti, Esther, tr. from ENG. 2003. (SPA.). (J). (gr. k-2). pap. 6.95 (978-1-930332-41-6(6)) Lectorum Pubns., Inc.

—Who's in Love with Arthur? (Arthur Chapter Bks. : Bk. 10). (J). 1999. (gr. 3-6). pap. 3.95 (978-0-316-10671-9(2)); 10th ed. 1998. (Illus.). 64p. (gr. 2-4). pap. 4.25 (978-0-316-11540-7(1)) Little, Brown Bks. for Young Readers.

—Who's in Love with Arthur? (Arthur Chapter Bks.: Bk. 10). 57p. (J). (gr. 3-6). pap. 3.95 (978-0-8072-1306-3(3) , Listening Library) Random Hse. Audio Publishing Group.

Brown, Marc & Sarfatti, Esther. Arturo y la Navidad. 2004. (SPA.). (J). pap. 6.95 (978-1-930332-48-5(3)) Lectorum Pubns., Inc.

Brown, Marc & Schulman, Janet. Arthur's Hiccups. Brown, Marc, illus. 2001. (Arthur Ser.). (Illus.). 24p. (J). (gr. k-3). lib. bdg. 11.99 (978-0-375-90698-5(3) , Random Hse. Bks. for Young Readers) Random Hse. Children's Bks.

Brown, Marc & Schulman, Lester. Arthur Breaks the Bank. 2004. (Arthur Ser.). (Illus.). 24p. (J). (gr. k-3). pap. 3.99 (978-0-375-81002-2(1)); lib. bdg. 11.99 (978-0-375-91002-9(6)) Random Hse. Children's Bks. (Random Hse. Bks. for Young Readers).

Brown, Marc, et al. Arthur & the Lost Diary. 9th ed. 1998. (Arthur Chapter Bks. : Bk. 9). (Illus.). 64p. (J). (gr. 2-4). 14.95 (978-0-316-11573-5(8)) Little, Brown Bks. for Young Readers.

—Buster Makes the Grade. Brown, Marc, illus. 16th ed. 1999. (Arthur Chapter Bks. : Bk. 16). (Illus.). 64p. (J). (gr. 2-4). 13.95 (978-0-316-11960-3(1)) Little, Brown Bks. for Young Readers.

deRubertis, Barbara. Marty Aardvark. Cockrille, Eva V., illus. 1998. (Let's Read Together Ser.). 32p. (J). (ps-3). pap. 4.95 (978-1-57565-042-5(8)); pap. 8.95 (978-1-57565-047-0(9)) Kane Pr., The.

George, Lindsay Barrett. Alfred Digs. 2008. 40p. (J). 16.99 ***(978-0-06-078760-8(0));** lib. bdg. 17.89 ***(978-0-06-078761-5(9))** HarperCollins Pubs. (Greenwillow Bks.).

Kennaway, Adrienne & Mwalimu. Awkward Aardvark. 2nd ed. 2005. (Illus.). 32p. (J). pap. 7.99 (978-0-340-52581-4(9) , Hodder Children's Books) Hodder Children's Division.

Krensky, Stephen. Arthur Accused! 1998. (Arthur Chapter Bks. : Bk. 5). (J). (gr. 3-6). pap. 3.95 (978-0-316-12150-7(9)); 5th ed. (Illus.). 64p. (gr. 2-4). pap. 4.25 (978-0-316-11556-8(8)) Little, Brown Bks. for Young Readers.

—Arthur & the Crunch Cereal Contest. 1998. (Arthur Chapter Bks. : Bk. 4). (J). (gr. 3-6). pap. 3.95 (978-0-316-10546-0(5)); Bk. 4. (Illus.). 64p. (gr. 2-4). pap. 4.25 (978-0-316-11553-7(3)) Little, Brown Bks. for Young Readers.

—Arthur & the Crunch Cereal Contest. 1998. (Arthur Chapter Bks.: Bk. 4). (J). (gr. 3-6). 11.05 (978-0-606-13150-6(7)) Tandem Library Bks.

—Arthur & the Scare-Your-Pants-off Club. 1998. (Arthur Chapter Bks. : Bk. 2). (J). (gr. 3-6). pap. 3.95 (978-0-316-10496-8(5)); (Illus.). 64p. (gr. 2-4). pap. 4.25 (978-0-316-11549-0(5)) Little, Brown Bks. for Young Readers.

—Arthur & the Scare-Your-Pants-off Club. unabr. ed. 1998. (Arthur Chapter Bks.: Bk. 2). 58p. (J). (gr. 2-4). pap. 17.00 incl. audio (978-0-8072-0376-7(9) , FTR188SP, Listening Library) Random Hse. Audio Publishing Group.

—Arthur & the Scare-Your-Pants-off Club. 1998. (Arthur Chapter Bks.: Bk. 2). (J). (gr. 3-6). 11.05 (978-0-606-13151-3(5)) Tandem Library Bks.

—Arthur Makes the Team. 2002. (Arthur Chapter Bks. : Bk. 3). (J). (gr. k-3). 14.95 (978-1-58605-914-9(9) , LeapFrog Schl. Hse.) LeapFrog Enterprises, Inc.

—Arthur Makes the Team. 1998. (Arthur Chapter Bks. : Bk. 3). (J). (gr. 3-6). pap. 3.95 (978-0-316-10536-1(8)); (Illus.). 64p. (gr. 2-4). pap. 4.25 (978-0-316-11551-3(7)) Little, Brown Bks. for Young Readers.

—Arthur Makes the Team. 1998. (Arthur Chapter Bks.: Bk. 3). (J). (gr. 3-6). 11.05 (978-0-606-13152-0(3)); (Illus.). 61p. (ps). lib. bdg. 12.10 (978-0-613-06884-0(X)) Tandem Library Bks.

—Arthur's Mystery Envelope. 1998. (Arthur Chapter Bks. : Bk. 1). (J). (gr. 3-6). pap. 3.95 (978-0-316-10464-7(7)); (Illus.). 64p. (gr. 2-4). pap. 4.25 (978-0-316-11547-6(9)) Little, Brown Bks. for Young Readers.

—Arthur's Mystery Envelope. 1998. (Arthur Chapter Bks.: Bk. 1). (J). (gr. 3-6). 11.05 (978-0-606-13154-4(X)) Tandem Library Bks.

—Locked in the Library! (Arthur Chapter Bks.: Bk. 6). 58p. (J). (gr. 3-6). pap. 3.95 (978-0-8072-1300-1(4) , Listening Library) Random Hse. Audio Publishing Group.

Krensky, Stephen & LeapFrog Staff. Arthur Makes the Team. 2001. (Arthur Chapter Bks. : Bk. 3). (J). (ps-2). spiral bd. 14.99 (978-1-58605-130-3(X)) LeapFrog Enterprises, Inc.

Moodie, Fiona. Noko & the Night Monster. Moodie, Fiona, illus. 2001. (Illus.). 32p. (J). (gr. k-3). 15.95 (978-0-7614-5093-1(9) , Cavendish Children's Bks.) Cavendish, Marshall Corp.

Richter, Dana. Arthur's Road Trip. Moroney, Christopher, illus. 2001. (J). (978-0-7853-4859-7(X)) Publications International, Ltd.

Tomlinson, Jill. The Aardvark Who Wasn't Sure. Howard, Paul, illus. 2005. 96p. (J). reprint ed. pap. 6.99 (978-1-4052-1084-3(2)) Egmont Bks., Ltd. GBR. *Dist:* Trafalgar Square Publishing.

AARON, HANK, 1934-

Benson, Michael. Hank Aaron, Baseball Player. 2004. (Ferguson Career Biographies Ser.). (Illus.). 128p. (J). (gr. 6-12). 25.00 (978-0-8160-5349-0(9) , Ferguson Publishing Co.) Facts On File, Inc.

Golenbock, Peter. Hank Aaron: Brave in Every Way. Lee, Paul, illus. 2005. 32p. (J). reprint ed. pap. 6.00 (978-0-15-205250-8(X) , Voyager Bks./Libros Viajeros) Harcourt Children's Bks.

Kappes, Serena. Hank Aaron. 2006. (Sports Heroes & Legends Ser.). (Illus.). 106p. (J). (gr. 3-7). 27.93 (978-0-8225-3069-5(4) , Lerner Pubns.) Lerner Publishing Group.

Morris, Roz. Henry Aaron: Dream Chaser. 2002. (Alabama Roots Biography Ser.). (Illus.). 120p. (J). per. 7.95 (978-1-878561-94-7(4)) Seacoast Publishing, Inc.

Poolos, J. Hank Aaron. 2007. (Baseball Superstars Ser.). 128p. (gr. 6-12). 30.00 ***(978-0-7910-9536-2(3)** , Chelsea Hse.) Facts On File, Inc.

Sweet, Kimberly. Hank Aaron: The Life of the Home Run King. 2001. (J). (gr. 4-7). pap. 7.95 (978-1-58838-022-7(X)) NewSouth, Inc.

ABACUS

Dalmatian Press Staff. Disney Baby Abacus BK. 2006. 10p. bds. 8.99 (978-1-4037-1935-5(7)) Dalmatian Pr.

ABANDONED CHILDREN

Warren, Andrea. The Orphan Train Rider: One Boy's True Story. 1998. (Illus.). 80p. (J). (gr. 4-6). pap. 8.95 (978-0-395-91362-8(4)) Houghton Mifflin Co. Trade & Reference Div.

ABANDONED CHILDREN—FICTION

Acheson, Alison. The Mud Girl. 2007. 328p. pap. 10.95 ***(978-1-55050-354-8(5))** Coteau Bks. CAN. *Dist:* Fitzhenry & Whiteside, Ltd.

Alger, Horatio. The Errand Boy: Or, How Phil Brent Won Success. 271p. reprint ed. pap. 79.00 (978-1-4047-3566-8(6)) Classic Textbooks.

Alonso, Manuel L. Rumbo Sur. 2005. ***(978-84-263-5948-3(5))** Vives, Luis Editorial (Edelvives).

Atwood, Margaret. Bashful Bob & Doleful Dorinda. Petricic, Dusan, illus. 2006. 32p. (J). (gr. 1-3). ***(978-1-55263-609-1(7))** Key Porter Bks.

Benedict, Helen. Opposite of Love. 2007. 256p. (J). (gr. 6 up). 16.99 ***(978-0-670-06135-8(2)** , Viking Juvenile) Penguin Group (USA) Inc.

Bowsher, Melodie. My Lost & Found Life. (YA). 2007. 320p. pap. 7.95 ***(978-1-59990-155-8(2));** 2006. 350p. 16.95 (978-1-58234-736-3(0)) Bloomsbury Publishing. (Bloomsbury Children).

Byars, Betsy. The Two-Thousand-Pound Goldfish. 2000. (Illus.). 160p. (J). (gr. 3 up). pap. 4.95 (978-0-06-440855-4(8) , Harper Trophy) HarperCollins Pubs.

—The Two-Thousand-Pound Goldfish. 2000. (978-0-606-18725-1(1)) Tandem Library Bks.

Clay, Ian. Coyote Lake. 2007. 104p. per. 9.95 ***(978-0-595-44590-5(X))** iUniverse, Inc.

Dessen, Sarah. Lock & Key. 2008. 432p. (YA). (gr. 7). 18.99 ***(978-0-670-01088-2(X)** , Viking Juvenile) Penguin Group (USA) Inc.

Dyer, Thomas A. A Way of His Own. 2001. 160p. (J). (gr. 5-9). pap. 6.95 (978-0-618-13132-7(9)) Houghton Mifflin Co. Trade & Reference Div.

Godfrey, Rebecca. Torn Skirt. 2002. (gr. 7-12). lib. bdg. 21.05 (978-0-613-60626-4(4)) Tandem Library Bks.

Horton, Babs. Dandelion Soup. l.t. ed. 2005. (Charnwood Large Print Ser.). (Illus.). 504p. 32.50 (978-1-84395-621-1(7)) Ulverscroft Large Print Bks. GBR. *Dist:* Ulverscroft Large Print Bks., Ltd.

Ibbotson, Eva. The Star of Kazan. 2006. (Illus.). 416p. (J). (gr. 3). reprint ed. 6.99 (978-0-14-240582-6(5) , Puffin) Penguin Group (USA) Inc.

The Last Wild Run. 2006. (J). per. 14.95 (978-1-933791-05-0(5)) Finial Publishing.

Leavitt, Martine. Heck, Superhero! 2004. 144p. (YA). 16.95 (978-1-886910-94-2(4) , Lemniscaat) Boyds Mills Pr.

Lyon, Steve. The Gift Moves. 2004. 240p. (YA). (gr. 5-9). tchr. ed. 15.00 (978-0-618-39128-8(2)) Houghton Mifflin Co. Trade & Reference Div.

McCaffrey, Anne. Acorna: The Unicorn Girl. 2001. (Acorna Ser.). lib. bdg. 15.90 (978-0-613-55549-4(X)) Tandem Library Bks.

McMullan, Margaret. When I Crossed No-Bob. 2007. 224p. (J). (gr. 5-9). 16.00 ***(978-0-618-71715-6(3))** Houghton Mifflin Co. Trade & Reference Div.

Nolan, Han. Born Blue. (YA). 2003. 300p. pap. 6.95 (978-0-15-204697-2(6) , Harcourt Paperbacks); 2001. 288p. (gr. 9 up). 17.00 (978-0-15-201916-7(2)) Harcourt Children's Bks.

—Born Blue. 2003. (gr. 7-12). lib. bdg. 15.25 (978-0-613-59882-8(2)) Tandem Library Bks.

Patron, Susan. The Higher Power of Lucky. Phelan, Matt, illus. 2006. 144p. (J). (gr. 4-6). 16.95 (978-1-4169-0194-5(9) , Atheneum/Richard Jackson Bks.) Simon & Schuster Children's Publishing.

Price, Susan. The Wolf's Footprint. 2003. (Illus.). 96p. pap. (978-0-340-85589-8(4) , Hodder Children's Books) Hodder Children's Division.

Stewart, Paul & Riddell, Chris. Edge Chronicles 1: Beyond the Deepwoods. 2008. (Edge Chronicles Ser.). 288p. (J). (gr. 5-7). 6.99 (***978-0-440-42087-3(3)*** , Yearling) Random Hse. Children's Bks.

Van Draanen, Wendelin. Sammy Keyes & the Search for Snake Eyes. VanDraanen, Wendelin, illus. 2003. (Sammy Keyes Ser.: Bk. 7). pap. 36.95 incl. audio (978-1-59112-273-9(2)); pap. 54.95 incl. audio compact disk (978-1-59112-281-4(3)) Live Oak Media.

—Sammy Keyes & the Search for Snake Eyes. (Sammy Keyes Ser.: Bk. 7). (gr. 5). 2003. 320p. (J). pap. 5.99 (978-0-440-41900-6(X) , Yearling); 2002. 272p. lib. bdg. 17.99 (978-0-375-91175-0(8) , Knopf Bks. for Young Readers) Random Hse. Children's Bks.

White, Ruth. The Search for Belle Prater. 2005. (Illus.). 176p. (J). (gr. 8-12). 16.00 (978-0-374-30853-7(5) , Farrar, Straus & Giroux (BYR)) Farrar, Straus & Giroux.

—The Search for Belle Prater. 2007. 176p. (J). (gr. 4-7). 6.50 (978-0-440-42164-1(0) , Yearling) Random Hse. Children's Bks.

—The Search for Belle Prater. l.t. ed. 2006. 205p. (J). 23.95 (978-0-7862-8278-4(9)) Thorndike Pr.

Williams, Carol Lynch. The True Colors of Caitlynne Jackson. 1998. (J). (978-0-606-13873-4(0)) Tandem Library Bks.

Wilson, Jacqueline. Dustbin Baby. Sharratt, Nick, illus. l.t. ed. 2002. (J). 16.95 (978-0-7540-7828-9(0) , Galaxy Children's Large Print) BBC Audiobooks America.

ABANDONED TOWNS

see Cities and Towns, Ruined, Extinct, Etc.

ABDUL-JABBAR, KAREEM, 1947-

Kneib, Martha. Kareem Abdul-Jabbar. 2002. (Basketball Hall of Famers Ser.). (Illus.). 112p. (YA). (gr. 5-8). lib. bdg. 29.25 (978-0-8239-3483-6(7) , Rosen Central) Rosen Publishing Group, Inc., The.

ABERNATHY, TEMPLE, 1904-1987

Jackson, Robert B. The Remarkable Ride of the Abernathy Boys. 2003. (Land We Belong to Is Grand Ser.). (Illus.). 69p. (J). pap. (978-1-57168-798-2(X) , Eakin Pr.) Eakin Pr.

ABNORMAL PSYCHOLOGY

see Psychology, Pathological

ABOLITION OF SLAVERY

see Abolitionists

ABOLITIONISTS

Adler, David A. Enemies of Slavery. Smith, Donald A., illus. 2004. 32p. (J). (gr. k-3). tchr. ed. 16.95 (978-0-8234-1596-0(1)) Holiday Hse., Inc.

—A Picture Book of Frederick Douglass. Byrd, Samuel, illus. unabr. ed. 2005. (Picture Book Readalongs Ser.). (J). (gr. k-4). 25.95 incl. audio (978-1-59519-373-5(1)); pap. 28.95 incl. audio compact disk (978-1-59519-377-3(4)); Set. pap. 37.95 incl. audio (978-1-59519-374-2(X)); Set. pap. 39.95 incl. audio compact disk (978-1-59519-378-0(2)) Live Oak Media.

—A Picture Book of Harriet Beecher Stowe. Bootman, Colin, illus. 2003. 32p. (J). (gr. k-3). 6.95 (978-0-8234-1878-7(2)); tchr. ed. 16.95 (978-0-8234-1646-2(1)) Holiday Hse., Inc.

Belmonte, Kevin Charles. A Journey Through the Life of William Wilberforce: The Abolitionist Who Changed the Face of a Nation. 2006. (Illus.). 122p. (J). (***978-0-89221-671-0(9)***) New Leaf Pr., Inc.

Brezina, Corona. Sojourner Truth's "Ain't I a Woman?" Speech: A Primary Source Investigation. 2004. (Great Historic Debates & Speeches Ser.). (Illus.). 64p. (J). lib. bdg. 29.95 (978-1-4042-0154-5(8)) Rosen Publishing Group, Inc., The.

Burgan, Michael. Escaping to Freedom: The Underground Railroad. 2006. (Slavery in the Americas Ser.). (Illus.). 112p. (J). (gr. 4-9). 35.00 (978-0-8160-6137-2(8)) Facts On File, Inc.

Butler, Mary G. Sojourner Truth: From Slave to Activist for Freedom. 2005. (Library of American Lives & Times). (Illus.). 112p. (YA). (gr. 4-8). lib. bdg. 31.95 (978-0-8239-5736-1(5)) Rosen Publishing Group, Inc., The.

Clinton, Catherine. Underground Railroad. 2007. 32p. (J). lib. bdg. 17.89 (978-0-06-050426-7(9)) HarperCollins Pubs.

—When Harriet Met Sojourner. Evans, Shane, illus. 2007. 32p. (J). (gr. k-2). 16.99 (978-0-06-050425-0(0)) HarperCollins Pubs.

Cloud Tapper, Suzanne. The Abolition of Slavery: Fighting for a Free America. 2006. (American Saga Ser.). (Illus.). 128p. (J). (gr. 5 up). lib. bdg. 31.93 (978-0-7660-2605-6(1)) Enslow Pubs., Inc.

Collins, Kathleen. Sojourner Truth: Equal Rights Advocate. 2003. (Famous People in American History Ser.). (Illus.). 32p. (J). pap. 6.50 (978-0-8239-4193-3(0)) Rosen Publishing Group, Inc., The.

De Angelis, Gina. Lucretia Mott: Woman Suffragist. 2000. (Women of Achievement Ser.). (Illus.). 112p. (J). (gr. 4-7). 30.00 (978-0-7910-5295-2(8) , Chelsea Hse.) Facts On File, Inc.

DeVillers, David. The John Brown Slavery Revolt Trial: A Headline Court Case. 2000. (Headline Court Cases Ser.). (Illus.). 104p. (YA). (gr. 6-12). lib. bdg. 26.60 (978-0-7660-1385-8(5)) Enslow Pubs., Inc.

Donlan, Leni. Following Freedom: The Underground Railroad. 2006. (American History Through Primary Sources Ser.). (Illus.). 32p. (J). (gr. 2-4). lib. bdg. 28.21 (978-1-4109-2418-6(1)) Raintree.

—Following Freedom: The Underground Railroad. 2006. (American History Through Primary Sources Ser.). (Illus.). 32p. (J). pap. 7.99 (978-1-4109-2429-2(7)) Steck-Vaughn.

Edwards, Judith. Abolitionists & Slave Resistance: Breaking the Chains of Slavery. 2004. (Slavery in American History Ser.). (Illus.). 128p. (J). lib. bdg. 26.60 (978-0-7660-2155-6(6)) Enslow Pubs., Inc.

Empak Publishing Company Staff. Historic Black Abolitionists: A Gift of Heritage. ("Black History" Publication Ser.). 2.50 (978-0-922162-80-2(8)) Empak Publishing Co.

Fauchald, Nick. William Lloyd Garrison: Abolitionist & Journalist. 2004. (Signature Lives Ser.). (Illus.). 112p. (J). 30.60 (978-0-7565-0819-7(3) , 1240146) Compass Point Bks.

Fleming, Alice Mulcahey. Frederick Douglass: From Slave to Statesman. 2005. (Library of American Lives & Times). (Illus.). 112p. (J). (gr. 4-8). lib. bdg. 31.95 (978-0-8239-6624-0(0)) Rosen Publishing Group, Inc., The.

Fradin, Dennis Brindell. Bound for the North Star: True Stories of Fugitive Slaves. 2000. (Illus.). 224p. (J). (gr. 7-12). tchr. ed. 20.00 (978-0-395-97017-1(2) , Clarion Bks.) Houghton Mifflin Co. Trade & Reference Div.

Frost, Helen. Sojourner Truth. Saunders-Smith, Gail, ed. 2003. (Famous Americans Ser.). (Illus.). 24p. (J). (gr. k-1). lib. bdg. 15.93 (978-0-7368-1640-3(2) , Pebble Bks.) Capstone Pr., Inc.

Gillis, Jennifer Blizin. Sojourner Truth. 2005. (Illus.). 32p. (J). (978-1-4034-6981-6(4)); pap. (978-1-4034-6988-5(1)) Heinemann Library.

Griskey, Michele. Harriet Beecher Stowe. 2005. (Classic Storytellers Ser.). (Illus.). 48p. (J). lib. bdg. 29.95 (978-1-58415-375-7(X)) Mitchell Lane Pubs., Inc.

Haugen, Brenda. Frederick Douglass: Slave, Writer, Abolitionist. 2004. (Signature Lives Ser.). (Illus.). 112p. (J). 30.60 (978-0-7565-0818-0(5) , 1240139) Compass Point Bks.

—Harriet Beecher Stowe: Author & Advocate. 2004. (Signature Lives Ser.). (Illus.). 112p. (J). 30.60 (978-0-7565-0822-7(3) , 1240140) Compass Point Bks.

Hill, Mary. Harriet Beecher Stowe. 2003. (Welcome Book Ser.). (Illus.). 24p. (J). 18.00 (978-0-516-25865-2(6) , Children's Pr.) Scholastic Library Publishing.

Jacobs, Harriet A. Narrative of the Life of Frederick Douglass, an American Slave & Incidents In. 2000. (gr. 7-12). lib. bdg. 19.90 (978-0-613-50133-0(0)) Tandem Library Bks.

Jaffe, Elizabeth Dana. Sojourner Truth. 2001. (Compass Point Early Biographies Ser.). (Illus.). 32p. (J). (gr. 2 up). lib. bdg. 21.26 (978-0-7565-0068-9(0)) Compass Point Bks.

Kallen, Stuart A. The Civil War & Reconstruction. 2001. (Black History Ser.). (Illus.). 48p. (J). (gr. 3-8). lib. bdg. 25.65 (978-1-57765-469-8(2) , ABDO & Daughters) ABDO Publishing Co.

Katz, William Loren. Black Pioneers: An Untold Story. 1999. (Illus.). 208p. (YA). (gr. 7 up). 21.99 (978-0-689-81410-5(0) , Atheneum) Simon & Schuster Children's Publishing.

Kiely Miller, Barbara. Frederick Douglass. 2007. (J). pap. (***978-0-8368-8322-0(5)*** , Weekly Reader Early Learning Library) Stevens, Gareth Inc.

Krass, Peter. Sojourner Truth. 2004. (Black Americans of Achievement Ser.). (Illus.). 112p. (J). (gr. 6-12). 30.00 (978-0-7910-8165-5(6) , Chelsea Hse.) Facts On File, Inc.

—Sojourner Truth: Antislavery Activist. 2005. (Black Americans of Achievement Ser.). (Illus.). 112p. (J). (gr. 6-12). pap. 13.25 (978-0-7910-8339-0(X) , Chelsea Hse.) Facts On File, Inc.

Krebs, Laurie. A Day in the Life of a Colonial Sailmaker. 2004. (Library of Living & Working in Colonial Times). (Illus.). 24p. (J). lib. bdg. 18.75 (978-0-8239-6231-0(8) , PowerKids Pr.) Rosen Publishing Group, Inc., The.

Krohn, Katherine E. Sojourner Truth. 2005. (Fact Finders Ser.). (Illus.). 32p. (J). (978-0-7368-4348-5(5)) Capstone Pr., Inc.

Kudlinski, Kathleen. Sojourner Truth. 2003. (gr. 3-6). lib. bdg. 13.00 (978-0-613-61658-4(8)) Tandem Library Bks.

—Sojourner Truth: Voice for Freedom. Wooden, Lenny, illus. 2003. (Childhood of Famous Americans Ser.). 160p. (Orig.). mass mkt. 5.99 (978-0-689-85274-9(6) , Aladdin) Simon & Schuster Children's Publishing.

Landau, Elaine. The Abolitionist Movement. 2004. (Cornerstones of Freedom Ser.). (Illus.). 48p. (J). 26.00 (978-0-516-24202-6(4) , Children's Pr.) Scholastic Library Publishing.

—Fleeing to Freedom on the Underground Railroad: The Courageous Slaves, Agents, & Conductors. 2006. (People's History Ser.). (Illus.). 88p. (J). 29.27 (978-0-8225-3490-7(8) , Twenty-First Century Bks.) Lerner Publishing Group.

Lassieur, Allison. The Underground Railroad: An Interactive History Adventure. 2008. (You Choose Bks.). 112p. (J). (gr. 3-7). lib. bdg. 27.23 (***978-1-4296-0164-1(7)***) Capstone Pr., Inc.

Leebrick, Kristal. Sojourner Truth. 2002. (Let Freedom Ring Ser.). (Illus.). 48p. (J). (gr. 3-4). lib. bdg. 22.60 (978-0-7368-1090-6(0) , Bridgestone Bks.) Capstone Pr., Inc.

Lilley, Stephen R. Fighters Against American Slavery. 1998. (History Makers Ser.). (Illus.). 128p. (YA). (gr. 7-10). 27.45 (978-1-56006-036-9(0) , Lucent Bks.) Thomson Gale.

Lutz, Norma Jean. Sojourner Truth. 2001. (gr. 5-8). lib. bdg. 17.60 (978-0-613-33074-9(9)) Tandem Library Bks.

—Sojourner Truth: Abolitionist, Suffragist, & Preacher. (Famous Figures of the Civil War Era Ser.). (Illus.). 80p. (J). (gr. 4-7). 2001. 25.00 (978-0-7910-6007-0(1)); 2000. pap. 25.00 (978-0-7910-6145-9(0)) Facts On File, Inc. (Chelsea Hse.).

Malam, John. Sojourner Truth. 2000. (Tell Me about Ser.). (Illus.). 22p. (J). 16.95 (978-0-237-51972-8(0) , Evans Brothers, Limited) Evans Publishing Group GBR. *Dist:* Independent Pubs. Group.

Mattern, Joanne. Sojourner Truth: Early Abolitionist. 2003. (Reading Power Ser.). (Illus.). 24p. (J). lib. bdg. 17.25 (978-0-8239-6502-1(3) , PowerKids Pr.) Rosen Publishing Group, Inc., The.

—Sojourner Truth: Early Abolitionist: Individual Title Six-Packs. (On Deck Ser.: Vol. 2). 24p. (gr. 4-5). 35.00 (978-0-7578-5846-8(5)) Rigby Education.

Mayer, Cassie. Frederick Douglass. 2007. (J). (***978-1-4034-9974-5(8)***); pap. (***978-1-4034-9983-7(7)***) Heinemann Library.

McDougal, Littell Staff, contrib. by. A Nation Dividing 1800-1860. 2004. (Stories in History Ser.). (Illus.). 176p. (gr. 6-12). 13.32 (978-0-618-14222-4(3) , 2-00242) McDougal Littell Inc.

McKissack, Patricia C. & McKissack, Fredrick L. Sojourner Truth: A Voice for Freedom. rev. ed. 2002. (Great African Americans Ser.). (Illus.). 32p. (J). (gr. 1-4). lib. bdg. 18.60 (978-0-7660-1693-4(5)) Enslow Pubs., Inc.

McPherson, Stephanie Sammartino. Sisters Against Slavery: A Story about Sarah & Angelina Grimke. Ritz, Karen, illus. 64p. (J). pap. 22.60 (978-1-57505-815-3(4)); 1999. (gr. 3-6). lib. bdg. 21.27 (978-1-57505-361-5(6) , Carolrhoda Bks.) Lerner Publishing Group.

Miller, Barbara Kiely. Frederick Douglass. 2007. (Great Americans Ser.). 24p. (J). (gr. 2-4). lib. bdg. 19.93 (***978-0-8368-8315-2(2)*** , Weekly Reader Early Learning Library) Stevens, Gareth Inc.

Moore, Barbara R. Sojourner Truth. 2005. (Illus.). 16p. (J). (***978-0-618-56039-4(4)***) Houghton Mifflin Co.

Pierce, Alan. The Underground Railroad. 2005. (American Moments Ser.). (Illus.). 48p. (J). (gr. 4-8). lib. bdg. 25.65 (978-1-59197-942-5(0)) ABDO Publishing Co.

Randolph, Ryan P. Harriet Beecher Stowe: Author & Abolitionist. 2005. (Library of American Lives & Times). (Illus.). 112p. (J). (gr. 4-8). lib. bdg. 31.95 (978-0-8239-6623-3(2)) Rosen Publishing Group, Inc., The.

Rappaport, Doreen. Freedom River. Collier, Bryan, illus. 32p. (gr. k-4). 2000. 14.99 (978-0-7868-0350-7(9)); 2007. pap. 6.99 (***978-1-4231-0634-0(2)***) Hyperion Bks. for Children. (Jump at the Sun).

Rau, Dana Meachen. Frederick Douglass. 2003. (Compass Point Early Biographies Ser.). (Illus.). 32p. (J). (gr. 2 up). lib. bdg. 21.26 (978-0-7565-0418-2(X)) Compass Point Bks.

Rockwell, Anne. Only Passing Through: The Story of Sojourner Truth. Christie, R. Gregory, illus. 2002. 40p. (J). (gr. 2-5). pap. 6.99 (978-0-440-41766-8(X) , Dragonfly Bks.) Random Hse. Children's Bks.

Rockwell, Anne F. Only Passing Through. 2002. (gr. 3-6). lib. bdg. 15.30 (978-0-613-86684-2(3)) Tandem Library Bks.

—Only Passing Through: The Story of Sojourner Truth. Siscoe, Nancy, ed. Christie, R. Gregory, illus. 2000. 40p. (J). (gr. 2-5). 16.95 (978-0-679-89186-4(2)); lib. bdg. 18.99 (978-0-679-99186-1(7)) Random Hse. Children's Bks. (Knopf Bks. for Young Readers).

Roop, Connie & Roop, Peter. Sojourner Truth. 2003. (In Their Own Words Ser.). (Illus.). 128p. (J). (gr. 2-5). 4.99 (978-0-439-26323-8(9) , Scholastic Nonfiction) Scholastic, Inc.

Roop, Peter. Sojourner Truth. 2002. (gr. 3-6). lib. bdg. 12.40 (978-0-613-66669-5(0)) Tandem Library Bks.

Rosen, Daniel. Dred Scott & the Supreme Court. 2006. (Navigators Ser.). (J). pap. 42.00 (***978-1-4108-6258-7(5)***) Benchmark Education Co.

Ruffin, Frances E. Frederick Douglass: Rising up from Slavery. 2008. (Sterling Biographies Ser.). (Illus.). 128p. (J). pap. 5.95 (***978-1-4027-4118-0(9)***) Sterling Publishing Co., Inc.

—Her Story, Her Words: The Narrative of Sojourner Truth. 2004. (Great Moments in American History Ser.). (Illus.). 32p. (gr. 4-8). lib. bdg. 21.25 (978-0-8239-4387-6(9) , Rosen Central) Rosen Publishing Group, Inc., The.

—Sojourner Truth. 2002. (American Legends Ser.). (Illus.). 24p. (J). (gr. 3). lib. bdg. 18.75 (978-0-8239-5826-9(4) , PowerKids Pr.) Rosen Publishing Group, Inc., The.

Russell, Sharman Apt. Frederick Douglass: Abolitionist Editor. (Black Americans of Achievement Ser.). (Illus.). 112p. (gr. 6-12). 2005. pap. 13.25 (978-0-7910-8331-4(4)); 2004. 30.00 (978-0-7910-8157-0(5)) Facts On File, Inc. (Chelsea Hse.).

Schaefer, Lola M. Frederick Douglass. Saunders-Smith, Gail, ed. 2002. (First Biographies Ser.). (Illus.). 24p. (J). (gr. k-1). lib. bdg. 15.93 (978-0-7368-1174-3(5) , Pebble Bks.) Capstone Pr., Inc.

Slade, Suzanne. Frederick Douglass: Writer, Speaker, & Opponent of Slavery. McGuire, Robert, illus. 2006. (Biographies Ser.). 24p. (J). (gr. k-3). lib. bdg. 23.93 (***978-1-4048-3102-5(9)***) Picture Window Bks.

—Sojourner Truth: Preacher for Freedom & Equality. Blanks, Natascha Alex, illus. 2007. (J). lib. bdg. (***978-1-4048-3726-3(4)***) Picture Window Bks.

Spengler, Kremena. Frederick Douglass: Voice for Freedom. 2006. (Fact Finders Ser.). (Illus.). 32p. (J). 22.60 (978-0-7368-5434-4(7) , Fact Finders) Capstone Pr., Inc.

Stein, R. Conrad. Escaping Slavery on the Underground Railroad. 2008. (From Many Cultures, One History Ser.). (Illus.). 128p. (J). (gr. 5 up). lib. bdg. 31.93 (***978-0-7660-2799-2(6)***) Enslow Pubs., Inc.

Stein, R. Conrad. John Brown's Raid on Harpers Ferry in American History. 1999. (In American History Ser.). (Illus.). 128p. (YA). (gr. 5-12). lib. bdg. 26.60 (978-0-7660-1123-6(2)) Enslow Pubs., Inc.

Strangis, Joel. Lewis Hayden & the War Against Slavery. 1999. (Illus.). xiv, 167p. (YA). (gr. 9 up). 25.00 (978-0-208-02430-5(1) , Linnet Bks.) Shoe String Pr., Inc.

Streissguth, Thomas. John Brown. Ramstad, Ralph L., illus. 1999. (On My Own Biographies Ser.). 48p. (J). (gr. 1-3). lib. bdg. 23.93 (978-1-57505-334-9(9) , Carolrhoda Bks.) Lerner Publishing Group.

Swain, Gwenyth. President of the Underground Railroad: A Story about Levi Coffin. Ramstad, Ralph L., illus. (Creative Minds Biographies Ser.). 64p. (J). (gr. 3-6). 2003. 6.95 (978-1-57505-552-7(X)); 2001. lib. bdg. 22.60 (978-1-57505-551-0(1) , Carolrhoda Bks.) Lerner Publishing Group.

—President of the Underground Railroad: A Story of Levi Coffin. 2001. (gr. 3-6). lib. bdg. 15.25 (978-0-613-68377-7(3)) Tandem Library Bks.

—Sojourner Truth. Archambault, Matthew, illus. 2005. (On My Own Biography Ser.). 48p. (J). (ps-ps). pap. 5.95 (978-1-57505-827-6(8)) Lerner Publishing Group.

—Sojourner Truth. 2005. (On My Own Biography Ser.). (Illus.). 48p. (J). 25.26 (978-1-57505-651-7(8) , Carolrhoda Bks.) Lerner Publishing Group.

Trumbauer, Lisa. Let's Meet Sojourner Truth. 2003. (Let's Meet Biographies Ser.). (Illus.). 32p. (gr. 2-4). 23.00 (978-0-7910-7323-0(8) , Chelsea Hse.) Facts On File, Inc.

Waxman, Laura Hamilton. Sojourner Truth. 2008. (History Maker Biographies Ser.). (J). lib. bdg. 26.60 (***978-0-8225-7172-8(2)*** , Lerner Pubns.) Lerner Publishing Group.

Weidt, Maryann N. Voice of Freedom: A Story about Frederick Douglass. Reeves, Jeni, illus. (Creative Minds Biographies Ser.). 64p. (J). (gr. 3-6). 2003. 6.95 (978-1-57505-553-4(8)); 2001. lib. bdg. 22.60 (978-1-57505-459-9(0) , Carolrhoda Bks.) Lerner Publishing Group.

—Voice of Freedom: A Story about Frederick Douglass. Reeves, Jeni, illus. 2001. 64p. (J). (ps-3). lib. bdg. 15.25 (978-0-613-68475-0(3)) Tandem Library Bks.

Welch, Catherine A. Frederick Douglass. 2003. (History Maker Bios Ser.). (Illus.). 48p. (J). (gr. 4-7). pap. 6.95 (978-0-8225-4802-7(X)); (gr. 3-5). lib. bdg. 26.60 (978-0-8225-4672-6(8)) Lerner Publishing Group.

Weymouth Seguin, Marilyn. The Freedom Stairs: The Story of Adam Lowry Rankin, Underground Railroad Conductor. 2004. (Illus.). 93p. (J). (ps-7). per. 12.95 net. (978-0-8283-2084-9(5)) Branden Bks.

Whalin, W. Terry. Sojourner Truth: American Abolitionist. Landgraf, Ken, illus. 1999. (Young Reader's Christian Library). 222p. (J). (gr. 8-12). pap. 1.39 (978-1-57748-515-5(7)) Barbour Publishing, Inc.

—Sojourner Truth: American Abolitionist. 1999. (Heroes of the Faith Ser.). 208p. (YA). (gr. 4-7). 14.95 (978-0-7910-5034-7(3) , Chelsea Hse.) Facts On File, Inc.

Wilson, Camilla. Frederick Douglass: A Voice for Freedom in the 1800s. 2003. (Scholastic Biography Ser.). (Illus.). 90p. (J). pap. (978-0-439-38082-9(0)) Scholastic, Inc.

Yancey, Diane. Frederick Douglass. 2002. (Heroes & Villains Ser.). (Illus.). 112p. (J). 28.70 (978-1-56006-950-8(3) , Lucent Bks.) Thomson Gale.

ABOLITIONISTS—FICTION

Bryant, Louella. Father by Blood. 1999. (Illus.). 160p. (YA). (gr. 6-8). pap. 12.95 (978-1-881535-33-1(9)) New England Pr., Inc., The.

Kay, Alan N. On the Trail of John Brown's Body. 2001. (Young Heroes of History Ser.: Vol. 2). (Illus.). 175p. (J). (gr. 4-7). pap. 5.95 (978-1-57249-239-4(2) , 1572492406, Burd Street Pr.) White Mane Publishing Co., Inc.

Kirby, Susan E. Hattie's Story. 2000. (American Quilts Ser.: Vol. 2). (J). 11.64 (978-0-606-20080-6(0)) Tandem Library Bks.

Lasky, Kathryn. True North: A Novel of the Underground Railroad. 1998. (J). (978-0-606-13874-1(9)) Tandem Library Bks.

Lyons, Mary E. & Branch, Muriel M. Dear Ellen Bee: A Civil War Scrapbook of Two Union Spies. Tauss, Marc, illus. 2000. 176p. (J). (gr. 4 up). 21.99 (978-0-689-82379-4(7) , Atheneum) Simon & Schuster Children's Publishing.

Pryor, Bonnie. Joseph: 1861 - A Rumble of War. Dodson, Bert, illus. 1999. (American Adventures Ser.). 176p. (J). (gr. 3-7). 14.95 (978-0-688-15671-8(1)) HarperCollins Pubs.

—Joseph: 1861 - A Rumble of War. 2000. (Illus.). (J). (978-0-606-17975-1(5)) Tandem Library Bks.

—Joseph: 1861—A Rumble of War. 2000. (American Adventures Ser.). (Illus.). 176p. (J). (gr. 3-7). pap. 4.50 (978-0-380-73103-9(7) , Harper Trophy) HarperCollins Pubs.

Rees, Douglas. Lightning Time. 1999. (J). (978-0-606-19069-5(4)) Tandem Library Bks.

Rinaldi, Ann. Mine Eyes Have Seen. 2002. (978-0-606-22271-6(5)) Tandem Library Bks.

Smiley, Jane. The All-True Travels & Adventures of Lidie Newton: A Novel. 1999. (gr. 7-12). lib. bdg. 23.45 (978-0-613-17077-2(6)) Tandem Library Bks.

ABORTION

Bacon, Lizzy. Abortion. 2004. (World Issues Ser.). (J). lib. bdg. 28.50 (978-1-59389-157-2(1)) Chrysalis Education.

Bernay, Emma. Abortion Controversy 2007. 2007. (Current Controversies Ser.). 240p. (J). (gr. 10-12). pap. 24.95 (***978-0-7377-3274-0(1)***); 36.20 (***978-0-7377-3273-3(3)***) Thomson Gale. (Greenhaven Pr., Inc.).

A B

Cassidy, Patrice. Teen Pregnancy. 2001. (Teen Issues Ser.). (Illus.). 104p. (J). (gr. 4-12). lib. bdg. 27.45 (978-1-56006-515-9(X) , LML00902-177873, Lucent Bks.) Thomson Gale.

Durrett, Deanne. The Abortion Conflict: A Pro/Con Issue. 2000. (Hot Pro/Con Issues Ser.). (Illus.). 64p. (J). (gr. 6-12). lib. bdg. 27.93 (978-0-7660-1193-9(3)) Enslow Pubs., Inc.

Gay, Kathlyn. Abortion: Understanding the Debate. 2004. (Issues in Focus Ser.). (Illus.). 128p. (J). lib. bdg. 26.60 (978-0-7660-2162-4(9)) Enslow Pubs., Inc.

Gold, Susan Dudley. Roe V. Wade: A Women's Choice. 2004. (Supreme Court Milestones Ser.). (Illus.). 144p. (J). 37.07 (978-0-7614-1839-9(3) , Benchmark Bks.) Cavendish, Marshall Corp.

Hitchcock, Susan Tyler & McNeese, Tim. Roe V. Wade: Protecting a Woman's Right to Choose. 2006. (Great Supreme Court Decisions Ser.). (Illus.). 128p. (J). (gr. 5-8). 30.00 (978-0-7910-9239-2(9) , Chelsea Hse.) Facts On File, Inc.

Juettner, Bonnie. Abortion. 2007. (J). ***(978-1-60217-020-9(7))*** Erickson Pr.

Lassieur, Allison. Abortion. rev. ed. 2001. (Overview Ser.). (Illus.). 96p. (YA). (gr. 6-9). lib. bdg. 29.95 (978-1-56006-818-1(3) , LML00902-178150, Lucent Bks.) Thomson Gale.

Marcovitz, Hal. Abortion. 2006. (Gallup Major Trends & Events Ser.). (Illus.). 112p. (J). (gr. 7 up). lib. bdg. (978-1-59084-962-0(0) , 1260827) Mason Crest Pubs.

Mary E. Williams. Abortion. 2006. (Writing the Critical Essay Ser.). 244p. (gr. 6-10). 29.95 (978-0-7377-3576-5(7) , Greenhaven Pr., Inc.) Thomson Gale.

Naden, Corinne J. Abortion. 2007. (Open for Debate Ser.). (J). lib. bdg. ***(978-0-7614-2573-1(X)*** , Benchmark Bks.) Cavendish, Marshall Corp.

Piehl, Norah. Abortion. 2006. (Social Issues Firsthand Ser.). 224p. 29.95 (978-0-7377-2492-9(7) , Greenhaven Pr., Inc.) Thomson Gale.

Reynolds, Marilyn. But What about Me? 2003. 192p. (J). (gr. 7-12). pap. 8.95 (978-1-885356-10-9(2) , 56102) Morning Glory Pr., Inc.

Torr, James D. Problems of Death. 2000. (Opposing Viewpoints Ser.). (Illus.). 189p. (YA). (gr. 10-12). pap. 24.95 (978-0-7377-0349-8(0)); 36.20 (978-0-7377-0350-4(4)) Thomson Gale. (Greenhaven Pr., Inc.).

ABORTION—FICTION

Brinkerhoff, Shirley. Second Choices. 2000. (Nikki Sheridan Ser.: Vol. 6). (Illus.). 160p. (YA). (gr. 9-13). pap. 5.99 (978-1-56179-880-3(0)) Bethany Hse. Pubs.

—Second Choices. 2000. (gr. 7-12). lib. bdg. 14.15 (978-0-613-82302-9(8)) Tandem Library Bks.

Cohn, Rachel. Gingerbread. 2002. (Illus.). 176p. (J). (gr. 9 up). 15.95 (978-0-689-84337-2(2)) Simon & Schuster Children's Publishing.

—Gingerbread. 2003. (gr. 7-12). lib. bdg. 15.30 (978-0-613-60473-4(3)) Tandem Library Bks.

Cohn, Rachel & Wattenberg, Jane. Gingerbread. 2003. 176p. (YA). pap. 6.99 (978-0-689-86020-1(X) , Simon Pulse) Simon & Schuster Children's Publishing.

Hamilton, Elizabeth L. Date with Responsibility. 2004. (Character-in-Action Ser.: No. 2). (Illus.). 384p. (YA). per. 19.95 (978-0-9713749-0-4(2) , Character-in-Action) Quiet Impact, Inc.

Reynolds, Marilyn. No More Sad Goodbyes. 2007. (Hamilton High Ser.). 192p. (YA). 18.95 ***(978-1-932538-72-4(0));*** pap. 9.95 ***(978-1-932538-71-7(2))*** Morning Glory Pr., Inc.

ABRAHAM (BIBLICAL PATRIARCH)

Abraham. (Divertidas Historias Biblicas para Ninos Ser.). (SPA.). (J). 3.49 (978-0-7899-0600-7(7) , 496647) Editorial Unilit.

Abraham: Serie para Ninos Amigos de la Biblia. 2000. pap. (978-1-57697-787-3(0)) United Bible Societies/ Americas Service Ctr.

Arthur, Kay & Arndt, Janna. Abraham - God's Brave Explorer: Genesis 11-25. 2003. (Discover 4 Yourself Inductive Bible Studies for Kids Ser.). 208p. pap., wbk. ed. 10.99 (978-0-7369-0936-5(2) , 6909362) Harvest Hse. Pubs.

Brand, Ruth Redding. Abraham. White, John & Tank, Darrel, illus. 2004. (Family Bible Story Ser.). 109p. (J). 19.99 (978-0-8280-1856-2(1) , 010-570) Review & Herald Publishing Assn.

De Graaf, Anne. Abraham. 1999. (Little Children's Bible Bks.). (Illus.). 38p. (J). 5.99 (978-0-8054-1897-2(0)) B&H Publishing Grp.

Frank, Penny. Abraham, Friend of God. 1999. (Lion Story Bible Ser.). (Illus.). 24p. pap. 2.99 (978-0-7459-4104-2(4) , Lion) Lion Hudson plc GBR. *Dist:* Independent Pubs. Group.

Haus, Cari. Father of Many Nations. 2007. (Illus.). 112p. (J). pap. 9.99 ***(978-0-8127-0468-6(1))*** Autumn Hse. Publishing Co.

Lepon, Shoshana. The Ten Tests of Avraham. Friedman, Aaron, illus. 2000. (J). (ps-3). 12.95 (978-1-880582-61-9(9)) Judaica Pr., Inc., The.

—The Ten Tests of Avraham. 2000. (J). (ps-3). pap. 9.95 (978-1-880582-70-1(8)) Judaica Pr., Inc., The.

Nederveld, Patricia L. Count the Stars! The Story of God's Promise to Abraham & Sarah. 1998. (God Loves Me Ser.). (Illus.). 24p. (J). (ps-3). pap. 2.95 (978-1-56212-276-8(2) , 001207, Faith Alive Christian Resources) CRC Pubns.

Racklin-Siegel, Carol, illus. Lech Lecha: The Story of Abraham & Rebecca. 2004. (HEB & ENG.). (J). per. 8.50 (978-0-939144-49-5(2)) EKS Publishing Co.

van Rijswijk, Cor. Abraham's Sacrifice. Visser, Rino, illus. 2001. 43p. (J). pap. (978-1-894666-21-3(6)) Inheritance Pubns.

White, John & Tank, Darrel, illus. Abraham. 2004. (Family Bible Story Ser.). 109p. (J). pap. (978-0-8280-1857-9(X)) Review & Herald Publishing Assn.

Zauderer, Moshe. Abraham: Lessons for Our Time. 2000. 254p. (YA). (gr. 5-10). 24.95 (978-0-9675202-0-9(7)) Zichron Avos-Jewish Interactive Studies Foundation, Inc.

ABSENCE FROM SCHOOL

see School Attendance

ABSTINENCE, SEXUAL

see Sexual Abstinence

ABSTRACT ART

see Art, Abstract

ACADIANS

Harcourt School Publishers Staff. The Cajuns. 3rd ed. 2002. (Horizons Ser.). (Illus.). (J). pap. 5.50 (978-0-15-333403-0(7)) Harcourt Schl. Pubs.

ACCIDENTS

see also Disasters

Beech, Sandy. Worst Class Trip Ever. 2005. 173p. (J). ***(978-1-4156-0619-3(6)*** , Aladdin) Simon & Schuster Children's Publishing.

Beylon, Cathy. Hospital Emergency Room Sticker Activity Book. 2001. (Illus.). 4p. (J). pap. 1.50 (978-0-486-41626-7(7)) Dover Pubns., Inc.

Bonder, Dianna. Accidental Alphabet. Bonder, Dianna, illus. 2nd ed. 2004. (Illus.). 32p. (J). (ps-2). pap. 8.95 (978-1-55285-596-6(1)) Whitecap Bks., Ltd. CAN. *Dist:* Firefly Bks., Ltd.

Brubaker, Paul E. Apollo 1 Tragedy: Fire in the Capsule. 2002. (American Disasters Ser.). (Illus.). 48p. (J). (gr. 4-10). lib. bdg. 23.93 (978-0-7660-1787-0(7)) Enslow Pubs., Inc.

Bryan, Nichol. Bhopal: Chemical Plant Accident. 2003. (Environmental Disasters Ser.). (Illus.). 48p. (gr. 5 up). (YA). lib. bdg. 30.00 (978-0-8368-5503-6(5)); (J). pap. 11.95 (978-0-8368-5510-4(8)) Stevens, Gareth Inc. (World Almanac Library).

—Exxon Valdez: Oil Spill. 2003. (Environmental Disasters Ser.). (Illus.). 48p. (gr. 5 up). (J). pap. 11.95 (978-0-8368-5513-5(2)); (YA). lib. bdg. 30.00 (978-0-8368-5506-7(X)) Stevens, Gareth Inc. (World Almanac Library).

Gogerly, Liz. When Disaster Struck: The Challenger 1986. 2006. (Illus.). 56p. (J). (978-1-4109-2279-3(0)) Steck-Vaughn.

Hardy, Caroline. Through the Peephole Dangerous Places (Home Safety) Daykin, Louise, illus. 2006. (Through the Peephole Ser.). 48p. 9.95 (978-1-84560-013-6(4)) Mercury Bks. Ltd. GBR. *Dist:* International Publishers Marketing.

Hardy, Caroline, et al. Busy Places: A Child Safety Book. 2006. (Through the Peephole Ser.). (Illus.). 48p. 9.95 (978-1-84560-015-0(0)) Mercury Bks. Ltd. GBR. *Dist:* International Publishers Marketing.

Higgins, Chris. Nuclear Submarine Disasters. 2001. (Great Disasters, Reforms & Ramifications Ser.). (Illus.). 112p. (J). (gr. 6 up). 30.00 (978-0-7910-6329-3(1) , Chelsea Hse.) Facts On File, Inc.

Kate Shelley & the Midnight Express. 9.95 (978-1-59112-169-5(8)) Live Oak Media.

Koh, Frederick. The 10 Most Disastrous Accidents. 2008. (Tentrade; Ser.). 48p. (J). pap. 14.99 ***(978-1-55448-479-9(0)*** , Watts, Franklin) Scholastic Library Publishing.

Landau, Elaine. Spinal Cord Injuries. 2001. (Diseases & People Ser.). (Illus.). 128p. (J). (gr. 6-12). lib. bdg. 26.60 (978-0-7660-1474-9(6)) Enslow Pubs., Inc.

Mason, Paul. In the Environment. 2002. (Young Library). (Illus.). 32p. (J). lib. bdg. 25.69 (978-0-7398-6316-9(9)) Raintree.

Nelson, Robin. Jugar Sin Peligro. 2005. (Libros para Avanzar (Pull Ahead Bks.)). (SPA & ENG., Illus.). 32p. (J). (gr. 3-7). lib. bdg. 22.60 (978-0-8225-3146-3(1) , Ediciones Lerner) Lerner Publishing Group.

Parker, Victoria. Chernobyl 1986: An Explosion at a Nuclear Power Station. 2006. (When Disaster Struck Ser.). (Illus.). 56p. (J). (978-1-4109-2275-5(8)) Steck-Vaughn.

Parks, Peggy J. Driving under the Influence. 2007. (J). ***(978-1-60217-013-1(4))*** Erickson Pr.

Raatma, Lucia. Emergencies/911 Safety. 2003. (Living Well). (Illus.). 32p. (J). (gr. 2-6). 27.07 (978-1-59296-087-3(1)) Child's World, Inc.

Raymer, Dottie. Staying Home Alone: A Girl's Guide to Staying Safe & Having Fun. Scheuer, Lauren, illus. 2002. (American Girl Library). 72p. (J). pap. 7.95 (978-1-58485-506-4(1)) American Girl Publishing, Inc.

Townsend, John. When Disaster Struck: The Exxon Valdez 1989. 2006. (Illus.). 56p. (978-1-4109-2280-9(4)) Steck-Vaughn.

Vize, Dania. Emergency. Tattam, Mark, ed. 2006. (Lift Stick & Learn Ser.). (Illus.). 12p. (J). (ps-k). 4.95 (978-1-905051-69-4(7)) Make Believe Ideas GBR. *Dist:* Ingram Pub. Services.

Vogt, Gregory L. Disasters in Space Exploration. 2001. (Enthusiastic Astronomy Ser.). (Illus.). 72p. (gr. 5-8). lib. bdg. (978-0-7613-1920-7(4) , Millbrook Pr.) Lerner Publishing Group.

Walker, Linda. Living after Chernobyl: Ira's Story. 2005. (Illus.). 48p. (YA). (gr. 6-9). lib. bdg. 30.00 (978-0-8368-5957-7(X) , World Almanac Library) Stevens, Gareth Inc.

Walker, Niki. Transportation Disaster Alert! 2005. (Disaster Alert Ser.). (Illus.). 32p. (J). pap. (978-0-7787-1616-7(3)) Crabtree Publishing Co.

Werther, Scott P. Jon Krakauer's Adventure on Mt. Everest. 2002. (Survivors Ser.). (Illus.). 48p. (YA). (gr. 7-12). 24.00 (978-0-516-23902-6(3)); pap. 6.95 (978-0-516-23488-5(9)) Scholastic Library Publishing. (Children's Pr.).

When Disaster Strikes! 2005. (Illus.). 48p. (gr. 5-8). lib. bdg. 143.70 (978-0-8239-3892-6(1)) Rosen Publishing Group, Inc., The.

Woodford, Chris. Space Dramas. 2002. (Young Library - Space Busters Ser.). (Illus.). 32p. (J). (gr. 3-5). lib. bdg. 25.69 (978-0-7398-4850-0(X)) Raintree.

Woods, Michael & Woods, Mary B. Disasters at Sea. 2008. (Disasters up Close Ser.). (J). lib. bdg. 27.93 ***(978-0-8225-6773-8(3)*** , Lerner Pubns.) Lerner Publishing Group.

ACCIDENTS—FICTION

Alcott, Louisa May. Jack & Jill. l.t. ed. 2005. 496p. pap. (978-1-84637-054-0(X)) Echo Library.

Bang, Molly Garrett. Tiger's Fall. Bang, Molly Garrett, illus. rev. ed. 2001. (Illus.). 112p. (J). (gr. 4-7). 15.95 (978-0-8050-6689-0(6) , Holt, Henry & Co. Bks. For Young Readers) Holt, Henry & Co.

Banks, Kimberly E. Mask Man. Wroe, Dameon K., ed. 2003. 57p. (YA). pap. 9.99 (978-0-9740685-0-3(0)) Another Ep Publishing.

Banscherus, Jurgen & Baron, Daniel C. The Mysterious Mask. Butschkow, Ralf, illus. 2007. 65p. (J). ***(978-1-59889-341-0(6));*** pap. ***(978-1-59889-440-0(4))*** Stone Arch Bks.

Blackwater Mine, 6 Pack. (Bookweb Ser.). 32p. (gr. 6 up). 34.00 (978-0-7578-0893-7(X)) Rigby Education.

Byars, Betsy. The Eighteenth Emergency. 1999. (J). (gr. 5-8). 21.25 (978-0-8446-7026-3(X)) Smith, Peter Pub., Inc.

Choyce, Lesley. Smoke & Mirrors. 2004. 200p. (YA). pap. 8.99 (978-1-55002-534-7(1)) Dundurn Group, The CAN. *Dist:* Univ. of Toronto Pr.

Coolidge, Susan. What Katy Did. 2006. 62.99 ***(978-1-4280-3108-1(1))*** IndyPublish.com.

Falcon, Marilyn Perez. Cui-Cui-Cuidado! Animales al Volante. Repiso, Elena, illus. 2002. (SPA.). 32p. (J). pap. (978-980-257-269-4(1)) Ekare, Ediciones.

Franek, Claire. El Desastre. 2002. (SPA.). 32p. (J). pap. (978-980-257-270-0(5)) Ekare, Ediciones.

Hall, Kirsten. The Big Race: All about Safety. Luedecke, Bev, illus. (Beastieville Ser.). (J). (gr. k-1). 2005. 32p. pap. 3.95 (978-0-516-25517-0(7)); 2004. 19.50 (978-0-516-23671-1(7)) Scholastic Library Publishing. (Children's Pr.).

Harcourt School Publishers Staff. Follow My Leader Level D. 2001. (Collections Ser.). (Illus.). pap., lib. bdg. 13.20 (978-0-15-314408-0(4)) Harcourt Schl. Pubs.

Harrell, Deborah A. Pintos Hope. 2003. 124p. (YA). pap. 10.95 (978-0-595-26514-5(6)) iUniverse, Inc.

Hill, David. Coming Back. 2007. 189p. pap. 18.95 ***(978-0-9542330-2-0(6))*** Aurora Metro Pubns. Ltd. GBR. *Dist:* Consortium Bk. Sales & Distribution.

Huxman, K. D. Grizzelda Gorilla. l.t. ed. 2007. (Illus.). 24p. (J). 24.99 ***(978-0-9794660-2-1(4));*** per. 12.99 ***(978-0-9794660-3-8(2))*** Dragonfly Publishing, Inc.

Ikumi, Mia & Yoshida, Reiko. Tokyo Mew Mew (en Español), Vol. 1. 2006. (SPA., Illus.). 176p. reprint ed. pap. 10.95 (978-1-59497-155-6(2)) Public Square Bks.

Jan Baer: And the Mystery of the Silent Circus. 2005. (J). per. 10.00 (978-1-930052-29-1(4)) Cherokee Bks.

Jeffs, Stephanie. Josh: Coming to Terms with the Death of a Friend. Thomas, Jacqui, illus. 2006. 32p. (ps-3). 14.00 (978-0-687-49719-5(1)) Abingdon Pr.

Lange, Willem. John & Tom. Dodson, Bert, illus. 2001. (Family Heritage Ser.). 36p. (J). (ps-2). 15.95 (978-0-916718-17-6(4)) Vermont Folklife Ctr.

Langston, Laura. Perfect Blue. 2008. 220p. pap. ***(978-1-55455-058-6(0))*** Fitzhenry & Whiteside, Ltd.

Marshall, Catherine. Midnight Rescue/the Proposal/Christy's Choice. 2005. (Christy Juvenile Ser.). 384p. (J). pap. 9.99 (978-1-4003-0773-9(2)) Nelson, Thomas Inc.

Mawson, Robert. Lazarus Child. 1999. (gr. 7-12). lib. bdg. 14.75 (978-0-613-21884-9(1)) Tandem Library Bks.

McBay, Bruce. Waiting for Sarah. 2003. (gr. 7-12). lib. bdg. 16.40 (978-0-613-83712-5(6)) Tandem Library Bks.

McNulty, Faith & Shiffman, Lena. Le Chant des Baleines. (Hello Reader! Ser.). (FRE., Illus.). 40p. (J). pap. 5.99 (978-0-590-16027-8(3)) Scholastic, Inc.

A Medal for Molly: Individual Chapter Book Title Six-Packs. Vol. 25. 32p. (gr. 3-4). 44.00 (978-0-7635-4475-1(2)) Rigby Education.

Mendes, Valerie. The Drowning. 2006. 256p. (J). pap. 8.99 (978-1-4169-0127-3(2)) Simon & Schuster, Ltd. GBR. *Dist:* Trafalgar Square Publishing.

Moore-Malinos, Jennifer & Roca, Nuria. Ganar no es Todo! Winning Isn't Everything (Spanish Edition) Fabrega, Marta, illus. 2007. (Vive y Aprende Ser.). (SPA.). 32p. (J). (ps-2). pap. 6.99 ***(978-0-7641-3792-1(1))*** Barron's Educational Series, Inc.

No Running! Individual Title Six-Pack Pouch - Level H. (Lighthouse Ser.). 16p. (gr. 1 up). 26.00 (978-0-7578-0850-0(6)) Rigby Education.

Oates, Joyce Carol. After the Wreck, I Picked Myself up, Spread My Wings, & Flew Away. 2006. 304p. (YA). lib. bdg. 17.89 (978-0-06-073526-5(0) , HarperTeen) HarperCollins Pubs.

—After the Wreck, I Picked Myself Up, Spread My Wings, & Flew Away. 2006. 304p. (YA). 16.99 (978-0-06-073525-8(2) , HarperTeen) HarperCollins Pubs.

Orme, Helen. Horsing Around. 2008. (Siti's Sisters Ser.). 36p. pap. 7.95 ***(978-1-84167-685-2(3))*** Ransom Publishing Ltd. GBR. *Dist:* International Publishers Marketing.

Otero, Rodolfo. La Travesia. (SPA.). 112p. (YA). (gr. 5-8). (978-84-279-3152-7(2) , NG3670) Noguer y Caralt Editores, S. A. ESP. *Dist:* Lectorum Pubns., Inc.

Park, Barbara. Mick Harte Was Here. 88p. (J). (gr. 4-6). pap. 4.99 (978-0-8072-1502-9(3) , Listening Library) Random Hse. Audio Publishing Group.

Park, Barbara, ed. Mick Harte Was Here. unabr. ed. 2004. (Middle Grade Cassette Librariestm Ser.). 88p. (J). (gr. 3-7). pap. 29.00 incl. audio (978-0-8072-7797-3(5) , S YA 922 SP, Listening Library) Random Hse. Audio Publishing Group.

Qualey, Marsha. Just Like That. 240p. (YA). (gr. 7). 2007. pap. 6.99 (978-0-14-240830-8(1) , Puffin); 2005. 16.99 (978-0-8037-2840-0(9) , Dial) Penguin Group (USA) Inc.

Repp, Janelle. Little Bear & the Springwood Spinners. Garvin, Elaine, illus. 2000. (Little Bear Adventure Ser.: Vol. 6). 32p. (J). (ps-1). pap. 6.49 (978-1-57924-439-2(4)) Jones, Bob Univ. Pr.

—Little Bear & the Springwood Spinners. 2001. (ps-2). lib. bdg. 13.55 (978-0-613-85511-2(6)) Tandem Library Bks.

Rue, Nancy N. M D Lily Robbins: Medical Dabbler. 2000. (gr. 7-12). lib. bdg. 13.00 (978-0-613-71717-5(1)) Tandem Library Bks.

Schroder, Jack. The Nasty Affair at the Lake, 1 bk. 2004. 152p. (J). per. 9.95 (978-0-9745665-8-0(6)) Catalpa Pr.

Shaffer, Neal. Last Exit Before Toll. 2003. (Illus.). 96p. pap. 9.95 (978-1-929998-70-8(8)) Oni Pr., Inc.

Sykes, Julie. Careful, Santa! Warnes, Tim, illus. 2002. 32p. (J). (ps-1). tchr. ed. 14.95 (978-1-58925-023-9(0) , tiger tales) ME Media LLC.

Thiesing, Lisa. All Better. 2000. (Road to Reading Ser.). (Illus.). (J). 10.79 (978-0-606-20539-9(X)) Tandem Library Bks.

Tiernan, Cate. A Circle of Ashes, No. 2. 2005. (Balefire Ser.). 224p. (YA). (gr. 7-12). mass mkt. 6.99 (978-1-59514-046-3(8) , Razorbill) Penguin Group (USA) Inc.

—A Feather of Stone, No. 3. 2005. (Balefire Ser.). 240p. (YA). (gr. 7-12). mass mkt. 5.99 (978-1-59514-047-0(6) , Razorbill) Penguin Group (USA) Inc.

Tolan, Stephanie S. Listen! 2006. 208p. (J). 15.99 (978-0-06-057935-7(8)); lib. bdg. 16.89 (978-0-06-057936-4(6)) HarperCollins Pubs.

Tristan, Sarah. Cheat Codes. 2003. 234p. (YA). pap. 15.95 (978-0-595-29670-5(X)) iUniverse, Inc.

Waring, Scott C. West's Time MacHine. 2007. 200p. 24.95 ***(978-0-595-88775-0(9));*** per. 14.95 ***(978-0-595-41887-9(2))*** iUniverse, Inc.

Wharton, Edith. Ethan Frome, Level 3. 2nd abr. ed. 2000. (Bookworms Ser.). (Illus.). 80p. 6.50 (978-0-19-423002-5(3)) Oxford Univ. Pr., Inc.

Wright, Randall. The Silver Penny. rev. ed. 2005. 208p. (J). 16.95 (978-0-8050-7391-1(4) , Holt, Henry & Co. Bks. For Young Readers) Holt, Henry & Co.

Zephaniah, Benjamin. Face. 2004. 208p. (J). reprint ed. pap. 6.95 (978-1-58234-921-3(5) , Bloomsbury Children) Bloomsbury Publishing.

ACCIDENTS—PREVENTION

see also Safety Education

Berry, Joy Wilt. A Book about Being Careless. 2005. (Illus.). (J). ***(978-0-7172-8582-2(0))*** Scholastic, Inc.

Burstein, John. Avoiding Injuries. 2006. (Illus.). 32p. (J). lib. bdg. ***(978-0-8368-7739-7(X))*** Stevens, Gareth Inc.

—Keeping Safe. 2006. (Illus.). 32p. (J). lib. bdg. ***(978-0-8368-7743-4(8))*** Stevens, Gareth Inc.

Chapman, Cindy. Play It Safe! 2003. (Compass Point Phonics Readers Ser.). (Illus.). 16p. (J). (gr. 1 up). 13.26 (978-0-7565-0520-2(8)) Compass Point Bks.

Gedatus, Gus. Travel Safety. 2000. (Perspectives on Violence Ser.). (Illus.). 64p. (J). (gr. 4-6). lib. bdg. 23.93 (978-0-7368-0426-4(9) , LifeMatters Bks.) Capstone Pr., Inc.

Harrison, Jean. Safety. 2004. (Children's Rights Ser.). (J). lib. bdg. 27.10 (978-1-58340-422-5(8)) Smart Apple Media.

Leaney, Cindy. Help! I Can't Swim! Safety in Water. Wilks, Peter, tr. Wilks, Peter, illus. 2003. 32p. (J). 28.50 (978-1-58952-743-0(7)) Rourke Publishing, LLC.

—Look Out! Safety on Bicycles. Wilks, Peter, tr. Wilks, Peter, illus. 2003. 32p. (J). 28.50 (978-1-58952-744-7(5)) Rourke Publishing, LLC.

Llewellyn, Claire. On the Road. Gordon, Mike, illus. 2006. (Watch Out! Bks.). 32p. (J). (gr. k-2). pap. 5.99 (978-0-7641-3324-4(1)) Barron's Educational Series, Inc.

—Watch Out! at Home. Gordon, Mike, illus. 2006. (Watch Out! Bks.). 32p. (J). pap. 5.99 (978-0-7641-3323-7(3)) Barron's Educational Series, Inc.

—Watch Out! near Water. Gordon, Mike, illus. 2006. (Watch Out! Bks.). 32p. (J). pap. 5.99 (978-0-7641-3327-5(6)) Barron's Educational Series, Inc.

Mattern, Joanne. Staying Safe at Home. 2006. (Illus.). 24p. (J). pap. ***(978-0-8368-7798-4(5));*** (ENG & SPA., pap. ***(978-0-8368-8063-2(3));*** lib. bdg. ***(978-0-8368-7791-5(8));*** (ENG & SPA., lib. bdg. ***(978-0-8368-8056-4(0))*** Stevens, Gareth Inc. (Weekly Reader Early Learning Library).

—Staying Safe on the Street. 2006. (Illus.). 24p. (J). pap. ***(978-0-8368-7803-5(5));*** (SPA & ENG., pap. ***(978-0-8368-8068-7(4));*** lib. bdg. ***(978-0-8368-7796-0(9));*** (SPA & ENG., lib. bdg. ***(978-0-8368-8061-8(7))*** Stevens, Gareth Inc. (Weekly Reader Early Learning Library).

McEwen, Rebecca. Safety First. 2004. (Spyglass Books). (Illus.). 24p. (J). (gr. 1 up). lib. bdg. 18.60 (978-0-7565-0626-1(3)) Compass Point Bks.

McKay, Sindy. We Both Read-Being Safe Big Book: Being Safe Big Book Edition. 2005. 44p. (J). (gr. 1-2). 29.95 (978-1-891327-92-6(5)) Treasure Bay, Inc.

Meiners, Cheri J. Be Careful & Stay Safe. 2006. (Learning to Get along(R) Ser.). (Illus.). 40p. (J). pap. 10.95 (978-1-57542-211-4(5)) Free Spirit Publishing, Inc.

Naik, Anita. Wise Guides: Personal Safety. 2005. (Illus.). (YA). pap. 12.00 (978-0-340-88436-2(3) , Hodder & Stoughton) Hodder General Publishing Division GBR. *Dist:* Trafalgar Square Publishing.

Nelson, Robin. Playing Safely. 2005. (Pull Ahead Books). (Illus.). 32p. (J). pap. 5.95 (978-0-8225-2770-1(7) , Lerner Pubns.) Lerner Publishing Group.

Olson, Karen W. Living Safe, Playing Safe. Hamelin, Marie-Micheline, illus. 2006. 20p. (J). pap. 10.95 (978-1-894778-33-6(2)) Theytus Bks., Ltd. CAN. *Dist:* Orca Bk. Pubs. USA.

Oregon Center for Applied Science, creator. Walk Smart: Children's Pedestrian Safety Program. 2005. (J). cd-rom 19.95 (***978-1-933898-10-0(0)***) Oregon Ctr. for Applied Science, Inc.

Pancella, Peggy. Be Safe!, 8 bks. 2004. (J). (gr. k-2). lib. bdg. 193.71 (978-1-4034-4937-5(6)) Heinemann Library.

—Bicycle Safety. 2004. (Heinemann First Library). (Illus.). 32p. (J). pap. 6.95 (978-1-4034-4939-9(2)); lib. bdg. 22.79 (978-1-4034-4930-6(9)) Heinemann Library.

—Home Safety. 2004. (Heinemann First Library). (Illus.). 32p. (J). 6.95 (978-1-4034-4941-2(4)); lib. bdg. 22.79 (978-1-4034-4932-0(5)) Heinemann Library.

—Playground Safety. 2004. (Heinemann First Library). (Illus.). 32p. (J). 6.95 (978-1-4034-4943-6(0)); lib. bdg. 22.79 (978-1-4034-4934-4(1)) Heinemann Library.

—Street Smarts. 2004. (Heinemann First Library). (Illus.). 32p. (J). 6.95 (978-1-4034-4942-9(2)); lib. bdg. 22.79 (978-1-4034-4933-7(3)) Heinemann Library.

—Water Safety. 2004. (Heinemann First Library). (Illus.). 32p. (J). 6.95 (978-1-4034-4945-0(7)); lib. bdg. 22.79 (978-1-4034-4936-8(8)) Heinemann Library.

Phillips, Robert. Security Officer's Handbook. 2005. (Illus.). 50p. (J). (ps-ps). per. 10.95 (978-1-56167-900-3(3)) American Literary Pr.

Raatma, Lucia. Bike Safety. 2003. (Living Well). (Illus.). 32p. (J). (gr. 2-6). 27.07 (978-1-59296-085-9(5)) Child's World, Inc.

—Emergencies/911 Safety. 2003. (Living Well). (Illus.). 32p. (J). (gr. 2-6). 27.07 (978-1-59296-087-3(1)) Child's World, Inc.

—Safety, 9 bks., Set. 1998. (J). (gr. 1-3). (978-0-516-29770-5(8) , Children's Pr.) Scholastic Library Publishing.

—School Safety. 2003. (Living Well). (Illus.). 32p. (J). (gr. 2-6). 27.07 (978-1-59296-089-7(8)) Child's World, Inc.

—Water Safety. 2003. (Living Well). (Illus.). 32p. (J). (gr. 2-6). 27.07 (978-1-59296-090-3(1)) Child's World, Inc.

SafeKids 101. . . Preparing Kids to Stay Safe at Home & in the Community! 2003. (J). stu. ed. (978-0-9729706-5-5(7)); (978-0-9729706-4-8(9)) Production 101, Inc.

Safety Always Matters (SAM), Vol. II. 12p. (J). (gr. k-3). 29.50 (978-1-883994-06-8(3)) Safety Always Matters, Inc.

Safety Makes Sense. (J). 29.50 (978-1-883994-10-5(1)); 29.50 (978-1-883994-11-2(X)) Safety Always Matters, Inc.

Simms, Mattie. The "Q" Kids: A Disaster Safety Workbook for Children of All Ages. 1998. 64p. (J). (gr. 1-6). pap. 7.00 (978-0-8059-4307-8(2)) Dorrance Publishing Co., Inc.

ACCLIMATIZATION

see Adaptation (Biology); Human Beings—Effect of Environment on; Plant Introduction

ACCOUNTING

Accounting, 11 vols., Set. 2004. (Illus.). (YA). (gr. 9-12). tchr. ed., stu. ed. 47.95 (978-0-7403-0196-4(9) , ES9315, Lifepac) Alpha Omega Pubns., Inc.

Barnard, Marietjie & Gous, M. M. Introduction to Accounting for the Senior Phase Learner's Book (Afrikaans Translation) 2007. pap. (***978-0-521-71064-0(2)***) Cambridge Univ. Pr.

Barnard, Marietjie & Gous, M.M. Introduction to Accounting for the Senior Phase Learner's Book. 2007. pap. (***978-0-521-71062-6(6)***) Cambridge Univ. Pr.

Conradie, Elsabé, et al. Study & Master Accounting Grade 10 Learner's Book. 2005. 424p. pap. 16.65 (978-0-521-67430-0(1)) Cambridge Univ. Pr.

Hendricks, Hansie. NSSC Accounting Answer Book. 2005. 147p. pap. 11.95 (978-0-521-68077-6(8)) Cambridge Univ. Pr.

—NSSC Accounting Module 1. 2005. 147p. pap. 13.80 (978-0-521-68074-5(3)) Cambridge Univ. Pr.

—NSSC Accounting Module 2. 2005. 147p. pap. 14.70 (978-0-521-68075-2(1)) Cambridge Univ. Pr.

—NSSC Accounting Module 3. 2005. 147p. pap. 12.90 (978-0-521-68076-9(X)) Cambridge Univ. Pr.

Larry, Sanford, creator. Accounting Fundamentals Crash Course. 2000. (YA). cd-rom (978-0-9707746-0-6(5)) Glolar Multimedia Productions.

McGraw-Hill Staff. Glencoe Accounting: 1st Year Course, Chapter Reviews & Working Papers 1-28. 4th ed. 1999. (C). pap. 37.32 (978-0-02-643970-1(0) , 9780026439701) Glencoe/McGraw-Hill.

Peterman, Lori. Practical Accounting Fundamentals. 2004. spiral bd. (978-0-9722058-7-0(X)) Peterman, Melvin G.

Romney, Marshall B. & Schiff, Andrew D. Casebook in Accounting Information Systems. 4th ed. 2003. 90p. (C). pap. 24.95 (978-0-7593-2017-8(9)) Thomson South-Western.

ACCOUNTING MACHINES

see Calculators

ACID RAIN

Acid Rain. (Our Planet in Peril Ser.). 24p. (YA). 7.95 (978-0-7368-3294-6(7)) Capstone Pr., Inc.

Acid Rain: Level M, 6 vols. (Wonder Worldtm Ser.). 16p. 34.95 (978-0-7802-2887-0(1)) Wright Group, The.

Capstone Press Editors. Our Planet in Peril, 4 bks. Incl. Acid Rain. lib. bdg. 22.60 (978-0-7368-1360-0(8)); Global Warming. lib. bdg. 22.60 (978-0-7368-1361-7(6)); Nuclear Waste. lib. bdg. 22.60 (978-0-7368-1362-4(4)); Oil Spills. lib. bdg. 22.60 (978-0-7368-1363-1(2)); 48p. (J). (gr. 3-4). 2002. (Illus.). 2002. Set lib. bdg. 90.40 (978-0-7368-1364-8(0) , Bridgestone Bks.) Capstone Pr., Inc.

DuTemple, Lesley A. Acid Rain. 2003. (Lucent Overview Ser.). (Illus.). 96p. (J). 29.95 (978-1-56006-502-9(8) , Lucent Bks.) Thomson Gale.

Hocking, Colin, et al. Acid Rain. Bergman, Lincoln & Fairwell, Kay, eds. Bevilacqua, Carol & Craig, Rose, illus. Bergman, Lincoln et al, photos by. rev. ed. 1999. (Great Explorations in Math & Science Ser.). 176p. (YA). (gr. 6-8). pap. 18.00 (978-0-924886-14-0(5) , GEMS) Univ. of California, Berkeley, Lawrence Hall of Science.

Morgan, Sally. Acid Rain. 2006. (Earth Watch Ser.). (Illus.). 32p. (978-1-59771-063-3(6)) Sea-To-Sea Pubns.

Parks, Peggy J. Acid Rain. 2005. (Our Environment Ser.). (Illus.). 48p. (J). (gr. 4-8). 26.20 (978-0-7377-2628-2(8) , Greenhaven Pr., Inc.) Thomson Gale.

ACOUSTICS

see Hearing; Sound

ACQUIRED IMMUNE DEFICIENCY SYNDROME

see AIDS (Disease)

ACTING

see also Actors and Actresses; Pageants; Theater

Ahart, John. The Director's Eye: A Comprehensive Textbook for Directors & Actors. 2001. (Illus.). 376p. pap. 24.95 (978-1-56608-071-2(1) , N-B246) Meriwether Publishing, Ltd.

Bolton, Martha. Humorous Monologues. Behr, Joyce, illus. 2003. 128p. (J). (gr. 2-7). 19.00 (978-0-8069-6750-9(1)) Sterling Publishing Co., Inc.

Caruso, Sandra & Kosoff, Susan. Young Actors Book of Improvisation: Dramatic Situations from Shakespeare to Spielberg. 1998. (Young Actor's Book of Improvisation Ser.: Vol. 1). 280p. (YA). (gr. 7-11). pap. 22.95 (978-0-325-00049-7(2) , E00049); 200p. (gr. 2-6). pap. 19.95 (978-0-325-00048-0(4) , E00048) Heinemann.

Cranium Inc. Staff. Cranium: the Star Performer Book of Outrageous Fun! Sing it, Dance it, Act It! Baseman, illus. 2006. 38p. (J). (gr. 2-17). 14.99 (978-0-316-05759-2(2)) Little, Brown Bks. for Young Readers.

Dabrowski, Kristen. Volume IV for Kids: 10+ Format Comedy. 2005. (Young Actor Ser.). 240p. 16.95 (978-1-57525-441-8(7)) Smith and Kraus Publishers, Incorporated.

—Volume V for Kids: 10+ Format Drama. 2005. (Young Actor Ser.: Vol. II). 16.95 (978-1-57525-438-8(7)) Smith and Kraus Publishers, Incorporated.

—Volume V for Middle School: 10+ Format Comedy. 2005. (Young Actor Ser.: Vol. 3). 16.95 (978-1-57525-442-5(5)) Smith and Kraus Publishers, Incorporated.

—Volume VII for Middle School: 10+ Format Drama. 2005. (Young Actor Ser.: Vol. IV). 240p. 16.95 (978-1-57525-439-5(5)) Smith and Kraus Publishers, Incorporated.

—111 One-Minute Monologues: The Ultimate Monologue Book for Middle School Actors, Vol. 3. 2004. (Ultimate Monologue Book for Middle School Actors Ser.: Vol. 1). 136p. (J). pap. 11.95 (978-1-57525-419-7(0)) Smith and Kraus Publishers, Incorporated.

Frick, Sheila M. & Kawar, Mary. Core Concepts in Action. 2004. (Illus.). spiral bd. 34.00 (978-0-9717653-0-6(8)) Vital Links.

Friedman, Lise & Dowdle, Mary. Break a Leg! The Kids' Guide to Acting & Stagecraft. Dowdle, Mary, photos by. 2001. (Illus.). 256p. (J). (gr. 4-7). pap. 14.95 (978-0-7611-2208-1(7) , 12208) Workman Publishing Co., Inc.

Gibbs, Adrea. Let's Put on a Show! A Beginner's Theatre Handbook for Young Actors. Melvin, Janice, illus. 1999. 160p. (gr. 6-12). pap. 19.95 (978-1-56608-052-1(5) , N-B231) Meriwether Publishing, Ltd.

Harvey, Anne, ed. The Methuen Book of Monologues for Young Actors. 2004. 192p. pap. 13.95 (978-0-413-77279-4(9)) Methuen Publishing Ltd. GBR. *Dist:* Consortium Bk. Sales & Distribution.

Horn, Geoffrey M. Movie Acting. 2006. (Making Movies Ser.). (Illus.). 32p. (J). (gr. 4-6). lib. bdg. 23.93 (978-0-8368-6836-4(6)) Stevens, Gareth Inc.

Howie, Diana M. Tight Spots: True-to-Life Monolog Characterizations for Student Actors. 1999. 116p. (gr. 9-12). pap. 14.95 (978-1-56608-054-5(1) , N-B233) Meriwether Publishing, Ltd.

Introduction to Theatre Arts 2 Student Handbook: An action handbook for middle grade & high school students & Teachers. 2007. pap., stu. ed. 24.95 (***978-1-56608-148-1(3)***) Meriwether Publishing, Ltd.

Jay, Annie & Feik, LuAnne. Stars in Your Eyes... Feet on the Ground: A Practical Guide for Teenage Actors (And Their Parents!) Crawford, Ron, illus. 1999. 160p. (YA). (gr. 8 up). pap. 16.95 (978-0-933919-42-6(5)) Theatre Directories Inc.

Lamedman, Debbie. The Ultimate Audition Book for Teens Vol. II: 111 Monologues from Classical Theater, 2 Minutes & Under. 2006. 11.95 (978-1-57525-458-6(1)) Smith and Kraus Publishers, Incorporated.

—The Ultimate Audition Book for Teens Vol. III: 111 Monologues from Classical Literature, 2 Minutes & Under. 2006. 11.95 (978-1-57525-459-3(X)) Smith and Kraus Publishers, Incorporated.

—The Ultimate Audition Book for Teens Vol. IX: 111 Monologues from Contemporary Literature, 2 Minutes & Under. 2006. 11.95 (978-1-57525-460-9(3)) Smith and Kraus Publishers, Incorporated.

—The Ultimate Audition Book for Teens IV: 111 One Minute Monologues. 2003. (Ultimate Audition Book for Teens Ser.: Vol. 4). viii, 117p. (J). 11.95 (978-1-57525-353-4(4)) Smith and Kraus Publishers, Incorporated.

Laurie, Rona. Auditioning: A Practical Guide for the Would-Be Actor & Drama Student. 2nd ed. 2003. (Illus.). 64p. (YA). (gr. 8-12). pap. 10.00 (978-0-85343-585-3(5)) Miller, J. Garnet Ltd. GBR. *Dist:* Empire Publishing Service.

Lindsay, David & Marlow, Jean. Satire of the Three Estates. McDiarmid, Matthew & Kemp, Robert, eds. 2000. 144p. (J). 17.95 (978-0-87830-114-0(3) , Theatre Arts Bks.) Routledge.

McCullough, L. E. The Ultimate Audition Book for Teens Vol. II: III One-Minute Monologues for Teens. 2000. (Young Actors Ser.). 128p. (J). pap. 11.95 (978-1-57525-237-7(6)) Smith and Kraus Publishers, Incorporated.

—Wild & Wacky Characters for Kids: 60 One-Minute Monologues. 2001. 63p. (J). 11.95 (978-1-57525-305-3(4)) Smith and Kraus Publishers, Incorporated.

Milstein, Janet B. Cool Characters for Kids: 60 One-Minute Monologues. 2001. xii, 78p. (J). (gr. k-6). 11.95 (978-1-57525-306-0(2)) Smith and Kraus Publishers, Incorporated.

Milstein, Karen Kaufman. Hot Spots for Teens: Cold Readings for Commercial Audition Success. 2006. 112p. 11.95 (978-1-57525-461-6(1)) Smith and Kraus Publishers, Incorporated.

Pierce, J. P. Killer Monologues: Highly Actable Monologues & Performance Tips to Give You an Almost Unfair Advantage in the Auditioning Game. 1998. 128p. (YA). (gr. 9-12). pap. 39.95 incl. VHS (978-1-892553-00-3(7)) Impact Films.

Polsky, Milton & Gilead, Jack. The Improv Workshop Handbook: Creative Movement & Verbal Interaction for Students K-8: The Object Is Teamwork. Cordero, Chris, ed. Rockwell, Richard, illus. l.t. ed. 2003. 112p. (J). (gr. k-8). pap. 15.00 (978-0-88734-691-0(X)) Players Pr., Inc.

Pomerance, Susan. More Monologues for Teenage Girls. 2002. 58p. (J). pap. 9.95 (978-0-940669-53-6(6)) Dramaline Pubns.

Quinn, Stephanie. Beginning Improv Workshop for Kids. 2008. per. (***978-0-9773099-4-8(0)***) Quinn Entertainment.

Silverberg, Larry. The 7 Simple Truths of Acting for the Teen Actor. 2006. (Young Actors Ser.). 96p. (YA). 14.95 (978-1-57525-462-3(X)) Smith and Kraus Publishers, Incorporated.

Slaight, Craig, ed. Great Scenes & Monologues for Children. 2000. (Young Actors Ser.: Vol. II). (Illus.). 224p. (J). (gr. 2). pap. 14.95 (978-1-57525-224-7(4)) Smith and Kraus Publishers, Incorporated.

Stephens, Heather. Cabbage & Other Scenes. 2003. 48p. (Orig.). (J). (gr. 3-9). pap. 12.00 (978-0-88734-656-9(1)) Players Pr., Inc.

Stevens, Chambers. Magnificent Monologues for Kids. 1999. (gr. 3-6). lib. bdg. 23.40 (978-0-613-80203-1(9)) Tandem Library Bks.

—Magnificent Monologues for Teens: The Teens' Monologue Source for Every Occasion! 2002. (Hollywood 101 Ser.: Vol. 4). 96p. (YA). per. 14.95 (978-1-883995-11-9(6)) Sandcastle Publishing.

—Sensational Scenes for Kids: The Scene Study-Guide for Young Actors! Hope, Nathan, photos by. 2003. (Hollywood 101 Ser.: 5). (Illus.). 112p. (J). per. 14.95 (978-1-883995-12-6(4)) Sandcastle Publishing.

—Sensational Scenes for Teens: The Scene Study-Guide for Teen Actors! Rolle-Whatley, Renee, ed. 2001. (Hollywood 101 Ser.: Vol. 3). (Illus.). 112p. (YA). (gr. 7-11). per. 14.95 (978-1-883995-10-2(8)) Sandcastle Publishing.

—The Ultimate Commercial Book for Kids & Teens: The Young Actors' Commercial Study-guide! Stevens, Chambers, ed. 2005. (Hollywood 101 Ser.: 6). (Illus.). 112p. (J). per. 14.95 (978-1-883995-13-3(2)) Sandcastle Publishing.

Surface, Mary H. Monologues & Scenes for Middle School Actors. 1999. (Young Actors Ser.). 256p. (YA). (gr. 7-8). pap. 11.95 (978-1-57525-179-0(5)) Smith and Kraus Publishers, Incorporated.

ACTING—FICTION

Bell, Alison. Zibby Payne & the Drama Trauma. 2007. 96p. (J). (gr. 4-6). pap. (978-1-897073-47-6(X)) Lobster Pr.

Caple, Kathy. Starring Hillary. Caple, Kathy, illus. 2003. (Picture Bks.). (Illus.). 28p. (J). (ps-3). 15.95 (978-1-57505-261-8(X) , Carolrhoda Bks.) Lerner Publishing Group.

Chute, Marchette. The Wonderful Winter. 2002. 256p. 12.95 (978-0-9714612-1-5(X)) Green Mansion Pr. LLC.

Cottringer, Anne. Mary Is Scary. Gale, Cathy, illus. 2005. 32p. (ps-k). 19.99 (978-0-7475-6464-5(7)) Bloomsbury Publishing Plc GBR. *Dist:* Independent Pubs. Group.

Davidson, Jody. Broadway Beginner. 2006. 172p. pap. 10.95 (978-1-59800-494-6(8)) Outskirts Press, Inc.

Dussling, Jennifer. The Longest Yawn. Sims, Blanche, illus. 2005. 32p. (J). lib. bdg. 20.00 (***978-1-4242-1095-4(X)***) Fitzgerald Bks.

—The Longest Yawn. Sims, Blanche, illus. 2006. (Science Solves It! Ser.). 32p. (J). pap. 4.99 (978-1-57565-160-6(2)) Kane Pr., The.

Hirsch, Odo. Antonio S. & the Mysterious Theodore Guzman. 2001. (Illus.). 224p. (J). lib. bdg. 16.49 (978-0-7868-2605-6(3)) Hyperion Bks. for Children.

—Antonio S. & the Mysterious Theodore Guzman. Hall, August, illus. 2001. 208p. (gr. 3-7). 15.99 (978-0-7868-0747-5(4)) Hyperion Bks. for Children.

Katschke, Judy. Bye-Bye Boyfriend. 2000. (gr. 3-6). lib. bdg. 13.00 (978-0-613-31037-6(3)) Tandem Library Bks.

L'Engle, Madeleine. The Joys of Love. 2008. 272p. (YA). 16.95 (***978-0-374-33870-1(1)***) Farrar, Straus & Giroux.

Lerangis, Peter. The Big Production, No. 2. 2007. (Drama Club Ser.). 240p. (YA). (gr. 7). 7.99 (***978-0-14-240887-2(5)*** , Puffin) Penguin Group (USA) Inc.

—The Fall Musical, No. 1. 2007. (Drama Club Ser.). 224p. (YA). (gr. 7). 7.99 (***978-0-14-240886-5(7)*** , Puffin) Penguin Group (USA) Inc.

Marshall, Catherine. Stage Fright/Goodbye, Sweet Prince/Brotherly Love. 2005. (Christy Juvenile Ser.). 368p. (J). (gr. 4-7). pap. 9.99 (978-1-4003-0775-3(9)) Nelson, Thomas Inc.

Martin, Ann M. Karen's Show & Share. 1999. (Baby-Sitters Little Sister Ser.: No. 109). 112p. (J). (gr. 3-7). pap. 3.99 (978-0-590-50061-6(9)) Scholastic, Inc.

Matlin, Marlee & Cooney, Doug. Leading Ladies. 2007. 288p. (J). (gr. 3-7). 15.99 (***978-0-689-86987-7(8)*** , Simon & Schuster Children's Publishing) Simon & Schuster Children's Publishing.

Murphy, Barbara Beasley & Wolkoff, Judie. Ace Hits Rock Bottom. 2003. (Can't Stop Ace Ser.: No. 2). 204p. (J). pap. 16.95 (978-0-86534-408-2(6)) Sunstone Pr.

Peterson, Shelley. Stagestruck. rev. ed. 2002. (Illus.). 262p. (J). pap. 9.95 (***978-1-55263-501-8(5)***) Key Porter Bks. CAN. *Dist:* Perseus Distribution.

Rallison, Janette. Fame, Glory & Other Things on My to Do List. 2005. 192p. (YA). 16.95 (978-0-8027-8991-4(9)) Walker & Co.

Rallison, Janette. Fame, Glory, & Other Things on My to Do List. 2007. 208p. (YA). pap. 6.95 (***978-0-8027-9682-0(6)***) Walker & Co.

Rue, Nancy N. Lily!lights, Action. 2002. (gr. 3-6). lib. bdg. 13.00 (978-0-613-71698-7(1)) Tandem Library Bks.

Sargent, Dave & Sargent, Pat. Gizmo: (Flea-bitten Dun) Don't Be Silly, 25 vols., Vol. 28. Lenoir, Jane, illus. 2001. (Saddle Up Ser.: 28). 36p. (J). pap. 6.95 (978-1-56763-654-3(3)); lib. bdg. 22.60 (978-1-56763-653-6(5)) Ozark Publishing.

Siebold, Jan. My Nights at the Improv. 2005. 98p. (YA). (gr. 6-9). lib. bdg. 14.95 (978-0-8075-5630-6(0)) Whitman, Albert & Co.

Strasser, Todd. Help! I'm Trapped in a Movie Star's Body. 1999. (Help! I'm Trapped Ser.). 144p. (J). (gr. 4-7). pap. 3.99 (978-0-590-97803-3(9)) Scholastic, Inc.

ACTING—VOCATIONAL GUIDANCE

Albert, Lisa Rondinelli. So You Want to Be a Film or TV Actor? 2008. (Careers in Film & Television Ser.). (Illus.). 128p. (J). (gr. 6 up). lib. bdg. 31.93 (***978-0-7660-2741-1(4)***) Enslow Pubs., Inc.

Howey, Bill. The Actor's Menu: A Character Preparation Handbook. 2005. 204p. pap. 14.95 (978-0-9753102-2-9(4)) Compass Publishing.

Lamedman, Debbie. A Teen Drama Student's Guide to Laying the Foundation for a. 2006. 192p. 16.95 (978-1-57525-463-0(8)) Smith and Kraus Publishers, Incorporated.

Maddox, Deborah. Audition Monologues: Power Pieces for Kids & Teens. 2002. (ENG.). 80p. (J). per. 12.95 (978-0-9716827-0-2(4)) Lucid Solutions.

Mayfield, Katherine. Acting A to Z (revised) The Young Person's Guide to a Stage or Screen Career. 2nd rev. ed. 2007. (Illus.). 192p. (YA). pap. 16.95 (***978-0-8230-8797-6(2)*** , Back Stage Bks.) Watson-Guptill Pubns., Inc.

Quinlan, Kathryn A. Actor. (Careers Without College Ser.). 48p. pap. 6.95 (978-0-7368-8017-6(8) , LifeMatters Bks.) Capstone Pr., Inc.

—Actor. 1998. (Careers Without College Ser.). (Illus.). 48p. (J). (gr. 3-7). pap. 19.00 (978-0-516-21278-4(8) , Children's Pr.) Scholastic Library Publishing.

Rauf, Don & Vescia, Monique. Virtual Apprentice. 2008. (Virtual Apprentice Ser.). 64p. (J). (gr. 6-12). 29.95 (***978-0-8160-6757-2(0)*** , Ferguson Publishing Co.) Facts On File, Inc.

ACTORS AND ACTRESSES

see also Acting; Acting—Vocational Guidance; African American Actors; Motion Pictures—Biography; Theater

Abraham, Philip. Christopher Reeve. 2002. (gr. k-3). lib. bdg. 12.95 (978-0-613-58826-3(6)) Tandem Library Bks.

—Tobey Maguire. 2003. (gr. 7-12). lib. bdg. 15.25 (978-0-613-67940-4(7)) Tandem Library Bks.

Abrams, Lea. Freddie Prinze Jr. 2001. (Latinos in the Limelight Ser.). (Illus.). 64p. (J). (gr. 4-7). 27.50 (978-0-7910-6479-5(4) , Chelsea Hse.) Facts On File, Inc.

Adams, Colleen. Jake Gyllenhaal. 2006. (Stars in the Spotlight Ser.). (Illus.). 32p. (J). lib. bdg. (978-1-4042-3514-4(0) , PowerKids Pr.) Rosen Publishing Group, Inc., The.

—Johnny Depp. 2006. (Tony Stead Nonfiction Independent Reading Collection). pap. (978-1-4042-5667-5(9)) Rosen Publishing Group, Inc., The.

Alexander, Lauren. Mad for Miley: An Unauthorized Biography. 2007. 128p. (J). pap. 4.99 (***978-0-8431-2684-6(1)*** , Price Stern Sloan) Penguin Group (USA) Inc.

Allison, Amy. Antonio Banderas. (Latinos in the Limelight Ser.). (Illus.). 64p. (J). 2001. (gr. 3 up). 27.50 (978-0-7910-6102-2(7)); 2000. pap. (978-0-7910-6103-9(5)) Facts On File, Inc. (Chelsea Hse.).

—John Leguizamo. 2001. (Latinos in the Limelight Ser.). (Illus.). 64p. (J). (gr. 6-9). 27.50 (978-0-7910-6477-1(8) , Chelsea Hse.) Facts On File, Inc.

Alter, Judith. Oprah Winfrey. 2008. (J). lib. bdg. 26.00 (***978-1-60279-069-8(8)***) Cherry Lake Publishing.

Alter, Judy. Audie Murphy: War Hero & Movie Star. 2007. 72p. (YA). 14.95 (***978-1-933337-19-7(2)***) State Hse. Pr.

Alter, Judy. Christopher Reeve: Triumph over Tragedy. 2000. (gr. 5-8). lib. bdg. 15.25 (978-0-613-54128-2(6)) Tandem Library Bks.

Anderson, Marilyn D. Chris Farley. 2000. (They Died Too Young Ser.). (Illus.). 48p. (J). (gr. 4-7). 21.95 (978-0-7910-5860-2(3) , Chelsea Hse.) Facts On File, Inc.

—Sarah Michelle Gellar. 2001. (Galaxy of Superstars Ser.). (Illus.). 64p. (YA). (gr. 5-9). 25.00 (978-0-7910-6461-0(1) , Chelsea Hse.) Facts On File, Inc.

—Will Smith. 2002. (People in the News Ser.). (Illus.). 112p. (J). (gr. 6-9). 27.45 (978-1-59018-140-9(9) , Lucent Bks.) Thomson Gale.

Apte, Sunita. Christopher Reeve: Don't Lose Hope! 2005. (Defining Moments Ser.). (Illus.). 32p. (J). lib. bdg. 25.27 (978-1-59716-074-2(1)) Bearport Publishing Co., Inc.

—Michael J. Fox: I Can Make a Difference! 2006. (Defining Moments Ser.). (Illus.). 32p. (J). lib. bdg. 25.27 (978-1-59716-269-2(8)) Bearport Publishing Co., Inc.

Aronson, Virginia. Drew Barrymore. (Overcoming Adversity Ser.). (Illus.). (YA). 2000. 112p. 30.00 (978-0-7910-5306-5(7)); 1999. 128p. pap. 30.00 (978-0-7910-5307-2(5)) Facts On File, Inc. (Chelsea Hse.).

—Drew Barrymore. 2000. (gr. 5-8). lib. bdg. 18.75 (978-0-613-21469-8(2)) Tandem Library Bks.

—Jennifer Love Hewitt. 1999. (Galaxy of Superstars Ser.). (Illus.). 64p. (J). (gr. 4-7). 25.00 (978-0-7910-5497-0(7) , Chelsea Hse.) Facts On File, Inc.

Asirvatham, Sandy. Bruce Willis. 2001. (Overcoming Adversity Ser.). (Illus.). (J). 110p. 19.95 (978-0-7910-6115-2(9)); 112p. 30.00 (978-0-7910-6114-5(0)) Facts On File, Inc. (Chelsea Hse.).

Bankston, John. Alyssa Milano. 2000. (Real-Life Reader Biography Ser.). (Illus.). 32p. (J). (gr. 3-8). lib. bdg. 15.95 (978-1-58415-040-4(8)) Mitchell Lane Pubs., Inc.

—Ben Stiller. l.t. ed. 2002. (Real-Life Reader Biography Ser.). (Illus.). 32p. (gr. 3-8). lib. bdg. 24.95 (978-1-58415-132-6(3)) Mitchell Lane Pubs., Inc.

—Daniel Radcliffe. l.t. ed. 2003. (Blue Banner Biography Ser.). (Illus.). 32p. (J). (gr. 3-8). lib. bdg. 25.70 (978-1-58415-250-7(8)) Mitchell Lane Pubs., Inc.

—Drew Barrymore. 2002. (Galaxy of Superstars Ser.). (Illus.). 64p. (J). 25.00 (978-0-7910-6772-7(6) , Chelsea Hse.) Facts On File, Inc.

—Heath Ledger. 2002. (Galaxy of Superstars Ser.). (Illus.). 64p. (J). 25.00 (978-0-7910-6769-7(6) , Chelsea Hse.) Facts On File, Inc.

—Julia Stiles. l.t. ed. 2002. (Real-Life Reader Biography Ser.). (Illus.). 32p. (gr. 3-8). lib. bdg. 24.95 (978-1-58415-130-2(7)) Mitchell Lane Pubs., Inc.

—Mandy Moore. 2001. (Real-Life Reader Biography Ser.). (Illus.). 32p. (gr. 3-8). lib. bdg. 15.95 (978-1-58415-073-2(4)) Mitchell Lane Pubs., Inc.

—Michael J. Fox. l.t. ed. 2002. (Real Life Reader Biography Ser.). (Illus.). 32p. (gr. 3-8). lib. bdg. 24.95 (978-1-58415-128-9(5)) Mitchell Lane Pubs., Inc.

Banting, Erinn. Halle Berry. 2005. (Great African American Women for Kids Ser.). (Illus.). 24p. (J). (ps-7). pap. 6.95 (978-1-59036-339-3(6)); lib. bdg. 26.00 (978-1-59036-333-1(7)) Weigl Pubs., Inc.

Barile, Louise. Meet the Stars of Dawson's Creek. 1998. (Illus.). 144p. (J). (gr. 5-9). pap. 4.99 (978-0-590-64269-9(3)) Scholastic, Inc.

Barker, John L. River Phoenix: Into the Sun. 1999. (Illus.). 148p. (J). (gr. 4-12). pap. 9.95 (978-0-9665612-3-4(6)) Phoenix Literary Productions.

Barnham, Kay. Jennifer Lopez. 2004. (Star Files Ser.). 29.93 (978-1-4109-1086-8(5)) Harcourt Schl. Pubs.

Berman, Connie. Cher. 2001. (Women of Achievement Ser.). (Illus.). 112p. (J). (gr. 8-12). pap. 9.95 (978-0-7910-5908-1(1) , Chelsea Hse.) Facts On File, Inc.

Berne, Emma Carlson. Paris & Nicky Hilton. 2007. (J). (***978-1-4222-0204-3(6)***) Mason Crest Pubs.

Beyer, Mark. Frankie Muniz. 2002. (gr. 7-12). lib. bdg. 15.25 (978-0-613-58697-9(2)) Tandem Library Bks.

Bial, Daniel. Arnold Schwarzenegger: Man of Action. 1999. (Book Report Biographies Ser.). (Illus.). 112p. (YA). (gr. 6-8). pap. 6.95 (978-0-531-15933-0(7) , Watts, Franklin) Scholastic Library Publishing.

Blakely, Gloria. Danny Glover. 2001. (Black Americans of Achievement Ser.). (Illus.). 112p. (J). 30.00 (978-0-7910-6285-2(6) , Chelsea Hse.) Facts On File, Inc.

Blashfield, Jean F. Oprah Winfrey. 2003. (Trailblazers of the Modern World Ser.). (ENG & SPA., Illus.). 48p. (J). (gr. 5 up). pap. 14.95 (978-0-8368-5247-9(8)); lib. bdg. 30.00 (978-0-8368-5087-1(4)) Stevens, Gareth Inc. (World Almanac Library).

—Shirley Temple Black: Actor & Diplomat. 2000. (Career Biographies Ser.). (Illus.). 128p. (J). (gr. 6-12). 25.00 (978-0-89434-338-4(6) , F408, Ferguson Publishing Co.) Facts On File, Inc.

Blue, Rose. Wesley Snipes. 2002. (gr. 5-8). lib. bdg. 18.75 (978-0-613-33213-2(X)) Tandem Library Bks.

Blue, Rose & Naden, Corinne J. Nicolas Cage. 2003. (Illus.). 112p. (J). (gr. 6-9). 32.45 (978-1-59018-136-2(0) , Lucent Bks.) Thomson Gale.

—Wesley Snipes. 2001. (Black Americans of Achievement Ser.). (Illus.). 104p. (J). (gr. 5 up). pap. 30.00 (978-0-7910-5801-5(8) , Chelsea Hse.) Facts On File, Inc.

Bonner, Mike. Jennifer Aniston. 2001. (Galaxy of Superstars Ser.). (Illus.). 64p. (J). 25.00 (978-0-7910-6465-8(4) , Chelsea Hse.) Facts On File, Inc.

Boulais, Sue. Katie Holmes. 2000. (Real-Life Reader Biography Ser.). (Illus.). 32p. (J). (gr. 3-8). lib. bdg. 15.95 (978-1-58415-038-1(6)) Mitchell Lane Pubs., Inc.

—Liv Tyler. 2000. (Real-Life Reader Biography Ser.). (Illus.). 32p. (J). (gr. 3-8). lib. bdg. 15.95 (978-1-58415-041-1(6)) Mitchell Lane Pubs., Inc.

Brighton, Catherine. Keep Your Eye on the Kid: The Early Years of Buster Keaton. 2008. 32p. (J). 16.95 (***978-1-59643-158-4(X)***) Roaring Brook Pr.

Britton, Tamara L., contrib. by. Mary-Kate & Ashley Olsen. 1999. (Young Profiles Ser.). (Illus.). 32p. (J). (gr. 3). lib. bdg. 21.35 (978-1-57765-351-6(3) , Checkerboard Library) ABDO Publishing Co.

Brown, Jonatha A. Oprah Winfrey. 2004. (Gente Que Hay Que Conocer Ser.). (ENG & SPA.). pap. 5.95 (978-0-8368-4361-3(4)) Stevens, Gareth Inc.

—Oprah Winfrey. Acosta, Tatiana & Gutierrez, Guillermo, trs. 2004. (Gente Que Hay Que Conocer Ser.). (ENG & SPA.). 24p. (J). lib. bdg. 19.33 (978-0-8368-4354-5(1)) Stevens, Gareth Inc.

—Oprah Winfrey. 2004. (Illus.). 24p. pap. (978-0-8368-4319-4(3)); (YA). lib. bdg. 19.33 (978-0-8368-4312-5(6)) Stevens, Gareth Inc.

Calderone, Samantha. Meet the Stars of Roswell: An Unauthorized Biography. 2000. (gr. 7-12). lib. bdg. 13.00 (978-0-613-89565-1(7)) Tandem Library Bks.

Caper, William. Whoopi Goldberg: Comedian & Movie Star. 1999. (African-American Biographies Ser.). (Illus.). 128p. (YA). (gr. 6-12). lib. bdg. 26.60 (978-0-7660-1205-9(0)) Enslow Pubs., Inc.

Clark, Travis. Will Ferrell. 2007. (J). (***978-1-4222-0202-9(X)***) Mason Crest Pubs.

Coco, Paul. Drama Queens. 2004. (Pop Zone Ser.). (Illus.). 32p. (J). (978-0-439-66976-4(6)) Scholastic, Inc.

Cohn, Gary. Michael J. Fox. 2000. (Overcoming Adversity Ser.). (Illus.). 112p. (J). (gr. 4-7). 30.00 (978-0-7910-5425-3(X) , Chelsea Hse.) Facts On File, Inc.

Cole, Melanie. Chuck Norris. 1998. (Real Life Reader Biography Ser.). (Illus.). 32p. (J). (gr. 4-7). lib. bdg. 15.95 (978-1-883845-91-9(2)) Mitchell Lane Pubs., Inc.

—Jimmy Smits. 1998. (Real-Life Reader Biographies Ser.). (Illus.). 32p. (J). (gr. 3-8). lib. bdg. 24.95 (978-1-883845-59-9(9)) Mitchell Lane Pubs., Inc.

Colon & Turner Classic Movies Staff. Leading Men: The 50 Most Unforgettable Actors of the Studio Era. 2006. (Illus.). 240p. pap. 19.95 (978-0-8118-5467-7(1)) Chronicle Bks. LLC.

Cooper, Ilene. Oprah Winfrey. 2007. (Up Close Ser.). (Illus.). 224p. (J). 15.99 (978-0-670-06162-4(X)) Penguin Group (USA) Inc.

Cooper, Ilene. Up Close: Oprah Winfrey: Oprah Winfrey. 2008. (Up Close Ser.). 208p. (J). (gr. 6). pap. 6.99 (***978-0-14-241045-5(4)*** , Puffin) Penguin Group (USA) Inc.

Corrigan, Jim. Will Smith. 2006. (Hip-Hop Ser.). (Illus.). 64p. (YA). (gr. 5 up). 22.95 (978-1-4222-0128-2(7)) Mason Crest Pubs.

Cruz, Barbara C. Raul Julia: Actor & Humanitarian. 1998. (Hispanic Biographies Ser.). (Illus.). 128p. (YA). (gr. 6-12). lib. bdg. 26.60 (978-0-7660-1040-6(6)) Enslow Pubs., Inc.

Davies, Ross. Andre the Giant. 2005. (Wrestling Greats Ser.). (Illus.). 112p. (YA). (gr. 7-12). lib. bdg. 25.25 (978-0-8239-3430-0(6)) Rosen Publishing Group, Inc., The.

De Angelis, Gina. Gregory Hines. 1999. (Black Americans of Achievement Ser.). (Illus.). 103p. (J). (gr. 5-9). pap. 9.95 (978-0-7910-5198-6(6)); (YA). (gr. 4 up). pap. 9.95 (978-0-7910-4966-2(3)); (Illus.). 112p. (J). (gr. 5-9). 30.00 (978-0-7910-5197-9(8)) Facts On File, Inc. (Chelsea Hse.).

De Angelis, Therese. Jodie Foster. 2000. (Illus.). 112p. (J). (ps-7). lib. bdg. 18.75 (978-0-613-21812-2(4)) Tandem Library Bks.

DeAngelis, Gina. Morgan Freeman: Actor. 1999. (Black Americans of Achievement Ser.). (Illus.). (gr. 4-7). 112p. (J). 30.00 (978-0-7910-4963-1(9)); 144p. (YA). pap. 30.00 (978-0-7910-4964-8(7)) Facts On File, Inc. (Chelsea Hse.).

—Robin Williams. 2000. (Overcoming Adversity Ser.). (Illus.). 112p. (J). 30.00 (978-0-7910-5308-9(3) , Chelsea Hse.) Facts On File, Inc.

DeBoer, Andy. Whoopi Goldberg. 1998. (Ovations Ser.: Vol. 8). (Illus.). 32p. (YA). (gr. 4-7). 21.30 (978-0-88682-696-3(9) , Creative Education) Creative Co., The.

Dempsey, Amy. Brad Pitt. 1999. (Superstars of Film Ser.). (Illus.). 48p. (YA). (gr. 5 up). lib. bdg. 18.65 (978-0-7910-4649-4(4) , Chelsea Hse.) Facts On File, Inc.

Doeden, Matt. Will Smith. 2007. (Just the Facts Biographies Ser.). (J). 27.93 (978-0-8225-6608-3(7) , Lerner Pubns.) Lerner Publishing Group.

Donaghey, Sean. The 10 Funniest People. 2008. (Tentrade; Ser.). 48p. (J). pap. 14.99 (***978-1-55448-474-4(X)*** , Watts, Franklin) Scholastic Library Publishing.

Dougherty, Terri. Ashton Kutcher. 2006. 112p. (J). (gr. 7-10). 32.45 (978-1-59018-718-0(0) , Lucent Bks.) Thomson Gale.

—Ben Stiller. 2007. (People in the News Ser.). 128p. (J). (gr. 7-10). 31.20 (***978-1-59018-723-4(7)*** , Lucent Bks.) Thomson Gale.

—Hillary Duff. 2007. (People in the News Ser.). (Illus.). 128p. (gr. 7-10). 31.20 (***978-1-4205-0012-7(0)*** , Lucent Bks.) Thomson Gale.

—Jennifer Lopez. 2007. (Twentieth Century Most Influential Hispanics Ser.). (Illus.). 128p. (J). (gr. 7-10). 31.20 (***978-1-4205-0021-9(X)*** , Lucent Bks.) Thomson Gale.

—Mary-Kate & Ashley Olsen. 2005. (People in the News Ser.). (Illus.). 112p. (YA). (gr. 7-10). lib. bdg. 32.45 (978-1-59018-720-3(2) , Lucent Bks.) Thomson Gale.

—Tim Allen. 2002. (People in the News Ser.). (Illus.). 112p. (J). (gr. 6-9). 32.45 (978-1-59018-241-3(3) , Lucent Bks.) Thomson Gale.

Dougherty, Terri. Zac Efron. 2007. (People in the News Ser.). (Illus.). 128p. (gr. 7-10). 31.20 (***978-1-4205-0017-2(1)*** , Lucent Bks.) Thomson Gale.

Dougherty, Terri & Dougherty, Denise. Brad Pitt. 2001. (People in the News Ser.). (Illus.). 112p. (J). (gr. 6-9). 27.45 (978-1-56006-867-9(1) , Lucent Bks.) Thomson Gale.

Dower, Laura. Hangin' with Hilary Duff. 2003. (Illus.). 48p. (J). pap. 5.99 (978-0-439-61732-1(4)) Scholastic, Inc.

Dupont, Connie Hull. Mike Myers. 1999. (Galaxy of Superstars Ser.). (Illus.). 64p. (YA). 25.00 (978-0-7910-5236-5(2) , Chelsea Hse.) Facts On File, Inc.

DuPont, Lonnie H. Mike Myers. 1999. (Galaxy of Superstars Ser.). (Illus.). 64p. (YA). pap. 25.00 (978-0-7910-5336-2(9) , Chelsea Hse.) Facts On File, Inc.

DuPont, Lonnie Hull. Mike Myers. 2000. (Illus.). 64p. (J). (ps-7). lib. bdg. 17.60 (978-0-613-22000-2(5)) Tandem Library Bks.

Dyson, Cindy. Brandon Lee. 2000. (They Died Too Young Ser.). (Illus.). 48p. (J). (gr. 4-7). pap. 18.65 (978-0-7910-5858-9(1) , Chelsea Hse.) Facts On File, Inc.

Eckel, Jessie, illus. How to be a Star in 7 Days or Less. 2006. (How to Be a... Ser.). 32p. (J). (gr. 3-5). 12.95 (978-0-7534-5956-0(6) , Kingfisher) Houghton Mifflin Co. Trade & Reference Div.

Edwards, Karen. Christopher Reeve: A Real-Life Superhero. 2005. (Illus.). 32p. (J). (978-0-669-51411-7(X)) Great Source Education Group, Inc.

Embacher, Eric. Will Smith: The Funny, Funky, & Confident Fresh Prince. 2003. (High Five Reading (Red Level) Ser.). (Illus.). (J). 64p. lib. bdg. 22.60 (978-0-7368-2786-7(2)); 48p. pap. 23.93 (978-0-7368-2829-1(X)) Capstone Pr., Inc.

Epstein, Dwayne. Adam Sandler. 2004. (Illus.). 112p. (J). 32.45 (978-1-59018-447-9(5) , Lucent Bks.) Thomson Gale.

—Hilary Swank. 2006. 112p. (gr. 7-10). 32.45 (978-1-59018-856-9(X) , Lucent Bks.) Thomson Gale.

—Will Ferrell. 2005. (People in the News Ser.). (Illus.). 112p. (YA). (gr. 7-10). lib. bdg. 32.45 (978-1-59018-716-6(4) , Lucent Bks.) Thomson Gale.

Feinstein, Stephen. Oprah Winfrey. 2007. (African-American Heroes Ser.). (Illus.). 24p. (J). (gr. 1-3). lib. bdg. 21.26 (978-0-7660-2764-0(3) , Enslow Elementary) Enslow Pubs., Inc.

Feinstein, Stephen. Will Smith. 2007. (African-American Heroes Ser.). (Illus.). 24p. (J). (gr. 1-3). lib. bdg. 21.26 (***978-0-7660-2765-7(1)*** , Enslow Elementary) Enslow Pubs., Inc.

Ferry, Joe. Rob Reiner. 2002. (Behind the Camera Ser.). (Illus.). 112p. (J). (gr. 6-12). 30.00 (978-0-7910-6717-8(3) , Chelsea Hse.) Facts On File, Inc.

Fingeroth, Danny. Elijah Wood. 2003. (High Interest Bks.). (Illus.). 48p. (YA). (gr. 7-12). pap. 6.95 (978-0-516-27858-2(4) , Children's Pr.) Scholastic Library Publishing.

—Elijah Wood. 2003. (gr. 7-12). lib. bdg. 15.25 (978-0-613-67884-1(2)) Tandem Library Bks.

—Liv Tyler. 2003. (gr. 7-12). lib. bdg. 15.25 (978-0-613-67909-1(1)) Tandem Library Bks.

Fishel, Danielle & Rizzo, Monica. A Teenager's Guide to Life. 1999. (Girls Get Real Ser.). (Illus.). 144p. (J). (gr. 3-9). pap. 5.99 (978-0-439-08788-9(0)) Scholastic, Inc.

Fitzgerald, Stephanie. Mary-Kate & Ashley Olsen. 2005. (Star Files Ser.). (Illus.). 48p. (J). (ps-1). lib. bdg. 31.43 (978-1-4109-1662-4(6)) Harcourt Schl. Pubs.

Ford, Carin T. Paul Robeson: I Want to Make Freedom Ring. 2007. (African-American Biography Library). (Illus.). 128p. (J). (gr. 6 up). lib. bdg. 31.93 (***978-0-7660-2703-9(1)***) Enslow Pubs., Inc.

Forkos, Heather. Tupac Shakur. 2000. (They Died Too Young Ser.). (Illus.). 48p. (J). (gr. 4-7). 21.95 (978-0-7910-5859-6(X) , Chelsea Hse.) Facts On File, Inc.

Freedman, Suzanne. Vanessa Williams: Singer. 1999. (Black Americans of Achievement Ser.). (Illus.). (YA). (gr. 4-7). 144p. pap. 9.95 (978-0-7910-4960-0(4)); 112p. 30.00 (978-0-7910-4959-4(0)) Facts On File, Inc. (Chelsea Hse.).

Friedman, Katherine. Hayden Christensen. 2002. (gr. 7-12). lib. bdg. 15.25 (978-0-613-58699-3(9)) Tandem Library Bks.

Friedrich, Belinda. Oprah Winfrey. 2001. (Women of Achievement Ser.). (Illus.). 112p. (J). pap. (978-0-7910-5892-3(1)); (gr. 4-7). 30.00 (978-0-7910-5891-6(3)) Facts On File, Inc. (Chelsea Hse.).

Furman, Leah. Jennifer Lopez. (Latinos in the Limelight Ser.). (Illus.). 64p. (J). 2002. pap. (978-0-7910-6111-4(6)); 2001. (gr. 3 up). 27.50 (978-0-7910-6110-7(8)) Facts On File, Inc. (Chelsea Hse.).

Gaines, Ann Graham. Drew Carey: Comedian/Performer. 1999. (Overcoming Adversity Ser.). (Illus.). 104p. (YA). (gr. 5 up). pap. 6.65 (978-0-7910-4943-3(4) , Chelsea Hse.) Facts On File, Inc.

—Hedy Lamarr. 2001. (Discover the Life of an Inventor Ser.). (Illus.). 24p. (J). (gr. 1-4). lib. bdg. 20.64 (978-1-58952-119-3(6)) Rourke Publishing, LLC.

—Hedy Lamarr. Sarfatti, Esther & de la Vega, Eida, trs. from ENG. 2001. (Inventores Famosos Ser.). (SPA., Illus.). 24p. (J). lib. bdg. 19.27 (978-1-58952-176-6(5) , RK7040) Rourke Publishing, LLC.

—Melissa Joan Hart. 2000. (Real-Life Reader Biography Ser.). (Illus.). 32p. (J). (gr. 3-8). lib. bdg. 15.95 (978-1-58415-036-7(X)) Mitchell Lane Pubs., Inc.

—Roseanne: Entertainer. 1999. (Overcoming Adversity Ser.). (Illus.). 128p. (YA). (gr. 5 up). pap. 8.95 (978-0-7910-4707-1(5)); lib. bdg. 21.95 (978-0-7910-4706-4(7)) Facts On File, Inc. (Chelsea Hse.).

—Steve Jobs: Real Life Reader Biography. 2000. (Real-Life Reader Biography Ser.). (Illus.). 32p. (J). (gr. 3-8). lib. bdg. 15.95 (978-1-58415-026-8(2)) Mitchell Lane Pubs., Inc.

—Whoopi Goldberg: Comedienne/Performer. 1999. (Overcoming Adversity Ser.). (Illus.). (YA). (gr. 5 up). 128p. pap. 6.65 (978-0-7910-4939-6(6)); 112p. lib. bdg. 21.95 (978-0-7910-4938-9(8)) Facts On File, Inc. (Chelsea Hse.).

Galaxy of Superstars. 2005. pap. 925.00 (978-0-7910-9145-6(7) , Chelsea Hse.) Facts On File, Inc.

Galaxy of Superstars, 6 bks., Set. Incl. Hanson. Powell, Phelan. (J). (gr. 3 up). pap. 25.00 (978-0-7910-5325-6(3)); Jonathan Taylor Thomas. Grabowski, John F. (YA). pap. 25.00 (978-0-7910-5330-0(X)); LeAnn Rimes. Zymet, Cathy Alter. (YA). (gr. 3). pap. 25.00 (978-0-7910-5327-0(X)); Leonardo DiCaprio. Stauffer, Stacey. (YA). pap. 25.00 (978-0-7910-5326-3(1)); Venus Williams. Aronson, Virginia. (J). pap. 25.00 (978-0-7910-5329-4(6)); 1999. (Illus.). 64p. 1999. Set pap. 59.70 (978-0-7910-5337-9(7) , Chelsea Hse.) Facts On File, Inc.

Giacobello, John. Melissa Joan Hart. 2002. (gr. 7-12). lib. bdg. 15.25 (978-0-613-58716-7(2)) Tandem Library Bks.

Giblin, James Cross. Good Brother, Bad Brother: The Story of Edwin Booth & John Wilkes Booth. 2005. (Illus.). 256p. (YA). (gr. 5-9). 22.00 (978-0-618-09642-8(6) , Clarion Bks.) Houghton Mifflin Co. Trade & Reference Div.

Girod, Christina M. Matt Damon. 2001. (People in the News Ser.). (Illus.). 112p. (J). (gr. 6-9). 32.45 (978-1-56006-774-0(8) , Lucent Bks.) Thomson Gale.

Gogerly, Liz. Halle Berrry. 2004. (Star Files Ser.). (Illus.). 48p. 29.93 (978-1-4109-1085-1(7)) Harcourt Schl. Pubs.

Gorman, Jacqueline Laks. The Olsen Twins. 2007. (Today's Superstars). 32p. (YA). (gr. 5 up). lib. bdg. 23.93 (***978-0-8368-8199-8(0)***) Stevens, Gareth Inc.

—Queen Latifah. 2006. (Today's Superstars). (Illus.). 32p. (J). (gr. 5 up). lib. bdg. 23.93 (***978-0-8368-7652-9(0)***) Stevens, Gareth Inc.

Grabowski, John. Jonathan Taylor Thomas. 1999. (gr. 5-8). lib. bdg. 17.60 (978-0-613-17686-6(3)) Tandem Library Bks.

Grabowski, John F. Jonathan Taylor Thomas. 1999. (Galaxy of Superstars Ser.). (Illus.). 64p. (YA). pap. 25.00 (978-0-7910-5330-0(X) , Chelsea Hse.) Facts On File, Inc.

Granados, Christine. Rosie O'Donnell. 1999. (Real-Life Reader Biography Ser.). (Illus.). 32p. (gr. 3-8). lib. bdg. 15.95 (978-1-883845-98-8(X)) Mitchell Lane Pubs., Inc.

Greene, Meg. Matt Damon. 2000. (Galaxy of Superstars Ser.). (Illus.). 64p. (J). pap. 9.95 (978-0-7910-5780-3(1)); (gr. 4-7). 25.00 (978-0-7910-5779-7(8)) Facts On File, Inc. (Chelsea Hse.).

—Will Smith. 2001. (Galaxy of Superstars Ser.). (Illus.). 64p. (J). 25.00 (978-0-7910-6469-6(7) , Chelsea Hse.) Facts On File, Inc.

Guzman, Lila & Guzman, Rick. George Lopez: Comedian & TV Star. 2006. (Famous Latinos Ser.). (Illus.). 32p. (J). lib. bdg. 22.60 (978-0-7660-2644-5(2) , Enslow Elementary) Enslow Pubs., Inc.

Guzman, Lila & Guzman, Rick. George Lopez: Comediante y estrella de TV. 2007. (Latinos Famosos Ser.). (Illus.). 32p. (J). (gr. 3-4). lib. bdg. 22.60 (***978-0-7660-2680-3(9)*** , Enslow Elementary) Enslow Pubs., Inc.

Hadley, Joyce M. Dorothy Arnold: Joe Dimaggio's First Wife. 2004. (Illus.). 189p. (YA). per. 16.95 (978-0-9667808-2-6(5)) Chauncey Park Pr.

Harrison, Paul. Mike Meyers. 2004. (Star Files Ser.). (Illus.). 48p. 29.93 (978-1-4109-1088-2(1)) Harcourt Schl. Pubs.

Hasday, Judy L. Extraordinary People in the Movies. 2003. (Extraordinary People Ser.). (Illus.). (J). (gr. 6 up). 288p. pap. 16.95 (978-0-516-27857-5(6)); 208-288p. 40.00 (978-0-516-22348-3(8)) Scholastic Library Publishing. (Children's Pr.).

—Extraordinary People in the Movies. 2003. (gr. 7-12). lib. bdg. 26.85 (978-0-613-67894-0(X)) Tandem Library Bks.

—Keri Russell. 2000. (Real-Life Reader Biography Ser.). (Illus.). 32p. (J). (gr. 3-8). lib. bdg. 15.95 (978-1-58415-033-6(5)) Mitchell Lane Pubs., Inc.

Hawes, Esme. Johnny Depp. 1999. (Superstars of Film Ser.). (Illus.). 48p. (YA). (gr. 5 up). 12.95 (978-0-7910-4648-7(6) , Chelsea Hse.) Facts On File, Inc.

—Pamela Anderson Lee. 1999. (Superstars of Film Ser.). (Illus.). 48p. (YA). (gr. 5 up). lib. bdg. 18.65 (978-0-7910-4647-0(8) , Chelsea Hse.) Facts On File, Inc.

Hayes, Donna. Brandy. 1999. (Real-Life Reader Biography Ser.). (Illus.). 32p. (J). (gr. 3-8). lib. bdg. 15.95 (978-1-883845-93-3(9)) Mitchell Lane Pubs., Inc.

Healy, Nick. Paul Robeson. 2003. (African-American Biographies Ser.). 64p. pap. 8.95 (978-1-4109-0040-1(1)); (Illus.). (J). lib. bdg. 28.56 (978-0-7398-6874-4(8)) Raintree.

Higgins, Kara. Jennifer Love Hewitt. 2003. (Illus.). 96p. (J). 32.45 (978-1-59018-324-3(X) , Lucent Bks.) Thomson Gale.

Hill, Anne E. Cameron Diaz. 1999. (Galaxy of Superstars Ser.). (Illus.). 64p. (YA). (gr. 3 up). pap. 25.00 (978-0-7910-5334-8(2)); 25.00 (978-0-7910-5234-1(6)) Facts On File, Inc. (Chelsea Hse.).

—Cameron Diaz. 2000. (gr. 5-8). lib. bdg. 17.60 (978-0-613-21283-0(5)) Tandem Library Bks.

—Drew Barrymore. 2001. (Illus.). 96p. (J). (gr. 4-12). 32.45 (978-1-56006-831-0(0) , Lucent Bks.) Thomson Gale.

—Gwyneth Paltrow. 2001. (Galaxy of Superstars Ser.). 64p. (J). 25.00 (978-0-7910-6463-4(8) , Chelsea Hse.) Facts On File, Inc.

—Kirsten Dunst. 2005. (People in the News Ser.). (Illus.). 112p. (YA). (gr. 7-10). lib. bdg. 32.45 (978-1-59018-715-9(6) , Lucent Bks.) Thomson Gale.

—Reese Witherspoon. 2003. (People in the News Ser.). (Illus.). 112p. (J). 32.45 (978-1-59018-450-9(5) , Lucent Bks.) Thomson Gale.

—Sandra Bullock. 2000. (People in the News Ser.). (Illus.). 96p. (J). (gr. 6-9). 27.45 (978-1-56006-711-5(X) , Lucent Bks.) Thomson Gale.

Holland, Gini. Oprah Winfrey. 2001. (Profiles Ser.). (Illus.). 56p. (J). (gr. 4-6). lib. bdg. 24.22 (978-1-58810-061-0(8)) Heinemann Library.

Holt, Julia. Jackie Chan, 6 vols. 2005. (Illus.). 32p. pap. (978-0-340-87655-8(7)) Cambridge Univ. Pr.

—Johnny Depp. 2001. (Livewire Ser.). (Illus.). 32p. pap. (978-0-340-80099-7(2) , Hodder Arnold) Hodder Education.

Holt, Julia & Basic Skills Agency Staff. Livewire. 2005. (Illus.). 32p. pap. (978-0-340-74729-2(3)) Cambridge Univ. Pr.

—Robbie Williams. 2005. (Illus.). 32p. pap. (978-0-340-77620-9(X)) Cambridge Univ. Pr.

Horn, Geoffrey M. Adam Sandler. 2005. (Today's Superstars). (Illus.). 32p. (J). (gr. 5 up). lib. bdg. 23.93 (978-0-8368-4234-0(0)) Stevens, Gareth Inc.

—Cameron Diaz. 2005. (Today's Superstars). (Illus.). 32p. (J). (gr. 5 up). lib. bdg. 23.93 (978-0-8368-4231-9(6)) Stevens, Gareth Inc.

—Jamie Foxx. 2005. (Today's Superstars). (Illus.). 32p. (J). (gr. 5 up). lib. bdg. 23.93 (978-0-8368-4232-6(4)) Stevens, Gareth Inc.

Horner, Matina S., intro. Rosie O'Donnell: Entertainer - Comedienne. 1999. (Women of Achievement Ser.). (Illus.). 112p. (YA). (gr. 4-7). pap. 9.95 (978-0-7910-4711-8(3), Chelsea Hse.) Facts On File, Inc.

Howard, Megan. Christopher Reeve. 1999. (Biography Ser.). (Illus.). 112p. (gr. 6-12). lib. bdg. 27.93 (978-0-8225-4945-1(X)) Lerner Publishing Group.

Hudak, Heather C. Oprah Winfrey. 2005. (Great African American Women for Kids Ser.). (Illus.). 24p. (J). (ps-7). pap. 6.95 (978-1-59036-341-6(8)); lib. bdg. 26.00 (978-1-59036-335-5(3)) Weigl Pubs., Inc.

Hunter, Matt. Jesse Ventura: The Story of the Wrestler They Call the Body. 2000. (gr. 5-8). lib. bdg. 17.60 (978-0-613-21049-2(2)) Tandem Library Bks.

—They Call Hollywood Hulk Hogan: Story of the Wrestler. 1999. (Pro Wrestling Legends Ser.). (Illus.). 64p. (YA). (gr. 3 up). 25.00 (978-0-7910-5406-2(3), Chelsea Hse.) Facts On File, Inc.

Hurst, Heidi. Jennifer Lopez. 2003. (People in the News Ser.). (Illus.). 112p. (J). 32.45 (978-1-59018-325-0(8), Lucent Bks.) Thomson Gale.

Israel, Elaine. Hilary Duff. 2006. (Today's Superstars). (Illus.). 32p. (J). (gr. 5 up). lib. bdg. 23.93 (***978-0-8368-7651-2(2)***) Stevens, Gareth Inc.

Jeffrey, Gary. Oprah Winfrey: The Life of a Media Superstar. 2006. 48p. (J). (978-1-4042-0924-4(7)); pap. (978-1-4042-0925-1(5)); lib. bdg. 29.95 (978-1-4042-0862-9(3)) Rosen Publishing Group, Inc., The.

Johns, Michael-Anne. Cool in School. 1999. (gr. 3-6). lib. bdg. 11.80 (978-0-613-24678-1(0)) Tandem Library Bks.

—Hangin' with Lindsay Lohan. 2004. (Illus.). 48p. (J). (978-0-439-72512-5(7)) Scholastic, Inc.

Jones, Veda Boyd. Ewan McGregor. (Galaxy of Superstars Ser.). (Illus.). 64p. (J). 2000. 25.00 (978-0-7910-5501-4(9)); 1999. pap. 25.00 (978-0-7910-5502-1(7)) Facts On File, Inc. (Chelsea Hse.).

—Ewan Mcgregor. 2000. (gr. 5-8). lib. bdg. 17.60 (978-0-613-21506-0(0)) Tandem Library Bks.

Joseph, Paul. Will Smith. 1999. (Young Profiles Ser.). (Illus.). 32p. (J). (gr. k-6). lib. bdg. 22.78 (978-1-57765-320-2(3), Checkerboard Library) ABDO Publishing Co.

Kara Higgins. Johnny Depp. 2004. (Illus.). 96p. 32.45 (978-1-59018-538-4(2)) Thomson Gale.

Kinstad-Pupeza, Lori. Brandy. 1999. (Young Profiles Ser.). (Illus.). 32p. (J). (gr. k-6). lib. bdg. 22.78 (978-1-57765-323-3(8), Checkerboard Library) ABDO Publishing Co.

—Leonardo DiCaprio. 1999. (Young Profiles Ser.). (Illus.). 32p. (J). (gr. k-6). lib. bdg. 22.78 (978-1-57765-322-6(X), Checkerboard Library) ABDO Publishing Co.

Kjelle, Marylou Morano. Brittany Murphy. 2006. (Robbie Reader Ser.). (Illus.). 32p. (J). (gr. 1-4). lib. bdg. (978-1-58415-520-1(5)) Mitchell Lane Pubs., Inc.

—Hilary Duff. 2004. (Robbie Reader Ser.). (Illus.). 32p. (J). (gr. 1-4). lib. bdg. 25.70 (978-1-58415-295-8(8)) Mitchell Lane Pubs., Inc.

Knelman, Martin. Mike's World: The Life of Mike Myers. 2003. (Illus.). 268p. (gr. 5-12). pap. 16.95 (978-1-55297-661-6(0)) Firefly Bks., Ltd.

Koopmans, Andy. Bruce Lee. 2001. (Importance of Ser.). (Illus.). 112p. (J). (gr. 7-10). 28.70 (978-1-59018-081-5(X), Lucent Bks.) Thomson Gale.

Kosek, Jane Kelly. Learning about Courage from the Life of Christopher Reeve. 1999. (Character Building Book Ser.). (Illus.). 24p. (J). (gr. 3). lib. bdg. 18.75 (978-0-8239-5346-2(7), PowerKids Pr.) Rosen Publishing Group, Inc., The.

Kozar, Richard. Michael J. Fox. 2001. (Overcoming Adversity Ser.). (Illus.). 110p. (YA). pap. 9.95 (978-0-7910-5426-0(8), Chelsea Hse.) Facts On File, Inc.

Kramer, Barbara. Michael J. Fox: Courage for Life. 2005. (Awesome Values in Famous Lives Ser.). (Illus.). 48p. (J). (gr. 3-4). lib. bdg. 23.93 (978-0-7660-2376-5(1), Enslow Elementary) Enslow Pubs., Inc.

—Oprah Winfrey: Reaching Out to Others. 2005. (Awesome Values in Famous Lives Ser.). (Illus.). 48p. (J). (gr. 3-4). lib. bdg. 23.93 (978-0-7660-2378-9(8), Enslow Elementary) Enslow Pubs., Inc.

—Ron Howard: Child Star & Hollywood Director. 1998. (People to Know Ser.). (Illus.). 112p. (YA). (gr. 6-12). lib. bdg. 26.60 (978-0-89490-981-8(9)) Enslow Pubs., Inc.

—Tom Hanks: Superstar. 2001. (People to Know Ser.). (Illus.). 112p. (J). (gr. 6-12). lib. bdg. 26.60 (978-0-7660-1436-7(3)) Enslow Pubs., Inc.

Krohn, Katherine. Oprah Winfrey. 2005. (Lighting Bolt Bios Ser.). (Illus.). 112p. (J). (gr. 6-12). 27.93 (978-0-8225-2472-4(4)) Lerner Publishing Group.

Krohn, Katherine E. Oprah Winfrey. (Biography Ser.). (Illus.). 112p. (J). (gr. 6 up). 2003. pap. 7.95 (978-0-8225-5000-6(8)); 2001. 27.93 (978-0-8225-4999-4(9), Lerner Pubns.) Lerner Publishing Group.

—Oprah Winfrey. 2002. (gr. 7-12). lib. bdg. 16.40 (978-0-613-84025-5(9)) Tandem Library Bks.

—Rosie O'Donnell. 2003. (Biography Ser.). (Illus.). 112p. (YA). (gr. 6 up). 7.95 (978-0-8225-9681-3(4), Carolrhoda Bks.) Lerner Publishing Group.

Krulik, Nancy E. Angels! The Inside Scoop on the Stars of Charlie's Angels. 2000. (gr. 5-8). lib. bdg. 13.00 (978-0-613-30949-3(9)) Tandem Library Bks.

—Heath Ledger: The Heath Is On! 2001. (gr. 3-6). lib. bdg. 13.00 (978-0-613-74241-2(9)) Tandem Library Bks.

—Second to None: Superstars on the Rise. 2000. (gr. 7-12). lib. bdg. 13.00 (978-0-613-73120-1(4)) Tandem Library Bks.

Kudlinski, Kathleen. Christopher Reeve: Young Actor. Henderson, Meryl, illus. 2007. (Childhood of Famous Americans Ser.). 224p. (J). pap. 5.99 (***978-1-4169-1544-7(3)***, Aladdin) Simon & Schuster Children's Publishing.

Laslo, Cynthia. Sarah Michelle Gellar. 2000. (Celebrity Bios Ser.). (Illus.). 48p. (J). pap. (978-0-531-17614-6(2), Watts, Franklin) Scholastic Library Publishing.

—Sarah Michelle Gellar. 2000. (gr. 7-12). lib. bdg. 15.25 (978-0-613-58730-3(8)) Tandem Library Bks.

Laslo, Cynthia, contrib. by. Sarah Michelle Gellar. 2000. (Celebrity Bios Ser.). (Illus.). 48p. (J). (978-0-531-12114-6(3), Watts, Franklin) Scholastic Library Publishing.

Latinos in the Limelight. 2005. pap. 357.50 (978-0-7910-8728-2(X), Chelsea Hse.) Facts On File, Inc.

Lawrence, Katherine Drobot. Jean-Claude Van Damme. 2005. (Martial Arts Masters Ser.). (Illus.). 112p. (YA). (gr. 7-12). lib. bdg. 25.25 (978-0-8239-3517-8(5)) Rosen Publishing Group, Inc., The.

Leavitt, Amie. Amanda Bynes. 2007. (Robbie Reader Ser.). (Illus.). 32p. (J). (gr. 1-4). lib. bdg. 25.70 (***978-1-58415-594-2(9)***) Mitchell Lane Pubs., Inc.

—Dylan & Cole Sprouse. 2007. (Robbie Reader Ser.). (Illus.). 32p. (J). (gr. 1-4). lib. bdg. 25.70 (***978-1-58415-591-1(4)***) Mitchell Lane Pubs., Inc.

—Miley Cyrus. 2007. (Robbie Reader Ser.). (Illus.). 32p. (J). (gr. 1-4). lib. bdg. 25.70 (***978-1-58415-590-4(6)***) Mitchell Lane Pubs., Inc.

—Raven-Symone. 2007. (Robbie Reader Ser.). (Illus.). 32p. (J). (gr. 1-4). lib. bdg. 25.70 (***978-1-58415-593-5(0)***) Mitchell Lane Pubs., Inc.

Lee, Sally. Arnold Schwarzenegger: From Superstar to Governor. 2006. (People to Know Today Ser.). (Illus.). 128p. (J). lib. bdg. 31.93 (978-0-7660-2625-4(6)) Enslow Pubs., Inc.

Lommel, Cookie. Cuba Gooding Jr. 1999. (Black Americans of Achievement Ser.). (Illus.). 104p. (J). (gr. 5-9). pap. 30.00 (978-0-7910-5276-1(1), Chelsea Hse.) Facts On File, Inc.

Lommel, Cookie & Edeison, Paula. Cuba Gooding Jr. 2000. (Black Americans of Achievement Ser.). (Illus.). 112p. (J). (gr. 4-7). 30.00 (978-0-7910-5275-4(3), Chelsea Hse.) Facts On File, Inc.

Lynette, Rachel. Angelina Jolie. 2006. (Illus.). 112p. (J). (gr. 7-10). 32.45 (978-1-59018-973-3(6), Lucent Bks.) Thomson Gale.

Madison, Taylor. Boys We Love: Today's Top 30 Hottest Stars. 2005. (Illus.). (J). (978-0-439-74864-3(X)) Scholastic, Inc.

Mara, Wil. Oprah Winfrey. 2005. (Rookie Biographies(R) Ser.). (Illus.). (gr. 1-2). 31p. (J). pap. 4.95 (978-0-516-25819-5(2)); 32p. 20.50 (978-0-516-21724-6(0)) Scholastic Library Publishing. (Children's Pr.).

Marcovitz, Hal. Lindsay Lohan. 2007. (J). (***978-1-4222-0206-7(2)***) Mason Crest Pubs.

—Owen & Luke Wilson. 2007. (J). (***978-1-4222-0210-4(0)***) Mason Crest Pubs.

Marcovitz, Hal. Ron Howard. 2002. (Behind the Camera Ser.). (Illus.). 112p. (YA). (gr. 6-12). 30.00 (978-0-7910-6716-1(5), Chelsea Hse.) Facts On File, Inc.

Marsh, Carole. Orson Welles. 2002. (One Thousand Readers Ser.). (Illus.). 12p. (J). (gr. k-4). 2.95 (978-0-635-01557-0(9), 15579) Gallopade International.

Marx, Christy. Jet Li. 2005. (Martial Arts Masters Ser.). (Illus.). 112p. (YA). (gr. 7-12). lib. bdg. 25.25 (978-0-8239-3519-2(1)) Rosen Publishing Group, Inc., The.

Mason, Paul. Sarah-Michelle Gellar. 2004. (Star Files Ser.). 20.95 (978-1-4109-1089-9(X)) Harcourt Schl. Pubs.

Mattern, Joanne. Dakota Fanning. 2006. (Robbie Reader Ser.). (Illus.). 32p. (J). (gr. 1-4). lib. bdg. (978-1-58415-519-5(1)) Mitchell Lane Pubs., Inc.

—Drake Bell & Josh Peck. 2007. (Robbie Reader Ser.). (Illus.). 32p. (J). (gr. 1-4). lib. bdg. 25.70 (***978-1-58415-592-8(2)***) Mitchell Lane Pubs., Inc.

—Orlando Bloom. 2007. (J). (***978-1-4222-0198-5(8)***) Mason Crest Pubs.

Mattern, Joanne. Tom Cruise. 2000. (People in the News Ser.). (Illus.). 96p. (J). (gr. 6-9). 32.45 (978-1-56006-827-3(2), Lucent Bks.) Thomson Gale.

McAvoy, Jim. Mel Gibson. 2001. (People in the News Ser.). (Illus.). 112p. (J). (gr. 6-9). 32.45 (978-1-56006-980-5(5), Lucent Bks.) Thomson Gale.

—Tom Hanks. 1999. (Galaxy of Superstars Ser.). (Illus.). 64p. (YA). pap. 25.00 (978-0-7910-5335-5(0)); 25.00 (978-0-7910-5235-8(4)) Facts On File, Inc. (Chelsea Hse.).

—Tom Hanks. 2000. (gr. 5-8). lib. bdg. 17.60 (978-0-613-22501-4(5)) Tandem Library Bks.

McCracken, Kristin. Freddie Prinze, Jr. 2001. (gr. 7-12). lib. bdg. 15.25 (978-0-613-52058-4(0)) Tandem Library Bks.

—James Van der Beek. 2001. (Celebrity Bios Ser.). (Illus.). 48p. (J). (gr. 7-12). 23.00 (978-0-516-23429-8(3)); pap. 6.95 (978-0-516-29604-3(3)) Scholastic Library Publishing. (Children's Pr.).

—James Van der Beek. 2001. (gr. 7-12). lib. bdg. 15.25 (978-0-613-58700-6(6)) Tandem Library Bks.

—Jennifer Love Hewitt. 2000. (High Interest Bks.). (Illus.). 48p. (YA). (gr. 7-12). 23.00 (978-0-516-23321-5(1)); pap. 6.95 (978-0-516-23521-9(4)) Scholastic Library Publishing. (Children's Pr.).

—Katie Holmes. 2001. (Celebrity Bios Ser.). 48p. (gr. 7-12). (YA). 23.00 (978-0-516-23426-7(9)); (Illus.). (J). pap. 6.95 (978-0-516-29601-2(9)) Scholastic Library Publishing. (Children's Pr.).

—Leonardo DiCaprio. 2000. (High Interest Bks.). (Illus.). 48p. (YA). (gr. 7-12). pap. 6.95 (978-0-516-23523-3(0), Children's Pr.); (J). (978-0-531-17611-5(8), Watts, Franklin); (J). (978-0-531-12111-5(9), Watts, Franklin) Scholastic Library Publishing.

McIntosh-Wooten, Sara. Oprah Winfrey: Talk Show Legend. 1999. (African-American Biographies Ser.). (Illus.). 128p. (YA). (gr. 6-12). lib. bdg. 26.60 (978-0-7660-1207-3(7)) Enslow Pubs., Inc.

McLeese, Don. Oprah Winfrey. 2002. (Discover the Life of an American Legend Ser.). (Illus.). 24p. (J). lib. bdg. 20.64 (978-1-58952-306-7(7)) Rourke Publishing, LLC.

Meachum, Virginia. Rosie O'Donnell: Talk Show Host & Comedian. 2000. (People to Know Ser.). (Illus.). 112p. (YA). (gr. 6-12). lib. bdg. 26.60 (978-0-7660-1148-9(8)) Enslow Pubs., Inc.

Membery, York. Keanu Reeves. 1999. (Superstars of Film Ser.). (Illus.). 48p. (YA). (gr. 5 up). lib. bdg. 18.65 (978-0-7910-4646-3(X), Chelsea Hse.) Facts On File, Inc.

Menard, Valerie. Cheech Marin. 2001. (Real-Life Reader Biography Ser.). (Illus.). 32p. (gr. 3-8). lib. bdg. 24.95 (978-1-58415-070-1(X)) Mitchell Lane Pubs., Inc.

—Jennifer Lopez. 2000. (Real-Life Reader Biography Ser.). (Illus.). 32p. (J). (gr. 3-8). lib. bdg. 15.95 (978-1-58415-025-1(4)) Mitchell Lane Pubs., Inc.

—Salma Hayek. 1999. (Real-Life Reader Biography Ser.). (Illus.). 32p. (J). (gr. 3-8). lib. bdg. 15.95 (978-1-58415-018-3(1)) Mitchell Lane Pubs., Inc.

—Winona Ryder. 2000. (Real-Life Reader Biography Ser.). (Illus.). 32p. (J). (gr. 3-8). lib. bdg. 15.95 (978-1-58415-039-8(4)) Mitchell Lane Pubs., Inc.

Mitchell, Susan K. Will Smith. 2006. (Today's Superstars). (Illus.). 32p. (J). (gr. 5 up). lib. bdg. 23.93 (***978-0-8368-7653-6(9)***) Stevens, Gareth Inc.

Mochizuki, Ken. Be Water, My Friend: The Early Years of Bruce Lee. Lee, Dom, illus. 2006. 32p. (J). 16.95 (978-1-58430-265-0(8)) Lee & Low Bks., Inc.

Morreale, Marie T. Class Acts: Celebrity Confession Sessions. 2000. (Illus.). 48p. (J). (gr. 3-9). pap. 5.99 (978-0-439-21027-0(5)) Scholastic, Inc.

Naden, Corinne J. Halle Berry. 2001. (gr. 3-6). lib. bdg. 18.75 (978-0-613-86157-1(4)) Tandem Library Bks.

Naden, Corinne J. & Blue, Rose. John Travolta. 2002. (People in the News Ser.). (Illus.). 112p. (YA). (gr. 6-9). 32.45 (978-1-56006-868-6(X), Lucent Bks.) Thomson Gale.

Napsha, Cheryl. Cher. 2001. (Women of Achievement Ser.). (Illus.). 112p. (J). (gr. 4-7). 30.00 (978-0-7910-5907-4(3), Chelsea Hse.) Facts On File, Inc.

Noble, Sandy. Mel Gibson. 1999. (Superstars of Film Ser.). (Illus.). 48p. (J). (gr. 4-7). lib. bdg. 18.65 (978-0-7910-4643-2(5), Chelsea Hse.) Facts On File, Inc.

Norwich, Grace. Amped up Aly & Aj Official Biography. 2007. 128p. (J). (gr. 3). 5.99 (***978-0-448-44841-1(6)***, Grosset & Dunlap) Penguin Group (USA) Inc.

—Ashley Tisdale: Life Is Sweet! An Unauthorized Biography. 2006. 128p. (J). pap. 4.99 (978-0-8431-2183-4(1), Price Stern Sloan) Penguin Group (USA) Inc.

—Daniel Radcliffe: No Ordinary Wizard. 2005. (Illus.). 128p. (J). pap. 4.99 (978-1-4169-1390-0(4), Simon Spotlight) Simon & Schuster Children's Publishing.

—Vanessa Hudgens: Breaking Free: An Unauthorized Biography. 2007. (Illus.). 128p. (J). pap. 4.99 (***978-0-8431-2668-6(X)***, Price Stern Sloan) Penguin Group (USA) Inc.

Norwich, Grace. Zac Attack: An Unauthorized Biography. 2006. (Illus.). 128p. (J). (gr. 3). pap. 4.99 (978-0-8431-2496-5(2), Price Stern Sloan) Penguin Group (USA) Inc.

Oleksy, Walter. Christopher Reeve. 1999. (People in the News Ser.). (Illus.). 112p. (YA). (gr. 6-9). 32.45 (978-1-56006-534-0(6), Lucent Bks.) Thomson Gale.

Oleksy, Walter G. James Dean. 2000. (Importance of Ser.). (Illus.). 112p. (J). (gr. 7-10). 27.45 (978-1-56006-698-9(9), Lucent Bks.) Thomson Gale.

Olsen, Mary-Kate & Olsen, Ashley. Mary-Kate & Ashley: Our Story: Mary-Kate & Ashley Olsen's Official Biography. 2000. (Illus.). 96p. (J). (gr. 3-7). mass mkt. 4.99 (978-0-06-107569-8(8)) HarperCollins Pubs.

Orr, Tamra. Ice Cube. 2006. (Blue Banner Biography Ser.). (Illus.). 32p. (J). (gr. 4-8). lib. bdg. (978-1-58415-517-1(5)) Mitchell Lane Pubs., Inc.

—Orlando Bloom. 2006. (Blue Banner Biography Ser.). (Illus.). 32p. (J). (gr. 4-8). lib. bdg. (978-1-58415-515-7(9)) Mitchell Lane Pubs., Inc.

Pappas, Rita. Barbra Streisand: Entertainer. 2000. (Women of Achievement Ser.). (Illus.). 112p. (J). (gr. 4-7). 30.00 (978-0-7910-5285-3(0), Chelsea Hse.) Facts On File, Inc.

Parish, James Robert. Jennifer Lopez: Actor & Singer. 2005. (Ferguson Career Biographies Ser.). (Illus.). 144p. (gr. 6-12). 25.00 (978-0-8160-5832-7(6), Ferguson Publishing Co.) Facts On File, Inc.

—Tom Hanks: Actor. 2004. (Ferguson Career Biographies Ser.). (Illus.). 128p. (J). (gr. 6-12). 25.00 (978-0-8160-5542-5(4), Ferguson Publishing Co.) Facts On File, Inc.

Parker, Judy. Keri Russell. 2001. (gr. 7-12). lib. bdg. 15.25 (978-0-613-58706-8(5)) Tandem Library Bks.

Poolos, J. Jackie Chan. 2005. (Martial Arts Masters Ser.). (Illus.). 112p. (YA). (gr. 7-12). lib. bdg. 25.25 (978-0-8239-3518-5(3)) Rosen Publishing Group, Inc., The.

Powell, Phelan. Alicia Silverstone. 2000. (Real-Life Reader Biography Ser.). (Illus.). 32p. (J). (gr. 3-8). lib. bdg. 15.95 (978-1-58415-037-4(8)) Mitchell Lane Pubs., Inc.

—Sarah Michelle Gellar. 2000. (Real-Life Reader Biography Ser.). (Illus.). 32p. (J). (gr. 3-8). lib. bdg. 15.95 (978-1-58415-034-3(3)) Mitchell Lane Pubs., Inc.

—Tom Cruise. 1999. (Overcoming Adversity Ser.). (978-0-606-18038-2(9)); (gr. 5-8). lib. bdg. 18.75 (978-0-613-12199-6(6)) Tandem Library Bks.

—Tom Cruise: Actor. 1999. (Overcoming Adversity Ser.). (Illus.). (YA). (gr. 5 up). 128p. pap. 30.00 (978-0-7910-4941-9(8)); 112p. 30.00 (978-0-7910-4940-2(X)) Facts On File, Inc. (Chelsea Hse.).

Reisfeld, Randi. Meet the Stars of Animorphs. 1999. (Animorphs Ser.). (J). (gr. 3-7). 144p. pap. 4.99 (978-0-439-06165-0(2)); pap. 59.88 (978-0-439-07272-4(7)) Scholastic, Inc.

—Sarah Michelle Gellar: She is the Slayer. 1998. (J). pap. 3.99 (978-0-590-64308-5(8)) Scholastic, Inc.

Rivera, Ursula. Rachel Leigh Cook. 2002. (gr. 7-12). lib. bdg. 15.25 (978-0-613-58725-9(1)) Tandem Library Bks.

—Reese Witherspoon. 2003. (High Interest Bks.). (Illus.). 48p. (YA). (gr. 7-12). pap. 6.95 (978-0-516-27860-5(6), Children's Pr.) Scholastic Library Publishing.

—Reese Witherspoon. 2003. (gr. 7-12). lib. bdg. 15.25 (978-0-613-67926-8(1)) Tandem Library Bks.

Rizzo, Monica. One Tree Hill: Meet the Stars of One Tree Hill. movie tie-in ed. 2005. (One Tree Hill Ser.). (Illus.). 160p. (J). pap. 5.99 (978-0-439-73036-5(8)) Scholastic, Inc.

Robbins, Trina. Hedy Lamarr & a Secret Communication System. 2007. (Illus.). 32p. (J). (***978-0-7368-9641-2(4)***) Capstone Pr., Inc.

—Hedy Lamarr & a Secret Communication System. Martin, Cynthia & Timmons, Anne, illus. 2007. (Graphic Library). 32p. (J). 25.26 (978-0-7368-6479-4(2)) Capstone Pr., Inc.

Roensch, Greg. Bruce Lee. 2005. (Martial Arts Masters Ser.). (Illus.). 112p. (YA). (gr. 7-12). lib. bdg. 25.25 (978-0-8239-3515-4(9)) Rosen Publishing Group, Inc., The.

Rozakis, Laurie E. & Rozakis, Samantha. Who Are You? Teen Magazine. 1999. 240p. (gr. 8-12). pap. (978-0-671-01193-2(6)) ibooks, Inc.

Salem, Jon. Adam Sandler: Not Too Shabby! 1999. (Illus.). 152p. (gr. 4-7). pap. 4.99 (978-0-439-10427-2(0)) Scholastic, Inc.

Sandison, David. Sharon Stone. 1999. (Superstars of Film Ser.). (Illus.). 48p. (YA). (gr. 5 up). 12.95 (978-0-7910-4650-0(8), Chelsea Hse.) Facts On File, Inc.

Scholastic, Inc. Staff. High School Musical: 101+ Secrets, Facts, & Buzz about High School Musical. 2007. (High School Musical Ser.). 48p. (J). pap. 5.99 (***978-0-545-03475-3(2)***) Scholastic, Inc.

Scholastic, Inc. Staff, ed. Lovin' Leo: Your Leonardo DiCaprio Scrapbook. 1998. (Illus.). 48p. (J). (gr. 4-7). pap. 5.99 (978-0-590-04855-2(4)) Scholastic, Inc.

Schuman, Michael. Will Smith: I Like Blending a Message with Comedy. 2006. (African-American Biography Library). (Illus.). 128p. (J). lib. bdg. 31.93 (978-0-7660-2465-6(2), 1250489) Enslow Pubs., Inc.

Scott, Kieran. Cameron Diaz. (Latinos in the Limelight Ser.). (Illus.). 64p. (J). 2002. pap. 27.50 (978-0-7910-6109-1(4)); 2001. (gr. 3 up). 19.75 (978-0-7910-6108-4(6), Chelsea Hse.) Facts On File, Inc.

—Salma Hayek. 2001. (Latinos in the Limelight Ser.). (Illus.). 64p. (J). (gr. 4-6). 27.50 (978-0-7910-6476-4(X), Chelsea Hse.) Facts On File, Inc.

Severs, Vesta-Nadine. Jennifer Love Hewitt. 2000. (Real-Life Reader Biography Ser.). (Illus.). 32p. (J). (gr. 3-8). lib. bdg. 24.95 (978-1-58415-032-9(7)) Mitchell Lane Pubs., Inc.

Sexton, Colleen A. Arnold Schwarzenegger. 2005. (A&E Biography Ser.). (Illus.). 112p. (J). (gr. 6-12). 29.27 (978-0-8225-1634-7(9)); (ENG & SPA., pap., lib. bdg. 27.93 (978-0-8225-5328-1(7)) Lerner Publishing Group.

Simmons, Alex. Denzel Washington. 1998. (Contemporary African Americans Ser.). (Illus.). 48p. (J). (gr. 3-7). pap. 7.95 (978-0-8172-6875-6(8)) Steck-Vaughn.

Singer, Linda-Marie. Elizabeth Taylor. 1999. (gr. 5-8). lib. bdg. 18.75 (978-0-613-11510-0(4)) Tandem Library Bks.

—Elizabeth Taylor: Actress/Activist. 1999. (Women of Achievement Ser.). (Illus.). 112p. (J). (gr. 4-7). pap. 30.00 (978-0-7910-4790-3(3), Chelsea Hse.) Facts On File, Inc.

Smith, Rod & Addison-Wesley Publishing Staff. Tom Cruise. 2002. (Illus.). 16p. (C). pap. 9.00 (978-0-582-50495-0(3)) Pearson ESL.

Smith, Terri Smith. Jessica Simpson. 2004. (J). pap. (978-1-932724-25-7(7), Bios for Kids) Panda Publishing, L.L.C.

Snyder, Gail. Queen Latifah. 2006. (Hip-Hop Ser.). (Illus.). 64p. (J). (gr. 5 up). 22.95 (978-1-4222-0126-8(0)) Mason Crest Pubs.

Stauffer, Stacey. Leonardo DiCaprio. 1999. (Galaxy of Superstars Ser.). (Illus.). 64p. (YA). pap. 25.00 (978-0-7910-5326-3(1)); (gr. 4-7). 25.00 (978-0-7910-5151-1(X)) Facts On File, Inc. (Chelsea Hse.).

Stevens, Larry P. & Stevens, Cara J. How to Reach Your Favorite Superstar. 1999. (Illus.). 95p. (J). pap. (978-0-7373-0332-2(8)) Lowell Hse.

Stevens, Larry P., et al. How to Reach Your Favorite Superstar. 2000. (Illus.). 95p. (J). (gr. 3-7). pap. 4.95 (978-0-7373-0456-5(1), 04561W, Roxbury Park Juvenile) Lowell Hse. Juvenile.

Stewart, Jeffrey C., ed. & intro. Paul Robeson: Artist & Citizen. Stewart, Jeffrey C., intro. 1998. (Illus.). 304p. (C). (gr. 10-12). pap. 22.00 (978-0-8135-2511-2(X)) Rutgers Univ. Pr.

Stewart, Mark. Will Smith. 2004. (Star Files Ser.). 29.93 (978-1-4109-1090-5(3)) Harcourt Schl. Pubs.

Stone, Amy. Jim Carrey. 2007. (Today's Superstars). 32p. (J). (gr. 5 up). lib. bdg. 23.93 (***978-0-8368-8197-4(4)***) Stevens, Gareth Inc.

Stone, Tanya Lee. Oprah Winfrey: Success with an Open Heart. 2001. (Gateway Biography Ser.). (Illus.). 48p. (gr. 2-4). (J). lib. bdg. 23.90 (978-0-7613-1814-9(3)); pap. (978-0-7613-1389-2(3)) Lerner Publishing Group. (Millbrook Pr.).

—Rosie O' Donnell: America's Favorite Grown-Up Kid. 2000. (Gateway Biography Ser.). (Illus.). 48p. (gr. 2-4). lib. bdg. 23.90 (978-0-7613-1724-1(4) , Millbrook Pr.) Lerner Publishing Group.

Tagliaferro, Linda. Bruce Lee. (Biography Ser.). (Illus.). 112p. (gr. 6-12). 2005. lib. bdg. 27.93 (978-0-8225-4948-2(4)); 2003. (YA). pap. 7.95 (978-0-8225-9688-2(1) , Carolrhoda Bks.) Lerner Publishing Group.

Taliadoros, Jenny, ed. Alice Faye: Glamorous Movie Star Paper Dolls & Costumes. Mingo, Norman & Ernst, Clara, illus. 2007. 8p. pap. 12.00 (*978-0-9795053-0-0(5)) Paper Studio Pr.

—Bette Davis Paper Dolls. Mingo, Norman & Ernst, Clara, illus. 2007. 8p. (J). pap. 12.00 (*978-0-9790668-2-5(4)) Paper Studio Pr.

—Betty Grable Paper Dolls. 2007. 8p. pap. 12.00 (*978-0-9790668-7-0(5)) Paper Studio Pr.

—Deanna Durbin Paper Dolls. Mingo, Norman & Ernst, Clara, illus. 2007. 8p. pap. 12.00 (*978-0-9790668-5-6(9)) Paper Studio Pr.

—Doris Day Paper Dolls. 2007. 8p. pap. 12.00 (*978-0-9790668-4-9(0)) Paper Studio Pr.

—Greer Garson Paper Dolls. Madan, Fredric & Ernst, Clara, illus. 2007. 8p. pap. 12.00 (*978-0-9790668-6-3(7)) Paper Studio Pr.

—Judy Garland Cut-Out Dolls. 2007. (Illus.). 8p. pap. 12.00 (*978-0-9790668-9-4(1)) Paper Studio Pr.

—Lana Turner Paper Dolls. Valliant, Regina & Meixner, Jo Hedwig, illus. 2007. 8p. (J). pap. 12.00 (*978-0-9790668-1-8(6)) Paper Studio Pr.

Taylor, Nancy & Addison-Wesley Publishing Staff. Julia Roberts, EasyStarts. 2002. (Illus.). 16p. (C). pap. 9.00 (978-0-582-50496-7(1)) Longman Publishing Group.

Tierney, Tom. Best Actresses of the 1990s Paper Dolls. 2006. 32p. (J). pap. 6.95 (978-0-486-44897-8(5)) Dover Pubns., Inc.

—Glamorous Latin Film Stars Paper Dolls. 2003. (Paper Dolls Ser.). (Illus.). 32p. (J). pap. 5.95 (978-0-486-43055-3(3)) Dover Pubns., Inc.

—Glamorous Movie Stars of the Nineties Paper Dolls. 2004. (Paper Dolls Ser.). (Illus.). 32p. (J). pap. 5.95 (978-0-486-43053-9(7)) Dover Pubns., Inc.

—Great Movie Dance Couples Paper Dolls. 2004. (Paper Dolls Ser.). (Illus.). 16p. (J). pap. 6.95 (978-0-486-43054-6(5)) Dover Pubns., Inc.

Torres, Jennifer. Ashton Kutcher. 2005. (Blue Banner Biography Ser.). (Illus.). 32p. (J). (gr. 3-8). lib. bdg. 25.70 (978-1-58415-380-1(6)) Mitchell Lane Pubs., Inc.

—Paris Hilton. 2005. (Blue Banner Biography Ser.). (Illus.). 32p. (J). (gr. 4-8). lib. bdg. 25.70 (978-1-58415-382-5(2)) Mitchell Lane Pubs., Inc.

Tracy, Kathleen. Aly & AJ. 2007. (Robbie Reader Ser.). (Illus.). 32p. (J). (gr. 1-4). lib. bdg. 25.70 (*978-1-58415-595-9(7)) Mitchell Lane Pubs., Inc.

—Johnny Depp. 2007. (Blue Banner Biography Ser.). (Illus.). 32p. (J). (gr. 4-8). lib. bdg. 25.70 (*978-1-58415-614-7(7)) Mitchell Lane Pubs., Inc.

—Lindsay Lohan. 2005. (Blue Banner Biography Ser.). (Illus.). 32p. (J). (gr. 3-8). lib. bdg. 25.70 (978-1-58415-393-1(8)) Mitchell Lane Pubs., Inc.

—Mary Kate & Ashley Olsen. l.t. ed. 2002. (Real-Life Reader Biography Ser.). (Illus.). 32p. (J). (gr. 3-8). lib. bdg. 15.95 (978-1-58415-124-1(2)) Mitchell Lane Pubs., Inc.

Tracy, Kathleen. Zac Efron. 2007. (Blue Banner Biography Ser.). (Illus.). 32p. (J). (gr. 4-8). lib. bdg. 25.70 (*978-1-58415-618-5(X)) Mitchell Lane Pubs., Inc.

Triumph Books Staff. Hilary Duff: Style, Fashion, Guys, & More! 2004. (Illus.). 80p. pap. 9.95 (978-1-57243-680-0(8)) Triumph Bks.

Tuttle, Dennis R. Angela Bassett. 2001. (Black Americans of Achievement Ser.). (Illus.). 106p. (J). (gr. 8-12). pap. 30.00 (978-0-7910-5811-4(5) , Chelsea Hse.) Facts On File, Inc.

Ward, Kristin. Learning about Assertiveness from the Life of Oprah Winfrey. 1999. (Character Building Book Ser.). (Illus.). 24p. (J). (gr. 3). lib. bdg. 18.75 (978-0-8239-5348-6(3) , PowerKids Pr.) Rosen Publishing Group, Inc., The.

Weber, Terri Smith. Frankie Muniz: Enjoying His Success. 2004. (J). pap. (978-1-932724-27-1(3)); lib. bdg. (978-1-932724-26-4(5)) Panda Publishing, L.L.C. (Bios for Kids).

—Hilary Duff: Branching Out. 2003. (J). pap. (978-1-932724-03-5(6)); lib. bdg. (978-1-932724-02-8(8) , Bios for Kids) Panda Publishing, L.L.C.

—Jennifer Lopez: Realizando Los Suenos. 2003. (SPA.). (J). pap. (978-0-9740180-4-1(X)); lib. bdg. (978-0-9740180-3-4(1)) Panda Publishing, L.L.C. (Bios for Kids).

—Jessica Simpson. 2004. (J). lib. bdg. (978-1-932724-24-0(9) , Bios for Kids) Panda Publishing, L.L.C.

Wellman, Sam. Ben Affleck. 1999. (Galaxy of Superstars Ser.). (Illus.). 64p. (YA). (gr. 4-7). pap. 25.00 (978-0-7910-5331-7(8)); (J). (gr. 10). 25.00 (978-0-7910-5231-0(1)) Facts On File, Inc. (Chelsea Hse.).

—Ben Affleck. 2000. (Galaxy of the Superstars Ser.). (gr. 5-8). lib. bdg. 17.60 (978-0-613-21191-8(X)) Tandem Library Bks.

West, Betsy. Corbin Bleu: To the Limit: An Unauthorized Biography. 2007. 128p. (J). pap. 4.99 (*978-0-8431-2685-3(X) , Price Stern Sloan) Penguin Group (USA) Inc.

—Jennifer Hudson: American Dream Girl: American Dream Girl An Unauthorized Biography. 2007. 128p. (J). (gr. 3). pap. 4.99 (*978-0-8431-2687-7(6) , Price Stern Sloan) Penguin Group (USA) Inc.

Westen, Robin. Oprah Winfrey: I Dont Believe in Failure. 2005. (African-American Biography Library). (Illus.). 128p. (J). (gr. 6-12). lib. bdg. 31.93 (978-0-7660-2462-5(8)) Enslow Pubs., Inc.

Wheeler, Jill C. Brad Pitt. 2003. (Star Tracks Ser.). (Illus.). 64p. (J). (gr. 3-8). lib. bdg. 25.65 (978-1-57765-769-9(1)) ABDO Publishing Co.

—Denzel Washington. 2003. (Star Tracks Ser.). (Illus.). 64p. (J). (gr. 3-8). lib. bdg. 25.65 (978-1-57765-772-9(1)) ABDO Publishing Co.

—Hilary Duff. 2004. (Young Profiles Ser.). (Illus.). 32p. (J). (gr. k-6). lib. bdg. 22.78 (978-1-59197-407-9(0)) ABDO Publishing Co.

—Jennifer Lopez. 2003. (Star Tracks Ser.). (Illus.). 64p. (J). (gr. 3-8). lib. bdg. 25.65 (978-1-57765-770-5(5)) ABDO Publishing Co.

—Jim Carrey. 2001. (Star Tracks Ser.). (Illus.). 64p. (J). (gr. 3-8). lib. bdg. 25.65 (978-1-57765-556-5(7) , ABDO & Daughters) ABDO Publishing Co.

—Julia Roberts. 2001. (Star Tracks Ser.). (Illus.). 64p. (J). (gr. 3-8). lib. bdg. 25.65 (978-1-57765-555-8(9) , ABDO & Daughters) ABDO Publishing Co.

—Lindsay Lohan. 2004. (Young Profiles Ser.). (Illus.). 32p. (J). (gr. k-6). 22.78 (978-1-59197-878-7(5)) ABDO Publishing Co.

—Madonna. 2003. (Star Tracks Ser.). (Illus.). 64p. (J). (gr. 3-8). lib. bdg. 25.65 (978-1-57765-768-2(3)) ABDO Publishing Co.

—Mel Gibson. 2003. (Star Tracks Ser.). (Illus.). 64p. (J). (gr. 3-8). lib. bdg. 25.65 (978-1-57765-767-5(5)) ABDO Publishing Co.

—Michael J. Fox. 2001. (Star Tracks Ser.). (Illus.). 64p. (J). (gr. 3-8). lib. bdg. 25.65 (978-1-57765-551-0(6) , ABDO & Daughters) ABDO Publishing Co.

—Star Tracks, Set. Incl. Jim Carrey. lib. bdg. 25.65 (978-1-57765-556-5(7)); Julia Roberts. lib. bdg. 25.65 (978-1-57765-555-8(9)); Michael J. Fox. lib. bdg. 25.65 (978-1-57765-551-0(6)); Shania Twain. lib. bdg. 25.65 (978-1-57765-552-7(4)); Tom Cruise. lib. bdg. 25.65 (978-1-57765-553-4(2)); Tom Hanks. lib. bdg. 25.65 (978-1-57765-554-1(0)); 64p. (J). (gr. 3-8). 2001. (Illus.). 2001. Set lib. bdg. 153.90 (978-1-57765-504-6(4) , ABDO & Daughters) ABDO Publishing Co.

—Tom Cruise. 2001. (Star Tracks Ser.). (Illus.). 64p. (J). (gr. 3-8). lib. bdg. 25.65 (978-1-57765-553-4(2) , ABDO & Daughters) ABDO Publishing Co.

—Tom Hanks. 2001. (Star Tracks Ser.). (Illus.). 64p. (J). (gr. 3-8). lib. bdg. 25.65 (978-1-57765-554-1(0) , ABDO & Daughters) ABDO Publishing Co.

Whiting, Jim. Hilary Duff. 2007. (J). (*978-1-4222-0201-2(1)) Mason Crest Pubs.

Wilson, Wayne. Bruce Lee. 2001. (Real-Life Reader Biography Ser.). (Illus.). 32p. (J). (gr. 3-8). lib. bdg. 15.95 (978-1-58415-066-4(1)) Mitchell Lane Pubs., Inc.

—Freddie Prinze, Jr. 2000. (Real-Life Reader Biography Ser.). (Illus.). 32p. (J). (gr. 3-8). lib. bdg. 15.95 (978-1-58415-063-3(7)) Mitchell Lane Pubs., Inc.

—Julia Roberts. 2000. (Real-Life Reader Biography Ser.). (Illus.). 32p. (J). (gr. 3-8). lib. bdg. 15.95 (978-1-58415-028-2(9)) Mitchell Lane Pubs., Inc.

Woog, Adam. Frank Sinatra. 2000. (Importance of Ser.). (Illus.). 112p. (YA). (gr. 7-10). 32.45 (978-1-56006-749-8(7) , Lucent Bks.) Thomson Gale.

Wooten, Sara McIntosh. Denzel Washington: Academy Award-Winning Actor. 2003. (African-American Biographies Ser.). (Illus.). 128p. (J). lib. bdg. 26.60 (978-0-7660-2131-0(9)) Enslow Pubs., Inc.

Woronoff, Kristen. Oprah Winfrey: Media Superstar. 2002. (Famous Women Juniors Ser.). (Illus.). 32p. (J). (gr. 3-5). 24.94 (978-1-56711-588-8(8) , Blackbirch Pr., Inc.) Thomson Gale.

Wren, Laura Lee. Christopher Reeve: Hollywood's Man of Courage. 1999. (People to Know Ser.). (Illus.). 112p. (YA). (gr. 6-12). lib. bdg. 26.60 (978-0-7660-1149-6(6)) Enslow Pubs., Inc.

Wukovits, John F. Jim Carrey. 1999. (People in the News Ser.). (Illus.). 112p. (YA). (gr. 6-9). 28.70 (978-1-56006-561-6(3) , Lucent Bks.) Thomson Gale.

—Michael J. Fox. 2002. (Illus.). 104p. (YA). (gr. 4-12). 32.45 (978-1-59018-200-0(6) , Lucent Bks.) Thomson Gale.

—Tobey Maguire. 2006. 112p. (J). (gr. 7-10). 32.45 (978-1-59018-719-7(9) , Lucent Bks.) Thomson Gale.

Young, Jeff C. Arnold Schwarzenegger. 2007. (Political Profiles Ser.). (Illus.). 112p. (YA). (gr. 5 up). lib. bdg. 27.95 (*978-1-59935-050-9(5)) Reynolds, Morgan Inc.

Zannos, Susan. Arnold Schwarzenegger. 1999. (Real-Life Reader Biography Ser.). (Illus.). 32p. (gr. 3-8). lib. bdg. 15.95 (978-1-883845-95-7(5)) Mitchell Lane Pubs., Inc.

—Drew Barrymore. 2000. (Real-Life Reader Biography Ser.). (Illus.). 32p. (J). (gr. 3-8). lib. bdg. 15.95 (978-1-58415-035-0(1)) Mitchell Lane Pubs., Inc.

—Robin Williams. 2000. (Real-Life Reader Biography Ser.). (Illus.). 32p. (J). (gr. 3-8). lib. bdg. 15.95 (978-1-58415-029-9(7)) Mitchell Lane Pubs., Inc.

—Sandra Bullock. 2000. (Real-Life Reader Biography Ser.). (Illus.). 32p. (J). (gr. 3-8). lib. bdg. 24.95 (978-1-58415-027-5(0)) Mitchell Lane Pubs., Inc.

ACTORS AND ACTRESSES—FICTION

Alger, Horatio. $500: Or, Jacob Marlowe's Secret. unabr. ed. 2002. (Polyglot Press Alger Ser.). (Illus.). (J). pap. 17.95 (978-1-931927-97-0(9)) Polyglot Pr., Inc.

Bell, Cece. Sock Monkey Goes to Hollywood: A Star Is Bathed. Bell, Cece, illus. 2003. (Illus.). 32p. (J). (ps). 13.99 (978-0-7636-1962-6(0)) Candlewick Pr.

—Sock Monkey Rides Again. Bell, Cece, illus. 2006. (Illus.). 32p. (J). (ps-2). 13.99 (978-0-7636-3089-8(6)) Candlewick Pr.

Blackwood, Gary L. The Shakespeare Stealer. 2000. (ps-7). 216p. (J). lib. bdg. 14.15 (978-0-613-28638-1(3)); (978-0-606-17870-9(8)) Tandem Library Bks.

—Shakespeare's Spy. 2005. 288p. (J). (gr. 5-9). pap. 6.99 (978-0-14-240311-2(3) , Puffin) Penguin Group (USA) Inc.

Blackwood, Gary L. & Alcorn, Stephen. The Shakespeare Stealer. 1998. 208p. (J). (gr. 4-6). 16.99 (978-0-525-45863-0(8) , Dutton Juvenile) Penguin Group (USA) Inc.

Block, Francesca Lia. Psyche in a Dress. 2006. 128p. (J). (gr. 9 up). 15.99 (978-0-06-076372-5(8)); lib. bdg. 16.89 (978-0-06-076373-2(6)) HarperCollins Pubs. (Cotler, Joanna Books).

Blumenthal, Deborah. Charlie Hits It Big. 2008. (Illus.). 32p. (J). 16.99 (*978-0-06-056353-0(2)); lib. bdg. 17.89 (*978-0-06-056354-7(0)) HarperCollins Pubs.

Bonk, John J. Dustin Grubbs: One Man Show. 2006. 272p. (J). (gr. 3-7). pap. 5.99 (978-0-316-15408-6(3)) Little Brown & Co.

Cabot, Meg. Teen Idol. (J). (gr. 7 up). 2004. 304p. 15.99 (978-0-06-009616-8(0)); 2005. (Illus.). 320p. reprint ed. pap. 8.99 (978-0-06-009618-2(7) , Harper Trophy) HarperCollins Pubs.

—Teen Idol. l.t. ed. 2006. 366p. (YA). 23.95 (978-0-7862-7760-5(2)) Thorndike Pr.

Calonita, Jen. Secrets of My Hollywood Life. 2006. 256p. (J). (gr. 7-17). 16.99 (978-0-316-15442-0(3)) Little Brown & Co.

—Secrets of My Hollywood Life. 2007. 256p. (J). (gr. 7 up). pap. 7.99 (*978-0-316-15443-7(1) , Poppy) Little, Brown Bks. for Young Readers.

—Secrets of My Hollywood Life: On Location. 2nd ed. 2007. 240p. (J). (gr. 7 up). 16.99 (*978-0-316-15439-0(3)) Little, Brown Bks. for Young Readers.

Clements, Bruce. What Erika Wants. 2005. 224p. (YA). (gr. 7-17). 16.00 (978-0-374-32304-2(6) , Farrar, Straus & Giroux (BYR)) Farrar, Straus & Giroux.

Coleman, Rowan. Ruby Parker Hits the Small Time. 2007. 240p. (J). (gr. 6-9). lib. bdg. 16.89 (978-0-06-077630-5(7)); (gr. 7 up). 15.99 (978-0-06-077628-2(5)) HarperCollins Pubs. (HarperTeen).

Collins, Yvonne & Rideout, Sandy. Introducing Vivien Leigh Reid: Daughter of the Diva. 2005. 240p. pap. 9.95 (978-0-312-33837-4(6) , St. Martin's Griffin) St. Martin's Pr.

—The New & Improved Vivien Leigh Reid: Diva in Control. 2007. 240p. (gr. 7-10). pap. 9.95 (978-0-312-35828-0(8) , St. Martin's Griffin); 231p. (YA). (*978-1-4287-1928-6(8)) St. Martin's Pr.

Conford, Ellen. Annabel the Actress: Starring in Gorilla My Dreams. 2000. (gr. k-3). lib. bdg. 11.80 (978-0-613-29876-6(4)) Tandem Library Bks.

—Annabel the Actress Starring in Gorilla My Dreams. Andriani, Renee W., illus. 2000. (Annabel the Actress Ser.). 64p. (J). (gr. 2-5). pap. 3.99 (978-0-689-83883-5(2) , Aladdin) Simon & Schuster Children's Publishing.

—Annabel the Actress Starring in Gorilla My Dreams. 2000. (Ready-for-Chapters Ser.). (J). 10.79 (978-0-606-20029-5(0)) Tandem Library Bks.

—Hound of the Barkervilles. Andriani, Renee W., illus. 2002. (Annabel the Actress Ser.). 96p. (J). (gr. 2-5). 15.00 (978-0-689-84734-9(3)) Simon & Schuster Children's Publishing.

Cooke, Jordan. Pilot Episode. 2008. 224p. (J). (gr. 9). pap. 6.99 (*978-0-448-44670-7(7) , Grosset & Dunlap) Penguin Group (USA) Inc.

Cooke, Marjorie Benton. Bambi. 2004. reprint ed. pap. 27.95 (978-1-4191-0885-3(9)); pap. 1.99 (978-1-4192-0885-0(3)) Kessinger Publishing, LLC.

Cooper, Susan. King of Shadows. 2005. 192p. (J). pap. 2.99 (978-1-4169-0532-5(4) , Aladdin) Simon & Schuster Children's Publishing.

—King of Shadows. Clapp, John, illus. 192p. (J). (gr. 5-9). 2001. mass mkt. 5.99 (978-0-689-84445-4(X) , Aladdin); 1999. 16.00 (978-0-689-82817-1(9) , McElderry, Margaret K.) Simon & Schuster Children's Publishing.

—King of Shadows. l.t. ed. 2000. (Thorndike Press Large Print Juvenile Ser.). (Illus.). 246p. (J). (gr. 8-12). 21.95 (978-0-7862-2706-8(0)) Thorndike Pr.

Craft, Elizabeth & Fain, Sarah. Bass Ackwards & Belly Up. 2006. 240p. (J). (gr. 7-17). 16.99 (978-0-316-05793-6(2)) Little Brown & Co.

—Bass Ackwards & Belly Up. 2007. 404p. (J). (gr. 10 up). pap. 8.99 (*978-0-316-05794-3(0) , Poppy) Little, Brown Bks. for Young Readers.

Czech, Jan. Grace Happens. 2007. 160p. (YA). pap. 6.99 (978-0-14-240752-3(6) , Puffin) Penguin Group (USA) Inc.

deGroat, Diane. Annie Pitts, Swamp Monster. 2001. (978-0-606-22334-8(7)) Tandem Library Bks.

Dhami, Narinder. Bollywood Babes. 224p. (J). 2006. (gr. 4-7). pap. 5.50 (978-0-440-42020-0(2) , Yearling); 2005. (gr. 3). 14.95 (978-0-385-73178-2(7) , Delacorte Bks. for Young Readers) Random Hse. Children's Bks.

Douglas, Lola. True Confessions of a Hollywood Starlet. (YA). (gr. 7-12). 2007. 272p. 6.99 (978-1-59514-153-8(7)); 2006. 288p. pap. 6.99 (978-1-59514-093-7(X)); 2005. 272p. 16.99 (978-1-59514-035-7(2)) Penguin Group (USA) Inc. (Razorbill).

DPWW, ed. High School Musical Actors' Biography. 2007. (J). (gr. 2-7). pap. 6.99 (*978-1-4231-0827-6(2)) Disney Pr.

Duder, Tessa. Tiggie Thompson All at Sea. 2001. 232p. (YA). pap. (978-0-14-131323-8(4) , Puffin) Penguin Group (USA) Inc.

Edwards, Julie Andrews. The Great American Mousical. Walton, Tony, illus. 2007. 160p. (J). pap. 5.99 (*978-0-06-057920-3(X) , Harper Trophy) HarperCollins Pubs.

Edwards, Julie Andrews & Hamilton, Emma Walton. The Great American Mousical. Walton, Tony, illus. 2006. (Julie Andrews Collection). 160p. (J). 15.99 (978-0-06-057918-0(8) , Julie Andrews Collection); lib. bdg. 16.89 (978-0-06-057919-7(6)) HarperCollins Pubs.

Fisher, Linda C. A Will of Her Own. 2006. (YA). pap. (978-0-88092-641-6(4)); lib. bdg. (978-0-88092-640-9(6)) Royal Fireworks Publishing Co.

Hagerup, Klaus. Markus & Diana. Chace, Tara, tr. from NOR. 2006. 192p. (J). 17.95 (978-1-932425-59-8(4) , Front Street) Boyds Mills Pr.

Hartinger, Brent. Split Screen: Attack of the Soul-Sucking Brain Zombies/Bride of the Soul-Sucking Brain Zombies. 2007. 304p. (J). (gr. 9 up). 16.99 (978-0-06-082408-2(5)); lib. bdg. 17.89 (978-0-06-082409-9(3)) HarperCollins Pubs. (HarperTeen).

Heyes, Eileen. O'Dwyer & Grady Starring In: Acting Innocent. Carver, Steve, illus. 2002. 176p. (J). (gr. 4-7). pap. 4.99 (978-0-689-84911-4(7) , Aladdin) Simon & Schuster Children's Publishing.

—O'Dwyer & Grady Starring in Acting Innocents. 2002. (gr. 3-6). lib. bdg. 13.00 (978-0-613-57433-4(8)) Tandem Library Bks.

—O'Dwyer & Grady Starring in Tough Act to Follow. 2003. (gr. 3-6). lib. bdg. 13.00 (978-0-613-66465-3(5)) Tandem Library Bks.

Hirsch, Odo. Antonio S. & the Mysterious Theodore Guzman. 2001. (Illus.). 224p. (J). lib. bdg. 16.49 (978-0-7868-2605-6(3)) Hyperion Bks. for Children.

—Antonio S. & the Mysterious Theodore Guzman. Hall, August, illus. 2001. 208p. (gr. 3-7). 15.99 (978-0-7868-0747-5(4)) Hyperion Bks. for Children.

Inches, Alison. Barbie: Super Spy. Wolcott, Karen, illus. 2005. (Starring Barbie Ser.: Vol. 4). (J). (*978-1-4155-7688-5(2) , Golden Bks.) Random Hse. Children's Bks.

Kennedy, Mary. Tales of a Hollywood Gossip Queen. 2006. 256p. (YA). (gr. 12). pap. 9.99 (978-0-425-20993-6(8) , Berkley Trade) Penguin Group (USA) Inc.

Krulik, Nancy E. Quiet on the Set!, No. 10. John and Wendy Staff, illus. 2003. (Katie Kazoo, Switcheroo Ser.: No. 10). 80p. (J). pap. 3.99 (978-0-448-43214-4(5) , Grosset & Dunlap) Penguin Group (USA) Inc.

Lambert, Janet. Stagestruck Parri. 2001. (Parri MacDonald Series by Janet Lambert: Vol. 3). (YA). pap. 12.95 (978-1-930009-43-1(7)) Image Cascade Publishing.

Lantz, Francess L. Lights, Camera, Love! 2000. (gr. 3-6). lib. bdg. 11.80 (978-0-613-21906-8(6)) Tandem Library Bks.

Lee, Tanith. Piratica: Being a Daring Tale of a Singular Girl's Adventure upon the High Seas. (Piratica Ser.: Vol. 1). 304p. (gr. 6). 2006. (YA). pap. 6.99 (978-0-14-240644-1(9) , Puffin); 2004. (Illus.). (J). 17.99 (978-0-525-47324-4(6) , Dutton Juvenile) Penguin Group (USA) Inc.

Littlesugar, Amy. The Tree of Hope. Cooper, Floyd, illus. 2001. 40p. (J). pap. 6.99 (978-0-698-11903-1(7) , Putnam Juvenile) Penguin Group (USA) Inc.

Lockhart, E. Dramarama. 2007. 320p. (gr. 7 up). 15.99 (978-0-7868-3815-8(9)) Hyperion Bks. for Children.

Lutz, Norma Jean. Elise the Actress: Climax of the Civil War. 2005. (Sisters in Time Ser.). 141p. (J). (*978-1-4156-0075-7(9)) Barbour Publishing, Inc.

Madison, Bennett. Lulu Dark & the Summer of the Fox. 2007. 208p. (YA). (gr. 7-12). 5.99 (978-1-59514-154-5(5) , Razorbill) Penguin Group (USA) Inc.

Manning, Sarra. Pretty Things (Splashproof Ed.) 2007. 1p. (YA). (gr. 7). pap. 6.99 (978-0-14-240859-9(X) , Puffin) Penguin Group (USA) Inc.

Martin, Ann M. Maggie: Diary Three. 1999. (California Diaries: Bk. 13). (Illus.). (YA). (gr. 6-8). (978-0-606-18524-0(0)) Tandem Library Bks.

Maxwell, Katie. The Year My Life Went down the Loo. 2003. (YA). pap. 5.99 (978-0-8439-5313-8(6)) Dorchester Publishing Co., Inc.

Pfeffer, Susan Beth. Revenge of the Aztecs. 2004. 118p. (J). lib. bdg. 16.92 (*978-1-4242-0763-3(0)) Fitzgerald Bks.

Pfeffer, Susan Beth. Revenge of the Aztecs: A Story of 1920s Hollywood. 2001. (American Portraits Ser.). (Illus.). 114p. (J). (gr. 5-8). 15.32 (978-0-8092-0586-8(6) , 9780809205868) Jamestown.

—Revenge of the Aztecs: A Story of 1920s Hollywood. 2004. (Jamestown's American Portraits Ser.). (Illus.). 120p. (J). (gr. 5-7). pap. 4.95 (978-0-7696-3431-9(1) , Waterbird Bks.) School Specialty Publishing.

—Revenge of the Aztecs: A Story of 1920s Hollywood. 2000. (978-0-606-21875-7(0)); (gr. 5-8). lib. bdg. 14.95 (978-0-613-36866-7(5)) Tandem Library Bks.

Pfeffer, Susan Beth & McGraw-Hill Staff. Revenge of the Aztecs: A Story of 1920s Hollywood. 2001. (Jamestown Classics Ser.). (Illus.). 114p. (J). (gr. 5-8). pap. 10.00 (978-0-8092-0627-8(7) , 9780809206278) Jamestown.

Pinder, Margaret. But I Don't Want to Be a Movie Star. 2006. 256p. (YA). (gr. 6-12). 15.99 (978-0-525-47634-4(2) , Dutton Juvenile) Penguin Group (USA) Inc.

Reisfeld, Randi. Starlet. 2007. 304p. (gr. 7 up). pap. 8.99 (*978-1-4231-0501-5(X)) Hyperion Pr.

Rocheleau, Nicole. Ollie Ollie in Come Free! 2006. 76p. pap. 14.95 (978-1-4241-0433-8(5)) PublishAmerica, Inc.

Scheunemann, Pam. Peacock Fan. Chawla, Neena, illus. (Fact & Fiction Ser.). 24p. (J). 2007. 21.35 (978-1-59928-460-6(X)); 2006. (978-1-59928-461-3(8)) ABDO Publishing Co.

Schwartz, Amy. Starring Miss Darlene. 2007. (Illus.). 32p. (J). (ps-3). 16.95 (*978-1-59643-230-7(6)) Roaring Brook Pr.

Selfors, Suzanne. Saving Juliet. 2008. 256p. (YA). 16.95 (*978-0-8027-9740-7(7)) Walker & Co.

Senate, Melissa. Theodora Twist. 224p. (YA). (gr. 9). 2007. pap. 7.99 (***978-0-385-73302-1(X));*** 2006. 15.95 (978-0-385-73301-4(1)); 2006. lib. bdg. 17.99 (978-0-385-90322-6(7)) Random Hse. Children's Bks. (Delacorte Bks. for Young Readers).

Sheldon, Dyan. Confessions of a Teenage Hollywood Star. 2007. (Illus.). 208p. (YA). (gr. 7 up). pap. 7.99 (***978-0-7636-3408-7(5))*** Candlewick Pr.

Sones, Sonya. One of Those Hideous Books Where the Mother Dies. 272p. (YA). 2004. (Illus.). 16.95 (978-0-689-85820-8(5)); 2005. (gr. 7-12). reprint ed. pap. 6.99 (978-1-4169-0788-6(2) , Simon Pulse) Simon & Schuster Children's Publishing.

Van Draanen, Wendelin. Sammy Keyes & the Hollywood Mummy. VanDraanen, Wendelin, illus. 2001. (Sammy Keyes Ser.: Bk. 6). pap. 36.95 incl. audio (978-0-87499-800-9(X)); pap. 54.95 incl. audio compact disk (978-0-87499-868-9(9)) Live Oak Media.

Waber, Bernard. Evie & Margie. Waber, Bernard, illus. 2003. (Illus.). 32p. (J). (gr. k-3). 15.00 (978-0-618-34124-5(2) , Walter Lorraine) Houghton Mifflin Co. Trade & Reference Div.

Warner, Gertrude Chandler. The Movie Star Mystery. 1999. (Boxcar Children Ser.: No. 69). (J). (gr. 2-5). (978-0-606-18762-6(6)) Tandem Library Bks.

—Movie Star Mystery. 1999. (gr. 3-6). lib. bdg. 11.80 (978-0-613-16285-2(4)) Tandem Library Bks.

Warner, Gertrude Chandler, creator. The Movie Star Mystery, Vol. 69. 1999. (Boxcar Children Ser.: No. 69). (Illus.). 128p. (J). (gr. 2-5). 14.95 (978-0-8075-5303-9(4)); pap. 4.50 (978-0-8075-5304-6(2)) Whitman, Albert & Co.

Wemmlinger, Raymond. Booth's Daughter. 2007. 210p. (YA). (gr. 7 up). 17.95 (978-1-932425-86-4(1) , Front Street) Boyds Mills Pr.

Wilcox, Mary. Caught on Tape. 2007. (Hollywood Sisters Ser.). 208p. (J). (gr. 5). 7.99 (***978-0-385-73356-4(9));*** lib. bdg. 10.99 (***978-0-385-90371-4(5))*** Random Hse. Children's Bks. (Delacorte Bks. for Young Readers).

—The Hollywood Sisters: Backstage Pass. 2006. 256p. (J). (gr. 5). 7.95 (978-0-385-73354-0(2)); lib. bdg. 9.99 (978-0-385-90369-1(3)) Random Hse. Children's Bks. (Delacorte Bks. for Young Readers).

—On Location. 2007. (Hollywood Sisters Ser.). 240p. (J). (gr. 5). 7.99 (978-0-385-73355-7(0) , Delacorte Bks. for Young Readers) Random Hse. Children's Bks.

Wilcox, Mary. Truth or Dare. 2008. (J). (***978-0-385-90514-5(9));*** pap. (***978-0-385-73528-5(6))*** Dell Publishing. (Delacorte Pr.).

Zindel, Lizabeth. Girl of the Moment. 288p. (YA). (gr. 7). 2008. pap. 8.99 (***978-0-14-241104-9(3)*** , Puffin); 2007. 16.99 (978-0-670-06210-2(3) , Viking Juvenile) Penguin Group (USA) Inc.

ADAGES

see Proverbs

ADAM (BIBLICAL FIGURE)

Bostrom, Kathleen Long. The Snake in the Grass: The Story of Adam & Eve. McKinsey, Dennis, illus. 2003. 48p. (J). 12.95 (978-0-664-22592-6(6)) Westminster John Knox Pr.

Frank, Penny. Adam & Eve. (Illus.). 24p. 2.99 (978-0-7459-4102-8(8) , Lion) Lion Hudson plc GBR. *Dist:* Trafalgar Square Publishing.

Freed, Shirley Ann & Moon, Louise. Adam Named the Animals. Morelan, Bill, ed. Butler, Steven, illus. l.t. ed. 2002. 8p. (J). (ps-k). pap. 3.99 (978-1-58938-000-4(2)) Concerned Communications.

Nederveld, Patricia L. Adam & Eve: The Story of the First Man & Woman. 1998. (God Loves Me Ser.). (Illus.). 24p. (J). (ps-3). pap. 2.95 (978-1-56212-272-0(X) , 001203, Faith Alive Christian Resources) CRC Pubns.

—Take Good Care of My World! The Story of Adam & Eve in the Garden. 1998. (God Loves Me Ser.). (Illus.). 24p. (J). (ps-3). pap. 2.95 (978-1-56212-273-7(8) , 001204, Faith Alive Christian Resources) CRC Pubns.

—A Very Sad Day: The Story of Adam & Eve's Disobedience. 1998. (God Loves Me Ser.). (Illus.). 24p. (J). (ps-3). pap. 2.95 (978-1-56212-274-4(6) , 001205, Faith Alive Christian Resources) CRC Pubns.

Pingry, Patricia A. The Story of Adam & Eve. Thornburgh, Rebecca McKillip, illus. 2002. 26p. (J). bds. 6.95 (978-0-8249-6280-7(X) , Candy Cane Pr.) Ideals Pubns.

Pulley, Kelly, illus. Adam & Eve in the Garden: My First I Can Read! 2008. 32p. (J). pap. (***978-0-310-71552-8(0))*** Zonderkidz.

Ray, Jane. Adam & Eve & the Garden of Eden. Ray, Jane, illus. 2005. (Illus.). 32p. (J). 17.00 (978-0-8028-5278-6(5)) Eerdmans, William B. Publishing Co.

—Adam & Eve & the Garden of Eden. 2006. (Illus.). 32p. (J). pap. (978-1-903919-07-1(X) , Eden Project Books) Transworld Publishers Ltd.

Sasso, Sandy Eisenberg. Adam & Eve's First Sunset: God's New Day. Rothenberg, Joani Keller, illus. 2003. 32p. (J). 17.95 (978-1-58023-177-0(2)) Jewish Lights Publishing.

—Adam & Eve's New Day. Rothenberg, Joani Keller, illus. 2006. 24p. (J). bds. 7.99 (978-1-59473-205-8(1)) SkyLight Paths Publishing.

Smart Kids Publishing Staff. Adam & Eve: All about Doing What's Right. 2006. 12p. (ps). bds. 14.95 (978-0-8249-6660-7(0) , Candy Cane Pr.) Ideals Pubns.

The Story of Adam & Eve. 2003. (Illus.). 24p. (J). bds. 6.95 (978-0-8249-4229-8(9)) Ideals Pubns.

Wilson, N. D. The Dragon & the Garden. 2007. (J). per. 12.00 (***978-1-59128-044-6(3))*** Canon Pr.

ADAMS, ABIGAIL, 1744-1818

Adler, David A. & Adler, Michael S. A Picture Book of John & Abigail Adams. Himler, Ronald, illus. 2007. (J). (978-0-8234-2007-0(8)) Holiday Hse., Inc.

Ashby, Ruth. John & Abigail Adams. 2005. (Illus.). 48p. (J). pap. (978-0-8368-5761-0(5)); lib. bdg. 30.00 (978-0-8368-5755-9(0)) Stevens, Gareth Inc. (World Almanac Library).

Bober, Natalie S. Abigail Adams: Witness to a Revolution. 1998. (Illus.). 272p. (YA). (gr. 7-12). pap. 9.99 (978-0-689-81916-2(1) , Simon Pulse) Simon & Schuster Children's Publishing.

—Abigail Adams: Witness to a Revolution. 1998. 16.64 (978-0-606-13106-3(X)) Tandem Library Bks.

Ching, Jacqueline. Abigail Adams: A Revolutionary Woman. 2005. (Library of American Lives & Times). (Illus.). 112p. (J). (gr. 4-8). lib. bdg. 31.95 (978-0-8239-5723-1(3)) Rosen Publishing Group, Inc., The.

Connell, Kate. Servant to Abigail Adams: The Early American Adventures of Hannah Cooper. 2004. (Illus.). 40p. (J). (gr. 4-8). pap. 7.00 (978-0-7567-8216-0(3)) DIANE Publishing Co.

Connell, Kate & Feresten, Nancy. Servant to Abigail Adams: The Early Colonial Adventures of Hannah Cooper. 2003. (I Am American Ser.). (Illus.). 40p. (J). (gr. 3-7). pap. 6.99 (978-0-7922-5828-5(2) , National Geographic Children's Bks.) National Geographic Society.

Davis, Kate. Abigail Adams. 2002. (Triangle History of the American Revolution Ser.). (Illus.). 104p. (J). 28.70 (978-1-56711-610-6(8) , Blackbirch Pr., Inc.) Thomson Gale.

Ferris, Jeri Chase. Remember the Ladies: A Story about Abigail Adams. Beier, Ellen, illus. (Creative Minds Biographies Ser.). 64p. (J). (gr. 3-6). 2003. pap. 6.95 (978-1-57505-558-9(9)); 2000. lib. bdg. 22.60 (978-1-57505-292-2(X) , Carolrhoda Bks.) Lerner Publishing Group.

—Remember the Ladies: A Story about Abigail Adams. 2001. (gr. 3-6). lib. bdg. 15.25 (978-0-613-68379-1(X)) Tandem Library Bks.

Glass, Maya. Abigail Adams: Famous First Lady. 2003. (Famous People in American History Ser.). (Illus.). 32p. (YA). pap. (978-0-8239-4172-8(8)) Rosen Publishing Group, Inc., The.

Lakin, Patricia. Abigail Adams: First Lady of the American Revolution. Bandelin, Debra & Dacey, Bob, illus. 2006. 48p. (J). lib. bdg. 15.00 (***978-1-4242-1560-7(9))*** Fitzgerald Bks.

—Abigail Adams: First Lady of the American Revolution. Dacey, Bob & Bandelin, Debra, illus. 2006. (Ready-to-read SOFA Ser.). 48p. (J). (gr. 1-3). pap. 3.99 (978-0-689-87032-3(9)); lib. bdg. 11.89 (978-0-689-87033-0(7)) Simon & Schuster Children's Publishing. (Aladdin).

Larkin, Tanya. What Was Cooking in Abigail Adam's White House? 2001. (Cooking Throughout American History Ser.). (Illus.). 24p. (J). (gr. 3). lib. bdg. 19.95 (978-0-8239-5607-4(5) , PowerKids Pr.) Rosen Publishing Group, Inc., The.

Manera, Alexandria. Abigail Adams. 2003. (Women of the Revolution Ser.). (J). pap. (978-1-58417-086-0(7)); lib. bdg. (978-1-58417-023-5(9)) Lake Street Pubs.

Mayer, Cassie. Abigail Adams. 2007. (J). (***978-1-4034-9971-4(3));*** pap. (***978-1-4034-9980-6(2))*** Heinemann Library.

McCarthy, Pat. Abigail Adams: First Lady & Patriot. 2002. (Historical American Biographies Ser.). (Illus.). 128p. (YA). (gr. 6-12). lib. bdg. 26.60 (978-0-7660-1618-7(8)) Enslow Pubs., Inc.

St. George, Judith. John & Abigail Adams: An American Love Story. 2001. (Illus.). 160p. (J). (gr. 4-6). tchr. ed. 22.95 (978-0-8234-1571-7(6)) Holiday Hse., Inc.

Sutcliffe, Jane. Abigail Adams. 2006. (History Maker Bios Ser.). (Illus.). 48p. (J). 26.60 (978-0-8225-5942-9(0) , Lerner Pubns.) Lerner Publishing Group.

Whiting, Jim. The Life & Times of Abigail Adams. 2007. (Profiles in American History Ser.). (Illus.). 48p. (J). lib. bdg. 29.95 (***978-1-58415-527-0(2))*** Mitchell Lane Pubs., Inc.

ADAMS, JOHN, 1735-1826

Adkins, Jan E. John Adams: Young Revolutionary. 2002. (gr. 3-6). lib. bdg. 13.00 (978-0-613-45074-4(4)) Tandem Library Bks.

Adler, David A. & Adler, Michael S. A Picture Book of John & Abigail Adams. Himler, Ronald, illus. 2007. (J). (978-0-8234-2007-0(8)) Holiday Hse., Inc.

Ashby, Ruth. John & Abigail Adams. 2005. (Illus.). 48p. (J). pap. (978-0-8368-5761-0(5)); lib. bdg. 30.00 (978-0-8368-5755-9(0)) Stevens, Gareth Inc. (World Almanac Library).

Behrman, Carol H. John Adams. 2004. (Presidential Leaders Ser.). (Illus.). 112p. (J). 29.27 (978-0-8225-0820-5(6) , Lerner Pubns.) Lerner Publishing Group.

Benge, Janet. John Adams: Independence Forever. 2003. (gr. 3-6). lib. bdg. 15.30 (978-0-613-83654-8(5)) Tandem Library Bks.

Benge, Janet & Benge, Geoff. John Adams: Independence Forever. 2002. (Illus.). 224p. pap. 8.99 (978-1-883002-51-0(6)) Emerald Bks.

Burgan, Michael. John Adams. 2000. (Revolutionary War Leaders Ser.). (Illus.). 80p. (J). (gr. 4-7). pap. 27.50 (978-0-7910-6128-2(0)); (gr. 8-12). 31.00 (978-0-7910-5970-8(7)) Facts On File, Inc. (Chelsea Hse.).

—John Adams: Second U. S. President. 2001. (gr. 5-8). lib. bdg. 17.60 (978-0-613-32724-4(1)) Tandem Library Bks.

Collard, Sneed B., III. John Adams: Our Second President. 2006. (American Heroes Ser.). (Illus.). 48p. (J). lib. bdg. 28.50 (***978-0-7614-2159-7(9)*** , Benchmark Bks.) Cavendish, Marshall Corp.

Connell, Kate. Servant to Abigail Adams: The Early American Adventures of Hannah Cooper. 2004. (Illus.). 40p. (J). (gr. 4-8). pap. 7.00 (978-0-7567-8216-0(3)) DIANE Publishing Co.

—The Spirit of a New Nation. 2002. (Voices from America's Past Ser.). (Illus.). 40p. (J). (978-0-7922-8684-4(7)) National Geographic Society.

Crompton, Samuel Willard. John Adams: American Patriot. 2005. (Leaders of the American Revolution Ser.). (Illus.). 136p. (J). (gr. 4-8). 30.00 (978-0-7910-8620-9(8) , Chelsea Hse.) Facts On File, Inc.

Dubois, Muriel L. John Adams. 2003. (Photo-Illustrated Biographies Ser.). (Illus.). 24p. (J). (gr. 2-3). lib. bdg. 18.60 (978-0-7368-1606-9(2) , Bridgestone Bks.) Capstone Pr., Inc.

Feinberg, Barbara Silberdick. John Adams. 2003. (Encyclopedia of Presidents Ser.: Vol. 2). (Illus.). 110p. (J). 34.00 (978-0-516-22680-4(0) , Children's Pr.) Scholastic Library Publishing.

Feinstein, Stephen. John Adams: A MyReportLinks.com Book. 2002. (Presidents Ser.). (Illus.). 48p. (J). (gr. 4-10). lib. bdg. 25.26 (978-0-7660-5001-3(7) , MyReportLinks.com Bks.) Enslow Pubs., Inc.

Gillis, Jennifer Blizin. John Adams. 2004. (American Lives Ser.). (Illus.). 32p. (J). pap. 7.50 (978-1-4034-5967-1(3)); lib. bdg. 24.22 (978-1-4034-5959-6(2)) Heinemann Library.

Glass, Maya. Abigail Adams: Famous First Lady. 2003. (Famous People in American History Ser.). (Illus.). 32p. (YA). pap. (978-0-8239-4172-8(8)) Rosen Publishing Group, Inc., The.

Harness, Cheryl. The Revolutionary John Adams. 2003. (Illus.). 48p. (J). (gr. 3-7). 17.95 (978-0-7922-6970-0(5) , National Geographic Children's Bks.) National Geographic Society.

—Revolutionary John Adams. 2006. 48p. (gr. 3). pap. 7.95 (978-0-7922-5491-1(0) , National Geographic Children's Bks.) National Geographic Society.

Kallen, Stuart A. John Adams. 2001. (Founding Fathers Ser.). (Illus.). 64p. (J). (gr. 3-8). lib. bdg. 25.65 (978-1-57765-007-2(7) , ABDO & Daughters) ABDO Publishing Co.

Kent, Zachary. John Adams: Creating a Nation. 2004. (America's Founding Fathers Ser.). (Illus.). 128p. (J). lib. bdg. 26.60 (978-0-7660-2183-9(1)) Enslow Pubs., Inc.

Lukes, Bonnie L. John Adams: Public Servant. 2004. (Notable Americans Ser.). (Illus.). 128p. (J). (gr. 6-12). 23.95 (978-1-883846-80-0(3) , First Biographies) Reynolds, Morgan Inc.

Lusted, Marcia Amidon. Revolution & the New Nation. 2007. (***978-1-59036-739-1(1));*** (***978-1-59036-740-7(5))*** Weigl Pubs., Inc.

Mara, Wil. John Adams. 2008. (J). (***978-0-7614-2840-4(2))*** Cavendish, Marshall Bks., Ltd.

Marcovitz, Hal. John Adams. 2003. (Childhoods of the Presidents Ser.). (Illus.). 48p. (J). (gr. 4 up). lib. bdg. (978-1-59084-268-3(5)) Mason Crest Pubs.

McCarthy, Pat. Abigail Adams: First Lady & Patriot. 2002. (Historical American Biographies Ser.). (Illus.). 128p. (YA). (gr. 6-12). lib. bdg. 26.60 (978-0-7660-1618-7(8)) Enslow Pubs., Inc.

Miller, Chuck. John Adams. 2003. (America's Founders Ser.). (J). pap. (978-1-58417-082-2(4)); lib. bdg. (978-1-58417-019-8(0)) Lake Street Pubs.

Randolph, Ryan P. How to Draw the Life & Times of John Adams. 2006. (Kid's Guide to Drawing the Presidents of the United States of America Ser.). (J). 25.25 (978-1-4042-2979-2(5) , PowerKids Pr.) Rosen Publishing Group, Inc., The.

Santella, Andrew. John Adams. 2002. (Profiles of the Presidents Ser.). (Illus.). 64p. (J). (gr. 4 up). lib. bdg. 23.93 (978-0-7565-0251-5(9)) Compass Point Bks.

St. George, Judith. John & Abigail Adams: An American Love Story. 2001. (Illus.). 160p. (J). (gr. 4-6). tchr. ed. 22.95 (978-0-8234-1571-7(6)) Holiday Hse., Inc.

Sutcliffe, Jane. John Adams. 2006. (History Maker Bios Ser.). (Illus.). 48p. (J). 26.60 (978-0-8225-5940-5(4) , Lerner Pubns.) Lerner Publishing Group.

Venezia, Mike. John Adams. Venezia, Mike, illus. 2005. (Getting to Know the U. S. Presidents Ser.). (Illus.). 32p. (J). (gr. 3-4). pap. 7.95 (978-0-516-27476-8(7) , Children's Pr.) Scholastic Library Publishing.

Venezia, Mike, illus. John Adams. 2004. (Gtk Us Presidents Ser.). (J). 27.00 (978-0-516-22607-1(X) , Children's Pr.) Scholastic Library Publishing.

Wagner, Heather Lehr. John Adams. 2003. (Great American Presidents Ser.). (Illus.). 100p. (J). pap. (978-0-7910-7787-0(X)); (gr. 4-8). 30.00 (978-0-7910-7603-3(2)) Facts On File, Inc. (Chelsea Hse.).

Walker, Jane C. John Adams. 2002. (United States Presidents Ser.). (Illus.). 128p. (J). (gr. 5 up). lib. bdg. 26.60 (978-0-7660-1704-7(4)) Enslow Pubs., Inc.

Welsbacher, Anne. John Adams. 1999. (United States Presidents Ser.). (Illus.). 32p. (J). (gr. k-6). lib. bdg. 22.78 (978-1-56239-738-8(9) , Checkerboard Library) ABDO Publishing Co.

Whiting, Jim. John Adams. 2006. (Profiles in American History Ser.). (Illus.). 48p. (J). (gr. 4-8). lib. bdg. 20.95 (978-1-58415-442-6(X)) Mitchell Lane Pubs., Inc.

ADAMS, JOHN, 1735-1826—FICTION

Adkins, Jan E. John Adams: Young Revolutionary. Henderson, Meryl, illus. 2002. (Childhood of Famous Americans Ser.). 256p. (gr. 3-7). mass mkt. 5.99 (978-0-689-85135-3(9) , Aladdin) Simon & Schuster Children's Publishing.

Hopkinson, Deborah. John Adams Speaks for Freedom. Orback, Craig, illus. ed. 2005. 32p. (J). lib. bdg. 15.00 (978-1-59054-992-6(9)) Fitzgerald Bks.

Krensky, Stephen. Dangerous Crossing: The Revolutionary Voyage of John & John Quincy Adams. Harlin, Greg, tr. Harlin, Greg, illus. 2004. 32p. (J). (gr. k). 16.99 (978-0-525-46966-7(4) , Dutton Juvenile) Penguin Group (USA) Inc.

ADAMS, JOHN QUINCY, 1767-1848

Burgan, Michael. John Quincy Adams. 2003. (Profiles of the Presidents Ser.). (Illus.). 64p. (J). (gr. 4 up). lib. bdg. 23.93 (978-0-7565-0254-6(3)) Compass Point Bks.

Feinstein, Stephen. John Quincy Adams: A MyReportLinks.com Book. 2002. (Presidents Ser.). (Illus.). 48p. (J). (gr. 4-10). lib. bdg. 25.26 (978-0-7660-5002-0(5) , MyReportLinks.com Bks.) Enslow Pubs., Inc.

Gherman, Beverly. First Son & President: A Story about John Quincy Adams. Bird, Matthew, illus. 2005. 64p. (J). (ps-7). pap. 6.95 (978-0-8225-3091-6(0)) Lerner Publishing Group.

Hewson, Martha S. John Quincy Adams. 2003. (Great American Presidents Ser.). (Illus.). 100p. (J). pap. (978-0-7910-7785-6(3)); (gr. 4-8). 30.00 (978-0-7910-7599-9(0)) Facts On File, Inc. (Chelsea Hse.).

Joseph, Paul. John Quincy Adams. 1999. (United States Presidents Ser.). (Illus.). 32p. (J). (gr. k-6). lib. bdg. 22.78 (978-1-57765-231-1(2) , Checkerboard Library) ABDO Publishing Co.

Levy, Debbie. John Quincy Adams. 2005. (Presidential Leaders Ser.). (Illus.). 112p. (J). lib. bdg. 29.27 (978-0-8225-0825-0(7)) Lerner Publishing Group.

McCollum, Sean. John Quincy Adams. 2003. (Encyclopedia of Presidents Ser.). (Illus.). 110p. (J). 34.00 (978-0-516-22867-9(6) , Children's Pr.) Scholastic Library Publishing.

Souter, Gerry & Souter, Janet. John Quincy Adams: Our Sixth President. 2001. (Spirit of America: Our Presidents Ser.). (Illus.). 48p. (J). (gr. 2-6). 28.50 (978-1-56766-846-9(1)) Child's World, Inc.

Tecco, Betsy Dru. How to Draw the Life & Times of John Quincy Adams. 2006. (Kid's Guide to Drawing the Presidents of the United States of America Ser.). (J). 25.25 (978-1-4042-2983-9(3) , PowerKids Pr.) Rosen Publishing Group, Inc., The.

Venezia, Mike. John Quincy Adams. Venezia, Mike, illus. 2005. (Getting to Know the U. S. Presidents Ser.). (Illus.). 32p. (J). (gr. 3-4). pap. 7.95 (978-0-516-27480-5(5) , Children's Pr.) Scholastic Library Publishing.

Venezia, Mike, tr. & illus. John Quincy Adams. Venezia, Mike, illus. 2004. (Gtk Us Presidents Ser.). 32p. (J). 27.00 (978-0-516-22611-8(8) , Children's Pr.) Scholastic Library Publishing.

Walker, Jane C. John Quincy Adams. 2000. (United States Presidents Ser.). (Illus.). 128p. (YA). (gr. 5-12). lib. bdg. 26.60 (978-0-7660-1161-8(5)) Enslow Pubs., Inc.

ADAMS, SAMUEL, 1722-1803

Adler, David A. & Adler, Michael S. A Picture Book of Samuel Adams. Himler, Ronald, illus. 2005. 32p. (J). 16.95 (978-0-8234-1846-6(4)) Holiday Hse., Inc.

Burgan, Michael. Samuel Adams: Patriot & Statesman. 2004. (Signature Lives Ser.). (Illus.). 112p. (J). 30.60 (978-0-7565-0823-4(1) , 1240135) Compass Point Bks.

Davis, Kate. Samuel Adams. 2002. (Triangle History of the American Revolution Ser.). (Illus.). 104p. (J). 28.70 (978-1-56711-612-0(4) , Blackbirch Pr., Inc.) Thomson Gale.

Doeden, Matt. Samuel Adams: Patriot & Statesman. 2007. (Graphic Library). 32p. (J). 25.26 (978-0-7368-6500-5(4)) Capstone Pr., Inc.

Fradin, Dennis Brindell. Samuel Adams: The Father of American Independence. 1998. (Illus.). 192p. (J). (gr. 4-6). 20.00 (978-0-395-82510-5(5) , Clarion Bks.) Houghton Mifflin Co. Trade & Reference Div.

Fritz, Jean. Why Don't You Get a Horse, Sam Adams? 2004. (J). (gr. 2-6). 24.95 incl. audio (978-1-55592-158-3(2)); 29.95 incl. cd-rom (978-1-55592-159-0(0)); pap. 14.95 incl. audio (978-1-55592-154-5(X)); pap. 18.95 incl. audio compact disk (978-1-55592-153-8(1)) Weston Woods Studios, Inc.

Gibson, Karen Bush. Samuel Adams. 2006. (Profiles in American History Ser.). (Illus.). 48p. (J). (gr. 4-8). lib. bdg. 20.95 (978-1-58415-440-2(3)) Mitchell Lane Pubs., Inc.

Gillis, Jennifer Blizin. Samuel Adams. 2004. (Illus.). 32p. (J). pap. 7.50 (978-1-4034-5970-1(3)); lib. bdg. 25.64 (978-1-4034-5962-6(2)) Heinemann Library.

Heinrichs, Ann. Samuel Adams: Father of the Revolution. 2004. (Our People Ser.). (Illus.). 32p. (J). (gr. 2-6). 27.07 (978-1-59296-177-1(0)) Child's World, Inc.

Irvin, Benjamin H. Samuel Adams: Son of Liberty, Father of Revolution. 2002. (Oxford Portraits Ser.). (Illus.). 176p. (YA). 28.00 (978-0-19-513225-0(4)) Oxford Univ. Pr., Inc.

Jones, Veda Boyd. Samuel Adams. 2001. (Revolutionary War Leaders Ser.). (Illus.). 80p. (J). pap. 27.50 (978-0-7910-6387-3(9)); 27.50 (978-0-7910-6386-6(0)) Facts On File, Inc. (Chelsea Hse.).

Kallen, Stuart A. Samuel Adams. 2001. (Founding Fathers Ser.). (Illus.). 64p. (J). (gr. 3-8). lib. bdg. 25.65 (978-1-57765-008-9(5) , ABDO & Daughters) ABDO Publishing Co.

Walsh, Kieran. Samuel Adams. (Discover the Life of a Colonial American Ser.). 24p. 2005. (Illus.). (J). (gr. 2-5). 14.95 (978-1-59515-135-3(4)); 2004. pap. 4.95 (978-1-59515-336-4(5)) Rourke Publishing, LLC.

Why Don't You Get a Horse, Sam Adams? 2004. 24.95 incl. audio (978-1-56008-216-3(X)); pap. 38.75 incl. audio compact disk (978-1-55592-648-9(7)); (J). pap. 14.95 incl. audio (978-1-56008-223-1(2)); (J). pap. 32.75 incl. audio (978-1-55592-359-4(3)) Weston Woods Studios, Inc.

ADAPTATION (BIOLOGY)

see also Human Beings—Effect of Environment on

Arnold, Caroline. Shockers of the Sea: And Other Electric Animals. Forest, Crista, illus. 1999. 32p. (J). (ps-3). 15.95 (978-0-88106-873-3(X)); pap. 6.95 (978-0-88106-874-0(8)) Charlesbridge Publishing, Inc.

Benchmark Education Staff. Adaptation. 2005. 2.00 (***978-1-4108-4676-1(8))*** Benchmark Education Co.

A B

Benchmark Education Staff, compiled by. Watery World & Animal Adaptations. 2005. spiral bd. 225.00 (***978-1-4108-5814-6(6)***) Benchmark Education Co.

Biskup, Agnieszka. A Journey into Adaptation with Max Axiom, Super Scientist. Martin, Cynthia & Schulz, Barbara Jo, illus. 2007. (J). (***978-0-7368-6840-2(2)***) Capstone Pr., Inc.

Bramwell, Martyn J. Planet Earth: The Complete Guide to Our Living World. 1999. (J). (978-1-84100-264-4(X)) Quadrillion Publishing.

Brannon, Barbara. Discover Adaptation. 2005. 39.00 (***978-1-4108-5122-2(2)***) Benchmark Education Co.

Burton, Jane & Taylor, Kim. The Nature & Science of Survival. 2001. (Exploring the Science of Nature Ser.). (Illus.). 32p. (J). (gr. 3 up). lib. bdg. 24.67 (978-0-8368-2211-3(0)) Stevens, Gareth Inc.

Chinery, Michael. How Animals Work. 2003. (Wild Animal Planet Ser.). (Illus.). 64p. (gr. 3-7). 14.99 (978-0-7548-1155-8(7)) Anness Publishing GBR. *Dist:* National Bk. Network.

Davies, Nicola. Extreme Animals: The Toughest Creatures on Earth. Layton, Neal, illus. 2006. 64p. (J). (gr. 4-6). 12.99 (978-0-7636-3067-6(5)) Candlewick Pr.

Field, Nancy, ed. Wild Stickers - Wetlands. Maydak, Michael S., illus. 1998. (Wild Stickers Ser.: Vol. 1). 8p. (J). (gr. k-6). pap. 2.50 (978-0-941042-21-5(9)) Dog-Eared Pubns.

Fullick, Ann. Adaptation & Competition. 2005. (Life Science In-Depth Ser.). (J). pap. (978-1-4034-7526-8(1)); (Illus.). 64p. (978-1-4034-7518-3(0)) Heinemann Library.

Goodman, Susan E. Claws, Coats, & Camouflage. Doolittle, Michael J., photos by. 2001. (Illus.). 48p. (gr. 2-4). lib. bdg. 22.90 (978-0-7613-1865-1(8), Millbrook Pr.) Lerner Publishing Group.

—Seeds, Stems, & Stamens: The Ways Plants Fit into Their World. Doolittle, Michael J., photos by. 2001. (Illus.). 48p. (gr. 2-4). lib. bdg. 22.90 (978-0-7613-1874-3(7), Millbrook Pr.) Lerner Publishing Group.

Hoff, Mary. Handling Heat. 2002. (Illus.). 32p. (J). lib. bdg. (978-1-58341-240-4(9), Creative Editions) Creative Co., The.

Knight, Tim. Super Survivors. 2003. (Amazing Nature Ser.). (Illus.). 32p. (J). lib. bdg. 24.22 (978-1-4034-0723-8(1)); pap. 6.95 (978-1-4034-3262-9(7)) Heinemann Library.

Lady Bird Johnson Wildflower Center Staff, Lady Bird Johnson, compiled by. Exploring the Native Plant World Grades 5-6: Adaptations. 2004. 72p. (J). pap. 14.95 (978-1-57168-851-4(X), Eakin Pr.) Eakin Pr.

Parker, Steve. Adaptation. (Life Processes Ser.). (Illus.). 32p. (J). 2006. (***978-1-4034-8843-5(6)***); 2003. (gr. 4-6). pap. 7.50 (978-1-4034-4071-6(9)); 2000. (gr. 4-6). lib. bdg. 21.36 (978-1-57572-335-8(2)) Heinemann Library.

Parker, Steve. Survival & Change. (Life Processes Ser.). 32p. pap. 7.50 (978-1-4034-4076-1(X)); 2000. (Illus.). (J). (gr. 4-6). lib. bdg. 21.36 (978-1-57572-340-2(9)) Heinemann Library.

Romero, Libby. Adaptation. 2005. 42.00 (***978-1-4108-4628-0(8)***) Benchmark Education Co.

Silverstein, Alvin, et al. Adaptation. 2007. (Science Concepts, Second Ser.). (Illus.). 112p. (YA). (gr. 6-8). lib. bdg. 31.93 (***978-0-8225-3434-1(7)***, Twenty-First Century Bks.) Lerner Publishing Group.

Townsend, John. Would You Survive? Animal & Plant Adaptation. 2005. (Illus.). 32p. (J). lib. bdg. (978-1-4109-1938-0(2)) Steck-Vaughn.

—Would You Survive? Living Things in Habitats. 2005. (Illus.). 32p. (J). (gr. 3-5). 7.85 (978-1-4109-1969-4(2)) Steck-Vaughn.

Winner, Cherie. Life on the Edge. 2006. (Cool Science Ser.). (Illus.). 48p. (J). (gr. 4-8). lib. bdg. 26.60 (978-0-8225-2499-1(6), Lerner Pubns.) Lerner Publishing Group.

ADD (CHILD BEHAVIOR DISORDER)

see Attention-Deficit Hyperactivity Disorder

ADDAMS, JANE, 1860-1935

Alter, Judy & Rosenberg, Pam. Pocahontas: Native American Peacemaker. 2003. (Spirit of America). (Illus.). 32p. (J). (gr. 2-6). 27.07 (978-1-59296-010-1(3)) Child's World, Inc.

Armentrout, David & Armentrout, Patricia. Jane Addams. 2002. (People Who Made a Difference Ser.). (Illus.). 24p. (gr. 2-5). 14.95 (978-1-58952-054-7(8)) Rourke Publishing, LLC.

—Jane Addams. Sarfatti, Esther & de la Vega, Eida, trs. 2001. (Personas que Cambiaron la Historia Ser.). (SPA., Illus.). 24p. (J). (gr. 1-4). lib. bdg. 19.27 (978-1-58952-165-0(X), RK7297) Rourke Publishing, LLC.

Caravantes, Peggy. Waging Peace: The Story of Jane Addams. 2004. (Illus.). 144p. (YA). (gr. 6-12). 23.95 (978-1-931798-40-2(0)) Reynolds, Morgan Inc.

Fradin, Dennis Brindell & Fradin, Judith Bloom. Jane Addams: Champion of Democracy. 2006. (Illus.). 192p. (J). (gr. 5-9). 21.00 (978-0-618-50436-7(2), Clarion Bks.) Houghton Mifflin Co. Trade & Reference Div.

Harvey, Bonnie Carman. Jane Addams: Nobel Prize Winner & Founder of Hull House. 1999. (Historical American Biographies Ser.). (Illus.). 128p. (YA). (gr. 6-12). lib. bdg. 26.60 (978-0-7660-1094-9(5)) Enslow Pubs., Inc.

Jane Addams. (Compass Point Early Biographies Ser.). 32p. (J). 7.95 (978-0-7565-1173-9(9)) Compass Point Bks.

Kishel, Ann-Marie. Jane Addams: A Life of Cooperation. 2007. (Pull Ahead Books). (Illus.). 32p. (J). 22.60 (978-0-8225-6382-2(7), Lerner Pubns.) Lerner Publishing Group.

Marsh, Carole. Jane Addams. 2002. (One Thousand Readers Ser.). (Illus.). 12p. (J). (gr. k-4). 2.95 (978-0-635-01472-6(6), 14726) Gallopade International.

—The Virginia Reader: Jane Addams. 2001. (Virginia Experience! Ser.). 12p. (J). (gr. k-5). pap. 2.95 (978-0-635-00353-9(8)) Gallopade International.

Raatma, Lucia. Jane Addams. 2004. (Compass Point Early Biographies Ser.). (Illus.). 32p. (J). (gr. 2 up). lib. bdg. 21.26 (978-0-7565-0566-0(6)) Compass Point Bks.

Riley, John B. Jane Addams: A Photo Biography. l.t. ed. 2004. (First Biographies Ser.). (Illus.). 24p. (YA). (gr. 5 up). 16.95 (978-1-883846-61-9(7), First Biographies) Reynolds, Morgan Inc.

Simon, Charman. Jane Addams: Pioneer Social Worker. 1998. (Community Builders Ser.). (Illus.). 48p. (J). (gr. 3-5). pap. 6.95 (978-0-516-26235-2(1), Children's Pr.) Scholastic Library Publishing.

ADDING MACHINES

see Calculators

ADHD (CHILD BEHAVIOR DISORDER)

see Attention-Deficit Hyperactivity Disorder

ADIRONDACK MOUNTAINS (N.Y.)

Amsel, Sheri. Adirondack Counting: A Counting Adventure to the 46 Highest Peaks of the Adirondacks. Amsel, Sheri, illus. 1998. (Illus.). 32p. (J). (ps-k). pap. 7.50 (978-0-925168-63-4(7)) North Country Bks., Inc.

MacMillan, Dianne M. Life in a Deciduous Forest. 2003. (Ecosystems in Action Ser.). (Illus.). 71p. (J). (gr. 6-12). 26.60 (978-0-8225-4684-9(1)) Lerner Publishing Group.

Weber, Sandra. Two in the Wilderness: Adventures of a Mother & Daughter in the Adirondack Mountains. Heilman, Carl, illus. 2005. 48p. (J). 19.95 (978-1-59078-182-1(1)) Boyds Mills Pr.

ADIRONDACK MOUNTAINS (N.Y.)—FICTION

The Adirondack. 2006. (YA). per. (978-1-59872-344-1(8)) Instantpublisher.com.

Bauer, Joan. Backwater. 2000. (978-0-606-20077-6(0)) Tandem Library Bks.

Bruchac, Joseph. Bearwalker. Comport, Sally Wern, illus. 2007. 224p. (J). (gr. 5-8). 15.99 (***978-0-06-112309-2(9)***); lib. bdg. 16.89 (***978-0-06-112311-5(0)***) HarperCollins Pubs.

Clark, N. Laurie. It's Wesley! The Adirondack Guide. Clark, N. Laurie, illus. 1998. (Illus.). 32p. (J). (gr. k up). per. 14.95 (978-0-9641197-1-0(4)) Clark Pubs.

De Witt, Peter. Isabella & the Room of Lost Brooms. 2007. 210p. (J). pap. 12.95 (***978-1-933255-35-4(8)***) DNA Pr.

Donnelly, Jennifer. A Northern Light. (YA). 2003. (Illus.). 400p. (gr. 9 up). 17.00 (978-0-15-216705-9(6)); 2004. 408p. reprint ed. pap. 8.95 (978-0-15-205310-9(7), Harcourt Paperbacks) Harcourt Children's Bks.

Fitzhugh, K. Percy. Tom Slade at Temple Camp. 2007. (ENG.). 136p. 95.99 (***978-1-4280-7410-1(4)***); per. 88.99 (***978-1-4280-7390-6(6)***) IndyPublish.com.

Frenette, Liza. Dangerous Falls Ahead: An Adirondack Canoeing Adventure. Gillis, Jane, illus. 2001. (J). pap. 11.95 (978-0-925168-79-5(3)) North Country Bks., Inc.

—Soft Shoulders: An Adirondack Story. 1998. (J). 9.95 (978-0-925168-70-2(X)) North Country Bks., Inc.

Granger, Persis R. Adirondack Gold. 2003. (Illus.). 168p. (J). (gr. 3-6). pap. 9.95 (978-0-9742085-0-3(7)) Beaver Meadow Publishing.

Leonard, Rebecca JoAnne. Adirondack Halloween: A Spooky Tale in the North Country. 2006. 48p. (J). pap. 7.95 (***978-1-4327-0139-0(8)***) Outskirts Press, Inc.

McGhee, Alison. All Rivers Flow to the Sea. 176p. (YA). (gr. 9 up). 2007. (Illus.). pap. 7.99 (***978-0-7636-3372-1(0)***); 2005. 15.99 (978-0-7636-2591-7(4)) Candlewick Pr.

Petrie, Lettie A. Let Me Tell You About "Minnie the Mule & the Erie Canal" Petrie, Beth L., illus. 2001. (Erie Canal Ser.). (YA). (gr. 5-10). pap. 9.95 (978-0-9711638-0-5(4)) Petrie Pr.

Richards, Zackary. Frostie the Deadman. 2004. 222p. (J). pap. 14.95 (978-0-9713069-8-1(2)) Burns, Nicholas K. Publishing.

VanRiper, Justin & VanRiper, Gary. The Adirondack Kids. 2001. (Adirondack Kids Ser.). (Illus.). 86p. (J). (ps-3). pap. 8.95 (978-0-9707044-0-5(2), ADK1) Adirondack Kids Pr.

Winfield, Arthur M. The Rover Boys in the Mountains: Or, A Hunt for Fun & Fortune. 2007. 170p. pap. 11.99 (***978-1-4264-7052-3(5)***); 188p. pap. 14.99 (***978-1-4264-7128-5(9)***) BiblioBazaar.

ADJUSTMENT, SOCIAL

see Social Adjustment

ADMINISTRATION

see Civil Service; Management; Political Science; Public Administration

see names of countries, cities, etc. with the subdivision Politics and Government, e.g. U. S.—Politics and Government; etc.

ADMINISTRATION OF JUSTICE

see Justice, Administration of

ADMIRALS

Alphin, Elaine Marie & Alphin, Arthur B. I Have Not Yet Begun to Fight: A Story about John Paul Jones. Casale, Paul, tr. Casale, Paul, illus. 2004. (Creative Minds Biography Ser.). 64p. (J). 22.60 (978-1-57505-601-2(1), Carolrhoda Bks.) Lerner Publishing Group.

Ashworth, Leon. Horatio Nelson. 2000. (British History Makers Ser.). (Illus.). 32p. (J). 22.95 (978-0-7451-5290-5(2), Cherrytree Books) Evans Publishing Group GBR. *Dist:* Independent Pubs. Group.

Brager, Bruce L. John Paul Jones: America's Sailor. 2006. (Illus.). 160p. (J). lib. bdg. 26.95 (978-1-931798-84-6(2)) Reynolds, Morgan Inc.

Cawthorne, Nigel. Military Commanders: The 100 Greatest Throughout History. 2004. (Illus.). 208p. 18.95 (978-1-59270-029-5(2)) Enchanted Lion Bks., LLC.

Cooper, Michael. Hero of the High Seas: John Paul Jones & the American Revolution. 2006. (Illus.). 128p. (J). (gr. 5). 32.90 (978-0-7922-5548-2(8)); pap. 21.95 (978-0-7922-5547-5(X)) National Geographic Society. (National Geographic Children's Bks.).

Crompton, Samuel Willard. Francis Drake & the Oceans of the World. 2005. (Explorers of New Worlds Ser.). (Illus.). 160p. (J). (gr. 4-8). 30.00 (978-0-7910-8615-5(1), Chelsea Hse.) Facts On File, Inc.

—100 Military Leaders Who Changed the World. 2003. (People Who Changed the World Ser.). (Illus.). 112p. (J). (gr. 5 up). lib. bdg. 30.00 (978-0-8368-5470-1(5), World Almanac Library) Stevens, Gareth Inc.

Harkins, Susan and William. The Life & Times of John Paul Jones. 2007. (Profiles in American History Ser.). (Illus.). 48p. (J). lib. bdg. 22.95 (***978-1-58415-529-4(9)***) Mitchell Lane Pubs., Inc.

Haugen, Brenda & Santella, Andrew. John Paul Jones: Father of the American Navy. 2004. (Signature Lives Ser.). (Illus.). 112p. (J). 30.60 (978-0-7565-0829-6(0)) Compass Point Bks.

Hoogenboom, Lynn. Sir Francis Drake: A Primary Source Portrait. 2006. (J). lib. bdg. (978-1-4042-3035-4(1), PowerKids Pr.) Rosen Publishing Group, Inc., The.

Ingram, Scott. John Paul Jones. 2002. (Triangle History of the American Revolution Ser.). (Illus.). 104p. (J). 28.70 (978-1-56711-609-0(4), Blackbirch Pr., Inc.) Thomson Gale.

Larkin, Tanya. Sir Francis Drake. 2001. (Famous Explorers Ser.). (Illus.). 24p. (J). (gr. 3). lib. bdg. 18.75 (978-0-8239-5556-5(7), PowerKids Pr.) Rosen Publishing Group, Inc., The.

Mattern, Joanne. Grace Hopper: Computer Pioneer. 2003. (Reading Power Ser.). (Illus.). 24p. (J). lib. bdg. 17.25 (978-0-8239-6505-2(8), PowerKids Pr.) Rosen Publishing Group, Inc., The.

Murphy, Patricia J. Grace Hopper: Computer Pioneer. 2004. (Famous Inventors Ser.). (Illus.). 32p. (J). lib. bdg. 22.60 (978-0-7660-2273-7(0)) Enslow Pubs., Inc.

Petrie, Kristin. Sir Francis Drake. 2004. (Explorers Ser.). (Illus.). 32p. (J). (gr. k-6). lib. bdg. 22.78 (978-1-59197-601-1(4), Checkerboard Library) ABDO Publishing Co.

Price Hossell, Karen. John Paul Jones. 2004. (American War Biographies Ser.). (J). pap. 8.50 (978-1-4034-5086-9(2)); lib. bdg. 29.93 (978-1-4034-5079-1(X)) Heinemann Library.

Riley, John B. John Paul Jones: A Photo Biography. l.t. ed. 2004. (First Biographies Ser.). (Illus.). 24p. (YA). (gr. 5 up). 16.95 (978-1-883846-63-3(3), First Biographies) Reynolds, Morgan Inc.

Rink, Paul. Admiral Richard Byrd: Alone in the Antarctic. 2006. (Sterling Point Bks.). (Illus.). 192p. (J). pap. 6.95 (978-1-4027-3610-0(X)) Sterling Publishing Co., Inc.

Sonneborn, Liz. John Paul Jones: American Naval Hero. 2005. (Leaders of the American Revolution Ser.). (Illus.). 123p. (J). (ps-8). lib. bdg. 30.00 (978-0-7910-8621-6(6), Chelsea Hse.) Facts On File, Inc.

Sperry, Armstrong. John Paul Jones: The Pirate Patriot. 2006. (Sterling Point Bks.). (Illus.). 176p. (J). 12.95 (978-1-4027-3185-3(X)); pap. 6.95 (978-1-4027-3615-5(0)) Sterling Publishing Co., Inc.

ADOLESCENCE

see also Puberty

Abrahams, George & Ahlbrand, Sheila. Boy v. Girl? How Gender Shapes Who We Are, What We Want, & How We Get Along. 2004. (Illus.). 208p. (YA). (gr. 5-10). pap. 14.95 (978-1-57542-104-9(6)) Free Spirit Publishing, Inc.

Allenbaugh, Kay. Chocolate for a Teen's Dreams: Heartwarming Stories about Making Your Wishes Come True. 2003. (Illus.). 224p. pap. 12.00 (978-0-7432-3703-1(X), Fireside) Simon & Schuster.

Anonymous. Diary of a Junior Year. (Real Teens Ser.: Vol. 4). (YA). (gr. 7 up). 2000. 196p. pap. 4.99 (978-0-439-08411-6(3), Scholastic Paperbacks); 1999. pap. 59.88 (978-0-439-13483-5(8)); 1999. mass mkt. 59.88 (978-0-439-11746-3(1)); 1999. mass mkt. 59.88 (978-0-439-09275-3(2)) Scholastic, Inc.

—Diary of a Junior Year. 1999. (Real Teens Ser.: Vol. 1). (YA). (gr. 7 up). 11.64 (978-0-606-17278-3(5)); (978-0-606-17547-0(4)) Tandem Library Bks.

Arthur, Kay, et al. How to Study Your Bible for Teens. 2004. 176p. (YA). pap. 9.99 (978-0-7369-0965-5(6)) Harvest Hse. Pubs.

Blackstone, Margaret. Girl Stuff: A Survival Guide to Growing Up. 2000. (J). 15.60 (978-0-606-19417-4(7)) Tandem Library Bks.

Bode, Janet. Kids Still Having Kids: People Talk about Teen Pregnancy. rev. ed. 1999. (Single Titles-Teen Issues Ser.). (Illus.). 160p. (YA). (gr. 8-12). pap. 9.95 (978-0-531-15973-6(6), Watts, Franklin) Scholastic Library Publishing.

Borden, Sarah & Miller, Sarah. Middle School: How to Deal. Nuts and Bolts Girls Staff, ed. Hatori, Yuki, illus. 2005. 96p. (J). pap. 9.95 (978-0-8118-4497-0(8)) Chronicle Bks. LLC.

Bradley, Michael J. Yes, Your Parents Are Crazy! A Teen Survival Handbook. Glasbergen, Randy, illus. 2004. 432p. pap. 14.95 (978-0-936197-48-7(X)) Harbor Pr., Inc.

Brecon, Connah. Tomorrow. 2005. (Illus.). 32p. (978-0-7344-0730-6(0), Lothian Bks.) Hachette Livre Australia.

Brown, Marty. Infogirl: A Girl's Guide to the Internet. rev. ed. 2005. (Girls' Guides). (Illus.). 48p. (YA). (gr. 5-8). lib. bdg. 23.95 (978-0-8239-2984-9(1), GGINGI) Rosen Publishing Group, Inc., The.

Bryan, Jenny. Adolescence. 1999. (Health & Fitness Ser.). (Illus.). 48p. (J). (gr. 4-6). lib. bdg. 27.12 (978-0-7398-1346-1(3)) Raintree.

Burgen, Jim. What's the Big Deal about My Parents? Reeves, Dale, ed. 2006. (What's the Big Deal Ser.). 160p. (gr. 7 up). pap. 10.99 (978-0-7847-1252-8(2), 23335) Standard Publishing.

Canfield, Jack L., et al. Una 2nd Racion de Sopa de Pollo para el Alma del Adolescente: Mas Relatos Sobre la Vida el Amour y el Aprendizaje. 2nd ed. 2003. Tr. of Chicken Soup for the Teenage Soul. (SPA., Illus.). 350p. (YA). pap. 12.95 (978-0-7573-0134-6(7)) Health Communications, Inc.

Carlson, Dale. The Teen Brain Book: Who & What Are You? Teasdale, Nancy, ed. Nicklaus, Carol, illus. 2004. 230p. (gr. 7-12). pap. 14.95 (978-1-884158-29-2(3)) Bick Publishing Hse.

Carlson, Dale B. & Carlson, Hannah. Where's Your Head? Teenage Psychology. Nicklaus, Carol, illus. 2nd rev. ed. 2000. (Psychology for Teenagers Ser.: Vol. 2). 298p. (gr. 8-12). pap. 14.95 (978-1-884158-19-3(6)) Bick Publishing Hse.

Case, Steve. Everything Counts: A Year's Worth of Devotions on Radical Living. 2003. (Invert Ser.). (Illus.). 384p. (YA). pap. 14.99 (978-0-310-25408-9(6)) Zondervan.

Conny, Beth Mende & Conny, Julia Mende. Girls Rule! 2000. (Journal Ser.). 128p. 12.99 (978-0-88088-261-3(1)) Peter Pauper Pr. Inc.

Conny, Beth Mende & Conny, Julia Mende, eds. Girls Rule! Barbas, Kerren, illus. 2000. (Charming Petites Ser.). 80p. (YA). 4.95 (978-0-88088-327-6(8)) Peter Pauper Pr. Inc.

Coon, Nora E. It's Your Rite: Girls' Coming-of-Age Stories. 2002. (gr. 7-12). lib. bdg. 18.75 (978-0-613-67097-5(3)) Tandem Library Bks.

Copeland, Mary Ellen & Copans, Stuart. Recovering from Depression: A Workbook for Teens. rev. ed. 2002. 192p. (YA). pap. 22.95 (978-1-55766-592-8(3)) Brookes, Paul H. Publishing Co.

CosmoGIRL! Editors. Ask CosmoGIRL! about Your Body: All the Answers to Your Most Intimate Questions. 2006. (Illus.). 144p. pap. 5.95 (978-1-58816-486-5(1)) Hearst Bks.

Crump, Marguerite. Don't Sweat It! Everybody's Answers to Questions You Don't Want to Ask: A Guide for Young People. 2004. (Laugh & Learn Ser.). (Illus.). 128p. (YA). (gr. 4-8). pap. 12.95 (978-1-57542-114-8(3)) Free Spirit Publishing, Inc.

—No B. O. ! The Head-to-Toe Book of Hygiene for Preteens. Verdick, Elizabeth, ed. 2005. (Illus.). 128p. (J). (gr. 4-8). pap. 12.95 (978-1-57542-175-9(5)) Free Spirit Publishing, Inc.

Daldry, Jeremy. The Teenage Guy's Survival Guide: The Real Deal on Girls, Growing up, & Other Guy Stuff. 1999. (978-0-606-17234-9(3)); (gr. 5-8). lib. bdg. 17.30 (978-0-613-15215-0(8)) Tandem Library Bks.

Davis, Rachel, creator. A Hero's Stand: An Experience of Self Discovery for Teens. 2004. (YA). spiral bd. 18.00 (978-0-9741833-1-2(8)) Thumbprint Publishing.

Diary of a Junior Year. 2000. (Real Teens Ser.: Vol. 6). 160p. (YA). (gr. 7 up). pap. 4.99 (978-0-439-08413-0(X)) Scholastic, Inc.

Diaz, Juan R. Amaneciendo en la Adolescencia: Comprendiendo la Adolescencia, 2004. (SPA.). 96p. (J). per. 12.00 (978-0-9758755-1-3(5)) Alpha Behavior Consultants.

Dobson, Danae. Let's Talk! Good Stuff for Girlfriends about God, Guys, & Growing Up. 2003. (gr. 7-12). lib. bdg. 22.25 (978-0-613-76820-7(5)) Tandem Library Bks.

—Let's Talk! Good Stuff for Girlfriends about God, Guys, & Growing Up. 2003. 208p. (YA). pap. 12.99 (978-0-8423-0818-2(0)) Tyndale Hse. Pubs.

Drill, Esther, et al. Deal with It! A Whole New Approach to Your Body, Brain & Life as a GURL. 1999. (Illus.). 320p. (YA). (gr. 7-12). pap. 19.95 (978-0-671-04157-1(6), Pocket) Simon & Schuster.

Dunagan, Cindy. Journaling Toward Moral Excellence Volume Two for Pre-Teens Vol. 2: A Character Building Workbook of 100 Thought-Provoking Questions to Help the Young Discover the Value of Moral Strength. 2004. (Journaling Toward Moral Excellence Ser.: Vol. 2). 107p. (J). (gr. 5-7). 11.95 (978-0-9759871-1-7(9)) Straight Paths Pr.

Edelson, Paula. Straight Talk about Teenage Pregnancy. 1998. (Straight Talk Ser.). (Illus.). 144p. (YA). (gr. 6-12). 27.45 (978-0-8160-3717-9(5)) Facts On File, Inc.

Egerstrom, Marisa. Lift Your Voice: The Issues Handbook for Middle School Girls. Egerstrom, Marisa, illus. 2000. (Illus.). 36p. (YA). (gr. 5-12). pap. 6.50 (978-1-883477-36-3(0)) Lone Oak Pr., Ltd.

Emp Emp Books Staff. Its All Good. 1999. (YA). pap. 20.76 (978-0-9667677-0-4(5)) Emp! Emp! Pr.

Erlbach, Arlene. The Middle School Survival Guide: How to Survive from the Day Elementary School Ends until the Second High School Begins. Flook, Helen, illus. 2003. 160p. (J). 16.95 (978-0-8027-8852-8(1)); pap. 8.95 (978-0-8027-7657-0(4)) Walker & Co.

Favor, Lesli J. Everything You Need to Know about Growth Spurts & Delayed Growth. 2005. (Need to Know Library). (Illus.). 64p. (YA). (gr. 4-6). lib. bdg. 25.25 (978-0-8239-3549-9(3)) Rosen Publishing Group, Inc., The.

Fox, Annie. Can You Relate? Real-World Advice for Teens on Guys, Girls, Growing up & Getting Along. 1999. (Illus.). 256p. (YA). (gr. 8-16). pap. 15.95 (978-1-57542-066-0(X)) Free Spirit Publishing, Inc.

Frankenberger, Elizabeth. Crushes, Creeps & Classmates: A Girl's Guide to Getting along with Boys. rev. ed. 2005. (Girls' Guides). (Illus.). 48p. (YA). (gr. 5-8). lib. bdg. 23.95 (978-0-8239-2980-1(9), GGCRCR) Rosen Publishing Group, Inc., The.

Fuyo Gaskins, Pearl, ed. What Are You? Voices of Mixed-Race Young People. rev. ed. 1999. (Illus.). 288p. (YA). (gr. 7-12). 18.95 (978-0-8050-5968-7(7), Holt, Henry & Co. Bks. For Young Readers) Holt, Henry & Co.

Gottfried, Ted. Teen Fathers Today. 2001. (Single Titles Ser.: up). (Illus.). 128p. (gr. 7 up). lib. bdg. 24.90 (978-0-7613-1901-6(8) , Twenty-First Century Bks.) Lerner Publishing Group.

Gravelle, Karen. Que Pasa Por Alla Abajo? 2003. Tr. of What's Going on Down There?. (SPA.). (gr. 5-8). lib. bdg. 17.60 (978-0-613-75342-5(9)) Tandem Library Bks.

—What's Going on down There? Answers to Questions Boys Find Hard to Ask. 1998. (gr. 5-8). lib. bdg. 17.60 (978-0-613-75331-9(3)) Tandem Library Bks.

Gravelle, Karen & Gravelle, Jennifer. El Libro del Periodo. Palen, Debbie, illus. 2003. (SPA.). 117p. (gr. 3 up). pap. 8.95 (978-0-8027-7650-1(7)) Walker & Co.

Gravelle, Karen, et al. What's Going on down There? Answers to Questions Boys Find Hard to Ask. Leighton, Robert, illus. 1998. (gr. 5-9). 128p. (J). 15.95 (978-0-8027-8671-5(5)); 160p. (YA). pap. 8.95 (978-0-8027-7540-5(3)) Walker & Co.

Hanan, Jessica. Coping with Changing Roles for Young Men & Women. 2005. (Coping Ser.). (Illus.). 192p. (YA). (gr. 7-12). lib. bdg. 26.50 (978-0-8239-2880-4(2) , COGERO) Rosen Publishing Group, Inc., The.

Hassett, Gail Daniels. Parent-Teen Relationships. Zanzig, Thomas, ed. Thiewes, Sam, illus. 2003. (Horizons Program : Level 1, Minicourse 4). 60p. (YA). (gr. 9-10). pap., stu. ed. 9.95 (978-0-88489-349-3(9)) St. Mary's Pr.

Hibbert, Adam. Puberty: It's Your Health. 2005. (Illus.). 48p. (YA). (gr. 6 up). lib. bdg. 29.95 (978-1-58340-592-5(5)) Smart Apple Media.

Hoolihan, Patricia. Teen Girls Only! Daily Thoughts for Teenage Girls. 2000. (Illus.). 388p. (gr. 7-12). pap. 12.00 (978-0-930100-31-5(X)) Holy Cow! Pr.

Hynes, Angela. Puberty: An Illustrated Manual for Parents & Daughters. Lloya, Gita, illus. 1999. 147p. (YA). (gr. 6-10). reprint ed. 13.00 (978-0-7881-6361-6(2)) DIANE Publishing Co.

Johnston, Andrea. Girls Speak Out: Finding Your True Self. 1999. (J). (978-0-606-16591-4(6)) Tandem Library Bks.

Jukes, Mavis. Guy Book. 2002. (gr. 7-12). lib. bdg. 22.20 (978-0-613-60561-8(6)) Tandem Library Bks.

Just Around the Corner: For Boys. 2000. (Health & Human Development Resource Library). (J). (gr. 3-5). tchr. ed. 69.95 (978-1-55942-126-3(6) , 9225V9) Marsh Media.

Just Around the Corner: For Girls. 2000. (Health & Human Development Resource Library). (J). (gr. 3-5). tchr. ed. 69.95 (978-1-55942-125-6(8) , 9224V9) Marsh Media.

Ladybird Books Staff. Hangin' with the Lil' Bratz. 2004. (Lil' Bratz Ser.). 32p. pap. 5.43 (978-1-84422-521-7(6) , Grosset & Dunlap) Penguin Group (USA) Inc.

LaFlamme, Linda M. Rites of Passage: A Celebration of Menarche. 2001. (Moontime Ser.). (Illus.). 80p. (J). (gr. 3-9). 19.95 (978-0-9673449-0-4(5)) Synchronicity Pr.

Lerman-Golomb, Barbara. Teen Hot Line, 12 bks., Set. 1999. (gr. 6-12). 215.78 (978-0-8114-3819-3(8)) Raintree.

Lewellen, Judie. The Teen Body Book: A Guide to Your Changing Body. 1999. (Your Body, Your Self Bks.). (Illus.). 144p. (YA). (gr. 4-9). pap. 11.95 (978-0-7373-0165-6(1) , 01651W) McGraw-Hill/Contemporary.

Lieberman, E. James & Troccoli, Karen L. Like It Is: A Teen Sex Guide. 1998. (Illus.). 216p. (C). (gr. 6 up). pap. 29.95 (978-0-7864-0526-8(0)) McFarland & Co., Inc. Pubs.

Lindsay, Jeanne Warren. Teenage Couples - Expectations & Reality: Teens' Views on Living Together, Roles, Work, Children, Jealousy, & Partner Abuse. 2003. (Teen Pregnancy & Parenting Series Ser.). (Illus.). 192p. (J). (gr. 7-12). pap. 14.95 (978-0-930934-98-9(9)) Morning Glory Pr., Inc.

Madaras, Lynda & Madaras, Area. My Body, My Self for Boys. (Illus.). 112p. 2nd ed. 2000. (gr. 4-7). reprint ed. 12.95 (978-1-55704-440-2(6) , Newmarket Shooting Scripts); 3rd rev. ed. 2007. (YA). pap. 12.95 (***978-1-55704-767-0(7)***) Newmarket Pr.

—My Body, My Self for Girls. 3rd rev. ed. 2007. (Illus.). 128p. (YA). pap. 12.95 (***978-1-55704-766-3(9)***) Newmarket Pr.

—The What's Happening to My Body Book for Boys. 3rd ed. 2007. (Illus.). 272p. (YA). 24.95 (***978-1-55704-769-4(3)***); pap. 12.95 (***978-1-55704-765-6(0)***) Newmarket Pr.

—The What's Happening to My Body Book for Girls. 3rd rev. ed. 2007. (Illus.). 304p. (YA). 24.95 (***978-1-55704-768-7(5)***); pap. 12.95 (***978-1-55704-764-9(2)***) Newmarket Pr.

Mayle, Peter. What's Happening to Me? The Answers to Some of the World's Most Embarrassing Questions. Walter, Paul & Robins, Arthur, illus. 2000. 1p. (gr. 4-7). pap. 9.95 (978-0-8184-0312-5(8)) Kensington Publishing Corp.

McCourt, Lisa, et al. Attitude: Tips to Help You Deal, Feel, & Be Real. 2000. (Attitude Ser.). (Illus.). 96p. (J). (gr. 3-7). pap. 6.95 (978-0-7373-0336-0(0) , 03360W, Roxbury Park Juvenile) Lowell Hse. Juvenile.

McCoy, Kathy & Wibbelsman, Charles. The Teenage Body Book. rev. ed. 1999. (Illus.). 1p. (J). (gr. 7-12). pap. 18.95 (978-0-399-52535-3(1) , Perigee Trade) Penguin Group (USA) Inc.

McGraw, Jay. Closing the Gap: A Strategy for Bringing Parents & Teens Together. 2001. (gr. 7-12). lib. bdg. 23.45 (978-0-613-84519-9(6)) Tandem Library Bks.

Meier, Katie. A Girl's Guide to Life: The Real Dish on Growing up, Being True, & Making Your Teen Years Fabulous! 2004. (Illus.). 208p. (YA). pap. 13.99 (978-0-8499-4443-7(0)) Nelson, Thomas Inc.

Meyer, Stephanie H. Teen Ink: What Matters. 2003. (gr. 7-12). lib. bdg. 22.20 (978-0-613-88132-6(X)) Tandem Library Bks.

Meyer, Stephanie H., et al. What Matters. 2003. (Teen Ink Ser.). (Illus.). 400p. (YA). pap. 12.95 (978-0-7573-0063-9(4)) Health Communications, Inc.

Mosatche, Harriet S. & Unger, Karen. Too Old for This, Too Young for That! Your Survival Guide for the Middle-School Years. Gordon, Mike, illus. 2004. 200p. (YA). (gr. 5-9). pap. 14.95 (978-1-57542-067-7(8)) Free Spirit Publishing, Inc.

Movsessian, Shushann. Puberty Girl. 2005. (Illus.). 128p. (J). (ps-7). mass mkt. 15.95 (978-1-74114-104-7(4)) Allen & Unwin AUS. *Dist:* Independent Pubs. Group.

Muharrar, Aisha. More Than a Label: Why What You Wear & Who You're with Doesn't Define Who You Are. 2004. (Illus.). 152p. (YA). (gr. 8 up). pap. 13.95 (978-1-57542-110-0(0)) Free Spirit Publishing, Inc.

Musgrave, Susan. Nerves Out Loud: Critical Moments in the Lives of Seven Teen Girls. 2001. (gr. 7-12). lib. bdg. 18.75 (978-0-613-62398-8(3)) Tandem Library Bks.

—You Be Me: Friendship in the Lives of Teen Girls. 2002. (gr. 7-12). lib. bdg. 16.40 (978-0-613-78373-6(5)) Tandem Library Bks.

Musgrave, Susan, ed. Nerves Out Loud: Critical Moments in the Lives of Seven Teen Girls. 2001. 112p. (YA). (gr. 9 up). 19.95 (978-1-55037-693-7(4)); (Illus.). pap. 9.95 (978-1-55037-692-0(6)) Annick Pr., Ltd. CAN. *Dist:* Firefly Bks., Ltd.

—You Be Me: Friendship in the Lives of Teen Girls. 2002. 128p. (YA). (gr. 10 up). 18.95 (978-1-55037-739-2(6)) Annick Pr., Ltd. CAN. *Dist:* Firefly Bks., Ltd.

Parents Don't Know Everything: A Teen Freedom of Expression Journal. 2004. spiral bd. 9.50 (978-0-9749216-1-7(0)) Swannee Rivers.

Pascoe, Elaine, ed. Teen Dreams: The Journey Through Puberty. 2003. (Body Story Ser.). (Illus.). 48p. (J). 24.95 (978-1-4103-0061-4(7)); pap. 11.20 (978-1-4103-0182-6(6)) Thomson Gale. (Blackbirch Pr., Inc.).

Pingry, Patricia A. The Power of Faith for Teens: True Stories. 2004. (Illus.). 160p. pap. 9.95 (978-0-8249-4622-7(7)) Ideals Pubns.

Rice, Ashley. Girls Rule: A Very Special Book Created Especially for Girls. Rice, Ashley, illus. (Illus.). 64p. (J). pap. 9.95 (978-0-88396-627-3(1) , Blue Mountain Pr.) Blue Mountain Arts Inc.

Rimm, Sylvia. See Jane Win for Girls: A Smart Girl's Guide to Success. 2004. (Illus.). 144p. (YA). (gr. 4-8). pap. 13.95 (978-1-57542-122-3(4)) Free Spirit Publishing, Inc.

—See Jane Win for Girls: A Smart Girl's Guide to Success. 2003. (gr. 7-12). lib. bdg. 23.40 (978-0-613-67161-3(9)) Tandem Library Bks.

Ross, Michael. Bloom: A Girl's Guide to Growing Up. 2003. (gr. 7-12). lib. bdg. 28.05 (978-0-613-79771-9(X)) Tandem Library Bks.

Shaw, Victoria. Body Talk: A Girl's Guide to What's Happening to Your Body. 1999. (Girls' Guides). (Illus.). 48p. (YA). (gr. 5-8). lib. bdg. 23.95 (978-0-8239-2977-1(9) , GGBOTA) Rosen Publishing Group, Inc., The.

Sheen, Barbara. Adolescence. 2007. (J). (***978-1-4034-9691-1(9)***); pap. (***978-1-4034-9698-0(6)***) Heinemann Library.

Smith, Erica. Write It Down! A Girl's Guide to Keeping a Journal. 1999. (Girls' Guides). (Illus.). 48p. (YA). (gr. 5-8). lib. bdg. 23.95 (978-0-8239-2979-5(5) , GGWRDO) Rosen Publishing Group, Inc., The.

Spence, Simone. A Children's Book about Growing Up. 2000. (Help Me Succeed Ser.). (Illus.). 230p. (J). (gr. 4-7). pap. 29.95 (978-0-9670647-1-0(6)) EggShell Pr.

—A Children's Book about Growing Up. Friedman, Staci, illus. deluxe ed. 2000. (Help Me Grow Ser.: Vol. 3). 240p. (J). (ps-5). pap. 49.95 incl. audio compact disk (978-0-9670647-2-7(4)) EggShell Pr.

Stern, Zoe. Protect This Girl: Words of Inspiration from Girl to Girl. 2004. (Illus.). 32p. (gr. 7-13). 9.95 (978-1-883672-81-2(3) , Tricycle Pr.) Ten Speed Pr.

Strazzabosco, Jeanne M. From Algebra to Zits: A Girl's Guide to Making the Most of Life at School. 1999. (Girls' Guides) (Illus.) 48p (YA) (gr. 5-8). lib. bdg. 23.95 (978-0-8239-2983-2(3) , GGALZI) Rosen Publishing Group, Inc., The.

Villegas, Maria & Kent, Jennie. Girl to Girl. Salom Safi, Ivette, illus. 2007. 336p. (J). spiral bd. 16.00 (***978-958-8306-03-2(5)***) Villegas Editores S.A. COL. *Dist:* Independent Pubs. Group.

Vizzini, Ned. Teen Angst? Naaah...A Quasi-autobiography. 2002. 288p. (YA). (gr. 7 up). mass mkt. 5.99 (978-0-440-23767-9(X) , Laurel Leaf) Random Hse. Children's Bks.

Ward, Kristin. Havin' Fun & Hangin' Out: A Girl's Guide to Cool Stuff to Do. 1999. (Girls' Guides). (Illus.). 48p. (YA). (gr. 5-8). lib. bdg. 23.95 (978-0-8239-2978-8(7) , GGHAOU) Rosen Publishing Group, Inc., The.

The Winners. 2005. (YA). 14.95 (***978-0-9661256-4-1(9)***) Youth Communication - New York Center.

Yeager, Selene. What's with My Body? The Girls' Book of Answers to Growing Up, Looking Good, & Feeling Great. 2002. (Illus.). 272p. pap. 12.95 (978-0-7615-3723-6(6) , Three Rivers Pr.) Crown Publishing Group.

Zep. What's Going on down There? All the Stuff Your Body Won't Tell You about Sex. Zimmerman, Dwight, ed. 2005. (Illus.). 96p. pap. 14.95 (978-1-4165-0458-0(3)) ibooks, Inc.

ADOLESCENCE—FICTION

Abrams, Teri & Schread, Diane. Girls Like Me. 2000. 160p. (Orig.). (YA). (gr. 8-12). pap. 9.95 (978-0-9703225-1-7(8)) Blue Swan Bks.

Adams, Ann. Obsessed with... 2001. (Illus.). 96p. pap. 9.95 (978-1-931497-43-5(5)) 17th Street Productions, An Alloy Online Inc. Co.

Akinyemi, Rowena. Love or Money?, Level 1. 2nd ed. 2000. (Bookworms Ser.). (Illus.). 64p. 6.50 (978-0-19-422946-3(7)) Oxford Univ. Pr., Inc.

Alford, Jan. I Can't Believe I Have to Do This. 1999. (J). (978-0-606-16801-4(X)); (gr. 5-8). lib. bdg. 14.15 (978-0-613-19374-0(1)) Tandem Library Bks.

Alger, Horatio. Driven from Home: Carl Crawford's Experience. reprint ed. pap. 79.00 (978-1-4047-3564-4(X)) Classic Textbooks.

—Driven from Home: Carl Crawford's Experience. 2006. pap. (***978-1-4065-0702-7(4)***) Dodo Pr.

Allen, Debbie. Brothers of the Knight. Sherry, Toby, ed. Nelson, Kadir A., illus. 1999. 40p. (J). (gr. k-4). 16.99 (978-0-8037-2488-4(8) , Dial) Penguin Group (USA) Inc.

Andrews, Kate. Cool It, Carrie. 1999. (Making Friends Ser.: No. 2). (Illus.). 128p. (J). (gr. 3-7). mass mkt. 3.99 (978-0-380-80931-8(1)) HarperCollins Pubs.

Anfousse, Ginette. Rosalie a la Belle Etoile. 2002. (Roman Jeunesse Ser.). 96p. (YA). (gr. 4-7). pap. (978-2-89021-314-2(5)) Diffusion du livre Mirabel.

Anonymous. Diary of a Senior Year. 2000. (Real Teens Ser.: Vol. 1). (YA). (gr. 7 up). pap. 4.99 (978-0-439-11458-5(6)) Scholastic, Inc.

Applegate, Katherine. Burn. 2001. (Making Waves Ser.: No. 8). 272p. mass mkt. 4.99 (978-1-931497-19-0(2)) 17th Street Productions, An Alloy Online Inc. Co.

—Don't Forget Lara. 2000. (Making Out Ser.: No. 25). 176p. (YA). (gr. 7-12). pap. 3.99 (978-0-380-81529-6(X)) HarperCollins Pubs.

—Heat. 2001. (Making Waves Ser.: No. 5). 272p. mass mkt. 4.99 (978-1-931497-16-9(8)) 17th Street Productions, An Alloy Online Inc. Co.

—Making Waves. 2001. (Making Waves Ser.: No. 1). 320p. (YA). mass mkt. 4.99 (978-1-931497-12-1(5)) 17th Street Productions, An Alloy Online Inc. Co.

—Now Zoey's Alone. 2000. (Making Out Ser.: No. 24). 176p. (YA). (gr. 7-12). pap. 3.99 (978-0-380-81528-9(1)) HarperCollins Pubs.

—Tease. 2001. (Making Waves Ser.: No. 2). 288p. (YA). mass mkt. 4.99 (978-1-931497-13-8(3)) 17th Street Productions, An Alloy Online Inc. Co.

—Trouble with Aaron. 2000. (Making Out Ser.: No. 21). 176p. (YA). (gr. 7-12). pap. 3.99 (978-0-380-81310-0(6)) HarperCollins Pubs.

—Wild. 2001. (Making Waves Ser.: No. 9). 256p. mass mkt. 4.99 (978-1-931497-20-6(6)) 17th Street Productions, An Alloy Online Inc. Co.

—Zoey's Broken Heart. 2000. (Making Out Ser.: No. 26). 176p. (YA). (gr. 7 up). pap. 3.99 (978-0-380-81530-2(3)) HarperCollins Pubs.

Archer, Chris. Fright Club No. 6: Dreadlocks. 2001. 160p. (J). (gr. 4-7). pap. 3.99 (978-1-931497-28-2(1)) 17th Street Productions, An Alloy Online Inc. Co.

Ashworth, Sherry. What's Your Problem. 2000. 132p. (J). pap. 11.99 (978-0-7043-4961-2(2)) Women's Pr., Ltd., The GBR. *Dist:* Independent Pubs. Group.

Bagdasarian, Adam. First French Kiss: And Other Traumas. 2002. 144p. (YA). (gr. 7 up). 16.00 (978-0-374-32338-7(0) , Farrar, Straus & Giroux (BYR)) Farrar, Straus & Giroux.

Bagdasarian, Adam & Best, Cari. Are You Going to Be Good? Karas, G. Brian, illus. 2005. 32p. (J). 16.00 (978-0-374-30394-5(0) , Farrar, Straus & Giroux (BYR)) Farrar, Straus & Giroux.

Bailey, Barbara. When I Get Older I'll Understand. 2000. 192p. (gr. 7-12). 7.95 (978-1-56315-211-5(8)) Sterling-House Pubs., Inc.

—When I Get Older I'll Understand. 2000. (gr. 7-12). lib. bdg. 16.40 (978-0-613-83337-0(6)) Tandem Library Bks.

Baras, Ronit. Be Special, Be Yourself for Teenagers. 2005. 171p. (YA). per. (***978-0-9757976-0-0(3)***) Be Happy in LIFE.

Barondes, Jessica. Lucy. 2000. (Sweet Sixteen Ser.: Vol. 2). 240p. (YA). (gr. 12 up). pap. 5.95 (978-0-06-440813-4(2) , Harper Trophy) HarperCollins Pubs.

Bauer, Cat. Harley, Like a Person. 2000. 248p. (J). (gr. 7 up). 16.95 (978-1-890817-48-0(1)); pap. 6.95 (978-1-890817-49-7(X)) Winslow Pr.

Bauer, Joan. Hope Was Here. 2002. (YA). 13.19 (978-1-4046-0748-4(X)) Book Wholesalers, Inc.

—Hope Was Here. 2005. 192p. (YA). (gr. 7-12). pap. 7.99 (978-0-14-240424-9(1) , Puffin) Penguin Group (USA) Inc.

—Hope Was Here. unabr. ed. 2004. 186p. (J). (gr. 7 up). pap. 36.00 incl. audio (978-0-8072-1706-1(9) , S YA 1013 SP, Listening Library) Random Hse. Audio Publishing Group.

—Hope Was Here. l.t. ed. 2001. (YA). (gr. 8-12). 22.95 (978-0-7862-3258-1(7)) Thorndike Pr.

Betancourt, Jeanne. The Newborn Pony. Bachem, Paul, illus. 2001. (Pony Pals Ser.: No. 28). 96p. (J). (gr. 7). pap. 3.99 (978-0-439-16571-6(7)) Scholastic, Inc.

Blume, Judy. Are You There God? It's Me, Margaret. 2002. (J). 13.94 (978-0-7587-9131-3(3)) Book Wholesalers, Inc.

—Are You There God? It's Me, Margaret. l.t. ed. 2002. (LRS Large Print Cornerstone Ser.). (J). lib. bdg. 28.95 (978-1-58118-088-6(8) , 24873) LRS.

—Then Again, Maybe I Won't. (J). 125p. pap. 3.99 (978-0-8072-1445-9(0)); 2004. 164p. (gr. 5-9). pap. 29.00 incl. audio (978-0-8072-0796-3(9) , LYA 354 SP) Random Hse. Audio Publishing Group. (Listening Library).

Boy Crazy! 3rd ed. 2001. 144p. pap. 4.99 (978-0-06-441051-9(X)) HarperCollins Pubs.

Brashares, Ann & Random House Staff. Keep in Touch: Letters, Notes, & More from the Sisterhood of the Traveling Pants. movie tie-in ed. 2005. (Illus.). 144p. (YA). (gr. 7). pap. 7.95 (978-0-553-37608-1(X) , Delacorte Bks. for Young Readers) Random Hse. Children's Bks.

Bray, Libba. Kari. 2000. (Sweet Sixteen Ser.: No. 3). 240p. (YA). (gr. 12 up). pap. 5.95 (978-0-06-440817-2(5) , Harper Trophy) HarperCollins Pubs.

Brooks, Bruce. The Moves Make the Man. (J). pap., stu. ed. (978-0-13-017518-2(8)); 3rd ed. pap. 3.95 (978-0-13-800079-0(4)) Prentice Hall (Schl. Div.).

Brooks, Kevin. Candy. 2006. 384p. (J). pap. 7.99 (978-0-439-68328-9(9) , PUSH); 2005. 368p. pap. 16.95 (978-0-439-68327-2(0) , Chicken Hse., The) Scholastic, Inc.

Brooks, Martha. Being with Henry. 1999. (J). (978-0-88899-377-9(3)) Douglas & McIntyre, Ltd.

—Being with Henry. pap. 8.95 (978-0-88899-502-5(4)) Groundwood Bks. CAN. *Dist:* Transition Vendor.

Brown, Amanda. Beach Blonde. 2006. (Legally Elle Woods Ser.: Vol. 1). 240p. (gr. 7-17). pap. 6.99 (978-0-7868-3843-1(4)); 2nd rev. ed. (gr. 3-7). pap. 6.99 (978-0-7868-3844-8(2)) Hyperion Pr.

—Family Trust. 2004. 336p. (gr. 12). pap. 14.00 (978-0-452-28553-8(4) , Plume) Penguin Group (USA) Inc.

Bruce, Jonathan C. There Is a Season. 2001. 324p. pap. 17.95 (978-0-595-17565-9(1) , Writers Club Pr.) iUniverse, Inc.

Bryant, Annie. Fashion Frenzy. (Beacon Street Girls Ser.: Bk. 9). 232p. (YA). pap. 7.99 (978-1-933566-02-3(7) , Beacon Street Girls) B*tween Productions, Inc.

Bryant, Bonnie. Course of Action. 1999. (Pine Hollow Ser.: No. 8). (YA). (gr. 7 up). (978-0-606-18959-0(9)) Tandem Library Bks.

Buchanan, Paul W. Snapshots. 2007. 216p. (J). (gr. 4-7). pap. 8.95 (***978-0-7387-1073-0(3)***) Llewellyn Pubns.

Bullock, Harold B. The Dreamweaver. Dumas, Barbara, ed. 2000. (Tarlian Adventures Ser.: Vol. 4). 120p. (J). (gr. 2-5). pap. (978-1-929248-06-3(7)) Golden Oak Pubs.

Cabot, Meg. In Love. 2002. (Princess Diaries: Vol. 3). 272p. (YA). (gr. 7 up). mass mkt. 5.99 (978-0-06-052568-2(1)) HarperCollins Pubs.

Cann, Kate. California Holiday: How the World's Worst Summer Job Gave Me a Great New Life. 2005. 416p. (YA). (gr. 8 up). pap. 5.99 (978-0-06-056161-1(0)) HarperCollins Pubs.

—Hard Cash. 2003. (Illus.). 336p. (YA). mass mkt. 5.99 (978-0-689-85905-2(8) , Simon Pulse) Simon & Schuster Children's Publishing.

—Hard Cash. 2003. (gr. 7-12). lib. bdg. 14.15 (978-0-613-73411-0(4)) Tandem Library Bks.

Carver, Peter, ed. Close-Ups: Best Stories for Teens. 2000. 224p. (YA). (gr. 5 up). pap. (978-0-88995-200-3(0)) Red Deer Pr.

Children's Television Workshop Staff. Anywhere I Am Is Here... Anywhere I'm Not Is There: The Eternal Wisdoms of Sesame Street. 2000. (Illus.). 176p. pap. 14.95 (978-0-7868-8334-9(0)) Hyperion Paperbacks for Children.

Circle of Blue. 2006. (J). (978-1-933343-37-2(0) , PONY) Stabenfeldt Inc.

Clamp, ed. Clover. 2003. (Illus.). (YA). 29.99 (978-1-59182-592-0(X)) TOKYOPOP, Inc.

Clarke, Nicole & Bourne, Cecile. High Fashion. 2006. (Flirt Ser.: No. 3). 224p. (J). (gr. 7). pap. 6.99 (978-0-448-44122-1(5) , Grosset & Dunlap) Penguin Group (USA) Inc.

Cleary, Beverly. Fifteen. 2000. (J). (978-0-606-19735-9(4)) Tandem Library Bks.

Cleary, Christopher. Writing on the Wall. 2007. 198p. (YA). per. 9.99 (***978-0-9795753-5-8(4)***) Immortality Pr.

Cohn, Rachel. Pop Princess. 2005. 320p. (J). reprint ed. pap. 6.99 (978-1-4169-0263-8(5) , Simon Pulse) Simon & Schuster Children's Publishing.

Coming of Age Vol. 1: Fiction about Youth & Adolescence. 2nd ed. Incl. 2nd ed. Emra, Bruce & McGraw-Hill Staff. 311p. (C). pap., stu. ed. 41.32 (978-0-8442-0361-4(0) , 9780844203614); Vol. 1. Coming of Age. Emra, Bruce, contrib. by. (J). (978-0-8442-0362-1(9) , C03629); 1999. Set stu. ed. 46.00 (978-0-8442-0360-7(2) , 9780844203607) Glencoe/McGraw-Hill.

Cormier, Robert. Fade. 2004. 320p. (YA). (gr. 9-17). pap. 7.99 (978-0-385-73134-8(5) , Delacorte Bks. for Young Readers) Random Hse. Children's Bks.

—Fade. 2002. 20.50 (978-0-8446-7216-8(5)) Smith, Peter Pub., Inc.

Corrigan, Eireann. Splintering. 192p. (J). 2005. pap. 7.99 (978-0-439-48992-8(X)); 2004. pap. 16.95 (978-0-439-53597-7(2)) Scholastic, Inc.

Crane, Dede. The 25 Pains of Kennedy Baines. 2007. 176p. (J). pap. 8.95 (978-1-55192-979-8(1)) Raincoast Bk. Distribution CAN. *Dist:* Perseus Distribution.

Davidson, A. L., et al. The Spirit Line. 2004. 224p. (YA). (gr. 7). 16.99 (978-0-670-03645-5(5) , Viking Juvenile) Penguin Group (USA) Inc.

Day, Lauren. Who Can You Trust? 1999. (Rockett's World Ser.: No. 1). (Illus.). 128p. (J). (gr. 4-7). pap. 3.99 (978-0-439-04405-9(7)) Scholastic, Inc.

—Who Can You Trust? 1999. (Rockett's World Ser.: No. 1). (J). (gr. 4-7). (978-0-606-17049-9(9)) Tandem Library Bks.

de la Cruz, Melissa. Fresh off the Boat. 2005. (Illus.). 256p. (J). (gr. 7 up). 15.99 (978-0-06-054540-6(2)) HarperCollins Pubs.

De Oliveira, Eddie. Johnny Hazzard. 2006. 352p. (J). pap. 8.99 (978-0-439-67362-4(3)) Scholastic, Inc.

Dean, Zoey. The A-List. 2003. (A-List Ser.: Bk. 1). 256p. (J). (gr. 10-17). pap. 9.99 (978-0-316-73435-6(7) , Poppy) Little, Brown Bks. for Young Readers.

DeClements, Barthe. Nothing's Fair in Fifth Grade. 137p. (J). (gr. 3-5). pap. 4.50 (978-0-8072-1413-8(2) , Listening Library) Random Hse. Audio Publishing Group.

DeFelice, Cynthia C. The Apprenticeship of Lucas Whitaker. 1998. (J). 12.64 (978-0-606-13078-3(0)) Tandem Library Bks.

Dessen, Sarah. How to Deal: Someone Like You; That Summer. movie tie-in ed. 2003. 496p. (YA). pap. 7.99 (978-0-14-250103-0(4) , Puffin) Penguin Group (USA) Inc.

—Someone Like You. 2003. (gr. 7-12). lib. bdg. 16.45 (978-0-613-66709-8(3)) Tandem Library Bks.

—The Truth about Forever. 2004. 384p. (J). (gr. 7). 16.99 (978-0-670-03639-4(0) , Viking Juvenile) Penguin Group (USA) Inc.

Dower, Laura. The Boy Next Door. 2007. (Candy Apple Ser.: No. 2). 176p. (J). pap. 4.99 (978-0-439-92929-5(6)) Scholastic, Inc.

—From the Files of Madison Finn: Give & Take. 2002. (gr. 3-6). lib. bdg. 13.00 (978-0-613-75024-0(1)) Tandem Library Bks.

—From the Files of Madison Finn Super Edition: To Have & to Hold. 2004. 320p. (J). (gr. 3-7). pap. 5.99 (978-0-7868-1785-6(2)) Hyperion Bks. for Children.

—Give & Take. rev. ed. 2002. (From the Files of Madison Finn Ser.: Bk. 10). (Illus.). 176p. (J). (gr. 3-7). pap. 4.99 (978-0-7868-1684-2(8) , Volo) Hyperion Bks. for Children.

—Heart to Heart. rev. ed. 2003. (From the Files of Madison Finn Ser.: Bk. 11). (Illus.). 176p. (J). (gr. 3-7). pap. 4.99 (978-0-7868-1685-9(6) , Volo) Hyperion Bks. for Children.

—Just Visiting. rev. ed. 2002. (From the Files of Madison Finn Ser.). 176p. (J). (gr. 3-7). pap. 4.99 (978-0-7868-1683-5(X) , Volo) Hyperion Bks. for Children.

—Just Visiting. 2002. (gr. 3-6). lib. bdg. 13.00 (978-0-613-90688-3(8)) Tandem Library Bks.

—Lights Out! 12th rev. ed. 2003. (From the Files of Madison Finn Ser.: Bk. 12). (Illus.). 176p. (gr. 3-7). pap. 4.99 (978-0-7868-1686-6(4) , Volo) Hyperion Bks. for Children.

—Lights Out! 2003. (gr. 3-6). lib. bdg. 13.00 (978-0-613-91013-2(3)) Tandem Library Bks.

—Picture-Perfect. rev. ed. 2002. (From the Files of Madison Finn Ser.). (Illus.). 176p. (J). (gr. 3-7). pap. 4.99 (978-0-7868-1682-8(1) , Volo) Hyperion Bks. for Children.

—Save the Date. 7th rev. ed. 2002. (From the Files of Madison Finn Ser.: No. 7). (Illus.). 176p. (gr. 3-7). pap. 4.99 (978-0-7868-1681-1(3) , Volo) Hyperion Bks. for Children.

—Scribbles & Secrets. Torrecilla, Pablo, illus. 2004. 96p. (J). 9.99 (978-0-439-56126-6(4) , Tangerine Pr.) Scholastic, Inc.

—Three's a Crowd, Bk. 16. rev. ed. 2004. (From the Files of Madison Finn Ser.: Vol. 16). 192p. (J). (gr. 3-7). pap. 4.99 (978-0-7868-0986-8(8)) Hyperion Bks. for Children.

Dower, Laura & Powers, Stephanie. Off the Wall. 15th rev. ed. 2004. (From the Files of Madison Finn Ser.: No. 15). (Illus.). 176p. (gr. 3-7). pap. 4.99 (978-0-7868-1737-5(2)) Hyperion Pr.

Doyle, Malachy. Who Is Jesse Flood. 2004. 176p. (J). pap. 6.95 (978-1-58234-922-0(3) , Bloomsbury Children) Bloomsbury Publishing.

Doyon, Stephanie. Taking Chances. 1999. (On the Road Ser.: No. 3). (978-0-606-18899-9(1)) Tandem Library Bks.

Duncan, Lois. Killing Mr. Griffin. 223p. (YA). (gr. 7 up). pap. 4.50 (978-0-8072-1373-5(X) , Listening Library) Random Hse. Audio Publishing Group.

—Locked in Time. 2002. (Illus.). (J). 13.38 (978-0-7587-4791-4(8)) Book Wholesalers, Inc.

Elkeles, Simone. How to Ruin My Teenage Life. 2007. 288p. (J). (gr. 7-10). pap. 8.95 (978-0-7387-1019-8(9) , Flux) Llewellyn Pubns.

Emmy's Question. 2007. (J). 16.99 (*978-0-9790395-2-2(5)) Morningtide Pr.

Emra, Bruce, contrib. by. Coming of Age, Vol. 1. 1999. (J). (978-0-8442-0362-1(9) , C03629) McGraw-Hill/ Contemporary.

Emra, Bruce & McGraw-Hill Staff. Coming of Age Vol. 1: Fiction about Youth & Adolescence. 2nd ed. 1999. 311p. (C). pap., stu. ed. 41.32 (978-0-8442-0361-4(0) , 9780844203614) Glencoe/McGraw-Hill.

Fifteen. 190p. (YA). (gr. 7 up). pap. 4.99 (978-0-8072-1361-2(6) , Listening Library) Random Hse. Audio Publishing Group.

Fine, Anne. Charm School. l.t. ed. 2005. (Illus.). 241p. (J). pap. (978-0-7540-6176-2(0) , CLP 369) BBC Audio.

Finley, Martha. Elsie's Stolen Heart, Bk. 4. 1999. (Elsie Dinsmore: Bk. 4). (Illus.). 224p. (YA). (gr. 5-9). 12.99 (978-1-928749-04-2(6)) Zonderkidz.

—Elsie's Tender Mercies, Bk. 7. 2001. (Elsie Dinsmore: Bk. 7). 224p. (J). (gr. 5-9). 12.99 (978-1-928749-07-3(0)) Zonderkidz.

—Elsie's Troubled Times, Bk. 6. 2000. (Elsie Dinsmore: Bk. 6). 224p. (YA). (gr. 5-9). 12.99 (978-1-928749-06-6(2)) Zonderkidz.

Fitzhugh, Louise. Long Secret. 2002. (gr. 5-8). lib. bdg. 14.15 (978-0-613-86230-1(9)) Tandem Library Bks.

Fleischman, Paul. A Fate Totally Worse Than Death. 2004. (Illus.). 128p. (YA). (gr. 9 up). reprint ed. pap. 5.99 (978-0-7636-2189-6(7)) Candlewick Pr.

Foon, Dennis. Skud. 2004. 176p. (YA). pap. 6.95 (978-0-88899-549-0(0)) Groundwood Bks. CAN. *Dist:* Perseus Distribution.

Friesen, Gayle. Men of Stone. 2000. (gr. 7-12). lib. bdg. 15.25 (978-0-613-44529-0(5)) Tandem Library Bks.

—Men of stone. 2000. (Gayle Friessen Ser.). (Illus.). 216p. (YA). (gr. 13 up). (978-1-55074-781-2(9)) Kids Can Pr., Ltd.

Garfinkle, Debra. The Band: Holding On. 2007. 240p. (YA). (gr. 12 up). pap. 9.99 (*978-0-425-21562-3(8) , Berkley Trade) Penguin Group (USA) Inc.

Gerritsen, Tess. Bloodstream: A Novel of Medical Suspense. 1999. (gr. 7-12). lib. bdg. 16.45 (978-0-613-24020-8(0)) Tandem Library Bks.

Golden, Christopher & Sniegoski, Thomas E. Force Majeure. 2002. mass mkt. 5.99 (978-0-7434-2671-8(1)); 400p. (YA). (gr. 11 up). pap. 5.99 (978-0-7434-2670-1(3)) Simon & Schuster Children's Publishing. (Simon Pulse).

Golding, Theresa Martin. Kat's Surrender. 2003. 184p. (YA). (gr. 4-6). pap. 9.95 (978-1-56397-074-0(0)); (J). (gr. 5-9). 16.95 (978-1-56397-755-8(9)) Boyds Mills Pr.

Goldsworthy, J. L. Approaching the Crossroads: Four Stories of Adolescence. 2000. 76p. (YA). (gr. 7-12). pap. 9.95 (978-0-595-14911-7(1) , Writer's Showcase Pr.) iUniverse, Inc.

Goobie, Beth. Hello, Groin. 2006. 224p. (YA). lib. bdg. 17.95 (978-1-55143-459-9(8)) Orca Bk. Pubs. USA.

—The Lottery. 2002. 272p. (J). (gr. 7-12). lib. bdg. 15.95 (978-1-55143-238-0(2)) Orca Bk. Pubs. USA.

—The Lottery. 2002. 264p. (YA). (gr. 7 up). 19.95 (978-1-55142-283-1(2)) Rodeo Chaps CAN. *Dist:* Orca Bk. Pubs. USA.

Graphis Staff. Bridget De Socio, Socio X. 2000. 224p. (J). 70.00 (978-0-06-019806-0(0)) HarperCollins Pubs.

Greenberg, Joanne. I Never Promised You a Rose Garden. 2004. 288p. (gr. 12). pap. 13.95 (978-0-451-21120-0(0) , N A L Trade) Penguin Group (USA) Inc.

—I Never Promised You a Rose Garden. 256p. (YA). (gr. 7 up). pap. 5.99 (978-0-8072-1362-9(4) , Listening Library) Random Hse. Audio Publishing Group.

Griffin, Adele. Sons of Liberty. 1998. 230p. (gr. 5-17). pap. 4.95 (978-0-7868-1300-1(8)) Disney Pr.

Griffith, Amanda. Two Truths & a Lie. 2006. pap. 15.95 (*978-1-4259-4458-2(2)) AuthorHouse.

Griffiths, Corinne Escobar. Corky Eckelsbriar. 2004. (J). pap. 6.95 (978-0-9760271-0-2(0)) Cappella Publishing, A.

Grossman, Linda Sky. I'm a Great Little Kid Series Set: (6 Picture Books & Guide) (Illus.). 1p. 79.95 (978-1-896764-75-7(4)); pap. 39.95 (978-1-896764-74-0(6)) Second Story Pr. CAN. *Dist:* Orca Bk. Pubs. USA.

Gutman, Dan. Johnny Hangtime. 2000. 144p. (J). (gr. 3-7). pap. 5.99 (978-0-380-81012-3(3) , Harper Trophy) HarperCollins Pubs.

—Johnny Hangtime. 2000. (gr. 3-6). lib. bdg. 12.95 (978-0-613-25818-0(5)); (Illus.). (J). 12.64 (978-0-606-18699-5(9)) Tandem Library Bks.

Hale, Stephanie. Revenge of the Homecoming Queen. 2007. 272p. (YA). (gr. 6 up). pap. 9.99 (*978-0-425-21615-6(2) , Berkley Trade) Penguin Group (USA) Inc.

Hamilton, Virginia. The Planet of Junior Brown. 1998. (J). pap. 4.50 (978-0-87628-347-9(4)) Ctr. for Applied Research in Education, The.

Hammomnd, John & Hutchison, Gary. The Live & Loves of Adam Carter. 2005. 203p. (YA). pap. 13.99 (978-1-885631-98-5(7)) Hutchison, G.F. Pr.

Hargrove, Jason. Looking Good, Cody Greer. 2006. 188p. pap. 19.95 (*978-1-4241-4013-8(7)) PublishAmerica, Inc.

Harimann, Sierra & Burns, Laura J. Go West, Darcy! 2006. (Darcy's Wild Life Ser.: No. 6). 160p. (J). (gr. 4-7). mass mkt. 4.99 (978-0-448-44353-9(8) , Grosset & Dunlap) Penguin Group (USA) Inc.

Hawkins, Karen. The Seduction of Sara. 2001. 384p. pap. 6.99 (978-0-380-81526-5(5)) HarperCollins Pubs.

Hawthorne, Rachel. Caribbean Cruising. 2004. 336p. (J). (gr. 8 up). pap. 5.99 (978-0-06-056507-7(1)) HarperCollins Pubs.

Hayes, Sonia. Ms. Thang. 2006. (ENG.). 192p. (YA). per. 9.95 (978-0-9777573-0-5(7)) NUA Multimedia.

Henighan, Stephen. The Places Where Names Vanish. 2004. 183p. pap. (978-1-895449-77-8(4)) Thistledown Pr., Ltd.

Herrick, Steven. The Simple Gift. 2004. 192p. (YA). pap. 6.99 (978-0-689-86867-2(7) , Simon Pulse) Simon & Schuster Children's Publishing.

Hicks, Betty. Busted ! rev. ed. 2004. 176p. (J). 15.95 (978-1-59643-004-4(4)) Roaring Brook Pr.

Hoffmann, Kerry Cohen. Easy. 2007. 176p. (YA). pap. 6.99 (*978-1-4169-1426-6(9) , Simon Pulse) Simon & Schuster Children's Publishing.

Holeman, Linda. Mercy's Birds. 1998. (gr. 5-8). lib. bdg. 15.25 (978-0-613-77269-3(5)) Tandem Library Bks.

—Mercy's Birds. 1998. 208p. (J). (gr. 6-9). pap. 6.95 (978-0-88776-463-9(0)) Tundra Bks., Inc./Livres Toundra, Inc. CAN. *Dist:* Random Hse., Inc.

Hollstein, Stephanie. Connections. 2001. 192p. (YA). pap. 13.95 (978-0-595-17152-1(4) , Writers Club Pr.) iUniverse, Inc.

Holly, Cate. You + Me = Heart Symbol. 2001. (Illus.). 80p. 5.99 (978-0-7407-1450-4(3)) Andrews McMeel Publishing.

Holman, Felice. Slake's Limbo. unabr. ed. 2004. 117p. (J). (gr. 7 up). pap. 29.00 incl. audio (978-0-8072-8744-6(X) , YA254SP, Listening Library) Random Hse. Audio Publishing Group.

Holohan, Maureen. Friday Nights. 2000. (Broadway Ballplayers Ser.). (Illus.). (J). (978-0-606-20666-2(3)) Tandem Library Bks.

Holt, Rinehart and Winston Staff. And Now Miguel. 3rd ed. 2003. (Illus.). 16.80 (978-0-03-035916-3(3)) Holt, Rinehart & Winston.

Hopkins, Cathy. Mates, Dates Simply Fabulous Bks. 1-4, Set: Mates, Dates, & Inflatable Bras; Mates, Dates, & Cosmic Kisses; Mates, Dates, & Portobello Princesses; Mates, Dates, & Sleepover Secrets. 2006. (Mates, Dates Ser.: Bks. 1-4). 736p. (YA). pap. 10.99 (978-1-4169-1829-5(9)) Simon & Schuster Children's Publishing.

—White Lies & Barefaced Truths. 2005. (Truth or Dare Ser.: No. 1). 176p. (YA). mass mkt. 3.99 (978-1-4169-1152-4(9) , Simon Pulse) Simon & Schuster Children's Publishing.

Horniman, Joanne. Secret Scribbled Notebooks. 2005. 228p. (Orig.). (YA). (gr. 7-17). pap. 7.95 (978-1-74114-406-2(X)) Allen & Unwin AUS. *Dist:* Independent Pubs. Group.

Howell, Robert. Third Times the Charm. 2007. 224p. (J). (gr. 1-7). pap. 10.95 (*978-1-897235-20-1(8)) Thistledown Pr., Ltd. CAN. *Dist:* Fitzhenry & Whiteside, Ltd.

Hunt, Scott, illus. Twice Told: Original Stories Inspired by Original Artwork. 2006. 272p. (YA). (gr. 6). 19.99 (978-0-525-46818-9(8) , Dutton Juvenile) Penguin Group (USA) Inc.

Hyde, Diana. Sex Without Love. 2001. 304p. pap. 12.95 (978-0-9705435-4-7(9)) Heicron, Inc.

Hyperion, ed. An Unexpected Return - #8: W. I. T. C. H. Graphic Novel. 8th rev. ed. 2007. 128p. (gr. 3-7). pap. 4.99 (*978-1-4231-0903-7(1)) Hyperion Pr.

Jacobs, Deborah Lynn. The Same Difference. 2000. 187p. (J). (ps-8). pap. 9.99 (978-0-88092-465-8(9)) Royal Fireworks Publishing Co.

James, Brian & Masino, Brian. Perfect World. 2004. 304p. (J). (gr. 7 up). pap. 16.95 (978-0-439-67364-8(X) , PUSH) Scholastic, Inc.

Jenkins, A. M. Damage. 2003. (gr. 7-12). lib. bdg. 15.30 (978-0-613-62741-2(5)) Tandem Library Bks.

—Damage. l.t. ed. 2002. 221p. (YA). 24.95 (978-0-7862-4749-3(5)) Thorndike Pr.

Johnston, Julie. Hero of Lesser Causes. pap. 6.95 (978-0-7737-5850-6(X)) Stoddart Kids CAN. *Dist:* Fitzhenry & Whiteside, Ltd.

—Hero of Lesser Causes. 2003. 232p. (J). (gr. 6). pap. 9.95 (978-0-88776-649-7(8)) Tundra Bks., Inc./Livres Toundra, Inc. CAN. *Dist:* Random Hse., Inc.

Joseph, Lynn. The Color of My Words. 2002. 144p. (J). (gr. 5 up). pap. 5.99 (978-0-06-447204-3(3) , Harper Trophy) HarperCollins Pubs.

—The Color of My Words. unabr. ed. 2004. 96p. (J). (gr. 3-7). pap. 29.00 incl. audio (978-0-8072-0659-1(8) , Listening Library) Random Hse. Audio Publishing Group.

Juckes, Deborah Sioux. Meesha, Guardian of Grand Mountain: Book One of the Guardian Series. McCleary, Twila, illus. 2005. (Guardian Ser.: Bk. 1). (YA). pap. 12.95 (978-0-9767748-0-8(1)) Red Earth Publishing.

—Meesha, Guardian of Grand Mountain: Book One of the Guardian Series. McCleary, Twila, illus. 2005. (YA). 18.95 (978-0-9767748-1-5(X)) Red Earth Publishing.

Jukes, Mavis. Expecting the Unexpected. 1999. (J). (978-0-606-15911-1(8)) Tandem Library Bks.

Kallok, Emma. The Diary of Chickabiddy Baby. 2004. (Illus.). 128p. (YA). (gr. 4-7). pap. 4.95 (978-1-883672-90-4(2) , Tricycle Pr.) Ten Speed Pr.

Kalman, Maira. Ooh-la-La! Max in Love. Kalman, Maira, illus. 2002. (Illus.). 40p. (J). pap. 6.99 (978-0-14-055537-0(4) , Puffin) Penguin Group (USA) Inc.

Kelley, Ann. The Burying Beetle. 2007. 192p. per. 16.95 (978-1-84282-099-5(0)) Luath Pr. Ltd. GBR. *Dist:* Ingram Pub. Services.

Kemp, Kristen. How to Create the Boy of Your Dreams. 2002. (Genny in a Bottle Ser.: Vol. 4). (Illus.). 128p. (J). (gr. 4-6). pap. 4.50 (978-0-439-21181-9(6)) Scholastic, Inc.

Kendrick, Rosalyn. Bride of the Nile. 1998. 176p. (YA). (gr. 9 up). pap. 6.95 (978-0-86327-622-4(9)) Wolfhound Pr. IRL. *Dist:* Irish American Bk. Co.

Kenner, Julie, et al. Fendi, Ferragamo, & Fangs. 2007. 288p. (YA). (gr. 6 up). pap. 9.99 (*978-0-425-21539-5(3) , Berkley Trade) Penguin Group (USA) Inc.

Kenny A Portrait of a Prodigy. 2004. per. (978-1-59581-010-6(2)) Brentwood Communications Group.

Kerr, Don. Candy on the Edge. 2005. 138p. (J). (gr. 5-8). 8.95 (978-1-55050-189-6(5)) Coteau Bks. CAN. *Dist:* Fitzhenry & Whiteside, Ltd.

Kita, Joy. Why Be Normal? 2005. 116p. pap. 16.95 (978-1-4137-8094-9(6)) PublishAmerica, Inc.

Klause, Annette Curtis. Freaks: Alive, on the Inside! 2006. 336p. (YA). 16.95 (978-0-689-05143-2(3) , McElderry, Margaret K.) Simon & Schuster Children's Publishing.

Koertge, Ronald. The Arizona Kid. 2005. 304p. (YA). (gr. 9-12). 16.99 (978-0-7636-2542-9(6)) Candlewick Pr.

—Arizona Kid. 2005. 304p. (YA). (gr. 9 up). pap. 6.99 (978-0-7636-2695-2(3)) Candlewick Pr.

Kroll, Steven & McGraw-Hill Staff. When I Dream of Heaven: Angelina's Story. 2001. (Jamestown Classics Ser.). (Illus.). 155p. (C). (gr. 5-8). pap. 10.00 (978-0-8092-0623-0(4) , 9780809206230) Jamestown.

Lantz, Francess L. Current Affairs. 2004. (Luna Bay Ser.: No. 9). 176p. mass mkt. 4.99 (978-0-06-059521-0(3) , Harper Entertainment) HarperCollins Pubs.

—Sea for Yourself. 2004. (Luna Bay Ser.: No. 8). 176p. mass mkt. 4.99 (978-0-06-059520-3(5) , Harper Entertainment) HarperCollins Pubs.

Lenington, Amber. The White Indian: Lost in the Reality of My Own Dream. 2005. (YA). (978-0-9616620-1-1(8)) Constellation Pr.

Lerangis, Peter. Too Hot, No. 3. 2008. (Drama Club Ser.). 224p. (YA). (gr. 7). 7.99 (*978-0-14-241051-6(9) , Puffin) Penguin Group (USA) Inc.

Levithan, David, ed. This Is PUSH: New Stories from the Edge. 2007. 240p. (J). (gr. 9 up). pap. 6.99 (978-0-439-89028-1(4) , PUSH) Scholastic, Inc.

Lost in the Wilderness. 2006. (J). (978-1-933343-39-6(7) , PONY) Stabenfeldt Inc.

Mackler, Carolyn. Vegan Virgin Valentine. 2004. (Illus.). 240p. (YA). (gr. 9 up). 16.99 (978-0-7636-2155-1(2)) Candlewick Pr.

Malik, S. A. Omari's Flight: The Mercy of Love. 2007. (Illus.). 81p. (YA). per. 7.98 (*978-0-9794615-0-7(2)) EDR.

Manning, Sarra. Guitar Girl. 2005. 240p. (YA). (gr. 9-12). reprint ed. pap. 6.99 (978-0-14-240318-1(0) , Puffin) Penguin Group (USA) Inc.

Marien, Donna. Waiting at the Bay: A Young Woman's Reflections on Journeys in the Sea of Life. 2003. 108p. (YA). pap. 10.95 (978-0-595-26304-2(6) , Writers Club Pr.) iUniverse, Inc.

Martinez, Victor. Parrot in the Oven: Mi Vida. Scott, Steve, illus. rev. ed. 1998. 240p. (J). (gr. 7 up). pap. 5.99 (978-0-06-447186-2(1) , Harper Trophy) HarperCollins Pubs.

Masson, Sophie. The First Day. 2000. (StarMaker Bks.). 98p. (J). (gr. 6-9). pap. 5.50 (978-0-88489-490-2(8)) St. Mary's Pr.

Mazer, Anne. Look Before You Leap. Gesue, Monica, illus. 2001. (Amazing Days of Abby Hayes Ser.: No. 5). 144p. (J). (gr. 4-7). pap. 4.99 (978-0-439-17881-5(9) , Scholastic Paperbacks) Scholastic, Inc.

—Look Before You Leap. 2001. (Amazing Days of Abby Hayes Ser.: No. 5). (gr. 3-6). lib. bdg. 12.40 (978-0-613-43846-9(9)) Tandem Library Bks.

—Some Things Never Change. 2004. (Amazing Days of Abby Hayes Ser.: No. 13). (Illus.). 101p. (J). 4.99 (978-0-439-48281-3(X) , Scholastic Paperbacks) Scholastic, Inc.

McCann, James. Rancour. 2005. (Illus.). 240p. (J). (gr. 10). pap. 10.95 (978-1-894965-31-6(0)) Simply Read Bks. CAN. *Dist:* Perseus Distribution.

McClintock, Norah. Bang. 2007. (Orca Soundings Ser.). 112p. (YA). (gr. 7 up). pap. (*978-1-55143-654-8(X)); lib. bdg. (*978-1-55143-656-2(6)) Orca Bk. Pubs.

McClymer, Kelly. Getting to Third Date. 2006. (Romantic Comedies Ser.). (Illus.). 304p. (YA). (gr. 9 up). pap. 5.99 (978-1-4169-1479-2(X) , Simon Pulse) Simon & Schuster Children's Publishing.

McCormick, Patricia. Cut. unabr. ed. 2004. 168p. (J). (gr. 7 up). pap. 36.00 incl. audio (978-0-8072-0868-7(X) , LYA 320 SP, Listening Library) Random Hse. Audio Publishing Group.

—Cut. 2002. (Illus.). 160p. (J). (gr. 7 up). pap. 6.99 (978-0-439-32459-5(9) , PUSH) Scholastic, Inc.

—Cut. 2002. 13.64 (978-0-606-22261-7(8)); (gr. 7-12). lib. bdg. 15.30 (978-0-613-49394-9(X)) Tandem Library Bks.

McDaniel, Lurlene. Don't Die, My Love. 2000. (YA). pap. 50.24 incl. audio (978-0-7887-4165-4(9) , 41101) Recorded Bks., LLC.

—The Girl Death Left Behind. 1999. 192p. (YA). (gr. 7-12). pap. 5.50 (978-0-553-57091-5(9) , Laurel Leaf) Random Hse. Children's Bks.

—The Girl Death Left Behind. 1999. (J). 11.64 (978-0-606-16371-2(9)) Tandem Library Bks.

McGowan, Sharlene. Macaroni Monday. 2007. 112p. (YA). per. 10.95 (*978-0-595-45984-1(6)) iUniverse, Inc.

Meeting Half Way. 1999. (SmartReader Ser.). (J). Level 1. pap., tchr. ed. 19.95 incl. audio (978-0-7887-1157-2(1) , 79418T3); Level 2. pap., tchr. ed. 19.95 incl. audio (978-0-7887-0123-8(1) , 79311T3) Recorded Bks., LLC.

Metz, Melinda. Julia. 2000. (Sweet Sixteen Ser.: No. 1'). 240p. (YA). (gr. 12 up). pap. 5.95 (978-0-06-440814-1(0) , Harper Trophy) HarperCollins Pubs.

Miklowitz, Gloria D. Camouflage. 1998. 166p. (YA). (gr. 7-12). 16.00 (978-0-15-201467-4(5)) Harcourt Trade Pubs.

Miller, Frances A. Aren't You the One Who...? 2001. 196p. (YA). pap. 14.95 (978-0-595-18548-1(7)) iUniverse, Inc.

Minchin, Adele. The Beat Goes On. 2004. (Illus.). 224p. (YA). 16.95 (978-0-689-86611-1(9)) Simon & Schuster Children's Publishing.

Moloney, James. Angela. 1998. (YA). 22.95 (978-0-7022-3082-0(0)) Univ. of Queensland Pr. AUS. *Dist:* International Specialized Bk. Services.

Moore, Martha A. Angels on the Roof. 1999. (J). 11.64 (978-0-606-17346-9(3)) Tandem Library Bks.

Morgan, Melissa J. And the Winner Is... 2007. (Camp Confidential Ser.: No. 18). 160p. (J). (gr. 4-7). pap. 4.99 (*978-0-448-44652-3(9) , Grosset & Dunlap) Penguin Group (USA) Inc.

—Freaky Tuesday. 2007. (Camp Confidential Ser.: No. 17). 160p. (J). (gr. 4-7). pap. 4.99 (*978-0-448-44651-6(0) , Grosset & Dunlap) Penguin Group (USA) Inc.

Morgan, Melissa J. Hide & Shriek No. 14: Super Special. 2007. (Camp Confidential Ser.). 256p. (J). pap. 5.99 (978-0-448-44452-9(6) , Grosset & Dunlap) Penguin Group (USA) Inc.

Morgan, Melissa J. & Bracken, Elizabeth. TTYL. 2005. (Camp Confidential Ser.: Bk. 5). 160p. (J). (gr. 4-7). pap. 4.99 (978-0-448-43961-7(1) , Grosset & Dunlap) Penguin Group (USA) Inc.

Morris, Taylor. Class Favorite. 2007. 304p. (J). (gr. 4-8). pap. 5.99 (*978-1-4169-3598-8(3) , Aladdin) Simon & Schuster Children's Publishing.

Mowry, Jess. Babylon Boyz. Gore, Leonid, illus. 1999. 192p. (YA). (gr. 8-12). mass mkt. 10.95 (978-0-689-82592-7(7) , 076714008007, Simon Pulse) Simon & Schuster Children's Publishing.

—Babylon Boyz. 1999. (J). (978-0-606-16318-7(2)) Tandem Library Bks.

Muldrow, Diane. Into the Mix. Pollak, Barbara, illus. 2007. (Dish! Ser.: No. 4). 160p. (J). (gr. 4-7). pap. 4.99 (978-0-448-44529-8(8) , Grosset & Dunlap) Penguin Group (USA) Inc.

Murray, Millie. Jade. 2000. 122p. (J). pap. 9.99 (978-0-7043-4967-4(1)) Women's Pr., Ltd., The GBR. *Dist:* Independent Pubs. Group.

My Crush Tacular Book of Valentines: Decorate Your Own Cards - Lizzie Style! 2003. (Lizzie McGuire Ser.). (Illus.). 32p. (ps-17). pap. 5.99 (978-0-7868-4613-9(5) , Disney Editions) Disney Pr.

Nabb, Magdalen. Josie Smith in Spring. l.t. ed. 2005. (Illus.). (J). pap. (978-0-7540-7802-9(7) , CLP 394) BBC Audio.

—Josie Smith in Spring. l.t. ed. 2003. pap. 24.95 incl. audio (978-0-7540-6248-6(1) , Galaxy Children's Large Print) BBC Audiobooks America.

—Josie Smith in Winter. 2000. (Illus.). 124p. (J). pap. 7.99 (978-0-00-675407-7(4)) HarperCollins Pubs. Ltd. GBR. *Dist:* Trafalgar Square Publishing.

Newton, Robert. Runner. 2007. 224p. (J). (gr. 5 up). 15.99 (978-0-375-83744-9(2) , Knopf Bks. for Young Readers) Random Hse. Children's Bks.

Oates, Joyce Carol. Small Avalanches & Other Stories. 2003. 400p. (YA). 17.89 (978-0-06-001218-2(8) , HarperTeen) HarperCollins Pubs.
—Small Avalanches & Other Stories. 2004. lib. bdg. 16.45 (978-0-613-71362-7(1)) Tandem Library Bks.
Okamoto, Kazuhiro. Translucent Volume 1. 2007. (Illus.). 192p. (J). pap. 9.95 (***978-1-59307-647-4(9)***) Dark Horse Comics.
Olsen, Mary-Kate & Olsen, Ashley. We Can't Wait. 2004. (Mary-Kate & Ashley Graduation Summer Ser.: No. 1). 144p. mass mkt. 4.99 (978-0-06-072282-1(7) , Harper Entertainment) HarperCollins Pubs.
Pascal, Francine. Alone. 2002. (gr. 7-12). lib. bdg. 14.15 (978-0-613-67047-0(7)) Tandem Library Bks.
—Flee. 2001. (Fearless Ser.: No. 17). (gr. 7-12). lib. bdg. 14.15 (978-0-613-67086-9(8)) Tandem Library Bks.
—Liar. 2000. (Fearless Ser.: No. 10). 240p. (YA). (gr. 7-12). mass mkt. 5.99 (978-0-671-03951-6(2) , Simon Pulse) Simon & Schuster Children's Publishing.
—Liar. 2000. (Fearless Ser.: No. 10). (gr. 7-12). lib. bdg. 14.15 (978-0-613-27936-9(0)) Tandem Library Bks.
—Love. 2001. (Fearless Ser.: No. 18). (gr. 7-12). lib. bdg. 14.15 (978-0-613-67101-9(5)) Tandem Library Bks.
—My Mother Was Never a Kid. 2003. 256p. (YA). mass mkt. 5.99 (978-0-689-85988-5(0) , Simon Pulse) Simon & Schuster Children's Publishing.
—My Mother Was Never a Kid. 2003. (Victoria Martin Trilogy: No. 1). (gr. 7-12). lib. bdg. 13.00 (978-0-613-66464-6(7)) Tandem Library Bks.
Patrick, John. Fresh N' Frisky. 2000. (Illus.). 575p. 14.95 (978-1-891855-05-4(0) , STARbooks Pr.) Florida Literary Foundation.
Paulsen, Gary. Lawn Boy. 2007. 96p. (YA). (gr. 5-11). 12.99 (978-0-385-74686-1(5)); lib. bdg. 15.99 (978-0-385-90923-5(3)) Random Hse. Children's Bks. (Lamb, Wendy).
—Tracker. l.t. ed. 2002. (LRS Large Print Cornerstone Ser.). (J). lib. bdg. 29.95 (978-1-58118-095-4(0) , 25332) LRS.
—Tracker. 2000. 96p. (YA). (gr. 7-12). 15.95 (978-0-689-84088-3(8) , Atheneum/Richard Jackson Bks.) Simon & Schuster Children's Publishing.
Pearce, Jacqueline. Weeds & Other Stories. 2005. 144p. pap. 7.95 (978-1-894345-64-4(9)) Thistledown Pr., Ltd. CAN. *Dist:* Literary Pr. Group of Canada.
Pearson-Rowe, Delphia. Black Sheep Talking. 2001. (Illus.). 231p. (YA). pap. 13.95 (978-1-881524-94-6(9)) Milligan Bks., Inc.
Peck, Richard. A Long Way from Chicago. unabr. ed. 2004. 176p. (J). (gr. 5-9). pap. 36.00 incl. audio (978-0-8072-8126-0(3) , Listening Library) Random Hse. Audio Publishing Group.
—A Long Way from Chicago. l.t. ed. 2001. 188p. (J). (gr. 8-12). 22.95 (978-0-7862-3249-9(8)) Thorndike Pr.
—Remembering the Good Times. 181p. (YA). (gr. 7 up). pap. 4.50 (978-0-8072-1380-3(2) , Listening Library) Random Hse. Audio Publishing Group.
—Strays Like Us. 2000. (Illus.). 160p. (J). (gr. 5-9). pap. 5.99 (978-0-14-130619-3(X) , Puffin) Penguin Group (USA) Inc.
—Strays Like Us. 2000. 155p. (J). (gr. 5-9). per. 13.00 (978-0-613-28660-2(X)); (978-0-606-17871-6(6)) Tandem Library Bks.
Peck, Robert Newton. A Day No Pigs Would Die. 139p. (YA). (gr. 7 up). pap. 4.99 (978-0-8072-1384-1(5)); pap. 4.99 (978-0-8072-1357-5(8)) Random Hse. Audio Publishing Group. (Listening Library).
Pennebaker, Ruth. Don't Think Twice. rev. ed. 2001. 272p. (YA). (gr. 7). pap. 7.95 (978-0-8050-6729-3(9) , Holt, Henry & Co. Bks. For Young Readers) Holt, Henry & Co.
Peretti, Frank E. Hangman's Curse. movie tie-in ed. 2003. (Veritas Project Ser.). 312p. (YA). pap. 9.99 (978-1-4003-0371-7(0)) Nelson, Thomas Inc.
—Hangman's Curse. 2003. (gr. 3-6). lib. bdg. 18.80 (978-0-613-77934-0(7)) Tandem Library Bks.
Pittel, Jamie. Marisa. 2000. (Sweet Sixteen Ser.: No. 5). 240p. (J). (gr. 12 up). pap. 5.95 (978-0-06-440816-5(7) , Harper Trophy) HarperCollins Pubs.
The Pony Winter. 2007. (J). (978-1-933343-42-6(7) , PONY) Stabenfeldt Inc.
Poulsen, David A. Last Sam's Cage. rev. ed. 2004. 224p. pap. 9.95 (***978-1-55263-611-4(9)***) Key Porter Bks. CAN. *Dist:* Perseus Distribution.
—Last Sam's Cage. 2001. 208p. (YA). pap. 8.95 (978-1-896184-78-4(2)) Roussan Pubs., Inc./Roussan Editeur, Inc. CAN. *Dist:* Orca Bk. Pubs. USA.
Reisfeld, Randi. Partiers Preferred. 2007. (Summer Share Ser.). 288p. (YA). pap. 8.99 (978-1-4169-0037-5(3) , Simon Pulse) Simon & Schuster Children's Publishing.
Rennison, Louise. Angus, Thongs & Full-Frontal Snogging: Confessions of Georgia Nicolson. 2000. (Confessions of Georgia Nicolson Ser.). 256p. (J). (gr. 7 up). 16.99 (978-0-06-028814-3(0)) HarperCollins Pubs.
Reynolds, Marilyn. Beyond Dreams. Manriquez, Laura, illus. 2003. (True-to-Life Series from Hamilton High). 192p. (J). (gr. 7-12). pap. 8.95 (978-1-885356-00-0(5)); 15.95 (978-1-885356-01-7(3)) Morning Glory Pr., Inc.
—If You Loved Me. 1999. (True-to-Life Series from Hamilton High: Vol. 7). 32p. (J). pap., tchr. ed. 2.50 (978-1-885356-59-8(5)) Morning Glory Pr., Inc.
Richard, Ilene, illus. My Totally Cool Room. 2001. (Sticker Stories Ser.). 20p. (J). mass mkt. 4.99 (978-0-448-42526-9(2) , Grosset & Dunlap) Penguin Group (USA) Inc.
Richardson, Dorothea M. Moose Girl. 2002. 108p. (YA). pap. 16.95 (978-1-58851-797-5(7)) PublishAmerica, Inc.
—Moose Girl. 2001. (gr. 7-12). lib. bdg. 26.85 (978-0-613-85254-8(0)) Tandem Library Bks.
Rillera, Catherine. Freedom. 2003. 440p. (YA). pap. 22.95 (978-0-595-27088-0(3)) iUniverse, Inc.
Rue, Nancy N. False Friends & True Strangers. 2004. (Invert / 'Nama Beach High Ser.). 192p. (J). pap. 6.99 (978-0-310-25180-4(X)) Zondervan.
Rushton, Rosie. I Think I'll Just Curl up & Die. 2005. 176p. (J). pap. 5.99 (978-0-7868-5188-1(0)) Hyperion Bks. for Children.
—Just Don't Make a Scene, Mum! 2005. 224p. (J). pap. 5.99 (978-0-7868-5186-7(4)) Hyperion Bks. for Children.
—Olivia. 2000. 224p. (gr. 5-9). pap. 4.99 (978-0-7868-1392-6(X)) Disney Pr.
Ryan, Sarah. The Rules for Hearts: A Family Drama. 2007. 224p. (YA). (gr. 9 up). 16.99 (978-0-670-05906-5(4) , Viking Juvenile) Penguin Group (USA) Inc.
Sackin, Jacob. Islands. 2008. 280p. (YA). pap. 14.99 (978-1-59092-392-4(8) , Blue Works) Windstorm Creative.
Saks, Diane. Obsessive. 2002. (ENG.). 188p. 23.95 (***978-0-595-65476-5(2)*** , Writers Club Pr.) iUniverse, Inc.
Schuck, Philip. A Ricochet from Circumstance. 2005. (YA). 19.95 (978-0-9764670-0-7(3)) Smithfield Capital Corp.
Scott, Nicole. A Moment of Silence. 2005. 182p. pap. 19.95 (978-1-4137-5766-8(9)) PublishAmerica, Inc.
Segal, Herbert Alexander. Hantu & Enofi: The Quest. 2000. 145p. (J). (gr. 4-8). pap. 12.95 (978-0-9648520-1-3(2)) Blue Dragonfly Pubs.
Shaw, Tucker. What's That Smell? Oh, It's Me: 50 Mortifying Situations & How to Deal. Reddy, Mike, ed. 2003. (Illus.). 160p. (J). pap. 7.99 (978-0-14-250011-8(9) , Puffin) Penguin Group (USA) Inc.
Sheldon, Dyan. Confessions of a Teenage Drama Queen. braille ed. 2003. (J). (gr. 2). spiral bd. (978-0-616-15873-9(4)) Canadian National Institute for the Blind/ Institut National Canadien pour les Aveugles.
—Confessions of a Teenage Drama Queen. 2002. (Illus.). 272p. (YA). (gr. 7-12). pap. 7.99 (978-0-7636-1848-3(9)) Candlewick Pr.
—Planet Janet in Orbit. 2005. 304p. (YA). (gr. 9 up). 15.99 (978-0-7636-2755-3(0)) Candlewick Pr.
Shipley, Jocelyn. Getting a Life. 2003. (gr. 7-12). lib. bdg. 16.40 (978-0-613-81037-1(6)) Tandem Library Bks.
Smith, Kirsten. The Geography of Girlhood. 2007. 192p. (J). (gr. 7-17). pap. 7.99 (978-0-316-01735-0(3)) Little Brown & Co.
Spinelli, Jerry. Crash. 2004. 176p. (YA). (gr. 7). mass mkt. 6.50 (978-0-440-23857-7(9) , Laurel Leaf) Random Hse. Children's Bks.
—Jason & Marceline. 2000. 233p. (J). (gr. 4-7). pap. 6.99 (978-0-316-80662-6(5)) Little Brown & Co.
—Space Station Seventh Grade. 2001. (J). (gr. 5-8). 22.50 (978-0-8446-7189-5(4)) Smith, Peter Pub., Inc.
—Space Station Seventh Grade: The Newbery Award-Winning Author of Maniac Magee. 2000. 235p. (J). (gr. 4-7). pap. 6.99 (978-0-316-80605-3(6)) Little Brown & Co.
Stacy, Lori. Island Girl. 2001. (Seasons: Vol. 2). 124p. pap. 4.95 (978-0-9678285-2-7(X)) Lunchbox Pr.
Steig, William. Made for Each Other. Steig, William, illus. 2000. (Illus.). 48p. (J). (ps-3). 13.89 (978-0-06-028513-5(3)) HarperCollins Pubs.
Stolz, Mary. The Edge of Next Year. 2000. 212p. (YA). (gr. 4-7). pap. 13.95 (978-0-595-13832-6(2) , Backinprint-.com) iUniverse, Inc.
Stone, Tanya Lee. A Bad Boy Can Be Good for a Girl. 240p. (YA). 2007. (gr. 7-11). pap. 7.99 (978-0-553-49509-6(7)); 2006. (gr. 9). 14.95 (978-0-385-74702-8(0)); 2006. (gr. 9). lib. bdg. 16.99 (978-0-385-90946-4(2)) Random Hse. Children's Bks. (Lamb, Wendy).
Strasser, Todd. Help! I'm Trapped in a Supermodel's Body. 2001. (Help! I'm Trapped Ser.). 144p. (gr. 4-7). pap. 4.50 (978-0-439-21035-5(6)) Scholastic, Inc.
Stratton, Allan. Leslie's Journal. 2000. (Doghouse Bks.). 176p. (YA). (gr. 8 up). 19.95 (978-1-55037-665-4(9)); pap. 8.95 (978-1-55037-664-7(0)) Annick Pr., Ltd. CAN. *Dist:* Firefly Bks., Ltd.
—Leslie's Journal. 2000. (gr. 7-12). lib. bdg. 17.60 (978-0-613-33925-4(8)) Tandem Library Bks.
Strauss, Linda Leopold. The Alexandra Ingredient. 2000. 148p. (gr. 4-7). pap. 10.95 (978-0-595-00778-3(3) , Backinprint.com) iUniverse, Inc.
Sweeney, Joyce. Players. 2001. (Illus.). 262p. (YA). (gr. 7 up). pap. 5.95 (978-1-58837-016-7(X)) Winslow Pr.
Sydor, Colleen. Fashion Fandango. Pavanel, Jane, ed. Langlois, Suzane & Vernex, Lenka, illus. 2000. (Generation Norah Ser.: Vol. 1). 112p. (J). (gr. 3-7). pap. 6.95 (978-1-894222-17-4(2)) Lobster Pr. CAN. *Dist:* Univ. of Toronto Pr.
Talley, Linda. Emily Breaks Free. Chase, Andra, illus. (Key Concepts in Personal Development Ser.). 2001. 32p. pap., tchr. ed. 89.95 incl. VHS (978-1-55942-158-4(4) , 9386); 2000. 30p. (J). 16.95 (978-1-55942-155-3(X) , 7667) Marsh Media.
Thorpe, Kiki. Totally Crushed: Junior Novel. 2nd rev. ed. 2002. (Lizzie McGuire Ser.). 128p. (gr. 3-7). pap. 4.99 (978-0-7868-4539-2(2)) Disney Pr.
Thrash, Jacquelyn R. Heaven's Thunder. 1999. (YA). 22.00 (978-0-9635247-9-9(8)) Three Pines Pr.
Tiernan, Cate. Origins. 2002. (gr. 7-12). lib. bdg. 13.00 (978-0-613-64091-6(8)) Tandem Library Bks.
Tilley, Jessica. You Have to Be Smart If You're Going to be Tall. Evans, Leslie, illus. 2006. 46p. (J). per. 16.99 (***978-1-59879-217-1(2)***) Lifevest Publishing, Inc.
Townsend, Sue. The Growing Pains of Adrian Mole. 2003. (gr. 7-12). lib. bdg. 15.30 (978-0-613-68427-9(3)) Tandem Library Bks.
Vickers, Maydie. My Name Is Judy Ophelia Horton, I Think. 2005. 234p. pap. 19.95 (978-1-4137-8503-6(4)) PublishAmerica, Inc.
Voigt, Cynthia. Dicey's Song. l.t. ed. 2002. (Tillerman Cycle Ser.: Bk. 2). 370p. (YA). lib. bdg. 35.95 (978-1-58118-106-7(X) , 25790) LRS.
—When She Hollers. 2003. 192p. (J). (gr. 7 up). pap. 5.99 (978-0-590-46715-5(8) , Scholastic Paperbacks) Scholastic, Inc.
von Ziegesar, Cecily. All I Want Is Everything. 2003. (Gossip Girl Ser.: No. 3). 224p. (YA). (gr. 10-17). pap. 9.99 (978-0-316-91212-9(3) , Poppy) Little, Brown Bks. for Young Readers.
—All I Want Is Everything. 2003. (Gossip Girl Ser.: No. 3). (YA). (gr. 7-12). lib. bdg. 17.60 (978-0-613-71823-3(2)) Tandem Library Bks.
—Because I'm Worth It. 2003. (Gossip Girl Ser.: No. 4). 240p. (YA). (gr. 10-17). pap. 10.99 (978-0-316-90968-6(8) , Poppy) Little, Brown Bks. for Young Readers.
—Because I'm Worth It. 2003. (Gossip Girl Ser.: No. 4). (YA). (gr. 7-12). lib. bdg. 17.60 (978-0-613-71821-9(6)) Tandem Library Bks.
—Gossip Girl. 2003. (Gossip Girl Ser.: No. 1). 288p. (gr. 8 up). mass mkt. 5.99 (978-0-446-61315-6(0)) Grand Central Publishing.
—Gossip Girl. 208p. 2002. (Gossip Girl Ser.: No. 1). (YA). (gr. 9-17). pap. 10.99 (978-0-316-91033-0(3)); No. 1. 2007. pap. 10.99 (***978-0-316-02456-3(2)***) Little, Brown Bks. for Young Readers. (Poppy).
—Gossip Girl. 2002. (Gossip Girl Ser.: No. 1). (YA). (gr. 7-12). lib. bdg. 17.35 (978-0-613-60559-5(4)) Tandem Library Bks.
—Gossip Girl: The Second Collection. 2004. (Gossip Girl Ser.). (YA). (gr. 10-17). pap. 29.99 (978-0-316-01026-9(X) , Poppy) Little, Brown Bks. for Young Readers.
—Gossip Girl: The Third Collection. 2006. (Gossip Girl Ser.). (YA). (gr. 10 up). pap. 29.99 (978-0-316-01653-7(5) , Poppy) Little, Brown Bks. for Young Readers.
—Gossip Girl Collection, 3 bks., Set. 2003. (Gossip Girl Ser.). (YA). (gr. 10-17). pap., pap. 29.99 (978-0-316-72271-1(5) , 53605112, Poppy) Little, Brown Bks. for Young Readers.
Von Ziegesar, Cecily. It Had to Be You: The Gossip Girl Prequel. 2007. 398p. (YA). (gr. 10-12). 17.99 (***978-0-316-01768-8(X)*** , Poppy) Little, Brown Bks. for Young Readers.
von Ziegesar, Cecily. You Know You Love Me. 2nd ed. 2002. (Gossip Girl Ser.: Bk. 2). (Illus.). 240p. (YA). (gr. 10-17). pap. 10.99 (978-0-316-91148-1(8) , Poppy) Little, Brown Bks. for Young Readers.
—You Know You Love Me. 2002. (Gossip Girl Ser.: No. 2). (YA). (gr. 7-12). lib. bdg. 17.35 (978-0-613-56955-2(5)) Tandem Library Bks.
Waltman, Kevin. Nowhere Fast. 2002. (Illus.). 208p. (YA). (gr. 6 up). pap. 7.99 (978-0-439-41424-1(5) , PUSH) Scholastic, Inc.
—Nowhere Fast. 2002. (gr. 7-12). lib. bdg. 15.30 (978-0-613-72069-4(5)) Tandem Library Bks.
Watch Out, Sara! 2006. (J). (978-1-933343-35-8(4) , PONY) Stabenfeldt Inc.
Weinstein, Lauren R. Girl Stories. 2006. (Illus.). 240p. (YA). pap. 16.95 (978-0-8050-7863-3(0)) Holt, Henry & Co.
Weir, Joan. The Brideship. 1999. (Illus.). 218p. (YA). (gr. 7 up). mass mkt. 5.95 (978-0-7736-7474-5(8)) Stoddart Kids CAN. *Dist:* Fitzhenry & Whiteside, Ltd.
Weiss, M. Jerry & Weiss, Helen S., eds. Lost & Found. 2001. 224p. 5.99 (978-0-8125-6866-0(4) , Forge Bks.) Doherty, Tom Assocs., LLC.
Weksler, Artur. Young Loves. 2001. 216p. (YA). pap. 16.95 (978-965-229-247-6(8)) Gefen Publishing Hse., Ltd ISR. *Dist:* Gefen Bks.
Westerfeld, Scott. Specials. 2006. (YA). (978-1-4169-2165-3(6)); 384p. (gr. 7 up). 15.95 (978-0-689-86540-4(6) , Simon Pulse) Simon & Schuster Children's Publishing.
Westerfeld, Scott. The Uglies Trilogy: Uglies, Pretties, Specials. 2007. 1216p. (YA). pap. 25.99 (***978-1-4169-3640-4(8)*** , Simon Pulse) Simon & Schuster Children's Publishing.
Wieler, Diana. Drive. 2001. 246p. (J). (gr. 8-13). pap. 6.95 (978-0-88899-348-9(X)) Groundwood Bks. CAN. *Dist:* Perseus Distribution.
—Drive. 1999. (gr. 7-12). lib. bdg. 14.10 (978-0-613-28825-5(4)) Tandem Library Bks.
Wilson, Jacqueline. Girls under Pressure. 2003. 224p. (YA). (gr. 7). pap. 5.50 (978-0-440-22958-2(8) , Laurel Leaf) Random Hse. Children's Bks.
—Girls under Pressure. 2003. (gr. 7-12). lib. bdg. 13.00 (978-0-613-72337-4(6)) Tandem Library Bks.
Withrow, Sarah. Bat Summer. 2000. 174p. (J). (gr. 4-7). pap. 5.95 (978-0-88899-352-6(8) , Libros Tigrillo) Groundwood Bks. CAN. *Dist:* Perseus Distribution.
Wittlinger, Ellen. Hard Love. 2001. (Illus.). 240p. (YA). (gr. 8-12). reprint ed. pap. 8.99 (978-0-689-84154-5(X) , Simon Pulse) Simon & Schuster Children's Publishing.
—Lombardo's Law. 2003. 144p. (YA). (gr. 5-9). pap. 5.95 (978-0-618-31108-8(4)) Houghton Mifflin Co. Trade & Reference Div.
Wolfer, Dianne. Border Line. 1998. 190p. (J). pap. 11.95 (978-1-86368-208-4(2)) Fremantle Pr. AUS. *Dist:* International Specialized Bk. Services.
Wolff, Virginia Euwer. Make Lemonade. unabr. ed. 2004. (Young Adult Cassette Librariestm Ser.). 200p. (J). (gr. 7 up). pap. 36.00 incl. audio (978-0-8072-0793-2(4) , S YA 348 SP, Listening Library) Random Hse. Audio Publishing Group.
Wyeth, Sharon Dennis. A Piece of Heaven. 2002. 208p. (gr. 5-8). pap. 5.50 (978-0-440-41869-6(0) , Yearling) Random Hse. Children's Bks.
Wynne-Jones, Tim. Lord of the Fries & Other Stories: Other Stories. pap. 9.95 (978-0-88899-274-1(2)) Groundwood Bks. CAN. *Dist:* Transition Vendor.
Yansky, Brian. Wonders of the World. 2007. 240p. (J). 16.95 (978-0-7387-1084-6(9) , Flux) Llewellyn Pubns.
Yolen, Jane. Armageddon Summer. 1999. (gr. 7-12). lib. bdg. 14.15 (978-0-613-19505-8(1)) Tandem Library Bks.
Yolen, Jane & Coville, Bruce. Armageddon Summer. 1999. 272p. (YA). (gr. 7-12). pap. 6.95 (978-0-15-202268-6(6) , Harcourt Paperbacks) Harcourt Children's Bks.
—Armageddon Summer. 1999. (YA). (gr. 7 up). pap., stu. ed. 60.24 incl. audio (978-0-7887-3002-3(9) , 40884) Recorded Bks., LLC.
—Armageddon Summer. 1999. 266p. per. 12.64 (978-0-606-17225-7(4)) Tandem Library Bks.
Youmans, Marly. Little Jordan. 1999. 112p. (YA). (gr. 7-12). pap. 6.99 (978-0-380-73136-7(3)) HarperCollins Pubs.
Zeiger, David. Senior Year. 2001. 25.00 (978-1-57500-198-2(5)) TV Bks., L.L.C.
Ziegesar, Cecily von. Gossip Girl #2: You Know You Love Me: A Gossip Girl Novel. 2008. 240p. pap. 10.99 (***978-0-316-02661-1(1)*** , Poppy) Little, Brown Bks. for Young Readers.
Zindel, Paul. Pardon Me, You're Stepping on My Eyeball! 1999. mass mkt. (978-0-553-14836-7(2)); mass mkt. (978-0-553-23975-1(9)) Random Hse., Inc.

ADOPTION

A. B. Publishing Staff. Adopting an Orphan. 1998. (J). (gr. 4-7). pap. 6.95 (978-1-881545-87-3(3)) A B Publishing.
Aldrich, Andrew R. How My Family Came to Be - Daddy, Papa & Me. 2003. (Illus.). 32p. (J). 19.95 (978-0-9742008-0-4(8)) New Family Pr.
Arnold, Lynda. Angels of Love: Celebrating Diversity & Adoption. Monahan, Ellen M. & Rosemont School of the Holy Child Staff, illus. 1998. 32p. (YA). (gr. k-1). 18.95 (978-1-892073-00-6(5)) Dream Publishing.
Burwash, Lynn & McMullin, Cie. All about Me. unabr. ed. 1998. (Illus.). 12p. (J). (ps-2). spiral bd. 10.95 (978-0-9668858-0-4(5)) All About Me.
Cassidy, Patrice. Teen Pregnancy. 2001. (Teen Issues Ser.). (Illus.). 104p. (J). (gr. 4-12). lib. bdg. 27.45 (978-1-56006-515-9(X) , LML00902-177873, Lucent Bks.) Thomson Gale.
Cole, Joanna. How I Was Adopted. Chambliss, Maxie, illus. 1999. 48p. (J). (ps-3). pap. 6.99 (978-0-688-17055-4(2) , Harper Trophy) HarperCollins Pubs.
Cosby, Eileen Tucker. A Is for Adopted. Strange, Norma S., illus. 2000. 56p. (J). (ps-5). 14.95 (978-0-9676385-0-8(X) , 1001) Swak Pak, LLC.
Dunn, Connie. Jessa Ying Comes from China. 1998. (Illus.). 17p. (J). (ps-1). pap. 10.00 (978-1-890641-04-7(9)) No Stress Pr.
Durrant, Jolene. Never Never Never Will She Stop Loving You: The Adoption Love Story of Angel Annie. Allred, Steve, photos by. rev. ed. 1999. (Illus.). 40p. (YA). (gr. k up). pap. 6.95 (978-0-9663567-9-3(9)) JoBiz!, Inc.
Hatkoff, Isabella, et al. Knut: How One Little Polar Bear Captivated the World. 2007. (Knut Ser.). 40p. (J). pap. 16.99 (***978-0-545-04716-6(1)*** , Scholastic Pr.) Scholastic, Inc.
Heegaard, Marge Eaton. Adopted & Wondering: Drawing Out Feelings. 2007. 40p. pap. 9.95 (978-1-57749-166-8(1)) Fairview Pr.
Helmer, Diana Star. Let's Talk about Adoption. 1999. (Let's Talk Library). (Illus.). 24p. (J). (gr. 3). lib. bdg. 18.75 (978-0-8239-5201-4(0) , PowerKids Pr.) Rosen Publishing Group, Inc., The.
Kaminker, Laura. Everything You Need to Know about Being Adopted. 1999. (Need to Know Library). (Illus.). 64p. (YA). (gr. 7-12). lib. bdg. 25.25 (978-0-8239-2834-7(9) , NTADOP) Rosen Publishing Group, Inc., The.
Katz, Karen. Over the Moon: An Adoption Tale. rev. ed. 2001. (Illus.). 32p. (J). (ps-3). pap. 7.95 (978-0-8050-6707-1(8) , Holt, Henry & Co. Bks. For Young Readers) Holt, Henry & Co.
Koh, Frances M. A China Adoption Story: Mommy, Why Do We Look Different? O'Brien, Anne Sibley, illus. 2000. 24p. (J). (gr. 1-2). lib. bdg. 15.95 (978-0-9606090-9-3(1)) EastWest Pr.
Levete, Sarah. Fostering & Adoption. 2007. (Illus.). 32p. (J). (***978-1-59604-085-4(8)***) Stargazer Bks.
Lodien, Jennie, des. I Am Chosen: Brights. 2003. 56p. (YA). ring bd. 29.95 (978-0-9746341-0-4(7)) Chin & A Pr.
McMahon, Patricia & McCarthy, Conor Clarke. Just Add One Chinese Sister. Jerome, Karen A., illus. 2005. 32p. (J). (ps-ps). 16.95 (978-1-56397-989-7(6)) Boyds Mills Pr.
Miner, Chalise. Rain Forest Girl: More Than an Adoption Story. 1998. (Illus.). 48p. (J). (gr. 4-6). pap. 12.95 (978-1-883845-81-0(5)) Mitchell Lane Pubs., Inc.
Moore-Malinos, Jennifer. Somos Adoptados: We Are Adopted (Spanish Edition) Fabrega, Marta, illus. 2007. (Let's Talk about It Bks.). 36p. (J). pap. 6.99 (***978-0-7641-3788-4(3)***) Barron's Educational Series, Inc.
—We Are Adopted. Fabrega, Marta, illus. 2007. (Let's Talk about It Bks.). 36p. (J). pap. 6.99 (***978-0-7641-3787-7(5)***) Barron's Educational Series, Inc.
Nemiroff, Marc A. & Annunziata, Jane. All about Adoption: How Families Are Made & How Kids Feel about It. Koeller, Carol, tr. Koeller, Carol, illus. 2004. 48p. (J). (gr. k-3). 14.95 (978-1-59147-058-8(7)); pap. 8.95 (978-1-59147-059-5(5)) American Psychological Assn. (Magination Pr.).
Nolan, Mary. Teen Pregnancy. 2002. (Just the Facts Ser.). (Illus.). 56p. (J). (gr. 6-8). lib. bdg. 25.64 (978-1-58810-682-7(9)) Heinemann Library.
Parr, Todd. We Belong Together: A Book About Adoption & Families. 2007. (Illus.). 32p. (J). (ps-1). 15.99 (***978-0-316-01668-1(3)***) Little, Brown Bks. For Young Readers.
Powell, Jillian. Adoption. 1999. (Talking about Ser.). (Illus.). 32p. (J). (gr. k-4). lib. bdg. 25.69 (978-0-8172-5890-0(6)) Raintree.
Rogers, Fred. Let's Talk about It: Adoption. 1998. (Mister Rogers' Neighborhood Ser.). (Illus.). 32p. (J). (ps-1). pap. 6.99 (978-0-698-11625-2(9) , Putnam Juvenile) Penguin Group (USA) Inc.

Schoettle, Marilyn. W. I. S. E. Up! Powerbook. Stanish, Julie, illus. 2000. 28p. (J). (gr. 2-7). pap. 14.00 (978-0-9711732-0-0(6)) Ctr. for Adoption Support & Education, Inc.

Sherman, Aliza. Everything You Need to Know about Placing Your Baby for Adoption. rev. ed. 2001. (Need to Know Library). (Illus.). 64p. (YA). (gr. 9 up). lib. bdg. 25.25 (978-0-8239-3465-2(9)) Rosen Publishing Group, Inc., The.

Slade, Suzanne Bucki. Adopted: The Ultimate Teen Guide. 2007. 288p. (J). 45.00 ***(978-0-8108-5774-2(X))** Scarecrow Pr., Inc.

Stinson, Kathy. I Feel Different: A Book about Being Adopted. Lewis, Robin Baird, illus. rev. ed. 1998. 27p. (J). (gr. k-6). pap. 12.95 (978-0-87424-355-0(6) , W-355) Manson Western Corp.

Thomas, Pat. My New Family: A First Look at Adoption. Harker, Lesley, illus. 2003. (First Look at Bks.). 32p. (J). pap. 6.99 (978-0-7641-2461-7(7)) Barron's Educational Series, Inc.

Tubbs, Janet. Adoption. 2000. 16p. (J). pap. 19.95 (978-1-881185-07-9(9)) Arcadia Pr.

Weiss, Ann E. Adoptions Today: Questions & Controversy. 2001. (Single Titles Ser.). (Illus.). 144p. (gr. 7 up). lib. bdg. 24.90 (978-0-7613-1914-6(X) , Twenty-First Century Bks.) Lerner Publishing Group.

Williams, Mary. Adoption. 2006. 244p. (gr. 10-12). 24.95 (978-0-7377-3302-0(0)); pap. 36.20 (978-0-7377-3301-3(2)) Thomson Gale. (Greenhaven Pr., Inc.).

ADOPTION—FICTION

see also Foster Home Care—Fiction

Alsius, Lourdes. Unos Padres Para Aruna. 2005. (SPA.). 32p. (J). 18.95 (978-84-8418-096-8(4)) Zendrera Zariquiey, Editorial ESP. *Dist:* Iaconi, Mariuccia Bk. Imports.

Alvarez, Julia. En Busca de Milagros. 2006. (SPA.). 224p. (YA). (gr. 7). lib. bdg. 17.99 (978-0-375-90003-7(9)); mass mkt. 6.50 (978-0-553-49407-5(4)) Random Hse. Children's Bks. (Laurel Leaf).

—Finding Miracles. (gr. 7). 2006. 288p. (YA). mass mkt. 6.50 (978-0-553-49406-8(6) , Laurel Leaf); 2004. 272p. (J). 15.95 (978-0-375-82760-0(9) , Knopf Bks. for Young Readers); 2004. 272p. (YA). 17.99 (978-0-375-92760-7(3) , Knopf Bks. for Young Readers) Random Hse. Children's Bks.

Arlette, Joan. Maybe, Molly & Must-Be-Red. 1998. (Illus.). 8p. (J). (ps-5). mass mkt. 7.00 (978-0-9700121-0-4(1) , 001) Light Years Ahead.

Baker, David. The Roos, A home for Baby. 2005. 14p. 12.49 (978-1-4116-2290-6(1)) Lulu.com.

Banks, Kate. Dillon Dillon. 160p. (J). 2002. (gr. 3-6). 16.00 (978-0-374-31786-7(0) , Farrar, Straus & Giroux (BYR)); 2005. reprint ed. pap. 5.95 (978-0-374-41715-4(6) , Sunburst) Farrar, Straus & Giroux.

Bauer, Cat. Harley, Like a Person. 2007. 288p. (gr. 9). (J). pap. 8.99 (978-0-375-83735-7(3)); (YA). 15.99 (978-0-375-93735-4(8)) Random Hse. Children's Bks. (Knopf Bks. for Young Readers).

—Harley, Like a Person. 2000. (Illus.). (J). 13.60 (978-0-606-20690-7(6)) Tandem Library Bks.

—Harley, Like a Person. 2000. (Illus.). 248p. (J). (gr. 7 up). pap. 5.95 (978-1-58837-005-1(4)) Winslow Pr.

Belton, Sandra. Store-Bought Baby. 2006. 256p. (J). 15.99 (978-0-06-085086-9(8)); lib. bdg. 16.89 (978-0-06-085087-6(6)) HarperCollins Pubs.

Blacker, Terence. The Angel Factory. (Illus.). 224p. 2003. (J). (gr. k-17). pap. 5.99 (978-0-689-86413-1(2) , Aladdin); 2002. (YA). (gr. 6-9). 16.95 (978-0-689-85171-1(5)) Simon & Schuster Children's Publishing.

Bob, Uncle. Tobi the Little Puppy Dog. 2006. (Illus.). 12p. (J). pap. 3.95 (978-1-930596-61-0(8)) Amherst Pr.

Bodett, Tom, reader. Saving Sweetness. 2005. (Live Oak Readalong Ser.). (Illus.). (J). pap. 16.95 incl. audio (978-0-87499-898-6(0)) BBC Audiobooks America.

—Saving Sweetness. 2002. (Illus.). (J). pap., tchr.'s planning gde. ed. 37.95 incl. audio (978-0-87499-900-6(6)); 25.95 incl. audio (978-0-87499-899-3(9)) Live Oak Media.

Bond, Juliet C. Sam's Sister. Majewski, Dawn, illus. 2004. (J). 18.00 (978-0-944934-30-2(7)) Perspectives Pr., Inc.

Bongiorno, Patti Lynn, text. Tangled Hearts. 2004. 288p. (YA). per. 12.95 (978-0-9715819-1-3(6)) Bongiorno Bks.

Brinkerhoff, Shirley. Mysterious Love. 1998. (Nikki Sheridan Ser.: Bk. 2). 192p. (J). (gr. 4-7). pap. (978-1-56179-485-0(6)) Focus on the Family Publishing.

—Second Choices. 2000. (Nikki Sheridan Ser.: Vol. 6). (Illus.). 160p. (YA). (gr. 9-13). pap. 5.99 (978-1-56179-880-3(0)) Bethany Hse. Pubs.

—Second Choices. 2000. (gr. 7-12). lib. bdg. 14.15 (978-0-613-82302-9(8)) Tandem Library Bks.

Burns, John. Runnerland. 2007. 218p. pap. 9.95 ***(978-1-55192-957-6(0))** Raincoast Bk. Distribution CAN. *Dist:* Perseus Distribution.

Capone, Deb. Families Are Forever. 2004. (J). 16.95 ***(978-0-9728666-6-8(3))** As Simple As That Publishing.

Carlson, Melody. Just Ask. 2005. (Diary of a Teenage Girl Ser.). 256p. (J). pap. 12.99 (978-1-59052-321-6(0) , Multnomah) WaterBrook Pr.

Carlson, Nancy. My Family Is Forever. 2006. 32p. (J). pap. 5.99 (978-0-14-240561-1(2) , Puffin) Penguin Group (USA) Inc.

—My Family Is Forever. Carlson, Nancy, illus. 2004. (Illus.). 32p. (J). 15.99 (978-0-670-03650-9(1) , Viking Juvenile) Penguin Group (USA) Inc.

Caseley, Judith. Sisters. Caseley, Judith, illus. 2004. 32p. (J). 15.99 (978-0-06-051046-6(3)); lib. bdg. 16.89 (978-0-06-051047-3(1)) HarperCollins Pubs.

Chapman, Mary Beth & Chapman, Steven Curtis. Shoey & Dot: A Thunder & Lightning Bug Story. Chapman, Jim, illus. 2006. 32p. (J). 10.99 (978-1-4003-0743-2(0)) Nelson, Thomas Inc.

Chapman, Steven Curtis & Chapman, Mary Beth. Shaoey & Dot: Bug Meets Bundle. 2004. (Illus.). 32p. (J). 16.99 (978-1-4003-0482-0(2)) Nelson, Thomas Inc.

Cole, Joanna. How I Was Adopted. 1999. (J). (978-0-606-17243-1(2)); lib. bdg. 14.15 (978-0-613-22872-5(3)) Tandem Library Bks.

Coste, Marion. Finding Joy. Chen, Yong, illus. 2006. 32p. (J). (gr. 1-3). 16.95 (978-1-59078-192-0(9)) Boyds Mills Pr.

Cray, Jordan. Most Wanted. 1998. (Danger.com Ser.: No. 7). (YA). (gr. 6 up). (978-0-606-13311-1(9)) Tandem Library Bks.

Crutcher, Chris. Whale Talk. 2001. 224p. (J). (gr. 7 up). 16.99 (978-0-688-18019-5(1)) HarperCollins Pubs.

—Whale Talk. 2004. 224p. (J). (gr. 7 up). pap. 38.00 incl. audio (978-0-8072-2289-8(5) , Listening Library) Random Hse. Audio Publishing Group.

—Whale Talk. 2002. 224p. (YA). (gr. 7). pap. 6.99 (978-0-440-22938-4(3) , Laurel Leaf) Random Hse. Children's Bks.

—Whale Talk. 2002. (gr. 5-8). lib. bdg. 13.55 (978-0-613-61739-0(8)) Tandem Library Bks.

Cummings, Mary. Three Names of Me. Wang, Lin, illus. 2006. (J). 15.95 (978-0-8075-7903-9(3)) Whitman, Albert & Co.

Cunningham, Laura Shaine. The Midnight Diary of Zoya Blume. 2006. 176p. (J). pap. 5.99 (978-0-06-072261-6(4) , Harper Trophy) HarperCollins Pubs.

Curtis, Jamie Lee. Cuentame Otra Vez la Noche en Que Naci. Cornell, Laura, illus. 1999. (SPA.). (J). (gr. 1-2). 14.95 (978-1-880507-63-6(3) , LC4416) Lectorum Pubns., Inc.

Czech, Jan M. The Coffee Can Kid. Manning, Maurie, illus. 2002. 24p. pap. 8.95 (978-0-87868-821-0(8) , 8218, Child & Family Pr.) Child Welfare League of America, Inc.

—Coffee Can Kid. 2002. (gr. k-3). lib. bdg. 17.60 (978-0-613-53419-2(0)) Tandem Library Bks.

Dalton, Annie & Dalton, Maria. Invisible Threads. 2006. 208p. (YA). (gr. 9). 15.95 (978-0-385-73286-4(4)); lib. bdg. 17.99 (978-0-385-90303-5(0)) Random Hse. Children's Bks. (Delacorte Bks. for Young Readers).

Daringer, Helen Fern. Adopted Jane. Seredy, Kate, illus. 2002. 224p. (gr. 3-6). reprint ed. 12.95 (978-0-9714612-4-6(4)) Green Mansion Pr. LLC.

Davis, Susan. I'm Adopted, You're Adopted: Welcome to God's Family. 2007. (ENG.). 79p. (J). (gr. 1-4). per. 8.99 ***(978-0-8127-0434-1(7))** Autumn Hse. Publishing Co.

de Paola, Tomie. A New Barker in the House. (Illus.). 32p. (J). (ps up). 2004. pap. 5.99 (978-0-14-240141-5(2) , Puffin); 2002. (SPA., 13.99 (978-0-399-23865-9(4) , Putnam Juvenile) Penguin Group (USA) Inc.

Diersch, Sandra. Home Court Advantage. 2001. (Sports Stories Ser.). 128p. (gr. 3-8). (J). ***(978-1-55028-749-3(4));** 7.95 (978-1-55028-748-6(6)) Lorimer, James & Co., Ltd., Pubs. CAN. *Dist:* Casemate Pubs. & Bk. Distributors, LLC.

Dukovich, Amanda J. A Star Named Little One: (Female Version) Pride, Mathew, illus. l.t. ed. 2006. 22p. (J). 15.99 (978-1-59879-090-0(0)) Lifevest Publishing, Inc.

—A Star Named Little One: (Male Version) Pride, Mathew, illus. l.t. ed. 2006. 22p. (J). 15.99 (978-1-59879-189-1(3)) Lifevest Publishing, Inc.

Eliot, George & West, Clare. Silas Marner: The Weaver of Raveloe, Level 4. 2nd ed. 2000. (Bookworms Ser.). (Illus.). 96p. 6.50 (978-0-19-423044-5(9)) Oxford Univ. Pr., Inc.

Elliott, David. Jeremy Cabbage & the Museum of Human Oddballs & Quadruped Delights. 2008. 320p. (J). (gr. 3-7). 15.99 ***(978-0-375-84333-4(7)** , Knopf Bks. for Young Readers) Random Hse. Children's Bks.

Ellis, Sarah. Out of the Blue. 2001. 120p. (J). (gr. 5-9). pap. 5.95 (978-0-88899-236-9(X)) Groundwood Bks. CAN. *Dist:* Perseus Distribution.

Enderle, Dotti. Hand of Fate, Vol. 4. Nightingale, Kimberly, ed. 2004. (Fortune Tellers Club Ser.). (Illus.). 144p. (gr. 8-12). pap. 4.99 (978-0-7387-0390-9(7)) Llewellyn Pubns.

Fennell, Kristen & Petruccelli, Jessica, illus. A World of Hope: Written by Hope's Parents Laurie & Mike. l.t. ed. 2005. 18p. (J). per. 9.99 (978-1-59879-069-6(2)) Lifevest Publishing, Inc.

Freer, Jeannette. When Harry Met the Potter. 2007. 76p. (J). per. 9.99 ***(978-1-933899-72-5(7))** Holy Fire Publishing.

Friedrich, Molly. You're Not My Real Mother! Hale, Christy, tr. Hale, Christy, illus. 2004. 32p. (J). (ps-3). 15.99 (978-0-316-60553-3(0) , Tingley, Megan Bks.) Little, Brown Bks. for Young Readers.

Fuqua, Jonathon Scott. Medusas Daughter: A Graphic Novel. Parke, Steven, illus. 2007. (Narrative, Ink Ser.). 128p. (YA). (gr. 10 up). pap. 17.95 ***(978-1-933368-92-4(6))** Counterpoint.

—Medusas Daughter Graphic Novella. Parke, Steven, illus. 2007. (Narrative, Ink Ser.). 64p. (J). ***(978-1-933368-93-1(4))** Counterpoint.

Good Morning, Vietnam, Good Afternoon, USA. 2000. (J). (978-0-9703585-0-9(4)) Hudson, Anna E.

Grace, Roz. Anthony's Surprise. Melvin, James, illus. l.t. ed. 1999. 32p. (J). (ps-3). 12.95 (978-0-9659181-2-1(2)) BMF Pr.

Gray, Kes. Our Twitchy. McQuillan, Mary, illus. rev. ed. 2003. 32p. (J). 15.95 (978-0-8050-7454-3(6) , Holt, Henry & Co. Bks. For Young Readers) Holt, Henry & Co.

Gregory, Deborah. Who's 'Bout to Bounce, Baby. 1999. (gr. 3-6). lib. bdg. 11.80 (978-0-613-22631-8(3)) Tandem Library Bks.

—Who's Bout to Bounce, Baby? 3rd rev. ed. 1999. (Cheetah Girls Ser.: No. 3). 160p. (gr. 3-7). pap. 3.99 (978-0-7868-1386-5(5)) Hyperion Bks. for Children.

Greulich, Deborah Ripoll. I Choose You. 2007. 28p. per. 12.99 ***(978-1-59886-953-8(1))** Tate Publishing & Enterprises, L.L.C.

Haan, Linda de & Nijland, Stern. King & King & Family. 2004. (Illus.). 32p. (J). 14.95 (978-1-58246-113-7(9) , Tricycle Pr.) Ten Speed Pr.

Halvorsen Schreck, Karen. Lucy's Family Tree. Gassler, Stephen, illus. 2006. 40p. (J). 7.95 ***(978-0-88448-292-5(8))** Tilbury Hse. Pubs.

Hamilton, Deborah E. Why are You my Mother? A Mother's Response to Her Adopted Daughter. Andrules, Jamie L., illus. 2006. (J). 9.99 net. (978-0-9789202-0-3(1)) Dreams Due Media Group, Inc.

Harper, Meg. My Mum & the Hound from Hell. 2003. (My Mum Ser.). 160p. (J). pap. 9.99 (978-0-7459-4799-0(9) , Lion) Lion Hudson plc GBR. *Dist:* Independent Pubs. Group.

Harrar, George. Parents Wanted. Murphy, Dan, illus. 2001. (J). (gr. 3-8). 288p. 17.95 (978-1-57131-632-5(9)); 320p. pap. 6.95 (978-1-57131-633-2(7)) Milkweed Editions.

Hassler, Donald & Hassler, Sara. Loving Marley. Newsom, Carol, illus. 2007. 32p. (J). (ps-3). 14.99 ***(978-0-9766390-7-7(6))** PugTale Publishing.

Hatley, Julie. Dasher Gets Adopted: A Story of Love, Trust & Family. Jones, Shay, illus. 2000. 32p. (J). (ps-3). 14.95 (978-0-9705188-0-4(3)) Shine Pubns.

Haywood, Carolyn. Here's a Penny. 2005. (Illus.). 160p. (J). 16.00 (978-0-15-205227-0(5) , Harcourt Young Classics); pap. 5.95 (978-0-15-205225-6(9) , Odyssey Classics) Harcourt Children's Bks.

—Penny & Peter. 2005. (Illus.). 160p. (J). 16.00 (978-0-15-205232-4(1) , Harcourt Young Classics); pap. 5.95 (978-0-15-205226-3(7) , Odyssey Classics) Harcourt Children's Bks.

Henson, Andora. Shelby's 'Doption Story. Moody, Julie, illus. 2004. (J). bds. 9.99 (978-1-4183-0013-5(6)) Christ Inspired, Inc.

Hicks, Betty. Get Real. 2006. 192p. (J). 16.95 (978-1-59643-089-1(3)) Roaring Brook Pr.

Hills, Jodi. Hope-So. Bjornson, Barbara, illus. 2004. 36p. (J). 16.95 (978-0-9726504-2-7(3)) Tristan Publishing, Inc.

Hite, Sid. The King of Slippery Falls. 2004. 224p. (J). pap. 16.95 (978-0-439-34257-5(0)) Scholastic, Inc.

Hodge, Deborah. Emma's Story. Zhang, Song Nan, illus. 2003. 24p. (J). (gr. k-3). 17.95 (978-0-88776-632-9(3)) Tundra Bks., Inc./Livres Toundra, Inc. CAN. *Dist:* Random Hse., Inc.

Howe, James. Pinky & Rex & the New Baby. 1999. (gr. k-3). lib. bdg. 11.80 (978-0-7857-3870-1(3)) Tandem Library Bks.

—Pinky & Rex & the New Baby. 2006. (J). (gr. 1-4). 24.21 (978-1-59961-076-4(0)) Spotlight.

Hrdlitschka, Shelley. Dancing Naked: A Novel. 2002. 256p. (J). (gr. 7-12). pap. 6.95 (978-1-55143-210-6(2)) Orca Bk. Pubs. USA.

—Dancing Naked: A Novel. 2002. (gr. 7-12). lib. bdg. 15.25 (978-0-613-60545-8(4)) Tandem Library Bks.

Humphry, Christy. Fire & Water. 2005. 161p. pap. 19.95 (978-1-4137-8740-5(1)) PublishAmerica, Inc.

I Love You Like Crazy Cakes. 2004. (J). 24.95 incl. audio (978-1-55592-095-1(0)); 29.95 incl. cd-rom (978-1-55592-135-4(3)) Weston Woods Studios, Inc.

Johns, Linda. Hannah West & the Belltown Towers. 2006. (Hannah West Mystery Ser.). 176p. (J). (gr. 5). pap. 5.99 (978-0-14-240637-3(6) , Puffin) Penguin Group (USA) Inc.

—Hannah West in Deep Water. 2006. (Hannah West Ser.). (Illus.). 160p. (J). (gr. 5). pap. 5.99 (978-0-14-240700-4(3) , Puffin) Penguin Group (USA) Inc.

Johnson, Angela. Heaven. 2002. (Illus.). 13.40 (978-0-7587-0359-0(7)) Book Wholesalers, Inc.

—Heaven. 1998. 144p. (YA). (gr. 7-12). 16.95 (978-0-689-82229-2(4)) Simon & Schuster Children's Publishing.

—Heaven. 2000. (gr. 7-12). lib. bdg. 13.00 (978-0-613-28517-9(4)); (Illus.). (YA). 11.64 (978-0-606-18799-2(5)) Tandem Library Bks.

—Heaven. l.t. ed. 2000. 157p. (J). (gr. 7-12). 20.95 (978-0-7862-2463-0(0)) Thorndike Pr.

Johnson, Angela & Palencia, John Jude. Heaven. 2000. (Illus.). 144p. (YA). (gr. 8-12). pap. 5.99 (978-0-689-82290-2(1) , Simon Pulse) Simon & Schuster Children's Publishing.

Jones, Diana Wynne. Archer's Goon. 2003. (gr. 5-8). lib. bdg. 14.15 (978-0-613-68402-6(8)) Tandem Library Bks.

Katz, Karen. Over the Moon: An Adoption Tale. 2001. lib. bdg. 15.25 (978-0-613-37027-1(9)); (J). (978-0-606-21373-8(2)) Tandem Library Bks.

Kennedy, Pamela. A Sister for Matthew: A Story about Adoption. Wummer, Amy, illus. 2006. 32p. (J). 8.95 (978-0-8249-5527-4(7) , 1256104, Guideposts) Ideals Pubns.

Kent, Rose. Kimchi & Calamari. 2007. 240p. (J). 15.99 (978-0-06-083769-3(1)); lib. bdg. 16.89 (978-0-06-083770-9(5)) HarperCollins Pubs.

Klein, Adria F. Max & the Adoption Day Party. 2007. (Read-It! Readers Ser.). (Illus.). 24p. (J). ***(978-1-4048-3283-1(1)** , 1265792) Picture Window Bks.

—Max & the Adoption Day Party. Gallagher-Cole, Mernie, illus. 2006. (Read-It! Readers Ser.). 24p. (J). (gr. k-2). lib. bdg. 19.93 ***(978-1-4048-3145-2(2)** , 1265792) Picture Window Bks.

Koski, Mary B. Impatient Pamela Wants a Bigger Family. Brown, Dan, illus. 2002. (Impatient Pamela Ser.). 32p. (J). (ps-3). 14.95 (978-1-930650-04-6(3)) Trellis Publishing, Inc.

Kregel Publications Staff. The Long Ride. 2004. 32p. 13.99 (978-0-8254-3577-5(3)) Kregel Pubns.

Krishnaswami, Uma. Bringing Asha Home. Akib, Jamal, illus. 2006. 32p. (J). (978-1-58430-259-9(3)) Lee & Low Bks., Inc.

Lasenby, Jack. Because We Were the Travellers. 160p. (YA). (gr. 8 up). pap. 13.00 (978-1-877135-02-6(X)) Longacre Pr. NZL. *Dist:* Pacific Island Bks.

Layne, Steven L. Over Land & Sea: The Story of International Adoption. Bower, Jan, illus. 2005. 32p. (J). 15.95 (978-1-58980-182-0(2)) Pelican Publishing Co., Inc.

Lears, Laurie. Megan's Birthday Tree: A Story about Open Adoption. Farnsworth, Bill, illus. 2005. 32p. (J). (ps-3). 15.95 (978-0-8075-5036-6(1)) Whitman, Albert & Co.

Leavitt, Caroline. Girls in Trouble: A Novel. 2005. 368p. pap. 13.95 (978-0-312-33973-9(9) , St. Martin's Paperbacks) St. Martin's Pr.

Lee, Marie Myung-Ok. Somebody's Daughter. 2006. 280p. pap. 14.00 (978-0-8070-8389-5(5)) Beacon Pr.

Lewin, Terry. God Remembered Us. Gumm, Susan Kathleen, illus. 2006. 36p. (J). per. 19.00 ***(978-0-9771482-1-9(1)** , Ithaca Pr.) Authors & Artists Publishers of New York, Inc.

Lewis, Rose. Te Quiero Nina Bonita. Dyer, Jane, illus. 2002. (J). (SPA.). 16p. 16.95 (978-84-8488-054-7(0)); (CAT.). 30p. 14.95 (978-84-8488-055-4(9)) Serres, Ediciones, S. L. ESP. *Dist:* Lectorum Pubns., Inc.

Lewis, Rose A. Every Year on Your Birthday. Dyer, Jane, illus. 2007. 32p. (J). (ps-3). 16.99 (978-0-316-52552-7(9)) Little Brown & Co.

—I Love You Like Crazy Cakes. Dyer, Jane, illus. 2000. 32p. (J). (ps-3). 16.99 (978-0-316-52538-1(3)) Little Brown & Co.

—I Love You Like Crazy Cakes. Dyer, Jane, illus. 2003. 12p. (J). (ps ps). bds. 6.99 (978-0-316-52576-3(6)) Little, Brown Bks. for Young Readers.

Lightle, Lugenia L. Ruguma: New to America. 2005. 135p. pap. 19.95 (978-1-4137-6723-0(0)) PublishAmerica, Inc.

Lin, Grace. Red Thread: An Adoption Fairy Tale. Lin, Grace, illus. 2007. (Illus.). 32p. (J). (ps-3). 16.95 ***(978-0-8075-6922-1(4))** Whitman, Albert & Co.

Little, Jean. Emma's Strange Pet. Plecas, Jennifer, illus. (I Can Read Bks.). 64p. (J). (gr. k-3). 2004. pap. 3.99 (978-0-06-444259-6(4) , Harper Trophy); 2003. 15.99 (978-0-06-028350-6(5)) HarperCollins Pubs.

Little, Jean & Little, Jean. Emma's Yucky Brother. Plecas, Jennifer, illus. 2002. 63p. (J). (ps-ps). lib. bdg. 11.80 (978-0-613-45486-5(3)) Tandem Library Bks.

Lobel, Steven. Remains of Elliot Brown. 2004. 135p. pap. 19.95 (978-1-4137-4999-1(2)) PublishAmerica, Inc.

Lucado, Max. Just the Way You Are. Martinez, Sergio, illus. 1999. Orig. Title: Children of the King. 31p. (ps-5). reprint ed. 15.99 (978-1-58134-114-0(8) , Crossway Bibles) Crossway Bks.

Macguire, Gregory. Missing Sisters. 1998. (J). (978-0-606-13612-9(6)) Tandem Library Bks.

MacKall, Dandi Daley. Home Is Where Your Horse Is, Vol. 6. 2000. (Horsefeathers Ser.: Vol. 6). (Illus.). 192p. (J). (gr. 7-11). 5.99 (978-0-570-07087-0(2)) Concordia Publishing Hse.

—Home Is Where Your Horse Is. 2000. (gr. 7-12). lib. bdg. 14.15 (978-0-613-72790-7(8)) Tandem Library Bks.

Madrid-Branch, Michelle. The Tummy Mummy. 2004. (Adoption Means Love Ser.). 32p. 14.95 (978-0-9747443-0-8(1)) Adoption Tribe Publishing.

McClain, Lee. My Loco Life. 2006. (YA). mass mkt. 5.99 (978-0-8439-5661-0(5) , SMOOCH) Dorchester Publishing Co., Inc.

McKay, Hilary. Saffy's Angel. 2004. 160p. (J). (gr. 4-7). pap. 36.00 incl. audio (978-0-8072-2098-6(1) , Listening Library) Random Hse. Audio Publishing Group.

—Saffy's Angel. 160p. (J). (gr. 3-7). 2003. (Illus.). pap. 4.99 (978-0-689-84934-3(6) , Aladdin); 2002. 16.99 (978-0-689-84933-6(8) , McElderry, Margaret K.) Simon & Schuster Children's Publishing.

—Saffy's Angel. l.t. ed. 2003. (Juvenile Ser.). 227p. (J). 21.95 (978-0-7862-5500-9(5)) Thorndike Pr.

McNamara, Joan. Borya & the Burps: An Eastern European Adoption Story. Majewski, Dawn, illus. 2005. 30p. (J). (ps-ps). 18.00 (978-0-944934-31-9(5)) Perspectives Pr., Inc.

Medler, John, Jr. The Mommy Mole. Wagoner, Kim, illus. 2004. (J). pap. 15.00 (978-0-8059-6664-0(1)) Dorrance Publishing Co., Inc.

Miles, Ellen. Snowball. 2006. (Puppy Place Ser.: Vol. 2). (Illus.). 80p. (J). pap. 4.99 (978-0-439-79380-3(7) , Scholastic Paperbacks) Scholastic, Inc.

Miller, Kathryn Ann. Did My First Mother Love Me? A Story for an Adopted Child. Moffett, Jamie, illus. 2003. 48p. (J). (ps-3). 12.95 (978-0-930934-85-9(7)); pap. 5.95 (978-0-930934-84-2(9)) Morning Glory Pr., Inc.

Mokosso, Henry Efesoa. One Child - One Wish: The Agony of a Single Child Family. 2006. 71p. per. 8.95 (978-1-59824-351-2(9)) E-BookTime LLC.

Moore, Stephanie Perry. Sweet Honesty. 2005. (Carmen Browne Ser.: No. 2). 160p. (YA). (gr. 7-12). pap. 5.99 (978-0-8024-8168-9(X)) Moody Pubs.

Mueller, Miranda, illus. Mishka: An Adoption Tale. 2007. 32p. (J). 16.95 (978-1-933084-01-5(4)) DRT Pr.

My Two Families: Individual Title Six-Packs. (gr. 3 up). 35.00 (978-0-7635-9661-3(2)) Rigby Education.

Nelson, R. A. Breathe My Name. 2007. 288p. (J). (gr. 7). 16.99 ***(978-1-59514-094-4(8)** , Razorbill) Penguin Group (USA) Inc.

Neveloff, Arlene. Jackson Finds a Home. Bolam, Emily, illus. 2007. (I'm Going to Read Ser.). 32p. (J). (gr. 2-3). pap. 3.95 ***(978-1-4027-3078-8(0))** Sterling Publishing Co., Inc.

Newman, Leslea. Felicia's Favorite Story. Romo, Adriana, illus. 2003. 24p. (J). pap. 9.95 (978-0-9674468-5-1(6)) Two Lives Publishing.

Nixon, Joan Lowery. The Haunting. Horowitz, Beverly, ed. 2000. 192p. (YA). (gr. 7-12). mass mkt. 5.99 (978-0-440-22008-4(4) , Laurel Leaf) Random Hse. Children's Bks.

—The Haunting. 2000. (YA). 11.64 (978-0-606-19191-3(7)) Tandem Library Bks.

Odone, Jamison. Honey Badgers. 2007. (Illus.). 32p. (J). (ps). 16.95 (978-1-932425-51-2(9) , Front Street) Boyds Mills Pr.

Okimoto, Jean Davies & Aoki, Elaine Mei. The White Swan Express: A Story about Adoption. So, Meilo, illus. 2002. 32p. (J). (gr. k-3). tchr. ed. 16.00 (978-0-618-16453-0(7) , Clarion Bks.) Houghton Mifflin Co. Trade & Reference Div.

Orem Werner, Teresa. A Quilt of Wishes. Tremlin, Nathan, illus. l.t. ed. 2005. 22p. 16.95 (978-1-59879-147-1(8)) Lifevest Publishing, Inc.

Peacock, Carol Antoinette. Mommy Far, Mommy Near: An Adoption Story. Brownell, Shawn Costello, illus. 2000. (Concept Book Ser.). 32p. (J). (ps-2). 15.95 (978-0-8075-5234-6(8)) Whitman, Albert & Co.

Peck, Robert Newton. Extra Innings. 2003. (gr. 5-8). lib. bdg. 14.15 (978-0-613-61762-8(2)) Tandem Library Bks.

Pennebaker, Ruth. Don't Think Twice. 1998. (978-0-606-13341-8(0)) Tandem Library Bks.

Perkins, Mitali. First Daughter: Extreme American Makeover. (YA). (gr. 7). 2008. 288p. pap. 7.99 (***978-0-14-241154-4(X)*** , Puffin); 2007. 192p. 16.99 (978-0-525-47800-3(0) , Dutton Juvenile) Penguin Group (USA) Inc.

Perry, Sarah Catherine. Clara's Test. 2006. (J). per. (978-1-55452-022-0(3)) Essence Publishing.

Pfeffer, Susan Beth. Devil's Den. 1998. 115p. (J). (gr. 3-7). 15.95 (978-0-8027-8650-0(2)) Walker & Co.

Poe, Roderick. Ben: A Novella from the Heart. 2006. 82p. pap. 14.95 (978-1-4241-3263-8(0)) PublishAmerica, Inc.

Prophet, John M. Body in the Salt Marsh Boatyard: A Casey Miller Mystery. 2004. 162p. (YA). pap. 13.95 (978-0-595-30991-7(7) , Mystery & Suspense Pr.) iUniverse, Inc.

Queralt, Elisenda & Adell, Montse. La Luna Contenta. 2005. (Caballo alado series-Al Galope Ser.). (SPA., Illus.). 24p. (J). (ps-ps). pap. 4.95 (978-84-7864-886-3(0)) Combel Editorial, S.A. ESP. *Dist:* Independent Pubs. Group.

Ray-Ray's Dream. 2002. 28p. (J). lib. bdg. 14.95 (978-0-9702601-2-3(1)) Lovegifts Publishing.

Reinhardt, Dana. A Brief Chapter in My Impossible Life. (gr. 7). 2007. 256p. (YA). pap. 8.99 (***978-0-375-84691-5(3));*** 2006. 240p. (J). 15.95 (978-0-385-74698-4(9)); 2006. 240p. (J). lib. bdg. 17.99 (978-0-385-90940-2(3)) Random Hse. Children's Bks. (Lamb, Wendy).

Reiss, Kathryn. Blackthorn Winter: A Murder Mystery. 2007. (Illus.). 348p. (YA). pap. 6.95 (***978-0-15-206109-8(6)*** , Harcourt Paperbacks) Harcourt Children's Bks.

Rizzo, Kay D. Bells & Whistles. 2003. 96p. (J). (978-0-8163-1984-8(7)) Pacific Pr. Publishing Assn.

Rogers, Joe. The Changeling. 2005. 183p. pap. 19.95 (978-1-4137-8032-1(6)) PublishAmerica, Inc.

Rosenberg, Liz. We Wanted You. 1999. (J). (978-0-7894-2600-0(5)) Dorling Kindersley Publishing, Inc.

Royster, D. A. Adoption Is... l.t. ed. 2005. (Illus.). 30p. (J). bds. 15.99 (978-0-9761538-0-1(7)) Unspeakable Joy Pr.

Rue, Nancy N. Horse Crazy Lily. 2003. (gr. 3-6). lib. bdg. 13.00 (978-0-613-71715-1(5)) Tandem Library Bks.

Rylant, Cynthia. The Whale. McDaniels, Preston, illus. 2003. (Lighthouse Family Ser.). 64p. (J). 14.95 (978-0-689-84881-0(1)) Simon & Schuster Children's Publishing.

Sansone, Adele. The Little Green Goose. 2001. (Illus.). (J). (978-0-606-20768-3(6)) Tandem Library Bks.

—The Little Green Goose. James, J. Alison, tr. Marks, Alan, illus. 2001. (J). (ps-ps). lib. bdg. 15.25 (978-0-613-36468-3(6)) Tandem Library Bks.

Sarta, Jon. Your Adoption Story. 2005. 20p. 9.99 (978-1-4116-6439-5(6)) Lulu.com.

Say, Allen. Allison. 2004. (Illus.). 32p. (J). (ps-ps). lib. bdg. 13.75 (978-0-606-32838-8(6)) Tandem Library Bks.

Shemin, Craig. Families Are Forever. McCoy, John, illus. l.t. ed. 2004. 34p. 9.95 (978-0-9728666-1-3(2) , 1) As Simple As That Publishing.

Shrom, LaJoyce. Learning about Life. 2005. (ENG., Illus.). 28p. per. 15.99 (978-1-4141-0338-9(7)) Pleasant Word.

Skurzynski, Gloria. Escape from Fear. 2002. (gr. 3-6). lib. bdg. 14.10 (978-0-613-62746-7(6)) Tandem Library Bks.

Skurzynski, Gloria & Ferguson, Alane. Escape from Fear. 2002. (Mysteries in Our National Parks Ser.: Vol. 9). 160p. (J). (gr. 3-7). 15.95 (978-0-7922-6780-5(X)); No. 9. pap. 5.95 (978-0-7922-6782-9(6)) National Geographic Society. (National Geographic Children's Bks.).

Sleator, William. Rewind. 2001. (J). (978-0-606-20883-3(6)); (gr. 5-8). lib. bdg. 14.15 (978-0-613-36007-4(9)) Tandem Library Bks.

Stoeke, Janet Morgan. Waiting for May. Stoeke, Janet Morgan, illus. 2007. 32p. (J). (gr. k). pap. 5.99 (978-0-14-240853-7(0) , Puffin) Penguin Group (USA) Inc.

Sugarman, Brynn Olenberg. Rebecca's Journey Home. Shapiro, Michelle, illus. 2006. 32p. (J). 17.95 (978-1-58013-157-5(3)) Kar-Ben Publishing.

Tesch, Lisa. The Little Princess. 2005. 54p. (J). per. 12.95 (978-1-933290-01-0(3)) Tate Publishing & Enterprises, L.L.C.

Thomas, Eliza. The Red Blanket. Cepeda, Joe, tr. Cepeda, Joe, illus. 2004. 32p. (J). pap. 15.95 (978-0-439-32253-9(7)) Scholastic, Inc.

Thrasher, Jenny & Thrasher, Phil. The Golden Egg: A Story about Adoption. Enroc Illustrations, illus. 2006. (ENG.). 24p. per. 10.95 (978-1-59800-468-7(9)) Outskirts Press, Inc.

Throckmorton, Sylvestra. Annie Cabannie's Star Baby. 2004. (Illus.). 23p. (J). per. 11.95 (978-0-9761723-0-7(5)) Greene, A.S. & Co.

—Star Baby. Throckmorton, Sylvestra et al, illus. 2006. (ENG & RAJ.). 16p. (J). 14.95 (978-0-9761723-1-4(3)) Greene, A.S. & Co.

Tiernan, Cate. Coven. 2001. (gr. 7-12). lib. bdg. 13.00 (978-0-613-31093-2(4)) Tandem Library Bks.

Tomey, Ingrid. The Queen of Dreamland. 2004. 179p. (YA). (gr. 6-10). reprint ed. 15.00 (978-0-7567-7151-5(X)) DIANE Publishing Co.

Vogel, Jane & Johnson, Lissa Halls. Fast Forward to Normal, Vol. 2. 2005. (Brio Girls Ser.). 192p. (YA). (gr. 7-11). pap. 7.99 (978-1-56179-952-7(1)) Focus on the Family Publishing.

Walker, Neva M. Grandma's Teddy Bear Tales. Coonce, Phillip, illus. 2002. 144p. (J). (gr. 2-7). pap. (978-0-9721303-0-1(6)) Neva's Arts & Crafts.

Willis, Wayne. This Is How We Became a Family: An Adoption Story. 2000. (Illus.). 32p. (J). pap. (978-1-55798-700-6(9) , 441-7009); (978-1-55798-666-5(5) , 441-6665) American Psychological Assn. (Magination Pr.).

Woolley, Barbara B. Freedom West. 2006. 22.99 (***978-1-4257-0124-6(8));*** pap. 15.99 (***978-1-4257-0123-9(X))*** Xlibris Corp.

Wright, Bil. When the Black Girl Sings. 2008. 272p. (YA). (gr. 7 up). 16.99 (***978-1-4169-3995-5(4)*** , Simon & Schuster Children's Publishing) Simon & Schuster Children's Publishing.

Wynne-Jones, Tim. The Boat in the Tree. Shelley, John, illus. 2007. 40p. (J). (ps-2). 17.95 (978-1-932425-49-9(7) , Front Street) Boyds Mills Pr.

Yarborough, N. Patricia. The Duck Wedding. Diaz, Rolando, illus. 2002. 24p. (J). (978-1-57864-167-3(5)) Donning Co. Pubs.

Ye, Ting-Xing. Throwaway Daughter. 2004. 320p. mass mkt. 5.99 (978-0-7704-2921-8(1) , Seal Bks) Doubleday Canada, Ltd. CAN. *Dist:* Random Hse., Inc.

Young, Ed. My Mei Mei. Young, Ed, illus. 2006. (Illus.). 40p. (J). (gr. 1). 16.99 (978-0-399-24339-4(9) , Philomel) Penguin Group (USA) Inc.

ADULTHOOD

Ross, Mandy. Coming of Age. 2003. (Rites of Passage Ser.). (Illus.). 32p. (J). pap. (978-1-4034-2511-9(6)); lib. bdg. 24.22 (978-1-4034-3986-4(9)) Heinemann Library.

—Coming of Age. 2003. (gr. k-3). lib. bdg. 15.90 (978-0-613-87168-6(5)) Tandem Library Bks.

Sita, Lisa. Coming of Age. 1998. (World Celebrations & Ceremonies Ser.). (Illus.). 24p. (J). (gr. 3-5). 21.20 (978-1-56711-276-4(5) , Blackbirch Pr., Inc.) Thomson Gale.

ADVENTURE AND ADVENTURERS

see also Discoveries in Geography; Escapes; Explorers; Frontier and Pioneer Life; Heroes; Sea Stories; Seafaring Life; Shipwrecks; Underwater Exploration; Voyages and Travels

Adventure Travel Christian Adventures in Learning Book. 2005. (J). 19.95 (978-1-59210-398-0(7)) Whispering Pine Pr., Inc.

Adventure Travel Christian Educational Curriculum Book. 2005. (J). 19.95 (978-1-59210-362-1(6)) Whispering Pine Pr., Inc.

Alger, Horatio. Joe the Hotel Boy: Or, Winning Out by Pluck. 363p. reprint ed. pap. 79.00 (978-1-4047-3578-1(X)) Classic Textbooks.

Alter, Judy. Extraordinary Explorers & Adventurers. 2001. (gr. 7-12). lib. bdg. 26.85 (978-0-613-52259-5(1)) Tandem Library Bks.

Ambrose, Stephen E. This Vast Land: A Young Man's Journal of the Lewis & Clark Expedition. l.t. ed. 2004. 265p. (J). 22.95 (978-0-7862-6139-0(0)) Thorndike Pr.

Ayer, Eleanor H. Parallel Journeys. 2000. (978-0-606-17933-1(X)) Tandem Library Bks.

Ayer, Eleanor H., et al. Parallel Journeys. 2000. (Illus.). 256p. (gr. 5). pap. 5.99 (978-0-689-83236-9(2) , Aladdin) Simon & Schuster Children's Publishing.

Baeten, Lieve. Where Is Tom? 1998. (Tom & Maggie Ser.). (Illus.). 8p. 3.95 (978-0-7641-5024-1(3)) Barron's Educational Series, Inc.

Billings. True Tales: Complete Classroom. 2001. (Illus.). (J). pap. (978-0-7398-3449-7(5)) Steck-Vaughn.

—True Tales: Science Classroom Library. 1999. (Illus.). (J). pap. (978-0-7398-2395-8(7)) Steck-Vaughn.

Blasingame, James B. Gary Paulsen. 2007. (Teen Reads: Student Companions to Young Adult Literature Ser.). 184p. (J). 45.00 (***978-0-313-33532-7(X)*** , GR3532, Greenwood Pr.) Greenwood Publishing Group, Inc.

Bledsoe, Lucy Jane. How to Survive in Antarctica. 2005. (Illus.). 96p. (J). (gr. 5-9). 16.95 (978-0-8234-1890-9(1)) Holiday Hse., Inc.

Blotnick, Elihu. Glimmins: Children of the Western Woods. Blotnick, Elihu, illus. 2001. (Illus.). 72p. (J). (gr. 1 up). pap. 11.95 (978-0-915090-18-1(X)) California Street.

Bowermaster, Jon. Aleutian Adventure: Kayaking in the Birthplace of the Winds. Tessman, Barry, photos by. 2001. (Illus.). 64p. (J). (gr. 7-7). 17.95 (978-0-7922-7999-0(9) , National Geographic Children's Bks.) National Geographic Society.

Brown, Chris. Shiver Me Timbers! A Funbook of Pirates-,Sailors & Other Sea-Farers. 2006. (Illus.). 32p. pap. 8.95 (978-0-7145-3303-2(3)) Consortium Bk. Sales & Distribution.

Burandt, Dale. Tales from the Homeplace: Adventures of a Texas Farm Girl. 1999. (978-0-606-16447-4(2)) Tandem Library Bks.

Calkhoven, Laurie. Miles of Smiles. 2007. 80p. (J). pap. 9.95 (***978-1-59369-170-7(X)*** , Pleasant Co.) American Girl Publishing, Inc.

Colman, Penny. Adventurous Women: Eight True Stories about Women Who Made a Difference. rev. ed. 2006. (Illus.). 192p. (J). 18.95 (978-0-8050-7744-5(8)) Holt, Henry & Co.

Colum, Padraic. Adventures of Odysseus & the Tale of T. 2006. pap. 35.99 (***978-1-4219-6450-8(3))*** IndyPublish.com.

Cummins, Julie. Women Daredevils. Harness, Cheryl, illus. 2008. 48p. (J). (gr. 3). 17.99 (***978-0-525-47948-2(1)*** , Dutton Juvenile) Penguin Group (USA) Inc.

Currie, Stephen. Travels to Distant Lands: 1000-1400. 2004. (Reading Expeditions Ser.). (Illus.). 32p. (J). (978-0-7922-4542-1(3)) National Geographic Society.

Dowswell, Paul. True Escape Stories. Tyler, Jenny, ed. 2004. (True Adventure Stories Ser.). (Illus.). 144p. (J). pap. 4.95 (978-0-7945-0087-0(0) , Usborne) EDC Publishing.

—True Polar Adventures. Woodcock, John, illus. 2004. (True Adventure Stories Ser.). 144p. (J). pap. 4.95 (978-0-7945-0404-5(3) , Usborne) EDC Publishing.

—True Stories of Sea Adventures. 2005. (True Adventure Stories Ser.). 144p. (J). pap. 4.95 (978-0-7945-0733-6(6) , Usborne) EDC Publishing.

Dowswell, Paul Et Al. True Adv Coll (Combined Volume) 2007. 432p. (J). pap. 9.99 (978-0-7945-1500-3(2) , Usborne) EDC Publishing.

Duder, Tessa, ed. Down to the Sea Again: True Sea Stories for Young Newzealanders. 2005. 256p. (J). (978-1-86950-476-2(3)) HarperCollins Pubs. New Zealand NZL. *Dist:* HarperCollins Canada, Ltd.

Fine, Anne. Stranger Danger. (Illus.). 44p. (J). 11.95 (978-0-241-12545-8(6) , Hamilton, Hamish) Penguin Bks., Ltd. GBR. *Dist:* Trafalgar Square Publishing.

Fine, Edith Hope. Gary Paulsen: Author & Wilderness Adventurer. 2000. (People to Know Ser.). (Illus.). 128p. (YA). (gr. 6-12). lib. bdg. 26.60 (978-0-7660-1146-5(1)) Enslow Pubs., Inc.

Fritz, Jean. Around the World in a Hundred Years: From Henry the Navigator to Magellan. Venti, Anthony B., illus. 1998. 128p. (J). (gr. 2-6). pap. 8.99 (978-0-698-11638-2(0) , Putnam Juvenile) Penguin Group (USA) Inc.

Gaines, Ann Graham. Gary Paulsen. 2001. (Real-Life Reader Biography Ser.). (Illus.). 32p. (J). (gr. 3-8). lib. bdg. 15.95 (978-1-58415-077-0(7)) Mitchell Lane Pubs., Inc.

Gallagher, Jim. The Search for Lost Treasure. 1999. (Costume, Tradition & Culture). (Illus.). 64p. (YA). (gr. 5 up). lib. bdg. 19.75 (978-0-7910-5167-2(6) , Chelsea Hse.) Facts On File, Inc.

Gerstein, Mordicai. The Man Who Walked Between the Towers. Gerstein, Mordicai, illus. rev. ed. 2003. (Illus.). 40p. (J). (gr. 1-3). 17.95 (978-0-7613-1791-3(0)) Roaring Brook Pr.

Giblin, James Cross. The Boy Who Saved Cleveland: Based on a True Story. Dooling, Michael, illus. rev. ed. 2006. 80p. (J). 15.95 (978-0-8050-7355-3(8) , Holt, Henry & Co. Bks. For Young Readers) Holt, Henry & Co.

Group/McGraw-Hill, Wright. Aunt Jewel's Ghost, 6 vols. (D-Man Beans Ser.). 47p. (gr. 4-6). 42.50 (978-0-322-06259-7(4)) Wright Group, The.

—Possibilities, 6 vols. (D-Man Beans Ser.). 47p. (gr. 4-6). 42.50 (978-0-322-06264-1(0)) Wright Group, The.

Hale, Marian. Dark Water Rising. rev. ed. 2006. (Illus.). 240p. (J). 16.95 (978-0-8050-7585-4(2) , Holt, Henry & Co. Bks. For Young Readers) Holt, Henry & Co.

Hanke & Leedham. Alligator Raggedy-Mouth: Making Music with Poems & Rhymes. (Illus.). 64p. (J). spiral bd. 15.95 (978-0-7136-4281-0(5)) A & C Black GBR. *Dist:* Lubrecht & Cramer, Ltd.

Harcourt School Publishers Staff. Girls to the Rescue On Level. 3rd ed. 2002. (Trophies Reading Program Ser.). (Illus.). pap. 5.10 (978-0-15-323448-4(2)) Harcourt Schl. Pubs.

—Hay Que Salvar Advanced Level. 3rd ed. 2002. (Trofeos Ser.). (SPA., Illus.). pap. 6.80 (978-0-15-324029-4(6)) Harcourt Schl. Pubs.

Harris, David. Great Escapes. 2005. (X-Zone Ser.). (Illus.). 30p. (gr. 4-8). 23.00 (978-0-7910-8979-8(7)) Facts On File, Inc.

Harvey, Gill. True Desert Adventures. Woodcock, John, illus. 2004. (True Adventure Stories Ser.). 144p. (J). pap. 4.95 (978-0-7945-0381-9(0) , Usborne) EDC Publishing.

Hays, J. W. Adventures of Prince Lazybones & Other. 2006. 78.99 (***978-1-4280-3786-1(1));*** pap. 71.99 (***978-1-4280-3813-4(2))*** IndyPublish.com.

Heaney, Jocelyn. Extreme Adventures: 25 True Stories. 2000. (Extreme Adventures Ser.). (Illus.). 144p. (J). (gr. 3-7). pap. 8.95 (978-0-7373-0401-5(4) , 04014W, Roxbury Park Juvenile) Lowell Hse. Juvenile.

Holdcroft, Tina. Hidden Treasures: Amazing Stories of Discovery. 2003. (gr. 3-6). lib. bdg. 15.25 (978-0-613-78464-1(2)) Tandem Library Bks.

Hood, Karen Jean Matsko. Fun with Foster Kids Adventures in Learning Book. (J). 2005. spiral bd. 19.95 (978-1-59210-325-6(1)); 2004. 19.95 (978-1-59210-324-9(3)) Whispering Pine Pr., Inc.

—Fun with Foster Kids Christian Adventures in Learning Book. (J). 2005. 19.95 (978-1-59210-416-1(9)); 2004. spiral bd. 19.95 (978-1-59210-417-8(7)) Whispering Pine Pr., Inc.

Horrigan, David J. The Spark in the Sea: Adventures in Marine Science, 1. 2003. 152p. pap. 24.00 (978-0-9743712-0-7(3) , 001) Home Planet Bks.

J. G. Ferguson Publishing Company Staff. Discovering Careers for Your Future/Adventure. 2001. (Discovering Careers for Your Future Ser.). (Illus.). 96p. (J). (gr. 4-9). 21.95 (978-0-89434-359-9(9) , F540, Ferguson Publishing Co.) Facts On File, Inc.

Johnson, Allen L. Willmore Horseback Adventure: Adventures with Grandchildren, 2004. (Illus.). 190p. 15.00 (978-1-880675-08-3(0)) Creative Enterprises.

Karnes, Frances A. & Bean, Suzanne M. Adventures & Challenges: Real Life Stories by Girls & Young Women. 2000. (Illus.). 208p. (YA). 12.95 (978-0-910707-35-0(9)) Great Potential Pr., Inc.

Kids Favorite Adventures Audio. 2004. pap. 22.50 (978-0-01-208207-2(4)) Your Story Hour Recordings.

Kraske, Robert. Marooned: The Strange but True Adventures of Alexander Selkirk, the Real Robinson Crusoe. Parker, Robert Andrew, illus. 2005. 128p. (J). (gr. 5-9). 15.00 (978-0-618-56843-7(3) , Clarion Bks.) Houghton Mifflin Co. Trade & Reference Div.

Lecuna, Vicente & Cumbre, Proyecto. Camino a la Cumbre. 2002. (SPA.). (YA). pap. (978-980-257-295-3(0)) Ekare, Ediciones.

Lesa, Ropeti F. Being a Boy in Samoa in the 1950s. Asuao, Kelcey, illus. 2003. (Polynesian Literature Ser.: Vol. 1). xiii, 197p. (J). pap. 19.95 (978-0-9728126-3-4(6)) Isles of the Sea Pubs.

Lithgow, John & Blackaby, Susan. Drop, Drip, an Underwater Trip: Level 3. 2007. (Lithgow Palooza Readers Ser.). (Illus.). 32p. (J). (gr. 1-2). pap. 3.95 (978-0-7696-4253-6(5)) School Specialty Publishing.

Macken, JoAnn Early. Gary Paulsen: Voice of Adventure & Survival. 2007. (Authors Teens Love Ser.). (Illus.). 104p. (J). (gr. 6 up). lib. bdg. 31.93 (978-0-7660-2721-3(X)) Enslow Pubs., Inc.

Madsen, Chris. Undersea Adventure. 2005. (Glow in the Dark Ser.). 24p. (J). 5.95 (978-1-902626-76-5(1)) Red Bird Publishing GBR. *Dist:* Perseus Distribution.

Martin, Sam. The Curious Boy's Book of Adventure: 100 Hijinks & Escapades. 2007. 160p. (J). (gr. 5). pap. 15.00 (***978-1-59514-206-1(1))*** Penguin Group (USA) Inc.

—The Curious Boy's Book of Exploration. 2008. 160p. pap. 15.00 (***978-1-59514-207-8(X)*** , Razorbill) Penguin Group (USA) Inc.

McCall, Edith. Adventures of Cowboys on Cattle Drivers, Vol. 5. 2001. (Adventures on the American Frontiers Ser.). (Illus.). 127p. (J). (gr. 3-7). pap. 9.99 (978-0-89824-306-2(8) , 306-8) Royal Fireworks Publishing Co.

—Adventures of Early Trappers & Traders. 2000. (Adventures on the American Frontiers Ser.). (Illus.). 128p. (J). (gr. 3-5). pap. 9.99 (978-0-89824-300-0(9) , 3009) Royal Fireworks Publishing Co.

—Adventures of Pioneering on the Plains, 20 vols. 2000. (Adventures on the American Frontiers Ser.: Vol. 4). (Illus.). 128p. (J). (gr. 8-10). pap. 9.99 (978-0-89824-302-4(5) , 3025) Royal Fireworks Publishing Co.

—Adventures of Pirates & Privateers, 20 vols. 2000. (Adventures on the American Frontiers Ser.: Vol. 2). (Illus.). 128p. (J). (gr. 3-5). pap. 9.99 (978-0-89824-301-7(7) , 301-7) Royal Fireworks Publishing Co.

McCann, Michelle Roehm. Going Places: True Tales from Young Travelers. 2003. (gr. 3-6). lib. bdg. 18.75 (978-0-613-82286-2(2)) Tandem Library Bks.

Michel, June, illus. Going Places: True Tales from Young Travelers. 2003. 160p. (J). (gr. 4-12). pap. (978-1-58270-070-0(2)) Beyond Words Publishing, Inc.

Molan, Chris, illus. Heroic Stories. 2004. (Red Hot Reads Ser.). 256p. (J). (gr. 4-8). pap. 6.95 (978-0-7534-5720-7(2) , Kingfisher) Houghton Mifflin Co. Trade & Reference Div.

Moranville, Sharelle Byars. A Higher Geometry. rev. ed. 2006. 224p. (YA). 16.95 (978-0-8050-7470-3(8) , Holt, Henry & Co. Bks. For Young Readers) Holt, Henry & Co.

Morris, Deborah. Horse Kick & Other True Stories, Vol. 7. l.t. ed. 2005. (Illus.). 154p. (J). (gr. 1-2). 20.95 (978-0-7862-8035-3(2) , Large Print Pr.) Thorndike Pr.

—Plane Crash & Other True Stories. l.t. ed. 2004. (Real Kids Real Adventures Ser.: No. 6). 132p. (J). 20.95 (978-0-7862-6177-2(3)) Thorndike Pr.

—Real Kids, Real Adventures in Texas. 2002. 102p. pap. 8.95 (978-1-55622-933-6(X) , Republic of Texas Pr.) Wordware Publishing, Inc.

—Real Kids Real Adventures in Texas: Blanco River Rescue. 2002. (gr. k-3). lib. bdg. 17.60 (978-0-613-87965-1(1)) Tandem Library Bks.

Morris, Gerald. The Squire's Tale. 1998. (Squire's Tales Ser.). 224p. (J). (gr. 5-9). tchr. ed. 16.00 (978-0-395-86959-8(5)) Houghton Mifflin Co. Trade & Reference Div.

Muir, John. Stickeen. Buell, Carl Dennis, illus. Date not set. 94p. (J). 16.95 (978-0-8488-2803-5(8)) Amereon LTD.

Myers, Janet Nuzum. Strange Stuff: True Stories of Odd Places & Things. Hagsted, Maj-Britt, illus. 1999. vii, 104p. (J). (gr. 4-7). 19.50 (978-0-208-02405-3(0) , Linnet Bks.) Shoe String Pr., Inc.

O'Shei, Tim. The World's Most Amazing Survival Stories. 2007. (Edge Books, the World's Top Ten). (Illus.). 32p. (J). 23.93 (978-0-7368-6437-4(7) , 1258961) Capstone Pr., Inc.

Otoshi, Kathryn. What Emily Saw. Otoshi, Kathryn, illus. 2004. (Illus.). 36p. (J). (ps-12). 16.95 (978-0-9723946-0-4(5)) KO Kids Bks.

Ouellette, Deborah. How Robin Saved Spring. Date not set. (J). 16.95 (978-0-8050-6970-9(4) , Holt, Henry & Co. Bks. For Young Readers) Holt, Henry & Co.

Parham, Jerrill. Thrills & Spills: Fast Sports. 2007. (Shockwave: the Human Experience Ser.). 36p. (J). pap. 6.95 (***978-0-531-18796-8(9)*** , Children's Pr.) Scholastic Library Publishing.

Paterra, Elizabeth. Gary Paulsen. 2002. (Who Wrote That? Ser.). (Illus.). 112p. (gr. 6-12). 30.00 (978-0-7910-6723-9(8) , Chelsea Hse.) Facts On File, Inc.

Paulsen, Gary. Guts: The True Stories Behind Hatchet & the Brian Books. 2002. (gr. 7-12). lib. bdg. 13.55 (978-0-613-57901-8(1)) Tandem Library Bks.

—Woodsong. unabr. ed. 2004. 132p. (J). (gr. 6 up). pap. 29.00 incl. audio (978-0-8072-0460-3(9) , Listening Library) Random Hse. Audio Publishing Group.

Raintree Steck-Vaughn Staff. True Tales from the Deserts. 1999. (Illus.). (J). pap. 13.00 (978-0-7398-0856-6(7)) Steck-Vaughn.

—True Tales from the Jungles. 1999. (Illus.). (J). pap. 13.00 (978-0-7398-0853-5(2)) Steck-Vaughn.

—True Tales from the Mountains. 1999. (Illus.). (J). pap. 13.00 (978-0-7398-0854-2(0)) Steck-Vaughn.

—True Tales from the Polar Regions. 1999. (Illus.). (J). pap. 13.00 (978-0-7398-0855-9(9)) Steck-Vaughn.

—True Tales from the Seas. 1999. (J). pap. 13.00 (978-0-7398-0852-8(4)) Steck-Vaughn.

Reeves, Diane Lindsey. Career Ideas for Kids Who Like Adventure & Travel. 2nd rev. ed. (Career Ideas for Kids Ser.). (gr. 4-9). 2008. 64p. pap. 9.95 (***978-0-8160-6548-6(9));*** 2007. 208p. 32.95 (***978-0-8160-6547-9(0))*** Facts On File, Inc. (Checkmark Bks.).

Reeves, Diane Lindsey & Heubeck, Nancy. Career Ideas for Kids Who Like Adventure. Bond, Nancy, illus. 2001. (Career Ideas for Kids Ser.). (J). (gr. 4-8). 170p. pap. 12.95 (978-0-8160-4322-4(1)); 176p. 23.00 (978-0-8160-4321-7(3)) Facts On File, Inc. (Checkmark Bks.).

Rough & Ready. (J). (gr. 5). 42.95 (978-0-673-72658-2(4) , Scott Foresman) Addison Wesley Schl.

Rumford, James. Traveling Man: The Journey of Ibn Battuta 1325-1354. 2004. (Illus.). 40p. (J). (gr. 1-5). pap. 6.95 (978-0-618-43233-2(7)) Houghton Mifflin Co. Trade & Reference Div.

Seletzky, Valentina. Mosaic: A Child's Recollections of the Russian Revolution. 2003. 132p. (YA). pap. 13.95 (978-0-595-30408-0(7)) iUniverse, Inc.

Slade, Suzanne. Adventures Outdoors, 6 bks., Set. Incl. Let's Go Camping. lib. bdg. 23.95 (978-1-4042-3650-9(3)); Let's Go Canoeing & Kayaking. lib. bdg. 23.95 (978-1-4042-3649-3(X)); Let's Go Fishing. lib. bdg. 23.95 (978-1-4042-3647-9(3)); Let's Go Hiking. lib. bdg. 23.95 (978-1-4042-3651-6(1)); Let's Go Hunting. lib. bdg. 23.95 (978-1-4042-3646-2(5)); Let's Go Snowboarding. lib. bdg. 23.95 (978-1-4042-3648-6(1)); (Illus.). 32p. (J). (gr. 4-6). 2007. 2007. Set lib. bdg. 143.70 (***978-1-4042-3603-5(1)*** , PowerKids Pr.) Rosen Publishing Group, Inc., The.

Slamp, Kathy. Little House in the Arctic: An Adventure Story. l.t. ed. 2004. Orig. Title: Our Little House in the Arctic. (Illus.). 228p. pap. 17.95 (978-0-9713345-3-3(6)) Vessel Ministries.

St. George, Judith. So You Want to Be an Explorer? Small, David, illus. 2005. 56p. (J). (gr. 3-6). 16.99 (978-0-399-23868-0(9) , Philomel) Penguin Group (USA) Inc.

Strom, Laura Layton. Racing on the Wind: Steve Fossett. 2007. (Shockwave: Life Stories Ser.). (Illus.). 36p. (J). (gr. 4-6). lib. bdg. 25.00 (***978-0-531-17774-7(2)*** , Children's Pr.) Scholastic Library Publishing.

Studio Mouse. Disney's Little Einsteins Explore with the Little Einsteins: Learn & Carry 4 Books with CD. rev. ed. 2007. 20p. 14.99 (***978-1-59069-563-0(1))*** Studio Mouse LLC.

Summers, Barbara, ed. Open the Unusual Door: True Life Stories of Challenge, Adventure, & Success by Black Americans. Triplett, Gina, illus. 2005. 224p. (YA). (gr. 7 up). pap. 7.99 (978-0-618-58531-1(1) , Graphia) Houghton Mifflin Co. Trade & Reference Div.

Surrell, Jason. Disney Mountains: Imagineering at Its Peak. Welcome Enterprises Staff, illus. 2007. 128p. (ps-17). pap. 19.95 (978-1-4231-0155-0(3) , Disney Editions) Disney Pr.

Takes, Toon, ed. Peel 'n Play Adventure Scenes: Adventure Scene Activity Book. Reagan, Dawn, illus. 1999. 20p. (J). (ps-4). pap. 15.50 (978-1-929456-05-5(0)) Myrtle-Seal Publishing.

—Peel 'n Play Bible Adventures: Adventure Scene Activity Book. Reagan, Dawn, illus. 1999. 20p. (J). (ps-4). pap. 15.50 (978-1-929456-02-4(6)) Myrtle-Seal Publishing.

Ury, Allen B. Dangerous Encounters: Grizzly Real-Life Animal Attacks. 1999. (Cinco Sentides del Mundo Animal Ser.: Vol. 1). (Illus.). 96p. (J). (gr. 3-7). pap. 5.95 (978-0-7373-0042-0(6) , 00426W) McGraw-Hill/Contemporary.

Vogel, Carole G. Dangerous Crossings. 2003. (Restless Sea Ser.). (gr. 5-8). pap. 12.95 (978-0-531-16679-6(1)); (Illus.). 80p. (J). 30.50 (978-0-531-12325-6(1)) Scholastic Library Publishing. (Watts, Franklin).

—Dangerous Crossings. 2003. (gr. 5-8). lib. bdg. 22.20 (978-0-613-67799-8(4)) Tandem Library Bks.

Weil, Ann. Great Adventurers. 2006. (Atomic Ser.). (Illus.). 32p. (J). (gr. 4-6). lib. bdg. 28.21 (978-1-4109-2511-4(0)) Raintree.

—Great Adventurers. 2006. (Illus.). 32p. (J). pap. (978-1-4109-2516-9(1)) Steck-Vaughn.

Williams, Marcia. El Arca de Noe. 2002. (SPA.). 32p. (J). 14.95 (978-84-261-2587-3(5)) Juventud, Editorial ESP. *Dist:* AIMS International Bks., Inc.

Windham, Ryder. What You Don't Know about Dangerous Places. 2002. (Illus.). 144p. (J). (gr. 3-7). pap. 4.50 (978-0-439-22541-0(8) , Scholastic Paperbacks) Scholastic, Inc.

Zaunders, Bo. Crocodiles, Camels & Dugout Canoes: Eight Adventurous Episodes. Munro, Roxie, illus. 2006. 48p. (J). (gr. 4-8). reprint ed. 17.00 (978-1-4223-5397-4(4)) DIANE Publishing Co.

Zhang, Charles Yu. An Adventure into Mediterranean Cultures: Lasting Memories of Our First European Adventure. 2nd num. l.t. ed. 2005. (Illus.). 84p. (YA). 15.98 (978-1-933361-00-0(X)) Lexington Pubs.

Zullo, Allan. Surviving Sharks & Other Dangerous Creatures. 2006. 151p. (J). (978-0-439-79207-3(X)) Scholastic, Inc.

ADVENTURE AND ADVENTURERS—FICTION

AaronG, Driftin'. Claude Henry, the Iditarod Mouse: The Adventures Begin. 2007. 108p. (J). per. 9.95 (***978-0-595-44990-3(5))*** iUniverse, Inc.

Abbot, Jax. SuperWhat? 2004. (YA). mass mkt. 5.99 (978-0-8439-5385-5(3)) Dorchester Publishing Co., Inc.

Abbott, Charles R. Patches & Leif. 2003. pap. 9.00 (978-0-8059-6077-8(5)) Dorrance Publishing Co., Inc.

Abbott, Jacob. Ellen Linn a Franconia Story. 2005. pap. 24.95 (978-1-4179-0056-5(3)) Kessinger Publishing, LLC.

Abbott, Tony. Flight of the Genie. Merrell, David, illus. 2004. (Secrets of Droon Ser.). 128p. (J). 3.99 (978-0-439-56043-6(8) , Scholastic Paperbacks) Scholastic, Inc.

—Flight of the Genie. 2003. (gr. 3-6). lib. bdg. 11.80 (978-0-613-87594-3(X)) Tandem Library Bks.

—Fortress of the Treasure Queen. Merrell, David, illus. 2004. (Secrets of Droon Ser.). 112p. (J). (gr. 2-5). 3.99 (978-0-439-66157-7(9) , Scholastic Paperbacks) Scholastic, Inc.

—Fortress of the Treasure Queen. Merrell, David, illus. 2004. 115p. (J). lib. bdg. 15.38 (***978-1-4242-0312-3(0))*** Fitzgerald Bks.

—The Hawk Bandits of Tarkoom. Jessell, Tim, illus. 2001. (Secrets of Droon Ser.: No. 11). 128p. (J). (gr. 2-5). pap. 3.99 (978-0-439-20785-0(1)) Scholastic, Inc.

—Into the Land of the Lost. 2000. (gr. 3-6). lib. bdg. 11.80 (978-0-613-32690-2(3)) Tandem Library Bks.

—The Isle of Mists. Merrell, David, illus. 2004. 121p. (J). lib. bdg. 15.38 (***978-1-4242-0313-0(9))*** Fitzgerald Bks.

—Journey to the Volcano Palace. Merrell, David & Jessell, Tim, illus. 1999. (Secrets of Droon Ser.: No. 2). 96p. (J). (gr. 2-5). pap. 3.99 (978-0-590-10841-6(7)) Scholastic, Inc.

—Journey to the Volcano Palace. 1999. (gr. 3-6). lib. bdg. 11.80 (978-0-613-16961-5(1)); (Secrets of Droon Ser.: No. 2). (J). (gr. 2-5). 10.79 (978-0-606-18604-9(2)) Tandem Library Bks.

—The Knights of Silversnow. 2002. (gr. 3-6). lib. bdg. 11.80 (978-0-613-50453-9(4)) Tandem Library Bks.

—The Magic Escapes. ed. 2002. (Secrets of Droon Ser.: Bk. 1). (Illus.). 176p. (J). pap. 5.99 (978-0-439-42077-8(6) , Scholastic Paperbacks) Scholastic, Inc.

—The Magic Escapes. 2002. (gr. 3-6). lib. bdg. 13.00 (978-0-613-58158-5(X)) Tandem Library Bks.

—The Mysterious Island. Merrell, David, illus. 1999. (Secrets of Droon Ser.: No. 3). 96p. (J). (gr. 2-5). pap. 3.99 (978-0-590-10840-9(9)) Scholastic, Inc.

—The Mysterious Island. 1999. (Secrets of Droon Ser.: No. 3). (J). (gr. 2-5). (978-0-606-18605-6(0)) Tandem Library Bks.

—Pirates of the Purple Dawn. 2007. (Secrets of Droon Ser.: No. 29). 128p. (J). pap. 3.99 (978-0-439-90250-2(9) , Scholastic Paperbacks) Scholastic, Inc.

—The Secrets of Droon: The Isle of Mists. Merrell, David, illus. 2004. (Secrets of Droon Ser.). 112p. (J). 3.99 (978-0-439-56048-1(9)) Scholastic, Inc.

—The Tower of the Elf King. 2000. (gr. 3-6). lib. bdg. 11.80 (978-0-613-33156-2(7)) Tandem Library Bks.

—The Voyage of the Jaffa Wind, No. 14. Merrell, David, illus. 2002. (Secrets of Droon Ser.: No. 14). 144p. (J). (gr. 2-5). pap. 3.99 (978-0-439-30607-2(8) , Scholastic Paperbacks) Scholastic, Inc.

—Wizard or Witch. Merrell, David & Jessell, Tim, illus. 2004. (Secrets of Droon Ser.: Special Edition #2). 176p. (J). pap. 5.99 (978-0-439-56049-8(7)) Scholastic, Inc.

Abbott, Tony & Gelsey, James. Escape from Jabar-Loo. 2007. (Secrets of Droon Ser.: No. 30). 128p. (J). pap. 3.99 (***978-0-439-90251-9(7)*** , Scholastic Paperbacks) Scholastic, Inc.

Abela, Deborah. Mission: The Amazon Experiment. O'Connor, George, illus. 2007. (Spy Force Ser.). 288p. (J). pap. 5.99 (978-0-689-87361-4(1) , Simon & Schuster/Paula Wiseman Bks.) Simon & Schuster Children's Publishing.

—Mission: the Nightmare Vortex. O'Connor, George, illus. 2007. (Spy Force Ser.). 256p. (J). pap. 5.99 (978-1-4169-3484-4(7) , Aladdin) Simon & Schuster Children's Publishing.

—The Nightmare Vortex. O'Connor, George, illus. 2005. (Spy Force Ser.). 256p. (J). (gr. 3-7). 9.95 (978-0-689-87359-1(X) , Simon & Schuster/Paula Wiseman Bks.) Simon & Schuster Children's Publishing.

Aboff, Marcie, ed. Animals with Attitude. 2006. (Over the Hedge Ser.: No. 1). (Illus.). 48p. (J). pap. 3.99 (978-0-439-80147-8(8)) Scholastic, Inc.

About Town with Benny Be. 2005. (J). bds. 15.99 (978-0-9774752-0-9(4)) Bentley, Trish.

Abshire, Lisa D. Sam's Magical Day. 2006. 48p. pap. 12.95 (978-1-4241-1484-9(5)) PublishAmerica, Inc.

Accola, Juli. The Adventures of Amanda Humperdink. 2002. (Illus.). 148p. (J). per. (978-1-888223-39-2(1)) McMillen Publishing.

Acker, Rick. The Lost Treasure of Fernando Montoya, Vol. 2. 2003. (Davis Detective Mysteries Ser.). 192p. pap. 7.99 (978-0-8254-2005-4(9)) Kregel Pubns.

The Acorn Story: An Adventure about Change. 2005. (J). 12.95 (978-0-9767769-0-1(1)) Rutigliano, Joe.

Action Adventures Theme Pack, 5 vols. 2001. (Illus.). (J). (gr. 8-9). 19.95 (978-1-56762-146-4(5)) Modern Learning Pr.

Ada, Alma Flor. After the Storm. 1998. (Stories the Year 'Round Ser.). (J). (gr. k-12). pap. 7.95 (978-1-56014-337-6(1)) Santillana USA Publishing Co., Inc.

Ada, Alma Flor & Campoy, F. Isabel. A New Home for the Seven Little Kids. (Gateways to the Sun). 32p. (J). (gr. k-6). pap. 13.95 (978-1-58105-960-1(4)) Santillana USA Publishing Co., Inc.

Adair Scott, Paula. Blue Button & Red Thread. 2004. (Illus.). 25p. (J). pap. 5.95 (978-0-9740419-1-9(2)) words4u.

Adams, Denise H. Itchy the Witch. 2007. (J). per. 13.99 (***978-1-59879-385-7(3))*** Lifevest Publishing, Inc.

Adams, Douglas. So Long, & Thanks for All the Fish. 1999. (gr. 7-12). lib. bdg. 15.30 (978-0-613-17519-7(0)) Tandem Library Bks.

Adams, Jean Ekman. Clarence Goes Out West & Meets a Purple Horse. 2000. (Illus.). 32p. (ps-1). 15.95 (978-0-87358-753-2(7) , Rising Moon Bks. for Young Readers) Northland Publishing.

Adams, Jeanette. Within the Circle, one. 2003. (Camelot Rabbitry Ser.: Two). 108p. (YA). per. 9.95 (978-0-9672375-2-7(1)) Camelot Tales.

Adams, Jefferson. National Treasure Original: the Golden Door - Novel #1. 2007. 288p. (YA). (gr. 7-17). pap. 7.99 (***978-1-4231-0814-6(0))*** Disney Pr.

Adams, Richard. Watership Down. 2001. (Perennial Classics Ser.). (Illus.). 512p. pap. 13.00 (978-0-06-093545-0(6)) HarperCollins Pubs.

Adams, W. Royce. Rairarubia Bk. 1: The Rairarubia Tales, 6 vols. 2nd ed. 2004. (Rairarubia Tales Ser.: 1). 138p. (J). pap. 10.95 (978-0-9712206-5-2(4)) Rairarubia Bks.

Adderson, Caroline. I, Bruno. Flook, Helen, illus. 2007. (Orca Echoes Ser.). 64p. (J). (gr. 2-4). pap. (***978-1-55143-501-5(2))*** Orca Bk. Pubs.

Adeney, Anne. Skulduggery. Smith, Wendy, illus. l.t. ed. 2005. 256p. (J). pap. (978-0-7540-6195-3(7) , CLP 384) BBC Audio.

Adler, David A. Cam Jansen & the Mystery of the Dinosaur Bones. 2004. (Cam Jansen Ser.: No. 3). (Illus.). 64p. (J). (gr. 2-4). pap. 3.99 (978-0-14-240012-8(2) , Puffin) Penguin Group (USA) Inc.

—Cam Jansen & the Mystery of the Television Dog. 2004. (Cam Jansen Ser.: No. 4). (Illus.). 64p. (J). (gr. 2-4). pap. 3.99 (978-0-14-240013-5(0) , Puffin) Penguin Group (USA) Inc.

—Cam Jansen & the Mystery of the UFO. Natti, Susanna, illus. 2004. (Cam Jansen Ser.: No. 2). 64p. (J). (gr. 2-4). pap. 3.99 (978-0-14-240011-1(4) , Puffin) Penguin Group (USA) Inc.

Adoff, Jaime. Jimi & Me. 2005. 336p. (gr. 7-17). 15.99 (978-0-7868-5214-7(3) , Jump at the Sun) Hyperion Bks. for Children.

Adpot-a-Hulk. 2003. (J). per. (978-1-57657-819-3(4)) Paradise Pr., Inc.

Advantage Publishers Group & Saidens, Amy. Surfer Girl Sticker Book. 2007. (Illus.). 24p. (J). 14.95 (978-1-59223-632-9(4) , Silver Dolphin Bks.) Advantage Pubs. Group.

Adventure of My Dentist & the Tooth Fairy Activity & Coloring Book, First Edition. 2005. (978-1-59649-533-3(2)) Whispering Pine Pr., Inc.

Adventure Travel Adventures in Learning Book. 2005. (J). 15.95 (978-1-59210-284-6(0)); spiral bd. 19.95 (978-1-59649-551-7(0)); cd-rom 13.95 (978-1-59649-552-4(9)) Whispering Pine Pr., Inc.

Adventure Travel Story Book. 2005. (J). 7.95 (978-1-59649-415-2(8)); spiral bd. 7.95 (978-1-59649-563-0(4)); per. 7.95 (978-1-59649-562-3(6)); cd-rom 7.95 (978-1-59649-564-7(2)) Whispering Pine Pr., Inc.

Adventurer Guide: Leader's Handbook. 2004. (Caravan Ser.). 308p. pap. 12.99 (978-0-8341-2117-1(4)) Beacon Hill Pr. of Kansas City.

Adventurer Pathfinder. 2004. (Caravan Ser.). 176p. pap., stu. ed. 9.50 (978-0-8341-2118-8(2)) Beacon Hill Pr. of Kansas City.

Adventurer Trailblazer. 2004. (Caravan Ser.). 168p. pap., stu. ed. 9.50 (978-0-8341-2119-5(0)) Beacon Hill Pr. of Kansas City.

Adventures in the Purple Forest. 2003. (J). (978-1-932570-06-9(3)) Literacy Footprints Inc.

The Adventures of Alexandra. 2005. (J). 21.95 (978-0-9761169-0-5(1)) Silhouette Pond Productions.

The Adventures of Chip Green the Forestry Kid, l.t. ed. 2005. (Illus.). 34p. (J). per. (978-0-9729753-8-4(1)) Really Big Coloring Bks., Inc.

The Adventures of Little Nina: Nina's First Trip. l.t. ed. 2005. (Illus.). 40p. (J). 16.95 (978-0-9769662-0-3(4)) Strategies Publishing Co.

The Adventures of Marc John Jefferies: The Missing Princess. l.t. ed. 2004. (Illus.). 110p. (YA). per. (978-0-9747218-3-5(2) , 100, Young Women Programming) Young Women Bks.

The Adventures of Max & Millie: At the Pond. 2003. (Illus.). 32p. (J). 8.95 (978-0-9744427-0-9(4)) music bks. & games.

The Adventures of Mr. Cheesehead: Mr. Cheesehead Goes for A Ride. 2004. Orig. Title: Mr. Cheesehead Goes for A Ride. (J). per. 9.99 (978-0-9764463-0-9(8)) Vertigo Publishing.

Adventures of My Dentist & the Tooth Fairy Adventures in Learning Book. 2005. (J). per. 19.95 (978-1-59649-537-1(5)) Whispering Pine Pr., Inc.

Adventures of My Dentist & the Tooth Fairy Educational Curriculum Book. 2005. per. 19.95 (978-1-59649-540-1(5)) Whispering Pine Pr., Inc.

The Adventures of Pipi & Pearl: Pipi & Pearl Go West. 2003. (J). per. 7.95 (978-0-9747378-0-5(1)) Iverson, Theodore.

The Adventures of Ricky Raccoon & Jodi the Cat. 2001. 28p. (J). 7.95 (978-0-9709408-0-3(7)) Pinetree Pubns.

The Adventures of Rowdy Raccoon. 2006. (J). per. 16.95 incl. audio compact disk (***978-0-9766823-8-7(9))*** Sable Creek Pr. LLC.

The Adventures of Sammy the Snowflake: The Facts of Life, Flying & Finding Weather. 2007. (J). 19.95 (***978-0-9795260-0-8(0))*** Courtyard Publishing, LLC.

Adventures of Suzy Starfish: The Sunken Ship. 2000. 24p. (J). (978-1-931015-04-2(X)) Distant Waters Publishing & Designs.

Adventures of Suzy Starfish No. 2: The Rescue. 2001. (J). (978-1-931015-05-9(8)) Distant Waters Publishing & Designs.

Adventures of the Robber Pig: Level J, 6 vols. (Leveled Books). 128p. (gr. 2-3). 41.95 (978-0-7699-0987-5(6)) Shortland Pubns. (U. S. A.) Inc.

The Adventures of Tom Sawyer. 2004. (Classic Retelling Ser.). (gr. 6-12). (978-0-618-12053-6(X) , 2-00218) McDougal Littell Inc.

The Adventures of Tom Sawyer. 1998. 44p. (YA). stu. ed. 11.95 (978-1-56137-528-8(4) , NU5284SP) Novel Units, Inc.

The Adventures of Tom Sawyer. 2004. (Literature Units Ser.). (Illus.). 48p. 7.99 (978-1-57690-637-8(X)) Teacher Created Materials, Inc.

The Adventures of Tony & Little Britches. 2000. (J). pap. (978-0-9700756-4-2(2)) Pajo Publishing Co.

Adventures of Wishbone, 14 bks. l.t. ed. Incl. Digging to the Center of the Earth. Steele, Michael Anthony. Punchatz, Don, illus. (gr. 4 up). lib. bdg. 22.60 (978-0-8368-2595-4(0)); Digging up the Past. Sathre, Vivian. 144p. (gr. 4 up). lib. bdg. 22.60 (978-0-8368-2302-8(8)); Dog Overboard! Sathre, Vivian. (gr. 4 up). lib. bdg. 22.60 (978-0-8368-2590-9(X)); Dr. Jekyll & Mr. Dog. Butcher, Nancy. (gr. 4 up). lib. bdg. 22.60 (978-0-8368-2592-3(6)); Gullifur's Travels. Strickland, Brad & Strickland, Barbara. (gr. 4 up). lib. bdg. 22.60 (978-0-8368-2596-1(9)); Homer Sweet Homer. Jablonski, Carla. Punchatz, Don, illus. (gr. 4 up). lib. bdg. 22.60 (978-0-8368-2591-6(8)); Hunchdog of Notre Dame. Friedman, Michael Jan. 139p. (gr. 4 up). lib. bdg. 22.60 (978-0-8368-2301-1(X)); Last of the Breed. Steele, Alexander. Punchatz, Don, illus. 163p. (gr. 4 up). lib. bdg. 22.60 (978-0-8368-2594-7(2)); Mutt in the Iron Muzzle. Friedman, Michael Jan. 144p. (gr. 4 up). lib. bdg. 22.60 (978-0-8368-2303-5(6)); Pawloined Paper. Litowinsky, Olga. (gr. 4 up). lib. bdg. 22.60 (978-0-8368-2589-3(6)); Prince & the Pooch. Leavitt, Caroline. 144p. (gr. 4 up). lib. bdg. 22.60 (978-0-8368-2299-1(4)); Pup in King Arthur's Court. Barkan, Joanne. 164p. (gr. 2-5). lib. bdg. 22.60 (978-0-8368-2593-0(4)); Robinhound Crusoe. Leavitt, Caroline. 144p. (gr. 4 up). lib. bdg. 22.60 (978-0-8368-2300-4(1)); Tale of Two Sitters. Barkan, Joanne. 144p. (gr. 4 up). lib. bdg. 22.60 (978-0-8368-2305-9(2)); (J). 1999. (Illus.). 1999. Set lib. bdg. 316.40 (978-0-8368-2654-8(X)) Stevens, Gareth Inc.

Adventures with Kat & Dex: The search for the key to Golden Gate Park. l.t. ed. 2004. (Illus.). 32p. (J). lib. bdg. 22.95 (978-0-9754853-0-9(X)) DeAngelis, Anthony.

Afetian, "Uncle Ted". The Adventures of Midas & the Little Red Airplane. 2005. (Illus.). 32p. (J). 16.95i (978-0-9752749-0-3(2)) Snyder-Winston Pr.

Agee, Jon. Z Goes Home. 2003. (Illus.). 32p. (J). (ps-17). (978-0-7868-1987-4(1)) Hyperion Bks. for Children.

Aguileta Estrada, Gabriela, tr. El Espejo en el Agua. De Gante, Guillermo, illus. rev. ed. 2006. (Castillo de la Lectura Naranja Ser.). (SPA.). 124p. (J). pap. 7.95 (978-970-20-0131-7(5)) Castillo, Ediciones, S. A. de C. V. MEX. *Dist:* Macmillan.

Agunzo, Marianna. Three Peas in a Pod Go to Paris. Rodriguez, Angelo F., illus. 2006. 26p. (J). per. 14.95 (***978-1-59453-909-1(X)*** , 2977, Airleaf Publishing) Airleaf Publishing & Bookselling.

Ahern, Dianne. Break-in at the Basilica: Adventures with Sister Philomena, Special Agent to the Pope. Larson, Katherine, illus. 2006. (J). (978-0-9679437-8-7(7)) Aunt Dee's Attic, Inc.

—Lost in Peter's Tomb: Adventures with Sister Philomena, Special Agent to the Pope. Larson, Katherine, illus. 2006. (J). pap. (978-0-9679437-9-4(5)) Aunt Dee's Attic, Inc.

Ahlman, Larry. Mittens at Sea, 1. 2004. (Illus.). 200p. (YA). per. 14.95 (978-0-9712906-1-7(X)) Ahlman Publishing.

—Mittens in the Boundary Waters. Larsen, Chuck, ed. Hanson, Dana, illus. 2001. 200p. (YA). (gr. 7-12). pap. 14.95 (978-0-9712906-0-0(1)) Ahlman Publishing.

Aigner-Clark, Julie. Word Adventure. Zaidi, Nadeem, illus. 2005. 10p. (ps-17). 14.99 (978-0-7868-5478-3(2)) Hyperion Bks. for Children.

Aiken, Joan. Black Hearts in Battersea. 1999. 240p. (J). (gr. 5-9). pap. 5.95 (978-0-395-97128-4(4)) Houghton Mifflin Co. Trade & Reference Div.

—Bridle the Wind. 2007. (Illus.). 352p. (YA). pap. 6.95 (978-0-15-206058-9(8)) Harcourt Trade Pubs.

—Dangerous Games. 2000. (978-0-606-20482-8(2)) Tandem Library Bks.

—Midwinter Nightingale. 256p. (gr. 5). 2003. 15.95 (978-0-385-73081-5(0) , Delacorte Bks. for Young Readers); 2003. lib. bdg. 17.99 (978-0-385-90103-1(8) , Delacorte Bks. for Young Readers); 2005. reprint ed. 5.99 (978-0-440-41928-0(X) , Yearling) Random Hse. Children's Bks.

—Nightbirds on Nantucket. 1999. (978-0-606-21728-6(2)) Tandem Library Bks.

—The Stolen Lake. 2000. (Illus.). 320p. (J). (gr. 5-9). pap. 5.95 (978-0-618-07021-3(4)) Houghton Mifflin Co. Trade & Reference Div.

—The Stolen Lake. 2000. (Illus.). (J). (978-0-606-21733-0(9)) Tandem Library Bks.

—Stolen Lake. 2000. (gr. 5-8). lib. bdg. 14.10 (978-0-613-31756-6(4)) Tandem Library Bks.

—The Teeth of the Gale. 2007. 352p. (YA). pap. 6.95 (978-0-15-206070-1(7)) Harcourt Trade Pubs.

—The Witch of Clatteringshaws. 2005. 144p. (J). (gr. 5). lib. bdg. 17.99 (978-0-385-90252-6(2) , Delacorte Bks. for Young Readers) Random Hse. Children's Bks.

—The Witch of Clatteringshaws. 2006. 160p. (gr. 4-7). 5.99 (978-0-440-42037-8(7) , Yearling) Random Hse. Children's Bks.

Aikins, Dave, illus. At the Carnival. 2005. (J). (***978-1-4156-0769-5(9)*** , Simon Spotlight/Nickelodeon) Simon & Schuster Children's Publishing.

—Bailando al Rescate (Dance to the Rescue) 2005. (Dora la Exploradora Ser.). (SPA.). 24p. (J). pap. 3.99 (978-1-4169-1504-1(4) , Libros Para Ninos) Simon & Schuster Children's Publishing.

—Dora's Pirate Adventure. 2005. (Dora the Explorer Ser.). 24p. (J). pap. 3.99 (978-0-689-87583-0(5) , Simon Spotlight/Nickelodeon) Simon & Schuster Children's Publishing.

Aimard, Gustave. The Indian Scout: a Story of the Aster City. 2006. (ENG.). 464p. per. 37.95 (***978-1-4286-1776-6(0))** Kessinger Publishing, LLC.

Aina, Olaiya E. Ijapa & the Tug of War. Perrin, Sharon, illus. 1999. 12p. (J). (gr. k-7). pap. 8.00 (978-0-9709944-0-0(0)) Dried Fish Pubns.

Aiosssa, Janet M. Deep in the Woods. Gabel, Deborah Boudreau, illus. l.t. ed. 2005. 24p. (J). lib. bdg. 16.95 (978-0-9769360-0-8(3) , 0503) Adam Hill Pubns.

Aker, Don. Stranger at Bay. unabr. ed. 1998. (Gemini Bks.). 246p. (YA). (gr. 7-9). mass mkt. 5.95 (978-0-7736-7468-4(3)) Stoddart Kids CAN. *Dist:* Fitzhenry & Whiteside, Ltd.

—Stranger at Bay. 1998. (gr. 7-12). lib. bdg. 12.95 (978-0-613-85639-3(2)) Tandem Library Bks.

Akinje, Wale. The Adventures of Imhotep. Young, Craig, illus. 2006. (J). (978-0-9768485-0-9(3)) Nile Publishing.

Alapont, Pasqual. Un Verano Sin Francesas. Sola, Raquel, tr. from CAT. Molinero, David, illus. 2000. (Periscopio Ser.).Tr. of Summer Without French Girls. (SPA.). 112p. (YA). (gr. 9 up). (978-84-236-5512-0(1)) Edebé ESP. *Dist:* Baker & Taylor Bks.

Albee, Sarah. It's Check-up Time, Elmo! Brannon, Tom, illus. rev. ed. 2005. 24p. (J). (ps-3). pap. 3.50 (978-1-4037-1608-8(0)) Dalmatian Pr.

—Kidoozle Kids & the Great Shape Rescue! 2004. (Illus.). 12p. bds. 9.95 (978-1-932915-02-0(8)) Sandvik Publishing.

Albee, Sarah & Lukas, Catherine. Who's Hiding, Little Bill? Goldberg, Barry, illus. 2001. (Little Bill Ser.). 12p. (J). (gr. k-3). bds. 10.95 (978-0-689-84321-1(6) , Simon Spotlight/Nickelodeon) Simon & Schuster Children's Publishing.

Albertson, Bernard. So, You Think There Is No Santa, Bk. 2. 2004. 96p. (J). pap. 7.95 (978-0-87714-744-2(2)) Denlingers Pubs., Ltd.

Albright, Rachelle. An Adventure to Treasure. 2002. 121p. (J). per. 10.00 (978-0-9713435-0-4(0)) Albright, Rachelle.

Alcantara, Ricardo. El Hijo Del Viento. 2003. (SPA., Illus.). 64p. (978-84-207-6971-4(1) , GS2762) Grupo Anaya, S.A. ESP. *Dist:* Lectorum Pubns., Inc.

Alden, Paul & Bird, Brad. The Incredibles. Eliopoulos, Chris, illus. 2005. 96p. pap. 9.95 (978-1-59307-354-1(2)) Dark Horse Comics.

Aldrich, Thomas Bail. The Story of a Bad Boy. 2006. pap. (***978-1-4065-0613-6(3))** Dodo Pr.

Aldridge, Janet. The Meadow-Brook Girls Afloat (Illustrat. 2006. pap. (***978-1-4065-0692-1(3))** Dodo Pr.

—The Meadow-Brook Girls Afloat or the Sto. 2006. 33.99 (***978-1-4280-0789-5(X));** pap. 26.99 (***978-1-4280-0811-3(X))** IndyPublish.com.

—MeadowBrook Girls under Canvas or Fun an. 2006. 78.99 (***978-1-4280-3182-1(0))** IndyPublish.com.

Alegria, Ciro. Sueno y Verdad de America. 2000. (SPA., Illus.). 150p. 8.95 (978-84-239-7085-8(X)) Espasa Calpe, S.A. ESP. *Dist:* Libros Sin Fronteras.

Alexander, Heather. The Case of the Unicorn Mystery. 2005. 82p. (J). (ps-7). lib. bdg. 11.64 (978-0-606-33342-9(8)) Tandem Library Bks.

Alexander, Lloyd. The Beggar Queen. 2002. (Westmark Trilogy: Vol. 3). (YA). (gr. 5-8). lib. bdg. 14.15 (978-0-613-63920-0(0)) Tandem Library Bks.

—The Black Cauldron. rev. ed. 1999. (Chronicles of Prydain Ser.: Bk. 2). (Illus.). 224p. (J). (gr. 3-7). 19.95 (978-0-8050-6131-4(2) , Holt, Henry & Co. Bks. For Young Readers) Holt, Henry & Co.

—The Black Cauldron. 2004. (Chronicles of Prydain Ser.: Bk. 2). 240p. (J). (gr. 4-7). pap. 38.00 incl. audio (978-1-4000-8636-8(1) , Listening Library) Random Hse. Audio Publishing Group.

—The Castle of Llyr. rev. ed. 1999. (Chronicles of Prydain Ser.: Bk. 3). (Illus.). 204p. (J). (gr. 3-7). 21.95 (978-0-8050-6133-8(9) , Holt, Henry & Co. Bks. For Young Readers) Holt, Henry & Co.

—The Castle of Llyr. 2004. (Chronicles of Prydain Ser.: Bk. 3). 208p. (J). (gr. 4-7). pap. 36.00 incl. audio (978-1-4000-9019-8(9) , Listening Library) Random Hse. Audio Publishing Group.

—The Chronicles of Prydain. rev. ed. 1999. (Chronicles of Prydain Ser.: Bk. 3). (Illus.). 224p. (J). (gr. 3-7). 19.95 (978-0-8050-6132-1(0) , Holt, Henry & Co. Bks. For Young Readers) Holt, Henry & Co.

—The Drackenberg Adventure. 2001. (Vesper Holly Ser.). (Illus.). 160p. (YA). (gr. 5-9). pap. 5.99 (978-0-14-130471-7(5) , Puffin) Penguin Group (USA) Inc.

—The Drackenberg Adventure. 2001. (Vesper Holly Ser.). (YA). (gr. 5-8). lib. bdg. 14.15 (978-0-613-35938-2(0)) Tandem Library Bks.

—The El Dorado Adventure. 2000. (Vesper Holly Ser.). (Illus.). 160p. (J). (gr. 5-9). pap. 5.99 (978-0-14-130463-2(4) , Puffin) Penguin Group (USA) Inc.

—The El Dorado Adventure. 2000. (Vesper Holly Ser.). (YA). (gr. 5-8). lib. bdg. 14.15 (978-0-613-33693-2(3)); (gr. 7 up). 12.64 (978-0-606-20357-9(5)) Tandem Library Bks.

—The Golden Dream of Carlo Chuchio. 2007. 320p. (J). (gr. 5 up). 18.95 (***978-0-8050-8333-0(2)** , Holt, Henry & Co. Bks. For Young Readers) Holt, Henry & Co.

—The High King. rev. ed. 1999. (Chronicles of Prydain Ser.: Bk. 5). (Illus.). 288p. (J). (gr. 3-7). 19.95 (978-0-8050-6135-2(5) , Holt, Henry & Co. Bks. For Young Readers) Holt, Henry & Co.

—The Illyrian Adventure. 2000. (Vesper Holly Ser.). (YA). (gr. 5-8). lib. bdg. 14.15 (978-0-8085-9586-1(5)) Tandem Library Bks.

—The Jedera Adventure. 2001. (Vesper Holly Ser.). (Illus.). 160p. (J). (gr. 5-9). pap. 5.99 (978-0-14-131238-5(6) , Puffin) Penguin Group (USA) Inc.

—The Kestrel. 2002. (Westmark Trilogy: Vol. 2). 256p. (J). (gr. 5 up). pap. 6.99 (978-0-14-131069-5(3) , Puffin) Penguin Group (USA) Inc.

—The Kestrel. 2002. (Westmark Trilogy: Vol. 2). (YA). (gr. 5-8). lib. bdg. 14.15 (978-0-613-63956-9(1)) Tandem Library Bks.

—The Marvelous Misadventures of Sebastian. 2000. (Illus.). 224p. (J). (gr. 5-9). pap. 5.99 (978-0-14-130816-6(8) , Puffin) Penguin Group (USA) Inc.

—The Marvelous Misadventures of Sebastian. 2001. (J). (gr. 4-8). 21.00 (978-0-8446-7163-5(0)) Smith, Peter Pub., Inc.

—The Marvelous Misadventures of Sebastian. 2000. (gr. 3-6). lib. bdg. 14.15 (978-0-8335-8963-7(6)) Tandem Library Bks.

—The Philadelphia Adventure. 2002. (Vesper Holly Ser.). (YA). (gr. 5-8). lib. bdg. 14.15 (978-0-613-51463-7(7)) Tandem Library Bks.

—The Remarkable Journey of Prince Jen. l.t. ed. 2002. (LRS Large Print Cornerstone Ser.). (J). lib. bdg. 32.95 (978-1-58118-104-3(3) , 25787) LRS.

—The Remarkable Journey of Prince Jen. 2004. (Illus.). 288p. (J). (gr. 5). pap. 6.99 (978-0-14-240225-2(7) , Puffin) Penguin Group (USA) Inc.

—The Rope Trick. (J). 2002. 192p. (gr. 3-6). 16.99 (978-0-525-47020-5(4) , Dutton Juvenile); 2004. 208p. (gr. 5 up). reprint ed. pap. 5.99 (978-0-14-240119-4(6) , Puffin) Penguin Group (USA) Inc.

—Taran Wanderer. (Chronicles of Prydain Ser.: Bk. 4). 256p. (J). rev. ed. 1999. (gr. 3-7). 19.95 (978-0-8050-6134-5(7)); 4th rev. ed. 2006. pap. 5.99 (978-0-8050-8051-3(1)) Holt, Henry & Co. (Holt, Henry & Co. Bks. For Young Readers).

—Westmark, Vol. 1. 2002. (Westmark Trilogy: Vol. 1). (Illus.). 192p. (YA). (gr. 7 up). pap. 6.99 (978-0-14-131068-8(5) , Puffin) Penguin Group (USA) Inc.

—The Xanadu Adventure. (Vesper Holly Ser.). 160p. (gr. 5-9). 2007. (YA). 5.99 (978-0-14-240786-8(0)); 2005. (Illus.). (J). 16.99 (978-0-525-47371-8(8)) Penguin Group (USA) Inc. (Dutton Juvenile).

Alexander, Lloyd, contrib. by. The Rope Trick. 2004. 195p. (J). (gr. 5). lib. bdg. 13.64 (978-0-606-30794-9(X)) Tandem Library Bks.

Alexander, R. W. Charm Hunter. 2004. 208p. (YA). pap. 14.95 (978-0-7414-2105-0(4)) Infinity Publishing.

Alexander, Samantha. Flying Start. 2003. 149p. (J). mass mkt. 6.99 (978-0-330-33639-0(8) , Pan) Pan Macmillan GBR. *Dist:* Trafalgar Square Publishing.

—The Mission. 2003. 128p. (J). pap. 6.99 (978-0-330-34199-8(5) , Pan) Pan Macmillan GBR. *Dist:* Trafalgar Square Publishing.

—Peak Performance, Bk. 3. 118p. (J). mass mkt. 6.99 (978-0-330-34535-4(4) , Pan) Pan Macmillan GBR. *Dist:* Trafalgar Square Publishing.

—Rising Star, Vol. 4. 134p. (J). mass mkt. 6.99 (978-0-330-34536-1(2) , Pan) Pan Macmillan GBR. *Dist:* Trafalgar Square Publishing.

—Trapped. 2003. 128p. (J). pap. 6.99 (978-0-330-34200-1(2) , Pan) Pan Macmillan GBR. *Dist:* Trafalgar Square Publishing.

Alexander, Wilma E. Run for Your Life. 1999. (On Time's Wing Ser.). (Illus.). 120p. (YA). (gr. 5-9). pap. 6.95 (978-1-896184-46-3(4)) Roussan Pubs., Inc./Roussan Editeur, Inc. CAN. *Dist:* Orca Bk. Pubs. USA.

Alfano, Maria B. Kids Next Door: How to Draw. S. I. International Staff, illus. 2005. (Codename Ser.). 32p. (J). (ps-k). pap. 4.99 (978-0-439-75548-1(4) , Scholastic Paperbacks) Scholastic, Inc.

Alfonseca, Manuel. El Rubi del Ganges. (SPA.). 136p. (YA). (gr. 5-8). (978-84-279-3189-3(1) , NG3495) Noguer y Caralt Editores, S. A. ESP. *Dist:* Lectorum Pubns., Inc.

Alfonsi, Alice. Over the Top: Junior Novel. 14th rev. ed. 2006. (That's So Raven Ser.: Bk. 14). (Illus.). 128p. (gr. 3-7). pap. 4.99 (978-0-7868-3600-0(8)) Disney Pr.

—Showtime! 9th rev. ed. 2005. (That's So Raven Ser.: Vol. 9). (Illus.). 144p. (gr. 3-7). pap. 4.99 (978-0-7868-4692-4(5)) Disney Pr.

Alfred Oscar Valentine: Tales from Spoon Creek. 2005. (J). (978-0-9766894-4-7(8)); (978-0-9766894-3-0(X)); (978-0-9766894-2-3(1)); (978-0-9766894-1-6(3)); (978-0-9766894-0-9(5)) Stanley, Donna Lacy.

Alfred Oscar Valentine: Tales from Spoon Creek: New Beginnings. 2006. (J). 12.00 (978-0-9766894-5-4(6)) Stanley, Donna Lacy.

Alfreda. Story Time Stories Without Rhyme. 2003. 21.95 (978-0-913597-90-3(2)) Prosperity & Profits Unlimited, Distribution Services.

Alger, Horatio. Do & Dare. 2006. pap. (***978-1-4250-1766-8(5));** pap. (***978-1-4250-2027-9(5));** pap. (***978-1-4250-2300-3(2));** pap. (***978-1-4250-2118-4(2))** Assistedreadingbooks.com Inc.

—Do & Dare: Or, A Brave Boy's Fight for Fortune. 2006. 182p. pap. 11.99 (978-1-4264-0880-9(3)); 170p. pap. 14.99 (978-1-4264-0861-8(7)) BiblioBazaar.

—Do & Dare: Or, A Brave Boy's Fight for Fortune. 2006. pap. (***978-1-4065-0701-0(6))** Dodo Pr.

—Do & Dare: Or, A Brave Boy's Fight for Fortune. unabr. ed. 2002. (Illus.). (J). pap. 17.95 (978-1-931927-90-1(1)) Polyglot Pr., Inc.

—The Errand Boy. 2005. 296p. pap. 13.95 (978-1-4218-0455-2(7) , 1st World Library - Literary Society) 1st World Publishing, Inc.

—Facing the World. 2006. pap. (***978-1-4250-2212-9(X))** Assistedreadingbooks.com Inc.

—Helping Himself. 2006. 170p. pap. 11.99 (978-1-4264-2793-0(X)); 190p. pap. 14.99 (978-1-4264-2831-9(6)) BiblioBazaar.

—Mark Manning's Mission: The Story of a Shoe Factory Boy. unabr. ed. 2002. (Polyglot Press Alger Ser.). (Illus.). (J). pap. 17.95 (978-1-4115-0022-8(9)) Polyglot Pr., Inc.

—Paul the Peddler: Or, The Fortunes of a Young Street Merchant. 2006. pap. (***978-1-4065-0718-8(0))** Dodo Pr.

—The Store Boy. 2006. 170p. pap. 11.99 (***978-1-4264-4359-6(5));** 182p. pap. 14.99 (***978-1-4264-4397-8(8))** BiblioBazaar.

—The Store Boy. 2006. pap. (***978-1-4065-0722-5(9))** Dodo Pr.

—Struggling Upward: Or, Luke Larkin's Luck. 2006. pap. (***978-1-4065-0723-2(7))** Dodo Pr.

—Struggling Upward: Or, Luke Larkin's Luck. unabr. ed. 2002. (Polyglot Press Alger Ser.). (Illus.). (J). pap. 17.95 (978-1-4115-0053-2(9)) Polyglot Pr., Inc.

—Tom Temple's Career. reprint ed. pap. 79.00 (978-1-4047-3611-5(5)) Classic Textbooks.

—Tom Temple's Career. l.t. ed. 2002. (Illus.). pap. 19.95 (978-1-4115-0422-6(4)); (J). pap. 17.95 (978-1-4115-0057-0(1)) Polyglot Pr., Inc.

Alger, Horatio. The Young Musician. reprint ed. pap. 79.00 (978-1-4047-3629-0(8)) Classic Textbooks.

—The Young Musician. 2006. pap. (***978-1-4068-0673-1(0))** Echo Library.

Algozin, Bruce. Claw of the Dragon. 2008. (Endless Quest Ser.). 192p. (J). (gr. 3-7). 5.99 (***978-0-7869-4719-5(5)** , Mirrorstone) Wizards of the Coast.

Alice's Adventures in Wonderland: Lifetime Series Classics. 2002. (J). (978-0-924967-73-3(0)) JMW Group, Inc.

All Aboard! Softi's Adventures. 2003. (J). mass mkt. (978-1-932233-36-0(9)) Aurora Libris Corp.

Allen, A. D. Last Day. 2000. x, 150p. (YA). pap. 12.95 (978-0-9704776-0-6(0)) Project Amigo, Inc.

Allen, Christina G. Hippos in the Night: Autobiographical Adventures in Africa. 2003. (Illus.). 144p. (J). 17.89 (978-0-688-17827-7(8)) HarperCollins Pubs.

Allen, J. Kent. Embritt Waters & the Mark of the Rattlesnake. 2006. 229p. (J). pap. 14.95 (978-0-7414-2769-4(9)) Infinity Publishing.

Allen, Jim. Up in Smoke. Allen, Jim & Spear, Phil, illus. 2002. 144p. (YA). (gr. 6 up). pap. 12.95 (978-0-9711159-0-3(7)) Trailhead Pr.

Allen, Quinc. The Outdoor Chums. 2006. pap. (***978-1-4065-0782-9(2))** Dodo Pr.

—The Outdoor Chums after Big Game (Illust. 2006. pap. (***978-1-4065-0780-5(6))** Dodo Pr.

—The Outdoor Chums on the Gulf. 2006. pap. (***978-1-4065-0781-2(4))** Dodo Pr.

Allen, Quincy. The Outdoor Chums: The First Tour of the Rod, Gun & Camera Club. l.t. ed. 2006. 160p. pap. 14.99 (***978-1-4264-4095-3(2))** BiblioBazaar.

—Outdoor Chums after Big Game or Perilous. 2006. 77.99 (***978-1-4280-3810-3(8));** pap. 71.99 (***978-1-4280-3804-2(3))** IndyPublish.com.

Allen, Tricia. The Children under the Playhouse. McAdoo, Grami, illus. l.t. ed. 2004. 128p. (J). pap. 9.95 (978-0-9714358-4-1(7)) Longhorn Creek Pr.

Allen, Will. Swords for Hire. 2003. (gr. 3-6). lib. bdg. 15.25 (978-0-613-90085-0(5)) Tandem Library Bks.

—Swords for Hire: Two of the Most Unlikely Heroes you'll ever Meet. Beck, David Michael, illus. 2003. 168p. (gr. 3 up). pap. 6.95 (978-0-9724882-0-4(0)) Centerpunch Pr.

Allende, Isabel. El Bosque de los Pigmeos.Tr. of Forest of the Pygmies. (SPA.). 304p. 2005. pap. 7.99 (978-0-06-081619-3(8)); 2004. 19.99 (978-0-06-076219-3(5)) HarperCollins Pubs. (Rayo).

—City of the Beasts. 2005. Tr. of Ciudad de las Bestias. 464p. (J). (gr. 7-17). pap. 7.99 (978-0-06-077645-9(5) , Rayo) HarperCollins Pubs.

—City of the Beasts. Peden, Margaret Sayers, tr. from SPA. 2002. Tr. of Ciudad de las Bestias. 416p. (J). (gr. 5 up). 19.99 (978-0-06-050918-7(X)) HarperCollins Pubs.

—City of the Beasts. l.t. ed. 2002. Tr. of Ciudad de las Bestias. 400p. (J). (gr. 5). pap. 19.99 (978-0-06-051195-1(8)) HarperCollins Pubs.

—City of the Beasts. Peden, Margaret Sayers, tr. from SPA. 2004. Tr. of Ciudad de las Bestias. 432p. (J). (gr. 5 up). reprint ed. pap. 7.99 (978-0-06-053503-2(2)) HarperCollins Pubs.

—City of the Beasts. 2004. Tr. of Ciudad de las Bestias. (gr. 5-8). lib. bdg. 16.45 (978-0-613-71427-3(X)) Tandem Library Bks.

—La Ciudad de las Bestias. 2002. (SPA., Illus.). 416p. 19.95 (978-0-06-051031-2(5) , Rayo) HarperCollins Pubs.

—La Ciudad de las Bestias. 2003. (SPA.). (gr. 5-8). lib. bdg. 16.45 (978-0-613-83866-5(1)) Tandem Library Bks.

—Forest of the Pygmies. Peden, Margaret Sayers, tr. from SPA. 2005. 304p. (J). (gr. 5 up). 19.99 (978-0-06-076196-7(2) , Rayo) HarperCollins Pubs.

—Forest of the Pygmies. l.t. ed. 2005. 304p. (J). (gr. 5 up). pap. 19.99 (978-0-06-076200-1(4) , Rayo) HarperCollins Pubs.

—Kingdom of the Golden Dragon. Peden, Margaret Sayers, tr. from SPA. 2004. (Illus.). 448p. (J). (gr. 5 up). lib. bdg. 20.89 (978-0-06-058943-1(4)) HarperCollins Pubs.

—El Reino del Dragon de Oro. 2003. (SPA.). 432p. 19.99 (978-0-06-059170-0(6)) HarperCollins Pubs.

Allende, Isabel & Vega, Diego. Young Zorro: The Iron Brand. 2007. 240p. (J). pap. 6.99 (978-0-06-083947-5(3) , Rayo) HarperCollins Pubs.

Allgeier, Steve. Christmas with Norky, the Adventure Begins... 2007. (J). per. 17.99 (***978-1-933156-25-5(2)** , Visikid Bks.) GSVQ Publishing.

Allie, Scott. Planet of the Apes Movie Adaptation. 2001. (gr. 7-12). lib. bdg. 15.25 (978-0-613-79091-8(X)) Tandem Library Bks.

Alllen, Katherine. Gloves down Under. Alllen, Katherine, illus. 2005. (Illus.). 32p. (J). 15.95 (978-0-9747278-9-9(X)) Diakonia Publishing.

Allred, Chris Ross. Sir E. Bobbo! 2004. 21p. pap. 14.95 (978-1-4137-2785-2(9)) PublishAmerica, Inc.

Allred, Mike. The Atomics: Spaced Out & Grounded in Snap City. 2003. (Illus.). 112p. pap. 12.95 (978-1-929998-67-8(8)) Oni Pr., Inc.

—Madman Adventures. 2002. (Illus.). 128p. pap. 14.95 (978-1-929998-29-6(5)) Oni Pr., Inc.

Allred, Mike, et al. Madman Boogaloo! 1999. 80p. (YA). (gr. 7 up). pap. 8.95 (978-1-56971-404-1(5)) Dark Horse Comics.

Almekinder, Stephen. Backyardia. 2003. 220p. (YA). pap. 12.95 (978-0-7599-3959-2(4)) Hard Shell Word Factory.

Almond, David. The Fire-Eaters. 2005. 224p. (gr. 4-7). reprint ed. 5.99 (978-0-440-42012-5(1) , Yearling) Random Hse. Children's Bks.

—Heaven Eyes. 2002. 256p. (YA). (gr. 5). mass mkt. 5.99 (978-0-440-22910-0(3) , Laurel Leaf) Random Hse. Children's Bks.

—Heaven Eyes. 2002. 233p. (J). (gr. k-17). lib. bdg. 13.55 (978-0-613-72281-0(7)) Tandem Library Bks.

—Heaven Eyes. l.t. ed. 2001. 263p. (J). 24.95 (978-0-7862-3696-1(5)) Thorndike Pr.

Alonso, Fernando. Las Raices del Mar. (SPA., Illus.). 196p. (J). (978-84-207-8468-7(0)) Grupo Anaya, S.A. ESP. *Dist:* Lectorum Pubns., Inc.

Alonso, Juan Ramon, illus. Miguel Hernandez para Ninos. 2003. (SPA.). 178p. (978-84-305-9548-8(1) , SU30133) Susaeta Ediciones, S.A. ESP. *Dist:* Lectorum Pubns., Inc.

Alonso, Manuel L. Tiempo de Nubes Negras. Gaban, Jesus, illus. Tr. of Time for Black Clouds. (SPA.). 176p. (J). pap. (978-84-667-0289-8(X)); 4th ed. 88p. (YA). (gr. 5-8). 7.16 (978-84-207-7770-2(6)) Grupo Anaya, S.A. ESP. *Dist:* Lectorum Pubns., Inc.

Alphin, Elaine Marie. Picture Perfect. 2006. 256p. (YA). (gr. 5-12). pap. 7.95 (978-0-8225-6468-3(8) , First Avenue Editions) Lerner Publishing Group.

Altan. Fairy Tale Timpa. Reynolds, Michael, tr. Altan, illus. 2007. 48p. pap. 14.95 (***978-1-933372-38-9(9))** Europa Editions, Inc.

—Timpa Goes to the Sea. 2007. 48p. (J). pap. 14.95 (***978-1-933372-32-7(X))** Europa Editions, Inc.

Alton, Steve. The Malifex. 2003. (Middle Readers Ser.). (Illus.). 182p. (J). (gr. 3-7). 14.95 (978-0-8225-0959-2(8)) Lerner Publishing Group.

Altsheler, Joseph A. The Free Rangers: A Story of the Early D. 2006. pap. (***978-1-4065-0811-6(X))** Dodo Pr.

Aluris: The Book of Annua, 1, 4. 2006. (Illus.). 320p. (YA). per. 20.00 (978-0-9786177-0-7(3)) Michalek, Curtis.

The American Adventure. 1999. (Illus.). 144p. (J). (gr. 3). 127.60 (978-0-7910-4917-4(5) , Chelsea Hse.) Facts On File, Inc.

American Sunday School Union. The Allis Family or Scenes of Western Life. 2004. reprint ed. pap. 1.99 (978-1-4192-5191-7(0)); pap. 15.95 (978-1-4191-5191-0(6)) Kessinger Publishing, LLC.

Amery, H. & Cartwright, S. The Royal Broomstick. 2004. (First Stories Ser.). 16p. (J). pap. 4.95 (978-0-7945-0519-6(8)) EDC Publishing.

Amma, Jill. The Indaba Tree Odyssey: An African Tale. 2006. 360p. pap. 18.95 (978-0-7414-3172-1(6)) Infinity Publishing.

Ammann, Michael. Exos. 2003. 108p. (YA). pap. 9.95 (978-0-595-27121-4(9) , Writers Club Pr.) iUniverse, Inc.

Amodeo, John, et al. Lost on Aquaria. 2004. (Zenda Ser.: No. 4). (Illus.). 144p. (J). (gr. 5 up). pap. 4.99 (978-0-448-43256-4(0) , Grosset & Dunlap) Penguin Group (USA) Inc.

Amon, Ras Ran. Gerald, Fish of the Spirit! A Caribbean Tale of Fortune & Greed. Betiku, Olatukunbo, illus. ed. 2006. Orig. Title: Gerald, Fish of the Spirit! A Caribbean Tale of Fortune & Greed. (ENG.). (J). 7.99 (***978-0-9776603-0-8(3))** One Love Assn. Books.

Amon, Ras Ran, adapted by. Gerald, Fish of the Spirit! A Caribbean Tale of Fortune & Greed. 2005. Orig. Title: Gerald, Fish of the Spirit! A Caribbean Tale of Fortune & Greed. (J). cd-rom 5.99 (978-0-9776603-1-5(1)) One Love Assn. Books.

Amstel, Marsha. Sybil Ludington's Midnight Ride. Beier, Ellen, illus. 2000. (On My Own History Ser.). 56p. (J). (gr. 1-3). lib. bdg. 23.93 (978-1-57505-211-3(3) , Carolrhoda Bks.) Lerner Publishing Group.

Amworks. Sinbad & Marina. 2003. (gr. 3-6). lib. bdg. 13.00 (978-0-613-89802-7(8)) Tandem Library Bks.

Anastasio, Dina. Wild, Wild West. 1999. (Illus.). 176p. (gr. 3-7). pap. 4.99 (978-0-439-08653-0(1)) Scholastic, Inc.

Anasti, Tedd, et al. Spider Riders Book Two: Quest of the Earthen. 2006. (Illus.). 224p. pap. 5.99 (978-1-55704-681-9(6)) Newmarket Pr.

Anawalt, Paula Bonnier. The Crystal Palace: A Tale from the Gold Country. 1999. (J). (gr. k-4). 48p. 16.95 (978-0-9668414-0-4(9)); 44p. pap. 9.95 (978-0-9668414-1-1(7)) Abongold Bks.

Ancona, George. Charro: The Mexican Cowboy. 1999. (Illus.). 48p. (J). (gr. 3-7). 18.98 (978-0-8172-3773-8(9)) Raintree.

—Charro: The Mexican Cowboy. 1999. (gr. 3-6). lib. bdg. 17.65 (978-0-613-15750-6(8)) Tandem Library Bks.

Anders, Bill. Grave Robbers: A Novel. 2005. 82p. pap. 14.95 (978-1-4137-7022-3(3)) PublishAmerica, Inc.

Anders, Charlie. Choir Boy. 2005. 280p. (YA). (gr. 8-17). (978-1-932360-81-3(6)) Counterpoint.

Andersen, D. R. Paul Bunyan Builds a Mighty Mountain. 2005. 40.00 (***978-1-4108-4205-3(3))** Benchmark Education Co.

Andersen, Hans Christian. Cuentos de Anderson. 2000. Tr. of Stories of Anderson. (SPA., Illus.). 240p. (J). 17.95 (978-84-261-0255-3(7)) Juventud, Editorial ESP. *Dist:* Distribooks, Inc.

—Snow Queen. 2006. (Illus.). 48p. (J). (ps-3). 16.95 (978-1-84732-001-8(5)) Carlton Bks., Ltd. GBR. *Dist:* Ingram Pub. Services.

Anderson, Al. Pegasus: Adventures with Bingo Borden. Kurzyca, Krystyna Emilia, illus. 2006. 77p. (J). per. 19.50 (****978-1-887250-46-7(8)***) Agora Pubns., Inc.

Anderson, Brian. The Adventures of Commander Zack Proton & the Red Giant. Holgate, Doug, illus. 2006. (Adventures of Commander Zack Proton Ser.). 128p. (J). (gr. 2-5). pap. 3.99 (978-1-4169-1364-1(5) , Aladdin) Simon & Schuster Children's Publishing.

—The Adventures of Commander Zack Proton & the Warlords of Nibblecheese. Holgate, Doug, illus. 2006. (Adventures of Commander Zack Proton Ser.). 112p. (J). pap. 3.99 (978-1-4169-1365-8(3) , Aladdin) Simon & Schuster Children's Publishing.

—The Adventures of Commander Zack Proton & the Wrong Planet. Holgate, Doug, illus. 2007. (Adventures of Commander Zack Proton Ser.). 112p. (J). pap. 4.99 (978-1-4169-1366-5(1) , Aladdin) Simon & Schuster Children's Publishing.

Anderson, C. W. Blaze & the Forest Fire. 1999. reprint ed. 21.95 (978-1-56849-718-1(0)) Buccaneer Bks., Inc.

—Blaze & the Forest Fire. 1999. (J). (gr. 1-4). 21.75 (978-0-8446-7000-3(6)) Smith, Peter Pub., Inc.

Anderson, Carolyn D. Granny¿s Favorite Tales. Anderson, Carolyn D. et al, illus. 2006. 156p. (J). per. 39.95 (****978-1-60002-098-8(4)*** , 3915, Airleaf Publishing) Airleaf Publishing & Bookselling.

Anderson, James O. Poggy, the Stuffed Donkey. 2005. 16p. pap. 4.95 (****978-1-57258-395-5(9)***) TEACH Services, Inc.

Anderson, John David. Standard Hero Behavior. 2007. 288p. (J). (gr. 5-9). 16.00 (****978-0-618-75920-0(4)*** , Clarion Bks.) Houghton Mifflin Co. Trade & Reference Div.

Anderson, Laurie Halse. Twisted. 2007. 272p. (YA). (gr. 7). 16.99 (978-0-670-06101-3(8) , Viking Juvenile) Penguin Group (USA) Inc.

Anderson, M. T. & Moore, Stephen. Whales on Stilts! Thrilling Tales. Cyrus, Kurt, illus. 2005. (M. T. Anderson's Thrilling Tales Ser.). 208p. (J). 15.00 (978-0-15-205340-6(9)) Harcourt Children's Bks.

Anderson, Max Elliot. Big Rig Rustlers. 2004. 144p. pap. 10.95 (978-0-9752880-1-6(6)) Baker Trittin Pr.

—Legend of the White Wolf. 2005. (Illus.). 125p. (J). (ps-7). pap. 10.95 (978-0-9752880-3-0(2)) Baker Trittin Pr.

—Secret of Abbott's Cave. 2005. 144p. pap. 10.95 (978-0-9752880-0-9(8)) Baker Trittin Pr.

Anderson, Sara. Noisy Country Day. 2006. (J). bds. 8.95 (978-1-59354-113-2(9)) Handprint Bks.

—Noisy Country Night. 2006. (J). bds. 8.95 (978-1-59354-114-9(7)) Handprint Bks.

Anderson, Steve. Dark Sighted. 2004. 198p. pap. 19.95 (978-1-4137-4411-8(7)) PublishAmerica, Inc.

Anderson, Wayne R. Paula's Perilous Adventure. 2006. 48p. (YA). 12.95 (978-0-9773478-0-3(X)); 19.95 incl. DVD (978-0-9773478-2-7(6)) IMAGECRAFTERS.

Andrade, Brigitte. The Adventures of Bibi & Friends: Summer Season in Miami Beach, 1 vol., 7 bks. 7th ed. 2004. Orig. Title: The Adventures of Bibi 7 Friends. (Illus.). 65p. per. 7.95 (978-0-9754329-0-7(7)) BB International Productions, Inc.

Andrea, Leona. El Club de Las Siete Gatas. 2004. Tr. of Seven Kittens Club. (SPA., Illus.). 176p. (978-84-95618-73-3(7) , Umbriel) Ediciones Urano S. A.

Andreae, Giles. Captain Flinn & the Pirate Dinosaurs. Ayto, Russell, illus. 2005. 32p. (J). (gr. k-3). 15.95 (978-1-4169-0713-8(0) , McElderry, Margaret K.) Simon & Schuster Children's Publishing.

Andrews, Jerome. The Initiation. 2006. 40p. pap. 8.50 (978-1-4116-9167-4(9)) Lulu.com.

Andrews, Julie. The Little Grey Men: A Story for the Young in Heart. Watkins-Pitchford, Denys, illus. 2004. 304p. (J). 17.89 (978-0-06-055449-1(5) , Julie Andrews Collection) HarperCollins Pubs.

Andrews, Julie & "BB". The Little Grey Men: A Story for the Young in Heart. Watkins-Pitchford, Denys, illus. ed. 2004. 304p. (J). 17.99 (978-0-06-055448-4(7) , Julie Andrews Collection) HarperCollins Pubs.

Andrews, Kaare. Spider-Man Legend of the Spider-Clan, 3 vols. Young, Skott, illus. 2003. (Mangaverse Ser.: Vol. 3). 128p. (YA). pap. 11.99 (978-0-7851-1114-6(X)) Marvel Enterprises, Inc.

Andrews, Roxanna. The Adventures of Super Pig. 2006. (Illus.). 68p. (J). 15.95 (978-1-59879-232-4(6)) Lifevest Publishing, Inc.

Angeles: Redemption/Redencion. 2004. (Angeles Ser.).Tr. of Angels. (SPA., Illus.). 48p. pap. 4.99 (978-0-8054-2839-1(9)) B&H Publishing Grp.

Angeles: The Secret/el Secreto. 2004. (Angeles Ser.).Tr. of Angels. (SPA., Illus.). 48p. pap. 4.99 (978-0-8054-2833-9(X)) B&H Publishing Grp.

Angeles: The Sin/el Pecado. 2004. (Angeles Ser.).Tr. of Angels. (SPA., Illus.). 48p. pap. 4.99 (978-0-8054-2838-4(0)) B&H Publishing Grp.

Angello, Mary L. Rings of Power. 2001. 108p. (J). (gr. 4-7). pap. 9.95 (978-0-595-20231-7(4) , Writers Club Pr.) iUniverse, Inc.

Angelo, Alyssa. Sherlock the Circus Dog. 2007. 108p. pap. 11.95 (****978-1-60145-137-8(7));*** pap. 21.95 (****978-1-60145-133-0(4)***) Booklocker.com, Inc.

Angstrom, Gwen R. The Eemlets & Grandma Eema Stories, Book 1: From Rainbow to Sunshine. 2006. 67p. pap. 14.95 (978-1-4241-1257-9(5)) PublishAmerica, Inc.

Animal Rage. 2003. (gr. 7-12). lib. bdg. 14.15 (978-0-613-50635-9(9)) Tandem Library Bks.

Animaniacs in Thingamagigging. (Look & Find Bks.). (Illus.). 24p. (J). (ps-1). 14.98 (978-0-7853-1623-7(X) , PI15) Publications International, Ltd.

Annfousse, Ginette. Les Extravagances de Rosalie. 2000. (Roman Jeunesse Ser.). (FRE.). 288p. (J). (gr. 4-7). pap. (978-2-89021-387-6(0)) Diffusion du livre Mirabel.

Anonymous. The Book of Enterprise & Adventure. 2004. reprint ed. pap. 15.95 (978-1-4191-5453-9(2)); pap. 1.99 (978-1-4192-5453-6(7)) Kessinger Publishing, LLC.

—Story Time Book: Rhyme Time & Story Time. 2004. reprint ed. pap. 15.95 (978-1-4191-1380-2(1)) Kessinger Publishing, LLC.

Anrias, Donnan. Targ - the King of Eagles. 2005. 138p. (YA). per. 23.00 (978-1-4116-1923-4(4)) Lulu.com.

Anthony, Piers. Key to Chroma. 2003. (ChroMagic Ser.: Bk. 2). 550p. (J). 34.99 (978-1-59426-017-9(6)) Mundania Pr.

Anthony, Ross. The Infinite Adventures of Rodney Appleseed in Nothing Happens. 2001. (YA). per. 9.95 (978-0-9727894-0-0(5)) Arizona Blueberry Studios.

Anyone's Guess Teen Kits: A Murderous Melodrama. 2004. 39.95 (978-1-932146-26-4(1) , Upstart Bks.) Highsmith Inc.

Anzai, Nobuyuki. Flame of Recca, Vol. 23. 2007. (Flame of Recca Ser.). 192p. (YA). pap. 9.99 (978-1-4215-0893-1(1)) Viz Media.

Anzaldua, Gloria. Prietita & the Ghost Woman (Prietita y la Llorona) Gonzalez, Maya Christina, illus. 2001. (ENG & SPA.). 32p. (J). (gr. 1 up). pap. 7.95 (978-0-89239-167-7(7)) Children's Bk. Pr.

Applegate, Katherine. Attitude. 2001. (Making Waves Ser.: No. 7). 272p. mass mkt. 4.99 (978-1-931497-18-3(4)) 17th Street Productions, An Alloy Online Inc. Co.

—The Escape. 1998. (Animorphs Ser.: No. 15). 170p. (J). (gr. 3-7). pap. 4.99 (978-0-590-49424-3(4)) Scholastic, Inc.

—The Extreme. 1999. (Animorphs Ser.: No. 25). (J). (gr. 3-7). pap. 179.64 (978-0-439-04365-6(4)) Scholastic, Inc.

—The Extreme. 1999. (Animorphs Ser.: No. 25). (J). (gr. 3-7). 11.64 (978-0-606-15437-6(X)) Tandem Library Bks.

—The Hork-Bajir Chronicles. deluxe ed. 1998. (Animorphs Ser.). (J). (gr. 3-7). 12.95 (978-0-590-38198-7(9)) Scholastic, Inc.

—Nowhere Land. 2002. (Remnants Ser.: No. 4). 176p. (J). (gr. 4-8). pap. 4.99 (978-0-590-88193-7(0) , Scholastic Paperbacks) Scholastic, Inc.

—The Secret. 2001. (Making Waves Ser.: No. 6). 272p. mass mkt. 4.99 (978-1-931497-17-6(6)) 17th Street Productions, An Alloy Online Inc. Co.

Appleton, Victor. The Alien Probe. (Tom Swift Ser.). (J). (gr. 3-7). 20.95 (978-0-88411-464-2(3)) Amereon LTD.

—The Astral Fortress. (Tom Swift Ser.). (J). (gr. 3-7). 20.95 (978-0-88411-461-1(9)) Amereon LTD.

—The City in the Stars. (Tom Swift Ser.). (J). (gr. 3-7). 20.95 (978-0-88411-463-5(5)) Amereon LTD.

—Into the Abyss. 2006. (Tom Swift, Young Inventor Ser.). 176p. (J). (gr. 3-7). pap. 4.99 (978-1-4169-1518-8(4) , Aladdin) Simon & Schuster Children's Publishing.

—The Moving Picture Boys at Panama. 2005. 27.95 (978-1-4218-1499-5(4)); 208p. pap. 12.95 (978-1-4218-1599-2(0)) 1st World Publishing, Inc. (1st World Library - Literary Society).

—Moving Picture Boys at Panama. 2006. pap. (****978-1-4065-0890-1(X)***) Dodo Pr.

—The Moving Picture Boys at Panama. 2004. reprint ed. pap. 20.95 (978-1-4191-7472-8(X)); pap. 1.99 (978-1-4192-7472-5(4)) Kessinger Publishing, LLC.

—Moving Picture Boys at Panama or Stirrin. 2006. pap. 26.99 (****978-1-4280-3337-5(8)***) IndyPublish.com.

—Moving Picture Boys on the War Front or. 2006. pap. (****978-1-4065-0891-8(8)***) Dodo Pr.

—The Rescue Mission. (Tom Swift Ser.). (J). (gr. 3-7). 20.95 (978-0-88411-458-1(9)) Amereon LTD.

—The Space Hotel. 2006. (Tom Swift, Young Inventor Ser.: No. 3). 160p. (J). pap. 4.99 (978-1-4169-1751-9(9) , Aladdin) Simon & Schuster Children's Publishing.

—Terror on the Moons of Jupiter. (Tom Swift Ser.). (J). (gr. 3-7). 20.95 (978-0-88411-460-4(0)) Amereon LTD.

—Tom Swift among the Diamond Makers or Th. 2006. pap. (****978-1-4065-0892-5(6)***) Dodo Pr.

—Tom Swift among the Fire Fighters. 2005. 27.95 (978-1-4218-1088-1(3)); 204p. pap. 12.95 (978-1-4218-1188-8(X)) 1st World Publishing, Inc. (1st World Library - Literary Society).

—Tom Swift among the Fire Fighters. 2006. (ENG.). pap. (****978-1-4068-0726-4(5)***) Echo Library.

—Tom Swift among the Fire Fighters. 2004. reprint ed. pap. 20.95 (978-1-4191-9047-6(4)); pap. 1.99 (978-1-4192-9047-3(9)) Kessinger Publishing, LLC.

—Tom Swift among the Fire Fighters or Bat. 2006. pap. (****978-1-4065-0893-2(4)***) Dodo Pr.

—Tom Swift & His Aerial Warship. 2005. 27.95 (978-1-4218-1092-8(1)); 212p. pap. 12.95 (978-1-4218-1192-5(8)) 1st World Publishing, Inc. (1st World Library - Literary Society).

—Tom Swift & His Aerial Warship. 2004. reprint ed. pap. 1.99 (978-1-4192-8451-9(7)) Kessinger Publishing, LLC.

—Tom Swift & His Aerial Warship or the. 2006. pap. (****978-1-4065-0894-9(2)***) Dodo Pr.

—Tom Swift & His Aerial Warship or the Naval Terror of the Seas. 2005. reprint ed. pap. 24.95 (978-0-7661-9446-5(9)) Kessinger Publishing, LLC.

—Tom Swift & His Air Glider. 2004. reprint ed. pap. 20.95 (978-1-4191-8452-9(0)); pap. 1.99 (978-1-4192-8452-6(5)) Kessinger Publishing, LLC.

—Tom Swift & His Air Glider or Seeking. 2006. pap. (****978-1-4065-0895-6(0)***) Dodo Pr.

—Tom Swift & His Air Scout. 2005. 27.95 (978-1-4218-1091-1(3)); 208p. pap. 12.95 (978-1-4218-1191-8(X)) 1st World Publishing, Inc. (1st World Library - Literary Society).

—Tom Swift & His Air Scout. 2004. reprint ed. pap. 20.95 (978-1-4191-9048-3(2)); pap. 1.99 (978-1-4192-9048-0(7)) Kessinger Publishing, LLC.

—Tom Swift & His Air Scout or Uncle Sam. 2006. pap. (****978-1-4065-0896-3(9)***) Dodo Pr.

—Tom Swift & His Airship. 2005. 27.95 (978-1-59540-801-3(0)); 200p. pap. 12.95 (978-1-59540-806-8(1)) 1st World Publishing, Inc. (1st World Library - Literary Society).

—Tom Swift & His Airship. 2004. (Tom Swift Original Ser.: No. 3). 216p. (J). (ps-3). 17.95 (978-1-55709-177-2(3)) Applewood Bks.

—Tom Swift & His Airship. 2006. pap. (****978-1-4065-0897-0(7)***) Dodo Pr.

—Tom Swift & His Airship. 2006. pap. (****978-1-4068-0725-7(7)***) Echo Library.

—Tom Swift & His Airship. 2002. (ENG.). 148p. 23.99 (****978-1-4043-3564-6(1)***) IndyPublish.com.

—Tom Swift & His Airship. 2004. reprint ed. pap. 20.95 (978-1-4191-8453-6(9)); pap. 1.99 (978-1-4192-8453-3(3)) Kessinger Publishing, LLC.

—Tom Swift & His Airship. 2000. (Tom Swift Original Ser.: Vol. No. 3). 118p. (gr. 3-7). 19.95 (978-1-57646-359-8(1)); 118p. (gr. 3-7). pap. 7.95 (978-1-57646-203-4(X)); 186p. pap. 12.99 (978-1-57646-360-4(5)) Quiet Vision Publishing.

—Tom Swift & His Airship. 2006. 224p. pap. 16.95 (978-1-59462-179-6(9) , 208, Book Jungle) Standard Pubns., Inc.

—Tom Swift & His Big Tunnel. 2005. 27.95 (978-1-4218-1093-5(X)); 216p. pap. 12.95 (978-1-4218-1193-2(6)) 1st World Publishing, Inc. (1st World Library - Literary Society).

—Tom Swift & His Big Tunnel. 2004. reprint ed. pap. 20.95 (978-1-4191-8454-3(7)); pap. 1.99 (978-1-4192-8454-0(1)) Kessinger Publishing, LLC.

—Tom Swift & His Big Tunnel or the Hidd. 2006. pap. (****978-1-4065-0898-7(5)***) Dodo Pr.

—Tom Swift & His Electric Locomotive or. 2006. pap. (****978-1-4065-0899-4(3)***) Dodo Pr.

—Tom Swift & His Electric Rifle. 2005. 26.95 (978-1-59540-802-0(9)); 192p. pap. 11.95 (978-1-59540-807-5(X)) 1st World Publishing, Inc. (1st World Library - Literary Society).

—Tom Swift & His Electric Rifle. 1998. (Tom Swift Original Ser.: No. 10). (J). (gr. 3-7). lib. bdg. 18.95 (978-1-56723-020-8(2)) Yestermorrow, Inc.

—Tom Swift & His Electric Runabout. 2004. reprint ed. pap. 20.95 (978-1-4191-8455-0(5)); pap. 1.99 (978-1-4192-8455-7(X)) Kessinger Publishing, LLC.

—Tom Swift & His Electronic Electroscope. (J). (gr. 5-6). 20.95 (978-0-88411-462-8(7)) Amereon LTD.

—Tom Swift & His Giant Cannon. 2005. 27.95 (978-1-4218-1089-8(1)); 204p. pap. 12.95 (978-1-4218-1189-5(8)) 1st World Publishing, Inc. (1st World Library - Literary Society).

—Tom Swift & His Giant Cannon. 2004. reprint ed. pap. 20.95 (978-1-4191-8456-7(3)); pap. 1.99 (978-1-4192-8456-4(8)) Kessinger Publishing, LLC.

—Tom Swift & His Giant Cannon or the lo. 2006. pap. (****978-1-4065-0902-1(7)***) Dodo Pr.

—Tom Swift & His Great Searchlight. 2005. 204p. pap. 12.95 (978-1-4218-1190-1(1) , 1st World Library - Literary Society) 1st World Publishing, Inc.

—Tom Swift & His Great Searchlight. 2004. reprint ed. pap. 20.95 (978-1-4191-8457-4(1)); pap. 1.99 (978-1-4192-8457-1(6)) Kessinger Publishing, LLC.

—Tom Swift & His Great Searchlight or O. 2006. pap. (****978-1-4065-0903-8(5)***) Dodo Pr.

—Tom Swift & His Motor Boat. 2004. (Tom Swift Original Ser.: No. 2). 212p. (J). (ps-3). 14.95 (978-1-55709-176-5(5)) Applewood Bks.

—Tom Swift & His Motor Boat. 2000. (Tom Swift Original Ser.: Vol. No. 2). 112p. (gr. 3-7). 19.95 (978-1-57646-356-7(7)); 112p. (gr. 3-7). pap. 7.95 (978-1-57646-202-7(1)); 182p. pap. 12.99 (978-1-57646-357-4(5)) Quiet Vision Publishing.

—Tom Swift & His Motor Cycle. 2004. (Tom Swift Original Ser.: No. 1). 206p. (J). (ps-3). 17.95 (978-1-55709-175-8(7)) Applewood Bks.

—Tom Swift & His Motor Cycle. 2004. reprint ed. pap. 1.99 (978-1-4192-8459-5(2)) Kessinger Publishing, LLC.

—Tom Swift & His Motor Cycle. 2000. (Tom Swift Original Ser.: Vol. No. 1). 114p. (gr. 3-7). 19.95 (978-1-57646-353-6(2)); 114p. (gr. 3-7). pap. 7.95 (978-1-57646-201-0(3)); 180p. pap. 12.99 (978-1-57646-354-3(0)) Quiet Vision Publishing.

—Tom Swift & His MotorBoat or the Rival. 2006. pap. (****978-1-4065-0904-5(3)***) Dodo Pr.

—Tom Swift & His MotorCycle. 2006. pap. (****978-1-4068-0727-1(3)***) Echo Library.

—Tom Swift & His MotorCycle or Fun and. 2006. pap. (****978-1-4065-0905-2(1)***) Dodo Pr.

—Tom Swift & His Photo Telephone. 1998. (Tom Swift Original Ser.: No. 17). (J). (gr. 3-7). lib. bdg. 18.95 (978-1-56723-022-2(9)) Yestermorrow, Inc.

—Tom Swift & His Photo Telephone or the. 2006. pap. (****978-1-4065-0906-9(X)***) Dodo Pr.

—Tom Swift & His Sky Racer. 2004. reprint ed. pap. 1.99 (978-1-4192-8461-8(4)) Kessinger Publishing, LLC.

—Tom Swift & His Sky Racer or the Quick. 2006. pap. (****978-1-4065-0907-6(8)***) Dodo Pr.

—Tom Swift & His Sky Racer or the Quickest Flight on Record. 2005. reprint ed. pap. 24.95 (978-0-7661-9445-8(0)) Kessinger Publishing, LLC.

—Tom Swift & His Space Solatron. (Tom Swift Ser.). (J). (gr. 5-6). 20.95 (978-0-88411-457-4(0)) Amereon LTD.

—Tom Swift & His Submarine Boat. 2004. reprint ed. pap. 20.95 (978-1-4191-8462-8(8)); pap. 1.99 (978-1-4192-8462-5(2)) Kessinger Publishing, LLC.

—Tom Swift & His Submarine Boat. 2000. (Tom Swift Original Ser.: Vol. No. 4). 114p. (gr. 3-7). pap. 7.95 (978-1-57646-204-1(8)) Quiet Vision Publishing.

—Tom Swift & His Triphibian Atomicar. (Tom Swift Ser.). (J). (gr. 5-6). 20.95 (978-0-88411-459-8(7)) Amereon LTD.

—Tom Swift & His War Tank. 2004. reprint ed. pap. 20.95 (978-1-4191-9054-4(7)); pap. 1.99 (978-1-4192-9054-1(1)) Kessinger Publishing, LLC.

—Tom Swift & His War Tank or Doing His. 2006. pap. (****978-1-4065-0910-6(8)***) Dodo Pr.

—Tom Swift & His Wireless Message or Th. 2006. pap. (****978-1-4065-0911-3(6)***) Dodo Pr.

—Tom Swift & His Wizard Camera or Thril. 2006. pap. (****978-1-4065-0912-0(4)***) Dodo Pr.

—Tom Swift & the Visitor from Planet X. 2006. pap. (****978-1-4065-0913-7(2)***) Dodo Pr.

—Tom Swift & the Visitor from Planet X. 2006. pap. (****978-1-4068-0728-8(1)***) Echo Library.

—Tom Swift in Captivity. 2005. 27.95 (978-1-4218-1508-4(7)); 200p. pap. 12.95 (978-1-4218-1608-1(3)) 1st World Publishing, Inc. (1st World Library - Literary Society).

—Tom Swift in Captivity. 2004. reprint ed. pap. 20.95 (978-1-4191-9056-8(3)); pap. 1.99 (978-1-4192-9056-5(8)) Kessinger Publishing, LLC.

—Tom Swift in Captivity or A Daring Escap. 2006. pap. (****978-1-4065-0914-4(0)***) Dodo Pr.

—Tom Swift in the Caves of Ice or the Wre. 2006. pap. (****978-1-4065-0915-1(9)***) Dodo Pr.

—Tom Swift in the City of Gold or Marvelo. 2006. pap. (****978-1-4065-0916-8(7)***) Dodo Pr.

—Tom Swift in the Land of Wonders. 2005. 27.95 (978-1-4218-1511-4(7)); 204p. pap. 12.95 (978-1-4218-1611-1(3)) 1st World Publishing, Inc. (1st World Library - Literary Society).

—Tom Swift in the Land of Wonders. 2004. reprint ed. pap. 20.95 (978-1-4191-9057-5(1)); pap. 1.99 (978-1-4192-9057-2(6)) Kessinger Publishing, LLC.

—Tom Swift in the Land of Wonders or the. 2006. pap. (****978-1-4065-0917-5(5)***) Dodo Pr.

Appleton, Victor. The War in Outer Space. (Tom Swift Ser.). (J). (gr. 3-7). 19.95 (978-0-88411-465-9(1)) Amereon LTD.

Aptekar, Devan. Brain Swap. 2006. (Teen Titans Ser.). (Illus.). 32p. (J). pap. 3.99 (978-0-439-83009-6(5)) Scholastic, Inc.

—Frostbite. 2006. (Batman Ser.: No. 1). (Illus.). 32p. (J). pap. 3.99 (978-0-439-78951-6(6)) Scholastic, Inc.

Arac de Nyeko, Monica. Children of the Red Fields. 2005. (Illus.). 99p. (978-9966-47-104-8(9)) Phoenix Pubs., Ltd.

Aragones, Sergio. The Most Intelligent Man in the World. 1998. (Groo Ser.). (Illus.). 112p. (YA). (gr. 5 up). pap. 9.95 (978-1-56971-294-8(8)) Dark Horse Comics.

Araki, Hirohiko. Bizarre Adventure, Vol. 4. 2006. (Jo Joo's Bizarre Adventure Ser.). 208p. (YA). pap. 7.99 (978-1-4215-0653-1(X)) Viz Media.

—Jojo's Bizarre Adventure, Vol. 5. 2006. (Jo Joo's Bizarre Adventure Ser.). 208p. (YA). pap. 7.99 (978-1-4215-0654-8(8)) Viz Media.

Aranha, Marc. The Queen of Spiders. 2003. 210p. pap. 14.95 (978-0-595-29275-2(5)) iUniverse, Inc.

Archer, Chris. The Secret City. 2003. (Pyrates Ser.: No. 1). (Illus.). 192p. (J). (gr. 3-7). pap. 4.99 (978-0-439-36851-3(0)) Scholastic, Inc.

Archer, Richard. The Island Home. 2004. reprint ed. pap. 27.95 (978-1-4191-6772-0(3)); pap. 1.99 (978-1-4192-6772-7(8)) Kessinger Publishing, LLC.

Archie in Help Wanted. 2007. (Illus.). 80p. (J). 24.21 (****978-1-59961-258-4(5)***) Spotlight.

Ardagh, Philip. Dreadful Acts. Roberts, David, illus. 2004. (Eddie Dickens Trilogy Ser.: Bk. 2). 144p. (J). reprint ed. mass mkt. 5.99 (978-0-439-53760-5(6)) Scholastic, Inc.

—A House Called Awful End. 2003. (Eddie Dickens Trilogy: Bk. 1). (gr. 3-6). lib. bdg. 14.15 (978-0-613-72215-5(9)) Tandem Library Bks.

Ardagh, Philip, et al. A House Called Awful End. Roberts, David, illus. 2003. (Eddie Dickens Trilogy Ser.: Bk. 1). 144p. (J). (gr. 3-6). mass mkt. 5.99 (978-0-439-53759-9(2) , Scholastic Paperbacks) Scholastic, Inc.

Ardizzone, Edward. Ship's Cook Ginger. 2008. (Illus.). 48p. (J). 16.95 (****978-1-84507-574-3(9)***) Lincoln, Frances Ltd. GBR. *Dist:* Perseus Distribution.

—Tim All Alone. 2006. (Little Tim Ser.). (Illus.). 48p. 15.95 (978-1-84507-546-0(3)) Lincoln, Frances Ltd. GBR. *Dist:* Perseus Distribution.

—Tim & Charlotte. 2006. (Little Tim Ser.). (Illus.). 48p. 15.95 (978-1-84507-545-3(5)) Lincoln, Frances Ltd. GBR. *Dist:* Perseus Distribution.

—Tim & Ginger. 2007. (Illus.). 48p. (J). 16.95 (978-1-84507-561-3(7)) Lincoln, Frances Ltd. GBR. *Dist:* Perseus Distribution.

—Tim in Danger. 2000. (Tim Bks.). (J). (ps-3). (Illus.). 48p. 15.95 (978-0-688-17675-4(5)); 15.89 (978-0-06-029206-5(7)) HarperCollins Pubs.

—Tim in Danger. 2006. (Little Tim Ser.). (Illus.). 48p. 15.95 (978-1-84507-544-6(7)) Lincoln, Frances Ltd. GBR. *Dist:* Perseus Distribution.

—Tim to the Lighthouse. 2006. (Little Tim Ser.). (Illus.). 48p. (J). 16.95 (978-1-84507-562-0(5)) Lincoln, Frances Ltd. GBR. *Dist:* Perseus Distribution.

—Tim to the Rescue. ed. 2006. (Little Tim Ser.). (Illus.). 48p. (J). 15.95 (978-1-84507-458-6(0)) Lincoln, Frances Ltd. GBR. *Dist:* Perseus Distribution.

Arengo, Sue. The Gingerbread Man Beginner Level 2. 1999. (Illus.). 24p. (J). 5.50 (978-0-19-422022-4(2)) Oxford Univ. Pr., Inc.

Arensen, Shel. The Secret Oath, Vol. 4. 2003. (Rugendo Rhino Ser.: Vol. 4). 112p. (J). pap. 5.99 (978-0-8254-2040-5(7)) Kregel Pubns.

Arenstam, Peter. Nicholas: A Massachusetts Tale. Holman, Karen Busch, illus. 2007. (J). 14.95 (*978-1-58726-519-8(2) , Mitten Pr.) Ann Arbor Media Group, LLC.

Arias, Carlos Ballesteros. The Magic Forest. 2006. (J). pap. 8.00 (*978-0-8059-7022-7(3)) Dorrance Publishing Co., Inc.

Armstrong, Alan W. Raleigh's Page. Jessell, Tim, illus. 2007. (J). 336p. (gr. 1-5). lib. bdg. 19.99 (978-0-375-93319-6(0)); 328p. (gr. 5-7). 16.99 (978-0-375-83319-9(6)) Random Hse. Children's Bks. (Random Hse. Bks. for Young Readers).

Armstrong, Cindy. Boudreaux & His Buddies. 2006. 98p. pap. 14.95 (978-1-4241-3906-4(6)) PublishAmerica, Inc.

Armstrong, Helen. Road to Adventure. Dell, Steve, illus. 2005. 144p. (J). pap. 9.99 (978-1-84255-227-8(9)) Dolphin Paperbacks GBR. *Dist:* Trafalgar Square Publishing.

—Road to Somewhere. Horse, Harry, illus. 2005. 96p. (J). pap. 9.99 (978-1-84255-052-6(7)) Dolphin Paperbacks GBR. *Dist:* Trafalgar Square Publishing.

—The Road to Somewhere. Horse, Harry, illus. l.t. ed. 2005. (J). pap. (978-0-7540-7827-2(2) , CLP 417) BBC Audio.

—Road to the River. Dell, Steve, illus. 2005. 128p. pap. 9.99 (978-1-84255-249-0(X)) Dolphin Paperbacks GBR. *Dist:* Trafalgar Square Publishing.

Arnaiz, Joaquin. Rosa de Estambul. 1999. Tr. of Rose of Istambul. (SPA., Illus.). 138p. 9.95 (978-84-239-9054-2(0)) Espasa Calpe, S.A. ESP. *Dist:* Libros Sin Fronteras.

—Rosa de Estambul. 1999. Tr. of Rose of Istambul. (978-0-606-17736-8(1)) Tandem Library Bks.

Arndt, Rhonda. Mac's Adventure. 2006. 48p. pap. 12.95 (978-1-4241-1321-7(0)) PublishAmerica, Inc.

Arnold, Adam. Aoi House, Vol. 1. 2006. (Illus.). 192p. (YA). pap. 10.99 (978-1-933164-12-0(3)) Seven Seas Entertainment, LLC.

Arnold, George. Los Gatos of the CIA. 2005. (SPA & ENG., Illus.). 225p. pap. 22.95 (978-1-57168-861-3(7) , Nortex Pr.) Eakin Pr.

Arnold, Michelle Lee. Mathew Sunburst & the Keepers of the Sky. 2003. 141p. (J). pap. 13.95 (978-0-7414-1575-2(5)) Infinity Publishing.

Arnold, Tedd. Hi, Fly Guy! 2006. (Scholastic Reader Collection Level 1 Ser.). (Illus.). 32p. (J). pap. 3.99 (978-0-439-85311-8(7) , Cartwheel Bks.) Scholastic, Inc.

Arrigan, Mary. Maeve & the Long Arm Folly. 2000. (Illus.). 144p. (J). (gr. 3-7). pap. 9.95 (978-1-901737-20-2(9)) Anvil Bks., Ltd. IRL. *Dist:* Dufour Editions, Inc.

Artful Doodlers, illus. Ice Age 2: Geyser Blast. 2006. 32p. (J). lib. bdg. 13.85 (*978-1-4242-0691-9(X)) Fitzgerald Bks.

Artful Doodlers Limited Staff. First Brat. 2006. (Totally Spies! Ser.). (Illus.). 64p. (J). pap. 4.99 (978-1-4169-0792-3(0) , Simon Spotlight) Simon & Schuster Children's Publishing.

Arthur M. Winfi Staff. Rover Boys on the Great Lakes or the Sec. 2006. 63.99 (*978-1-4219-9685-1(5)) IndyPublish.com.

Artifact Group. Atlantis SquarePantis. 2007. (SpongeBob SquarePants Ser.). 24p. (J). pap. 3.99 (*978-1-4169-3799-9(4) , Simon Spotlight/Nickelodeon) Simon & Schuster Children's Publishing.

Artifact Group. The Crystal Caper: A Lift-the-Flap Story. 2006. (LazyTown Ser.). 16p. (J). pap. 6.99 (978-1-4169-2464-7(7) , Simon Spotlight/Nickelodeon) Simon & Schuster Children's Publishing.

Aryal, Aimee. Cort Spells It Out. De Angel, Miguel, illus. 2006. (J). pap. 5.95 (978-1-932888-62-1(4) , 91-101-01) Mascot Bks., Inc.

—Hello Big Jay! 2005. (J). 14.95 (978-1-932888-41-6(1)) Mascot Bks., Inc.

—Hello Herbie Husker! 2005. (J). 14.95 (978-1-932888-43-0(8)) Mascot Bks., Inc.

—Let's Go Irish! Shrestha, Anuj, illus. 2004. (J). 19.95 (978-0-9743442-5-6(7)) Mascot Bks., Inc.

Aryal, Aimee & Halligan, Chris. Meet Cort the Sport. 2006. (J). pap. 5.95 (978-1-932888-61-4(6) , 91-100-01) Mascot Bks., Inc.

Asad, Megan Emily. The Juggler's Journey. 2005. 144p. pap. 9.95 (978-0-7599-4470-1(9)) Hard Shell Word Factory.

Asai, Carrie. The Book of the Flame. Verhoye, Annabelle & Alarcao, Renato, illus. 2003. (Samurai Girl Ser.). 224p. (YA). pap. 6.99 (978-0-689-86713-2(1) , Simon Pulse) Simon & Schuster Children's Publishing.

—Book of the Flame. 2004. lib. bdg. 15.30 (978-0-613-73423-3(8)) Tandem Library Bks.

—Book of the Heart. 2004. lib. bdg. 15.30 (978-0-613-73422-6(X)) Tandem Library Bks.

—The Book of the Heart: Heaven's Mission: To Sharpen Her Senses. Alarcao, Renato, illus. 2004. (Samurai Girl Ser.). 240p. (YA). pap. 6.99 (978-0-689-86712-5(3) , Simon Pulse) Simon & Schuster Children's Publishing.

—The Book of the Pearl. Verhoye, Annabelle & Alarcao, Renato, illus. 2003. (Samurai Girl Ser.: Bk. 3). 240p. (YA). pap. 6.99 (978-0-689-86432-2(9) , Simon Pulse) Simon & Schuster Children's Publishing.

—Book of the Pearl. 2003. lib. bdg. 15.30 (978-0-613-73440-0(8)) Tandem Library Bks.

—The Book of the Sword. Verhoye, Annabelle, illus. 2003. (Samurai Girl Ser.). 224p. (YA). pap. 6.99 (978-0-689-85948-9(1) , Simon Pulse) Simon & Schuster Children's Publishing.

—The Book of the Sword Vol. 5: Samurai Girl, l.t. ed. 2004. 302p. 20.95 (978-0-7862-6684-5(8) , Large Print Pr.) Thorndike Pr.

Asai, Carrie & Gray, Mitchel. The Book of the Wind. Verhoye, Annabelle & Alarcao, Renato, illus. 2003. (Samurai Girl Ser.). 224p. (YA). pap. 6.99 (978-0-689-86433-9(7) , Simon Pulse) Simon & Schuster Children's Publishing.

Asare, Meshack. Kwajo & the Brassman's Secret: A Tale of Old Ashanti Wisdom & Gold. 2002. (Illus.). 45p. pap. (978-9988-550-43-1(X)) Sub-Saharan Pubs. & Traders.

Ashby, John. Sea Gift. 2003. (Illus.). 208p. (J). (gr. 5-9). tchr. ed. 15.00 (978-0-395-77603-2(1) , Clarion Bks.) Houghton Mifflin Co. Trade & Reference Div.

Ashby, R. S. Stronger Than Stone. 2002. (gr. 3-6). lib. bdg. 13.00 (978-0-613-72455-5(0)) Tandem Library Bks.

Ashcroft, Eagle. Nibs Goes to London. 2007. 104p. pap. 11.00 (*978-1-60047-075-2(0)) Wasteland Pr.

Ashe, Gregory. The Imagineer (Fire Eye Edition) A Book of Miracles. Whittaker, Kay, illus. 3rd ed. 2005. 198p. pap. (978-1-905532-01-8(6) , Whitenoise) Humdrumming, Ltd.

—The Imagineer (Snow Scene Edition) A Book of Miracles. Whittaker, Kay, illus. 2nd ed. 2005. 198p. (YA). pap. (978-1-905532-00-1(8) , Whitenoise) Humdrumming, Ltd.

Asher Penny. No More Pacifier. 2006. 32p. 12.95 (978-0-9755902-3-2(5)) Change Is Strange, Inc.

Ashford, Kathy. Jackdaw Jinx. Kitamura, Satoshi, illus. 2007. (Tiger Ser.). 128p. (J). 9.95 (*978-1-84270-540-7(7)) Transworld Publishers Ltd. GBR. *Dist:* Independent Pubs. Group.

Ashton, Rudy. Todd & Joey: A Teen Adventure. 1998. 128p. (J). pap. 12.00 (978-0-8059-4387-0(0)) Dorrance Publishing Co., Inc.

Askounis, Christina. The Dream of the Stone. 2007. 304p. (YA). pap. 8.99 (978-1-4169-1187-6(1)) Simon & Schuster Children's Publishing.

Asquith, Ros. Water Boy. Andrew, Ian, illus. 2007. 32p. 17.95 (*978-1-894965-67-5(1)) Simply Read Bks. CAN. *Dist:* Perseus Distribution.

Atanacio, Frank. Aggravating Factors: From the Nick Barnum Sealed Case File a Nick Barnum Novel II. 2003. 128p. (YA). pap. 10.95 (978-0-595-26985-3(0)) iUniverse, Inc.

Atwater, Paret Emily. How Sammy Went to CoralLand. 2006. pap. 33.99 (*978-1-4280-3232-3(0)) IndyPublish.com.

Atwood, Margaret. For the Birds. (J). pap. 4.99 (978-0-88894-825-0(5)) Douglas & McIntyre, Ltd. CAN. *Dist:* Transition Vendor.

Auch, Mary Jane. Journey to Nowhere. 1998. (Illus.). 208p. (J). (gr. 5-9). 4.99 (978-0-440-41491-9(1) , Yearling) Random Hse. Children's Bks.

Auerbach, Annie. Grosse Adventures, the Volume 3: Trouble at Twilight Cave. 2007. (Illus.). 96p. pap. 4.99 (*978-1-59816-051-2(6) , Tokyopop Kids) TOKYOPOP, Inc.

—The Unauthorized Biography. 2007. (Surf's Up Ser.). 64p. (J). pap. 4.99 (*978-0-06-115329-7(X) , Harper Entertainment) HarperCollins Pubs.

Auerbach, Annie & Houghton Mifflin Company Staff. Zathura the Movie Shadowbook: An Intergalactic Shadow-Casting Adventure. Noble, Steven, illus. 2005. 6p. (J). (gr. 3-5). 14.99 (978-0-618-60583-5(5)) Houghton Mifflin Co. Trade & Reference Div.

Auerbacher, Inge. Running Against the Wind: The True Story of Twin Sisters from Brooklyn Who Changed the Lives of Thousands of African-American Youngsters in New York City. 2000. (Illus.). 117p. (J). (ps-10). pap. 9.99 (978-0-88092-437-5(3) , 4373) Royal Fireworks Publishing Co.

August, Elaine Schiller. Southern Mischief. 2005. 78p. pap. 14.95 (978-1-4137-7893-9(3)) PublishAmerica, Inc.

Augustyn, Brian. Justice League the Swarm: 8x8 Storybook. Armstrong, Jason, illus. rev. ed. 2003. (Justice League Ser.). 24p. (J). per. 2.99 (978-1-4037-0298-2(5)) Dalmatian Pr.

—Justice League Total Eclipse: 8x8 Storybook. Armstrong, Jason, illus. 2003. (Justice League Ser.). 24p. (J). per. 2.99 (978-1-4037-0299-9(3)) Dalmatian Pr.

—The One-Man Justice League: 8x8 Storybook. Rousseau, Craig, illus. 2003. (Justice League Ser.). 24p. (J). per. 2.99 (978-1-4037-0297-5(7)) Dalmatian Pr.

Ausbun, Nellie M. Skip & Meow. 2001. 22p. (J). per. 8.95 (978-0-7414-0613-2(6)) Infinity Publishing.

Auxier, Bryan. Three Days & Four Knights. Daniels, Regina, illus. 2004. 66p. (J). pap. 3.95 (978-0-9719144-2-1(7)) Where? Pr., Inc.

La Aventura de Pimienta, 6 Pcks. (Coleccion Pm Ser.).Tr. of Pepper's adventure. (SPA.). 16p. (gr. 1 up). 26.00 (978-0-7578-3051-8(X)) Rigby Education.

Averett, Edward. The Rhyming Season. 2005. 224p. (YA). (gr. 7-7). 16.00 (978-0-618-46948-2(6) , Clarion Bks.) Houghton Mifflin Co. Trade & Reference Div.

Avey, F. M. The Harlequin's Nutcracker. Hart, Shawn, illus. 2002. 50p. (J). 18.95 (978-1-930758-66-7(9) , Yeva Kids) Yeva Corp.

Avi. A Beginning, a Muddle, & an End: The Return of the End of the Beginning. Tusa, Tricia, illus. 2008. 176p. (J). 14.95 (*978-0-15-205555-4(X)) Harcourt Trade Pubs.

—The End of the Beginning: Being the Adventures of a Small Snail (and an Even Smaller Ant) Tusa, Tricia, illus. 144p. (J). 2008. pap. 6.95 (*978-0-15-205532-5(0) , Harcourt Paperbacks); 2004. 14.95 (978-0-15-204968-3(1)) Harcourt Children's Bks.

—Perloo the Bold. Reed, Marcy, illus. 1999. 240p. (J). (gr. 3-7). pap. 4.99 (978-0-590-11003-7(9) , Scholastic Paperbacks) Scholastic, Inc.

—La Rata de Navidad. (SPA.). 156p. (J). (978-84-348-7858-7(5) , SM31137) SM Ediciones ESP. *Dist:* Lectorum Pubns., Inc.

—The True Confessions of Charlotte Doyle. (J). pap. (978-0-13-667429-0(1)); pap. 23.94 (978-0-13-667403-0(8)); 3rd ed. (J). pap. 3.99 (978-0-13-800012-7(3)) Prentice Hall (Schl. Div.).

—The True Confessions of Charlotte Doyle. 2003. 20.75 (978-0-8446-7235-9(1)) Smith, Peter Pub., Inc.

Aviles, Donna Nordmark. Fly Little Bird, Fly! 2004. 80p. per. 10.00 (978-1-932852-07-3(7)) Wasteland Pr.

Awdry, Wilbert V. Better View for Gordon Book & CD. 2005. (Illus.). 24p. (J). (ps-2). 9.95 (978-0-375-83501-8(6) , Random Hse. Bks. for Young Readers) Random Hse. Children's Bks.

Azzarello, Brian. A Forgone Tomorrow. Risso, Eduardo, illus. rev. ed. 2002. 264p. pap. 17.99 (978-1-56389-827-3(6)) DC Comics.

Azzopardi, Jeannie. Maricio & the Magic Suitcase. l.t. ed. 2004. (Illus.). 93p. (J). per. 14.00 incl. cd-rom (978-0-9744391-3-6(4) , MAR-BKCD-1st, Once Upon A Time in a Classroom) Interactive Media Publishing.

Baccalario, Pierdomenico. The Door to Time. Dunfey, Beth, ed. Janeczko, Leah, tr. from ITA. Bruno, Iacopo, illus. 2006. (Ulysses Moore Ser.: No. 1). 240p. (J). (gr. 4-7). pap. 12.99 (978-0-439-77438-3(1)) Scholastic, Inc.

Backyard Stories. 2007. (Backyardigans Ser.). 128p. (J). pap. 7.99 (978-1-4169-3561-2(4) , Simon Spotlight/ Nickelodeon) Simon & Schuster Children's Publishing.

Backyardigans, 5 bks., Set. 2007. (J). 128.10 (*978-1-59961-156-3(2)) Spotlight.

Bacon, Thomas. Of monsters, magik & Nano-technology. 2007. 114p. pap. 17.95 (978-0-533-15467-8(7)) Vantage Pr., Inc.

Bagley, Conor. Ziggy McFinster's Nantucket Adventure. Westcott, Nadine Bernard, illus. 2008. 40p. (*978-1-56625-315-4(2) , Volt Pr.) Bonus Bks., Inc.

Baglio, Ben M. Goose on the Loose. McNicholas, Shelagh, illus. 2000. (Animal Ark Ser.: No. 14). 160p. (J). (gr. 3-6). pap. 3.99 (978-0-439-09699-7(5)) Scholastic, Inc.

—Husky in a Hut. Baglio, Ben M. & Baum, Ann, illus. 2005. (Animal Ark Ser.: Vol. 36). 144p. (J). pap. 3.99 (978-0-439-44894-9(8)) Scholastic, Inc.

—Husky in a Hut. Baum, Ann, illus. 2005. 131p. (J). (ps-k). lib. bdg. 10.64 (978-0-606-33289-7(8)) Tandem Library Bks.

—Owl in the Office. 1999. (Animal Ark Ser.: No. 11). (J). (gr. 3-5). (978-0-606-19934-6(9)) Tandem Library Bks.

—Polars on the Path. Baum, Ann, illus. 2005. (Animal Ark Hauntings Ser.). 144p. 3.99 (978-0-439-44895-6(6)) Scholastic, Inc.

Bahrampour, Ali. Luna Likes Bugs. 2008. (J). (978-0-374-34672-0(0) , Farrar, Straus & Giroux (BYR)) Farrar, Straus & Giroux.

Baicker, Karen. Pea Pod Babies. Williams, Sam, illus. 2003. 32p. (J). (ps-2). 15.95 (978-1-59354-003-6(5)) Handprint Bks.

Bailey, Carolyn Sherwin. Stories of Great Adventures. Burd, Clara M., illus. 2005. reprint ed. pap. 24.95 (978-1-4179-0215-6(9)) Kessinger Publishing, LLC.

Bailey, Chris. Major Damage, Vol. 1. 2004. 96p. (YA). pap. 14.95 (978-0-9721831-4-7(0)); pap. 29.95 (978-0-9721831-5-4(9)) sky-dog.

Bailey, Helen. Takes a Break. 2007. (Topaz Ser.: Vol. 4). (Illus.). 144p. pap. 7.95 (*978-0-340-91733-6(4)) Hodder Children's Division GBR. *Dist:* Independent Pubs. Group.

Bailie, Helen. The Azura Stones. 2007. 212p. (YA). per. 18.00 (*978-1-58982-374-7(5) , Bedside Bks.) American Bk. Publishing Group.

Bain, Michelle. The Adventures of Thumbs up Johnnie: Banker Bill's Guide to Common Cents. Lizana, Lorenzo, illus. 2007. (J). 14.95 (*978-0-9761421-9-5(8)) Pixie Stuff LLC.

—The Adventures of Thumbs up Johnnie: Jimmy Jam Germ & the Happy Handshake Version 2. Lizana, Lorenzo, illus. 2007. (J). 14.95 (*978-0-9761421-7-1(1)) Pixie Stuff LLC.

—The Adventures of Thumbs up Johnnie: Johnnie Finds A Buddy Color Version 2. Lizana, Lorenzo, illus. 2007. (J). 14.95 (*978-0-9761421-6-4(3)) Pixie Stuff LLC.

—The Adventures of Thumbs up Johnnie: Johnnie's Missing Boot! Lizana, Lorenzo, illus. 2007. (J). 14.95 (*978-0-9761421-8-8(X)) Pixie Stuff LLC.

Bain, Michelle. Las aventuras de Juanito el Pulgarcito: Juanito encuentra un Compañerito. Lizana, Lorenzo, illus. 2006. Tr. of Johnnie Finds a Buddy. (SPA.). (J). 16.95 (978-0-9761421-4-0(7)) Pixie Stuff LLC.

Baird, Alison. White as the Waves: A Novel of Moby Dick. 1999. 288p. (J). pap. (978-1-894294-03-4(3)) Creative Bk. Publishing.

Baker, Dierdre. Becca at Sea. 2007. 165p. (J). (gr. 3-7). 16.95 (*978-0-88899-737-1(X)) Groundwood Bks. CAN. *Dist:* Perseus Distribution.

Baker, E. D. Once upon a Curse: More Tales of the Frog Princess. 2004. (Illus.). 225p. (J). 15.95 (978-1-58234-892-6(8) , Bloomsbury Children) Bloomsbury Publishing.

Baker, Elliott, adapted by. The Adventures of Doctor Dolittle. 2002. 104p. (YA). pap. 6.95 (978-1-58342-113-0(0) , A03) Dramatic Publishing Co.

Baker-Smith, Grahame. Little Pilot: George's Magic Day. (Illus.). 32p. 16.99 (*978-0-340-87549-0(6)); pap. 6.99 (*978-0-340-87550-6(X)) Hodder General Publishing Division GBR. (Hodder & Stoughton). *Dist:* Trafalgar Square Publishing.

Balaban, Bob. Beware of Dog. 2002. (gr. 3-6). lib. bdg. 13.00 (978-0-613-72091-5(1)) Tandem Library Bks.

Balaban, Mariah, ed. Dragonfire. 2006. (Duel Masters Ser.). (Illus.). 32p. (J). pap. 3.99 (978-0-439-78956-1(7) , Scholastic) Scholastic, Inc.

—Scooby-doo Pirates Ahoy. 2006. (Scooby-doo 8x8 Video Tie-in Ser.). (J). 24p. pap. 3.99 (978-0-439-83993-8(9)); 64p. pap. 3.99 (978-0-439-83992-1(0)) Scholastic, Inc.

Balan, Bruce. In Pursuit of Picasso. 1998. (Cyber Kdz Ser.). 176p. pap. 3.99 (978-0-380-79499-7(3)) HarperCollins Pubs.

Ballantyne, Michael. Blown to Bits or the Lonely Man of Rakat. 2006. 36.99 (*978-1-4280-4221-6(0)); pap. 30.99 (*978-1-4280-4226-1(1)) IndyPublish.com.

Ballantyne, R. The Coral Island. 2006. pap. 14.95 (*978-1-55742-666-6(X)) Wildside Pr.

Ballantyne, R. M. The Battle & the Breeze. 2004. reprint ed. pap. 15.95 (978-1-4191-5365-5(X)); pap. 1.99 (978-1-4192-5365-2(4)) Kessinger Publishing, LLC.

—Blown to Bits; or, the Lonely Man of Rak. 2006. pap. (*978-1-4065-0515-3(3)) Dodo Pr.

—The Dog Crusoe (Illustrated Edition) (Do. 2006. pap. (*978-1-4065-0529-0(3)) Dodo Pr.

—Fort Desolation. 2004. reprint ed. pap. 15.95 (978-1-4191-2037-4(9)); pap. 1.99 (978-1-4192-2037-1(3)) Kessinger Publishing, LLC.

—Gascoyne, the Sandal-Wood Trader. 2006. pap. (*978-1-4065-0530-6(7)) Dodo Pr.

—The Lighthouse. 2006. pap. (*978-1-4065-0531-3(5)) Dodo Pr.

—The Lighthouse. l.t. ed. 2006. 504p. pap. (978-1-84702-270-7(7)) Echo Library.

—The Norsemen in the West or America Before Columbus. 2004. reprint ed. pap. 1.99 (978-1-4192-7571-5(2)) Kessinger Publishing, LLC.

—Saved by the Lifeboat. 2004. reprint ed. pap. 15.95 (978-1-4191-4624-4(6)); pap. 1.99 (978-1-4192-4624-1(0)) Kessinger Publishing, LLC.

Ballantyne, R. M. The World of Ice (Illustrated Edition) (2006. pap. (*978-1-4065-0533-7(1)) Dodo Pr.

Ballard, John. Skateman: In the City of Angels. 1999. (Skateman: 1). (Illus.). (YA). (978-0-932279-60-6(0)) World Citizens.

—Soul Survivors: Real Love Knows No Boundaries. 1999. (Soul to Soul Adventure Ser.: 3). (Illus.). (YA). (gr. 7-13). (978-0-932279-13-2(9)) World Citizens.

Balloon Books Staff. Scout Visits the Farm: 100 Removable Stickers. 2003. (Illus.). 18p. (J). pap. 4.95 (978-1-4027-0487-1(9) , Balloon Bks.) Sterling Publishing Co., Inc.

Balocco, Patrizia & Francia, Giada, eds. Alex & Penny Ballooning over Italy. 2007. (Illus.). 80p. (J). (gr. 2-5). 14.95 (978-88-544-0160-0(9) , White Star) Rizzoli International Pubns., Inc.

Baltazar, Art & Franco, Aureliani. Patrick the Wolf Boy, Vol. 4. 2007. (Illus.). 144p. pap. 12.99 (978-1-932796-83-4(5)) Devil's Due Publishing, Inc.

Banks, Lynne Reid. The Adventures of King Midas. 153p. (J). pap. 4.50 (978-0-8072-1468-8(X) , Listening Library) Random Hse. Audio Publishing Group.

—The Farthest-Away Mountain. 130p. (J). (gr. 3-5). pap. 4.50 (978-0-8072-1499-2(X) , Listening Library) Random Hse. Audio Publishing Group.

—The Farthest-Away Mountain. 2004. 160p. (gr. 4-7). pap. 4.99 (978-0-440-41926-6(3) , Yearling) Random Hse. Children's Bks.

—Harry the Poisonous Centipede: A Story to Make You Squirm. Ross, Tony, illus. l.t. ed. 2005. 176p. (J). pap. (978-0-7540-6148-9(5) , CLP 341) BBC Audio.

—Harry the Poisonous Centipede: A Story to Make You Squirm. Ross, Tony, illus. 1998. 128p. (J). (gr. 3-7). pap., pap. 5.99 incl. audio (978-0-380-72734-6(X) , Harper Trophy) HarperCollins Pubs.

—Harry the Poisonous Centipede: A Story to Make You Squirm. (J). (gr. 1-3). 118p. pap. 4.50 (978-0-8072-1523-4(6)); 1998. pap. 23.00 incl. audio (978-0-8072-7997-7(8) , YA962SP) Random Hse. Audio Publishing Group. (Listening Library).

—The Key to the Indian. unabr. ed. 1999. (Indian in the Cupboard Ser.: No. 5). 240p. (J). (gr. 3-7). pap. 38.00 incl. audio (978-0-8072-8076-8(3) , YA995SP, Listening Library) Random Hse. Audio Publishing Group.

Banks, Steven. Love Potion. Sasic, Natasha, illus. ed. 2005. (Adventures of Jimmy Neutron Ser.: 7). 24p. (J). lib. bdg. 15.00 (978-1-59054-784-7(5)) Fitzgerald Bks.

—Love Potion. Sasic, Natasha, illus. 2003. (Jimmy Neutron Boy Genius Ser.). 24p. (J). pap. 3.99 (978-0-689-86317-2(9) , Simon Spotlight/Nickelodeon) Simon & Schuster Children's Publishing.

—Sandy's Rocket. 2001. (gr. 3-6). lib. bdg. 11.80 (978-0-613-43971-8(6)) Tandem Library Bks.

Bannerman, Helen. La Historia del Pequeno Babachi. 2001. Tr. of Story of Little Babaji. (SPA.). (J). (gr. 2-4). 16.76 (978-84-261-3064-8(X)) Juventud, Editorial ESP. *Dist:* Lectorum Pubns., Inc.

Bannister, Bram. Rupert, the Alien & the Bank Robbery. 2007. 56p. per. 8.95 (*978-0-595-44839-5(9)) iUniverse, Inc.

Banta, Byron. Tales from the High Meadows. 2005. 48p. (J). per. 13.99 (978-1-58930-149-8(8)) Selah Publishing Group, LLC.

Banyai, Istvan. Zoom. 1998. (J). (978-0-606-13944-1(3)) Tandem Library Bks.

Baranda, Maria. Tulia y la Tecla Magica. Martin, Mary Rodriguez, illus. rev. ed. 2006. (Castillo de la Lectura, Serie Naranja). (SPA.). 160p. (J). pap. 7.95 (978-970-20-0177-5(3)) Castillo, Ediciones, S. A. de C. V. MEX. *Dist:* Macmillan.

Baranello, Pat. The Adventures of Bible Buddy. 2004. pap. 15.00 (978-0-8059-6568-1(8)) Dorrance Publishing Co., Inc.

Barba, Rick. The Doomsday Dust. 2006. (Spy Gear Adventures Ser.). 208p. (J). pap. 4.99 (978-1-4169-0890-6(0) , Aladdin) Simon & Schuster Children's Publishing.

—The Massively Multiplayer Mystery. Steccati, Eve, illus. 2006. (Spy Gear Adventures Ser.). 240p. (J). pap. 4.99 (978-1-4169-0888-3(9) , Aladdin) Simon & Schuster Children's Publishing.

—The Secret of Stoneship Woods. Steccati, Eve, illus. 2006. (Spy Gear Adventures Ser.). 160p. (J). pap. 4.99 (978-1-4169-0887-6(0) , Aladdin) Simon & Schuster Children's Publishing.

Barba, Rick & Yuen Jr., Sammy. The Shrieking Shadow. Fischer, Scott M., illus. 2007. (Spy Gear Adventures Ser.). 176p. (J). pap. 4.99 (978-1-4169-0891-3(9) , Aladdin) Simon & Schuster Children's Publishing.

Barbauld, Anna. Little Stories for Children; Being Easy. 2004. reprint ed. pap. 20.95 (978-0-7661-9037-5(4)) Kessinger Publishing, LLC.

Barbetta, Sue. Surprise under the Sea. Wrzesniewski, Phyllis, illus. 1999. (Undersea Adventure Ser.). 48p. (J). (gr. 1-2). pap. 6.95 (978-1-892774-01-9(1)) Creative Publishing Services.

Barbie Preschool Educational. 2004. (J). (978-0-7666-1353-9(4) , 64065) Modern Publishing.

Barbour, Ralph Henry. The Adventure Club Afloat. 2006. (Illus.). pap. (*978-1-4065-0774-4(1)) Dodo Pr.

—The Adventure Club Afloat. 2006. 78.99 (*978-1-4280-1948-5(0)) IndyPublish.com.

—The New Boy at Hilltop & Other Stories. 2006. 62.99 (*978-1-4219-9700-1(2)); pap. 56.99 (*978-1-4219-9701-8(0)) IndyPublish.com.

Barclay Family Adventures Resource Guide. 2003. (Barclay Family Adventure Ser.). 48p. (YA). tchr. ed., per. 9.95 (978-1-56254-560-4(4) , SP 5604) Saddleback Educational Publishing.

Barclay Family Adventures Series 2 Resource Guide. 2004. 48p. (YA). per. 9.95 (978-1-56254-813-1(1) , SP8131) Saddleback Educational Publishing.

Bardwell, Harrison. The Lurtiss Field Mystery. 2003. 248p. (J). pap. 13.95 (978-1-55753-336-4(9)) Purdue Univ. Pr.

—The Mystery of Seal Islands. 2003. 223p. (J). pap. 13.95 (978-1-55753-337-1(7)) Purdue Univ. Pr.

—The Mystery Ship. 2003. 214p. (J). pap. 13.95 (978-1-55753-338-8(5)) Purdue Univ. Pr.

—Roberta's Flying Courage. 2003. 248p. (J). pap. 13.95 (978-1-55753-335-7(0)) Purdue Univ. Pr.

Barham, Lisa. A Girl Like Moi: The Fashion-Forward Adventures of Imogene. Rim, Sujean, illus. 2006. (Fashion-Forward Adventures of Imogene Ser.). 272p. (YA). (gr. 6-10). pap. 8.99 (978-1-4169-1443-3(9) , Simon Pulse) Simon & Schuster Children's Publishing.

—Project Paris: The Fashion-Forward Adventures of Imogene. Rim, Sujean, illus. 2007. (Fashion-Forward Adventures of Imogene Ser.). 224p. (YA). (gr. 6-10). pap. 9.99 (978-1-4169-1444-0(7) , Simon Pulse) Simon & Schuster Children's Publishing.

Barkan, Joanne. A Tale of Two Sitters. l.t. ed. 1999. (Adventures of Wishbone Ser.: No. 9). (Illus.). 144p. (J). (gr. 4 up). lib. bdg. 22.60 (978-0-8368-2305-9(2)) Stevens, Gareth Inc.

Barker. Sharp Stuff. 1999. 155p. (J). pap. 8.99 (978-0-552-54642-3(9)) Transworld Publishers Ltd. GBR. *Dist:* Independent Pubs. Group.

Barker, Cicely Mary. Flower Fairies Musical Treasure Chest. 2005. 1p. (J). pap. 12.99 (978-0-7232-5384-6(6) , Warne) Penguin Group (USA) Inc.

Barker, Cicely Mary. Lily's Seaside Adventure: A Flower Fairies Friends Chapter Book. 2008. (Flower Fairies Ser.). 80p. (J). (gr. 2). pap. 3.99 (*978-0-7232-6286-2(1) , Warne) Penguin Group (USA) Inc.

Barker, Cicely Mary & Le Quesne, Pippa. Zinnia's Magical Adventure: A Flower Fairy Chapter Book. 2006. 80p. (J). (gr. 7). 3.99 (978-0-7232-5774-5(4) , Warne) Penguin Group (USA) Inc.

Barker, Clive. Days of Magic, Nights of War. Barker, Clive, illus. 2005. (Abarat Ser.). 512p. (J). pap. 11.99 (978-0-06-440932-2(5) , Harper Trophy) HarperCollins Pubs.

Barkley, Roger C. Johnny Grasshopper. 2006. 52p. pap. 12.95 (978-1-4241-0221-1(9)) PublishAmerica, Inc.

Barlow, Galon L., Jr. The Adventures of Levi & Nathan from the Cape of Cod to the Outer Banks. Guthrie, Adam C., illus. l.t. ed. 1998. (YA). (gr. 6 up). mass mkt. 7.95 (978-0-9666020-2-9(1)) Farewell Pr.

Barlow, Steve L. & Skidmore, Steve. Friend or Foe? 2002. (Outernet Ser.: No. 1). (Illus.). 176p. (J). (gr. 3-7). pap. 4.99 (978-0-439-34351-0(8)) Scholastic, Inc.

—Mad Myths: A Touch of Wind! Ross, Tony, illus. l.t. ed. 2000. 95p. (J). pap. (978-0-7540-6116-8(7) , CLP 310) BBC Audio.

—Odyssey. 2002. (Outernet Ser.: No. 3). 192p. (J). (gr. 3-7). pap. 4.99 (978-0-439-34353-4(4) , Chicken Hse., The) Scholastic, Inc.

—Star Bores: The Novel. 1999. (Illus.). 128p. (J). (gr. 5-9). mass mkt. 4.95 (978-1-902618-76-0(9)) Element Children's Bks.

Barnes, Peter W. & Barnes, Cheryl Shaw. Where's Nat? A Nat, Nat, the Nantucket Cat Adventure Book. Arciero, Susan, illus. 2007. 32p. (J). 17.95 (*978-1-893622-19-7(3) , VSP Bks.) Vacation Spot Publishing.

Barnes, Susan. Kelly Karate: Discovers the Ice Princess. 2004. 138p. (J). (gr. 4-8). pap. 5.95 (978-0-9705777-3-3(7)) McBook Pubs., LLC.

Barnett, Gary W. Princess of the Lights: Fantasy Adventure. 2007. 324p. 29.95 (*978-0-595-68957-6(4)) iUniverse, Inc.

Barnum, P. T. Dick Broadhead: A Story of Perilous Adve. 2006. pap. 30.95 (*978-1-4286-1959-3(3)) Kessinger Publishing, LLC.

—Jack in the Jungle: A Tale of Land & S. 2006. pap. 33.95 (*978-1-4286-0764-4(1)) Kessinger Publishing, LLC.

Barnum, Richard. Mappo the Merry Monkey Illustrated Editi. 2006. (Illus.). pap. (*978-1-4065-0920-5(5)) Dodo Pr.

—Squinty the Comical Pig. 2004. reprint ed. pap. 15.95 (978-1-4191-4865-1(6)); pap. 1.99 (978-1-4192-4865-8(0)) Kessinger Publishing, LLC.

Barnum, Richard. Squinty the Comical Pig Illustrated Edit. 2006. (Illus.). pap. (*978-1-4065-0921-2(3)) Dodo Pr.

Baron, Andrew, illus. The Adventures of Octopus Rex. 2003. (J). per. 17.95 (978-0-9760348-0-3(8)) BaHart Pubns. / Eight Legs Publishing.

Barr, Mabel. Hamster Huey & the Gooey Kablooie: The Renowned Hero's Most Famous Adventure. l.t. ed. 2004. (Illus.). 8p. (J). 6.95 (978-0-9749090-0-4(9) , 214) Hamster Huey Pr.

Barr, Robert. The Clue of the Silver Spoons. 2004. reprint ed. pap. 15.95 (978-1-4191-5701-1(9)); pap. 1.99 (978-1-4192-5701-8(3)) Kessinger Publishing, LLC.

Barracca, Debra. Maxi, the Star. Buehner, Mark, illus. 2002. 13.19 (978-1-4046-0284-7(4)) Book Wholesalers, Inc.

Barrie, J. M. The Adventures of Peter Pan. 2004. 220p. pap. 12.95 (978-1-59540-036-9(2) , 1st World Library - Literary Society) 1st World Publishing, Inc.

—Peter Pan. 2007. (Illus.). 192p. pap. 14.95 (*978-0-413-73550-8(8)) A & C Black GBR. *Dist:* Consortium Bk. Sales & Distribution.

—Peter Pan. 1999. (Illus.). 160p. (J). (gr. 4-7). pap. 2.50 (978-0-486-40783-8(7)) Dover Pubns., Inc.

—Peter Pan. (J). 9.95 (978-1-56156-305-0(6)) Kidsbooks, Inc.

—Peter Pan. 2003. (gr. 3-6). lib. bdg. 14.15 (978-0-613-85653-9(8)); lib. bdg. 11.80 (978-0-613-86964-5(8)) Tandem Library Bks.

—Peter Pan: The Original Story. 2003. (gr. 3-6). lib. bdg. 13.00 (978-0-613-71839-4(9)) Tandem Library Bks.

—Peter Pan y Wendy. 2003. (SPA.). 64p. (J). 17.95 (978-84-233-2394-4(3)) Ediciones Destino ESP. *Dist:* Planeta Publishing Corp.

—Peter Pan y Wendy. (Coleccion Cuentos Universales). (SPA.). 190p. (YA). (gr. 4 up). (978-84-261-5584-9(7) , JV30117) Juventud, Editorial ESP. *Dist:* Lectorum Pubns., Inc.

—Peter Pan y Wendy: Edicion del Centenario. Gomez Aragon, Carmen, tr. from ENG. Ingpen, Robert R., illus. 2006. (SPA.). 218p. (J). (ps-7). 29.95 (978-84-89396-04-3(3)) Blume ESP. *Dist:* Independent Pubs. Group.

Barrie, J. M. & Scholastic, Inc. Staff. Peter Pan & Wendy. Geist, Ken, ed. 2004. (Illus.). 224p. (J). (ps up). 17.95 (978-0-439-67257-3(0) , Orchard Bks.) Scholastic, Inc.

Barron, T. A. The Day the Stones Walked: A Tale of Easter Island. Low, William, illus. 2007. 32p. (J). (gr. 1-4). 16.99 (978-0-399-24263-2(5) , Philomel) Penguin Group (USA) Inc.

—High As a Hawk: A Brave Girl's Historic Climb. Lewin, Ted, tr. Lewin, Ted, illus. 2004. 32p. (J). (ps-3). 16.99 (978-0-399-23704-1(6) , Philomel) Penguin Group (USA) Inc.

Barry, Dave & Pearson, Ridley. Cave of the Dark Wind: A Never Land Adventure. Call, Greg, illus. 2007. 176p. (gr. 3 up). 9.99 (978-0-7868-3790-8(X)) Hyperion Bks. for Children.

—Escape from the Carnivale: A Never Land Book. Call, Greg, illus. 2006. 144p. (gr. 3-17). 9.99 (978-0-7868-3789-2(6)) Hyperion Bks. for Children.

—Peter & the Secret of Rundoon. rev. ed. 2007. 496p. (YA). (gr. 7-17). 18.99 (*978-0-7868-3788-5(8) , Disney Editions) Disney Pr.

Barry, Dave & Pearson, Ridley. Peter & the Shadow Thieves. rev. ed. 2007. 592p. (gr. 5 up). pap. 8.99 (*978-1-4231-0855-9(8) , Disney Editions) Disney Pr.

—Peter & the Shadow Thieves. Call, Greg, illus. 2006. 576p. (gr. 5-17). 18.99 (978-0-7868-3787-8(X)) Hyperion Bks. for Children.

Barry, Maureen. Freddie the Frog's Adventure. 2007. (J). pap. 10.00 net. (*978-1-60402-177-6(2)) Independent Pub.

Barshaw, Ruth McNally. Ellie McDoodle: Have Pen, Will Travel. Barshaw, Ruth McNally, illus. 2007. (Illus.). 176p. (J). (gr. 3-7). 11.95 (*978-1-58234-745-5(X)) Bloomsbury Publishing.

Barth, Jeff. The Missionary Adventures of Bob & Arty Vol. 3: Mission Alaska. Barth, Marge, ed. 1998. (Illus.). 293p. (J). (gr. 4-12). pap. 10.00 (978-0-9624067-8-2(3)) Barth Family Ministries.

—The Missionary Adventures of Bob & Arty Vol. 4: The Storm! Barth, Marge, ed. 1999. (Illus.). 392p. (J). (gr. 4-12). pap. 10.00 (978-1-891484-01-8(X)) Barth Family Ministries.

Bartlett, Craig. Return of the Sewer King. 2000. (gr. 3-6). lib. bdg. 11.80 (978-0-613-31639-2(8)) Tandem Library Bks.

Bartlett, Jean. IndiAsia & the Dragon. Maravelias, Monica, illus. 2001. i, 31p. (J). (gr. 2-9). 19.95 (978-0-9713851-0-8(6)) Wolf Road.

Barton, Janet. Boathouse. 2001. (gr. 7-12). lib. bdg. 24.55 (978-0-613-82472-9(5)) Tandem Library Bks.

Barwin, Gary. The Magic Mustache. Jorisch, Stephane, illus. 1999. 32p. (J). (ps-2). lib. bdg. 17.95 (978-1-55037-607-4(1)) Annick Pr., Ltd. CAN. *Dist:* Firefly Bks., Ltd.

Bass, Jules. Herb, the Vegetarian Dragon: Book & Bendo Gift Set. Harter, Debbie, illus. 2005. 32p. (J). pap. 14.99 (978-1-905236-43-5(3)) Barefoot Bks., Inc.

Basu, Jayinee. HJBRL - A Nonsense Story by Sukumar Ray. 2005. 68p. pap. 10.98 (978-1-4116-3983-6(9)) Lulu.com.

Bateman, Colin. Running with the Reservoir Pups. 2006. 272p. (J). (gr. 4-7). 5.99 (978-0-440-42048-4(2) , Yearling) Random Hse. Children's Bks.

Bates, Cynthia. Courage on the Line. 1999. (Sports Stories Ser.). 117p. (J). (gr. 3-8). 7.95 (978-1-55028-648-9(X)); (*978-1-55028-649-6(8)) Lorimer, James & Co., Ltd., Pubs. CAN. *Dist:* Casemate Pubs. & Bk. Distributors, LLC.

—Courage on the Line. 1999. (gr. 3-6). lib. bdg. 13.55 (978-0-613-29585-7(4)) Tandem Library Bks.

Bates, Gordon. The Khaki Boys over the Top: Doing & Daring for Uncle Sam. 2007. 140p. pap. 10.99 (*978-1-4264-6542-0(4)) BiblioBazaar.

Bates, Michelle. Ride by Moonlight. Leigh, Susannah, ed. Woodcock, John, illus. rev. ed. 2004. (Sandy Lane Stables Ser.). 128p. (J). pap. 4.95 (978-0-7945-0547-9(3) , Usborne) EDC Publishing.

Bateson-Hill, Margaret. Shota & the Star Quilt. (Folk Tales Ser.). (Illus.). 32p. (J). (gr. k up). 2001. pap. 7.95 (978-1-84089-023-5(1)); 1998. 14.95 (978-1-84089-021-1(5)) Evans Publishing Group GBR. (Zero to Ten, Limited). *Dist:* Independent Pubs. Group.

Batory, Edward. Genevieve in Ashram. 2001. 276p. (J). pap. 15.95 (978-0-595-19209-0(2) , Authors Choice Pr.) iUniverse, Inc.

Batson, Susann. Gilly the Seasick Fish. l.t. ed. 2006. (Illus.). (J). 28p. 15.99 (978-1-933090-22-1(7)); 32p. E-Book 5.00 incl. cd-rom (978-1-933090-37-5(5)) Guardian Angel Publishing, Inc.

Batson, Wayne Thomas. The Door Within. 2005. (Door Within Trilogy: Bk. 1). (Illus.). 320p. (J). 16.99 (978-1-4003-0659-6(0)) Nelson, Thomas Inc.

Bauer, Christina. The Pirate Queen: A Timewalker Journey. 2005. 280p. (YA). pap. 14.99 (978-1-59092-224-8(7) , Blue Works) Windstorm Creative.

Bauer, Joan. Backwater. 1999. 192p. (J). (gr. 7-12). 18.99 (978-0-399-23141-4(2) , Putnam Juvenile) Penguin Group (USA) Inc.

Bauer, Marion Dane. Christmas Lights. Mitchell, Susan, illus. 2006. 12p. (J). 12.99 (978-0-689-86942-6(8) , Little Simon) Simon & Schuster Children's Publishing.

—Palabra de Honor. 1998. (SPA., Illus.). 88p. (J). (gr. k-2). (978-84-279-3234-0(0) , NG8010) Noguer y Caralt Editores, S. A. ESP. *Dist:* Lectorum Pubns., Inc.

Bauld, Jane Scoggins. Voyage of the Third Seed. Darr, Cynthia G., illus. l.t. ed. 2000. 32p. (J). 17.95 (978-1-929701-02-5(0)) Under the Green Umbrella.

Baum, L. Frank. The Enchanted Island of Yew. l.t. ed. 2005. 228p. pap. (978-1-84637-102-8(3)) Echo Library.

—Sky Island. 2004. (Twelve-Point Ser.). lib. bdg. 24.00 (978-1-58287-280-3(5)); lib. bdg. 25.00 (978-1-58287-792-1(0)) North Bks.

Bauman, Marty. The Crater Kid Collection. 2004. (Illus.). 144p. pap. 14.99 (978-0-9728585-0-2(4)) Dinoship, Inc.

Bawden, Nina. Off the Road. l.t. ed. 2005. (Illus.). 251p. (J). pap. (978-0-7540-6172-4(8) , CLP 364) BBC Audio.

Bayle, B. J. Perilous Passage. 2007. 176p. (YA). pap. 11.99 (*978-1-55002-689-4(5) , Sandcastle Bks.) Dundurn Group, The CAN. *Dist:* Univ. of Toronto Pr.

Beaman, Cliff. The Boy Who Grew Too Small. 2006. 51p. (J). pap. 12.95 (978-0-9777290-4-3(4) , 349-021) High-Pitched Hum Inc.

Beamer, Cheryl & Beamer, Frank. Yea, It's Hokie Game Day! De Angel, Miguel, illus. 2006. (J). 17.95 (978-1-932888-44-7(6)) Mascot Bks., Inc.

Bearstone. 1999. (J). 9.95 (978-1-56137-725-1(2)) Novel Units, Inc.

Beasley, Cheryl. Piano Paradise: My Piano Has a Big Secret. 2006. (ENG.). 52p. per. 12.95 (*978-1-4241-4590-4(2)) PublishAmerica, Inc.

The Beast. 2003. (J). per. (978-1-57657-864-3(X)) Paradise Pr., Inc.

Beast Quest 6 & Blade, Adam. Beast Quest #6 Epos the Winged Flame. 2008. (Beast Quest Ser.). 96p. (J). pap. 4.99 (*978-0-439-02458-7(7) , Scholastic Paperbacks) Scholastic, Inc.

Beaudoin, Beau. The Url King. 2006. (Illus.). 56p. (J). per. 15.95 (*978-0-9788401-0-5(0)) Red Ink Pr.

Beautiful Book Staff. Pistenbully Comes to the Rescue. 2006. (PistonBully Ser.). (Illus.). 24p. pap. 8.95 (978-0-9549476-6-8(5)) Beautiful Bks. GBR. *Dist:* International Publishers Marketing.

Beauty & the Boy: An old man's story for a dying Boy. 2006. (Illus.). 270p. (YA). per. 19.95 (978-0-9759902-0-9(9)) Before Christmas Pr.

Because of Walter, 6 Packs. (Action Packs Ser.). 104p. (gr. 3-5). 44.00 (978-0-7635-8402-3(9)) Rigby Education.

Because of Winn Dixie. 2005. (J). (978-1-59564-832-7(1)) Steps To Literacy, LLC.

Beck, Andrea. Elliot's Emergency. ed. 2004. (J). (gr. k-3). spiral bd. (978-0-616-01542-1(9)); spiral bd. (978-0-616-01543-8(7)) Canadian National Institute for the Blind/Institut National Canadien pour les Aveugles.

Beck, Ian. Home Before Dark. 2001. (Illus.). (J). pap. (978-0-439-17523-4(2)); 32p. pap. 15.95 (978-0-439-17522-7(4)) Scholastic, Inc.

Becker, Walt William. Link. 2000. (Illus.). (J). (978-0-606-17976-8(3)) Tandem Library Bks.

Beckerman, Menucha. Crankytown. 2004. (My Smiling World Ser.: No. 2). (Illus.). 32p. (J). 11.95 (978-1-931681-52-0(X)) Israel Bk. Shop.

Becket, Jim. Inca Gold: Choose Your Own Adventure #20. 2007. (Choose Your Own Adventure Ser.: 20). (Illus.). 144p. (J). per. 6.99 (*978-1-933390-20-8(4) , CHCL20) Chooseco LLC.

Beckham, David. Charlie Barker & the Secret of the Deep Dark Woods. 2006. 570p. pap. (*978-1-4120-9264-7(7)) Trafford Publishing.

Bedford, Annie North. Scamp: The Adventures of a Little Puppy. Walt Disney Company Staff, illus. 2004. 24p. (J). (gr. k-k). 2.99 (978-0-7364-2311-3(7) , Golden/Disney) Random Hse. Children's Bks.

Beech, Sandy. Isle Be Seeing You. Holder, Jimmy, illus. 2005. (Castaways Ser.). 192p. mass mkt. 4.99 (978-0-689-87598-4(3) , Aladdin) Simon & Schuster Children's Publishing.

—Worst Class Trip Ever. Holder, Jimmy, illus. 2005. (Castaways Ser.). 176p. pap. 4.99 (978-0-689-87596-0(7) , Aladdin) Simon & Schuster Children's Publishing.

Beechen, Adam. Jimmy on Ice. Marderosian, Mark, illus. 2003. (Jimmy Neutron Ser.: Vol. 2). 32p. (J). pap. 3.99 (978-0-689-85294-7(0) , Simon Spotlight/Nickelodeon) Simon & Schuster Children's Publishing.

—Jimmy on Ice. 2003. (ps-2). lib. bdg. 11.80 (978-0-613-58154-7(7)) Tandem Library Bks.

—What I Did on My Hypergalactic Interstellar Summer Vacation. Hipp, Dan, illus. 2006. 129p. (J). 12.95 (978-0-9742803-6-3(4)) Komikwerks, LLC.

Beecroft, Simon. Greatest Battles. 2008. (Dk Readers Ser.). 48p. (J). (ps-12). 14.99 (*978-0-7566-3606-7(X)); pap. 3.99 (*978-0-7566-3603-6(5)) Dorling Kindersley Publishing, Inc.

—Ready, Set, Podrace! 2007. (DK Readers: Level 1 (Paperback) Ser.). (Illus.). 32p. (J). (gr. 4-7). pap. 3.99 (*978-0-7566-3274-8(9)); (ps-3). 14.99 (*978-0-7566-3275-5(7)) Dorling Kindersley Publishing, Inc.

Beekman, Kelley Lee. Sir Eli & the Halloween Dragon: The Legend of the Toasted Marshmallow. 2006. 55p. pap. 12.95 (*978-1-4241-4047-3(1)) PublishAmerica, Inc.

Beer, Hans. Kleiner eisbar wohin fahrst Du. pap. 17.95 (978-3-423-07954-9(1)) Deutscher Taschenbuch Verlag GmbH & Co KG DEU. *Dist:* Distribooks, Inc.

Beetle Dan & the Big Purple Slide. 2006. 32p. pap. 14.99 (978-1-59185-921-5(2) , Creation Hse.) Strang Communications Co.

Behn, Rosa & Graham, Dora. The Adventures of Jenny Duck. 2006. 109p. pap. 16.95 (978-1-4137-9450-2(5)) PublishAmerica, Inc.

Beinstein, Phoebe. Dora's Color Adventure! Hall, Susan T., illus. 2002. (Dora the Explorer Ser.). 20p. (J). bds. 6.99 (978-0-689-84663-2(0) , Simon Spotlight/Nickelodeon) Simon & Schuster Children's Publishing.

—What Will I Be? Dora's Book about Jobs. Saunders, Zina, illus. 2004. (Dora the Explorer Ser.). 22p. (J). bds. 4.99 (978-0-689-86501-5(5) , Simon Spotlight/Nickelodeon) Simon & Schuster Children's Publishing.

Beiter, Anna M. & Beiter, Elizabeth A. The Story of the Star-Spangled Banner. 2005. (J). pap. 8.00 (978-0-8059-6727-2(3)) Dorrance Publishing Co., Inc.

Belch, Cheryl Renee. The Heroic Adventures of Dizzy Jr. 2007. 20.00 (*978-0-8059-8977-9(3)) Dorrance Publishing Co., Inc.

Belgue, Nancy. The Scream of the Hawk. 2003. (Sports Stories Ser.). 144p. (J). (gr. 3-7). pap. 6.95 (978-1-55143-257-1(9)) Orca Bk. Pubs. USA.

Bell, A. L. The Adventures of Captain Zero: I'm the Hero (Special Edition Cover) 2005. 45p. 17.00 (978-1-4116-3732-0(1)) Lulu.com.

Bell, David. Dawn Grays Cosmic Adventure 1. 2007. (Dawn Gray Trilogy Ser.). (Illus.). 260p. pap. 11.95 (*978-1-84167-558-9(X)) Ransom Publishing Ltd. GBR. *Dist:* International Publishers Marketing.

—Pink Alert! 2007. (Dawn Gray Trilogy Ser.). 260p. pap. 11.95 (*978-1-84167-581-7(4)) Ransom Publishing Ltd. GBR. *Dist:* International Publishers Marketing.

—Pyjamas in Space. 2007. (Dawn Gray Trilogy Ser.). 260p. pap. 11.95 (*978-1-84167-580-0(6)) Ransom Publishing Ltd. GBR. *Dist:* International Publishers Marketing.

Bell, Frank. How Slip Slap Slop Got His Name. Seaman, Paul, illus. 2004. 24p. pap. 7.00 (978-1-84161-069-6(0)) Ravette Publishing, Ltd. GBR. *Dist:* Parkwest Pubns., Inc.

Bell, Hilari. Fall of a Kingdom. 2004. (Farsala Trilogy Ser.). 352p. (YA). 16.95 (978-1-4169-0545-5(6)) Simon & Schuster Children's Publishing.

—Fall of a Kingdom. 2005. 422p. (YA). (gr. 7-12). per. 14.45 (978-1-4176-5288-4(8)) Tandem Library Bks.

—Forging the Sword. (Farsala Trilogy Ser.: No. 3). (YA). 2007. 624p. mass mkt. 6.99 (978-0-689-85418-7(8) , Simon & Schuster Children's Publishing); 2006. 512p. 17.99 (978-0-689-85416-3(1)) Simon & Schuster Children's Publishing.

Bell, Joanne. Breaking Trail. 2005. (J). 136p. pap. 6.95 (978-0-88899-662-6(4)); 160p. 15.95 (978-0-88899-630-5(6)) Groundwood Bks. CAN. *Dist:* Perseus Distribution.

Bell, Michele Ashman. Dragon's Jaw: A Heart-Pounding Adventure. 2005. 241p. (J). (978-1-59156-880-3(3)) Covenant Communications.

Bell-Myers, Darcy, illus. Higgledy-Piggledy: Mabel's World. 2006. 32p. 16.95 (978-0-9716631-1-4(4)) Attitude Pr., Inc.

Bell, Rebecca. Message from Miami - the Adventures of Sharp-Eye - Book2. Bell, Rebecca, illus. 2005. (Adventures of Sharp-Eye). 30p. (J). per. 9.95 (*978-1-934138-09-0(6)) Bouncing Ball Bks., Inc.

—A Regular Bug - the Adventures of Sharp-Eye - Book1. Bell, Rebecca, illus. 2005. (Adventures of Sharp-Eye: Bk. 1). (Illus.). 25p. (J). per. 9.95 (*978-1-934138-08-3(8)) Bouncing Ball Bks., Inc.

Bell, William. Crabbe. 1999. 169p. (YA). (gr. 7-12). mass mkt. 5.95 (978-0-7736-7483-7(7)) Stoddart Kids CAN. *Dist:* Fitzhenry & Whiteside, Ltd.

Bell, William, ed. Crabbe. 20th rev. anniv. ed. 2006. 176p. pap. 9.95 (978-1-55005-051-6(6)) Fitzhenry & Whiteside, Ltd. CAN. *Dist:* F & W Pubns., Inc.

Bendis, Brian Michael. Daredevil, Vol. 2. Maleev, Alex, illus. 288p. (YA). 29.99 (978-0-7851-0926-6(9)) Marvel Enterprises, Inc.

—Daredevil, Vol. 3. Youngquist, Jeff, ed. Maleev, Alex, illus. 320p. (YA). 29.99 (978-0-7851-1106-1(9)) Marvel Enterprises, Inc.

—Daredevil, Vol. 5. (Illus.). 256p. 29.99 (978-0-7851-2110-7(2)) Marvel Enterprises, Inc.

—Hollywood. Bagley, Mark, illus. 2004. 100p. lib. bdg. 24.35 (978-1-4176-6037-7(6)) Tandem Library Bks.

—Lowlife, 6 vols. Maleev, Alex, illus. 120p. (YA). 13.99 (978-0-7851-1105-4(0)) Marvel Enterprises, Inc.

—The Man Without Fear! Vol. 4. 40th ed. (Illus.). 280p. (YA). 29.99 (978-0-7851-1342-3(8)) Marvel Enterprises, Inc.

—The Murdock Papers. (Illus.). 152p. pap. 14.99 (978-0-7851-1810-7(1)) Marvel Enterprises, Inc.

—Public Scrutiny, 5 Vol. 5. Bagley, Mark, illus. 2003. (Ultimate Spider-man Ser.). 128p. (J). pap. 11.99 (978-0-7851-1087-3(9)) Marvel Enterprises, Inc.

—Ultimate Spider-Man, 2 vols., Vol. 2. Bagley, Mark, illus. 2003. (Ultimate Spider-man Ser.). 336p. 29.99 (978-0-7851-1061-3(5)) Marvel Enterprises, Inc.

Bendis, Brian Michael, et al. What If... ? Why Not?, Vol. 1. 2005. (Marvel Heroes Ser.). (Illus.). 152p. pap. 16.99 (978-0-7851-1593-9(5)) Marvel Enterprises, Inc.

Benedetti, Marie. Fishing with Grandpapa: The Most Important Rules. 2007. (J). per. 8.99 ***(978-1-59886-975-0(2))*** Tate Publishing & Enterprises, L.L.C.

Benintendi, Stephen F. PowerMark Seeker Series Issue 4: Redemption. 2003. (ENG & SPA.). (J). 1.75 (978-0-9729135-4-6(8)) PowerMark Productions.

—PowerMark Seeker Series Issue 5: Transformation. 2003. (ENG & SPA.). (J). 1.75 (978-0-9729135-5-3(6)) PowerMark Productions.

—PowerMark Seeker Series Issue 6: The Pathway. 2003. (ENG & SPA.). (J). 1.75 (978-0-9729135-6-0(4)) PowerMark Productions.

—PowerMark Series One Autographed Box Set: Issues 1-12. aut. ed. 2003. 50.00 (978-0-9717876-4-3(6)) PowerMark Productions.

Benintendi, Steve. PM Seeker Series # 7 Masquerade: Halloween Edition. 2005. (Illus.). 20p. (J). pap. 7.25 (978-0-9749339-1-7(0)) PowerMark Productions.

Benjamin, Matthew C. Andy's Discovery. del Conte, Mia, illus. 2003. 78p. (J). per. 8.95 (978-0-9744672-0-7(0)) Adventure & Discovery Pr.

—Ricky's Adventure. del Conte, Mia, illus. 2003. 94p. (J). per. 8.95 (978-0-9744672-1-4(9)) Adventure & Discovery Pr.

Bennett, Dean. The Late Loon. 2006. (Illus.). 32p. 15.95 (978-0-89272-730-8(6)) Down East Bks.

Bennett, Debra J. Hip, Hop & Flop's Many Adventures. 2007. (ENG.). 60p. per. 12.95 ***(978-1-4241-6564-3(4))*** PublishAmerica, Inc.

Bennett, Holly. The Bonemender's Choice. 2007. 240p. (YA). (gr. 7 up). pap. ***(978-1-55143-718-7(X))*** Orca Bk. Pubs.

—The Warrior's Daughter. 2007. 240p. (YA). (gr. 7 up). pap. ***(978-1-55143-607-4(8))*** Orca Bk. Pubs.

Bennett, Maureen A. Oliver & Audrey's First Adventure. Bennett, Exlus S., illus. 1998. (Oliver & Audrey Otter's Adventures Presents Ser.: Vol. 1). 58p. (J). (ps-6). pap. 14.95 (978-1-929914-01-2(6) , Ruf-Fur Pubns) Megaverse City Studios.

Bennett, Steven. The Adventures of Super Dad: Colossal Encounters (Book #1) 2005. 98p. pap. 10.49 (978-1-4116-5947-6(3)) Lulu.com.

Bennett, W. J., Jr. Sydney & Garrett's Great Arkansas Adventury. 2005. (J). pap. ***(978-0-9794044-6-7(0))*** Archeological Assessments, Inc.

Benson, E. F. The Confession of Charles Linkworth. 2004. reprint ed. pap. 15.95 (978-1-4191-5738-7(8)); pap. 1.99 (978-1-4192-5738-4(2)) Kessinger Publishing, LLC.

Benson, Elliott Iren. Ethel Hollister's Second Summer As a Cam. 2006. 77.99 ***(978-1-4280-2013-9(6))*** IndyPublish.com.

Bent, Ruth. Llama Hiking with Katie. 2000. 28p. (J). (gr. 1-3). pap. 8.00 (978-0-615-11191-9(2)) Sijama Publishing.

Bentley, Susan E. The Adventures of Twitcher & Solomon. 2005. 96p. (J). pap. 10.99 (978-1-4141-0467-6(7)) Pleasant Word.

Bently, Dawn. Kirsty's Big Adventure. Kemly, Kathleen, illus. 2005. (Woodkins Ser.). 12p. (J). bds. 14.95 (978-1-59354-049-4(3)) Handprint Bks.

Benton, Jim. The Fran with Four Brains. Benton, Jim, illus. 2006. (Franny K. Stein, Mad Scientist Ser.: Bk. 6). 112p. (J). 14.95 (978-1-4169-0231-7(7)) Simon & Schuster Children's Publishing.

—Franny K. Stein's Crate of Danger Set: Lunch Walks among Us; Attack of the 50-Ft. Cupid; the Invisible Fran; the Fran That Time Forgot. Benton, Jim, illus. 2005. (Franny K. Stein, Mad Scientist Ser.). 448p. (J). pap. 14.99 (978-1-4169-1402-0(1) , Aladdin) Simon & Schuster Children's Publishing.

—Frantastic Voyage. Benton, Jim, illus. (Franny K. Stein, Mad Scientist Ser.: Bk. 5). (Illus.). 112p. (J). 2006. pap. 3.99 (978-1-4169-0230-0(9) , Aladdin); 2005. 14.95 (978-1-4169-0229-4(5)) Simon & Schuster Children's Publishing.

—The Invisible Fran. Benton, Jim, illus. (Franny K. Stein, Mad Scientist Ser.: Bk. 3). (Illus.). 112p. (J). (gr. 2-5). 2005. pap. 3.99 (978-0-689-86297-7(0) , Aladdin); 2004. 14.95 (978-0-689-86293-9(8)) Simon & Schuster Children's Publishing.

Benz, Derek & Lewis, J. S. Revenge of the Shadow King Audio (library Edition) 2006. (Grey Griffins Ser.). (J). 84.95 (978-0-439-87913-2(3)) Scholastic, Inc.

BEOBI & the Magic Coloring Book Our First Adventure. 2005. (J). cd-rom 15.99 (978-0-9743847-9-5(8)) Cohn, Tricia.

Beobi & the Magic Coloring Book Our First Adventure. 2005. (J). 3.99 (978-0-9743847-2-6(0)) Cohn, Tricia.

Berenstain, Stan & Berenstain, Jan. The Berenstain Bears' Dinosaur Coloring Adventure. 2005. (Berenstain Bears Ser.). (Illus.). 32p. (J). pap. 3.99 (978-0-06-057413-0(5) , Harper Festival) HarperCollins Pubs.

—The Berenstain Bears Ride the Thunderbolt. 1998. (Berenstain Bears Ser.). (Illus.). 32p. (J). (ps-1). pap. 3.99 (978-0-679-88718-8(0) , Random Hse. Bks. for Young Readers) Random Hse. Children's Bks.

—The Berenstain Bears Ride the Thunderbolt. 1998. (Early Step into Reading Ser.). (J). (ps-k). 10.79 (978-0-606-13956-4(7)) Tandem Library Bks.

Beres, Lisa. My Body My House. 2006. 16.95 (978-0-9772392-0-7(9)) Green Nest LLC.

Bergen, Lara. Get Giggly with Piggley: A Jakers! Joke Book. Entara Ltd. Staff, photos by. 2006. (Jakers! Ser.). 48p. (J). pap. 3.99 (978-0-689-87707-0(2) , Simon Spotlight) Simon & Schuster Children's Publishing.

—Phonics Comics: Fearless Four - Level 2. Semple, Dave, illus. 2007. 24p. (J). (gr. 1-17). pap. 3.99 (978-1-58476-564-6(X)) Innovative Kids.

Bergen, Lara Rice. Into the Woods. 2000. (Back to Sherwood Ser.: 1). 176p. (J). (gr. 5-9). pap. 3.99 (978-0-440-22853-0(0) , Laurel Leaf) Random Hse. Children's Bks.

—Lost & Found. 2001. (gr. k-3). lib. bdg. 11.25 (978-0-613-43938-1(4)) Tandem Library Bks.

—The Trouble with Brenan. 2000. (Back to Sherwood Ser.: 2). (J). (gr. 5-9). pap. 3.99 (978-0-440-22856-1(5) , Laurel Leaf) Random Hse. Children's Bks.

Bergen, Lara Rice & Rodriguez, Robert. The Island of Lost Dreams: The Official Movie Storybook. movie tie-in ed. 2002. (Spy Kids 2 Ser.). (Illus.). 32p. pap. 5.99 (978-0-7868-1726-9(7)) Hyperion Bks. for Children.

Berger, Gilda & Berger, Melvin. Vivio Algun Dinosaurio Cerca de Tu Casa. 2007. 48p. (J). pap. 5.99 ***(978-0-439-85314-9(1)*** , Scholastic en Espanol) Scholastic, Inc.

Berkeley, Jon. The Palace of Laughter: The Wednesday Tales No. 1. Dorman, Brandon, illus. (J). 2007. 464p. (gr. 3-7). pap. 7.99 ***(978-0-06-075509-6(1)*** , Harper Trophy); 2006. 448p. 16.99 (978-0-06-075507-2(5) , Julie Andrews Collection); 2006. 448p. lib. bdg. 17.89 (978-0-06-075508-9(3) , Julie Andrews Collection) HarperCollins Pubs.

—The Tiger's Egg. Dorman, Brandon, illus. 2007. 416p. (J). (gr. 3-7). lib. bdg. 17.89 ***(978-0-06-075511-9(3));*** (Wednesday Tales Ser.: No. 2). 16.99 ***(978-0-06-075510-2(5))*** HarperCollins Pubs. (Julie Andrews Collection).

Berkeley, Laura. The Keeper of Wisdom. Dexter, Alison, illus. 2000. 32p. (J). (ps-3). 15.95 (978-1-84148-203-3(X)) Barefoot Bks., Inc.

Bern, Dave. Best Friends. 2006. 28p. pap. 9.95 ***(978-1-4327-0036-2(7))*** Outskirts Press, Inc.

Bernard, Greg. Alpha Summer. 2005. (YA). per. 12.95 (978-0-926147-21-8(8)) Loonfeather Pr.

Berndt, Ted. Search for the City. 2001. 100p. (YA). pap. 10.95 (978-1-58275-059-0(9) , Segen Bks.) Black Forest Pr.

Bernhardt, William. Princess Alice & the Dreadful Dragon. McGhee, Kerry, illus. 2007. 36p. (J). 19.95 ***(978-1-930709-65-2(X))*** HAWK Publishing Group.

Berry, Bob, illus. Pooh 'Where Are You Roo?' 14p. (J). bds. 15.98 (978-0-7853-8449-6(9) , 7186100) Publications International, Ltd.

Bertha Bantam. 2003. (J). 9.99 (978-0-9740847-7-0(8)) GiGi Bks.

Beskow, Elsa. Peter & Lotta's Adventure. 2003. (Illus.). 32p. (J). 17.95 (978-0-86315-398-3(4)) Floris Bks. GBR. *Dist:* SteinerBooks, Inc.

Bessen, Luc. Arthur & the Minimoys. Sowchek, Ellen, tr. from FRE. 2005. 240p. (J). 15.99 (978-0-06-059623-1(6)) HarperCollins Pubs.

Bessey, Sian Ann. Escape from Germany. 2004. 183p. (J). (978-1-59156-436-2(0)) Covenant Communications.

—Uprising in Samoa: A Novel. 2004. 178p. (J). (978-1-59156-890-2(0)) Covenant Communications.

Besson, Luc. Arthur & the Forbidden City. (Illus.). 192p. (J). 2006. pap. 5.99 (978-0-06-059628-6(7) , Harper Trophy); 2005. 15.99 (978-0-06-059626-2(0)); 2005. lib. bdg. 16.89 (978-0-06-059627-9(9)) HarperCollins Pubs.

—Arthur & the Invisibles. movie tie-in ed. 2006. 416p. (J). pap. 7.99 (978-0-06-122726-4(9)) HarperCollins Pubs.

—Arthur & the Minimoys. (Illus.). (J). 2006. 256p. pap. 6.99 (978-0-06-059625-5(2) , Harper Trophy); 2005. 240p. lib. bdg. 16.89 (978-0-06-059624-8(4)) HarperCollins Pubs.

Bester, Alfred. The Deceivers. 1999. 272p. pap. 14.00 (978-0-671-03889-2(3)) ibooks, Inc.

Bibee, John. The Spirit Flyer Series, 8 bks. 2005. (Illus.). 8p. pap. 80.00 (978-0-8308-1200-4(8) , 1200) InterVarsity Pr.

—The Spirit Flyer Series. Turnbaugh, Paul, illus. gif. ed. 2005. 4p. Bks. 1-4. pap. 40.00 (978-0-8308-1208-0(3) , 1208); Bks. 5-8. pap. 40.00 (978-0-8308-1289-9(X) , 1289) InterVarsity Pr.

Biddle, Kelly & Beach, Julia, eds. We Ain't Kiddin' 2000. 64p. (J). pap. 9.95 (978-1-57072-156-4(4)) Overmountain Pr.

Bidoli, Katie. Karate Adventures of Kisho, Hana, & Nobu: Karate Is for Everyone! 2006. (Illus.). 16p. (J). 10.00 ***(978-1-60243-029-7(2))*** Keen's Martial Arts Academy.

Bidwell, Dafne. Danger Unlimited: Action, Mystery & Adventure. 2007. 181p. pap. 15.50 ***(978-1-921064-89-0(7))*** Fremantle Pr. AUS. *Dist:* International Specialized Bk. Services.

Biegel, Paul. El Pais de las Siete Torres.Tr. of Land of Seven Towers. (SPA.). 120p. (YA). (gr. 5). (978-84-279-3248-7(0) , NG0325) Noguer y Caralt Editores, S. A. ESP. *Dist:* Lectorum Pubns., Inc.

Big Book of Backyard Adventures. 2007. (Backyardigans Ser.). 192p. (J). 10.99 ***(978-1-4169-3842-2(7)*** , Simon Spotlight/Nickelodeon) Simon & Schuster Children's Publishing.

Biggs, Pauline. A Wild Ride. Mayne, Michael, illus. 2004. 20p. (J). per. 12.95 (978-0-9760129-0-0(1)) Avant Garde Publishing.

Billie's World. 2005. (J). pap. 8.99 (978-0-9766295-0-4(X)) My Journey Bks.

Billiot, Wendy Wilson. Before the Saltwater Came. l.t. ed. 2005. (Illus.). 32p. (J). 19.95 (978-0-9762592-0-6(6)) Billiot, Wendy Wilson.

Billy & Baxter All Around Town, 4 vols. 2005. (Illus.). 24p. (J). (ps-ps). 8.95 (978-1-58087-098-6(8)) Stampley, C.D. Enterprises, Inc.

Billy & Baxter at the Airport, 4 vols. 2005. (Illus.). 24p. (J). (ps-7). 8.95 (978-1-58087-100-6(3)) Stampley, C.D. Enterprises, Inc.

Binaohan, Simon. The Misadventures of Miss Millicent Maddin, No. 2. 2003. 160p. (J). 15.99 (978-0-06-073914-0(2)); 16.89 (978-0-06-073915-7(0)); pap. 5.99 (978-0-06-073916-4(9) , Harper Trophy) HarperCollins Pubs.

Bishop, Mary Harelkin. Tunnels of Terror: Another Moose Jaw Adventure. 2005. 312p. (J). (gr. 6-8). pap. 7.95 (978-1-55050-193-3(3)) Coteau Bks. CAN. *Dist:* Fitzhenry & Whiteside, Ltd.

—Tunnels of Time. 2000. (gr. 5-8). lib. bdg. 15.25 (978-0-613-78444-3(8)) Tandem Library Bks.

—Tunnels of Time: A Moose Jaw Adventure. 2005. (Illus.). 282p. (J). (gr. 5 up). pap. 6.95 (978-1-55050-164-3(X)) Coteau Bks. CAN. *Dist:* Fitzhenry & Whiteside, Ltd.

Bisson, Terry. Crossfire. 2003. (Star Wars Ser.). 144p. mass mkt. 5.99 (978-0-439-39002-6(8)) Scholastic, Inc.

Bitetto, Marco A. V., ed. Black Watch. braille ed. 2000. (J). (978-1-58578-070-9(7)) Institute of Cybernetics Research, Inc.

Bjerkvold, Belinda & Stevenson, Robert Louis. Treasure Island. Tod, Lluis M. & Andrada, Javier, illus. 2006. 36p. (J). lib. bdg. ***(978-0-8368-7665-9(2))*** Stevens, Gareth Inc.

Bjerkvold, Belinda & Verne, Jules. Around the World in 80 Days. Desclot, Miquel & Andrada, Javier, illus. 2006. (J). lib. bdg. ***(978-0-8368-7662-8(8))*** Stevens, Gareth Inc.

Bjork, Linda. Salmon Cavern. 2006. 92p. pap. 10.95 (978-1-59800-546-2(4)) Outskirts Press, Inc.

Bjornson, Nancy. Mustangs, Fires & Snakes. 2007. (J). ***(*978-1-930596-84-9(7))*** Amherst Pr.

—Sleds, Skins & Snow. 2007. (J). ***(*978-1-930596-83-2(9))*** Amherst Pr.

Black, Chuck. Kingdom's Hope, 4 bks. Black, Andrea & Black, Brittney, eds. Johnson, Marcella, illus. Black, Chuck, photos by. 2002. (Kingdom Ser.: 2). 154p. (J). per. 8.95 (978-0-9679240-2-1(2)) Perfect Praise Publishing.

—Kingdom's Reign, 4 bks. Black, Andrea & Black, Brittney, eds. Johnson, Marcella, illus. 2004. 160p. (YA). per. 9.95 (978-0-9679240-3-8(0)) Perfect Praise Publishing.

Black, Holly & DiTerlizzi, Tony. The Chronicles of Spiderwick: A Grand Tour of the Enchanted World, Navigated by Thimbletack. 2007. (Spiderwick Chronicles). 32p. (J). 21.99 ***(*978-1-4169-5038-7(9))*** Simon & Schuster Children's Publishing.

—The Nixie's Song. DiTerlizzi, Tony, illus. 2007. (Beyond the Spiderwick Chronicles Ser.). (Illus.). 192p. (J). (gr. 2). 10.99 ***(*978-0-689-87131-3(7))*** Simon & Schuster Children's Publishing.

Black, Jake. Leonardo Returns. Jourdan, Diego, illus. 2007. (Teenage Mutant Ninja Turtles Ser.). 32p. (J). pap. 3.99 (978-1-4169-4056-2(1) , Simon Spotlight) Simon & Schuster Children's Publishing.

Black, Jessica L. What Can Baby Do? Metzger, Jeanne, illus. 2000. (J). bds. (978-1-57332-167-9(2)) HighReach Learning, Inc.

Blackford, Ami. Quest for the Elfin Elixir: A Duncan Family Adventure. Blackford, Ami, illus. 2007. 80p. (J). (gr. 3-7). 16.95 ***(*978-1-60108-021-9(2))*** Red Cygnet Pr.

Blackman, Hacker. 2000. 199p. (J). pap. 9.95 (978-0-552-52751-4(3)) Transworld Publishers Ltd. GBR. *Dist:* Independent Pubs. Group.

Blackman, Malorie. Operation Gadgetman! 2000. (Corgi Yearling Ser.). (Illus.). 144p. (J). pap. 9.99 (978-0-440-86307-6(4) , Corgi) Transworld Publishers Ltd. GBR. *Dist:* Trafalgar Square Publishing.

Blackmoor, Brandon & Blackmoor, Susan. Warlock: Black Spiral. 1999. 250p. (YA). (gr. 10 up). pap. 25.00 (978-0-9641722-4-1(0)) Black Gate Publishing.

Blackwood, Gary L. Shakespeare's Spy, Vol. 3. 2003. (Shakespeare Stealer Ser.). 288p. (J). (gr. 4-6). 16.99 (978-0-525-47145-5(6) , Dutton Juvenile) Penguin Group (USA) Inc.

Blade, Adam. Sepron the Sea Serpent. 2007. (Beast Quest Ser.: No. 2). 80p. (J). pap. 4.99 (978-0-439-90654-8(7) , Scholastic Paperbacks) Scholastic, Inc.

Blaine, John. The Boy Scouts on a Submarine. 2006. 62.99 ***(*978-1-4280-0926-4(4));*** pap. 55.99 ***(*978-1-4280-0929-5(9))*** IndyPublish.com.

Blair, Eric. Pecos Bill. Chambers-Goldberg, Micah, illus. 2006. (Read-It! Readers en Espanol Ser.).Tr. of Pecos Bill. (SPA.). 32p. (J). (ps-3). 19.95 (978-1-4048-1658-9(5)) Picture Window Bks.

Blair, Thomas L. The Sabatini Prophecy. 2006. 480p. (YA). 22.95 (978-0-9760237-1-5(7)) Axiom Hse.

Blake, Heather Lynn. Anne's Quest: The Wishing Stone. 2005. 153p. pap. 19.95 (978-1-4137-5749-1(9)) PublishAmerica, Inc.

Blake, Jon. Mystery Guest at the House of Fun. 2007. (Illus.). 128p. pap. 6.95 ***(*978-0-340-88461-4(4))*** Hodder Children's Division GBR. *Dist:* Independent Pubs. Group.

Blake, Sandy Ebelt. The Adventures of Santa & Rudolph. 2007. 38p. pap. 7.95 ***(*978-0-533-15684-9(X))*** Vantage Pr., Inc.

Bland, Caleb & Streit, Wendy. Skarskantuana. Bland, Caleb, illus. l.t. ed. 2002. (Great Lakes Ser.: Bk. 1). (Illus.). 26p. (YA). (gr. 3-9). spiral bd. 21.95 (978-0-9720790-0-6(9)) o-ho-lee-ab Publishing.

Blankenau, Gail. Mountain Pirates. 2001. 108p. (gr. 4-7). pap. 9.95 (978-0-595-16537-7(0)) iUniverse, Inc.

Blasing, George. Dinosaur George Prehistoric Safari: Raptor Island. Ramirez, Alberto, illus. 2007. (J). 4.95 ***(*978-0-9797304-2-9(2))*** Raining Popcorn Media.

Blaylock, Josh. G. I. Joe Vol. 1: A Real American Hero. 2002. 112p. (YA). pap. 14.95 (978-1-58240-252-9(3)) Image Comics.

Blaylock, Kathy. Adventures of Buddy Fairy & Friends. 2007. 48p. 12.95 ***(*978-1-4137-9195-2(6))*** PublishAmerica, Inc.

Blenkhorn, Les. The Adventures of Tracker. 2006. 26.99 ***(*978-1-4259-6605-8(5));*** pap. 16.99 ***(*978-1-4259-6604-1(7))*** AuthorHouse.

Bliss, Bob, illus. The Hardest Lessons: The Lost Babies Series #3. 2007. 118p. (J). per. 5.99 ***(*978-0-9792499-2-1(9))*** Howell, M Kay.

—The Ruby Hind: The Lost Babies Series #1. 2007. 116p. (J). per. 5.99 ***(*978-0-9792499-0-7(2))*** Howell, M Kay.

—Too Many Parents: The Lost Babies Series #2. 2007. 109p. (J). per. 5.99 ***(*978-0-9792499-1-4(0))*** Howell, M Kay.

Block, Francesca Lia. The Hanged Man. 1999. (Illus.). 160p. (J). (gr. 5 up). pap. 8.99 (978-0-06-440832-5(9)) HarperCollins Pubs.

—The Hanged Man. 1999. (Illus.). 137p. (YA). (gr. 7-12). per. 17.60 (978-0-613-21671-5(7)) Tandem Library Bks.

Bloomfield, Susanne George & Reed, Melvin, eds. Adventures in the West: Stories for Young Readers. 2007. (Illus.). 302p. (gr. 3 up). pap. 19.95 ***(*978-0-8032-5974-4(3)*** , Bison Bks.) Univ. of Nebraska Pr.

Blossom, F. Blossom Kingdom: The Adventures of Emily. 2005. 189p. pap. 19.95 (978-1-4241-1112-1(9)) PublishAmerica, Inc.

Blotcky, Mark. Cameron & Her Missing Shoes. 2006. 28p. pap. 9.95 ***(*978-1-4327-0035-5(9))*** Outskirts Press, Inc.

—Erin & Her Shoe Laces. 2006. 28p. pap. 9.95 ***(*978-1-4327-0034-8(0))*** Outskirts Press, Inc.

Blumberg, Rhoda. Commodore Perry in the Land of the Shogun. 2003. (Illus.). 144p. (J). (gr. 3 up). pap. 8.99 (978-0-06-008625-1(4) , Harper Trophy) HarperCollins Pubs.

Blumenstock, Jacqueline & Pool, David. Making New Friends. 2nd ed. 2005. (Illus.). 32p. (J). per. 5.95 (978-0-9764647-0-9(5)) Big Brown Box, Inc., The.

—Making New Friends. Madden, Colleen, illus. 2nd ed. 2005. 32p. (J). lib. bdg. 14.95 (978-0-9764647-1-6(3)) Big Brown Box, Inc., The.

Blumer, J. Michael. The Book of Broken Promises, Bk. 2. 2007. 280p. (YA). pap. 14.99 (978-1-59092-540-9(8) , Blue Works) Windstorm Creative.

—The Book of Second Chances, Bk. 1. 2006. 380p. pap. 14.99 (978-1-59092-317-7(0) , Blue Works) Windstorm Creative.

Blundell, Judy & Watson, Jude. Against the Empire. 2007. (Star Wars Ser.: No. 8). 160p. (J). pap. 5.99 ***(*978-0-439-68141-4(3))*** Scholastic, Inc.

Blunt, Patricia. George the Jackdaw. 2005. (Illus.). 52p. pap. ***(*978-1-84401-540-5(8))*** Athena Pr.

Bly, Leon. Jenny Turnbull Vol. 2: Kurdistan Mission. 180p. (YA). pap. 9.00 (978-0-9621505-4-8(1)) Schwarz Pauper Pr.

Bly, Stephen A. The Secret of the Old Rifle. 2004. (Lewis & Clark Squad Ser.: No. 2). 160p. (gr. 4-9). 4.99 (978-0-89107-940-8(8)) Crossway Bks.

—Treachery at the River Canyon. 2004. (Lewis & Clark Squad Ser.: No.3). 160p. (YA). (gr. 4-9). 4.99 (978-0-89107-941-5(6)) Crossway Bks.

Blyton, Enid. The Adventure of the Secret Necklace. (Illus.). 84p. (J). pap. 7.99 (978-0-7475-3211-8(7)) Bloomsbury Publishing Plc GBR. *Dist:* Trafalgar Square Publishing.

—The Adventures of Binkle & Flip. (Illus.). 137p. (J). pap. 5.95 (978-0-7475-3221-7(4)) Bloomsbury Publishing Plc GBR. *Dist:* Trafalgar Square Publishing.

—The Adventures of Mr. Pinkwhistle. (Illus.). 121p. (J). pap. 6.95 (978-0-7475-3219-4(2)) Bloomsbury Publishing Plc GBR. *Dist:* Trafalgar Square Publishing.

—The Boy Who Wanted a Dog. (Illus.). 91p. (J). pap. 7.99 (978-0-7475-3213-2(3)) Bloomsbury Publishing Plc GBR. *Dist:* Trafalgar Square Publishing.

—Castle of Adventure. 2006. (Adventure Ser.). 288p. (J). pap. 9.99 ***(*978-0-330-44630-3(4))*** Macmillan Publishers Ltd. GBR. *Dist:* Independent Pubs. Group.

—A Castle of Adventure. 13th rev. ed. 2003. (Adventure Series [3] Ser.). 192p. (J). pap. 9.99 (978-0-330-30178-7(0)) Pan Macmillan GBR. *Dist:* Trafalgar Square Publishing.

—The Children of St. Kidillin. (Illus.). 110p. (J). pap. 7.99 (978-0-7475-3216-3(8)) Bloomsbury Publishing Plc GBR. *Dist:* Trafalgar Square Publishing.

—The Circus of Adventure & the River of Adventure, 2 vols. 2003. (Adventure Series [3] Ser.). (Illus.). 352p. (J). pap. 13.99 (978-0-330-39838-1(5)) Pan Macmillan GBR. *Dist:* Trafalgar Square Publishing.

—Enid Blyton Adventure Omnibus. (Illus.). 136p. (J). 8.95 (978-0-09-921981-1(6)) Random Hse. GBR. *Dist:* Trafalgar Square Publishing.

—Five Get into a Fix. l.t. ed. 2005. 285p. (J). pap. (978-0-7540-6050-5(0) , CLP 252) BBC Audio.

—Five Go to Demon's Rocks. l.t. ed. 1999. (Illus.). 284p. (J). pap. (978-0-7540-6082-6(9) , CLP 281) BBC Audio.

—Five Have a Mystery to Solve. l.t. ed. 2000. (Famous Five Adventure Ser.). (Illus.). 263p. (J). pap. (978-0-7540-6094-9(2) , CLP 293) BBC Audio.

—Good Old Secret Seven. l.t. ed. 2005. 112p. (J). pap. (978-0-7540-6134-2(5) , CLP 327) BBC Audio.

—Good Work, Secret Seven. l.t. ed. 2005. 117p. (J). pap. (978-0-7540-6051-2(9) , CLP 257) BBC Audio.

—Good Work, Secret Seven. unabr. ed. 2003. (Read-Along Ser.). (J). pap. 24.95 incl. audio (978-0-7540-6215-8(5) , Galaxy Children's Large Print) BBC Audiobooks America.

A B

—Hedgerow Tales. (Illus.). 118p. (J). pap. 5.95 (978-0-09-973580-9(6)) Random Hse. GBR. *Dist:* Trafalgar Square Publishing.

—Hello Mr Twiddle. (Illus.). 118p. (J). pap. 7.99 (978-0-7475-3218-7(4)) Bloomsbury Publishing Plc GBR. *Dist:* Trafalgar Square Publishing.

—The Island of Adventure. 2006. 304p. (J). pap. 9.95 (*978-0-330-44629-7(0)) Macmillan Publishers Ltd. GBR. *Dist:* Independent Pubs. Group.

—The Island of Adventure & the Castle of Adventure, 2 vols. 2003. (Illus.). 384p. (J). pap. 13.99 (978-0-330-39835-0(0)) Pan Macmillan GBR. *Dist:* Trafalgar Square Publishing.

—Look Out, Secret Seven. l.t. ed. 2005. (Illus.). 144p. (J). pap. (978-0-7540-6167-0(1) , CLP 360) BBC Audio.

—More Hedgerow Tales. (Illus.). 112p. (J). pap. 5.95 (978-0-09-980880-0(3)) Random Hse. GBR. *Dist:* Trafalgar Square Publishing.

—The Mountain of Adventure. rev. ed. 2003. 187p. (J). 6.95 (978-0-333-73272-4(3)) Macmillan Publishers Ltd. GBR. *Dist:* Trafalgar Square Publishing.

—The Mountain of Adventure & the Ship of Adventure, 2 vols. 2003. (Adventure Series [3] Ser.). (Illus.). 384p. (J). pap. 13.99 (978-0-330-39837-4(7)) Pan Macmillan GBR. *Dist:* Trafalgar Square Publishing.

—The Sea of Adventure. 2007. 288p. (J). pap. 9.95 (*978-0-330-44836-9(6)) Macmillan Publishers Ltd. GBR. *Dist:* Independent Pubs. Group.

—The Sea of Adventure. 7th rev. ed. 2003. (Adventure Series [3] Ser.). 192p. (J). pap. 9.99 (978-0-330-30173-2(X)) Pan Macmillan GBR. *Dist:* Trafalgar Square Publishing.

—The Secret of Cliff Castle. (Illus.). 117p. (J). pap. 7.99 (978-0-7475-3214-9(1)) Bloomsbury Publishing Plc GBR. *Dist:* Trafalgar Square Publishing.

—Secret Seven. l.t. ed. (J). 2000. (Illus.). 121p. pap. 16.95 (978-0-7540-6098-7(5)); 2003. 24.95 incl. audio (978-0-7540-6203-5(1) , CCA3463) BBC Audiobooks America. (Galaxy Children's Large Print).

—Secret Seven Adventure. l.t. ed. 1998. (Illus.). 117p. (J). pap. (978-0-7540-6015-4(2) , CLP 218) BBC Audio.

—Secret Seven Fireworks. l.t. ed. 2000. 154p. (J). pap. (978-0-7540-6117-5(5) , CLP 312) BBC Audio.

—Secret Seven on the Trail. l.t. ed. 2005. 144p. (J). pap. (978-0-7540-7818-0(3) , CLP 408) BBC Audio.

—Secret Seven on the Trail. l.t. ed. 2003. pap. 24.95 incl. audio (978-0-7540-6263-9(5) , Galaxy Children's Large Print) BBC Audiobooks America.

—Secret Seven Win Through. l.t. ed. 1999. 167p. (J). pap. (978-0-7540-6068-0(3) , CLP 271) BBC Audio.

—Secret Seven Win Through. unabr. ed. 2000. (Read-Along Ser.). 120p. (J). pap. 24.95 incl. audio (978-0-7540-6221-9(X) , RA022, Chivers Children's Audio Bks.) BBC Audiobooks America.

—Three Cheers, Secret Seven. l.t. ed. 1999. (Illus.). 124p. (J). pap. (978-0-7540-6085-7(3) , CLP 284) BBC Audio.

—The Valley of Adventure. 2008. 304p. (J). pap. 9.95 (*978-0-330-44835-2(8)) Macmillan Publishers Ltd. GBR. *Dist:* Independent Pubs. Group.

Blyton, Enid. The Valley of Adventure & The Sea of Adventure. 2003. (Illus.). 387p. (J). pap. 17.95 (978-0-330-39836-7(9)) Pan Macmillan GBR. *Dist:* Trans-Atlantic Pubns., Inc.

Bob Jones University Staff. Up the Ladder. 2000. (J). (ps-1). pap. 12.95 (978-0-89084-950-7(1) , 109223) Jones, Bob Univ. Pr.

Bobadilla, Selene. Cuentos de Estraterrestres para Ninos. 1999. (Stories for Children Ser.).Tr. of Alien Stories for Kids. (SPA.). 125p. (J). mass mkt. 7.95 (978-970-643-166-0(7)) Selector, S.A. de C.V. MEX. *Dist:* Libros Sin Fronteras.

Boczkowski, Tricia. Fish Happens! Meurer, Caleb, illus. 2003. (SpongeBob SquarePants Ser.). 32p. (J). 6.99 (978-0-689-85996-0(1) , Simon Spotlight/Nickelodeon) Simon & Schuster Children's Publishing.

Bode, Mark & McCormick, Carlo. The Lizard of Oz. 2004. (Illus.). 64p. 12.95 (978-1-56097-595-3(4)) Fantagraphics Bks.

Bode, N. E. The Slippery Map. 2007. 288p. (J). lib. bdg. 17.89 (*978-0-06-079109-4(8)) HarperCollins Pubs.

—The Slippery Map. Dorman, Brandon, illus. 2007. 288p. (J). (gr. 3-7). 16.99 (*978-0-06-079108-7(X)) HarperCollins Pubs.

Boerner, Matthew. The Great Dolphin Door: The Adventures of Frostfin & Silverbeak. Cameron, Vinya, illus. 2006. 52p. (J). pap. 9.95 (978-0-9778525-5-0(5)) Peppertree Pr., The.

Bogart, Jo Ellen & Bogart, Jill. Out & about with the Big Tree Gang. Griffiths, Dean, illus. 2006. 64p. (J). pap. 4.99 (978-1-55143-603-6(5)) Orca Bk. Pubs. USA.

Bogumill, Mark P. KingMaker: The Swamp Crusade, 4 vols. 2003. 310p. (YA). bds. 25.00 (978-0-9744870-0-7(7)) KingMaker Bks. LLC.

Boix, Armando. Aprendiz de Marinero. Vila Delclos, Jordi, illus. 2000. (Periscopio Ser.).Tr. of Sailor's Apprentice. (SPA.). 189p. (YA). (gr. 9 up). pap. (978-84-236-5513-7(X)) Edebé ESP. *Dist:* Baker & Taylor Bks.

Bond, Douglas. Mr. Pipes & Psalms & Hymns of the Reformation. 2000. (Mr. Pipes Ser.: Vol. 2). (Illus.). 256p. (YA). (gr. 8-11). pap. 9.95 (978-1-930367-52-4(X) , CLP29770) Christian Liberty Pr.

Bond, Juliana. Salad Cream. 2005. 31p. spiral bd. 12.28 (978-1-4116-6047-2(1)) Lulu.com.

Bondoux, Anne-Laure. The Princetta. 2008. 448p. (YA). pap. 8.95 (*978-1-59990-098-8(X) , Bloomsbury Children) Bloomsbury Publishing.

—The Princetta. Bell, Anthea, tr. from FRE. 2006. 500p. (YA). 17.95 (978-1-58234-924-4(X) , Bloomsbury Children) Bloomsbury Publishing.

Bone, Thomas H., III, illus. Why Can't I Spray Today. 1999. (Pee Wee Pipes Adventure Ser.). 32p. (J). (ps-3). per. 15.00 (978-0-9674602-0-8(4)) Blue Marlin Pubns.

Bonehill, Ralph. Guns & Snowshoes. 2006. (Illus.). 252p. (J). pap. 14.95 (978-1-55753-391-3(1)) Purdue Univ. Pr.

—Out with Gun & Camera. 2006. 264p. (C). pap. 14.95 (978-1-55753-392-0(X)) Purdue Univ. Pr.

Bonham, Frank. Durango Street. 187p. (YA). (gr. 7 up). pap. 4.99 (978-0-8072-1549-4(X) , Listening Library) Random Hse. Audio Publishing Group.

—Durango Street. 1999. (gr. 7-12). lib. bdg. 14.15 (978-0-613-11499-8(X)) Tandem Library Bks.

Boniface, William. The Return of Meteor Boy? Gilpin, Stephen, illus. 2007. (Extraordinary Adventures of Ordinary Boy Ser.). 352p. (J). (gr. 3-7). lib. bdg. 17.89 (978-0-06-077468-4(1)); 16.99 (978-0-06-077467-7(3)) HarperCollins Pubs.

The Boogly, 6 pack. (Literatura 2000 Ser.). (gr. k-1). 28.00 (978-0-7635-0045-0(3)) Rigby Education.

Book Company Staff. Hoppity Hop. 2003. (Novelty Bks.). (Illus.). (J). 15.95 (978-1-74047-233-3(0)) Book Co. Publishing Pty, Ltd., The AUS. *Dist:* Penton Overseas, Inc.

—Stella Stars: Charm Treasury Adventure Book with Bracelet. 2002. (Novelty Bks.). 20p. (J). 12.95 (978-1-74047-177-0(6)) Book Co. Publishing Pty, Ltd., The AUS. *Dist:* Penton Overseas, Inc.

Book, Jennie Hale. Baby Dog Beans Comes Home: A Paul & Beans Adventure. 2005. (J). per. 13.95 (978-0-9767514-2-7(9) , 2000) Abbott Avenue Pr.

The Book of Lulu. 2001. (J). cd-rom 19.95 (978-0-9669744-6-1(8)) Harbor Electronic Publishing.

Boot Seeds. 2005. (J). 15.00 (978-0-9771015-2-8(5)) Let's Learn Library of Knowledge Series.

Booth, Martin. Coyote Moon. 2005. 272p. (J). (gr. 4-6). pap. 8.99 (978-0-552-55001-7(9) , Corgi) Transworld Publishers Ltd. GBR. *Dist:* Independent Pubs. Group.

—Doctor Illuminatus. 2006. (Alchemist's Son Ser.: Pt. 1). 192p. (J). (gr. 4-9). pap. 6.99 (978-0-316-01285-0(8)) Little Brown & Co.

—Pow. l.t. ed. 2001. 224p. (J). 16.95 (978-0-7540-6160-1(4) , Galaxy Children's Large Print) BBC Audiobooks America.

—Soul Stealer. 2006. (Alchemist's Son Ser.: Pt. 2). 256p. (J). (gr. 5-9). pap. 6.99 (978-0-316-05993-0(5)) Little Brown & Co.

Borgeas, Ted. Grandma Is a Giggle, 5 bks. 2005. 100p. (978-0-9764475-9-7(2)) Cameltrotters Publishing.

Borgia, Mary. Tales of the Texas Mermaid: The Boot. 2006. (Illus.). 47p. (J). 17.95 (978-0-9778451-0-1(9)) Goretti Publishing.

Boris, Papa. Adventures of the Soupman Pt. 1: Applications. 2005. 67p. pap. 14.95 (978-1-4137-7496-2(2)) PublishAmerica, Inc.

Bosley, Katherine. Uben Schoomer. 2004. 29p. pap. 14.95 (978-1-4137-0345-0(3)) PublishAmerica, Inc.

Bosonnet, Margot. The Scrabblemongers. 2002. 176p. (J). (gr. 3-7). pap. 6.95 (978-0-86327-880-8(9)) Interlink Publishing Group, Inc.

Bossley, Michele Martin. Jumper. 2006. 144p. (J). pap. 8.95 (978-1-55143-620-3(5)) Orca Bk. Pubs. USA.

Boston, Lucy M. River at Green Knowe. 2002. (gr. 3-6). lib. bdg. 14.15 (978-0-613-54444-3(7)) Tandem Library Bks.

—The River at Green Knowe. Boston, Peter, illus. 2002. (Green Knowe Ser.). 176p. (YA). (gr. 4-7). reprint ed. pap. 6.00 (978-0-15-202607-3(X) , Odyssey Classics) Harcourt Children's Bks.

Botsford, Matthew. Johnny Rocket & His Comrades in Faith. 2005. (ENG.). 160p. pap. 11.99 (978-88-89127-07-0(4)) Destiny Image Europe ITA. *Dist:* Destiny Image Pubs.

Boughn, Michael. Into the World of the Dead: Astonishing Adventures in the Underworld. 2006. (Illus.). 48p. (J). (gr. 5-7). pap. 12.95 (978-1-55037-958-7(5)); lib. bdg. 24.95 (978-1-55037-959-4(3)) Annick Pr., Ltd. CAN. *Dist:* Firefly Bks., Ltd.

Boulden, Jim & Boulden, Joan. A Deadly Secret. Kennedy, Kari, ed. Drengenberg, Heiko, illus. 1999. 32p. (YA). (gr. 7-11). 4.95 (978-1-892421-11-1(9) , 119) Boulden Publishing.

Bow, Patricia. The Ruby Kingdom. 2007. 256p. (J). pap. 12.99 (*978-1-55002-667-2(4) , Boardwalk Bks.) Dundurn Group, The CAN. *Dist:* Univ. of Toronto Pr.

Bowdish, Lynea. Downey & Buttercup's Adventure. 1998. (Illus.). 24p. (J). (gr. k-2). pap. 3.99 (978-0-87406-893-1(2) , Willowisp Pr.) Darby Creek Publishing.

Bowler, Ann Martin. Adventures of the Treasure Fleet: China Discovers the World. Tay-Audouard, Lak-Khee, illus. 2007. 32p. 19.95 (978-0-8048-3673-9(6)) Tuttle Publishing.

Bowman, Robert. The Three Vests: The New Brilliants. 2003. 224p. (J). pap. 7.95 (978-0-9713530-2-2(6)) Smart & Smarter Publishing.

Bowman, Vicki. Julie Through the Looking Glass. 2005. 55p. pap. 12.95 (978-1-4137-4679-2(9)) PublishAmerica, Inc.

Bowness, Kim. The Brave Engineers. 2007. (Illus.). 30p. (J). lib. bdg. 19.95 (*978-1-933732-36-7(9) , Bear Hug Bks.) MidAmerica Publishing Co.

Bowyer, Clifford. The Spread of Darkness: The Imperium Saga: the Adventures of Kyria. 2007. (Adventures of Kyria: 7). 168p. (YA). pap. 5.99 (*978-0-9787782-1-7(9) , BK0022) Silver Leaf Bks., LLC.

Bowyer, Clifford B. The Apprentice of Zoldex: The Imperium Saga: the Adventures of Kyria. 2008. (Adventures of Kyria: 8). 208p. (YA). pap. 5.99 (*978-0-9787782-2-4(7) , BK0023) Silver Leaf Bks., LLC.

—The Awakening: The Imperium Saga: the Adventures of Kyria. 2004. (Adventures of Kyria: Bk. 2). 192p. (J). pap. 5.99 (978-0-9744354-1-1(4) , BK0004) Silver Leaf Bks., LLC.

—Quest for the Shard: The Imperium Saga: the Adventures of Kyria. 2007. (Adventures of Kyria: 6). 176p. (YA). pap. 5.99 (978-0-9744354-8-0(1) , BK0020) Silver Leaf Bks., LLC.

—The Shard of Time: The Imperium Saga: the Adventures of Kyria. 2005. (Adventures of Kyria: Vol. 4). 192p. (J). pap. 5.99 (978-0-9744354-3-5(0) , BK0007) Silver Leaf Bks., LLC.

—Trapped in Time: The Imperium Saga: the Adventures of Kyria. 2006. (Adventures of Kyria: 5). 160p. (YA). pap. 5.99 (978-0-9744354-7-3(3) , BK0008) Silver Leaf Bks., LLC.

The Boy Who Tricked the Ghosts. 2003. (J). 14.99 (978-0-89610-769-4(8)) Island Heritage Publishing.

Boyce, Catherine & Boyce, Peter. A Royal Tea. Sibert, Stephanie Grace, illus. 2006. 32p. (J). per. 16.95 (978-0-9778420-1-8(0)) Semper Studio.

Boyce, Frank Cottrell. Millions. (gr. 3 up). 2004. (Illus.). 256p. (J). 15.99 (978-0-06-073330-8(6)); 2004. (Illus.). 256p. (J). lib. bdg. 16.89 (978-0-06-073331-5(4)); 2005. 272p. (YA). reprint ed. pap. 6.99 (978-0-06-073332-2(2) , Harper Trophy) HarperCollins Pubs.

Boyd, David. Spellbound. 2002. (gr. 3-6). lib. bdg. 12.95 (978-0-613-77599-1(6)) Tandem Library Bks.

Boyd, Kate & Brixton, Iris. The Quercus Quest. 2006. 159p. pap. 12.72 (978-1-4116-8843-8(0)) Lulu.com.

Braddock, Paige. Jane's World, Vol. 4. 2006. (Illus.). 160p. pap. 15.00 (978-0-9766707-3-5(9)) Girl Twirl Comics.

Bradfield, Roger. The Flying Hockey Stick. Bradfield, Roger, illus. 2006. (J). 18.95 (978-1-930900-31-8(7)) Purple Hse. Pr.

Bradford, Emma. Kat & the Emperor's Gift. Sano, Kazuhiko, illus. 1998. (Stardust Classics). 117p. (J). (gr. 2-6). 12.95 (978-1-889514-19-2(5)); pap. 5.95 (978-1-889514-20-8(9)) Dolls Corp.

—Kat & the Secrets of the Nile. Sano, Kazuhiko, illus. 1998. (Stardust Classics). 116p. (J). (gr. 2-6). 12.95 (978-1-889514-13-0(6)); pap. 5.95 (978-1-889514-14-7(4)) Dolls Corp.

Bradley, Alex. 24 Girls in 7 Days (Splashproof Ed) 2007. 1p. (YA). (gr. 7). pap. 5.99 (978-0-14-240834-6(4) , Puffin) Penguin Group (USA) Inc.

Bradman, Tony. Tommy Niner & the Moon of Doom. 1998. (Illus.). 98p. (J). 7.95 (978-0-14-037592-3(9)) Penguin Bks., Ltd. GBR. *Dist:* Trafalgar Square Publishing.

Brady, Laurel. Bronson Row. Date not set. 144p. (YA). (gr. 5 up). 14.99 (978-0-06-029234-8(2)); lib. bdg. 15.89 (978-0-06-029235-5(0)); mass mkt. 4.99 (978-0-06-440949-0(X)) HarperCollins Pubs.

Braga, Joyce. The Friary. 2000. 187p. (YA). (gr. 6 up). 9.99 (978-0-88092-302-6(4) , 3024) Royal Fireworks Publishing Co.

Bram, Christopher. Notorious Dr August: His Real Life & Crimes. 2001. (gr. 7-12). lib. bdg. 23.45 (978-0-613-37021-9(X)) Tandem Library Bks.

Bramble bear; the Missing Necklace. 2006. (J). per. 3.99 (978-1-934004-12-8(X)) Byeway Bks.

Branch, Beverly, illus. Thumbelina: A Tale about Being Nice. 2006. (J). 6.99 (978-1-59939-024-6(8)) Reader's Digest Young Families, Inc.

Brandeis, Madeline. Shaun O'Day of Ireland. 2004. reprint ed. pap. 22.95 (978-1-4179-2725-8(9)) Kessinger Publishing, LLC.

Brandreth, Gyles. Bruno Bruin Discovers America. Dennis, Peter, illus. 1999. 48p. (J). 16.99 (978-0-233-99533-5(1)) Andre Deutsch GBR. *Dist:* Independent Pubs. Group.

Brashear Hopper, Celia. The Merry Adventures of Blade & Friends. 2007. (YA). lib. bdg. 26.95 (*978-0-9795460-1-3(X)) Creative Bk. Pubs.

Braswell, Robert William. Jeffrey: Out from the Depths of Innocence. 2003. (gr. 7-12). lib. bdg. 30.35 (978-0-613-89759-4(5)) Tandem Library Bks.

—Jeffrey: Out from the Depths of Innocence. 2003. 358p. (YA). pap. 19.95 (978-0-595-26734-7(3) , Writers Club Pr.) iUniverse, Inc.

Brazil, Angela. Monitress Merle. 2004. reprint ed. pap. 1.99 (978-1-4192-3491-0(9)) Kessinger Publishing, LLC.

Breathed, Berkeley. The Last Basselope: One Ferocious Story. Breathed, Berkeley, illus. 2001. (Illus.). 32p. (J). (ps-17). pap. 6.99 (978-0-316-12664-9(0)) Little Brown & Co.

—Last Basselope: One Ferocious Story. 2001. (gr. 3-6). lib. bdg. 14.10 (978-0-613-35643-5(8)) Tandem Library Bks.

Breckenridge, Gerald. Radio Boys on the Mexican Border. 2006. 78.99 (*978-1-4280-2532-5(4)) IndyPublish.com.

Bredsdorff, Bodil. The Crow-Girl: The Children of Crow Cove. Ingwersen, Faith, tr. from DAN. 2004. (Illus.). 160p. (J). 16.00 (978-0-374-31247-3(8) , Farrar, Straus & Giroux (BYR)) Farrar, Straus & Giroux.

Breen-Bond, Tecia. Cousins: A Swift, Sweet Story. 2002. 138p. (J). pap. 10.95 (978-0-595-21207-1(7) , Writers Club Pr.) iUniverse, Inc.

Brege, Brege. Mick Morris Myth Solver #4 Grudge of the Gremlins. 2007. pap. 6.99 (*978-0-9774119-3-1(1)) Team B Creative LLC.

Brennan, Herbie. Faerie Wars. 2004. 368p. (J). reprint ed. pap. 8.95 (978-1-58234-943-5(6) , Bloomsbury Children) Bloomsbury Publishing.

—El Monstruo del Pantano. (Raton de Biblioteca Coleccion). (SPA.). 128p. (J). (gr. 3). 7.95 (978-84-88061-87-4(0)) Serres, Ediciones, S. L. ESP. *Dist:* Lectorum Pubns., Inc.

—The Purple Emperor: Faerie Wars II. 2004. 400p. (J). 17.95 (978-1-58234-880-3(4) , Bloomsbury Children) Bloomsbury Publishing.

Brenner, Barbara, et al. Bunny Tails. Munsinger, Lynn, illus. 2005. 32p. 15.95 (978-0-689-03925-6(5) , Milk & Cookies) ibooks, Inc.

Brett, Jan. The Trouble with Trolls. Brett, Jan, illus. 1999. (Illus.). 32p. (J). (ps-3). pap. 6.99 (978-0-698-11791-4(3) , Putnam Juvenile) Penguin Group (USA) Inc.

—The Trouble with Trolls. 1999. (978-0-606-17433-6(8)) Tandem Library Bks.

Brewster, Joy, et al. Summer Fun: Sticker Storybook. Binder, Eric & Thompson Brothers Staff, illus. 2003. (Powerpuff Girls Ser.). 24p. (J). pap. 5.99 (978-0-439-44934-2(0)) Scholastic, Inc.

Brezina, Thomas. El Ataque del Caballero de Piedra (The Attack of the Stone Knight) Jos, A. Santiago Tagle, tr. Kruger, Dietmar, illus. 2001. (Corazon de Dragon Ser.: No. 3). (SPA.). 126p. 11.95 (978-84-348-7826-6(7)) SM Ediciones ESP. *Dist:* AIMS International Bks., Inc.

—Who Can Save Vincent's Hidden Treasure? Museum of Adventures. Sartin, Laurence, illus. 2005. 96p. (J). (gr. 4-7). pap. 16.95 (978-3-7913-3432-5(8)) Prestel Publishing.

Brezina, Thomas & Sartin, Laurence. Who Will Find Vincent's Treasury of Colors? 2005. (Illus.). 96p. pap. 16.95 (978-3-7913-3433-2(6)) Prestel Publishing.

Bricker, Chris. The Leaping Frogs of Calameris County. 2006. 48p. pap. 12.95 (978-1-4241-2408-4(5)) PublishAmerica, Inc.

Briggs, Molly Anne. Momma's Favorite Rock. 2006. (J). pap. 8.00 (978-0-8059-7070-8(3)) Dorrance Publishing Co., Inc.

Bright, J. E. All or Nothing. 2000. (NASCAR Racers Ser.: Vol. 5). 144p. (J). (gr. 4-7). pap. 4.50 (978-0-06-107197-3(8)) HarperCollins Pubs.

—High Stakes. 2001. (NASCAR Racers Ser.: No. 8). 144p. (J). (gr. 2-6). 4.50 (978-0-06-107202-4(8) , Harper Entertainment) HarperCollins Pubs.

Brighter Minds, creator. Land Before Time Multimedia. gif. ed. 2005. (Illus.). 32p. (J). cd-rom 9.99 (978-1-57791-165-4(2)) Brighter Minds Children's Publishing.

Brightwood, Laura, illus. Mousanga Bira Mousa. Brightwood, Laura, . 2006. (J). (978-0-9789871-1-4(X)) 3-C Institute for Social Development.

Brimmer, Debi & Coleson, Julie. How Six Little Ipu Got Their Names. 2005. (Illus.). 32p. (J). 16.95 incl. audio compact disk (978-1-57306-186-5(7)) Bess Pr., Inc.

Brin, Susannah. Bronco Buster. rev. ed. 1999. (Take Ten Ser.). 64p. (YA). (gr. 4-12). pap. 3.95 (978-1-58659-041-3(3)) Artesian Pr.

—Climb. 2000. (gr. 5-8). lib. bdg. 11.80 (978-0-613-51205-3(7)) Tandem Library Bks.

—The Climb. rev. ed. 1999. (Take Ten Ser.). 61p. (YA). (gr. 4-12). pap. 3.95 (978-1-58659-042-0(1)) Artesian Pr.

—Seal Killers. 2000. (gr. 5-8). lib. bdg. 11.80 (978-0-613-51223-7(5)) Tandem Library Bks.

—Search & Rescue. rev. ed. 1999. (Take Ten Ser.). 62p. (YA). (gr. 4-12). pap. 3.95 (978-1-58659-043-7(X)) Artesian Pr.

—Search & Rescue. 2000. (gr. 7-12). lib. bdg. 11.80 (978-0-613-51055-4(0)) Tandem Library Bks.

—Tough Guy. rev. ed. 1999. (Take Ten Ser.). 62p. (YA). (gr. 4-12). pap. 3.95 (978-1-58659-045-1(6)) Artesian Pr.

Brink, Hazel. The Runaway Little Red Lawnmower. 2005. 32p. (J). 15.95 (978-1-931945-46-2(2)) Expert Publishing, Inc.

Brinley, Bertrand R. The New Adventures of the Mad Scientists' Club. Geer, Charles, illus. 2002. 210p. (J). 17.95 (978-1-930900-11-0(2)) Purple Hse. Pr.

Brinson, Heather. The Adventure of the Poisoned Drink. 2005. 59p. pap. 12.95 (978-1-4137-9239-3(1)) PublishAmerica, Inc.

Britt, Ruben, Jr. Lakota. Ardison, Darrell K., ed. Williams, Khary, illus. 2000. 38p. (J). pap. 8.99 (978-0-9705317-0-4(2) , 11452) Genesis Group.

Broadhurst, D. T. The Faringo Kid. 2006. pap. 13.49 (*978-1-4259-1836-1(0)) AuthorHouse.

Brock, J. Judd. Ima Toothlusa Is My Name. 2007. (Illus.). 38p. (J). per. 11.99 (*978-1-59879-247-8(4)) Lifevest Publishing, Inc.

Bromell, Jan. Naturally Plum Persuasion. 2002. 32p. (J). pap. 9.00 (978-0-8059-5415-9(5)) Dorrance Publishing Co., Inc.

Brook, Harry, retold by. Kidnapped. 2004. (Paperback Classics Ser.). 144p. (J). lib. bdg. 12.95 (978-1-58086-640-8(9) , Usborne) EDC Publishing.

Brook, Henry, retold by. Moby Dick. 2005. (Paperback Classics Ser.). 144p. (J). pap. 4.95 (978-0-7945-0899-9(5) , Usborne) EDC Publishing.

Brookes, Diane. It Was a Lemon. Lewis, Stephen, illus. l.t. ed. 1999. 24p. (J). (ps-3). pap. (978-1-894303-03-3(2)) Raven Rock Publishing.

—Spring Blizzard. Wilcox, Betty M., illus. l.t. ed. 1999. 24p. (J). (ps-3). pap. (978-1-894303-04-0(0)) Raven Rock Publishing.

Brookes, Diane & Dahl, Roald. A Novel Study for Grades One & Two Based on Esio Trot. Blake, Quentin, illus. 1998. (J). pap., tchr. ed. (978-0-9683449-3-4(3)) Raven Rock Publishing.

Brooks, Bruce. Asylum for Nightface. 1999. (J). (978-0-606-17459-6(1)) Tandem Library Bks.

Brooks, Felicity. Jason & the Argonauts. Humphreys, Graham, illus. 2005. 144p. (J). pap. 4.95 (978-0-7945-0275-1(X) , Usborne) EDC Publishing.

Brooks, Jillian. Troublemaker. 2002. (Wondergirls Ser.: No. 3). (J). (gr. 3-7). pap. 4.99 (978-0-439-35491-2(9) , Scholastic Paperbacks) Scholastic, Inc.

Brooks, Kevin. Being. 2007. 336p. (J). (gr. 7 up). pap. 16.99 (978-0-439-89973-4(7) , Chicken Hse., The) Scholastic, Inc.

Brooks, Stephen J. Alexander Asenby Saves the Day. 2007. (J). 16.95 (978-0-9769017-5-4(7)) Purple Sky Publishing.

Brooks, Walter R. Freddy & the Dragon. Wiese, Kurt, illus. 2000. 239p. (J). (gr. 3 up). 23.95 (978-1-58567-026-0(X)) Overlook Pr., The.

—Freddy & the Perilous Adventure. Wiese, Kurt, illus. 2001. 245p. (J). 23.95 (978-1-58567-178-6(9)) Overlook Pr., The.

—Freddy Goes to the North Pole. Wiese, Kurt, illus. 2001. 306p. (J). 23.95 (978-1-58567-104-5(5)) Overlook Pr., The.

Brooksbank, Angela. I've Lost My Yellow Zebra. 1999. (Illus.). 32p. (J). (ps-k). pap. 6.95 (978-0-7641-0875-4(1)) Barron's Educational Series, Inc.

Brother, Ernest. Dick of Copper Gap. 2005. pap. 24.95 (978-1-4179-8824-2(X)) Kessinger Publishing, LLC.

Brothers Grimm Staff. The Fisherman & His Wife/ el pescador y su Esposa. 2004. (Illus.). (J). (978-1-933530-20-8(0)) Bingo Bks., Inc.

—Hansel & Gretel/Hansel y Gretel. 2004. (Illus.). (J). (978-1-933530-14-7(6)) Bingo Bks., Inc.

—Little Red Riding Hood/Caperucita Roja. 2004. (Illus.). (J). (978-1-933530-15-4(4)) Bingo Bks., Inc.

—Rapunzel/Raponchigo. 2004. (Illus.). (J). (978-1-933530-16-1(2)) Bingo Bks., Inc.

—Rumpelstiltskin. 2004. (Illus.). (J). (978-1-933530-17-8(0)) Bingo Bks., Inc.

—Snow White/Blancanieves. 2004. (Illus.). (J). (978-1-933530-19-2(7)) Bingo Bks., Inc.

—Tom Thumb/Pulgarcito. 2004. (Illus.). (J). (978-1-933530-24-6(3)) Bingo Bks., Inc.

—The Water of Life/ el aqua de Vida. 2004. (Illus.). (J). (978-1-933530-23-9(5)) Bingo Bks., Inc.

Brouwer, Sigmund. Madness at Moonshiner's Bay. 2003. (Accidental Detectives Ser.). 144p. (J). pap. 5.99 (978-0-7642-2571-0(5)) Bethany Hse. Pubs.

—Madness at Moonshiner's Bay. 2003. (gr. 5-8). lib. bdg. 14.15 (978-0-613-84510-6(2)) Tandem Library Bks.

—Mystery Tribe of Camp Blackeagle. 2003. (gr. 5-8). lib. bdg. 14.15 (978-0-613-84509-0(9)) Tandem Library Bks.

—Wired. 2005. (Orca Currents Ser.). 112p. (J). (gr. 4-10). pap. 7.95 (978-1-55143-478-0(4)) Orca Bk. Pubs. USA.

Brower, Douglas. Backyard Friends. 2006. pap. 8.95 (978-0-533-15454-8(5)) Vantage Pr., Inc.

Brown, Abbie Farwell. Tales of the Red Children. 2006. pap. 20.95 (***978-1-4286-1602-8(0)***) Kessinger Publishing, LLC.

Brown, Alvin R. Native American Action Stories: Exciting Events in Nine Different Tribes. 2005. 254p. per. 15.95 (978-1-59453-885-8(9) , 3307, Airleaf Publishing) Airleaf Publishing & Bookselling.

Brown, Anne. The Dumari Chronicles: Year One: Year One. 2007. 376p. (YA). per. 20.95 (***978-0-595-45725-0(8)***) iUniverse, Inc.

Brown, Corinne. Let's Keep This Secret. 2004. (J). per. 5.95 (978-0-9745951-5-3(2)) All For One Pr.

Brown, Debbie T. Johnny & the Gnome: The Beginning of an Ordian Adventure. Khoury, Elysaar, illus. 1998. 134p. (J). (gr. k-6). pap. 5.95 (978-0-9640537-9-3(9)) Monterey Publishing.

Brown, Don. Alice Ramsey's Grand Adventure. 2000. (Illus.). 32p. (J). (gr. k-3). pap. 6.95 (978-0-618-07316-0(7)) Houghton Mifflin Co. Trade & Reference Div.

Brown, Elizabeth. Susan¿s Big Adventure. 2004. 32p. (J). per. (978-1-55306-837-2(8) , Epic Pr.) Essence Publishing.

Brown, Joe. The Flights of Marceau: Week One. 2007. (Illus.). 56p. (J). 22.50 (***978-0-9797495-0-6(6)***) Majestic Eagle Publishing.

Brown, Kelly. Kit & Caboodle. 2005. 50p. pap. 12.95 (978-1-4137-3689-2(0)) PublishAmerica, Inc.

Brown, Kevin. In a Field of Sunflowers. 2006. pap. 9.00 (978-0-8059-6921-4(7)) Dorrance Publishing Co., Inc.

Brown, Marc. Arthur to the Rescue. 13th ed. 2006. (Illus.). 24p. (J). (ps-1). mass mkt. 3.99 (978-0-316-05773-8(8)) Little Brown & Co.

—Arthur Writes a Story. 1998. (Arthur Adventure Ser.). (J). (gr. k-3). 12.75 (978-0-606-13153-7(1)) Tandem Library Bks.

—Binky Rules. 2000. (Arthur Chapter Bks.: Bk. 24). (J). pap. 3.95 (978-0-316-12244-3(0)) Little Brown & Co.

Brown, Marcia, et al. Children's Classics II, 5 bks., Set. unabr. ed. 1999. (Illus.). (J). (ps-3). pap. 76.95 incl. audio (978-0-87499-495-7(0)) Live Oak Media.

Brown, Margaret Wise. The Little Scarecrow Boy. Diaz, David, illus. 2005. 40p. (J). (ps-2). reprint ed. pap. 6.99 (978-0-06-077891-0(1) , Harper Trophy) HarperCollins Pubs.

—Sneakers, the Seaside Cat. Mortimer, Anne, illus. 32p. (J). (ps-ps). 2005. pap. 6.99 (978-0-06-443622-9(5)); 2003. 16.99 (978-0-06-028692-7(X)) HarperCollins Pubs.

Brown, Monica. Chavela's Magic Chick. Morales, Magaly, illus. 2008. (ENG & SPA.). (J). 15.95 (***978-0-87358-918-5(1)*** , Luna Rising) Northland Publishing.

Brown, Philip. Franky Franklyn's Fantastic Adventure. 2007. 118p. (J). pap. 10.99 (***978-1-60247-322-5(6)***) Tate Publishing & Enterprises, L.L.C.

Brown, Ruth. Night Time Tale. 2005. (Illus.). 32p. (J). 19.99 (***978-1-84270-344-1(7)***) Transworld Publishers Ltd. GBR. *Dist:* Independent Pubs. Group.

Brown, Sally. Alexandra's Travel Adventure: Making Friends in Mexico. Lyons, Deborah, illus. 2005. 32p. (J). pap. 9.95 (978-1-57860-232-2(7)) Emmis Bks.

Brown, Tony. Water's Edge. 2006. 180p. per. (***978-1-84685-163-6(7)*** , Exposure Publishing) Meadow Bks.

Brown, Wanda E. The Great Escape (from Loneliness) A Dragon Safe Ending Book. 2003. 24p. (J). per. 39.95 (978-1-59196-272-4(2)) Instantpublisher.com.

Browne, A. A. Beginnings. 2001. 108p. (J). pap. 9.95 (978-0-595-16544-5(3)) iUniverse, Inc.

Browne, Anthony. Into the Forest. Browne, Anthony, illus. 2004. (Illus.). 32p. (J). (gr. k-3). 16.99 (978-0-7636-2511-5(6)) Candlewick Pr.

—King Kong. Segovia, Francisco, tr. 2006. (SPA., Illus.). 92p. (J). (978-968-16-7987-3(3)) Fondo de Cultura Economica.

Brownlow, Brooke. The Magic of Old Oak Hill. 2005. 48p. pap. 12.95 (978-1-4241-0223-5(5)) PublishAmerica, Inc.

Brozek, Joan Bartlett. Hiram & the Rattales. 1999. (Illus.). 84p. (J). reprint ed. pap. 7.95 (978-0-913507-39-1(3)) New Forums Pr.

Brozon, M. B. Odisea Por el Espacio Inexistente. (la Orilla Del Viento Ser.). (SPA., Illus.). 200p. (J). 6.99 (978-968-16-6149-6(4) , 134) Fondo de Cultura Economica USA.

Bruce, Jonathan C. There Is a Season. 2001. 324p. pap. 17.95 (978-0-595-17565-9(1) , Writers Club Pr.) iUniverse, Inc.

Bruce, Karl. Annie Apple & the Teleportation Phantoms from Outer Space. 2006. (YA). pap. 16.00 (978-0-8059-7156-9(4)) Dorrance Publishing Co., Inc.

Bruchac, Joseph. Heroes & Heroines, Monsters & Magic: Native American Legends & Folktales. Burgevin, Daniel, illus. 2004. 200p. (gr. 3-7). reprint ed. pap. 12.95 (978-0-89594-995-0(4) , Crossing Pr., Inc.) Ten Speed Pr.

—Sacajawea. 2000. (Illus.). 208p. (YA). (gr. 7-12). 17.00 (978-0-15-202234-1(1) , Silver Whistle) Harcourt Trade Pubs.

Brumett, Jonas O. The Legend of Kittyfish: A Learning Storybook. Johnson, Sandra L., illus. l.t. ed. 2002. 64p. (J). (ps-3). 16.95 (978-1-892812-01-8(0)) Froginhood & Friends, Inc.

Bruna, Dick. Hide & See. 2004. (Illus.). 12p. 6.99 (978-1-59226-042-3(X)) Big Tent Entertainment, Inc.

—Let's Learn: Animals. 2004. (Illus.). 24p. pap. 4.99 (978-1-59226-167-3(1)) Big Tent Entertainment, Inc.

—Let's Learn: Boris in the Forest. 2004. (Illus.). 24p. pap. 4.99 (978-1-59226-174-1(4)) Big Tent Entertainment, Inc.

—Let's Learn: Miffy Looks Around. 2004. (Illus.). 24p. pap. 4.99 (978-1-59226-173-4(6)) Big Tent Entertainment, Inc.

—Let's Learn: Miffy's Adventure. 2004. (Illus.). 24p. pap. 4.99 (978-1-59226-171-0(X)) Big Tent Entertainment, Inc.

—Let's Learn: Miffy's Day. 2004. (Illus.). 24p. pap. 4.99 (978-1-59226-170-3(1)) Big Tent Entertainment, Inc.

—Let's Learn: School Time. 2004. (Illus.). 24p. pap. 4.99 (978-1-59226-172-7(8)) Big Tent Entertainment, Inc.

—Miffy. 2004. (Illus.). 24p. (J). 7.99 (978-1-59226-022-5(5)) Big Tent Entertainment, Inc.

Brundage, Jerome. The Princess & the Bear: Book I: the Battle for Aradam. 2007. (ENG.). 148p. per. 19.95 (***978-1-4241-6346-5(3)***) PublishAmerica, Inc.

Bryan, Jennifer. The Different Dragon. Hosler, Danamarie, illus. 2006. (J). pap. 10.95 (978-0-9674468-6-8(4)) Two Lives Publishing.

Bryant, Annie. Freestyle with Avery. 2007. (Beacon Street Girls Ser.). 240p. (J). (gr. 4-8). pap. 7.99 (***978-1-933566-01-6(9)***) B*tween Productions, Inc.

—Green Algae & Bubblegum Wars. 2007. 240p. (J). pap. 7.99 (978-0-9758511-8-0(7)) B*tween Productions, Inc.

Bryant, Annie. Maeve on the Red Carpet. 2007. 240p. pap. 7.10 (***978-1-933566-08-5(6)***) B*tween Productions, Inc.

Bryant, Bonnie. Dude Ranch. 2007. (Saddle Club Ser.: No. 6). 144p. (J). (gr. 4-6). lib. bdg. 11.99 (978-0-385-90422-3(3) , Yearling) Random Hse. Children's Bks.

Buchanan, Paul. Ask Willie. 1999. (gr. 3-6). lib. bdg. 14.15 (978-0-613-72656-6(1)) Tandem Library Bks.

—Heads I Win, Tails You Lose. 1999. (gr. 3-6). lib. bdg. 14.15 (978-0-613-72655-9(3)) Tandem Library Bks.

Buchanan, Paul & Randall, Rod. Ask Willie, Vol. 12. 1999. (Misadventures of Willie Plummett Ser.: Bk. 12). 128p. (J). (gr. 3-7). 5.99 (978-0-570-05478-8(8) , 56-1941GJ) Concordia Publishing Hse.

—Heads I Win, Tails You Lose, Vol. 11. 1999. (Misadventures of Willie Plummett Ser.: Bk. 11). 128p. (J). (gr. 3-7). 5.99 (978-0-570-05477-1(X) , 56-1940GJ) Concordia Publishing Hse.

Buchanan, Steve. More True Tales of Shorty Stevens the le. 2006. pap. 15.50 (***978-1-4259-8161-7(5)***) AuthorHouse.

Buchholz, Quint. Duerme Bien, Pequeño Oso. 2nd ed. 2003. (Rosa y Manzana Ser.). (SPA., Illus.). 208p. 15.16 (978-84-89804-10-4(9)) Loguez Ediciones ESP. *Dist:* Lectorum Pubns., Inc.

Buchwald, Claire. Max Talks to Me. Ritz, Karen, illus. 2007. (Sit! Stay! Read! Ser.). 24p. (J). 15.95 (***978-0-940719-03-3(7)***) Gryphon Pr., The.

Buckingham, Matt. Bright Stanley. Buckingham, Matt, illus. 2006. (Illus.). 32p. (J). (ps-2). 15.95 (978-1-58925-059-8(1) , tiger tales) ME Media LLC.

Bucky Badger a Children's Story: The Storm. 2005. (J). 9.99 (978-0-9765510-3-4(9)) Badgerland Bks. LLC.

Bucky Badger A Children's Story: Treasure. 2005. (J). 9.99 (978-0-9765510-2-7(0)) Badgerland Bks. LLC.

Bucky Badger A Children's Story: Yard Sale. 2005. (J). 9.99 (978-0-9765510-1-0(2)) Badgerland Bks. LLC.

Budig, Greg. I Hear the Wind. unabr. ed. 2005. (Illus.). 34p. (J). 18.95 (978-0-88045-164-2(5)) Stemmer Hse. Pubs., Inc.

Buehner, Caralyn. Snowmen at Night Jigsaw Puzzle Book. Buehner, Mark, illus. 2007. 12p. (J). (ps). 10.99 (***978-0-8037-3254-4(6)*** , Dial) Penguin Group (USA) Inc.

Buel, Hubert & Erskine, Dorothy Ward. North with de Anza. 2004. (Illus.). 234p. (J). (gr. 6-10). pap. 9.95 (978-0-8263-3631-6(0)) Univ. of New Mexico Pr.

Bugbee, M. Howe. Beyond the Road: Mayhaven Award for Children's Fiction. 2006. 288p. (YA). 23.95 (978-1-932278-08-8(7)) Mayhaven Publishing.

Buja, John E. & Morrison, Melody. Ballcourt of Death: Novel. 2000. (Illus.). 128p. (J). (gr. 7-12). pap. (978-1-894303-23-1(7)) Raven Rock Publishing.

Bujor, Flavia. The Prophecy of the Stones: A Novel. Coverdale, Linda, tr. from FRE. 2004. Tr. of Prophetie des Pierres. 400p. (gr. 5-17). 16.95 (978-0-7868-1835-8(2)) Hyperion Bks. for Children.

Buklis, Lawrence S. Mysteries from the Yukon: Three Fisheries Adventures for Students. 2003. 217p. (J). pap. 21.00 (978-1-888569-52-0(2)) American Fisheries Society.

Bulla, Clyde Robert. The Sword in the Tree. Bowles, Bruce, illus. 2000. (Trophy Chapter Bks.). 112p. (J). (gr. 2-5). pap. 4.99 (978-0-06-442132-4(5) , Harper Trophy) HarperCollins Pubs.

—The Sword in the Tree. 2000. (978-0-606-18723-7(5)) Tandem Library Bks.

Buller, Laura. What's Weirder Than A Wookiee? 2005. (Dk Readers Ser.). (Illus.). 32p. (J). 14.99 (978-0-7566-1146-0(6) , 1241626) Dorling Kindersley Publishing, Inc.

Buller, Laura & Simkins, Kate. What Is a Wookiee? 2005. (Dk Readers Ser.). (Illus.). 32p. (Orig.). (J). (ps-12). pap. 3.99 (978-0-7566-1157-6(1) , 1241626) Dorling Kindersley Publishing, Inc.

Bullis, J. Noah Peepkin - a Small Adventure. 2003. (Illus.). 20p. (J). per. 12.00 (978-0-9747878-6-2(8)) Jeremy's Things.

Bullock, Harold B. The Battle for the Worlds. Anderson, Jean, ed. 2nd rev. ed. Date not set. (Tarlian Adventures Ser.: Vol. 1). 120p. (J). (gr. 2-5). reprint ed. pap. (978-1-929248-00-1(8)) Golden Oak Pubs.

—The City in the Clouds. Dumas, Barbara, ed. 2001. (Tarlian Adventures Ser.: Vol. 5). 120p. (J). (gr. 2-5). pap. (978-1-929248-08-7(3)) Golden Oak Pubs.

—The Crystal Castle. Dumas, Barbara, ed. 1999. (Tarlian Adventures Ser.: Vol. 2). 140p. (J). (gr. 2-5). pap. (978-1-929248-02-5(4)) Golden Oak Pubs.

—The Dragon of Raldan. Dumas, Barbara, ed. 1999. (Tarlian Adventures Ser.: Vol. 3). 120p. (J). (gr. 2-5). pap. (978-1-929248-04-9(0)) Golden Oak Pubs.

Bully Busters in the Adventures of Wooly Bully. 2003. (Illus.). 100p. (J). per. 8.95 (978-0-9770294-0-2(9)) Better Me Bks., Inc.

Bulwer-Lytton, Edward. Los Ultimos Dias de Pompeya. (SPA., Illus.). 168p. (YA). 14.95 (978-84-7281-129-4(8) , AF1129) Auriga, Ediciones S.A. ESP. *Dist:* Continental Bk. Co., Inc.

Bunting, Eve. Blackwater. 2000. 160p. (J). (gr. 5 up). pap. 5.99 (978-0-06-440890-5(6) , Harper Trophy) HarperCollins Pubs.

—Emma's Turtle. Winborn, Marsha, illus. 2007. 32p. (J). (ps-2). 15.95 (***978-1-59078-350-4(6)***) Boyds Mills Pr.

—The Hideout. unabr. ed. 2000. (YA). pap. 41.25 incl. audio (978-0-7887-3213-3(7) , 95847X4) Recorded Bks., LLC.

—Noche de Humo. Andujar, Gloria de Aragon, tr. Diaz, David, illus. 1999. (SPA.). 36p. (J). (gr. 2-4). pap. 7.00 (978-0-15-201946-4(4) , Voyager Bks./Libros Viajeros) Harcourt Children's Bks.

—Noche de Humo. 1999. (978-0-606-16516-7(9)); (SPA.). lib. bdg. 14.15 (978-0-613-16782-6(1)) Tandem Library Bks.

—Smoky Night. 2002. (Illus.). (J). 13.19 (978-0-7587-0073-5(3)) Book Wholesalers, Inc.

—Smoky Night. Diaz, David, illus. 1999. 36p. (J). (ps-3). pap. 7.00 (978-0-15-201884-9(0) , Harcourt Paperbacks) Harcourt Children's Bks.

—Smoky Night. 1999. (978-0-606-16515-0(0)); lib. bdg. 14.15 (978-0-613-18279-9(0)) Tandem Library Bks.

Bunton, M. Catherine. The Little Maestro. 2000. 108p. pap. 9.95 (978-0-595-13855-5(1)) iUniverse, Inc.

Burch, Sharon. Freddie the Frog & the Bass Clef Monster: 2nd Adventure: Bass Clef Monster. Harris, Tiffany, illus. 2006. (J). 23.95 (978-0-9747454-8-0(0)) Mystic Publishing.

—Freddie the Frog & the Thump in the Night. 2004. (Illus.). (J). 23.95 incl. audio compact disk (978-0-9747454-9-7(9)) Mystic Publishing.

Burch, Steve, et al. Mercury's Fire. 2001. (Pendragon Tales Ser.: Vol. 2). 317p. (YA). pap. 13.99 (978-0-9708834-1-4(2)) SPYMYTHS, Inc.

Burchell, Graham. The Ice Spells of Krollinad. 2005. 213p. pap. 11.99 (978-1-4116-5258-3(4)) Lulu.com.

Burchett, Loni R. Bear & Katie in a Day at Nestlenook Farm. l.t. ed. 2004. (Illus.). 76p. (J). per. 11.95 (978-0-9742815-1-3(4)) Black Lab Publishing LLC.

Burden, Sara. Tom's Wheels. 2003. 16p. (J). per. 12.95 (978-1-56167-755-9(8)) American Literary Pr.

Burgan, Michael. Hot Iron: The Adventures of a Civil War Powder Boy. Rodríquez, Pedro, illus. 2007. (J). pap. (***978-1-59889-406-6(4)***); 56p. (gr. 3-6). 23.93 (***978-1-59889-311-3(4)***) Stone Arch Bks.

Burger, Sharon. The Five Amigos: A Funeral at Midnight. 2005. 48p. pap. 12.95 (978-1-4137-7101-5(7)) PublishAmerica, Inc.

—Five Amigos: The Mystery of Taboo Island. 2005. 48p. pap. 12.95 (978-1-4137-6300-3(6)) PublishAmerica, Inc.

Burgess, Karin Whiting. It's Always a Good Day for Crabbing. 2005. (J). 16.95 (978-0-9718303-4-9(7)) Flat Hammock Pr.

Burgess, Melvin. Bloodsong. 2007. 384p. (YA). (gr. 9 up). pap. 7.99 (***978-1-4169-3616-9(5)*** , Simon Pulse) Simon & Schuster Children's Publishing.

Burgess, Melvin. The Copper Treasure. Williams, Richard, illus. rev. ed. 2000. 112p. (YA). (gr. 4-7). 15.95 (978-0-8050-6381-3(1) , Holt, Henry & Co. Bks. For Young Readers) Holt, Henry & Co.

Burgess, Robert F. The Mystery of Mound Key. 2000. (Illus.). 192p. (gr. 4-7). pap. 12.95 (978-0-595-00348-8(6) , Backinprint.com) iUniverse, Inc.

Burgess, Thornton W. The Adventures of Reddy Fox. 2005. 26.95 (978-1-4218-0995-3(8) , 1st World Library - Literary Society) 1st World Publishing, Inc.

—The Adventures of Sammy Jay. 2006. (Dover Children's Thrift Classics Ser.). 96p. (J). (gr. 3-6). pap. 2.00 (978-0-486-44946-3(7)) Dover Pubns., Inc.

Burghardt, Frances. Pushie the Kitten-Cat. 2000. (J). pap. 8.00 (978-0-8059-4857-8(0)) Dorrance Publishing Co., Inc.

Burgoyne, Tom. The Adventures of Super Phanatic. Epstein, Len, illus. 2007. 32p. (***978-0-9705804-7-4(9)***) Middle Atlantic Pr.

Burkett & Watson. Emergency in Escape Pod Four. 1999. (Star Wars Science Adventures Ser.). (978-0-606-16615-7(7)) Tandem Library Bks.

Burkett, Kathy. Dive! Ethan Flask & Professor Von Offel's Underwater Adventures. 2001. (Mad Science Ser.). (Illus.). 68p. (J). pap. (978-0-439-27090-8(1)) Scholastic, Inc.

—The Doomed Tower: Ethan Flask & Professor Von Offel's Adventures in Engineering. 2001. (Mad Science Ser.). (Illus.). 68p. (J). pap. (978-0-439-23580-8(4)) Scholastic, Inc.

Burkhardt, Al. The Archimedeams. Burkhardt, Al, illus. 1999. (Illus.). 32p. (YA). (gr. 8-12). pap. 18.95 (978-0-914534-17-4(3) , 130) Stokes Publishing Co., Inc.

Burks, Brian. Walks Alone. 2000. 144p. (YA). (gr. 6 up). pap. 6.00 (978-0-15-202472-7(7) , Harcourt Paperbacks) Harcourt Children's Bks.

—Walks Alone. 2000. (978-0-606-20336-4(2)); (gr. 5-8). lib. bdg. 14.15 (978-0-613-30180-0(3)) Tandem Library Bks.

Burleigh, Robert. Into the Woods: John James Audubon Lives His Dream. Minor, Wendell, illus. 2003. 40p. (J). (gr. 2-5). 16.95 (978-0-689-83040-2(8) , Atheneum) Simon & Schuster Children's Publishing.

Burnard, Damon. The Amazing Adventures of Soupy Boy. 2000. (Illus.). 96p. (J). pap. 8.99 (978-0-440-86365-6(1)) Transworld Publishers Ltd. GBR. *Dist:* Trafalgar Square Publishing.

Burnett, Eric. Trapped in Tenochtitlan: An Aztec Adventure. 2002. 113p. pap. 9.95 (978-0-595-22161-5(0) , Writers Club Pr.) iUniverse, Inc.

Burnford, Sheila. The Incredible Journey. 148p. (J). pap. 4.99 (978-0-8072-8323-3(1) , Listening Library) Random Hse. Audio Publishing Group.

Burningham, John. Borka. 40th anniv. ed. 2004. (Illus.). 32p. 16.99 (978-0-224-06494-1(0) , Jonathan Cape) Random Hse. Children's Bks. GBR. *Dist:* Trafalgar Square Publishing.

—Trubloff. 2001. (Illus.). 32p. (J). pap. 8.99 (978-0-09-941428-5(7) , Red Fox) Random Hse. Children's Bks. GBR. *Dist:* Trafalgar Square Publishing.

—Would You Rather. 2003. (Illus.). 32p. (J). (gr. k-3). 6.95 (978-1-58717-217-5(8) , SeaStar Bks.) Chronicle Bks. LLC.

—Would You Rather. 2003. (gr. k-3). lib. bdg. 14.10 (978-0-613-87928-6(7)) Tandem Library Bks.

Burns, Brian. My Blankey & Me. 2004. 20p. pap. 14.95 (978-1-4137-3675-5(0)) PublishAmerica, Inc.

Burns, Emily. Manitou Art Caper. 2003. (Rocky Mountain Mysteries Ser.: 2). 128p. (J). per. 4.95 (978-0-9723259-1-2(3) , RMM2) Covered Wagon Publishing LLC.

Burns, John. The Many Adventures of Pengey Penguin. Coles, James, illus. 2005. 207p. (J). per. 17.95 (978-0-9774227-0-8(4)) San Francisco Story Works.

Burroughs, Edgar Rice. At the Earth's Core. 2001. Tr. of 184. (gr. 3-6). lib. bdg. 9.50 (978-0-613-88729-8(8)) Tandem Library Bks.

Burshek, Edward & Burshek, Tonja. Explorers of the Word: Episode 1: the Creation. Peterson, Melanie, illus. 2007. (ENG.). 76p. per. 14.95 (***978-1-4241-6691-6(8)***) PublishAmerica, Inc.

Burton, Rick. Running on Empty. 2005. 72p. pap. 14.95 (978-1-4137-6600-4(5)) PublishAmerica, Inc.

Bury, Laurie D. The Adventures of Dalbert Juan: Dalbert Goes to Arizona. Gallo, Karen A., illus. 2000. (J). (ps-2). 12.95 (978-0-9702319-2-5(X)) Rhette Enterprises, Inc.

—The Adventures of Dalbert Juan: Enjoying Michigan. Gallo, Karen A., illus. 2000. (J). 12.95 (978-0-9702319-1-8(1)) Rhette Enterprises, Inc.

—The Adventures of Dalbert Juan: Passport. Gallo, Karen A., illus. 2000. (J). (ps-2). 12.95 (978-0-9702319-3-2(8)) Rhette Enterprises, Inc.

Bushell, Sharon. Bernie Jones & the Blazing Bandits. 2005. (Illus.). 152p. (J). per. 6.99 (978-0-9721725-5-4(6)) Road Tunes Media.

—The Trouble with Bernie. 2004. (Illus.). 160p. (J). per. 6.99 (978-0-9721725-2-3(1)) Road Tunes Media.

Busy Builders. (Flip Flap Fun Book Ser.). 10p. (J). bds. (978-2-7643-0138-8(3)) Phidal Publishing, Inc./Editions Phidal, Inc.

Busy City. (Flip Flap Fun Book Ser.). 10p. (J). bds. (978-2-89393-820-2(5)) Phidal Publishing, Inc./Editions Phidal, Inc.

Butcher, A. J. The Serpent Scenario. 2004. (Spy High Ser.: Vol. 3). 224p. (J). (gr. 5-8). pap. 6.99 (978-0-316-73766-1(6)) Little, Brown Bks. for Young Readers.

Butcher, Nancy. Dr. Jekyll & Mr. Dog. l.t. ed. 1999. (Adventures of Wishbone Ser.: No. 14). (Illus.). (J). (gr. 4 up). lib. bdg. 22.60 (978-0-8368-2592-3(6)) Stevens, Gareth Inc.

—It's Snow Problem. 2001. (gr. 3-6). lib. bdg. 13.00 (978-0-613-43934-3(1)) Tandem Library Bks.

Butineau, W. Turning Thirteen. 2005. 165p. pap. 19.95 (978-1-4137-5817-7(7)) PublishAmerica, Inc.

Butler, Berwyn. Dinky the Doorknob: The Adventures of Sir Dinkum Wilhelm, the Third Earl of Surridge. 2005. (J). per. 11.99 (***978-1-933732-02-2(4)*** , Round Rock Chapter Bks.) MidAmerica Publishing Co.

A B

Butler, Berwyn & McClean, Shorty. Dinky the Doorknob. 2006. (J). lib. bdg. 21.95 (*978-1-933732-04-6(0)) , Round Rock Chapter Bks.) MidAmerica Publishing Co.

Butler, Tammi. I Am a Ward of the Court. 2003. (YA). pap. (978-0-9729847-0-6(4)) Sundance Entertainment.

Butler, Ted D. The Pandora Project, Bk. 5. 2007. 280p. (YA). pap. 14.99 (978-1-59092-292-7(1) , Blue Works) Windstorm Creative.

Butler, William S. Scraper Jones: Treasure Hunter. 2007. 320p. pap. 19.95 (*978-1-59663-770-2(6) , Castle Keep Pr.) Rock, James A. & Co. Pubs.

Butt, Fanny. Adventures at Smiths Bridge. 2004. 205p. pap. 19.95 (978-1-4137-5018-8(4)) PublishAmerica, Inc.

The Butterfly Pyramid, 6 vols. (Multicultural Programs Ser.). 16p. (gr. 1-6). 42.50 (978-0-7802-8326-8(0)) Wright Group, The.

Byers, Carla Rae. The Golden Word of My Way Vol. 3: The Adventures of Snowflake & Astar. l.t. ed. 2001. (gr. 3 up). 7.95 (978-1-930910-14-0(2)) Heyokah Publishing Co.

—Swiss Cheese Heart! The Adventures of Snowflake & Astar. Kepler, Kit, ed. l.t. ed. 2000. Vol. 3. 14p. (gr. 6 up). 7.95 (978-0-9656124-8-7(1)) Heyokah Publishing Co.

—What Color Are Your Bones? The Adventures of Snowflake & Astar. Kepler, Kit, ed. l.t. ed. 2000. Vol. 1. 19p. (gr. 1 up). 7.95 (978-0-9656124-5-6(7)) Heyokah Publishing Co.

Byers, Letha. Tesa, the Adopted Cow-bird. 2007. pap. 9.00 (*978-0-8059-8438-5(0)) Dorrance Publishing Co., Inc.

Byers, Rob. The Adventures of Pork & Bean. 2006. (ENG.). 124p. (J). per. 13.99 (*978-1-4141-0769-1(2)) Pleasant Word.

Byng, Georgia. Molly Moon's Hypnotic Time Travel Adventure. 2007. 400p. (J). (gr. 3-7). pap. 6.99 (978-0-06-075034-3(0) , Harper Trophy) HarperCollins Pubs.

Byrd, Robert. The Hero & the Minotaur: The Fantastic Adventures of Theseus. Byrd, Robert, illus. 2005. (Illus.). 40p. (J). (gr. 1-ps). 17.99 (978-0-525-47391-6(2) , Dutton Juvenile) Penguin Group (USA) Inc.

Byrd, Sandra. Just Between Friends. 2001. (gr. 3-6). lib. bdg. 13.00 (978-0-613-82434-7(2)) Tandem Library Bks.

Bywaters, Mayer. Tempest. (J). 16.95 (978-1-58717-206-9(2) , SeaStar Bks.) Chronicle Bks. LLC.

Bywaters, Mayer & Mayer, Marianna. Tempest. Bywaters, Lynn, illus. 2005. 40p. (J). 16.95 (978-0-8118-5054-4(4) , SeaStar Bks.) Chronicle Bks. LLC.

C D Stampley Enterprises, creator. Billy & Baxter Learn to Build, 4 vols. 2005. (Illus.). 24p. (J). (ps-ps). 8.95 (978-1-58087-099-3(6)) Stampley, C.D. Enterprises, Inc.

—Billy & Baxter on City Streets, 4 vols. 2005. (Illus.). 24p. (J). (ps-ps). 8.95 (978-1-58087-101-3(1)) Stampley, C.D. Enterprises, Inc.

Cabell, James Branch. The Jewel Merchants. 2004. reprint ed. pap. 15.95 (978-1-4191-6788-1(X)); pap. 1.99 (978-1-4192-6788-8(4)) Kessinger Publishing, LLC.

Cabeza de Vaca: el conquistador Gentil: Libros Aventuras (Adventure Books) 2000. (MacMillan/McGraw-Hill. Estudios Sociales Ser.). (ENG & SPA.). (gr. 5 up). (978-0-02-148716-5(2)) Macmillan/McGraw-Hill Schl. Div.

Cabot, Meg. Missing You. 2007. (1-800-Where-R-You Ser.: No. 5). 288p. (J). pap. 6.99 (978-0-06-087430-8(9) , HarperTeen) HarperCollins Pubs.

Caddy, David. Whacko! 2001. (Illus.). 136p. pap. 10.95 (978-1-86368-308-1(9)) Fremantle Pr. AUS. *Dist:* International Specialized Bk. Services.

Cadnum, Michael. Daughter of the Wind. 2003. 272p. (J). pap. 17.95 (978-0-439-35224-6(X) , Orchard Bks.) Scholastic, Inc.

—Zero at the Bone. 1998. (978-0-606-13943-4(5)) Tandem Library Bks.

Cahill, Timothy. Johnny Tractor & Friends: Taking Over. Linden, Pat, ed. Barron, Kurt, illus. 1998. (John Deere Storybook for Little Folks Ser.). 20p. (J). (gr. 2 up). 6.95 (978-1-887327-19-0(3)) Ertl Co., Inc.

—Johnny Tractor & Friends: Working Together. Linden, Pat, ed. Barron, Kurt, illus. 1998. (John Deere Storybook for Little Folks Ser.). 20p. (J). (gr. 2 up). 6.95 (978-1-887327-20-6(7)) Ertl Co., Inc.

Caldwell, V. M. Solar-Powered Sam. Morrison, Cathy, illus. 1999. (Books for Young Learners). 12p. (J). (gr. k-2). pap. 5.00 (978-1-57274-282-6(8) , A2498) Owen, Richard C. Pubs., Inc.

Calero, Dennis. You're Not the Captain of Me! 2006. 272p. pap. 9.95 (978-1-59687-375-9(2)) ibooks, Inc.

Calhoun, Dia. Firegold. Blondon, Herve, illus. 1999. (J). (gr. 7-12). 285p. 15.95 (978-1-890817-10-7(4)); 286p. pap. 9.95 (978-1-890817-28-2(7)) Winslow Pr.

Calhoun, T. B. Race Ready. 1998. (NASCAR Pole Position Adventure Ser.). 128p. (YA). (gr. 3-7). pap. 3.99 (978-0-06-105959-9(5) , Harper Entertainment) HarperCollins Pubs.

Calu, John & Hart, Dave. The Treasure of Tucker's Island. 2003. 80p. (YA). pap. 8.95 (978-0-595-27953-1(8)) iUniverse, Inc.

Cameron, Ian. Stirling Bridge. (Illus.). 32p. pap. 6.95 (978-1-899827-07-7(2)) Scottish Children's Pr. GBR. *Dist:* Wilson & Assocs.

Camp, Lindsay. Rambling Ted's Terrible Mix-Up. 2001. (Illus.). 25p. pap. 6.95 (978-0-00-664700-3(6)) Zondervan.

Campbell, Joanna. Samantha's Irish Luck. 2004. (Thoroughbred Ser.: No. 66). 176p. mass mkt. 4.99 (978-0-06-059525-8(6) , Harper Entertainment) HarperCollins Pubs.

Campdepadros, Jorgelina & Campdepadros, Eduardo. Descubriendo Tesoros. 2000. (Treehouse Gang Ser.).Tr. of Discovering Treasures. (SPA.). 32p. pap. 3.99 (978-0-8254-1139-7(4) , Editorial Portavoz) Kregel Pubns.

—El Misterioso Senor Robles. 2000. (Treehouse Gang Ser.).Tr. of Mysterious Mr. Robles. (SPA.). 32p. pap. 3.99 (978-0-8254-1138-0(6) , Editorial Portavoz) Kregel Pubns.

—Rescatemos a Windy. 2000. (Treehouse Gang Ser.).Tr. of Rescuing Windy. (SPA.). 32p. pap. 3.99 (978-0-8254-1140-3(8) , Editorial Portavoz) Kregel Pubns.

Campos, Jacqueline. The Adventures of Lil' Wolf, Twinkie, to. 2005. 63p. pap. 12.95 (978-1-4137-8494-7(1)) PublishAmerica, Inc.

Canela. Barco Pirata. 2002. (SPA.). 64p. (J). pap. 6.95 (978-1-4000-0015-9(7)) Random Hse., Inc.

Caniff, Milton. The Complete Terry & the Pirates Vol. 1: 1934 - 1936 a Library of American Comics Original. 2007. 368p. 49.99 (*978-1-60010-100-7(3)) Diamond Bk. Distributors.

Cann, Jonathan V. Night of the Crimson Twig. 2000. (Illus.). 378p. (YA). pap. 17.95 (978-0-595-12057-4(1)) iUniverse, Inc.

Cannon, Janell. Crickwing. 2000. (Illus.). 48p. (J). (gr. 1-4). 16.00 (978-0-15-201790-3(9)) Harcourt Children's Bks.

Canyons. 1999. (YA). 9.95 (978-1-56137-482-3(2)) Novel Units, Inc.

Capcom, et al, creators. Devil May Cry. 2006. pap. 7.99 (978-1-59816-450-3(3) , Tokyopop Adult) TOKYOPOP, Inc.

Capdevila, Paco. Nene, Nena y Guau. 2000. (SPA.). 120p. (J). (ps-k). Vol. 4. 12.76 net. (978-84-392-8368-3(7)); Vol. 5. 12.76 net. (978-84-392-8369-0(5)); Vol. 6. 12.76 net. (978-84-392-8370-6(9)) Lectorum Pubns., Inc.

Capdevila, Roser & Vendrell, Maria Martinez. Cambios y Distancias. 97th ed. 2003. Tr. of Changes & Distances. (SPA.). 24p. pap. 22.30 (978-84-233-1625-0(4)) Harcourt Schl. Pubs.

—Como Duele... 2003. Tr. of Does It Hurt.... (SPA.). 24p. (J). 7.95 (978-84-233-1566-6(5)) Ediciones Destino ESP. *Dist:* Planeta Publishing Corp.

— Uno Mas.Tr. of One More. (SPA., Illus.). 24p. (J). 7.95 (978-84-233-1508-6(8)) Ediciones Destino ESP. *Dist:* Planeta Publishing Corp.

Capeci, Anne. The Cascade Mountain Railroad Mysteries: Danger! Dynamite! 2003. (Cascade Moutain Railroad Mystery Ser.: No. 1). (Illus.). 144p. (J). (gr. 1-5). 12.95 (978-1-56145-288-0(2)) Peachtree Pubs., Ltd.

—Daredevils. Casale, Paul, illus. 2004. (Cascade Mountain Railroad Mysteries Ser.). 144p. (J). (gr. 2-3). 12.95 (978-1-56145-307-8(2)) Peachtree Pubs., Ltd.

—The Magic School Bus Chapter Book No.17: Food Chain Frenzy. 2004. (gr. 3-6). lib. bdg. 11.80 (978-0-613-87596-7(6)) Tandem Library Bks.

Capitol Mysteries. 2005. (J). (978-1-59564-732-0(5)) Steps To Literacy, LLC.

Capotosto, Anthony. No Shoes Required. 2005. 49p. pap. 8.00 (978-1-4116-2523-5(4)) Lulu.com.

Capriola, Arlene & Swenson, Rigmor. The Gingerbread Man. Mastry, Cherisse, ed. Burns, Kathy, illus. 1998. (Once upon a Time Ser.). (J). (gr. k-2). pap., wbk. ed. 12.95 incl. audio (978-1-57022-173-6(1)) ECS Learning Systems, Inc.

—Jack & the Beanstalk. Mastry, Cherisse, ed. Burns, Kathy, illus. 1998. (Once upon a Time Ser.). (J). (gr. k-2). pap., wbk. ed. 12.95 incl. audio (978-1-57022-174-3(X)) ECS Learning Systems, Inc.

Captain America. 2003. (J). per. (978-1-57657-906-0(9)) Paradise Pr., Inc.

Capucilli, Alyssa Satin. Biscuit Visits the Farm. Schories, Pat, illus. 2002. (Biscuit Ser.). 20p. (J). (ps-1). pap. 6.99 (978-0-694-01526-9(1)) HarperCollins Pubs.

Cardosi, Calesse. The Gifts. 2007. 192p. (YA). 16.95 (*978-0-9776281-3-1(2)) HPH Publishing.

Carey, John. Cook Spies. 2005. 34p. (J). per. (978-0-9773723-2-4(4)) Trent's Prints.

Cargile, Michael E. Spike's Erie Adventure: On the Steamship William G. Mather. Campbell, Jenny, illus. 2000. 32p. (J). (ps-6). pap. 9.95 (978-0-9665995-1-0(9)) Spike Enterprises.

—Spike's Grand Adventure. Shephard, Tom, illus. 1998. 32p. (J). (ps-6). pap. 9.95 (978-0-9665995-0-3(0)) Spike Enterprises.

Cargill, Linda. Jason & Medea. 2001. 157p. (YA). (gr. 7 up). 9.99 (978-0-88092-548-8(5) , 5485) Royal Fireworks Publishing Co.

Carignan, Michael J. The First Witness. Fuller, Ann, illus. 1998. (J). (ps-6). mass mkt. 4.95 (978-1-892589-00-2(1)) Madjec Jet Publishing Co.

Carle, Eric. From Head to Toe Soft Book. 2005. (J). 20.00 (978-0-9774677-2-3(4)) Small World Toys.

—Rooster's off to See the World. Carle, Eric, illus. 2002. (Illus.). (J). 15.53 (978-0-7587-3530-0(8)) Book Wholesalers, Inc.

—Rooster's off to See the World. Carle, Eric, illus. 2002. (Classic Board Bks.). (Illus.). 26p. (J). bds. 7.99 (978-0-689-84901-5(X) , Little Simon) Simon & Schuster Children's Publishing.

—Rooster's off to See the World. 1999. (978-0-606-16316-3(6)); lib. bdg. 15.30 (978-0-613-18325-3(8)) Tandem Library Bks.

Carlson, Amanda. Sultenfuss Moose's Lost Slipper. 2006. 26p. 18.03 (978-1-4116-7729-6(3)) Lulu.com.

Carman, Patrick. Beyond the Valley of Thorns. 2005. (Land of Elyon Ser.: Bk. 2). (Illus.). 240p. (J). (ps-7). pap. 11.99 (978-0-439-70094-8(9) , Orchard Bks.) Scholastic, Inc.

—Beyond the Valley of Thorns (Mas Alla Del Valle de Espinos) 2006. (Tierra de Elyon Ser.: Bk. 2). 224p. (J). pap. 6.99 (978-0-439-87480-9(7) , Scholastic en Espanol) Scholastic, Inc.

Carman, Patrick. Into the Mist. 2007. 304p. (J). (gr. 4-7). pap. 11.99 (*978-0-439-89952-9(4) , Orchard Bks.) Scholastic, Inc.

Carmody, Isobelle. A Fox Called Sorrow. (Little Fur Ser.). (Illus.). (J). (gr. 1-7). 2008. 272p. 5.99 (978-0-375-83857-6(0)); 2007. 256p. 14.99 (978-0-375-83856-9(2) , Random Hse. Bks. for Young Readers); 2007. 256p. lib. bdg. 16.99 (978-0-375-93856-6(7) , Random Hse. Bks. for Young Readers) Random Hse. Children's Bks.

Carmody, Isobelle. A Mystery of Wolves: Little Fur #3. 2008. (J). pap. (*978-0-375-83859-0(7)); (Little Fur: 3). 12.99 (*978-0-375-83858-3(9)); (Little Fur: 3). lib. bdg. 15.99 (*978-0-375-93858-0(3)) Random Hse., Inc.

Carpenter, Phyllis & Ford, Marti. Sparky's Excellent Misadventures: My A. D. D. Journal by Me (Sparky) Horjas, Peter, illus. 1999. 32p. (J). (gr. k-6). pap. (978-1-55798-606-1(1) , 441-6061, Magination Pr.) American Psychological Assn.

Carr, Paul C. The Adventures of Three Cousins. 2006. 24.00 (978-0-8059-9032-4(1)) Dorrance Publishing Co., Inc.

Carradice, Phil. The Pirates of Thorne Island. 2002. 109p. pap. 12.95 (978-1-85902-979-4(5)) Beekman Bks., Inc.

Carrero, Jorge & Cody, William. Buffalo Bill. 2003. (Timeless Classics Ser.). (SPA., Illus.). 92p. (J). (gr. 5-8). pap. 12.95 (978-84-204-5778-9(7)) Santillana USA Publishing Co., Inc.

Carrol, Jacqueline. Enter the Viper with Cards. 2001. (gr. k-3). lib. bdg. 13.00 (978-0-613-72449-4(6)) Tandem Library Bks.

—Strongest Evil. 2003. (gr. 3-6). lib. bdg. 13.00 (978-0-613-72477-7(1)) Tandem Library Bks.

—Uncle's Big Surprise. 2002. (gr. k-3). lib. bdg. 13.00 (978-0-613-72494-4(1)) Tandem Library Bks.

Carroll, John. The Adventures of Robbie the Raindrop. 2006. 32p. (J). 19.99 (*978-1-59886-991-0(4)); per. 21.99 (*978-1-59886-706-0(7)) Tate Publishing & Enterprises, L.L.C.

Carroll, Lewis, pseud. Alice's Adventures in Wonderland. Oxenbury, Helen, illus. 2003. 207p. (J). (gr. 4-7). per. 22.25 (978-0-613-60270-9(6)) Tandem Library Bks.

—Alice's Adventures in Wonderland. 2000. (gr. 3-6). lib. bdg. 11.80 (978-0-613-63173-0(0)) Tandem Library Bks.

—Alice's Adventures in Wonderland / Through the Looking Glass & What Alice Found There. Bachelier, Anne, illus. 2005. (J). per. (978-0-9769071-1-4(9)); (978-0-9728620-8-0(0)); (978-0-9769071-0-7(0)); im. lthr. (978-0-9728620-9-7(9)) CFM.

—Alice's Adventures in Wonderland & Through the Looking-Glass: The Classic Collection. 2005. 256p. (J). pap. 7.99 (978-1-4003-0753-1(8)) Nelson, Thomas Inc.

—The Story of Sylvie & Bruno. 2005. pap. 31.95 (978-0-7661-9697-1(6)) Kessinger Publishing, LLC.

—Through the Looking-Glass. 140p. 2005. 26.95 (978-1-4218-0656-3(8)); 2004. pap. 10.95 (978-1-59540-106-9(7)) 1st World Publishing, Inc. (1st World Library - Literary Society).

—Through the Looking-Glass. 1999. (gr. 7-12). lib. bdg. 9.50 (978-0-613-82766-9(X)) Tandem Library Bks.

Carroll, Michael. Gathering. 2008. (Quantum Prophecy Ser.). 224p. (YA). (gr. 5). 16.99 (*978-0-399-24726-2(2) , Philomel) Penguin Group (USA) Inc.

Carroll, Michael. Quantum Prophecy: the Awakening: The Awakening. 2007. (Quantum Prophecy Ser.). 304p. (YA). (gr. 5). 16.99 (978-0-399-24725-5(4) , Philomel) Penguin Group (USA) Inc.

Carse, Jodi & Gallagher, Maria. Catch That Kid! Spangler, Brie, illus. 2006. (Stinky Boys Club Ser.: Vol. 4). 64p. (J). pap. 4.99 (978-0-448-43355-4(9) , Grosset & Dunlap) Penguin Group (USA) Inc.

Cart, Michael. Rush Hour: Reckless. 2006. 224p. (YA). (gr. 9). lib. bdg. 12.99 (978-0-385-90184-0(4) , Delacorte Bks. for Young Readers) Random Hse. Children's Bks.

Carter, Alden R. Between a Rock & a Hard Place. 1999. (Illus.). 224p. (J). (gr. 5-9). reprint ed. pap. 4.99 (978-0-590-37486-6(9)) Scholastic, Inc.

Carter, Anne Laurel. Under a Prairie Sky. Daniel, Alan & Daniel, Lea, illus. 2004. 32p. (J). (ps-ps). lib. bdg. 15.15 (978-0-606-30126-8(7)) Tandem Library Bks.

Carter, Herbert. The Boy Scouts on Sturgeon Island. 2004. reprint ed. pap. 21.95 (978-1-4191-5507-9(5)); pap. 1.99 (978-1-4192-5507-6(X)) Kessinger Publishing, LLC.

Carter, Jay. The Bully Caterpillar: An Adventurous Journey of the Inner Child. l.t. ed. 2003. (Illus.). 48p. reprint ed. pap. 7.95 (978-0-937004-17-3(0)) Unicorn Pr.

Carter, Joey. The Great Airboat Ride! A Cantor Kids! Book. 2006. 72p. pap. 9.95 (978-1-59800-523-3(5)) Outskirts Press, Inc.

—Lost in a Submarine! A Cantor Kids! Book. 2006. 56p. pap. 9.95 (978-1-59800-312-3(7)) Outskirts Press, Inc.

Carter, John C. R. Julio. 2001. (YA). pap. (978-1-56765-065-5(1) , R694P) AMSCO Schl. Pubns., Inc.

Cartoon Network Staff & Dower, Laura. Bubble Trouble. 2000. (Powerpuff Girls Ser.: Vol. 2). (Illus.). 32p. (J). (ps-3). pap. 3.50 (978-0-439-17306-3(X)) Scholastic, Inc.

Cartwright, Stephen, illus. Hercules. 2004. (Young Reading Series Two Ser.). 64p. (J). (gr. 2 up). pap. 5.95 (978-0-7945-0453-3(1) , Usborne) EDC Publishing.

—Jason & the Golden Fleece. 2004. (Young Reading Series Two Ser.). 64p. (J). (gr. 2 up). pap. 5.95 (978-0-7945-0451-9(5) , Usborne) EDC Publishing.

—Ulysses. 2004. (Young Reading Series Two Ser.). 64p. (J). (gr. 2 up). pap. 5.95 (978-0-7945-0452-6(3) , Usborne) EDC Publishing.

Caruso, D. A. The Burning House. 2005. pap. 14.99 (978-0-9765953-1-1(1)) Educational Adventures.

—Cool by the Pool. 2005. pap. 19.99 (978-0-9765953-0-4(3)) Educational Adventures.

Casanova, Mary. Danger at Snow Hill. Rayyan, Omar, illus. 2006. (Dog Watch Ser.: No. 3). 128p. (J). pap. 4.99 (978-0-689-86812-2(X) , Aladdin) Simon & Schuster Children's Publishing.

—Dog-Napped! Rayyan, Omar, illus. 2006. (Dog Watch Ser.: No. 2). 144p. (J). pap. 4.99 (978-0-689-86811-5(1) , Aladdin) Simon & Schuster Children's Publishing.

—To Catch a Burglar. Rayyan, Omar, illus. 2007. (Dog Watch Ser.: No. 4). 144p. (J). pap. 4.99 (978-0-689-86813-9(8) , Aladdin) Simon & Schuster Children's Publishing.

Case, Linda. Brigits Day of Fun. 2006. 28p. pap. 9.95 (*978-1-4327-0001-0(4)) Outskirts Press, Inc.

Cason, Anjanette. Praise Puppy's Adventure in Praise. 2007. (J). (*978-0-9755234-7-6(3)) DOMINIONHOUSE Publishing & Design.

Casperson, Lana. Shelter from the Storm. Miller, Margaret, illus. 1999. 256p. (J). (gr. 7-12). pap. 7.95 (978-0-9621392-1-5(1)) Lighthouse Christian Publishing.

Cassidy, Catherine. Indigo Blue. 2005. 256p. (YA). (gr. 5). 15.99 (978-0-670-05927-0(7) , Viking Juvenile) Penguin Group (USA) Inc.

Cassidy, Cathy. Dizzy. 2005. 272p. (J). (gr. 3-6). pap. 6.99 (978-0-14-240474-4(8) , Puffin) Penguin Group (USA) Inc.

Castilla, Julia Mercedes. Luisa Viaja en Tren. 2003. (SPA.). 128p. (978-958-30-0795-8(1) , PV30463) Panamericana Editorial COL. *Dist:* Lectorum Pubns., Inc.

—El Tesoro de la Pordiosera. Diaz, Carlos Manuel, illus. 2002. (SPA.). 118p. pap. 5.30 (978-958-04-6889-9(3)) Norma S.A. COL. *Dist:* Lectorum Pubns., Inc.

Castillo, Patricia. La Alimentacion de Tu Hijo. 1999. (SPA., Illus.). 324p. (978-84-08-01601-4(6)) GeoPlaneta, Editorial, S. A.

Castleberry, Stephen B., Sr. & Castleberry, Susie L. Weighty Matters. 2003. (Farm Mystery Ser.). 155p. (YA). per. 8.50 (978-1-891907-13-5(1)) Castleberry Farms Pr.

Castlemon, Harry. The Boy Trapper. 2006. (Illus.). pap. (*978-1-4065-1308-0(3)) Dodo Pr.

Castro, Griselda. De Como Nacieron las Sirenas. Roldan, Gustavo, illus. 2000. (Tren Azul Ser.). (SPA.). 32p. (J). (ps-2). (978-84-236-5492-5(3)) Edebé ESP. *Dist:* Baker & Taylor Bks., Lectorum Pubns., Inc.

Castro, Ramon. Uncle Moncho's Treasure Chest. 1999. (Illus.). 100p. (J). (gr. 2-6). pap. 7.99 (978-1-893181-31-1(6) , Lagesse Stevens) Martell Publishing Co.

Caszatt-Allen, Wendy. Fort Brokenheart. 2007. 120p. (J). pap. 6.95 (*978-1-934133-09-5(4)) Mackinac Island Pr., Inc.

Catanese, P. W. The Brave Apprentice. 2005. 240p. (J). (gr. 4-7). pap. 4.99 (978-0-689-87174-0(0) , Aladdin) Simon & Schuster Children's Publishing.

—The Eye of the Warlock. 2005. 256p. (J). (gr. 5-9). pap. 4.99 (978-0-689-87175-7(9) , Aladdin) Simon & Schuster Children's Publishing.

—The Mirror's Tale. 2006. 288p. (J). (gr. 4-8). pap. 4.99 (978-1-4169-1251-4(7) , Aladdin) Simon & Schuster Children's Publishing.

—The Riddle of the Gnome. 2007. 256p. (J). pap. 5.99 (978-1-4169-1252-1(5) , Aladdin) Simon & Schuster Children's Publishing.

—The Thief & the Beanstalk. 288p. (J). 2006. pap. 2.99 (978-1-4169-2500-2(7)); 2005. (gr. 4-7). pap. 4.99 (978-0-689-87173-3(2)) Simon & Schuster Children's Publishing. (Aladdin).

Catherall, Arthur. The Strange Intruder. 2006. (Adventure Library). (J). pap. 11.95 (978-1-883937-97-3(3)) Bethlehem Bks.

Cathie & Jessie's Noisy New England Adventure. 2006. (Illus.). 32p. (J). cd-rom 12.99 (978-0-9773526-1-6(7)) Diversified A+ Pubns.

Catran, Ken. Voyage with Jason. 2006. 208p. (J). 16.95 (978-1-894965-43-9(4)) Simply Read Bks. CAN. *Dist:* Perseus Distribution.

Catran, Wendy. Not Raining Today. 2002. (Takeaways Ser.). (Illus.). 160p. (YA). pap. (978-0-7344-0260-8(0) , Lothian Bks.) Hachette Livre Australia.

Cauldwell, E. S. Alma Mae & the Golden Treasure. Myers, Shari, illus. 2007. (J). per. 19.95 (*978-0-9788985-8-8(3)) A Better Be Write Pub.

Cavele, Keith. Storm Child. Bock, Jean-Marc, illus. 1999. (Tales of the 21st Century Ser.). 75p. (J). (gr. 4-7). pap. (978-1-894155-01-4(7)) Cethial & Bossche Co.

Cavender-Jenkin, Barbara. A Is for Abe. 2005. 77p. pap. 14.95 (978-1-4137-7763-6(X)) PublishAmerica, Inc.

Cazet, Denys. Minnie & Moo Adventure Series. Cazet, Denys, illus. 2004. (Illus.). pap. 45.95 incl. audio (978-1-59112-849-6(8)); pap. 51.95 incl. audio compact disk (978-1-59112-850-2(1)) Live Oak Media.

Center for Learning Network Staff. Cold Mountain: Curriculum Unit. 2000. (Novel Ser.). 78p. (YA). (gr. 9-12). spiral bd. 19.95 (978-1-56077-631-4(5)) Ctr. for Learning, The.

—A Connecticut Yankee in King Arthur's Court: Curriculum Unit —Teacher Guide. 2001. (Novel Ser.). 57p. (YA). tchr. ed., spiral bd. 19.95 (978-1-56077-690-1(0)) Ctr. for Learning, The.

—The Unvanquished: Curriculum Unit. 2000. (Novel Ser.). 78p. (YA). (gr. 9-12). spiral bd. 19.95 (978-1-56077-632-1(3)) Ctr. for Learning, The.

Cerasini, Marc. Nacho Libre Movie Novelization. 2006. 128p. (J). pap. 4.99 (978-1-4169-2762-4(X) , Simon Spotlight) Simon & Schuster Children's Publishing.

—The SpongeBob Squarepants Movie: A Novelization of the Hit Movie! novel ed. 2004. (Spongebob Squarepants Ser.). (Illus.). 144p. (J). pap. 4.99 (978-0-689-86840-5(5) , Simon Spotlight) Simon & Schuster Children's Publishing.

Cerasini, Marc, et al. The Getaway. Christmas, Lawrence & Johnson, Shane L., illus. 2007. (Sprouse Bros. 47 R. O. N. I. N. Ser.). 112p. (J). pap. 5.99 (*978-1-4169-3902-3(4) , Simon Spotlight) Simon & Schuster Children's Publishing.

—The Revelation. Pierandrei, Natalia & Christmas, Lawrence, illus. 2007. (Sprouse Bros. 47 R. O. N. I. N. Ser.). 128p. (J). (gr. 4-9). pap. 5.99 (978-1-4169-3607-7(6) , Simon Spotlight) Simon & Schuster Children's Publishing.

Cerasini, Marc, et al. The Siege. Christmas, Lawrence & Panosian, Dan, illus. 2007. (Sprouse Bros. 47 R. O. N. I. N. Ser.). 112p. (J). pap. 5.99 (*978-1-4169-3903-0(2) , Simon Spotlight) Simon & Schuster Children's Publishing.

Cervantes Saavedra, Miguel de. Rinconete y Cortadillo Level 2. 1998. (SPA.). (gr. 7-12). lib. bdg. 14.10 (978-0-613-80727-2(8)) Tandem Library Bks.

Chad Borrows Money. l.t. ed. 2003. (Illus.). 16p. (J). ring bd. 15.95 (978-0-9722829-6-3(3)) Red Carpet Publishing.

Chadwick, Robert. Vengeful Impulse. 2003. 70p. pap. 8.95 (978-0-595-27876-3(0)) iUniverse, Inc.

Chambers, Aidan. Postcards from No Man's Land. 2002. 320p. (J). (gr. 9-12). 19.99 (978-0-525-46863-9(3) , Dutton Juvenile) Penguin Group (USA) Inc.

Chananie, Gloria. Fearful Frannie & Her Fateful Trip to Maui. 2003. 57p. 9.95 (978-1-4137-0162-3(0)) PublishAmerica, Inc.

—Fearful Frannie's African Safari. 2006. 95p. pap. 14.95 (978-1-4241-2617-0(7)) PublishAmerica, Inc.

Chanda, J-P. The Big Sewer Surprise. Spaziante, Patrick, illus. 2004. (Teenage Mutant Ninja Turtles Ser.). 14p. (J). bds. 5.99 (978-0-689-87366-9(2) , Simon Spotlight) Simon & Schuster Children's Publishing.

Chandler, Andrew and Amanda. Gertrude & Abigail (the Adventures Thereof) 2006. 35p. (J). 18.90 (978-1-4116-7572-8(X)) Lulu.com.

Chapman, Allen. Bart Stirlings Road to Success or the Yo. 2007. pap. (*978-1-4065-1430-8(6)) Dodo Pr.

—Radio Boys First Wireless or Winning the. 2007. pap. (*978-1-4065-1432-2(2)) Dodo Pr.

Chapman, Andrew. Heroic Feats. 2005. (Thrillogy Ser.). (Illus.). 48p. (gr. 4-8). 17.50 (978-0-7910-8889-0(8)) Facts On File, Inc.

—Heroic Feats. 2000. (gr. 7-12). lib. bdg. 12.10 (978-0-613-28872-9(6)) Tandem Library Bks.

Chapman, Bob. Visitors. 2006. 304p. pap. (*978-1-84401-693-8(5)) Athena Pr.

Chapman, Brenda. Where Trouble Leads. 2007. (Illus.). 136p. (YA). (gr. 5 up). pap. 8.95 (*978-1-894917-44-5(8)) Napoleon Publishing/Rendezvous Pr. CAN. *Dist:* AtlasBooks Distribution.

Chapman, Tessie L. Guardians of the Enchanted Island. 2006. 89p. pap. 14.95 (978-1-4137-7104-6(1)) PublishAmerica, Inc.

Charbonnet, Gabrielle. Adventure in Walt Disney World. 7th ed. 1999. (Disney Girls Ser.). 128p. (J). (gr. 2-5). pap. 3.99 (978-0-7868-4390-9(X)) Disney Pr.

Charles, Donald. Adventures in a Bubble. 2007. (J). per. 7.99 (*978-1-59886-877-7(2)) Tate Publishing & Enterprises, L.L.C.

Charlie & the Kitten. 2006. (Charlie's Great Adventures: 5). (Illus.). 96p. (J). per. 5.95 (978-0-9702546-6-5(0)) GoodyGoody Bks.

Chaucer, Geoffrey. The Canterbury Tales - Literary Touchstone Edition. 2005. 128p. (YA). per. 3.99 (978-1-58049-396-3(3) , PWH3963) Prestwick Hse., Inc.

Cherubini, E. Pinocchio in Africa. 2007. pap. (*978-1-4065-1442-1(X)) Dodo Pr.

Cheryl, Bustle. Ralphie Goes on a Boat Ride. 2007. (J). pap. 7.99 (*978-1-60247-243-3(2)) Tate Publishing & Enterprises, L.L.C.

Chester, Laura. Hiding Glory. Lippincott, Gary, illus. 2007. 160p. (J). 18.95 (*978-1-59543-616-0(2)) Willow Creek Pr., Inc.

Chesterfield, Sadie. The Legend of Big Z. 2007. (Surf's Up Ser.). 24p. (J). pap. 3.99 (*978-0-06-115330-3(3) , Harper Entertainment) HarperCollins Pubs.

—Lion, the Witch, & the Wardrobe. Marderosian, Mark, illus. movie tie-in ed. 2005. (Narnia Ser.). 32p. (J). pap., act. bk. ed. 4.99 (978-0-06-076557-6(7)) Zonderkidz.

—Meet the Characters. 2006. (Ice Age 2 Ser.). 18p. (J). pap. 6.99 (978-0-06-083976-5(7)) HarperCollins Pubs.

Chetwin, Grace. Gerrad's Quest. Chetwin, Grace, illus. 1998. (Ulm Ser.). (Illus.). 151p. (J). pap. 20.00 (978-0-9649349-7-9(3) , Rivet Bks.) Feral Pr., Inc.

Chew, E. B. Daniel & the Grubby Old Book. 2007. 196p. per. 14.95 (*978-0-595-34880-0(7)) iUniverse, Inc.

Chiaramonti, Gregory. Probie: the Space Probe, Mission One: the Ocean of Europa. 2007. 32p. (J). 16.72 (*978-0-615-13848-0(9)) Chiaramonti, Gregory.

Chick, Bryan. The Secret Zoo. 2007. 252p. pap. 5.99 (*978-0-9791887-3-2(3)) Second Wish Pr.

Chickasaw Adventures: More than Warriors. 2005. (J). (978-1-4265-0002-2(5)) Layne Morgan Media, Inc.

Chickasaw Adventures: Tears at Fort Coffee. 2004. (J). (978-0-9762904-2-1(1)) Layne Morgan Media, Inc.

Chickasaw Adventures: The Battle of Akia. 2004. (J). (978-0-9762904-1-4(3)) Layne Morgan Media, Inc.

Chickasaw Adventures: The Civil War. 2005. (J). (978-1-4265-0000-8(9)) Layne Morgan Media, Inc.

Chickasaw Adventures: The Making of a Storyteller. 2004. (J). (978-0-9762904-3-8(X)) Layne Morgan Media, Inc.

Chickasaw Adventures: War with the Creeks. 2005. (J). (978-1-4265-0001-5(7)) Layne Morgan Media, Inc.

Chickasaw Adventures No. 1: The Journey Begins. 2004. (J). (978-0-9762904-0-7(5)) Layne Morgan Media, Inc.

Chihak, Sheena, ed. Bee Movie: Deluxe Sound Storybook. 2007. 22p. (J). 15.95 (*978-0-696-23384-5(3)) Meredith Bks.

—Bee Movie Book with Activity Kit. 2007. 32p. (J). 14.99 (*978-0-696-23386-9(X)) Meredith Bks.

Chikere, Chidi. The Adventures of Alfalfa. 1999. (Illus.). 100p. pap. 10.95 (978-1-58521-000-8(5)) Books for Black Children, Inc.

Child, Lauren. Quién Teme al Libro Feroz? 2004. (SPA., Illus.). 32p. (J). 17.99 (978-84-8488-075-2(3)) Serres, Ediciones, S. L. ESP. *Dist:* Lectorum Pubns., Inc.

Children's Magic Adventures. 2002. (J). per. (978-1-931456-09-8(7)) Athena Pr.

Childress, Jamie. Galactic Treasure Hunt: Lost City of Atlantis. Braun, Chris, illus. 2006. 120p. (J). pap. 4.99 (978-1-931882-62-0(2)) Adventures Unlimited Pr.

—Galactic Treasure Hunt: Lost City of the Moon. Braun, Chris, illus. 2005. 115p. (J). (ps-7). pap. 4.99 (978-1-931882-45-3(2)) Adventures Unlimited Pr.

Chima, Ahiru & Misu, Max. Ellena__- Ellen meets Frog King - 2005. 32p. pap. 14.99 (978-1-4116-4050-4(0)) Lulu.com.

Chima, Cinda Williams. Disney Adventure Stories. Disney Press Staff, ed. 2007. 320p. (ps-17). 15.99 (*978-1-4231-0436-0(6)) Disney Pr.

—Wizard Heir. 2007. 464p. (gr. 5-17). 17.99 (*978-1-4231-0487-2(0)) Hyperion Pr.

Chin, Oliver Clyde. The Adventures of Wonderbaby: From A to Z. Chiodo, Joe Allen, illus. 2005. 32p. bds. 8.95 (978-1-59702-001-5(X)) Immedium.

Chinchinian, Harry. Holly Brown & the Dragon Dingle. 1998. (Heather & Hally Brown Ser.). (Illus.). 134p. (J). (gr. k-3). pap. 9.95 (978-0-9653535-9-5(1) , 1883697) Plum Tree Pr.

Ching, Jacqueline. Cloned. 12th rev. ed. 2006. (Kim Possible Ser.: Bk. 12). 80p. (gr. 2-5). pap. 3.99 (978-0-7868-4691-7(7)) Disney Pr.

Ching, Jacqueline & Bones, Bess. Pirates of the Caribbean: A Storm at Sea. 2007. 32p. (gr. k-2). pap. 3.99 (*978-1-4231-0619-7(9)) Disney Pr.

Chisel Hedgehog Crazy Great Summer, 1. 2008. (Illus.). 256p. (J). per. 18.95 (*978-0-9794191-7-1(4)) McKellen-Caffey.

Cho, Takara. Warrior Chosen, Tekkan Wing: First Blood. 2002. 198p. (YA). pap. 13.95 (978-0-595-25017-2(3) , Writers Club Pr.) iUniverse, Inc.

Chosen. 1999. (YA). 9.95 (978-1-56137-746-6(5)); 11.95 (978-1-56137-747-3(3)) Novel Units, Inc.

Christen, Dennis H. Lundon's Bridge & the Three Keys. 2005. (YA). lib. bdg., act. bk. ed. 24.95 (978-0-9718151-3-1(5)); 2006. (ENG.). (J). per. 12.95 (978-0-9718151-2-4(7)) CG Star, L.L.C.

Christopher, Matt. Centering Court Sting. 1998. 11.15 (978-0-606-13260-2(0)) Tandem Library Bks.

—Tough to Tackle. 139p. (J). (gr. 3-5). pap. 3.95 (978-0-8072-1463-3(9) , Listening Library) Random Hse. Audio Publishing Group.

Christopherson, Keven. Adventures of the Sky Kids: Lost Treasure of Kolob Canyon. 2005. 58p. pap. 12.95 (978-1-4137-6514-4(9)) PublishAmerica, Inc.

Chronicle Books LLC Staff. Casey & Derek on the Ice. 2008. (J). 16.95 (978-0-8118-5132-9(X)) Chronicle Bks. LLC.

El Cid. (SPA., Illus.). 128p. (J). 11.95 (978-84-7281-098-3(4) , AF1098) Auriga, Ediciones S.A. ESP. *Dist:* Continental Bk. Co., Inc.

Ciminera, Siobhan. Franny in the Pumpkin Patch. 2008. 32p. (J). (ps-k). 3.99 (*978-0-448-44836-7(X) , Grosset & Dunlap) Penguin Group (USA) Inc.

Cincotta, Wendy. The Rescue of Georgeonus. 2002. (Adventures in Evergreen Ser.: Bk. 3). 128p. (J). (gr. 3-7). pap. 9.95 (978-0-9723010-2-2(X)) Evergreen Bks.

Cisco's Adventure Downunder. 2002. (Illus.). 80p. (J). per. 5.99 (978-0-9707924-2-6(5)) Tail it Like it is, Publishing.

Cizmich, Marilyne. Sonia, the Church Cat. 2007. (Illus.). 28p. (J). per. 9.99 (*978-1-60247-096-5(0)) Tate Publishing & Enterprises, L.L.C.

CK Books. The Adventures of Brady Bean: Operation: Canine Caper. Myers, Alishea, illus. 2007. (J). pap. 5.95 (*978-0-9797580-1-0(7)) CK Bks.

Claire, Elizabeth. The New Boy Is Lost! Reader/Teacher's Guide/CD Package: An ESL Picture Novel. 2005. pap. 39.00 incl. audio compact disk (978-0-86647-194-7(4)) Pro Lingua Assocs., Inc.

Clamp. Angelic Layer, 5 vols. (gr. 2-6). Vol. 1. 2002. (Illus.). 180p. pap. 9.99 (978-1-931514-47-7(X)); Vol. 3. 3rd rev. ed. 2002. 192p. (J). pap. 9.99 (978-1-59182-004-8(9)); Vol. 5. rev. ed. 2003. (Illus.). 196p. pap. 9.99 (978-1-59182-152-6(5)) TOKYOPOP, Inc. (Tokyopop Kids).

—Cardcaptor Sakura: Anime, 10 bks. 2002. Bk. 4. 148p. pap. 14.99 (978-1-59182-043-7(X)); Bk. 5. 148p. pap. 14.99 (978-1-59182-044-4(8)); Bk. 6. 148p. pap. 14.99 (978-1-59182-045-1(6)); Bk. 7. 148p. pap. 14.99 (978-1-59182-046-8(4)); Bk. 8. 148p. pap. 14.99 (978-1-59182-047-5(2)); Vol. 6. 184p. (gr. 2-6). pap. 9.99 (978-1-892213-74-7(5)) TOKYOPOP, Inc.

—Cardcaptor Sakura: Master of the Clow, 6 vols. (Illus.). 192p. (gr. 2-6). Vol. 1. 2002. pap. 9.99 (978-1-892213-75-4(3)); Vol. 3. 2003. pap. 9.99 (978-1-892213-77-8(X)); Vol. 4. 2003. pap. 9.99 (978-1-892213-78-5(8)) TOKYOPOP, Inc. (Tokyopop Kids).

—Cardcaptor Sakura Vol. 6, 6 vols. 6th rev. ed. 2003. (Master of the Clow Ser.). (Illus.). (gr. 2 up). pap. 9.99 (978-1-892213-80-8(X) , Tokyopop Kids) TOKYOPOP, Inc.

Clamp, creator. Angelic Layer, 5 vols., Vol. 4. rev. ed. 2003. (Illus.). 192p. (gr. 2 up). pap. 9.99 (978-1-59182-086-4(3) , Tokyopop Kids) TOKYOPOP, Inc.

—CardCaptor Sakura, 6 vols., Vol. 5. 2001. 184p. pap. 9.99 (978-1-892213-73-0(7)) TOKYOPOP, Inc.

—Legend of Chun Hyang, Vol. 1. 2004. (Illus.). 192p. (gr. 2-5). pap. 9.99 (978-1-59182-763-4(9) , Tokyopop Adult) TOKYOPOP, Inc.

Clamp, et al. Cardcaptor Sakura: Master of the Clow, 6 vols., Vol. 2. rev. ed. 2002. (Illus.). 192p. (gr. 2-6). pap. 9.99 (978-1-892213-76-1(1) , Tokyopop Kids) TOKYOPOP, Inc.

Clampitt, Ed & Fortier, Robert. Team Dawg Stranger Danger. ed. 2005. (Illus.). 30p. (J). per. 14.99 (978-0-9749378-1-6(9)) Team Dawg Productions, Inc.

Clancy, Tom. The Great Race. 1999. (Tom Clancy's Net Force Ser.). (978-0-606-20420-0(2)) Tandem Library Bks.

—Hidden Agendas. 1999. (gr. 7-12). lib. bdg. 16.45 (978-0-613-33473-0(6)) Tandem Library Bks.

—Safe House. 2000. (Tom Clancy's Net Force Ser.). (978-0-606-20427-9(X)); (gr. 7-12). lib. bdg. 13.00 (978-0-613-33493-8(0)) Tandem Library Bks.

Clancy, Tom, et al. Gameprey. 2000. (Tom Clancy's Net Force Ser.). 1p. mass mkt. 4.99 (978-0-425-17514-9(6) , Berkley) Penguin Group (USA) Inc.

—Private Lives. 2000. (Tom Clancy's Net Force Ser.: Vol. 9). 1p. (gr. 7-12). mass mkt. 4.99 (978-0-425-17367-1(4) , Berkley) Penguin Group (USA) Inc.

—Virtual Vandals. 1999. (Tom Clancy's Net Force Ser.: Vol. 1). 1p. (gr. 7-12). mass mkt. 4.99 (978-0-425-16173-9(0) , Berkley) Penguin Group (USA) Inc.

Clark, Betsy Huhn. Lizzie's Extraordinary Adventure. 2006. (Illus.). 24p. (J). 9.99 (978-1-4276-0116-2(X)) Aardvark Global Publishing.

Clark, Catherine. Icing on the Lake. 2005. 368p. (YA). (gr. 8 up). pap. 5.99 (978-0-06-081534-9(5)) HarperCollins Pubs.

Clark, Clara Gillow. Hill Hawk Hattie. Clark, Clara Gillow, illus. 2004. (Illus.). 176p. (J). (gr. 5 up). pap. 5.99 (978-0-7636-2559-7(0)) Candlewick Pr.

Clark, Gina Beth. Hannah's Quest. 2003. 261p. per. 19.95 (978-1-59453-026-5(2) , 1348) Airleaf Publishing & Bookselling.

Clark, John, ed. Donald Duck Adventures, Vol. 15. 2005. 128p. (YA). pap. 7.95 (978-0-911903-99-7(2)) Gemstone Publishing, Inc.

Clark, Kenneth L. The Adventures in Nit Picky: Home of the Fighting Tomcats. 2002. (Illus.). 162p. pap. 11.95 (978-0-9720043-0-5(0)) Clark, Kenneth L.

Clark, Malcolm. Bounty's Cave. 2007. (ENG.). 156p. per. 19.95 (*978-1-932762-82-2(5)) Elderberry Press, Inc.

Clark, Margaret. Care Factor Zero. 2000. 192p. (J). (gr. 4-6). pap. 6.99 (978-0-380-81390-2(4)) HarperCollins Pubs.

—The Gutless Gladiator: Fighting Is Not for the Faint of Heart! Denton, Terry, illus. 2006. (Bites Ser.). 96p. (J). pap. 3.95 (978-0-7624-2650-8(0) , Running Pr. Kids) Running Pr. Bk. Pubs.

Clark, Sheryl. Asking for Trouble: Prove It!, Take a Hike!, Knock It Off! 2005. (Triple Play-Yellow Ser.). (Illus.). 48p. (gr. 4-8). 41.85 (978-0-7910-9079-4(5)) Facts On File, Inc.

Clarke, Catherine. Ninja Turtles: The Next Mutation. 1998. (J). 3.99 (978-0-679-89301-1(6) , Random Hse. Bks. for Young Readers) Random Hse. Children's Bks.

Clarke, Gus. Nothing but Trouble. 1998. (Illus.). 32p. (J). (ps-1). pap. 9.95 (978-0-86264-841-1(6)) Andersen GBR. *Dist:* Trafalgar Square Publishing.

—The Sun Robbers. 2000. (Illus.). 64p. (J). 13.99 (978-0-86264-954-8(4)) Andersen GBR. *Dist:* Independent Pubs. Group.

Clarke, Pauline. The Return of the Twelves. Bryson, Bernarda, illus. 2001. (Company of Books Ser.). 296p. (YA). (gr. 5 up). 24.95 (978-1-58579-021-0(4) , Common Reader Editions) Akadine Pr., The.

Clasicos de Adventura. (Clasicos Juveniles Coleccion). (SPA.). (YA). (gr. 5-8). pap. (978-950-11-1300-6(0) , SG4723) Sigmar ARG. *Dist:* Lectorum Pubns., Inc.

Claybourne, Anna. Adventures of Ulysses. 2005. 144p. (J). pap. 4.95 (978-0-7945-0322-2(5) , Usborne) EDC Publishing.

Claycomb, Patty. My Magic Carpet Adventure. McMahon, Kelly, illus. 2002. (Two Can Read Ser.). 16p. (J). 2.99 (978-1-56472-657-5(6)) Edupress, Inc.

—My Night Adventure. McMahon, Kelly, illus. 2002. (Two Can Read Ser.). 16p. (J). 2.99 (978-1-56472-656-8(8)) Edupress, Inc.

—My Sidewalk Adventure. McMahon, Kelly, illus. 2002. (Two Can Read Ser.). 16p. (J). 2.99 (978-1-56472-658-2(4)) Edupress, Inc.

Clayton, A. J. An Egg-Citing Dream. 2006. 17.00 (*978-0-8059-9127-7(1)) Dorrance Publishing Co., Inc.

Cle, Troy. The Marvelous Effect. 2007. (Marvelous World Ser.: No. 1). 384p. (J). (gr. 5 up). 14.99 (978-1-4169-3958-0(X)) Simon & Schuster Children's Publishing.

Cleaning House. 2003. (J). per. (978-1-57657-964-0(6)) Paradise Pr., Inc.

Cleary, Beverly. Ramona's World. Dockray, Tracy, illus. 2006. 209p. (J). lib. bdg. 20.00 (*978-1-4242-0407-6(0)) Fitzgerald Bks.

Clemens, James. Wit'ch War. 2001. (Banned & the Banished Ser.: Vol. 3). (Illus.). 560p. pap. 7.99 (978-0-345-41710-7(0) , Del Rey) Random House Publishing Group.

Clement-Davies, David. Fell. 2007. 432p. (YA). pap. 19.95 (*978-0-8109-9470-6(4)) Abrams, Harry N. , Inc.

—Fire Bringer. 2002. 498p. (YA). (gr. 8-12). lib. bdg. 15.30 (978-0-613-44450-7(7)) Tandem Library Bks.

Clement-Davies, David. The Telling Pool. (gr. 7-17). 2007. 382p. (YA). pap. 7.95 (*978-0-8109-9257-3(4)); 2005. (Illus.). 376p. (J). 19.95 (978-0-8109-5758-9(2) , Abrams Bks. for Young Readers) Abrams, Harry N. , Inc.

Clements, Becky. A Picnic with Friends: Alaska Adventure Bears. 2003. (Alaska Adventure Bears Ser.). 16p. pap. 9.95 (978-1-888125-87-0(X)) Publication Consultants.

Clifford, Eth. Help! I'm a Prisoner in the Library. Hughes, George, illus. 2004. (Jo-Beth & Mary Rose Mystery Ser.). 112p. (J). (gr. 3-5). pap. 5.95 (978-0-618-49482-8(0)) Houghton Mifflin Co. Trade & Reference Div.

Clifford, Mary. Lonesome Road. 2005. 185p. pap. 19.95 (978-1-4137-6419-2(3)) PublishAmerica, Inc.

Clifford, Mary Louise. The Shalamar Code. 2006. 192p. (J). (gr. 7 up). pap. 8.95 (978-0-7387-0934-5(4) , Flux) Llewellyn Pubns.

Climent, Paco. El Tesoro del Capitan Nemo. 2003. (SPA.). 128p. (978-84-279-3246-3(4) , NG3561) Noguer y Caralt Editores, S. A. ESP. *Dist:* Lectorum Pubns., Inc.

—El Tesoror del Capitan Nemo.Tr. of Captain Nemo's Treasure. (SPA.). 123p. (YA). (gr. 5-8). 6.80 (978-84-279-3164-0(6)) Noguer y Caralt Editores, S. A. ESP. *Dist:* Lectorum Pubns., Inc.

Climo. Pandora's Gift. Date not set. 64p. (J). pap. 3.99 (978-0-06-444271-8(3)) HarperCollins Pubs.

Climo, Shirley. Pandora's Gift. 2001. 64p. (J). lib. bdg. 14.89 (978-0-06-028633-0(4)) HarperCollins Pubs.

Clish, Marian L. Brice & Breezy: The Mall Adventure. Robinson, Lori Clish, illus. unabr. ed. 2000. (J). (gr. k-3). pap. 10.95 incl. audio (978-1-928632-47-4(5)); pap. 14.95 incl. audio compact disk (978-1-928632-48-1(3)) Writers Marketplace:Consulting, Critiquing & Publishing.

—Brice & Breezy: The Mall Adventure. Clish-Robinson, Lori, illus. unabr. l.t. ed. 2000. 41p. (J). (gr. k-3). per. 7.95 (978-1-928632-46-7(7)) Writers Marketplace:Consulting, Critiquing & Publishing.

—Brice & Breezy Set: The Mall Adventure. Robinson, Lori Clish, illus. 2000. (Brice & Breezy Ser.). 41p. (J). (gr. k-3). pap. 7.95 (978-1-928632-45-0(9)) Writers Marketplace:Consulting, Critiquing & Publishing.

—You Choose the Way: A Book That Reads Like a Game - Mazash the Wizard. Anderson, Jan, illus. l.t. ed. 1999. (J). (gr. k-5). 56p. pap. 7.95 (978-1-928632-07-8(6)); pap. 14.95 incl. audio compact disk (978-1-928632-09-2(2)) Writers Marketplace:Consulting, Critiquing & Publishing.

—You Choose the Way: A Book That Reads Like a Game: Mazash the Wizard. 1999. (J). (gr. 2-7). 22.95 incl. cd-rom (978-1-928632-25-2(4)) Writers Marketplace:Consulting, Critiquing & Publishing.

—You Choose the Way: A Book That Reads Like a Game: Mazash the Wizard. Anderson, Jan, illus. unabr. ed. 1999. (J). (gr. 2-7). 18.95 incl. audio (978-1-928632-24-5(6)); (gr. 3-5). 15.95 (978-1-928632-23-8(8)) Writers Marketplace:Consulting, Critiquing & Publishing.

Clizbe, Kent. Xrina at Hagar Qim: The Temple Builders of Malta. Konstantinov, Ignat, illus. 1998. (Children of Malta Ser.: Vol. 1). 40p. (J). (gr. k-5). pap. 12.95 (978-0-9656252-1-0(4) , MAL001) O.T.S.

Clueless George Goes to War. 2005. (Illus.). 32p. (J). (ps-3). per. 7.95 (978-0-9744860-5-5(1)) White Horse Bks.

Coates, Theresa. Imaginary Time of Life. 2007. 102p. pap. 10.95 (*978-0-7414-4067-9(9)) Infinity Publishing.

Coatsworth, Elizabeth. The Wonderful Day. 2006. pap. 11.99 (978-1-883937-87-4(6)) Bethlehem Bks.

Cobb, Debbie. Gracie's Big Adventure... with Augustine the Beaver. Ferchaud, Steve, illus. 2006. (J). per. 10.95 (978-0-9787376-0-3(1)) Laurob Pr.

Coburn, Ann. Glint. (J). 2007. 432p. (gr. 6-8). 17.99 (978-0-06-084723-4(9)); 2007. 432p. (gr. 6-8). lib. bdg. 18.89 (978-0-06-084724-1(7)); 2005. 336p. pap. 6.99 (978-0-06-084725-8(5)) HarperCollins Pubs.

Coburn, Catherine Jane. The Adventures of Monterey Jack: Jack's Original Recipe for Rescue. Bondarenko-Machado, Ana, illus. 2002. (YA). per. 19.95 (978-0-9715735-0-5(6)) Destiny Publishing.

Cockley, David H. Over the Falls: A Child's Storybook Guide to Chagrin Falls. Ascherman, Herbert, Jr., tr. 2000. (Illus.). 24p. (J). (ps-10). pap. 5.95 (978-0-9700846-1-3(7)) Fireside Book Shop, Inc.

Codell, Esmé Raji. Hanukkah, Shmanukkah! Pham, LeUyen, illus. 2005. 64p. (ps-2). 16.99 (978-0-7868-5179-9(1)) Hyperion Pr.

Cody, William. Buffalo Bill. 2001. (SPA., Illus.). 182p. (YA). (gr. 5-8). 12.95 (978-84-372-2234-9(6)) Altea, Ediciones, S.A. - Grupo Santillana ESP. *Dist:* Santillana USA Publishing Co., Inc.

Coelho, Paulo. Warrior of the Light: A Manual. 2004. 160p. pap. 11.95 (978-0-06-052798-3(6)) HarperCollins Pubs.

Coerr, Eleanor. Mieko & the Fifth Treasure. 2003. (Illus.). 80p. (J). (gr. 4-7). pap. 5.99 (978-0-698-11990-1(8) , Puffin) Penguin Group (USA) Inc.

—Mieko & the Fifth Treasure. 2003. (gr. 3-6). lib. bdg. 14.15 (978-0-613-61642-3(1)) Tandem Library Bks.

—Sadako & the Thousand Paper Cranes 25th Anniversary Edition. 25th anniv. ed. 2002. 80p. (J). 16.99 (978-0-399-23799-7(2) , Putnam Juvenile) Penguin Group (USA) Inc.

Cofer, Amadeus. Aloha Adventure: The Magic of Imagination on a Rainy Day. l.t. ed. 2004. (Illus.). 36p. (J). 14.00 (978-1-932957-01-3(4)) Legacy Pubs.

Coffel, Michael. The Unwritten Books of Thalk & Wink. 2005. 28.00 (978-0-8059-9727-9(X)) Dorrance Publishing Co., Inc.

Cogar, Tubal U., et al. The Journeys of Wobblefoot the Beginning. Cogar, Karen S., ed. O'Connor, Tim, illus. 2003. (J). pap. 17.50 (978-0-9747149-0-5(9)) Wobblefoot Ltd.

Cohon, Mary E. & Cohon, Helen S. Mud Bud & Poxie: Their Very First Adventure. Cohon, Helen S., illus. 1998. (Illus.). 30p. (J). (ps-k). pap. 5.99 (978-0-9663116-0-0(4)) Little Idea Co., The.

Coia, Kristina. Lymeria. 2007. 120p. (YA). 20.95 (*978-0-595-69347-4(4)); per. 10.95 (*978-0-595-45268-2(X)) iUniverse, Inc.

Cola, Arthur. Papa & the Gingerbread Man. 2006. 14.95 (*978-0-9789423-0-4(2)) Cola, Arthur.

Colbert, Norman. Norman Okay, Not Today. 2001. 109p. pap. 10.95 (978-0-7414-0674-3(8)) Infinity Publishing.

Colby's Egypt Adventures. 2005. (J). kivar 17.95 (978-0-9746810-4-7(0)) Versait Pr. LLC.

Cole, Brock. Buttons. 2001. (J). (ps-3). 26.90 incl. audio (978-0-8045-6881-4(2) , 6881) Spoken Arts, Inc.

A B

Cole, Grace. Bill the Bull. Miller, Lelia, illus. 2002. 4.95 (978-0-9712923-2-1(9)) Taylor-Dth Publishing.

Cole, James. The Lost Island. 2005. 180p. pap. 19.95 (978-1-4137-7572-3(1)) PublishAmerica, Inc.

Cole, Joanna. El Autobus Magico Explora los Sentidos. Degen, Bruce, illus. 1999. (Coleccion El Autobus Magico). (SPA.). 48p. (J). (gr. 3-5). pap. 4.99 (978-0-439-08780-3(5) , SO30009) Scholastic, Inc.

Cole, Joanna & Calmenson, Stephanie. Fun on the Run: Travel Games & Songs. Tiegreen, Alan, illus. 1999. 126p. (J). (gr. k-3). 17.00 (978-0-688-14660-3(0)) HarperCollins Pubs.

Cole, Joanna & Capeci, Anne. The Giant Germ. Degen, Bruce, illus. 2001. (Magic School Bus Chapter Bks.: No. 6). 80p. (J). (gr. 1-4). pap. 4.99 (978-0-439-20420-0(8)) Scholastic, Inc.

Cole, Stephen. The Adventures of Mr. Bean. 2002. (Illus.). 64p. (J). pap. 6.99 (978-1-84222-657-5(6)) Carlton Bks., Ltd. GBR. *Dist:* Independent Pubs. Group.

—Thieves Like Us. 352p. (YA). 2007. (Illus.). pap. 7.95 (978-1-59990-041-4(6)); 2006. 16.95 (978-1-58234-653-3(4)) Bloomsbury Publishing. (Bloomsbury Children).

Cole, Stephen. Thieves Till We Die. 2007. 320p. (YA). 16.95 (***978-1-59990-082-7(3)*** , Bloomsbury Children) Bloomsbury Publishing.

Coleman, Alice Scovell. Engraved in Stone. Armand, Anjale Renee, illus. 2003. 152p. (J). 14.95 (978-0-9729846-0-7(7)) Tiara Bks. LLC.

Coleman, James. The Circle. 2000. 120p. (YA). (gr. 7-12). pap. 9.95 (978-0-595-01081-3(4)) iUniverse, Inc.

Coleman, Michael. Weirdo's War. 1998. (Illus.). 192p. (J). (gr. 4-8). pap. 16.95 (978-0-531-30103-6(6) , Orchard Bks.) Scholastic, Inc.

Colfer, Eoin. Airman. rev. ed. 2008. 416p. 17.99 (***978-1-4231-0750-7(0)***) Hyperion Bks. for Children.

—The Arctic Incident. 2004. (Artemis Fowl Ser.: Bk. 2). 416p. (J). (gr. 8-17). reprint ed. pap. 5.99 (978-0-7868-5147-8(3)) Hyperion Bks. for Children.

—Artemis Fowl. 2002. (Artemis Fowl Ser.: Bk. 1). 277p. (YA). (gr. 8-12). lib. bdg. 14.39 (978-0-606-24618-7(5)) Tandem Library Bks.

—Benny & Omar. 2007. 288p. (gr. 5-17). 18.95 (***978-1-4231-0281-6(9)***); pap. 7.95 (***978-1-4231-0282-3(7)***) Miramax Bks.

—Benny & Omar. 2003. 240p. (YA). (gr. 5 up). pap. 7.95 (978-0-86278-567-3(7)) O'Brien Pr., Ltd., The IRL. *Dist:* Independent Pubs. Group.

—The Eternity Code. (Artemis Fowl Ser.: Bk. 3). 320p. 2003. (ps-17). 16.95 (978-0-7868-1914-0(6)); 2004. (Illus.). (J). (gr. 5-17). reprint ed. pap. 7.99 (978-0-7868-1493-0(4)) Hyperion Bks. for Children.

—The Eternity Code. l.t. ed. 2003. (Artemis Fowl Ser.: Bk. 3). 349p. (J). 25.95 (978-0-7862-5920-5(5)) Thorndike Pr.

—The Lost Colony. (Artemis Fowl Ser.: Bk. 5). 400p. (J). 2006. (gr. 5-17). 16.95 (978-0-7868-4956-7(8)); 2008. (gr. 2-7). pap. 7.99 (***978-0-7868-4959-8(2)***) Miramax Bks.

—El Mundo Subterraneo. 2005. (Artemis Fowl Ser.). (SPA., Illus.). 288p. (J). pap. 13.95 (978-0-307-34309-3(X) , Montena) Random House Mondadori ESP. *Dist:* Random Hse., Inc.

Colfer, Eoin. The Opal Deception. (Artemis Fowl Ser.). (gr. 5 up). 2007. 528p. pap. 5.99 (***978-1-4231-0399-8(8)***); 2006. 352p. (J). reprint ed. pap. 7.99 (978-0-7868-5290-1(9)) Miramax Bks.

—The Opal Deception. l.t. ed. 2005. (Artemis Fowl Ser.: Bk. 4). 421p. (J). 23.95 (978-0-7862-7754-4(8) , Large Print Pr.) Thorndike Pr.

Coll, Ivar Da. Bien Vestidos. (SPA.). (J). bds. (978-958-04-4911-9(2)) Norma S.A. COL. *Dist:* Lectorum Pubns., Inc.

Coll, L. & Coll, C. Beware the Unknown: The Landing. 2003. (Illus.). 144p. (J). per. 12.95 (978-0-9729965-0-1(8)) White Line Productions Inc.

Colledge, Anne. Northern Lights. 2000. (Illus.). (YA). 94p. (gr. 3 up). (978-1-902628-75-2(6)); 2nd l.t. ed. 94p. pap. (978-1-902628-81-3(0)); 3rd l.t. ed. 124p. per. (978-1-902628-83-7(7)) Pipers' Ash, Ltd.

Collier, Christine. Adventure on Apple Orchard Road. 2003. 50p. pap. 8.95 (978-0-595-27725-4(X) , Mystery & Suspense Pr.) iUniverse, Inc.

Collins, Anthony. Rip Power: Reading gave him the strength to fight Back! 2006. 178p. per. 12.99 (978-1-59886-469-4(6)) Tate Publishing & Enterprises, L.L.C.

Collins, Charles. Hover for a Day. Seltzer, Jerry, illus. 2006. (J). 19.95 (978-1-60131-004-0(8)) Big Tent Bks.

Collins, Suzanne. Gregor & the Prophecy of Bane. 2004. (Underland Chronicles: Bk. 1). 320p. (J). pap. 6.99 (978-0-439-67813-1(7) , Scholastic Paperbacks) Scholastic, Inc.

Collins, Terry. Chew on This! 2003. (ps-2). lib. bdg. 11.25 (978-0-613-58145-5(8)) Tandem Library Bks.

—Jimmy Neutron: Movie Storybook. 2001. (Illus.). 32p. (J). 7.99 (978-0-689-85016-5(6) , Simon Spotlight/ Nickelodeon) Simon & Schuster Children's Publishing.

—Tea at the Treedome. O'Hare, Mark, illus. 2000. (SpongeBob SquarePants Chapter Bks.: No. 1). 64p. (J). (gr. 4-6). pap. 3.99 (978-0-689-84015-9(2) , Simon Spotlight) Simon & Schuster Children's Publishing.

—Tea at the Treedome. 2000. (gr. 3-6). lib. bdg. 11.80 (978-0-613-31787-0(4)) Tandem Library Bks.

—The World's Greatest Valentine, Vol. 4. 2004. 64p. (J). (gr. 2-5). pap. 17.00 incl. audio (978-0-8072-1989-8(4) , Listening Library) Random Hse. Audio Publishing Group.

Collodi, C. The Adventures of Pinocchio. Della Chiesa, Carol, tr. 2007. (ENG.). 160p. per. (***978-1-4065-1463-6(2)***) Dodo Pr.

Collodi, Carlo. The Adventures of Pinocchio. 2004. 216p. per. 12.95 (978-1-59540-008-6(7)) 1st World Publishing, Inc.

—The Adventures of Pinocchio. 2004. reprint ed. pap. 21.95 (978-1-4191-5159-0(2)); pap. 1.99 (978-1-4192-5159-7(7)) Kessinger Publishing, LLC.

—The Adventures of Pinocchio. Ghiuselev, Iassen, illus. 2nd unabr. ed. 2002. 160p. 24.95 (978-0-9688768-0-0(3)) Simply Read Bks. CAN. *Dist:* Perseus Distribution.

—Las Aventuras de Pinocho Great Read. 2005. (Great Classics for Children Ser.). (SPA., Illus.). 160p. (J). 5.99 (978-1-4037-1148-9(8)) Dalmatian Pr.

—Avventure Di Pinocchio. pap. 19.95 (978-88-451-2911-7(X)) Fabbri - RCS Libri ITA. *Dist:* Distribooks, Inc.

—Pinocho. 2003. Tr. of Pinocchio. (SPA.). 284p. (978-958-30-0803-0(6) , PV30464) Centro de Informacion y Desarrollo de la Comunicacion y la Literatura MEX. *Dist:* Lectorum Pubns., Inc.

Colum, Padraic. The Children's Homer: The Adventures of Odysseus & the Tale of Troy. Pogany, Willy, illus. 2004. 256p. (J). pap. 9.95 (978-0-689-86883-2(9) , Aladdin) Simon & Schuster Children's Publishing.

—The Golden Fleece: And the Heroes Who Lived Before Achilles. Pogany, Willy, illus. 2004. 320p. (J). pap. 9.95 (978-0-689-86884-9(7) , Aladdin) Simon & Schuster Children's Publishing.

Comerford, Kevin. Halcyon. 2003. 158p. pap. 19.95 (978-1-4137-0675-8(4)) PublishAmerica, Inc.

Comic Debris Staff. The Boring Issue. 2005. (Illus.). 48p. (J). pap. 7.95 (978-1-59307-323-7(2)) Dark Horse Comics.

Como los ratones robaron el Fuego: Aventuras (Adventure Books) 2000. (Aventuras A Traves Del Tiempo Ser.). (ENG & SPA.). (gr. 4 up). (978-0-02-148709-7(X)) Macmillan/McGraw-Hill Schl. Div.

Como nacio la Orca: Aventuras (Adventure Books) 2000. (Aventuras A Traves Del Tiempo Ser.). (ENG & SPA.). (gr. 5 up). (978-0-02-148723-3(5)) Macmillan/McGraw-Hill Schl. Div.

Condon, Bill. Time Travelers: The Jungle Goes Bananas, Sherwood Forest Goes to Pieces, the Wild West Goes Crazy. 2005. (Triple Play Ser.). (Illus.). 48p. (gr. 4-8). 41.85 (978-0-7910-9076-3(0)) Facts On File, Inc.

Conejito Azul: Y la Aventura de Pap Conejo.Tr. of Bunny Rabbit-Father's Adventure. (SPA.). (J). 2.98 (978-970-22-0019-2(9)) Larousse, Ediciones, S. A. de C. V. MEX. *Dist:* Continental Bk. Co., Inc.

Conford, Ellen. A Case for Jenny Archer. Palmisciano, Diane, illus. 2nd ed. 2006. 64p. (J). (gr. 1-4). pap. 3.99 (978-0-316-01486-1(9)) Little Brown & Co.

Conger, Donna. Jared's Adventure. 2004. (Illus.). 40p. (J). (ps-7). per. 5.95 (978-1-59466-016-0(6) , Growing Years) Port Town Publishing.

Conley, Deane W. Angelino Courage to Fly. 2007. (J). lib. bdg. 19.95 (***978-1-933732-27-5(X)*** , Bear Hug Bks.) MidAmerica Publishing Co.

—Angelino Flies Again. 2007. (J). lib. bdg. 19.95 (***978-1-933732-26-8(1)*** , Bear Hug Bks.) MidAmerica Publishing Co.

Conly, Jane Leslie. In the Night, on Lanvale Street. 2005. 256p. (J). 16.95 (978-0-8050-7464-2(3) , Holt, Henry & Co. Bks. For Young Readers) Holt, Henry & Co.

Connell, Richard. Most Dangerous Game. 2006. pap. 15.95 (***978-1-4304-5151-8(3)***) Kessinger Publishing, LLC.

Connelly, Valerie. Arthur, the Christmas Elf: A Christmas Adventure. 2006. (Illus.). 60p. (J). per. 24.95 (978-1-933449-23-4(3)) Nightengale Pr.

Conner, Jimmie L. The Adventures of Captain Computerman & His Sidekick Mouseman: The Saving of the Toy Websites. 2005. 77p. pap. 14.95 (978-1-4137-7457-3(1)) PublishAmerica, Inc.

Constantine. Kiquoti & the Coati. 2001. 40p. (J). (gr. k-3). pap. 5.95 (978-0-06-443552-9(0)); lib. bdg. 15.89 (978-0-06-028310-0(6)) HarperCollins Pubs.

Contender. 1999. (YA). 11.95 (978-1-56137-608-7(6)) Novel Units, Inc.

Cook, Paul T. The Adventures of Mon & Tauk. 2005. 16.95 (978-0-533-14937-7(1)) Vantage Pr., Inc.

Cook, Sherry & Johnson, Martin. Underwater Utley, 26. Kuhn, Jesse, illus. l.t. ed. 2006. (Quirkles—Exploring Phonics through Science Ser.: 21). 32p. (J). 7.99 (978-1-933815-20-6(5) , Quirkles, The) Creative 3, LLC.

Cook, Vivian E. The Journey Home. Nelson, Grace I., illus. 1999. (Adventures of Spencer, Private Eye & His Psychic Sister, Tiffany Ser.: No. 2). 50p. (J). (gr. 3-5). pap. 7.95 (978-1-928659-01-3(2)) Two Sisters Publishing.

—Rescue from Rapid Gully. Nelson, Grace I., illus. 1999. (Adventures of Spencer, Private Eye & His Psychic Sister, Tiffany Ser.: No. 3). 56p. (J). (gr. 3-5). pap. 7.95 (978-1-928659-02-0(0)) Two Sisters Publishing.

Cooke, Darwyn, et al. Spider-Man's Tangled Web, 4 vols., Vol. 4. Cooke, Darwyn et al, illus. 2003. (Spider-Man's Tangled Web Ser.). 176p. (YA). 15.99 (978-0-7851-1064-4(X)) Marvel Enterprises, Inc.

Cooke, Trish. Zoom! 2001. (Illus.). 25p. (J). pap. 9.99 (978-0-00-664621-1(2)) HarperCollins Pubs. Ltd. GBR. *Dist:* Independent Pubs. Group.

Cookson, Catherine. Joe & the Gladiator. 2000. (J). 176p. 16.95 (978-0-385-40178-4(7)); 171p. pap. 5.95 (978-0-552-52617-3(7)) Transworld Publishers Ltd. GBR. *Dist:* Trafalgar Square Publishing.

Cool by the Pool: Coloring/Activity Book. 2005. (Illus.). (J). (978-0-9770455-2-5(8)) Educational Adventures.

Cool by the Pool: Picture Book (English) 2005. (Illus.). 47p. (J). (978-0-9770455-3-2(6)) Educational Adventures.

Coon, Thomas & Coon, Helene. Two of Our Friends Are Doves. MacMenamin, John, illus. 2003. 64p. (J). per. (978-1-932077-17-9(0)) Athena Pr.

Cooney, Caroline B. Code Orange. 2005. 208p. (gr. 7-12). (J). lib. bdg. 17.99 (978-0-385-90277-9(8)); (YA). 15.95 (978-0-385-73259-8(7)) Random Hse. Children's Bks. (Delacorte Bks. for Young Readers).

Cooper, Helen. Donde Esta Tatty Ratty? Bourgeois, Elodie, tr. 2005. (SPA.). (J). (gr. k-2). 20.95 (978-84-261-3260-4(X)) Juventud, Editorial ESP. *Dist:* Iaconi, Mariuccia Bk. Imports.

—Historias de Juguetes. (SPA., Illus.). 80p. (J). (gr. k-2). 23.95 (978-84-261-3127-0(1) , JV1108) Juventud, Editorial ESP. *Dist:* Lectorum Pubns., Inc.

Cooper, Ilene. Lucy on the Loose. Harvey, Amanda, illus. 2000. (Road to Reading Ser.). 80p. (J). (gr. 2-5). 11.99 (978-0-307-46508-5(X) , Golden Bks.) Random Hse. Children's Bks.

Cooper, James Fenimore & Bowler, Bill. The Last of the Mohicans. 2003. (Illus.). 80p. 6.50 (978-0-19-424403-9(2)) Oxford Univ. Pr., Inc.

Cooper, Merian C. & Wallace, Edgar. King Kong. 2005. (Illus.). 160p. (J). (ps-7). pap. 9.95 (978-1-887424-91-2(1)) Underwood Books.

Cooper, Paul Fenimore. Tal, His Marvelous Adventures with Noom-Zor-Noom. Reeves, Ruth, illus. 2001. 320p. (J). (gr. 3-7). 20.00 (978-1-930900-08-0(2)) Purple Hse. Pr.

Cooper, Susan. The Boggart. 196p. (YA). (gr. 5 up). pap. 3.95 (978-0-8072-1465-7(5) , Listening Library) Random Hse. Audio Publishing Group.

—The Boggart. Rayyan, Omar, illus. 2004. 208p. (J). pap. 5.99 (978-0-689-86930-3(4) , Aladdin) Simon & Schuster Children's Publishing.

—The Boggart & the Monster. 185p. (J). (gr. 4-6). pap. 3.95 (978-0-8072-1531-9(7) , Listening Library) Random Hse. Audio Publishing Group.

—The Boggart & the Monster. Rayyan, Omar, illus. 2004. 192p. (J). pap. 5.99 (978-0-689-86931-0(2) , Aladdin) Simon & Schuster Children's Publishing.

—The Magician's Boy. Riglietti, Serena, illus. 2005. 112p. (J). (gr. 3-7). 15.99 (978-0-689-87622-6(X) , McElderry, Margaret K.) Simon & Schuster Children's Publishing.

Copeland, Kenneth. Quest for the Second Half. 1999. (Superkids Novels Ser.). 116p. (J). (gr. 3-7). pap. 7.99 (978-1-57794-150-7(0)) Harrison Hse., Inc.

Corbett, Sue. Free Baseball. 2006. 160p. (J). (gr. 3). 15.99 (978-0-525-47120-2(0) , Dutton Juvenile) Penguin Group (USA) Inc.

Cordoves, Barbara, pseud & Cordoves, Gladys M. The Legend of Zias. Cordoves, Barbara & Cordoves, Gladys M., illus. (Zias' Adventures Ser.). (Illus.). 44p. (J). pap. 7.99 (978-0-9637252-0-2(3)) Cordoves, Barbara & Gladys M.

Corman, Dick. Fountain of Age. 2006. 185p. (YA). pap. 12.95 (***978-0-9655749-2-1(X)***) Corman Productions.

Cormier, Robert. Beyond the Chocolate War. 2000. (YA). 22.25 (978-0-8446-7140-6(1)) Smith, Peter Pub., Inc.

—I Am the Cheese. l.t. ed. 2005. 255p. pap. 10.95 (978-0-7862-7336-2(4) , Large Print Pr.) Thorndike Pr.

Cornwell, Autumn. Carpe Diem. 2007. 368p. (YA). (gr. 7 up). 16.95 (***978-0-312-36792-3(9)***) Feiwel & Friends.

Corwin, Katherine. River of Glass. Jasuna, Aija, illus. 2006. (J). 12.95 (978-1-60131-002-6(1)) Big Tent Bks.

Corwin, Susan Simon. The Cryptic Cat. Corwin, Stuart, illus. 2006. 99p. (YA). (***978-0-9790632-0-6(5)***) Lucky Duck Designs.

Cosentino, Ralph. Batman. 2008. 40p. (J). (ps). 15.99 (***978-0-670-06255-3(3)*** , Viking Juvenile) Penguin Group (USA) Inc.

Cosentino, Ralph. The Marvelous Misadventures of Fun Boy. 2006. (Illus.). 32p. (J). (ps-1). 15.99 (978-0-670-05961-4(7) , Viking Juvenile) Penguin Group (USA) Inc.

Costantino, Eric. Beeboo Bear Dreamed A Dream. 2004. 31p. pap. 17.95 (978-1-4137-3649-6(1)) PublishAmerica, Inc.

Cote, Denis. Descente Aux Enfers. 2003. (Roman Plus Ser.). (FRE.). 160p. (YA). (gr. 8 up). pap. (978-2-89021-208-4(4)) Diffusion du livre Mirabel.

—La Foret aux Cent Perils. Poulin, Stephane, tr. 2003. (Roman Jeunesse Ser.). (FRE., Illus.). 96p. (J). (gr. 4-7). pap. (978-2-89021-647-1(0)) Diffusion du livre Mirabel.

—L' Isle du Savant Fou. Poulin, Stephane, illus. 2002. (Roman Jeunesse Ser.). (FRE.). 96p. (YA). (gr. 4-7). pap. (978-2-89021-275-6(0)) Diffusion du livre Mirabel.

—Un Parfum de Mystere. 2003. (Premier Roman Ser.). (Illus.). 64p. (J). (gr. 2-5). pap. (978-2-89021-352-4(8)) Diffusion du livre Mirabel.

—Le Retour des Inactifs. 2002. (Roman Plus Ser.). (FRE.). 160p. (YA). (gr. 8 up). pap. (978-2-89021-142-1(8)) Diffusion du livre Mirabel.

—La Revolte des Inactifs. 2002. (Roman Jeunesse Ser.). (FRE.). 160p. (YA). (gr. 8 up). pap. (978-2-89021-127-8(4)) Diffusion du livre Mirabel.

—Terminus Cauchemar. 2002. (Roman Plus Ser.). (FRE.). 160p. (YA). (gr. 8 up). pap. (978-2-89021-149-0(5)) Diffusion du livre Mirabel.

Cote, Denis & Poulin, Stephane, eds. Les Otages de la Terreur. 2003. (Roman Jeunesse Ser.). (Illus.). 96p. (YA). (gr. 4-7). pap. (978-2-89021-341-8(2)) Diffusion du livre Mirabel.

Cote, M. Theresa. Scooter's New Clothes. Roux, Lynn M., illus. 2001. 48p. (J). (ps-5). pap. 9.95 (978-0-9601302-5-2(X)) Adventures Into Time.

Couloumbis, Audrey. Maude March on the Run! 2007. (Illus.). 320p. (J). (gr. 3-7). 15.99 (978-0-375-83246-8(7) , Random Hse. Bks. for Young Readers) Random Hse. Children's Bks.

—Maude March on the Run!, or, Trouble Is Her Middle Name. 2007. (Illus.). 309p. (J). pap. (978-0-375-83248-2(3)) Random Hse., Inc.

—Maude March on the Run!, Or, Trouble Is Her Middle Name. 2007. (Illus.). 320p. (J). (gr. 3-7). lib. bdg. 17.99 (978-0-375-93246-5(1) , Random Hse. Bks. for Young Readers) Random Hse. Children's Bks.

—The Misadventures of Maude March: Or Trouble Rides a Fast Horse. 2005. (Illus.). 304p. (J). (gr. 5-9). 15.95 (978-0-375-83245-1(9)); lib. bdg. 17.99 (978-0-375-93245-8(3)) Random Hse. Children's Bks. (Random Hse. Bks. for Young Readers).

—The Misadventures of Maude Marche. 2007. (Illus.). 320p. (J). (gr. 3-7). 6.50 (978-0-375-83247-5(5) , Yearling) Random Hse. Children's Bks.

Coulton, Mia. Danny Can Sort. Coulton, Mia, photos by. 2003. (J). 4.95 (978-0-9720295-6-8(7)) Maryruth Bks., Inc.

—Danny's Big Adventure. Coulton, Mia, photos by. 2004. (J). per. 14.95 (978-0-9746475-0-0(0)) Maryruth Bks., Inc.

—Danny's Timeline. Coulton, Mia, photos by. 2004. (J). 4.95 (978-0-9746475-2-4(7)) Maryruth Bks., Inc.

The Count of Monte Cristo. 2000. (Illus.). (YA). 80p. per. 6.95 (978-1-56254-283-2(4) , SP2834); 48p. per. 17.95 (978-1-56254-284-9(2) , SP2842) Saddleback Educational Publishing.

Counter, Ben. Grey Knights. 2004. 416p. mass mkt. 7.99 (978-1-84416-087-7(4) , Games Workshop) Simon & Schuster.

Coursen, Valerie. Mordant's Wish. rev. ed. 2001. (Illus.). 40p. (J). (ps-2). reprint ed. pap. 6.95 (978-0-8050-6706-4(X) , Holt, Henry & Co. Bks. For Young Readers) Holt, Henry & Co.

Courtin, Thierry. Decouvre les contraires Avec. (FRE.). pap. (978-2-09-202276-4(8)) Editions Rouge et Or.

Courtney, Kateri. Welby & the Knobby King. 2003. pap. 14.95 (978-0-9743588-0-2(0)) Castlegate Pr.

Courtney, Richard. Down at the Docks. 2003. (ps-2). lib. bdg. 10.95 (978-0-613-87810-4(8)) Tandem Library Bks.

Cousins, Lucy. La Nochebuena de Maisy. 2004. (SPA., Illus.). 32p. (J). 16.99 (978-84-8488-106-3(7)) Serres, Ediciones, S. L. ESP. *Dist:* Lectorum Pubns., Inc.

—Sueños de Colores. 2004. (SPA., Illus.). 32p. (J). 18.99 (978-84-8488-108-7(3)) Serres, Ediciones, S. L. ESP. *Dist:* Lectorum Pubns., Inc.

—Sweet Dreams, Maisy. Cousins, Lucy, illus. 2005. (Illus.). 16p. (J). (ps-k). 12.99 (978-0-7636-2874-1(3)) Candlewick Pr.

Coveleskie, Sally & Goodrich, Peter. Henry the Steinway Tours the World. Friedman, Laura, illus. 2005. (Henry the Steinway Ser.: 3). 32p. (J). (ps-ps). 15.95 (978-0-9729427-8-2(5)) Yorkville Pr.

Coville, Bruce. My Teacher Fried My Brains. Pierard, John, illus. 2005. (My teacher Bks.). 144p. (J). (ps-7). pap. 4.99 (978-1-4169-0332-1(1) , Aladdin) Simon & Schuster Children's Publishing.

—My Teacher Glows in the Dark. Pierard, John, illus. 2005. (My teacher Bks.). 144p. (J). (ps-7). pap. 4.99 (978-1-4169-0333-8(X) , Aladdin) Simon & Schuster Children's Publishing.

—My Teacher Is an Alien. Wimmer, Mike, illus. 2005. 124p. (J). (ps-7). lib. bdg. 12.04 (978-0-606-33889-9(6)) Tandem Library Bks.

—The Weeping Werewolf. Coville, Katherine, illus. 2004. (Moongobble & Me Ser.). 80p. (J). (gr. 1-4). 15.99 (978-0-689-85756-0(X)) Simon & Schuster Children's Publishing.

Cowell, Cressida. Heroic Misadventures of Hiccup the Viking, the: the First Collection Boxed Set. 2007. (gr. 3-7). 28.99 (***978-0-316-00592-0(4)***) Little, Brown Bks. for Young Readers.

Cowley, Stewart. Bronty: Share the Adventures of Bronty Brontosaurus & His Friends. 2001. (Dinosaur Friends Ser.). (Illus.). 32p. (J). 7.95 (978-1-57717-178-2(0)) New Line Bks.

—Steggy: Share the Adventures of Steggy Stegasaurus & Her Friends. 2001. (Dinosaur Friends Ser.). (Illus.). 32p. (J). 7.95 (978-1-57717-179-9(9)) New Line Bks.

—Trisha: Share the Adventures of Trisha Triceratops & Her Friends. 2001. (Dinosaur Friends Ser.). (Illus.). 32p. (J). 7.95 (978-1-57717-177-5(2)) New Line Bks.

—Tyro: Share the Adventures of Tyro Tyrannosaurus & His Friends. 2001. (Dinosaur Friends Ser.). (Illus.). 32p. (J). 7.95 (978-1-57717-180-5(2)) New Line Bks.

Cox, Buddy. Quicksilver Deep, 2004. 401p. per. 19.95 (978-0-9709104-3-1(6)) Hickory Tales Publishing.

Cox, Jon, illus. Crazy Man & the Plums. 2005. (Wind River Stories Ser.). (ENG & ARP.). 32p. (J). 14.95 (978-0-9759806-1-3(0)) Painted Pony, Inc.

Cox, Joseph J. Grobar & the Mind Control Potion. Becker, Rebecca J., illus. 2005. 168p. (J). per. 9.95 (978-0-9764659-3-5(0)) Suckerfish Bks.

Cox, Judy. The Mystery of the Burmese Bandicoot. Rayyan, Omar, illus. 2007. (Tails of frederick & Ishbu Ser.). 256p. (YA). (gr. 5 up). 16.99 (***978-0-7614-5376-5(8)***) Cavendish, Marshall Corp.

Cox, Stephen Angus. The Dare Boys of 1776. 2004. reprint ed. pap. 15.95 (978-1-4191-5856-8(2)); pap. 1.99 (978-1-4192-5856-5(7)) Kessinger Publishing, LLC.

Cozzens, Woodworth Samu. Young Trail Hunters or the Wild Riders O. 2006. pap. 26.99 (***978-1-4280-3343-6(2)***) IndyPublish.com.

Crabtree, Zona Mae. The Travelers. 2004. (Corn Cave Ser.: 2). (Illus.). 155p. (YA). per. 8.00 (978-0-9726826-1-9(9)) Owl Hollow Publishing.

—White Dove. 2005. (Corn Cave Ser.: 3). (Illus.). (YA). per. 8.00 (978-0-9726826-2-6(7)) Owl Hollow Publishing.

Craig, Joe. Jimmy Coates: Assassin? 2005. 224p. (J). (gr. 5 up). 15.99 (978-0-06-077263-5(8)) HarperCollins Pubs.

—Jimmy Coates: Target. 2007. 272p. (J). 15.99 (978-0-06-077266-6(2)); lib. bdg. 16.89 (978-0-06-077267-3(0)) HarperCollins Pubs.

—Jimmy Coates: Assassin? 2006. 224p. (J). pap. 5.99 (978-0-06-077265-9(4) , Harper Trophy) HarperCollins Pubs.

Craig, Mary J. When Megan Had to Move. 2006. pap. (978-0-533-15400-5(6)) Vantage Pr., Inc.

Craik, Dinah Maria Mulock. The Little Lame Prince & the Adventures of a Brownie. Date not set. lib. bdg. 25.95 (978-0-8488-2095-4(9)) Amereon LTD.

Craine, E. J. Airplane Boys at Belize. 2003. 224p. (J). pap. 13.95 (978-1-55753-323-4(7)) Purdue Univ. Pr.

—Airplane Boys at Cap Rock. 2002. 248p. (J). pap. 13.95 (978-1-55753-317-3(2)) Purdue Univ. Pr.

—Airplane Boys at Platinum River. 2003. 200p. (J). pap. 13.95 (978-1-55753-320-3(2)) Purdue Univ. Pr.

—Airplane Boys Discover the Secrets of Cuzco. 2003. 246p. (J). pap. 13.95 (978-1-55753-318-0(0)) Purdue Univ. Pr.

—Airplane Boys Flying to Amy-Ran Fastness. 2003. 245p. (J). pap. 13.95 (978-1-55753-319-7(9)) Purdue Univ. Pr.

—Airplane Boys in the Black Woods. 2003. 209p. (J). pap. 13.95 (978-1-55753-322-7(9)) Purdue Univ. Pr.

—Airplane Boys on the Border Line. 2003. 246p. (J). pap. 13.95 (978-1-55753-316-6(4)) Purdue Univ. Pr.

—Airplane Boys with the Revolutionists in Bolivia. 2003. 201p. (J). pap. 13.95 (978-1-55753-321-0(0)) Purdue Univ. Pr.

Craven, Georgina. Adventures & Rhymes with Grandmother. 2006. (Illus.). 76p. pap. (*978-1-84401-648-8(X)) Athena Pr.

Cray, Jordan. Bad Intent. 1998. (Danger.com Ser.: No. 6). (YA). (gr. 6 up). (978-0-606-13310-4(0)) Tandem Library Bks.

Cree, Ronald. Desert Blood 10pm/9c. 2006. (Illus.). 320p. (YA). pap. 7.99 (978-1-4169-1156-2(1) , Simon Pulse) Simon & Schuster Children's Publishing.

Creech, Sharon. Chasing Redbird. 261p. (J). (gr. 4-6). pap. 4.95 (978-0-8072-1532-6(5)); 1999. pap. 38.00 incl. audio (978-0-8072-8057-7(7) , YA989SP) Random Hse. Audio Publishing Group. (Listening Library).

Creed, Julie. Danny the Dump Truck. Hastings, Ken, illus. 2003. per. (978-0-9728181-0-0(3)) Creed, Julie.

Crews, Nina. Below. rev. ed. 2006. (Illus.). 32p. (J). 16.95 (978-0-8050-7728-5(6)) Holt, Henry & Co.

Crider, Bill. Muttketeer! l.t. ed. 1999. (Adventures of Wishbone Ser.: No. 8). (Illus.). 144p. (J). (gr. 4 up). lib. bdg. 22.60 (978-0-8368-2304-2(4)) Stevens, Gareth Inc.

Crilley, Mark. Akiko, Vol. 6. 2003. (Illus.). 136p. pap. 14.95 (978-1-57989-057-5(1)) Sirius Entertainment, Inc.

—Akiko Vol. 7: The Battle for Boach's Keep. 2004. (Illus.). 144p. pap. 14.95 (978-1-57989-064-3(4)) Sirius Entertainment, Inc.

—Akiko & the Alpha Centauri 5000. Crilley, Mark, illus. 2004. (Illus.). 176p. (gr. 3). pap. 5.50 (978-0-440-41892-4(5) , Yearling) Random Hse. Children's Bks.

—Akiko & the Great Wall of Trudd. Crilley, Mark, illus. 2002. (Illus.). 176p. (gr. 3-12). 5.50 (978-0-440-41654-8(X) , Yearling) Random Hse. Children's Bks.

—Akiko & the Great Wall of Trudd. 2002. (gr. 3-6). lib. bdg. 13.00 (978-0-613-50400-3(3)) Tandem Library Bks.

—Akiko & the Intergalactic Zoo. Crilley, Mark, illus. 2003. (Illus.). 160p. (gr. 3 up). pap. 5.50 (978-0-440-41891-7(7) , Yearling) Random Hse. Children's Bks.

—Akiko & the Intergalactic Zoo. 2003. (gr. k-3). lib. bdg. 13.00 (978-0-613-82973-1(5)) Tandem Library Bks.

—Akiko & the Journey to Toog. Crilley, Mark, illus. (Illus.). (gr. 3 up). 2005. 192p. 5.50 (978-0-440-41893-1(3) , Yearling); 2003. 176p. 9.95 (978-0-385-73042-6(X) , Delacorte Bks. for Young Readers) Random Hse. Children's Bks.

—Akiko in the Castle of Alia Rellapor. 2002. (gr. 3-6). lib. bdg. 13.00 (978-0-613-49540-0(3)) Tandem Library Bks.

—Akiko in the Sprubly Islands. Crilley, Mark, illus. 2001. (Akiko Ser.: Vol. 2). (Illus.). 176p. (J). (gr. 3-3). pap. 5.50 (978-0-440-41651-7(5) , Yearling) Random Hse. Children's Bks.

—Akiko in the Sprubly Islands. 2001. (Illus.). 146p. (J). (gr. 4-7). lib. bdg. 13.00 (978-0-613-42696-1(7)) Tandem Library Bks.

—Akiko on the Planet Smoo. Crilley, Mark, illus. 2001. (Akiko Ser.: Vol. 1). (Illus.). 176p. (J). (gr. 3-3). pap. 5.50 (978-0-440-41648-7(5) , Yearling) Random Hse. Children's Bks.

—Akiko on the Planet Smoo. 2001. (gr. 3-6). lib. bdg. 13.00 (978-0-613-42697-8(5)) Tandem Library Bks.

—Akiko: Pieces of Gax. Crilley, Mark, illus. 2006. (Illus.). 224p. (J). (gr. 3). 9.95 (978-0-385-73044-0(6) , Delacorte Bks. for Young Readers) Random Hse. Children's Bks.

—Akiko Pocket-Size. 2004. (Illus.). 192p. pap. 11.95 (978-1-57989-067-4(9)) Sirius Entertainment, Inc.

—Akiko: The Training Master. Crilley, Mark, illus. 2006. (Illus.). 224p. (gr. 3). 5.50 (978-0-440-41894-8(1) , Yearling) Random Hse. Children's Bks.

—Billy Clikk: Creatch Battler. 2006. (Illus.). 246p. (J). (*978-1-4156-5030-1(6) , Yearling) Random Hse. Children's Bks.

—Bornstone's Elixir. 2001. (gr. 3-6). lib. bdg. 22.20 (978-0-613-50412-6(7)) Tandem Library Bks.

—Creatch Battler. 2006. (Illus.). 272p. (J). (gr. 4-7). 5.99 (978-0-440-41953-2(0) , Yearling) Random Hse. Children's Bks.

—Rogmasher Rampage. 2007. (Billy Clikk Ser.). 224p. (J). (gr. 4-7). 5.99 (978-0-440-41955-6(7) , Yearling) Random Hse. Children's Bks.

—The Training Master. Crilley, Mark, illus. 2005. (Akiko Ser.). (Illus.). 224p. (J). (gr. 3). 9.95 (978-0-385-73043-3(8) , Delacorte Bks. for Young Readers) Random Hse. Children's Bks.

Crisp, Marty. Private Captain. 2002. 304p. (J). (gr. 5-9). 6.99 (978-0-698-11969-7(X) , Putnam Juvenile) Penguin Group (USA) Inc.

—Private Captain: A Story of Gettysburg. 2002. (gr. 7-12). lib. bdg. 15.30 (978-0-613-60830-5(5)) Tandem Library Bks.

Croce, Warren. Opposite Day. 2007. (ENG.). 28p. per. 14.90 (*978-1-4303-0659-7(9)) Lulu.com.

Crockett, Johns. Harold et le crayon Rose. pap. 13.95 (978-2-266-09592-1(7)) Presses Pocket FRA. *Dist:* Distribooks, Inc.

Crockett, S. R. The Surprising Adventures of Sir Toady L. 2005. pap. 30.95 (978-1-4179-5884-9(7)) Kessinger Publishing, LLC.

Crompton, Paul. Remarkable for Short. 2005. 113p. pap. 16.95 (978-1-4241-0287-7(1)) PublishAmerica, Inc.

Crompton, Richmal. Just Jimmy Again. Henry, Thomas, illus. 2003. 257p. (J). 16.95 (978-0-333-71231-3(5)) Macmillan Publishers Ltd. GBR. *Dist:* Trafalgar Square Publishing.

Cronin, Susan L. Gidget Goes Away. 2006. 54p. pap. 12.95 (978-1-4137-9878-4(0)) PublishAmerica, Inc.

Crosby, Vernon H. The Adventures of Scurry Little: Lost in my Dream. l.t. ed. 2004. 40p. (J). per. 10.95 (978-1-59196-819-1(4)) Instantpublisher.com.

The Cross & the Spy (2000-2001 Children's Reading Book) 2000. 80p. (J). pap. 6.90 (978-0-8341-1858-4(0)) Beacon Hill Pr. of Kansas City.

Cross, Frances. Boy the Witch & the Blobber 1. 2007. (Blobber Trilogy Ser.). (Illus.). 96p. pap. 7.95 (*978-1-84167-560-2(1)) Ransom Publishing Ltd. GBR. *Dist:* International Publishers Marketing.

—Butternut Blobber & the Blue Jade. 2007. (Blobber Trilogy Ser.). 98p. pap. 7.95 (*978-1-84167-561-9(X)) Ransom Publishing Ltd. GBR. *Dist:* International Publishers Marketing.

—Mystery of the Green Elephant. 2007. (Blobber Trilogy Ser.). 96p. pap. 7.95 (*978-1-84167-559-6(8)) Ransom Publishing Ltd. GBR. *Dist:* International Publishers Marketing.

Cross, Gillian. The Black Room: The Lost. 2006. (Dark Ground Ser.). 256p. (YA). (gr. 6). 16.99 (978-0-525-47487-6(0) , Dutton Juvenile) Penguin Group (USA) Inc.

—Pictures in the Dark. 208p. (978-0-19-275428-8(9)) Oxford Univ. Pr., Inc.

Cross, Nicholas. The Boy & the Dog Who Walked to the Moon. 2000. (Illus.). 160p. (J). (gr. 3 up). pap. (978-0-86315-314-3(3)) Floris Bks. GBR. *Dist:* SteinerBooks, Inc.

Cross, Steve. Walt Michaels Is A Wienie. 2007. (YA). pap. 13.95 (*978-1-59705-808-7(4)) Wings ePress, Inc.

Crossley-Holland, Kevin. The Seeing Stone. unabr. ed. 2004. (Young Adult Cassette Librariestm Ser.). 352p. (J). (gr. 6 up). pap. 48.00 incl. audio (978-0-8072-0999-8(6) , S YA 327 SP, Listening Library) Random Hse. Audio Publishing Group.

—The Seeing Stone. 2002. (Arthur Trilogy: Bk.1). (J). 17.95 (978-0-439-43037-1(2)) Scholastic, Inc.

Croteau-Fleury, Marie-Danielle & St. Aubin, Bruno. Ma Nuit Dans les Glaces. 2001. (FRE., Illus.). 64p. (J). pap. (978-2-89021-506-1(7)) Diffusion du livre Mirabel.

Croteau, Marie-Danielle. La Grande Aventure d'un Petit Mouton Noir. ed. 2004. (FRE., Illus.). (J). (ps-3). spiral bd. (978-0-616-07260-8(0)) Canadian National Institute for the Blind/Institut National Canadien pour les Aveugles.

Crovi, Chantal. Sept Mamm-Goz & La Pate... 2000. Tr. of Seven Breton Grandma's. (FRE.). (J). 19.95 (978-2-86726-550-1(9)) Editions Milan FRA. *Dist:* AIMS International Bks., Inc.

Crow, E. J. The Eye Pocket: The Fantastic Society of Peculiar Adventurers. 2006. (Illus.). 48p. (J). pap. 7.95 (978-1-933255-17-0(X)) DNA Pr.

Crow, Elmay. Speck the Brownie & His Friends. Crow, Elmay, illus. 2000. 32p. (J). pap. 9.00 (978-1-892657-12-1(0)) Town Bk. Pr. The.

Crow, Gary & Crow, Brock. JimJim Meets PosterGuy. 2006. 100p. (J). pap. 14.95 (978-0-9759621-5-2(9)) Koenisha Pubns.

Crowder, Jack L. Haskle Runs Away. 1999. (SPA, ENG & NAV., Illus.). 64p. (J). (gr. k-3). pap. 8.95 (978-0-9616589-2-2(4)) Crowder, Jack L.

Crowe, Duane E. Catfish Annie to the Rescue. Ackison, Wendy Wassink, illus. 2004. (Back River Adventures of Catfish Annie Ser.). 48p. (J). (gr. k-5). (978-0-9672882-0-8(7)) Back River Company, The, LLC.

Crowell, Peter Thomas. Haunted Mountain: The Tales of True Adventure, Book Two. 2006. (J). 19.95 (*978-0-9740290-8-5(4)) Crowell, Peter T. Pubns.

Crowson, Andrew & Ward, Beck. Spaceman Sam. 2005. 8p. (J). 12.95 (978-0-7624-2408-5(7) , Running Pr. Kids) Running Pr. Bk. Pubs.

Crumbaugh, David. The Primrose Kids. 2006. 81p. pap. 14.95 (978-1-4241-3250-8(9)) PublishAmerica, Inc.

Crusoe, Kristen. The Maggie Tales: Morgan & the Sneaker Wave. 2007. (Illus.). 20p. pap. 14.95 (*978-1-59299-286-7(2)) Inkwater Pr.

Crutcher, Chris. Stotan! 2003. 272p. (J). pap. 7.99 (978-0-06-009492-8(3)) HarperCollins Pubs.

—Stotan! 2003. (gr. 7-12). lib. bdg. 15.30 (978-0-613-71360-3(5)) Tandem Library Bks.

Cry of the Falcon. 2006. 208p. (J). pap. 9.95 (978-0-9788541-0-2(1)) m.d. hughes.

Cue, Ian J. The Renewal: First Encounter. 2003. 192p. (YA). per. 9.95 (978-0-9741989-0-3(0)) Mill Creek Metro Publishing.

Culbertson, Jan E. The Legend of the Lost Tiki. 2006. 95p. (YA). pap. 13.95 (978-1-58909-315-7(1)) Bookstand Publishing.

Cullimore, Stan. Killer Sharks. Savage, Paul, illus. 2006. 40p. (J). (gr. 2-3). lib. bdg. (978-1-59889-013-6(1)) Stone Arch Bks.

Cumberland, Heather. The Adventures of Bethany Bunny. Cumberland, Bo, illus. l.t. ed. 2002. 31p. per. 9.95 (978-1-932344-07-3(1)) Thornton Publishing.

Cumyn, Alan. The Secret Life of Owen Skye. 2004. 176p. (J). pap. 5.95 (978-0-88899-517-9(2)) Groundwood Bks. CAN. *Dist:* Perseus Distribution.

Cunliffe, John. Postman Pat Suit of Armour, Bk. 2. (Illus.). 32p. (J). pap. 8.99 (978-0-340-70383-0(0) , Hodder & Stoughton) Hodder General Publishing Division GBR. *Dist:* Trafalgar Square Publishing.

Cunningham, Kay. Bucky, the Adventures of the Dinosaur Cowboy. Wilson, Mary Ann, illus. 2004. 32p. (J). 18.99 (978-1-57860-173-8(8) , Guild Pr. of Indiana); pap. 12.99 (978-1-57860-174-5(6)) Emmis Bks.

Cupper, Karin. The Thrilling Adventures of Life in Eidl. 2005. 151p. pap. 19.95 (978-1-4137-6862-6(8)) PublishAmerica, Inc.

Curley, Marianne. The Dark. 2005. (Guardians of Time Trilogy: Bk. 2). 336p. (J). pap. 8.95 (978-1-58234-664-9(X) , Bloomsbury Children) Bloomsbury Publishing.

Curriculum Corporation. Tai Hao Le! 2005. pap. 79.95 incl. audio compact disk (978-1-86366-402-8(5)) Curriculum Corporation AUS. *Dist:* Cheng & Tsui Co.

Curry, Don, ed. Bee Movie. 2007. (I Can Find It Ser.). 22p. (J). 7.99 (*978-0-696-23385-2(1)) Meredith Bks.

—The Legend of Shrek. 2007. 32p. (J). 19.99 (*978-0-696-23934-2(5)) Meredith Bks.

Curry, Don, ed. Lucky's Pirate Adventure. 2006. 22p. (J). 14.95 (978-0-696-23423-1(8)) Meredith Bks.

Curtis, Jennifer. Scute Salute. 2005. (J). pap. (978-0-9703021-2-0(6)) Captain Caleb Communications.

Curtis, Patricia Gregory. A Secret from the Deep. 2004. 154p. pap. 19.95 (978-1-4137-2293-2(8)) PublishAmerica, Inc.

Curtis, S. R. El Zorro: El Origen de la Leyenda. 1999. (978-0-606-17646-0(2)) Tandem Library Bks.

Curwood, James Oliver. Baree: The Story of a Wolf-Dog. 2005. (Medallion Edition Ser.). 256p. (YA). (gr. 4-7). pap. 5.95 (978-1-55704-132-6(6)) Newmarket Pr.

Cushman, Karen. Matilda Huesos. 2004. Tr. of Matilda Bone. (SPA.). (YA). pap. 7.99 (978-84-348-9080-0(1)) SM Ediciones ESP. *Dist:* Lectorum Pubns., Inc.

Cussler, Clive. The Adventures of Vin Fiz. Farnsworth, William, illus. 2006. 144p. (J). (gr. 3). 15.99 (978-0-399-24474-2(3) , Philomel) Penguin Group (USA) Inc.

—The Adventures of Vin Fizz. Farnsworth, Bill, illus. 2007. 176p. (J). (gr. 2 up). 6.99 (978-0-14-240774-5(7) , Puffin) Penguin Group (USA) Inc.

Cuthbert, Jennifer. The Adventures of Lollipop. 2004. 28p. 4.95 (978-0-9732053-0-5(X)) Peppermint Publishing CAN. *Dist:* Hushion Hse. Publishing, Ltd.

Cutler, Jane. Leap, Frog. Pearson, Tracey Campbell, illus. 2002. 208p. (J). (gr. 2-5). 16.00 (978-0-374-34362-0(4) , Farrar, Straus & Giroux (BYR)) Farrar, Straus & Giroux.

Cyanne Bandanna Kindergartner always Tell the Truth. 2005. (YA). per. (978-1-59872-133-1(X)) Instantpublisher.com.

Cyr, Lynne G. Drako's ABC Adventures as an Iguana. ed. 2006. (Illus.). 37p. (J). spiral bd. 21.95 (978-0-9774543-0-3(4)) Cyr Design Publishing.

Da Coll, Ivar. Jose Tomillo, Maria Juana. Da Coll, Ivar, illus. 2004. (SPA., Illus.). 53p. pap. (978-958-04-7662-7(4)) Norma S.A.

Dabb, Andrew, et al. Depth. 2007. (G. I. Joe SIGMA 6 Ser.). 24p. (J). (gr. 3-6). 21.35 (*978-1-59961-370-3(0)) Spotlight.

Dadey, Debbie & Jones, Marcia Thornton. Goblins Don't Play Video Games. 1999. (Bailey School Kids Ser.: No.37). (gr. 3-6). lib. bdg. 11.80 (978-0-613-17914-0(5)) Tandem Library Bks.

—Hercules Doesn't Pull Teeth. 1998. (Adventures of the Bailey School Kids Ser.: No. 30). (J). (gr. 2-4). 10.79 (978-0-606-13475-0(1)) Tandem Library Bks.

—Leprechauns Don't Play Fetch. 2003. (Bailey School Kids Holiday Special Ser.). (Illus.). 96p. (J). (gr. 2-4). pap. 3.99 (978-0-439-40833-2(4) , Scholastic Paperbacks) Scholastic, Inc.

—Leprechauns Don't Play Fetch. 2002. (Bailey School Kids Holiday Special Ser.). (gr. 3-6). lib. bdg. 11.80 (978-0-613-63312-3(1)) Tandem Library Bks.

—Mrs. Jeepers' Secret Cave. Gurney, John Steven, illus. 1998. (Adventures of the Bailey School Kids Super Special Ser.: No. 3). 128p. (J). (gr. 2-4). pap. 4.99 (978-0-590-11712-8(2) , Scholastic Paperbacks) Scholastic, Inc.

—Ninjas Don't Bake Pumpkin Pies. Gurney, John Steven, illus. 1999. (Adventures of the Bailey School Kids Ser.: No. 38). 80p. (J). (gr. 2-4). 3.99 (978-0-439-04398-4(0)) Scholastic, Inc.

—Ninjas Don't Bake Pumpkin Pies. 1999. (gr. 3-6). lib. bdg. 11.80 (978-0-613-22101-6(X)); (Adventures of the Bailey School Kids Ser.: No. 38). (J). (gr. 2-4). (978-0-606-18588-2(7)) Tandem Library Bks.

—Trolls Don't Ride Roller Coasters. Gurney, John Steven, illus. 1999. (Adventures of the Bailey School Kids Ser.: No. 35). 80p. (J). (gr. 2-4). 3.99 (978-0-590-18985-9(9) , Scholastic Paperbacks) Scholastic, Inc.

—Trolls Don't Ride Roller Coasters. 1999. (Adventures of the Bailey School Kids Ser.: No. 35). (J). (gr. 2-4). (978-0-606-16587-7(8)); (gr. 3-6). lib. bdg. 11.80 (978-0-613-17030-7(X)) Tandem Library Bks.

—Vikings Don't Wear Wrestling Belts. Gurney, John Steven, illus. 2001. (Adventures of the Bailey School Kids Ser.: No. 43). 80p. (J). 3.99 (978-0-439-21583-1(8) , Scholastic Paperbacks) Scholastic, Inc.

Dagg, Stephanie. Beat the Hackers. 2001. 96p. (J). (gr. 4-8). per. (978-1-84210-073-8(4)) Mentor Bks.

Dah Doo-ay Earth Adventure. Date not set. (Furby Storybooks Ser.). (Illus.). 24p. (J). pap. (978-0-7666-0435-3(7) , Honey Bear Bks.) Modern Publishing.

Daher, Anita. Racing for Diamonds. 2007. (Orca Young Readers Ser.). 128p. (J). pap. (*978-1-55143-675-3(2)) Orca Bk. Pubs.

Dahl, Roald. Charlie y la Fabrica de Chocolate. (SPA.). (J). 8.95 (978-968-6026-71-9(1)) Santillana USA Publishing Co., Inc.

—Danny the Champion of the World. Blake, Quentin, illus. collector's ed. 2002. 224p. (J). (gr. 3-7). 15.95 (978-0-375-81425-9(6) , Knopf Bks. for Young Readers) Random Hse. Children's Bks.

—James et la Grosse Peche.Tr. of James & the Giant Peach. (FRE.). (J). pap. 17.95 (978-2-07-051374-1(2)) Gallimard, Editions FRA. *Dist:* Distribooks, Inc.

—La Jirafa, el Pelicano y el Mono. Blake, Quentin, illus. 2003. (SPA.). 67p. (J). (gr. 3-5). pap. 10.95 (978-968-19-0756-3(6)) Santillana USA Publishing Co., Inc.

—A Novel Study for Grades Two & Three Based on James & the Giant Peach. Brookes, Diane, ed. 1998. (J). pap., tchr. ed. (978-0-9683234-9-6(9)) Raven Rock Publishing.

Dahlquist, Kathleen C. "Hop-a-Long's Adventures" Erickson, Beverly H., ed. Tuokey, Eleonor, illus. 2000. 81p. (J). (gr. 1-4). pap. 7.95 (978-1-885527-18-9(7)) Feather Fables Publishing Company.

—Tales of Erin: March 17th. Erickson, Beverly H., ed. Anthony, Ruth, illus. l.t. ed. 2000. 80p. (J). (gr. 1-5). pap. 15.00 (978-1-885527-20-2(9)) Feather Fables Publishing Company.

Dakin, Glenn. Ice Age No. 2: The Essential Guide. 2006. (Illus.). 48p. (J). 12.99 (978-0-7566-1747-9(2)) Dorling Kindersley Publishing, Inc.

Daley, Michael. Shanghaied to the Moon. 2007. 256p. (YA). 16.99 (978-0-399-24619-7(3) , Putnam Juvenile) Penguin Group (USA) Inc.

Dalmatian Press Staff. Justice League: Saving the World. 2005. (Justice League Ser.). (Illus.). 400p. (J). pap. 5.99 (978-1-4037-0537-2(2)) Dalmatian Pr.

—Never Give Up: Wild Force. 2003. (Power Rangers Wild Force Ser.). 24p. (J). pap. 2.99 (978-1-57759-813-8(X)) Dalmatian Pr.

—Power Ranger: Operation Overdrive. 2007. 24p. pap. 3.50 (*978-1-4037-3569-0(7)) Dalmatian Pr.

—Power Rangers: Space Patrol Delta. 2006. 24p. pap. 3.50 (978-1-4037-2886-9(0)) Dalmatian Pr.

—Power Rangers: Transforming Time. 2007. 24p. pap. 3.50 (*978-1-4037-3704-5(5)) Dalmatian Pr.

—Power Rangers Carry-along Stories: 6 Stoybooks in a Box! Spanish Edition. rev. ed. 2007. 144p. pap. 9.99 (*978-1-4037-3273-6(6)) Dalmatian Pr.

—Red Lion Roar: Wild Force. 2003. (Power Rangers Wild Force Ser.). 24p. (J). pap. 2.99 (978-1-57759-812-1(1)) Dalmatian Pr.

—Scooby-Doo: Key Chain Book. rev. ed. 2003. (Scooby-Doo! Ser.). 48p. (J). 3.99 (978-1-4037-0195-4(4)) Dalmatian Pr.

—Scooby Doo Shadow Mystery: Window Board Book. 2003. (Scooby-Doo! Ser.). (Illus.). 14p. (J). bds. 7.99 (978-1-4037-0332-3(9)) Dalmatian Pr.

—Storm Power: Ninja Storm. 2003. (Power Rangers Ninja Storm Ser.). 24p. (J). pap. 2.99 (978-1-4037-0355-2(8)) Dalmatian Pr.

—Storm Strike: Sticker Story Book to Color. 2003. (Power Rangers Ninja Storm Ser.). (Illus.). 16p. (J). pap. 2.99 (978-1-57759-253-2(0)) Dalmatian Pr.

Dalmatian Press Staff, adapted by. Oliver Twist. Date not set. (C). pap. (978-0-7593-9612-8(4) , Thomson Learning) CENGAGE Learning.

Dalmatian Press Staff, ed. Power Rangers: Magic Masters. 2006. 24p. pap. 3.50 (978-1-4037-2887-6(9)) Dalmatian Pr.

—Spooky Critters. 2006. 48p. (J). 2.99 (978-1-4037-2462-5(8)) Dalmatian Pr.

Daloisio, Denis. Melanie's Magic Stones. 2003. 55p. pap. 9.95 (978-1-4137-0223-1(6)) PublishAmerica, Inc.

Dalrymple, Farel. Pop Gun War. 2003. (Illus.). 136p. (gr. 11 up). pap. 13.95 (978-1-56971-934-3(9)) Dark Horse Comics.

Dalton, Andrew. Temples of Malplaquet. 2005. 192p. (YA). 14.50 (978-0-7188-3046-5(6)); pap. 7.50 (978-0-7188-3047-2(4)) Lutherworth Pr., The GBR. *Dist:* Parkwest Pubns., Inc.

Dalton, Annie. Angels Unlimited: Losing the Plot. l.t. ed. 2005. 164p. (J). pap. (978-1-4056-6047-1(3)) BBC Audio.

—Calling the Shots. 2003. (Angels Unlimited Ser.: No. 4). (Illus.). 160p. (J). pap. 4.99 (978-0-06-008818-7(4)) HarperCollins Pubs.

Dalton, Annie. The Heavenly Collection. 2008. 400p. (J). pap. 19.95 (*978-0-00-723307-6(8)) HarperCollins Pubs. Ltd. GBR. *Dist:* Independent Pubs. Group.

Daly, Joseph M. Strange Town Volume One: The Woods Behind Trevor Malone's House. 2007. 265p. (YA). pap. (*978-0-9779921-0-2(1)) Wolfs Corner Publishing.

Daly, Kerry. Finding Feldspar. 2005. (Illus.). 22p. (J). per. 8.99 (978-1-932338-91-1(8)) Lifevest Publishing, Inc.

Daly-Weir, Catherine. Coat of Arms. Crosby, Jeff, illus. 2000. 32p. (J). (gr. 2-6). pap. 6.99 (978-0-448-41975-6(0) , Grosset & Dunlap) Penguin Group (USA) Inc.

D'Amico, Carmela & D'Amico, Steven. Ella Sets the Stage. 2006. (Illus.). 48p. (J). pap. 16.99 (978-0-439-83152-9(0) , Levine, Arthur A. Bks.) Scholastic, Inc.

Damitz, Charlie. The Shot Not Heard Around the World. 1999. 86p. (YA). (gr. 5 up). 9.99 (978-0-88092-440-5(3) , 4403) Royal Fireworks Publishing Co.

Dammann, Anke. Chester Crumbleberry, Dammann, Anke, illus. 2005. (Illus.). 32p. 15.95 (978-1-893815-11-7(0)) Pie in the Sky Publishing, LLC.

Dana, Jane. Jane on a Crane. Bakhtin, Viktor, illus. 2005. 87p. (J). bds. 25.00 (978-0-9761000-0-3(2)) Green Troubadour Pr.

A B

Danger Alert: Coloring/Activity Book. 2006. (Illus.). (J). (978-1-933934-05-1(0)) Educational Adventures.

Danger Alert: Picture Book (English) 2006. (Illus.). 47p. (J). (978-1-933934-03-7(4)) Educational Adventures.

Daniel, Claire. The Chick That Wouldn't Hatch. Ernst, Lisa Campbell, illus. 2003. (Green Light Readers Level 2 Ser.). 24p. (J). 11.95 (978-0-15-204871-6(5)); pap. 3.95 (978-0-15-204831-0(6)) Harcourt Children's Bks. (Green Light Readers).

Daniels, Patricia A. Voices in the Solemn Wind. Mackey, Rosella, ed. Daniels, Sterling N., 2nd, illus. 96p. (Orig.). (J). pap. 10.00 (978-0-9628081-1-1(3)) Daw Enterprises.

Daniels, Sterling N., 2nd. Yas. Daniels, Sterling N., 2nd, illus. (Illus.). 36p. (J). (gr. k-3). pap. 4.95 (978-0-9628081-2-8(1)) Daw Enterprises.

Danko, Dan. Take It to the Max. Mason, Tom, illus. 2001. (Max Steel Ser.: No. 2). 48p. (J). pap. 3.99 (978-0-439-22565-6(5)) Scholastic, Inc.

Danko, Dan & Mason, Tom. Sidekicks, Vol. 3. 2004. (Illus.). 112p. (J). 13.95 (978-0-316-73426-4(8)) Little Brown & Co.

—Sidekicks 6: Invasion of the Evil Teachers from Planet Buttface. 2005. 128p. (J). pap. 4.99 (978-0-316-15896-1(8)) Little Brown & Co.

Dankyi, Jane Osafoa. Incredible Adventures of Wapi. 2004. (ENG., Illus.). Bk. 1. 60p. per. (*978-9964-70-122-2(5)); Bk. 2. 52p. (gr. 3-7). per. (*978-9964-70-123-9(3)); Bk. 3. 52p. per. (*978-9964-70-124-6(1)) Afram Pubns. Ghana, Ltd.

Dann, Colin. Copycat. 1999. 165p. mass mkt. 8.95 (978-0-09-921212-6(9)) Random Hse. GBR. *Dist:* Trafalgar Square Publishing.

—Lion Country. 2000. (Illus.). 128p. (J). (gr. 3-6). 19.99 (978-0-09-176807-2(1) , Hutchinson) Random Hse. GBR. *Dist:* Independent Pubs. Group.

Dann, Penny, illus. Me Lees un Cuento, Por Favor? (SPA.). (gr. k-3). Vol. 1. (J). (978-84-480-1622-7(X) , TM7339); Vol. 2. 96p. (J). (978-84-480-1624-1(6) , TM0700); Vol. 3. 2003. 96p. (978-84-480-1626-5(2) , TM3568) Timun Mas, Editorial S.A. ESP. *Dist:* Lectorum Pubns., Inc.

Dark Horse Comics Staff. Xena: Warrior Princess. 2001. (Illus.). pap. 12.95 (978-1-56971-537-6(8)) Dark Horse Comics.

Darlington, Edgar B. P. The Circus Boys Across Continent or Making the Start in the Sawdust Life. 2004. reprint ed. pap. 22.95 (978-1-4191-5679-3(9)); pap. 1.99 (978-1-4192-5679-0(3)) Kessinger Publishing, LLC.

—The Circus Boys in Dixie Land or Winning the Plaudits of the Sunny South. 2004. reprint ed. pap. 22.95 (978-1-4191-5680-9(2)); pap. 1.99 (978-1-4192-5680-6(7)) Kessinger Publishing, LLC.

—The Circus Boys on the Mississippi or Afloat with the Big Show on the Big River. 2004. reprint ed. pap. 22.95 (978-1-4191-5681-6(0)); pap. 1.99 (978-1-4192-5681-3(5)) Kessinger Publishing, LLC.

—The Circus Boys on the Plains or the Young Advance Agents Ahead of the Show. 2004. reprint ed. pap. 22.95 (978-1-4191-5682-3(9)); pap. 1.99 (978-1-4192-5682-0(3)) Kessinger Publishing, LLC.

Dashner, James. War of the Black Curtain: Book Four - Jimmy Fincher Saga. Phipps, Michael, illus. 2005. (YA). per. 14.99 (978-1-55517-879-6(0) , Bonneville Bks.) Cedar Fort, Inc./CFI Distribution.

David, Christopher. Denholme & the Skeleton Mystery. 2006. 274p. pap. (*978-1-4120-8014-9(2)) Trafford Publishing.

David, James F. Ship of the Damned. 2001. (gr. 7-12). lib. bdg. 15.30 (978-0-613-42792-0(0)) Tandem Library Bks.

David, Lawrence. Terror of the Pink Dodo Balloons. Gott, Barry, illus. 3rd ed. 2003. (Horace Splattly Ser.: No. 3). 160p. (J). pap. 4.99 (978-0-14-250001-9(1) , Puffin) Penguin Group (USA) Inc.

—When Second Graders Attack. Gott, Barry, illus. 2nd ed. 2002. (Horace Splattly Ser.). 160p. (J). pap. 4.99 (978-0-14-230118-0(3) , Puffin) Penguin Group (USA) Inc.

David, Peter. Nothing to Lose. Cross, Chris, illus. 2003. (Captain Marvel Ser.). 144p. (YA). pap. 12.99 (978-0-7851-1104-7(2)) Marvel Enterprises, Inc.

Davidson, Ellen. When the Third Moon Wanes. 2004. 123p. pap. 17.95 (978-1-4137-2233-8(4)) PublishAmerica, Inc.

Davidson, Halsey. Navy Boys Behind the Big Guns or Sinking. 2006. 95.99 (*978-1-4280-1601-9(5)); pap. 89.99 (*978-1-4280-1600-2(7)) IndyPublish.com.

Davidson, Susanna. Dolls. Wanert, Amandine, illus. 2006. 48p. (J). 8.99 (978-0-7945-1327-6(1) , Usborne) EDC Publishing.

Davie, Jan. The Nexus Facilitator. 2006. 96p. pap. (*978-1-84401-798-0(2)) Athena Pr.

Davies, Michael J. Mashu & the Mystery of the Missing Image. 2005. (YA). pap. 13.95 (978-1-59088-611-3(9)) Wings ePress, Inc.

Davies, Robert, adapted by. Lit a Shuck for Texas: Adapted Louis l'Amour Short Stories Series. 2003. (Adapted Louis L'Amour Short Stories Ser.). (Illus.). 56p. (YA). (978-1-57035-983-5(0) , 233LIT) Sopris West Educational Services.

—Merrano of the Dry Country: Adapted Louis l'Amour Short Story Series. 2003. (Adapted Louis L'Amour Short Stories Ser.). (Illus.). 60p. (J). (978-1-57035-985-9(7) , 233MERRANO) Sopris West Educational Services.

—A Trail to the West: Adapted Louis l'Amour Short Stories Series. 2003. (Adapted Louis L'Amour Short Stories Ser.). (Illus.). 56p. (J). (978-1-57035-984-2(9) , 233TRAIL) Sopris West Educational Services.

Davis, Alan. Killraven. Davis, Alan, illus. 2003. (Spider-Man Ser.). (Illus.). 144p. (YA). pap. 16.99 (978-0-7851-1083-5(6)) Marvel Enterprises, Inc.

Davis, L. Mitchell. Mouse Adventures: The Tale of Micah Mouse. 2007. 32p. per. 13.99 (*978-1-59886-655-1(9)) Tate Publishing & Enterprises, L.L.C.

Davis, Tanita S. A la Carte. 2008. 288p. (J). (gr. 7). 15.99 (*978-0-375-84815-5(0) , Knopf Bks. for Young Readers) Random Hse. Children's Bks.

Davis, Terry. Camping with Dad: The Mystery of Valley Gulch. 2006. (ENG.). 148p. per. 19.95 (*978-1-4241-5659-7(9)) PublishAmerica, Inc.

Davoll, Barbara. A Load of Trouble. Hockerman, Dennis, illus. 1999. (Christopher Churchmouse Classics Ser.). 24p. (J). (ps-3). 7.99 (978-0-8024-4932-0(8)) Moody Pubs.

—Rainy Day Rescue. Hockerman, Dennis, illus. 1999. (Christopher Churchmouse Classics Ser.). 24p. (J). (ps-3). 7.99 (978-0-8024-4933-7(6)) Moody Pubs.

—Stowaways, Vol. 2. Hockerman, Dennis, illus. 1999. (New Christopher Churchmouse Adventures Ser.: Vol. 2). 24p. (J). (ps-3). 9.99 (978-0-8024-5397-6(X)) Moody Pubs.

—The Unplanned Voyage. Hockerman, Dennis, illus. 1999. (New Christopher Churchmouse Adventures Ser.: Vol. 1). 24p. (J). (ps-3). 9.99 (978-0-8024-5396-9(1)) Moody Pubs.

Dawes, Claiborne. Daniel on the Run: Louisa, Will, & the Underground Railroad. 2001. (Illus.). 40p. (J). pap. 7.95 (978-1-57960-078-5(6)) History Compass, LLC.

Dawn, Marion. Gleaning Up! 1998. (Continuing Adventures of Timothy Glean Ser.). 38p. (J). (gr. k-3). pap. 6.95 (978-1-885986-02-3(5)) Glean Pubns., Ltd.

Dawson, JoAnn S. Lady's Big Surprise. 2004. 288p. pap. 8.95 (978-0-9746561-6-8(X)); (Illus.). 15.95 (978-0-9746561-5-1(1)) FT Richards Publishing.

—Star of Wonder. 2005. (Illus.). 268p. pap. 8.95 (978-0-9746561-4-4(3)) FT Richards Publishing.

Day, Alexandra. Carl's Summer Vacation. Day, Alexandra, illus. 2008. (Carl Ser.). (Illus.). 32p. (J). 12.95 (*978-0-374-31085-1(8) , Farrar, Straus & Giroux (BYR)) Farrar, Straus & Giroux.

Day, Jan. Pirate Pink & Treasures of the Reef. Mason, Janeen I., illus. 2003. 32p. (J). pap. 14.95 (978-1-58980-086-1(9)) Pelican Publishing Co., Inc.

Day, Roger. Anurada negotiates our wobbly Planet. 2006. 393p. pap. 12.40 (978-1-4116-7916-0(4)) Lulu.com.

Daynes, Katie, retold by. Pinocchio. 2005. (Young Reading Gift Books Ser.). 64p. (J). (gr. 2 up). 8.95 (978-0-7945-0887-6(1) , Usborne) EDC Publishing.

Dayton, Dorothy. The Legend of Farmer Will. 2006. 70p. pap. 14.95 (978-1-4241-0985-2(X)) PublishAmerica, Inc.

DC Comics Staff, et al. Flight. 3rd ed. 2002. (Smallville Ser.: No. 3). 192p. (J). (gr. 7-17). mass mkt. 5.99 (978-0-316-17468-8(8)) Little, Brown Bks. for Young Readers.

De Armond, Garry E. Bugaroos: The Adventure Begins. Huff, Nichalos, illus. 2000. 32p. (YA). (gr. k-4). 19.95 (978-0-9676287-0-7(9)) De Armond, Garry.

de Brun, Kieran Christopher. The Talking Llama: la Llama Que Habla. de Brun, Brendan Joseph, illus. 2005. (J). pap. 16.00 (978-0-8059-6910-8(1)) Dorrance Publishing Co., Inc.

De Foreest, Rosalie A. That's Not Alice. 1998. (Illus.). 16p. (J). (gr. 1-3). pap. 6.00 (978-0-8059-4522-5(9)) Dorrance Publishing Co., Inc.

de la Luz Uribe, Maria. El Cururia. 2002. (SPA., Illus.). 48p. (J). 6.50 (978-980-257-060-7(5) , EK3154) Ekare, Ediciones VEN. *Dist:* Lectorum Pubns., Inc.

de las Casas, Diane. Cajun Cornbread Boy. de las Casas, Diane, illus. 2005. (Illus.). 32p. (J). 15.95 (978-1-58980-224-7(1)) Pelican Publishing Co., Inc.

De Lint, Charles. Wolf Moon. 2004. (Illus.). 256p. (Orig.). (YA). pap. 6.99 (978-0-14-240077-7(7) , Puffin) Penguin Group (USA) Inc.

De Oliveira, Eddie. Johnny Hazzard. 2006. 352p. (J). pap. 8.99 (978-0-439-67362-4(3)) Scholastic, Inc.

de Paola, Tomie. Jamie O'Rourke & the Pooka. 2002. 32p. (J). pap. 6.99 (978-0-698-11924-6(X) , Putnam Juvenile) Penguin Group (USA) Inc.

—Jamie O'Rourke & the Pooka. 2002. (gr. k-3). lib. bdg. 15.30 (978-0-613-50539-0(5)) Tandem Library Bks.

De Rolf, Shane. Blackboard Jungle. 1998. (978-0-679-88450-7(5) , Random Hse. Bks. for Young Readers) Random Hse. Children's Bks.

De Santis, Pablo. El Ultimo Espia. 2002. (SPA.). 72p. (J). pap. (978-1-4000-0026-5(2)) Editorial Sudamericana S.A.

Dead Man's Chest. 2007. (Pirates of the Caribbean Ser.). 160p. pap. 4.99 (*978-1-4231-1106-1(0)) Disney Publishing Worldwide.

Deal, Carla. A Pig's Tale. 2004. (Illus.). 42p. (J). spiral bd. 22.95 (978-1-932373-65-3(9) , Cedar Hill Pr.) Cedar Hill Publishing.

Dean, Carol S. The Live Bale of Hay: A Real Maine Adventure. Dunn, Sandra, illus. 2005. 32p. (ps-ps). 15.95 (978-0-89272-674-5(1)) Down East Bks.

Dean, Zoey. American Beauty. 7th ed. 2006. (A-List Ser.: No. 7). 288p. (J). (gr. 9-17). pap. 9.99 (978-0-316-01094-8(4) , Poppy) Little, Brown Bks. for Young Readers.

Deary, Terry. Flight of the Fire Thief. 2006. (Fire Thief Ser.). 240p. (J). (gr. 5). 9.95 (978-0-7534-5819-8(5) , Kingfisher) Houghton Mifflin Co. Trade & Reference Div.

—Vanished! 2004. (Classified Ser.). 96p. (J). (gr. 5-9). pap. 4.95 (978-0-7534-5825-9(X) , Kingfisher) Houghton Mifflin Co. Trade & Reference Div.

Deathwatch. 1999. (YA). 9.95 (978-1-56137-140-2(8)) Novel Units, Inc.

Décary, Marie. Adam's Tropical Adventure. Cummins, Sarah, tr. from FRE. Beshwaty, Steve, illus. 2005. (First Novel Ser.). 64p. (gr. 2-5). (*978-0-88780-687-2(2)); (J). 4.95 (978-0-88780-686-5(4)) Formac Publishing Co., Ltd. CAN. *Dist:* Casemate Pubs. & Bk. Distributors, LLC.

Decary, Marie. Le Combats des Chocolats. Brignaud, Pierre, illus. 2003. (Roman Jeunesse Ser.). (FRE.). 96p. (J). (gr. 4-7). pap. (978-2-89021-611-2(X)) Diffusion du livre Mirabel.

—Rendez-Vous sur Planete Terre. 1998. (Roman + Ser.). (Illus.). 160p. (YA). (gr. 8 up). pap. (978-2-89021-321-0(8)) Diffusion du livre Mirabel.

Decker, Wendy. The Bedazzling Bowl. 2006. pap. 13.99 (*978-1-60034-468-8(2)) Xulon Pr., Inc.

Decter, Ed. Expedition to Blue Cave. Yuen, Sammy, Jr., illus. 2007. (Outriders Ser.). 208p. (J). (gr. 3-7). pap. 4.99 (978-1-4169-1305-4(X) , Aladdin) Simon & Schuster Children's Publishing.

—Expedition to Pine Hollow. Yuen, Sammy, Jr., illus. 2007. (Outriders Ser.). 240p. (J). pap. 4.99 (978-1-4169-1307-8(6) , Aladdin) Simon & Schuster Children's Publishing.

—Expedition to Surf Island. Yuen Jr., Sammy, illus. 2009. (Outriders Ser.). 224p. (J). pap. 4.99 (*978-1-4169-1308-5(4) , Aladdin) Simon & Schuster Children's Publishing.

Decter, Ed. Expedition to Willow Key, Vol. 2. Yuen, Sammy, Jr., illus. 2007. (Outriders Ser.). 224p. (J). (gr. 3-7). pap. 4.99 (978-1-4169-1306-1(8) , Aladdin) Simon & Schuster Children's Publishing.

DeFalco, Tom. Fun 'N' Games with the Fantastic Five! 2006. (Illus.). (J). (gr. 2-6). 21.35 (978-1-59961-030-6(2)) Spotlight.

—Legacy... in Black & White. 2006. (Illus.). (J). (gr. 2-6). 21.35 (978-1-59961-029-0(9)) Spotlight.

—Touch of Venom. 2006. (Illus.). (J). (gr. 2-6). 21.35 (978-1-59961-026-9(4)) Spotlight.

DeFalco, Tom & Frenz, Ron. Spider-Girl Presents Avengers Next Vol. 1: Second Coming Digest. 2006. (Illus.). 144p. pap. 7.99 (978-0-7851-2131-2(5)) Marvel Enterprises, Inc.

DeFalco, Tom, et al. Spider-Girl Volume 6: Too Many Spiders! Digest: Too Many Spiders! Digest. 2006. (Illus.). 144p. pap. 7.99 (978-0-7851-2156-5(0)) Marvel Enterprises, Inc.

DeFelice, Jennie & Landry, Jennifer. The Adventures of Zsa-Zsa & Gabby-Lou: Dangers at the Seashore. DeFelice, Bonnie, illus. 2005. (J). lib. bdg. 19.95 (978-0-9767072-0-2(9)) Two Dogz.

Defelice, Jennie & Landry, Jennifer. The Adventures of Zsa Zsa & Gabby Lou a Country Harvest. 2006. (J). lib. bdg. 20.00 (978-0-9767072-2-6(5)) Two Dogz.

—The Adventures of Zsa Zsa & Gabby Lou in New Orleans. Defelice, Bonnie, illus. 2006. (J). lib. bdg. 21.95 (978-0-9767072-1-9(7)) Two Dogz.

Defoe, Daniel. The Adventures of Robinson Crusoe. 2002. (Great Illustrated Classics Ser.).Tr. of Robinson Crusoe. (Illus.). 240p. (J). (gr. 3-8). 21.35 (978-1-57765-677-7(6) , ABDO & Daughters) ABDO Publishing Co.

—The Farther Adventures of Robinson Crusoe. (Illus.). (J). reprint ed. 32.50 (978-0-404-07912-3(1)) AMS Pr., Inc.

—Robinson Crusoe. Heller, Julek, illus. 1998. (Eyewitness Classics Ser.).Tr. of Robinson Crusoe. 64p. (J). (gr. 3-6). 14.95 (978-0-7894-3625-2(6)) Dorling Kindersley Publishing, Inc.

—Robinson Crusoe. 2004. Tr. of Robinson Crusoe. (SPA., Illus.). 284p. (J). (ps-7). pap. (978-958-30-0091-1(4)) Panamericana Editorial.

—Robinson Crusoe. 2001. (Modern Library Classics Ser.).Tr. of Robinson Crusoe. 320p. pap. 7.95 (978-0-375-75732-7(5) , Modern Library) Random House Publishing Group.

—Robinson Crusoe. 2nd ed. 2003. (Historias de Siempre Ser.).Tr. of Robinson Crusoe. (SPA., Illus.). 92p. (J). (gr. 5-8). pap. 12.95 (978-84-204-5723-9(X)) Santillana USA Publishing Co., Inc.

—Robinson Crusoe. Grandville, J. J., illus. 2001. (Junior Classics Ser.).Tr. of Robinson Crusoe. 128p. (J). (gr. 8). mass mkt. 3.99 (978-0-439-23621-8(5)) Scholastic, Inc.

—Robinson Crusoe. 2001. (Classics Ser.).Tr. of Robinson Crusoe. 304p. (YA). (gr. 3-7). pap. 5.99 (978-0-689-84408-9(5) , Aladdin) Simon & Schuster Children's Publishing.

—Robinson Crusoe. Akib, Jamel, illus. 2006. (Classic Starts Ser.).Tr. of Robinson Crusoe. 160p. (J). 4.95 (978-1-4027-2664-4(3)) Sterling Publishing Co., Inc.

—Robinson Crusoe. 2000. (Coleccion "Clasicos Juveniles" Ser.).Tr. of Robinson Crusoe. (SPA., Illus.). 288p. (YA). (gr. 4-7). pap. 13.95 (978-1-58348-782-2(4)) iUniverse, Inc.

Defoe, Daniel, et al. Robinson Crusoe. (Classics Illustrated Ser.).Tr. of Robinson Crusoe. (Illus.). 52p. (YA). pap. 4.95 (978-1-57209-021-7(9)) Classics International Entertainment, Inc.

Deford, Ted. Po & the Gang: In Two Big Adventures. 2005. 49p. pap. 12.95 (978-1-4137-9068-9(2)) PublishAmerica, Inc.

Degen, Bruce, illus. Commander Toad & the Space Pirates. 2002. (Commander Toad Ser.). (J). 13.19 (978-0-7587-1080-2(1)) Book Wholesalers, Inc.

—Commander Toad & the Voyage Home. 2002. (Commander Toad Ser.). (J). 13.19 (978-0-7587-1077-2(1)) Book Wholesalers, Inc.

DeGrazia, John. The Three Little Tigers Go Fishing. Spirin, Ilya, illus. 1999. (Three Little Tigers Ser.: Vol. 2). 15p. (J). (gr. 1-8). pap. 5.00 (978-0-9670522-1-2(1)) Big Cats Publishing.

deGroat, Diane. Good Night, Sleep Tight, Don't Let the Bed Bugs Bite! deGroat, Diane, illus. 2006. (Illus.). 27p. (J). (gr. k-4). reprint ed. 16.00 (978-0-7567-9991-5(0)) DIANE Publishing Co.

Degruy, David. As the Sparks Fly Upward: The Jimmy & Johnny Adventure Stories. 2003. (Illus.). 104p. pap. 12.95 (978-0-929292-55-7(3) , 800-747-0738) Hannibal Bks.

Deiss, A. G. & Emi. The Sad Tale of Emmaline Austin, Monkey-Girl. 2005. 23p. 10.67 (978-1-4116-5439-6(0)) Lulu.com.

Del Amo, Montserrat. El Nudo. (SPA.). 94p. (YA). (gr. 5-8). (978-84-261-1691-8(4) , JV2941) Juventud, Editorial ESP. *Dist:* Lectorum Pubns., Inc.

Del Rio, Adam. Teo in Palo Verde. Ill, Noel, illus. 2008. Tr. of Teo en Palo Verde. (ENG & SPA.). 28p. 15.95 (*978-1-60448-000-9(9)) Lectura Bks.

De'Leon, Lunden. Oops Loops. 2006. 28p. pap. 9.95 (*978-1-4327-0114-7(2)) Outskirts Press, Inc.

Delessert, Etienne. Humpty Dumpty. 2006. (Illus.). 32p. (J). (gr. k-3). 17.00 (978-0-618-56987-8(1)) Houghton Mifflin Co.

Delgado, Josep Francesc. Nima, El Sherpa. 2003. (SPA.). 168p. (978-84-8453-060-2(4) , PT31196) Ediciones del Bronce ESP. *Dist:* Lectorum Pubns., Inc.

Della-Sera, Robert. The Giant Behind the House. 2001. 116p. (J). pap. 9.95 (978-0-595-20582-0(8) , Authors Choice Pr.) iUniverse, Inc.

DeLorge, Jaqueline. Gilfinton under the Sea. 2005. (Illus.). 28p. (J). per. 7.99 (978-1-932338-97-3(7)) Lifevest Publishing, Inc.

Delton, Judy. Back Yard Angel. 1999. (gr. 3-6). lib. bdg. 12.95 (978-0-613-18239-3(1)) Tandem Library Bks.

Delval, Marie He. Lili et Mistigri jouent a Cache. (FRE.). pap. 14.95 (978-2-227-75602-1(0)) Bayard Editions FRA. *Dist:* Distribooks, Inc.

Demarest, Chris L. Supertwins Meet the Bad Dogs from Space. 2003. (gr. k-3). lib. bdg. 11.80 (978-0-613-72178-3(0)) Tandem Library Bks.

DeMatteis, J.M. Stardust Kid. 2008. (Stardust Kind Ser. : Ser.). (Illus.). 128p. pap. 14.99 (*978-1-934506-04-2(4)) Boom! Studios.

Deming, Lynette. Day in Matthews Shoes. 2006. 28p. pap. 9.95 (*978-1-4327-0100-0(2)) Outskirts Press, Inc.

deNiord, Lyman & DeNord, Pam Rodgers. The Adventures of Garth Oglie: History Rewritten. DeNord, Pam Rodgers, illus. 2001. 59p. (J). pap. 14.95 (978-1-58851-114-0(6)) PublishAmerica, Inc.

Denny, Joe. Triune: Jimmy's Escape. 2005. 80p. (J). pap. (978-0-9772240-0-5(7)) RS Publishing.

—Triune 2: Journey to the Unknown. 2005. (J). per. 5.95 (978-0-9772240-1-2(5)) RS Publishing.

Denson, Abby. Cover Up. Marderosian, Marc, illus. 2002. (Powerpuff Girls Ser.). 24p. (J). (ps-3). pap. 5.99 (978-0-439-37230-5(5)) Scholastic, Inc.

Dent, Jenny. Adventures of Hoppy the Gnome. (Illus.). 16p. (J). (gr. k-3). 1.75 (978-0-85487-048-6(2)) White Eagle Publishing Trust GBR. *Dist:* DeVorss & Co.

Denton, Terry. The Minotaur's Maze. 2004. (Storymaze Ser.). (Illus.). 144p. (J). pap. 6.95 (978-1-74114-088-0(9)) Allen & Unwin AUS. *Dist:* Independent Pubs. Group.

—The Obelisk of Eeeno. 2004. (Storymaze Ser.). (Illus.). 144p. (J). pap. 6.95 (978-1-74114-089-7(7)) Allen & Unwin AUS. *Dist:* Independent Pubs. Group.

Derksen, Barbara Ann. Alexis Learns to Trust: Shih-Tzu Puppy Adventures. 2007. (J). 9.99 (*978-1-59872-845-3(8)) Instantpublisher.com.

Derwent, Lavinia. Return to Sula. 2003. (Kelpies Ser.). (Illus.). 128p. pap. 10.00 (978-0-86315-424-9(7)) Floris Bks. GBR. *Dist:* SteinerBooks, Inc.

DeSio, Dolores. Rescue of the Gem Children. 1998. (Illus.). 35p. (J). (gr. 3-6). pap. 10.00 (978-0-9670347-0-6(1)) De Sio, Anthony W. & Delores J. Foundation.

Desrosiers, Sylvie. Les Extraterrestres Sont-ils des Voleurs? 2000. (Roman Jeunesse Ser.). (FRE.). 96p. (J). (gr. 4-7). pap. (978-2-89021-410-1(9)) Diffusion du livre Mirabel.

—Quatre Jours de Liberté. 2001. (Roman + — Special Editions Ser.). (FRE.). 96p. (YA). (gr. 8). pap. (978-2-89021-511-5(3)) Diffusion du livre Mirabel.

Desrosiers, Sylvie & Franson, Leanne. Au Revoir, Camille! 2000. (Premier Roman Ser.). 64p. (J). (gr. 2-5). pap. (978-2-89021-399-9(4)) Diffusion du livre Mirabel.

Deutsch, David. In Search of the Little People. l.t. ed. 2005. (Illus.). 60p. (J). per. 13.95 (978-1-59879-013-9(7)) Lifevest Publishing, Inc.

Deutsch, Stacia & Cohon, Rhody. Bell's Breakthrough. Wenzel, David, illus. 2005. (Blast to the Past Ser.). 112p. (J). pap. 3.99 (978-0-689-87026-2(4) , Aladdin) Simon & Schuster Children's Publishing.

—Ben Franklin's Fame. Francis, Guy, illus. 2006. (Blast to the Past Ser.). 128p. (J). pap. 3.99 (978-1-4169-1804-2(3) , Aladdin) Simon & Schuster Children's Publishing.

—Disney's Dream. Wenzel, David, illus. 2005. (Blast to the Past Ser.). 112p. (J). pap. 3.99 (978-0-689-87025-5(6) , Aladdin) Simon & Schuster Children's Publishing.

—King's Courage. Wenzel, David, illus. 2005. (Blast to the Past Ser.). 112p. (J). pap. 3.99 (978-1-4169-1269-9(X) , Aladdin) Simon & Schuster Children's Publishing.

—Lincoln's Legacy. Wenzel, David, illus. 2005. (Blast to the Past Ser.). 80p. (J). pap. 3.99 (978-0-689-87024-8(8) , Aladdin) Simon & Schuster Children's Publishing.

—Sacagawea's Strength. Wenzel, David, illus. 2006. (Blast to the Past Ser.). 128p. (J). pap. 3.99 (978-1-4169-1270-5(3) , Aladdin) Simon & Schuster Children's Publishing.

Deutsch/Cohon. Lincoln's Legacy. Wenzel, David, illus. 2005. 104p. (J). lib. bdg. 16.92 (*978-1-4242-1716-8(4)) Fitzgerald Bks.

Developing Set 3. 2001. (978-1-58453-164-7(9)) Pioneer Valley Educational Pr., Inc.

Deveze, Winky. Hewitch. Neate, Andy, illus. 2006. (J). (978-0-9787174-0-7(6)) Love Bug Bks.

Devor, Nina. It Must Be Mary Margaret. Cochran, Donna Eastman, illus. 2000. (Mary Margaret Adventure Stories Ser.). (J). (ps-k). pap. 6.50 (978-0-9676428-0-2(9)) Devor, Nina.

Dewin, Howie. The Circus Comes to Town. 2007. (One Piece Ser.: No. 2). 112p. (J). pap. 4.99 (978-0-439-89726-6(2) , Scholastic Paperbacks) Scholastic, Inc.

Dewin, Howie & Howie, Betsy. Mewtwo Returns. movie tie-in ed. 2002. (Pokemon Ser.). (Illus.). 80p. (J). pap. 4.50 (978-0-439-38564-0(4)) Scholastic, Inc.

Dezago, Todd. Spidey Strikes Back! 2006. (Illus.). (J). (gr. 2-6). 21.35 (978-1-59961-017-7(5)) Spotlight.

Dezago, Todd & Raicht, Mike. Spidey Strikes Back!, Vol. 5. 2005. (Spider-Man Ser.). (Illus.). 96p. pap. 5.99 (978-0-7851-1632-5(X)) Marvel Enterprises, Inc.

Di Maggio, S. J. Rob's Trilogy. 2006. 196p. (YA). per. 13.95 (978-0-9786593-1-8(7)) Omniland Bks.

Diablo - the Bequest. 2006. (J). (978-1-933343-14-3(1)) Stabenfeldt Inc.

Diablo - the Secret of Echo Lake. 2006. (J). (978-1-933343-21-1(4)) Stabenfeldt Inc.

Diamond Hunter: MainSails Individual Title Six-Packs. (Sails Literacy Ser.). (gr. 5 up). 37.00 (978-0-7578-8063-6(0)) Rigby Education.

Diaz, Gloria Cecilia. El Valle de los Cocuyos. (Barco de Vapor). (SPA.). 136p. (YA). (gr. 5-8). (978-84-348-1939-9(2)) SM Ediciones.

Diaz, Mariano. The Adventures of KCTMJ: Kitty, China, Tina, & Mary Jane. 2006. 125p. pap. 10.50 (978-1-4116-7620-6(3)) Lulu.com.

DiCamillo, Kate. The Miraculous Journey of Edward Tulane. Ibatoulline, Bagram, illus. 2006. 228p. (J). (gr. 2). 18.99 (978-0-7636-2589-4(2)) Candlewick Pr.

Dickens, Charles. A Tale of Two Cities. Hegarty, Carol, ed. 1998. (Classics Ser.: Set I). (Illus.). 80p. (YA). (gr. 5-12). pap. 6.95 (978-1-56254-277-1(X) , SP277X) Saddleback Educational Publishing.

Dickens, Charles, ed. Oliver Twist: Juvenile Classic. 2004. (Great Classics for Children Ser.). (Illus.). 182p. (J). 5.99 (978-1-4037-0794-9(4)) Dalmatian Pr.

Dier, Debra. The Sorcerer's Lady. 1999. (Timeswept Ser.). 448p. mass mkt. 5.50 (978-0-505-52305-1(1) , Love Spell) Dorchester Publishing Co., Inc.

DiGiacomo, Anthony W. Powerful Girls Adventures. DiGiacomo, Rachel Alison, illus. 2000. 50p. (J). (gr. 5-7). pap. 6.00 (978-1-58265-025-8(X) , 0112) Orphan Pr.

Dillingham, Mike. Rivers Book Two: Through the Eyes of a Blind Sled Dog. 2003. 13.95 (978-1-59433-004-9(2)) Publication Consultants.

Dillon, Eilis. Island of Horses. 2004. (New York Review Children's Collection). 224p. (J). pap. 17.95 (978-1-59017-102-8(0) , NYR Children's Collection) New York Review of Bks., Inc., The.

—The Lost Island. 2006. (New York Review Children's Collection). 208p. (J). (gr. 5). 17.95 (978-1-59017-205-6(1) , NYR Children's Collection) New York Review of Bks., Inc., The.

Dinges, Jason. Paleo Pals: The Adventures of Bill & Beryl. 2004. (Illus.). 34p. (J). pap. 14.95 (978-1-932373-71-4(3) , Cedar Hill Pr.) Cedar Hill Publishing.

Dinsdale, Christopher. Stolen Away. 2006. (Illus.). 229p. (YA). pap. 8.95 (978-1-894917-20-9(0)) Napoleon Publishing/Rendezvous Pr. CAN. *Dist:* AtlasBooks Distribution.

Discovering Dinos. (Flip Flap Fun Book Ser.). 10p. (J). bds. (978-2-7643-0137-1(5)) Phidal Publishing, Inc./Editions Phidal, Inc.

Disney Classics Collection Boxed Set. 1999. (Illus.). (J). (ps-3). pap. 3.99 (978-0-307-15891-8(8) , Golden Bks.) Random Hse. Children's Bks.

Disney Press, ed. Pirates of the Caribbean Film - Box Set. rev. ed. 2007. 496p. (gr. 3-7). pap. 12.99 (*978-1-4231-0926-6(0)) Disney Pr.

—Pirates of the Caribbean: GN - at Worlds End. rev. ed. 2007. 48p. (gr. 1). pap. 3.99 (*978-1-4231-0449-0(8)) Disney Pr.

Disney Press Staff. Dead Man's Chest. 2007. 48p. (ps-3). 12.99 incl. audio compact disk (978-1-4231-0368-4(8)) Disney Pr.

—Disney Trivia Challenge. 2006. 128p. (gr. k-17). 19.99 (978-0-7868-3848-6(5)) Disney Pr.

—Disney's Lilo & Stitch. 2006. (Disney Adventure Ser.: No.1). 96p. (gr. 3-7). pap. 4.99 (978-0-7868-4719-8(0)) Disney Pr.

Disney Press Staff, ed. Pirates of the Caribbean: At World's End Storybook. rev. ed. 2007. 48p. (J). (gr. 1-4). 12.99 (*978-1-4231-0918-1(X)) Disney Pr.

—Pirates of the Caribbean 3: Swann. 2007. 24p. (J). (ps-2). pap. 3.99 (*978-1-4231-0375-2(0)) Disney Pr.

Disney Press Staff & Beechwood, Beth. Check It Out, Bk. 5. 5th rev. ed. 2007. 80p. (gr. 2-5). pap. 3.99 (978-0-7868-4939-0(8)) Disney Pr.

Disney Press Staff & King, M. C. Truth or Dare. 4th rev. ed. 2007. (Hannah Montana Ser.: No. 4). 128p. (gr. 3-7). pap. 4.99 (978-1-4231-0277-9(0)) Disney Pr.

Disney Staff. Aladdin. (FRE.). 96p. (J). (gr. k-5). pap. 9.95 (978-0-7859-8852-6(1)) French & European Pubns., Inc.

—Gorilla, Gorilla. 2006. (Disney Adventure Ser.: Vol. 2). 96p. (gr. 3-7). pap. 4.99 (978-0-7868-4720-4(4)) Disney Pr.

—Tarzan, Me & You. 1999. (Illus.). 10p. (J). (ps). 3.99 (978-0-7364-0132-6(6)) Mouse Works.

—Tarzan's Jungle Adventure. 1999. (Giant Lift-the-Flap Ser.). (Illus.). 10p. (J). (ps). bds. 8.99 (978-0-7364-0066-4(4)) Mouse Works.

Disney Staff & McCoy, Glenn. Disney's Tall Tails. 2006. (Disney Adventure Ser.: Vol. 3). 96p. (gr. 3-7). pap. 4.99 (978-0-7868-3766-3(7)) Disney Pr.

Disney Staff & Walker, Landry Quinn. Kid Gravity. Jones, Eric, illus. 2006. (Disney Adventure Ser.: Vol. 4). 96p. (gr. 3-7). pap. 4.99 (978-0-7868-3765-6(9)) Disney Pr.

Disney Storybook Artists Staff, ed. Remy's Adventure in Paris: A Magnetic Book. 2007. 10p. (ps-2). 12.99 (*978-1-4231-0655-5(5)) Disney Pr.

DiTerlizzi, Tony. G Is for One Gzonk! An Alpha-Number-Bet Book. DiTerlizzi, Tony, illus. 2006. 80p. (J). (ps-2). (Illus.). 16.95 (978-0-689-85290-9(8)) ; 150.00 (978-1-4169-2471-5(X)) Simon & Schuster Children's Publishing.

—Jimmy Zangwow's Out-of-This-World Moon-Pie Adventure. DiTerlizzi, Tony, illus. 2005. (Stories to Go! Ser.). 40p. (J). 4.99 (978-0-689-87830-5(3) , Aladdin) Simon & Schuster Children's Publishing.

—Moon Pie Adventure. DiTerlizzi, Tony, illus. 2000. (Illus.). 40p. (J). (gr. k-3). 17.99 (978-0-689-82215-5(4)) Simon & Schuster Children's Publishing.

—The Wrath of Mulgarath. 2004. (Spiderwick Chronicles: Bk. 5). (Illus.). 160p. (gr. 1-5). 10.99 (978-0-689-85940-3(6)) Simon & Schuster Children's Publishing.

DiTerlizzi, Tony & Black, Holly. The Spiderwick Chronicles Boxed Set: The Field Guide; The Seeing Stone; Lucinda's Secret; The Ironwood Tree; The Wrath of Mulgrath, Vol. 1-5. DiTerlizzi, Tony & Black, Holly, illus. 2004. (Spiderwick Chronicles). (Illus.). 672p. (J). 49.99 (978-0-689-04034-4(2)) Simon & Schuster Children's Publishing.

Divakaruni, Chitra Banerjee. The Conch Bearer. rev. ed. 2003. (Illus.). 272p. (J). (gr. 3 up). 16.95 (978-0-7613-1935-1(2)) Roaring Brook Pr.

—The Conch Bearer. 2005. 272p. (J). reprint ed. pap. 5.99 (978-0-689-87242-6(9) , Aladdin) Simon & Schuster Children's Publishing.

Dixon, Chuck. El Cazador. Epting, Stephen, illus. rev. ed. 2007. 144p. (J). (gr. 5 up). pap. 12.99 (*978-1-4231-0927-3(9)) Hyperion Pr.

Dixon, Franklin W. The Dangerous Transmission. 2004. (Hardy Boys Ser.). (Illus.). 160p. (J). pap. 4.99 (978-0-689-86378-3(0) , Aladdin) Simon & Schuster Children's Publishing.

—The Dangerous Transmission. 2004. (gr. 3-6). lib. bdg. 13.00 (978-0-613-86965-2(6)) Tandem Library Bks.

—Double Jeopardy. 2003. (Hardy Boys Ser.: No. 181). 160p. (J). pap. 4.99 (978-0-689-85780-5(2) , Aladdin) Simon & Schuster Children's Publishing.

—Double Jeopardy. 2003. 150p. (J). (gr. 3-7). per. 13.00 (978-0-613-89000-7(0)) Tandem Library Bks.

—Farming Fear. 2004. (Hardy Boys Ser.: No. 188). 160p. (J). pap. 4.99 (978-0-689-86739-2(5) , Aladdin) Simon & Schuster Children's Publishing.

—Feeding Frenzy. 2008. (Hardy Boys (All New) Undercover Brothers Ser.). 160p. (J). pap. 4.99 (*978-1-4169-5499-6(6) , Aladdin) Simon & Schuster Children's Publishing.

—Figure in Hiding, Vol. 16. Laune, Paul, illus. 2005. (Hardy Boys (Hardcover) Ser.). 212p. (J). (gr. 3-9). 17.95 (978-1-55709-274-8(5)) Applewood Bks.

—Hardy Boys Starter Set. 2007. (Hardy Boys Ser.). 128p. (J). lthr. 25.98 (*978-0-448-44820-6(3) , Grosset & Dunlap) Penguin Group (USA) Inc.

—Hidden Mountain. 2004. (Hardy Boys Ser.: No. 186). (Illus.). 160p. (J). pap. 4.99 (978-0-689-86737-8(9) , Aladdin) Simon & Schuster Children's Publishing.

—Hurricane Joe. 2006. (Hardy Boys (All New) Undercover Brothers Ser.: No.11). 160p. (J). pap. 4.99 (978-1-4169-1174-6(X) , Aladdin) Simon & Schuster Children's Publishing.

—In Plane Sight. 2002. 148p. (gr. 5-8). lib. bdg. 13.00 (978-0-613-63303-1(2)) Tandem Library Bks.

—Motocross Madness. 2005. (Hardy Boys Ser.). 160p. (J). pap. 4.99 (978-0-689-87365-2(4) , Aladdin) Simon & Schuster Children's Publishing.

—No Way Out. 2004. (Hardy Boys Ser.: No. 187). 160p. (J). pap. 4.99 (978-0-689-86738-5(7) , Aladdin) Simon & Schuster Children's Publishing.

—Operation: Survival. 2005. (Hardy Boys Ser.: No. 7). (Illus.). 160p. (J). (gr. 3-7). pap. 4.99 (978-1-4169-0067-2(5) , Aladdin) Simon & Schuster Children's Publishing.

—Pushed. 2007. (Hardy Boys (All New) Undercover Brothers Ser.). 154p. (J). (gr. 3-7). per. 4.99 (*978-1-4169-4802-5(3) , Aladdin) Simon & Schuster Children's Publishing.

—Rocky Road. 2005. (Hardy Boys Ser.: Bk. 5). (Illus.). 160p. pap. 4.99 (978-1-4169-0006-1(3) , Aladdin) Simon & Schuster Children's Publishing.

—Running on Fumes, Vol. 2. 2005. (Hardy Boys Ser.). 160p. pap. 4.99 (978-1-4169-0003-0(9) , Aladdin) Simon & Schuster Children's Publishing.

—The Secret of the Soldier's Gold. 2003. (gr. 3-6). lib. bdg. 13.00 (978-0-613-90468-1(0)) Tandem Library Bks.

—Thrill Ride, Vol. 4. 2005. (Hardy Boys Ser.). 160p. pap. 4.99 (978-1-4169-0005-4(5) , Aladdin) Simon & Schuster Children's Publishing.

—Trick-or-Trouble, Vol. 175. 2002. (Hardy Boys Ser.). 160p. (J). pap. 4.99 (978-0-7434-3759-2(4) , Aladdin) Simon & Schuster Children's Publishing.

—Trick-or-Trouble. 2002. (gr. 5-8). lib. bdg. 13.00 (978-0-613-63359-8(8)) Tandem Library Bks.

—Wreck & Roll. 2004. (Hardy Boys Ser.: No. 185). (Illus.). 160p. (J). pap. 4.99 (978-0-689-86736-1(0) , Aladdin) Simon & Schuster Children's Publishing.

Dixon, Franklin W. & Walker, Jeff. The Secret of the Soldier's Gold. 2003. (Hardy Boys Ser.). (Illus.). 160p. (J). pap. 4.99 (978-0-689-85885-7(X) , Aladdin) Simon & Schuster Children's Publishing.

Dixon, Sean. The Feathered Cloak. rev. ed. 2007. (Trilogy of the Tree Ser.: Pt. 1). 200p. (J). (gr. 7 up). 12.95 (*978-1-55263-936-8(3)) Key Porter Bks. CAN. *Dist:* Perseus Distribution.

Dixon, Steve. Out of the Shadows. 2003. (Rumours of the King Trilogy Ser.). 128p. 6.99 (978-1-85999-671-3(X)) Scripture Union GBR. *Dist:* Gabriel Resources.

DK Publishing. Glow-in-the-Dark Indiana Jones. 2008. (Ultimate Sticker Bks.). 16p. (J). (ps-12). pap. 6.99 (*978-0-7566-3498-8(9)) Dorling Kindersley Publishing, Inc.

—Indiana Jones. 2008. (Ultimate Sticker Bks.). 16p. (J). (ps-12). pap. 6.99 (*978-0-7566-3499-5(7)) Dorling Kindersley Publishing, Inc.

—Indiana Jones: The Ultimate Guide. 2008. 144p. (J). 24.99 (*978-0-7566-3500-8(4)) Dorling Kindersley Publishing, Inc.

—Kung Fu Panda Ultimate Sticker Book. 2008. (Ultimate Sticker Bks.). 16p. (J). (gr. 2-6). pap. 6.99 (*978-0-7566-3824-5(0)) Dorling Kindersley Publishing, Inc.

—Power Rangers. 2008. (Dk Readers Ser.). 32p. (J). 14.99 (*978-0-7566-3489-6(X)); 14.99 (*978-0-7566-3493-3(8)); pap. 3.99 (*978-0-7566-3488-9(1)); pap. 3.99 (*978-0-7566-3492-6(X)) Dorling Kindersley Publishing, Inc.

DK Publishing Staff. Magic Toy Shop. 2007. 12p. (J). (ps-3). 14.99 (*978-0-7566-3179-6(3)) Dorling Kindersley Publishing, Inc.

Do, Kim-Thu, tr. Tang Monk Disciples Monkey King: English/Vietnamese. Ma, Wenhai, illus. 2005. (Adventures of Monkey King Ser.: No. 3). (ENG & VIE.). 32p. (J). 16.95 (978-1-57227-087-9(X)) Pan Asia Pubns. (USA), Inc.

Dodds, Dayle Ann. Great Divide: A Mathematical Marathon. Mitchell, Tracy, illus. 2005. 32p. (J). (gr. k-5). reprint ed. pap. 6.99 (978-0-7636-1592-5(7)) Candlewick Pr.

Dodds, Robert. The Secret of Iguando. 2005. 128p. (J). pap. 8.99 (978-1-84270-327-4(7)) Andersen GBR. *Dist:* Trafalgar Square Publishing.

Dodee. That Big Old Round Orange Thing: A Mrs. Tockalocka Adventure. 2006. 64p. (J). per. 9.95 (978-1-60002-129-9(8) , 3931, Airleaf Publishing) Airleaf Publishing & Bookselling.

Doder, Joshua. A Dog Called Grk. (Grk Bks.). (J). (gr. 4-7). 2008. 240p. 6.50 (*978-0-440-42147-4(0) , Yearling); 2007. 272p. 14.99 (978-0-385-73359-5(3) , Delacorte Bks. for Young Readers); 2007. 272p. lib. bdg. 18.99 (978-0-385-90374-5(X) , Delacorte Bks. for Young Readers) Random Hse. Children's Bks.

—Grk & the Hotdog Trail. 2008. (J). (*978-0-385-73361-8(5)); (*978-0-385-90376-9(6)); pap. (*978-0-440-42150-4(0)) Dell Publishing. (Delacorte Pr.).

—Grk & the Pelotti Brothers. 2006. 240p. (J). pap. (978-1-84270-527-8(X)) Andersen.

Doder, Joshua. Grk & the Pelotti Gang. 2007. (Grk Bks.). 208p. (J). (gr. 4-7). 14.99 (*978-0-385-73360-1(7)); lib. bdg. 17.99 (*978-0-385-90375-2(8)) Random Hse. Children's Bks. (Delacorte Bks. for Young Readers).

Dodge, Mary Mapes. Po No Kah an Indian Tale of Long Ago. 2004. reprint ed. pap. 15.95 (978-1-4191-4185-0(6)) Kessinger Publishing, LLC.

Doherty, Berlie. The Famous Adventures of Jack. unabr. l.t. ed. 2001. (Read-Along Ser.). 128p. (J). 24.95 incl. audio (978-0-7540-6237-0(6) , RAO38, Chivers Children's Audio Bks.) BBC Audiobooks America.

—The Snake-Stone. 1998. (J). (978-0-606-13086-8(1)) Tandem Library Bks.

Domnauer, Teresa & Lithgow, John. Rock, Rag, & Swing, Level 4: A Musical Adventure. 2005. (Lithgow Palooza Readers Ser.). (Illus.). 32p. (J). (gr. 2-3). pap. 3.95 (978-0-7696-4234-5(9)) School Specialty Publishing.

—Sounds of Celebration!, Level 3: A Musical Adventure. 2005. (Lithgow Palooza Readers Ser.). (Illus.). 32p. (J). (gr. 1-2). pap. 3.95 (978-0-7696-4233-8(0)) School Specialty Publishing.

—Tweet, Oompa, Bumpety-Boom! Level 2: A Musical Adventure. 2005. (Lithgow Palooza Readers Ser.). (Illus.). 32p. (J). (gr. k-1). pap. 3.95 (978-0-7696-4222-2(5)) School Specialty Publishing.

Donaki & Rosenberry, Donald. Spectacular Journey. Rosenberry, Akiko & Rosenberry, Susan, illus. 2006. (J). per. 20.00 (*978-0-9771482-6-4(2) , Ithaca Pr.) Authors & Artists Publishers of New York, Inc.

Donald Duck Adventures, Vol. 2. 2003. (Illus.). 128p. pap. 7.95 (978-0-911903-11-9(9)) Diamond Bk. Distributors.

Donaldson, Julia. Charlie Cook's Favorite Book. Scheffler, Axel, illus. 2008. 32p. (J). (ps-k). pap. 6.99 (*978-0-14-241138-4(8) , Puffin) Penguin Group (USA) Inc.

Donaldson, Julia. The Gruffalo. Scheffler, Axel, illus. 2003. 24p. (J). pap. 11.99 (978-0-333-71093-7(2)) Macmillan Publishers Ltd. GBR. *Dist:* Trafalgar Square Publishing.

—The Gruffalo. Scheffler, Axel, illus. 2005. 24p. (J). (ps). bds. 6.99 (978-0-8037-3047-2(0) , Dial) Penguin Group (USA) Inc.

Donaldson, Julia & Richards, Lucy. The Quick Brown Fox Club. 2006. (Red Bananas Ser.). (Illus.). 48p. (J). (978-0-7787-1080-6(7)) Crabtree Publishing Co.

Dong, Claxton. Save Our Star. 2002. 144p. (YA). (gr. 5-9). pap. 5.99 (978-0-9717993-0-1(X)) Brown Swan Pubs.

Donovan, Stacey. Dive. 2000. (gr. 7-12). lib. bdg. 25.70 (978-0-613-87317-8(3)) Tandem Library Bks.

—Dive. 2001. 256p. (gr. 7-12). pap. 15.95 (978-0-595-16557-5(5) , Backinprint.com) iUniverse, Inc.

Dooley, Sarah. Wilfred & Harold's Dinner Party Disaster. 2004. 35p. pap. 17.95 (978-1-4137-1585-9(0)) PublishAmerica, Inc.

Doran, Colleen. A Distant Soil Vol. 4: Coda Limited Edition. ltd. ed. 2006. 164p. (YA). 29.95 (978-1-58240-525-4(5)) Image Comics.

Dora's Ready-to-Read Adventures. 2005. (Dora the Explorer Ser.). (Illus.). 128p. (J). pap. 7.99 (978-0-689-87815-2(X) , Simon Spotlight/Nickelodeon) Simon & Schuster Children's Publishing.

Dora's Stories: A Boxed Set. 2005. (Dora the Explorer Ser.). 56p. (J). bds. 9.99 (978-1-4169-0035-1(7) , Simon Spotlight/Nickelodeon) Simon & Schuster Children's Publishing.

Dora's Storytime Collection. 2003. (Dora the Explorer Ser.). (Illus.). 160p. (J). 10.95 (978-0-689-86623-4(2) , Simon Spotlight/Nickelodeon) Simon & Schuster Children's Publishing.

Dorling Kindersley Publishing Staff. Flushed Away Essential Guide. 2006. (Illus.). 48p. (J). 12.99 (978-0-7566-2243-5(3)) Dorling Kindersley Publishing, Inc.

—Over the Edge. 2006. (Ultimate Sticker Bks.). 16p. (J). pap. 6.99 (978-0-7566-2123-0(2)) Dorling Kindersley Publishing, Inc.

—The Wild. 2006. (Ultimate Sticker Bks.). 16p. (J). pap. 6.99 (978-0-7566-1836-0(3)) Dorling Kindersley Publishing, Inc.

Dorris, Michael. A Yellow Raft in Blue Water: A Novel. 1999. (YA). 9.95 (978-1-56137-933-0(6)) Novel Units, Inc.

Dotlich, Rebecca Kai. Away We Go! Yaccarino, Dan, illus. 2000. (Growing Tree Ser.). 24p. (J). (ps). 9.95 (978-0-694-01393-7(5) , Harper Festival) HarperCollins Pubs.

Dotlich, Rebecca Kai. Peanut & Pearl's Picnic Adventure. Alley, R. W., illus. 2007. (My First I Can Read Bks.). 32p. (J). lib. bdg. 16.89 (*978-0-06-054921-3(1)); 15.99 (*978-0-06-054920-6(3)) HarperCollins Pubs.

Dotrice, Roy, narrated by. The Little Mermaid: Read Along. 2001. (Illus.). 32p. (J). pap. 9.98 incl. audio compact disk (978-0-7634-0799-5(2)) Walt Disney Records.

Doty, Linda. The Christmas Doll. 2005. 124p. pap. 17.95 (978-1-4137-7790-1(2)) PublishAmerica, Inc.

Douglas, Carole Nelson. The Cat & the Jack of Spades. 2000. (Midnight Louie Mystery Ser.: Bk. 4). 206p. 22.95 (978-0-7862-2896-6(2) , Five Star) Thomson Gale.

Douglas, H. I. Voyage to the Stars: David's First Adventure. 2006. 156p. pap. 19.95 (978-1-4241-1176-3(5)) PublishAmerica, Inc.

Doust, Jon & Spillman, Ken. Magwheel Madness. 2005. (Illus.). 128p. (J). pap. 13.50 (978-1-920731-76-2(8)) Fremantle Pr. AUS. *Dist:* International Specialized Bk. Services.

Douthit, George. Boy Who Slept with Bears. 2005. 60p. pap. 12.95 (978-0-9700127-3-9(X)) Sweet Success Pr.

Dowell, Michael. Moodoo: The Marvelous World of Moodoo. 2005. (Illus.). 128p. (J). per. 13.99 (*978-0-9762454-2-1(6) , b-001) Moodoo Productions, Inc.

Dower, Laura. Fishy Business. 2001. (Powerpuff Girls Ser.). 32p. (J). (ps-3). pap. 3.50 (978-0-439-29590-1(4)) Scholastic, Inc.

—Mojo Jojo's Rising. 2000. (gr. k-3). lib. bdg. 11.25 (978-0-613-26246-0(8)) Tandem Library Bks.

—Paste Makes Waste. 2000. (ps-2). lib. bdg. 11.25 (978-0-613-32931-6(7)) Tandem Library Bks.

Downer, Ann. Hatching Magic. 2004. 256p. (J). reprint ed. pap. 5.99 (978-0-689-87057-6(4) , Aladdin) Simon & Schuster Children's Publishing.

Dowswell, P. & Allan, Tony. True Ghost Stories. 2004. (True Adventure Stories Ser.). 144p. (J). lib. bdg. 12.95 (978-1-58086-601-9(8)) EDC Publishing.

Dowswell, Paul. Powder Monkey: Adventures of a Young Sailor. 2006. 288p. (YA). pap. 7.95 (978-1-58234-748-6(4) , Bloomsbury Children) Bloomsbury Publishing.

—Prison Ship: Adventures of a Young Sailor. 2006. 300p. (YA). 16.95 (978-1-58234-676-2(3) , Bloomsbury Children) Bloomsbury Publishing.

Dowswell, Paul & Harvey, Gill. True Adventure Stories. 2004. 144p. (YA). (gr. 4 up). lib. bdg. 20.95 (978-1-58086-703-0(0)) EDC Publishing.

Doyle, Arthur Conan. The Adventure of the Speckled Band. Stemach, Jerry, ed. Letwenko, Michael, illus. 2000. 65.00 incl. audio, cd-rom (978-1-58702-338-5(5)); 2002. 104p. 150.00 (978-1-58702-041-4(6)); 2000. 104p. 50.00 (978-1-58702-496-2(9)) Johnston, Don Inc.

—The Adventures & Memoirs of Sherlock Holmes. 2001. (gr. 7-12). lib. bdg. 22.25 (978-0-613-64240-8(6)) Tandem Library Bks.

Doyle, Brian. Dam Lies. 1999. 128p. (J). (gr. 4 up). 15.95 (978-0-88899-349-6(8)) ; pap. (978-0-88899-350-2(1)) Groundwood Bks. CAN. *Dist:* Transition Vendor.

—The Low Life: From up & down the River. 2002. (Illus.). (J). pap. (978-0-88899-498-1(2)) Douglas & McIntyre, Ltd.

Doyon, Stephanie. Making Waves. 1999. (On the Road Ser.: No. 4). (978-0-606-16905-9(9)) Tandem Library Bks.

DPWW. Tarzan. 1999. (Disney Chapters Ser.). (Illus.). 48p. (J). (gr. 2-4). pap. 3.95 (978-0-7868-4289-6(X)) Disney Pr.

Dragon: Enter the Realm. 2007. (YA). per. (*978-1-934345-43-6(1)) SouthWest Pubns.

Dragon: The Fantasy Continues. 2007. (YA). per. (*978-1-934345-44-3(X)) SouthWest Pubns.

Dragonwings. 1999. (YA). 9.95 (978-1-56137-073-3(8)) Novel Units, Inc.

Drake, David. Disaster at Disappearing Creek. 2001. 115p. (YA). (gr. 8-12). pap. 9.99 (978-1-885631-07-7(3) , Family Of Man Pr., The) Hutchison, G.F. Pr.

—The Great Balloon Adventure. 2002. (Cricket of Dew Drop Dell Ser.). (Illus.). 32p. (J). 3.49 (978-1-885631-62-6(6) , Family Of Man Pr., The) Hutchison, G.F. Pr.

—Kidd's Grand Adventure. 2003. 190p. (YA). mass mkt. 13.99 (978-1-885631-71-8(5)) Hutchison, G.F. Pr.

—Tommy Powers & the Mutant Stranger. 2005. 213p. (J). pap. 14.95 (978-1-885631-90-9(1) , Family Of Man Pr., The) Hutchison, G.F. Pr.

—Tommy Powers & the Replicator of Rio Azul. 2005. 210p. (YA). pap. 14.99 (978-1-885631-93-0(6)) Hutchison, G.F. Pr.

Draper, Sharon M. The Backyard Animal Show. Watson, Jesse Joshua, illus. 2006. (Ziggy & the Black Dinosaurs Ser.). 128p. (J). pap. 4.99 (978-1-4169-0000-9(4) , Aladdin) ; lib. bdg. 11.89 (978-1-4169-2754-9(9) , Aladdin Library) Simon & Schuster Children's Publishing.

—The Space Mission Adventure. Watson, Jesse Joshua, illus. 2006. (Ziggy & the Black Dinosaurs Ser.). 128p. (J). lib. bdg. 11.89 (978-1-4169-2458-6(2) , Aladdin Library); pap. 4.99 (978-0-689-87914-2(8) , Aladdin) Simon & Schuster Children's Publishing.

—Stars & Sparks on Stage. Watson, Jesse Joshua, illus. 2007. (Ziggy & the Black Dinosaurs Ser.). 160p. (J). lib. bdg. 11.89 (978-1-4169-2755-6(7) , Aladdin Library) Simon & Schuster Children's Publishing.

—Stars & Sparks Onstage. Watson, Jesse Joshua, illus. 2007. (Ziggy & the Black Dinosaurs Ser.). 160p. (J). pap. 4.99 (978-1-4169-0001-6(2) , Aladdin) Simon & Schuster Children's Publishing.

Dravis, Betty. The Toonies Invade Silicon Valley. 2005. (Illus.). 168p. (J). per. 14.95 (978-1-932586-29-9(6) , Just My Bk., Inc.) Just My Best Bk. Publishing Co.

Drawson, Blair. All along the River. Drawson, Blair, illus. 2003. (Illus.). 36p. (J). (ps-2). 16.95 (978-0-88899-546-9(6)) Groundwood Bks. CAN. *Dist:* Perseus Distribution.

—Flying Dimitri. (Illus.). (J). 16.95 (978-0-88899-284-0(X)) Groundwood Bks. CAN. *Dist:* Transition Vendor.

The Dreamer Who Unlocked the Secrets of the Universe... 2004. (Illus.). 126p. (YA). pap. 11.11 (978-0-9749196-1-4(6)) Don Quixote Publishing Co. Inc.

Dreams of Glory: A Penny Parrish Story. 2001. (Penny Parrish Story). 190p. (YA). pap. 12.95 (978-1-930009-27-1(5)) Image Cascade Publishing.

Dress, Robert, illus. Mars, Here We Come! 2006. (Backyardigans Ser.). 16p. (J). bds. 7.99 (978-1-4169-1471-6(4) , Simon Spotlight/Nickelodeon) Simon & Schuster Children's Publishing.

Drew, Alejandrina. Abra Cadabra, Patas De Cabra: A Spanish, English Story for Young Readers. Satcher, David & Ford, Richard, trs. Mora, Mauricio, illus. 41p. (J). pap. 15.95 (978-1-57168-505-6(7)); 2001. (ENG & SPA.). 46p. (gr. 2-4). 18.95 (978-1-57168-506-3(5)) Eakin Pr.

Driggs, Scout. Peter Pan: Adventures in Neverland. 2003. (gr. 3-6). lib. bdg. 13.00 (978-0-613-71458-7(X)) Tandem Library Bks.

—Power Up! 2004. (Astro Boy Ser.). (Illus.). 24p. (J). pap. 3.50 (978-0-06-072525-9(7) , Harper Festival) HarperCollins Pubs.

Driscoll, Laura. All Aboard the Circus Train! A Foldout Book with Flaps! Roper, Robert, illus. 2004. (Dora the Explorer Ser.). 14p. (J). bds. 6.99 (978-0-689-86868-9(5) , Simon Spotlight/Nickelodeon) Simon & Schuster Children's Publishing.

—Dora Helps Diego! Mangano, Tom, illus. 2007. (Ready-To-Read Ser.). 24p. (J). pap. 3.99 (978-1-4169-1509-6(5) , Simon Spotlight/Nickelodeon) Simon & Schuster Children's Publishing.

Druitt, Tobias. Corydon & the Fall of Atlantis. 2007. 352p. (J). (gr. 5). 15.99 (978-0-375-83383-0(8)); lib. bdg. 18.99 (978-0-375-93383-7(2)) Random Hse. Children's Bks. (Knopf Bks. for Young Readers).

The Drums of Legenderry. 2006. (J). per. (978-0-9776967-0-3(7)) Legenderry.com.

Du Bois, Thaddeus. Thaddeus' Weekend Adventures. 2002. 120p. (YA). per. 19.95 (978-0-9653074-9-9(2)) Northbooks.

Duane, Diane. A Wizard Alone. 2003. (Young Wizards Ser.: Bk. 6). (gr. 7-12). lib. bdg. 15.25 (978-0-613-71627-7(2)) Tandem Library Bks.

Duarte, Pamela, illus. Beyond the Clouds. Mattel Photo Studio, photos by. 2005. 32p. (J). (ps-2). pap. 3.99 (978-0-375-83362-5(5) , Golden Bks.) Random Hse. Children's Bks.

Dube, Jasmine & Barrette, Doris. Grattelle au Bois Mordant. 1998. (Etait une Fois Ser.). (Illus.). 24p. (J). pap. (978-2-89021-332-6(3)) Diffusion du livre Mirabel.

Dube, Jasmine & Paré, Roger. Elvis Fait des Acrobaties. 2000. (Elvis Ser.). (FRE., Illus.). 24p. (YA). (ps up). pap. (978-2-89021-420-0(6)) Diffusion du livre Mirabel.

DuBose, Sara A. Where Hearts Live. 2002. 184p. pap. 19.95 (978-1-59129-219-7(0)) PublishAmerica, Inc.

Dubowski, Cathy East. Hanging onto Home. 2001. (gr. 3-6). lib. bdg. 11.80 (978-0-613-51308-1(8)) Tandem Library Bks.

Dubowski, Cathy East & Dubowski, Mark. Ice Mummy: The Discovery of a 5,000 Year-Old Man. 1998. (Step into Reading Step 3 Bks.). (Illus.). 48p. (J). (gr. 2-4). pap. 3.99 (978-0-679-85647-4(1) , Random Hse. Bks. for Young Readers) Random Hse. Children's Bks.

Dubya, Jay. Pot of Gold. 2001. 182p. pap. 16.95 (978-1-58909-174-0(4)) Bookstand Publishing.

Duce, Gillian. Magic & Mayhem. 2006. 208p. per. (*978-1-894936-64-4(7)) Saga Bks.

Duckett, Brenda. Summit Lane. 2005. 79p. pap. 10.99 (978-1-4116-3897-6(2)) Lulu.com.

Dudley, Maywill. The Story of Little Red Riding Hood. 2005. reprint ed. pap. 15.95 (978-1-4191-5430-0(3)) Kessinger Publishing, LLC.

Duey, Kathleen. Arthur. Epstein, Eugene, illus. Gould, Robert, photos by. 2005. (Time Soldiers Ser.: Vol. 4). 96p. (J). (gr. 3-4). pap. 5.95 (978-1-929945-56-6(6)) Big Guy Bks., Inc.

—Arthur. 2007. (Illus.). 96p. (J). 24.21 (978-1-59961-224-9(0)) Spotlight.

—Castle Avamir. Rayyan, Omar, illus. 2003. (Unicorn's Secret Ser.). 80p. (J). pap. 3.99 (978-0-689-85372-2(6) , Aladdin) Simon & Schuster Children's Publishing.

—Mummy. 2007. (Illus.). 96p. (J). 24.21 (978-1-59961-225-6(9)) Spotlight.

—Patch. Epstein, Eugene, illus. Gould, Robert, photos by. 2005. (Time Soldiers Ser.: Bk. 3). 96p. (J). (gr. 3-4). pap. 5.95 (978-1-929945-55-9(8)) Big Guy Bks., Inc.

—Patch. 2007. (Illus.). 96p. (J). 24.21 (978-1-59961-226-3(7)) Spotlight.

—Patch. 2003. (gr. k-3). lib. bdg. 17.60 (978-0-613-70790-9(7)) Tandem Library Bks.

—Pony Express: Time Soldiers Book #7. 2007. (Time Soldiers Ser.). (Illus.). (J). 48p. 15.95 (978-1-929945-68-9(X)); 96p. pap. 5.95 (978-1-929945-69-6(8)) Big Guy Bks., Inc.

—Rex. Epstein, Eugene, illus. Gould, Robert, photos by. 2000. (Time Soldiers Ser.: Bk. 1). 48p. (J). (ps-5). 12.95 (978-1-929945-18-4(3)) Big Guy Bks., Inc.

—Rex. Epstein, Eugene, illus. Gould, Robert, photos by. (Time Soldiers Ser.: Bk. 1). (J). 2005. 96p. (gr. 3-4). pap. 5.95 (978-1-929945-53-5(1)); 2003. 48p. (ps-5). pap. 7.95 (978-1-929945-20-7(5)) Big Guy Bks., Inc.

—Rex 2. Epstein, Eugene, illus. Gould, Robert, photos by. 2003. (Time Soldiers Ser.: Bk. 2). 48p. (J). (ps-5). pap. 8.95 (978-1-929945-27-6(2)) Big Guy Bks., Inc.

—Rex 2. Epstein, Eugene, illus. Gould, Robert, photos by. (Time Soldiers Ser.: Bk. 2). (J). 2005. (ENG.). 96p. (gr. 3-4). pap. 5.95 (978-1-929945-54-2(X)); 2nd rev. ed. 2000. 48p. (ps-5). 12.95 (978-1-929945-19-1(1)) Big Guy Bks., Inc.

—Rex, Rex 2, Patch, Set. Epstein, Eugene, illus. Gould, Robert, photos by. gif. ed. 2003. (Time Soldiers Ser.). 144p. (J). 32.95 (978-1-929945-23-8(X)) Big Guy Bks., Inc.

—Samurai. 2007. (Illus.). 96p. (J). 24.21 (978-1-59961-229-4(1)) Spotlight.

—The Sunset Gates. Rayyan, Omar, illus. ed. 2005. 76p. (J). lib. bdg. 15.00 (978-1-59054-918-6(X)) Fitzgerald Bks.

—True Heart. Rayyan, Omar, illus. 2003. (Unicorn's Secret Ser.). 80p. (J). pap. 3.99 (978-0-689-85370-8(X) , Aladdin) Simon & Schuster Children's Publishing.

—True Heart. 2003. (gr. 3-6). lib. bdg. 11.80 (978-0-613-61664-5(2)) Tandem Library Bks.

Duey, Kathleen, et al. Katie & the Mustang. 2004. (Hoofbeats Ser.: Bk. 4). (J). 140p. (gr. 3 up). pap. 4.99 (978-0-14-240093-7(9)); Bk. 2. 144p. pap. 4.99 (978-0-14-240091-3(2)); Bk. 3. 144p. pap. 4.99 (978-0-14-240092-0(0)) Penguin Group (USA) Inc. (Puffin).

Duffield, W. J. The Radio Boys in the Thousand Islands O. 2006. pap. 71.99 (*978-1-4219-9966-1(8)) IndyPublish.com.

—Radio Boys in the Thousand Islands or Th. 2006. 78.99 (*978-1-4219-9957-9(9)) IndyPublish.com.

Duggan, Matt. The Royal Woods. rev. ed. 2007. 244p. (gr. 7-12). 12.95 (*978-1-55263-826-2(X)) Key Porter Bks. CAN. *Dist:* Perseus Distribution.

Duhon, Joe. The T-graben: Discovery & Exploration of the Mammalian Graben. Loren, illus. 2002. 189p. (YA). pap. 14.95 (978-1-58736-109-8(4) , Starbound Bks.) Wheatmark.

Dumas, Alexandre. Classic Starts: the Three Musketeers. Akib, Jamel, illus. 2007. (Classic Starts Ser.). 160p. (J). 4.95 (978-1-4027-3695-7(9)) Sterling Publishing Co., Inc.

—The Count of Monte Cristo. 2002. (Great Illustrated Classics Ser.). (Illus.). 240p. (J). (gr. 3-8). 21.35 (978-1-57765-684-5(9) , ABDO & Daughters) ABDO Publishing Co.

—The Man in the Iron Mask. 1998. (978-0-606-13594-8(4)) Tandem Library Bks.

—Man in the Iron Mask. Lynch, Brendan, illus. 2005. (Great Illustrated Classics Ser.). 238p. (J). (gr. 3-8). 21.35 (978-1-59679-247-0(7) , ABDO & Daughters) ABDO Publishing Co.

—The Man in the Iron Mask. Ho, Oliver & Howell, Troy, illus. 2008. (Classic Starts Ser.). 160p. (J). 5.95 (*978-1-4027-4579-9(6)) Sterling Publishing Co., Inc.

—The Three Musketeers. 2002. (Great Illustrated Classics Ser.). (Illus.). 240p. (J). (gr. 3-8). 21.35 (978-1-57765-803-0(5) , ABDO & Daughters) ABDO Publishing Co.

—The Three Musketeers. Nino, Alex, illus. 2nd ed. 1998. (Illustrated Classic Book Ser.). 61p. (J). (gr. 3 up). reprint ed. pap. 4.95 (978-1-56767-251-0(5)) Educational Insights, Inc.

—The Three Musketeers. Bair, Lowell, tr. Kidd, Thomas, illus. 1998. (Books of Wonder). 656p. (J). (gr. 4-7). 25.00 (978-0-688-14583-5(3)) HarperCollins Pubs.

—The Three Musketeers. 2004. reprint ed. pap. 1.99 (978-1-4192-8527-1(0)) Kessinger Publishing, LLC.

—The Three Musketeers. (Classics Ser.). (Illus.). 56p. (J). 3.50 (978-0-7214-1753-0(1) , Dutton Juvenile); 2006. 656p. (gr. 12). pap. 6.95 (978-0-451-53003-5(9) , Signet Classics) Penguin Group (USA) Inc.

—The Three Musketeers. Le Clercq, Jacques, tr. from ENG. 1999. (Modern Library Ser.). 624p. (J). (gr. 4-11). 24.95 (978-0-679-60332-0(8) , Modern Library) Random House Publishing Group.

—The Three Musketeers. 2001. (Saddleback Classics). (Illus.). (J). (978-0-606-21573-2(5)) Tandem Library Bks.

—Los Tres Mosqueteros. (SPA.). (J). 2.49 (978-968-890-125-0(3)) Edivision Compania Editorial, S.A. de C.V. MEX. *Dist:* Continental Bk. Co., Inc., Giron Bks.

Dumas, Alexandre & Mantell, Paul. The Man in the Iron Mask. abr. ed. 1998. (Stepping Stone Book Classic Ser.). (Illus.). 128p. (J). (gr. 2-4). pap. 3.99 (978-0-679-89433-9(0) , Random Hse. Bks. for Young Readers) Random Hse. Children's Bks.

Dumont, Jean-Francois. A Blue So Blue. 2005. (Illus.). 32p. 14.95 (978-1-4027-2139-7(0)) Sterling Publishing Co., Inc.

Dumont, Naomi K. Mr. Kitty & the Magical Island. 2005. 39p. pap. 17.95 (978-1-4137-3294-8(1)) PublishAmerica, Inc.

Dunagan, Ted. A Yellow Watermelon. 2007. 256p. (J). 23.95 (*978-1-58838-197-2(8) , Junebug Bks.) NewSouth, Inc.

Dunbar, Jake. Crashers. 1999. 160p. (J). (gr. 3-7). pap. 4.95 (978-0-7373-0303-2(4) , 03034W, Roxbury Park) Lowell Hse.

Dunbar, Joyce. Muy Chiquitin. Gliori, Debi, illus. 2003. (SPA.). 32p. (J). (gr. k-2). (978-84-480-1646-3(7) , TM30375) Timun Mas, Editorial S.A. ESP. *Dist:* Lectorum Pubns., Inc.

Duncan, Lois. Don't Look Behind You. 2002. (Illus.). (J). 13.40 (978-0-7587-4789-1(6)) Book Wholesalers, Inc.

—Trapped! Cages of Mind & Body. 1999. (978-0-606-17321-6(8)) Tandem Library Bks.

Duncan, Sandy Frances. Gold Rush Orphan. 2005. (Illus.). 280p. (J). pap. 10.95 (978-1-55380-012-5(5)) Ronsdale Pr. CAN. *Dist:* Literary Pr. Group of Canada.

Duncklee, John. Forced Journey. Duncklee, Penny, illus. 2000. (J). (gr. 7-12). pap. 8.95 (978-0-9678566-3-6(9)) Barbed Wire Publishing.

Dunevant, Darlene J. An A+ Alaskan Adventure. 2002. 110p. pap. 9.95 (978-0-595-22991-8(3) , Writers Club Pr.) iUniverse, Inc.

Dunfey, Beth, ed. Codename: Kids Next Door Sooper Secrets & Boomerang Bloopers. 2006. (Codename Ser.). (Illus.). 64p. (J). pap. 4.99 (978-0-439-82962-5(3)) Scholastic, Inc.

—Hi Hi Puffy Amiyumi Chapter Book. 2006. (Illus.). 64p. (J). pap. 3.99 (978-0-439-75021-9(0) , Scholastic Paperbacks) Scholastic, Inc.

Dunmore, Helen. Ingo. 2006. 336p. (J). 16.99 (978-0-06-081852-4(2)); lib. bdg. 17.89 (978-0-06-081853-1(0)) HarperCollins Pubs.

Dunn, Diane E. The Adventures of a Harp Mouse. Endres, Linda Carollo, illus. 2005. (J). 14.95 (978-0-9742174-3-7(3)) Heart & Harp LLC.

Dunn, Mary. Magical Message Machine: Book One. 2007. 120p. (YA). pap. 14.99 (978-1-59092-402-0(9) , Blue Works) Windstorm Creative.

Dunn, Matthew. Day One. 2007. 192p. (YA). per. 15.00 (*978-0-9794908-0-4(4)) Onondaga Hill Publishing.

Dunphy, Catherine. Caitlin. 2006. (Degrassi Junior High Ser.). 184p. (YA). (gr. 5-10). 7.95 (978-1-55028-923-7(3)) Lorimer, James & Co., Ltd., Pubs. CAN. *Dist:* Casemate Pubs. & Bk. Distributors, LLC.

Duran Armengol, Teresa. El Pinguino. 2002. Tr. of Penguin. (SPA., Illus.). 24p. (J). 6.50 (978-84-246-1723-3(1)) La Galera, S.A. Editorial ESP. *Dist:* AIMS International Bks., Inc.

Duran, Teresa. Fabulame un Fabula. Espluga, Maria, illus. 2003. (SPA.). 96p. (978-84-480-1638-8(6) , TM30428) Timun Mas, Editorial S.A. ESP. *Dist:* Lectorum Pubns., Inc.

Durrell, Gerald. The Battle for Castle Cockatrice. 1999. 208p. (J). (gr. 5 up). pap. 4.95 (978-0-06-440780-9(2) , Harper Trophy) HarperCollins Pubs.

Durrenmatt, Fried. Hund/der Tunnel/Panne. pap. 18.95 (978-3-257-23061-1(3)) Diogenes Verlag AG CHE. *Dist:* Distribooks, Inc.

Durston, George. Boy Scout Aviators. 2006. 62.99 (*978-1-4280-2433-5(6)) IndyPublish.com.

Dussling, Jennifer. Which Way, Wendy? Thornburgh, Rebecca McKillip, illus. 2005. (Social Studies Connects). 32p. (J). pap. 4.99 (978-1-57565-147-7(5)) Kane Pr., The.

Dutka, Pamela. Madame Cecil's Swamp. 2005. 48p. pap. 12.95 (978-1-4137-9701-5(6)) PublishAmerica, Inc.

Dutton, John. Tiger's Island. Dutton, John, illus. unabr. ed. Date not set. (Dreamguard Trilogy Ser.: Vol. 2). (Illus.). viii, 245p. (J). pap. 12.95 (978-0-9577556-1-1(9)) Samara Pr.

Dutton, Louise. The Wishing Moon. 2005. pap. 31.95 (978-1-4191-5933-6(X)) Kessinger Publishing, LLC.

Duvall, Deborah L. Rabbit Goes to Kansas. 2007. (Illus.). 32p. (J). (gr. 1 up). 16.95 (*978-0-8263-4181-5(0)) Univ. of New Mexico Pr.

Dwyer, Mary. Barnyard Bash. Dwyer, Michael, illus. 2006. (J). spiral bd. incl. cd-rom (978-1-933843-00-1(4)) That's Me Publishing, LLC.

Dyahnne. Sweetie's Place: A Moving Adventure. 2004. 26p. (J). per. 7.99 (978-1-4116-0760-6(0)) Lulu.com.

Dyan, Penelope, creator. For Love of Pete! The Story of the Boy Who Played the Taps on Iwo Jima. 2005. 292p. (YA). per. 15.95 (978-0-9768417-9-1(7)) Bellissima Publishing, LLC.

Dyer, Thomas A. A Way of His Own. 2001. 160p. (J). (gr. 5-9). pap. 6.95 (978-0-618-13132-7(9)) Houghton Mifflin Co. Trade & Reference Div.

Dygard, Thomas J. Running Wild. 1998. (978-0-606-13753-9(X)) Tandem Library Bks.

Dyson, Tony. The Crystal Wand. 2005. 242p. pap. 14.01 (978-1-4116-5596-6(6)) Lulu.com.

Eager, Edward. Magic or Not? 1999. (gr. 3-6). lib. bdg. 14.15 (978-0-613-21946-4(5)) Tandem Library Bks.

Easley, Mary Ann. Belly Up! 2000. 154p. (YA). (gr. 5-8). 9.99 (978-0-88092-551-8(5) , 5515) Royal Fireworks Publishing Co.

Eastwood, J. G. Dragon: Enter the Realm. 2007. (YA). per. (*978-0-9792030-7-7(4)) Light Sword Publishing LLC.

Eaton, Walter Prichard. Boy Scouts in the White Mountains: the Story of a Long Hike. Merrill, Frank T., illus. 2006. (ENG.). 316p. per. 30.95 (*978-1-4286-4117-4(3)) Kessinger Publishing, LLC.

Ebeling, Vicki. The Winners Group. 2007. (J). per. 7.95 (978-0-9779768-0-5(7)) Pier Avenue Publishing.

Ebeltoft, Christine. Koo & Jay in the Rainforest. 2004. 34p. pap. 17.95 (978-1-4137-3698-4(X)) PublishAmerica, Inc.

Eberhart, Nancy. The Adventures of Granny: Granny Goes to the Zoo. 2007. (J). per. 13.99 (*978-1-59879-373-4(X)) Lifevest Publishing, Inc.

Ede, Allan. Rosalund's Raiders. 2002. 112p. (YA). pap. 9.95 (978-0-595-21749-6(4) , Writers Club Pr.) iUniverse, Inc.

Edens, Cooper, compiled by. Sea Stories: A Classic Illustrated Edition. 2007. (Illus.). 148p. (J). 19.95 (978-0-8118-5634-8(8)) Chronicle Bks. LLC.

Edmond, Wally. Cuddles the Chocolate Cow & Friends. Melinda, Sheffler, illus. 2006. 39p. (J). 14.95 (978-1-59879-108-2(7)); per. 9.99 (978-1-59879-125-9(7)) Lifevest Publishing, Inc.

Edmonds, Walter D. The Matchlock Gun. Lantz, Paul, illus. 1998. 64p. (J). (gr. 3-7). pap. 6.99 (978-0-698-11680-1(1) , Putnam Juvenile) Penguin Group (USA) Inc.

Ed's Terrestrials. 2006. (J). per. 19.99 net. (978-0-9789168-1-7(6)) Blue Dream Studios.

Educational Adventures, creator. Blazin' Hot: Picture Book (Spanish) 9x9. 2006. (SPA., Illus.). (J). (*978-0-9770455-4-9(4)) Educational Adventures.

—Poison Patrol: Coloring/Activity Book (Spanish) w/ Snipe. 2006. (Illus.). (J). (*978-1-933934-02-0(6)) Educational Adventures.

—Poison Patrol: Picture Book (Spanish) 9x9. 2006. (Illus.). (J). (*978-1-933934-00-6(X)) Educational Adventures.

Edwards, Byron. The Mystery of Melissa's First Date: Book One. 2001. 108p. pap. 9.95 (978-0-595-18836-9(2) , Writers Club Pr.) iUniverse, Inc.

Edwards, Carol. Jacy's Search for Jesus, Frey, Daniel J., illus. 2005. 32p. (J). 15.95 (978-0-9755314-0-2(9)) Majestic Publishing, LLC.

Edwards, Frank B. Robin Hood with Lots of Dogs. Bianchi, John, illus. 1999. (Dog Eared Classics Ser.). 32p. (J). (gr. 3-6). pap. 15.95 (978-1-894323-09-3(2)) Pokeweed Pr. CAN. *Dist:* Fitzhenry & Whiteside, Ltd.

Edwards, Frank B. & Bianchi, John. Robin Hood with Lots of Dogs. 1999. (Dog Eared Classics Ser.). (Illus.). 32p. (J). (gr. 3-6). pap. 5.95 (978-1-894323-08-6(4)) Pokeweed Pr. CAN. *Dist:* Fitzhenry & Whiteside, Ltd.

—Treasure Island with Lots of Dogs. 1999. (Dog Eared Classics Ser.). (Illus.). 32p. (J). (gr. 3-6). pap. 5.95 (978-1-894323-10-9(6)); lib. bdg. 15.95 (978-1-894323-11-6(4)) Pokeweed Pr. CAN. *Dist:* Fitzhenry & Whiteside, Ltd.

Edwards, Michelle. Misha the Minstrel. 2004. (Illus.). (gr. 3-7). 8.95 (978-0-930100-19-3(0)) Holy Cow! Pr.

Edwards, Pat & Edwards, LaVell. Hello, Cosmo! De Angel, Miguel, illus. 2006. (J). 17.95 (978-1-932888-45-4(4)) Mascot Bks., Inc.

Egan, Kate. The Movie Storybook. 2006. (Open Season Ser.). 48p. (J). 8.99 (978-0-06-084609-1(7)) HarperCollins Pubs.

—Spider-Man 2: Hands off, Doc Ock! Mones, Isidre et al, illus. 2004. (Spider-Man Ser.). 24p. (J). (ps-2). pap. 3.99 (978-0-06-057138-2(1) , Harper Festival) HarperCollins Pubs.

—Spider-Man 3: The Movie Storybook. 2007. (Spider-Man Ser.). 48p. (J). pap. 8.99 (978-0-06-083723-5(3) , Harper Entertainment) HarperCollins Pubs.

Egan, Tim. Dodsworth in New York. 2007. (Illus.). 48p. (J). (gr. 3-5). 15.00 (*978-0-618-77708-2(3)) Houghton Mifflin Co.

Ehlin, Gina. Emma & Friends: Emma's Airport Adventure. Ayzenberg, Nina, illus. l.t. ed. 2005. 32p. (J). lib. bdg. 15.99 (978-1-59879-015-3(3)); per. 10.99 (978-1-59879-014-6(5)) Lifevest Publishing, Inc.

—Emma & Friends; Emma Rescues Cali. Ayzenberg, Nina, illus. l.t. ed. 2006. 24p. (J). per. 10.99 (978-1-59879-112-9(5)) Lifevest Publishing, Inc.

Ehrbar, Greg, et al. Disney's Atlantis the Lost Empire. 2001. (Illus.). 156p. (J). pap. 6.95 (978-1-56971-625-0(0)) Dark Horse Comics.

Ehrenhaft, Daniel. 10 Things to Do Before I Die. 2004. 224p. (YA). (gr. 7). 15.95 (978-0-385-73007-5(1) , Delacorte Bks. for Young Readers) Random Hse. Children's Bks.

Ehrlich, Fred. You Can't Use Your Brain If You're a Jellyfish. 2005. (Illus.). 44p. 15.95 (978-1-59354-090-6(6)) Blue Apple Bks.

Ehrmantraut, Brenda. Night Catch. Wehrman, Vicki, illus. 2005. 32p. (J). lib. bdg. 15.95 (978-0-9729833-9-6(2)) Bubble Gum Pr.

Ejersbo, Jakob & Liberman, Wili. Get Outta Town! Mr. X; Episode One. 2005. pap. (978-1-55278-548-5(3)) McArthur & Co. CAN. *Dist:* National Bk. Network.

Elboz, Stephen. Clever Monkeys. Bowman, Pete, illus. 2006. (Read-It! Chapter Books). 64p. (J). (*978-1-4048-3115-5(0) , 1265802) Picture Window Bks.

Elkington, Sandra. The Adventures of Pedro in Ecuador. 2003. (YA). per. 9.95 (978-1-59453-005-0(X) , 1113) Airleaf Publishing & Bookselling.

Ellie. Bengal & Sengal. 2006. (J). pap. 8.00 (*978-0-8059-7273-3(0)) Dorrance Publishing Co., Inc.

Elliott, David. Jeremy Cabbage & the Museum of Human Oddballs & Quadruped Delights. 2008. 320p. (J). (gr. 3-7). 15.99 (*978-0-375-84333-4(7) , Knopf Bks. for Young Readers) Random Hse. Children's Bks.

Elliott, John C. Ri Ra: An Adventure Begins. 2006. 48p. pap. 12.95 (978-1-4241-2771-9(8)) PublishAmerica, Inc.

Elliott, Laura. Give Me Liberty. 2006. (Illus.). 384p. (J). 16.99 (978-0-06-074421-2(9)); lib. bdg. 17.89 (978-0-06-074422-9(7)) HarperCollins Pubs. (Tegen, Katherine Bks).

Elliott, Louise. Mr. Hornbeams Treasure Hunt. (Illus.). 96p. pap. 10.95 (978-0-7022-2587-1(8)) Univ. of Queensland Pr. AUS. *Dist:* International Specialized Bk. Services.

Elliott, Patricia. Ice Boy. 2002. (J). pap. 9.99 (978-0-340-85424-2(3) , Hodder & Stoughton) Hodder General Publishing Division GBR. *Dist:* Trafalgar Square Publishing.

Ellis, Deborah. Looking for X. 2001. 132p. (J). (gr. 4-7). pap. 5.95 (978-0-88899-382-3(X)) Groundwood Bks. CAN. *Dist:* Perseus Distribution.

—Looking for X. 2000. (gr. 5-8). lib. bdg. 14.10 (978-0-613-62637-8(0)) Tandem Library Bks.

Ellis, Mary. Lily Dragon. Phillips, Rachael, illus. 2000. 139p. (J). (gr. 3-5). pap. 7.99 (978-0-00-675458-9(9)) HarperCollins Pubs. Ltd. GBR. *Dist:* Trafalgar Square Publishing.

Ellis, Sarah. Next Stop! Ohi, Ruth, illus. 2000. 32p. (J). (ps-k). (978-1-55041-539-1(5)) Fitzhenry & Whiteside, Ltd.

—The Several Lives of Orphan Jack. St. Aubin, Bruno, illus. 2005. 88p. (J). pap. 6.95 (978-0-88899-618-3(7)) Groundwood Bks. CAN. *Dist:* Perseus Distribution.

Elmer, Robert. Adventures down Under, 4 vols., Vols. 1-4. 1998. (Adventures down under Ser.). (J). (gr. 4-7). pap. 23.99 (978-0-7642-8307-9(3) , 258307) Bethany Hse. Pubs.

—Hyperlinkz Bk. 2: Fudge Factor. 2004. 128p. pap. 5.99 (978-1-57856-748-5(3) , WaterBrook Pr.) WaterBrook Pr.

—Hyperlinkz Bk. 3: Web Jam. 2004. 128p. (J). 5.99 (978-1-57856-749-2(1) , WaterBrook Pr.) WaterBrook Pr.

—Hyperlinkz Bk. 4: Spam Alert. 2004. 128p. (J). 5.99 (978-1-57856-750-8(5) , WaterBrook Pr.) WaterBrook Pr.

—Panic at EMU Flat, Vol. 8. 1999. (Adventures down under Ser.: Vol. 8). (Illus.). 160p. (J). (gr. 3-8). pap. 5.99 (978-0-7642-2106-4(X)) Bethany Hse. Pubs.

Elms, Mae D. And Donna Makes Five. l.t. ed. 2000. (Adventure Ser.). 31p. (J). (gr. 1-6). pap. 22.95 (978-1-930002-30-2(0)) I & L Publishing.

—A Candle in the Dark. 2000. 70p. (J). (gr. k-6). pap. 13.95 (978-1-930002-17-3(3)) I & L Publishing.

—Travel into Adventure Land. l.t. ed. 2000. (Illus.). 150p. (J). (gr. 2-9). pap. 19.95 (978-1-930002-08-1(4)) I & L Publishing.

Elson, William H. The Elson Readers, Vol. 5. 2004. reprint ed. pap. 1.99 (978-1-4192-6079-7(0)) Kessinger Publishing, LLC.

Emergency. 2001. (Illus.). 48p. (J). (gr. 1-3). pap. 19.99 (978-1-903276-72-3(1)) Lego Media International, Inc.

Emerson, Alice B. Betty Gordon in Washington. 2004. reprint ed. pap. 20.95 (978-1-4191-0977-5(4)); pap. 1.99 (978-1-4192-0977-2(9)) Kessinger Publishing, LLC.

—Ruth Fielding on the St. Lawrence or the. 2005. pap. 24.95 (978-0-7661-9911-8(8)) Kessinger Publishing, LLC.

Emerson, B. Alice. Ruth Fielding in Moving Pictures or Help. 2006. 32.99 (*978-1-4280-2942-2(7)) IndyPublish.com.

—Ruth Fielding on Cliff Island or the Old. 2006. 32.99 (*978-1-4280-2823-4(4)) IndyPublish.com.

Emesse, Tea. Nova Rocks. 2005. (Star Sisterz Ser.: Bk. 1). (Illus.). 192p. (J). pap. 5.99 (978-0-7869-3625-0(8)) Wizards of the Coast.

Emmet, Laura. Julie Trent & the Lightning. 2003. 148p. pap. 11.95 (978-0-595-27380-5(7)) iUniverse, Inc.

The Emperor's Fruits. 2002. (YA). pap. 14.00 (978-1-59268-004-7(6)) GMA Publishing & Inspiration Pr.

Ende, Michael. El Largo Camino Hacia Santa Cruz. Kehn, Regina, illus. (SPA.). 64p. (J). (gr. 3-5). 6.95 (978-84-241-3354-2(4) , EV3073) Everest de Ediciones y Distribucion, S.L. ESP. *Dist:* Lectorum Pubns., Inc.

Enderle, Dotti. The Ghost of Shady Lane. 2005. (Fortune Tellers Club Ser.: book 7). (Illus.). 160p. pap. 4.99 (978-0-7387-0590-3(X) , 1241933) Llewellyn Pubns.

—Secrets of Lost Arrow. Nightingale, Kimberly, ed. 2004. (Fortune Tellers Club Ser.: Bk. 4). (Illus.). 144p. pap. 4.99 (978-0-7387-0389-3(3)) Llewellyn Pubns.

Endoh, Minari. Dazzle, Vol. 1. 2006. (Illus.). (YA). (gr. 8 up). pap. 9.99 (978-1-59816-092-5(3) , Tokyopop Kids) TOKYOPOP, Inc.

Endraske, Jackie. Dudley. 2006. 80p. pap. 12.95 (978-0-9769460-0-7(9)); 2005. (J). lib. bdg. 19.95 net. (978-0-9769460-1-4(7)) Loma, LLC.

England-Lord, Susan. The Adventures of Andrew: Breezy's Day Out. 2004. 23p. pap. 14.95 (978-1-4137-3285-6(2)) PublishAmerica, Inc.

Engle, Janice. Rainbows Stories & Poetry for Children. 2004. 277p. (J). pap. 15.08 (978-1-4116-8612-0(8)) Lulu.com.

Englehart, Steve & Englehart, Terry. The DNAgers. 2001. 128p. (YA). (gr. 4-7). pap. 9.95 (978-0-595-16697-8(0)) iUniverse, Inc.

Englehart, Steve & Warner, John. Captain America & the Falcon: Nomad TPB: Nomad TPB. 2007. (Illus.). 192p. pap. 24.99 (978-0-7851-2197-8(8)) Marvel Enterprises, Inc.

Eno, Paul F. The Kitleys & the Gate of the Poltergeist. 2006. (ENG.). (YA). pap. 12.95 (978-1-891724-04-6(5) , 5,000) New River Pr.

Enright, Elizabeth. The Four-Story Mistake. 2008. (Melendy Quartet Ser.). (Illus.). 224p. (J). pap. 6.99 (*978-0-312-37599-7(9)) Square Fish.

—Gone-Away Lake. Krush, Beth & Krush, Joe, illus. 2000. (Gone-Away Lake Bks.). 272p. (YA). (gr. 3-7). pap. 6.00 (978-0-15-202272-3(4) , Odyssey Classics) Harcourt Children's Bks.

—Return to Gone-Away. Krush, Beth & Krush, Joe, illus. 2000. (Gone-Away Lake Bks.). 224p. (YA). (gr. 3-7). 17.00 (978-0-15-202263-1(5)); pap. 6.95 (978-0-15-202256-3(2)) Harcourt Children's Bks. (Odyssey Classics).

—Return to Gone-Away. 2000. (gr. 3-6). lib. bdg. 14.15 (978-0-613-14145-1(8)) Tandem Library Bks.

Ensler. V. 1998. (J). 17.95 (978-0-7868-6324-2(2)) Hyperion Pr.

Ensor, Rod. Getting It. 2007. 216p. per. 14.95 (*978-0-595-44800-5(3)) iUniverse, Inc.

Entara Ltd., illus. Piggley's Treasure Hunt. 2007. (Jakers! Ser.). 24p. (J). pap. 3.99 (*978-0-689-87612-7(2) , Simon Spotlight) Simon & Schuster Children's Publishing.

Entara Ltd. Staff, photos by. Ferny Gets a Crush. 2006. (Jakers! Ser.). 16p. (J). pap. 5.99 (978-1-4169-0384-0(4) , Simon Spotlight) Simon & Schuster Children's Publishing.

Enzensberger, Hans Magnus. The Number Devil: A Mathematical Adventure. Heim, Michael Henry, tr. Berner, Rotraut Susanne, illus. rev. ed. 2000. 264p. (J). (gr. 5-9). pap. 18.00 (978-0-8050-6299-1(8) , Owl Bks.) Holt, Henry & Co.

Epner, Paul. Herbert Hilligan & His Magical Adventure. Kuon, Vuthy & Nguyen, Duke, illus. 2003. 32p. (J). 15.95 (978-0-9743335-0-2(6)) Imaginative Publishing, Ltd.

—Herbert Hilligan's Prehistoric Adventure, Vol. 2. Walker, Jennifer, illus. rev. ed. 1999. (Herbert Hilligan Ser.). 24p. (gr. 1-4). 15.95 (978-1-57168-256-7(2)) Eakin Pr.

—Herbert Hilligan's Prehistoric Adventure. Kuon, Vuthy & Nguyen, Duke, illus. 2003. 32p. (J). 15.95 (978-0-9743335-1-9(4)) Imaginative Publishing, Ltd.

—Herbert Hilligan's SeaWorld Adventure. Reed, Bill, illus. 2005. (J). 16.95 (978-0-9743335-9-5(X)) Imaginative Publishing, Ltd.

Epner, Paul & Kuon, Vuthy. Herbert Hilligan's Prehistoric Adventure. 32p. (J). 15.95 (978-1-57168-474-5(3)) Eakin Pr.

Epstein, Robin. Growing up Groovy: An Out of This World Adventure. 2005. 60p. (J). (978-0-439-65795-2(4)) Scholastic, Inc.

Equipo Staff. Aprende las Horas con Winnie Pooh. 2000. (Adventures of Winnie the Pooh! Ser.). (SPA., Illus.). 124p. (J). 16.95 (978-84-488-0671-2(9)) Beascoa, Ediciones S.A. ESP. *Dist:* Distribooks, Inc.

Erenberger, Timothy D. Abacar the Wizard Book One: A Tale of Magic, War, Elves, Goblins, Orcs, Monsters, Fantasy, & Adventure. 2001. 210p. pap. 14.95 (978-0-595-21261-3(1) , Writer's Showcase Pr.) iUniverse, Inc.

Erickson, Byron, et al. Mickey Mouse Adventures, Vol. 9. 2006. (Illus.). 128p. (YA). pap. 7.95 (978-1-888472-10-3(3)) Gemstone Publishing, Inc.

Erickson, John R. The Dungeon of Doom. Holmes, Gerald L., illus. 2004. (Hank the Cowdog Ser.: No. 44). 144p. (J). (gr. 3-7). 15.99 (978-0-670-05881-5(5) , Viking Juvenile); pap. 4.99 (978-0-14-240134-7(X) , Puffin) Penguin Group (USA) Inc.

—Slim's Good-Bye. 2000. (Hank the Cowdog Ser.: No. 34). (gr. 3-6). lib. bdg. 13.00 (978-0-613-22391-1(8)) Tandem Library Bks.

—Las Verdaderas Aventuras de Hank el Perro Vaquero. Holmes, Gerald L., illus. 2000. (Hank the Cowdog Ser.: No. 1). (SPA.). 160p. (J). (gr. 2-5). pap. 6.99 (978-0-14-130699-5(8) , Puffin) Penguin Group (USA) Inc.

Erickson, Lori. The Adventures of Sandy Clown Bk. 1: The Journey Home. 2002. (Illus.). 144p. (J). 14.95 (978-1-58930-076-7(9)) Selah Publishing Group, LLC.

Erickson, Robert. Fluke Family Hero: Book Two in the Saga of Maynerd Dumsted. 2003. 276p. 27.95 (978-0-595-66108-4(4)); pap. 17.95 (978-0-595-30005-1(7)) iUniverse, Inc.

Eric's Travel Diary 6 Pks: Individual Chapter Book Title. Vol. 29. 32p. (gr. 5 up). 44.00 (978-0-7578-0977-4(4)) Rigby Education.

Ering, Timothy B. Necks Out for Adventure: The True Story of Edwin Wiggleskin. 2007. 48p. (J). (*978-0-7636-2355-5(5)) Candlewick Pr.

Erkert, A. Islas de Relajacion. (Crecer Jugando Ser.). (SPA.). 94p. 9.90 (978-84-95456-83-0(4) , (87901)) Ediciones Oniro S.A. ESP. *Dist:* Bilingual Pubns. Co., The, Lectorum Pubns., Inc., Libros Sin Fronteras.

Ervin, Imogene. Charlie & Chu Chu's Day of Adventure. Ervin, Keith, illus. 2005. (J). 7.00 (978-0-9771549-0-6(4)) Finer Moments.

Escondete y Grita, Vol. II. (Fantasmas de Fear Street Coleccion: No. 1). (SPA.). (J). (gr. 4-7). pap. 7.95 (978-950-04-1999-4(8) , EM4474) Emecé Editores S.A. ARG. *Dist:* Lectorum Pubns., Inc., Planeta Publishing Corp.

Estefan, Gloria & Garland, Michael. Noelle's Treasure Tale: A New Magically Mysterious Adventure. 2006. (Illus.). 32p. (ps-1). 17.95 (978-0-06-112614-7(4) , Rayo) HarperCollins Pubs.

Estes, Eleanor. The Curious Adventures of Jimmy Mcgee. O'Brien, John, illus. 2005. 224p. (J). (ps-17). 17.00 (978-0-15-205523-3(1) , Harcourt Young Classics); pap. 5.95 (978-0-15-205517-2(7) , Odyssey Classics) Harcourt Children's Bks.

—The Tunnel of Hugsy Goode. Ardizzone, Edward, illus. 2003. 256p. (J). 17.00 (978-0-15-204914-0(2) , Harcourt Young Classics); pap. 6.95 (978-0-15-204916-4(9) , Odyssey Classics) Harcourt Children's Bks.

—The Tunnel of Hugsy Goode. 2003. (gr. 3-6). lib. bdg. 14.10 (978-0-613-70526-4(2)) Tandem Library Bks.

Evangel - the Smallest Angel. 2006. (J). (*978-0-9790210-0-8(6)) Evening Star Enterprise, Inc.

Evans, Douglas. MVP: Magellan Voyage Project. Shelley, John, illus. 2004. 232p. (J). 16.95 (978-1-932425-13-0(6) , Lemniscaat) Boyds Mills Pr.

Evans, Robert J. Dorothy's Mystical Adventures in Oz. 2004. reprint ed. pap. 1.99 (978-1-4192-1658-9(9)) Kessinger Publishing, LLC.

Evans, Shane W. Travelin' Man. 2007. (Illus.). 32p. 15.99 (978-0-7868-0679-9(6)) Disney Pr.

Evarts, Hal G. Smuggler's Road. 2000. (J). pap. 1.95 (978-0-590-04503-2(2)) Scholastic, Inc.

Everett Hale, Edward. Last of the Peterkins with Others of the. 2006. pap. (*978-1-4068-1087-5(8)) Echo Library.

Evernden, Margery. Wilderness Boy. 2001. 192p. (J). pap. 9.95 (978-0-8229-5754-6(X)) Univ. of Pittsburgh Pr.

Evers, Alf. Treasure of Watchdog Mountain: The Story of a Mountain in the Catskills. Yanow-Schwartz, Jo & Schwartz, Arthur, eds. 2006. 76p. (J). 16.95 (978-1-879504-19-6(7)) Woodstocker Books/Arthur Schwartz & Company.

Eversole, Barbara. Adventures of Zorro. 2005. 42p. 14.49 (978-1-4116-5523-2(0)) Lulu.com.

Ewing, Susan. Ten Rowdy Ravens. Zerbetz, Evon, illus. 2005. 32p. (J). (ps-1). pap. 8.95 (978-0-88240-610-7(8) , Alaska Northwest Bks.) Graphic Arts Ctr. Publishing Co.

Explorers, 4 bks. (J). (gr. 5-7). Set 1. (Illus.). lib. bdg. 102.56 (978-1-58810-137-2(1)); Set 1-4. 2003. lib. bdg. 487.26 (978-1-4034-0245-5(0)); Set 3. 2002. lib. bdg. 189.49 (978-1-58810-429-8(X)); Set 4. 2002. lib. bdg. 81.21 (978-1-4034-0246-2(9)) Heinemann Library.

Explorers. 1998. (Hot Wheels Ser.). (Illus.). 24p. (J). (ps-1). (978-0-7666-0107-9(2) , 19605) Modern Publishing.

Explorers in Dinosaur World. 2005. (J). audio, cd-rom 25.95 (978-0-9771381-2-8(7)) Williams, Geoffrey T.

Fabra, Jordi Sierra. La Asombrosa Historia del Viajero de las Estrellas. (SPA.). (YA). 8.95 (978-958-04-6872-1(9)) Norma S.A. COL. *Dist:* Distribuidora Norma, Inc.

The Face That Stopped Time. 2001. 32p. (YA). (gr. 6-12). pap. (978-0-8224-3465-8(2)) Globe Fearon Educational Publishing.

Fagan, Cary. Directed by Kaspar Snit. 2007. 160p. (J). (gr. 3-7). pap. 9.95 (978-0-88776-753-1(2) , Delacorte Bks. for Young Readers) Random Hse. Children's Bks.

—The Fortress of Kaspar Snit. 2004. (gr. 3-6). lib. bdg. 18.75 (978-0-613-77346-1(2)) Tandem Library Bks.

—The Fortress of Kaspar Snit. 2004. 176p. (J). (gr. 3-7). pap. 8.95 (978-0-88776-665-7(X)) Tundra Bks., Inc./Livres Toundra, Inc. CAN. *Dist:* Random Hse., Inc.

Fairbanks, Randy. The Weird Club: The Search for the Jersey Devil. 2007. (Weird Ser.). (Illus.). 144p. (J). (gr. 3-7). 12.95 (978-1-4027-4228-6(2)) Sterling Publishing Co., Inc.

Fairy Tale- Aladdin. 2005. (J). bds. (978-1-4194-0037-7(1)) Paradise Pr., Inc.

Falcone, L. M. The Devil, the Banshee & Me. 2006. 192p. (J). (gr. 4-7). (978-1-55337-894-5(6)) Kids Can Pr., Ltd.

—The Devil, the Banshee & Me. 2006. 192p. 6.95 (978-1-55337-895-2(4)) Kids Can Pr., Ltd. CAN. *Dist:* Wybel Marketing Group.

Falkner, John Meade. Moonfleet. (Twelve-Point Ser.). 2002. (YA). lib. bdg. 25.00 (978-1-58287-175-2(2)); 2004. 370p. 26.00 (978-1-58287-658-0(4)) North Bks.

Faller, Régis. The Adventures of Polo. Faller, Régis, illus. 2006. (Illus.). 80p. (J). (gr. k-2). 16.95 (978-1-59643-160-7(1)) Roaring Brook Pr.

Fancher, Joseph. Sydney's Travels Through Dreamland Part. 2006. 48p. pap. 12.95 (978-1-4241-3690-2(3)) PublishAmerica, Inc.

Fanning, Kieran. Voyage to Victory. 2001. 128p. (J). (gr. 4-8). per. (978-1-84210-085-1(8)) Mentor Bks.

Fant, Donna. Scotty's Dream. McKeown, David, illus. 2004. 16p. (J). 14.99 (*978-1-931844-17-8(8) , PP1034) Piano Pr.

Farber, Erica. The Alien from Outer Space. Mayer, Mercer, illus. 2006. (Critter Kids Adventure Ser.). 32p. (J). (gr. 2-3). pap. 4.95 (978-0-7696-4763-0(4) , Gingham Dog Pr.) School Specialty Publishing.

—The Jaguar Paw Puzzle. Mayer, Mercer, illus. 2006. (Critter Kids Adventure Ser.). 32p. (J). (gr. 2-5). pap. 4.95 (978-0-7696-4765-4(0) , Gingham Dog Pr.) School Specialty Publishing.

—The Prince. Mayer, Mercer, illus. 2006. (Critter Kids Adventure Ser.). 32p. (J). (gr. 2-5). pap. 4.95 (978-0-7696-4767-8(7) , Gingham Dog Pr.) School Specialty Publishing.

Fardell, John. Flight of the Silver Turtle. 2006. 212p. (J). (gr. 3). 15.99 (978-0-399-24382-0(8) , Putnam Juvenile) Penguin Group (USA) Inc.

—Seven Professors of the Far North. 2006. 240p. (J). pap. 6.99 (978-0-14-240735-6(6) , Puffin) Penguin Group (USA) Inc.

Faris, Debi. Kaya & Nannas First Excellent Adventur. 2006. pap. 18.99 (*978-1-4259-7780-1(4)) AuthorHouse.

Farland, David. Of Mice & Magic. Lyon, Howard, illus. 2005. (Ravenspell Ser.: Bk. 1). 276p. (J). 16.95 (978-1-57734-918-1(0)) Covenant Communications, Inc.

Farley, Terri. Blue Wings. 2006. (Phantom Stallion Ser.). (Illus.). 256p. (J). pap. 4.99 (978-0-06-075848-6(1)) HarperCollins Pubs.

—Gypsy Gold. 2006. (Phantom Stallion Ser.). 240p. (J). pap. 4.99 (978-0-06-081540-0(X) , Harper Trophy) HarperCollins Pubs.

—Moonrise, Vol. 14. 2005. (Phantom Stallion Ser.). (Illus.). 208p. (gr. 5 up). pap. 4.99 (978-0-06-058315-6(0)) HarperCollins Pubs.

—Phantom Stallion Box Set: The Wild One; Mustang Moon; Dark Sunshine. Call, Greg, illus. 2004. (Phantom Stallion Ser.). 704p. (J). (gr. 5 up). pap. 14.99 (978-0-06-059504-3(3) , HarperCollins) HarperCollins Pubs.

—Phantom Stallion: Wild Horse Island #5: Fire Maiden. 2008. (Phantom Stallion: Wild Horse Island Ser.). 272p. (J). pap. 4.99 (*978-0-06-088618-9(8) , Harper Trophy) HarperCollins Pubs.

—Renegade. 2003. (gr. 5-8). lib. bdg. 13.00 (978-0-613-66731-9(X)) Tandem Library Bks.

—Secret Star. 2006. (Phantom Stallion Ser.). (Illus.). 224p. (J). pap. 4.99 (978-0-06-075847-9(3)) HarperCollins Pubs.

Farley, Walter. Black Stallion Adventure Set. 2005. (J). (gr. 3-7). 23.96 (978-0-375-83406-6(0) , Yearling) Random Hse. Children's Bks.

Farmer, Gayle. SHOWTIME at Indio! 2004. (YA). per. 12.95 (978-0-9748728-1-0(4)) Jeff & Gayle Farmer.

Farmer, Nancy. The Ear, the Eye & the Arm. 2002. (Firebird Ser.). 320p. (J). pap. 6.99 (978-0-14-131109-8(6) , Puffin) Penguin Group (USA) Inc.

—The Ear, the Eye & the Arm. 2004. (Orchard Classics Ser.). 320p. (J). pap. 9.95 (978-0-439-53064-4(4)) Scholastic, Inc.

—The Ear, the Eye & the Arm. l.t. ed. 2005. 479p. (J). 22.95 (978-0-7862-7580-9(4)) Thorndike Pr.

Farnsworth, Frances Joyce. Cubby in Wonderland. 3rd ed. 2001. (Cubby Ser.). (Illus.). 128p. (J). (gr. 2 up). pap. 14.95 (978-0-943972-72-5(8)) Homestead Publishing.

Farquhar-Claypool, Kris. Everglades Environmental Storybook: Upland & Inland Creatures. l.t. ed. 1999. (Voices of the Earth Ser.: Vol. II). (Illus.). 48p. (J). (gr. k-4). pap. 6.95 (978-0-9666720-0-8(3)) Earthwing Pubns.

Farren, Rick. Eliza's Wish. 2005. 154p. (J). per. 14.95 (978-0-9772078-0-0(3)) Journey Pubns., LLC.

—The Secret of the Lighthouse. 2004. (J). per. 12.95 (978-0-9748087-3-4(3)) Journey Pubns., LLC.

Farrow, Edward Georg. The Mysterious Shin Shira. 2006. 40.99 (*978-1-4280-1467-1(5)); pap. 34.99 (*978-1-4280-1471-8(3)) IndyPublish.com.

Farshtey, Greg. Bionicle Adventures: Challenge of the Hordika, Vol. 8. 2005. (Bionicle Ser.). 112p. (J). 4.99 (978-0-439-69621-0(6)) Scholastic, Inc.

—Bionicle Adventures: Web of the Visorak. 7th ed. 2005. (Bionicle Ser.). 112p. (J). 4.99 (978-0-439-69619-7(4)) Scholastic, Inc.

—Bionicle Legends: Island of Doom. 2006. 128p. (J). pap. 4.99 (978-0-439-74560-4(8)) Scholastic, Inc.

—Dark Hunters. Simpson, Fiona, ed. 2006. (Bionicle Ser.: No. 4). (Illus.). 128p. (J). pap. 6.99 (978-0-439-82803-1(1) , Scholastic) Scholastic, Inc.

—Exo-Force: Attack of the Robots. 2006. (Lego Ser.). 64p. (J). pap. 3.99 (978-0-439-82809-3(0) , Scholastic) Scholastic, Inc.

—Ghost of the Past. 2007. (Lego Ser.: No. 4). 64p. (J). pap. 3.99 (*978-0-439-92326-2(3)) Scholastic, Inc.

—Island of Doom. 2007. (Bionicle Adventures Ser.: No. 1). 128p. (J). pap. 2.99 (*978-0-545-01315-4(1)) Scholastic, Inc.

—Legacy of Evil. 2006. (Bionicle Legends Ser.). 128p. (J). pap. 4.99 (978-0-439-82807-9(4)) Scholastic, Inc.

—Maze of Shadows. 2004. (Bionicle Ser.). 128p. (J). (gr. 4-7). 4.99 (978-0-439-68023-3(9)) Scholastic, Inc.

—Power Play. 2006. (Bionicle Legends Ser.: No. 3). (Illus.). 128p. (J). pap. 4.99 (978-0-439-82804-8(X) , Scholastic) Scholastic, Inc.

—Search for the Golden City. 2007. (Lego Ser.: No. 3). (Illus.). 64p. (J). pap. 3.99 (*978-0-439-89203-2(1)) Scholastic, Inc.

Farshtey, Greg. Web of Shadows. 2005. (Bionicle Adventures Ser.: Vol. 9). 144p. (J). (ps-7). pap. 4.99 (978-0-439-74558-1(6)) Scholastic, Inc.

Farshtey, Greg & James, Jeff. Rahi Beasts. 2005. (Illus.). (J). (Bionicle Ser.: No. 3). 112p. (gr. 2-5). pap. 5.99 (978-0-439-69622-7(4)); 103p. (*978-1-4156-0534-9(3)) Scholastic, Inc.

Fast & Mysty. Night Ride. 2001. 32p. (YA). (gr. 6-12). pap. (978-0-8224-3767-3(8)) Globe Fearon Educational Publishing.

Faye. Jazzy Shoes. l.t. ed. 2006. (ENG., Illus.). 28p. per. 9.95 (*978-1-4327-0176-5(2)) Outskirts Press, Inc.

Faye, Thomas. Pirates of the Caribbean: The Secret Files of the East India Trading Company. rev. ed. 2007. 28p. (gr. 8). 19.99 (*978-1-4231-0499-5(4)) Disney Pr.

Fears & Phantoms. 2006. (J). (978-1-933343-20-4(6)) Stabenfeldt Inc.

Feiffer, Jules. A Barrel of Laughs, a Vale of Tears. Feiffer, Jules, illus. 1998. (Illus.). 192p. (gr. 4-7). pap. 11.99 (978-0-06-205926-0(2)) HarperCollins Pubs.

—Meanwhile... Feiffer, Jules, illus. 1999. (Michael di Capua Bks.). (Illus.). 32p. (J). (ps-k). pap. 6.99 (978-0-06-205933-8(5)) HarperCollins Pubs.

—Meanwhile... 1999. (978-0-606-17882-2(1)); lib. bdg. 14.15 (978-0-613-22891-6(X)) Tandem Library Bks.

Feinstein, John. Cover-up: Mystery at the Super Bowl. 2007. 304p. (J). (gr. 5). lib. bdg. 19.99 (*978-0-375-94247-1(5) , Knopf Bks. for Young Readers) Random Hse. Children's Bks.

—Cover-Up: Mystery at the Super Bowl. 2007. 304p. (J). (gr. 5 up). 16.99 (*978-0-375-84247-4(0) , Knopf Bks. for Young Readers) Random Hse. Children's Bks.

Feinstein, Stephen. Call of the Wild. abr. ed. 1999. (gr. 7-12). lib. bdg. 15.25 (978-0-613-32365-9(3)) Tandem Library Bks.

Feld, Ellen F. Shadow. The Curious Morgan Horse. 2006. (Illus.). 32p. (J). 15.95 (978-0-9709002-6-5(0)) Willow Bend Publishing.

Feldman, Thea. A Kite-Tacular Adventure. rev. ed. 2007. 10p. (ps-1). 12.99 (*978-1-4231-0904-4(X)) Disney Pr.

Feldman, Thea. A Visit to the Farm. 2006. 3p. 5.99 (978-1-932915-32-7(X)) Sandvik Publishing.

Feldstein, Al. The EC Archives Vol. 2: Shock Suspenstories. 2007. (Illus.). 212p. (YA). 49.95 (*978-1-888472-70-7(7)) Gemstone Publishing, Inc.

Feliciano, Luis. The Adventures of the Three Angels. 2005. (J). pap. 8.00 (978-0-8059-6676-3(5)) Dorrance Publishing Co., Inc.

Felipe, Nersys. Cuentos de Guane (Stories of Guane) (SPA.). (J). 4.95 (978-950-581-518-0(2)) Colihue ARG. *Dist:* AIMS International Bks., Inc.

Fenton, Karen B. It's Raining Outside & I'm Gonna Be Bored! Roth, Stacy Schulstrom, illus. 2006. (J). lib. bdg. 16.82 (978-0-9778196-4-5(7)) Harbour Arts, LLC.

Ferguson, Will. I Was a Teenage Katima-Victim. pap. 19.95 (978-1-55054-652-1(X)) Douglas & McIntyre, Ltd. CAN. *Dist:* Transition Vendor.

Ferris, James Cody. The X Bar X Boys on Big Bison Trail. Rogers, Walter S., illus. 2004. reprint ed. pap. 24.95 (978-1-4179-3953-4(2)) Kessinger Publishing, LLC.

Fetty, Margaret & Jasinski, Diane. Three Cheers for August: Prek-K. 2006. (Illus.). 96p. (ps-k). pap. 12.99 (978-0-7398-9827-7(2)) Steck-Vaughn.

Feutl, Rita. Rescue at Fort Edmonton. 2004. (Juvenile Novel Ser.). (Illus.). 192p. (J). (gr. 4-8). pap. 7.95 (978-1-55050-308-1(1)) Coteau Bks. CAN. *Dist:* Fitzhenry & Whiteside, Ltd.

Fforde, Jasper. The Eyre Affair. 2003. 374p. (gr. 7-12). per. 23.45 (978-0-613-62901-0(9)) Tandem Library Bks.

Ficklin, Jonene H. Orinoco Intrigue. 2005. (YA). 14.95 (978-0-9761188-1-7(5)) Victor's Crown Publishing.

Fidler, Kathleen. The Desperate Journey. 2001. (Kelpies Ser.). (Illus.). 192p. pap. 10.00 (978-0-86315-401-0(8)) Floris Bks. GBR. *Dist:* SteinerBooks, Inc.

Fidler, Mark. The Call of Sagarmatha. 2002. 142p. pap. 11.95 (978-0-595-25281-7(8) , Writers Club Pr.) iUniverse, Inc.

Field, Rachel. Calico Bush. Lewis, Allen, illus. 1998. 224p. (J). (gr. 5-9). pap. 5.99 (978-0-689-82285-8(5) , Aladdin) Simon & Schuster Children's Publishing.

Fienberg, Anna. Horrendo's Curse. Gamble, Kim, illus. 2002. 160p. (J). (gr. 2-6). 18.95 (978-1-55037-773-6(6)); pap. 6.95 (978-1-55037-772-9(8)) Annick Pr., Ltd. CAN. *Dist:* Firefly Bks., Ltd.

Fienberg, Anna & Fienberg, Barbara. Tashi & the Ghosts. Gamble, Kim, illus. 2003. (Tashi Ser.). 64p. (J). (gr. 1-4). pap. 4.95 (978-1-86448-090-0(4)) Allen & Unwin AUS. *Dist:* Independent Pubs. Group.

Fienberg, Anna & Fienberg, Barbara. Tashi Lost in the City. Gamble, Kim, illus. (Tashi Ser.). 64p. (J). (gr. k-2). 2007. pap. 5.95 (*978-1-74114-963-0(0)); 2005. pap. 5.95 (978-1-74114-401-7(9)) Allen & Unwin AUS. *Dist:* Independent Pubs. Group.

Figueredo, D. H. Un Mundo Nuevo. ed. 2004. (SPA., Illus.). (J). (ps-4). spiral bd. (978-0-616-07276-9(7)) Canadian National Institute for the Blind/Institut National Canadien pour les Aveugles.

Figueroa, Acton. I Am Astro. 2004. (Festival Reader Ser.). (Illus.). 32p. (J). pap. 3.99 (978-0-06-072526-6(5) , Harper Festival) HarperCollins Pubs.

—Rocket Ball. 2004. (Astro Boy Ser.). (Illus.). 24p. (J). pap. 3.50 (978-0-06-072524-2(9) , Harper Festival) HarperCollins Pubs.

The Fijiboat Adventure. 2004. 56p. pap. 6.99 (978-0-8341-2092-1(5)) Beacon Hill Pr. of Kansas City.

Filaretos, William. The Potion of Time: A Story of Demetrios. 2006. per. 12.95 (978-0-9724520-0-7(1)) Filaretos, William.

Filella, Nacho & Garcia, Gloria. El Cumpleaños. 2005. (SPA.). 6p. 9.95 (978-84-272-6684-1(7)) Molino, Editorial ESP. *Dist:* Distribooks, Inc., Santillana USA Publishing Co., Inc.

Filippello, Mike. Miratambo Moonsong. 2004. 39p. pap. 17.95 (978-1-4137-2421-9(3)) PublishAmerica, Inc.

Finding Conway: Seek the Truth. 2006. (YA). (978-0-9771114-1-1(5)) LIP Publishing LLC.

Fine, Anne. Jamie & Angus Together. Dale, Penny, illus. 2007. 112p. (J). (ps-1). 15.99 (*978-0-7636-3374-5(7)) Candlewick Pr.

Fingeroth, Danny. The New Goblin. 2007. (Spider-Man Ser.: No. 3). 64p. (J). pap. 4.99 (978-0-06-083724-2(1) , Harper Entertainment) HarperCollins Pubs.

Fink, B. Turning the World Upside Down. 2001. 112p. (YA). pap. 9.95 (978-0-595-15094-6(2)) iUniverse, Inc.

Finkelstein, Chaim. The Burksfield Bike Club, Book 2: Lost & Found. Jennings, R. W., illus. 2007. 224p. (J). 15.95 (978-1-932443-69-1(X) , BBC1H) Judaica Pr., Inc., The.

Finley, Martha. Violet's Bumpy Ride, Bk. 6. 2005. (Life of Faith Ser.). (Illus.). 224p. (YA). (gr. 7-17). 12.99 (978-1-928749-22-6(4)) Zonderkidz.

—Violet's Foreign Intrigue, Bk. 8. 2006. (Life of Faith Ser.). 224p. (J). 12.99 (978-1-928749-24-0(0)) Zonderkidz.

Finn, Rebecca, illus. Jolly Snowman. 2005. 6p. (J). 6.95 (978-1-58925-752-8(9) , tiger tales) ME Media LLC.

—Santa's Day. 2005. 6p. (J). 6.95 (978-1-58925-753-5(7) , tiger tales) ME Media LLC.

Finnemore, John. Jack Haydons Quest. 2006. pap. 15.95 (*978-0-8095-0116-8(3)) Wildside Pr.

Finsterbusch, Monika. Princess Lillifee's Secret. 2006. 28p. (J). (ps-3). 12.95 (978-0-8109-5724-4(8) , Abrams Bks. for Young Readers) Abrams, Harry N. , Inc.

Fiorello, Frank. Pumpkin Patch Scarecrows. Fiorello, Frank, illus. 1998. (Illus.). 40p. (J). (ps-1). pap. 7.95 (978-0-9646300-3-1(6)) Pumpkin Patch Publishing.

Fisch, Sholly. Batman Beyond: Grounded. Delaney, John et al, illus. 2002. (Pictureback Ser.). 24p. (J). (ps-3). pap. 3.25 (978-0-375-80655-1(5) , Random Hse. Bks. for Young Readers) Random Hse. Children's Bks.

—No Place Like Home. 2000. (gr. k-3). lib. bdg. 10.95 (978-0-613-32901-9(5)) Tandem Library Bks.

Fischer, Debbie. Swimming with the Sharks. 2008. 264p. (J). pap. 9.95 (*978-0-7387-1161-4(6) , Flux) Llewellyn Pubns.

Fishel, Dennis. Russell's Revenge, 1. 2005. (YA). 17.95 (978-0-9763398-2-3(X)) Dragonon, Inc.

Fisher, Cyrus. The Avion My Uncle Flew. Floethe, Richard, illus. 2004. 252p. (YA). pap. 6.95 (978-0-8027-7693-8(0)) Walker & Co.

Fisher, Diane. Aja's Dragon. Levy, Michael, illus. 1998. 58p. (J). (ps-3). pap. 10.95 (978-1-892137-11-1(9)) Muse Press.

Fisher, Leonard Everett. William Tell. Fisher, Leonard Everett, illus. 2006. (Illus.). 28p. (J). reprint ed. 16.00 (978-0-7567-9880-2(9)) DIANE Publishing Co.

Fisher, Norma Grusy. Anna's Amazing Journey. Knudson, Rachel, tr. Perry, Judy, illus. unabr. ed. 1998. 16p. (Orig.). (J). (gr. 3-5). pap. 5.95 (978-0-9664797-9-9(3)) Roaninn Pubns.

Fisher-Price Rescue Heroes Coloring & Activity Books. 2004. (J). act. bk. ed. (978-0-7666-0514-5(0) , 99570); act. bk. ed. (978-0-7666-0515-2(9) , 99570); act. bk. ed. (978-0-7666-0516-9(7) , 99570); act. bk. ed. (978-0-7666-0517-6(5) , 99570) Modern Publishing.

Fisher, Susan. The Little Lost Kiss. 2006. (Illus.). 20p. (J). per. 19.95 (978-1-59453-964-0(2) , Airleaf Publishing) Airleaf Publishing & Bookselling.

Fisk, Scott. Herman the Homeless Hermit Crab. 2004. 17p. 7.99 (978-1-4116-1770-4(3)) Lulu.com.

Fitzgerald, John D. More Adventures of the Great Brain. Mayer, Mercer, illus. (Great Brain Ser.). 160p. (J). 2004. (gr. 3-7). pap. 4.99 (978-0-14-240065-4(3) , Puffin); 2000. (ps-3). 9.99 (978-0-8037-2591-1(4) , Dial) Penguin Group (USA) Inc.

—More Adventures of the Great Brain. 2004. (Great Brain Ser.). 142p. (J). (gr. 3-7). pap., tchr.'s training gde. ed. 36.00 incl. audio (978-0-8072-0860-1(4) , Listening Library) Random Hse. Audio Publishing Group.

—More Adventures of the Great Brain. 2004. (gr. 3-6). lib. bdg. 14.15 (978-0-613-83003-4(2)) Tandem Library Bks.

Fitzhugh, K. Percy. Tom Slade with the Boys over There. 2006. 95.99 (*978-1-4280-5001-3(9)); pap. 88.99 (*978-1-4280-5003-7(5)) IndyPublish.com.

Fitzhugh, Keese Perc. Pee-Wee Harris Adrift. 2006. 41.99 (*978-1-4280-1435-0(7)); pap. 35.99 (*978-1-4280-1445-9(4)) IndyPublish.com.

—Roy Blakeley's Adventures in Camp. 2006. 95.99 (*978-1-4219-7388-3(X)); pap. 89.99 (*978-1-4219-7381-4(2)) IndyPublish.com.

Fitzhugh, Keese Percy. PeeWee Harris. 2006. 62.99 (*978-1-4280-2454-0(9)) IndyPublish.com.

—Tom Slade at Black Lake. 2006. 94.99 (*978-1-4280-5015-0(9)); pap. 88.99 (*978-1-4280-5030-3(2)) IndyPublish.com.

—Tom Slade on Mystery Trail. 2006. 94.99 (*978-1-4280-2385-7(2)); pap. 88.99 (*978-1-4280-2365-9(8)) IndyPublish.com.

Fitzhugh, Percy K. Pee-Wee Harris. 2004. reprint ed. pap. 1.99 (978-1-4192-4057-7(9)); pap. 15.95 (978-1-4191-4057-0(4)) Kessinger Publishing, LLC.

—Roy Blakeley. 2004. reprint ed. pap. 19.95 (978-1-4191-4560-5(6)); pap. 1.99 (978-1-4192-4560-2(0)) Kessinger Publishing, LLC.

—Roy Blakeley's Adventures in Camp. 2004. reprint ed. pap. 20.95 (978-1-4191-4561-2(4)) Kessinger Publishing, LLC.

Fitzhugh, Percy Keese. Roy Blakeley. 2006. 134p. pap. 10.99 (*978-1-4264-4185-1(1)); 148p. pap. 13.99 (*978-1-4264-4226-1(2)) BiblioBazaar.

Flack, Marjorie. Angus & the Ducks. Flack, Marjorie, illus. 2002. (Illus.). (J). 14.43 (978-0-7587-9219-8(0)) Book Wholesalers, Inc.

—Angus & the Ducks. unabr. ed. 1998. (J). (ps-2). pap. 14.95 incl. audio (978-0-7882-0694-8(X) , PRA039) Weston Woods Studios, Inc.

Flake, Sharon G. Bang! 2005. 320p. (gr. 7-17). 16.99 (978-0-7868-1844-0(1) , Jump at the Sun) Hyperion Bks. for Children.

Flaker, Tracey. Around the Corner: Gwenever's Quest. 2006. 55p. pap. 12.95 (978-1-4241-1886-1(7)) PublishAmerica, Inc.

Flanagan, John. The Burning Bridge. 2006. (Ranger's Apprentice Ser.: Bk. 2). 256p. (YA). (gr. 5). 16.99 (978-0-399-24455-1(7) , Philomel) Penguin Group (USA) Inc.

—The Ruins of Gorlan. 2005. (Ranger's Apprentice Ser.: Bk. 1). 256p. (J). (gr. 6). 15.99 (978-0-399-24454-4(9) , Philomel) Penguin Group (USA) Inc.

Flat Kid Action Figure. 2004. (J). ring bd. 3.50 (978-0-9763328-1-7(7)) Smart Smiles Co., The.

Flat Stanley. 1998. (J). (gr. 3). pap. 3.95 (978-0-439-04444-8(8)) Scholastic, Inc.

Fleischman, Sid. Bandit's Moon. Smith, Jos. A., illus. 1998. 144p. (J). (gr. 3 up). 16.99 (978-0-688-15830-9(7)) HarperCollins Pubs.

—Disappearing Act. 2004. 128p. (J). (gr. 3 up). reprint ed. pap. 5.99 (978-0-06-051964-3(9) , Harper Trophy) HarperCollins Pubs.

Fleming, Ian. Chitty Chitty Bang Bang. l.t. ed. 2002. (Illus.). 80p. (J). 16.95 (978-0-7540-7831-9(0) , Galaxy Children's Large Print) BBC Audiobooks America.

—Chitty Chitty Bang Bang. Selznick, Brian, illus. 2005. 160p. (J). (gr. 3). 5.99 (978-0-375-83283-3(1) , Random Hse. Bks. for Young Readers) Random Hse. Children's Bks.

Fleming, Sarah. The Moons of Jupiter. 2000. (Cambridge Reading Ser.). (Illus.). 14p. pap. 5.00 (978-0-521-77448-2(9)); Pack. 12p. pap. 28.00 (978-0-521-78766-6(1)) Cambridge Univ. Pr.

Fleming, Sean & Ewald, Jenny, eds. To Catch a Mall Thief. 2004. 85p. (YA). pap. 9.95 (978-0-7414-2196-8(8)) Infinity Publishing.

Flesh, Chris P. The Mystery of the Mystery Meat #3. 2008. 176p. (J). (gr. 3). pap. 4.99 (*978-0-448-44811-4(4) , Grosset & Dunlap) Penguin Group (USA) Inc.

Fletcher, Lee Archib. Boy Scouts in the Coal Caverns or the Li. 2006. 25.99 (*978-1-4280-0741-3(5)); pap. 18.99 (*978-1-4280-0750-5(4)) IndyPublish.com.

Fletcher, Lee Archibald. Boy Scouts on A Long Hike or to the Resc. 2006. 94.99 (*978-1-4280-5014-3(0)); pap. 88.99 (*978-1-4280-5033-4(7)) IndyPublish.com.

Fletcher, Susan. Sign of the Dove. 1999. 224p. (J). (gr. 5-9). pap. 5.99 (978-0-689-82449-4(1) , Aladdin) Simon & Schuster Children's Publishing.

—Sign of the Dove. 1999. (978-0-606-16295-1(X)); (gr. 5-8). lib. bdg. 13.00 (978-0-613-17857-0(2)) Tandem Library Bks.

Fleuriel, Allison. Are You Done Sleeping? 2006. (J). pap. 16.00 (978-0-8059-7115-6(7)) Dorrance Publishing Co., Inc.

Flexer, Michael. Lucy's Adventure: The Search for Aslan. Baynes, Pauline, illus. 2006. (Narnia Ser.). 96p. (J). 14.99 (978-0-06-085234-4(8)); pap. 3.99 (978-0-06-085233-7(X) , Harper Trophy) HarperCollins Pubs.

Flinn, Alex. Breaking Point. 2003. 256p. (J). pap. 6.99 (978-0-06-447371-2(6)) HarperCollins Pubs.

Florkoski, Anthony. The Adventures of Macho Mutt. 2002. 59p. (YA). pap. 9.95 (978-0-7414-1166-2(0)) Infinity Publishing.

Flower, Jessie Graham. Grace Harlowe's Senior Year at High School. 2006. 156p. pap. 11.99 (978-1-4264-1912-6(0)) BiblioBazaar.

—Grace Harlowe's Senior Year at High School. 2004. reprint ed. pap. 21.95 (978-1-4191-2224-8(X)); pap. 1.99 (978-1-4192-2224-5(4)) Kessinger Publishing, LLC.

Flycatcher: Tales from the Grand Adventure of Frederick the French Frog. 2001. 87p. pap. 16.95 (978-1-928888-00-0(3)) Heart Gallery Pr.

Flying Rhinoceros Inc. Staff. Bug Book Adventure Pack. 2000. (Illus.). 24p. (J). (gr. k-2). pap. 5.00 (978-1-883772-71-0(0)) Flying Rhinoceros, Inc.

—I Am Hercules Adventure Pack. 2000. 24p. (J). (gr. k-2). pap. 5.00 (978-1-883772-67-3(2)) Flying Rhinoceros, Inc.

—I Am Jenny Adventure Pack. 2000. (Illus.). 24p. (J). (gr. k-2). pap. 5.00 (978-1-883772-69-7(9)) Flying Rhinoceros, Inc.

—I Am Porkchop Adventure Pack. 2000. (Illus.). 24p. (J). (gr. k-2). pap. 5.00 (978-1-883772-68-0(0)) Flying Rhinoceros, Inc.

—I Am Sam Adventure Pack. 2000. (Illus.). 24p. (J). (gr. k-2). pap., wbk. ed. 5.00 (978-1-883772-66-6(4)) Flying Rhinoceros, Inc.

—Today I Will Moo Adventure Pack. 2000. (Illus.). 24p. (J). (gr. k-2). pap. 5.00 (978-1-883772-70-3(2)) Flying Rhinoceros, Inc.

Flying Rhinoceros Productions. The Horned Avenger: The Battle Against VonBoredom! 2005. 64p. (J). 9.99 (978-1-4003-0662-6(0)) Nelson, Thomas Inc.

Flynn, Arthur. Achill Adventure. 2001. 128p. (YA). (gr. 5-9). per. (978-0-947548-97-1(1)) Mentor Bks.

Flynn, Warren. Escaping Paradise. 2001. 256p. (J). pap. 13.95 (978-1-86368-280-0(5)) Fremantle Pr. AUS. *Dist:* International Specialized Bk. Services.

Fogerty, Ramona. Come to Galapagos at Sea to See. Hayden, Seitu, illus. 2004. (SPA.). (J). pap. 22.95 (978-0-9759889-1-6(3)) Potenial Psychotherapy Counseling & Remedial Serv.

Fogg, K. L. Serpent Tide. 2006. 16.95 (978-1-59156-861-2(7)) Covenant Communications, Inc.

Follen, Eliza Lee. The Pedler of Dust Sticks. 2006. (ENG.). pap. (*978-1-4250-2996-8(5)) Assistedreadingbooks.com Inc.

—The Pedler of Dust Sticks. 2004. reprint ed. pap. 15.95 (978-1-4191-7694-4(3)) Kessinger Publishing, LLC.

—The Talkative Wig. 2004. reprint ed. pap. 15.95 (978-1-4191-8483-3(0)) Kessinger Publishing, LLC.

Folmsbee, Sharene. Checkerboard Charlie. 2004. 53p. pap. 12.95 (978-1-4137-5583-1(6)) PublishAmerica, Inc.

Fontenay, Charles L. Kipton & the Martian Maidens, 18 vols. 1999. (Kipton Chronicles Ser.: Bk. 16). 183p. (J). (gr. 5 up). pap. 9.99 (978-0-88092-417-7(9)) Royal Fireworks Publishing Co.

Fontes, Justine. Cheerios Action Park Adventure. 2005. (Picture Clue Math Reader Ser.). (Illus.). 28p. (J). pap. (*978-0-439-70343-7(3)) Scholastic, Inc.

Fontes, Justine & Fontes, Ron. Danger Ahead! Mitchell, Redondo, illus. 2001. (Tonka Joe Adventures Ser.). 24p. (J). (ps-3). pap. 3.50 (978-0-439-25910-1(X)) Scholastic, Inc.

Fools Bounty. 2003. (Star Wars Ser.: Vol. 5). (Illus.). 376p. (Orig.). (J). (gr. 3 up). pap. 29.95 (978-1-56971-906-0(3)) Dark Horse Comics.

Foon, Dennis. Double or Nothing. 2000. 144p. (YA). (gr. 7 up). 17.95 (978-1-55037-627-2(6)); pap. 6.95 (978-1-55037-626-5(8)) Annick Pr., Ltd. CAN. *Dist:* Firefly Bks., Ltd.

—Double or Nothing. 2000. (gr. 7-12). lib. bdg. 15.25 (978-0-613-51820-8(9)) Tandem Library Bks.

—Freewalker. 2004. (Longlight Legacy Ser.). 320p. (YA). (gr. 6). 19.95 (978-1-55037-885-6(6)); pap. 9.95 (978-1-55037-884-9(8)) Annick Pr., Ltd. CAN. *Dist:* Firefly Bks., Ltd.

Forbes, Lucie E. The Adventures of Jesse & Teri. 2005. 16.95 (978-0-533-14957-5(6)) Vantage Pr., Inc.

Ford, Laura. Buster Brown & Tige in Misfit Heroes. 2004. (Illus.). 320p. 19.95 (978-1-881554-28-8(7)) Skyward Publishing Co.

Ford, Robert. Adventures of Hit the Road Jack. l.t. ed. 2003. (Illus.). 40p. per. 10.00 (978-1-932338-11-9(X)) Lifevest Publishing, Inc.

Ford, Sandy Lee, illus. Gullah, the Nawleans Cat Meets Katrina. 2007. 32p. (J). (*978-0-9793637-0-2(5)) Hart Street Pubs.

Foreman, B. Tracy Barton & the Ninja Secret Formulas. 2005. 197p. pap. 19.95 (978-1-4137-2861-3(8)) PublishAmerica, Inc.

Foreman, Michael. Hola, Mundo. 2004. (SPA., Illus.). 28p. (J). 19.99 (978-84-88342-41-6(1)) S.A. Kokinos ESP. *Dist:* Lectorum Pubns., Inc.

—Saving Sinbad! 2002. (Illus.). 32p. (J). 15.95 (978-1-929132-34-8(4)) Kane/Miller Bk. Pubs., Inc.

The Forest of the Frendibles. 2006. (J). mass mkt. (*978-0-9791982-0-5(8)) Donnellan, Martha.

Forester, Victoria. The Girl Who Could Fly. 2008. 208p. (J). 16.95 (*978-0-312-37462-4(3)) Feiwel & Friends.

Forge, Joni. Andie's Amazing Discovery. 2000. (Illus.). 28p. (J). (gr. 1-7). pap. 7.99 (978-0-9674180-0-1(3)) Wordsmith Publishing.

Forgey, Winchester. Chronicle of the Bent Nail. 2004. (J). per. (978-0-9666572-7-2(6)) Acacia Publishing, Inc.

Forgotten Door. 1999. (J). 9.95 (978-1-56137-283-6(8)) Novel Units, Inc.

Forrest, Rayzelle. The Adventures of Zana the Great: Everyone in the House Except Me. 2000. 20p. (J). (gr. 2-10). 15.99 (978-0-9702628-1-3(7)) Onyx Pubns.

Forrester, Sandra. The Witches of Bailiwick. 2005. (Adventures of Beatrice Bailey Ser.). (Illus.). 240p. (J). pap. 4.95 (978-0-7641-3025-0(0)) Barron's Educational Series, Inc.

Forst, Arthur & Patterson, Renee. Pippin & Peanut: The Adventure Begins. 2000. 108p. (J). (gr. 4-7). pap. 9.95 (978-0-595-14537-9(X)) iUniverse, Inc.

Forsyth, C. A. Adrenaline High. 2003. (SideStreets Ser.). 128p. (YA). (gr. 5-9). (*978-1-55028-793-6(1)); (gr. 7-12). 7.95 (978-1-55028-792-9(3)) Lorimer, James & Co., Ltd., Pubs. CAN. *Dist:* Casemate Pubs. & Bk. Distributors, LLC.

Fort, Gloria. El Mago Decibelio. 2000. (Dulces Suenos Collection). (SPA., Illus.). 18p. (J). 7.95 (978-84-348-6259-3(X)) SM Ediciones ESP. *Dist:* Distribooks, Inc.

El Fortin Musical: Aventura 1: el Viaje a la Coleccion de Liderazgo. 2004. (SPA.). (J). per. 12.95 (978-0-9727273-6-5(1)) Leadership Loft, The.

Foster, Alan Dean. Hand of Dinotopia. 2002. (Dinotopia Ser.). (Illus.). 416p. (J). (gr. 5 up). pap. 7.99 (978-0-06-051851-6(0)) HarperCollins Pubs.

Fowler. Little Chick's Big Adventure. 2000. (Illus.). 18p. (J). 10.95 (978-0-385-40728-1(9)) Transworld Publishers Ltd. GBR. *Dist:* Trafalgar Square Publishing.

Fowler, Charles. Plenty of Room Between the Trees. 1999. (Illus.). 36p. (J). (gr. k-6). pap. 15.00 (978-0-9675506-9-5(6)) House of Mirth.

Fowles, Shelley, illus. The Seven Voyages of Sinbad. 2008. 64p. (J). 18.95 (*978-1-84507-531-6(5)) Lincoln, Frances Ltd. GBR. *Dist:* Perseus Distribution.

Fox, L. B. The Adventures of Marky, Slash & Levy. 2006. (ENG.). 184p. per. 19.95 (*978-1-4241-4992-6(4)) PublishAmerica, Inc.

Fox, Lee White. Toby Erdrich & the Golden Eclipse. Selyov, Trebor E., ed. 2005. 170p. (YA). (gr. 7-12). pap. 11.95 (978-0-9665055-7-3(3) , 5) Hallmark Emporium.

Fox, Mary Virginia. A Desert Adventure. McMahon, Kelly, illus. 2002. (Two Can Read Ser.). 16p. (J). 2.99 (978-1-56472-659-9(2)) Edupress, Inc.

—A Fishing Adventure. McMahon, Kelly, illus. 2002. (Two Can Read Ser.). 16p. 2.99 (978-1-56472-661-2(4)) Edupress, Inc.

Fox, Michael H. TomorrowChild. 2001. 348p. pap. 18.95 (978-0-595-20103-7(2) , Writers Club Pr.) iUniverse, Inc.

Fox, Molly & Fox, Samantha. The Raft: A Companion Guide to the Boathouse. 2002. 171p. pap. 13.95 (978-0-595-21165-4(8) , Writers Club Pr.) iUniverse, Inc.

Fox, Paula. Portrait of Ivan. 2004. 160p. (J). reprint ed. pap. 7.95 (978-1-886910-60-7(X) , Lemniscaat) Boyds Mills Pr.

Foyt, Victoria. The Virtual Life of Lexie Diamond. 2007. 320p. (J). 16.99 (978-0-06-082563-8(4)); lib. bdg. 17.89 (978-0-06-082564-5(2)) HarperCollins Pubs. (HarperTeen).

Framke, Jilly. Prayer Power: With Nehemiah the Praying Mantis. 2007. (J). pap. 14.99 (*978-1-60247-304-1(8)) Tate Publishing & Enterprises, L.L.C.

Francis, Dick. Blood Sport. 1999. (gr. 7-12). lib. bdg. 15.30 (978-0-613-12525-3(8)) Tandem Library Bks.

Francis, Pauline. Sam Stars at Shakespeare's Globe. Tattersfield, Jane, illus. 2006. 32p. (J). 15.95 (978-1-84507-406-7(8)) Lincoln, Frances Ltd. GBR. *Dist:* Perseus Distribution.

Francis, Pauline & Verne, Jules. Journey to the Center of the Earth. 2003. (Fast Track Classics Ser.). (Illus.). 48p. (YA). pap. 9.99 (978-0-237-52534-7(8) , Evans Brothers, Limited) Evans Publishing Group GBR. *Dist:* Independent Pubs. Group.

Franklin, Shawna. Catching Achoo. 2006. (ENG.). 28p. per. 11.95 (*978-1-59800-492-2(1)) Outskirts Press, Inc.

Frantz, Jennifer. The Lion, the Witch & the Wardrobe: Tea with Mr. Tumnus. Downer, Maggie, illus. 2005. (Festival Reader Ser.). 32p. (J). 14.99 (978-0-06-079117-9(9)) Zonderkidz.

Fraser, Frank. Bearista: A Grand Adventure. Fraser, Frank, illus. 2003. (J). pap. 14.95 (978-0-9726394-0-8(3)) Starbucks Coffee Co.

Frazier, Breen. Infiltration. 2004. (Alias Ser.). 240p. (YA). (gr. 7). mass mkt. 5.99 (978-0-553-49437-2(6) , Bantam Bks. for Young Readers) Random Hse. Children's Bks.

Frazier, Jan. The Adventures of JC Van Winkler, Vol. 3. 2005. 192p. pap. 8.95 (978-1-56315-374-7(2)) SterlingHouse Pubs., Inc.

—Ghost of a Chance Vol. 2: The Adventure of J. C. Van Winkler, 2004. 192p. pap. 8.95 (978-1-56315-317-4(3)) SterlingHouse Pubs., Inc.

Freaked Out. 2006. (J). pap. 7.99 (978-0-9758511-7-3(9)) B*tween Productions, Inc.

Frederick, Heather Vogel. The Education of Patience Goodspeed. 2004. (Illus.). 320p. (J). 16.95 (978-0-689-86411-7(6)) Simon & Schuster Children's Publishing.

Free, Zaccai. Mbutu's Mangos. Vasudevan, Vidya, illus. 2006. 24p. (J). per. 12.95 (978-0-9785326-0-4(0)) Solar Publishing LLC.

Freeland, Alan W. Pursuit up North. 2000. 120p. (gr. 4-7). pap. 9.95 (978-0-595-12901-0(3)) iUniverse, Inc.

—Warrior's Hill. 2001. 108p. (YA). pap. 9.95 (978-0-595-18296-1(8) , Writers Club Pr.) iUniverse, Inc.

Freeman, Bill. Ambush in the Foothills. 2000. (Bains Ser.). (Illus.). 163p. (gr. 3-8). 6.95 (978-1-55028-716-5(8)); (*978-1-55028-717-2(6)) Lorimer, James & Co., Ltd., Pubs. CAN. *Dist:* Casemate Pubs. & Bk. Distributors, LLC.

Freeman, Marilyn. Pasquale's Journey. 2003. 49p. pap. 8.95 (978-0-595-30311-3(0)) iUniverse, Inc.

French, Claire. The Queen of the Silver Castle. 1999. (Illus.). 128p. (J). pap. 9.95 (978-0-86315-291-7(0)) Floris Bks. GBR. *Dist:* SteinerBooks, Inc.

French, Simon. Change the Locks. 2006. 112p. (J). pap. 15.00 (978-0-14-330172-1(1) , Penguin Global) Penguin Group (USA) Inc.

French, Vivian. Alegre Roger y el Tesoro Submarino. 2003. (la Orilla Del Viento Ser.). (SPA., Illus.). 56p. (J). 3.99 (978-968-16-6837-2(5) , 163) Fondo de Cultura Economica USA.

—Henny Penny. Windham, Sophie, illus. 2006. 32p. (J). 16.95 (978-1-58234-706-6(9) , Bloomsbury Children) Bloomsbury Publishing.

—Space Dog Visits Planet Earth. Heap, Sue, illus. 2000. (Space Dog Ser.: No. 4). 64p. (J). (ps-3). pap. 3.99 (978-0-439-13086-8(7) , Scholastic Paperbacks) Scholastic, Inc.

—Whale Journey. Flather, Lisa, illus. 2001. (Fantastic Journeys Ser.). 32p. (J). pap. 7.95 (978-1-84089-214-7(5) , Zero to Ten, Limited) Evans Publishing Group GBR. *Dist:* Independent Pubs. Group.

Frey, Hildegard G. The Camp Fire Girls at Camp Keewaydin: Or, Paddles Down. 2006. 156p. pap. 11.99 (*978-1-4264-4283-4(1)); 174p. pap. 14.99 (*978-1-4264-4347-3(1)) BiblioBazaar.

Fricke, Anna. Bayou Blues. 2001. (gr. 7-12). lib. bdg. 14.15 (978-0-613-74185-9(4)) Tandem Library Bks.

Fricke, Anna & Siebertz, Barbara. Bayou Blues. 2001. (Dawson's Creek Suspense Ser.: No. 2). (Illus.). 272p. (YA). (gr. 8 up). mass mkt. 5.99 (978-0-7434-1695-5(3) , Simon Pulse) Simon & Schuster Children's Publishing.

Friday, Stormy. Signal's Airport Adventure. Speer, Phyllis, illus. 2006. (J). 14.95 (*978-0-9717047-5-6(9)) Bay Media, Inc.

Fridman, Sashi. Fishy Friday. Klausner, April Stewart, illus. 2000. 32p. (J). (ps-2). 12.95 (978-0-8266-0027-1(1)) Merkos L'Inyonei Chinuch.

Friedman, Mel. The Mystery of the Backlot Banshee: A ClueFinders Mystery Adventure. 2004. (Illus.). 96p. (J). pap. 4.99 (978-0-7630-7620-7(1)) Learning Co. Bks.

Friedman, Michael Jan. Hunchdog of Notre Dame. l.t. ed. 1999. (Adventures of Wishbone Ser.: No. 5). (Illus.). 139p. (J). (gr. 4 up). lib. bdg. 22.60 (978-0-8368-2301-1(X)) Stevens, Gareth Inc.

—The Stolen Trophy. l.t. ed. 1999. (Wishbone Mysteries Ser.: No. 5). 144p. (J). (gr. 4 up). lib. bdg. 23.33 (978-0-8368-2386-8(9)) Stevens, Gareth Inc.

—The Stolen Trophy, 1998. (Wishbone Mysteries Ser.: No. 5). (J). (gr. 2-5). (978-0-606-12859-9(X)) Tandem Library Bks.

—Superman's First Flight. 2000. (Hello Reader! Ser.). (978-0-606-18609-4(3)) Tandem Library Bks.

Friedman, Michael Jan & Motter, Dean, illus. Superman's First Flight. 2000. (Hello Reader! Ser.). 32p. (J). (gr. 1-3). pap. 3.99 (978-0-439-09550-1(6)) Scholastic, Inc.

Friesen, Michael. I'm Theman! 2002. 108p. pap. 9.95 (978-0-595-21496-9(7) , Writer's Showcase Pr.) iUniverse, Inc.

Friesen, Ray. Another Dirt Sandwich: Some Rambling & Hilarious Exploits of Thyrd Fearlessness, 2008. (ENG., Illus.). 100p. pap. 12.95 (978-0-9728177-4-5(3)) Don't Eat Any Bugs Prodns.

—RQW, Vol. 3. 2003. (YA). 2.95 (978-0-9728177-2-1(7)) Don't Eat Any Bugs Prodns.

Friesner, Esther M. Nobody's Princess. (gr. 7-11). 2008. 336p. (J). pap. 7.99 (978-0-375-87529-8(8)); 2007. 320p. (J). lib. bdg. 19.99 (978-0-375-97528-8(4)); 2007. 320p. (YA). 16.99 (978-0-375-87528-1(X)) Random Hse. Children's Bks. (Random Hse. Bks. for Young Readers).

Friesner, Esther M. Nobody's Prize. 2008. (J). (*978-0-375-87531-1(X)); (*978-0-375-87533-5(6)); pap. (*978-0-375-87532-8(8)); lib. bdg. (*978-0-375-97531-8(4)) Random Hse., Inc.

Fritz, Jean. Early Thunder. 2001. (YA). (gr. 5-9). 19.75 (978-0-8446-7174-1(6)) Smith, Peter Pub., Inc.

Fritz, Kevin. The Newf & the Dane. 2003. 108p. (J). pap. 9.95 (978-0-595-27050-7(6) , Writers Club Pr.) iUniverse, Inc.

Frolick, Vernon. Fire into Ice: Charles Fipke & the Great Diamond Hunt. 2002. (Illus.). 376p. pap. 14.95 (978-1-55192-334-5(3)) Raincoast Bk. Distribution CAN. *Dist:* Transition Vendor.

From Ship to Shore. 2007. (Pirates of the Caribbean Ser.). 10p. (ps-3). 12.99 (*978-1-4231-0807-8(8)) Disney Pr.

Fronte, Kathy. Bella's Bow Tie Bears: Three Magnificent Tales of Adventure, Dreams & Magic. 2006. (Illus.). 36p. (J). pap. 12.95 (978-0-9727725-0-1(2)) Fronte, Kathy.

Frontiera, Deborah. Eric & the Enchanted Leaf. 2002. (Illus.). 20p. 4.99 (978-1-58608-653-4(7)) New Concepts Publishing.

Frood, Earle. The Wabasca Adventure. unabr. ed. 176p. (J). pap. (978-0-920576-49-6(4)) Caitlin Pr., Inc.

Frosty: The Adventures of a Morgan Horse. (Illus.). (J). 2003. 199p. per. 9.95 (978-0-9709002-2-7(8)); 2nd ed. 2007. 232p. per. 9.95 (*978-0-9709002-7-2(9)) Willow Bend Publishing.

Fry, Sonali. Dora the Detective. Fruchter, Jason, illus. 2004. (Dora the Explorer Ser.). 10p. (J). bds. 8.99 (978-0-689-86531-2(7) , Simon Spotlight/Nickelodeon) Simon & Schuster Children's Publishing.

—Wheel of Wishes. Saunders, Zina, illus. 2005. (Spongebob Squarepants Ser.). 14p. (J). 5.99 (978-0-689-87420-8(0) , Simon Spotlight/Nickelodeon) Simon & Schuster Children's Publishing.

Fry, Sonali, adapted by. All Aboard! ed. 2005. (Rubbadubbers Ser.: 2). (Illus.). 24p. (J). lib. bdg. 15.00 (978-1-59054-820-2(5)) Fitzgerald Bks.

Frye, Tom. The Kid, the Cop & the Con. 2000. 256p. (YA). pap. 12.95 (978-0-595-12903-4(X) , Writer's Showcase Pr.) iUniverse, Inc.

Fryer, Mary B. Buckskin Pimpernel: The Exploits of Justus Sherwood, Loyalist Spy. 2004. 288p. pap. 6.99 (978-0-919670-57-0(1)) Dundurn Group, The CAN. *Dist:* Univ. of Toronto Pr.

Fuchs, Menucha. Chatzkel, Mendel & Me: An adventure Story. Daykin, Rachmiel, tr. from HEB. Hechtkopf, H., illus. 2005. Orig. Title: Mah Shekarah Ba'Ayarah. 192p. (J). 15.95 (978-1-932443-39-4(8) , CHMH) Judaica Pr., Inc., The.

—The Yellow Ball & Other Summer Adventures. Shlomo, Bat, illus. 2000. (Children's Learning Ser.: Vol. 11). 48p. (J). (gr. k-5). pap. 4.95 (978-1-880582-53-4(8)) Judaica Pr., Inc., The.

Fuertes, Gloria. El Cuarto del Bebe. 2000. (Cuentos de Ahora Ser.).Tr. of Bebe's Quarter. (SPA., Illus.). 22p. (J). 12.95 (978-84-348-6011-7(2)) SM Ediciones ESP. *Dist:* Distribooks, Inc.

Fujishima, Kosuke. Oh My Goddess! Childhood's End. 2002. (gr. 7-12). lib. bdg. 25.70 (978-0-613-55151-9(6)) Tandem Library Bks.

—Oh My Goddess! Devil in Miss Urd. 2001. (gr. 7-12). lib. bdg. 24.55 (978-0-613-55156-4(7)) Tandem Library Bks.

—Oh My Goddess! Fourth Goddess. 2001. (gr. 7-12). lib. bdg. 29.20 (978-0-613-55165-6(6)) Tandem Library Bks.

—Oh My Goddess! Queen of Vengeance. 1999. (gr. 7-12). lib. bdg. 23.40 (978-0-613-55186-1(9)) Tandem Library Bks.

—Sympathy for the Devil. 1998. (Illus.). 100p. (gr. 7-12). lib. bdg. 23.40 (978-0-613-55196-0(6)) Tandem Library Bks.

Fulcher, Dean. The Grand Island Adventure. 2006. 238p. (J). per. 18.95 (978-1-59886-074-0(7)) Tate Publishing & Enterprises, L.L.C.

Fullerton, Charlotte. Aqua Planet. 2006. (Sonic X Ser.). (Illus.). 48p. (J). (gr. 1-3). pap. 4.99 (978-0-448-44254-9(X) , Grosset & Dunlap) Penguin Group (USA) Inc.

—Desperately Seeking Sonic. 2007. (Sonic X Ser.). 48p. (J). pap. 4.99 (978-0-448-44479-6(8) , Grosset & Dunlap) Penguin Group (USA) Inc.

—Dr. Eggman Goes to War. 2006. (Sonic X Ser.). (Illus.). 48p. (J). (gr. 1-3). pap. 4.99 (978-0-448-44327-0(9) , Grosset & Dunlap) Penguin Group (USA) Inc.

Fullmer, Howard, retold by. The King's Highway. Fullmer, Howard, . 2006. 32p. (J). 17.95 (978-1-59038-631-6(0) , Shadow Mountain) Deseret Bk. Co.

Fun on the Slide. 2000. (J). (978-1-58453-090-9(1)) Pioneer Valley Educational Pr., Inc.

Fun with Foster Kids Chapter Book. 2005. (J). 12.95 (978-1-59808-395-8(3)); spiral bd. 12.95 (978-1-59808-394-1(5)); per. 12.95 (978-1-59808-393-4(7)); cd-rom 10.95 (978-1-59808-396-5(1)) Whispering Pine Pr., Inc.

Funke, Cornelia. The Thief Lord. Latsch, Oliver, tr. from GER. Burmingham, Christian, illus. (J). 2002. 352p. (gr. 4-7). pap. 16.95 (978-0-439-40437-2(1)); 2003. 376p. (gr. 3-6). reprint ed. 6.99 (978-0-439-42089-1(X)) Scholastic, Inc. (Chicken Hse., The).

Funkhouser, Allison. Zealk & the Humans. 2005. 60p. 16.99 (978-1-58752-111-9(3)) Timberwolf Pr., Inc.

Furgang, Kathy, told to. Paul Bunyan. ed. 2003. (Early Connections Ser.). (J). pap. 33.00 (978-1-4108-1360-2(6)) Benchmark Education Co.

Gaetz, Dayle. Crossbow. 2007. (Orca Currents Ser.). 112p. (YA). (gr. 5 up). pap. (*978-1-55143-841-2(0)); lib. bdg. (*978-1-55143-843-6(7)) Orca Bk. Pubs.

Gaetz, Dayle Campbell. Spoiled Rotten. 2005. (Orca Currents Ser.). 112p. (J). (gr. 4-10). pap. 7.95 (978-1-55143-474-2(1)) Orca Bk. Pubs. USA.

Gaiman, Neil. Dangerous Alphabet. Grimly, Gris, illus. 2008. 32p. (J). 17.99 (*978-0-06-078333-4(8)); lib. bdg. 18.89 (*978-0-06-078334-1(6)) HarperCollins Pubs.

Gaiman, Neil. Stardust. 2005. (Single Volume Ser.). (SPA., Illus.). 210p. pap. 16.95 (978-1-59497-097-9(1)) Public Square Bks.

Gaited Horse Activity & Coloring Book-English/German/Spanish Edition. 2006. (ENG, GER & SPA.). (J). spiral bd. 17.95 (978-1-59210-287-7(5)) Whispering Pine Pr., Inc.

The Galactic Adventures of Team Energy: Episode I: Dr. Slouch & the Candy Factory. 2007. (J). 16.95 (*978-0-9778776-1-4(2)) LGE Performance Systems, Inc.

Gallagher, Diana G. Spaceship Blue Typhoon. 2005. (Sonic X Ser.). 48p. (J). (gr. 1-3). pap. 4.99 (978-0-448-43997-6(2) , Grosset & Dunlap) Penguin Group (USA) Inc.

Gallagher, Diana G. & Burge, Constance M. Beware What You Wish. 2001. (Charmed Ser.). 192p. (YA). (gr. 7 up). pap. 6.99 (978-0-7434-1238-4(9) , Simon Pulse) Simon & Schuster Children's Publishing.

Gallagher, Michael. X-Men, Scourge of the Savage Land. Severin, Marie, illus. 24p. (YA). (gr. k up). 12.95 (978-0-9627001-7-0(7)) Futech Educational Products, Inc.

Gallagher, Mike. Sonic the Hedgehog Archives, Vol. 1. 2006. 112p. pap. 7.49 (978-1-879794-20-7(9)) Archie Comic Pubns., Inc.

Gallagher, Mike & DeCesare, Angelo. Sonic the Hedgehog Archives, Vol. 2. 2006. 112p. pap. 7.49 (978-1-879794-21-4(7)) Archie Comic Pubns., Inc.

Gallego Garcia, Laura. La Hijas de Tara. 2004. (SPA.). 272p. (YA). 9.99 (978-84-348-8629-2(4)) SM Ediciones ESP. *Dist:* Lectorum Pubns., Inc.

Gallo, Donald R. No Easy Answers. 1999. (978-0-606-15903-6(7)) Tandem Library Bks.

—No Easy Answers: Short Stories about Teenagers Making Tough Choices. 1999. 336p. (YA). (gr. 7-12). pap. 6.50 (978-0-440-41305-9(2) , Laurel Leaf) Random Hse. Children's Bks.

Gallop to the Sea. 2005. (J). (978-1-933343-12-9(5)) Stabenfeldt Inc.

Galvin, Laura Gates. Ankylosaurus Fights Back. Chesterman, Adrian, illus. 2007. 36p. 14.95 (*978-1-59249-679-2(2)); 2.95 (*978-1-59249-682-2(2)); pap. 6.95 (*978-1-59249-680-8(6)) Soundprints.

—Ankylosaurus Fights Back: Paperback with CD. Chesterman, Adrian, illus. 2007. 36p. 8.95 (*978-1-59249-681-5(4)) Soundprints.

Gamer, Ron. One Last Chance: Trapped by a Blowdown. 2007. 240p. (YA). per. 8.95 (*978-1-59193-211-6(4)) Adventure Pubns., Inc.

Gamer, Ron. Wild Chance: Whitewater Awakening. 2005. 260p. (J). (ps-7). pap. 14.95 (978-1-59193-128-7(2)) Adventure Pubns., Inc.

Gannett, Ruth Stiles. My Father's Dragon: Books 1 & 2: #1 My Father's Dragon #2 Elmer & the Dragon. 2005. (Illus.). 96p. (J). (gr. 5). 6.50 (978-0-440-42121-4(7) , Yearling) Random Hse. Children's Bks.

Gantos, Jack. La Nueva Fuerza de Jack. (Torre de Papel Ser.). (SPA., Illus.). (YA). (gr. 5-8). 8.95 (978-958-04-5636-0(4) , NR30644) Norma S.A. COL. *Dist:* Distribuidora Norma, Inc., Lectorum Pubns., Inc.

Gapanowicz, Delores. The Finchley House Mystery. 2005. 112p. (J). per. 13.95 (978-1-933449-06-7(3)) Nightengale Pr.

Garcia, Belinda. Alyson's Adventures in Computer Land. 2005. 184p. (J). pap. 15.95 (978-1-58736-484-6(0) , Hats Off Bks.) Wheatmark.

Garcia-Huidobro, Beatriz. Misterio en el Campamento. 2002. (J). (978-956-240-348-1(3)) Arrayan Editores S.A.

Garcia, R. M. The Steamer Trunk Adventures #1: The Trunk & the Tortoise. 2006. 76p. pap. 14.95 (978-1-4241-0614-1(1)) PublishAmerica, Inc.

Garcia, Randolph. The Steamer Trunk Adventures #2: The Ghosts of Machu Picchu. 2006. (ENG.). 88p. per. 14.95 (*978-1-4241-1843-4(3)) PublishAmerica, Inc.

Garcia-Weed, Barbara. Zeroid & the Gold-Fanged Frock. 2003. pap. 13.95 (978-0-533-13491-5(9)) Vantage Pr., Inc.

Garden, Nancy. The Case of the Stolen Scarab: A Candlestone Inn Mystery. 2004. (J). pap. 8.95 (978-0-9674468-7-5(2)) Two Lives Publishing.

Gardner, Esther. I with Sword: A Novel for the Middle-Grade Child. 1999. 119p. (J). (gr. 3-6). pap. 9.95 (978-1-890622-77-0(X)) Leathers Publishing.

Gardner, J. J. Quest for Camelot. 1998. (Quest for Camelot Ser.). (Illus.). (J). (gr. 2-5). pap. 3.98 (978-0-590-12058-6(1)) Scholastic, Inc.

Gardner, Sally. Countess's Calamity. 2003. (gr. 3-6). lib. bdg. 15.25 (978-0-613-63271-3(0)) Tandem Library Bks.

Garis, C. Lillian. The Girl Scout Pioneers or Winning the F. 2006. 25.99 (*978-1-4280-1682-8(1)) IndyPublish.com.

Garis, Howard Roger. Buddy & His Winter Fun or a Boy in a Snow Camp. 2005. reprint ed. pap. 24.95 (978-1-4179-0679-6(0)) Kessinger Publishing, LLC.

—The Curlytops at Uncle Frank's Ranch. 2005. 26.95 (978-1-4218-1466-7(8) , 1st World Library - Literary Society) 1st World Publishing, Inc.

—The Curlytops at Uncle Frank's Ranch. 2004. reprint ed. pap. 21.95 (978-1-4191-5842-1(2)); pap. 1.99 (978-1-4192-5842-8(7)) Kessinger Publishing, LLC.

—The Curlytops on Star Island. 2005. 26.95 (978-1-4218-1467-4(6)); 192p. pap. 11.95 (978-1-4218-1567-1(2)) 1st World Publishing, Inc. (1st World Library - Literary Society).

—The Curlytops on Star Island. 2004. reprint ed. pap. 1.99 (978-1-4192-5843-5(5)) Kessinger Publishing, LLC.

—Uncle Wiggily's Adventures. Date not set. 192p. (J). 20.95 (978-0-8488-2281-1(1)) Amereon LTD.

Garland, Mark. Rescue Party. 1999. (Dinotopia Ser.: No. 9). (J). (gr. 3-6). (978-0-606-16862-5(1)) Tandem Library Bks.

Garland, Michael. The Big Stone. 1999. (Single Titles Ser.: 3). (Illus.). 32p. (gr. k-3). lib. bdg. 22.90 (978-0-7613-1261-1(7) , Millbrook Pr.) Lerner Publishing Group.

Garland, Sarah. Splash! 2006. (Illus.). 16p. (J). bds. 5.95 (978-1-84507-345-9(2)) Lincoln, Frances Ltd. GBR. *Dist:* Perseus Distribution.

Garlington, William R. The Great Divide: Coloring & Activity Book. 2004. (Illus.). (J). 5.95 (978-0-9708395-4-1(5)) Legacy Publishing Services, Inc.

—The Great Divide: The Adventures of Billy Bean & Bobby Nut. 2004. (Illus.). 127p. (J). pap. 12.95 (978-0-9708395-2-7(9)) Legacy Publishing Services, Inc.

Garthwaite, Lynn D. Dirkle Smat Inside Mount Flatbottom. Howarth, Craig, illus. 2006. 48p. (J). pap. 9.95 (978-1-59663-512-8(6) , Castle Keep Pr.) Rock, James A. & Co. Pubs.

Garton, Kevan. The Cockleton Mystery. 2006. 68p. pap. (*978-1-84401-788-1(5)) Athena Pr.

Gates, Phil. Terror on the Amazon. 2000. (gr. k-3). lib. bdg. 11.80 (978-0-613-33130-2(3)) Tandem Library Bks.

—Terror on the Amazon: The Quest for el Dorado. Martin, Linda, ed. 2000. (Readers Ser.). (Illus.). 48p. (J). (gr. 2-3). pap. 3.99 (978-0-7894-6638-9(4)) Dorling Kindersley Publishing, Inc.

Gates, Phil & Dorling Kindersley Publishing Staff. Terror on the Amazon: The quest for el Dorado. 2000. (Eyewitness Readers). (Illus.). 48p. (J). (gr. 2-3). 12.95 (978-0-7894-6639-6(2)) Dorling Kindersley Publishing, Inc.

Gathorne-Hardy, Jonathan. Jane's Adventures: Jane's Adventures in & Out of the Book, Jane's Adventures on the Island of Peeg, & Jane's Adventures in a Balloon. 2006. (Illus.). 588p. (J). 27.95 (978-1-58567-798-6(6)) Overlook Pr., The.

Gatou, Shouji. Full Metal Panic! Tateo, Retsu, illus. (YA). Vol. 2. 2003. 200p. pap. (978-1-4139-0006-4(2)); Vol. 3. 2004. 178p. pap. (978-1-4139-0007-1(0)) ADV Manga.

—Full Metal Panic, Vol. 9. 2006. (Illus.). 184p. (YA). pap. (978-1-4139-0338-6(X)) ADV Manga.

Gatou, Shouji & Kaisyaku. Full Metal Panic!, Vol. 1. 2003. (Illus.). 168p. (YA). pap. (978-1-4139-0001-9(1) , MFP/001) ADV Manga.

Gauch, Patricia Lee. This Time, Tempe Wick? Tomes, Margot, illus. 2003. 48p. (YA). (gr. 4-6). 16.95 (978-1-59078-179-1(1)); pap. 9.95 (978-1-59078-185-2(6)) Boyds Mills Pr.

—This Time, Tempe Wick? 2003. (gr. 3-6). lib. bdg. 18.75 (978-0-613-79892-1(9)) Tandem Library Bks.

Gauthier, Gilles. Missing Mooch. Cummins, Sarah, tr. Deromer, Pierre-André, illus. 1999. (First Novels Ser.: Vol. 31). 61p. (J). (gr. 1-5). (978-0-88780-485-4(3)) Formac Publishing Co., Ltd. CAN. *Dist:* Casemate Pubs. & Bk. Distributors, LLC.

—Missing Mooch. Cummins, Sarah, tr. Derome, Pierre-Andre, illus. 1999. (First Novels Ser.: Vol. 31). 61p. (gr. 1-5). 4.95 (978-0-88780-484-7(5)) Formac Publishing Co., Ltd. CAN. *Dist:* Casemate Pubs. & Bk. Distributors, LLC.

Gavin, Rebecca Thompson. The Adventures of Oakey Dokey Acorn: Oakey & Ivy. Gavin, Rebecca Thompson, illus. 2003. (Illus.). 64p. (J). (978-1-57579-255-2(9)) Pine Hill Pr., Inc.

Gavlas, Kathleen M. Eagle Mountain. 2002. 206p. pap. 19.95 (978-1-58851-321-2(1)) PublishAmerica, Inc.

Gay, Marie-Louise. Estela, Hada del Bosque. 2002. (SPA.). 36p. (J). pap. (978-980-257-272-4(1)) Ekare, Ediciones.

Gay, Michel. Croninon. 2003. (SPA.). 40p. (978-84-8470-001-2(1)) Corimbo, Editorial S.L.

—Una Vez Mas. 2003. (SPA.). 32p. (978-84-95150-42-4(5)) Corimbo, Editorial S.L.

Gebhart, Adalgiza. Gotta Have Hearts: Three Picture Stories for Preschoolers. Gebhart, Adalgiza, illus. l.t. ed. 2005. (Illus.). 76p. (J). 27.95 (978-0-922993-38-3(6)); per. 19.95 (978-0-922993-37-6(8)) Marquette Bks., LLC.

Geibler, Peter. Yours & Mine. Kunert, Almud, illus. 2005. 40p. (J). 16.95 (978-1-84507-323-7(1)) Lincoln, Frances Ltd. GBR. *Dist:* Perseus Distribution.

Geist, Ken, ed. Friends Forever: 4 Favorite Stories. 2005. (Scholastic Reader Collection Level 3 Ser.). 160p. (J). pap. 6.99 (978-0-439-76314-1(2) , Cartwheel Bks.) Scholastic, Inc.

Gemstone Publishing, creator. Donald Duck Adventures, Vol. 14. 2005. (Illus.). 128p. (YA). (gr. 4-7). pap. 7.95 (978-0-911903-94-2(1)) Gemstone Publishing, Inc.

—Mickey Mouse Adventures, Vol. 6. 2005. (Illus.). 128p. (YA). pap. 7.95 (978-0-911903-71-3(2)) Gemstone Publishing, Inc.

Gentile, Joe. Werewolf the Apocalypse Fang & Claw Vol. 1: Raging Fury. 2003. (Illus.). 168p. (gr. 11 up). pap. 15.95 (978-0-9721668-7-4(4)) Moonstone.

Gentry, Stephen. Journey to the Stars & Back. 2005. 52p. (J). pap. 16.49 (978-1-4116-5985-8(6)) Lulu.com.

George, Jean Craighead. Crowbar. 2020. (Illus.). 32p. (J). (ps-17). 14.99 (978-0-7868-0378-1(9)) Disney Pr.

—Crowbar. 2020. 32p. (J). (ps-17). 15.49 (978-0-7868-2326-0(7)) Hyperion Bks. for Children.

—Gorilla Gang. 1999. (Illus.). 32p. (J). 14.49 (978-0-7868-5078-5(7)) Disney Pr.

—My Side of the Mountain. 2001. (Illus.). 192p. (J). (gr. 4-7). reprint ed. pap. 6.99 (978-0-14-131242-2(4) , Puffin) Penguin Group (USA) Inc.

—My Side of the Mountain Trilogy. 2000. (Illus.). 1p. (J). (gr. 4-7). 24.99 (978-0-525-46269-9(4) , Dutton Juvenile) Penguin Group (USA) Inc.

—On the Far Side of the Mountain. 2002. (YA). 13.28 (978-0-7587-9152-8(6)) Book Wholesalers, Inc.

—On the Far Side of the Mountain. 2001. (Illus.). 144p. (gr. 4-7). reprint ed. pap. 6.99 (978-0-14-131241-5(6) , Puffin) Penguin Group (USA) Inc.

George Ramey. The Friendly Dragon. 2006. (ENG.). 28p. per. 13.99 (*978-1-4259-7967-6(X)) AuthorHouse.

Gerber, Linda. Death by Bikini. 2008. 272p. (J). (gr. 7). pap. 7.99 (*978-0-14-241117-9(5) , Puffin) Penguin Group (USA) Inc.

Geringswald, Rita T. The Adventures of Ali Alligator. 2007. (Illus.). 33p. (J). 6.95 (*978-0-9797566-1-0(8)) R & D Publishing of Lakeland, Florida.

Gernhart, Cyndi. The Adventures of Gertrude Mccluck, Chicken in Charge Vol. 4: A Midwinter Light's Dream, 4 vols. Gernhart, Carlie, illus. l.t. ed. 2006. 52p. (J). 8.00 (978-0-9778240-4-5(7)) Prairie Winds Publishing.

Gershon, Neil. The Other Side of the Frame. 2007. 184p. (J). per. 13.95 (*978-0-595-40618-0(1)) iUniverse, Inc.

Gerstein, Sherry. Brainbenders from the Four Nations. 2008. (Avatar Ser.). 48p. (J). pap. 3.99 (*978-1-4169-5350-0(7) , Simon Spotlight) Simon & Schuster Children's Publishing.

Gerwitz, Felice & Gerwitz, Christina. Dinosaur Quest at Diamond Peak, 3, Vol. 2. 2nd rev. ed. 2007. (Truth Seeker's Mystery Ser.). 208p. (YA). per. 8.99 (*978-1-931941-11-2(4)) Media Angels, Inc.

—The Missing Link: Found, 3, Vol. 1. 2nd rev. ed. 2004. (Truth Seeker's Mystery Ser.). 208p. (YA). per. 8.99 (*978-1-931941-08-2(4)) Media Angels, Inc.

Geshell, Carmen. Muffin's Makapu'u Adventure. 1998. (Illus.). 40p. (J). (gr. k-6). 8.95 (978-0-9665686-0-8(5)) Muffin & Co.

Get Ready for Hulk. 2003. (J). per. (978-1-57657-860-5(7)) Paradise Pr., Inc.

Getz, David. Floating Home. 2000. (gr. 3-6). lib. bdg. 15.25 (978-0-613-30408-5(X)) Tandem Library Bks.

Ghazi, Suhaib Hamid. Ramadan. Rayyan, Omar, illus. 32p. (J). (gr. k-3). pap. 6.95 (978-0-8234-1275-4(X)) Holiday Hse., Inc.

Gibbons, Alan. Dark Beneath. 2006. (Illus.). 192p. (J). pap. 11.99 (*978-1-84255-097-7(7)) Orion Publishing Group, Ltd. GBR. *Dist:* Independent Pubs. Group.

Gibson, D. W., et al. Fundorado Island. 2006. (Illus.). 224p. (J). (gr. 3). lib. bdg. 16.99 (978-0-385-90284-7(0) , Delacorte Bks. for Young Readers) Random Hse. Children's Bks.

Gibson, Kari Smalley. Mooki the Berry Bandit. 2001. 40p. (J). 12.99 (978-0-310-70100-2(7)) Zondervan.

A B

Giff, Patricia Reilly. Kidnap at the Catfish Cafe. Cravath, Lynne W., illus. unabr. ed. (Adventures of Minnie & Max Ser.). (J). (gr. 4-7). 2000. pap., tchr. ed. 32.95 incl. audio (978-0-87499-555-8(8)); 1999. 30.95 incl. audio (978-0-87499-554-1(X)) Live Oak Media.

Gifford, Christopher. Swiper, No Swiping! Fruchter, Jason, illus. 2003. (Dora the Explorer Ser.). 14p. (J). bds. 12.95 (978-0-689-84773-8(4) , Simon Spotlight/ Nickelodeon) Simon & Schuster Children's Publishing.

A Gift to Share. 2005. (J). 17.00 (978-0-9721457-1-8(0)) Silent Moon Bks.

Gil, Alejandra & Magnasco, Carlos. Misterio en la profundidad de mi Cama. 2005. (SPA., Illus.). 28p. (J). 14.95 (978-9974-7799-3-8(6)) Hardenville SA URY. *Dist:* Independent Pubs. Group.

Gilbert, Marcie. Zee: Adventure One: Borrowing China. Krebs, Patricia, illus. l.t. ed. 2006. 48p. (J). per. 16.99 (978-0-9771566-0-3(5)) Librujas.

Gilbert, William. The Last Lords of Gardonal. 2006. (ENG.). pap. (*978-1-4250-2621-9(4)) Assistedreadingbooks.com Inc.

—The Last Lords of Gardonal. 2004. reprint ed. pap. 15.95 (978-1-4191-6872-7(X)); pap. 1.99 (978-1-4192-6872-4(4)) Kessinger Publishing, LLC.

Gildea, Kathy. The Adventures of Baylee Beagle—Annabelle Beagle. Larson, Amanda, illus. 2005. 28p. (J). 7.95 (978-0-9767096-1-9(9)) Maxim Pr.

—The Adventures of Baylee Beagle—Greenville. 2005. (Illus.). 20p. (J). 7.95 (978-0-9767096-0-2(0)) Maxim Pr.

—The Adventures of Baylee Beagle—Hurricane Hound. Larson, Amanda, illus. 2005. 28p. (J). 7.95 (978-0-9767096-2-6(7)) Maxim Pr.

Giles, Mike & Ruiz, Aristides, illus. Comic Book Heroes. 2005. (Teenage Mutant Ninja Turtles Ser.). 32p. (J). pap. 3.99 (978-1-4169-0074-0(8) , Simon Spotlight) Simon & Schuster Children's Publishing.

Giles, S. A. A Home for All: How a Little Puppy Finds a Home. 2006. 20.00 (978-0-8059-9076-8(3)) Dorrance Publishing Co., Inc.

Gill, Margaret. Return of the Quetzal. 2003. (ENG.). 184p. 22.95 (*978-0-595-65609-7(9)); 182p. (YA). pap. 12.95 (978-0-595-26531-2(6)) iUniverse, Inc. (Writers Club Pr.).

Gill, Paul. The Centaurs: An Adventure Fantasy. 2003. 54p. pap. 8.95 (978-0-595-30260-4(2)) iUniverse, Inc.

Gill, Shelley. Sitka Rose. Cartwright, Shannon, illus. 2005. (J). 16.95 (978-1-57091-353-2(6)); 32p. pap. 7.95 (978-1-57091-364-8(1)) Charlesbridge Publishing, Inc.

Gilligan, Shannon. Struggle down Under. 2007. (Choose Your Own Adventure Ser.: No. 21). (Illus.). 144p. (J). (gr. 3-7). pap. 6.99 (*978-1-933390-21-5(2)) Chooseco LLC.

Gilman, Laura Anne. The Shadow Companion. 2006. (Grail Quest Trilogy Ser.: No. 3). 256p. (J). 10.99 (978-0-06-077285-7(9)); lib. bdg. 14.89 (978-0-06-077286-4(7)) HarperCollins Pubs.

Gilman, Phoebe. Pirate Pearl. ed. 2004. (J). (gr. k-3). spiral bd. (978-0-616-01657-2(3)); spiral bd. (978-0-616-01658-9(1)) Canadian National Institute for the Blind/ Institut National Canadien pour les Aveugles.

Gilmer, Evelyn. Maggie: The Beagle with a Broken Tail. 2007. (J). per. 6.99 (*978-1-60247-310-2(2)) Tate Publishing & Enterprises, L.L.C.

Gilmore, Dorina Lazo. A Stone in the Soup. Hires, Josh, illus. 2006. 39p. per. 15.00 (*978-0-938911-29-6(5)) Individualized Education Systems/Poppy Lane Publishing.

Gilmore, Rachna. The Sower of Tales. 2005. 348p. (J). (978-1-55041-945-0(5)) Fitzhenry & Whiteside, Ltd.

Girard, Jeremy. The Key to Slumber: The Tales of Slumber. 2005. 201p. pap. 19.95 (978-1-4137-7243-2(9)) PublishAmerica, Inc.

Girard, Lawrence Vijay. The Adventures of Harry Fruitgarden Bk. 1: What's It All About? 2002. (J). (gr. 5-10). pap. 12.95 (978-0-9646457-4-5(2)) Fruitgarden Pub.

Girard, Philippe. Gustave et le Capitaine Planète. Girard, Philippe, illus. 2004. (Mon Roman Ser.). (FRE., Illus.). 96p. (J). (gr. 2). pap. (978-2-89021-649-5(7)) Diffusion du livre Mirabel.

Girls Can Do Adventures in Learning Book. 2005. (J). 15.95 (978-1-59210-285-3(9)) Whispering Pine Pr., Inc.

Gisbert, Joan Manuel. El Misterio de la Isla Tokland. 1998. (SPA.). 288p. (J). 8.95 (978-84-395-0817-5(4)) Lectorum Pubns., Inc.

Given, Cate. The Great Pogo Stick. Hill-Peterson, Jodi, illus. 2006. (J). (*978-0-9790057-0-1(1)) Paws In the Sand Publishing.

Gladiators. (Awesome Adventures Ser.). 16p. (J). (978-2-7643-0169-2(3)) Phidal Publishing, Inc./Editions Phidal, Inc.

Glass, Beth Raisner & Lubner, Susan. Noises at Night. Whatley, Bruce, illus. 2005. 32p. (J). (ps-3). 15.95 (978-0-8109-5750-3(7) , Abrams Bks. for Young Readers) Abrams, Harry N. , Inc.

Gleitzman, Morris. Toad Away. 208p. (J). (gr. 3-7). 2007. 4.99 (978-0-375-82767-9(6) , Yearling); 2006. 14.95 (978-0-375-82766-2(8) , Random Hse. Bks. for Young Readers); 2006. lib. bdg. 16.99 (978-0-375-92766-9(2) , Random Hse. Bks. for Young Readers) Random Hse. Children's Bks.

—Toad Heaven. 2006. 208p. (J). (gr. 3-7). reprint ed. 4.99 (978-0-375-82765-5(X) , Yearling) Random Hse. Children's Bks.

—Toad Rage. l.t. ed. 2005. (J). pap. (978-0-7540-7844-9(2) , CLP 434) BBC Audio.

—Toad Rage. 2005. 176p. (J). (gr. 3-7). 5.50 (978-0-375-82763-1(3) , Yearling) Random Hse. Children's Bks.

—Worry Warts. l.t. ed. 2005. 160p. (J). pap. (978-0-7540-7881-4(7) , CLP 458) BBC Audio.

Gleitzman, Morris & Jennings, Paul. Deadly!, 6 Bks in 1. 2004. (Deadly! Ser.). (Illus.). 444p. pap. 12.99 (978-0-14-330024-5(3) , Penguin Global) Penguin Group (USA) Inc.

Glencoe McGraw-Hill Staff & McGraw-Hill - Jamestown Education Staff. Topics from the Restless, Bk. 2. unabr. ed. 1999. (Wordsworth Classics Ser.). (gr. 10 up). pap. 24.64 (978-0-89061-117-3(3) , 9780890611173) Jamestown.

Glocke, Robin. Tiny Fish. 2006. 56p. pap. 12.95 (978-1-4241-3777-0(2)) PublishAmerica, Inc.

Godby, Ron. The King of Imperial Hill. 2006. 76p. pap. 14.95 (978-1-4241-1061-2(0)) PublishAmerica, Inc.

Godon, Ingrid. Neli y Gus: Saltar, Bailar y Otras Aventuras. (SPA.). (J). bds. (978-84-246-8833-2(3)); 2001. 24p. (978-84-246-8832-5(5)) La Galera, S.A. Editorial ESP. *Dist:* Lectorum Pubns., Inc.

Gold, Becky. Babies in Reptarland. Goldberg, Barry, illus. 2000. (Rugrats Ser.). 32p. (J). (ps-2). 5.99 (978-0-689-83337-3(7) , Simon Spotlight/Nickelodeon) Simon & Schuster Children's Publishing.

—Babies in Reptarland. 2000. (gr. k-3). lib. bdg. 14.15 (978-0-613-30972-1(3)) Tandem Library Bks.

—Tommy's Bestest Adventure. 2000. (gr. k-3). lib. bdg. 11.25 (978-0-613-31825-9(0)); (Illus.). (J). (978-0-606-20948-9(4)) Tandem Library Bks.

Gold, Jeffrey. Brianna & the Search for the Cloudmaker. Date not set. (Illus.). (J). (ps-8). (978-0-615-11213-8(7)) Spoon Publishing Hse.

Goldbeck, Anneliese. Scotty's Adventure in the Forest. Pery, Charles, ed. Frazier, Mike, illus. l.t. ed. 1999. 36p. (J). (ps up). pap. 6.95 (978-0-9673977-0-2(7)) Spiegel Publishing Co.

Goldberg, Malky. What Do I Say. Argoff, Patti, illus. 2006. (J). 9.95 (978-1-929628-24-7(2)) Hachai Publishing.

Goldblum, Jeff. Read-Along Storybook & Audio Tape: Prince of Egypt. 1998. (Prince of Egypt Ser.). (Illus.). 32p. (J). (ps-3). 7.99 incl. audio (978-0-8499-5896-0(2)) Nelson, Thomas Inc.

Golden Books Staff. Against All Odds. 2000. (Disney Ser.). (Illus.). 32p. (ps-3). pap. 3.99 (978-0-307-09224-3(0) , 09224, Golden Bks.) Random Hse. Children's Bks.

—All Around the World! 2007. (Book & CD Ser.). (Illus.). 32p. (J). (ps-2). 9.99 (978-0-375-84026-5(5) , Golden Bks.) Random Hse. Children's Bks.

—Backyard Adventures. 2005. (Illus.). 2p. (J). (ps-2). pap. 4.99 (978-0-375-83472-1(9) , Golden Bks.) Random Hse. Children's Bks.

—Battle of the Benders. 2008. 24p. (J). (gr. k-5). pap. 5.99 (*978-0-375-84331-0(0) , Golden Bks.) Random Hse., Inc.

—The Beast of Blueberry Heights. 2000. (Scooby-Doo Ser.). (Illus.). 12p. (J). (ps-3). pap. 9.99 (978-0-307-10143-3(6) , 10143, Golden Bks.) Random Hse. Children's Bks.

—Big Terrible Trouble. 2000. (Powerpuff Girls Ser.). (Illus.). (J). (ps-3). bds. 3.99 (978-0-307-16613-5(9)); 16p. bds. 2.99 (978-0-307-99500-1(3)) Random Hse. Children's Bks. (Golden Bks.).

—Christmas Book Bag. 2006. (Illus.). 32p. (J). (ps-2). pap. 4.99 (978-0-375-83710-4(8) , Golden Bks.) Random Hse. Children's Bks.

—Dynamo Destruction: The Powerpuff Girls. 2000. (Powerpuff Girls Ser.). (Illus.). 32p. (J). (ps-3). pap. 3.99 (978-0-307-20005-1(1) , 20005, Golden Bks.) Random Hse. Children's Bks.

—Fire & Ice: The Powerpuff Girls. 2000. (Powerpuff Girls Ser.). (Illus.). 32p. (J). (ps-3). pap. 4.99 (978-0-307-10412-0(5) , 10412, Golden Bks.) Random Hse. Children's Bks.

—Fun on the Go! 2006. (Illus.). 32p. (J). (ps-3). 4.99 (978-0-375-83661-9(6) , Golden Bks.) Random Hse. Children's Bks.

—Hop to It! Zalme, Ron, illus. 2006. (Color Plus Chunky Crayons Ser.). 32p. (J). (ps-2). pap. 3.99 (978-0-375-83589-6(X) , Golden Bks.) Random Hse. Children's Bks.

—Jewel of the Sea. 1999. (Disney Ser.). (Illus.). 56p. (ps-3). pap. 3.99 (978-0-307-27615-5(5)) Whitman Publishing LLC.

—Look, Listen & Love: The Powerpuff Girls. 2000. (Illus.). 10p. (J). (ps-k). bds. 9.99 (978-0-307-10107-5(X) , 10107, Golden Bks.) Random Hse. Children's Bks.

—Magical Treasures. Duarte, Pamela, illus. 2005. (Deluxe Coloring Book Ser.). 64p. (J). (ps-2). pap. 3.99 (978-0-375-83356-4(0) , Golden Bks.) Random Hse. Children's Bks.

—Make a Wish. 2005. (Illus.). 24p. (J). (ps-2). pap. 9.95 (978-0-375-83281-9(5) , Golden Bks.) Random Hse. Children's Bks.

—Picture Perfect: The Powerpuff Girls. 2000. (Illus.). (J). bds. 5.99 (978-0-307-10146-4(0) , Golden Bks.) Random Hse. Children's Bks.

—Ready, Set, Race! 2008. (Color Plus Ser.). (Illus.). 48p. (J). (ps-3). pap. 4.99 (*978-0-375-84577-2(1) , Golden Bks.) Random Hse. Children's Bks.

—Snack Time Adventure. 2006. (Illus.). 32p. (J). (ps-2). pap. 4.99 (978-0-375-83585-8(7) , Golden Bks.) Random Hse. Children's Bks.

—Spy Race! 2008. (Color Plus Chunky Crayons Ser.). (Illus.). 48p. (J). (ps-2). pap. 3.99 (*978-0-375-84008-1(7) , Golden Bks.) Random Hse., Inc.

—Super Blue to the Rescue. 2001. (Blue's Clues Ser.). 32p. (ps-3). pap. 3.99 (978-0-307-27612-4(0) , Golden Bks.) Random Hse. Children's Bks.

—Thomas' ABCs. 2006. (Color Plus Sticker Roll Ser.). (Illus.). 32p. (J). (ps-2). pap. 4.99 (978-0-375-83475-2(3) , Golden Bks.) Random Hse. Children's Bks.

—Travel with Thomas. 2007. (Deluxe Coloring Book Ser.). (Illus.). 96p. (J). (ps-2). pap. 3.99 (978-0-375-83953-5(4) , Golden Bks.) Random Hse. Children's Bks.

—Trick or Treat. Borlasca, Hector, illus. 2006. 12p. (J). (gr. k-1). bds. 3.99 (978-0-375-87490-1(9) , Golden Bks.) Random Hse. Children's Bks.

Golden, Christopher. Predator & Prey. 2001. (Prowlers Ser.: Vol. 3). 304p. (YA). pap. 5.99 (978-0-7434-0366-5(5) , Simon Pulse) Simon & Schuster Children's Publishing.

Golden, Christopher & Sniegoski, Thomas E. Dragon Secrets. 2004. (Outcasts Ser.: Bk. 02). 240p. (J). pap. 5.99 (978-0-689-86662-3(3) , Aladdin) Simon & Schuster Children's Publishing.

—The Un-Magician. 2004. (Outcasts Ser.). (Illus.). 240p. (J). pap. 12.95 (978-0-689-86661-6(5) , Aladdin) Simon & Schuster Children's Publishing.

Golden, Christopher, et al. Wurm War. 2005. (OutCast Ser.). 208p. (J). pap. 5.99 (978-0-689-86664-7(X) , Aladdin) Simon & Schuster Children's Publishing.

Golden Goblet. 1999. (J). 9.95 (978-1-56137-615-5(9)) Novel Units, Inc.

Goldman, Leslie. Toy Story 2: Junior Novel Book. 1999. (J). pap. 4.99 (978-0-7868-4394-7(2)) Disney Pr.

Goldstein, Alrica, ed. Polly Lodge: Snowed In! 2008. 32p. (J). pap. 3.99 (*978-0-696-23894-9(2)) Meredith Bks.

—Whirlwind World Tour. 2007. 32p. (J). pap. 3.99 (*978-0-696-23646-4(X)) Meredith Bks.

Goldwell, Bruce. Dragon Keepers. 2005. (Illus.). (YA). (978-1-894936-43-9(4)) Saga Bks.

Gomez de Salazar, Carmen & Martilotti, Carla. Pinky Pig: Lost in the City! 2006. (ENG.). 32p. per. 12.95 (978-1-59800-118-1(3)) Outskirts Press, Inc.

Gonder, Glen W. Poudre Canyon. Gonder, Sharon J., ed. Grove, Gladys, illus. Date not set. (Adventures of Willy Whacker Ser.: Vol. 9). 161p. (YA). (gr. 6-8). lib. bdg. 8.95 (978-1-58389-004-2(1)) Osage Bend Publishing Co.

Gonzales, Alysia. Mikey & Monster Vacuum. Cook, Joel, illus. 2004. 28p. 15.95 (978-0-9707906-0-6(0)) Providence Publishing.

Gonzalez, Ada Acosta. Mayte & the Bogeyman: Mayte y el Cuco. Rodriguez, Christina, illus. (ENG & SPA.). (J). 15.95 (978-1-55885-442-0(8) , Piñata Books) Arte Publico Pr.

Gonzalez, Xose Manuel & Thomassen, Hellen. Eleven Adventurous Ladies. 2002. (Illus.). 32p. (J). 14.95 (978-84-95730-21-3(9)) Kalandraka Catalunya, Edicions, S.L. ESP. *Dist:* Independent Pubs. Group.

Good, Merle. Reuben & the Fire. Moss, P. Buckley, illus. 2003. (Bestselling Children's Book Ser.). 32p. (J). 7.95 (978-1-56148-388-4(5)) Good Bks.

—Reuben & the Fire. 2003. (gr. k-3). lib. bdg. 16.40 (978-0-613-84738-4(5)) Tandem Library Bks.

Good, Merle, et al. Dan's Pants: The Adventures of Dan, the Fabric Man. Benner, Cheryl A., illus. 2004. 32p. (J). 6.95 (978-1-56148-413-3(X)) Good Bks.

Goodman, Alison. Eon: the Last Dragoneye: The Last Dragoneye. 2008. (YA). (gr. 7). 19.99 (*978-0-670-06227-0(8) , Viking Juvenile) Penguin Group (USA) Inc.

Goodman, Deborah Lerme. The Throne of Zeus. 1999. (Illus.). 118p. mass mkt. (978-0-553-24679-7(8)) Random Hse., Inc.

Goodman, Joan Elizabeth. Paradise. 2006. 224p. (J). (gr. 7). pap. 7.99 (978-0-618-49481-1(2)) Houghton Mifflin Co.

Goodridge, Jim. A Sterling Plan: The Yankees, the Durang. 2005. 156p. pap. 19.95 (978-1-4137-4088-2(X)) PublishAmerica, Inc.

Goodwin, Carol. Does This Belong Here? A Twiggyleaf Adventure. McDaniel, Thomas, illus. l.t. ed. 2003. 32p. (J). 14.95 (978-0-9741072-1-9(2)) CornerWind Media, L.L.C.

—The Great Acorn: A Twiggyleaf Adventure. McDaniel, Thomas, illus. l.t. ed. 2004. 32p. (J). 14.95 (978-0-9741072-2-6(0)) CornerWind Media, L.L.C.

—Tippy Needs A Home: A Twiggyleaf Adventure. McDaniel, Thomas, illus. l.t. ed. 32p. (J). 2004. 14.95 (978-0-9741072-3-3(9)); 2003. per. 14.95 (978-0-09-741072-2(1)) CornerWind Media, L.L.C.

—What's the Hurry, Furry? A Twiggyleaf Adventure. McDaniel, Thomas, illus. l.t. ed. 2003. 32p. (J). 14.95 (978-0-9741072-0-2(4)) CornerWind Media, L.L.C.

Goody, C. A. Charlie Goes Camping: Charlie's Great Adventure #4. 2004. (Charlie's Great Adventures). (Illus.). 112p. (J). per. 5.95 (978-0-9702546-0-3(1)) Goody-Goody Bks.

Gopnik, Adam. The King in the Window. 2005. (Illus.). 416p. (gr. 5-17). 19.95 (978-0-7868-1862-4(X)) Hyperion Bks. for Children.

—The King in the Window. Rayyan, Omar, illus. 2006. 416p. (gr. 5-17). reprint ed. pap. 9.99 (978-0-7868-3894-3(9)) Miramax Bks.

Gorbachev, Valeri. Christopher Counting. Gorbachev, Valeri, illus. 2008. 32p. (J). (ps). 15.99 (*978-0-399-24629-6(0) , Philomel) Penguin Group (USA) Inc.

Gordon, Roderick. Tunnels. 2008. 480p. (J). pap. 17.99 (*978-0-439-87177-8(8) , Chicken Hse., The) Scholastic, Inc.

Gormley, Greg. Mummy's Big Day Out. 2007. (Fantastic Phones Ser.). (Illus.). 12p. (J). 9.99 (*978-0-7475-8380-6(3)) Bloomsbury Publishing Plc GBR. *Dist:* Independent Pubs. Group.

Goscinny, René & Uderzo, Albert. Asterix & the Class Act. 2005. (Illus.). 56p. pap. 9.95 (978-0-7528-6640-6(0)) Orion Bks. Ltd. GBR. *Dist:* Sterling Publishing Co., Inc.

—Asterix & the Class Act. Bell, Anthea & Hockridge, Derek, trs. from FRE. Uderzo, Albert, illus. 2004. (Illus.). 56p. 12.95 (978-0-7528-6068-8(2)) Orion Bks. Ltd. GBR. *Dist:* Sterling Publishing Co., Inc.

—Asterix Omnibus 1. 2008. (Illus.). 144p. 27.95 (*978-0-7528-9154-5(5)) Orion Bks. Ltd. GBR. *Dist:* Sterling Publishing Co., Inc.

—Asterix Omnibus 2. 2008. (Illus.). 144p. 27.95 (*978-0-7528-9156-9(1)) Orion Bks. Ltd. GBR. *Dist:* Sterling Publishing Co., Inc.

Gotsubo, Masaru. Samurai Champloo, Vol. 2. 2nd rev. ed. 2006. (Illus.). (YA). pap. 9.99 (978-1-59816-215-8(2) , Tokyopop Adult) TOKYOPOP, Inc.

Gould, Cecily. Island of the White Toothed Shrew. 2003. (ENG.). 132p. 20.95 (*978-0-595-65469-7(X)); 128p. pap. 10.95 (978-0-595-25963-2(4)) iUniverse, Inc. (Writers Club Pr.).

Gould, Emily & Jaffrey, Zareen. Hex Education. 2007. 192p. (YA). pap. 8.99 (978-1-59514-118-7(9) , Razorbill) Penguin Group (USA) Inc.

Goulis, Julie. Something Shiny, Something Round. Ferguson, John, illus. 2005. 32p. (J). (gr. 3-7). 14.99 (978-0-9754621-1-9(3)) Bubblegum Bks.

—The Things a String Can Be. Ferguson, John, illus. 2005. 32p. (J). 14.99 (978-0-9754621-0-2(5)) Bubblegum Bks.

—The Topsy-Turvy Towel. Ferguson, John H., illus. 2006. 32p. (J). 14.95 (978-0-9754621-2-6(1)) Bubblegum Bks.

Gownley, Jimmy. Amelia Rules! Vol. 3: Superheroes. 2006. (Illus.). 176p. (J). pap. (978-0-9712169-6-9(7)) Renaissance Pr.

—Amelia Rules! Superheroes. 2006. 176p. (J). (978-0-9712169-7-6(5)) Renaissance Pr.

Gownley, Jimmy, illus. Amelia Rules! Book 3: Super Heroes. 2006. 176p. pap. 14.95 (978-1-59687-830-3(4) , ipicturebooks) ibooks, Inc.

Grace, N. B. Blast from the Past: Junior Novel. 3rd rev. ed. 2006. (Phil of the Future Ser.: Bk. 3). 128p. (gr. 3-7). pap. 4.99 (978-0-7868-3847-9(7)) Disney Pr.

Graeber, Mark. Collin Conway: The First Adventure with. 2005. 77p. pap. 14.95 (978-1-4137-9542-4(0)) PublishAmerica, Inc.

Graf, Mike. Yellowstone: Eye of the Grizzly. Leggitt, Marjorie, illus. 2007. (Adventures with the Parkers Ser.). 93p. (J). (gr. 4-7). pap. 9.95 (978-1-55591-568-1(X)) Fulcrum Publishing.

—Yosemite: Harrowing Ascent of Half Dome. Leggitt, Marjorie, illus. 2007. (Adventures with the Parkers Ser.). 93p. (J). (gr. 4-7). pap. 9.95 (978-1-55591-609-1(0)) Fulcrum Publishing.

Graham, Craig. Peter's Destiny: The Battle for Narnia. Baynes, Pauline, illus. 2006. (Narnia Ser.). 96p. (J). 14.99 (978-0-06-085236-8(4)) HarperCollins Pubs.

Graham, Lorenz. North Town. Graham, Lorenz, illus. 2003. (Illus.). 188p. (YA). (gr. 6-9). 16.95 (978-1-59078-162-3(7)) Boyds Mills Pr.

Graham, Wendy. High Jinx: Sloanes Beach, Skateboard Hero, Rock on, Bearded Toad. 2005. (Triple Play Ser.). (Illus.). 48p. (gr. 4-8). 41.85 (978-0-7910-9074-9(4)) Facts On File, Inc.

Graham, Wylie T. E. The Adventures of Sam & Hungry. Fallis, Margo & Kuehn, John, eds. Adle, Mary Ann, illus. l.t. ed. 2002. 37p. (J). (ps-4). pap. (978-0-9715665-0-7(X)) Schuerholz Graphics.

Grahame, Kenneth. Dream Days. 2005. (ENG.). 32.99 (*978-1-4219-0459-7(4)) IndyPublish.com.

—Dream Days. Shepard, Ernest H., illus. 2004. reprint ed. pap. 21.95 (978-1-4179-0979-7(X)) Kessinger Publishing, LLC.

—Open Road Bk. 2. Iosa, Ann, illus. 2006. (Easy Reader Classics Ser.). 32p. (J). pap. 3.95 (978-1-4027-3294-2(5)) Sterling Publishing Co., Inc.

—The Wind in the Willows. Leplar, Anna, illus. 256p. (J). (978-1-4054-3774-5(X)) Parragon, Inc.

—The Wind in the Willows Vol. 3: The Wild Wood. Iosa, Ann, illus. 2007. (Easy Reader Classics Ser.). 32p. (J). pap. 3.95 (978-1-4027-3295-9(3)) Sterling Publishing Co., Inc.

—The Wind in the Willows Vol. 4: Home Sweet Home. Iosa, Ann, illus. 2007. (Easy Reader Classics Ser.). 32p. (J). pap. 3.95 (978-1-4027-3296-6(1)) Sterling Publishing Co., Inc.

Gram, Peter. Gladiator, Level 4. 2001. (Illus.). 80p. (C). pap. 9.00 (978-0-582-47117-7(6)) Longman Publishing Group.

Gramatky, Hardie. Tub Time with Little Toot. Long, Laurie Struck, illus. 1999. 8p. (J). (ps). 4.99 (978-0-448-41550-5(X) , Grosset & Dunlap) Penguin Group (USA) Inc.

The Grand Escape. 2002. (J). (gr. 3-4). tchr.'s training gde. ed. (978-1-56137-723-7(6)) Novel Units, Inc.

Grant, Blake F. Windriders. 1998. (Illus.). 200p. (J). (gr. 5-7). pap. 12.95 (978-0-943864-97-6(6)) Davenport, May Pubs.

Grant, Crystal. Warrior Boy. 2007. (ENG.). 92p. per. 14.95 (*978-1-4241-3978-1(3)) PublishAmerica, Inc.

Grant, George, et al. Going Somewhere: A Dan & Bea Adventure. 1999. 287p. pap. 12.95 (978-1-58182-030-0(5)) Cumberland Hse. Publishing.

Grant, K. M. How the Hangman Lost His Heart. 2007. 256p. (YA). (gr. 7 up). 16.95 (*978-0-8027-9672-1(9)) Walker & Co.

Grant, Myrna. Ivan & the Daring Escape. 128p. (YA). mass mkt. 5.99 (978-1-85792-620-0(X) , Christian Focus) Christian Focus Pubns. GBR. *Dist:* Riverside.

—Ivan & the Informer. (Illus.). 160p. (YA). mass mkt. 5.99 (978-1-85792-624-8(2) , Christian Focus) Christian Focus Pubns. GBR. *Dist:* Riverside.

Grantham, Jared James. Ashley & the Dollmaker. 2004. (J). 14.95 (978-1-58597-270-8(3)) Leathers Publishing.

Graver, Fred. The Journey to Stonehenge. 1999. (Illus.). 111p. mass mkt. (978-0-553-24484-7(1)) Random Hse., Inc.

Graves, Pat R. Telemachus Joe - I Knew You Would Come. 2001. 55p. pap. 13.95 (978-1-58877-165-0(2)) enovel.com.

Gravley, Debbie Bybee. Golden Lace & the Magical Mossy Woods. 2005. 25.00 (978-0-9771793-0-5(3)) Gravley, Debbie Bybee.

Graziani, Maria. The Adventures of Valeria Veterinarian: Las Aventuras de Valeria Veterinaria, 1. Elejalde, Eliana, illus. l.t. ed. 2004. (SPA.). 23p. (J). 7.00 (978-0-9762361-0-8(9)) Ed. Acespanish S.A.C.- Lima, Peru.

The Great Bird Adventure. 2003. (J). lib. bdg. 18.95 (978-0-9725485-1-9(3)) Waterfall Ridge.

The Great Caterpillar Adventure. 2002. (J). lib. bdg. 13.95 (978-0-9725485-0-2(5)) Waterfall Ridge.

The Great Gilly Hopkins. 1999. (YA). 11.95 (978-1-56137-837-1(2)) Novel Units, Inc.

Green, Corey. Managing Stan. 2007. 162p. (J). 16.95 (****978-1-934437-01-8(8));*** pap. 7.99 (****978-1-934437-02-5(6))*** Abligio Bks.

Green, Jim. The Ghost Dancer. 2007. (YA). pap. 15.95 (****978-1-59705-923-7(4))*** Wings ePress, Inc.

—Shadows of the Moon... Dancing. 2007. (YA). pap. 14.95 (****978-1-59705-872-8(6))*** Wings ePress, Inc.

Green, Timothy. The Legend of Wingz. 2001. (Illus.). 32p. 17.95 (978-1-57174-275-9(1)) Hampton Roads Publishing Co., Inc.

Greenberg, Martin H. & Waugh, Charles. Lighthouse Island & Other Selections. l.t. ed. 2001. (Newbery Authors Collection: No. 4). 160p. (J). (gr. 4 up). lib. bdg. 23.33 (978-0-8368-2858-0(5)) Stevens, Gareth Inc.

Greenburg, Dan. The Boy Who Cried Bigfoot. Davis, Jack E., illus. 2000. (Zack Files Ser.: No. 19). 64p. (J). (gr. 2-5). pap. 4.99 (978-0-448-42041-7(4) , Grosset & Dunlap) Penguin Group (USA) Inc.

—The Boy Who Cried Bigfoot. 2000. (Zack Files Ser.: No. 19). (J). (gr. 2-5). 11.79 (978-0-606-18475-5(9)) Tandem Library Bks.

—Claws. 2006. 208p. (YA). (gr. 5). 15.95 (978-0-375-83410-3(9) , Random Hse. Bks. for Young Readers) Random Hse. Children's Bks.

—Elvis, the Turnip...and Me, Vol. 14. Davis, Jack E., illus. 1998. (Zack Files Ser.: No. 14). 64p. (J). (gr. 2-5). pap. 4.99 (978-0-448-41749-3(9) , Grosset & Dunlap) Penguin Group (USA) Inc.

—The Hijacking of Manhattan. 2001. (Maximum Boy Ser.: No. 1). (Illus.). 96p. (J). (gr. 2-4). pap. 3.99 (978-0-439-21944-0(2)) Scholastic, Inc.

—The Hijacking of Manhattan. 2001. (Maximum Boy Ser.). (Illus.). (J). (978-0-606-21319-6(8)) Tandem Library Bks.

—Just Add Water...and Scream! 2002. (gr. 3-6). lib. bdg. 13.00 (978-0-613-61637-9(5)) Tandem Library Bks.

—Maximum Girl Unmasked. 2002. (978-0-606-22272-3(3)) Tandem Library Bks.

Greenburg, J. C. In the Bathroom. 2002. (Andrew Lost Ser.: Bk. 1). (Illus.). 96p. (J). (gr. 2-5). lib. bdg. 11.99 (978-0-375-91278-8(9) , Random Hse. Bks. for Young Readers) Random Hse. Children's Bks.

—In the Bathroom, No. 2. Palen, Debbie, illus. 2002. (Andrew Lost Ser.: Bk. 1). 96p. (J). (gr. 2-5). pap. 3.99 (978-0-375-81278-1(4) , Random Hse. Bks. for Young Readers) Random Hse. Children's Bks.

—In the Garbage. Gerardi, Jan, illus. 2006. (Andrew Lost Ser.: Bk. 13). 96p. (J). (gr. 2-4). 3.99 (978-0-375-83562-9(8)); lib. bdg. 11.99 (978-0-375-93562-6(2)) Random Hse. Children's Bks. (Random Hse. Bks. for Young Readers).

—With the Bats. Gerardi, Jan, illus. 2006. (Andrew Lost Ser.: Bk. 14). 96p. (J). (gr. 2-4). 3.99 (978-0-375-83563-6(6)); No. 14. lib. bdg. 11.99 (978-0-375-93563-3(0)) Random Hse. Children's Bks. (Random Hse. Bks. for Young Readers).

Greene, Brenda. Dog Gone: Boomer's Story. Cheryl H. Hahn, illus. 2005. 127p. (YA). per. 8.99 (978-0-9770279-0-3(2)) Three Willows Pr.

Greene, Janice. Breaking Point: Set 3. 2002. 32p. (YA). 2.95 (978-1-56254-426-3(8) , SP 4268) Saddleback Educational Publishing.

—The Dark Lady. 2004. (Illus.). 32p. (YA). 2.95 (978-1-56254-741-7(0) , SP7410) Saddleback Educational Publishing.

—I Spy, E-Spy. 2001. (gr. 7-12). lib. bdg. 11.80 (978-0-613-34276-6(3)); (Illus.). (J). 10.75 (978-0-606-21555-8(7)) Tandem Library Bks.

—I Spy, E-spy. 2001. (PageTurner Spy Ser.). 80p. (YA). per. 3.95 (978-1-56254-138-5(2) , SP 1382) Saddleback Educational Publishing.

—White Fang. 2003. (gr. 7-12). lib. bdg. 15.25 (978-0-613-65750-1(0)) Tandem Library Bks.

Greene, John McBride. Encounter at Ogre Island. Julich, Jenniffer, illus. 2006. 96p. pap. 9.50 (978-0-9772809-0-2(X)) Comprecom.

Greene, Karen. The Adventures of Jack. 2003. pap. 15.00 (978-0-8059-6322-9(7)) Dorrance Publishing Co., Inc.

Greene, Richard. Lawrence the Locomotive. 2004. 49p. pap. 12.95 (978-1-4137-5704-0(9)) PublishAmerica, Inc.

Greene, Sefton. Space Painters. 2003. 18p. bds. (978-1-904502-30-2(X)) MediaWorld/BestBooks.

Greene, Stephanie. Owen Foote, Frontiersman. Weston, Martha, illus. 2002. 96p. (J). (gr. k-3). pap. 4.95 (978-0-618-24620-5(7) , Clarion Bks.) Houghton Mifflin Co. Trade & Reference Div.

—Owen Foote, Frontiersman. 2002. (gr. k-3). lib. bdg. 12.95 (978-0-613-72910-9(2)) Tandem Library Bks.

Greenwood, Anna. Beyond the Grey Wall. 2007. (ENG.). 292p. (YA). per. 21.95 (****978-1-58736-729-8(7))*** Wheatmark.

Greenwood, Kerry. Alien Invasions. 2005. (Thrillogy Ser.). (Illus.). 48p. (gr. 4-8). 17.50 (978-0-7910-8865-4(0)) Facts On File, Inc.

Greer, Tom C. Honey's Peanut Butter Adventure. Faust, Laurie A., illus. 2007. (J). per. 9.95 (****978-0-9789227-1-9(9))*** Weeping Willow Publishing.

Gregar, Steve. Al the Alien. 2004. 23p. pap. 14.98 (978-1-4116-1149-8(7)) Lulu.com.

Gregg, Kelly. Thaddeus Mouskin: An Eventful Life. 2005. 57p. pap. 12.95 (978-1-4137-6737-7(0)) PublishAmerica, Inc.

Gregory, David. Visions of Reality. 2007. 236p. per. 15.95 (****978-0-595-44969-9(7))*** iUniverse, Inc.

Gregory, Deborah & Alfonsi, Alice. The Cheetah Girls, Vol. 2. 2nd rev. ed. 2006. (Illus.). 128p. (gr. 3-7). pap. 4.99 (978-1-4231-0080-5(8)) Disney Pr.

Gregory, Kristiana. Legend of Jimmy Spoon. 2002. (gr. 3-6). lib. bdg. 14.15 (978-0-613-58069-4(9)) Tandem Library Bks.

—The Stowaway: A Tale of California Pirates. 2003. (Stowaway Ser.). 144p. (J). (gr. 4-7). pap. 4.50 (978-0-590-48823-5(6) , Scholastic Paperbacks) Scholastic, Inc.

Greig, Allison. Stacey's Adventures. 2006. (Illus.). 64p. pap. (****978-1-84401-035-6(X))*** Athena Pr.

Gresham, P. A. Anything Could Be Any Thing. 2005. 128p. pap. 12.95 (978-1-4116-4353-6(4)) Lulu.com.

Grey, Mini. The Adventures of the Dish & the Spoon. 2006. (Illus.). 32p. (J). (gr. 1). 16.95 (978-0-375-83691-6(8)); lib. bdg. 18.99 (978-0-375-93691-3(2)) Random Hse. Children's Bks. (Knopf Bks. for Young Readers).

Griffin, Daniel. The Adventures of Merlin the Mouse, 2005. (Illus.). 44p. (J). (978-0-9768348-0-9(4)) DiGuiseppi, Joseph.

Griffin, Dawnell. Osenplots! 2003. pap. 9.00 (978-0-8059-6220-8(4)) Dorrance Publishing Co., Inc.

Griffin, Judith Berry. Phoebe the Spy. 1998. (J). (gr. 4). pap. 3.95 (978-0-439-04466-0(9)) Scholastic, Inc.

Griffin, Margot. Dancing for Danger. Burden, P. John, illus. 2001. (Meggy Tales Ser.). 94p. (J). (gr. 3-6). pap. 6.95 (978-0-7737-6136-0(5)) Stoddart Kids CAN. *Dist:* Fitzhenry & Whiteside, Ltd.

—Secret of the Crystal Cave: A Meggy Tale. Burden, P. John, illus. 2002. 164p. (J). (gr. 3-6). pap. 7.95 (978-0-7737-6226-8(4)) Stoddart Kids CAN. *Dist:* Fitzhenry & Whiteside, Ltd.

Griffin, W. Marooned on Earth: The Adventures of O-Boo & U-Boo. 2005. 109p. pap. 16.95 (978-1-4137-6814-5(8)) PublishAmerica, Inc.

Griffiths, Andy. The Day My Butt Went Psycho. 2003. (gr. 5-8). lib. bdg. 13.00 (978-0-613-62939-3(6)) Tandem Library Bks.

—The Day My Butt Went Psycho! 2003. 240p. (J). (gr. 4-7). 4.99 (978-0-439-42469-1(0)) Scholastic, Inc.

—Just Wacky! Denton, Terry, illus. 2004. 144p. (J). (gr. 4-7). 4.99 (978-0-439-42473-8(9) , Scholastic Paperbacks) Scholastic, Inc.

Griffiths, Robert. Adventures of Clive. 2005. 45p. (J). pap. 10.01 (978-1-4116-5332-0(7)); 89p. pap. 8.81 (978-1-4116-5191-3(X)) Lulu.com.

Griggs, Joyce. Imanis Good Deed. 2006. pap. 9.95 (****978-1-4327-0071-3(5))*** Outskirts Press, Inc.

Griggs, Terry. The Silver Door. 2004. (Cat's Eye Corner Ser.). (Illus.). 192p. pap. 7.95 (978-1-55192-685-8(7)) Raincoast Bk. Distribution CAN. *Dist:* Perseus Distribution.

—The Silver Door Teacher Guide. 2004. 4p. pap. (978-1-55192-705-3(5)) Raincoast Bk. Distribution CAN. *Dist:* Transition Vendor.

Grimm, Jacob W. Tom Thumb/Pulgarcito. 2004. (Illus.). (J). cd-rom (978-1-933530-38-3(3)) Bingo Bks., Inc.

Grinnell, George Bird. Jack in the Rockies or A Boys Adventures. 2006. (Illus.). pap. 28.95 (****978-1-4286-2952-3(1))*** Kessinger Publishing, LLC.

Grisham, John. The Testament. 2000. (gr. 7-12). lib. bdg. 16.45 (978-0-613-23044-5(2)) Tandem Library Bks.

Gritton, Steve. Plain Fish. 2007. (J). 17.95 (****978-0-9795361-2-0(X))*** Bad Frog Art/SMG Bks.

Grizzell, Larry. What Would You Like to Do Today? Fun in the Snow. 2006. (Illus.). 30p. (J). 16.95 (978-0-9759542-1-8(0)) Adventures Galore.

Groffman, Simcha. Awesome Days. 164p. 19.99 (978-1-58330-713-7(3)) Feldheim Pubs.

Grogan, Marijo. As Strong As the Wind, As Deep As a Canyon: A Girl's Adventure Story. 1999. (Illus.). 127p. (YA). (gr. 5-8). 24.95 (978-0-9678801-0-5(6)) Acorn Publishing.

Grosgebauer, Clare Ham. Snickerdoodle & the Roller-Skating Horse! Rissing, Karen, illus. 3rd ed. 2005. 36p. (gr. k-3). 12.99 (978-0-9741888-4-3(0)) Small Wonders Enterprises.

Group/McGraw-Hill, Wright. Crazy Adventurers: Magazine Anthology: Level 6, 6 vols. (Comprehension Strand Ser.). (gr. 4-8). 54.00 (978-0-322-09860-2(2)) Wright Group, The.

—Secrets & Strays, 6 vols. (D-Man Beans Ser.). 47p. (gr. 4-6). 42.50 (978-0-322-06258-0(6)) Wright Group, The.

Gruber, Zaque. Blindsided. Wise, Noreen, ed. Gruber, Zaque, illus. 2002. (Lemonade Collection). (Illus.). 128p. (YA). pap. 9.95 (978-1-58584-268-1(0)) Huckleberry Pr.

Guardiola, Pepa. Los Ojos de la Nereida. 2000. Tr. of Eyes of the Sea Nymph. (SPA.). 92p. (J). (gr. 3-5). 9.95 (978-84-236-5503-8(2)) Baker & Taylor Bks.

Guilin, Peadar O. The Inferior. 2008. 448p. (J). (gr. 7). lib. bdg. 19.99 (****978-0-385-75146-9(X)*** , Fickling, David Bks.) Random Hse. Children's Bks.

Guillain, Adam. Bella Balistica & the African Safari. 2007. (Bella Balistica Ser.). (Illus.). 234p. (J). (gr. 5-8). pap. 9.95 (978-1-84059-482-9(9)) Milet Publishing.

—Bella Balistica & the Indian Summer. 2005. (Bella Balistica Ser.). (Illus.). 272p. (J). pap. 9.95 (978-1-84059-407-2(1)) Milet Publishing.

Guillaume, Robert, narrated by. Lion King: Read Along. 2001. (Illus.). 32p. (J). pap. 9.98 incl. audio compact disk (978-0-7634-0735-3(6)) Walt Disney Records.

Guilloppé, Antoine. One Scary Night. 2005. (Illus.). 32p. 15.95 (978-1-59687-185-4(7) , Milk & Cookies) ibooks, Inc.

Gulliver's Travels Study Guide. 2000. (Illus.). 48p. (YA). per. 17.95 (978-1-56254-286-3(9) , SP2869) Saddleback Educational Publishing.

Gunderson, Jessica. The Last Rider: The Final Days of the Pony Express. Ocampo Ruiz, José Alfonso, illus. 2007. (J). 56p. 23.93 (****978-1-59889-312-0(2));*** 49p. pap. (****978-1-59889-407-3(2))*** Stone Arch Bks.

Gureke, Mankin. Imperfect Hero, Vol. 3. 2005. (Illus.). 208p. (YA). pap. 9.95 (978-1-59796-094-6(2)) DrMaster Pubns. Inc.

Gureke, Nankin. Imperfect Hero, Vol. 2. 2006. (Illus.). 208p. pap. 9.95 (978-1-58899-247-5(0)) DrMaster Pubns. Inc.

Gurney, James. Dinotopia: Journey to Chandara. 2007. (Illus.). 160p. 29.95 (****978-0-7407-6431-8(4))*** Andrews McMeel Publishing.

Gurney, John Steven. Storyland Adventure. 1998. (J). pap. 3.25 (978-0-679-88823-9(3) , Random Hse. Bks. for Young Readers) Random Hse. Children's Bks.

Gurney, Stella. Marinera Sandra, Level P. Worsley, Belinda, illus. 2006. (Lightning Readers Ser.). 32p. (J). (gr. k-k). pap. 3.95 (978-0-7696-4215-4(2) , Gingham Dog Pr.) School Specialty Publishing.

Gustaveson, Dave. The Himalayan Rescue. 2000. (Reel Kids Adventures Ser.: Bk. 10). 168p. (gr. 5-7). pap. 6.99 (978-1-57658-027-1(X)) YWAM Publishing.

—Reel Kids Adventures, 5 vols. 2000. (Reel Kids Adventures Ser.). (gr. 5-7). 34.95 (978-1-57658-013-4(X)) YWAM Publishing.

Gutman, Dan. Casey Back at the Bat. Johnson, Steve & Fancher, Lou, illus. 2007. 32p. (J). (gr. k-4). 16.99 (978-0-06-056025-6(8) , HarperCollins); lib. bdg. 17.89 (978-0-06-056026-3(6)) HarperCollins Pubs.

Guy, Glen E. Adventure Gold: The Adventures of Dusty Sourdough, 3 vols. Totten, Dave, illus. 1999. 128p. (gr. 4-7). reprint ed. 9.95 (978-1-888125-22-1(5)) Publication Consultants.

Haber, Melissa. Heroic Adventures of Hercules Amsterdam. 2004. 224p. (J). (gr. 5). pap. 5.99 (978-0-14-240216-0(8) , Puffin) Penguin Group (USA) Inc.

Haddix, Margaret Peterson. Among the Brave. (Shadow Children Ser.). (Illus.). 240p. (J). (gr. 3-7). 2005. pap. 5.99 (978-0-689-85795-9(0) , Aladdin); 2004. 15.95 (978-0-689-85794-2(2)) Simon & Schuster Children's Publishing.

—Among the Hidden. 2000. (Shadow Children Ser.: No. 1). 12.64 (978-0-606-17823-5(6)) Tandem Library Bks.

—Among the Hidden. l.t. ed. 2000. (Shadow Children Ser.). 185p. (YA). (gr. 5-8). 20.95 (978-0-7862-3051-8(7)) Thorndike Pr.

—Running Out of Time. 184p. (gr. 5 up). (YA). pap. 4.99 (978-0-8072-1529-6(5)); 1998. (J). pap. 38.00 incl. audio (978-0-8072-8032-4(1) , YA972SP) Random Hse. Audio Publishing Group. (Listening Library).

Haddon, Mark. Agent Z Goes Wild. 1999. (Illus.). 170p. (J). pap. (978-0-09-940073-8(1) , Red Fox) Random Hse. Children's Bks.

—The Ice Bear's Cave. Axtell, David, illus. 2002. 30p. (J). (gr. k-2). pap. 9.99 (978-0-00-664628-0(X)) HarperCollins Pubs. Ltd. GBR. *Dist:* Trafalgar Square Publishing.

Hadley, Amy. Fool's Gold. 2006. (Illus.). pap. 9.99 (978-1-59816-585-2(2) , Tokyopop Adult) TOKYOPOP, Inc.

Haggard, H. Rider. King Solomon's Mines. Marcos, Pablo, illus. 2005. (Great Illustrated Classics Ser.). 239p. (J). (gr. 3-8). 21.35 (978-1-59679-244-9(2) , ABDO & Daughters) ABDO Publishing Co.

—Pearl-Maiden. Kou, Christopher D. & McHugh, Michael J., eds. 2003. 372p. (YA). pap. 9.95 (978-1-930367-89-0(9)) Christian Liberty Pr.

Haggarty, Holly. Summer Dragons. 2007. 144p. (J). (gr. 3 up). pap. 7.98 (****978-1-894917-52-0(9))*** Napoleon Publishing/Rendezvous Pr. CAN. *Dist:* AtlasBooks Distribution.

Hahn, Mary Downing. The Gentleman Outlaw & Me: A Story of the Old West. 2007. 224p. (YA). (gr. 7-9). pap. 6.95 (978-0-618-83000-8(6) , Clarion Bks.) Houghton Mifflin Co. Trade & Reference Div.

A Hair-Raising Tale. 2001. 24p. (J). 12.99 (978-0-307-20048-8(5) , 20048, Golden Bks.) Random Hse. Children's Bks.

Halam, Ann. Siberia: A Novel. 2005. (J). (gr. 7). 272p. 16.95 (978-0-385-74650-2(4)); 262p. lib. bdg. 18.99 (978-0-385-90885-6(7)) Random Hse. Children's Bks. (Lamb, Wendy).

Hale, Bruce. The Chameleon Wore Chartreuse: A Chet Gecko Mystery. unabr. ed. 2004. (Chet Gecko, Private Eye Ser.: No. 1). 112p. (J). (gr. 3-6). pap. 17.00 incl. audio (978-0-8072-0342-2(4) , Listening Library) Random Hse. Audio Publishing Group.

—Pirates of Underwhere. Hillman, Shane, illus. 2008. (Underwhere Ser.). 160p. (J). 15.99 (****978-0-06-085127-9(9));*** lib. bdg. 16.89 (****978-0-06-085128-6(7))*** HarperCollins Pubs.

—Prince of Underwhere. Hillman, Shane, illus. 2008. (Underwhere Ser.). 176p. (J). lib. bdg. 16.89 (****978-0-06-085125-5(2));*** (gr. 3-7). 15.99 (****978-0-06-085124-8(4))*** HarperCollins Pubs.

Hale, Daniel J. & LaBrot, Matthew. Red Card. 2004. (Zeke Armstrong Mysteries Ser.: Vol. 1). 170p. (gr. 4-9). 8.95 (978-1-929976-15-7(1)) Top Pubns., Ltd.

Hale, Shannon & Smith, James Noel. Book of a Thousand Days. 2007. (Illus.). 320p. (YA). (gr. 7 up). 17.95 (****978-1-59990-051-3(3))*** Bloomsbury Publishing.

Halfmann, Janet. Ogre Hunter No. 2: With Stencils. Karl, Linda, illus. 2004. (Shrek 2 Ser.). 32p. (J). act. bk. ed. 3.99 (978-0-439-57633-8(4)) Scholastic, Inc.

Hall. Here Comes Zelda Claus: And Other Holiday Disasters. 2001. (J). pap. (978-0-15-216468-3(5)) Harcourt Trade Pubs.

Hall, Donald. Ox-Cart Man. 1999. (J). 9.95 (978-1-56137-457-1(1)) Novel Units, Inc.

Hall, John. Jeffrey Takes on the World. 2005. 48p. pap. 12.95 (978-1-4137-9832-6(2)) PublishAmerica, Inc.

Hall, John & Gilpin, Stephen. If the Earth Had a Zipper. 2006. (Illus.). 48p. 15.99 (978-1-59379-069-1(4)) White Stone Bks.

Hall, Kirsten. Help! All about Telling Time. 2004. (Beastieville Ser.). (J). (gr. k-1). pap. 3.95 (978-0-516-24655-0(0) , Children's Pr.) Scholastic Library Publishing.

Hall, Marjorie. The Talismon Tales No. 1: Wiggleton's Courageous Adventure. 2003. 146p. 21.95 (978-0-595-65790-2(7)); pap. 11.95 (978-0-595-28414-6(0)) iUniverse, Inc.

Hall, Susan', illus. Diego Saves the Tree Frogs. 2006. (Go, Diego, Go! Ser.). 24p. (J). pap. 3.99 (978-1-4169-1574-4(5) , Simon Spotlight/Nickelodeon) Simon & Schuster Children's Publishing.

Hallagin, Janet. The Way of Courage. 2006. 30.99 (****978-1-4257-1249-5(5));*** pap. 20.99 (****978-1-4257-1248-8(7))*** Xlibris Corp.

Hallam, Gwion. Disgwyl a Disgwyl. 2005. (WEL., Illus.). 16p. (978-1-85644-750-8(2)) Univ. of Wales, Aberystwyth, Centre for Educational Studies.

Haller, Reese. Fred the Mouse: The Adventures Begin. 2005. (Illus.). 108p. (J). lib. bdg. 4.97 (978-0-9616046-8-4(9)) Personal Power Pr.

Halperin, Michael. Black Wheels. 2003. (gr. 7-12). lib. bdg. 31.55 (978-0-613-77954-8(1)) Tandem Library Bks.

Halvorson, Marilyn. Blue Moon. 2004. (Orca Soundings Ser.). 112p. (J). (gr. 7-12). pap. 7.95 (978-1-55143-320-2(6) , 1234488) Orca Bk. Pubs. USA.

—Stranger on the Run. unabr. ed. 1998. (Gemini Bks.). 191p. (YA). (gr. 7-9). mass mkt. 5.95 (978-0-7736-7471-4(3)) Stoddart Kids CAN. *Dist:* Fitzhenry & Whiteside, Ltd.

Hamburger, Carole. The Zippity-Do-Dot: The Dot Who Dared to Pick Her Knows. Hamburger, Carole, illus. 2008. (Illus.). 40p. (J). 16.95 (****978-0-9764921-1-5(3))*** Cherry Street Pr.

Hamidi, Sarah. The Things Jordan Does. 2002. 108p. (J). (gr. 4-7). pap. 16.95 (978-1-59129-285-2(9)) PublishAmerica, Inc.

Hamilton, Elizabeth L. Secret of Cachuma Lake. 2001. (Travel Adventure Ser.: Bk. 1). (Illus.). 144p. (YA). per. 9.95 (978-0-9713749-7-3(X)) Quiet Impact, Inc.

Hamilton, Leo. Leo Hamilton Presents: Children's Dream Adventures, Larkin, Jessica, illus. l.t. ed. 2002. 40p. (J). (ps-5). pap. 8.99 (978-0-9671660-2-5(0)) Story Place, The.

Hamilton, Leslie. The Story of Peter Little Bear: A Lamprey River Adventure. 2005. (J). per. 12.95 (978-1-933002-02-6(6)) PublishingWorks.

Hamilton, Morse. The Garden of Eden Motel. 1999. (Illus.). 160p. (J). (gr. 5 up). 16.00 (978-0-688-16814-8(0)) HarperCollins Pubs.

Hamilton, Tisha. Piratas del Caribe. el viaje al fin del Mundo: Pirates of the Caribbean: at the World's End. 2007. (Illus.). 38p. (J). 24.95 (****978-970-718-532-6(5)*** , Silver Dolphin en Español) Advanced Marketing, S. de R. L. de C. V. MEX. *Dist:* Perseus Distribution.

Hamilton, Tisha. Pirate Island Storybook & Dress up Kit. 2006. (Storybook & Dress-up Kit Ser.). 24p. (J). pap. 18.99 (978-0-7944-1105-3(3)) Reader's Digest Assn., Inc., The.

Hamilton, Tisha & Artful Doodlers Limited Staff. TMNT: the Nightwatcher. 2007. (Teenage Mutant Ninja Turtles Ser.). 48p. (J). 3.99 (978-1-4169-3415-8(4) , Simon Scribbles) Simon & Schuster Children's Publishing.

Hamilton, Tisha & Primeau, Chuck. Shrek the Third Storybook & Viewer. Laguna, Fabio, illus. 2007. (RD Innovative Book & Player Format Ser.). 40p. (J). (ps-3). 24.99 (978-0-7944-1279-1(3)) Reader's Digest Assn., Inc., The.

Hamilton, Virginia. Dustland. 1998. (Justice Cycle Ser.: Bk. 2). 214p. (YA). (gr. 6-12). pap. 4.50 (978-0-590-36217-7(8)) Scholastic, Inc.

—Dustland. 1998. (Justice Cycle Ser.). (978-0-606-12927-5(8)) Tandem Library Bks.

—The Gathering. 1998. (Justice Cycle Ser.: Bk. 3). 214p. (J). (gr. 6-12). mass mkt. 4.50 (978-0-590-36216-0(X)) Scholastic, Inc.

—The Gathering. 1998. (Justice Cycle Ser.). (978-0-606-13414-9(X)) Tandem Library Bks.

Hammock, Sarah Owens. You Can't Get into More Trouble Than Gator Pervis!! Cocciolone, Kathy Roberts, illus. 2007. 32p. (J). 12.95 (****978-1-934246-27-6(1))*** Peppertree Pr., The.

Hammond, John & Hutchison, Gary. The Bewildering Bond: A Novel for Teenagers. 2004. 182p. (YA). pap. 13.99 (978-1-885631-86-2(3)) Hutchison, G.F. Pr.

Hammond, Ron J. The Dig: Journey of a Lost Tribe. unabr. ed. 2004. 186p. (YA). pap. 10.95 (978-1-932280-47-0(2) , 80472) Granite Publishing & Distribution.

Hampshire, Anthony. Fast Track. 2004. (Redline Racing Ser.: Bk. 1). (Illus.). 104p. (YA). pap. 3.99 (978-1-55305-007-0(X)) Cygnet Publishing Group, Inc./Coolreading.com CAN. *Dist:* Orca Bk. Pubs. USA.

—Fast Track. 2005. (Redline Racing Ser.: Bk. 1). (Illus.). 138p. (YA). (gr. 6 up). pap. (****978-1-55041-570-4(0))*** Fitzhenry & Whiteside, Ltd.

—Full Throttle. 2004. (Redline Racing Ser.: Bk. 2). (Illus.). 108p. (YA). pap. 3.99 (978-1-55305-008-7(8)) Cygnet Publishing Group, Inc./Coolreading.com CAN. *Dist:* Orca Bk. Pubs. USA.

—Full Throttle. 2005. (Redline Racing Ser.: Bk. 2). (Illus.). 138p. (YA). (gr. 6 up). pap. (****978-1-55041-564-3(6))*** Fitzhenry & Whiteside, Ltd.

Hancock, Irving H. Dave Darrin's First Year at Annapolis. 2006. 78.99 (****978-1-4219-9882-4(3));*** pap. 72.99 (****978-1-4219-9880-0(7))*** IndyPublish.com.

—Dave Darrin's Fourth Year at Annapolis (2006. 78.99 (***978-1-4219-9801-5(7)***); pap. 72.99 (***978-1-4219-9805-3(X)***) IndyPublish.com.

—Dave Darrin's Second Year at Annapolis O. 2006. 95.99 (***978-1-4280-1562-3(0)***); pap. 89.99 (***978-1-4280-1578-4(7)***) IndyPublish.com.

—Dave Darrin's Third Year at Annapolis or. 2006. 95.99 (***978-1-4219-7420-0(7)***); pap. 89.99 (***978-1-4219-7419-4(3)***) IndyPublish.com.

—The High School Boys' Training Hike or M. 2006. 78.99 (***978-1-4219-9925-8(0)***); pap. 72.99 (***978-1-4219-9909-8(9)***) IndyPublish.com.

—The Young Engineers in Colorado or at Ra. 2006. pap. 72.99 (***978-1-4219-9888-6(2)***) IndyPublish.com.

—Young Engineers in Colorado or at Railwo. 2006. 78.99 (***978-1-4219-9872-5(6)***) IndyPublish.com.

—Young Engineers in Mexico or Fighting Th. 2006. 78.99 (***978-1-4219-9889-3(0)***) IndyPublish.com.

—Young Engineers in Nevada or Seeking for. 2006. 78.99 (***978-1-4219-9871-8(8)***) IndyPublish.com.

—Young Engineers on the Gulf or the Dread. 2006. 78.99 (***978-1-4280-2538-7(3)***) IndyPublish.com.

Handy, Robert Watts. River Raft Pack of Weeping Water Flat. 2001. 340p. (YA). pap. 18.95 (978-0-595-18792-8(7)) iUniverse, Inc.

Hanel, Wolfram. Rescue at Sea! 2000. (gr. 3-6). lib. bdg. 14.10 (978-0-613-30107-7(2)) Tandem Library Bks.

Hanington, John G. The Adventures of Quick Fox. 2006 80p. pap. 9.95 (***978-0-7414-3223-0(4)***) Infinity Publishing.

Hannan, Peter. Goofballs in Paradise. Hannan, Peter, illus. 2007. (Super Goofballs Ser.: Bk. 2). (Illus.). 176p. (J). (gr. 2-6). 15.99 (978-0-06-085214-6(3)) HarperCollins Pubs.

—That Stinking Feeling. Hannan, Peter, illus. 2007. (Super Goofballs Ser.: Bk. 1). (Illus.). 160p. (J). (gr. 2-6). 15.99 (978-0-06-085212-2(7)) HarperCollins Pubs.

Hansen, Eric. The Isle of Nam. Meier, Paul, illus. 2004. (J). bds. 9.99 (978-1-4183-0016-6(0)) Christ Inspired, Inc.

Hansen, Francis & Hansen, Caroline. Old Rowdy the Hero. 2001. (Illus.). 84p. (J). (gr. 3-8). per. (978-0-9722501-0-8(7)) Backwoods Publishing Co.

Hansen, Marc. Ralph Snart Adventures: Comic Collection #2. 2007. (Illus.). 128p. (YA). pap. 14.95 (***978-0-9794643-1-7(5)***) Hansen, Marc Stuff!.

Hansen, Marc. Ralph Snart Adventures: Comic Collection #1. Hansen, Marc, . 2007. (YA). per. 14.95 (***978-0-9794643-0-0(7)***) Hansen, Marc Stuff!.

Hanson, Bonnie Compton. Lost on Monster Mountain. 2004. (Ponytail Girls Ser.). (Illus.). 208p. (J). pap. 7.99 (978-1-58411-031-6(7) , Legacy Pr.) Rainbow Pubs. & Legacy Pr.

Hanson, Ed. Amazon Adventure. 2003. (Barclay Family Adventure Ser.: Bk. 1). 64p. (J). (gr. k-6). per. 3.95 (978-1-56254-550-5(7) , SP 5507) Saddleback Educational Publishing.

—Danger at 20 Fathoms. 2003. (Barclay Family Adventure Ser.: Bk. 2). 64p. (J). (gr. k-6). per. 3.95 (978-1-56254-551-2(5) , SP 5515) Saddleback Educational Publishing.

—Falsely Accused. 2004. 64p. (YA). per. 3.95 (978-1-56254-802-5(6) , SP8026) Saddleback Educational Publishing.

—Free Fall. 2004. 64p. (YA). per. 3.95 (978-1-56254-804-9(2) , SP8042) Saddleback Educational Publishing.

—Iron Mountain. 2004. 64p. (YA). per. 3.95 (978-1-56254-806-3(9) , SP8069) Saddleback Educational Publishing.

—Lost at Sea. 2003. (Barclay Family Adventure Ser.: Bk. 6). 64p. (J). (gr. k-6). per. 3.95 (978-1-56254-555-0(8) , SP 5558) Saddleback Educational Publishing.

—The Pass. 2003. (Barclay Family Adventure Ser.: Bk. 9). 64p. (J). (gr. k-6). per. 3.95 (978-1-56254-557-4(4) , SP 5574) Saddleback Educational Publishing.

—The Swamp. 2003. (Barclay Family Adventure Ser.: Bk. 10). 64p. (J). (gr. k-6). per. 3.95 (978-1-56254-558-1(2)) Saddleback Educational Publishing.

—Tornado. 2003. (Barclay Family Adventure Ser.: Bk. 8). 64p. (J). (gr. k-6). per. 3.95 (978-1-56254-559-8(0) , SP 5590) Saddleback Educational Publishing.

Hapka, C. A. Makuta's Revenge. 2003. (gr. 3-6). lib. bdg. 13.00 (978-0-613-89581-1(9)) Tandem Library Bks.

—Tale of the Toa. 2003. (gr. 3-6). lib. bdg. 13.00 (978-0-613-85392-7(X)) Tandem Library Bks.

Hapka, Catherine. Shrek Babies. 2007. (I Can Read Bks.). 32p. (J). pap. 3.99 (***978-0-06-143687-1(9)***, Harper Trophy) HarperCollins Pubs.

—Wildfire Showoff, No. 1. 2006. 256p. (gr. 7-17). pap. 5.99 (978-1-4231-0188-8(X)) Disney Pr.

—Wildfire Track Record, No. 2. 2nd rev. ed. 2007. 256p. (gr. 7-17). pap. 5.99 (978-1-4231-0189-5(8)) Disney Pr.

Hapka, Cathy. Beware the Bohrok: Chronicles 2. 2003. (Bionicle Chronicles: No. 2). 96p. (J). (gr. 2-5). 4.99 (978-0-439-50117-0(2)) Scholastic, Inc.

—Tale of the Toa. 2003. (Bionicle Chronicles: Bk. 1). 128p. (J). (gr. 2-5). pap. 4.99 (978-0-439-50116-3(4)) Scholastic, Inc.

Happily Ever After Agency. Hoodwinked! The True Story of Little Red Riding Hood. 2005. 32p. (J). (gr. 1-6). pap. 9.95 (978-1-57178-188-8(9)) Council Oak Bks.

—Hoodwinked: The True Story of Red Riding Hood. 2005. 32p. (J). (gr. 1-6). 14.95 (978-1-57178-174-1(9)) Council Oak Bks.

Harbo, Gary. The Northern Woods Adventure: Advanced Reader, 6 vols. Harbo, Gary, illus. l.t. ed. 2004. (If You Want to Succeed, You Need to Read! Ser.: 6). (Illus.). 33p. (J). per. 10.95 (978-1-884149-15-3(4)) Kutie Kari Bks., Inc.

—The Northern Woods Adventure: Early Reader. Harbo, Gary, illus. l.t. ed. 2004. (If You Want to Succeed, You Need to Read! Ser.: 6). (Illus.). 33p. (J). 10.95 (978-1-884149-16-0(2)) Kutie Kari Bks., Inc.

Harcourt School Publishers Staff. Adventure in Alaska: Take-Home Book. 2001. (Collections Ser.). (Illus.). (J). pap. 1.90 (978-0-15-319520-4(7)) Harcourt Schl. Pubs.

—Aventura en Alaska: Take-Home Book. 2001. (Vamos Ser.). (SPA., Illus.). (J). pap. 2.80 (978-0-15-319952-3(0)) Harcourt Schl. Pubs.

—Bronco Buster: Take-Home Book. 2001. (Collections Ser.). (Illus.). (J). (gr. 6). pap. 1.90 (978-0-15-319666-9(1)) Harcourt Schl. Pubs.

—The Crater: Take-Home Book. 2001. (Collections Ser.). (Illus.). (J). pap. 1.90 (978-0-15-319558-7(4)) Harcourt Schl. Pubs.

—The Crater Below Level. 3rd ed. 2002. (Trophies Reading Program Ser.). (Illus.). pap. 5.10 (978-0-15-323416-3(4)) Harcourt Schl. Pubs.

—Desert Letters On Level. 3rd ed. 2002. (Trophies Reading Program Ser.). (Illus.). pap. 5.10 (978-0-15-323280-0(3)) Harcourt Schl. Pubs.

—Egyptian Adventure Advanced Level. 3rd ed. 2002. (Trophies Reading Program Ser.). (Illus.). pap. 5.10 (978-0-15-323473-6(3)) Harcourt Schl. Pubs.

—The Mayflower Surprise Advanced Level. 3rd ed. 2002. (Trophies Reading Program Ser.). (Illus.). pap. 5.10 (978-0-15-323396-8(6)) Harcourt Schl. Pubs.

—My Surprising Vacation Below Level. 3rd ed. 2002. (Trophies Reading Program Ser.). (Illus.). pap. 5.10 (978-0-15-323339-5(7)) Harcourt Schl. Pubs.

—Rebecca's Story Below Level. 3rd ed. 2002. (Trophies Reading Program Ser.). (Illus.). pap. 5.10 (978-0-15-323146-9(7)) Harcourt Schl. Pubs.

—The Stowaway: Take-Home Book. 2001. (Collections Ser.). (Illus.). (J). pap. 1.90 (978-0-15-319538-9(X)) Harcourt Schl. Pubs.

—Walking Thru the Jungle: Little Book. 2000. (Collections Ser.). (Illus.). (J). pap. 10.20 (978-0-15-314502-5(1)) Harcourt Schl. Pubs.

Harding, Sandy Bacon. A Stick, a Stone & a Bone. Mickelson, Brenda, illus. 1999. (Farm Adventures Ser.: Vol. 2). 79p. (J). (gr. 1-6). pap. 6.95 (978-1-890609-08-5(0) , Lion's Paw Bks.) Coronet Bks. & Pubns.

Hardouin, Benny. Safari Slim & the Search for the Fat-Loss Secret. Lardner, Walt, illus. 1998. 154p. (J). (ps-6). pap. 19.95 (978-1-889636-09-2(6) , HN001) Youthlight, Inc.

Hardy, Emelia J. The Adventures of Maureen & Maury: For Children of All Ages! 2003. 158p. (J). pap. 12.95 (978-0-595-29536-4(3)) iUniverse, Inc.

Hardy, Jonathan. Cyril Bonhamy & Operation Ping. Blake, Quentin, illus. 2000. 128p. (J). 5.99 (978-0-09-979180-5(3)) Random Hse. GBR. *Dist:* Independent Pubs. Group.

Hardy, Robert. Todd & the TimbaThump. 2001. 20p. pap. 25.00 (978-0-9656945-6-8(9)) LHA Bks.

Hardy, Zoey. Brockway High. 2006. 344p. (YA). per. 12.95 (978-0-9765423-1-5(5)) Eudon Publishing.

Hargreaves, Roger. Mr. Clever. Hargreaves, Roger, illus. 2001. (Mr. Men & Little Miss Ser.). (Illus.). 32p. (J). pap. 3.99 (978-0-8431-7671-1(7) , Price Stern Sloan) Penguin Group (USA) Inc.

—Mr. Dizzy. Hargreaves, Roger, illus. 2001. (Mr. Men & Little Miss Ser.). (Illus.). 32p. (J). pap. 3.99 (978-0-8431-7670-4(9) , Price Stern Sloan) Penguin Group (USA) Inc.

—Mr. Happy & the Wizard. 2007. (Mr. Men & Little Miss Ser.). 32p. (J). (ps). pap. 3.99 (978-0-8431-2491-0(1) , Price Stern Sloan) Penguin Group (USA) Inc.

Harkness, Peter T. Andy the Acrobat: Out with the Greatest Show on Earth. 2007. 162p. pap. 11.99 (***978-1-4264-4077-9(4)***); 180p. pap. 14.99 (***978-1-4264-4136-3(3)***) BiblioBazaar.

Harkness, T. Peter. Andy the Acrobat or Out with the Greates. 2006. pap. 89.99 (***978-1-4280-0385-9(1)***) IndyPublish.com.

Harlin, Kathy. Maverick's Secret Treasure. 2005. 148p. pap. 19.95 (978-1-4137-7248-7(X)) PublishAmerica, Inc.

Harman, Chuck. Lost City. 2000. (Adventures of Artie the Airplane & His Friends Ser.). (Illus.). 40p. (J). (ps-6). pap. 6.95 (978-1-891736-10-0(8)) Studio Five/Fourteen.

—Trick or Treat. 2000. (Adventures of Artie the Airplane & His Friends Ser.). (Illus.). 32p. (J). (ps-6). pap. 6.95 (978-1-891736-09-4(4)) Studio Five/Fourteen.

Harmening, William M. The Misadventure of Salem Jack & Finnigan Reeves. 2000. 202p. (YA). pap. (978-0-9639377-1-1(5)) Big Rock Pr.

Harms, John, II. The Saving of Sly Manatee. Belizar, Denise H., ed. Makowski, Robin Lee, illus. 1998. 32p. (J). (gr. 2-5). 14.95 (978-0-9653871-3-2(5)) Frederick Pr.

Harp, O. J. Across Time: Love Eternal. 2002. pap. 19.95 (978-1-885778-97-0(X)) Seaburn Pubs.

Harper, Benjamin. Battling the Bad Guys: Storybook & Dvd. 2006. (Marvel Heroes Ser.). (Illus.). 32p. (J). bds. 17.99 (978-0-7944-1136-7(3)) Reader's Digest Assn., Inc., The.

—Marvel Swinging into Action. 2007. 10p. (J). bds. 14.99 (978-0-7944-1228-9(9)) Reader's Digest Assn., Inc., The.

Harper, Charise Mericle. Good Night, Leo: A Swashbuckling Bedtime Adventure. 2008. (Illus.). 24p. (J). (gr. k-k). bds. 6.99 (***978-0-375-84234-4(9)***, Robin Corey Bks.) Random Hse. Children's Bks.

Harper-Deiters, Cyndi. River Turtle. 2000. (Clara Browning Ser.: Bk. 1). 224p. (YA). pap. 8.95 (978-1-888831-00-9(6)) Country Home Pubs.

—Unnamed Warrior. 2000. (Clara Browning Ser.: Bk. 2). 224p. (J). pap. 8.95 (978-1-888831-03-0(0)) Country Home Pubs.

Harper, Max. The Mushpluk. 2002. (J). per. 12.95 (978-0-9717436-1-8(4)) James, Hugo Publishing.

Harperfestival. Hulk: The Junior Novel. 2003. (gr. 3-6). lib. bdg. 13.00 (978-0-613-83868-9(8)) Tandem Library Bks.

—Hulk: The Movie Storybook. 2003. (gr. 3-6). lib. bdg. 16.45 (978-0-613-83869-6(6)) Tandem Library Bks.

Harris, Ann Marie, ed. Short-Circuit Chef. 2006. (Teen Titans Ser.). 32p. (J). pap. 3.99 (978-0-439-78961-5(3)) Scholastic, Inc.

—Teen Titans: Calm Before the Storm. 2006. (Teen Titans Ser.). 48p. (J). pap. 3.99 (978-0-439-78962-2(1)) Scholastic, Inc.

—Teen Titans: How to Draw. 2006. (Teen Titans Ser.). 32p. (J). pap. 4.99 (978-0-439-78963-9(X)) Scholastic, Inc.

Harris, Christine. Undercover Girl #5: Twisted. 2007. 136p. (J). per. 10.95 (***978-1-59594-151-0(7)***, Wingspan Pr.) WingSpan Publishing.

Harris-Davies, Dafydd, et al. Caleb a Tyg. 2005. (WEL., Illus.). 23p. (978-0-86381-854-7(4)) Gwasg Carreg Gwalch.

Harris, Joan. Moving Day: An Alfie & Roxy Adventure. Santeramo, Rich, illus. 2007. 16p. (J). 12.95 (***978-0-9796994-9-8(5)***) TRIAD Publishing Group.

Harris, Joe. Narda. 2005. (J). (978-0-9772259-0-3(9)) Character Arts.

Harris, Mark. Dario Figg & the Phantom of Murk. 2001. 192p. pap. 13.95 (978-0-595-18933-5(4) , Writers Club Pr.) iUniverse, Inc.

Harris, Mark J. The Amazing Adventure in Tovia. 2001. 168p. pap. 12.95 (978-0-595-19230-4(0) , Writers Club Pr.) iUniverse, Inc.

Harris, Nelson. Andrew of the Antimites. 2006. 83p. pap. 14.95 (978 1 4241-3129-8(3)) PublishAmerica, Inc.

Harris, Peter. The Night Pirates. Allwright, Deborah, illus. 2006. 32p. (J). (ps-2). 16.99 (978-0-439-79959-1(7) , Scholastic Pr.) Scholastic, Inc.

Harris, Terry. The Lonliest Leprechaun. 2002. pap. 10.95 (978-0-7414-0930-0(5)) Infinity Publishing.

Harris, Tumeka. The Broken Law. Sea Breeze Productions & Phelps, Janice, eds. Miller, Linzi, illus. ed. 2006. 32p. (J). 14.95 (978-0-9769366-0-2(7)) Volare, LLC.

—The Goody Bag. Sea Breeze Productions, ed. Miller, Linzi, illus. 2006. 36p. (J). 14.95 (978-0-9769366-2-6(3)) Volare, LLC.

—Home Sweet Home. Sea Breeze Productions, ed. Miller, Linzi, illus. 2006. 36p. (J). 14.95 (978-0-9769366-3-3(1)) Volare, LLC.

—Trouble in Paradise. Sea Breeze Productions & Phelps, Janice, eds. Miller, Linzi, illus. 2006. 36p. (J). 14.95 (978-0-9769366-1-9(5)) Volare, LLC.

Harris, Whittney N., et al. Chocolate Covered Adventures: Tyco's Search for the Ark of the Covenant. 1999. (Illus.). 32p. (J). pap. 6.00 (978-0-9677469-4-4(9)) Van Buren California Publishing.

—Chocolate Covered Christmas. 1999. (Chocolate Covered Adventures Ser.). (Illus.). 40p. (J). pap. 6.00 (978-0-9677469-2-0(2)) Van Buren California Publishing.

Harrison, Charles C. Dick Turpin. 2003. (Historias de Siempre Ser.). (SPA., Illus.). 92p. (J). (gr. 5-8). pap. 12.95 (978-84-204-5701-7(9)) Santillana USA Publishing Co., Inc.

Harrison, Cora. The Viking at Drumshee. 2001. 128p. (J). pap. 7.95 (978-0-86327-788-7(8)) Interlink Publishing Group, Inc.

Harrison, Emma. Close Quarters: A Michael Vaughn Novel. 2003. (Alias Ser.). 192p. (YA). (gr. 7). mass mkt. 5.99 (978-0-553-49403-7(1) , Bantam Bks. for Young Readers) Random Hse. Children's Bks.

Harrison, F. Bayford. The Battlefield Treasure. 2004. reprint ed. pap. 15.95 (978-1-4191-5373-0(0)); pap. 1.99 (978-1-4192-5373-7(5)) Kessinger Publishing, LLC.

Harrison, J. The Adventurous Journey of Willowby Went. 2005. 350p. pap. 24.95 (978-1-4137-7249-4(8)) PublishAmerica, Inc.

Harrison, Michael. Facing the Dark. 1999. (Illus.). 128p. (J). (gr. 7-12). tchr. ed. 15.95 (978-0-8234-1491-8(4)) Holiday Hse., Inc.

Harriton, Maxine. A School Trip to the Fruit Planet, 1. l.t. ed. 2006. 34p. (J). (ps-1). lib. bdg. 18.95 (978-0-9787248-0-1(1) , 00-01-851-447X) UpTree Publishing.

Harry How Books. Just Luke. l.t. ed. 2006. (ENG., Illus.). 28p. per. 9.95 (***978-1-4327-0178-9(9)***) Outskirts Press, Inc.

Harshfield, James B. The Rock Street Five: The Mystery of the Computer Disks. 2000. 136p. (YA). pap. 9.95 (978-0-595-09688-6(3) , Writer's Showcase Pr.) iUniverse, Inc.

Hart, Anne. Four Astronauts & a Kitten. 2001. 144p. (J). pap. 11.95 (978-0-595-19202-1(5) , Authors Choice Pr.) iUniverse, Inc.

Harter, Debbie. De paseo por la selva (Walking through the Jungle) Ugalde, Raquel, tr. Harter, Debbie, illus. 2003. (SPA., Illus.). 32p. (J). 6.99 (978-1-84148-995-7(6)) Barefoot Bks., Inc.

Hartland, Patricia. The Adventures of Captain Love & Dr. Smart, Vol. 1. Foster, Rollen, ed. l.t. ed. 1998. (Illus.). 32p. (J). (ps up). pap. 8.95 (978-1-891806-01-8(7)) LittleKid Pr.

—Jungle Bungle Vol. 2: The Adventures of Captain Love & Dr. Smart. Foster, Rollen, ed. l.t. ed. 1998. (Illus.). 32p. (J). (ps up). pap. 8.95 (978-1-891806-02-5(5)) LittleKid Pr.

Hartley, Susan. Abby's Adventures: Abby the Pirate. Kane, Brenden, illus. 2005. 37p. pap. 17.95 (978-1-4137-4491-0(5)) PublishAmerica, Inc.

Hartry, Nancy & Kilby, Don. Hold on, McGinty! 1999. (Illus.). 32p. (J). pap. 6.95 (978-0-385-25710-7(4) , Doubleday Can) Doubleday Canada, Ltd. CAN. *Dist:* Random Hse., Inc.

Harvey, M. A. Attack of the Jaguar: Dare to Take the Test. 2004. (Illus.). 128p. (J). pap. (978-1-84458-051-4(2)) Chrysalis Children's Bks.

—The Scorpion Secret: Dare to Take the Test. 2004. (Illus.). 128p. (J). pap. (978-1-84458-050-7(4)) Chrysalis Children's Bks.

Harvie, Ronald Anthony. The Adventures of Peter Potato & Friends. 2005. (Illus.). 71p. (J). per. 15.95 (978-0-9771939-0-5(X) , 0002) New World Publishing.

Hassett, John & Hassett, Ann. Charles of the Wild. 2000. (Illus.). 32p. (J). (gr. k-3). pap. 5.95 (978-0-618-08222-3(0) , Walter Lorraine) Houghton Mifflin Co. Trade & Reference Div.

Hassinger, Peter W. The Book of Alfar: A Tale of the Hudson Highlands. 2002. (Illus.). 272p. (J). (gr. 4 up). 15.89 (978-0-06-028470-1(6) , Geringer, Laura Book) HarperCollins Pubs.

Haswell, Peter. Megamogs & the Dangerous Doughnut. 2000. (Illus.). 32p. (J). pap. 8.99 (978-0-09-953951-3(9) , Red Fox) Random Hse. Children's Bks. GBR. *Dist:* Trafalgar Square Publishing.

Hathaway, William. CD-Ring. 2006. 144p. (YA). (gr. 9-12). pap. (978-1-897073-29-2(1)) Lobster Pr.

Hathorn, Libby. The River. Wong, Stanley, illus. 2003. 40p. 28.95 (978-1-86366-516-2(1)) Curriculum Corporation AUS. *Dist:* Cheng & Tsui Co.

Hauser, Judy. The Legend of Punzel's Pond. 2005. (Illus.). 126p. (YA). per. 9.95 (978-0-9713603-0-3(8)) Fen's Rim.

Havel, Geoff. Babies Bite. 2004. (Illus.). 146p. (J). pap. 13.50 (978-1-920731-87-8(3)) Fremantle Pr. AUS. *Dist:* International Specialized Bk. Services.

Hawes, Charles Boardman. The Dark Frigate. unabr. ed. 2004. 246p. (J). (gr. 7 up). pap. 38.00 incl. audio (978-0-8072-0448-1(X) , Listening Library) Random Hse. Audio Publishing Group.

Hawking, Stephen & Hawking, Lucy. George's Secret Key to the Universe. Parsons, Gary, illus. 2007. 304p. (J). (gr. 3 up). 17.99 (***978-1-4169-5462-0(7)***) Simon & Schuster Children's Publishing.

Hawkins, Colin. Pirate Ship: A Pop-up Adventure. Hawkins, Colin et al, illus. 2006. 28p. (J). (gr. 4-8). reprint ed. 20.00 (978-0-7567-9827-7(2)) DIANE Publishing Co.

Hay, Louise L. & Olmos, Dan. The Adventures of Lulu. Smith-Moore, J. J., illus. 2005. 99p. pap. 12.95 (978-1-4019-0553-8(6)) Hay Hse., Inc.

Hay, Samantha. Hocus-Pocus Hound. Reed, Nathan, illus. 2006. (I Am Reading Ser.). 48p. (J). (gr. k-3). pap. 3.95 (978-0-7534-5957-7(4) , Kingfisher) Houghton Mifflin Co. Trade & Reference Div.

Hayes, Clyde & Jacobson, Pat. The Tunnels of Tecsuna. 2003. 122p. (J). pap. 9.95 (978-1-55517-739-3(5) , 1232038, Bonneville Bks.) Cedar Fort, Inc./CFI Distribution.

Hayes, James A., Jr. Up in the Air with the Flying Mingling Brothers. 2005. (J). 39.95 (978-0-9765720-0-8(1)) Hayes, Jamie Gallery, LLC.

Hayes, Ladene. The Continuing Saga of Rikki Tikki Tavi. 2007. 20p. (J). per. 10.99 (***978-1-59886-786-2(5)***) Tate Publishing & Enterprises, L.L.C.

Hayes, Malcolm. The Dreamcatchers. 2006. 282p. pap. (***978-1-4120-8320-1(6)***) Trafford Publishing.

Hayley, Barbara. Boot Camp. 2006. 128p. mass mkt. (978-1-84550-128-0(4)) Christian Focus Pubns.

Haynes, Cate. Groovy Granny. Tholen, Shane, illus. 2003. 32p. (J). pap. 13.50 (978-1-86368-332-6(1)) Fremantle Pr. AUS. *Dist:* International Specialized Bk. Services.

Hays, Steve. Beauty & the Boy: An Old Man's Story for a Dying Boy. 2006. (YA). 24.95 (978-0-9759902-1-6(7)) Before Christmas Pr.

Hazell, Mark. Miners of the Rainbow Stone (the Forest Children Series) 2006. 308p. pap. (***978-1-84401-625-9(0)***) Athena Pr.

Hazen, Lynn E. Mermaid Mary Margaret. 2004. (Illus.). 96p. (J). (gr. 2-5). 14.95 (978-1-58234-869-8(3) , Bloomsbury Children) Bloomsbury Publishing.

Healy, Sherry. Confident Child: A Tale & Affirmations to Build a Child's Self Esteem. 2002. 108p. (J). pap. 9.95 (978-0-595-22476-0(8) , Writers Club Pr.) iUniverse, Inc.

Heape, David. R. That's What Friends Do. l.t. ed. 2006. (ENG., Illus.). 28p. per. 9.95 (***978-1-4327-0177-2(0)***) Outskirts Press, Inc.

Hearn, Julie & Yankus, Marc. Sign of the Raven. 2005. (Illus.). 336p. (YA). 16.95 (978-0-689-85734-8(9) , Atheneum) Simon & Schuster Children's Publishing.

Hearn, Lian. Battle for Marnyama. 2006. (Brilliance of the Moon Ser.: Episode 1). (Illus.). 256p. (YA). (gr. 7). pap. 6.50 (978-0-14-240623-6(6) , Puffin) Penguin Group (USA) Inc.

—Leyendas de los Otori I. (SPA.). 312p. (J). (gr. 8-12). pap. 13.95 (978-956-239-300-3(3)) Santillana USA Publishing Co., Inc.

—Scars of Victory. 2006. (Brilliance of the Moon Ser.: Episode 2). (Illus.). 320p. (YA). (gr. 7). pap. 6.50 (978-0-14-240594-9(9) , Puffin) Penguin Group (USA) Inc.

Heath, Kathy. Camp Crazy Kids. 2006. 157p. pap. 19.95 (978-1-4241-0260-0(X)) PublishAmerica, Inc.

Heaton, Layce D. The Many Tracks of Lap'n Tap, 1. Heaton, Layce D., illus. 2006. (Illus.). 32p. (J). lib. bdg. 18.95 (978-0-9761128-3-9(3)) Hafabanana Pr.

Hébert, Marie-Francine & Germaine, Philippe. Un Cheval dans la Bataille. 2001. (Premier Roman Ser.). (FRE.). 64p. (J). (gr. 1-4). pap. (978-2-89021-433-0(8)) Diffusion du livre Mirabel.

Hebert, Pamela. Elliot Finley's Jus' Plain Ole Daisy. 2005. pap. 14.95 (978-0-9767696-0-6(3)) Oak Court Pr.

Hecker, Howard. Mike McGill, Pirate. Falkey, Mark, illus. 2000. 240p. (YA). (gr. 6-11). pap. 5.99 (978-0-9676870-3-2(9)) Chesire Pr.

Hedderwick, Mairi. Katie Morag's Island World: Four More of Your Favourite Katie Morag Adventures. 2004. (Illus.). 112p. (J). pap. 14.99 (978-0-09-943303-3(6) , Red Fox) Random Hse. Children's Bks. GBR. *Dist:* Trafalgar Square Publishing.

Heddle, Rebecca. Puzzle Journey through Time. Spenceley, Annabel, illus. 2003. 32p. (J). pap. 6.95 (978-0-7945-0440-3(X) , Usborne) EDC Publishing.
Hees, Miriam. The Adventures of Jilly & Brad: Noises in the Attic. Kinneman, D. Michael, illus. 2003. 128p. (J). pap. 5.95 (978-0-9718348-4-2(9)) Blooming Tree Pr.
Heide, Florence Parry. The Shrinking of Treehorn. 60p. (J). (gr. 1-3). pap. 6.95 (978-0-8072-1327-8(6) , Listening Library) Random Hse. Audio Publishing Group.
Heil, Christopher. Wish Rings: A Second Beginning. 2003. 196p. pap. 14.95 (978-0-595-29582-1(7)) iUniverse, Inc.
Heimerdinger, Chris. Daniel & Nephi. 2004. pap. 13.95 (978-1-57734-821-4(4)) Covenant Communications, Inc.
Hein, Connie L. Toliver in Time; for a Journey West: History in a Nutshell. Theobald, Denise, illus. l.t. ed. 2005. 28p. (J). lib. bdg. 17.95 (978-0-9740855-6-2(1)); per. 9.95 (978-0-9740855-7-9(X)) Still Water Publishing.
Heinlein, Robert A. Sixth Column. lib. bdg. 22.95 (978-0-8488-1982-8(9)) Amereon LTD.
Heintze, Ty. Lios. Heintze, Ty, illus. 1998. (Illus.). (YA). (gr. 3-11). pap. 9.95 (978-0-9665317-0-1(1)) Bateman Pr.
Heinz, Brian J. Butternut Hollow Pond. Marstall, Bob, illus. 2000. 32p. (gr. 2-6). lib. bdg. 22.90 (978-0-7613-0268-1(9) , Millbrook Pr.) Lerner Publishing Group.
The Heir of King Meldh: Book One of the Geometry of Power. 2004. (YA). per. 10.95 (978-0-9747441-0-0(7)) Brainerd Enterprises.
Heisler, Edith. Mystery at the Old Estate. 2002. 129p. pap. 17.95 (978-1-59129-275-3(1)) PublishAmerica, Inc.
Helakoski, Leslie. Woolbur. Harper, Lee, illus. 2008. 32p. (J). 17.89 (*978-0-06-084727-2(1)) HarperCollins Pubs.
Heller, Andrew. A Fine Mess. 2003. (J). 7.99 (978-0-9722038-6-9(9)) Mr Do It All, Inc.
Heller, Sarah E. & Cristaldi, Kathryn. Around the World in Tweety Time: Tattoo Storybook. Batcheller, Keith, illus. 2000. 24p. (J). (ps-3). pap. 5.99 (978-0-439-20282-4(5)) Scholastic, Inc.
—Tweety's High Flying Adventures. Summers, Ethan, illus. 2000. 32p. (J). (ps-3). pap. 3.50 (978-0-439-20281-7(7)) Scholastic, Inc.
Hempel, Linda K. Have Fries - Will Travel! The Adventures of a Veggie-Powered Car & an Eco-Rap Star. Dotson, Kathy, illus. 2005. 72p. (J). (ps-7). (978-0-86571-549-3(1)) New Society Pubs., Ltd.
Hemphill, Rick, illus. The Adventures of Kirra & Rincon: Li'l Kids, Big Waves. 2005. 32p. (J). 17.99 (978-0-9766408-0-6(5)) Kerr, Justin & Shelley.
Hemyng, Bracebridge. Jack Harkaway & His Son's Escape from the Brigands of Greece. 2004. reprint ed. pap. 37.95 (978-1-4191-2705-2(5)) Kessinger Publishing, LLC.
Henderson, Dianne. The Frightening Old Mansion. 2006. 116p. pap. 16.95 (978-1-4241-2486-2(7)) PublishAmerica, Inc.
Hendley, Jeff. Stump. Hendley, Tess, illus. 2007. (J). pap. (*978-0-9762014-7-2(X)) L'Edge Pr.
Hendrickson, Jean A. Tales of the Sea Patrol. 2001. (Angell Ser.). (Illus.). 32p. (J). (gr. k up). pap. (978-1-929953-03-5(8)) Gates & Bridges Inc.
Hendry, Diana. You Can't Kiss It Better. l.t. ed. 2005. (Illus.). 232p. (J). pap. incl. audio (978-0-7540-7872-2(8) , CLP 453) BBC Audio.
Hendry, Frances. Quest for a Queen: The Lark. 2006. pap. (*978-1-905665-04-4(0)) Pollinger In Print.
Heneghan, James. Safe House. 2006. 176p. (J). pap. 7.95 (978-1-55143-640-1(X)) Orca Bk. Pubs. USA.
Heneghan, James & McBay, Bruce. The Nannycatch Chronicles. Valerio, Geraldo, illus. 2006. 96p. (J). (978-1-896580-56-2(4)) Tradewind Bks.
Henighan, Tom. Viking Quest. 2005. 120p. (YA). pap., tchr. ed. (978-0-88878-421-6(X) , Sandcastle Bks.) Dundurn Group, The.
Henkes, Kevin. Lilly's Big Day Standee. 2006. (J). (978-0-06-087311-0(6)) HarperCollins Pubs.
Henley, Christian A. Adventures with Norky: Teamwork. 2005. (J). pap. 7.99 (978-0-9744178-2-0(3)) Daughters Arise, LLC.
Henley, Karyn. Twigs Has an Adventure. 2000. (Tails Ser.). (Illus.). 28p. (J). (ps-5). 9.99 (978-0-8054-2284-9(6)) B&H Publishing Grp.
Hennelly, Nilsson. Rafters. 1998. (Rafters Ser.: Vol. 1). (Illus.). 120p. (J). (gr. 3-8). pap. 5.95 (978-1-56565-947-6(3) , 09473W, Roxbury Park Juvenile) Lowell Hse. Juvenile.
Henny, Rose. Teddy Finds His Way: A Teddy Tale. Henny, Rose, illus. l.t. ed. 2005. (Illus.). 22p. (J). per. 12.95 (978-0-9705458-7-9(8)) Royalty Bks. International.
Henry, Heather French. Claire's Magic Shoes. Henry, Heather French, illus. 2004. (Claire's Everyday Adventures Ser.). (Illus.). 32p. (gr. k-4). 15.95 (978-0-9706341-3-9(7) , 1231609) Cubbie Blue Publishing.
Henry, Patrick. The Spectacular Adventures of John Cross. 2005. (J). per. 8.99 (978-0-9773990-1-7(X)) Mother's Hse. Publishing.
Henry, T. K. Rickey & Rachel, the Cats without Tails & Their Awesome Adventure. 2007. 40p. (J). pap. 8.00 (*978-0-8059-7224-5(2)) Dorrance Publishing Co., Inc.
Henty, A. G. Under Drakes Flag A Tale of the Spanish. 2007. 97.99 (*978-1-4280-5259-8(3)); pap. 91.99 (*978-1-4280-5245-1(3)) IndyPublish.com.
Henty, G. A. Bravest of the Brave. 2006. pap. (*978-1-4068-1274-9(9)) Echo Library.
—The Cat of Bubastes: A Tale of Ancient Egypt. 2002. 370p. 29.95 (978-1-59087-113-3(8) , GAH113); per. 19.95 (978-1-59087-112-6(X) , GAH112) Althouse Pr.
—The Cat of Bubastes: A Tale of Ancient Egypt. 2002. 320p. (J). (gr. 4-7). pap. 6.95 (978-0-486-42363-0(8)) Dover Pubns., Inc.
—The Cat of Bubastes: A Tale of Ancient Egypt. 2006. (ENG.). pap. 33.95 (*978-1-4286-0382-0(4)) Kessinger Publishing, LLC.
—The Cat of Bubastes: A Tale of Ancient Egypt. collector's ed. 2002. (Illus.). im. lthr. 38.85 (978-1-4115-1348-8(7)); pap. 19.95 (978-1-4115-0588-9(3)); 25.95 (978-1-4115-0918-4(8)); pap. 17.95 (978-1-4115-0097-6(0)) Polyglot Pr., Inc.
—The Cat of Bubastes: A Tale of Ancient Egypt. 2000. 294p. (YA). 7.99 (978-1-887159-68-5(1)) Preston-Speed Pubns.
—The Cat of Bubastes: A Tale of Ancient Egypt. Preston Speed Publications Staff, ed. Weguelin, J. R., illus. 1998. 339p. (YA). pap. 14.99 (978-1-887159-23-4(1)) Preston-Speed Pubns.
—The Cat of Bubastes: A Tale of Ancient Egypt. 1998. (Illus.). 339p. (J). lib. bdg. 20.99 (978-1-887159-16-6(9)) Preston-Speed Pubns.
—In Freedom's Cause: A Story of Wallace & Bruce. 2004. reprint ed. pap. 1.99 (978-1-4192-2572-7(3)) Kessinger Publishing, LLC.
—In the Heart of the Rockies. 2002. 370p. 29.95 (978-1-59087-073-0(5) , GAH073); per. 19.95 (978-1-59087-072-3(7) , GAH072) Althouse Pr.
—In the Heart of the Rockies. l.t. ed. 2006. 322p. pap. 17.99 (978-1-4264-3253-8(4)) BiblioBazaar.
—In the Heart of the Rockies. 2005. 304p. (gr. 3-7). pap. 6.95 (978-0-486-44214-3(4)) Dover Pubns., Inc.
—In the Heart of the Rockies. 2003. (ENG.). pap. 15.99 (*978-1-4142-0081-1(1)) IndyPublish.com.
—In the Heart of the Rockies. 2004. reprint ed. pap. 27.95 (978-1-4191-2600-0(8)); pap. 1.99 (978-1-4192-2600-7(2)) Kessinger Publishing, LLC.
—In the Heart of the Rockies. Hindley, G. C.., illus. 1998. 388p. (YA). (gr. 8-12). reprint ed. per. 16.95 (978-1-890623-08-1(3)) Lost Classics Bk. Co.
—In the Heart of the Rockies. collector's ed. 2002. (Illus.). im. lthr. 38.85 (978-1-4115-1341-9(X)); pap. 19.95 (978-1-4115-0577-3(8)); 25.95 (978-1-4115-0949-8(8)); pap. 17.95 (978-1-4115-0174-4(8)) Polyglot Pr., Inc.
—A Knight of the White Cross: A Tale of the Siege of Rhodes. Peacock, Ralph & Fitterling, Michael A., illus. 1999. 487p. (J). (gr. 4-7). reprint ed. per. 16.95 (978-1-890623-06-7(7)) Lost Classics Bk. Co.
—A Knight of the White Cross: A Tale of the Siege of Rhodes. Preston Speed Publications Staff, ed. Peacock, Ralph, illus. 1999. 336p. (YA). 21.99 (978-1-887159-24-1(X)) Preston-Speed Pubns.
—A March on London: A Story of Wat Tyler's Insurrection. l.t. ed. 2005. 596p. pap. (978-1-84637-209-4(7)) Echo Library.
—A March on London: A Story of Wat Tyler's Insurrection. (ENG.). 2004. 98.99 (*978-1-4142-1634-8(3)); 2003. 272p. pap. 14.99 (*978-1-4043-8185-8(6)) IndyPublish.com.
—A March on London: A Story of Wat Tyler's Insurrection. 2004. reprint ed. pap. 27.95 (978-1-4191-0224-0(9)); pap. 1.99 (978-1-4192-0224-7(3)) Kessinger Publishing, LLC.
—The Stone Chest or the Secret of Cedar Island. 2004. reprint ed. pap. 15.95 (978-1-4191-8354-6(0)); pap. 1.99 (978-1-4192-8354-3(5)) Kessinger Publishing, LLC.
—Under Drake's Flag: A Tale of the Spanish Main. Brown, Gordon, illus. 2005. 304p. (J). pap. 6.95 (978-0-486-44215-0(2)) Dover Pubns., Inc.
Henty, G. A. & Fitterling, Michael A. For the Temple: A Tale of the Fall of Jerusalem. Fitterling, Michael A. & Solomon, Solomon J., illus. 1999. 403p. (J). (gr. 4-7). reprint ed. per. 16.95 (978-1-890623-07-4(5)) Lost Classics Bk. Co.
Hepworth, David G. The Picture Stone. 2006. (Illus.). 76p. pap. (*978-1-4120-9053-7(9)) Trafford Publishing.
Herbel, K.C. With a Jester of Kindness Book One: The Jester King. 2004. 400p. pap. 17.95 net. (978-1-59113-551-7(6)) Booklocker.com, Inc.
Herbert Hilligan & His Magical Adventure Curriculum Guide. 2004. ring bd. 24.95 (978-0-9743335-4-0(9)) Imaginative Publishing, Ltd.
Herbert Hilligan's Lone Star Adventure Curriculum Guide. 2004. ring bd. 24.95 (978-0-9743335-7-1(3)) Imaginative Publishing, Ltd.
Herbert Hilligan's Prehistoric Adventure Curriculum Guide. 2004. ring bd. 24.95 (978-0-9743335-5-7(7)) Imaginative Publishing, Ltd.
Herbert Hilligan's Tropical Adventure Curriculum Guide. 2004. ring bd. 24.95 (978-0-9743335-6-4(5)) Imaginative Publishing, Ltd.
Hereford, L. F. Gerry the Grape. Skardarasy, Doreen L., illus. 2005. (J). pap. (978-0-9728969-9-3(6)) Acorn Publishing.
Hergé. The Adventures of Tintin in the Congo: Reporter for Le Petit Vingtieme. 2004. (Adventures of Tintin Ser.). (Illus.). 120p. (J). 24.95 (978-0-86719-902-4(4)) Last Gasp of San Francisco.
—L' Affaire Tournesol. 1999. (Tintin Ser.).Tr. of Calculus Affair. (FRE.). (J). (gr. 4-7). 21.95 (978-2-203-00117-6(8)) Casterman, Editions FRA. Dist: Distribooks, Inc.
—Der Arumbaya-Fetisch. (GER., Illus.). 62p. (J). pap. 19.95 (978-0-8288-5008-7(9)) French & European Pubns., Inc.
—El Asunto Tornasol. (SPA., Illus.). 62p. (J). 19.95 (978-0-8288-5009-4(7)) French & European Pubns., Inc.
—El Asunto Tornasol. (Tintin Ser.). (SPA.). (J). pap. 14.95 (978-84-261-1413-6(X)) Juventud, Editorial ESP. Dist: Distribooks, Inc.
—Aterrizaje en la Luna. (SPA., Illus.). 62p. (J). 19.95 (978-0-8288-5010-0(0)) French & European Pubns., Inc.
—Les Bijoux de la Castafiore. 1999. (Tintin Ser.).Tr. of Castafiore Emerald. (FRE.). (J). (gr. 4-7). 21.95 (978-2-203-00120-6(8)) Casterman, Editions FRA. Dist: Distribooks, Inc.
—The Black Island. (Illus.). 62p. (J). 19.95 (978-0-8288-5012-4(7)) French & European Pubns., Inc.
—Der Blaue Lotos. (GER., Illus.). 62p. (J). pap. 19.95 (978-0-8288-5013-1(5)) French & European Pubns., Inc.
—The Blue Lotus. (Illus.). (J). 19.95 (978-0-8288-5480-1(7)) French & European Pubns., Inc.
—The Broken Ear. (Illus.). 62p. (J). 24.95 (978-0-8288-5086-5(0)) French & European Pubns., Inc.
—The Calculus Affair. (Illus.). 62p. (J). 19.95 (978-0-8288-5014-8(3)) French & European Pubns., Inc.
—El Cangrejo Pinzas Oro. (SPA., Illus.). 62p. (J). 19.95 (978-0-8288-5015-5(1)) French & European Pubns., Inc.
—The Castafiore Emerald. (Illus.). 62p. (J). 19.95 (978-0-8288-5016-2(X)) French & European Pubns., Inc.
—El Cetro de Ottokar. (SPA., Illus.). 62p. (J). 19.95 (978-0-8288-5017-9(8)) French & European Pubns., Inc.
—El Cetro de Ottokar. (Tintin Ser.). (SPA.). 64p. (J). 14.95 (978-84-261-1415-0(6)) Juventud, Editorial ESP. Dist: Distribooks, Inc.
—Les Cigares du Pharaon. 1999. (Tintin Ser.).Tr. of Cigars of the Pharaoh. (FRE., Illus.). 62p. (J). (gr. 4-7). 21.95 (978-2-203-00103-9(8)) Casterman, Editions FRA. Dist: Distribooks, Inc.
—Les Cigares du Pharaon.Tr. of Cigars of the Pharaoh. (FRE., Illus.). 62p. (J). 19.95 (978-0-8288-5020-9(8)) French & European Pubns., Inc.
—Los Cigarros del Faraon. (SPA., Illus.). 62p. (J). 19.95 (978-0-8288-5019-3(4)) French & European Pubns., Inc.
—Los Cigarros del Faraon. (Tintin Ser.). (SPA.). 46p. (J). 14.95 (978-84-261-1406-8(7)) Juventud, Editorial ESP. Dist: Distribooks, Inc.
—Cigars of the Pharaoh.Tr. of Cigares du Pharoan. (Illus.). 62p. (J). 19.95 (978-0-8288-5021-6(6)) French & European Pubns., Inc.
—Coke en Stock. 1999. (Tintin Ser.). (FRE., Illus.). 62p. (J). (gr. 4-7). 21.95 (978-2-203-00118-3(6)) Casterman, Editions FRA. Dist: Distribooks, Inc.
—The Crab with the Golden Claws. (Illus.). 62p. (J). (gr. 3-8). 19.95 (978-0-8288-5023-0(2)) French & European Pubns., Inc.
—Le Crabe aux Pinces d'Or. 1999. (Tintin Ser.).Tr. of Crab with the Golden Claws. (FRE.). (J). (gr. 4-7). 21.95 (978-2-203-00108-4(9)) Casterman, Editions FRA. Dist: Distribooks, Inc.
—Le Crabe aux Pinces d'Or.Tr. of Crab with the Golden Claws. (FRE., Illus.). (J). (gr. 7-9). ring bd. 19.95 (978-0-8288-5025-4(9)) French & European Pubns., Inc.
—Destination Moon.Tr. of Objectif Lune. (J). (gr. 3-8). ring bd. 19.95 (978-0-8288-5026-1(7)); (Illus.). 62p. 19.95 (978-0-8288-5027-8(5)) French & European Pubns., Inc.
—Il Drago Blu. (ITA., Illus.). 62p. (J). pap. 19.95 (978-0-8288-5028-5(3)) French & European Pubns., Inc.
—La Estrella Misteriosa. (SPA., Illus.). 62p. (J). 19.95 (978-0-8288-5029-2(1)) French & European Pubns., Inc.
—La Estrella Misteriosa. (Tintin Ser.). (SPA.). 64p. (J). 14.95 (978-84-261-1416-7(4)) Juventud, Editorial ESP. Dist: Distribooks, Inc.
—L' Etoile Mysterieuse. 1999. (Tintin Ser.).Tr. of Mysterious Star. (FRE., Illus.). 62p. (J). (gr. 4-7). pap. 21.95 (978-2-203-00109-1(7)) Casterman, Editions FRA. Dist: Distribooks, Inc.
—Explorers of the Moon. (Illus.). 62p. (J). 19.95 (978-0-8288-5031-5(3)) French & European Pubns., Inc.
—Der Fall Bienlein. (GER., Illus.). 62p. (J). pap. 19.95 (978-0-8288-5033-9(X)) French & European Pubns., Inc.
—Flight 714. (Illus.). 62p. (J). 19.95 (978-0-8288-5034-6(8)) French & European Pubns., Inc.
—Flug 714 nach Sydney. (GER., Illus.). 62p. (J). pap. 19.95 (978-0-8288-5035-3(6)) French & European Pubns., Inc.
—Das Geheimnis der "Einhorn" (GER., Illus.). 62p. (J). pap. 19.95 (978-0-8288-5036-0(4)) French & European Pubns., Inc.
—Der Geheimnisvolle Stern. (GER., Illus.). 62p. (J). pap. 19.95 (978-0-8288-5037-7(2)) French & European Pubns., Inc.
—Il Granchio d'Oro. (ITA., Illus.). 62p. (J). pap. 19.95 (978-0-8288-5038-4(0)) French & European Pubns., Inc.
—L' Ile Noire. 1999. (Tintin Ser.).Tr. of Black Island. (FRE., Illus.). (J). (gr. 4-7). pap. 21.95 (978-2-203-00106-0(2)) Casterman, Editions FRA. Dist: Distribooks, Inc.
—L' Ile Noire.Tr. of Black Island. (FRE., Illus.). (J). (gr. 7-9). ring bd. 19.95 (978-0-8288-5039-1(9)) French & European Pubns., Inc.
—Im Reiche des Schwarzen Goldes. (GER., Illus.). 62p. (J). pap. 19.95 (978-0-8288-5040-7(2)) French & European Pubns., Inc.
—La Isla Negra. (SPA., Illus.). 62p. (J). 19.95 (978-0-8288-5041-4(0)) French & European Pubns., Inc.
—La Isla Negra. (Tintin Ser.). (SPA.). 64p. (J). 14.95 (978-84-261-1417-4(2)) Juventud, Editorial ESP. Dist: Distribooks, Inc.
—Las Joyas de la Castafiore. (SPA., Illus.). 62p. (J). 19.95 (978-0-8288-5042-1(9)) French & European Pubns., Inc.
—Las Joyas de la Castafiore. (Tintin Ser.). (SPA.). 64p. (J). 14.95 (978-84-261-1421-1(0)) Juventud, Editorial ESP. Dist: Distribooks, Inc.
—Die Juwelen der Sangerin. (GER., Illus.). 62p. (J). pap. 19.95 (978-0-8288-5043-8(7)) French & European Pubns., Inc.
—King Ottokars Sceptre. Orig. Title: Sceptre d'Ottokar. (Illus.). 62p. (J). 19.95 (978-0-8288-5044-5(5)) French & European Pubns., Inc.
—Kohle an Bord. (GER., Illus.). 62p. (J). pap. 19.95 (978-0-8288-5045-2(3)) French & European Pubns., Inc.
—Konig Ottokar's Zepter. (GER., Illus.). 62p. (J). pap. 19.95 (978-0-8288-5046-9(1)) French & European Pubns., Inc.
—Die Krabbe mit den Goldenen Scheren. (GER., Illus.). 62p. (J). pap. 19.95 (978-0-8288-5047-6(X)) French & European Pubns., Inc.
—Land of Black Gold. Orig. Title: Tintin au Pays de l'Or Noir. (Illus.). 62p. (J). 19.95 (978-0-8288-5048-3(8)) French & European Pubns., Inc.
—Lo Scettro di Ottokar. (ITA., Illus.). 62p. (J). pap. 19.95 (978-0-8288-5061-2(5)) French & European Pubns., Inc.
—El Loto Azul.Tr. of Blue Lotus. (SPA., Illus.). 62p. (J). 19.95 (978-0-8288-5049-0(6)) French & European Pubns., Inc.
—El Loto Azul. (Tintin Ser.).Tr. of Blue Lotus. (SPA.). 64p. (J). 14.95 (978-84-261-1418-1(0)) Juventud, Editorial ESP. Dist: Distribooks, Inc.
—Le Lotus Bleu. 1999. (Tintin Ser.).Tr. of Blue Lotus. (FRE.). (J). (gr. 4-7). 21.95 (978-2-203-00104-6(6)) Casterman, Editions FRA. Dist: Distribooks, Inc.
—Le Lotus Bleu.Tr. of Blue Lotus. (FRE.). (J). (gr. 2-9). 19.95 (978-0-8288-5050-6(X)) French & European Pubns., Inc.
—Objectif Lune. 1999. (Tintin Ser.).Tr. of Destination Moon. (FRE., Illus.). 62p. (J). (gr. 4-7). 21.95 (978-2-203-00115-2(1)) Casterman, Editions FRA. Dist: Distribooks, Inc.
—Objectif Lune.Tr. of Destination Moon. (FRE., Illus.). (J). (gr. 7-9). ring bd. 19.95 (978-0-8288-5051-3(8)) French & European Pubns., Inc.
—Objetivo la Luna. (SPA., Illus.). 62p. (J). 19.95 (978-0-8288-5052-0(6)) French & European Pubns., Inc.
—Objetivo la Luna. (Tintin Ser.). (SPA.). 64p. (J). 14.95 (978-84-261-1419-8(9)) Juventud, Editorial ESP. Dist: Distribooks, Inc.
—On a Marche sur la Lune. (Tintin Ser.).Tr. of Explorers on the Moon. (FRE.). (J). pap. 21.95 (978-2-203-00116-9(X)) Casterman, Editions FRA. Dist: Distribooks, Inc.
—On a Marche sur la Lune.Tr. of Explorers on the Moon. (FRE., Illus.). (J). (gr. 7-9). ring bd. 19.95 (978-0-8288-5053-7(4)) French & European Pubns., Inc.
—L' Oreille Cassee.Tr. of Broken Ear. (FRE., Illus.). 62p. (J). 19.95 (978-0-8288-5054-4(2)) French & European Pubns., Inc.
—La Oreja Rota. (SPA., Illus.). 62p. (J). 19.95 (978-0-8288-5055-1(0)) French & European Pubns., Inc.
—La Oreja Rota. (Tintin Ser.). (SPA.). 64p. (J). 14.95 (978-84-261-1424-2(5)) Juventud, Editorial ESP. Dist: Distribooks, Inc.
—Prisoners of the Sun. (Illus.). 62p. (J). 24.95 (978-0-8288-5056-8(9)) French & European Pubns., Inc.
—Red Rackham's Treasure. Orig. Title: Tresor de Rackham le Rouge. (Illus.). 62p. (J). 24.95 (978-0-8288-5057-5(7)) French & European Pubns., Inc.
—The Red Sea Sharks. (Illus.). (J). (gr. 3-8). 24.95 (978-0-8288-5058-2(5)) French & European Pubns., Inc.
—Reiseziel Mond. (GER., Illus.). 62p. (J). pap. 24.95 (978-0-8288-5059-9(3)) French & European Pubns., Inc.
—Le Sceptre d' Ottokar.Tr. of King Ottokar's Sceptre. (FRE., Illus.). (J). (gr. 7-9). ring bd. 24.95 (978-0-8288-5060-5(7)) French & European Pubns., Inc.
—Le Sceptre d'Ottokar. 1999. (Tintin Ser.).Tr. of King Ottokar's Sceptre. (FRE., Illus.). (J). (gr. 4-7). 21.95 (978-2-203-00107-7(0)) Casterman, Editions FRA. Dist: Distribooks, Inc.
—Der Schatz Rackhams des Roten. (GER., Illus.). 62p. (J). pap. 24.95 (978-0-8288-5062-9(3)) French & European Pubns., Inc.
—Schritte auf dem Mond. (GER., Illus.). 62p. (J). pap. 24.95 (978-0-8288-5063-6(1)) French & European Pubns., Inc.
—Die Schwarze Insel. (GER., Illus.). 62p. (J). pap. 24.95 (978-0-8288-5064-3(X)) French & European Pubns., Inc.
—Secret de la Licorne.Tr. of Secret of the Unicorn. (FRE., Illus.). (J). (gr. 7-9). 24.95 (978-0-8288-5065-0(8)) French & European Pubns., Inc.
—La Secret de la Licorne. 1999. (Tintin Ser.).Tr. of Secret of the Unicorn. (FRE., Illus.). (J). (gr. 4-7). 21.95 (978-2-203-00110-7(0)) Casterman, Editions FRA. Dist: Distribooks, Inc.
—The Secret of the Unicorn. Orig. Title: Secret de la Licorne. (Illus.). 62p. (J). 24.95 (978-0-8288-5066-7(6)) French & European Pubns., Inc.
—El Secreto del Unicornio. (SPA., Illus.). 62p. (J). 24.95 (978-0-8288-5067-4(4)) French & European Pubns., Inc.
—El Secreto del Unicornio. (Tintin Ser.). (SPA.). 64p. (J). 14.95 (978 84-261-1420-4(2)) Juventud, Editorial ESP. Dist: Distribooks, Inc.
—Il Segreto del Liocorno. (ITA., Illus.). 62p. (J). pap. 24.95 (978-0-8288-5068-1(2)) French & European Pubns., Inc.
—Sept Boules de Cristal. (FRE., Illus.). (J). (gr. 7-9). 24.95 (978-0-8288-5069-8(0)) French & European Pubns., Inc.
—Les Sept Boules de Cristal. 1999. (Tintin Ser.). (FRE., Illus.). (J). (gr. 4-7). 21.95 (978-2-203-00112-1(7)) Casterman, Editions FRA. Dist: Distribooks, Inc.
—Le Sette Sfere di Cristallo. (ITA., Illus.). 62p. (J). pap. 24.95 (978-0-8288-5070-4(4)) French & European Pubns., Inc.
—The Seven Crystal Balls. (Illus.). 62p. (J). (gr. 3-8). 24.95 (978-0-8288-5071-1(2)) French & European Pubns., Inc.
—The Shooting Star. (Illus.). (J). (gr. 3-8). ring bd. 24.95 (978-0-8288-5073-5(9)) French & European Pubns., Inc.
—Die Sieben Kristallkugeln. (GER., Illus.). 62p. (J). pap. 24.95 (978-0-8288-5072-8(0)) French & European Pubns., Inc.
—Las Siete Bolas de Cristal. (SPA., Illus.). 62p. (J). 24.95 (978-0-8288-5074-2(7)) French & European Pubns., Inc.
—Las Siete Bolas de Cristal. (Tintin Ser.). (SPA.). 64p. (J). 14.95 (978-84-261-1423-5(7)) Juventud, Editorial ESP. Dist: Distribooks, Inc.
—I Sigari del Faraone. (ITA., Illus.). 62p. (J). pap. 24.95 (978-0-8288-5075-9(5)) French & European Pubns., Inc.
—Der Sonnentempel. (GER., Illus.). 62p. (J). pap. 24.95 (978-0-8288-5076-6(3)) French & European Pubns., Inc.
—Stock de Coque. (FRE., Illus.). 62p. (J). 24.95 (978-0-8288-5077-3(1)) French & European Pubns., Inc.
—Stock de Coque. (Tintin Ser.). (FRE & SPA.). (J). pap. 14.95 (978-84-261-1422-8(9)) Juventud, Editorial ESP. Dist: Distribooks, Inc.
—Temple du Soleil. (FRE., Illus.). (J). (gr. 7-9). 24.95 (978-0-8288-5078-0(X)) French & European Pubns., Inc.

A
B

—Le Temple du Soleil. 1999. (Tintin Ser.). (FRE.). (J). (gr. 4-7). 21.95 (978-2-203-00113-8(5)) Casterman, Editions FRA. *Dist:* Distribooks, Inc.

—El Templo del Sol. (SPA., Illus.). 62p. (J). 24.95 (978-0-8288-5079-7(8)) French & European Pubns., Inc.

—El Templo del Sol. (Tintin Ser.). (SPA.). 64p. (J). 14.95 (978-84-261-1405-1(9)) Juventud, Editorial ESP. *Dist:* Distribooks, Inc.

—Il Templo del Sol. (ITA., Illus.). 62p. (J). pap. 24.95 (978-0-8288-5080-3(1)) French & European Pubns., Inc.

—El Tesoro de Rackham el Rojo. (SPA., Illus.). 62p. (J). 24.95 (978-0-8288-5081-0(X)) French & European Pubns., Inc.

—El Tesoro de Rackham el Rojo. (Tintin Ser.). (SPA.). 4p. (J). 14.95 (978-84-261-1399-3(0)) Juventud, Editorial ESP. *Dist:* Distribooks, Inc.

—Il Tesoro di Rakam. (ITA., Illus.). 62p. (J). pap. 24.95 (978-0-8288-5082-7(8)) French & European Pubns., Inc.

—Tim in Tibet. (GER., Illus.). 62p. (J). pap. 24.95 (978-0-8288-5083-4(6)) French & European Pubns., Inc.

—Tim und der Haifschsee. (GER., Illus.). 62p. (J). pap. 24.95 (978-0-8288-5084-1(4)) French & European Pubns., Inc.

—Tim und die Picaros. (GER., Illus.). 62p. (J). pap. 24.95 (978-0-8288-5085-8(2)) French & European Pubns., Inc.

—Tintín: El cangrejo de las pinzas de Oro. 2007. (SPA., Illus.). 64p. reprint ed. 22.95 ***(*978-1-59497-346-8(6))*** Public Square Bks.

—Tintín: El cetro de Ottokar. 2007. (SPA., Illus.). 64p. reprint ed. 22.95 ***(*978-1-59497-345-1(8))*** Public Square Bks.

—Tintín: La isla Negra. 2007. (SPA., Illus.). 64p. reprint ed. 22.95 ***(*978-1-59497-344-4(X))*** Public Square Bks.

—Tintin & the Golden Fleece. (J). (gr. 3-8). 24.95 (978-0-8288-5087-2(9)) French & European Pubns., Inc.

—Tintin & the Lake of Sharks. (Illus.). 62p. (J). 24.95 (978-0-416-78950-8(1)) French & European Pubns., Inc.

—Tintin & the Picaros. Orig. Title: Tintin et les Picaros. (Illus.). 62p. (J). 24.95 (978-0-8288-5089-6(5)) French & European Pubns., Inc.

—Tintin au Congo. 1999. (Tintin Ser.). (FRE., Illus.). 62p. (J). (gr. 4-7). 21.95 (978-2-203-00101-5(1)) Casterman, Editions FRA. *Dist:* Distribooks, Inc.

—Tintin au Congo. (FRE., Illus.). (J). (gr. 7-9). 24.95 (978-0-8288-5090-2(9)) French & European Pubns., Inc.

—Tintin au Pays de l'Or Noir. 1999. (Tintin Ser.).Tr. of Land of Black Gold. (FRE., Illus.). 62p. (J). (gr. 4-7). 21.95 (978-2-203-00114-5(3)) Casterman, Editions FRA. *Dist:* Distribooks, Inc.

—Tintin au Pays de l'Or Noir.Tr. of Land of Black Gold. (FRE.). (J). (gr. 7-9). 24.95 (978-0-8288-5091-9(7)) French & European Pubns., Inc.

—Tintin au Pays des Soviets. 1999. (Tintin Ser.). (FRE.). (J). (gr. 4-7). pap. 29.95 (978-2-203-01101-4(7)) Casterman, Editions FRA. *Dist:* Distribooks, Inc.

—Tintin au Tibet. 1999. (Tintin Ser.).Tr. of Tintin in Tibet. (FRE.). (J). (gr. 4-7). pap. 21.95 (978-2-203-00119-0(4)) Casterman, Editions FRA. *Dist:* Distribooks, Inc.

—Tintin au Tibet.Tr. of Tintin in Tibet. (J). (gr. 7-9). ring bd. 24.95 (978-0-8288-5092-6(5)) French & European Pubns., Inc.

Herge. Tintin Boxed Set Of 8. 2007. (ps-17). 150.00 ***(*978-0-316-00668-2(8))*** Little, Brown Bks. for Young Readers.

Hergé. Tintin en Amerique. 1999. (Tintin Ser.). Orig. Title: Tintin in America. (FRE., Illus.). 62p. (J). (gr. 4-7). pap. 21.95 (978-2-203-00102-2(X)) Casterman, Editions FRA. *Dist:* Distribooks, Inc.

—Tintin en Amerique. Orig. Title: Tintin in America. (Illus.). 62p. (J). (FRE.). 24.95 (978-0-8288-5093-3(3)); (SPA., 24.95 (978-0-8288-5094-0(1)) French & European Pubns., Inc.

—Tintin en Amerique. (Tintin Ser.). Orig. Title: Tintin in America. (SPA.). 64p. (J). 14.95 (978-84-261-1400-6(8)) Juventud, Editorial ESP. *Dist:* Distribooks, Inc.

—Tintin en el Congo. (SPA., Illus.). 62p. (J). 24.95 (978-0-8288-5095-7(X)) French & European Pubns., Inc.

—Tintin en el Congo. (Tintin Ser.). (SPA.). 64p. (J). 14.95 (978-84-261-1401-3(6)) Juventud, Editorial ESP. *Dist:* Distribooks, Inc.

—Tintin en el Pais del Oro Negro.Tr. of Land of Black Gold. (SPA., Illus.). 62p. (J). 24.95 (978-0-8288-4995-1(1)) French & European Pubns., Inc.

—Tintin en Tibet. (SPA., Illus.). 62p. (J). 24.95 (978-0-8288-4996-8(X)) French & European Pubns., Inc.

—Tintin en Tibet. (Tintin Ser.). (SPA.). 64p. (J). 14.95 (978-84-261-1403-7(2)) Juventud, Editorial ESP. *Dist:* Distribooks, Inc.

—Tintin et les Picaros. 1999. (Tintin Ser.).Tr. of Tintin & the Picaros. (FRE.). (J). (gr. 4-7). 21.95 (978-2-203-00123-7(2)) Casterman, Editions FRA. *Dist:* Distribooks, Inc.

—Tintin et les Picaros.Tr. of Tintin & the Picaros. (FRE., Illus.). 62p. (J). 24.95 (978-0-8288-4997-5(8)) French & European Pubns., Inc.

—Tintin im Amerika.Tr. of Tintin in America. (GER., Illus.). 62p. (J). pap. 24.95 (978-0-8288-4999-9(4)) French & European Pubns., Inc.

—Tintin im Kongo. (GER., Illus.). 62p. (J). pap. 24.95 (978-0-8288-4998-2(6)) French & European Pubns., Inc.

—Tintin in America. Orig. Title: Tintin en Amerique. (Illus.). 62p. (J). 24.95 (978-0-8288-5000-1(3)) French & European Pubns., Inc.

—Tintin in the Land of the Soviets: Reporter for Le Petit Vingtieme. fac. ed. 2004. (Adventures of Tintin Ser.). (Illus.). 138p. (J). reprint ed. 24.95 (978-0-86719-903-1(2)) Last Gasp of San Francisco.

—Tintin in Tibet. Orig. Title: Tintin au Tibet. (Illus.). 62p. (J). 24.95 (978-0-8288-5001-8(1)) French & European Pubns., Inc.

—Tintin y los Picaros. (SPA., Illus.). 62p. (J). 24.95 (978-0-8288-5002-5(X)) French & European Pubns., Inc.

—Tintin y los Picaros. (Tintin Ser.). (SPA.). 64p. (J). 14.95 (978-84-261-1389-4(3)) Juventud, Editorial ESP. *Dist:* Distribooks, Inc.

—Tresor de Rackham le Rouge.Tr. of Red Rackham's Treasure. (FRE., Illus.). 62p. (J). (gr. 7-9). 24.95 (978-0-8288-5003-2(8)) French & European Pubns., Inc.

—Vol 714 Pour Sydney Vol. 714: Flight 714 for Sydney. (FRE., Illus.). 62p. 21.95 (978-2-203-00121-3(6)) Casterman, Editions FRA. *Dist:* Distribooks, Inc.

—Vuelo 714 para Sidney. (SPA., Illus.). 62p. (J). 24.95 (978-0-8288-5004-9(6)) French & European Pubns., Inc.

—Vuelo 714 para Sidney. (Tintin Ser.). (SPA.). 64p. (J). 14.95 (978-84-261-1404-4(0)) Juventud, Editorial ESP. *Dist:* Distribooks, Inc.

—Y las Naranjas Azules. (SPA., Illus.). 62p. (J). 24.95 (978-0-8288-5005-6(4)) French & European Pubns., Inc.

—Die Zigarren des Pharaos. (GER., Illus.). 62p. (J). pap. 24.95 (978-0-8288-5006-3(2)) French & European Pubns., Inc.

Hergé, illus. Tintin & Snowy: Album 1. 2006. 68p. (J). pap. 9.99 (978-0-86719-668-9(8)) Last Gasp of San Francisco.

Hergenroeder, Ernie, illus. Little Drop of Water. 2007. 24p. (J). 15.00 ***(*978-0-9724272-4-1(4))*** Katydid Publishing LLC.

Herman, Gail. Look Out, Earth-Below! 2000. (Fairy School Ser.). (Illus.). (J). (978-0-606-21635-7(9)) Tandem Library Bks.

Herman, Gail. Silvermist & the Ladybug Curse. 2008. (Stepping Stone Book(TM) Ser.). 128p. (J). (gr. 1-5). 5.99 ***(*978-0-7364-2508-7(X)*** , RH/Disney) Random Hse. Children's Bks.

Hermes, Patricia. Untitled Chapter Book - Patricia Hermes. 1999. (J). (978-0-316-35931-3(9)) Little Brown & Co.

Hernandez, David. Land of the Pharaohs. 2003. (Adventures of Toby Digz Ser.). (Illus.). 96p. (J). pap. 5.99 (978-1-4003-0195-9(5)) Nelson, Thomas Inc.

Hernandez, Natalie. Las Aventuras con Padre Serra. Hernandez, Tony Y., tr. Nolan, Claudia, illus. 1999. (ENG & SPA.). 112p. (Orig.). (J). (gr. 3-8). pap. 9.95 (978-0-9644386-1-3(5)) Santa Ines Pubns.

—Stowaway to California: Adventures with Father Junipero Serra, 3. 2003. (Illus.). 138p. (J). per. 10.95 (978-1-885852-29-8(0)) James Stevenson Pub.

Hernandez, Natalie Nelson. Captain Sutter's Fort: Adventures with John A. Sutter. 2003. (Illus.). 108p. (J). per. 9.95 (978-1-885852-28-1(2)) James Stevenson Pub.

—Captain Sutter's Fort: Adventures with John A. Sutter. 1999. (Illus.). 107p. (J). (gr. 4-6). pap. 9.95 (978-0-9644386-3-7(1)) Santa Ines Pubns.

—Mapmakers of the Western Trails: Adventures with John Chrles Fremont, 3 bks. 2003. (Illus.). 130p. (J). per. 10.95 (978-1-885852-31-1(2)) James Stevenson Pub.

Hernandez, Regina. Texas Roundup: Jake the Beagle's Crazy Adventures. Woods, Carol, ed. Fetherston, Catherine & Miller, Tom, illus. 2003. (Jake the Beagle Crazy Adventure Ser.: 2). 90p. (J). pap. 5.99 (978-0-9727771-2-4(1)) Regal Enterprises.

Herrera, Joaquin. Horris, Little Eli & the Lens of Truth. 2007. (DreamFever Chronicles Ser.: Bk. 1). 208p. (978-1-59258-245-7(1)) Hylas Publishing.

Herrick, Ann. Walk Softly & Watch Out for Bigfoot. 2006. (YA). pap. 9.95 (978-0-7599-4489-3(X)) Hard Shell Word Factory.

Herrington, Chris. Harry & Hannah: The Christmas Adventure. 2003. 72p. 15.00 (978-0-9722343-2-0(2)) Herrington Teddy Bears.

Herrington, Nancy. An Alphabet Adventure with Rose. Herrington, Nancy, illus. 2002. (Laughing & Learning Ser.: Vol. 1). (Illus.). 26p. (J). pap. 6.95 (978-0-9711299-0-0(8)) Herrington, Nancy Publishing.

Hess, Brian F. Lynquest & the Search for Greatness. 2006. (ENG.). 116p. per. 16.95 (978-1-4241-4503-4(1)) PublishAmerica, Inc.

Hest, Amy. You Can Do It, Sam. Jeram, Anita, illus. 2007. (Sam Bks.). 32p. (J). (ps). pap. 4.99 ***(*978-0-7636-3688-3(6))*** Candlewick Pr.

Heuck, Sigrid. El Poni, el Oso y el Manzano. 2001. Tr. of Who Stole the Apples. (SPA., Illus.). 32p. (J). 9.20 (978-84-261-1738-0(4)) Juventud, Editorial ESP. *Dist:* Lectorum Pubns., Inc.

Heuer, Christoph, illus. Lola & Fred & Tom. 2007. 48p. (J). 15.95 (978-0-9741319-9-3(7)) 4N Publishing LLC.

Heyliger, William. Don Strong, Patrol Leader. 2006. 32.99 ***(*978-1-4280-1775-7(5))*** IndyPublish.com.

Heyman, Alissa. The Big Book of Adventure. Rodriguez, Pedro, illus. 2008. 112p. (J). 12.95 ***(*978-1-4027-5156-1(7))*** Sterling Publishing Co., Inc.

Hickery Dickery. 2004. (J). per. (978-1-57657-426-3(1)) Paradise Pr., Inc.

Hickey, Joshalyn M. Good Morning Lovey! Chaveevah, Banks Ferguson, illus. 2005. 28p. (J). 12.00 (978-0-9718939-3-1(4)) BaHar Publishing, L.C.

Hicks, Esther & Hicks, Jerry. Sara Bk. 2: Solomon's Fine Featherless Friends. 2007. (Illus.). 256p. pap. 14.95 (978-1-4019-1159-1(5)) Hay Hse., Inc.

—Sara, Book 1: The Foreverness of Friends of a Feather. 2007. (Illus.). 192p. pap. 14.95 (978-1-4019-1158-4(7)) Hay Hse., Inc.

Hicks, John. Divided World. 2003. 192p. (YA). per. 6.50 (978-0-9742829-1-6(X)) Quiet Man Publishing.

—My Buddypack. ltd. ed. 2003. (Illus.). 160p. (J). per. 5.99 (978-0-9742829-0-9(1)) Quiet Man Publishing.

Hicks, John Bryant. The Day Charlie Lost His Weirdness. 2nd ed. 2007. (J). per. 5.99 ***(*978-0-9742829-4-7(4))*** Quiet Man Publishing.

Higashi/Glaser Design Inc. Staff. Hello Kitty Haiku: Note Cards. 2005. (Illus.). 15p. (J). (gr. 2-10). 12.95 (978-0-8109-8806-4(2) , Abrams Gifts and Stationery) Abrams, Harry N. , Inc.

Higashi/Glaser Design Inc. Staff. Hello Kitty Hello Nature! Explorer Kit. 2007. 16p. (J). (ps-3). 14.95 ***(*978-0-8109-9365-5(1))*** Abrams, Harry N. , Inc.

Higgins, Richard P. Weekend in the Wild. 2000. 152p. (YA). pap. 9.95 (978-0-595-13808-1(X)) iUniverse, Inc.

Higginson, Sheila. Up, up, & Away! Disney Storybook Artists Staff, illus. 2007. 24p. (J). (ps-k). pap. 3.99 ***(*978-1-4231-0647-0(4))*** Disney Pr.

High, Linda Oatman. The Girl on the High-Diving Horse. Lewin, Ted, illus. 2005. 40p. (J). (ps-ps). pap. 6.99 (978-0-14-240278-8(8) , Puffin) Penguin Group (USA) Inc.

Highstreet, Harry. Read Aloud Series. 2006. pap. 28.95 ***(*978-1-84728-641-3(0))*** Lulu.com.

Higson, Charlie. Blood Fever. 2006. 368p. (gr. 5-17). 16.95 (978-0-7868-3662-8(8)) Hyperion Bks. for Children.

—A James Bond Adventure. 2006. 368p. (gr. 5-17). pap. 6.99 (978-0-7868-3866-0(3)) Miramax Bks.

—Silverfin: A James Bond Adventure. 2005. (J). pap. 7.99 (978-0-7868-3814-1(0)) Miramax Bks.

Hikawa, Kyoko. From Far Away, Vol. 11. Hikawa, Kyoko, illus. 2006. (From Far Away Ser.). 208p. (YA). pap. 9.99 (978-1-4215-0538-1(X)) Viz Media.

—From Far Away, Vol. 12. 2006. (From Far Away Ser.). 208p. (YA). pap. 9.99 (978-1-4215-0539-8(8)) Viz Media.

Hilbrandt, Sarah Perrin. Jack & the Taloon. 2006. 24p. per. 11.99 ***(*978-1-59886-818-0(7))*** Tate Publishing & Enterprises, L.L.C.

Hilderbrand, Barbara. Paul's Missionary Adventure. 2003. (Pencil Fun Bks.: Vol. 10). 16p. (J). (ps-3). pap., pap. 9.90 (978-1-55513-270-5(7) , 1555132707) Cook, David C. Publishing Co.

Hill, Donna. Shipwreck Season. 1998. 224p. (J). (gr. 4-6). tchr. ed. 16.00 (978-0-395-86614-6(6) , Clarion Bks.) Houghton Mifflin Co. Trade & Reference Div.

Hill, Stuart. The Cry of the Icemark. l.t. ed. 2005. 611p. (YA). 22.95 (978-0-7862-8089-6(1)) Thorndike Pr.

Hillary, Robert. The Ugly Banana. 2005. 20p. per. 9.95 (978-1-59453-700-4(3) , 2815) Airleaf Publishing & Bookselling.

Hillert, Margaret. The Boy & the Goats. Miyake, Yoshi, illus. rev. exp. ed. 2007. (Beginning to Read Ser.). 32p. (J). lib. bdg. (978-1-59953-053-6(8)) Norwood Hse. Pr.

—The Cookie House: Hansel & Gretel Retold. Craft, Kinuko, illus. rev. exp. ed. 2007. (Beginning to Read Ser.). 28p. (J). lib. bdg. (978-1-59953-051-2(1)) Norwood Hse. Pr.

Hillier. Homeland. 2000. 352p. pap. 8.99 (978-0-7515-2235-8(X) , Warner Books) Little, Brown Bk. Group Ltd. GBR. *Dist:* Independent Pubs. Group.

Hillman, Jack. There Are Giants in This Valley. 2005. 256p. (YA). 26.99 (978-1-59507-096-8(6) , ArcheBooks) ArcheBooks Publishing.

Himmelman, John. The Animal Rescue Club. 1998. (I Can Read Bks.). (Illus.). 48p. (J). (gr. 3-4). 14.95 (978-0-06-027408-5(5)); 15.89 (978-0-06-027409-2(3)) HarperCollins Pubs.

Hinchliffe, Polly. Trio Theo in the Grip of Terror. 2003. 150p. pap. 12.95 (978-0-595-28727-7(1)) iUniverse, Inc.

Hinkler Books Staff, reader. Barney's Outer Space Adventure. 2004. (J). 9.99 incl. audio compact disk (978-1-86515-996-6(4)) Hinkler Bks. Pty. Ltd. AUS. *Dist:* Penton Overseas, Inc.

Hinnen, Brandy & Kahn, Karen, illus. The Adventures of Travel Tiger. 2002. 34p. per. 16.99 (978-1-931540-85-8(3)) SynergEbks.

Hinojosa, Francisco. Las Orejas de Urbano. 2002. (SPA., Illus.). 48p. (J). (gr. 3-5). 12.95 (978-968-19-1015-0(X)) Aguilar Editorial MEX. *Dist:* Santillana USA Publishing Co., Inc.

Hinton, Nigel. Collision Course. 2005. 160p. (J). (gr. 5-8). pap., pap. 5.95 (978-1-903015-42-1(1)) Barn Owl Bks, London GBR. *Dist:* Independent Pubs. Group.

Hinton, S. E. Hawkes Harbor. 2005. 304p. pap. 7.99 (978-0-7653-4472-4(6) , Tor Bks.) Doherty, Tom Assocs., LLC.

—Rebeldes. 2003. (SPA., Illus.). 192p. (YA). (gr. 5-8). pap. 13.95 (978-968-19-0831-7(7) , AF4535) Aguilar Editorial MEX. *Dist:* Lectorum Pubns., Inc., Santillana USA Publishing Co., Inc.

—Rebeldes. 2nd ed. (SPA., Illus.). 200p. (YA). (gr. 5-8). 13.95 (978-84-204-4797-1(8)) Alfaguara, Ediciones, S.A.- Grupo Santillana ESP. *Dist:* Lectorum Pubns., Inc., Santillana USA Publishing Co., Inc.

Hippely, Hilary Horder. Adventure on Klickitat Island. Upton, Barbara, illus. 2000. (Picture Puffin Ser.). 32p. (J). (ps-3). pap. 6.99 (978-0-14-056633-8(3) , Puffin) Penguin Group (USA) Inc.

Hiriart, Hugo. Muneco de Don Bepo. (SPA.). 72p. (J). 5.95 (978-84-348-1287-1(8)) SM Ediciones ESP. *Dist:* AIMS International Bks., Inc., Lectorum Pubns., Inc.

Hirsch, Odo. Bartlett & the City of Flames. McLean, Andrew, illus. 2003. 150p. (J). 15.95 (978-1-58234-831-5(6) , Bloomsbury Children) Bloomsbury Publishing.

—Bartlett & the Ice Voyage. McLean, Andrew, illus. 2003. 175p. (J). (gr. 3-9). 14.95 (978-1-58234-797-4(2) , Bloomsbury Children) Bloomsbury Publishing.

—Something's Fishy, Hazel Green. 2006. 208p. (J). (gr. 3-6). pap. 6.95 (978-1-58234-947-3(9) , Bloomsbury Children) Bloomsbury Publishing.

—Something's Fishy Hazel Green. 2005. 208p. (J). (gr. 3-6). 15.95 (978-1-58234-928-2(2) , Bloomsbury Children) Bloomsbury Publishing.

Hitchcock, Alfred. Misterio de la Arana de Plata. (Alfred Hitchcock y los Tres Investigadores Ser.). (SPA.). (YA). 8.95 (978-84-272-4908-0(X) , MO60) Molino, Editorial ESP. *Dist:* Continental Bk. Co., Inc.

—Misterio de la Calavera Parlante. (Alfred Hitchcock y los Tres Investigadores Ser.). (SPA.). (YA). 8.95 (978-84-272-4911-0(X) , MO63) Molino, Editorial ESP. *Dist:* Continental Bk. Co., Inc.

—Misterio de la Cueva de los Lamentos. (Alfred Hitchcock y los Tres Investigadores Ser.). (SPA.). 160p. (YA). 8.95 (978-84-272-4910-3(1) , MO62) Molino, Editorial ESP. *Dist:* Continental Bk. Co., Inc.

—Misterio de la Montana del Monstruo. (Alfred Hitchcock y los Tres Investigadores Ser.). (SPA.). (YA). 8.95 (978-84-272-4920-2(9) , MO72) Molino, Editorial ESP. *Dist:* Continental Bk. Co., Inc.

—Misterio de Leon Mervioso. (Alfred Hitchcock y los Tres Investigadores Ser.). (SPA.). 192p. (YA). 8.95 (978-84-272-4916-5(0) , MO68) Molino, Editorial ESP. *Dist:* Continental Bk. Co., Inc.

—Misterio del Dragon. (Alfred Hitchcock y los Tres Investigadores Ser.). (SPA.). 176p. (YA). 8.95 (978-84-272-4914-1(4) , MO66) Molino, Editorial ESP. *Dist:* Continental Bk. Co., Inc.

—Misterio del Gato de Trapo. (Alfred Hitchcock y los Tres Investigadores Ser.). (SPA.). 152p. (YA). 8.95 (978-84-272-4913-4(6) , MO65) Molino, Editorial ESP. *Dist:* Continental Bk. Co., Inc.

Hite, Sid. Stick & Whittle. 2001. 208p. (J). (gr. 5 up). pap. 4.99 (978-0-439-09829-8(7)) Scholastic, Inc.

—Stick & Whittle. 2001. (gr. 5-8). lib. bdg. 13.00 (978-0-613-53868-8(4)) Tandem Library Bks.

Hiti, Samuel, creator. End Times - Tiempos Finales Vol. 1: English / Spanish. 2004. Orig. Title: Bloody Demon Guts. (Illus.). 128p. (YA). per. 9.95 net. (978-0-9755193-0-1(1)) La Luz comics.

Hixson, Jon, et al. The Adventures of Caterpillar Jones. 2000. 154p. (J). (gr. 3-7). pap. (978-1-892714-12-1(4)) Onjinjinkta Publishing.

—Caterpillar Jones & the Adventures of Nut E. Squirrel. 2002. (Mulberry Meadow Ser.: Vol. 2). iv, 184p. (J). (gr. 2-6). pap. 8.95 (978-0-9718774-0-5(8)) Foundation Publishing.

Ho, Minfong. The Clay Marble. unabr. ed. 1998. (J). 107.30 incl. audio (978-0-7887-2554-8(8) , 46724); (gr. 6). 50.20 incl. audio (978-0-7887-2250-9(6) , 40734) Recorded Bks., LLC.

Ho, Oliver & Dumas, Alexandre. The Three Musketeers. Akib, Jamel, illus. 2007. (Classic Starts Ser.). 151p. (J). ***(*978-1-4287-4206-2(9))*** Sterling Publishing Co., Inc.

Hoadley, Jo. Miss Creant: The Adventures of a little Red Hen. l.t. ed. 2004. (Illus.). 127p. (J). per. 15.99 (978-0-9765088-0-9(X)) Billy Jo Bks.

Hobbs, Leigh. Old Tom's Guide to Being Good. Hobbs, Leigh, illus. 2006. 96p. (gr. 1-3). pap. 3.99 (978-0-7868-5694-7(7)) Hyperion Pr.

Hobbs, Valerie. Sheep. 2006. 128p. (J). 16.00 (978-0-374-36777-0(9) , Farrar, Straus & Giroux (BYR)) Farrar, Straus & Giroux.

Hobbs, Will. Beardance. 2004. (Illus.). 208p. (J). pap. 5.99 (978-0-689-87072-9(8) , Aladdin) Simon & Schuster Children's Publishing.

—The Big Wander. 2004. (Illus.). 192p. (J). pap. 5.99 (978-0-689-87070-5(1) , Aladdin) Simon & Schuster Children's Publishing.

—River Thunder. 1999. (Learn-Along Board Bks. Ser.). 224p. (YA). (gr. 7-12). pap. 5.99 (978-0-440-22681-9(3) , Laurel Leaf) Random Hse. Children's Bks.

Hobbs, William. Ghost Canoe. 1998. (Avon Camelot Bks.). 208p. (J). (gr. 5-9). pap. 5.99 (978-0-380-72537-3(1)) HarperCollins Pubs.

—Ghost Canoe. 1998. (J). 12.64 (978-0-606-13420-0(4)) Tandem Library Bks.

Hoberman, Mary Ann. It's Simple, Said Simon. So, Meilo, illus. 2003. 40p. (J). (ps-2). pap. 6.99 (978-0-440-41772-9(4) , Dragonfly Bks.) Random Hse. Children's Bks.

Hochenauer, Mary & Hochenauer-Fox, Lois. Sunny & Wondrous, Cat Cousins. 2006. (J). 15.95 (978-0-9778005-0-6(4)) Gnatcatcher Children'S Bks.

Hock, Dan. The Afternoon Auction: An Iggy & Igor Mystery. 2004. (Illus.). 48p. (J). per. 4.99 (978-0-9754046-0-7(1)) Anticipation Pr.

Hockenberger, Henry. The Gold Case. 2006. (YA). pap. 15.95 (978-1-58736-584-3(7)) Wheatmark.

Hodes, Loren. Thirty-One Cakes: A Hashvas Aveida Adventure. Rosenfeld, Devorah Leah, ed. Klineman, Harvey, illus. 2003. (J). 9.95 (978-1-929628-13-1(7)) Hachai Publishing.

Hodges, James. The Trail of Truth. 2004. 36p. (J). pap. 18.99 (978-1-4141-0284-9(4)) Pleasant Word.

Hodgson, Linda Beyer. The Adventures of Sheldon, the Time Traveling Turtle. 2006. pap. 8.95 (978-0-533-15414-2(6)) Vantage Pr., Inc.

Hodgson, William Hope. The Sea Horses. 2004. reprint ed. pap. 1.99 (978-1-4192-8166-2(6)) Kessinger Publishing, LLC.

Hodson, Christopher. Lizo's Song: Chilomwe Version. Nkhoma, Wilson, tr. 1999. (Cambridge Reading Routes Ser.). (Illus.). 16p. pap. 3.70 (978-0-521-66854-5(9)) Cambridge Univ. Pr.

—Lizo's Song: Chitumbuka Version. Chirambo, Reuben, tr. 1999. (Cambridge Reading Routes Ser.). (Illus.). 16p. pap. 3.70 (978-0-521-66872-9(7)) Cambridge Univ. Pr.

—Lizo's Song: Chiyao Version. Mjaya, Ahmmardouh, tr. 1999. (Cambridge Reading Routes Ser.). (Illus.). 16p. pap. 3.70 (978-0-521-66865-1(4)) Cambridge Univ. Pr.

Hoeye, Michael. No Time Like Showtime. 2006. (Illus.). 288p. (YA). (gr. 7). pap. 7.99 (978-0-14-240563-5(9) , Puffin) Penguin Group (USA) Inc.

Hofer, Nelly & Hofer, Ernst, illus. Clever Katarina: A Tale in Six Parts. 2006. 40p. (J). (gr. 3-5). 17.95 (978-0-88776-764-7(8)) Tundra Bks., Inc./Livres Toundra, Inc. CAN. *Dist:* Random Hse., Inc.

Hoffman, Eric. Heroinas y Heroes. 1999. Tr. of Heroines & Heroes. (SPA.). (gr. k-3). lib. bdg. 19.90 (978-0-613-80188-1(1)) Tandem Library Bks.

Hoffman, Mary. Bravo, Grace! 2005. (Illus.). 96p. (J). 14.95 (978-1-84507-057-1(7)) Lincoln, Frances Ltd. GBR. *Dist:* Perseus Distribution.

Hoffmann, Arthur W. The Blue King. 2003. (Illus.). 31p. (J). 21.95 incl. audio compact disk (978-0-9742967-0-8(8)) ASK Publishing, L.L.C.

Hoffmann, Dana. The Golden Tale: A Goldentail Adventure Story Book. O'Leary Brown, Erin, illus. 2004. 44p. (J). lib. bdg. 19.95 (978-0-9753106-0-1(7)) Hoffmann Partnership, The.

Hoffmann, Dana Marie. El Cuento Dorado, un Libro de Aventura, la Historia de Goldentail. O'Leary Brown, Erin, illus. 2004. (SPA.). 42p. (J). 9.95 (978-0-9753106-1-8(5)) Hoffmann Partnership, The.

—The Golden Tale, A Goldentail Adventure Story Book. O'Leary Brown, Erin, illus. 2004. 42p. (J). 9.95 (978-0-9753106-3-2(1)) Hoffmann Partnership, The.

Hofkin, Sabrina. Magnolia, 1. 2005. 168p. (YA). per. 9.95 (978-0-9763916-0-9(0)) Manzanita Falls Pubs.

Hofmeister, Alan, et al. The Mask. (Reading for All Learners Ser.). (Illus.). (J). pap. (978-1-56861-139-6(0)) Swift Learning Resources.

—Ruff. (Reading for All Learners Ser.). (Illus.). (J). pap. (978-1-56861-137-2(4)) Swift Learning Resources.

—Run, Feet, Run. (Reading for All Learners Ser.). (Illus.). (J). pap. (978-1-56861-095-5(5)) Swift Learning Resources.

—We Will Run. (Reading for All Learners Ser.). (Illus.). (J). pap. (978-1-56861-099-3(8)) Swift Learning Resources.

Hohlbein, Wolfgang. Avalon Projekt. pap. 30.95 (978-3-426-61866-0(4)) Droemersche Verlagsanstalt Th. Knaur Nachf. - GmbH & Co. DEU. *Dist:* Distribooks, Inc.

Hokenson, Terry. The Winter Road. 2006. 176p. (J). 16.95 (978-1-932425-45-1(4) , Front Street) Boyds Mills Pr.

Holbrook, Bill. Tomb Raiding for Fun & Profit Vol. 2: On the Fastrack. 2000. (On the Fastrack Ser.). (Illus.). 152p. (J). 12.95 (978-1-929462-12-4(3)) Plan Nine Publishing, Inc.

Holbrook, Sara. Nothing's the End of the World. Smith-Moore, J. J., illus. 2003. 48p. (YA). (gr. 4-6). pap. 8.95 (978-1-56397-198-3(4)) Boyds Mills Pr.

Holden, George P. The Idyl of the Split Bamboo. 1998. (Illus.). 294p. reprint ed. 24.95 (978-1-55709-492-6(6)) Applewood Bks.

Holder, Nancy. Blood & Fog. 2003. (gr. 7-12). lib. bdg. 15.30 (978-0-613-65071-7(9)) Tandem Library Bks.

Holland, Maryjo. Susannah & Henry: Making the Best of T. 2005. 73p. pap. 14.95 (978-1-4137-6485-7(1)) PublishAmerica, Inc.

Holland, Steve. London Adventure. 2001. (Kenan & Kel Ser.: Vol. 10). (YA). pap. 4.50 (978-0-7434-0604-8(4) , Simon Pulse) Simon & Schuster Children's Publishing.

Hollaway, David. Pete Has Big Feet. 2006. (J). per. 8.95 (978-1-933211-06-0(7)) Quackenworth Publishing.

—Quigley Mccormick: And the Curse of the Polka Dotted Pig, 3 vols. l.t. ed. 2005. (Illus.). 156p. (J). per. 15.95 (978-1-933211-54-1(7)) Quackenworth Publishing.

—Quigley Mccormick & the Stuperton Conspiracy. 2006. (J). per. 15.95 (978-1-933211-56-5(3)) Quackenworth Publishing.

Hollins, Jack. Charlie¿s christmas Adventure. 2006. 16.95 (978-0-9788725-0-2(9)) Alli Kat Publishing.

Holsather, Kent /Wilson. Sara's Moon. 2007. (Illus.). 176p. (YA). per. 12.95 ***(978-0-9729101-3-2(1))*** Lonejack Mountain Pr.

Holt, Rinehart and Winston Staff. The Adventures of Tom Sawyer: With Connections. 1998. pap., stu. ed. 13.20 (978-0-03-054047-9(X)) Holt, Rinehart & Winston.

Holub, Josef. The Robber & Me. 1999. (J). (gr. 4-7). 19.25 (978-0-8446-7007-2(3)) Smith, Peter Pub., Inc.

—The Robber & Me. 1999. (978-0-606-15909-8(6)) Tandem Library Bks.

Homer. La Iliada. (SPA., Illus.). 192p. (YA). 11.95 (978-84-7281-104-1(2) , AF1104) Auriga, Ediciones S.A. ESP. *Dist:* Continental Bk. Co., Inc.

—La Odisea. (SPA., Illus.). 192p. (YA). 11.95 (978-84-7281-079-2(8) , AF1079) Auriga, Ediciones S.A. ESP. *Dist:* Continental Bk. Co., Inc.

Honey, Elizabeth. Remote Man. 2004. (Illus.). 272p. (J). (gr. 5). 4.99 (978-0-440-41901-3(8) , Yearling) Random Hse. Children's Bks.

—Remote Man. 2004. (gr. 5-8). lib. bdg. 13.00 (978-0-613-86686-6(X)) Tandem Library Bks.

Hoobler, David. Zonk & the Secret Lagoon: The Further Adventures of Zonk the Dreaming Tortoise. l.t. ed. 2005. (Illus.). 32p. (J). lib. bdg. 16.95 (978-0-9706537-1-0(9)) Zonk Galleries.

Hood, Karen Jean Matsko. Adventure Travel Activity & Coloring Book First Edition: Activity & Coloring Book Series. braille ed. 2006. (J). spiral bd. 22.95 (978-1-59808-637-9(5)) Whispering Pine Pr., Inc.

—Adventure Travel Annual 2003 Book. 2003. (YA). 15.95 (978-1-59210-456-7(8)) ; (JPN & ENG.). cd-rom 13.95 (978-1-59434-050-5(1)) Whispering Pine Pr., Inc.

—Adventure Travel International: A Daily Journal. 2003. (J). 15.95 (978-1-59434-596-8(1)) Whispering Pine Pr., Inc.

—Adventure Travel International: Annual 2003 Book. 2003. (J). 15.95 (978-1-59210-454-3(1)) ; (JPN.). cd-rom 13.95 (978-1-59434-192-2(3)) Whispering Pine Pr., Inc.

—Adventure Travel USA: A Daily Journal. 2003. (JPN & ENG.). (YA). (978-1-59434-599-9(6)) Whispering Pine Pr., Inc.

—Adventures of My Dentist & the Tooth Fairy Activity & Coloring Book Second Edition. 2nd rev. ed. 2005. (Educational Activity & Coloring Book Ser.).Tr. of Japanese. (J). 15.95 (978-1-930948-59-4(X)) Whispering Pine Pr., Inc.

—Adventures of My Dentist & the Tooth Fairy Adventures in Learning Book. 2005. (J). 15.95 (978-1-59210-282-2(4)) ; spiral bd. 15.95 (978-1-59210-306-5(5)) ; cd-rom 13.95 (978-1-59649-328-5(3)) Whispering Pine Pr., Inc.

—Adventures of My Dentist & the Tooth Fairy Christian Adventures in Learning Book: Christian Educational Learning Series. 2005. (J). spiral bd. 15.95 (978-1-59210-393-5(6)) ; cd-rom 13.95 (978-1-59649-329-2(1)) Whispering Pine Pr., Inc.

—Adventures of My Dentist & the Tooth Fairy Christian Adventures in Learning Books: Christian Educational Learning Series. 2005. (J). 15.95 (978-1-59210-392-8(8)) Whispering Pine Pr., Inc.

—Goodnight, I Wish You Goodnight. 2005. (Illus.). 32p. (J). 15.95 (978-1-930948-83-9(2)) Whispering Pine Pr., Inc.

—Goodnight, I Wish You Goodnight. Keyama, Hiroshi Hata, illus. 2005. 32p. (J). 24.95 (978-1-930948-97-6(2)) Whispering Pine Pr., Inc.

—Goodnight, I Wish You Goodnight. 2002. (J). per. 15.95 (978-1-59210-500-7(9)) Whispering Pine Pr., Inc.

—Jesus Loves the Little Children Activity & Coloring Book. 2005. (Educational Little Activity & Coloring Book Ser.). (ENG & SPA.). (J). spiral bd. 15.95 (978-1-59649-607-1(X)) ; cd-rom 7.95 (978-1-59434-087-1(0)) Whispering Pine Pr., Inc.

—Spokane Falls Falcon: Mysteries of the Brothers Hood-Children's Fiction. 2006. (J). 19.95 (978-1-59434-220-2(2)) ; 24.95 (978-1-59434-228-8(8)) ; per. 19.95 (978-1-59434-226-4(1)) ; ring bd. 24.95 (978-1-59434-223-3(7)) ; cd-rom 13.95 (978-1-59434-221-9(0)) Whispering Pine Pr., Inc.

—Wilbur's Great Adventure. 2006. (J). 19.95 (978-1-59434-388-9(8)) ; spiral bd. 19.95 (978-1-59434-386-5(1)) ; per. 19.95 (978-1-59434-312-4(8)) ; cd-rom 13.95 (978-1-59434-389-6(6)) Whispering Pine Pr., Inc.

—Wilbur's Great Adventure: Large Print Edition. l.t. ed. 2006. spiral bd. 22.95 (978-1-59434-730-6(1)) Whispering Pine Pr., Inc.

—Wilbur's Great Adventure - Braille Edition. braille ed. 2006. spiral bd. 22.95 (978-1-59434-732-0(8)) Whispering Pine Pr., Inc.

Hoogstad, Alice. BOLDER & BOAT. 2008. 32p. 13.95 ***(978-1-60136-015-1(0))*** Mars Media Pubs.

Hook. Wrinkled Crinkled Grapes: A Purple Monster. 2007. 52p. per. 8.95 ***(978-0-595-42310-1(8))*** iUniverse, Inc.

Hooper. Pole-Seekers. 2000. (Illus.). 165p. pap. 8.99 (978-0-340-75734-5(5) , Hodder & Stoughton) Hodder General Publishing Division GBR. *Dist:* Trafalgar Square Publishing.

Hooper, Mary. Spook Summer. Hillard, Susan, illus. l.t. ed. 2005. 96p. (J). pap. (978-0-7540-7811-1(6) , CLP 397) BBC Audio.

Hope-Hawkins, Anthony & Hope, Anthony. The Prisoner of Zenda, Level 3. 2nd abr. ed. 2000. (Bookworms Ser.). (Illus.). 80p. 6.50 (978-0-19-423012-4(0)) Oxford Univ. Pr., Inc.

Hope, Laura Lee. The Bobbsey Twins' Adventure in the Country, Vol. 2. 2004. (Bobbsey Twins Ser.: Vol. 2). (Illus.). 196p. (J). (gr. 3-8). 5.99 (978-0-448-43753-8(8) , Grosset & Dunlap) Penguin Group (USA) Inc.

—The Bobbsey Twins' Adventure in Washington, Vol. 12. 2004. (Bobbsey Twins Ser.: Vol. 12). (Illus.). 182p. (J). (gr. 3-8). 5.99 (978-0-448-43763-7(5) , Grosset & Dunlap) Penguin Group (USA) Inc.

—The Bobbsey Twins & the Mystery at Snow Lodge, Vol. 5. 2004. (Bobbsey Twins Ser.: Vol. 5). (Illus.). 196p. (J). (gr. 3-8). 5.99 (978-0-448-43756-9(2) , Grosset & Dunlap) Penguin Group (USA) Inc.

—The Bobbsey Twins' Big Adventure at Home, Vol. 8. 2004. (Bobbsey Twins Ser.: Vol. 8). (Illus.). 196p. (J). (gr. 3-8). 5.99 (978-0-448-43759-0(7) , Grosset & Dunlap) Penguin Group (USA) Inc.

—The Bobbsey Twins' Mystery at School. 2004. (Bobbsey Twins Ser.: Vol. 4). (Illus.). 196p. (J). (gr. 3-8). 5.99 (978-0-448-43755-2(4) , Grosset & Dunlap) Penguin Group (USA) Inc.

—The Bobbsey Twins of Lakeport: The Bobbsey Twins, 1. 2004. (Bobbsey Twins Ser.: Vol. 1). (Illus.). 196p. (J). (gr. 3-8). 5.99 (978-0-448-43752-1(X) , Grosset & Dunlap) Penguin Group (USA) Inc.

—The Bobbsey Twins' Search in the Great City: The Bobbsey Twins, Vol. 9. 2004. (Bobbsey Twins Ser.: Vol. 9). (Illus.). 192p. (J). 5.99 (978-0-448-43760-6(0) , Grosset & Dunlap) Penguin Group (USA) Inc.

—Outdoor Girls at Ocean View or the Box T. 2007. 95.99 ***(978-1-4280-5332-8(8))*** ; pap. 89.99 ***(978-1-4280-5327-4(1))*** IndyPublish.com.

—The Outdoor Girls at the Hostess House: Or, doing their best for the Soldiers. 2007. 138p. pap. 10.99 ***(978-1-4264-7589-4(6))*** BiblioBazaar.

—The Outdoor Girls at the Hostess House O. 2006. 77.99 ***(978-1-4280-2008-5(X))*** IndyPublish.com.

—The Outdoor Girls of Deepdale or Camping. 2006. 41.99 ***(978-1-4280-0232-6(4))*** ; pap. 35.99 ***(978-1-4280-0258-6(8))*** IndyPublish.com.

—Outdoor Girls on Pine Island or A Cave A. 2007. 95.99 ***(978-1-4280-5320-5(4))*** ; pap. 89.99 ***(978-1-4280-5317-5(4))*** IndyPublish.com.

—The Secret at the Seashore. 2004. (Bobbsey Twins Ser.: Vol. 3). (Illus.). 182p. (J). (gr. 3-8). 5.99 (978-0-448-43754-5(6) , Grosset & Dunlap) Penguin Group (USA) Inc.

—Six Little Bunkers at Cousin Tom's. rev. ed. 2006. 192p. 26.95 (978-1-4218-1795-8(0)) ; pap. 11.95 (978-1-4218-1895-5(7)) 1st World Publishing, Inc. (1st World Library - Literary Society).

Hopkins, Cathy. Double Dare. 2005. (Truth or Dare Ser.: No. 5). 240p. (YA). (gr. 7 up). mass mkt. 5.99 (978-1-4169-0653-7(3) , Simon Pulse) Simon & Schuster Children's Publishing.

—Mates, Dates & Great Escapes. 2005. (Mates, Dates Ser.). 224p. (YA). (gr. 7-12). pap. 5.99 (978-0-689-87695-0(5) , Simon Pulse) Simon & Schuster Children's Publishing.

—Mates, Dates & Tempting Trouble. 2005. (Mates, Dates Ser.). 256p. (YA). mass mkt. 5.99 (978-0-689-87062-0(0) , Simon Pulse) Simon & Schuster Children's Publishing.

Hopkins, David. Emily Edison. Rizy, Brock, illus. 2006. 144p. (YA). (gr. 8 up). per. 12.95 (978-0-9777883-2-3(6)) Viper Comics.

Hopkins, Nicolia. What was Grandma Doing? eVision, ed. Wiggins, Margaret W., illus. 2007. (J). per. 9.99 ***(978-0-9768579-8-3(7))*** eVision, LLC.

Hopkinson, Deborah. Adventure in Gold Town. Farnsworth, Bill, illus. ed. 2005. 84p. (J). lib. bdg. 15.00 (978-1-59054-895-0(7)) Fitzgerald Bks.

—The Long Trail. Farnsworth, Bill, illus. ed. 2005. 2004p. (J). lib. bdg. 15.00 (978-1-59054-904-9(X)) Fitzgerald Bks.

—Maria's Comet. 2003. (gr. k-3). lib. bdg. 15.30 (978-0-613-60426-0(1)) Tandem Library Bks.

—Our Kansas Home. Faricy, Patrick, illus. 2003. (Prairie Skies Ser.: Bk. 3). 80p. (J). pap. 3.99 (978-0-689-84353-2(4) , Aladdin) Simon & Schuster Children's Publishing.

—Saving Strawberry Farm. Isadora, Rachel, illus. 2005. 32p. (J). 16.99 (978-0-688-17400-2(0)) HarperCollins Pubs.

Hoppe, Paul & Johnson, Henry. Travis & Freddy's Adventures in Vegas. 2006. 224p. (J). (gr. 5). 15.99 (978-0-525-47646-7(6) , Dutton Juvenile) Penguin Group (USA) Inc.

Hopper, Celia. The Merry Adventures of Blade & Friends. 2006. (J). lib. bdg. 26.95 (978-0-9779662-8-8(3)) Creative Bk. Pubs.

Hord, Donald. Shortcut & Friends Australian Outback. 2006. pap. 12.99 ***(978-1-4259-6355-2(2))*** AuthorHouse.

Hornung, E. W. The Return Match. 2004. reprint ed. pap. 15.95 (978-1-4191-8039-2(8)) ; pap. 1.99 (978-1-4192-8039-9(2)) Kessinger Publishing, LLC.

Horowitz, Anthony. Ark Angel. (Alex Rider Ser.: Bk. 6). 2007. 336p. (J). 7.99 (978-0-14-240738-7(0) , Puffin); 2006. 326p. (YA). (gr. 5). 17.99 (978-0-399-24152-9(3) , Philomel) Penguin Group (USA) Inc.

—The Devil & His Boy. 2007. 192p. (J). 6.99 (978-0-14-240797-4(6) , Puffin); 2000. 1p. (YA). (gr. 5-9). 17.99 (978-0-399-23432-3(2) , Philomel) Penguin Group (USA) Inc.

—The Devil & His Boy. 2001. (978-0-606-22508-3(0)) ; (gr. 5-8). lib. bdg. 14.15 (978-0-613-44387-6(X)) Tandem Library Bks.

—Eagle Strike. (Alex Rider Ser.: Bk. 4). 2006. 352p. (J). (gr. 7). pap. 7.99 (978-0-14-240613-7(9) , Puffin); 2004. (Illus.). 272p. (YA). (gr. 4). 17.99 (978-0-399-23979-3(0) , Philomel) Penguin Group (USA) Inc.

—Eagle Strike. 2003. 352p. (YA). pap. (978-0-7445-9057-9(4)) Walker & Co.

—The Falcon's Malteser. 2004. (Diamond Brothers Ser.: No. 1). 208p. (J). (gr. 3-6). pap. 6.99 (978-0-14-240219-1(2) , Puffin) Penguin Group (USA) Inc.

—Gadgets. 2006. (Alex Rider Ser.). (Illus.). 56p. (J). (gr. 5). 15.99 (978-0-399-24486-5(7) , Philomel) Penguin Group (USA) Inc.

Horowitz, Anthony. Snakehead. 2007. 400p. (J). (gr. 5). 17.99 ***(978-0-399-24161-1(2)*** , Philomel) Penguin Group (USA) Inc.

Horowitz, Anthony & Johnston, Antony. Point Blank: the Graphic Novel: The Graphic Novel. Kanako & Yuzuru, illus. 2007. 144p. (J). (gr. 4). pap. 14.99 ***(978-0-399-25026-2(3)*** , Philomel) Penguin Group (USA) Inc.

Horowitz, Jeanine. Latch Key Kid. 2006. 75p. (YA). lib. bdg. 12.99 ***(978-1-934190-10-4(1))*** Ocean Front Bk. Publishing, Inc.

Horowitz, Rebecca & McCarthy, Rebecca. The World According to Bean: Mr. Bean's Holiday. 2007. 48p. (J). (gr. 2-5). pap. 5.99 (978-0-8431-2524-5(1) , Price Stern Sloan) Penguin Group (USA) Inc.

Hosler, Jay, creator. The Sandwalk Adventures. 2003. (Illus.). 152p. pap. 20.00 (978-0-9677255-1-2(8)) Active Synapse.

Hotaling, Billie. Be Like the Bats. 2002. (gr. 7-12). lib. bdg. 25.70 (978-0-613-78097-1(3)) Tandem Library Bks.

Hough, Emerson. Girl at the Halfway House. 2006. 79.99 ***(978-1-4280-3184-5(7))*** IndyPublish.com.

Houghton Mifflin Company Staff. Zathura the Movie Sticker Book. 2005. (Illus.). 8p. (J). (ps-k). 6.99 (978-0-618-60582-8(7)) Houghton Mifflin Co. Trade & Reference Div.

—Zorgons Attack! 2005. (Illus.). 24p. (J). (gr. k-3). 3.99 (978-0-618-60581-1(9)) Houghton Mifflin Co. Trade & Reference Div.

Houghton Mifflin Company Staff & Rey, Margret. Curious George the Movie: A Junior Novel. 2006. (Illus.). 128p. (J). (gr. k-3). pap. 4.99 (978-0-618-60591-0(6)) Houghton Mifflin Co. Trade & Reference Div.

—Curious George the Movie: Curious George's Big Adventure. 2006. (Illus.). 24p. (J). (ps-k). pap. 3.99 (978-0-618-63449-1(5)) Houghton Mifflin Co. Trade & Reference Div.

Houghton Mifflin Company Staff & Weiss, Ellen. Zathura the Movie: Junior Novel. 2005. (Illus.). 128p. (J). (gr. 5). pap. 4.99 (978-0-618-60579-8(7)) Houghton Mifflin Co. Trade & Reference Div.

House, David James. The Key to Space. 2006. (ENM.). 364p. (YA). 24.95 (978-0-9777086-0-4(8)) House, David.

Houston, James A. James Houston's Treasury of Inuit Legends. 2006. (Illus.). 304p. (J). 18.00 (978-0-15-205924-8(5) , Harcourt Young Classics) Harcourt Children's Bks.

How Mog & Nan Made Our Numbers. 2005. (AFA.). (J). (978-0-9650298-4-1(0)) MBAR Publishing.

Howard, Peggy Ann. Zorees: Land of Dreams. 2007. (YA). per. 16.95 ***(978-0-9795519-0-1(0))*** Dream Scape Publishing.

Howard, Rushton. Sebastian Reckless. Howard, Rushton, illus. 2005. (Illus.). 263p. (J). per. 8.99 (978-0-9768088-0-0(3)) Abdiel Productions.

Howat, Irene. Adoniram Judson: Danger on the Streets of Gold. 160p. (J). mass mkt. 5.99 (978-1-85792-660-6(9) , Christian Focus) Christian Focus Pubns. GBR. *Dist:* Riverside.

Howe, Norma. The Adventures of Blue Avenger. 2000. 240p. (J). (gr. 7 up). pap. 7.99 (978-0-06-447225-8(6) , HarperTeen) HarperCollins Pubs.

Howe, Tina Field. Snailsworth, a Slow Little Story. Howe, Tina Field, illus. l.t. ed. 2005. (Illus.). 24p. (J). 12.95 (978-0-9768585-0-8(9) , 001) Howe, Tina Field.

Howell, David. Swan Songs-in Search of the Staffstone. 2005. per. 13.99 (978-1-59781-002-9(9)) Xulon Pr., Inc.

Howell, Theresa. I Don't See Any Bears Do You? A Yellowstone, Grand Teton, Glacier Adventure. Jones, Larry, illus. 2004. 12p. (J). reprint ed. bds. 7.95 (978-0-87358-886-7(X) , Rising Moon Bks. for Young Readers) Northland Publishing.

Hoylie, Gerry. Byron Unleashed. 2005. 60p. pap. 14.95 (978-1-59113-670-5(9)) Booklocker.com, Inc.

Huang, Kathryn. A Guide Book to the Great Tree. 2007. (Guardians of Ga'Hoole Ser.). 208p. (J). pap. 7.99 ***(978-0-439-93188-5(6))*** Scholastic, Inc.

Huband, Sue. Arabellas Stories. 2006. pap. 14.49 ***(978-1-4259-6597-6(0))*** AuthorHouse.

Hubbard, Coleen. Rush for Gold. Rabinowitz, Sandy & Keiffer, Christa, illus. l.t. ed. 1999. (Treasured Horses Collection). 128p. (J). (gr. 4 up). lib. bdg. 23.33 (978-0-8368-2405-6(9)) Stevens, Gareth Inc.

Hubbard, Sharron/Y. Link & Rosie Pick Berries. Schleihs, Krostin, illus. 2007. (J). bds. 7.95 ***(978-0-9762434-2-7(3))*** Link & Rosie Pr.

Hubley, Mary. Brad & Emily's Treasure Adventure. Hubley, Mary, illus. 2001. (Illus.). 32p. (J). (ps-2). 15.95 (978-0-9707267-0-4(8)) Bluefish Bay Publishing.

Huckleberry Finn. (ARA., Illus.). 48p. (J). 12.00 (978-0-86685-623-2(4)) International Bk. Ctr., Inc.

Hudson, B. Saint Tamika & Josh: Heaven & Christmas. 2006. 16p. per. 9.99 ***(978-1-59886-745-9(8))*** Tate Publishing & Enterprises, L.L.C.

Hughes, Carol. Jack Black & the Ship of Thieves. 2001. 240p. (J). (gr. 3-8). 5.99 (978-0-375-80473-1(0) , Yearling) Random Hse. Children's Bks.

—Jack Black & the Ship of Thieves. 1999. 11.64 (978-0-606-21803-0(3)) Tandem Library Bks.

Hughes, Dean. No Easy Out. 1999. (Scrappers Ser.: No. 6). (J). (gr. 3-7). (978-0-606-16299-9(2)) Tandem Library Bks.

—No Fear. 1999. (Scrappers Ser.: No. 8). (J). (gr. 3-7). (978-0-606-17513-5(X)) Tandem Library Bks.

—Take Your Base. 1999. (Scrappers Ser.: No. 7). 120p. (J). (gr. 3-7). pap. 3.99 (978-0-689-81940-7(4) , 076714003996, Simon Pulse) Simon & Schuster Children's Publishing.

—Take Your Base. 1999. (Scrappers Ser.: No. 7). (J). (gr. 3-7). (978-0-606-16300-2(X)) Tandem Library Bks.

Hughes, Diane Marie. Meet Wilbur the Squirrel. 2004. 21p. pap. 14.95 (978-1-4137-2758-6(1)) PublishAmerica, Inc.

Hughes, Shirley. Alfie's World. 2007. (Illus.). 48p. (J). 19.95 ***(978-0-370-32894-2(9))*** Transworld Publishers Ltd. GBR. *Dist:* Independent Pubs. Group.

Hughes, Thomas. Tom Brown's School Days by an Old Boy. 2004. reprint ed. pap. 1.99 (978-1-4192-9039-8(8)) Kessinger Publishing, LLC.

Hughes, Walker. Sea to Shining Sea with Sticker. 2003. (gr. 3-6). lib. bdg. 11.80 (978-0-613-72162-2(4)) Tandem Library Bks.

Hulk. 2003. (J). per. (978-1-57657-856-8(9)) Paradise Pr., Inc.

Hulk the Hero. 2003. (J). per. (978-1-57657-821-6(6)) Paradise Pr., Inc.

Hulk to the Rescue. 2003. (J). per. (978-1-57657-811-7(9)) Paradise Pr., Inc.

Hulk's Big Mess. 2003. (J). per. (978-1-57657-822-3(4)) Paradise Pr., Inc.

Hull, Maureen. Wild Cameron Women. Mills, Judith Christine, illus. 2000. 30p. (J). (ps-3). 14.95 (978-0-7737-3219-3(5)) Stoddart Kids CAN. *Dist:* Fitzhenry & Whiteside, Ltd.

Hume, Mark. River of the Angry Moon. 2004. (978-1-55054-660-6(0) , Greystone Bks.) Douglas & McIntyre, Ltd.

Humphreys, C. C. The Fetch. 2006. (Runestone Saga Ser.: No. 1). (Illus.). 368p. (YA). (gr. 7). 15.95 (978-0-375-83292-5(0)) ; lib. bdg. 17.99 (978-0-375-93292-2(5)) Random Hse. Children's Bks. (Knopf Bks. for Young Readers).

Humphreys, Chris. The Fetch. 2007. 384p. (J). (gr. 7-11). pap. 8.99 ***(978-0-553-49475-4(9)*** , Knopf Bks. for Young Readers) Random Hse. Children's Bks.

—Vendetta. 2007. (Runestone Saga Ser.: No. 2). 336p. (YA). (gr. 7 up). 15.99 ***(978-0-375-83293-2(9))*** ; lib. bdg. 18.99 ***(978-0-375-93293-9(3))*** Random Hse. Children's Bks. (Knopf Bks. for Young Readers).

The Hunchback of Notre Dame. 2002. 376p. (J). (978-1-58726-015-5(8) , Mundus) Ann Arbor Media Group, LLC.

Huneck, Stephen. Sally's Snow Adventure. 2006. (Illus.). 32p. (J). (ps-3). 15.95 (978-0-8109-7061-8(9)) Abrams, Harry N., Inc.

Hunt, Brian. Joker's Wild. DC Comics Staff, illus. 2006. (Batman Ser.: No. 2). 24p. (J). pap. 3.50 (978-0-439-78950-9(8)) Scholastic, Inc.

Hunt, Elizabeth Singer. The Escape of the Deadly Dinosaur. 2007. (Secret Agent Jack Stalwart Ser.). 128p. (J). (gr. 1-4). pap. 4.99 ***(978-1-60286-004-9(1))*** Weinstein Bks.

—The Mystery of the Mona Lisa. 2007. (Secret Agent Jack Stalwart Ser.). 128p. (J). (gr. 1-4). pap. 4.99 ***(978-1-60286-001-8(7))*** Weinstein Bks.

—The Search for the Sunken Treasure. 2007. (Secret Agent Jack Stalwart Ser.). 128p. (J). (gr. 1-4). pap. 4.99 (***978-1-60286-002-5(5)***) Weinstein Bks.

The Hunt for Pirate Gold, 6 vols., Vol. 2. (Woodland Mysteriestm Ser.). 133p. (gr. 3-7). 42.50 (978-0-7802-7934-6(4)) Wright Group, The.

Hunt, L. J. The Abernathy Boys. 2004. (Abernathy Boys Ser.). 208p. (J). 15.99 (978-0-06-440953-7(8)); (Illus.). lib. bdg. 16.89 (978-0-06-029259-1(8)) HarperCollins Pubs.

Hunter, Bernice Thurman. The Girls They Left Behind. 2005. (Illus.). 192p. (J). pap. (978-1-55041-927-6(7)) Fitzhenry & Whiteside, Ltd.

Hunter, Derek. Pirate Club Vol. 2: Brainwash Escape Victims. 2006. (Illus.). 144p. (YA). pap. 12.95 (978-1-59362-051-6(9)) Slave Labor Bks.

Hunter, Erin. Dark River. 2008. (Warriors Ser.: Bk. 2). 352p. (J). (gr. 5 up). 16.99 (***978-0-06-089205-0(6)***) HarperCollins Pubs.

—Forest of Secrets. 2004. (Warriors Ser.: Bk. 3). 336p. (J). (gr. 5 up). pap. 6.99 (978-0-06-052561-3(4)) HarperCollins Pubs.

—Into the Wild. 2004. (Warriors Ser.: Bk. 1). 288p. (J). (gr. 5 up). pap. 6.99 (978-0-06-052550-7(9)) HarperCollins Pubs.

—The Lost Warrior. 2007. (Warriors Manga Ser.: No. 1). (J). (***978-0-06-124061-4(3)***) HarperCollins Pubs.

—Moonrise. (Warriors Ser.: Bk. 2). (J). 2006. 320p. pap. 6.99 (978-0-06-074454-0(5) , Harper Trophy); 2005. (Illus.). 304p. (gr. 5 up). lib. bdg. 17.89 (978-0-06-074453-3(7)) HarperCollins Pubs.

—Sunset. 2007. (Warriors Ser.: Bk. 6). (Illus.). 320p. (J). 16.99 (978-0-06-082769-4(6)); lib. bdg. 17.89 (978-0-06-082770-0(X)) HarperCollins Pubs.

—Warriors, Vols. 1-3, Set. 2006. (Warriors Ser.). (J). pap. 15.99 (978-0-06-089190-9(4) , Harper Trophy) HarperCollins Pubs.

Hunter, S.C. The Little Cow in Valle Grande: El Becerrito en Valle Grande. Ritthaler, Sarah Pilcher, tr. from ENG. Sundstrom, Mary, illus. 2006. (SPA & ENG.). 32p. (J). (978-0-8263-4044-3(X)) Univ. of New Mexico Pr.

Hurcomb, Fran. One Lucky Fish. Schlagintweit, Kris, illus. l.t. ed. 1999. 32p. (J). (gr. k-5). pap. (978-1-894303-15-6(6)) Raven Rock Publishing.

Hurd, Thacher. Mystery on the Docks. Hurd, Thacher, illus. 2001. (Illus.). pap. 39.95 incl. audio compact disk (978-1-59112-529-7(4)); (J). pap. 18.95 incl. audio compact disk (978-1-59112-322-4(4)); (J). pap. 37.95 incl. audio (978-0-87499-752-1(6)); (J). pap. 16.95 incl. audio (978-0-87499-751-4(8)) Live Oak Media.

Hurston, Nancy. The Enchanted Pixie Gardens: Hide & Seek. 2007. 32p. per. 13.99 (***978-1-59886-807-4(1)***) Tate Publishing & Enterprises, L.L.C.

Hurwitz, Johanna. Pee Wee & Plush. Brewster, Patience, illus. 2004. (Park Pals Adventure Ser.). 144p. (J). (ps-k). pap. 4.95 (978-1-58717-243-4(7) , SeaStar Bks.) Chronicle Bks. LLC.

—Russell Rides Again. 1999. (Beech Tree Chapter Bks.). (Illus.). (J). (978-0-606-21760-6(6)) Tandem Library Bks.

—Russell Sprouts. 2001. (gr. 3-6). lib. bdg. 12.10 (978-0-613-43875-9(2)); (Illus.). (J). (978-0-606-22037-8(2)) Tandem Library Bks.

Hussey, Charmian. The Valley of Secrets. Crump, Christopher, illus. 400p. 2006. (J). pap. 9.99 (978-1-4169-0015-3(2) , Simon Pulse); 2005. (YA). 17.95 (978-0-689-87862-6(1)) Simon & Schuster Children's Publishing.

Hutchens, Paul. The Battle of the Bees. rev. ed. 1999. (Sugar Creek Gang Ser.: No. 32). (J). (gr. 4-7). 144p. 4.99 (978-0-8024-7035-5(1)); 112p. 4.99 (978-0-8024-7036-2(X)) Moody Pubs.

—The Bull Fighter. 1998. (gr. 3-6). lib. bdg. 13.00 (978-0-613-90324-0(2)) Tandem Library Bks.

—The Ghost Dog. 1998. (gr. 3-6). lib. bdg. 13.00 (978-0-613-90866-5(X)) Tandem Library Bks.

—Locked in the Attic. rev. ed. 1999. (Sugar Creek Gang Ser.: No. 35). 96p. (J). (gr. 4-7). 4.99 (978-0-8024-7039-3(4)) Moody Pubs.

—Locked in the Attic. 1999. (gr. 3-6). lib. bdg. 13.00 (978-0-613-90556-5(3)) Tandem Library Bks.

—The Sugar Creek Gang, Vols. 13-18. rev. ed. 1998. (Sugar Creek Gang Ser.). 640p. (J). (gr. 4-7). 24.99 (978-0-8024-6996-0(5)) Moody Pubs.

—Thousand Dollar Fish. 1998. (gr. 3-6). lib. bdg. 13.00 (978-0-613-88120-3(6)) Tandem Library Bks.

—The Treasure Hunt. 1998. (gr. 3-6). lib. bdg. 13.00 (978-0-613-90127-7(4)) Tandem Library Bks.

—The Watermelon Mystery. 1998. (gr. 3-6). lib. bdg. 13.00 (978-0-613-88823-3(5)) Tandem Library Bks.

—The White Boat Rescue. 1998. (gr. 3-6). lib. bdg. 13.00 (978-0-613-90326-4(9)) Tandem Library Bks.

Hutchins, H. J. TJ & the Quiz Kids. 2007. (Orca Young Readers Ser.). 144p. (J). (gr. 3-6). pap. (***978-1-55143-731-6(7)***) Orca Bk. Pubs.

Hutchins, Hazel J. Two So Small. Ohi, Ruth, illus. 2000. 32p. (J). (ps-1). pap. 7.95 (978-1-55037-650-0(0)) Annick Pr., Ltd. CAN. *Dist:* Firefly Bks., Ltd.

Hutchinson, Emily. Last of the Mohicans. abr. ed. 2001. (gr. 7-12). lib. bdg. 15.25 (978-0-613-36461-4(9)) Tandem Library Bks.

—Swiss Family Robinson. 2003. (gr. 7-12). lib. bdg. 15.25 (978-0-613-65747-1(0)) Tandem Library Bks.

Hutsell-Manning, Linda. Jason & the Deadly Diamonds. 2004. (Juvenile Novel Ser.: Vol. 2). (Illus.). 256p. (J). (gr. 4-6). pap. 8.95 (978-1-55050-307-4(3)) Coteau Bks. CAN. *Dist:* Fitzhenry & Whiteside, Ltd.

Hwang, Mina. Redmoon. (YA). Vol. 2. 2001. 200p. pap. 11.95 (978-1-58899-094-5(X)); Vol. 3. 2001. 201p. pap. 11.95 (978-1-58899-095-2(8)); Vol. 4. 2002. 201p. pap. 11.95 (978-1-58899-096-9(6)); Vol. 5. 2002. 206p. pap. 11.95 (978-1-58899-097-6(4)) ComicsOne Corp./Dr. Masters.

Hyde, Dayton. Island of the Loons. 2002. (gr. 5-8). lib. bdg. 18.75 (978-0-613-57307-8(2)) Tandem Library Bks.

Hyde, E. A. Watson. Little Sisters to the Camp Fire Girls. 2004. reprint ed. pap. 15.95 (978-1-4179-9442-7(8)) Kessinger Publishing, LLC.

Hyde, Ray. The CRIMEBUSTERS Club. 2006. (ENG.). 184p. per. 14.95 (***978-1-59800-970-5(2)***) Outskirts Press, Inc.

Hyman, Fracaswell. Adventure with Captain Brainstorm! 2001. (gr. k-3). lib. bdg. 14.15 (978-0-613-50399-0(6)) Tandem Library Bks.

Hyperion Staff & Ring, Susan. Australian Adventure. Song, Aram, illus. 2006. 24p. (ps-k). 12.99 (978-0-7868-4972-7(X)) Disney Pr.

—Birthday Machine. Okabe, Anna, illus. 2006. 12p. (ps-k). 5.99 (978-0-7868-4971-0(1)) Disney Pr.

—Farmer Annie's Garden. Mastrocinque, Andy, illus. 2006. 12p. (ps-k). 5.99 (978-0-7868-4970-3(3)) Disney Pr.

—Galactic Goodnight. Etienne, Kirk-Albert, illus. 2006. (Disney's Little Einsteins Ser.). 24p. (ps-17). 12.99 (978-0-7868-4973-4(8)) Disney Pr.

Ibach, Max. The Castaway. 2000. 288p. (J). (gr. 7-12). pap. 16.95 (978-1-893162-12-9(5)) Erica Hse.

Ibbotson, Eva. Journey to the River Sea. Hawkes, Kevin, illus. 2003. 304p. (J). (gr. 3-7). pap. 5.99 (978-0-14-250184-9(0) , Puffin) Penguin Group (USA) Inc.

Icelandic Horse Adventures in Learning Book. 2005. (J). 15.95 (978-1-59649-224-0(4)) Whispering Pine Pr., Inc.

Icelandic Horse Christian Adventures in Learning Book. 2005. (J). 19.95 (978-1-59210-395-9(2)) Whispering Pine Pr., Inc.

If You're Gonna be a Monster do it Right. 2005. (YA). per. (978-1-59872-088-4(0)) Instantpublisher.com.

Ikumi, Mia. Tokyo Mew Mew. 2006. (SPA., Illus.). reprint ed. 6. 192p. pap. 10.95 (978-1-59497-174-7(9)); Vol. 7. 176p. pap. 10.95 (978-1-59497-198-3(6)) Public Square Bks.

—Tokyo Mew Mew (en Español) 2006. (SPA., Illus.). reprint ed. Vol. 2. 176p. pap. 10.95 (978-1-59497-170-9(6)); Vol. 3. 176p. pap. 10.95 (978-1-59497-171-6(4)); Vol. 4. 184p. pap. 10.95 (978-1-59497-172-3(2)) Public Square Bks.

Ilich, Marjorie. Muttwutter's Adventure in Wappleland. Ilich, Mark, illus. 1998. (Muttwutter Tales Ser.: No. 3). 60p. (J). (gr. 1-4). 13.95 (978-0-935650-52-5(0)) Bengal Pr., Inc.

Ilich, Marjorie & Ilich, Mark. Shoebox Shugroo in Veedoo Land. 2001. (Muttwutter Tales Ser.: Vol. 4). (Illus.). 69p. (J). (gr. k-4). (978-0-935650-53-2(9)) Bengal Pr., Inc.

I'm Just the Right Size. 2004. Tr. of Soy del tamano correcto!. (SPA.). 24p. 8.99 (978-1-59185-423-4(7) , Casa Creacion) Strang Communications Co.

Imagine This, James Robert: Individual Title, 6 packs. (Action Packs Ser.). 120p. (gr. 3-5). 44.00 (978-0-7635-8418-4(5)) Rigby Education.

In Search of the Little People & the Normand Key. 2005. (Illus.). 170p. (J). per. (978-0-9760045-2-3(6) , Reluctant Reader Bks.) e-Pluribus Unum Publishing Co.

In the Clubhouse. 2003. (J). per. (978-1-57657-872-8(0)) Paradise Pr., Inc.

Inagaki, Riichiro. Eyeshield 21, Volume 12. 2007. (Eyeshield 21 Ser.). 208p. (YA). pap. 7.99 (978-1-4215-1061-3(8)) Viz Media.

—Eyeshield 21, Volume 13. 2007. (Eyeshield 21 Ser.). 216p. (YA). pap. 7.99 (978-1-4215-1062-0(6)) Viz Media.

Inches, Alison. Castaways! 2006. (Illus.). 24p. (J). lib. bdg. 9.00 (***978-1-4242-0950-7(1)***) Fitzgerald Bks.

—Diego's Buzzing Bee Adventure. Zalme, Ron, illus. 2008. (Go, Diego, Go! Ser.). 24p. (J). pap. 3.99 (***978-1-4169-4776-9(0)*** , Simon Spotlight/Nickelodeon) Simon & Schuster Children's Publishing.

Inches, Alison. Dora's Treasure Hunt. Hall, Susan', illus. 2002. (Dora the Explorer Ser.). 12p. (J). 5.99 (978-0-689-84664-9(9) , Simon Spotlight/Nickelodeon) Simon & Schuster Children's Publishing.

The Incredible Hulk Storm. 2003. (J). per. (978-1-57657-812-4(7)) Paradise Pr., Inc.

The Infinite Adventures of Rodney Appleseed in Something Happens. 2007. (YA). per. (***978-0-9727894-5-5(6)***) Arizona Blueberry Studios.

Ingelow, Jean. Mopsa the Fairy. 2006. pap. 19.95 (***978-1-4304-4177-9(1)***) Kessinger Publishing, LLC.

Inkpen, Mick. Beachmoles & Bellvine. 2006. (Blue Nose Island Ser.: Bk. 2). (Illus.). (J). (ps). pap. 9.99 (978-0-340-87866-8(5) , Hodder & Stoughton) Hodder General Publishing Division GBR. *Dist:* Trafalgar Square Publishing.

—Blue Nose Island Ploo & the Terrible Gnobbler. 2006. (Blue Nose Island Ser.: Bk. 1). (Illus.). (J). (ps). pap. 9.99 (978-0-340-87900-9(9) , Hodder & Stoughton) Hodder General Publishing Division GBR. *Dist:* Trafalgar Square Publishing.

—Kipper's A to Z: An Alphabet Adventure. 2005. (Kipper Ser.). (Illus.). 64p. (J). (ps-ps). pap. 7.00 (978-0-15-205441-0(3) , Red Wagon Bks.) Harcourt Children's Bks.

—Ploo & the Terrible Gnobbler. 2006. (Blue Nose Island Ser.: Bk. 1). (Illus.). (J). (ps). 19.99 (978-0-340-85573-7(8)); pap. 11.95 (978-1-84032-988-9(2)) Hodder General Publishing Division GBR. (Hodder & Stoughton). *Dist:* Trafalgar Square Publishing.

Inner Voice. 80p. (YA). (gr. 6-12). pap. 10.50 (978-0-8224-3927-1(1)) Globe Fearon Educational Publishing.

Innes, Grant. The Flight of the Whirligigs. Innes, Grant, illus. 1999. (Illus.). 24p. (J). (ps-k). pap. 6.95 (978-1-55037-586-2(5)) Annick Pr., Ltd. CAN. *Dist:* Firefly Bks., Ltd.

Inns, Dennis & Kanaan, Salah. Fattish & Fattoush: The Revelation. 2005. 143p. pap. 19.95 (978-1-4137-4397-5(8)) PublishAmerica, Inc.

Iribarren, Elena, ed. Mambru se fue a la Guerra. Calderon, Gloria, illus. 2005. (SPA.). 27p. (ps-2). reprint ed. pap. 14.00 (978-0-7567-8948-0(6)) DIANE Publishing Co.

Ironman. 2000. (J). stu. ed. 11.95 (978-1-58130-561-6(3)); pap., tchr. ed., wbk. ed. (978-1-58130-560-9(5)) Novel Units, Inc.

Irvin-Marston, Hope. My Little Book of River Otters. Magdalena-Brown, Maria, illus. 2nd ed. 2004. 32p. (J). pap. 7.95 (978-0-89317-051-6(8) , WW-0518, Windward Publishing) Finney Co., Inc.

Irvin, William. The Adventures of Winston & Hazel: Episode 1: the Silver Medallion. 2006. 11.00 (978-0-8059-8220-6(5)) Dorrance Publishing Co., Inc.

Irwin, Daniel. The Adventures of Tylor Bear & Mana. 2004. 144p. pap. 19.95 (978-1-4137-5580-0(1)) PublishAmerica, Inc.

Ishwaran, Wobine. Spunky Sprout in India. 2006. pap. 19.50 (***978-1-4259-4237-3(7)***) AuthorHouse.

Ives, Bob. The Three Ants & the Cat. Fairy, Meg, illus. 2003. 40p. (J). (978-1-920832-07-0(6)) Four Heads Publishing Group Pty, Ltd.

Ives, David. Scrib. 2005. 208p. (J). (gr. 5 up). 16.99 (978-0-06-059841-9(7)); lib. bdg. 17.89 (978-0-06-059842-6(5)) HarperCollins Pubs.

Jablonski, Carla. Bindings. 2003. (gr. 7-12). lib. bdg. 14.15 (978-0-613-65686-3(5)) Tandem Library Bks.

—Homer Sweet Homer. Punchatz, Don, illus. l.t. ed. 1999. (Adventures of Wishbone Ser.: No. 13). (J). (gr. 4 up). lib. bdg. 22.60 (978-0-8368-2591-6(8)) Stevens, Gareth Inc.

Jablonski, Carla & Burge, Constance M. The Gypsy Enchantment. 2001. (Charmed Ser.: Vol. 7). 192p. (YA). (gr. 7 up). pap. 10.95 (978-0-7434-1235-3(4) , Simon Pulse) Simon & Schuster Children's Publishing.

Jackson, Dave & Jackson, Neta. Trailblazer Books Boxed Set: The Drummer Boy's Battle; Traitor in the Tower; Defeat of the Ghost Riders; The Fate of the Yellow Woodbee; The Gold Miners' Rescue. McLaughlin, Catherine R., illus. 1998. (Trailblazer Bks.: Vol. 21-25). (J). (gr. 3-7). pap. 29.99 (978-0-7642-8308-6(1) , 258308) Bethany Hse. Pubs.

Jackson, Gary. The Sunny Side of the Apple. 2005. 28p. (J). per. 14.99 net. (978-1-59975-034-7(1)) Independent Pub.

Jackson, Marjorie. Beach Feet. Cohen, Lynda, illus. 2005. 8p. (J). pap. 5.00 (978-1-57274-750-0(1) , 2123, Bks. for Young Learners) Owen, Richard C. Pubs., Inc.

Jackson, Melanie. The Summer of the Spotted Owl. 2005. (Orca Young Readers Ser.: Book 4). (Illus.). 176p. (J). (gr. 3-7). pap. 6.95 (978-1-55143-412-4(1)) Orca Bk. Pubs. USA.

Jackson, Paul B. Luke & Mcnashty's Treasure. 2006. 96p. pap. 14.95 (978-1-4241-2909-6(5)) PublishAmerica, Inc.

Jackson, Stephen. Mundoespejo. Abreu, Carlos, tr. 2005. (SPA., Illus.). 28p. (J). (gr. 2-4). 15.95 (978-84-666-1495-5(8)) Ediciones B ESP. *Dist:* Independent Pubs. Group.

Jacobson, Jack. No Ordinary Boy. 2003. 188p. (YA). pap. 13.95 (978-1-58736-165-4(5) , Starbound Bks.) Wheatmark.

Jacobson, John & Brymer, Mark A. The Quest: Adventure Story & Songs. Wilson, Roberta, illus. 2005. (J). (978-1-4234-0019-6(4)) Leonard, Hal Corp.

Jacques, Brian. The Bellmaker. Curless, Allan, illus. 2004. (Redwall Ser.). 352p. (YA). reprint ed. 8.99 (978-0-14-240030-2(0) , Puffin) Penguin Group (USA) Inc.

—High Rhulain. 2005. (Redwall Ser.). 352p. (YA). (gr. 4). 23.99 (978-0-399-24208-3(2) , Philomel) Penguin Group (USA) Inc.

—The Legend of Luke. 2001. (Redwall Ser.). (gr. 5-8). lib. bdg. 15.30 (978-0-613-33924-7(X)) Tandem Library Bks.

—Lord Brocktree. 2002. (Redwall Ser.). 15.23 (978-1-4046-1587-8(3)) Book Wholesalers, Inc.

—Marlfox. 2000. (Redwall Ser.). (Illus.). 365p. (YA). (gr. 7-12). per. 13.64 (978-0-606-17602-6(0)) Tandem Library Bks.

—Die Mauer. pap. 19.95 (978-3-570-26021-0(6)) Bertelsman, Verlagsgruppe C. GmbH DEU. *Dist:* Distribooks, Inc.

—Mossflower. 2002. (Redwall Ser.). (gr. 3-6). lib. bdg. 16.45 (978-0-613-71582-9(9)) Tandem Library Bks.

—Outcast of Redwall. 2004. (Redwall Ser.). (Illus.). 368p. (J). (gr. 5 up). pap. 8.99 (978-0-14-240142-2(0) , Puffin) Penguin Group (USA) Inc.

—Pearls of Lutra. 2004. (Redwall Ser.). (Illus.). 416p. (J). (gr. 5 up). pap. 8.99 (978-0-14-240144-6(7) , Puffin) Penguin Group (USA) Inc.

—Redwall: The Graphic Novel. Blevins, Bret, illus. 2007. (Redwall Ser.). 148p. (YA). (gr. 3 up). 12.99 (***978-0-399-24481-0(6)*** , Philomel) Penguin Group (USA) Inc.

Jacques, Brian. Voyage of Slaves. (Castaways of the Flying Dutchman Ser.: No. 3). 2007. 320p. (gr. 12). mass mkt. 7.99 (***978-0-441-01528-3(X)*** , Ace Bks.); 2006. (Illus.). 368p. (YA). (gr. 5). 23.99 (978-0-399-24549-7(9) , Philomel) Penguin Group (USA) Inc.

Jacques, Marcie. Booba-Lou. 2005. (Illus.). (J). bds. 9.95 (978-0-9764114-0-6(7)) Little People Bks.

Jaffe, Nina. The Rain Forest. Caldwell, Ben, illus. 2004. (Festival Reader Ser.). 32p. (J). (ps-2). pap. 3.99 (978-0-06-056520-6(9) , Harper Festival) HarperCollins Pubs.

Jaggi, Harleen. Mystery at the Book Store. 2007. (J). per. (***978-0-9790896-0-2(3)***) Booksmart Pubns.

Jahn, Jazmine. Sneakers. 2006. (ENG.). 32p. per. 19.99 (***978-1-4259-3098-1(0)***) AuthorHouse.

Jaimie Hope, Jaimie. Adventures of Baby Jaimie. 2006. pap. 12.99 (***978-1-4259-5947-0(4)***) AuthorHouse.

James, B. J. Supertwins Meet the Dangerous Dino-Robots. 2003. (gr. k-3). lib. bdg. 11.80 (978-0-613-72179-0(9)) Tandem Library Bks.

James, Brian. Attack on the High Seas. Zivoin, Jennifer, illus. 2007. (Pirate School Ser.: No. 3). 64p. (J). (gr. 1-3). pap. 3.99 (***978-0-448-44645-5(6)*** , Grosset & Dunlap) Penguin Group (USA) Inc.

—The Curse of Snake Island. Zivoin, Jennifer, illus. 2007. (Pirate School Ser.: No. 1). 64p. (J). (gr. 1-3). pap. 3.99 (978-0-448-44574-8(3) , Grosset & Dunlap) Penguin Group (USA) Inc.

—Port of Spies. Zivoin, Jennifer, illus. 2007. (Pirate School Ser.: No. 4). 64p. (J). (gr. 1-3). pap. 3.99 (***978-0-448-44646-2(4)*** , Grosset & Dunlap) Penguin Group (USA) Inc.

—Treasure Trouble. Zivoin, Jennifer, illus. 2008. (Pirate School Ser.). 64p. (J). (gr. 1-3). 3.99 (***978-0-448-44782-7(7)*** , Grosset & Dunlap) Penguin Group (USA) Inc.

James, Henry. The Turn of the Screw. 2005. 96p. per. 4.95 (978-1-4209-2244-8(0)) Digireads.com.

—The Turn of the Screw. l.t. ed. 2006. 240p. pap. (978-1-84637-294-0(1)) Echo Library.

James, Martha. Jack Tenfield's Star: A Story of Yankee. 2005. pap. 30.95 (978-1-4179-9285-0(9)) Kessinger Publishing, LLC.

James, Richard E., III. Adventures of the Elements Vol. 3: Dangerous Games. Lyle, Maryann, ed. Welch, Chad, illus. 2004. 169p. (YA). (gr. 3-12). pap. 5.95 (978-0-9675901-2-7(4)) Three Rivers Council, BSA, Inc.

James, William. Adam's Apples. 2003. (Dream Doors Ser.: Bk. 1). 133p. pap. 16.95 (978-1-59286-912-1(2)) PublishAmerica, Inc.

Jamieson, B. Goldstrike. (Illus.). xiii, 252p. (J). (gr. k-6). 39.95 (978-0-09-174260-7(9) , Arrow Bks., Ltd.) Random Hse. GBR. *Dist:* Trafalgar Square Publishing.

Janicke, Gregory. Attack of the Shadow Beasts. 2007. 280p. (YA). (***978-983-3318-64-3(9)***) Cavendish, Marshall Corp.

—The Shadow Beasts. 2007. (Outcasts Ser.: Bk. 1). 276p. (YA). (gr. 5 up). pap. 6.99 (***978-0-7614-5364-2(4)***) Cavendish, Marshall Corp.

—The Survivors. 2007. (Outcasts Ser.: Bk. 2). 276p. (YA). (gr. 5 up). 6.99 (***978-0-7614-5365-9(2)***) Cavendish, Marshall Corp.

Jantti, Mariana. Pope y su oveja Ba. 2005. (Grandes lugares para la Aventura Ser.). (SPA., Illus.). 28p. (J). 14.95 (978-84-933955-9-9(5)) Hardenville SA URY. *Dist:* Independent Pubs. Group.

—What Is Miranda Looking At? Jantti, Mariana, illus. 2005. (Illus.). 28p. (J). (ps-ps). 12.95 (978-9974-7896-1-6(3)) Hardenville SA URY. *Dist:* Independent Pubs. Group.

Jardine, Alan. Sloop John B: A Pirate's Tale. Pickering, Jimmy, illus. 2005. 32p. 17.95 (978-0-689-03596-8(9) , Milk & Cookies) ibooks, Inc.

Jarmes, Jon Jeffery. Jason Post: Magic at the Downs. 2006. (YA). 19.95 (978-0-9770483-0-4(6)) Speech Publishing Hse.

Jaroszko, Mike. Children's Classics. 2002. (Illus.). 96p. (J). 12.98 (978-0-7853-6910-3(4) , 7168400) Publications International, Ltd.

Jarrell, Pamela R. The Tod Squad Can Pretend. 2006. (J). bds. 7.99 (978-1-57332-413-7(2)) HighReach Learning, Inc.

—The Tod Squad Can Pretend Book with Game Cards. 2006. (J). bds. (978-1-57332-406-9(X)) HighReach Learning, Inc.

Jarvis, Carol & Flosi, Jeanne. Ellie Rose & the Terrible Stomach Ache. 2006. (ENG., Illus.). 40p. (J). per. 13.95 (***978-1-59800-760-2(2)***) Outskirts Press, Inc.

Jarvis, James. Vortigern¿s Machine & the Great Sage of Wisdom. 2006. (Illus.). 48p. pap. 24.00 (978-3-89955-098-6(6)) Die Gestalten Verlag DEU. *Dist:* Prestel Publishing.

Jarvis, Martin & Crompton, Richmal. William & the Hidden Treasure & Other Stories, No. 2. Ross, Tony, illus. 2003. (Meet Just William Ser.). 81p. (J). pap. 8.99 (978-0-330-39100-9(3) , Pan) Pan Macmillan GBR. *Dist:* Trafalgar Square Publishing.

—William's Day off & Other Stories, No. 6. Ross, Tony, illus. 2003. (Meet Just William Ser.). 83p. (J). pap. 8.99 (978-0-330-39099-6(6) , Pan) Pan Macmillan GBR. *Dist:* Trafalgar Square Publishing.

Jarvis, Robin. Thomas. 2006. 400p. (J). 17.95 (978-0-8118-5412-2(4)) Chronicle Bks. LLC.

Jeapes, Ben. Xenocide Mission. 2004. (gr. 7-12). lib. bdg. 14.75 (978-0-613-72334-3(1)) Tandem Library Bks.

Jenck, Heidi Shelton. Pets on Vacation. 2007. (Illus.). 32p. (J). (***978-1-4048-1236-9(9)***) Picture Window Bks.

—Pets on Vacation. Blanks, Natascha Alex, illus. 2006. 32p. (J). lib. bdg. (***978-1-4048-3141-4(X)***) Picture Window Bks.

Jenkins, Amanda. Pecos Bill & Sluefoot Sue: An AMER Tall Tale. 2006. spiral bd. 23.00 (***978-1-4108-7158-9(4)***) Benchmark Education Co.

Jenkins Bathe, Bettina. Violet the Pilot in Canada. 2004. (Illus.). 20p. (J). (978-1-4120-3215-5(6)) Trafford Publishing.

Jenkins, Beverly. Before the Dawn. 2001. 384p. mass mkt. 7.99 (978-0-380-81375-9(0)) HarperCollins Pubs.

Jenkins, Emily. Five Creatures. Bogacki, Tomek, illus. 2001. 32p. (J). (ps-1). 16.00 (978-0-374-32341-7(0) , Farrar, Straus & Giroux (BYR)) Farrar, Straus & Giroux.

—Five Creatures. abr. ed. 2004. (J). 24.95 incl. audio (978-1-55592-147-7(7)); 24.95 incl. audio (978-1-55592-148-4(5)) Weston Woods Studios, Inc.

—Toys Go Out: Being the Adventures of a Knowledgeable Stingray, a Toughy Little Buffalo, & Someone Called Plastic. Zelinsky, Paul O., illus. 2006. 128p. (J). (gr. 1-4). 16.95 (978-0-375-83604-6(7)); lib. bdg. 18.99 (978-0-375-93604-3(1)) Random Hse. Children's Bks. (Schwartz & Wade Bks.).

Jenkins, Jerry B. Crash at Cannibal Valley. 2006. (AirQuest Adventures Ser.). 160p. (J). pap. 6.99 (978-0-310-71347-0(1)) Zonderkidz.

—Disaster in the Yukon, Bk. 3. 2006. (AirQuest Adventures Ser.). (Illus.). 160p. (J). pap. 6.99 (978-0-310-71345-6(5)) Zonderkidz.

—Terror in Branco Grande, Bk. 3. 2006. (AirQuest Adventures Ser.). (Illus.). 160p. (J). pap. 6.99 (978-0-310-71346-3(3)) Zonderkidz.

Jenkins, Jerry B. & Fabry, Chris. The Book of the King. 2007. (Wormling Ser.). 288p. (J). (gr. 5-9). pap. 7.99 (*978-1-4143-0155-6(3)) Tyndale Hse. Pubs.

—The Changeling. 2007. (Wormling Ser.). 336p. (J). (gr. 5-9). pap. 7.99 (*978-1-4143-0157-0(X)) Tyndale Hse. Pubs.

—The Sword of the Wormling. 2007. (Wormling Ser.). 336p. (J). (gr. 5-9). pap. 7.99 (*978-1-4143-0156-3(1)) Tyndale Hse. Pubs.

Jenkins, Jerry B. & LaHaye, Tim. Arrived. 2005. (Left Behind Ser.). 480p. (YA). 14.99 (978-1-4143-0273-7(8)) Tyndale Hse. Pubs.

—Breakout! Believers in Danger. 2003. (Left Behind Ser.: Bk. 29). 168p. (J). pap. 5.99 (978-0-8423-5793-7(9) , 75 5793-9) Tyndale Hse. Pubs.

—Darkening Skies: Judgment of Ice. 2001. (Left Behind Ser.: Bk. 18). 176p. (J). (gr. 4-7). mass mkt. 5.99 (978-0-8423-4312-1(1)) Tyndale Hse. Pubs.

—Death Strike: The Young Trib Force Faces War. 2000. (Left Behind Ser.: Bk. 8). (Illus.). 144p. (J). (gr. 4-7). mass mkt. 5.99 (978-0-8423-4328-2(8)) Tyndale Hse. Pubs.

—Escape from New Babylon: Discovering New Believers. 2002. (Left Behind Ser.: Bk. 22). (gr. 3-6). lib. bdg. 14.15 (978-0-613-59298-7(0)) Tandem Library Bks.

—Escape to Masada: Joining Operation Eagle. 2003. (Left Behind Ser.: Bk. 31). (gr. 5-8). lib. bdg. 14.15 (978-0-613-76889-4(2)) Tandem Library Bks.

—Fire from Heaven: Deceiving the Enemy. 2001. (Left Behind Ser.: Bk. 16). (Illus.). 160p. (J). (gr. 5-9). mass mkt. 5.99 (978-0-8423-4297-1(4)) Tyndale Hse. Pubs.

—Into the Storm: The Search for Secret Documents. 2000. (Left Behind Ser.: Bk. 11). (Illus.). 160p. (J). (gr. 4-7). mass mkt. 5.99 (978-0-8423-4331-2(8)) Tyndale Hse. Pubs.

—Judgment Day: Into Raging Waters. 2001. (Left Behind Ser.: Bk. 14). (gr. 5-8). lib. bdg. 14.15 (978-0-613-33304-7(7)) Tandem Library Bks.

—Judgment Day: Into Raging Waters. 2001. (Left Behind Ser.: Bk. 14). (Illus.). 144p. (J). (gr. 4-7). mass mkt. 5.99 (978-0-8423-4295-7(8)) Tyndale Hse. Pubs.

—Murder in the Holy Place: Carpathia's Deadly Deception. 2003. (Left Behind Ser.: Bk. 30). 168p. (J). mass mkt. 5.99 (978-0-8423-5794-4(7) , 75 5797-4) Tyndale Hse. Pubs.

—On the Run: The Kids Are on the Run. 2000. (Left Behind Ser.: Bk. 10). 160p. (J). (gr. k-9). lib. bdg. 12.64 (978-0-606-21868-9(8)); (gr. 5-8). lib. bdg. 14.15 (978-0-613-33310-8(1)) Tandem Library Bks.

—The Search: The Struggle to Survive. 2000. (Left Behind Ser.: Bk. 9). (gr. 5-8). lib. bdg. 14.15 (978-0-613-33315-3(2)) Tandem Library Bks.

—Shaken. 2005. (Left Behind Ser.). 384p. (YA). 14.99 (978-1-4143-0268-3(1)) Tyndale Hse. Pubs.

—The Showdown: Behind Enemy Lines. 2001. (Left Behind Ser.: Bk. 13). (Illus.). 152p. (J). (gr. 4-7). pap. 5.99 (978-0-8423-4294-0(X)) Tyndale Hse. Pubs.

—Terror in the Stadium: Witnesses under Fire. 2001. (Left Behind Ser.: Bk. 17). 176p. (J). (gr. 4-7). mass mkt. 5.99 (978-0-8423-4299-5(0)) Tyndale Hse. Pubs.

—The Underground: The Young Trib Force Fights Back. 1999. (Left Behind Ser.: Bk. 6). (Illus.). 128p. (J). (gr. 4-7). mass mkt. 5.99 (978-0-8423-4326-8(1)) Tyndale Hse. Pubs.

Jenkins, Jerry B., et al. On the Run: The Kids Are on the Run. 2000. (Left Behind Ser.: Bk. 10). (Illus.). 176p. (J). (gr. 4-7). mass mkt. 5.99 (978-0-8423-4330-5(X)) Tyndale Hse. Pubs.

Jenkins, Paul. Trials & Tribulations, 4 vols., Vol. 4. Buckingham, Mark, illus. 2003. (Peter Parker, Spider-Man Ser.: Vol. 4). 128p. (YA). 11.99 (978-0-7851-1150-4(6)) Marvel Enterprises, Inc.

Jennings, Richard W. Ferret Island. 2007. 192p. (J). (gr. 4-6). 16.00 (*978-0-618-80632-4(6) , Walter Lorraine) Houghton Mifflin Co. Trade & Reference Div.

Jennings, Sharon. Bats & Burglars. Mardon, John, illus. 2000. 40p. (YA). (gr. 2 up). pap. (978-1-55041-644-2(8)) Fitzhenry & Whiteside, Ltd.

—Bats & Burglars. 2000. (gr. k-3). lib. bdg. 11.80 (978-0-613-90067-6(7)) Tandem Library Bks.

—Bats Out the Window. Mardon, John, illus. 2001. (First Flight Bks.). 64p. (J). (gr. 3-6). pap. (978-1-55041-678-7(2)) Fitzhenry & Whiteside, Ltd.

Jennings, Sharon, et al. Franklin & the Stopwatch. Jeffrey, Sean et al, illus. 2007. 32p. pap. (*978-1-55337-891-4(1)) Kids Can Pr., Ltd.

Jennings, Steven J. The Bodacious Adventures of Joe & Barb. 2006. 399p. 38.00 (978-1-4116-7509-4(6)) Lulu.com.

Jensen, Lars, et al. Donald Duck Adventures, Vol. 18. 2006. (Illus.). 128p. (YA). pap. 7.95 (978-1-888472-30-1(8)) Gemstone Publishing, Inc.

Jenson, Jeff. X-Factor. Ranson, Arthur, illus. 2003. (X-Men Ser.: Vol. 1). 96p. (YA). pap. 9.99 (978-0-7851-1016-3(X)) Marvel Enterprises, Inc.

Jeremiatt, Omani. Paper Boy. Rollins, Bernic, illus. 2003. 40p. (J). (gr. 6-8). pap. 10.00 (978-1-929188-09-3(9)) Morton Bks.

Jeremy Thatcher, Dragon Hatcher. 1999. (J). 9.95 (978-1-56137-840-1(2)) Novel Units, Inc.

Jett Jackson, Bk. 3. 2005. 96p. (J). pap. 4.99 (978-0-7868-4435-7(3)) Disney Pr.

Jewett, Sarah Orne. Betty Leicester: A Story for Girls. 2004. reprint ed. pap. 20.95 (978-1-4191-0978-2(2)); pap. 1.99 (978-1-4192-0978-9(7)) Kessinger Publishing, LLC.

Jinks, Catherine. Pagan in Exile. 2005. (Pagan Chronicles Ser.: Bk. 2). (Illus.). 336p. (J). (gr. 7 up). reprint ed. pap. 6.99 (978-0-7636-2691-4(0)) Candlewick Pr.

—Pagan's Crusade. 2000. (Pagan Chronicles Ser.: Bk. 1). 156p. (J). (gr. 6-9). pap. 5.50 (978-0-88489-506-0(8)) St. Mary's Pr.

Jocson, Antonio. Dancing Blues. 1998. (Muddy Tom's Wacky Adventure Ser.). (J). 14.95 (978-1-890963-04-0(6)) Liberty Bell Productions.

Jocson, Antonio & Christian, J. E. The Egg Thief. Swanson, John, illus. 1998. (Muddy Tom's Wacky Adventures Ser.: Vol. 4). 31p. (J). (gr. 1-3). 14.95 (978-1-890963-03-3(8) , LB Bks.) Liberty Bell Productions.

Jocson, Antonio, et al. Richard, Prince of Thieves. Vasquez, Jorge & Romano, Miriam, illus. 1999. 92p. (J). (gr. 1-5). 19.95 (978-1-890963-25-5(9)) Liberty Bell Productions.

Johansen, K. V. The Drone War: A Cassandra Virus Novel. 2007. (Cassandra Virus Ser.). 150p. (YA). pap. 9.95 (*978-0-9739505-2-6(8)) Sybertooth Inc. CAN. *Dist:* Lightning Source, Inc.

Johansen, K. V. Torrie & the Firebird. Delezenne, Christine, illus. 2006. (Torrie Quests Ser.). 195p. (J). (gr. 3-5). 18.95 (978-1-55037-961-7(5)); pap. 7.95 (978-1-55037-960-0(7)) Annick Pr., Ltd. CAN. *Dist:* Firefly Bks., Ltd.

Johansen, Krista. Torrie & the Pirate Queen. Delezenne, Christine, illus. 2005. (Torrie Quests Ser.). 144p. (J). (gr. 4-6). 18.95 (978-1-55037-901-3(1)); pap. 7.95 (978-1-55037-900-6(3)) Annick Pr., Ltd. CAN. *Dist:* Firefly Bks., Ltd.

Johansen, Zdenka. When You Give of Yourself. 2006. 28p. pap. 9.95 (*978-1-4327-0059-1(6)) Outskirts Press, Inc.

John Brown Publishing Ltd. Diego in Action! Follow the Reader Level II. 2007. (Go, Diego, Go! Ser.). 24p. (J). 24.99 (*978-1-4169-4993-0(3) , Simon Scribbles) Simon & Schuster Children's Publishing.

—Diego's Rescue Games: Follow the Reader Level I. 2007. (Go, Diego, Go! Ser.). 24p. (J). 24.99 (*978-1-4169-4989-3(5) , Simon Scribbles) Simon & Schuster Children's Publishing.

John Brown Publishing Ltd. & Murphy, Harriet. Dora's Enchanted Adventure: Follow the Reader Level II. 2007. (Dora the Explorer Ser.). 24p. (J). 24.99 (*978-1-4169-4992-3(5) , Simon Scribbles) Simon & Schuster Children's Publishing.

Johns, Geoff. A Kid's Game. rev. ed. 2004. (Teen Titans Go! Ser.). (Illus.). 192p. pap. 9.99 (978-1-4012-0308-5(6)) DC Comics.

Johns, Linda. Carmen Dives In. 2005. (Star Sisterz Ser.: Bk. 2). (Illus.). 192p. (J). pap. 5.99 (978-0-7869-3714-1(9)) Wizards of the Coast.

—Postcard Clues. ed. 2004. (Shared Connections Ser.). (J). pap. 27.00 (978-1-4108-1644-3(3)) Benchmark Education Co.

—Postcard Clues (Big Book) ed. 2004. (Shared Connections Ser.). (J). pap., instr.'s gde. ed. 27.00 (978-1-4108-1620-7(6)) Benchmark Education Co.

Johns, W. E. Biggles & the Missing Millionaire. 2001. iii, 148p. pap. (978-0-7551-0713-1(6)) House of Stratus, Inc.

—Biggles Breaks the Silence. 2001. 156p. pap. (978-0-7551-0716-2(0)) House of Stratus, Inc.

—Biggles Gets His Men. 2001. 166p. pap. (978-0-7551-0820-6(5)) House of Stratus, Inc.

—Biggles of the Interpol. 2000. 193p. pap. (978-0-7551-0720-9(9)) House of Stratus, Inc.

—Biggles of the Special Air Police. 2001. 184p. pap. (978-0-7551-0721-6(7)) House of Stratus, Inc.

—Biggles Sorts It Out. 2001. ii, 158p. pap. (978-0-7551-0727-8(6)) House of Stratus, Inc.

—Biggles Works It Out. 2001. 174p. pap. (978-0-7551-0734-6(9)) House of Stratus, Inc.

—The Boy Biggles. 2001. 148p. pap. (978-0-7551-0735-3(7)) House of Stratus, Inc.

Johnson, Amy. The Geewhizkids in Shapeland. 2002. 32p. (J). mass mkt. 12.95 (978-0-9712677-9-4(0)) Shapeland Publishing.

Johnson, Bob. The Castle of Gallimaufry Bk. 4: The Squatland Chronicles. l.t. ed. 2005. 56p. per. 11.00 (978-1-59453-510-9(8) , 2549) Airleaf Publishing & Bookselling.

Johnson, Jay, illus. King Funshine Bear. 2004. (Care Bears Ser.). 48p. (J). (ps-3). pap. 7.99 (978-0-439-62490-9(8)) Scholastic, Inc.

Johnson, Judith C. Poppel. Moriarity, Aaron Joel, illus. 2002. 32p. (J). (ps-4). 16.95 (978-0-9724193-0-7(6)) Poppel Pr.

Johnson, Kylie. Fit for a Princess. 2007. (J). per. 11.99 (*978-1-60247-275-4(0)) Tate Publishing & Enterprises, L.L.C.

Johnson, Pete. Trust Me I'm a Troublemaker. 2005. 209p. (J). pap. 8.99 (978-0-440-86626-8(X) , Corgi) Transworld Publishers Ltd. GBR. *Dist:* Trafalgar Square Publishing.

Johnson, Rand. Great Lakes Ghost Ship. 2005. (Michigan Chillers: No. 11). 208p. pap. (978-1-893699-84-7(6)) AudioCraft Publishing, Inc.

Johnson, Sandi. Doctor Hop. Johnson, Britt, illus. 1999. 12p. (J). (ps-6). spiral bd. 8.99 (978-1-929063-47-5(4) , 147) Moons & Stars Publishing For Children.

Johnson, Stephen T. My Little Yellow Taxi. 2006. (Illus.). 14p. (J). 19.95 (978-0-15-216465-2(0) , Red Wagon Bks.) Harcourt Children's Bks.

Johnson, William Crow. The Adventures of Sara Springborn & Mr. Wollo Bushtail. 2001. 208p. (gr. 7). pap. 14.95 (978-0-595-17616-8(X)) iUniverse, Inc.

Johnston-Brown, A. M. Life at Pleasant Grove. 2005. (J). per. 15.95 (978-0-9760718-1-5(9)) Retriever Pr.

Johnston, Fellows Annie. Little Colonels Hero. 2006. pap. 27.99 (*978-1-4280-3363-4(7)) IndyPublish.com.

Johnston, Mark & Spizman, Robyn Freedman. The Secret Agents Strike Back. 2008. 160p. (J). (gr. 4-7). 16.99 (978-1-4169-0086-3(1) , Atheneum) Simon & Schuster Children's Publishing.

Johnston, Tony. Amber on the Mountain. 1998. (Picture Puffin Ser.). (J). 13.79 (978-0-606-13119-3(1)) Tandem Library Bks.

Jolley, Dan. Iron Man: The Movie Storybook. 2008. (Iron Man Ser.). 256p. (J). 6.99 (*978-0-06-082198-2(1) , Harper Entertainment) HarperCollins Pubs.

Jones, Brenda. The Adventures of Murphy the Mouse. Moore, Dwain, illus. 2007. (J). per. 12.99 (*978-1-59712-069-2(3)) Catawba Publishing Co.

Jones, Bruce & Austen, Chuck. The Call of Duty Vol. 2: The Precinct, 2 vols. Mandrake, Tom & Zezelj, Danijel, illus. 2003. (Call Ser.). 128p. (YA). pap. 9.99 (978-0-7851-0974-7(9)) Marvel Enterprises, Inc.

Jones, Carol. Lake of the Lost. 2005. (Illus.). 160p. pap. (978-0-7344-0646-0(0) , Lothian Bks.) Hachette Livre Australia.

Jones, Christianne C. Caleb's Race. Lewis, Janie, illus. 2006. 24p. (J). (*978-1-4048-3135-3(5)) Picture Window Bks.

Jones, Christianne C. John Henry. Peterson, Ben, illus. 2006. (Read-It! Readers en Espanol Ser.).Tr. of John Henry. (SPA.). 32p. (J). (ps-3). 19.95 (978-1-4048-1654-1(2)) Picture Window Bks.

Jones, Dennis. The Life of Socks. 2004. 27p. pap. 14.95 (978-1-4137-2774-6(3)) PublishAmerica, Inc.

Jones, E. Payson, 3rd. The Penny Tree Stories: Bumble Bunny & the Enchanted Forest. 2002. ring bd. 20.00 (978-0-9729194-0-1(6)) Jones, E. Payson.

Jones, Gwyneth. The Hidden Ones. (Livewire Ser.). 144p. (YA). (gr. 6-9). pap. 7.99 (978-0-7043-4910-0(8)) Women's Pr., Ltd., The GBR. *Dist:* Trafalgar Square Publishing.

Jones, Jasmine. The Last Stand: Fight the Cure. 2006. (X Men Ser.: No. 2). 64p. (J). pap. 4.99 (978-0-06-082207-1(4)) HarperCollins Pubs.

—Stuck in Time Bk. 1: Junior Novel. 2005. (Phil of the Future Ser.). (Illus.). 128p. (gr. 3-7). pap. 4.99 (978-0-7868-4725-9(5)) Disney Pr.

Jones, Jenny. Shadowsong. 128p. (J). pap. 8.99 (978-1-85881-708-8(0)) Orion Bks. Ltd. GBR. *Dist:* Trafalgar Square Publishing.

Jones, Marcia Thornton & Dadey, Debbie. Werewolves Don't Run for President. Gurney, John Steven, illus. 2004. (Baily School Kids Ser.). 96p. (J). (gr. 2-5). pap. 3.99 (978-0-439-65036-6(4) , Scholastic Paperbacks) Scholastic, Inc.

Jones, Michael. Finding Imagine Nation. 2007. (YA). per. 10.95 (*978-0-9789386-4-2(X)) Lucy Rose Publishing LLC.

Jones, Stephen M. Charlemagne Mack: Rise of the Queen, Personal Journal #1. 2007. 178p. (J). (gr. 4-7). per. 14.95 (*978-1-933002-41-5(7)) PublishingWorks.

Jones, T. W. Derth. 2006. 165p. pap. 19.95 (978-1-4241-0806-0(3)) PublishAmerica, Inc.

Jones, Veda Boyd. Betsy's River Adventure: The Journey Westward. 2004. (Sisters in Time Ser.). 144p. (J). pap. 4.97 (978-1-59310-207-4(0)) Barbour Publishing, Inc.

Jopling, John Perry & Jopling, Hazel Joan. John, the Airport Kid: A Magical Adventure. 2007. (YA). per. (*978-0-9778070-4-8(5)) SilverBear.

Jordan, Charles, illus. Daniel el Descortes: Rude Ralph. 2005. (Rookie Reader Espanol Ser.). (SPA & ESP.). 31p. (J). (gr. k-2). pap. 4.95 (978-0-516-24693-2(3) , Children's Pr.) Scholastic Library Publishing.

Jordan, Lana. The Sleepytime Ponies Trick a Trickster. Allen, Kd & Giraud, Teresa, illus. 2004. 32p. (J). 12.95 (978-0-9710696-1-9(1)) Jorlan Publishing, Inc.

Jorgensen, Norman. A Fine Mess. 2004. 192p. (J). pap. 13.50 (978-1-920731-02-1(4)) Fremantle Pr. AUS. *Dist:* International Specialized Bk. Services.

Journey to see the King. 2006. (J). (*978-0-9791168-0-3(5)) Lighthouse Bk. Publishing.

Jowett, Simon. Over the Hedge Essential Guide. 2006. (Illus.). 48p. (J). 12.99 (978-0-7566-2122-3(4)) Dorling Kindersley Publishing, Inc.

Joyal, Lisa. Swahili for Beginners: A Young Adult Novel. 2007. (Illus.). 176p. pap. 9.95 (*978-1-894549-69-1(4)) Sumach Pr. CAN. *Dist:* Univ. of Toronto Pr.

A Jugar! Aventuras (Adventure Books) 2000. (Aventuras A Traves Del Tiempo Ser.). (ENG & SPA.). (gr. k up). (978-0-02-148657-1(3)) Macmillan/McGraw-Hill Schl. Div.

Jukes, Mavis. Expecting the Unexpected. 1999. (J). (978-0-606-15911-1(8)) Tandem Library Bks.

Jullie A. Smith. The Magic Carpet Adventures: A Trip to the Park. 2007. (ENG.). 32p. per. 12.99 (*978-1-4259-7358-2(2)) AuthorHouse.

Jumbo & the Stranger. 2004. (J). per. 15.99 (978-0-9744205-5-4(7)) Golden Eagle Publishing Hse., Inc.

Jumbo Fun. 2003. (J). per. (978-1-884907-22-7(9)); per. (978-1-884907-23-4(7)) Paradise Pr., Inc.

Jumbo, the Kids & the Babysitter. 2004. (J). per. 15.99 (978-0-9744205-8-5(1)) Golden Eagle Publishing Hse., Inc.

Junge, Alexandra. A Night-Time Tale. Connolly, Kate, tr. from GER. 2006. (Picture books from around the World Seri Ser.). (Illus.). 36p. (J). 16.95 (978-1-905341-06-1(7)) WingedChariot Pr. GBR. *Dist:* Independent Pubs. Group.

Jungle Book. 2000. (Illus.). 48p. (YA). stu. ed., per. 6.95 (978-1-56254-292-4(3) , SP2923) Saddleback Educational Publishing.

Juravel, Rabbi. A Journey with Rabbi Juravel II: Adventure in the Sky & other Stories. 2003. (Illus.). 254p. (J). 21.95 (978-1-931681-50-6(3)) Israel Bk. Shop.

—A Journey with Rabbi Juravel III: The Great Escape & Other Stories. 2004. (Illus.). 252p. (J). 21.95 (978-1-931681-63-6(5)) Israel Bk. Shop.

Jurgens, Dan, et al. Thor Vol. 3: Gods on Earth, 3 vols. Raney, Tom & Bennett, Davis, illus. 2003. (Thor Ser.). 248p. (YA). pap. 21.99 (978-0-7851-1126-9(3)) Marvel Enterprises, Inc.

Kaaberbol, Lene. Heartbreak Island, Vol. 2. rev. ed. 2005. (W. I. T. C. H. Adventures Ser. : Bk. 3). (Illus.). 112p. (J). (gr. 3-7). pap. 4.99 (978-0-7868-0981-3(7) , Volo) Hyperion Bks. for Children.

—The Shamer's Daughter. 2006. (Shamer Chronicles Ser.). 240p. (J). pap. 7.95 (978-0-8050-8111-4(9) , Holt, Henry & Co. Bks. For Young Readers) Holt, Henry & Co.

—Stolen Spring. rev. ed. 2005. (W. I. T. C. H. Adventures Ser. : Bk. 3). (Illus.). 112p. (gr. 3-7). pap. 4.99 (978-0-7868-0980-6(9) , Volo) Hyperion Bks. for Children.

Kaczmarczyk, Kyle J. The Misadventures of Silent Boy - Volume II: the Stupid Strikes Back. 2005. 52p. (YA). pap. 17.99 (978-1-4116-5231-6(2)) Lulu.com.

Kahler, Janet C. 1918 Covered Wagon Adventure. 2006. (Illus.). 94p. (J). per. 10.95 (978-1-57258-444-0(0) , 945-6305) TEACH Services, Inc.

Kain, Wallace M. The Red Column: A Young Woman's Capture, Imprisonment & Escape in the Amazon Jungle. 2006. (YA). per. 12.95 (978-0-9742148-1-8(7)) Inkberry Pr.

Kalkipsakis, Thalia. Go Girl! #8 - Catch Me If You Can. Oswald, Ash, illus. 2008. (Go Girl! Ser.). 96p. (J). pap. 3.99 (*978-0-312-34654-6(9)) Feiwel & Friends.

Kamens, Gerald. Leopold & Clinton. 2007. 44p. (J). pap. 8.99 (978-1-59092-395-5(2) , Little Blue Works) Windstorm Creative.

Kaminski, Tom. Miss Olivia, the Little Red Poodle: Her First Big Adventure. Fallon, Lisa, illus. 2006. (J). pap. 16.00 (*978-0-8059-7253-5(6)) Dorrance Publishing Co., Inc.

Kampmann, Durten. Adventures of moxie Mouse. Kampmann, Durten, illus. 2006. (Illus.). 32p. 9.95 (978-1-57188-389-6(4) , MM) Amato, Frank Pubns., Inc.

Kanaan, Hanan S. The Jewel of Love. 2003. (Illus.). 114p. (J). per. 11.95 (978-1-59405-000-8(7) , New Age World Pr.) New Age World Publishing.

Kane, James. Ellie's Magic Kingdom. 2005. 73p. pap. 14.95 (978-1-4137-6420-8(7)) PublishAmerica, Inc.

—Tom & Katie's Greatest Adventure. 2005. 73p. pap. 14.95 (978-1-4241-0776-6(8)) PublishAmerica, Inc.

Kane, Tracy. The Magic of Color. Kane, Tracy, illus. l.t. ed. 2005. (Illus.). 40p. (J). (gr. 1-3). 17.95 (978-0-9766289-0-3(2)) Light-Beams Publishing.

Karbo, Karen. Minerva Clark Gets a Clue. 2005. 224p. (J). (ps-7). 16.95 (978-1-58234-677-9(1) , Bloomsbury Children) Bloomsbury Publishing.

Karecki, Jason, illus. The Adventures of Drake Montana Vol. 1: The Great Migration. 1998. 24p. (J). (gr. k-5). (978-1-890716-07-3(3)) K&M International.

—The Adventures of Drake Montana Vol. 2: Asian Mountains. 1998. 24p. (J). (gr. k-5). (978-1-890716-08-0(1)) K&M International.

—The Adventures of Drake Montana Vol. 3: North American Forests. 1998. 24p. (J). (gr. k-5). (978-1-890716-10-3(3)) K&M International.

—The Adventures of Drake Montana Vol. 4: The Pacific Ocean. 1998. 24p. (J). (gr. k-5). (978-1-890716-11-0(1)) K&M International.

Karr, D. The Adventures of Barrett: The Racehorse. 2005. 63p. pap. 12.95 (978-1-4137-7743-7(0)) PublishAmerica, Inc.

Karr, D. A. The Legend of Pendyne: The King, the Horse, the Boy, & the Legend. 2006. 153p. pap. 19.95 (*978-1-4241-5161-5(9)) PublishAmerica, Inc.

Karr, Kathleen. Bone Dry. 2002. (Illus.). 240p. (gr. 5-9). 15.99 (978-0-7868-0776-5(8)) Hyperion Bks. for Children.

—Bone Dry. 2002. lib. bdg. 14.15 (978-0-613-68195-7(9)) Tandem Library Bks.

—Born for Adventure. 2007. (Illus.). 208p. (J). (gr. 7 up). 16.99 (*978-0-7614-5348-2(2)) Cavendish, Marshall Corp.

Karr, Kathleen. Skullduggery. Howell, Troy, illus. 2000. 272p. (gr. 3-17). 15.99 (978-0-7868-0506-8(4)) Hyperion Bks. for Children.

—Skullduggery. 2002. (gr. 5-8). lib. bdg. 14.15 (978-0-613-68287-9(4)) Tandem Library Bks.

Kasser, Carol. Broccoliosaur Stories. 2007. pap. 26.49 (*978-1-4259-7933-1(5)) AuthorHouse.

Kasten, Victoria. Mighty Stallion. 2005. 70p. (J). per. 7.95 (978-0-9788850-0-7(7)) Kasten, Victoria.

—Mighty Stallion 2 Fury's Journey. 2006. 72p. (J). per. 7.95 (978-0-9788850-1-4(5)) Kasten, Victoria.

Kastigar, Jessica. The King of Hearts. 2006. 49p. pap. 12.95 (978-1-4241-3875-3(2)) PublishAmerica, Inc.

Kathleen, Jo Ann. Buddy Can't Tie Shoes. l.t. ed. 2006. (ENG., Illus.). 28p. per. 9.95 (*978-1-4327-0238-0(6)) Outskirts Press, Inc.

—NATALIA, O' MIA, WHITE LACES & SHOES. l.t. ed. 2006. (ENG., Illus.). 28p. per. 9.95 (*978-1-4327-0314-1(5)) Outskirts Press, Inc.

Katschke, Judy. The Adventures of Astro. 2004. (Astro Boy Ser.). (Illus.). 64p. (J). pap. 4.99 (978-0-06-072528-0(1) , Harper Festival) HarperCollins Pubs.

—No Wimps Allowed! Tales of Courage. 1999. (One Saturday Morning Ser.: Vol. 1). (Illus.). 103p. (J). (gr. 2-5). pap. 3.99 (978-0-7868-4307-7(1)) Hyperion Pr.

—Soaring Summer. 2000. (Adventure Ser.). (Illus.). (J). pap. 3.41 (978-0-8114-9319-2(9)) Steck-Vaughn.

—Surf's up: The Movie Storybook. 2007. (Surf's Up Ser.). 48p. (J). 8.99 (*978-0-06-115333-4(8)) , Harper Entertainment) HarperCollins Pubs.

Katschke, Judy. Tarzan Goes Bananas: Disney First Reader Ser. 1999. (Disney's Tarzan Ser.). (Illus.). 32p. (J). (gr. k-2). pap. 2.99 (978-0-7868-4281-0(4)) Hyperion Pr.

Katschke, Judy & Artifact Group. Camp Sportacus. 2006. (LazyTown Ser.). 14p. (J). bds. 5.99 (978-1-4169-0662-9(2) , Simon Spotlight/Nickelodeon) Simon & Schuster Children's Publishing.

Katschke, Judy & Children School Staff, School. Junior Novel. 2006. (Open Season Ser.). 144p. (J). pap. 4.99 (978-0-06-084608-4(9)) HarperCollins Pubs.

Katula, Bob. Larry y el Increible Ataque de los Tapa Oidos. 2003. Tr. of Larry Boy & the Awful Earwacks Attacks. (SPA.). pap. 5.49 (978-0-8297-3747-9(2)) Vida Pubs.

Katz, Welwyn W. Sun God, Moon Witch. (J). pap. 7.95 (978-0-88899-246-8(7)) Groundwood Bks. CAN. *Dist:* Transition Vendor.

Kaulfersch, Ron & Schwark, Mike. Van Von Hunter. 2007. (Kaplan SAT/ACT Score-Raising Manga Ser.: Vol. 1). 192p. pap. 9.99 (*978-1-4277-5494-3(2)) Kaplan Publishing.

Kay, Elizabeth. Back to the Divide. 2004. 384p. (J). pap. 15.95 (978-0-439-63410-6(5)) Scholastic, Inc.

Kay, Ross. Go Ahead Boys & Simons Mine. 2006. 78.99 (*978-1-4280-3199-9(5)) IndyPublish.com.

Kaye, David. The High Fallutin' Adventures of Armadillo Al & the Kilgore Kid. 1999. 46p. (J). pap. 7.00 (978-1-58193-187-7(5)) Brown Bag Productions.

Kaye, Michael. Summer Camp Race of Horror. 2002. 108p. pap. 9.95 (978-0-595-23726-5(6) , Writers Club Pr.) iUniverse, Inc.

Kaye, Steven. The Narrow Road. 2002. 341p. per. 15.95 (978-0-9674467-1-4(6)) Creative Passages, Inc.

Kayser, Eric. Champion: Graphic Novel Series. 3rd ed. 2007. (YA). 2.95 (*978-0-9785605-2-2(3)) Oasis Studios Inc.

Kayser, Eric, creator. Champion: Graphic Novel Series. 2007. (Illus.). 28p. (YA). 2.95 (*978-0-9785605-4-6(X)); abr. ed. 2.95 (*978-0-9785605-3-9(1)); 2nd abr. ed. 2.95 (*978-0-9785605-1-5(5)) Oasis Studios Inc.

Kazenbroot, Nelly. Down the Chimney with Googal & Googolplex. 2004. 63p. (J). lib. bdg. 20.00 (*978-1-4242-1257-6(X)) Fitzgerald Bks.

Kchodl, Joseph 'PaleoJoe' & Caszatt-Allen, Wendy. Raptor's Revenge. 2007. (Illus.). 160p. (J). pap. 6.95 (*978-1-934133-37-8(X)) Mackinac Island Pr., Inc.

Kean, Lorraine. Spiders in the Woods. 2002. 113p. pap. 16.95 (978-1-59129-580-8(7)) PublishAmerica, Inc.

Kearney Cooper, Nicole. Time for Bed: Andrew & April's Adventures. Broadnax, Charles, illus. 2005. (J). 7.00 (978-0-9766086-7-7(7)) Play Bks.

Keehn, Sally M. Gnat Stokes & the Foggy Bottom Swamp Queen. 2005. 160p. (YA). (gr. 5-7). 16.99 (978-0-399-24287-8(2) , Philomel) Penguin Group (USA) Inc.

—Moon of Two Dark Horses. 2002. (Illus.). 240p. (YA). (gr. 5-9). pap. 6.99 (978-0-698-11949-9(5) , Putnam Juvenile) Penguin Group (USA) Inc.

—Moon of Two Dark Horses. 2002. (gr. 3-6). lib. bdg. 14.15 (978-0-613-45344-8(1)) Tandem Library Bks.

Keely, Jeannie & Arnold, Terry. Melanie Runs Away. 2004. (Illus.). 21p. (J). spiral bd. 19.95 (978-1-932373-74-5(8)) Cedar Hill Publishing.

Keene, Carolyn. Action!, No. 6. 2004. (Nancy Drew Ser.: No. 6). 144p. (J). pap. 4.99 (978-0-689-86571-8(6) , Aladdin) Simon & Schuster Children's Publishing.

—Bad Times, Big Crimes. 2005. (Nancy Drew Ser.: Vol. 14). 160p. (J). (gr. 3-7). pap. 4.99 (978-0-689-87883-1(4) , Aladdin) Simon & Schuster Children's Publishing.

—False Notes. ed. 2005. (Nancy Drew Ser.: 3). 154p. (J). lib. bdg. 15.00 (978-1-59054-810-3(8)) Fitzgerald Bks.

—False Notes. 2004. (Nancy Drew Ser.: No. 3). 160p. (J). pap. 4.99 (978-0-689-86568-8(6) , Aladdin) Simon & Schuster Children's Publishing.

—The Lost Files of Nancy Drew. 2007. (Nancy Drew Mystery Stories). 32p. (J). (gr. 3-9). 19.99 (*978-0-448-44647-9(2) , Grosset & Dunlap) Penguin Group (USA) Inc.

—Nancy Drew Girl Detective (Boxed Set) Sleuth Set: Without a Trace; A Race Against Time; False Notes; High Risk. 2004. (Nancy Drew Ser.). (Illus.). 640p. (J). pap. 19.99 (978-0-689-03691-0(4) , Aladdin) Simon & Schuster Children's Publishing.

—A Race Against Time. 2004. (Nancy Drew Ser.: No. 2). 160p. (J). (gr. 3-7). pap. 4.99 (978-0-689-86567-1(8) , Aladdin) Simon & Schuster Children's Publishing.

—Riverboat Ruse, Vol. 11. 2005. (Nancy Drew Ser.). 160p. (ps-7). pap. 4.99 (978-0-689-87335-5(2) , Aladdin) Simon & Schuster Children's Publishing.

—A Taste of Danger. 2003. (Nancy Drew Mystery Stories: No. 174). 176p. (J). pap. 4.99 (978-0-689-86154-3(0) , Aladdin) Simon & Schuster Children's Publishing.

—Trade Wind Danger. 2005. (Nancy Drew Ser.: No. 13). 160p. (J). pap. 4.99 (978-0-689-87641-7(6) , Aladdin) Simon & Schuster Children's Publishing.

—Uncivil Acts. 2005. (Nancy Drew Ser.). 160p. (J). pap. 4.99 (978-0-689-86937-2(1) , Aladdin) Simon & Schuster Children's Publishing.

—Werewolf in a Winter Wonderland. 2003. (Nancy Drew Mystery Stories). 160p. (J). pap. 4.99 (978-0-689-86182-6(6) , Aladdin) Simon & Schuster Children's Publishing.

—Where's Nancy? 2005. (Nancy Drew Ser.). 176p. (J). pap. 4.99 (978-1-4169-0034-4(9) , Aladdin) Simon & Schuster Children's Publishing.

—Without a Trace. 2004. (Nancy Drew Ser.: No. 1). 160p. (J). pap. 4.99 (978-0-689-86566-4(X) , Aladdin) Simon & Schuster Children's Publishing.

Keene, Carolyn & Drew, Nancy. Lights, Camera. 2004. (Nancy Drew Ser.). (Illus.). 160p. (J). pap. 4.99 (978-0-689-86570-1(8) , Aladdin) Simon & Schuster Children's Publishing.

Keene, Carolyn & Frost, Michael. Stop the Clock, Vol. 12. 2005. (Nancy Drew Ser.). 160p. (J). pap. 4.99 (978-0-689-87336-2(0) , Aladdin) Simon & Schuster Children's Publishing.

Keep, Linda Lowery & Keep, Richard Cleminson. The Tale of La Llorona: A Mexican Folktale. Porter, Janice Lee, illus. 2007. (On My Own Folklore Ser.). 48p. (J). (gr. 2-5). lib. bdg. 25.26 (978-0-8225-6378-5(9) , Millbrook Pr.) Lerner Publishing Group.

The Keeper of Names. 2005. (YA). per. (978-0-9744448-3-3(9)) McCourtie, Anne.

Kehret, Peg. Don't Tell Anyone. 2002. 13.19 (978-1-4046-0954-9(7)) Book Wholesalers, Inc.

—Don't Tell Anyone. (Illus.). 144p. 2001. (J). pap. 5.99 (978-0-14-230031-2(4) , Puffin); 2000. (YA). (gr. 5-9). 15.99 (978-0-525-46388-7(7) , Dutton Juvenile) Penguin Group (USA) Inc.

—Don't Tell Anyone. 2001. (gr. 5-8). lib. bdg. 14.15 (978-0-613-44388-3(8)) Tandem Library Bks.

—Nightmare Mountain. abr. ed. 1999. (Illus.). 176p. (J). (gr. 3-7). pap. 5.99 (978-0-14-130645-2(9) , Puffin) Penguin Group (USA) Inc.

—Nightmare Mountain. 1999. (gr. 3-6). lib. bdg. 13.00 (978-0-613-23019-3(1)) Tandem Library Bks.

—The Secret Journey. 2000. (J). (978-0-606-19874-5(1)) Tandem Library Bks.

—The Secret Journey. l.t. ed. 2003. 190p. (J). 22.95 (978-0-7862-5605-1(2)) Thorndike Pr.

—Spy Cat. 2004. 192p. (J). (gr. 3 up). pap. 5.99 (978-0-14-240151-4(X) , Puffin) Penguin Group (USA) Inc.

Keith, Don. White Lightning. 1999. (gr. 7-12). lib. bdg. 14.15 (978-0-613-17594-4(8)) Tandem Library Bks.

Keller, John E. The Emperor's Elephant. 2006. 127p. (YA). per. 12.95 (978-0-942566-45-1(9)) LinguaText, Ltd.

Kelley, Ellen A. My Life As a Chicken. Slack, Michael H., illus. 2007. 40p. (J). (ps-2). 16.00 (978-0-15-205306-2(9)) Harcourt Trade Pubs.

Kellogg, Elijah. The Ark of Elm Island. 2005. reprint ed. pap. 28.95 (978-1-4191-1833-3(1)) Kessinger Publishing, LLC.

Kelly, Charles. Legend of Otherland: Adventure Underground. 2003. 193 p. pap. 19.95 (978-1-4137-0540-9(5)) PublishAmerica, Inc.

Kelly, John & Simkins, Kate. Wagon Train Adventure. Inklink, illus. 2008. 48p. (J). (gr. 3-4). 14.99 (*978-0-7566-3852-8(6)); pap. 3.99 (*978-0-7566-3851-1(8)) Dorling Kindersley Publishing, Inc.

Kelly, Kc. Action Adventures: Magnetic Book & Playset. 2006. (Marvel Heroes Ser.). (Illus.). 16p. (J). bds. 14.99 (978-0-7944-1134-3(7)) Reader's Digest Assn., Inc., The.

Kelly, Marylee A. Quest to Obsidia: The Second Peter Mcfall Adventure. 2003. 126p. pap. 10.95 (978-0-595-29402-2(2) , Writers Club Pr.) iUniverse, Inc.

Kelly, Neil. Evil Adversaries. 2007. 48p. (J). 14.99 (978-0-7566-2701-0(X)) Dorling Kindersley Publishing, Inc.

—The World's Greatest Superteam. 2007. 48p. (J). 14.99 (978-0-7566-2700-3(1)); pap. 3.99 (978-0-7566-2699-0(4)) Dorling Kindersley Publishing, Inc.

Kelly, Neil & Beecroft, Simon. Evil Adversaries. 2007. 48p. (J). pap. 3.99 (978-0-7566-2702-7(8)) Dorling Kindersley Publishing, Inc.

Kelly, Stephen M. Symbala's River. 2006. (YA). lib. bdg. 6.99 (978-1-4276-0237-4(9)) Aardvark Global Publishing.

Kelman, Marcy. Disney's Little Einsteins: Annie's Solo Mission. rev. ed. 2007. 24p. (J). (ps-1). pap. 3.99 (*978-1-4231-0214-4(2)) Disney Pr.

—Disney's Little Einsteins: Christmas Wish. rev. ed. 2007. 24p. (J). (ps-1). pap. 4.99 (*978-1-4231-0210-6(X)) Disney Pr.

—Disney's Little Einsteins: Pirate's Treasure. rev. ed. 2007. 16p. (ps-1). pap. 4.99 (*978-1-4231-0211-3(8)) Disney Pr.

—Disney's Little Einsteins: Quincy's Dream. rev. ed. 2007. 24p. (ps-1). pap. 3.99 (*978-1-4231-0216-8(9)) Disney Pr.

—Disney's Little Einsteins: the Firebird. rev. ed. 2007. 24p. (ps-1). pap. 3.99 (*978-1-4231-0209-0(6)) Disney Pr.

—Power Rangers: Operation Overdrive Adventure. rev. ed. 2007. 10p. (ps-1). 12.99 (*978-1-4231-0835-1(3)) Disney Pr.

Kemler, Nancy. Dragon Box: The Key to Magic. 2005. 108p. pap. 16.95 (978-1-4137-8445-9(3)) PublishAmerica, Inc.

Kemp, Jane & Walters, Clare. 99 Mostly Fun Things I'll Do Today. Uff, Caroline, illus. 2007. 32p. (J). 22.95 (*978-1-4052-2806-0(7)); pap. 12.95 (*978-1-4052-2807-7(5)) Egmont Bks., Ltd. GBR. *Dist:* Independent Pubs. Group.

Kempton, Linda. Jessica Sweetapple & the Battle. (Illus.). 183p. (J). 8.99 (978-0-7497-3905-8(3)) Egmont Bks., Ltd. GBR. *Dist:* Trafalgar Square Publishing.

Kenah, Katharine & Lithgow, John. The Amazing, Incredible You! Level 3: A "Being Unique" Adventure. 2005. (Lithgow Palooza Readers Ser.). (Illus.). 32p. (J). (gr. 1-2). pap. 3.95 (978-0-7696-4273-4(X)) School Specialty Publishing.

—A Crash, a Roar & So Much More! Level 2: An Animal Adventure, Level 2. 2005. (Lithgow Palooza Readers Ser.). (Illus.). 32p. (J). (gr. k-1). pap. 3.95 (978-0-7696-4262-8(4)) School Specialty Publishing.

—Slither, Slide, Hop & Run Level 2: An Animal Adventure. 2005. (Lithgow Palooza Readers Ser.). (Illus.). 32p. (J). (gr. k-1). pap. 3.95 (978-0-7696-4272-7(1)) School Specialty Publishing.

Kendall, Cassie. Laurel. 1999. (Stardust Classics). (J). 16.95 (978-1-889514-22-2(5)) Dolls Corp.

—Laurel Rescues the Pixies. Spector, Joel, illus. 1998. (Stardust Classics). 105p. (J). (gr. 2-6). 12.95 (978-1-889514-17-8(9)); pap. 5.95 (978-1-889514-18-5(7)) Dolls Corp.

Kendall, Sarita H. Al Rescate de Omacha. (SPA.). (YA). (gr. 5-8). 8.95 (978-958-04-2930-2(8) , NR2139) Norma S.A. COL. *Dist:* Distribuidora Norma, Inc., Lectorum Pubns., Inc.

Kendall, Stan P. Samson Gets a Family. 2005. 22p. (J). 13.50 (978-1-4116-5756-4(X)) Lulu.com.

Kendrick, Robert. Treasure Quest: Journey to the Jungle. 2004. 46p. pap. 19.95 (978-1-4137-1467-8(6)) PublishAmerica, Inc.

Kennedy, Kim. Pirate Pete's Giant Adventure. Kennedy, Doug, illus. 2006. 36p. (J). (ps-3). 15.95 (978-0-8109-5965-1(8)) Abrams, Harry N. , Inc.

Kennedy, Shannon. Colt Class Capers. 2000. (Horse Country Top-Hands Ser.: Vol. 3). (Illus.). 100p. (J). (gr. 5 up). pap. 5.99 (978-0-9653703-4-9(8)) Copalis Publishing.

Kennedy Tosten, S. Troy's Amazing Universe: A for Aliens. 2005. 124p. pap. 12.95 (978-1-59113-672-9(5)) Booklocker.com, Inc.

Kenney, Cindy. A Very Veggie Family Adventure. 2002. (Illus.). (J). pap. 19.99 (978-0-310-70464-5(2)) Zonderkidz.

—3-2-1 Penguins! Family Adventures. 2003. (Illus.). 96p. (J). pap. 9.99 (978-0-310-70694-6(7)) Zonderkidz.

Kenny, Michael. The Misadventures of Mocha the Mouse. 2000. 160p. (J). (gr. 4-7). pap. 10.95 (978-0-595-13472-4(6)) iUniverse, Inc.

Kenrick, Angela Mastrodonato, creator. Flannery Fiddlesticks Goes on Strike. 2nd ed. 2002. 30p. (J). per. 12.99 (978-0-9707914-6-7(1)) Litterateur Pubns., Inc.

—Flannery Fiddlesticks Meets the Cliffhanger. 2002. 30p. per. 12.99 (978-0-9707914-7-4(X)) Litterateur Pubns., Inc.

Kent, Deborah. Saddle, Stars & Stripes on the Edge of Revolution. 2006. (Saddles, Stars, & Stripes Ser.). 176p. (J). (gr. 4-6). 8.95 (978-0-7534-6000-9(9) , Kingfisher) Houghton Mifflin Co. Trade & Reference Div.

Kermani, Arax. League of the Spirit Hunters. 2002. 172p. (YA). pap. 12.95 (978-0-595-26183-3(3) , Writers Club Pr.) iUniverse, Inc.

—The Wyrm, Bk. 1. 2003. 134p. (YA). pap. 10.95 (978-0-595-26775-0(0) , Writers Club Pr.) iUniverse, Inc.

Kerr, P. B. Blue Djinn of Baby. 2006. (Children of the Lamp Ser.: No. 2). 384p. (J). pap. 6.99 (978-0-439-67022-7(5)) Scholastic, Inc.

—The Blue Djinn of Babylon. 2006. (Children of the Lamp Ser.: Bk. 2). 384p. (J). (gr. 4-7). pap. 16.99 (978-0-439-67021-0(7) , Orchard Bks.) Scholastic, Inc.

—Children of the Lamp: The Akhenaten Adventure. 2005. (Children of the Lamp Ser.). 384p. (J). pap. 6.99 (978-0-439-67020-3(9) , Scholastic Paperbacks) Scholastic, Inc.

—One Small Step. 2008. 304p. (J). 16.99 (978-1-4169-4213-9(0)) Simon & Schuster Children's Publishing.

Kerr, Pat. Down to Earth. (Illus.). xii, 180p. (J). (gr. k-6). 29.95 (978-0-09-175159-3(4)) Random Hse. GBR. *Dist:* Trafalgar Square Publishing.

Kerrin, Jessica Scott. Martin Bridge: Blazing Ahead! Kelly, Joseph, illus. 2006. 112p. (978-1-55337-962-1(4)); (978-1-55337-961-4(6)) Kids Can Pr., Ltd.

Kessler, Leonard P. Mrs. Pine Takes a Trip. Kessler, Leonard P., illus. 2005. (Illus.). (J). 16.00 (978-1-930900-25-7(2)) Purple Hse. Pr.

Ketcham, Donald. Adventures of Daniel Kroff: The Kid & the Old Man. 2000. 164p. (YA). pap. 10.95 (978-0-595-15049-6(7) , Writers Club Pr.) iUniverse, Inc.

Ketter-Brust, Sandra. Sir Guinness of Wildridge. 2006. 48p. pap. 12.95 (*978-1-4241-4626-0(7)) PublishAmerica, Inc.

Khing, T. T. Where Is the Cake? 2007. (Illus.). 28p. (J). (ps-3). 12.95 (*978-0-8109-1798-9(X) , Abrams Bks. for Young Readers) Abrams, Harry N. , Inc.

Kibera, Ngumi. Shaza's Trials. 2005. (Phoenix Young Readers Library). (Illus.). 103p. (978-9966-47-023-2(9)) Phoenix Pubs., Ltd.

Kibuishi, Kazu, ed. Flight Explorer: Vol. 1. 2008. 112p. pap. 9.95 (*978-0-345-50313-8(9) , Villard Bks.) Random House Publishing Group.

Kidd, Richard. Almost Famous Daisy: Around the World in Famous Paintings. Kidd, Richard, illus. 2000. (Illus.). 32p. (J). (gr. k-4). pap. 9.99 (978-0-7112-1070-7(5)) Lincoln, Frances Ltd. GBR. *Dist:* Transition Vendor.

Kidd, Rob. The Age of Bronze. 5th rev. ed. 2006. (Pirates of the Caribbean Ser.: Bk. 5). 144p. (gr. 3-7). pap. 4.99 (978-1-4231-0168-0(5)) Disney Pr.

—City of Gold. Orpinas, Jean-Paul, illus. 7th rev. ed. 2007. (Pirates of the Caribbean Ser.: Bk. 7). 128p. (gr. 3-7). pap. 4.99 (978-1-4231-0170-3(7)) Disney Pr.

—The Coming Storm. 2006. (Pirates of the Caribbean Ser.: Bk. 1). (Illus.). 144p. (gr. 3-7). pap. 4.99 (978-1-4231-0018-8(2)) Disney Pr.

—Dance of the Hours. Orpinas, Jean-Paul, illus. 9th rev. ed. 2007. 139p. (J). (gr. 3-7). per. 4.99 (*978-1-4231-0367-7(X)) Disney Pr.

—The Pirate Chase. 3rd rev. ed. 2006. (Pirates of the Caribbean Ser.: Bk. 3). (Illus.). 128p. (gr. 3-7). pap. 4.99 (978-1-4231-0020-1(4)) Disney Pr.

—Pirates of the Caribbean: Sins of the Fathers - Jack Sparrows #10. 10th rev. ed. 2007. 144p. (gr. 2-7). pap. 4.99 (*978-1-4231-0455-1(2)) Disney Pr.

—The Quest for the Sword of Cortes, Set. 2006. (Pirates of the Caribbean Ser.). 528p. (gr. 3-7). pap. 15.99 (978-1-4231-0656-2(3)) Disney Pr.

—Silver. 6th rev. ed. 2007. (Pirates of the Caribbean Ser.: Bk. 7). 128p. (gr. 3-7). pap. 4.99 (978-1-4231-0169-7(3)) Disney Pr.

—The Siren Song. 2nd rev. ed. 2006. (Pirates of the Caribbean Ser.: Vol. 2). (Illus.). 128p. (gr. 3-7). pap. 4.99 (978-1-4231-0019-5(0)) Disney Pr.

—The Sword of Cortes. 4th rev. ed. 2006. (Pirates of the Caribbean Ser.: Bk. 4). (Illus.). 128p. (gr. 3-7). pap. 4.99 (978-1-4231-0061-4(1)) Disney Pr.

Kidd, Rob. The Timekeeper. Orpinas, Jean-Paul, illus. 8th rev. ed. 2007. 128p. (gr. 3-7). pap. 4.99 (*978-1-4231-0366-0(1)) Disney Pr.

Kidd, Rob & Ching, Jacqueline. Ghost Ship. 2007. 32p. (gr. k-2). pap. 3.99 (*978-1-4231-0620-3(2)) Disney Pr.

—Pirates of the Caribbean: The Missing Pirate. Disney Storybook Artists Staff, illus. 2007. 32p. (gr. k-2). pap. 3.99 (*978-1-4231-0621-0(0)) Disney Pr.

Kidd, Rob, et al. Pirates of the Caribbean: Escape from Davy Jones. 2007. 32p. (gr. k-2). pap. 3.99 (*978-1-4231-0622-7(9)) Disney Pr.

Kid's Kindness Christian Adventures in Learning Book. 2005. (J). 15.95 (978-1-59210-419-2(3)) Whispering Pine Pr., Inc.

Kieper, Rienhold Richard. Blue Thunder One. 2004. 30p. (J). pap. (978-0-9719284-0-4(1)) Blue Thunder One, Inc.

Kiley, Christian Kennedy. Little Trixie's Big Adventure. 2004. (J). per. 10.99 (978-0-9758888-0-3(3)) IFLY Bks.

Kilpatrick, Irene. A Is for Adventure. Hall, Susan', illus. 2007. (Backyardigans Ser.). 26p. (J). bds. 5.99 (978-1-4169-2779-2(4) , Simon Spotlight/Nickelodeon) Simon & Schuster Children's Publishing.

—TMNT Movie Sticker Book. Style Guide, illus. 2007. (Teenage Mutant Ninja Turtles Ser.). 8p. (J). 6.99 (978-1-4169-4055-5(3) , Simon Spotlight) Simon & Schuster Children's Publishing.

Kilworth, Garry. Attica. 2006. 352p. (YA). pap. 17.95 (*978-1-904233-81-7(3)) Little, Brown Bk. Group Ltd. GBR. *Dist:* Independent Pubs. Group.

Kim, F. S. Blueberry Muffin's Book: An Adventure in Blue. 2005. 39p. lib. bdg. (*978-0-439-70468-7(5)) Scholastic, Inc.

Kimmons, Janet M. The Jewel in the Attic & the Adventures of Tiger. Farmer, Zoe, illus. 2007. 108p. (J). (gr. 1-3). pap. (978-1-58690-028-1(5)) Mould, Paul Publishing.

Kimpton, Diana. Princess Ellie's Starlight Adventure. Finlay, Lizzie, illus. 4th rev. ed. 2006. 96p. (gr. 1-4). pap. 3.99 (978-0-7868-4873-7(1)) Hyperion Pr.

—A Surprise for Princess Ellie. Finlay, Lizzie, illus. 6th rev. ed. 2007. 96p. (gr. 1-4). pap. 3.99 (978-0-7868-4875-1(8)) Hyperion Pr.

King, Charles. The Amazing Adventures of Joey & Joy. 2003. 128p. (J). pap. 9.99 (978-1-58832-087-2(1)); 19.99 (978-1-58832-086-5(3)) Unlimited Publishing LLC.

King, Christopher. Joey's Adventures. McGinty, Paul, illus. 2001. 32p. (J). pap. 9.00 (978-0-8059-5503-3(8)) Dorrance Publishing Co., Inc.

King, Douglas. Smile, God Loves You! And the Adventure Begins. 2000. (Snugeldorfs Ser.). (J). 14.99 (978-0-9662913-8-4(7)) Cela Distribution Services.

King, Frank. Nina & Skeezix: The Problem of the Lost Ring. 2005. pap. 26.95 (978-1-4179-9654-4(4)) Kessinger Publishing, LLC.

King, Paulk, Sr. The Hero. 2005. per. 5.95 (978-0-9771476-1-8(4)) LJK Publishing LLC.

King-Smith, Dick. The Stray. 139p. (J). (gr. 3-5). pap. 4.99 (978-0-8072-1507-4(4) , Listening Library) Random Hse. Audio Publishing Group.

King, Steve. The Stone Dragon. 2005. 80p. pap. 14.95 (978-1-4137-9628-5(1)) PublishAmerica, Inc.

Kingsley, Kaza. Erec Rex: The Dragon's Eye. Payne, John, ed. Grant, Melvyn, illus. 2006. 360p. (J). 17.99 (978-0-9786555-6-3(7)) Firelight Press, Inc.

Kingsley, Mike. Countdown to Midnight. 2002. (Ace Adventures Ser.). 64p. (J). (gr. 4-6). (978-1-876367-55-8(5)) Wizard Bks.

—The Haunted House. (Ace Adventures Ser.). (Illus.). 64p. (J). (gr. 4-6). (978-1-876367-21-3(0)) Wizard Bks.

—The Secret of Shark Island. 2002. (Ace Adventures Ser.). 64p. (J). (gr. 4-6). (978-1-876367-54-1(7)) Wizard Bks.

—The Treasure of King Midas. (Ace Adventures Ser.). (Illus.). 64p. (J). (gr. 4-6). pap. (978-1-876367-12-1(1)) Wizard Bks.

Kingston, W. Aventuras en la Selva. (SPA., Illus.). 160p. (YA). 14.95 (978-84-7281-182-9(4) , AF1182) Auriga, Ediciones S.A. ESP. *Dist:* Continental Bk. Co., Inc.

Kinsella, Sheralyn Mary. A Coloring Adventure with the Coralville Kids: The Coralville Kids in a Coloring Adventure True Colors, an Odyssey in the Sea Coloring & Activity Book. Davis, Bob, illus. 2002. 38p. (J). spiral bd., act. bk. ed. (978-0-9666841-2-4(5)) Odyssey Tales, LLC.

Kipling, Rudyard. Capitanes Intrepidos. 2002. (Classics for Young Readers Ser.). (SPA.). (YA). 14.95 (978-84-392-0922-5(3) , EV30593) Gaviota Ediciones ESP. *Dist:* Lectorum Pubns., Inc.

—The Jungle Book. Alexander, Gregory, illus. 2000. Tr. of 192. 160p. (J). pap. 8.99 (978-1-85793-998-9(0) , Pavilion Bks., Ltd.) Anova Bks. GBR. *Dist:* Trafalgar Square Publishing.

—Kim. unabr. ed. 1998. (Wordsworth Classics Ser.).Tr. of 384. (YA). (gr. 6-12). 5.27 (978-0-89061-099-2(1) , R0991WW) Jamestown.

—Puck of Pook's Hill. 2001. (Collected Works of Rudyard Kipling: Vol. 23). reprint ed. pap. 28.00 (978-0-7426-7852-1(0)) Classic Bks.

—Rikki Tikki Tavi & the Mystery in the Garden. Madsen, Jim, illus. 2006. (Easy Reader Classics Ser.: No. 2). 32p. (J). pap. 3.95 (978-1-4027-3290-4(2)) Sterling Publishing Co., Inc.

—Rikki Tikki Tavi Moves In No. 1, No. 1. Madsen, Jim, illus. 2006. (Easy Reader Classics Ser.). 32p. (J). pap. 3.95 (978-1-4027-3289-8(9)) Sterling Publishing Co., Inc.

Kir-On, Calanitte. The Adventures of the Gimmel Gang II: The Secret in the Basement. 2002. (Illus.). 110p. (J). pap. 8.95 (978-1-931681-36-0(8)) Israel Bk. Shop.

Kirkman, Robert. Freedom Ring, Vol. 4. 2007. (Illus.). 168p. pap. 17.99 (978-0-7851-1990-6(6)) Marvel Enterprises, Inc.

Kishimoto, Seishi. O-Parts Hunter. 2007. (O-Parts Hunter Ser.). 200p. (YA). Vol. 2. pap. 9.99 (978-1-4215-0856-6(7)); Vol. 3. pap. 9.99 (978-1-4215-0857-3(5)) Viz Media.

Kitoh, Mohiro. Nothing but Truth. 2003. (Shadow Star Ser.: Vol. 4). (Illus.). 160p. (YA). (gr. 8 up). pap. 14.95 (978-1-56971-920-6(9)) Dark Horse Comics.

Kiwak, Barbara. Classic Adventures: A Collection of Action-Packed Adventures. Bledsoe, Glen et al, eds. 2000. (Roxbury Park Bks.). (Illus.). 122p. (J). (gr. 3-7). pap. 5.95 (978-0-7373-0275-2(5) , 02755W, Roxbury Park Juvenile) Lowell Hse. Juvenile.

Klaassen, Mike. The Brute. 2005. 180p. (YA). pap. 14.99 (978-1-59092-225-5(5) , Blue Works) Windstorm Creative.

—Cracks. 2006. 142p. (YA). pap. 14.99 (978-1-59092-171-5(2) , Blue Works) Windstorm Creative.

Klar, Elizabeth. A Long Way from Chicago. Robbins, Dawn Michelle, ed. 2000. (J). 9.95 (978-1-58130-628-6(8)); 11.95 (978-1-58130-629-3(6)) Novel Units, Inc.

Klass, David. Whirlwind. 2008. (Caretaker Trilogy Ser.). 304p. (YA). 17.95 (*978-0-374-32308-0(9)) Farrar, Straus & Giroux.

Klause, Annette Curtis. Freaks: Alive, on the Inside! 336p. (YA). 2007. pap. 6.99 (*978-0-689-87038-5(8) , Simon Pulse); 2006. (gr. 8 up). 16.95 (978-0-689-87037-8(X) , McElderry, Margaret K.) Simon & Schuster Children's Publishing.

Klein, Abby. Ready, Freddy! McKinley, John, illus. 2004. (Ready, Freddy! Ser.: No. 3). 96p. (J). pap. 3.99 (978-0-439-55600-2(7) , Blue Sky Pr., The) Scholastic, Inc.

Klein, Grady. The Snodgrass Conspiracy Bk. 1. collector's ed. 2006. (Lost Colony Ser.). (Illus.). 128p. (YA). 25.00 (978-1-59643-172-0(5) , First Second Bks.) Roaring Brook Pr.

Klett, David. The Adventures of Willy & Billy Bk. 1: The Lake Lure Chronicles - Book 1. Lang, Carole, illus. l.t. ed. 2006. 32p. (J). lib. bdg. 17.95 (978-0-9779325-0-4(8)) Five Oaks Pr.

Klim, Christopher. Firecracker Jones Is on the Case. 2006. (Illus.). 116p. (J). lib. bdg. 19.95 (978-1-933435-11-4(9)) Hopewell Pubns., LLC.

Kline, Suzy. Horrible Harry & the Mud Gremlins. Remkiewicz, Frank, illus. 2004. 64p. (J). (gr. 2 up). pap. 3.99 (978-0-14-240123-1(4) , Puffin) Penguin Group (USA) Inc.

Klink, Angie. I Found U, 1. Birch, Joe, illus. l.t. ed. 2006. 20p. (J). bds. 14.95 (*978-0-9762636-1-6(0)) Mascots for Kids.

Klink, Angie. Purdue Pete Finds His Hammer, 1. Birch, Joe, illus. l.t. ed. 2005. 20p. (J). bds. 14.95 (978-0-9762636-0-9(2)) Mascots for Kids.

Klise, Kate & Klise, M. Sarah. Regarding the Trees: A Splintered Saga Rooted in Secrets. 2005. (Regarding The ... Ser.). (Illus.). 160p. (YA). (ps-7). 15.00 (978-0-15-205163-1(5) , Gulliver Bks.) Harcourt Children's Bks.

The Klondike Kid. 2005. (J). pap. (*978-1-60015-070-8(5)) Steps To Literacy, LLC.

Klott, A. J. It's Fun to Be A Kid. Taylor, Rosie, illus. 2001. (J). 5.95 (978-0-9768860-0-6(6)) Two Guys With Flys.

Knaak, Richard A. & Kim, Jae-Hwan. Warcraft Vol. 1: Dragon Hunt : SAT/ACT Vocabulary-Building Manga. 2007. (Kaplan SAT/ACT Score-Raising Manga Ser.). 160p. pap. 9.99 (*978-1-4277-5495-0(0)) Kaplan Publishing.

Knee-Knock Rise. 133p. (J). (gr. 4-6). pap. 4.95 (978-0-8072-1488-6(4) , Listening Library) Random Hse. Audio Publishing Group.

Knife & Packer. Captain Fact: Space Adventure. 2004. (Illus.). 103p. (J). (*978-1-4156-0561-5(0)) Hyperion Bks. for Children.

Knife and Packer Staff. Creepy-Crawly Adventure, Bk. 3. 3rd rev. ed. 2005. (Illus.). 112p. (gr. 2-5). pap. 4.99 (978-0-7868-5573-5(8) , Volo) Hyperion Bks. for Children.

—Dinosaur Adventure. 2005. (Captain Fact Ser.: Bk. 2). (Illus.). 112p. (gr. 2-5). pap. 4.99 (978-0-7868-5512-4(6) , Volo) Hyperion Bks. for Children.

—Egyptian Adventure. 4th rev. ed. 2005. (Captain Fact Ser.: Bk. 4). (Illus.). 112p. (gr. 2-5). pap. 4.99 (978-0-7868-5574-2(6) , Volo) Hyperion Bks. for Children.

—Space Adventure. 2005. (Captain Fact Ser.: Bk. 1). (Illus.). 112p. (gr. 2-5). pap. 4.99 (978-0-7868-5511-7(8) , Volo) Hyperion Bks. for Children.

Knight, Dawn. Mischief, Mad Mary, & Me. 1998. (Avon Camelot Bks.). (Illus.). 96p. (gr. 2-6). pap. 3.99 (978-0-380-73135-0(5)) HarperCollins Pubs.

Knight, Sarah Kemble. The Journal of Madam Knight. 1998. 72p. reprint ed. per. 9.95 (978-1-55709-115-4(3)) Applewood Bks.

Knisley, Eric. The Adventures of Furlington Mackelthwaite. 2005. 40p. pap. 19.95 (978-1-4116-4792-3(0)) Lulu.com.

Knox, Thomas W. The Young Nimrods Around the World. 2005. reprint ed. pap. 28.95 (978-1-4179-6340-9(9)) Kessinger Publishing, LLC.

Kobert, Michael Gilead & Donato, Dona. Who Goes with That Nose? The Wild Adventures of Juicy Coppertoes. Fuller, Laurie, illus. 2005. 40p. (J). per. 9.95 (978-0-9770700-0-8(X)) Giggling Gorilla Productions, LLC.

Koepp, David & Kamps, John. Brothers Together: Zathura the Movie. 2005. (Illus.). 24p. (J). (gr. k-3). pap. 3.99 (978-0-618-60580-4(0)) Houghton Mifflin Co. Trade & Reference Div.

Koeppel, Ruth. Time Pincher. 2003. (ps-2). lib. bdg. 11.80 (978-0-613-58169-1(5)) Tandem Library Bks.

Koeppel, Ruth & Reader's Digest Editors. Exploring with Dora. 2007. (Readers Book & DVD Ser.). 32p. (J). 17.99 (978-0-7944-1280-7(7)) Reader's Digest Assn., Inc., The.

Koge-Donbo, illus. & creator. Pita Ten Official Fan Book, Vol. 2. Koge-Donbo, creator. 2nd rev. ed. 2006. pap. 9.99 (978-1-59816-107-6(5) , Tokyopop Kids) TOKYOPOP, Inc.

Koger, Danny K. The Misadventures of Carson & C J Crenshaw: In Search of the Book of Life. 2007. 184p. per. 13.95 (*978-0-595-42365-1(5)) iUniverse, Inc.

Kohlhepp, Michael G. Within the Hearthstone Book 2: The Fountain of Balance. 2007. (ENG.). 184p. per. 19.95 (*978-1-4241-4446-4(9)) PublishAmerica, Inc.

Kohlmann, Krista. Mapsurne: Unscramble the Hero. 2003. 118p. (YA). pap. 10.95 (978-0-595-27182-5(0)) iUniverse, Inc.

Koike, Kazuo. Echo of the Assassin. 2001. (Lone Wolf & Cub Ser.: Vol. 9). (Illus.). 304p. pap. 9.95 (978-1-56971-510-9(6)) Dark Horse Comics.

Kolar, Marsha. Little Brave Bear. Di Marco, Audrey, illus. 2005. 17p. (J). per. (978-0-9766804-0-6(8)) CottonWood Publishing Co.

Koller, Jackie French. A Wizard Named Nell. Guay, Rebecca, illus. 2003. (Keepers Ser.: Bk. 1). 208p. pap. 11.95 (978-0-689-85591-7(5) , Aladdin) Simon & Schuster Children's Publishing.

—The Wizard's Apprentice. Guay, Rebecca, illus. 2003. 192p. (J). pap. 4.99 (978-0-689-85592-4(3) , Aladdin) Simon & Schuster Children's Publishing.

—The Wizard's Scepter. 2004. (Keepers Ser.: No. 3). (Illus.). 176p. (J). pap. 4.99 (978-0-689-85593-1(1) , Aladdin) Simon & Schuster Children's Publishing.

Konigsburg, E. L. From the Mixed-Up Files of Mrs. Basil E. Frankweiler. Konigsburg, E. L., illus. 2002. (Illus.). 13.40 (978-0-7587-0182-4(9)) Book Wholesalers, Inc.

—From the Mixed-Up Files of Mrs. Basil E. Frankweiler. 159p. (J). (gr. 4-6). pap. 4.99 (978-0-8072-1386-5(1) , Listening Library) Random Hse. Audio Publishing Group.

—From the Mixed-Up Files of Mrs. Basil E. Frankweiler. l.t. ed. 2005. 186p. pap. 10.95 (978-0-7862-7358-4(5) , Large Print Pr.) Thorndike Pr.

—Up from Jericho Tel. 1998. 192p. (J). (gr. 5-9). pap. 5.99 (978-0-689-82332-9(0) , Aladdin) Simon & Schuster Children's Publishing.

Korbel, Wendy. Gus: Adventures on the Farm. 2007. 24p. (J). pap. 8.99 (*978-1-59886-999-6(X)) Tate Publishing & Enterprises, L.L.C.

Korman, Gordon. The Abduction. 2006. (Kidnapped Ser.: No. 1). 144p. (J). pap. 4.99 (978-0-439-84777-3(X)) Scholastic, Inc.

—The Climb. 2002. (Everest Ser.: Bk. 2). (gr. 3-6). lib. bdg. 12.40 (978-0-613-58466-1(X)) Tandem Library Bks.

—The Contest. 2002. (Everest Ser.: Bk. 1). 146p. (gr. 3-8). pap. 4.99 (978-0-439-40139-5(9)) Scholastic, Inc.

—The Contest. 2002. (Everest Ser.: Bk. 1). (gr. 3-6). lib. bdg. 12.40 (978-0-613-58945-1(9)) Tandem Library Bks.

—The Danger. 2003. (Dive Ser.: No. 3). 144p. (J). pap. 4.99 (978-0-439-50724-0(3)) Scholastic, Inc.

—The Danger. 2003. (Dive Ser.: No. 3). (gr. 3-6). lib. bdg. 12.40 (978-0-613-67482-9(0)) Tandem Library Bks.

—The Discovery. 2003. (Dive Ser.: No. 1). (gr. 3-6). lib. bdg. 12.40 (978-0-613-67481-2(2)) Tandem Library Bks.

—Escape. 2001. (Island Ser.: Vol. 3). 144p. (J). pap. 4.99 (978-0-439-16452-8(4) , Scholastic Paperbacks) Scholastic, Inc.

—Escape. 2001. (gr. 3-6). lib. bdg. 12.40 (978-0-613-35733-3(7)) Tandem Library Bks.

—The Fugitive Factor. 2005. (On the Run Ser.: No. 2). 160p. 4.99 (978-0-439-65137-0(9) , Scholastic Paperbacks); 148p. (J). (978-1-4156-0396-3(0)) Scholastic, Inc.

—Hunting the Hunter. 2006. (On the Run Ser.: No. 6). 160p. (J). pap. 4.99 (978-0-439-65141-7(7) , Scholastic Paperbacks) Scholastic, Inc.

—Now You See Them, Now You Don't. 2005. (On the Run Ser.: No. 3). (ps-7). 160p. mass mkt. 4.99 (978-0-439-65138-7(7) , Scholastic Paperbacks); 146p. (J). (978-1-4156-1599-7(3)) Scholastic, Inc.

—Now You See Them, Now You Don't. 2005. (On the Run Ser.: No. 3). 146p. (J). (gr. 4-7). per. 12.04 (978-0-606-33834-9(9)) Tandem Library Bks.

—The Rescue. 2006. (Kidnapped Ser.: No. 3). 160p. (J). pap. 4.99 (978-0-439-84779-7(6)) Scholastic, Inc.

—Shipwreck. 2001. (Island Ser.: Bk. 1). 143p. (J). (gr. 3-7). pap. 4.99 (978-0-439-16456-6(7)) Scholastic, Inc.

—Shipwreck. 2001. (gr. 3-6). lib. bdg. 12.40 (978-0-613-36068-5(0)) Tandem Library Bks.

—The Summit. 2002. (Everest Ser.). (gr. 3-6). lib. bdg. 12.40 (978-0-613-58505-7(4)) Tandem Library Bks.

—Survival. 2001. (Island Ser.). 144p. (J). (gr. 4-7). pap. 4.99 (978-0-439-16457-3(5)) Scholastic, Inc.

—Survival. 2001. (gr. 3-6). lib. bdg. 12.40 (978-0-613-35732-6(9)) Tandem Library Bks.

Korman, Gordon. Swindle. 2008. 256p. (J). pap. 16.99 (*978-0-439-90344-8(0) , Scholastic Pr.) Scholastic, Inc.

Korman, Justine. Spring Is Here, Grumpy Bunny! 2008. (Clifford's Bedtime Ser.). 64p. (J). pap. 4.99 (*978-0-545-03402-9(7) , Cartwheel Bks.) Scholastic, Inc.

Korman, Susan. Jewel of the Sea Cruise. 1999. (Magic Attic Club Ser.). (J). (gr. 2-6). (978-0-606-16951-6(2)) Tandem Library Bks.

Korman, Susan. The Life & Times of Cody Maverick. 2007. (Surf's Up Ser.). 144p. (J). pap. 4.99 (*978-0-06-115332-7(X) , Harper Entertainment) HarperCollins Pubs.

Koski, Mary B. Stowaway Fairy Goes to Japan. 2002. (J). 8.99 (978-0-89610-203-3(3)) Island Heritage Publishing.

Kovac, Tommy. Wonderland #1. 2006. (Illus.). 24p. (YA). pap. 3.50 (978-1-59362-039-4(X) , Slave Labor Graphics) Slave Labor Bks.

—Wonderland #2: The Tulgey Wood & the Treacle Well. 2006. (Illus.). 3.50 (978-1-59362-050-9(0)) Slave Labor Bks.

Kovalski, Maryann. Jenny & Joanna Album. 2005. (978-1-55041-941-2(2)) Fitzhenry & Whiteside, Ltd.

Kowitt, Holly. Road Trip Vol. 2. 2006. (Teenick Ser.). 128p. (J). pap. 4.99 (978-0-439-89041-0(1) , Scholastic) Scholastic, Inc.

Kratzer, Mary. The Adventure Club Catches the Poachers. 2006. 76p. pap. 14.95 (978-1-4137-7376-7(1)) PublishAmerica, Inc.

Kravetz, Nathan. Moscow, Farewell! A Russian Boy's Adventure in Times Past. 2000. (gr. 7-12). lib. bdg. 31.55 (978-0-613-73907-8(8)) Tandem Library Bks.

Kreschner, Bill & Kreschner, Phyllis. Plucky-lucky duck's amazing Adventures. 2007. 16.95 (*978-0-533-15647-4(5)) Vantage Pr., Inc.

Kress, Adrienne. Alex & the Ironic Gentleman. 2007. 320p. (YA). (gr. 3-7). 16.95 (*978-1-60286-005-6(X)) Weinstein Bks.

Krill, Darren. Escape from Treasure Island. 2006. 336p. (J). (gr. 3-7). pap. (978-1-897073-31-5(3)) Lobster Pr.

Krings, Antoon. Abeja Teresa. 2005. (Bichitos curiosos Ser.). (SPA., Illus.). 32p. (J). 5.95 (978-84-932442-7-9(9)) Blume ESP. *Dist:* Independent Pubs. Group.

—Gilberto Mariposa. 2005. (Bichitos curiosos Ser.). (SPA., Illus.). 32p. (J). 5.95 (978-84-932442-9-3(5)) Blume ESP. *Dist:* Independent Pubs. Group.

Kropp, Joseph. Bowlegs' Bounty. 2005. 192p. (J). pap. 9.95 (978-1-890905-24-8(0)) Day to Day Enterprises.

Kropp, Paul. Moonkid & Prometheus. unabr. ed. 1998. (Gemini Bks.). 294p. (gr. 7-9). mass mkt. 5.95 (978-0-7736-7465-3(9)) Stoddart Kids CAN. *Dist:* Fitzhenry & Whiteside, Ltd.

Krug, R. Lyding. The Treasure of Ferson Creek. 2006. 133p. (YA). pap. 9.95 (978-1-4116-3683-5(X)) Lulu.com.

Krymski, Walter A. The Adventures of Peter Pangler Puncker: Discovering the Pumping Heart. 2005. (Illus.). 16p. (J). 17.00 (978-0-8059-9940-2(X) , RoseDog Bks.) Dorrance Publishing Co., Inc.

Kubert, Joe. The Adventures of Yaakov & Isaac. 64p. 9.99 (978-1-58330-741-0(9)) Feldheim Pubs.

Kubik, Dorothy. The Adventures of Elbert & Leopoldina. James, Annie, illus. 2006. 104p. (J). per. 15.00 (*978-0-9790775-1-7(6)) Touchstone Communications.

Kubler, Annie. Busy Builders. 1999. (Illus.). 44p. (ps-k). 4.99 (978-0-85953-882-4(6)) Child's Play International Ltd. GBR. *Dist:* Child's Play-International.

Kuchman, D. S. Krystal Steps: The Journey Begins. 2006. 57p. pap. 12.95 (*978-1-4241-5135-6(X)) PublishAmerica, Inc.

Kulling, Monica. Sea of Ice: The Wreck of the Endurance. 1999. (Step into Reading Ser.). (978-0-606-18503-5(8)) Tandem Library Bks.

Kunda, Shmuel. Boruch Learns about Pesach. 2001. (Illus.). 40p. (J). 13.95 (978-1-932443-19-6(3) , BLPH) Judaica Pr., Inc., The.

Kunkel, Mike. Inheritance. 2003. (gr. k-3). lib. bdg. 30.35 (978-0-613-77882-4(0)) Tandem Library Bks.

Kunneman, Hank. La Cosa Mas Grande de Todos! Las Adventures de Mazfi y Milo. Wilson, David, illus. 1999. (Adventures of Mutzsphey & Milo Ser.). (SPA.). 32p. (J). (gr. k-5). 10.95 (978-1-930120-03-7(6)) Great Adventures Pubn.

—En la Busqueda del Regalo Gratis: Las Adventuras de Mazfi y Milo. Wilson, David, illus. 1999. (Adventures of Mutzsphey & Milo Ser.). (SPA.). 48p. (J). (gr. k-5). 13.95 (978-1-930120-01-3(X)) Great Adventures Pubn.

—The Greatest Thing of All. Wilson, David, illus. 1999. (Adventures of Mutzsphey & Milo Ser.). 32p. (J). (gr. k-5). 10.95 (978-1-930120-02-0(8)) Great Adventures Pubn.

—In Search of the Free Gift. Wilson, David, illus. 1999. (Adventures of Mutzsphey & Milo Ser.). 48p. (J). (gr. k-5). 13.95 (978-1-930120-00-6(1)) Great Adventures Pubn.

Kurtz, Scott. PvP Rides Again, Vol. 3. (Illus.). 144p. pap. 11.95 (978-1-58240-553-7(0)) Image Comics.

Kusaka, Hidenori. Pokemon Yellow Caballero: Blue Returns. MATO Staff, illus. 2002. (Pokemon Adventures Ser.). 54p. (YA). (gr. 4-7). pap. 4.95 (978-1-56931-564-4(7)) Viz Media.

—Saffron City Siege. MATO Staff, illus. 2001. (Pokemon Adventures Ser.: Vol. 3). 224p. (YA). (gr. 4-7). pap. 13.95 (978-1-56931-560-6(4)) Viz Media.

—Yellow Caballero: The Seafoam Encounter. MATO Staff, illus. 2002. (Pokemon Adventures Ser.: Vol. 5). 49p. (YA). pap. 4.95 (978-1-56931-726-6(7)) Viz Media.

—Yellow Caballero Vol. 7: The Pokemon Elite. MATO Staff, illus. 2003. (Pokemon Adventures Ser.). 208p. (YA). pap. 13.95 (978-1-56931-851-5(4)) Viz Media.

Kwiat, C. R. Saber's Edge. 2006. 212p. (YA). pap. 13.00 (978-1-4116-9668-6(9)) Lulu.com.

Kyne, Peter B. The Three Godfathers. 2005. reprint ed. pap. 15.95 (978-1-4179-0351-1(1)) Kessinger Publishing, LLC.

La Brack, Joy. Elmo's Animal Adventures. DiCiccio, Sue, illus. 2000. (Baby Fingers Ser.). 14p. (J). (gr. k-ps). bds. 4.99 (978-0-375-80331-4(9) , Random Hse. Bks. for Young Readers) Random Hse. Children's Bks.

La Fon-Cox, Angelique. A Tale of Kooshla & Saboo: in Heavenly Castles. 2006. (ENG.). 48p. per. 19.99 (*978-1-4259-7997-3(1)) AuthorHouse.

Labatt, Mary. Weekend at the Grand Hotel. 2001. (gr. 3-6). lib. bdg. 12.95 (978-0-613-37071-4(6)) Tandem Library Bks.

LaBrot, Matthew & Daniel, Hale. Green Streak. 2004. (Zeke Armstrong Mysteries Ser.: 2). 236p. (J). per. 8.95 (978-1-929976-28-7(3)) Top Pubns., Ltd.

Lade, Linda. Peter Bunny: Adventures in the Kudzu Pat. 2006. 82p. pap. 14.95 (978-1-4241-3818-0(3)) PublishAmerica, Inc.

Ladew, Donald. Troop 402: A Novel. 2003. 178p. (YA). pap. 13.95 (978-0-595-27317-1(3)) iUniverse, Inc.

LaFevers, R. L. The Secrets of Grim Wood. 2006. (Lowthar's Blade Ser.: Bk. 2). 160p. (J). (gr. 2). pap. 5.99 (978-0-14-240558-1(2) , Puffin) Penguin Group (USA) Inc.

LaFevers, R. L. Theodosia & the Serpents of Chaos. Tanaka, Yoko, illus. 2007. 368p. (J). (gr. 5-7). 16.00 (*978-0-618-75638-4(8)) Houghton Mifflin Co. Trade & Reference Div.

Lagerlof, Selma. The Further Adventures of Nils. 2005. pap. 31.95 (978-1-4179-9042-9(2)) Kessinger Publishing, LLC.

—The Further Adventures of Nils. 2006. 384p. pap. 25.45 (*978-1-59462-402-5(X) , 438, Book Jungle) Standard Pubns., Inc.

Lagoon Books Staff, ed. Dr. C. K. Fortune & the Lost City Labyrinth. Lee, Brian, illus. 2000. (Soft Bath Book Ser.). 20p. (J). (gr. 2-9). 9.95 (978-1-902813-12-7(X)) Lagoon Bks. GBR. *Dist:* Midpoint Trade Bks., Inc.

LaHaye, Tim & Jenkins, Jerry B. El Clandestino. 2000. (Dejados Atras los Chicos Ser.: Vol. 6). (SPA.). (J). (gr. 4-7). pap. 4.99 (978-0-7899-0724-0(0)) Spanish Hse. Distributors.

—Dejados Atras. 2003. (Left Behind Ser.).Tr. of Left Behind. (SPA., Illus.). 48p. 4.99 (978-0-8054-2843-8(7)); Vol. 2. pap. 4.99 (978-0-8054-2847-6(X)); Vol. 3. 4.99 (978-0-8054-2844-5(5)) B&H Publishing Grp.

—Secundaria Nicolas. 2000. (Dejados Atras los Chicos Ser.: Vol. 5). (SPA.). (J). (gr. 4-7). pap. 4.99 (978-0-7899-0723-3(2)) Spanish Hse. Distributors.

Lahey, Thomas A. King of the Pygmies. 2005. pap. 28.95 (978-1-4179-9360-4(X)) Kessinger Publishing, LLC.

Laird, Elizabeth. Simon & the Spy. 2002. (Illus.). 16p. pap. (978-0-582-40291-1(3) , Putnam Juvenile) Penguin Group (USA) Inc.

Laird, Marnie. Water Rat. 2001. 192p. (J). (gr. 4-7). pap. 5.95 (978-1-58837-002-0(X)) Winslow Pr.

Lakin, Patricia. Stuart's Wild Ride. 2002. (ps-2). lib. bdg. 11.80 (978-0-613-50511-6(5)) Tandem Library Bks.

Lamb, Dorothy M. The Call of the Mountain. 1999. (Illus.). (J). (gr. k-3). 10.95 (978-0-533-12938-6(9)) Vantage Pr., Inc.

Lamb, Tanya. Kyle's One Day Adventures. 2005. (J). pap. 16.00 (978-0-8059-6683-1(8)) Dorrance Publishing Co., Inc.

Lambert, Ian. Viajes y Adventuras. Lambert, Ian, illus. 2001. (SPA., Illus.). 32p. (J). (ps-3). pap. 7.50 (978-1-884083-48-8(X)) Maval Publishing, Inc.

Lambert, Janet. A Bright Tomorrow. 2001. (Jordon Ser.: Vol. 9). (YA). pap. 12.95 (978-1-930009-40-0(2)) Image Cascade Publishing.

—One for the Money. 2001. (Candy Kane Ser.: Vol. 3). (YA). pap. 12.95 (978-1-930009-47-9(X)) Image Cascade Publishing.

Lambert, Patricia. The Blue Ribbon Chicken. 2005. 36p. (J). pap. 14.93 (978-1-4116-6163-9(X)) Lulu.com.

Lamensdorf, Len. The Crouching Dragon. 1999. (Will to Conquer Ser.: Bk. 1). (Illus.). 278p. (YA). (gr. 7-12). 19.95 (978-0-9669741-5-7(8)) SeaScape Pr., Ltd.

L'Amour, Louis. Hanging Woman Creek. 1999. (gr. 7-12). lib. bdg. 12.40 (978-0-8085-1672-9(8)) Tandem Library Bks.

Lampman, Evelyn Sibley. The Shy Stegosaurus of Cricket Creek. Buel, Hubert, illus. 2001. 220p. (J). 17.95 (978-1-930900-09-7(0)) Purple Hse. Pr.

Lamson, Sharon. Squiggz Rides the Big Storm: A Story about Overcoming Fear. Barry, Bruce, illus. 2006. 32p. (J). 7.99 (978-0-310-71005-9(7)) Zonderkidz.

Lancaster, Janie. Julie & the Lost Fairy Tale. 2006. (Illus.). 116p. (J). per. 10.95 (*978-1-932993-60-8(6)) Star Publish LLC.

Lancaster, Susan. The Caves & the Skull. 2004. 160p. pap. 12.95 (978-0-9730350-1-8(3)) Snosrap Publishing CAN. *Dist:* Hushion Hse. Publishing, Ltd.

—Caves & the Skull. 2003. (gr. 7-12). lib. bdg. 22.20 (978-0-613-83368-4(6)) Tandem Library Bks.

Lancett, Peter. Dark Machine. 2007. (Dark Man Ser.). 36p. pap. 6.95 (*978-1-84167-601-2(2)) Ransom Publishing Ltd. GBR. *Dist:* International Publishers Marketing.

—Day Is Dark. 2007. (Dark Man Ser.). 36p. pap. 6.95 (*978-1-84167-606-7(3)) Ransom Publishing Ltd. GBR. *Dist:* International Publishers Marketing.

—Dying for the Dark. 2007. (Dark Man Ser.). 36p. pap. 6.95 (*978-1-84167-604-3(7)) Ransom Publishing Ltd. GBR. *Dist:* International Publishers Marketing.

The Land Beyond Forever. 2006. 25.00 (*978-0-9785570-0-3(X)) Three Sisters Publishing Hse., Ltd.

Land, David, et al. Star Wars Infinities: The Empire Strikes Back. Fabbri, Davide & Vecchia, Christian Della, illus. 2003. 96p. (YA). (gr. 3 up). pap. 12.95 (978-1-56971-904-6(7)) Dark Horse Comics.

Lander, C. F. Willow & the Ice Fairies. 2004. 88p. pap. 14.95 (978-1-4137-1638-2(5)) PublishAmerica, Inc.

Landes, David. The Three Little Fish. 2007. (Illus.). 22p. (J). per. 8.99 (*978-1-60247-117-7(7)) Tate Publishing & Enterprises, L.L.C.

Lane, Jeanette. Magic School Bus & the Missing Tooth. 2007. (Magic School Bus Ser.). 32p. (J). pap. 3.99 (978-0-439-80107-2(9) , Cartwheel Bks.) Scholastic, Inc.

Lane, Leonie. Tom Turner & the Dream Box. 2006. 119p. pap. (*978-1-84685-460-6(1) , Exposure Publishing) Meadow Bks.

Lang, Andrew. Prince Prigio. 2004. reprint ed. pap. 19.95 (978-1-4179-0522-5(0)) Kessinger Publishing, LLC.
Langan, Paul. Summer of Secrets. Langan, Paul, ed. 2004. (Bluford Ser.: 10). 142p. (YA). mass mkt. 4.95 (978-1-59194-018-0(4)) Townsend Pr.
Langan, Paul & Blackwell, D. M. Blood Is Thicker. Langan, Paul, ed. 2004. (Bluford Ser.: 8). 156p. (YA). mass mkt. 4.95 (978-1-59194-016-6(8)) Townsend Pr.
Langen, Annette. Felix Explores Planet Earth. Droop, Constanza, illus. 2004. (Perfect for Earth Day Promotions! Ser.). 47p. (J). 14.99 (978-1-59384-030-3(6)) Parklane Publishing.
Langrish, Katherine. Troll Blood. Stevens, Tim, illus. 2008. 352p. (J). 16.99 ***(978-0-06-111674-2(2)***); lib. bdg. 17.89 ***(978-0-06-111675-9(0))*** HarperCollins Pubs. (Eos).
Langworthy, John Luther. The Aeroplane Boys Flight. 2004. reprint ed. pap. 1.99 (978-1-4192-5169-6(4)) Kessinger Publishing, LLC.
Lanse, Hal W. Penelope Quagmire & the Lizard Men from Outer Space. (J). 2004. 15.00 (978-1-893896-40-6(4)); 2001. 172p. (gr. 4-7). pap. 10.50 (978-1-893896-46-8(3)) ImaJinn Bks.
Lansing, Richard, Jr. The Brown Mud Chickens. Lansing, Randy, illus. 2000. 48p. per. 6.00 (978-0-9661844-6-4(7)) Purple Gorilla, LLC, The.
Lansing, Richard D., Jr. The Black Catskill Cat. Lansing, Randy, illus. 2000. 48p. (J). per. 6.00 (978-0-9661844-7-1(5)) Purple Gorilla, LLC, The.
—The Green Curly-Tailed Lizard. Lansing, Randy, illus. 1999. 48p. (J). (ps-4). mass mkt. 6.00 (978-0-9661844-4-0(0)) Purple Gorilla, LLC, The.
Lansky, Bruce. Girls to the Rescue, Bk. 7. 2000. (Illus.). 120p. (J). (gr. 3-7). pap. 3.95 (978-0-689-84079-1(9)) Meadowbrook Pr.
—Girls to the Rescue, No. 6. 1999. (978-0-606-17665-1(9)) Tandem Library Bks.
—Girls to the Rescue: Folk Tales from Around the World. 1999. (Illus.). (J). 78.00 (978-0-684-81211-3(8)) Meadowbrook Pr.
Lansky, Bruce, ed. Girls to the Rescue. 1998. (J). Bk. 1. 3.95 (978-0-88166-314-3(X)); Bk. 4. 112p. (gr. 3-6). pap. 3.95 (978-0-88166-301-3(8)) Meadowbrook Pr.
Lansky, Bruce & Johnson, Martha. Girls to the Rescue, Bk. 5. 108p. (J). pap. (978-0-88166-315-0(8)) Meadowbrook Pr.
Lapid, Koty. The Wild Virtual Enchanted Garden. 2005. 41p. (J). per. 16.18 (978-1-4116-2068-1(2)) Lulu.com.
LaRocque, Greg. Crybaby: Extinction. Castillo, Cesar & Burruss, Melissa, illus. 2005. (YA). per. 9.99 (978-1-933570-86-0(5)) Aardvark Global Publishing.
Larousse Mexico Staff, ed. El Conde de Montecristo. 2004. (Encuentro con la Lectura Ser.).Tr. of Count of Montecristo. (SPA., Illus.). 48p. pap. 6.50 (978-970-22-0730-6(4)) Larousse, Ediciones, S. A. de C. V. MEX. *Dist:* Houghton Mifflin Co. Trade & Reference Div.
—Viaje al Centro de la Tierra. 2004. (Encuentro Con la Lectura Ser.). (SPA., Illus.). 48p. (gr. 4-9). pap. 6.50 (978-970-22-0529-6(8)) Larousse, Ediciones, S. A. de C. V. MEX. *Dist:* Houghton Mifflin Co. Trade & Reference Div.
Larry's Adventure (a Carpet Dweller's Tale) 2002. (J). per. 9.97 (978-0-9723929-0-7(4)) MTW Investments.
Larsen, Alison. Thomas the Turtle's Adventures. 2006. (Illus.). 30p. (J). per. 14.95 (978-1-60002-096-4(8) , 3962, Airleaf Publishing) Airleaf Publishing & Bookselling.
Larsen, Erik, et al. Image Comics. ltd. ed. 2005. 128p. (YA). 75.00 (978-1-58240-257-4(4)) Image Comics.
Larsen, Kirsten. Dora's Rainbow Egg Hunt. Savitsky, Steven, illus. 2006. (Dora the Explorer Ser.). 14p. (J). bds. 6.99 (978-1-4169-0798-5(X) , Simon Spotlight/ Nickelodeon) Simon & Schuster Children's Publishing.
Larsen, Sandy. The Dark Lighthouse. Taylor, Wanda, illus. 2000. (Jackpine Point Adventure Ser.: Vol. 4). 128p. (J). (gr. 5-9). pap. 5.99 (978-0-9666677-3-8(5)) Merritt Park Pr.
—The Re-Appearing Statue. Taylor, Wanda, illus. 1998. (Jackpine Point Adventure Ser.: Vol. 1). 120p. (J). (gr. 6-9). pap. 5.99 (978-0-9666677-0-7(0)) Merritt Park Pr.
—Something's Fishy. Taylor, Wanda, illus. 1999. (Jackpine Point Adventure Ser.: Vol. 3). 128p. (J). (gr. 6-9). pap. 5.99 (978-0-9666677-2-1(7)) Merritt Park Pr.
Larson, Cynthia Sue. Karen Kimball. 2003. (gr. 7-12). lib. bdg. 22.20 (978-0-613-85680-5(5)) Tandem Library Bks.
Lasher, Sylvia E. The Little Garden Snake's First Adventure. 2000. (J). pap. 7.00 (978-0-8059-4699-4(3)) Dorrance Publishing Co., Inc.
Lasky, Kathryn. Blood Secret. 2004. (Illus.). 256p. (J). (gr. 7 up). 15.99 (978-0-06-000066-0(X)); lib. bdg. 16.89 (978-0-06-000065-3(1)) HarperCollins Pubs.
—The Burning. 2004. (Guardians of Ga'Hoole Ser.: Bk. 6). (Illus.). 224p. (J). (gr. 4-7). pap. 4.99 (978-0-439-40562-1(9) , Scholastic Paperbacks) Scholastic, Inc.
—The Capture. 2003. (Guardians of Ga'Hoole Ser.: Bk. 1). 240p. (gr. 3-7). mass mkt. 5.99 (978-0-439-40557-7(2) , Scholastic Paperbacks) Scholastic, Inc.
—The First Collier. 2006. (Guardians of Ga'Hoole Ser.: Bk. 9). 208p. (J). (gr. 4-7). pap. 4.99 (978-0-439-79568-5(0) , Scholastic Paperbacks) Scholastic, Inc.
Lassen C R Staff. Bountiful Sea. 2002. (Illus.). 20p. (J). 8.95 (978-1-74047-139-8(3)) Book Co. Publishing Pty, Ltd., The AUS. *Dist:* Leonard, Hal Corp.
Lassieur, Allison. Exo-Force. collector's ed. 2007. (Lego Ser.). 80p. (J). pap. 5.99 (978-0-439-82811-6(2)) Scholastic, Inc.
—Exo-force: Race to the Golden City. 2007. (Lego Ser.). 64p. (J). pap. 3.99 ***(978-0-439-92328-6(X))*** Scholastic, Inc.
—Secret of the Golden Tower. 2007. (Lego Ser.). 48p. (J). pap. 3.99 ***(978-0-439-92329-3(8))*** Scholastic, Inc.
Lassiter, Erin & Garcia, Jolanda. EarTwiggle's Adventure 1: The Treasure Hunt. 2004. (Illus.). (J). 12.99 (978-0-9762573-0-1(0)) Ear Twiggles Productions, Inc.
Lassiter, Rhiannon. Shadows. Gerber, Mark, illus. 2002. (Hex Ser.: Vol. 2). 272p. (YA). (gr. 5-8). mass mkt. 4.99 (978-0-7434-2212-3(0) , Simon Pulse) Simon & Schuster Children's Publishing.
Latorre, Jose Maria. La Incognita del Volcan. Ibarz, Miguel, illus. 2000. (Periscopio Ser.).Tr. of Mystery of the Volcano. (SPA.). 236p. (YA). (gr. 9 up). (978-84-236-5517-5(2)) Edebé ESP. *Dist:* Baker & Taylor Bks.
The Laughing Snowman. 2003. (J). per. (978-1-57657-924-4(7)) Paradise Pr., Inc.
Laury, Jean R., et al. No Dragons on My Quilt. rev. ed. 2000. (Illus.). 52p. (gr. k-2). 16.95 (978-0-89145-967-5(7) , 0891459677, American Quilter's Society) Collector Bks.
Lavette, Lavaille. The Adventures of Roopster Roux: Escape from Vulture's Roost. Mitchell, Louis H., illus. 1998. (Adventures of Roopster Roux Ser.). 32p. (J). (ps-3). pap. 5.95 (978-1-56554-360-7(2)) Pelican Publishing Co., Inc.
—The Adventures of Roopster Roux: Slammin' Slime. Mitchell, Louis H., illus. 1998. (Adventures of Roopster Roux Ser.). 32p. (J). (ps-3). pap. 5.95 (978-1-56554-359-1(9)) Pelican Publishing Co., Inc.
—The Adventures of Roopster Roux: Surfing the Net. Mitchell, Louis H., illus. 1998. (Adventures of Roopster Roux Ser.). 32p. (J). (ps-3). pap. 5.95 (978-1-56554-361-4(0)) Pelican Publishing Co., Inc.
—The Adventures of Roopster Roux: The Monster All-Stars. Mitchell, Louis H., illus. 1998. (Adventures of Roopster Roux Ser.). 32p. (J). (ps-3). pap. 5.95 (978-1-56554-362-1(9)) Pelican Publishing Co., Inc.
Lawlor, Laurie. Adventure on the Wilderness Road 1775. 2001. (American Sisters Ser.). (Illus.). 185p. (J). (ps-ps). lib. bdg. 11.15 (978-0-606-21015-7(6)) Tandem Library Bks.
—Crossing the Colorado Rockies 1864. 2001. (American Sisters Ser.). (Illus.). (J). 11.15 (978-0-606-21131-4(4)) Tandem Library Bks.
—Horseback on the Boston Post Road 1704. Lyall, Dennis, illus. 2002. (American Sisters Ser.: Vol. 7). 208p. (J). pap. 4.99 (978-0-7434-3626-7(1) , Aladdin) Simon & Schuster Children's Publishing.
Lawrence, Iain. The Buccaneers. (Illus.). 256p. (gr. 5-9). 2003. 5.99 (978-0-440-41671-5(X) , Yearling); 2001. 16.95 (978-0-385-32736-7(6) , Delacorte Bks. for Young Readers) Random Hse. Children's Bks.
—Buccaneers. 2003. (gr. 5-8). lib. bdg. 13.55 (978-0-613-64433-4(6)) Tandem Library Bks.
—The Buccaneers. l.t. ed. 2001. (Illus.). 320p. (J). 23.95 (978-0-7862-3464-6(4)) Thorndike Pr.
—The Cannibals. 2005. 240p. (J). (gr. 7-9). lib. bdg. 17.99 (978-0-385-90110-9(0) , Delacorte Bks. for Young Readers) Random Hse. Children's Bks.
—The Cannibals: The Curse of the Jolly Stone Trilogy. 2007. (Curse of the Jolly Stone Trilogy Ser.: Bk. II). 240p. (YA). (gr. 7 up). mass mkt. 6.50 (978-0-440-41933-4(6) , Laurel Leaf) Random Hse. Children's Bks.
—The Castaways. 2007. 256p. (YA). (gr. 7). 15.99 ***(978-0-385-73090-7(X)***); lib. bdg. 18.99 ***(978-0-385-90112-3(7))*** Random Hse. Children's Bks. (Delacorte Bks. for Young Readers).
—Ghost Boy. 2002. 352p. (YA). (gr. 7). reprint ed. pap. 6.50 (978-0-440-41668-5(X) , Laurel Leaf) Random Hse. Children's Bks.
—Ghost Boy. 2002. (gr. 7-12). lib. bdg. 14.15 (978-0-613-58216-2(0)) Tandem Library Bks.
—The Smugglers. (Illus.). (J). (gr. 5-9). 2000. 208p. 5.99 (978-0-440-41596-1(9) , Yearling); 1999. 192p. 15.95 (978-0-385-32663-6(7) , Delacorte Bks. for Young Readers) Random Hse. Children's Bks.
—The Smugglers. 2000. 184p. (J). (ps-7). lib. bdg. 12.15 (978-0-606-19693-2(5)) Tandem Library Bks.
—Smugglers. 2000. (gr. 5-8). lib. bdg. 13.55 (978-0-613-30132-9(3)) Tandem Library Bks.
—The Smugglers. l.t. ed. 2001. (Illus.). 246p. (J). 22.95 (978-0-7862-3465-3(2)) Thorndike Pr.
Lawrence, Kevin. Julianna's Quest: The Rescue of Queen Catherine. 2001. 116p. (J). pap. 9.95 (978-0-595-19540-4(7) , Writers Club Pr.) iUniverse, Inc.
Lawrence, Michael. The Poltergoose. l.t. ed. 2005. (Illus.). 168p. (J). pap. (978-0-7540-7836-4(1) , CLP 427) BBC Audio.
Lawrence, Mike. The Macaroni Disaster! 2006. 44p. pap. 12.00 (978-1-4116-8613-7(6)) Lulu.com.
Lawrie, Robin. Ballerina Biker. 2003. (Chain Gang Ser.). (Illus.). 32p. (YA). pap. 9.99 (978-0-237-52561-3(5) , Evans Brothers, Limited) Evans Publishing Group GBR. *Dist:* Independent Pubs. Group.
—First among Losers. 2003. (Chain Gang Ser.). (Illus.). 32p. (YA). pap. 9.99 (978-0-237-52562-0(3) , Evans Brothers, Limited) Evans Publishing Group GBR. *Dist:* Independent Pubs. Group.
—Gone Green. 2003. (Chain Gang Ser.). (Illus.). 32p. (YA). pap. 9.99 (978-0-237-52563-7(1) , Evans Brothers, Limited) Evans Publishing Group GBR. *Dist:* Independent Pubs. Group.
—Paintball Panic. 2003. (Chain Gang Ser.). (Illus.). 32p. (YA). pap. 11.00 (978-0-237-52559-0(3) , Evans Brothers, Limited) Evans Publishing Group GBR. *Dist:* Independent Pubs. Group.
—Radar Riders. 2003. (Chain Gang Ser.). (Illus.). 32p. (YA). pap. 9.99 (978-0-237-52560-6(7) , Evans Brothers, Limited) Evans Publishing Group GBR. *Dist:* Independent Pubs. Group.
—Treetop Trauma. 2003. (Chain Gang Ser.). (Illus.). 32p. (YA). pap. 9.99 (978-0-237-52564-4(X) , Evans Brothers, Limited) Evans Publishing Group GBR. *Dist:* Independent Pubs. Group.
Lawrie, Robin & Lawrie, Chris, illus. Chain Reaction. 32p. pap. (978-0-237-52110-3(5) , Evans Brothers, Limited) Evans Publishing Group.
—Fear 3.1. 32p. (J). pap. (978-0-237-52107-3(5) , Evans Brothers, Limited) Evans Publishing Group.
—Muddy Mayhem. 32p. (J). pap. (978-0-237-52105-9(9) , Evans Brothers, Limited) Evans Publishing Group.
—Shock Tactic. 2000. (Chain Gang Ser.). 32p. (J). pap. 7.99 (978-0-237-52108-0(3) , Evans Brothers, Limited) Evans Publishing Group GBR. *Dist:* Independent Pubs. Group.
—Winged Avenger. 32p. pap. (978-0-237-52106-6(7) , Evans Brothers, Limited) Evans Publishing Group.
Lawrie, Robin & Lawrie, Christine. Paintball Panic. Lawrie, Robin, illus. 2007. (Illus.). 32p. (J). (gr. 3-8). lib. bdg. 19.93 (978-1-59889-126-3(X)) Stone Arch Bks.
—Treetop Trauma. Lawrie, Robin, illus. 2007. (Illus.). 32p. (J). (gr. 3-8). lib. bdg. 19.93 (978-1-59889-128-7(6)) Stone Arch Bks.
Lawrie, Robin & Lawrie, Christine, illus. Block Busters. 2001. (Chain Gang Ser.). 32p. pap. 7.99 (978-0-237-52263-6(2) , Evans Brothers, Limited) Evans Publishing Group GBR. *Dist:* Independent Pubs. Group.
—Cheat Challenge. 2001. (Chain Gang Ser.). 30p. pap. 7.99 (978-0-237-52259-9(4) , Evans Brothers, Limited) Evans Publishing Group GBR. *Dist:* Independent Pubs. Group.
—Return Descender. 2001. (Chain Gang Ser.). 32p. pap. 7.99 (978-0-237-52262-9(4) , Evans Brothers, Limited) Evans Publishing Group GBR. *Dist:* Independent Pubs. Group.
—Snow Bored. 2001. 32p. pap. (978-0-237-52261-2(6) , Evans Brothers, Limited) Evans Publishing Group.
—Sweet Revenge. 2001. 32p. (J). pap. (978-0-237-52264-3(0) , Evans Brothers, Limited) Evans Publishing Group.
—2 XC 4 My Shirt. 2001. (Chain Gang Ser.). 32p. pap. 7.99 (978-0-237-52260-5(8) , Evans Brothers, Limited) Evans Publishing Group GBR. *Dist:* Independent Pubs. Group.
Lawson, Julie. Goldstone. unabr. ed. 1998. 170p. (J). (gr. 5-9). pap. 7.95 (978-0-7737-5891-9(7)) Stoddart Kids CAN. *Dist:* Fitzhenry & Whiteside, Ltd.
Lawton, Wilbur. The Boy Aviators' Polar Dash or Facing Death in the Antarctic. 2004. reprint ed. pap. 1.99 (978-1-4192-5497-0(9)) Kessinger Publishing, LLC.
Lawton, Wilbur Capta. The Boy Aviators in Africa or an Aerial. 2006. 25.99 ***(978-1-4219-7625-9(0)***); pap. 19.99 ***(978-1-4219-7629-7(3))*** IndyPublish.com.
Layden, Joseph Lyon. The Other Side of Yore. 2007. 156p. pap. 14.95 ***(978-1-60145-122-4(9))*** Booklocker.com, Inc.
Layne, Steven L. Mergers. 2006. 200p. (YA). (gr. 5-12). 15.95 (978-1-58980-183-7(0)) Pelican Publishing Co., Inc.
Layton, Dan. Adventures in the Kingdom, the Dreamer. 2004. 64p. pap. 5.99 (978-0-9707919-4-8(1)) Mercy Place, Inc.
Layton, Dian. Adventures in the Kingdom: In Search of Wanderer. 2001. (J). pap. 4.99 (978-0-9677402-8-7(2)) Mercy Place, Inc.
—Seeker's Great Adventure. 2005. (Illus.). 64p. (J). (gr. 2-5). pap. 4.99 (978-0-9677402-1-8(5)) Destiny Image Pubs.
Layton, Neal. Bartholomew & the Bug. 2006. (Illus.). (J). (ps). pap. 9.99 (978-0-340-87329-8(9) , Hodder & Stoughton) Hodder General Publishing Division GBR. *Dist:* Trafalgar Square Publishing.
Lazewnik, Libby. Three Cheers for Shira! 611p. 11.99 (978-1-58330-628-4(5)) Feldheim Pubs.
Lazewnik, Libby, et al. Baker's Dozen: Three-in-One: On Our Own; Ghosthunters; And the Winners. 1999. (Illus.). 139p. (J). (gr. 3-9). 16.99 (978-1-56871-190-4(5)) Targum Pr., Inc.
Le Gallienne, Richard. The Book Bills of Narcissus. 2004. reprint ed. pap. 15.95 (978-1-4191-5479-9(6)); pap. 1.99 (978-1-4192-5479-6(0)) Kessinger Publishing, LLC.
Le Guin, Ursula K. Catwings Return. 2003. (Catwings Ser.: No. 2). 56p. (J). pap. 3.99 (978-0-439-55190-8(0)) Scholastic, Inc.
—Catwings Return. 1999. (Catwings Ser.: No. 2). (J). (978-0-606-17402-2(8)) Tandem Library Bks.
—Wonderful Alexander & the Catwings. 2003. (Catwings Ser.: No. 3). 48p. (J). pap. 3.99 (978-0-439-55191-5(9)) Scholastic, Inc.
—Wonderful Alexander & the Catwings. 1999. (Catwings Ser.: No. 3). (978-0-606-17403-9(6)) Tandem Library Bks.
Leavey, Peggy Dymond. Treasure at Turtle Lake. 2007. 146p. (J). (gr. 4 up). pap. 7.95 ***(978-1-894917-49-0(9))*** Napoleon Publishing/Rendezvous Pr. CAN. *Dist:* Atlas-Books Distribution.
Leavitt, Caroline. The Prince & the Pooch. l.t. ed. 1999. (Adventures of Wishbone Ser.: No. 3). (Illus.). 144p. (J). (gr. 4 up). lib. bdg. 22.60 (978-0-8368-2299-1(4)) Stevens, Gareth Inc.
Leberer, Sigrid. The Adventures of the Three Best Friends. 2004. (Charming Collection of Five Short Stories Ser.). (Illus.). 22p. (J). bds. 6.99 (978-1-59384-056-3(X)) Parklane Publishing.
Leblanc, Louise & Brochard, Philippe. Cinema Chez les Vampires. 2002. (Premier Roman Ser.). (Illus.). 64p. (J). (gr. 2-5). pap. (978-2-89021-322-7(6)) Diffusion du livre Mirabel.
Leblanc, Margaret. Ms. Maddy Comes to Town. 2006. 76p. pap. 14.95 (978-1-4241-4103-6(6)) PublishAmerica, Inc.
Lebscky, Ibi. Amadeus. Cardoni, Paolo, illus. (Coleccion Seran Famosos). (SPA.). 32p. (J). (gr. 2-4). 14.95 (978-84-233-1262-7(3)) Ediciones Destino ESP. *Dist:* AIMS International Bks., Inc., Lectorum Pubns., Inc.
Lechner, John. A Froggy Fable. Lechner, John, illus. 2005. (Illus.). 32p. (J). (ps up). 14.99 (978-0-7636-2123-0(4)) Candlewick Pr.
Ledbetter, Penny S. Mushroom's Day Away. Garrett, Caroline S., illus. 2005. 32p. (J). 9.95 (978-1-933251-19-6(0)) Parkway Pubs., Inc.
Lee, Betsy S. Off the Track. 2007. 107p. pap. 13.95 ***(978-0-7414-3817-1(8))*** Infinity Publishing.
Lee Follen, Eliza. The Pedler of Dust Sticks. 2004. reprint ed. pap. 1.99 (978-1-4192-7694-1(8)) Kessinger Publishing, LLC.
—The Talkative Wig. 2004. reprint ed. pap. 1.99 (978-1-4192-8483-0(5)) Kessinger Publishing, LLC.
Lee, Huy Voun. In the Leaves. rev. ed. 2005. (Illus.). 32p. (J). (ps-ps). 16.95 (978-0-8050-6764-4(7) , Holt, Henry & Co. Bks. For Young Readers) Holt, Henry & Co.
Lee, Ingrid. George, the Best of All! Denis, Stephané, illus. 2006. 64p. (J). pap. 4.99 (978-1-55143-623-4(X)) Orca Bk. Pubs. USA.
—The True Story of George. Denis, Stephane, illus. 2004. (Orca Echoes Ser.). 64p. (J). (gr. 2-3). pap. 4.99 (978-1-55143-293-9(5)) Orca Bk. Pubs. USA.
Lee, Jeanie. Now It's Fall! Valerio, Geraldo, illus. 2007. (Flips & Flaps Book Ser.). 12p. (J). (ps-2). 9.99 ***(978-1-4169-0934-7(6)*** , Little Simon) Simon & Schuster Children's Publishing.
Lee, Kang-Woo. Rebirth, 11 vols., Vol. 1. 2003. (Illus.). 192p. (gr. 8 up). pap. 9.99 (978-1-59182-216-5(5) , Tokyopop Adult) TOKYOPOP, Inc.
—Rebirth, 11 vols., Vol. 4. Ryu, Youngju, tr. from JPN. rev. ed. 2003. (Illus.). 176p. pap. 9.99 (978-1-59182-219-6(X) , Tokyopop Adult) TOKYOPOP, Inc.
—Rebirth, 11 vols., Vol. 5. Lee, Kang-Woo, illus. 5th rev. ed. 2003. (Illus.). 176p. pap. 9.99 (978-1-59182-220-2(3) , Tokyopop Adult) TOKYOPOP, Inc.
—Rebirth, 11 vols. rev. ed. 2004. (Illus.). 176p. Vol. 8. pap. 9.99 (978-1-59182-526-5(1)); Vol. 9. pap. 9.99 (978-1-59182-527-2(X)) TOKYOPOP, Inc. (Tokyopop Adult).
Lee, Myung-Jin, creator. Ragnarok: Memories of Shadow, Vol. 10. rev. ed. 2004. (Illus.). 192p. pap. 9.99 (978-1-59182-209-7(2) , Tokyopop Adult) TOKYOPOP, Inc.
Lee, Nancy. Baby Chipmunks & Backyard Friends. 2005. (J). 9.95 (978-0-9772078-2-4(X)) Journey Pubns., LLC.
Lee, Quinlan B. Dazzle. 2005. (Boohbah Ser.). 12p. (J). pap. 9.99 (978-0-439-74412-6(1)) Scholastic, Inc.
—Go, Diego, Go!, Set. 2007. (Go, Diego, Go! Ser.). (J). 12.99 ***(978-0-439-91304-1(7))*** Scholastic, Inc.
—Rainbow Brite: Adventures in Rainbow Land. Albrecht, Jeff, illus. 2005. (Rainbow Brite Ser.). 18p. (J). 5.99 (978-0-439-65934-5(5)) Scholastic, Inc.
Lee, Quinlan B. Superstars! 2007. (Doodlebops Ser.). 32p. (J). pap. 3.99 ***(978-0-545-00901-0(4))*** Scholastic, Inc.
Lee, Rex. Rann Braden Circus Showman A Circus Adve. 2006. (Illus.). pap. 27.95 ***(978-1-4286-5861-5(0))*** Kessinger Publishing, LLC.
Lee, Shell. Teenie's Treehouse Adventures: The Magic Begins. 2004. 37p. pap. 17.95 (978-1-4137-2879-8(0)) PublishAmerica, Inc.
Lee, Stan. Thor, Vol. 2. 2005. (Thor Ser.). (Illus.). 584p. pap. 16.99 (978-0-7851-1591-5(9)) Marvel Enterprises, Inc.
Lee, Suzy. The Zoo. Lee, Suzy, illus. 2007. (Illus.). 32p. (J). (gr. 2-5). 15.95 (978-1-933605-28-9(6) , 05289) Kane/ Miller Bk. Pubs., Inc.
Lee, Tanith. Piratica: Being a Daring Tale of a Singular Girl's Adventure upon the High Seas. (Piratica Ser.: Vol. 1). 304p. (gr. 6). 2006. (YA). pap. 6.99 (978-0-14-240644-1(9) , Puffin); 2004. (Illus.). (J). 17.99 (978-0-525-47324-4(6) , Dutton Juvenile) Penguin Group (USA) Inc.
—Return to Parrot Island. (Piratica Ser.: Vol. 2). (YA). (gr. 7). 2008. 368p. 6.99 ***(978-0-14-241094-3(2)*** , Puffin); 2006. 360p. 17.99 (978-0-525-47769-3(1) , Dutton Juvenile) Penguin Group (USA) Inc.
—Wolf Star. 2002. (Claidi Journals: Bk. 2). 240p. (YA). pap. 6.99 (978-0-14-230152-4(3) , Puffin) Penguin Group (USA) Inc.
—Wolf Tower. 2001. (Claiddi Journals: Bk. 1). (Illus.). 240p. (J). pap. 6.99 (978-0-14-230030-5(6) , Puffin) Penguin Group (USA) Inc.
Leeds, Jonathan M. Close to the Edge. 2001. (YA). pap. (978-1-56765-070-9(8) , R709P) AMSCO Schl. Pubns., Inc.
—Hyperlink. 2001. (YA). pap. (978-1-56765-064-8(3) , R693P) AMSCO Schl. Pubns., Inc.
Leeson, Robert. Lucky Lad. l.t. ed. 1999. (Galaxy Children's Large Print Ser.). (Illus.). 100p. (J). pap. (978-0-7540-6042-0(X) , CLP 247) BBC Audio.
Legault, Anne & Franson, Leanne. Une Premiere pour Etamine Leger. 2002. (Roman Jeunesse Ser.). (Illus.). 96p. (YA). (gr. 4-7). pap. (978-2-89021-327-2(7)) Diffusion du livre Mirabel.
The Legend of the Great Salt Mountain. 2005. (J). pap. (978-0-9771804-1-7(7)) Terra Tales.
Lego Staff. Fantastic Fliers. 2000. (Illus.). 24p. (J). spiral bd. 7.99 (978-1-903276-11-2(X)) Lego Media International, Inc.
LeGrand, Hank, 3rd. Paddle Tail's First Winter Adventure. Fair, Patricia Lynn, illus. 2006. (J). per. 7.95 (978-1-59466-082-5(4) , Growing Years) Port Town Publishing.
Lehman, Barbara. Rainstorm. 2007. (Illus.). (J). (ps-k). 32p. 16.00 (978-0-618-75639-1(6)); 30p. ***(978-1-4287-3564-4(X))*** Houghton Mifflin Co.
Lehnert, R. B. The Adventures of Billy Butterfly. Garcia, Marc Khayam, illus. 2003. (J). per. (978-0-9747628-2-1(2)) BKB Group, Inc., The.
Lehr, Norma. Dance of the Crystal Skull. rev. exp. ed. 2003. (Illus.). 238p. (J). (gr. 3-7). lib. bdg. 15.95 (978-0-87358-724-2(3) , Rising Moon Bks. for Young Readers) Northland Publishing.
—Dance of the Crystal Skull. 1999. (Illus.). (J). (978-0-606-18310-9(8)) Tandem Library Bks.

A Lei of Dancers: Aventuras (Adventure Books) 2000. (Aventuras A Traves Del Tiempo Ser.). (ENG & SPA.). (gr. 4 up). (978-0-02-148914-5(9)) Macmillan/McGraw-Hill Schl. Div.

Leibold, Jay. Secret of the Ninja No. 16: Choose Your Own Adventure #16. 2007. (Choose Your Own Adventure Ser.: Vol. 16). (Illus.). 144p. (J). mass mkt. 5.99 (978-1-933390-16-1(6)) Chooseco LLC.

Leigh, Emma & Artifact Group. Clowning Around. 2007. (Backyardigans Ser.). 12p. (J). 7.99 (*978-1-4169-3352-6(2) , Simon Spotlight/Nickelodeon) Simon & Schuster Children's Publishing.

Leigh, S. Runaway Pony. 2004. (Sandy Lane Stables Ser.). 100p. (J). pap. 4.95 (978-0-7945-0507-3(4)); lib. bdg. 12.95 (978-1-58086-575-3(5)) EDC Publishing.

—Uncle Pete's Pirate Adventure. rev. ed. 2004. (Young Puzzle Adventures Ser.). 32p. (J). (gr. 2 up). pap. 4.95 (978-0-7945-0401-4(9)); lib. bdg. 12.95 (978-1-58086-545-6(3)) EDC Publishing.

Leigh, Susannah. Puzzle Mountain. Haw, Brenda, illus. 2003. 32p. (J). pap. 6.95 (978-0-7945-0713-8(1) , Usborne) EDC Publishing.

Leigh, Susannah. Uncle Pete's Pirate Adventure. rev. ed. 2007. (Young Puzzle Adventures Ser.). 32p. (J). pap. 4.99 (*978-0-7945-1848-6(6) , Usborne) EDC Publishing.

Leigh, Susannah, et al. Young Puzzle Adventures: Combined Volume. 2004. (Young Puzzle Adventures Ser.). (Illus.). 128p. (J). (gr. 2 up). pap. 12.95 (978-0-7945-0698-8(4) , Usborne) EDC Publishing.

Leighton, Robert. Bravest Boy in the Camp A Story of Adven. 2006. pap. 28.95 (*978-1-4286-5937-7(4)) Kessinger Publishing, LLC.

Leininger, Tracy M. A Light Kindled: The Story of Pricilla Mullins. 2nd ed. 2000. (Illus.). 64p. (J). mass mkt. 15.99 (978-0-9724287-2-9(0)) His Seasons.

Leiterman, Robert S. Operation Redwood Quest: Search for Answers. 2003. 351p. (YA). pap. 20.95 (978-0-595-30513-1(X)) iUniverse, Inc.

—Yeti or Not, Here We Come! Bigfoot in the Redwoods. 2003. 275p. (YA). pap. 16.95 (978-0-595-26561-9(8) , Writers Club Pr.) iUniverse, Inc.

Leloup, Roger. Yoko Tsuno: On the Edge of Life. Spear, Luke, tr. from FRE. 2007. (Illus.). 48p. pap. 9.99 (*978-1-905460-32-8(5)) CineBook GBR. *Dist:* Biblio Distribution.

Lemieux, Michele. Stormy Night. 1999. (Illus.). 240p. (J). (gr. 4-6). (978-1-55074-692-1(8)) Kids Can Pr., Ltd.

LeMonde, Stephanie. Misty Forest. Fryba, Borivoj, illus. 2007. (YA). per. 14.95 (*978-1-934138-13-7(4)) Bouncing Ball Bks., Inc.

Lenhard, Elizabeth. Freeze Frame. 8th rev. ed. 2004. (Spy Kids Adventures Ser.: No. 8). (Illus.). 144p. (gr. 3-7). pap. 4.99 (978-0-7868-1806-8(9) , Disney Editions) Disney Pr.

—Spring Fever. 9th rev. ed. 2004. (Spykids Adventures Ser.: Bk. 9). (Illus.). 144p. (gr. 3-7). pap. 4.99 (978-0-7868-0989-9(2)) Hyperion Bks. for Children.

—Spy TV. 6th rev. ed. 2003. (Spy Kids Adventures Ser.: No. 6). (Illus.). 144p. (gr. 3-7). pap. 4.99 (978-0-7868-1804-4(2) , Disney Editions) Disney Pr.

—Spy TV. 2003. (gr. 3-6). lib. bdg. 13.00 (978-0-613-68291-6(2)) Tandem Library Bks.

—Superstar Spies. 7th rev. ed. 2004. (Spy Kids Adventures Ser.: No. 7). (Illus.). 144p. (gr. 3-7). pap. 4.99 (978-0-7868-1805-1(0) , Disney Editions) Disney Pr.

Lenhard, Elizabeth & Kaaberbol, Lene. When Lightning Strikes. 2004. (W. I. T. C. H. Adventures Ser. : Bk. 1). (Illus.). 112p. (J). (gr. 3-7). pap. 4.99 (978-0-7868-0977-6(9) , Volo) Hyperion Bks. for Children.

Lenhard, Elizabeth, et al. The Power of Five. 2004. (W. I. T. C. H. Ser.: Bk. 1). (Illus.). 158p. (J). (gr. 3-7). pap. 4.99 (978-0-7868-5257-4(7) , Volo) Hyperion Bks. for Children.

Lenkov, Peter. R. I. P. D. 2003. (Illus.). 96p. (J). (gr. 7 up). pap. 12.95 (978-1-56971-928-2(4)) Dark Horse Comics.

Lenkov, Peter M. Fort: Prophet of the Unexplained. 2003. (Illus.). 96p. (YA). (gr. 7 up). pap. 9.95 (978-1-56971-781-3(8)) Dark Horse Comics.

Leonard, Elise. Killer Lunch Lady. 2007. (Al's World Ser.: No. 2). 144p. (J). (gr. 5-9). pap. 5.99 (*978-1-4169-3465-3(0) , Aladdin) Simon & Schuster Children's Publishing.

—Monday Morning Blitz. 2007. (Al's World Ser.). 144p. (J). (gr. 5-9). pap. 5.99 (*978-1-4169-3464-6(2) , Aladdin) Simon & Schuster Children's Publishing.

—Scared Stiff. 2007. (Al's World Ser.). 132p. (J). (gr. 5-9). per. 5.99 (*978-1-4169-3466-0(9) , Aladdin) Simon & Schuster Children's Publishing.

Leone, Jason, illus. the Enchantress of Caratunk. Manna, Elizabeth, photos by. 2003. 30p. (J). (gr. 1-5). pap. 9.95 (978-0-9729807-0-8(9)) Murray, David M.

Leopold, Astara Ladyvienna. The Stardream Chronicles, Vol. 2. Date not set. 128p. (J). (gr. 1-8). pap. 12.95 (978-1-885226-45-7(4)) StarLineage Pubns.

Lerangis, Peter. Escape from Disaster. 2000. (Antarctica Ser. : Vol. 2). (Illus.). 160p. (J). (gr. 4-7). pap. 4.50 (978-0-439-16388-0(9)) Scholastic, Inc.

—Escape from Disaster. 2000. (Illus.). (J). (978-0-606-18865-4(7)) Tandem Library Bks.

—Island. 1999. (Watchers Ser.: No. 5). 156p. (J). (gr. 4-7). pap. 4.50 (978-0-590-11500-1(6)) Scholastic, Inc.

—Journey to the North Pole. 2000. (Illus.). (J). (978-0-606-18864-7(9)) Tandem Library Bks.

Leslie, J. Lawrence. In Camp on the Big Sunflower. 2006. 24.99 (*978-1-4219-7624-2(2)); pap. 18.99 (*978-1-4219-7630-3(7)) IndyPublish.com.

Leslie, Lawrence J. With Trapper Jim in the North Woods. 2004. reprint ed. pap. 19.95 (978-1-4191-9451-1(8)); pap. 1.99 (978-1-4192-9451-8(2)) Kessinger Publishing, LLC.

Leslie, Robyn. Rinny & the Trail of Clues. 2003. Orig. Title: Miss President & the Trail of Clues. (Illus.). 192p. (J). pap. 7.95 (978-0-9727388-8-0(6)) Sugar Ducky Bks., Inc.

Let the Circle Be Unbroken. 1999. (J). 9.95 (978-1-56137-660-5(4)) Novel Units, Inc.

Lethcoe, Jason. Amazing Adventures from Zoom's Academy. 2005. (Illus.). 160p. (J). pap. 12.95 (978-0-345-48355-3(3) , Ballantine Bks.) Random House Publishing Group.

Lethcoe, Jason. Wish You Were Here, No. 4. 2008. (Benjamin Bartholomew Piff Ser.). 240p. (J). (gr. 3-6). 9.99 (*978-0-448-44499-4(2) , Grosset & Dunlap) Penguin Group (USA) Inc.

Levering-Duff, Judy. The Medallion of Tiben: Book Two of the Adventures of Princess Isabella. 2004. (YA). 265p. 16.50 (978-0-9725874-9-5(7)); pap. 9.50 (978-1-932672-00-8(1)) Outskirts Press, Inc.

Levert, Mireille. An Island in the Soup. 2002. (Illus.). 24p. (J). (ps-k). pap. 5.95 (978-0-88899-505-6(9)) Groundwood Bks. CAN. *Dist:* Perseus Distribution.

Levine, Heather F. Sophie's Castle. Drummond, J. K., illus. 2005. 32p. (J). (ps-1). 9.95 (978-0-7607-6692-7(4)) Friedman, Michael Publishing Group, Inc.

Levithan, David. Are We There Yet? 2005. 224p. (YA). (gr. 7-12). 15.95 (978-0-375-82846-1(X) , Knopf Bks. for Young Readers) Random Hse. Children's Bks.

—Charlie's Angels: Full Throttle. 2003. (gr. 3-6). lib. bdg. 13.00 (978-0-613-66449-3(3)) Tandem Library Bks.

Levy, Michael. The Inspiring Story of Little Goody Two Shoes. 2007. 139p. (YA). per. 12.95 (*978-0-9668069-9-1(9)) Point of Life, Inc.

Lewis, C. S. The Chronicles of Narnia: Based on the Books by C. S. Lewis. Sabuda, Robert & Armstrong, Matthew, illus. 2007. (Narnia Ser.). 14p. (J). (ps-3). 29.99 (*978-0-06-117612-8(5)) HarperCollins Pubs.

—The Complete Chronicles of Narnia. 2002. (Chronicles of Narnia Ser.). pap. 29.99 (978-0-06-051758-8(1)) HarperCollins Pubs.

—The Horse & His Boy. Baynes, Pauline, illus. 240p. 2006. (Narnia Ser.). (J). 11.99 (978-0-06-112524-9(5)); 2000. (Chronicles of Narnia Ser.: Bk. 5). (YA). (gr. 3 up). pap. 8.99 (978-0-06-440940-7(6) , Harper Trophy) HarperCollins Pubs.

—The Horse & His Boy. 2000. (Chronicles of Narnia Ser.: Bk.5). (J). (gr. 4-8). (978-0-606-19976-6(4)) Tandem Library Bks.

—The Horse & His Boy. Baynes, Pauline, illus. l.t. ed. 2000. (Chronicles of Narnia Ser.: Bk. 5). 253p. (J). (gr. 4-8). 21.95 (978-0-7862-2233-9(6)) Thorndike Pr.

—The Last Battle. Baynes, Pauline, illus. 2006. (Narnia Ser.). 224p. (J). 11.99 (978-0-06-112529-4(6)) HarperCollins Pubs.

—El Leon, la Bruja y el Ropero. 2005. (ESP & SPA.). 208p. pap. 9.95 (978-0-06-084253-6(9) , Rayo) HarperCollins Pubs.

—The Magician's Nephew. Baynes, Pauline, illus. 2006. (Narnia Ser.). 208p. (J). 11.99 (978-0-06-112526-3(1)) HarperCollins Pubs.

—The Magician's Nephew Read-Aloud Edition. Baynes, Pauline, illus. 2006. (Narnia Ser.). 208p. (J). 15.99 (978-0-06-087588-6(7)) HarperCollins Pubs.

—Prince Caspian (paper-over-board) The Return to Narnia. Baynes, Pauline, illus. 2006. (Narnia Ser.). 240p. (J). 11.99 (978-0-06-112525-6(3)) HarperCollins Pubs.

—The Return to Narnia: The Rescue of Prince Caspian. Armstrong, Matthew, illus. 2006. (Narnia Ser.). 32p. (J). 16.99 (978-0-06-113110-3(5)); lib. bdg. 17.89 (978-0-06-113111-0(3)) HarperCollins Pubs.

—The Silver Chair. Baynes, Pauline, illus. 2006. (Narnia Ser.). 256p. (J). 11.99 (978-0-06-112528-7(8)) HarperCollins Pubs.

—The Voyage of the Dawn Treader. Baynes, Pauline, illus. 2006. (Narnia Ser.). 256p. (J). 11.99 (978-0-06-112527-0(X)) HarperCollins Pubs.

Lewis, Calvin, Jr. & Wilhite, Susan L. It Comes in the Night: Speaking Eagle, Book One. 2006. pap. 9.95 (*978-1-934130-03-2(6) , 3002) Flood Crest Pr.

Lewis, Carolyn. Hairy Beary Book Two Bk. 2,Vol. 2: The Great Waterfall, 3 bks. DeVince, James, ed. Porcheron, Tammy, illus. 2003. (Hairy Beary Ser.: 2). 42p. (J). pap. 9.95 (978-0-9712641-1-3(2)) J M D's Business Services.

Lewis, Carolyn & DeVince, James. The Hairy Beary Adventure Series, 3 bks. DeVince, James, ed. Porcheron, Tammy, illus. 2005. 122p. (J). pap. 24.95 (978-0-9712641-3-7(9)) J M D's Business Services.

—Hairy Beary Book Three: The Blue Ribbon Hero, 3 bks., Vol. 3. DeVince, James, ed. Porcheron, Tammy, illus. 2003. (Hairy Beary Ser.: 3). 46p. (J). pap. 9.95 (978-0-9712641-2-0(0)) J M D's Business Services.

Lewis, David & Dugas, Lisa, eds. Hill House Speaks. 2006. 156p. (YA). pap. 18.00 (978-0-9769114-7-0(7)) Leonard Pr.

Lewis, Megan. The Girl Who Could Fly. l.t. ed. 2005. (Illus.). 30p. (J). per. 9.99 (978-1-59879-029-0(3)) Lifevest Publishing, Inc.

Lewis, Omar. Myat & the Art Lesson, Vol. 3, Lewis, Omar, illus. l.t. ed. 2001. Tr. of Wonderful World of Myat. 36p. (J). 5.99 (978-1-886433-89-2(5)) A & B Distributors & Pubs. Group.

—The Wonderful World of Myat: Myat & Her Fear of the Dark, 6 vols. Lewis, Omar, illus. l.t. ed. 2001. 36p. (J). 5.99 (978-1-886433-87-8(9)) A & B Distributors & Pubs. Group.

Lewis, Phyllis. Legend of the Aneeka. 2003. 173p. pap. 16.95 (978-1-59286-519-2(4)) PublishAmerica, Inc.

Lewman, David. Case of the Missing Gold. 2000. (gr. 3-6). lib. bdg. 11.80 (978-0-613-24494-7(X)) Tandem Library Bks.

—The Three Little Neighbors. DePorter, Vince, illus. 2006. (SpongeBob SquarePants Ser.). 20p. (J). 8.99 (978-1-4169-0688-9(6) , Simon Spotlight/Nickelodeon) Simon & Schuster Children's Publishing.

Leyendas Nordicas. (SPA., Illus.). 160p. (YA). 11.95 (978-84-7281-056-3(9) , AF1056) Auriga, Ediciones S.A. ESP. *Dist:* Continental Bk. Co., Inc.

Liess, Claudia. A Stranger on Planet Earth. 2006. 76p. pap. 14.95 (978-1-4241-0987-6(6)) PublishAmerica, Inc.

Lift & Listen. pap. 15.98 (978-0-7853-4251-9(6)) Publications International, Ltd.

Light, John & Light, Marilyn. TT Triangle. 2005. (Illus.). 26p. (978-1-897968-27-7(2)) Photon Pr.

Light's Adventures: Light's Adventures with Doom & Gloom. 2003. (J). spiral bd. 7.00 (978-0-9743223-0-8(X)) Jones, Augustine R.

Light's Adventures on the Playground. 2004. (J). spiral bd. 7.00 net. (978-0-9743223-1-5(8)) Jones, Augustine R.

Light's Adventure's with Friends. 2005. (J). spiral bd. 7.00 (978-0-9743223-2-2(6)) Jones, Augustine R.

Lime, Harry. The Last Stand: Meet the X-Men. Gordon, Steven E., illus. 2006. (I Can Read Bks.). 32p. (J). pap. 3.99 (978-0-06-082204-0(X) , Harper Trophy) HarperCollins Pubs.

—The Last Stand: Rogue Finds a Home. Kirkland, Boyd, illus. 2006. (I Can Read Bks.). 32p. (J). pap. 3.99 (978-0-06-082205-7(8) , Harper Trophy) HarperCollins Pubs.

Lincoln, Jacqueline Michelle. The Adventures of Sheila the Awesome (Aussie) Dog. 2005. (J). 7.95 (978-0-9748426-3-9(X)) Accent Pubns.

Lincoln, Nan. Cecily's Summer. Wynne, Patricia J., illus. 2005. 40p. 16.95 (978-1-59373-047-5(0)) Bunker Hill Publishing, Inc.

Linda, Brooks. Meet Toado & Friends. l.t. ed. 2006. (Illus.). 34p. (J). per. 12.99 (*978-1-59879-314-7(4)) Lifevest Publishing, Inc.

Linder, Cori. Bobby the Blue Bus. 2005. 21p. 10.75 (978-1-4116-3564-7(7)) Lulu.com.

Lindgren, Astrid. Mio, My Son. Wikland, Ilon, illus. 2003. Tr. of Mio, Min Mio. 179p. (J). 17.95 (978-1-930900-23-3(6)) Purple Hse. Pr.

—Pippi Goes on Board. (Pippi Longstocking Ser.). 140p. (J). (gr. 3-5). pap. 3.99 (978-0-8072-1401-5(9) , Listening Library) Random Hse. Audio Publishing Group.

—Pippi Goes to the Circus. Chesworth, Michael, illus. 2000. (Pippi Longstocking Storybooks). 32p. (J). (gr. k-2). pap. 6.99 (978-0-14-130243-0(7) , Puffin) Penguin Group (USA) Inc.

—Pippi in the South Seas. (Pippi Longstocking Ser.). 125p. (J). (gr. 3-5). pap. 3.99 (978-0-8072-1392-6(6) , Listening Library) Random Hse. Audio Publishing Group.

—Pippi Longstocking. Nunally, Tina, tr. from SWE. 2007. 208p. (J). (gr. k). 25.00 (*978-0-670-06276-8(6) , Viking Juvenile) Penguin Group (USA) Inc.

—Pippi Longstocking. (Pippi Longstocking Ser.). 160p. (J). (gr. 3-5). pap. 4.99 (978-0-8072-1431-2(0) , Listening Library) Random Hse. Audio Publishing Group.

—Pippi's Extraordinary Ordinary Day. 1999. (Pippi Longstocking Storybooks). (Illus.). 64p. (J). (gr. k-2). 14.99 (978-0-670-88073-7(6) , Viking Juvenile) Penguin Group (USA) Inc.

Lindner, Brooke. Dora's Sweet Adventure: A Scratch & Sniff Board Book. Mangano, Tom, illus. 2007. (Dora the Explorer Ser.). 14p. (J). bds. 7.99 (978-1-4169-2747-1(6) , Simon Spotlight/Nickelodeon) Simon & Schuster Children's Publishing.

Lindner, Simone. Aelin the Water Fairy. Unzner, Christa, illus. 2008. 32p. (J). (ps). 9.99 (*978-0-698-40070-2(4) , Minedition) Penguin Group (USA) Inc.

—Gobulus the Earth Fairy. Unzner, Christa, illus. 2008. 32p. (J). (ps). 9.99 (*978-0-698-40072-6(0) , Minedition) Penguin Group (USA) Inc.

—Runia the Fire Fairy. Unzner, Christa, illus. 2008. 32p. (J). (ps). 9.99 (*978-0-698-40071-9(2) , Minedition) Penguin Group (USA) Inc.

—Tara the Air Fairy. Unzner, Christa, illus. 2008. 32p. (J). (ps). 9.99 (*978-0-698-40069-6(0) , Minedition) Penguin Group (USA) Inc.

Lininger, Dianne. The Kingdom of Cydinah. 2006. (J). (*978-0-9790337-0-4(5)) Crosam Pr.

Linsner, Joseph Michael. Three Tiers. (Dawn Ser.: Vol. 3). 176p. (YA). (Illus.). 39.99 (978-1-58240-573-5(5)); 2006. 69.99 (978-1-58240-574-2(3)) Image Comics.

Linz, Kathryn. Jim Brandon's Adventures. 2006. (ENG.). 100p. per. 14.95 (*978-1-4241-3160-0(X)) PublishAmerica, Inc.

Lionni, Leo. Tico & the Golden Wings. Slattery, Joan, ed. Lionni, Leo, illus. 2000. (Pinwheel Bks.). (Illus.). 32p. (J). (gr. k-3). pap. 5.99 (978-0-394-83078-0(4) , Dragonfly Bks.) Random Hse. Children's Bks.

Lipp, Douglas. Northeast of the Lobster Pot. 2006. pap. 15.99 (*978-1-4259-8681-0(1)) AuthorHouse.

Liput, Andrew L. Evie the Evergreen's Christmas Adventure. 2002. 31p. (J). pap. 9.95 (978-0-7414-1034-4(6)) Infinity Publishing.

Lisle, Holly. Vengeance of Dragons. 2000. (gr. 7-12). lib. bdg. 15.30 (978-0-613-29378-5(9)) Tandem Library Bks.

Lisle, Janet Taylor. Black Duck. (J). (gr. 5 up). 2007. 256p. 6.99 (*978-0-14-240902-2(2) , Puffin); 2006. 240p. 15.99 (978-0-399-23963-2(4) , Philomel) Penguin Group (USA) Inc.

Lisle, Rebecca. Amethyst. 2007. 176p. (J). (gr. 4-7). pap. 7.95 (*978-1-84270-541-4(5)) Andersen GBR. *Dist:* Independent Pubs. Group.

Lisle, Rebecca. Dogs Don't Do Dishes. 2004. (Illus.). 64p. (J). pap. 8.99 (978-1-84270-314-4(5)) Andersen GBR. *Dist:* Independent Pubs. Group.

Litchmore, Michael. The MB Force: Heroes at the Best! 2007. 56p. pap. 9.00 (*978-0-8059-7399-0(0)) Dorrance Publishing Co., Inc.

Literature Connections English: Johnny Tremain. 2004. (gr. 6-12). (978-0-395-77535-6(3) , 2-80104) McDougal Littell Inc.

Literature Connections Spanish: Las Aventuras de Huckleberry Finn (the Adventures of Huckleberry Finn) 2004. (gr. 6-12). (978-0-395-81742-1(0) , 2-70492) McDougal Littell Inc.

Litowinsky, Olga. The Pawloined Paper. l.t. ed. 1999. (Adventures of Wishbone Ser.: No. 11). (Illus.). (J). (gr. 4 up). lib. bdg. 22.60 (978-0-8368-2589-3(6)) Stevens, Gareth Inc.

Litteken, Erin. Stinky Mcpew Is Not Gonna Move! 2005. 48p. pap. 12.95 (978-1-4137-6432-1(0)) PublishAmerica, Inc.

A Little Adventure: Individual Title Six-Packs. (gr. 3 up). 35.00 (978-0-7635-9656-9(6)) Rigby Education.

Little Airplane Productions Staff & Selig, Josh. Teamwork Saves the Day! Book & Beanie Baby Gift Set. Oxley, Jennifer, illus. 2008. (Wonder Pets! Ser.). 12p. (J). bds. 12.99 (*978-1-4169-4797-4(3) , Simon Spotlight/Nickelodeon) Simon & Schuster Children's Publishing.

Little Farm down the Lane, Bk. III. 2005. pap. 10.99 (978-1-59781-702-8(3)) Xulon Pr., Inc.

Little, Jean. Somebody Else's Summer. 2007. 192p. (J). 16.00 (978-0-670-04466-5(0) , Penguin Global) Penguin Group (USA) Inc.

Little Reader Digital Storybook: Beauty & the Beast. 2005. (J). cd-rom 9.99 (978-0-9767657-2-1(1) , oatb-ctvol1) Mullings Media.

Little Reader Digital Storybook: Rumplestiltskin. 2005. (J). cd-rom 7.99 (978-0-9767657-6-9(4) , rum-cfvol1) Mullings Media.

Little, Rich. Will's New Backpack. Lenoir, Jane, illus. 2000. (J). cd-rom 9.95 (978-1-58338-246-2(1)) Crossroads-Pub.com.

The Littles Go Exploring. 2002. (Littles Ser.). (Illus.). (J). 12.17 (978-0-7587-8432-2(5)) Book Wholesalers, Inc.

Littleton, Mark. Tracks in the Sand. 2001. (Ally OConnor Adventures Ser.: Vol. 1). 128p. (J). (gr. 4-7). pap. 5.99 (978-0-8010-4490-8(1)) Baker Bks.

Llewellyn, Claire. Shadow Play. 2000. (Cambridge Reading Ser.). (Illus.). 14p. pap. 5.00 (978-0-521-77450-5(0)); Pack. 12p. pap. 28.00 (978-0-521-78762-8(9)) Cambridge Univ. Pr.

Llewellyn, Sam. Pegleg. 2001. (Illus.). 173p. pap. (978-0-7551-0011-8(5)) House of Stratus, Inc.

—The Return of Death Eric. 2006. 258p. (YA). 16.95 (978-0-8027-8951-8(X)) Walker & Co.

Lloyd, Ann. National Treasure 2: Book of Secrets. 2nd rev. ed. 2007. 160p. (J). (gr. 3-7). pap. 4.99 (*978-1-4231-0627-2(X)) Disney Pr.

Lloyd-Jones, Sally. Handbag Friends. Heap, Sue, illus. 2006. 64p. (J). bds. 11.95 (978-0-385-75096-7(X) , Fickling, David Bks.) Random Hse. Children's Bks.

Lloyd-Kyi, Tanya. The Crystal Connection. 2nd ed. 2003. (Science Squad Adventure Ser.). (Illus.). 160p. (J). (gr. 3-2). pap. 6.95 (978-1-55285-511-9(2)) Whitecap Bks., Ltd. CAN. *Dist:* Firefly Bks., Ltd.

Lluch, Alex. Alexander, It's Time for Bed! 2006. 30p. 14.95 (978-1-887169-59-2(8)) Wedding Solutions Publishing, Inc.

Lo Raso, Carlo, illus. We Love a Luau! 2007. (Backyardigans Ser.). 16p. (J). pap. 6.99 (978-1-4169-3365-6(4) , Simon Spotlight) Simon & Schuster Children's Publishing.

Lobdell, Scott. Flesh & Blood, 3. 5. (Illus.). 464p. (Orig.). pap. 24.99 (978-1-58240-538-4(7)) Image Comics.

—The Opposite Numbers. Rendon, Daniel, illus. 7th rev. ed. 2006. (Hardy Boys Ser.: No. 7). 96p. (J). pap. 7.95 (978-1-59707-034-8(3)) Papercutz.

—The Oppsite Numbers. Rendon, Daniel, illus. 7th rev. ed. 2006. (Hardy Boys Ser.: No. 7). 96p. (J). 12.95 (978-1-59707-035-5(1)) Papercutz.

Lobdell, Scott & Baron, Mike. Kiss Vol. 3: Men & Monsters. 2003. 96p. (YA). pap. 12.95 (978-1-56971-971-8(3)) Dark Horse Comics.

Lobdell, Scott & Rendon, Daniel. Hyde & Shriek. 6th rev. ed. 2006. (Hardy Boys Ser.: No. 6). (Illus.). 96p. (J). 12.95 (978-1-59707-029-4(7)) Papercutz.

Lobel, Arnold. Adventure Stories That Will Thrill You. 2001. (gr. 3-6). lib. bdg. 11.80 (978-0-613-56166-2(X)) Tandem Library Bks.

Locke, Terry. Spencer Hurley & the Aliens: Book One: the Abduction. 2007. (Spencer Hurley & the Aliens Ser.: 1). (Illus.). 224p. (YA). 12.95 (978-0-9786940-0-5(7) , SHAB1V1E1CB) Dream Workshop Publishing Co., LLC, The.

Locker, Thomas. Water Dance. 2002. (Illus.). 32p. (J). pap. 7.00 (978-0-15-216396-9(4) , Voyager Bks./Libros Viajeros) Harcourt Children's Bks.

—Water Dance. 2002. (gr. 3-6). lib. bdg. 14.15 (978-0-613-44346-3(2)) Tandem Library Bks.

Lockwood, Cara. The Scarlet Letterman. 2007. (Bard Academy Ser.). 320p. pap. 9.95 (978-1-4165-2490-8(8) , MTV) Simon & Schuster.

LoDestro, Christine. The Littlest Cloud. 2005. 15p. (J). 12.01 (978-1-4116-6377-0(2)) Lulu.com.

Loeb, Jeph. Blue. Sale, Tim, illus. 2003. (Spider-Man Ser.). 160p. (YA). 21.99 (978-0-7851-1062-0(3)) Marvel Enterprises, Inc.

Lofting, Hugh. La Historia del Doctor Dolittle. (SPA.). 136p. 12.95 (978-84-239-9048-1(6)); (Illus.). 184p. (YA). (gr. 5-8). 11.95 (978-84-239-2733-3(4) , EC2743) Espasa Calpe, S.A. ESP. *Dist:* Planeta Publishing Corp., Continental Bk. Co., Inc., Lectorum Pubns., Inc.

—The Voyages of Doctor Dolittle. 2004. (Illus.). 224p. (J). pap. 3.95 (978-0-486-43491-9(5)) Dover Pubns., Inc.

—Voyages of Doctor Dolittle. 2004. lib. bdg. 12.95 (978-0-613-90738-5(8)); 2000. (gr. 3-6). lib. bdg. 14.15 (978-0-7857-5056-7(8)) Tandem Library Bks.

Logan, June. Billy & His Underwater Adventures. 2005. (J). 9.00 (978-1-59971-046-4(3)) Aardvark Global Publishing.

Lohans, Alison. No Place for Kids. 1999. (Middle Readers Ser.). 98p. (J). (gr. 3-5). pap. 4.95 (978-1-896184-50-0(2)) Roussan Pubs., Inc./Roussan Editeur, Inc. CAN. *Dist:* Orca Bk. Pubs. USA.

Lojeski, Lynne & O'Donnell, Thomas. Sneak Force, Mission Infinity: The Legend. 2004. (J). lib. bdg. 28.95 (978-1-932303-17-9(0)) Media Creations, Inc.

Lomba, Ana. Easy French Storybook: Little Red Riding Hood. 2005. (ENG & FRE., Illus.). 41p. 14.95 incl. cd-rom (978-0-07-146167-2(1) , 9780071461672) McGraw-Hill Cos., The.

—Easy Spanish Storybook: Little Red Riding Hood. 2005. (ENG & SPA., Illus.). 41p. 14.95 incl. cd-rom (978-0-07-146164-1(7) , 9780071461641) McGraw-Hill Cos., The.

Lombardo, G. Where the Trees Grow Gumballs. 2006. 57p. pap. 12.95 (978-1-4241-2978-2(8)) PublishAmerica, Inc.

London. Old Man Tiger. (J). 15.95 (978-0-8118-4902-9(3)) Chronicle Bks. LLC.

London, Jack. Call of the Wild. (Illus.). 184p. (J). 9.95 (978-1-56156-370-8(6)) Kidsbooks, Inc.

—Call of the Wild. 2003. (gr. 3-6). lib. bdg. 11.80 (978-0-613-61610-2(3)); 2000. (gr. 5-8). lib. bdg. 11.80 (978-0-613-66693-0(3)) Tandem Library Bks.

—The Call of the Wild. 2001. (Classics Ser.). (Illus.). 192p. (J). (gr. 10). pap. 4.99 (978-0-439-22714-8(3)) Scholastic, Inc.

—The Call of the Wild. Hegarty, Carol, ed. 1998. (Classics Ser.: Set I). (Illus.). 79p. (YA). (gr. 5-12). pap. 6.95 (978-1-56254-254-2(0) , SP2540) Saddleback Educational Publishing.

—The Call of the Wild. 1999. 65p. (J). reprint ed. pap. 8.95 (978-1-57002-094-0(9)) University Publishing Hse., Inc.

—The Call of the Wild: Prestwick House Literary Touchstone Edition. 2005. 100p. (YA). per. 3.99 (978-1-58049-584-4(2) , PWH5842) Prestwick Hse., Inc.

—The Call of the Wild - Spotlight Edition. Grudzina, Douglas, ed. 2005. 100p. (YA). per. 5.95 (978-1-58049-552-3(4) , PWH5524) Prestwick Hse., Inc.

—Jack London. 2003. cd-rom 19.00 (978-0-931968-52-5(6)) B & R Samizdat Express.

—Jack London. 10th ed. 2003. (Selected Words Ser.). (SPA & ENG.). 528p. 12.95 (978-84-8403-704-0(5)) Edimat Libros, S. A. ESP. *Dist:* Independent Pubs. Group.

—Jack London's The Call of the Wild. 2006. (J). (gr. 4-8). 24.21 (978-1-59961-114-3(7)) Spotlight.

—La Llamada de la Selva. (SPA.). (YA). 8.00 (978-958-04-6747-2(1)) Norma S.A. COL. *Dist:* Distribuidora Norma, Inc.

—La Llamada de la Selva. 2002. (SPA., Illus.). 124p. (J). (ps-7). per. (978-958-30-0163-5(5)) Panamericana Editorial.

—La Quimera del Oro. (SPA.). 256p. (YA). (978-84-7525-004-5(1)) Ediciones Generales Anaya SA.

—To Build a Fire. abr. ed. 1999. mass mkt. 3.99 (978-0-8125-6993-3(8) , Tor Bks.) Doherty, Tom Assocs., LLC.

—To Build a Fire. 2003. (gr. 3-6). lib. bdg. 13.00 (978-0-613-89665-8(3)) Tandem Library Bks.

—To Build a Fire & Other Stories. 1999. (gr. 7-12). lib. bdg. 11.80 (978-0-613-17557-9(3)) Tandem Library Bks.

—White Fang. l.t. ed. 2005. 354p. (J). 20.95 (978-0-7862-7540-3(5)) Thorndike Pr.

London, Jack, ed. Call of the Wild Great Read. 2004. (Great Classics for Children Ser.). 128p. (J). 5.99 (978-1-4037-0983-7(1)) Dalmatian Pr.

London, Jonathan. Froggy Goes to Camp. Remkiewicz, Frank, illus. 2008. (Froggy Ser.). 32p. (J). (ps-k). 15.99 (***978-0-670-01098-1(7)*** , Viking Juvenile) Penguin Group (USA) Inc.

Long, Christopher E. Blackfoot Braves Society: Spirit Totems. Geiger, Michael, illus. 2006. 127p. (J). 12.95 (978-0-9742803-9-4(9) , Actionopolis) Komikwerks, LLC.

Long, Cliff. Broadside Ben & the Big Brass Cannon. 2004. (Illus.). 46p. (J). per. 8.95 (978-0-9754400-0-1(4)) Watermark Cruises.

Long, Melinda. How I Became a Pirate. Shannon, David, illus. 2003. 44p. (J). (ps-3). 16.00 (978-0-15-201848-1(4)) Harcourt Children's Bks.

Long, Sanford. The Adventures of Vox & Enduro. 2004. 134p. pap. 19.95 (978-1-4137-0467-9(0)) PublishAmerica, Inc.

Lopez, David Mark. Maddie's Magic Markers: Ride Like an Indian. 2006. (J). (gr. 3-7). (***978-0-9744097-1-9(5)***) Lopez, David.

—Walk Like an Egyptian. 2006. (J). (gr. 3-7). (***978-0-9744097-0-2(7)***) Lopez, David.

Loranger, Marc J. Diamond in the Rough. 2004. (J). (978-1-59196-741-5(4)) Instantpublisher.com.

Lord of the Flies. 1998. 40p. (YA). 11.95 (978-1-56137-384-0(2) , NU3842SP) Novel Units, Inc.

Lorenzo, Mike. Allison's Summer Of '53. 2005. 53p. pap. 12.95 (978-1-4241-1074-2(2)) PublishAmerica, Inc.

Lorimer, Janet. Boneyard. 2003. (Illus.). 80p. (YA). per. 3.95 (978-1-56254-700-4(3) , SP7003) Saddleback Educational Publishing.

—Empty Eyes: Set 1. 2002. 32p. (YA). 2.95 (978-1-56254-407-2(1) , SP 4071) Saddleback Educational Publishing.

The Lost Children. 1999. (J). (gr. 4-7). pap. 6.95 (978-1-881545-97-2(0)) A B Publishing.

Lost in the Woods CONNECT-IT. 2005. (J). per. 24.95 (978-0-9749412-2-6(0)) EDCO Publishing, Inc.

Lotz, Dana. What It's Like to Still Be a Kid. 2005. 61p. pap. 12.95 (978-1-4137-9257-7(X)) PublishAmerica, Inc.

Louchard, Anto. Plume dans le Whisky. pap. 12.95 (978-2-84146-723-5(6)) Editions Milan FRA. *Dist:* Distribooks, Inc.

Lourie, Peter. The Lost Treasure of Captain Kidd. 2003. (Illus.). 96p. (YA). (gr. 4-6). pap. 9.95 (978-1-56397-851-7(2)) Boyds Mills Pr.

Louvier, Randy. The Many Misadventures of Randy Rabbit. 2005. 71p. pap. 14.95 (978-1-4137-3776-9(5)) PublishAmerica, Inc.

Love, D. Anne. The Secret Prince. 2005. 240p. (J). 16.95 (978-0-689-84426-3(3) , McElderry, Margaret K.) Simon & Schuster Children's Publishing.

Love, Hallie. Watakame's Journey: The Story of the Great Flood & the World. Huichol Artists Staff, illus. 1999. 84p. (J). (gr. 4-7). 14.95 (978-1-57416-029-1(X)) Clear Light Pubs.

Love, Judy. Praise Be & Rainbows. 2006. 51p. pap. 12.95 (978-1-4241-0333-1(9)) PublishAmerica, Inc.

Lovell, H. N. Wootie's Great Adventure: Escape to Freedom. 2006. (J). pap. 12.95 (978-0-9761182-1-3(1)) Alpha Run Pr., LLC.

Lovett, Darrell. Hi, I'm Alex. l.t. ed. 2006. (ENG., Illus.). 28p. per. 9.95 (***978-1-4327-0195-6(9)***) Outskirts Press, Inc.

—My Dog Tony. l.t. ed. 2006. (ENG., Illus.). 28p. per. 9.95 (***978-1-4327-0187-1(8)***) Outskirts Press, Inc.

Lovhaug, Lewis J. Angel Armor: Just a Boy. 2003. 224p. (YA). pap. 15.95 (978-0-595-28475-7(2)) iUniverse, Inc.

Low, Vicki. First Emperor. Mayhew, Sara E., illus. 2007. 48p. (J). lib. bdg. 23.08 (***978-1-4242-1626-0(5)***) Fitzgerald Bks.

Lowe, Lana. The Three Little Girls & the Giant Sea Turtle. Beaumont, Peter, illus. 2006. (J). (978-0-9777274-0-7(8)) Lone Star Publishing Co.

Lowe, Wesley. The Griffin's Gauntlet. 2003. (YA). per. 14.95 (978-1-59453-013-5(0) , 1171) Airleaf Publishing & Bookselling.

Lowell, Melissa. Silver Blades, 10 bks. l.t. ed. Incl. Breaking the Ice. 144p. lib. bdg. 23.33 (978-0-8368-2063-8(0)); . Center Ice. 144p. lib. bdg. 23.33 (978-0-8368-2099-7(1)); Competition. lib. bdg. 23.33 (978-0-8368-2065-2(7)); Going for the Gold. 128p. lib. bdg. 23.33 (978-0-8368-2066-9(5)); Ice Princess. 144p. lib. bdg. 23.33 (978-0-8368-2096-6(7)); In the Spotlight. 128p. lib. bdg. 23.33 (978-0-8368-2064-5(9)); Perfect Pair. 96p. lib. bdg. 23.33 (978-0-8368-2067-6(3)); Rumors at the Rink. 144p. lib. bdg. 23.33 (978-0-8368-2097-3(5)); Skating Camp. 96p. lib. bdg. 23.33 (978-0-8368-2068-3(1)); Spring Break. 144p. lib. bdg. 23.33 (978-0-8368-2098-0(3)); (J). (gr. 4 up). 1998. Set lib. bdg. 233.30 (978-0-8368-2062-1(2)) Stevens, Gareth Inc.

Lowry, Lois. Anastasia Vive Aqui. Alonso, Juan Ramon, illus. 2003. (SPA.). 160p. (J). 9.95 (978-84-670-0073-3(2)) Espasa Calpe, S.A. ESP. *Dist:* Lectorum Pubns., Inc., Planeta Publishing Corp.

Lowry, Mark & Bolton, Martha. Piper's Great Adventures. Myers, Kristen, illus. 2005. (Adventures of Piper the Hyper Mouse Ser.). 124p. (J). 11.99 (978-1-58229-474-2(7)) Simon & Schuster.

Loyd, Mark. Big Ben: A Little Known Story. Loyd, Mark, illus. ed. 2005. (J). (978-0-9773317-1-0(7)) Too Fun Publshing.

Loyie, Larry. As Long as the Rivers Flow. Holmlund, Heather D., illus. 2005. 40p. (J). pap. 8.95 (978-0-88899-696-1(9)) Groundwood Bks. CAN. *Dist:* Perseus Distribution.

Lubar, David. Punished! 2006. 96p. (J). (gr. 2-5). 15.95 (978-1-58196-042-6(5)) Darby Creek Publishing.

Lucas, David. Lying Carpet. 2007. (Illus.). 48p. (J). (978-1-84270-441-7(9)) Andersen.

Luceno, James. Mask of Zorro. 1998. (978-0-606-13600-6(2)) Tandem Library Bks.

Luceno, James. Movie Novelization. 2008. (Indiana Jones Ser.). 160p. (J). 6.99 (***978-0-545-00701-6(1)*** , Scholastic) Scholastic, Inc.

Luciani, Brigitte. How Will Get Beach. 2006. (J). pap. 6.95 (978-0-7358-2038-8(4)) North-South Bks., Inc.

Luckett, Dave. Girl the Queen & the Castle. 2004. (Rhianna Ser.: No. 3). 144p. (J). pap. 4.99 (978-0-439-41189-9(0) , Scholastic Paperbacks) Scholastic, Inc.

Lucky Foot Stable & Lady's Big Surprise. 2003. (J). (978-0-9746561-7-5(8)) FT Richards Publishing.

Lucretius Carus, Titus. Of the Nature of Things. 2006. pap. 47.99 (***978-1-4219-7900-7(4)***) IndyPublish.com.

Ludwig, Charles. Leopard Glue & Cannibal County. 2001. (Illus.). 149p. (YA). (gr. 6-9). pap. 7.95 (978-0-9673806-2-9(6)) King's Bookshelf Pubns.

Ludy, Mark. Jujo: Of the Jungle. 2007. (Illus.). 32p. (J). 16.95 (978-0-9664276-5-3(3)) Green Pastures Publishing, Inc.

Luisi, Nancy. Unwanted Changes. 2005. 131p. pap. 19.95 (978-1-4137-8250-9(7)) PublishAmerica, Inc.

Lujan, Jorge. Palabras Manzana. Marín, Manuel, illus. 2004. (SPA.). 96p. (J). 5.95 (978-84-667-2474-6(5)) Grupo Anaya, S.A. ESP. *Dist:* Lectorum Pubns., Inc.

Lukas, Catherine. Race to the Tower of Power. 2007. 24p. (J). 21.35 (***978-1-59961-159-4(7)***) Spotlight.

Luke, Judy. Teddy Goes to Monaco. 2006. (Illus.). 116p. (YA). per. 12.95 (978-0-9769645-6-8(2)) Flo's Productions.

Luke's Adventures: Individual Title Six-Packs. (ps-2). 27.00 (978-0-7635-9460-2(1)) Rigby Education.

Lumry, Amanda. Polar Bear Puzzle. 2007. (Adventures of Riley Ser.). 36p. (ps-3). 18.95 (***978-1-60040-005-6(1)***); 15.95 (***978-1-60040-004-9(3)***) Eaglemont Pr.

Lumry, Amanda & Hurwitz, Laura. Amazon River Rescue. McIntyre, Sarah, illus. 2004. (Adventures of Riley Ser.). 36p. 15.95 (978-0-9662257-9-2(1)) Eaglemont Pr.

Lunn, John. The Mariner's Curse. 2004. 216p. (J). (gr. 4-7). pap. 8.95 (978-0-88776-672-5(2)) Tundra Bks., Inc./Livres Toundra, Inc. CAN. *Dist:* Random Hse., Inc.

Lutz II, William. Quest of Brothers. 2007. 346p. pap. 18.99 (***978-0-615-15622-4(3)***) Lutz, William G.

Luxa, Sue. A Cabin in Cripple Creek. 2004. (Illus.). 99p. (J). pap. 8.95 (978-1-932738-04-9(5) , 1234249) Western Reflections Publishing Co.

Lyle-Soffe, Shari. The Misadventures of Rooter & Snuffle. Collier, Kevin Scott, illus. 2006. 28p. (J). E-Book 5.00 incl. cd-rom (***978-1-933090-43-6(X)***) Guardian Angel Publishing, Inc.

Lynch, Keven R. What's a Buffalo Soldier? The Historical Adventures of Amber & Trevor. 2005. (J). pap. 12.00 (978-0-8059-6750-0(8)) Dorrance Publishing Co., Inc.

Lynn, Jeffrey. The Adventures of Pablo. . the Ecuadorian Panda. 2004. (YA). per. (978-0-9763025-0-6(0)) Penner/Lynn Publishing.

Lyttleton, Kay. Jean Craig in New York. 2005. pap. 24.95 (978-1-4179-9293-5(X)) Kessinger Publishing, LLC.

Ma, Wenhai, illus. Tang Monk Disciples Monkey King. 2005. (Adventures of Monkey King Ser.: No. 3). 32p. (J). 16.95 (978-1-57227-084-8(5)) Pan Asia Pubns. (USA), Inc.

—Tang Monk Disciples Monkey King: English/Chinese. 2005. (Adventures of Monkey King Ser.: No. 3). (ENG & CHI.). 32p. (J). 16.95 (978-1-57227-086-2(1)) Pan Asia Pubns. (USA), Inc.

Ma, Wing Shing. Black Leopard #4. 2005. 160p. (YA). pap. 14.95 (978-1-58899-336-6(1)) ComicsOne Corp./Dr. Masters.

—A Tale of No Name, Vol. 1. 2005. (Storm Riders Ser.). (Illus.). 300p. (YA). pap. 7.95 (978-1-58899-375-5(2)) ComicsOne Corp./Dr. Masters.

Mabie, Hamilton Wright. Heroes Every Child Should Know. 2005. 368p. pap. 15.95 (978-1-59540-641-5(7) , 1st World Library - Literary Society) 1st World Publishing, Inc.

—Heroes Every Child Should Know. 2006. 268p. pap. 13.99 (978-1-4264-1392-6(0)) BiblioBazaar.

—Heroes Every Child Should Know. 2004. reprint ed. pap. 26.95 (978-1-4191-2360-3(2)); pap. 1.99 (978-1-4192-2360-0(7)) Kessinger Publishing, LLC.

Macan, Darko. Soldier X. Kordey, Igor, illus. 2003. 144p. (YA). pap. 12.99 (978-0-7851-1013-2(5)) Marvel Enterprises, Inc.

MacArthur, Nancy. Adventure of the Big Snow. 1998. (J). (gr. 2-4). pap. 3.99 (978-0-590-37209-1(2)) Scholastic, Inc.

MacDonald, George. At the Back of the North Wind. Hughes, Arthur, illus. 2001. (Everyman's Library Children's Classics). 352p. 14.95 (978-0-375-41335-3(9) , Everyman's Library) Knopf Publishing Group.

—At the Back of the North Wind. 1998. (Twelve-Point Ser.). 280p. reprint ed. lib. bdg. 25.00 (978-1-58287-015-1(2)) North Bks.

—Double Story. 2006. 62.99 (***978-1-4280-2469-4(7)***) IndyPublish.com.

MacDonald, George. Sir Gibbie. Lindskoog, Kathryn, ed. Wynne, Patrick, illus. 2001. (Classics for Young Readers Ser.). 224p. (J). (gr. 3-6). pap. 7.99 (978-0-87552-726-0(4)) P & R Publishing.

MacDonald, James. Levi, Adventures of a Police Dog. 2005. 96p. (J). 16.95 (978-0-9716923-1-2(9)) Regency Hse., Ltd.

Macfarlane, Stuart & Macfarlane, Linda. The Secret Diary of Adrian Cat. 2006. 286p. (YA). (gr. 5-8). 24.95 (978-1-933255-23-1(4)) DNA Pr.

MacGregor, Roy. Attack on the Tower of London, Vol. 19. 2004. (Illus.). 128p. (YA). mass mkt. 4.95 (978-0-7710-5648-2(6) , Screech Owls) McClelland & Stewart CAN. *Dist:* Random Hse., Inc.

—The Complete Screech Owls, Vol. 4. 2006. 488p. (J). pap. 15.95 (978-0-7710-5491-4(2) , Screech Owls) McClelland & Stewart CAN. *Dist:* Random Hse., Inc.

—Danger in Dinosaur Valley. Banning, Gregory C., illus. 1999. (Screech Owls Ser.: No. 10). 128p. (J). (gr. 4-7). mass mkt. 4.95 (978-0-7710-5620-8(6) , Screech Owls) McClelland & Stewart CAN. *Dist:* Random Hse., Inc.

—Nightmare in Nagano. Banning, Gregory C., illus. 1998. (Screech Owls Ser.: No. 9). 120p. (J). (gr. 4-7). mass mkt. 3.95 (978-0-7710-5619-2(2) , Screech Owls) McClelland & Stewart CAN. *Dist:* Random Hse., Inc.

—The Screech Owls' Reunion. 2004. (Illus.). 144p. (YA). mass mkt. 4.95 (978-0-7710-5649-9(4) , Screech Owls) McClelland & Stewart CAN. *Dist:* Random Hse., Inc.

—The West Coast Murders. Banning, Gregory C., illus. 2000. (Screech Owls Ser.: No. 12). 128p. (J). (gr. 4-7). mass mkt. 4.95 (978-0-7710-5623-9(0) , Screech Owls) McClelland & Stewart CAN. *Dist:* Random Hse., Inc.

MacHado, Ana Maria. Aunque Parezca Mentira. (SPA., Illus.). 64p. (J). 16.95 (978-84-207-4412-4(3)) Grupo Anaya, S.A. ESP. *Dist:* Distribooks, Inc., Lectorum Pubns., Inc.

MacHale, D. J. Black Water. 2004. (Pendragon Ser.: Bk. 5). 448p. (gr. 3-6). pap. 7.99 (978-0-689-86911-2(8) , Aladdin) Simon & Schuster Children's Publishing.

—Black Water. 2004. (Pendragon Ser. : Bk. 5). 200p. (J). (gr. k-9). lib. bdg. 14.30 (978-1-4176-2874-2(X)) Tandem Library Bks.

—The Guide to the Territories of Halla. Ferguson, Peter, illus. 2005. (Pendragon Ser.). 48p. (J). pap. 7.99 (978-1-4169-0014-6(4) , Aladdin) Simon & Schuster Children's Publishing.

—The Lost City of Faar. 2007. (Pendragon Ser.: Bk. 2). 400p. (J). 16.99 (978-1-4169-3626-8(2)) Simon & Schuster Children's Publishing.

—The Lost City of Faar. 2003. (Pendragon Ser. : Bk. 2). 384p. (J). (gr. 4-7). per. 14.15 (978-0-613-61640-9(5)) Tandem Library Bks.

—The Merchant of Death. (Pendragon Ser.: Bk. 1). (J). 2007. 384p. 16.99 (978-1-4169-3625-1(4)); 2006. 400p. pap. 2.99 (978-1-4169-2495-1(7) , Aladdin) Simon & Schuster Children's Publishing.

—The Merchant of Death & The Lost City of Faar: Journal of an Adventure through Time & Space. 2005. (Pendragon Ser.: Bks. 1-2). 758p. (YA). 9.99 (978-0-681-05434-9(4)) Borders Pr.

—The Never War. 2003. (Pendragon Ser.: Bk. 3). (Illus.). 352p. (J). pap. 7.99 (978-0-7434-3733-2(0) , Aladdin) Simon & Schuster Children's Publishing.

—Pendragon: The Merchant of Death; the Lost City of Faar; the Never War. 2004. (Pendragon Ser.: Bks. 1-3). (Illus.). 1136p. (J). 15.95 (978-0-689-03808-2(9) , Aladdin) Simon & Schuster Children's Publishing.

—The Pilgrims of Rayne. 2007. (Pendragon Ser.: Bk. 8). 560p. (J). 16.99 (978-1-4169-1416-7(1)) Simon & Schuster Children's Publishing.

—The Quillan Games. (Pendragon Ser.: Bk. 7). 496p. (J). 2007. pap. 8.99 (***978-0-689-86913-6(4)*** , Aladdin); 2006. (gr. 5-9). 16.99 (978-1-4169-1423-5(4)) Simon & Schuster Children's Publishing.

—The Reality Bug, Vol. 4. 2003. (Pendragon Ser.: Bk. 4). 384p. pap. 6.99 (978-0-7434-3734-9(9) , Aladdin) Simon & Schuster Children's Publishing.

—The Reality Bug. 2003. (Pendragon Ser. : Bk. 4). (gr. 5-8). lib. bdg. 14.15 (978-0-613-90177-2(0)) Tandem Library Bks.

—The Rivers of Zadaa. (Pendragon Ser.: Bk. 6). 416p. (J). 2006. pap. 6.99 (978-0-689-86912-9(6) , Aladdin); 2005. 14.95 (978-1-4169-0710-7(6)) Simon & Schuster Children's Publishing.

MacHale, D. J. & Sorrells, Walter. Static, No. 1. 2006. (Flight 29 Down Ser.: Vol. 1). (Illus.). 224p. (J). (gr. 4-7). pap. 5.99 (978-0-448-44106-1(3) , Grosset & Dunlap) Penguin Group (USA) Inc.

MacInnis, Katherine Grace. Kelsar. 2006. 140p. 19.95 (978-1-58939-877-1(7)) Virtualbookworm.com Publishing, Inc.

Mack, David. Skin Deep. 1999. (Illus.). 112p. (YA). 23.95 (978-1-58240-073-0(3)) Image Comics.

Mack, Paulette. Cookout at Grandma's House: The Adventures of Mielle & Cheeky. 2006. (ENG., Illus.). 24p. per. 10.95 (***978-1-59800-998-9(2)***) Outskirts Press, Inc.

Mackenzie, Catherine. The Big Green Tree at No.11: Tammy & Jake Learn about Life & Death. (Illus.). 144p. (J). mass mkt. 5.99 (978-1-85792-731-3(1) , Christian Focus) Christian Focus Pubns. GBR. *Dist:* Riverside.

MacKenzie, Catherine. The Lonely Grey Dog at No. 6: Tammy & Jake Learn about Love & Loyalty. 2005. (Illus.). 157p. (J). mass mkt. (978-1-84550-103-7(9) , Christian Focus) Christian Focus Pubns.

Mackinnon, Bernard. The Boy Who Turned Green. 2005. 119p. pap. 16.95 (978-1-4137-7262-3(5)) PublishAmerica, Inc.

MacLean, Alistair. Boondini. Bowser, Milton, illus. l.t. ed. 1998. 72p. (YA). 10.00 (978-0-940178-60-1(5) , BDNI) Sitare, Ltd.

—Circus. (J). 24.95 (978-0-89190-672-8(X)) Amereon LTD.

MacNeil, Stephen. Woolies & Worms. 2007. 192p. (J). (gr. 2-5). 16.95 (***978-0-8126-2751-0(2)***) Cricket Bks.

Mad Dash. 2005. (J). 4.95 (978-1-59792-011-7(8)) F.A.S.T. Learning LLLC.

Madden, Kerry. Jessie's Mountain. 2008. (J). (gr. 3). 16.99 (***978-0-670-06154-9(9)*** , Viking Juvenile) Penguin Group (USA) Inc.

Maddern, Eric. The Fire Children: A West African Tale. Lessac, Frane, illus. 2006. 32p. (J). pap. 7.95 (978-1-84507-514-9(5)) Lincoln, Frances Ltd. GBR. *Dist:* Perseus Distribution.

Maden, Mary. The Great Manatee Rescue. Schroeder, Eric, ed. Geib, Stephanie K., illus. 1999. (Earth/Ocean Adventures Ser.: Vol. 2). (J). (gr. 1-7). pap. 5.95 (978-1-890479-58-9(6)) Dog & Pony Publishing.

—The Great Pirate Adventure. Schroeder, Eric, ed. 1999. (Outer Banks Animal Adventure Ser.: Vol. 7). (Illus.). 24p. (J). (gr. k-6). pap. 5.95 (978-1-890479-56-5(X)) Dog & Pony Publishing.

—The Great Shark Adventure. Geib, Stephanie K., illus. 1999. (Earth/Ocean Adventures Ser.: Vol. 1). (J). (gr. 1-7). pap. 5.95 (978-1-890479-60-2(8)) Dog & Pony Publishing.

Madonna. The Adventures of Abdi, the (Las Avunturas de Abdi) Dugina, Olga & Dugin, Andrej, illus. 2004. 40p. (J). (ps-6). 19.95 (978-0-670-05889-1(0)) Callaway Editions, Inc.

The Magical Adventures of Samuel the Squirrel & Oscar the Owl Journey to Mars. 2005. (J). per. 12.95 (978-0-9762929-0-6(4)) Morning Glory Pubns.

Magness, Lee. Silver Dasher. 2003. 164p. pap. 12.95 (978-0-595-29043-7(4)) iUniverse, Inc.

Maguire, Thomas Aquinas. A Growling Place. 2007. (Illus.). 32p. (J). (gr. k up). 16.95 (***978-1-894965-74-3(4)***) Simply Read Bks. CAN. *Dist:* Perseus Distribution.

Maher, Alex, illus. Diego's Safari Rescue. 2007. (Go, Diego, Go! Ser.). 24p. (J). pap. 3.99 (***978-1-4169-3818-7(4)*** , Simon Spotlight/Nickelodeon) Simon & Schuster Children's Publishing.

Maher, Mickle Brandt. Master Stitchum & the Moon. Dousias, Spiro, illus. 2003. (J). 19.99 (978-1-932188-01-1(0)) Bollix Bks.

Mahto, Jamison C. The Misadventures of Bonehead Bear. 2002. (Illus.). 24p. (J). (ps-3). 14.95 (978-1-889401-10-2(2)); pap. 7.95 (978-1-889401-11-9(0)) Spirit Bear.

Mahy, Margaret. Down the Dragon's Tongue. MacCarthy, Patricia, illus. 2000. 32p. (J). pap. (978-0-7322-7052-0(9)) HarperCollins Pubs.

Mahy, Margaret & MacCarthy, Patricia. Down the Dragon's Tongue. 2000. (Illus.). 32p. (J). (ps-2). pap. 15.95 (978-0-531-30272-9(5) , Orchard Bks.) Scholastic, Inc.

Maisner, Heather. Diary of a Princess: A Tale from Marco Polo's Travels. Moxley, Sheila, illus. 2004. 32p. (J). (978-0-7112-1854-3(4)); pap. 7.95 (978-1-84507-148-6(4)) Lincoln, Frances Ltd. GBR. *Dist:* Transition Vendor, Perseus Distribution.

Maizels, Jennie. The Journey to Jigsaw Town. 1999. (Jigsaw Bks.). (Illus.). 14p. (J). (ps-k). bds. 10.95 (978-1-86233-073-5(5)) Sterling Publishing Co., Inc.

Major, David L. The Day of the Nefilim. 2002. 343p. (YA). pap. (978-0-9579858-9-6(4)) Metropolis Ink.

Major, Kevin. Far from Shore. 2004. 250p. (YA). pap. 6.95 (978-0-88899-568-1(7)) Groundwood Bks. CAN. *Dist:* Perseus Distribution.

—Hold Fast. 2004. 204p. (YA). pap. 6.95 (978-0-88899-580-3(6)); 25th anniv. ed. 2003. 192p. (J). 16.95 (978-0-88899-579-7(2)) Groundwood Bks. CAN. *Dist:* Perseus Distribution.

Makranczy, Judit. We Have to Escape. 1999. 185p. (J). (gr. k-17). pap. 9.99 (978-0-88092-373-6(3) , 3733) Royal Fireworks Publishing Co.

Makumi, Joel. The Return of Njaga. 2005. (Phoenix Young Readers Library). (Illus.). 179p. (978-9966-47-113-0(8)) Phoenix Pubs., Ltd.

Malaika: Safari Adventure to Kenya. 2006. (J). 4.99 (978-0-9765982-0-6(5)) Simba Publishing Co.

Malcolm, Jahnna N. The Sapphire Princess Hunts for Treasure. 1998. (Jewel Kingdom Ser.: No. 6). (J). (gr. 3-5). 3.99 (978-0-590-11714-2(9)) Scholastic, Inc.

Malea. Princess Melia. 2007. 145p. (J). pap. 15.95 (***978-1-58909-367-6(4)***) Bookstand Publishing.

Malison, Anna. Through Thick & Thin. 2006. (ENG.). 136p. per. (978-1-897117-14-9(0)) Gospel Folio Pr.

Malkin, Arlene Swinson. Adventures with Grandma & Grandpa: The Secret of the Old Trunk. 2006. 48p. pap. 12.95 (978-1-4241-1621-8(X)) PublishAmerica, Inc.

Malokas, Ann. The Tag-a-long Trio: Zak, Lizze & Ben Too! Nicholas, Corasue, illus. 2007. (J). 15.95 (***978-0-9708415-8-2(2)***) Guilty Mom Pr.

Malone, Geoffrey. Elephant Ben. 2nd ed. 2002. 160p. (J). pap. (978-0-340-86059-5(6) , Hodder & Stoughton) Hodder General Publishing Division.

Malot, Hector & Crewe-Jones, Florence. Nobody's Boy: Companion Story to Nobody's Girl. Gooch, Thelma & Gruelle, Johnny, illus. 2006. 237p. (J). pap. (978-1-894666-75-6(5)) Inheritance Pubns.

—Nobody's Girl: Companion Story to Nobody's Boy. Gooch, Thelma, illus. 2006. 220p. (J). pap. (978-1-894666-76-3(3)) Inheritance Pubns.

Maloy, Karen. Are You Afraid of the Dark, Too? Prouty, Jan, illus. 2002. (J). (978-0-9709940-7-3(9)) Salt Pubs.

Malz, Betty. Angels Watching over Me. 2000. 128p. (gr. 13 up). mass mkt. 4.99 (978-0-8007-8678-6(5) , Spire) Revell.

Man-Kong, Mary. Dora the Explorer Sponge Art Kit. 2006. (Illus.). 24p. (J). (gr. k-ps). 9.99 (978-0-375-83537-7(7) , Golden Bks.) Random Hse. Children's Bks.

Mancusi, Mari. Stake That! 2006. 288p. (YA). (gr. 12). pap. 9.99 (978-0-425-21210-3(6) , Berkley Trade) Penguin Group (USA) Inc.

Manfredi, Federica, illus. Kat & Mouse. 2006. (Kat & Mouse Ser.: Vol. 1). pap. 5.99 (978-1-59816-548-7(8) , Tokyopop Kids) TOKYOPOP, Inc.

Mangano, J. M. Crossing Cadogan Bay. 2002. 222p. pap. 14.95 (978-0-595-22370-1(2) , Writer's Showcase Pr.) iUniverse, Inc.

Mangano, Tom, illus. Dora explora el mundo. 2006. (Dora la Exploradora Ser.). (SPA.). 24p. (J). pap. 3.99 (978-1-4169-2448-7(5) , Libros Para Ninos) Simon & Schuster Children's Publishing.

—Dora's World Adventure! 2006. (Dora the Explorer Ser.). 24p. (J). pap. 3.99 (978-1-4169-2447-0(7) , Simon Spotlight/Nickelodeon) Simon & Schuster Children's Publishing.

Maniac Magee. 1999. (J). 9.95 (978-1-56137-348-2(6)) Novel Units, Inc.

Mankamyer, Laura. The Adventures of the Stonycreek Gang. Mankamyer, Laura, illus. l.t. ed. 2003. (Illus.). 84p. (J). 12.99 (978-0-9728431-4-0(0)) Mankamyer, Laura.

Mann, Seymour. The Purple Automobile & the Newspaper Girl. 2003. 112p. 20.95 (978-0-595-66076-6(2)); pap. 10.95 (978-0-595-29907-2(5)) iUniverse, Inc.

Mansell, Lisa, ed. Bimini Twist. 1999. (Illus.). 280p. (YA). 22.50 (978-0-9676853-0-4(3)) Bimini Twist Adventures, Inc.

Mantell, Paul. The Man in the Iron Mask. 1998. (Bullseye Step into Classics Ser.). (J). (978-0-606-13965-6(6)) Tandem Library Bks.

Manus, Willard. A Dog Called Leka. 2007. (ENG.). 122p. pap. 7.99 (***978-0-9740551-3-8(1)***) Smith, Viveca Publishing.

The Many Tracks of Lap'n Tap. 2007. (J). per. 10.95 (***978-0-9761128-4-6(1)***) Hafabanana Pr.

Mappin, Don. Mortal Enemies: Sentinels. 1999. 150p. (YA). (gr. 10 up). pap. 15.00 (978-0-9641722-2-7(4)) Black Gate Publishing.

Mara, Sarah Robinson. A Snug Little Island, Hammond, Nancy Robinson, illus. 2005. 60p. (J). 18.50 (978-0-9766737-0-5(3)) Pink Granite Pr.

Marbury, Stephon & Dean, Marshall. The Adventures of Young Starbury: Practice Makes Perfect. Nakai, Ryan, illus. 2007. 36p. (J). 12.99 (***978-0-9798250-0-2(8)***) Godspeed Pr.

Marcinko, Richard & Weisman, John. Detachment Bravo. 2001. 416p. pap. 7.99 (978-0-671-00075-2(6) , Pocket Star) Simon & Schuster.

Marderosian, Mark & Giles, Mike, illus. Who Took the Cake? 2006. (LazyTown Ser.). 24p. (J). pap. 3.99 (978-1-4169-0694-0(0) , Simon Spotlight/Nickelodeon) Simon & Schuster Children's Publishing.

Maresca, Wendi S. Alphabet Silly Time. 2005. (J). pap. (978-0-9772897-0-7(2)) Maresca, Wendi.

Margie BluePockets. 2004. (J). (978-0-9744448-1-9(2)) McCourtie, Anne.

Mariotte, Jeff. Sanctuary. 2003. (gr. 7-12). lib. bdg. 14.15 (978-0-613-61812-0(2)) Tandem Library Bks.

—Summer. Frost, Michael, photos by. 2004. (Witch Season Ser.). 320p. (YA). mass mkt. 5.99 (978-0-689-86665-4(8) , Simon Pulse) Simon & Schuster Children's Publishing.

—Winter. Frost, Michael, photos by. 2005. (Witch Season Ser.). 288p. (YA). mass mkt. 5.99 (978-0-689-86725-5(5) , Simon Pulse) Simon & Schuster Children's Publishing.

Mariotte, Jeff & Frost, Michael. Spring. 2005. (Witch Season Ser.). 272p. (YA). mass mkt. 5.99 (978-0-689-86726-2(3) , Simon Pulse) Simon & Schuster Children's Publishing.

Markas, Jenny. Scooby-Doo & the Monster of Mexico Jr Novelization. 2003. (gr. k-3). lib. bdg. 13.00 (978-0-613-66378-6(0)) Tandem Library Bks.

Marks, Melanie. Super Sam. Collins, Daryll, illus. 2006. (Phonics Comics Ser.). 24p. (J). (gr. 1-17). pap. 3.99 (978-1-58476-420-5(1) , IKIDS) Innovative Kids.

Markun, Alan F. New Revolution. (J). 8.95 (978-0-8022-1062-3(7)) Philosophical Library, Inc.

Marlow, Herb & Marlow, Lynn. Max the Skydiving Mouse. Newberry, Loretta, illus. l.t. ed. 2002. 28p. (J). lib. bdg. 14.95 (978-1-893595-19-4(6)) Four Seasons Bks., Inc.

Marquess, Dana. Night of the Lighted Freedom: A Firefly Fantasy. 2006. (Illus.). 32p. (J). 19.95 (978-1-932278-06-4(0)) Mayhaven Publishing.

Marr, Ella J. The Adventures of Curtis & Grammy. 2006. 57p. pap. 12.95 (***978-1-4241-4743-4(3)***) PublishAmerica, Inc.

Marriott, Donna. 100 Years Ago, Vol. 4416. Kupperstein, Joel, ed. Treatner, Meryl, illus. 1998. (Learn to Read Social Studies). 16p. (J). (ps-2). pap. 2.99 (978-1-57471-339-8(6) , 4416) Creative Teaching Pr., Inc.

Marryat, Frederick. Masterman Ready. l.t. ed. 2006. 276p. pap. 16.99 (978-1-4264-0573-0(1)) BiblioBazaar.

Marsano, Daniel T. Sir Day the Knight. Stroschin, Jane H., illus. rev. ed. 2000. 48p. (J). (gr. k-6). lib. bdg. 15.00 (978-1-883960-20-9(7)) Henry Quill Pr.

Marsden, John. Burning for Revenge. 2006. (Tomorrow Ser.). 272p. (J). pap. 8.99 (978-0-439-85803-8(8) , Scholastic Paperbacks) Scholastic, Inc.

Marsh, Carole. The Goshawful Gold Rush MYST. 2007. 160p. pap. 5.95 (***978-0-635-06334-2(4)***) Gallopade International.

—To a Pioneer Praire! 2007. 128p. pap. 5.99 (***978-0-635-06337-3(9)***) Gallopade International.

—To the Eight Wonders of the World. 2007. 128p. pap. 5.99 (***978-0-635-06335-9(2)***) Gallopade International.

—To the Planet Mars! 2007. 128p. pap. 5.99 (***978-0-635-06336-6(0)***) Gallopade International.

—The Treacherous Tornado Mystery! 2007. 128p. pap. 5.99 (***978-0-635-06338-0(7)***) Gallopade International.

Marsh, David. Into the Abyss. 2004. (YA). 23.95 (978-0-9742909-0-4(4)) Sea Chest Bks.

Marsh, T. F. Quest for Courage. Marsh, T. F., illus. 2006. (Amazing Travels of Wannabeb Ser.). (Illus.). 32p. (J). 8.99 (978-0-7847-1801-8(6) , 04127) Standard Publishing.

Marshall, Catherine. The Princess Club/Family Secrets/ Mountain Madness. 2005. (Christy Juvenile Ser.). 368p. (J). pap. 9.99 (978-1-4003-0774-6(0)) Nelson, Thomas Inc.

Marshall, James. George & Martha: Round & Round Early Reader #3. 2008. 32p. (J). (ps-3). 15.00 (***978-0-618-98505-0(0)***) Houghton Mifflin Co. Trade & Reference Div.

—George & Martha: the Best of Friends Early Reader #4. 2008. 24p. (J). (ps-3). 15.00 (***978-0-618-98451-0(8)***) Houghton Mifflin Co. Trade & Reference Div.

Marshall, James. Taking Care of Carruthers. 2000. (J). (978-0-606-19365-8(0)) Tandem Library Bks.

Marshall, Ken. The Adventures of Maya & Grampa. 2005. 64p. pap. 9.95 (978-0-7414-2472-3(X)) Infinity Publishing.

Marshall, Kenneth L. The Adventures of Maya & Grandpa, Bk. II. 2005. 65p. pap. 9.95 (978-0-7414-2238-5(7)) Infinity Publishing.

Martel, Suzanne. King's Daughter. 1998. (gr. 5-9). 14.95 (978-0-88899-323-6(4) , Libros Tigrillo) Groundwood Bks. CAN. *Dist:* Transition Vendor.

—The King's Daughter. rev. ed. 1998. 232p. (J). (gr. 5-9). pap. 5.95 (978-0-88899-218-5(1) , Libros Tigrillo) Groundwood Bks. CAN. *Dist:* Perseus Distribution.

Martel, Yann. Life of Pi: A Novel. 2003. (gr. 7-12). lib. bdg. 23.45 (978-0-613-59907-8(1)) Tandem Library Bks.

Martens, Floyd. The Adventures of Freddie & Carlos: Danger in the Sun. 2005. 144p. (J). per. (978-1-55306-867-9(X)) Essence Publishing.

—Finding Real Treasure: Book 2 of the Adventures of Freddie & Carlos. 2006. 160p. (J). per. (978-1-55452-011-4(8)) Essence Publishing.

Martin, Ann M. Upon a Midnight Clear. Date not set. (J). 15.95 (978-0-8050-6898-6(8) , Holt, Henry & Co. Bks. For Young Readers) Holt, Henry & Co.

Martin, Cynthia Bloom. Tryloc: The Quest. ed. 2006. (J). per. 22.95 (978-0-9787015-0-5(X)) T.C. McSears Publishing.

Martin, Gary & Pennebaker, H. I. Professor Tyme's Timeless Tales: Revenge of the Sargasso Sea Ogre. 2006. (ENG.). 160p. per. 19.95 (***978-1-4241-5701-3(3)***) PublishAmerica, Inc.

Martin, Herbert. Catch A Falling Leaf. 2006. (J). lib. bdg. 20.00 (978-0-9761765-1-0(3)) Smartinbooks, Inc.

Martin, JoElle. Moonlight in the Forest. 2009. 280p. (YA). pap. 14.99 (978-1-59092-563-8(7) , Blue Works) Windstorm Creative.

Martin, Patricia. Travels with Rainie Marie. 1999. (978-0-606-17388-9(9)) Tandem Library Bks.

Martin, Rebella. Joanna's Journey. Yoder, Laura, illus. 2006. 168p. (YA). pap. 10.99 (978-1-933753-01-0(3)) Carlisle Pr.- Walnut Creek.

Martin, S. R. Frozen. 1999. (Insomniacs Ser.: No. 2). 80p. (gr. 7-12). pap. 2.99 (978-0-590-69141-3(4)) Scholastic, Inc.

—Road Kill. 1999. (Insomniacs Ser.: No. 1). 80p. (gr. 7-12). pap. 2.99 (978-0-590-69130-7(9)) Scholastic, Inc.

—Swampland. 2000. 112p. (J). (gr. 7-12). pap. 4.50 (978-0-439-04393-9(X)) Scholastic, Inc.

—Tunnel, No. 4. 1999. (Insomniacs Ser.: No. 4). 80p. (gr. 7-12). pap. 2.99 (978-0-590-69149-9(X)) Scholastic, Inc.

Martin, Sharene. Lilah Birdsong's Original Little Perrytales. 2004. 49p. pap. 12.95 (978-1-4137-1367-1(X)) PublishAmerica, Inc.

Martinez, Shawna Joy. Lemur's Legacy: A Savior Is Born. l.t. ed. 2003. (Illus.). 176p. (YA). per. 11.00 (978-0-9729057-0-1(7)) Training Grounds.

—Lemur's Legacy: The Final Outcome. l.t. ed. 2003. (Illus.). 176p. (YA). per. 11.00 (978-0-9729057-2-5(3)) Training Grounds.

—Lemur's Legacy: The Training Begins. l.t. ed. 2003. (Illus.). 176p. (YA). per. 11.00 (978-0-9729057-1-8(5)) Training Grounds.

Martone, Ginny. The White Stallion. 2006. (ENG.). 60p. per. 12.95 (***978-1-4241-4332-0(2)***) PublishAmerica, Inc.

Marz, Ron & Robinson, James. Wildstorm Rising. 1999. (Orig.). (YA). pap. 19.95 (978-1-56389-588-3(9)) DC Comics.

Marzollo, Jean. I Spy Little Numbers. Wick, Walter, illus. 1999. (I Spy Bks.). 26p. (J). (ps). bds. 6.99 (978-0-590-68714-0(X) , Cartwheel Bks.) Scholastic, Inc.

Marzollo, Jean & Wick, Walter. I Spy Year-Round Challenger! A Book of Picture Riddles. Wick, Walter, illus. 2001. (I Spy Ser.). (Illus.). 40p. (J). (gr. k-2). pap. 13.95 (978-0-439-31634-7(0) , Cartwheel Bks.) Scholastic, Inc.

Maselli, Christopher P. N. Choke Hold Bk. 7: They Must Not Surrender to Fear's Grip. 2004. 128p. (J). pap. 4.99 (978-0-310-70666-3(1)) Zonderkidz.

—Shut Down! Bk. 8: True Courage Reveals the Laptop's Truth. 2004. 128p. (J). pap. 4.99 (978-0-310-70667-0(X)) Zonderkidz.

Mashima, Hiro. En Espanol, Vol. 5. 2006. (SPA., Illus.). 192p. reprint ed. pap. 10.95 (978-1-59497-179-2(X)) Public Square Bks.

—Rave Master. 2006. (SPA., Illus.). reprint ed. Vol. 7. 200p. pap. 10.95 (978-1-59497-199-0(4)); Vol. 8. 186p. pap. 10.95 (978-1-59497-200-3(1)); Vol. 9. 192p. pap. 10.95 (978-1-59497-201-0(X)) Public Square Bks.

—Rave Master (En Español) 2006. (SPA., Illus.). reprint ed. Vol. 1. 192p. pap. 10.95 (978-1-59497-175-4(7)); Vol. 2. 192p. pap. 10.95 (978-1-59497-176-1(5)); Vol. 3. 184p. pap. 10.95 (978-1-59497-177-8(3)); Vol. 4. 192p. pap. 10.95 (978-1-59497-178-5(1)); Vol. 6. 200p. pap. 10.95 (978-1-59497-180-8(3)) Public Square Bks.

Masini, Beatrice. A Brave Little Princess. Handley, Diana, tr. Monaco, Octavia, illus. 2000. 32p. (J). (gr. k-2). lib. bdg. 16.99 (978-1-84148-267-5(6)) Barefoot Bks., Inc.

Mason, Hazel M. The Adventures of Hamhocks & Henry. 2002. 114p. pap. 9.95 (978-0-595-23718-0(5) , Writers Club Pr.) iUniverse, Inc.

Mason, Simon. The Quigleys at Large. Stephens, Helen, illus. 2003. 160p. (J). (gr. k-7). 14.95 (978-0-385-75022-6(6) , Fickling, David Bks.) Random Hse. Children's Bks.

Mason, Tom. Going Turbo. Danko, Dan, illus. 2001. (Max Steel Ser.). 48p. (Orig.). (J). pap. 3.99 (978-0-439-22561-8(2)) Scholastic, Inc.

—Take It to the Max. 2001. (gr. 3-6). lib. bdg. 11.80 (978-0-613-87080-1(8)) Tandem Library Bks.

Mason, Tom & Danko, Dan. The Lost Scrolls: Fire. Spaziante, Patrick, illus. 2006. (Avatar Ser.). 64p. (J). pap. 4.99 (978-1-4169-1880-6(9) , Simon Spotlight) Simon & Schuster Children's Publishing.

—The Lost Scrolls: Air. Yee, Josie & Johnson, Shane L., illus. 2007. (Avatar Ser.). 64p. (J). pap. 4.99 (978-1-4169-1879 0(5) , Simon Spotlight) Simon & Schuster Children's Publishing.

Mason, Tom & Danko, Dan. The Ultimate Pocket Guide. 2007. (Avatar Ser.). 48p. (J). pap. 3.99 (***978-1-4169-4736-3(1)*** , Simon Spotlight) Simon & Schuster Children's Publishing.

Massey, Howard C. Deep Woods. 2005. 217p. pap. 19.95 (978-1-4137-7618-8(3)) PublishAmerica, Inc.

Masson, Sophie. Serafin. 2000. (StarMaker Bks.). 140p. (J). (gr. 6-9). pap. 5.50 (978-0-88489-567-1(X)) St. Mary's Pr.

Masters, Anthony. Doughnut Danger. Fisher, Chris, illus. 2004. (I Am Reading Ser.). 48p. (J). (gr. k-3). pap. 3.95 (978-0-7534-5821-1(7) , Kingfisher) Houghton Mifflin Co. Trade & Reference Div.

—Ricky's Rat Gang. Fisher, Chris, illus. 2004. (I Am Reading Ser.). 48p. (J). (gr. 1-3). pap. 3.95 (978-0-7534-5800-6(4) , Kingfisher) Houghton Mifflin Co. Trade & Reference Div.

Mateboer, Hans. Peter the Cruise Ship. 2007. (J). 16.95 (***978-0-9759487-1-2(7)***) Mateboer, Johannes Aart.

Matheson, Richard. Abu & the 7 Marvels. Stout, William, illus. 2003. 128p. (YA). pap. 21.95 (978-1-887368-49-0(3)) Gauntlet, Inc.

Matheson, Shirlee Smith. Fastback Beach. 2006. (Orca Soundings Ser.). 112p. (YA). lib. bdg. 14.95 (978-1-55143-580-0(2)) Orca Bk. Pubs. USA.

Matott, Justin, Jr., illus. The Tales of Mr. Murphy. 2005. 145p. (YA). 17.50 (978-1-889191-17-1(5)) Clove Pubns.

Matsumoto, Lisa. The Adventures of Gary & Harry: A Tale of Two Turtles. Furuya, Michael, illus. 2006. (J). 16.95 (978-0-9647491-4-6(9)) Lehua, Inc.

Matsumoto, Lisa & Furuya, Michael. The Adventures of Gary & Harry. 2002. (J). (ps-3). 16.95 (978-0-9705015-2-3(8)) B-52 Entertainment, LLC.

Matsumoto, Tomo. Beauty Is the Beast, Vol. 4. 2006. (Beauty Is the Beast Ser.). 208p. (YA). pap. 8.99 (978-1-4215-0354-7(9)) Viz Media.

Matsuoka, Kyoko. Where Is Little Toko. 2005. (Illus.). 27p. (J). 11.95 (978-4-902216-11-0(6)) R.I.C. Publications Asia Co, Inc. JPN. *Dist:* Continental Enterprises Group, Inc. (CEG).

Matt Drives the Car. 2001. (978-1-58453-160-9(6)) Pioneer Valley Educational Pr., Inc.

Mattel, creator. Barbie Box - the Enchanted Collection. 2005. (Illus.). 288p. pap. 19.99 (978-1-59816-408-4(2)) TOKYOPOP, Inc.

Matthew, Patricia D. THG-Mystery... Treehouse Gargoyle. 2006. 150p. pap. 19.95 (978-1-4241-2587-6(1)) PublishAmerica, Inc.

Matthews, T. J. The Canoeing Safari. Rheburg, Judy, illus. 2004. (J). (978-0-938978-35-0(7)) Wycliffe Bible Translators.

—The Village Safari. Rheburg, Judy, illus. 2005. (J). (978-0-938978-36-7(5)) Wycliffe Bible Translators.

Matthies, Don-Oliver. Detective Mazes. 2004. (Maze Craze Book Ser.). (Illus.). 40p. pap. 3.95 (978-1-4027-1293-7(6)) Sterling Publishing Co., Inc.

Mauner, Claudia & Smalley, Elisa. Zoe Sophia's Scrapbook. Mauner, Claudia, illus. 2006. (Illus.). 40p. (J). reprint ed. pap. 6.95 (978-0-8118-5304-0(7)) Chronicle Bks. LLC.

Maupin Schmid, Susan. Lost Time. 2008. 224p. (J). (gr. 5-8). 16.99 (***978-0-399-24460-5(3)*** , Philomel) Penguin Group (USA) Inc.

Mawhinney, Art, illus. Diego's Wolf Pup Rescue. 2006. (Go, Diego, Go! Ser.). 24p. (J). pap. 3.99 (978-1-4169-1559-1(1) , Simon Spotlight/Nickelodeon) Simon & Schuster Children's Publishing.

Max & Mintie, 6 Pks. (gr. k-1). 23.00 (978-0-7635-9054-3(1)) Rigby Education.

May, Jenny. Earth Adventures of Seedwin the Nix. 2000. 36p. (J). (ps-3). pap. (978-0-9684804-1-0(1)) Ogo Bks.

May, Scott. Sten Gizzle- Time Traveller: The Egyptian Adventure. 2000. mass mkt. 8.95 (978-1-931179-08-9(5)) Long Hill Productions, Inc.

May, Sophie. Dotty Dimple Out West. 2005. reprint ed. pap. 22.95 (978-1-4179-8845-7(2)) Kessinger Publishing, LLC.

Mayer, Marianna. The Adventures of Tom Thumb. Craft, Kinuko Y., illus. 2005. 28p. (J). (gr. k-4). reprint ed. 16.00 (978-0-7567-9642-6(3)) DIANE Publishing Co.

Mayes, Walter M. Walter the Giant Storyteller's Giant Book of Giant Stories. O'Malley, Kevin, illus. 2005. 48p. (J). (gr. 1-5). 19.85 (978-0-8027-8975-4(7)) Walker & Co.

Mayher, Lauren. The Legend of Darien: A Hero Rises. 2007. pap. 12.95 (***978-0-9794545-0-9(6)***) Blue Eyed Mayhem Publishing.

Mayhew, James. Miranda Da la Vuelta Al Mundo. 2004. (SPA., Illus.). (J). 17.99 (978-84-8488-094-3(X)) Serres, Ediciones, S. L. ESP. *Dist:* Lectorum Pubns., Inc.

Mayoral, Juana Aurora. Tres Monedas de un Penique. (SPA.). 160p. (YA). (gr. 5-8). (978-84-216-2066-3(5) , BU6190) Bruño, Editorial ESP. *Dist:* Lectorum Pubns., Inc.

Mayowa-Harrison, Lady Paula Merry. The Buckaroos. 2006. (J). pap. 8.00 (***978-0-8059-6978-8(0)***) Dorrance Publishing Co., Inc.

Mayper, Monica. Come & See: A Christmas Story. 1999. (Illus.). 32p. (J). (ps-3). 14.95 (978-0-06-023526-0(8)) HarperCollins Pubs.

Mays, Stan. Wicked Little Camp Story. 2005. 248p. pap. 14.95 (978-1-59113-674-3(1)) Booklocker.com, Inc.

The Maze of Terror. 2001. (YA). (gr. 6-12). pap. (978-0-8224-6407-5(1)) Globe Fearon Educational Publishing.

Mazer, Anne. What Goes up Must Go Down. 2008. (Amazing Days of Abby Hayes Ser.: No. 18). 128p. (J). 4.99 (***978-0-439-82926-7(7)*** , Scholastic Paperbacks) Scholastic, Inc.

Mazur, Kathy. My Story... I'd like to Tell. 2005. (J). bds. 8.95 (978-0-9761076-1-3(9)) Spring Ducks Bks., LLC.

Mazzola, Lori. Tales of the Tree People to Tree... or. 2006. 48p. pap. 12.95 (***978-1-4241-5065-6(5)***) PublishAmerica, Inc.

McAdams Moore, Carol. Phonics Comics: Cave Dave - Level 1. Dammer, Mike, illus. 2007. 24p. (J). (gr. 1-17). pap. 3.99 (978-1-58476-552-3(6)) Innovative Kids.

McAdoo, Grami. Adventures of Sergeant Socks: The Journey Home. 2003. (gr. 5-8). lib. bdg. 18.75 (978-0-613-85568-6(X)) Tandem Library Bks.

McAdoo, Grami & Mcadoo, Opa. The Adventures of Sergeant Socks Bk. 2: The Bravest Heart. McAdoo, Grami, illus. l.t. ed. 2004. (Illus.). 122p. (J). pap. 9.95 (978-0-9714358-5-8(5)) Longhorn Creek Pr.

McAdoo, Grami & McAdoo, O'Pa. The Adventures of Sergeants Socks: The Journey Home. McAdoo, Grami, illus. l.t. ed. 2003. (Illus.). 122p. (J). pap. 9.95 (978-0-9714358-3-4(9)) Longhorn Creek Pr.

McAllister, M. I. The Urchin & the Heartstone. Rayyan, Omar, illus. 2nd rev. ed. 2006. (Mistmantle Chronicles Ser.: Bk. 2). 304p. (gr. 3-7). 17.95 (978-0-7868-5488-2(X)) Hyperion Bks. for Children.

McArthur, Cathy E. The Adventures of Elvis the Groundhog: The Golden Glow. 2005. 9.00 (978-0-8059-8154-4(3)) Dorrance Publishing Co., Inc.

McArthur, Nancy. The Secret of the Plant That Ate Dirty Socks. 2001. 144p. (YA). (gr. 4-7). pap. 12.95 (978-0-595-20185-3(7) , Backinprint.com) iUniverse, Inc.

McBride, Earvin, Jr. The Adventurous Cyborg. McBride, Earvin, Jr., illus. 2nd unabr. ed. 2003. (Amazing Sci-Fi & Adventure Heroes Ser.). (Illus.). 43p. (YA). (gr. 7-12). 4.95 (978-1-892511-06-5(1)) MacBride, E. J. Pubn., Inc.

—Earvin MacBride's Fun Fun Lovable Cartoons, 4 vols., Set. McBride, Earvin, Jr., illus. unabr. ed. 2002. (Illus.). (J). (gr. 7-12). pap. 16.95 (978-1-892511-00-3(2)) MacBride, E. J. Pubn., Inc.

—The Eerie Adventures of Detective Omar Mendez. McBride, Earvin, Jr., illus. 2nd unabr. ed. 2003. (Earvin MacBride's Amazing Sci-Fi & Adventure Heroes Ser.). (Illus.). 329p. (J). (gr. 7-12). pap. 5.95 (978-1-892511-08-9(8)) MacBride, E. J. Pubn., Inc.

McBride, R. J. Temple of the Rainbow. 2004. 151p. pap. 19.95 (978-1-4137-1934-5(1)) PublishAmerica, Inc.

McBrier, Page. Beatrice's Goast. unabr. ed. 2005. (J). (ps-3). 27.95 incl. audio (978-0-8045-6938-5(X)) Spoken Arts, Inc.

McCall, Edith. Adventures on the Waterways. 2000. (Adventures on the American Frontiers Ser.: Vol. 3). (Illus.). 128p. (J). (gr. 8-10). pap. 9.99 (978-0-89824-303-1(3), 3033) Royal Fireworks Publishing Co.

McCann, James. Pyre. 2007. 180p. (J). pap. 8.95 (978-1-894965-66-8(3)) Simply Read Bks. CAN. *Dist:* Perseus Distribution.

McCann, Jesse Leon. Dragon Ball Sticker Book. collector's ed. 2003. (Dragon Ball Z Ser.). (Illus.). 32p. (J). pap. 5.99 (978-0-439-46519-9(2)) Scholastic, Inc.

—Ghastly Giant. del Sur, Duendes, illus. 2003. (Scooby Doo Ser.). 32p. (J). pap. 3.50 (978-0-439-45523-7(5)) Scholastic, Inc.

—Ghastly Giant. 2003. (gr. k-3). lib. bdg. 11.25 (978-0-613-66376-2(4)) Tandem Library Bks.

—Glow in the Dark: Scooby Doo & the Invisible Android. Musacchia, Vince, illus. 2002. (Scooby-Doo Ser.). 24p. (J). (ps). pap. 5.99 (978-0-439-31725-2(8)) Scholastic, Inc.

—Scooby-Doo & the Legend of Vampire Rock. 2003. (gr. 3-6). lib. bdg. 11.25 (978-0-613-58167-7(9)) Tandem Library Bks.

—Scooby-Doo & the Monster of Mexico. 2003. (gr. 3-6). lib. bdg. 11.25 (978-0-613-66377-9(2)) Tandem Library Bks.

McCann, Jesse Leon, et al. Batman No. 1: Time Thaw. Byrne, John, illus. 2003. (Scholastic Reader Ser.). 40p. (J). pap. 3.99 (978-0-439-47096-4(X), Cartwheel Bks.) Scholastic, Inc.

McCarthy, Meghan. Adventures of Patty & the Big Red Bus. 2005. (Illus.). 40p. (J). (ps-1). 12.95 (978-0-375-82939-0(3)); lib. bdg. 14.99 (978-0-375-92939-7(8)) Random Hse. Children's Bks. (Knopf Bks. for Young Readers).

McCarthy, Ralph F. Adventure of Momotaro, the Peach Boy. Saito, Ioe, illus. 2000. (Kodansha Children's Bilingual Classics Ser.). 48p. (ps-3). 9.95 (978-4-7700-2098-7(8)) Kodansha International JPN. *Dist:* Oxford Univ. Pr., Inc.

—Kintaro, the Nature Boy. Yonai, Suiho, illus. 2000. (Kodansha Children's Bilingual Classics Ser.). 48p. 9.95 (978-4-7700-2102-1(X)) Kodansha International JPN. *Dist:* Oxford Univ. Pr., Inc.

McCarthy, Tara. Bridge to Terabithia: Everything You Need for Successful Literature Circles That Get Kids Thinking, Talking, Writing-and Loving Literature. 2002. (Literature Circle Guides Ser.). (Illus.). 32p. (gr. 4-8). pap. 5.95 (978-0-439-27171-4(1)) Scholastic, Inc.

McCartney, Paul, et al. High in the Clouds. 2005. (Illus.). 96p. (J). (gr. 1-5). 19.99 (978-0-525-47733-4(0), Dutton Juvenile) Penguin Group (USA) Inc.

McCarty, Jerry. A Dog to Treasure. 2003. 130p. per. 14.95 (978-1-59196-228-1(5)) Instantpublisher.com.

McCarty, Peter. Fabian Escapes. rev. ed. 2007. (Illus.). 40p. (J). (ps-1). 16.95 (*978-0-8050-7713-1(8)), Holt, Henry & Co. Bks. For Young Readers) Holt, Henry & Co.

McCaughrean, Geraldine. Blue Moon Mountain. Palin, Nicki & Tomic, Tomislav, illus. 2nd ed. 2006. 32p. (J). (gr. 1-4). 16.95 (978-1-894965-56-9(6)) Simply Read Bks. CAN. *Dist:* Perseus Distribution.

—One Thousand & One Arabian Nights. Fowler, Rosamund, illus. 1999. (Oxford Story Collections). 288p. (YA). 13.95 (978-0-19-275013-6(5)) Oxford Univ. Pr., Inc.

—Peter Pan in Scarlet. Fischer, Scott M., illus. 2006. 320p. (J). (gr. 4-9). 17.99 (978-1-4169-1808-0(6), McElderry, Margaret K.) Simon & Schuster Children's Publishing.

McCaughrean, Geraldine & Ross. Las Aventuras de Ulises. 2005. (Mythology Series Collection Mitos Ser.). (SPA., Illus.). 50p. (J). (gr. 2-3). 9.95 (978-84-348-6426-9(6)) SM Ediciones ESP. *Dist:* Iaconi, Mariuccia Bk. Imports.

McCaughren, Tom. Ride a Pale Horse. 1999. (Illus.). 144p. (YA). (gr. 4 up). 14.95 (978-1-901737-08-0(X)) Anvil Bks., Ltd. IRL. *Dist:* Dufour Editions, Inc., Irish Bks. & Media, Inc.

—Ride a Pale Horse. 2001. (Illus.). 144p. pap. 11.95 (978-1-901737-09-7(8)) Dufour Editions, Inc.

McCay, Bill & Simmons, Alex. The Raven League. 2006. 192p. (J). (gr. 4-7). 10.99 (978-1-59514-072-2(7), Razorbill) Penguin Group (USA) Inc.

McCay, Bill, et al. Cold Case. 2001. (Tom Clancy's Net Force Ser.: Vol. 15). 208p. (gr. 7-12). mass mkt. 4.99 (978-0-425-17879-9(X), Berkley) Penguin Group (USA) Inc.

McCay, William. Young Indiana Jones & the Mask of the Madman. 1998. (Young Indiana Jones Ser.: No. 18). (J). (gr. 4-6). pap. 3.99 (978-0-679-87907-7(2), Random Hse. Bks. for Young Readers) Random Hse. Children's Bks.

McClanahan, Teel, 3rd. Dragons' Truth. 2007. 208p. (YA). per. 12.99 (*978-1-934516-02-7(3)) Modern Evil Pr.

McClatchy, Lisa. Eloise's Pirate Adventure. Lyon, Tammie, illus. 2007. (Eloise Ser.). 32p. (J). (ps-1). pap. 3.99 (*978-1-4169-4979-4(8), Aladdin) Simon & Schuster Children's Publishing.

McCloskey, John J. Warrior Ching. 2006. 179p. pap. 19.95 (978-1-4241-2389-6(5)) PublishAmerica, Inc.

McClure, Brian D. The Raindrop. 2006. (Illus.). 36p. (J). 14.95 (978-1-933426-01-3(2)) Universal Flag Publishing.

McCluskey, J. E. The Adventures of Peter the Pleasant Platypus & Friends: First Adventure, Tidy Time. 2004. 48p. pap. 19.95 (978-1-4137-2546-9(5)) PublishAmerica, Inc.

McCluskey, Jeffrey. The Adventures of Peter the Pleasant Platypus & Friends, Second Adventure: Brown Water. 2005. 52p. pap. 19.95 (978-1-4116-4880-7(3)) Lulu.com.

McConnell, Edith J. Their Times. 2004. 44p. (J). per. 11.66 (978-1-4116-1370-6(8)) Lulu.com.

McConnell, Sarah. Don't Mention Pirates. 2006. (Illus.). 32p. (J). 14.99 (978-0-7641-5945-9(3)) Barron's Educational Series, Inc.

McCorkle, Barbara. Bandit Raccoon. Taylor, David, illus. l.t. ed. 2006. 39p. (J). 19.95 (*978-1-59879-170-9(2)); per. 13.99 (*978-1-59879-123-5(0)) Lifevest Publishing, Inc.

McCorkle, Mark & Schooley, Bob. Grudge Match. 2005. (Illus.). 80p. (J). (978-1-4155-9100-0(8)) Disney Pr.

McCracken, Craig. Bubbles Keychain Book. Romano, Lou, illus. 2000. (Powerpuff Girls Ser.). 48p. (J). (ps-3). 3.99 (978-0-307-10241-6(6), 10241, Golden Bks.) Random Hse. Children's Bks.

McCullagh, Sheila. Griffin. 2007. (Three Pirates Ser.). (Illus.). 48p. 15.95 (*978-1-84560-044-0(4)) Mercury Bks. Ltd. GBR. *Dist:* International Publishers Marketing.

—Wild Pirates Attack. 2007. (Illus.). 48p. 15.95 (*978-1-84560-045-7(2)) Mercury Bks. Ltd. GBR. *Dist:* International Publishers Marketing.

McCulley, Johnston. The Mark of Zorro. 1998. (978-0-606-13597-9(9)) Tandem Library Bks.

—Zorro! (FRE.). pap. 19.95 incl. audio compact disk (978-88-7754-819-1(3)) Cideb ITA. *Dist:* Distribooks, Inc.

—Zorro. (SPA.). pap. 20.95 incl. audio compact disk (978-88-7754-895-5(9)) Cideb ITA. *Dist:* Distribooks, Inc.

McCusker, Paul. Annison's Risk. 2005. (Adventures in Odyssey Passages Ser.). 192p. (J). pap. 7.99 (978-1-58997-169-1(8)) Focus on the Family Publishing.

Mccutcheon, George B. The Purple Parasol. 2004. reprint ed. pap. 15.95 (978-1-4191-7949-5(7)) Kessinger Publishing, LLC.

McCutcheon, George Barr. The Purple Parasol. 2004. reprint ed. pap. 1.99 (978-1-4192-7949-2(1)) Kessinger Publishing, LLC.

McDaid, Mark. Billy the Bus. 2006. (Illus.). 48p. pap. (*978-1-84401-714-0(1)) Athena Pr.

McDermott, John Francis. The Adventures of Izzy & Bitty Bee. 2007. (J). 0.01 net. (*978-1-60402-094-6(6)) Independent Pub.

McDonald, Ann-Eve. MaGook. 2005. (J). (978-0-9770158-6-3(6)) BeachWalk Bks. Inc.

—The Tale of the Black Square. 2004. (J). (978-0-9770158-2-5(3)) BeachWalk Bks. Inc.

McDonald, Janet. A Chill Wind. 2006. 144p. (YA). reprint ed. pap. 6.95 (978-0-374-41183-1(2)) Macmillan.

McDonald, Megan. The Judy Moody Star-Studded Collection: Judy Moody; Judy Moody Gets Famous!; Judy Moody Saves the World! Reynolds, Peter H., illus. 2004. (Judy Moody Ser.). 464p. (J). (gr. 1-5). pap. 17.97 (978-0-7636-2563-4(9)) Candlewick Pr.

—When the Library Lights Go Out. Tillotson, Katherine, tr. Tillotson, Katherine, illus. 2005. 40p. (J). 16.95 (978-0-689-86170-3(2), Atheneum/Richard Jackson Bks.) Simon & Schuster Children's Publishing.

McDonnell, Vincent. Can Timmy Save Toyland? 2006. (Illus.). 185p. pap. 11.95 (978-1-903464-86-1(2)) Collins Pr., The IRL. *Dist:* Dufour Editions, Inc.

—Children of Stone. 2006. 206p. (J). pap. 9.95 (978-1-903464-88-5(9)) Collins Pr., The IRL. *Dist:* Dufour Editions, Inc.

—The Knock Airport Mystery. 2006. (Illus.). 203p. (J). pap. 9.95 (978-1-903464-87-8(0)) Collins Pr., The IRL. *Dist:* Dufour Editions, Inc.

McElroy, Laurie. Go Hollywood. 2006. (Teenick Ser.: No. 3). 112p. (J). pap. 4.99 (978-0-439-89043-4(8)) Scholastic, Inc.

McEwan, Ian. The Daydreamer. 2003. (gr. 3-6). lib. bdg. 14.15 (978-0-613-58678-8(6)) Tandem Library Bks.

McFadden, Deanna & Verne, Jules. Around the World in 80 Days. Akib, Jamel, illus. 2007. (Classic Starts Ser.). 151p. (J). (*978-1-4287-4207-9(7)) Sterling Publishing Co., Inc.

McFall, Jessica & McFall, Ernest. Unselfish Love. l.t. ed. 2006. (ENG., Illus.). 28p. per. 9.95 (*978-1-4327-0076-8(6)) Outskirts Press, Inc.

McFarlane, Brian. Fire in the North. 2007. (Mitchell Brothers Ser.). 220p. pap. 6.99 (*978-1-55168-243-3(5)) Key Porter Bks. CAN. *Dist:* Perseus Distribution.

—On the Hockey Highway, Vol. 2. 2nd ed. 2007. (Mitchell Brothers Ser.). 220p. pap. 6.95 (*978-1-55168-245-7(1)) Key Porter Bks. CAN. *Dist:* Perseus Distribution.

—Trouble at Tumbling Waters. 3rd ed. 2007. (Illus.). 200p. pap. 6.99 (*978-1-55168-251-8(6)) Key Porter Bks. CAN. *Dist:* Perseus Distribution.

—Wizard the Wonder Horse. 2007. 162p. pap. 6.99 (*978-1-55168-253-2(2)) Key Porter Bks. CAN. *Dist:* Perseus Distribution.

McFarlane, Leslie. McGonigle Scores! 2006. 256p. (J). pap. 9.95 (*978-1-55263-834-7(0)) Key Porter Bks. CAN. *Dist:* Perseus Distribution.

McGahan, Mary. Raid at Red Mill. Butterfield, Ned, illus. 2001. (Adventures in America Ser.). 96p. (J). (gr. 3-7). lib. bdg. 14.95 (978-1-893110-11-3(7)) Silver Moon Pr.

McGee, Warner, illus. Hide & Go Boo! 2006. (Backyardigans Ser.). 16p. (J). pap. 5.99 (978-1-4169-1229-3(0), Simon Spotlight/Nickelodeon) Simon & Schuster Children's Publishing.

—The Mystery of the Jeweled Eggs. 2007. (Backyardigans Ser.). 24p. (J). pap. 3.99 (978-1-4169-4070-8(7), Simon Spotlight/Nickelodeon) Simon & Schuster Children's Publishing.

—The Polka Palace Party: An Adventure in Teamwork. 2006. (Backyardigans Ser.). 24p. (J). pap. 3.99 (978-1-4169-1799-1(3), Simon Spotlight/Nickelodeon) Simon & Schuster Children's Publishing.

McGhee, Heather. The Wild Adventures of a Curious Princess. Myers, Shari, illus. 2007. (J). per. 19.95 (*978-0-9788985-9-5(1)) A Better Be Write Pub.

McGillicuddy, Barbara. Adventures in the Kingdom of Mim: Buddie Saves the Day. 2006. (J). per. 13.95 (978-0-9774513-7-1(2)) Changing Lives Publishing.

McGinley, Carol. Allyn's Embarrassing & Mysterious Irish Adventures. Murray, Linda, illus. 1999. 202p. (J). (gr. 4-6). pap. 7.95 (978-1-892671-00-4(X)) AGA Publishing.

McGirr, Randel W. Bible Camp. 2007. 176p. per. 13.95 (*978-0-595-44663-6(9)) iUniverse, Inc.

McGraw, Eloise Jarvis. The Golden Goblet. l.t. ed. 2003. (LRS Large Print Cornerstone Ser.). 318p. (J). lib. bdg. 35.95 (978-1-58118-113-5(2)) LRS.

McGreal, Pat, et al. Donald Duck Adventures, Vol. 19. 2006. (Illus.). 128p. (YA). pap. 7.95 (978-1-888472-31-8(6)) Gemstone Publishing, Inc.

—Mickey Mouse Adventures, Vol. 10. 2006. (Illus.). 128p. (YA). pap. 7.95 (978-1-888472-32-5(4)) Gemstone Publishing, Inc.

McGregor, Don. Drownings. Lima, Sidney, illus. 2nd rev. ed. 2006. (Zorro Graphic Novel Ser.: No. 2). 96p. (J). pap. 7.95 (978-1-59707-018-8(1)) Papercutz.

—Sabre 20th Anniversary. anniv. ed. 1999. (Illus.). 48p. pap. 12.95 (978-1-58240-059-4(8)) Image Comics.

—Zorro: Drownings. Lima, Sidney, illus. 2nd rev. ed. 2006. (Zorro Graphic Novel Ser.: No. 2). 96p. (J). 12.95 (978-1-59707-019-5(X)) Papercutz.

McGregor, Don & Lima, Sidney. Zorro: Flights. 4th rev. ed. 2006. (Zorro Ser.). (Illus.). 96p. (J). 12.95 (978-1-59707-027-0(0)); pap. 7.95 (978-1-59707-026-3(2)) Papercutz.

McGuinness, Jeff. Paddy the Penguin's Adventure. Starr, Lisa, illus. l.t. ed. 2006. 33p. (J). per. 15.95 (*978-1-59879-229-4(6)) Lifevest Publishing, Inc.

—Paddy, the Penguin's Adventure. Starr, Lisa, illus. l.t. ed. 2006. 33p. (J). 27.95 (*978-1-59879-231-7(8)) Lifevest Publishing, Inc.

McHaney, Eric & McHaney, Mandy. Rich the Itch. Smith, Jordyn, illus. l.t. ed. 2005. 20p. (J). (978-0-9769086-0-9(3)) RTI Publishing, LLC.

McIlvenna, Dorothy A. The Secret Cave: The Kids from Silversand Lake. 2000. 80p. (YA). (gr. 7-11). 10.00 (978-0-9679412-0-2(2)) Leapfrog Pr.

McIntosh, C. Ruth Bay & the Minotaur. 2004. 91p. pap. 14.95 (978-1-4137-4811-6(2)) PublishAmerica, Inc.

Mcintyre, Sterlynett. The Closing Argument. 2005. 97p. pap. 14.95 (978-1-4137-9216-4(2)) PublishAmerica, Inc.

Mckay, Malcolm. Thistown. 2006. (Illus.). 285p. pap. 16.95 (978-0-9546912-5-7(3)) Aurora Metro Pubns. Ltd. GBR. *Dist:* Consortium Bk. Sales & Distribution.

McKee, David. Two Can Toucan. 2001. (Illus.). 32p. (J). pap. 9.99 (978-1-84270-036-5(7)) Andersen GBR. *Dist:* Trafalgar Square Publishing.

McKernan, Victoria. Shackleton's Stowaway. 336p. (gr. 7-11). 2006. (YA). pap. 5.99 (978-0-440-41984-6(0), Laurel Leaf); 2005. (J). lib. bdg. 17.99 (978-0-375-92691-4(7), Knopf Bks. for Young Readers); 2005. (YA). 15.95 (978-0-375-82691-7(2), Knopf Bks. for Young Readers) Random Hse. Children's Bks.

McKinney, Mary. Shadow of Fear. 2002. 135p. (gr. 4-7). pap. 14.95 (978-1-59129-107-7(0)) PublishAmerica, Inc.

McKinstry, J. A. The Adventures of the 31st Street Saints: Book 1: the Eno. 2007. pap. 10.99 (*978-1-59886-892-0(6)) Tate Publishing & Enterprises, L.L.C.

McLaughlin, Julie. Mr. Gator's up the Creek. McKay, Ann Marie, illus. 2005. (J). 15.99 (978-0-933101-23-4(6)) Legacy Pubns.

McLaughlin, Vicki. The Dancer of Her Dreams. 2006. 48p. pap. 12.95 (978-1-4241-2723-8(8)) PublishAmerica, Inc.

McLellan, John. The Adventures of Mike & Tim: A Boy & His Shadow. Draaistra, Sylvia, illus. 2004. 48p. (J). (978-1-55306-679-8(0), Epic Pr.) Essence Publishing.

McMahan, Stephanie K. The Mystery of the Golden Rings. 2007. 140p. 21.95 (*978-0-595-68451-9(3)); per. 11.95 (*978-0-595-43998-0(5)) iUniverse, Inc.

McMahen, Chris. Klutzhood. 2007. 160p. (J). (gr. 4-7). pap. (*978-1-55143-710-1(4)) Orca Bk. Pubs.

McMahon, Kara. Big Sister Blue. Kanemoto, Dan, illus. 2007. (Blue's Clues Ser.). 12p. (J). (ps-k). bds. 5.99 (*978-1-4169-3820-0(6), Simon Spotlight/Nickelodeon) Simon & Schuster Children's Publishing.

—Diego Discovers. McGee, Warner, illus. 2008. (Go, Diego, Go! Ser.). 12p. (J). 12.99 (*978-1-4169-4940-4(2), Simon Spotlight/Nickelodeon) Simon & Schuster Children's Publishing.

McMahon, Kara. The Mud Monster: A Bath Book. Lo Raso, Carlo, illus. 2007. (Backyardigans Ser.). 8p. (J). 6.99 (978-1-4169-3979-5(2), Simon Spotlight/Nickelodeon) Simon & Schuster Children's Publishing.

McMahon, Kara & Artful Doodlers Limited Staff. Diego's Animal Science Book. 2007. (Go, Diego, Go! Ser.). 16p. (J). pap. 6.99 (978-1-4169-4119-4(3), Simon Spotlight/Nickelodeon) Simon & Schuster Children's Publishing.

McMillen, Charlotte Palmer. The Little Sea Rock & His Friend Arena. 2005. (Illus.). 32p. (J). per. 14.95 (978-0-9771939-4-3(2), 003) New World Publishing.

McMullan, Kate. Double Dragon Trouble. Basso, Bill, illus. 2005. (Dragon Slayers' Academy Ser.: No. 15). 112p. (J). (gr. 2-5). pap. 4.99 (978-0-448-43821-4(6), Grosset & Dunlap) Penguin Group (USA) Inc.

—Dragon Slayers' Academy. Basso, Bill, illus. 2005. (Dragon Slayers' Academy Ser.). 112p. (J). lthr. 19.96 (978-0-448-43976-1(X), Grosset & Dunlap) Penguin Group (USA) Inc.

—The Ghost of Sir Herbert Dungeonstone, Vol. 12. Basso, Bill, illus. 2004. (Dragon Slayers' Academy Ser.: No. 12). 112p. (J). (gr. 2-5). pap. 4.99 (978-0-448-43530-5(6), Grosset & Dunlap) Penguin Group (USA) Inc.

—Hail! Hail! Camp Dragononka! Basso, Bill, illus. 2006. (Dragon Slayers' Academy Ser.: No. 17). 224p. (J). (gr. 2-5). pap. 5.99 (978-0-448-44124-5(1), Grosset & Dunlap) Penguin Group (USA) Inc.

—Never Trust a Troll! Basso, Bill, illus. 2006. (Dragon Slayers' Academy Ser.: No. 18). 112p. (J). (gr. 2-5). pap. 4.99 (978-0-448-44393-5(7), Grosset & Dunlap) Penguin Group (USA) Inc.

—Revenge of the Dragon Lady. Basso, Bill, illus. 2003. (Dragon Slayers' Academy Ser.: No. 2). 112p. (J). (gr. 1-4). mass mkt. 4.99 (978-0-448-43109-3(2), Grosset & Dunlap) Penguin Group (USA) Inc.

—Revenge of the Dragon Lady. 2007. (Dragon Slayers' Academy Ser.: No. 2). 112p. (J). (gr. 1-6). 24.21 (*978-1-59961-378-9(6)) Spotlight.

—Revenge of the Dragon Lady. 2003. (Dragon Slayers' Academy Ser.: No. 2). (gr. 3-6). lib. bdg. 13.00 (978-0-613-72539-2(5)) Tandem Library Bks.

McMullen, Jill. Toby & Friends: Therapy Dogs. 2007. (J). pap. 7.99 (*978-1-60247-241-9(6)) Tate Publishing & Enterprises, L.L.C.

McNab, Andy & Rigby, Robert. Avenger. 2007. 272p. (YA). (gr. 7). 16.99 (*978-0-399-24685-2(1), Putnam Juvenile) Penguin Group (USA) Inc.

—Payback. 2007. 288p. (YA). (gr. 7). 7.99 (*978-0-14-240914-5(6), Puffin) Penguin Group (USA) Inc.

McNamara, Jeannette B. Caitlin's Country. 1999. (gr. 7-12). lib. bdg. 19.80 (978-0-613-79685-9(3)) Tandem Library Bks.

McNamee, Eoin. The Navigator. 2007. 352p. (gr. 4-7). (J). lib. bdg. 18.99 (978-0-375-93910-5(5)); (Illus.). (YA). 15.99 (978-0-375-83910-8(0)) Random Hse. Children's Bks. (Lamb, Wendy).

McNamee, Graham. Acelercion. (SPA.). (YA). 9.95 (978-958-04-7608-5(X)) Norma S.A. COL. *Dist:* Distribuidora Norma, Inc.

McNaughton, Colin. De Repente! (Buenas Noches Coleccion). (SPA.). (J). (gr. 1-3). 8.95 (978-958-04-5627-8(5)) Norma S.A. COL. *Dist:* Distribuidora Norma, Inc., Lectorum Pubns., Inc.

McNaughton, Janet. To Dance at the Palais Royale. 1999. (Illus.). 216p. (YA). (gr. 7-9). mass mkt. 5.95 (978-0-7736-7473-8(X)) Stoddart Kids CAN. *Dist:* Fitzhenry & Whiteside, Ltd.

McNish, Cliff. Silver City. 2007. (Exceptional Reading & Language Arts Titles for Intermediate Grades Ser.). 256p. (J). (gr. 4-8). pap. 6.95 (*978-0-8225-6780-6(6), First Avenue Editions) Lerner Publishing Group.

McNish, Cliff. Silver City: Book Two of the Silver Sequence. 2006. (Silver Sequence: Bk. 2). 256p. (J). 15.95 (978-1-57505-926-6(6), Carolrhoda Bks.) Lerner Publishing Group.

McPhail, David. Boy on the Brink. 2006. (Illus.). (J). (*978-1-4156-7145-0(1)); 32p. 15.95 (978-0-8050-7618-9(2)) Holt, Henry & Co.

McPhate, Paul. The Puggles: The Adventures of Carly & Vinigin. 2006. (ENG.). 48p. per. 12.95 (*978-1-4241-4481-5(7)) PublishAmerica, Inc.

McPhee, Peter. Out of Time. 2003. (SideStreets Ser.). 168p. (YA). (gr. 5). 7.95 (978-1-55028-796-7(6)); (gr. 7-12). (*978-1-55028-797-4(4)) Lorimer, James & Co., Ltd., Pubs. CAN. *Dist:* Casemate Pubs. & Bk. Distributors, LLC.

—Runner. 1999. (SideStreets Ser.). 160p. (gr. 7-12). 7.95 (978-1-55028-674-8(9)) Lorimer, James & Co., Ltd., Pubs. CAN. *Dist:* Casemate Pubs. & Bk. Distributors, LLC.

McPherson, Missie & O'Neill, Elizabeth. Alfred Visits Washington D. C. 2006. 24p. (J). pap. 12.00 (978-0-9771836-1-6(0)) Funny Bone Bks.

McQuerry, Maureen Doyle. Wolfproof. Murphy, John, illus. 2006. (J). 183p. 24.95 (978-1-59597-006-0(1)); 176p. per. 14.95 (978-1-59597-009-1(6)) Idylls Pr.

Mcshane, Pol. The Magic Elevator: The Adventures of Johnny & Joey. 2005. 129p. pap. 17.95 (978-1-4241-0014-9(3)) PublishAmerica, Inc.

McShane, Pol. Return to Animal Land: The Adventures of Johnny & Joey. 2007. 132p. (J). per. 10.95 (*978-0-595-45804-2(1)) iUniverse, Inc.

McSpadden, J. Walker & Hildebrandt, Greg. The Adventures of Robin Hood. gif. ed. 2004. (Illus.). 64p. (J). 9.98 (978-0-7624-2197-8(5), Courage Bks.) Running Pr. Bk. Pubs.

McSwigan, Marie. Snow Treasure. 2005. 208p. (J). (gr. 3-6). 10.99 (978-0-525-47626-9(1), Dutton Juvenile) Penguin Group (USA) Inc.

McTague, Charles. Bernard Overall: The Russian Tom Sawyer. 2004. (J). pap. 7.00 (978-0-8059-6404-2(5)) Dorrance Publishing Co., Inc.

Meade, L. T. Red Rose & Tiger Lily or in a Wider Wo. 2004. reprint ed. pap. 28.95 (978-0-7661-8345-2(9)) Kessinger Publishing, LLC.

Meadowbrook Press. Meadowbrook Kids Three Book Back to School Set. 2005. 250p. pap. 26.85 (978-0-689-05307-8(X)) Meadowbrook Pr.

Meadows, Daisy. Amber the Orange Fairy. Ripper, Georgie, illus. 2nd ed. 2005. (Rainbow Magic Ser.: No. 2). 80p. (J). 4.99 (978-0-439-74465-2(2)) Scholastic, Inc.

—Ruby the Red Fairy, Vol. 1. Ripper, Georgie, illus. 2005. (Rainbow Magic Ser.). 80p. (Orig.). (J). (ps-ps). pap. 4.99 (978-0-439-73861-3(X)) Scholastic, Inc.

Meadows, Melissa. What's the Word, Thunderbird? 2007. (Illus.). 80p. (J). pap. 4.99 (*978-1-934517-00-0(3)) Firelight Press, Inc.

Means, Elizabeth R. The Youngest Hobos: A Story of Survival. Cowan, Nancy, illus. 2000. 150p. (YA). (gr. 4-12). pap. (978-0-9652561-2-4(X)) Pelican Pr.

Meckler, Linda. Ghost Kids Trilogy. 2004. 139p. (YA). pap. 11.95 (978-0-7414-2273-6(5)) Infinity Publishing.

Mehr, Bethany. Adventures of Reggie Elder & the Sourc. 2007. 126p. pap. 17.95 (*978-1-4241-5599-6(1)) PublishAmerica, Inc.

Meissner, Amy, illus. Seldovia Sam & Wildfire Escape. 2005. (Misadventures of Seldovia Sam Ser.: Bk. 3). 64p. (J). (ps-ps). pap. 6.95 (978-0-88240-601-5(9)) Graphic Arts Ctr. Publishing Co.

Melling, David. Good Knight, Sleep Tight. 2005. (Illus.). 32p. (J). (ps-2). 14.99 (978-0-7641-5878-0(3)) Barron's Educational Series, Inc.

Melodies. 2005. (J). 6.50 (978-0-9776472-1-7(8)) Myth-Series.

Melville, Herman. Moby Dick: Juvenile Classic. 2005. (Illus.). 192p. (J). 5.99 (978-1-4037-1441-1(X)) Dalmatian Pr.

—Moby Dick, or the Whale. 2005. (J). Pt. 1. pap. 9.95 (978-1-4105-0263-6(5)); Pt. 1. cd-rom (978-1-4105-0265-0(1)); Pt. 2. pap. 9.95 (978-1-4105-0267-4(8)); Pt. 2. cd-rom (978-1-4105-0269-8(4)) Johnston, Don Inc.

Melville, Herman & Huth, Michael. Moby Dick. 2004. (GER., Illus.). 92p. (978-3-921743-52-2(4)) Maximilian-Gesellschaft e. V.

Menefee, Angelo K. Billy's First Summer Vacation. 2007. (J). per. 16.95 (*978-1-60002-249-4(9) , Airleaf Publishing) Airleaf Publishing & Bookselling.

Meredith Books Staff. Shrek the Third. Marshall, Paula, ed. 2007. (I Can Find It Ser.). 24p. (J). pap. 4.99 (*978-0-696-23729-4(6)) Meredith Bks.

—Superman Returns. Curry, Don, ed. 2007. (I Can Find It Ser.). 24p. (J). pap. 4.99 (*978-0-696-23728-7(8)) Meredith Bks.

Meredith Books Staff, ed. I Can Find It Kung Fu Panda. 2008. 22p. 7.99 (*978-0-696-23484-2(X)) Meredith Bks.

—Kung Fu Panda 3-D Puzzle BK. 2008. 10p. 9.99 (*978-0-696-23485-9(8)) Meredith Bks.

—Kung Fu Panda BK w/Activity Kit. 2008. 32p. 14.99 (*978-0-696-23483-5(1)) Meredith Bks.

—Kung Fu Panda Soundbook. 2008. 22p. 15.95 (*978-0-696-23482-8(3)) Meredith Bks.

Meredith Books Staff & Marvel Books Staff. The Hulk vs. Hulk. Curry, Don, ed. 2006. (Incredible Hulk Ser.). 24p. (J). pap. 3.99 (978-0-696-22985-5(4)) Meredith Bks.

Meredith-Markowitz, Susan. Charlie's Museum Adventure. ed. 2003. (Early Connections Ser.). (J). pap. 33.00 (978-1-4108-1367-1(3)) Benchmark Education Co.

Meredith, Randy. Marvel Puzzle Peril. 2007. (Illus.). 10p. (J). (gr. 1-5). ring bd. 9.95 (*978-1-57791-377-1(9)) Brighter Minds Children's Publishing.

Meres, Jonathan. My Grandpa Was an Astronaut. 2005. (Illus.). 32p. (J). (978-0-09-188499-4(3) , Hutchinson) Random Hse.

Merilatt, James & Frainier, Tamara. Miles Grand Adventures: The Denver Broncos Mascot's A-to-Z Journey Around Colorado. Malone, Kyle, illus. 2004. 32p. (J). 19.95 (978-0-9759579-2-9(9)) Denver Broncos.

Merrell, Mar'ce & Holmes, Ron. Max's Misadventures. 2000. (Illus.). vi, 49p. (J). pap. 5.95 (978-0-9686899-0-5(6)) Hodgepog Bks. CAN. *Dist:* Coteau Bks.

Messick, Maxine. Use Your Noodle! The Adventures of a Hollywood Poodle Named Doodle. Hodsdon-Carr, Sandra, ed. Urrwin-Camara, Nancy, tr. Carrillo, J. Raul, illus. 2004. (SPA.). 90p. 15.00 (978-0-9753508-0-5(3)) Aurora Bks.

Metzenthen, David. Bay Boys: Big Wave Day, Adrian over the Top, Adrian Goes Out There! 2005. (Triple Play-Yellow Ser.). (Illus.). 48p. (gr. 4-8). 41.85 (978-0-7910-9080-0(9)) Facts On File, Inc.

Metzger, Steve. Little Snowflake's Big Adventure. 2005. (Illus.). (*978-0-439-67619-9(3)) Scholastic, Inc.

Metzler, Rosemary. The Dangerous Ride: A Snooty the Fox Adventure. Lankenau, Gaynel, illus. 2002. (J). (gr. 3-5). pap. 10.95 (978-0-88100-128-0(7)) National Writers Pr., The.

Meyer, Louis A. Bloody Jack: Being an Account of the Curious Adventures of Mary Jacky Faber, Ship's Boy. 2004. (Illus.). 301p. (YA). (gr. 8-12). lib. bdg. 15.25 (978-0-613-71640-6(X)) Tandem Library Bks.

—Curse of the Blue Tattoo: Being an Account of the Misadventures of Jacky Faber, Midshipman & Fine Lady. 2005. (Bloody Jack Adventures Ser.). (Illus.). 512p. (YA). (gr. 7-12). reprint ed. pap. 6.95 (978-0-15-205459-5(6) , Harcourt Paperbacks) Harcourt Children's Bks.

Meyers, Elizabeth Ann. The Adventures of Winky & Binky. 2003. (J). 16.95 (978-0-533-14170-8(2)) Vantage Pr., Inc.

Michalak, Jamie. Larry & Rita. Newton, Jill, illus. 2007. (Brand New Readers Ser.). 1p. (J). (ps-2). pap. 5.99 (*978-0-7636-2964-9(2)) Candlewick Pr.

Michot, Fabienne, et al. I Love to Walk. Michot, Fabienne & Brasset, Doris, illus. 2000. (Maki Ser.). 14p. (J). (ps up). bds. (978-1-894363-35-8(3)) Dominique & Friends.

Mickey Mouse Adventures, Vol. 5. 2005. 128p. (YA). pap. 7.95 (978-0-911903-70-6(4)) Gemstone Publishing, Inc.

Midnight at the August Tree House. 2004. (Illus.). 100p. (J). per. 15.95 (978-0-9754823-1-5(9)) Pumpkin Patch Publishing.

Miglis, Jenny. Return of the Pumpkin Head. Destefano, Stephen & Giles, Mike, illus. ed. 2005. (Adventures of Jimmy Neutron Ser.: 5). 24p. (J). lib. bdg. 15.00 (978-1-59054-785-4(3)) Fitzgerald Bks.

Miglis Sandvik, Jenny. Midnight Mayhem No. 4: Color Activity Book with Iron-On Transfer. Karl, Linda, illus. 2004. (Shrek 2 Ser.). 32p. (J). act. bk. ed. 3.99 (978-0-439-57635-2(0)) Scholastic, Inc.

Mihara, Mitsukazu. Beautiful People. 2006. (Illus.). pap. 9.99 (978-1-59816-243-1(8) , Tokyopop Adult) TOKYOPOP, Inc.

Mihelic, Mira. Come My Gentle Ariel. MacKinnon, Alasdair, tr. from SLV. Abaza, Dasa, illus. 2002. 132p. (YA). 34.95 net. (978-961-6463-02-7(0)) Bks. of Slovenia.

Mika, Sharon Ann. Penny's Big Day. Wilson, Kay, illus. 2003. (J). 8.95 (978-0-9747836-0-4(9)) Button Flower Pr.

Mikaelsen, Ben. Sparrow Hawk Red. 1999. 192p. pap. 5.99 (978-0-7868-1002-4(5)) Hyperion Pr.

Miles, Elizabeth & Noon, Steve. Villains Masks. 2001. (Big Book of... Ser.). (Illus.). 24p. (J). pap. 9.95 (978-1-901323-17-7(X)) Orpheus Bks., Ltd. GBR. *Dist:* CPG Publishing, Inc.

Miles, Ellen. Cheer Fever. 2000. (Illus.). 144p. (J). (gr. 4-7). pap. 4.99 (978-0-439-19454-9(7)) Scholastic, Inc.

—Taylor-Made Tales. 2006. 144p. (J). pap. 4.99 (978-0-439-59710-4(2) , Scholastic Paperbacks) Scholastic, Inc.

Miles, Victoria. Magnifico. 2007. 264p. pap. (*978-1-55041-991-7(9)) Fitzhenry & Whiteside, Ltd.

—Magnifico. 2006. 176p. (J). 15.95 (978-1-55041-960-3(9)) Fitzhenry & Whiteside, Ltd. CAN. *Dist:* F & W Pubns., Inc.

Milgrim, David. Swing Otto Swing! Milgrim, David, illus. 2005. (Adventures of Otto Ser.). (Illus.). 32p. (J). pap. 3.99 (978-0-689-85565-8(6) , Aladdin) Simon & Schuster Children's Publishing.

Millar, Mark. Hellfire & Brimstone, 4 vols., Vol. 4. Kubert, Adam et al, illus. 2003. (Ultimate X-Men Ser.: Vol. 4). 144p. (YA). pap. 12.99 (978-0-7851-1089-7(5)) Marvel Enterprises, Inc.

—Ultimate War, 6 vols., Vol. 5. Bachalo, Chris, illus. 2003. (Ultimate X-Men Ser.: Vol. 5). 112p. (J). pap. 10.99 (978-0-7851-1129-0(8)) Marvel Enterprises, Inc.

—Ultimate X-Men, 3 vols., Vol. 3. 2003. (Ultimate X-men Ser.). (Illus.). 312p. 29.99 (978-0-7851-1131-3(X)) Marvel Enterprises, Inc.

—Ultimate X-Men: The Tomorrow People. 2002. (gr. 5-8). lib. bdg. 24.55 (978-0-613-53690-5(8)) Tandem Library Bks.

Millar, Mark & Austen, Chuck. Ultimate X-Men, 2 vols., Vol. 2. Kubert, Adam et al, illus. 2003. (Ultimate X-men Ser.). 336p. (YA). 29.99 (978-0-7851-1130-6(1)) Marvel Enterprises, Inc.

Miller, Alan. The Litluns & the Golden Spider Web. 2005. 61p. pap. 12.95 (978-1-4137-6444-4(4)) PublishAmerica, Inc.

Miller, Carol A. Maurice the Mole: Can You Guess Series. Miller, Carol A., illus. 2007. 24p. 18.95 (*978-0-9771641-3-4(6)) Defiance In Print.

Miller, Dorothy Anne. Stories to Read 'Round the Campfire. 2006. pap. 12.95 (978-1-4137-7554-9(3)) PublishAmerica, Inc.

Miller, Gary & Miller, Lynda. The Adventures of Bob & Betty. 2006. (J). spiral bd. (978-1-933594-92-7(6)) Faith Baptist Church Publns.

Miller, Kyle Linda. Dillo: A Baby Armadillo's Adventure on Sanibel Island. Eddy, Randon, illus. l.t. ed. 2005. 64p. (J). per. 16.95 (978-0-9769332-0-5(9)) Jungle Hse. Pubns.

Miller, Larry, Jr. Long Live the Queen. 2003. 162p. (YA). pap. 12.95 (978-0-595-27449-9(8)) iUniverse, Inc.

Miller, Lisa K. The Range of Light. 2005. (Illus.). 112p. (YA). pap. 11.95 (978-1-58736-538-6(3)) Wheatmark.

Miller, Mike. Joshua's Surprise: A Tomas the Tortoise Adventure. Miller, Mike, illus. 2003. 32p. (J). 15.95 (978-1-932173-23-9(4)) Stephens Pr. LLC.

—My Big Book of the Desert: A Tomas the Tortoise Adventure. 2004. pap. 15.95 (978-1-932173-38-3(2)) Stephens Pr. LLC.

—One Hot Day: A Tomas the Tortoise Adventure. Miller, Mike, illus. 2004. 32p. (J). 15.95 (978-1-932173-21-5(8) , 702-387-5260) Stephens Pr. LLC.

—Tales for Tomas: A Tomas the Tortoise Adventure. 2004. 15.95 (978-1-932173-37-6(4)) Stephens Pr. LLC.

Miller, Mike, told to. Tomas & the Ghost Town: A Tomas the Tortoise Adventure. 2004. 15.95 (978-1-932173-36-9(6)) Stephens Pr. LLC.

Miller, Ron Jay. The Medallion. 2003. 210p. (YA). pap. 14.95 (978-1-55517-737-9(9) , 77379, Bonneville Bks.) Cedar Fort, Inc./CFI Distribution.

Miller, Sara Swan. Three Stories You Can Read to Your Teddy Bear. Kelley, True, tr. Kelley, True, illus. 2004. 48p. (J). (gr. k-3). tchr. ed. 15.00 (978-0-618-30397-7(9)) Houghton Mifflin Co. Trade & Reference Div.

Miller, Wiley. The Extraordinary Adventures of Ordinary Basil: The Impossible Flight to Helios. 2006. (Illus.). 128p. (J). pap. 14.99 (978-0-439-85665-2(5) , Blue Sky Pr., The) Scholastic, Inc.

Miller, Wiley. The Extraordinary Adventures of Ordinary Basil Vol. 2: Island of the Volcano Monkeys. 2008. (Extraordinary Adventures of Ordinary Bas Ser.). 128p. (J). pap. 14.99 (*978-0-439-86132-8(2) , Blue Sky Pr., The) Scholastic, Inc.

Milligan, Peter. Good Omens. Allred, Mike, illus. 2003. (X-Statix Ser.). 128p. (YA). 11.99 (978-0-7851-1059-0(3)) Marvel Enterprises, Inc.

—X-Force: Famous, Mutant & Mortal. Allred, Mike, illus. 2003. (X-Statix Ser.). 352p. (YA). 29.99 (978-0-7851-1023-1(2)) Marvel Enterprises, Inc.

Millin, Christopher. The King of Arugula. 2007. 208p. (J). (gr. 1-7). pap. 10.95 (*978-1-897235-21-8(6)) Thistledown Pr., Ltd. CAN. *Dist:* Fitzhenry & Whiteside, Ltd.

Millionaire, Tony. Sock Monkey. 2001. (Illus.). 80p. (J). pap. 9.95 (978-1-56971-549-9(1)) Dark Horse Comics.

Millman, Calanitte. The Adventures of the Gimmel Gang IV: Triple Trouble, Vol. 4. 2007. (J). pap. 10.95 (*978-1-60091-005-0(X)) Israel Bk. Shop.

Millman, Dan. El Secreto Del Guerrero Pacifico. 2004. (SPA.). 32p. (978-84-7720-903-4(0)) Obelisco, Ediciones S.A.

Millman, M. C. Always Something Else: The whimsical adventures of Elisheva Raskin. 2005. (Illus.). 160p. (J). 14.95 (978-1-932443-23-3(1) , ASEH) Judaica Pr., Inc., The.

Mills, Claudia. 7 x 9 = Trouble! Karas, Brain G., illus. 2004. 112p. (J). pap. 5.95 (978-0-374-46452-3(9) , Sunburst) Farrar, Straus & Giroux.

Mills, Dorothy Jane. The Tent. Holman, Nance, illus. 2003. 32p. (J). (ps-7). per. 14.25 (978-1-932301-47-2(X) , 1274) Airleaf Publishing & Bookselling.

Mills, Linda Sue. Meet Toado & Friends. Mills, Lori, illus. l.t. ed. 2006. 34p. (J). 23.99 (*978-1-59879-246-1(6)) Lifevest Publishing, Inc.

Mills, Paul A. Chipper & Fluffy's Big Adventure. 2003. per. (978-1-59196-255-7(2)) Instantpublisher.com.

Milne, A. A. A Gallery of Children. Le Mair, Henriette Willebeek, illus. 2006. 79p. (J). (gr. k-4). reprint ed. 20.00 (978-1-4223-5106-2(8)) DIANE Publishing Co.

Milnes, Ellen. Tarzan Jungle Jam. Emslie, Peter, illus. 1999. (Chunky Roly-Poly Book Ser.). 16p. (J). bds. 3.50 (978-0-7364-0048-0(6)) Mouse Works.

Milord, Susan. If I Could. Denise, Christopher, illus. 2008. 32p. (J). (gr. k-1). 15.99 (978-0-7636-2348-7(2)) Candlewick Pr.

Miner, Sharon. Octavia's Quest. 2005. 113p. pap. 11.95 (978-0-7414-2647-5(1)) Infinity Publishing.

Minich, Eric. Digger & the Search for Home. 2006. 48p. pap. 12.95 (978-1-4241-0321-8(5)) PublishAmerica, Inc.

Minnie, Dana, creator. Mook, the Environmental Adventure. 2nd ed. 2001. per. 12.95 (978-0-9707914-2-9(9)) Litterateur Pubns., Inc.

Minshall, Caleigh. Blue: Voyage to the Sky. 2005. 54p. (J). pap. 19.95 net. (978-1-59975-284-6(0)) Independent Pub.

Minter, J. Break Every Rule. 2005. 300p. (YA). pap. 8.95 (978-1-58234-667-0(4) , Bloomsbury Children) Bloomsbury Publishing.

Miranda, Twyla. Longfeather Ponds: A Chipmunk's Tale. 2006. 82p. pap. 14.95 (978-1-4241-1785-7(2)) PublishAmerica, Inc.

Mirarchi, Anthony J. The King's Challenge. 2007. (Illus.). 220p. (J). (gr. 5-7). per. 9.95 (*978-1-933255-32-3(3)) DNA Pr.

Mirkov, Nadia. Cuentos de Encuentros Cercanos para Ninos. 1999. (Stories for Children Ser.).Tr. of Stories of Close Encounters. (SPA.). 125p. (J). mass mkt. 7.95 (978-970-643-172-1(1)) Selector, S.A. de C.V. MEX. *Dist:* Libros Sin Fronteras.

Miro. The Watermelon Story. Brown, Nick, illus. 2003. 103p. (J). pap. (978-1-84426-258-8(8)) Upfront Publishing Ltd.

The Misadventures of Wags & Freckles. (J). 4.00 (978-1-56230-043-2(1)) Syndistar, Inc.

Mishkin, Dan. The Forest King: Woodlark's Shadow. Mandrake, Tom, illus. 2006. 101p. (J). (gr. 5-8). 12.95 (978-0-9742803-5-6(6)) Komikwerks, LLC.

The Missing Earrings. 2005. (J). (978-1-932570-39-7(X)) Literacy Footprints Inc.

Missing Pieces. 2002. (Illus.). (J). pap. (978-0-7398-5067-1(9)) Steck-Vaughn.

Mitchelhill, Barbara. Kids on the Run. 2005. 160p. (J). pap. 8.99 (*978-1-84270-388-5(9)) Transworld Publishers Ltd. GBR. *Dist:* Independent Pubs. Group.

Mitchell, Carolyn. The Tale of the Pumpkin Seed Squad. 2006. (ENG.). 40p. per. 16.99 (*978-1-4259-7004-8(4)) AuthorHouse.

Mitchell, Kathleen Riley. Island Adventure. Gormley, Mary, ed. Bogdanffy, Marilyn, illus. 2nd ed. 2000. 48p. (J). (ps-7). 18.00 (978-0-9669648-1-3(0)) Mitchell, Kathleen Riley.

Mitchell, Mark E. The Curious Flame of King Pellimore, 5 vols. 1998. (Chronicles of the House of Chax Ser.: Bk. 5). 88p. (J). (ps-k). pap. 9.99 (978-0-88092-353-8(9) , 3539) Royal Fireworks Publishing Co.

Mitchell, Mary Esther. The Adventures of Timmy Gills. 2005. (J). pap. 20.00 (978-0-8059-9660-9(5) , RoseDog Bks.) Dorrance Publishing Co., Inc.

Mitchell, N. J. W. The Adventures of Princess Nightshade. 2000. 264p. (J). pap. 13.95 (978-0-595-14024-6(0)) iUniverse, Inc.

—Fuzbud & the Wizard: A Sequel to the Adventures of Princess Nightshade. 2001. 168p. (J). pap. 12.95 (978-0-595-19111-6(8)) iUniverse, Inc.

—Hannah, the Witch, & the Unicorn: A Sequel to the Adventures of Princess Nightshade & Fuzbud & the Wizard. 2002. 154p. (J). pap. 11.95 (978-0-595-21186-9(0) , Writer's Showcase Pr.) iUniverse, Inc.

—The Search. 2003. 110p. pap. 9.95 (978-0-595-27251-8(7)) iUniverse, Inc.

Mitchum, Lynn Tyner. Happy Being Me. Mitchum, Lynn Tyner, illus. 2006. (Illus.). 21.95 (978-0-9745191-0-4(3)) Lynn Tyner Mitchum & James Rogers.

Miyazaki, Hayao. Castle in the Sky. Miyazaki, Hayao, illus. 2003. (Castle in the Sky Ser.). (Illus.). 164p. (YA). Vol. 1. pap. 9.95 (978-1-59116-170-7(3)); Vol. 2. pap. 9.95 (978-1-59116-171-4(1)); Vol. 3. pap. 9.95 (978-1-59116-172-1(X)); Vol. 4. pap. 9.95 (978-1-59116-173-8(8)) Viz Media.

—Spirited Away. Orig. Title: Sen to Chihiro no kamikakushi. (gr. 3-6). 2003. lib. bdg. 18.75 (978-0-613-79014-7(6)); 2002. lib. bdg. 18.75 (978-0-613-79012-3(X)); 2002. lib. bdg. 18.75 (978-0-613-79013-0(8)); 2002. lib. bdg. 18.75 (978-0-613-79011-6(1)) Tandem Library Bks.

—Spirited Away. Miyazaki, Hayao, illus. (Spirited Away Ser.). Orig. Title: Sen to Chihiro no kamikakushi. (Illus.). (YA). Vol. 1. 2002. 172p. pap. 9.95 (978-1-56931-791-4(7)); Vol. 2. 2002. 172p. pap. 9.95 (978-1-56931-792-1(5)); Vol. 3. 2003. 172p. pap. 9.95 (978-1-56931-793-8(3)); Vol. 4. 2003. 172p. pap. 9.95 (978-1-56931-794-5(1)); Vol. 5. 2003. 184p. pap. 9.95 (978-1-56931-795-2(X)) Viz Media.

Moby Dick. (Great Classics for Children Ser.). (Illus.). 192p. (J). (978-1-4037-0597-6(6)) Dalmatian Pr.

Moffett, Slyvia. The Missionary Kids Adventure Series: Bo. 2006. 48p. pap. 12.95 (978-1-4241-2854-9(4)) PublishAmerica, Inc.

Molla, Jean. Sobibor. 2006. 174p. pap. 14.95 (978-0-9546912-4-0(5)) Aurora Metro Pubns. Ltd. GBR. *Dist:* Consortium Bk. Sales & Distribution.

Moloney, James. The Book of Lies. 2007. 368p. (J). (gr. 4-8). 16.99 (978-0-06-057842-8(4)); lib. bdg. 17.89 (978-0-06-057843-5(2)) HarperCollins Pubs.

—Crossfire. 1998. 160p. (YA). reprint ed. pap. 18.95 (978-0-7022-2384-6(0)) Univ. of Queensland Pr. AUS. *Dist:* International Specialized Bk. Services.

Moloney, James. Scream World: Prepare for the Ride of Your Life! 2007. 72p. (J). pap. 3.95 (*978-0-7624-2926-4(7) , Running Pr. Kids) Running Pr. Bk. Pubs.

Momi a Hawaiian Mermaid in the Land of Delight. 2001. (J). 8.99 (978-0-89610-356-6(0)) Island Heritage Publishing.

Monge, Nieves. The Adventures of Three Raccoons Raised by a Human Mother. 2004. (J). pap. 8.00 (978-0-8059-6472-1(X)) Dorrance Publishing Co., Inc.

Mongillo, Michael. The Philistine: Anthology/Chronology, 1 book. Zittel, Michael, illus. 2003. 216p. (YA). pap. 24.95 (978-0-9743086-0-9(9)) United Comics.

Monk, Carol. The Walking Adventures of Ruthie & Coco. 2005. (Illus.). 29p. (J). pap. 12.95 (978-1-56167-881-5(3)) American Literary Pr.

Monkey Business. 2005. (J). 4.95 (978-1-59792-015-5(0)) F.A.S.T. Learning LLLC.

Monnin, Sheena. Discover Your Destiny. 2007. (Illus.). 40p. (J). per. 12.99 (*978-1-60247-121-4(5)) Tate Publishing & Enterprises, L.L.C.

Monsen, Annie. Captain Blye & the Friendly Fly. 2004. 11p. per. 5.00 (978-1-59453-613-7(9) , 2808) Airleaf Publishing & Bookselling.

Monsters Inc. Read Along. 2001. (J). pap. 9.98 incl. audio compact disk (978-0-7634-1828-1(5)) Walt Disney Records.

Montes, Graciela. Había una vez una Nube. 2006. 26p. 8.95 (978-1-59820-214-4(6) , Alfaguara) Santillana USA Publishing Co., Inc.

—Había una vez una Princesa. 2006. 26p. 8.95 (978-1-59820-215-1(4) , Alfaguara) Santillana USA Publishing Co., Inc.

Montgomery, Bobbie. Fruit Tramp Kids. 2000. (Pathfinder Junior Book Club Ser.). 143p. (J). (gr. 4-7). pap. 6.99 (978-0-8280-1422-9(1)) Review & Herald Publishing Assn.

Montgomery, L. M. The Blue Castle. Date not set. (J). 22.95 (978-0-8488-2370-2(2)) Amereon LTD.

Montgomery, R. A. Behind the Wheel. 2008. (Choose Your Own Adventure Ser.: No. 26). (Illus.). 144p. (J). per. 5.99 (*978-1-933390-26-0(3)) Chooseco LLC.

—Beyond Escape. 2007. (Choose Your Own Adventure Ser.: No. 15). (Illus.). 144p. (J). mass mkt. 5.99 (978-1-933390-15-4(8) , CHCL15) Chooseco LLC.

—Beyond Escape. 2005. (Illus.). 118p. (J). pap. (*978-0-7608-9703-4(4)) Sundance/Newbridge Educational Publishing.

—The Brilliant Dr. Wogan. 2007. (Choose Your Own Adventure Ser.: No. 17). (Illus.). 144p. (J). mass mkt. 5.99 (978-1-933390-17-8(4) , CHC:17) Chooseco LLC.

—Caravan. 2007. (Choose Your Own Adventure - Dragonlarks Ser.). (Illus.). 64p. (J). pap. 5.99 (*978-1-933390-54-3(9)) Chooseco LLC.

—Choose Your Own Adventure Four Book Boxed Set #1: The Abominable Snowman, Journey under the Sea, Space & Beyond, the Lost Jewels of Nabooti. 2006. 576p. (J). per. 19.95 (*978-1-933390-94-9(8)) Chooseco LLC.

—Choose Your Own Adventure Four Book Boxed Set #2: Mystery of the Maya, House of Danger, Race Forever, Escape. 2006. 576p. (J). per. 19.95 (*978-1-933390-95-6(6)) Chooseco LLC.

—Escape. 2006. (Choose Your Own Adventure Ser.: No. 8). (Illus.). 144p. (J). mass mkt. 5.99 (978-1-933390-08-6(5) , CHCL08) Chooseco LLC.

—Escape. 2005. (Illus.). 127p. (J). pap. (*978-0-7608-9696-9(8)) Sundance/Newbridge Educational Publishing.

—The Haunted House. 2007. (Choose Your Own Adventure Ser.). (Illus.). 64p. (J). pap. 5.99 (*978-1-933390-51-2(4)) Chooseco LLC.

—House of Danger. 2006. (Choose Your Own Adventure Ser.: No. 6). (Illus.). 144p. (J). mass mkt. 5.99 (978-1-933390-06-2(9) , CHCL06) Chooseco LLC.

—Indian Trail. 2007. (Choose Your Own Adventure - Dragonlarks Ser.). (Illus.). 64p. (J). pap. 5.99 (*978-1-933390-53-6(0)) Chooseco LLC.

—Journey under the Sea. 1999. mass mkt. (978-0-553-23229-5(0)) Random Hse., Inc.

—The Lost Jewels of Nabooti. 2006. (Choose Your Own Adventure Ser.: No. 4). (Illus.). 144p. (J). mass mkt. 5.99 (978-1-933390-04-8(2) , CHCL04) Chooseco LLC.

—Prisoner of the Ant People. 2006. (Choose Your Own Adventure Ser.: No. 10). (Illus.). 144p. (J). mass mkt. 5.99 (978-1-933390-10-9(7) , CHCL10) Chooseco LLC.

—Prisoner of the Ant People. 1999. (Illus.). 115p. mass mkt. (978-0-553-23661-3(X)) Random Hse., Inc.

—Return to Atlantis. 2007. (Choose Your Own Adventure Ser.: No. 18). (Illus.). 144p. (J). mass mkt. 5.99 (978-1-933390-18-5(2) , CHCL18) Chooseco LLC.

—Tattoo of Death. 2007. (Choose Your Own Adventure Ser.: No. 22). (Illus.). 144p. (J). (gr. 3-7). pap. 6.99 (*978-1-933390-22-2(0)) Chooseco LLC.

—Your Purrr-fect Birthday. 2007. (Dragonlarks Ser.). (Illus.). 64p. (J). (gr. k-3). pap. 6.99 (*978-1-933390-55-0(7)) Chooseco LLC.

—Your Very Own Robot. 2007. (Choose Your Own Adventure Ser.). (Illus.). 64p. (J). pap. 5.99 (*978-1-933390-52-9(2)) Chooseco LLC.

Montgomery, Trego Frances. Billy Whiskers Adventures. 2006. 94.99 (*978-1-4280-5032-7(9)); pap. 88.99 (*978-1-4280-5036-5(1)) IndyPublish.com.

—Billy Whiskers the Autobiography of A Go. 2007. 40.99 (*978-1-4280-5180-5(5)); pap. 34.99 (*978-1-4280-5194-2(5)) IndyPublish.com.

Moody, Ron. The Amazon Box. 1998. (Illus.). 278p. (Orig.). (J). (gr. 4-7). (978-1-86105-049-6(6) , Robson Bks. Ltd.) Anova Bks.

Moon, Catherine R. & Everette, Maureen C. The Adventures of NanaCat & Her Children: Someone New. Richardson, Kara, illus. 2004. 32p. (J). per. 6.95 (978-0-930507-02-2(9)) Currier Davis Publishing.

Mooney, E. S. Blossom to the Rescue. Alger, Bill, illus. 2001. (Powerpuff Girls Storybks.). 16p. (J). (ps-3). 7.99 (978-0-439-25057-3(9)) Scholastic, Inc.

—Blossoming Out. 2000. (gr. k-3). lib. bdg. 11.80 (978-0-613-32329-1(7)) Tandem Library Bks.

—Cartoon Crazy. 2000. (gr. k-3). lib. bdg. 11.80 (978-0-613-32373-4(4)) Tandem Library Bks.

—Mojo & Mini-Mo. 2003. (gr. k-3). lib. bdg. 11.80 (978-0-613-66424-0(8)) Tandem Library Bks.

—Mojo Mayhem. 2002. (gr. k-3). lib. bdg. 11.80 (978-0-613-43852-0(3)) Tandem Library Bks.

—Shrinky Jinx. 2002. (gr. k-3). lib. bdg. 11.80 (978-0-613-50500-0(X)) Tandem Library Bks.

—Snow-off. 2000. (gr. k-3). lib. bdg. 11.25 (978-0-613-33069-5(2)) Tandem Library Bks.

—Teacher's Pest, No. 5. Maher, Alex, illus. 2001. (Powerpuff Girls Chapter Bks.: Vol. 5). 64p. (J). (ps-2). pap. 3.99 (978-0-439-24325-4(4)) Scholastic, Inc.

Moonshower, Candie. The Legend of Zoey. 2006. 224p. (J). (gr. 4-7). 15.95 (978-0-385-73280-2(5)); lib. bdg. 17.99 (978-0-385-90298-4(0)) Random Hse. Children's Bks. (Delacorte Bks. for Young Readers).

Moore, Alan & Gray, Mick. Promethea Book 2, Vol. 2. Williams, J. H., illus. 2nd rev. ed. 2003. 176p. pap. 14.99 (978-1-56389-957-7(4)) DC Comics.

Moore, Alan & Veitch, Rick. Greyshirt: Indigo Sunset. 2003. (Illus.). 224p. pap. 19.95 (978-1-56389-909-6(4)) DC Comics.

Moore, Cathy. The Daring Escape of Ellen Craft. Young, Mary O'Keefe, illus. 2003. (On My Own History Ser.). 48p. (J). (gr. 1-3). pap. 5.95 (978-0-87614-787-0(2) , Carolrhoda Bks.) Lerner Publishing Group.

Moore, Diane. Sophie's Sojourn in Persia. 2004. 143p. pap. 19.95 (978-1-4137-4458-3(3)) PublishAmerica, Inc.

Moore, Robin. The Man with the Silver Oar. 2002. 192p. (J). (gr. 5 up). 15.89 (978-0-06-000048-6(1)) HarperCollins Pubs.

Moore, Sherry. The Crab Is Back in Town. 2007. (J). per. (*978-1-894936-78-1(7)) Saga Bks.

Moore, Ulysses. The Door to Time. 2006. (Ulysses Moore Ser.: No. 1). 226p. (J). 155.88 (978-0-439-83978-5(5)) Scholastic, Inc.

Moore, Ulysses. House of Mirrors. 2007. (Ulysses Moore Ser.: No. 3). 256p. (J). pap. 5.99 (*978-0-439-77672-1(4)) Scholastic, Inc.

Mora, Pat. La Noche Que Se Cayo La. ed. 2001. (J). (gr. 1). spiral bd. (978-0-616-07279-0(1)) Canadian National Institute for the Blind/Institut National Canadien pour les Aveugles.

Moreau, Chris. The Professor's Telescope. Marek, Jane, illus. 2006. (YA). 10.95 (978-0-9785399-0-0(7)); cd-rom 7.95 (978-0-9785399-2-4(3)) Windows of Discovery.

Morgan, Allan. Tiens-Toi Bien, Mathieu! 1999. (Illus.). 24p. (J). pap. (978-2-89021-316-6(1)) Diffusion du livre Mirabel.

Morgan, Allen. Matthew & the Midnight Firefighter. Martchenko, Michael, tr. Martchenko, Michael, illus. 2003. (Wild Midnight Adventure Ser.). (J). 46p. pap. (978-1-55041-877-4(7)); 40p. lib. bdg. (978-1-55041-875-0(0)) Fitzhenry & Whiteside, Ltd.

—Matthew & the Midnight Firefighter. Martchenko, Michael, illus. 2000. (Matthew's Midnight Adventures Ser.). 32p. (J). (ps-3). 6.99 (978-0-7737-6090-5(3)) Stoddart Kids CAN. Dist: Fitzhenry & Whiteside, Ltd.

—Matthew & the Midnight Firefighter. 2003. (gr. k-3). lib. bdg. 12.95 (978-0-613-81245-0(X)) Tandem Library Bks.

—Matthew & the Midnight Firefighters. ed. 2004. (Illus.). (J). (gr. k-3). spiral bd. (978-0-616-07242-4(2)) Canadian National Institute for the Blind/Institut National Canadien pour les Aveugles.

—Matthew & the Midnight Wrestlers. 2000. (gr. k-3). lib. bdg. 15.30 (978-0-613-84051-4(8)) Tandem Library Bks.

—Matthew's Midnight Adventures. Martchenko, Michael, illus. 2001. 80p. (J). (ps-2). 19.95 (978-1-55037-699-9(3)) Annick Pr., Ltd. CAN. Dist: Firefly Bks., Ltd.

Morgan, Allen & Longval, Raymonde. En Avant, Pirates! 1998. (Droles D'Histories Ser.). (Illus.). 24p. (J). pap. (978-2-89021-340-1(4)) Diffusion du livre Mirabel.

Morgan, Allen & Martchenko, Michael. Matthew & the Midnight Wrestlers. 2000. (Matthew's Midnight Adventures Ser.). (Illus.). 32p. (J). (ps-3). 6.99 (978-0-7737-6053-0(9)) Stoddart Kids CAN. Dist: Fitzhenry & Whiteside, Ltd.

Morgan, Allen, et al. Au Feu, Mathieu! 2001. (Drtles d'Histoires Ser.). (FRE., Illus.). 24p. (YA). (ps up). pap. (978-2-89021-418-7(4)) Diffusion du livre Mirabel.

Morgan, Beverly. Gregory & the Stars: A Little Story about Independence. Joyful Noise, ed. 2005. (Illus.). 26p. (J). 4.95 (978-0-9772109-0-9(1)) Joyful Noise.

Morgan, C. M. Silver Doorway #3: An Elf's Adventure. 2004. 104p. (J). pap. 6.99 (978-0-9702189-4-0(X)) Sabledrake Enterprises.

MOrgan, C. M. Silver Doorway #4: Dragon on the Loose. 2004. 104p. (J). pap. 6.99 (978-0-9702189-7-1(4)) Sabledrake Enterprises.

Morgan, Clay. The Boy Who Spoke Dog: Return to Dog Island. 2007. 176p. (J). (gr. 4). 16.99 (*978-0-525-47401-2(3) , Dutton Juvenile) Penguin Group (USA) Inc.

Morgan, Melissa J. Second Time's the Charm. 2006. (Camp Confidential Ser.: No. 7). 160p. (J). (gr. 4-7). pap. 4.99 (978-0-448-44265-5(5) , Grosset & Dunlap) Penguin Group (USA) Inc.

Morgan, Richard & Rose, Maddy. What's in a Nickname? 2007. (Illus.). 24p. (J). pap. 9.95 (*978-1-86230-159-7(X)) Transworld Publishers Ltd. GBR. Dist: Independent Pubs. Group.

Morgan, Ruth. Jess & the Bean Root. 2005. (Illus.). 24p. (J). lib. bdg. 22.65 (*978-1-59646-732-3(0)) Dingles & Co.

Morgan, Ruth. Things That Go Bump in the Night. Glyn, Chris, illus. 2001. 48p. pap. 11.95 (978-1-85902-944-2(2)) Beekman Bks., Inc.

Morice, Dave. Visit from St Alphabet. 2005. 24p. 9.95 (978-1-56689-179-0(5)) Coffee Hse. Pr.

Morley, Linda. The White Pair with Colorful Dinosaurs. Reyes, Joe, illus. l.t. ed. 2002. 36p. (J). (ps-2). pap. 7.99 (978-0-9662888-3-4(1)) Morley Pr.

Morningforest, Chris & Raymond, Rebecca. Princess Underdrawers & the Dragon. 2006. 37p. (J). pap. 15.58 (978-1-4116-8837-7(6)) Lulu.com.

Morpurgo, Michael. Kenshuke's Kingdom. 2003. 176p. (J). (gr. 3-6). 16.95 (978-0-439-38202-1(5) , Scholastic Pr.) Scholastic, Inc.

—Kensuke's Kingdom. Foreman, Michael, illus. l.t. ed. 2000. 215p. (J). pap. (978-0-7540-6096-3(9) , CLP 295) BBC Audio.

—Kensuke's Kingdom. 2005. (Illus.). 176p. (J). pap. (*978-1-4052-2174-0(7)) Egmont Bks., Ltd.

—Kensuke's Kingdom. 2004. 176p. (J). mass mkt. 4.99 (978-0-439-59181-2(3) , Scholastic Paperbacks) Scholastic, Inc.

—The Marble Crusher. 2004. (Illus.). 96p. (J). pap. 7.50 (978-1-4052-0187-2(8)) Egmont Bks., Ltd. GBR. Dist: Trafalgar Square Publishing.

—The Nine Lives of Montezuma. 2004. (Illus.). 120p. pap. 8.99 (978-1-4052-0189-6(4)) Egmont Bks., Ltd. GBR. Dist: Trafalgar Square Publishing.

Morris, April. Eldon the Elephant. 2004. (J). lib. bdg. 25.95 (978-1-893595-49-1(8)) Four Seasons Bks., Inc.

Morris, Deborah. Whirlpool: Real Kids Real Adventures. 2002. (Juvenile Ser.). (Illus.). (J). 22.95 (978-0-7862-4423-2(2)) Thorndike Pr.

Morris, Gerald. The Lioness & Her Knight. 2005. (Squire's Tales Ser.). 352p. (J). (gr. 5-7). 16.00 (978-0-618-50772-6(8)) Houghton Mifflin Co. Trade & Reference Div.

—The Quest of the Fair Unknown. 2006. 278p. (J). (gr. 5). 16.00 (978-0-618-63152-0(6)) Houghton Mifflin Co. Trade & Reference Div.

Morris, Gilbert. The Spell of the Crystal Chair. 2000. (Seven Sleepers the Lost Chronicles Ser.: Vol. 1). (Illus.). 160p. (J). (gr. 7-12). pap. 5.99 (978-0-8024-3667-2(6)) Moody Pubs.

—Spell of the Crystal Chair. 2000. (gr. 7-12). lib. bdg. 14.15 (978-0-613-88611-6(9)) Tandem Library Bks.

—Strange Creatures of Dr Korbo. 2000. (gr. 7-12). lib. bdg. 14.15 (978-0-613-88022-0(6)) Tandem Library Bks.

—Terrible Beast of Zor. 2000. (gr. 3-6). lib. bdg. 14.15 (978-0-613-88615-4(1)) Tandem Library Bks.

—Victims of Nimbo. 2000. (gr. 3-6). lib. bdg. 14.15 (978-0-613-88614-7(3)) Tandem Library Bks.

Morris, Karen. Perils from the Seven Seas, Vol. 2. 2005. 127p. pap. 17.95 (978-1-4137-4663-1(2)) PublishAmerica, Inc.

Morris, Kerry Nicole. The Baby Who Just... WON't Sleep! Parker's Story. 2004. 35p. pap. 17.95 (978-1-4137-3724-0(2)) PublishAmerica, Inc.

Morris, Kimberly. Beck Beyond the Sea. Clarke, Judith, illus. 2007. 128p. (J). (gr. 1-5). 5.99 (*978-0-7364-2456-1(3) , RH/Disney) Random Hse. Children's Bks.

Morris, Kimberly. The Real Deal: Junior Novel. 13th rev. ed. 2006. (That's So Raven Ser.: No. 13). (Illus.). 128p. (gr. 3-7). pap. 4.99 (978-0-7868-3599-7(0)) Disney Pr.

Morrison, Ellen M. Murder's Take: The First Adventure of Sam & Sam. 2000. 108p. (gr. 4-7). pap. 9.95 (978-0-595-16322-9(X)) iUniverse, Inc.

Morrison, Grant. Riot at Xavier's, 4 vols., Vol. 4. Quitely, Frank, illus. 2003. (New X-Men Ser.: Vol. 4). 120p. (YA). 11.99 (978-0-7851-1067-5(4)) Marvel Enterprises, Inc.

Morrison, P. R. Wave Traveller. 2007. 300p. (J). (gr. 3-7). 16.95 (*978-1-59990-123-7(4)) Bloomsbury Publishing.

Morse, Scott. Complete Soulwind. 2003. 520p. (YA). pap. 29.95 (978-1-929998-73-9(2)) Oni Pr., Inc.

Mortenson, R. K. Landon Snow & the Auctor's Riddle. 2005. (Landon Now Ser.). (Illus.). 224p. (J). (gr. 4-7). 9.97 (978-1-59310-881-6(8)) Barbour Publishing, Inc.

—Landon Snow & the Igneus Forest. 2007. 224p. (J). 9.97 (978-1-59789-296-4(3) , Barbour Bks.) Barbour Publishing, Inc.

Mortenson, Randall Kent. Landon Snow & the Island of Arcanum. 2006. 224p. (J). 9.97 (978-1-59789-358-9(7) , Barbour Bks.) Barbour Publishing, Inc.

Morton, Elizabeth. Anne: The Animated Series. 2001. pap. 4.99 (978-0-06-442162-1(7)) HarperCollins Pubs.

—Anne & the Hunt for the Golden Crown: The Animated Series. 2001. (J). (gr. 2-5). pap. 4.99 (978-0-06-442161-4(9)) HarperCollins Pubs.

Morton, Jane & Dreier, Ted. Moozie's Kind Adventure. Royse, Jane, illus. deluxe ed. 1999. (Moozie Adventures Ser.). 28p. (J). (ps-3). 14.95 (978-0-9662268-1-2(X)) Best Friends Bks.

Moshonas, Spyridon. Escape from Argopoli. 2002. 108p. pap. 16.95 (978-1-59129-661-4(7)) PublishAmerica, Inc.

Mostoller, Gordon. Randy Walter & Rex. 2006. pap. 12.95 (*978-1-4259-6498-6(2)) AuthorHouse.

Mother Goose. Sugar & Spice, 6 Bks. 2005. (Illus.). (J). bds. 12.95 incl. audio compact disk (978-1-59249-471-2(4) , 1D100) Soundprints.

Mothershead, Martha Fulford. Petoskey Stone Soup. Clarkson, Janet M., illus. 2006. 32p. (J). 18.95 (978-0-9785465-0-2(4)) Whaleback Pr.

Moulton, Eugena. The Age of Merrik: The Anointing. 2007. 200p. 24.95 (*978-0-595-67899-0(8)); per. 14.95 (*978-0-595-41367-6(6)) iUniverse, Inc.

Moulton, Mark Kimball. The Night at Humpback Bridge. Winget, Susan, illus. 2001. 48p. (J). (gr. k-3). 22.00 (978-0-7412-0823-1(7)) Lang Graphics, Ltd.

Moulton, Mike. Tina Talinka's Travels Vol. 1: Tina Talinka & the Knights of Sacrifice & Tina Talinka & the Echo of the Allohom. 2004. 260p. (YA). 27.99 (978-1-59507-044-9(3) , ArcheBooks) ArcheBooks Publishing.

Mount, Jill. The Mystery of the Dirty Bike. 2005. 9.00 (978-0-8059-9778-1(4)) Dorrance Publishing Co., Inc.

The Mountain Hike. 2000. (J). (978-1-58453-133-3(9)) Pioneer Valley Educational Pr., Inc.

Mouse Works Staff. Tarzan. 1999. (Spanish Read-Aloud Storybook Classics). (SPA., Illus.). 64p. (J). (ps-2). 6.99 (978-0-7364-0057-2(5)) Mouse Works.

—Tarzan. 1999. (Disney's Read-Aloud Storybooks Ser.). (Illus.). 72p. (J). (ps-2). 8.99 (978-0-7364-0047-3(8) , RH/Disney) Random Hse. Children's Bks.

—Toy Story 2: Punchout Play. 1999. (J). 8.99 (978-0-7364-0175-3(X)) Mouse Works.

Movies in My Mind Vol. 2: Audio Adventures for Children. 2002. (YA). pap. 19.95 incl. audio (978-1-931184-04-5(6)) Imagination Development Group, LLC.

Movies in My Mind Vol. 3: Audio Adventures for Children. 2002. (YA). pap. 19.95 incl. audio (978-1-931184-05-2(4)) Imagination Development Group, LLC.

Mowll, Joshua. Operation Red Jericho. Heller, Julek et al, illus. 2005. (Guild Trilogy Ser.: Bk. 1). 288p. (YA). (gr. 7-8). 15.99 (978-0-7636-2634-1(1)) Candlewick Pr.

—Operation Red Jericho: The Guide of Specialists Book 1. Heller, Julek & Puttapipat, Niroot, illus. 2007. 288p. (J). (gr. 5). pap. 8.99 (*978-0-7636-3475-9(1)) Candlewick Pr.

Mowll, Joshua. Operation Typhoon Shore. Mowll, Joshua et al, illus. 2006. (Guild of Specialists Ser.). 288p. (YA). (gr. 5 up). 15.99 (978-0-7636-3122-2(1)) Candlewick Pr.

Mowry, Jess. Tyger Tales. 2007. 280p. (YA). pap. 14.99 (978-1-59092-358-0(8) , Blue Works) Windstorm Creative.

Moyer, Bess. Gypsies of the Air. 2004. reprint ed. pap. 19.95 (978-1-4179-9112-9(7)) Kessinger Publishing, LLC.

Mr. Cheesehead Goes for a Ride... 2nd rev. ed. 2005. (Illus.). 32p. (J). 12.99 (978-0-9764463-1-6(6)) Vertigo Publishing.

Muchamore, Robert. The Dealer. 2005. (Cherub Ser.). 320p. (YA). mass mkt. 6.99 (978-0-689-87780-3(3) , Simon Pulse) Simon & Schuster Children's Publishing.

—Divine Madness. 2006. (Cherub Ser.). 400p. (YA). mass mkt. 5.99 (978-1-4169-2724-2(7) , Simon Pulse) Simon & Schuster Children's Publishing.

—Man vs. Beast. 2007. (Cherub Ser.). 336p. (YA). mass mkt. 5.99 (978-1-4169-2725-9(5) , Simon Pulse) Simon & Schuster Children's Publishing.

—The Recruit. 2005. (Cherub Ser.). 352p. (YA). mass mkt. 6.99 (978-0-689-87779-7(X) , Simon Pulse) Simon & Schuster Children's Publishing.

Mudd, Missy. Candy Bar Caper. 2007. (J). per. 7.99 (*978-1-59886-843-2(8)) Tate Publishing & Enterprises, L.L.C.

Mueller, Doris. Marryin' Sam. 2005. 61p. pap. 12.95 (978-1-4137-7557-0(8)) PublishAmerica, Inc.

Muench-Williams, Heather & Jarrell, Pamela R. Caillou's Hiking Adventure. Storch, Ellen N., illus. l.t. ed. 2005. (Hrl Board Book Ser.). (J). (gr. k up). pap. 10.95 (978-1-57332-329-1(2)) HighReach Learning, Inc.

Muhammad, Shahid. The Adventures of the Math Doctor: Book One: King Jafiz & the Evil Farmer Nimra. 2007. (J). per. 7.95 (*978-1-59872-778-4(8)) Instantpublisher.com.

Muir, Sabine. Matthew & the Highland Rescue: The Time Gate Series. 2005. 131p. pap. 16.95 (978-1-4137-5916-7(5)) PublishAmerica, Inc.

—Meeting Wolfie: A Story about Mozart. 2006. 129p. pap. 16.95 (978-1-4241-3968-2(6)) PublishAmerica, Inc.

Mukerji, Dhan Gopal. Jungle Beasts & Men. Allen, J. E., illus. 2005. reprint ed. pap. 22.95 (978-0-7661-9403-8(5)) Kessinger Publishing, LLC.

Muldrow, Diane. Recipe for Trouble. Pollak, Barbara, illus. 2007. (Dish Ser.: No. 7). 160p. (J). pap. 4.99 (978-0-448-44532-8(8) , Grosset & Dunlap) Penguin Group (USA) Inc.

Mull, Brandon. The Candy Shop War. 2007. 358p. (YA). (gr. 4 up). 17.95 (*978-1-59038-783-2(X) , Shadow Mountain) Deseret Bk. Co.

Mullican, Judy. Riding the Range. Carroll, Ken, Jr., illus. 1998. (Big Bks.). 8p. (J). (ps-k). pap. 10.95 (978-1-57332-104-4(4)) HighReach Learning, Inc.

Mulligan, Glori. The Challenge of the Dragons: Book Two of the Trilogy of the Dragons. 2007. (Illus.). 48p. (J). per. 19.95 (*978-1-933324-73-9(2)) Cedar Hill Publishing.

Mullin, Penn. River & the Trace. 1999. (gr. 7-12). lib. bdg. 11.60 (978-0-613-29037-1(2)) Tandem Library Bks.

Mullins, Norman D. Mountain Boy: The Adventures of Orion Saddler. 2004. 104p. (YA). per. 9.95 (978-0-9724867-4-3(7)) Woodland Pr. LLC.

Munch, Donna. Dark Tales of the Tower. 2005. (J). pap. 9.95 (978-1-932196-71-9(4)) WordWright.biz, Inc.

Mundy, Talbot. For the Salt He Had Eaten. 2004. reprint ed. pap. 15.95 (978-1-4191-2024-4(7)); pap. 1.99 (978-1-4192-2024-1(1)) Kessinger Publishing, LLC.

Munnik, Hema. Bhole: Adventures of a Young Yogi. 2006. 352p. pap. 18.95 (978-81-88157-37-2(6)) Lotus Pr.

Munro, Ken. Fireball. 2003. (Sammy & Brian Mystery Ser.: No. 15). (J). pap. 5.95 (978-1-930353-84-8(7)) Masthof Pr.

Munzel, Alexander. Where the Holy Thistle Blooms. 2003. (Illus.). 98p. (J). per. (978-0-9672566-1-0(5)) Technical Software, Inc.

Muralidharan, Anuradha. The Coconut Cutter & Other Stories. 2000. 98p. (J). (978-81-87075-47-9(3)) Srishti Pubs. & Distributors IND. Dist: Nesma Bks. India.

Murdocca, Sal & Osborne, Mary Pope. Dinosaurs Before Dark Book & CD. 2008. (Stepping Stone Book(TM) Ser.). (J). (gr. k-3). 9.99 (*978-0-375-84405-8(8) , Random Hse. Bks. for Young Readers) Random Hse. Children's Bks.

Murphy, Breena. The Fairy Seekers - the Sand Fairy. Waid, Sara Joyce & Waid, Antoinette M., illus. l.t. ed. 2006. 284p. (J). 24.95 (978-0-9788010-1-4(6)) Edes Publishing Co.

—The Fairy Seekers - the Sand Fairy, 1. Waid, Sara J. & Waid, Antoinette M., illus. l.t. ed. 2006. 284p. (J). per. 14.95 (978-0-9788010-0-7(8)) Edes Publishing Co.

Murphy, Francis X. There's Hair Out There: A Chubby's World Adventure. Robidas, Ted, illus. 1998. (Chubby's World Adventure Ser.). 24p. (J). (gr. 2-4). 8.95 (978-0-9667642-0-8(X) , CWA001) Xavier Shott, Inc.

Murphy, Jill. Lista para Salir. (SPA., Illus.). (J). (gr. k-2). (978-84-350-9192-3(9) , EH0377) Edhasa ESP. Dist: Lectorum Pubns., Inc.

Murphy, Mary. I Like It When. 2005. (Illus.). 22p. (J). (ps-ps). bds. 6.95 (978-0-15-205649-0(1) , Red Wagon Bks.) Harcourt Children's Bks.

Murphy, Peg. I Can Do Anything. l.t. ed. 2006. (ENG., Illus.). 28p. per. 9.95 (*978-1-4327-0175-8(4)) Outskirts Press, Inc.

Murphy, Stephen. Secret. 2004. (gr. k-3). lib. bdg. 11.80 (978-0-613-88302-3(0)) Tandem Library Bks.

Murphy, Steve. Shadows over Chinatown. Spaziante, Patrick, illus. 2005. (Teenage Mutant Ninja Turtles Ser.). 128p. (J). pap. 4.99 (978-0-689-87209-9(7) , Simon Spotlight) Simon & Schuster Children's Publishing.

Murphy, Steve, adapted by. TMNT Movie Novelization. movie tie-in ed. 2007. (Teenage Mutant Ninja Turtles Ser.). 128p. (J). pap. 5.99 (978-1-4169-4057-9(X) , Simon Spotlight) Simon & Schuster Children's Publishing.

Murphy, Stuart J. Treasure Map. Tusa, Tricia, illus. 2004. (MathStart 3 Ser.). 40p. (J). (gr. 2 up). pap. 5.99 (978-0-06-446738-4(4) , Harper Trophy) HarperCollins Pubs.

Murphy, T. M. The Secrets of Code Z. 2001. (Belltown Mystery Ser.: Vol. 5). 144p. (J). (gr. 4-7). pap. 9.95 (978-1-880158-33-3(7)) Townsend, J.N. Publishing.

Murray, Betty Jean. The Little Raccoon: A True Story. Douthit, Karen, illus. 2005. (J). pap. 10.95 (978-1-933916-63-7(X) , Ferne Pr.) Nelson Publishing & Marketing.

Murray, Peter J. Mokee Joe No. 3: The Doomsday Trail. 2006. (Mokee Joe Ser.: Bk. 3). (Illus.). 192p. (J). (gr. 4-6). pap. 9.99 (978-0-340-89305-0(2) , Hodder & Stoughton) Hodder General Publishing Division GBR. Dist: Trafalgar Square Publishing.

Murray, Regina Waldron. The Very Exciting Train Ride: An Adventure. 2006. (J). per. 15.95 (*978-0-9664042-1-0(1)) Murray, Regina Waldron.

Murray, Susan. Chaos in Cancun. 1998. (gr. 7-12). lib. bdg. 14.15 (978-0-613-78577-8(0)) Tandem Library Bks.

—Panic in Puerto Vallarta: Quebec's Intelligentsia & the Fascist Temptation, 19. 1998. (gr. 7-12). lib. bdg. 15.30 (978-0-613-78576-1(2)) Tandem Library Bks.

Murray, Susan & Davies, Robert. Outrage in Orlando. 2000. (KC Flanagan Girl Detective Ser.). 192p. (YA). (gr. 5-11). pap. (978-1-55207-023-9(9)) Studio 9 Bks.

Muschinske, Victoria. Honey Pie Pony's Book: A Fun with Fillies Adventure. 2005. (Illus.). 39p. (*978-0-439-70471-7(5)) Scholastic, Inc.

Muschla, Gary Robert. Crusader. 2006. (YA). pap. (978-0-88092-491-7(8)) Royal Fireworks Publishing Co.

Mussi, Sarah. The Door of No Return. 2008. (YA). (*978-1-4169-1550-8(8) , McElderry, Margaret K.) Simon & Schuster Children's Publishing.

The Mutant Race. 2003. (J). per. (978-1-57657-865-0(8)) Paradise Pr., Inc.

Mutchnick, Brenda & Casden, Ron. A Noteworthy Tale. Penney, Ian, illus. 2004. 30p. (J). (gr. k-4). reprint ed. 19.00 (978-0-7567-7654-1(6)) DIANE Publishing Co.

Mwangi, Meja. The Mzungu Boy. (J). 2006. 152p. pap. 6.95 (978-0-88899-664-0(0)); 2005. 160p. 15.95 (978-0-88899-653-4(5)) Groundwood Bks. CAN. Dist: Perseus Distribution.

My Day- Pillow Fight. 2003. (J). per. (978-1-57657-159-0(9)) Paradise Pr., Inc.

My First Busy Book- Dual Spanish/English. 2004. (J). (978-1-59292-000-6(4)) SoftPlay, Inc.

Myers, Bill. My Life As a Prickly Porcupine from the Planet Pluto. 2004. (Incredible Worlds of Wally McDoogle Ser.). 128p. (J). pap. 6.99 (978-0-8499-5994-3(2)) Nelson, Thomas Inc.

—My Life as a Walrus Whoopee Cushion, Vol. 16. 1999. (Incredible Worlds of Wally McDoogle Ser.: No. 16). 128p. (J). (gr. 3-7). pap. 6.99 (978-0-8499-4025-5(7)) Nelson, Thomas Inc.

Myers, Edward. Survival of the Fittest. 2000. 172p. (J). (gr. 4-8). pap. 11.95 (978-0-9674477-2-8(0) , 0-9674477-2-0) Montemayor Pr.

Myers, Walter Dean & Myers, Walter Dean. Fallen Angels. 2003. 309p. (YA). (gr. 8-12). lib. bdg. 14.15 (978-0-8335-3180-3(8)) Tandem Library Bks.

Myracle, Lauren. Rodney's SsssSolution. 2001. (J). (978-1-884272-34-9(7)) Premier Schl. Agendas.

—Rodney's SsssSolution - Big Book. Renooy, "Cosmic" Ray, illus. 2003. (J). spiral bd. (978-1-884272-88-2(6)) Premier Schl. Agendas.

Mysterious Chills & Thrills: 10 creepy, strange, adventurous short stories for kids to tickle the Imagination. 2004. (J). per. 6.95 (978-0-9749013-0-5(X)) LH Pubns. & Productions.

Mystery of the Maya: Choose Your Own Adventure. 2004. per. 5.95 (978-0-9745356-3-0(X)) Chooseco LLC.

Mystical World of Nebe: Sky of Dreams. 2006. (YA). 14.95 (978-0-9779369-0-8(2)) Adamson, Mac.

Naas, Nancy. The Clubhouse. 2006. pap. 7.95 (978-0-533-15395-4(6)) Vantage Pr., Inc.

Nadja. Cinco Deditos. (SPA.). 12p. (978-84-8470-019-7(4)) Corimbo, Editorial S.L.

Naifeh, Ted. Courtney Crumrin & the Coven of Mystics, 2 vols., Vol. 2. Naifeh, Ted, illus. 2003. (Illus.). 128p. (YA). pap. 11.95 (978-1-929998-59-3(7)) Oni Pr., Inc.

Najar, Qasim M. The Army of Lions. 1998. (Illus.). 190p. (YA). (gr. 6-11). mass mkt. 9.95 (978-1-889720-15-9(1)) Amirah Publishing.

Nakagawa, Rieko. Guri & Gura's Seaside Adventure. Yamawaki, Yuriko, illus. 2003. (Guri & Gura Ser.). 32p. 10.95 (978-0-8048-3354-7(0)) Tuttle Publishing.

Napoli, Donna Jo. Flamingo Dream. Felstead, Cathie, illus. 2002. 32p. (J). (gr. k up). 15.95 (978-0-688-16796-7(9)); (gr. 2 up). 16.89 (978-0-688-17863-5(4)) HarperCollins Pubs.

Narvick, the Whark (or a Shwale) 2003. (J). 8.95 (978-0-9729703-1-0(2)) Kidderature Publishing.

Nash, David. A Pete & Charley Adventure: The Sheri. 2005. 131p. pap. 19.95 (978-1-4137-9449-6(1)) PublishAmerica, Inc.

Nash, Naomi. I Am SO Jinxed! 2006. (YA). mass mkt. 5.99 (978-0-8439-5405-0(1)) Dorchester Publishing Co., Inc.

—You Are So Cursed! 2004. (YA). mass mkt. 5.99 (978-0-8439-5310-7(1)) Dorchester Publishing Co., Inc.

Naylor, Phyllis Reynolds. Carlotta's Kittens. Daniel, Alan, illus. 2000. (Cat Pack Ser.). 144p. (J). (gr. 3-5). 16.99 (978-0-689-83269-7(9), Atheneum) Simon & Schuster Children's Publishing.

—Carlotta's Kittens. 2002. (gr. 3-6). lib. bdg. 13.00 (978-0-613-45019-5(1)) Tandem Library Bks.

—The Grand Escape. Daniel, Alan, illus. 2005. (Cat Pack Ser.). 160p. (J). pap. 4.99 (978-0-689-87407-9(3), Aladdin) Simon & Schuster Children's Publishing.

—The Great Chicken Debacle. 2003. (gr. 3-6). lib. bdg. 14.10 (978-0-613-82436-1(9)) Tandem Library Bks.

—The Healing of Texas Jake. Daniel, Alan, illus. 2005. (Cat Pack Ser.). 128p. (J). pap. 4.99 (978-0-689-87406-2(5), Aladdin) Simon & Schuster Children's Publishing.

—Polo's Mother. Daniel, Alan, illus. (Cat Pack Ser.). 176p. (J). 2006. pap. 5.99 (978-0-689-87404-8(9), Aladdin); 2005. 15.95 (978-0-689-86555-8(4), Atheneum) Simon & Schuster Children's Publishing.

Naylor, Phyllis Reynolds. Roxie & the Hooligans. Boiger, Alexandra, illus. 128p. (J). 2007. (gr. 3-5). pap. 4.99 (***978-1-4169-0244-7(9)***, Aladdin); 2006. (gr. 2-5). 16.99 (978-1-4169-0243-0(0), Atheneum) Simon & Schuster Children's Publishing.

Neale, Jonathan. Himalaya. 2004. 160p. (J). (gr. 5-9). 16.00 (978-0-618-55203-0(0)) Houghton Mifflin Co. Trade & Reference Div.

Needham, Dorothy. Adventures in Ruyton XI Towns. 2007. 200p. per. (***978-1-84685-532-0(2)***, Exposure Publishing) Meadow Bks.

Neimark, Susie. The Adventures of Sunny & the Chocolate Dog: Sunny & the Chocolate Dog Go to the Beach. Hammerstrom, Kent, illus. 2003. per. (978-0-9725945-1-6(5)) Sunny & The Chocolate Dog, LLC.

—The Adventures of Sunny & the Chocolate Dog: Sunny & the Chocolate Dog Go to the Doctor. Hammerstrom, Kent, illus. 2003. per. (978-0-9725945-2-3(3)) Sunny & The Chocolate Dog, LLC.

—The Adventures of Sunny & the Chocolate Dog: Sunny Meets Her Baby Sister. Hammerstrom, Kent, illus. 2003. per. (978-0-9725945-0-9(7)) Sunny & The Chocolate Dog, LLC.

Nejime, Shoichi. Bit by Bit. Castles, Heather, illus. 2005. 32p. (J). (ps-k). pap. 7.95 (978-1-55037-906-8(2)); lib. bdg. 19.95 (978-1-55037-907-5(0)) Annick Pr., Ltd. CAN. *Dist:* Firefly Bks., Ltd.

Nekrasov, Andrei. The Adventures of Captain Vrungel. Kay, Nicole, tr. from ENG. 2006. (RUS.). (J). (978-0-9754433-1-6(3), Language Transformer Bks.) Velichko, Vera.

Nelson, Jim. Crosstown Crush. 2005. 82p. Vol. 1, Bk. 1. (YA). pap. 9.00 (978-1-4116-5266-8(5)); Vol. 1,Bk. 2. pap. 9.00 (978-1-4116-6654-2(2)) Lulu.com.

Nelson, Ray, et al. The Internal Adventures of Marcus Snarkis. McLane, Mike, ed. Nelson, Ray et al, illus. 2000. (Farmer Bob Ser.). 48p. (J). (gr. 3-6). 18.00 (978-1-883772-14-7(1)) Flying Rhinoceros, Inc.

Nelson, Theresa. Devil Storm. 2000. 228p. (YA). (gr. 4-7). pap. 14.95 (978-0-595-14413-6(6), Backinprint.com) iUniverse, Inc.

Nemec, Thomas F., creator. Owenopolis: A New Childrens Book, Created by Thomas Nemec-N. Y. C. ed. 2007. (J). lib. bdg. 15.00 (***978-0-9791612-0-9(7)***) Goon Dog Publishing.

Nesbit. The Story of Treasure Seekers, Level 2. 2000. (C). pap. 9.00 (978-0-582-41666-6(3)) Longman Publishing Group.

Nesbit, E. Magic City. 2000. 212p. (gr. 3-6). lib. bdg. 18.75 (978-0-613-32808-1(6)) Tandem Library Bks.

—Story of the Treasure Seekers. Browne, Gordon & Baumer, Lewis Christopher Edward, illus. 2006. 196p. (J). 14.95 (978-0-8118-5415-3(9)); pap. 9.95 (978-0-8118-5416-0(7)) Chronicle Bks. LLC. (SeaStar Bks.).

—The Wouldbegoods. 1999. 272p. (J). 9.95 (978-0-233-99237-2(5)) Andre Deutsch GBR. *Dist:* Trafalgar Square Publishing.

—The Wouldbegoods. l.t. ed. 2005. 428p. pap. (978-1-84637-208-7(9)) Echo Library.

Nesbit, E. & Hedge, Tricia. Five Children & IT, Level 2. 2nd ed. 2000. (Bookworms Ser.). (Illus.). 6.25 (978-0-19-422973-9(4)) Oxford Univ. Pr., Inc.

Nesbitth. Melisenda. 2000. (SPA.). lib. bdg. 21.50 (978-0-613-80754-8(5)) Tandem Library Bks.

Nestor, Gregg. All Hands on Deck: Become Part of a Caribbean Sailing Adventure. 2005. (Illus.). 72p. (J). (ps-7). pap. 29.00 (978-1-4208-2407-0(4)) AuthorHouse.

Nettrour, Nelani. Banshees Bk. 2: Dragon Lands. Nettrour, Heather, illus. l.t. ed. 2003. 114p. (J). pap. 11.95 (978-1-932657-03-6(7)) Third Millennium Pubns.

—Nunkey's Adventures, Bk. 1. Nettrour, Autumn, illus. 2003. 70p. (J). pap. 11.95 (978-1-929381-17-3(4), Third Millennium Publishing) Sci Fi-Arizona, Inc.

Nettrour, Nelani. Sun Griffins: Dragonlands, Book 4. 2007. (Illus.). 190p. (J). pap. 16.95 (***978-1-932657-90-6(8)***) Third Millennium Pubns.

Neumann, Jeff. How Do You Do? 2005. 39p. 8.00 (978-1-4116-6201-8(5)) Lulu.com.

Nevins, Paul. Dante's War. 2003. 168p. (YA). pap. 12.95 (978-0-595-26743-9(2), Writers Club Pr.) iUniverse, Inc.

Newcomb, Ambrose. Flying the Coast Skyways or Jack Ralston. 2005. pap. 26.95 (978-1-4179-8975-1(0)) Kessinger Publishing, LLC.

Newcomb, Kristene. Molly Q's Trash Travels Through the Water Cycle. Paschall, Patricia, ed. Newcomb, Kristene, illus. 2007. (Illus.). 32p. (J). per. 8.00 (***978-0-9760790-9-5(7)***) Folsom Fallies Pr.

Newcome, Joey. Sueno y Vuelos. Maval Publishing Inc. Staff, illus. 2001. Tr. of Flight Dreams. (SPA.). (J). (ps-3). pap. 7.50 (978-1-884083-82-2(X)) Maval Publishing, Inc.

—Suenos y Vuelos. Maval Publishing Inc. Staff, illus. 2001. Tr. of Flight Dreams. (SPA.). 32p. (J). (ps-3). pap. 7.50 (978-1-59134-012-6(8)) Maval Publishing, Inc.

Nguy, Hoa X. The Bamboo Girl. 2007. 84p. (J). pap. 20.00 (***978-0-8059-7562-8(4)***) Dorrance Publishing Co., Inc.

Nicholls, Stan. The Book of Shadows. l.t. ed. 2000. (Illus.). 344p. 18.99 (978-0-7089-9526-6(8)) Ulverscroft Large Print Bks. GBR. *Dist:* Ulverscroft Large Print Bks., Ltd.

—Fade to Black. l.t. ed. 1998. (Illus.). 274p. (J). pap. 16.95 (978-0-7540-6016-1(0), Galaxy Children's Large Print) BBC Audiobooks America.

Nichols, John. Eggbee's Dream. McKenzie, Darrell-Lee, ed. Rolston, Ken, illus. 2001. (Cackleberies Ser.). 32p. (J). (ps-3). pap. (978-0-9686876-0-4(1)) Cackleberry Pr.

—Rockhopper Rangers Map the Town. McKenzie, Darrell-Lee, ed. Rolston, Ken, illus. 2001. (Cackleberies Ser.: No. 2). 32p. (J). (ps-3). pap. 5.95 (978-0-9686876-2-8(8)) Cackleberry Pr. CAN. *Dist:* Hushion Hse. Publishing, Ltd.

Nichols, Niki. Your Karma, DeeDee. 2005. 141p. pap. 19.95 (978-1-4137-9690-2(7)) PublishAmerica, Inc.

Nichols, Willie Charles. The Adventures of Bo & His Pal Boboy. 2004. pap. 8.00 (978-0-8059-6175-1(5)) Dorrance Publishing Co., Inc.

Nicholson, William. El Silbador del Viento. Manero Jimenez, Laura, tr. 3rd ed. 2005. (Escritura desatada Ser.). (SPA.). 336p. (J). (ps-8). 17.95 (978-84-666-0279-2(8)) Ediciones B ESP. *Dist:* Independent Pubs. Group.

—Viento en Llamas: Son del Fuego. Manero Jimenez, Laura, tr. 2005. (Escritura desatada Ser.). (SPA.). 368p. (J). 17.95 (978-84-666-1232-6(7)) Ediciones B ESP. *Dist:* Independent Pubs. Group.

Nickel, Scott. Double Trouble. Harpster, Steve, illus. 2007. (J). 40p. (***978-1-59889-314-4(9)***); 33p. pap. (***978-1-59889-409-7(9)***) Stone Arch Bks.

—The Super-Powered Sneeze. Harpster, Steve, illus. 2007. 33p. (J). pap. (***978-1-59889-411-0(0)***); (gr. 2-4). lib. bdg. 21.26 (***978-1-59889-316-8(5)***) Stone Arch Bks.

Nickel, Scott & Artful Doodlers Limited Staff. TMNT: Cowabunga! 2007. (Teenage Mutant Ninja Turtles Ser.). 32p. (J). 3.99 (978-1-4169-3414-1(6), Simon Scribbles) Simon & Schuster Children's Publishing.

Nickles, Clay & Ayres, Ella. Ali's Treasure. l.t. ed. 2005. (Illus.). 38p. (J). per. 16.95 (978-1-59879-006-1(4)) Lifevest Publishing, Inc.

Nicolas, Ron. Northern Lights: A Wilderness Adventure. 2005. 228p. (YA). per. 15.85 (978-0-9770043-2-4(5)) New Global Publishing.

Night Beast. 2005. (J). 4.95 (978-1-59792-018-6(5)) F.A.S.T. Learning LLLC.

Night of the Cougar. 2005. (J). 4.95 (978-1-59792-014-8(2)) F.A.S.T. Learning LLLC.

Night Visitor. 2005. (J). 4.95 (978-1-59792-019-3(3)) F.A.S.T. Learning LLLC.

Nightmare: Individual Title Six-Packs. (Action Packs Ser.). 120p. (gr. 3-5). 44.00 (978-0-7635-8392-7(8)) Rigby Education.

Nihart, Gene. The Fox Island Cup. 2004. (YA). pap. (978-1-59404-023-8(0)) Peanut Butter Publishing.

Nikola-Lisa, W. Bein' with You This Way, 2 bks. Bryant, Michael, illus. 1999. (SPA.). (J). (gr. k-3). 25.95 incl. audio (978-0-87499-546-6(9)); pap. 16.95 incl. audio (978-0-87499-545-9(0)) Live Oak Media.

Niland, Deborah. Let's Play. Niland, Deborah, illus. 2007. (Illus.). 24p. (Orig.). (J). (ps). pap. 4.99 (***978-1-933605-47-0(2)***) Kane/Miller Bk. Pubs., Inc.

Nimmo, Jenny. The Box Boys & the Magic Shell. (Box Boys Ser.). (Illus.). 64p. (J). pap. (978-0-340-73290-8(3), Hodder & Stoughton) Hodder General Publishing Division.

—Charlie Bone & the Beast. 2007. (Children of the Red King Ser.: Bk. 6). 464p. (J). 10.99 (***978-0-439-84665-3(X)***, Orchard Bks.) Scholastic, Inc.

Nimmo, Jenny. Charlie Bone & the Invisible Boy. 2004. (Children of the Red King Ser.: Bk. 3). (Illus.). 432p. (J). 9.95 (978-0-439-54526-6(9), Orchard Bks.) Scholastic, Inc.

Nino, Jairo Anibal. Zoro. 2003. (SPA., Illus.). 97p. (J). (ps-7). pap. (978-958-30-0291-5(7), PV4489) Panamericana Editorial COL. *Dist:* Lectorum Pubns., Inc.

The Ninth Life. 2005. (J). 4.95 (978-1-59792-017-9(7)) F.A.S.T. Learning LLLC.

Nix, Garth. Above the Veil. Rawlings, Steve, illus. 2001. (Seventh Tower Ser.: Bk. 4). 256p. (J). (gr. 3-7). pap. 4.99 (978-0-439-17685-9(9), Scholastic Pr.) Scholastic, Inc.

—Across the Wall: A Tale of the Abhorsen & Other Stories. 2006. 432p. (J). pap. 7.99 (978-0-06-074715-2(3)) HarperCollins Pubs.

—Grim Tuesday. 2004. (Keys to the Kingdom Ser.: No. 2). 336p. (J). 5.99 (978-0-439-43655-7(9), Scholastic Paperbacks) Scholastic, Inc.

—Grim Tuesday. 2004. (Keys to the Kingdom Ser.: No. 2). (gr. 3-6). lib. bdg. 14.15 (978-0-613-70969-9(1)) Tandem Library Bks.

Nixon, Hershell. The Long Way West. 2003. (Illus.). 176p. (J). 16.95 (978-0-89672-508-9(1)) Texas Tech Univ. Pr.

Nixon, Joan Lowery. Caught in the Act. l.t. ed. 1999. (Orphan Train Adventures Ser.: No. 2). 150p. (J). (gr. 4 up). lib. bdg. 23.33 (978-0-8368-2639-5(6)) Stevens, Gareth Inc.

—A Dangerous Promise. l.t. ed. 1999. (Orphan Train Adventures Ser.: No. 5). 148p. (J). (gr. 4 up). lib. bdg. 23.33 (978-0-8368-2642-5(6)) Stevens, Gareth Inc.

—A Family Apart. 2000. (Orphan Train Adventures Ser.: Bk. 1). (YA). (gr. 5 up). pap. 49.75 incl. audio (978-0-7887-4331-3(7), 41126) Recorded Bks., LLC.

—A Family Apart. l.t. ed. 1999. (Orphan Train Adventures Ser.: No. 1). 162p. (J). (gr. 4 up). lib. bdg. 23.33 (978-0-8368-2638-8(8)) Stevens, Gareth Inc.

—In the Face of Danger. l.t. ed. 1999. (Orphan Train Adventures Ser.: No. 3). (J). (gr. 4 up). lib. bdg. 23.33 (978-0-8368-2640-1(X)) Stevens, Gareth Inc.

—Keeping Secrets. l.t. ed. 1999. (Orphan Train Adventures Ser.: No. 6). 163p. (J). (gr. 4 up). lib. bdg. 23.33 (978-0-8368-2643-2(4)) Stevens, Gareth Inc.

—A Place to Belong. l.t. ed. 1999. (Orphan Train Adventures Ser.: No. 4). (J). (gr. 4 up). lib. bdg. 23.33 (978-0-8368-2641-8(8)) Stevens, Gareth Inc.

—The Seance. 2004. 224p. (YA). pap. 5.95 (978-0-15-205029-0(9), Harcourt Paperbacks) Harcourt Children's Bks.

Noah's Freezer. 2005. (978-0-9765358-0-5(7)) Strategic Dreamers, LLC.

Noble, Sarah. Hannah & Horatio Pea. 2006. (Illus.). 336p. pap. (***978-1-84401-673-0(0)***) Athena Pr.

Nocenti, Ann. Typhoid Mary, 4 vols. Romita, John, Jr., illus. 2003. (Daredevil Legends Ser.: Vol. 4). 224p. (YA). pap. 19.99 (978-0-7851-1041-5(0)) Marvel Enterprises, Inc.

Noland, Charles. The Adventures of Drew & Ellie: The Daring Rescue. Moyer, Tom, illus. 2nd ed. 2006. (J). per. 7.95 (***978-0-9789297-2-5(1)***) TMD Enterprises.

Noland, Charles. The Adventures of Drew & Ellie: The Magical Dress. Baker, Sherri, illus. 2006. (J). (978-0-9789297-1-8(3)); 2nd rev. ed. per. 7.95 (978-0-9789297-0-1(5)) TMD Enterprises.

Noland, Monica. Slide. 2006. 116p. pap. 16.95 (***978-1-4241-4966-7(5)***) PublishAmerica, Inc.

Noll, Katherine. The Amazon. 2005. (Survivor Ser.). 144p. (J). mass mkt. 4.99 (978-0-689-87731-5(5), Simon Spotlight) Simon & Schuster Children's Publishing.

—Haunted Park. 2003. (gr. 3-6). lib. bdg. 13.00 (978-0-613-72479-1(8)) Tandem Library Bks.

Norfolk, Bobby. Anansi & the Tug O' War. 2007. (Story Cove Ser.). 32p. (J). pap. 3.95 (***978-0-87483-825-1(8)***) August Hse. Pubs., Inc.

Norman, Dayle. Tre's Surprise the Move. l.t. ed. 2005. 35p. (J). per. 8.00 (978-1-59196-896-2(8)) Instantpublisher.com.

Norris, Christine. Talisman of Zandria, 1. Nagy, Robert, illus. 2005. 187p. (YA). pap. 14.95 (978-1-885093-44-8(6), LBF/Hadrosaur) Hadrosaur Pr.

Norris, L. Wayne. The Adventures of Ricky Raccoon & Jodi the Cat with Boomer. l.t. ed. 2003. (Illus.). 36p. (J). pap. (978-0-9709408-1-0(5)) Pinetree Pubns.

Northwestern Band of Shoshoni Nation of Utah (Washakie) Staff, contrib. by. Coyote Steals Fire: A Shoshone Tale. 2005. (Illus.). 32p. (J). 17.95 (978-0-87421-618-9(4)) Utah State Univ. Pr.

Norton, Andre. Ralestone Luck. 2006. 96.99 (***978-1-4280-4411-1(6)***); pap. 89.99 (***978-1-4280-4419-7(1)***) Indy-Publish.com.

Norton, George. Papa Golley's Journey Home. Hutcherson, Darren, illus. Date not set. 14.95 (978-1-889506-06-7(0)) Kendar Publishing, Inc.

Norton, Jack, Jr., as told by. Brave from Thunders. 2003. pap. 15.00 (978-0-9740071-3-7(7)) Ctr. for the Affirmation of Responsible Education.

Norton, Mary. The Borrowers. Krush, Beth & Krush, Joe, illus. 2003. (Borrowers Ser.). 192p. (J). pap. 5.95 (978-0-15-204737-5(9), Odyssey Classics) Harcourt Children's Bks.

—Borrowers. 50th anniv. ed. 2003. (Illus.). (YA). (978-0-15-204768-9(9), Harcourt Children's Bks.) Harcourt Children's Bks.

—The Borrowers. Stanley, Diana, illus. 50th anniv. gif. ed. 2003. (Borrowers Ser.). 176p. (J). 19.95 (978-0-15-204928-7(2)) Harcourt Children's Bks.

—The Borrowers Afield. Krush, Beth & Krush, Joe, illus. 50th anniv. ed. 2003. (Borrowers Ser.). 224p. (J). pap. 5.95 (978-0-15-204732-0(8), Odyssey Classics) Harcourt Children's Bks.

—The Borrowers Afloat. Krush, Beth & Krush, Joe, illus. 2003. (Borrowers Ser.). 192p. (J). pap. 5.95 (978-0-15-204733-7(6), Odyssey Classics) Harcourt Children's Bks.

—The Borrowers Avenged. Krush, Joe & Krush, Beth, illus. 50th anniv. ed. 2003. (Borrowers Ser.). 304p. (J). pap. 5.95 (978-0-15-204731-3(X), Odyssey Classics) Harcourt Children's Bks.

Norville, Rod. Moonshine Express: Revised Edition with a History of Moonshine Today & Yesterday. 2003. 178p. (YA). per. 13.95 (978-1-891929-99-1(2)) Four Seasons Pubs.

Nosov, Nikolai. The Adventures of Dunno & His Friends. Kay, Nicole, tr. from ENG. 2006. (RUS.). (J). (978-0-9754433-2-3(1), Language Transformer Bks.) Velichko, Vera.

Novara, Joe. Road Wrangler: Cowboys on Wheels. Lawson, Robert & Spatrisano, Kimberly, illus. 2007. (J). pap. 7.95 (***978-1-58980-507-1(0)***) Pelican Publishing Co., Inc.

Noyes, Alfred. The Highwayman. Kimber, Murray, illus. 2005. 48p. (gr. 5 up). (978-1-55337-425-1(8)) Kids Can Pr., Ltd.

—The Highwayman. Keeping, Charles, illus. 2nd ed. 1999. 32p. (YA). 12.95 (978-0-19-272370-3(7)) Oxford Univ. Pr., Inc.

Nunn, Paul E., illus. Forest Adventure. 2008. 16p. (J). (ps-2). pap. 5.99 (***978-0-448-44779-7(7)***, Grosset & Dunlap) Penguin Group (USA) Inc.

Nusz, Janean. The Littlest Cowboy. 2005. 26p. 12.30 (978-1-4116-4019-1(5)) Lulu.com.

Nwapa-Ibuaka, Njideka. Tales from Animal Kingdom. l.t. unabr. ed. 2003. (Illus.). 30p. (gr. 2-5). pap. 7.95 (978-0-9661598-5-1(3)) Ekwike Bks. & Publishing.

Nybo, B. J. Elmo Jackson Great Yellow Ball. 2005. (978-0-9742322-0-1(3)) New Art & Vision, LLC.

Nyikos, Stacy Ann, Dizzy. Lee, Kary, illus. l.t. ed. 2007. 32p. (J). lib. bdg. 15.95 (***978-0-9764199-2-1(0)***, 888-867-1927) Stonehorse Publishing, LLC.

Nyquist, Kate. Maggie's Coral Reef Adventure. McCord, Kathleen, illus. 2001. 32p. (J). (ps-1). 12.95 (978-1-878244-34-5(5)) Monterey Bay Aquarium.

Oberne, Sharon. Kelsey. 2006. 88p. (YA). pap. 13.95 (978-1-58909-340-9(2)) Bookstand Publishing.

O'Berry, Jan. The Journey Home. 2003. 198p. pap. 13.95 (978-0-595-27195-5(2)) iUniverse, Inc.

Obrien, Elaime F. Anita of Ranch Del Mar. 2005. 171p. (J). (gr. 5-6). reprint ed. pap. 995.00 (978-1-885375-14-8(X), Shore Line Pr.) Pacific Bks.

O'Brien, Robert C. Mrs. Frisby & the Rats of Nimh. Bernstein, Zena, illus. 2002. (J). 13.94 (978-0-7587-0205-0(1)) Book Wholesalers, Inc.

—The Silver Crown. 2001. (gr. 5-8). lib. bdg. 13.00 (978-0-613-37168-1(2)) Tandem Library Bks.

O'Brien, Sandy. Thorvo. 1998. (J). pap. 8.95 (978-0-533-12558-6(8)) Vantage Pr., Inc.

Ocean Front Books. Coloring Book. l.t. ed. 2006. (J). lib. bdg. (***978-1-934190-02-9(0)***) Ocean Front Bk. Publishing, Inc.

O'Conner, John. Three Classic Thrillers. Calcutt, David, ed. 1999. (Dramascripts Classic Texts Ser.). 82p. (J). (gr. 6-9). pap. 17.95 (978-0-17-432598-7(3)) Nelson Thornes Ltd. GBR. *Dist:* Trans-Atlantic Pubns., Inc.

O'Connor, Carol M. Hedgehog Day. O'Connor, Carol M., illus. 1999. 8p. (J). (gr. k-2). pap. 3.75 (978-1-880612-93-4(3), Seedling Pubns.) Continental Pr., Inc.

O'Connor, George. Ker-splash! O'Connor, George, illus. 2005. (Illus.). 40p. (J). 14.95 (978-0-689-87682-0(3)) Simon & Schuster Children's Publishing.

O'Connor, Ilett. The Dancer 2 Cristina & the Magic Ball. unabr. ed. 2002. 45p. (J). pap. 12.00 (978-0-9717003-5-2(4)) O'Connor, Ilett K.

O'Connor, Kerrie. Through the Tiger's Eye. Wagner, Erica, tr. 2005. (Telares Ser.: Bk. 1). (Illus.). 288p. (Orig.). (J). (ps-7). pap. 9.95 (978-1-86508-538-8(3)) Allen & Unwin AUS. *Dist:* Independent Pubs. Group.

O'Dell, Scott. The Black Pearl. 2002. (Illus.). (J). 13.40 (978-0-7587-0242-5(6)) Book Wholesalers, Inc.

Odom, Mel. A Conspiracy Revealed. 2005. (Hunter's League Ser.). 256p. (YA). mass mkt. 5.99 (978-0-689-86608-1(9), Simon Pulse) Simon & Schuster Children's Publishing.

—His Legacy Avenged, No. 4. 2006. (Hunter's League Ser.). 256p. (YA). mass mkt. 5.99 (978-0-689-86635-7(6), Simon Pulse) Simon & Schuster Children's Publishing.

Odom, Mel & Seeley, Dave. The Mystery Unravels. 2005. (Hunter's League Ser.). 256p. (YA). mass mkt. 5.99 (978-0-689-86633-3(X), Simon Pulse) Simon & Schuster Children's Publishing.

—The Secret Explodes. 2005. (Hunter's League Ser.). 240p. (YA). mass mkt. 5.99 (978-0-689-86634-0(8), Simon Pulse) Simon & Schuster Children's Publishing.

O'Donnell, E. E. Father Browne's Galway. 2006. (Illus.). 112p. 38.95 (978-1-85607-938-9(4)) Currach Pr. IRL. *Dist:* Dufour Editions, Inc.

O'Donnell, Liam. United Force. Rooth, Mike, illus. 2007. 44p. (J). lib. bdg. 23.08 (***978-1-4242-1633-8(8)***) Fitzgerald Bks.

Oeming, Michael Avon. Thor Blood Oath. 2007. (Illus.). 144p. pap. 14.99 (978-0-7851-1852-7(7)) Marvel Enterprises, Inc.

O'Fearghail, Charles. The Discovery Bk. 1: The Santa Claus Chronicles. 2003. 216p. (J). per. 18.00 (978-1-58982-009-8(6), Bedside Bks.) American Bk. Publishing Group.

A B

Ogden, Charles. Rare Beasts. Carton, Rick, illus. ed. 2005. (Edgar & Ellen Ser.). 144p. (J). 9.95 (978-1-4169-1409-9(9) , Aladdin) Simon & Schuster Children's Publishing.

—Tourist Trap. Carton, Rick, illus. ed. 2005. (Edgar & Ellen Ser.). 176p. (J). 9.95 (978-1-4169-1411-2(0) , Aladdin) Simon & Schuster Children's Publishing.

—Under Town. Carton, Rick, illus. ed. 2006. (Edgar & Ellen Ser.). 160p. (J). 9.95 (978-1-4169-1412-9(9) , Aladdin) Simon & Schuster Children's Publishing.

Ogilvy, Ian. Measle & the Dragodon. 2005. 352p. (J). (ps-8). 15.99 (978-0-06-058688-1(5)) HarperCollins Pubs.

—Measle & the Mallockee. 2006. 384p. (J). lib. bdg. 16.89 (978-0-06-058692-8(3)) HarperCollins Pubs.

O'Grady, Standish Hayes. The Pursuit of the Gilla Decair & His Horse. 2004. reprint ed. pap. 15.95 (978-1-4191-7950-1(0)); pap. 1.99 (978-1-4192-7950-8(5)) Kessinger Publishing, LLC.

Ohkami, Mineko. Dragon Knights. Ohkami, Mineko, illus. (Illus.). 210p. Vol. 12. 2004. lib. bdg. 20.90 (978-1-4176-5944-9(0)); Vol. 14. 2004. lib. bdg. 20.90 (978-1-4176-5945-6(9)); Vol. 16. 2004. lib. bdg. 20.90 (978-1-4176-5946-3(7)); Vol. 18. 2005. lib. bdg. 20.90 (978-1-4176-5947-0(5)) Tandem Library Bks.

Ohnogi, Hiroki. Raxephon Novel, Vol. 1. 2005. 200p. (YA). pap. 7.95 (978-1-59796-000-7(4)) DrMaster Pubns. Inc.

Okamoto, Rod. Kingdom of Nu - TJ's Tale: TJ's Tale. Okamoto, Alan, illus. 2006. (J). per. 19.95 (978-0-9764116-0-4(1)) Nutrishare Publishing.

Okaty, Nicole. Custard & Pupcake's Book: A Pet Pals Adventure. 2005. 39p. (*978-0-439-70470-0(7)) Scholastic, Inc.

Okorafor-Mbachu, Nnedi. Zahrah the Windseeker. Cooper, Stephanie & Hall, Amanda, illus. 2005. 320p. (YA). (gr. 5-7). 16.00 (978-0-618-34090-3(4)) Houghton Mifflin Co. Trade & Reference Div.

The Old Man & the Sea. 1998. 36p. (YA). 11.95 (978-1-56137-404-5(0) , NU4040SP) Novel Units, Inc.

Old Man Winter: The New Season. 2005. (Illus.). 32p. (J). bds. 15.99 (978-1-933079-03-5(7)) Core Publishing & Consulting, Inc.

Old Mcdonald. 2004. (J). per. (978-1-57657-425-6(3)) Paradise Pr., Inc.

Oldenburg, Claes & Milne, A. A. Winnie the Pooh's Baby Days. Shepard, Ernest H., illus. 2004. 64p. (J). (ps). 15.99 (978-0-525-47325-1(4) , Dutton Juvenile) Penguin Group (USA) Inc.

Olds, Sara V. Anna - a Farewell to Juarez. Roy, T. M., illus. 2003. Orig. Title: Hanne's Farewell to Juarez. (J). pap. 10.50 (978-0-9715433-7-9(2) , AFJ-TP) Zapstone Productions.

O'Leary-Coggins, Annette C. Nanny Reilly. 2007. 116p. per. 10.95 (*978-0-595-44994-1(8)) iUniverse, Inc.

O'Leary, John. En busca del tesoro del Pirata! 2005. (SPA., Illus.). 14p. (J). bds. 13.95 (978-84-7864-794-1(5)) Combel Editorial, S.A. ESP. *Dist:* Independent Pubs. Group.

Olesha, Yuri. The Three Fat Men. Kay, Nicole, tr. from RUS. 2006. (J). (978-0-9754433-0-9(5) , Language Transformer Bks.) Velichko, Vera.

Oleson, Susan. Sammy Tails: Finding a Home, 1. ed. 2006. (Illus.). 28p. (J). pap. (978-0-9779251-0-0(2)) Oleson, Susan.

Oliva, Nephi. Elder Teddy & His First Companion. Maruyama, Jerrod, illus. 2005. 32p. (J). per. 4.95 (978-1-886249-30-1(X)) WindRiver Publishing.

Olive Branch Publishing, ed. Boogalaboo Meets Ranger Bob. 2007. (Adventures of Boogalaboo Ser.). (Illus.). 32p. (J). (*978-0-9793147-0-4(4)) Olive Branch Publishing, LLC.

Oliver, Andrew. Haunted Hill. 2006. (Sam & Stephanie Mystery Ser.). 268p. (J). (gr. 5-9). per. 12.95 (978-0-9661009-7-6(2)) Adams-Pomeroy Pr.

—If Photos Could Talk. 2005. (Sam & Stephanie Mystery Ser.). 264p. (J). per. 12.95 (978-0-9661009-6-9(4)) Adams-Pomeroy Pr.

Oliver, Lin. Beezy's Big Boy. Dodge, Bill, illus. l.t. ed. 2000. 32p. (J). pap. 14.99 incl. audio (978-1-890647-61-2(6)); 14.95 (978-1-890647-60-5(8)) RC2 Corp.

—Daylight Limited. 1999. pap. 14.95 (978-1-56799-866-5(6) , Friedman-Fairfax) Friedman, Michael Publishing Group, Inc.

—Journey of the Jupiter. Dodge, Bill, illus. l.t. ed. 2000. 32p. (J). pap. 14.99 incl. audio (978-1-890647-59-9(4)); 14.95 (978-1-890647-58-2(6)) RC2 Corp.

Oliver Twist. 2000. (Illus.). 80p. (YA). per. 6.95 (978-1-56254-295-5(8) , SP2958) Saddleback Educational Publishing.

Olmstead, Kathleen & Twain, Mark. The Prince & the Pauper. Akib, Jamel, illus. 2007. (Classic Starts Ser.). 152p. (J). (*978-1-4287-4214-7(X)) Sterling Publishing Co., Inc.

Olsen, Ashley & Olsen, Mary-Kate. The Dream Date Debate. 2003. (Two of a Kind Ser.: Vol. 28). (Illus.). 112p. mass mkt. 4.99 (978-0-06-009324-2(2) , Harper Entertainment) HarperCollins Pubs.

Olsen, Ashley, et al. The Case of the Hollywood Who-Done-It. 2003. (New Adventures of Mary-Kate & Ashley Ser.: No. 33). (Illus.). 96p. mass mkt. 4.50 (978-0-06-009331-0(5) , Harper Entertainment) HarperCollins Pubs.

Olsen, Mary-Kate. Love-Set-Match. 2003. (gr. 5-8). lib. bdg. 13.00 (978-0-613-64745-8(9)) Tandem Library Bks.

—Password: Red Hot. 2003. (gr. k-3). lib. bdg. 12.40 (978-0-613-68458-3(3)) Tandem Library Bks.

Olsen, Mary-Kate & Olsen, Ashley. New Adventures, 20 Copies, Vol. 36. 2003. pap. 90.00 (978-0-06-057176-4(4) , Harper Entertainment) HarperCollins Pubs.

—Password: Red Hot. 2003. (In Action Ser.: No. 7). (Illus.). 64p. 4.50 (978-0-06-009308-2(0) , Harper Entertainment) HarperCollins Pubs.

—Two of a Kind No. 33: Heart to Heart. 2004. (gr. 3-6). lib. bdg. 13.00 (978-0-613-71364-1(8)) Tandem Library Bks.

—Two of a Kind Box. 2001. pap. 19.22 (978-0-06-009014-2(6)) HarperCollins Pubs.

Olson, Kevin Noel. Eerey Tocsin in the Cryptoid Zoo. Hammack, Debi, illus. 2006. (YA). per. 15.95 (*978-1-887560-17-7(3) , Cornerstone Bk. Publishers) Poll, Michael Publishing.

Olson, Marianne. Over the Waves. Kazal, Pamela, illus. 1999. iv, 147p. (YA). (gr. 4 up). pap. 9.95 (978-0-9673497-0-1(2)) Rafter Five Pr.

Olswanger, Anna. Shlemiel Crooks. Koz, Paula Goodman, illus. 2005. 36p. (J). (ps-7). 15.95 (978-1-58838-165-1(X)) NewSouth, Inc.

O'Mahony, Carol. A Dee Dee & Clark Delay Magical Myster. 2006. 73p. pap. 14.95 (*978-1-4241-5119-6(8)) PublishAmerica, Inc.

Once upon a Time Spanish Version-Little Red Riding Hood. 2005. (J). (978-1-57022-562-8(1)) ECS Learning Systems, Inc.

Once upon a Time Spanish Version-the Three Little Pigs. 2005. (J). (978-1-57022-565-9(6)) ECS Learning Systems, Inc.

Once upon My Summer Camp Dream. 2003. spiral bd. 14.95 (978-0-9744437-1-3(9)) Imagination Workshop, The.

Oppel, Kenneth. Firewing. 2008. 320p. (J). pap. 6.99 (*978-1-4169-4999-2(2) , Aladdin) Simon & Schuster Children's Publishing.

Optic, Oliver. Duty Bound: The Lightning Express. unabr. ed. 1998. (Lakeshore Ser.: Vol. 2). (Illus.). 312p. reprint ed. 15.00 (978-1-889128-51-1(1)) Mantle Ministries.

—Haste & Waste or the Young Pilot of Lake Champlain A Story for Young People. 2004. reprint ed. pap. 1.99 (978-1-4192-2291-7(0)) Kessinger Publishing, LLC.

—Taken by the Enemy. Shute, A. B., illus. 1998. (Blue & the Gray Ser.). 351p. (J). (gr. 4-7). reprint ed. per. 14.95 (978-1-890623-03-6(2)) Lost Classics Bk. Co.

Orban, Marianne. To Earn a Star. 2000. 172p. (YA). pap. 14.95 (978-0-595-17080-7(3)) iUniverse, Inc.

O'Reilly, Sean. Ezra: Egyptian Exchange. 2005. (YA). 9.95 (978-0-9763095-4-3(8)) Arcana Studio, Inc.

Orliac, Catherine. Te Tumu o Rapa Nui: El Arbolito de Rapa Nui. the Little Tree of Rapa Nui. le Petit Arbre de Rapa Nui. Haoa Cardinali, Viki et al, trs. Willemin, Veronique, illus. 2005. (FRE, SPA & ENG.). 40p. (J). spiral bd. 12.00 (978-1-880636-02-2(6)) Easter Island Foundation.

Orloff, Erica. Balloonatiks: The 1st Goopy, Goofy, Loopy Adventure. 2002. 128p. (J). pap. 5.95 (978-0-9703338-1-0(1) , 174-001) Animagic Entertainment Group, Inc.

Orloff, Erica & Diloia, Tony. The Balloonatiks: The 1st Goopy, Goofy, Loopy Adventures. 2001. 126p. (J). (gr. 3-7). pap. 5.95 (978-0-9703338-0-3(3)) Animagic Entertainment Group, Inc.

Orme, David. Boffin Boy & the Ice Caves of Pluto. 2007. (Boffin Boy Ser.). (Illus.). 36p. pap. 7.95 (*978-1-84167-626-5(8)) Ransom Publishing Ltd. GBR. *Dist:* International Publishers Marketing.

—Boffin Boy & the Quest for Wisdom. 2007. (Boffin Boy Ser.). (Illus.). 36p. pap. 7.95 (*978-1-84167-628-9(4)) Ransom Publishing Ltd. GBR. *Dist:* International Publishers Marketing.

Orme, Helen. Wet! 2008. (Siti's Sisters Ser.). 36p. pap. 7.95 (*978-1-84167-688-3(8)) Ransom Publishing Ltd. GBR. *Dist:* International Publishers Marketing.

Ormondroyd, Edward. Castaways on Long Ago. 2003. (Illus.). 188p. (gr. 5 up). 12.95 (978-0-9714612-8-4(7)) Green Mansion Pr. LLC.

O'Rourke, Carol J. Sea Critters Vol. 2: The Splangywangba Adventure. 1998. (Illus.). 14p. (J). (gr. k-4). pap. 2.95 (978-0-9665692-1-6(0)) Sea Critters.

Orr, Ryan. Beyond the Oasis. Hernandez, Carlos, illus. 2002. 353p. (YA). per. 24.95 (978-0-9641861-1-8(X) , RWP Bks.) Redhawk Publishing.

—Grimaldi Land of the Dragons. Hernandez, Carlos, illus. 1998. 372p. (YA). (gr. 6 up). reprint ed. per. 24.95 (978-0-9641861-6-3(0) , RWP Bks.) Redhawk Publishing.

—Jeremy Ruhl Africa. 2004. 420p. (YA). per. 25.95 (978-0-9641861-9-4(5) , RWP Bks.) Redhawk Publishing.

—Jeremy Ruhl Savannah Wars, 1. 2005. 400p. (YA). per. 25.95 net. (978-0-9641861-3-2(6) , JRSW, RWP Bks.) Redhawk Publishing.

—The Life & Times of Jeremy Ruhl. Hernandez, Carlos, illus. 2002. 387p. (YA). per. 24.95 (978-0-9641861-5-6(2) , 0964186152) Redhawk Publishing.

Orr, Wendy. Nim at Sea. Millard, Kerry, illus. 2008. 192p. (J). (gr. 3-7). 12.99 (*978-0-440-42232-7(9) , Knopf Bks. for Young Readers) Random Hse. Children's Bks.

Orr, Wendy. Spook's Shack. Millard, Kerry, illus. 2005. 120p. (J). (ps-ps). pap. 6.95 (978-1-86508-645-3(2)) Allen & Unwin AUS. *Dist:* Independent Pubs. Group.

Ortiz, Carolyn. Cat's Got My Tongue! 2006. (ENG., Illus.). 40p. per. 13.90 (978-1-4208-7851-6(4)) AuthorHouse.

Osborne, Mary Pope. Afternoon on the Amazon. unabr. ed. 2004. (Magic Tree House Ser. : No. 6). 67p. (J). (gr. k-3). pap. 17.00 incl. audio (978-0-8072-0339-2(4) , S FTR 217 SP, Listening Library) Random Hse. Audio Publishing Group.

—The Final Battle. Howell, Troy, illus. 6th rev. ed. 2005. (Tales from the Odyssey Ser.: Bk. 6). 112p. (gr. 3-6). pap. 4.99 (978-0-7868-0994-3(9)) Hyperion Bks. for Children.

—Magic Tree House #9-12, No. 3, Bks. 9-12. 2003. (Magic Tree House Ser.). (Illus.). (J). (gr. 1-4). pap. 15.96 (978-0-375-82553-8(3) , Random Hse. Bks. for Young Readers) Random Hse. Children's Bks.

—The Mysteries of Spider Kane. 2006. 240p. (J). (gr. 4-7). 5.99 (978-0-440-42097-2(0) , Yearling) Random Hse. Children's Bks.

—Night of the Ninjas, Vol. 5. unabr. ed. 2004. (Magic Tree House Ser. : No. 5). 69p. (J). (gr. k-3). pap. 17.00 incl. audio (978-0-8072-0338-5(6) , Listening Library) Random Hse. Audio Publishing Group.

—Sunset of the Sabertooth, Vol. 7. unabr. ed. 2004. (Magic Tree House Ser. : No. 7). 67p. (J). (gr. k-3). pap. 17.00 incl. audio (978-0-8072-0340-8(8) , Listening Library) Random Hse. Audio Publishing Group.

O'Shields, Charlie. The Curious Case of Miser Snoot & the Bibliomaniacs. 2002. 186p. pap. 13.95 (978-0-595-22250-6(1) , Writers Club Pr.) iUniverse, Inc.

Osorio, Rick. The Great Adventure of Sally Rock & el Lobo. 2007. (ENG.). 96p. per. 14.95 (*978-1-4241-5869-0(9)) PublishAmerica, Inc.

Osorio, Rick. The Great Adventure of Sally Rock & the Cretaceous Chicken. 2006. 65p. pap. 12.95 (978-1-4241-0971-5(X)) PublishAmerica, Inc.

Ostby, Kristin & Piper, Watty. Ride along with the Little Engine That Could. Ong, Cristina & Artful Doodlers Limited Staff, illus. 2005. (Little Engine That Could Ser.). 10p. (J). (ps). bds. 6.99 (978-0-448-43845-0(3) , Grosset & Dunlap) Penguin Group (USA) Inc.

Ostow, Micol & Burge, Constance M. House of Shards. 2006. (Charmed Ser.). 192p. (YA). pap. 6.99 (978-1-4169-2531-6(7) , Simon Spotlight Entertainment) Simon & Schuster.

Ostrander, P. Martin. P Martin Ostrander's Dangerous Four Series: Book #1. 2007. 112p. 20.95 (*978-0-595-68250-8(2)); per. 10.95 (*978-0-595-43582-1(3)) iUniverse, Inc.

Ostrom, Bob, illus. Friends till the End! 2004. (Teenage Mutant Ninja Turtles Ser.). 24p. (J). pap. 3.99 (978-0-689-87006-4(X) , Simon Spotlight) Simon & Schuster Children's Publishing.

—Spider-Man 2: Hurry up, Spider-Man! 2004. (Spider-Man Ser.). 24p. (J). (ps-2). pap. 3.99 (978-0-06-057137-5(3) , Harper Festival) HarperCollins Pubs.

Ostrow, Kim & Burnett, Mark. Marquesas. 2005. (Survivor—Outwit, Outplay, Outlast Ser.: Vol. 2). 143p. (J). (978-1-4155-7990-9(3) , Simon Spotlight) Simon & Schuster Children's Publishing.

Ostrowski-Young, Lori. Aboo & Sidekick. 2007. (YA). per. 6.99 (*978-1-59886-753-4(9)) Tate Publishing & Enterprises, L.L.C.

Otis, James. District Messenger Boy & A Necktie Par. 2006. pap. (*978-1-4250-1843-6(2)); pap. (*978-1-4250-2095-8(X)); pap. (*978-1-4250-2386-7(X)); pap. (*978-1-4250-1391-2(0)) Assistedreadingbooks.com Inc.

Otte, Kathleen M. The Tod Squad Can Explore. 2006. (J). bds. (978-1-57332-416-8(7)) HighReach Learning, Inc.

Otto, Carolyn B., et al. Big Box of Backyard Animals, 4 bks., Set. Sherrow, Victoria et al, illus. 2002. (Big Box of Board Bks.). 10p. (J). (ps-k). bds. (978-1-59069-177-9(6)) Studio Mouse LLC.

Our Story... for All to See. 2005. (J). bds. 8.95 (978-0-9761076-2-0(7)) Spring Ducks Bks., LLC.

Overton, Max & Overton, Ariana. Glass House. 2003. 208p. 22.00 (978-1-59426-010-0(9) , gh-hc) Mundania Pr.

Owen, Dan. Ellen. 2006. 32p. (J). pap. 11.99 (978-1-4116-9069-1(9)) Lulu.com.

Owens Hammock, Sarah. You Can't Get into More Trouble Than Gator Pervis. Roberts Cocciolone, Kathy, illus. 2007. 32p. (J). 12.95 (*978-0-9796994-4-3(4)) TRIAD Publishing Group.

Owens, M. T. The Great Tome. 2006. (YA). per. 11.99 (978-0-9768589-2-8(4)) Montage Publishing International.

Oxley, MacDonald J. Young Woodsman or Life in the Forests of. 2006. 24.99 (*978-1-4280-3300-9(9)); pap. 18.99 (*978-1-4280-3280-4(0)) IndyPublish.com.

Pachela, Czes, illus. The Rainy Day Adventure. 2001. 24p. (J). pap. 3.50 (978-1-58925-362-9(0) , tiger tales) ME Media LLC.

Packard, Edward. Supercomputer. 1999. (Illus.). 118p. (Orig.). mass mkt. (978-0-553-24678-0(X)) Random Hse., Inc.

—Underground Kingdom. 1999. (Illus.). 108p. mass mkt. (978-0-553-23292-9(4)) Bantam Bks.

& Packer, Knife & McCoshan, Duncan. Captain Fact's Creepy Crawly Adventure. 2004. (Illus.). 96p. (J). pap. (*978-1-4052-0834-5(1)) Egmont Bks., Ltd.

Padilla, Claudia. Las Aventuras de Ceci y Azul. 2003. 96p. (J). per. (978-1-931456-45-6(3)) Athena Pr.

Page, Marion. The Printer's Devil. Dodge, Chris, illus. 2002. 171p. (YA). (gr. 6-9). 9.99 (978-0-88092-464-1(0) , 4640) Royal Fireworks Publishing Co.

Page, Via, et al, eds. The Adventures of Big Shot & Teeny Weeny. Arinsberg, Norman, illus. 2002. 94p. (J). (gr. 2-4). pap. 15.00 incl. audio compact disk (978-0-9667442-1-7(7)) Curen Enterprises.

Pagliarulo, Antonio. A Different Kind of Heat. 2006. 192p. (YA). (gr. 9). pap. 7.50 (978-0-385-73298-7(8)); lib. bdg. 9.99 (978-0-385-90319-6(7)) Random Hse. Children's Bks. (Delacorte Bks. for Young Readers).

Paine, Walter. Cousin John: The Story of a Boy & A Small Smart Pig. 2006. 96p. 17.95 (978-1-59373-057-4(8)) Bunker Hill Publishing, Inc.

Pajaroflor. 2003. (SPA.). pap. (978-956-13-1080-3(5) , AB8005) Bello, Andres CHL. *Dist:* Lectorum Pubns., Inc.

Pallas-Luke, Barbara. Cryptic Society. ed. 2005. (YA). 5.00 (978-0-9765637-0-9(3)) Iris Pallas-Luke E-Writings/E-Literature.

Palmer, Slim. Albert Tales Too. 2006. (Illus.). 240p. (J). per. 15.99 (978-1-905363-84-1(2) , Exposure Publishing) Meadow Bks. GBR. *Dist:* Ingram Bk. Co.

Palmer, Slim. Kryptos: An Albert Tale. 2007. per. (*978-1-84685-384-5(2) , Exposure Publishing) Meadow Bks.

Palmerlee, B. P. Legend of Darious: The First Part of the Chronicles of Arattoss. 2006. 69p. pap. 14.95 (978-1-4241-1464-1(0)) PublishAmerica, Inc.

Panagopoulos, Janie Lynn. North to Iron Country: A Dream-Quest Adventure. 1998. (Dream-Quest Adventure Ser.). 224p. (J). (gr. 3-7). pap. 7.95 (978-0-938682-48-6(2) , 682-48-2) River Road Pubns., Inc.

—Train to Midnight: A Dream-Quest Adventure. 1999. 208p. (J). (gr. 3-8). 15.95 (978-0-938682-53-0(9)) River Road Pubns., Inc.

Panamkat, Matthew. Karan Quma & the Meluha Tree. 2007. 348p. per. 19.95 (*978-0-595-41816-9(3)) iUniverse, Inc.

Pandell, Karen. Peekaboo, Stretch! Mcelmurry, Jill, illus. 2006. 18p. (J). (gr. k-k). 9.99 (978-0-7636-1593-2(5)) Candlewick Pr.

Panev, Aleksandar. Queen Nzinga. Stefflbauer, Thomas, illus. 2007. 48p. (J). lib. bdg. 23.08 (*978-1-4242-1641-3(9)) Fitzgerald Bks.

Panik, Alison Saeger. Berry Best Friends Book: A Fun with Friends Adventure. 2005. 39p. lib. bdg. (*978-0-439-70469-4(3)) Scholastic, Inc.

Pannell, Michael. Wilbur the Brushhound. 2005. 312p. (J). per. 14.95 (978-1-59453-920-6(0) , Airleaf Publishing) Airleaf Publishing & Bookselling.

Pantelo, Amber. The Totally Meaningless Summer. 2004. 75p. (YA). pap. 12.95 (978-0-7414-1914-9(9)) Infinity Publishing.

Paolini, Christopher. Eldest. (Inheritance Trilogy: Bk. 2). (gr. 7 up). 2007. 704p. (YA). pap. 12.99 (978-0-375-84040-1(0)); 2006. 736p. (J). 24.00 (978-0-375-84060-9(5)); 2006. 736p. (J). lib. bdg. 27.99 (978-0-375-94060-6(X)) Random Hse. Children's Bks. (Knopf Bks. for Young Readers).

—Eragon. (Inheritance Trilogy: Bk. 1). (YA). (gr. 7 up). 2007. 768p. mass mkt. 6.99 (*978-0-440-24073-0(5) , Laurel Leaf); 2003. (Illus.). 544p. 18.95 (978-0-375-82668-9(8) , Knopf Bks. for Young Readers); 2006. (Illus.). 528p. pap. 10.95 (978-0-375-84054-8(0) , Knopf Bks. for Young Readers) Random Hse. Children's Bks.

Papademetriou, Lisa. Ultimate Adventures Digiarmor Energize! 2001. 96p. (gr. 4-7). pap. 4.50 (978-0-06-107204-8(4)) HarperCollins Pubs.

Papademetriou, Lisa & Jones, Jasmine. Spider-Man 3: The Junior Novel. 2007. (Spider-Man Ser.: Vol. 3). 144p. (J). pap. 4.99 (978-0-06-083725-9(X) , Harper Entertainment) HarperCollins Pubs.

Papaj, Dana. Blackjack's Hare Raising Adventure. Dixon, Gary, illus. 2005. (J). (978-1-932583-20-5(3)) digital@batesjackson llc.

Papineau, Lucie. Gontrand et le Croissant des Cavernes. ed. 2004. (FRE., Illus.). (J). (gr. k-3). spiral bd. (978-0-616-11145-1(2)) Canadian National Institute for the Blind/Institut National Canadien pour les Aveugles.

Papp, Robert, illus. The Game Store Mystery, 104. 2005. (Boxcar Children Mysteries Ser.: No. 104). 131p. (J). (gr. 2-7). pap. 4.50 (978-0-8075-2739-9(4)); lib. bdg. 14.95 (978-0-8075-2738-2(6)) Whitman, Albert & Co.

Pardoe, David. Jasper Tippett's Amazing Journey to Page 42. 2006. (Illus.). 132p. pap. (*978-1-84401-785-0(0)) Athena Pr.

Parfitt, Tim. Spanish Vogue Book. 2006. 254p. pap. 22.00 (*978-1-4050-4619-0(8)) Macmillan Publishers Ltd. GBR. *Dist:* Independent Pubs. Group.

Parish, Margaret. Adventures of Amelia Bedelia, 2 vols., Vol. 2. 2001. 27.65 (978-0-06-001318-9(4)) HarperCollins Pubs.

Park, Barbara. Junie B. , First Grader (at Last!) unabr. ed. 2004. (Junie B. Jones Ser.: No. 18). 70p. (J). (gr. k-3). pap. 17.00 incl. audio (978-0-8072-1020-8(X) , S FTR 258 SP, Listening Library) Random Hse. Audio Publishing Group.

—Junie B., First Grader: Jingle Bells, Batman Smells! (P. S. So Does May.) Brunkus, Denise, illus. 2005. (Junie B. Jones Ser.: No. 25). 128p. (J). (gr. k-3). lib. bdg. 13.99 (978-0-375-92808-6(1) , Random Hse. Bks. for Young Readers) Random Hse. Children's Bks.

—Junie B., First Grader: Jingle Bells, Batman Smells! (P.S. So Does May.) Brunkus, Denise, illus. 2005. (Junie B. Jones Ser.: No. 25). 128p. (J). (gr. k-3). 11.95 (978-0-375-82808-9(7) , Random Hse. Bks. for Young Readers) Random Hse. Children's Bks.

—Junie B. Jones Is a Graduation Girl. unabr. ed. 2004. (Junie B. Jones Ser.: No. 17). 69p. (J). (gr. k-3). pap. 17.00 incl. audio (978-0-8072-1019-2(6) , S FTR 257 SP, Listening Library) Random Hse. Audio Publishing Group.

—Junie B. Jones Is Captain Field Day. unabr. ed. 2004. (Junie B. Jones Ser.: No. 16). 80p. (J). (gr. k-3). pap. 17.00 incl. audio (978-0-8072-0337-8(8) , Listening Library) Random Hse. Audio Publishing Group.

—Junie B. Jones Is Captain Field Day. Brunkus, Denise, illus. 2001. (Junie B. Jones Ser.: No. 16). 80p. (J). (gr. k-3). pap. 3.99 (978-0-375-80291-1(6)); lib. bdg. 11.99 (978-0-375-90291-8(0)) Random Hse. Children's Bks. (Random Hse. Bks. for Young Readers).

Park, Linda Sue. Clicks. 2007. (J). (*978-0-439-41139-4(4) , Levine, Arthur A. Bks.) Scholastic, Inc.

Park, Linda Sue. The Kite Fighters. 2002. 144p. (J). (gr. 4-7). pap. 5.50 (978-0-440-41813-9(5) , Yearling) Random Hse. Children's Bks.

Park, Linda Sue, et al. Click. 2007. 224p. (J). (gr. 5 up). pap. 16.99 (*978-0-439-41138-7(6) , Levine, Arthur A. Bks.) Scholastic, Inc.

Park, Yong-gi. The Secrets Behind Number 64. Suh, Paul, tr. from KOR. 2005. (Illus.). 164p. (YA). pap. 20.00 (978-0-89581-832-4(9)) Jain Publishing Company, Inc.

Parker, Andy. Ciberbichos: Cyber Bugs, Spanish-Language Edition. 2005. (Mekanimals Ser.). (SPA., Illus.). 8p. (J). bds. 12.95 (978-970-718-323-0(3) , Silver Dolphin en Español) Advanced Marketing, S. de R. L. de C. V. MEX. *Dist:* Perseus Distribution.

Parker, Jeff. Interman. 2003. (gr. 7-12). lib. bdg. 30.35 (978-0-613-66783-8(2)) Tandem Library Bks.
—The Leader Has a Big Head. 2007. (Avengers Ser.). 24p. (J). (gr. 2-6). 21.35 (***978-1-59961-384-0(0)***) Spotlight.
—The Master of Sound. 2007. (Fantastic Four Set II Ser.). 24p. (J). (gr. 2-6). 21.35 (***978-1-59961-391-8(3)***) Spotlight.
—The Masters of Evil. 2007. (Avengers Ser.). 24p. (J). (gr. 2-6). 21.35 (***978-1-59961-385-7(9)***) Spotlight.
—The Replacements. 2007. (Avengers Ser.). 24p. (J). (gr. 2-6). 21.35 (***978-1-59961-386-4(7)***) Spotlight.
Parker, John. Gwoppy. 2003. 79 p. pap. 14.95 (978-1-4137-0795-3(5)) PublishAmerica, Inc.
Parkinson, Curtis. Sea Chase. 2004. 192p. (J). (gr. 5). pap. 8.95 (978-0-88776-682-4(X)) Tundra Bks., Inc./Livres Toundra, Inc. CAN. *Dist:* Random Hse., Inc.
—Storm-Blast. 2003. (gr. 3-6). lib. bdg. 16.40 (978-0-613-77301-0(2)) Tandem Library Bks.
—Storm-Blast. 2003. (Illus.). 160p. (J). (gr. 5-9). pap. 7.95 (978-0-88776-630-5(7)) Tundra Bks., Inc./Livres Toundra, Inc. CAN. *Dist:* Random Hse., Inc.
Parra, Jen. Crazy Old Lou. Meier, Paul, illus. 2005. (J). bds. 9.99 (978-1-4183-0063-0(2)) Christ Inspired, Inc.
Parus, M. V. The Adventures of Mamma Simone, Jodie & Zed: The Mystery of the Pirate's Lost Treasure. 2006. 115p. (YA). per. 12.95 (***978-1-58374-148-1(8)***) Chicago Spectrum Pr.
Parvensky Barwell, Catherine A. Tommi Goes Camping, 4 vols. Barwell, Matthew W. et al, eds. Parvensky Barwell, Catherine A., illus. 2006. (Illus.). 40p. (J). 14.95 (978-0-9774409-3-1(1) , TL004) ILT Publishing.
—Tommi Goes to the Beach, 4 vols. Barwell, Matthew W. & Parvensky, Mary T., eds. 2006. (Illus.). 40p. (J). (978-0-9774409-2-4(3) , TL003) ILT Publishing.
—Tommi Lance Grows Up, 4 vols. 2006. (Illus.). 30p. (J). (978-0-9774409-0-0(7) , TL001) ILT Publishing.
—Tommi's First Snowfall, 4 vols. 2006. (Illus.). 32p. (J). (978-0-9774409-1-7(5) , TL002) ILT Publishing.
Pascal, Francine. Agent Out. 2006. (Fearless FBI Ser.: Vol. 3). 256p. (YA). pap. 7.99 (978-0-689-87823-7(0) , Simon Pulse) Simon & Schuster Children's Publishing.
—Blind. 2002. (Fearless Ser.: No. 21). (gr. 7-12). lib. bdg. 14.15 (978-0-613-67068-5(X)) Tandem Library Bks.
—Fearless Super Edition #3. 2004. (Fearless Ser.). 320p. (YA). mass mkt. 6.99 (978-0-689-86824-5(3) , Simon Pulse) Simon & Schuster Children's Publishing.
—Kill Game: A Gaia Moore Novel. 2005. (Fearless FBI Ser.). 272p. (YA). pap. 8.99 (978-0-689-87821-3(4) , Simon Pulse) Simon & Schuster Children's Publishing.
—Lucha por la Fama. Orig. Title: Claim to Fame. (SPA.). 128p. (J). 6.95 (978-84-272-3793-3(6)) Molino, Editorial ESP. *Dist:* AIMS International Bks., Inc.
—Missing. 2001. (Fearless Ser.: No. 14). (gr. 7-12). lib. bdg. 14.15 (978-0-613-67104-0(X)) Tandem Library Bks.
—Mocosos. Orig. Title: Jessica & the Brat Attack. (SPA.). 112p. (J). 6.95 (978-84-272-3590-8(9)) Molino, Editorial ESP. *Dist:* AIMS International Bks., Inc.
—Naked Eye. 2006. (Fearless FBI Ser.: No. 4). 240p. (YA). pap. 7.99 (978-0-689-87824-4(9) , Simon Pulse) Simon & Schuster Children's Publishing.
—Rebel. 2000. (Fearless Ser.: No. 7). 215p. (YA). (gr. 7-12). pap. (978-0-671-77341-0(0) , Simon & Schuster Children's Publishing) Simon & Schuster Children's Publishing.
—Run. 2000. 206p. pap. (978-0-671-03748-2(X) , Simon & Schuster Children's Publishing) Simon & Schuster Children's Publishing.
—Sam. 2003. (Secret Love Diaries). lib. bdg. 14.15 (978-0-613-73395-3(9)) Tandem Library Bks.
—Sex. 2002. (Fearless Ser.: No. 20). (gr. 7-12). lib. bdg. 14.15 (978-0-613-67120-0(1)) Tandem Library Bks.
Pascal, Francine & Frost, Michael. Live Bait. 2005. (Fearless FBI Ser.). 208p. (YA). pap. 7.99 (978-0-689-87822-0(2) , Simon Pulse) Simon & Schuster Children's Publishing.
Paschkis, Julie. Play All Day. Paschkis, Julie, illus. 1998. (Illus.). 32p. (J). (ps-k). 14.95 (978-0-316-69043-0(0)) Little Brown & Co.
Pasha, Georgia. Jelly Bean & Key Mystery. 2005. 17.00 (978-0-8059-9909-9(4) , RoseDog Bks.) Dorrance Publishing Co., Inc.
Pass, Erica. My Animal Friends: Storybook & Spotting Scope. 2007. (Nick Jr. Ser.). 32p. (YA). 24.99 (***978-0-7944-1319-4(6)***) Reader's Digest Assn., Inc., The.
A Pat on the Back. 2003. (J). per. (978-1-57657-879-7(8)) Paradise Pr., Inc.
Patchin, Gee Frank. The Pony Rider Boys in the Grand Canyon. 2006. 33.99 (***978-1-4219-7869-7(5)***); pap. 27.99 (***978-1-4219-7871-0(7)***) IndyPublish.com.
—The Pony Rider Boys in the Rockies. 2006. 63.99 (***978-1-4280-0930-1(2)***); pap. 57.99 (***978-1-4280-0940-0(X)***) IndyPublish.com.
—The Pony Rider Boys with the Texas Range. 2006. 78.99 (***978-1-4280-0012-4(7)***); pap. 72.99 (***978-1-4280-0014-8(3)***) IndyPublish.com.
Paterson, Brian. Ziggy Hunts for Treasure. 2003. (Illus.). 32p. (J). (ps). pap. 8.99 (978-0-00-713181-5(X) , HarperCollins Children's Bks.) HarperCollins Pubs. Ltd. GBR. *Dist:* Independent Pubs. Group.
Patrick, David. Nero Demare & the Legend of the Vampires. 2007. 284p. (YA). per. 17.95 (***978-0-595-42014-8(1)***) iUniverse, Inc.
Patrick, James. Osmosis Jones. novel ed. 2001. (Illus.). 112p. (J). (gr. 4-7). pap. 4.99 (978-0-439-26090-9(6)) Scholastic, Inc.
—Osmosis Jones: Graphic Novel. 2001. (Illus.). 48p. (J). (gr. 4-7). pap. 5.99 (978-0-439-24997-3(X)) Scholastic, Inc.
—Osmosis Jones: Graphic Novel. 2001. (J). (978-0-606-21956-3(0)) Tandem Library Bks.
Patrick, James & Chapman, Vera. Quest for Camelot. deluxe ed. 1998. (Quest for Camelot Ser.). (Illus.). 64p. (J). (gr. k-3). pap. 5.98 (978-0-590-12060-9(3)) Scholastic, Inc.
Patten, Laurien. The Left Hand of Aneryn. Date not set. (Illus.). 352p. (YA). (978-1-885173-95-9(4)) Write Way Publishing.
Patterson, Don. Dawson's Down! Parenteau, Mary, ed. Schug, Sonny, illus. 2000. (Tales of the R. A. F. Ser.). 98p. (J). (gr. 3-7). per. 7.95 (978-1-929031-36-8(X)) Hindsight, Ltd.
—Night Mission. Parenteau, Mary, ed. Schug, Sonny, illus. 2001. (Tales of the R. A. F. Ser. : Bk. 5). 98p. (J). (gr. 3 up). per. 7.95 (978-1-929031-27-6(0)) Hindsight, Ltd.
Patterson, James. The Angel Experiment. (Maximum Ride Ser.: No. 1). 2005. 432p. (YA). (gr. 5-17). 16.99 (978-0-316-15556-4(X)); 2006. 464p. (gr. 8-17). reprint ed. mass mkt. 6.99 (978-0-446-61779-6(2)) Little Brown & Co.
—The Angel Experiment. 2nd rev. ed. 2007. (Maximum Ride Ser.: No. 1). 464p. (YA). (gr. 4-7). pap. 7.99 (***978-0-316-06795-9(4)***) Little, Brown Bks. for Young Readers.
—The Angel Experiment. l.t. ed. 2006. (Maximum Ride Ser.: No. 1). 495p. 23.95 (978-0-7862-8292-0(4)) Thorndike Pr.
—Black Friday. 2000. (gr. 7-12). lib. bdg. 16.45 (978-0-613-27743-3(0)) Tandem Library Bks.
—Saving the World & Other Extreme Sports. 3rd ed. 2008. (Maximum Ride Novel Ser.). 432p. mass mkt. 7.99 (***978-0-446-19404-4(2)***); 2007. (Maximum Ride Ser.: No. 3). 416p. (J). (gr. 5 up). 16.99 (***978-0-316-15560-1(8)***) Little, Brown Bks. for Young Readers.
Patterson, James. School's Out - Forever. 2nd ed. 2006. (Maximum Ride Ser.: No. 2). 416p. (J). (gr. 5-17). 16.99 (978-0-316-15559-5(4)) Little Brown & Co.
—School's Out - Forever. 2nd ed. 2007. (Maximum Ride Ser.: No. 2). (YA). 368p. mass mkt. 6.99 (***978-0-446-61889-2(6)***); 448p. (gr. 7-17). pap. 7.99 (***978-0-316-06796-6(2)***) Little, Brown Bks. for Young Readers.
Patton, Rick E. The Adventures of Joey Panda: Crisis in Panda Valley. 2002. 200p. pap. 13.95 (978-0-595-20528-8(3) , Writers Club Pr.) iUniverse, Inc.
—Mythenea Awakens: The Adventure Begins. 2002. 114p. pap. 9.95 (978-0-595-26078-2(0) , Writers Club Pr.) iUniverse, Inc.
—The Warlock Crystal: An Unexpected Journey. 2002. 116p. pap. 9.95 (978-0-595-26076-8(4) , Writers Club Pr.) iUniverse, Inc.
—Warlock Crystal: An Unexpected Journey. 2002. lib. bdg. 18.75 (978-0-613-81385-3(5)) Tandem Library Bks.
Pattou, Edith. Fire Arrow: The Second Song of Eirren. 2005. (Illus.). 348p. (J). (gr. 7-12). pap. 7.95 (978-0-15-205530-1(4) , Magic Carpet Bks.) Harcourt Children's Bks.
Paul, Eric. Lemons to Lemonade. 2005. 108p. pap. 16.95 (978-1-4137-6921-0(7)) PublishAmerica, Inc.
Paul Ponderosa. 2005. 60p. (J). per. 9.95 (978-1-933290-91-1(9)) Tate Publishing & Enterprises, L.L.C.
Paulding, James Kirke. Westward Ho! 2004. reprint ed. pap. 26.95 (978-1-4191-9343-9(0)); pap. 1.99 (978-1-4192-9343-6(5)) Kessinger Publishing, LLC.
Paulsen, Gary. Brian's Hunt. 2003. 112p. (YA). (gr. 5). 14.95 (978-0-385-74647-2(4)); lib. bdg. 16.99 (978-0-385-90882-5(2)) Random Hse. Children's Bks. (Lamb, Wendy).
—Brian's Return. (J). (gr. 5-9). 1999. 128p. 15.95 (978-0-385-32500-4(2) , Delacorte Bks. for Young Readers); 2001. 144p. reprint ed. pap. 5.99 (978-0-440-41379-0(6) , Laurel Leaf) Random Hse. Children's Bks.
—Captive! Gary Paulsen World of Adventure. 2001. 68p. (gr. 3-7). pap. 12.00 (978-0-375-89510-4(8) , Yearling) Random Hse. Children's Bks.
—Dogsong. 1999. (YA). 9.95 (978-1-56137-342-0(7)) Novel Units, Inc.
—Dogsong. 2000. 192p. (YA). (gr. 7 up). 17.99 (978-0-689-83960-3(X) , Atheneum/Richard Jackson Bks.) Simon & Schuster Children's Publishing.
—Dogsong. 1999. (J). 11.64 (978-0-606-16328-6(X)) Tandem Library Bks.
—Dogsong. l.t. ed. 2000. (Illus.). 184p. (J). (gr. 8-12). 21.95 (978-0-7862-2845-4(8)) Thorndike Pr.
—The Legend of Bass Reeves. 2006. 160p. (YA). (gr. 7). lib. bdg. 17.99 (978-0-385-90898-6(9) , Lamb, Wendy) Random Hse. Children's Bks.
—Literature Guide: Hatchet. 1999. (Illus.). 16p. (J). pap. 3.95 (978-0-590-38924-2(6)) Scholastic, Inc.
—The River. unabr. ed. 2004. (Middle Grade Cassette Librariestm Ser.). 132p. (J). (gr. 5-9). pap. 29.00 incl. audio (978-0-8072-8704-0(0) , S YA 241 SP, Listening Library) Random Hse. Audio Publishing Group.
—The Schernoff Discoveries. 1998. 112p. (gr. 5-9). 4.99 (978-0-440-41463-6(6) , Yearling) Random Hse. Children's Bks.
—Tucket's Ride. 1998. (Tucket Adventures Ser.: Vol. 3). (Illus.). 112p. (gr. 3-7). reprint ed. 5.50 (978-0-440-41147-5(5) , Yearling) Random Hse. Children's Bks.
—Tucket's Ride, 3. 1998. (Tucket Adventures Ser.). (J). (978-0-606-13877-2(3)) Tandem Library Bks.
—Tucket's Travels Bks.1-5: Francis Tucket's Adventures in the West, 1847-1849, Bks. 1-5. 2003. 560p. (YA). (gr. 4-7). pap. 7.50 (978-0-440-41967-9(0) , Yearling) Random Hse. Children's Bks.
—The White Fox Chronicles. 2002. 288p. (YA). (gr. 5-9). mass mkt. 5.99 (978-0-440-41248-9(X) , Laurel Leaf) Random Hse. Children's Bks.
—The Winter Room. 2001. pap., tchr. ed., wbk. ed. (978-1-56137-596-7(9)) Novel Units, Inc.
—World of Adventure Omni, Vol. 2. 2006. 208p. (J). (gr. 3-7). 5.99 (978-0-440-42123-8(3) , Yearling) Random Hse. Children's Bks.
Paulsen, Gary & Roberts, Esyllt Nest. Craig y Diafol. 2005. (WEL.). 62p. (978-0-86381-684-0(3)) Gwasg Carreg Gwalch.
—Plygu Amser. 2005. (WEL.). 77p. (978-0-86381-683-3(5)) Gwasg Carreg Gwalch.
Paulsen, Gary, et al. Parasiwt! 2005. (WEL.). 60p. (978-0-86381-685-7(1)) Gwasg Carreg Gwalch.
Paulson, Michael William. The Baker Street Bunch & the Missing Bracelet Mystery. 2005. (Illus.). (J). per. (978-0-9754241-2-4(2)) MiMar Publishing.
Pavelka, Patricia. The Adventures of Victor. 2003. (Illus.). 32p. (J). per. 7.99 (978-0-9722918-1-1(4)) Husky Trail Pr. LLC.
Pavelka, Pavelka. Foodle. 2004. (Illus.). 32p. (J). per. 7.99 (978-0-9722918-2-8(2)) Husky Trail Pr. LLC.
Pavlova, Elena. Adventures at Tall Oaks: New Friends. 2004. (Illus.). 80p. (J). 19.95 (978-0-9755839-0-6(5)) Read 2 Children.
Payne, Raymond. Shelter from the Storm. rev. ed. 2004. 144p. (YA). pap. 9.95 (978-0-9740552-1-3(2)) Harbourside Pr.
Payson, Lieutenent H. The Boy Scouts at the Panama Canal. 2005. reprint ed. pap. 30.95 (978-1-4179-2457-8(8)) Kessinger Publishing, LLC.
Pean, Stanley. Le Temps s'Enfuit. 2000. (Roman Plus Ser.). (Illus.). 160p. (YA). (gr. 8 up). pap. (978-2-89021-350-0(1)) Diffusion du livre Mirabel.
Pearce, Jacqueline. Emily's Dream. 2005. (Orca Young Readers Ser.: Sequel to Discovering Emily). (Illus.). 128p. (J). (gr. 3-6). pap. 5.95 (978-1-55143-368-4(0)) Orca Bk. Pubs. USA.
Pearce, Jonathan. Nobody's Fault: Surprises from the Earth & the Heart. 2006. 234p. (YA). per. (978-0-9765479-3-8(7)) Balona Bks.
Pearce, Philippa. The Battle of Bubble & Squeak. Baker, Alan, illus. l.t. ed. 1999. 112p. (J). pap. (978-0-7540-6059-8(4) , CLP 276) BBC Audio.
Pearson, Susan. Hooray for Feet! 2005. (Illus.). 36p. (J). 12.95 (978-1-59354-093-7(0)) Blue Apple Bks.
Peck, Lisa J. CTR Club Adventure Series: (Four-book Set), 4 bks. 2005. (J). pap. 24.95 (***978-0-9749241-9-9(9)***) Golden Wings Enterprises.
Pecos Bill. 1999. (J). 9.95 (978-1-56137-333-8(8)) Novel Units, Inc.
Pederson, Katie. The Point of No Return. 2006. 304p. pap. 24.95 (978-1-4137-9945-3(0)) PublishAmerica, Inc.
Peebles, Joseph. The Stickman & the Crow. 2004. (ENG.). (YA). 10.95 (978-0-9644758-4-7(7)) Peebco Publishing Hse., The.
Peek-a-Boo, Hulk. 2003. (J). per. (978-1-57657-816-2(X)) Paradise Pr., Inc.
Peel, John. Book of Magic, Vol. 3. Karre, Andrew, ed. 2004. (Diadem Worlds of Magic Ser.). 208p. pap. 4.99 (978-0-7387-0615-3(9)) Llewellyn Pubns.
—Book of Signs, Vol. 2. Karre, Andrew, ed. 2004. (Diadem Worlds of Magic Ser.). (Illus.). 208p. pap. 5.99 (978-0-7387-0616-0(7)) Llewellyn Pubns.
—Doomsday. 1999. (Twenty Ninety-Nine Ser.: Bk. 1). 192p. (J). (gr. 3-7). pap. 4.99 (978-0-439-06030-1(3)) Scholastic, Inc.
—Double Disaster! Gurney, John Steven, illus. 2001. (Magical States of America Ser.: Vol. 3). 176p. (J). pap. 9.95 (978-0-7434-1764-8(X) , Aladdin) Simon & Schuster Children's Publishing.
—The Innocent. 1998. (Outer Limits Ser.: No. 6). (J). (gr. 4-7). (978-0-606-13690-7(8)) Tandem Library Bks.
—The Invaders. 1998. (Outer Limits Ser.: No. 5). (J). (gr. 4-7). (978-0-606-13689-1(4)) Tandem Library Bks.
Peep for Keeps. 2005. 43p. (J). 3.99 (978-0-9763213-4-7(3)) OHC Group LLC.
Peirce-Bale, Mary. Wilma Wombat's Trek to Back of Beyond. 2006. (J). 9.90 (978-0-9773990-4-8(4)) Mother's Hse. Publishing.
Pelelo-Ray, Sam. Athenrei. 2006. 56p. pap. 12.95 (978-1-4137-9946-0(9)) PublishAmerica, Inc.
Pelham, David. Trail: A Classic Collectible Pop-up. Pelham, David, illus. 2007. 12p. (J). (ps). 26.99 (***978-1-4169-4894-0(5)***, Little Simon) Simon & Schuster Children's Publishing.
Pella, Judith & Peterson, T. Ribbons of Steel, 3 vols., Vols. 1-3. 1998. (Ribbons of Steel Ser.). (J). pap. 38.99 (978-0-7642-8309-3(X) , 258309) Bethany Hse. Pubs.
Penn, Audrey. Blackbeard & the Sandstone Pillar: When Lightning Strikes. Howard, Philip, illus. 2007. 400p. (gr. 3-7). 15.95 (***978-1-933718-08-8(0)***) Tanglewood Pr.
—Mystery at Blackbeard's Cove. 2006. (Illus.). 200p. (J). 14.95 (978-0-9749303-1-2(8)) American Media Intl.
—Mystery at Blackbeard's Cove. 2007. 347p. pap. 7.95 (***978-1-933718-09-5(9)***) Tanglewood Pr.
Pennell, Kathleen. Reflecto Man. Pennell, Lauren, illus. 2001. (Pony Investigators Ser.: No. 2). 95p. (J). (gr. 2-5). pap. 5.95 (978-1-930353-34-3(0)) Masthof Pr.
Penner, Fred. Proud. Bolling, Vickey, illus. 2001. 32p. (J). (ps). pap. 4.95 (978-1-55285-274-3(1)) Whitecap Bks., Ltd. CAN. *Dist:* Firefly Bks., Ltd.
Pennington, Kate. Nightingale's Song. 2007. 284p. (YA). (gr. 7 up). pap. 9.95 (***978-0-340-87875-0(4)***) Hodder Children's Division GBR. *Dist:* Independent Pubs. Group.
Pennypacker, Sara. Stuart's Cape. Matje, Martin, illus. 2004. 64p. (J). (ps-3). reprint ed. pap. 3.99 (978-0-439-30181-7(5) , Scholastic Paperbacks) Scholastic, Inc.
Penrose, Margaret. Dorothy Dale: A Girl of To-day. 2006. 152p. pap. 11.99 (978-1-4264-1944-7(9)) BiblioBazaar.
—Dorothy Dale (a Girl of to-Day) 2006. 63.99 (***978-1-4280-1166-3(8)***); pap. 56.99 (***978-1-4280-1169-4(2)***) IndyPublish.com.
—The Motor Girls. 2006. 152p. pap. 11.99 (978-1-4264-1903-4(1)) BiblioBazaar.
—The Motor Girls. 2004. reprint ed. pap. 21.95 (978-1-4191-7466-7(5)); pap. 1.99 (978-1-4192-7466-4(X)) Kessinger Publishing, LLC.
—The Motor Girls on Cedar Lake, or the He. 2006. 63.99 (***978-1-4219-9401-7(1)***); pap. 56.99 (***978-1-4219-9422-2(4)***) IndyPublish.com.
Penrose, Margaret. The Motor Girls on Waters Blue. rev. ed. 2006. 228p. 27.95 (978-1-4218-1802-3(7)); pap. 12.95 (978-1-4218-1902-0(3)) 1st World Publishing, Inc. (1st World Library - Literary Society).
—The Motor Girls on Waters Blue. 2006. 164p. pap. 11.99 (978-1-4264-2184-6(2)) BiblioBazaar.
—The Motor Girls on Waters Blue. 2004. reprint ed. pap. 22.95 (978-1-4191-7467-4(3)); pap. 1.99 (978-1-4192-7467-1(8)) Kessinger Publishing, LLC.
Peoples, Camette. Thomas' Dinosaur Days; Thomas' Beach Days; Thomas' Trip to Europe, 3 vols., 3 volume set. Samuel, Arthur, illus. 2002. (Thomas' Ser.: 3). (ENG.). 17p. (J). (ps-8). lib. bdg. 7.00 (978-0-9722724-1-4(0)) Blackfoot Burkino Cherokee Publishing.
Pepper, Sly. Dugan Peckles Through the Manhole. 2004. 190p. (gr. 4-6). pap. 5.99 (978-0-9747668-0-5(1)) Mind-Maze Publishing Co.
Percy, Carrie. Ridley Bluefox & the Flying Fish of Fortune Falls. 2007. 96p. (J). (gr. 2-5). pap. (978-1-897073-59-9(3)) Lobster Pr.
Percy, Richard & Baudet. The Rescue of Maid Marian. 1999. 128p. (J). pap. 7.99 (978-0-233-99514-4(5)) Andre Deutsch GBR. *Dist:* Independent Pubs. Group.
—The Silver Arrow. (Illus.). 128p. (J). pap. 7.95 (978-0-233-99516-8(1)) Andre Deutsch GBR. *Dist:* Trafalgar Square Publishing.
—The Tresure Chest: Adventures of Young Robin. 1999. 128p. (J). pap. 7.99 (978-0-233-99515-1(3)) Andre Deutsch GBR. *Dist:* Independent Pubs. Group.
Pereira, William. The Adventures of LC, the Lucky Calf. Bowlsby, Tina Marie, illus. 2005. (J). 18.95 (978-0-9773133-0-3(1)) Little Tule Bks.
Perera, Hilda. Mumu. (SPA.). (YA). (gr. 5-8). 128p. 8.95 (978-84-216-1207-1(7) , BU3780); 100p. (978-84-216-2557-6(8) , BU1696); 64p. 8.76 (978-84-216-1611-6(0) , BU4757) Bruño, Editorial ESP. *Dist:* Lectorum Pubns., Inc.
Peretti, Frank. Deadly Curse of Toco Rey: Cooper Kids #6. Life Publishers International, tr. from ENG. 2005. (RUS., Illus.). 156p. (J). (978-0-7361-0347-3(3)) Life Pubs. International.
Peretti, Frank E. The Cooper Kids Adventure Series. 2004. (Cooper Kids Adventure Ser.). (gr. 5-7). 23.96 (978-0-89107-901-9(7)) Crossway Bks.
—Cooper Kids Adventure Series, 4 vols. 2005. 23.96 (978-1-58134-691-6(3) , Crossway Bibles) Crossway Bks.
—The Door in the Dragon's Throat. 2005. (Cooper Kids Adventure Ser.: Vol. 1). 128p. (gr. 3-6). pap. 5.99 (978-1-58134-618-3(2) , Crossway Bibles) Crossway Bks.
—Escape from the Island of Aquarius, Vol. 2. 2005. (Cooper Kids Adventure Ser.: Vol. 2). 160p. pap. 5.99 (978-1-58134-619-0(0) , Crossway Bibles) Crossway Bks.
—The Tombs of Anak. 2004. (Cooper Kids Adventure Ser.: No. 3). 144p. (gr. 4-7). 5.99 (978-0-89107-593-6(3)) Crossway Bks.
—The Tombs of Anak. Life Publishers International Staff, tr. 1999. (Cooper Kids Adventure Ser.: Vol. 4). (RUS., Illus.). 206p. (J). (gr. 3-12). pap. (978-0-7361-0127-1(6)) Life Pubs. International.
—Trapped at the Bottom of the Sea. 144p. 2004. (Cooper Kids Adventures Ser.: No. 4). (gr. 4-7). 5.99 (978-0-89107-594-3(1)); Vol. 4. 2005. (Cooper Kids Adventure Ser.: Vol. 4). (gr. 3-6). pap. 5.99 (978-1-58134-621-3(2) , Crossway Bibles) Crossway Bks.
—Trapped at the Bottom of the Sea: Russian Language Edition. Life Publishers International Staff, tr. 1999. (Cooper Kids Adventure Ser.: Vol. 3). (RUS., Illus.). 206p. (J). (gr. 3-12). pap. (978-0-7361-0126-4(8)) Life Pubs. International.
Perez Lugin, Alejandro. La Casa de la Troya Level 3. 1998. (SPA.). (gr. 7-12). lib. bdg. 14.10 (978-0-613-80657-2(3)) Tandem Library Bks.
Perkins, Lucy Fitch. Eskimo Twins. 2006. 62.99 (***978-1-4280-3721-2(7)***); pap. 55.99 (***978-1-4280-3694-9(6)***) IndyPublish.com.
Perrault, Charles. Pulgarcito. 2006. Tr. of Tom Thumb. (SPA., Illus.). 40p. (J). 14.95 (978-84-9801-035-0(7)) Blume ESP. *Dist:* Independent Pubs. Group.
Perry, Caroline. Johnny's Real Adventure. 2004. 48p. pap. 12.95 (978-1-4137-5021-8(4)) PublishAmerica, Inc.
Perry, Dennis. Yakabou Must Choose: An African Adventure for Boys & Girls. 2004. 108p. (YA). pap. 10.95 (978-0-7414-1766-4(9)) Infinity Publishing.
Perry, Holly Lynn. Spinner's Mystic Travels: Lost in the Black Forest. 2003. pap. 9.00 (978-0-8059-6291-8(3)) Dorrance Publishing Co., Inc.
Perry, M. LaVora. Taneesha's Treasures of the Heart. 2006. 56p. pap. 5.65 (978-0-9759251-9-5(9)) Forest Hill Publishing, LLC.
Perry, Shelly. Duckling's First Adventure. Loebel, Bonnie, illus. 2006. (ENG.). 56p. (J). per. 9.95 (978-0-9787740-3-5(5)) Peppertree Pr., The.
Peter & the Wolf. 2004. (Illus.). (J). (978-1-84458-040-8(7)) Chrysalis Children's Bks.
Peter Pan. 2003. (Illus.). 12.99 (978-0-7868-3479-2(X)) Disney Pr.
Peter Piper: 6 Small Books. (gr. k-2). 23.00 (978-0-7635-8495-5(9)) Rigby Education.
Peters, Elizabeth, pseud. The Falcon at the Portal. 2000. 450p. (gr. 7-12). per. 15.90 (978-0-613-25117-4(2)) Tandem Library Bks.
Petersen, P. J. Rising Water. 2003. (Illus.). 128p. (J). pap. 4.99 (978-0-689-86356-1(X) , Aladdin) Simon & Schuster Children's Publishing.

A
B

—White Water. 1999. (978-0-606-16710-9(2)) Tandem Library Bks.

Peterson, Jim. Kittens in the Mall. 2006. 76p. pap. 14.95 (978-1-4241-2604-0(5)) PublishAmerica, Inc.

Peterson, Ruth. Its Time for Bed Stephanie... but First. 2005. (J). per. (978-1-932721-64-5(9)) My Heart Yours Publishing.

Peterson, Sara Budinger. The Journey of Perm. Kaufman, Mary Bee, illus. 2004. 96p. pap. 11.95 (978-0-9665282-3-7(9)) Saranjon Publishing.

Peterson, Scott. Batman: The Story of Batman. 2006. (Scholastic Reader Ser.). (Illus.). 40p. (J). pap. 3.99 (978-0-439-47104-6(4) , Cartwheel Bks.) Scholastic, Inc.

—Batman Beyond: New Hero in Town. Kruse, Brandon et al, illus. 2000. (Pictureback Ser.). 24p. (J). (ps-3). pap. 3.99 (978-0-375-80653-7(9) , Random Hse. Bks. for Young Readers) Random Hse. Children's Bks.

—Blackout! Spaziante, Patrick, illus. 2005. (Teenage Mutant Ninja Turtles Ser.). 24p. (J). pap. 3.99 (978-0-689-87329-4(8) , Simon Spotlight) Simon & Schuster Children's Publishing.

—New Hero in Town. 2000. (gr. k-3). lib. bdg. 10.95 (978-0-613-32879-1(5)) Tandem Library Bks.

—Royally Enchanted Cartoon Tales. 4th rev. ed. 2006. (Disney Princess Ser.: Vol. 44). (Illus.). 192p. (gr. 1-5). 14.99 (978-0-7868-3715-1(2)) Disney Pr.

Petri, Michelle. The Fvantom: Omegapocalypse. 2007. 212p. per. 14.95 (*978-0-595-45723-6(1)) iUniverse, Inc.

Petrie, Glen. Lucy & the Pirates. Harrison, Matilda, illus. 32p. (J). (gr. k-5). 2001. pap. (978-1-896580-38-8(6)); 2000. (978-1-896580-02-9(5)) Tradewind Bks.

Petruccio, Steven James. Tarzan Sticker Activity Book. 1999. (Dover Little Activity Bks.). (Illus.). 4p. (J). act. bk. ed. 1.00 (978-0-486-40933-7(3)) Dover Pubns., Inc.

Petrucha, Stefan. BlindSighted. 2006. (Timetripper Ser.). 240p. (YA). (gr. 7-12). mass mkt. 5.99 (978-1-59514-079-1(4) , Razorbill) Penguin Group (USA) Inc.

—The Charmed Bracelet. Ross, Vaughn, illus. 2006. (Nancy Drew Ser.). 96p. (J). rev. ed. 12.95 (978-1-59707-037-9(8)); 7th rev. ed. pap. 7.95 (978-1-59707-036-2(X)) Papercutz.

Petrucha, Stefan & Murase, Sho. Mr. Cheeters Is Missing. 6th rev. ed. 2006. (Nancy Drew Ser.: No. 6). (Illus.). 96p. (J). 12.95 (978-1-59707-031-7(9)) Papercutz.

Pettee, Sandra. Imagination. Com. 2005. 48p. pap. 12.95 (978-1-4137-7124-4(6)) PublishAmerica, Inc.

Petty, Kate. The Nightspinners. Smith, Mary Claire, illus. 2004. 32p. (J). pap. 8.99 (978-1-84255-105-9(1)) Dolphin Paperbacks GBR. *Dist:* Trafalgar Square Publishing.

Pfeffer, Wendy. Light So Bright. Date not set. (J). pap. 4.99 (978-0-06-440924-7(4) , Harper Trophy); 40p. lib. bdg. 16.89 (978-0-06-029122-8(2)) HarperCollins Pubs.

Pfister, Marcus. The Rainbow Fish. Pfister, Marcus, illus. ed. 2000. (Rainbow Fish Ser.). (Illus.). 32p. (J). (ps-3). 8.95 (978-0-7358-1232-1(2)) North-South Bks., Inc.

—Rainbow Fish Finds His Way. James, J. Alison, tr. from GER. 2006. (Illus.). 32p. (J). 18.95 (978-0-7358-2084-5(8)) North-South Bks., Inc.

—Rainbow Fish Finds His Way. 2006. (Illus.). 32p. (J). 18.88 (978-0-7358-2085-2(6)) North-South Bks., Inc.

Pfitsch, Patricia Curtis. Riding the Flume. 2004. (Illus.). 240p. (J). pap. 4.99 (978-0-689-86692-0(5) , Aladdin) Simon & Schuster Children's Publishing.

Pharaohs. (Awesome Adventures Ser.). 16p. (J). (978-2-7643-0166-1(9)) Phidal Publishing, Inc./Editions Phidal, Inc.

Philbrick, Rodman. Freak the Mighty. 169p. (J). pap. 4.99 (978-0-8072-1521-0(X)); 1998. (gr. 7 up). pap. 29.00 incl. audio (978-0-8072-7982-3(X) , YA959SP) Random Hse. Audio Publishing Group. (Listening Library).

—Freak the Mighty. (Scholastic Signature Ser.). 2001. 176p. (gr. 5-9). 5.99 (978-0-439-28606-0(9)); 1998. (Illus.). 169p. (YA). (gr. 7-12). pap. 4.50 (978-0-590-11022-8(5)) Scholastic, Inc.

—Freak the Mighty. 2001. (gr. 3-6). lib. bdg. 13.00 (978-0-613-36061-6(3)) Tandem Library Bks.

—Max the Mighty. 1998. 176p. (J). (gr. 7-12). pap. 5.99 (978-0-590-57964-3(9)) Scholastic, Inc.

Philbrick, Rodman, et al. Abduction. 1998. 320p. (J). (gr. 6 up). pap. 5.99 (978-0-590-34808-9(6) , 893382) Scholastic, Inc.

Philipson, Sandra. Max's Wild Goose Chase. Takatch, Robert, illus. 1999. (J). (gr. k-4). 17.95 (978-1-929821-01-3(8)) Chagrin River Publishing Co.

The Phillie Phanatic's Phantastic Journey. 2005. (J). (978-0-9705804-9-8(5)) Middle Atlantic Pr.

Phillips, Don. I, Tutus: Book One: the Son of Heaven. 2005. 263p. pap. 21.95 (978-1-4137-5932-7(7)) PublishAmerica, Inc.

Phillips, Terrie. The Ski Trip. 2006. (Illus.). 38p. (J). lib. bdg. 12.95 (*978-0-9789449-0-2(9)) Tbooks Publishing Co.

Philpot, Graham, illus. Hansel & Gretel. 2007. (First Fairy Tales Ser.). 31p. (J). (*978-1-59771-075-6(X)) Sea-To-Sea Pubns.

Phleger, Marjorie. Pilot Down, Presumed Dead. 206p. (J). (gr. 5-6). pap. 5.95 (978-0-8072-1426-8(4)) Random Hse. Audio Publishing Group.

Photo Novel. 2007. (Transformers Ser.). 96p. (J). (gr. 2-5). pap. 7.99 (*978-0-06-088805-3(9) , Harper Entertainment) HarperCollins Pubs.

Picard, Anne M. Peace & Pancakes. 2006. 48p. bds. 25.00 (978-1-59298-149-6(6)) Beaver's Pond Pr., Inc.

Pickup, Michael. The Adventures of Bhakta Musika & the Lion. 1998. (Illus.). 40p. (J). (ps-5). pap. 4.95 (978-81-87216-03-2(4)) Torchlight Publishing.

—The Adventures of Bhakta Musika & the Terrible Snake. 1998. (Illus.). 38p. (J). (ps-5). pap. 4.95 (978-81-87216-08-7(5)) Torchlight Publishing.

Pierce, Tamora. Emperor Mage. 2003. (Immortals Ser.: No. 3). (Illus.). 320p. (YA). 10.95 (978-0-689-85613-6(X) , Atheneum) Simon & Schuster Children's Publishing.

—Emperor Mage. 2002. (Immortals Ser.: No. 3). 20.50 (978-0-8446-7227-4(0)) Smith, Peter Pub., Inc.

—First Test. 2004. (Protector of the Small Ser.: No. 1). 240p. (YA). (gr. 7). pap. 8.95 (978-0-375-82905-5(9) , Random Hse. Bks. for Young Readers) Random Hse. Children's Bks.

—Lady Knight. 2004. (Protector of the Small Ser.: No. 4). 464p. (YA). (gr. 7-12). pap. 8.95 (978-0-375-82908-6(3) , Random Hse. Bks. for Young Readers) Random Hse. Children's Bks.

—Page. 2004. (Protector of the Small Ser.: No. 2). 288p. (YA). (gr. 7). pap. 8.95 (978-0-375-82907-9(5) , Random Hse. Bks. for Young Readers) Random Hse. Children's Bks.

—The Realms of the Gods. (Immortals Ser.: No. 4). (YA). 2005. 368p. mass mkt. 6.99 (978-1-4169-0817-3(X) , Simon Pulse); 2003. (Illus.). 288p. 10.95 (978-0-689-86209-0(1) , Atheneum) Simon & Schuster Children's Publishing.

—Squire. 2004. (Protector of the Small Ser.: No. 3). 432p. (YA). (gr. 7). pap. 8.95 (978-0-375-82906-2(7) , Random Hse. Bks. for Young Readers) Random Hse. Children's Bks.

—Wild Magic. 2003. (Immortals Ser.: No. 1). (Illus.). 320p. (YA). 11.99 (978-0-689-85611-2(3) , Atheneum) Simon & Schuster Children's Publishing.

—Wolf-Speaker. 2005. (Immortals Ser.: No. 2). 368p. (YA). pap. 6.99 (978-1-4169-0344-4(5) , Simon Pulse) Simon & Schuster Children's Publishing.

Pierre, Dana. Mousey, Mousey Finds Cheese? Illustrated by Wellon Pierre. 2006. 17.00 (978-0-8059-9867-2(5)) Dorrance Publishing Co., Inc.

Pierson, Jan. The Carson Kids & the Mystery of Five Finger Island. 2000. (Carson Kids Ser.: Vol. 1). (Illus.). 128p. (gr. 4-7). pap. 9.95 (978-0-595-09075-4(3) , Backinprint.com) iUniverse, Inc.

—Carson Kids & the Shipwreck on Grizzly Island. 2000. (Carson Kids Ser.: Vol. 5). (Illus.). 116p. pap. 9.95 (978-0-595-09072-3(9) , Backinprint.com) iUniverse, Inc.

—The Haunted Horse of Gold Hill (Gold Hill, Nevada) 2006. (Ghostowners Ser.: Vol. 4). (Illus.). 109p. pap. 9.95 (978-0-9721800-3-0(6)) WildWest Publishing.

Pighin, Marcel. Tickles the Bear Goes on a Cruise, 1 bk. Mitchell, Hazel, illus. 2006. 48p. (J). per. 10.49 (*978-0-9776679-7-0(9)) MP2ME Enterprise.

Pike, Christopher, pseud. The Shaktra. 2006. (Alosha Trilogy: No. 2). 336p. (YA). 6.99 (978-0-7653-4961-3(2) , Tor Bks.) Doherty, Tom Assocs., LLC.

Pilgrim, Elza. The China Doll. Segovia, Carmen, illus. 2005. 32p. (J). (gr. k-2). 14.95 (978-1-4027-2223-3(0)) Sterling Publishing Co., Inc.

Pilkey, Dav. The Adventures of Captain Underpants: An Epic Novel. Pilkey, Dav, illus. ed. 2005. (Captain Underpants Ser.: No. 1). (Illus.). 128p. (J). pap. 9.99 (978-0-439-75668-6(5) , Blue Sky Pr., The) Scholastic, Inc.

—The Adventures of Super Diaper Baby. 2003. (Super Diaper Baby Ser.). (SPA., Illus.). 128p. (J). mass mkt. 4.99 (978-0-439-55120-5(X) , Scholastic en Espanol) Scholastic, Inc.

—The Adventures of Super Diaper Baby. 2002. (gr. 3-6). lib. bdg. 13.00 (978-0-613-45569-5(X)) Tandem Library Bks.

—El Capitan Calzoncillos y el Perverso Plan del Profesor Pipicaca. 2002. (Captain Underpants Ser.: No. 4). (SPA.). 160p. (J). (gr. 1-5). pap. 4.99 (978-0-439-41037-3(1) , Scholastic en Espanol) Scholastic, Inc.

—El Capitan Calzoncillos y la Feroz Batalla Contra el Nino Mocobionico Pt. 2: La Venganza de los Ridiculos Mocorobots. Azaola, Miguel, tr. Pilkey, Dav, illus. 2005. (Captain Underpants Ser.: Bk. 7). Orig. Title: Captain Underpants & the Big, Bad Battle of the Bionic Booger Boy, Part 2: The Revenge of the Ridiculous Robo-Boogers. (Illus.). 176p. (J). pap. 4.99 (978-0-439-66205-5(2) , Scholastic en Espanol) Scholastic, Inc.

—Captain Underpants & the Attack of the Talking Toilets. ed. 2005. (Captain Underpants Ser.: No. 2). (Illus.). 140p. (J). lib. bdg. 15.00 (978-1-59054-657-4(1)) Fitzgerald Bks.

—The First Captain Underpants Collection: Captain Underpants & the Perilous Plot of Professor Poopypants; Captain Underpants & the Invasion of the Incredibly Naughty Cafeteria Ladies from Outer Space; Captain Underpants & the Attack of the Talking Toilets; The Adventures of Captain Underpants. 2004. (Captain Underpants Ser.). (Illus.). (J). 19.96 (978-0-439-69862-7(6)) Scholastic, Inc.

—Ricky Ricotta's Giant Robot vs. the Voodoo Vultures from Venus. 2001. (Ricky Ricotta Ser.: No. 3). (gr. 3-6). lib. bdg. 11.80 (978-0-613-32998-9(8)); (J). (ps-3). (978-0-606-20065-3(7)) Tandem Library Bks.

—Ricky Ricotta's Mighty Robot vs. the Voodoo Vultures from Venus. Ontiveros, Martin, illus. 2001. (Ricky Ricotta Ser.: No. 3). 128p. (J). (ps-3). pap. 3.99 (978-0-439-23625-6(8)) Scholastic, Inc.

—The Second Captain Underpants Collection: The Adventures of Super Diaper Baby; Captain Underpants & the Big, Bad Battle of the Bionic Booger Boy Part 2; Captain Underpants & the Big, Bad Battle of the Bionic Booger Boy Part 1; Captain Underpants & the Wrath of the Wicked Wedgie Woman. 2004. (Captain Underpants Ser.). (Illus.). 525p. (J). (gr. 3 up). 19.96 (978-0-439-69054-6(4) , Scholastic Paperbacks) Scholastic, Inc.

Pilkey, Dav, illus. Make Way for Dumb Bunnies. 2002. (Dumb Bunnies Ser.). (J). 20.49 (978-0-7587-3078-7(0)) Book Wholesalers, Inc.

Pilling, Ann. The Year of the Worm. 176p. (J). (gr. 4-7). pap. 7.50 (978-0-7459-4294-0(6) , Lion) Lion Hudson plc GBR. *Dist:* Trafalgar Square Publishing.

Pillsbury, Samuel H. Mission to California. Kantrowitz, David, illus. 2003. (Planet Wampetter Adventure Ser.). 140p. (J). pap. 8.95 (978-1-930085-03-9(6)) Perspective Publishing, Inc.

Pingry, Patricia A. The Story of Joshua & the Bugles of Jericho. Spence, Jim, illus. 2001. (J). (ps-3). pap. 4.95 (978-0-8249-5412-3(2) , Ideals Children's Bks.) Ideals Pubns.

Pini, Wendy & Pini, Richard. Hunters' Dawn. 1998. (Elfquest Ser.: No. 6). pap. 10.99 (978-0-8125-2349-2(0) , Tor Bks.) Doherty, Tom Assocs., LLC.

Pinkney, Brian. Adventures of Sparrow Boy. 2000. (J). 13.79 (978-0-606-19246-0(8)) Tandem Library Bks.

Piper, Deb. Those Sevy Blues, Vol. 2. 2001. 91p. (J). (gr. 5-7). 9.99 (978-0-88092-422-1(5) , 4225) Royal Fireworks Publishing Co.

Pippen, Scottie. Out of the Shadows. 2000. 256p. (J). 22.95 (978-0-7868-6618-2(7)) Disney Pr.

Pirates of the Caribbean: The Black Pearl - a Pop-up Pirate Ship. 2007. 4p. (ps-3). 12.99 (*978-1-4231-0808-5(6)) Disney Pr.

Pirates of the Caribbean: Poster Book. 2007. 24p. (ps-17). pap. 7.99 (*978-1-4231-0793-4(4)) Disney Pr.

Pisarik, Michael E. Loonhaunt. 2006. (J). per. 19.95 (978-1-59872-600-8(5)) Instantpublisher.com.

Pittar, Gill. Milly & Molly Go Camping (book W/dolls) 2006. 28p. pap. (978-1-86972-097-1(0)) Milly Molly Bks.

—Milly, Molly & Beefy. 2004. (Illus.). 28p. (978-1-86972-006-3(7)) Milly Molly Bks.

—Milly, Molly & Betelgeuse. 2004. (Illus.). 28p. (978-1-86972-005-6(9)) Milly Molly Bks.

—Milly, Molly & Taffy Bogle. 2004. (Illus.). 28p. (978-1-86972-001-8(6)) Milly Molly Bks.

—Milly, Molly & the Tree Hut. 2004. 28p. (978-1-86972-028-5(8)) Milly Molly Bks.

—Milly, Molly & What Was That? 2004. 28p. (978-1-86972-031-5(8)) Milly Molly Bks.

Pitzorno, Bianca. La Casa del Arbol. Blake, Quentin, illus. 4th ed. (SPA.). 128p. (J). (978-84-207-7771-9(4)) Grupo Anaya, S.A. ESP. *Dist:* Lectorum Pubns., Inc.

Plant, Timothy. Beyond the Wall. 2005. (Illus.). 192p. pap. 8.95 (978-1-56315-368-6(8)) SterlingHouse Pubs., Inc.

Plante, Raymond. Marilou, Iguana Hunter. Cummins, Sarah, tr. from FRE. Favreau, Marie-Claude, illus. 2001. (First Novels Ser.: Vol. 41). 64p. (gr. 1-5). (J). (978-0-88780-553-0(1)); 4.95 (978-0-88780-552-3(3)) Formac Publishing Co., Ltd. CAN. *Dist:* Casemate Pubs. & Bk. Distributors, LLC.

Plante, Raymond & Delezenne, Christine. Les Rats du Yellow Star. 2001. (Roman Jeunesse Ser.). (FRE., Illus.). 96p. (J). pap. (978-2-89021-480-4(X)) Diffusion du livre Mirabel.

Platt, Kin. The Blue Man. 3rd collector's ed. 2005. (YA). 125.00 (978-1-59885-000-0(8)); 192p. 24.95 (978-1-59885-001-7(6)) Two Lakes Pr., Inc.

Pledger, Maurice. Pledger sounds of wild Nighttime. 2007. (Illus.). 16p. (J). 16.95 (*978-1-59223-471-4(2) , Silver Dolphin Bks.) Advantage Pubs. Group.

Pledger, Maurice, illus. In the Ocean: A Touch-and-Feel Adventure. 2002. (Nature Trails Ser.). 16p. (J). (ps-1). 12.95 (978-1-57145-453-9(5)) Advantage Pubs. Group.

Pliszka, Jodi. Bella & Gizmo's Adventures — Bella Gets A New Sweater. 2005. 32p. (J). per. 18.95 (978-1-933449-26-5(8)) Nightengale Pr.

—Bella & Gizmo's Adventures — the Hairless Sphynx Cats. 2005. (Illus.). 30p. (J). per. 18.95 (978-1-933449-27-2(6)) Nightengale Pr.

Plourde, Josee. Solitaire a l'Infini. 1998. (Roman + Ser.). (Illus.). 160p. (YA). (gr. 8 up). pap. (978-2-89021-329-6(3)) Diffusion du livre Mirabel.

Plourde, Josee & Barrette, Doris. Une Ombre au Tableau. 2003. (Roman Jeunesse Ser.). (FRE., Illus.). 96p. (J). (gr. 4-7). pap. (978-2-89021-616-7(0)) Diffusion du livre Mirabel.

Pociask, Stephen. Black Hole of Sacred Mountain. 2005. 109p. 18.95 (978-0-9763811-0-5(9)) Loquacious Publishing Co.

Poe, Edgar Allan. Las Aventuras de Arthur Gordon Pym. 2000. (SPA., Illus.). 196p. (gr. 4-7). pap. 11.95 (978-0-595-13917-0(5)) iUniverse, Inc.

Pogo the Clown. Along Little Dogie: Harley's Great Adventures. Miller, Richard, illus. 2005. (J). 12.95 (978-0-9755253-3-3(6)) Chiliric Pubns.

—A Brave Little Lion: Harley's Great Adventures. Miller, Richard D., illus. 2005. (J). 12.95 (978-0-9755253-5-7(2)) Chiliric Pubns.

—The Great Blue Sky: Harley's Great Adventures. Miller, Richard D., illus. 2005. (J). 12.95 (978-0-9755253-6-4(0)) Chiliric Pubns.

—A Little Gray Mouse: Harley's Great Adventures. Miller, Richard D., illus. 2005. (J). 12.95 (978-0-9755253-7-1(9)) Chiliric Pubns.

—A Taste of Shrimp: Harley's Great Adventures. Miller, Richard D., illus. 2005. (J). 12.95 (978-0-9755253-4-0(4)) Chiliric Pubns.

Pohlig, Thomas. Tweeker the Speaker. 2006. 22p. 17.01 (978-1-4116-8140-8(1)) Lulu.com.

Poison Patrol: Coloring/Activity Book (English) 2005. (Illus.). (J). (978-1-933934-01-3(8)) Educational Adventures.

Poison Patrol: Coloring/Activity (English) Incl. Posters, Stickers. 2007. (J). (*978-1-933934-53-2(0)) Educational Adventures.

Poison Patrol: Picture Book 8x8. 2007. (J). (*978-1-933934-40-2(9)) Educational Adventures.

Poison Patrol: Picture Book (English) 9x9 with Snipe. 2007. (J). (*978-1-933934-50-1(6)) Educational Adventures.

Poison Safe! Life Safety Coloring/Activity Book. 2007. (Illus.). (J). (*978-1-933934-33-4(6)) Educational Adventures.

Polacco, Patricia. Thunder Cake. Polacco, Patricia, illus. 2002. (Illus.). (J). 14.04 (978-0-7587-3808-0(0)) Book Wholesalers, Inc.

Polak, Monique. No More Pranks. 2006. (Orca Soundings Ser.). 112p. (YA). lib. bdg. 14.95 (978-1-55143-584-8(5)) Orca Bk. Pubs. USA.

Polette, Keith. Paco & the Giant Chile Plant/Paco y las Planta de Chile Gigante. de la Vega, Eida, tr. Dulemba, Elizabeth, illus. 2008. (SPA.). (J). lib. bdg. 16.95 (978-0-9770906-2-4(0)) Raven Tree Pr.

Pollack, P. & Belviso, M. Friends Are Forever. 2006. (Junior Chapter Bk.). (Illus.). 64p. (J). pap. 3.99 (978-0-439-75057-8(1) , Scholastic Paperbacks) Scholastic, Inc.

Pollack, P., et al. Bloo Done It. 2007. (Foster's Home for Imaginary Friends Ser.: No. 3). 48p. (J). pap. 3.99 (978-0-439-89948-2(6)) Scholastic, Inc.

—Too Cool for School. 2007. (Foster's Home for Imaginary Friends Ser.: No. 4). 48p. (J). pap. 3.99 (978-0-439-90371-4(8)) Scholastic, Inc.

Polland, Madeleine A. Beorn the Proud. Drennen, Joan Coppa, illus. 1999. x, 185p. (J). (gr. 5-9). pap. 12.95 (978-1-883937-08-9(6) , 08-6) Bethlehem Bks.

Polston, Deborah Ehler. Eagle Child Series 1-3. 2006. 182p. per. 12.95 (978-1-933290-26-3(9)) Tate Publishing & Enterprises, L.L.C.

Poole, Jack. Las Primas de Loreto. 2000. (SPA.). 120p. (gr. 4-7). pap. 7.95 (978-1-58348-610-8(0)) iUniverse, Inc.

Pope, Elizabeth Marie. The Perilous Gard. 2001. (Illus.). 320p. (J). (gr. 5-9). tchr. ed. 16.00 (978-0-618-16967-2(9)) Houghton Mifflin Co. Trade & Reference Div.

—The Perilous Gard. Cuffari, Richard, illus. 2001. 288p. (YA). (gr. 5-9). tchr. ed. 18.00 (978-0-618-17736-3(1)); pap. 5.95 (978-0-618-15073-1(0)) Houghton Mifflin Co. Trade & Reference Div.

Popper, Garry. High Noon in Didley Pidley. Forshaw, John, illus. 2004. (Bret the Vet Ser.). 40p. 7.00 (978-1-84161-013-9(5)) Ravette Publishing, Ltd. GBR. *Dist:* Parkwest Pubns., Inc.

Porter, Eleanor H. Pollyanna Book & Charm. 2006. (Charming Classics). 272p. (J). pap. 6.99 (978-0-06-088216-7(6) , Harper Festival) HarperCollins Pubs.

Portman, Michelle Eva. Compost, by Gosh! An Adventure with Vermicomposting. Portman, Michelle Eva, illus. l.t. ed. 2004. (Illus.). 42p. 16.95 (978-0-942256-16-1(6)) Flowerfield Enterprises.

Posner-Sanchez, Andrea. Banana Hunt. 2001. (Illus.). 32p. (J). 3.99 (978-0-7364-1174-5(7) , RH/Disney) Random Hse. Children's Bks.

Posner-Sanchez, Andrea. Tales from the Track. Random House Disney Staff, illus. 2007. (Toddler Board Bks.). 30p. (J). (gr. k-k). bds. 11.99 (*978-0-7364-2510-0(1) , RH/Disney) Random Hse. Children's Bks.

Posner-Sanchez, Andrea & Golden Books Staff. Sea Captain Ned. 2004. (Illus.). 24p. (J). (ps-2). pap. 3.99 (978-0-375-82954-3(7) , Golden Bks.) Random Hse. Children's Bks.

Poth, Karen. The Pirates Who Don't Do Anything & Me! 2004. (Illus.). 32p. 7.99 (978-0-310-70725-7(0)) Zonderkidz.

Potter, Alan Mitchell & Williams, Virginia. Hoo-Hoo Hooty-Hoo-Who. 2005. 9.00 (978-0-8059-9807-8(1)) Dorrance Publishing Co., Inc.

Potter, Beatrix. El Conejo Pedro. 2003. (Coleccion el Mundo de Peter Rabbit). (SPA., Illus.). (J). (gr. k-2). pap. (978-950-07-1718-2(2) , SA30684) Editorial Sudamericana S.A. ARG. *Dist:* Lectorum Pubns., Inc.

—The Peter Rabbit & Friends Treasury. Potter, Beatrix, illus. 2006. (Illus.). 240p. (J). (gr. k-4). reprint ed. 20.00 (978-1-4223-5452-0(0)) DIANE Publishing Co.

—The Tale of Peter Rabbit. 2006. (Pop-Up Ser.). (Illus.). 8p. (J). 15.99 (978-0-7232-5704-2(3)) Penguin Group (USA) Inc.

Potter, George. The Wisemen of Bountiful. Harmon, Glenn, illus. 2005. per. 11.99 (978-1-55517-814-7(6) , Cedar Fort, Inc.) Cedar Fort, Inc./CFI Distribution.

Potters, Harry. Tory the Little Dust Devil. 2006. pap. 15.30 (*978-1-84728-571-3(6)) Lulu.com.

Potters, Harry P. Tory. 2006. 85p. 22.96 (978-1-4116-7958-0(X)) Lulu.com.

Poulsen, David A. No Time Like the Past. 3rd rev. ed. 2007. (Salt & Pepper Chronicles). 160p. (gr. 3-7). pap. 6.95 (*978-1-55263-807-1(3)) Key Porter Bks. CAN. *Dist:* Perseus Distribution.

Powell, Jillian. Code Breakers. Savage, Paul, illus. 2006. 40p. (J). (*978-1-59889-182-9(0)) Stone Arch Bks.

The Power of Chocolate. 2005. (YA). (978-0-9771020-0-6(9)) Savas, Bachtsoglou.

The Power of Friendship. 2005. (W. I. T. C. H. Graphic Novels Ser.: Bk. 1). (Illus.). 128p. (gr. 3-7). pap. 4.99 (978-0-7868-3674-1(1) , Volo) Hyperion Bks. for Children.

Power Ranger Operation Overdrive. 2007. 48p. pap. 3.99 (*978-1-4037-3570-6(0)) Dalmatian Pr.

Power Rangers: Super Legends. 2007. 224p. (J). mass mkt. 4.99 (*978-1-4037-3897-4(1)) Dalmatian Pr.

PowerMark Issue 11 Vol. 1, Issue 11: Trojan Horse. 2001. 32p. (J). pap. 2.95 (978-0-9713412-0-3(6)) PowerMark Productions.

PowerMark Issue 12 Vol. 1, Issue 12: Redemption. 2001. 32p. (J). pap. 2.95 (978-0-9713412-1-0(4)) PowerMark Productions.

PowerMark Issue 13 Vol. 1, Issue 13: Standing Tall. 2002. 32p. (J). pap. 2.95 (978-0-9713412-2-7(2)) PowerMark Productions.

Powermark Issue 14 Vol. 2, Issue 14: Sinister Plans. 2002. 32p. (J). pap. 2.95 (978-0-9713412-3-4(0)) PowerMark Productions.

PowerMark Issue 15 Vol. 1, Issue 15: Break Out. 2002. 32p. (J). pap. 2.95 (978-0-9713412-4-1(9)) PowerMark Productions.

PowerMark Issue 16 Vol. 1, Issue 16: Sacrifice. 2002. 32p. (J). pap. 2.95 (978-0-9713412-5-8(7)) PowerMark Productions.

PowerMark Issue 17 Vol. 1, Issue 17: My Brother's Keeper. 2002. 32p. (J). pap. 2.95 (978-0-9713412-6-5(5)) PowerMark Productions.

PowerMark Issue 18 Vol. 2, Issue 18: Playing with Fire. 2002. 32p. (J). pap. 2.95 (978-0-9713412-7-2(3)) PowerMark Productions.

PowerMark Issue 19 Vol. 1, Issue 19: The Den. 2002. 32p. (J). pap. 2.95 (978-0-9713412-8-9(1)) PowerMark Productions.

PowerMark Issue 20 Vol. 1, Issue 20: Redeemer. 2002. 32p. (J). pap. 2.95 (978-0-9713412-9-6(X)) PowerMark Productions.

Powerpuff Girls: A Little Monstrous Problem. 2000. (Golden Super Shape Book Ser.). (Illus.). 24p. (J). (ps-3). pap. 3.29 (978-0-307-13330-4(3) , Golden Bks.) Random Hse. Children's Bks.

Pratcher, Birgit. Matt & Spencer in Their Great Adventur. 2005. 153p. pap. 19.95 (978-1-4137-6638-7(2)) PublishAmerica, Inc.

Pratchett, Terry. A Hat Full of Sky. 2005. 448p. (gr. 7 up). pap. 6.99 (978-0-06-058662-1(1) , Harper Trophy) HarperCollins Pubs.

—Truckers. 2004. (Bromeliad Trilogy Ser.). 288p. (J). (gr. 5 up). reprint ed. pap. 6.99 (978-0-06-009496-6(6) , Harper Trophy) HarperCollins Pubs.

Pratt, Pierre. Marcel et Andre. 2003. (Picture Bks.). (FRE., Illus.). 32p. (J). (ps). (978-2-89021-633-4(0)) Diffusion du livre Mirabel.

Prehistoria. 2005. (Coleccion Las Grandes Aventuras Ser.). (SPA.). (J). 21.95 (978-968-7381-52-7(3)); pap. 17.95 (978-968-7381-48-0(5)) Tecolote, Ediciones, S.A. de C.V. MEX. *Dist:* Iaconi, Mariuccia Bk. Imports.

Preisler, Jerome. Zorro & the Jaguar Warriors. 1998. 224p. mass mkt. 4.99 (978-0-8125-6767-0(6) , Forge Bks.) Doherty, Tom Assocs., LLC.

—Zorro & the Jaguar Warriors. 1998. (J). (978-0-606-13946-5(X)) Tandem Library Bks.

—Zorro & the Shadow Riders. 1998. (978-0-606-13947-2(8)) Tandem Library Bks.

Preller, James. The Case of the Spoiled Rotten Spy. 2007. (Jigsaw Jones Ser.: No. 31). 80p. (J). pap. 3.99 (978-0-439-89623-8(1) , Scholastic Paperbacks) Scholastic, Inc.

Prentice, Amy. Mouser Cats' Story. 2004. reprint ed. pap. 15.95 (978-1-4191-3542-2(2)); pap. 1.99 (978-1-4192-3542-9(7)) Kessinger Publishing, LLC.

Prenzlau & Suttom. The by Times' Kid Sisters: Three-in-One 1-3, 4-6, 7-9, 10-12, 12 vols. 355p. 15.99 (978-1-56871-239-0(1)) Targum Pr., Inc.

Press, Skip. Cliffhanger. Taylor, Marjorie, illus. 1999. (Take Ten Ser.). 47p. (YA). (gr. 4 up). pap. 3.95 (978-1-58659-011-6(1)) Artesian Pr.

—Cliffhanger. 2000. (gr. 5-8). lib. bdg. 11.80 (978-0-613-51204-6(9)) Tandem Library Bks.

Preston, Douglas & Child, Lincoln. The Ice Limit. 2001. (gr. 7-12). lib. bdg. 16.45 (978-0-613-49415-1(6)) Tandem Library Bks.

—Thunderhead. 2000. (gr. 7-12). lib. bdg. 15.90 (978-0-613-28102-7(0)) Tandem Library Bks.

Price & Wilkinson. The Saga of Aslak. 2004. (Illus.). 96p. bds. 8.95 (978-0-7136-4076-2(6)) A & C Black GBR. *Dist:* Consortium Bk. Sales & Distribution.

Price, Iain. Johnny the Pookie. 2005. 155p. (J). (978-1-905203-15-4(2)) Pen Pr. Pubs., Ltd.

Price, Margaret Evans. The Angora Twinnies. Price, Margaret Evans, illus. 2005. (Illus.). 16p. (J). (ps-3). 9.00 (978-1-59583-046-3(4)) Laughing Elephant.

Price, Roger & Stern, Leonard. Mr. Bean's Holiday Mad Libs. 2007. (Mad Libs Ser.). 48p. (J). (gr. 2-5). pap. 3.99 (978-0-8431-2522-1(5) , Price Stern Sloan) Penguin Group (USA) Inc.

Priddy, Roger. Cloth Book Big Rex. rev. ed. 2004. 10p. (J). 8.95 (978-0-312-49260-1(X) , Priddy Bks.) St. Martin's Pr.

Priest, Christopher. Black Panther: The Client. 2001. (gr. 5-8). lib. bdg. 24.55 (978-0-613-53671-4(1)) Tandem Library Bks.

Priest, Nancy. Where Can Bebe Be: The Tale of Bebe's Great Adventures. 2004. (Illus.). 16p. (J). pap. 14.95 (978-1-932373-62-2(4) , Cedar Hill Pr.) Cedar Hill Publishing.

Primavera, Elise. Secret Order Gumm Street Girl, No. 2. 2006. (978-0-06-056949-5(2)); (978-0-06-056950-1(6)) HarperCollins Canada, Ltd.

Prins, Piet. The Search for Sheltie. Kramer, Jaap, illus. 2006. 137p. (J). pap. (978-1-894666-43-5(7)) Inheritance Pubns.

Prior, Natalie Jane. Lily Quench & the Lighthouse of Skellig Mor, Vol. 4. 2004. (Illus.). 160p. (J). (gr. 3-7). pap. 4.99 (978-0-14-240059-3(9) , Puffin) Penguin Group (USA) Inc.

Prior, Natalie Jane & Dawson, Kathy. Lily Quench & the Magician's Pyramid, Vol. 5. 2004. (Illus.). 176p. (Orig.). (J). (gr. 3 up). pap. 4.99 (978-0-14-240163-7(3) , Puffin) Penguin Group (USA) Inc.

Proimos, James. Many Adventures of Johnny Mutton. 2001. (gr. k-3). lib. bdg. 14.15 (978-0-613-35535-3(0)) Tandem Library Bks.

Project-00. 2003. (J). 15.95 (978-0-9743843-0-6(5)) Endeavor Publishing.

Proysen, Alf. Mrs. Pepperpot & the Hidden Treasure. Offen, Hilda, illus. 2007. 32p. pap. 4.99 (***978-0-09-945159-4(X)***) Transworld Publishers Ltd. GBR. *Dist:* Independent Pubs. Group.

Prude, Marsha A. C. C. bee moves to honey town & the adventures of grampa Bumble. 2007. pap. 7.95 (***978-0-533-15345-9(X)***) Vantage Pr., Inc.

Psomas, Paul P. A Boy Named Wolf. 2001. 132p. pap. 10.95 (978-0-595-19827-6(9) , Writers Club Pr.) iUniverse, Inc.

Publishing Company Staff. Scooby-Doo! 2000. (Illus.). (J). pap. 3.99 (978-0-307-44532-2(1) , Golden Bks.) Random Hse. Children's Bks.

Puckett, Annie Marie. Pedro Learns about Salvation. 2006. 56p. per. 9.95 (***978-1-57258-453-2(X)*** , 945-6314) TEACH Services, Inc.

Puebla, Teo, illus. Antonio Machado para Ninos. 2003. (SPA.). 248p. (978-84-305-9532-7(5) , SU30132) Susaeta Ediciones, S.A. ESP. *Dist:* Lectorum Pubns., Inc.

Puffy. 2006. (J). (***978-0-9779521-0-6(X)***) City on a Hill, Inc.

Puffy: The Cloud That Couldn't Rain. 2005. (J). 8.95 (978-0-9755348-0-9(7)) Kids Life Pr.

Pugh, Tracey D. A Show & Tell Lesson. McCracken, Jaime, photos by. l.t. ed. 2006. (Illus.). 32p. (J). 12.95 (978-1-59879-105-1(2)) Lifevest Publishing, Inc.

Pugh, Tracey D. & McCracken, Jaime, photos by. A Show & Tell Lesson. l.t. ed. 2006. (Illus.). 32p. (J). per. 12.95 (978-1-59879-134-1(6)) Lifevest Publishing, Inc.

Pugin-Rodas, M. C. The Eight Ball Club: Ocean of Fire. 2007. (Illus.). 144p. pap. 15.95 (***978-0-9793761-2-2(2)***) ESOL Publishing.

Pullman, Philip. Count Karlstein. Bryan, Diana, illus. 2000. 256p. (YA). (gr. 5-8). 5.99 (978-0-375-80348-2(3) , Yearling) Random Hse. Children's Bks.

—Count Karlstein. 1998. 256p. (J). (gr. 5-8). 17.00 (978-0-679-89255-7(9) , Knopf Bks. for Young Readers) Random Hse. Children's Bks.

—Count Karlstein. 2000. 12.64 (978-0-606-17845-7(7)); (gr. 7-12). lib. bdg. 14.15 (978-0-613-28451-6(8)) Tandem Library Bks.

—The Firework-Maker's Daughter. 1999. 120p. (J). 16.95 (978-0-7540-6055-0(1) , Galaxy Children's Large Print) BBC Audiobooks America.

—The Firework-Maker's Daughter. Gallagher, Susan Saelig, illus. 1999. (J). pap. (978-0-590-12943-5(0) , Levine, Arthur A. Bks.) Scholastic, Inc.

—The Firework-Maker's Daughter. 2001. 11.64 (978-0-606-21186-4(1)) Tandem Library Bks.

—His Dark Materials Omnibus. 2007. (His Dark Materials Ser.: Bks. 1-3). 944p. (YA). (gr. 7-12). pap. 21.99 (***978-0-375-84722-6(7)*** , Knopf Bks. for Young Readers) Random Hse. Children's Bks.

—Once Upon a Time in the North. 2008. 112p. (J). (gr. 7). 12.99 (***978-0-375-84510-9(0)*** , Knopf Bks. for Young Readers) Random Hse. Children's Bks.

—Les Royaumes du Nord. (FRE.). pap. 19.95 (978-2-07-054188-1(6)) Gallimard, Editions FRA. *Dist:* Distribooks, Inc.

—The Scarecrow & His Servant. Bailey, Peter, illus. 240p. (J). (gr. 3-7). 2007. 6.50 (978-0-440-42130-6(6) , Yearling); 2005. 15.95 (978-0-375-81531-7(7) , Knopf Bks. for Young Readers); 2005. lib. bdg. 17.99 (978-0-375-91531-4(1) , Knopf Bks. for Young Readers) Random Hse. Children's Bks.

—The Subtle Knife. (His Dark Materials Ser.: Bk. 2). (YA). (gr. 7-12). 2003. lib. bdg. 15.30 (978-0-613-72255-1(8)); 2002. lib. bdg. 21.05 (978-0-613-71929-2(8)) Tandem Library Bks.

—La Tour des Anges. (FRE.). pap. 19.95 (978-2-07-054189-8(4)) Gallimard, Editions FRA. *Dist:* Distribooks, Inc.

—Yo Era una Rata. Azaola, Miguel, tr. Bailey, Peter, illus. 2001. (Barco de Vapor: No. 22). Orig. Title: I Was a Rat!. (SPA.). 178p. 9.95 (978-84-348-7811-2(9)) SM Ediciones ESP. *Dist:* AIMS International Bks., Inc.

Punnett, Dick. Count the Possums: A Talk-along Book. Punnett, Yvonne, ed. 2nd ed. 2005. (Talk-Along Bks.). (Illus.). 32p. (J). pap. 6.99 (978-0-9657211-4-1(0)) Tomoka Pr.

—Help Jumbo Escape: A Talk-along Book. Dunnington, Tom, illus. 2nd ed. 2005. (Talk-Along Bks.). 32p. (J). pap. 6.99 (978-0-9657211-2-7(4)) Tomoka Pr.

Punter, Russell. Pirate Adv. Fox, Christyan, illus. 2007. 48p. (J). pap. 5.99 (978-0-7945-1447-1(2) , Usborne) EDC Publishing.

Purdie, Keith. Willo. 2005. (Cygnet Young Fiction Ser.). (Illus.). 88p. (Orig.). pap. 13.50 (978-1-920694-53-1(6)) Univ. of Western Australia Pr. AUS. *Dist:* International Specialized Bk. Services.

Purney, Dawn. Lost & Found. 2004. 64p. (YA). per. 3.95 (978-1-56254-822-3(0) , SP8220) Saddleback Educational Publishing.

Puttock, Simon. Horsey. Julian, Russell, illus. 2004. 32p. (J). 17.99 (978-1-4052-1058-4(3)) Egmont Bks., Ltd. GBR. *Dist:* Independent Pubs. Group.

Puzzle Track Staff, ed. Adv with Little Duck. 2007. (Puzzle Track Ser.). 20p. (J). bds. 18.95 (***978-0-7696-5619-9(6)***) School Specialty Publishing.

—Red Car Ride. 2007. (Puzzle Track Ser.). 20p. (J). bds. 18.95 (***978-0-7696-5579-6(3)***) School Specialty Publishing.

Pyle, Howard. The Story of Jack Ballister's Fortunes. 2007. (YA). (***978-0-486-45467-2(3)***) Dover Pubns., Inc.

—Twilight Land. 2006. (ENG.). pap. (***978-1-4068-3431-4(9)***) Echo Library.

Pyle, Howard. Within the Capes. 2004. reprint ed. pap. 27.95 (978-1-4179-3855-1(2)) Kessinger Publishing, LLC.

Pyle, Hugh F. The Crooked Cave Caper! 2000. 159p. (J). (gr. 4-7). pap. 4.95 (978-0-87398-130-9(8)) Sword of the Lord Pubs.

Pyne, Erin A. A Fandom of Magical Proportions: S: an Unauthorized History of the Harry Potter Phenomenon. 2007. (Illus.). 84p. (J). per. 8.36 (***978-0-9788138-8-8(X)***) Nimble Bks. LLC.

Q. T. Pie's Rescue Adventure. 2003. (Illus.). 36p. (J). (ps-6). mass mkt. 4.99 (978-0-9670875-3-5(8) , 313-533-7383) SanPaul Group, LLC, The.

Quattlebaum, Mary. Underground Train. Smith, Cat Bowman, illus. 1999. (J). (ps-ps). lib. bdg. 12.54 (978-0-606-20025-7(8)) Tandem Library Bks.

Quest for God's Hidden Creatures: The Legacy of the Doors. 2006. (J). per. 9.95 (978-0-9777725-0-6(0)) bazow, thomas.

Quest for Gold. 2003. (J). per. (978-1-57657-976-3(X)) Paradise Pr., Inc.

The Quest for Seven Castles. 2006. (J). per. 7.99 (978-0-9785523-1-2(8)) Dunlop, Edward.

Quinn, Zoe. The Caped 6th Grader: Lightning Strikes! 2006. (Illus.). 128p. (J). (gr. 4-7). lib. bdg. 11.99 (978-0-385-90306-6(5) , Yearling) Random Hse. Children's Bks.

—Totally Toxic. 2006. (Caped 6th Grader Ser.). (Illus.). 160p. (J). (gr. 4-7). pap. 4.99 (978-0-440-42080-4(6) , Yearling) Random Hse. Children's Bks.

Quinones, Juan Carlos. The Gang & the Biggest Book in the World. Montanez, Nivea Ortiz, illus. 2004. (Purple Ser.). 48p. (J). (978-1-57581-438-4(2)) Ediciones Santillana, Inc.

—The Gang under the Tree. Montanez, Nivea Ortiz, illus. 2004. (Purple Ser.). (SPA.). 44p. (J). (gr. 3-5). pap. 5.95 (978-1-57581-439-1(0)) Santillana USA Publishing Co., Inc.

—La Pandilla Bajo el Arbol. 2003. (SPA.). (gr. 3-6). lib. bdg. 14.10 (978-0-613-79282-0(3)) Tandem Library Bks.

Quintanilla, Efren. Aventuras de Bartolillo. (SPA.). (J). 7.95 (978-84-241-5634-3(X)) Torres, Eliseo & Sons.

Quisenberry, Stacey. Dinosaur George Pre-hysterical Adventures: What Color Were Dinosaurs? Browning, Suzan, illus. 2007. (J). 3.95 (***978-0-9797304-3-6(0)***) Raining Popcorn Media.

Ra, In-Soo. King of Hell, Vol. 13. Kim, Jae-Hwan, illus. 13th rev. ed. 2006. pap. 9.99 (978-1-59816-061-1(3) , Tokyopop Adult) TOKYOPOP, Inc.

Rabley, Stephen. The Barcelona Game. 2002. (Illus.). 16p. pap. (978-0-582-42771-6(1) , Putnam Juvenile) Penguin Group (USA) Inc.

—The Troy Stone. 2002. (Illus.). 16p. pap. (978-0-582-40287-4(5) , Putnam Juvenile) Penguin Group (USA) Inc.

Raboy, Mac. Mac Raboy's Flash Gordon, Vol. 2. 2003. (Illus.). 256p. (YA). (gr. 8 up). pap. 19.95 (978-1-56971-911-4(X)) Dark Horse Comics.

Race to Moonrise Rev. 2006. 9.95 (978-1-932738-31-5(2)) Western Reflections Publishing Co.

Rackham, Katelyn. The Storyteller. 2007. 275p. pap. 15.95 (***978-0-7414-3845-4(3)***) Infinity Publishing.

Rae, Jaci. Collista's Search for the True Meaning of Christmas. 2007. (Illus.). 59p. per. 14.95 (***978-0-9746229-1-0(5)***) North Shore Records, Inc.

Raffle, Diana. Moondragon. 2006. 161p. pap. 19.95 (978-1-4241-0626-4(5)) PublishAmerica, Inc.

Ragin, M. K. Mildred Row & Improper Bounds. 2006. 185p. pap. 19.95 (978-1-4137-9724-4(5)) PublishAmerica, Inc.

Raicht, Mike. Grotesque Adventure of the Green Goblin! 2006. (Illus.). (J). (gr. 2-6). 21.35 (978-1-59961-020-7(5)) Spotlight.

The Rainbow's End. 2003. 14.95 (978-1-929489-75-6(7)) Platinum Medallion Children's Bks.

Raintree Steck-Vaughn Staff. Knight Moves. 2000. (Adventure Ser.). (Illus.). (J). pap. 3.41 (978-0-8114-9317-8(2)) Steck-Vaughn.

—Road Rally. 2000. (Adventure Ser.). (Illus.). (J). pap. 3.41 (978-0-8114-9314-7(8)) Steck-Vaughn.

—Soaring Summer. 2000. (Adventure Ser.). (Illus.). (J). pap. 3.41 (978-0-8114-9316-1(4)) Steck-Vaughn.

Raintree Steck-Vaughn Staff, ed. Salvaged!, 6 bks., Set. 1998. (Illus.). (gr. 1-6). 89.88 (978-0-8172-4552-8(9)) Raintree.

The Rainy Day Adventure: Third Grade Guided Reading Level O. (On Our Way to English Ser.). (gr. 3 up). 34.50 (978-0-7578-7140-5(2)) Rigby Education.

Ralles, H. J. Keeper of the Island. 2007. (Who? What? When? Where? Ser.). (YA). per. 10.95 (***978-1-929976-39-3(9)*** , TOP) Top Pubns., Ltd.

Ralles, H. J. Keeper of the Realm, Vol. 2. 2003. (Illus.). 248p. (J). pap. 9.95 (978-1-929976-21-8(6)) Top Pubns., Ltd.

Ralph, Brian. Cave-In. 1999. (Illus.). 96p. pap. 12.95 (978-0-9665363-3-1(9)) Highwater Bks.

Ralphson, Harvey G. Boy Scouts in Southern Waters or Spaniar. 2006. 78.99 (***978-1-4280-1931-7(6)***) IndyPublish.com.

Ramblin' Rose: The Porcelain Mines in Russia. 2007. 196p. (YA). pap. 8.99 (***978-0-9776043-7-1(3)***) Aspirations Media, Inc.

Ramblin' Rose: The Wire Forests of Peru. 2007. 200p. (YA). pap. 8.99 (***978-0-9776043-9-5(X)***) Aspirations Media, Inc.

The Rambunctious Tommy Turnpike. 2nd ed. 2005. (J). (978-0-9773760-0-1(1)) Johnson, Anthony.

Rameaka, T. Where's Dorothy? 2005. 73p. pap. 14.95 (978-1-4137-9117-4(4)) PublishAmerica, Inc.

Ramee, De La Louise. Bimbi (Stories for Children) 2006. 62.99 (***978-1-4280-1006-2(8)***); pap. 55.99 (***978-1-4280-1036-9(X)***) IndyPublish.com.

Ramos, Ian. Adventures of the G.C. Boys: The Cure for Death. 2001. 188p. (J). pap. 19.95 (978-1-58851-040-2(9)) PublishAmerica, Inc.

Ramsey, Dave. Dave Ramsey's 6 Kids Books Boxed Set. 2005. (J). 59.99 (978-0-9774895-8-9(2)) Lampo Group Inc., The.

Ramsey, R. M. The Browser Bunch: The Browser Files Presents... the Big Lie. 2006. (J). pap. 8.00 (***978-0-8059-7172-9(6)***) Dorrance Publishing Co., Inc.

Rancourt, Heather & Gauches, Claudia. The Fossibles - Bursting from Extinction to Distinction. 2007. (J). per. 8.85 (***978-0-9702654-4-9(1)***) 360 Marketing, LLC.

Rand, Johnathan. Kreepy Klowns of Kalamazoo. 2000. (Michigan Chillers: Vol. 7). 216p. (YA). pap. 5.99 (978-1-893699-13-7(7)) AudioCraft Publishing, Inc.

—Mayhem on Mackinac Island. 1999. (Michigan Chillers: Vol. 1). 160p. (YA). pap. 5.99 (978-1-893699-05-2(6)) AudioCraft Publishing, Inc.

—Poltergeists of Petoskey. 1999. (Michigan Chillers: Vol. 3). 224p. (J). pap. 5.99 (978-1-893699-08-3(0)) AudioCraft Publishing, Inc.

—Strange Spirits of St. Ignace. 2000. (Michigan Chillers: Vol. 6). 208p. (YA). pap. 5.99 (978-1-893699-11-3(0)) AudioCraft Publishing, Inc.

—Terror Stalks Traverse City. 1999. (Michigan Chillers: Vol. 2). 208p. (J). pap. 5.99 (978-1-893699-07-6(2)) AudioCraft Publishing, Inc.

Rand, Jonathan. The Magical Wading Pool, Freddie Fernortner Bk 7: Fearless First Grader. 2007. pap. 4.99 (***978-1-893699-91-5(9)***) AudioCraft Publishing, Inc.

Randall, Bob. Tracker Tjugingji. 2003. 32p. 22.50 incl. audio compact disk (978-1-86465-030-3(3)) IAD Pr. AUS. *Dist:* International Specialized Bk. Services.

Randall, Homer. Army Boys on Our Doughboys Q. 2006. 62.99 (***978-1-4280-2321-5(6)***) IndyPublish.com.

Randall, Rod. The Mysterious Treasure of the Slimy Sea Cave. 1999. (Heebie Jeebies Ser.: Vol. 3). 144p. (YA). pap. 5.99 (978-0-8054-1000-6(7)) B&H Publishing Grp.

Random House Disney Staff. Battle for the High Seas. 2007. (Illus.). 24p. (J). (gr. k-7). pap. 5.99 (***978-0-7364-2461-5(X)*** , RH/Disney) Random Hse. Children's Bks.

—The Big Blue. 2003. (Illus.). 12p. (J). (ps-2). pap. 6.99 (978-0-7364-2167-6(X) , RH/Disney) Random Hse. Children's Bks.

—The Big Game. 2005. (Illus.). 16p. (J). (ps-2). pap. 3.99 (978-0-7364-2322-9(2) , RH/Disney) Random Hse. Children's Bks.

—Davy Jones's Curse. Disney Storybook Artists Staff, illus. 2006. 32p. (J). (ps-3). pap. 3.99 (978-0-7364-2386-1(9) , Golden/Disney) Random Hse. Children's Bks.

—Dream Dance. 2003. (Disney Princess Ser.). (Illus.). 32p. (J). (ps-3). pap. 4.99 (978-0-7364-2118-8(1) , Golden/Disney) Random Hse. Children's Bks.

—Enchanting Treasures. 2002. (Disney Princess Ser.). (Illus.). 12p. (J). (ps-3). pap. 6.99 (978-0-7364-2050-1(9) , RH/Disney) Random Hse. Children's Bks.

—The Final Showdown. 2007. (Pirates of the Caribbean Ser.: No. 3). (Illus.). 48p. (J). (ps-2). pap. 3.99 (***978-0-7364-2451-6(2)*** , RH/Disney) Random Hse. Children's Bks.

—Finding Nemo. 2004. (Disney Read-Aloud Board Books). (Illus.). 24p. (J). (gr. k-k). bds. 4.99 (978-0-7364-2249-9(8) , RH/Disney) Random Hse. Children's Bks.

—Happy Hugs. Yee, Josie, illus. 2001. (Disney's Winnie the Pooh Ser.). 32p. (J). (gr. k-1). pap. 3.99 (978-0-7364-1136-3(4) , Golden/Disney) Random Hse. Children's Bks.

—Pixar Book Bag. 2006. (Bookbag Ser.). (Illus.). 32p. (J). (ps-2). pap. 4.99 (978-0-7364-2401-1(6) , Golden/Disney) Random Hse. Children's Bks.

—Rogue Robots! 2008. 24p. (J). (ps-2). pap. 3.99 (***978-0-7364-2519-3(5)*** , RH/Disney) Random Hse. Children's Bks.

—Sarge's Boot Camp/Al's Sky-High Adventure. 2008. (Pictureback(R) Ser.). 32p. (J). (ps-2). pap. 4.99 (***978-0-7364-2526-1(8)*** , RH/Disney) Random Hse. Children's Bks.

—Search for Jack Sparrow. Disney Storybook Artists Staff, illus. deluxe ed. 2006. 64p. (J). (ps-3). pap. 3.99 (978-0-7364-2384-7(2) , Golden/Disney) Random Hse. Children's Bks.

—Thunder & Lightning. 2006. (Random House Pictureback Book Ser.). (Illus.). 24p. (J). (ps-2). pap. 3.99 (978-0-7364-2321-2(4) , RH/Disney) Random Hse. Children's Bks.

Random House Disney Staff. Wall-E. 2008. (Read-Aloud Storybook Ser.). 72p. (J). (ps-3). 8.99 (***978-0-7364-2528-5(4)*** , RH/Disney) Random Hse. Children's Bks.

Random House Disney Staff & McVeigh, Mark. Buzz Lightyear vs. Torque: One on One? 2002. (Step into Reading Ser.). (Illus.). 48p. (J). (gr. 1-3). lib. bdg. 11.99 (978-0-7364-8007-9(2) , Random Hse. Bks. for Young Readers) Random Hse. Children's Bks.

Random House Value Publishing Staff & Stevenson, Robert Louis. Treasure Island. 1998. (Children's Classics Ser.). (Illus.). 272p. (J). (gr. 5-9). 5.99 (978-0-517-18963-4(1) , Children's Classics) Random Hse. Value Publishing.

Ranieri, Nik. The Great Elephant. Ranieri, Nik, illus. 2005. (Illus.). 46p. (J). (ps-7). 19.95 (978-1-57921-780-8(X)) WinePress Publishing.

Ransom, Candice. Bones in the Badlands. Call, Greg, illus. 2006. 128p. (J). (gr. 2-4). pap. 4.99 (978-0-7869-4028-8(X) , Mirrorstone) Wizards of the Coast.

Ransom, Candice F. Rescue on the Outer Banks. Ritz, Karen, illus. 2003. (On My Own History Ser.). 48p. (J). (gr. 1-3). pap. 5.95 (978-0-87614-815-0(1) , Carolrhoda Bks.) Lerner Publishing Group.

Ransome, Arthur. Great Northern? 2003. (Swallows & Amazons Ser.). (Illus.). 352p. (J). pap. 14.95 (978-1-56792-259-2(7)) Godine, David R. Pub.

—Missee Lee. 2002. (Swallows & Amazons Ser.). (Illus.). 352p. (J). pap. 14.95 (978-1-56792-196-0(5)) Godine, David R. Pub.

—Swallows & Amazons. 1998. (Swallows & Amazons Ser.). (gr. 3-6). lib. bdg. 24.55 (978-0-613-77196-2(6)) Tandem Library Bks.

Rao, Chatura. Amie & the Chawl of Colour. Pathak, Ashutosh, illus. 2004. 100p. pap. (978-0-14-333592-4(8) , Puffin) Penguin Group (USA) Inc.

Rao, Lisa. Island Adventures. 2007. (Surf's Up Ser.). 32p. (J). pap. 3.99 (***978-0-06-115327-3(3)*** , Harper Trophy) HarperCollins Pubs.

A B

Rappaport, Doreen. Freedom River. Date not set. (Illus.). 32p. (J). pap. 4.99 (978-0-7868-1229-5(X)) Hyperion Paperbacks for Children.

Rapson, Helen. One Lucky Goose. 2005. 31p. pap. 17.95 (978-1-4137-2852-1(9)) PublishAmerica, Inc.

Rash, Brett. The Dragon Lords. 2007. 160p. per. 12.95 (*978-0-595-43842-6(3)) iUniverse, Inc.

Raskin, Lawrie & Pearson, Debora. 52 Days by Camel: My Sahara Adventure. Raskin, Lawrie, photos by. 1998. (Adventure Travel Ser.). (Illus.). 88p. (J). (gr. 3-7). pap. 14.95 (978-1-55037-518-3(0)) Annick Pr., Ltd. CAN. *Dist:* Firefly Bks., Ltd.

Raspe, Rudolph. Surprising Adventures of Baron Munchause. 2006. 62.99 (*978-1-4219-8906-8(9)) IndyPublish.com.

Ratoff, Michael. Caspar & the Sun: An Adventure, 3 vols. Painter, Laurie, illus. l.t. ed. 2001. (Every Thing in an Empty Box Ser.). 56p. (J). (ps-3). lib. bdg. 9.95 (978-0-9627986-3-4(0)) Rebel Butterfly Pr.

El Raton. 2002. Tr. of Mouse. (SPA., Illus.). 22p. (J). 6.50 (978-84-246-1724-0(X)) La Galera, S.A. Editorial ESP. *Dist:* AIMS International Bks., Inc.

Rau, Dana Meachen. The Secret Code. Weissman, Bari, illus. 1998. (Rookie Reader Skill Set Ser.). 32p. (J). (gr. k-2). pap. 4.95 (978-0-516-26362-5(5) , Children's Pr.) Scholastic Library Publishing.

Rautenberg, Karen Rita. Lady Lucy's Gallant Knight. 2007. 156p. (J). pap. 7.95 (978-1-933255-22-4(6)) DNA Pr.

Rauzon, Mark. The Sky's the Limit: All about the Atmosphere. 1999. (Our World Ser.). (Illus.). 32p. (gr. 2-4). lib. bdg. 22.90 (978-0-7613-1263-5(3) , Millbrook Pr.) Lerner Publishing Group.

Ravel, Edeet. The Secret Journey of Pauline Siddhartha. 2007. 224p. pap. 9.95 (*978-1-55192-974-3(0)) Raincoast Bk. Distribution CAN. *Dist:* Perseus Distribution.

Ray, Baltazar, creator. The Adventures of the FancyCrazyHydrants: The Mission, 2004. (Illus.). 162p. (J). per. 17.95 (978-0-9745386-9-3(8)) FancyCrazy Publishing.

Raye, Donna. Edison the Firefly: And His Buddy Bell. 2007. (J). pap. 7.99 (*978-1-60247-097-2(9)) Tate Publishing & Enterprises, L.L.C.

Raymond, N. T. The Winning Wave. 2007. (Surf's Up Ser.). 24p. (J). pap. 3.99 (*978-0-06-115331-0(1) , Harper Entertainment) HarperCollins Pubs.

RAZ. 'Cuz That's Just My Way. Kerchner, Janet Hall, illus. 2005. 32p. (J). bds. 15.95 (978-0-9712070-4-2(6)) B2Z Publishing, Inc.

Razzell, Mary. Runaway at Sea. unabr. ed. 2005. (Illus.). 150p. (YA). (gr. 7-9). 9.95 (978-1-55017-327-7(8)) Harbour Publishing Co., Ltd. CAN. *Dist:* Graphic Arts Ctr. Publishing Co.

Reader's Digest Children's Books, creator. Little People Welcome to Our Town: A Look-Inside Book. 2007. (Fisher Price Lift the Flap Ser.). (Illus.). 20p. (J). (ps-k). bds. 9.99 (*978-0-7944-1360-6(9)) Reader's Digest Assn., Inc., The.

Reader's Digest Staff. Shrek the Halls: Lift-the-Flap. 2007. 10p. (J). (ps-k). bds. 9.99 (*978-0-7944-1365-1(X)) Reader's Digest Assn., Inc., The.

Readler, Blaine C. Under the Radar: The Spy Drone Adventure. 2006. 248p. (J). pap. 14.95 (978-1-933255-18-7(8)) DNA Pr.

RealBuzz Studios Staff. Out of the Soup. 2007. (Goofyfoot Gurl Ser.: No. 4). 96p. (YA). pap. 4.97 (978-1-59789-576-7(8)) Barbour Publishing, Inc.

Reberg, Evelyne. Tom Tom et la impossible Na. pap. 21.95 (978-2-227-73101-1(X)) Bayard Editions FRA. *Dist:* Distribooks, Inc.

—Tom Tom et les idees Explosi. pap. 21.95 (978-2-227-73106-6(0)) Bayard Editions FRA. *Dist:* Distribooks, Inc.

Redbank, Tennant. Dead Man's Chest - the Chase Is On. 2nd rev. ed. 2006. (Pirates of the Carribean Ser.). 32p. (gr. k-2). pap. 3.99 (978-1-4231-0089-8(1)) Disney Pr.

Reddy's Golden Adventure. 2004. (J). 15.95 (978-0-9639670-0-8(2)) twhiteart.

Redmon, Angela M., illus. The Adventures of Margaret Mouse: School Days. l.t. ed. 2004. 32p. (J). 6.95 (978-0-9761326-0-8(5)) www.margaretmouse.com publishing co.

—The Adventures of Margaret Mouse: The Picnic. 2004. 32p. (J). 6.95 (978-0-9761326-1-5(3)) www.margaretmouse.com publishing co.

Redmond, Zelie. The Adventures of Sister Regina Marie: Sister Finds a Friend. Redmond, Zelie, . 2005. (J). per. 6.95 (978-0-9774345-0-3(8)) Joy of my Youth Pubns., The.

Reece, Colleen L. Sarah's New World: The Mayflower Adventure. 2004. (Sisters in Time Ser.). 144p. (J). pap. 4.97 (978-1-59310-203-6(8)) Barbour Publishing, Inc.

Reece, Stephen. Mudflap & Logjam to the Rescue. 1998. (Illus.). 12p. (J). (ps-3). pap. 3.65 (978-1-892388-05-6(7)) Little Trucker Bks.

Reed, Don C. The Kraken. Hunt, Judith, illus. 2003. 224p. (YA). (gr. 5-9). pap. 7.95 (978-1-56397-693-3(5)) Boyds Mills Pr.

Reed, Gary. Spirit of the Samurai: Of Swords & Rings. Hoberg, Rick, illus. 2006. 107p. (J). 12.95 (978-0-9778809-9-7(0) , Actionopolis) Komikwerks, LLC.

Reed, Jennifer. Hadi's Journey. 2003. 110p. pap. 10.95 (978-0-595-29375-9(1)) iUniverse, Inc.

Reeder, Carolyn. Captain Kate. 2002. 210p. (J). (gr. 4-7). reprint ed. pap. 6.50 (978-1-890920-14-2(2)) Children's Literature.

—Captain Kate. 2000. 224p. (J). (gr. 3-7). pap. 4.99 (978-0-380-79668-7(6)) HarperCollins Pubs.

—Captain Kate. 1999. (Illus.). (J). (978-0-606-17963-8(1)) Tandem Library Bks.

Rees. Something Secret. 2000. (Illus.). 137p. (J). pap. 6.99 (978-0-440-86339-7(2)) Transworld Publishers Ltd. GBR. *Dist:* Trafalgar Square Publishing.

Rees, Celia. Pirates! 2003. 340p. (J). 16.95 (978-1-58234-816-2(2)); 2005. 384p. (YA). (gr. 9-12). reprint ed. pap. 8.95 (978-1-58234-665-6(8)) Bloomsbury Publishing. (Bloomsbury Children).

—The Wish House. 2006. 272p. (YA). (gr. 9). 15.99 (978-0-7636-2951-9(0)) Candlewick Pr.

Rees, Douglas. Smoking Mirror. 2005. (Art Encounters Ser.). (Illus.). 176p. (YA). 15.95 (978-0-8230-4863-2(2)) Watson-Guptill Pubns., Inc.

Reetz, Kurt & Schure, Kimberley. Kasey & the Dream Forest: The First Dream. Voelker, Marty, illus. 2000. 24p. (J). (gr. 1-3). pap. (978-0-9701450-0-0(4)) Long Hill Productions, Inc.

Reetz, Kurt & Schure, Kimberly. Kasey & the Dream Forest: The First Dream. 2000. mass mkt. 8.95 incl. audio compact disk (978-1-931179-05-8(0)) Long Hill Productions, Inc.

Reeve, Philip. Larklight: A Rousing Tale of Dauntless Pluck in the Farthest Reaches of Space. Wyatt, David, illus. 2007. 416p. (J). (gr. 5 up). pap. 7.95 (*978-1-59990-145-9(5) , Bloomsbury Children) Bloomsbury Publishing.

Reeve, Philip & Yancey, Rick. Larklight: A Rousing Tale of Dauntless Pluck in the Farthest Reaches of Space. Wyatt, David, illus. 2006. 250p. (YA). 16.95 (978-1-59990-020-9(3) , Bloomsbury Children) Bloomsbury Publishing.

Reeves, Claire. Adventures of Boots the One Eyed Cat, 2003. (Illus.). 32p. (J). 15.95 (978-0-9743048-1-6(6)) LTI Publishing.

Reeves, Jeni, illus. Anansi & the Box of Stories. 2007. (On My Own Folklore Ser.). 48p. (J). (gr. 2-5). lib. bdg. 25.26 (*978-0-8225-6741-7(5) , Millbrook Pr.) Lerner Publishing Group.

Regan, Peter. A Fresh Start. Myler, Terry, illus. 2004. 112p. pap. 9.95 (978-1-901737-49-3(7)) Anvil Bks., Ltd. IRL. *Dist:* Dufour Editions, Inc.

—Riverside: Setbacks. 2002. (Illus.). 128p. (YA). (gr. 7 up). pap. 7.95 (978-1-901737-32-5(2)) Anvil Bks., Ltd. IRL. *Dist:* Dufour Editions, Inc.

—Something New, Vol. 2. Myler, Terry, illus. 2004. (Shannon Harps Ser.). 112p. pap. 9.95 (978-1-901737-52-3(7)) Anvil Bks., Ltd. IRL. *Dist:* Dufour Editions, Inc.

Rehnert, Anne M. Witchworks Perilous Journeys. 2002. 235p. (YA). pap. 9.95 (978-1-892614-36-0(7)) Briarwood Pubns.

Reich, J. J. Deer Dad: Kampp Tales; Outdoor Adventures. Johnathan, Kuehl, illus. 2006. (BAT.). 32p. (J). (*978-0-9762971-0-9(8)) Outdoor Originals LLC.

Reiche, Dietlof. The Haunting of Freddy. 2007. (Golden Hamster Saga Ser.: Bk. 4). 320p. (J). pap. 5.99 (978-0-439-53160-3(8) , Scholastic Paperbacks) Scholastic, Inc.

Reid, Barbara. The Subway Mouse. Reid, Barbara, illus. 2005. (Illus.). 40p. (J). 15.95 (978-0-439-72827-0(4)) Scholastic, Inc.

—The Subway Mouse. 2005. (Illus.). (J). (978-0-439-77430-7(6)) Scholastic, Inc.

Reid, Mayne. The Boy Hunters or Adventures in Search of a White Buffalo. 2005. reprint ed. pap. 30.95 (978-1-4179-0412-9(7)) Kessinger Publishing, LLC.

Reid, Mayne. Young Yagers or A Narrative of Hunting A. 2006. (Illus.). pap. 31.95 (*978-1-4286-2205-0(5)) Kessinger Publishing, LLC.

Reid, Roger. Longleaf. 2006. 136p. (J). 19.95 (978-1-58838-194-1(3) , Junebug Bks.) NewSouth, Inc.

Reid, Thomas M. Forged. 2003. 320p. (YA). per. 7.99 (978-1-59263-010-3(3)) Bastion Pr., Inc.

Reidy, Hannah. Crazy Creature Capers. Mackie, Clare, illus. 2003. (Crazy Creatures Ser.). 26p. (J). pap. (978-1-84089-222-2(6) , Zero to Ten, Limited) Evans Publishing Group.

Reilly, Matthew. Crash Course. Raimondi, Pablo, illus. 2006. (Hover Car Racer Ser.). 240p. (J). pap. 5.99 (978-1-4169-0226-3(0) , Aladdin) Simon & Schuster Children's Publishing.

Reinhart, Matthew. The Jungle Book. Reinhart, Matthew, illus. ltd. ed. 2006. 12p. (J). 250.00 (978-1-4169-2543-9(0) , Little Simon) Simon & Schuster Children's Publishing.

—The Jungle Book: A Pop-up Adventure. Reinhart, Matthew, illus. 2006. 12p. (J). 26.95 (978-1-4169-1824-0(8) , Little Simon) Simon & Schuster Children's Publishing.

Reinheimer, Melinda T. Little Blue Kite Makes A Friend: Another Adventure of the Little Blue Kite. 2005. 24p. (J). per. 9.95 (978-1-59196-908-2(5)) Instantpublisher.com.

Reiss, Johanna. La Habitacion de Arriba. (SPA., Illus.). 213p. (YA). (gr. 5-8). pap. (978-84-239-8852-5(X) , EC0945) Espasa Calpe, S.A. ESP. *Dist:* Lectorum Pubns., Inc.

Reiss, Kathryn. Pale Phoenix. 2003. (gr. 7-12). lib. bdg. 14.10 (978-0-613-67837-7(0)) Tandem Library Bks.

Remender, Rick. Girl Afraid Vol. 1. (Illus.). 104p. (YA). pap. 12.99 (978-1-58240-543-8(3)) Image Comics.

Remnant-Ashton, Rod. The Roseland Mysteries. 2005. 128p. (J). pap. 15.00 (978-1-4116-5166-1(9)) Lulu.com.

Rene, Richard. The Nightmare Tree. 2007. 240p. (YA). (gr. 5-8). 8.95 (*978-1-55050-363-0(4)) Coteau Bks. CAN. *Dist:* Fitzhenry & Whiteside, Ltd.

Rennie, Gordon. Rain Dogs. 2002. 52p. 14.95 (978-1-56971-697-7(8)) Dark Horse Comics.

Renninson, Lou. Frontalknutschen. pap. 17.95 (978-3-570-30008-4(0)) Bertelsman, Verlagsgruppe C. GmbH DEU. *Dist:* Distribooks, Inc.

Renshaw, Ken. The Yosemite Adventure of Spotty Bat. Rosenthal, Robert, illus. 2005. 104p. per. 10.95 (978-0-9616620-2-8(6)) Constellation Pr.

Rescue Flight! 2003. 150p. (J). (gr. 4-6). per. 12.95 (978-0-9740202-0-4(6)) Skyword Pr.

Rex, Adam. The True Meaning of Smekday. Rex, Adam, illus. rev. ed. 2007. 432p. (gr. 2-7). 16.99 (*978-0-7868-4900-0(2)) Hyperion Pr.

Rex, Annmarie. Black's Adventure in the Big, Scary, Hairy World. 2007. 46p. (J). 19.99 (*978-1-59879-365-9(9)); per. 15.99 (*978-1-59879-364-2(0)) Lifevest Publishing, Inc. (Lifevest).

Rey, H. A. & Rey, Margret. Curious George to the Rescue: A Slide & Peek Adventure. 2007. (Curious George Ser.). (Illus.). 12p. (J). (ps-k). bds. 8.99 (978-0-618-72401-7(X)) Houghton Mifflin Co. Trade & Reference Div.

—The New Adventures of Curious George 2006. 2006. (Illus.). 208p. (J). (ps-k). 10.99 (978-0-618-66373-6(8)) Houghton Mifflin Co. Trade & Reference Div.

—Whiteblack the Penguin Sees the World. 2004. (Illus.). 32p. (J). (gr. k-3). reprint ed. pap. 5.95 (978-0-618-07390-0(6)) Houghton Mifflin Co. Trade & Reference Div.

Rey, H. A. and Margret. Curious George Shapes: CG TV Board Book #5. 2008. 10p. (J). (gr. k-ps). bds. 6.99 (*978-0-618-89198-6(6)) Houghton Mifflin Co. Trade & Reference Div.

—Curious George/Jorge el curioso Bilingual Edition. 2008. 64p. (J). (gr. k-3). 16.00 (*978-0-618-88410-0(6)); pap. 6.95 (*978-0-618-88411-7(4)) Houghton Mifflin Co. Trade & Reference Div.

Reynolds, Mignon C. Life as Bonkers. 2006. 137p. pap. 12.95 (978-1-4116-7357-1(3)) Lulu.com.

Reynolds, Peter H. The Dot. Reynolds, Peter H., illus. 2005. (Illus.). 34p. (J). bds. 19.95 (978-0-9769313-0-0(3)) BrailleInk.

Rhae, Sympne. My Name Is Johnson? l.t. ed. 2006. (Illus.). 53p. (J). per. 13.75 (978-0-9770043-9-3(2)) New Global Publishing.

Rhead, Louis. Robin Hood & His Outlaw Band. Exams Unlimited, Inc. Staff, ed. 2001. 274p. (J). reprint ed. cd-rom 6.94 (978-1-885343-11-6(6)) Exams Unlimited, Inc.

Rhee, Nami, illus. & retold by. Woodcutter & Tiger Brother. Rhee, Nami, retold by. 1999. 32p. (J). (ps-1). 18.50 (978-1-56591-093-5(1)) Hollym International Corp.

Rhue, Morton. Welle Bericht Uber Einen. (GER.). pap. 14.95 (978-3-473-58008-8(2)) Ravensburger Buchverlag Otto Maier GmbH DEU. *Dist:* Distribooks, Inc.

Rhymer-Martin, Marie. The Franklin Adventures: Strictly Mangoes. 2006. pap. 7.95 (978-0-533-14992-6(4)) Vantage Pr., Inc.

Rhyne, Nancy. The Crab Boys. 2007. (J). pap. (*978-0-87844-183-9(2)) Sandlapper Publishing Co., Inc.

Ribar, Sandy. Operation - Rescue in the Redwoods: Readalong - Singalong Pack. unabr. ed. 1999. (Kids on Assignment - The Adventures of Rex & Ruby Ser.: Vol. 1). (J). (ps-5). pap. 11.49 incl. audio (978-1-893401-08-2(1) , KOA000RR) Pure & Simple Productions.

Ricci, Christine. The Backyardigans Music Player Storybook. 2006. (Music Player Storybook Ser.). 40p. (J). 24.99 (978-0-7944-1110-7(X)) Reader's Digest Assn., Inc., The.

—Dora in the Deep Sea. Roper, Robert, illus. 2003. (Dora the Explorer Ser.: Vol. 3). 24p. (J). pap. 3.99 (978-0-689-85845-1(0) , Simon Spotlight/Nickelodeon) Simon & Schuster Children's Publishing.

—Dora in the Deep Sea. 2003. (ps-2). lib. bdg. 11.80 (978-0-613-73392-2(4)) Tandem Library Bks.

—Dora's Christmas Adventure. Piluso, Piero, illus. 2006. (Dora the Explorer Ser.). 14p. (J). bds. 6.99 (978-1-4169-1755-7(1) , Simon Spotlight/Nickelodeon) Simon & Schuster Children's Publishing.

—Dora's Costume Party! Saunders, Zina, illus. 2005. 24p. (J). lib. bdg. 9.00 (*978-1-4242-0978-1(1)) Fitzgerald Bks.

—Dora's Costume Party. 2006. (J). (ps-2). 21.35 (978-1-59961-071-9(X)) Spotlight.

—Dora's Fairy-Tale Adventure. Hall, Susan', illus. ed. 2005. (Dora the Explorer Ser.: No. 9). 22p. (J). lib. bdg. 15.00 (978-1-59054-795-3(0)) Fitzgerald Bks.

—Dora's Favorite Adventures! Miller, Victoria, illus. 2007. (Dora the Explorer Ser.). 14p. (J). bds. 7.99 (*978-1-4169-3802-6(8) , Simon Spotlight/Nickelodeon) Simon & Schuster Children's Publishing.

—Dora's Mystery of the Missing Shoes. Savitsky, Steven, illus. 2007. (Dora the Explorer Ser.). 24p. (J). pap. 3.99 (*978-1-4169-3824-8(9) , Simon Spotlight/Nickelodeon) Simon & Schuster Children's Publishing.

—Dora's River Race. Roper, Robert, illus. 2006. (Dora the Explorer Ser.). 16p. (J). pap. 5.99 (978-1-4169-1208-8(8) , Simon Spotlight/Nickelodeon) Simon & Schuster Children's Publishing.

—Follow Those Feet! Hall, Susan', illus. ed. 2005. 22p. (J). lib. bdg. 15.00 (978-1-59054-974-2(0)) Fitzgerald Bks.

—Legend Hunters! McGee, Warner, illus. 2007. (Backyardigans Ser.). 24p. (J). pap. 3.99 (978-1-4169-4058-6(8) , Simon Spotlight/Nickelodeon) Simon & Schuster Children's Publishing.

Ricci, Christine & A&J Studios Staff. Dora's Valentine Adventure. 2006. (Dora the Explorer Ser.). 14p. (J). bds. 6.99 (978-1-4169-1754-0(3) , Simon Spotlight/ Nickelodeon) Simon & Schuster Children's Publishing.

Ricci, Laura. Dr. Mike's Adventures. 2006. 63p. pap. 12.95 (978-1-4241-2653-8(3)) PublishAmerica, Inc.

Rice, Doris House. Doogie: The Sea Is Calling Me. Marable, Joseph & Wilson, Sean, illus. 2000. (Doogie Adventures Ser.: Vol. 3). 40p. (J). (gr. 1-6). 20.00 (978-0-9700851-0-8(9)) Toothpick Productions.

Rice, Melinda. Marooned on the Pirate Coast. 2002. (Lone Star Heroine Ser.: No. 4). 123p. (gr. 4-7). pap. 8.95 (978-1-55622-935-0(6) , Republic of Texas Pr.) Wordware Publishing, Inc.

Rich, Francine Poppo. Pee Wee Pipes & the Wing Thing. Bone, Thomas H., III, illus. 2000. (Pee Wee Pipes Adventure Ser.: Vol. 2). 32p. (J). (ps-2). per. 15.00 (978-0-9674602-1-5(2)) Blue Marlin Pubns.

Richards, Jane. Tombs, Temples, & Thrones. 2005. 125p. pap. 17.95 (978-1-4137-9084-9(4)) PublishAmerica, Inc.

Richards, Justin. The Chaos Code. 2007. 416p. (YA). (gr. 7 up). 17.95 (*978-1-59990-124-4(2)) Bloomsbury Publishing.

Richards, Kitty. Lites & Camera. Goldberg, Barry, illus. 2000. (Rugrats Ser.). 32p. (J). (gr. k-3). per. 3.99 (978-0-7434-0802-8(0) , Simon & Schuster Children's Publishing) Simon & Schuster Children's Publishing.

—One of a Kind. 2001. (gr. 3-6). lib. bdg. 11.80 (978-0-613-43946-6(5)) Tandem Library Bks.

Richards, L. B. The Adventures of Charley Tooth, Vol. 1. 2004. (Illus.). mass mkt. 12.95 (978-0-8439-5136-3(2)) Dorchester Publishing Co., Inc.

Richards, Laura E. Captain January. 2004. reprint ed. pap. 15.95 (978-1-4191-1199-0(X)) Kessinger Publishing, LLC.

Richardson, A. A. Slingshot Home, 1 vol. 2003. 164p. (YA). pap. 8.99 (978-0-9745281-0-6(2)) WSI Educational Bks.

Richardson, Duncan. Revenge. Edwards, Rebecca, illus. 2005. 30p. (J). pap. (978-1-876682-69-9(8)) Post Pressed.

Richardson, Steve. Alexander Trout's Amazing Adventure. Lowe, Wesley, illus. 2007. 75p. 16.95 (*978-0-9786422-2-8(8)) Impossible Dreams Publishing Co.

Richemont, Enid. Jamie & the Whippersnapper. 2000. (Illus.). 64p. (J). pap. 6.99 (978-0-09-940098-1(7)) Random Hse. GBR. *Dist:* Independent Pubs. Group.

Richler, Mordecai. Jacob Two-Two Meets the Hooded Fang. Wegner, Fritz, illus. movie tie-in ed. 1999. (Jacob Two-Two Adventures Ser.). 96p. (J). (gr. 3-7). pap. 6.95 (978-0-88776-481-3(9)) Tundra Bks., Inc./Livres Toundra, Inc. CAN. *Dist:* Random Hse., Inc.

—Jacob Two-Two Meets the Hooded Fang. Wegner, Fritz, tr. Wegner, Fritz, illus. 4th ed. 2003. 96p. (J). (gr. 3-7). pap. 6.95 (978-0-88776-686-2(2)) Tundra Bks., Inc./ Livres Toundra, Inc. CAN. *Dist:* Random Hse., Inc.

Richmond, Marianne R. My Shoes Take Me Where I Want to Go! A Journey Through the Imagination. Richmond, Marianne R., illus. 2006. (Illus.). 40p. (J). 15.95 (978-0-9753528-6-1(5)) Marianne Richmond Studios, Inc.

Richter, Conrad. The Light in the Forest. (YA). (gr. 7 up). 21.95 (978-0-89190-333-8(X)) Amereon LTD.

Riddell, J. H. The Open Door. 2004. reprint ed. pap. 1.99 (978-1-4192-7623-1(9)) Kessinger Publishing, LLC.

Ridden, Brian. Blind Fear. 2002. (Crime Waves Ser.). (Illus.). 96p. (YA). pap. (978-0-7344-0276-9(7) , Lothian Bks.) Hachette Livre Australia.

Riddle, A. Yogi & Me. 2006. 48p. pap. 12.95 (978-1-4241-0565-6(X)) PublishAmerica, Inc.

Ridgeway, Krishmatie & Ridgeway, Doug. Shiva's Dance: A Young Girl's Troubled Life. 2002. 230p. pap. 14.95 (978-0-595-24306-8(1) , Writers Club Pr.) iUniverse, Inc.

Ridley, Susan. Suzie's Adventures in Space: the Forbidden Planet. 2007. 80p. pap. 8.99 (*978-0-615-15328-5(3)) Arts & Health Publishing.

Rieback, Milton. The Adventures of Webb Ellis, a Tale from the Heart of Africa: The Return of the Protectors. Crowley, Cheryl, illus. 2006. (J). lib. bdg. 19.95 (978-0-9777440-0-8(0)) Inyati Press.

Rigby & Gem: A Guberif Adventure. 2005. (J). (978-0-9773775-0-3(4)) Don Rand's Classy Collectibles.

Rigby Education Staff. Peter Piper. (gr. k-2). 21.00 (978-0-7635-2407-4(7)) Rigby Education.

Riggs, Darla L. Hooney Bacooney: Caught Red Handed. 2004. (Illus.). 12p. (J). 4.98 (978-0-9747883-0-2(9)) Little League Pr.

Riley, Lehman, et al. The Adventures of Papa Lemon's Little Wanderers Bk. 2: The Dangerous Escape from Slavery. 2005. 52p. pap. 5.99 (978-0-9760523-1-9(8)) Matter of Africa America Time.

Rinaldo, Luana, illus. Clackers: BEE. 2008. (Clackers Ser.). 14p. (J). (gr. k-ps). bds. 4.99 (*978-0-375-84229-0(2) , Robin Corey Bks.) Random Hse. Children's Bks.

—Clackers: FISH. 2008. (Clackers Ser.). 14p. (J). (gr. k-ps). bds. 4.99 (*978-0-375-84230-6(6) , Robin Corey Bks.) Random Hse. Children's Bks.

Ring, Susan. Disney's Little Einsteins: Mission: Color Discoveries. Benica, Barrett & Song, Aram, illus. 2006. (Art for Children Ser.). 32p. (ps-17). 9.99 (978-0-7868-5540-7(1)) Disney Pr.

—Innovative Kids Readers: the Great Barrier Reef - an Undersea Adventure. 2007. 32p. (J). (gr. 1-3). pap. 6.99 (978-1-58476-543-1(7)) Innovative Kids.

Rip Squeak & His Friends Discover the Treasure. 2003. Tr. of Rip Squeak y Sus Amigos Descubren un Tesoro. per. 16.95 (978-0-9672422-5-5(8)) Rip Squeak, Inc.

Rissman, Angelica. Julius & the Lost Letter to Santa. 2003. (J). 7.99 (978-1-59384-019-5(5)) Parklane Publishing.

Ritchie, Joseph R. Knock, Knock, Who's There? Rose, Drew, illus. 2005. 14p. (J). bds. 7.95 (978-0-8249-6613-3(9)) Ideals Pubns.

Rivas y Salazar, Larissa. Cuentos de Robots para Ninos. 2000. (Stories for Children Ser.).Tr. of Robot Stories for Kids. (SPA., Illus.). 125p. (J). (gr. 3-7). 7.98 (978-970-643-215-5(9)) Selector, S.A. de C.V. MEX. *Dist:* Giron Bks., Libros Sin Fronteras.

Rivera, Raquel. Orphan Ahwak. 2007. 144p. (J). (gr. 4-8). pap. (*978-1-55143-653-1(1)) Orca Bk. Pubs.

Rivers, Karen. Dream Water. 2000. 176p. (J). (gr. 7-10). lib. bdg. 14.95 (978-1-55143-160-4(2)) Orca Bk. Pubs. USA.

Rivers, Katie. A Winter's Dream. 2005. 31p. (J). per. 2.95 (978-0-9721640-1-6(4)) Whispering Wind Publishing Inc.

Rizner, Staci. Last Chance Out. 2002. (gr. 7-12). lib. bdg. 24.55 (978-0-613-81754-7(0)) Tandem Library Bks.

Road Trip. 2003. (J). per. (978-1-57657-958-9(1)) Paradise Pr., Inc.

Robbins, Neal. The Island of the Three Sapphires. Mayfield, Helen, illus. 98p. (J). (gr. 6 up). pap. 4.00 (978-1-884993-04-6(4)) Koldarana Pubns.

Robbins, Trina. The Odyssey: A Graphic Classic. 2002. (Read 180 Ser.). (Illus.). 24p. (J). (978-0-439-12336-5(4)) Scholastic, Inc.

Roberts, Allyson. Leroy the Labrador - the Big Move. 2005. 14.95 (978-0-9759305-1-9(6)) Maximum Potential, Inc.

Roberts, Barbara A. Phoebe's Lost Treasure. Sternberg, Kate, illus. 1999. (Phoebe Flower's Adventures Ser.). 68p. (gr. 2-4). pap. 5.95 (978-0-9660366-6-4(2)) National Bk. Network.

Roberts, Bethany. May Belle & the Ogre. Winborn, Marsha, illus. 2003. (Dutton Easy Reader Ser.). 48p. (J). (gr. 1-3). 14.99 (978-0-525-46855-4(2) , Dutton Juvenile) Penguin Group (USA) Inc.

Roberts, Christa. Free Fall. 2004. (Prequel Ser.). 192p. (YA). (gr. 7). mass mkt. 5.99 (978-0-553-49405-1(8) , Bantam Bks. for Young Readers) Random Hse. Children's Bks.

—Free Fall. 2004. (gr. 7-12). lib. bdg. 14.15 (978-0-613-82961-8(1)) Tandem Library Bks.

Roberts, Curt. The Story of Scruffy of Smithfield, Virginia. Traylor, Waverley, ed. Roberts, Curt & Traylor, Waverley, illus. l.t. ed. 2005. 14p. (J). (gr. k-6). pap. 3.95 (978-0-9715068-4-8(1)) Traylor, Waverley Publishing.

Roberts, Judson. Dragons from the Sea. 2007. (Strongbow Saga Ser.: Bk. 2). 352p. (gr. 9 up). (J). 16.99 (*978-0-06-081300-0(8)); (YA). lib. bdg. 17.89 (*978-0-06-081302-4(4)) HarperCollins Pubs. (HarperTeen).

Roberts, Katherine. The Babylon Game. 2002. (Seven Fabulous Wonders Ser.). (Illus.). 310p. pap. 11.00 (978-0-00-711279-1(3)) HarperCollins Pubs. Ltd. GBR. *Dist:* Independent Pubs. Group.

—The Cleopatra Curse. 2006. (Seven Fabulous Wonders Ser.). (Illus.). 288p. (J). pap. 11.99 (978-0-00-711284-5(X) , HarperCollins Children's Bks.) HarperCollins Pubs. Ltd. GBR. *Dist:* Independent Pubs. Group.

—Seven Fabulous Wonders Great. 2001. (Seven Fabulous Wonders Ser.). (Illus.). 298p. (J). pap. 11.00 (978-0-00-711278-4(5)) HarperCollins Pubs. Ltd. GBR. *Dist:* Trafalgar Square Publishing.

—Seven Fabulous Wonders Temple. 2002. (Seven Fabulous Wonders Ser.). (Illus.). 298p. (J). pap. 11.00 (978-0-00-711280-7(7)) HarperCollins Pubs. Ltd. GBR. *Dist:* Trafalgar Square Publishing.

Roberts, Kerry Daniel. Room of the Eyes. 2006. (Knights of the Silver Dragon Ser.). 192p. (YA). pap. 4.99 (978-0-7869-4185-8(5) , Mirrorstone) Wizards of the Coast.

Roberts, Laura Peyton. Secret Life. 2003. (gr. 7-12). lib. bdg. 14.15 (978-0-613-72716-7(9)) Tandem Library Bks.

Roberts, Nora. The Reef. 1999. (gr. 7-12). lib. bdg. 16.45 (978-0-613-22257-0(1)) Tandem Library Bks.

Roberts, Phyllis. Teeny Tiny Star. 2007. (Illus.). 30p. (J). lib. bdg. 19.95 (*978-1-933732-40-4(7) , Bear Hug Bks.) MidAmerica Publishing Co.

Roberts, Rachel. Circles in the Stream. 2003. (Avalon Ser.: Bk. 1). 244p. (J). (gr. 3-7). pap. 4.99 (978-1-59315-003-7(2)) Perseus Bks. Group.

—Circles in the Stream. 2001. (Avalon Ser.: Bk. 1). (Illus.). 160p. (J). pap. 4.99 (978-0-439-22165-8(X) , Scholastic Paperbacks) Scholastic, Inc.

—Circles in the Stream. 2007. (Avalon Ser.: Bk. 1). 175p. (J). 9.99 (*978-1-933164-64-9(6)) Seven Seas Entertainment, LLC.

Roberts, Rachel. Cry of the Wolf. 2003. (Avalon Ser.: Bk. 3). 189p. (J). (gr. 3-7). pap. 4.99 (978-1-59315-005-1(9)) Perseus Bks. Group.

—Cry of the Wolf. 2001. (Avalon Ser.: Bk. 3). 176p. (J). pap. 4.99 (978-0-439-22168-9(4)) Scholastic, Inc.

Roberts, Tim. The Portal to Chalicu. 2005. 218p. pap. 19.95 (978-1-4137-9680-3(X)) PublishAmerica, Inc.

Roberts, Willo Davis. The Kidnappers: A Mystery. 1999. 144p. (J). (gr. 3-7). pap. 4.99 (978-0-689-81393-1(7) , Aladdin) Simon & Schuster Children's Publishing.

—Undercurrents. 2003. (Illus.). 240p. (J). pap. 4.99 (978-0-689-85994-6(5) , Aladdin) Simon & Schuster Children's Publishing.

—Undercurrents. Downey, Mark, illus. 2002. 240p. (J). (gr. 5-8). 16.95 (978-0-689-81671-0(5) , Atheneum) Simon & Schuster Children's Publishing.

—Undercurrents. 2002. (gr. 3-6). lib. bdg. 13.00 (978-0-613-66553-7(8)) Tandem Library Bks.

Robertson, Elysia Hill. Dottie Goes to School. Robertson, Elysia Hill, illus. 2005. (Illus.). 30p. (J). per. 6.95 (978-0-9764444-8-0(8)) E. J. Publishing.

Robinet, Harriette Gillem. Twelve Travelers, Twenty Horses. 208p. (J). 2005. pap. 4.99 (978-0-689-87607-3(6) , Aladdin); 2003. (Illus.). 16.95 (978-0-689-84561-1(8) , Atheneum) Simon & Schuster Children's Publishing.

Robins, Eleanor. It Does Matter. 2004. (Illus.). 48p. (YA). per. 3.95 (978-1-56254-770-7(4) , SP7704) Saddleback Educational Publishing.

Robinson, Amy. Bobby's Biking Lesson. Carrozza, Kyle A., illus. 2001. 36p. (J). 9.95 (978-1-58284-005-5(9) , BBL001, Thoughtful Education Pr., The) Silver Strong & Assocs.

Robinson, Gwen. The Renshaw Diversion. 2007. 204p. per. (*978-0-7552-0275-1(9)) Authors OnLine, Ltd.

Robinson, Kelley. The Magic of Lo: Book 1, lo Trilogy. l.t. ed. 2004. (Illus.). 160p. (YA). per. 9.95 (978-0-9745865-0-2(1) , SarahRose Children's Bks.) SarahRose Publishing.

Robinson, Lee. Gateway. 1998. (978-0-606-13413-2(1)) Tandem Library Bks.

Robinson, Marcus. Samurai Baby the Adventure Begins. 2007. 87p. pap. 11.98 (*978-1-4303-0350-3(6)) Lulu.com.

Robinson, Patrick. Shark Mutiny. 2002. (gr. 7-12). lib. bdg. 16.45 (978-0-613-62158-8(1)) Tandem Library Bks.

Robinson, Sabra A. Micky, Ticky, Boo! Says Hello. 2003. (J). per. 9.99 (978-1-59196-230-4(7)) Instantpublisher.com.

Robson, Jerry. Adventures of Mr. Penwiggles: A Recipe for Danger. 2004. 75p. pap. 14.95 (978-1-4137-3588-8(6)) PublishAmerica, Inc.

Robson, Walter. Ear2ear & the Gem1's. 2005. (ENG.). 192p. per. (*978-1-904988-05-2(9)) Donard Publishing.

Rockliff, Mara. Pieces of Another World. Alikhan, Salima, illus. 2005. 32p. (J). 15.95 (978-0-9764943-2-4(9)) Sylvan Dell Pubng.

The Rocks. 2005. (J). 4.95 (978-1-59792-013-1(4)) F.A.S.T. Learning LLLC.

Rockwell, Carey. Revolt on Venus. 2006. 95.99 (*978-1-4280-5054-9(X)); pap. 89.99 (*978-1-4280-5053-2(1)) IndyPublish.com.

—Sabotage in Space. 2006. 95.99 (*978-1-4280-3661-1(X)); pap. 89.99 (*978-1-4280-3670-3(9)) IndyPublish.com.

—Stand by for Mars! 2007. (ENG.). 208p. per. 89.99 (*978-1-4280-7416-3(3)) IndyPublish.com.

Rockwell, D. R. The Jessicas: The Adventures of Five City Girls. 2005. (J). pap. 9.95 (978-0-9767711-0-4(1)) CLOJ Publishing.

Rockwood, Roy. Jack North's Treasure Hunt: Or, Daring Adventures in South America. 2006. 142p. pap. 10.99 (978-1-4264-2654-4(2)); 146p. pap. 13.99 (978-1-4264-2711-4(5)) BiblioBazaar.

Rocky & Bullwinkle, Bk. 2. 1999. (Illus.). (J). mass mkt. 3.99 (978-0-689-82513-2(7) , Simon Spotlight) Simon & Schuster Children's Publishing.

Rocky, Bullwinkle, Dudley Do Right, No. 3. movie tie-in ed. 1999. (J). pap. (978-0-689-82520-0(X) , Simon Spotlight) Simon & Schuster Children's Publishing.

Rodda, Emily. City of the Rats. 2001. (Deltora Quest Ser.: No. 3). (Illus.). 144p. (J). (gr. 3-7). pap. 5.99 (978-0-439-25325-3(X)) Scholastic, Inc.

—City of the Rats. 2001. (gr. 5-8). lib. bdg. 13.00 (978-0-613-36052-4(4)) Tandem Library Bks.

—Dragon's Nest. McBride, Marc, illus. 2004. (Deltora Quest, Dragons Of Ser.: No. 1). 192p. (J). pap. 4.99 (978-0-439-63373-4(7) , Scholastic Paperbacks) Scholastic, Inc.

—Enter the Realm: Three Fairy Realm Adventures. Vitale, Raoul, illus. 2007. (Fairy Realm Ser.). 352p. (J). 9.99 (*978-0-06-120845-4(0)) HarperCollins Pubs.

—The Key to Rondo. 2008. (J). (*978-0-545-03536-1(8)); 224p. pap. 16.99 (*978-0-545-03535-4(X)) Scholastic, Inc. (Scholastic Pr.).

Rodriguez, Raul. Runaway Baby / el Bebe' Travieso. 2005. (SPA., Illus.). 13p. (J). per. 9.99 (978-1-932338-63-8(2)) Lifevest Publishing, Inc.

Rodriguez, Robert. One Agent Too Many. 2003. (gr. 3-6). lib. bdg. 13.00 (978-0-613-68272-5(6)) Tandem Library Bks.

Rodriguez, Robert & Rodriguez, Racer. The Adventures of Shark Boy & Lava Girl: The Movie Storybook. 2005. (Illus.). 65p. (J). (978-1-933104-02-7(3)) Troublemaker Publishing, LP.

Rodriguez, Robert, et al. The Day Dreamer. Toader, Alex, illus. 2005. (Shark Boy & Lava Girl Adventures Ser.: Bk. 1). 162p. (J). (ps-7). per. (978-1-933104-04-1(X)) Troublemaker Publishing, LP.

Roeder, Mark. The Summer of My Discontent: A Better Place II. 2003. 294p. (YA). 28.95 (978-0-595-66057-5(6)); pap. 18.95 (978-0-595-29806-8(0)) iUniverse, Inc.

Rogan, Sally Jones. The Daring Adventures of Penhaligon Brush. Slade, Christian, illus. 2007. 230p. (J). (gr. 3-7). 15.99 (*978-0-375-84344-0(2)); lib. bdg. 18.99 (*978-0-375-94344-7(7)) Random Hse. Children's Bks. (Knopf Bks. for Young Readers).

Rogers, Alan. El Hipopotamo Amarillo. 2004. (Pequenos Gigantes Ser.).Tr. of Yellow Hippo. (SPA., Illus.). 16p. (ps-k). (J). pap. 3.95 (978-1-58728-956-9(3)); 5.95 (978-1-58728-142-6(2)) T&N Children's Publishing. (Two Can Publishing).

—El Hipopotamo Amarillo. Rogers, Alan, illus. 2000. (Pequenos Gigantes Ser.).Tr. of Yellow Hippo. (SPA., Illus.). 15p. (J). (ps-ps). lib. bdg. 10.75 (978-0-606-20704-1(X)) Tandem Library Bks.

—El Oso Verde. 2004. (Pequenos Gigantes Ser.).Tr. of Green Bear. (SPA., Illus.). 16p. (ps-k). (J). pap. 3.95 (978-1-58728-957-6(1)); 5.95 (978-1-58728-143-3(0)) T&N Children's Publishing. (Two Can Publishing).

—El Oso Verde. Rogers, Alan, illus. 2000. (Pequenos Gigantes Ser.).Tr. of Green Bear. (Illus.). 15p. (J). (ps-ps). lib. bdg. 10.75 (978-0-606-20836-9(4)) Tandem Library Bks.

—El Rinoceronte Rojo. 2004. (Pequenos Gigantes Ser.).Tr. of Red Rhino. (SPA., Illus.). 16p. (ps-k). (J). pap. 3.95 (978-1-58728-958-3(X)); 5.95 (978-1-58728-144-0(9)) T&N Children's Publishing. (Two Can Publishing).

—El Rinoceronte Rojo. Rogers, Alan, illus. 2000. (Pequenos Gigantes Ser.).Tr. of Red Rhino. (Illus.). 15p. (J). (ps-ps). lib. bdg. 10.75 (978-0-606-20885-7(2)) Tandem Library Bks.

—La Tortuga Azul. 2004. (Pequenos Gigantes Ser.). (SPA., Illus.). 16p. (ps-k). (J). pap. 3.95 (978-1-58728-959-0(8)); 5.95 (978-1-58728-145-7(7)) T&N Children's Publishing. (Two Can Publishing).

Rogers, Christopher M., illus. Homer the Helicopter Grand Canyon Adventures: N/a. 2007. Tr. of N/a. 72p. (J). 18.95 (*978-0-9786352-3-7(X)) Buscher, Julie W.

Rogers, Gregory. The Boy, the Bear, the Baron, the Bard. Rogers, Gregory, illus. rev. ed. 2004. (Illus.). 32p. (J). 16.95 (978-1-59643-009-9(5)) Roaring Brook Pr.

Rogers, Joe. The War of the Elves (Book Two of the Changeling) 2006. 221p. pap. (978-1-84685-164-3(5) , Exposure Publishing) Meadow Bks.

Rogers, Jonathan. The Bark of the Bog Owl. 2005. (Wilderking Trilogy: Bk. 1). (Illus.). 240p. pap. 9.97 (978-0-8054-3131-5(4)) B&H Publishing Grp.

—The Secret of the Swamp King 2: The Wilderking Trilogy. 2005. 240p. pap. 9.97 (978-0-8054-3132-2(2)) B&H Publishing Grp.

—The Way of the Wilderking. 2006. (Wilderking Trilogy: Vol. 3). 24p. (J). 9.97 (978-0-8054-3133-9(0)) B&H Publishing Grp.

Rogers, Paul & Rogers, Emma. La Torre de Zoe. Cornfield, Robin Bell, illus. 2001. (SPA.). (J). (gr. k-1). (978-84-88342-01-0(2) , KK1290) S.A. Kokinos ESP. *Dist:* Lectorum Pubns., Inc.

Rogers, Wanda Gayle. Miss Bean & the Great Tricycle Rescue: The Great Tricycle Rescue. 2007. (J). 7.95 (*978-1-59872-735-7(4)) Instantpublisher.com.

Rogerson, George. Stillness of the Dawn - Book One - White Man Coming. 2007. 144p. (YA). pap. 12.95 (*978-1-60145-165-1(2)) Booklocker.com, Inc.

Roginsky, Renata. The Simulacrum & the Book of Spells. 2005. 173p. pap. 9.25 (978-1-4116-2451-1(3)) Lulu.com.

Rohmann, Eric. Cinder-Eyed Cat. 2001. (gr. k-3). lib. bdg. 15.30 (978-0-613-36797-4(9)) Tandem Library Bks.

Rohmer, Sax, pseud, et al. Adventure Classics, Vol. 12. Pomplun, Tom, ed. 2005. (Graphic Classics Ser.: Vol. 12). (Illus.). 144p. pap. 11.95 (978-0-9746648-4-2(7) , Graphic Classics) Eureka Productions.

Roland-James, Patricia & James, Robert L. Something Wicked in the Land of Picatrix. Chidgey, Scarlett, ed. Verhoef, Sharon & Pinkham, Pamela, illus. 2007. 281p. (J). pap. 12.95 (*978-0-9760789-9-9(6)) Aquila Ink Publishing.

Roldan, Gustavo. Cuentos de Pedro Urdemales. Roldan, Gustavo, Jr., illus. 2000. (Cuentamerica Ser.). (SPA.). 62p. (YA). (gr. 4 up). pap. 7.95 (978-950-07-1760-1(3) , SA30060) Editorial Sudamericana S.A. ARG. *Dist:* Lectorum Pubns., Inc.

Rolfs, Judith. Adventures of Tommy Smurlee. 2003. (ENG.). 208p. 23.95 (*978-0-595-74482-4(6)); 206p. pap. 13.95 (978-0-595-26303-5(8)) iUniverse, Inc. (Writers Club Pr.).

—Tommy Smurlee & the Missing Statue. 2007. 216p. (J). per. 13.95 (*978-0-595-45250-7(7)) iUniverse, Inc.

Roman, Javier. Adventures of Tinturu & Kumachan the M. 2007. (Illus.). 48p. pap. 12.95 (*978-1-4241-1626-3(0)) PublishAmerica, Inc.

Roman, Stacey. Some of Us Want Wrinkles. Wurster, Laurie, illus. 2005. (J). per. 16.95 (978-1-59858-033-4(7)) Dog Ear Publishing, LLC.

Roman, Steven A. Sunn. Lau, Kevin et al, illus. 2003. 192p. (gr. 7). pap. 9.95 (978-1-59687-814-3(2)) ibooks, Inc.

Romano, Lou, illus. Blossom Keychain Book. 2000. (Powerpuff Girls Ser.). 48p. (J). (ps-3). 3.99 (978-0-307-10240-9(8) , 10240, Golden Bks.) Random Hse. Children's Bks.

Roman's Hook. 2001. 290p. (YA). (gr. 6 up). pap. 10.00 (978-0-9633479-6-1(9)) Dummer Publishing.

Romansky, Sally Rosenberg. Invincible. Ott, Margot Janet, illus. 2006. (J). pap. 8.95 (978-0-9723729-4-7(6)) Imagination Stage, Inc.

Romay, Alexis. Diego Saves the Sloth! Mawhinney, Art, illus. 2007. (Go, Diego, Go! Ser.). 24p. (J). pap. 3.99 (978-1-4169-3470-7(7) , Simon Spotlight/Nickelodeon) Simon & Schuster Children's Publishing.

Romeu, Emma. A Mississippi por el Mar. 2003. (SPA., Illus.). 150p. (J). (gr. 5-8). pap. 11.95 (978-968-19-0554-5(7)) Santillana USA Publishing Co., Inc.

—Naufragio en las Filipinas. 2003. Tr. of Shipwrecked in the Philippines. (SPA., Illus.). 162p. (J). (gr. 5-8). pap. 9.95 (978-968-19-0555-2(5)) Santillana USA Publishing Co., Inc.

—Naufragio en las Filipinas. 2002. Tr. of Shipwrecked in the Philippines. (SPA.). (gr. 5-8). lib. bdg. 18.75 (978-0-613-71354-2(0)) Tandem Library Bks.

Romoulous. Katalambano: Invasion of the Terror Dome. 2005. (YA). (978-0-9773064-5-9(3)) Miroglyphics.

Roome, Diana Reynolds. Tulliver's Tunnel. Winter, Susan, illus. 2006. 32p. (ps-1). 15.95 (978-1-84507-400-5(9)) Lincoln, Frances Ltd. GBR. *Dist:* Perseus Distribution.

Roper, Robert, illus. Space Case. 2006. (Totally Spies! Ser.). 32p. (J). pap. 3.99 (978-1-4169-1571-3(0) , Simon Spotlight) Simon & Schuster Children's Publishing.

Rosa-Leigh. The Briar & the Rose. 2006. 62p. pap. 12.95 (978-1-4137-7230-2(7)) PublishAmerica, Inc.

Rosano, John. Molly Monkey. 2008. (Illus.). (J). 14.95 (*978-1-60131-013-2(7)) Big Tent Bks.

Rose, Bubba. Penguin Adventures. 2005. 44p. pap. 8.95 (978-1-59453-746-2(1) , 3221) Airleaf Publishing & Bookselling.

Rose, Gerald. Captain Cool & the Robogang. 1998. (Cambridge Reading Ser.). (Illus.). 64p. (gr. 2-6). pap. 12.00 (978-0-521-55648-4(1)) Cambridge Univ. Pr.

Rose, Maddy. Adventures of Pinkie: Sandcastle Fun. 2008. 24p. (J). pap. 9.95 (*978-1-86230-492-5(0)) Transworld Publishers Ltd. GBR. *Dist:* Independent Pubs. Group.

—The Adventures of Pinkie: Tricky Tricksters. 2008. 24p. (J). pap. 9.95 (*978-1-86230-489-5(0)) Transworld Publishers Ltd. GBR. *Dist:* Independent Pubs. Group.

Rose, Malcolm. The Alibi: The Perfect Murder... l.t. ed. 2000. (Illus.). 302p. (J). pap. (978-0-7540-6099-4(3) , CLP 297) BBC Audio.

—Final Lap. 2007. (Traces Ser.). 232p. (J). (gr. 7). pap. 5.95 (978-0-7534-6005-4(X) , Kingfisher) Houghton Mifflin Co. Trade & Reference Div.

—The Smoking Gun. l.t. ed. 1998. (Illus.). 228p. (J). pap. 16.95 (978-0-7540-6009-3(8) , Galaxy Children's Large Print) BBC Audiobooks America.

Rose, Simon. The Clone Conspiracy. 2006. 96p. (J). (gr. 4-7). pap. (978-1-896580-80-7(7)) Tradewind Bks.

Rosell, Joel Franz. Vuela, Ertico, Vuela. (SPA.). 64p. (J). (978-84-348-5268-6(3)) SM Ediciones ESP. *Dist:* Lectorum Pubns., Inc.

Rosellini, Eleanor. The Mystery of the Ancient Coins. 2003. 124p. (J). 18.95 (978-1-57860-125-7(8)) Emmis Bks.

Rosenblatt, Jason Hernandez. Justice League Mirror, Mirror: 8x8 Storybook. 2003. (Justice League Ser.). (Illus.). 24p. (J). pap. 2.99 (978-1-4037-0300-2(0)) Dalmatian Pr.

Rosenlund, Barbara F. Shadow Across the Land. 2000. 130p. (YA). (gr. 6-12). pap. 8.95 (978-0-9679354-0-9(7)) Coastline Pubs.

Ross, D. K. Beirut Middle School. 2003. 117p. pap. 16.95 (978-1-59286-640-3(9)) PublishAmerica, Inc.

Ross, David & Cattell, Bob. Red Hot. 2000. (Strikers Ser.). (Illus.). 128p. (J). pap. 7.99 (978-0-233-99695-0(8)) Andre Deutsch GBR. *Dist:* Independent Pubs. Group.

—Shoot-out. 2000. (Strikers Ser.). (Illus.). 128p. (J). pap. 7.99 (978-0-233-99694-3(X)) Andre Deutsch GBR. *Dist:* Independent Pubs. Group.

—Young Blood. 1999. 128p. (J). pap. 7.99 (978-0-233-99508-3(0)) Andre Deutsch GBR. *Dist:* Independent Pubs. Group.

Ross, Dev. We Both Read-Frank & the Giant. Reinhart, Larry, illus. 2005. (We Both Read Ser.). 44p. (J). (gr. k-1). 7.99 (978-1-891327-59-9(3)); pap. 3.99 (978-1-891327-60-5(7)) Treasure Bay, Inc.

Ross, Harriet, ed. Great Adventure Stories. Bolle, Frank, illus. 2002. 160p. (J). (gr. 3-9). pap. 4.50 (978-0-87460-181-7(9)); lib. bdg. 11.95 (978-0-87460-180-0(0)) Lion Bks.

Ross, Jillian. Alissa & the Dungeons of Grimrock. Backes, Nick, illus. 1998. (Stardust Classics). 106p. (J). (gr. 2-6). pap. 5.95 (978-1-889514-16-1(0)) Dolls Corp.

Ross, Pat. M & M & the Mummy Mess. Hafner, Marylin, illus. 1999. (Puffin Chapters Ser.). 48p. (J). (gr. 2-5). pap. 4.99 (978-0-14-130654-4(8) , Puffin) Penguin Group (USA) Inc.

Ross, Sharon, contrib. by. Diapie Tales: A Rugrats Storybook. 2003. (Rugrats Ser.). (Illus.). 160p. (J). (gr. k-3). 10.95 (978-0-689-85729-4(2) , Simon Spotlight/ Nickelodeon) Simon & Schuster Children's Publishing.

Ross, Sherry Lazarus. The Light of Lucinda. Date not set. (Illus.). 253p. (J). (gr. 2-6). pap. (978-0-615-11146-9(7)) Well Fire Pubns.

Ross, Tony. Say Please! Ross, Tony, illus. 2006. (People Love Little Princess Books! Ser.: 6). (Illus.). 28p. (J). pap. 4.95 (978-1-933605-16-6(2)) Kane/Miller Bk. Pubs., Inc.

Rossell, Judith. The Haunted Castle of Count Viper: A Spooky Maze Adventure. 2007. (Illus.). 32p. (Orig.). (J). pap. 4.95 (978-1-57990-950-5(7)) Lark Bks.

—Jack Jones & the Pirate Curse. 2007. 176p. (J). (gr. 3-6). 15.95 (*978-0-8027-9661-5(3)) Walker & Co.

Rossell, Judith. The Lost Treasure of the Green Iguana: A Jungle Maze Adventure. 2007. (Illus.). 32p. (Orig.). (J). pap. 4.95 (978-1-57990-949-9(3)) Lark Bks.

Rostam, Search for the King: Tales from the Shahnameh. 2007. (Illus.). 32p. (YA). 5.95 (*978-0-9770213-2-1(7)) hyperwerks.

Roth, Carol. In Search of Katherine: The Sequel to "Forget Me Not" 2000. 240p. (YA). (gr. 7-12). pap. 11.95 (978-0-9667555-3-4(7)) Clouse Publishing.

Roth, Matthue. Candy in Action. 2007. 224p. (YA). (gr. 9 up). 15.95 (978-1-933368-63-4(2)) Counterpoint.

Rough Riders. 2005. (J). 4.95 (978-1-59792-020-9(7)) F.A.S.T. Learning LLLC.

Rouse, Marisa K. Hildigarde of Willow Hollow. 2007. 64p. pap. 9.95 (*978-1-4327-0127-7(4)) Outskirts Press, Inc.

Rousseau, Leon. Fritz Deelman en Die Woestynrowers. 2004. 160p. pap. (978-0-7981-4425-4(4)) Human & Rousseau.

Rovetch, L. Bob. Hot Dog & Bob: And the Particularly Pesky Attack of the Pencil People. Whamond, Dave, illus. 2006. 96p. (J). pap. 4.95 (978-0-8118-5322-4(5)) Chronicle Bks. LLC.

—Hot Dog & Bob: And the Seriously Scary Attack of the Evil Alien Pizza Person. Whamond, Dave, illus. 2006. 96p. (J). pap. 4.95 (978-0-8118-5156-5(7)) Chronicle Bks. LLC.

—Hot Dog & Bob & the Surprisingly Slobbery Attack of the Dog-Wash Doggies. Whamond, Dave, illus. 2007. (Hot Dog & Bob Ser.: No. 5). 96p. (J). (gr. 1-5). 15.50 (978-0-8118-5745-1(X)); pap. 4.95 (978-0-8118-5746-8(8)) Chronicle Bks. LLC.

Rovetch, Lissa. Hot Dog & Bob Adventure, No. 6. Whamond, Dave, illus. 2008. (J). pap. 4.95 (978-0-8118-5748-2(4)) Chronicle Bks. LLC.

—Hot Dog & Bob Adventure 6 Le. Whamond, Dave, illus. 2008. (J). 15.50 (978-0-8118-5747-5(6)) Chronicle Bks. LLC.

Rowling, J. K. Harry Potter agus an Orebloch. 2004. (GAE.). 300p. (J). (gr. 5 up). 21.95 (978-1-58234-828-5(6) , Bloomsbury Children) Bloomsbury Publishing.

—Harry Potter & the Philosopher's Stone. 2004. (GRE & GEC.). 300p. (J). (gr. 3-6). 21.95 (978-1-58234-826-1(X) , Bloomsbury Children) Bloomsbury Publishing.

—Harry Potter y el Caliz de Fuego. 2004. (Harry Potter Ser.). (SPA., Illus.). 240p. (YA). 19.95 (978-84-7888-645-6(1) , SAL30169) Emece Editores ESP. *Dist:* Lectorum Pubns., Inc.

Rox, Steven. The Adventures of Grassie Green in the Colored Worlds: The Flower Country & the Green World, 3 vols. 500th ed. 2006. Orig. Title: The Flower Country & the Green World. (Illus.). 437p. (YA). cd-rom 14.95 (978-0-9773406-0-6(0)) SR Publishing Co.

Roy, James. Almost Wednesday. 2001. 152p. (YA). reprint ed. pap. 15.95 (978-0-7022-3272-5(6)) Univ. of Queensland Pr. AUS. *Dist:* International Specialized Bk. Services.

—Full Moon Racing. 1998. 208p. (YA). reprint ed. pap. 16.95 (978-0-7022-2974-9(1)) Univ. of Queensland Pr. AUS. *Dist:* International Specialized Bk. Services.

Roy, Lillian Elizabeth. Polly in New York. Barbour, H. S., illus. 2004. reprint ed. pap. 28.95 (978-1-4179-0068-8(7)) Kessinger Publishing, LLC.

Roy, Sandy & Roy, Pat. Jonathan Park & the Secret of the Hidden Cave. 1999. (Illus.). 112p. (J). (gr. 5-9). pap. 8.99 (978-0-89051-263-0(9)) Master Bks.

Royce, Richard. Hard Day for Harry. 2006. (J). spiral bd. (978-0-9777735-1-0(5)) Everwas Publishing.

Rubalcaba, Jill. The Wadjet Eye. 160p. (J). (gr. 4-6). 2006. pap. 5.95 (978-0-618-68927-9(3)); 2000. (Illus.). tchr. ed. 15.00 (978-0-395-68942-4(2)) Houghton Mifflin Co. Trade & Reference Div. (Clarion Bks.).

Ruby, Anne. Children of the Sea. Meier, Ty, illus. 2007. (YA). per. (978-0-9787881-0-0(9)) Seachild.

Ruck-Pauquet, Gina. Los Ninos Mas Encantadores del Mundo. 2003. (SPA.). 192p. (J). (gr. 3-5). 8.95 (978-84-204-4772-8(2)) Alfaguara, Ediciones, S.A.- Grupo Santillana ESP. *Dist:* Santillana USA Publishing Co., Inc.

Rucka, Greg. Introspect. Austen, Chuck, illus. 2002. (Elektra Ser.: Vol. 1). 160p. 16.99 (978-0-7851-0973-0(0)) Marvel Enterprises, Inc.

Rucker, Noah. Mystery of the Shadows. 2005. 27p. (J). 5.00 (978-1-882695-21-8(6)) Patagonia Pr.

Rucker, William. Sea Dog... Arctic Action. 2002. (Illus.). 306p. per. 16.00 (978-0-9672110-4-6(2)) Sea Dog Pr.

Ruditis, Paul. Meteor Shower Messenger. 2005. (Sonic X Ser.). 48p. (J). (gr. 1-3). pap. 4.99 (978-0-448-43996-9(4), Grosset & Dunlap) Penguin Group (USA) Inc.

Rudkin, Nancy. A Dragon at School. 2005. 28p. (J). 9.95 (978-1-4116-3877-8(8)) Lulu.com.

Rue, Nancy N. The Chase. 1999. (Christian Heritage Ser.). 192p. (J). (gr. 3-7). pap. (978-1-56179-735-6(9)) Focus on the Family Publishing.

—Lily's Church Camp Adventure. 2003. (gr. 3-6). lib. bdg. 13.00 (978-0-613-71663-5(9)) Tandem Library Bks.

Ruelle, Karen Gray. Easter Egg Disaster: A Harry & Emily Adventure. Ruelle, Karen Gray, illus. (Holiday House Readers Ser.). (Illus.). 32p. (J). (gr. k-3). pap. 4.95 (978-0-8234-1823-7(5)) Holiday Hse., Inc.

Ruiz, John. Escape. 1999. (Illus.). 24p. (J). (gr. k-6). pap. 3.99 (978-0-9715245-1-4(3)) Teamwork Foundation, Inc.

—Tommy's Firehouse Adventure. 1999. (Illus.). 24p. (J). (gr. k-6). 3.99 (978-0-9715245-2-1(1)) ; pap. 3.99 (978-0-9715245-5-2(6)) Teamwork Foundation, Inc.

Rumble, Chris. The Good, the Bad, & the Smelly. 2005. (Adventures of Uncle Stinky Ser.). (Illus.). 96p. (J). 15.95 (978-1-58246-120-5(1)); 5.95 (978-1-58246-122-9(8)) Ten Speed Pr. (Tricycle Pr.).

—Moby Stink. 2005. (Illus.). 96p. (J). (ps-7). pap. 5.95 (978-1-58246-145-8(7) , Tricycle Pr.) Ten Speed Pr.

—Stink Trek: The Adventures of Uncle Stinky #2. 2005. (Illus.). 96p. (J). 5.95 (978-1-58246-123-6(6) , Tricycle Pr.) Ten Speed Pr.

Rundstrom, T. S. The Adventures of Tommy Toad. Marshall, Setsu, illus. 2002. 34p. (J). per. 16.00 (978-1-932062-03-8(3)) Hability Solution Services, Inc.

—Sherman the Sheep: A Sheep Adventure Story about Dreams, Doing Stuff & Happiness. Miller, Bryan & Marshall, H. Keene, illus. l.t. ed. 2002. per. (978-1-932062-00-7(9) , 02-0232SH) Hability Solution Services, Inc.

Rundstrom, Teressa. The Adventures of Tommy Toad. Marshall, Setsu, illus. 2004. 40p. (J). per. (978-1-932062-41-0(6)) Hability Solution Services, Inc.

—I Love to Leap! Miller, Bryan, illus. 2004. 35p. (J). per. (978-1-932062-42-7(4)) Hability Solution Services, Inc.

—Sherman the Sheep. Marshall, H. Keene & Miller, Bryan, illus. 2002. 35p. (J). per. (978-1-932062-38-0(6)) Hability Solution Services, Inc.

Rupp, Rebecca. The Dragon of Lonely Island. ed. 2006. 192p. (J). (gr. 3-6). pap. 5.99 (978-0-7636-2805-5(0)) Candlewick Pr.

Ruppelius, Jeffrey & Ruppelius, Conrad. Conrad's Hiking Adventure. Ruppelius, Conrad, illus. 2006. (Illus.). (J). per. 12.95 (978-0-9774143-3-8(7)) Little Dog Pubns.

Russell, Elaine. Martin Mcmillan & the Lost Inca City. Cornell du Houx, Emily M. D., illus. 2005. 128p. (gr. 5 up). pap. 10.00 (978-1-882190-86-7(6)) Polar Bear & Co.

Russell, Ginny. The Money Boot. Mardon, John, illus. 1999. (First Flight Ser.). 64p. (J). pap. (978-1-55041-370-0(8)) Fitzhenry & Whiteside, Ltd.

Russo, Anthony. Abby. Sampson, Jody, illus. 2003. 18p. (J). 7.95 (978-1-59466-006-1(9) , Little Ones) Port Town Publishing.

Russo, Anthony & Derbyshire, Myra. Aerobella. Baumgardner, Mary Alice, illus. l.t. ed. 2002. 14p. (J). (978-0-9725990-1-6(0)) Port Town Publishing.

Rutledge, Margie & Cowan, Maxine. The Great Laundry Adventure. 2004. (Illus.). 174p. (J). (gr. 5-8). pap. 7.95 (978-0-929141-67-1(9)) Napoleon Publishing/ Rendezvous Pr. CAN. *Dist:* AtlasBooks Distribution.

Ryan. Me Two. Sauber, Rob, illus. 2001. 192p. (YA). (gr. 4-7). pap. 14.95 (978-0-595-17594-9(5)) iUniverse, Inc.

Ryan-Herndon, Lisa. Codename Kids Next Door: Coloring Book. Roper, Bob, illus. 2005. (Codename Ser.). 80p. (J). pap. 2.99 (978-0-439-75546-7(8) , Scholastic Paperbacks) Scholastic, Inc.

Ryan, Margaret. Kat McCrumble. 2004. (Kat Mccrumble Ser.). (Illus.). (J). pap. (978-0-340-87827-9(4) , Hodder Children's Books) Hodder Children's Division.

Ryan, Pam Muñoz. Un Caballo Llamado Libertad. 2001. (SPA.). (J). 11.64 (978-0-606-21096-6(2)) Tandem Library Bks.

Ryland, John B., told to. Wisdom for the Little People. 2005. (Illus.). (J). pap. (978-0-9743985-2-5(7)) DJ Blues Publishing.

Rylant, Cynthia. Days with Henry & Mudge, 4 bks. Stevenson, Sucie, illus. 2000. (Henry & Mudge Ser.). (J). (gr. k-3). pap. 61.95 incl. audio (978-0-87499-705-7(4)) Live Oak Media.

—The High-Rise Private Eyes Series. Karas, G. Brian, illus. 2003. pap. 61.95 incl. audio (978-1-59112-430-6(1)); pap. 68.95 incl. audio compact disk (978-1-59112-858-8(7)) Live Oak Media.

—La Tormenta.Tr. of Storm. (SPA.). (J). 7.95 (978-958-04-7077-9(4)) Norma S.A. COL. *Dist:* Distribuidora Norma, Inc.

—The Whale. McDaniels, Preston, illus. 2003. (Lighthouse Family Ser.). 64p. (J). 14.95 (978-0-689-84881-0(1)) Simon & Schuster Children's Publishing.

Rylant, Cynthia & McDaniels, Preston. The Whale. 2004. (Lighthouse Family Ser.). (Illus.). 96p. (J). pap. 3.99 (978-0-689-84883-4(8) , Aladdin) Simon & Schuster Children's Publishing.

Rymas-Loomis, Cathy. Calamity Clancey: The Calamity Cat from Kalvesta Kansas. 2007. 40p. per. 12.97 (*978-1-932344-85-1(3)) Thornton Publishing.

Rymond, Lynda Gene. Oscar & the Mooncats. Ceccoli, Nicoletta, illus. 2007. 40p. (J). (gr. k-3). 16.00 (*978-0-618-56316-6(4)) Houghton Mifflin Co.

Sachar, Louis. Holes. 2002. (Illus.). (J). 15.00 (978-0-7587-0192-3(6)) Book Wholesalers, Inc.

—Holes. unabr. ed. 2004. 240p. (J). (gr. 5-9). pap. 36.00 incl. audio (978-0-8072-8072-0(0) , Listening Library) Random Hse. Audio Publishing Group.

—Holes. 2001. tchr. ed. 0.00 (978-0-385-38025-6(9) , Dell Books for Young Readers); 2001. 256p. (YA). (gr. 5 up). mass mkt. 6.99 (978-0-440-22859-2(X) , Laurel Leaf); 2003. (Illus.). 240p. (gr. 5 up). pap. 6.50 (978-0-440-41946-4(8) , Yearling) Random Hse. Children's Bks.

—Holes. 2001. (gr. 5-8). lib. bdg. 14.75 (978-0-613-87297-3(5)); 2000. 233p. (J). (gr. k-9). per. 14.75 (978-0-613-23669-6(0)); 2000. 13.15 (978-0-606-18910-1(6)) Tandem Library Bks.

Sachi. 2006. 26p. 10.05 (978-1-4116-7248-2(8)) Lulu.com.

Sage, Angie. Frognapped. Pickering, Jimmy, illus. 2007. (Araminta Spookie Ser.: Bk. 3). (J). (gr. 2-5). 128p. 8.99 (*978-0-06-077487-5(8)); 208p. lib. bdg. 14.89 (*978-0-06-077488-2(6)) HarperCollins Pubs. (Tegen, Katherine Bks).

—My Haunted House. Pickering, Jimmy, illus. 2006. (Araminta Spookie Ser.: Bk. 1). 144p. (J). (gr. 2-5). lib. bdg. 14.89 (978-0-06-077482-0(7)) HarperCollins Pubs.

—The Sword in the Grotto. Pickering, Jimmy, illus. 2006. (Araminta Spookie Ser.: Bk. 2). 160p. (J). (gr. 2-5). 8.99 (978-0-06-077484-4(3) , Tegen, Katherine Bks); lib. bdg. 14.89 (978-0-06-077485-1(1)) HarperCollins Pubs.

Sage, Angie. Vampire Brat. 2007. (Araminta Spookie Ser.: Bk. 4). (Illus.). 208p. (J). (gr. 2-5). lib. bdg. 14.89 (*978-0-06-077491-2(6)) HarperCollins Pubs.

—Vampire Brat, No. 4. Pickering, Jimmy, illus. 2007. (Araminta Spookie Ser.: Bk. 4). 128p. (J). (gr. 2-5). 8.99 (*978-0-06-077490-5(8)) HarperCollins Pubs.

Said, S. F. The Outlaw Varjak Paw. McKean, Dave, illus. 2007. 272p. (J). (gr. 3-7). 6.50 (978-0-440-42172-6(1) , Yearling) Random Hse. Children's Bks.

Saintil-van Goodman, Claire J. Mariel & the Cookie. 2003. (J). pap. 10.00 (978-0-8059-9230-4(8) , RoseDog Bks.) Dorrance Publishing Co., Inc.

Sakai, Stan. Duel at Kitanoji. 2003. (Usagi Yojimbo Ser.). (Illus.). 224p. (YA). pap. 16.95 (978-1-56971-973-2(X)) Dark Horse Comics.

—Travels with Jotaro. 2004. (Usagi Yojimbo Ser.: Vol. 18). (Illus.). 208p. (YA). pap. 15.95 (978-1-59307-220-9(1)) Dark Horse Comics.

—Usagi Yojimbo Vol. 4: Estaciones. 2007. (SPA., Illus.). 200p. reprint ed. pap. 15.95 (*978-1-59497-320-8(2)) Public Square Bks.

—Usagi Yojimbo Vol. 5: Segadora. 2007. (SPA., Illus.). 256p. reprint ed. pap. 17.95 (*978-1-59497-321-5(0)) Public Square Bks.

—Usagi Yojimbo Vol. 6: Primeras Andanzas. 2007. (SPA., Illus.). 128p. reprint ed. pap. 12.95 (*978-1-59497-322-2(9)) Public Square Bks.

—Usagi Yojimbo Vol. 7: Samurai (en Español) 2007. (SPA., Illus.). 144p. reprint ed. pap. 14.95 (*978-1-59497-323-9(7)) Public Square Bks.

Salerno, Tony. Dog Tired: A Learning Adventure in Perseverance, 4 vols. 2005. 56p. (J). 14.99 (978-0-89221-605-5(0)) New Leaf Pr., Inc.

—A Sticky Situation: A Learning Adventure in Honesty. 2005. 56p. (J). 14.99 (978-0-89221-606-2(9)) New Leaf Pr., Inc.

—Wise Quacks: A Learning Adventure in Self-Control, 4 vols. 2005. 56p. (J). 14.99 (978-0-89221-604-8(2)) New Leaf Pr., Inc.

Salgari, Emilio. El Corsario Negro. 2002. (Classics for Young Readers Ser.). (SPA.). (YA). 14.95 (978-84-392-0931-7(2) , EV30598) Lectorum Pubns., Inc.

—El Corsario Negro. 2000. (Coleccion "Clasicos Juveniles" Ser.). (SPA., Illus.). 108p. (gr. 4-7). pap. 8.95 (978-1-58348-826-3(X)) iUniverse, Inc.

Salmassian, Jennifer. Sally Saves the Mice. 2007. (J). per. 0.01 net. (*978-1-60402-115-8(2)) Independent Pub.

—Sally the Firefighter. 2007. (J). per. 0.01 net. (*978-1-60402-164-6(0)) Independent Pub.

Salvatore, R. A. Vector Prime. 2000. (Star Wars Ser.: Bk. 1). (gr. 7-12). lib. bdg. 15.90 (978-0-613-29377-8(0)) Tandem Library Bks.

Samantha's Arizona Adventure. 1998. (Illus.). 2p. (J). (ps-1). 15.00 (978-1-888074-84-0(1)) Pockets of Learning.

Samantha's Colorado Adventure. 1998. (Illus.). 2p. (J). (ps-1). 15.00 (978-1-888074-85-7(X)) Pockets of Learning.

Samantha's Florida Adventure. 1998. (Illus.). 2p. (J). (ps-1). 15.00 (978-1-888074-86-4(8)) Pockets of Learning.

Samantha's Hawaii Adventure. 1998. (Illus.). 2p. (J). (ps-1). 15.00 (978-1-888074-87-1(6)) Pockets of Learning.

Samantha's New York Adventure. 1998. (Illus.). 2p. (J). (ps-1). 15.00 (978-1-888074-88-8(4)) Pockets of Learning.

Samantha's Vermont Adventure. 1998. (Illus.). 2p. (J). (ps-1). 15.00 (978-1-888074-89-5(2)) Pockets of Learning.

Sampson, Brent. Aidan's Shoes. Switzer, Bobbi, illus. 2006. (ENG.). 28p. per. 12.95 (*978-1-59800-684-1(3)) Outskirts Press, Inc.

Sampson, Fay. Sorcerers Trap. 2005. 224p. (J). pap. 9.99 (978-0-7459-4985-7(1)) Lion Hudson plc GBR. *Dist:* Independent Pubs. Group.

Sampson, Jeff. The Ebony Eye. 2007. (Suncatcher Trilogy Ser.: Vol. 2). 256p. (YA). pap. 5.99 (978-0-7869-4255-8(X) , Mirrorstone) Wizards of the Coast.

Samuel, Catherine. Timmy's Eggs-Ray Vision. Saunders, Zina, illus. 2005. (Fairly OddParents Ser.). 16p. (J). pap. 5.99 (978-0-689-87229-7(1) , Simon Spotlight/ Nickelodeon) Simon & Schuster Children's Publishing.

Samuels, Vallerie. The Village of Time. 2005. 9.00 (978-0-8059-9709-5(1)) Dorrance Publishing Co., Inc.

Samura, Hiroaki. Last Blood. Lewis, Dana & Smith, Toren, trs. Samura, Hiroaki, illus. 2005. (Illus.). per. 30.15 (978-1-4176-5923-4(8)) Tandem Library Bks.

Samurai's Tale. 1999. (YA). 9.95 (978-1-56137-818-0(6)) Novel Units, Inc.

Sanchez, Gloria. Chinto y Tom. (SPA.). 80p. (J). (978-84-348-8101-3(2)) SM Ediciones ESP. *Dist:* Lectorum Pubns., Inc.

Sancho the Snowboarder. 2005. (J). 15.95 (978-0-9773243-0-9(5)) Sancho Storybooks.

Sanders, Alex. Un Lobo! (SPA.). 36p. (978-84-95150-34-9(4)) Corimbo, Editorial S.L.

—Un Lobo! (SPA.). 36p. 16.95 (978-84-95150-24-0(7)) Corimbo, Editorial S.L. ESP. *Dist:* Distribooks, Inc.

Sanders, Marty Beatty. Misty of Chincoteague. Castanares, Ana, illus. 1999. (Literature Units Ser.). 48p. (J). (gr. 3-5). pap., tchr. ed. 7.99 (978-1-57690-624-8(8) , TCA2624) Teacher Created Materials, Inc.

Sanders, Stephanie. Q. T. Pie Catches the Rainbow. Pauling, Galen T., illus. 2001. 24p. (J). pap. 3.99 (978-0-9670875-2-8(X)) SanPaul Group, LLC, The.

Sanjo, Riku. Beet the Vandel Buster. Inada, Koji, illus. 2005. (Beet the Vandel Buster Ser.). 208p. (YA). pap. 7.99 (978-1-59116-750-1(7)) Viz Media.

Sanschagrin, Joceline. Mission Audacieuse. 1998. (Roman Jeunesse Ser.). (FRE., Illus.). 96p. (J). (gr. 4-7). pap. (978-2-89021-156-8(8)) Diffusion du livre Mirabel.

Sanschagrin, Joceline & Pratt, Pierre. Le Labyrinthe des Reves. 2000. (Roman Jeunesse Ser.). (FRE.). 96p. (J). (gr. 4-7). pap. (978-2-89021-409-5(5)) Diffusion du livre Mirabel.

Santangelo, Colony Elliott. Brother Wolf of Gubbio: A Legend of Saint Francis. 2000. (Illus.). 32p. (J). (gr. 1-5). 15.95 (978-1-929766-07-9(6)) Handprint Bks.

Santiago, Chiori. Home to Medicine Mountain. Lowry, Judith, illus. 2002. 32p. (J). (gr. 1 up). pap. 7.95 (978-0-89239-176-9(6)) Children's Bk. Pr.

Santina. Momaguin. 2001. (gr. 7-12). lib. bdg. 21.60 (978-0-613-74621-2(X)) Tandem Library Bks.

Santoro, Lucio, et al. Journey to the Moon: A Roaring, Soaring Ride. 2007. 14p. (J). (ps). 26.99 (*978-1-4169-4721-9(3) , Little Simon) Simon & Schuster Children's Publishing.

Sapp, Brent. Teknon & the Champion Warriors. Cariello, Sergio, illus. 2003. 7.99 (978-1-57229-219-2(9)) FamilyLife.

Sargent, Dave. Hiding Place #4, 10 vols. 2007. (Little Stinker Ser.: 4). (J). lib. bdg. 22.60 (*978-1-59381-282-9(5)) Ozark Publishing.

—Hiding Place #4 (PB), 10 vols. 2007. (Little Stinker Ser.: 4). (J). pap. 9.95 (*978-1-59381-283-6(3)) Ozark Publishing.

—Sammy's Hiding Place #9, 10 vols. 2007. (Little Stinker Ser.: 9). (J). lib. bdg. 22.60 (*978-1-59381-297-3(3)) Ozark Publishing.

—Sammy's Hiding Place #9 (PB), 10 vols. 2007. (Little Stinker Ser.: 9). (J). pap. 9.95 (*978-1-59381-298-0(1)) Ozark Publishing.

Sargent, Dave. Tornado & Sweep, Bk. II. Bowen, Debbie, ed. Zapata, Miguel, tr. from ENG. Lenoir, Jane, illus. (SPA.). (Orig.). (J). (gr. k-6). pap. 6.95 (978-1-56763-123-4(1)); pap. 6.95 (978-1-56763-126-5(6)) Ozark Publishing.

Sargent, Dave & Sargent, Pat. Big Jake: I'm Very Curious, 56 vols., Vol. 12. Huff, Jeane, illus. 2nd rev. ed. 2003. (Animal Pride Ser.: 12). 42p. (J). lib. bdg. 19.95 (978-1-56763-781-6(7)) Ozark Publishing.

—The Chuck Wagon: Don't Be Stubborn, 10. Lenoir, Jane, illus. 2005. (Colorado Cowboys Ser.: 7). 32p. (J). 7. lib. bdg. 22.60 (978-1-59381-098-6(9)); Vol. 7. pap. 9.95 (978-1-59381-099-3(7)) Ozark Publishing.

—The Colorado Blizzard: Be Determined, 10 vols., Vol. 8. Lenoir, Jane, illus. 2005. (Colorado Cowboys Ser.: 10). 32p. (J). pap. 9.95 (978-1-59381-027-6(X)) Ozark Publishing.

—The Drought: Have Faith, 10. Lenoir, Jane, illus. 2005. (Colorado Cowboys Ser.: 9). 32p. (J). 9. lib. bdg. 22.60 (978-1-59381-102-0(0)); Vol. 9. pap. 9.95 (978-1-59381-103-7(9)) Ozark Publishing.

—The Fire: A Second Chance, 10 vols., Vol. 10. Lenoir, Jane, illus. 2005. (Colorado Cowboys Ser.: 10). 32p. (J). pap. 9.95 (978-1-59381-105-1(5)) Ozark Publishing.

—Valley Oak Acorns: (Maidu) Be Helpful, 20, Vol. 20. Lenoir, Jane, illus. l.t. ed. 2005. (Story Keeper Ser.: 20). 42p. (J). (ps-ps). lib. bdg. 22.60 (978-1-56763-941-4(0)) Ozark Publishing.

Sargent, Dave, et al. Fierce Warriors Vol. 7: (Comanche) Learn Skills, 20 bks. Lenoir, Jane, illus. l.t. ed. 2004. (Story Keeper Ser.: 7). 48p. (J). pap. 6.95 (978-1-56763-916-2(X)) Ozark Publishing.

—Fierce Warriors Vol. 7: Learn Skills, 20 bks. Lenoir, Jane, illus. l.t. ed. 2004. (Story Keeper Ser.: 7). 48p. (J). lib. bdg. 22.60 (978-1-56763-915-5(1)) Ozark Publishing.

—Summer Milky Way: (Blackfeet) Be Compassionate, 20, Vol. 16. Lenoir, Jane, illus. l.t. ed. 2004. (Story Keeper Ser.). 48p. (J). lib. bdg. 22.60 (978-1-56763-933-9(X)); pap. 6.95 (978-1-56763-934-6(8)) Ozark Publishing.

—Truth, Power & Freedom Vol. 19: (Sioux) Show Respect, 20. Lenoir, Jane, illus. l.t. ed. 2004. (Story Keeper Ser.: 19). 42p. (J). 19. lib. bdg. 22.60 (978-1-56763-939-1(9)); Vol. 19. pap. 6.95 (978-1-56763-940-7(2)) Ozark Publishing.

—Valley Oaks Acorns Vol. 20: (Maidu) Be Helpful, 20. Lenoir, Jane, illus. l.t. ed. 2004. (Story Keeper Ser.: 20). 48p. (J). pap. 6.95 (978-1-56763-942-1(9)) Ozark Publishing.

Sargent, Pamela. Farseed. 2007. (Seed Trilogy Ser.). 288p. (YA). (gr. 7 up). 17.95 (978-0-7653-1427-7(4) , Tor Teen) Doherty, Tom Assocs., LLC.

Sathre, Vivian. Dog Overboard! l.t. ed. 1999. (Adventures of Wishbone Ser.: No. 12). (Illus.). (J). (gr. 4 up). lib. bdg. 22.60 (978-0-8368-2590-9(X)) Stevens, Gareth Inc.

Sato, Wakiko. Grandma Baba's Amazing Scarf!, Vol. 10. 2004. (Grandma Baba Ser.: Bk. 10). (Illus.). 28p. 12.95 (978-0-8048-3566-4(7)) Tuttle Publishing.

Satterwhite, William. Stealth,, Vol. 1. 2005. 44p. (YA). pap. 5.75 (978-1-4116-2395-8(9)) Lulu.com.

Saunders, Catherine. The Story of Darth Vader. 2008. (Dk Readers Ser.). 48p. (J). 14.99 (*978-0-7566-3605-0(1)); pap. 3.99 (*978-0-7566-3602-9(7)) Dorling Kindersley Publishing, Inc.

Saunders, Joanne. The Secret at the Winthrop House, Independence Day: Book 2. 2007. 208p. (YA). per. 13.99 (*978-1-59886-935-4(3)) Tate Publishing & Enterprises, L.L.C.

Saunders, Joanne D. Secret at the Winthrop House. 2007. 192p. per. 12.99 (*978-1-59886-622-3(2)) Tate Publishing & Enterprises, L.L.C.

Saunders, Susan. All-American Puppies: On The Scent of Trouble. 2001. (All-American Puppies Ser.: Vol. 2). (Illus.). 96p. (J). (gr. 2-5). pap. 3.99 (978-0-06-440885-1(X)) HarperCollins Pubs.

—Chilling Tale of Crescent Pond. 1998. (Black Cat Club Ser.: Vol. 8). (J). (978-0-606-13205-3(8)) Tandem Library Bks.

—Disaster at Parson's Point. 1998. (Neptune Adventures Ser.: No. 2). 96p. (J). (gr. 3-7). pap. 3.99 (978-0-380-79489-8(6)) HarperCollins Pubs.

—Stranding on Cedar Point, No. 4. 1998. (Neptune Adventures Ser.: No. 4). 96p. (J). (gr. 3-7). pap. 3.99 (978-0-380-79492-8(6)) HarperCollins Pubs.

Saunders, Zina, illus. Cops & Robots. 2006. (Backyardigans Ser.). 14p. (J). bds. 6.99 (978-1-4169-1572-0(9) , Simon Spotlight/Nickelodeon) Simon & Schuster Children's Publishing.

—Go, Team, Go! 2005. (Dora the Explorer Ser.). 10p. (J). bds. 7.99 (978-1-4169-0394-9(1) , Simon Spotlight/ Nickelodeon) Simon & Schuster Children's Publishing.

—Secret Agents. 2006. (Backyardigans Ser.). 24p. (J). pap. 3.99 (978-1-4169-1226-2(6) , Simon Spotlight/ Nickelodeon) Simon & Schuster Children's Publishing.

Sautel, Anne & Chouinard, Catherine. The Wombat Takes on Tasmania. Stewart, Scott, illus. 2006. 96p. (J). (gr. 2-4). pap. (978-1-897073-32-2(1)) Lobster Pr.

Savage, Bridgette Z. Fly Like the Wind. Savage, Bridgette Z., illus. 2005. (Illus.). 112p. (J). per. 16.99 (978-0-9771494-0-7(4)) Buckbeech Studios.

Savage, Tawanna. Anna Mischievous: The Early Years. 2005. Orig. Title: ANNA MISCHIEVOUS: the Early Years. (J). spiral bd. (978-0-9754147-9-8(8)) ASP Corp. Entertainment Group, Inc.

Savageau, Tony. The Mud House Mystery: A Wild Bunch Adventure. Raditz, JoAnne, illus. 2004. (J). pap. 9.95 (978-0-9759737-0-7(3)) Blue Mustang Pr.

Saving the Zog. 2002. (Illus.). (J). pap. (978-0-7398-5104-3(7)) Steck-Vaughn.

Sawler, Kimberley. Rocket & the Magical Cosmic Candies. 2007. (YA). 18.95 (*978-1-933285-51-1(6)) Brown Bks. Publishing Group.

Sawyer, Walter. La Tormenta. Romo, Alberto, tr. O'Malley, Kathleen, illus. 1999. (Books for Young Learners).Tr. of Storm. (SPA.). 8p. (J). (gr. k-2). pap. 5.00 (978-1-57274-346-5(8) , A2912) Owen, Richard C. Pubs., Inc.

Saxon, Victoria. Tigger's Tall Tales: Chuncky Roly Poly Book. 1999. (Learn & Grow Ser.). (Illus.). 16p. (J). (ps-k). 3.50 (978-0-7364-0153-1(9)) Mouse Works.

Sayers, Susan. Adventures. 2000. (Living Word Living Water Ser.). 144p. (YA). pap. 24.95 (978-1-58595-105-5(6)) Twenty-Third Pubns./Bayard.

Sayger, Jack. Fountain of Youth. 2002. (978-0-9711403-0-1(8)) Sayger, Jack.

Scafuro, Lisa. Adventures at Cedar Hollow: Tigre Encounters the Great Horned Owl. 2005. (J). 18.00 (978-0-8059-6635-0(8)) Dorrance Publishing Co., Inc.

Scanes, Amy. The Chosen: Book Two of the Abon Trilogy. 2007. 304p. per. 18.95 (*978-0-595-45990-2(0)) iUniverse, Inc.

Scarry, Richard. Richard Scarry's Busiest Pop-up Ever! 2007. (Richard Scarry Ser.). 10p. (J). (ps-2). 19.99 (*978-0-375-84120-0(2) , Golden Bks.) Random Hse. Children's Bks.

Schaaf, Ron. Tiger's Quest: Rounding Cape Horn. 2007. (J). (*978-0-9787555-0-8(2)) Hickory Tales Publishing.

Schachner, Judy. Skippyjon Jones & the Treasure Hunt. 2008. 16p. (J). (ps-1). 9.99 (*978-0-448-44817-6(3) , Grosset & Dunlap) Penguin Group (USA) Inc.
—A Surprise for Mama. 2008. 16p. (J). (ps-1). pap. 5.99 (*978-0-448-44816-9(5) , Grosset & Dunlap) Penguin Group (USA) Inc.
Schade, Susan. Faradawn. Buller, Jon, illus. 2007. (Fog Mound Ser.: No. 2). 208p. (J). (gr. 3-7). 15.99 (978-0-689-87686-8(6)) Simon & Schuster Children's Publishing.
—Travels of Thelonious. Buller, Jon, illus. 2007. (Fog Mound Ser.: No. 1). 224p. (J). (gr. 3-7). pap. 7.99 (978-0-689-87685-1(8) , Simon & Schuster Children's Publishing) Simon & Schuster Children's Publishing.
Schade, Susan & Buller, Jon. The Travels of Thelonious. 2006. (Fog Mound Ser.: No. 1). (Illus.). 224p. (J). (gr. 3-7). 14.95 (978-0-689-87684-4(X)) Simon & Schuster Children's Publishing.
Schaller, Bob. The Adventures of Jack & Diane: A Christian Children's Story about Sports. 2000. 108p. (gr. 4-7). pap. 9.95 (978-0-595-12756-6(8) , Writer's Showcase Pr.) iUniverse, Inc.
—Arlington Family Adventures, 4 vols. 2000. (J). (gr. 4-7). 19.95 (978-0-8010-8493-5(8)) Baker Bks.
Schalow, Al. The Adventure down Crunchy Road. 2004. (Illus.). vii, 69p. (J). 19.95 (978-0-9654963-4-6(1)) Medwag Publishing.
Schandle, Julie. Little Wishes Big Dreams: Around the World. 2005. (Illus.). 22p. (J). 11.95 (978-0-9771868-0-8(6) , 303-503-3289) Big Dreams Publishing.
Scheber, George. Earl Joins the Circus. Spicer, Bridgett, illus. l.t. ed. 2005. (Adventures of Earl the Squirrel Ser.). 32p. (J). (ps-3). 12.95 (978-1-878847-01-0(5)) Make Me A Story Pr.
Scherer, Catherine W. Simon & Barklee in China, Book 2 - the Mountains. 2008. (Another Country Calling Ser.). (J). per. 15.00 (978-0-9714502-7-1(7) , Explorer Media) Simon & Barklee, Inc./ExplorerMedia.
—Simon & Barklee in China, Book 3 - the North. 2008. (Another Country Calling Ser.). (J). per. 15.00 (978-0-9714502-8-8(5) , Explorer Media) Simon & Barklee, Inc./ExplorerMedia.
Schermbrucker, Reviva. An African Christmas Cloth. 2007. 36p. 27.95 (978-1-77009-081-1(9)); (Illus.). 40p. pap. 19.95 (978-1-77009-151-1(3)) Jacana Media ZAF. *Dist:* Independent Pubs. Group.
Scheving, Magnus & Artful Doodlers Limited Staff. It's Sports Day! 2006. (LazyTown Ser.). (Illus.). 16p. (J). pap. 4.99 (978-1-4169-0721-3(1) , Simon Spotlight/Nickelodeon) Simon & Schuster Children's Publishing.
Schexnayder, Paul, illus. The Kajun Kween. 2003. 100p. (J). per. 22.00 (978-0-9650977-1-0(4)) Border Pr.
Schifferli, Paul Phillip. Darryl's Daring Deed. Schifferli, Paul Phillip, illus. 2006. (J). 9.95 (*978-0-9765304-7-3(3)) Windsor Media Enterprises, LLC.
Schiller, Friedrich. Guilermo Tell.Tr. of William Tell. (SPA., Illus.). 160p. (YA). 11.95 (978-84-7281-088-4(7) , AF1088) Auriga, Ediciones S.A. ESP. *Dist:* Continental Bk. Co., Inc.
Schisgall, Jim. Spritzer Rides Again. Timmins, John, illus. 2000. 32p. (J). pap. 6.95 (978-1-890997-05-2(6)); 15.95 (978-1-890997-04-5(8)) Hardy Hill Enterprises, Inc.
Schlesinger, Gretchen. Send Me the Soap #2: The Amazon Adventure. Pietila, David, illus. 2007. (J). 11.95 (*978-0-9778536-2-5(4)) Eco-thumb Publishing Co.
Schlossberg Tamberrino, Suzanne. Firestorm. 2004. 61p. pap. 12.95 (978-1-4137-6008-8(2)) PublishAmerica, Inc.
Schmidt, Werner. The Forests of Adventure. 2005. 137p. pap. 12.50 (978-1-4116-4721-3(1)) Lulu.com.
—Prisoners of the Witchaliks. 2005. 173p. pap. 12.50 (978-1-4116-4728-2(9)) Lulu.com.
Schneider, Howie. Wilky the White House Cockroach. Schneider, Howie, illus. 2006. (Illus.). 32p. (J). (ps-3). 16.99 (978-0-399-24388-2(7)) Penguin Group (USA) Inc.
Schnitzler, Arthur. Meisterzahlungen. pap. 25.95 (978-3-257-21016-3(7)) Diogenes Verlag AG CHE. *Dist:* Distribooks, Inc.
Schnur, Steven. Mrs. Popham's Library. 2003. 48p. (J). pap. 8.95 (978-0-595-30163-8(0)) iUniverse, Inc.
Schofield, S. M. Race to Eagle Mountain. 2007. (ENG.). 184p. (J). per. 16.99 (*978-1-4141-0814-8(1)) Pleasant Word.
Scholastic Editorial Staff. Super Spooky Double Storybook. 2008. (Puppy Place Ser.). 48p. (J). pap. 4.99 (*978-0-545-03153-0(2)) Scholastic, Inc.
Scholastic, Inc. Staff. Adventures in Care-a-Lot Sticker Storybook. Swendsen, Silje, ed. 2004. (Care Bears Ser.). 16p. (J). pap. 5.99 (978-0-439-62489-3(4)) Scholastic, Inc.
—Adventures in Care-a-Lot Sticker Storybook. 2004. (gr. k-3). lib. bdg. 14.15 (978-0-613-82750-8(3)) Tandem Library Bks.
—Battle for Morcia. 2006. (Knights' Kingdom Ser.). 4p. (J). bds. 9.99 (978-0-439-82814-7(7)) Scholastic, Inc.
—Create & Trace. Jayatilleke, Ruwan, ed. 2003. (G. I. Joe Ser.). (Illus.). 32p. (J). pap. 2.99 (978-0-439-44929-8(4)) Scholastic, Inc.
—The Door to Time. 2007. (Ulysses Moore Ser.: Bk. 1). 240p. (J). pap. 2.99 (*978-0-439-93020-8(0)) Scholastic, Inc.
—Harry Potter & the Prisoner of Azkaban Color & Activity Book: With Stickers. Reisfeld, Randi, ed. 2004. (Harry Potter Ser.). 32p. (J). 3.99 (978-0-439-62561-6(0) , Scholastic Paperbacks) Scholastic, Inc.
—I Challenge You. 2007. (Yu-Gi-Oh Gx Ser.). 32p. (J). pap. 3.99 (*978-0-439-88839-4(5)) Scholastic, Inc.
—Undefeated Hero, Bk. 4. 2007. (Yu-Gi-Oh Gx Ser.). 96p. (J). pap. 4.99 (*978-0-439-88833-2(6)) Scholastic, Inc.
Scholastic, Inc. Staff, ed. Charlie's Ticket to Literacy. 1999. (J). pap. 9.95 (978-0-590-73095-2(9)) Scholastic, Inc.
Scholastic, Inc. Staff & Blade, Adam. Cypher the Mountain Giant. 2007. (Beast Quest Ser.: No. 3). 80p. (J). pap. 4.99 (*978-0-439-92225-8(9)) Scholastic, Inc.
Scholastic, Inc. Staff & Farshtey, Greg. Bionicle Adventures: The Darkness Below. 2004. (Bionicle Ser.). (Illus.). 96p. (J). 4.99 (978-0-439-60733-9(7)) Scholastic, Inc.
—Mystery of Metru Nui: Bionicle Adventures. 2004. (Bionicle Adventures Ser.: Vol. 1). (Illus.). 96p. (J). 4.99 (978-0-439-60731-5(0)) Scholastic, Inc.
Scholastic, Inc. Staff & West, Tracey. Cyborg, Come Home! MacKenzie, Kevin, illus. 2004. (Teen Titans Ser.). 64p. (J). 3.99 (978-0-439-63620-9(5) , Scholastic Paperbacks) Scholastic, Inc.
—Teen Titans, Bk. 2. MacKenzie, Kevin, illus. 2004. (Teen Titans Ser.). 64p. (J). pap. 3.99 (978-0-439-63618-6(3) , Scholastic Paperbacks) Scholastic, Inc.
Scholastic, Inc. Staff & Windham, Ryder. Return of the Jedi. novel ed. 2004. (Star Wars Ser.). 176p. (J). (gr. 4-7). pap. 5.99 (978-0-439-68126-1(X)) Scholastic, Inc.
Schooley, Bob & McCorkle, Mark. Liar of Kudzu. 2007. 192p. (J). 15.99 (978-1-4169-1488-4(9)) Simon & Schuster Children's Publishing.
Schraff, Anne. A Horse Called Courage. 2001. (PageTurner Adventure Ser.). 80p. (YA). per. 3.95 (978-1-56254-187-3(0) , SP 1870) Saddleback Educational Publishing.
—Swamp Furies. Parker, Liz, ed. Taylor, Marjorie, illus. rev. ed. 1999. (Take Ten Ser.). 55p. (YA). (gr. 4 up). pap. 3.95 (978-1-58659-013-0(8)) Artesian Pr.
—Swamp Furies. 2000. (gr. 5-8). lib. bdg. 11.80 (978-0-613-51226-8(X)) Tandem Library Bks.
—Terrible Orchid Sky. 2001. (gr. 7-12). lib. bdg. 11.80 (978-0-613-33129-6(X)) Tandem Library Bks.
—Up Rattler Mountain. 2001. (PageTurner Adventure Ser.). 80p. (YA). per. 3.95 (978-1-56254-183-5(8) , SP 1838) Saddleback Educational Publishing.
—Up Rattler Mountain. 2001. (gr. 7-12). lib. bdg. 11.80 (978-0-613-33178-4(8)); (Illus.). 75p. (J). (gr. 4-7). lib. bdg. 11.15 (978-0-606-21578-7(6)) Tandem Library Bks.
—Who Has Seen the Beast? 2001. (PageTurner Adventure Ser.). 80p. (YA). per. 3.95 (978-1-56254-186-6(2) , SP 1862) Saddleback Educational Publishing.
—Who Has Seen the Beast? 2001. (gr. 7-12). lib. bdg. 11.80 (978-0-613-33243-9(1)) Tandem Library Bks.
Schroeder, Erin, illus. & des. Oh no! it's the helpful hound... & the days of the Week. Schroeder, Erin, des. 2006. (FRE, JPN, SPA & GER.). 27p. (J). per. 7.95 (*978-0-9779155-0-7(6)) Erinsillart.
Schurch, Maylan. Danger Signals in Belize. 2002. (Justin Case Adventures Ser.: 3). 121p. (YA). pap. 7.99 (978-0-8280-1613-1(5)) Review & Herald Publishing Assn.
Schuster, Judith. The Eddie Brewster Adventures, Bk. 1. 2006. 142p. pap. 19.95 (*978-1-4241-4418-1(3)) PublishAmerica, Inc.
Schwartz, Lew Sayre. Moby Dick: Based on the Novel by Herman Melville. 2002. (gr. 5-8). lib. bdg. 15.25 (978-0-613-70733-6(8)) Tandem Library Bks.
Schwartz, Roslyn. The Complete Adventures of the Mole Sisters. Schwartz, Roslyn, illus. 2004. (Mole Sisters Ser.). (Illus.). 168p. (J). (ps-k). 19.95 (978-1-55037-883-2(X)) Annick Pr., Ltd. CAN. *Dist:* Firefly Bks., Ltd.
Schwartz, Suzanne & Schwartz, Robert. My Friend Hibby: A Tropical Adventure. Schwartz, Suzanne & Schwartz, Robert, illus. 2005. (Illus.). 20p. (J). spiral bd. 6.00 (978-0-9764152-0-6(8)) Seascay Productions.
Schwarz, Laurence & KOL (AOL Kids) Staff. Can It: As Seen on Cartoon Network. 5th ed. 2006. (Princess Natasha Ser.: No. 6). (Illus.). 80p. (J). (gr. 3-7). pap. 3.99 (978-0-316-15509-0(8)) Little Brown & Co.
—Game Over: As Seen on Cartoon Network. 3rd ed. 2006. (Princess Natasha Ser.: No. 3). (Illus.). 80p. (J). (gr. 3-7). pap. 3.99 (978-0-316-15506-9(3)) Little Brown & Co.
—Thunderstruck: As Seen on Cartoon Network. 4th ed. 2006. (Princess Natasha Ser.: No. 4). (Illus.). 80p. (J). (gr. 3-7). pap. 3.99 (978-0-316-15508-3(X)) Little Brown & Co.
Schwarz, Viviane. Shark & Lobster's Amazing Undersea Adventure. Schwarz, Viviane & Stewart, Joel, illus. 2006. 40p. (J). (ps-1). 15.99 (978-0-7636-2910-6(3)) Candlewick Pr.
Scieszka, Jon. Ay, Samuray!Tr. of Sam Samurai. (SPA.). (J). 7.95 (978-958-04-6867-7(2)) Norma S.A. COL. *Dist:* Distribuidora Norma, Inc.
—Domingo, el Dia del Vikingo. (SPA.). (J). 7.95 (978-958-04-7448-7(6)) Norma S.A. COL. *Dist:* Distribuidora Norma, Inc.
—Harem Scare'em. 2007. (Time Warp Trio). 80p. (J). pap. 4.99 (*978-0-06-111649-0(1) , Harper Trophy) HarperCollins Pubs.
—Lewis & Clark... & Jodie, Freddi, & Samantha. 2006. (Time Warp Trio: No. 2). 80p. (J). pap. 4.99 (978-0-06-111638-4(6) , Harper Trophy) HarperCollins Pubs.
—Meet You at Waterloo. 2007. (Time Warp Trio: Vol. 4). 96p. (J). pap. 6.99 (*978-0-06-111646-9(7) , Harper Trophy) HarperCollins Pubs.
—Nightmare on Joe's Street. 2006. (Time Warp Trio: Vol. 1). 96p. (J). (gr. 3-6). pap. 6.99 (978-0-06-111639-1(4) , Harper Trophy) HarperCollins Pubs.
—The Not-So-Jolly Roger, Vol. 2. 2004. (Time Warp Trio Ser.: No. 2). (Illus.). 64p. (J). (gr. 2-6). pap. 4.99 (978-0-14-240045-6(9) , Puffin) Penguin Group (USA) Inc.
—The Not-So-Jolly Roger. unabr. ed. (Time Warp Trio Ser.: No. 2). (J). (gr. 2-4). 1999. pap. 29.98 incl. audio (978-0-8072-1302-5(0) , EFTR194MP); 1998. 57p. pap. 17.00 incl. audio (978-0-8072-0394-1(7) , EFTR194SP) Random Hse. Audio Publishing Group. (Listening Library).
—Oh Say, I Can't See. McCauley, Adam, illus. 2005. (Time Warp Trio Ser.: No. 15). 80p. (J). (gr. 2). 14.99 (978-0-670-06025-2(9) , Viking Juvenile) Penguin Group (USA) Inc.
—The Seven Blunders of the World. 2006. (Time Warp Trio: Vol. 2). 96p. (J). pap. 6.99 (978-0-06-111637-7(8) , Harper Trophy) HarperCollins Pubs.
—Tu Mama Era Neanderthal. Smith, Lane, illus. (SPA.). (J). (gr. 5-8). 7.95 (978-958-04-5045-0(5) , NR3076) Norma S.A. COL. *Dist:* Distribuidora Norma, Inc., Lectorum Pubns., Inc.
—Tut, Tut. Smith, Lane, illus. (SPA.). (J). (gr. 5-8). 7.95 (978-958-04-5046-7(3) , NR7010) Norma S.A. COL. *Dist:* Distribuidora Norma, Inc., Lectorum Pubns., Inc.
—Tut, Tut. Smith, Lane, illus. 2004. (Time Warp Trio Ser.: No. 6). 80p. (J). (gr. 2-6). pap. 4.99 (978-0-14-240047-0(5) , Puffin) Penguin Group (USA) Inc.
—Tut, Tut. Smith, Lane, illus. 2004. (Time Warp Trio Ser.: No. 6). 74p. (J). (ps-7). lib. bdg. 11.79 (978-0-606-30136-7(4)) Tandem Library Bks.
—Tut, Tut. 1998. (Time Warp Trio Ser.: No. 6). (978-0-606-13879-6(X)) Tandem Library Bks.
—What's So Great about Peter? 2007. (Time Warp Trio). 96p. (J). pap. 6.99 (*978-0-06-111651-3(3) , Harper Trophy) HarperCollins Pubs.
—Wushu Were Here. 2007. (Time Warp Trio: No. 3). 80p. (J). pap. 4.99 (*978-0-06-111645-2(9) , Harper Trophy) HarperCollins Pubs.
Scieszka, Jon & Kaemon, Amy Court. Plaid to the Bone. 2007. (Time Warp Trio: Vol. 3). 96p. (J). pap. 6.99 (978-0-06-111642-1(4) , Harper Trophy) HarperCollins Pubs.
Scieszka, Jon, et al. The High & the Flighty. Scieszka, Jon, illus. 2007. (Time Warp Trio). (Illus.). 48p. (J). (gr. k-2). 15.99 (*978-0-06-111644-5(0)); pap. 3.99 (*978-0-06-111643-8(2) , Harper Trophy) HarperCollins Pubs.
Scorcia, Yvonne. Joey's Big Adventure. 2001. 56p. (J). pap. 9.00 (978-0-8059-5485-2(6)) Dorrance Publishing Co., Inc.
Scott, Ann Herbert. Someday Rider. 2000. (978-0-606-18046-7(X)) Tandem Library Bks.
Scott, Carlton T. Little Big Wolf. Scott, Carlton T., illus. 1999. (Illus.). 32p. (J). (gr. k-5). 9.95 (978-0-9636652-8-7(6)) Ends of the Earth Books.com.
Scott, Deborah. The California Kid Fights Back. 1998. (J). (gr. 3-7). pap. 3.99 (978-0-380-72851-0(6)) HarperCollins Pubs.
Scott, James. Demian: Reproducible Teaching Unit. 2001. 53p. tchr. ed., ring bd. 29.50 (978-1-58049-284-3(3) , TU170) Prestwick Hse., Inc.
Scott, Mavis. Magic Palace. Spoor, Mike, illus. 96p. pap. 8.95 (978-0-7022-2528-4(2)) Univ. of Queensland Pr. AUS. *Dist:* International Specialized Bk. Services.
Scott, Terrence. Bryce Coris Blessing. 2006. 28p. pap. 9.95 (*978-1-4327-0000-3(6)) Outskirts Press, Inc.
Scott, Walter, Sr. Ivanhoe. 2000. (SPA.). 384p. (gr. 4-7). pap. 17.95 (978-1-58348-783-9(2)) iUniverse, Inc.
Scrimger, Richard. From Charlie's Point of View. 2005. 224p. (J). (gr. 3). 10.99 (978-0-525-47374-9(2) , Dutton Juvenile) Penguin Group (USA) Inc.
—Into the Ravine. 2007. 144p. (YA). (gr. 6 up). pap. 9.95 (*978-0-88776-822-4(9)) Tundra Bks., Inc./Livres Toundra, Inc. CAN. *Dist:* Random Hse., Inc.
Scrimger, Richard. Princess Bun Bun. Johnson, Gillian, illus. 2002. 24p. (J). (ps-1). 12.95 (978-0-88776-543-8(2)) Tundra Bks., Inc./Livres Toundra, Inc. CAN. *Dist:* Random Hse., Inc.
Scudamore, Beverly. Ice Dreams. 2003. (Sports Stories Ser.). 112p. (J). (gr. 4-8). 7.95 (978-1-55028-812-4(1)); (*978-1-55028-813-1(X)) Lorimer, James & Co., Ltd., Pubs. CAN. *Dist:* Casemate Pubs. & Bk. Distributors, LLC.
Secret of the Ancient Crowns. 2006. per. 14.95 (*978-1-59352-263-6(0)) Christian Services Publishing.
Secrets Of Droon #28 Staff & Abbott, Tony. In the Shadow of Goll. 2006. (Secrets of Droon Ser.: No. 28). (Illus.). 112p. (J). pap. 3.99 (978-0-439-67176-7(0) , Scholastic Paperbacks) Scholastic, Inc.
Sedgwick, Marcus. The Dark Horse. 2004. 224p. (YA). (gr. 5). mass mkt. 5.99 (978-0-440-41908-2(5) , Laurel Leaf) Random Hse. Children's Bks.
—Floodland. unabr. ed. 2004. (Middle Grade Cassette Librariestm Ser.). 154p. (J). (gr. 4-7). pap. 29.00 incl. audio (978-0-8072-0979-0(1) , S YA 282 SP, Listening Library) Random Hse. Audio Publishing Group.
—The Foreshadowing. 2006. 304p. (gr. 4-7). lib. bdg. 18.99 (978-0-385-90881-8(4)); (YA). (gr. 7 up). 16.95 (978-0-385-74646-5(6)) Random Hse. Children's Bks. (Lamb, Wendy).
See, Ee Lin. My Kiasu Teenage Life in Singapore. 2005. (Illus.). 176p. pap. 12.95 (978-981-05-3016-7(1)) Monsoon Bks. Pte. Ltd. SGP. *Dist:* Biblio Distribution.
See No Evil. 2002. (gr. 7-12). lib. bdg. 14.15 (978-0-613-50641-0(3)) Tandem Library Bks.
Seewald, Jacqueline. A Devil in the Pines. Cunningham, Patricia & Cunningham, Lisa, eds. Rosenfeld, Jason, illus. 1999. 32p. (J). (gr. 2-5). pap. 19.95 (978-0-89359-013-0(4)) Afton Publishing.
Segal, John. Alistair & Kip's Great Adventure. Segal, John, illus. 2008. 32p. (J). 15.99 (978-1-4169-0280-5(5) , McElderry, Margaret K.) Simon & Schuster Children's Publishing.
Seider, Sharon J. The Door in the Garden Wall. 2003. 139p. (J). pap. 13.95 (978-0-7414-1712-1(X)) Infinity Publishing.
Seidman, David. Kong: The 8th Wonder of the World Deluxe Sound Storybook. Curry, Don, ed. Bollinger, Peter & Papp, Robert, illus. 2005. 22p. (J). (ps-3). 15.95 (978-0-696-22813-1(0)) Meredith Bks.
Seigelson, Kim. Trembling Earth. 2004. 160p. (YA). (gr. 5). 17.99 (978-0-399-24021-8(7) , Philomel) Penguin Group (USA) Inc.
Seleccion de Oro: Libro Morado.Tr. of Golden Selection: Purple Book. (SPA.). (J). 13.48 (978-84-8426-240-4(5)) Susaeta Ediciones, S.A. ESP. *Dist:* AIMS International Bks., Inc.
Sell, Jeff. The Quarry Cave. 2006. 51p. pap. 12.95 (978-1-4241-1188-6(9)) PublishAmerica, Inc.
Semerad, Emma & Semerad, Johnnie. Josh W. Time Out. Semerad, Johnnie, illus. 2003. (Illus.). 32p. (J). 15.00 (978-0-9744251-0-8(9)) Quiet Man.
Send Me the Soap #2: The Amazon Adventure (lib. Binding) 2007. (J). lib. bdg. 11.95 (*978-0-9778536-3-2(2)) Eco-thumb Publishing Co.
Sender, Ruth Minsky. To Life. 2000. (978-0-606-17940-9(2)) Tandem Library Bks.
Sennell, Joles. El Bosque Encantado. 4th ed. 1998. (Espasa Juvenil Ser.: Vol. 62). (SPA., Illus.). 116p. (J). (gr. 4-7). 7.95 (978-84-239-9033-7(8)) i.b.d., Ltd.
Seppala, Ray. Willowrun Tales. 2006. (Illus.). 122p. (YA). per. 9.95 (978-1-933324-47-0(3)) Cedar Hill Publishing.
Serafin, Michael. 4 Seasons of Baghdad. 2007. (ENG.). 60p. per. 12.95 (*978-1-4241-2303-2(8)) PublishAmerica, Inc.
Sergeant, Kate. It's a Very Good Night. 2005. (J). (978-0-9770158-5-6(8)) BeachWalk Bks. Inc.
Serrano, Tomas. Salfon el Limpiador de Tejados. (SPA.). 48p. (J). (gr. 1-3). pap. (978-84-264-3746-4(X)) Editorial Lumen ESP. *Dist:* Lectorum Pubns., Inc.
Seuss, Dr. Gatola da Cartola. pap. 23.95 (978-85-7406-085-9(2)) Schwarcz, Editora Ltda, Companhia das Letrinhas BRA. *Dist:* Distribooks, Inc.
The Seven Little Kids. 2005. (J). (978-1-58453-305-4(6)) Pioneer Valley Educational Pr., Inc.
Severine Rugumamu. Further Adventures of the Black Hand Gang. 2005. 64p. pap. 12.95 (978-9966-25-422-1(6)) Heinemann Kenya, Limited (East African Educational Publishers Ltd E.A.E.P.) KEN. *Dist:* Michigan State Univ. Pr.
Sewell, Anna. Black Beauty. 2004. 224p. (J). 5.99 (978-1-4037-0982-0(3)) Dalmatian Pr.
Seymour, Lee. Monster Lake. 2005. 212p. (J). pap. 12.00 (978-1-889186-56-6(2) , Little Devil Books) Necro Pubns.
Shaboo, Joseph R. Shalamazoo. Churchill, Jessica, photos by. Date not set. (Illus.). 56p. (J). (gr. 2-5). (978-0-9700380-0-5(3)) Purple Pig Publishing.
Shacter, Sara F. Heading to the Wedding: You're invited to join Patrick & Evie on the Great Adventure of Becoming (almost) perfect Guests. Thornton, Christine, illus. 2006. 32p. 18.95 (978-1-933176-05-5(9) , Red Pebble Bks.) Red Rock Pr., Inc.
Shaffert, Charles F. Googus to the Rescue. Stringer, Margaret, illus. l.t. ed. 2005. 31p. (J). per. 10.00 (978-1-59879-043-6(9)) Lifevest Publishing, Inc.
Shaler, Robert. The Boy Scouts As Country Fair Guides. 2005. pap. 21.95 (978-1-4191-2256-9(8)) Kessinger Publishing, LLC.
—The Boy Scouts in the Great Flood. 2005. pap. 21.95 (978-1-4191-2257-6(6)) Kessinger Publishing, LLC.
Shan, Darren, pseud. Cirque du Freak: Book 1, 2, 3. 2007. 736p. pap. 7.95 (*978-0-316-02304-7(3)) Little, Brown Bks. for Young Readers.
Shannon, Ronnie Jay. Samurai Force: the Final Hope: The Junior Novel. 2007. (ENG.). 76p. per. 14.95 (*978-1-4241-6528-5(8)) PublishAmerica, Inc.
Sharkey, Niamh. Santasaurus. Sharkey, Niamh, illus. 2005. (Illus.). 32p. (J). (ps-1). 15.99 (978-0-7636-2671-6(6)) Candlewick Pr.
Sharmat, Marjorie Weinman. Nate the Great Goes Undercover. Simont, Marc, illus. unabr. ed. 2004. (Nate the Great Ser.). 48p. (J). (gr. 1-3). pap. 17.00 incl. audio (978-0-8072-0201-2(0) , FTR172SP, Listening Library) Random Hse. Audio Publishing Group.
Sharp, Thelma & Laner, Doris. The Saturday Appaloosa. Graham, Georgia, illus. 2004. (Northern Lights Books for Children Ser.). 32p. (J). (ps-1). 16.95 (978-0-88995-213-3(2)) Red Deer Pr. CAN. *Dist:* Fitzhenry & Whiteside, Ltd.
Sharpe, Gerald. What Lies Beneath the Bed: Parade of Lights. 2007. 496p. (YA). pap. 11.00 (*978-1-933894-01-0(6)) IJN Publishing, Inc.
Sharpe, Gerald. What Lies Beneath the Bed: Tommy's Tales. 2006. 304p. (YA). pap. 7.00 (978-1-933894-00-3(8)) IJN Publishing, Inc.
Sharratt, Nick. Stack-a-Rocket. 1999. 38p. (J). 12.95 (978-1-86233-161-7(8)) Sterling Publishing Co., Inc.
—Stack-a-Sub. 1999. 36p. (J). 12.95 (978-1-86233-028-3(X)) Sterling Publishing Co., Inc.
Shasek, Judy & Schulz, Wendy Anderson. E-Wally & the Renegades. 2003. per. (978-0-9729599-0-2(4)) invenTEAM, LLC.
Shaw, Daniel, illus. Journey to Pansophigus. ed. 2005. (J). per. 9.95 (978-0-9772168-0-2(2)) Water Lily Pr., Inc.
Shaw-MacKinnon, Margaret & Gal, Laszlo. Tiktala. (Illus.). 30p. 13.95 (978-0-7737-2920-9(8)) Stoddart Kids CAN. *Dist:* Fitzhenry & Whiteside, Ltd.
Shaw, Nancy E. Sheep Blast off! HC. Apple, Margot, illus. 2008. 32p. (J). 15.00 (*978-0-618-13168-6(X)) Houghton Mifflin Co. Trade & Reference Div.
Shea, Chris. The Adventures of Davey Prickle. Shea, Chris, illus. 1999. (Illus.). 24p. (J). (ps-k). 8.50 (978-0-9657012-2-8(0)) Lifesighs Cards.
Shealy, Dennis R. Dare the Day! 2007. (Illus.). 32p. (J). (ps-2). lib. bdg. 11.99 (978-0-375-93793-4(5) , Golden Bks.) Random Hse. Children's Bks.
—Dare the Day! Walston, Dave, illus. 2007. 32p. (J). (ps-2). pap. 3.99 (978-0-375-83793-7(0) , Golden Bks.) Random Hse. Children's Bks.

A B

Shearer, Alex. Sea Legs. 320p. (J). 2006. pap. 5.99 (978-0-689-87144-3(9) , Aladdin); 2005. 16.95 (978-0-689-87143-6(0)) Simon & Schuster Children's Publishing.

Sheehan, Jennifer E. Chicky Dickey's Animal Pancakes. 2003. (Illus.). 32p. (J). 15.95 (978-0-9700952-9-9(5)) Bumples.

Shelby, Anne. The Adventures of Molly Whuppie, & Other Appalachian Folktales. McArdle, Paula, illus. 2007. 96p. (J). 14.95 (*978-0-8078-3163-2(8)) Univ. of North Carolina Pr.

Sheldon, Heather Barlow. Seymour's Night Flight: The Adventures of a Nantucket Seagull. 2004. (J). kivar 16.95 (978-0-9761820-0-9(9)) Cassiopeia Pr.

Sheley, Kristen. No Time Like the Present. 2002. (Partners in Time Ser.). 262p. (YA). pap. 14.95 (978-0-595-24687-8(7) , Writer's Showcase Pr.) iUniverse, Inc.

Shelton, Lee. The Little Thomas Adventures. 2002. 320p. (J). pap. 17.95 (978-1-59113-273-8(8)) Booklocker.com, Inc.

Shelton, Rick. Hoggle's Christmas. Gates, Donald, illus. 2007. 80p. (J). pap. 11.95 (*978-1-60306-026-4(X)) NewSouth, Inc.

Shepard, Aaron. The Adventures of Mouse Deer. Gamble, Kim, illus. 2005. 56p. (J). pap. 6.00 (978-0-938497-32-5(4) , Skyhook Pr.) Shepard Pubns.

—The Adventures of Mouse Deer: Tales of Indonesia & Malaysia (or Indonesian & Malaysian Folktales) Gamble, Kim, illus. 2006. 56p. (J). lib. bdg. 15.00 (978-0-938497-31-8(6) , Skyhook Pr.) Shepard Pubns.

—The Legend of Lightning Larry. Goffe, Toni, illus. 50p. (J). 2006. lib. bdg. 15.00 (978-0-938497-27-1(8)); 2005. pap. 6.00 (978-0-938497-28-8(6)) Shepard Pubns. (Skyhook Pr.).

Shepherd, JaiLeen. Lea's Song: The Life of a Special Little Horse. 2006. (J). per. 13.95 (978-1-889743-54-7(2)) Robbie Dean Pr.

Shepperson, Jacqueline Ruth. The Blue Jay Tales. 2005. 89p. pap. 14.95 (978-1-4137-3884-1(2)) PublishAmerica, Inc.

Sherman, Josepha. Land of Endless Night. 2007. 124p. pap. 4.99 (*978-1-931567-68-8(9)) Sovereign Pr.

Sherrill, Rusty & Miers, Doug. Kid Nitro & the Sinister Slorp. Sherrill, Cathy, ed. Sherrill, Rusty, illus. 2007. (Illus.). 273p. (YA). per. 14.95 (*978-0-9787729-0-1(3)) RS Art Studio.

Shi, Sharon. The Brave Messenger. Rapier, Tracey, illus. 1998. (J). (gr. k-3). (978-1-892800-05-3(5)) Tattoo Manufacturing.

—Sam Starlight's Great Adventure. Jones, David Phillip, illus. 2000. 24p. (J). (gr. k-3). mass mkt. 4.99 (978-0-9678636-9-6(4) , B010) Tattoo Manufacturing.

Shickman, Allan Richard. Zan-Gah: A Prehistoric Adventure. 2007. 160p. pap. 9.95 (*978-0-9790357-0-8(8)) Earthshaker Bks.

Shields, Lew. Legend of Pleasant Island. 2004. 203p. (YA). pap. 18.95 (978-1-930002-55-5(6)) I & L Publishing.

Shifting Ground. 2002. (Illus.). (J). pap. (978-0-7398-5139-5(X)) Steck-Vaughn.

Shigeno, Shuichi. Initial D, Vol. 17. Shigeno, Shuichi, illus. 2005. (Illus.). 212p. lib. bdg. 20.90 (978-1-4176-5264-8(0)) Tandem Library Bks.

Shimizu, Toshimitsu. Red Prowling Devil. (Illus.). 200p. Vol. 1. 2002. pap. 9.95 (978-1-58899-284-0(5)); Vol. 2. 2003. pap. 9.95 (978-1-58899-285-7(3)); Vol. 3. 2003. pap. 9.95 (978-1-58899-286-4(1)); Vol. 4. 2003. (gr. 12 up). pap. 9.95 (978-1-58899-287-1(X)); Vol. 6. 2003. pap. 9.95 (978-1-58899-289-5(6)) ComicsOne Corp./Dr. Masters.

Shimizu, Toshimitzu. Red Prowling Devil, Vol. 5. 2003. (Illus.). 200p. (gr. 11 up). pap. 9.95 (978-1-58899-288-8(8)) ComicsOne Corp./Dr. Masters.

Shinn, Sharon. Safe-Keeper's Secret. 2004. 224p. (J). (gr. 7). 16.99 (978-0-670-05910-2(2) , Viking Juvenile) Penguin Group (USA) Inc.

Shiozu, Shuri. Eerie Queerie!, 4 vols., Vol. 1. 2004. (Illus.). 192p. pap. 9.99 (978-1-59182-719-1(1) , Tokyopop Adult) TOKYOPOP, Inc.

—Eerie Queerie!, 3, Vol. 2. Yamaguchi, Heidi, tr. from JPN. rev. ed. 2004. (Illus.). 192p. pap. 9.99 (978-1-59182-720-7(5) , Tokyopop Adult) TOKYOPOP, Inc.

—Eerie Queerie!, 3 , Vol. 3. rev. ed. 2004. (Illus.). 192p. pap. 9.99 (978-1-59182-721-4(3) , Tokyopop Adult) TOKYOPOP, Inc.

Shoelace, CM. Thumper: The Story of a Curious Little Bunny. 2002. 108p. (J). pap. 9.95 (978-0-595-21234-7(4)) iUniverse, Inc.

Shotwell, Mary. Summer Expedition. 2007. (J). per. 6.99 (*978-1-59886-921-7(3)) Tate Publishing & Enterprises, L.L.C.

Shoup, Andrew J. Andy & Elmer's Apple Dumpling Adventure. 2nd ed. 2007. (J). 16.95 (*978-0-9720436-3-2(2)) TokoBooks.

—Andy & Elmer's Apple Dumpling Adventure Coloring & Activity Book. Shoup, Andrew J., illus. 2007. (Illus.). 36p. (J). 3.95 (*978-0-9720436-2-5(4)) TokoBooks.

Shoup, Gary. Suma. 2006. (J). bds. (978-0-9762544-1-6(7)) Garden Fleetfoot Pr.

Shreeve, Elizabeth. Hector Afloat. Levy, Pamela R., illus. 2004. (Ready-for-Chapters Ser.). 64p. (J). pap. 3.99 (978-0-689-86416-2(7) , Aladdin) Simon & Schuster Children's Publishing.

Shua, Ana Maria. Expedicion al Amazonas. 2002. (SPA.). 64p. (J). pap. (978-1-4000-0056-2(4)) Editorial Sudamericana S.A.

—Expedicion al Amazonas. 2002. (SPA.). (gr. 3-6). lib. bdg. 15.25 (978-0-613-88201-9(6)) Tandem Library Bks.

Shuff, Lana Tanaka. Kira Helps A Friend. l.t. ed. 2007. (ENG., Illus.). 28p. (J). per. 9.95 (*978-1-4327-0810-8(4)) Outskirts Press, Inc.

Shukla, Subir. The Boy Who Loved Colour. Sabnani, Nina, illus. 2004. (ENG & HIN.). (J). (978-81-8146-042-4(1)) Tulika Pubs.

Shumaker, Bob. The Legend of the Schmooney. Webb, Hannah, illus. 2005. (ENG.). 44p. (J). per. 21.50 (978-1-4208-5219-6(1)) AuthorHouse.

Shusterman, Neal. Speeding Bullet. 2004. 208p. (YA). mass mkt. 11.95 (978-0-689-87348-5(4) , Simon Pulse) Simon & Schuster Children's Publishing.

Siamon, Sharon. Dark Horse. 2005. (Mustang Mountain Ser.). 176p. (J). (gr. 3-7). pap. 6.95 (978-1-55285-720-5(4) , Walrus Bks.) Whitecap Bks., Ltd. CAN. *Dist:* Firefly Bks., Ltd.

—Gallop to the Sea. 2006. (Saddle Island Ser.). 168p. (J). (gr. 3-7). pap. 6.95 (978-1-55285-713-7(1) , Walrus Bks.) Whitecap Bks., Ltd. CAN. *Dist:* Firefly Bks., Ltd.

—Mustang Mountain Vol. 7: Free Horse. 2004. (Mustang Mountain Ser.). 160p. (J). (gr. 3-7). pap. 6.95 (978-1-55285-608-6(9)) Whitecap Bks., Ltd. CAN. *Dist:* Firefly Bks., Ltd.

—Race to the Rescue. 2007. (Saddle Island Ser.). 172p. (J). (gr. 3-7). pap. 6.95 (*978-1-55285-855-4(3) , Walrus Bks.) Whitecap Bks., Ltd. CAN. *Dist:* Firefly Bks., Ltd.

Siamon, Sharon. Secrets in the Sand. 2006. (Saddle Island Ser.). 208p. (J). (gr. 3-7). pap. 6.95 (978-1-55285-714-4(X) , Walrus Bks.) Whitecap Bks., Ltd. CAN. *Dist:* Firefly Bks., Ltd.

Sibley, Jerry. The Adventures of Harley Earle. 2006. 170p. 25.95 (978-1-59824-230-0(X)); per. 12.95 (978-1-59824-229-4(6)) E-BookTime LLC.

Sidney, Maragret. Five Little Peppers Abroad. 2006. 236p. pap. 12.99 (*978-1-4264-5079-2(6)); 262p. pap. 16.99 (*978-1-4264-5380-9(9)) BiblioBazaar.

Sidney, Margaret. The Adventures of Joel Pepper. 2006. 234p. pap. 12.99 (978-1-4264-2360-4(8)); 250p. pap. 16.99 (978-1-4264-2408-3(6)) BiblioBazaar.

—Margaret Sidney: Little Peppers. 2003. (J). cd-rom 19.00 (978-0-931968-61-7(5)) B & R Samizdat Express.

Sidon, Ephraim. Colina Calva. Cazes, Heidi, tr. Carlucho, illus. 1998. (la Orilla Del Viento Ser.). (SPA.). 39p. (J). reprint ed. pap. 6.99 (978-968-16-4724-7(6) , 100) Fondo de Cultura Economica USA.

Siefken, Paul. Smashing Lumpkins. 2001. (gr. k-3). lib. bdg. 11.80 (978-0-613-43890-2(6)) Tandem Library Bks.

Siegel, Rv. A Bee Called Kangaroo. 2005. 81p. pap. 9.16 (978-1-4116-2890-8(X)) Lulu.com.

Siert, Kara Grace ManJian. Tales of Cunburra & Other Stories. 2006. 240p. pap. (*978-1-84549-114-7(9)) arima publishing.

Silberberg, Alan. Pond Scum. 2005. (Illus.). 288p. (gr. 3-7). 15.99 (978-0-7868-5634-3(3)) Hyperion Pr.

Silk, Max V. Whiskers. Hirsch, Kerry, illus. 2004. (J). pap. 12.00 (978-0-9748524-6-1(5)) Biblio Bks. International.

Silver Dolphin en Español Editors. Caritas felices: Simba: Happy Faces: Simba, Spanish-Language Edition. 2007. (Illus.). 8p. (J). bds. 7.95 (*978-970-718-392-6(6) , Silver Dolphin en Español) Advanced Marketing, S. de R. L. de C. V. MEX. *Dist:* Perseus Distribution.

—Disney princesas: Felices para Siempre: Disney Princesses: Happily Ever after, Spanish-Language Editon. 2007. (Illus.). 5p. (J). 14.99 (*978-970-718-448-0(5) , Silver Dolphin en Español) Advanced Marketing, S. de R. L. de C. V. MEX. *Dist:* Perseus Distribution.

Silver Dolphin en Español Editors. Magical Magnets: Pixar. 2006. (SPA., Illus.). 8p. (J). bds. 12.95 (978-970-718-319-3(5)) Advantage Pubs. Group.

Silver Dolphin en Español Staff. Musica en casa: Disney, cuentos de Animales: Music Player: Animal Friends. 2007. (Illus.). 38p. (J). 24.95 (*978-970-718-494-7(9) , Silver Dolphin en Español) Advanced Marketing, S. de R. L. de C. V. MEX. *Dist:* Perseus Distribution.

Silver Dolphin en Español Staff, ed. Cine en casa: Cars: Movie Theater: Cars. 2007. (Cine en casa Disney Ser.). (Illus.). 46p. (J). 24.95 (*978-970-718-508-1(2) , Silver Dolphin en Español) Advanced Marketing, S. de R. L. de C. V. MEX. *Dist:* Perseus Distribution.

Silverhardt, Lauryn. SpongeBob's Best Day Ever! Reiss, William & Greenblatt, C. H., illus. 2004. (SpongeBob SquarePants Ser.). 12p. (J). bds. 6.99 (978-0-689-86754-5(9) , Simon Spotlight/Nickelodeon) Simon & Schuster Children's Publishing.

—Winona Makes Waves! Style Guide Staff, illus. 2005. (Rubbadubbers Ser.). 8p. (J). 6.99 (978-0-689-87616-5(5) , Simon Spotlight) Simon & Schuster Children's Publishing.

Silverthorne, Judith. Dinosaur Hideout. 2003. (Dinosaur Adventure Ser.). 192p. (J). (gr. 4-6). pap. 6.95 (978-1-55050-226-8(3)) Coteau Bks. CAN. *Dist:* Fitzhenry & Whiteside, Ltd.

Silvestre, R. Un Secreto en la Tormenta. (Raton de Biblioteca Coleccion). (SPA., Illus.). 128p. (J). (gr. 3). 7.95 (978-84-88061-69-0(2)) Serres, Ediciones, S. L. ESP. *Dist:* Lectorum Pubns., Inc.

Silvey, Diane. Spirit Quest. Silvey, Joe, illus. 2006. 64p. (J). (gr. 2-5). pap., tchr. ed. 5.95 (978-0-88878-376-9(0) , Sandcastle Bks.) Dundurn Group, The CAN. *Dist:* Univ. of Toronto Pr.

Simmons, Alexander. Red Nights. 1998. (J). 5.99 (978-0-679-88205-3(7) , Random Hse. Bks. for Young Readers) Random Hse. Children's Bks.

Simmons, Andrew. Bullseye Express. 2001. (Woody's Roundup Ser.: Bk. 5). (Illus.). 64p. (gr. 2-5). reprint ed. pap. 4.99 (978-0-7868-4457-9(4)) Disney Pr.

Simmons, Celeste. The Adventures of Booger Malone: Busted in the Backseat. 2007. (J). per. 10.95 (*978-0-9777041-2-5(2)) Third Dimension Publishing.

Simmons, Lisa M. Kip MacAllister: Bodyguard. 2001. (Kip MacAllister adventures). 132p. (YA). pap. 10.95 (978-0-595-20376-5(0) , Writers Club Pr.) iUniverse, Inc.

Simmons, Michael. Finding Lubchenko. (YA). (gr. 7-12). 2006. 304p. pap. 8.99 (978-1-59514-075-3(1)); 2005. 288p. 16.99 (978-1-59514-021-0(2)) Penguin Group (USA) Inc. (Razorbill).

—The Rise of Lubchenko. 2006. 224p. (YA). (gr. 7-12). 16.99 (978-1-59514-061-6(1) , Razorbill) Penguin Group (USA) Inc.

Simon and Schuster Children's Staff, ed. Adventures in Bikini Bottom. 2006. (SpongeBob SquarePants Ser.). 144p. (J). pap. 7.99 (978-1-4169-1562-1(1) , Simon Spotlight/Nickelodeon) Simon & Schuster Children's Publishing.

Simon and Schuster Staff, ed. Adventures to Go! 2006. (Nick Jr. Carry-along Boxed Set Ser.). 144p. (J). pap. 9.99 (978-1-4169-1558-4(3) , Simon Spotlight/ Nickelodeon) Simon & Schuster Children's Publishing.

—Cuentos de Dora y sus amigos. 2006. (Dora la Exploradora Ser.).Tr. of Dora's Storytime Collection. (SPA.). 160p. (J). 10.95 (978-1-4169-1564-5(8) , Libros Para Ninos) Simon & Schuster Children's Publishing.

—Learn & Grow on the Go! 2007. (Nick Jr. Carry-along Boxed Set Ser.). 144p. (J). pap. 9.99 (978-1-4169-2780-8(8) , Simon Spotlight/Nickelodeon) Simon & Schuster Children's Publishing.

Simon, Jay. Deep Freeze. 2004. 255p. (YA). per. 7.99 (978-0-931764-17-2(3)) Roberts Publishing Co.

Simon-Kerr, Julia. The Lion, the Witch, & the Wardrobe: Coloring & Activity Book & Magnets. Redondo, Jesus, illus. movie tie-in ed. 2005. (Narnia Ser.). 32p. (J). pap., act. bk. ed. 4.99 (978-0-06-076558-3(5)) Zonderkidz.

Simon, Les. The Secret of the Red Silk Pouch. 1998. 157p. (YA). (gr. 8-12). pap. 9.99 (978-0-88092-362-0(8) , 3628) Royal Fireworks Publishing Co.

Simonson, Louise. Extreme Monsters Battling Bigfoot. Elston, James W., illus. 2007. 96p. (J). (gr. 2-5). pap. 3.99 (978-1-57791-275-0(6) , Penny Candy Pr.) Brighter Minds Children's Publishing.

—Extreme Monsters Chapter, Vol. 3. Elston, James W., illus. gif. ed. 2006. 96p. (J). per. 3.99 (978-1-57791-255-2(1)) Brighter Minds Children's Publishing.

Simonson, Walter. Meltdown, 3 vols. Simonson, Louise et al, illus. 2003. (Wolverine Legends Ser.: Vol. 2). 200p. (YA). 19.99 (978-0-7851-1048-4(8)) Marvel Enterprises, Inc.

Simpson, Fiona, ed. Knights Kingdom Punch Out Book. 2006. 17p. (J). pap. 5.99 (978-0-439-78802-1(1)) Scholastic, Inc.

Simpson, Sue. Keepers of the Quantum: Lizard's Leap Two. 2003. 151p. (YA). pap. 12.95 (978-0-595-29752-8(8)) iUniverse, Inc.

Simpson-Tweedie, Karen. Treasure on Chincoteague Island. 2003. (Illus.). 153p. (J). per. 12.95 (978-0-9742205-0-5(7)) Sheepdog Pr.

Sims, L. Island Adventure. 2004. (Puzzle Adventures Ser.). 48p. (J). lib. bdg. 12.95 (978-1-58086-463-3(5)) EDC Publishing.

Sims, Lesley. Island Adventures. 2004. (Puzzle Adventures Ser.). (Illus.). 48p. (J). pap. 4.95 (978-0-7945-0091-7(9) , Usborne) EDC Publishing.

—Skull Island. 1998. (Adventure Fiction Ser.). 144p. (J). (gr. 3-7). lib. bdg. 12.95 (978-0-88110-863-7(4)); (Illus.). pap. 4.95 (978-0-7460-2460-7(6)) EDC Publishing.

Sims, Matt. Bass Lake. 1999. (gr. 3-6). lib. bdg. 10.85 (978-0-613-30258-6(3)) Tandem Library Bks.

—Red Gem Mine. 1999. (gr. 3-6). lib. bdg. 10.85 (978-0-613-30697-3(X)) Tandem Library Bks.

Singer, Isaac Bashevis. Mazel y Schlimazel. (SPA.). 30p. (YA). (gr. 5 up). 17.75 (978-84-264-3574-3(2) , LM3116) Editorial Lumen ESP. *Dist:* Lectorum Pubns., Inc.

Singleton, Mikey. Zac Master in the Quest. 2005. 190p. pap. 19.95 (978-1-4137-4966-3(6)) PublishAmerica, Inc.

Sis, Peter. Lighthouse. 2007. (978-0-374-34460-3(4) , Farrar, Straus & Giroux (BYR)) Farrar, Straus & Giroux.

—An Ocean World. Sis, Peter, illus. 2002. (Illus.). (YA). 14.43 (978-1-4046-0278-6(X)) Book Wholesalers, Inc.

Siu-Chong, Ken. Street Fighter, Vol. 1. 2006. (Illus.). 144p. pap. 9.99 (*978-0-9738652-0-2(2)) URON Entertainment Corp. CAN. *Dist:* Diamond Bk. Distributors.

—Street Fighter Volume 2. 2006. (Illus.). 200p. pap. 13.99 (*978-0-9738652-7-1(X)) URON Entertainment Corp. CAN. *Dist:* Diamond Bk. Distributors.

—Street Fighter Volume 3: Fighter's Destiny: Fighter's Destiny. 2007. 160p. (YA). pap. 13.99 (*978-0-9738652-8-8(8)) URON Entertainment Corp. CAN. *Dist:* Diamond Bk. Distributors.

Siwinski, Deborah. The Adventures of Teddy & Freddy Summer Safari. Siwinski, Deborah, illus. l.t. ed. 2006. (Illus.). 41p. (J). per. 8.95 (978-1-59879-097-9(8)) Lifevest Publishing, Inc.

Skewes, John & Schwartz, Robert. Larry Gets Lost in Seattle. 2007. (Illus.). 32p. 16.95 (*978-1-57061-483-5(0)) Sasquatch Bks.

Skinner, Daphne, adapted by. The Adventures of Stuart Little. 1999. (Stuart-Little Ser.). (Illus.). 64p. (J). (gr. 2 up). pap. 3.99 (978-0-06-440827-1(2)) HarperCollins Pubs.

Skudera, George. The Adventures of Freddie the Little Fir. 2006. pap. 10.49 (*978-1-4259-5950-0(4)) AuthorHouse.

Skurnick, Elizabeth. Alias: The Pursuit. 2003. (gr. 7-12). lib. bdg. 14.15 (978-0-613-72721-1(5)) Tandem Library Bks.

Skurzynski, Gloria. The Choice. 2006. (Virtual War Chronologs Ser.: Bk. 4). 240p. (YA). 16.95 (978-0-689-84267-2(8) , Atheneum) Simon & Schuster Children's Publishing.

—Cliff-Hanger. 2001. (gr. 3-6). lib. bdg. 14.10 (978-0-613-81326-6(X)) Tandem Library Bks.

Sky Rock. 2005. (J). 4.95 (978-1-59792-012-4(6)) F.A.S.T. Learning LLLC.

Skye, Obert. Leven Thumps & the Eyes of the Want. 2007. (Leven Thumps Ser.: Bk. 3). (Illus.). 406p. (J). (gr. 5 up). 18.95 (*978-1-59038-800-6(3) , Shadow Mountain) Deseret Bk. Co.

Slack, David. Shendu Escapes! with Cards. 2002. (gr. 3-6). lib. bdg. 13.00 (978-0-613-72451-7(8)) Tandem Library Bks.

Slade, Arthur. Megiddo's Shadow. 2006. (Illus.). 304p. (J). (gr. 7). 15.95 (978-0-385-74701-1(2)); lib. bdg. 17.99 (978-0-385-90945-7(4)) Random Hse. Children's Bks. (Lamb, Wendy).

Slanina, Anne M. The Adventures of Annie Mouse: Baby Brother Goes to the Hospital. Agnew, Alicia, illus. 2007. 28p. (J). 16.99 (*978-0-9793379-1-8(7)); per. 9.99 (*978-0-9793379-0-1(9)) Annie Mouse Bks.

Slater, David Michael. Cheese Louise! Cowden, Steve, illus. 2005. 32p. (J). (gr. 2-4). pap. 8.95 (978-1-55285-721-2(2) , Walrus Bks.) Whitecap Bks., Ltd. CAN. *Dist:* Firefly Bks., Ltd.

Slater, Jean M. The Adventures of Hopper. Slater, Jean M., illus. 2003. (Illus.). 8p. (J). bds. 16.00 (978-0-9743149-3-8(5)) Slater Software. Inc.

Sloan, Glenna. Stealing Time. 1998. 126p. (YA). (gr. 7-17). pap. 9.99 (978-0-88092-266-1(4) , 2664) Royal Fireworks Publishing Co.

Small, Pauline & Abalama, Katherine. At the Mountains (Cupik) Shantz, Joy, illus. l.t. ed. 2000. (ESK.). 8p. (J). (gr. k-3). pap. 6.00 (978-1-58084-196-2(1)) Lower Kuskokwim Schl. District.

Small, Pauline, et al. At the Mountains. Shantz, Joy, illus. l.t. ed. 2000. 8p. (J). (gr. k-3). pap. 6.00 (978-1-58084-191-7(0)) Lower Kuskokwim Schl. District.

Smalley, Roger. Big Cat Trouble. Shaw, Charles, illus. 2005. (J). (978-1-933248-13-4(0)) World Quest Learning.

—Rick's Dream Adventure. 2005. (J). (978-1-933248-10-3(6)) World Quest Learning.

Smallwood, Edward. J. Frankles: Space Adventures. 2003. (Illus.). 24p. (J). 9.95 (978-0-9741282-0-7(1) , 00001) Smallwood, Edward.

The Smile of A Golden Child. 2004. (J). per. 16.99 (978-0-9753533-6-3(5)) Golden Eagle Publishing Hse., Inc.

Smiley, Jane. The All-True Travels & Adventures of Lidie Newton: A Novel. 1999. (gr. 7-12). lib. bdg. 23.45 (978-0-613-17077-2(6)) Tandem Library Bks.

Smiley, Sophie & Foreman, Michael. Man of the Match. 2005. (Illus.). 64p. (J). pap. 8.99 (*978-1-84270-420-2(6)) Transworld Publishers Ltd. GBR. *Dist:* Independent Pubs. Group.

Smileytooth & the Plaque Attack: The Adventures of Smileytooth. 2006. (J). 6.95 (978-0-9778456-0-6(5)) Pontrelli, Jeany.

Smith, Bryon. Dark Matter: The Adventures of Megan Martin. 2004. 672p. (YA). pap. 24.00 (978-0-9745434-8-2(9)) Sweetgrass Pr., L.L.C.

—Night Visions Bk. 5: The Adventures of Megan Martin. 2003. 524p. (YA). pap. 20.00 (978-0-9745434-1-3(1)) Sweetgrass Pr., L.L.C.

—A Space in Time: The Adventures of Megan Martin. 2003. pap. 18.00 (978-0-9723376-5-6(2)) Sweetgrass Pr., L.L.C.

Smith, Carrie. Going to the Beach. ed. 2004. (Shared Connections Ser.). (J). pap. 27.00 (978-1-4108-1639-9(7)) Benchmark Education Co.

Smith, David R. The Door to Andara. 2005. 180p. pap. 8.14 (978-1-4116-1894-7(7)) Lulu.com.

Smith, Dianne M. Stuck! 2004. 20p. (J). per. (978-1-59196-580-0(2)) Instantpublisher.com.

Smith, Duane. Heritage Revealed Series, 3. (J). (gr. 2-9). pap. 13.95 (978-1-886218-00-0(5)) Azimuth Pr.

Smith, Frank Dabba & Kuhn-Leitz, Elsie. Elsie's War. 2004. (Illus.). 32p. (J). 15.95 (978-1-84507-190-5(5)) Lincoln, Frances Ltd. GBR. *Dist:* Perseus Distribution.

Smith, Geof. City Tales. Sorra, Kristin, illus. 2002. 16p. (J). (978-0-439-35145-4(6)) Scholastic, Inc.

—Scooby-Doo! & the Cyber Chase. 2001. 16p. (J). (ps-3). pap. 3.99 (978-0-307-25301-9(5) , Golden Bks.) Random Hse. Children's Bks.

Smith, George Harmon. Bayou Belle. 2000. 196p. (YA). (gr. 4-7). pap. 11.95 (978-0-595-00756-1(2) , Writer's Showcase Pr.) iUniverse, Inc.

—The Voice of Turtle Ann. 2001. 127p. (YA). pap. 10.95 (978-0-595-20757-2(X) , Writers Club Pr.) iUniverse, Inc.

Smith, Goerky. Danger Follows. 1999. 98p. (YA). (gr. 7 up). pap. 6.49 (978-1-57924-070-7(4) , 109835) Jones, Bob Univ. Pr.

Smith, I. J. The Legend of Scary Mary: The Journey to Leadership Collection Adventure 2. Pollard, Deborah Hanna, illus. 2004. 96p. (J). 16.95 (978-0-9727273-1-0(0)) Leadership Loft, The.

—The Musical Fort. Pollard, Deborah Hanna, illus. 2003. 53p. (J). 14.95 (978-0-9727273-0-3(2)) Leadership Loft, The.

Smith, J. E. Complex City: All in a Day's Work. 2003. 120p. per. 12.95 (978-0-9728070-0-5(4)) Better Comics.

Smith, Jane. Adventure on White High Island. 2006. (YA). per. (978-0-9777074-0-9(7)) Beverly Hills Publishing.

Smith, Jeff. Eyes of the Storm. 2006. (Bone Ser.: No. 3). (Illus.). 192p. (J). pap. 9.99 (978-0-439-70638-4(6)); (gr. 4-7). pap. 18.99 (978-0-439-70625-4(4)) Scholastic, Inc. (Graphix).

—The Great Cow Race. Hamaker, Steve, illus. 2005. (Bone Ser.: No. 2). 144p. (J). (ps-7). pap. 19.95 (978-0-439-70624-7(6) , Graphix) Scholastic, Inc.

—Rock Jaw: Master of the Eastern Border. 2007. (Bone Ser.: No. 5). 128p. (J). pap. 9.99 (978-0-439-70636-0(X) , Graphix) Scholastic, Inc.

—Rock Jaw: Master of the Eastern Border. Smith, Jeff, illus. 2007. (Bone Ser.: No. 5). (Illus.). 128p. (J). (gr. 4-7). pap. 18.99 (978-0-439-70627-8(0) , Graphix) Scholastic, Inc.

Smith, Josephine A. It's Okay on a Winters Day! Hickle Pickle Books Presents Adventures of Hickle the Pickle. 2005. (J). per. (978-1-881958-10-9(8)) Hickle Pickle Publishing.

Smith, Jullie. The Magic Carpet Adventures: Finding the Magic Carpet, Vol. 1. 2005. (ENG., Illus.). 36p. per. 19.25 (978-1-4208-6725-1(3)) AuthorHouse.

Smith, Lauren E. Ashley Enright Investigations. 2006. 48p. pap. 12.95 (978-1-4241-2963-8(X)) PublishAmerica, Inc.

Smith, Peggy. The Champ: The Adventures of a Boy & His New Puppy. Told in One-syllable Words for the Barton Reading & Spelling System. 2003. (J). pap. 7.95 (978-0-9744343-3-9(7) , SA-304) Bright Solutions for Dyslexia, LLC.

Smith, Rick. Shuck Unmasked. 2003. (Illus.). 168p. pap. 14.95 (978-1-891830-47-1(3)) Top Shelf Productions.

Smith, Roland. Jaguar. 1999. 256p. (gr. 4-7). pap. 5.95 (978-0-7868-1312-4(1)) Disney Pr.

—Walkabout. 2020. 224p. (J). 15.99 (978-0-7868-0588-4(9)) Hyperion Bks. for Children.

Smith, Sherri L. Lucy the Giant. 2003. 224p. (YA). (gr. 9). mass mkt. 5.50 (978-0-440-22927-8(8) , Laurel Leaf) Random Hse. Children's Bks.

Smith, Sherwood. Wren's Quest. 2001. (Illus.). 199p. (YA). (gr. 6-8). 17.00 (978-0-7567-5193-7(4)) DIANE Publishing Co.

Smith, Stevie. Johnnie & Will: Curse of the Devil's Son. 2004. 80p. pap. 14.95 (978-1-4137-2322-9(5)) PublishAmerica, Inc.

Smith, Susan. Katie's Wish. 2004. 60p. pap. 12.95 (978-1-4137-3270-2(4)) PublishAmerica, Inc.

Smith, Timothy R. The Salmon Stop Running. 2007. (Illus.). 80p. (J). pap. 5.95 (***978-1-934133-34-7(5)***) Mackinac Island Pr., Inc.

Snead, D. J. E. D. Nasty Nathan (the No-good Gnat who Never Listened to Nobody) 2005. (Illus.). 34p. (J). per. 11.95 (978-0-9769033-0-7(X)) Moonwater Products.

Snedeker, Caroline Dale. The White Isle. Elkorek, Alexander, illus. 2002. 208p. (J). per. 14.95 (978-0-9667067-3-4(0)) American Home-School Publishing, LLC.

Snell, J. Roy. Curlie Carson Listens In. 2007. (ENG.). 136p. 41.99 (***978-1-4280-7269-5(1)***); per. 34.99 (***978-1-4280-7273-2(X)***) IndyPublish.com.

—Triple Spies. 2006. 32.99 (***978-1-4280-1776-4(3)***) IndyPublish.com.

Snicket, Lemony, pseud. Una Academia Muy Austera. 2004. (Coleccion Una Serie de Catastroficas Desdichas A Series of Unfortunate Events Ser.). (SPA., Illus.). 189p. (YA). 12.95 (978-84-8441-214-4(8)) Grijalbo Mondadori, S.A.-Montena ESP. *Dist:* Lectorum Pubns., Inc.

—Una Academia Muy Austera. Canales, Veronica, tr. Helquist, Brett, illus. 2004. (Catastroficas Desdichas Ser.). (SPA.). 224p. (J). pap. 7.95 (978-0-307-20936-8(9) , Montena) Random House Mondadori ESP. *Dist:* Random Hse., Inc.

—The Complete Wreck, Bks. 1-13. Helquist, Brett, illus. 2006. (Series of Unfortunate Events Ser.). (J). 150.00 (978-0-06-111906-4(7)) HarperCollins Pubs.

—The Grim Grotto. Helquist, Brett, illus. 2004. (Series of Unfortunate Events Ser.: Bk. 11). 352p. (YA). (gr. 3-6). 12.99 (978-0-06-441014-4(5) , HarperCollins) HarperCollins Pubs.

—La Habitacion de los Reptiles. Busquets, Nestor, tr. Helquist, Brett, illus. 2004. (Catastroficas Desdichas Ser.). (SPA.). 208p. (J). pap. 7.95 (978-0-307-20935-1(0) , Montena) Random House Mondadori ESP. *Dist:* Random Hse., Inc.

—Lemony Snicket: The Unauthorized Autobiography. Helquist, Brett, illus. 2003. (Series of Unfortunate Events Ser.). 240p. (J). (gr. 3-6). pap. 6.99 (978-0-06-056225-0(0)) HarperCollins Pubs.

—A Library of Unfortunate Events. 2002. 98.91 (978-0-06-053759-3(0)) HarperCollins Pubs.

—The Penultimate Peril. Helquist, Brett, illus. 2005. (Series of Unfortunate Events Ser.: Bk. 12). 368p. (J). lib. bdg. 15.89 (978-0-06-029643-8(7)) HarperCollins Pubs.

—Piege au College. pap. 24.95 (978-2-09-282599-0(2)) Nathan, Fernand FRA. *Dist:* Distribooks, Inc.

—Tout Commence Mal. (FRE.). pap. (978-2-09-282353-8(1)) Editions Rouge et Or.

—El Ventanal. Busquets, Nestor, tr. Helquist, Brett, illus. 2004. (Catastroficas Desdichas Ser.). (SPA.). 224p. (J). pap. 7.95 (978-0-307-20937-5(7) , Montena) Random House Mondadori ESP. *Dist:* Random Hse., Inc.

Snicket, Lemony, pseud, creator. Lemony Snicket: The Unauthorized Autobiography. 2003. (gr. 5-8). lib. bdg. 15.30 (978-0-613-67209-2(7)) Tandem Library Bks.

Sniegoski, Tom. Sleeper Agenda. 2006. (Sleeper Conspiracy Ser.: Pt. II). 320p. (YA). (gr. 7-12). pap. 6.99 (978-1-59514-053-1(0) , Razorbill) Penguin Group (USA) Inc.

—Sleeper Code. 2006. (Sleeper Conspiracy Ser.: Pt. I). 304p. (YA). (gr. 7-12). pap. 6.99 (978-1-59514-052-4(2) , Razorbill) Penguin Group (USA) Inc.

Snyder, Lavinia Branca. The King of New York: Softi's Adventures, 2002. (Illus.). (J). mass mkt. (978-1-932233-34-6(2)) Aurora Libris Corp.

—Mission in Space: Softi's Adventures. 2003. (Illus.). (J). mass mkt. (978-1-932233-35-3(0)) Aurora Libris Corp.

Snyder, Paul A. Courageous Journey. 2000. 216p. (J). (gr. 7-10). pap. 9.99 (978-0-88092-360-6(1)) Royal Fireworks Publishing Co.

Sobczak, Charles. Way under Contract. 2000. 432p. (YA). pap. 14.95 (978-0-9676199-4-1(7)) Indigo Pr., LC.

Sobel, Gerrie. Jacob & His Magical Flying Bears: A Christmas Story. Torres, Dottie, illus. 2007. 32p. (J). 12.95 (***978-0-9798244-4-9(3)***) TRIAD Publishing Group.

Sobol, Donald J. Encyclopedia Brown Cracks the Case. 2007. 128p. (J). (gr. 3). 15.99 (***978-0-525-47924-6(4)*** , Dutton Juvenile) Penguin Group (USA) Inc.

Soesbee, Ree. City of Fortune. 2006. (Elidor Trilogy Ser.: Vol. 3). (Illus.). 256p. (YA). pap. 5.99 (978-0-7869-4026-4(3) , Mirrorstone) Wizards of the Coast.

Sohn, Emily. Adventures in Sound with Max Axiom, Super Scientist. Martin, Cynthia & Timmons, Anne, illus. 2007. (J). (***978-0-7368-6836-5(4)***) Capstone Pr., Inc.

—A Crash Course in Forces & Motion with Max Axiom, Super Scientist. 2007. (Graphic Library). (Illus.). 32p. (J). (***978-0-7368-7890-6(4)*** , 1264931) Capstone Pr., Inc.

Solice, Deborah. The Eye of the Undead: The Hidden Channel: an Adventure Series in Time. l.t. ed. 2005. (ENG., Illus.). 100p. (J). per. 7.59 (978-1-933300-01-6(9)) Wandering Sage Bookstore & More, LLC.

Solitaire, Jenna. Keeper of the Earth. 2006. (Guardian of the Boards Ser.). 256p. (YA). mass mkt. 6.99 (978-0-7653-5360-3(1) , Tor Teen) Doherty, Tom Assocs., LLC.

—Keeper of the Flames. 3rd rev. ed. 2006. (Guardian of the Boards Ser.). 272p. (YA). 6.99 (978-0-7653-5358-0(X) , Tor Teen) Doherty, Tom Assocs., LLC.

—Keeper of the Waters. 3rd rev. ed. 2006. (Guardian of the Boards Ser.). 256p. (YA). 6.99 (978-0-7653-5359-7(8) , Tor Teen) Doherty, Tom Assocs., LLC.

Sollinger, Emily. Dance! Dora's Pop-up Dancing Adventure. Aikins, Dave, illus. 2007. (Dora the Explorer Ser.). 12p. (J). 12.99 (***978-1-4169-4717-2(5)*** , Simon Spotlight/Nickelodeon) Simon & Schuster Children's Publishing.

—Diego's Arctic Adventure: A Book of Facts about Arctic Animals. Mawhinney, Art, illus. 2007. (Go, Diego, Go! Ser.). 16p. (J). pap. 6.99 (***978-1-4169-3822-4(2)*** , Simon Spotlight/Nickelodeon) Simon & Schuster Children's Publishing.

Sollinger, Emily & Hot Animation Staff, Animation. Arctic Adventure! 2004. (Rubbadubbers Ser.). 12p. (J). bds. 10.95 (978-0-689-87182-5(1) , Simon Spotlight) Simon & Schuster Children's Publishing.

Soloman, Ms Debra. Don't Look under the Bridge. 2006. 25p. 17.00 (978-1-4116-7114-0(7)) Lulu.com.

Song Ha. Indebted As Lord Chom/No Nhu Chua Chom: The Legend of the Forbidden Street. Smith, William, tr. from VIE. Ly, Thu Ha, illus. 2006. (ENG & VIE.). 32p. (J). (gr. 1-4). 16.95 (978-0-9701654-6-6(3)) East West Discovery Pr.

Sorensen, Launa. The King's First Journey, Bk. 1. 2007. 280p. (YA). pap. 15.99 (978-1-59092-572-0(6) , Blue Works) Windstorm Creative.

Sorrells, Walter. First Shot. 2007. 279p. (YA). (gr. 7-12). 16.99 (***978-0-525-47801-0(9)*** , Dutton Juvenile) Penguin Group (USA) Inc.

Sorrells, Walter. Survival. 2007. (Flight 29 Down Ser.: Vol. 7). 224p. (J). pap. 5.99 (978-0-448-44432-1(1) , Grosset & Dunlap) Penguin Group (USA) Inc.

Sorrells, Walter & MacHale, D. J. On Fire, Vol. 6. 2007. (Flight 29 Down Ser.). 256p. (J). pap. 5.99 (978-0-448-44431-4(3) , Grosset & Dunlap) Penguin Group (USA) Inc.

—Scratch. 2006. (Flight 29 Down Ser.: Vol. 5). 224p. (J). (gr. 4-7). pap. 5.99 (978-0-448-44403-1(8) , Grosset & Dunlap) Penguin Group (USA) Inc.

—Ten Rules. 2006. (Flight 29 Down Ser.). 224p. (J). (gr. 4-7). pap. 5.99 (978-0-448-44402-4(X) , Grosset & Dunlap) Penguin Group (USA) Inc.

Sosna, Marvin. Brandon's Trail. 2006. 220p. per. 13.95 (978-1-58939-875-7(0)) Virtualbookworm.com Publishing, Inc.

Soto, Gary. Crazy Weekend. 2003. 160p. (gr. 4-9). pap. 8.95 (978-0-89255-286-3(7)) Persea Bks., Inc.

—Crazy Weekend. 2003. (gr. 5-8). lib. bdg. 17.60 (978-0-613-87186-0(3)) Tandem Library Bks.

Souhami, Jessica. Sausages. 2006. (Illus.). 32p. (ps-2). 15.95 (978-1-84507-397-8(5)) Lincoln, Frances Ltd. GBR. *Dist:* Perseus Distribution.

Southall, Donna. The Buibble Trailer. 2004. (J). 15.00 (978-0-8059-6585-8(8)) Dorrance Publishing Co., Inc.

Space Jam Audio Action Adventure. (Illus.). 28p. (J). (gr. 1-7). pap. 9.89 incl. audio (978-1-56826-707-4(X) , KR1) Rhino Entertainment Co, A Warner Music Group Co.

Spalding, Andrea. Behind the Sorcerer's Cloak. 2006. 192p. (J). pap. 8.95 (978-1-55143-627-2(2)) Orca Bk. Pubs. USA.

Spalding, Andrea & Spalding, David. The Silver Boulder. (Adventure Net Ser.). 8p. tchr. ed. 3.95 (978-1-55285-160-9(5) , Walrus Bks.); 2000. (Illus.). 128p. (J). (gr. 3-2). pap. 6.95 (978-1-55285-105-0(2)) Whitecap Bks., Ltd. CAN. *Dist:* Graphic Arts Ctr. Publishing Co., Firefly Bks., Ltd.

Spangenberg, Greg. A Christmas Eve Victory: The Adventures of Churchy Church Mouse & His Cousin Tootsie. Lodwick, Sarah, illus. l.t. ed. 2006. 34p. (J). 16.99 (978-1-59879-140-2(0)) Lifevest Publishing, Inc.

Spann, Bill. The Agents of Little Woods. 2005. 116p. pap. 16.95 (978-1-4137-6574-8(2)) PublishAmerica, Inc.

The Sparkling Beauty. 2006. Orig. Title: Televisual Book. (J). 18.99 (978-0-9779672-0-9(4)) Karsonkina, Tatiana.

Sparks, Beatrice. Finding Katie: The Diary of Anonymous, a Teenager in Foster Care. 2005. (Illus.). 192p. (J). pap. 5.99 (978-0-06-050721-3(7)) HarperCollins Pubs.

Spaziante, Patrick, illus. Meet Leatherhead. 2005. (Teenage Mutant Ninja Turtles Ser.). 24p. pap. 3.99 (978-0-689-87711-7(0) , Simon Spotlight) Simon & Schuster Children's Publishing.

—Super Slam Turtles! 2005. (Teenage Mutant Ninja Turtles Ser.). 24p. (J). pap. 3.99 (978-1-4169-0502-8(2) , Simon Spotlight) Simon & Schuster Children's Publishing.

Spellman, Frankie. Pinky & Bubs' Stinky Night Out: Adventures on Martha's Vineyard. Spellman, Susan, illus. 2005. (J). per. 12.95 (978-1-933002-16-3(6)) PublishingWorks.

Spelvin, Justin. Deep-Sea Countdown. McGee, Warner, illus. 2006. (Backyardigans Ser.). 26p. (J). bds. 5.99 (978-1-4169-1484-6(6) , Simon Spotlight/Nickelodeon) Simon & Schuster Children's Publishing.

—Pirate Treasure. 2007. 24p. (J). 21.35 (***978-1-59961-158-7(9)***) Spotlight.

—Riding the Range. 2006. (Illus.). 24p. (J). lib. bdg. 9.00 (***978-1-4242-0248-5(5)***) Fitzgerald Bks.

Spence, Stephen Mark. African Knights. 2005. 340p. (J). pap. 14.95 (978-0-9705324-4-2(X)) Spence, Stephen Mark.

Spencer, Pamela. Timeless Treasures. 2005. (J). per. 13.95 (978-0-9748426-5-3(6)) Accent Pubns.

Spencer, Robert. Bravo Persevere! Musgrave, Michael, illus. 1998. 32p. (J). pap. 8.00 (978-0-7188-2971-1(9)) Lutherworth Pr., The GBR. *Dist:* Parkwest Pubns., Inc.

Spendlove, Owen. Stanley Brambles & the Pirate's Treasure. 2007. 320p. per. 18.95 (***978-0-595-43792-4(3)***) iUniverse, Inc.

Spiegelman, Art. Big Fat Little Lit. Mouly, Francoise, ed. 2006. (Illus.). 144p. (J). (gr. k). pap. 14.99 (978-0-14-240706-6(2) , Puffin) Penguin Group (USA) Inc.

Spiegle, Dan, et al. Historical Adventure. 2006. (Illus.). 56p. pap. (***978-0-8368-7934-6(1)***); (YA). (gr. 4 up). lib. bdg. 29.27 (***978-0-8368-7927-8(9)***) Stevens, Gareth Inc. (World Almanac Library).

Spiewak, Chet. An Ornaments' Tale. 2006. 32p. pap. 16.95 (978-0-9785827-0-8(5)) CWS Studios, Inc.

Spikes, James L. The Adventures of LemonHead & Mudd Duck: What to do if Someone Tries to Grab You. 2005. 36p. (J). lib. bdg. 19.95 net. (978-0-9749202-7-6(4)) Excel Digital Pr., Inc.

Spilny, Yuri. River of Fire. Schreiber, Catherine, ed. Balzhak, Anna & Balzhak, Nadezhda, illus. 1998. (Incredible Adventures of Kitto Ser.: Vol. 3). 52p. (J). (gr. 3-6). pap. 12.95 (978-1-892316-02-8(1)) Rama Pr., Inc.

—Sorceress's Spell. Schreiber, Catherine, ed. Balzhak, Anna & Balzhak, Nadezhda, illus. 1998. (Incredible Adventures of Kitto Ser.: Vol. 1). 48p. (J). (gr. 3-6). pap. 12.95 (978-1-892316-00-4(5)) Rama Pr., Inc.

—The Toynapers. Schreiber, Catherine, ed. Balzhak, Anna & Balzhak, Nadezhda, illus. 1998. (Incredible Adventures of Kitto Ser.: Vol. 2). 52p. (J). (gr. 3-6). pap. 12.95 (978-1-892316-01-1(3)) Rama Pr., Inc.

Spinelli, Jerry. The Bathwater Gang. Johnson, Meredith, illus. 2005. 64p. (J). (gr. 4-7). pap. 3.99 (978-0-316-01442-7(7)) Little Brown & Co.

The Spirited Little Fisherman: A Pip Adventure. 2005. lib. bdg. 11.95 (978-1-932341-00-3(5)) Lotti, Marc.

Spirn, Michele. Racing Against the Light. 2001. (YA). pap. (978-1-56765-066-2(X) , R695P) AMSCO Schl. Pubns., Inc.

—Wait till the Midnight Hour. 2001. (YA). pap. (978-1-56765-069-3(4) , R698P) AMSCO Schl. Pubns., Inc.

Spirn, Michele & Spirn, Michele, illus. All Washed Up. 2000. (gr. k-3). lib. bdg. 11.25 (978-0-613-30925-7(1)) Tandem Library Bks.

Spoon, Cynthia. The Can-Do Stories. 2005. (Illus.). 72p. (J). per. 12.95 (978-1-59453-912-1(X) , Airleaf Publishing) Airleaf Publishing & Bookselling.

Springer, Nancy. Lionclaw. (Tales of Rowan Hood Ser.: No. 2). 2004. 128p. (J). pap. 5.99 (978-0-14-240053-1(X) , Puffin); 2002. 160p. (YA). (gr. 4-7). 16.99 (978-0-399-23716-4(X) , Philomel) Penguin Group (USA) Inc.

—Rowan Hood: Outlaw Girl of Sherwood Forest. 2002. (Tales of Rowan Hood Ser.: No. 1). 192p. (J). (ps-7). pap. 5.99 (978-0-698-11972-7(X) , Putnam Juvenile) Penguin Group (USA) Inc.

—Rowan Hood: Outlaw Girl of Sherwood Forest. 2002. (Tales of Rowan Hood Ser.: No. 1). (gr. 5-8). lib. bdg. 14.15 (978-0-613-53860-2(9)) Tandem Library Bks.

—Rowan Hood Returns: The Final Chapter. (Tales of Rowan Hood Ser.: No. 5). 2006. 176p. (J). (gr. 3). pap. 5.99 (978-0-14-240685-4(6) , Puffin); 2005. 170p. (YA). (gr. 5). 16.99 (978-0-399-24206-9(6) , Philomel) Penguin Group (USA) Inc.

—Wild Boy: A Tale of Rowan Hood. 2005. (Tales of Rowan Hood Ser.: No. 4). 160p. (J). (gr. 3). pap. 5.99 (978-0-14-240395-2(4) , Puffin) Penguin Group (USA) Inc.

Springer, Paul. Ink Thief. 2003. (Illus.). 176p. mass mkt. 6.99 (978-0-330-33714-4(9) , Pan) Pan Macmillan GBR. *Dist:* Trafalgar Square Publishing.

Spyri, Johanna. Otra Vez Heidi. (SPA., Illus.). 160p. (YA). 11.95 (978-84-7281-091-4(7) , AF1091) Auriga, Ediciones S.A. ESP. *Dist:* Continental Bk. Co., Inc.

Stack, Edward. Food, Spirits, Lodging. 2003. (YA). per. 19.95 (978-1-929374-18-2(6)) Fire Mountain Pr.

Stacy, Dorothy. Erie Canal Cousins. Stacy, Dorothy, illus. 2007. (Illus.). 110p. (J). per. 9.95 (***978-0-9792947-0-9(3)***) Blackberry Hill Pr.

Stadther, Michael. Official Solution Book to A Treasure's Trove. Stadther, Michael, illus. 2005. (Treasure's Trove Ser.). (Illus.). 96p. (J). 14.99 (978-0-9760618-5-4(6)) Simon & Schuster, Inc.

Stafford, Mary. Lincoln & the Lilac Lilies. Dennis, Nadine, illus. 2005. (Fantastic World of Lincoln Llama Ser.). 24p. 6.95 (978-0-9735663-0-7(2)) Amethyst Hse Publishing, Inc. CAN. *Dist:* Hushion Hse. Publishing, Ltd.

—Lincoln's Day of Discovery, Vol. 2. Dennis, Nadine, illus. 2005. (Fantastic World of Lincoln Llama Ser.). 24p. 6.95 (978-0-9735663-1-4(0)) Amethyst Hse Publishing, Inc. CAN. *Dist:* Hushion Hse. Publishing, Ltd.

—Lincoln's Journey of Journeys, Vol. 3. Dennis, Nadine, illus. 2005. (Fantastic World of Lincoln Llama Ser.). 24p. 6.95 (978-0-9735663-2-1(9)) Amethyst Hse Publishing, Inc. CAN. *Dist:* Hushion Hse. Publishing, Ltd.

Stahnke, Rich. Furious Fist of the Drunken Monkey: Origin of the Species #3. 2007. 2.95 (***978-0-9791192-4-8(3)***) Silent Devil Productions.

Stainer, M. L. The Lyon's Throne. Melvin, James, illus. 1999. (Lyon Saga Ser.: Bk. 4). 153p. (YA). (gr. 5-9). lib. bdg. 9.95 (978-1-893337-01-5(4)) Chicken Soup Pr., Inc.

Stamper, Judith Bauer & Keenan. Hercules & the Maze of the Minotaur. 1998. (Disney's First Readers Ser.: Vol. 3). 40p. (J). (gr. 2-4). pap. 3.50 (978-0-7868-4171-4(0)) Disney Pr.

Stamper, Judith Bauer & Sol Studios Staff. Hercules & the Maze of the Minotaur. 1999. (Illus.). (J). (978-0-590-39387-4(1)) Scholastic, Inc.

Standish, Burt L. Dick Merriwell Abroad. Rudman, Jack, ed. 2003. (Frank Merriwell Ser.). pap. 9.95 (978-0-8373-9118-2(0)) Merriwell, Frank Inc.

—Dick Merriwell Adrift. Rudman, Jack, ed. 2003. (Frank Merriwell Ser.). pap. 9.95 (978-0-8373-9154-0(7)) Merriwell, Frank Inc.

—Dick Merriwell at Fardale. Rudman, Jack, ed. 2003. (Frank Merriwell Ser.). 29.95 (978-0-8373-9376-6(0)); pap. 9.95 (978-0-8373-9076-5(1)) Merriwell, Frank Inc.

—Dick Merriwell Doubted. Rudman, Jack, ed. 2003. (Frank Merriwell Ser.). pap. 9.95 (978-0-8373-9164-9(4)) Merriwell, Frank Inc.

—Dick Merriwell, Freshman. Rudman, Jack, ed. 2003. (Frank Merriwell Ser.). pap. 9.95 (978-0-8373-9142-7(3)) Merriwell, Frank Inc.

—Dick Merriwell in the Wilds. Rudman, Jack, ed. 2003. (Frank Merriwell Ser.). pap. 9.95 (978-0-8373-9167-0(9)) Merriwell, Frank Inc.

—Dick Merriwell on the Gridiron. Rudman, Jack, ed. 2003. (Frank Merriwell Ser.). pap. 9.95 (978-0-8373-9102-1(4)) Merriwell, Frank Inc.

—Dick Merriwell, the Wizard. Rudman, Jack, ed. 2003. (Frank Merriwell Ser.). pap. 9.95 (978-0-8373-9126-7(1)) Merriwell, Frank Inc.

—Dick Merriwell's Ability. Rudman, Jack, ed. 2003. (Frank Merriwell Ser.). 29.95 (978-0-8373-9390-2(6)); pap. 9.95 (978-0-8373-9090-1(7)) Merriwell, Frank Inc.

—Dick Merriwell's Assurance. Rudman, Jack, ed. 2003. (Frank Merriwell Ser.). pap. 9.95 (978-0-8373-9109-0(1)) Merriwell, Frank Inc.

—Dick Merriwell's Backers. Rudman, Jack, ed. 2003. (Frank Merriwell Ser.). pap. 9.95 (978-0-8373-9149-6(0)) Merriwell, Frank Inc.

—Dick Merriwell's Backstop. Rudman, Jack, ed. 2003. (Frank Merriwell Ser.). 29.95 (978-0-8373-9396-4(5)); pap. 9.95 (978-0-8373-9096-3(6)) Merriwell, Frank Inc.

—Dick Merriwell's Best Work. Rudman, Jack, ed. 2003. (Frank Merriwell Ser.). pap. 9.95 (978-0-8373-9150-2(4)) Merriwell, Frank Inc.

—Dick Merriwell's Black Star. Rudman, Jack, ed. 2003. (Frank Merriwell Ser.). pap. 9.95 (978-0-8373-9158-8(X)) Merriwell, Frank Inc.

—Dick Merriwell's Cleverness. Rudman, Jack, ed. 2003. (Frank Merriwell Ser.). pap. 9.95 (978-0-8373-9124-3(5)) Merriwell, Frank Inc.

—Dick Merriwell's Close Call. Rudman, Jack, ed. 2003. (Frank Merriwell Ser.). pap. 9.95 (978-0-8373-9156-4(3)) Merriwell, Frank Inc.

—Dick Merriwell's Dare. Rudman, Jack, ed. 2003. (Frank Merriwell Ser.). pap. 9.95 (978-0-8373-9136-6(9)) Merriwell, Frank Inc.

—Dick Merriwell's Dash. Rudman, Jack, ed. 2003. (Frank Merriwell Ser.). 29.95 (978-0-8373-9389-6(2)); pap. 9.95 (978-0-8373-9089-5(3)) Merriwell, Frank Inc.

—Dick Merriwell's Day. Rudman, Jack, ed. 2003. (Frank Merriwell Ser.). pap. 9.95 (978-0-8373-9114-4(8)) Merriwell, Frank Inc.

—Dick Merriwell's Debt. Rudman, Jack, ed. 2003. (Frank Merriwell Ser.). pap. 9.95 (978-0-8373-9152-6(0)) Merriwell, Frank Inc.

—Dick Merriwell's Defense. Rudman, Jack, ed. 2003. (Frank Merriwell Ser.). 29.95 (978-0-8373-9392-6(2)); pap. 9.95 (978-0-8373-9092-5(3)) Merriwell, Frank Inc.

—Dick Merriwell's Delivery. Rudman, Jack, ed. 2003. (Frank Merriwell Ser.). 29.95 (978-0-8373-9384-1(1)); pap. 9.95 (978-0-8373-9084-0(2)) Merriwell, Frank Inc.

—Dick Merriwell's Diamond. Rudman, Jack, ed. 2003. (Frank Merriwell Ser.). 29.95 (978-0-8373-9387-2(6)); pap. 9.95 (978-0-8373-9087-1(7)) Merriwell, Frank Inc.

—Dick Merriwell's Disguise. Rudman, Jack, ed. 2003. (Frank Merriwell Ser.). pap. 9.95 (978-0-8373-9103-8(2)) Merriwell, Frank Inc.

—Dick Merriwell's Distrust. Rudman, Jack, ed. 2003. (Frank Merriwell Ser.). pap. 9.95 (978-0-8373-9151-9(2)) Merriwell, Frank Inc.

—Dick Merriwell's Downfall. Rudman, Jack, ed. 2003. (Frank Merriwell Ser.). pap. 9.95 (978-0-8373-9116-8(4)) Merriwell, Frank Inc.

—Dick Merriwell's Example. Rudman, Jack, ed. 2003. (Frank Merriwell Ser.). pap. 9.95 (978-0-8373-9166-3(0)) Merriwell, Frank Inc.

—Dick Merriwell's Five. Rudman, Jack, ed. 2003. (Frank Merriwell Ser.). pap. 9.95 (978-0-8373-9130-4(X)) Merriwell, Frank Inc.

—Dick Merriwell's Glory. Rudman, Jack, ed. 2003. (Frank Merriwell Ser.). 29.95 (978-0-8373-9377-3(9)); pap. 9.95 (978-0-8373-9077-2(X)) Merriwell, Frank Inc.

—Dick Merriwell's Grit. Rudman, Jack, ed. 2003. (Frank Merriwell Ser.). pap. 9.95 (978-0-8373-9108-3(3)) Merriwell, Frank Inc.

—Dick Merriwell's Home Run. Rudman, Jack, ed. 2003. (Frank Merriwell Ser.). pap. 9.95 (978-0-8373-9135-9(0)) Merriwell, Frank Inc.

—Dick Merriwell's Honors. Rudman, Jack, ed. 2003. (Frank Merriwell Ser.). pap. 9.95 (978-0-8373-9173-1(3)) Merriwell, Frank Inc.

—Dick Merriwell's Influence. Rudman, Jack, ed. 2003. (Frank Merriwell Ser.). pap. 9.95 (978-0-8373-9141-0(5)) Merriwell, Frank Inc.

—Dick Merriwell's Joke. Rudman, Jack, ed. 2003. (Frank Merriwell Ser.). pap. 9.95 (978-0-8373-9144-1(X)) Merriwell, Frank Inc.

—Dick Merriwell's Long Slide. Rudman, Jack, ed. 2003. (Frank Merriwell Ser.). pap. 9.95 (978-0-8373-9110-6(5)) Merriwell, Frank Inc.

—Dick Merriwell's Magnetism. Rudman, Jack, ed. 2003. (Frank Merriwell Ser.). pap. 9.95 (978-0-8373-9148-9(2)) Merriwell, Frank Inc.

—Dick Merriwell's Marked Money. Rudman, Jack, ed. 2003. (Frank Merriwell Ser.). pap. 9.95 (978-0-8373-9100-7(8)) Merriwell, Frank Inc.

—Dick Merriwell's Mastery. Rudman, Jack, ed. 2003. (Frank Merriwell Ser.). pap. 9.95 (978-0-8373-9153-3(9)) Merriwell, Frank Inc.

—Dick Merriwell's Model. Rudman, Jack, ed. 2003. (Frank Merriwell Ser.). 29.95 (978-0-8373-9393-3(0)); pap. 9.95 (978-0-8373-9093-2(1)) Merriwell, Frank Inc.

—Dick Merriwell's Mystery. Rudman, Jack, ed. 2003. (Frank Merriwell Ser.). 29.95 (978-0-8373-9394-0(9)); pap. 9.95 (978-0-8373-9094-9(X)) Merriwell, Frank Inc.

—Dick Merriwell's Narrow Escape. Rudman, Jack, ed. 2003. (Frank Merriwell Ser.). 29.95 (978-0-8373-9380-3(9)); pap. 9.95 (978-0-8373-9080-2(X)) Merriwell, Frank Inc.

—Dick Merriwell's Persistence. Rudman, Jack, ed. 2003. (Frank Merriwell Ser.). pap. 9.95 (978-0-8373-9113-7(X)) Merriwell, Frank Inc.

—Dick Merriwell's Polo Team. Rudman, Jack, ed. 2003. (Frank Merriwell Ser.). pap. 9.95 (978-0-8373-9132-8(6)) Merriwell, Frank Inc.

—Dick Merriwell's Pranks. Rudman, Jack, ed. 2003. (Frank Merriwell Ser.). pap. 9.95 (978-0-8373-9120-5(2)) Merriwell, Frank Inc.

—Dick Merriwell's Promise. Rudman, Jack, ed. 2003. (Frank Merriwell Ser.). 29.95 (978-0-8373-9378-0(7)); pap. 9.95 (978-0-8373-9078-9(8)) Merriwell, Frank Inc.

—Dick Merriwell's Racket. Rudman, Jack, ed. 2003. (Frank Merriwell Ser.). 29.95 (978-0-8373-9381-0(7)); pap. 9.95 (978-0-8373-9081-9(8)) Merriwell, Frank Inc.

—Dick Merriwell's Regret. Rudman, Jack, ed. 2003. (Frank Merriwell Ser.). pap. 9.95 (978-0-8373-9147-2(4)) Merriwell, Frank Inc.

—Dick Merriwell's Reputation. Rudman, Jack, ed. 2003. (Frank Merriwell Ser.). pap. 9.95 (978-0-8373-9171-7(7)) Merriwell, Frank Inc.

—Dick Merriwell's Rescue. Rudman, Jack, ed. 2003. (Frank Merriwell Ser.). 29.95 (978-0-8373-9379-7(5)); pap. 9.95 (978-0-8373-9079-6(6)) Merriwell, Frank Inc.

—Dick Merriwell's Resource. Rudman, Jack, ed. 2003. (Frank Merriwell Ser.). pap. 9.95 (978-0-8373-9129-8(6)) Merriwell, Frank Inc.

—Dick Merriwell's Return. Rudman, Jack, ed. 2003. (Frank Merriwell Ser.). pap. 9.95 (978-0-8373-9128-1(8)) Merriwell, Frank Inc.

—Dick Merriwell's Ruse. Rudman, Jack, ed. 2003. (Frank Merriwell Ser.). 29.95 (978-0-8373-9383-4(3)); pap. 9.95 (978-0-8373-9083-3(4)) Merriwell, Frank Inc.

—Dick Merriwell's Stanchness. Rudman, Jack, ed. 2003. (Frank Merriwell Ser.). pap. 9.95 (978-0-8373-9161-8(X)) Merriwell, Frank Inc.

—Dick Merriwell's Threat. Rudman, Jack, ed. 2003. (Frank Merriwell Ser.). pap. 9.95 (978-0-8373-9112-0(1)) Merriwell, Frank Inc.

—Dick Merriwell's Trap. Rudman, Jack, ed. 2003. (Frank Merriwell Ser.). 29.95 (978-0-8373-9391-9(4)); pap. 9.95 (978-0-8373-9091-8(5)) Merriwell, Frank Inc.

—Dick Merriwell's Way. Rudman, Jack, ed. 2003. (Frank Merriwell Ser.). pap. 9.95 (978-0-8373-9169-4(5)) Merriwell, Frank Inc.

—Dick Merriwell's Western Mission. Rudman, Jack, ed. 2003. (Frank Merriwell Ser.). 29.95 (978-0-8373-9397-1(3)); pap. 9.95 (978-0-8373-9097-0(4)) Merriwell, Frank Inc.

—Dick Merriwell's Wonders. Rudman, Jack, ed. 2003. (Frank Merriwell Ser.). 29.95 (978-0-8373-9385-8(X)); pap. 9.95 (978-0-8373-9085-7(0)) Merriwell, Frank Inc.

—Frank Merriwell in Maine. Rudman, Jack, ed. 2003. (Frank Merriwell Ser.). (YA). (gr. 9 up). 29.95 (978-0-8373-9328-5(0)); pap. 9.95 (978-0-8373-9028-4(1) , FM-028) Merriwell, Frank Inc.

—Frank Merriwell in the Rockies. Rudman, Jack, ed. 2003. (Frank Merriwell Ser.). pap. 9.95 (978-0-8373-9119-9(9)) Merriwell, Frank Inc.

—Frank Merriwell on the Boulevards. Rudman, Jack, ed. 2003. (Frank Merriwell Ser.). pap. 9.95 (978-0-8373-9045-1(1)) Merriwell, Frank Inc.

—Frank Merriwell on the Road. Rudman, Jack, ed. 2003. (Frank Merriwell Ser.). 29.95 (978-0-8373-9334-6(5)); pap. 9.95 (978-0-8373-9034-5(6)) Merriwell, Frank Inc.

—Frank Merriwell on Top. Rudman, Jack, ed. 2003. (Frank Merriwell Ser.). 29.95 (978-0-8373-9355-1(8)); pap. 9.95 (978-0-8373-9055-0(9)) Merriwell, Frank Inc.

—Frank Merriwell's Air Voyage. Rudman, Jack, ed. 2003. (Frank Merriwell Ser.). pap. 9.95 (978-0-8373-9157-1(1)) Merriwell, Frank Inc.

—Frank Merriwell's Alarm. Rudman, Jack, ed. 2003. (Frank Merriwell Ser.). (YA). (gr. 9 up). 29.95 (978-0-8373-9316-2(7)); pap. 9.95 (978-0-8373-9016-1(8) , FM-016) Merriwell, Frank Inc.

—Frank Merriwell's Athletes. Rudman, Jack, ed. 2003. (Frank Merriwell Ser.). (YA). (gr. 9 up). 29.95 (978-0-8373-9317-9(5)); pap. 9.95 (978-0-8373-9017-8(6) , FM-017) Merriwell, Frank Inc.

—Frank Merriwell's Backers. Rudman, Jack, ed. 2003. (Frank Merriwell Ser.). 296.95 (978-0-8373-9395-7(7)); pap. 9.95 (978-0-8373-9095-6(8)) Merriwell, Frank Inc.

—Frank Merriwell's Bicycle Tour. Rudman, Jack, ed. 2003. (Frank Merriwell Ser.). (YA). (gr. 9 up). 29.95 (978-0-8373-9313-1(2)); pap. 9.95 (978-0-8373-9013-0(3) , FM-013) Merriwell, Frank Inc.

—Frank Merriwell's Brother. Rudman, Jack, ed. 2003. (Frank Merriwell Ser.). 29.95 (978-0-8373-9373-5(6)); pap. 9.95 (978-0-8373-9073-4(7)) Merriwell, Frank Inc.

—Frank Merriwell's Challengers. Rudman, Jack, ed. 2003. (Frank Merriwell Ser.). pap. 9.95 (978-0-8373-9122-9(9)) Merriwell, Frank Inc.

—Frank Merriwell's Champions. Rudman, Jack, ed. 2003. (Frank Merriwell Ser.). (YA). (gr. 9 up). 29.95 (978-0-8373-9319-3(1)); pap. 9.95 (978-0-8373-9019-2(2) , FM-019) Merriwell, Frank Inc.

—Frank Merriwell's Chase. Rudman, Jack, ed. 2003. (Frank Merriwell Ser.). (YA). (gr. 9 up). 29.95 (978-0-8373-9327-8(2)); pap. 9.95 (978-0-8373-9027-7(3) , FM-027) Merriwell, Frank Inc.

—Frank Merriwell's Club. Rudman, Jack, ed. 2003. (Frank Merriwell Ser.). 29.95 (978-0-8373-9368-1(X)); pap. 9.95 (978-0-8373-9068-0(0)) Merriwell, Frank Inc.

—Frank Merriwell's Courage. Rudman, Jack, ed. 2003. (Frank Merriwell Ser.). (YA). (gr. 9 up). 29.95 (978-0-8373-9314-8(0)); pap. 9.95 (978-0-8373-9014-7(1) , FM-014) Merriwell, Frank Inc.

—Frank Merriwell's Cruise. Rudman, Jack, ed. 2003. (Frank Merriwell Ser.). (YA). (gr. 9 up). 29.95 (978-0-8373-9326-1(4)); pap. 9.95 (978-0-8373-9026-0(5) , FM-026) Merriwell, Frank Inc.

—Frank Merriwell's Danger. Rudman, Jack, ed. 2003. (Frank Merriwell Ser.). (YA). (gr. 9 up). 29.95 (978-0-8373-9322-3(1)); pap. 9.95 (978-0-8373-9022-2(2) , FM-022) Merriwell, Frank Inc.

—Frank Merriwell's Daring. Rudman, Jack, ed. 2003. (Frank Merriwell Ser.). (YA). (gr. 9 up). 29.95 (978-0-8373-9315-5(9)); pap. 9.95 (978-0-8373-9015-4(X) , FM-015) Merriwell, Frank Inc.

—Frank Merriwell's Duel. Rudman, Jack, ed. 2003. (Frank Merriwell Ser.). 29.95 (978-0-8373-9346-9(9)); pap. 9.95 (978-0-8373-9046-8(X)) Merriwell, Frank Inc.

—Frank Merriwell's Encounter. Rudman, Jack, ed. 2003. (Frank Merriwell Ser.). 29.95 (978-0-8373-9399-5(X)); pap. 9.95 (978-0-8373-9099-4(0)) Merriwell, Frank Inc.

—Frank Merriwell's Encouragement. Rudman, Jack, ed. 2003. (Frank Merriwell Ser.). pap. 9.95 (978-0-8373-9172-4(5)) Merriwell, Frank Inc.

—Frank Merriwell's Endurance. Rudman, Jack, ed. 2003. (Frank Merriwell Ser.). pap. 9.95 (978-0-8373-9123-6(7)) Merriwell, Frank Inc.

—Frank Merriwell's Fortune. Rudman, Jack, ed. 2003. (Frank Merriwell Ser.). 29.95 (978-0-8373-9339-1(6)); pap. 9.95 (978-0-8373-9039-0(7)) Merriwell, Frank Inc.

—Frank Merriwell's Fun. Rudman, Jack, ed. 2003. (Frank Merriwell Ser.). 29.95 (978-0-8373-9351-3(5)); pap. 9.95 (978-0-8373-9051-2(6)) Merriwell, Frank Inc.

—Frank Merriwell's Great Scheme. Rudman, Jack, ed. 2003. (Frank Merriwell Ser.). 29.95 (978-0-8373-9343-8(4)); pap. 9.95 (978-0-8373-9043-7(5)) Merriwell, Frank Inc.

—Frank Merriwell's Hard Case. Rudman, Jack, ed. 2003. (Frank Merriwell Ser.). pap. 9.95 (978-0-8373-9162-5(8)) Merriwell, Frank Inc.

—Frank Merriwell's Iron Nerve. Rudman, Jack, ed. 2003. (Frank Merriwell Ser.). 29.95 (978-0-8373-9362-9(0)); pap. 9.95 (978-0-8373-9062-8(1)) Merriwell, Frank Inc.

—Frank Merriwell's Loyalty. Rudman, Jack, ed. 2003. (Frank Merriwell Ser.). (YA). (gr. 9 up). 29.95 (978-0-8373-9323-0(X)); pap. 9.95 (978-0-8373-9023-9(0) , FM-023) Merriwell, Frank Inc.

—Frank Merriwell's Marvel. Rudman, Jack, ed. 2003. (Frank Merriwell Ser.). 29.95 (978-0-8373-9374-2(4)); pap. 9.95 (978-0-8373-9074-1(5)) Merriwell, Frank Inc.

—Frank Merriwell's Mascot. Rudman, Jack, ed. 2003. (Frank Merriwell Ser.). 29.95 (978-0-8373-9357-5(4)); pap. 9.95 (978-0-8373-9057-4(5)) Merriwell, Frank Inc.

—Frank Merriwell's New Comedian. Rudman, Jack, ed. 2003. (Frank Merriwell Ser.). 29.95 (978-0-8373-9340-7(X)); pap. 29.95 (978-0-8373-9040-6(0)) Merriwell, Frank Inc.

—Frank Merriwell's Nomads. Rudman, Jack, ed. 2003. (Frank Merriwell Ser.). pap. 9.95 (978-0-8373-9101-4(6)) Merriwell, Frank Inc.

—Frank Merriwell's Opportunity. Rudman, Jack, ed. 2003. (Frank Merriwell Ser.). 29.95 (978-0-8373-9331-5(0)); pap. 9.95 (978-0-8373-9031-4(1)) Merriwell, Frank Inc.

—Frank Merriwell's Own Company. Rudman, Jack, ed. 2003. (Frank Merriwell Ser.). 29.95 (978-0-8373-9335-3(3)); pap. 9.95 (978-0-8373-9035-2(4)) Merriwell, Frank Inc.

—Frank Merriwell's Party. Rudman, Jack, ed. 2003. (Frank Merriwell Ser.). (YA). (gr. 9 up). 29.95 (978-0-8373-9312-4(4)); pap. 29.95 (978-0-8373-9012-3(5) , FM-012) Merriwell, Frank Inc.

—Frank Merriwell's Peril. Rudman, Jack, ed. 2003. (Frank Merriwell Ser.). pap. 9.95 (978-0-8373-9115-1(6)) Merriwell, Frank Inc.

—Frank Merriwell's Phantom. Rudman, Jack, ed. 2003. (Frank Merriwell Ser.). 29.95 (978-0-8373-9359-9(0)); pap. 9.95 (978-0-8373-9059-8(1)) Merriwell, Frank Inc.

—Frank Merriwell's Power. Rudman, Jack, ed. 2003. (Frank Merriwell Ser.). 29.95 (978-0-8373-9364-3(7)); pap. 9.95 (978-0-8373-9064-2(8)) Merriwell, Frank Inc.

—Frank Merriwell's Pride. Rudman, Jack, ed. 2003. (Frank Merriwell Ser.). pap. 9.95 (978-0-8373-9121-2(0)) Merriwell, Frank Inc.

—Frank Merriwell's Problem. Rudman, Jack, ed. 2003. (Frank Merriwell Ser.). 29.95 (978-0-8373-9338-4(8)); pap. 9.95 (978-0-8373-9038-3(9)) Merriwell, Frank Inc.

—Frank Merriwell's Prosperity. Rudman, Jack, ed. 2003. (Frank Merriwell Ser.). 29.95 (978-0-8373-9341-4(8)); pap. 9.95 (978-0-8373-9041-3(9)) Merriwell, Frank Inc.

—Frank Merriwell's Protege. Rudman, Jack, ed. 2003. (Frank Merriwell Ser.). 29.95 (978-0-8373-9333-9(7)); pap. 9.95 (978-0-8373-9033-8(8)) Merriwell, Frank Inc.

—Frank Merriwell's Pursuit. Rudman, Jack, ed. 2003. (Frank Merriwell Ser.). pap. 9.95 (978-0-8373-9117-5(2)) Merriwell, Frank Inc.

—Frank Merriwell's Races. Rudman, Jack, ed. 2003. (Frank Merriwell Ser.). (YA). (gr. 9 up). 29.95 (978-0-8373-9311-7(6)); pap. 9.95 (978-0-8373-9011-6(7) , FM-011) Merriwell, Frank Inc.

—Frank Merriwell's Rescue. Rudman, Jack, ed. 2003. (Frank Merriwell Ser.). 29.95 (978-0-8373-9398-8(1)); pap. 9.95 (978-0-8373-9098-7(2)) Merriwell, Frank Inc.

—Frank Merriwell's Return to Yale. Rudman, Jack, ed. 2003. (Frank Merriwell Ser.). (YA). (gr. 9 up). 29.95 (978-0-8373-9320-9(5)); pap. 9.95 (978-0-8373-9020-8(6) , FM-020) Merriwell, Frank Inc.

—Frank Merriwell's Reward. Rudman, Jack, ed. 2003. (Frank Merriwell Ser.). 29.95 (978-0-8373-9358-2(2)); pap. 9.95 (978-0-8373-9058-1(3)) Merriwell, Frank Inc.

—Frank Merriwell's Rough Deal. Rudman, Jack, ed. 2003. (Frank Merriwell Ser.). pap. 9.95 (978-0-8373-9111-3(3)) Merriwell, Frank Inc.

—Frank Merriwell's Search. Rudman, Jack, ed. 2003. (Frank Merriwell Ser.). 29.95 (978-0-8373-9367-4(1)); pap. 9.95 (978-0-8373-9067-3(2)) Merriwell, Frank Inc.

—Frank Merriwell's Secret. Rudman, Jack, ed. 2003. (Frank Merriwell Ser.). (YA). (gr. 9). 29.95 (978-0-8373-9321-6(3)); pap. 9.95 (978-0-8373-9021-5(4) , FM-021) Merriwell, Frank Inc.

—Frank Merriwell's Setback. Rudman, Jack, ed. 2003. (Frank Merriwell Ser.). 29.95 (978-0-8373-9366-7(3)); pap. 9.95 (978-0-8373-9066-6(4)) Merriwell, Frank Inc.

—Frank Merriwell's Shrewdness. Rudman, Jack, ed. 2003. (Frank Merriwell Ser.). 29.95 (978-0-8373-9365-0(5)); pap. 9.95 (978-0-8373-9065-9(6)) Merriwell, Frank Inc.

—Frank Merriwell's Skill. Rudman, Jack, ed. 2003. (Frank Merriwell Ser.). (YA). (gr. 9 up). 29.95 (978-0-8373-9318-6(3)); pap. 9.95 (978-0-8373-9018-5(4) , FM-018) Merriwell, Frank Inc.

—Frank Merriwell's Stage Hit. Rudman, Jack, ed. 2003. (Frank Merriwell Ser.). 29.95 (978-0-8373-9342-1(6)); pap. 9.95 (978-0-8373-9042-0(7)) Merriwell, Frank Inc.

—Frank Merriwell's Steadying Hand. Rudman, Jack, ed. 2003. (Frank Merriwell Ser.). pap. 9.95 (978-0-8373-9165-6(2)) Merriwell, Frank Inc.

—Frank Merriwell's Strategy. Rudman, Jack, ed. 2003. (Frank Merriwell Ser.). pap. 9.95 (978-0-8373-9106-9(7)) Merriwell, Frank Inc.

—Frank Merriwell's Strong Arm. Rudman, Jack, ed. 2003. (Frank Merriwell Ser.). 29.95 (978-0-8373-9371-1(X)); pap. 9.95 (978-0-8373-9071-0(0)) Merriwell, Frank Inc.

—Frank Merriwell's Struggle. Rudman, Jack, ed. 2003. (Frank Merriwell Ser.). (YA). (gr. 9 up). pap. 9.95 (978-0-8373-9029-1(X)) Merriwell, Frank Inc.

—Frank Merriwell's Support. Rudman, Jack, ed. 2003. (Frank Merriwell Ser.). 29.95 (978-0-8373-9375-9(2)); pap. 9.95 (978-0-8373-9075-8(3)) Merriwell, Frank Inc.

—Frank Merriwell's Talisman. Rudman, Jack, ed. 2003. (Frank Merriwell Ser.). pap. 9.95 (978-0-8373-9145-8(8)) Merriwell, Frank Inc.

—Frank Merriwell's Temptation. Rudman, Jack, ed. 2003. (Frank Merriwell Ser.). 29.95 (978-0-8373-9354-4(X)); pap. 9.95 (978-0-8373-9054-3(0)) Merriwell, Frank Inc.

—Frank Merriwell's Tigers. Rudman, Jack, ed. 2003. (Frank Merriwell Ser.). pap. 9.95 (978-0-8373-9131-1(8)) Merriwell, Frank Inc.

—Frank Merriwell's Tricks. Rudman, Jack, ed. 2003. (Frank Merriwell Ser.). 29.95 (978-0-8373-9353-7(1)); pap. 9.95 (978-0-8373-9053-6(2)) Merriwell, Frank Inc.

—Frank Merriwell's Trip West. Rudman, Jack, ed. (Frank Merriwell Ser.). (YA). (gr. 9 up). 29.95 (978-0-8373-9304-9(3)); pap. 9.95 (978-0-8373-9004-8(4) , FM-004) Merriwell, Frank Inc.

—Frank Merriwell's Triumph. Rudman, Jack, ed. 2003. (Frank Merriwell Ser.). pap. 9.95 (978-0-8373-9107-6(5)) Merriwell, Frank Inc.

—Frank Merriwell's Trump Card. Rudman, Jack, ed. 2003. (Frank Merriwell Ser.). pap. 9.95 (978-0-8373-9105-2(9)) Merriwell, Frank Inc.

—Frank Merriwell's Trust. Rudman, Jack, ed. 2003. (Frank Merriwell Ser.). 29.95 (978-0-8373-9369-8(8)); pap. 9.95 (978-0-8373-9069-7(9)) Merriwell, Frank Inc.

—Frank Merriwell's Vacation. Rudman, Jack, ed. 2003. (Frank Merriwell Ser.). (YA). (gr. 9 up). 29.95 (978-0-8373-9325-4(6)); pap. 9.95 (978-0-8373-9025-3(7) , FM-025) Merriwell, Frank Inc.

—Frank Merriwell's Victories. Rudman, Jack, ed. 2003. (Frank Merriwell Ser.). 29.95 (978-0-8373-9361-2(2)); pap. 9.95 (978-0-8373-9061-1(3)) Merriwell, Frank Inc.

—Frank Merriwell's Winners. Rudman, Jack, ed. 2003. (Frank Merriwell Ser.). 29.95 (978-0-8373-9388-9(4)); pap. 9.95 (978-0-8373-9088-8(5)) Merriwell, Frank Inc.

—Frank Merriwell's Wizard. Rudman, Jack, ed. 2003. (Frank Merriwell Ser.). pap. 9.95 (978-0-8373-9174-8(1)) Merriwell, Frank Inc.

—Frank Merriwell's Worst Boy. Rudman, Jack, ed. 2003. (Frank Merriwell Ser.). pap. 9.95 (978-0-8373-9155-7(5)) Merriwell, Frank Inc.

Standish, Burt L. & Rudman, Jack. Frank Merriwell on the Boulevards. 2003. (Frank Merriwell Ser.). 29.95 (978-0-8373-9345-2(0)) Merriwell, Frank Inc.

Standish, L. Burt. Frank Merriwell's Chums. 2007. (ENG.). 268p. 97.99 (*978-1-4280-7372-2(8)); per. 91.99 (*978-1-4280-7378-4(7)) IndyPublish.com.

Stanek, Mary Beth. The Fire Keepers: Mystery at Manitou Beach. Stanek, Mary Beth, illus. Stanek, Linda, photos by. 2003. (J). pap. 20.00 (978-0-9747556-0-1(5)) Stanek, Mary Beth.

Stanek, Robert. The Elf Queen & the King. (Ruin Mist Chronicles: Bk. 1). (YA). 2003. pap. 23.50 (978-1-57545-076-6(3)); 2002. 300p. pap. 15.00 (978-1-57545-061-2(5)) Reagent Pr.

—The Elf Queen & the King II. (Ruin Mist Chronicles). (YA). 2003. 23.50 (978-1-57545-077-3(1)); 2002. 300p. pap. 15.00 (978-1-57545-062-9(3)) Reagent Pr.

—The Elf Queen & the King III. 2007. 232p. (YA). pap. 15.00 (978-1-57545-086-5(0)) Reagent Pr.

—The Elf Queen & the King IV. 2008. 238p. (YA). pap. 15.00 (978-1-57545-087-2(9)) Reagent Pr.

—Into the Stone Land. 2006. (Best Fantasy Ser.: Bk. 2). 152p. (J). pap. 11.00 (978-1-57545-092-6(5)) Reagent Pr.

—Journey Beyond the Beyond: Magic Lands Book #1. ed. 2006. (Illus.). 112p. (J). pap. 18.95 (978-1-57545-108-4(5)) Reagent Pr.

—Magic Lands: Journey Beyond the Beyond. 2002. (Best Fantasy Ser.: Vol. 1). 180p. (J). pap. 11.00 (978-1-57545-064-3(X)) Reagent Pr.

—Magic Lands: Journey Beyond the Beyond. 2002. (gr. 3-6). lib. bdg. 19.95 (978-0-613-79225-7(4)) Tandem Library Bks.

—The Secrets, Mysteries & Magic of Robert Stanek's Ruin Mist. 2007. 200p. (YA). pap. 15.00 (978-1-57545-037-7(2) , Ruin Mist Pubns.) Reagent Pr.

—Student's Classroom Handbook for the Kingdoms & the Elves of the Reaches 2. 2007. 128p. pap. 15.00 (978-1-57545-036-0(4) , Ruin Mist Pubns.) Reagent Pr.

Stangherlin, Tonia. T-Bird & the Island of Lost Cats. 2006. 116p. pap. 14.99 (978-1-4116-6697-9(6)) Lulu.com.

Stanley, Andy. Go Fish Study Guide: Because of What's on the Line. 2005. 96p. pap. 9.99 (978-1-59052-548-7(5) , Multnomah) WaterBrook Pr.

Stanley, George Edward. Adam Sharp No. 4: Operation Spy School. 2003. (gr. k-3). lib. bdg. 11.80 (978-0-613-87820-3(5)) Tandem Library Bks.

Stanley, John. Little Lulu Vol. 14: Queen Lulu. 2007. 240p. pap. 9.95 (978-1-59307-683-2(5)) Dark Horse Comics.

Stanley, Mandy. Playtime. Fairley, Melissa, ed. 2003. (Illus.). 12p. (J). (ps-k). 3.95 (978-0-7534-5680-4(X) , Kingfisher) Houghton Mifflin Co. Trade & Reference Div.

Stanley's Adventure: Sticker Book to Color. (Playhouse Disney Ser.). 16p. (J). 2.99 (978-1-4037-0710-9(3)) Dalmatian Pr.

Stanley's Great Adventures: Stanley Dreams. 2001. (J). spiral bd. 15.95 net. (978-0-9705225-2-8(5)) Harvest Inspirational Publishing, Inc.

Stansfield, David. The Amazing Adventures of Boogie One Shoe & Munch the Mouse. 2006. 48p. pap. 12.95 (978-1-4241-2404-6(2)) PublishAmerica, Inc.

Stanton, Mary. By Moonlight, by Fire. 1999. (Unicorns of Balinor Ser.: No. 4). 144p. (J). (gr. 3-7). pap. 4.50 (978-0-439-06283-1(7)) Scholastic, Inc.

—The Road to Balinor. 1999. (Unicorns of Balinor Ser.: No. 1). (978-0-606-17550-0(4)) Tandem Library Bks.

—Search for the Star. Craig, D., illus. 1999. (Unicorns of Balinor Ser.: Vol. 5). 128p. (J). (gr. 3-7). pap. 4.99 (978-0-439-12047-0(0)) Scholastic, Inc.

—Sunchaser's Quest. 1999. (Unicorns of Balinor Ser.: No. 2). 160p. (J). (gr. 3-7). pap. 4.50 (978-0-439-06281-7(0)) Scholastic, Inc.

—Sunchaser's Quest. 1999. (Unicorns of Balinor Ser.: No. 2). (978-0-606-17551-7(2)) Tandem Library Bks.

—Valley of Fear No.3. 1999. (gr. 5-8). lib. bdg. 12.40 (978-0-613-16870-0(4)) Tandem Library Bks.

Stanwood Pier, Arthu. The Jester of St. Timothy's. 2006. pap. 14.95 (*978-1-55742-546-1(9)) Wildside Pr.

Starke, Ruth. Chomps: Catland: Can Rose pull off her purrfect Plan? 2007. 96p. (J). pap. 3.95 (*978-0-7624-2925-7(9) , Running Pr. Kids) Running Pr. Bk. Pubs.

Starr, Sandra. Leigh's Triumph. 2006. 295p. pap. 24.95 (978-1-4137-4660-0(8)) PublishAmerica, Inc.

Staton, Debbie. Twiggle. Patzelt, Kasie, illus. l.t. ed. 2006. 26p. (J). per. 12.99 (*978-1-59879-199-0(0)) Lifevest Publishing, Inc.

Staunton, Ted. Forgive Us Our Travises. Lafontaine, Roger, illus. 2004. (Monkey Mountain Bks.). 64p. (J). (gr. 2-5). pap. 4.95 (978-0-88995-207-2(8)) Red Deer Pr. CAN. *Dist:* Fitzhenry & Whiteside, Ltd.

Stead. The End of The Century at the End of the World. 1999. 2220p. (YA). pap. 24.95 (978-1-86950-299-7(X)) HarperCollins Pubs. New Zealand NZL. *Dist:* Antipodes Bks. & Beyond.

Stead, Rebecca. First Light. 2007. 336p. (J). (gr. 4-7). 15.99 (*978-0-375-84017-3(6)); lib. bdg. 18.99 (*978-0-375-94017-0(0)) Random Hse. Children's Bks. (Lamb, Wendy).

Steck-Vaughn Staff. Classic Adventure: New York Edition. 2002. (J). (gr. 3). pap. 150.00 (978-1-58702-943-1(X)) Johnston, Don Inc.

—Classic Adventures: Book Pack. 2001. (J). (gr. 3). pap. 30.00 (978-1-58702-751-2(8)) Johnston, Don Inc.

—Classic Adventures: Reading Group Pack. 2001. (J). (gr. 3). pap. 399.00 (978-1-58702-752-9(6)) Johnston, Don Inc.

—Classic Adventures: Single User Packs. 2001. (J). (gr. 3). pap. 174.00 (978-1-58702-750-5(X)) Johnston, Don Inc.

—Jojos Road Trips/Tony's Yellow. 1999. (Take Me Home Ser.). (Illus.). (J). pap. (978-0-7398-2679-9(4)) Steck-Vaughn.

—Three Cheers for May. 2005. (ps-k). pap. 12.99 (978-0-7398-9825-3(6)) Harcourt Schl. Pubs.

Steele, Alexander. The Last of the Breed. Punchatz, Don, illus. l.t. ed. 1999. (Adventures of Wishbone Ser.: No. 16). 163p. (J). (gr. 4 up). lib. bdg. 22.60 (978-0-8368-2594-7(2)) Stevens, Gareth Inc.

—Moby Dog. l.t. ed. 1999. (Adventures of Wishbone Ser.: No. 10). (Illus.). 144p. (J). (gr. 4 up). lib. bdg. 22.60 (978-0-8368-2306-6(0)) Stevens, Gareth Inc.

—Tale of the Missing Mascot. l.t. ed. 1999. (Wishbone Mysteries Ser.: No. 4). 144p. (J). (gr. 4 up). lib. bdg. 23.33 (978-0-8368-2385-1(0)) Stevens, Gareth Inc.

Steele, Giselle. The off-Limits Watermelon Patch. 2006. (Illus.). 35p. (J). per. 12.95 (978-0-9769949-0-9(9)) Stuart & Weitz Publishing Group.

Steele, Giselle V. Nicholas & the Magical Wind. 2005. 32p. 23.95 (978-1-58275-093-4(9)) Stuart & Weitz Publishing Group.

Steele, Michael Anthony. Agent Cody Banks 2: Junior Novelization. novel ed. 2004. 112p. (J). pap. 4.99 (978-0-439-65125-7(5)) Scholastic, Inc.

—Digging to the Center of the Earth. Punchatz, Don, illus. l.t. ed. 1999. (Adventures of Wishbone Ser.: No. 17). (J). (gr. 4 up). lib. bdg. 22.60 (978-0-8368-2595-4(0)) Stevens, Gareth Inc.

—Fire & Ice. 2006. (Winx Club Ser.). (Illus.). 152p. (J). pap. 4.99 (978-0-439-78781-9(5)) Scholastic, Inc.

—The Magic of the Tower. 2006. (Knights' Kingdom Ser.). 24p. (J). pap. 4.99 (978-0-439-82812-3(0)) Scholastic, Inc.

—Quest for the Tower. Schutz, Samantha, ed. 2006. (Knights' Kingdom Ser.). 24p. (J). pap. 3.99 (978-0-439-78801-4(3)) Scholastic, Inc.

Steele, Philip & MacDonald, Fiona. Raiders of the North. 2001. (Illus.). 128p. pap. 12.95 (978-1-84215-401-4(X), Southwater) Anness Publishing GBR. *Dist:* National Bk. Network.

Steele, William O. The Buffalo Knife. 2004. (Illus.). 144p. (J). 17.00 (978-0-15-205214-0(3), Harcourt Young Classics); pap. 5.95 (978-0-15-205215-7(1), Odyssey Classics) Harcourt Children's Bks.

Steffen, Tim & Thornton, Susan. The Adventures of Baby Cat in Cherry Grove: Home Sweet Home. 2006. (Illus.). (J). per. 15.00 (978-0-9779518-0-2(4)) Baby Cat Books.

Steffen, Tim & Thornton, Susan Ann. The Adventures of Baby Cat in Cherry Grove: Finding Faith. Thornton, Susan Ann, illus. 2007. (Illus.). 50p. (J). per. 12.00 (***978-0-9779518-1-9(2)***) Baby Cat Books.

Steig, William. Dominic. 2007. (Illus.). 160p. (J). pap. 5.99 (***978-0-312-37144-9(6)***) Square Fish.

Stein, Aidel, et al. Baker's Dozen Three-in-One: Ima Come Home; Hey, Walter!; Through Thick & Thin, 3 vols. 2000. (Illus.). 143p. 16.99 (978-1-56871-285-7(5)) Targum Pr., Inc.

—Baker's Dozen Three-in-One: Stars in Their Eyes; The Inside Story; Trapped, 3 vols. 2000. (Illus.). 169p. (gr. 3-9). 16.99 (978-1-56871-163-8(8)) Targum Pr., Inc.

Steinberg, David. Mac Attack! Smith, Brian, illus. 2008. 96p. (J). (gr. 3-6). pap. 5.99 (***978-0-448-44699-8(5)***, Grosset & Dunlap) Penguin Group (USA) Inc.

Stellinga, Mark. Buster Boogernose & the Junkyard. 2007. (J). per. 9.95 (***978-0-9796421-6-6(7)***) Stellinga, Mark.

—Buster Boogernose & the Old Mansion. 2007. (J). per. 9.95 (***978-0-9796421-5-9(9)***) Stellinga, Mark.

—Buster Boogernose & the Secret Cave. 2007. (J). per. 9.95 (***978-0-9796421-8-0(3)***) Stellinga, Mark.

Stem, Jacqueline. The Secret of the Dragonfly Pin. 2006. (Hollow Tree Mystery Ser.: 7). 122p. (J). pap. 12.95 (978-1-57168-264-2(3), Eakin Pr.) Eakin Pr.

Stemach, Jerry. Alcatraz, the Book. Stemach, Jerry et al, eds. Dizick, Phillip, illus. 2002. (Start-to-Finish Books: Vol. 3). (J). (gr. 2-3). 100.00 (978-1-58702-981-3(2)) Johnston, Don Inc.

Stephens, Jay. Atomic City Tales Vol. 2: Doc Phantom. 2003. (Illus.). 80p. (gr. 12 up). pap. 12.95 (978-1-929998-27-2(9)) Oni Pr., Inc.

Stephens, Monique Z. The Incredible Mr. E! 2006. (I Can Read Bks.). 32p. (J). pap. 3.99 (978-0-06-084605-3(4), Harper Trophy) HarperCollins Pubs.

—Meet the Characters. 2006. (I Can Read Bks.). 32p. (J). pap. 3.99 (978-0-06-084606-0(2), Harper Trophy) HarperCollins Pubs.

Sterling Publishing Co., Inc. Naughty Kitten: A Touch & Feel Adventure. 2005. (Illus.). 16p. (J). 12.95 (978-1-4027-2454-1(3)) Sterling Publishing Co., Inc.

—Playful Puppy: A Touch & Feel Adventure. 2005. (Illus.). 16p. (J). 12.95 (978-1-4027-2455-8(1)) Sterling Publishing Co., Inc.

Sterling Publishing Co., Inc. & Fernleigh Books Staff. Goldilocks: A Magic 3-Dimensional Fairy-Tale World. 2006. (Step Inside Ser.). (Illus.). 12p. (J). 9.95 (978-1-4027-3657-5(6)) Sterling Publishing Co., Inc.

Stern, Shirley. Around the World. 2008. (Franny's Feet Ser.). 224p. (J). (ps-1). 4.99 (***978-1-4169-4919-0(4)***, Simon Scribbles) Simon & Schuster Children's Publishing.

—Giddy-Up! 2008. (Franny's Feet Ser.). 32p. (J). (ps-1). 3.99 (***978-1-4169-4916-9(X)***, Simon Scribbles) Simon & Schuster Children's Publishing.

Stern, Steven L. The Earth Project. 2001. (YA). pap. (978-1-56765-068-6(6), R697P) AMSCO Schl. Pubns., Inc.

Sternfeld, Nathan. All about Motti & His Adventures with Rebbe Mendel. Bichman, David, illus. 2004. 220p. (J). 20.99 (978-1-58330-669-7(2)) Feldheim Pubs.

Stevenson, James. The Castaway. Stevenson, James, illus. 2002. (Illus.). 32p. (J). (gr. 2 up). 15.95 (978-0-688-16965-7(1)) HarperCollins Pubs.

Stevenson, Robert Louis. The Black Arrow. l.t. ed. 2005. 448p. pap. (978-1-84637-164-6(3)) Echo Library.

—La Flecha Negra.Tr. of Black Arrow. (SPA., Illus.). 160p. (YA). 11.95 (978-84-7281-142-3(5), AF1142) Auriga, Ediciones S.A. ESP. *Dist:* Continental Bk. Co., Inc.

—La Flecha Negra. 1999. Tr. of Black Arrow. (SPA.). 182p. 11.95 (978-84-239-7076-6(0)) Espasa Calpe, S.A. ESP. *Dist:* Libros Sin Fronteras.

—La Flecha Negra. 2002. (Classics for Young Readers Ser.).Tr. of Black Arrow. (SPA.). (YA). 14.95 (978-84-392-0927-0(4), EV30605) Gaviota Ediciones ESP. *Dist:* Lectorum Pubns., Inc.

—La Flecha Negra. (Coleccion Clasicos de la Juventud).Tr. of Black Arrow. (SPA., Illus.). (J). 12.95 (978-84-7189-100-6(X), ORT304) Ortells, Alfredo Editorial S.L. ESP. *Dist:* Continental Bk. Co., Inc.

—Isla del Tesoro. 1999. Tr. of Treasure Island. 18.60 (978-0-606-17595-1(4)) Tandem Library Bks.

—La Isla del Tesoro. 2001. (SPA., Illus.). 166p. (YA). (gr. 5-8). 12.95 (978-84-372-2236-3(2)) Altea, Ediciones, S.A. - Grupo Santillana ESP. *Dist:* Santillana USA Publishing Co., Inc.

—La Isla del Tesoro. (Coleccion Clasicos de la Juventud). (SPA., Illus.). 188p. (J). 12.95 (978-84-7189-017-7(8), ORT301) Ortells, Alfredo Editorial S.L. ESP. *Dist:* Continental Bk. Co., Inc.

—La Isla del Tesoro. (Coleccion Estrella). (SPA., Illus.). 64p. (J). 14.95 (978-950-11-0009-9(X), SGM009) Sigmar ARG. *Dist:* Continental Bk. Co., Inc.

—La Isla del Tesoro. 2000. (Coleccion "Clasicos Juveniles" Ser.). (SPA., Illus.). 192p. (gr. 4-7). pap. 9.95 (978-1-58348-832-4(4)) iUniverse, Inc.

—Kidnapped. 2002. (Great Illustrated Classics Ser.). (Illus.). 240p. (J). (gr. 3-8). 21.35 (978-1-57765-690-6(3), ABDO & Daughters) ABDO Publishing Co.

—Kidnapped. 1999. (Illus.). 208p. 19.95 (978-1-85149-708-9(0)) Antique Collectors' Club.

—Kidnapped. 2000. (Classics Ser.). 240p. mass mkt. 3.95 (978-0-451-52768-4(2), Signet Classics) Penguin Group (USA) Inc.

—Kidnapped. 2006. per. 8.95 (978-1-57646-970-5(0)) Quiet Vision Publishing.

—Kidnapped. 2002. (Scholastic Classics Ser.). 288p. (J). (gr. 5). pap. 3.99 (978-0-439-29578-9(5)) Scholastic, Inc.

—Kidnapped. 1998. (Children's Classics). (ENG.). 224p. (YA). (ps up). pap. (978-1-85326-117-6(3), 1173WW) Wordsworth Editions, Ltd.

—Kidnapped. 2004. (Fast Track Classics Ser.). (Illus.). 48p. (J). pap. 8.99 (978-0-237-52403-6(1), Evans Brothers, Limited) Evans Publishing Group GBR. *Dist:* Independent Pubs. Group.

—Kidnapped. Kennedy, Cam, illus. 2007. 64p. (J). (gr. 5). pap. 11.95 (***978-0-88776-843-9(1)***) Tundra Bks., Inc./Livres Toundra, Inc. CAN. *Dist:* Random Hse., Inc.

—Kidnapped. unabr. ed. 2000. (Dover Juvenile Classics Ser.). (Illus.). 256p. (J). (gr. 4-7). pap. 2.50 (978-0-486-41026-5(9)) Dover Pubns., Inc.

—Kidnapped Promotion: Being Memoirs of the Adventures of David Balfour in the Year 1751. 2000. (Cageworld Ser.). 336p. (J). pap. 2.99 (978-0-14-130936-1(9), Puffin) Penguin Group (USA) Inc.

—Robert Louis Stevenson's Treasure Island: The Graphic Novel. 2005. (Puffin Graphics Ser.). (Illus.). 176p. (978-1-4156-2620-7(0), Puffin) Penguin Group (USA) Inc.

—Robert Louis Stevenson/Treasure Island. Cruz, Nardo, illus. 2005. 48p. (J). (gr. 5-8). 25.50 (978-0-7910-9107-4(0)) Facts On File, Inc.

—Secuestrado. 3rd ed. (Coleccion Clasicos en Accion). (SPA., Illus.). 80p. (YA). (gr. 5-8). 15.95 (978-84-241-5781-4(8), EV1487) Everest de Ediciones y Distribucion, S.L. ESP. *Dist:* Lectorum Pubns., Inc.

—Secuestrado. 2002. (Clover Ser.). (SPA., Illus.). 156p. (YA). 11.50 (978-84-392-8006-4(8), EV5548) Lectorum Pubns., Inc.

—The Strange Case of Dr. Jekyll & Mr. Hyde (Quality Library Classics) 2008. (YA). pap. 14.95 (978-1-57545-703-1(2)) Reagent Pr.

—Treasure Island. McAllister, A. J., illus. 2002. (Great Illustrated Classics Ser.). 240p. (J). (gr. 3-8). 21.35 (978-1-57765-805-4(1), ABDO & Daughters) ABDO Publishing Co.

—Treasure Island. Todd, Justin, illus. 1999. (Abbeville Classics Ser.). 176p. (J). pap. 7.95 (978-0-7892-0551-3(3), Abbeville Kids) Abbeville Pr., Inc.

—Treasure Island. Date not set. (Nelson Readers Ser.). (J). pap. (978-0-17-556699-0(2)) Addison-Wesley Longman, Inc.

—Treasure Island. Todd, Justin, illus. 2000. 192p. (J). pap. 8.95 (978-1-86205-007-5(4), Pavilion Bks., Ltd.) Anova Bks. GBR. *Dist:* Trafalgar Square Publishing.

—Treasure Island. 2005. 116p. per. 5.95 (978-1-4209-2258-5(0)) Digireads.com.

—Treasure Island. 2001. (YA). (gr. 5-12). pap. 8.50 (978-0-8359-0234-2(X)) Globe Fearon Educational Publishing.

Treasure Island. Lawrence, John, illus. 2001. (Kingfisher Classics Ser.). 352p. (J). (gr. 4-6). tchr. ed. 15.95 (978-0-7534-5380-3(0), Kingfisher) Houghton Mifflin Co. Trade & Reference Div.

—Treasure Island. (Young Collector's Illustrated Classics Ser.). (Illus.). 192p. (J). (gr. 3-7). 9.95 (978-1-56156-456-9(7)) Kidsbooks, Inc.

—Treasure Island. 2007. (Oxford Children's Classics). (Illus.). 288p. (YA). 9.95 (***978-0-19-271998-0(X)***) Oxford Univ. Pr., Inc.

—Treasure Island. Ingpen, Robert, illus. 2006. 192p. (J). 19.95 (978-0-9545103-6-7(4)) Palazzo Editions, Ltd. GBR. *Dist:* Trafalgar Square Publishing.

—Treasure Island. Chapman, Neil, illus. 2004. 320p. (J). (978-1-4054-3773-8(1)) Parragon, Inc.

—Treasure Island. Seelye, John, ed. 1999. (Classics Ser.). (Illus.). 240p. (gr. 12). pap. 7.00 (978-0-14-043768-3(1), Penguin Classics) Penguin Group (USA) Inc.

—Treasure Island. 1999. 1p. (J). (gr. 4-7). 2.99 (978-0-14-130545-5(2), Puffin); 1998. 224p. mass mkt. 3.95 (978-0-451-52704-2(6), Signet Classics) Penguin Group (USA) Inc.

—Treasure Island. Winter, Milo, illus. 2002. (Illustrated Library for Children). 272p. (J). 12.99 (978-0-517-22114-3(4), Gramercy) Random Hse. Value Publishing.

—Treasure Island. 2006. (Scholastic Classics Ser.). (Illus.). x, 205p. (J). (gr. 9-12). 25.00 (978-0-531-16961-2(8), Watts, Franklin) Scholastic Library Publishing.

—Treasure Island. 2005. (Enriched Classics Ser.). 304p. mass mkt. 3.95 (978-1-4165-0029-2(4), Pocket) Simon & Schuster.

—Treasure Island. Wyeth, N. C., illus. 2000. (Aladdin Classics Ser.). 368p. (gr. 3-7). mass mkt. 5.99 (978-0-689-83212-3(5), Aladdin) Simon & Schuster Children's Publishing.

—Treasure Island. 2006. (J). (gr. 4-8). 24.21 (978-1-59961-119-8(8)) Spotlight.

—Treasure Island. 1998. (Children's Classics). (ENG., Illus.). 224p. (J). (gr. 3-7). pap. (978-1-85326-103-9(3), 1033WW) Wordsworth Editions, Ltd.

—Treasure Island. Corvino, Lucy, illus. 2005. (Classic Starts Ser.). 160p. 4.95 (978-1-4027-1318-7(5)) Sterling Publishing Co., Inc.

—Treasure Island. Cruz, Nardo, illus. 2nd ed. 1998. (Illustrated Classic Book Ser.). 61p. (J). (gr. 3 up). reprint ed. pap. 4.95 (978-1-56767-239-8(6)) Educational Insights, Inc.

—Treasure Island. unabr. ed. 1998. (Wordsworth Classics Ser.). (YA). (gr. 6-12). 5.27 (978-0-89061-103-6(3), R1033WW) Jamestown.

—Treasure Island. 2004. reprint ed. pap. 1.99 (978-1-4192-9097-8(5)) Kessinger Publishing, LLC.

—Treasure Island. 1999. (Illus.). 240p. (YA). (gr. 3 up). reprint ed. 7.95 (978-1-56852-233-3(9), Konecky & Konecky) Konecky, William S. Assocs., Inc.

—Treasure Island. 1998. (Twelve-Point Ser.). 204p. reprint ed. lib. bdg. 25.00 (978-1-58287-075-5(6)) North Bks.

—Treasure Island: A Young Reader's Edition of the Classic Adventure. Wyeth, N. C., illus. 2004. 47p. (J). (gr. 4-8). reprint ed. 17.00 (978-0-7567-8010-4(1)) DIANE Publishing Co.

—Treasure Island: With a Discussion of Courage. 2003. (Values in Action Illustrated Classics Ser.). (J). (978-1-59203-054-5(8)) Learning Challenge, Inc.

—Treasure Island: With Story of the Treasure of Normon Island. Date not set. (J). (gr. 5-6). reprint ed. lib. bdg. 22.95 (978-0-89190-236-2(8), American Reprint Co.) Amereon LTD.

—Treasure Island #3: on the Island. Comport, Sally Wern, illus. 2007. (Easy Reader Classics Ser.). 32p. (J). pap. 3.95 (978-1-4027-4119-7(7)) Sterling Publishing Co., Inc.

—Treasure Island #4: Pirate Attack. Comport, Sally Wern, illus. 2007. (Easy Reader Classics Ser.). 32p. (J). pap. 3.95 (978-1-4027-4120-3(0)) Sterling Publishing Co., Inc.

—Treasure Island (Quality Library Classics) 2005. (YA). pap. 14.95 (978-1-57545-701-7(6)) Reagent Pr.

Stevenson, Robert Louis. Treausre Island: #1 the Treasure Map. 2007. (Easy Reader Classics Ser.). 32p. (J). (ps-3). 21.35 (***978-1-59961-342-0(5)***) Spotlight.

Stevenson, Robert Louis, intro. Kidnapped: Catriona. 2007. 480p. pap. 15.00 (***978-1-84697-033-7(4)***) BirlinnPolygon GBR. *Dist:* Interlink Publishing Group, Inc.

Stevenson, Robert Louis & Brook, Henry. Treasure Island. 2006. 160p. (J). pap. 4.99 (978-0-7945-1230-9(5), Usborne) EDC Publishing.

Stevenson, Robert Louis & Hitchner, Earle. Treasure Island. 1999. (Illus.). 245p. (J). (978-0-03-054463-7(7)) Holt, Rinehart & Winston.

Stevenson, Robert Louis & Wyeth, N. C. Kidnapped. 2004. (Scribner Storybook Classic Ser.). (Illus.). 64p. (J). 18.95 (978-0-689-86542-8(2), Atheneum) Simon & Schuster Children's Publishing.

Stewart, Angela. The Curious Adventures of India Sophia. Stuart, Mitchell, illus. 2004. (Juvenile Novel Ser.). 176p. (J). (gr. 4-6). pap. 9.95 (978-1-895836-78-3(6)) River Bks. CAN. *Dist:* Coteau Bks., Fitzhenry & Whiteside, Ltd.

Stewart, Jane L. A Campfire Girl's Test of Friendship. 2004. reprint ed. pap. 26.95 (978-1-4179-3874-2(9)) Kessinger Publishing, LLC.

Stewart, Jennifer. If That Breathes Fire, We're Toast! 2001. 128p. (gr. 4-7). pap. 4.50 (978-0-439-17482-4(1)) Scholastic, Inc.

Stewart, Paul. Joust of Honor. Riddell, Chris, illus. 2005. (Knight's Story Ser.: Bk. 2). 144p. (J). 9.95 (978-0-689-87240-2(2), Atheneum) Simon & Schuster Children's Publishing.

—Midnight Hand. 2000. (Yearling Book Ser.). (Illus.). 187p. (J). pap. 8.99 (978-0-440-86348-9(1)) Transworld Publishers Ltd. GBR. *Dist:* Trafalgar Square Publishing.

Stewart, Paul & Riddell, Chris. Blobheads Go Boing! l.t. ed. 2005. (J). pap. (978-1-4056-6002-0(3)) BBC Audio.

—Dragon's Hoard. 2005. (Knight's Story Ser.). (Illus.). 144p. (J). 9.95 (978-0-689-87241-9(0), Atheneum) Simon & Schuster Children's Publishing.

—Far-Flung Adventures: Fergus Crane. 2006. (Illus.). 240p. (J). (gr. 3-7). 14.95 (978-0-385-75088-2(9)); lib. bdg. 17.99 (978-0-385-75089-9(7)) Random Hse. Children's Bks. (Fickling, David Bks.).

—Fergus Crane. 2004. (Illus.). 160p. (J). (978-0-385-60719-3(9)) Doubleday Publishing.

—Hugo Pepper. 2007. (Far-Flung Adventures Ser.). (Illus.). 272p. (J). (gr. 3-7). 14.99 (978-0-385-75092-9(7)); lib. bdg. 16.99 (978-0-385-75093-6(5)) Random Hse. Children's Bks. (Fickling, David Bks.).

Stewart, Sean & Weisman, Jordan. Cathy's Book: If Found Call 650-266-8233. 2006. (Illus.). 144p. (YA). 17.95 (978-0-7624-2656-0(X)) Running Pr. Bk. Pubs.

Stewart, Shawn. Donny & the Doorman's Nightmare. 2004. 54p. pap. 8.11 (978-1-4116-2188-6(3)) Lulu.com.

Stewart, Trenton Lee. The Mysterious Benedict Society. Ellis, Carson, illus. 2007. 496p. (J). (gr. 3-7). 16.99 (978-0-316-05777-6(0), Tingley, Megan Bks.) Little, Brown Bks. for Young Readers.

—The Mysterious Benedict Society. 2006. (978-0-307-28440-2(9), Listening Library) Random Hse. Audio Publishing Group.

Stewart, Trenton Lee. Mysterious Benedict Society 2. 2008. 448p. 16.99 (***978-0-316-05780-6(0)***) Little Brown & Co.

Stier, Roy E. Son of Bunyan & the Sacred Moonstone. 2003. (Illus.). 158p. (J). per. 15.95 (978-1-892264-10-7(2)) Timeless Voyager Pr.

Stierle, Cynthia. Stepan's Story: Mr. Bean's Holiday. 2007. 48p. (J). (gr. 1-4). pap. 3.99 (978-0-8431-2523-8(3), Price Stern Sloan) Penguin Group (USA) Inc.

Stierle, Cynthia & Disney Pixar Artists. Disney Pixar Cars Movie Theater Storybook & Movie Projector. 2006. (RD Innovative Book & Player Format Ser.). 48p. (J). (ps-3). 24.99 (978-0-7944-1269-2(6)) Reader's Digest Assn., Inc., The.

Still, James. Sporty Creek. Johnson, Paul Brett, illus. 1999. 119p. (YA). (gr. 8-12). pap. 14.00 (978-0-8131-0965-7(5)) Univ. Pr. of Kentucky.

Stilton, Geronimo. All Because of a Cup of Coffee. 2004. (Geronimo Stilton Ser.: No. 10). (Illus.). 112p. (J). (gr. 2-5). lib. bdg. 13.94 (978-0-606-33273-6(1)) Tandem Library Bks.

—Attack of the Bandit Cats. Wolf, Matt, illus. 2004. (Geronimo Stilton Ser.: No. 8). 115p. (J). lib. bdg. 10.00 (***978-1-4242-0277-5(9)***) Fitzgerald Bks.

—Attack of the Bandit Cats. 2004. (Geronimo Stilton Ser.: No. 8). (Illus.). 128p. (J). pap. 5.99 (978-0-439-55970-6(7), Scholastic Paperbacks) Scholastic, Inc.

—Cat & Mouse in a Haunted House. 2004. (Geronimo Stilton Ser.: No. 3). (gr. 3-6). lib. bdg. 14.15 (978-0-613-72224-7(8)) Tandem Library Bks.

—The Christmas Toy Factory. 2006. (Geronimo Stilton Ser.: No. 27). (Illus.). 95p. (J). (***978-1-4156-8969-1(5)***) Scholastic, Inc.

—The Curse of the Cheese Pyramid. Wolf, Matt, illus. 2004. (Geronimo Stilton Ser.: No. 2). 113p. (J). lib. bdg. 10.00 (***978-1-4242-0696-4(0)***) Fitzgerald Bks.

—The Curse of the Cheese Pyramid. 2004. (Geronimo Stilton Ser.: No. 2). (gr. 3-6). lib. bdg. 14.15 (978-0-613-72223-0(X)) Tandem Library Bks.

—Down & Out down under. 2007. (Geronimo Stilton Ser.: No. 29). (Illus.). 128p. (J). pap. 6.99 (978-0-439-84120-7(8), Scholastic Paperbacks) Scholastic, Inc.

—A Fabumouse Vacation for Geronimo. Keys, Larry, illus. 2004. (Geronimo Stilton Ser.: No. 9). 128p. (J). pap. 6.99 (978-0-439-55971-3(5), Scholastic Paperbacks) Scholastic, Inc.

—Four Mice Deep in the Jungle. Wolf, Matt & Keys, Larry, illus. 2004. (Geronimo Stilton Ser.: No. 5). 128p. (J). pap. 6.99 (978-0-439-55967-6(7), Scholastic Paperbacks) Scholastic, Inc.

—Un granizado de moscas para el Conde. Wolf, Matt, illus. (SPA.). 128p. (J). (gr. 3-5). pap. 7.95 (978-1-59437-452-4(X)) Santillana USA Publishing Co., Inc.

—I'm Too Fond of My Fur! Wolf, Matt, illus. 2004. (Geronimo Stilton Ser.: No. 4). 116p. (J). lib. bdg. 10.00 (***978-1-4242-0698-8(7)***) Fitzgerald Bks.

—I'm Too Fond of My Fur! Wolf, Matt & Keys, Larry, illus. 2004. (Geronimo Stilton Ser.: No. 4). 128p. (J). pap. 6.99 (978-0-439-55966-9(9), Scholastic Paperbacks) Scholastic, Inc.

—I'm Too Fond of My Fur! 2004. (Geronimo Stilton Ser.: No. 4). (gr. 3-6). lib. bdg. 14.15 (978-0-613-72225-4(6)) Tandem Library Bks.

—Lost Treasure of the Emerald Eye. Wolf, Matt, illus. 2004. (Geronimo Stilton Ser.: No. 1). 116p. (J). lib. bdg. 10.00 (***978-1-4242-0695-7(2)***) Fitzgerald Bks.

—Lost Treasure of the Emerald Eye. 2007. (Geronimo Stilton Ser.: No. 1). 128p. (J). pap. 2.99 (***978-0-545-01032-0(2)***, Scholastic Paperbacks) Scholastic, Inc.

—Lost Treasure of the Emerald Eye. Wolf, Matt & Keys, Larry, illus. 2004. (Geronimo Stilton Ser.: No. 1). 128p. (J). (gr. 2-5). pap. 6.99 (978-0-439-55963-8(4), Scholastic Paperbacks) Scholastic, Inc.

—El Misterio Del Ojo Esmeralda. (SPA., Illus.). 128p. (J). (gr. 3-5). pap. 7.95 (978-1-59437-453-1(8)) Santillana USA Publishing Co., Inc.

—The Mummy with No Name. 2006. (Geronimo Stilton Ser.: No. 26). 128p. (J). pap. 6.99 (978-0-439-84117-7(8), Scholastic Paperbacks) Scholastic, Inc.

—The Mysterious Cheese Thief. 2007. (Geronimo Stilton Ser.: No. 31). 128p. (J). pap. 6.99 (***978-0-439-02312-2(2)***) Scholastic, Inc.

—The Secret of Cacklefur Castle. 2005. (Geronimo Stilton Ser.: No. 22). (Illus.). 128p. (ps-k). pap. 6.99 (978-0-439-69145-1(1), Scholastic Paperbacks) Scholastic, Inc.

—The Temple of the Ruby of Fire. Wolf, Matt, illus. 2004. (Geronimo Stilton Ser.: No. 14). 109p. (J). lib. bdg. 10.00 (***978-1-4242-0283-6(3)***) Fitzgerald Bks.

—The Temple of the Ruby of Fire. 2004. (Geronimo Stilton Ser.: No. 14). (Illus.). 128p. (J). (gr. 2-5). pap. 6.99 (978-0-439-66163-8(3), Scholastic Paperbacks) Scholastic, Inc.

—The Temple of the Ruby of Fire. 2004. (Geronimo Stilton Ser.: No. 14). (Illus.). 106p. (J). (gr. 2-5). lib. bdg. 13.94 (978-0-606-33277-4(4)) Tandem Library Bks.

—The Wild, Wild West. 2005. (Geronimo Stilton Ser.: No. 21). (Illus.). 128p. (J). 5.99 (978-0-439-69144-4(3), Scholastic Paperbacks) Scholastic, Inc.

—The Wild, Wild West. Keys, Larry & Rattonchi, Ratterto, illus. 2005. (Geronimo Stilton Ser.: No. 21). 100p. (J). (ps-k). lib. bdg. 13.94 (978-0-606-33824-0(1)) Tandem Library Bks.

Stilton, Geronimo, text. A Cheese-Colored Camper. 2005. (Geronimo Stilton Ser.: No. 16). (Illus.). 111p. (J). (ps-k). lib. bdg. 12.64 (978-0-606-33281-1(2)) Tandem Library Bks.

Stilton, Geronimo & Wolf, Matt. All Because of a Cup of Coffee. 2004. (Geronimo Stilton Ser.: No. 10). (Illus.). 112p. (J). lib. bdg. 10.00 (***978-1-4242-0279-9(5)***) Fitzgerald Bks.

Stine, Megan. Power of the Rat. 2002. (gr. 3-6). lib. bdg. 13.00 (978-0-613-72454-8(2)) Tandem Library Bks.

—Sign of the Ox. 2001. (gr. k-3). lib. bdg. 13.00 (978-0-613-72448-7(8)) Tandem Library Bks.

Stine, Megan & Stine, H. William. Young Indiana Jones & the Ring of Power. 1999. (Young Indiana Jones Ser.). (J). (gr. 4-6). pap. 3.99 (978-0-679-89049-2(1)); lib. bdg. 11.99 (978-0-679-99049-9(6)) Random Hse. Children's Bks. (Random Hse. Bks. for Young Readers).

Stine, R. L. Attack of the Mutant. 2004. (Goosebumps Ser.). 144p. (J). 4.99 (978-0-439-66215-4(X)) Scholastic, Inc.

—Into the Twister of Terror. 1999. (Give Yourself Goosebumps Ser.: No. 38). 144p. (gr. 3-7). pap. 3.99 (978-0-590-51706-5(6)) Scholastic, Inc.

—My Hairiest Adventure. 2006. (Goosebumps Ser.). 144p. (J). pap. 4.99 (978-0-439-86394-0(5) , Scholastic Paperbacks) Scholastic, Inc.

Stockham, Jessica, illus. Little Red Riding Hood. 2005. 24p. pap. (978-1-904550-22-8(3)) Child's Play-International.

Stockton, Frank Richard. The Associate Hermits. 2005. pap. 27.95 (978-1-4179-2511-7(6)) Kessinger Publishing, LLC.

—The Captain's Toll Gate. 2005. pap. 31.95 (978-1-4179-2498-1(5)) Kessinger Publishing, LLC.

—The Lady or the Tiger. 1999. (J). (978-0-606-12387-7(3)) Tandem Library Bks.

Stockton, Lucille. Hallo, Mallo & Pallo: The Ostracized Ostrich Family. Sampson, April, illus. ed. 2005. 31p. (J). 19.95 (978-1-59408-511-6(0)) Cork Hill Pr.

Stockton, Mary Peck. Tootletown Tales: A Storybook Adventure Helping your Child Develop Moral Character. Berg, Sara, illus. unabr. ed. 2002. ix, 130p. (J). (ps-6). pap. 14.95 (978-0-9709709-0-9(0)) Tamaltree Bks.

Stockton, Sally, retold by. Robin Hood. 2nd ed. 2000. (Green Apple). 92p. (YA). pap. (978-1-57159-009-1(9)) Los Andes Publishing Co.

Stockwell, Jeff. Fandango: The Key to the Wind. Stockwell, Pel, illus. 2007. 58p. (YA). per. 22.50 (***978-0-9785594-0-3(1)***) Stockwell Publishing.

Stohler, Dolores. The Land That Might Have Been. 2003. 168p. pap. 16.95 (978-1-4137-0047-3(0)) PublishAmerica, Inc.

Stokes, Jeremiah & Jones, Denise G. Thunder Cave: The Thrilling Adventures of Jasper & Zebbie & the Good Giant Wigwah. Sears, Jack, illus. 2001. (YA). (gr. 4-12). 44.95 (978-0-9718474-0-8(1)) Kitkooh Pubns.

Stokes, Katherine. Motor Maids in Fair Japan. 2006. pap. (***978-1-4068-3090-3(9)***) Echo Library.

Stokoe, Julian & Chambers, Brent. Tamatoa & the Great Tree. 2000. (Illus.). (J). pap. 12.95 (978-1-86950-346-8(5)) HarperCollins Pubs. New Zealand NZL. *Dist:* Antipodes Bks. & Beyond.

Stone, Charlene. The Greatest Fishing Adventure of a Lifetime: American Kids Greatest Adventures. 2004. 47p. pap. 19.95 (978-1-4137-2862-0(6)) PublishAmerica, Inc.

Stone, David Lee. The Ratastrophe Catastrophe. Lea, Bob, illus. 2004. (Illmoor Chronicles Ser.: Bk. 1). 288p. (gr. 5-9). 16.99 (978-0-7868-5128-7(7)) Hyperion Bks. for Children.

Stone, Jeff. Crane. 2007. (Five Ancestors Ser.: Bk. 4). 256p. (J). (gr. 5-9). 15.99 (978-0-375-83077-8(4) , Random Hse. Bks. for Young Readers) Random Hse. Children's Bks.

Stone, Jeff. Eagle. 2008. (Five Ancestors Ser.). 224p. (J). (gr. 5). 15.99 (***978-0-375-83083-9(9)***); lib. bdg. 18.99 (***978-0-375-93083-6(3)***) Random Hse. Children's Bks. (Random Hse. Bks. for Young Readers).

Stones, Tad & Pascoe, Jim. Hellboy Animated Volume 2: the Judgement Bell: The Judgement Bell. 2007. 80p. (J). pap. 6.95 (***978-1-59307-799-0(8)***) Dark Horse Comics.

Storad, Conrad J. Lizards for Lunch: A Roadrunner's Tale. 1999. 32p. (J). (ps-3). 15.95 (978-1-891795-02-2(3)) RGU Group, The.

—Lizards for Lunch: A Roadrunner's Tale. 1999. (gr. k-3). lib. bdg. 15.25 (978-0-613-61916-5(1)) Tandem Library Bks.

Storer, Megan. Cowbelle - Snow Day. 2005. (Illus.). 54p. (J). per. 6.99 (978-0-9769856-0-0(8) , 0-9769856-0-8) Little River Bookshelf.

Storm Is Coming. 2003. (J). per. (978-1-57657-866-7(6)) Paradise Pr., Inc.

Storm, Michael. The Roboshop. 2005. (J). 12.95 (978-0-9744929-5-7(7)) Leeway Pubs.

Stormer, Kate. Casey's Unexpected Friend. Lowes, Tom, illus. l.t. ed. 2003. 38p. (J). 16.95 (978-0-9722099-7-7(2) , CUF) Caseys World Bks.

A Stormy Adventure: Facing the Fear of Storms. 2004. (J). 6.99 (978-0-9753870-3-0(0)) Write On!.

Story Lady. Adventures down Nursery Rhyme Lane. 2001. 108p. (J). pap. 9.95 (978-0-595-19866-5(X) , Writers Club Pr.) iUniverse, Inc.

—The House of the Seven Cats: An Adventure. 2001. 132p. pap. 10.95 (978-0-595-20681-0(6) , Writers Club Pr.) iUniverse, Inc.

The Story of the Incredible Hulk. 2003. (Dk Readers Ser.). (J). pap. 3.99 (978-0-7894-3974-1(3)) Dorling Kindersley Publishing, Inc.

Stouffer, N. K. The Legend of Rah & the Muggles. Stouffer, N. K., illus. 2001. (Illus.). 288p. (J). 19.95 (978-1-58989-400-6(6)) Thurman Hse., LLC.

St.Pierre, Joe, creator. Bold Blood. 2005. (YA). per. 5.95 (978-0-9772727-0-9(2)) Astronaut Ink.

Strachan, Linda. Edinburgh Adventure. 2005. (Illus.). 32p. pap. 9.00 (978-0-9546701-7-7(5)) GW Publishing GBR. *Dist:* Wilson & Assocs.

—Ghost of Glamis. 2005. (Illus.). 32p. pap. 9.00 (978-0-9546701-9-1(1)) GW Publishing GBR. *Dist:* Wilson & Assocs.

—Serach for Loch Ness Monster. 2005. (Illus.). 32p. pap. 9.00 (978-0-9546701-5-3(9)) GW Publishing GBR. *Dist:* Wilson & Assocs.

—Skye Surprise. 2005. (Illus.). 32p. pap. 9.00 (978-0-9546701-8-4(3)) GW Publishing GBR. *Dist:* Wilson & Assocs.

Straczynski, J. Michael. Amazing Spider-Man: The Life & Death of Spiders, 4 vols., Vol. 4. Romita, John, Jr., illus. 2003. (Amazing Spider-man Ser.). 120p. (YA). 11.99 (978-0-7851-1097-2(6)) Marvel Enterprises, Inc.

—Best of Spider-Man, Vol. 3. Youngquist, Jeff, ed. 2004. (Spider-Man Ser.). (Illus.). 368p. (YA). 29.99 (978-0-7851-1339-3(8)) Marvel Enterprises, Inc.

—The Book of Ezekiel, Vol. 7. Romita, John, Jr., illus. 2004. (Spider-Man Ser.). 144p. (YA). 12.99 (978-0-7851-1525-0(0)) Marvel Enterprises, Inc.

Straczynski, J. Michael & Jenkins, Paul. Best of Spider-Man, 2 vols., Vol. 2. annual Romita, John, Jr. & Ramos, Humberto, illus. 2003. (Spider-Man Ser.: Vol. 2). 368p. (YA). 29.99 (978-0-7851-1100-9(X)) Marvel Enterprises, Inc.

Strang, Herbert. Round the World in Seven Days. 2006. pap. (***978-1-4068-2304-2(X)***) Echo Library.

Strangway, Melissa. 56 Water Street. 2007. 104p. per. 9.95 (***978-0-595-42429-0(5)***) iUniverse, Inc.

Strasser, Todd. Battle Drift. Phillips, Craig, illus. 2006. (DriftX Ser.). 224p. (YA). pap. 6.99 (978-1-4169-0582-0(0) , Simon Pulse) Simon & Schuster Children's Publishing.

—Close Call. 1999. 11.64 (978-0-606-17627-9(6)) Tandem Library Bks.

—Cut Back. 2004. 320p. (YA). pap. 5.99 (978-0-689-87030-9(2) , Simon Pulse) Simon & Schuster Children's Publishing.

—Kidnap Kids. 1999. (978-0-606-17564-7(4)) Tandem Library Bks.

—Slide or Die. Phillips, Craig, illus. 2006. (DriftX Ser.). 224p. (YA). (gr. 9 up). pap. 6.99 (978-1-4169-0581-3(2) , Simon Pulse) Simon & Schuster Children's Publishing.

—Take Off. 320p. (YA). 2005. mass mkt. 3.99 (978-1-4169-0523-3(5)); 2004. pap. 5.99 (978-0-689-87029-3(9)) Simon & Schuster Children's Publishing. (Simon Pulse).

—Y2K-9: The Dog Who Saved the World. 1999. (YA). pap. 4.50 (978-0-439-14247-2(4)) Scholastic, Inc.

—Y2K-9: The Dog Who Saved the World. 1999. (978-0-606-18619-3(0)) Tandem Library Bks.

Stratemeyer, Edward. Richard Dare's Venture. 2004. reprint ed. pap. 21.95 (978-1-4191-4479-0(0)); pap. 1.99 (978-1-4192-4479-7(5)) Kessinger Publishing, LLC.

—Richard Dare's Venture or Striking Out F. 2006. 63.99 (***978-1-4219-9741-4(X)***); pap. 57.99 (***978-1-4219-9724-7(X)***) IndyPublish.com.

—The Rover Boys at College or the Right R. 2004. reprint ed. pap. 22.95 (978-1-4191-8114-6(9)) Kessinger Publishing, LLC.

—The Rover Boys at College or the Right Road & the Wrong. 2004. reprint ed. pap. 1.99 (978-1-4192-8114-3(3)) Kessinger Publishing, LLC.

—The Rover Boys at School: Or the Cadets of Putnam Hall. 2006. 164p. pap. 11.99 (978-1-4264-2004-7(8)) BiblioBazaar.

—The Rover Boys in Business or the Search. 2004. reprint ed. pap. 22.95 (978-1-4191-8116-0(5)) Kessinger Publishing, LLC.

—The Rover Boys in Business or the Search for the Missing Bonds. 2004. reprint ed. pap. 1.99 (978-1-4192-8116-7(X)) Kessinger Publishing, LLC.

—The Rover Boys on the Ocean: Or, a Chase for a Fortune. 2006. 158p. pap. 11.99 (978-1-4264-2766-4(2)); 170p. pap. 14.99 (978-1-4264-2804-3(9)) BiblioBazaar.

Streit, Jakob. Puck trhe Gnome. Mitchell, David S., ed. Kuettel, Nina, tr. 2004. Orig. Title: Puck der Zwerg. (J). per. 14.00 (978-1-888365-54-2(4)) Assn. of Waldorf Schls. of North America Pubns. (AWSNA).

Strickland, Brad. Be a Wolf! l.t. ed. 1999. (Adventures of Wishbone Ser.: No. 1). (Illus.). 144p. (J). (gr. 4 up). lib. bdg. 22.60 (978-0-8368-2297-8(3)) Stevens, Gareth Inc.

—Guns of Tortuga. 2003. (gr. 3-6). lib. bdg. 13.00 (978-0-613-60418-5(0)) Tandem Library Bks.

—Mutiny! Fuller, Thomas E. & Saponaro, Dominick, illus. 2002. 208p. (J). (gr. 3-6). pap. 4.99 (978-0-689-85296-1(7) , Aladdin) Simon & Schuster Children's Publishing.

—Salty Dog. l.t. ed. 1999. (Adventures of Wishbone Ser.: No. 2). (Illus.). 140p. (J). (gr. 4 up). lib. bdg. 22.60 (978-0-8368-2298-4(5)) Stevens, Gareth Inc.

—Terrier of the Lost Mines. 1999. (Adventures of Wishbone Ser.: No. 19). (J). (gr. 2-5). (978-0-606-19457-0(6)) Tandem Library Bks.

Strickland, Brad & Fuller, Thomas E. The Guns of Tortuga, No. 2. Saponaro, Dominick, illus. 2003. (Pirate Hunter). 208p. (J). pap. 4.99 (978-0-689-85297-8(5) , Aladdin) Simon & Schuster Children's Publishing.

—Marooned! 2004. (Mars Year One Ser.: No. 1). (Illus.). 192p. (J). pap. 4.99 (978-0-689-86400-1(0) , Aladdin) Simon & Schuster Children's Publishing.

—The Treasure of Skeleton Reef. l.t. ed. 1999. (Wishbone Mysteries Ser.: No. 1). 144p. (J). (gr. 4 up). lib. bdg. 23.33 (978-0-8368-2382-0(0)) Stevens, Gareth Inc.

Strickland, Brad & Strickland, Barbara. Gullifur's Travels. l.t. ed. 1999. (Adventures of Wishbone Ser.: No. 18). (Illus.). (J). (gr. 4 up). lib. bdg. 22.60 (978-0-8368-2596-1(9)) Stevens, Gareth Inc.

Strickland, Brad, et al. Drive-In of Doom. l.t. ed. 1999. (Wishbone Mysteries Ser.: No. 7). 144p. (J). (gr. 4 up). lib. bdg. 23.33 (978-0-8368-2388-2(5)) Stevens, Gareth Inc.

Strickland, Brad, et al. The Storm: A Novelization. 2006. (Flight 29 down Ser.: Vol. 4). 224p. (J). (***978-1-4156-8721-5(8)*** , Grosset & Dunlap) Penguin Group (USA) Inc.

Strickland, Deborah. Mary Reeder, Prairie Girl. 2007. 68p. per. 8.95 (***978-0-595-44514-1(4)***) iUniverse, Inc.

Strong, Jeremy. Don't Go in the Cellar. Anderson, Scoular, illus. 2006. 72;88p. (J). (gr. 2-3). lib. bdg. 21.26 (978-1-59889-002-0(6)) Stone Arch Bks.

—Karate Princess in Monsta Trouble. Sharratt, Nick, illus. l.t. ed. 2005. 112p. (J). pap. (978-0-7540-6183-0(3) , CLP 375) BBC Audio.

—Krazy Kow Saves the World - Well, Almost. l.t. ed. 2003. (Illus.). 152p. (J). 16.95 (978-0-7540-7841-8(8) , Galaxy Children's Large Print) BBC Audiobooks America.

Strong, Louise. The Island Adventures of Frodo Mcadoo. 2005. (Illus.). 196p. (J). per. 12.95 (978-0-9770950-0-1(2)) Strong, Louise dev.

The Strongest of Them All. 2003. (J). per. (978-1-57657-862-9(3)) Paradise Pr., Inc.

Stroschin, Jane H. Atsa & Ga: A Story from the High Desert. Stich, Carolyn R., illus. 2005. 32p. (J). (gr. k-6). (978-1-883960-29-2(0)) Henry Quill Pr.

Stroud, Jonathan. The Amulet of Samarkand. 2004. (Bartimaeus Trilogy Ser.: Bk. 1). 480p. (gr. 5-17). reprint ed. pap. 7.99 (978-0-7868-5255-0(0)) Miramax Bks.

—The Last Siege. 2006. 288p. (gr. 7-17). pap. 6.95 (978-1-4231-0107-9(3)) Miramax Bks.

—Ptolemy's Gate. 3rd rev. ed. (Bartimaeus Trilogy Ser.: Bk. 3). 512p. (gr. 5-17). 2007. pap. 8.99 (978-0-7868-3868-4(X)); 2006. 17.95 (978-0-7868-1861-7(1)) Miramax Bks.

Strunk, Peter, illus. & creator. Two Inch Hero: The Adventures of Lorenzo Lizard. Strunk, Peter, creator. 2006. (J). 17.95 (***978-0-9785961-0-1(2)***) Smile Time Publishing.

Stuart-Russell, C. Playtime with the Animals. 2007. 61p. pap. 12.95 (***978-1-4241-5473-9(1)***) PublishAmerica, Inc.

Stuart, W. Howard & Burden, Walter. T-Rex VI: Wonders of an Ancient World. 2000. (T-Rex Ser.: Vol. 6). (Illus.). 176p. (J). (gr. 4-9). pap. (978-0-9696800-6-2(6)) Youth Academy Books, Limited.

Stull, Judy. From Darkness to Color: A Trilogy. 2005. (J). per. (978-0-9765738-3-8(0)) Stull, Judy.

—The Gray World. 2005. (Illus.). (J). per. (978-0-9765738-0-7(6)) Stull, Judy.

—The Great Connection. 2005. (J). per. (978-0-9765738-2-1(2)) Stull, Judy.

—The Secret Mission. 2005. (J). per. (978-0-9765738-1-4(4)) Stull, Judy.

Sturm, James. Unstable Molecules. Davis, Guy & Sikoryak, Bob, illus. 2003. (Fantastic Four Legends Ser.: Vol. 1). 128p. (YA). pap. 13.99 (978-0-7851-1112-2(3)) Marvel Enterprises, Inc.

Style Guide Staff, illus. Leonardo! 2005. (Teenage Mutant Ninja Turtles Ser.). 16p. (J). pap. 6.99 (978-0-689-86901-3(0) , Simon Spotlight) Simon & Schuster Children's Publishing.

Styles, Showell. The Flying Ensign: Greencoats Against Napoleon. 2003. (Budget Bks.). Orig. Title: Greencoat Against Napoleon. 340p. (J). pap. 14.95 (978-1-883937-70-6(1)) Bethlehem Bks.

—The Midshipman Quinn Collection: Four Complete Adventures. Saponaro, Dominick, illus. 1999. (Bethlehem Budget Bks.). 616p. (YA). (gr. 7-12). pap. 19.95 (978-1-883937-45-4(0) , 45-0) Bethlehem Bks.

Suben, Eric, et al, illus. Tarzan. 1999. (Disney Ser.). 24p. (J). (ps-3). pap. 3.29 (978-0-307-13194-2(7) , Golden Bks.) Random Hse. Children's Bks.

Sugisaki, Yukiru. D. N. Angel, Vol. 11. 11th rev. ed. 2006. pap. 9.99 (978-1-59816-810-5(X) , Tokyopop Adult) TOKYOPOP, Inc.

Sula, Sondra & Sula, Robert. Briny Town: Shark Showdown. Sula, Robert, illus. 2000. (Illus.). 32p. (J). (gr. 1-3). pap. (978-0-9701450-6-2(3)) Long Hill Productions, Inc.

Sullivan, told to. The Adventures of the Pink Shovel & the Red Pail. 2004. (J). pap. 9.00 (978-0-8059-6263-5(8)) Dorrance Publishing Co., Inc.

Sullivan, George E. Trapped. 1998. (Illus.). 128p. (J). (gr. 3-9). pap. 4.50 (978-0-590-29894-0(1) , 893376) Scholastic, Inc.

—Trapped. 1998. (978-0-606-13861-1(7)) Tandem Library Bks.

Sullivan, Michael. Escapade Johnson & Mayhem at Mount Moosilauke. Kolitsky, Joy, illus. 2007. (Escapade Johnson Ser.). 96p. (J). pap. 3.95 (978-1-929945-70-2(1)) Big Guy Bks., Inc.

Sullivan, Stephen D. Fantastic Four: The Junior Novel. 2005. (Fantastic Four Ser.). (Illus.). 144p. pap. 4.99 (978-0-06-078619-9(1)) HarperCollins Pubs.

—Iron Man: The Junior Novel. 2008. (Iron Man Ser.). 144p. (J). pap. 4.99 (***978-0-06-082197-5(3)*** , Harper Entertainment) HarperCollins Pubs.

Sullivan, Stephen D. Warrior's Blood. 2007. (Goodlund Trilogy Ser.: Vol. 2). 256p. (YA). pap. 5.99 (978-0-7869-4300-5(9) , Mirrorstone) Wizards of the Coast.

Sullivan, Steve. Warrior's Heart. 2006. (Illus.). 256p. (J). (gr. 5). pap. 5.99 (978-0-7869-4187-2(1) , Mirrorstone) Wizards of the Coast.

Sultemeier, Annette. Miss Molly's Secret Adventure. Laredo Publishing Staff, ed. Orchard, Joyce, illus. 1998. 19p. (J). (ps-3). pap. 9.95 (978-0-9662426-0-7(2)) Sultemeier, Annette.

Sumerak, Mark. End of the Rainbow. 2006. (Illus.). (J). (gr. 2-6). 21.35 (978-1-59961-032-0(9)) Spotlight.

Summers, Everette. Grandaddy's Short Stories. 2006. 48p. pap. 12.95 (978-1-4241-2468-8(9)) PublishAmerica, Inc.

Surrell, Jason. Pirates of the Caribbean: from the Magic Kindom to the Movies. 2006. (Illus.). 148p. (ps-17). pap. 22.95 (978-1-4231-0709-5(8) , Disney Editions) Disney Pr.

Suter, Joanne. Adventures of Tom Sawyer. abr. ed. 1999. (gr. 7-12). lib. bdg. 15.25 (978-0-613-32246-1(0)) Tandem Library Bks.

—War of the Worlds. 2003. (gr. 7-12). lib. bdg. 15.25 (978-0-613-65749-5(7)) Tandem Library Bks.

Sutherland, David. Samantha Cardigan & the Genie's Revenge. Roberts, David, illus. 2005. (Red Bananas Ser.). 48p. (J). (978-0-7787-1070-7(X)) Crabtree Publishing Co.

—Samantha Cardigan & the Genie's Revenge. 2005. (Red Bananas Ser.). (Illus.). 48p. (J). (ps). pap. (978-0-7787-1086-8(6)) Crabtree Publishing Co.

—Samantha Cardigan & the Ghastly Twirling Sickness. Roberts, David, illus. 2005. (Red Bananas Ser.). 48p. (J). (978-0-7787-1069-1(6)) Crabtree Publishing Co.

—Samantha Cardigan & the Ghastly Twirling Sickness. 2005. (Red Bananas Ser.). (Illus.). 48p. (J). (ps). pap. (978-0-7787-1085-1(8)) Crabtree Publishing Co.

Sutherland, David, et al. Siriol Llywelyn a Dial y Bwgan. 2005. (WEL., Illus.). 47p. (978-1-85596-678-9(6)) Dref Wen.

—Siriol Llywelyn a'r Salwch Chwyrlio Erchyll. 2005. (WEL., Illus.). 45p. (978-1-85596-679-6(4)) Dref Wen.

Sutherland, Robert. A River Apart. 2000. 178p. (YA). (gr. 5-8). (978-1-55041-652-7(9)) Fitzhenry & Whiteside, Ltd.

Sutherland, T. T. Pirates of the Caribbean 3: At World's End. Disney Press Staff, ed. 2007. 176p. (gr. 4-7). pap. 4.99 (***978-1-4231-0377-6(7)***) Disney Pr.

—Pirates of the Caribbean 3: Turner. Disney Press Staff, ed. 2007. 24p. (ps-2). pap. 3.99 (***978-1-4231-0376-9(9)***) Disney Pr.

—Pirates of the Caribbean At World's End: Saving Jack Sparrow. Disney Press Staff, ed. 2007. 24p. (ps-2). pap. 3.99 (***978-1-4231-0374-5(2)***) Disney Pr.

—Pirates of the Caribbean At World's End: Singapore! Disney Press Staff, ed. 2007. 32p. (gr. 1-4). pap. 3.99 (***978-1-4231-0379-0(3)***) Disney Pr.

—Pirates of the Caribbean At World's End: The Movie Storybook. Disney Press Staff, ed. 2007. 64p. (gr. 5-17). 8.99 (***978-1-4231-0378-3(5)***) Disney Pr.

—Pirates of the Caribbean At World's End: The Mystic's Journey. Disney Press Staff, ed. 2007. 32p. (gr. 1-4). pap. 3.99 (***978-1-4231-0380-6(7)***) Disney Pr.

Sutton, Scott E. Danger: Dinky Diplodocus. 2007. (Adventures of Dinosaur Dog Ser.). 144p. (J). pap. 5.99 (***978-1-888045-52-9(3)***) Action Publishing, LLC.

—Death by Deinonychus. 2007. (Adventures of Dinosaur Dog Ser.). 144p. (J). pap. 5.99 (***978-1-888045-54-3(X)***) Action Publishing, LLC.

—Trouble with Pteranodons. 2007. (Adventures of Dinosaur Dog Ser.). 144p. (Orig.). (J). pap. 5.99 (***978-1-888045-53-6(1)***) Action Publishing, LLC.

—Tyrannosaurus Forest. 2007. (Adventures of Dinosaur Dog Ser.). 144p. (J). (gr. 3-6). pap. 5.99 (***978-1-888045-51-2(5)***) Action Publishing, LLC.

Swallow, Su. La escalera de mano de Lucas, Level P. Nascimbeni, Barbara, illus. 2006. (Lightning Readers Ser.). 32p. (J). pap. 3.95 (978-0-7696-4206-2(3) , Gingham Dog Pr.) School Specialty Publishing.

Swamp Stomp. 2002. (Illus.). (J). pap. (978-0-7398-5141-8(1)) Steck-Vaughn.

Swan, Bill. Off Track. 2003. (Sports Stories Ser.). 112p. (J). (gr. 4-8). (***978-1-55028-807-0(5)***); 7.95 (978-1-55028-806-3(7)) Lorimer, James & Co., Ltd., Pubs. CAN. *Dist:* Casemate Pubs. & Bk. Distributors, LLC.

Sweeney, Joyce. Players. 2001. (Illus.). 262p. (YA). (gr. 7 up). pap. 5.95 (978-1-58837-016-7(X)) Winslow Pr.

Sweet, Karen. The Adventures of Little AMP: The Sparrow Electric Car. Speckles, Jenny, illus. l.t. ed. 2002. 12p. (J). 8.95 (978-0-9714378-0-7(7)) Sweet Sommer Productions.

Swift, Carolyn. Robbers in the House. (Illus.). 96p. 2.95 (978-0-900068-59-1(0)) Penguin Group (USA) Inc.

Swift, Jonathan. Gulliver's Travels. 1999. (YA). 11.95 (978-1-56137-922-4(0)); 9.95 (978-1-56137-921-7(2)) Novel Units, Inc.

—Gulliver's Travels. (gr. k-3). 2003. lib. bdg. 14.10 (978-0-613-67626-7(2)); 2001. (Illus.). (J). 13.75 (978-0-606-21553-4(0)) Tandem Library Bks.

Swindells, Robert. Ruby Tanya. 2006. 256p. (J). (gr. 4-6). pap. 8.99 (978-0-440-86398-4(8) , Corgi) Transworld Publishers Ltd. GBR. *Dist:* Trafalgar Square Publishing.

Sykes, Harold S. The Beacon of Airport Seven. 2004. reprint ed. pap. 15.95 (978-1-4191-5375-4(7)); pap. 1.99 (978-1-4192-5375-1(1)) Kessinger Publishing, LLC.

Sylvia, Dean Jason. Just for Kicks: The Adventures of Sami Sidekick. 2001. (gr. 7-12). lib. bdg. 25.15 (978-0-613-74590-1(6)) Tandem Library Bks.

Symes, Sally. Caterpillar to Butterfly: A Colorful Adventure. Harmer, Sharon, illus. 2008. 16p. (J). bds. 8.99 (***978-1-4169-4753-0(1)*** , Little Simon) Simon & Schuster Children's Publishing.

Symes, Sally. Harry's Coin. 2006. (Illus.). 16p. pap. 12.95 (978-0-7624-2657-7(8)) Running Pr. Bk. Pubs.

Szarka, Marion L. Buddy's Adventures. 2006. pap. 7.95 (978-0-533-15271-1(2)) Vantage Pr., Inc.

Szymanski, Lois K. Charming Ponies: A Pony Named Patches. 2008. (Charming Ponies Ser.). 96p. (J). pap. 4.99 (***978-0-06-128871-5(3)*** , Harper Festival) HarperCollins Pubs.

Taback, Simms. Kibitzers & Fools: Tales My Zayda Told Me. 2005. (Illus.). 48p. (J). (gr. 1-6). 16.99 (978-0-670-05955-3(2) , Viking Juvenile) Penguin Group (USA) Inc.

Tabb, Robert C. The Rules: Trust No One. 2007. 156p. per. 11.95 (***978-0-595-44797-8(X)***) iUniverse, Inc.

Tachibana, Yutaka. Gacchagacha. 2006. (Illus.). pap. 9.99 (978-1-59816-153-3(9) , Tokyopop Kids) TOKYOPOP, Inc.

Tachibana, Yutaka, illus. & creator. Gatcha Gacha. Tachibana, Yutaka, creator. 2nd rev. ed. 2006. pap. 9.99 (978-1-59816-154-0(7) , Tokyopop Kids) TOKYOPOP, Inc.

Takacs, Dalma. Meet Me at the Globe: A Novel for Young People. 2002. 204p. (YA). pap. 13.95 (978-0-595-21155-5(0) , Writer's Showcase Pr.) iUniverse, Inc.

Takahashi, Kazuki. Monster Fight. Takahashi, Kazuki, illus. 2004. (Illus.). 200p. lib. bdg. 18.55 (978-1-4176-5897-8(5)) Tandem Library Bks.

Takahashi, Rumiko. Inu Yasha. Takahashi, Rumiko, illus. 2004. (Illus.). 190p. per. 19.70 (978-1-4176-5276-1(4)); 184p. per. 19.70 (978-1-4176-5272-3(1)) Tandem Library Bks.

—Inu Yasha. 2003. (Illus.). 188p. per. 19.70 (978-1-4176-5645-5(X)) Tandem Library Bks.

—Inu Yasha. Takahashi, Rumiko, illus. 2003. (Illus.). 188p. per. 19.70 (978-1-4176-5646-2(8)); 182p. per. 19.70 (978-1-4176-5274-7(8)); 185p. per. 19.70 (978-1-4176-5273-0(X)); 186p. per. 19.70 (978-1-4176-5271-6(3)); 189p. per. 19.70 (978-1-4176-5648-6(4)); 181p. per. 19.70 (978-1-4176-5082-8(6)) Tandem Library Bks.

—Inu Yasha: Volume 12. Takahashi, Rumiko, illus. 2004. (Illus.). 200p. lib. bdg. 19.70 (978-1-4176-5992-0(0)) Tandem Library Bks.

—Inu Yasha Ani-Manga. Takahashi, Rumiko, illus. 2004. (Illus.). 206p. per. 21.35 (978-1-4176-6422-1(3)) Tandem Library Bks.

—Inuyasha, Vol. 29. 2007. (Inuyasha Ser.). 192p. (YA). pap. 8.95 (978-1-4215-0900-6(8)) Viz Media.

Talbott, Hudson. Safari Journal. 2003. (Illus.). 64p. (J). 18.00 (978-0-15-216393-8(X)) Harcourt Children's Bks.

The Tale of Jackie Berry. 2005. (J). per. 12.95 (978-0-9677047-5-3(8)) Marble House Editions.

Tamura, Yumi. Chicago Book of Justice, Vol. 2. Tamura, Yumi, illus. 2003. (Chicago Ser.: Vol. 2). (Illus.). 200p. (YA). pap. 15.95 (978-1-56931-829-4(8)) Viz Media.

Tanos, Elaine. Anadarko & Pugwash: The Delbert Adventures. 2006. (J). spiral bd. 6.79 (978-0-9764666-6-6(X)) TanosBooks Publishing.

Tapp, Kathy Kennedy & Newsom, Carol. Deadbolts & Dinkles. 2000. (Illus.). 64p. (J). (ps-3). pap. 3.95 (978-1-57255-774-1(5)) Mondo Publishing.

Tarbett, Debbie. Ten Wriggly Wiggly Caterpillars. (Illus.). 24p. (J). bds. 19.95 (978-1-84506-027-5(X)) Little Tiger Pr.

Tasker, Rod. Jack's Book. 2003. 60p. pap. 9.95 (978-1-59286-966-4(1)) PublishAmerica, Inc.

Tate & Tini's Learning Journey Five Storybook Set. 2001. (J). (978-0-9768948-0-3(7)) Broken Wing Enterprises, Inc.

Tate, Cynthia Wagoner. Gordy's Grimy but Groovy Adventure. 2006. 24p. 12.98 (978-1-4116-6297-1(0)) Lulu-.com.

Tate, Nikki. The Battle for Carnillo. Williams, E. Colin, illus. 2003. 322p. (J). pap. 8.95 (978-1-55039-127-5(5)) Sono Nis Pr. CAN. *Dist:* Orca Bk. Pubs. USA.

Tavares, Wendy. Stories for My Son. 2006. 40p. 8.29 (978-1-4116-7660-2(2)) Lulu.com.

Taylor, Cora. Adventure in Istanbul No. 1: The Spy Who Wasn't There. 2005. (Juvenile Novel, Ser.). (Illus.). 176p. (J). (gr. 4-6). pap. 7.95 (978-1-55050-315-9(4)) Coteau Bks. CAN. *Dist:* Fitzhenry & Whiteside, Ltd.

—Ghost Voyages. 2005. 120p. (J). pap. 5.95 (978-1-55050-197-1(6)) Coteau Bks. CAN. *Dist:* Fitzhenry & Whiteside, Ltd.

—Ghost Voyages II: The Matthew. 2005. (Ghost Voyages Ser.). 120p. (J). pap. 5.95 (978-1-55050-198-8(4)) Coteau Bks. CAN. *Dist:* Fitzhenry & Whiteside, Ltd.

Taylor, Edward C. Ted Strong's Motor Car or Fast & Furio. 2006. pap. (***978-1-4068-0774-5(5)***) Echo Library.

Taylor, G. P. The Tizzle Sisters & Erik. 2007. 188p. (***978-1-905692-22-4(6)***) Markosia Enterprises Ltd.

—Wormwood. 2004. (Illus.). 320p. (J). pap. (***978-0-571-22150-9(5)***) Faber & Faber, Ltd.

—Wormwood. 2004. (Illus.). 272p. (J). (gr. 3-6). 17.99 (978-1-59185-626-9(4)) Strang Communications Co.

Taylor, Jennifer. Dragon Sitter. 2005. 36p. (J). 14.99 (978-1-4116-6449-4(3)) Lulu.com.

Taylor, K. C. Easier Without. 2005. 177p. (YA). lib. bdg. 12.95 (978-0-9728549-2-4(4)) GND Publishing.

Taylor, Kim. Accion. (SPA., Illus.). (J). (gr. 5-8). pap. (978-84-216-1812-7(1) , BU4732) Bruño, Editorial ESP. *Dist:* Lectorum Pubns., Inc.

Taylor, Mari Jo. Not One of the Robot Children. 2005. 11.00 (978-0-8059-9791-0(1)) Dorrance Publishing Co., Inc.

Taylor, Mildred D. Roll of Thunder, Hear My Cry. 25th anniv. ed. 2004. (Illus.). 288p. (J). (gr. 3). pap. 7.99 (978-0-14-240112-5(9) , Puffin) Penguin Group (USA) Inc.

Taylor, Orpheus. The Heart & Soul of Aman. Taylor, Orpheus, ed. McGhie, Melissa, illus. McGhie, Melissa, photos by. 2000. 39p. (YA). pap. 13.00 (978-0-9700319-0-7(4)) Black-Out Media.

Taylor, S. G. Books of Merlin I. 2006. pap. 10.49 (***978-1-4259-6740-6(X)***) AuthorHouse.

Taylor, Theodore. Billy the Kid: A Novel. (Illus.). 224p. 2005. (YA). (gr. 7-12). 17.00 (978-0-15-204930-0(4)); 2006. (J). reprint ed. pap. 6.95 (978-0-15-205651-3(3) , Harcourt Paperbacks) Harcourt Children's Bks.

Taylor, Theodore. Rogue Wave: And Other Red-Blooded Sea Stories. 2009. (Illus.). 192p. (YA). pap. 6.95 (***978-0-15-206254-5(8)*** , Harcourt Paperbacks) Harcourt Children's Bks.

Tbd. I Am Iron Man. 2008. (I Can Read Bks.). 32p. (J). pap. 3.99 (***978-0-06-082193-7(0)*** , Harper Trophy) Harper-Collins Pubs.

T'choupi Est Trop Groumand. 2000. (FRE.). (J). (978-2-09-202025-8(0)) Nathan, Fernand FRA. *Dist:* Distribooks, Inc.

Teague, Mark. The Secret Shortcut. Teague, Mark, illus. 1999. (Illus.). 32p. (J). (gr. 1-4). pap. 5.99 (978-0-439-11091-4(2)) Scholastic, Inc.

—The Secret Shortcut. 1999. (978-0-606-17446-6(X)) Tandem Library Bks.

—Secret Shortcut. 1999. (gr. k-3). lib. bdg. 14.15 (978-0-613-22932-6(0)) Tandem Library Bks.

—The Secret Shortcut. ed. 2004. (J). (gr. k-3). spiral bd. (978-0-616-03059-2(2)); spiral bd. (978-0-616-04563-3(8)) Canadian National Institute for the Blind/Institut National Canadien pour les Aveugles.

Teitelbaum, Michael. Batman Beyond: The Return of the Joker. 2000. 144p. (J). (gr. 4-7). pap. 4.99 (978-0-439-20769-0(X)) Scholastic, Inc.

—Cine en casa: Heroes de Cine: Movie Theater: Marvel Heroes. 2007. (Cine en casa Disney Ser.). (Illus.). 46p. (J). 24.95 (***978-970-718-535-7(X)*** , Silver Dolphin en Español) Advanced Marketing, S. de R. L. de C. V. MEX. *Dist:* Perseus Distribution.

—City at War. Giles, Mike & George, Chris, illus. 2005. (Teenage Mutant Ninja Turtles Ser.). 128p. pap. 4.99 (978-0-689-87714-8(5) , Simon Spotlight) Simon & Schuster Children's Publishing.

—Draganta Revealed! 1999. (Mystic Knights of Tir Na Nog Ser.: No. 5). 96p. (gr. 1-5). pap. 4.25 (978-0-06-107164-5(1) , Harper Entertainment) HarperCollins Pubs.

—The Earth Kingdom Chronicles: The Tale of Aang. Spaziante, Patrick, illus. 2007. (Avatar Ser.). 96p. (J). pap. 5.99 (978-1-4169-3606-0(8) , Simon Spotlight) Simon & Schuster Children's Publishing.

—The Earth Kingdom Chronicles: The Tale of Sokka. Spaziante, Patrick, illus. 2007. (Avatar Ser.). 96p. (J). (gr. 2-6). pap. 5.99 (***978-1-4169-3829-3(X)*** , Simon Spotlight) Simon & Schuster Children's Publishing.

—The Earth Kingdom Chronicles: The Tale of Toph. Spaziante, Patrick, illus. 2007. (Avatar Ser.). 96p. (J). (gr. 2-6). pap. 5.99 (***978-1-4169-3797-5(8)*** , Simon Spotlight) Simon & Schuster Children's Publishing.

—Legend Begins. 2002. (gr. 3-6). lib. bdg. 12.40 (978-0-613-50455-3(0)) Tandem Library Bks.

—The Legend Begins. 2002. (Samurai Jack Ser.). (Illus.). 80p. (J). (gr. 3-7). pap. 4.50 (978-0-439-40972-8(1)) Scholastic, Inc.

—The Littlest Ninja, Vol. 3. Aikins, Dave, illus. 2005. (Teenage Mutant Ninja Turtles Ser.). 128p. (J). pap. 4.99 (978-1-4169-0217-1(1) , Simon Spotlight) Simon & Schuster Children's Publishing.

—The Lost Scrolls: Water. Spaziante, Patrick, illus. 2006. (Avatar Ser.). 64p. (J). pap. 4.99 (978-1-4169-1878-3(7) , Simon Spotlight) Simon & Schuster Children's Publishing.

—The Lost Scrolls: Earth. Johnson, Shane L., illus. 2007. (Avatar Ser.). 64p. (J). pap. 4.99 (978-1-4169-1877-6(9) , Simon Spotlight) Simon & Schuster Children's Publishing.

—Red Flag. 2001. (NASCAR Racers Ser.: Vol. 7). (Illus.). 128p. (J). (gr. 2-6). pap. 4.50 (978-0-06-107201-7(X) , Harper Entertainment) HarperCollins Pubs.

—Spider-Man. Mada Design Staff, illus. 2004. (Spider Man Ser.). 32p. (J). 3.99 (978-0-439-32953-8(1) , Scholastic Paperbacks) Scholastic, Inc.

—The Spy Who Was Me. Goldberg, Barry, illus. ed. 2005. (Adventures of Jimmy Neutron Ser.: 8). 24p. (J). lib. bdg. 15.00 (978-1-59054-788-5(8)) Fitzgerald Bks.

—The Spy Who Was Me. Goldberg, Barry, illus. 2004. (Jimmy Neutron Boy Genius Ser.). 24p. (J). pap. 3.50 (978-0-689-86318-9(7) , Simon Spotlight/Nickelodeon) Simon & Schuster Children's Publishing.

—Volcano Rescue!, No. 2. Roper, Marty, illus. 2001. 24p. (ps-3). pap. 3.50 (978-0-439-25911-8(8)) Scholastic, Inc.

Temperley, Alan. Huntress of the Sea. l.t. ed. 2000. (Illus.). 189p. (J). pap. (978-0-7540-6097-0(7) , CLP 298) BBC Audio.

—The Magician of Samarkand. l.t. ed. 2005. 216p. (J). pap. (978-0-7540-7883-8(3) , CLP 459) BBC Audio.

—The Magician of Samarkand. 2004. (J). pap. 29.95 incl. audio (978-0-7540-6279-0(1) , Chivers Children's Audio Bks.) BBC Audiobooks America.

Temple, Frances. The Beduins' Gazelle. Bowers, David, illus. 1998. (Harper Trophy Bks.). 160p. (J). (gr. 7 up). pap. 5.99 (978-0-06-440669-7(5) , Harper Trophy) HarperCollins Pubs.

Tennyson, Patrick & Bickford, Nicole. Tarantula Tracks: Rosie's Wild Adventure. l.t. ed. 2004. (Illus.). 32p. (J). 2.95 (978-0-9729000-1-0(2)) Butterfly Pavilion.

Teply, George. The Lost Crown of Meleor. Teply, George, illus. 2000. (Illus.). 32p. (J). (ps-2). lib. bdg. 16.95 (978-1-55037-601-2(2)) Annick Pr., Ltd. CAN. *Dist:* Firefly Bks., Ltd.

Testa, Dom. Galahad 1: The Comet's Curse. 2005. 224p. (YA). per. 8.95 (978-0-9760564-0-9(2)) Profound Impact Group.

—Galahad 2: The Web of Titan. 2006. (YA). per. 8.95 (978-0-9760564-1-6(0)) Profound Impact Group.

Testa, Dom. Galahad 3: The Cassini Code. 2008. 272p. (YA). pap. 9.95 (***978-0-9760564-4-7(5)***) Profound Impact Group.

Tezuka, Osamu. Astro Boy. 2003. (Illus.). 224p. (YA). Vol. 12. pap. 9.95 (978-1-56971-813-1(X)); Vol. 13. (gr. 9 up). pap. 9.95 (978-1-56971-894-0(6)) Dark Horse Comics.

—Metropolis. 2003. (Illus.). 169p. (YA). (gr. 8 up). pap. 13.95 (978-1-56971-864-3(4)) Dark Horse Comics.

Thal, Lilli. Mimus. Brownjohn, John, tr. from GER. 2005. 398p. (YA). (gr. 7-10). 19.95 (978-1-55037-925-9(9)) Annick Pr., Ltd. CAN. *Dist:* Firefly Bks., Ltd.

—Mimus. Brownjohn, John, tr. from GER. 2005. 398p. (YA). (gr. 7-10). pap. 9.95 (978-1-55037-924-2(0)) Annick Pr., Ltd. CAN. *Dist:* Firefly Bks., Ltd.

Thaler, Mike. The Class Trip from the Black Lagoon. D. Lee, Jared, illus. 2004. (Black Lagoon Ser.). 64p. (J). pap. 3.99 (978-0-439-42927-6(7) , Scholastic Paperbacks) Scholastic, Inc.

Thames, S. R. Crystal Star: Legend of the Mecha Fighters. 2002. 148p. pap. 11.95 (978-0-595-26119-2(1) , Writers Club Pr.) iUniverse, Inc.

Thank You, Thank You, Thank You. 2003. (J). 10.95 (978-0-9745798-0-1(7)) Pen & Sword Publishing Co., The.

Tharp, Barbara, et al. Tillena Lou's Day in the Sun. Denk, James, ed. Lewis, T., illus. 2006. (My World & Me Ser.). 32p. (J). pap. (978-1-888997-44-6(3) , BioEd) Baylor College of Medicine.

Thiele, Colin. River Murray Mary. (Illus.). 160p. pap. (978-0-7344-0414-5(X) , Lothian Bks.) Hachette Livre Australia.

Thierry, Raphael. Green Butterfly: A Superdog Adventure. 2007. (Superdog Adventure Ser.). (Illus.). 32p. (J). (ps-k). pap. 6.99 (***978-1-84270-449-3(4)***) Transworld Publishers Ltd. GBR. *Dist:* Independent Pubs. Group.

Thinking Publications. The Deciders Take on Concepts Mission I: Goobie Troubles. 2001. 27p. cd-rom 99.00 (978-1-888222-59-3(X)) Super Duper Pubns.

—The Deciders Take on Concepts Mission II: Clutterbug's Catastrophe. 2001. 27p. cd-rom 99.00 (978-1-888222-67-8(0)) Super Duper Pubns.

Thomas - Captain Kate Pack. 2000. (J). pap. 9.49 (978-0-06-449119-8(6) , Harper Trophy) HarperCollins Pubs.

Thomas, Alisa. The Adventures of Tom Sawyer. 2001. 80p. (J). stu. ed., ring bd. 12.99 (978-1-58609-174-3(3)) Progeny Pr.

Thomas, Janet. Can I Play? Bartlett, Alison, illus. 32p. (J). 2005. 8.99 (978-1-4052-0597-9(0)); 2003. 16.99 (978-1-4052-0537-5(7)) Egmont Bks., Ltd. GBR. *Dist:* Trafalgar Square Publishing, Independent Pubs. Group.

Thomas, Jim. Super Slam Turtles! Spaziante, Patrick, illus. 2005. 22p. (J). lib. bdg. 15.00 (***978-1-4242-0971-2(4)***) Fitzgerald Bks.

Thomas, Jim. Turtle Power! A Scrapbook by Leonardo. George, Chris & Giles, Mike, illus. 2004. (Teenage Mutant Ninja Turtles Ser.). 24p. (J). 5.99 (978-0-689-86898-6(7) , Simon Spotlight) Simon & Schuster Children's Publishing.

Thomas, Marian. Adventure Writer. (J). (gr. 4-6). pap. (978-1-875739-93-6(9)) Wizard Bks.

Thomas, Nigel. Tom Travis: The Lost People of Orion. 2006. 193p. pap. 19.95 (978-1-4241-0382-9(7)) PublishAmerica, Inc.

Thomas, Pat. Share a Story: Dial D for Disaster. (Illus.). 32p. (J). pap. 7.95 (978-0-14-038877-0(X)) Penguin Bks., Ltd. GBR. *Dist:* Trafalgar Square Publishing.

Thomas, Sue. Secesh. 2001. 120p. (J). (gr. 3-7). pap. 9.99 (978-0-88092-540-2(X)) Royal Fireworks Publishing Co.

Thompson Brothers Staff, illus. On the Road. movie tie-in ed. 2004. (Clifford Ser.). 24p. (J). pap. 4.99 (978-0-439-62815-0(6)) Scholastic, Inc.

Thompson, D. R. My New Town: A Flying Naptime Adventure. Thompson, D. R. & Thompson, Dave, illus. 2003. (Naptime Adventure Ser.: Vol. 1). 32p. 14.95 (978-0-9723252-0-2(4)) This New World Publishing, LLC.

—Our Picnic Lunch: An Ant-Sized Naptime Adventure, Vol. 3. Thompson, D. R. & Thompson, Dave, illus. 2005. (Naptime Adventure Ser.: 3). 32p. (J). 14.95 (978-0-9723252-1-9(2)) This New World Publishing, LLC.

Thompson, Jenean. All in a Day's Play. Thompson, Jenean, illus. l.t. ed. 2005. (Illus.). 40p. (J). 14.95 (978-1-59879-066-5(8)) Lifevest Publishing, Inc.

Thompson, Jill. Scary Godmother: Ghoul's Out for Summer. 2002. (Illus.). 128p. pap. 14.95 (978-1-57989-052-0(0)) Sirius Entertainment, Inc.

Thompson, John. Shadow Warriors II: Deadly. 2005. 252p. pap. 15.95 (978-1-59113-832-7(9)) Booklocker.com, Inc.

Thompson, Karen & Mitzo Thompson, Kim. A Pilot Flies Her Plane. 2006. (Read & Sing along Board Books with CDs Ser.). (Illus.). 18p. (J). bds. 7.49 (978-0-7696-4583-4(6)) School Specialty Publishing.

Thompson, Kay. Eloise the Ultimate Edition. Knight, Hilary, illus. 2000. 304p. (J). (ps-3). 39.99 (978-0-689-83990-0(1)) Simon & Schuster Children's Publishing.

Thompson, Keith. Bells Lake Treasure. 2007. per. 14.99 (***978-1-59886-565-3(X)***) Tate Publishing & Enterprises, L.L.C.

Thompson, Lisa. Amazing Africa. Harvey, Roger, illus. 2006. 80p. (J). (gr. 2-4). 19.95 (978-1-4048-1674-9(7)) Picture Window Bks.

—Lookout London. Jurevicius, Nathan, illus. 2006. (Read-It! Chapter Books). 80p. (J). (gr. 2-4). 19.95 (978-1-4048-1672-5(0)) Picture Window Bks.

—Saving Atlantis. Cantell, Brenda, illus. 2005. (Treasure Trackers Ser.). 80p. (J). (gr. 5-9). 19.00 (978-0-7910-8878-4(2)) Facts On File, Inc.

—Sent to Sydney. Squire, Stan, illus. 2006. (Read-It! Chapter Books). 80p. (J). (gr. 2-4). 19.95 (978-1-4048-1671-8(2)) Picture Window Bks.

—Spectacular Spain. Jones, Helen, illus. 2006. 80p. (J). (gr. 2-4). 19.95 (978-1-4048-1675-6(5)) Picture Window Bks.

—Taste of Thailand. Cantell, Brenda, illus. 2006. (Read-It! Chapter Books). 80p. (J). (gr. 2-4). 19.95 (978-1-4048-1677-0(1)) Picture Window Bks.

—Tokyo Techno. Chan, Jimmy, illus. 2006. (Read-It! Chapter Books). 80p. (J). (gr. 2-4). 19.95 (978-1-4048-1673-2(9)) Picture Window Bks.

Thompson, Lisa, illus. Incredible India. 2006. (Read-It! Chapter Books). 80p. (J). (gr. 2-4). 19.95 (978-1-4048-1676-3(3)) Picture Window Bks.

—New York City. 2006. (Read-It! Chapter Books). 80p. (J). (gr. 2-4). 19.95 (978-1-4048-1670-1(4)) Picture Window Bks.

Thompson, Teresa. The Adventures of Shasta & Nikki: A True Friendship. 2004. 34p. pap. 17.95 (978-1-4137-1967-3(8)) PublishAmerica, Inc.

Thomson, Celia. The Fallen. 2004. (Nine Lives of Chloe King Ser.: No. 1). 256p. (YA). pap. 12.95 (978-0-689-86658-6(5) , Simon Pulse) Simon & Schuster Children's Publishing.

Thor, Son of Asgard. 2007. (J). 128.10 (***978-1-59961-285-0(2)***) Spotlight.

Thornton, Duncan. Captain Jenny & the Sea of Wonders. Noblet, Yves, illus. 2005. 312p. (J). (gr. 5 up). pap. 8.95 (978-1-55050-194-0(1)) Coteau Bks. CAN. *Dist:* Fitzhenry & Whiteside, Ltd.

Thorpe, Kiki. The Island of Lost Dreams: The Official Movie Storybook - Junior Novel. novel ed. 2002. (Spy Kids 2 Ser.). (Illus.). 144p. pap. 4.99 (978-0-7868-1725-2(9) , Volo) Hyperion Bks. for Children.

—No Cowgirls Allowed! 2001. (Woody's Roundup Ser.: Bk. 7). (Illus.). 64p. (gr. 2-5). reprint ed. pap. 4.99 (978-0-7868-4460-9(4)) Disney Pr.

—Tink, North of Never Land. Disney Storybook Artists Staff, illus. 2007. 128p. (J). (gr. 1-5). 5.99 (***978-0-7364-2455-4(5)*** , RH/Disney) Random Hse. Children's Bks.

Thorpe, Kiki. Treasure Planet: Jim's Journal. 2002. (ps-2). lib. bdg. 11.80 (978-0-613-50576-5(X)) Tandem Library Bks.

Thoughts Staff. PNUT BUDDY & JUDDY (the adventures Of) #1. 2005. 38p. (J). pap. 16.99 (978-1-4116-2574-7(9)) Lulu.com.

Threatt, Cedric Lanier, Sr. A Journey Through the States with Harlo & Nate. 2005. (J). 17.95 (978-0-9720543-4-8(0)) Threatt, Cedric L.

The Thrill of the Ride. 2002. (Illus.). (J). pap. (978-0-7398-5070-1(9)) Steck-Vaughn.

Thuswalder, Werner. Silent Night, Holy Night. Ingpen, Robert R., illus. 2005. 48p. (J). (ps). 16.99 (978-0-698-40032-0(1) , Minedition) Penguin Group (USA) Inc.

Tibo, Gilles. Le Grand Voyage de Monsieur. ed. 2004. (FRE., Illus.). (J). (gr. k-3). spiral bd. (978-0-616-14600-2(0)) Canadian National Institute for the Blind/Institut National Canadien pour les Aveugles.

—Naomi & the Secret Message. Ouriou, Susan, tr. from FRE. Laliberte, Louise-Andree, illus. 2004. 168p. (J). (gr. 1-4). pap. 7.95 (978-0-88776-668-8(4)) Tundra Bks., Inc./Livres Toundra, Inc. CAN. *Dist:* Random Hse., Inc.

Tich, Jan. Pope Meets Pin. 2006. (Adventures in Unusual Places Ser.). (Illus.). 28p. (J). 12.95 (978-9974-7925-7-9(6)) Hardenville SA URY. *Dist:* Independent Pubs. Group.

Tidball, Lee. Windfork Secrets. Calderon, Dimitri, illus. unabr. ed. 1998. 280p. (J). pap. 16.95 (978-1-892896-06-3(0)) Infinity Publishing.

Tieri, Frank. Law of the Jungle, 3 vols. Chen, Sean, illus. 2003. (Wolverine Legends Ser.: Vol. 3). 144p. (YA). 12.99 (978-0-7851-1135-1(2)) Marvel Enterprises, Inc.

—Weapon X: The Underground, Vol. 2. Youngquist, Jeff, ed. Jeanty, Georges, illus. 2004. (X-Men Ser.). 184p. pap. 19.99 (978-0-7851-1253-2(7)) Marvel Enterprises, Inc.

Tiernan, Cate. Awakening. 2001. 192p. (YA). (gr. 7 up). pap. 5.99 (978-0-14-230045-9(4) , Puffin) Penguin Group (USA) Inc.

—Awakening. 2001. (gr. 7-12). lib. bdg. 13.00 (978-0-613-64018-3(7)) Tandem Library Bks.

Tigger & Pooh 100 Acre Woods Friends. 2007. 48p. pap. 3.99 (***978-1-4037-3227-9(2)***) Dalmatian Pr.

Tikki Tikki Tembo. 2000. (J). 9.95 (978-1-56137-021-4(5)) Novel Units, Inc.

Till, Danelle. Max's Moving Adventure: A Coloring Book for Kids on the Move. Spooner, Joe, illus. 2006. 52p. (J). 8.95 (978-0-912301-64-8(3)) First Bks.

Tiller, Steve. La Colonia de Arco Iris. Cremeans, Robert, illus. Date not set. (SPA.). (J). 15.95 (978-1-932317-02-2(3)) MichaelsMind LLC.

—Rainbows Landing. Tecosky, Kathryn, ed. Cremeans, Robert, illus. 2002. 36p. (J). pap. 7.95 (978-0-9704597-4-9(2)); 15.95 (978-0-9704597-5-6(0)) MichaelsMind LLC.

Tim, Tornado. Tornado Chaser: Life on the Edge. 2003. 92p. (YA). pap. 8.95 (978-0-595-27381-2(5)) iUniverse, Inc.

Time Soldiers. 2007. 145.26 (978-1-59961-223-2(2)) Spotlight.

Time Soldiers Book: Rex. 2003. tchr. ed. (978-1-929945-30-6(2)) Big Guy Bks., Inc.

Time Soldiers Book Vol. 2: Rex 2. 2003. tchr. ed. (978-1-929945-31-3(0)) Big Guy Bks., Inc.

Timmers, Leo. Happy with Me. 2002. (Illus.). 32p. (J). 16.95 (978-1-931290-08-1(3)) Tallfellow Pr.

Tina Modotti, Roses. 2002. 14.95 (978-0-7893-0697-5(2)) Universe Publishing.

Tindall, Steve. The Quest of the Black Knight. 2006. (ENG.). 168p. (J). per. (978-1-84685-303-6(6) , Exposure Publishing) Meadow Bks.

Tingwald, Jady Ann. The Adventures of Rady Red Comb. Powell, James, illus. 2005. 33p. (J). (gr. 1-6). 9.00 (978-0-9706728-1-0(0)) New Millenium Pr., The.

Tinkler, David. Revenge of the Dinner Ladies. unabr. ed. 2003. (J). pap. 24.95 incl. audio (978-0-7540-6200-4(7) , Galaxy Children's Large Print) BBC Audiobooks America.

Tisopulos, Tara. Finding a Family. Tokar, Rob, photos by. 1999. (Adventures of Buddi the Greyhound Ser.). (Illus.). 22p. (J). (gr. 1-5). 14.95 (978-0-9678057-0-2(8)) Great Dog Publishing.

Tito Vuela al Sur. 2002. (Let's Start Teacher's Pets Ser.).Tr. of Timothy Flies South. (SPA., Illus.). 32p. (J). (ps-3). (978-968-5308-17-5(9) , Silver Dolphin en Español) Advanced Marketing, S. de R. L. de C. V.

Todd, Barbara. Roger Gets Carried Away. Roge, illus. 2005. 32p. (J). (ps-2). pap. 7.95 (978-1-55037-898-6(8)); lib. bdg. 19.95 (978-1-55037-899-3(6)) Annick Pr., Ltd. CAN. *Dist:* Firefly Bks., Ltd.

Todd, John. The Zoo Savers. 2007. 140p. (J). per. (***978-0-9779680-8-4(1)***) Global Authors Pubns.

Todorov, Boriana & Todorov, Vladimir. The Moon Rock. 2007. (Illus.). 96p. (J). (gr. 7 up). 19.95 (***978-1-894965-77-4(9)***) Simply Read Bks. CAN. *Dist:* Perseus Distribution.

Toews, Marj. Black & White Blanche. Bonder, Dianna, illus. 2006. 32p. 16.95 (978-1-55005-132-2(6)) Fitzhenry & Whiteside, Ltd. CAN. *Dist:* F & W Pubns., Inc.

Tofte, Mavis. Doogie Dork & Marta. 2005. (Illus.). 64p. (J). per. 5.75 (978-0-9709906-4-8(2)) Creative Quill Publishing, Inc.

—Doogie Dork & the Storm. Tofte, Mavis, illus. 2006. (Illus.). 64p. (J). per. 6.75 (978-0-9709906-5-5(0)) Creative Quill Publishing, Inc.

—Doogie Dork's Wish. Tofte, Mavis, illus. 2003. (J). per. 5.75 (978-0-9709906-2-4(6)) Creative Quill Publishing, Inc.

Tofte, Mavis. Franny Frumpel's Secret. 2007. (Illus.). 64p. (J). per. 6.00 (***978-0-9709906-7-9(7)***) Creative Quill Publishing, Inc.

Toki, Wilfred. Hana & the Honu. Toki, Wilfred, illus. 2004.

(Illus.).32p. (J). 12.95 (978-0-9729905-8-5(5)) Beachhouse Publishing, LLC.

Tokoro, Juzo. Spawn Manga, Vol. 1. (Illus.). 200p. (YA). pap. 9.99 (978-1-58240-571-1(9)) Image Comics.

Tokyopop Staff, ed. Jackie Chan Adventures, 3 vols., Vol. 2. 2004. (Illus.). 128p. pap. 7.99 (978-1-59182-403-9(6)) TOKYOPOP, Inc.

—Jackie Chan Adventures Vol. 3: Jackie & Jade Save the Day, 4 vols. 2004. (Illus.). 96p. pap. 7.99 (978-1-59182-404-6(4)) TOKYOPOP, Inc.

Tolkien, J. R. R. Las Aventuras de Tom Bombadil. Baynes, Pauline, illus. 2005. (SPA.). 157p. (J). 22.95 (978-84-450-7194-6(7)) Minotauro Ediciones ESP. *Dist:* Planeta Publishing Corp.

—Senhor dos Aneis, Vol. 3. pap. 34.95 (978-85-336-1339-3(3)) Livraria Martins Editora BRA. *Dist:* Distribooks, Inc.

Tolson, Aaron J. Washington Putter. 2005. 248p. (YA). per. 22.00 (978-1-58982-243-6(9) , Bedside Bks.) American Bk. Publishing Group.

Tomasso, Phillip. King Gauthier & the Little Dragon Slayer. l.t. ed. 2003. (Illus.). 61p. (J). per. (978-0-9740833-5-3(6)) Port Town Publishing.

Tomizawa, Hitoshi. Treasure Hunter 1: Eternal Youth, 3 vols., Vol. 1. Pannone, Frank, ed. Kobayashi, Mayumi, tr. from JPN. Tomizawa, Hitoshi, illus. 2004. Orig. Title: Hizenya Jyubei 2. (Illus.). 200p. pap. 9.99 (978-1-58664-921-0(3) , CMX 65101G, CPM Manga) Central Park Media Corp.

—Treasure Hunter 2: Figurehead of Souls, 3 vols., Vol. 2. Pannone, Frank, ed. Kobayashi, Mayumi, tr. from JPN. Tomizawa, Hitoshi, illus. 2004. Orig. Title: Hizenya Jyubei 2. (Illus.). 200p. pap. 9.99 (978-1-58664-922-7(1) , CMX 65102G, CPM Manga) Central Park Media Corp.

—Treasure Hunter 3: The Last Crusade, 3 vols., Vol. 3. Pannone, Frank, ed. Kobayashi, Mayumi, tr. from JPN. Tomizawa, Hitoshi, illus. 2004. Orig. Title: Hizenya Jyubei 2. (Illus.). 216p. pap. 9.99 (978-1-58664-923-4(X) , CMX 65103G, CPM Manga) Central Park Media Corp.

Tomlinson, Jill. Cat Wanted to Go Home - Picture Boo. Howard, Paul, illus. 2004. 32p. (J). (ps). pap. 9.99 (978-1-4052-1873-3(8)) Egmont Bks., Ltd. GBR. *Dist:* Independent Pubs. Group.

Tomlinson, Theresa. Child of the May. 1998. (Illus.). 128p. (YA). (gr. 5-9). pap. 15.95 (978-0-531-30118-0(4) , Orchard Bks.) Scholastic, Inc.

Tompkins, Robyn Lee. Miss Molly's Adventure in the Park: Another Great Adventure Brought to You by Miss Molly & Her Dog Reyburn, 10 vols. Carson, Shawn K., illus. l.t. ed. 2005. (ENG.). 60p. (J). per. (978-0-9741647-6-2(3)) NRG Pubns.

Tompkins, Robyn Lee. Miss Molly's Adventure on the Farm: Another great adventure brought to you by Miss Molly & her dog Reyburn. Carson, Shawn, illus. 2006. (J). per. (***978-0-9741647-7-9(1)***) NRG Pubns.

Top That Publishing Staff, ed. Snowman. Briggs, Raymond, illus. 2006. 8p. (978-1-84666-214-0(1)) Top That! Publishing PLC.

Torba, Ed. The Magic Trip. Hansen, Kate, illus. 2002. (YA). per. 15.00 (978-0-9765748-0-4(2)) Torba Publishing.

Toriyama, Akira. Dragon Ball Z. Toriyama, Akira, illus. 2004. (Illus.). Vol. 15. 200p. lib. bdg. 18.55 (978-1-4176-5214-3(4)); Vol. 16. 200p. lib. bdg. 18.55 (978-1-4176-5215-0(2)); Vol. 17. 200p. lib. bdg. 18.55 (978-1-4176-5216-7(0)); Vol. 18. lib. bdg. 18.55 (978-1-4176-5213-6(6)) Tandem Library Bks.

—Dragon Ball Z, Vol. 26. 2006. (Dragon Ball Z Ser.). 208p. (YA). pap. 7.95 (978-1-4215-0636-4(X)) Viz Media.

Torphy, William & Gowack, Paul. Snakebite. 2005. (Illus.). 116p. (J). per. 16.95 (978-0-9749502-4-2(6)) Ithuriel's Spear.

Torres, J. Boy Wonder. Staton, Joe et al, illus. 2005. (Teen Titans Ser.: No. 2). 80p. (J). (ps-ps). mass mkt. 2.99 (978-0-439-74573-4(X)) Scholastic, Inc.

—Machina Ex Deus. 2003. (Jason & the Argobots Ser.: Vol. 2). (Illus.). 88p. pap. 11.95 (978-1-929998-56-2(2)) Oni Pr., Inc.

Torres, Jotam. Weagol's Big Mess. 2007. 28p. per. 12.99 (***978-1-59886-758-9(X)***) Tate Publishing & Enterprises, L.L.C.

Torres, Leyla. Saturday Sancocho. 1999. (gr. k-3). lib. bdg. 14.10 (978-0-613-84583-0(8)); (978-0-606-16472-6(3)) Tandem Library Bks.

Torres, Melissa & A&J Studios Staff. Under the Sea. 2006. (Dora the Explorer Ser.). 8p. (J). 6.99 (978-1-4169-1427-3(7) , Simon Spotlight/Nickelodeon) Simon & Schuster Children's Publishing.

Torrey, Michele. Bottles of Eight & Pieces of Rum. 1998. 138p. (J). (ps-7). pap. 9.99 (978-0-88092-321-7(0) , 3210) Royal Fireworks Publishing Co.

Touma, Patricia. Happy Times, the Adventures of Ish & Mish Vol. 1: Ish & Mish Go to the Circus. 2005. per. 7.00 (978-1-58396-873-4(3)) Blue Unicorn Edition, LLC.

Townson, Hazel. Dark Deeds at Deathwood. 2006. (Sequel to Deathwood Letters Ser.). 92p. (J). pap. 8.99 (***978-1-84270-486-8(9)***) Andersen GBR. *Dist:* Independent Pubs. Group.

—Diamond Hunt. 2003. 188p. (YA). pap. 9.99 (978-1-84270-302-1(1)) Andersen GBR. *Dist:* Independent Pubs. Group.

—The Secret Room. Salisbury, Martin, illus. 2006. (Pathway Books). 75p. (J). 21.26 (978-1-59889-003-7(4)) Stone Arch Bks.

Toybox Innovations. Disney Pixar's Toy Story. 2006. (Disney's Read Along Ser.). (Illus.). (J). (ps-3). audio compact disk 7.99 (978-0-7634-2179-3(0)) Walt Disney Records.

ToyBox Innovations, creator. The Curse of the Black Pearl. 2006. (Pirates of the Caribbean (Audio) Ser.). (Illus.). 24p. (J). (ps-3). audio compact disk 7.99 (978-0-7634-2176-2(6)) Walt Disney Records.

The Transformation. 2003. (J). per. (978-1-57657-863-6(1)) Paradise Pr., Inc.

Travis, Alva. Secret of the Hidden Chamber. 2006. pap. 12.95 (978-1-4241-2071-0(3)) PublishAmerica, Inc.

Trayer, Edward. The Struggles of Felicity Brady. 2004. (YA). per. 14.95 (978-1-59571-043-7(4)) Word Association Pubs.

Trayer, Edward H. Struggles of Felicity Brady: Articulus Quest. 2005. (YA). per. 14.95 (978-1-59571-091-8(4)) Word Association Pubs.

Trease, Christine K. Mike E. Meanderer Meets. Trease, Christine K., illus. 1999. (Adventure Ser.: Vol. No. 2). (Illus.). 21p. (J). (ps-7). cd-rom 14.95 (978-1-929450-03-9(6)) Lexico.

—Mike E. Meanderer Meets the Cow in the Flannel Nightgown. Trease, Christine K., illus. 1999. (Illus.). 21p. (J). (ps-7). 14.95 (978-1-929450-02-2(8)) Lexico.

—Pandemonium in Pleasant Valley. 2000. (Illus.). 29p. (J). (ps-10). cd-rom 14.95 (978-1-929450-13-8(3)) Lexico.

Treasure Found. 2005. 32p. (J). 12.99 (978-0-9758709-2-1(0) , A.W.A. Gang) Journey Stone Creations, LLC.

Treasure Trackers. 2006. (Illus.). (gr. 5-9). 111.60 (978-0-7910-9082-4(5)) Facts On File, Inc.

Treasures. ed. 2005. (J). 6.50 (978-0-9776472-0-0(X)) Myth-Series.

Treece, Amy L. Winds Day. Raymer, M. Loys, illus. 123p. (J). (gr. 3-7). pap. 9.95 (978-0-9677982-0-2(5)) Treece, Amy L.

Treggiari, Jo. The Curious Misadventures of Feltus Ovalton. Baldwin, Alisa, illus. 2006. 336p. (J). (gr. 3-7). pap. (978-1-897073-43-8(7)) Lobster Pr.

Trejo, Delia. A Fairy Tale for Artemis. 2002. 238p. pap. 14.95 (978-0-595-23437-0(2) , Writer's Showcase Pr.) iUniverse, Inc.

Tremblay, Alain Ulysse. Le Don de Jonathan. Malepart, Celine, tr. 2003. (Roman Jeunesse Ser.). (FRE., Illus.). 96p. (J). (gr. 4-7). pap. (978-2-89021-635-8(7)) Diffusion du livre Mirabel.

Tremblay, Carole. Mary Baba & the 40 Sailors. 2000. (Illus.). 32p. (J). (ps-3). pap. (978-1-894363-30-3(2)) Dominique & Friends.

Trevor, Meriol. Following the Phoenix. 1998. (Letzenstein Chronicles Ser.: No. 2). 200p. (J). (gr. 4-7). pap. 11.95 (978-1-883937-26-3(4) , 26-4) Bethlehem Bks.

—The Rose & Crown. 1999. (Letzenstein Chronicles Ser.: No. 4). 199p. (J). (gr. 4-7). pap. 11.95 (978-1-883937-28-7(0) , 28-0) Bethlehem Bks.

Triple Play. 2006. (Illus.). (gr. 4-8). 167.40 (978-0-7910-9072-5(8)) Facts On File, Inc.

Triple Play-Yellow. 2006. (Illus.). (gr. 4-8). 167.40 (978-0-7910-9077-0(9)) Facts On File, Inc.

Trondheim, Lewis. Kaput & Zosky. 2008. 80p. (J). pap. 13.95 (***978-1-59643-132-4(6)*** , First Second Bks.) Roaring Brook Pr.

Trottier, Maxine. By the Standing Stone. 2001. (Circle of Silver Chronicles Ser.). (Illus.). 246p. (YA). (gr. 7-12). pap. 7.95 (978-0-7737-6138-4(1)) Stoddart Kids CAN. *Dist:* Fitzhenry & Whiteside, Ltd.

—By the Standing Stone. 2001. (gr. 3-6). lib. bdg. 16.40 (978-0-613-51481-1(5)) Tandem Library Bks.

—Dreamstones. East, Stella, illus. 2000. 22p. (J). (ps-3). 8.95 (978-0-7737-6141-4(1)) Stoddart Kids CAN. *Dist:* Fitzhenry & Whiteside, Ltd.

—Dreamstones. 2000. (gr. 3-6). lib. bdg. 16.40 (978-0-613-49487-8(3)) Tandem Library Bks.

Trout, Richard. Sign of the Dragon. 2007. (J). 15.95 (***978-1-58980-476-0(7)***) Pelican Publishing Co., Inc.

Trout, Richard E. Cayman Gold: Lost Treasure of Devil's Grotto. 2005. (MacGregor Family Adventure Ser.). (Illus.). 224p. (YA). (gr. 14 up). 15.95 (978-1-58980-323-7(X)) Pelican Publishing Co., Inc.

—Czar of Alaska: The Cross of Charlemagne. 2005. 248p. (J). (gr. 5-8). 15.95 (978-1-58980-328-2(0)) Pelican Publishing Co., Inc.

Truckey, Don. The Adventures of Caraway Kim— Southpaw. 2005. 192p. pap. 8.95 (978-1-894345-90-3(8)) Thistledown Pr., Ltd. CAN. *Dist:* Literary Pr. Group of Canada.

Trudel, Sylvain. Le Roi Qui Venait du Bout du Monde. Langlois, Suzane, illus. 2002. (Premier Roman Ser.). (FRE.). 64p. (J). (gr. 2-5). pap. (978-2-89021-279-4(3)) Diffusion du livre Mirabel.

Trudel, Sylvain & Langlois, Suzane. L' Iti de Mes Dix Ans. 2002. (Premier Roman Ser.). (FRE., Illus.). 64p. pap. (978-2-89021-519-1(9)) Diffusion du livre Mirabel.

True, John Preston. The Iron Star. 2004. reprint ed. pap. 15.95 (978-1-4191-6767-6(7)); pap. 1.99 (978-1-4192-6767-3(1)) Kessinger Publishing, LLC.

Trujillo Stephens, Kristina. The Tod Squad Can Go. 2006. (J). bds. (978-1-57332-415-1(9)) HighReach Learning, Inc.

—The Tod Squad Can Go Book with Game Cards. 2006. (J). bds. (978-1-57332-408-3(6)) HighReach Learning, Inc.

Tryon, Micro, et al. Fundorado Island. 2006. (Illus.). 224p. (J). (gr. 3). 14.95 (978-0-385-73267-3(8) , Delacorte Bks. for Young Readers) Random Hse. Children's Bks.

Tsukirino, Yumi. Arbok's First Love, Pt. 2. Tsukirino, Yumi, illus. 2000. (Magical Pokemon Journey : No. 3, pt. 2). (Illus.). 40p. (YA). (ps up). pap. 4.95 (978-1-56931-483-8(7)) Viz Media.

Tuck Everlasting. 1998. (J). 9.95 (978-1-56137-251-5(X)) Novel Units, Inc.

Tuck Everlasting. 8.97 (978-0-13-437487-1(8)) Prentice Hall PTR.

Tuck, Helen. The House at the Bend of Contently Creek. Melton, Eric, illus. 2003. 107p. (J). pap. 11.95 (978-0-7414-1682-7(4)) Infinity Publishing.

Tuck, Pamela M. The Adventure of Sheldon, the Mushroom. Alford, Joann M., illus. 2005. 30p. (J). per. 13.99 (978-1-59879-072-6(2)) Lifevest Publishing, Inc.

Tucker, Mark. Super Phil. Petete, Christine, illus. 2003. (J). 4.50 (978-1-882440-00-9(5)) God's World Pubns. Inc.

—Super Phil & the Missing Mom. Patete, Christine, illus. 2003. 24p. (J). 4.50 (978-1-882440-01-6(3)) God's World Pubns. Inc.

—Super Phil & the Sphiddle of the Rinks. Patete, Christine, illus. 2003. (J). 4.50 (978-1-882440-02-3(1)) God's World Pubns. Inc.

Tugman, Etta. Smokey Mountain Bears. 2006. 9.00 (978-0-8059-8189-6(6)) Dorrance Publishing Co., Inc.

Tuitel, Johnnie. Searching the Noonday Trail. 2000. (Gun Lake Adventure Ser.: Bk. 4). 112p. (J). (gr. 4-7). pap. 5.99 (978-0-9658075-3-1(3)) Cedar Tree Publishing.

Tuitel, Johnnie & Lamson, Sharon. The Light in Bradford Manor. 2004. 135p. pap. 5.99 (978-0-9658075-5-5(X)) Cedar Tree Publishing.

Tuitel, Johnnie & Lamson, Sharon E. Mystery Explosion. Sharp, Dan, illus. 1998. (Gun Lake Adventure Ser.: No. 2). 121p. (J). (gr. 3-7). pap. 5.99 (978-0-9658075-1-7(7)) Cedar Tree Publishing.

Tukan, Jaytoe Anthony, Sr. Little Bernice Animal Book. Tukan, Jaytoe Anthony, Sr., illus. 2002. (J). per. 7.95 (978-0-9665909-3-7(7)) Kalawantis Publishing Services, Inc.

Tullson, Diane. The Darwin Expedition. 2007. (Orca Sports Ser.). 112p. (YA). (gr. 7 up). pap. (***978-1-55143-676-0(0)***); lib. bdg. (***978-1-55143-678-4(7)***) Orca Bk. Pubs.

Tullson, Diane. Red Sea. 2005. 176p. (J). (gr. 7-12). pap. 7.95 (978-1-55143-331-8(1)) Orca Bk. Pubs. USA.

Turkovitz, Karen. Oh, Frannie! Ryan, Linda et al, eds. rev. ed. 2000. (Frannie Flotnick Adventure Ser.). (Illus.). 36p. (YA). (gr. 5-12). pap. 12.95 (978-0-9679115-7-1(5)) Five Degrees of Frannie.

Turner, Ethel. Seven Little Australians. 2005. 27.95 (978-1-4218-0333-3(X)); 204p. pap. 12.95 (978-1-4218-0433-0(6)) 1st World Publishing, Inc. (1st World Library - Literary Society).

—Seven Little Australians. 2006. 142p. pap. 10.99 (978-1-4264-1638-5(5)) BiblioBazaar.

—Seven Little Australians. 2004. (ENG.). pap. 35.99 (***978-1-4142-8241-1(9)***) IndyPublish.com.

—Seven Little Australians. 2004. reprint ed. pap. 20.95 (978-1-4191-4679-4(3)); pap. 1.99 (978-1-4192-4679-1(8)) Kessinger Publishing, LLC.

Turner, Jessie E. Moon in the Day Sky. 2006. 19p. (YA). pap. 19.95 (***978-1-59299-238-6(2)***) Inkwater Pr.

Turner, Julie Anne. A Tale of Summerland. 2007. (Illus.). 72p. pap. (***978-1-84401-902-1(0)***) Athena Pr.

Turner, Megan Whalen. The King of Attolia. 400p. (J). 2007. (gr. 5 up). pap. 7.99 (***978-0-06-083579-8(6)*** , Eos); 2006. 16.99 (978-0-06-083577-4(X)); 2006. lib. bdg. 17.89 (978-0-06-083578-1(8)) HarperCollins Pubs.

—The Queen of Attolia. 2000. 288p. (J). (gr. 5 up). 15.95 (978-0-688-17423-1(X)) HarperCollins Pubs.

—Queen of Attolia. 2006. 368p. (J). pap. 6.99 (978-0-06-084182-9(6)) HarperCollins Pubs.

Turner Sinnenburg, Kris, illus. Aero & Officer Mike: Police Partners. Plummer, Joan & Russell, P., photos by. 2003. 32p. (J). (ps up). 17.95 (978-1-56397-931-6(4)) Boyds Mills Pr.

Twain, Mark. Die Abenteuer von Tom Sawyer. 2000. Tr. of Adventures of Tom Sawyer. (GER.). (J). pap. 14.95 (978-3-596-50166-3(0)) Fischer Taschenbuch Verlag DEU. *Dist:* Distribooks, Inc.

—The Adventures of Huckleberry Finn. Pablo Marcos Studio Staff, illus. 2002. (Great Illustrated Classics Ser.). 240p. (J). (gr. 3-8). 21.35 (978-1-57765-676-0(8) , ABDO & Daughters) ABDO Publishing Co.

—The Adventures of Huckleberry Finn. 2001. (SPA., Illus.). 192p. (YA). (gr. 5-8). 12.95 (978-84-372-2257-8(5)) Altea, Ediciones, S.A. - Grupo Santillana ESP. *Dist:* Santillana USA Publishing Co., Inc.

—The Adventures of Huckleberry Finn. Redondo, Francisco, illus. 2nd ed. 1998. (Illustrated Classic Book Ser.). 61p. (J). (gr. 3 up). reprint ed. pap. 4.95 (978-1-56767-255-8(8)) Educational Insights, Inc.

—The Adventures of Huckleberry Finn. 96p. (J). pap. 4.95 (978-0-7910-4108-6(5) , Chelsea Hse.) Facts On File, Inc.

—The Adventures of Huckleberry Finn. (Coleccion Clasicos de la Juventud). (SPA., Illus.). 192p. (J). 12.95 (978-84-7189-027-6(5) , ORT313) Ortells, Alfredo Editorial S.L. ESP. *Dist:* Continental Bk. Co., Inc.

—The Adventures of Huckleberry Finn. 1999. (Aladdin Classics Ser.). 544p. (YA). (gr. 4-7). pap. 5.99 (978-0-689-83139-3(0) , Aladdin) Simon & Schuster Children's Publishing.

—The Adventures of Huckleberry Finn. McKowen, Scott, illus. 2006. (Unabridged Classics Ser.). 320p. 9.95 (978-1-4027-2600-2(7)) Sterling Publishing Co., Inc.

—The Adventures of Huckleberry Finn. 2003. (gr. 7-12). lib. bdg. 14.15 (978-0-613-64012-1(8)); 1999. 10.64 (978-0-606-17508-1(3)); 1999. (gr. 3-6). lib. bdg. 11.80 (978-0-613-63171-6(4)); 1999. (gr. 7-12). lib. bdg. 15.25 (978-0-613-32245-4(2)) Tandem Library Bks.

—The Adventures of Huckleberry Finn: Juvenile Classic. 2005. (Illus.). 192p. (J). 5.99 (978-1-4037-1383-4(9)) Dalmatian Pr.

—The Adventures of Huckleberry Finn: Level. 3. abr. ed. 2000. (Illus.). vii, 54p. (C). pap. 9.00 (978-0-582-42050-2(4)) Pearson ESL.

—The Adventures of Tom Sawyer. 2004. 264p. pap. 13.95 (978-1-59540-318-6(3) , 1st World Library - Literary Society) 1st World Publishing, Inc.

—The Adventures of Tom Sawyer. Pablo Marcos Studio Staff, illus. 2002. (Great Illustrated Classics Ser.). 240p. (J). (gr. 3-8). 21.35 (978-1-57765-679-1(2) , ABDO & Daughters) ABDO Publishing Co.

—The Adventures of Tom Sawyer. 1999. (Andre Deutsch Classics). (Illus.). 272p. (J). 9.95 (978-0-233-99242-6(1)) Andre Deutsch GBR. *Dist:* Trafalgar Square Publishing.

—The Adventures of Tom Sawyer. (Great Classics for Children Ser.). (Illus.). 192p. (J). 5.99 (978-1-4037-0598-3(4)) Dalmatian Pr.

—The Adventures of Tom Sawyer. 2001. (Paperback Classics Ser.). (Illus.). 304p. pap. 6.95 (978-0-375-75681-8(7) , Modern Library) Random House Publishing Group.

—The Adventures of Tom Sawyer. 2006. (Scholastic Classics Ser.). (Illus.). vi, 219p. (J). (gr. 9-12). 25.00 (978-0-531-16978-0(2) , Watts, Franklin) Scholastic Library Publishing.

—The Adventures of Tom Sawyer. 2001. (Aladdin Classics Ser.). 272p. (J). (gr. 4-7). pap. 4.99 (978-0-689-84224-5(4) , Aladdin) Simon & Schuster Children's Publishing.

—The Adventures of Tom Sawyer. 2001. (gr. 3-6). lib. bdg. 11.80 (978-0-613-63172-3(2)); 1999. (gr. 5-8). lib. bdg. 11.80 (978-0-613-66685-5(2)) Tandem Library Bks.

—The Adventures of Tom Sawyer. 2001. 184p. pap. 9.95 (978-1-57002-169-5(4)) University Publishing Hse., Inc.

—The Adventures of Tom Sawyer. Corvino, Lucy, illus. 2005. (Classic Starts Ser.). 160p. 4.95 (978-1-4027-1216-6(2)) Sterling Publishing Co., Inc.

—The Adventures of Tom Sawyer. 1999. reprint ed. pap. 28.00 (978-1-4047-1117-4(1)) Classic Textbooks.

—The Adventures of Tom Sawyer. l.t. ed. 2006. 510p. 22.95 (978-0-7862-8640-9(7)) Thorndike Pr.

—The Adventures of Tom Sawyer. Williams, True W., illus. 2nd rev. ed. 2002. (Mark Twain Library). 288p. pap. 15.95 (978-0-520-23575-5(4)) Univ. of California Pr.

—The Adventures of Tom Sawyer: Juvenile Classic. 2005. (Illus.). 192p. (J). 5.99 (978-1-4037-1382-7(0)) Dalmatian Pr.

—The Adventures of Tom Sawyer - Literary Touchstone Edition. 2005. 216p. (YA). per. 4.99 (978-1-58049-596-7(6) , PWH5966) Prestwick Hse., Inc.

—The Adventures of Tom Sawyer; Adventures of Huckleberry Finn. 2002. 544p. mass mkt. 5.95 (978-0-451-52864-3(6) , Signet Classics) Penguin Group (USA) Inc.

—The Adventures of Tom Sawyer, Complete. l.t. ed. 2006. 408p. pap. (978-1-84637-320-6(4)) Echo Library.

—Las Aventuras de Huckleberry Finn. 2002. (Classics for Young Readers Ser.). (SPA.). (YA). 14.95 (978-84-392-0925-6(8) , EV30617) Gaviota Ediciones ESP. *Dist:* Lectorum Pubns., Inc.

—Las Aventuras de Huckleberry Finn. 2000. (SPA.). 352p. (YA). 15.95 (978-84-207-3396-8(2)) Grupo Anaya, S.A. ESP. *Dist:* AIMS International Bks., Inc.

—Las Aventuras de Huckleberry Finn. 2000. (SPA.). 244p. (YA). 13.95 (978-84-348-2796-7(4)) SM Ediciones ESP. *Dist:* AIMS International Bks., Inc.

—Las Aventuras de Tom Sawyer. 2002. (SPA.). (YA). 7.95 (978-956-13-1069-8(4)) Bello, Andres CHL. *Dist:* AIMS International Bks., Inc.

—Las Aventuras de Tom Sawyer. 2000. (SPA., Illus.). 272p. (J). 7.95 (978-84-406-8397-7(9)) Ediciones B ESP. *Dist:* Distribooks, Inc.

—Las Aventuras de Tom Sawyer. 2003. (Advanced Reading Ser.). (SPA.). 124p. (J). 11.95 (978-84-239-9045-0(1)) Espasa Calpe, S.A. ESP. *Dist:* Planeta Publishing Corp.

—Las Aventuras de Tom Sawyer. 2002. (Classics for Young Readers Ser.). (SPA.). (YA). 13.99 (978-84-392-0908-9(8) , EV30591) Gaviota Ediciones ESP. *Dist:* Lectorum Pubns., Inc.

—Las Aventuras de Tom Sawyer. (Coleccion Estrella). (SPA., Illus.). 64p. (YA). 14.95 (978-950-11-0012-9(X) , SGM012) Sigmar ARG. *Dist:* Continental Bk. Co., Inc.

—Avventure di Tom Sawyer. pap. 15.95 (978-88-451-2151-7(8)) Fabbri - RCS Libri ITA. *Dist:* Distribooks, Inc.

—The Best Fence Painter. Bates, Amy June, illus. 2006. (Adventures of Tom Sawyer Ser.: Bk. 2). 32p. (J). pap. 3.95 (978-1-4027-3288-1(0)) Sterling Publishing Co., Inc.

—Mark Twain/the Adventures of Tom Sawyer. Cruz, E. R., illus. 2005. 48p. (gr. 5-8). 25.50 (978-0-7910-9102-9(3)) Facts On File, Inc.

—The Mysterious Stranger. 2004. 160p. pap. 11.95 (978-1-59540-326-1(4) , 1st World Library - Literary Society) 1st World Publishing, Inc.

—Penguin Young Readers Sample Adventures Tom Sawyer. 2000. (YA). (978-0-582-46867-2(1)) Pearson Education.

—Personal Recollections of Joan of Arc. 1999. reprint ed. pap. 28.00 (978-1-4047-1122-8(8)); pap. 28.00 (978-1-4047-1123-5(6)) Classic Textbooks.

—The Prince & the Pauper. Lynch, Brendan, illus. 2002. (Great Illustrated Classics Ser.). 240p. (J). (gr. 3-8). 21.35 (978-1-57765-698-2(9) , ABDO & Daughters) ABDO Publishing Co.

—The Prince & the Pauper. (J). 19.95 (978-0-8488-0849-5(5)) Amereon LTD.

—The Prince & the Pauper. 2007. (Bantam Classics Ser.). 224p. (J). (gr. 4-11). pap. 3.95 (978-0-553-21256-3(7) , Bantam Classics) Bantam Bks.

—The Prince & the Pauper. 1999. reprint ed. pap. 28.00 (978-1-4047-1120-4(1)) Classic Textbooks.

—The Prince & the Pauper. 2000. (Thrift Edition Ser.). 176p. (gr. 6). pap. 2.50 (978-0-486-41110-1(9)) Dover Pubns., Inc.

—The Prince & the Pauper. (YA). (gr. 5-12). pap. 6.50 (978-0-8224-9344-0(6)) Globe Fearon Educational Publishing.

—The Prince & the Pauper. (J). 9.95 (978-1-56156-311-1(0)) Kidsbooks, Inc.

—The Prince & the Pauper. l.t. ed. 2000. (Large Print Heritage Ser.). 364p. (J). lib. bdg. 33.95 (978-1-58118-068-8(3) , 23662) LRS.

—The Prince & the Pauper. 2003. (Modern Library Classics). (Illus.). 240p. pap. 8.95 (978-0-375-76112-6(8) , Modern Library) Random House Publishing Group.

—The Prince & the Pauper. Akib, Jamel, illus. 2007. (Classic Starts Ser.). 160p. (J). 4.95 (978-1-4027-3687-2(8)) Sterling Publishing Co., Inc.

—The Prince & the Pauper. abr. ed. 2001. (gr. 7-12). lib. bdg. 15.25 (978-0-613-43870-4(1)) Tandem Library Bks.

—The Prince & the Pauper. l.t. ed. 2000. (Perennial Bestsellers Ser.). 307p. (J). 26.95 (978-0-7838-9061-6(3)) Thorndike Pr.

—The Prince & the Pauper. 1998. (Children's Library). 288p. (J). pap. 3.95 (978-1-85326-147-3(5) , 1475WW) Wordsworth Editions, Ltd. GBR. *Dist:* Combined Publishing.

—The Prince & the Pauper: With a Discussion of Respect. 2003. (Values in Action Illustrated Classics Ser.). (J). (978-1-59203-052-1(1)) Learning Challenge, Inc.

—El Principe y el Mendigo.Tr. of Prince & the Pauper. (SPA., Illus.). 144p. (YA). 11.95 (978-84-7281-073-0(9) , AF1073) Auriga, Ediciones S.A. ESP. *Dist:* Continental Bk. Co., Inc.

—A Song for Aunt Polly. Bates, Amy June, illus. 2006. (Adventures of Tom Sawyer Ser.: Bk. 1). 32p. (J). pap. 3.95 (978-1-4027-3287-4(2)) Sterling Publishing Co., Inc.

—Tom Sawyer. Cruz, E. R., illus. 2nd ed. 1998. (Illustrated Classic Book Ser.). 61p. (J). (gr. 3 up). reprint ed. pap. 4.95 (978-1-56767-263-3(9)) Educational Insights, Inc.

—Tom Sawyer. adapted ed. (YA). (gr. 5-12). pap. 8.50 (978-0-8359-0212-0(9)) Globe Fearon Educational Publishing.

—Tom Sawyer. (Coleccion Clasicos de la Juventud). (SPA., Illus.). 220p. (J). 12.95 (978-84-7189-029-0(1) , ORT310) Ortells, Alfredo Editorial S.L. ESP. *Dist:* Continental Bk. Co., Inc.

—Tom Sawyer. 2003. (Timeless Classics Ser.). (SPA., Illus.). 95p. (J). (gr. 5-8). pap. 12.95 (978-84-372-2235-6(4)) Santillana USA Publishing Co., Inc.

—Tom Sawyer. 1999. (Illus.). 336p. (J). (gr. 4-7). pap. 4.99 (978-0-439-09940-0(4)) Scholastic, Inc.

—Tom Sawyer. unabr. ed. 2002. (YA). pap. incl. audio compact disk (978-1-58472-341-7(6) , In Audio) Sound Room Pubs., Inc.

—Tom Sawyer Abroad. 1999. reprint ed. pap. 28.00 (978-1-4047-1125-9(2)) Classic Textbooks.

—Tom Sawyer Abroad & Tom Sawyer, Detective. l.t. ed. 1999. (Large Print Heritage Ser.). 265p. (YA). (gr. 7-12). lib. bdg. 29.95 (978-1-58118-046-6(2) , 22515) LRS.

—Tom Sawyer & Huckleberry Finn. unabr. ed. 1998. (Wordsworth Classics Ser.). (YA). (gr. 6-12). 5.27 (978-0-89061-011-4(8) , R0118WW) Jamestown.

—Tom Sawyer, Detective. (SPA., Illus.). 160p. (YA). 11.95 (978-84-7281-062-4(3) , AF0623) Auriga, Ediciones S.A. ESP. *Dist:* Continental Bk. Co., Inc.

—Tom Sawyer, Detective. unabr. ed. 2002. (Dover Juvenile Classics Ser.). 80p. (J). (gr. 4-7). pap. 2.00 (978-0-486-42109-4(0)) Dover Pubns., Inc.

—Tom Sawyer, Detective. 2002. (gr. 3-6). lib. bdg. 9.50 (978-0-613-90063-8(4)) Tandem Library Bks.

'Twas the Night Before Testing. l.t. ed. 2001. 44p. (J). pap. 12.00 (978-0-9705117-0-6(1)) FUNdamentals in Education.

Tytler, Sarah. Girlhood & Womanhood the Story of Some. 2007. 43.99 (***978-1-4280-5160-7(0)***); pap. 36.99 (***978-1-4280-5161-4(9))*** IndyPublish.com.

Udry, Janice May. Thump & Plunk. Hayes, Geoffrey, illus. 2000. (My First I Can Read Bks.). 32p. (J). (ps up). 12.95 (978-0-06-028528-9(1)) HarperCollins Pubs.

Ueyama, Michiro. Chaotic Century. Ueyama, Michiro, illus. (Zoids Ser.). (Illus.). (YA). Vol. 11. 2004. 82p. pap. 5.95 (978-1-56931-858-4(1)); Vol. 12. 2003. 72p. pap. 5.95 (978-1-56931-867-6(0)) Viz Media.

Ugon, Gabriela Armand. El Secreto de la Casa Gris. (SPA.). (J). 8.95 (978-958-04-7349-7(8)) Norma S.A. COL. *Dist:* Distribuidora Norma, Inc.

Ullrich, Hortense. La Aventura de Lorenzo. (SPA.). (J). 7.95 (978-958-04-7447-0(8)) Norma S.A. COL. *Dist:* Distribuidora Norma, Inc.

Umansky, Kaye. Pongwiffy & the Goblin's Revenge. Smedley, Chris, illus. 2002. 160p. (J). pap. 4.50 (978-0-7434-1913-0(8) , Aladdin) Simon & Schuster Children's Publishing.

—Prince Dandypants & the Masked Avenger. Dunton, Trevor, illus. l.t. ed. 2002. 224p. (J). 16.95 (978-0-7540-7825-8(6) , Galaxy Children's Large Print) BBC Audiobooks America.

Umhau, Jan Fleet. The Adventures of Henry Fleete: Potomac Captive. 1999. (Illus.). 162p. (J). pap. 17.95 (978-0-87517-108-1(7)) Dietz Pr.

Uncle Markie. Piglletté & Bobo Christmas in Palm Springs. 2003. (YA). ring bd. 9.95 (978-1-933129-10-5(7)) Studio 403.

—Piglletté & Bobo in Estonia. 2003. (YA). ring bd. 9.95 (978-1-933129-13-6(1)) Studio 403.

—Piglletté & Bobo in Kansas City. 2003. (YA). ring bd. 9.95 (978-1-933129-08-2(5)) Studio 403.

—Piglletté & Bobo in Sud Africa. 2003. (YA). ring bd. 9.95 (978-1-933129-15-0(8)) Studio 403.

—Piglletté & Bobo in the New Territories. 2003. (YA). ring bd. 9.95 (978-1-933129-06-8(9)) Studio 403.

—Piglletté & Bobo in the United Kingdom. 2003. (YA). ring bd. 9.95 (978-1-933129-14-3(X)) Studio 403.

—Piglletté & Bobo on Safari. 2003. (YA). ring bd. 9.95 (978-1-933129-16-7(6)) Studio 403.

Under the Blood-Red Sun. 1999. (J). 9.95 (978-1-56137-904-0(2)) Novel Units, Inc.

Under the Lilacs. 2005. (J). 19.95 (978-1-59808-649-2(9)); spiral bd. 19.95 (978-1-59808-648-5(0)); cd-rom 13.95 (978-1-59808-650-8(2)) Whispering Pine Pr., Inc.

Unknown. Corduroy's Alphabet Hunt. 2008. 12p. (J). (ps-1). 9.99 (***978-0-448-44882-4(3)*** , Grosset & Dunlap) Penguin Group (USA) Inc.

Unknown 02. Franny's Frantabulous Shoes. 2008. 12p. (J). (ps-k). bds. 5.99 (***978-0-448-44838-1(6)*** , Grosset & Dunlap) Penguin Group (USA) Inc.

Updale, Eleanor. Montmorency & the Assassins, Bk. 3. 2007. (Montmorency & the Assassins Ser.). 416p. (J). pap. 6.99 (***978-0-439-68344-9(0))*** Scholastic, Inc.

Upton, Joe. Runaways on the Inside Passage. 2005. (Illus.). 304p. (gr. 5 up). 17.95 (978-0-88240-564-3(0)); pap. 9.95 (978-0-88240-565-0(9)) Graphic Arts Ctr. Publishing Co.

Urbach, Jourdan. Leaving Jeremiah. 2003. (Illus.). 108p. (J). 19.95 (978-1-930648-57-9(X) , 207-832-6665); per. 10.95 (978-1-930648-50-0(2) , 207-832-6665) Goose River Pr.

Urberuaga, Emilio. Pluma y Tapon. (Mi Primera Sopa de Libros Coleccion). (SPA., Illus.). 24p. (J). (ps). (978-84-207-9244-6(6) , GS6867) Grupo Anaya, S.A. ESP. *Dist:* Lectorum Pubns., Inc.

Ursu, Anne. The Siren Song. Fortune, Eric, illus. 2007. (Cronus Chronicles Ser.). 448p. (J). (gr. 3-7). 16.99 (978-1-4169-0589-9(8)) Simon & Schuster Children's Publishing.

Uwuigiaren, Omoruyi. The Adventures of Nihu. Ayalomeh, Shedrach, illus. 2007. (YA). per. 16.95 (***978-1-934138-15-1(0))*** Bouncing Ball Bks., Inc.

Vachon, Mary Beth. Mac s Mackinac Island Adventure. Rusky, Ann G., illus. 2005. 216p. (J). pap. 17.95 (978-0-9766104-1-0(8)) Arbutus Pr.

Vail, Rachel. The Sort-Of-Super Snowman. Bjorkman, Steve, illus. 2002. 32p. (J). (978-0-439-38472-8(9)) Scholastic, Inc.

Valdes, Leslie. At the Carnival. Roper, Robert, illus. 2005. 24p. (J). lib. bdg. 9.00 (***978-1-4242-0982-8(X))*** Fitzgerald Bks.

—Dora's Pirate Adventure. 2006. (Illus.). (J). (ps-2). 21.35 (978-1-59961-072-6(8)) Spotlight.

—Meet Diego! Hall, Susan T., illus. 2003. (Dora the Explorer Ser.). 24p. (J). pap. 3.50 (978-0-689-85993-9(7) , Simon Spotlight/Nickelodeon) Simon & Schuster Children's Publishing.

—Meet Diego! 2003. (ps-2). lib. bdg. 11.25 (978-0-613-73344-1(4)) Tandem Library Bks.

Valdez, Ricardo, illus. The Journey: Skillcastle Vol. 1: The Adventures of Matthew McCloud. 2000. 280p. (J). (ps-4). pap. 19.95 (978-0-9700939-1-2(8)) Parent 2 Child Bks.

Valentine, James. Don't Touch Anything. Koopman, Caia, illus. 2004. (Jump-Man Ser.: No. 1). 272p. (J). 14.95 (978-0-689-86872-6(3)) Simon & Schuster Children's Publishing.

Valeska, John & Fripp, Jean. The Secret of the Sand. Fripp, Jean, ed. Moussa, Karen M., illus. 2003. (Dolphin Watch Ser.). 32p. (J). (gr. k-5). pap. 5.99 (978-0-9701008-2-5(5)) Bicast, Inc.

Van Allsburg, Chris. Jumanji. Van Allsburg, Chris, illus. 2002. (Illus.). (J). 25.28 (978-0-7587-6813-1(3)) Book Wholesalers, Inc.

—The Polar Express. Van Allsburg, Chris, illus. 1999. pap., tchr. ed. 9.95 (978-1-56137-196-9(3)) Novel Units, Inc.

Van Allsburg, Chris & Houghton Mifflin Company Staff. Zathura: The Movie Deluxe Storybook. deluxe ed. 2005. (Illus.). 48p. (J). (gr. k-3). 9.99 (978-0-618-60578-1(9)) Houghton Mifflin Co. Trade & Reference Div.

Van Draanen, Wendelin. Attack of the Tagger. 2004. (Shredderman Ser.: Bk. 2). (Illus.). 176p. (J). (gr. 2-5). lib. bdg. 14.99 (978-0-375-92352-4(7) , Knopf Bks. for Young Readers) Random Hse. Children's Bks.

—Attack of the Tagger. Biggs, Brian, illus. 2004. (Shredderman Ser.: Bk. 2). 176p. (J). (gr. 2-5). 12.95 (978-0-375-82352-7(2) , Knopf Bks. for Young Readers) Random Hse. Children's Bks.

—Enemy Spy. 2005. (Shredderman Ser.: Bk. 4). (Illus.). 192p. (J). (gr. 2-5). 12.95 (978-0-375-82354-1(9)); lib. bdg. 14.99 (978-0-375-92354-8(3)) Random Hse. Children's Bks. (Knopf Bks. for Young Readers).

—Meet the Gecko. Biggs, Brian, illus. 2005. (Shredderman Ser.: Bk. 3). 176p. (J). (gr. 2-5). 12.95 (978-0-375-82353-4(0)); lib. bdg. 14.99 (978-0-375-92353-1(5)) Random Hse. Children's Bks. (Knopf Bks. for Young Readers).

—Sammy Keyes & the Runaway Elf. unabr. ed. 2001. (Sammy Keyes Ser.: Bk. 4). (Illus.). (J). (gr. 4-7). 38.95 incl. audio (978-0-87499-736-1(4)); 186p. pap. 30.95 incl. audio (978-0-87499-735-4(6)) Live Oak Media.

—Sammy Keyes & the Sisters of Mercy. unabr. ed. 2001. (Sammy Keyes Ser.: Bk. 3). (Illus.). 44.95 incl. audio (978-0-87499-729-3(1)); (J). pap. 36.95 incl. audio (978-0-87499-728-6(3)); Set. pap. 49.95 incl. audio (978-0-87499-730-9(5)) Live Oak Media.

—Sammy Keyes & the Sisters of Mercy. 1999. (Sammy Keyes Ser.: Bk. 3). (J). (gr. 4-7). (978-0-606-19439-6(8)) Tandem Library Bks.

—Swear to Howdy. 144p. (J). (gr. 5). 2003. (Illus.). 15.95 (978-0-375-82505-7(3) , Knopf Bks. for Young Readers); 2003. (Illus.). lib. bdg. 17.99 (978-0-375-92505-4(8) , Knopf Bks. for Young Readers); 2005. reprint ed. pap. 5.99 (978-0-440-41943-3(3) , Yearling) Random Hse. Children's Bks.

—Swear to Howdy. l.t. ed. 2004. 145p. (J). (gr. 4-6). 23.95 (978-0-7862-6141-3(2)) Thorndike Pr.

Van Genechten, Guido. Floppy. 2004. (CHI & ENG., Illus.). (J). (978-1-85269-550-7(1)) Mantra Publishing, Ltd.

Van Hauten, Jacques. Llega el Zorro. 2003. (SPA., Illus.). 144p. (J). (gr. 5-8). 9.95 (978-84-372-2192-2(7) , SAN1927) Altea, Ediciones, S.A. - Grupo Santillana ESP. *Dist:* Santillana USA Publishing Co., Inc.

Van Patten, Barbara. Whoo Saves the Symphony. 2007. (J). per. 9.99 (***978-1-60247-150-4(9))*** Tate Publishing & Enterprises, L.L.C.

Van Steenhoven, Tom. Moon Adventure. 1999. (Billy Bks.). (Illus.). (J). 15.99 (978-0-9672652-0-9(7)) Nation of Imagi, LLC, The.

Van Straaten, Harmen. Tough guy Tim. 2008. 24p. 12.95 (***978-1-60136-002-1(9))*** Mars Media Pubs.

Vance, Kristina. Shipwreck. 1998. (gr. 7-12). lib. bdg. 18.80 (978-0-613-84721-6(0)) Tandem Library Bks.

Vandercook, Margaret. Camp Fire Girls at Sunrise Hill, the (Fi. 2006. pap. 55.99 (***978-1-4219-9140-5(3))*** IndyPublish.com.

Vanderdoes, Amanda & Ratcliffe, T. J., Jr. The Adventures of Makui. Vanderdoes, Amanda & Ratcliffe, T. J., Jr., illus. l.t. ed. 1999. (Illus.). 40p. (J). (gr. k-5). pap. 5.95 (978-1-928632-16-0(5)) Writers Marketplace:Consulting, Critiquing & Publishing.

Vandersteen, Willy. The Circle of Power. Geerts, Paul, illus. 1998. (Greatest Adventures of Spike & Suzy Ser.: Vol. 2). 56p. (J). (gr. 2-9). 11.95 (978-0-9533178-1-3(1)) Intes International (UK) Ltd. GBR. *Dist:* Diamond Comic Distributors, Inc.

—Sagarmatha. Geerts, Paul, illus. 1998. (Greatest Adventures of Spike & Suzy Ser.: Vol. 1). 56p. (J). (gr. 2-9). 11.95 (978-0-9533178-0-6(3)) Intes International (UK) Ltd. GBR. *Dist:* Diamond Comic Distributors, Inc.

—The Secret of the Incas. Geerts, Paul, illus. 1998. (Greatest Adventures of Spike & Suzy Ser.: Vol. 3). 56p. (J). (gr. 2-9). 11.95 (978-0-9533178-2-0(X)) Intes International (UK) Ltd. GBR. *Dist:* Diamond Comic Distributors, Inc.

Vanier, Jolie. Puwaii Adventures with Joliea & Friends. 2006. 16.95 (***978-0-9787949-1-0(5))*** Puwaii International, LLC.

VanRiper, Justin & VanRiper, Gary. The Adirondack Kids. 2001. (Adirondack Kids Ser.). (Illus.). 86p. (J). (ps-3). pap. 8.95 (978-0-9707044-0-5(2) , ADK1) Adirondack Kids Pr.

—The Lost Lighthouse. Gary, Glenn, illus. 2003. (Adirondack Kids Ser. : Vol. 3). 82p. pap. 8.95 (978-0-9707044-2-9(9) , ADK3) Adirondack Kids Pr.

Vargas, Jay. Cantalina: The Author's Edition. Muniz, Jim, illus. 2001. 48p. (YA). (gr. 4 up). pap. 6.95 (978-0-9674768-1-0(X)) Creative Endeavors Publishing.

Varios. Mi Primera Biblioteca Coleccion, 12 vols., Set. (SPA.). 288p. (J). (gr. k-3). (978-84-392-8300-3(8) , EV31247) Gaviota Ediciones ESP. *Dist:* Lectorum Pubns., Inc.

Varsell, Linda. A Journey for Rainbows. Curtis, E., illus. 2003. 166p. (YA). per. 6.00 (978-0-9725479-1-8(6)) Rainbow Communications.

Vasey, Tony. The Adventures of Lily Lifeboat. Baines, Jacqueline, illus. 1999. 12p. (J). (ps-1). pap. 21.00 (978-1-85072-187-1(4)) Sessions, William Ltd. GBR. *Dist:* State Mutual Bk. & Periodical Service, Ltd.

Vaughn, Deborah. Sneaky Secret Steff & Her Problem Solving Adventure. 2004. (J). per. 7.95 (978-1-932560-25-1(4)) Media Creations, Inc.

Vazov, George D. The Other Side of the Mushroom. 2006. 12.00 (978-0-8059-9018-8(6)) Dorrance Publishing Co., Inc.

Vazquez, Diana. Lost in Sierra. Jaramillo, German, illus. 2005. (In the Same Boat Ser.: No. 2). 184p. (J). (gr. 4-6). pap. 7.95 (978-1-55050-184-1(4)) Coteau Bks. CAN. *Dist:* Fitzhenry & Whiteside, Ltd.

Vedder, G. M. Kaylee Shares Her Sadness. Vedder, G. M., illus. 1999. (Adventures in Learning with Miss Lucy & the Village Children Ser.: Vol. I). (Illus.). 75p. (J). (gr. k-6). spiral bd. 12.95 (978-0-9679091-0-3(4)) A Miracle Cub.

Vega, Diego. Young Zorro: The Iron Brand. 2006. (Illus.). 240p. (YA). 15.99 (978-0-06-083945-1(7)); lib. bdg. 16.89 (978-0-06-083946-8(5)) HarperCollins Pubs. (Rayo).

Vega, Diego & Adkins, Jan. Young Zorro (Spanish Edition) El joven Zorro: la marca de Hierro. 2007. (SPA.). 256p. (J). pap. 6.99 (***978-0-06-115378-5(8)*** , Rayo) HarperCollins Pubs.

Velasco. La Medalla de Ambar. 1999. Tr. of Amber Medallion. (978-0-606-17687-3(X)) Tandem Library Bks.

Velasco, Francisco Ruiz. Battle Gods: Warriors of the Chaak. 2001. (Illus.). 240p. (YA). pap. 19.95 (978-1-56971-562-8(9)) Dark Horse Comics.

Velez, Walter, illus. Little Red Riding Hood: A Tale about Staying Safe. 2006. (J). 6.99 (978-1-59939-021-5(3) , Reader's Digest Young Families, Inc.) Reader's Digest Children's Publishing, Inc.

Vendrell, Maria Martinez & Capdevila, Roser. La Noche. 2003. Tr. of Night. (SPA.). 24p. (J). 7.95 (978-84-233-1455-3(3)) Ediciones Destino ESP. *Dist:* Planeta Publishing Corp.

Veneziano, Chuckie. My Time on Nantucket. 2005. (Illus.). 56p. (J). lib. bdg. 17.95 (978-0-9755078-0-3(X)) Sweet Punkin Pr.

Venn, Cecilia. Puppy Parade, Level 2. 1998. (Disney's First Readers Ser.). (Illus.). 32p. (J). (gr. 1-3). pap. 2.95 (978-0-7868-4170-7(2)) Disney Pr.

Verne, Jules. Around the World in 80 Days. l.t. ed. 1999. (Large Print Heritage Ser.). 325p. (gr. 7-12). lib. bdg. 32.95 (978-1-58118-040-4(3) , 22509) LRS.

—Around the World in 80 Days Great Read. 2004. (Great Classics for Children Ser.). 224p. (J). 5.99 (978-1-4037-0981-3(5)) Dalmatian Pr.

—Around the World in Eighty Days. 2002. (Great Illustrated Classics Ser.). (Illus.). 240p. (J). (gr. 3-8). 21.35 (978-1-57765-680-7(6) , ABDO & Daughters) ABDO Publishing Co.

—Around the World in Eighty Days. 2004. (Young Reading Series Two Ser.). 64p. (J). (gr. 2 up). pap. 5.95 (978-0-7945-0741-1(7) , Usborne) EDC Publishing.

—Around the World in Eighty Days. unabr. ed. 1998. (Wordsworth Classics Ser.). (YA). (gr. 6-12). 5.27 (978-0-89061-090-9(8) , R0908WW) Jamestown.

—Un Capitan de Quince Anos.Tr. of Fifteen Year Old Captain. (SPA., Illus.). (YA). 14.95 (978-84-7281-049-5(6) , AF1049) Auriga, Ediciones S.A. ESP. *Dist:* Continental Bk. Co., Inc.

—Classic Starts: Around the World in 80 Days. Akib, Jamel, illus. 2007. (Classic Starts Ser.). 160p. (J). 4.95 (978-1-4027-3689-6(4)) Sterling Publishing Co., Inc.

—Dick Sands: The Boy Captain. ELLEN E. FREWER, tr. 2006. 298p. pap. 13.99 (978-1-4264-3403-7(0)) BiblioBazaar.

—Dick Sands: The Boy Captain. Frewer, Ellen E., tr. l.t. ed. 2006. 328p. pap. 18.99 (978-1-4264-3453-2(7)) BiblioBazaar.

—The Field of Ice: Part II of the Adventures of Captain Hatteras. 2006. 154p. pap. 11.99 (***978-1-4264-3591-1(6)***); 168p. pap. 12.99 (***978-1-4264-3642-0(4))*** BiblioBazaar.

—Los Hijos del Capitan Grant. 2002. (Classics for Young Readers Ser.). (SPA.). (YA). 14.95 (978-84-392-0918-8(5) , EV30596) Lectorum Pubns., Inc.

—Los Hijos del Capitan Grant. (Coleccion Clasicos de la Juventud). (SPA., Illus.). 324p. (J). 12.95 (978-84-7189-098-6(4) , ORT314) Ortells, Alfredo Editorial S.L. ESP. *Dist:* Continental Bk. Co., Inc.

—La Isla Misteriosa. (SPA., Illus.). 192p. (YA). 11.95 (978-84-7281-105-8(0) , AF1105) Auriga, Ediciones S.A. ESP. *Dist:* Continental Bk. Co., Inc.

—Journey to the Center of the Earth. Calaguian, Val, illus. 2nd ed. 1998. (Illustrated Classic Book Ser.). 61p. (J). (gr. 3 up). reprint ed. pap. 4.95 (978-1-56767-259-6(0)) Educational Insights, Inc.

—Miguel Strogoff. (SPA., Illus.). 176p. (YA). 11.95 (978-84-7281-109-6(3) , AF1109) Auriga, Ediciones S.A. ESP. *Dist:* Continental Bk. Co., Inc.

—Miguel Strogoff. 2002. (SPA.). 14.95 (978-84-392-0915-7(0) , EV30597); 2001. (978-84-305-2204-0(2)) Lectorum Pubns., Inc.

—Miguel Strogoff. (Coleccion Clasicos de la Juventud). (SPA., Illus.). 236p. (J). 12.95 (978-84-7189-106-8(9) , ORT305) Ortells, Alfredo Editorial S.L. ESP. *Dist:* Continental Bk. Co., Inc.

—Viaje al Centro de la Tierra. Orig. Title: Journey to the Center of the Earth. (SPA., Illus.). 160p. (YA). 11.95 (978-84-7281-084-6(4) , AF1084) Auriga, Ediciones S.A. ESP. *Dist:* Continental Bk. Co., Inc.

—Viaje al Centro de la Tierra. 1999. (Coleccion "Clasicos Juveniles" Ser.). Orig. Title: Journey to the Center of the Earth. (SPA & ENG.). 192p. (gr. 4-7). pap. 10.95 (978-1-58348-780-8(8)) iUniverse, Inc.

—Viaje Al Centro de la Tierra. 2004. (Illus.). 48p. (J). (ps-ps). lib. bdg. 12.75 (978-0-606-30424-5(X)) Tandem Library Bks.

—20,000 Leagues under the Sea. Marcos, Pablo, illus. 2002. (Great Illustrated Classics Ser.). 240p. (J). (gr. 3-8). 21.35 (978-1-57765-806-1(X) , ABDO & Daughters) ABDO Publishing Co.

—20,000 Leagues under the Sea. Gambog, Romie, illus. 2nd ed. 1998. (Illustrated Classic Book Ser.). 61p. (J). (gr. 3 up). reprint ed. pap. 4.95 (978-1-56767-243-5(4)) Educational Insights, Inc.

—20,000 Leagues under the Sea. 2000. (J). lib. bdg. 15.89 (978-0-06-029204-1(0)) HarperCollins Pubs.

—20,000 Leagues under the Sea. (Illus.). (J). 9.95 (978-1-56156-307-4(2)) Kidsbooks, Inc.

—20,000 Leagues under the Sea. 2003. (Scholastic Classics Ser.). 448p. (J). pap. 4.99 (978-0-439-22715-5(1) , Scholastic Paperbacks) Scholastic, Inc.

—20,000 Leguas de Viaje Submarino. 2002. (Classics for Young Readers Ser.). (SPA.). (YA). 14.95 (978-84-392-0910-2(X) , EV30604) Gaviota Ediciones ESP. *Dist:* Lectorum Pubns., Inc.

—20,000 Leguas de Viaje Submarino. (Coleccion Clasicos de la Juventud). (SPA., Illus.). 232p. (J). 12.95 (978-84-7189-019-1(4) , ORT309) Ortells, Alfredo Editorial S.L. ESP. *Dist:* Continental Bk. Co., Inc.

—20,000 Leguas de Viaje Submarino. 1999. (SPA.). (gr. 3-6). lib. bdg. 24.55 (978-0-613-85424-5(1)) Tandem Library Bks.

Vescio & LohnRiver, Jenna. Rainbow Journey Screen Play (with Pictures) 2005. 65p. pap. 20.00 (978-1-4116-3288-2(5)) Lulu.com.

Viagem de Babar. pap. 19.95 (978-85-85466-78-7(2)) Companhia das Letras BRA. *Dist:* Distribooks, Inc.

Vicary, Tim. White Death, Level 1. 2000. (Bookworms Ser.). (Illus.). 64p. 6.50 (978-0-19-422956-2(4)) Oxford Univ. Pr., Inc.

Vick, Helen Hughes. Walker's Journey Home. 1998. (Illus.). 192p. (gr. 7 up). pap. 9.95 (978-1-57140-001-7(X)) Rinehart, Roberts Pubs.

Victor, Ralph. Boy Scouts Patrol. 2006. 62.99 ***(978-1-4280-2470-0(0))*** IndyPublish.com.

Vili, Fane. Mano: The Awakening. Frakes, Clint, ed. 2006. (YA). per. 19.95 (978-0-9774074-0-8(3)) Plankton Pr.

Villar Liebana, Luisa. El Ladron Sin Huellas. 2005. (Investigator Big Ears Ser.). (SPA., Illus.). 78p. (J). (gr. 2-3). 8.95 (978-84-348-9434-1(3)) SM Ediciones ESP. *Dist:* Iaconi, Mariuccia Bk. Imports.

Vincent, Annie. Adventures at Honeybee Hive: Trouble in the New Forest. 2004. 69p. pap. 14.95 (978-1-4137-4676-1(4)) PublishAmerica, Inc.

Vines, Connie. Un Murmullo Sobre el Agua. Perez, Laura C., tr. 2005. (SPA & ENG.). 144p. (YA). per. 9.95 (978-0-7599-3932-5(2)) Hard Shell Word Factory.

Vinette, Arnold D. Reid's Adventures - 1st Year Breaking in Your New Parents. Vinette, Dorothy V., ed. 2004. (J). 576p. 35.99 (978-1-4149-0002-5(3)); 592p. pap. 24.50 (978-1-4149-0004-9(X)) Time Capsule eBooks, Inc. (Time Capsule Bks.).

Vischer, Lisa. Three Pirates & You! 2004. (Illus.). 32p. 7.99 (978-0-310-70724-0(2)) Zonderkidz.

Voelkel, J&P. Middleworld. 2007. (Jaguar Stones Trilogy Ser.: Bk. 1). (Illus.). 400p. (J). (gr. 6-9). 17.95 ***(978-1-57525-561-3(8))*** Smith and Kraus Publishers, Incorporated.

Voigt, Cynthia. Elske: A Novel of the Kingdom. Vermeer, Jan, illus. 2003. (Kingdom Ser.). 320p. (YA). mass mkt. 5.99 (978-0-689-86438-4(8) , Simon Pulse) Simon & Schuster Children's Publishing.

—Elske: A Novel of the Kingdom. (Kingdom Ser.). (gr. 7-12). 2003. lib. bdg. 14.15 (978-0-613-73442-4(4)); 2001. lib. bdg. 18.80 (978-0-613-73327-4(4)) Tandem Library Bks.

—On Fortune's Wheel. 1999. (Kingdom Ser.). (Illus.). 304p. (YA). (gr. 7-12). pap. 6.99 (978-0-689-82957-4(4) , Simon Pulse) Simon & Schuster Children's Publishing.

—On Fortune's Wheel. 1999. (Kingdom Ser.). (978-0-606-17193-9(2)); (gr. 7-12). lib. bdg. 13.55 (978-0-613-22911-1(8)) Tandem Library Bks.

Volo, creator. Crushes. 2005. (Illus.). 96p. (gr. 3-7). pap. 4.99 (978-0-7868-5282-6(8) , Volo) Hyperion Bks. for Children.

von Bissing, Ronimund. La Tierra del Oro Ardiente. (SPA.). 184p. (YA). (gr. 5-8). (978-84-216-1045-9(7) , BU4764) Bruño, Editorial ESP. *Dist:* Lectorum Pubns., Inc.

Von Burg, Frederick E. Keep My White Sneakers, Kit Carson: An Adventure with the Blackfeet. 2002. 160p. pap. 12.95 (978-0-595-24264-1(2) , Writers Club Pr.) iUniverse, Inc.

von Zennenfels, Skye. Crystal's Adventure: Includes Toy. Aranda, Shane & Cluff, Jon, illus. 2000. (Pixie Tales of the Mystical Forest Ser.). v, 23p. (J). (ps-6). pap. 14.99 (978-0-9678580-3-6(8) , MY9001, IPI Toys) Interstellar Productions, Inc.

Vornholt, John. Dolphin Watch. 2002. (gr. 5-8). lib. bdg. 11.80 (978-0-613-70888-3(1)) Tandem Library Bks.

—Joyride. 1999. (gr. 3-6). lib. bdg. 11.80 (978-0-613-21826-9(4)) Tandem Library Bks.

Vornholt, John & MacHale, D. J. The Return, No. 3. 2006. (Flight 29 Down Ser.: Vol. 3). 224p. (J). (gr. 4-7). pap. 5.99 (978-0-448-44129-0(2) , Grosset & Dunlap) Penguin Group (USA) Inc.

—The Seven, No. 2. 2006. (Flight 29 Down Ser.: Vol. 2). 224p. (J). (gr. 4-7). pap. 5.99 (978-0-448-44107-8(1) , Grosset & Dunlap) Penguin Group (USA) Inc.

Vornholt, John & Rayyan, Omar. The Troll Treasure. 2003. (Illus.). 160p. (J). pap. 4.99 (978-0-689-85834-5(5) , Aladdin) Simon & Schuster Children's Publishing.

Vv. Las Cosas de la Cocina. (SPA.). 24p. 7.95 (978-84-488-1107-5(0)) Beascoa, Ediciones S.A. ESP. *Dist:* Distribooks, Inc.

—Cuentos de Elfos y Gnomos. 2nd ed. 2004. (SPA., Illus.). 128p. (978-84-9777-013-2(7)) Obelisco, Ediciones S.A.

—Guia Del Entrenador Pokemon. (SPA.). 102p. 9.95 (978-84-488-1003-0(1)) Beascoa, Ediciones S.A. ESP. *Dist:* Distribooks, Inc.

—La Prueba Continua. (SPA.). 62p. 4.95 (978-84-488-1002-3(3)) Beascoa, Ediciones S.A. ESP. *Dist:* Distribooks, Inc.

—El Viaje de Ash. (SPA.). 62p. 4.95 (978-84-488-1001-6(5)) Beascoa, Ediciones S.A. ESP. *Dist:* Distribooks, Inc.

Wach, Martin & Wach, Delia. The Great West Virginia Snow Adventure. Wach, Delia, illus. 2006. (Illus.). 32p. (J). 16.95 (978-0-929915-42-5(9)) Headline Bks., Inc.

Wacker, Mary Langley. Landmarks. 2002. 211p. (gr. 8-12). pap. 19.95 (978-1-59129-374-3(X)) PublishAmerica, Inc.

Wackwitz, Winnie. The Creature of Lost Bayou. 2004. (YA). pap. 12.95 (978-1-58752-107-2(5)) Timberwolf Pr., Inc.

Waddell, Martin. Tough Ronald. Mould, Chris, illus. 2006. (Read-It! Chapter Books). 64p. (J). lib. bdg. ***(978-1-4048-3127-8(4)*** , 1265816) Picture Window Bks.

Waechter, Philip. Rosie & the Nightmares. 2005. (Illus.). 32p. (J). (ps-2). 16.50 (978-1-59354-130-9(9)) Handprint Bks.

Wafer, C. K. & Wafer, C. K. The Adventures of Brady Bean: Operation: Georgie Porgie. Myers, Alishea, illus. 2007. (J). pap. 5.95 ***(978-0-9797580-0-3(9))*** CK Bks.

Wagner, Jerri. The Adventures of "Jako", the Florida Troll. 1999. 53p. (J). pap. 9.95 (978-0-7414-0111-3(8)) Infinity Publishing.

—Jako's Vacation. 2001. 58p. pap. 9.95 (978-0-7414-0704-7(3)) Infinity Publishing.

Wagner, John. Predator vs. Judge Dredd. 1998. (Predator Ser.). (Illus.). 80p. (YA). (gr. 9 up). pap. 9.95 (978-1-56971-345-7(6)) Dark Horse Comics.

Wagoner, Timothy Allen. The Adventures of Jacque & Wanderwan Bk. 1: Naoo. 2005. (J). pap. (978-0-9761739-2-2(1)) Grandoc Publishing.

Waid, Mark. Imaginauts. Wieringo, Mike, illus. 2003. (Fantastic Four Ser.: Vol. 1). 144p. (YA). pap. 12.99 (978-0-7851-1063-7(1)) Marvel Enterprises, Inc.

—Supreme Justice. 2001. lib. bdg. 28.00 (978-0-613-92134-3(8)) Tandem Library Bks.

Walker, Brian, illus. Adventure Stories. 2004. (Red Hot Reads Ser.). 256p. (J). (gr. 5-9). pap. 6.95 (978-0-7534-5718-4(0) , Kingfisher) Houghton Mifflin Co. Trade & Reference Div.

Walker, Craig, ed. Fantastic Tales for Boys. 2006. 736p. (J). pap. 5.99 (978-0-439-85862-5(3) , Scholastic) Scholastic, Inc.

—Tales of Suspense for Boys. 2006. 448p. (J). pap. 5.99 (978-0-439-85860-1(7) , Scholastic) Scholastic, Inc.

Walker, E. G. & Wilham, Nancy J. Mario & the Road Runner. 2002. (Illus.). 50p. (J). (gr. k-7). pap. 6.95 (978-0-9716071-4-9(1)) Walker, Esther.

Walker, Nicole. Gingersnap. 2005. (YA). per. 15.99 (978-0-9677379-2-8(3)) North Gap Publishing.

Walker, Pamela. Veil of Secrets #3. 2006. (Illus.). 224p. (J). (gr. 7). pap. 6.99 (978-0-448-44141-2(1) , Grosset & Dunlap) Penguin Group (USA) Inc.

Walker, Peter. The Magic Airplane. 2006. (ENG.). 160p. per. 12.95 ***(978-1-59526-416-9(7))*** Media Creations, Inc.

Walker, Peter Lancaster. Space Travelers Land at Buckingham Palace. Dixit, Rama, illus. 2007. (YA). per. 19.95 ***(978-1-934138-12-0(6))*** Bouncing Ball Bks., Inc.

Walker, Robert W. Daniel Webster Jackson & the Wrong Way Railroad. 2000. (YA). (gr. 6-9). pap. 9.99 (978-0-88092-554-9(X) , 554X) Royal Fireworks Publishing Co.

—Gideon Tell & the Siege of Vicksburg. 2000. 190p. (YA). (gr. 8 up). 9.99 (978-0-88092-555-6(8)) Royal Fireworks Publishing Co.

Walker, Russell D. Michelle & the Magic Timepiece. 2006. 108p. pap. 16.95 (978-1-4241-3143-3(X)) PublishAmerica, Inc.

Wall, Cynthia. A Spark to the Past. 1998. 184p. (J). (gr. 5-8). pap. 6.95 (978-0-931625-34-3(3)) DIMI Pr.

Wallace, Barbara Brooks. The Interesting Thing That Happened at Perfect Acres, Inc. 2007. 148p. per. 11.95 ***(978-0-595-45763-2(0)*** , Backinprint.com) iUniverse, Inc.

Wallace, Barbara Brooks. Palmer Patch. 2000. (Illus.). 132p. (J). (gr. 4-7). pap. 9.95 (978-0-595-09573-5(9) , Backinprint.com) iUniverse, Inc.

Wallace, Bill. Coyote Autumn. 2000. (Illus.). 208p. (J). (gr. 4-6). tchr. ed. 16.95 (978-0-8234-1628-8(3)) Holiday Hse., Inc.

—The Legend of Thunderfoot. 2006. 160p. (J). 15.95 (978-1-4169-0691-9(6)) Simon & Schuster Children's Publishing.

—Trapped in Death Cave. 2002. 176p. (J). pap. 5.99 (978-0-689-85341-8(6) , Aladdin) Simon & Schuster Children's Publishing.

—Trapped in Death Cave. 2002. (gr. 3-6). lib. bdg. 13.00 (978-0-613-87051-1(4)) Tandem Library Bks.

Wallace, Bill & Wallace, Carol. Bub, Snow, & the Burly Bear Scare. Gurney, John Steven, illus. 2003. 128p. (J). pap. 4.99 (978-0-7434-0640-6(0) , Aladdin) Simon & Schuster Children's Publishing.

Wallace, Carol & Wallace, Bill. The Flying Flea, Callie & Me. 1999. (Gray Cat Ser.: Vol. 1). 96p. (J). (gr. 3-6). pap. 4.99 (978-0-671-03968-4(7) , Aladdin) Simon & Schuster Children's Publishing.

—The Flying Flea, Callie & Me. 1999. (Illus.). (J). 11.79 (978-0-606-18368-0(X)) Tandem Library Bks.

Wallace, Ivy. Pookie. (Illus.). 32p. 2002. pap. 9.99 (978-0-00-664731-7(6)); 2001. (J). 19.99 (978-0-00-198377-9(6)) HarperCollins Pubs. Ltd. GBR. *Dist:* Trafalgar Square Publishing.

Wallace, James. Tsunami: Ghost Eagle 1. 2003. 149p. (YA). pap. 11.95 (978-0-595-27372-0(6)) iUniverse, Inc.

Wallace, Jim. Terror on the Titanic. 2007. (Choose Your Own Adventure Ser.: No. 24). (Illus.). 144p. (J). (gr. 3-7). pap. 6.99 ***(978-1-933390-24-6(7))*** Chooseco LLC.

Wallace, John. Pirate Boy. (Illus.). 32p. (J). 2003. pap. 9.99 (978-0-00-664776-8(6)); 2002. 19.99 (978-0-00-198421-9(7)) HarperCollins Pubs. Ltd. GBR. *Dist:* Independent Pubs. Group, Trafalgar Square Publishing.

Wallace, Karen. Freaky Families - Uncle Douglas & Au. 1999. (Illus.). 64p. (J). 7.95 (978-0-14-038757-5(9)) Penguin Bks., Ltd. GBR. *Dist:* Trafalgar Square Publishing.

—Freaky Families- Cousin Cedric Goes. (Illus.). 64p. (J). 7.95 (978-0-14-038500-7(2)) Penguin Bks., Ltd. GBR. *Dist:* Trafalgar Square Publishing.

Wallace, Karen. The Secret of the Crocodiles. 2007. (Lady Violet's Casebook Ser.). 208p. (J). (gr. 4-7). pap. 9.95 ***(978-0-689-87483-3(9))*** Simon & Schuster, Ltd. GBR. *Dist:* Independent Pubs. Group.

Wallace, Sheila Ryan. Miss Abigail's Antique Treasures. 2007. 133p. pap. 15.95 ***(978-0-7414-3942-0(5))*** Infinity Publishing.

Waller, J. Sludge Culpers. 2000. 272p. (J). (gr. 4-7). mass mkt. (978-0-330-34428-9(5) , Macmillan Children's Bks.) Pan Macmillan.

Walls, Pamela June. Sp Abby Lost at Sea. 2003. (Abby Ser.). pap. 6.99 (978-0-7899-0967-1(7)) Editorial Unilit.

—Sp Abby Secret at Cutter Grove. 2003. (Abby Ser.). pap. 6.99 (978-0-7899-0970-1(7)) Editorial Unilit.

—Trouble in Tahiti. 2002. (gr. 3-6). lib. bdg. 14.15 (978-0-613-76806-1(X)) Tandem Library Bks.

—Trouble in Tahiti. 2002. (Abby & the South Seas Adventures Ser.: Vol. 7). 208p. (J). mass mkt. 5.99 (978-0-8423-3632-1(X)) Tyndale Hse. Pubs.

Wally the Walleye. 2004. (J). lib. bdg. 14.95 (978-0-9725485-3-3(X)) Waterfall Ridge.

Walsh, Ann. The Doctors Apprentice. 2007. 160p. (J). pap. 9.99 ***(978-1-55002-633-7(X)*** , Sandcastle Bks.) Dundurn Group, The CAN. *Dist:* Univ. of Toronto Pr.

Walsh, Ellen Stoll. Pintura de Raton. Campoy, F. Isabel, tr. 2006. (Illus.). 30p. (J). bds. 6.95 (978-0-15-205743-5(9) , Voyager Bks./Libros Viajeros) Harcourt Children's Bks.

Walsh, Maria Elena. Manuelita, Donde Vas? Ink, Lancman, illus. 2003. (SPA.). 136p. (J). (gr. 3-5). pap. 11.95 (978-950-511-631-7(4)) Santillana USA Publishing Co., Inc.

Walsh, Paton Jill. Pepi & the Secret Names. French, Fiona, illus. 2001. 32p. (J). (ps-3). pap. 8.99 (978-0-7112-1089-9(6)) Lincoln, Frances Ltd. GBR. *Dist:* Antique Collectors' Club.

Walsh, Sheila. Will, God's Mighty Warrior. 2006. (Will, God's Mighty Warrior Ser.). (Illus.). 32p. (J). 12.99 (978-1-4003-0805-7(4)) Nelson, Thomas Inc.

Walt Disney Company Staff. Treasure Planet: A Pop-Up Adventure. 2002. 12p. (J). bds. 8.99 (978-0-7364-2014-3(2) , RH/Disney) Random Hse. Children's Bks.

Walt Disney Company Staff, creator. Lady & the Tramp. 2006. (Illus.). 32p. pap. 3.99 (978-1-59816-443-5(0) , Tokyopop Kids) TOKYOPOP, Inc.

Walt Disney Company Staff & Disney Staff. Classic Disney Adventures CD Storybook: Lion King, Aladdin, Little Mermaid & Toy Story. Hinkler Books Staff, ed. rev. ed. 2004. (Disney CD Storybooks Ser.). (Illus.). 128p. (J). (gr. 4-12). 14.95 incl. cd-rom (978-1-86515-304-9(4)) Hinkler Bks. Pty, Ltd. AUS. *Dist:* Penton Overseas, Inc.

Walters, Clare & Kemp, Jane. I Very Really Miss You. Langley, Jonathan, illus. 2006. 32p. (J). (ps-1). 15.95 ***(978-1-84507-260-5(X))*** Lincoln, Frances Ltd. GBR. *Dist:* Perseus Distribution.

Walters, Eric. Caged Eagles. 2001. (gr. 7-12). lib. bdg. 16.40 (978-0-613-86415-2(8)) Tandem Library Bks.

—Diamonds in the Rough. 1998. (Gemini Bks.). 252p. (YA). (gr. 7-10). mass mkt. 6.95 (978-0-7736-7470-7(5)) Stoddart Kids CAN. *Dist:* Fitzhenry & Whiteside, Ltd., Stoddart Publishing.

—Diamonds in the Rough. 1998. (gr. 7-12). lib. bdg. 14.10 (978-0-613-85640-9(6)) Tandem Library Bks.

—I've Got an Idea. 2004. 166p. (J). pap. ***(978-0-00-639196-8(6)*** , HarperTrophy) HarperCollins Canada, Ltd.

—Overdrive. 2004. (Orca Soundings Ser.). 112p. (J). (gr. 7-12). pap. 7.95 (978-1-55143-318-9(4)) Orca Bk. Pubs. USA.

—Stranded. 2000. 288p. (J). mass mkt. 5.99 (978-0-00-638592-9(3)) HarperCollins Pubs.

—Stranded. 1998. 128p. (J). pap. (978-0-00-648110-2(8)) Zondervan.

—Tiger Town. 2006. 168p. (YA). pap. 10.99 ***(978-1-55002-631-3(3)*** , Sandcastle Bks.) Dundurn Group, The CAN. *Dist:* Univ. of Toronto Pr.

—Tiger Trap. 2007. 168p. (YA). pap. 11.99 ***(978-1-55002-673-3(9)*** , Sandcastle Bks.) Dundurn Group, The CAN. *Dist:* Univ. of Toronto Pr.

Walters, Eric. Trapped in Ice. 2003. 224p. mass mkt. 4.99 (978-0-14-038626-4(2) , Penguin Global) Penguin Group (USA) Inc.

Ward, Beck. Submarine Sam. Crowson, Andrew, illus. 2005. 8p. (J). (ps-k). 12.95 (978-0-7624-2418-4(4) , Running Pr. Kids) Running Pr. Bk. Pubs.

Ward, Jean Elizabeth. A Barbara Anne Bushy Tale: Book #2 in a Series. 2007. 188p. per. 16.95 ***(978-0-595-45726-7(6))*** iUniverse, Inc.

Ward-O-Brien, Jo-Lynn M. The Adventures of Hopper & other Children's Stories. 2005. pap. 7.95 (978-0-533-14787-8(5)) Vantage Pr., Inc.

Ward, Ruth. The Adventures of Bloor Bone. 2005. (J). lib. bdg. 18.00 (978-1-59094-105-8(5)) Jawbone Publishing Corp.

Ware, Jim. Canyon Quest. 2004. (Last Chance Detectives Ser.). 272p. (YA). per. 7.99 (978-1-58997-239-1(2)) Focus on the Family Publishing.

Wargin, Kathy-Jo. Mitt & Minn at the Wisconsin Cheese Jamboree. Busch Holman, Karen, illus. 2007. 144p. (J). 14.95 ***(978-1-58726-305-7(X)*** , Mitten Pr.) Ann Arbor Media Group, LLC.

—Mitt & Minn's Illinois Adventure. Holman, Karen Busch, illus. 2007. 144p. (J). 14.95 ***(978-1-58726-306-4(8)*** , Mitten Pr.) Ann Arbor Media Group, LLC.

Warner Brothers Staff. Battle for Camelot. Schonzeit, Marcia, ed. 1998. (Quest for Camelot Ser.). (Illus.). 32p. (gr. k-3). pap. 3.50 (978-0-590-12059-3(X)) Scholastic, Inc.

Warner, Gertrude Chandler. The Cereal Box Mystery. Tang, Charles, illus. 1998. 111p. (J). (ps-7). per. 11.80 (978-0-613-07455-1(6)) Tandem Library Bks.

The Wars. Date not set. (J). (978-0-679-40067-7(2) , Random Hse. Bks. for Young Readers) Random Hse. Children's Bks.

Wasburn, Connie. Hoob & Brabble. 2003. 62p. pap. 12.95 (978-1-59286-650-2(6)) PublishAmerica, Inc.

Washer, S. N. The Wingate Adventures: Our New Friends. 2006. 164p. pap. 11.95 (978-1-59800-510-3(3)) Outskirts Press, Inc.

Washington State Adventures in Learning Book. 2005. (J). 15.95 (978-1-59210-336-2(7)) Whispering Pine Pr., Inc.

Wasserman, Robin. Awakening. 2007. (Chasing Yesterday Ser.: No. 1). 224p. (J). pap. 5.99 ***(978-0-439-93338-4(2)*** , Scholastic Paperbacks) Scholastic, Inc.

—Betrayal. 2007. (Chasing Yesterday Ser.: Bk. 2). 224p. (J). 5.99 ***(978-0-439-93341-4(2))*** Scholastic, Inc.

—Truth. 2007. (Chasing Yesterday Ser.). 240p. (J). pap. 5.99 ***(978-0-439-93342-1(0)*** , Scholastic Paperbacks) Scholastic, Inc.

Watanabe, Yoshitomo, illus. & creator. Beyond the Beyond. Watanabe, Yoshitomo, creator. 2006. pap. 9.99 (978-1-59816-371-1(X) , Tokyopop Kids) TOKYOPOP, Inc.

Watase, Yu. Enemy, Vol. 10. Watase, Yu, illus. 2004. (Illus.). 200p. lib. bdg. 20.85 (978-1-4176-5241-9(1)) Tandem Library Bks.

—Oracle: Vol. 2. Watase, Yu, illus. 2004. (Illus.). 200p. lib. bdg. 20.85 (978-1-4176-5230-3(6)) Tandem Library Bks.

Watase, Yuu. Alice 19th Vol. 2: Inner Heart. JN Productions Staff, tr. 2003. (Alice 19th Ser.). (Illus.). 200p. (YA). pap. 9.95 (978-1-59116-229-2(7)) Viz Media.

Waterton, Betty. Quincy Rumpel. 2000. (Quincy Rumpel Bks.). (Illus.). 144p. (J). (gr. 3-7). pap. 3.95 (978-0-88899-393-9(5) , Libros Tigrillo) Groundwood Bks. CAN. *Dist:* Transition Vendor.

Watkins, Dawn L. A King for Brass Cobweb, 2 vols., Set. 2000. (Illus.). (J). (ps-3). pap. 14.98 incl. audio (978-0-89084-904-0(8) , 100073) Jones, Bob Univ. Pr.

Watkins, Janet & Banks, Courtney Brea. There's Something in My Closet: A Courtney B Adventure Book. Watkins, Janet, ed. 2nd ed. 2002. (J). spiral bd. (978-0-9767545-1-0(7)) JDW Collaborative.

Watkins, Tesha. Joey & the Ancient Horn / Mystery Revealed. 2006. (YA). pap. 12.95 (978-0-9762788-0-1(4)) Great I-AM Publishing Co., The.

Watlington, Elizabeth. Binky's Big Adventure. 2004. (YA). pap. 7.95 (978-0-9723102-3-9(1)) Bush Publishing Inc.

Watson, Dolores. The Country Life. 2004. 52p. (YA). pap. 9.95 (978-1-932373-04-2(7) , Cedar Hill Pr.) Cedar Hill Publishing.

Watson, Don. The Legend of Red Leaf. Robbins, Ashley, illus. l.t. ed. 2005. 125p. (J). pap. 9.95 (978-0-9714358-6-5(3)) Longhorn Creek Pr.

Watson, Gayle. Catie Corn & the Corn Cops. Fautsch, Jackie, illus. l.t. ed. 22p. (J). 2006. 15.99 (978-1-59879-098-6(6)); 2005. per. 9.99 (978-1-59879-079-5(X)) Lifevest Publishing, Inc.

Watson, H. B. Marrio. The Stone Chamber. 2006. (ENG.). pap. ***(978-1-4250-1466-7(6))*** Assistedreadingbooks.com Inc.

—The Stone Chamber. 2004. reprint ed. pap. 15.95 (978-1-4191-8353-9(2)) Kessinger Publishing, LLC.

Watson, H. B. Marriott. The Stone Chamber. 2004. reprint ed. pap. 1.99 (978-1-4192-8353-6(7)) Kessinger Publishing, LLC.

Watson, Jude. Death on Naboo. 2006. (Star Wars Ser.: No. 4). 160p. (J). pap. 5.99 (978-0-439-68137-7(5)) Scholastic, Inc.

—Deception. Nielsen, Cliff, illus. ed. 2001. (Star Wars Ser.: Bk. 1 Special Edition). 192p. (J). (gr. 4-7). pap. 5.99 (978-0-439-13938-0(4)) Scholastic, Inc.

—The Defenders of the Dead. 1999. (Star Wars Ser.: Bk. 5). 11.64 (978-0-606-18608-7(5)) Tandem Library Bks.

—Emergency in Escape Pod Four. 1999. (Star Wars Science Adventures Ser.). (Illus.). 96p. (gr. 3-7). pap. 3.99 (978-0-590-20227-5(8)) Scholastic, Inc.

—Legacy of the Jedi. Mattingly, David, illus. 2003. (Star Wars Ser.). 208p. (J). (gr. 3-7). pap. 12.95 (978-0-439-53666-0(9)) Scholastic, Inc.

—Return of the Dark Side. 2006. (Star Wars Ser.: No. 6). 160p. (J). pap. 5.99 (978-0-439-68139-1(1)) Scholastic, Inc.

—The School of Fear. 2003. (Star Wars Ser.: No. 5). (gr. 3-6). lib. bdg. 13.00 (978-0-613-58164-6(4)) Tandem Library Bks.

—Secret Weapon. 2007. (Star Wars Ser.: No. 7). 149p. (J). pap. 5.99 (978-0-439-68140-7(5) , Scholastic Paperbacks) Scholastic, Inc.

—The Shadow Trap. Buelow, Alice & Mattingly, David, illus. 2003. (Star Wars Ser.: No. 6). 144p. (J). pap. 4.99 (978-0-439-33922-3(7)) Scholastic, Inc.

—A Tangled Web. 2006. (Star Wars Ser.: No. 5). 160p. (J). pap. 5.99 (978-0-439-68138-4(3) , Scholastic) Scholastic, Inc.

Watson, Pat. The Scarlet Pimpernel. Robbins, Dawn Michelle, ed. 2000. (YA). 9.95 (978-1-58130-638-5(5)); 11.95 (978-1-58130-639-2(3)) Novel Units, Inc.

Watsuki, Nobuhiro. In the 11th Year of Meiji, May 14th. Watsuki, Nobuhiro, illus. 2004. (Illus.). 200p. lib. bdg. 18.55 (978-1-4176-5888-6(6)) Tandem Library Bks.

—Mitsurugi, Master & Student. Watsuki, Nobuhiro, illus. 2005. (Illus.). 200p. lib. bdg. 18.55 (978-1-4176-5890-9(8)) Tandem Library Bks.

—On the East Sea Road. Watsuki, Nobuhiro, illus. 2005. (Illus.). 185p. per. 18.55 (978-1-4176-5889-3(4)) Tandem Library Bks.

Watt, J. S. The Hall of Sorrows. 2006. 67p. pap. 14.95 (978-1-4241-2984-3(2)) PublishAmerica, Inc.

Wax, Wendy. Fashion Headquarters. Artful Doodlers Limited Staff, illus. 2005. (Totally Spies! Ser.). 16p. (J). pap. 5.99 (978-1-4169-0821-0(8) , Simon Spotlight) Simon & Schuster Children's Publishing.

—A Royal Valentine. Hall, Susan', illus. 2006. 24p. (J). lib. bdg. 9.00 ***(978-1-4242-0951-4(X))*** Fitzgerald Bks.

—Secret Agents. 2007. 24p. (J). 21.35 ***(978-1-59961-161-7(9))*** Spotlight.

Wax, Wendy. Sticky Situations: A Totally Spies! Guide to Getting Out in a Clutch! Style Guide Staff, illus. 2006. (Totally Spies! Ser.). 64p. (J). pap. 6.99 (978-1-4169-0840-1(4) , Simon Spotlight) Simon & Schuster Children's Publishing.

Wax, Wendy & A&J Studios Staff. Diego to the Rescue! 2006. (Go, Diego, Go! Ser.). 12p. (J). bds. 10.95 (978-1-4169-1790-8(X) , Simon Spotlight/Nickelodeon) Simon & Schuster Children's Publishing.

Way, Daniel. Ghost Rider Vicious Cycl, Vol. 1. 2007. (Illus.). 120p. pap. 13.99 (978-0-7851-2296-8(6)) Marvel Enterprises, Inc.

We Both Read-My Day Big Book: My Day Big Book Edition. 2006. (We Both Read Ser.). (J). pap. 29.95 (978-1-891327-93-3(3)) Treasure Bay, Inc.

Wealth, Viktoria. Aadorn Kingdom of the Dragons' Light: Book-I. 2003. 214p. (YA). pap. 14.95 (978-0-595-28175-6(3)) iUniverse, Inc.

Weathers, Andrea. Hermy the Hermit Crab: The Adventure Begins. 2004. (J). pap. 15.99 (978-0-933101-22-7(8)) Legacy Pubns.

Weaver, Patricia. Ashaki, African Princess. 2001. 164p. (YA). pap. 12.95 (978-0-595-18283-1(6) , Writer's Showcase Pr.) iUniverse, Inc.

Webb, Leonard. Corinthia: My Name Is Corinthia. 2005. 72p. pap. 11.95 (978-1-59113-693-4(8)) Booklocker-.com, Inc.

Webb, Mack H., Jr. Webb's Wondrous Tales Book 2. Webb, Celia, illus. 2007. 156p. (J). per. 14.95 (*978-0-9779576-3-7(2)) Pilinut Pr., Inc.

Webb, Tracy. Weathering the Storms. 2005. 148p. (YA). pap. 13.99 (978-1-4141-0393-8(X)) Pleasant Word.

Weber, Jen Funk. Hogsqueal's Activity Book. 2008. (Spiderwick Chronicles). 64p. 4.99 (*978-1-4169-4951-0(8) , Simon Scribbles) Simon & Schuster Children's Publishing.

Weber, Lenora Mattingly. Beany & the Beckoning Road. 1999. (Beany Malone Ser.). 277p. (J). reprint ed. pap. 12.95 (978-0-9639607-6-4(8)) Image Cascade Publishing.

—Beany Malone. Howe, Gertrude, illus. 1999. (Beany Malone Ser.). 220p. (J). reprint ed. pap. 12.95 (978-0-9639607-4-0(1)) Image Cascade Publishing.

—Leave It to Beany! 1999. (Beany Malone Ser.). 266p. (J). reprint ed. pap. 12.95 (978-0-9639607-5-7(X)) Image Cascade Publishing.

—Meet the Malones. Howe, Gertrude, photos by. 1999. (Beany Malone Ser.). (Illus.). 282p. (J). reprint ed. pap. 12.95 (978-0-9639607-3-3(3)) Image Cascade Publishing.

Weber, Lou, ed. Teenage Mutant Ninja Turtles: Interactive Play-a-Sound. 24p. (J). 15.98 (978-1-4127-3240-6(9) , 7236000) Publications International, Ltd.

—Weebles Zuzie Q Big Delivery. 2005. 10p. (J). bds. 9.98 (978-1-4127-3356-4(1) , 7250000) Publications International, Ltd.

Webster, David. Book One of the Naxos Island Mages: The Grand Adventure. 2003. 200p. 24.95 (978-0-595-75137-2(7)) iUniverse, Inc.

—Book One of the Naxos Island Mages: The Grand Adventure. 2003. 200p. pap. 14.95 (978-0-595-29933-1(4)) iUniverse, Inc.

—Book Two of the Naxos Island Mages: The War of the Dark Mages. 2004. 190p. pap. 13.95 (978-0-595-31302-0(7)) iUniverse, Inc.

Webster, Jean. Papaito-Piernas-Largas. (SPA.). (YA). (gr. 5-8). pap. (978-950-08-1515-4(X) , AA7255) Atlantida ARG. *Dist:* Lectorum Pubns., Inc.

Webster, V. Frank. The Boys of Bellwood School or Frank Jor. 2006. 62.99 (*978-1-4219-9655-4(3)); pap. 56.99 (*978-1-4219-9645-5(6)) IndyPublish.com.

Wechsler, Nathalie. Once upon A Fly: The Adventures of Lamouche. Wechsler, Nathalie, illus. 2005. (Illus.). 24p. (J). per. 7.99 (978-0-9766998-1-1(8)) Finlay Prints, Inc.

—Once upon A Fly - Hardcover: The Adventures of Lamouche. Wechsler, Nathalie, illus. 2005. (Illus.). 24p. (J). 10.95 (978-0-9766998-0-4(X)) Finlay Prints, Inc.

Weeks, Sarah. The Brass Bone. Date not set. (J). 15.99 (978-0-06-025007-2(0)); 16.89 (978-0-06-025008-9(9)) HarperCollins Pubs.

Weeks, Timothy A. The Wise Mullet of Cook Bayou, l.t. ed. 2004. (Illus.). 48p. (J). per. (978-0-9713573-8-9(2)) Thomas Expressions, Inc.

Weil, Eric. Christmas with Little Bill. Kanemoto, Dan, illus. 2002. (Little Bill Ser.). 12p. (J). 5.99 (978-0-689-84084-5(5) , Simon Spotlight/Nickelodeon) Simon & Schuster Children's Publishing.

Wein, Elizabeth E. The Lion Hunter. 2007. (Mark of Solomon Ser.: Bk. 1). 208p. (YA). (gr. 7 up). 16.99 (978-0-670-06163-1(8) , Viking Juvenile) Penguin Group (USA) Inc.

Weinberg, Moshe. The Unforgettable Journey. 142p. 12.95 (978-1-56871-306-9(1)) Targum Pr., Inc.

Weinman, Logan & Bennett, Jeffrey. Max's Ice Age Adventure. 2007. (Science Adventures Written by Kids Ser.). (Illus.). 32p. (J). pap. 12.00 (*978-0-9721819-2-1(X)) Big Kid Science.

Weir, Joan. Principal's Kid. 1999. (gr. 3-6). lib. bdg. 15.25 (978-0-613-29326-6(6)) Tandem Library Bks.

Weise, Selene H. C. Gold for a Boat. 2001. (Illus.). 68p. (J). (gr. 1-6). 5.95 (978-1-57249-270-7(8) , Burd Street Pr.) White Mane Publishing Co., Inc.

Weisman, Greg. Gargoyles #1. 2006. (Illus.). 24p. (YA). pap. 3.50 (978-1-59362-040-0(3) , Slave Labor Graphics) Slave Labor Bks.

Weiss, Bobbi J. G. Knights of the Periodic Table. 2003. (gr. k-3). lib. bdg. 14.15 (978-0-613-72109-7(8)) Tandem Library Bks.

Weiss, Ellen. The Mystery of Microsneezia: A ClueFinders Mystery Adventure. 2004. (Illus.). 96p. (J). pap. 4.99 (978-0-7630-7619-1(8)) Learning Co. Bks.

Weiss, Jim, reader. The Treasure. 2001. (Illus.). (J). (ps-4). pap. 16.95 incl. audio (978-0-87499-754-5(2) , 1124-LL2) Live Oak Media.

Weissmann, Joe, illus. The Gingerbread Man. 2005. (J). 7.95 (978-0-9770473-0-7(X)) Heersink, Roland.

—Three Tales of Adventure. 2005. (Once-upon-a-Time Ser.). 32p. (J). (gr. k-3). (978-1-55074-945-8(5)) Kids Can Pr., Ltd.

Welsh Books Staff. Llyfr Lliwio Sali Mali. 2nd ed. 2005. (WEL., Illus.). 22p. (978-1-902416-88-5(0)) Cymdeithas Lyfrau Ceredigion.

Wenger, Brahm. Dewey's Magical Sleigh. 2005. 32p. 15.95 (978-0-9745143-5-2(7)) RandallFraser Publishing.

Wengerd, Marvin, ed. Invisibles. Fabian, Melinda, illus. 2000. 32p. (J). (ps-8). pap. 4.00 (978-1-890050-38-2(5)) Carlisle Pr.- Walnut Creek.

Weninger, Brigitte. Bye-Bye Binky. Yonezu, Yusuke, illus. 2007. 32p. (J). 15.99 (978-0-698-40048-1(8) , Minedition) Penguin Group (USA) Inc.

Wensel, Bill. Adventure Is Adventure: The Sea Stories of Captain Bill. 2002. 185p. per. 14.95 net. (978-1-931934-09-1(6)) Back Yard Pub.

Wenzell, Tim. Absent Children. 2000. 316p. (YA). pap. 15.95 (978-0-595-12142-7(X)) iUniverse, Inc.

Werkley, Vicki. Girl-on-Fire. Laidig, Jean & HighPine, Gayle, eds. 1999. 230p. (YA). pap. 14.95 (978-1-58436-400-9(9)) Haven Bks.

Wert, Richard. The Boxer's Backyard. 2007. (J). pap. 8.99 (*978-1-60247-023-1(5)) Tate Publishing & Enterprises, L.L.C.

West, Cathy. Jade's Secret Power. 2001. (gr. k-3). lib. bdg. 13.00 (978-0-613-72446-3(1)) Tandem Library Bks.

West, Colin. Toby & His Old Tin Tub. West, Colin, illus. 2005. (Read-It! Chapter Bks.). (Illus.). 52p. (J). (ps-k). lib. bdg. 19.95 (978-1-4048-1279-6(2)) Picture Window Bks.

West, Elizabeth. The ARUN Project. 2002. 184p. (YA). per. 9.99 (978-0-9720919-0-9(4)) West, Elizabeth.

West, Greg. Hooky. 2000. (gr. 7-12). lib. bdg. 21.60 (978-0-613-79758-0(2)) Tandem Library Bks.

West, Joyce. The Drovers Road Collection: Three New Zealand Adventures, 3 books under one cover. 2003. (Bethlehem Budget Bks.). (Illus.). 448p. (YA). pap. 16.95 (978-1-883937-69-0(8)) Bethlehem Bks.

West, Keith. Kidnapped: A Classic Tale. Boucher, William, illus. 2000. (Star Plays Ser.). 48p. (YA). (gr. 4-6). pap. 8.99 (978-0-237-52193-6(8) , Evans Brothers, Limited) Evans Publishing Group GBR. *Dist:* Independent Pubs. Group.

—Mirror World: A Science-Fiction Drama. Buckley, Harriet, illus. 2001. (Star Plays Ser.). 48p. (gr. 4-6). pap. 8.99 (978-0-237-52189-9(X) , Evans Brothers, Limited) Evans Publishing Group GBR. *Dist:* Independent Pubs. Group.

—Young Runaways: A Teenage Adventure. Andrews, Gary, illus. 2001. (Star Plays Ser.). 48p. (gr. 4-6). pap. 8.99 (978-0-237-52191-2(1) , Evans Brothers, Limited) Evans Publishing Group GBR. *Dist:* Independent Pubs. Group.

West, Kim. A Home for Pup E. Dog. West, Kim, illus. l.t. ed. 2002. (Illus.). 39p. (J). 9.50 (978-0-9743905-0-5(X) , 1500) West, Kim.

West, Nancy. Chips - the War Dog: Based on the True-Life Adventures of the World War II K-9 Hero. 2nd ed. 2004. 183p. (J). per. 8.95 (978-0-9743659-1-6(2)) Hero Dog Pubns.

West, Tracey. The Code Caper. Style Guide Staff, illus. 2006. (Totally Spies! Ser.). 48p. (YA). pap. 4.99 (978-1-4169-1881-3(7) , Simon Spotlight) Simon & Schuster Children's Publishing.

—Foster's Home for Imaginary Friends Sticker Storybook: Mix & Match Imaginary Friends. 2006. 18p. (J). pap. 4.99 (978-0-439-74664-9(7) , Scholastic Paperbacks) Scholastic, Inc.

—Go West, Young Ash. 2001. (Pokemon Chapter Bks.: Vol. 17). (Illus.). 96p. (J). (gr. 2-7). pap. 4.50 (978-0-439-20093-6(8)) Scholastic, Inc.

—The Haunted Gym. 2003. (Pokemon Readers Ser.: No. 3). 32p. (J). pap. 3.99 (978-0-439-42988-7(9)) Scholastic, Inc.

—Jelly-Bean Jam. Durk, Jim & Roper, Robert, illus. 2008. (Totally Spies! Ser.). 24p. (J). pap. 5.99 (978-1-4169-3340-3(9) , Simon Spotlight) Simon & Schuster Children's Publishing.

—Journey to the Impossible Islands. 2003. (gr. 3-6). lib. bdg. 12.40 (978-0-613-72173-8(X)) Tandem Library Bks.

—Mario & the Incredible Rescue. 2006. 76p. (J). pap. (*978-0-439-84366-9(9)) Scholastic, Inc.

—Mayor Is Missing. 2003. (gr. 3-6). lib. bdg. 11.80 (978-0-613-58159-2(8)) Tandem Library Bks.

—The Mayor Is Missing. Thompson Brothers Staff, illus. 2003. (Powerpuff Girls Readers: No. 7). 32p. (J). (gr. 1-4). pap. 3.99 (978-0-439-44223-7(0)) Scholastic, Inc.

—The Outback. 2005. (Survivor Ser.). 144p. (J). (ps-6). mass mkt. 4.99 (978-0-689-87730-8(7) , Simon Spotlight) Simon & Schuster Children's Publishing.

—Pokemon Reader No.6: Get Well, Pikachu! 2004. (gr. k-3). lib. bdg. 11.80 (978-0-613-84568-7(4)) Tandem Library Bks.

—Power Pals. Marderosian, Marc, illus. 2002. (Powerpuff Girls Ser.: No. 13). 32p. (J). (gr. 4-6). pap. 3.50 (978-0-439-37229-9(1)) Scholastic, Inc.

—Power Pals. 2002. (gr. k-3). lib. bdg. 11.25 (978-0-613-50486-7(0)) Tandem Library Bks.

—Prepare for Trouble. 2001. (Pokemon Chapter Bks.: Vol. 19). (Illus.). 96p. (J). (gr. 2-7). pap. 4.50 (978-0-439-22033-0(5)) Scholastic, Inc.

—The Return of Sailor Moon. 2001. (Sailor Moon Junior Chapter Bks.). (Illus.). 48p. (J). (gr. 5-8). pap. 3.99 (978-0-439-22452-9(7)) Scholastic, Inc.

—Sailor Scouts Unite! 2001. (Sailor Moon Junior Chapter Bks.: No. 2). (Illus.). 48p. (YA). (gr. 5-8). pap. 3.99 (978-0-439-22448-2(9)) Scholastic, Inc.

—Scrambled Brains! Roper, Robert, illus. 2006. (Totally Spies! Ser.). 64p. (J). pap. 4.99 (978-1-4169-1313-9(0) , Simon Spotlight) Simon & Schuster Children's Publishing.

—The Seven Labors of Jack. Rodriguez, Angel, illus. 2003. (Samurai Jack Chapter Bks.: No. 2). 80p. (J). (gr. 3-7). pap. 4.50 (978-0-439-40974-2(8)) Scholastic, Inc.

—Shadow Riders. 2007. (Yu-gi-oh Ser.). (Illus.). 96p. (J). pap. 4.99 (*978-0-439-88831-8(X)) Scholastic, Inc.

—Team Rocket Truce. 2007. (Pokemon Junior Chapter Bks.: No. 1). 48p. (J). pap. 3.99 (*978-0-545-00073-4(4)) Scholastic, Inc.

—Teeth Thief. Alger, Bill, illus. 2002. (Powerpuff Girls Ser.). 32p. (J). (ps-3). pap. 3.50 (978-0-439-34433-3(6) , Cartwheel Bks.) Scholastic, Inc.

—Welcome to Sinnoh. 2008. (Pokemon Ser.). 32p. (J). pap. 3.99 (*978-0-545-01414-4(X)) Scholastic, Inc.

—Where Is Chicken Pox? 2001. (gr. k-3). lib. bdg. 11.80 (978-0-613-43911-4(2)) Tandem Library Bks.

West, Tracey. Yu-Gi-Oh Gx Ch Bk #5 Nightshroud's Secret. 2008. 96p. pap. 4.99 (*978-0-545-04406-6(5) , Scholastic) Scholastic, Inc.

West, Tracey, adapted by. The Chikorita Challenge. 2001. (Pokemon Chapter Bks.: Vol. 21). (Illus.). 96p. (J). (gr. 2-7). pap. 4.50 (978-0-439-22113-9(7)) Scholastic, Inc.

Westerfeld, Scott. Blue Noon. 2006. (Midnighters Ser.). 384p. (J). lib. bdg. 17.89 (978-0-06-051958-2(4)); (YA). 16.99 (978-0-06-051957-5(6)) HarperCollins Pubs.

—Pretties. 2005. 384p. (YA). (gr. 9 up). pap. 8.99 (978-0-689-86539-8(2) , Simon Pulse) Simon & Schuster Children's Publishing.

—So Yesterday. 240p. (gr. 7-12). 2004. (J). 16.99 (978-1-59514-000-5(X)); 2005. (YA). reprint ed. pap. 7.99 (978-1-59514-032-6(8)) Penguin Group (USA) Inc. (Razorbill).

—Uglies. 2005. 448p. (YA). (gr. 7 up). pap. 8.99 (978-0-689-86538-1(4) , Simon Pulse) Simon & Schuster Children's Publishing.

Westra, Elizabeth. Alexander & the Stallion. Ampel, Kenneth Robert, illus. 2003. (Books for Young Learners). 16p. (J). per. 5.00 net. (978-1-57274-534-6(7) , 2721) Owen, Richard C. Pubs., Inc.

Wetterer, Margaret K. Historical Fiction Series, 3 bks., Set. 2000. (Illus.). (J). (gr. 1-6). pap. 45.95 incl. audio (978-0-87499-580-0(9)) Live Oak Media.

Wetterer, Margaret K., et al. Historical Fiction Series. Young, Mary O. et al, illus. 2000. pap. 51.95 incl. audio compact disk (978-1-59112-859-5(5)) Live Oak Media.

Wetz, Juliann. Boot Camp: A Robbie & Marshall Adventure. 2002. (J). mass mkt. 4.95 (978-0-9716397-1-3(X)) Wetz, Juliann.

—Genuine Swiss Army: A Robbie & Marshall Adventure. 2002. 64p. (J). mass mkt. 4.95 (978-0-9716397-0-6(1)) Wetz, Juliann.

Weyn, Suzanne. Indiana Jones: Temple of Doom Novelization: Temple of Doom Novelization. 2008. (Indiana Jones Ser.). 176p. (J). 6.99 (*978-0-545-04255-0(0) , Scholastic) Scholastic, Inc.

Weyn, Suzanne. Mission Without Permission. 2004. (Illus.). 128p. (J). 4.99 (978-0-439-58811-9(1)) Scholastic, Inc.

Whalen, Erin T. Charlie Gets Spooked, 3 vols. 2004. (Illus.). 32p. (J). (gr. k-3). 16.95 (978-1-929265-04-6(2)); pap. 8.95 (978-1-929265-05-3(0)) Lily & Co. Publishing.

What Can I Do. 2002. (J). 4.95 (978-0-9725121-2-1(8)) PowerMark Productions.

Wheeler, Chase. Challenge of the Masked Racer #2. 2008. 144p. (J). (gr. 2-5). 6.99 (*978-0-448-44805-3(X) , Grosset & Dunlap) Penguin Group (USA) Inc.

—The Great Plan #1. 2008. 144p. (J). (gr. 2-5). 6.99 (*978-0-448-44804-6(1) , Grosset & Dunlap) Penguin Group (USA) Inc.

—The Most Dangerous Race #5. 2008. 144p. (J). (gr. 2-5). 6.99 (*978-0-448-44808-4(4) , Grosset & Dunlap) Penguin Group (USA) Inc.

Wheelus, Doris. The Plum Jelly Kids. 2005. 223p. pap. 19.95 (978-1-4137-5649-4(2)) PublishAmerica, Inc.

Wheetley, Jennifer. Ancestor Adventure. 2000. (Illus.). (J). (gr. 2-4). 53.00 (978-1-57336-351-8(0) , 3009) Interaction Pubs., Inc.

When all the locusts had Eaten. 2006. (YA). per. 12.99 (978-1-59872-460-8(6)) Instantpublisher.com.

When All the Locusts Had Eaten. 2006. (YA). per. 13.99 (978-1-59872-534-6(3)) Instantpublisher.com.

When Kids Dream & Trucks Fly. 2007. per. 14.99 (*978-0-9792258-6-4(8)) Bezalel Bks.

When the Legends Die. 1999. (YA). 11.95 (978-1-56137-423-6(7)) Novel Units, Inc.

Where Red Fern Grows. 1998. (J). pap. 3.95 (978-0-439-04478-3(2)) Scholastic, Inc.

Where the Leprechauns Hide. 2007. pap. 12.99 (*978-0-9792258-9-5(2)) Bezalel Bks.

Where the Sky Meets the Sea: Where Time Meets Eternity. 2001. 120p. (YA). (gr. 11 up). pap. 3.95 (978-0-9701168-1-9(0)) Horley, Robert E.

Wherry, Alwyn. The Hungry Little Mouse. 2006. 17p. (J). 12.08 (978-1-4116-8056-2(1)) Lulu.com.

Whipping Boy. 1999. (J). 11.95 (978-1-56137-711-4(2)) Novel Units, Inc.

Whipple, Wayne. Radio Boys Cronies. 2004. reprint ed. pap. 1.99 (978-1-4192-4378-3(0)) Kessinger Publishing, LLC.

White, Debra. Nobody's Pets. 2001. (Illus.). 127p. (YA). (gr. 5 up). pap. 8.95 net. (978-0-9707758-0-1(6)) Four Footed Friends.

White, E. B. Le Avventure di Stuart Little.Tr. of Stuart Little. (ITA.). pap. 17.95 (978-88-451-2736-6(2)); 2000. (J). pap. 15.95 (978-88-452-3861-1(X)) Fabbri - RCS Libri ITA. *Dist:* Distribooks, Inc.

White, Graham. Asalto al Castillo. 2003. (FRE.). 32p. 14.95 (978-84-89396-96-8(5)) Blume ESP. *Dist:* Independent Pubs. Group.

White, Jane Nixon. Taming of Corky. 2001. (gr. 3-6). lib. bdg. 21.60 (978-0-613-74558-1(2)) Tandem Library Bks.

White, Jeanne M. The Journey to Vida. Pinheiro, Atini, illus. 1999. 54p. (J). (ps-6). pap. 6.95 (978-1-891929-24-3(0)) Four Seasons Pubs.

White, T. Diogenes in a Barrel of Fun. 2004. (J). 15.95 (978-0-9639670-2-2(9)) twhiteart.

White, Tom. Lost in the Texas Desert. 2004. (Illus.). 132p. per. 7.95 (978-0-9753611-0-8(4)) Arlington Pubns.

Whitehouse, Howard. The Strictest School in the World: Being the Tale of a Clever Girl, a Rubber Boy & a Collection of Flying Machines,Mostly Broken. Slavin, Bill, illus. 2006. 256p. (978-1-55337-883-9(0)); (978-1-55337-882-2(2)) Kids Can Pr., Ltd.

Whitethrow, Lord. Cuentos Escalofriantes para Ninos. 1999. (Stories for Children Ser.).Tr. of Scary Stories for Kids. (SPA.). 125p. (J). mass mkt. 7.95 (978-970-643-149-3(7)) Selector, S.A. de C.V. MEX. *Dist:* Libros Sin Fronteras.

Whittemore, JoAnne. Onaj's Horn. 2007. 312p. pap. 8.95 (978-0-7387-1125-6(X) , Flux) Llewellyn Pubns.

Who's My Opposite? (Peek A Boo Pockets Ser.). 12p. (J). bds. (978-2-89393-973-5(2)) Phidal Publishing, Inc./ Editions Phidal, Inc.

Whybrow, Ian. Little Wolf's Haunted Hall for Small Horrors. Ross, Tony, illus. 2004. (Middle Grade Fiction Ser.). 132p. (J). (gr. 2-6). pap. 6.95 (978-1-57505-794-1(8)) Lerner Publishing Group.

—Malicia para Principiantes: Una Aventura de Lobito y Apestosito. 2005. (Libros Ilustrados (Picture Bks.)). (SPA., Illus.). 32p. (gr. k-2). 16.95 (978-0-8225-3211-8(5) , Ediciones Lerner) Lerner Publishing Group.

Whyte, John. Buddy's Adventures in Reading. 2007. pap. 8.95 (*978-0-533-15641-2(6)) Vantage Pr., Inc.

Wiberg, Harald, illus. The Tomten. 2nd rev. ed. 32p. (J). 17.95 (978-0-86315-153-8(1)) Floris Bks. GBR. *Dist:* SteinerBooks, Inc.

Wick. Elfish Fantasy: The Great Chocolate Caper. 2003. 128p. (YA). pap. 11.95 (978-0-595-29038-3(8)) iUniverse, Inc.

Wicke, Ed. Akayzia Adams & the Masterdragon's Secret. Warne, Tom, illus. 2003. 280p. (J). per. 9.99 (978-0-9677652-3-5(4) , Blacknblue Pr. UK) Blacknblue Pr.

—Mattie & the Highwaymen. Warne, Tom, illus. 2003. 232p. (J). per. 8.99 (978-0-9677652-1-1(8) , BlacknBlue Pr. UK) Blacknblue Pr.

Wicks, Ben. Dawn of the Promised Land: The Creation of Israel. 1998. 256p. 24.95 (978-0-7868-6322-8(6)) Disney Pr.

Wieler, Diana. Ranvan: Magic Nation. 1998. 229p. (J). (gr. 7-12). pap. 5.95 (978-0-88899-316-8(1) , Libros Tigrillo) Groundwood Bks. CAN. *Dist:* Transition Vendor.

Wielkiewicz, Richard M. Okay, Riders, Set 'Em Up: A Nate Walker BMX Adventure. Dwyer, Corinne et al, illus. 2005. 140p. (J). pap. 12.95 (978-0-9774129-0-7(3)) Main Event Pr.

Wiesner, David. Flotsam. Cushman, Doug, illus. 2006. 40p. (J). (gr. k-3). 17.00 (978-0-618-19457-5(6) , Clarion Bks.) Houghton Mifflin Co. Trade & Reference Div.

—Los Tres Cerditos. 2004. Tr. of Three Little Pigs. (SPA.). (J). (gr. k-2). 21.95 (978-84-261-3291-8(X)) Juventud, Editorial ESP. *Dist:* Lectorum Pubns., Inc., Iaconi, Mariuccia Bk. Imports.

Wiggin, Kate Douglas. New Chronicles of Rebecca. 2006. (ENG.). 300p. per. 21.45 (978-1-59462-367-7(8) , 403); per. 21.45 (978-1-59462-368-4(6) , 404) Standard Pubns., Inc. (Book Jungle).

Wilcox, John. Charlie the Chinook. Wiker, Betty, illus. l.t. ed. 1998. (J). (ps-3). pap. (978-0-9683640-7-9(1)) Raven Rock Publishing.

Wilder, Alice. It's Present Day. Levy, David B., illus. 1999. (Blue's Clues Ser.). 16p. (J). (ps-k). pap. 5.99 (978-0-689-82898-0(5) , Simon Spotlight/Nickelodeon) Simon & Schuster Children's Publishing.

Wiley. The Extraordinary Adventures of Ordinary Basil: Island of the Volcano Monkeys. 2007. (J). pap. (*978-0-439-86133-5(0)) Blue Sky Pr.

Wilhelm, Hans. I Am Lost. 2004. 32p. (J). lib. bdg. 15.00 (978-1-59054-352-8(1)) Fitzgerald Bks.

—I'm Not Scared! 2005. (Illus.). 32p. (J). (ps-ps). pap. 3.99 (978-0-439-44334-0(2) , Cartwheel Bks.) Scholastic, Inc.

Wilkens, S. Kyle XY Novel. 2008. (Kyle XY Ser.). 192p. (YA). (gr. 9 up). pap. 5.99 (*978-0-06-143033-6(1) , Harper Entertainment) HarperCollins Pubs.

Wilkes, Irene. Elvie, Santa's Ninth Reindeer. Montgomery, Jason, illus. 2006. 28p. (J). 19.95 (*978-1-59299-227-0(7)) Inkwater Pr.

Wilkey, David. Through the Black Hole: The Incredible Adventures of Justin Hart. 2003. 154p. pap. 12.95 (978-0-595-29497-8(9)) iUniverse, Inc.

Wilkins, Kim. Ghost Ship: Sunken Kingdom #1. Cornish, D. M., illus. 2008. 96p. (J). (gr. 4-7). pap. 5.99 (*978-0-375-84806-3(1) , Random Hse. Bks. for Young Readers) Random Hse. Children's Bks.

—Ghost Ship: Sunken Kingdom #1. Cornish, D. M., illus. 2008. 96p. (J). (gr. 4-7). lib. bdg. 11.99 (*978-0-375-94806-0(6) , Random Hse. Bks. for Young Readers) Random Hse. Children's Bks.

Wilkins, Lisa. The Key Seekers. 2005. 68p. pap. 14.95 (978-1-4137-8681-1(2)) PublishAmerica, Inc.

Will I Ever. 2003. per. (978-0-9740182-0-1(1)) HuntForMo Creations.

Willard, Eliza. Revenge of the Dark Hand with Cards. 2002. (gr. 3-6). lib. bdg. 13.00 (978-0-613-72453-1(4)) Tandem Library Bks.

Willever, Lisa. Nicky Fifth's Garden State Adventure. 2004. 160p. 5.95 (978-0-9760469-2-9(X) , 329-005) Franklin Mason Pr.

Williams, Ann. The Multifarious Adventures of Fred the Raindrop. 2005. 22p. (J). 8.00 (978-1-4116-4175-4(2)) Lulu.com.

Williams, Brenda Gail. Little Mo Weep. 2004. (J). per. 7.95 (978-1-59427-027-7(9)) Aglob Publishing.

Williams, Carol. Dickey. 2005. 16.00 (978-0-8059-9830-6(6)) Dorrance Publishing Co., Inc.

Williams, D. Disillusions. 2005. 164p. pap. 19.95 (978-1-4137-7187-9(4)) PublishAmerica, Inc.

Williams, Jeff E. The Unknown Priestess. 1998. (Illus.). (J). pap. 8.80 (978-1-56763-343-6(9)); lib. bdg. 25.25 (978-1-56763-342-9(0)) Ozark Publishing.

Williams, Jennifer. Stringbean's Trip to the Shining Sea. Williams, Vera B., illus. 1999. 48p. (J). (ps-3). pap. 6.99 (978-0-688-16701-1(2) , Harper Trophy) HarperCollins Pubs.

Williams, John F. The Fantastic Space Travels of Caleb McDougal Episode I: The Ruby Crystals. 2001. 123p. pap. 10.95 (978-0-595-21007-7(4) , Writers Club Pr.) iUniverse, Inc.

Williams, Joyce Hall & West, Nancy. Ruffitt versus Do-Well: In the Cradle of Mankind. 2001. 79p. per. 10.95 (978-0-7414-0641-5(1)) Infinity Publishing.

Williams, Juliet. Mouse House: An Extravagant Lift-the-Flap Hide-and-Seek Adventure. 2005. (Illus.). 7p. (J). bds. 9.95 (978-1-59354-082-1(5)) Handprint Bks.

Williams, Larry. The League of Clique. Williams, Larry, illus. 2007. (ENG., Illus.). 80p. per. 19.95 (*978-1-4241-5976-5(8)) PublishAmerica, Inc.

Williams, Levester. The Adventures od Crunchy & Munchy Squirrel: Field Nuts. 2005. pap. (*978-0-9774418-0-8(6)) L.Patrick Publishing.

Williams, Linda. The Mustard Seed Adventure. 2000. (J). pap. 9.00 (978-0-8059-4983-4(6)) Dorrance Publishing Co., Inc.

Williams, Maiya. The Hour of the Cobra. (YA). 2007. 320p. (gr. 2-7). pap. 5.95 (*978-0-8109-9362-4(7)); 2006. 312p. (gr. 4-9). 16.95 (978-0-8109-5970-5(4) , Amulet Bks.) Abrams, Harry N. , Inc.

—The Hour of the Outlaw. 2007. 360p. (YA). (gr. 4-9). 16.95 (*978-0-8109-9355-6(4)) Abrams, Harry N. , Inc.

Williams, Sue. I Went Walking. Vivas, Julie, illus. 2002. (J). 14.79 (978-0-7587-2823-4(9)) Book Wholesalers, Inc.

—I Went Walking, 2 bks., Set. Vivas, Julie, illus. unabr. ed. 2000. (ENG & SPA.). (J). (gr. k-3). pap. 33.95 incl. audio (978-0-87499-666-1(X)) Live Oak Media.

Williams, Suzanne. The Gigantic, Genuine Genie. Gonzales, Chuck, illus. 2007. (Princess Power Ser.: No. 6). 128p. (J). 15.99 (*978-0-06-078309-9(5)); (gr. 3-7). pap. 4.99 (*978-0-06-078308-2(7) , Harper Trophy) HarperCollins Pubs.

—Human or Alien? Carter, Abby, illus. 2004. (Ready-for-Chapters Ser.). 64p. (J). pap. 3.99 (978-0-689-86337-0(3) , Aladdin) Simon & Schuster Children's Publishing.

Williams, Suzanne. The Stubbornly Secretive Servant. Gonzales, Chuck, illus. 2007. (Princess Power Ser.). 128p. (J). 15.99 (*978-0-06-078307-5(9)); pap. 4.99 (*978-0-06-078306-8(0) , Harper Trophy) HarperCollins Pubs.

Williams, Vera B. Stringbean's Trip to the Shining Sea. 1999. (978-0-606-16744-4(7)); lib. bdg. 14.10 (978-0-613-18280-5(4)) Tandem Library Bks.

Williamson, Greg. How Do I Cure This Cold? Popko, Wendy, illus. 2005. (J). 7.99 (978-0-9666076-4-2(3)) Peerless Publishing, L.L.C.

Willis, Dan. The Dragon Well. 2004. (Dragonlance Ser.). (Illus.). 256p. (YA). pap. 5.99 (978-0-7869-3354-9(2)) Wizards of the Coast.

Willis, Jeanne. Adventures of Jimmy Scar. 2003. (Illus.). 160p. (J). pap. 8.99 (978-1-84270-230-7(0)) Andersen GBR. Dist: Independent Pubs. Group.

Willis, Patricia. Danger along the Ohio. 1999. 192p. (J). (gr. 3-7). pap. 6.99 (978-0-380-73151-0(7) , Harper Trophy) HarperCollins Pubs.

—Danger along the Ohio. 1999. (J). 12.64 (978-0-606-16343-9(3)); (gr. 3-6). lib. bdg. 14.15 (978-0-7857-0159-0(1)) Tandem Library Bks.

Willis, Wren. Why Is My Name September? 2005. 155p. pap. 11.39 (978-1-4116-6534-7(1)) Lulu.com.

Willoughby, Bebe. Saving Emma. Dacus, Bobbie, illus. 2005. (J). pap. 12.95 (978-0-9763945-0-1(2)) King St Bks./Stabler-Leadbeater Apothecary Museum.

Willowbough, W. K. A Day at the Old Man's Garden. 2005. (J). 19.95 (978-0-9761138-0-5(5)) Kaseberg, W. G. Publishing.

Wills, David. Fern's Dragon. 2005. 55p. pap. 12.95 (978-1-4137-7017-9(7)) PublishAmerica, Inc.

Willson, Sarah. Costume Capers. Artful Doodlers Limited Staff, illus. 2005. (Totally Spies! Ser.). 16p. (J). pap. 5.99 (978-0-689-87728-5(5) , Simon Spotlight) Simon & Schuster Children's Publishing.

—Dora's Halloween Adventure. Savitsky, Steven, illus. 2003. (Dora the Explorer Ser.). 14p. (J). bds. 5.99 (978-0-689-85844-4(2) , Simon Spotlight/Nickelodeon) Simon & Schuster Children's Publishing.

Willson, Sarah & Artful Doodlers Limited Staff. Mystery Messages. 2006. (Totally Spies! Ser.). (Illus.). 48p. (J). pap. 3.99 (978-1-4169-1188-3(X) , Simon Spotlight) Simon & Schuster Children's Publishing.

Wilson, Barbara. Sugarfootn' Hampson, Glenn C., ed. Curry, Garrett, illus. 2001. 7p. (J). (gr. k-3). pap. 6.50 (978-0-9653869-8-2(8)) Castle Pacific Publishing.

Wilson, Bob. Fearless Dave. 2006. (Illus.). 36p. 15.95 (978-1-84507-496-8(3)) Lincoln, Frances Ltd. GBR. Dist: Perseus Distribution.

—Stanley Bagshaw & the Fourteen-Foot Wheel. 2005. (Stanley Bagshaw Ser.). (Illus.). 32p. (J). (ps-k). pap. 5.95 (978-1-903015-40-7(5)) Barn Owl Bks, London GBR. Dist: Independent Pubs. Group.

Wilson, Budge. The Long Wait. Fernandes, Eugenie, illus. 32p. (J). (ps up). (978-0-7737-5851-3(8)) Stoddart Kids.

Wilson, David J. Lucky & the Trials of Life. 2000. (Illus.). 24p. (J). (gr. k-3). pap. 5.95 (978-0-9704761-0-4(8)) Pink Flamingo.

Wilson, Douglas. Blackthorn Winter. Bentley, Peter, illus. 2003. 141p. (J). per. 12.00 (978-1-932168-10-5(9)) Veritas Pr., Inc.

Wilson, Eric. Kootenay Kidnapper. 2001. (gr. 3-6). lib. bdg. 13.00 (978-0-613-54818-2(3)) Tandem Library Bks.

Wilson, Eric G. Pesadilla en Vancuver. 2001. Tr. of Vancouver Nightmare. (SPA.). 168p. (J). 6.95 (978-84-348-1138-6(3)) SM Ediciones ESP. Dist: AIMS International Bks., Inc.

Wilson, Greg. Three Sensible Adventures. Lytle, William S., illus. 1999. 56p. (J). (gr. k-3). pap. 7.95 (978-1-55037-598-5(9)); lib. bdg. 18.95 (978-1-55037-599-2(7)) Annick Pr., Ltd. CAN. Dist: Firefly Bks., Ltd.

—Three Sensible Adventures. 1999. (gr. k-3). lib. bdg. 16.40 (978-0-613-27242-1(0)) Tandem Library Bks.

Wilson, J. M. & Zolkowski, Cathy A. Blue: Adventures of a Gymnast. 2004. 150p. (YA). per. 11.95 (978-0-9667037-5-7(8)) Verona (Bk.) Publishing, Inc.

Wilson, Jacqueline. Buried Alive! l.t. ed. 2001. (Illus.). 192p. (J). 16.95 (978-0-7540-6157-1(4) , Galaxy Children's Large Print) BBC Audiobooks America.

—Cliffhanger. Sharratt, Nick, illus. l.t. ed. 2000. 86p. (J). pap. 16.95 (978-0-7540-6120-5(5) , Galaxy Children's Large Print) BBC Audiobooks America.

—Cliffhanger. 2000. (Yearling Book Ser.). (Illus.). 128p. (J). 8.99 (978-0-440-86338-0(4) , Corgi) Transworld Publishers Ltd. GBR. Dist: Trafalgar Square Publishing.

—The Dare Game. l.t. ed. 2001. (Illus.). 297p. (J). 16.95 (978-0-7540-6171-7(X) , Galaxy Children's Large Print) BBC Audiobooks America.

—Glubbslyme. 2000. (Corgi Yearling Ser.). (Illus.). 32p. (J). pap. 9.99 (978-0-440-86231-4(0) , Corgi) Transworld Publishers Ltd. GBR. Dist: Trafalgar Square Publishing.

Wilson, John. Lost in Spain. (Illus.). 174p. 2000. (YA). (gr. 8-12). (978-1-55041-550-6(6)); 1999. (gr. 7-10). (978-1-55041-523-0(9)) Fitzhenry & Whiteside, Ltd.

—Lost in Spain. 2001. (gr. 7-12). lib. bdg. 18.75 (978-0-613-43694-6(6)) Tandem Library Bks.

Wilson, Lynda. The Virtural Zone: In Search of Klondike Gold. 2001. (On Time's Wing Ser.). (Illus.). 72p. (J). (gr. 3-7). pap. (978-1-896184-70-8(7)) Roussan Pubs., Inc./Roussan Editeur, Inc.

Wilson, N. D. Leepike Ridge. 2007. (Illus.). 240p. (J). (gr. 3-7). 15.99 (978-0-375-83873-6(2)); lib. bdg. 18.99 (978-0-375-93873-3(7)) Random Hse. Children's Bks. (Random Hse. Bks. for Young Readers).

—Leepike Ridge. 2007. (Illus.). 224p. (J). pap. (978-0-375-83874-3(0)) Random Hse., Inc.

Wilson, Ryan. The Legendary Blobshocker. 1999. (Illus.). 20p. (gr. 1-4). pap. 16.95 (978-1-885477-51-4(1)) Future Horizons, Inc.

Windham, Ryder. The Hostage Princess. 2002. 90p. (J). (978-0-439-45881-8(1)) Scholastic, Inc.

—Indiana Jones: Last Crusade Novelization: Last Crusade Novelization. 2008. (Indiana Jones Ser.). 176p. (J). 6.99 (*978-0-545-04256-7(9) , Scholastic) Scholastic, Inc.

—Indiana Jones: Raiders of the Lost Ark Novelizat: Raiders of the Lost Ark Novelizat. 2008. (Indiana Jones Ser.). 176p. (J). 6.99 (*978-0-545-00700-9(3) , Scholastic) Scholastic, Inc.

Windle, Jeanette. Captured in Colombia, Vol. 3. 2002. (Parker Twins Ser.: No. 3). 160p. (gr. 3-8). pap. 5.99 (978-0-8254-4147-9(1)) Kregel Pubns.

Windsor, Patricia. Nightwood. 2006. 256p. (YA). (gr. 9). pap. 7.95 (978-0-385-73312-0(7)); lib. bdg. 9.99 (978-0-385-90331-8(6)) Random Hse. Children's Bks. (Delacorte Bks. for Young Readers).

Winfield (Edward Str Staff. The Rover Boys in the Jungle or Stirring. 2006. 63.99 (*978-1-4280-1844-0(1)) IndyPublish.com.

—The Rover Boys on the Ocean or a Chase F. 2006. 63.99 (*978-1-4280-1827-3(1)) IndyPublish.com.

Winfield, Arthur M. Putnam Hall Champions or Bound to Win Ou. 2006. pap. 28.95 (*978-1-4286-2346-0(9)) Kessinger Publishing, LLC.

Winfield, Arthur M. The Rover Boys in the Jungle. 2004. reprint ed. pap. 21.95 (978-1-4191-8118-4(1)); pap. 1.99 (978-1-4192-8118-1(6)) Kessinger Publishing, LLC.

Winfield, Arthur M. The Rover Boys in the Mountains or a Hunt for Fun & Fortune. 2006. (ENG.). 268p. per. 27.95 (*978-1-4286-4100-6(9)) Kessinger Publishing, LLC.

—The Rover Boys on the Plains or the Mystery of Red Rock Ranch. 2004. reprint ed. pap. 27.95 (978-1-4179-2626-8(0)) Kessinger Publishing, LLC.

—The Rover Boys Out West. 2004. reprint ed. pap. 21.95 (978-1-4191-8120-7(3)) Kessinger Publishing, LLC.

Winfield, Arthur M. The Rover Boys Out West. 2004. reprint ed. pap. 1.99 (978-1-4192-8120-4(8)) Kessinger Publishing, LLC.

Winfield, M. Arthur. The Rover Boys in the Mountains or a Hun. 2006. 78.99 (*978-1-4280-1209-7(5)); pap. 72.99 (*978-1-4280-1205-9(2)) IndyPublish.com.

—The Rover Boys Out West or the Search Fo. 2006. 63.99 (*978-1-4280-1837-2(9)) IndyPublish.com.

Wingfield, Albert B. A Real Win. Ramey, Lisa L., illus. 2000. 16p. (J). pap. 7.95 (978-1-930260-06-1(7)) CTS Family Pr.

Wininger, Stephen T. The Adventure of Pirate Pete Moss. 2004. (J). pap. (978-1-59196-466-7(0)) Instantpublisher.com.

Winkler, Henry & Oliver, Lin. The Life of Me: Enter at Your Own Risk. Watson, Jesse Joshua, illus. 2008. (Hank Zipzer Ser.: No. 14). 256p. (J). 14.99 (*978-0-448-44377-5(5)); (gr. 3-7). pap. 5.99 (*978-0-448-44376-8(7)) Penguin Group (USA) Inc. (Grosset & Dunlap).

Winn, L. B. Butterpod Jerome & the Planet of Gabool. Winn, L. B., illus. 2007. (J). pap. 18.95 (*978-0-9791884-0-4(7)) Winn, Lynnette.

Winnard, Rebecca Victoria & Winnard, Linda. Giraffe Liberation: An Act of Freedom. 2006. 53p. pap. 12.95 (978-1-4241-0552-6(8)) PublishAmerica, Inc.

Winnick, Karen B. Sybil's Night Ride. Winnick, Karen B., illus. 2003. (Illus.). 32p. (J). (gr. k-2). 15.95 (978-1-56397-697-1(8)) Boyds Mills Pr.

Winston, Annie. Admiral Wright's Heroical Storicals: Daniel Boone & the Battle of Boonesborough. 2nd ed. 2002. (Illus.). 192p. (J). per. 7.95 (978-0-9725719-7-5(3) , Sonship Pr.) 21st Century Pr.

Winter, Karen Knight & Winter, William B. Amazon Rush. 2005. 122p. pap. 17.95 (978-1-4137-7503-7(9)) PublishAmerica, Inc.

Winterson, Jeanette. Tanglewreck. 2006. 250p. (J). 16.95 (978-1-58234-919-0(3) , Bloomsbury Children) Bloomsbury Publishing.

Wisemon, Tamar. Y. A. D. Investigators. 2002. (Illus.). 235p. 15.95 (978-0-9707572-6-5(3)) Jerusalem Pubns.

Wishinsky, Frieda. Flying High! Griffiths, Dean, illus. 2007. (Canadian Flyer Adventures Ser.: No. 5). 96p. (J). (gr. 1-4). 16.95 (*978-1-897066-98-0(8)); pap. 6.95 (*978-1-897066-99-7(6)) Maple Tree Pr. CAN. Dist: Perseus Distribution.

Wishinsky, Frieda. A Quest in Time. Slavin, Bill, illus. 2000. 72p. (J). (gr. 3-7). 22.95 (978-1-894379-07-6(1) , Owl Bks.) Maple Tree Pr. CAN. Dist: Firefly Bks., Ltd.

Wisler, G. Clifton. Mustang Flats. 1999. (J). (978-0-606-16769-7(2)) Tandem Library Bks.

Wisner, Helyn. Seaside Sleuths: The Bald Head Island G. 2006. pap. 11.50 (*978-1-4259-1097-6(1)) AuthorHouse.

Withers, Pam. Adrenalin Ride. 2004. (Take It to the Extreme Ser.). 176p. (YA). (gr. 7-11). pap. 6.95 (978-1-55285-604-8(6)) Whitecap Bks., Ltd. CAN. Dist: Firefly Bks., Ltd.

—BMX Tunnel Run. 2007. (Take It to the Xtreme Ser.). 231p. (YA). (gr. 7-10). pap. 6.95 (*978-1-55285-904-9(5) , Walrus Bks.) Whitecap Bks., Ltd. CAN. Dist: Firefly Bks., Ltd.

—Daredevil Club. 2006. 112p. (J). pap. 8.95 (978-1-55143-614-2(0)); lib. bdg. 14.95 (978-1-55143-618-0(3)) Orca Bk. Pubs. USA.

—Surf Zone. 2005. (Take it to the Extreme Ser.). 160p. (YA). (gr. 7-10). pap. 6.95 (978-1-55285-718-2(2) , Walrus Bks.) Whitecap Bks., Ltd. CAN. Dist: Firefly Bks., Ltd.

—Vertical Limits. 2006. (Take it to the Extreme Ser.). 226p. (YA). (gr. 7-12). pap. 6.95 (978-1-55285-783-0(2) , Walrus Bks.) Whitecap Bks., Ltd. CAN. Dist: Firefly Bks., Ltd.

Withers, Pam. Wake's Edge. 2007. (Take It to the Xtreme Ser.). 196p. (YA). (gr. 7-10). pap. 6.95 (*978-1-55285-856-1(1) , Walrus Bks.) Whitecap Bks., Ltd. CAN. Dist: Firefly Bks., Ltd.

Witschen, Kay. Clinker's Dragon. 2006. (J). 6.95 (978-0-9741352-2-9(4)) Dwitt Publishing.

Wittner, Shirley. Kemira & the Ancient Book of Spells. 2006. 51p. pap. 12.95 (*978-1-4241-4840-0(5)) PublishAmerica, Inc.

Wohl, David, et al. Top Cows Best of Michael Turner. 2005. (Illus.). 240p. (YA). pap. 24.99 (978-1-58240-544-5(1)) Image Comics.

Wojciechowska, Maia. Shadow of the Bull. 141p. (YA). (gr. 5 up). pap. 3.95 (978-0-8072-1506-7(6) , Listening Library) Random Hse. Audio Publishing Group.

Wolder, Dianne & Harrison-Lever, Brian. Photographs in the Mud. 2005. (Illus.). 32p. (J). 24.25 (978-1-920731-20-5(2)) Fremantle Pr. AUS. Dist: International Specialized Bk. Services.

Wolfe, Corey & Mawhinney, Art, illus. The Rainforest Race. 2006. (Ready-To-Read Ser.). 24p. (J). pap. 3.99 (978-1-4169-1756-4(X) , Simon Spotlight/Nickelodeon) Simon & Schuster Children's Publishing.

Wolfe, D. K. Flap Doodle & the Incredible Kibbll Caper. 2005. (Illus.). 247p. (J). (gr. 4-6). 16.95 (978-1-59810-031-0(9)) Jeriger Pr.

Wolfel, Ursula. Fliegender Stern. pap. 14.95 (978-3-570-26064-7(X)) Bertelsman, Verlagsgruppe C. GmbH DEU. Dist: Distribooks, Inc.

Wolo, Elaine Armour. John & the Diamonds. Weah, Leo Gmi, illus. 2001. 24p. (J). (ps-6). pap. 4.00 (978-0-9708998-1-1(5)) Wolo, Armour Foundation.

The Wonderful Wizard of OZ: Twiggle Book. 2004. (Illus.). 26p. (J). 1.99 (978-0-9762573-2-5(7)) Ear Twiggles Productions, Inc.

Woo. Rebirth, 11 vols. rev. ed. 2003. (Illus.). 176p. Vol. 2. (gr. 8 up). pap. 9.99 (978-1-59182-217-2(3)); Vol. 3. (gr. 9 up). pap. 9.99 (978-1-59182-218-9(1)) TOKYOPOP, Inc. (Tokyopop Adult).

Wood, Amanda. Amazing Baby Look & Play! 2005. (Illus.). 12p. (J). 15.95 (978-1-59223-528-5(X) , Silver Dolphin Bks.) Advantage Pubs. Group.

—Amazing Baby Touch & Play! 2005. (Illus.). 12p. (J). 15.95 (978-1-59223-529-2(8) , Silver Dolphin Bks.) Advantage Pubs. Group.

Wood, Beverley & Wood, Chris. Golden Boy. 2007. (Sirius Mystery Ser.). 276p. (J). pap. 8.95 (978-1-55192-953-8(8) , Polestar Book Pubs.) Raincoast Bk. Distribution CAN. Dist: Perseus Distribution.

Wood, Francis Eugene. The Nipkins, Vol. II. Pickett, Elizabeth, ed. McDermott, Robert W., illus. Wood, Chris, photos by. rev. ed. 2002. 140p. (J). pap. 12.00 (978-0-9657047-8-6(5)) Tip-Of-The-Moon Publishing Co.

—Return to Winterville. Pickett, Elizabeth & Dean, Tina, eds. Larsen, Dan, illus. 2004. 96p. (YA). per. 14.95 net. (978-0-9746372-1-1(1)) Tip-Of-The-Moon Publishing Co.

Wood, Maggie L. The Princess Pawn. 2004. 299p. (J). pap. 9.95 (978-1-894549-29-5(5)) Sumach Pr. CAN. Dist: Orca Bk. Pubs. USA.

Wood, Wally. T. H. U. N. D. E. R. Agents. rev. ed. 2002. (Archives Ser.: Vol. 1). (Illus.). 248p. 49.95 (978-1-56389-903-4(5)) DC Comics.

Woodberry, Gareth. Gakeva Gluntok's New School. 2005. 65p. pap. 12.95 (978-1-4137-9894-4(2)) PublishAmerica, Inc.

Woodfield, Gary. The Time Thief. 2004. (J). per. 19.95 (978-0-9761289-2-2(6)); (Illus.). (YA). 26.95 (978-0-9743348-9-9(8)) Nightengale Pr.

Wooding, Chris. Survive. 2000. (Broken Sky Ser.: No. 2). (Illus.). 160p. (gr. 4-7). (J). pap. 4.50 (978-0-439-12864-3(1)); (J). pap. 4.50 (978-0-439-12865-0(X) , Scholastic Paperbacks); (YA). pap. 4.50 (978-0-439-13998-4(8)) Scholastic, Inc.

—Survive. (Broken Sky Ser.: No. 1). (J). (gr. 4-7). No. 1. 1999. (978-0-606-19543-0(2)); No. 2. 2000. (978-0-606-19544-7(0)); No. 3. 2000. (978-0-606-19545-4(9)); No. 4. 2000. (978-0-606-19546-1(7)); No. 5. 2000. (978-0-606-19547-8(5)) Tandem Library Bks.

Wooding, Chris & Kyte, Steve. Survive, No. 7. 2001. 432p. pap. 4.50 (978-0-439-12869-8(2) , Scholastic Paperbacks) Scholastic, Inc.

Woodruff, Elvira. Fearless. 2008. 240p. (J). 16.99 (978-0-439-67703-5(3) , Scholastic Pr.) Scholastic, Inc.

Woodruff, Paul M. Monsters, Myths & Mysteries: A Tangled Tour Maze Book. 2007. (Illus.). 80p. (J). pap. 5.95 (978-1-4027-3803-6(X)) Sterling Publishing Co., Inc.

Woodson, Frank. Mean Waters. Taylor, Marjorie, illus. rev. ed. 1999. (Take Ten Ser.). 54p. (YA). (gr. 4-12). pap. 3.95 (978-1-58659-015-4(4)) Artesian Pr.

—Mean Waters. 2000. (gr. 5-8). lib. bdg. 11.80 (978-0-613-51218-3(9)) Tandem Library Bks.

Woodson, Jacqueline. The House You Pass on the Way. 1999. (J). (978-0-606-16085-8(X)) Tandem Library Bks.

Woodward, J. Howland. A Moment in Time. 2006. 55p. pap. 12.95 (978-1-4241-1334-7(2)) PublishAmerica, Inc.

Woodward, Susan. Seldovia Sam & Blueberry Bear, Vol. 4. Meissner, Amy, illus. 2005. 64p. (J). pap. 6.95 (978-0-88240-603-9(5) , Alaska Northwest Bks.) Graphic Arts Ctr. Publishing Co.

Wookie World. 2003. (Star Wars Ser.: Vol. 6). (Illus.). 360p. pap. 29.95 (978-1-56971-907-7(1)) Dark Horse Comics.

Worcester, Daryl D. The Story of the Famous Travels Travlslot. 2006. 48p. pap. 12.95 (978-1-4241-2417-6(4)) PublishAmerica, Inc.

Worcester, Donald Emmet. Lone Hunter Books: War Pony. 2000. Tr. of Lone Hunter's Gray Pony. (gr. 3-6). lib. bdg. 32.65 (978-0-613-90540-4(7)) Tandem Library Bks.

Worley, Rob. Heir to Fire: Gila Flats. Dubisch, Mike, illus. 2006. 129p. (J). (gr. 5-8). 12.95 (978-0-9742803-7-0(2) , Actionopolis) Komikwerks, LLC.

Worley, Roger. The Wishbone Journal II. 2005. 76p. pap. 14.95 (978-1-4137-6314-0(6)) PublishAmerica, Inc.

Wormell, Christopher. The Sea Monster. 2006. (Illus.). 32p. pap. 8.99 (978-0-09-945147-1(6) , Red Fox) Random Hse. Children's Bks. GBR. Dist: Trafalgar Square Publishing.

Worthfields, Mark. Willy the Blue-Speckled Worm. 2004. 57p. pap. 12.95 (978-1-4137-1547-7(8)) PublishAmerica, Inc.

Wright, Chris. Operation Overflow. 2003. per. 14.25 (978-1-932301-90-8(9) , 1555) Airleaf Publishing & Bookselling.

Wright Johnson, Shelli. Falcon in the Nest: A Story of Bes Adventure. 2004. 273p. pap. 21.95 (978-1-4137-5263-2(2)) PublishAmerica, Inc.

Wright, Lisa. A Christmas Vacation. 2003. (J). per. 11.00 (978-1-4116-0306-6(0)) Lulu.com.

Wright, Mary J. The Brave Knight. 2005. 108p. pap. 16.95 (978-1-4137-8185-4(3)) PublishAmerica, Inc.

Wright, Randall. Hunchback. rev. ed. 2004. (Illus.). 256p. (J). 16.95 (978-0-8050-7232-7(2) , Holt, Henry & Co. Bks. For Young Readers) Holt, Henry & Co.

Wright, Sean. Jesse Jameson & the Golden Glow, Bk.1. Wright, Trisha & Cole, Patricia Natalie, eds. 2003. (ENG., Illus.). 182p. pap. (*978-0-9544374-0-4(3)) Crowswing Bks.

Wright, Terry. The One-Eyed Monster. 2006. 48p. pap. 12.95 (978-1-4241-3696-4(2)) PublishAmerica, Inc.

Wright, Timothy. Childish Things. 2006. 163p. pap. 11.49 (978-1-4116-6987-1(8)) Lulu.com.

Wyatt, Cherokee, as told by. The Adventures of Margaret Mouse: Harvest Carnival. l.t. ed. 2006. (Illus.). 32p. (J). 6.95 (978-0-9761326-5-3(6)) www.margaretmouse.com publishing co.

—The Adventures of Margaret Mouse: The Magic Star. l.t. ed. 2006. (Illus.). 32p. (J). 6.95 (978-0-9761326-6-0(4)) www.margaretmouse.com publishing co.

Wyke-Smith, E. A. The Marvellous Land of Snergs. Morrow, George, illus. 2006. 224p. (J). pap. 9.95 (978-0-486-45255-5(7)) Dover Pubns., Inc.

Wyre, Yvonne. The Further Adventures of Cuthbert the Coal Lorry & all His Friends. 2007. (Illus.). 204p. pap. (*978-1-84401-801-7(6)) Athena Pr.

Wyss, Johann David. The Swiss Family Robinson. 2006. (Charming Classics). 208p. (J). pap. 6.99 (978-0-06-087587-9(9) , Harper Festival) HarperCollins Pubs.

Wyss, Johann David. The Swiss Family Robinson: Or Adventures in a Desert Island. l.t. ed. 2006. 354p. pap. 18.99 (*978-1-4264-5633-6(6)) BiblioBazaar.

Wyss, Tyan. Night Flyer. Immelman, Sarita, illus. 2006. 40p. (J). per. 14.95 (*978-1-58939-916-7(1)) Virtualbookworm.com Publishing, Inc.

Yaccarino, Dan. Where the 4 Winds Blow. 2000. mass mkt. 6.95 (978-0-06-443841-4(4)) HarperCollins Pubs.

Yackety-Yak, the Alien's Back. 2005. (Illus.). (J). lib. bdg. 27.10 (978-1-59389-141-1(5)) Chrysalis Education.

Yaeger, Stephen S. Ian & the Woodins. 2001. 152p. (Orig.). pap. 11.95 (978-0-595-18366-1(2) , Writers Club Pr.) iUniverse, Inc.

Yago, Norihiro. Claymore. 2007. (Claymore Ser.). 200p. (YA). Vol. 6. pap. 7.99 (978-1-4215-1048-4(0)); Vol. 7. pap. 7.99 (978-1-4215-1049-1(9)) Viz Media.

Yan, Wing. King of Fighters 2003, Vol. 4. 2008. (Illus.). 128p. (YA). pap. 13.95 (***978-1-59796-010-6(1)***) DrMaster Pubns. Inc.

Yancey, Rick. Alfred Kropp No. 2: The Seal of Solomon. 2007. 336p. (J). (gr. 7 up). 16.95 (***978-1-59990-045-2(9)***) Bloomsbury Publishing.

Yancey, Rick. The Extraordinary Adventures of Alfred Kropp. 2005. 375p. (J). (gr. 7-12). 16.95 (978-1-58234-693-9(3)); 2006. (Illus.). 352p. (YA). reprint ed. pap. 7.95 (978-1-59990-044-5(0)) Bloomsbury Publishing. (Bloomsbury Children).

Yasuhiko, Yoshikazu. Gundam No. 9, No. 10: The Origin. 2004. (gr. 7-12). lib. bdg. 16.40 (978-0-613-88462-4(0)) Tandem Library Bks.

Yates, Lady. Earthsong, Vol. 1. 2006. (Illus.). 160p. (YA). pap. 14.99 (978-1-933164-15-1(8)) Seven Seas Entertainment, LLC.

Yee, Linda L. Big Red Things. 2005. 20.00 (978-0-8059-9855-9(1)) Dorrance Publishing Co., Inc.

Yeh, Julie. Poppie's Adventures: Serpents in Paradise. Hsu, Jack, illus. 2003. 48p. (J). per. (978-0-9742386-0-9(0)) Way Out Comics.

Yep, Laurence. The Red Warrior. 2002. (YA). (gr. 5-9). 14.89 (978-0-06-027521-1(9)); 14.95 (978-0-06-027520-4(0)) HarperCollins Pubs.

Yerges, Karen. The Adventures of Scooper the Beagle Dog: Las aventuras de Scooper el perrito Beagle. 2004. (SPA., Illus.). 60p. (J). per. 19.95 (978-0-9764384-0-3(2)) Mitre's Touch Gallery, The.

Yerkes, Lane. Don't Make a Sound. 2000. (Talking Pages Deluxe Ser.). (Illus.). (J). (ps-3). 11.00 (978-1-58224-129-6(5)) Futech Interactive Products, Inc.

YKids Staff. Gulliver's Travels. 2007. (Manga Literary Classics Ser.). 148p. (J). (gr. 4-7). pap. 14.95 (***978-981-05-4941-1(5)***) Youngjin (Singapore) Pte Ltd. SGP. *Dist:* Independent Pubs. Group.

—Prince & the Pauper. 2008. (Manga Literary Classics Ser.). 144p. (J). (gr. 4-7). pap. 14.95 (***978-981-05-7553-3(X)***) Youngjin (Singapore) Pte Ltd. SGP. *Dist:* Independent Pubs. Group.

—Treasure Island. 2007. (Manga Literary Classics Ser.). 148p. (J). (gr. 4-7). pap. 14.95 (***978-981-05-4942-8(3)***) Youngjin (Singapore) Pte Ltd. SGP. *Dist:* Independent Pubs. Group.

—20,000 Leagues under the Sea. 2008. (Manga Literary Classics Ser.). 144p. (J). pap. 14.95 (***978-981-05-7556-4(4)***) Youngjin (Singapore) Pte Ltd. SGP. *Dist:* Independent Pubs. Group.

Ylvisaker, Anne. Little Klein. 2007. (Illus.). 192p. (J). (gr. 3-7). 15.99 (***978-0-7636-3359-2(3)***) Candlewick Pr.

Yoder, Greg, illus. The Swing: A Storybook to Color. 2003. (J). 8.99 (978-1-930353-88-6(X)) Masthof Pr.

Yoder, Karen L. Fire Kids! The Adventures of Hose Company No. 2. 2002. 124p. (J). 15.95 (978-0-9700487-4-5(2)) Stoney Creek Pr.

Yolen, Jane. Atalanta & the Arcadian Beast. 2004. (gr. 3-6). lib. bdg. 14.15 (978-0-613-83009-6(1)) Tandem Library Bks.

—Commander Toad & the Voyage Home. Degen, Bruce, illus. 1998. 64p. (J). (gr. 2-5). pap. 5.99 (978-0-698-11602-3(X) , Putnam Juvenile) Penguin Group (USA) Inc.

—Commander Toad & the Voyage Home. 1999. (Illus.). (J). (978-0-606-15489-5(2)) Tandem Library Bks.

—Dragon's Blood. 2004. (Pit Dragon Chronicles: Vol. 1). (Illus.). 320p. (YA). pap. 6.95 (978-0-15-205126-6(0) , Magic Carpet Bks.) Harcourt Children's Bks.

—Heart's Blood. 2004. (Pit Dragon Chronicles: Vol. 2). (Illus.). 368p. (YA). pap. 6.95 (978-0-15-205118-1(X) , Magic Carpet Bks.) Harcourt Children's Bks.

—Pictish Child. 2002. (gr. 3-6). lib. bdg. 14.10 (978-0-613-53854-1(4)) Tandem Library Bks.

—A Sending of Dragons. 2004. (Pit Dragon Chronicles: Vol. 3). (Illus.). 312p. (YA). pap. 6.95 (978-0-15-205128-0(7) , Magic Carpet Bks.) Harcourt Children's Bks.

—The Wizard's Map. 2002. (Tartan Magic Ser.: Bk. 1). 156p. (YA). pap. 5.95 (978-0-15-216365-5(4) , Magic Carpet Bks.) Harcourt Children's Bks.

Yolen, Jane & Harris, Robert J. Atalanta & the Arcadian Beast. 2003. (Young Heroes Ser.: Bk. 3). 256p. (J). 15.99 (978-0-06-029454-0(X)) HarperCollins Pubs.

Yolen, Jane & Harris, Robert J. The Rogues. 2007. 277p. (J). (gr. 6-9). 18.99 (***978-0-399-23898-7(0)*** , Philomel) Penguin Group (USA) Inc.

Yost-Filgate, Susan. A Good Day for Abbey. Filgate, Leonard, illus. 2004. 14p. (J). bds. 6.99 (978-0-9672422-8-6(2)) Rip Squeak, Inc.

—Rip Squeak & His Friends off on Adventure. Filgate, Leonard, illus. 2004. 32p. (J). 16.99 (978-0-9672422-9-3(0)) Rip Squeak, Inc.

—The Treasure. Filgate, Leonard, illus. 2005. 32p. (J). (ps-3). 14.99 (978-0-9747825-1-5(3)) Rip Squeak, Inc.

Young, Brett. The Twontle. 2005. (Illus.). 40p. (J). 10.99 (978-0-9725230-7-3(3)) Wandering Sage Bookstore & More, LLC.

Young, Emma. STORM: the Infinity Code: The Infinity Code. 2008. (J). (gr. 5). 16.99 (***978-0-8037-3265-0(1)*** , Dial) Penguin Group (USA) Inc.

Young, Joseph R. Legend of the Lost Josephine Mine: A Fascinating Adventure. 2001. 221p. (J). pap. 13.95 (978-1-55517-550-4(3) , Bonneville Bks.) Cedar Fort, Inc./CFI Distribution.

Young, Kristi. The Secret Club - the Powder Puff Club Book 1. 2007. 140p. (J). per. 12.95 (***978-1-59594-070-4(7)*** , Wingspan Pr.) WingSpan Publishing.

Young, Lauren. Ally M. & Ally G. Rooney, Sandra, illus. 2006. 20p. (J). (***978-1-4120-8518-2(7)***) Trafford Publishing.

Young, Steve. Winchell Mink: The Misadventure Begins. 2004. 144p. (J). 16.89 (978-0-06-053500-1(8)) HarperCollins Pubs.

Youngberg, Norma. The Tiger of Bitter Valley. 2004. (Illus.). 251p. (J). (gr. 3-6). reprint ed. per. 13.95 (978-1-57258-186-9(7) , 945-6048) TEACH Services, Inc.

Yourgrau, Barry. Another NASTYbook: The Curse of the Tweeties. DeJesus, Robert, illus. 2006. 176p. (J). 11.99 (978-0-06-057981-4(1)); lib. bdg. 13.89 (978-0-06-057982-1(X)) HarperCollins Pubs. (Cotler, Joanna Books).

—Nasty Book. 2005. 192p. (J). (gr. k-9). 11.99 (978-0-06-057978-4(1) , Cotler, Joanna Books) HarperCollins Pubs.

—Nasty Book, No. 3. Swaab, Neil, illus. 2007. 160p. (J). 12.99 (***978-0-06-077676-3(5)*** , Cotler, Joanna Books) HarperCollins Pubs.

—NASTYbook. 2007. 192p. (J). pap. 5.99 (***978-0-06-057980-7(3)*** , Harper Trophy) HarperCollins Pubs.

Yourzek, Tammy. Dragons of the Soul. 2006. 192p. (YA). pap. 9.95 (978-1-56315-382-2(3)) SterlingHouse Pubs., Inc.

YoYo Books. Princess Charlotte's Journey Through History. 2005. 32p. 9.95 (978-90-5843-458-6(3)) YoYo Bks. BEL. *Dist:* National Bk. Network.

Yu, Li, et al. The Holy Spark: Rogel & the Goddess of Liberty. 2006. (J). (978-1-931907-42-2(0)) Homa & Sekey Bks.

Zabrosky, Joseph. Herbie Hanson, 1 vol., 4 bks. l.t. ed. 2005. (Illus.). 32p. (J). per. (978-0-9768831-0-4(4)) Elohim Bks.

Zahn, Timothy. Dragon & Herdsman. 2007. (Dragonback Ser.). 304p. (J). mass mkt. 5.99 (***978-0-7653-5276-7(1)*** , Starscape) Doherty, Tom Assocs., LLC.

—Dragon & Judge. 2007. (Dragonback Ser.). 320p. (J). 17.95 (***978-0-7653-1418-5(5)*** , Starscape) Doherty, Tom Assocs., LLC.

—Dragon & Slave: The Third Dragonback Adventure. rev. ed. 2005. (Dragonback Ser.). 304p. (J). 17.95 (978-0-7653-0126-0(1) , Tor Bks.) Doherty, Tom Assocs., LLC.

—Dragon & Soldier. 2005. (Dragonback Ser.). 304p. (J). 5.99 (978-0-7653-5017-6(3) , Starscape) Doherty, Tom Assocs., LLC.

—Dragon & Soldier: The Second Dragonback Adventure. rev. ed. 2004. (Dragonback Ser.). 304p. (J). 17.95 (978-0-7653-0125-3(3) , Tor Bks.) Doherty, Tom Assocs., LLC.

Zakon, Miriam, creator. Baker's Dozen: Three-in-One 1-3, 4-6, 7-9, 10-12, 13-15, 16-17, 3 vols. Vols. 1-3. 16.95 (978-1-56871-200-6(0)); Vols. 10-12. 16.99 (978-1-56871-297-0(9)); Vols. 13-15. 16.99 (978-1-56871-266-6(9)) Targum Pr., Inc.

Zalme, Ron, illus. Around the World! 2006. (Dora the Explorer Ser.). 24p. (J). pap. 3.99 (978-1-4169-2478-4(7) , Simon Spotlight/Nickelodeon) Simon & Schuster Children's Publishing.

Zappa, Ahmet. The Monstrous Memoirs of a Mighty McFearless. 2006. (Illus.). 224p. (J). (gr. 3-7). 12.95 (978-0-375-83287-1(4) , Random Hse. Bks. for Young Readers) Random Hse. Children's Bks.

Zarley, Jacqualynn. Adventures with Lucy the Llama: Book One: Justice for the Great Forest. 2004. 56p. pap. 12.95 (978-1-4137-4906-9(2)) PublishAmerica, Inc.

Zarley, Jacqualynn R. Adventures with Lucy the Llama Book Two: Shung the Trickster. 2006. 54p. pap. 12.95 (978-1-4137-5996-9(3)) PublishAmerica, Inc.

Zaugg, Sandra L. A Prayer for Mother. 2005. (Illus.). 95p. (J). (978-0-8163-2056-1(X)) Pacific Pr. Pubns.

Zdenek, Joseph. Heart of Courage: The Narscix War. 2007. 372p. (ps-7). per. 20.95 (***978-0-595-43187-8(9)***) iUniverse, Inc.

Zellers, Michelle. Maya's Magic Carpet. 2006. (J). per. 11.95 (978-1-889743-48-6(8)) Robbie Dean Pr.

Zeman, Ludmila. Gilgamesh the King. Zeman, Ludmila, illus. 1998. (Epic of Gilgamesh Ser.: Vol. 1). (Illus.). 24p. (J). (gr. 3-7). reprint ed. pap. 8.95 (978-0-88776-437-0(1)) Tundra Bks., Inc./Livres Toundra, Inc. CAN. *Dist:* Random Hse., Inc.

—The Last Quest of Gilgamesh, Book 3. Zeman, Ludmila, illus. 1998. (Epic of Gilgamesh Ser.: Vol. 3). (Illus.). 24p. (J). (gr. 3-7). reprint ed. pap. 8.95 (978-0-88776-380-9(4)) Tundra Bks., Inc./Livres Toundra, Inc. CAN. *Dist:* Random Hse., Inc.

—Sindbad: From the Tales of the Thousand & One Nights. Zeman, Ludmila, illus. 1999. (Illus.). 32p. (J). (gr. 1-3). 17.95 (978-0-88776-460-8(6)) Tundra Bks., Inc./Livres Toundra, Inc. CAN. *Dist:* Random Hse., Inc.

Zeman, Ludmila, illus. & retold by. Sinbad's Secret. Zeman, Ludmila, retold by. 2003. 32p. (J). (gr. 1 up). 17.95 (978-0-88776-462-2(2)) Tundra Bks., Inc./Livres Toundra, Inc. CAN. *Dist:* Random Hse., Inc.

Zeman, Ludmila & Levesque, Suzanne. Sinbad et les Geants. 2001. (FRE & SPA., Illus.). 32p. (J). (gr. 1). 19.95 (978-0-88776-525-4(4) , Livres Toundra) Tundra Bks., Inc./Livres Toundra, Inc. CAN. *Dist:* Random Hse., Inc.

Zemeckis, Robert, et al. The Polar Express Movie Shadowbook: An Interactive Shadow-Casting Bedtime Story. Allsburg, ChrisVan, illus. 2006. 12p. (J). (gr. 4 up). reprint ed. 13.00 (978-1-4223-5172-7(6)) DIANE Publishing Co.

Zevy, Aaron. A Light in the Darkness. Tebbutt, Susan, illus. 1998. pap. 5.95 (978-0-9680678-9-5(1)) Tumbleweed Pr.

Zick, Bruce, illus. The Anubis Tapestry: Between Twilights. 2006. 152p. (J). 12.95 (978-0-9742803-8-7(0) , Actionopolis) Komikwerks, LLC.

Ziefert, Harriet. William & the Dragon. Brown, Richard, illus. 2005. 36p. (ps-ps). 15.95 (978-1-59354-089-0(2)) Blue Apple Bks.

Ziefert, Harriet & Taback, Simms. Beach Party! 2005. (Illus.). 7p. (J). bds. 8.95 (978-1-59354-067-8(1)) Blue Apple Bks.

Ziegler, Argentina Palacios, tr. Aventura magica de Dora (Dora's Fairy-Tale Adventure) Hall, Susan', illus. 2006. (Dora la Exploradora Ser.). (SPA.). 24p. (J). pap. 3.99 (978-1-4169-1184-5(7) , Libros Para Ninos) Simon & Schuster Children's Publishing.

Zierfert, Harriet. The Biggest Job of All. Brown, Lauren, illus. 2005. 40p. (J). 15.95 (978-1-59354-100-2(7)) Blue Apple Bks.

Zimmerman, Ron. Ultimate Adventures Vol. 1: One Tin Soldier. 2005. (Hank Kipple Ser.). (Illus.). 144p. (YA). pap. 12.99 (978-0-7851-1043-9(7)) Marvel Enterprises, Inc.

Zimmerman, W. Frederick. Unauthorized Harry Potter & the Alchemist's Cell News: Half-Blood Prince Analysis & Speculation. 2006. 160p. per. 14.94 (978-0-9777424-7-9(4)) Nimble Bks. LLC.

—Unauthorized Harry Potter & the Chariots of Light News: Half-Blood Prince Analysis & Speculation. 2006. 160p. per. 14.94 (978-0-9777424-8-6(2)) Nimble Bks. LLC.

Zindel, Paul. The Effect of Gamma Rays on Man-in-the-Moon Marigolds. 1999. 17p. (J). (gr. 8-12). 9.95 (978-1-56137-150-1(5) , BK8184) Novel Units, Inc.

—The Pigman's Legacy. 2005. 168p. (YA). (gr. 7-12). lib. bdg. 13.04 (978-0-606-33946-9(9)) Tandem Library Bks.

—Raptor, No. 1. 1999. (Raptor Ser.: Vol. 1). 176p. (gr. 5-9). pap. 4.99 (978-0-7868-1224-0(9)) Disney Pr.

—Raptor. unabr. ed. 2000. (J). pap., stu. ed. 42.24 incl. audio (978-0-7887-4185-2(3) , 41098) Recorded Bks., LLC.

—Raptor. 1999. 170p. (J). (ps-7). per. 11.64 (978-0-606-17385-8(4)); (gr. 5-8). lib. bdg. 13.00 (978-0-613-22241-9(5)) Tandem Library Bks.

—Raptor Paperback Club. 1999. (Illus.). 176p. (J). pap. 4.99 (978-0-7868-1471-8(3)) Disney Pr.

—Reef of Death. 1998. (Illus.). 192p. (J). (gr. 3 up). 15.95 (978-0-06-024728-7(2)); (gr. 6-10). lib. bdg. 15.89 (978-0-06-024733-1(9)) HarperCollins Pubs.

—Reef of Death. 1999. (978-0-606-16669-0(6)) Tandem Library Bks.

Zocchi, Judy M. Paulie & Sasha: The Rescue. Vannozzi, Don, illus. 1999. (Paulie & Sasha Ser.). 32p. (J). (gr. k-3). 15.95 (978-1-891997-04-4(1)) Dingles & Co.

Zoehfeld, Kathleen Weidner, adapted by. Tarzan. 1999. (Illus.). 48p. (J). (ps-3). 10.99 (978-0-7868-3220-0(7)) Disney Pr.

Zondervan. Elephant's Big Ride. Pulley, Kelly, illus. 2006. (Beginner's Bible' Ser.). 20p. (J). 6.99 (978-0-310-71340-1(4)) Zonderkidz.

—Soul Gear Assortment AMS. 2004. (J). pap. 95.88 (978-0-310-60306-1(4)) Zonderkidz.

—2:52 Laptop 1 Reality Shift/Laptop 2 Double Take - Focus on the Family: 52 Laptop 1 Reality Shift/Laptop 2 Double Take - Focus on the Family. 2004. (J). pap. 9.98 (978-0-310-70934-3(2)) Zonderkidz.

Zorn, Steven & Defoe, Daniel. Robinson Crusoe. Wyeth, N. C., illus. 2002. 48p. (J). 9.98 (978-0-7624-1419-2(7) , Courage Bks.) Running Pr. Bk. Pubs.

Zorro: Crypts. 2006. (J). pap. 7.95 (978-1-59707-032-4(7)) NBM Publishing Co.

Zucker, Jonny. Alien Attack. Smith, Pete, illus. 2007. 35p. (J). pap. (***978-1-59889-425-7(0)***); 40p. (YA). (gr. 5-9). lib. bdg. 21.26 (***978-1-59889-329-8(7)***) Stone Arch Bks.

—Creature Chase. Troiano, Enzo, illus. 2007. 33p. (J). pap. (***978-1-59889-424-0(2)***); 40p. (YA). (gr. 5-9). 21.26 (***978-1-59889-336-6(X)***) Stone Arch Bks.

—Cut-Throat Pirates. Smith, Pete, illus. 2007. 33p. (J). pap. (***978-1-59889-428-8(5)***); 40p. (YA). (gr. 5-9). lib. bdg. 21.26 (***978 1 59889-332-8(7)***) Stone Arch Bks.

—Inside the Game. Smith, Pete, illus. 2007. 33p. (J). pap. (***978-1-59889-426-4(9)***); 40p. (YA). (gr. 5-9). lib. bdg. 21.26 (***978-1-59889-330-4(0)***) Stone Arch Bks.

—Safecrackers. Troiano, Enzo, illus. 2007. 33p. (J). pap. (***978-1-59889-427-1(7)***); 40p. (YA). (gr. 5-9). lib. bdg. 21.26 (***978-1-59889-331-1(9)***) Stone Arch Bks.

—Soccer Showdown. Troiano, Enzo, illus. 2007. 33p. (J). pap. (***978-1-59889-430-1(7)***); 40p. (YA). (gr. 5-9). lib. bdg. 21.26 (***978-1-59889-334-2(3)***) Stone Arch Bks.

—Speed Star. Troiano, Enzo, illus. 2007. 33p. (J). pap. (***978-1-59889-431-8(5)*** , 1264997); 40p. (YA). (gr. 5-9). lib. bdg. 21.26 (***978-1-59889-335-9(1)*** , 1264997) Stone Arch Bks.

—Spin Off. Troiano, Enzo, illus. 2007. 33p. (J). pap. (***978-1-59889-429-5(3)***); 40p. (YA). (gr. 5-9). lib. bdg. 21.26 (***978-1-59889-333-5(5)***) Stone Arch Bks.

Zucker, Zoey. Daffy Does It Again. Style Guide Staff, illus. 2006. (Baby Looney Tunes Ser.). 48p. (J). act. bk. ed. 3.99 (978-1-4169-1843-1(4) , Simon Scribbles) Simon & Schuster Children's Publishing.

Zuckerman, Lilla & Zuckerman, Nora. Beauty Queen Blowout. 2003. (Miss Adventures Ser.: Bk. 2). 240p. pap. 9.95 (978-0-7432-3846-5(X) , Fireside) Simon & Schuster.

Zuhdi, Darla. A South Sea Adventure, Vol. 4. 2005. (Cat Detectives Present Ser.: 4). (Illus.). 104p. (J). per. 6.99 (978-0-9706062-6-6(5)) Aloha Publications.

Zuhdi, Darla L. Finding Your Dream. 2nd l.t. ed. 2001. (Cat Detectives Present Ser.). 88p. (J). (gr. 4-7). per. 6.99 (978-0-9706062-1-1(4)) Aloha Publications.

Zuravicky, Orli. Blue Says. Craig, Karen, illus. 2007. (Blue's Clues Ser.). 12p. (J). bds. 6.99 (978-1-4169-4127-9(4) , Simon Spotlight/Nickelodeon) Simon & Schuster Children's Publishing.

Zusak, Markus. Fighting Ruben Wolfe. 2001. (Illus.). 208p. (YA). (gr. 5-10). pap. 15.95 (978-0-439-24188-5(X) , Levine, Arthur A. Bks.) Scholastic, Inc.

ADVERTISING

see also Marketing; Posters; Propaganda; Sales Personnel; Signs and Signboards

Advertisements, 6, Pack. (Sails Literacy Ser.). (gr. 5 up). 37.00 (978-0-7578-8062-9(2)) Rigby Education.

Day, Nancy. Advertising: Information or Manipulation? 1999. (Issues in Focus Ser.). (Illus.). 128p. (YA). (gr. 6-12). lib. bdg. 26.60 (978-0-7660-1106-9(2)) Enslow Pubs., Inc.

Eleanor Stanford. Advertising. 2007. (Introducing Issues with Opposing Viewpoints Ser.). (Illus.). 244p. (gr. 7-10). 33.70 (978-0-7377-3572-7(4) , Greenhaven Pr., Inc.) Thomson Gale.

Gifford, Clive. Advertising & Marketing: Developing the Marketplace. 2005. (Influence & Persuasion Ser.). (Illus.). 64p. (J). (gr. 6-8). lib. bdg. 31.43 (978-1-4034-7651-7(9)) Heinemann Library.

Graydon, Shari. Made You Look: How Advertising Works & Why You Should Know. Clark, Warren, illus. 2003. 120p. (J). (gr. 4-7). 24.95 (978-1-55037-815-3(5)); pap. 14.95 (978-1-55037-814-6(7)) Annick Pr., Ltd. CAN. *Dist:* Firefly Bks., Ltd.

—Made You Look: How Advertising Works & Why You Should Know. 2003. (gr. 3-6). lib. bdg. 24.55 (978-0-613-78467-2(7)) Tandem Library Bks.

Harcourt School Publishers Staff. Advertising in Action On Level. 3rd ed. 2002. (Trophies Reading Program Ser.). (Illus.). pap. 5.10 (978-0-15-323361-6(3)) Harcourt Schl. Pubs.

Mierau, Christina B. Accept No Substitutes! The History of American Advertising. 2005. (People's History Ser.). (Illus.). 96p. (gr. 6-12). lib. bdg. 26.60 (978-0-8225-1742-9(6)) Lerner Publishing Group.

Milton, Bess. Advertising. 2004. (High Interest Bks.). (Illus.). 48p. (J). (gr. 7-12). pap. 6.95 (978-0-516-25943-7(1) , Children's Pr.) Scholastic Library Publishing.

Understanding Advertising: History, Persuasion Techniques, Mass Media, Target Audiences, Ad Creation. 2000. (J). per. 10.95 (978-1-883055-37-0(7)) Dandy Lion Pubns.

ADVERTISING—FICTION

Brown, Marc. Arthur's TV Trouble. Brown, Marc, illus. 2002. (Arthur Adventure Ser.). (Illus.). (J). 13.15 (978-0-7587-1990-4(6)) Book Wholesalers, Inc.

—Arthur's TV Trouble. Brown, Marc, illus. 1999. (Arthur Adventure Ser.). (Illus.). 32p. (J). (ps-3). 9.95 (978-0-316-11594-0(0)) Little, Brown Bks. for Young Readers.

Carmichael, Claire. Leaving Simplicity. 2007. 256p. (J). (gr. 6-12). 21.95 (***978-1-55451-090-0(2)***); pap. 10.95 (***978-1-55451-089-4(9)***) Annick Pr., Ltd. CAN. *Dist:* Firefly Bks., Ltd.

Dalmatian Press Staff, adapted by. Oliver Twist. 2002. (Spot the Classics Ser.). (Illus.). 182p. (J). (gr. k-5). 4.99 (978-1-57759-554-0(8)) Dalmatian Pr.

Farmer, Gayle. Showtime! 2004. (YA). per. 12.95 (978-0-9748728-0-3(6)) Jeff & Gayle Farmer.

Hanson, Ed. Hostages. 2003. (Barclay Family Adventure Ser.: Bk. 5). 64p. (J). (gr. k-6). per. 3.95 (978-1-56254-554-3(X) , SP 554X) Saddleback Educational Publishing.

Langston, Laura. The Trouble with Cupid. 2008. 240p. (YA). (gr. 5-8). pap. (***978-1-55455-059-3(9)***) Fitzhenry & Whiteside, Ltd.

Naylor, Phyllis Reynolds. Anyone Can Eat Squid! Ramsey, Marcy Dunn, illus. 2005. 80p. (J). 14.95 (978-0-7614-5182-2(X)) Cavendish, Marshall Corp.

Reilly, Matthew. Crash Course. Raimondi, Pablo, illus. 2006. (Hover Car Racer Ser.). 240p. (J). pap. 2.99 (978-1-4169-2503-3(1) , Aladdin) Simon & Schuster Children's Publishing.

Shapiro, Laurie Gwen. Brand X: The Boyfriend Account. 2006. 240p. (YA). (gr. 7). 15.95 (978-0-385-73288-8(0)); lib. bdg. 17.99 (978-0-385-90309-7(X)) Random Hse. Children's Bks. (Delacorte Bks. for Young Readers).

Standish, Burt L. Dick Merriwell's Revenge. Rudman, Jack, ed. 2003. (Frank Merriwell Ser.). 29.95 (978-0-8373-9382-7(5)); pap. 9.95 (978-0-8373-9082-6(6)) Merriwell, Frank Inc.

Taha, Karen T. Hotdog on TV. Takahashi, Hideko, illus. 2005. (Easy-to-Read, Dial Ser.). 40p. (J). (ps). 14.99 (978-0-8037-2933-9(2) , Dial) Penguin Group (USA) Inc.

Waid, Mark, et al. Terror Incognita. Hitch, Brian, illus. rev. ed. 2002. (Justice League Adventures Ser.: Vol. 9). 144p. pap. 12.99 (978-1-56389-936-2(1)) DC Comics.

ADVERTISING, PICTORIAL

see Posters

ADVERTISING—VOCATIONAL GUIDANCE

Ferguson, creator. Discovering Careers for Your Future: Advertising & Marketing. 2005. (Discovering Careers for Your Future Ser.). (Illus.). 92p. (YA). (gr. 4-9). 21.95 (978-0-8160-5847-1(4) , Ferguson Publishing Co.) Facts On File, Inc.

Haegele, Katie. E-Advertising & E-Marketing: Online Opportunities. 2005. (Library of E-Commerce & Internet Careers). (Illus.). 64p. (YA). (gr. 7-12). lib. bdg. 26.50 (978-0-8239-3426-3(8)) Rosen Publishing Group, Inc., The.

J. G. Ferguson Publishing Company Staff, contrib. by. Careers in Focus. 2003. (Careers in Focus Ser.). (Illus.). 192p. (J). (gr. 6-12). 22.95 (978-0-8160-5482-4(7) , Ferguson Publishing Co.) Facts On File, Inc.

Petley, Julian. Advertising. 2003. (Media Wise Ser.). 64p. (J). lib. bdg. 28.50 (978-1-58340-255-9(1)) Smart Apple Media.

AENEAS (LEGENDARY CHARACTER)

Hoena, B. A. Aeneas. 2004. (Illus.). 24p. (J). 14.95 (978-0-7368-2496-5(0)) Capstone Pr., Inc.

Lively, Penelope. In Search of a Homeland: The Story of the Aeneid. Andrews, Ian, illus. 2001. 119p. (J). (978-0-385-72930-7(8) , Delacorte Pr.) Dell Publishing.

—In Search of a Homeland: The Story of the Aeneid. Andrew, Ian, illus. 2006. 128p. 19.95 (978-1-84507-685-6(0)) Lincoln, Frances Ltd. GBR. *Dist:* Perseus Distribution.

Williams, Rose. The Labors of Aeneas: What a Pain It Was to Found the Roman Race. 2003. (Illus.). (YA). 14.00 (978-0-86516-556-4(4)) Bolchazy-Carducci Pubs.

AERIAL PHOTOGRAPHY

Arthus-Bertrand, Yann. The Future of the Earth: An Introduction to Sustainable Development for Young Readers. Bataille, Sylvia, illus. 2004. 76p. (J). (gr. 3-7). 16.95 (978-0-8109-5018-4(9)) Abrams, Harry N., Inc.

Charlotte a Complete Photo Tour Book. 1998. (Illus.). 32p. (YA). (gr. 7-12). pap. 5.95 (978-1-880970-41-6(4)) Aerial Photography Services, Inc.

AERIAL ROCKETS

see Rockets (Aeronautics)

AERODYNAMICS

see also Aeronautics

Matthews, Stuart. Aerodynamics. 2001. (How Does It Work? Ser.). (Illus.). 24p. (J). (gr. 2-7). lib. bdg. 21.30 (978-1-58340-065-4(6)) Smart Apple Media.

Parker, Steve. The Science of Air: Projects & Experiments on Air & Flight. 2005. (Tabletop Scientist Ser.). (Illus.). 32p. (J). (gr. 4-7). lib. bdg. 27.79 (978-1-4034-7280-9(7)); (ps-6). pap. 7.95 (978-1-4034-7287-8(4)) Heinemann Library.

Sobey, Edwin J. C. Fantastic Flying Fun with Science: 69 Projects You Can Fly, Spin, Launch, & Ri. 2000. (gr. 5-8). lib. bdg. 21.05 (978-0-613-71530-0(6)) Tandem Library Bks.

Wallace, Lane E. Wild Blue Wonders: Exploring the Magic of Flight. 2001. (Illus.). 164p. (J). per. 19.95 (978-1-58932-002-4(6)) EAA (Experimental Aircraft Assn.).

Willis, Shirley. Dime por Que Tienen Alas los Aviones. (Los Estupendos Whiz Kids, Spanish Edition Ser.). (SPA., Illus.). 32p. (J). 2000. (gr. 1-3). pap. 5.95 (978-0-531-15998-9(1) , OD30032); 1999. (gr. 2-4). 20.00 (978-0-531-11848-1(7) , OD30033) Scholastic Library Publishing. (Watts, Franklin).

—Dime por Que Tienen Alas los Aviones. 2000. (Estupendos Ser.). (J). 12.75 (978-0-606-20151-3(3)) Tandem Library Bks.

AERODYNAMICS, SUPERSONIC

Herold, Vickey. Discover the Sound Barrier. 2006. pap. 39.00 (***978-1-4108-6490-1(1)***) Benchmark Education Co.

Pierce, Alan. Breaking the Sound Barrier. 2005. (American Moments Ser.). (J). (gr. 4-8). lib. bdg. 25.65 (978-1-59197-730-8(4)) ABDO Publishing Co.

AERONAUTICAL SPORTS

see also names of specific sports, e.g. Airplane Racing; Skydiving; etc.

Hansen, Ole Steen. Flying for Fun. 2003. (Story of Flight Ser.). (Illus.). 32p. (J). (gr. 4). pap. (978-0-7787-1227-5(3)); lib. bdg. (978-0-7787-1211-4(7)) Crabtree Publishing Co.

—Flying for Fun. 2003. (gr. 3-6). lib. bdg. 17.60 (978-0-613-87233-1(9)) Tandem Library Bks.

Jefferis, David. Air Sports. 2001. (Young Library - Super Sports). (Illus.). 32p. (J). 25.69 (978-0-7398-4343-7(5)) Raintree.

Kalman, Bobbie & Crossingham, John. Extreme Skydiving. 2006. (Extreme Sports No Limits! Ser.). (Illus.). 32p. (J). (gr. 3-9). pap. (978-0-7787-1730-0(5)); (978-0-7787-1684-6(8)) Crabtree Publishing Co.

AERONAUTICS

see also Aerodynamics; Aeronautical Sports; Airplanes; Airships; Astronautics; Balloons; Flight; Gliders (Aeronautics); Helicopters; High Speed Aeronautics; Kites; Parachutes; Rocketry; Rockets (Aeronautics); Unidentified Flying Objects

Alcraft, Rob. Flight. 2004. (Twenty4Sevens Ser.). (Illus.). 48p. (J). pap. (978-0-439-68103-2(0)) Scholastic, Inc.

Amato, William. Aviones Supersonicos. 2004. (Vehiculos de Alta Tecnologia Ser.). (SPA & ENG., Illus.). 24p. (J). (gr. 3-6). lib. bdg. 17.25 (978-0-8239-6880-0(4) , Buenas Letra) Rosen Publishing Group, Inc., The.

Andersen, Ashley C. First Book of Flight: A Child's History of Aviation & Flight Log. 2000. (Illus.). 48p. (J). (ps-3). pap. 7.95 (978-1-882663-48-4(9)) Plymouth Toy & Book.

Ashley, Susan. Going by Plane. 2003. (Going Places Ser.). (Illus.). 24p. (YA). (gr. 2 up). lib. bdg. 19.33 (978-0-8368-3731-5(2) , Weekly Reader Early Learning Library) Stevens, Gareth Inc.

Berger, Samantha. In the Air. 1999. (J). pap. 2.50 (978-0-439-08124-5(6)) Scholastic, Inc.

—In the Air. 1999. (gr. 3-6). lib. bdg. 10.10 (978-0-613-54814-4(0)) Tandem Library Bks.

Binns, Tristan Boyer. The FAA: Federal Aviation Administration. (Government Agencies Ser.). 48p. (J). (gr. 3-5). 2003. (Illus.). lib. bdg. 27.07 (978-1-58810-498-4(2)); 2002. pap. 7.95 (978-1-58810-982-8(8) , 91597) Heinemann Library.

Bitetto, Marco A. V., ed. A Joystick Nation. braille ed. 2000. (J). (978-1-58578-085-3(5)) Institute of Cybernetics Research, Inc.

Blair, Margaret. The Roaring Twenty: The First Cross-Country Air Race for Women. 2006. 112p. (gr. 5). 32.90 (978-0-7922-5390-7(6)); (Illus.). (J). 21.95 (978-0-7922-5389-1(2)) National Geographic Society. (National Geographic Children's Bks.).

Bledsoe, Karen & Bledsoe, Glen. Airplane Adventures. 2001. (Dangerous Adventures Ser.). (Illus.). 48p. (J). (gr. 3-4). lib. bdg. 21.26 (978-0-7368-0903-0(1) , Capstone High-Interest Bks.) Capstone Pr., Inc.

Bruce, Linda. Space Technology. 2006. (How Does It Work? Ser.). (Illus.). 32p. (J). (978-1-58340-795-0(2)) Smart Apple Media.

Clemson, Wendy & Clemson, David. Rocket to the Moon. 2006. (Illus.). 32p. (J). pap. (***978-0-8368-8140-0(0)***); lib. bdg. (***978-0-8368-7841-7(8)***) Stevens, Gareth Inc.

Collins, Francis. The Boys' Book of Model Aeroplanes: How to Build & Fly Them: with the Story of the Evolution of the Flying Machine. 2004. (Illus.). 308p. (YA). per. 16.95 (978-0-9758914-3-8(X)) Gustav's Library.

Coupe, Robert. Exploring Space. 2002. (Junior Adventure Ser.). (Illus.). 32p. (J). (gr. 3 up). lib. bdg. (978-1-59084-189-1(1)) Mason Crest Pubs.

Crompton, Samuel Willard. The Wright Brothers: First in Flight. 2007. (Milestones in American History Ser.). 120p. (gr. 6-12). 35.00 (***978-0-7910-9356-6(5)*** , Chelsea Hse.) Facts On File, Inc.

Dailey, Franklyn E., Jr. The Triumph of Instrument Flight: A Retrospective in the Century of U. S. Aviation. 2004. (Illus.). 335p. per. 18.95 (978-0-9666251-3-4(7)) Dailey International Pubs.

Dibben, Colin. Flight. 2007. (J). (***978-1-60044-259-9(5)***) Rourke Publishing, LLC.

Dixon-Engel, Tara & Jackson, Mike. Sterling Biographies: the Wright Brothers: First in Flight. 2007. (Sterling Biographies Ser.). (Illus.). 128p. (J). pap. 5.95 (***978-1-4027-3231-7(7)***) Sterling Publishing Co., Inc.

Dorling Kindersley Publishing Staff. Aircraft. 2005. (Ultimate sticker Bks.). 16p. (J). pap. 6.99 (978-0-7566-1511-6(9)) Dorling Kindersley Publishing, Inc.

—Flight. 2006. (Experience Ser.). (Illus.). 64p. (J). 15.99 (978-0-7566-1411-9(2)) Dorling Kindersley Publishing, Inc.

—Flight. 2003. (gr. 3-6). lib. bdg. 14.15 (978-0-613-75204-6(X)) Tandem Library Bks.

Edwards, Pamela Duncan. The Wright Brothers. Cole, Henry, illus. 2003. 40p. (gr. k-4). 16.49 (978-0-7868-2682-7(7)) Hyperion Bks. for Children.

Farndon, John. Flight. 2001. (Science Experiments Ser.). (Illus.). 32p. (J). (gr. 3-5). lib. bdg. 25.64 (978-0-7614-1342-4(1) , Benchmark Bks.) Cavendish, Marshall Corp.

Flight Path: Individual Title Six-Packs. (Rigby Infoquest Ser.). 32p. (gr. 4 up). 37.00 (978-0-7578-5727-0(2)) Rigby Education.

Flying Machines. (First Facts about Ser.). 24p. (J). (gr. 3-7). pap. (978-1-882210-17-6(4)) Action Publishing, Inc.

Flying Machines. Date not set. (I Can Draw Ser.). 32p. (J). 4.98 (978-1-4054-0019-0(6)) Parragon, Inc.

Flying Machines, 6 bks., Set. 2001. (J). (gr. 1-4). lib. bdg. 123.86 (978-1-58952-000-4(9)) Rourke Publishing, LLC.

Forden, Lesley, told to. The Ford Air Tours, 1925-1931: A Complete Narrative & Pictorial History of the Seven National Air Tour Competitions for the Edsel B. Ford Trophy. 2003rd rev. ed. 2002. (Illus.). 218p. per. 19.95 (978-0-9725249-1-9(6) , 2) Aviation Foundation of America.

Gaffney, Timothy R. Amazing Agricultural Aircraft. 2001. (Aircraft Ser.). (Illus.). 48p. (J). (gr. 4-10). lib. bdg. 23.93 (978-0-7660-1608-6(0)) Enslow Pubs., Inc.

Goodman, Susan E. Blasting off to Space Academy, Vol. 5. Doolittle, Michael J., illus. 2001. (Ultimate Field Trip Ser.: Vol. 5). 48p. (J). (gr. 5-8). 17.00 (978-0-689-83044-0(0) , Atheneum) Simon & Schuster Children's Publishing.

Graham, Ian. Aircraft. Connell, Tom, illus. 1998. (Built for Speed Ser.). 32p. (J). (gr. 3-7). pap. 10.80 (978-0-8172-8072-7(3)) Steck-Vaughn.

—Flight. 2001. (Single Subject References Ser.). (Illus.). 64p. (J). (gr. 4-8). tchr. ed. 16.95 (978-0-7534-5326-1(6) , Kingfisher) Houghton Mifflin Co. Trade & Reference Div.

—In the Air: Machines at Work. 2007. (QEB Machines at Work Ser.). (J). lib. bdg. 19.95 (978-1-59566-315-3(0)) QEB Publishing Inc.

Grist, Julie. Flying: Just Plane Fun. 2006. (Illus.). 24p. (J). pap. 8.95 (978-0-9725750-2-7(2)) Spoonbender Bks.

—Flying: Just Plane Fun. Grist, Julie, illus. 2003. (Illus.). 24p. (J). (gr. 1-7). 17.95 (978-0-9725750-0-3(6)) Spoonbender Bks.

Group/McGraw-Hill, Wright. Great Aviators Take Flight, 6 vols. (Book2WebTM Ser.). (gr. 4-8). 36.50 (978-0-322-04467-8(7)) Wright Group, The.

Haddrick Taylor, Michael Johnn. Chronology of Flight: 1940 to the Present. 1999. (World's Greatest Aircraft Ser.). (Illus.). 62p. (J). (gr. 5 up). 12.95 (978-0-7910-5424-6(1) , Chelsea Hse.) Facts On File, Inc.

—Chronology of Flight: c. 843 B.C.-1939. 1999. (World's Greatest Aircraft Ser.). (Illus.). 64p. (J). (gr. 5 up). 24.15 (978-0-7910-5423-9(3) , Chelsea Hse.) Facts On File, Inc.

Hansen, Ole Steen. Air Combat. 2003. (Story of Flight Ser.). (Illus.). 32p. (J). (gr. 4). pap. (978-0-7787-1222-0(2)) Crabtree Publishing Co.

—Flying for Fun. 2003. (Story of Flight Ser.). (Illus.). 32p. (J). (gr. 4). pap. (978-0-7787-1227-5(3)); lib. bdg. (978-0-7787-1211-4(7)) Crabtree Publishing Co.

—Flying for Fun. 2003. (gr. 3-6). lib. bdg. 17.60 (978-0-613-87233-1(9)) Tandem Library Bks.

—Seaplanes & Naval Aviation. 2003. (Story of Flight Ser.). (Illus.). 32p. (J). (gr. 4). pap. (978-0-7787-1225-1(7)) Crabtree Publishing Co.

Harding, Les. McCurdy & the silver dart. 1999. (Illus.). 126p. (J). (gr. 4-7). pap. (978-0-920336-69-4(8)) Cape Breton Univ. Pr.

Haslam, Andrew. Flight. 2004. (Make It Work! Science Ser.). (Illus.). 48p. (J). (gr. 3-6). 12.95 (978-1-58728-371-0(9)); pap. 6.95 (978-1-58728-355-0(7)) T&N Children's Publishing. (Two Can Publishing).

High Flying: Level P, 6 vols., Vol. 3. (Explorers Ser.). 32p. (gr. 3-6). 44.95 (978-0-7699-0619-5(2)) Shortland Pubns. (U. S. A.) Inc.

Hill, Lee Sullivan. The Flyer Flew! The Invention of the Airplane. Naprstek, Joel, illus. (On My Own Science Ser.). 48p. (J). 2007. pap. 5.95 (978-1-57505-855-9(3) , First Avenue Editions); 2006. (gr. 2-4). lib. bdg. 25.26 (978-1-57505-758-3(1) , Millbrook Pr.) Lerner Publishing Group.

—Get Around in Air & Space. 1999. (Get Around Bks.). (Illus.). 32p. (J). (gr. 3-6). lib. bdg. 14.60 (978-1-57505-310-3(1) , Carolrhoda Bks.) Lerner Publishing Group.

Holden, Henry M. Crime-Fighting Aircraft. 2002. (Aircraft Ser.). (Illus.). 48p. (J). (gr. 4-10). lib. bdg. 23.93 (978-0-7660-1718-4(4)) Enslow Pubs., Inc.

—Fire-Fighting Aircraft & Smoke Jumpers. 2002. (Aircraft Ser.). (Illus.). 48p. (J). (gr. 4-10). lib. bdg. 23.93 (978-0-7660-1720-7(6)) Enslow Pubs., Inc.

Howatson, Ian & Quigley, Sebastian, illus. The World of Flight. 2001. (Inside Look Ser.). 48p. (J). (gr. 4 up). lib. bdg. 26.00 (978-0-8368-2903-7(4)) Stevens, Gareth Inc.

Humphreys, Pauline A. Romance of the Airman. 2005. pap. 43.95 (978-1-4191-0278-3(8)) Kessinger Publishing, LLC.

Hunter, Ryan Ann, et al. Into the Air: An Illustrated Timeline of Flight. Nascimbene, Yan, illus. 2003. 48p. (J). (ps-3). 16.95 (978-0-7922-5120-0(2) , National Geographic Children's Bks.) National Geographic Society.

Jepson, Edgar. Admirable Tinker Child of the World. 2006. 95.99 (***978-1-4280-4993-2(2)***); pap. 89.99 (***978-1-4280-5011-2(6)***) IndyPublish.com.

Kaleidoscope, 20 bks., Set. 2001. (Illus.). (J). (gr. 3 up). lib. bdg. 455.71 (978-0-7614-1049-2(X) , Benchmark Bks.) Cavendish, Marshall Corp.

Kids Can Press Staff, Press Can, ed. This Is Daniel Cook on a Plane. 2006. (Illus.). 24p. (J). (978-1-55453-081-6(4)) Kids Can Pr., Ltd.

—This Is Daniel Cook on A Plane. 2006. (Illus.). 24p. (J). (978-1-55453-082-3(2)) Kids Can Pr., Ltd.

Kinmont, Ritchie. Every Kid Needs Things That Fly. Casey, Robert, photos by. 2005. (Illus.). 136p. (J). 14.95 (978-1-58685-509-3(3) , 1241179) Gibbs Smith, Publisher.

Loves, June. Flight Series, 6 bks. Incl. Airplanes. 32p. (YA). 22.95 (978-0-7910-6560-0(X) , 010301); Balloons, Kites, Airships & Gliders. (J). 27.00 (978-0-7910-6563-1(4) , 010302); Flying Animals. 32p. (J). 22.95 (978-0-7910-6561-7(8) , 010303); Helicopters. 32p. (J). 22.95 (978-0-7910-6562-4(6) , 010304); Military Aircraft. 32p. (J). 22.95 (978-0-7910-6559-4(6) , 010305); (gr. 5 up). 2001. (Illus.). 101.70 (978-0-7910-6557-0(X) , 101300S, Chelsea Hse.) Facts On File, Inc.

MacLeod, Elizabeth. The Wright Brothers. Krystoforski, Andrej, illus. 2008. 32p. pap. (***978-1-55453-054-0(7)***) Kids Can Pr., Ltd.

Martin, Michael J. The Wright Brothers. 2002. (Importance of Ser.). (Illus.). 112p. (J). (gr. 7-10). 32.45 (978-1-56006-847-1(7) , Lucent Bks.) Thomson Gale.

Maynard, Christopher. Aircraft. 1999. (Need for Speed Ser.). (Illus.). 32p. (gr. 3-6). (J). pap. 7.95 (978-0-8225-9855-8(8)); lib. bdg. 23.93 (978-0-8225-2485-4(6)) Lerner Publishing Group.

—Aircraft. 1999. (gr. 5-8). lib. bdg. 16.40 (978-0-613-84024-8(0)); (Illus.). (J). (978-0-606-18812-8(6)) Tandem Library Bks.

—I Wonder Why Planes Have Wings: And Other Questions about Transportation. 2003. (I Wonder Why Ser.). (Illus.). 32p. (J). (gr. k-3). 6.95 (978-0-7534-5662-0(1) , Kingfisher) Houghton Mifflin Co. Trade & Reference Div.

McHaffie, Natalie. C-Growl: The Daring Little Airplane. McHaffie, Natalie, illus. 1999. (Illus.). 32p. (J). (978-1-55125-015-1(2)) Vanwell Publishing, Ltd.

Mellett, Peter. Flight. Bowyer, Dave, illus. 1998. (Young Scientist Concepts & Projects Ser.). 68p. (J). (gr. 4 up). lib. bdg. 27.33 (978-0-8368-2162-8(9)) Stevens, Gareth Inc.

Milbourne, Anna. Viaje a la Luna. 2005. (SPA.). 24p. (J). 9.99 (978-0-7460-6632-4(5) , Usborne) EDC Publishing.

Molzahn, Arlene Bourgeois. Airplanes. 2003. (Transportation & Communication Ser.). (Illus.). 48p. (J). (gr. 1-4). lib. bdg. 23.93 (978-0-7660-2026-9(6)) Enslow Pubs., Inc.

Moss, Marissa. Brave Harriet: The First Woman to Fly the English Channel. Payne, C. F., illus. 2001. 32p. (J). (gr. 1-4). 17.00 (978-0-15-202380-5(1) , Silver Whistle) Harcourt Trade Pubs.

Murray, Jennifer. Flight & Fancy: The Airline Industry. 2007. (Shockwave: Economics & Geography Ser.). (Illus.). 36p. (J). (gr. 4-6). lib. bdg. 25.00 (***978-0-531-17796-9(3)*** , Children's Pr.) Scholastic Library Publishing.

Nahum, Andrew & Dorling Kindersley Publishing Staff. Flying Machine. 2004. (Dk Eyewitness Books Ser.). (Illus.). 72p. (J). 15.99 (978-0-7566-0680-0(2)) Dorling Kindersley Publishing, Inc.

O'Brien, Patrick. Fantastic Flights: One Hundred Years of Flying on the Edge. 2003. (Illus.). 40p. (J). 18.85 (978-0-8027-8881-8(5)) Walker & Co.

O'Hern, Kerri & Mayo, Gretchen. The Wright Brothers. 2006. (Illus.). (J). pap. (978-0-8368-6251-5(1) , World Almanac Library) Stevens, Gareth Inc.

Penguin Books Staff, ed. Things That Fly. (Information Activity Ser.). 24p. (J). 3.50 (978-0-7214-3443-8(6) , Dutton Juvenile) Penguin Group (USA) Inc.

Reed, Jennifer. Wilbur & Orville Wright: Trailblazers of the Sky. 2007. (Inventors Who Changed the World Ser.). (Illus.). 128p. (J). (gr. 5). lib. bdg. 33.27 (***978-1-59845-054-5(9)*** , MyReportLinks.com Bks.) Enslow Pubs., Inc.

Rees, Peter. How Does It Fly? The Science of Flight. 2007. (Shockwave: Technology & Manufacturing Ser.). (Illus.). 36p. (J). (gr. 4-6). lib. bdg. 25.00 (***978-0-531-17587-3(1)*** , Children's Pr.) Scholastic Library Publishing.

Roza, Greg. The Incredible Story of Jets. 2004. (Kid's Guide to Incredible Technology Ser.). (Illus.). 24p. (J). lib. bdg. 19.95 (978-0-8239-6713-1(1) , PowerKids Pr.) Rosen Publishing Group, Inc., The.

Ryan, Bernard. The Wright Brothers: Inventors of the Airplane. 2003. (Great Life Stories Ser.). (Illus.). 128p. (J). 30.50 (978-0-531-12254-9(9) , Watts, Franklin) Scholastic Library Publishing.

Saunders-Smith, Gail. Airplanes. 1998. (J). pap. 13.25 (978-0-516-21229-6(X) , Children's Pr.) Scholastic Library Publishing.

Schleifer, Jay. Wings, 4 bks. Incl. Bomber Planes. lib. bdg. 21.26 (978-1-56065-303-5(5)); Combat Helicopters. lib. bdg. 21.26 (978-1-56065-305-9(1)); Fighter Planes. lib. bdg. 21.26 (978-1-56065-304-2(3)); Spy Planes. lib. bdg. 21.26 (978-1-56065-302-8(7)); 48p. (J). (gr. 3-4). 1996. (Illus.). Set lib. bdg. 85.04 (978-1-56065-669-2(7) , Capstone High-Interest Bks.) Capstone Pr., Inc.

Sibila, Tom. SpaceShipOne: Making History in Outer Space. 2005. (High Five Reading Ser.). (Illus.). 48p. (J). (978-0-7368-5744-4(3)); (978-0-7368-5734-5(6)) Capstone Pr., Inc.

Smith, Robert W. The Wright Brothers. 2003. (Spotlight on America Ser.). (Illus.). 48p. pap. 8.99 (978-0-7439-3210-3(2)) Teacher Created Materials, Inc.

Sobey, Edwin J. C. Just Plane Smart! Activities for Kids in the Air & on the Ground. 1998. (Illus.). 96p. (gr. 3-12). pap. 7.95 (978-0-07-059598-9(4) , 9780070595989) McGraw-Hill Cos., The.

Spizzirri, Peter M. Aircraft. Spizzirri, Linda, ed. unabr. ed. (Educational Coloring Book & Cassette Ser.). (J). (gr. 1-8). pap. 6.95 incl. audio (978-0-86545-109-4(5)) Spizzirri Pr., Inc.

Sproule, Anna. The Wright Brothers. 2005. (Giants of Science Bilingual Ser.). (J). 9.95 (978-1-4103-0507-7(4) , Blackbirch Pr., Inc.) Thomson Gale.

Steers, Billy. The Little Book of Planes. Steers, Billy, illus. 1999. (Jellybean Bks.). (Illus.). 24p. (J). (ps-k). lib. bdg. 7.99 (978-0-375-90219-2(8) , Random Hse. Bks. for Young Readers) Random Hse. Children's Bks.

Taking to the Air: Individual Title Six-Packs. (Action Packs Ser.). 120p. (gr. 3-5). 44.00 (978-0-7635-8396-5(0)) Rigby Education.

Taylor-Miller, Sandra. Are We There Yet? The Wright Brothers' National Memorial Park, Kill Devil Hills, North Carolina, Site of the First Heavier-Than-Air Machine-Powered Flight. 2004. (Illus.). 56p. (J). 9.95 (978-1-887905-87-9(1)) Parkway Pubs., Inc.

Tiner, John Hudson. Airplanes. (Illus.). 32p. 2004. pap. 8.95 (978-0-89812-387-6(9) , Creative Paperbacks); 2003. (J). lib. bdg. 18.95 (978-1-58341-258-9(1) , Creative Education) Creative Co., The.

Tuxworth, Nicola & Lorenz Editors. Flying Machines. 2002. (Let's Look at Board Bks.). (Illus.). 20p. (ps-3). 5.95 (978-0-7548-1031-5(3) , Lorenz Bks.) Anness Publishing GBR. *Dist:* National Bk. Network.

Williams, Zachary. How Do Airplanes Fly? 2002. (Reading Room Collection). (Illus.). 24p. (J). pap. (978-0-8239-8160-1(6)); lib. bdg. 18.75 (978-0-8239-3723-3(2)) Rosen Publishing Group, Inc., The.

Willis, Shirley. Tell Me Why Planes Have Wings. 2000. (Whiz Kids Ser.). (Illus.). 32p. (J). (gr. 1-3). pap. 5.95 (978-0-531-15981-1(7) , Watts, Franklin) Scholastic Library Publishing.

Winchester, Jim. Record Breakers. 2006. (Aircraft of the World Ser.). (Illus.). 32p. (J). lib. bdg. (978-0-8368-6905-7(2)) Stevens, Gareth Inc.

Wyborny, Sheila. The Wright Brothers. 2002. (Inventors & Creators Ser.). (Illus.). 48p. (J). (gr. 3-5). 18.96 (978-0-7377-1369-5(0) , Kidhaven) Thomson Gale.

Yes Mag Editors. Amazing International Space Station. 2003. (gr. 3-6). lib. bdg. 25.70 (978-0-613-87147-1(2)) Tandem Library Bks.

3,2,1 Liftoff! Level M, 6 vols. 128p. (gr. 2-3). 41.95 (978-0-7699-1024-6(6)) Shortland Pubns. (U. S. A.) Inc.

AERONAUTICS—ACCIDENTS

see Aircraft Accidents

AERONAUTICS—BIOGRAPHY

see also Air Pilots; Women in Aeronautics

Benge, Janet & Benge, Geoff. Orville Wright: The Flyer. 2006. (J). pap. (978-1-932096-34-7(5)) Emerald Bks.

Brown, Jonatha A. The Wright Brothers. 2004. (Illus.). 24p. (J). pap. (978-0-8368-4321-7(5)); (YA). lib. bdg. 19.33 (978-0-8368-4314-9(2)) Stevens, Gareth Inc.

Burleigh, Robert. Into the Air: The Story of the Wright Brothers' First Flight. Wylie, Bill, illus. 2002. (American Heroes Ser.). 48p. (J). (gr. 3-7). pap. 6.00 (978-0-15-216803-2(6) , 53227831, Silver Whistle) Harcourt Trade Pubs.

Collins, Mary. Airborne: A Photobiography of Wilbur & Orville Wright. 2003. (Illus.). 64p. (J). (gr. 5). 18.95 (978-0-7922-6957-1(8) , 53238483, National Geographic Children's Bks.) National Geographic Society.

Dixon-Engel, Tara & Jackson, Mike. Sterling Biographies: the Wright Brothers: First in Flight. 2007. (Sterling Biographies Ser.). (Illus.). 128p. (J). 12.95 (***978-1-4027-4954-4(6)***); pap. 5.95 (***978-1-4027-3231-7(7)***) Sterling Publishing Co., Inc.

Dunn, Joeming W. The Wright Brothers. Dunn, Joeming W. & Dunn, Ben, illus. 2007. (Bio-Graphics Ser.). 32p. (J). (gr. 3-6). lib. bdg. 27.07 (***978-1-60270-071-0(0)***, Graphic Planet) Magic Wagon.

Gaines, Ann Graham. Orville & Wilbur Wright. 2001. (Illus.). 24p. (J). (gr. 1-4). lib. bdg. 20.64 (978-1-58952-121-6(8)) Rourke Publishing, LLC.

—Orville y Wilbur Wright. 2001. (Inventores Famosos Ser.). (SPA & ENG., Illus.). 24p. (J). (gr. 1-4). lib. bdg. 19.27 (978-1-58952-178-0(1) , RK5957) Rourke Publishing, LLC.

—Orville y Wilbur Wright. 2002. (SPA.). (gr. k-3). lib. bdg. 14.10 (978-0-613-79816-7(3)) Tandem Library Bks.

Los Hermanos Wright. 2006. (People We Should Know Ser.).Tr. of Wright Brothers. (SPA.). (J). (gr. 3-4). 4.76 (978-0-8368-4363-7(0) , GHS33824) Stevens, Gareth Inc.

Jenner, Caryn. First Flight: The Wright Brothers. 2003. (gr. k-3). lib. bdg. 11.80 (978-0-613-67328-0(X)) Tandem Library Bks.

—First Flight Vol. 4: The Story of the Wright Brothers. 2003. (DK Readers Ser.). (Illus.). 48p. (J). (gr. 5). pap. 3.99 (978-0-7894-9291-3(1)) Dorling Kindersley Publishing, Inc.

Jenner, Caryn & Dorling Kindersley Publishing Staff. First Flight: The Wright Brothers. 2003. (Readers Ser.). (Illus.). 48p. (J). 14.99 (978-0-7894-9541-9(4)) Dorling Kindersley Publishing, Inc.

Lynch, Emma. The Wright Brothers. 2005. (Illus.). 32p. (J). (978-1-4034-6354-8(9)); pap. (978-1-4034-6368-5(9)) Heinemann Library.

Mayo, Gretchen Will. The Wright Brothers. 2003. (Trailblazers of the Modern World Ser.). (Illus.). 48p. (J). (gr. 5 up). lib. bdg. 30.00 (978-0-8368-5094-9(7)); pap. 11.95 (978-0-8368-5254-7(0)) Stevens, Gareth Inc. (World Almanac Library).

McCormick, Lisa Wade. Wright Brothers. 2005. (Scholastic News Nonfiction Readers Ser.). (Illus.). 24p. (J). pap. (978-0-516-24786-1(7)) Children's Pr., Ltd.

McPherson, Stephanie Sammartino & Gardner, Joseph Sammartino. Wilbur & Orville Wright: Taking Flight. 2004. (Trailblazer Biography Ser.). (Illus.). 120p. (J). 30.60 (978-1-57505-443-8(4) , Carolrhoda Bks.) Lerner Publishing Group.

Niz, Xavier. The Wright Brothers & the Airplane. Erwin, Steve & Barnett, Charles, illus. 2007. 32p. (J). (978-0-7368-6845-7(3)) Capstone Publishing.

O'Hern, Kerri & Mayo, Gretchen. The Wright Brothers. 2006. (Illus.). 32p. (J). lib. bdg. 26.00 (978-0-8368-6199-0(X) , World Almanac Library) Stevens, Gareth Inc.

Old, Wendie C. To Fly: The Story of the Wright Brothers. Parker, Robert Andrew, illus. 2002. 48p. (J). (gr. 3-5). tchr. ed. 16.00 (978-0-618-13347-5(X) , Clarion Bks.) Houghton Mifflin Co. Trade & Reference Div.

—The Wright Brothers: Inventors of the Airplane. 2000. (Historical American Biographies Ser.). (Illus.). 128p. (J). (gr. 6-12). lib. bdg. 26.60 (978-0-7660-1095-6(3)) Enslow Pubs., Inc.

Orr, Tamra B. The Dawn of Aviation: The Story of the Wright Brothers. 2005. (Illus.). 48p. (YA). (ps-7). lib. bdg. 29.95 (978-1-58415-396-2(2) , 1244922) Mitchell Lane Pubs., Inc.

Rausch, Monica. The Wright Brothers & the Airplane. 2006. (Illus.). 24p. (J). pap. (***978-0-8368-7733-5(0)***); lib. bdg. (***978-0-8368-7502-7(8)***) Stevens, Gareth Inc. (Weekly Reader Early Learning Library).

Ryan, Bernard. The Wright Brothers: Inventors of the Airplane. 2003. (Great Life Stories Ser.). (Illus.). 128p. (J). 30.50 (978-0-531-12254-9(9) , Watts, Franklin) Scholastic Library Publishing.

Seymour, Tres. Our Neighbor Is a Strange, Strange Man. Krudop, Walter Lyon, illus. 1999. 32p. (J). (gr. k-4). 16.99 (978-0-531-33107-1(5)); pap. 15.95 (978-0-531-30107-4(9)) Scholastic, Inc. (Orchard Bks.).

Sproule, Anna. The Wright Brothers. 2005. (Gigantes de Ciencia Ser.). (ENG & SPA., Illus.). 64p. (J). (gr. 5-7). 28.70 (978-1-4103-0501-5(5) , Blackbirch Pr., Inc.) Thomson Gale.

—The Wright Brothers: The Birth of Modern Aviation. 1999. (Giants of Science Ser.). (Illus.). 64p. (YA). (gr. 5-8). 24.95 (978-1-56711-328-0(1) , Blackbirch Pr., Inc.) Thomson Gale.

Tieck, Sarah. The Wright Brothers. 2007. (First Biographies Ser.). (Illus.). 32p. (J). (gr. k-3). lib. bdg. 22.78 (978-1-59679-790-1(8)) ABDO Publishing Co.

Van Steenwyk, Elizabeth. One Fine Day: A Radio Play. Farnsworth, Bill, illus. 2004. 32p. (gr. 3-5). 16.00 (978-0-8028-5234-2(3)) Eerdmans, William B. Publishing Co.

Wadsworth, Ginger. The Wright Brothers. 2004. (History Maker Bios Ser.). (Illus.). 47p. (J). 26.60 (978-0-8225-0199-2(6) , Lerner Pubns.) Lerner Publishing Group.

Yolen, Jane. My Brothers' Flying Machine: Wilbur, Orville, & Me. Burke, Jim, illus. 2003. 32p. (J). (gr. 1-4). 17.99 (978-0-316-97159-1(6)) Little, Brown Bks. for Young Readers.

AERONAUTICS, COMMERCIAL

Canavan, Andrea. The Federal Aviation Administration. 2002. (Your Government Ser.). (Illus.). 64p. (J). 25.00 (978-0-7910-6795-6(5) , Chelsea Hse.) Facts On File, Inc.

—The Federal Aviation Administration: Your Government: How it Works. 2006. (Illus.). 64p. (J). (gr. 4-8). reprint ed. 20.00 (978-1-4223-5544-2(6)) DIANE Publishing Co.

Going on an Airplane. 2003. (First Time Ser.). (Illus.). 24p. (J). (ps-1). lib. bdg. 18.50 (978-1-4034-3866-9(8)) Heinemann Library.

Hansen, Ole Steen. Commercial Aviation. 2003. (Story of Flight Ser.). (Illus.). 32p. (J). (gr. 4). pap. (978-0-7787-1221-3(4)); lib. bdg. (978-0-7787-1205-3(2)) Crabtree Publishing Co.

—Commercial Aviation: Military Aircraft of World War One. 2003. (Illus.). (J). (gr. 3-6). lib. bdg. 17.60 (978-0-613-59064-8(3)) Tandem Library Bks.

Wright, John. The U. S. Transportation Security Administration. 2003. (Rescue & Prevention Ser.). (Illus.). 96p. (J). (gr. 7 up). lib. bdg. (978-1-59084-412-0(2)) Mason Crest Pubs.

AERONAUTICS—FICTION

Appleton, Victor. Tom Swift among the Diamond Makers or Th. 2006. pap. (***978-1-4065-0892-5(6)***) Dodo Pr.

—Tom Swift & His Air Scout or Uncle Sam. 2006. pap. (***978-1-4065-0896-3(9)***) Dodo Pr.

—Tom Swift & His Sky Racer or the Quick. 2006. pap. (***978-1-4065-0907-6(8)***) Dodo Pr.

Baggette, Susan K. Jonathan Goes to the Airport. Moriarty, William J., photos by. 1998. (Jonathan Adventures Ser.). (Illus.). 16p. (J). (ps-k). bds. 5.95 (978-0-9660172-6-7(9)) Brookfield Reader, Inc., The.

Brier, Howard M. Skycruiser. 2005. pap. 26.95 (978-1-4191-1033-7(0)) Kessinger Publishing, LLC.

Carlson, Glenn E. Angie the Aviator. Robinson, Helen, ed. Storey, Linda & Nielson, Doug, illus. l.t. ed. 2004. 55p. (J). (gr. 2-9). 21.95 (978-0-9611954-4-1(4)) Watosh Publishing.

Doyle, Bill. Nabbed! The 1925 Journal of G. Codd Fitzmorgan. Lewis, Anthony, illus. 2006. 125p. (J). lib. bdg. 18.46 (***978-1-4242-1735-9(0)***) Fitzgerald Bks.

Hickam, Homer H., Jr. October Sky. 1999. Orig. Title: Rocket Boys. (gr. 7-12). lib. bdg. 15.90 (978-0-613-16784-0(8)) Tandem Library Bks.

Langworthy, Luther J. The Aeroplane Boys Flight or a Hydroplan. 2006. 95.99 (***978-1-4280-0352-1(5)***); pap. 89.99 (***978-1-4280-0353-8(3)***) IndyPublish.com.

—The Aeroplane Boys on the Wing or Aeropl. 2006. 41.99 (***978-1-4280-0509-9(9)***); pap. 35.99 (***978-1-4280-0512-9(9)***) IndyPublish.com.

Lawton, Wilbur Capta. The Boy Aviators in Africa or an Aerial. 2006. 25.99 (***978-1-4219-7625-9(0)***); pap. 19.99 (***978-1-4219-7629-7(3)***) IndyPublish.com.

—The Boy Aviators' Treasure Quest or the. 2006. 25.99 (***978-1-4280-0557-0(9)***); pap. 19.99 (***978-1-4280-0560-0(9)***) IndyPublish.com.

Mathiews, Franklin K. Skyward Ho! 2005. pap. 26.95 (978-1-4191-1034-4(9)) Kessinger Publishing, LLC.

Montgomery, R. A. Silver Wings. 2007. (Choose Your Own Adventure Ser.: No. 23). (Illus.). 144p. (J). (gr. 3-7). pap. 6.99 (***978-1-933390-23-9(9)***) Chooseco LLC.

Reid, Charles. Hurricanes over London. 2005. (Illus.). 152p. (J). (gr. 3-9). pap., tchr. ed. 8.95 (978-0-921870-82-1(5)) Ronsdale Pr. CAN. *Dist:* Literary Pr. Group of Canada.

Schotter, Roni. Captain Bob Takes Flight. Cepeda, Joe, illus. 2003. 32p. (J). (ps-2). 15.95 (978-0-689-83388-5(1) , Atheneum/Anne Schwartz Bks.) Simon & Schuster Children's Publishing.

Seidler, Tor. The Silent Spillbills. 1998. 224p. (J). (gr. 3-7). 14.95 (978-0-06-205180-6(6)) HarperCollins Pubs.

Semel, Nava. Flying Lessons. Halkin, Hillel, tr. 1999. Orig. Title: Moris Havivel Melamid La-uf. 119p. (J). (gr. 6-9). reprint ed. 14.00 (978-0-7881-6625-9(5)) DIANE Publishing Co.

Winfield, Arthur M. The Rover Boys in the Air or from College Campus to the Clouds. 2006. (ENG.). 316p. per. 30.95 (***978-1-4286-4103-7(3)***) Kessinger Publishing, LLC.

AERONAUTICS—FLIGHTS

see also Space Flight

Borden, Louise, et al. Touching the Sky. 2003. (Illus.). 64p. (J). (gr. k-3). 18.95 (978-0-689-84876-6(5) , McElderry, Margaret K.) Simon & Schuster Children's Publishing.

Davis, Lucile. Charles Lindbergh. 1999. (Photo-Illustrated Biographies Ser.). (Illus.). 24p. (J). (gr. 2-3). lib. bdg. 18.60 (978-0-7368-0204-8(5) , Bridgestone Bks.) Capstone Pr., Inc.

Finkelstein, Norman H. Three Across: The Great Transatlantic Air Race of 1927. 2008. (***978-1-59078-462-4(6)***, Calkins Creek) Boyds Mills Pr.

Koestler-Grack, Rachel A. Spirit of St. Louis. 2005. (American Moments Ser.). (Illus.). 48p. (J). (gr. 4-8). lib. bdg. 25.65 (978-1-59197-940-1(4)) ABDO Publishing Co.

Rice, Mel. Secrets in the Sky. 2001. (gr. 3-6). lib. bdg. 17.60 (978-0-613-86877-8(3)) Tandem Library Bks.

—Secrets in the Sky. 2001. (Lone Star Heroine Ser.). (Illus.). 116p. (gr. 4-7). pap. 8.95 (978-1-55622-787-5(6) , Republic of Texas Pr.) Wordware Publishing, Inc.

AERONAUTICS, HIGH SPEED

see High Speed Aeronautics

AERONAUTICS—HISTORY

Berger, Melvin & Berger, Gilda. Can You Fly High, Wright Brothers? 2007. (Scholastic Science Super Giants Ser.: Vol. 1). 48p. (J). pap. 4.99 (978-0-439-83378-3(7)) Scholastic, Inc.

Bledsoe, Karen E. Daredevils of the Air: Thrilling Tales of Pioneer Aviators. 2003. (Avisson Young Adult Ser.). (Illus.). 155p. (J). pap. 19.95 (978-1-888105-58-2(5)) Avisson Pr., Inc.

Brown, Jonatha A. The Wright Brothers. 2004. (Illus.). 24p. (J). pap. (978-0-8368-4321-7(5)); (YA). lib. bdg. 19.33 (978-0-8368-4314-9(2)) Stevens, Gareth Inc.

Carson, Mary Kay. The Wright Brothers for Kids: How They Invented the Airplane: 21 Activities Exploring the Science & History of Flight. 2003. (Illus.). 146p. (J). (gr. 4-7). lib. bdg. 24.55 (978-0-613-63373-4(3)) Tandem Library Bks.

Dixon-Engel, Tara & Jackson, Mike. Sterling Biographies: the Wright Brothers: First in Flight. 2007. (Sterling Biographies Ser.). (Illus.). 128p. (J). 12.95 (***978-1-4027-4954-4(6)***); pap. 5.95 (***978-1-4027-3231-7(7)***) Sterling Publishing Co., Inc.

Finkelstein, Norman H. Three Across: The Great Transatlantic Air Race of 1927. 2008. (***978-1-59078-462-4(6)***, Calkins Creek) Boyds Mills Pr.

Ford, Carin T. The Wright Brothers: Heroes of Flight. 2003. (Famous Inventors Ser.). (Illus.). 32p. (J) (gr. 1-4). lib. bdg. 22.60 (978-0-7660-2002-3(9)) Enslow Pubs., Inc.

Fraterrigo, Elizabeth. Beyond Kitty Hawk: Inventing Flight at Huffman Prairie Flying Field. 2002. (Illus.). 44p. (YA). 4.95 (978-1-888213-98-0(1)) Eastern National.

The Future Takes Wing: San Diego International Airport - 75 Years of Flight. 2nd ed. 2003. per. (978-0-9745294-0-0(0)) San Diego County Regional Airport Authority.

Hamen, Susan E. The Wright Brothers. 2007. (Essential Lives Ser.). (ENG., Illus.). 112p. (YA). (gr. 8-12). lib. bdg. 32.79 (***978-1-59928-846-8(X)*** , Essential Library) ABDO Publishing Co.

Hansen, Ole Steen. Amazing Flights: The Golden Age. 2003. (Story of Flight Ser.). (Illus.). 32p. (J). (gr. 4). pap. (978-0-7787-1218-3(4)); lib. bdg. (978-0-7787-1202-2(8)) Crabtree Publishing Co.

—Commercial Aviation. 2003. (Story of Flight Ser.). (Illus.). 32p. (J). (gr. 4). lib. bdg. (978-0-7787-1205-3(2)) Crabtree Publishing Co.

—The Story of Flight. 2003. (Illus.). 190p. (J). (978-0-7787-1212-1(5)) Crabtree Publishing Co.

—The Story of Flight, 12 bks. Incl. Air Combat. (gr. 4). lib. bdg. (978-0-7787-1206-0(0)); Amazing Flights : The Golden Age. (gr. 4). lib. bdg. (978-0-7787-1202-2(8)); Commercial Aviation. (gr. 4). lib. bdg. (978-0-7787-1205-3(2)); Flying for Fun. (gr. 4). lib. bdg. (978-0-7787-1211-4(7)); Helicopters. (gr. 4). lib. bdg. (978-0-7787-1208-4(7)); Military Aircraft of WWI. (gr. 4). lib. bdg. (978-0-7787-1201-5(X)); Military Aircraft of WWII. (gr. 4). lib. bdg. (978-0-7787-1203-9(6)); Modern Military Aircraft. (gr. 4). lib. bdg. (978-0-7787-1204-6(4)); Seaplanes & Naval Aviation. (gr. 4). lib. bdg. (978-0-7787-1209-1(5)); Space Flight. (gr. 2-9). lib. bdg. (978-0-7787-1207-7(9)); Weird & Wonderful Aircraft. (gr. 4). lib. bdg. (978-0-7787-1210-7(9)); Wright Brothers & Other Pioneers of Flight. (gr. 4). lib. bdg. (978-0-7787-1200-8(1)); 32p. (J). 2003. (Illus.). 2003. (978-0-7787-1198-8(6)); Set pap. (978-0-7787-1214-5(1)) Crabtree Publishing Co.

—The Wright Brothers & Other Pioneers of Flight. 2003. (Story of Flight Ser.). (Illus.). 32p. (J). (gr. 4). pap. (978-0-7787-1216-9(8)); lib. bdg. (978-0-7787-1200-8(1)) Crabtree Publishing Co.

—Wright Brothers & Other Pioneers of Flight. 2003. (gr. 3-6). lib. bdg. 17.60 (978-0-613-59120-1(8)) Tandem Library Bks.

Hofer, Charles. Airplanes. 2008. (J). lib. bdg. (***978-1-4042-4173-2(6)*** , PowerKids Pr.) Rosen Publishing Group, Inc., The.

Howe, Jane Moore. Amelia Earhart: Young Air Pioneer. Underdown, Harold, ed. Morrison, Cathy, illus. 2nd rev. ed. 2000. (Young Patriots Ser.). 111p. (J). (gr. 5 up). 15.95 (978-1-882859-02-3(2)) Patria Pr., Inc.

Hulls, John R. Rider in the Sky: How an American Cowboy Built England's First Airplane. Weitzman, David L., illus. 2003. 112p. (J). (gr. 5-8). 16.95 (978-0-375-81106-7(0) , Crown Books For Young Readers) Random Hse. Children's Bks.

Jeffrey, Gary. The History of Flight. 2007. (Graphic Discoveries Ser.). (J). (Illus.). 48p. (J). (gr. 3-7). lib. bdg. (***978-1-4042-1087-5(3)***); (***978-1-4042-9590-2(9)***); pap. (***978-1-4042-9589-6(5)***) Rosen Publishing Group, Inc., The.

Kent, Zachary. Charles Lindbergh & the Spirit of St. Louis in American History. 2001. (In American History Ser.). (Illus.). 128p. (YA). (gr. 5-12). lib. bdg. 26.60 (978-0-7660-1683-5(8)) Enslow Pubs., Inc.

McCormick, Lisa Wade. Wright Brothers. 2005. (Scholastic News Nonfiction Readers Ser.). (Illus.). 24p. (J). (gr. 1-2). 19.00 (978-0-516-24937-7(1) , Children's Pr.) Scholastic Library Publishing.

Morris, Neil. Air Pioneers. (Illus.). 48p. (YA). (gr. 5 up). lib. bdg. 29.95 (978-1-932333-81-7(9)) Chrysalis Education.

O'Brien, Patrick. Fantastic Flights: One Hundred Years of Flying on the Edge. O'Brien, Patrick, illus. 2003. (Illus.). 40p. (J). 17.95 (978-0-8027-8880-1(7)) Walker & Co.

—Fantastic Flights: One Hundred Years of Flying on the Edge. 2003. (Illus.). 40p. (J). 18.85 (978-0-8027-8881-8(5)) Walker & Co.

Price Hossell, Karen. Kitty Hawk: The Flight of the Wright Brothers. 2003. (Point of Impact Ser.). (Illus.). 32p. (J). (gr. 5-7). lib. bdg. 25.64 (978-1-58810-907-1(0)) Heinemann Library.

Rinard, Judith. The Story of Flight: From the Smithsonian National Air & Space Museum. 2002. (Illus.). 64p. (J). (gr. 3-6). 16.95 (978-1-55297-642-5(4)); pap. 8.95 (978-1-55297-694-4(7)) Firefly Bks., Ltd.

Robinson Masters, Nancy. The Airplane, 80 vols. 2004. (Inventions That Shaped the World Ser.). (Illus.). 8p. (J). 30.50 (978-0-531-12360-7(X) , Watts, Franklin) Scholastic Library Publishing.

Robinson Masters, Nancy. Airplanes. 2008. (J). lib. bdg. 25.26 (***978-1-60279-119-0(8)***) Cherry Lake Publishing.

Sandler, Martin W. Flying over the USA: Airplanes in American Life. 2006. (Illus.). 61p. (J). (gr. 4-8). reprint ed. 20.00 (978-1-4223-5623-4(X)) DIANE Publishing Co.

—Flying over the USA: Airplanes in American Life. 2004. (Transportation in America Ser.). (Illus.). 64p. (YA). 21.95 (978-0-19-513231-1(9)) Oxford Univ. Pr., Inc.

Shuter. Flying High. 2004. (Technology Through Time Ser.). (Illus.). pap. 7.50 (978-1-4109-0978-7(6)) Raintree.

Shuter, Jane. Flying High: Travel by Air. 2004. (Technology Through Time Ser.). (Illus.). 32p. (J). lib. bdg. 25.70 (978-1-4109-0579-6(9)) Raintree.

Sproule, Anna. The Wright Brothers. 2005. (Gigantes de Ciencia Ser.). (ENG & SPA., Illus.). 64p. (J). (gr. 5-7). 28.70 (978-1-4103-0501-5(5) , Blackbirch Pr., Inc.) Thomson Gale.

Thomson, Sarah L. Extreme Aircraft Q & A. 2007. 48p. (J). 16.99 (978-0-06-089943-1(3)); pap. 6.99 (978-0-06-089939-4(5)) HarperCollins Pubs.

Tieck, Sarah. The Wright Brothers. 2007. (First Biographies Ser.). (Illus.). 32p. (J). (gr. k-3). lib. bdg. 22.78 (978-1-59679-790-1(8)) ABDO Publishing Co.

Weitzman, David. Jenny: The Airplane That Taught America to Fly. Weitzman, David, illus. 2006. (Illus.). 27p. (J). (gr. k-4). reprint ed. 19.00 (978-1-4223-5582-4(9)) DIANE Publishing Co.

Weitzman, David L. Jenny: The Airplane That Taught America to Fly. Weitzman, David L., illus. rev. ed. 2002. (Illus.). 40p. (J). (gr. 1-4). 17.95 (978-0-7613-1547-6(0)) Roaring Brook Pr.

Woodford, Chris. Air & Space Travel. 2004. (History of Invention Ser.). (Illus.). 96p. (YA). (gr. 6-12). 35.00 (978-0-8160-5436-7(3)) Facts On File, Inc.

Yenne, Bill. The History of Flight. 2002. (Illus.). 48p. (J). (gr. 3-6). 18.95 (978-1-58728-412-0(X)); pap. 9.95 (978-1-58728-413-7(8)) T&N Children's Publishing. (Two Can Publishing).

AERONAUTICS, MILITARY

see also Aircraft Carriers; Airplanes, Military; Parachute Troops

also names of wars with the subdivision Aerial Operations

Anderson, Jameson. Fighter Pilot. 2006. (Illus.). 32p. (J). (978-1-4109-2496-4(3)); pap. (978-1-4109-2501-5(3)) Steck-Vaughn.

Bledsoe, Karen & Bledsoe, Glen. The Blue Angels: The U. S. Navy Flight Demonstration Squadron. 2001. (Serving Your Country Ser.). (Illus.). 48p. (J). (gr. 3-4). lib. bdg. 21.26 (978-0-7368-0773-9(X) , Capstone High-Interest Bks.) Capstone Pr., Inc.

Haberlen, Klaus. A Luftwaffe Bomber Pilot Remembers: World War Two from the Cockpit. 2001. (Schiffer Military History Ser.). (Illus.). 208p. (gr. 10-13). 29.95 (978-0-7643-1393-6(2)) Schiffer Publishing, Ltd.

Hansen, Ole Steen. Air Combat. 2003. (Story of Flight Ser.). (Illus.). 32p. (J). (gr. 4). pap. (978-0-7787-1222-0(2)); lib. bdg. (978-0-7787-1206-0(0)) Crabtree Publishing Co.

—Seaplanes & Naval Aviation. 2003. (Story of Flight Ser.). (Illus.). 32p. (J). (gr. 4). pap. (978-0-7787-1225-1(7)); lib. bdg. (978-0-7787-1209-1(5)) Crabtree Publishing Co.

Holden, Henry M. Black Hawk Helicopter. 2002. (Aircraft Ser.). (Illus.). 48p. (J). (gr. 4-10). lib. bdg. 23.93 (978-0-7660-1568-5(8)) Enslow Pubs., Inc.

Holder, Bill & Vadnais, Scott. Air Launch! A Pictorial History of Airborne Weapons. 2001. (Schiffer Military History Book Ser.). (Illus.). 96p. (gr. 10-13). pap. 19.95 (978-0-7643-1392-9(4)) Schiffer Publishing, Ltd.

Miller, Roger G. Billy Mitchell: Evangelist of Airpower. 2007. (Illus.). 152p. (YA). (gr. 10 up). lib. bdg. 25.95 (***978-1-59556-025-4(4)***) OTTN Publishing.

O'Connor, Neal W. Aviation Awards of Imperial Germany in WWI & the Men Who Earned Them, Vol. 7. 2002. (Illus.). 528p. (gr. 10-13). 69.95 (978-0-7643-1626-5(5)) Schiffer Publishing, Ltd.

Parks, Peggy J. Fighter Pilot. 2005. (Exploring Careers Ser.). (Illus.). 48p. (J). (gr. 4-8). lib. bdg. 26.20 (978-0-7377-3079-1(X) , Kidhaven) Thomson Gale.

WWII Airplanes. (Color & Learn Ser.). 36p. (J). (gr. 1-5). pap. (978-1-882210-01-5(8)) Action Publishing, Inc.

AERONAUTICS, NAVAL

see Aeronautics, Military

AERONAUTICS—PILOTING

see Airplanes—Piloting

AERONAUTICS—SAFETY MEASURES

Beyer, Mark. Sky Marshals. 2003. (High Interest Bks.). (Illus.). 48p. (J). 23.00 (978-0-516-24314-6(4)); (YA). (gr. 7-12). pap. 6.95 (978-0-516-24377-1(2)) Scholastic Library Publishing. (Children's Pr.).

Gaffney, Timothy R. Air Safety: Preventing Future Disasters. 1999. (Issues in Focus Ser.). (Illus.). 128p. (YA). (gr. 6-12). lib. bdg. 26.60 (978-0-7660-1108-3(9)) Enslow Pubs., Inc.

AERONAUTICS—VOCATIONAL GUIDANCE

Casil, Amy Sterling. Choosing a Career in Aircraft Mechanic. 2005. (World of Work Ser.). (Illus.). 64p. (YA). (gr. 7-12). lib. bdg. 25.25 (978-0-8239-3567-3(1)) Rosen Publishing Group, Inc., The.

Jaffe, Elizabeth Dana. Pilots. 2001. (Community Workers Ser.). (Illus.). 32p. (J). (gr. 1 up). lib. bdg. 21.26 (978-0-7565-0065-8(6)) Compass Point Bks.

Mattern, Joanne. Pilots. 2002. (Reading Power Ser.). (Illus.). 24p. (J). lib. bdg. 17.25 (978-0-8239-5979-2(1) , PowerKids Pr.) Rosen Publishing Group, Inc., The.

Schomp, Virginia. If You Were a Pilot. 2000. (If You Were A... Ser.). (Illus.). 32p. (J). (gr. 2-4). lib. bdg. 22.79 (978-0-7614-0919-9(X) , Benchmark Bks.) Cavendish, Marshall Corp.

Tetrick, Byron. Choosing a Career as a Pilot. 2005. (World of Work Ser.). (Illus.). 64p. (YA). (gr. 7-12). lib. bdg. 25.25 (978-0-8239-3571-0(X)) Rosen Publishing Group, Inc., The.

AERONAUTICS—VOYAGES

see Aeronautics—Flights

AB

AERONAUTICS IN METEOROLOGY

Gaffney, Timothy R. Hurricane Hunters. 2001. (Aircraft Ser.). (Illus.). 48p. (YA). (gr. 4-10). lib. bdg. 23.93 (978-0-7660-1569-2(6)) Enslow Pubs., Inc.

AFFECTION

see Friendship; Love

AFGHANISTAN

Adams, Simon. Afghanistan. 2007. (J). (***978-1-59920-014-9(7)***) Smart Apple Media.

Afganistan. 2002. (Countries of the World Ser.). (Illus.). 96p. (J). (gr. 6 up). lib. bdg. 30.00 (978-0-8368-2357-8(5)) Stevens, Gareth Inc.

Ali, Sharifah Enayat. Afghanistan. 2nd ed. 2006. (Cultures of the World Ser.). 144p. (YA). (gr. 5-9). lib. bdg. 39.93 (978-0-7614-2064-4(9) , Benchmark Bks.) Cavendish, Marshall Corp.

Banting, Erinn. Afghanistan: The Culture. 2003. (gr. 3-6). lib. bdg. 16.40 (978-0-613-59037-2(6)) Tandem Library Bks.

—Afghanistan: The People. 2003. (gr. 3-6). lib. bdg. 16.40 (978-0-613-59036-5(8)) Tandem Library Bks.

—Afghanistan - The Culture. 2003. (Lands, Peoples & Cultures Ser.). (Illus.). 32p. (J). (gr. 4-5). (978-0-7787-9337-3(0)) Crabtree Publishing Co.

—Afghanistan - The Land. 2003. (Lands, Peoples & Cultures Ser.). (Illus.). 32p. (J). (gr. 2-9). (978-0-7787-9335-9(4)); pap. (978-0-7787-9703-6(1)) Crabtree Publishing Co.

—Afghanistan - The People. 2003. (Lands, Peoples & Cultures Ser.). (Illus.). 32p. (J). (gr. 2-9). (978-0-7787-9336-6(2)); pap. (978-0-7787-9704-3(X)) Crabtree Publishing Co.

—Afghanistan -The Culture. 2003. (Lands, Peoples & Cultures Ser.). (Illus.). 32p. (J). (gr. 4-5). pap. (978-0-7787-9705-0(8)) Crabtree Publishing Co.

Behnke, Alison. Afghanistan in Pictures. 2nd ed. 2003. (Visual Geography Ser.). (Illus.). 80p. (J). (gr. 5-12). 27.93 (978-0-8225-4683-2(3)) Lerner Publishing Group.

Brimson, Samuel. Afghanistan-Botswana, 8 vols. 2003. (Nations of the World Ser.: Vol. 1). (Illus.). 64p. (J). (gr. 5 up). lib. bdg. 30.00 (978-0-8368-5485-5(3) , World Almanac Library) Stevens, Gareth Inc.

Downing, David. Afghanistan. 2004. (Illus.). 56p. (J). pap. 8.95 (978-1-4034-5523-9(6)); lib. bdg. (978-1-4034-4864-4(7)) Heinemann Library.

Englar, Mary. Afghanistan. 2003. (Countries & Cultures Ser.). (Illus.). 64p. (J). lib. bdg. 25.26 (978-0-7368-2174-2(0) , Bridgestone Bks.) Capstone Pr., Inc.

Fordyce, Deborah & Kazem, Halima. Welcome to Afghanistan. 2004. (Welcome to My Country Ser.). (Illus.). 48p. (J). (gr. 2 up). lib. bdg. 26.00 (978-0-8368-2557-2(8)) Stevens, Gareth Inc.

Gaag, Nikki Van Der. Focus on Afghanistan. 2007. (J). pap. (***978-0-8368-6755-8(6));*** 64p. (gr. 5-8). lib. bdg. 33.27 (***978-0-8368-6748-0(3)***) Stevens, Gareth Inc. (World Almanac Library).

Gritzner, Jeffrey A. Afghanistan. 2002. (Modern World Nations Ser.). (Illus.). 112p. (J). pap. 30.00 (978-0-7910-7104-5(9)); 150p. (gr. 6-12). 30.00 (978-0-7910-6774-1(2)) Facts On File, Inc. (Chelsea Hse.).

Gritzner, Jeffrey A. & Shroder, John F. Afghanistan. 2nd rev. ed. 2006. (Modern World Nations Ser.). (Illus.). 120p. (J). (gr. 6-12). 30.00 (978-0-7910-9209-5(7) , Chelsea Hse.) Facts On File, Inc.

Gunderson, Cory Gideon. Afghanistan's Struggles. 2004. (World in Conflict (Edina, Minn.) Ser.). (Illus.). 48p. (J). (gr. 4-8). lib. bdg. 25.65 (978-1-59197-410-9(0)) ABDO Publishing Co.

Haskins, James & Benson, Kathleen. Count Your Way Through Afghanistan. Moore, Megan, illus. 2007. (Count Your Way Ser.). 24p. (J). 19.93 (978-1-57505-880-1(4) , Millbrook Pr.) Lerner Publishing Group.

Howard, Helen, et al. Living As a Refugee in America: Mohammed's Story. 2005. (J). lib. bdg. 30.00 (978-0-8368-5959-1(6) , World Almanac Library) Stevens, Gareth Inc.

Italia, Bob. Afghanistan. 2002. (Countries Ser.). (Illus.). 40p. (J). (gr. k-6). lib. bdg. 22.78 (978-1-57765-653-1(9) , Checkerboard Library) ABDO Publishing Co.

Knox, Barbara. Afghanistan. 2004. (Many Cultures, One World Ser.). (Illus.). 32p. (J). (gr. 2-3). lib. bdg. 23.93 (978-0-7368-2448-4(0) , Bridgestone Bks.) Capstone Pr., Inc.

Marsh, Carole. Afghanistan: A Country at the Crossroads of War & Peace. 2002. (Here & Now Ser.). 32p. (YA). (gr. 3-8). pap. 9.95 (978-0-635-01079-7(8)) Gallopade International.

Miller, Raymond H. The War in Afghanistan. 2003. (American War Library). (Illus.). 112p. (J). 29.95 (978-1-59018-331-1(2) , Lucent Bks.) Thomson Gale.

Olson, Gillia M. Afghanistan: A Question & Answer Book. 2004. (Fact Finders Ser.). (Illus.). 32p. (J). lib. bdg. 22.60 (978-0-7368-2685-3(8)) Capstone Pr., Inc.

Parks, Peggy J. Afghanistan. 2003. (Nations in Conflict Ser.). (Illus.). 48p. (J). 24.95 (978-1-56711-499-7(7) , Blackbirch Pr., Inc.) Thomson Gale.

Piddock, Charles. Afghanistan. 2006. (Illus.). 48p. (J). pap. (978-0-8368-6713-8(0)); lib. bdg. (978-0-8368-6706-0(8)) Stevens, Gareth Inc (World Almanac Library).

Roraback, Amanda. Afghanistan in a Nutshell. (Nutshell Notes). 2004. (Illus.). 60p. (YA). pap. 7.95 (978-0-9702908-7-8(X)); 2001. 24p. pap. 4.95 (978-0-9702908-0-9(2)) Enisen Publishing.

Stewart, Gail B. Life under the Taliban. 2004. (Way People Live Ser.). (Illus.). 112p. (J). (gr. 7-10). 29.95 (978-1-59018-291-8(X) , Lucent Bks.) Thomson Gale.

Todd, Anne M. Hamid Karzai. 2003. (Major World Leaders Ser.). (Illus.). 112p. (J). (gr. 6-12). 30.00 (978-0-7910-7649-1(0) , Chelsea Hse.) Facts On File, Inc.

Wahab, Shaista & Youngerman, Barry. A Brief History of Afghanistan. 2007. (Brief History Ser.). 320p. (gr. 9). 45.00 (978-0-8160-5761-0(3)) Facts On File, Inc.

Walsh, Kieran. Afghanistan. 2003. (Countries in the News Ser.). (Illus.). 24p. (J). 25.64 (978-1-58952-676-1(7)) Rourke Publishing, LLC.

Weber, Valerie J. I Come from Afghanistan. 2006. (This Is My Story Ser.). (Illus.). 24p. (J). (gr. k-2). pap. 5.95 (978-0-8368-7240-8(1)); lib. bdg. 19.93 (978-0-8368-7233-0(9)) Stevens, Gareth Inc. (Weekly Reader Early Learning Library).

Whitehead, Kim. Afghanistan. 2005. (Growth & Influence of Islam in the Nations of Asia & Central Asia Ser.). (Illus.). 128p. (J). lib. bdg. 25.95 (978-1-59084-833-3(0)) Mason Crest Pubs.

Willis, Terri. Afghanistan. 2007. (Enchantment of the World, Second Ser.). 144p. (J). spiral bd. 37.00 (***978-0-531-18483-7(8)*** , Children's Pr.) Scholastic Library Publishing.

Wolny, Philip. American Troops in Afghanistan: Building a New Nation. 2004. (Frontline Coverage of Current Events Ser.). (Illus.). 48p. (J). lib. bdg. 26.50 (978-1-4042-0343-3(5)) Rosen Publishing Group, Inc., The.

Wolny, Philip. Hamid Karzai: President of Afghanistan. 2007. (J). (***978-1-4042-1902-1(1)***) Rosen Publishing Group, Inc., The.

Woodward, John. Afghanistan. 2006. (Illus.). 244p. (gr. 10-12). 24.95 (978-0-7377-3304-4(7)); pap. 36.20 (978-0-7377-3303-7(9)) Thomson Gale. (Greenhaven Pr., Inc.).

AFGHANISTAN—FICTION

Ellis, Deborah. The Breadwinner. 2001. 170p. (YA). (gr. 4-7). pap. 8.95 (978-0-88899-416-5(8)); (Illus.). (J). (gr. 5-7). 15.95 (978-0-88899-419-6(2)) Groundwood Bks. CAN. *Dist:* Perseus Distribution, Transition Vendor, Perseus Distribution.

—The Breadwinner. unabr. ed. 2004. 170p. (J). (gr. 5-7). pap. 29.00 incl. audio (978-0-8072-0982-0(1) , S YA 411 SP, Listening Library) Random Hse. Audio Publishing Group.

—The Breadwinner. 2002. (gr. 3-6). lib. bdg. 14.10 (978-0-613-44488-0(4)) Tandem Library Bks.

—Jackal in the Garden: An Encounter with Bihzad. 2006. (Art Encounters Ser.). (Illus.). 176p. (YA). (gr. 7 up). 16.95 (978-0-8230-0415-7(5)) Watson-Guptill Pubns., Inc.

—Mud City. (Illus.). 176p. 2004. (J). pap. 5.95 (978-0-88899-542-1(3)); 2003. (gr. 5-9). 15.95 (978-0-88899-518-6(0)) Groundwood Bks. CAN. *Dist:* Perseus Distribution.

—Parvana's Journey. 2003. 176p. (J). (gr. 5-9). pap. 6.95 (978-0-88899-519-3(9)) Groundwood Bks. CAN. *Dist:* Perseus Distribution.

—Parvana's Journey. 2003. (gr. 5-8). lib. bdg. 14.10 (978-0-613-88800-4(6)) Tandem Library Bks.

Khan, Rukhsana. The Roses in My Carpets. Himler, Ronald, illus. 1998. 32p. (J). (ps-3). 15.95 (978-0-8234-1399-7(3)) Holiday Hse., Inc.

—The Roses in My Carpets. Himler, Ronald, illus. 26p. 16.95 (978-0-7737-3092-2(3)) Stoddart Kids CAN. *Dist:* Fitzhenry & Whiteside, Ltd.

Staples, Suzanne Fisher. Under the Persimmon Tree. 2005. (Illus.). 288p. (YA). 17.00 (978-0-374-38025-0(2)) Farrar, Straus & Giroux.

—Under the Persimmon Tree. 2008. 304p. (YA). pap. 7.99 (***978-0-312-37776-2(2)***) Square Fish.

Stine, Catherine. Refugees. 288p. (gr. 7). 2006. (YA). pap. 5.99 (978-0-440-23876-8(5) , Laurel Leaf); 2005. (J). 15.95 (978-0-385-73179-9(5) , Delacorte Bks. for Young Readers); 2005. (YA). 17.99 (978-0-385-90216-8(6) , Delacorte Bks. for Young Readers) Random Hse. Children's Bks.

Tilly, Meg. Porcupine. 2007. 192p. (J). (gr. 5-9). 15.95 (***978-0-88776-810-1(5)***) Tundra Bks., Inc./Livres Toundra, Inc. CAN. *Dist:* Random Hse., Inc.

AFRICA

Adam, Winky. African Activity Book. 1999. (Illus.). 64p. (J). pap. 1.50 (978-0-486-40492-9(7)) Dover Pubns., Inc.

Africa: Progress & Problems, 13 vols., Set. Incl. AIDS & Health Issues in Africa. Gelletly, LeeAnne. (Illus.). (J). (gr. 7 up). 2006. lib. bdg. 24.95 (978-1-59084-954-5(X)); Civil Wars in Africa. Habeeb, William Mark. (Illus.). (YA). (gr. 7 up). 2006. lib. bdg. 24.95 (978-1-59084-955-2(8)); Ecological Issues in Africa. Gelletly, LeeAnne. (Illus.). (YA). (gr. 7 up). 2006. lib. bdg. 24.95 (978-1-59084-956-9(6)); Education in Africa. Lewis, Suzanne Grant. (Illus.). (YA). (gr. 7 up). 2006. lib bdg. 24.95 (978-1-59084-959-0(0)); Ethnic Groups in Africa : Africa: Progress & Problems. Obadina, Elizabeth. (Illus.). (J). (gr. 7 up). 2006. (978-1-59084-996-5(5)); Governance & Leadership in Africa. Rotberg, Robert I. (Illus.). (YA). (gr. 7 up). 2006. lib. bdg. 24.95 (978-1-59084-957-6(4)); Helping Africa Help Itself : A Global Effort. Sah, Anup. (Illus.). (YA). (gr. 7 up). 2007. lib. bdg. 24.95 (978-1-59084-923-1(X)); Human Rights. Baughan, Brian. (YA). (gr. 7 up). 2006. lib. bdg. 24.95 (978-1-59084-960-6(4)); Islam in Africa. Mazrui, Ali. (Illus.). (YA). (gr. 9 up). 2006. lib. bdg. 24.95 (***978-1-59084-999-6(X));*** Making of Africa. Obadina, Tunde. (Illus.). (J). (gr. 7 up). 2007. lib. bdg. 24.95 (978-1-59084-998-9(1)); Population & Overcrowding. Obadina, Tunde. (YA). (gr. 7 up). 2007. lib. bdg. 24.95 (978-1-59084-997-2(3)); Poverty & Economic Issues in Africa. Obadina, Tunde. (Illus.). (YA). (gr. 7 up). 2006. lib. bdg. 24.95 (978-1-59084-953-8(1)); Religions of Africa. Cavanaugh, Dorothy. (J). (gr. 7 up). 2006. lib. bdg. 24.95 (***978-1-59084-958-3(2));*** 112p. 2006. Set lib. bdg. 324.35 (***978-1-59084-952-1(3)***) Mason Crest Pubs.

African Kings & Queens. 2000. (My Ancestors—My Heroes Ser.: Vol. 1). (J). (gr. 3-4). (978-1-893091-00-9(7)) Parker Publishing Co.

African Safari, 6, Pack. 32p. (gr. 5 up). 44.00 (978-0-7578-0988-0(X)) Rigby Education.

African Villages & Peoples. 2000. (My Ancestors—My Heroes Ser.: Vol. 2). (J). (gr. 3-4). (978-1-893091-01-6(5)) Parker Publishing Co.

Aspen-Baxter, Linda. Africa. (Illus.). 32p. (J). 2006. (gr. 4-6). lib. bdg. 26.00 (978-1-59036-316-4(7)); 2005. (ps-7). pap. 7.95 (978-1-59036-323-2(X)) Weigl Pubs., Inc.

Ayo, Yvonne. Africa. 2000. (Eyewitness Bks.). (Illus.). 64p. (J). (gr. 3-12). 15.99 (978-0-7894-6030-1(0)) Dorling Kindersley Publishing, Inc.

Ayo, Yvonne & Dorling Kindersley Publishing Staff. Africa. 2000. (Eyewitness Bks.). (Illus.). 64p. (J). (gr. 3-12). lib. bdg. 19.99 (978-0-7894-6610-5(4)) Dorling Kindersley Publishing, Inc.

Barnett, Michelle Noble, et al. Theme Pockets - September: School Days; Africa; Whales. Evans, Marilyn, ed. Larsen, Jo, illus. 1999. (Making Books with Pockets). 96p. (J). (gr. 1-3). pap., tchr. ed. 12.99 (978-1-55799-706-7(3) , EMC 592) Evan-Moor Educational Pubs.

Barron's Educational Editorial Staff. Exploration of Africa. 1998. (Great Explorers Ser.). (Illus.). 32p. (YA). (gr. 5-9). pap. 5.95 (978-0-7641-0632-3(5)) Barron's Educational Series, Inc.

Bateman, Helen & Denshire, Jayne. Africa. 2006. (J). (978-1-58340-799-8(5)) Smart Apple Media.

Bowden, Rob. Africa. (Illus.). 64p. (J). 2006. (gr. 7-10). lib. bdg. 32.67 (978-0-8368-5910-2(3)); 2005. pap. (978-0-8368-5917-1(0)) Stevens, Gareth Inc. (World Almanac Library).

Bramwell, Martyn. Africa. 2000. (World in Maps Ser.). (Illus.). 56p. (J). (gr. 5-12). lib. bdg. 23.93 (978-0-8225-2914-9(9) , Lerner Pubns.) Lerner Publishing Group.

Brimson, Samuel. Niger-Seychelles, 8 vols. 2003. (Nations of the World Ser.: Vol. 6). (Illus.). 64p. (J). (gr. 5 up). lib. bdg. 30.00 (978-0-8368-5490-9(X) , World Almanac Library) Stevens, Gareth Inc.

Brown, Barbara & Brown, Shirley. Into the Bush. 2000. (Illus.). 26p. (J). (gr. 2-6). lib. bdg. 20.00 (978-0-9704872-1-6(5)) Brown's Graphics & Printing.

Brown, Don. Uncommon Traveler: Mary Kingsley in Africa. 2003. (Illus.). 32p. (J). (gr. k-3). 5.95 (978-0-618-36916-4(3)) Houghton Mifflin Co. Trade & Reference Div.

Bull, Schuyler. Along the Luangwa: A Story of an African Floodplain. Male, Alan, illus. 1999. (Nature Conservancy Habitat Ser.: No. 13). 36p. (J). (gr. 1-4). 15.95 (978-1-56899-776-6(0)) Soundprints.

Chait, Thelma. Call of Africa. Wells, Malcolm, illus. Chait, Thelma, photos by. 1998. 64p. (J). (gr. 4-8). pap. 10.95 (978-1-880812-29-7(0)) Storytellers Ink, Inc.

Chanek, Sherilin. Africa. 2003. (National Geographic Reading Expeditions Ser.). (Illus.). 64p. (J). (978-0-7922-4364-9(1)) National Geographic Society.

Chapman, Simon. On Safari. Chapman, Simon, illus. 2005. (Illus.). 111p. (J). lib. bdg. 20.00 (***978-1-4242-0633-9(2)***) Fitzgerald Bks.

Chelsea House Publishing Staff. Congo & Angola Regions. 1999. (Exploration of Africa). (Illus.). 144p. (YA). (gr. 7-12). 29.95 (978-0-7910-5742-1(9) , Chelsea Hse.) Facts On File, Inc.

—Southeast Africa. 2002. (Exploration of Africa). (Illus.). 112p. (YA). (gr. 7-12). 35.00 (978-0-7910-5747-6(X) , Chelsea Hse.) Facts On File, Inc.

—Sudan. 2001. (Exploration of Africa). (Illus.). 112p. (J). (gr. 7 up). 35.00 (978-0-7910-5453-6(5) , Chelsea Hse.) Facts On File, Inc.

Costain, Meredith. African Grasslands. 2000. (gr. k-3). lib. bdg. 11.80 (978-0-613-30211-1(7)) Tandem Library Bks.

Croze, Harvey. Africa for Kids: Exploring a Vibrant Continent, 19 Activities. 2006. (For Kids Ser.). (Illus.). 144p. (J). pap. 17.95 (978-1-55652-598-8(2)) Chicago Review Pr., Inc.

De Villiers, Les. Africa 2004. 4th ed. 2004. (Illus.). 400p. pap. 28.95 (978-0-916673-13-0(8)) Business Bks. International.

Deady, Kathleen W. Rwanda. 2005. (Fact Finders Ser.). (Illus.). 32p. (J). 22.60 (978-0-7368-3759-0(0)) Capstone Pr., Inc.

Di Piazza, Francesca. Sudan in Pictures. 2006. (Visual Geography Ser.). (Illus.). 80p. (J). 27.93 (978-0-8225-2678-0(6) , Twenty-First Century Bks.) Lerner Publishing Group.

Donaldson, Madeline. Africa. 2005. (Pull Ahead Bks.). (Illus.). 32p. (J). (gr. k-3). lib. bdg. 22.60 (978-0-8225-4720-4(1)) Lerner Publishing Group.

Dudley, William. Africa. 2000. (Opposing Viewpoints Ser.). (Illus.). 312p. (gr. 10-12). pap. 21.20 (978-0-7377-0118-0(8)); 212p. (gr. 9-12). lib. bdg. (978-0-7377-0119-7(6)) Thomson Gale. (Greenhaven Pr., Inc.).

Ellis, Veronica Freeman. Afro-Bets First Book about Africa. Ford, George, illus. 2003. 32p. (J). (gr. 1-3). pap. 5.99 (978-0-439-42918-4(8) , Cartwheel Bks.) Scholastic, Inc.

Encyclopaedia Britannica Publishers, Inc. Staff. Views of Africa. 2004. (Britannica Learning Library). (Illus.). (J). lib. bdg. 14.95 (978-1-59339-011-2(4)) Encyclopaedia Britannica, Inc.

Foster, Leila Merrell. Africa. (Illus.). 32p. (J). 2006. (***978-1-4034-8539-7(9));*** 2001. lib. bdg. 21.36 (978-1-57572-446-1(4)) Heinemann Library.

Foster, Leila Merrell & Fox, Mary Virginia. Africa. 2002. (Continents Ser.). (Illus.). 32p. (J). (gr. k-2). pap. 6.95 (978-1-58810-945-3(3) , 91435) Heinemann Library.

Fowler, Allan. Africa. (Rookie Read-About Geography Ser.). (Illus.). 32p. (J). (gr. 1-2). 2002. pap. 5.95 (978-0-516-25979-6(2)); 2001. 20.50 (978-0-516-22238-7(4)) Scholastic Library Publishing. (Children's Pr.).

—Africa. 2001. (gr. k-3). lib. bdg. 14.10 (978-0-613-53898-5(6)) Tandem Library Bks.

Graf, Mike. Africa. 2002. (Continents Ser.). (Illus.). 79p. (J). (gr. 1-2). 18.60 (978-0-7368-1414-0(0) , Bridgestone Bks.) Capstone Pr., Inc.

—Somalia. 2002. (Countries of the World Ser.). (Illus.). 24p. (J). (gr. 2-3). lib. bdg. 18.60 (978-0-7368-1108-8(7) , Bridgestone Bks.) Capstone Pr., Inc.

Habeeb, William Mark. Africa: Facts & Figures. 2004. (Africa Ser.). (Illus.). 87p. (J). lib. bdg. (978-1-59084-817-3(9)) Mason Crest Pubs.

Hassig, Susan M. & Latif, Zawiah Abdul. Somalia. 2nd ed. 2007. (Cultures of the World Ser.). 144p. (J). lib. bdg. 39.93 (***978-0-7614-2082-8(7)*** , Benchmark Bks.) Cavendish, Marshall Corp.

Heinrichs, Ann. Niger: Enchantment of the World. 2001. (Enchantment of the World, Second Ser.). (Illus.). 144p. (J). (gr. 5-9). 36.00 (978-0-516-21633-1(3) , Children's Pr.) Scholastic Library Publishing.

Hovanec, Erin M. An Online Visit to Africa. (Internet Field Trips Ser.). 24p. (J). 2002. lib. bdg. 18.75 (978-0-8239-6420-8(5)); 2001. (Illus.). (gr. 3). lib. bdg. 18.75 (978-0-8239-5651-7(2)) Rosen Publishing Group, Inc., The. (PowerKids Pr.).

Hughes, Christopher. Sudan. 2005. (Nations in Conflict Ser.). (Illus.). 48p. (J). (gr. 5-8). lib. bdg. 24.95 (978-1-4103-0553-4(8) , Blackbirch Pr., Inc.) Thomson Gale.

Ibazebo, Isimene. Africa. 2000. (Exploration Into... Ser.). (Illus.). 48p. (J). (gr. 4-7). 25.00 (978-0-7910-6019-3(5) , Chelsea Hse.) Facts On File, Inc.

James, Roger S. Mozambique. 1999. (Major World Nations Ser.). (Illus.). 144p. (YA). (gr. 4-7). 29.95 (978-0-7910-4744-6(X) , Chelsea Hse.) Facts On File, Inc.

Jenson-Elliott, Cynthia L. Southern Africa. 2002. (Indigenous Peoples of Africa Ser.). (Illus.). 112p. (J). 29.95 (978-1-59018-084-6(4) , Lucent Bks.) Thomson Gale.

Kalman, Bobbie & Sjonger, Rebecca. Explore Africa. 2007. (Explore the Continents Ser.). (Illus.). 32p. (J). (gr. 1-7). (***978-0-7787-3070-5(0));*** pap. (***978-0-7787-3084-2(0)***) Crabtree Publishing Co.

Karmiol, Sheri Metzger. The Africans. 2006. (Illus.). 112p. (gr. 10-12). 34.95 (978-0-7377-3497-3(3) , Greenhaven Pr., Inc.) Thomson Gale.

Kavanagh, James. African Animal Tracks: An Introduction to the Tracks & Dung of Familiar Species. Leung, Raymond, illus. 2001. (Pocket Traveller Ser.). 12p. pap. 5.95 (978-1-58355-037-3(2)) Waterford Pr., Ltd.

—African Birds: An Introduction to Familiar Species. Leung, Raymond, illus. 2001. (Pocket Traveller Ser.). 12p. pap. 5.95 (978-1-58355-033-5(X)) Waterford Pr., Ltd.

—African Wildlife: An Introduction to Familiar Species. Leung, Raymond, illus. 2001. (Pocket Traveller Ser.). 12p. pap. 5.95 (978-1-58355-032-8(1)) Waterford Pr., Ltd.

Klingel, Cynthia Fitterer. Africa. 2003. (Continents Ser.). (Illus.). 32p. (J). (gr. 2-6). 27.07 (978-1-59296-059-0(6)) Child's World, Inc.

Kneib, Martha. Benin. 2007. (Cultures of the World Ser.). (Illus.). 128p. (J). lib. bdg. 39.93 (978-0-7614-2328-7(1) , Benchmark Bks.) Cavendish, Marshall Corp.

Knight, Margy Burns. Africa Is Not a Country. 2002. (gr. 3-6). lib. bdg. 18.75 (978-0-613-90445-2(1)) Tandem Library Bks.

Knight, Margy Burns & Melnicove, Mark. Africa Is Not a Country. O'Brien, Anne Sibley, illus. 2002. 48p. (J). (gr. 3-6). pap. 9.95 (978-0-7613-1647-3(7) , Millbrook Pr.) Lerner Publishing Group.

Knight, Margy Burns, et al. Africa Is Not a Country. O'Brien, Anne Sibley, illus. 2000. 48p. (gr. 3-6). lib. bdg. (978-0-7613-1266-6(8) , Millbrook Pr.) Lerner Publishing Group.

Know the Self, Afrikan: Knowledge, the Prerequisite of Freedom. 2001. 45p. (YA). (gr. 9 up). pap. 8.00 (978-0-9658331-4-1(3)) Starlight Communications.

Levy, Patricia & Latif, Zawiah Abdul. Sudan. 2nd ed. 2007. (Cultures of the World Ser.). 144p. (J). lib. bdg. 39.93 (***978-0-7614-2083-5(5)*** , Benchmark Bks.) Cavendish, Marshall Corp.

MacDonald, Fiona & Wood, Gerald. An Ancient African Town. 1999. (Metropolis Ser.). (Illus.). 48p. (J). (gr. 5-7). pap. 8.95 (978-0-531-15360-4(6) , Watts, Franklin) Scholastic Library Publishing.

Macken, JoAnn Early. African Animals. Hess, Paul, illus. 2002. (Animal Worlds Ser.). 24p. (J). (ps up). lib. bdg. 20.67 (978-0-8368-3038-5(5)) Stevens, Gareth Inc.

Mattern, Joanne. Animal Geography: Africa. 2000. 56p. (YA). (gr. 5-12). pap. 8.95 (978-0-7891-5331-9(9)); (Illus.). (J). (gr. 4-7). lib. bdg. 17.95 (978-0-7807-9713-0(2)) Perfection Learning Corp.

McGraw-Hill Staff. Exploring Our World, Eastern Hemisphere, Interactive Tutor Self Assessment CD-ROM. 2007. (C). cd-rom 93.32 (***978-0-07-879098-0(0)*** , 9780078790980) Glencoe/McGraw-Hill.

—Exploring Our World, Eastern Hemisphere, Reading Essentials & Note-Taking Guide Workbook. 2007. (C). pap. 18.00 (***978-0-07-878166-7(3)*** , 9780078781667) Glencoe/McGraw-Hill.

—Exploring Our World, Eastern Hemisphere, Standardized Test Practice Workbook. 2007. (C). pap. 10.00 (***978-0-07-877743-1(7)*** , 9780078777431) Glencoe/McGraw-Hill.

—Exploring Our World, Eastern Hemisphere, Student Edition. 2nd ed. 2007. 69.32 (***978-0-07-874578-2(0)*** , 9780078745782) Glencoe/McGraw-Hill.

McNeil, Niki, et al. HOCPP 1052 Africa. 2005. spiral bd. 24.00 (***978-1-60308-052-1(X)***) In the Hands of a Child.

Middleton, John, ed. Africa: An Encyclopedia for Students, 4 vols. 2001. (Illus.). (J). (978-0-684-80651-8(7)); (978-0-684-80652-5(5)); (978-0-684-80653-2(3)); (978-0-684-80654-9(1)) Simon & Schuster. (Scribner).

Moore, Jo Ellen. Africa. Evans, Marilyn, ed. Davis, Cindy & Winters, Keli, illus. 1999. (Geography Units Ser.). 80p. (J). (gr. 3-6). pap., tchr. ed. 12.95 (978-1-55799-716-6(0) , EMC 769) Evan-Moor Educational Pubs.

Mulroy, Tanya. Mozambique. 2007. (J). (978-1-4222-0090-2(6)) Mason Crest Pubs.

Murray, Jocelyn & Sheehan, Sean. Africa. 2nd rev. ed. 2003. (Cultural Atlas for Young People Ser.). (Illus.). 96p. (J). (gr. 4-9). 35.00 (978-0-8160-5151-9(8)) Facts On File, Inc.

Obadina, Elizabeth. Ethnic Groups in Africa: Africa: Progress & Problems. 2006. (Africa Ser.). (Illus.). 112p. (J). (gr. 7 up). (978-1-59084-996-5(5)) Mason Crest Pubs.

Onyefulu, Ifeoma. Triangle for Adaora: An African Book of Shapes. 2007. (Illus.). 32p. (J). pap. 7.95 (978-1-84507-738-9(5)) Lincoln, Frances Ltd. GBR. *Dist:* Perseus Distribution.

Pelusey, Michael & Pelusey, Jane. Africa. 2004. (Continents Ser.). (Illus.). 32p. (J). (gr. 2-4). 23.00 (978-0-7910-8281-2(4), Chelsea Hse.) Facts On File, Inc.

Petersen, David. Africa. Taft, James, ed. 1998. (True Bks.). (Illus.). 48p. (J). (gr. 3-5). pap. 6.95 (978-0-516-26369-4(2), Children's Pr.) Scholastic Library Publishing.

Prebeg, Rick. Into the Jungle. Prebeg, Rick, photos by. 2005. (J). (978-1-933248-05-9(X)) World Quest Learning.

Rappoport, Bernice. Habitats of Africa. 2005. (Navigators Ser.). (J). pap. 38.00 (*978-1-4108-5074-4(9)) Benchmark Education Co.

Rodin, Ermila. Sunset on an African Horizon. 1999. (Illus.). 120p. pap. 8.95 (978-1-58521-010-7(2)) Books for Black Children, Inc.

Sammis, Fran. Africa. 1998. (Mapping Our World Ser.). (Illus.). 64p. (J). (gr. 4-8). lib. bdg. 27.07 (978-0-7614-0372-2(8), Benchmark Bks.) Cavendish, Marshall Corp.

Sayre, April Pulley. Africa. 1999. (Seven Continents Ser.: 8). (Illus.). 64p. (gr. 5-8). lib. bdg. 25.90 (978-0-7613-1367-0(2), Millbrook Pr.) Lerner Publishing Group.

—Good Morning, Africa! 2003. 32p. (J). (gr. 2-5). pap. 7.95 (978-0-7613-1993-1(X)); (Celebrate the Continents Ser.: 4). (Illus.). lib. bdg. 21.90 (978-0-7613-2121-7(7)) Lerner Publishing Group. (Millbrook Pr.).

—Good Morning, Africa! 2003. (gr. k-3). lib. bdg. 16.40 (978-0-613-90691-3(8)) Tandem Library Bks.

Schaefer, A. R. Africa. 2006. (Illus.). 24p. (J). (978-0-7368-5425-2(8)) Capstone Pr., Inc.

Schemenauer, Elma. Welcome to Russia. 2007. (Welcome to the World Ser.). 32p. (J). (gr. 1-5). 27.07 (*978-1-59296-921-0(6)) Child's World, Inc.

—Welcome to Somalia. 2008. (Welcome to the World Ser.). 32p. (J). (gr. 1-5). 27.07 (*978-1-59296-976-0(3)) Child's World, Inc.

Sheehan, Sean. Angola. 1999. (Cultures of the World Ser.). (Illus.). 128p. (J). (gr. k-17). lib. bdg. 37.07 (978-0-7614-0953-3(X), Benchmark Bks.) Cavendish, Marshall Corp.

Smith, A. G. African Village Sticker Picture. 1998. (Illus.). (J). 4.50 (978-0-486-40377-9(7)) Dover Pubns., Inc.

Snyder, Gail. Sudan. 2003. (Modern Middle East Nations & Their Strategic Place in the World Ser.). (Illus.). 112,128p. (YA). (gr. 7 up). lib. bdg. (978-1-59084-519-6(6)) Mason Crest Pubs.

Striveildi, Cheryl. Africa. 2003. (Continents Ser.). (Illus.). 32p. (J). (gr. k-4). lib. bdg. 22.78 (978-1-57765-958-7(9)) ABDO Publishing Co.

Underwood, Deborah. Africa. 2006. (Illus.). 32p. (J). (978-1-4034-8241-9(1)); pap. (978-1-4034-8249-5(7)) Heinemann Library.

Vierow, Wendy. Africa. 2004. (Atlas of the Seven Continents Ser.). (Illus.). 24p. (J). lib. bdg. 21.25 (978-0-8239-6687-5(9), PowerKids Pr.) Rosen Publishing Group, Inc., The.

Watson, Galadriel Findlay. The Bushmen of South Africa. 2005. (Indigenous Peoples Ser.). 32p. pap. 7.95 (978-1-59036-254-9(3)) Weigl Pubs., Inc.

Weintraub, Aileen. Discovering Africa's Land, People, & Wildlife: A MyReportLinks. com Book. 2004. (Continents of the World Ser.). (Illus.). 48p. (J). lib. bdg. 25.26 (978-0-7660-5204-8(4), MyReportLinks.com Bks.) Enslow Pubs., Inc.

World Book, Inc Staff, contrib. by. Wild Animals. 2007. (J). (*978-0-7166-7733-8(4)) World Bk., Inc.

Zwier, Lawrence J. Sudan: North Against South. 1999. (World in Conflict Ser.). (Illus.). 80p. (YA). (gr. 7-12). 25.26 (978-0-8225-3559-1(9), Lerner Pubns.) Lerner Publishing Group.

AFRICA—ANTIQUITIES

Pacchini, Fiorenzo. A Day with Homo Habilis: Life 2,000,000 Years Ago. 2003. (Early Humans Ser.). (Illus.). 48p. (gr. 6 up). lib. bdg. 23.90 (978-0-7613-2765-3(7), Twenty-First Century Bks.) Lerner Publishing Group.

AFRICA—BIOGRAPHY

Abella, Tomas. E de Escuela. 2005. (SPA.). 26p. (J). (gr. 2-7). 18.95 (978-84-89970-69-4(6)) Fundacion Intermon ESP. *Dist:* Iaconi, Mariuccia Bk. Imports.

Briscoe, Diana. Jane Goodall: Finding Hope in the Wilds of Africa, 6 vols. (gr. 4 up). 49.95 (978-0-7368-3869-6(4), High Five) Red Brick Learning.

Collin, Grace. Man of Destiny: The Life of Leopold Sedar Senghor. Bostic, Alex, illus. 2006. 32p. (J). lib. bdg. 16.95 (978-1-886366-15-2(2)) Sights Productions.

Diouf, Sylviane A. Kings & Queens of East Africa. (Watts Library). (Illus.). 64p. (J). (gr. 5-7). 2001. pap. 8.95 (978-0-531-16534-8(5)); 2000. 25.50 (978-0-531-20373-6(5)) Scholastic Library Publishing. (Watts, Franklin).

—Kings & Queens of Southern Africa. (Watts Library). (Illus.). 64p. (J). (gr. 5-7). 2001. pap. 8.95 (978-0-531-16535-5(3)); 2000. 25.50 (978-0-531-20374-3(3)) Scholastic Library Publishing. (Watts, Franklin).

Hall, Lynn Bradford. Shaka, Warrior King of the Zulu. Hermans, Rene, illus. 2006. 32p. (J). (gr. 4-7). pap. 11.00 (978-1-86825-418-7(6)) Struik Pubs. ZAF. *Dist:* International Publishers Marketing.

Hansen, Joyce. African Princess: The Amazing Lives of Africa's Royal Women. McGaw, Laurie, illus. 2004. 48p. (gr. 3-17). 16.99 (978-0-7868-5116-4(3)) Hyperion Bks. for Children.

Howat, Irene. John Newton, a Slave Set Free. 144p. (J). mass mkt. 5.99 (978-1-85792-834-1(2), Christian Focus) Christian Focus Pubns. GBR. *Dist:* Riverside.

Leidenfrost, Lisa. At the Edge of the Village: Musings of a Missionary Wife. 2004. Orig. Title: African Sketches. (Illus.). 212p. (YA). per. 12.00 (978-1-59128-017-0(6)) Canon Pr.

Otfinoski, Steven. David Livingstone: Deep in the Heart of Africa. 2006. (Great Explorations Ser.). (Illus.). 80p. (YA). (gr. 5-9). lib. bdg. 32.79 (978-0-7614-2226-6(9), Benchmark Bks.) Cavendish, Marshall Corp.

Rosenberg, Aaron. Taig Khris:In-Line Skating. 2005. (Illus.). 64p. (J). (gr. 5-8). lib. bdg. 26.50 (978-1-4042-0069-2(X)) Rosen Publishing Group, Inc., The.

AFRICA, CENTRAL

Barber, Nicola. Central Africa. 2005. (Illus.). 44p. (J). (gr. 6-9). lib. bdg. 29.95 (978-1-58340-607-6(7)) Smart Apple Media.

Bodnarchuk, Kari J. Rwanda: A Country Torn Apart. 1999. (World in Conflict Ser.). (Illus.). 96p. (YA). (gr. 7-12). 25.26 (978-0-8225-3557-7(2), Lerner Pubns.) Lerner Publishing Group.

Cook, Diane. Cameroon. 2007. (J). (978-1-4222-0089-6(2)) Mason Crest Pubs.

Diouf, Sylviane A. Kings & Queens of Central Africa. 2000. (Kings & Queens of Africa Ser.). (Illus.). 64p. (J). (gr. 5-7). 25.50 (978-0-531-20372-9(7), Watts, Franklin) Scholastic Library Publishing.

Fish, Bruce & Fish, Becky Durost. The Congo. 2001. (Exploration of Africa Ser.). (Illus.). 112p. (J). 35.00 (978-0-7910-6198-5(1), Chelsea Hse.) Facts On File, Inc.

Freeman, Charles. Crisis in Rwanda. 1998. (New Perspectives Ser.). (Illus.). 64p. (YA). (gr. 4-7). lib. bdg. 28.54 (978-0-8172-5020-1(4)) Raintree.

Harmon, Daniel E. Central & East Africa. 2001. (Exploration of Africa Ser.). (Illus.). 112p. (J). (gr. 7-12). 35.00 (978-0-7910-5743-8(7), Chelsea Hse.) Facts On File, Inc.

Hughes, Christopher. Rwanda. 2003. (Nations in Conflict Ser.). 48p. (J). 26.19 (978-1-56711-542-0(X), Blackbirch Pr., Inc.) Thomson Gale.

Kneib, Martha. Chad. 2007. (Cultures of the World Ser.). (Illus.). 128p. (J). lib. bdg. 39.93 (978-0-7614-2327-0(3), Benchmark Bks.) Cavendish, Marshall Corp.

Koopmans, Andy. Rwanda. 2004. (Africa Ser.). (Illus.). 87p. (J). lib. bdg. (978-1-59084-812-8(8)) Mason Crest Pubs.

AFRICA, CENTRAL—FICTION

Karr, Kathleen. Born for Adventure. 2007. (Illus.). 208p. (J). (gr. 7 up). 16.99 (*978-0-7614-5348-2(2)) Cavendish, Marshall Corp.

AFRICA, EAST

Britton, Tamara L. Somalia. 2003. (Countries Ser.). (Illus.). 40p. (J). (gr. k-6). lib. bdg. 22.78 (978-1-57765-844-3(2)) ABDO Publishing Co.

Bull, Schuyler. Through Tsavo: A Story of an East African Savanna. Kratter, Paul, illus. 1998. (Habitat Ser.). (J). (gr. 1-4). 32p. 19.95 incl. audio (978-1-56899-554-0(7), BC7008); Incl. toy. 36p. 26.95 (978-1-56899-556-4(3)) Soundprints.

Cobb, Vicki. This Place Is Wild: East Africa. 2000. (Imagine Living Here Ser.). (978-0-606-18744-2(8)); (gr. 3-6). lib. bdg. 16.40 (978-0-613-27231-5(5)) Tandem Library Bks.

—This Place Is Wild: East Africa. Lavallee, Barbara, illus. 1998. (Imagine Living Here Ser.: Vol. 7). 33p. (J). (gr. k-3). lib. bdg. 16.85 (978-0-8027-8633-3(2)); 15.95 (978-0-8027-8632-6(4)) Walker & Co.

Cobb, Vicki & Lavallee, Barbara. This Place Is Wild: East Africa. 2000. (Imagine Living Here Ser.). (Illus.). 32p. (J). (gr. 2-5). pap. 7.95 (978-0-8027-7579-5(9)) Walker & Co.

Dahl, Roald. Going Solo. 1999. (Illus.). 224p. (gr. 7-12). pap. 6.99 (978-0-14-130310-9(7), Puffin) Penguin Group (USA) Inc.

—Going Solo. 1998. (Illus.). 209p. (YA). (gr. 7-12). per. 15.30 (978-0-613-10109-7(X)) Tandem Library Bks.

Diouf, Sylviane A. Kings & Queens of East Africa. (Watts Library). (Illus.). 64p. (J). (gr. 5-7). 2001. pap. 8.95 (978-0-531-16534-8(5)); 2000. 25.50 (978-0-531-20373-6(5)) Scholastic Library Publishing. (Watts, Franklin).

Feelings, Muriel L. Moja Means One: Swahili Counting Book. Feelings, Tom, illus. 2004. 20p. (J). (gr. k-4). reprint ed. pap. 5.00 (978-0-7567-7108-9(0)) DIANE Publishing Co.

Fitzgibbon. East Africa: Paper Application. 2002. (Illus.). 450p. (J). pap. (978-0-12-257885-4(6)) Harcourt Trade Pubs.

Hamilton, Janice. Somalia in Pictures. 2007. (Visual Geography Ser.). (Illus.). 80p. (J). (gr. 5-12). 27.93 (978-0-8225-6586-4(2), Twenty-First Century Bks.) Lerner Publishing Group.

Harmon, Daniel E. Central & East Africa. 2001. (Exploration of Africa Ser.). (Illus.). 112p. (J). (gr. 7-12). 35.00 (978-0-7910-5743-8(7), Chelsea Hse.) Facts On File, Inc.

Heale, Jay. Tanzania. 1998. (Cultures of the World Ser.). (Illus.). 128p. (gr. 5-12). lib. bdg. 37.07 (978-0-7614-0809-3(6), Benchmark Bks.) Cavendish, Marshall Corp.

Kavanaugh, Dorothy. Sudan. 2007. (978-1-4222-0085-8(X)) Mason Crest Pubs.

Montgomery, Bertha Vining & Nabwire, Constance R. Cooking the East African Way. 2nd rev. exp. ed. 2002. (Easy Menu Ethnic Cookbooks). (Illus.). 72p. (J). (gr. 5-12). 25.26 (978-0-8225-4164-6(5)) Lerner Publishing Group.

Morrow, James. Djibouti. 2003. (Modern Middle East Nations & Their Strategic Place in the World Ser.). (Illus.). 112,128p. (YA). (gr. 7 up). lib. bdg. (978-1-59084-525-7(0)) Mason Crest Pubs.

Moss, Miriam. This Is the Tree. Kennaway, Adrienne, illus. 2005. 32p. (J). pap. 7.95 (978-1-929132-77-5(8)) Kane/Miller Bk. Pubs., Inc.

Nnoromele, Salome. Sudan. 2004. (Modern Nations of the World Ser.). (Illus.). 112p. (J). 29.95 (978-1-59018-338-0(X), Lucent Bks.) Thomson Gale.

Pacchini, Fiorenzo. A Day with Homo Habilis: Life 2,000,000 Years Ago. 2003. (Early Humans Ser.). (Illus.). 48p. (gr. 6 up). lib. bdg. 23.90 (978-0-7613-2765-3(7), Twenty-First Century Bks.) Lerner Publishing Group.

AFRICA, EAST—FICTION

Bull, Schuyler. Through Tsavo: A Story of an East African Savanna. 2005. (Soundprints' Wild Habitats Ser.). (Illus.). 32p. (J). (gr. 1-4). 8.95 incl. audio (978-1-59249-096-7(4), SC7008) Soundprints.

Jomo & Mata: Evaluation Guide. 2006. (J). (978-1-55942-411-0(7)) Marsh Media.

Whelan, Gloria. Listening for Lions. 208p. (J). 2006. pap. 5.99 (978-0-06-058176-3(X), Harper Trophy); 2005. (gr. 5 up). 15.99 (978-0-06-058174-9(3)); 2005. (Illus.). (gr. 5 up). lib. bdg. 16.89 (978-0-06-058175-6(1)) HarperCollins Pubs.

AFRICA—FICTION

Adlerman, Daniel. Africa Calling, Nighttime Falling. Adlerman, Kim, illus. 2001. 32p. (J). (ps-2). pap. 6.95 (978-1-58089-025-0(3)) Charlesbridge Publishing, Inc.

Adlerman, Daniel, ed. Africa Calling, Nighttime Falling. 2001. (J). 13.75 (978-0-606-20533-7(0)) Tandem Library Bks.

Alakija, Polly. Catch That Goat! (Illus.). 32p. (J). 2004. pap. 6.99 (978-1-84148-161-6(0)); 2002. 16.99 (978-1-84148-908-7(5)) Barefoot Bks., Inc.

Alexander, Lloyd. The Fortune-Tellers. Hyman, Trina Schart, illus. 2005. 28p. (J). (gr. k-4). reprint ed. 16.00 (978-0-7567-9706-5(3)) DIANE Publishing Co.

Allen, Christina G. Hippos in the Night: Autobiographical Adventures in Africa. 2003. (Illus.). 144p. (J). 17.89 (978-0-688-17827-7(8)) HarperCollins Pubs.

Alvin, John & Alvin, Andrea, illus. Simba's Pride. 1998. (Classic Storybook Ser.). 96p. (J). (ps-3). 7.99 (978-1-57082-876-8(8)) Mouse Works.

Ambatchew, Daniel M. Bongani in Addis. 1999. (Illus.). 16p. pap. (978-1-77905-072-4(0)) SAPES Books, Zimbabwe.

Anderson, Bob. Obo. Anderson, Bob, illus. 1999. (Illus.). 48p. (J). (ps-5). bds. 16.00 (978-1-57174-124-0(0)) Hampton Roads Publishing Co., Inc.

Anderson, Jane. Anansi the Spider & the Sky King: A Tale from Africa. 2006. 23.00 (*978-1-4108-6175-7(9)) Benchmark Education Co.

Asare, Meshack. L' Appel de Sosu (Sosu's Call) Keita, Fatou, tr. 2003. (Illus.). 37p. pap. (978-9988-550-48-6(0)) Sub-Saharan Pubs. & Traders.

—Cat in Search of a Friend. 1999. Tr. of Die Katze Sucht Sich Einen Freund. pap. (978-9988-550-18-9(9)) Sub-Saharan Pubs. & Traders.

—Meliga's Day. 2000. (Illus.). 31p. pap. (978-9988-550-20-2(0)) Sub-Saharan Pubs. & Traders.

—Sosu's Call. Asare, Meshack, illus. 2002. (Illus.). 40p. (J). (gr. k-4). 15.95 (978-1-929132-21-8(2)) Kane/Miller Bk. Pubs., Inc.

Ashley, Bernard. Little Soldier: A Novel. 2002. (Illus.). 240p. (J). (gr. 9 up). pap. 16.95 (978-0-439-22424-6(1), Scholastic Pr.) Scholastic, Inc.

Atungsiri's Ghost & Other Tales. 2002. (J). pap. 5.95 net. (978-0-620-29636-6(4)) African Artistic Ventures.

Ausbeth-Ajagu, Anuli C. The King's Verdict. 2003. (Illus.). 31p. pap. (978-978-2951-65-6(X)) CSS Bookshops, Ltd., Agency & Publishing Div.

Axtell, David. We're Going on A Lion Hunt. 2007. (Illus.). 32p. (J). pap. 7.95 (*978-0-8050-8219-7(0), Holt, Henry & Co. Bks. For Young Readers) Holt, Henry & Co.

Ballantyne, R. M. Gorilla Hunters A Tale of the Wilds of A. 2006. pap. 36.95 (*978-1-4286-5952-0(8)) Kessinger Publishing, LLC.

Base, Graeme. Jungle Drums. 2004. (Illus.). 40p. (J). (ps-3). 18.95 (978-0-8109-5044-3(8)) Abrams, Harry N., Inc.

Beake, Lesley. Home Now. Littlewood, Karin, illus. 2007. 32p. (J). (gr. k-3). 16.95 (978-1-58089-162-2(4)); pap. 6.95 (*978-1-58089-163-9(2)) Charlesbridge Publishing, Inc.

Bess, Clayton. Story for a Black Night. Crevelier, Solvej & Ahumada, Manuel, illus. 2nd rev. ed. 2002. (J). (978-1-882405-03-9(X)) Lookout Pr.

Birch, Beverley. Rift. 2008. (Illus.). 224p. (YA). pap. 9.95 (*978-1-4052-1589-3(5)) Egmont Bks., Ltd. GBR. *Dist:* Independent Pubs. Group.

Bognomo, Joel Ebouerne. Madoulina: A Girl Who Wanted to Go to School. 2003. (Illus.). 32p. (J). (gr. 2-4). 14.95 (978-1-56397-769-5(9)) Boyds Mills Pr.

—Madoulina: A Girl Who Wanted to Go to School. 1999. (978-0-606-17704-7(3)); lib. bdg. 17.60 (978-0-613-23339-2(5)) Tandem Library Bks.

Brailsford, David. Confessions of Anansi. 2004. (Illus.). 136p. 6.99 (978-976-8184-51-1(5)) Penguin Group (USA) Inc.

Brett, Jan. Honey... Honey... Lion! Brett, Jan, illus. 2005. (Illus.). 36p. (J). (ps-3). 16.99 (978-0-399-24463-6(8), Putnam Juvenile) Penguin Group (USA) Inc.

Brother to the Wind. 2004. (J). 24.95 incl. audio (978-1-56008-169-2(4)) Weston Woods Studios, Inc.

Brouillet, Chrystine. Secrets D'Afrique. 2002. (Roman Jeunesse Ser.). (FRE., Illus.). 96p. (YA). (gr. 4-7). pap. (978-2-89021-248-0(3)) Diffusion du livre Mirabel.

Bull, Schuyler. Through Tsavo: A Story of an East African Savanna. Kratter, Paul, illus. 1998. (Habitat Ser.). 32p. (J). (gr. 1-4). 15.95 (978-1-56899-552-6(0), B7008) Soundprints.

Castle, Caroline. Snip, Snap, Croc. 2007. (J). lib. bdg. 16.95 (*978-1-59566-367-2(3)) QEB Publishing Inc.

Chambers, Veronica. Amistad Rising: A Story of Freedom. 1998. (Illus.). 40p. (J). (gr. 4-7). lib. bdg. (978-0-8172-5510-7(9)) Raintree.

Chananie, Gloria. Fearful Frannie's African Safari. 2006. 95p. pap. 14.95 (978-1-4241-2617-0(7)) PublishAmerica, Inc.

Cherubini. Pinocchio in Africa. 2006. (ENG.). 62.99 (*978-1-4280-1918-8(9)) IndyPublish.com.

—Pinocchio in Africa. 2004. reprint ed. pap. 15.95 (978-1-4191-4166-9(X)); pap. 1.99 (978-1-4192-4166-6(4)) Kessinger Publishing, LLC.

Cherubini, E. Pinocchio in Africa. 2007. pap. (*978-1-4065-1442-1(X)) Dodo Pr.

Chidebelu-Eze, Obi. The Tales of Tortoise: Inspirtional Words of Wisdom. 2005. (Illus.). 76p. (J). 16.00 (978-0-9766578-0-4(5)) Dove Publishing, Inc.

Chukovskii, Kornei. Doctor Ouch. Seabaugh, Jan, tr. from RUS. Seabaugh, Jan, illus. 2004. (Children's International Ser.: 1). Orig. Title: Aibolit. 50p. (J). pap. 6.99 (978-0-9740551-0-7(7)) Smith, Viveca Publishing.

Conway, David. The Most Important Gift of All. Littlewood, Karin, illus. 2006. 32p. (J). 15.95 (978-0-7696-4618-3(2), Gingham Dog Pr.) School Specialty Publishing.

Cornwell, Nikki. Christophe's Story. Littlewood, Karin, illus. 2007. 96p. (J). (gr. 3 up). 14.95 (*978-1-84507-765-5(2)) Lincoln, Frances Ltd. GBR. *Dist:* Perseus Distribution.

Courlander, Harold & Herzog, George. The Cow-Tail Switch: And Other West African Stories. Chastain, Madye Lee, illus. 2008. 160p. (J). pap. 6.99 (*978-0-312-38006-9(2)) Square Fish.

Croall, Marie P. & Lago, Ray, texts. Marwe: Into the Land of the Dead: An East African Folktale. 2007. (Graphic Myths & Legends Ser.). (J). 26.60 (*978-0-8225-7134-6(X), Graphic Universe) Lerner Publishing Group.

Daly, Niki. Pretty Salma: A Little Red Riding Hood Story from Africa. Daly, Niki, illus. 2007. (Illus.). 32p. (J). (gr. k-3). 16.00 (978-0-618-72345-4(5), Clarion Bks.) Houghton Mifflin Co. Trade & Reference Div.

—Welcome to Zanzibar Road. 2006. (Illus.). 40p. (J). (gr. k-3). 16.00 (978-0-618-64926-6(3), Clarion Bks.) Houghton Mifflin Co. Trade & Reference Div.

Davis, Cynthia. Drink the Rain. 2007. 256p. (YA). per. 12.95 (*978-0-9712163-1-0(2)) Greenroom Bks.

De Matos, Isabel Freire. Una Carta de Delke. Saez, Sofia, illus. 2004. (SPA.). 32p. pap. 6.95 (978-1-57581-573-2(7)) Santillana USA Publishing Co., Inc.

Delaney, Michael. Birdbrain Amos: Mr. Fun. 2006. (Illus.). 160p. (J). (gr. 3). 15.99 (978-0-399-24278-6(3), Philomel) Penguin Group (USA) Inc.

Dent, Jenny. Peter Parrot Visits Africa. 2001. (Peter Parrot Ser.). (Illus.). 32p. (J). (gr. k-3). 12.95 (978-0-85487-120-9(9)) White Eagle Publishing Trust GBR. *Dist:* DeVorss & Co.

Diakite, Penda. I Lost My Tooth in Africa. Diakite, Baba Wague, illus. 2006. 32p. (J). (ps-3). pap. 16.99 (978-0-439-66226-0(5), Scholastic Pr.) Scholastic, Inc.

Disney Staff. Tarzan, Me & You. 1999. (Illus.). 10p. (J). (ps). 3.99 (978-0-7364-0132-6(6)) Mouse Works.

—Tarzan's Jungle Adventure. 1999. (Giant Lift-the-Flap Ser.). (Illus.). 10p. (J). (ps). bds. 8.99 (978-0-7364-0066-4(4)) Mouse Works.

DPWW. Tarzan. 1999. (Disney Chapters Ser.). (Illus.). 48p. (J). (gr. 2-4). pap. 3.95 (978-0-7868-4289-6(X)) Disney Pr.

Echewa, T. Obinkaram. How Tables Came to Umu Madu. (Young Reader's Ser.). (Illus.). 90p. (J). (gr. 5 up). 19.95 (978-0-86543-127-0(?)) Africa World Pr.

Ferrone, John M. Margo Goes on Safari. Ferrone, John M., illus. Date not set. (Illus.). 36p. (J). (ps-5). pap. 16.95 (978-1-928811-04-6(3)) Story Stuff, Inc.

Flegg, Aubrey. The Cinnamon Tree: A Novel Set in Africa. 2003. 208p. (YA). reprint ed. pap. 7.95 (978-0-86278-657-1(6)) O'Brien Pr., Ltd., The IRL. *Dist:* Independent Pubs. Group.

Fox, Mem. A Particular Cow. Denton, Terry, illus. 2000. 40p. (J). 16.00 (978-0-15-200250-3(2)) Harcourt Trade Pubs.

Geraghty, Paul. Yamina. 2nd ed. 2001. (SPA., Illus.). 32p. (J). (gr. 2-4). (978-84-89675-77-3(5)) Zendrera Zariquiey, Editorial ESP. *Dist:* Lectorum Pubns., Inc.

Gleeson, Brian. Koi & the Kola Nuts. Ruffins, Reynold, illus. 2007. (J). 25.65 (978-1-59961-310-9(7)) ABDO Publishing Co.

Gomez Cerda, Alfredo. Luna's Braids. (SPA.). (J). pap. (978-84-241-7934-2(X)) Everest de Ediciones y Distribucion, S.L. ESP. *Dist:* Lectorum Pubns., Inc.

Gomez, Luis Marcelino. Memorias de Angola: Cuentos Africanos. Vallejo, Esperanza, illus. 2004. (SPA.). 131p. (J). (ps-7). pap. (978-958-30-1257-0(2)) Panamericana Editorial.

Gonzalez Vela, Helena. Mala Suerte. 1998. (SPA.). (gr. 7-12). lib. bdg. 14.10 (978-0-613-80662-6(X)) Tandem Library Bks.

Gravett, Emily. Meerkat Mail. Gravett, Emily, illus. 2007. (Illus.). 24p. (J). (ps-3). 17.99 (*978-1-4169-3473-8(1)) Simon & Schuster Children's Publishing.

Grifalconi, Ann. The Village That Vanished. Nelson, Kadir A., illus. 2002. 40p. (J). (gr. k up). 16.99 (978-0-8037-2623-9(6), Dial) Penguin Group (USA) Inc.

—The Village That Vanished. Nelson, Kadir A., illus. 2004. 40p. (J). reprint ed. pap. 6.99 (978-0-14-240190-3(0), Puffin) Penguin Group (USA) Inc.

Hagen, Michael. The African Term. Kemnitz, Myrna, ed. 1998. 81p. (YA). (gr. 8 up). 9.99 (978-0-88092-368-2(7)) Royal Fireworks Publishing Co.

Hanson, Ed. African Safari. 2004. 64p. (YA). per. 3.95 (978-1-56254-800-1(X) , SP800X) Saddleback Educational Publishing.

Harcourt School Publishers Staff. Journey to Kush: Take-Home Book. 2001. (Collections Ser.). (Illus.). (J). pap. 1.90 (978-0-15-319555-6(X)) Harcourt Schl. Pubs.

Hassan, Marian A. Bright Star, Blue Sky. 2005. Tr. of Xidig Bidhaanta, Cir Buluug Ah. (SOM.). 7.00 (978-0-9766616-0-3(8)) Hassan, Marian.

Hawksley, Gerald. See Through Safari. Spengler, Margaret, illus. 2005. (J). bds. (978-1-890647-15-5(2)) RC2 Corp.

Hoffman, Mary. Boundless Grace. Binch, Caroline, illus. 2002. (J). 25.45 (978-0-7587-2139-6(0)) Book Wholesalers, Inc.

—Boundless Grace. Binch, Caroline, illus. 2000. 32p. (J). (ps-3). pap. 6.99 (978-0-14-055667-4(2) , Puffin) Penguin Group (USA) Inc.

—Boundless Grace. Binch, Caroline, illus. 2000. (J). (ps-ps). 26p. 12.79 (978-0-606-20350-0(8)); lib. bdg. 14.15 (978-0-613-33678-9(X)) Tandem Library Bks.

—Boundless Grace. 2000. (J). (978-0-606-20224-4(2)) Tandem Library Bks.

Hoosier, Wanda M. Princess Mandisa. McCabe, Pat, illus. 1999. 34p. (J). 15.00 (978-1-56469-070-8(9)) Harmony Hse. Pubs.

Intercambio Cultural. 2001. (la Orilla Del Viento Ser.).Tr. of Cultural Exchange. (SPA., Illus.). 31p. (J). (ps-ps). pap. 6.99 (978-968-16-6261-5(X) , 136) Fondo de Cultura Economica USA.

Jansen, Hanna. Over a Thousand Hills I Walk with You. Crawford, Elizabeth D., tr. from GER. 2006. 344p. (YA). lib. bdg. 16.95 (978-1-57505-927-3(4) , Carolrhoda Bks.) Lerner Publishing Group.

Johnson, Julia. Cheetah's Tale. Keeble, Suzie, illus. 2004. 56p. pap. 16.95 (978-1-900988-87-2(9)) Stacey International Pubs. GBR. *Dist:* Interlink Publishing Group, Inc.

Johnson, Sandi. The Peaceful Lion. Johnson, Britt, ed. Kraft, Lauri, illus. l.t. ed. 2003. 28p. (J). (gr. k-5). spiral bd. 8.99 (978-1-929063-95-6(4) , 325) Moons & Stars Publishing For Children.

Joosse, Barbara M. & Lavallee, Barbara. Papa Do You Love Me? Lavallee, Barbara, illus. 2005. (Illus.). 36p. (J). 15.95 (978-0-8118-4265-5(7)) Chronicle Bks. LLC.

Jordan, Apple. Bug Stew! 2003. (gr. k-3). lib. bdg. 11.80 (978-0-613-73701-2(6)) Tandem Library Bks.

Jorisch, Stephane, illus. The Trial of the Stone: A Folk Tale. 2000. 32p. (J). (ps-1). lib. bdg. 19.95 (978-1-55037-647-0(0)) Annick Pr., Ltd. CAN. *Dist:* Firefly Bks., Ltd.

Katschke, Judy. Tarzan Goes Bananas: Disney First Reader Ser. 1999. (Disney's Tarzan Ser.). (Illus.). 32p. (J). (gr. k-2). pap. 2.99 (978-0-7868-4281-0(4)) Hyperion Pr.

Kessler, Cristina. Jubela. Stammen, JoEllen McAllister, illus. 2004. 32p. (J). reprint ed. pap. 6.99 (978-0-689-86690-6(9) , Aladdin) Simon & Schuster Children's Publishing.

—Jubela. 2004. (gr. k-3). lib. bdg. 15.30 (978-0-613-88065-7(X)) Tandem Library Bks.

Kroll, Virginia K. Faraway Drums. Cooper, Floyd, illus. 1998. 32p. (J). (ps-3). 14.95 (978-0-316-50449-2(1)) Little Brown & Co.

Landstrom, Lena. A Hippo's Tale. Sandin, Joan, tr. from SWE. 2007. (Illus.). 32p. (J). (ps-1). 15.00 (***978-91-29-66603-8(1)***) R & S Bks. SWE. *Dist:* Macmillan.

Lawton, Wilbur Capta. The Boy Aviators in Africa or an Aerial. 2006. 25.99 (***978-1-4219-7625-9(0));*** pap. 19.99 (***978-1-4219-7629-7(3)***) IndyPublish.com.

Learning Through Literature: Mufaro's Beautiful Daughters. 2004. pap. 32.75 incl. audio (978-1-55592-525-3(1)) Weston Woods Studios, Inc.

Lee, Evelyn. Mountain Mists: A Story of the Virungas. Kratter, Paul, illus. 1999. (Habitat Ser.: No. 14). 36p. (J). (gr. 1-4). 26.95 (978-1-56899-789-6(2)); (ps-3). 15.95 (978-1-56899-785-8(X)); (ps-3). pap. 5.95 (978-1-56899-786-5(8)) Soundprints.

—Mountain Mists: A Story of the Virungas. 1999. (gr. k-3). lib. bdg. 15.25 (978-0-613-56927-9(X)) Tandem Library Bks.

The Legend of the Great Salt Mountain. 2005. (J). pap. (978-0-9771804-1-7(7)) Terra Tales.

Leonard, Marie. Tibili: The Little Boy Who Didn't Want to Go to School. Prigent, Andree, illus. 2002. 36p. (J). (ps-2). 15.95 (978-1-929132-20-1(4)) Kane/Miller Bk. Pubs., Inc.

Lester, Julius. Shining. Clapp, John, illus. 2007. 32p. (J). pap. 6.00 (***978-0-15-206077-0(4)***) , Voyager Bks./Libros Viajeros) Harcourt Children's Bks.

—Shining. Shaffer, Terea D. & Clapp, John, illus. 2003. 32p. (J). 17.00 (978-0-15-200773-7(3) , Silver Whistle) Harcourt Trade Pubs.

Lincoln, Hazel. Little Elephant's Trunk. Lincoln, Hazel, illus. 2006. (Illus.). 32p. (J). 15.95 (978-0-8075-4591-1(0)) Whitman, Albert & Co.

Lindy, Elaine L. A Caterpillar's Voice: A Folk Tale from Africa. 2002. (Whootie Owl's Test Prep Storytime Ser.). 32p. (J). 4.99 (978-0-9672831-4-2(0)) Whootie Owl International, LLC.

Lochmandy, Paula. What Come Out Dah Bottle. Miller, Jeffrey A., ed. Lochmandy, Paula, illus. 1998. (Illus.). (J). (gr. 2-6). ltd. ed. 30p. ring bd. 12.00 (978-0-9639890-5-5(7)); 2nd ed. 35p. pap. 13.50 (978-0-9639890-9-3(X)) Tattersall Pr.

Lumry, Amanda, et al. Safari in South Africa. 2003. (Adventures of Riley Ser.: Bk. 2). (Illus.). 36p. (gr. k-3). 15.95 (978-0-9662257-8-5(3)) Eaglemont Pr.

Mabalani, Kazi. Journey to Ahkabah: The Map & the Riddle. 2001. 236p. (J). pap. 11.95 (978-0-9709160-0-6(0)) Tusktown Publishing.

Maddern, Eric. The Fire Children: A West African Tale. Lessac, Frane, illus. 2006. 32p. (J). pap. 7.95 (978-1-84507-514-9(5)) Lincoln, Frances Ltd. GBR. *Dist:* Perseus Distribution.

Mary, Nanette. Ashby, the Happy Little Elephant. 2007. (Illus.). 40p. (J). per. 12.95 (***978-0-9787112-7-6(0)***, 01002) New World Publishing.

Masilela, Johnny. We Shall Not Weep. 2003. 132p. pap. 17.00 (978-0-7957-0147-4(0)) Kwela Bks. ZAF. *Dist:* Independent Pubs. Group.

Matovu, Gerald M. M. How Namudiguli Saved her Sister. 2000. (Illus.). 10p. pap. (978-9970-02-129-1(X)) Fountain Pubs. Ltd.

Mbairamadji, Koffi. African Savannah Stories. 2006. (Illus.). 46p. (J). per. 17.49 (***978-1-59879-277-5(6)***) Lifevest Publishing, Inc.

Mbanze, Dinah M., et al. The Magic Pot: Three African Tales. 2002. (Illus.). 48p. 11.95 (978-0-7957-0099-6(7)) Kwela Bks. ZAF. *Dist:* Independent Pubs. Group.

McBrier, Page. Beatrice's Goat. Lohstoeter, Lori, illus. 2004. 34p. (J). (ps-ps). lib. bdg. 15.60 (978-1-4176-3045-5(0)) Tandem Library Bks.

McCormick, Wendy. Daddy, Will You Miss Me? 2002. (gr. k-3). lib. bdg. 15.30 (978-0-613-53803-9(X)) Tandem Library Bks.

McDaniel, Lurlene. Angel of Hope. 2000. (Mercy Trilogy). 240p. (YA). (gr. 7-12). pap. 4.99 (978-0-553-57148-6(6) , Laurel Leaf) Random Hse. Children's Bks.

—Angel of Hope. 2000. (Mercy Trilogy). (gr. 7-12). lib. bdg. 13.00 (978-0-613-24184-7(3)); (Illus.). (J). 11.64 (978-0-606-17991-1(7)) Tandem Library Bks.

—Journey of Hope: Two Novels: Angel of Mercy & Angel of Hope. 2004. (Mercy Trilogy). 448p. (YA). (gr. 7). mass mkt. 7.99 (978-0-553-49451-8(1) , Laurel Leaf) Random Hse. Children's Bks.

McIntosh, Gavin. Hausaland Tales from the Nigerian Market Place. 2005. (Illus.). 98p. (J). (gr. 5-9). reprint ed. 22.00 (978-0-7567-9714-0(4)) DIANE Publishing Co.

McKenzie, Lyn. Lavinia's Shoes. 2007. (J). pap. 12.95 (***978-0-9788628-5-5(6)***) Just Write Bks.

McKissack, Patricia C. Nzingha, Warrior Queen of Matamba - Angola 1595. 2000. (Royal Diaries Ser.). (Illus.). 144p. (J). (gr. 4-8). pap. 10.95 (978-0-439-11210-9(9)) Scholastic, Inc.

McMahan, Virginia, told to. Mushgnome Legend of the African Spear. 2003. 38p. pap. 15.56 (978-1-4116-0222-9(6)) Lulu.com.

McMullan, Kate. A Wedding for Wiglaf? 2007. (Dragon Slayers' Academy Ser.: No. 4). 112p. (J). (gr. 1-6). 24.21 (***978-1-59961-380-2(8)***) Spotlight.

Mead, Alice. Year of No Rain. 2005. 144p. (J). (gr. 4-7). pap. 5.50 (978-0-440-42004-0(0) , Yearling) Random Hse. Children's Bks.

Mead, Alice & Weber James, Alice. Year of No Rain. 2003. 144p. (J). 16.00 (978-0-374-37288-0(8) , Farrar, Straus & Giroux (BYR)) Farrar, Straus & Giroux.

Milnes, Ellen. Tarzan Jungle Jam. Emslie, Peter, illus. 1999. (Chunky Roly-Poly Book Ser.). 16p. (J). bds. 3.50 (978-0-7364-0048-0(6)) Mouse Works.

Milway, Katie Smith. One Hen: How One Small Loan Made a Big Difference. Fernandes, Eugenie, illus. 2008. 32p. (***978-1-55453-028-1(8)***) Kids Can Pr., Ltd.

Montgomery, R. A. Race Forever. 2006. (Choose Your Own Adventure Ser.: No. 7). (Illus.). 144p. (J). mass mkt. 5.99 (978-1-933390-07-9(7) , CHCL07) Chooseco LLC.

—Race Forever. 2005. (Illus.). 122p. (J). (***978-0-7608-9695-2(X)***) Sundance/Newbridge Educational Publishing.

Morpurgo, Michael. Dear Olly. Birmingham, Christian, illus. 2001. 128p. (J). mass mkt. 7.99 (978-0-00-675333-9(7)) HarperCollins Pubs. Ltd. GBR. *Dist:* Independent Pubs. Group.

Mouse Works Staff. Tarzan. 1999. (Spanish Read-Aloud Storybook Classics). (SPA., Illus.). 64p. (J). (ps-2). 6.99 (978-0-7364-0057-2(5)) Mouse Works.

—Tarzan. 1999. (Disney's Read-Aloud Storybooks Ser.). (Illus.). 72p. (J). (ps-2). 8.99 (978-0-7364-0047-3(8) , RH/Disney) Random Hse. Children's Bks.

Mufari's Beautiful Daughters. 2004. pap. 14.95 incl. audio (978-1-55592-052-4(7)) Weston Woods Studios, Inc.

Mufaro Beautiful. 1998. (J). pap. 3.95 (978-0-439-04448-6(0)) HarperCollins Pubs.

Mufaro's Beautiful Daughters. 2004. pap. 32.75 incl. audio (978-1-55592-280-1(5)) Weston Woods Studios, Inc.

Musariri, Blessing. Going Home: A Tree's Story. 2005. (Illus.). 29p. pap. 12.95 (978-1-77922-042-4(1)) Weaver Pr. ZWE. *Dist:* Michigan State Univ. Pr.

My African Safari. 2004. (J). ring bd. 3.25 (978-0-9762740-4-9(3) , Flat Kids) Smart Smiles Co., The.

Myers, Bill. My Life as a Belching Baboon with Bad Breath. 2006. (Incredible Worlds of Wally McDoogle Ser.). pap. 6.99 (978-1-4003-0907-8(7)) Nelson, Thomas Inc.

Newman, Gwill York. Bingo Bear Was Here: A Toy Bear's Climb to the Top of Africa's Highest Mountain. Babcock, Jeff, illus. 2003. 48p. (J). pap. 8.95 (978-0-86534-395-5(0)) Sunstone Pr.

Njeng, Pierre Yves. Vacation in the Village: A Story from West Africa. 2003. (Illus.). 24p. (J). (gr. 2-4). pap. 6.95 (978-1-56397-823-4(7)) Boyds Mills Pr.

Ocelot, Michel. Kirikou et la Sorciere. pap. 14.95 (978-2-01-321877-1(X)) Hachette Groupe Livre FRA. *Dist:* Distribooks, Inc.

Oram, Hiawyn. Counting Leopard's Spots & other Stories. Warnes, Tim, illus. 2005. 96p. (J). (gr. k-4). reprint ed. 17.00 (978-0-7567-9252-7(5)) DIANE Publishing Co.

Ormsby, Nathaniel Hosea. Timeless Tales of Anansi: Ancestral Realm of Africa. 2006. 108p. pap. 16.95 (978-1-4241-3396-3(3)) PublishAmerica, Inc.

Orr, Ryan. Beyond the Oasis. Hernandez, Carlos, illus. 2002. 353p. (YA). per. 24.95 (978-0-9641861-1-8(X) , RWP Bks.) Redhawk Publishing.

Peretti, Frank E. The Secret of the Desert Stone. 2005. (Cooper Kids Adventure Ser.: Vol. 5). 160p. (J). pap. 6.99 (978-1-4003-0574-2(8)) Nelson, Thomas Inc.

Petruccio, Steven James. Tarzan Sticker Activity Book. 1999. (Dover Little Activity Bks.). (Illus.). 4p. (J). act. bk. ed. 1.00 (978-0-486-40933-7(3)) Dover Pubns., Inc.

Pinguilly, Yves. Contes et legendes d Afrique. pap. 19.95 (978-2-09-282309-5(4)) Nathan, Fernand FRA. *Dist:* Distribooks, Inc.

Pirotta, Saviour & Marks, Alan. The Enchanted Gazelle. 2007. (J). (***978-1-59771-081-7(4)***) Sea-To-Sea Pubns.

Price, Matt. Out on a Limb. 2006. 32p. 4.50 (978-0-8341-2229-1(4)) Beacon Hill Pr. of Kansas City.

Rau, Dana Meachen. The Lion in the Grass. 2006. (Nature Ser.). (Illus.). 24p. (J). lib. bdg. 22.79 (978-0-7614-2305-8(2) , Benchmark Bks.) Cavendish, Marshall Corp.

Reid, Carolyn. Busy in the Bushveld: South African Edition. 1998. (Cambridge Reading Routes Ser.). (Illus.). 16p. pap. 5.45 (978-0-521-63680-3(9)) Cambridge Univ. Pr.

Reno, Dawn E. The Candace: Warrior Queens of the Kingdom of Kush. 1999. (Illus.). 120p. pap. 8.95 (978-1-58521-009-1(9)) Books for Black Children, Inc.

Richardson, Dick. The Oglin: A Hero's Journey Across Africa... Towards the Tomorrows. Feek, Cathy, illus. 2004. 417p. (J). 24.95 (978-0-9759440-3-5(7)) Savanna Pr.

Rodanas, Kristina. The Blind Hunter. 2003. (Illus.). 32p. (J). 16.95 (978-0-7614-5132-7(3)) Cavendish, Marshall Corp.

Rodrigues, Ann & Winch, John. What Little Rhino Sees. 2002. (J). 15.99 (978-0-7636-1396-9(7)) Candlewick Pr.

Ross, Stewart. The Curse of the Crocodile God. 2007. 48p. (J). pap. 3.99 (978-0-7566-2563-4(7)); pap. 14.99 (978-0-7566-2564-1(5)) Dorling Kindersley Publishing, Inc.

Rumford, James. Calabash Cat. 2003. (ENG & ARA., Illus.). 32p. (J). (gr. k-3). 16.00 (978-0-618-22423-4(8)) Houghton Mifflin Co. Trade & Reference Div.

Schade, Susan. Bungee Baboon Rescue. Buller, Jon, illus. 2002. (Danger Joe Show Ser.: No. 2). 112p. (J). pap. 3.99 (978-0-439-40976-6(4) , Scholastic Paperbacks) Scholastic, Inc.

—Bungee Baboon Rescue. 2002. (gr. k-3). lib. bdg. 11.80 (978-0-613-72067-0(9)) Tandem Library Bks.

Schaefer, Carole Lexa. Cool Time Song. Morgan, Pierr, illus. 2005. 32p. (J). (ps-2). 15.99 (978-0-670-05928-7(5) , Viking Juvenile) Penguin Group (USA) Inc.

Schein, Herman, et al. Story for a Black Night. 2004. 112p. (YA). (gr. 7). pap. 6.99 (978-0-618-49483-5(9) , Graphia) Houghton Mifflin Co. Trade & Reference Div.

Severine Rugumamu. Further Adventures of the Black Hand Gang. 2005. 64p. pap. 12.95 (978-9966-25-422-1(6)) Heinemann Kenya, Limited (East African Educational Publishers Ltd E.A.E.P.) KEN. *Dist:* Michigan State Univ. Pr.

Shea-Gass, Lucille. How Animals Sleep Vol. 1: In Africa. 2004. 48p. pap. 19.95 (978-1-4137-2039-6(0)) PublishAmerica, Inc.

The Smartest Thing. 2004. (YA). (978-0-9762904-8-3(0)) Layne Morgan Media, Inc.

Smith, Alexander McCall. Akimbo & the Crocodile Man. Pham, LeUyen, illus. 80p. (J). 2007. pap. 4.95 (***978-1-59990-033-9(5)***, Bloomsbury Children); 2006. 9.95 (978-1-58234-692-2(5)) Bloomsbury Publishing.

—Akimbo & the Elephants. Pham, LeUyen, illus. 2007. (Akimbo Ser.). 80p. (J). (gr. 2-4). pap. 4.95 (978-1-59990-031-5(9) , Bloomsbury Children) Bloomsbury Publishing.

—Akimbo & the Elephants. Pham, LeUyen, illus. 2005. 80p. (J). (ps-7). 9.95 (978-1-58234-686-1(0)) Bloomsbury Publishing.

—Akimbo & the Lions. Pham, LeUyen, illus. (Akimbo Ser.). 80p. (J). 2007. pap. 4.95 (978-1-59990-032-2(7) , Bloomsbury Children); 2005. 9.95 (978-1-58234-687-8(9)) Bloomsbury Publishing.

—Akimbo & the Snakes. Pham, LeUyen, illus. (Akimbo Ser.). 80p. (J). 2007. pap. 4.95 (***978-1-59990-034-6(3));*** 2006. 9.95 (978-1-58234-705-9(0)) Bloomsbury Publishing. (Bloomsbury Children).

Smith, Roland. Cryptid Hunters. 2006. 352p. (gr. 5-17). pap. 5.99 (978-0-7868-5162-1(7)) Hyperion Pr.

Souci, Robert D. San & Burroughs, Edgar Rice. Tarzan. McCurdy, Michael, illus. 2004. 31p. (J). (gr. k-4). reprint ed. 16.00 (978-0-7567-7576-6(0)) DIANE Publishing Co.

Spalding, Andrea. An Island of My Own. 2007. 112p. (YA). pap. 11.99 (***978-1-55002-635-1(6)***, Sandcastle Bks.) Dundurn Group, The CAN. *Dist:* Univ. of Toronto Pr.

Spence, Stephen Mark. African Knights. 2005. 340p. (J). pap. 14.95 (978-0-9705324-4-2(X)) Spence, Stephen Mark.

St. John, Patricia. I Needed a Neighbour. 2003. 128p. 6.49 (978-0-86201-454-4(9)) Scripture Union GBR. *Dist:* Gabriel Resources.

Stassen, Jean-Philippe. Deogratias. 2006. (Illus.). 96p. (J). pap. (***978-0-330-44467-5(0)***, First Second Bks.) Roaring Brook Pr.

Steptoe, John. Mufaro's Beautiful Daughters. Steptoe, John, illus. 2001. Tr. of Las Bellas Hijas De Mufaro. (Illus.). 28.95 incl. audio compact disk (978-1-59112-542-6(1)); pap. 35.95 incl. audio compact disk (978-1-59112-541-9(3)); pap. 33.95 incl. audio (978-1-59112-132-9(9)) Live Oak Media.

Stewart, Dianne. The Dove. Daly, Jude, illus. 2005. 32p. (J). (ps-3). pap. 7.95 (978-1-84507-022-9(4)) Lincoln, Frances Ltd. GBR. *Dist:* Perseus Distribution.

Stewart, Dianne & Heale, Jay. African Myths & Legends. 2004. (Illus.). 96p. 10.00 (978-1-86872-705-6(X)) Struik Pubs. ZAF. *Dist:* Continental Enterprises Group, Inc. (CEG).

Stojic, Manya. Rain. Stojic, Manya, illus. 2000. (Illus.). 32p. (J). (gr. k-3). 15.95 (978-0-517-80085-0(3) , Crown Books For Young Readers) Random Hse. Children's Bks.

Stratton, Allan. Chanda's Secrets. 2004. 196p. (YA). (gr. 9). 19.95 (978-1-55037-835-1(X)); pap. 10.95 (978-1-55037-834-4(1)) Annick Pr., Ltd. CAN. *Dist:* Firefly Bks., Ltd.

Stratton, Allan. Chanda's Wars. 2008. 400p. (J). 17.99 (***978-0-06-087262-5(4));*** lib. bdg. 18.89 (***978-0-06-087264-9(0)***) HarperCollins Pubs.

Stuyvesant, Carolyn. Storytime in Africa. 2002. (Illus.). (J). Bk. 1. 64p. pap. (978-1-883012-03-8(1)); Bk. 2. 96p. pap. (978-1-883012-04-5(X)) Remnant Pubns.

Suben, Eric, et al, illus. Tarzan. 1999. (Disney Ser.). 24p. (J). (ps-3). pap. 3.29 (978-0-307-13194-2(7) , Golden Bks.) Random Hse. Children's Bks.

Thompson, Lisa. Amazing Africa. Harvey, Roger, illus. 2006. 80p. (J). (gr. 2-4). 19.95 (978-1-4048-1674-9(7)) Picture Window Bks.

Trebi-Ollennu, Flora. A Big Christmas Surprise for Sweetie Awo. Burgesson, Kate & Adu Nyarko, Margaret M., illus. 2000. (Sunbeamy Kids Ser.). 90p. (J). (gr. 4-6). pap. (978-1-894718-00-4(3)) Amerley Treb Bks.

Udo, Victoria. The Children & the Yard Animals: Children of an African Village Volume 1. 2004. 31p. pap. 17.95 (978-1-4137-3215-3(1)) PublishAmerica, Inc.

Villalobos, Ligiah. Save the Elephants. Zalme, Ronald, illus. 2007. (Go, Diego, Go! Ser.). 24p. (J). pap. 3.99 (***978-1-4169-3821-7(4)***, Simon Spotlight) Simon & Schuster Children's Publishing.

Wein, Elizabeth. The Sunbird. 2006. 208p. (YA). (gr. 7 up). pap. 6.99 (978-0-14-240171-2(4) , Puffin) Penguin Group (USA) Inc.

Whelan, Gloria. Yatandou. rev. ed. 2007. (Tales of the World Ser.). 32p. (J). (gr. 3-7). 17.95 (***978-1-58536-211-0(5)***) Sleeping Bear Pr.

Winfield (Edward Str Staff. The Rover Boys in the Jungle or Stirring. 2006. 63.99 (***978-1-4280-1844-0(1)***) IndyPublish.com.

Winter, Jeanette. Elsina's Clouds. 2004. (Illus.). 40p. (J). 16.00 (978-0-374-32118-5(3) , Farrar, Straus & Giroux (BYR)) Farrar, Straus & Giroux.

Wooden, Itanza L. The Chill Street Gang Spring Break Vacation. 2006. (J). pap. 6.99 (978-0-9664506-3-7(9)) Dukes World, Inc.

Wyss, Tyan. African Dream. Immelman, Sarita, illus. 2006. 48p. (J). pap. 15.95 (***978-1-58939-915-0(3)***) Virtualbookworm.com Publishing, Inc.

Youree, Barbara. Senegal Sleuths. 2006. 56p. 7.75 (978-0-8341-2226-0(X)) Beacon Hill Pr. of Kansas City.

Zocchi, Judy. Paulie & Sasha: The Rescue. Vannozzi, Don, illus. 2001. (Paulie & Sasha Ser.). 32p. (J). lib. bdg. 23.00 (978-1-891997-15-0(7)) Dingles & Co.

Zoehfeld, Kathleen Weidner, adapted by. Tarzan. 1999. (Illus.). 48p. (J). (ps-3). 10.99 (978-0-7868-3220-0(7)) Disney Pr.

AFRICA—HISTORY

Ahiagble, Gilbert & Meyer, Louise. Master Weaver from Ghana. Hernandez, Nestor, photos by. 1998. (Illus.). 32p. (YA). (gr. 2-8). 18.00 (978-0-940880-61-0(X)) Open Hand Publishing, LLC.

Allen, John. Idi Amin. 2003. (History's Villains Ser.). (Illus.). 112p. (J). 28.70 (978-1-56711-759-2(7) , Blackbirch Pr., Inc.) Thomson Gale.

Altman, Susan. Encyclopedia of African-American Heritage. 2nd ed. 2000. (Illus.). 368p. (YA). (gr. 6-12). 45.00 (978-0-8160-4125-1(3)) Facts On File, Inc.

Barr, Gary. History & Activities of the West African Kingdoms. 2006. (Hands-On Ancient History Ser.). (Illus.). 32p. (J). pap. (978-1-4034-7933-4(X)); (gr. 3-6). lib. bdg. 28.21 (978-1-4034-7925-9(9)) Heinemann Library.

Barron's Educational Editorial Staff. Exploration of Africa. 1998. (Great Explorers Ser.). (Illus.). 32p. (YA). (gr. 5-9). pap. 5.95 (978-0-7641-0632-3(5)) Barron's Educational Series, Inc.

Brennan, Kristine. Burundi. 2004. (Africa Ser.). (Illus.). 79p. (J). lib. bdg. 19.95 (978-1-59084-820-3(9)) Mason Crest Pubs.

Cairns, Conrad. African Knights: The Armies of Sokoto, Bornu & Bagirmi in the 19th Century. 2006. (Illus.). 64p. pap. 24.95 (***978-1-901543-08-7(0)***) Foundry Bks. GBR. *Dist:* Casemate Pubs. & Bk. Distributors, LLC.

Coletti, Sharon. Everything You Need to Teach Africa. 2005. (YA). ring bd. 149.95 (978-1-933558-00-4(8)) InspirEd Educators.

Conklin, Wendy. China * India * Mesopotamia * Africa: All-in-One Resource with Background Information, Map Activities, Simulations & Games, & a Read-Aloud Play to Support Comprehension & Critical Thinking in Social Studies. 2006. (Ancient Civilizations Ser.). 96p. pap. 13.99 (978-0-439-53993-7(5) , Teaching Resources) Scholastic, Inc.

Dalton, David. Living in a Refugee Camp: Carbino's Story. 2005. (Illus.). 48p. (J). lib. bdg. 30.00 (978-0-8368-5960-7(X) , World Almanac Library) Stevens, Gareth Inc.

Davenport, John. A Brief Political & Geographic History of Africa: Where Are the Belgian Congo, Rhodesia, & Kush? 2007. (Places in Time Ser.). (Illus.). 112p. (YA). (gr. 5-10). lib. bdg. 37.10 (***978-1-58415-624-6(4)***) Mitchell Lane Pubs., Inc.

Diouf, Sylviane A. Kings & Queens of East Africa. 2001. (Watts Library). (Illus.). 64p. (J). (gr. 5-7). pap. 8.95 (978-0-531-16534-8(5) , Watts, Franklin) Scholastic Library Publishing.

Dorling Kindersley Publishing Staff. El Mundo Antiguo de Egipto. 2004. (Dk Eyewitness Books Ser.). 72p. (J). 15.99 (978-0-7566-0792-0(2)) Dorling Kindersley Publishing, Inc.

Exploration of Africa: The Emerging Nations. 2005. 112-144p. pap. 385.00 (978-0-7910-6267-8(8) , Chelsea Hse.) Facts On File, Inc.

Ferry, Joseph. Somalia. 2003. (Modern Middle East Nations & Their Strategic Place in the World Ser.). (Illus.). 112,128p. (YA). (gr. 7 up). lib. bdg. (978-1-59084-520-2(X)) Mason Crest Pubs.

Fish, Bruce & Fish, Becky Durost. Angola, 1880 to the Present: Slavery, Exploitation & Revolt. 2001. (Exploration of Africa). (Illus.). 112p. (J). 35.00 (978-0-7910-6197-8(3) , Chelsea Hse.) Facts On File, Inc.

Freedman, Frances. David Livingstone. 2002. (Great Explorers Ser.). (Illus.). 48p. (J). (gr. 5 up). pap. 14.60 (978-0-8368-5175-5(7) , World Almanac Library) Stevens, Gareth Inc.

Group/McGraw-Hill, Wright. Africa: Rich in Land & History, 6 vols. (Book2WebTM Ser.). (gr. 4-8). 36.50 (978-0-322-04439-5(1)) Wright Group, The.

Haskins, James & Benson, Kathleen. African Beginnings. Cooper, Floyd, illus. 2007. 48p. (J). pap. 7.99 (978-0-06-113612-2(3) , Amistad) HarperCollins Pubs.

Haywood, John. West African Kingdoms. 2007. (J). ***978-1-4109-2912-9(4));** pap. (***978-1-4109-2918-1(3))** Steck-Vaughn.

Icy, prod. Apartheid Revisited. (YA). (978-0-7365-4406-1(2)) Films Media Group.

Innes, William. Liberia or the Early History & Signal Preservation of the American Colony of Free Negroes on the Coast of Africa. 2006. cd-rom (978-1-892824-47-9(7)) AFCHRON.

Kalman, Bobbie & Sjonger, Rebecca. Explora Africa. 2007. (SPA.). 32p. (gr. 6-10). pap. (***978-0-7787-8295-7(6))** Crabtree Publishing Co.

Katis, Alex. Fandex Africa. 2005. (Illus.). 50p. 9.95 (978-0-7611-3978-2(8) , 13978) Workman Publishing Co., Inc.

Kiflom, Shegitu. My African Heritage. 2000. (ENG., Illus.). 26p. (J). (ps-5). pap. 7.00 (978-0-9675581-0-3(7)) Papyrus Publishing, Inc.

King, David C. Mozambique. 2007. (Illus.). 128p. (J). lib. bdg. 39.93 (978-0-7614-2331-7(1) , Benchmark Bks.) Cavendish, Marshall Corp.

—Rwanda. 2007. (Cultures of the World Ser.). (Illus.). 128p. (J). lib. bdg. 39.93 (978-0-7614-2333-1(8) , Benchmark Bks.) Cavendish, Marshall Corp.

Lekuton, Joseph Lemasolai & Viola, Herman. Facing the Lion: Growing up Maasai on the African Savanna. 2005. 128p. (YA). (gr. 7-12). pap. 6.95 (978-0-7922-7297-7(8) , National Geographic Children's Bks.) National Geographic Society.

Martin, Michael. Apartheid in South Africa. 2006. (World History Ser.). 112p. (J). (gr. 7-10). 32.45 (978-1-59018-696-1(6) , Lucent Bks.) Thomson Gale.

Matthews, Caitlin & Williams, Sophy. Secret Bride, Runaway Princess: Two Stories from Rwanda. 2006. (J). (978-1-905236-90-9(5)) Barefoot Bks., Inc.

Medieval Africa DBA. 2003. spiral bd. 16.95 (978-1-56004-170-2(6)) Social Studies Schl. Service.

Miller, Danny. African Journeys: 1850-1900. 2004. (National Geographic Reading Expeditions Ser.). (Illus.). 32p. (J). pap. (978-0-7922-4545-2(8)) National Geographic Society.

Murray, Jocelyn & Stewart, Brian A. Africa. 3rd rev. ed. 2007. (Cultural Atlas for Young People Ser.). (Illus.). 96p. (YA). (gr. 5-8). 35.00 (***978-0-8160-6826-5(7)** , Chelsea Hse.) Facts On File, Inc.

Obadina, Tunde. The Making of Africa. 2007. (Africa Ser.). (Illus.). 112p. (J). (gr. 7 up). lib. bdg. 24.95 (978-1-59084-999-9(0)) Mason Crest Pubs.

Pancella, Peggy. Mansa Musa. 2003. (Historical Biographies Ser.). (Illus.). 32p. (J). pap. 7.50 (978-1-4034-3711-2(4)); lib. bdg. 22.79 (978-1-4034-3703-7(3)) Heinemann Library.

Reef, Catherine. Africans in American: The Spread of People & Culture. 1998. (Library of African-American History). (Illus.). 144p. (J). (gr. 7-12). 25.00 (978-0-8160-3772-8(8)) Facts On File, Inc.

Richardson, Hazel. Life in Ancient Africa. 2005. (Peoples of the Ancient World Ser.). (Illus.). 32p. (J). (978-0-7787-2043-0(8)); pap. (978-0-7787-2073-7(X)) Crabtree Publishing Co.

Roberts, Russell. The African Union. 2007. (J). (***978-1-4222-0093-3(0))** Mason Crest Pubs.

Rotberg, Robert I., ed. Africa: Continent in the Balance, 13 vols., Set. 2005. (Illus.). 88p. (YA). lib. bdg. (978-1-59084-807-4(1)) Mason Crest Pubs.

Sherrow, Victoria. Ancient Africa: Archaeology Unlocks the Secrets of Africa's Past. 2007. (National Geographic Investigates Ser.). 64p. (YA). (gr. 5 up). lib. bdg. 27.90 (978-0-7922-5399-0(X)); (Illus.). (J). (gr. 1-5). 17.95 (978-0-7922-5384-6(1)) National Geographic Society. (National Geographic Children's Bks.).

Shuter, Jane. Ancient West African Kingdoms. 2003. (History Opens Windows Ser.). (Illus.). 32p. (J). (gr. 2-4). lib. bdg. 22.79 (978-1-4034-0255-4(8)); pap. 7.50 (978-1-4034-0083-3(0)) Heinemann Library.

Thoennes Keller, Kristin. The Slave Trade in Early America. 2004. (Let Freedom Ring Ser.). (Illus.). 48p. (J). 17.95 (978-0-7368-2465-1(0) , Bridgestone Bks.) Capstone Pr., Inc.

Thomson Gale Staff. Junior Worldmark Visual Reference of the States. 2006. 85.00 (978-1-4144-1133-0(2) , UXL) Thomson Gale.

White, Ellen G. The Spirit of Prophecy the Great Controversy Between Christ & His Angels & Satan & His Angels, Vol. 1. 2005. cd-rom (978-1-892824-84-4(1)) AFCHRON.

Wildlife Safari Africa, Swahili & English: Who's Who in the African Jungle & Savanna, a Swahili/English Multicultural Book. 2004. (J). per. 9.95 (978-0-9742688-2-8(8)) Ndegwa, Catherine W.

Wisniewski, David, retold by. Sundiata: Lion King of Mali. 1999. (Illus.). 32p. (J). (gr. k-3). 6.95 (978-0-395-76481-7(5) , Clarion Bks.) Houghton Mifflin Co. Trade & Reference Div.

World History: Patterns of Interaction: Early African History in-Depth Resources. 2003. (gr. 6-12). (978-0-618-06841-8(4) , 2-81191) McDougal Littell Inc.

World History: Patterns of Interaction: Early African History to 1500, PE. 2003. (gr. 6-12). (978-0-618-06839-5(2) , 2-81189) McDougal Littell Inc.

Worth, Richard. Stanley & Livingstone & the Exploration of Africa in World History. 2000. (In World History Ser.). (Illus.). 128p. (YA). (gr. 5-12). lib. bdg. 26.60 (978-0-7660-1400-8(2)) Enslow Pubs., Inc.

AFRICA—NATIVE RACES

Green, Jen. The Africans. 2000. (We Came to North America Ser.). (Illus.). 32p. (J). (gr. 4). pap. (978-0-7787-0198-9(0)) Crabtree Publishing Co.

Marshall Cavendish Corporation Staff, contrib. by. Peoples of Africa, 11 vols., Set. 2000. (Illus.). 700p. (gr. 4-8). 471.36 (978-0-7614-7158-5(8) , Cavendish, Marshall Reference Bks.) Cavendish, Marshall Corp.

Parker, Linda. The San of Africa. 2002. (First Peoples Ser.). (Illus.). 48p. (J). (gr. 4-8). 23.93 (978-0-8225-4177-6(7)) Lerner Publishing Group.

AFRICA, NORTH

Benchmark Education Staff. Kingdom of Kush. 2005. 2.00 (***978-1-4108-4654-9(7))** Benchmark Education Co.

Bowden, Rob. The Middle East & North Africa. 2007. (J). (***978-1-4034-9902-8(0));** (Illus.). 64p. (gr. 4-7). pap. (***978-1-4034-9911-0(X))** Heinemann Library.

Brannon, Barbara. Discover the Kingdom of Kush. 2005. 39.00 (***978-1-4108-5160-4(5))** Benchmark Education Co.

Chelsea House Publishing Staff. North Africa. 2002. (Exploration of Africa). (Illus.). 112p. (J). (gr. 7-12). 35.00 (978-0-7910-5746-9(1) , Chelsea Hse.) Facts On File, Inc.

Connolly, Sean. Sudan. 2008. (J). (***978-1-60044-618-4(3))** Rourke Publishing, LLC.

Forester, C. S. Sterling Point Books: the Barbary Pirates. 2007. (Sterling Point Bks.). (Illus.). 176p. (J). 12.95 (978-1-4027-4522-5(2)); pap. 6.95 (978-1-4027-4142-5(1)) Sterling Publishing Co., Inc.

Gritzner, Jeffrey A. & Gritzner, Charles F. North Africa & the Middle East. 2006. (Modern World Cultures Ser.). (Illus.). 128p. (J). (gr. 6-12). 30.00 (978-0-7910-8145-7(1) , Chelsea Hse.) Facts On File, Inc.

Piddock, Charles. Sudan. 2006. 48p. (J). pap. (978-0-8368-6718-3(1)); lib. bdg. (978-0-8368-6711-4(4)) Stevens, Gareth Inc. (World Almanac Library).

Ryall, Michael. The Kingdom of Kush. 2005. 39.00 (***978-1-4108-4606-8(7))** Benchmark Education Co.

AFRICA, NORTH—FICTION

Alexander, Lloyd. The Jedera Adventure. 2001. (Vesper Holly Ser.). (J). (gr. 3-6). lib. bdg. 14.15 (978-0-613-43837-7(X)) Tandem Library Bks.

Grant, Karima. Sofie & the City. Montecalvo, Janet, illus. 2006. 32p. (J). 15.95 (978-1-59078-273-6(9)) Boyds Mills Pr.

St. John, Patricia. Secret of the Fourth Candle. rev. ed. 2003. (Illus.). 96p. 6.49 (978-1-85999-511-2(X)) Scripture Union GBR. *Dist:* Gabriel Resources.

AFRICA—SOCIAL LIFE AND CUSTOMS

African Languages & Cultural Beliefs. 2000. (My Ancestors—My Heroes Ser.: Vol. 3). (J). (gr. 3-4). (978-1-893091-02-3(3)) Parker Publishing Co.

Alexanyan, Karina. An African Odyssey. 2004. 96p. pap. (978-0-9688648-6-9(4)) Parkhurst Publishing, Ltd.

Ashanti to Zulu. 2004. (J). pap. 14.95 incl. audio (978-0-7882-0674-0(5)) Weston Woods Studios, Inc.

Ashanti to Zulu: African Traditions. 2004. (J). 24.95 incl. audio (978-1-56008-159-3(7)) Weston Woods Studios, Inc.

Barr, Gary. History & Activities of the West African Kingdoms. 2006. (Hands-On Ancient History Ser.). (Illus.). 32p. (J). pap. (978-1-4034-7933-4(X)); (gr. 3-6). lib. bdg. 28.21 (978-1-4034-7925-9(9)) Heinemann Library.

Brownlie, Alison. Kenya. 2004. (Letters from Around the World Ser.). (Illus.). 32p. (J). (978-1-84234-252-7(5) , Cherrytree Books) Evans Publishing Group.

Cavanaugh, Dorothy. Religions of Africa. 2006. (Africa Ser.). 112p. (J). (gr. 7 up). lib. bdg. 24.95 (***978-1-59084-958-3(2))** Mason Crest Pubs.

CultureGrams 2006 World Edition - the Americas. 2005. (YA). per. 129.99 (978-1-931694-93-3(1) , CultureGrams World Edition) ProQuest CSA.

Devisch, Rene & Brodeur, Claude. The Law of the Lifegivers: The Domestication of Desire. 1999. (Illus.). 288p. (J). pap. 27.00 (978-90-5702-423-8(3)) Gordon & Breach Publishing Group.

—Law of the Lifegivers: The Domestication of Desire. 1999. (Illus.). 261p. (C). (gr. 13 up). 60.00 (978-90-5702-422-1(5) , Harwood Academic Pubs.) Gordon & Breach Publishing Group.

Golding, Vivien. Traditions from Africa. 1999. (Cultural Journeys Ser.). (Illus.). 48p. (J). (gr. 3-7). lib. bdg. 27.12 (978-0-8172-5382-0(3)) Raintree.

Grieg, Charlotte. Africa. 2002. (Cultures & Costumes Ser.). (Illus.). 64p. (J). (gr. 7 up). lib. bdg. (978-1-59084-433-5(5)) Mason Crest Pubs.

Grolier Educational Staff, contrib. by. Tunisia. 2003. (Illus.). 32p. (J). (978-0-7172-5804-8(1) , Grolier) Scholastic Library Publishing.

Hansen, Joyce. African Princess: The Amazing Lives of Africa's Royal Women. McGaw, Laurie, illus. 2004. 48p. (gr. 3-17). 16.99 (978-0-7868-5116-4(3)) Hyperion Bks. for Children.

Harcourt School Publishers Staff. Life in the City. 3rd ed. 2002. (Horizons Ser.). (Illus.). (J). pap. 7.30 (978-0-15-333632-4(3)) Harcourt Schl. Pubs.

—A New Day for South Africa. 3rd ed. 2002. (Horizons Ser.). (Illus.). (J). pap. 7.30 (978-0-15-333630-0(7)) Harcourt Schl. Pubs.

Harvey, Miles. Look What Came from Africa. 2003. (Look What Came from Ser.). (Illus.). 32p. (J). (gr. 2-4). pap. 6.95 (978-0-531-16626-0(0) , Watts, Franklin) Scholastic Library Publishing.

—Look What Came from Africa. 2002. (gr. 3-6). lib. bdg. 15.25 (978-0-613-59506-3(8)) Tandem Library Bks.

Herrera, Susana. Mango Elephants in the Sun: How Life in an African Village Let Me Be in My Skin. 2000. (Illus.). 280p. pap. 22.95 (978-1-57062-572-5(7)) Shambhala Pubns., Inc.

Hinds, Kathryn. The Pharaoh's Court. 2006. (Life in Ancient Egypt Ser.). (Illus.). 80p. (J). lib. bdg. 32.79 (978-0-7614-2183-2(1) , Benchmark Bks.) Cavendish, Marshall Corp.

Lekuton, Joseph Lemasolai. Facing the Lion: Growing up Maasai on the African Savanna. 2003. (Illus.). 144p. (J). (gr. 7 up). 15.95 (978-0-7922-5125-5(3) , National Geographic Children's Bks.) National Geographic Society.

Lugira, Aloysius Muzzanganda. African Religion. 2nd rev. ed. 2004. (World Religions Ser.). (Illus.). 144p. (J). (gr. 6-12). per. 30.00 (978-0-8160-5729-0(X)) Facts On File, Inc.

Lynch, Emma. We're from Kenya. 2005. (We're from Ser.). (Illus.). 32p. (J). pap. (978-1-4034-5815-5(4)); lib. bdg. (978-1-4034-5806-3(5)) Heinemann Library.

Marshall Cavendish Corporation Staff, contrib. by. Peoples of Africa, 11 vols., Set. 2000. (Illus.). 700p. (gr. 4-8). 471.36 (978-0-7614-7158-5(8) , Cavendish, Marshall Reference Bks.) Cavendish, Marshall Corp.

Mazrui, Ali. Islam in Africa. 2006. (Africa Ser.). (Illus.). 112p. (YA). (gr. 9 up). lib. bdg. 24.95 (***978-1-59084-999-6(X))** Mason Crest Pubs.

Meade, Deborah. Africa. 2003. (National Geographic Reading Expeditions Ser.). (Illus.). 64p. (J). (978-0-7922-4365-6(X)) National Geographic Society.

Musgrove, Margaret. Ashanti to Zulu: African Traditions. Dillon, Leo & Dillon, Diane, illus. 2004. 28p. (YA). (gr. 4-8). reprint ed. pap. 14.00 (978-0-7567-7106-5(4)) DIANE Publishing Co.

Onyefulu, Ifeoma. A de Africa. 2005. (SPA.). 28p. (J). (gr. 2-7). 18.95 (978-84-89970-67-0(X)) Fundacion Intermon ESP. *Dist:* Iaconi, Mariuccia Bk. Imports.

—Emeka's Gift: An African Counting Book. 1999. (Illus.). 24p. (J). (ps-3). pap. 6.99 (978-0-14-056500-3(0) , Puffin) Penguin Group (USA) Inc.

—Emeka's Gift: An African Counting Story. 1999. (Illus.). (J). (978-0-606-22074-3(7)) Tandem Library Bks.

—My Grandfather Is a Magician: Work & Wisdom in an African Village. Onyefulu, Ifeoma, illus. 2006. (Illus.). 32p. (J). pap. 7.95 (978-1-84507-510-1(2)) Lincoln, Frances Ltd. GBR. *Dist:* Perseus Distribution.

—Your Name Is Dede: An African Baby's Naming Ceremony. 2003. (Illus.). 32p. (J). 14.95 (978-0-7112-1938-0(9)) Lincoln, Frances Ltd. GBR. *Dist:* Transition Vendor.

Rich, Susan, et al. Africa South of the Sahara: Understanding Geography & History Through Art. 1999. (Artisans Around the World Ser.). (Illus.). 48p. (J). (gr. 4-8). lib. bdg. 27.12 (978-0-7398-0118-5(X)) Raintree.

Rivers, Freya A. KMT: Our African Heritage. Brooks, Julian A. & Rivers, Shariba W., eds. Rivers, Freya A. & Moore, La Mailede, illus. Moore, La Mailede, photos by. 1999. 73p. (J). (gr. 2-8). pap. 30.00 (978-0-9667215-3-9(5)) Sankofa Publishing Co.

Sheehan, Sean. Benin & Other African Kingdoms. 1999. (Ancient World Ser.). (Illus.). 64p. (978-0-7502-2172-6(0)) Steck-Vaughn.

—Great African Kingdoms. 1999. (Ancient World Ser.). (Illus.). 63p. (J). (gr. 5-10). lib. bdg. 27.12 (978-0-8172-5124-6(3)) Raintree.

Shoveller, Herb. Ryan & Jimmy: And the Well in Africa That Brought Them Together. 2006. (Illus.). 56p. (J). (gr. 3-7). (978-1-55337-967-6(5)) Kids Can Pr., Ltd.

Welcome to Africa, Swahili & English: Fun & Adventure, a Swahili/English Multicultural Book. 2004. (J). per. 9.95 (978-0-9742688-1-1(X)) Ndegwa, Catherine W.

Winget, Mary. Cooking the North African Way. 2nd rev. ed. 2004. (Easy Menu Ethnic Cookbooks). (Illus.). 72p. (J). 25.26 (978-0-8225-4169-1(6) , Lerner Pubns.) Lerner Publishing Group.

AFRICA, SOUTHERN

Here are entered works on the area south of Congo (Democratic Republic) and Tanzania. Works on the Republic of South Africa are entered under South Africa.

Binns, Tony & Bowden, Rob. South Africa. 2002. (Changing Face Of... Ser.). (Illus.). 48p. (J). 27.12 (978-0-7398-4968-2(9)) Raintree.

Britton, Tamara L. South Africa. 2004. (Countries Ser.). (Illus.). 40p. (J). (gr. k-6). lib. bdg. 22.78 (978-1-59197-297-6(3)) ABDO Publishing Co.

Brownlie, Alison. South Africa. 2000. (We Come from Ser.). (Illus.). 32p. (J). (gr. 1-4). lib. bdg. 25.69 (978-0-8172-5221-2(5)) Raintree.

Clark, Domini. South Africa - The Culture. 1999. (Lands, Peoples & Cultures Ser.). (Illus.). 32p. (J). (gr. 4-5). (978-0-86505-237-6(9)); pap. (978-0-86505-317-5(0)) Crabtree Publishing Co.

—South Africa - The Land. 1999. (Lands, Peoples & Cultures Ser.). (Illus.). 32p. (J). (gr. 4-5). (978-0-86505-235-2(2)); pap. (978-0-86505-315-1(4)) Crabtree Publishing Co.

—South Africa - The People. 1999. (Lands, Peoples & Cultures Ser.). (Illus.). 32p. (J). (gr. 4-5). (978-0-86505-236-9(0)); pap. (978-0-86505-316-8(2)) Crabtree Publishing Co.

Cornell, Kari & Thomas, Peter. Cooking the Southern African Way. 2nd rev. ed. 2005. (Easy Menu Ethnic Cookbooks). (Illus.). 72p. (J). 25.26 (978-0-8225-1239-4(4) , Lerner Pubns.) Lerner Publishing Group.

Corona, Laurel. South Africa. 1999. (Modern Nations of the World Ser.). (Illus.). 112p. (YA). (gr. 7-10). 27.45 (978-1-56006-601-9(6) , Lucent Bks.) Thomson Gale.

Costain, Meredith & Collins, Paul. Welcome to South Africa. 2001. (Countries of the World Ser.). (Illus.). (J). (gr. 4 up). 28.00 (978-0-7910-6540-2(5) , 010210, Chelsea Hse.) Facts On File, Inc.

Fish, Bruce & Fish, Becky Durost. South Africa: 1800 to the Present: Imperialism, Nationalism, & Apartheid. 2000. (Exploration of Africa). (Illus.). 112p. (YA). (gr. 7 up). 35.00 (978-0-7910-5676-9(7) , Chelsea Hse.) Facts On File, Inc.

Gaines, Ann Graham. Nelson Mandela & Apartheid in World History. 2001. (In World History Ser.). (Illus.). 128p. (J). (gr. 5-12). lib. bdg. 26.60 (978-0-7660-1463-3(0)) Enslow Pubs., Inc.

Hamilton, Janice. South Africa in Pictures. 2nd ed. 2004. (Visual Geography Series, Second Ser.). (Illus.). 80p. (J). (gr. 5-12). 27.93 (978-0-8225-0938-7(5)) Lerner Publishing Group.

Leslie, Tonya. South Africa. 2002. (Steadwell Books World Tour). (Illus.). 48p. (J). lib. bdg. 24.26 (978-0-7398-5756-4(8)) Raintree.

Mulla-Feroze, Umaima & Stotko, Mary-Ann. Welcome to South Africa. 2003. (Welcome to My Country Ser.). (Illus.). 48p. (J). (gr. 2 up). lib. bdg. 26.00 (978-0-8368-2547-3(0)) Stevens, Gareth Inc.

Oluonye, Mary N. South Africa. 1999. (Ticket to Ser.). (Illus.). 48p. (gr. 2-4). lib. bdg. 22.60 (978-1-57505-141-3(9)); (J). (gr. 3-5). lib. bdg. 22.60 (978-1-57505-116-1(8) , Carolrhoda Bks.) Lerner Publishing Group.

Park, Ted. Taking Your Camera to South Africa. Sloan, Frank, ed. 2001. (Taking Your Camera to Ser.). (Illus.). 32p. (J). (gr. 4-7). lib. bdg. 22.83 (978-0-7398-3571-5(8)) Raintree.

Raatma, Lucia. South Africa. 2001. (First Reports). (Illus.). 48p. (J). (gr. 3 up). lib. bdg. 21.26 (978-0-7565-0131-0(8)) Compass Point Bks.

Stotko, Mary-Ann. South Africa. 2002. (Countries of the World Ser.). (Illus.). 96p. (J). (gr. 6 up). lib. bdg. 30.00 (978-0-8368-2347-9(8)) Stevens, Gareth Inc.

AFRICA, SOUTHERN—FICTION

Haggard, H. Rider. King Solomon's Mines. Marcos, Pablo, illus. 2005. (Great Illustrated Classics Ser.). 239p. (J). (gr. 3-8). 21.35 (978-1-59679-244-9(2) , ABDO & Daughters) ABDO Publishing Co.

AFRICA, SOUTHERN—HISTORY

Connolly. Apartheid in South Africa. 2002. (Troubled World Ser.). (Illus.). 64p. (J). (gr. 6 up). lib. bdg. 28.54 (978-0-7398-6339-8(8)) Raintree.

Diouf, Sylviane A. Kings & Queens of Southern Africa. (Watts Library). (Illus.). 64p. (J). (gr. 5-7). 2001. pap. 8.95 (978-0-531-16535-5(3)); 2000. 25.50 (978-0-531-20374-3(3)) Scholastic Library Publishing. (Watts, Franklin).

—Kings & Queens of Southern Africa. 2000. (gr. 3-6). lib. bdg. 17.60 (978-0-613-54600-3(8)) Tandem Library Bks.

Malam, John. The Release of Nelson Mandela. 2002. (Dates with History Ser.). (Illus.). 31p. (J). lib. bdg. 24.25 (978-1-58340-216-0(0)) Smart Apple Media.

Nicholson, Michael. Mahatma Gandhi. (Pacificadores Mundiales Ser.). 64p. (gr. 5-8). 28.70 (978-1-4103-0541-1(4) , Blackbirch Pr., Inc.) Thomson Gale.

AFRICA, SOUTHWEST

Staeger, Rob. Angola. 2007. (J). (978-1-4222-0086-5(8)) Mason Crest Pubs.

AFRICA, SOUTHWEST—FICTION

Totemeyer, Andree-Jeanne. Under the Story Tree: Readathon Stories. 2005. (Illus.). 93p. (***978-99916-0-509-8(6))** Namibian Children's Bk. Forum.

AFRICA, SUB-SAHARAN

Bowden, Rob. Africa South of the Sahara. 2007. (J). (***978-1-4034-9901-1(2));** pap. (***978-1-4034-9910-3(1))** Heinemann Library.

Ellis, Deborah. Our Stories, Our Songs: African Children Talk About AIDS. 2005. (Illus.). 112p. (YA). (978-1-55041-913-9(7)) Fitzhenry & Whiteside, Ltd.

Gordon, Kevin. Not Yet African: The Long Voyage Home. unabr. ed. 1998. 192p. (gr. 9-12). pap. 14.00 (978-1-57889-013-2(6)) Passeggiata Pr.

Oppong, Joseph R. Africa South of the Sahara. 2005. (Modern World Cultures Ser.). (Illus.). 136p. (J). (gr. 6-12). 30.00 (978-0-7910-8146-4(X) , Chelsea Hse.) Facts On File, Inc.

Peters, Georgia, illus. African Myths & Legends. 2001. (World Book Myths & Legends Ser.). 64p. (J). (978-0-7166-2605-3(5)) World Bk., Inc.

AFRICA, SUB-SAHARAN—HISTORY

Nelson. West African Kingdoms. 2001. (Ancient Civilizations Ser.). (Illus.). (J). pap. (978-0-7398-4152-5(1)) Steck-Vaughn.

Nelson, Julie. Great African Kingdoms. 2001. (Ancient Civilizations Ser.). (Illus.). 48p. (J). lib. bdg. 22.83 (978-0-7398-3581-4(5)) Raintree.

Sub-Saharan Africa: Regions of the World. 2003. spiral bd. 16.95 (978-1-56004-161-0(7)) Social Studies Schl. Service.

AFRICA, WEST

Brownlie, Alison. West Africa. 1999. (Food & Festivals Ser.). (Illus.). 32p. (J). (gr. 1-4). lib. bdg. 25.69 (978-0-8172-5552-7(4)) Raintree.

Chambers, Catherine. West African States: 15th Century to the Colonial Era. 1998. (Looking Back Ser.). (Illus.). 64p. (YA). (gr. 6-9). 19.98 (978-0-8172-5427-8(7)) Raintree.

Chelsea House Publishing Staff. West Africa. 2001. (Exploration of Africa). (Illus.). 112p. (J). (gr. 7-12). 35.00 (978-0-7910-5748-3(8) , Chelsea Hse.) Facts On File, Inc.

Conrad, David C. Empires of Medieval West Africa: Ghana, Mali, & Songhay. 2005. (Great Empires of the Past Ser.). (Illus.). 128p. (J). (gr. 6-12). 35.00 (978-0-8160-5562-3(9)) Facts On File, Inc.

Diakite, Baba Wague. The Hatseller & the Monkeys. Diakite, Baba Wague, illus. 1999. (Illus.). 32p. (J). (ps-2). pap. 16.95 (978-0-590-96069-4(5)) Scholastic, Inc.

Diouf, Sylviane A. Kings & Queens of West Africa. (Watts Library). (Illus.). 64p. (J). (gr. 5-7). 2001. pap. 8.95 (978-0-531-16536-2(1)); 2000. 25.50 (978-0-531-20375-0(1)) Scholastic Library Publishing. (Watts, Franklin).

Kummer, Patricia K. Cameroon. 2004. (Enchantment of the World, Second Ser.). 144p. (YA). (gr. 5-9). 36.00 (978-0-516-24256-9(3) , Children's Pr.) Scholastic Library Publishing.

Lerner Publications, Department of Geography Staff. Cote d'Ivoire in Pictures. 1999. (Visual Geography Ser.). (Illus.). 64p. (YA). (gr. 6-12). (978-0-8225-1828-0(7) , Lerner Pubns.) Lerner Publishing Group.

Levy, Patricia. Liberia. 1998. (Cultures of the World Ser.). (Illus.). 128p. (gr. 5-12). lib. bdg. 37.07 (978-0-7614-0810-9(X) , Benchmark Bks.) Cavendish, Marshall Corp.

Montgomery, Bertha Vining, et al. Cooking the West African Way. 2nd rev. exp. ed. 2002. (Easy Menu Ethnic Cookbooks). (Illus.). 72p. (J). (gr. 5-12). 25.26 (978-0-8225-4163-9(7) , Lerner Pubns.) Lerner Publishing Group.

Nnoromele, Salome C. Somalia. 1999. (Modern Nations of the World Ser.). (Illus.). 112p. (YA). (gr. 7-10). 27.45 (978-1-56006-396-4(3) , Lucent Bks.) Thomson Gale.

Quigley, Mary. Ancient West African Kingdoms. 2002. (Understanding People in the Past Ser.). (Illus.). 64p. (J). (gr. 4-6). pap. 8.95 (978-1-4034-0098-7(9) , 91673) Heinemann Library.

—Ancient West African Kingdoms: Ghana, Mali, & Songhai. 2002. (Understanding People in the Past Ser.). (Illus.). 64p. (J). (gr. 4-6). lib. bdg. 28.50 (978-1-58810-425-0(7)) Heinemann Library.

Reece, Katherine E. West African Kingdom: Empires of Gold & Trade. 2005. (Ancient Civilizations Ser.). (Illus.). 48p. (J). (gr. 4-8). 20.95 (978-1-59515-508-5(2)) Rourke Publishing, LLC.

Seffal, Rabah. Niger. 2000. (Cultures of the World Ser.). (Illus.). 128p. (gr. 5-12). lib. bdg. 37.07 (978-0-7614-0995-3(5) , Benchmark Bks.) Cavendish, Marshall Corp.

Shuter, Jane. Ancient West African Kingdoms. 2003. (History Opens Windows Ser.). (Illus.). 32p. (J). (gr. 2-4). lib. bdg. 22.79 (978-1-4034-0255-4(8)); pap. 7.50 (978-1-4034-0083-3(0)) Heinemann Library.

Zurlo, Tony. Native Peoples of West Africa. 2001. (Indigenous Peoples of Africa Ser.). (Illus.). 112p. (J). (gr. 4-12). 29.95 (978-1-56006-832-7(9) , LML00902-178164, Lucent Bks.) Thomson Gale.

AFRICA, WEST—BIOGRAPHY

Diouf, Sylviane A. Kings & Queens of West Africa. (Watts Library). (Illus.). 64p. (J). (gr. 5-7). 2001. pap. 8.95 (978-0-531-16536-2(1)); 2000. 25.50 (978-0-531-20375-0(1)) Scholastic Library Publishing. (Watts, Franklin).

Hicks, Kyra E. Martha Ann's Quilt for Queen Victoria. 2006. (J). 16.95 (978-1-933285-59-7(1)) Brown Bks. Publishing Group.

AFRICA, WEST—FICTION

Aardema, Verna. Why Mosquitoes Buzz in People's Ears. 2004. 29.95 incl. cd-rom (978-1-55592-491-1(3)); pap. 32.75 incl. audio (978-1-55592-494-2(8)) Weston Woods Studios, Inc.

Azasu, Kwakuvi. Sweet Justice. 2000. pap. (978-9964-978-74-7(X)) Woeli Publishing Services.

Burns, Khephra. Mansa Musa: The Lion of Mali. Dillon, Leo & Dillon, Diane, illus. 2001. 56p. (J). (gr. 3-5). 18.00 (978-0-15-200375-3(4) , Gulliver Bks.) Harcourt Children's Bks.

Cleveland, Robert. Clever Monkey. Hoffmire, Baird, illus. 2006. 32p. (J). pap. 3.95 (978-0-87483-801-5(0)) August Hse. Pubs., Inc.

Cumberbatch, Judy. Can You Hear the Sea? Wilson-Max, Ken, illus. 2006. 32p. (J). (gr. k-3). 15.95 (978-1-58234-703-5(4) , Bloomsbury Children) Bloomsbury Publishing.

Hergé. Tintin au Congo. 1999. (Tintin Ser.). (FRE., Illus.). 62p. (J). (gr. 4-7). 21.95 (978-2-203-00101-5(1)) Casterman, Editions FRA. *Dist:* Distribooks, Inc.

—Tintin im Kongo. (GER., Illus.). 62p. (J). pap. 24.95 (978-0-8288-4998-2(6)) French & European Pubns., Inc.

Kimmel, Eric A. Anansi's Party Time. Stevens, Janet, illus. 2008. (J). (***978-0-8234-1922-7(3)***) Holiday Hse., Inc.

Lippert, Margaret H. Talking Vegetables. Paye, Won-Ldy, ed. Paschkis, Julie, illus. rev. ed. 2006. 32p. (J). 16.95 (978-0-8050-7742-1(1)) Holt, Henry & Co.

Norfolk, Bobby. Anansi Goes to Lunch. 2007. 32p. (J). pap. 3.95 (***978-0-87483-852-7(5)***) August Hse. Pubs., Inc.

Nwokolo, Nwanneka. Zara: The Girl Traveller. 2004. (ENG.). 76p. per. (***978-1-904744-58-0(3)***) Troubador Publishing Ltd.

Onyefulu, Ifeoma, illus. Here Comes Our Bride an African Wedding Story. 2004. 32p. (J). 15.95 (978-1-84507-047-2(X)) Lincoln, Frances Ltd. GBR. *Dist:* Perseus Distribution.

Polisar, Barry Louis. Stolen Man: The Story of the Amistad Rebellion. 2007. 32p. (J). (gr. 3-5). pap. 7.95 (***978-0-938663-50-8(X)***) Rainbow Morning Music Alternatives.

Scherer, Catherine W. Simon & Barklee in West Africa. Richardson, Kara, illus. 2006. (Another Country Calling Ser.). 80p. (J). per. 15.00 (978-0-9714502-4-0(2) , Explorer Media) Simon & Barklee, Inc./ExplorerMedia.

Watson, Peter & Watson, Mary. Heart of the Lion. Watson, Peter, illus. 2005. (Illus.). 32p. 15.95 (978-0-9726614-1-6(7)) Shenanigan Bks.

AFRICAN AMERICAN ACTORS

African American Actors & Actresses. 2000. (My Ancestors—My Heroes Ser.: Vol. 27). (J). (gr. 3-4). (978-1-893091-26-9(0)) Parker Publishing Co.

Blue, Rose. Halle Berry. 2001. (Black Americans of Achievement Ser.). (Illus.). 112p. (J). (gr. 4-7). 30.00 (978-0-7910-5802-2(6) , Chelsea Hse.) Facts On File, Inc.

—Wesley Snipes. 2001. (Black Americans of Achievement Ser.). (Illus.). 112p. (J). (gr. 4-7). 30.00 (978-0-7910-5800-8(X) , Chelsea Hse.) Facts On File, Inc.

Brooks, Philip. Oprah Winfrey: A Voice for the People. 2000. (Book Report Bios Ppbk Ser.). (Illus.). (YA). pap. 6.95 (978-0-531-16406-8(3) , Watts, Franklin) Scholastic Library Publishing.

—Oprah Winfrey: A Voice for the People. 1999. (978-0-606-18159-4(8)) Tandem Library Bks.

De Angelis, Gina. Gregory Hines. 1999. (Black Americans of Achievement Ser.). (YA). (gr. 4 up). lib. bdg. 19.95 (978-0-7910-4965-5(5) , Chelsea Hse.) Facts On File, Inc.

Dean, Tanya. Della Reese. 2001. (Black Americans of Achievement Ser.). 112p. (J). 30.00 (978-0-7910-6291-3(0) , Chelsea Hse.) Facts On File, Inc.

Dils, Tracy. Samuel L. Jackson: Actor. (Black Americans of Achievement Ser.). (Illus.). 2000. 112p. (J). (gr. 4-7). 30.00 (978-0-7910-5281-5(8)); 1999. 104p. (YA). (gr. 5 up). pap. 30.00 (978-0-7910-5282-2(6)) Facts On File, Inc. (Chelsea Hse.).

Edelson, Paula. Cuba Gooding JR. 2000. (Illus.). 104p. (J). (gr. k-9). lib. bdg. 18.75 (978-0-613-21388-2(2)) Tandem Library Bks.

Feinstein, Stephen. Oprah Winfrey. 2007. (African-American Heroes Ser.). (Illus.). 24p. (J). (gr. 1-3). lib. bdg. 21.26 (978-0-7660-2764-0(3) , Enslow Elementary) Enslow Pubs., Inc.

Feinstein, Stephen. Will Smith. 2007. (African-American Heroes Ser.). (Illus.). 24p. (J). (gr. 1-3). lib. bdg. 21.26 (***978-0-7660-2765-7(1)*** , Enslow Elementary) Enslow Pubs., Inc.

Fitzgerald, Dawn. Angela Bassett. 2001. (Black Americans of Achievement Ser.). (Illus.). 112p. (J). (gr. 4-7). 30.00 (978-0-7910-5810-7(7) , Chelsea Hse.) Facts On File, Inc.

Gaines, Ann Graham. Whoopi Goldberg. 2000. (Illus.). 112p. (J). (ps-7). per. 18.75 (978-0-613-12278-8(X)) Tandem Library Bks.

Guilfoyle, Peg. Oprah Winfrey. 1999. (Ovations Ser.). (Illus.). 32p. (YA). (gr. 4-7). pap. (978-0-88682-941-4(0) , Creative Education) Creative Co., The.

Hasday, Judy L. James Earl Jones: Actor. 1999. (Overcoming Adversity Ser.). (Illus.). 128p. (YA). (gr. 5 up). 32.00 (978-0-7910-4702-6(4)); pap. 6.65 (978-0-7910-4703-3(2)) Facts On File, Inc. (Chelsea Hse.).

Hill, Anne E. Denzel Washington: Actor. 1999. (Black Americans of Achievement Ser.). (Illus.). 96p. (J). (gr. 4-7). pap. 9.95 (978-0-7910-4693-7(1)); 32.00 (978-0-7910-4692-0(3)) Facts On File, Inc. (Chelsea Hse.).

Leavitt, Amie. Raven-Symone. 2007. (Robbie Reader Ser.). (Illus.). 32p. (J). (gr. 1-4). lib. bdg. 25.70 (***978-1-58415-593-5(0)***) Mitchell Lane Pubs., Inc.

Paprocki, Sherry. Oprah Winfrey. 2006. (Black Americans of Achievement, Legacy Edition Ser.). (Illus.). 112p. (gr. 6-12). 30.00 (978-0-7910-9226-2(7) , Chelsea Hse.) Facts On File, Inc.

Presnall, Judith Janda. Oprah Winfrey. 1998. (People in the News Ser.). (Illus.). 112p. (YA). (gr. 6-9). 27.45 (978-1-56006-360-5(2) , Lucent Bks.) Thomson Gale.

Schoell, William. Heartbreaker: The Dorothy Dandridge Story. 2002. (Illus.). 127p. (Orig.). (J). (gr. 6-12). pap. 19.95 (978-1-888105-51-3(8)) Avisson Pr., Inc.

Stewart, Jeffrey C., ed. & intro. Paul Robeson: Artist & Citizen. Stewart, Jeffrey C., intro. 1998. (Illus.). 304p. (C). (gr. 10-12). pap. 22.00 (978-0-8135-2511-2(X)) Rutgers Univ. Pr.

Westen, Robin. Oprah Winfrey: I Dont Believe in Failure. 2005. (African-American Biography Library). (Illus.). 128p. (J). (gr. 6-12). lib. bdg. 31.93 (978-0-7660-2462-5(8)) Enslow Pubs., Inc.

Wheeler, Jill C. Oprah Winfrey. 2002. (Breaking Barriers Ser.). (Illus.). 64p. (J). (gr. 3-8). lib. bdg. 25.65 (978-1-57765-319-6(X) , ABDO & Daughters) ABDO Publishing Co.

Wooten, Sara McIntosh. Denzel Washington: Academy Award-Winning Actor. 2003. (African-American Biographies Ser.). (Illus.). 128p. (J). lib. bdg. 26.60 (978-0-7660-2131-0(9)) Enslow Pubs., Inc.

AFRICAN AMERICAN ART

Bolden, Tonya. Wake up Our Souls: A Celebration of Black American Artists. 2004. (Illus.). 128p. (J). (gr. 5-17). 24.95 (978-0-8109-4527-2(4)) Abrams, Harry N. , Inc.

Butler, Jerry. A Drawing in the Sand: A Story of African American Art. Butler, Jerry, illus. 1998. (Illus.). 64p. (J). (gr. 3-7). 24.95 (978-1-55933-216-3(6) , 2166BK) Zino Pr. Children's Bks.

Haskins, James. Harlem Renaissance. 2004. (J). pap. 10.95 (978-0-940975-95-8(5) , Sankofa Bks.) Just Us Bks., Inc.

Jordan, Denise M. Harlem Renaissance Artists. 2002. (Artists in Profile Ser.). (Illus.). 64p. (J). lib. bdg. 28.50 (978-1-58810-649-0(7)) Heinemann Library.

Kallen, Stuart A. A Travel Guide to Harlem Renaissance. 2003. (J). 29.95 (978-1-59018-358-8(4) , Lucent Bks.) Thomson Gale.

Marsh, Carole. Color Purple & All That Jazz! African American Achievements in the Arts. 2003. (gr. 5-8). lib. bdg. 22.20 (978-0-613-73033-4(X)) Tandem Library Bks.

Nichols, Catherine. African American Culture. 2006. (Discovering the Arts Ser.). (gr. 4-8). 125.70 (978-1-59515-516-0(3)); (Illus.). 48p. 20.95 (978-1-59515-517-7(1)) Rourke Publishing, LLC.

Price, Sean. Rebirth of a People: Harlem Renaissance. 2006. (American History Through Primary Sources Ser.). (Illus.). 32p. (J). (978-1-4109-2415-5(7)) Raintree.

—Rebirth of a People: Harlem Renaissance. 2006. (American History Through Primary Sources Ser.). (Illus.). 32p. (J). pap. (978-1-4109-2426-1(2)) Steck-Vaughn.

Slovey, Christine. Harlem Renaissance. 2000. (Illus.). xxix, 293p. (J). (gr. 4-7). 67.00 (978-0-7876-4836-7(1) , GML00502-114880, UXL) Thomson Gale.

Sullivan, Charles. Children of Promise: African-American Literature & Art for Young People. 2002. (Illus.). 126p. 12.98 (978-0-8109-8221-5(8)) Abrams, Harry N. , Inc.

Wilson, Sule Greg C. African-American Quilting: The Warmth of Tradition. 1999. (Library of African American Arts & Culture). (Illus.). 64p. (YA). (gr. 7-12). lib. bdg. 26.50 (978-0-8239-1854-6(8) , AAQUCR) Rosen Publishing Group, Inc., The.

Worth, Richard. Harlem Renaissance: An Explosion of African-American Culture. 2008. (J). (***978-0-7660-2907-1(7)***) Enslow Pubs., Inc.

AFRICAN AMERICAN ARTISTS

African-American Artists. 2000. (My Ancestors—My Heroes Ser.: Vol. 10). (J). (gr. 3-4). (978-1-893091-09-2(0)) Parker Publishing Co.

Chandler, Alton. A Salute to African American Architects: Learning Activities. Chapman, Loring F., ed. Still, Wayne A., illus. 24p. (Orig.). (J). (gr. 3-8). pap. 1.75 (978-1-877804-16-8(9)) Chandler/White Publishing Co.

Duggleby, John. Story Painter: The Life of Jacob Lawrence. 1998. (Illus.). 64p. (J). (gr. 1-7). 16.95 (978-0-8118-2082-0(3)) Chronicle Bks. LLC.

Greenberg, Jan. Romare Bearden: Collage of Memories. Bearden, Romare, illus. 2003. 52p. (J). (gr. 1-5). 17.95 (978-0-8109-4589-0(4)) Abrams, Harry N. , Inc.

Haskins, Jim, et al. Black Stars of the Harlem Renaissance. 2002. (Illus.). 122p. (J). (ps-7). per. 22.20 (978-0-613-84109-2(3)) Tandem Library Bks.

—Black Stars of the Harlem Renaissance. 2002. (Black Stars Ser.). (Illus.). 128p. pap. 12.95 (978-0-471-21152-5(4) , Pfeiffer) Wiley, John & Sons, Inc.

Igus, Toyomi, ed. Going Back Home: An Artist Returns to the South. Wood, Michele, illus. 2004. 32p. (J). (gr. 1 up). pap. 7.95 (978-0-89239-197-4(9)) Children's Bk. Pr.

Jordan, Denise M. Harlem Renaissance Artists. 2002. (Artists in Profile Ser.). (Illus.). 64p. (J). lib. bdg. 28.50 (978-1-58810-649-0(7)) Heinemann Library.

Rembert, Winfred. Don't Hold Me Back: My Life & Art. Rembert, Winfred, illus. 2003. (Illus.). 48p. 19.95 (978-0-8126-2703-9(2)) Cricket Bks.

Roy, Jennifer Rozines & Roy, Gregory. Jacob Lawrence: Painter of African-American Life. 2003. (J). 18.95 (978-0-7660-1878-5(4)) Enslow Pubs., Inc.

Schaefer, A. R. Jacob Lawrence. 2002. (Life & Work of. . . Ser.). (J). pap. 6.50 (978-1-4034-0496-1(8)); 32p. lib. bdg. 21.36 (978-1-4034-0290-5(6)) Heinemann Library.

Slovey, Christine. Harlem Renaissance. 2000. (Illus.). xxix, 293p. (J). (gr. 4-7). 67.00 (978-0-7876-4836-7(1) , GML00502-114880, UXL) Thomson Gale.

Todd, Anne M. Chris Rock. 2006. (Black Americans of Achievement, Legacy Edition Ser.). (Illus.). 104p. (gr. 6-12). 30.00 (978-0-7910-9225-5(9) , Chelsea Hse.) Facts On File, Inc.

Venezia, Mike. Faith Ringgold. 2008. (Getting to Know the World's Greatest Artists Ser.). 32p. (J). pap. 6.95 (***978-0-531-14757-3(6)*** , Children's Pr.) Scholastic Library Publishing.

—Horace Pippin. 2008. (Getting to Know the World's Greatest Artists Ser.). 32p. (J). pap. 6.95 (***978-0-531-14758-0(4)*** , Children's Pr.) Scholastic Library Publishing.

Venezia, Mike. Jacob Lawrence. (Getting to Know the World's Greatest Artists Ser.). (Illus.). 32p. (J). (gr. 3-4). 2000. pap. 6.95 (978-0-516-26533-9(4)); 1999. 27.00 (978-0-516-21012-4(2)) Scholastic Library Publishing. (Children's Pr.).

—Jacob Lawrence. 1999. (gr. 3-6). lib. bdg. 15.25 (978-0-613-39504-5(2)) Tandem Library Bks.

AFRICAN AMERICAN ATHLETES

African American Athletes. 2000. (My Ancestors—My Heroes Ser.: Vol. 25). (J). (gr. 3-4). (978-1-893091-24-5(4)) Parker Publishing Co.

Auerbacher, Inge. Running Against the Wind: The True Story of Twin Sisters from Brooklyn Who Changed the Lives of Thousands of African-American Youngsters in New York City. 2000. (Illus.). 117p. (J). (ps-10). pap. 9.99 (978-0-88092-437-5(3) , 4373) Royal Fireworks Publishing Co.

Bernstein, Ross. Randy Moss: Star Wide Receiver. 2002. (Sports Reports). (Illus.). 104p. (J). (gr. 4-10). lib. bdg. 26.60 (978-0-7660-1503-6(3)) Enslow Pubs., Inc.

Daly, Chuck, intro. Alonzo Mourning. 1999. (Basketball Legends Ser.). (Illus.). 64p. (YA). (gr. 4-7). 12.95 (978-0-7910-4577-0(3) , Chelsea Hse.) Facts On File, Inc.

—Gary Payton. 1999. (Basketball Legends Ser.). (Illus.). 64p. (YA). (gr. 4-7). 12.95 (978-0-7910-4578-7(1) , Chelsea Hse.) Facts On File, Inc.

—Juwan Howard. 1999. (Basketball Legends Ser.). (Illus.). 64p. (YA). (gr. 4-7). lib. bdg. 18.65 (978-0-7910-4575-6(7) , Chelsea Hse.) Facts On File, Inc.

—Shawn Kemp. 1999. (Basketball Legends Ser.). (Illus.). 64p. (YA). (gr. 4-7). 12.95 (978-0-7910-4576-3(5) , Chelsea Hse.) Facts On File, Inc.

Elster, Jean Alicia. Just Call Me Joe Joe. Tadgell, Nicole, illus. 2001. (Joe Joe in the City Ser.). 32p. (gr. 1-5). 12.00 (978-0-8170-1398-1(9)) Judson Pr.

Frisaro, Joe. Reggie Miller: From Downtown. 2003. (Superstar Ser.: Vol. 6). (Illus.). 96p. (gr. 4-7). pap. 4.95 (978-1-58261-180-8(7)) Sports Publishing, LLC.

Gormley, Beatrice. Althea Gibson: Young Tennis Player. Henderson, Meryl, illus. 2005. 214p. (J). (gr. 3-7). lib. bdg. 12.04 (978-0-606-33374-0(6)) Tandem Library Bks.

Gottfried, Ted. Earvin "Magic" Johnson: Champion & Crusader. 2001. (Book Report Biographies Ser.). (Illus.). 100p. (YA). (gr. 6-8). pap. 6.95 (978-0-531-15550-9(1) , Watts, Franklin) Scholastic Library Publishing.

Kernan, Kevin. Tim Duncan: Slam Duncan. 2000. (SuperStar Ser.: Vol. 5). (Illus.). 96p. (J). (gr. 4-7). per. 4.95 (978-1-58261-179-2(3)) Sports Publishing, LLC.

Lowenstein, Felicia. Super Sports Star Grant Hill. 2001. (Super Sports Star Ser.). (Illus.). 48p. (J). (gr. 1-4). lib. bdg. 23.93 (978-0-7660-1517-3(3)) Enslow Pubs., Inc.

Macnow, Glen. Sports Great Kevin Garnett. 2000. (Sports Great Bks.). (Illus.). 64p. (YA). (gr. 4-10). lib. bdg. 17.95 (978-0-7660-1263-9(8)) Enslow Pubs., Inc.

Mandell, Judith J. Super Sports Star Alonzo Mourning. 2002. (Super Sports Star Ser.). (Illus.). 48p. (J). (gr. 1-4). lib. bdg. 18.95 (978-0-7660-1518-0(1)) Enslow Pubs., Inc.

Raatma, Lucia. Jesse Owens: Track-and-Field Olympian. 2003. (Journey to Freedom Ser.). (Illus.). 40p. (J). (gr. 3-7). 28.50 (978-1-56766-532-1(2)) Child's World, Inc.

Rappoport, Ken. Super Sports Star Penny Hardaway. 2001. (Super Sports Star Ser.). (Illus.). 48p. (J). (gr. 1-4). lib. bdg. 23.93 (978-0-7660-1516-6(5)) Enslow Pubs., Inc.

Rosenthal, Bert. Tim Hardaway: Star Guard. 2001. (Sports Reports). (Illus.). 104p. (J). (gr. 4-10). lib. bdg 26.60 (978-0-7660-1500-5(9)) Enslow Pubs., Inc.

Savage, Jeff. Top 10 African-American Men's Athletes. 2001. (Sports Top 10 Ser.). (Illus.). 48p. (J). (gr. 4-10). lib. bdg. 23.93 (978-0-7660-1494-7(0)) Enslow Pubs., Inc.

Smallwood. NBA - Yesterday's Heroes: A Journey Through the History of African-American Superstars in the NBA. 2000. (J). (978-0-606-19933-9(0)) Tandem Library Bks.

Time for Kids Editors. Jesse Owens: Running into History. 2008. (Time for Kids Ser.). (Illus.). 48p. (J). 15.99 (***978-0-06-057621-9(9)***); pap. 3.99 (***978-0-06-057620-2(0)*** , Collins) HarperCollins Pubs.

Weatherford, Carole Boston. A Negro League Scrapbook. 2004. (Illus.). 48p. (YA). 19.95 (978-1-59078-091-6(4)) Boyds Mills Pr.

Winter, Jonah. Fair Ball! 14 Great Stars from Baseball's Negro Leagues. 2002. (J). pap. 5.99 (978-0-590-39465-9(7) , Levine, Arthur A. Bks.); 32p. (gr. 2-5). pap. 5.99 (978-0-439-37604-4(1)) Scholastic, Inc.

—Fair Ball! 14 Great Stars from Baseball's Negro Leagues. Winter, Jonah, illus. 1999. (Illus.). (J). (gr. 2-5). pap. 15.95 (978-0-590-39464-2(9)) Scholastic, Inc.

AFRICAN AMERICAN AUTHORS

Angelou, Maya & Kirkpatrick, Patricia. Maya Angelou. 2003. (Voices of Poetry Ser.). (Illus.). 48p. 19.95 (978-1-58341-281-7(6) , Creative Education) Creative Co., The.

Brezina, Corona. Sojourner Truth's "Ain't I a Woman?" Speech: A Primary Source Investigation. 2004. (Great Historic Debates & Speeches Ser.). (Illus.). 64p. (J). lib. bdg. 29.95 (978-1-4042-0154-5(8)) Rosen Publishing Group, Inc., The.

Bryant, Philip S. Zora Neale Hurston. 2003. (African-American Biographies Ser.). (Illus.). 64p. (J). 28.56 (978-0-7398-6872-0(1)) Raintree.

Cannarella, Deborah. James Baldwin: African-American Writer & Activist. 2003. (Journey to Freedom Ser.). (Illus.). 40p. (J). (gr. 3-7). 28.50 (978-1-56766-531-4(4)) Child's World, Inc.

—Zora Neale Hurston: African-American Writer. 2002. (Journey to Freedom Ser.). (Illus.). 40p. (J). (gr. 3-7). 28.50 (978-1-56766-649-6(3)) Child's World, Inc.

Douglass, Frederick. Great Black Authors. 2001. (J). pap. 4.95 (978-0-88388-200-9(0)) Bellerophon Bks.

Fish, Bruce. Terry McMillan. 2001. (Black Americans of Achievement Ser.). (Illus.). 112p. (J). (gr. 4-7). 30.00 (978-0-7910-5804-6(2) , Chelsea Hse.) Facts On File, Inc.

Fish, Bruce & Fish, Becky Durost. Terry McMillan. 2001. (Black Americans of Achievement Ser.). (Illus.). (YA). (gr. 8-12). pap. 30.00 (978-0-7910-5805-3(0) , Chelsea Hse.) Facts On File, Inc.

—Terry Mcmillan. 2001. (Illus.). 112p. (J). (gr. 4-7). lib. bdg. 18.75 (978-0-613-33131-9(1)) Tandem Library Bks.

Fullen, Marilyn K. Great Black Writers. 2002. (Contributions Ser.). (Illus.). 64p. (J). 12.95 (978-0-940880-66-5(0)); pap. 6.95 (978-0-940880-67-2(9)) Open Hand Publishing, LLC.

Gaines, Ann. Christopher Paul Curtis. 2004. (Blue Banner Biography Ser.). (Illus.). 32p. (J). lib. bdg. (978-1-58415-330-6(X)) Mitchell Lane Pubs., Inc.

Gaines, Ann Graham. Christopher Paul Curtis. 2001. (Real-Life Reader Biography Ser.). (Illus.). 32p. (J). (gr. 3-8). lib. bdg. 15.95 (978-1-58415-076-3(9)) Mitchell Lane Pubs., Inc.

Harkins, Susan and William. Walter Dean Myers. 2007. (YA). lib. bdg. (***978-1-58415-534-8(5)***) Mitchell Lane Pubs., Inc.

Hart, Joyce. Native Son: The Story of Richard Wright. 2004. (World Writers Ser.). (Illus.). 128p. (YA). (gr. 6-12). 23.95 (978-1-931798-06-8(0)) Reynolds, Morgan Inc.

Haskins, Jim, et al. Black Stars of the Harlem Renaissance. 2002. (Illus.). 122p. (J). (ps-7). per. 22.20 (978-0-613-84109-2(3)) Tandem Library Bks.

—Black Stars of the Harlem Renaissance. 2002. (Black Stars Ser.). (Illus.). 128p. pap. 12.95 (978-0-471-21152-5(4) , Pfeiffer) Wiley, John & Sons, Inc.

Herron, Carolivia. Always an Olivia: A Remarkable Family History. Tugeau, Jeremy, illus. 2007. (Jewish Identity Ser.). 32p. (J). (gr. 2-5). 17.95 (***978-0-8225-7049-3(1)***) Kar-Ben Publishing.

Houghton, Gillian. Mildred Taylor. 2004. (Library of Author Biographies). (Illus.). 112p. (YA). 26.50 (978-1-4042-0330-3(3)) Rosen Publishing, Inc.

Jones, Lynda & Garnett, Ron. Five Famous Writers. 2001. (Great Black Heroes Ser.). (Illus.). 48p. (J). (978-0-590-48035-2(9)) Scholastic, Inc.

Kite, L. Patricia. Maya Angelou. 2006. (Just the Facts Biographies Ser.). (Illus.). 112p. (J). 27.93 (978-0-8225-3426-6(6)); pap. (***978-0-8225-5997-9(8)***) Lerner Publishing Group. (Lerner Pubns.).

Kjelle, Marylou Morano. Henry Louis Gates, Jr. 2003. (African American Leaders Ser.). (Illus.). 112p. (gr. 6-12). 30.00 (978-0-7910-7687-3(3) , Chelsea Hse.) Facts On File, Inc.

Levin, Judy & Draper, Allison Stark. Christopher Paul Curtis. annot. ed. 2005. (Library of Author Biographies). (Illus.). 112p. (YA). (ps-ps). lib. bdg. 26.50 (978-1-4042-0458-4(X)) Rosen Publishing Group, Inc., The.

Levy, Debbie. Richard Wright. 2007. (Literary Greats Ser.). 160p. (YA). (gr. 7-12). lib. bdg. 33.26 (***978-0-8225-6793-6(8)*** , Twenty-First Century Bks.) Lerner Publishing Group.

Litwin, Laura Baskes. Zora Neale Hurston: I Have Been in Sorrow's Kitchen. 2007. (African-American Biography Library). (Illus.). 128p. (YA). (gr. 6 up). lib. bdg. 31.93 (978-0-7660-2536-3(5)) Enslow Pubs., Inc.

Loos, Pamela. A Reader's Guide to Lorraine Hansberry's A Raisin in the Sun. 2008. (Multicultural Literature Ser.). (Illus.). 128p. (YA). (gr. 9-12). lib. bdg. 31.93 (978-0-7660-2830-2(5)) Enslow Pubs., Inc.

Mangal, Melina. Mildred Taylor. 2004. (Classic Storytellers Ser.). (Illus.). 48p. (J). (gr. 4-8). lib. bdg. 20.95 (978-1-58415-311-5(3)) Mitchell Lane Pubs., Inc.

—Virginia Hamilton. 2002. (Real Life Reader Biography Ser.). (Illus.). 32p. (J). (gr. 3-8). lib. bdg. 24.95 (978-1-58415-170-8(6)) Mitchell Lane Pubs., Inc.

Marinelli, Deborah A. Virginia Hamilton. 2003. (Library of Author Biographies). (Illus.). 112p. (YA). (gr. 5-8). lib. bdg. 26.50 (978-0-8239-3777-6(1) , Rosen Central) Rosen Publishing Group, Inc., The.

McKissack, Patricia C. & McKissack, Fredrick L. Young, Black & Determined: A Biography of Lorraine Hansberry. 1998. (Illus.). 156p. (YA). (gr. 5 up). tchr. ed. 18.95 (978-0-8234-1300-3(4)) Holiday Hse., Inc.

Miller, William. Zora Hurston & the Chinaberry Tree. ed. 2004. (Illus.). (J). (gr. k-3). spiral bd. (978-0-616-03099-8(1)) Canadian National Institute for the Blind/Institut National Canadien pour les Aveugles.

—Zora Hurston y El Arbol Sonador. Hu, Ying-Hwa & Van Wright, Cornelius, illus. 2001. (SPA.). 32p. (J). (gr. 3-5). 15.95 (978-1-58430-029-8(9) , LW30399); pap. 6.95 (978-1-58430-030-4(2) , LW30398) Lee & Low Bks., Inc.

Myers, Walter Dean. Bad Boy: A Memoir. 2001. (Amistad Ser.). 224p. (YA). (gr. 7 up). 16.99 (978-0-06-029523-3(6)) HarperCollins Pubs.

—Bad Boy: A Memoir. l.t. ed. 2005. (Thorndike Press Large Print the Literacy Bridge Ser.). 269p. (978-0-7862-7537-3(5)) Thorndike Pr.

Raatma, Lucia. Alice Walker: African-American Author & Activist. 2003. (Journey to Freedom Ser.). (Illus.). 40p. (J). (gr. 3-7). 28.50 (978-1-56766-512-3(8)) Child's World, Inc.

Sickels, Amy. Walter Dean Myers. 2008. (Who Wrote That? Ser.). 128p. (gr. 6-12). 30.00 (***978-0-7910-9524-9(X)*** , Chelsea Hse.) Facts On File, Inc.

Walker, Alice. Langston Hughes: American Poet. Deeter, Catherine, illus. rev. ed. 2002. (Amistad Ser.). 48p. (J). (gr. 4 up). 16.99 (978-0-06-021518-7(6) , Amistad) HarperCollins Pubs.

Watson, Galadriel Findlay. Toni Morrison. 2005. (Great African American Women for Kids Ser.). (Illus.). 24p. (J). (ps-7). pap. 6.95 (978-1-59036-340-9(X)); lib. bdg. 26.00 (978-1-59036-334-8(5)) Weigl Pubs., Inc.

AFRICAN AMERICAN COOKERY

Hunt, Sharon. Dinner Cookbook for Men at Work: Menus, Recipes & Market Orders. 1999. pap. (978-0-9654517-2-7(0)) African American Queen Hunt Production, Inc.

Raabe, Emily. A Kwanzaa Holiday Cookbook. 2002. (Festive Foods for the Holidays Ser.). (Illus.). 24p. (J). (gr. 2-5). lib. bdg. 19.95 (978-0-8239-5629-6(6) , PowerKids Pr.) Rosen Publishing Group, Inc., The.

Sanna, Ellyn, compiled by. African American. 2005. (American Regional Cooking Library). (Illus.). 72p. (J). lib. bdg. (978-1-59084-610-0(9)) Mason Crest Pubs.

Weber, Valerie & Jackson, Jeraldine. Food in Grandma's Day. 1999. (In Grandma's Day Ser.). (Illus.). 32p. (J). (gr. 2-4). lib. bdg. 21.27 (978-1-57505-328-8(4) , Carolrhoda Bks.) Lerner Publishing Group.

AFRICAN AMERICAN FOLKLORE

see African Americans—Folklore

AFRICAN AMERICAN LITERATURE (ENGLISH)

see American Literature—African American Authors

AFRICAN AMERICAN MUSIC

see African Americans—Music

AFRICAN AMERICAN MUSICIANS

African-American Musicians. 2000. (My Ancestors—My Heroes Ser.: Vol. 26). (J). (gr. 3-4). (978-1-893091-25-2(2)) Parker Publishing Co.

Ayazi-Hashjin, Sherry. Rap & Hip Hop: The Voice of a Generation. 1999. (Library of African American Arts & Culture). (Illus.). 64p. (YA). (gr. 7-12). lib. bdg. 26.50 (978-0-8239-1855-3(6) , AARAHI) Rosen Publishing Group, Inc., The.

Ellis, Veronica Freeman. Wynton Marsalis. 1998. (Contemporary African Americans Ser.). (Illus.). 48p. (J). (gr. 3-7). pap. 7.95 (978-0-8172-6877-0(4)) Steck-Vaughn.

Embacher, Eric. Will Smith: The Funny, Funky, & Confident Fresh Prince. 2003. (High Five Reading (Red Level) Ser.). (Illus.). (J). 64p. lib. bdg. 22.60 (978-0-7368-2786-7(2)); 48p. pap. 23.93 (978-0-7368-2829-1(X)) Capstone Pr., Inc.

Ford, Carin T. Duke Ellington: I Live with Music. 2007. (African-American Biography Library). (Illus.). 128p. (J). (gr. 6 up). lib. bdg. 31.93 (978-0-7660-2702-2(3)) Enslow Pubs., Inc.

Gelfand, Dale Evva. Jimi Hendrix. 2006. (Black Americans of Achievement Ser.). (Illus.). 128p. (J). (gr. 6-12). 30.00 (978-0-7910-9214-9(3) , Chelsea Hse.) Facts On File, Inc.

Gourse, Leslie. Wynton Marsalis: Trumpet Genius. (Book Report Biographies Ser.). (Illus.). 112p. (YA). (gr. 6-8). 2000. pap. 6.95 (978-0-531-16407-5(1)); 1999. 18.95 (978-0-531-11673-9(5)) Scholastic Library Publishing. (Watts, Franklin).

Harrah, Madge. Blind Boone: Piano Prodigy. 2004. (Trailblazers Biographies Ser.). (Illus.). 112p. (J). (gr. 5-9). lib. bdg. 30.60 (978-1-57505-057-7(9)) Lerner Publishing Group.

Higginsen, V. & Johnson, H. A Harlem Century. 2000. (J). lib. bdg. 21.99 (978-0-517-70950-4(3) , Random Hse. Bks. for Young Readers) Random Hse. Children's Bks.

Holland, Gini. Louis Armstrong. 2003. (Trailblazers of the Modern World Ser.). (Illus.). 48p. (J). (gr. 5 up). pap. 11.95 (978-0-8368-5249-3(4)); lib. bdg. 30.00 (978-0-8368-5089-5(0)) Stevens, Gareth Inc. (World Almanac Library).

Josephson, Judith Pinkerton. Louis Armstrong. 2008. (History Maker Biographies Ser.). (J). lib. bdg. 26.60 (***978-0-8225-7169-8(2)*** , Lerner Pubns.) Lerner Publishing Group.

Kavanaugh, Lee Hill. Quincy Jones: Musician, Composer, Producer. 1998. (African-American Biographies Ser.). (Illus.). 128p. (YA). (gr. 6-12). lib. bdg. 20.95 (978-0-89490-814-9(6)) Enslow Pubs., Inc.

Morreale, Marie. Hangin' with Lil' Bow Wow. 2002. (Backstage Pass Ser.). (Illus.). 48p. (J). pap. 8.95 (978-0-439-37959-5(8)) Scholastic, Inc.

Old, Wendie C. Louis Armstrong: King of Jazz. 1998. (African-American Biographies Ser.). (Illus.). 128p. (YA). (gr. 6-12). lib. bdg. 26.60 (978-0-89490-997-9(5)) Enslow Pubs., Inc.

Orgill, Roxane. If I Only Had a Horn: Young Louis Armstrong. Jenkins, Leonard, illus. 2002. 32p. (J). (gr. 4-6). pap. 5.95 (978-0-618-25076-9(X)) Houghton Mifflin Co. Trade & Reference Div.

—If I Only Had a Horn: Young Louis Armstrong. 2002. (gr. k-3). lib. bdg. 14.10 (978-0-613-70726-8(5)) Tandem Library Bks.

—Mahalia: A Life in Gospel Music. 2004. (Illus.). 132p. (gr. 4-8). reprint ed. 20.00 (978-0-7567-7945-0(6)) DIANE Publishing Co.

Raschka, Chris. Charlie Parker Played Be Bop. 2004. 14p. (J). pap. 6.99 (978-0-439-57823-3(X)) Scholastic, Inc.

Still, Judith A. Little David Had No Fear. Magruder, Lea W., illus. 1999. 118p. (Orig.). (J). (gr. 3-8). pap. 19.95 (978-1-877873-03-4(9)) Master-Player Library, The.

Stockdale, Tom. Jimi Hendrix. 1999. (They Died Too Young Ser.). (Illus.). 48p. (YA). (gr. 5 up). lib. bdg. 18.65 (978-0-7910-4632-6(X) , Chelsea Hse.) Facts On File, Inc.

—Marvin Gaye. 1999. (They Died Too Young Ser.). (Illus.). 48p. (YA). 27.00 (978-0-7910-5227-3(3) , Chelsea Hse.) Facts On File, Inc.

Terrill, Richard. Duke Ellington. 2003. (African-American Biographies Ser.). 64p. pap. 8.95 (978-1-4109-0035-7(5)) Raintree.

Wilder, Stephanie. Legends of the Blues. 2005. (Illus.). 24p. (J). (***978-0-328-13542-4(9)*** , Scott Foresman) Addison-Wesley Educational Pubs., Inc.

AFRICAN AMERICAN MUSICIANS—FICTION

Levine, Gail Carson. Dave at Night. 2001. 304p. (J). (gr. 3-7). reprint ed. pap. 6.99 (978-0-06-440747-2(0) , Harper Trophy) HarperCollins Pubs.

—Dave at Night. unabr. ed. 2004. 278p. (J). (gr. 4-7). pap. 38.00 incl. audio (978-0-8072-8379-0(7) , YA174SP, Listening Library) Random Hse. Audio Publishing Group.

—Dave at Night. 1999. (YA). pap., stu. ed. 69.95 incl. audio (978-0-7887-3794-7(5) , 41038) Recorded Bks., LLC.

AFRICAN AMERICAN POETRY (ENGLISH)

see American Poetry—African American Authors

AFRICAN AMERICAN SCIENTISTS

African-American Scientist. 2000. (My Ancestors—My Heroes Ser.: Vol. 12). (J). (gr. 3-4). (978-1-893091-11-5(2)) Parker Publishing Co.

Blue, Rose & Naden, Corinne J. Benjamin Banneker: Mathematician & Stargazer. 2001. (Gateway Biography Ser.). (Illus.). 48p. (gr. 2-4). lib. bdg. 23.90 (978-0-7613-1805-7(4) , Millbrook Pr.) Lerner Publishing Group.

Braun, Eric. Benjamin Banneker. 2005. (Pebble Books). (Illus.). 24p. (J). (978-0-7368-4233-4(0) , Pebble Bks.) Capstone Pr., Inc.

Haskins, Jim. Outward Dreams: Black Inventors & Their Inventions. 2003. (gr. 5-8). lib. bdg. 17.60 (978-0-613-75330-2(5)) Tandem Library Bks.

—Outward Dreams: Black Inventors & Their Inventions. 2003. (Illus.). 112p. (J). pap. 8.95 (978-0-8027-7673-0(6)) Walker & Co.

Hinman, Bonnie. Benjamin Banneker. 1999. (Colonial Leaders Ser.). (Illus.). 79p. (J). (gr. 3 up). pap. 8.95 (978-0-7910-5691-2(0) , Chelsea Hse.) Facts On File, Inc.

—Benjamin Banneker: American Mathematician & Astronomer. 2000. (Colonial Leaders Ser.). (Illus.). 80p. (J). (gr. 3 up). 27.50 (978-0-7910-5348-5(2) , Chelsea Hse.) Facts On File, Inc.

Jones, Lynda. Great Black Heroes: Five Brilliant Scientists. Garnett, Ron, illus. 2000. (Great Black Heroes Ser.). 48p. (J). (gr. 2-4). pap. 3.99 (978-0-590-48031-4(6)) Scholastic, Inc.

Krapp, Kristine, ed. Notable Black American Scientists. 1998. (Illus.). xxvi, 349p. (J). 157.00 (978-0-7876-2789-8(5) , GML00502-112329) Thomson Gale.

Litwin, Laura Baskes. Benjamin Banneker: Astronomer & Mathematician. 1999. (African-American Biographies Ser.). (Illus.). 112p. (YA). (gr. 6-12). lib. bdg. 26.60 (978-0-7660-1208-0(5)) Enslow Pubs., Inc.

Pinkney, Andrea Davis. Dear Benjamin Banneker. Pinkney, Brian, illus. 1998. 32p. (J). (gr. 1-5). pap. 7.00 (978-0-15-201892-4(1) , Harcourt Paperbacks) Harcourt Children's Bks.

—Dear Benjamin Banneker. 1998. 12.80 (978-0-606-13324-1(0)) Tandem Library Bks.

Wadsworth, Ginger. Benjamin Banneker: Pioneering Scientist. Orback, Craig, illus. 2003. (On My Own Biographies Ser.). 48p. (J). (gr. 2-5). 25.26 (978-0-87614-916-4(6)) Lerner Publishing Group.

Webster, Raymond B. African-American Firsts in Science & Technology. 1999. (Illus.). 462p. (J). 105.00 (978-0-7876-3876-4(5) , GML00502-113669, Gale Research International, Ltd.) Thomson Gale.

Welch, Catherine A. Benjamin Banneker. 2008. (History Maker Biographies Ser.). (J). lib. bdg. 26.60 (***978-0-8225-7167-4(6)*** , Lerner Pubns.) Lerner Publishing Group.

AFRICAN AMERICAN SOLDIERS

Bodie, Idella. Brave Black Patriots. 2002. (Illus.). 78p. (J). (978-0-87844-159-4(X)) Sandlapper Publishing Co., Inc.

Bruning, John Robert, Jr. Elusive Glory: African-American Heroes of World War II. 2001. (Illus.). 144p. (J). (gr. 6-12). pap. 19.95 (978-1-888105-48-3(8)) Avisson Pr., Inc.

Buffalo Soldiers & the Western Frontier Vol. 2: Individual Title Six-Packs. (On Deck Ser.: Vol. 2). 24p. (gr. 4-5). 35.00 (978-0-7578-5805-5(8)) Rigby Education.

Clinton, Catherine. Hold the Flag High. Evans, Shane W., illus. 2005. 32p. (J). (ps-2). 15.99 (978-0-06-050428-1(5) , Amistad) HarperCollins Pubs.

DeAngelis, Gina. The Massachusetts 54th: African American Soldiers of the Union. 2002. (Let Freedom Ring Ser.). (Illus.). 48p. (J). (gr. 3-4). lib. bdg. 22.60 (978-0-7368-1343-3(8) , Bridgestone Bks.) Capstone Pr., Inc.

Drama of African-American History, 5 bks., Set. Incl. Africa : A Look Back. Haskins, James & Benson, Kathleen. lib. bdg. 34.21 (978-0-7614-2148-1(3)); Civil War. Jordan, Anne Devereaux & Schomp, Virginia. lib. bdg. 34.21 (978-0-7614-2179-5(3)); Reconstruction ERA. Stroud, Bettye & Schomp, Virginia. lib. bdg. 34.21 (978-0-7614-2181-8(5)); Slave Trade & the Middle Passage. Sharp, S. Pearl & Schomp, Virginia. lib. bdg. 34.21 (978-0-7614-2176-4(9)); Slavery & Resistance. Jordan, Anne Devereaux & Schomp, Virginia. lib. bdg. 34.21 (978-0-7614-2178-8(5)); (Illus.). 80p. (J). 2006. 2007. Set lib. bdg. 171.07 (***978-0-7614-2174-0(2)*** , Benchmark Bks.) Cavendish, Marshall Corp.

Flanagan, Alice K. The Buffalo Soldiers. 2004. (We the People Ser.). (Illus.). 48p. (J). 22.60 (978-0-7565-0833-3(9)) Compass Point Bks.

Ford, Carin T. African-American Soldiers in the Civil War: Fighting for Freedom. 2004. (Civil War Library Ser.). (Illus.). 48p. (J). lib. bdg. 23.93 (978-0-7660-2254-6(4)) Enslow Pubs., Inc.

Homan, Lynn M. & Reilly, Thomas. Tuskegee Airmen: American Heroes. Shepherd, Rosalie M., illus. 2002. 96p. (J). 14.95 (978-1-56554-994-4(5)) Pelican Publishing Co., Inc.

—The Tuskegee Airmen Story. Shepherd, Rosalie M., illus. 2002. 32p. (J). 15.95 (978-1-58980-005-2(2)) Pelican Publishing Co., Inc.

Lewis, Noah & Graham, Loretta. Edward Ned Hector. 2005. (ENG., Illus.). 36p. (J). per. 19.99 (***978-1-4208-6817-3(9)***) AuthorHouse.

Massachusetts 54th: African American Soldiers of the Union. (Civil War Ser.). 48p. (YA). 7.95 (978-0-7368-4518-2(6)) Capstone Pr., Inc.

Nell, William C. Black Patriots of the American Revolution, with Sketches of Several Distinguished Black Persons to Which Is Added a Brief Survey of the Condition & Prospects of Black Americans. 2006. (Illus.). 396p. (YA). cd-rom (978-1-892824-87-5(6)) AFCHRON.

Raabe, Emily. Buffalo Soldiers & the Western Frontier. 2003. (Reading Power Ser.). (Illus.). 24p. (J). lib. bdg. 17.25 (978-0-8239-6495-6(7) , PowerKids Pr.) Rosen Publishing Group, Inc., The.

AFRICAN AMERICAN SOLDIERS—FICTION

Bohjalian, Chris. The Buffalo Soldier: A Novel. 2003. (gr. 7-12). lib. bdg. 23.40 (978-0-613-70910-1(1)) Tandem Library Bks.

Garland, Sherry. The Buffalo Soldier. Himler, Ronald, illus. 2006. 32p. (J). (gr. 3-6). 15.95 (978-1-58980-391-6(4)) Pelican Publishing Co., Inc.

AFRICAN AMERICAN SONGS

see African Americans—Music

AFRICAN AMERICAN SPIRITUALS

see Spirituals (Songs)

AFRICAN AMERICANS

Here are entered works on citizens of the United States of black African descent. Works on blacks outside the United States are entered under Blacks.

African-American Achievers. (Illus.). (gr. 6-12). lib. bdg. 69.65 (978-0-7910-8444-1(2)); 2005. 104 - 144p. pap. 270.00 (978-0-7910-7720-7(9)) Facts On File, Inc. (Chelsea Hse.).

African American & American Indian Relations. 2000. (My Ancestors—My Heroes Ser.: Vol. 50). (J). (gr. 3-4). (978-1-893091-49-8(X)) Parker Publishing Co.

African-American Contributions. 2005. (Illus.). 112p. (gr. 6-12). pap. 180.00 (978-0-7910-7271-4(1) , Chelsea Hse.) Facts On File, Inc.

African-Americans in Oil Drilling. 2000. (My Ancestors—My Heroes Ser.: Vol. 30). (J). (gr. 3-4). (978-1-893091-29-0(5)) Parker Publishing Co.

African-Americans in Waste Management Treatment. 2000. (My Ancestors—My Heroes Ser.: Vol. 31). (J). (gr. 3-4). (978-1-893091-30-6(9)) Parker Publishing Co.

Allen, Thomas B. Harriet Tubman, Secret Agent: How Daring Slaves & Free Blacks Spied for the Union During the Civil War. Bauer, Carla, illus. 2006. (National Geographic Ser.). 192p. (J). (gr. 5-8). 16.95 (978-0-7922-7889-4(5)); 25.90 (978-0-7922-7890-0(9)) National Geographic Society. (National Geographic Children's Bks.).

Alonzo, Tamara. Just Imagine... a World Without the Contributions of Black People! 1999. (Illus.). 20p. (J). (gr. 3-8). pap. 7.97 (978-0-9673627-0-0(9)) Good Stuff Desktop Publishing.

Baker, Henry E. American Black Inventors Pictorials Drawings & Illustrations Volume I. 2007. (Illus.). 369p. (YA). lib. bdg. (978-1-892824-30-1(2) , AFCHRON.COM) AFCHRON.

Banting, Erinn. Halle Berry. 2005. (Great African American Women for Kids Ser.). (Illus.). 24p. (J). (ps-7). pap. 6.95 (978-1-59036-339-3(6)); lib. bdg. 26.00 (978-1-59036-333-1(7)) Weigl Pubs., Inc.

Bell, Nasherrall, compiled by. African American Leaders. 2002. (Illus.). 32p. 6.95 (978-0-9727833-6-1(9)) Really Big Coloring Bks., Inc.

Bloom, Harold. Gwendolyn Brooks. 2000. (Bloom's Modern Critical Views Ser.). 200p. (J). 45.00 (978-0-7910-5656-1(2) , Chelsea Hse.) Facts On File, Inc.

Bloom, Harold, ed. Bloom's Literary Criticism 20th Anniversary Collection. (Illus.). (gr. 9-13). pap. (978-0-7910-8394-9(2) , Chelsea Hse.) Facts On File, Inc.

Bloom's Literary Criticism. 20th anniv. ed. Incl. Dramatists & Drama. Bloom, Harold, ed. 200p. 45.00 (978-0-7910-8226-3(1) , Checkmark Bks.); Epic. 266p. (YA). 2004. bds. 45.00 (978-0-7910-8229-4(6) , Chelsea Hse.); Essayists & Prophets. Bloom, Harold, ed. 200p. 2004. 45.00 (978-0-7910-8523-3(6) , Chelsea Hse.); Novelists & Novels. Bloom, Harold, ed. 200p. 45.00 (978-0-7910-8227-0(X) , Checkmark Bks.); Poets & Poems. 488p. (YA). 2004. bds. 45.00 (978-0-7910-8225-6(3) , Chelsea Hse.); Short Story Writers & Short Stories. Bloom, Harold. 189p. (YA). 2004. bds. 45.00 (978-0-7910-8228-7(8) , Chelsea Hse.); (gr. 9-14). (Illus.). 200-300p. 2005. 270.00 (978-0-7910-8480-9(9) , Chelsea Hse.) Facts On File, Inc.

Bolden, Tonya. Tell All the Children Our Story: Memories & Mementos of Being Young & Black in America. 2002. (Illus.). 128p. (J). (gr. 5-17). 24.95 (978-0-8109-4496-1(0)) Abrams, Harry N. , Inc.

Bowen, Richard. The African Americans. 2002. (Welcome to America Ser.). (Illus.). 64p. (YA). (gr. 5 up). lib. bdg. (978-1-59084-116-7(6)) Mason Crest Pubs.

Braun, Eric. Booker T. Washington: Great American Educator. Martin, Cynthia, illus. 2005. (Graphic Library). 32p. (J). (gr. 3-7). lib. bdg. 25.26 (978-0-7368-4630-1(1)) Capstone Pr., Inc.

Brooks, Philip. The Tuskegee Airmen. 2004. (Illus.). 48p. (J). (gr. 4 up). lib. bdg. 22.60 (978-0-7565-0683-4(2)) Compass Point Bks.

Brown, Margery W. Afro-Bets Book of Shapes. Blair, Culverson & Simpson, Howard, illus. 2nd ed. 2004. (Afro-Bets Ser.). 24p. (J). (ps-1). pap. 3.95 (978-0-940975-58-3(0) , Sankofa Bks.) Just Us Bks., Inc.

—Book of Colors: Meet the Color Family. Blair, Culverson & Simpson, Howard, illus. 2nd ed. 2004. (Afro-Bets Ser.). 24p. (J). (ps-1). pap. 3.95 (978-0-940975-57-6(2) , Sankofa Bks.) Just Us Bks., Inc.

Burgan, Michael. African Americans. 2003. (Spirit of America). (Illus.). 32p. (J). (gr. 2-6). 27.07 (978-1-59296-012-5(X)) Child's World, Inc.

Chandler, Alton. A Salute to African American in Medicine: Learning. Chapman, L., ed. Still, Wayne A., illus. 24p. (Orig.). (J). (gr. 3-8). pap. 1.75 (978-1-877804-17-5(7)) Chandler/White Publishing Co.

Cooper, Ilene. Up Close: Oprah Winfrey: Oprah Winfrey. 2008. (Up Close Ser.). 208p. (J). (gr. 6). pap. 6.99 (***978-0-14-241045-5(4)*** , Puffin) Penguin Group (USA) Inc.

Crowe, Chris. Getting Away with Murder: The True Story of the Emmett till Case. 2003. (Illus.). 128p. (J). (gr. 5). 18.99 (978-0-8037-2804-2(2) , Dial) Penguin Group (USA) Inc.

Downing, David. Martin Luther King, Jr. 2002. (Leading Lives Ser.). 64p. (J). (gr. 5-7). pap. 8.95 (978-1-4034-0123-6(3) , 91614) Heinemann Library.

Edward, Davis. I'm Black What's Wrong. 2001. 36p. (J). per. 12.95 (978-0-7414-0625-5(X)) Infinity Publishing.

Famous Black Americans. 24p. (gr. k-1). 5.99 (978-0-7682-0511-4(5) , FS8500); (gr. 1-2). 5.99 (978-0-7682-0510-7(7) , FS8499); (gr. 2-3). 5.99 (978-0-7682-0509-1(3) , FS8498); (gr. 3-4). 5.99 (978-0-7682-0515-2(8) , FS8615) Schaffer, Frank Pubns.

Garrison, Mary. Slaves Who Dared: The Stories of Ten African-American Heroes. 2002. (Illus.). 150p. (J). (gr. 4-6). lib. bdg. 19.95 (978-1-57249-272-1(4) , White Mane Kids) White Mane Publishing Co., Inc.

Glencoe McGraw-Hill Staff. Glencoe African American Literature. 2002. 388p. 31.96 (978-0-07-822925-1(1) , 9780078229251) Glencoe/McGraw-Hill.

Green, Jen. The Africans: We Came to North America. 2006. (Illus.). 32p. (J). (gr. 4-8). reprint ed. pap. 19.00 (978-0-7567-9901-4(5)) DIANE Publishing Co.

Greenfield, Eloise. How They Got Over: African Americans & the Call of the Sea. Date not set. 80p. (J). pap. 6.99 (978-0-06-443693-9(4)) HarperCollins Pubs.

Hansen-Krening, Nancy, et al, eds. Kaleidoscope: A Multicultural Booklist for Grades K-8. 4th ed. 2003. (NCTE Bibliography Ser.). (Illus.). 118p. (J). pap. 30.95 (978-0-8141-2539-7(5) , 25395) National Council of Teachers of English.

Harcourt School Publishers Staff. Black Cowboys & Wild Horses Level D: Readers. 2001. (Collections Ser.). (Illus.). pap. 12.10 (978-0-15-314379-3(7)) Harcourt Schl. Pubs.

Hasan, Rashad, ed. African-American Chronicle Quarterly Magazine. 2005. (ENG.). (YA). lib. bdg. 120.00 (978-1-892824-28-8(0)) AFCHRON.

Haskins, James. African American Assortment. 1999. 540.00 (978-0-688-17361-6(6)) HarperCollins Pubs.

Hill, Laban Carrick. Harlem Stomp! A Cultural History of the Harlem Renaissance. Myers, Christopher, illus. 2004. 160p. (J). (gr. 7-17). 18.99 (978-0-316-81411-9(3)) Little Brown & Co.

Horton, David, 2nd. Negro Intellect: A Guide for Young Black Males. 2004. 114p. (YA). per. 11.95 (978-0-9763583-0-5(1) , 395) Horton, David.

Hudak, Heather C. Oprah Winfrey. 2005. (Great African American Women for Kids Ser.). (Illus.). 24p. (J). (ps-7). pap. 6.95 (978-1-59036-341-6(8)); lib. bdg. 26.00 (978-1-59036-335-5(3)) Weigl Pubs., Inc.

Hudson, Cheryl Willis. Afro-Bets 1 2 3 Book. rev. ed. 2000. (Afro-Bets Ser.). (Illus.). 24p. (J). (ps-3). pap. 3.95 (978-0-940975-98-9(X)) Just Us Bks., Inc.

—Afro-Bets A, B, C Book. Hudson, Cheryl Willis, illus. 2002. (Afro-Bets Ser.). (Illus.). 24p. (J). (ps-1). pap. 3.50 (978-0-439-42917-7(X) , Cartwheel Bks.) Scholastic, Inc.

—Afro-Bets A B C Book. rev. ed. 1999. (Illus.). 24p. (J). (ps-1). pap. 3.95 (978-0-940975-88-0(2)) Just Us Bks., Inc.

Johnson, et al. Love Through the Generations: The Inspirational Journey of an African-American Family for Children of All Ages. Minter, Amani, illus. Minter, Kendall, photos by. 2001. 104p. pap. 8.95 (978-0-9655064-8-9(7)) Amber Bks.

Johnson, Angela. In Daddy's Arms, I Am Tall. ed. 2004. (Illus.). (J). (gr. k-3). spiral bd. (978-0-616-03094-3(0)) Canadian National Institute for the Blind/Institut National Canadien pour les Aveugles.

Johnson, Angela & Adedjouma, Davida, contrib. by. In Daddy's Arms, I Am Tall. 2002. (Illus.). (J). (ps). 25.95 incl. audio (978-0-87499-895-5(6)); pap., tchr.'s planning gde. ed. 37.95 incl. audio (978-0-87499-896-2(4)); pap. 16.95 incl. audio (978-0-87499-894-8(8)) Live Oak Media.

Jones, Brenn. Learning about Achievement from the Life of Maya Angelou. 2002. (Character Building Book Ser.). (Illus.). 24p. (J). (gr. 3). lib. bdg. 18.75 (978-0-8239-5780-4(2) , PowerKids Pr.) Rosen Publishing Group, Inc., The.

Kallen, Stuart A. A Travel Guide to Harlem Renaissance. 2003. (J). 29.95 (978-1-59018-358-8(4) , Lucent Bks.) Thomson Gale.

King, Wilma. Children of the Emancipation. 2005. (Picture the American Past Ser.). (Illus.). 48p. (gr. 2-5). 22.60 (978-1-57505-396-7(9)) Lerner Publishing Group.

Koopmans, Andy. The Harlem Renaissance. 2005. (Lucent Library of Black History). (Illus.). 112p. (YA). (gr. 7-10). lib. bdg. 32.45 (978-1-59018-702-9(4) , Lucent Bks.) Thomson Gale.

Krull, Kathleen. Wilma Sin Limites. 2000. Tr. of Wilma Unlimited. (SPA.). (gr. 3-6). lib. bdg. 14.15 (978-0-613-27592-7(6)) Tandem Library Bks.

Lane, Mitchell. Contemporary African-American Collection, 14 vols., Set. 2003. (Illus.). (J). (gr. 3-8). lib. bdg. 223.30 (978-1-58415-189-0(7)) Mitchell Lane Pubs., Inc.

Laslo, Cynthia, contrib. by. Lauryn Hill. 2000. (J). (978-0-531-12110-8(0) , Orchard Bks.) Scholastic, Inc.

Macmillan General Reference Staff. African-American Culture & History: A Student's Guide, 4 vols., Set. Salzman, Jack, ed. 2000. (Illus.). xix, 1082p. (J). stu. ed. 460.00 (978-0-02-865531-4(1) , GML00502-171695, Macmillan Reference USA) Thomson Gale.

Magee, Kanika A. M. Today I Got Saved, 1 book. Thomas, Sonya, illus. 2003. 20p. (J). 10.00 net. (978-0-9748834-0-3(9)) Ebenezer A.M.E. Church.

Marbury, Ja'Nitta. All Mixed Up. Marbury, Ja'Nitta, illus. 2003. 22p. (J). pap. 22.50 (978-0-9718307-3-8(8)) Shades of Me Publishing.

Marsh, Carole. Color Purple & All That Jazz! African American Achievements in the Arts. 2003. (gr. 5-8). lib. bdg. 22.20 (978-0-613-73033-4(X)) Tandem Library Bks.

—Quilt Our African American. 2002. 36p. (gr. 3-8). pap. 7.95 (978-0-635-01577-8(3)) Gallopade International.

Mayer, Cassie. Harriet Tubman. 2007. (J). ***978-1-4034-9973-8(X)**); pap. (***978-1-4034-9982-0(9)**) Heinemann Library.

McGill, Alice. Here We Go Round. Evans, Shane W., illus. 2002. 128p. (J). (gr. 3-5). 15.00 (978-0-618-16064-8(7)) Houghton Mifflin Co. Trade & Reference Div.

McLendon, Jacquelyn Y. Phillis Wheatley: A Revolutionary Poet. 2005. (Library of American Lives & Times). (Illus.). 112p. (YA). (gr. 4-8). lib. bdg. 31.95 (978-0-8239-5750-7(0)) Rosen Publishing Group, Inc., The.

Metcalf, Doris H. Portraits of African American Achievers. 2001. 144p. tchr. ed. 14.99 (978-0-86653-815-2(1) , GA1507, Milestone) Schaffer, Frank Pubns.

Miller, Calvin Craig. No Easy Answers: Bayard Rustin & the Civil Rights Movement. 2005. (Civil Rights Leaders Ser.). (Illus.). 160p. (J). (gr. 6-12). 26.95 (978-1-931798-43-3(5)) Reynolds, Morgan Inc.

Monroe, Judy. George Washington Carver. 2005. (Fact Finders Ser.). (Illus.). 32p. (J). (978-0-7368-4345-4(0)) Capstone Pr., Inc.

Nell, William C. Black Patriots of the American Revolution, with Sketches of Several Distinguished Black Persons to Which Is Added a Brief Survey of the Condition & Prospects of Black Americans. 2006. (Illus.). 396p. (YA). cd-rom (978-1-892824-87-5(6)) AFCHRON.

Nelson, Kadir. Golden Age of the Negro League. Nelson, Kadir, illus. 2008. (Illus.). 96p. 18.99 (978-0-7868-0832-8(2)) Disney Pr.

Nobisso, Josephine & Nobisso, Joi. John Blair & the Great Hinckley Fire. Rose, Ted, illus. 2000. 32p. (J). (gr. 4-6). tchr. ed. 16.00 (978-0-618-01560-3(4)) Houghton Mifflin Co. Trade & Reference Div.

Ovations. Incl. Barry Bonds. Goodman, Michael E. lib. bdg. 21.30 (978-0-88682-694-9(2)); Grant Hill. Goodman, Michael E. lib. bdg. (978-0-88682-831-8(7)); Hillary Rodham Clinton. Loewen, Nancy. lib. bdg. (978-0-88682-636-9(5)); Jeff Gordon. Bach, Julie S. pap. (978-0-88682-939-1(9)); Monica Seles. Goodman, Michael E. lib. bdg. 21.30 (978-0-88682-699-4(3)); Shaquille O'Neal. Goodman, Michael E. lib. bdg. (978-0-88682-633-8(0)); Spike Lee. Chapman, Ferguson. lib. bdg. (978-0-88682-697-0(7)); Whoopi Goldberg. DeBoer, Andy. 21.30 (978-0-88682-696-3(9)); (Illus.). 32p. (YA). (gr. 4-7). 1998. 59.80 (978-0-88682-693-2(4) , Creative Education) Creative Co., The.

Rau, Dana Meachen. Climb up a Mountain. 2000. (Adventurers Ser.). (Illus.). 24p. (J). (gr. k-2). lib. bdg. 19.27 (978-1-57103-317-8(3)) Rourke Publishing, LLC.

Reef, Catherine. This Our Dark Country: The American Settlers of Liberia. 2002. (Illus.). 144p. (J). (gr. 5-9). tchr. ed. 17.00 (978-0-618-14785-4(3) , Clarion Bks.) Houghton Mifflin Co. Trade & Reference Div.

The River Is My Life: Six-Pack. (Greetings Ser.: Vol. 3). (gr. 3-5). 31.00 (978-0-7635-1823-3(9)) Rigby Education.

Ross, Kathy. Crafts That Celebrate Black History. Stow, Jenny, illus. 2002. 48p. (J). (ps-3). pap. 8.95 (978-0-7613-1681-7(7) , First Avenue Editions) Lerner Publishing Group.

Rossi, Ann. Freedom Struggle: The Anti-Slavery Movement 1830-1865. 2005. (Crossroads America Ser.). (Illus.). 40p. (gr. 5-9). (J). 12.95 (978-0-7922-7828-3(3)); 21.90 (978-0-7922-8061-3(X)) National Geographic Society. (National Geographic Children's Bks.).

Sanders, Nancy I. D Is for Drinking Gourd: An African American Alphabet. Lewis, Earl B, illus. 2007. (General Alphabet Ser.). 40p. (J). (gr. 1-7). 17.95 (***978-1-58536-293-6(X)**) Sleeping Bear Pr.

Schaefer, Lola M. Kwanzaa. Saunders-Smith, Gail, ed. 2000. (Holidays & Celebrations Ser.). (Illus.). 24p. (J). (gr. k-1). lib. bdg. 15.93 (978-0-7368-0663-3(6) , Pebble Bks.) Capstone Pr., Inc.

Schnidman, Ellen. African American Answer Book, 6 bks. 1999. (Illus.). 64p. (J). (gr. 5-12). pap. 29.70 (978-0-7910-3765-2(7) , Chelsea Hse.) Facts On File, Inc.

Shone, Rob & Ganeri, Anita. Harriet Tubman: The Life of an African-American Abolitionist. 2005. (Graphic Nonfiction Ser.). (Illus.). 48p. (J). (gr. 4-6). lib. bdg. 26.50 (978-1-4042-0245-0(5)) Rosen Publishing Group, Inc., The.

Steptoe, Javaka. Sweet, Sweet Baby! Fabric Petals with Fun Sounds & a Mylar Mirror! Steptoe, Javaka, illus. 2005. (Illus.). 4p. (J). bds. 12.95 (978-0-439-65086-1(0) , Cartwheel Bks.) Scholastic, Inc.

Taylor-Butler, Christine. Thurgood Marshall. 2006. 32p. (YA). (gr. 1-2). pap. 4.95 (978-0-516-27099-9(0) , Children's Pr.) Scholastic Library Publishing.

Toussaint, Pamela. Great Books for African Americans. 1999. (J). (978-0-606-17070-3(7)) Tandem Library Bks.

Ueda, Reed & Stotsky, Sandra, eds. African-American Answer Book. 1999. (Ethnic Answer Book Ser.). (Illus.). 136p. (YA). (gr. 5 up). pap. 9.95 (978-0-7910-4913-6(2)); lib. bdg. 19.75 (978-0-7910-4912-9(4)) Facts On File, Inc. (Chelsea Hse.).

Walbridge, Mike. African-American Heroes of the Civil War. 2000. 144p. (gr. 6-12). tchr. ed. 21.99 (978-0-8251-4145-4(1) , 0-41451) Walch Publishing.

Wheeler, Jill C. Thurgood Marshall. 2003. (Breaking Barriers Ser.). (Illus.). 64p. (J). (gr. 3-8). lib. bdg. 25.65 (978-1-57765-907-5(4)) ABDO Publishing Co.

AFRICAN AMERICANS—ALABAMA

Miller, Jake. The March from Selma to Montgomery: African Americans Demand the Vote. 2004. (Library of the Civil Rights Movement Ser.). (Illus.). 24p. (J). lib. bdg. 19.95 (978-0-8239-6254-9(7) , PowerKids Pr.) Rosen Publishing Group, Inc., The.

Pingry, Patricia A. The Story of Rosa Parks. Walker, Steven, illus. 2007. 24p. (J). (ps-k). bds. 6.99 (***978-0-8249-6687-4(2)** , Candy Cane Pr.) Ideals Pubns.

Whiting, Jim. Rosa Parks. 2007. (What's So Great About... ? Ser.). (J). lib. bdg. 25.70 (***978-1-58415-573-7(6)**) Mitchell Lane Pubs., Inc.

AFRICAN AMERICANS—ALABAMA—MONTGOMERY

Banting, Erinn. Rosa Parks. 2005. (Great African American Women for Kids Ser.). (Illus.). 24p. (J). (ps-7). pap. 6.95 (978-1-59036-342-3(6)); lib. bdg. 26.00 (978-1-59036-336-2(1)) Weigl Pubs., Inc.

Donovan, Sandy. Rosa Parks. 2003. (Illus.). 64p. (J). (gr. 4-7). pap. 9.50 (978-1-4109-0320-4(6)); lib. bdg. 28.56 (978-0-7398-7032-7(7)) Raintree.

Dubois, Muriel L. Rosa Parks. 2003. (Photo-Illustrated Biographies Ser.). (Illus.). 24p. (J). (gr. 2-3). lib. bdg. 18.60 (978-0-7368-1607-6(0) , Bridgestone Bks.) Capstone Pr., Inc.

Dubowski, Cathy East. Rosa Parks: Don't Give In! 2005. (Defining Moments Ser.). (Illus.). 32p. (J). lib. bdg. 25.27 (978-1-59716-078-0(4)) Bearport Publishing Co., Inc.

Edwards, Pamela Duncan. The Bus Ride That Changed History: The Story of Rosa Parks. Shanahan, Danny, illus. 2005. 32p. (J). (gr. k-3). 16.00 (978-0-618-44911-8(6)) Houghton Mifflin Co. Trade & Reference Div.

Fine, Edith Hope. Rosa Parks: Meet a Civil Rights Hero. 2004. (Meeting Famous People Ser.). (Illus.). 32p. (J). lib. bdg. 22.60 (978-0-7660-2099-3(1)) Enslow Pubs., Inc.

Giovanni, Nikki. Rosa. Collier, Bryan, illus. rev. ed. 2005. 40p. (J). (gr. 4-7). 16.95 (978-0-8050-7106-1(7) , Holt, Henry & Co. Bks. For Young Readers) Holt, Henry & Co.

Greenfield, Eloise. Rosa Parks. Ashby, Gil, illus. 2002. 12.62 (978-0-7587-0755-0(X)) Book Wholesalers, Inc.

Hull, Mary E. Rosa Parks: Civil Rights Leader. (Black Americans of Achievement Ser.). (Illus.). 112p. (J). (gr. 6-12). 2005. pap. 13.25 (978-0-7910-8338-3(1)); 2004. 30.00 (978-0-7910-8164-8(8)) Facts On File, Inc. (Chelsea Hse.).

Kishel, Ann-Marie. Rosa Parks: A Life of Courage. 2006. (Pull Ahead Books). (Illus.). 32p. (J). 22.60 (978-0-8225-3478-5(9) , Lerner Pubns.) Lerner Publishing Group.

—Rosa Parks: Una Vida de Valentía. 2006. (Libros para Avanzar Ser.). (ENG & SPA.). 32p. (J). lib. bdg. 22.60 (978-0-8225-6239-9(1)) Lerner Publishing Group.

Kudlinski, Kathleen V. Rosa Parks. Henderson, Meryl, illus. 2001. (Childhood of Famous Americans Ser.). 224p. (gr. 3-7). mass mkt. 5.99 (978-0-689-83925-2(1) , Aladdin) Simon & Schuster Children's Publishing.

Mara, Wil. Rosa Parks. (Rookie Biographies Ser.). (Illus.). (J). 2004. 31p. (gr. 1-2). pap. 4.95 (978-0-516-27916-9(5)); 2003. 32p. 19.50 (978-0-516-25876-8(1)) Scholastic Library Publishing. (Children's Pr.).

McLeese, Don. Rosa Parks. 2002. (Rourke Discovery Library). (Illus.). 24p. (J). lib. bdg. 20.64 (978-1-58952-287-9(7)) Rourke Publishing, LLC.

Morris, Roz. Rosa Parks: Mother of the Civil Rights Movement. 2003. (Alabama Roots Biography Ser.). (Illus.). 109p. (J). (978-1-878561-57-2(X)) Seacoast Publishing, Inc.

Nobleman, Marc Tyler. Rosa Parks. 2002. (Trailblazers of the Modern World Ser.). (Illus.). 48p. (J). (gr. 5 up). pap. 14.95 (978-0-8368-5231-8(1)); lib. bdg. 30.00 (978-0-8368-5071-0(8)) Stevens, Gareth Inc. (World Almanac Library).

—Rosa Parks. 2002. (gr. 3-6). lib. bdg. 19.90 (978-0-613-76804-7(3)) Tandem Library Bks.

Parks, Rosa. I Am Rosa Parks. 2000. (gr. k-3). lib. bdg. 11.80 (978-0-613-22996-8(7)); (Illus.). (J). 10.79 (978-0-606-18410-6(4)) Tandem Library Bks.

Parks, Rosa & Haskins, Jim. I Am Rosa Parks. Clay, Wil, illus. 1999. (Easy-to-Read Ser.). 48p. (J). (gr. 1-3). pap. 3.99 (978-0-14-130710-7(2) , Puffin) Penguin Group (USA) Inc.

Rinaldo, Denise. Rosa Parks: With a Discussion of Courage. 2003. (Values in Action Ser.). (J). (978-1-59203-061-3(0)) Learning Challenge, Inc.

Ringgold, Faith. If a Bus Could Talk: The Story of Rosa Parks. Ringgold, Faith, illus. (Illus.). 32p. (J). 2003. (gr. k-4). pap. 7.99 (978-0-689-85676-1(8) , Aladdin); 1999. (gr. 1-4). 16.00 (978-0-689-81892-9(0)) Simon & Schuster Children's Publishing.

—If a Bus Could Talk: The Story of Rosa Parks. 2003. (gr. k-3). lib. bdg. 15.30 (978-0-613-61633-1(2)) Tandem Library Bks.

Schaefer, Lola M. Rosa Parks. Saunders-Smith, Gail, ed. 2002. (First Biographies Ser.). (Illus.). 24p. (J). (gr. k-1). lib. bdg. 15.93 (978-0-7368-1176-7(1) , Pebble Bks.) Capstone Pr., Inc.

Schraff, Anne E. Rosa Parks: Tired of Giving In. 2005. (African-American Biography Library). (Illus.). 128p. (J). (gr. 6-12). lib. bdg. 31.93 (978-0-7660-2463-2(6)) Enslow Pubs., Inc.

Shores, Erika L. Rosa Parks: Civil Rights Poineer. 2005. (Fact Finders Ser.). (Illus.). 32p. (J). (ps-7). lib. bdg. 22.60 (978-0-7368-3746-0(9)) Capstone Pr., Inc.

Steele, Phillip. Rosa Parks & Her Protest for Civil Rights. 2002. (Dates with History Ser.). (Illus.). 31p. (J). lib. bdg. 24.25 (978-1-58340-215-3(2)) Smart Apple Media.

Weidt, Maryann N. Rosa Parks. 2003. (History Maker Bios Ser.). (Illus.). 47p. (J). 26.60 (978-0-8225-4673-3(6) , Lerner Pubns.) Lerner Publishing Group.

Wheeler, Jill C. Rosa Parks, Set II. 2003. (Breaking Barriers Ser.). (Illus.). 64p. (J). (gr. 3-8). lib. bdg. 25.65 (978-1-57765-640-1(7)) ABDO Publishing Co.

Wilson, Cammie. Rosa Parks: From the Back of the Bus to the Front of a Movement. 2001. (Scholastic Biography Ser.). (Illus.). 88p. (J). (gr. 3-7). pap. 4.50 (978-0-439-16330-9(7)) Scholastic, Inc.

AFRICAN AMERICANS—BIOGRAPHY

Abnett, Dan. Harriet Tubman & the Underground Railroad. 2007. (Jr. Graphic Biographies Ser.). (Illus.). 24p. (J). (978-1-4042-2336-3(3)); pap. (978-1-4042-2146-8(8)); (gr. 2-6). lib. bdg. 21.25 (978-1-4042-3393-5(8)) Rosen Publishing Group, Inc., The. (PowerKids Pr.).

Abraham, Philip. Jackie Robinson. 2002. (Wel-Real People Ser.). (Illus.). 24p. (J). (ps-2). 18.00 (978-0-516-23950-7(3)); pap. 4.95 (978-0-516-23605-6(9)) Scholastic Library Publishing. (Children's Pr.).

—Jackie Robinson. 2002. (gr. k-3). lib. bdg. 12.95 (978-0-613-58845-4(2)) Tandem Library Bks.

Acker, Kerry. Nina Simone. (Women in the Arts Ser.). (Illus.). 112p. 2004. pap. 30.00 (978-0-7910-7952-2(X)); 2003. (gr. 6-12). 30.00 (978-0-7910-7456-5(0)) Facts On File, Inc. (Chelsea Hse.).

Adler, David A. Dr. Martin Luther King, Jr. Level 2: A House House Reader. Bootman, Colin, illus. 2001. (Reader Ser.). 48p. (J). (gr. k-3). tchr. ed. 15.95 (978-0-8234-1572-4(4)) Holiday Hse., Inc.

—Heroes for Civil Rights. Farnsworth, Bill, illus. 2007. 32p. (J). (gr. 1-5). 16.95 (***978-0-8234-2008-7(6)**) Holiday Hse., Inc.

—A Picture Book of Frederick Douglass. Byrd, Samuel, illus. unabr. ed. 2005. (Picture Book Readalongs Ser.). (J). (gr. k-4). 25.95 incl. audio (978-1-59519-373-5(1)); pap. 28.95 incl. audio compact disk (978-1-59519-377-3(4)); Set. pap. 37.95 incl. audio (978-1-59519-374-2(X)); Set. pap. 39.95 incl. audio compact disk (978-1-59519-378-0(2)) Live Oak Media.

—A Picture Book of Rosa Parks. Casilla, Robert, illus. 2004. 28.95 incl. audio compact disk (978-1-59112-762-8(9)) Live Oak Media.

Adler, David A. & Berkower, Amy. Joe Louis: America's Fighter. Widener, Terry, illus. 2005. 32p. (J). (gr. 2-6). 16.00 (978-0-15-216480-5(4)) Harcourt Children's Bks.

African-American Architects. 2000. (My Ancestors—My Heroes Ser.: Vol. 40). (J). (gr. 3-4). (978-1-893091-39-9(2)) Parker Publishing Co.

African American Astronauts. 2000. (My Ancestors—My Heroes Ser.: Vol. 19). (J). (gr. 3-4). (978-1-893091-18-4(X)) Parker Publishing Co.

African-American Biographies, 8 vols. 2003. (Illus.). pap. 56.30 (978-1-4109-0428-7(8)) Raintree.

African American Biographies. 2003. (Illus.). pap. 50.00 (978-1-4109-0144-6(0)) Raintree.

African-American Biographies, 43 bks., Set. (Illus.). (YA). (gr. 6-12). lib. bdg. 900.85 (978-0-89490-775-3(1)) Enslow Pubs., Inc.

African-American Biographies 6-Pack (96 Books), Set. 2003. (Illus.). (J). pap. 773.30 (978-1-4109-1245-9(0)) Raintree.

African-American Biographies Series, Set. 2003. (Illus.). pap. 128.90 (978-1-4109-0429-4(6)); Set. 228.48 (978-0-7398-6876-8(4)) Raintree.

African-American Biographies Set. 2003. (Illus.). (YA). 456.96 (978-1-4109-0706-6(6)) Raintree.

African American Business Persons. 2000. (My Ancestors—My Heroes Ser.: Vol. 16). (J). (gr. 3-4). (978-1-893091-15-3(5)) Parker Publishing Co.

African-American Doctors. 2000. (My Ancestors—My Heroes Ser.: Vol. 13). (J). (gr. 3-4). (978-1-893091-12-2(0)) Parker Publishing Co.

African-American Engineers. 2000. (My Ancestors—My Heroes Ser.: Vol. 15). (J). (gr. 3-4). (978-1-893091-14-6(7)) Parker Publishing Co.

African-American Environmentalists. Date not set. (My Ancestors—My Heroes Ser.: Vol. 32). (J). (gr. 3-4). (978-1-893091-31-3(7)) Parker Publishing Co.

African-American Farmers. 2000. (My Ancestors—My Heroes Ser.: Vol. 34). (J). (gr. 3-4). (978-1-893091-33-7(3)) Parker Publishing Co.

African-American Freedom Fighters. 2000. (My Ancestors—My Heroes Ser.: Vol. 7). (J). (gr. 3-4). (978-1-893091-06-1(6)) Parker Publishing Co.

African-American International Business Leaders. 2000. (My Ancestors—My Heroes Ser.: Vol. 35). (J). (gr. 3-4). (978-1-893091-34-4(1)) Parker Publishing Co.

African-American Journalists. 2000. (My Ancestors—My Heroes Ser.: Vol. 17). (J). (gr. 3-4). (978-1-893091-16-0(3)) Parker Publishing Co.

African-American Lawyers. 2000. (My Ancestors—My Heroes Ser.: Vol. 14). (J). (gr. 3-4). (978-1-893091-13-9(9)) Parker Publishing Co.

African-American Makeup Manufacturers. 2000. (My Ancestors—My Heroes Ser.: Vol. 41). (J). (gr. 3-4). (978-1-893091-40-5(6)) Parker Publishing Co.

African-American Music Producers. 2000. (My Ancestors—My Heroes Ser.: Vol. 43). (J). (gr. 3-4). (978-1-893091-42-9(2)) Parker Publishing Co.

African-American Nobel Peace Prize Winners. 2000. (My Ancestors—My Heroes Ser.: Vol. 44). (J). (gr. 3-4). (978-1-893091-43-6(0)) Parker Publishing Co.

African-American Pharmacists. 2000. (My Ancestors—My Heroes Ser.: Vol. 29). (J). (gr. 3-4). (978-1-893091-28-3(7)) Parker Publishing Co.

African-American Scientist. 2000. (My Ancestors—My Heroes Ser.: Vol. 12). (J). (gr. 3-4). (978-1-893091-11-5(2)) Parker Publishing Co.

African-American Seamstress. 2000. (My Ancestors—My Heroes Ser.: Vol. 28). (J). (gr. 3-4). (978-1-893091-27-6(9)) Parker Publishing Co.

African-American Singers. 2000. (My Ancestors—My Heroes Ser.: Vol. 38). (J). (gr. 3-4). (978-1-893091-37-5(6)) Parker Publishing Co.

African-American Surgeons. 2000. (My Ancestors—My Heroes Ser.: Vol. 18). (J). (gr. 3-4). (978-1-893091-17-7(1)) Parker Publishing Co.

African-American Teachers. 2000. (My Ancestors—My Heroes Ser.: Vol. 36). (J). (gr. 3-4). (978-1-893091-35-1(X)) Parker Publishing Co.

African-American Veterinarians. 2000. (My Ancestors—My Heroes Ser.: Vol. 33). (J). (gr. 3-4). (978-1-893091-32-0(5)) Parker Publishing Co.

Ali, Maryum. I Shook up the World: The Incredible Life of Muhammad Ali. Johnson, Patrick, illus. 2004. 32p. (J). 16.95 (978-1-58270-090-8(7)) Beyond Words Publishing, Inc.

—I Shook up the World: The Incredible Life of Muhammad Ali. Johnson, Patrick, illus. 2004. 32p. (J). (gr. 3 up). lib. bdg. 24.67 (978-0-8368-4098-8(4)) Stevens, Gareth Inc.

Aller, Susan Bivin. Madam C. J. Walker. 2007. (History Maker Biographies Ser.). (J). 26.60 (978-0-8225-6582-6(X) , Lerner Pubns.) Lerner Publishing Group.

Alter, Judy. Great Women of the Old West. 2001. (We the People Ser.). (Illus.). 48p. (J). (gr. 4 up). lib. bdg. 22.60 (978-0-7565-0099-3(0)) Compass Point Bks.

Altman, Susan. Extraordinary African-Americans: From Colonial to Contemporary Times. 2001. (gr. 7-12). lib. bdg. 26.85 (978-0-613-52258-8(3)) Tandem Library Bks.

Amper, Thomas. Booker T. Washington. Reeves, Jeni, illus. (On My Own Biographies Ser.). 48p. 2003. (J). (gr. 1-3). pap. 5.95 (978-0-87614-534-0(9) , Carolrhoda Bks.); 1998. (gr. 2-5). lib. bdg. 23.93 (978-1-57505-094-2(3)) Lerner Publishing Group.

Anastasio, Dina. Harriet Tubman. Morgan, Jacqui, illus. 2002. 16p. (J). pap. (978-0-439-35163-8(4)) Scholastic, Inc.

Anderson, Wayne & Abrams, Dennis. Jay-Z. 2007. (Hip-Hop Stars Ser.). 112p. (J). (gr. 6-12). 30.00 (***978-0-7910-9551-5(7)*** , Chelsea Hse.) Facts On File, Inc.

Anderson, Wayne A., et al. Tupac Shakur. 2007. (Hip-Hop Stars Ser.). 112p. (J). (gr. 6-12). 30.00 (***978-0-7910-9495-2(2)*** , Chelsea Hse.) Facts On File, Inc.

Ansary, Mir Tamim. El Día de Martin Luther King, Jr. 2003. Tr. of Martin Luther King, Jr. Day. (SPA., Illus.). 32p. (J). lib. bdg. 22.79 (978-1-4034-3004-5(7)) Heinemann Library.

Ansary, Mir Tamim. Martin Luther King, Jr. Day. 2006. (Illus.). 32p. (J). (***978-1-4034-8889-3(4)***) Heinemann Library.

Armentrout, David & Armentrout, Patricia. Coretta Scott King. 2004. (Discover the Life of an American Legend Ser.). (Illus.). 24p. (gr. 2-5). 20.64 (978-1-58952-659-4(7)) Rourke Publishing, LLC.

Armentrout, David & Armentrout, Patricia, trs. Venus & Serena Williams. 2003. (Discover the Life of a Sports Star Ser.). (Illus.). 24p. (J). 20.64 (978-1-58952-655-6(4)) Rourke Publishing, LLC.

Aronson, Virginia. Venus & Serena Williams. 2000. (Women Who Win Ser.). (Illus.). 64p. (J). (gr. 4-7). pap. 25.00 (978-0-7910-6158-9(2)); 25.00 (978-0-7910-5799-5(2)) Facts On File, Inc. (Chelsea Hse.).

—Venus & Serena Williams. 2000. (Illus.). 64p. (J). (gr. 4-7). lib. bdg. 17.60 (978-0-613-33180-7(X)) Tandem Library Bks.

—Venus Williams. 1999. (Galaxy of Superstars Ser.). (Illus.). 64p. (J). pap. 25.00 (978-0-7910-5329-4(6)); (YA). (gr. 4-7). 25.00 (978-0-7910-5153-5(6)) Facts On File, Inc. (Chelsea Hse.).

—Venus Williams. 1999. (Galaxy of Superstars Ser.). (978-0-606-16419-1(7)); (gr. 5-8). lib. bdg. 17.60 (978-0-613-17759-7(2)) Tandem Library Bks.

Ashby, Ruth. Rosa Parks: Freedom Rider. 2008. (Sterling Biographies Ser.). (Illus.). 128p. (J). pap. 5.95 (***978-1-4027-4865-3(5)***) Sterling Publishing Co., Inc.

Asirvatham, Sandy. Venus Williams. 2001. (Black Americans of Achievement Ser.). (Illus.). (J). 104p. pap. 30.00 (978-0-7910-6290-6(2)); 112p. 30.00 (978-0-7910-6289-0(9)) Facts On File, Inc. (Chelsea Hse.).

Ayers, Samuel J. Roscoe Wilson: Champion of the Law, Education & Community Service. l.t. ed. 2000. (Illus.). 32p. (J). (gr. 3-8). 14.00 (978-0-9667681-2-1(4)) Hermosa Creations.

Bader, Bonnie. Who Was Martin Luther King Jr. Harrison, Nancy & Wolf, Elizaabeth, illus. 2007. (Who Was... ? Ser.). 112p. (J). (gr. 2-5). 4.99 (***978-0-448-44723-0(1)*** , Grosset & Dunlap) Penguin Group (USA) Inc.

Bailey, Tom. A.G. Gaston: Visionary Businessman. 2003. (Alabama Roots Biography Ser.). (Illus.). 111p. (J). pap. (978-1-878561-99-2(5)) Seacoast Publishing, Inc.

Baker, Courtney. Let's Read About— Rosa Parks. Hunt, Robert, illus. 2004. (Scholastic First Biographies Ser.). 29p. (J). pap. (978-0-439-56413-7(1) , Cartwheel Bks.) Scholastic, Inc.

—Let's Read about Martin Luther King, Jr. Hu, Ying-Hwa & Van Wright, Cornelius, illus. 2001. (First Biographies Ser.). (J). pap. (978-0-439-22112-2(9)) Scholastic, Inc.

Bankston, John. Bow Wow. l.t. ed. 2004. (Blue Banner Biography Ser.). (Illus.). 32p. (J). (gr. 3-8). lib. bdg. 25.70 (978-1-58415-220-0(6)) Mitchell Lane Pubs., Inc.

—Ja Rule. l.t. ed. 2004. (Blue Banner Biography Ser.). (Illus.). 32p. (J). (gr. 3-8). lib. bdg. 25.70 (978-1-58415-221-7(4)) Mitchell Lane Pubs., Inc.

—Jay-Z. 2004. (Blue Banner Biography Ser.). (Illus.). 32p. (gr. 3-8). lib. bdg. 25.70 (978-1-58415-223-1(0)) Mitchell Lane Pubs., Inc.

—The Life & Times of Duke Ellington. 2004. (Masters of Music Ser.). (Illus.). 48p. (gr. 4-8). lib. bdg. 20.95 (978-1-58415-248-4(6)) Mitchell Lane Pubs., Inc.

—The Life & Times of Scott Joplin. 2004. (Masters of Music Ser.). (Illus.). 48p. (gr. 4-8). lib. bdg. 20.95 (978-1-58415-270-5(2)) Mitchell Lane Pubs., Inc.

—Missy Elliott: Hip-Hop Superstar. l.t. ed. 2004. (Blue Banner Biography Ser.). (Illus.). 32p. (J). (gr. 3-8). lib. bdg. 25.70 (978-1-58415-219-4(2)) Mitchell Lane Pubs., Inc.

—Venus Williams. l.t. ed. 2002. (Real Life Reader Biography Ser.). (Illus.). 32p. (gr. 3-8). lib. bdg. 15.95 (978-1-58415-129-6(3)) Mitchell Lane Pubs., Inc.

Banting, Erinn. Condoleezza Rice. 2007. (J). (***978-1-59036-639-4(5)); (*978-1-59036-640-0(9)***) Weigl Pubs., Inc.

Banting, Erinn. Rosa Parks. 2005. (Great African American Women for Kids Ser.). (Illus.). 24p. (J). (ps-7). pap. 6.95 (978-1-59036-342-3(6)); lib. bdg. 26.00 (978-1-59036-336-2(1)) Weigl Pubs., Inc.

Barasch, Lynne. Knockin' on Wood: Starring Peg Leg Bates. 2004. (Illus.). 32p. (J). 16.95 (978-1-58430-170-7(8)) Lee & Low Bks., Inc.

Barber, Tiki & Barber, Ronde. By My Brother's Side. Root, Barry, illus. 2004. 32p. (J). (gr. 1-5). 16.95 (978-0-689-86559-6(7) , Simon & Schuster/Paula Wiseman Bks.) Simon & Schuster Children's Publishing.

Barbour, Karen. Mr. Williams. rev. ed. 2005. (Illus.). 32p. (J). 16.95 (978-0-8050-6773-6(6) , Holt, Henry & Co. Bks. For Young Readers) Holt, Henry & Co.

Beckner, Chrisanne. 100 African Americans Who Changed History. 2005. (People Who Changed History Ser.). (Illus.). 112p. (J). lib. bdg. 30.00 (978-0-8368-5767-2(4) , World Almanac Library) Stevens, Gareth Inc.

Bedesky, Baron. Peary & Henson: The Race to the North Pole. 2006. (In the Footsteps of Explorers Ser.). (Illus.). 32p. (J). (gr. 3-9). (978-0-7787-2426-1(3)) Crabtree Publishing Co.

Beier, Anne. Crispus Attucks: Hero of the Boston Massacre. (Primary Sources of Famous People in American History Ser.). (Illus.). 32p. 2004. (gr. 4-8). lib. bdg. 21.25 (978-0-8239-4106-3(X) , Rosen Central); 2004. (SPA & ENG., (gr. 4-8). lib. bdg. 21.25 (978-0-8239-4154-4(X) , Buenas Letra); 2003. (YA). pap. (978-0-8239-4178-0(7)) Rosen Publishing Group, Inc., The.

Bello, M. A. Of Hope, Courage & Life. 2001. 464p. (J). pap. 24.95 (978-1-56167-666-8(7)) American Literary Pr.

Benge, Janet & Benge, Geoffrey Francis. George Washington Carver: From Slave to Scientist. 2001. 192p. pap. 8.99 (978-1-883002-78-7(8)) Emerald Bks.

Benjamin Banneker 24: Leveled Books. 2001. (McGraw-Hill. Lectura Ser.). (ENG & SPA.). (gr. 1 up). (978-0-02-188001-0(8)) Macmillan/McGraw-Hill Schl. Div.

Benjamin, Lisa. Jackie Robinson: Changing the Game. 2005. (Voices Reading Ser.). (Illus.). 32p. (J). (978-0-7367-2937-6(2)) Zaner-Bloser, Inc.

Benson, Michael. Hank Aaron, Baseball Player. 2004. (Ferguson Career Biographies Ser.). (Illus.). 128p. (J). (gr. 6-12). 25.00 (978-0-8160-5349-0(9) , Ferguson Publishing Co.) Facts On File, Inc.

—Malcolm X. 2001. (Biography Ser.). (Illus.). 112p. (YA). (gr. 6-12). 27.93 (978-0-8225-5025-9(3) , Lerner Pubns.) Lerner Publishing Group.

Bernard, Catherine J. Sojourner Truth: Abolitionist & Women's Rights Activist. 2001. (Historical American Biographies Ser.). (Illus.). 112p. (YA). (gr. 6-12). lib. bdg. 26.60 (978-0-7660-1257-8(3)) Enslow Pubs., Inc.

Bernstein, Ross. Barry Bonds. 2004. (Sports Heroes & Legends Ser.). (Illus.). 112p. (J). (gr. 6-12). lib. bdg. 27.93 (978-0-8225-1791-7(4)) Lerner Publishing Group.

—Gary Payton: Star Guard. 2000. (Sports Reports). (Illus.). 104p. (YA). (gr. 4-10). lib. bdg. 20.95 (978-0-7660-1330-8(8)) Enslow Pubs., Inc.

—Shaquille O'Neal. 2005. (Amazing Athletes Ser.). (Illus.). 32p. (gr. 3-4). lib. bdg. 22.60 (978-0-8225-3689-5(7)) Lerner Publishing Group.

—Sports Great Daunte Culpepper. 2003. (Sports Great Books). (Illus.). 64p. (J). lib. bdg. 22.60 (978-0-7660-2037-5(1)) Enslow Pubs., Inc.

Beyer, Mark. Ray Charles. 2006. (Rock & Roll Hall of Famers Ser.). (Illus.). 112p. (YA). (gr. 5-8). lib. bdg. 29.25 (978-0-8239-3642-7(2)) Rosen Publishing Group, Inc., The.

—Stevie Wonder. 2006. (Rock & Roll Hall of Famers Ser.). (Illus.). 112p. (YA). (gr. 5-8). lib. bdg. 29.25 (978-0-8239-3525-3(6)) Rosen Publishing Group, Inc., The.

Bigmama's. 1998. (J). pap. 3.95 (978-0-439-04436-3(7)) Scholastic, Inc.

Billus, Kathleen. Judy Johnson. 2002. (Baseball Hall of Famers of the Negro League Ser.). (Illus.). 112p. (YA). (gr. 5-8). lib. bdg. 29.25 (978-0-8239-3476-8(4) , Rosen Central) Rosen Publishing Group, Inc., The.

Bjornlund, Lydia D. Women of the Suffrage Movement. 2003. (Women in History Ser.). (Illus.). 112p. (J). 32.45 (978-1-59018-173-7(5) , Lucent Bks.) Thomson Gale.

Black Americans of Achievement. (Illus.). 104-144p. (J). (gr. 5). 219.45 (978-0-7910-5216-7(8)); (Illus.). 40p. (J). (gr. 5). pap. 109.45 (978-0-7910-5217-4(6)); (Illus.). (gr. 6-12). pap. 119.40 (978-0-7910-8396-3(9)); (Illus.). (gr. 6-12). lib. bdg. 275.40 (978-0-7910-8419-9(1)); 2005. pap. 1440.00 (978-0-7910-9139-5(2)) Facts On File, Inc. (Chelsea Hse.).

Black Americans of Achievement, Legacy Edition. 2005. 112p. pap. 540.00 (978-0-7910-8735-0(2) , Chelsea Hse.) Facts On File, Inc.

Black Americans of Achievement-the Game. 1999. (J). (gr. 5). 24.95 (978-0-7910-3350-0(3) , Chelsea Hse.) Facts On File, Inc.

Black, Sonia W. Mae Jemison. 2000. (Illus.). 64p. (J). (gr. 3-7). pap. 3.95 (978-1-57255-801-4(6)) Mondo Publishing.

—Mae Jemison. 2000. (978-0-606-22649-3(4)); (gr. 3-6). lib. bdg. 11.80 (978-0-613-35854-5(6)) Tandem Library Bks.

Blakely, Gloria. Condoleezza Rice. 2003. (African American Leaders Ser.). (Illus.). 112p. (gr. 6-12). 30.00 (978-0-7910-7683-5(0) , Chelsea Hse.) Facts On File, Inc.

—Danny Glover. 2001. (Black Americans of Achievement Ser.). (Illus.). 112p. (J). 30.00 (978-0-7910-6285-2(6) , Chelsea Hse.) Facts On File, Inc.

Blashfield, Jean F. Oprah Winfrey. 2003. (Trailblazers of the Modern World Ser.). (ENG & SPA., Illus.). 48p. (J). (gr. 5 up). pap. 14.95 (978-0-8368-5247-9(8)); lib. bdg. 30.00 (978-0-8368-5087-1(4)) Stevens, Gareth Inc. (World Almanac Library).

Bloom, Harold. Gwendolyn Brooks. 2004. (Bloom's BioCritiques Ser.). (Illus.). 112p. (YA). (gr. 9-13). 35.00 (978-0-7910-8114-3(1) , Chelsea Hse.) Facts On File, Inc.

Bloom, Harold, ed. Bloom's BioCritiques. (Illus.). (gr. 9-13). pap. (978-0-7910-8483-0(3)); lib. bdg. 1115.85 (978-0-7910-8482-3(5)) Facts On File, Inc. (Chelsea Hse.).

—Bloom's Guides. (Illus.). (gr. 9-13). pap. (978-0-7910-8068-9(4)); lib. bdg. 527.85 (978-0-7910-8481-6(7)) Facts On File, Inc. (Chelsea Hse.).

—Bloom's Major Literary Characters. (Illus.). 180p. (gr. 9-13). lib. bdg. 383.40 (978-0-7910-7881-5(7)); lib. bdg. 111.60 (978-0-7910-8070-2(6)) Facts On File, Inc. (Chelsea Hse.).

Bloom, Sarah R. Queen Latifah. 2001. (Black Americans of Achievement Ser.). 112p. (YA). (gr. 6-10). 30.00 (978-0-7910-6287-6(2) , Chelsea Hse.) Facts On File, Inc.

Blue. Toni Morrison. 2004. (African-American Biographies Ser.). 64p. pap. 9.50 (978-1-4109-1120-9(9)) Raintree.

Blue, Rose. Wesley Snipes. 2002. (gr. 5-8). lib. bdg. 18.75 (978-0-613-33213-2(X)) Tandem Library Bks.

Blue, Rose & Naden, Corinne J. Benjamin Banneker: Mathematician & Stargazer. 2001. (Gateway Biography Ser.). (Illus.). 48p. (gr. 2-4). lib. bdg. 23.90 (978-0-7613-1805-7(4) , Millbrook Pr.) Lerner Publishing Group.

—Chris Rock. 1999. (Black Americans of Achievement Ser.). (Illus.). 104p. (J). 9.95 (978-0-7910-5278-5(8) , Chelsea Hse.) Facts On File, Inc.

—Henry Louis Gates. 2004. (African-American Biographies Ser.). 64p. pap. 9.50 (978-1-4109-1121-6(7)) Raintree.

—Wesley Snipes. 2001. (Black Americans of Achievement Ser.). (Illus.). 104p. (J). (gr. 5 up). pap. 30.00 (978-0-7910-5801-5(8) , Chelsea Hse.) Facts On File, Inc.

Blumberg, Rhoda. York's Adventures with Lewis & Clark: An African-American's Part in the Great Expedition. 2007. 96p. (J). pap. 7.99 (978-0-06-009113-2(4)) HarperCollins Pubs.

Boekhoff, P. M. & Kallen, Stuart A. Venus Williams. 2002. (Stars of Sports Ser.). (Illus.). 48p. (J). 26.20 (978-0-7377-1395-4(X) , Greenhaven Pr., Inc.) Thomson Gale.

Bohannon, Lisa Frederiksen. Freedom Cannot Rest: Ella Baker & the Civil Rights Movement. 2005. (Civil Rights Leaders Ser.). (Illus.). 176p. (J). (gr. 6-12). lib. bdg. 26.95 (978-1-931798-71-6(0)) Reynolds, Morgan Inc.

Bolden, Tonya. And Not Afraid to Dare: The Stories of Ten African-American Women. 2003. (Illus.). 224p. (J). (gr. 4-8). pap. 4.99 (978-0-439-47139-8(7) , Scholastic Paperbacks) Scholastic, Inc.

—The Champ. Christie, R. Gregory, illus. 2004. 40p. (J). (gr. k-3). 17.95 (978-0-375-82401-2(4) , Knopf Bks. for Young Readers) Random Hse. Children's Bks.

—The Champ: The Story of Muhammad Ali. Christie, R. Gregory, illus. 2004. 40p. (J). (gr. k-3). 19.99 (978-0-375-92401-9(9) , Knopf Bks. for Young Readers) Random Hse. Children's Bks.

—M. L. K. The Journey of a King. Adelman, Bob, ed. 2007. 128p. (J). (gr. 5-9). 19.95 (978-0-8109-5476-2(1) , Abrams Bks. for Young Readers) Abrams, Harry N. , Inc.

—Maritcha: A Nineteenth-Century American Girl. 2005. (Illus.). 48p. (J). (gr. k-4). 17.95 (978-0-8109-5045-0(6)) Abrams, Harry N. , Inc.

—Portraits of African-American Heroes. Pitcairn, Ansel, illus. (J). (gr. 2). 2005. 96p. pap. 11.99 (978-0-14-240473-7(X) , Puffin); 2003. 88p. 18.99 (978-0-525-47043-4(3) , Dutton Juvenile) Penguin Group (USA) Inc.

Booker T Washington. (Photo Illustrated Biographies Ser.). 24p. (J). 6.95 (978-1-56065-942-6(4)); 32p. (YA). 7.95 (978-0-7368-6190-8(4)); Vol. 2. 2005. (YA). (978-0-7368-3379-0(X) , Pebble Bks.) Capstone Pr., Inc.

Bowdish, Lynea. George Washington Carver. 2004. (Rookie Biographies Ser.). (Illus.). 31p. (J). 20.50 (978-0-516-23610-0(5) , Children's Pr.) Scholastic Library Publishing.

Boyd, Herb. Martin Luther King, Jr. Marcos, Pablo, illus. 2005. (Heroes of America Ser.). 240p. (J). (gr. 3-8). lib. bdg. 21.35 (978-1-59679-258-6(2)) ABDO Publishing Co.

Bozzuti-Jones, Mark Francisco. The Miter Fits Just Fine: A Story about the Rt. Rev. Barbara Clementine Harris, Suffragan Bishop, Diocese of Massachusetts. 2003. 86p. pap. 10.95 (978-1-56101-220-6(3)) Cowley Pubns.

Bradley, Michael. Donovan McNabb. 2004. (Illus.). 48p. (J). 27.07 (978-0-7614-1756-9(7) , Benchmark Bks.) Cavendish, Marshall Corp.

Brager, Bruce L. Bessie Coleman. Mazellan, Ron, illus. 2002. 16p. (J). (978-0-439-35155-3(3)) Scholastic, Inc.

Brandt, Keith & Mattern, Joanne. Rosa Parks: Freedom Rider. Griffith, Gershom, illus. 2006. 54p. (J). pap. (***978-0-439-66045-7(9)***) Scholastic, Inc.

Braun, Eric. Benjamin Banneker. 2005. (Pebble Books). (Illus.). 24p. (J). (978-0-7368-4233-4(0) , Pebble Bks.) Capstone Pr., Inc.

Brenner, Richard J. Michael Jordan. (J). 2000. 25.01 (978-0-688-16586-4(9)); 1999. (Illus.). 32p. pap. 3.95 (978-0-688-16587-1(7)) HarperCollins Pubs.

—Michael Jordan. 1999. (978-0-606-17077-2(4)) Tandem Library Bks.

Brezina, Corona. Sojourner Truth's "Ain't I a Woman?" Speech: A Primary Source Investigation. 2004. (Great Historic Debates & Speeches Ser.). (Illus.). 64p. (J). lib. bdg. 29.95 (978-1-4042-0154-5(8)) Rosen Publishing Group, Inc., The.

Bridges, Ruby & Maccarone, Grace. Let's Read About— Ruby Bridges. Van Wright, Cornelius & Hu, Ying-Hwa, illus. 2003. (Scholastic First Biographies Ser.). (J). (978-0-439-51362-3(6)) Scholastic, Inc.

Brill, Marlene Targ. Barack Obama. 2006. (J). pap. 6.95 (978-0-8225-6056-2(9) , First Avenue Editions) Lerner Publishing Group.

—Barack Obama: Working to Make a Difference. 2006. (Gateway Biographies Ser.). (Illus.). 48p. (J). 23.93 (978-0-8225-3417-4(7)) Lerner Publishing Group.

—Marshall Major Taylor: Bicycle Superstar. 2007. (Trailblazer Biographies Ser.). 112p. (YA). (gr. 5-9). lib. bdg. 31.93 (978-0-8225-6610-6(9) , Twenty-First Century Bks.) Lerner Publishing Group.

Brimner, Larry Dane. We Are One: The Story of Bayard Rustin. 2007. 48p. (YA). (gr. 3 up). 17.95 (***978-1-59078-498-3(7)***) Boyds Mills Pr.

Broadwater, Andrea. Marian Anderson: Singer & Humanitarian. 2000. (African-American Biographies Ser.). (Illus.). 128p. (YA). (gr. 6-12). lib. bdg. 26.60 (978-0-7660-1211-0(5)) Enslow Pubs., Inc.

Brooks, Philip. Oprah Winfrey: A Voice for the People. 2000. (Book Report Bios Ppbk Ser.). (Illus.). (YA). pap. 6.95 (978-0-531-16406-8(3) , Watts, Franklin) Scholastic Library Publishing.

—Oprah Winfrey: A Voice for the People. 1999. (978-0-606-18159-4(8)) Tandem Library Bks.

Brown, Gene. Duke Ellington: Jazz Master. 2001. (Giants of Art & Culture Ser.). (Illus.). 128p. (J). (gr. 5-8). 28.70 (978-1-56711-505-5(5) , Blackbirch Pr., Inc.) Thomson Gale.

Brown, Jonatha A. Martin Luther King, Jr. 2005. (Illus.). 24p. (ENG & SPA.). (J). pap. (978-0-8368-4590-7(0)); (J). lib. bdg. (978-0-8368-4474-0(2)); (ENG & SPA., (J). lib. bdg. 19.33 (978-0-8368-4583-9(8)); (YA). lib. bdg. 19.33 (978-0-8368-4467-2(X) , Weekly Reader Early Learning Library) Stevens, Gareth Inc.

—Muhammad Ali. 2005. (Illus.). 24p. (J). pap. (978-0-8368-4750-5(4)); lib. bdg. 19.33 (978-0-8368-4743-7(1)) Stevens, Gareth Inc.

—Rosa Parks. 2005. (Illus.). 24p. (J). (ENG & SPA.). pap. (978-0-8368-4769-7(5)); (ENG & SPA., lib. bdg. 19.33 (978-0-8368-4762-8(8)); pap. (978-0-8368-4755-0(5)); lib. bdg. 19.33 (978-0-8368-4748-2(2)) Stevens, Gareth Inc.

Brown, Jonatha A. & Raatma, Lucia. Jackie Robinson. 2004. (Illus.). 24p. (J). pap. (978-0-8368-4318-7(5)); (YA). lib. bdg. 19.33 (978-0-8368-4311-8(8)) Stevens, Gareth Inc.

Brown, Susan Taylor. Robert Smalls Sails to Freedom. Marshall, Felicia, illus. 2006. (On My Own History Ser.). 48p. (J). 25.26 (978-1-57505-872-6(3)) Lerner Publishing Group.

Brown, Warren. Colin Powell: Soldier & Statesman. (Black Americans of Achievement Ser.). (Illus.). 112p. (J). (gr. 6-12). 2005. pap. 13.25 (978-0-7910-8373-4(X)); 2004. 30.00 (978-0-7910-8254-6(7)) Facts On File, Inc. (Chelsea Hse.).

Brown, William Wells. Narrative of William Wells Brown. 2006. (Illus.). (YA). cd-rom (978-1-892824-80-6(9)) AFCHRON.

Bruchac, Joseph. Jim Thorpe's Bright Path. Nelson, S. D., tr. Nelson, S. D., illus. 2004. 40p. (J). 17.95 (978-1-58430-166-0(X)) Lee & Low Bks., Inc.

Bryant, Philip. Langston Hughes. 2003. (African-American Biographies Ser.). 64p. pap. 8.95 (978-1-4109-0037-1(1)) Raintree.

—Zora Neale Hurston. 2003. (African-American Biographies Ser.). 64p. pap. 8.95 (978-1-4109-0041-8(X)) Raintree.

Bryant, Philip S. Langston Hughes. 2003. (African-American Biographies Ser.). (Illus.). 64p. (J). lib. bdg. 28.56 (978-0-7398-6871-3(3)) Raintree.

—Zora Neale Hurston. 2003. (African-American Biographies Ser.). (Illus.). 64p. (J). 28.56 (978-0-7398-6872-0(1)) Raintree.

Buckley, Annie. Robert L. Johnson. 2008. (J). lib. bdg. 26.00 (***978-1-60279-072-8(8)***) Cherry Lake Publishing.

Buckley, James. Muhammad Ali. 2004. (Trailblazers of the Modern World Ser.). (Illus.). 48p. (J). (gr. 5 up). pap. 11.95 (978-0-8368-5256-1(7)); lib. bdg. 30.00 (978-0-8368-5096-3(3)) Stevens, Gareth Inc. (World Almanac Library).

Buckley, James, Jr. Venus & Serena Williams. 2003. (Trailblazers of the Modern World Ser.). (Illus.). 48p. (J). (gr. 5 up). pap. 14.95 (978-0-8368-5246-2(X)); lib. bdg. 30.00 (978-0-8368-5086-4(6)) Stevens, Gareth Inc. (World Almanac Library).

Burgan, Michael. George Washington Carver: Scientist, Inventor, & Teacher. (Signature Lives Ser.). (Illus.). 112p. (J). 2007. pap. (***978-0-7565-1986-5(1)*** , 1265882); 2006. (978-0-7565-1882-0(2) , 1265882) Compass Point Bks.

Burgan, Michael. Sheryl Swoopes. 2000. (Women Who Win Ser.). (Illus.). 64p. (J). (gr. 4-7). pap. 25.00 (978-0-7910-6155-8(8)); 25.00 (978-0-7910-5795-7(X)) Facts On File, Inc. (Chelsea Hse.).

—Sheryl Swoopes. 2001. (gr. 3-6). lib. bdg. 17.60 (978-0-613-33051-0(X)) Tandem Library Bks.

Burke, Rick. Benjamin Banneker. 2003. (American Lives Ser.). (Illus.). 32p. (J). lib. bdg. 24.22 (978-1-4034-0725-2(8)); pap. 6.50 (978-1-4034-3100-4(0)) Heinemann Library.

—James Beckwourth. 2003. (American Lives Ser.). 32p. pap. 6.95 (978-1-4034-4199-7(5)); (Illus.). (J). pap. 112.59 (978-1-4034-4204-8(5)); (Illus.). (J). lib. bdg. 24.22 (978-1-4034-4191-1(X)) Heinemann Library.

—Phillis Wheatley. 2003. (American Lives Ser.). (Illus.). 32p. (J). lib. bdg. 24.22 (978-1-4034-0730-6(4)); pap. 6.50 (978-1-4034-3105-9(1)) Heinemann Library.

Burleigh, Robert. Langston's Train Ride. Jenkins, Leonard, tr. Jenkins, Leonard, illus. 2004. 32p. (J). (ps-3). pap. 16.95 (978-0-439-35239-0(8) , Orchard Bks.) Scholastic, Inc.

Butler, Jerry. A Drawing in the Sand: A Story of African American Art. Butler, Jerry, illus. 1998. (Illus.). 64p. (J). (gr. 3-7). 24.95 (978-1-55933-216-3(6) , 2166BK) Zino Pr. Children's Bks.

Butler, Mary G. Sojourner Truth: From Slave to Activist for Freedom. 2005. (Library of American Lives & Times). (Illus.). 112p. (YA). (gr. 4-8). lib. bdg. 31.95 (978-0-8239-5736-1(5)) Rosen Publishing Group, Inc., The.

Button, Beth. Notable Black Americans. Rogers, Kathy, ed. Adams, Elizabeth, illus. 2000. (Famous Faces Ser.). 8p. (J). pap. 6.95 (978-1-56472-279-9(1)) Edupress, Inc.

Calkhoven, Laurie. Harriet Tubman: Leading the Way to Freedom. 2008. (Sterling Biographies Ser.). (Illus.). 128p. (J). pap. 5.95 (***978-1-4027-4117-3(0)***) Sterling Publishing Co., Inc.

Cameron, Mike & Brown, Greg. Mike Cameron: It Takes a Team. 2002. (Illus.). 48p. (J). 15.95 (978-1-57243-502-5(X) , Benchmark Pr.) Triumph Bks.

Cannarella, Deborah. James Baldwin: African-American Writer & Activist. 2003. (Journey to Freedom Ser.). (Illus.). 40p. (J). (gr. 3-7). 28.50 (978-1-56766-531-4(4)) Child's World, Inc.

Caravantes, Peggy. Marcus Garvey: Black Nationalist. 2004. (Twentieth Century Leaders Ser.). (Illus.). 128p. (YA). (gr. 6-12). 23.95 (978-1-931798-14-3(1)) Reynolds, Morgan Inc.

Carroll, Jillian. Aretha Franklin. 2003. (Illus.). 64p. (J). pap. 8.95 (978-1-4109-0314-3(1)); lib. bdg. 28.56 (978-0-7398-7029-7(7)) Raintree.

—Aretha Franklin. 2003. (gr. 3-6). lib. bdg. 18.20 (978-0-613-78176-3(7)) Tandem Library Bks.

Carter, Andy. George Washington Carver. 2000. (gr. 3-6). lib. bdg. 14.10 (978-0-613-79176-2(2)) Tandem Library Bks.

Carter, Andy, et al. George Washington Carver. Paladino, Lance, illus. (On My Own Biographies Ser.). 48p. (J). (gr. 1-3). 2003. 5.95 (978-1-57505-458-2(2)); 2000. lib. bdg. 23.93 (978-1-57505-427-8(2) , Carolrhoda Bks.) Lerner Publishing Group.

Casilla, Robert, illus. A Picture Book of Martin Luther King, Jr. 2004. (J). pap. 18.95 incl. audio compact disk (978-1-59112-773-4(4)) Live Oak Media.

Cefrey, Holly. The Inventions of Granville Woods: The Railroad Telegraph System & the "Third Rail" 2003. (19th Century American Inventors Ser.). (Illus.). 24p. (J). lib. bdg. 17.25 (978-0-8239-6442-0(6) , PowerKids Pr.) Rosen Publishing Group, Inc., The.

Chanko, Pamela. Easy Reader Biographies: Rosa Parks: Bus Ride to Freedom. 2007. 16p. pap. 2.99 (***978-0-439-77420-8(9)*** , Teaching Resources) Scholastic, Inc.

Ching, Jacqueline. The Assassination of Martin Luther King, Jr. 2003. (Library of Political Assassinations). (Illus.). 64p. (YA). (gr. 7-12). lib. bdg. 26.50 (978-0-8239-3543-7(4)) Rosen Publishing Group, Inc., The.

Christopher, Matt. In the Goal with... Brianna Scurry. 2000. (YA). 11.60 (978-0-606-19839-4(3)) Tandem Library Bks.

—On the Court with... Kobe Bryant. 2001. (978-0-606-22562-5(5)); (gr. 3-6). lib. bdg. 13.00 (978-0-613-44172-8(9)) Tandem Library Bks.

—On the Court with... Shaquille O'Neil. 2003. (Illus.). 128p. (J). (gr. 3-7). pap. 4.99 (978-0-316-16473-3(9)) Little Brown & Co.

—On the Court with... Venus & Serena Williams. 2002. (Matt Christopher Sports Biographies Ser.). (Illus.). 112p. (J). (gr. 4-7). pap. 4.99 (978-0-316-13814-7(2)) Little, Brown Bks. for Young Readers.

—On the Court with... Venus & Serena Williams. 2002. (gr. 3-6). lib. bdg. 12.95 (978-0-613-70947-7(0)) Tandem Library Bks.

Claybourne, Anna. Martin Luther King, Jr. Civil Rights Hero. 2001. (Famous Lives Ser.). (Illus.). 48p. (J). (gr. 4-6). lib. bdg. 27.12 (978-0-7398-4433-5(4)) Raintree.

Cline-Ransome, Lesa. Major Taylor, Champion Cyclist. Ransome, James E., illus. 2003. 40p. (J). 16.95 (978-0-689-83159-1(5) , Atheneum/Anne Schwartz Bks.) Simon & Schuster Children's Publishing.

—Satchel Paige. Ransome, James E., illus. 2004. 31p. (J). (gr. k-4). reprint ed. pap. 7.00 (978-0-7567-7799-9(2)) DIANE Publishing Co.

—Satchel Paige. Ransome, James E., illus. 40p. (J). (gr. 1-5). 2003. 6.99 (978-0-689-85681-5(4) , Aladdin); 2000. 17.99 (978-0-689-81151-7(9)) Simon & Schuster Children's Publishing.

—Satchel Paige. 2003. (gr. 3-6). lib. bdg. 15.30 (978-0-613-55361-2(6)) Tandem Library Bks.

Clinton, Catherine. Underground Railroad. 2007. 32p. (J). lib. bdg. 17.89 (978-0-06-050426-7(9)) HarperCollins Pubs.

—When Harriet Met Sojourner. Evans, Shane, illus. 2007. 32p. (J). (gr. k-2). 16.99 (978-0-06-050425-0(0)) HarperCollins Pubs.

Clinton, Catherine, illus. Phillis's Big Test. 2008. 32p. (J). (gr. k-3). 16.00 (***978-0-618-73739-0(1)***) Houghton Mifflin Co.

Cloud Tapper, Suzanne. Voices from Slavery's Past: Yearning to Be Heard. 2004. (Slavery in American History Ser.). (Illus.). 128p. (J). lib. bdg. 26.60 (978-0-7660-2157-0(2)) Enslow Pubs., Inc.

Cohen, Joel H. Oscar Robertson. 2002. (Basketball Hall of Famers Ser.). (Illus.). 112p. (YA). (gr. 5-8). lib. bdg. 29.25 (978-0-8239-3485-0(3) , Rosen Central) Rosen Publishing Group, Inc., The.

Cole, Melanie. Sinbad. 1998. (Real-Life Reader Biographies Ser.). (Illus.). 32p. (J). (gr. 3-8). lib. bdg. 24.95 (978-1-883845-73-5(4)) Mitchell Lane Pubs., Inc.

Collard, Sneed B., III. Rosa Parks: The Courage to Make a Difference. 2006. (American Heroes Ser.). (Illus.). 48p. (J). (gr. 3-5). lib. bdg. 28.50 (978-0-7614-2163-4(7) , Benchmark Bks.) Cavendish, Marshall Corp.

Collins, Ace & Hillman, John. Blackball Superstars: Legendary Players of the Negro Baseball Leagues. 1999. (Illus.). 141p. (J). (gr. 6-12). lib. bdg. 19.95 (978-1-888105-38-4(0)) Avisson Pr., Inc.

Collins, Kathleen. Sojourner Truth: Equal Rights Advocate. 2003. (Famous People in American History Ser.). (Illus.). 32p. (J). pap. 6.50 (978-0-8239-4193-3(0)) Rosen Publishing Group, Inc., The.

Cooper, Floyd. Jump! From the Life of Michael Jordan. Cooper, Floyd, illus. 2004. (Illus.). 40p. (J). (gr. 1-5). 15.99 (978-0-399-24230-4(9) , Philomel) Penguin Group (USA) Inc.

Cooper, Michael L. Slave Spirituals & the Jubilee Singers. 2001. (Illus.). 96p. (J). (gr. 5-9). tchr. ed. 16.00 (978-0-395-97829-0(7) , Clarion Bks.) Houghton Mifflin Co. Trade & Reference Div.

Cornelius, Kay. Chamique Holdsclaw. 2000. (Women Who Win Ser.). (Illus.). 64p. (J). (gr. 4-7). pap. 25.00 (978-0-7910-6153-4(1)); (gr. 3 up). 25.00 (978-0-7910-5793-3(3)) Facts On File, Inc. (Chelsea Hse.).

—Chamique Holdsclaw. 2001. (gr. 3-6). lib. bdg. 17.60 (978-0-613-32387-1(4)) Tandem Library Bks.

Cox, Vicki. Maya Angelou. 2006. (Black Americans of Achievement, Legacy Edition Ser.). (Illus.). 128p. (gr. 6-12). 30.00 (978-0-7910-9224-8(0) , Chelsea Hse.) Facts On File, Inc.

Crawford, Ann Fears. Barbara Jordan: Breaking the Barriers. 2002. (J). (978-1-57168-570-4(7) , Eakin Pr.) Eakin Pr.

—Barbara Jordan: Breaking the Barriers. 2003. (Illus.). 90p. (J). (gr. 7-9). lib. bdg. 19.95 (978-1-931823-11-1(1)) Halcyon Pr., Ltd.

Crews, Donald. Bigmama's. 2001. (J). (gr. k-3). pap. 16.90 incl. audio (978-0-8045-6840-1(5) , 6840) Spoken Arts, Inc.

Crow, Joseph Medicine & Viola, Herman. Counting Coup: Becoming a Crow Chief on the Reservation & Beyond. 2006. (Illus.). 128p. (J). (gr. k-4). 15.95 (978-0-7922-5391-4(4)); 23.90 (978-0-7922-5392-1(2)) National Geographic Society. (National Geographic Children's Bks.).

Cruz, Barbara C. Alvin Ailey: Celebrating African-American Culture in Dance. 2004. (African-American Biographies Ser.). (Illus.). 112p. (J). lib. bdg. 26.60 (978-0-7660-2293-5(5)) Enslow Pubs., Inc.

Daly, Chuck, intro. Juwan Howard. 1999. (Basketball Legends Ser.). (Illus.). 64p. (YA). (gr. 4-7). lib. bdg. 18.65 (978-0-7910-4575-6(7) , Chelsea Hse.) Facts On File, Inc.

Davis, Kenneth C. Don't Know Much about Martin Luther King Jr., Vol. 6. Kodaira, Machiyo, illus. 2006. (Don't Know Much About Ser.). 144p. (J). (gr. 2-5). lib. bdg. 16.89 (978-0-06-028822-8(1)) HarperCollins Pubs.

Dawson, George. Life Is So Good. 2001. (gr. 7-12). lib. bdg. 23.45 (978-0-613-36465-2(1)) Tandem Library Bks.

de Kay, James T. Meet Martin Luther King, Jr. 2001. (Landmark Bks.). (Illus.). (J). (978-0-606-20793-5(7)) Tandem Library Bks.

Deane, Bill. Sports Great Frank Thomas. 2000. (Sports Great Bks.). (Illus.). 64p. (YA). (gr. 4-10). lib. bdg. 22.60 (978-0-7660-1269-1(7)) Enslow Pubs., Inc.

DeAngelis, Gina. Jackie Robinson. 2000. (Overcoming Adversity Ser.). (Illus.). (J). 104p. (gr. 8-12). pap. 30.00 (978-0-7910-5898-5(0)); 112p. (gr. 4-7). 30.00 (978-0-7910-5897-8(2)) Facts On File, Inc. (Chelsea Hse.).

Deangelis, Gina. Jackie Robinson. 2001. (gr. 5-8). lib. bdg. 18.75 (978-0-613-32699-5(7)) Tandem Library Bks.

DeAngelis, Therese. Louis Farrakhan: Political Activist. 1999. (Black Americans of Achievement Ser.). (Illus.). 144p. (YA). (gr. 5 up). pap. 9.95 (978-0-7910-4689-0(3)); 32.00 (978-0-7910-4688-3(5)) Facts On File, Inc. (Chelsea Hse.).

Deans, Karen. Playing to Win: The Story of Althea Gibson. Brown, Elbrite, illus. 2007. 32p. (J). (ps-3). 16.95 (978-0-8234-1926-5(6)) Holiday Hse., Inc.

DeBoer, Andy. Whoopi Goldberg. 1998. (Ovations Ser.: Vol. 8). (Illus.). 32p. (YA). (gr. 4-7). 21.30 (978-0-88682-696-3(9) , Creative Education) Creative Co., The.

DeGezelle, Terri. Life in the Time of Rosa Parks & the Civil Rights Movement. 2007. (J). (***978-1-4034-9671-3(4));*** pap. (***978-1-4034-9679-9(X)***) Heinemann Library.

Devaney, Sherri. Barack Obama. 2006. (Illus.). 112p. (J). (gr. 7-10). 32.45 (978-1-59018-937-5(X) , Lucent Bks.) Thomson Gale.

Devillier, Christy. Martin Luther King, Jr. 2001. (First Biographies Ser.). (Illus.). 32p. (J). (gr. k-4). lib. bdg. 22.78 (978-1-57765-592-3(3) , Buddy Bks.) ABDO Publishing Co.

Ditchfield, Christin. Condoleezza Rice: America's Leading Stateswoman. 2006. (Great Life Stories Ser.). (Illus.). 111p. (J). (gr. 5-8). 30.50 (978-0-531-13874-8(7) , Watts, Franklin) Scholastic Library Publishing.

—Condoleezza Rice: National Security Advisor. 2003. (Great Life Stories: Political Figures Ser.). (Illus.). 112p. (J). 30.50 (978-0-531-12307-2(3) , Watts, Franklin) Scholastic Library Publishing.

Doeden, Matt. George Washington Carver. 2007. (History Maker Biographies Ser.). (J). 26.60 (***978-0-8225-7605-1(8)*** , Lerner Pubns.) Lerner Publishing Group.

Donaldson, Madeline. Venus & Serena Williams. 2005. (Amazing Athletes Ser.). (Illus.). 32p. (gr. 3-4). lib. bdg. 22.60 (978-0-8225-3316-0(2)) Lerner Publishing Group.

—Venus & Serena Williams. 2004. (Illus.). 32p. (J). (ps-6). lib. bdg. 12.75 (978-0-606-30527-3(0)) Tandem Library Bks.

Donnelly, Karen. Deacon Jones. 2003. (Football Hall of Famers Ser.). (Illus.). 112p. (YA). (gr. 5-8). lib. bdg. 29.25 (978-0-8239-3606-9(6) , Rosen Central) Rosen Publishing Group, Inc., The.

Donovan, Sandy. Fannie Lou Hamer. 2003. (Illus.). 64p. (J). pap. 8.95 (978-1-4109-0316-7(8)); lib. bdg. 28.56 (978-0-7398-7030-3(0)) Raintree.

—Marcus Garvey. 2003. (African-American Biographies Ser.). 64p. pap. 8.95 (978-1-4109-0038-8(X)); (Illus.). (J). 28.56 (978-0-7398-6870-6(5)) Raintree.

—Mary McLeod Bethune. 2003. (African-American Biographies Ser.). 64p. (YA). pap. 8.95 (978-1-4109-0039-5(8)) Raintree.

—Rosa Parks. 2003. (Illus.). 64p. (J). (gr. 4-7). pap. 9.50 (978-1-4109-0320-4(6)); lib. bdg. 28.56 (978-0-7398-7032-7(7)) Raintree.

D'Orio, Wayne. Carol Moseley-Braun. 2003. (African American Leaders Ser.). (Illus.). 112p. (gr. 6-12). 30.00 (978-0-7910-7684-2(9) , Chelsea Hse.) Facts On File, Inc.

Dorrie, Roxanne. Venus & Serena Williams: The Smashing Sisters. 2003. (High Five Reading (Red Level) Ser.). (Illus.). (J). 64p. lib. bdg. 22.60 (978-0-7368-2784-3(6)); 48p. pap. 23.93 (978-0-7368-2827-7(3)) Capstone Pr., Inc.

Dougherty, Denis. Michael Jordan. 1999. (Jam Session Ser.). (Illus.). 32p. (J). (gr. 3-8). lib. bdg. 24.21 (978-1-57765-038-6(7) , ABDO & Daughters) ABDO Publishing Co.

Dougherty, Terri. Barry Bonds. 2002. (Jam Session Ser.). (Illus.). 32p. (J). (gr. 3-8). lib. bdg. 24.21 (978-1-57765-675-3(X) , ABDO & Daughters) ABDO Publishing Co.

—Ken Griffey, Jr. 2001. (Jam Session Ser.). (Illus.). 32p. (J). (gr. 3-8). lib. bdg. 24.21 (978-1-57765-472-8(2) , ABDO & Daughters) ABDO Publishing Co.

—Lisa Leslie. 1999. (Jam Session Ser.). (Illus.). 32p. (J). (gr. 3-8). lib. bdg. 24.21 (978-1-57765-313-4(0) , ABDO & Daughters) ABDO Publishing Co.

Downing, David. Malcolm X. 2003. (Leading Lives Ser.). (Illus.). 64p. (J). lib. bdg. 28.50 (978-1-58810-579-0(2)) Heinemann Library.

—Malcolm X. 2003. (gr. 5-8). lib. bdg. 17.60 (978-0-613-60899-2(2)) Tandem Library Bks.

—Martin Luther King, Jr. 2002. (Leading Lives Ser.). (Illus.). 64p. (J). (gr. 5-7). lib. bdg. 28.50 (978-1-58810-580-6(6)) Heinemann Library.

Doyle, Alfreda C. Black American Inventors - Based on Black American Inventors - A Rhyme. 1999. (Illus.). 20p. pap., wbk. ed. 15.95 (978-1-56820-389-8(6)) Story Time Stories That Rhyme.

Dray, Philip. Daughter of Freedom: The Life & Times of Ida B. Wells. Alcorn, Stephen, illus. 2007. (J). (***978-1-56145-417-4(6)***) Peachtree Pubs., Ltd.

Driscoll, Laura. The Negro Leagues: All-Black Baseball. Mitchell, Tracy, illus. 2002. (Smart about History Ser.). 32p. (J). pap. 5.99 (978-0-448-42684-6(6) , Grosset & Dunlap) Penguin Group (USA) Inc.

Dubois, Muriel L. Rosa Parks. 2003. (Photo-Illustrated Biographies Ser.). (Illus.). 24p. (J). (gr. 2-3). lib. bdg. 18.60 (978-0-7368-1607-6(0) , Bridgestone Bks.) Capstone Pr., Inc.

Dubowski, Cathy East. Rosa Parks: Don't Give In! 2005. (Defining Moments Ser.). (Illus.). 32p. (J). lib. bdg. 25.27 (978-1-59716-078-0(4)) Bearport Publishing Co., Inc.

Duggleby, John. Story Painter: The Life of Jacob Lawrence. 1998. (Illus.). 64p. (J). (gr. 1-7). 16.95 (978-0-8118-2082-0(3)) Chronicle Bks. LLC.

Dumas, Bianca. Robert Moses. 2003. (African-American Biographies Ser.). (Illus.). 64p. (J). lib. bdg. 28.56 (978-0-7398-7031-0(9)) Raintree.

—Robert Parris Moses. 2003. (African-American Biographies Ser.). (Illus.). 64p. (J). (ps-7). pap. 9.50 (978-1-4109-0319-8(2)) Raintree.

Dunn, Herb. Jackie Robinson: Young Sports Trailblazer. Henderson, Meryl, illus. 1999. (Childhood of Famous Americans Ser.). 192p. (J). (gr. 3-7). pap. 5.99 (978-0-689-82453-1(X) , Aladdin) Simon & Schuster Children's Publishing.

—Jackie Robinson: Young Sports Trailblazer. 1999. (Childhood of Famous Americans Ser.). (J). 11.64 (978-0-606-16287-6(9)); (gr. 3-6). lib. bdg. 13.00 (978-0-613-15849-7(0)) Tandem Library Bks.

Dunn, Joe. Jackie Robinson. Espinosa, Rod, illus. 2007. (Bio-Graphics Ser.). 32p. (J). (gr. 3-6). lib. bdg. 27.07 (***978-1-60270-068-0(0)*** , Graphic Planet) Magic Wagon.

Dyson, Cindy. Janet Jackson: Singer. 2000. (Black Americans of Achievement Ser.). (Illus.). 144p. (J). (gr. 4-7). 32.00 (978-0-7910-5283-9(4)); (YA). (gr. 5 up). pap. 30.00 (978-0-7910-5284-6(2)) Facts On File, Inc. (Chelsea Hse.).

Edelman, Marian Wright. Lanterns: A Memoir of Mentors. 2000. (gr. 7-12). lib. bdg. 23.45 (978-0-613-31403-9(4)) Tandem Library Bks.

Edwards, Pamela Duncan. The Bus Ride That Changed History: The Story of Rosa Parks. Shanahan, Danny, illus. 2005. 32p. (J). (gr. k-3). 16.00 (978-0-618-44911-8(6)) Houghton Mifflin Co. Trade & Reference Div.

Edwards, Roberta. Barack Obama: An American Story. Call, Ken, illus. 2007. (All Aboard Reading Ser.). 48p. (J). (gr. 1-3). pap. 3.99 (***978-0-448-44799-5(1)*** , Grosset & Dunlap) Penguin Group (USA) Inc.

Ella Fitzgerald: The Tale of a Vocal Virtuosa. 2004. 29.95 incl. cd-rom (978-1-55592-498-0(0)) Weston Woods Studios, Inc.

Ellis, Rex M. With a Banjo on My Knee: A Musical Journey from Slavery to Freedom. 2001. (Single Titles Social Studies Ser.). (Illus.). 160p. (YA). (gr. 9-12). 28.00 (978-0-531-11747-7(2) , Watts, Franklin) Scholastic Library Publishing.

Embacher, Eric. Will Smith: The Funny, Funky, & Confident Fresh Prince. 2003. (High Five Reading (Red Level) Ser.). (Illus.). (J). 64p. lib. bdg. 22.60 (978-0-7368-2786-7(2)); 48p. pap. 23.93 (978-0-7368-2829-1(X)) Capstone Pr., Inc.

Empak Publishing Company Staff. Black Civil Rights Leaders. (J). 2.50 (978-0-922162-78-9(6)) Empak Publishing Co.

—Black Pioneers. (J). 2.50 (978-0-922162-77-2(8)) Empak Publishing Co.

—Historic Black Abolitionists: A Gift of Heritage. ("Black History" Publication Ser.). 2.50 (978-0-922162-80-2(8)) Empak Publishing Co.

—Historic Black Firsts: A Gift of Heritage. ("Black History" Publication Ser.). (J). 2.50 (978-0-922162-82-6(4)) Empak Publishing Co.

—Historic Black Women. (J). 2.50 (978-0-922162-75-8(1)) Empak Publishing Co.

Eskridge, Ann E. Slave Uprisings & Runaways: Fighting for Freedom & the Underground Railroad. 2004. (Slavery in American History Ser.). (Illus.). 128p. (J). lib. bdg. 26.60 (978-0-7660-2154-9(8)) Enslow Pubs., Inc.

Evento, Susan. Mary McLeod Bethune. 2004. (Rookie Biographies Ser.). (Illus.). 31p. (J). 20.50 (978-0-516-21720-8(8) , Children's Pr.) Scholastic Library Publishing.

Fact Finders Biographies: Great African Americans. 2005. (Fact Finders Ser.). (Illus.). (J). (gr. 3-4). lib. bdg. 271.20 (978-0-7368-4424-6(4)) Capstone Pr., Inc.

Fandel, Jennifer. James Brown. 2003. (Illus.). 64p. (J). pap. 9.50 (978-1-4109-0317-4(6)); lib. bdg. 28.56 (978-0-7398-7027-3(0)) Raintree.

—Martin Luther King, Jr. 2005. (Genius Ser.). (Illus.). 48p. (gr. 5-9). 21.95 (978-1-58341-329-6(4) , Creative Education) Creative Co., The.

—Martin Luther King, Jr: Great Civil Rights Leader. 2007. (Graphic Library). (Illus.). 32p. (J). (978-0-7368-6498-5(9)) Capstone Pr., Inc.

Farris, Christine King. My Brother Martin: A Sister Remembers Growing up with the Rev. Dr. Martin Luther King Jr. Soentpiet, Chris K., illus. 2003. 40p. (J). 17.95 (978-0-689-84387-7(9)) Simon & Schuster Children's Publishing.

Feeney, Kathy. Martin Luther King, Jr. 2002. (Photo-Illustrated Biographies Ser.). (Illus.). 24p. (J). (gr. 2-3). lib. bdg. 18.60 (978-0-7368-1111-8(7) , Bridgestone Bks.) Capstone Pr., Inc.

Feinstein, Stephen. Colin Powell. 2007. (African-American Heroes Ser.). (Illus.). 24p. (J). (gr. 1-3). lib. bdg. 21.26 (978-0-7660-2761-9(9) , Enslow Elementary) Enslow Pubs., Inc.

—Lee sobre Martin Luther King, Jr./Read about Martin Luther King, Jr. 2006. (I Like Biographies! Bilingual Ser.). (ENG & SPA., Illus.). 24p. (J). (gr. 1-3). lib. bdg. 21.26 (978-0-7660-2745-9(7) , Enslow Elementary) Enslow Pubs., Inc.

—Mae Jemison. 2007. (African-American Heroes Ser.). (Illus.). 24p. (J). (gr. 1-3). lib. bdg. 21.26 (978-0-7660-2762-6(7) , Enslow Elementary) Enslow Pubs., Inc.

—Oprah Winfrey. 2007. (African-American Heroes Ser.). (Illus.). 24p. (J). (gr. 1-3). lib. bdg. 21.26 (978-0-7660-2764-0(3) , Enslow Elementary) Enslow Pubs., Inc.

—Read about George Washington Carver. 2006. (I Like Biographies! Ser.). (Illus.). 24p. (J). (978-0-7660-2897-5(6)) Enslow Pubs., Inc.

—Read about Harriet Tubman. 2005. (I Like Biographies! Ser.). (Illus.). 24p. (J). lib. bdg. 21.26 (978-0-7660-2591-2(8) , Enslow Elementary) Enslow Pubs., Inc.

—Read about Martin Luther King, Jr. 2004. (I Like Biographies Ser.!). (Illus.). 24p. (J). lib. bdg. 24.95 (978-0-7660-2300-0(1)) Enslow Pubs., Inc.

Feinstein, Stephen. Wynton Marsalis. 2007. (African-American Heroes Ser.). (Illus.). 24p. (J). (gr. 1-3). lib. bdg. 21.26 (***978-0-7660-2766-4(X)*** , Enslow Elementary) Enslow Pubs., Inc.

Feldman, Heather. Marion Jones: World-Class Runner. 2001. (Reading Power Ser.). (Illus.). 24p. (J). (gr. 1). lib. bdg. 17.25 (978-0-8239-5718-7(7) , PKMAJO, PowerKids Pr.) Rosen Publishing Group, Inc., The.

—Marion Jones, Atleta de Categoria Internacional. 2002. (Coleccion Power Kids). (SPA & ENG., Illus.). 24p. (J). (gr. k-2). lib. bdg. 17.25 (978-0-8239-6141-2(9) , RN31310, Buenas Letra) Rosen Publishing Group, Inc., The.

—Venus Williams: Campeona del Tenis. 2002. (Superestrellas del Deporte Ser.).Tr. of Venus Williams: Tennis Champion. (SPA.). 24p. (J). lib. bdg. 17.25 (978-0-8239-6120-7(6) , Buenas Letra) Rosen Publishing Group, Inc., The.

—Venus Williams: Campeona del Tenis. de Leon, Mauricio V., tr. 2001. Tr. of Venus Williams: Tennis Champion. (SPA.). 24p. 11.95 Rosen Publishing Group, Inc., The.

—Venus Williams: Tennis Champion. 2001. (Reading Power Ser.). (Illus.). 24p. (J). (gr. 1). lib. bdg. 17.25 (978-0-8239-5717-0(9) , PKSUST, PowerKids Pr.) Rosen Publishing Group, Inc., The.

—Venus Williams, Campeona del Tenis. 2002. (Coleccion Power Kids). (SPA & ENG., Illus.). 24p. (J). (gr. k-2). lib. bdg. 17.25 (978-0-8239-6138-2(9) , RN31300, Buenas Letra) Rosen Publishing Group, Inc., The.

Feldman, Ruth Tenzer. Thurgood Marshall. 2001. (Biography Ser.). (Illus.). 112p. (J). (gr. 6-12). lib. bdg. 27.93 (978-0-8225-4989-5(1) , Lerner Pubns.) Lerner Publishing Group.

Ferris, Jeri Chase. Demanding Justice: A Story about Mary Ann Shadd Cary. Smith, Kimanne, illus. 2003. 64p. (J). 6.95 (978-0-87614-928-7(X) , Carolrhoda Bks.); (gr. 4-8). 22.60 (978-1-57505-177-2(X)) Lerner Publishing Group.

—Demanding Justice: A Story about Mary Ann Shadd Cary. 2003. (gr. 3-6). lib. bdg. 14.10 (978-0-613-58898-0(3)) Tandem Library Bks.

Figley, Marty Rhodes. Prisoner for Liberty. Orback, Craig, illus. 2008. (On My Own History Ser.). (J). lib. bdg. 25.26 (***978-0-8225-7280-0(X)*** , Millbrook Pr.) Lerner Publishing Group.

Figley, Marty Rhodes. Washington Is Burning. Orback, Craig, illus. 2006. (On My Own History Ser.). 48p. (J). 25.26 (978-1-57505-875-7(8)) Lerner Publishing Group.

Fillon, Mike. Young Superstars of Tennis: The Venus & Serena Williams Story. 1999. (Illus.). 144p. (YA). (gr. 6-12). lib. bdg. 19.95 (978-1-888105-43-8(7)) Avisson Pr., Inc.

Findley, Violet. Easy Reader Biographies: Harriet Tubman: Follow the North Star. 2007. 16p. pap. 2.99 (***978-0-439-92330-9(1)*** , Teaching Resources) Scholastic, Inc.

Fine, Edith Hope. Martin Luther King, Jr: Champion of Civil Rights. 2006. (Heroes of American History Ser.). (Illus.). 32p. (J). lib. bdg. 22.60 (978-0-7660-2466-3(0) , Enslow Elementary) Enslow Pubs., Inc.

—Rosa Parks: Meet a Civil Rights Hero. 2004. (Meeting Famous People Ser.). (Illus.). 32p. (J). lib. bdg. 22.60 (978-0-7660-2099-3(1)) Enslow Pubs., Inc.

Finlayson, Reggie. Colin Powell. 2005. (Biography Ser.). (Illus.). 112p. (gr. 6-12). lib. bdg. 27.93 (978-0-8225-4966-6(2)) Lerner Publishing Group.

—Colin Powell. 2004. (gr. 7-12). lib. bdg. 16.40 (978-0-613-76660-9(1)) Tandem Library Bks.

Fisher, Antwone Quenton. Finding Fish: A Memoir. 2001. (gr. 7-12). lib. bdg. 23.40 (978-0-613-49314-7(1)) Tandem Library Bks.

Fitzgerald, Dawn. Destiny's Child. 2002. (Galaxy of Superstars Ser.). (Illus.). 64p. (J). 25.00 (978-0-7910-6770-3(X) , Chelsea Hse.) Facts On File, Inc.

Flanagan, Alice K. Colin Powell: U. S. Army General & Secretary of State. 2001. (Career Biographies Ser.). (Illus.). 128p. (J). (gr. 6-12). 25.00 (978-0-89434-372-8(6) , F415, Ferguson Publishing Co.) Facts On File, Inc.

Fleming, Alice Mulcahey. Martin Luther King, Jr. A Dream of Hope. 2008. (Sterling Biographies Ser.). (Illus.). 128p. (J). pap. 5.95 (***978-1-4027-4439-6(0)***) Sterling Publishing Co., Inc.

Ford, Carin T. Muhammad Ali: I Am the Greatest. 2006. (African-American Biography Library). (Illus.). 128p. (J). lib. bdg. 31.93 (978-0-7660-2460-1(1)) Enslow Pubs., Inc.

—Paul Robeson: I Want to Make Freedom Ring. 2007. (African-American Biography Library). (Illus.). 128p. (J). (gr 6 up). lib. bdg. 31.93 (***978-0-7660-2703-9(1)***) Enslow Pubs., Inc.

Ford, Carin T. Ray Charles: I Was Born with Music Inside Me. 2007. (African-American Biography Library). (Illus.). 128p. (J). lib. bdg. 31.93 (978-0-7660-2701-5(5)) Enslow Pubs., Inc.

Forkos, Heather. Tupac Shakur. 2000. (They Died Too Young Ser.). (Illus.). 48p. (J). (gr. 4-7). 21.95 (978-0-7910-5859-6(X) , Chelsea Hse.) Facts On File, Inc.

Forten, Charlotte L., et al. A Free Black Girl Before the Civil War: The Diary of Charlotte Forten, 1854. Steele, Christy & Graves, Kerry, eds. 2000. (Blue Earth Books). (Illus.). 32p. (J). (gr. 3-4). lib. bdg. 22.60 (978-0-7368-0345-8(9) , Bridgestone Bks.) Capstone Pr., Inc.

Fradin, Dennis Brindell. My Family Shall Be Free! The Life of Peter Still. 2001. (gr. 5 up). (Illus.). 208p. (J). 17.89 (978-0-06-029328-4(4)); (YA). pap. 16.95 (978-0-06-447262-3(0)) HarperCollins Pubs.

Fradin, Dennis Brindell & Fradin, Judith Bloom. Ida B. Wells: Mother of the Civil Rights Movement. 2000. (Illus.). 192p. (J). (gr. 5-9). tchr. ed. 19.00 (978-0-395-89898-7(6) , Clarion Bks.) Houghton Mifflin Co. Trade & Reference Div.

Fradin, Judith Bloom & Fradin, Dennis Brindell. The Power of One: Daisy Bates & the Little Rock Nine. 2004. (Illus.). 192p. (YA). (gr. 5-9). tchr. ed. 19.00 (978-0-618-31556-7(X) , Clarion Bks.) Houghton Mifflin Co. Trade & Reference Div.

Franzen, Lenore. Venus Williams. 2003. (Ovations Ser.). (Illus.). 32p. (J). (978-1-58341-249-7(2) , Creative Education) Creative Co., The.

Freedman, Russell. Freedom Walkers: The Story of the Montgomery Bus Boycott. 2006. (Illus.). 112p. (J). (gr. 3-7). 18.95 (978-0-8234-2031-5(0)) Holiday Hse., Inc.

—The Voice That Challenged a Nation: Marian Anderson & the Struggle for Equal Rights. 2004. (Illus.). 128p. (J). (gr. 4-6). tchr. ed. 18.00 (978-0-618-15976-5(2) , Clarion Bks.) Houghton Mifflin Co. Trade & Reference Div.

Friedrich, Belinda. Oprah Winfrey. 2001. (Women of Achievement Ser.). (Illus.). 112p. (J). pap. (978-0-7910-5892-3(1)); (gr. 4-7). 30.00 (978-0-7910-5891-6(3)) Facts On File, Inc. (Chelsea Hse.).

Frost, Helen. Let's Meet Booker T. Washington. 2003. (Let's Meet Biographies Ser.). (Illus.). 32p. (gr. 2-4). 23.00 (978-0-7910-7318-6(1) , Chelsea Hse.) Facts On File, Inc.

—Let's Meet Ida B. Wells-Barnett. 2003. (Let's Meet Biographies Ser.). (Illus.). 32p. (gr. 2-4). 23.00 (978-0-7910-7320-9(3) , Chelsea Hse.) Facts On File, Inc.

—Let's Meet Jackie Robinson. 2003. (Let's Meet Biographies Ser.). (Illus.). 32p. (gr. 2-4). 23.00 (978-0-7910-7321-6(1) , Chelsea Hse.) Facts On File, Inc.

—Sojourner Truth. Saunders-Smith, Gail, ed. 2003. (Famous Americans Ser.). (Illus.). 24p. (J). (gr. k-1). lib. bdg. 15.93 (978-0-7368-1640-3(2) , Pebble Bks.) Capstone Pr., Inc.

—Thurgood Marshall. Saunders-Smith, Gail, ed. 2003. (Famous Americans Ser.). (Illus.). 24p. (J). (gr. k-1). lib. bdg. 15.93 (978-0-7368-1643-4(7) , Pebble Bks.) Capstone Pr., Inc.

Fullen, Marilyn K. Great Black Writers. 2002. (Contributions Ser.). (Illus.). 64p. (J). 12.95 (978-0-940880-66-5(0)); pap. 6.95 (978-0-940880-67-2(9)) Open Hand Publishing, LLC.

Fuller, Barbara. Great Britain. 2004. (Illus.). (J). 48p. 27.07 (978-0-7614-1760-6(5)); 2nd ed. 144p. 37.07 (978-0-7614-1845-0(8)) Cavendish, Marshall Corp. (Benchmark Bks.).

Gaines, Ann Graham. Allen Iverson. l.t. ed. 2002. (Real Life Reader Biographies Ser.). (Illus.). 32p. (gr. 3-8). lib. bdg. 15.95 (978-1-58415-134-0(X)) Mitchell Lane Pubs., Inc.

—Whoopi Goldberg. 2000. (Illus.). 112p. (J). (ps-7). per. 18.75 (978-0-613-12278-8(X)) Tandem Library Bks.

Gallagher, Aileen. Walter Payton. 2003. (Football Hall of Famers Ser.). (Illus.). 112p. (YA). (gr. 5-8). lib. bdg. 29.25 (978-0-8239-3611-3(2) , Rosen Central) Rosen Publishing Group, Inc., The.

Ganeri, Anita. Martin Luther King, Jr. 2003. (Twentieth Century History Makers Ser.). (Illus.). 112p. (J). lib. bdg. 32.85 (978-0-7398-5257-6(4)) Raintree.

Garcia, Kimberly. Janet Jackson. 2002. (Real-Life Reader Biography Ser.). (Illus.). 32p. (J). (gr. 3-8). lib. bdg. 15.95 (978-1-58415-113-5(7)) Mitchell Lane Pubs., Inc.

Garrett, Leslie. Story of Muhammad Ali. 2002. (gr. k-3). lib. bdg. 11.80 (978-0-613-45625-8(4)) Tandem Library Bks.

Garrett, Leslie & Dorling Kindersley Publishing Staff. The Story of Muhammad Ali. 2002. (Readers Ser.). (Illus.). 48p. (J). (gr. 1-4). 12.99 (978-0-7894-8516-8(8)); Vol. 4. pap. 3.99 (978-0-7894-8517-5(6)) Dorling Kindersley Publishing, Inc.

Gatto, Kimberly. Emmitt Smith. 2003. (Stars of Sport Ser.). (Illus.). 48p. (J). 26.20 (978-0-7377-2084-6(0) , Greenhaven Pr., Inc.) Thomson Gale.

Gayle, Sharon. Harriet Tubman & the Freedom Train. Marshall, Felicia, illus. 2003. (Ready-to-Read Ser.). 32p. (J). pap. 3.99 (978-0-689-85480-4(3) , Aladdin) Simon & Schuster Children's Publishing.

Gelfand, Dale Evva & Rhodes, Lisa Renee. Coretta Scott King: Civil Rights Activist. 2nd rev. ed. 2006. (Black Americans of Achievement, Legacy Edition Ser.). (Illus.). 144p. (J). (gr. 6-12). 30.00 (978-0-7910-9522-5(3) , Chelsea Hse.) Facts On File, Inc.

Gelletly, LeeAnne. Mae Jemison. 2002. (Black Americans of Achievement Ser.). (Illus.). 112p. (J). 30.00 (978-0-7910-6293-7(7) , Chelsea Hse.) Facts On File, Inc.

Gentry, Tony. Jesse Owens: Champion Athlete. 2005. (Black Americans of Achievement Ser.). (Illus.). 112p. (J). (gr. 6-12). 30.00 (978-0-7910-8252-2(0)); pap. 13.25 (978-0-7910-8372-7(1)) Facts On File, Inc. (Chelsea Hse.).

Gillis, Jennifer Blizin. Jesse Jackson. 2005. (Illus.). 32p. (J). (978-1-4034-6983-0(0)); pap. (978-1-4034-6990-8(3)) Heinemann Library.

—Sojourner Truth. 2005. (Illus.). 32p. (J). (978-1-4034-6981-6(4)); pap. (978-1-4034-6988-5(1)) Heinemann Library.

—W.E.B. Dubois. 2005. (Illus.). 32p. (J). (978-1-4034-6982-3(2)); pap. (978-1-4034-6989-2(X)) Heinemann Library.

Giovanni, Nikki. Rosa. Collier, Bryan, illus. rev. ed. 2005. 40p. (J). (gr. 4-7). 16.95 (978-0-8050-7106-1(7) , Holt, Henry & Co. Bks. For Young Readers) Holt, Henry & Co.

—Rosa. Collier, Bryan, illus. 2007. 40p. (J). pap. 7.99 (***978-0-312-37602-4(2)***) Square Fish.

Glover, Maria Robinson. Who Do I Want to Be? Contemporary Black Women from A to Z. Glover, Maria Robinson, illus. 2006. (J). 16.95 (978-0-9787940-0-2(1)) Hot-Comb Pr.

Golenbock, Peter. Hank Aaron: Brave in Every Way. Lee, Paul, illus. 2005. 32p. (J). reprint ed. pap. 6.00 (978-0-15-205250-8(X) , Voyager Bks./Libros Viajeros) Harcourt Children's Bks.

—Teammates. 1998. (Illus.). 32p. (ps-3). 16.98 (978-0-8172-4092-9(6)) Raintree.

Gomez, Rebecca. Jackie Robinson. 2003. (First Biographies Ser.). (Illus.). 32p. (J). (gr. k-4). lib. bdg. 22.78 (978-1-57765-949-5(X)) ABDO Publishing Co.

Goodman, Michael E. Barry Bonds. 1998. (Ovations Ser.). (Illus.). 32p. (YA). (gr. 4-7). lib. bdg. 21.30 (978-0-88682-694-9(2) , Creative Education) Creative Co., The.

—Grant Hill. 1998. (Ovations Ser.). (Illus.). 32p. (YA). (gr. 4-7). lib. bdg. (978-0-88682-831-8(7) , Creative Education) Creative Co., The.

—Kobe Bryant. 2003. (Ovations Ser.). (Illus.). 32p. (J). lib. bdg. (978-1-58341-248-0(4) , Creative Education) Creative Co., The.

Gordon, Kevin. Not Yet African: The Long Voyage Home. unabr. ed. 1998. 192p. (gr. 9-12). pap. 14.00 (978-1-57889-013-2(6)) Passeggiata Pr.

Gorman, Jacqueline Laks. Queen Latifah. 2006. (Today's Superstars). (Illus.). 32p. (J). (gr. 5 up). lib. bdg. 23.93 (***978-0-8368-7652-9(0)***) Stevens, Gareth Inc.

Gormley, Beatrice. Althea Gibson: Young Tennis Player. Henderson, Meryl, illus. 2005. 214p. (J). (gr. 3-7). lib. bdg. 12.04 (978-0-606-33374-0(6)) Tandem Library Bks.

Gormley, Beatrice. Malcolm X: A Revolutionary Voice. 2008. (Sterling Biographies Ser.). (Illus.). 128p. (J). pap. 5.95 (***978-1-4027-4589-8(3)***) Sterling Publishing Co., Inc.

Gosda, Randy T. Booker T. Washington. 2002. (First Biographies Ser.). (Illus.). 32p. (J). (gr. k-4). lib. bdg. 22.78 (978-1-57765-734-7(9) , Buddy Bks.) ABDO Publishing Co.

Gotsch, Patrice. Martin Luther King, Jr: Changing Lives. Arreola, Gil, illus. 2005. 19p. (J). pap. (***978-1-55501-779-8(7)***) Ballard & Tighe Pubs.

Granger, Stacey. Colin Powell. l.t. ed. 2002. (Real-Life Reader Biography Ser.). (Illus.). 32p. (J). (gr. 3-8). lib. bdg. 15.95 (978-1-58415-144-9(7)) Mitchell Lane Pubs., Inc.

Graves, Jeseca, illus. Bessie Coleman: The Story of an Aviation Pioneer. 2007. 24p. (J). (***978-0-9745294-1-7(9)***) San Diego County Regional Airport Authority.

Graves, Karen Marie. Michael Jackson. 2000. (People in the News Ser.). (Illus.). 112p. (J). (gr. 6-9). (978-1-56006-707-8(1) , Lucent Bks.) Thomson Gale.

Graves, Renee. Malcolm X. 2007. (Cornerstones of Freedomtrade;, Second Ser.). 48p. (J). 5.95 (***978-0-531-18691-6(1)*** , Children's Pr.) Scholastic Library Publishing.

Green, Michelle Y. A Strong Right Arm: The Story of Mamie "Peanut" Johnson. Nelson, Kadir, illus. 128p. (J). 2004. (gr. 3-6). pap. 5.99 (978-0-14-240072-2(6) , Puffin); 2002. (gr. 4-7). 15.99 (978-0-8037-2661-1(9) , Dial) Penguin Group (USA) Inc.

—A Strong Right Arm: The Story of Mamie "Peanut" Johnson. 2004. (gr. 5-8). lib. bdg. 14.15 (978-0-613-83004-1(0)) Tandem Library Bks.

Green, Richard L., et al, eds. A Salute to Black Civil Rights Leaders. Dobson, S. Gaston, illus. (Empak "Black History" Publication). (J). pap. 1.00 (978-0-9616156-3-5(X)) Empak Publishing Co.

Greene, Meg. Lauryn Hill. (Galaxy of Superstars Ser.). (Illus.). 2000. 64p. (YA). 25.00 (978-0-7910-5495-6(0)); 1999. 64p. (J). pap. 25.00 (978-0-7910-5496-3(9)) Facts On File, Inc. (Chelsea Hse.).

—Lauryn Hill. 2000. (gr. 5-8). lib. bdg. 17.60 (978-0-613-21883-2(3)) Tandem Library Bks.

Greenfield, Eloise. How They Got Over: African Americans & the Call of the Sea. Gilchrist, Jan Spivey, illus. 2003. 128p. (J). (gr. 3-5). 16.99 (978-0-06-028991-1(0)) HarperCollins Pubs.

—Rosa Parks. Ashby, Gil, illus. 2002. 12.62 (978-0-7587-0755-0(X)) Book Wholesalers, Inc.

Gregson, Susan R. James Beckwourth: Mountaineer, Scout & Pioneer. 2005. (Signature Lives Ser.). (Illus.). 112p. (J). (gr. 5-7). (978-0-7565-1000-8(7)) Compass Point Bks.

Griffin, Gwen. Barry Sanders. 1999. (Ovations Ser.). (Illus.). 32p. (YA). (gr. 4-7). pap. (978-0-88682-938-4(0) , Creative Education) Creative Co., The.

Guilfoyle, Peg. Oprah Winfrey. 1999. (Ovations Ser.). (Illus.). 32p. (YA). (gr. 4-7). pap. (978-0-88682-941-4(0) , Creative Education) Creative Co., The.

Gutman, Bill. Ken Griffey, Jr. A Biography. 1998. (J). (978-0-606-13550-4(2)) Tandem Library Bks.

—Ken Griffey, Jr. Baseball's Best. 1998. (Millbrook Sports World Ser.). (Illus.). 48p. (J). (gr. 3-6). lib. bdg. 22.90 (978-0-7613-0415-9(0) , Millbrook Pr.) Lerner Publishing Group.

—Marion Jones: The Fastest Woman in the World. 2000. (YA). (978-0-606-19499-0(1)) Tandem Library Bks.

—Michael Jordan & Scottie Pippen. 1998. (Teammates Ser.). (Illus.). 112p. (gr. 4-6). lib. bdg. 23.90 (978-0-7613-0420-3(7) , Millbrook Pr.) Lerner Publishing Group.

—Venus & Serena: The Grand Slam Williams Sisters. 2001. (Scholastic Biography Ser.). (Illus.). 144p. (J). (gr. 3-7). pap. 4.50 (978-0-439-27152-3(5)) Scholastic, Inc.

—Venus & Serena: The Grand Slam Williams Sisters. 2001. (Illus.). (978-0-606-21502-2(6)) Tandem Library Bks.

Gutman, Dan. Jackie Robinson & the Big Game. Garvin, Elaine, illus. 2006. 32p. (J). lib. bdg. 15.00 (***978-1-4242-0957-6(9)***) Fitzgerald Bks.

—Jackie Robinson & the Big Game. Garvin, Elaine, illus. 2006. (Ready-to-Read Cofa Ser.). 32p. (J). pap. 3.99 (978-0-689-86239-7(3) , Aladdin); lib. bdg. 11.89 (978-0-689-86240-3(7) , Aladdin Library) Simon & Schuster Children's Publishing.

Haegele, Katie. Monte Irvin. 2002. (Baseball Hall of Famers of the Negro League Ser.). (Illus.). 112p. (YA). (gr. 5-8). lib. bdg. 29.25 (978-0-8239-3477-5(2) , Rosen Central) Rosen Publishing Group, Inc., The.

Hall, Margaret. Madam C. J. Walker. 2003. (Lives & Times Ser.). (Illus.). (J). 24p. pap. (978-1-4034-4257-4(6)); 32p. lib. bdg. 22.79 (978-1-4034-3252-0(X)) Heinemann Library.

Halvorsen, Lisa. George Washington Carver: Innovator in Agriculture. 2002. (Giants of Science Ser.). (Illus.). 64p. (J). 26.20 (978-1-56711-657-1(4) , Blackbirch Pr., Inc.) Thomson Gale.

Hanft, Joshua E. Jackie Robinson. Marcos, Pablo, illus. 2005. (Heroes of America Ser.). 240p. (J). (gr. 3-8). lib. bdg. 21.35 (978-1-59679-259-3(0)) ABDO Publishing Co.

Hansen, Joyce. African Americans Who Made a Difference. 2007. (Women of Hope Ser.). 32p. (J). pap. 6.99 (***978-0-590-93974-4(2)***) Scholastic, Inc.

Hansen, Joyce & Bread and Roses Staff. African Americans Who Made a Difference. 1998. (Illus.). 32p. (J). (gr. 3-7). pap. 16.95 (978-0-590-93973-7(4)) Scholastic, Inc.

Hanson, Joyce Ann. Mary McLeod Bethune & Black Women's Political Activism. 2003. (Illus.). 256p. 32.50 (978-0-8262-1451-5(7)) Univ. of Missouri Pr.

Harcourt School Publishers Staff. Booker T. Washington: Library Edition. 1999. (Collections Ser.). (Illus.). (J). 5.30 (978-0-15-314344-1(4)) Harcourt Schl. Pubs.

—Guion Bluford: A Space Biography. 2001. (Reader's Choice Bks.). (Illus.). (J). pap. 7.20 (978-0-15-314430-1(0)) Harcourt Schl. Pubs.

—Horizons: Madame C. J. Walker. 3rd ed. 2002. (Illus.). pap. 5.60 (978-0-15-333529-7(7)) Harcourt Schl. Pubs.

Hareas, John. All-Star Allen Iverson. 2003. (NBA Reader Ser.). 40p. (J). pap. 3.99 (978-0-439-44301-2(6)) Scholastic, Inc.

—All-Star Allen Iverson. 2003. (gr. k-3). lib. bdg. 11.80 (978-0-613-72200-1(0)) Tandem Library Bks.

Harmon, Rod. American Civil Rights Leaders. 2000. (Collective Biographies Ser.). (Illus.). 104p. (J). (gr. 6-12). lib. bdg. 26.60 (978-0-7660-1381-0(2)) Enslow Pubs., Inc.

Harriet Tubman & the Underground Railroad. (Graphic History Ser.). 32p. (YA). 7.95 (978-0-7368-5245-6(X)) Capstone Pr., Inc.

Hart, Joyce. Native Son: The Story of Richard Wright. 2004. (World Writers Ser.). (Illus.). 128p. (YA). (gr. 6-12). 23.95 (978-1-931798-06-8(0)) Reynolds, Morgan Inc.

Haskins, James. Champion: The Story of Muhammad Ali. Velasquez, Eric, illus. 2001. (J). (gr. 1-5). 18.85 (978-0-8027-8785-9(1)) Walker & Co.

Haskins, James & Benson, Kathleen. Conjure Times: Black Magicians in America. 2001. (Illus.). 192p. (J). (gr. 5-10). 17.85 (978-0-8027-8763-7(0)) Walker & Co.

—Conjure Times: The History of Black Magicians in America. 2001. (Illus.). 192p. (J). (gr. 5-10). 16.95 (978-0-8027-8762-0(2)) Walker & Co.

Haskins, James & Poole, Cecil F. Cecil Poole: A Life in the Law. 2002. (Illus.). xii, 172p. (YA). 15.00 (978-0-9635086-2-1(8)) Ninth Judicial Circuit Historical Society.

Haskins, Jim. Against All Opposition: Black Explorers in America. 2003. (gr. 5-8). lib. bdg. 17.60 (978-0-613-91054-5(0)) Tandem Library Bks.

—Black Stars. 2001. (Black Stars Ser.: Vol. 1). 272p. 59.95 (978-0-471-21145-7(1) , Wiley) Wiley, John & Sons, Inc.

—Outward Dreams: Black Inventors & Their Inventions. 2003. (gr. 5-8). lib. bdg. 17.60 (978-0-613-75330-2(5)) Tandem Library Bks.

—Outward Dreams: Black Inventors & Their Inventions. 2003. (Illus.). 112p. (J). pap. 8.95 (978-0-8027-7673-0(6)) Walker & Co.

Haskins, Jim & Benson, Kathleen. John Lewis in the Lead: A Story of the Civil Rights Movement. Andrews, Benny, illus. 2006. 40p. (J). 17.95 (978-1-58430-250-6(X)) Lee & Low Bks., Inc.

Hatt, Christine. Martin Luther King, Jr. 2004. (Judge for Yourself Ser.). (Illus.). 64p. (J). pap. (978-0-8368-5565-4(5)); (gr. 5 up). lib. bdg. 30.00 (978-0-8368-5562-3(0)) Stevens, Gareth Inc. (World Almanac Library).

Haugen, Brenda. Langston Hughes: The Voice of Harlem. 2005. (Signature Lives Ser.). (Illus.). 112p. (J). (gr. 5-7). 30.60 (978-0-7565-0993-4(9)) Compass Point Bks.

Haugen, Brenda. Thurgood Marshall: Civil Rights Lawyer & Supreme Court Justice. 2006. (Illus.). 112p. (J). lib. bdg. (***978-0-7565-1877-6(6)***) Compass Point Bks.

Hayes, Donna. Brandy. 1999. (Real-Life Reader Biography Ser.). (Illus.). 32p. (J). (gr. 3-8). lib. bdg. 15.95 (978-1-883845-93-3(9)) Mitchell Lane Pubs., Inc.

Hayhurst, Chris. Bill Russell. 2002. (Basketball Hall of Famers Ser.). (Illus.). 112p. (YA). (gr. 5-8). lib. bdg. 29.25 (978-0-8239-3480-5(2) , Rosen Central) Rosen Publishing Group, Inc., The.

Healy, Nick. Bill Russell. 2003. (Illus.). 64p. (J). pap. 9.50 (978-1-4109-0315-0(X)); lib. bdg. 28.56 (978-0-7398-7034-1(3)) Raintree.

—Bill Russell. 2003. (gr. 3-6). lib. bdg. 18.20 (978-0-613-78179-4(1)) Tandem Library Bks.

—Harriet Tubman. 2005. (Fact Finders Ser.). (Illus.). 32p. (J). 22.60 (978-0-7368-3743-9(4)) Capstone Pr., Inc.

—Jack Johnson. 2003. (African-American Biographies Ser.). (Illus.). 64p. pap. 8.95 (978-1-4109-0036-4(3)); (J). lib. bdg. 28.56 (978-0-7398-6873-7(X)) Raintree.

—Muhammad Ali. 2005. (Genius Ser.). (Illus.). 48p. (gr. 5-9). 21.95 (978-1-58341-333-3(2) , Creative Education) Creative Co., The.

—Paul Robeson. 2003. (African-American Biographies Ser.). 64p. pap. 8.95 (978-1-4109-0040-1(1)) Raintree.

Hearth, Amy Hill. The Delany Sisters Reach High. Ladwig, Tim, illus. 2004. 32p. 17.00 (978-0-687-03074-3(9)) Abingdon Pr.

Hicks, Kyra E. Martha Ann's Quilt for Queen Victoria. 2006. (J). 16.95 (978-1-933285-59-7(1)) Brown Bks. Publishing Group.

Hill, Christine M. Gwendolyn Brooks: Poetry Is Life Distilled. 2005. (African-American Biography Library). (Illus.). 128p. (J). (gr. 6-12). lib. bdg. 31.93 (978-0-7660-2292-8(7)) Enslow Pubs., Inc.

Hill, Mary. Colin Powell. 2003. (gr. k-3). lib. bdg. 12.95 (978-0-613-67704-2(8)) Tandem Library Bks.

—Serena & Venus Williams. 2003. (Welcome Bks.). (Illus.). 24p. (J). (ps-2). pap. 4.95 (978-0-516-27889-6(4) , Children's Pr.) Scholastic Library Publishing.

—Serena & Venus Williams. 2003. (gr. k-3). lib. bdg. 12.95 (978-0-613-67764-6(1)) Tandem Library Bks.

Hind, Devon & Bergstresser, Kate, trs. Jesse Owens: World's Fastest Human. 2003. (Alabama Roots Biography Ser.). (Illus.). 120p. (J). (978-1-878561-38-1(3)) Seacoast Publishing, Inc.

Hinman, Bonnie. Benjamin Banneker. 1999. (Colonial Leaders Ser.). (Illus.). 79p. (J). (gr. 3 up). pap. 8.95 (978-0-7910-5691-2(0) , Chelsea Hse.) Facts On File, Inc.

—Benjamin Banneker: American Mathematician & Astronomer. 2000. (Colonial Leaders Ser.). (Illus.). 80p. (J). (gr. 3 up). 27.50 (978-0-7910-5348-5(2) , Chelsea Hse.) Facts On File, Inc.

—A Stranger in My Own House: The Story of W. E. B. du Bois. 2005. (Civil Rights Leaders Ser.). (Illus.). 176p. (J). (gr. 6-12). 26.95 (978-1-931798-45-7(1)) Reynolds, Morgan Inc.

Hinton-Johnson, Kaavonia. Jacqueline Woodson. 2007. (Classic Storytellers Ser.). (Illus.). 48p. (J). lib. bdg. 29.95 (***978-1-58415-533-1(7)***) Mitchell Lane Pubs., Inc.

Hoena, B. A. Matthew Henson. 2005. (Illus.). 24p. (J). (ps-7). lib. bdg. 15.93 (978-0-7368-5249-4(2) , Pebble Bks.) Capstone Pr., Inc.

—Matthew Henson: Arctic Adventurer. Miller, Phil & Barnett, Charles, III, illus. 2005. (Graphic Library). 32p. (J). (gr. 3-7). lib. bdg. 25.26 (978-0-7368-4634-9(4)) Capstone Pr., Inc.

Holland, Gini. Louis Armstrong. 2003. (Trailblazers of the Modern World Ser.). (Illus.). 48p. (J). (gr. 5 up). pap. 11.95 (978-0-8368-5249-3(4) , World Almanac Library) Stevens, Gareth Inc.

—Oprah Winfrey. 2001. (Profiles Ser.). (Illus.). 56p. (J). (gr. 4-6). lib. bdg. 24.22 (978-1-58810-061-0(8)) Heinemann Library.

Holliday, Laurel. Dreaming in Color, Living in Black & White. 2000. (gr. 3-6). lib. bdg. 13.00 (978-0-613-21468-1(4)) Tandem Library Bks.

—Dreaming in Color Living in Black & White: Our Own Stories of Growing up Black in America. 2000. (J). 12.15 (978-0-606-19494-5(0)) Tandem Library Bks.

Homemaker, Nellie. Journey with a Woman of the Gullah Cultu. 2006. pap. 10.00 (***978-1-4257-1916-6(3)***) Xlibris Corp.

Hook, Jason. Muhammad Ali: The Greatest. 2001. (Famous Lives Ser.). (Illus.). 48p. (J). (gr. 3-7). lib. bdg. 27.12 (978-0-8172-5717-0(9)) Raintree.

Hopkinson, Deborah. Sweet Land of Liberty. Jenkins, Leonard, illus. 2007. 32p. (J). (gr. 1-5). 16.95 (978-1-56145-395-5(1) , Peachtree Junior) Peachtree Pubs., Ltd.

Horn, Geoffrey M. Colin Powell. 2004. (Trailblazers of the Modern World Ser.). (Illus.). 48p. (J). pap. 11.95 (978-0-8368-5267-7(2)); (YA). lib. bdg. 30.00 (978-0-8368-5498-5(5)) Stevens, Gareth Inc. (World Almanac Library).

—Thurgood Marshall. 2004. (Trailblazers of the Modern World Ser.). (Illus.). 48p. (J). (gr. 5 up). pap. 11.95 (978-0-8368-5258-5(3)); lib. bdg. 30.00 (978-0-8368-5098-7(X)) Stevens, Gareth Inc. (World Almanac Library).

Houghton, Sarah. Michael Jordan: The Best Ever. 2001. (Illus.). 64p. (J). pap. (978-0-7368-9502-6(7)); (gr. 4-5). lib. bdg. 22.60 (978-0-7368-4002-6(8) , Capstone High-Interest Bks.) Capstone Pr., Inc.

Hubbard, Crystal. Jimmy Winkfield: The Last Black King of the Kentucky Derby. Oyler, Tami, illus. 2007. (J). (*978-1-58430-274-2(7)) Lee & Low Bks., Inc.

Hudson, Wade. Five Bold Freedom Fighters. Garnett, Ron, illus. 2003. 48p. (J). (ps-ps). lib. bdg. 11.80 (978-0-613-63544-8(2)) Tandem Library Bks.

—Great Black Heroes: Five Bold Freedom Fighters. Garnett, Ron, illus. 2003. (Hello Reader! Ser.: Vol. 4). 48p. (J). (gr. 2-4). pap. 3.99 (978-0-590-48026-0(X) , Cartwheel Bks.) Scholastic, Inc.

—Great Black Heroes: Five Brave Explorers. Garnett, Ron, illus. 2004. 48p. (J). lib. bdg. 15.00 (978-1-59054-529-4(X)) Fitzgerald Bks.

—Scientists Healers & Inventors, Vol. 3. 2004. (Book of Black Heroes Ser.: Vol. 3). (Illus.). 72p. (J). (gr. 4-7). pap. 9.95 (978-0-940975-97-2(1) , Sankofa Bks.) Just Us Bks., Inc.

Hull, Mary, et al. Rosa Parks: Civil Rights Leader. 2nd rev. ed. 2006. (Black Americans of Achievement: Ser.). 128p. (J). (gr. 6-12). 30.00 (*978-0-7910-9523-2(1) , Chelsea Hse.) Facts On File, Inc.

Hull, Mary E. Rosa Parks: Civil Rights Leader. (Black Americans of Achievement Ser.). (Illus.). 112p. (J). (gr. 6-12). 2005. pap. 13.25 (978-0-7910-8338-3(1)); 2004. 30.00 (978-0-7910-8164-8(8)) Facts On File, Inc. (Chelsea Hse.).

Hunt, Rameck, et al. We Beat the Street: How a Friendship Pact Led to Success. 2006. (Illus.). 208p. (J). (gr. 5). pap. 6.99 (978-0-14-240627-4(9) , Puffin) Penguin Group (USA) Inc.

Jackie Robinson. 1999. (SmartReader Ser.). (J). Level 1. pap., tchr. ed. 19.95 incl. audio (978-0-7887-1156-5(3) , 79417T3); Level 2. pap., tchr. ed. 19.95 incl. audio (978-0-7887-0280-8(7) , 79320T3) Recorded Bks., LLC.

Jackson, Garnet N. Martin Luther King, Jr. A Man of Peace. Ford, George Cephas, illus. 2001. (Hello Reader! Ser.). 48p. (J). (978-0-439-20643-3(X)) Scholastic, Inc.

Jacobs, Harriet A. Incidents in the Life of a Slave Girl. 2000. (gr. 7-12). lib. bdg. 14.10 (978-0-613-21756-9(X)) Tandem Library Bks.

—Narrative of the Life of Frederick Douglass, an American Slave & Incidents In. 2000. (gr. 7-12). lib. bdg. 19.90 (978-0-613-50133-0(0)) Tandem Library Bks.

Jaffe, Elizabeth Dana. Sojourner Truth. 2001. (Compass Point Early Biographies Ser.). (Illus.). 32p. (J). (gr. 2 up). lib. bdg. 21.26 (978-0-7565-0068-9(0)) Compass Point Bks.

Jakoubek, Robert. Jesse Jackson: Civil Rights Leader & Politician. (Black Americans of Achievement Ser.). (Illus.). 112p. (gr. 6-12). 2005. pap. 13.25 (978-0-7910-8334-5(9)); 2004. (J). 30.00 (978-0-7910-8160-0(5)) Facts On File, Inc. (Chelsea Hse.).

Jakoubek, Robert E. Martin Luther King, Jr. Civil Rights Leader. (Black Americans of Achievement Ser.). (Illus.). 112p. (gr. 6-12). 2005. pap. 13.25 (978-0-7910-8335-2(7)); 2004. 30.00 (978-0-7910-8161-7(3)) Facts On File, Inc. (Chelsea Hse.).

January, Brendan. Martin Luther King, Jr. Minister & Civil Rights Activist. 2000. (Career Biographies Ser.). (Illus.). 128p. (J). (gr. 6-12). 25.00 (978-0-89434-342-1(4) , F405, Ferguson Publishing Co.) Facts On File, Inc.

Jarnow, Jesse. Phillis Wheatley. 2003. (Primary Sources of Famous People in American History Ser.). (Illus.). 32p. (J). pap. 6.50 (978-0-8239-4191-9(4)) Rosen Publishing Group, Inc., The.

Jeffrey, Gary. Martin Luther King, Jr: The Life of a Civil Rights Leader. Riley, Terry, illus. 2006. (Graphic Biographies Ser.). 48p. (J). lib. bdg. 29.95 (978-1-4042-0858-2(5)) Rosen Publishing Group, Inc., The.

—Martin Luther King Jr: The Life of a Civil Rights Leader. Forsey, Christopher, illus. 2006. 48p. (J). (978-1-4042-0920-6(4)); pap. (978-1-4042-0921-3(2)) Rosen Publishing Group, Inc., The.

Jeffrey, Laura S. Betty Shabazz: Sharing the Vision of Malcolm X. 2000. (African-American Biographies Ser.). (Illus.). 128p. (YA). (gr. 6-12). lib. bdg. 26.60 (978-0-7660-1210-3(7)) Enslow Pubs., Inc.

Jemison, Mae. Find Where the Wind Goes: Moments from My Life. (Find Where the Wind Goes Ser.). (Illus.). 208p. (J). 2003. pap. 4.99 (978-0-439-13196-4(0) , Scholastic Paperbacks); 2001. (gr. 5-9). pap. 16.95 (978-0-439-13195-7(2)) Scholastic, Inc.

—Find Where the Wind Goes: Moments from My Life. 2003. (gr. 5-8). lib. bdg. 13.00 (978-0-613-72017-5(2)) Tandem Library Bks.

Johnson, Dolores. Onward: A Photobiography of African-American Polar Explorer Matthew Henson. 2005. (National Geographic Photographer Ser.). (Illus.). 64p. (J). (gr. k-3). 17.95 (978-0-7922-7914-3(X)); 27.90 (978-0-7922-7915-0(8)) National Geographic Society. (National Geographic Children's Bks.).

Jones, Rob Lloyd. Martin Luther King, Jr. 2006. (Illus.). 62p. (J). pap. (*978-0-439-02299-6(1)) Scholastic, Inc.

Jones, Steven L. Football's Fallen Hero: The Jack Trice Story. 2000. (Cover-to-Cover Bks.). (Illus.). 64p. (J). (gr. 4-7). lib. bdg. 17.95 (978-0-7807-9043-8(X)) Perfection Learning Corp.

Jones, Veda Boyd. Jazz Age Poet: A Story about Langston Hughes. Kiwak, Barbara, illus. 2006. (Creative Minds Biography Ser.). 64p. (J). (ps-7). 22.60 (978-1-57505-757-6(3) , Carolrhoda Bks.) Lerner Publishing Group.

Jones, Victoria Garrett. Marian Anderson: A Voice Uplifted. 2008. (Sterling Biographies Ser.). (Illus.). 128p. (J). pap. 5.95 (*978-1-4027-4239-2(8)) Sterling Publishing Co., Inc.

Jordan, Denise M. Julian Bond: Civil Rights Activist & Chairman of the NAACP. 2001. (African-American Biographies Ser.). (Illus.). 128p. (J). (gr. 6-12). lib. bdg. 26.60 (978-0-7660-1549-4(1)) Enslow Pubs., Inc.

—Muhammad Ali: Meet the Champion. 2003. (Meeting Famous People Ser.). (Illus.). 32p. (J). lib. bdg. 22.60 (978-0-7660-2272-0(2)) Enslow Pubs., Inc.

Jordan, June. Soldier: A Poet's Childhood. 2000. (gr. 7-12). lib. bdg. 22.25 (978-0-613-34957-4(1)) Tandem Library Bks.

Josephson, Judith Pinkerton. Nikki Giovanni: Poet of the People. 2000. (African-American Biographies Ser.). (Illus.). 128p. (J). (gr. 6-12). lib. bdg. 26.60 (978-0-7660-1238-7(7)) Enslow Pubs., Inc.

Judge for Yourself New Releases: Martin Luther King, Jr.; Mahatma Gandhi, 2 bks. 2004. (Illus.). (J). (gr. 5 up). lib. bdg. 58.53 (978-0-8368-5560-9(4) , World Almanac Library) Stevens, Gareth Inc.

Kallen, Stuart A. Marcus Garvey & the Back to Africa Movement. 2006. (Lucent Library of Black History). (Illus.). 112p. (J). (gr. 7-10). 32.45 (978-1-59018-838-5(1) , Lucent Bks.) Thomson Gale.

Kelley, Brent. Lisa Leslie. 2000. (Illus.). 64p. (J). (gr. 4-7). lib. bdg. 17.60 (978-0-613-32788-6(8)) Tandem Library Bks.

Kelley, Brent P. Lisa Leslie. 2000. (Women Who Win Ser.). (Illus.). 64p. (gr. 4-7). (J). pap. 25.00 (978-0-7910-6154-1(X)); (YA). 25.00 (978-0-7910-5794-0(1)) Facts On File, Inc. (Chelsea Hse.).

Kent, Daniel T. Muhammad Ali & Laila Ali. 2004. (Famous Families Ser.). (Illus.). 48p. (J). lib. bdg. 25.25 (978-1-4042-0261-0(7)) Rosen Publishing Group, Inc., The.

Kent, Deborah. Phillis Wheatley: First Published African-American Poet. 2003. (Spirit of America). (Illus.). 32p. (J). (gr. 2-6). 27.07 (978-1-59296-009-5(X)) Child's World, Inc.

Kent, Jacqueline C. Phillis Wheatley. 2003. (Women of the Revolution Ser.). (J). pap. (978-1-58417-089-1(1)); lib. bdg. (978-1-58417-026-6(3)) Lake Street Pubs.

Kernan, Elizabeth. Harriet Tubman: A Lesson in Bravery. 2002. (Reading Room Collection). (Illus.). 24p. (J). pap. (978-0-8239-8229-5(7)); lib. bdg. 18.75 (978-0-8239-3750-9(X)) Rosen Publishing Group, Inc., The.

Kiely Miller, Barbara. Frederick Douglass. 2007. (J). pap. (*978-0-8368-8322-0(5) , Weekly Reader Early Learning Library) Stevens, Gareth Inc.

—George Washington Carver. 2007. (J). pap. (*978-0-8368-8320-6(9) , Weekly Reader Early Learning Library) Stevens, Gareth Inc.

King, Meet Martin Luther, Jr. Meet Martin Luther King Jr. 2004. 32p. (J). 7.95 (978-0-8249-5486-4(6)) Ideals Pubns.

Kinstad-Pupeza, Lori. Brandy. 1999. (Young Profiles Ser.). (Illus.). 32p. (J). (gr. k-6). lib. bdg. 22.78 (978-1-57765-323-3(8) , Checkerboard Library) ABDO Publishing Co.

Kirkpatrick, Rob. Evander Holyfield: Heavyweight Champion. 2000. (Reading Power Ser.). (Illus.). 24p. (J). (gr. 1). lib. bdg. 17.25 (978-0-8239-5542-8(7) , PowerKids Pr.) Rosen Publishing Group, Inc., The.

—Evander Holyfield, Campeon de los Pesos Pesados. 2002. (Coleccion Power Kids). (SPA & ENG., Illus.). 24p. (J). (gr. k-2). lib. bdg. 17.25 (978-0-8239-6148-1(6) , RN31316, Buenas Letra) Rosen Publishing Group, Inc., The.

—Grant Hill: Basketball All-Star. 2003. (Reading Power Ser.). (Illus.). 24p. (J). (gr. 1). lib. bdg. 17.25 (978-0-8239-5538-1(9) , PowerKids Pr.) Rosen Publishing Group, Inc., The.

—Kobe Bryant: "Slam Dunk" Champion. 2000. (Reading Power Ser.). (Illus.). 24p. (J). (gr. 1). lib. bdg. 17.25 (978-0-8239-5539-8(7) , PowerKids Pr.) Rosen Publishing Group, Inc., The.

—Kobe Bryant, Campeon del "Slam Dunk" 2002. (Coleccion Power Kids). (SPA & ENG., Illus.). 24p. (J). (gr. k-2). lib. bdg. 17.25 (978-0-8239-6142-9(7) , RN31311, Buenas Letra) Rosen Publishing Group, Inc., The.

—Terrell Davis: Super Bowl Running Back. (Deportistas de Poder Ser.). 24p. (J). 2002. (SPA.). lib. bdg. 17.25 (978-0-8239-6126-9(5) , Buenas Letra); 2000. (Illus.). (gr. 1). lib. bdg. 17.25 (978-0-8239-5536-7(2) , PowerKids Pr.) Rosen Publishing Group, Inc., The.

—Terrell Davis, Corredor de Super Bowl. 2002. (Coleccion Power Kids). (SPA & ENG., Illus.). 24p. (J). (gr. k-2). lib. bdg. 17.25 (978-0-8239-6144-3(3) , RN31313, Buenas Letra) Rosen Publishing Group, Inc., The.

Kirkpatrick, Rob, et al, contrib. by. Michael Jordan, Basketball Superstar: Rob Kirkpatrick. 2001. (Great Record Breakers in Sports Ser.). (Illus.). 24p. (J). lib. bdg. 18.75 (978-0-8239-5633-3(4) , PowerKids Pr.) Rosen Publishing Group, Inc., The.

Kishel, Ann-Marie. Rosa Parks: A Life of Courage. 2006. (Pull Ahead Books). (Illus.). 32p. (J). 22.60 (978-0-8225-3478-5(9) , Lerner Pubns.) Lerner Publishing Group.

Kite, L. Patricia. Maya Angelou. 2006. (Just the Facts Biographies Ser.). (Illus.). 112p. (J). pap. (*978-0-8225-5997-9(8) , Lerner Pubns.) Lerner Publishing Group.

Kittinger, Jo S. George Washington Carver. 2005. (Scholastic News Nonfiction Readers Ser.). (Illus.). 24p. (J). (gr. 1-2). 19.00 (978-0-516-24939-1(8) , Children's Pr.) Scholastic Library Publishing.

Kjelle, Marylou Morano. Henry Louis Gates, Jr. 2003. (African American Leaders Ser.). (Illus.). 112p. (gr. 6-12). 30.00 (978-0-7910-7687-3(3) , Chelsea Hse.) Facts On File, Inc.

Klingel, Cynthia Fitterer. Harriet Tubman: Abolitionist & Underground Railroad Conductor. 2003. (Spirit of America). (Illus.). 32p. (J). (gr. 2-6). 27.07 (978-1-59296-004-0(9)) Child's World, Inc.

Klingel, Cynthia Fitterer & Noyed, Robert B. Jackie Robinson. 2001. (Wonder Books Level 2: Biographies Ser.). (Illus.). 24p. (J). (ps-3). 22.79 (978-1-56766-953-4(0)) Child's World, Inc.

Kneib, Martha. Kareem Abdul-Jabbar. 2002. (Basketball Hall of Famers Ser.). (Illus.). 112p. (YA). (gr. 5-8). lib. bdg. 29.25 (978-0-8239-3483-6(7) , Rosen Central) Rosen Publishing Group, Inc., The.

Knox, Barbara. Jackie Robinson. 2003. (Photo-Illustrated Biographies Ser.). (Illus.). 24p. (J). lib. bdg. 19.93 (978-0-7368-2224-4(0) , Bridgestone Bks.) Capstone Pr., Inc.

Korb, Rena B. Pulling down the Walls: The Struggle of African American Performers. 2005. (Illus.). 24p. (J). (*978-0-328-13625-4(5) , Scott Foresman) Addison-Wesley Educational Pubs., Inc.

Kovatch, Sarah & Crumpler, Rebecca Lee. Rebecca Lee Crumpler. 2005. (Illus.). 16p. (J). (*978-0-7367-2891-1(0)) Zaner-Bloser, Inc.

Kramer, Barbara. Mahalia Jackson: The Voice of Gospel & Civil Rights. 2003. (African-American Biographies Ser.). (Illus.). 128p. (J). lib. bdg. 26.60 (978-0-7660-2115-0(7)) Enslow Pubs., Inc.

Krass, Peter. Sojourner Truth. 2004. (Black Americans of Achievement Ser.). (Illus.). 112p. (J). (gr. 6-12). 30.00 (978-0-7910-8165-5(6) , Chelsea Hse.) Facts On File, Inc.

Krebs, Laurie. A Day in the Life of a Colonial Sailmaker. 2004. (Library of Living & Working in Colonial Times). (Illus.). 24p. (J). lib. bdg. 18.75 (978-0-8239-6231-0(8) , PowerKids Pr.) Rosen Publishing Group, Inc., The.

Krensky, Stephen. Man for All Seasons. 2008. 32p. (J). (gr. k-4). lib. bdg. 17.89 (978-0-06-027886-1(2)) HarperCollins Pubs.

—Man for All Seasons. Clay, Wil, illus. 2008. 32p. (J). (gr. k-4). 16.99 (978-0-06-027885-4(4)) HarperCollins Pubs.

Krohn, Katherine E. Ella Fitzgerald: First Lady of Song. 2005. (Lerner Biographies Ser.). (Illus.). 128p. (gr. 6-12). lib. bdg. 27.93 (978-0-8225-4933-8(6)) Lerner Publishing Group.

—Madam C.J. Walker & New Cosmetics. Dominguez, Richard & Barnett, Charles, illus. 2007. (Graphic Library). 32p. 25.26 (978-0-7368-6485-5(7)) Capstone Pr., Inc.

—Madam C.J. Walker & New Cosmetics. Dominguez, Richard, illus. 2007. (Graphic Library). 32p. (*978-0-7368-9647-4(3)) Capstone Pr., Inc.

—Oprah Winfrey. (Biography Ser.). (Illus.). 112p. (J). (gr. 6 up). 2003. pap. 7.95 (978-0-8225-5000-6(8)); 2001. 27.93 (978-0-8225-4999-4(9) , Lerner Pubns.) Lerner Publishing Group.

—Oprah Winfrey. 2002. (gr. 7-12). lib. bdg. 16.40 (978-0-613-84025-5(9)) Tandem Library Bks.

—Sojourner Truth. 2005. (Fact Finders Ser.). (Illus.). 32p. (J). (978-0-7368-4348-5(5)) Capstone Pr., Inc.

Krull, Kathleen. Wilma Sin Limites. 2000. Tr. of Wilma Unlimited. (978-0-606-18197-6(0)) Tandem Library Bks.

—Wilma Sin Limites: Como Wilma Rudolph Se Convirtio en la Mujer Mas Rapida del Mundo. Ada, Alma Flor & Campoy, F. Isabel, trs. Diaz, David, illus. 2000. (SPA.). 44p. (J). (gr. 2-4). pap. 7.00 (978-0-15-202360-7(7) , HB30426, Voyager Bks./Libros Viajeros) Harcourt Children's Bks.

—Wilma Unlimited. 2000. (978-0-606-18198-3(9)) Tandem Library Bks.

Kudlinski, Kathleen. Rosa Parks: Young Rebel. 2001. (gr. 3-6). lib. bdg. 13.00 (978-0-613-31647-7(9)) Tandem Library Bks.

—Sojourner Truth. 2003. (gr. 3-6). lib. bdg. 13.00 (978-0-613-61658-4(8)) Tandem Library Bks.

—Sojourner Truth: Voice for Freedom. Wooden, Lenny, illus. 2003. (Childhood of Famous Americans Ser.). 160p. (Orig.). mass mkt. 5.99 (978-0-689-85274-9(6) , Aladdin) Simon & Schuster Children's Publishing.

Kudlinski, Kathleen V. Rosa Parks. Henderson, Meryl, illus. 2001. (Childhood of Famous Americans Ser.). 224p. (gr. 3-7). mass mkt. 5.99 (978-0-689-83925-2(1) , Aladdin) Simon & Schuster Children's Publishing.

—Rosa Parks: Young Rebel. 2001. (Childhood of Famous Americans Ser.). (Illus.). (J). (978-0-606-20891-8(7)) Tandem Library Bks.

Kulling, Monica. Escape North! The Story of Harriet Tubman. Corey, Shana, ed. Flavin, Teresa, illus. 2000. (Step into Reading Step 3 Bks.). 48p. (J). (gr. 2-4). pap. 3.99 (978-0-375-80154-9(5) , Random Hse. Bks. for Young Readers) Random Hse. Children's Bks.

—Escape North! The Story of Harriet Tubman. Flavin, Teresa, illus. 2000. (Step into Reading Ser.). (J). 10.79 (978-0-606-19895-0(4)) Tandem Library Bks.

—Escape North! the Story of Harriet Tubman. 2000. (gr. k-3). lib. bdg. 11.80 (978-0-613-32507-3(9)) Tandem Library Bks.

Lasky, Kathryn. Vision of Beauty: The Story of Sarah Breedlove Walker. Bennett, Nneka, illus. 48p. (J). (gr. 3-7). 2003. pap. 6.99 (978-0-7636-1834-6(9)); 2000. 17.99 (978-0-7636-0253-6(1)) Candlewick Pr.

—Vision of Beauty: The Story of Sarah Breedlove Walker. 2003. (gr. 3-6). lib. bdg. 15.30 (978-0-613-74818-6(2)) Tandem Library Bks.

—A Voice of Her Own: The Story of Phillis Wheatley, Slave Poet. Lee, Paul, illus. 2005. 40p. (J). (gr. 3-7). reprint ed. pap. 6.99 (978-0-7636-2878-9(0)) Candlewick Pr.

Laslo, Cynthia. Brandy. 2000. (High Interest Bks.). (Illus.). 48p. (YA). (gr. 7-12). pap. 6.95 (978-0-516-23520-2(6) , Children's Pr.); (J). pap. (978-0-531-17608-5(8) , Watts, Franklin) Scholastic Library Publishing.

Laslo, Cynthia, contrib. by. Brandy. 2000. (J). (978-0-531-12108-5(9) , Watts, Franklin) Scholastic Library Publishing.

Lassieur, Allison. Benjamin Banneker: Astronomer & Mathematician. 2006. (Fact Finders Ser.). (Illus.). 32p. (J). (978-0-7368-5432-0(0)) Capstone Pr., Inc.

Lawler, Mary. Marcus Garvey: Black Nationalist Leader. (Black Americans of Achievement Ser.). (Illus.). 112p. (J). (gr. 6-12). 2005. pap. 13.25 (978-0-7910-8333-8(0)); 2004. 30.00 (978-0-7910-8159-4(1)) Facts On File, Inc. (Chelsea Hse.).

Lazo, Caroline Evensen. Alice Walker: Freedom Writer. 2005. (Lerner Biographies Ser.). (Illus.). 128p. (gr. 6-12). 27.93 (978-0-8225-4960-4(3)) Lerner Publishing Group.

Leavitt, Amie. George Washington Carver. 2007. (What's So Great About... ? Ser.). (J). lib. bdg. 25.70 (*978-1-58415-580-5(9)) Mitchell Lane Pubs., Inc.

—Harriet Tubman. 2007. (What's So Great About... ? Ser.). (J). lib. bdg. 25.70 (*978-1-58415-577-5(9)) Mitchell Lane Pubs., Inc.

Leebrick, Kristal. Sojourner Truth. 2002. (Let Freedom Ring Ser.). (Illus.). 48p. (J). (gr. 3-4). lib. bdg. 22.60 (978-0-7368-1090-6(0) , Bridgestone Bks.) Capstone Pr., Inc.

The Legend of Jocko: Hero of the American Revolution. 2003. (YA). pap. 9.95 (978-0-9761778-0-7(3)) Lefall and Co., Inc.

Lemke, Donald B. The Brave Escape of Ellen & William Craft. Barnett, Charles, III et al, illus. 2005. (Graphic Library). 32p. (J). (gr. 3-7). lib. bdg. 25.26 (978-0-7368-4973-9(4)) Capstone Pr., Inc.

Lester, Julius. The Blues Singers: Ten Who Rocked the World. Cohen, Lisa, illus. 2001. 48p. (gr. k-17). 16.49 (978-0-7868-2405-2(0) , Jump at the Sun) Hyperion Bks. for Children.

Levadi, Barbara, et al. African American Biographies: A Collection of Mini-Books. 2001. 48p. (J). (gr. 1-5). pap. 6.99 (978-0-7424-0082-5(4) , IF2822) School Specialty Publishing.

Levin, Pamela. Tyra Banks: Model. 1999. (Black Americans of Achievement Ser.). (Illus.). (YA). (gr. 5-9). 144p. pap. 30.00 (978-0-7910-5196-2(X)); 112p. 30.00 (978-0-7910-5195-5(1)) Facts On File, Inc. (Chelsea Hse.).

Levy, Debbie. Richard Wright. 2007. (Literary Greats Ser.). 160p. (YA). (gr. 7-12). lib. bdg. 33.26 (*978-0-8225-6793-6(8) , Twenty-First Century Bks.) Lerner Publishing Group.

Lewis, Jon E. Muhammad Ali. 1999. (Life & Times of Ser.). (Illus.). 48p. (YA). (gr. 5 up). 12.95 (978-0-7910-4641-8(9) , Chelsea Hse.) Facts On File, Inc.

Linney, Susan. Martin Luther King, Jr: With a Discussion of Responsibility. 2004. (Values in Action Ser.). (J). (978-1-59203-069-9(6)) Learning Challenge, Inc.

Litwin, Laura Baskes. Benjamin Banneker: Astronomer & Mathematician. 1999. (African-American Biographies Ser.). (Illus.). 112p. (YA). (gr. 6-12). lib. bdg. 26.60 (978-0-7660-1208-0(5)) Enslow Pubs., Inc.

—Fannie Lou Hamer: Fighting for the Right to Vote. 2002. (African-American Biographies Ser.). (Illus.). 128p. (J). (gr. 6-12). lib. bdg. 26.60 (978-0-7660-1772-6(9)) Enslow Pubs., Inc.

—Matthew Henson: Co-Discoverer of the North Pole. 2001. (African-American Biographies Ser.). (Illus.). 128p. (J). (gr. 6-12). lib. bdg. 26.60 (978-0-7660-1546-3(7)) Enslow Pubs., Inc.

Livorse, Kay. Let Freedom Sing. Copeland, Greg, illus. 2002. 16p. (J). (978-0-439-35159-1(6)) Scholastic, Inc.

Lohse, Joyce B. Justina Ford, Medical Pioneer. 2005. (Now You Know Bio Ser.). (Illus.). 56p. (J). pap. (978-0-86541-074-9(7)) Filter Pr., LLC.

Lommel, Cookie. Cuba Gooding Jr. 1999. (Black Americans of Achievement Ser.). (Illus.). 104p. (J). (gr. 5-9). pap. 30.00 (978-0-7910-5276-1(1) , Chelsea Hse.) Facts On File, Inc.

—Johnnie Cochran: Lawyer. 1999. (Black Americans of Achievement Ser.). (Illus.). 117p. (J). (gr. 4 up). 21.95 (978-0-7910-5279-2(6)); (gr. 5 up). pap. 30.00 (978-0-7910-5280-8(X)) Facts On File, Inc. (Chelsea Hse.).

Lommel, Cookie & Edeison, Paula. Cuba Gooding Jr. 2000. (Black Americans of Achievement Ser.). (Illus.). 112p. (J). (gr. 4-7). 30.00 (978-0-7910-5275-4(3) , Chelsea Hse.) Facts On File, Inc.

Lovitt, Chip. Michael Jordan. (Scholastic Biography Ser.). (Illus.). (gr. 4-9). 2nd rev. ed. 1998. 213p. (YA). pap. 4.50 (978-0-590-59644-2(6)); 3rd rev. ed. 1999. 224p. (J). pap. 4.50 (978-0-439-12961-9(3)) Scholastic, Inc.

—Michael Jordan. 1999. (978-0-606-17877-8(5)) Tandem Library Bks.

Lowenstein, Felicia. Super Sports Star Grant Hill. 2001. (Super Sports Star Ser.). (Illus.). 48p. (J). (gr. 1-4). lib. bdg. 23.93 (978-0-7660-1517-3(3)) Enslow Pubs., Inc.

—Super Sports Star Terrell Davis. 2003. (Super Sports Star Ser.). (Illus.). 48p. (J). lib. bdg. 18.95 (978-0-7660-2052-8(5)) Enslow Pubs., Inc.

Lowery, Linda. Martin Luther King Jr Day. 2004. (gr. k-3). lib. bdg. 14.10 (978-0-613-79212-7(2)) Tandem Library Bks.

Lucas, Eileen. Prudence Crandall: Teacher for Equal Rights. Smith, Kimanne, illus. 2001. (On My Own Biographies Ser.). 48p. (J). (gr. 2-5). pap. 5.95 (978-1-57505-479-7(5) , Carolrhoda Bks.) Lerner Publishing Group.

Lutz, Norma Jean. J. C. Watts: Politician. 2000. (Black Americans of Achievement Ser.). (Illus.). 112p. (J). (gr. 4-7). 30.00 (978-0-7910-5338-6(5) , Chelsea Hse.) Facts On File, Inc.

—Sojourner Truth. 2001. (gr. 5-8). lib. bdg. 17.60 (978-0-613-33074-9(9)) Tandem Library Bks.

—Sojourner Truth: Abolitionist, Suffragist, & Preacher. (Famous Figures of the Civil War Era Ser.). (Illus.). 80p. (J). (gr. 4-7). 2001. 25.00 (978-0-7910-6007-0(1)); 2000. pap. 25.00 (978-0-7910-6145-9(0)) Facts On File, Inc. (Chelsea Hse.).

Lynch, Emma. Harriet Tubman. 2005. (J). pap. (978-1-4034-6367-8(0)); (Illus.). 32p. lib. bdg. 25.36 (978-1-4034-6353-1(0)) Heinemann Library.

Lynch, Emma, et al. Martin Luther King, Jr. 2005. (Illus.). 32p. (J). (978-1-4034-6351-7(4)); pap. (978-1-4034-6365-4(4)) Heinemann Library.

MacLeod, Elizabeth. George Washington Carver: An Innovative Life. 2007. (Illus.). 32p. (J). (gr. 3-7). ***(978-1-55337-906-5(3)); (978-1-55337-907-2(1))*** Kids Can Pr., Ltd.

MacMillan, Dianne M. Martin Luther King, Jr. Day. 2nd ed. 2008. (Best Holiday Books Ser.). 48p. (J). (gr. 3-4). lib. bdg. 23.93 ***(978-0-7660-3043-5(1))*** Enslow Pubs., Inc.

Macnow, Glen. Sports Great Allen Iverson. 2003. (Sports Great Books). (Illus.). 64p. (J). (gr. 4-10). lib. bdg. 22.60 (978-0-7660-2063-4(0)) Enslow Pubs., Inc.

Malam, John. Sojourner Truth. 2000. (Tell Me about Ser.). (Illus.). 22p. (J). 16.95 (978-0-237-51972-8(0) , Evans Brothers, Limited) Evans Publishing Group GBR. *Dist:* Independent Pubs. Group.

Mallin, Jay. Al Sharpton: Community Activist. 2007. (Great Life Stories Ser.). (Illus.). 111p. (J). ***(978-0-531-13672-0(8)*** , Franklin Watts) Hodder Children's Division.

—Al Sharpton: Community Activist. 2006. (Great Life Stories Ser.). (Illus.). 111p. (YA). (gr. 6 up). 30.50 (978-0-531-13872-4(0) , Watts, Franklin) Scholastic Library Publishing.

Mandel, Peter. Say Hey! A Song of Willie Mays. Tate, Don, illus. 2004. 30p. (J). (gr. k-2). reprint ed. 16.00 (978-0-7567-8162-0(0)) DIANE Publishing Co.

Mandell, Judith J. Super Sports Star Alonzo Mourning. 2002. (Super Sports Star Ser.). (Illus.). 48p. (J). (gr. 1-4). lib. bdg. 18.95 (978-0-7660-1518-0(1)) Enslow Pubs., Inc.

Manera, Alexandria. Bessie Smith. 2003. (African-American Biographies Ser.). (Illus.). 64p. pap. 8.95 (978-1-4109-0034-0(7)); (J). lib. bdg. 28.56 (978-0-7398-6875-1(6)) Raintree.

Mangal, Melina. Mildred Taylor. 2004. (Classic Storytellers Ser.). (Illus.). 48p. (J). (gr. 4-8). lib. bdg. 20.95 (978-1-58415-311-5(3)) Mitchell Lane Pubs., Inc.

—Virginia Hamilton. 2002. (Real Life Reader Biography Ser.). (Illus.). 32p. (J). (gr. 3-8). lib. bdg. 24.95 (978-1-58415-170-8(6)) Mitchell Lane Pubs., Inc.

Manheimer, Ann S. James Beckwourth: Legendary Mountain Man. 2006. (Trailblazer Biography Ser.). (Illus.). 112p. (J). (ps-7). 30.60 (978-1-57505-892-4(8) , Twenty-First Century Bks.) Lerner Publishing Group.

—Martin Luther King Jr: Dreaming of Equality. 2005. (Trailblazer Biography Ser.). (Illus.). 112p. (J). 30.60 (978-1-57505-627-2(5) , Carolrhoda Bks.) Lerner Publishing Group.

Manolis, Kay. Rosa Parks: A Life of Courage. 2007. (Illus.). 24p. (J). lib. bdg. 19.95 (978-1-60014-088-4(2)) Bellwether Media.

Mantell, Paul. Arthur Ashe: Young Tennis Champion. Henderson, Meryl, illus. 2006. (Childhood of Famous Americans Ser.). 224p. (J). pap. 5.99 (978-0-689-87346-1(8) , Aladdin) Simon & Schuster Children's Publishing.

Mara, Wil. Colin Powell. 2004. (Rookie Biographies Ser.). (Illus.). 31p. (J). (gr. 1-2). pap. 4.95 (978-0-516-27918-3(1) , Children's Pr.) Scholastic Library Publishing.

—Jackie Robinson. 2003. (Rookie Biographies Ser.). (Illus.). 32p. (J). (gr. 1-2). pap. 4.95 (978-0-516-27336-5(1) , Children's Pr.) Scholastic Library Publishing.

—Jackie Robinson. 2003. (Illus.). 31p. (J). (ps-3). lib. bdg. 12.95 (978-0-613-59501-8(7)) Tandem Library Bks.

—Martin Luther King, Jr. (Rookie Biographies Ser.). (Illus.). 32p. (J). (gr. 1-2). 2003. pap. 4.95 (978-0-516-27333-4(7)); 2002. 20.50 (978-0-516-22517-3(0)) Scholastic Library Publishing. (Children's Pr.).

—Rosa Parks. 2006. (Rookie Biography Ser.). (Illus.). 31p. (J). (978-0-531-12451-2(7)) Children's Pr., Ltd.

—Rosa Parks. (Rookie Biographies Ser.). (Illus.). (J). 2004. 31p. (gr. 1-2). pap. 4.95 (978-0-516-27916-9(5)); 2003. 32p. 19.50 (978-0-516-25876-8(1)) Scholastic Library Publishing. (Children's Pr.).

—Thurgood Marshall: Champion for Civil Rights. 2004. (Great Life Stories Ser.). (Illus.). 125p. (J). 30.50 (978-0-531-12058-3(9) , Watts, Franklin) Scholastic Library Publishing.

Marcovitz, Hal. Al Sharpton. 2001. (Black Americans of Achievement Ser.). (Illus.). 112p. (YA). (gr. 6 up). pap. 30.00 (978-0-7910-6296-8(1)); 30.00 (978-0-7910-6295-1(3)) Facts On File, Inc. (Chelsea Hse.).

—Al Sharpton. 2001. (gr. 3-6). lib. bdg. 18.75 (978-0-613-85632-4(5)) Tandem Library Bks.

Markel, Rita J. Jimi Hendrix. 2005. (Biography Ser.). (Illus.). 112p. (J). (gr. 6-12). lib. bdg. 27.93 (978-0-8225-4990-1(5)) Lerner Publishing Group.

Marsh, Carole. Booker T. Washington. 2002. (One Thousand Readers Ser.). (Illus.). 12p. (J). (gr. k-4). 2.95 (978-0-635-01479-5(3) , 14793) Gallopade International.

—Condoleezza Rice. 2003. 12p. (gr. k-4). 2.95 ***(978-0-635-02385-8(7))*** Gallopade International.

—Harold Washington. 2002. (One Thousand Readers Ser.). (Illus.). 12p. (J). (gr. k-4). 2.95 (978-0-635-01504-4(8) , 15048) Gallopade International.

—Harriet Tubman. 2002. (One Thousand Readers Ser.). (Illus.). 12p. (J). (gr. k-4). 2.95 (978-0-635-01480-1(7) , 14807) Gallopade International.

—Jackie Robinson. 2002. (One Thousand Readers Ser.). (Illus.). 12p. (J). (gr. k-4). 2.95 (978-0-635-01529-7(3) , 15293) Gallopade International.

—Vel Phillips. 2002. (One Thousand Readers Ser.). (Illus.). 12p. (J). (gr. k-4). 2.95 (978-0-635-01553-2(6) , 15536) Gallopade International.

—The Virginia Reader: L. Douglas Wilder. 2001. (Virginia Experience! Ser.). 12p. (J). (gr. k-4). pap. 2.95 (978-0-635-00365-2(1)) Gallopade International.

Marshall, Thurgood. Thurgood Marshall: Supreme Court Justice. 2005. (Black Americans of Achievement Ser.). (Illus.). 112p. (J). (gr. 6-12). pap. 13.25 (978-0-7910-8337-6(3) , Chelsea Hse.) Facts On File, Inc.

Marsico, Katie. Madame C. J. Walker. 2008. (J). lib. bdg. 26.00 ***(978-1-60279-074-2(4))*** Cherry Lake Publishing.

Martin Luther King, Jr, Vol. 3. 2005. (First Biographies Ser.). (YA). (gr. k-3). (978-0-7368-8112-8(3) , Pebble Bks.) Capstone Pr., Inc.

Martin, Michael. Harriet Tubman & the Underground Railroad. 2005. (Graphic Library). (Illus.). 31p. (J). 22.60 (978-0-7368-3829-0(5)) Capstone Pr., Inc.

Martin, Oscar, Jr., creator. Doctors, l.t. ed. 2003. (Illus.). 25p. (J). E-Book 19.95 incl. cd-rom (978-0-9748416-5-6(X)) Build Your Story.

—Famous Women, l.t. ed. 2003. (Illus.). 25p. (J). E-Book 19.95 incl. cd-rom (978-0-9748416-8-7(4)) Build Your Story.

Martin's Big Words. 2004. pap. 38.75 incl. audio compact disk (978-1-55592-637-3(1)); pap. 32.75 incl. audio (978-1-55592-367-9(4)); pap. 14.95 incl. audio (978-1-55592-169-9(8)) Weston Woods Studios, Inc.

Mattern, Joanne. Coretta Scott King: Civil Rights Activist. 2003. (Reading Power Ser.). (Illus.). 24p. (J). lib. bdg. 17.25 (978-0-8239-6504-5(X) , PowerKids Pr.) Rosen Publishing Group, Inc., The.

—The Cost of Freedom: Crispus Attucks & the Boston Massacre. 2004. (Great Moments in American History Ser.). (Illus.). 32p. (gr. 4-8). lib. bdg. 21.25 (978-0-8239-4341-8(0) , Rosen Central) Rosen Publishing Group, Inc., The.

—Donovan Mcnabb. 2004. (Robbie Reader Ser.). (Illus.). 32p. (J). (gr. 1-4). lib. bdg. 25.70 (978-1-58415-294-1(X)) Mitchell Lane Pubs., Inc.

—Oprah Winfrey. 2006. (Biography Ser.). 128p. (J). 14.99 (978-0-7566-1494-2(5)) Dorling Kindersley Publishing, Inc.

—Sojourner Truth: Early Abolitionist. 2003. (Reading Power Ser.). (Illus.). 24p. (J). lib. bdg. 17.25 (978-0-8239-6502-1(3) , PowerKids Pr.) Rosen Publishing Group, Inc., The.

Mayer, Cassie. Frederick Douglass. 2007. (J). ***(978-1-4034-9974-5(8));*** pap. ***(978-1-4034-9983-7(7))*** Heinemann Library.

McCormack, Shaun. Cool Papa Bell. 2002. (Baseball Hall of Famers of the Negro League Ser.). (Illus.). 112p. (YA). (gr. 5-8). lib. bdg. 29.25 (978-0-8239-3474-4(8) , Rosen Central) Rosen Publishing Group, Inc., The.

McDonough, Yona Zeldis. Sisters in Strength: American Women Who Made a Difference. Zeldis, Malcah, illus. rev. ed. 2000. 48p. (J). (gr. 1-5). pap. 17.95 (978-0-8050-6102-4(9) , Holt, Henry & Co. Bks. For Young Readers) Holt, Henry & Co.

—Who Was Louis Armstrong? O'Brien, John & Harrison, Nancy, illus. 2004. (Who Was...? Ser.). 112p. (J). 13.89 (978-0-448-43560-2(8)); (gr. 3-7). pap. 4.99 (978-0-448-43368-4(0)) Penguin Group (USA) Inc. (Grosset & Dunlap).

McIntosh-Wooten, Sara. Oprah Winfrey: Talk Show Legend. 1999. (African-American Biographies Ser.). (Illus.). 128p. (YA). (gr. 6-12). lib. bdg. 26.60 (978-0-7660-1207-3(7)) Enslow Pubs., Inc.

McKissack, Lisa Beringer. Women of the Harlem Renaissance. 2006. 48p. (J). (978-0-7565-2034-2(7)) Compass Point Bks.

McKissack, Patricia C. Black Diamond: The Story of the Negro Baseball Leagues. 1998. (gr. 5-8). lib. bdg. 14.15 (978-0-613-70493-9(2)) Tandem Library Bks.

McKissack, Patricia C. & McKissack, Frederick. Black Diamond: The Story of the Negro Baseball Leagues. 1998. 192p. (J). pap. 5.99 (978-0-590-68213-8(X)) Scholastic, Inc.

McKissack, Patricia C. & McKissack, Fredrick L. Booker T. Washington: Leader & Educator. rev. ed. 2001. (Great African Americans Ser.). (Illus.). 32p. (J). (gr. 1-4). lib. bdg. 18.60 (978-0-7660-1679-8(X)) Enslow Pubs., Inc.

—Ida B. Wells-Barnett: A Voice Against Violence. rev. ed. 2001. (Great African Americans Ser.). (Illus.). 32p. (J). (gr. 1-4). lib. bdg. 18.60 (978-0-7660-1677-4(3)) Enslow Pubs., Inc.

—Jesse Owens: Olympic Star. rev. ed. 2001. (Great African Americans Ser.). (Illus.). 32p. (J). (gr. 1-4). lib. bdg. 18.60 (978-0-7660-1681-1(1)) Enslow Pubs., Inc.

—Madam C. J. Walker: Self-Made Millionaire. rev. ed. 2001. (Great African Americans Ser.). (Illus.). 32p. (J). (gr. 1-4). lib. bdg. 18.60 (978-0-7660-1682-8(X)) Enslow Pubs., Inc.

—Martin Luther King, Jr. Man of Peace. rev. ed. 2001. (Great African Americans Ser.). (Illus.). 32p. (J). (gr. 1-4). lib. bdg. 18.60 (978-0-7660-1678-1(1)) Enslow Pubs., Inc.

—Mary Church Terrell: Leader for Equality. rev. ed. 2002. (Great African Americans Ser.). (Illus.). 32p. (J). (gr. 1-4). lib. bdg. 18.60 (978-0-7660-1697-2(8)) Enslow Pubs., Inc.

—Paul Robeson: A Voice to Remember. rev. ed. 2001. (Great African Americans Ser.). (Illus.). 32p. (J). (gr. 1-4). lib. bdg. 18.60 (978-0-7660-1674-3(9)) Enslow Pubs., Inc.

—Sojourner Truth: A Voice for Freedom. rev. ed. 2002. (Great African Americans Ser.). (Illus.). 32p. (J). (gr. 1-4). lib. bdg. 18.60 (978-0-7660-1693-4(5)) Enslow Pubs., Inc.

McLeese, Don. Crispus Attucks. 2005. (Heroes of the American Revolution Ser.). (Illus.). 32p. (gr. 2-5). 19.95 (978-1-59515-218-3(0)) Rourke Publishing, LLC.

—Jackie Robinson. 2002. (Illus.). 24p. (J). (ps-3). lib. bdg. 20.64 (978-1-58952-288-6(5)) Rourke Publishing, LLC.

—Martin Luther King, Jr. 2002. (Illus.). 24p. (J). lib. bdg. 20.64 (978-1-58952-286-2(9)) Rourke Publishing, LLC.

—Oprah Winfrey. 2002. (Discover the Life of an American Legend Ser.). (Illus.). 24p. (J). lib. bdg. 20.64 (978-1-58952-306-7(7)) Rourke Publishing, LLC.

—Rosa Parks. 2002. (Rourke Discovery Library). (Illus.). 24p. (J). lib. bdg. 20.64 (978-1-58952-287-9(7)) Rourke Publishing, LLC.

McLeese, Don & Marshall, Thurgood. Thurgood Marshall. 2003. (Rourke Discovery Library). (Illus.). 24p. (gr. 2-5). 14.95 (978-1-58952-303-6(2)) Rourke Publishing, LLC.

McPherson, Stephanie Sammartino. Coretta Scott King. 2007. (J). lib. bdg. ***(978-0-8225-7156-8(0))*** Twenty First Century Bks.

Medearis, Angela Shelf. Dare to Dream: Coretta Scott King & the Civil Rights Movement. Rich, Anna, illus. 1999. (Rainbow Biography Ser.). 64p. (J). (gr. 3-7). pap. 4.99 (978-0-14-130202-7(X) , Puffin) Penguin Group (USA) Inc.

—Dare to Dream: Coretta Scott King & the Civil Rights Movement. 1999. (gr. 3-6). lib. bdg. 13.00 (978-0-613-14663-0(8)) Tandem Library Bks.

Mendelsohn, James. Barbara Jordan: Getting Things Done. 2000. (Single Titles Ser.: up). (Illus.). 192p. (J). (gr. 7 up). lib. bdg. (978-0-7613-1467-7(9) , Twenty-First Century Bks.) Lerner Publishing Group.

Metcalf, Doris H. Portraits of Contemporary African Americans. 2001. 144p. (J). (gr. 4-8). tchr. ed. 14.99 (978-0-86653-723-0(6) , GA1442, Milestone) Schaffer, Frank Pubns.

Michelson, Richard. As Good as Anybody. 2008. 40p. (J). (gr. 1-5). lib. bdg. 19.99 ***(978-0-375-93335-6(2)*** , Knopf Bks. for Young Readers) Random Hse. Children's Bks.

Miller, Barbara Kiely. Frederick Douglass. 2007. (Great Americans Ser.). 24p. (J). (gr. 2-4). lib. bdg. 19.93 ***(978-0-8368-8315-2(2)*** , Weekly Reader Early Learning Library) Stevens, Gareth Inc.

—George Washington Carver. 2007. (Great Americans Ser.). 24p. (J). (gr. 2-4). lib. bdg. 19.93 ***(978-0-8368-8313-8(6)*** , Weekly Reader Early Learning Library) Stevens, Gareth Inc.

Miller, Calvin Craig. A. Philip Randolph & the African American Labor Movement. 2005. (Civil Rights Leaders Ser.). (Illus.). 160p. (YA). (gr. 6-12). 26.95 (978-1-931798-50-1(8)) Reynolds, Morgan Inc.

—Roy Wilkins: Leader of the NAACP. 2005. (Civil Rights Leaders Ser.). (Illus.). 176p. (J). (gr. 6-12). 26.95 (978-1-931798-49-5(4)) Reynolds, Morgan Inc.

Miller, Connie Colwell. Rosa Parks & the Montgomery Bus Boycott. 2007. (Graphic Library). (Illus.). 32p. (J). 25.26 (978-0-7368-6495-4(4)) Capstone Pr., Inc.

Miller, Ray. Shaquille O'Neal. 2002. (Stars of Sports Ser.). (Illus.). 48p. (J). 26.20 (978-0-7377-1422-7(0) , Kidhaven) Thomson Gale.

Miller, Raymond H. Barry Bonds. 2002. (Stars of Sports Ser.). (Illus.). 48p. (J). 26.20 (978-0-7377-1393-0(3) , Greenhaven Pr., Inc.) Thomson Gale.

—George Washington Carver. 2005. (Inventors & Creators Ser.). (Illus.). 48p. (J). (ps-8). lib. bdg. 26.20 (978-0-7377-3160-6(5) , Greenhaven Pr., Inc.) Thomson Gale.

—Kobe Bryant. 2003. (Stars of Sports Ser.). (Illus.). 48p. (J). 26.20 (978-0-7377-1538-5(3) , Greenhaven Pr., Inc.) Thomson Gale.

Miller, Robert H. Reflections of a Black Cowboy: Buffalo Soldiers. 2004. (J). pap. 9.95 (978-0-940975-69-9(6) , Sankofa Bks.) Just Us Bks., Inc.

—Reflections of a Black Cowboy: Cowboys. 2004. (J). pap. 9.95 (978-0-940975-70-5(X) , Sankofa Bks.) Just Us Bks., Inc.

Miller, William. Zora Hurston & the Chinaberry Tree. ed. 2004. (Illus.). (J). (gr. k-3). spiral bd. (978-0-616-03099-8(1)) Canadian National Institute for the Blind/Institut National Canadien pour les Aveugles.

—Zora Hurston Y el Arbol Sonador. 2001. (SPA.). (gr. k-3). lib. bdg. 15.25 (978-0-613-36034-0(6)) Tandem Library Bks.

Mir Tamim Ansary. Martin Luther King Jr. Day. 2nd ed. 2006. (Illus.). 32p. (J). pap. ***(978-1-4034-8902-9(5))*** Heinemann Library.

Mohamed, Paloma. A Man Called Garvey: The Life & Times of the Great Leader Marcus Garvey. Braithwaite, Barrington, illus. l.t. ed. 2004. (Majority Press Inc., Wisdom for Children Ser.: No. 1). 32p. (J). 12.95 (978-0-912469-40-9(4)) Majority Pr., Inc., The.

Molzahn, Arlene Bourgeois. Kevin Garnett. 2001. (Sports Heroes Ser.). (Illus.). 48p. (J). (gr. 3-4). lib. bdg. 21.26 (978-0-7368-0778-4(0) , Capstone High-Interest Bks.) Capstone Pr., Inc.

—Randy Moss. 2002. (Sports Heroes Ser.). (Illus.). 48p. (J). (gr. 3-4). lib. bdg. 21.26 (978-0-7368-1053-1(6) , Capstone High-Interest Bks.) Capstone Pr., Inc.

Monceaux, Morgan & Katcher, Ruth. My Heroes, My People: African Americans & Native Americans in Thewest. Monceaux, Morgan, illus. 2004. (Illus.). 63p. (J). (gr. k-4). reprint ed. 18.00 (978-0-7567-7868-2(9)) DIANE Publishing Co.

Monroe, Judy. Thurgood Marshall. 2005. (Fact Finders Ser.). (Illus.). 32p. (J). (978-0-7368-4349-2(3)) Capstone Pr., Inc.

Moore, Barbara R. Sojourner Truth. 2005. (Illus.). 16p. (J). ***(978-0-618-56039-4(4))*** Houghton Mifflin Co.

Moore, Cathy. The Daring Escape of Ellen Craft. Young, Mary O'Keefe, illus. 2002. (On My Own History Ser.). 48p. (J). (gr. 1-3). lib. bdg. 23.93 (978-0-87614-462-6(8) , Carolrhoda Bks.) Lerner Publishing Group.

—Daring Escape of Ellen Craft. 2002. (gr. 3-6). lib. bdg. 14.10 (978-0-613-46125-2(8)) Tandem Library Bks.

Moore, Heidi. Ida B. Wells-Barnett. 2004. (Illus.). 32p. (J). pap. 6.95 (978-1-4034-5706-6(9)); lib. bdg. (978-1-4034-4997-9(X)) Heinemann Library.

—Medgar Evers. 2005. (Illus.). (J). 32p. (978-1-4034-7272-4(6)); 64p. pap. (978-1-4034-7273-1(4)) Heinemann Library.

Moore, Mary. Blacks in Ohio II, Vol. 1. Caesor, Ebraska, ed. Clay, Cliff, illus. (YA). (gr. 6 up). pap. 12.95 (978-0-913678-31-2(7)) New Day Pr.

Morelli, Jack. Heroes of the Negro Leagues. 2007. 128p. 19.95 ***(978-0-8109-9434-8(8))*** Abrams, Harry N. , Inc.

Morgan, Terri. Venus & Serena Williams. 2003. (gr. 3-6). lib. bdg. 14.10 (978-0-613-76644-9(X)) Tandem Library Bks.

—Venus & Serena Williams: Grand Slam Sisters. (Sports Achievers Biographies Ser.). (Illus.). 2005. 80p. (gr. 7-12). lib. bdg. 22.60 (978-0-8225-3684-0(6)); 2003. 64p. (J). (gr. 4-9). pap. 5.95 (978-0-8225-9866-4(3) , Carolrhoda Bks.) Lerner Publishing Group.

Morris, Ann. Grandma Lois Remembers: An African-American Family Story. Linenthal, Peter, illus. 2002. (What Was It Like, Grandma? Ser.). 32p. (gr. k-3). lib. bdg. 22.90 (978-0-7613-2316-7(3) , Millbrook Pr.) Lerner Publishing Group.

Morris, Roz. Henry Aaron: Dream Chaser. 2002. (Alabama Roots Biography Ser.). (Illus.). 120p. (J). per. 7.95 (978-1-878561-94-7(4)) Seacoast Publishing, Inc.

—Rosa Parks: Mother of the Civil Rights Movement. 2003. (Alabama Roots Biography Ser.). (Illus.). 109p. (J). (978-1-878561-57-2(X)) Seacoast Publishing, Inc.

Morrison, John. Cornel West. 2003. (African American Leaders Ser.). (Illus.). 112p. (J). (gr. 6-12). 30.00 (978-0-7910-7686-6(5) , Chelsea Hse.) Facts On File, Inc.

Mortensen, Lori. George Washington Carver: Teacher, Scientist, & Inventor. O'Connor, Niamh, illus. 2007. (J). lib. bdg. ***(978-1-4048-3725-6(6))*** Picture Window Bks.

—Harriet Tubman: Hero of the Underground Railroad. Moore, Frances, illus. 2006. (Biographies Ser.). 24p. (J). (gr. k-3). lib. bdg. 23.93 ***(978-1-4048-3103-2(7))*** Picture Window Bks.

Murcia, Rebecca Thatcher. The Civil Rights Movement. 2005. (Monumental Milestones Ser.). (Illus.). 48p. (YA). (ps-7). lib. bdg. (978-1-58415-401-3(2)) Mitchell Lane Pubs., Inc.

Murphy, Claire Rudolf. I Am Sacagawea, I Am York: Our Journey West with Lewis & Clark. Bond, Higgins, illus. 2005. 32p. (J). (gr. 3-5). 17.85 (978-0-8027-8921-1(8)); 16.95 (978-0-8027-8919-8(6)) Walker & Co.

Murphy, Nora & Murphy-Gnatz, Mary, contrib. by. Meet African Americans in Minnesota: Telling Our Own Stories. 2000. (Illus.). 88p. (J). (gr. 3-7). pap. 12.95 (978-0-87351-380-7(0) , 380-0, Borealis Bk.) Minnesota Historical Society Pr.

Murphy, Patricia J. Garrett Morgan: Inventor of the Traffic Light & Gas Mask. 2004. (Famous Inventors Ser.). (Illus.). 32p. (J). lib. bdg. 22.60 (978-0-7660-2274-4(9)) Enslow Pubs., Inc.

Myers, Walter Dean. Bad Boy: A Memoir. 2002. (Amistad Ser.). 224p. (J). (gr. 7 up). reprint ed. pap. 7.99 (978-0-06-447288-3(4) , HarperTeen) HarperCollins Pubs.

—Bad Boy: A Memoir. 2002. (gr. 7-12). lib. bdg. 15.25 (978-0-613-62375-9(4)) Tandem Library Bks.

—The Greatest: Muhammad Ali. 2001. (Greatest Ser.). (Illus.). 192p. (J). (gr. 7 up). pap. 4.99 (978-0-590-54343-9(1) , Scholastic Paperbacks) Scholastic, Inc.

—Greatest: Muhammad Ali. 2001. (gr. 5-8). lib. bdg. 13.00 (978-0-613-49432-8(6)) Tandem Library Bks.

—The Greatest: Muhammed Ali. 2001. 11.64 (978-0-606-22250-1(2)) Tandem Library Bks.

—I've Seen the Promised Land: The Life of Dr. Martin Luther King, Jr. Jenkins, Leonard, illus. 2004. 40p. (J). (gr. k-3). lib. bdg. 17.89 (978-0-06-027704-8(1)) HarperCollins Pubs.

—Muhammad Ali Biography. Date not set. 40p. (J). (gr. k-3). 15.99 (978-0-06-029131-0(1)); 16.89 (978-0-06-029132-7(X)); pap. 5.99 (978-0-06-443718-9(3)) HarperCollins Pubs.

Naden, Corinne J. Halle Berry. 2001. (gr. 3-6). lib. bdg. 18.75 (978-0-613-86157-1(4)) Tandem Library Bks.

Naden, Corinne J. & Blue, Rose. Condoleeza Rice. 2004. (African-American Biographies Ser.). (Illus.). 64p. (J). 28.56 (978-1-4109-1039-4(3)) Raintree.

—Cornel West. 2004. (African-American Biographies Ser.). (Illus.). 64p. (J). (gr. 4-7). 32.86 (978-1-4109-1040-0(7)) Raintree.

—Henri Louis Gates. 2004. (African-American Biographies Ser.). (Illus.). 64p. (J). (gr. 4-7). 32.86 (978-1-4109-1041-7(5)) Raintree.

—Mae Jeminson: Out of This World. 2003. (Gateway Biography Ser.: 4). (Illus.). 48p. lib. bdg. 23.90 (978-0-7613-2570-3(0) , Millbrook Pr.) Lerner Publishing Group.

—Maya Angelou. (African-American Biographies Ser.). (Illus.). (J). 2005. 64p. (gr. 6-9). pap. 9.50 (978-1-4109-1119-3(5)); 2004. 28.56 (978-1-4109-1042-4(3)) Raintree.

—Toni Morrison. 2004. (African-American Biographies Ser.). (Illus.). 64p. (J). (gr. 4-7). 32.86 (978-1-4109-1043-1(1)) Raintree.

Nelson, Kristi. WNBA: The Chamique Holdsclaw Story. 2000. 11.79 (978-0-606-18616-2(6)) Tandem Library Bks.

Nelson, Richard. Harriet Tubman. 2007. (Essential Lives Ser.). (ENG., Illus.). 112p. (YA). (gr. 8-12). lib. bdg. 32.79 ***(978-1-59928-842-0(7)*** , Essential Library) ABDO Publishing Co.

Nelson, Robin. George Washington Carver: A Life of Devotion. 2007. (Pull Ahead Books-Biographies Ser.). (J). 22.60 (978-0-8225-6461-4(0) , Lerner Pubns.) Lerner Publishing Group.

A B

Neri, Greg. Yummy: The Last Days of a Southside Shorty. DuBurke, Randy, illus. 2007. (J). (978-1-58430-266-7(6)); pap. (978-1-58430-267-4(4)) Lee & Low Bks., Inc.

Newman, Matthew. Brandy. 2000. (Galaxy of Superstars Ser.). (J). (Illus.). pap. 9.95 (978-0-7910-5782-7(8)); 64p. (gr. 4-7). 25.00 (978-0-7910-5781-0(X)) Facts On File, Inc. (Chelsea Hse.).

Nichols, Catherine. Madam C.J. Walker. 2005. (Scholastic News Nonfiction Readers Ser.). (Illus.). 24p. (J). pap. (978-0-516-24784-7(0)) Children's Pr., Ltd.

—Madame C. J. Walker. 2005. (Scholastic News Nonfiction Readers Ser.). (Illus.). 24p. (J). (gr. 1-2). 19.00 (978-0-516-24941-4(X) , Children's Pr.) Scholastic Library Publishing.

Nicholson, Lois P. Booker T. Washington - Educator/ Activist: A Modern Moses. 1998. (Junior Black Americans of Achievement Ser.). (Illus.). 80p. (J). (gr. 3-6). pap. 10.20 (978-0-7910-4461-2(0) , Chelsea Hse.) Facts On File, Inc.

Nobleman, Marc Tyler. Rosa Parks. 2002. (Trailblazers of the Modern World Ser.). (Illus.). 48p. (J). (gr. 5 up). pap. 14.95 (978-0-8368-5231-8(1)); lib. bdg. 30.00 (978-0-8368-5071-0(8)) Stevens, Gareth Inc. (World Almanac Library).

—Rosa Parks. 2002. (gr. 3-6). lib. bdg. 19.90 (978-0-613-76804-7(3)) Tandem Library Bks.

O'Hern, Kerri & Raatma, Lucia. Jackie Robinson. 2006. (Illus.). 31p. (J). pap. (978-0-8368-6250-8(3) , World Almanac Library) Stevens, Gareth Inc.

Olson, Nathan. George Washington Carver: Ingenious Inventor. 2006. (Graphic Library). (Illus.). 32p. (J). 25.26 (978-0-7368-5484-9(3)) Capstone Pr., Inc.

—Tupac Shakur. 2004. (Edge Books, Rock Music Library). (Illus.). 32p. (J). lib. bdg. 22.60 (978-0-7368-2703-4(X)) Capstone Pr., Inc.

Orgill, Roxane. Mahalia: A Life in Gospel Music. 2004. (Illus.). 132p. (gr. 4-8). reprint ed. 20.00 (978-0-7567-7945-0(6)) DIANE Publishing Co.

Parks, Rosa. I Am Rosa Parks. 2000. (gr. k-3). lib. bdg. 11.80 (978-0-613-22996-8(7)); (Illus.). (J). 10.79 (978-0-606-18410-6(4)) Tandem Library Bks.

—Rosa Parks: My Story. 1999. (Illus.). 200p. (YA). (gr. 5-9). pap. 6.99 (978-0-14-130120-4(1) , Puffin) Penguin Group (USA) Inc.

—Rosa Parks: My Story. 1999. (978-0-606-15995-1(9)); (gr. 5-8). lib. bdg. 15.30 (978-0-613-15120-7(8)) Tandem Library Bks.

Parks, Rosa & Haskins, Jim. I Am Rosa Parks. Clay, Wil, illus. 1999. (Easy-to-Read Ser.). 48p. (J). (gr. 1-3). pap. 3.99 (978-0-14-130710-7(2) , Puffin) Penguin Group (USA) Inc.

Paterra, M. Elizabeth. Kweisi Mfume: Congressman & NAACP Leader. 2001. (African-American Biographies Ser.). (Illus.). 104p. (J). (gr. 6-12). lib. bdg. 26.60 (978-0-7660-1237-0(9)) Enslow Pubs., Inc.

Patrick, Denise Lewis. Jackie Robinson Strong Inside & Out. 2005. 44p. (J). lib. bdg. 15.00 (*978-1-4242-0850-0(5)) Fitzgerald Bks.

—A Lesson for Martin Luther King, Jr. Pate, Rodney S., illus. 2003. (Ready-to-Read Ser.). 32p. (J). pap. 3.99 (978-0-689-85397-5(1) , Aladdin) Simon & Schuster Children's Publishing.

—Lesson for Martin Luther King Jr. 2003. (gr. k-3). lib. bdg. 11.80 (978-0-613-73360-1(6)) Tandem Library Bks.

Patrick, Denise Lewis & Time for Kids Editors. Jackie Robinson: Strong Inside & Out. 2005. (Time for Kids Ser.). (Illus.). 48p. (J). 15.99 (978-0-06-057601-1(4)); pap. 3.99 (978-0-06-057600-4(6)) HarperCollins Pubs.

Payment, Simone. Buck Leonard. 2002. (Baseball Hall of Famers of the Negro League Ser.). (Illus.). 112p. (YA). (gr. 5-8). lib. bdg. 29.25 (978-0-8239-3473-7(X) , Rosen Central) Rosen Publishing Group, Inc., The.

Peacock, Nancy. Chris Rock. 2000. (Black Americans of Achievement Ser.). (Illus.). 112p. (J). (gr. 4-7). 30.00 (978-0-7910-5277-8(X) , Chelsea Hse.) Facts On File, Inc.

Pellowski, Michael J. Super Sports Star Latrell Sprewell. 2002. (Super Sports Star Ser.). (Illus.). 48p. (J). (gr. 1-4). lib. bdg. 23.93 (978-0-7660-1811-2(3)) Enslow Pubs., Inc.

Petry, Ann. Harriet Tubman: Conductor on the Underground Railroad. 1999. (YA). pap. 59.20 incl. audio (978-0-7887-3011-5(8) , 40893) Recorded Bks., LLC.

Pettit, Jayne. Martin Luther King, Jr. A Man with a Dream. 2001. (Book Report Biographies Ser.). (Illus.). 100p. (J). (gr. 6-8). pap. 6.95 (978-0-531-15553-0(6) , Watts, Franklin) Scholastic Library Publishing.

Pingry, Patricia A. The Story of Coretta Scott King. Walker, Steven, illus. 2007. 26p. (J). (ps-k). bds. 6.99 (*978-0-8249-6717-8(8) , Candy Cane Pr.) Ideals Pubns.

—The Story of Rosa Parks. Walker, Steven, illus. 2007. 24p. (J). (ps-k). bds. 6.99 (*978-0-8249-6687-4(2) , Candy Cane Pr.) Ideals Pubns.

Pinkney, Andrea Davis. Bill Pickett: Rodeo-Ridin' Cowboy. Pinkney, Brian, illus. 1999. (J). (gr. 5-8). lib. bdg. 14.15 (978-0-613-22822-0(7)) Tandem Library Bks.

—Bill Pickett: Rodeo-Ridin' Cowboy. 1999. (J). 12.80 (978-0-606-17356-8(0)) Tandem Library Bks.

—Dear Benjamin Banneker. Pinkney, Brian, illus. 1998. 32p. (J). (gr. 1-5). pap. 7.00 (978-0-15-201892-4(1) , Harcourt Paperbacks) Harcourt Children's Bks.

—Dear Benjamin Banneker. 1998. 12.80 (978-0-606-13324-1(0)) Tandem Library Bks.

—Duke Ellington: The Piano Prince & His Orchestra. Pinkney, Brian, illus. 1999. 32p. (gr. k-4). 15.95 (978-0-7868-0178-7(6) , Jump at the Sun) Hyperion Bks. for Children.

—Duke Ellington: The Piano Prince & His Orchestra. Pinkney, Brian, illus. 2007. 32p. (gr. k-4). pap. 5.99 (978-0-7868-1420-6(9)) Hyperion Pr.

—Ella Fitzgerald: The Tale of a Vocal Virtuosa. Pinkney, Brian, illus. 2007. 32p. (gr. k-4). pap. 5.99 (978-0-7868-1416-9(0)) Disney Pr.

—Ella Fitzgerald: The Tale of a Vocal Virtuosa. Pinkney, Brian, illus. 2002. 32p. (gr. k-4). 17.49 (978-0-7868-2493-9(X)); 16.99 (978-0-7868-0568-6(4)) Hyperion Bks. for Children. (Jump at the Sun).

—Let It Shine: Stories of Black Women Freedom Fighters. 2000. (Illus.). 128p. (J). (ps-3). 22.98 (978-0-7398-3073-4(2)) Raintree.

Pittman, Rickey E. & Hierstein, Judith. Jim Limber Davis: A Black Orphan in the Confederate White House. 2007. (Illus.). 32p. (J). (gr. 2-4). 15.95 (978-1-58980-435-7(X)) Pelican Publishing Co., Inc.

Plantz, Connie. Bessie Coleman: First Black Woman Pilot. 2001. (African-American Biographies Ser.). (Illus.). 128p. (J). (gr. 6-12). lib. bdg. 26.60 (978-0-7660-1545-6(9)) Enslow Pubs., Inc.

Plowden, Martha Ward. Famous Firsts of Black Women. Jones, Ronald, illus. 2nd ed. 2002. 176p. (J). (gr. 5-9). pap. 18.95 (978-1-56554-197-9(9)) Pelican Publishing Co., Inc.

Plum-Ucci, Carol. Super Sports Star Stephon Marbury. 2002. (Super Sports Star Ser.). (Illus.). 48p. (J). (gr. 1-4). lib. bdg. 23.93 (978-0-7660-1810-5(5)) Enslow Pubs., Inc.

Polakow, Amy. Daisy Bates: Civil Rights Crusader. 2002. (Illus.). 128p. (J). 25.00 (978-0-208-02513-5(8) , Linnet Bks.) Shoe String Pr., Inc.

Poolos, J. Hank Aaron. 2007. (Baseball Superstars Ser.). 128p. (gr. 6-12). 30.00 (*978-0-7910-9536-2(3) , Chelsea Hse.) Facts On File, Inc.

Presnall, Judith Janda. Oprah Winfrey. 1998. (People in the News Ser.). (Illus.). 112p. (YA). (gr. 6-9). 27.45 (978-1-56006-360-5(2) , Lucent Bks.) Thomson Gale.

Press, Petra. Coretta Scott King: An Unauthorized Biography. 1999. (Profiles Ser.). (Illus.). 56p. (J). (gr. 4-6). lib. bdg. 24.22 (978-1-57572-496-6(0)) Heinemann Library.

Price Hossell, Karen. I Have a Dream. 2005. (Illus.). 48p. (J). (978-1-4034-6811-6(7)); pap. (978-1-4034-6816-1(8)) Heinemann Library.

Prince, April Jones. Jackie Robinson: He Led the Way. Casilla, Robert, illus. 2007. (All Aboard Reading Ser.). 48p. (J). (gr. 1-3). pap. 3.99 (*978-0-448-44721-6(5) , Grosset & Dunlap) Penguin Group (USA) Inc.

Prince, Mary. The History of Mary Prince, a West Indian Slave, Related by Herself. 2001. (Penguin Classics Ser.). (Illus.). (J). (978-0-606-20705-8(8)) Tandem Library Bks.

Project Boy: Too Blessed to be Stressed, 1 bk. 2004. 117p. pap. 10.00 (978-0-9760441-0-9(2)) In The Hse. Publishing Co.

Pyle, Lydia. Kobe Bryant. 2004. (Awesome Athletes Ser.). (Illus.). 32p. (J). (gr. k-6). lib. bdg. 22.78 (978-1-59197-488-8(7)) ABDO Publishing Co.

—Venus & Serena Williams. 2004. (Awesome Athletes Ser.). (Illus.). 32p. (J). (gr. k-6). lib. bdg. 22.78 (978-1-59197-486-4(0)) ABDO Publishing Co.

Raatma, Lucia. Alice Walker: African-American Author & Activist. 2003. (Journey to Freedom Ser.). (Illus.). 40p. (J). (gr. 3-7). 28.50 (978-1-56766-512-3(8)) Child's World, Inc.

—Jackie Robinson. 2000. (Compass Point Early Biographies Ser.). (Illus.). 32p. (J). (gr. 2 up). lib. bdg. 21.26 (978-0-7565-0016-0(8)) Compass Point Bks.

—Jackie Robinson. 2002. (Trailblazers of the Modern World Ser.). (Illus.). 48p. (J). (gr. 5 up). pap. 14.95 (978-0-8368-5232-5(X)); lib. bdg. 30.00 (978-0-8368-5072-7(6)) Stevens, Gareth Inc. (World Almanac Library).

—Jackie Robinson. 2002. (gr. 3-6). lib. bdg. 16.40 (978-0-613-76805-4(1)) Tandem Library Bks.

—Jesse Owens: Track-and-Field Olympian. 2003. (Journey to Freedom Ser.). (Illus.). 40p. (J). (gr. 3-7). 28.50 (978-1-56766-532-1(2)) Child's World, Inc.

—Martin Luther King, Jr. 2001. (Compass Point Early Biographies Ser.). (Illus.). 32p. (J). (gr. 2 up). lib. bdg. 21.26 (978-0-7565-0114-3(8)) Compass Point Bks.

Raber, Thomas R. Michael Jordan: Basketball Skywalker. 3rd rev. exp. ed. 1999. (Sports Achievers Biographies Ser.). (Illus.). 80p. (gr. 4-9). (978-0-8225-9846-6(9) , LernerSports) Lerner Publishing Group.

—Michael Jordan: Returning Champion. 4th rev. ed. 2005. (Sports Achievers Biographies Ser.). (Illus.). 80p. (gr. 7-12). 22.60 (978-0-8225-0473-3(1)) Lerner Publishing Group.

—Michael Jordan: Returning Champion. 2002. (gr. 5-8). lib. bdg. 14.10 (978-0-613-46151-1(7)) Tandem Library Bks.

Raintree IL Staff. Connections: African-American Biographies. 2003. (Illus.). pap. 5.95 (978-1-4109-0792-9(9)) Raintree.

Raintree Steck-Vaughn Staff. Overcoming Challenges: The Life of Charles F. Bolden, Jr. 1999. (Illus.). (J). pap. 35.60 (978-0-7398-0910-5(5)) Steck-Vaughn.

Rapoport, Ron. See How She Runs: Marion Jones & the Making of a Champion. 2001. (J). (978-0-606-21706-4(1)) Tandem Library Bks.

Rappaport, Doreen. Freedom River. Collier, Bryan, illus. 32p. (gr. k-4). 2000. 14.99 (978-0-7868-0350-7(9)); 2007. pap. 6.99 (*978-1-4231-0634-0(2)) Hyperion Bks. for Children. (Jump at the Sun).

—Martin's Big Words: The Life of Dr. Martin Luther King Jr. Collier, Bryan, illus. 2001. 40p. (gr. k-4). 15.99 (978-0-7868-0714-7(8)) Hyperion Bks. for Children.

Rappaport, Doreen. Martin's Big Words: The Life of Dr. Martin Luther King Jr. Collier, Bryan, illus. rev. ed. 2007. 40p. (ps-17). pap. 6.99 (*978-1-4231-0635-7(0) , Jump at the Sun) Hyperion Bks. for Children.

Rappoport, Ken. Super Sports Star Glen Rice. 2002. (Super Sports Star Ser.). (Illus.). 48p. (J). (gr. 1-4). lib. bdg. 23.93 (978-0-7660-1808-2(3)) Enslow Pubs., Inc.

—Super Sports Star Penny Hardaway. 2001. (Super Sports Star Ser.). (Illus.). 48p. (J). (gr. 1-4). lib. bdg. 23.93 (978-0-7660-1516-6(5)) Enslow Pubs., Inc.

Raschka, Chris. Charlie Parker Played Be Bop. Raschka, Chris, illus. 2000. (Live Oak Readalong Ser.). (Illus.). (J). pap. 18.95 incl. audio compact disk (978-1-59112-419-1(0)) Live Oak Media.

—Charlie Parker Played Be-Bop. Raschka, Chris, illus. 2000. (Illus.). 28.95 incl. audio compact disk (978-1-59112-425-2(5)); pap. 35.95 incl. audio compact disk (978-1-59112-602-7(9)) Live Oak Media.

—Mysterious Thelonious. Raschka, Chris, illus. (Illus.). pap. 18.95 incl. audio compact disk (978-1-59112-421-4(2)); 2000. 28.95 incl. audio compact disk (978-1-59112-422-1(0)) Live Oak Media.

Raum, Elizabeth. Louis Armstrong: Jazz Legend. 2006. (Fact Finders Ser.). (Illus.). 32p. (J). 22.60 (978-0-7368-6419-0(9)) Capstone Pr., Inc.

—Mae Jemison. 2005. (American Lives Ser.). (Illus.). 32p. (J). (978-1-4034-6942-7(3)); pap. (978-1-4034-6949-6(0)) Heinemann Library.

Rausch, Monica. Crispus Attucks. 2006. (Illus.). 24p. (J). pap. (*978-0-8368-7688-8(1)); lib. bdg. (*978-0-8368-7681-9(4)) Stevens, Gareth Inc. (Weekly Reader Early Learning Library).

—Hariet Tubman. 2006. (ENG & SPA.). (J). pap. (*978-0-8368-7992-6(9)); lib. bdg. (*978-0-8368-7985-8(6)) Stevens, Gareth Inc. (Weekly Reader Early Learning Library).

—Harriet Tubman. 2006. 24p. (J). pap. (*978-0-8368-7693-2(8)); lib. bdg. (*978-0-8368-7686-4(5)) Stevens, Gareth Inc. (Weekly Reader Early Learning Library).

Reef, Catherine. A. Philip Randolph: Union Leader & Civil Rights Crusader. 2001. (African-American Biographies Ser.). (Illus.). 128p. (J). (gr. 6-12). lib. bdg. 26.60 (978-0-7660-1544-9(0)) Enslow Pubs., Inc.

—Paul Laurence Dunbar: Portrait of a Poet. 2000. (African-American Biographies Ser.). (Illus.). 128p. (J). (gr. 6-12). lib. bdg. 26.60 (978-0-7660-1350-6(2)) Enslow Pubs., Inc.

—William Grant Still: African-American Composer. 2004. (Modern Music Masters Ser.). (Illus.). 112p. (YA). (gr. 6-12). 23.95 (978-1-931798-11-2(7)) Reynolds, Morgan Inc.

Regis, Frankye. A Voice from the Civil Rights Era. 2004. (Voices of Twentieth-Century Conflict Ser.). (Illus.). 184p. 36.95 (978-0-313-32998-2(2) , GR2998, Praeger Pubs.) Greenwood Publishing Group, Inc.

Rhodes, Lisa Renee. Coretta Scott King: Civil Rights Activist. (Black Americans of Achievement Ser.). (Illus.). 112p. (J). (gr. 6-12). 2005. pap. 13.25 (978-0-7910-8371-0(3)); 2004. 30.00 (978-0-7910-8251-5(2)) Facts On File, Inc. (Chelsea Hse.).

—Coretta Scott King: Humanitarian. 1999. (Black Americans of Achievement Ser.). (Illus.). 144p. (YA). (gr. 4-7). 30.00 (978-0-7910-4690-6(7)); (gr. 5 up). pap. 6.65 (978-0-7910-4691-3(5)) Facts On File, Inc. (Chelsea Hse.).

Rhynes, Martha E. Gwendolyn Brooks: Poet from Chicago. 2004. (World Writers Ser.). (Illus.). 112p. (YA). (gr. 6-12). 23.95 (978-1-931798-05-1(2)) Reynolds, Morgan Inc.

Rigby Education Staff. John Henry. (Illus.). 16p. (J). pap. 30.00 (978-0-7635-6490-2(7) , 764907C99) Rigby Education.

Riley, John B. George Washington Carver: A Photo Biography. l.t. ed. 2004. (First Biographies Ser.). (Illus.). 24p. (YA). (gr. 5 up). 16.95 (978-1-883846-62-6(5) , First Biographies) Reynolds, Morgan Inc.

Rinaldo, Denise. Rosa Parks: With a Discussion of Courage. 2003. (Values in Action Ser.). (J). (978-1-59203-061-3(0)) Learning Challenge, Inc.

Ringgold, Faith. If a Bus Could Talk: The Story of Rosa Parks. Ringgold, Faith, illus. (Illus.). 32p. (J). 2003. (gr. k-4). pap. 7.99 (978-0-689-85676-1(8) , Aladdin); 1999. (gr. 1-4). 16.00 (978-0-689-81892-9(0)) Simon & Schuster Children's Publishing.

—If a Bus Could Talk: The Story of Rosa Parks. 2003. (gr. k-3). lib. bdg. 15.30 (978-0-613-61633-1(2)) Tandem Library Bks.

Riordan, James. The Story of Martin Luther King. 2001. (Illus.). 48p. (J). lib. bdg. 24.25 (978-1-930643-24-6(1)) Chrysalis Education.

Rivera, Sheila. Martin Luther King Jr. A Life of Determination. 2006. (Pull Ahead Books). (Illus.). 32p. (J). 22.60 (978-0-8225-3477-8(0) , Lerner Pubns.) Lerner Publishing Group.

Rivera, Ursula. Aretha Franklin. 2006. (Rock & Roll Hall of Famers Ser.). (Illus.). 112p. (YA). (gr. 5-8). lib. bdg. 29.25 (978-0-8239-3639-7(2)) Rosen Publishing Group, Inc., The.

—The Supremes. 2006. (Rock & Roll Hall of Famers Ser.). (Illus.). 112p. (YA). (gr. 5-8). lib. bdg. 29.25 (978-0-8239-3527-7(2)) Rosen Publishing Group, Inc., The.

Robbins, Trina. Bessie Coleman: Daring Stunt Pilot. Steacy, Ken, illus. 2007. (Graphic Library). 32p. (J). (gr. 3-5). lib. bdg. 25.26 (978-0-7368-6851-8(8)); pap. 7.95 (*978-0-7368-7903-3(X)) Capstone Pr., Inc.

Robert Smalls Sails to Freedom. 2007. (J). pap. 5.95 (*978-0-8225-6051-7(8) , First Avenue Editions) Lerner Publishing Group.

Robertson, Theda Robinson. Journey to a Free Land: The Story of Nicodemus, the First All Black Town West of the Mississippi. 2006. (Illus.). (J). (978-0-9705721-6-5(6)) Written Images, Inc.

Robinson, Sharon. Jackie Robinson's Values to Live By: Becoming Your Best Self. 2002. (Jackie's 9 Ser.). 192p. (J). (gr. 4-9). pap. 4.99 (978-0-439-38550-3(4)) Scholastic, Inc.

—Jackie's Nine: Jackie Robinson's Values to Live By. 2002. (gr. 5-8). lib. bdg. 13.00 (978-0-613-50333-4(3)) Tandem Library Bks.

—Promises to Keep: How Jackie Robinson Changed America. 2004. (Illus.). 64p. (YA). pap. 16.95 (978-0-439-42592-6(1)) Scholastic, Inc.

Rockwell, Anne. Only Passing Through: The Story of Sojourner Truth. Christie, R. Gregory, illus. 2002. 40p. (J). (gr. 2-5). pap. 6.99 (978-0-440-41766-8(X) , Dragonfly Bks.) Random Hse. Children's Bks.

Rockwell, Anne F. Only Passing Through. 2002. (gr. 3-6). lib. bdg. 15.30 (978-0-613-86684-2(3)) Tandem Library Bks.

—Only Passing Through: The Story of Sojourner Truth. Siscoe, Nancy, ed. Christie, R. Gregory, illus. 2000. 40p. (J). (gr. 2-5). 16.95 (978-0-679-89186-4(2)); lib. bdg. 18.99 (978-0-679-99186-1(7)) Random Hse. Children's Bks. (Knopf Bks. for Young Readers).

Rolfe, John & Ross, Dalton. Grant Hill: Superstar Forward. 2005. (Sports Illustrated for Kids Bks.). (Illus.). 176p. (YA). (gr. 7-12). lib. bdg. 30.50 (978-0-8239-3578-9(7)) Rosen Publishing Group, Inc., The.

Rolfe, John, et al. Ken Griffey, Jr. 2000. 112p. (J). pap. 3.99 (978-1-930623-07-1(0)) Sports Illustrated For Kids.

—Ken Griffey, Jr. Superstar Centerfielder. 2005. (Sports Illustrated for Kids Bks.). (Illus.). 176p. (YA). (gr. 7-12). lib. bdg. 30.50 (978-0-8239-3687-8(2)) Rosen Publishing Group, Inc., The.

Roop, Connie & Roop, Peter. Sojourner Truth. 2003. (In Their Own Words Ser.). (Illus.). 128p. (J). (gr. 2-5). 4.99 (978-0-439-26323-8(9) , Scholastic Nonfiction) Scholastic, Inc.

Roop, Peter. Sojourner Truth. 2002. (gr. 3-6). lib. bdg. 12.40 (978-0-613-66669-5(0)) Tandem Library Bks.

Rosenthal. Michael Johnson: Sprinter Deluxe. 2000. (Sport Snaps Ser.). (J). (978-0-606-20158-2(0)) Tandem Library Bks.

Rosenthal, Bert. Tim Hardaway: Star Guard. 2001. (Sports Reports). (Illus.). 104p. (J). (gr. 4-10). lib. bdg. 26.60 (978-0-7660-1500-5(9)) Enslow Pubs., Inc.

Rowley, John. Harriet Tubman. 2002. (Lives & Times Ser.). (Illus.). 24p. (J). (gr. k-3). pap. 6.50 (978-1-4034-0029-1(6) , 91473) Heinemann Library.

Roza, Greg. Venus & Serena Williams: The Sisters of Tennis. 2006. (Tony Stead Nonfiction Independent Reading Collection). (J). pap. (978-1-4042-5537-1(0)) Rosen Publishing Group, Inc., The.

Ruffin, Frances E. Frederick Douglass: Rising up from Slavery. 2008. (Sterling Biographies Ser.). (Illus.). 128p. (J). pap. 5.95 (*978-1-4027-4118-0(9)) Sterling Publishing Co., Inc.

—Her Story, Her Words: The Narrative of Sojourner Truth. 2004. (Great Moments in American History Ser.). (Illus.). 32p. (gr. 4-8). lib. bdg. 21.25 (978-0-8239-4387-6(9) , Rosen Central) Rosen Publishing Group, Inc., The.

—Sally Hemings. 2002. (American Legends Ser.). (Illus.). 24p. (J). (gr. 3). lib. bdg. 18.75 (978-0-8239-5828-3(0) , PowerKids Pr.) Rosen Publishing Group, Inc., The.

Rummel, Jack. Muhammad Ali. (Black Americans of Achievement Ser.). (Illus.). 112p. (J). (gr. 6-12). 2005. pap. 13.25 (978-0-7910-8330-7(6)); 2004. 30.00 (978-0-7910-8156-3(7)) Facts On File, Inc. (Chelsea Hse.).

Ruth, Amy. Queen Latifah. 2000. (Biography Ser.). (Illus.). 112p. (YA). (gr. 6-12). lib. bdg. 27.93 (978-0-8225-4988-8(3) , Lerner Pubns.) Lerner Publishing Group.

Ryan, Bernard. Condoleeza Rice: National Security Advisor & Musician. 2003. (Ferguson Career Biographies Ser.). (Illus.). 160p. (J). (gr. 6-12). 25.00 (978-0-8160-5480-0(0) , Ferguson Publishing Co.) Facts On File, Inc.

Ryan, Pam Muñoz. When Marian Sang: The True Recital of Marian Anderson. Selznick, Brian, illus. pap. 16.95 incl. audio (978-1-59112-943-1(5)); pap. incl. audio (978-1-59112-945-5(1)); pap. 18.95 incl. audio compact disk (978-1-59112-947-9(8)); pap. incl. audio compact disk (978-1-59112-949-3(4)) Live Oak Media.

—When Marian Sang: The True Recital of Marian Anderson. Selznick, Brian, illus. 2002. 40p. (J). (gr. 1-5). pap. 16.95 (978-0-439-26967-4(9) , Scholastic Pr.) Scholastic, Inc.

Salas, Laura Purdie. Charles Drew: Pioneer in Medicine. 2006. (Fact Finders Ser.). (Illus.). 32p. (J). (978-0-7368-5433-7(9)) Capstone Pr., Inc.

—Phillis Wheatley: Colonial American Poet. 2006. (Fact Finders Ser.). (Illus.). 32p. (J). (978-0-7368-5435-1(5)) Capstone Pr., Inc.

Salisbury, Cynthia. Phillis Wheatley: Legendary African-American Poet. 2001. (Historical American Biographies Ser.). (Illus.). 112p. (J). (gr. 6-12). lib. bdg. 26.60 (978-0-7660-1394-0(4)) Enslow Pubs., Inc.

Santella, Andrew. Martin Luther King Jr. Civil Rights Leader & Nobel Prize Winner. 2003. (Journey to Freedom). (Illus.). 40p. (J). (gr. 3-7). 28.50 (978-1-56766-539-0(X)) Child's World, Inc.

Sapet, Kerrily. Barack Obama. 2007. (Political Profiles Ser.). (Illus.). 128p. (YA). (gr. 5 up). lib. bdg. 27.95 (*978-1-59935-045-5(9)) Reynolds, Morgan Inc.

Savage, Jeff. Barry Bonds. 2004. (Amazing Athletes Ser.). (Illus.). 32p. (J). (gr. 3-4). lib. bdg. 23.93 (978-0-8225-3688-8(9)) Lerner Publishing Group.

—Barry Bonds: Record Breaker. 2nd rev. ed. 2003. (Sports Achievers Biographies Ser.). (Illus.). 64p. (J). (gr. 4-9). 5.95 (978-0-8225-0472-6(3) , Carolrhoda Bks.) Lerner Publishing Group.

—Kobe Bryant. 2005. (Amazing Athletes Ser.). (Illus.). 32p. (gr. 3-4). lib. bdg. 22.60 (978-0-8225-1300-1(5)) Lerner Publishing Group.

—Sports Great Ken Griffey, Jr. 2000. (Sports Great Bks.). (Illus.). 64p. (YA). (gr. 4-10). lib. bdg. 22.60 (978-0-7660-1266-0(2)) Enslow Pubs., Inc.

—Sports Great Stephon Marbury. 2000. (Sports Great Bks.). (Illus.). 64p. (YA). (gr. 4-10). lib. bdg. 22.60 (978-0-7660-1265-3(4)) Enslow Pubs., Inc.

—Terrell Davis: TD! 1999. (Sports Achievers Biographies Ser.). (Illus.). 80p. (YA). (gr. 4-9). pap. (978-0-8225-9847-3(7) , LernerSports) Lerner Publishing Group.

—Top 10 African-American Men's Athletes. 2001. (Sports Top 10 Ser.). (Illus.). 48p. (J). (gr. 4-10). lib. bdg. 23.93 (978-0-7660-1494-7(0)) Enslow Pubs., Inc.

Sawyer, Kem Knapp. Oprah Winfrey. 2006. (Biography Ser.). 128p. (J). pap. 4.99 (978-0-7566-1497-3(X)) Dorling Kindersley Publishing, Inc.

Schaefer, A. R. Jacob Lawrence. 2002. (Life & Work of. . . Ser.). (J). pap. 6.50 (978-1-4034-0496-1(8)); 32p. lib. bdg. 21.36 (978-1-4034-0290-5(6)) Heinemann Library.

—Ken Griffey, Jr. 2002. (Sports Heroes Ser.). (Illus.). 48p. (J). (gr. 3-4). lib. bdg. 21.26 (978-0-7368-1294-8(6) , Capstone High-Interest Bks.) Capstone Pr., Inc.

—Kobe Bryant. 2002. (Sports Heroes Ser.). (Illus.). 48p. (J). (gr. 3-4). lib. bdg. 21.26 (978-0-7368-1052-4(8) , Capstone High-Interest Bks.) Capstone Pr., Inc.

—Serena & Venus Williams. 2002. (Sports Heroes Ser.). (Illus.). 48p. (J). (gr. 3-4). lib. bdg. 21.26 (978-0-7368-1054-8(4) , Capstone High-Interest Bks.) Capstone Pr., Inc.

—Shaquille O'Neal. 2002. (Sports Heroes Ser.). (Illus.). 48p. (J). (gr. 3-4). lib. bdg. 21.26 (978-0-7368-1297-9(0) , Capstone High-Interest Bks.) Capstone Pr., Inc.

Schaefer, Lola M. Booker T. Washington. Saunders-Smith, Gail, ed. 2003. (First Biographies Ser.). (Illus.). 24p. (J). (gr. k-1). lib. bdg. 15.93 (978-0-7368-1647-2(X) , Pebble Bks.) Capstone Pr., Inc.

—Frederick Douglass. 2005. (First Biographies Ser.). 24p. (YA). (gr. k-3). pap. (978-0-7368-9370-1(9) , Pebble Bks.) Capstone Pr., Inc.

—Frederick Douglass. Saunders-Smith, Gail, ed. 2002. (First Biographies Ser.). (Illus.). 24p. (J). (gr. k-1). lib. bdg. 15.93 (978-0-7368-1174-3(5) , Pebble Bks.) Capstone Pr., Inc.

—Jackie Robinson. Saunders-Smith, Gail, ed. 2002. (First Biographies Ser.). (Illus.). 24p. (J). (gr. k-1). lib. bdg. 15.93 (978-0-7368-1435-5(3) , Pebble Bks.) Capstone Pr., Inc.

—Rosa Parks. Saunders-Smith, Gail, ed. 2002. (First Biographies Ser.). (Illus.). 24p. (J). (gr. k-1). lib. bdg. 15.93 (978-0-7368-1176-7(1) , Pebble Bks.) Capstone Pr., Inc.

Schlissel, Lillian. Black Frontiers. 2000. (Illus.). 80p. (J). (gr. 3-7). pap. 7.99 (978-0-689-83315-1(6) , Aladdin) Simon & Schuster Children's Publishing.

—Black Frontiers: A History of African American Heroes in the Old West. 2000. (gr. 3-6). lib. bdg. 16.45 (978-0-613-21229-8(0)); (Illus.). (J). 14.79 (978-0-606-17914-0(3)) Tandem Library Bks.

Schnakenberg, Robert. Cynthia Cooper. 2000. (Illus.). 64p. (J). (gr. 4-7). lib. bdg. 17.60 (978-0-613-32432-8(3)) Tandem Library Bks.

Schnakenberg, Robert E. Cynthia Cooper. 2000. (Women Who Win Ser.). (Illus.). 64p. (gr. 4-7). (YA). pap. 25.00 (978-0-7910-6156-5(6)); (J). 25.00 (978-0-7910-5796-4(8)) Facts On File, Inc. (Chelsea Hse.).

Schoell, William. "I Can Do Anything" The Sammy Davis, Jr. Story. 2004. (Avisson Young Adult Ser.). (Illus.). 116p. (J). pap. 19.95 (978-1-888105-61-2(5)) Avisson Pr., Inc.

Scholastic Library Publishing Staff, contrib. by. African American Biographies, 10 vols. 2006. (Illus.). (YA). (gr. 6-12). 449.00 (978-0-7172-6090-4(9) , Grolier Online) Scholastic Library Publishing.

Schraff, Anne. Charles Drew: Pioneer in Medicine. 2003. (Famous Inventors Ser.). (Illus.). 32p. (J). (gr. 1-4). lib. bdg. 22.60 (978-0-7660-2008-5(8)) Enslow Pubs., Inc.

—Dr. Charles Drew: Blood Bank Innovator. 2003. (African-American Biographies Ser.). (Illus.). 128p. (J). (gr. 6-12). lib. bdg. 26.60 (978-0-7660-2117-4(3)) Enslow Pubs., Inc.

—Harriet Tubman: Moses of the Underground Railroad. 2001. (African-American Biographies Ser.). (Illus.). 128p. (J). (gr. 6-12). lib. bdg. 26.60 (978-0-7660-1548-7(3)) Enslow Pubs., Inc.

—Marcus Garvey: Controversial Champion of Black Pride. 2004. (African-American Biographies Ser.). (Illus.). 128p. (J). lib. bdg. 26.60 (978-0-7660-2168-6(8)) Enslow Pubs., Inc.

—Wilma Rudolph: The Greatest Woman Sprinter in History. 2004. (African-American Biographies Ser.). (Illus.). 112p. (J). lib. bdg. 26.60 (978-0-7660-2291-1(9)) Enslow Pubs., Inc.

Schraff, Anne E. Booker T. Washington: Character Is Power. 2006. (African-American Biography Library). (Illus.). 128p. (J). lib. bdg. 31.93 (978-0-7660-2535-6(7)) Enslow Pubs., Inc.

—Ida B. Wells-Barnett: Strike a Blow Against Glaring Evil. 2008. (African-American Biography Library). (Illus.). 128p. (J). (gr. 6 up). lib. bdg. 31.93 (***978-0-7660-2704-6(X)***) Enslow Pubs., Inc.

—Martin Luther King, JR: We Shall Overcome. 2005. (African-American Biography Library). (Illus.). 128p. (J). (gr. 6-13). lib. bdg. 31.93 (978-0-7660-1774-0(5)) Enslow Pubs., Inc.

—Rosa Parks: Tired of Giving In. 2005. (African-American Biography Library). (Illus.). 128p. (J). (gr. 6-12). lib. bdg. 31.93 (978-0-7660-2463-2(6)) Enslow Pubs., Inc.

Schroeder, Alan. Booker T. Washington: Educator & Racial Spokesman. (Black Americans of Achievement Ser.). (Illus.). 112p. (J). (gr. 6-12). 2005. pap. 13.25 (978-0-7910-8374-1(8)); 2004. 30.00 (978-0-7910-8253-9(9)) Facts On File, Inc. (Chelsea Hse.).

—Minty: A Story of Young Harriet Tubman. Pinkney, Jerry, illus. 2002. (YA). 25.45 (978-0-7587-0382-8(1)) Book Wholesalers, Inc.

—Minty: A Story of Young Harriet Tubman. Pinkney, Jerry, illus. 2000. (J). (ps-ps). lib. bdg. 15.30 (978-0-613-33712-0(3)) Tandem Library Bks.

—Minty: A Story of Young Harriet Tubman. 2000. (978-0-606-20365-4(6)); (YA). (978-0-606-20246-6(3)) Tandem Library Bks.

Schroeder, Alan & Wagner, Heather Lehr. Josephine Baker. 2006. (Black Americans of Achievement Ser.). (Illus.). 128p. (J). (gr. 6-12). 30.00 (978-0-7910-9212-5(7) , Chelsea Hse.) Facts On File, Inc.

Schuldt, Lori Meek. Martin Luther King, Jr: With Profiles of Mohandas K. Gandhi & Nelson Mandela. 2006. (Biographical Connections Ser.). (Illus.). 112p. (J). (978-0-7166-1822-5(2)) World Bk., Inc.

Schulman, Arlene. Muhammad Ali. (Just the Facts Biographies Ser.). (Illus.). (J). (gr. 6-12). 2005. 112p. 27.93 (978-0-8225-2448-9(1)); 2003. 128p. pap. 7.95 (978-0-8225-9693-6(8) , Lerner Pubns.) Lerner Publishing Group.

Schuman, Michael. Barack Obama: We Are One People. 2008. (African-American Biography Library). (Illus.). 128p. (J). (gr. 6 up). lib. bdg. 31.93 (***978-0-7660-2891-3(7)***) Enslow Pubs., Inc.

—Halle Berry: Beauty Is Not Just Physical. 2006. (African-American Biography Library). (Illus.). 112p. (YA). lib. bdg. 31.93 (978-0-7660-2467-0(9)) Enslow Pubs., Inc.

—Will Smith: I Like Blending a Message with Comedy. 2006. (African-American Biography Library). (Illus.). 128p. (J). lib. bdg. 31.93 (978-0-7660-2465-6(2) , 1250489) Enslow Pubs., Inc.

Sexton, Colleen. Jackie Robinson: A Life of Determination. 2007. (Illus.). 24p. (J). lib. bdg. 19.95 (978-1-60014-089-1(0)) Bellwether Media.

Sexton, Colleen A. Let's Meet Martin Luther King, Jr. 2003. (Let's Meet Biographies Ser.). (Illus.). 32p. (gr. 2-4). 23.00 (978-0-7910-7322-3(X) , Chelsea Hse.) Facts On File, Inc.

Shafer, Susan. Jesse Owens: Fastest Human. 2005. 22.00 (***978-1-4108-4207-7(X)***) Benchmark Education Co.

Sharp, Anne Wallace. Condoleezza Rice. 2007. (People in the News Ser.). (Illus.). 128p. (gr. 7-10). 31.20 (***978-1-59018-521-6(8)*** , Lucent Bks.) Thomson Gale.

Sharpten, Al. African-American Civil Rights Activists: Black Panthers. 2000. (My Ancestors—My Heroes Ser.: Vol. 39). (J). (gr. 3-4). (978-1-893091-38-2(4)) Parker Publishing Co.

Sherman, Josepha. Terrell Davis. 2001. (Sports Files Ser.). (Illus.). 32p. (J). (gr. 1-3). lib. bdg. (978-1-58810-115-0(0)) Heinemann Library.

—Venus Williams. 2001. (Sports Files Ser.). (Illus.). 32p. (J). (gr. 1-3). lib. bdg. (978-1-58810-116-7(9)) Heinemann Library.

Sherrow, Victoria. Wilma Rudolph. Johnson, Larry, illus. (On My Own Biographies Ser.). (J). (gr. 1-3). 2003. 48p. 5.95 (978-1-57505-442-1(6)); 2000. 56p. lib. bdg. 23.93 (978-1-57505-246-5(6) , Carolrhoda Bks.) Lerner Publishing Group.

—Wilma Rudolph. 1999. (Illus.). 48p. (gr. 4-7). pap. 5.95 (978-1-57505-264-9(4)) Lerner Publishing Group.

—Wilma Rudolph. 2000. (gr. k-3). lib. bdg. 14.10 (978-0-613-79246-2(7)); 2000. (gr. 3-6). lib. bdg. 14.10 (978-0-613-68304-3(8)); 1999. (gr. 3-6). lib. bdg. 14.10 (978-0-613-79247-9(5)) Tandem Library Bks.

Shirley, David. Alex Haley: Author. 2005. (Black Americans of Achievement Ser.). (Illus.). 112p. (J). (gr. 6-12). 30.00 (978-0-7910-8249-2(0)); pap. 13.25 (978-0-7910-8369-7(1)) Facts On File, Inc. (Chelsea Hse.).

Shone, Rob. Rosa Parks: The Life of a Civil Rights Heroine. Spender, Nik, illus. 2006. 48p. (J). (978-1-4042-0926-8(3)); pap. (978-1-4042-0927-5(1)); (gr. 3-8). lib. bdg. 29.95 (978-1-4042-0864-3(X)) Rosen Publishing Group, Inc., The.

Shores, Erika L. Rosa Parks: Civil Rights Poineer. 2005. (Fact Finders Ser.). (Illus.). 32p. (J). (ps-7). lib. bdg. 22.60 (978-0-7368-3746-0(9)) Capstone Pr., Inc.

Sickels, Amy. Walter Dean Myers. 2008. (Who Wrote That? Ser.). 128p. (gr. 6-12). 30.00 (***978-0-7910-9524-9(X)*** , Chelsea Hse.) Facts On File, Inc.

Sidwell, Mark Free Indeed: Heroes of Black Christian History. exp. ed. 2001. vi, 154p. (J). (gr. 3-6). 10.95 (978-1-57924-734-8(2)) Jones, Bob Univ. Pr.

Simms, Patsy Ford. Harriet's Freedom Train. 2000. (J). stu. ed. 12.50 (978-0-7692-9377-6(8)); tchr. ed. 24.95 (978-0-7692-9376-9(X)) Alfred Publishing Co., Inc. (Warner Bros. Pubns.).

Simpkins, Daphne. Nat King Cole: An Unforgettable Life of Music. 2001. (J). (gr. 4-7). pap. 7.95 (978-1-58838-023-4(8) , Junebug Bks.) NewSouth, Inc.

Sinnott, Susan. Lorraine Hansberry: Award-Winning Playwright & Civil Rights Activist. 1999. (J). (978-0-606-19366-5(9)) Tandem Library Bks.

Skelton, Renee. Harriet Tubman: A Woman of Courage. 2005. (Time for Kids Ser.). (Illus.). 48p. (J). pap. 3.99 (978-0-06-057607-3(3)) HarperCollins Pubs.

Skelton, Renee. Harriet Tubman A Woman of Courage. 2005. 2005p. (J). lib. bdg. 15.00 (***978-1-4242-0849-4(1)***) Fitzgerald Bks.

Skelton, Renee & Time for Kids Editors. Harriet Tubman: A Woman of Courage. 2005. (Time for Kids Ser.). (Illus.). 48p. (J). 15.99 (978-0-06-057608-0(1)) HarperCollins Pubs.

Slade, Suzanne. Frederick Douglass: Writer, Speaker, & Opponent of Slavery. McGuire, Robert, illus. 2006. (Biographies Ser.). 24p. (J). (gr. k-3). lib. bdg. 23.93 (***978-1-4048-3102-5(9)***) Picture Window Bks.

—Sojourner Truth: Preacher for Freedom & Equality. Blanks, Natascha Alex, illus. 2007. (J). lib. bdg. (***978-1-4048-3726-3(4)***) Picture Window Bks.

Slavicek, Louise Chipley. Harriet Tubman & the Underground Railroad. 2006. (Lucent Library of Black History). 112p. (J). (gr. 7-10). 32.45 (978-1-59018-927-6(2) , Lucent Bks.) Thomson Gale.

Sloate, Susan. Ray Charles: Young Musician. Henderson, Meryl, illus. 2007. (Childhood of Famous Americans Ser.). 176p. (J). pap. 5.99 (978-1-4169-1437-2(4) , Aladdin) Simon & Schuster Children's Publishing.

Smallwood. NBA - Yesterday's Heroes: A Journey Through the History of African-American Superstars in the NBA. 2000. (J). (978-0-606-19933-9(0)) Tandem Library Bks.

Smallwood, John, Jr. Yesterday's Heroes: A Journey Through the History of African-American Superstars in the NBA. 2001. (NBA Ser.). (Illus.). 80p. (J). (gr. 3-7). pap. 4.99 (978-0-439-24110-6(3)) Scholastic, Inc.

Smith, Pohla & Wilson, Steve. Shaquille O'Neal: Superhero at Center. 2005. (Sports Illustrated for Kids Bks.). (Illus.). 176p. (YA). (gr. 7-12). lib. bdg. 25.25 (978-0-8239-3577-2(9)) Rosen Publishing Group, Inc., The.

Somervill, Barbara A. Mary McLeod Bethune: African-American Educator. 2003. (Spirit of America). (Illus.). 32p. (J). (gr. 2-6). 27.07 (978-1-59296-008-8(1)) Child's World, Inc.

St. Lawrence, Genevieve. Medgar Evers. 2003. (gr. 3-6). lib. bdg. 18.20 (978-0-613-78291-3(7)) Tandem Library Bks.

Stafford, Mark & Davenport, John, texts. W. E. B. Du Bois: Scholar & Activist. (Black Americans of Achievement Ser.). (Illus.). 112p. (J). (gr. 6-12). 2005. pap. 13.25 (978-0-7910-8332-1(2)); 2004. 30.00 (978-0-7910-8158-7(3)) Facts On File, Inc. (Chelsea Hse.).

Stauffacher, Sue. Nothing but Trouble: The Story of Althea Gibson. Couch, Greg, illus. 2007. 40p. (J). (gr. k-3). lib. bdg. 19.99 (978-0-375-93408-7(1)); 16.99 (978-0-375-83408-0(7)) Random Hse. Children's Bks. (Knopf Bks. for Young Readers).

Stearns, Dan. Harriet Tubman & the Underground Railroad. 2006. (In the Footsteps of American Heroes Ser.). (Illus.). 64p. (J). pap. 11.95 (978-0-8368-6433-5(6)); lib. bdg. 32.67 (978-0-8368-6428-1(X)) Stevens, Gareth Inc. (World Almanac Library).

Steele, Christy & Graves, Kerry, eds. A Free Black Girl Before the Civil War: The Diary of Charlotte Forten, 1854. 1999. (Diaries, Letters & Memoirs Ser.). 32p. (J). (gr. 2-7). pap. 21.00 (978-0-516-21339-2(3) , Children's Pr.) Scholastic Library Publishing.

Steele, Philip. Jesse Owens. 2001. (Profiles Ser.). (Illus.). 56p. (J). (gr. 4-6). lib. bdg. (978-1-58810-059-7(6)) Heinemann Library.

Steele, Phillip. Rosa Parks & Her Protest for Civil Rights. 2002. (Dates with History Ser.). (Illus.). 31p. (J). lib. bdg. 24.25 (978-1-58340-215-3(2)) Smart Apple Media.

Steenkamer, Paul. Sports Great Donovan Mcnabb. 2003. (Sports Great Books). (Illus.). 64p. (J). lib. bdg. 22.60 (978-0-7660-2114-3(9)) Enslow Pubs., Inc.

Sterling, Kristin. Mary McLeod Bethune: A Life of Resourcefulness. 2008. (Pull Ahead Books-Biographies Ser.). (J). lib. bdg. 22.60 (***978-0-8225-8588-6(X)*** , Lerner Pubns.) Lerner Publishing Group.

Stewart, Mark. Chamique Holdsclaw: Driving Force. 2000. (New Wave Ser.). (Illus.). 48p. (gr. 4 up). lib. bdg. 22.90 (978-0-7613-1801-9(1) , Millbrook Pr.) Lerner Publishing Group.

—Daunte Culpepper: Command & Control. 2002. (New Wave Ser.). (Illus.). 48p. (gr. 4 up). lib. bdg. 22.90 (978-0-7613-2613-7(8) , Millbrook Pr.) Lerner Publishing Group.

—Jevon Kearse: Force of One. 2001. (New Wave Ser.). (Illus.). 48p. (gr. 4 up). lib. bdg. 22.90 (978-0-7613-2269-6(8) , Millbrook Pr.) Lerner Publishing Group.

—Kevin Garnett/Shake up the Game. 2002. (New Wave Ser.). (Illus.). 48p. (gr. 4 up). lib. bdg. 22.90 (978-0-7613-2615-1(4) , Millbrook Pr.) Lerner Publishing Group.

—Kobe Bryant: Hard to the Hoop. 2000. (Basketball's New Wave Ser.: up). (Illus.). 48p. (J). (gr. 4-8). pap. 6.95 (978-0-7613-1380-9(X) , Millbrook Pr.) Lerner Publishing Group.

—Kobe Bryant: Hard to the Hoop. 2000. (J). (978 0 606-20194-0(7)); (gr. 3-6). lib. bdg. 15.25 (978-0-613-25901-9(7)) Tandem Library Bks.

—Lisa Leslie. 1998. (gr. 3-6). lib. bdg. 14.10 (978-0-613-90733-0(7)) Tandem Library Bks.

—Marion Jones: Fast & Fearless. 2000. (New Wave Ser.). (Illus.). 48p. (gr. 4 up). lib. bdg. 22.90 (978-0-7613-1870-5(4) , Millbrook Pr.) Lerner Publishing Group.

—Randy Moss: First in Flight. 2000. (New Wave Ser.). (Illus.). 48p. (gr. 4 up). lib. bdg. 22.90 (978-0-7613-1518-6(7) , Millbrook Pr.) Lerner Publishing Group.

—Terrell Davis: Toughing It Out. 1999. (New Wave Ser.). (Illus.). 48p. (gr. 4 up). lib. bdg. 22.90 (978-0-7613-1514-8(4) , Millbrook Pr.) Lerner Publishing Group.

—Venus & Serena Williams: Sisters in Arms. 2000. (New Wave Ser.). (Illus.). 48p. (gr. 4 up). lib. bdg. 22.90 (978-0-7613-1803-3(8) , Millbrook Pr.) Lerner Publishing Group.

Stewart, Mark Alan. Kordell Stewart: Steelers Sensation. 1999. (Sports Stars Ser.). (Illus.). 48p. (J). (gr. 3-4). 22.00 (978-0-516-21553-2(1) , Children's Pr.) Scholastic Library Publishing.

—Lisa Leslie: Queen of the Court. 1998. (Sports Stars Ser.). (Illus.). 48p. (J). (gr. 3-4). 19.50 (978-0-516-20585-4(4) , Children's Pr.) Scholastic Library Publishing.

—Marion Jones: Sprinting Sensation. 2000. (Sports Stars Ser.). (Illus.). 48p. (J). (gr. 3-4). pap. 5.95 (978-0-516-27004-3(4) , Children's Pr.) Scholastic Library Publishing.

—Randy Moss: First in Flight. 2000. (J). (978-0-606-19170-8(4)) Tandem Library Bks.

Stille, Darlene R. Madam C.J. Walker: Entrepreneur & Millionaire. (Signature Lives Ser.). (Illus.). 112p. (J). 2007. pap. (***978-0-7565-2203-2(X)*** , 1265883); 2006. (***978-0-7565-1883-7(0)*** , 1265883) Compass Point Bks.

Stone, Tanya Lee. Oprah Winfrey: Success with an Open Heart. 2001. (Gateway Biography Ser.). (Illus.). 48p. (gr. 2-4). (J). lib. bdg. 23.90 (978-0-7613-1814-9(3)); pap. (978-0-7613-1389-2(3)) Lerner Publishing Group. (Millbrook Pr.).

The Story of Martin Luther King, Jr. 2001. (Illus.). 24p. (J). (ps-k). 6.95 (978-0-8249-4144-4(6)) Ideals Pubns.

Stout, Glenn & Christopher, Matt. Muhammad Ali: Legends in Sports. 2005. (Matt Christopher Legends of Sports Ser.). (Illus.). 128p. (J). (gr. 5-8). pap. 4.99 (978-0-316-10843-0(X)) Little Brown & Co.

Streissguth, Thomas. Jesse Owens. 1999. (Biography Ser.). (Illus.). 112p. (gr. 6-12). lib. bdg. 27.93 (978-0-8225-4940-6(9)) Lerner Publishing Group.

—Mae Jemison. 2003. (Explore Space! Ser.). (Illus.). 24p. (J). (gr. 1-2). lib. bdg. 18.60 (978-0-7368-1626-7(7) , Bridgestone Bks.) Capstone Pr., Inc.

Streissguth, Tom. Jesse Owens. 2005. (Bios for Challenged Readers Ser.). (Illus.). 112p. (J). (gr. 6-12). lib. bdg. 27.93 (978-0-8225-2256-0(X)) Lerner Publishing Group.

Strong, Mike. Colin Powell: It Can Be Done! 2002. (High Five Reading Ser.). (Illus.). 48p. (J). (gr. 3-4). lib. bdg. 22.60 (978-0-7368-9551-4(5) , Capstone High-Interest Bks.); pap. (978-0-7368-9529-3(9)) Capstone Pr., Inc.

Summers, Barbara, ed. Open the Unusual Door: True Life Stories of Challenge, Adventure, & Success by Black Americans. Triplett, Gina, illus. 2005. 224p. (YA). (gr. 7 up). pap. 7.99 (978-0-618-58531-1(1) , Graphia) Houghton Mifflin Co. Trade & Reference Div.

Suskind, Ron. Hope in the Unseen: An American Odyssey from the Inner City to the Ivy League. 1999. 373p. (YA). (gr. 8-12). per. 24.55 (978-0-613-51076-9(3)) Tandem Library Bks.

Sutcliffe, Jane. Jesse Owens. Porter, Janice Lee, illus. (On My Own Biographies Ser.). 48p. (J). (gr. 1-3). 2003. 5.95 (978-1-57505-487-2(6)); 2000. lib. bdg. 23.93 (978-1-57505-451-3(5) , Carolrhoda Bks.) Lerner Publishing Group.

—Jesse Owens. 2000. (gr. 3-6). lib. bdg. 15.25 (978-0-613-79243-1(2)) Tandem Library Bks.

Sutcliffe, Jane. Marian Anderson. 2008. (History Maker Biographies Ser.). (J). lib. bdg. 26.60 (***978-0-8225-7170-4(6)*** , Lerner Pubns.) Lerner Publishing Group.

Swain, Gwenyth. Civil Rights Pioneer: A Story about Mary Church Terrell. Beier, Ellen, illus. 64p. (J). pap. 6.95 (978-0-8225-4170-7(X)); 1999. (gr. 4-8). lib. bdg. 22.60 (978-1-57505-355-4(1)) Lerner Publishing Group.

—Civil Rights Pioneer: A Story about Mary Church Terrell. 1999. (gr. 3-6). lib. bdg. 15.25 (978-0-613-68325-8(0)) Tandem Library Bks.

—Dred & Harriet Scott: A Family's Struggle for Freedom. 2004. (Illus.). 102p. pap. 12.95 (978-0-87351-483-5(1) , Borealis Bk.) Minnesota Historical Society Pr.

—A Hunger for Learning: A Story about Booker T. Washington. Johnson, Larry, illus. (Creative Minds Biography Ser.). 64p. (J). 2006. (gr. 3-7). lib. bdg. 22.60 (978-1-57505-754-5(9)); 2005. (gr. 4-8). pap. 6.95 (978-0-8225-3090-9(2)) Lerner Publishing Group.

—Sojourner Truth. Archambault, Matthew, illus. 2005. (On My Own Biography Ser.). 48p. (J). (ps-ps). pap. 5.95 (978-1-57505-827-6(8)) Lerner Publishing Group.

—Sojourner Truth. 2005. (On My Own Biography Ser.). (Illus.). 48p. (J). 25.26 (978-1-57505-651-7(8) , Carolrhoda Bks.) Lerner Publishing Group.

Swanson, June. Venus & Serena Williams. Burke, Susan S., illus. 2003. (You Must Be Joking! Riddle Bks.). 32p. (J). (gr. 2-5). pap. 5.95 (978-0-8225-9842-8(6)) Lerner Publishing Group.

Sweeney, Alyse. Easy Reader Biographies: Martin Luther King, Jr: A Man with a Dream. 2007. 16p. pap. 2.99 (***978-0-439-77419-2(5)*** , Teaching Resources) Scholastic, Inc.

Sweet, Kimberly. Hank Aaron: The Life of the Home Run King. 2001. (J). (gr. 4-7). pap. 7.95 (978-1-58838-022-7(X)) NewSouth, Inc.

Talmadge, Morgan. Usher. 2001. (gr. 7-12). lib. bdg. 15.25 (978-0-613-52213-7(3)) Tandem Library Bks.

Taylor-Butler, Christine. Booker T. Washington. 2006. (Illus.). 31p. (J). (978-0-516-29842-9(X)) Children's Pr., Ltd.

—Thurgood Marshall. 2006. (Rookie Biographies Ser.). (Illus.). 32p. (J). (gr. 1-2). 20.50 (978-0-516-25015-1(9) , Children's Pr.) Scholastic Library Publishing.

Taylor, Marian. Harriet Tubman. (Black Americans of Achievement Ser.). (Illus.). 112p. (J). (gr. 6-12). 2005. pap. 13.25 (978-0-7910-8340-6(3)); 2004. 30.00 (978-0-7910-8166-2(4)) Facts On File, Inc. (Chelsea Hse.).

Taylor, Yuval, ed. Growing up in Slavery: Stories of Young Slaves as Told by Themselves. 2007. (Illus.). 256p. (J). pap. 9.95 (978-1-55652-635-0(0) , Hill, Lawrence Bks.) Chicago Review Pr., Inc.

Terrill, Richard. Duke Ellington. 2003. (African-American Biographies Ser.). 64p. pap. 8.95 (978-1-4109-0035-7(5)); (Illus.). (J). lib. bdg. 28.56 (978-0-7398-6869-0(1)) Raintree.

Tessitore, John. Muhammad Ali: The World's Champion. 1999. (Single Titles-Biography Ser.). (Illus.). 144p. (YA). (gr. 8-12). pap. 9.95 (978-0-531-15927-9(2) , Watts, Franklin) Scholastic Library Publishing.

Thoennes Keller, Kristin. Booker T. Washington. 2005. (Fact Finders Ser.). (Illus.). 32p. (J). (978-0-7368-4343-0(4)) Capstone Pr., Inc.

—Booker T. Washington: Innovative Educator. 2006. (J). (978-0-7565-1881-3(4)) Compass Point Bks.

—Malcolm X. 2005. (Fact Finders Ser.). (Illus.). 32p. (J). (978-0-7368-4347-8(7)) Capstone Pr., Inc.

Thompson, Craig. The ABCs of Black History: A Children's Guide. 2005. (Illus.). 32p. (J). 14.95 (978-0-931761-72-0(7) , 194-022) Beckham Pubns. Group, Inc.

Thornley, Stew. Grant Hill: Star Forward. 1999. (Sports Reports). (Illus.). 104p. (YA). (gr. 4-10). lib. bdg. 20.95 (978-0-7660-1078-9(3)) Enslow Pubs., Inc.

—Super Sports Star Barry Bonds. 2004. (Super Sports Star Ser.). (Illus.). 48p. (J). lib. bdg. 23.93 (978-0-7660-2132-7(7)) Enslow Pubs., Inc.

—Super Sports Star Chris Webber. 2002. (Super Sports Star Ser.). (Illus.). 48p. (J). (gr. 1-4). lib. bdg. 23.93 (978-0-7660-1807-5(5)) Enslow Pubs., Inc.

—Super Sports Star Daunte Culpepper. 2003. (Super Sports Star Ser.). (Illus.). 48p. (J). (gr. 1-4). lib. bdg. 23.93 (978-0-7660-2051-1(7)) Enslow Pubs., Inc.

—Super Sports Star Eddie George. 2003. (Super Sports Star Ser.). (Illus.). 48p. (J). (gr. 1-4). lib. bdg. 23.93 (978-0-7660-2050-4(9)) Enslow Pubs., Inc.

—Super Sports Star Ken Griffey, Jr. 2004. (Super Sports Star Ser.). (Illus.). 48p. (J). lib. bdg. 23.93 (978-0-7660-2133-4(5)) Enslow Pubs., Inc.

—Super Sports Star Randy Moss. 2003. (Super Sports Star Ser.). (Illus.). 48p. (J). (gr. 1-4). lib. bdg. 23.93 (978-0-7660-2049-8(5)) Enslow Pubs., Inc.

Tieck, Sarah. Rosa Parks. 2007. (Buddy Book Ser.). (Illus.). 32p. (J). 22.78 (978-1-59679-788-8(6)) ABDO Publishing Co.

Tillage, Leon Walter. Leon's Story. Roth, Susan L., illus. 2000. 112p. (J). (gr. 3-7). pap. 5.95 (978-0-374-44330-6(0) , Sunburst) Farrar, Straus & Giroux.

—Leon's Story. 2000. (978-0-606-20397-5(4)); (J). (978-0-606-20134-6(3)); (gr. 3-6). lib. bdg. 12.95 (978-0-613-30550-1(7)) Tandem Library Bks.

Todd, Anne M. Chris Rock. 2006. (Black Americans of Achievement, Legacy Edition Ser.). (Illus.). 104p. (gr. 6-12). 30.00 (978-0-7910-9225-5(9) , Chelsea Hse.) Facts On File, Inc.

Torres, John Albert. Allen Iverson: Never Give Up. 2004. (Sports Leaders Ser.). (Illus.). 104p. (J). lib. bdg. 26.60 (978-0-7660-2174-7(2)) Enslow Pubs., Inc.

—Shaquille O'Neal: Gentle Giant. 2004. (Sports Leaders Ser.). (Illus.). 104p. (J). lib. bdg. 26.60 (978-0-7660-2175-4(0)) Enslow Pubs., Inc.

—Sheryl Swoopes. 2001. (Real-Life Reader Biography Ser.). (Illus.). 32p. (gr. 3-8). lib. bdg. 15.95 (978-1-58415-068-8(8)) Mitchell Lane Pubs., Inc.

—Sports Great Grant Hill. 2001. (Sports Great Bks.). (Illus.). 64p. (YA). (gr. 4-10). lib. bdg. 22.60 (978-0-7660-1467-1(3)) Enslow Pubs., Inc.

—Vince Carter: Slam Dunk Artist. 2004. (Sports Leaders Ser.). (Illus.). 104p. (J). lib. bdg. 26.60 (978-0-7660-2173-0(4)) Enslow Pubs., Inc.

Tracy, Kathleen. Queen Latifah. 2004. (Blue Banner Biography Ser.). (Illus.). 32p. (J). (gr. 3-8). lib. bdg. 25.70 (978-1-58415-313-9(X)) Mitchell Lane Pubs., Inc.

Trice, Linda. Charles Drew. 2000. (Ideas on Trial Ser.). (Illus.). 121p. (C). (gr. 8-12). pap. 8.95 (978-0-07-135317-5(8)) McGraw-Hill Cos., The.

Triumph Books Staff. Allen Iverson. 2002. 48p. 12.95 (978-1-57243-492-9(9)) Triumph Bks.

Troupe, Quincy. Little Stevie Wonder. Cohen, Lisa, illus. 2005. 32p. (J). (gr. k-3). 18.00 (978-0-618-34060-6(2)) Houghton Mifflin Co. Trade & Reference Div.

Troy, Don. Harriet Ross Tubman. 1999. (Journey to Freedom Ser.). (Illus.). 40p. (J). (gr. 3-7). 28.50 (978-1-56766-568-0(3)) Child's World, Inc.

Trueit, Trudi Strain. Martin Luther King, Jr. Day. 2007. (Holidays, Festivals, & Celebrations Ser.). 32p. (J). (gr. k-4). 22.79 (*978-1-59296-814-5(7)) Child's World, Inc.

Trumbauer, Lisa. Let's Meet Frederick Douglass. 2003. (Let's Meet Biographies Ser.). (Illus.). 32p. (gr. 2-4). 23.00 (978-0-7910-7319-3(X) , Chelsea Hse.) Facts On File, Inc.

—Let's Meet Sojourner Truth. 2003. (Let's Meet Biographies Ser.). (Illus.). 32p. (gr. 2-4). 23.00 (978-0-7910-7323-0(8) , Chelsea Hse.) Facts On File, Inc.

Turner, Glennette Tilley. An Apple for Harriet Tubman. Keeter, Susan, illus. 2006. 24p. (J). 15.95 (978-0-8075-0395-9(9)) Whitman, Albert & Co.

—Follow in Their Footsteps: Biographies of Ten Outstanding African Americans. 1999. (J). (978-0-606-15994-4(0)) Tandem Library Bks.

Turner, Morrie. Explore Black History with Wee Pals. 1998. (Illus.). 64p. (J). (gr. 1-7). pap. 5.95 (978-0-940975-79-8(3) , Sankofa Bks.) Just Us Bks., Inc.

Tuttle, Dennis R. Angela Bassett. 2001. (Black Americans of Achievement Ser.). (Illus.). 106p. (J). (gr. 8-12). pap. 30.00 (978-0-7910-5811-4(5) , Chelsea Hse.) Facts On File, Inc.

Twemlow, Nick. Josh Gibson. 2002. (Baseball Hall of Famers of the Negro League Ser.). (Illus.). 112p. (YA). (gr. 5-8). lib. bdg. 29.25 (978-0-8239-3475-1(6) , Rosen Central) Rosen Publishing Group, Inc., The.

Underwood, Deborah. Nat Love. 2008. (History Maker Biographies Ser.). (J). lib. bdg. 26.60 (*978-0-8225-7171-1(4) , Lerner Pubns.) Lerner Publishing Group.

Uschan, Michael V. Martin Luther King, Jr. 2003. (Heroes & Villains Ser.). (Illus.). 112p. (J). 29.95 (978-1-59018-257-4(X) , Lucent Bks.) Thomson Gale.

Uzoigwe, Chioma. The Ship Is Healy "Hell Roaring Mike" the Forgotten Hero. 1999. (Illus.). 70p. (YA). (gr. 5-8). 10.00 (978-0-9675252-0-4(9)) Uzoigwe, Chioma.

Vaughn, Wally G. & Davis, Mattie Campbell, eds. The Selma Campaign, 1963-1965: The Decisive Battle of the Civil Rights Movement. 2006. 261p. pap. 19.95 (978-0-912469-44-7(7)) Majority Pr., Inc., The.

Venezia, Mike. Faith Ringgold. Venezia, Mike, illus. 2007. (Getting to Know the World's Greatest Artists Ser.). 32p. (J). 28.00 (*978-0-531-18526-1(5) , Children's Pr.) Scholastic Library Publishing.

—Horace Pippin. Venezia, Mike, illus. 2007. (Getting to Know the World's Greatest Artists Ser.). 32p. (J). 28.00 (*978-0-531-18527-8(3) , Children's Pr.) Scholastic Library Publishing.

Wade, Linda R. Condoleeza Rice. l.t. ed. 2002. (Real-Life Reader Biography Ser.). (Illus.). 32p. (gr. 3-8). lib. bdg. 15.95 (978-1-58415-145-6(5)) Mitchell Lane Pubs., Inc.

—Condoleezza Rice. 2004. (Illus.). 32p. (J). lib. bdg. (978-1-58415-332-0(6)) Mitchell Lane Pubs., Inc.

Wade, Mary. Condoleeza Rice: Being the Best. 2003. (gr. 3-6). lib. bdg. 17.60 (978-0-613-58959-8(9)) Tandem Library Bks.

Wade, Mary Dodson. Condoleezza Rice. rev. ed. 2005. (Illus.). 48p. (J). (ps-7). pap. 6.95 (978-0-7613-9549-2(0) , First Avenue Editions) Lerner Publishing Group.

—Condoleezza Rice: Being the Best. 2003. (Gateway Biography Ser.: 4). 48p. lib. bdg. 23.90 (978-0-7613-2619-9(7)); (Illus.). (gr. 2-4). pap. (978-0-7613-1927-6(1)) Lerner Publishing Group. (Millbrook Pr.).

Wadsworth, Ginger. Benjamin Banneker: Pioneering Scientist. Orback, Craig, illus. 2003. (On My Own Biographies Ser.). 48p. (J). (gr. 1-3). 5.95 (978-0-87614-104-5(1) , Carolrhoda Bks.); (gr. 2-5). 25.26 (978-0-87614-916-4(6)) Lerner Publishing Group.

—Benjamin Banneker: Pioneering Scientist. 2003. (gr. 3-6). lib. bdg. 14.10 (978-0-613-58889-8(4)) Tandem Library Bks.

Wagner, Heather Lehr. Benjamin Hooks. 2003. (African American Leaders Ser.). (Illus.). 112p. (gr. 6-12). 30.00 (978-0-7910-7685-9(7) , Chelsea Hse.) Facts On File, Inc.

Walker, Alice. Langston Hughes: American Poet. Deeter, Catherine, illus. 2006. 48p. (J). reprint ed. pap. 7.99 (978-0-06-079889-5(0) , Amistad) HarperCollins Pubs.

Walker, Rebecca. Black, White, & Jewish: Autobiography of A Shifting Self. 2002. (gr. 7-12). lib. bdg. 23.45 (978-0-613-49405-2(9)) Tandem Library Bks.

Walker, Sally M. Bessie Coleman: Daring to Fly. Porter, Janice Lee, illus. 2005. (On My Own Biographies Ser.). 48p. (gr. 2-5). lib. bdg. 23.93 (978-0-87614-919-5(0)) Lerner Publishing Group.

—Bessie Coleman: Daring to Fly. 2003. (gr. 3-6). lib. bdg. 14.10 (978-0-613-58890-4(8)) Tandem Library Bks.

—Jackie Robinson. Pate, Rodney S., illus. 2005. (Yo Solo (On My Own) Ser.). (SPA & ENG.). 48p. (J). (gr. 2-5). lib. bdg. 23.93 (978-0-8225-3126-5(7) , Ediciones Lerner) Lerner Publishing Group.

—Jackie Robinson. Pate, Rodney, illus. 2002. (On My Own Biographies Ser.). 48p. (J). lib. bdg. 23.93 (978-0-87614-599-9(3) , Carolrhoda Bks.) Lerner Publishing Group.

—Jackie Robinson. Pate, Rodney S., illus. 2002. 48p. (J). (ps-3). lib. bdg. 14.10 (978-0-613-52412-4(8)) Tandem Library Bks.

Wallace, Maurice O. Langston Hughes: The Harlem Renaissance. 2007. (Writers & Their Works). 160p. (YA). (gr. 9 up). lib. bdg. 39.93 (*978-0-7614-2591-5(8) , Benchmark Bks.) Cavendish, Marshall Corp.

Wallner, Rosemary. Sheryl Swoopes. 2001. (Sports Heroes Ser.). (Illus.). 48p. (J). (gr. 3-4). lib. bdg. 21.26 (978-0-7368-0780-7(2) , Capstone High-Interest Bks.) Capstone Pr., Inc.

Walters, John. LeBron James. 2006. (World's Greatest Athletes Ser.). (Illus.). 32p. (J). (gr. 1-5). 27.07 (978-1-59296-756-8(6)) Child's World, Inc.

Walton, Darwin McBeth. Overcoming Challenges: The Life of Charles F. Bolden, Jr. 2000. (Pair-It Books). (Illus.). 40p. (J). (978-0-7398-0879-5(6)) Steck-Vaughn.

Washington Is Burning. 2007. (J). pap. 5.95 (*978-0-8225-6050-0(X) , First Avenue Editions) Lerner Publishing Group.

Watson, Galadriel Findlay. Venus & Serena Williams. 2005. (Great African American Women for Kids Ser.). (Illus.). 24p. (J). (978-1-59036-338-6(8)); lib. bdg. 26.00 (978-1-59036-332-4(9)) Weigl Pubs., Inc.

Waxman, Laura Hamilton. Colin Powell. 2005. (History Maker Bios Ser.). 48p. (J). pap. 6.95 (978-0-8225-5463-9(1)); (Illus.). 26.60 (978-0-8225-2433-5(3) , Lerner Pubns.) Lerner Publishing Group.

—Coretta Scott King. 2008. (History Maker Biographies Ser.). (J). lib. bdg. 26.60 (*978-0-8225-7168-1(4) , Lerner Pubns.) Lerner Publishing Group.

—Sojourner Truth. 2008. (History Maker Biographies Ser.). (J). lib. bdg. 26.60 (*978-0-8225-7172-8(2) , Lerner Pubns.) Lerner Publishing Group.

Weatherford, Carole Boston. Great African-American Lawyers: Raising the Bar of Freedom. 2003. (Collective Biographies Ser.). (Illus.). 112p. (YA). (gr. 6-12). lib. bdg. 26.60 (978-0-7660-1837-2(7)) Enslow Pubs., Inc.

Weatherford, Carole Boston. I, Matthew Henson. Velasquez, Eric, illus. 2007. 32p. (J). 16.95 (*978-0-8027-9688-2(5)); 17.85 (*978-0-8027-9689-9(3)) Walker & Co.

Weatherly, Myra. Benjamin Banneker: American Scientific Pioneer. 2006. (Signature Lives Ser.). (Illus.). 112p. (J). (gr. 5-7). 30.60 (978-0-7565-1579-9(3)) Compass Point Bks.

Weber, Terri Smith. Halle Berry: Fighting for First. 2003. (J). pap. (978-0-9740180-8-9(2)); lib. bdg. (978-0-9740180-7-2(4)) Panda Publishing, L.L.C. (Bios for Kids).

Weber, Valerie & Jackson, Jeraldine. Food in Grandma's Day. 1999. (In Grandma's Day Ser.). (Illus.). 32p. (J). (gr. 2-4). lib. bdg. 21.27 (978-1-57505-328-8(4) , Carolrhoda Bks.) Lerner Publishing Group.

Weidt, Maryann N. Harriet Tubman. (History Maker Bios Ser.). (Illus.). (J). 2003. 47p. 26.60 (978-0-8225-4676-4(0)); 2002. 48p. pap. 6.95 (978-0-8225-4803-4(8)) Lerner Publishing Group. (Lerner Pubns.).

—Matthew Henson. 2002. (History Maker Bios Ser.). (Illus.). 48p. (J). pap. 6.95 (978-0-8225-1565-4(2) , Lerner Pubns.) Lerner Publishing Group.

—Rosa Parks. 2003. (History Maker Bios Ser.). (Illus.). 47p. (J). 26.60 (978-0-8225-4673-3(6) , Lerner Pubns.) Lerner Publishing Group.

—Voice of Freedom: A Story about Frederick Douglass. Reeves, Jeni, illus. (Creative Minds Biographies Ser.). 64p. (J). (gr. 3-6). 2003. 6.95 (978-1-57505-553-4(8)); 2001. lib. bdg. 22.60 (978-1-57505-459-9(0) , Carolrhoda Bks.) Lerner Publishing Group.

—Voice of Freedom: A Story about Frederick Douglass. Reeves, Jeni, illus. 2001. 64p. (J). (ps-3). lib. bdg. 15.25 (978-0-613-68475-0(3)) Tandem Library Bks.

Welch, Catherine A. Frederick Douglass. 2003. (History Maker Bios Ser.). (Illus.). 48p. (J). (gr. 4-7). pap. 6.95 (978-0-8225-4802-7(X)); (gr. 3-5). lib. bdg. 26.60 (978-0-8225-4672-6(8)) Lerner Publishing Group.

Wellman, Sam. J. C. Watts: Politician. 1999. (Black Americans of Achievement Ser.). (Illus.). 110p. (J). (gr. 5 up). pap. 30.00 (978-0-7910-5339-3(3) , Chelsea Hse.) Facts On File, Inc.

—T. D. Jakes: Religious Leader. (Black Americans of Achievement Ser.). (Illus.). (J). 2000. 112p. (gr. 4-7). 30.00 (978-0-7910-5362-1(8)); 1999. 103p. (gr. 5 up). pap. 30.00 (978-0-7910-5363-8(6)) Facts On File, Inc. (Chelsea Hse.).

Westen, Robin. Oprah Winfrey: I Dont Believe in Failure. 2005. (African-American Biography Library). (Illus.). 128p. (J). (gr. 6-12). lib. bdg. 31.93 (978-0-7660-2462-5(8)) Enslow Pubs., Inc.

Whalin, W. Terry. Sojourner Truth: American Abolitionist. Landgraf, Ken, illus. 1999. (Young Reader's Christian Library). 222p. (J). (gr. 8-12). pap. 1.39 (978-1-57748-515-5(7)) Barbour Publishing, Inc.

—Sojourner Truth: American Abolitionist. 1999. (Heroes of the Faith Ser.). 208p. (YA). (gr. 4-7). 14.95 (978-0-7910-5034-7(3) , Chelsea Hse.) Facts On File, Inc.

Wheeler, Irvin, illus. Justina's Dream. 2005. 30p. (J). (*978-1-887302-12-8(3)) Western Images Pubns., Inc.

Wheeler, Jill C. Breaking Barriers Set III. 2003. (J). (gr. 3-8). lib. bdg. 153.90 (978-1-57765-902-0(3) , ABDO & Daughters) ABDO Publishing Co.

—Condoleezza Rice. 2004. (Women of the World Ser.). (J). (978-1-59197-616-5(2)) ABDO Publishing Co.

—Denzel Washington. 2003. (Star Tracks Ser.). (Illus.). 64p. (J). (gr. 3-8). lib. bdg. 25.65 (978-1-57765-772-9(1)) ABDO Publishing Co.

—Jackie Robinson. 2003. (Breaking Barriers Ser.). (Illus.). 64p. (J). (gr. 3-8). lib. bdg. 25.65 (978-1-57765-739-2(X)) ABDO Publishing Co.

—Lebron James. 2007. (Awesome Athletes Ser.). (Illus.). 32p. (J). 22.78 (978-1-59928-306-7(9)) ABDO Publishing Co.

—Oprah Winfrey. 2002. (Breaking Barriers Ser.). (Illus.). 64p. (J). (gr. 3-8). lib. bdg. 25.65 (978-1-57765-319-6(X) , ABDO & Daughters) ABDO Publishing Co.

—Rosa Parks, Set II. 2003. (Breaking Barriers Ser.). (Illus.). 64p. (J). (gr. 3-8). lib. bdg. 25.65 (978-1-57765-640-1(7)) ABDO Publishing Co.

Whipple, John. Free Trade in Money, or Note-shaving, the Great cause of Fraud, Poverty & Ruin. 2006. 36p. cd-rom (978-1-892824-73-8(6)) AFCHRON.

Whitehead, Kathy. Art from Her Heart: Folk Artist Clementine Hunter. Evans, Shane, illus. 2008. (J). (*978-0-399-24219-9(8) , Putnam Juvenile) Penguin Group (USA) Inc.

Whiting, Jim. Rosa Parks. 2007. (What's So Great About... ? Ser.). (J). lib. bdg. 25.70 (*978-1-58415-573-7(6)) Mitchell Lane Pubs., Inc.

Wilds, Mary. A Forgotten Champion: The Story of Major Taylor, Fastest Bicycle Racer in the World. 2002. (Illus.). 100p. (J). (gr. 6-12). 19.95 (978-1-888105-52-0(6)) Avisson Pr., Inc.

—I Dare Not Fail: Notable African American Women Educators. 2004. (Avisson Young Adult Ser.). 139p. (J). pap. 19.95 (978-1-888105-64-3(X)) Avisson Pr., Inc.

Williams, Tenley. Stevie Wonder. 2001. (Overcoming Adversity Ser.). (Illus.). 112p. (J). 30.00 (978-0-7910-5903-6(0) , Chelsea Hse.) Facts On File, Inc.

Williams, Teresa A. J. Hugh Granville Tilley North Carolina House of Representatives 1887 And 1889, 1 book. l.t. ed. 2007. 17p. lib. bdg. 15.00 (978-0-9722724-3-8(7)) Blackfoot Burkino Cherokee Publishing.

Wilma Rudolph. 2006. (J). pap. 5.95 (978-0-8225-6623-6(0) , Ediciones Lerner) Lerner Publishing Group.

Wilmore, Kathy. Jackie Robinson: With a Discussion of Respect. 2004. (Values in Action Ser.). (J). (978-1-59203-071-2(8)) Learning Challenge, Inc.

—Muhammad Ali: With a Discussion of Honesty. 2003. (Values in Action Ser.). (J). (978-1-59203-065-1(3)) Learning Challenge, Inc.

Wilson, Camilla. Frederick Douglass: A Voice for Freedom in the 1800s. 2003. (Scholastic Biography Ser.). (Illus.). 90p. (J). pap. (978-0-439-38082-9(0)) Scholastic, Inc.

—George Washington Carver: The Genius Behind the Peanut. 2003. (Scholastic Biography Ser.). (Illus.). 101p. (J). pap. (978-0-439-28722-7(7)) Scholastic, Inc.

Wilson, Cammie. Rosa Parks: From the Back of the Bus to the Front of a Movement. 2001. (Scholastic Biography Ser.). (Illus.). 88p. (J). (gr. 3-7). pap. 4.50 (978-0-439-16330-9(7)) Scholastic, Inc.

Wilson, Mike. The Williams Sisters: Venus & Serena. 2005. (Illus.). 32p. pap. 8.50 (978-0-340-84876-0(6)) Cambridge Univ. Pr.

Winget, Mary. Martin Luther King, Jr. 2003. (History Maker Bios Ser.). (Illus.). 47p. (J). 26.60 (978-0-8225-4674-0(4) , Lerner Pubns.) Lerner Publishing Group.

—Martin Luther King, Jr. 2004. (History Maker Bios Ser.). (Illus.). 48p. (J). pap. (978-0-8225-4804-1(6) , Lerner Pubns.) Lerner Publishing Group.

Winter, Jonah. Dizzy. Qualls, Sean, illus. 2006. 48p. (J). (gr. 3-8). pap. 16.99 (978-0-439-50737-0(5) , Levine, Arthur A. Bks.) Scholastic, Inc.

—Fair Ball! 14 Great Stars from Baseball's Negro Leagues. 2002. (J). pap. 5.99 (978-0-590-39465-9(7) , Levine, Arthur A. Bks.); 32p. (gr. 2-5). pap. 5.99 (978-0-439-37604-4(1)) Scholastic, Inc.

—Fair Ball! 14 Great Stars from Baseball's Negro Leagues. Winter, Jonah, illus. 1999. (Illus.). 32p. (J). (gr. 2-5). pap. 15.95 (978-0-590-39464-2(9)) Scholastic, Inc.

Woog, Dan. Jesse Jackson. 1999. (People in the News Ser.). (Illus.). 118p. (YA). (gr. 6-9). 32.45 (978-1-56006-631-6(8) , Lucent Bks.) Thomson Gale.

Woronoff, Kristen. Leontyne Price: Singing Star. 2002. (Famous Women Juniors Ser.). (Illus.). 32p. (J). (gr. 3-5). 23.70 (978-1-56711-589-5(6) , Blackbirch Pr., Inc.) Thomson Gale.

—Oprah Winfrey: Media Superstar. 2002. (Famous Women Juniors Ser.). (Illus.). 32p. (J). (gr. 3-5). 24.94 (978-1-56711-588-8(8) , Blackbirch Pr., Inc.) Thomson Gale.

Worth, Richard. Gail Devers. 2001. (Overcoming Adversity Ser.). (Illus.). 112p. (J). 30.00 (978-0-7910-6305-7(4) , Chelsea Hse.) Facts On File, Inc.

Wukovits, John F. Colin Powell. 1999. (People in the News Ser.). (Illus.). 112p. (YA). (gr. 6-9). 32.45 (978-1-56006-632-3(6) , Lucent Bks.) Thomson Gale.

Wynn, Mychal. Follow Your Dreams: Lessons I Learned in School. 2001. 210p. (J). pap. 7.95 (978-1-880463-51-2(2)) Rising Sun Publishing, Inc.

Yancey, Diane. Frederick Douglass. 2002. (Heroes & Villains Ser.). (Illus.). 112p. (J). 28.70 (978-1-56006-950-8(3) , Lucent Bks.) Thomson Gale.

Yannuzzi, Della A. Madam C. J. Walker: Self-Made Businesswoman. 2000. (African-American Biographies Ser.). (Illus.). 112p. (J). (gr. 6-12). lib. bdg. 26.60 (978-0-7660-1204-2(2)) Enslow Pubs., Inc.

Young, Jeff C. Inspiring African-American Inventors. 2008. (J). (*978-1-59845-080-4(8)) Enslow Pubs., Inc.

Your Little Black Book on African American Inventions & Inventors. 2006. (J). per. 9.95 (*978-0-9791883-0-5(X)) Disciple One Publishing.

AFRICAN AMERICANS—CALIFORNIA

Haskins, James & Poole, Cecil F. Cecil Poole: A Life in the Law. 2002. (Illus.). xii, 172p. (YA). 15.00 (978-0-9635086-2-1(8)) Ninth Judicial Circuit Historical Society.

AFRICAN AMERICANS—CIVIL RIGHTS

Adler, David A. Dr. Martin Luther King, Jr. Level 2: A House House Reader. Bootman, Colin, illus. 2001. (Reader Ser.). 48p. (J). (gr. k-3). tchr. ed. 15.95 (978-0-8234-1572-4(4)) Holiday Hse., Inc.

—Heroes for Civil Rights. Farnsworth, Bill, illus. 2007. 32p. (J). (gr. 1-5). 16.95 (*978-0-8234-2008-7(6)) Holiday Hse., Inc.

Adler, David A. A Picture Book of Rosa Parks. Casilla, Robert, illus. 2004. (J). (ps-3). audio compact disk 18.95 (978-1-59112-761-1(0)) Live Oak Media.

Alexander, Florence. Dare to Be. . . Martin Luther King Jr. Whitmore, Yvette, illus. 2003. (ENG & SPA.). 17p. (J). 3.99 (978-0-915960-65-1(6)) Ebon Research Systems Publishing, LLC.

Anderson, Dale. Freedom Rides: Campaign for Equality. 2007. (J). lib. bdg. (*978-0-7565-3333-5(3)) Compass Point Bks.

Anderson, Wayne. Fighting Racial Discrimination: Treating All Americans Fairly under the Law. 2004. (Progressive Movement, 1900-1920 Ser.). (Illus.). 32p. (J). lib. bdg. (978-1-4042-0189-7(0)) Rosen Publishing Group, Inc., The.

Aretha, David. Freedom Summer. 2007. (J). (*978-1-59935-059-2(9)) Reynolds, Morgan Inc.

—Selma & the Voting Rights ACT. 2007. (J). (*978-1-59935-056-1(4)) Reynolds, Morgan Inc.

Armentrout, David & Armentrout, Patricia. Coretta Scott King. 2004. (Discover the Life of an American Legend Ser.). (Illus.). 24p. (gr. 2-5). 20.64 (978-1-58952-659-4(7)) Rourke Publishing, LLC.

Ashby, Ruth. Rosa Parks: Freedom Rider. 2008. (Sterling Biographies Ser.). (Illus.). 128p. (J). pap. 5.95 (*978-1-4027-4865-3(5)) Sterling Publishing Co., Inc.

Baker, Courtney. Let's Read About— Rosa Parks. Hunt, Robert, illus. 2004. (Scholastic First Biographies Ser.). 29p. (J). pap. (978-0-439-56413-7(1) , Cartwheel Bks.) Scholastic, Inc.

Banting, Erinn. Rosa Parks. 2005. (Great African American Women for Kids Ser.). (Illus.). 24p. (J). (ps-7). pap. 6.95 (978-1-59036-342-3(6)); lib. bdg. 26.00 (978-1-59036-336-2(1)) Weigl Pubs., Inc.

Bjornlund, Lydia. Rosa Parks & the Montgomery Bus Boycott. 2007. (Lucent Library of Black History Ser.). (Illus.). 128p. (J). (gr. 7-10). 28.70 (*978-1-4205-0010-3(4) , Lucent Bks.) Thomson Gale.

Bolden, Tonya. M. L. K. The Journey of a King. Adelman, Bob, ed. 2007. 128p. (J). (gr. 5-9). 19.95 (978-0-8109-5476-2(1) , Abrams Bks. for Young Readers) Abrams, Harry N. , Inc.

Brandt, Keith & Mattern, Joanne. Rosa Parks: Freedom Rider. Griffith, Gershom, illus. 2006. 54p. (J). pap. (*978-0-439-66045-7(9)) Scholastic, Inc.

Brown, Jonatha A. Martin Luther King, Jr. 2005. (Illus.). 24p. (ENG & SPA.). (J). pap. (978-0-8368-4590-7(0)); (J). lib. bdg. (978-0-8368-4474-0(2)); (ENG & SPA., (J). lib. bdg. 19.33 (978-0-8368-4583-9(8)); (YA). lib. bdg. 19.33 (978-0-8368-4467-2(X) , Weekly Reader Early Learning Library) Stevens, Gareth Inc.

—Rosa Parks. 2005. (Illus.). 24p. (J). (ENG & SPA.). pap. (978-0-8368-4769-7(5)); (ENG & SPA., lib. bdg. 19.33 (978-0-8368-4762-8(8)); pap. (978-0-8368-4755-0(5)); lib. bdg. 19.33 (978-0-8368-4748-2(2)) Stevens, Gareth Inc.

Caravantes, Peggy. Marcus Garvey: Black Nationalist. 2004. (Twentieth Century Leaders Ser.). (Illus.). 128p. (YA). (gr. 6-12). 23.95 (978-1-931798-14-3(1)) Reynolds, Morgan Inc.

Clare, John D. The Black Peoples of America. 2001. (Illus.). 48p. pap. 23.50 (***978-0-340-79033-5(4)***, Hodder Murray) Hodder Education GBR. *Dist:* Trans-Atlantic Pubns., Inc.

Coleman, Wim & Perrin, Pat. Martin Luther King, Jr. National Historic Site: A MyReportLinks.com Book. 2005. (Virtual Field Trips Ser.). (Illus.). 48p. (J). (gr. 4-10). lib. bdg. 25.26 (978-0-7660-5225-3(7), MyReportLinks.com Bks.) Enslow Pubs., Inc.

Collier, Christopher & Collier, James Lincoln. Reconstruction & the Rise of Jim Crow: 1864-1896. 1999. (Drama of American History Ser.). (Illus.). 96p. (YA). (gr. 5-9). lib. bdg. 31.36 (978-0-7614-0819-2(3), Benchmark Bks.) Cavendish, Marshall Corp.

Conaway, Judith. Brown V. Board of Education: The Case for Integration. 2006. 96p. lib. bdg. (978-0-7565-2448-7(2)) Compass Point Bks.

Creative Media Applications. Beginning a New Life: African Americans During Reconstruction. 2006. (Slavery in the Americas Ser.). (Illus.). 112p. (J). (gr. 4-9). 35.00 (978-0-8160-6139-6(4)) Facts On File, Inc.

Crewe, Sabrina & Ingram, Scott. The 1963 Civil Rights March. 2005. (Events That Shaped America Ser.). (Illus.). 32p. (J). lib. bdg. 24.67 (978-0-8368-3411-6(9)) Stevens, Gareth Inc.

Crewe, Sabrina & Walsh, Frank. The Montgomery Bus Boycott. 2003. (Events That Shaped America Ser.). (Illus.). 32p. (gr. 3 up). lib. bdg. 24.67 (978-0-8368-3394-2(5)) Stevens, Gareth Inc.

Davis, W. Harry. Changemaker: W. Harry Davis. Sturdevant, Lori, ed. 2004. (Illus.). 136p. (J). pap. 17.95 (978-1-890434-60-1(4)) Afton Historical Society Pr.

Doak, Robin S. The March on Washington: Uniting Against Racism. 2007. (J). lib. bdg. (***978-0-7565-3339-7(2)***) Compass Point Bks.

Donovan, Sandy. Rosa Parks. 2003. (Illus.). 64p. (J). (gr. 4-7). pap. 9.50 (978-1-4109-0320-4(6)); lib. bdg. 28.56 (978-0-7398-7032-7(7)) Raintree.

Dubois, Muriel L. Rosa Parks. 2003. (Photo-Illustrated Biographies Ser.). (Illus.). 24p. (J). (gr. 2-3). lib. bdg. 18.60 (978-0-7368-1607-6(0), Bridgestone Bks.) Capstone Pr., Inc.

Dubowski, Cathy East. Rosa Parks: Don't Give In! 2005. (Defining Moments Ser.). (Illus.). 32p. (J). lib. bdg. 25.27 (978-1-59716-078-0(4)) Bearport Publishing Co., Inc.

Edwards, Pamela Duncan. The Bus Ride That Changed History: The Story of Rosa Parks. Shanahan, Danny, illus. 2005. 32p. (J). (gr. k-3). 16.00 (978-0-618-44911-8(6)) Houghton Mifflin Co. Trade & Reference Div.

Evento, Susan. Mary McLeod Bethune. 2004. (Rookie Biographies Ser.). (Illus.). 31p. (J). 20.50 (978-0-516-21720-8(8), Children's Pr.) Scholastic Library Publishing.

Fandel, Jennifer. Martin Luther King, Jr: Great Civil Rights Leader. 2007. (Graphic Library). (Illus.). 32p. (J). (978-0-7368-6498-5(9)) Capstone Pr., Inc.

Featonby, Douglas & Whittock, Martyn. The Black Peoples of America. 2001. (Illus.). 48p. pap. 23.50 (***978-0-340-79034-2(2)***, Hodder Murray) Hodder Education GBR. *Dist:* Trans-Atlantic Pubns., Inc.

Feinstein, Stephen. Lee sobre Martin Luther King, Jr./Read about Martin Luther King, Jr. 2006. (I Like Biographies! Bilingual Ser.). (ENG & SPA., Illus.). 24p. (J). (gr. 1-3). lib. bdg. 21.26 (978-0-7660-2745-9(7), Enslow Elementary) Enslow Pubs., Inc.

—Read about Martin Luther King, Jr. 2004. (I Like Biographies Ser.!). (Illus.). 24p. (J). lib. bdg. 24.95 (978-0-7660-2300-0(1)) Enslow Pubs., Inc.

Ferris, Jeri Chase. Demanding Justice: A Story about Mary Ann Shadd Cary. Smith, Kimanne, illus. 2003. 64p. (J). 6.95 (978-0-87614-928-7(X), Carolrhoda Bks.); (gr. 4-8). 22.60 (978-1-57505-177-2(X)) Lerner Publishing Group.

—Demanding Justice: A Story about Mary Ann Shadd Cary. 2003. (gr. 3-6). lib. bdg. 14.10 (978-0-613-58898-0(3)) Tandem Library Bks.

Fine, Edith Hope. Martin Luther King, Jr: Champion of Civil Rights. 2006. (Heroes of American History Ser.) (Illus.). 32p. (J). lib. bdg. 22.60 (978-0-7660-2466-3(0), Enslow Elementary) Enslow Pubs., Inc.

—Rosa Parks: Meet a Civil Rights Hero. 2004. (Meeting Famous People Ser.). (Illus.). 32p. (J). lib. bdg. 22.60 (978-0-7660-2099-3(1)) Enslow Pubs., Inc.

Finlayson, Reggie. We Shall Overcome: The History of the American Civil Rights Movement. 2005. (People's History Ser.). (Illus.). 96p. (gr. 6-12). lib. bdg. 26.60 (978-0-8225-0647-8(5)) Lerner Publishing Group.

Fiorelli, June Estep. Fannie Lou Hamer: A Voice for Freedom. 2004. (Avisson Young Adult Ser.). (Illus.). 117p. (J). pap. 19.95 (978-1-888105-62-9(3)) Avisson Pr., Inc.

Fireside, Harvey. The Mississippi Burning Civil Rights Murder Conspiracy Trial. 2002. (Headline Court Cases Ser.). (Illus.). 112p. (YA). (gr. 6-12). lib. bdg. 26.60 (978-0-7660-1762-7(1)) Enslow Pubs., Inc.

Fitzgerald, Stephanie. Struggling for Civil Rights. 2004. (On the Front Line Ser.). (Illus.). 48p. (J). (gr. 4-6). 29.93 (978-1-4109-1467-5(4)) Raintree.

—Struggling for Civil Rights. 2006. (On the Front Line Ser.). (Illus.). 48p. (J). (978-1-4109-2196-3(4)); pap. (978-1-4109-2203-8(0)) Steck-Vaughn.

Fleming, Alice Mulcahey. Martin Luther King, Jr. A Dream of Hope. 2008. (Sterling Biographies Ser.). (Illus.). 128p. (J). pap. 5.95 (***978-1-4027-4439-6(0)***) Sterling Publishing Co., Inc.

Freedman, Russell. Freedom Walkers: The Story of the Montgomery Bus Boycott. 2006. (Illus.). 112p. (J). (gr. 3-7). 18.95 (978-0-8234-2031-5(0)) Holiday Hse., Inc.

Gelfand, Dale Evva & Rhodes, Lisa Renee. Coretta Scott King: Civil Rights Activist. 2nd rev. ed. 2006. (Black Americans of Achievement, Legacy Edition Ser.). (Illus.). 144p. (J). (gr. 6-12). 30.00 (978-0-7910-9522-5(3), Chelsea Hse.) Facts On File, Inc.

George, Charles. Life under the Jim Crow Laws. 1999. (Way People Live Ser.). (Illus.). 96p. (YA). (gr. 7-10). 27.45 (978-1-56006-499-2(4), LML00902-177862, Lucent Bks.) Thomson Gale.

George, Linda. Civil Rights Marches. 1999. (gr. 3-6). lib. bdg. 14.10 (978-0-613-52007-2(6)) Tandem Library Bks.

George, Linda & George, Charles. Civil Rights Marches. 2000. (Cornerstones of Freedom Ser.). (Illus.). 32p. (J). (gr. 4-6). pap. 5.95 (978-0-516-26516-2(4), Children's Pr.) Scholastic Library Publishing.

Giovanni, Nikki. Rosa. Collier, Bryan, illus. rev. ed. 2005. 40p. (J). (gr. 4-7). 16.95 (978-0-8050-7106-1(7), Holt, Henry & Co. Bks. For Young Readers) Holt, Henry & Co.

—Rosa. Collier, Bryan, illus. 2007. 40p. (J). pap. 7.99 (***978-0-312-37602-4(2)***) Square Fish.

Gold, Susan Dudley. Brown V. Board of Education: Separate but Equal? 2004. (Supreme Court Milestones Ser.). (Illus.). 143p. (J). 37.07 (978-0-7614-1842-9(3), Benchmark Bks.) Cavendish, Marshall Corp.

Good, Diane L. Brown v. Board of Education. 2007. (Cornerstones of Freedomtrade;, Second Ser.). 48p. (J). (gr. 4-6). pap. 5.95 (***978-0-531-18686-2(5)***, Children's Pr.) Scholastic Library Publishing.

Good, Diane L. Brown vs. Board of Education: A Civil Rights Milestone. 2004. (Cornerstones of Freedom Ser.). (J). 26.00 (978-0-516-24225-5(3), Children's Pr.) Scholastic Library Publishing.

Gotsch, Patrice. Martin Luther King, Jr: Changing Lives. Arreola, Gil, illus. 2005. 19p. (J). pap. (***978-1-55501-779-8(7)***) Ballard & Tighe Pubs.

Green, Richard L., et al, eds. A Salute to Black Civil Rights Leaders. Dobson, S. Gaston, illus. (Empak "Black History" Publication). (J). pap. 1.00 (978-0-9616156-3-5(X)) Empak Publishing Co.

Greenfield, Eloise. Rosa Parks. Ashby, Gil, illus. 2002. 12.62 (978-0-7587-0755-0(X)) Book Wholesalers, Inc.

Hardy, P. Stephen & Hardy, Sheila Jackson. Extraordinary People of the Civil Rights Movement. 2006. (Extraordinary People Ser.). (Illus.). 288p. (YA). (gr. 9 up). (978-0-516-25461-6(8)) Children's Pr., Ltd.

Haskins, James. Freedom Rides: Journey for Justice. 2005. (Illus.). 88p. (J). (ps-17). pap. 10.95 (978-0-940975-94-1(7), Sankofa Bks.) Just Us Bks., Inc.

—Separate but Not Equal: The Dream & the Struggle. 2002. (Illus.). 184p. (J). (ps-7). lib. bdg. 13.00 (978-0-613-49773-2(2)) Tandem Library Bks.

Haskins, James & Haskins, Jim. Separate but Not Equal: The Dream & the Struggle. 2002. (Illus.). 192p. (J). (gr. 3-7). mass mkt. 4.99 (978-0-590-45911-2(2)) Scholastic, Inc.

Haskins, Jim. Black Stars of the Civil Rights Movement. 2003. (gr. 3-6). lib. bdg. 22.20 (978-0-613-81938-1(1)) Tandem Library Bks.

—Black Stars of the Civil Rights Movement. 2003. (Black Stars Ser.). (Illus.). 128p. pap. 12.95 (978-0-471-22068-8(X), Wiley-Interscience) Wiley, John & Sons, Inc.

—Delivering Justice: W. W. Law & the Fight for Civil Rights. Andrews, Benny, illus. 2005. 32p. (J). (gr. k-3). 17.99 (978-0-7636-2592-4(2)) Candlewick Pr.

Haskins, Jim & Benson, Kathleen. John Lewis in the Lead: A Story of the Civil Rights Movement. Andrews, Benny, illus. 2006. 40p. (J). 17.95 (978-1-58430-250-6(X)) Lee & Low Bks., Inc.

Hatt, Christine. Martin Luther King, Jr. 2004. (Judge for Yourself Ser.). (Illus.). 64p. (J). pap. (978-0-8368-5565-4(5)); (gr. 5 up). lib. bdg. 30.00 (978-0-8368-5562-3(0)) Stevens, Gareth Inc. (World Almanac Library).

Hermann, Spring. The Struggle for Equality: Women & Minorities in America. 2006. (American Saga Ser.). (Illus.). 128p. (J). lib. bdg. 31.93 (978-0-7660-2573-8(X)) Enslow Pubs., Inc.

Hopkinson, Deborah. Sweet Land of Liberty. Jenkins, Leonard, illus. 2007. 32p. (J). (gr. 1-5). 16.95 (978-1-56145-395-5(1), Peachtree Junior) Peachtree Pubs., Ltd.

Howard, Melanie A. Civil Rights Marches. 2005. (American Moments Ser.). (Illus.). (J). (gr. 4-8). lib. bdg. 25.65 (978-1-59197-282-2(5), ABDO & Daughters) ABDO Publishing Co.

Hudson, David L., Jr. The Fourteenth Amendment: Equal Protection under the Law. 2002. (Constitution Ser.). (Illus.). 128p. (J). (gr. 6-12). lib. bdg. 26.60 (978-0-7660-1904-1(7)) Enslow Pubs., Inc.

Hughes, Langston. Black Misery. 2001. (Illus.). (J). 14.75 (978-0-606-20572-6(1)) Tandem Library Bks.

Hull, Mary, et al. Rosa Parks: Civil Rights Leader. 2nd rev. ed. 2006. (Black Americans of Achievement: Ser.). 128p. (J). (gr. 6-12). 30.00 (***978-0-7910-9523-2(1)***, Chelsea Hse.) Facts On File, Inc.

Hull, Mary E. Rosa Parks: Civil Rights Leader. (Black Americans of Achievement Ser.). (Illus.). 112p. (J). (gr. 6-12). 2005. pap. 13.25 (978-0-7910-8338-3(1)); 2004. 30.00 (978-0-7910-8164-8(8)) Facts On File, Inc. (Chelsea Hse.).

Ingram, Scott. The 1963 Civil Rights March. 2004. (Landmark Events in American History Ser.). (Illus.). 48p. (J). 11.95 (978-0-8368-5420-6(9)); lib. bdg. 30.00 (978-0-8368-5392-6(X)) Stevens, Gareth Inc. (World Almanac Library).

Jakoubek, Robert E. Martin Luther King, Jr. Civil Rights Leader. (Black Americans of Achievement Ser.). (Illus.). 112p. (gr. 6-12). 2005. pap. 13.25 (978-0-7910-8335-2(7)); 2004. 30.00 (978-0-7910-8161-7(3)) Facts On File, Inc. (Chelsea Hse.).

January, Brendan. Civil Rights. 2003. (Illus.). 56p. (J). pap. 8.50 (978-1-4034-4574-2(5)); lib. bdg. 27.07 (978-1-4034-4566-7(4)) Heinemann Library.

—Civil Rights. 2003. (gr. 5-8). lib. bdg. 17.60 (978-0-613-88218-7(0)) Tandem Library Bks.

—Martin Luther King, Jr. Minister & Civil Rights Activist. 2000. (Career Biographies Ser.). (Illus.). 128p. (J). (gr. 6-12). 25.00 (978-0-89434-342-1(4), F405, Ferguson Publishing Co.) Facts On File, Inc.

Jeffrey, Gary. Martin Luther King, Jr: The Life of a Civil Rights Leader. Riley, Terry, illus. 2006. (Graphic Biographies Ser.). 48p. (J). lib. bdg. 29.95 (978-1-4042-0858-2(5)) Rosen Publishing Group, Inc., The.

—Martin Luther King Jr: The Life of a Civil Rights Leader. Forsey, Christopher, illus. 2006. 48p. (J). (978-1-4042-0920-6(4)); pap. (978-1-4042-0921-3(2)) Rosen Publishing Group, Inc., The.

Johnson, James Weldon. Lift Every Voice & Sing. 2002. (978-0-606-22268-6(5)) Tandem Library Bks.

Jones, Rob Lloyd. Martin Luther King, Jr. 2006. (Illus.). 62p. (J). pap. (***978-0-439-02299-6(1)***) Scholastic, Inc.

Jordan, Denise M. Julian Bond: Civil Rights Activist & Chairman of the NAACP. 2001. (African-American Biographies Ser.). (Illus.). 128p. (J). (gr. 6-12). lib. bdg. 26.60 (978-0-7660-1549-4(1)) Enslow Pubs., Inc.

Kallen, Stuart A. Marcus Garvey & the Back to Africa Movement. 2006. (Lucent Library of Black History). (Illus.). 112p. (J). (gr. 7-10). 32.45 (978-1-59018-838-5(1), Lucent Bks.) Thomson Gale.

—Women of the Civil Rights Movement. 2005. (Women in History Ser.). (Illus.). 112p. (YA). (gr. 7-10). lib. bdg. 32.45 (978-1-59018-569-8(2), Lucent Bks.) Thomson Gale.

Kelso, Richard. Days of Courage: The Little Rock Story. 2001. (Nonfiction Bookbag Ser.). (J). (gr. 6-7). per. 8.45 (978-1-58830-208-3(3)) Metropolitan Teaching & Learning Co.

—Walking for Freedom: The Montgomery Bus Boycott. (Nonfiction Bookbag Ser.). (J). (gr. 5-6). 2001. per. 8.45 (978-1-58830-202-1(4)); 2002. per. (978-1-58120-806-1(5)) Metropolitan Teaching & Learning Co.

King, Martin Luther, Jr. Why We Can't Wait. 2000. (gr. 7-12). lib. bdg. 15.25 (978-0-613-22632-5(1)) Tandem Library Bks.

King, Wilma. Children of the Emancipation. 2005. (Picture the American Past Ser.). (Illus.). 48p. (gr. 2-5). 22.60 (978-1-57505-396-7(9)) Lerner Publishing Group.

Kishel, Ann-Marie. Rosa Parks: A Life of Courage. 2006. (Pull Ahead Books). (Illus.). 32p. (J). 22.60 (978-0-8225-3478-5(9), Lerner Pubns.) Lerner Publishing Group.

—Rosa Parks: Una Vida de Valentía. 2006. (Libros para Avanzar Ser.). (ENG & SPA.). 32p. (J). lib. bdg. 22.60 (978-0-8225-6239-9(1)) Lerner Publishing Group.

Kudlinski, Kathleen V. Rosa Parks. Henderson, Meryl, illus. 2001. (Childhood of Famous Americans Ser.). 224p. (gr. 3-7). mass mkt. 5.99 (978-0-689-83925-2(1), Aladdin) Simon & Schuster Children's Publishing.

Landau, Elaine. The Civil Rights Movement in America. 2007. (Cornerstones of Freedomtrade;, Second Ser.). 48p. (J). pap. 5.95 (***978-0-531-18765-4(9)***, Children's Pr.) Scholastic Library Publishing.

Levine, Ellen. Freedom's Children: Young Civil Rights Activists Tell Their Own Stories. 2000. 14.64 (978-0-606-20359-3(1)); (gr. 7-12). lib. bdg. 15.30 (978-0-613-33699-4(2)) Tandem Library Bks.

Linney, Susan. Martin Luther King, Jr: With a Discussion of Responsibility. 2004. (Values in Action Ser.). (J). (978-1-59203-069-9(6)) Learning Challenge, Inc.

Lowery, Linda. Martin Luther King Jr Day. 2004. (gr. k-3). lib. bdg. 14.10 (978-0-613-79212-7(2)) Tandem Library Bks.

Lucas, Eileen. Cracking the Wall: The Story of the Little Rock Nine. Anthony, Mark, illus. 2007. pap. 16.95 incl. audio (***978-1-59519-937-9(3)***); pap. 18.95 incl. audio compact disk (***978-1-59519-941-6(1)***) Live Oak Media.

—Cracking the Wall (4 PB/1 Cass) Anthony, Mark, illus. 2007. pap. 37.95 incl. audio (***978-1-59519-939-3(X)***) Live Oak Media.

—Cracking the Wall (4 PB/1 CD) Anthony, Mark, illus. 2007. pap. 39.95 incl. audio compact disk (***978-1-59519-943-0(8)***) Live Oak Media.

Lynch, Emma, et al. Martin Luther King, Jr. 2005. (Illus.). 32p. (J). (978-1-4034-6351-7(4)); pap. (978-1-4034-6365-4(4)) Heinemann Library.

Manheimer, Ann S. Martin Luther King Jr: Dreaming of Equality. 2005. (Trailblazer Biography Ser.). (Illus.). 112p. (J). 30.60 (978-1-57505-627-2(5), Carolrhoda Bks.) Lerner Publishing Group.

Mara, Wil. Rosa Parks. 2006. (Rookie Biography Ser.). (Illus.). 31p. (J). (978-0-531-12451-2(7)) Children's Pr., Ltd.

—Rosa Parks. (Rookie Biographies Ser.). (Illus.). (J). 2004. 31p. (gr. 1-2). pap. 4.95 (978-0-516-27916-9(5)); 2003. 32p. 19.50 (978-0-516-25876-8(1)) Scholastic Library Publishing. (Children's Pr.).

March on Washington. 2002. (History in the Headlines Ser.). 32p. (gr. 6-8). 6.99 (978-0-7682-0469-8(0), GA131694) School Specialty Publishing.

Matthews, Sherrie Voss, ed. Free at Last: The Struggle for Civil Rights. 2000. (Literature & Thought Ser.). (Illus.). 144p. (J). (978-0-7807-9633-1(0)); (978-0-7891-5213-8(4)); pap. (978-0-7891-5212-1(6)) Perfection Learning Corp.

Mayer, Robert H. When the Children Marched: The Birmingham Civil Rights Movement. 2008. (Prime Ser.). (Illus.). 160p. (J). (gr. 5 up). lib. bdg. 34.60 (***978-0-7660-2930-9(1)***) Enslow Pubs., Inc.

McLeese, Don. Rosa Parks. 2002. (Rourke Discovery Library). (Illus.). 24p. (J). lib. bdg. 20.64 (978-1-58952-287-9(7)) Rourke Publishing, LLC.

McNeese, Tim. Brown V. Board of Education. 2006. (Great Supreme Court Decisions Ser.). 144p. (J). (gr. 5-8). 30.00 (978-0-7910-9238-5(0), Chelsea Hse.) Facts On File, Inc.

McPherson, Stephanie Sammartino. Coretta Scott King. 2007. (J). lib. bdg. (***978-0-8225-7156-8(0)***) Twenty First Century Bks.

Medearis, Angela Shelf. Dare to Dream: Coretta Scott King & the Civil Rights Movement. Rich, Anna, illus. 1999. (Rainbow Biography Ser.). 64p. (J). (gr. 3-7). pap. 4.99 (978-0-14-130202-7(X), Puffin) Penguin Group (USA) Inc.

—Dare to Dream: Coretta Scott King & the Civil Rights Movement. 1999. (gr. 3-6). lib. bdg. 13.00 (978-0-613-14663-0(8)) Tandem Library Bks.

Michelson, Richard. As Good as Anybody. 2008. 40p. (J). (gr. 1-5). lib. bdg. 19.99 (***978-0-375-93335-6(2)***, Knopf Bks. for Young Readers) Random Hse. Children's Bks.

Miller, Calvin Craig. A. Philip Randolph & the African American Labor Movement. 2005. (Civil Rights Leaders Ser.). (Illus.). 160p. (YA). (gr. 6-12). 26.95 (978-1-931798-50-1(8)) Reynolds, Morgan Inc.

—Roy Wilkins: Leader of the NAACP. 2005. (Civil Rights Leaders Ser.). (Illus.). 176p. (J). (gr. 6-12). 26.95 (978-1-931798-49-5(4)) Reynolds, Morgan Inc.

Miller, Connie Colwell. Rosa Parks & the Montgomery Bus Boycott. 2007. (Graphic Library). (Illus.). 32p. (J). 25.26 (978-0-7368-6495-4(4)) Capstone Pr., Inc.

Miller, Jake. The Little Rock Nine: Young Champions for School Integration. 2004. (Library of the Civil Rights Movement Ser.). (Illus.). 24p. (J). lib. bdg. 19.95 (978-0-8239-6252-5(0), PowerKids Pr.) Rosen Publishing Group, Inc., The.

—The March from Selma to Montgomery: African Americans Demand the Vote. 2004. (Library of the Civil Rights Movement Ser.). (Illus.). 24p. (J). lib. bdg. 19.95 (978-0-8239-6254-9(7), PowerKids Pr.) Rosen Publishing Group, Inc., The.

—The Montgomery Bus Boycott: Integrating Public Buses. 2004. (Library of the Civil Rights Movement Ser.). (Illus.). 24p. (J). lib. bdg. 19.95 (978-0-8239-6251-8(2), PowerKids Pr.) Rosen Publishing Group, Inc., The.

—Sit-Ins & Freedom Rides: The Power of Nonviolent Resistance. 2004. (Library of the Civil Rights Movement Ser.). (Illus.). 24p. (J). lib. bdg. 19.95 (978-0-8239-6253-2(9), PowerKids Pr.) Rosen Publishing Group, Inc., The.

—The 1963 March on Washington: Speeches & Songs for Civil Rights. 2004. (Library of the Civil Rights Movement Ser.). (Illus.). 24p. (J). lib. bdg. 19.95 (978-0-8239-6255-6(5), PowerKids Pr.) Rosen Publishing Group, Inc., The.

Moore, Heidi. Ida B. Wells-Barnett. 2004. (Illus.). 32p. (J). pap. 6.95 (978-1-4034-5706-6(9)); lib. bdg. (978-1-4034-4997-9(X)) Heinemann Library.

Morris, Roz. Rosa Parks: Mother of the Civil Rights Movement. 2003. (Alabama Roots Biography Ser.). (Illus.). 109p. (J). (978-1-878561-57-2(X)) Seacoast Publishing, Inc.

Nobleman, Marc Tyler. Rosa Parks. 2002. (Trailblazers of the Modern World Ser.). (Illus.). 48p. (J). (gr. 5 up). pap. 14.95 (978-0-8368-5231-8(1)); lib. bdg. 30.00 (978-0-8368-5071-0(8)) Stevens, Gareth Inc. (World Almanac Library).

—Rosa Parks. 2002. (gr. 3-6). lib. bdg. 19.90 (978-0-613-76804-7(3)) Tandem Library Bks.

O'Hern, Kerri & Walsh, Frank. The Montgomery Bus Boycott. 2006. (Graphic Histories Ser.). (Illus.). (J). pap. (978-0-8368-6257-7(0)); 32p. lib. bdg. 26.00 (978-0-8368-6205-8(8)) Stevens, Gareth Inc. (World Almanac Library).

Parks, Rosa. I Am Rosa Parks. 2000. (gr. k-3). lib. bdg. 11.80 (978-0-613-22996-8(7)); (Illus.). (J). 10.79 (978-0-606-18410-6(4)) Tandem Library Bks.

—Rosa Parks: My Story. 1999. (Illus.). 200p. (YA). (gr. 5-9). pap. 6.99 (978-0-14-130120-4(1), Puffin) Penguin Group (USA) Inc.

—Rosa Parks: My Story. 1999. (978-0-606-15995-1(9)); (gr. 5-8). lib. bdg. 15.30 (978-0-613-15120-7(8)) Tandem Library Bks.

Parks, Rosa & Haskins, Jim. I Am Rosa Parks. Clay, Wil, illus. 1999. (Easy-to-Read Ser.). 48p. (J). (gr. 1-3). pap. 3.99 (978-0-14-130710-7(2), Puffin) Penguin Group (USA) Inc.

Pierce, Alan. The Montgomery Bus Boycott. 2005. (American Moments Ser.). (Illus.). 48p. (J). (gr. 4-8). lib. bdg. 25.65 (978-1-59197-935-7(8)) ABDO Publishing Co.

Pingry, Patricia A. The Story of Coretta Scott King. Walker, Steven, illus. 2007. 26p. (J). (ps-k). bds. 6.99 (***978-0-8249-6717-8(8)***, Candy Cane Pr.) Ideals Pubns.

—The Story of Rosa Parks. Walker, Steven, illus. 2007. 24p. (J). (ps-k). bds. 6.99 (***978-0-8249-6687-4(2)***, Candy Cane Pr.) Ideals Pubns.

Pinkney, Andrea Davis. Let It Shine: Stories of Black Women Freedom Fighters. 2000. (Illus.). 128p. (J). (ps-3). 22.98 (978-0-7398-3073-4(2)) Raintree.

Price, Sean. When Will I Get In? Segregation & Civil Rights. 2006. (American History Through Primary Sources Ser.). (Illus.). 32p. (J). (978-1-4109-2414-8(9)); pap. (978-1-4109-2425-4(4)) Steck-Vaughn.

Rappaport, Doreen. Free at Last! Stories & Songs of Emancipation. Evans, Shane W., illus. 2006. 64p. (J). (gr. 4-7). pap. 7.99 (978-0-7636-3147-5(7)) Candlewick Pr.

—Free at Last! Stories & Songs of Emancipation. Evans, Shane, tr. Evans, Shane, illus. 2003. 64p. (J). (gr. 4-7). 19.99 (978-0-7636-1440-9(8)) Candlewick Pr.

—Martin's Big Words: The Life of Dr. Martin Luther King Jr. Collier, Bryan, illus. rev. ed. 2007. 40p. (ps-17). pap. 6.99 (***978-1-4231-0635-7(0)***, Jump at the Sun) Hyperion Bks. for Children.

Rappaport, Doreen. Nobody Gonna Turn Me 'Round: Stories & Songs of the Civil Rights Movement. Evans, Shane W., illus. 2006. 64p. (J). (gr. 4-7). 19.99 (978-0-7636-1927-5(2)) Candlewick Pr.

Rinaldo, Denise. Rosa Parks: With a Discussion of Courage. 2003. (Values in Action Ser.). (J). (978-1-59203-061-3(0)) Learning Challenge, Inc.

Ringgold, Faith. If a Bus Could Talk: The Story of Rosa Parks. Ringgold, Faith, illus. (Illus.). 32p. (J). 2003. (gr. k-4). pap. 7.99 (978-0-689-85676-1(8) , Aladdin); 1999. (gr. 1-4). 16.00 (978-0-689-81892-9(0)) Simon & Schuster Children's Publishing.

—If a Bus Could Talk: The Story of Rosa Parks. 2003. (gr. k-3). lib. bdg. 15.30 (978-0-613-61633-1(2)) Tandem Library Bks.

Santella, Andrew. The NAACP: An Organization Working to End Discrimination. 2003. (Journey to Freedom). (Illus.). 40p. (J). (gr. 3-7). 28.50 (978-1-56766-540-6(3)) Child's World, Inc.

Schaefer, Lola M. Rosa Parks. Saunders-Smith, Gail, ed. 2002. (First Biographies Ser.). (Illus.). 24p. (J). (gr. k-1). lib. bdg. 15.93 (978-0-7368-1176-7(1) , Pebble Bks.) Capstone Pr., Inc.

Schraff, Anne E. Martin Luther King, JR: We Shall Overcome. 2005. (African-American Biography Library). (Illus.). 128p. (J). (gr. 6-13). lib. bdg. 31.93 (978-0-7660-1774-0(5)) Enslow Pubs., Inc.

—Rosa Parks: Tired of Giving In. 2005. (African-American Biography Library). (Illus.). 128p. (J). (gr. 6-12). lib. bdg. 31.93 (978-0-7660-2463-2(6)) Enslow Pubs., Inc.

Schuldt, Lori Meek. Martin Luther King, Jr: With Profiles of Mohandas K. Gandhi & Nelson Mandela. 2006. (Biographical Connections Ser.). (Illus.). 112p. (J). (978-0-7166-1822-5(2)) World Bk., Inc.

Sharp, Anne Wallace. A Dream Deferred: the Jim Crow Era. 2005. (Lucent Library of Black History). (Illus.). 112p. (YA). (gr. 7-10). lib. bdg. 32.45 (978-1-59018-700-5(8) , Lucent Bks.) Thomson Gale.

Shone, Rob. Rosa Parks: The Life of a Civil Rights Heroine. Spender, Nik, illus. 2006. 48p. (J). (978-1-4042-0926-8(3)); pap. (978-1-4042-0927-5(1)); (gr. 3-8). lib. bdg. 29.95 (978-1-4042-0864-3(X)) Rosen Publishing Group, Inc., The.

Shores, Erika L. Rosa Parks: Civil Rights Poineer. 2005. (Fact Finders Ser.). (Illus.). 32p. (J). (ps-7). lib. bdg. 22.60 (978-0-7368-3746-0(9)) Capstone Pr., Inc.

Steele, Phillip. Rosa Parks & Her Protest for Civil Rights. 2002. (Dates with History Ser.). (Illus.). 31p. (J). lib. bdg. 24.25 (978-1-58340-215-3(2)) Smart Apple Media.

Sterling, Kristin. Mary McLeod Bethune: A Life of Resourcefulness. 2008. (Pull Ahead Books-Biographies Ser.). (J). lib. bdg. 22.60 (*978-0-8225-8588-6(X) , Lerner Pubns.) Lerner Publishing Group.

Stroud, Bettye & Schomp, Virginia. The Reconstruction ERA. 2006. (Drama of African-American History Ser.). (Illus.). 80p. (J). lib. bdg. 34.21 (978-0-7614-2181-8(5) , Benchmark Bks.) Cavendish, Marshall Corp.

Supples, Kevin. The Civil Rights Movement. 2003. (People Who Changed America Ser.). (Illus.). 40p. (J). (978-0-7922-8628-8(6)) National Geographic Society.

—Speaking Out: The Civil Rights Movement 1950-1964. 2005. (Crossroads America Ser.). (Illus.). 40p. (J). (gr. k-3). 12.95 (978-0-7922-8279-2(5)); 21.90 (978-0-7922-8359-1(7)) National Geographic Society. (National Geographic Children's Bks.).

Tackach, James. Early Black Reformers. 2003. (gr. 7-12). lib. bdg. 33.25 (978-0-613-73930-6(2)) Tandem Library Bks.

—Early Black Reformers. 2003. (History Firsthand Ser.). (Illus.). (YA). 224p. pap. 24.95 (978-0-7377-1598-9(7)); 202p. lib. bdg. 36.20 (978-0-7377-1597-2(9)) Thomson Gale. (Greenhaven Pr., Inc.).

Tembo, Limbiko & Venable, Rose. The Civil Rights Movement. 2001. (Journey to Freedom Ser.). (Illus.). 40p. (J). (gr. 3-7). 28.50 (978-1-56766-917-6(4)) Child's World, Inc.

Tieck, Sarah. Rosa Parks. 2007. (Buddy Book Ser.). (Illus.). 32p. (J). 22.78 (978-1-59679-788-8(6)) ABDO Publishing Co.

Tillage, Leon Walter. Leon's Story. Roth, Susan L., illus. 2000. 112p. (J). (gr. 3-7). pap. 5.95 (978-0-374-44330-6(0) , Sunburst) Farrar, Straus & Giroux.

Time for Kids Editors. Rosa Parks: Civil Rights Pioneer. 2007. (Time for Kids Ser.). (Illus.). 48p. (J). 14.99 (978-0-06-057625-7(1)); pap. 3.99 (978-0-06-057624-0(3)) HarperCollins Pubs.

Turck, Mary. Civil Rights Movement for Kids: A History with 21 Activities. 2000. (For Kids Ser.). (Illus.). 208p. (J). (gr. 4-8). pap. 14.95 (978-1-55652-370-0(X)) Chicago Review Pr., Inc.

Upchurch, Thomas Adams. The Encyclopedia of African-American Civil Rights: From Emancipation to the Twenty-First Century, 2 vols., Vol. 1. Lowery, Charles D. & Marszalek, John F., eds. 2nd ed. 2003. (Illus.). xxviii, 920p. lib. bdg. 175.00 (978-0-313-32766-7(1)) Greenwood Publishing Group, Inc.

Uschan, Michael V. Life on the Front Lines: The Fight for Civil Rights. 2004. (Illus.). 112p. (J). 32.45 (978-1-59018-387-8(8) , Lucent Bks.) Thomson Gale.

—The Scottsboro Case. 2004. (Landmark Events in American History Ser.). (Illus.). 48p. (J). (gr. 5 up). pap. 11.95 (978-0-8368-5416-9(0)); lib. bdg. 30.00 (978-0-8368-5388-9(1)) Stevens, Gareth Inc. (World Almanac Library).

Vaughn, Wally G. & Davis, Mattie Campbell, eds. The Selma Campaign, 1963-1965: The Decisive Battle of the Civil Rights Movement. 2006. 261p. pap. 19.95 (978-0-912469-44-7(7)) Majority Pr., Inc., The.

Wagner, Heather Lehr. Benjamin Hooks. 2003. (African American Leaders Ser.). (Illus.). 112p. (gr. 6-12). 30.00 (978-0-7910-7685-9(7) , Chelsea Hse.) Facts On File, Inc.

Waldstreicher, David. The Struggle Against Slavery: A History in Documents. 2001. (Pages from History Ser.). (Illus.). 176p. (gr. 7 up). reprint ed. 36.95 (978-0-19-510850-7(7)) Oxford Univ. Pr., Inc.

Walewander, James. Free at Last. 1999. (Illus.). 60p. pap. 7.95 (978-1-58521-013-8(7)) Books for Black Children, Inc.

Walsh, Frank. The Montgomery Bus Boycott. 2003. (Landmark Events in American History Ser.). (Illus.). 48p. (J). (gr. 5 up). pap. 14.95 (978-0-8368-5403-9(9)); lib. bdg. 30.00 (978-0-8368-5375-9(X)) Stevens, Gareth Inc. (World Almanac Library).

Waxman, Laura Hamilton. Coretta Scott King. 2008. (History Maker Biographies Ser.). (J). lib. bdg. 26.60 (*978-0-8225-7168-1(4) , Lerner Pubns.) Lerner Publishing Group.

Weidt, Maryann N. Rosa Parks. 2003. (History Maker Bios Ser.). (Illus.). 47p. (J). 26.60 (978-0-8225-4673-3(6) , Lerner Pubns.) Lerner Publishing Group.

Welch, Catherine A. Children of the Civil Rights Era. 2005. (Picture the American Past Ser.). (Illus.). 48p. (J). (gr. 2-5). lib. bdg. 22.60 (978-1-57505-481-0(7)) Lerner Publishing Group.

Wheeler, Jill C. Rosa Parks, Set II. 2003. (Breaking Barriers Ser.). (Illus.). 64p. (J). (gr. 3-8). lib. bdg. 25.65 (978-1-57765-640-1(7)) ABDO Publishing Co.

Whiting, Jim. Rosa Parks. 2007. (What's So Great About... ? Ser.). (J). lib. bdg. 25.70 (*978-1-58415-573-7(6)) Mitchell Lane Pubs., Inc.

Wilson, Cammie. Rosa Parks: From the Back of the Bus to the Front of a Movement. 2001. (Scholastic Biography Ser.). (Illus.). 88p. (J). (gr. 3-7). pap. 4.50 (978-0-439-16330-9(7)) Scholastic, Inc.

Winget, Mary. Martin Luther King, Jr. 2003. (History Maker Bios Ser.). (Illus.). 47p. (J). 26.60 (978-0-8225-4674-0(4) , Lerner Pubns.) Lerner Publishing Group.

—Martin Luther King, Jr. 2004. (History Maker Bios Ser.). (Illus.). 48p. (J). pap. (978-0-8225-4804-1(6) , Lerner Pubns.) Lerner Publishing Group.

Woog, Adam. The Fight Renewed: the Civil Rights Movement. 2005. (Lucent Library of Black History). (Illus.). 112p. (YA). (gr. 7-10). lib. bdg. 32.45 (978-1-59018-701-2(6) , Lucent Bks.) Thomson Gale.

AFRICAN AMERICANS—DICTIONARIES

Rasmussen, R. Kent, ed. The African American Encyclopedia, 10 vols. 2nd rev. ed. (Illus.). Set. 3000p. (J). lib. bdg. 459.95 (978-1-76147-208-4(9)); Vol. 1. 2001. (978-0-7614-7209-4(6)); Vol. 2. 2001. (978-0-7614-7210-0(X)); Vol. 3. 2001. (978-0-7614-7211-7(8)); Vol. 4. 2001. (978-0-7614-7212-4(6)); Vol. 5. 2001. (978-0-7614-7213-1(4)); Vol. 6. 2001. (978-0-7614-7214-8(2)); Vol. 7. 2001. (978-0-7614-7215-5(0)); Vol. 8. 2001. (978-0-7614-7216-2(9)); Vol. 9. 2001. (978-0-7614-7217-9(7)); Vol. 10. 2001. (978-0-7614-7218-6(5)) Cavendish, Marshall Corp.

—The African American Encyclopedia, 10 vols. 2nd ed. Incl. Vol. 1. (978-0-7614-7209-4(6)); Vol. 2. (978-0-7614-7210-0(X)); Vol. 3. (978-0-7614-7211-7(8)); Vol. 4. (978-0-7614-7212-4(6)); Vol. 5. (978-0-7614-7213-1(4)); Vol. 6. (978-0-7614-7214-8(2)); Vol. 7. (978-0-7614-7215-5(0)); Vol. 8. (978-0-7614-7216-2(9)); Vol. 9. (978-0-7614-7217-9(7)); Vol. 10. (978-0-7614-7218-6(5)); 2001. (Illus.). 3,000p. 2001. 599.93 (978-0-7614-7208-7(8) , Cavendish, Marshall Reference Bks.) Cavendish, Marshall Corp.

AFRICAN AMERICANS—DRAMA

Kamerman, Sylvia E., ed. Plays of Black Americans. rev. enl. ed. 2001. 157p. (gr. 4-9). 13.95 (978-0-8238-0301-9(5)) Kalmbach Publishing Co., Bks. Div.

Katzenbach, John. Hart's War. 2000. (gr. 7-12). lib. bdg. 16.45 (978-0-613-34760-0(9)) Tandem Library Bks.

AFRICAN AMERICANS—EDUCATION

Bridges, Ruby. Through My Eyes. 1999. (Illus.). 64p. (J). (gr. 3-7). pap. 16.95 (978-0-590-18923-1(9)) Scholastic, Inc.

Conaway, Judith. Brown V. Board of Education: The Case for Integration. 2006. 96p. lib. bdg. (978-0-7565-2448-7(2)) Compass Point Bks.

Evento, Susan. Mary McLeod Bethune. 2004. (Rookie Biographies Ser.). (Illus.). 31p. (J). 20.50 (978-0-516-21720-8(8) , Children's Pr.) Scholastic Library Publishing.

Jurmain, Suzanne. The Forbidden Schoolhouse: The True & Dramatic Story of Prudence Crandall & Her Students. 2005. (Illus.). 160p. (J). (gr. 5-6). 18.00 (978-0-618-47302-1(5)) Houghton Mifflin Co. Trade & Reference Div.

Miller, Mara. School Desegregation & the Story of the Little Rock Nine. 2008. (From Many Cultures, One History Ser.). (Illus.). 128p. (J). (gr. 5 up). lib. bdg. 31.93 (*978-0-7660-2835-7(6)) Enslow Pubs., Inc.

Peltak, Jennifer. History of African American Colleges & Universities. 2003. (American Mosaic Ser.). (Illus.). 112p. (gr. 6-12). 30.00 (978-0-7910-7269-1(X) , Chelsea Hse.) Facts On File, Inc.

Rappaport, Doreen. The School Is Not White! A True Story of the Civil Rights Movement. James, Curtis, illus. 2005. 32p. (gr. 2-7). 16.99 (978-0-7868-1838-9(7) , Jump at the Sun) Hyperion Bks. for Children.

Stroud, Bettye. A Personal Tour of Tuskegee Institute. 2001. (How It Was Ser.). (Illus.). (J). (gr. 4-6). lib. bdg. 25.26 (978-0-8225-3585-0(8)) Lerner Publishing Group.

Visions: Early Emergent - Complete Kit. (gr. k up). 319.50 (978-0-7802-9397-7(5)) Wright Group, The.

AFRICAN AMERICANS—EDUCATION—FICTION

Burton, Jennifer. Princess's Journey. 2003. (Topeka Heights Ser.). (YA). (gr. 9-12). pap. 10.99 (978-0-9724733-0-9(0)) Allen Publishing, USA.

Per, Sharon Mills. Darkness Before Dawn. 2002. (gr. 7-12). lib. bdg. 14.15 (978-0-613-53804-6(8)) Tandem Library Bks.

Waldron, Ann. The Integration of Mary-Larkin Thornhill. 2000. 148p. pap. 10.95 (978-0-595-00069-2(X)) iUniverse, Inc.

AFRICAN AMERICANS—EMPLOYMENT

Buckley, Annie. Robert L. Johnson. 2008. (J). lib. bdg. 26.00 (*978-1-60279-072-8(8)) Cherry Lake Publishing.

Marsh, Carole. Black Business: African American Entrepreneurs & Their Amazing Success! 2003. (gr. 5-8). lib. bdg. 22.20 (978-0-613-73035-8(6)) Tandem Library Bks.

AFRICAN AMERICANS—FOLKLORE

Farmer, Nancy. Casey Jones's Fireman: The Story of Sim Webb. Fogelman, Phyllis, ed. Bernardin, James, illus. 1999. 40p. (J). (ps-3). 16.99 (978-0-8037-1929-3(9) , Dial) Penguin Group (USA) Inc.

Hamilton, Virginia. The People Could Fly: American Black Folktales. Schulman, Janet, ed. Dillon, Leo & Dillon, Diane, illus. 2000. 192p. (YA). (gr. 3 up). 24.95 (978-0-375-80471-7(4) , Knopf Bks. for Young Readers) Random Hse. Children's Bks.

—The People Could Fly: The Picture Book. Dillon, Leo & Dillon, Diane, illus. 32p. (J). 2007. audio compact disk 20.99 (*978-0-375-94553-3(9)); 2004. 16.95 (978-0-375-82405-0(7)) Random Hse. Children's Bks. (Knopf Bks. for Young Readers).

Hamilton, Virginia. Second Cousins. 1998. (Virginia Hamilton Ser.: Vol. 3). (Illus.). 160p. (YA). (gr. 5-9). pap. 14.95 (978-0-590-47368-2(9) , Blue Sky Pr., The) Scholastic, Inc.

Harris, Joel Chandler. The Complete Tales of Uncle Remus. 2002. (Illus.). 848p. (YA). 35.00 (978-0-618-15429-6(9)) Houghton Mifflin Co. Trade & Reference Div.

—Uncle Remus: His Songs & His Sayings. Date not set. (J). lib. bdg. 24.95 (978-0-8488-0711-5(1)) Amereon LTD.

—Uncle Remus: His Songs & His Sayings. 265p. (J). 18.00 (978-0-9645990-0-0(7)) Historic Pr.-South.

—Uncle Remus: Tales. 1999. (Illus.). 234p. (J). reprint ed. 30.00 (978-0-88322-041-2(5)) Beehive Pr., The.

—Uncle Remus & Brer Rabbit. 1999. (Illus.). 64p. (J). (gr. 4-7). reprint ed. 19.95 (978-1-55709-491-9(8)) Applewood Bks.

Haskins, James. Moaning Bones: African-American Ghost Stories. Marshall, Felicia, illus. 1998. 64p. (YA). (gr. 2 up). 14.00 (978-0-688-16021-0(2)) HarperCollins Pubs.

Hurston, Zora Neale. What's the Hurry, Fox? And Other Animal Stories. Collier, Bryan, illus. 2004. 32p. (J). 16.99 (978-0-06-000643-3(9)) HarperCollins Pubs.

Krensky, Stephen, adapted by. John Henry. 2007. (On My Own Folklore Ser.). (Illus.). 48p. (J). (gr. 2-5). lib. bdg. 25.26 (978-1-57505-887-0(1) , Millbrook Pr.) Lerner Publishing Group.

Lester, Julius. John Henry. Pinkney, Jerry, illus. 2002. (J). 14.04 (978-0-7587-0123-7(3)) Book Wholesalers, Inc.

—John Henry. Pinkney, Jerry, illus. 1999. 40p. (J). (ps-17). pap. 7.99 (978-0-14-056622-2(8) , Puffin) Penguin Group (USA) Inc.

—John Henry. 1999. (ps-2). lib. bdg. 16.45 (978-0-7857-1862-8(1)) Tandem Library Bks.

—John Henry. unabr. ed. 1998. (Illus.). (J). (ps-4). 24.95 incl. audio (978-0-7882-0682-5(6) , HRA377) Weston Woods Studios, Inc.

—The Tales of Uncle Remus: The Adventures of Brer Rabbit. Pinkney, Jerry, illus. 1999. 176p. (J). (gr. 3-7). pap. 8.99 (978-0-14-130347-5(6) , Puffin) Penguin Group (USA) Inc.

—Tales of Uncle Remus: The Adventures of Brer Rabbit. Pinkney, Jerry, illus. 2006. (Puffin Modern Classics Ser.). 160p. (J). (gr. 3). pap. 5.99 (978-0-14-240720-2(8) , Puffin) Penguin Group (USA) Inc.

—Uncle Remus: The Complete Tales. Fogelman, Phyllis, ed. Pinkney, Jerry, illus. 1999. 720p. (J). (ps-3). 35.00 (978-0-8037-2451-8(9) , Dial) Penguin Group (USA) Inc.

McGill, Alice. Sure as Sunrise: Stories of Bruh Rabbit & His Walkin' Talkin' Friends. Tate, Don, tr. Tate, Don, illus. 2004. 48p. (J). (gr. k-3). tchr. ed. 17.00 (978-0-618-21196-8(9)) Houghton Mifflin Co. Trade & Reference Div.

—Way up & over Everything. 2005. (J). (978-0-618-38796-0(X)) Houghton Mifflin Co.

Rayner, Olivia, illus. North American Myths & Legends. 2001. (World Book Myths & Legends Ser.). 64p. (J). (978-0-7166-2611-4(X)) World Bk., Inc.

Robbins, Sandra. Big Annie: An American Tall Tale. Oseki, Iku, illus. 1998. (See-More's Stories Ser.). 32p. (J). (ps-4). pap. 6.95 (978-1-882601-25-7(4)); pap. 11.95 incl. audio (978-1-882601-27-1(0)) See-More's Workshop.

San Souci, Robert D. The Secret of the Stones: A Folktale. 2000. (Illus.). 40p. (J). (ps-3). 16.99 (978-0-8037-1640-7(0) , Dial) Penguin Group (USA) Inc.

AFRICAN AMERICANS—FICTION

Ackerman, Karen. By the Dawn's Early Light: Al Amanecer. 1999. (J). (978-0-606-15924-1(X)) Tandem Library Bks.

Adebayo, Yinka. Age Ain't Nothin' but a Number. 1998. (Drummond Hill Crew Ser.). 144p. (J). (978-1-874509-33-2(6)) X Pr., The.

—Livin' Large. 1998. 144p. (J). (978-1-874509-34-9(4)) X Pr., The.

Adlerman, Daniel, ed. Africa Calling, Nighttime Falling. 2001. (J). 13.75 (978-0-606-20533-7(0)) Tandem Library Bks.

Alcantara, Ignacio, illus. My Very Breast Friend. 2005. 40p. (J). 17.00 (978-0-9659538-5-6(8)) Soul Vision Works Publishing.

Altman, Linda Jacobs. The Legend of Freedom Hill. Van Wright, Cornelius, illus. 2003. 32p. (J). (978-1-58430-169-1(4)) Lee & Low Bks., Inc.

—The Legend of Freedom Hill. Van Wright, Cornelius & Hu, Ying-Hwa, illus. 2000. 32p. (J). (ps up). 15.95 (978-1-58430-003-8(5)) Lee & Low Bks., Inc.

—The Legend of Freedom Hill. Van Wright, Cornelius et al, illus. 2004. 32p. (J). (ps-k). lib. bdg. 13.75 (978-0-606-30127-5(5)) Tandem Library Bks.

—The Legend of Freedom Hill. 2003. (gr. k-3). lib. bdg. 15.25 (978-0-613-85872-4(7)) Tandem Library Bks.

—Singin' with Momma Lou. Johnson, Larry, illus. 2002. 32p. (J). (gr. 1-5). 16.95 (978-1-58430-040-3(X)) Lee & Low Bks., Inc.

American Tract Society Staff. Step by Step or Tidy's Way to Freedom. 2006. 50.99 (*978-1-4219-8162-8(9)); pap. 44.99 (*978-1-4219-8160-4(2)) IndyPublish.com.

Anderson, M. T. The Astonishing Life of Octavian Nothing, Traitor to the Nation. 2006. (Pox Party Ser.: Vol. 1). (Illus.). 368p. (YA). (gr. 9). 17.99 (978-0-7636-2402-6(0)) Candlewick Pr.

Anderson, M. T. Astonishing Life of Octavian Nothing, Traitor to the Nation: The Pox Party. rev. l.t. ed. 2007. (Astonishing Life of Octavian Nothing Ser.). 500p. (YA). 23.95 (*978-0-7862-9552-4(X)) Thorndike Pr.

Anderson, Pamela Dell. My New School: Afro Boy. Lee, Hanlim & WU, Stacie, illus. 2003. 24p. (J). 12.95 (978-1-932555-01-1(3)) Watch Me Grow Kids.

—My New School: Afro Girl. Lee, Hanlim & WU, Stacie, illus. 2003. 24p. (J). 12.95 (978-1-932555-00-4(5)) Watch Me Grow Kids.

Andrews, V. C. Star. 1999. (978-0-606-17533-3(4)) Tandem Library Bks.

Applegate, Katherine. Home of the Brave. 2007. 256p. (J). (gr. 5-9). 16.95 (*978-0-312-36765-7(1)) Feiwel & Friends.

Armistead, John. The Return of Gabriel. Gregory, Fran, illus. 2002. 240p. (J). (gr. 3-8). 17.95 (978-1-57131-637-0(X)); pap. 6.95 (978-1-57131-638-7(8)) Milkweed Editions.

Armstrong, William H. Sounder. 2001. (Perennial Classics Ser.). 96p. (gr. 4-7). pap. 7.00 (978-0-06-093548-1(0)) HarperCollins Pubs.

—Sounder. Barkley, James, illus. l.t. ed. 1999. (LRS Large Print Cornerstone Ser.). 230p. (YA). (gr. 6-12). lib. bdg. 27.95 (978-1-58118-054-1(3) , 22768) LRS.

—Sounder. 2001. (gr. 3-6). lib. bdg. 15.30 (978-0-613-85745-1(3)) Tandem Library Bks.

—Sounder. l.t. ed. 2005. 111p. (YA). pap. 10.95 (978-0-7862-7915-9(X)) Thorndike Pr.

Arterburn, Stephen & Hunt, Angela Elwell. Taz. 2004. (Young Believer on Tour Ser.). (J). pap. 3.99 (978-0-8423-8340-0(9)) Tyndale Hse. Pubs.

Aston, Dianna Hutts. When You Were Born. Lewis, Earl, illus. 2004. 32p. (J). (ps up). 15.99 (978-0-7636-1438-6(6)) Candlewick Pr.

Baicker, Karen. I Can Do It Too! Wilson-Max, Ken, illus. 2003. 24p. (J). 13.95 (978-1-929766-83-3(1)) Handprint Bks.

Bailey, Barbara. When I Get Older I'll Understand. 2000. 192p. (gr. 7-12). 7.95 (978-1-56315-211-5(8)) Sterling-House Pubs., Inc.

—When I Get Older I'll Understand. 2000. (gr. 7-12). lib. bdg. 16.40 (978-0-613-83337-0(6)) Tandem Library Bks.

Banks, Jacqueline Turner. Egg-Drop Blues. 2003. 128p. (J). (gr. 4-6). pap. 4.95 (978-0-618-25080-6(8)); 15.00 (978-0-618-34885-5(9)) Houghton Mifflin Co. Trade & Reference Div.

Barber, Barbara E. Allie's Basketball Dream. Ligasan, Darryl, illus. 1998. 32p. (J). (ps-5). 6.95 (978-1-880000-72-4(5)) Lee & Low Bks., Inc.

—Saturday at the New You. Rich, Anna, illus. 2002. (J). 14.66 (978-0-7587-3566-9(9)) Book Wholesalers, Inc.

Barnes, Derrick. The Low-down, Bad-Day Blues. Boyd, Aaron, illus. 2004. 32p. (J). (gr. k-1). lib. bdg. 11.19 (978-0-606-33352-8(5)) Tandem Library Bks.

Barnes, Derrick D. The Low-down, Bad-Day Blues. Boyd, Aaron, illus. 2004. 32p. (J). lib. bdg. 15.00 (*978-1-4242-0222-5(1)) Fitzgerald Bks.

—Stop, Drop, & Chill. Phillips-Duke, Barbara Jean, illus. 2004. 32p. (J). lib. bdg. 15.00 (*978-1-4242-0231-7(0)) Fitzgerald Bks.

Barnes, Joyce Annette. Promise Me the Moon. 1999. (978-0-606-14297-7(5)) Tandem Library Bks.

Barnwell, Ysaye M. No Mirrors in My Nana's House. Saint James, Synthia, illus. 1998. 32p. (J). (gr. k-3). 18.00 (978-0-15-201825-2(5)) Harcourt Children's Bks.

—No Mirrors in My Nana's House: Musical CD & Book. Saint James, Synthia, illus. 2005. 32p. (J). reprint ed. 8.00 (978-0-15-205243-0(7) , Voyager Bks./Libros Viajeros) Harcourt Children's Bks.

Battle-Lavert, Gwendolyn. The Barber's Cutting Edge. Holbert, Raymond, illus. 2004. 32p. (J). pap. 7.95 (978-0-89239-196-7(0)) Children's Bk. Pr.

—The Music in Derrick's Heart. Bootman, Colin, illus. 2000. 32p. (J). (gr. k-3). tchr. ed. 16.95 (978-0-8234-1353-9(5)) Holiday Hse., Inc.

—Papa's Mark. Bootman, Colin, illus. 2003. 32p. (J). (gr. k-3). tchr. ed. 16.95 (978-0-8234-1650-9(X)) Holiday Hse., Inc.

Belton, Sandra. Beauty, Her Basket. Cabrera, Cozbi A., illus. 2004. 32p. (J). 15.99 (978-0-688-17821-5(9)); lib. bdg. 16.89 (978-0-688-17822-2(7)) HarperCollins Pubs.

—Pictures for Miss Josie. Andrews, Benny, illus. 2003. 40p. (J). (gr. k-3). 17.99 (978-0-688-17480-4(9)) HarperCollins Pubs.

—Store-Bought Baby. 2006. 256p. (J). 15.99 (978-0-06-085086-9(8)); lib. bdg. 16.89 (978-0-06-085087-6(6)) HarperCollins Pubs.

Belton, Sandra. The Tallest Tree: The Paul Robeson Story. 2008. 160p. (J). lib. bdg. 17.89 (*978-0-06-052750-1(1) , Amistad) HarperCollins Pubs.

Bermiss, Aamir. I Hate to Be Sick! Wilson-Max, Ken, illus. 2004. 32p. (J). (gr. k-1). lib. bdg. 11.19 (978-0-606-33350-4(9)) Tandem Library Bks.

Bermiss, Aamir Lee. I Hate to Be Sick! Wilson-Max, Ken, illus. 2004. 32p. (J). lib. bdg. 15.00 (*978-1-4242-0220-1(5)) Fitzgerald Bks.

Billingsley, ReShonda Tate. Blessings in Disguise. 2007. 192p. (YA). pap. 9.95 (978-1-4165-2561-5(0) , Pocket) Simon & Schuster.

—With Friends Like These. 2007. 256p. pap. 9.95 (978-1-4165-2562-2(9) , Pocket) Simon & Schuster.

Birtha, Becky. Grandmama's Pride. Bootman, Colin, illus. 2005. 32p. (J). (gr. 7-10). 16.95 (978-0-8075-3028-3(X)) Whitman, Albert & Co.

Black, Sonia W. Jumping the Broom. Wright and Hu, Cornelius Van and Ying-Hwa, illus. 2004. 32p. (J). lib. bdg. 15.00 (***978-1-4242-0234-8(5)***) Fitzgerald Bks.

—Mommy's Bed. Kindert, Jennifer, illus. 2004. 32p. (J), lib. bdg. 15.00 (***978-1-4242-0223-2(X)***) Fitzgerald Bks.

Blackaby, Susan. Greg Gets a Hint. Trover, Zachary, illus. 2006. (Read-It! Readers Ser.). (J). 19.93 (978-1-4048-2411-9(1)) Picture Window Bks.

Blakeslee, Ann R. Summer Battles. 2000. (Illus.). 128p. (YA). (gr. 5-9). 14.95 (978-0-7614-5064-1(5) , Cavendish Children's Bks.) Cavendish, Marshall Corp.

Bolden, Tonya. Through Loona's Door: A Tammy & Owen Adventure with Carter G. Woodson. Simpson, Howard, illus. 2005. (J). per. 11.95 (978-0-9740212-2-5(9)) Cedar Grove Bks.

Boles, Philana Marie. Little Divas. 2006. 176p. (J). 15.99 (978-0-06-073299-8(7) , Amistad); lib. bdg. 16.89 (978-0-06-073300-1(4)) HarperCollins Pubs.

Bond, Katherine Grace & Tate, Don, II. The Legend of the Valentine: An Inspirational Story of Love & Reconciliation. 2002. (Illus.). 32p. (J). 15.99 (978-0-310-70039-5(6)) Zonderkidz.

Bonham, Frank. Durango Street. 1999. 192p. (YA). (gr. 7-12). pap. 5.99 (978-0-14-130309-3(3) , Puffin) Penguin Group (USA) Inc.

Bontemps, Arna. Chariot in the Sky: A Story of the Jubilee Singers. 2002. (Iona & Peter Opie Library of Children's Literature). (Illus.). 240p. (YA). 22.95 (978-0-19-515658-4(7)) Oxford Univ. Pr., Inc.

Booth, Coe. Tyrell. 2006. 320p. (J). pap. 16.99 (978-0-439-83879-5(7) , PUSH) Scholastic, Inc.

Boyd, Dee. Only the Stars. Rich, Anna, illus. 2004. 32p. (J). lib. bdg. 15.00 (***978-1-4242-0230-0(2)***) Fitzgerald Bks.

Bradby, Marie. Momma, Where Are You From. Soentpiet, Chris K., illus. 2000. 32p. (J). (ps-2). pap. 16.95 (978-0-531-30105-0(2) , Orchard Bks.) Scholastic, Inc.

—Some Friend. 2007. 240p. (J). pap. 5.99 (978-1-4169-3452-3(9) , Aladdin) Simon & Schuster Children's Publishing.

—Some Friend. Frederick, Brooks, illus. 2004. 240p. (J). 15.95 (978-0-689-85615-0(6) , Atheneum/Richard Jackson Bks.) Simon & Schuster Children's Publishing.

Bray, Jeannine D. Superfro. Kenyatta, Imani, ed. Mitchell, Denise B., illus. 1998. 72p. (J). (gr. k-6). 14.95 (978-1-886580-10-7(3)) Pinnacle-Syatt Pubns.

Brooks, Bruce. Prince. 1998. (Wolfbay Wings Ser.: No. 5). (Illus.). 144p. (J). (gr. 4-7). pap. 4.50 (978-0-06-440600-0(8)) HarperCollins Pubs.

—Prince. 1998. (Wolfbay Wings Ser.: No. 5). (J). (gr. 4-7). (978-0-606-13925-0(7)) Tandem Library Bks.

Brooks, Regina. Never Finished, Never Done! Borgella, Marjorie, illus. 2004. 32p. (J). lib. bdg. 15.00 (***978-1-4242-0229-4(9)***) Fitzgerald Bks.

Brown, Marc. D. W. the Big Boss. 2005. (Arthur's 8 x 8 Bks.). (Illus.). 24p. (J). (ps-3). pap. 3.99 (978-0-316-73395-3(4)) Little Brown & Co.

Broyles, Anne. Priscilla & the Hollyhocks. Alter, Anna, illus. 2008. (J). (***978-1-57091-675-5(6)***) Charlesbridge Publishing, Inc.

Bryant, Bonnie. Carole: The Inside Story. 1999. (J). (978-0-606-19288-0(3)) Tandem Library Bks.

Buckley, Helen. Grandfather & I. 2000. (ps-2). lib. bdg. 14.10 (978-0-613-28503-2(4)) Tandem Library Bks.

—Grandmother & I. 2000. (ps-2). lib. bdg. 14.10 (978-0-613-28504-9(2)) Tandem Library Bks.

Buckley, Helen E. Grandfather & I. Ormerod, Jan, illus. 2000. 24p. (J). (ps-3). pap. 6.99 (978-0-688-17526-9(0) , Harper Trophy) HarperCollins Pubs.

—Grandmother & I. Ormerod, Jan, illus. 2000. 24p. (J). (ps-3). pap. 6.99 (978-0-688-17525-2(2) , Harper Trophy) HarperCollins Pubs.

Bunting, Eve. Flower Garden. 2002. (Illus.). (J). 13.19 (978-0-7587-2519-6(1)) Book Wholesalers, Inc.

—Flower Garden. Hewitt, Kathryn, illus. 2000. 32p. (J). (ps-3). pap. 7.00 (978-0-15-202372-0(0)) Harcourt Children's Bks.

—Flower Garden. Hewitt, Kathryn, illus. 1999. 32p. (J). (ps-3). 25.95 (978-0-15-201968-6(5)) Harcourt Trade Pubs.

—Flower Garden. Hewitt, Kathryn, illus. 2000. (J). (ps-ps). lib. bdg. 14.15 (978-0-613-28490-5(9)) Tandem Library Bks.

—Flower Garden. 2000. 12.80 (978-0-606-17842-6(2)) Tandem Library Bks.

—Flower Garden: Lap-Sized Board Book. Hewitt, Kathryn, illus. 2008. 30p. (J). bds. 10.95 (***978-0-15-206516-4(4)*** , Red Wagon Bks.) Harcourt Children's Bks.

—Two Different Girls. 2001. 32p. (YA). (gr. 6-12). pap. (978-0-8224-3535-8(7)) Globe Fearon Educational Publishing.

—Your Move. Ransome, James E., illus. 1998. 32p. (J). (gr. 1-5). 17.00 (978-0-15-200181-0(6)) Harcourt Children's Bks.

Burden-Patmon, Denise. Imani's Gift at Kwanzaa. (J). 48.95 (978-0-8136-2248-4(4)) Modern Curriculum Pr.

Cameron, Ann. Gloria Rising. Toft, Lis, illus. 2002. 112p. (J). (gr. 2-5). 15.00 (978-0-374-32675-3(4) , Farrar, Straus & Giroux (BYR)) Farrar, Straus & Giroux.

—Gloria Rising. 2004. 112p. (J). (gr. 1-4). pap. 4.99 (978-0-440-41998-3(0) , Random Hse. Bks. for Young Readers) Random Hse. Children's Bks.

—Gloria's Way. 2002. (Illus.). 12.34 (978-1-4046-0952-5(0)) Book Wholesalers, Inc.

—Gloria's Way. Toft, Lis, illus. 2000. 112p. (J). (ps-3). 15.00 (978-0-374-32670-8(3) , Farrar, Straus & Giroux (BYR)) Farrar, Straus & Giroux.

—Julian, Dream Doctor. 2002. (J). 12.32 (978-0-7587-6155-2(4)) Book Wholesalers, Inc.

—Julian, Secret Agent. 2002. (Illus.). (J). 12.87 (978-0-7587-1353-7(3)) Book Wholesalers, Inc.

—Julian's Glorious Summer. 2002. (Illus.). (J). 12.87 (978-0-7587-1354-4(1)) Book Wholesalers, Inc.

—More Stories Huey Tells. Toft, Lis, illus. 1999. 128p. (J). (gr. k-4). pap. 4.99 (978-0-679-88363-0(0) , Random Hse. Bks. for Young Readers) Random Hse. Children's Bks.

—More Stories Huey Tells. 1998. (J). pap. 4.99 (978-0-679-88576-4(5) , Knopf Bks. for Young Readers) Random Hse. Children's Bks.

—More Stories Huey Tells. 1999. (J). (978-0-606-16567-9(3)) Tandem Library Bks.

—More Stories Huey Tells. Toft, Lis, illus. 1999. 117p. (J). (ps-ps). per. 13.00 (978-0-613-10978-9(3)) Tandem Library Bks.

—The Stories Julian Tells. 1999. (J). 9.95 (978-1-56137-671-1(X)) Novel Units, Inc.

Cameron, Ann & Toft, Lis. Gloria's Way. 2001. (Chapters Ser.). (Illus.). 112p. (J). pap. 4.99 (978-0-14-230023-7(3) , Puffin) Penguin Group (USA) Inc.

Campbell, Bebe Moore. Sometimes My Mommy Gets Angry. Lewis, E. B., illus. 2005. 32p. (J). pap. 5.99 (978-0-14-240359-4(8) , Puffin) Penguin Group (USA) Inc.

—Sometimes My Mommy Gets Angry. Lewis, Earl, illus. 2003. 32p. (J). (ps-3). 16.99 (978-0-399-23972-4(3) , Putnam Juvenile) Penguin Group (USA) Inc.

—Stompin' at the Savoy. Yarde, Richard, illus. 2006. 40p. (J). (gr. 1-4). 16.99 (978-0-399-24197-0(3) , Philomel) Penguin Group (USA) Inc.

Campbell, Charles K. La Magic Coin. 2004. (YA). (gr. 3 up). per. 15.00 (978-0-9742064-3-1(1)) Unmistakably C K C.

Campbell, Terry. Harlem & Momma: A Short Children Story. 2005. 42p. (J). pap. 10.00 (978-0-9761560-0-0(8)) Sweet T. C. Campbell.

Campoy, F. Isabel, et al. Celebra Kwanzaa con Botitas y Sus Gatitos. Docampo, Valeria, illus. 2006. (J). (978-1-59820-123-9(9)) Santillana USA Publishing Co., Inc.

—Celebrate Kwanzaa with Boots & Her Kittens. Docampo, Valeria, illus. 2006. 31p. (J). (978-1-59820-135-2(2)) Santillana USA Publishing Co., Inc.

Carbone, Elisa. Last Dance on Holladay Street. 208p. (gr. 7-11). 2006. (YA). mass mkt. 5.99 (978-0-553-49426-6(0) , Laurel Leaf); 2005. (J). 15.95 (978-0-375-82896-6(6) , Knopf Bks. for Young Readers) Random Hse. Children's Bks.

—Night Running: How James Escaped with the Help of His Faithful Dog. Lewis, Earl, illus. 2007. (J). (978-0-375-82247-6(X)); lib. bdg. (978-0-375-92247-3(4)) Knopf, Alfred A. Inc.

—Stealing Freedom. 2002. (EMC Masterpiece Series Access Editions). (Illus.). xix, 284p. (J). 14.60 (978-0-8219-2507-2(5)) EMC/Paradigm Publishing.

—Stealing Freedom. 2001. (gr. 5-8). lib. bdg. 13.55 (978-0-613-33729-8(8)) Tandem Library Bks.

—Stealing Freedom. l.t. ed. 2005. 346p. pap. 10.95 (978-0-7862-7314-0(3) , Large Print Pr.) Thorndike Pr.

—Storm Warriors. 2002. (gr. 5-8). lib. bdg. 13.55 (978-0-613-61730-7(4)) Tandem Library Bks.

Carlson, Judy. Life with Max. 2000. (Metro Reading Program Ser.). (J). (gr. k). 7.98 (978-1-58120-973-0(8)); 45.95 (978-1-58830-031-7(5)) Metropolitan Teaching & Learning Co.

Carlson, Margaret. The Canning Season. Smith, Kimanne, illus. 1999. (First Person Ser.). 32p. (J). (gr. 2-4). pap. 7.95 (978-1-57505-283-0(0) , Carolrhoda Bks.) Lerner Publishing Group.

Carlson, Nolan. Lame Eagle & Wind Chaser. 2005. (YA). per. (978-0-9772745-1-2(9)) Mennonite Pr. Inc.

Carr, Pat M. If We Must Die: A Novel. 2004. (Chaparral Book for Young Readers Ser.). 168p. (C). pap. 15.95 (978-0-87565-262-7(X)) Texas Christian Univ. Pr.

Carroll, Jonathan. Meet Julius Carmichael: First Day Blues. Koltun, Amy, illus. 2003. 96p. (J). (gr. 3-6). pap. 6.95 (978-0-9724935-0-5(6)) Striking Presence Pubns.

Carter, Cassandra. 16 Isn't Always Sweet. 2008. 256p. pap. 9.99 (***978-0-373-83097-8(1)***) Harlequin Enterprises, Ltd. CAN. *Dist:* Simon & Schuster, Inc.

Carter, Dorothy. Grandma's General Store - The Ark. Allen, Thomas B., illus. 2005. 144p. (J). 16.00 (978-0-374-32766-8(1) , Farrar, Straus & Giroux (BYR)) Farrar, Straus & Giroux.

—Wilhe'mina Miles: After the Stork Night. Stevenson, Harvey, illus. 2005. 30p. (J). (gr. k-4). reprint ed. 16.00 (978-0-7567-9421-7(8)) DIANE Publishing Co.

Center for Learning Network Staff & Ellison, Ralph. Invisible Man: Curriculum Unit. 1998. 63p. (YA). (gr. 9-12). tchr. ed., spiral bd. 19.95 (978-1-56077-561-4(0)) Ctr. for Learning, The.

Childrens Press Staff, ed. Messy Bessey. 2005. (Rookie Reader Ser.). 96p. (J). (ps-2). pap. 9.95 (978-0-516-25328-2(X) , Children's Pr.) Scholastic Library Publishing.

Childress, Alice. A Hero Ain't Nothin' but a Sandwich. 2000. 128p. (J). (gr. 7-12). pap. 5.99 (978-0-698-11854-6(5) , Putnam Juvenile) Penguin Group (USA) Inc.

—A Hero Ain't Nothin' but a Sandwich. 2000. 12.64 (978-0-606-17821-1(X)) Tandem Library Bks.

Christopher, Matt. Fairway Phenom. 2003. (gr. 3-6). lib. bdg. 12.40 (978-0-613-71602-4(7)) Tandem Library Bks.

Clifton, Lucille. One of the Problems of Everett Anderson. Grifalconi, Ann, illus. rev. ed. 2001. 32p. (J). (gr. k-3). 16.95 (978-0-8050-5201-5(1) , Holt, Henry & Co. Bks. For Young Readers) Holt, Henry & Co.

Clovis, Donna L. Locket of Dreams: A Modern African American Fairy Tale. 1999. (Illus.). 24p. (J). (gr. 3-8). pap. 9.95 (978-1-58521-001-5(3)) Books for Black Children, Inc.

Codell, Esmé Raji. Sahara Special. (gr. 3-7). 2004. 192p. (J). pap. 5.99 (978-0-7868-1611-8(2)); 2003. (Illus.). 208p. (J). lib. bdg. 16.49 (978-0-7868-2627-8(4)); 2003. (Illus.). 192p. 15.99 (978-0-7868-0793-2(8)) Hyperion Bks. for Children.

—Sahara Special. 2003. (gr. 3-6). lib. bdg. 14.10 (978-0-613-65611-5(3)) Tandem Library Bks.

—Vive la Paris! 2006. 224p. (J). (gr. 3-7). 15.99 (978-0-7868-5124-9(4)) Hyperion Pr.

Coker, Deborah Connor. Aunt Mattie's Present. Joysmith, Brenda, illus. 1998. (J). (978-0-316-23498-6(2)) Little Brown & Co.

Coleman, Evelyn. Born in Sin. Duffy, Tony, illus. 2001. 240p. (YA). (gr. 7-12). 16.00 (978-0-689-83833-0(6) , Atheneum/Richard Jackson Bks.) Simon & Schuster Children's Publishing.

—Circle of Fire. 2001. (American Girl Collection). (Illus.). (J). 12.60 (978-0-606-21249-6(3)) Tandem Library Bks.

—Mystery of the Dark Tower. 2000. (History Mysteries Ser.). (978-0-606-18356-7(6)) Tandem Library Bks.

—Shadows on Society Hill: An Addy Mystery. 2007. 192p. (J). 10.95 (***978-1-59369-163-9(7)***); pap. 6.95 (***978-1-59369-162-2(9)***) American Girl Publishing, Inc. (American Girl).

—To Be a Drum. Robinson, Aminah B., illus. 1998. 32p. (YA). (gr. k-3). lib. bdg. 16.95 (978-0-8075-8006-6(6)) Whitman, Albert & Co.

—To Be a Drum. Robinson, Aminah B., illus. 2004. 32p. (J). (gr. k up). pap. 6.95 (978-0-8075-8007-3(4)) Whitman, Albert & Co.

—White Socks Only. Geter, Tyrone, illus. 2004. (Prairie Paperback Bks.). 32p. (J). (gr. k-4). pap. 6.95 (978-0-8075-8956-4(X)) Whitman, Albert & Co.

Collier, Bryan. Uptown. rev. ed. (Illus.). 32p. (J). 2004. pap. 7.95 (978-0-8050-7399-7(X)); 2000. 17.95 (978-0-8050-5721-8(8)) Holt, Henry & Co. (Holt, Henry & Co. Bks. For Young Readers).

—Uptown. 2004. (gr. k-3). lib. bdg. 15.25 (978-0-613-75623-5(1)) Tandem Library Bks.

Collier, James Lincoln. Who Is Carrie? 2001. (gr. 5-8). lib. bdg. 21.10 (978-0-613-86696-5(7)) Tandem Library Bks.

Collier, James Lincoln & Collier, Christopher. Who Is Carrie? 2001. 176p. (J). (gr. 5-7). 12.00 (978-0-375-89503-6(5) , Delacorte Bks. for Young Readers) Random Hse. Children's Bks.

Collier, Kristi. Jericho Walls. 2007. 224p. (YA). pap. 7.95 (***978-0-8050-8184-8(4)*** , Holt, Henry & Co. Bks. For Young Readers) Holt, Henry & Co.

Come on Rain. 2004. (J). pap. 14.95 incl. audio (978-0-7882-0513-2(7)) Weston Woods Studios, Inc.

Condon, Bill. Holly & Mac. Gordon, Gus, illus. 1999. (Supa Doopers Ser.). 64p. (J). (978-0-7608-1924-1(6)) Sundance/Newbridge Educational Publishing.

—Holly & Mac. 1999. (gr. 3-6). lib. bdg. 12.60 (978-0-613-19373-3(3)) Tandem Library Bks.

Connelly, Bernardine. Follow the Drinking Gourd. Buchanan, Yvonne, illus. 2005. (Rabbit Ears-A Classic Tale Ser.). 40p. (J). (gr. k-5). 25.65 (978-1-59197-763-6(0)) Spotlight.

Cooke, Trish. Full of Love. Howard, Paul, illus. 2003. 32p. (J). (ps). 15.99 (978-0-7636-1851-3(9)) Candlewick Pr.

Cooney, Caroline B. Burning Up. 1999. (YA). pap., stu. ed. 68.99 incl. audio (978-0-7887-3190-7(4) , 40925) Recorded Bks., LLC.

—Burning Up. 2001. (YA). 12.15 (978-0-606-20585-6(3)) Tandem Library Bks.

Cooney, Caroline B. Diamonds in the Shadow. 2007. 228p. (YA). (gr. 7-12). 15.99 (***978-0-385-73261-1(9)*** , Delacorte Bks. for Young Readers) Random Hse. Children's Bks.

Cooper, Melrose. Gettin' Through Thursday. 2000. (Illus.). 32p. (J). (ps-5). 6.95 (978-1-58430-014-4(0)) Lee & Low Bks., Inc.

—Gettin' Through Thursday. Bennett, Nneka, illus. 1999. 32p. (J). (ps-5). 15.95 (978-1-880000-67-0(9)) Lee & Low Bks., Inc.

—Gettin' Through Thursday. Bennett, Nneka, illus. 2000. (J). 13.75 (978-0-606-19831-8(3)) Tandem Library Bks.

Cosby, Bill. The Day I Saw My Father Cry. 2000. (Little Bill Books for Beginning Readers Ser.). (Illus.). (J). 10.79 (978-0-606-20470-5(9)) Tandem Library Bks.

—The Day I Was Rich. Honeywood, Varnette P., illus. 1999. (J). (ps-k). lib. bdg. 11.80 (978-0-613-16653-9(1)) Tandem Library Bks.

—Hooray for the Dandelion Warriors! Honeywood, Varnette P., illus. 1999. (Little Bill Books for Beginning Readers Ser.: No. 11). 40p. (J). (gr. 1-5). pap. 3.99 (978-0-590-52194-9(2) , Cartwheel Bks.) Scholastic, Inc.

—Money Troubles. Honeywood, Varnette P., illus. 1998. (Little Bill Books for Beginning Readers Ser.). 40p. (J). (gr. k-3). pap. 13.95 (978-0-590-16402-3(3)) Scholastic, Inc.

—Money Troubles. Honeywood, Varnette P., illus. 1998. (Little Bill Books for Beginning Readers Ser.). (J). (gr. k-3). (978-0-606-13615-0(0)) Tandem Library Bks.

—Money Troubles, Level. 3. Honeywood, Varnette P., illus. 1998. (Little Bill Books for Beginning Readers Ser.: No. 6). 40p. (J). (gr. k-3). pap. 3.99 (978-0-590-95623-9(X)) Scholastic, Inc.

—My Big Lie. Honeywood, Varnette P., illus. 1999. (Little Bill Books for Beginning Readers Ser.). 40p. (J). (gr. k-3). pap. 15.95 (978-0-590-52160-4(8)); (gr. 1-5). pap. 3.99 (978-0-590-52161-1(6)) Scholastic, Inc.

—My Big Lie. 1999. (gr. k-3). lib. bdg. 11.80 (978-0-613-16979-0(4)); (J). (978-0-606-16631-7(9)) Tandem Library Bks.

—One Dark & Scary Night. 1999. (Little Bill Books for Beginning Readers Ser.). (J). (gr. k-3). pap. 47.88 (978-0-439-04655-8(6) , Cartwheel Bks.) Scholastic, Inc.

—One Dark & Scary Night. 1999. (Little Bill Books for Beginning Readers Ser.). (J). (gr. k-3). (978-0-606-15831-2(6)) Tandem Library Bks.

—One Dark & Scary Night: Level. 3. Honeywood, Varnette P., illus. 1999. (Little Bill Books for Beginning Readers Ser.: No. 7). 40p. (J). (gr. k-3). pap. 3.99 (978-0-590-51476-7(8) , Cartwheel Bks.) Scholastic, Inc.

—Shipwreck Saturday. Honeywood, Varnette P., illus. 1998. (Little Bill Books for Beginning Readers Ser.). 40p. (J). (gr. k-3). pap. 13.95 (978-0-590-16400-9(7)); pap. 3.99 (978-0-590-95620-8(5)) Scholastic, Inc.

—The Worst Day of My Life. Honeywood, Varnette P., illus. 1999. (Little Bill Books for Beginning Readers Ser.: No. 10). 40p. (J). (gr. k-3). pap. 3.99 (978-0-590-52190-1(X) , Cartwheel Bks.) Scholastic, Inc.

Cosby, Bill & Honeywood, Varnette P. The Day I Saw My Father Cry. 2000. (Little Bill Books for Beginning Readers Ser.). (Illus.). 40p. (J). (gr. k-3). pap. 15.95 (978-0-590-52197-0(7)) Scholastic, Inc.

—One Dark & Scary Night. 1999. (Little Bill Books for Beginning Readers Ser.). (Illus.). (J). (gr. k-3). pap. 13.95 (978-0-590-51475-0(X)) Scholastic, Inc.

Cousain, Hattie M. When I Was Little. (J). 8.95 (978-0-9640459-0-3(7)) Cole's, C. Consultant & Pubns.

Cousin. My Teacher Helps Me. 2004. 8p. (gr. k-2). 20.95 (978-0-322-00311-8(3)) Wright Group, The.

Coy, John, et al. Directo Al Aro. Jean-Bart, Leslie, illus. 2002. (SPA & ENG.). (J). 16.95 (978-1-58430-082-3(5)); pap. 6.95 (978-1-58430-083-0(3)) Lee & Low Bks., Inc.

Crawford, Ann Fears. Keechee: The Witch of the Woods. 2005. (J). (978-1-931823-21-0(9)) Halcyon Pr.

Cross, Cecil, II. First Semester. 2007. 256p. pap. 9.99 (***978-0-373-83082-4(3)*** , Kimani) Harlequin Enterprises, Ltd. CAN. *Dist:* Simon & Schuster, Inc.

Crowe, Chris. The Mississippi Trial, 1955. 2003. 240p. (YA). pap. 5.99 (978-0-14-250192-4(1) , Puffin) Penguin Group (USA) Inc.

—The Mississippi Trial, 1955. 2003. (gr. 7-12). lib. bdg. 14.15 (978-0-613-86522-7(7)) Tandem Library Bks.

Crump, Fred, Jr. Brave Toy Soldier. 2006. (Illus.). 32p. (J). pap. 9.95 (978-1-932715-82-8(7)) UMI (Urban Ministries, Inc.).

Crutcher, Chris. Crazy Horse Electric Game. 2003. (gr. 7-12). lib. bdg. 15.30 (978-0-613-66954-2(1)) Tandem Library Bks.

Cummings, Pat. Angel Baby. 2000. (Illus.). 24p. (J). (gr. k-2). 15.89 (978-0-688-14822-5(0)) HarperCollins Pubs.

—Clean Your Room, Harvey Moon! Cummings, Pat, illus. 2002. (Illus.). (J). 14.47 (978-0-7587-2248-5(6)) Book Wholesalers, Inc.

—Clean Your Room, Harvey Moon! 1998. (J). pap. 4.95 (978-0-87628-335-6(0)) Ctr. for Applied Research in Education, The.

Curry, Kenneth. The Legend of the Dancing Trees: An African American Folk Tale. 2007. 111p. (J). per. 14.95 (***978-0-9798364-0-4(9)***) Curry Brothers Publishing.

Curry, Kenneth, et al. The Legend of the Dancing Tees Teachers Resource: The Legend of the Dancing Trees. 2007. Tr. of Teachers Resource. per. 19.95 (***978-0-9798364-1-1(7)***) Curry Brothers Publishing.

Curtis, Christopher. Bud Not Buddy. l.t. ed. 2003. 278p. pap. 10.95 (978-0-7862-6191-8(9)) Thorndike Pr.

Curtis, Christopher Paul. Bucking the Sarge. 2004. 272p. (YA). (gr. 7). lib. bdg. 17.99 (978-0-385-90159-8(3) , Lamb, Wendy) Random Hse. Children's Bks.

—Bucking the Sarge. l.t. ed. 2005. 325p. 23.95 (978-0-7862-7148-1(5) , Large Print Pr.) Thorndike Pr.

—Bud, Not Buddy. 2002. (Illus.). 14.47 (978-1-4046-1884-8(8)) Book Wholesalers, Inc.

—Bud, Not Buddy. 1999. (Illus.). 256p. (J). (gr. 4-7). 16.95 (978-0-385-32306-2(9) , Delacorte Bks. for Young Readers) Random Hse. Children's Bks.

—Bud, Not Buddy. 2002. (gr. 5-8). lib. bdg. 14.15 (978-0-613-36783-7(9)) Tandem Library Bks.

—Bud, Not Buddy. l.t. ed. 2000. (Illus.). 279p. (J). (gr. 8-12). 22.95 (978-0-7862-2574-3(2)) Thorndike Pr.

—Mr. Chickee's Funny Money. 2007. 160p. (gr. 4-7). 6.50 (978-0-440-22919-3(7) , Yearling) Random Hse. Children's Bks.

—Mr. Chickee's Funny Money. l.t. ed. 2006. 190p. 23.95 (978-0-7862-8670-6(9)) Thorndike Pr.

—Mr. Chickee's Messy Mission. 2008. 240p. (J). (gr. 4-7). 6.50 (***978-0-440-22922-3(7)*** , Yearling) Random Hse. Children's Bks.

Curtis, Christopher Paul. The Watsons Go to Birmingham - 1963. 2002. (Illus.). (J). 14.47 (978-0-7587-0328-6(7)) Book Wholesalers, Inc.

—The Watsons Go to Birmingham - 1963. 1998. 15p. pap., stu. ed., tchr.'s training gde. ed. 15.95 (978-1-58303-068-4(9)) Pathways Publishing.

—The Watsons Go to Birmingham - 1963. 210p. (YA). (gr. 5 up). pap. 5.50 (978-0-8072-8336-3(3)); 2004. (J). (gr. 4 up). pap. 38.00 incl. audio (978-0-8072-8335-6(5) , YA166SP) Random Hse. Audio Publishing Group. (Listening Library).

—The Watsons Go to Birmingham - 1963. 2000. 224p. (YA). (gr. 5-7). pap. 6.50 (978-0-440-22800-4(X) , Laurel Leaf) Random Hse. Children's Bks.

—The Watsons Go to Birmingham - 1963. 2000. (gr. 5-8). lib. bdg. 14.15 (978-0-613-85111-4(0)) Tandem Library Bks.

—The Watsons Go to Birmingham - 1963. l.t. ed. 2004. 254p. pap. 10.95 (978-0-7862-6406-3(3)) Thorndike Pr.

Curtis, Gavin. The Bat Boy & His Violin. Lewis, Earl, illus. (J). (ps-3). 2001. 32p. 7.99 (978-0-689-84115-6(9) , Aladdin); 1999. mass mkt. 6.99 (978-0-689-83012-9(2) , Aladdin); 1998. 32p. 16.95 (978-0-689-80099-3(1)) Simon & Schuster Children's Publishing.

—Bat Boy & His Violin. 2001. (gr. 3-6). lib. bdg. 15.30 (978-0-613-33669-7(0)) Tandem Library Bks.

Curtis, Matt. Six Empty Pockets. Newell, Mary J., illus. 1998. (Rookie Reader Skill Set Ser.). 32p. (J). (gr. k-2). pap. 4.95 (978-0-516-26253-6(X) , Children's Pr.) Scholastic Library Publishing.

—Six Empty Pockets. DePalma, Mary Newell, illus. 1998. 32p. (J). (gr. k-3). lib. bdg. 12.95 (978-0-613-37539-9(4)) Tandem Library Bks.

Dahlberg, Maurine F. The Story of Jonas. 2007. (Illus.). 160p. (J). (gr. 4-7). 16.00 (978-0-374-37264-4(0) , Farrar, Straus & Giroux (BYR)) Farrar, Straus & Giroux.

Davidson, Dana. Jason & Kyra. 2005. 352p. (gr. 7-17). pap. 5.99 (978-0-7868-3653-6(9) , Jump at the Sun) Hyperion Bks. for Children.

Davis, Ossie. Just Like Martin. (J). 2002. 176p. 15.99 (978-0-7868-0812-0(8)); 2001. pap. (978-0-7868-1642-2(2)) Hyperion Bks. for Children. (Jump at the Sun).

Davis, Tanita S. A la Carte. 2008. 288p. (J). (gr. 7). 15.99 (***978-0-375-84815-5(0)*** , Knopf Bks. for Young Readers) Random Hse. Children's Bks.

de Alcantara, Pedro. Befiddled. 2007. 192p. (J). (gr. 4-7). 5.99 (***978-0-440-42057-6(1)*** , Yearling) Random Hse. Children's Bks.

DeGross, Monalisa. Donavans Double Trouble. Bates, Amy, illus. 2008. 192p. (J). 15.99 (***978-0-06-077293-2(X))*** HarperCollins Pubs.

—Donavan's Double Trouble. Bates, Amy June, illus. 2008. 192p. (J). lib. bdg. 16.89 (***978-0-06-077294-9(8)*** , Amistad) HarperCollins Pubs.

Dell, Pamela. Shaky Bones: A Story of the Harlem Renaissance. 2003. (Scrapbooks of America Ser.). (Illus.). 48p. (J). (gr. 2-6). 28.50 (978-1-59187-040-1(2)) Child's World, Inc.

Dennis-Wyeth, Sharon. Something Beautiful. 2002. 32p. (J). (gr. 2-4). pap. 6.99 (978-0-440-41210-6(2) , Dragonfly Bks.) Random Hse. Children's Bks.

Derby, Sally. Mi Escalera. de la Vega, Eida, tr. Burrowes, Adjoa J., illus. 1998. (SPA & ENG.). 32p. (J). (ps-3). 15.95 (978-1-880000-74-8(1) , LW7547); pap. 6.95 (978-1-880000-75-5(X) , LW7771) Lee & Low Bks., Inc.

—My Steps. Burrowes, Adjoa J., illus. 1999. 32p. (J). (gr. 1-4). (978-1-880000-84-7(9)); (ps-4). 15.95 (978-1-880000-40-3(7)) Lee & Low Bks., Inc.

Deutsch, Stacia & Cohon, Rhody. Sacagawea's Strength. Wenzel, David, illus. 2006. (Blast to the Past Ser.). 128p. (J). pap. 3.99 (978-1-4169-1270-5(3) , Aladdin) Simon & Schuster Children's Publishing.

Devard, Nancy, et al, illus. I Told You I Can Play. 2006. (ENM.). 32p. (J). 16.95 (***978-1-933491-06-6(X))*** Just Us Bks., Inc.

Dike, Tina. His Greatest Challenge. Schulman, Cory & Johnstone, Sandy, eds. 2000. 125p. (YA). (gr. 7-9). pap. 9.95 (978-0-9642997-1-9(2)) Best Seller Pubns., Inc.

Dillon, Leo & Dillon, Diane. Rap a Tap Tap: Here's Bojangles - Think of That! 2005. (J). 25.95 incl. audio (978-1-59519-365-0(0)); 28.95 incl. audio compact disk (978-1-59519-369-8(3)) Live Oak Media.

—Rap a Tap Tap: Here's Bojangles - Think of That! Dillon, Leo & Dillon, Diane, illus. 2002. (Illus.). 32p. (J). pap. 15.95 (978-0-590-47883-0(4) , Blue Sky Pr., The) Scholastic, Inc.

Disney Press Staff, creator. The Cheetah Girls Quiz Book. 2005. 80p. (gr. 3-7). pap. 3.99 (978-0-7868-4718-1(2) , Jump at the Sun) Hyperion Bks. for Children.

Dougherty, Terri. Emily's Pictures. Rooney, Ronnie, illus. 2006. (Read-It! Readers Ser.). (J). 19.93 (978-1-4048-2409-6(X)) Picture Window Bks.

Doyle, Edwina Ann. The Bless Mark. 2006. (YA). pap. 14.95 (978-1-58736-674-1(6)) Wheatmark.

Draper, Sharon. Fire from the Rock. 2007. 240p. (YA). (gr. 7). 16.99 (***978-0-525-47720-4(9)*** , Dutton Juvenile) Penguin Group (USA) Inc.

Draper, Sharon M. The Backyard Animal Show. Watson, Jesse Joshua, illus. 2006. (Ziggy & the Black Dinosaurs Ser.). 128p. (J). pap. 4.99 (978-1-4169-0000-9(4) , Aladdin); lib. bdg. 11.89 (978-1-4169-2754-9(9) , Aladdin Library) Simon & Schuster Children's Publishing.

—The Buried Bones Mystery. Watson, Jesse Joshua, illus. 2006. (Ziggy & the Black Dinosaurs Ser.: Vol. 1). 112p. (J). pap. 4.99 (978-0-689-87910-4(5)) Simon & Schuster Children's Publishing.

—Copper Sun. 2008. 336p. (YA). pap. 8.99 (***978-1-4169-5348-7(5)*** , Simon Pulse) Simon & Schuster Children's Publishing.

—Copper Sun. l.t. ed. 2006. 358p. (YA). (gr. 8 up). 22.95 (978-0-7862-8948-6(1)) Thorndike Pr.

—Darkness Before Dawn. (Hazelwood High Trilogy: Bk. 3). (YA). (gr. 7 up). 2002. 288p. pap. 5.99 (978-0-689-85134-6(0) , Simon Pulse); 2001. 240p. 17.95 (978-0-689-83080-8(7) , Atheneum) Simon & Schuster Children's Publishing.

—Darkness Before Dawn. l.t. ed. 2006. 199p. pap. 10.95 (978-0-7862-8364-4(5)); 2005. 304p. (YA). (gr. 8-12). per. 22.95 (978-0-7862-7416-1(6) , Large Print Pr.) Thorndike Pr.

—Double Dutch. 2003. 192p. (J). pap. 5.99 (978-0-689-84231-3(7) , Aladdin) Simon & Schuster Children's Publishing.

—Double Dutch. Gabbidon, O'Lanso, illus. 2002. 192p. (J). (gr. 7 up). 16.99 (978-0-689-84230-6(9) , Atheneum) Simon & Schuster Children's Publishing.

—Forged by Fire. 2002. (Illus.). (J). 13.40 (978-0-7587-0354-5(6)) Book Wholesalers, Inc.

—Forged by Fire. l.t. ed. 2006. 199p. pap. 10.95 (978-0-7862-8358-3(0)) Thorndike Pr.

—Forged by Fire No. 2: Hazelwood High Trilogy. l.t. ed. 2005. 199p. 21.95 (978-0-7862-7417-8(4)) Thorndike Pr.

—Jazz Imagination: A Journal to Read & Write. 2000. 81p. (J). (gr. 3-7). pap. 12.95 (978-0-439-06130-8(X)) Scholastic, Inc.

—Jazzimagination: A Journal to Read & Write. 2002. 128p. (J). pap. 4.50 (978-0-439-26577-5(0)) Scholastic, Inc.

—November Blues. 2007. 320p. (YA). (gr. 7 up). 16.99 (***978-1-4169-0698-8(3)*** , Atheneum) Simon & Schuster Children's Publishing.

—Romiette & Julio. 2009. 320p. (YA). pap. 8.99 (***978-1-4169-5514-6(3)*** , Simon Pulse) Simon & Schuster Children's Publishing.

—Romiette & Julio. Lowenbein, Adam, illus. (YA). (gr. 7-12). 2001. 336p. mass mkt. 6.99 (978-0-689-84209-2(0) , Simon Pulse); 1999. 240p. 18.99 (978-0-689-82180-6(8) , Atheneum) Simon & Schuster Children's Publishing.

—Shadows of Caesar's Creek. Watson, Jesse Joshua, illus. 2006. (Ziggy & the Black Dinosaurs Ser.: No. 3). 128p. (J). pap. 4.99 (978-0-689-87913-5(X) , Aladdin) Simon & Schuster Children's Publishing.

—The Space Mission Adventure. Watson, Jesse Joshua, illus. 2006. (Ziggy & the Black Dinosaurs Ser.). 128p. (J). lib. bdg. 11.89 (978-1-4169-2458-6(2) , Aladdin Library); pap. 4.99 (978-0-689-87914-2(8) , Aladdin) Simon & Schuster Children's Publishing.

—Tears of a Tiger. l.t. ed. 219p. 2006. pap. 10.95 (978-0-7862-8361-3(0)); 2005. 20.95 (978-0-7862-7418-5(2) , Large Print Pr.) Thorndike Pr.

Dudley, David L. The Bicycle Man. 2005. 256p. (J). (gr. 5-9). 16.00 (978-0-618-54233-8(7) , Clarion Bks.) Houghton Mifflin Co. Trade & Reference Div.

Duey, Kathleen & Bale, Karen A. Flood: Mississippi 1927. 1998. (Survival! Ser.: No. 5). 176p. (J). (gr. 4-7). pap. 4.99 (978-0-689-82116-5(6) , Aladdin) Simon & Schuster Children's Publishing.

—Flood, Mississippi, 1927. 1998. (Survival! Ser.: No. 5). (J). (gr. 4-7). 10.64 (978-0-606-13829-1(3)) Tandem Library Bks.

Dugdale, John, concept. Jump at the Sun: An African American Picture Book Collection. 2001. (Illus.). 208p. (J). (ps-17). 16.99 (978-0-7868-0754-3(7) , Jump at the Sun) Hyperion Bks. for Children.

Dukes, LeRoy. The Chill Street Gang. 2005. (Illus.). 40p. (J). 6.99 (978-0-9664506-1-3(2)) Dukes World, Inc.

Dunbar, Paul Laurence. The Sport of the Gods. 1999. (gr. 7-12). lib. bdg. 14.10 (978-0-613-22425-3(6)) Tandem Library Bks.

Durham, David. Gabriel's Story. 2002. (gr. 7-12). lib. bdg. 22.25 (978-0-613-49406-9(7)) Tandem Library Bks.

Ehrhardt, Karen. This Jazz Man. Roth, Robert, illus. 2006. 32p. (J). (ps-2). 16.00 (978-0-15-205307-9(7)) Harcourt Trade Pubs.

Ellison, James W. Akeelah & the Bee. 2006. (Illus.). 192p. pap. 6.95 (978-1-55704-729-8(4)) Newmarket Pr.

Elster, Jean Alicia. I Have a Dream, Too! Tadgell, Nicole, illus. 2002. (Joe Joe in the City Ser.: No. 2). 32p. (gr. 1-5). 12.00 (978-0-8170-1397-4(0)) Judson Pr.

—I'll Do the Right Thing. Tadgell, Nicole, illus. 2003. (Joe Joe in the City Ser.). 32p. (gr. 1-5). 12.00 (978-0-8170-1408-7(X)) Judson Pr.

—I'll Fly My Own Plane. Tadgell, Nicole, illus. 2002. (Joe Joe in the City Ser.: 3). 32p. 12.00 (978-0-8170-1407-0(1)) Judson Pr.

—Just Call Me Joe Joe. Tadgell, Nicole, illus. 2001. (Joe Joe in the City Ser.). 32p. (gr. 1-5). 12.00 (978-0-8170-1398-1(9)) Judson Pr.

English, Karen. The Baby on the Way. Qualls, Sean, illus. 2005. 32p. (J). (ps-1). 16.00 (978-0-374-37361-0(2) , Farrar, Straus & Giroux (BYR)) Farrar, Straus & Giroux.

—Francie. 2002. (Illus.). (J). 25.45 (978-0-7587-0355-2(4)) Book Wholesalers, Inc.

—Francie. 2002. 208p. (J). pap. 5.95 (978-0-374-42459-6(4) , Sunburst) Farrar, Straus & Giroux.

—Francie. 2007. 224p. (J). pap. 6.99 (***978-0-312-37383-2(X))*** Square Fish.

—Francie. 2002. (gr. 5-8). lib. bdg. 14.10 (978-0-613-54223-4(1)) Tandem Library Bks.

—Francie. l.t. ed. 2002. 220p. (J). 21.95 (978-0-7862-3717-3(1)) Thomson Gale.

—Hot Day on Abbott Avenue. Steptoe, Javaka, illus. 2004. 32p. (J). (gr. k-3). 16.00 (978-0-395-98527-4(7) , Clarion Bks.) Houghton Mifflin Co. Trade & Reference Div.

—Just Right Stew. Rich, Anna, illus. 32p. (J). (gr. k-2). pap. 8.95 (978-1-59078-168-5(6)) Boyds Mills Pr.

—Just Right Stew. 2003. (Illus.). 32p. (J). (gr. k-4). 15.95 (978-1-56397-487-8(8)) Boyds Mills Pr.

—Neeny Coming, Neeny Going. 1998. (978-0-606-13656-3(8)) Tandem Library Bks.

Evans, Freddi Williams. A Bus of Our Own. Costello, Shawn, illus. 2001. 32p. (J). (gr. 1-5). pap. 6.95 (978-0-8075-0971-5(X)) Whitman, Albert & Co.

Evans, Mari. I'm Late: The Story of LeNeese & Moonlight & Alisha Who Didn't Have Anyone of Her Own. Honeywood, Varnette P., illus. 2006. 86p. (YA). (gr. 7 up). 14.95 (978-1-933491-00-4(0)) Just Us Bks., Inc.

Falwell, Cathryn. David's Drawings. 2001. (Illus.). 32p. (J). (ps-3). 16.00 (978-1-58430-031-1(0)) Lee & Low Bks., Inc.

—Los Dibujos de David. de la Vega, Eida, tr. Falwell, Cathryn, illus. 2005. (Illus.). 32p. (J). (ps-k). pap. 7.95 (978-1-58430-258-2(5)) Lee & Low Bks., Inc.

—Feast for 10. Falwell, Cathryn, illus. 2002. (Illus.). (J). 14.74 (978-0-7587-2485-4(3)) Book Wholesalers, Inc.

—Feast for 10. Falwell, Cathryn, illus. 2003. (Illus.). 28p. (J). (gr. k-ps). bds. 4.95 (978-0-618-38226-2(7) , Clarion Bks.) Houghton Mifflin Co. Trade & Reference Div.

Falwell, Cathryn, illus. & text. David's Drawings. Falwell, Cathryn, text. 2005. 32p. (J). (ps-ps). pap. 7.95 (978-1-58430-261-2(5)) Lee & Low Bks., Inc.

Fenner, Carol. Yolonda's Genius. Colon, Raul, illus. 2002. (J). 14.47 (978-0-7587-0333-0(3)) Book Wholesalers, Inc.

Ferguson, Dwayne. The Werewolf of PS 40, Vol. 2. 1998. (Kid Caramel: Vol. 2). 72p. (J). (gr. 4-7). pap. 4.50 (978-0-940975-82-8(3) , Sankofa Bks.) Just Us Bks., Inc.

Flake, Sharon G. Bang! 2005. 320p. (gr. 7-17). 16.99 (978-0-7868-1844-0(1) , Jump at the Sun) Hyperion Bks. for Children.

—The Broken Bike Boy & the Queen of 33rd Street. Bootman, Colin, illus. 2007. 144p. (gr. 3-7). 15.99 (***978-1-4231-0032-4(8)*** , Jump at the Sun) Hyperion Bks. for Children.

—Money Hungry. (J). 2003. 208p. (gr. 5-17). pap. 5.99 (978-0-7868-1503-6(5)); 2001. 192p. (gr. 3-7). 15.99 (978-0-7868-0548-8(X) , Jump at the Sun) Hyperion Bks. for Children.

—The Skin I'm In. 176p. (gr. 5-17). 2000. pap. 5.99 (978-0-7868-1307-0(5)); 1999. 14.95 (978-0-7868-0444-3(0)) Hyperion Pr.

—The Skin I'm In. 2000. 171p. (J). (gr. 5-9). lib. bdg. 13.94 (978-0-606-17605-7(5)) Tandem Library Bks.

—Skin I'm In. 2000. (gr. 5-8). lib. bdg. 14.15 (978-0-613-28643-5(X)) Tandem Library Bks.

—The Skin I'm In. l.t. ed. 1999. 173p. (J). (gr. 7-12). 20.95 (978-0-7862-2179-0(8)) Thorndike Pr.

Fleischner, Jennifer. Nobody's Boy. 2006. (Illus.). 96p. (J). pap. 12.95 (978-1-883982-58-4(8)) Missouri Historical Society Pr.

Flood, Pansie Hart. Secret Holes. Marshall, Felicia, illus. 2004. 128p. (J). (gr. 3-6). 15.95 (978-0-87614-923-2(9) , Carolrhoda Bks.) Lerner Publishing Group.

—Sometimey Friend. Marshall, Felicia, illus. 2005. 128p. (J). (gr. 4-6). 15.95 (978-1-57505-866-5(9)) Lerner Publishing Group.

—Sylvia & Miz Lula Maye. Marshall, Felicia, illus. 2003. (Middle Grade Fiction Ser.). 120p. (J). (gr. 3-6). 15.95 (978-0-87614-204-2(8) , Carolrhoda Bks.) Lerner Publishing Group.

Flossie & the Fox. 2004. (J). pap. 18.95 incl. audio compact disk (978-1-55592-772-1(6)); pap. 38.75 incl. audio compact disk (978-1-55592-787-5(4)); pap. 32.75 incl. audio (978-1-55592-224-5(4)); pap. 14.95 incl. audio (978-1-55592-051-7(9)) Weston Woods Studios, Inc.

Fogelin, Adrian. Crossing Jordan. Schultz, Suzy, illus. (J). 160p. pap. 6.95 (978-1-56145-281-1(5) , Q23381); 2000. 140p. (gr. 3-7). 14.95 (978-1-56145-215-6(7) , Q23381) Peachtree Pubs., Ltd.

—Crossing Jordan. 2002. (gr. 3-6). lib. bdg. 15.25 (978-0-613-54154-1(5)) Tandem Library Bks.

Ford, Bernette. Don't Hit Me! Grier, Gary, illus. 2004. 32p. (J). lib. bdg. 15.00 (***978-1-4242-0218-8(3))*** Fitzgerald Bks.

Ford, Bernette G. Hurry Up! Kindert, Jennifer C., illus. 2004. (Just for You! Ser.). 32p. pap. 3.99 (978-0-439-56849-4(8) , Teaching Resources) Scholastic, Inc.

Ford, Juwanda G. Shop Talk. Hoston, Jim, illus. 2004. 32p. (J). lib. bdg. 15.00 (***978-1-4242-0236-2(1))*** Fitzgerald Bks.

Foster, Cassandra. Do You Know Us? A Collection of Short Stories. 2006. (Illus.). 48p. (YA). per. 8.00 (978-0-9778641-1-9(1)) Smith, Mildred C.

—A Good Story: A Collection of Short Short Stories. 2006. (Illus.). 37p. (YA). per. 8.00 (978-0-9778641-0-2(3)) Smith, Mildred C.

Fox, Paula. How Many Miles to Babylon? 2005. 104p. (J). pap. (978-1-932425-39-0(X) , Lemniscaat) Boyds Mills Pr.

Frame, Jeron Ashford. Yesterday I Had the Blues. Christie, Gregory R., illus. 2004. 30p. (J). (gr. k-3). 14.95 (978-1-58246-084-0(1) , Tricycle Pr.) Ten Speed Pr.

Free & Sparks Taylor, Chandra. Spin It Like That. 2007. 256p. pap. 9.99 (***978-0-373-83080-0(7))*** Harlequin Enterprises, Ltd. CAN. *Dist:* Simon & Schuster, Inc.

Fuqua, Jonathan Scott. Darby. 2002. 256p. (J). (gr. 5 up). 16.99 (978-0-7636-1417-1(3)) Candlewick Pr.

Fuqua, Jonathon Scott. Darby. 2006. 256p. (J). (gr. 5). 5.99 (978-0-7636-2290-9(7)) Candlewick Pr.

—Reappearance of Sam Webber. 1999. (Illus.). 232p. (YA). pap. 23.95 (978-1-890862-03-9(7)) Bancroft Pr.

—The Reappearance of Sam Webber. 2001. (Illus.). 288p. (J). (gr. 5). reprint ed. pap. 9.99 (978-0-7636-1424-9(6)) Candlewick Pr.

Gaudissart, Martine. Kanyon & the Rainbow Stone. Gaudissart, Martine, illus. 2000. (Illus.). 64p. (J). (gr. k-3). 17.95 (978-0-9677547-0-3(4)) Angie Blue Bks., LLC.

Gayle, Sharon Shavers. Emma's Escape: A Story of America's Underground Railroad. Velasquez, Eric, illus. 3rd ed. 2005. (Soundprints' Read-and-Discover Ser.). 48p. (J). (gr. 2-4). pap. 3.95 (978-1-59249-021-9(2) , S2009) Soundprints.

—Escape! A Story of the Underground Railroad. Velasquez, Eric, illus. 1999. (Smithsonian Odyssey Ser.: Vol. 11). 32p. (J). (gr. 2-5). 14.95 (978-1-56899-622-6(5) , B6009); (ps-3). pap. 5.95 (978-1-56899-623-3(3)) Soundprints.

George, Olivia. The Bravest Girls in the World. DuBurke, Randy, illus. 2004. 32p. (J). lib. bdg. 15.00 (***978-1-4242-0241-6(8))*** Fitzgerald Bks.

Gershator, Phillis. Someday Cyril. Lucas, Cedric, illus. 2000. (MONDO Chapter Books). 46p. (J). (978-1-57255-748-2(6)) Mondo Publishing.

Gilchrist, Jan Spivey. Indigo & Moonlight Gold. 2000. (gr. k-3). lib. bdg. 15.25 (978-0-613-27899-7(2)) Tandem Library Bks.

Giovanni, Nikki. The Girls in the Circle. Johnson, Cathy Ann, illus. 2004. 32p. (J). lib. bdg. 15.00 (***978-1-4242-0232-4(9))*** Fitzgerald Bks.

Glasthal, Jacqueline B. Liberty on 23rd Street. Reingold, Alan, illus. 2006. (Adventures in America Ser.). (J). (978-1-893110-45-8(1)) Silver Moon Pr.

Goggles! 2004. (J). pap. 18.95 incl. audio compact disk (978-1-55592-417-1(4)); pap. 38.75 incl. audio compact disk (978-1-55592-418-8(2)); pap. 32.75 incl. audio (978-1-55592-232-0(5)); pap. 14.95 incl. audio (978-1-56008-084-8(1)) Weston Woods Studios, Inc.

Going, K. L. The Liberation of Gabriel King. 2007. 160p. (J). (gr. 3 up). pap. 6.99 (978-0-14-240766-0(6) , Puffin) Penguin Group (USA) Inc.

Gore, Elizabeth Griffin. Niara. Brown, Marietta, ed. 2000. 227p. (YA). (gr. 8 up). pap. (978-0-9701447-0-6(9)) Gore Pubns.

Gorman, Carol & Findley, Ron. The Stumptown Kid. 2005. 224p. (J). (gr. 3-7). 14.95 (978-1-56145-337-5(4)) Peachtree Pubs., Ltd.

Graham, Lorenz. Return to South Town. Graham, Lorenz, illus. 2003. (Illus.). 240p. (YA). (gr. 6-9). 16.95 (978-1-59078-164-7(3)) Boyds Mills Pr.

—South Town. Graham, Lorenz, illus. 2003. (Illus.). 188p. (YA). (gr. 6-9). 16.95 (978-1-59078-161-6(9)) Boyds Mills Pr.

Graham, Wendy. My Weird Mother. Burgemeestre, Kevin, illus. 1999. (Supa Doopers Ser.). 56p. (J). (978-0-7608-1921-0(1)) Sundance/Newbridge Educational Publishing.

Grant, Karima. Sofie & the City. Montecalvo, Janet, illus. 2006. 32p. (J). 15.95 (978-1-59078-273-6(9)) Boyds Mills Pr.

Grant, Larry. Hewie Goes to the Million Man March. Byers, Reggie, illus. 1998. 48p. (Orig.). (J). (gr. 1-5). pap. 8.95 (978-1-889851-05-1(1)) SolidGumboWorks.

Gray, Libba Moore. Dear Willie Rudd. 2000. (gr. k-3). lib. bdg. 15.30 (978-0-613-22980-7(0)) Tandem Library Bks.

—Miss Tizzy. Rowland, Jada, illus. 1998. 40p. (J). (ps-3). 6.99 (978-0-689-81897-4(1) , Aladdin) Simon & Schuster Children's Publishing.

—Miss Tizzy. 1998. (978-0-606-13611-2(8)) Tandem Library Bks.

Green, Debra. Maya Made Over. 2007. (Star Sisterz Ser.: Bk. 9). 144p. (J). (gr. 3-7). pap. 4.99 (978-0-7869-4162-9(6) , Mirrorstone) Wizards of the Coast.

Greenberg, Polly. Oh Lord, I Wish I Was a Buzzard. Aliki, illus. 2002. 32p. (J). (gr. k-3). 15.95 (978-1-58717-122-2(8) , SeaStar Bks.) Chronicle Bks. LLC.

Greene, Bette. I've Already Forgotten Your Name, Philip Hall! Jenkins, Leonard, illus. 2004. 176p. (J). (gr. 5 up). 15.99 (978-0-06-051835-6(9)) HarperCollins Pubs.

Greenfield, Eloise. Grandmama's Joy. 1999. (J). 12.79 (978-0-606-16847-2(8)) Tandem Library Bks.

—Me & Neesie. Gilchrist, Jan Spivey, illus. 2005. (Amistad Ser.). 32p. (J). (ps-3). lib. bdg. 16.89 (978-0-06-000702-7(8)); 15.99 (978-0-06-000701-0(X) , Amistad) HarperCollins Pubs.

—William & the Good Old Days. Date not set. (Illus.). 32p. (J). (gr. k-3). pap. 4.99 (978-0-06-443453-9(2)) HarperCollins Pubs.

Gregory, Deborah. The Cheetah Girls, No. 2, Bks. 5-8. 2003. 624p. (J). (gr. 3-7). pap. 9.99 (978-0-7868-1790-0(9)) Hyperion Bks. for Children.

—Cheetah Girls No.13: OOPS, Doggy Dog! 2002. (gr. 3-6). lib. bdg. 11.80 (978-0-613-91004-0(4)) Tandem Library Bks.

—Cheetah Girls Bind Up No.1, Bks. 1-4: Livin' Large! 2003. lib. bdg. 18.80 (978-0-613-75036-3(5)) Tandem Library Bks.

—Cheetah Girls Bind Up No.2: Supa Dupa Sparkle! Book 5-8. 2003. (gr. 3-6). lib. bdg. 18.80 (978-0-613-74957-2(X)) Tandem Library Bks.

—The Cheetah Girls Livin' Large, No. 1, Bks. 1-4. 2003. 576p. (J). (gr. 3-7). pap. 9.99 (978-0-7868-1789-4(5)) Hyperion Bks. for Children.

—Hey, Ho Hollywood! 1999. (gr. 3-6). lib. bdg. 11.80 (978-0-613-21701-9(2)) Tandem Library Bks.

—Off the Hook! 2005. 672p. (gr. 3-7). pap. 9.99 (978-0-7868-5654-1(8) , Jump at the Sun) Hyperion Bks. for Children.

—Oops, Doggy Dog! 2002. (Cheetah Girls Ser.: Bk. 13). 160p. (gr. 3-7). pap. 3.99 (978-0-7868-1484-8(5)) Hyperion Bks. for Children.

—Showdown at the Okie Dokie. 2000. (Cheetah Girls Ser.: Bk. 9). 160p. (J). (gr. 3-7). pap. 3.99 (978-0-7868-1475-6(6) , Jump at the Sun) Hyperion Bks. for Children.

—Showdown at the Okie Dokie. 2001. (gr. 3-6). lib. bdg. 11.80 (978-0-613-31700-9(9)) Tandem Library Bks.

—Who's 'Bout to Bounce, Baby. 1999. (gr. 3-6). lib. bdg. 11.80 (978-0-613-22631-8(3)) Tandem Library Bks.

—Who's Bout to Bounce, Baby? 3rd rev. ed. 1999. (Cheetah Girls Ser.: No. 3). 160p. (gr. 3-7). pap. 3.99 (978-0-7868-1386-5(5)) Hyperion Bks. for Children.

Grifalconi, Ann. Tiny's Hat. Grifalconi, Ann, illus. 1999. (Illus.). 32p. (J). (gr. k-3). 14.89 (978-0-06-027655-3(X)) HarperCollins Pubs.

Grimes, Nikki. Bronx Masquerade. 2003. 176p. (YA). (gr. 6-11). pap. 5.99 (978-0-14-250189-4(1) , Puffin) Penguin Group (USA) Inc.

—Bronx Masquerade. Myers, Chris, illus. 2001. 176p. (J). (gr. 7 up). 16.99 (978-0-8037-2569-0(8) , Dial) Penguin Group (USA) Inc.

—Bronx Masquerade. 2003. (gr. 7-12). lib. bdg. 14.15 (978-0-613-81701-1(X)) Tandem Library Bks.

—Danitra Brown, Class Clown. Lewis, Earl, illus. 2005. 32p. (J). 16.99 (978-0-688-17290-9(3)); lib. bdg. 16.89 (978-0-688-17291-6(1)) HarperCollins Pubs.

—Dark Sons. 2005. 224p. (gr. 7-17). 15.99 (978-0-7868-1888-4(3)) Hyperion Bks. for Children.

—Jazmin's Notebook. 2002. (Illus.). (J). 12.34 (978-0-7587-0368-2(6)) Book Wholesalers, Inc.

—Jazmin's Notebook. 112p. (J). 1998. (gr. 8-12). 15.99 (978-0-8037-2224-8(9) , Dial); 2000. (gr. 5-9). reprint ed. pap. 5.99 (978-0-14-130702-2(1) , Puffin) Penguin Group (USA) Inc.

—Jazmin's Notebook. 2000. (gr. 7-12). lib. bdg. 14.15 (978-0-613-23623-2(8)); (Illus.). (J). 12.64 (978-0-606-18414-4(7)) Tandem Library Bks.

—The Road to Paris. 2008. 160p. (J). (gr. 3). 6.99 (***978-0-14-241082-0(9)*** , Puffin) Penguin Group (USA) Inc.

—When Gorilla Goes Walking. Evans, Shane, illus. 2007. 32p. (J). (ps-3). pap. 16.99 (978-0-439-31770-2(3) , Orchard Bks.) Scholastic, Inc.

—Wild, Wild Hair. Ford, George, illus. 2002. (J). 11.91 (978-0-7587-1855-6(1)) Book Wholesalers, Inc.

Grove, Vicki. The Starplace. 2000. (Illus.). 224p. (J). (gr. 5-9). pap. 6.99 (978-0-698-11868-3(5) , Putnam Juvenile) Penguin Group (USA) Inc.

—The Starplace. 2000. (978-0-606-20373-9(7)); (J). (978-0-606-20257-2(9)) Tandem Library Bks.

—Starplace. 2000. (gr. 5-8). lib. bdg. 14.15 (978-0-613-30759-8(3)) Tandem Library Bks.

Guilford, Jd. The Edification of Sonya Crane. 2007. 256p. pap. 9.99 (***978-0-373-83077-0(7)***) Harlequin Enterprises, Ltd. CAN. *Dist:* Simon & Schuster, Inc.

Gutman, Dan. Jackie & Me. 2005. (Baseball Card Adventures Ser.). (Illus.). 145p. (YA). (gr. 4-8). reprint ed. 20.00 (978-0-7567-9569-6(9)) DIANE Publishing Co.

—Jackie & Me. (Baseball Card Adventures Ser.). 160p. (J). 2000. (gr. 3-7). pap. 5.99 (978-0-380-80084-1(5)); 1999. (Illus.). (gr. 4-7). 16.99 (978-0-380-97685-0(4)) HarperCollins Pubs.

—Jackie & Me. 2000. (Baseball Card Adventures Ser.). (gr. 5-8). lib. bdg. 14.15 (978-0-613-27912-3(3)); (Illus.). (J). 12.64 (978-0-606-17974-4(7)) Tandem Library Bks.

—Satch & Me. 2006. (Baseball Card Adventures Ser.). (Illus.). 192p. (J). 15.99 (978-0-06-059491-6(8)); lib. bdg. 16.89 (978-0-06-059492-3(6)) HarperCollins Pubs.

Hahn, Mary Downing. Promises to the Dead. 2000. 208p. (J). (gr. 5-9). tchr. ed. 15.00 (978-0-395-96394-4(X) , Clarion Bks.) Houghton Mifflin Co. Trade & Reference Div.

Haislip, Phyllis Hall. Lottie's Courage: A Contraband Slave's Story. 2003. (Illus.). 120p. (J). pap. 7.95 (978-1-57249-311-7(9) , White Mane Kids) White Mane Publishing Co., Inc.

Half Baked Sistas-in the Beginning. 2004. 242p. (YA). lib. bdg. 12.99 (978-0-9761819-0-3(8) , 002) Smart Publishing.

Halperin, Michael. Black Wheels. 2003. (gr. 7-12). lib. bdg. 31.55 (978-0-613-77954-8(1)) Tandem Library Bks.

Hamilton, Patricia Birdsong. Why do you Walk Funny? l.t. ed. 2006. (Ataxia: A Lifestyle Change). 38p. (J). 16.95 (978-1-889826-91-2(X)) Scripts Publishing.

Hamilton, Virginia. Bluish. Dillon, Leo & Dillon, Diane, illus. 1999. 128p. (J). (gr. 4-9). pap. 16.95 (978-0-590-28879-8(2) , Blue Sky Pr., The) Scholastic, Inc.

—Bluish. 2002. (gr. 5-8). lib. bdg. 13.00 (978-0-613-53797-1(1)) Tandem Library Bks.

—Dustland. 1998. (Justice Cycle Ser.: Bk. 2). 214p. (YA). (gr. 6-12). pap. 4.50 (978-0-590-36217-7(8)) Scholastic, Inc.

—Dustland. 1998. (Justice Cycle Ser.). (978-0-606-12927-5(8)) Tandem Library Bks.

—The Gathering. 1998. (Justice Cycle Ser.: Bk. 3). 214p. (J). (gr. 6-12). mass mkt. 4.50 (978-0-590-36216-0(X)) Scholastic, Inc.

—The Gathering. 1998. (Justice Cycle Ser.). (978-0-606-13414-9(X)) Tandem Library Bks.

—The House of Dies Drear. 1998. 32p. (J). 9.95 (978-1-56137-516-5(0) , NU5168) Novel Units, Inc.

—The House of Dies Drear. 2001. (Assessment Packs Ser.). 15p. pap. 15.95 (978-1-58303-122-3(7)) Pathways Publishing.

—The House of Dies Drear. 8.97 (978-0-13-437491-8(6)) Prentice Hall PTR.

—The House of Dies Drear. 2006. 256p. (J). pap. 5.99 (978-1-4169-1405-1(6) , Aladdin) Simon & Schuster Children's Publishing.

—M. C. Higgins, the Great. 1998. (J). pap. 4.50 (978-0-87628-568-8(X)) Ctr. for Applied Research in Education, The.

—M. C. Higgins, the Great. (J). pap., stu. ed. (978-0-13-620246-2(2)); 3rd ed. pap. 23.70 (978-0-13-620220-2(9)); 3rd ed. pap. 3.95 (978-0-13-800137-7(5)) Prentice Hall (Schl. Div.).

—M. C. Higgins, the Great. 2006. (Illus.). 288p. (J). pap. 5.99 (978-1-4169-1407-5(2) , Aladdin) Simon & Schuster Children's Publishing.

—M. C. Higgins, the Great. Palencar, John J., illus. 25th anniv. ed. 1999. 240p. (J). (gr. 7). 19.99 (978-0-689-83074-7(2)) Simon & Schuster Children's Publishing.

—The Magical Adventures of Pretty Pearl. 1999. (J). (gr. 5 up). 21.50 (978-0-8446-6998-4(9)) Smith, Peter Pub., Inc.

—The People Could Fly Picture. Dillon, Leo & Dillon, Diane, illus. 2007. 32p. (J). 17.99 incl. audio compact disk (***978-0-375-84553-6(4)*** , Knopf Bks. for Young Readers) Random Hse. Children's Bks.

—Plain City. (Barco de Vapor). (SPA.). 176p. (YA). (gr. 5-8). 6.95 (978-84-348-4686-9(1) , LEC6861) SM Ediciones ESP. *Dist:* Continental Bk. Co., Inc.

—Plain City. 2003. 208p. (J). (gr. 4-7). pap. 5.99 (978-0-590-47365-1(4) , Scholastic Paperbacks) Scholastic, Inc.

—The Planet of Junior Brown. 1998. (J). pap. 4.50 (978-0-87628-347-9(4)) Ctr. for Applied Research in Education, The.

—The Planet of Junior Brown. 2006. (Illus.). 224p. (J). pap. 5.99 (978-1-4169-1410-5(2) , Aladdin) Simon & Schuster Children's Publishing.

—Second Cousins. 2000. (gr. 5-8). lib. bdg. 13.00 (978-0-613-29054-8(2)) Tandem Library Bks.

—Sweet Whispers, Brother Rush. 1999. (J). (gr. 4-7). pap. 12.25 (978-0-88103-610-7(2)) Tandem Library Bks.

—A White Romance. 1998. (Point Signature Ser.). 450p. (YA). (gr. 8-12). pap. 4.50 (978-0-590-13005-9(6)) Scholastic, Inc.

—Zeely. 1998. (C). pap. 3.95 (978-0-87628-345-5(8)) Simon & Schuster.

—Zeely. Shimin, Symeon, illus. 2006. 128p. (J). pap. 4.99 (978-1-4169 1413-6(7) , Aladdin) Simon & Schuster Children's Publishing.

—Zeely. 2005. (Illus.). 128p. (J). (gr. 2-6). 21.75 (978-0-8446-7277-9(7) , 3592) Smith, Peter Pub., Inc.

Hansen, Joyce. The Gift-Giver. 2005. 128p. (J). (gr. 5-9). pap. 6.95 (978-0-618-61123-2(1) , Clarion Bks.) Houghton Mifflin Co. Trade & Reference Div.

—The Heart Calls Home. 1999. viii, 175p. (J). (gr. 7-12). 16.95 (978-0-8027-8636-4(7)) Walker & Co.

—One True Friend. 2005. 160p. (J). (gr. 5-9). pap. 6.95 (978-0-618-60991-8(1) , Clarion Bks.) Houghton Mifflin Co. Trade & Reference Div.

—Yellow Bird & Me. 2005. 168p. (J). (gr. 5-9). pap. 6.95 (978-0-618-61116-4(9) , Clarion Bks.) Houghton Mifflin Co. Trade & Reference Div.

Harcourt School Publishers Staff. Bill Pickett Advanced Level. 3rd ed. 2002. (Trophies Reading Program Ser.). (Illus.). pap. 5.10 (978-0-15-323124-7(6)) Harcourt Schl. Pubs.

—With Love, J On Leve: Letters from the Past. 3rd ed. 2002. (Trophies Reading Program Ser.). (Illus.). pap. 5.10 (978-0-15-323370-8(2)) Harcourt Schl. Pubs.

Harper, Donna A., ed. The Later Simple Stories, Vol. 8. 2005. (Collected Works of Langston Hughes: Vol. 8). (Illus.). 384p. 34.95 (978-0-8262-1409-6(6)) Univ. of Missouri Pr.

Harrington, Janice N. & Lagarrigue, Jerome. Going North. 2004. (Illus.). 40p. (J). 16.00 (978-0-374-32681-4(9) , Farrar, Straus & Giroux (BYR)) Farrar, Straus & Giroux.

Harris, Joel Chandle. Told by Uncle Remus: New Stories of the. 2006. (Illus.). pap. 31.95 (***978-1-4254-9964-8(3)***) Kessinger Publishing, LLC.

Harris, Joel Chandler. Uncle Remus His Songs & His Sayings. 2006. (Illus.). (YA). cd-rom (978-1-892824-57-8(4)) AFCHRON.

Harrison, Emma. The Cheetah Girls Supa-Star Scrapbook. 2005. (Illus.). 48p. (J). (gr. 3-7). pap. 6.99 (978-0-7868-4717-4(4)) Disney Pr.

Harrison, Marie Joseph. Mosanna & Me. 2003. 160p. pap. 12.95 (978-0-916251-62-8(4)) Sunbelt Pubns., Inc.

—Mosanna & Me. 2003. (gr. 7-12). lib. bdg. 22.20 (978-0-613-89684-9(X)) Tandem Library Bks.

Hart, Alison. Gabriel's Horses. 2007. 224p. (J). (gr. 3-7). 14.95 (***978-1-56145-398-6(6)*** , Peachtree Junior) Peachtree Pubs., Ltd.

—Gabriel's Triumph. 2007. 160p. (J). (gr. 3-7). 14.95 (***978-1-56145-410-5(9)*** , Peachtree Junior) Peachtree Pubs., Ltd.

Haskins, James. The March on Washington. 2004. (Illus.). 192p. (J). (gr. 5 up). pap. 10.95 (978-0-940975-93-4(9) , Sankofa Bks.) Just Us Bks., Inc.

Hathaway, Barbara. Missy Violet & Me. 112p. (J). (gr. 3-5). 2008. pap. 6.95 (***978-0-618-80919-6(8)***); 2004. tchr. ed. 15.00 (978-0-618-37163-1(X)) Houghton Mifflin Co. Trade & Reference Div.

Haugaard, Kay. The Day the Dragon Danced. Barritt, Carolyn Reed, illus. 2006. (J). (gr. 2-4). 16.95 (978-1-885008-30-5(9)) Shen's Bks.

Havill, Juanita. Jamaica's Blue Marker. O'Brien, Anne Sibley, illus. 2003. 32p. (J). (gr. k-3). pap. 6.95 (978-0-618-36917-1(1)) Houghton Mifflin Co. Trade & Reference Div.

Hayden. A Matter of Attitude. 2008. 256p. pap. 9.99 (***978-0-373-83089-3(0)***) Harlequin Enterprises, Ltd. CAN. *Dist:* Simon & Schuster, Inc.

Hayes, Sonia. Ms. Thang. 2006. (ENG.). 192p. (YA). per. 9.95 (978-0-9777573-0-5(7)) NUA Multimedia.

Hayes, Sonia. Urban Goddess. 2007. 224p. (YA). per. 9.95 (***978-0-9777573-1-2(5)***) NUA Multimedia.

Haynes, Henry L. If I Grow Up. 1999. (Illus.). 150p. pap. 10.95 (978-1-58521-004-6(8)) Books for Black Children, Inc.

Heath, Lorraine. Avon True Romance: An Amelia & the Outlaw. 2003. (gr. 7-12). lib. bdg. 13.00 (978-0-613-71381-8(8)) Tandem Library Bks.

Hedstrom-Page, Deborah. From Slavery to Freedom with Harriet Tubman. Martinez, Sergio, illus. 2007. 80p. (J). (gr. 3-8). 9.99 (978-0-8054-3268-8(X)) B&H Publishing Grp.

Hegamin, Tonya. Most Loved in All the World. Cohen, Lisa, illus. 2010. (J). (978-0-618-41903-6(9)) Houghton Mifflin Co.

Helmso, Candy G. Saltar la Escoba. Romo, Alberto, tr. Friar, Joanne, illus. 1998. (Books for Young Learners).Tr. of Jump the Broom. (SPA.). 16p. (J). (gr. k-2). pap. 5.00 (978-1-57274-202-4(X) , A2900) Owen, Richard C. Pubs., Inc.

Helmso, Candy Grant. Cakewalk. Taylor, Stephen, illus. 2003. (Books for Young Learners). 16p. (J). pap. 5.00 net. (978-1-57274-250-5(X) , 2727) Owen, Richard C. Pubs., Inc.

Henderson, Alicia Terry, 1st. Call Me Black Call Me Beautiful, 1. Kindert, Jennifer, illus. 2002. 28p. (J). (gr. k-3). lib. bdg. 9.95 (978-0-9719490-1-0(8)) Royal Regal Bks.

Herron, Carolivia. Nappy Hair. 1998. (Dragonfly Books Ser.). (Illus.). 32p. (J). (gr. k-3). pap. 6.99 (978-0-679-89445-2(4) , Dragonfly Bks.) Random Hse. Children's Bks.

—Nappy Hair. 1999. (J). (978-0-606-16082-7(5)) Tandem Library Bks.

Hesse, Karen. Come on, Rain! 2004. (J). 24.95 incl. audio (978-1-55592-177-4(9)); 29.95 incl. cd-rom (978-1-55592-500-0(6)) Weston Woods Studios, Inc.

Hest, Amy. Jamaica Louise James. (gr. k-3). lib. bdg. 14.15 (978-0-613-70961-3(6)) Tandem Library Bks.

—Mr. George Baker. Muth, Jon J., illus. 2004. 32p. (J). (gr. k-3). 16.99 (978-0-7636-1233-7(2)) Candlewick Pr.

—Mr. George Baker. Muth, Jon J., illus. 2007. 32p. (J). (gr. k-3). pap. 6.99 (978-0-7636-3308-0(9)) Candlewick Pr.

Hester, Denia Lewis. Grandma Lena's Big Ol' Turnip. Urbanovic, Jackie, illus. 2005. 32p. (J). (ps-3). 16.95 (978-0-8075-3027-6(1)) Whitman, Albert & Co.

Hewett, Lorri. Dancer: Everybody Has a Dream. 2001. 224p. (YA). (gr. 8-12). pap. 5.99 (978-0-14-131085-5(5) , Puffin) Penguin Group (USA) Inc.

—Lives of Our Own. 2000. (J). (978-0-606-19695-6(1)) Tandem Library Bks.

Hicks, Benjamin & Hicks, Rosetta. Byron's Tie. Hicks, Benjamin, ed. 2006. 35p. pap. 8.95 (978-1-929883-08-0(0)) Ingleside Pr.

Hill, Clarissa. God Deserves Your Best. Hill, Stephanie, illus. 2005. (ENG.). 20p. (J). pap. 11.00 (***978-0-9785539-0-6(X)***) Hill, Stephanie & Clarissa.

Hill, Pamela Smith. A Voice from the Border. 2000. (J). (978-0-606-20004-2(5)) Tandem Library Bks.

Hines, Thomas, illus. The Bubble Machine. l.t. ed. 2003. 26p. (J). per. (978-1-887636-02-5(1)) Creative Writing & Publishing Co.

Hoffman, Mary. Amazing Grace. (Illus.). 32p. (J). (ARA & ENG.). (978-1-85430-334-9(1) , 93433); (ENG & VIE., (978-1-85430-340-0(6) , 93435) Magi Pubns.

—Amazing Grace. Binch, Caroline, illus. 1998. (ENG & TUR.). 32p. (J). (ps-3). (978-1-85430-338-7(4)) Magi Pubns.

—Amazing Grace. 1999. (YA). pap. 32.99 incl. audio (978-0-7887-4097-8(0) , 41103) Recorded Bks., LLC.

—Boundless Grace. Binch, Caroline, illus. 2002. (J). 25.45 (978-0-7587-2139-6(0)) Book Wholesalers, Inc.

—Boundless Grace. Binch, Caroline, illus. 2000. 32p. (J). (ps-3). pap. 6.99 (978-0-14-055667-4(2) , Puffin) Penguin Group (USA) Inc.

—Boundless Grace. Binch, Caroline, illus. 2000. (J). (ps-ps). 26p. 12.79 (978-0-606-20350-0(8)); lib. bdg. 14.15 (978-0-613-33678-9(X)) Tandem Library Bks.

—Boundless Grace. 2000. (J). (978-0-606-20224-4(2)) Tandem Library Bks.

—Princess Grace. Van Wright, Cornelius & Hu, Ying-Hwa, illus. 2008. 32p. (J). (ps). 16.99 (***978-0-8037-3260-5(0)*** , Dial) Penguin Group (USA) Inc.

Hoffman, Mary. Starring Grace. Binch, Caroline, illus. (Chapters Ser.). 96p. (J). 2001. (gr. 2-6). pap. 4.99 (978-0-14-230022-0(5) , Puffin); 2000. (gr. k-4). 14.99 (978-0-8037-2559-1(0) , Dial) Penguin Group (USA) Inc.

—Starring Grace. 2001. (gr. 3-6). lib. bdg. 13.00 (978-0-613-44418-7(3)) Tandem Library Bks.

Hoffman, Mary & Youngblood, Shay. Amazing Grace. 1998. 44p. pap. 6.25 (978-0-87129-809-6(0) , A64) Dramatic Publishing Co.

Holman, John. Luminous Mysteries. 2000. (gr. 7-12). lib. bdg. 21.10 (978-0-613-21942-6(2)) Tandem Library Bks.

Holman, Sandy Lynne. Grandpa, Is Everything Black Bad? Holman, Sandy Lynne, ed. Kometiani, Lela, illus. 1998. 32p. (J). (gr. 2-6). lib. bdg. 18.95 (978-0-9644655-0-3(7)) Culture C.O.-O.P., The.

Holt, Kimberly Willis. Mister & Me. 2000. (gr. 3-6). lib. bdg. 13.00 (978-0-613-33713-7(1)) Tandem Library Bks.

Holt, Rinehart and Winston Staff. Slave Dancer. 3rd ed. 2003. (Illus.). 16.75 (978-0-03-035274-4(6)) Holt, Rinehart & Winston

Honeywood, Varnette P., illus. The Best Way to Play. 2002. (Little Bill Ser.). (J). 11.91 (978-0-7587-0983-7(8)) Book Wholesalers, Inc.

—The Day I Saw My Father Cry. 2002. (Little Bill Ser.). (J). 11.91 (978-0-7587-1093-2(3)) Book Wholesalers, Inc.

—The Day I Was Rich. 2002. (Little Bill Ser.). (J). 11.91 (978-0-7587-1094-9(1)) Book Wholesalers, Inc.

—Hooray for the Dandelion Warriors! 2002. (Little Bill Ser.). (J). 11.91 (978-0-7587-1286-8(3)) Book Wholesalers, Inc.

—Money Troubles. 2002. (Little Bill Ser.). (J). 11.91 (978-0-7587-1452-7(1)) Book Wholesalers, Inc.

—One Dark & Scary Night. 2002. (Little Bill Ser.). (J). 11.91 (978-0-7587-1525-8(0)) Book Wholesalers, Inc.

Hoobler, Dorothy & Hoobler, Thomas. The 1920s: Luck. Hoffman, Robin, illus. 2000. (Century Kids Ser.). 160p. (J). (gr. 5-8). lib. bdg. 22.90 (978-0-7613-1602-2(7) , Twenty-First Century Bks.) Lerner Publishing Group.

—The 1950's: Music. Hoffman, Robin, illus. 2001. (Century Kids Ser.). 160p. (J). (gr. 5-8). lib. bdg. 22.90 (978-0-7613-1605-3(1) , Twenty-First Century Bks.) Lerner Publishing Group.

—The 1960's: Rebels. Hoffman, Robin, illus. 2001. (Century Kids Ser.). 160p. (J). (gr. 5-8). lib. bdg. 22.90 (978-0-7613-1606-0(X) , Twenty-First Century Bks.) Lerner Publishing Group.

Hood, Susan. Look! I Can Read! Wummer, Amy, illus. 2000. (All Aboard Reading Ser.). 32p. (J). (ps-3). mass mkt. 3.99 (978-0-448-41967-1(X) , Grosset & Dunlap) Penguin Group (USA) Inc.

—Look! I Can Read! 2000. (gr. k-3). lib. bdg. 11.80 (978-0-613-26053-4(8)); field. (Illus.). (J). (978-0-606-18470-0(8)) Tandem Library Bks.

hooks, bell. Be Boy Buzz. Raschka, Chris, tr. Raschka, Chris, illus. 2002. (J). 17.49 (978-0-7868-2633-9(9)) Hyperion Bks. for Children.

—Be Boy Buzz. Raschka, Chris, tr. Raschka, Chris, illus. 2005. 32p. (ps-3). pap. 6.99 (978-0-7868-1643-9(0)) Hyperion Bks. for Children.

—Homemade Love. Evans, Shane W., illus. 2003. 32p. (ps-3). 16.99 (978-0-7868-0643-0(5)) Hyperion Bks. for Children.

Hooks, Gwendolyn. Three's a Crowd. Walker, Sylvia, illus. 2004. 32p. (J). lib. bdg. 15.00 (***978-1-4242-0240-9(X)***) Fitzgerald Bks.

Hopkinson, Deborah. A Band of Angels: A Story Inspired by the Jubilee Singers. Colon, Raul, illus. 1999. (Anne Schwartz Bks.). 40p. (J). (gr. 1-4). 16.95 (978-0-689-81062-6(8) , Atheneum/Anne Schwartz Bks.) Simon & Schuster Children's Publishing.

—Band of Angels: A Story Inspired by the Jubilee Singers. 2002. (gr. k-3). lib. bdg. 15.30 (978-0-613-90188-8(6)) Tandem Library Bks.

—From Slave to Soldier: Based on a True Civil War Story. Floca, Brian, illus. (Ready-to-Reads Ser.). 48p. (J). 2007. pap. 3.99 (978-0-689-83966-5(9) , Aladdin); 2005. 14.95 (978-0-689-83965-8(0) , Atheneum) Simon & Schuster Children's Publishing.

—Under the Quilt of Night. Ransome, James E., illus. 40p. (J). 2002. 18.99 (978-0-689-82227-8(8) , Atheneum/Anne Schwartz Bks.); 2005. reprint ed. 7.99 (978-0-689-87700-1(5) , Aladdin) Simon & Schuster Children's Publishing.

Houston, Gloria M. Bright Freedom's Song: A Story of the Underground Railroad. 1998. (Illus.). 160p. (YA). (gr. 5 up). 17.00 (978-0-15-201812-2(3) , Silver Whistle) Harcourt Trade Pubs.

Houston, Julian. New Boy. 288p. (J). (gr. 7). 2008. pap. 7.99 (***978-0-618-88405-6(X)***); 2005. 16.00 (978-0-618-43253-0(1)) Houghton Mifflin Co. Trade & Reference Div.

Howard, Annabelle. Keelboat Annie: An AMER Tall Tale. 2006. 42.00 (***978-1-4108-6169-6(4)***) Benchmark Education Co.

Howard, Elizabeth Fitzgerald. Aunt Flossie's Hats (and Crab Cakes Later) Ransome, James E., illus. 10th anniv. ed. 2001. 40p. (J). (gr. k-3). tchr. ed. 16.00 (978-0-618-12038-3(6) , Clarion Bks.) Houghton Mifflin Co. Trade & Reference Div.

—The Train to Lulu's. 1998. (J). pap. 4.95 (978-0-87628-336-3(9)) Simon & Schuster.

—Virgie Goes to School with Us Boys. Lewis, Earl, illus. 2002. (J). 25.11 (978-0-7587-3907-0(9)) Book Wholesalers, Inc.

—Virgie Goes to School with Us Boys. Lewis, E. B., illus. 2005. 32p. (J). reprint ed. pap. 6.99 (978-0-689-87793-3(5) , Aladdin) Simon & Schuster Children's Publishing.

—What's in Aunt Mary's Room? Lucas, Cedric, illus. 2002. 32p. (J). (gr. k-3). pap. 5.95 (978-0-618-24621-2(5) , Clarion Bks.) Houghton Mifflin Co. Trade & Reference Div.

—What's in Aunt Mary's Room? 2002. (gr. k-3). lib. bdg. 14.10 (978-0-613-72911-6(0)) Tandem Library Bks.

—When Will Sarah Come. Crews, Nina, photos by. 1999. (Illus.). 24p. (J). (ps-3). 16.00 (978-0-688-16180-4(4)); 15.89 (978-0-688-16181-1(2)) HarperCollins Pubs.

Howard, Elizabeth Fitzgerald & Lewis, Earl. Virgie Goes to School with Us Boys. 2000. (Illus.). 32p. (J). (gr. k-3). 17.99 (978-0-689-80076-4(2)) Simon & Schuster Children's Publishing.

Hubbell, Patricia. Black All Around! Tate, Don, illus. 2003. 32p. (J). 16.95 (978-1-58430-048-9(5)) Lee & Low Bks., Inc.

Hubler, Marsha. Teamwork at Camp Tioga. 2005. (Keystone Stables Ser.). (Illus.). 128p. (J). pap. 4.99 (978-0-310-70575-8(4)) Zonderkidz.

—Trouble Times Two. 2005. (Keystone Stables Ser.). (Illus.). 128p. (J). pap. 4.99 (978-0-310-70574-1(6)) Zondervan.

Hudson, Cheryl Willis. What Do You Know? Snow! Walker, Sylvia, illus. 2004. 32p. (J). (ps-ps). lib. bdg. 10.79 (978-0-606-30031-5(7)) Tandem Library Bks.

Hudson, Cheryl Willis. What Do You Know? SNOW! Walker, Sylvia, illus. 2004. 32p. (J). lib. bdg. 15.00 (***978-1-4242-0233-1(7)***) Fitzgerald Bks.

Hudson, Wade. The Two Tyrones. Page, Mark, illus. 2004. 32p. (J). lib. bdg. 15.00 (***978-1-4242-0239-3(6)***) Fitzgerald Bks.

—The Two Tyrones. Page, Mark, illus. 2004. 32p. (J). (gr. 2). lib. bdg. 11.19 (978-0-606-33361-0(4)) Tandem Library Bks.

Hughes, Langston. Simple Speaks His Mind. (J). (gr. 5-6). reprint ed. lib. bdg. 22.95 (978-0-88411-061-3(3)) Amereon LTD.

Hurston, Zora Neale. The Six Fools. Tanksley, Ann, illus. 2006. 40p. (J). 15.99 (978-0-06-000646-4(3)) HarperCollins Pubs.

Hurston, Zora Neale & Thomas, Joyce Carol. The Six Fools. Tanksley, Ann, illus. 2006. 40p. (J). lib. bdg. 16.89 (978-0-06-000647-1(1)) HarperCollins Pubs.

I Like Me. 2004. (J). per. (978-1-57657-395-2(8)) Paradise Pr., Inc.

I Like Me. 2004. 8p. (gr. k-2). 20.95 (978-0-322-00630-0(9)) Wright Group, The.

Igus, Toyomi. Two Mrs Gibsons. 2001. (gr. k-3). lib. bdg. 16.40 (978-0-613-65372-5(6)) Tandem Library Bks.

Imes, Jarod. Age Ain't Nothing but a Number. 2007. 148p. (YA). pap. 10.99 (***978-1-934195-04-8(9)***) Abednego's Free.

Imes, Jarold. Hold on Be Strong. 2007. 192p. per. 14.99 (***978-1-934195-05-5(7)***) Abednego's Free.

—Johnny Appleseed. 2008. (YA). per. 10.99 (***978-1-934195-08-6(1)***) Abednego's Free.

—Rollin' Wit' the Punches. 2008. (YA). per. 10.99 (*978-1-934195-09-3(X)) Abednego's Free.

—Runnin' Wit No Breaks. 2007. (YA). per. 10.99 (*978-1-934195-06-2(5)) Abednego's Free.

Imes, Jarold. Worth Fighting 4. 2007. 168p. (YA). pap. 10.99 (978-1-934195-01-7(4)) Abednego's Free.

Imes, Jarold, adapted by. U Can't Break Me. 2007. 148p. (YA). pap. 10.99 (*978-1-934195-03-1(0)) Abednego's Free.

In One Day. 2002. (Illus.). 33p. (J). pap. 9.95 (978-0-9723826-0-1(7)) Tajiri Ventures LLC.

Isadora, Rachel. Bring on That Beat. 2002. (Illus.). 32p. (J). (ps-3). 15.99 (978-0-399-23232-9(X) , Putnam Juvenile) Penguin Group (USA) Inc.

—Peekaboo Morning. Isadora, Rachel, illus. 32p. (J). (ps-ps). 2008. bds. 6.99 (*978-0-399-25153-5(7)); 2002. (Illus.). 15.99 (978-0-399-23602-0(3)) Penguin Group (USA) Inc. (Putnam Juvenile).

—Uh-Oh! 2008. (J). (*978-0-15-205765-7(X)) Harcourt Trade Pubs.

Isadora, Rachel. Yo, Jo! 2007. (Illus.). 40p. (J). 16.00 (978-0-15-205783-1(8)) Harcourt Children's Bks.

Jackson, Brian. Walking Through Mirrors. 1999. (gr. 7-12). lib. bdg. 23.45 (978-0-613-24002-4(2)) Tandem Library Bks.

Jackson, Dave & Jackson, Neta. The Forty-Acre Swindle: George Washington Carver. McLaughlin, Catherine R., illus. 2000. (Trailblazer Bks.: Vol. 31). 144p. (J). (gr. 3-7). pap. 6.99 (978-0-7642-2264-1(3)) Bethany Hse. Pubs.

Jeremiah, Omari. Paperboy 3: The School of Doom. Rollins, Bernie, illus. 2006. 75p. pap. 12.99 (978-1-929188-13-0(7)) Morton Bks.

John Henry. (Guided Reading Levels Ser.). 8.48 (978-0-7362-1770-5(3)); 50.88 (978-0-7362-2173-3(5)) Hampton-Brown Bks.

Johnson, Angela. Bird. 2004. 144p. (J). (gr. 4). 16.99 (978-0-8037-2847-9(6) , Dial) Penguin Group (USA) Inc.

—Daddy Calls Me Man. Mitchell, Rhonda, illus. 2000. (Richard Jackson Bks.). 32p. (J). (ps-k). pap. 6.95 (978-0-531-07175-5(8) , Orchard Bks.) Scholastic, Inc.

—Daddy Calls Me Man. 2000. (J). 13.75 (978-0-606-19856-1(3)); lib. bdg. 15.25 (978-0-613-44555-9(4)) Tandem Library Bks.

—The First Part Last. 144p. (YA). 2003. (Illus.). (gr. 6 up). 15.95 (978-0-689-84922-0(2)); 2004. reprint ed. pap. 5.99 (978-0-689-84923-7(0) , Simon Pulse) Simon & Schuster Children's Publishing.

—The First Part Last. l.t. ed. 241p. 2005. pap. 10.95 (978-0-7862-7379-9(8) , Large Print Pr.); 2004. 22.95 (978-0-7862-6510-7(8)) Thorndike Pr.

—Heaven. 2002. (Illus.). 13.40 (978-0-7587-0359-0(7)) Book Wholesalers, Inc.

—Heaven. 1998. 144p. (YA). (gr. 7-12). 16.95 (978-0-689-82229-2(4)) Simon & Schuster Children's Publishing.

—Heaven. 2000. (gr. 7-12). lib. bdg. 13.00 (978-0-613-28517-9(4)); (Illus.). (YA). 11.64 (978-0-606-18799-2(5)) Tandem Library Bks.

—Heaven. l.t. ed. 2000. 157p. (J). (gr. 7-12). 20.95 (978-0-7862-2463-0(0)) Thorndike Pr.

—Just Like Josh Gibson. Peck, Beth, illus. 32p. (J). 2004. 15.95 (978-0-689-82628-3(1)); 2007. reprint ed. 6.99 (978-1-4169-2728-0(X) , Aladdin) Simon & Schuster Children's Publishing.

—Lily Brown's Paintings. Lewis, E. B., illus. 2007. 32p. (J). (ps-3). pap. 16.99 (978-0-439-78225-8(2) , Orchard Bks.) Scholastic, Inc.

—Looking for Red. 128p. (YA). 2003. (Illus.). pap. 8.95 (978-0-689-86388-2(8) , Simon Pulse); 2002. (gr. 7 up). 15.95 (978-0-689-83253-6(2)) Simon & Schuster Children's Publishing.

—Looking for Red. 2003. (gr. 7-12). lib. bdg. 13.00 (978-0-613-73436-3(X)) Tandem Library Bks.

—Looking for Red. l.t. ed. 2003. 117p. (J). 24.95 (978-0-7862-5603-7(6)) Thorndike Pr.

—Maniac Monkeys on Magnolia Street. Ward, John, illus. 2000. 97p. (J). (ps-7). 12.04 (978-0-606-19829-5(6)) Tandem Library Bks.

—Songs of Faith. 1998. (Illus.). 112p. (J). (gr. 3-7). 16.99 (978-0-531-33023-4(0)); pap. 15.95 (978-0-531-30023-7(4)) Scholastic, Inc. (Orchard Bks.).

—Songs of Faith. 1999. (978-0-606-17374-2(9)) Tandem Library Bks.

—A Sweet Smell of Roses. Velasquez, Eric, illus. 32p. (J). 2007. 6.99 (*978-1-4169-5361-6(2) , Aladdin); 2004. 17.99 (978-0-689-83252-9(4)) Simon & Schuster Children's Publishing.

—Toning the Sweep. 2002. (J). 13.19 (978-0-7587-0401-6(1)) Book Wholesalers, Inc.

—Toning the Sweep. 2003. 112p. (J). (gr. 7 up). pap. 5.99 (978-0-590-48142-7(8) , Scholastic Paperbacks) Scholastic, Inc.

—The Wedding. Soman, David, illus. 1999. 32p. (J). (ps-2). 17.99 (978-0-531-33139-2(3)); pap. 16.95 (978-0-531-30139-5(7)) Scholastic, Inc. (Orchard Bks.).

—Wind Flyers. Long, Loren, illus. 2007. 32p. (J). 16.99 (978-0-689-84879-7(X)) Simon & Schuster Children's Publishing.

Johnson, Angela & Palencar, John Jude. Heaven. 2000. (Illus.). 144p. (YA). (gr. 8-12). pap. 5.99 (978-0-689-82290-2(1) , Simon Pulse) Simon & Schuster Children's Publishing.

Johnson, Dolores. Now Let Me Fly: The Story of a Slave Family. 1998. pap. 5.99 (978-0-87628-977-8(4)) Ctr. for Applied Research in Education, The.

Johnson, Dolores, illus. Grandma's Hands. 1998. (Accelerated Reader Bks.). 32p. (J). (gr. 1-4). 15.95 (978-0-7614-5025-2(4) , Cavendish Children's Bks.) Cavendish, Marshall Corp.

Johnston, Tony. Angel City. Byard, Carole M., illus. 2006. 40p. (J). (ps). 15.99 (978-0-399-23405-7(5) , Philomel) Penguin Group (USA) Inc.

—The Wagon. 1999. (Illus.). 40p. (J). (ps-3). pap. 5.95 (978-0-688-16694-6(6)) HarperCollins Pubs.

Jonas, Ann. The Quilt. Jonas, Ann, illus. 2002. (Illus.). (J). 13.19 (978-0-7587-3478-5(6)) Book Wholesalers, Inc.

Jones, Christianne C. Back to School. Haugen, Ryan, illus. 2005. (Read-It! Readers Ser.). 24p. (J). (ps-ps). lib. bdg. 18.60 (978-1-4048-1166-9(4)) Picture Window Bks.

Jones, Jasmine. The Cheetah Girls Movie: Junior Novel. 2004. (Illus.). 128p. (gr. 3-7). pap. 4.99 (978-0-7868-4713-6(1)) Disney Pr.

Jones, Traci L. Standing Against the Wind. 2006. 192p. (J). 16.00 (978-0-374-37174-6(1)) Farrar, Straus & Giroux.

Joosse, Barbara M. Hot City. Gauch, Patricia Lee, ed. Christie, Gregory R., illus. 2004. 32p. (J). (ps-3). 16.99 (978-0-399-23640-2(6) , Philomel) Penguin Group (USA) Inc.

—Snow Day! Plecas, Jennifer, illus. 1999. 32p. (J). (gr. k-3). pap. 5.95 (978-0-395-96890-1(9) , Clarion Bks.) Houghton Mifflin Co. Trade & Reference Div.

Jordan, Rosa. Lost Goat Lane. 2004. 192p. (J). 14.95 (978-1-56145-325-2(0)) Peachtree Pubs., Ltd.

Justus, Adalu. The Storyteller House. Justus, Adalu, illus. 1999. 180p. (YA). (gr. 5-12). per. (978-0-937109-11-3(8)) Ike, J. Bks.

Kantor, Susan, et al, eds. An Illustrated Treasury of African American Read-Aloud Stories: More Than 40 of the World's Best -Loved Stories for Parent & Child to Share. Kantor, Christian & Hale, Christy, illus. 2003. (Read Aloud Library Ser.). 192p. tchr. ed. 14.95 (978-1-57912-347-5(3) , 81347) Black Dog & Leventhal Pubs., Inc.

Katz, Karen. My First Kwanzaa. Katz, Karen, illus. rev. ed. 2003. (Illus.). 32p. (J). 14.95 (978-0-8050-7077-4(X) , Holt, Henry & Co. Bks. For Young Readers) Holt, Henry & Co.

Kay, Alan N. Send 'Em South. 2001. (Young Heroes of History Ser.: Vol. 1). (Illus.). 145p. (J). (gr. 3-6). pap. 7.95 (978-1-57249-208-0(2) , White Mane Kids) White Mane Publishing Co., Inc.

Keats, Ezra Jack. Goggles. Keats, Ezra Jack, illus. 1998. (Illus.). 40p. (J). 16.99 (978-0-670-88062-1(0) , Viking Juvenile) ; pap. 6.99 (978-0-14-056440-2(3) , Puffin) Penguin Group (USA) Inc.

—Goggles! Keats, Ezra Jack, illus. 2002. (Illus.). (J). 14.04 (978-0-7587-0111-4(X)) Book Wholesalers, Inc.

—Hi, Cat! Keats, Ezra Jack, illus. 2002. (Illus.). (J). 22.72 (978-0-7587-6792-9(7)) Book Wholesalers, Inc.

—Hi, Cat! Keats, Ezra Jack, illus. unabr. ed. 1998. (Illus.). (J). (gr. k-3). 25.95 incl. audio (978-0-87499-180-2(3)) Live Oak Media.

—Hi, Cat! Keats, Ezra Jack, illus. 1999. (Illus.). 40p. (J). (ps-3). 15.99 (978-0-670-88546-6(0) , Viking Juvenile) Penguin Group (USA) Inc.

—Pet Show! 2001. (978-0-606-22504-5(8)) Tandem Library Bks.

—Peter's Chair. 2006. 32p. (J). (ps-ps). bds. 6.99 (978-0-670-06190-7(5) , Viking Juvenile) Penguin Group (USA) Inc.

—The Snowy Day. Keats, Ezra Jack, illus. 2002. (Illus.). (J). 12.40 (978-0-7587-0027-8(X)) Book Wholesalers, Inc.

—The Snowy Day. 2000. (J). pap. 19.97 incl. audio (978-0-7366-9215-1(0)) Books on Tape, Inc.

—The Snowy Day/Whistle for Willie DVD & Book Gift Set. 2007. 64p. (J). (gr. 12). 19.99 (*978-0-670-06253-9(7) , Viking Juvenile) Penguin Group (USA) Inc.

Keats, Ezra Jack. Whistle for Willie. Keats, Ezra Jack, illus. 2002. (Illus.). (J). 13.19 (978-0-7587-4003-8(4)) Book Wholesalers, Inc.

—Whistle for Willie. 2000. (J). pap. 19.97 incl. audio (978-0-7366-9211-3(8)) Books on Tape, Inc.

—Whistle for Willie. Keats, Ezra Jack, illus. 1998. (Illus.). 32p. (J). (ps-k). bds. 7.99 (978-0-670-88046-1(9) , Viking Juvenile) Penguin Group (USA) Inc.

Keats, Ezra Jack & Keats, Ezra Jack. Goggles! 1998. (Illus.). (J). (ps-ps). lib. bdg. 15.30 (978-0-8085-2315-4(5)) Tandem Library Bks.

Kelley, Gloria. Beverly Babes & Guys: Alicia's Thirtee. 2006. 64p. pap. 12.95 (978-1-4241-2610-1(X)) PublishAmerica, Inc.

Kelly, Claire. Nellie in the News. Hicks, Faith, illus. 2007. 48p. (J). lib. bdg. 23.08 (*978-1-4242-1631-4(1)) Fitzgerald Bks.

Klass, David. Danger Zone. 1998. (J). 11.64 (978-0-606-13080-6(2)) Tandem Library Bks.

Klein, Adria F. Max Stays Overnight. 2007. (Read-It! Readers Ser.). (Illus.). 24p. (J). (*978-1-4048-3547-4(4) , 1265796) Picture Window Bks.

—Max Stays Overnight. Gallagher-Cole, Mernie, illus. 2006. (Read-It! Readers Ser.). 24p. (J). (*978-1-4048-3149-0(5) , 1265796) Picture Window Bks.

—Max's Fun Day. 2007. (Read-It! Readers Ser.). (Illus.). 24p. (J). (*978-1-4048-3549-8(0) , 1265797) Picture Window Bks.

—Max's Fun Day. Gallagher-Cole, Mernie, illus. 2006. (Read-It! Readers Ser.). 24p. (J). (*978-1-4048-3150-6(9) , 1265797) Picture Window Bks.

Koertge, Ronald. The Heart of the City. 1998. 128p. (J). (gr. 3-7). 16.99 (978-0-531-33078-4(8) , Orchard Bks.) Scholastic, Inc.

Konigsburg, E. L. Jennifer, Hecate, Macbeth, William McKinley, & Me, Elizabeth. (J). 177p. (gr. 3-6). pap. 4.99 (978-0-8072-1524-1(4)); 117p. (gr. 3-6). pap. 4.99 (978-0-8072-1417-6(5)); 1998. 177p. (gr. 4-7). pap. 29.00 incl. audio (978-0-8072-8001-0(1) , YA963SP) Random Hse. Audio Publishing Group. (Listening Library).

—Jennifer, Hecate, Macbeth, William McKinley, & Me, Elizabeth. 128p. (J). 2007. pap. 2.99 (*978-1-4169-4829-2(5)); 2007. pap. 5.99 (978-1-4169-3396-0(4)); 2001. (Illus.). pap. 5.99 (978-0-689-84625-0(8)) Simon & Schuster Children's Publishing. (Aladdin).

Krensky Stephen. John Henry. Oldroyd, Mark, illus. 2007. (On My Own Folklore Ser.). (J). pap. 6.95 (*978-0-8225-6477-5(7) , First Avenue Editions) Lerner Publishing Group.

Kroll. Masai & I. 1998. pap. 4.99 (978-0-87628-558-9(2)) Ctr. for Applied Research in Education, The.

Kroll, Virginia K. Faraway Drums. Cooper, Floyd, illus. 1998. 32p. (J). (ps-3). 14.95 (978-0-316-50449-2(1)) Little Brown & Co.

Kurtz, Jane. Faraway Home. Lewis, Earl, illus. 2000. 32p. (J). (gr. 1-5). 17.00 (978-0-15-200036-3(4) , Gulliver Bks.) Harcourt Children's Bks.

—The Storyteller's Beads. Van Doren, Liz, ed. Bryant, Michael, illus. 1998. 160p. (YA). (gr. 3-7). 16.00 (978-0-15-201074-4(2) , Gulliver Bks.) Harcourt Children's Bks.

Lasky, Kathryn. True North: A Novel of the Underground Railroad. 1998. (J). (978-0-606-13874-1(9)) Tandem Library Bks.

Lattany, Kristin Hunter. Kinfolks. 2000. (gr. 7-12). lib. bdg. 15.30 (978-0-613-21861-0(2)) Tandem Library Bks.

Lee, Spike & Lee, Tonya Lewis. Please, Baby, Please. Nelson, Kadir, illus. 2002. 32p. (J). 16.95 (978-0-689-83233-8(8)) Simon & Schuster Children's Publishing.

Lee, Spike & Lee, Tonya Lewis. Please, Baby, Please. Nelson, Kadir, illus. 2007. (Classic Board Bks.). 32p. (J). bds. 7.99 (*978-1-4169-4911-4(9) , Little Simon) Simon & Schuster Children's Publishing.

Leonard Marcia. Mi día de campamento (My Camp-Out) 2007. (Lecturas para niños de verdad - Nivel 1 (Real Kids Readers - Level 1) Ser.). (J). pap. 5.95 (*978-0-8225-7798-0(4) , Ediciones Lerner) Lerner Publishing Group.

Leonard, Marcia. My Camp-Out. Handelman, Dorothy, photos by. 1999. (Real Kids Readers Ser.). (Illus.). 32p. (ps-1). lib. bdg. 18.90 (978-0-7613-2052-4(0)); (J). pap. 4.99 (978-0-7613-2077-7(6)) Lerner Publishing Group. (Millbrook Pr.).

—My Camp-Out. 1999. (J). (978-0-606-19165-4(8)); lib. bdg. 13.00 (978-0-613-16774-1(0)) Tandem Library Bks.

Lester, Julius. Black Cowboy, Wild Horses. Pinkney, Jerry, illus. 1998. 32p. (J). (gr. k-3). 18.99 (978-0-8037-1787-9(3) , Dial) Penguin Group (USA) Inc.

—Long Journey Home: Stories from Black History. 2000. (J). (gr. 6 up). 20.75 (978-0-8446-7148-2(7)) Smith, Peter Pub., Inc.

—This Strange New Feeling: Three Love Stories from Black History. 2006. 208p. (YA). 16.99 (978-0-8037-3172-1(8) , Dial) Penguin Group (USA) Inc.

—Time's Memory. 2006. (Illus.). 240p. (YA). 17.00 (978-0-374-37178-4(4) , Farrar, Straus & Giroux (BYR)) Farrar, Straus & Giroux.

—Why Heaven Is Far Away. Cepeda, Joe, illus. 2002. 40p. (J). (gr. 1-3). pap. 16.95 (978-0-439-17871-6(1) , Scholastic Pr.) Scholastic, Inc.

Levine, Ellen. Henry's Freedom Box: A True Story. Nelson, Kadir, illus. 2007. 40p. (J). (ps-3). pap. 16.99 (978-0-439-77733-9(X) , Scholastic Pr.) Scholastic, Inc.

Levine, Gail Carson. Dave at Night. 1999. (YA). pap., stu. ed. 69.95 incl. audio (978-0-7887-3794-7(5) , 41038) Recorded Bks., LLC.

Lieurance, Suzanne. Shoelaces. Girouard, Patrick, illus. 2000. (Rookie Reader Skill Set Ser.). 32p. (J). (gr. k-2). pap. 4.95 (978-0-516-26546-9(6)); (gr. 1-2). 19.50 (978-0-516-21613-3(9)) Scholastic Library Publishing. (Children's Pr.).

—Shoelaces. 2000. (gr. k-3). lib. bdg. 12.95 (978-0-613-54659-1(8)) Tandem Library Bks.

The Lil Dudes. 2006. (YA). per. (978-1-59872-308-3(1)) Instantpublisher.com.

Lindbergh, Reeve. Nobody Owns the Sky. Paparone, Pamela, illus. 2004. 32p. (J). (VIE, CHI, BEN, GUJ & ENG.). (978-1-85269-342-8(8)); (VIE, CHI, BEN, GUJ & ENG.). (978-1-85269-343-5(6)); (VIE, CHI, BEN, GUJ & ENG.). (978-1-85269-344-2(4)); (CHI, VIE, BEN, GUJ & ENG.). (978-1-85269-345-9(2)); (VIE, CHI, BEN, GUJ & ENG.). (978-1-85269-347-3(9)) Mantra Publishing, Ltd.

Lindsey, Kathleen D. Sweet Potato Pie. Riley-Webb, Charlotte, illus. 2003. (J). 16.95 (978-1-58430-061-8(2)) Lee & Low Bks., Inc.

Literature Connections English: The Glory Field. 2004. (gr. 6-12). (978-0-395-78374-0(7) , 2-70257) McDougal Littell Inc.

Literature Connections Spanish: Lloro por la Tierra (Roll of Thunder, Hear My Cry) 2004. (gr. 6-12). (978-0-395-80048-5(X) , 2-70467) McDougal Littell Inc.

Littlesugar, Amy. Tree of Hope. 2001. (gr. k-3). lib. bdg. 15.30 (978-0-613-44423-1(X)) Tandem Library Bks.

—The Tree of Hope. Cooper, Floyd, illus. 2001. 40p. (J). pap. 6.99 (978-0-698-11903-1(7) , Putnam Juvenile) Penguin Group (USA) Inc.

Lombard, Jenny. Drita, My Homegirl. 2008. 144p. (J). (gr. 4-6). pap. 5.99 (*978-0-14-240905-3(7) , Puffin) Penguin Group (USA) Inc.

Lou Weber Staff, ed. African American Children's Stories: A Treasury of Tradition & Pride. 2004. (Illus.). 320p. (J). 15.98 (978-0-7853-5239-6(2) , 7137100) Publications International, Ltd.

Lukas, Catherine. Hooray for Mother's Day! 2003. (gr. k-3). lib. bdg. 14.15 (978-0-613-63298-0(2)) Tandem Library Bks.

Lutz, Norma Jean. Escape from Slavery: A Family's Fight for Freedom. 1999. (American Adventure Ser.: No. 16). 144p. (J). (gr. 3-7). 11.95 (978-0-7910-5590-8(6) , Chelsea Hse.) Facts On File, Inc.

Lynch, Marcia. United in Freedom. Cornelison, Sue F., illus. 2000. (Cover-to-Cover Bks.). 92p. (J). pap. (978-0-7891-5102-5(2)); (gr. 2-5). lib. bdg. 13.95 (978-0-7807-9068-1(5)) Perfection Learning Corp.

Lyons, Mary E. Letters from a Slave Boy: The Story of Joseph Jacobs. 2007. 208p. (YA). (gr. 4-8). 15.99 (978-0-689-87867-1(2) , Atheneum) Simon & Schuster Children's Publishing.

—Letters from a Slave Girl: The Story of Harriet Jacobs. 2007. 192p. (YA). pap. 5.99 (978-1-4169-3637-4(8) , Simon Pulse) Simon & Schuster Children's Publishing.

—Roy Makes a Car. Widener, Terry, illus. 2005. 32p. (J). 16.95 (978-0-689-84640-3(1) , Atheneum) Simon & Schuster Children's Publishing.

Maddox, Jake. Slam Dunk Shoes. Tiffany, Sean, illus. 2008. (J). (*978-1-59889-842-2(6)); pap. (*978-1-59889-894-1(9)) Stone Arch Bks.

Mahony, Mary. Stand Tall, Harry. Pasternack, Susan, ed. Larkin, Catherine, illus. 2002. 200p. (J). (gr. 4). pap. 14.95 (978-0-9658879-2-2(8)) Redding Pr.

Marbury, Ja'Nitta. Shades of Me: Coloring the Self-Esteem of African American Children. Marbury, Ja'Nitta, illus. l.t. ed. 2002. (Illus.). 22p. (J). pap. 20.00 (978-0-9718307-2-1(X)) Shades of Me Publishing.

Marshall, Bill. The Oyster Man. 2000. 159p. pap. (978-9964-70-223-6(X)) Afram Pubns. Ghana, Ltd.

Martin, Ann M. Belle Teale. 2001. 224p. (J). (gr. 5-9). pap. 16.95 (978-0-439-09823-6(8)) Scholastic, Inc.

—Claudia & Crazy Peaches. 1999. (Baby-Sitters Club Ser.: No. 78). 138p. (J). (gr. 3-7). pap. 3.99 (978-0-590-92610-2(1)) Scholastic, Inc.

—Claudia & the Little Liar. 1999. (Baby-Sitters Club Ser.: No. 128). 114p. (J). (gr. 3-7). pap. 4.50 (978-0-590-50351-8(0)) Scholastic, Inc.

—Claudia & the Terrible Truth. 1998. (Baby-Sitters Club Ser.: No. 117). (J). (gr. 3-7). pap. 4.50 (978-0-590-05995-4(5) , Scholastic Paperbacks) Scholastic, Inc.

—Kristy & the Cat Burglar. 1998. (Baby-Sitters Club Mystery Ser.: No. 36). (J). (gr. 3-7). pap. 3.99 (978-0-590-05976-3(9) , Scholastic Paperbacks) Scholastic, Inc.

—Mary Anne & the Haunted Bookstore. 1998. (Baby-Sitters Club Mystery Ser.: No. 34). (J). (gr. 3-7). pap. 3.99 (978-0-590-05974-9(2) , Scholastic Paperbacks) Scholastic, Inc.

—Mary Anne & the Playground Fight. 1998. (Baby-Sitters Club Ser.: No. 120). (J). (gr. 3-7). pap. 3.99 (978-0-590-05998-5(X) , Scholastic Paperbacks) Scholastic, Inc.

—Mary Anne & the Playground Fight. 1998. (Baby-Sitters Club Ser.: No. 120). (J). (gr. 3-7). (978-0-606-13164-3(7)) Tandem Library Bks.

—Mary Anne in the Middle. 1998. (Baby-Sitters Club Ser.: No. 125). (Illus.). 121p. (J). (gr. 3-7). pap. 3.99 (978-0-590-50179-8(8)) Scholastic, Inc.

Marzollo, Jean. Doctor Show, No. 2. Evans, Shane W., illus. 2001. 24p. (J). lib. bdg. 13.49 (978-0-7868-2548-6(0) , Jump at the Sun) Hyperion Bks. for Children.

—Hip, Hop, Hooray! 2004. (Shanna Show! Ser.). (Illus.). 32p. (ps-1). pap. 3.99 (978-0-7868-1830-3(1)) Hyperion Bks. for Children.

—Shanna's Animal Riddles. Roos, Maryn, illus. 2004. (J). (ps-ps). lib. bdg. 10.79 (978-0-606-30551-8(3)) Tandem Library Bks.

—Shanna's Party Surprise. 2004. (Shanna Show! Ser.). (Illus.). 32p. (ps-1). pap. 3.99 (978-0-7868-1828-0(X)) Hyperion Bks. for Children.

—Shanna's Princess Show. No. 1. Evans, Shane W., illus. 2001. 24p. (J). 13.49 (978-0-7868-2549-3(9) , Jump at the Sun) Hyperion Bks. for Children.

—Shanna's Princess Show. 2003. (ps-2). lib. bdg. 11.25 (978-0-613-91009-5(5)) Tandem Library Bks.

Masters, Susan Rowan. Night Journey to Vicksburg. Killcoyne, Hope L., ed. Smith, Duane A., illus. 2003. (Adventures in America Ser.). 74p. (J). 14.95 (978-1-893110-30-4(3)) Silver Moon Pr.

Mather, Melissa. One Summer in Between. 2000. 228p. (YA). pap. 14.95 (978-0-595-09384-7(1) , Backinprint.com) iUniverse, Inc.

Matthews, Steve. Brain-in-A-Box. 1999. (gr. 3-6). lib. bdg. 12.60 (978-0-613-19342-9(3)) Tandem Library Bks.

Maxson, H. A. & Young, Claudia H. Antoni: Resource Guide. Kosits, Andrew, illus. 2001. 30p. (J). 13.95 (978-0-9704692-5-0(X)) Bay Oak Pubs., Ltd.

Mazellan, Ron, illus. We Will Walk. 2005. 16p. (J). pap. (*978-0-7367-2919-2(4)) Zaner-Bloser, Inc.

McCully, Emily Arnold. The Escape of Oney Judge: Martha Washington's Slave Finds Freedom. 2007. (Illus.). 32p. (J). (gr. 1). 16.00 (978-0-374-32225-0(2) , Farrar, Straus & Giroux (BYR)) Farrar, Straus & Giroux.

McCurty, Darlene M. I'm Special Too. 2003. 55p. (J). (gr. 4-8). pap. 6.95 (978-0-913543-27-6(6)) African American Images.

McDaniels, William. Abdul & the Designer Tennis Shoes. 2003. (Illus.). 33p. (J). (gr. 2-12). pap. 6.95 (978-0-913543-15-3(2)) African American Images.

McDonald, Janet. Brother Hood. 2004. 176p. (YA). 16.00 (978-0-374-30995-4(7) , Frances Foster Bks.) Farrar, Straus & Giroux.

—Brother Hood. l.t. ed. 2005. 179p. 20.95 (978-0-7862-7334-8(8) , Large Print Pr.) Thorndike Pr.

—Chill Wind. l.t. ed. 2003. 165p. (J). 24.95 (978-0-7862-5502-3(1)) Thorndike Pr.

—Twists & Turns. 144p. (YA). 2006. pap. 6.95 (978-0-374-40006-4(7)); 2003. 16.00 (978-0-374-39955-9(7)) Farrar, Straus & Giroux. (Farrar, Straus & Giroux (BYR)).

—Twists & Turns, Vol. 5. l.t. ed. 2004. 147p. 21.95 (978-0-7862-6664-7(3) , Large Print Pr.) Thorndike Pr.

McDonald, Joyce. Devil on My Heels. 272p. (YA). (gr. 7 up). 2005. pap. 6.50 (978-0-440-23829-4(3) , Laurel Leaf); 2004. 15.95 (978-0-385-73107-2(8) , Delacorte Bks. for Young Readers) Random Hse. Children's Bks.

McGuigan, Mary Ann. Morning in a Different Place. 2008. (J). (*978-1-59078-551-5(7)* , Front Street) Boyds Mills Pr.

McKay, Sindy & Johnson, Meredith. We Both Read-Baseball Fever. 2003. (Illus.). 44p. (J). (gr. 1-2). 7.99 (978-1-891327-45-2(3)) Treasure Bay, Inc.

McKayhan, Monica. Trouble Follows. 2007. 256p. pap. 9.99 (*978-0-373-83087-9(4))* Harlequin Enterprises, Ltd. CAN. *Dist:* Simon & Schuster, Inc.

McKissack, Frederick. This Generation of Americans: A Story of the Civil Rights Movement. 2000. (gr. 5-8). lib. bdg. 14.95 (978-0-613-36884-1(3)) Tandem Library Bks.

McKissack, Fredrick L. This Generation of Americans. 2004. 150p. (J). lib. bdg. 16.92 (*978-1-4242-0769-5(X))* Fitzgerald Bks.

McKissack, Fredrick L. This Generation of Americans: A Story of the Civil Rights Movement. 2004. (Jamestown's American Portraits Ser.). (Illus.). 152p. (J). (gr. 5-7). pap. 4.95 (978-0-7696-3441-8(9) , Waterbird Bks.) School Specialty Publishing.

McKissack, Pat. The All-I'll-Ever-Want Christmas Doll. Pinkney, Jerry, illus. 2007. (J). (*978-0-375-83615-2(2)* , Schwartz & Wade Bks.) Random Hse. Children's Bks.

—Stitchin' & Pullin' A Gee's Bend Quilt. Cabrera, Cozbi S., illus. 2007. (J). (*978-0-375-83163-8(0));* lib. bdg. (*978-0-375-93163-5(5))* Random Hse., Inc.

McKissack, Patricia. Abby Takes a Stand. James, Gordon C., illus. 2006. (Scraps of Time Ser.). 112p. (J). (gr. 3). pap. 4.99 (978-0-14-240687-8(2) , Puffin) Penguin Group (USA) Inc.

—The All-I'll-Ever-Want Christmas Doll. Pinkney, Jerry, illus. 2007. 40p. (J). (ps-3). lib. bdg. 19.99 (*978-0-375-93759-0(5));* 16.99 (*978-0-375-83759-3(0))* Random Hse. Children's Bks. (Schwartz & Wade Bks.).

McKissack, Patricia. Away West. James, Gordon, illus. 2006. (Scraps of Time Ser.). 128p. (J). (gr. 3). pap. 4.99 (978-0-14-240688-5(0) , Puffin) Penguin Group (USA) Inc.

McKissack, Patricia C. Abby Takes a Stand. James, Gordon C., illus. 2005. (Scraps of Time Ser.). 112p. (J). (gr. 3). 14.99 (978-0-670-06011-5(9) , Viking Juvenile) Penguin Group (USA) Inc.

—Bessey, la Desordenada. 2002. Tr. of Messy Bessey. (SPA.). (gr. k-3). lib. bdg. 12.95 (978-0-613-59452-3(5)) Tandem Library Bks.

—Color Me Dark: The Diary of Nellie Lee Love, the Great Migration North, Chicago, Illinois, 1919. 2000. (Dear America Ser.). (J). 9.95 (978-0-439-26653-6(X)) Scholastic, Inc.

—Color Me Dark: The Diary of Nellie Lee Love, the Great Migration North, Chicago, Illinois, 1919. 2000. (Dear America Ser.). (Illus.). 224p. (J). (gr. 4-9). pap. 10.95 (978-0-590-51159-9(9)) Scholastic, Inc.

—The Dark-Thirty. Pinkney, Brian, illus. 2001. 176p. (J). (gr. 5). 6.50 (978-0-679-89006-5(8) , Yearling) Random Hse. Children's Bks.

—The Dark-Thirty: Southern Tales of the Supernatural. Pinkney, Brian, illus. 2004. 122p. (J). (gr. 5-8). reprint ed. pap. 17.00 (978-0-7567-7601-5(5)) DIANE Publishing Co.

—Dark-Thirty Southern Tales of the Supernatural. 2001. (gr. 5-8). lib. bdg. 13.55 (978-0-613-33690-1(9)) Tandem Library Bks.

—Flossie & the Fox. 2002. (Illus.). (J). 24.43 (978-0-7587-2518-9(3)) Book Wholesalers, Inc.

—A Friendship for Today. 2007. 240p. (J). (gr. 4-7). pap. 16.99 (978-0-439-66098-3(X) , Scholastic Pr.) Scholastic, Inc.

—The Honest-to-Goodness Truth. 2002. (Illus.). (J). 25.11 (978-0-7587-2741-1(0)) Book Wholesalers, Inc.

—The Honest-to-Goodness Truth. Potter, Giselle, illus. 2000. 40p. (J). (ps-3). 16.00 (978-0-689-82668-9(0) , Atheneum/Anne Schwartz Bks.) Simon & Schuster Children's Publishing.

—The Honest-to-Goodness Truth. 2003. (gr. k-3). lib. bdg. 15.30 (978-0-613-61627-0(8)) Tandem Library Bks.

—Ma Dear's Aprons. 2002. (Illus.). (J). 14.47 (978-0-7587-5149-2(4)) Book Wholesalers, Inc.

—Ma Dear's Aprons. 2000. (gr. k-3). lib. bdg. 14.15 (978-0-613 23015-5(9)); (Illus.). (J). (978-0-606-17928-7(3)) Tandem Library Bks.

—Messy Bessey. rev. ed. 1999. (gr. k-3). lib. bdg. 12.95 (978-0-613-37455-2(X)) Tandem Library Bks.

—Messy Bessey's Closet. 2001. (gr. k-3). lib. bdg. 12.95 (978-0-613-54440-5(4)) Tandem Library Bks.

—Messy Bessey's Garden. 2002. (gr. k-3). lib. bdg. 12.95 (978-0-613-53836-7(6)) Tandem Library Bks.

—Messy Bessey's Holidays. 1999. (gr. k-3). lib. bdg. 12.95 (978-0-613-37457-6(6)) Tandem Library Bks.

—Miami Gets It Straight. 2000. (Road to Reading Ser.). (Illus.). (J). (978-0-606-20444-6(X)) Tandem Library Bks.

—Miami Makes the Play. 2001. (gr. k-3). lib. bdg. 11.80 (978-0-613-43071-5(9)) Tandem Library Bks.

—Miami Sees It Through. 2002. (gr. k-3). lib. bdg. 11.80 (978-0-613-82723-2(6)) Tandem Library Bks.

—Porch Lies: Tales of Slicksters, Tricksters, & Other Wily Characters. Carrilho, André, illus. 2006. 160p. (J). (gr. 3-7). 18.95 (978-0-375-83619-0(5) , Schwartz & Wade Bks.) Random Hse. Children's Bks.

—Porch Lies: Tales of Slicksters, Tricksters, & Other Wily Characters. Carrilho, Andre, illus. 2006. 160p. (J). (gr. 3-7). lib. bdg. 20.99 (978-0-375-93619-7(X) , Schwartz & Wade Bks.) Random Hse. Children's Bks.

—Porch Lies: Tales of Slicksters, Tricksters, & Other Wily Characters. Carrilho, André, illus. 2006. xii, 146p. (J). (*978-1-4156-9337-7(4)* , Schwartz & Wade Bks.) Random Hse. Children's Bks.

McKissack, Patricia C. & Cooper, Floyd. Ma Dear's Aprons. 2000. (Illus.). 32p. (J). (ps-3). reprint ed. pap. 7.99 (978-0-689-83262-8(1) , Aladdin) Simon & Schuster Children's Publishing.

McKissack, Patricia C. & McKissack, Frederick. Miami Gets It Straight. Chesworth, Michael, illus. 2004. 89p. (J). (gr. 4-7). lib. bdg. 11.80 (978-0-613-27975-8(1)) Tandem Library Bks.

McKissack, Patricia C. & McKissack, Fredrick L. Christmas in the Big House: Christmas in the Quarters. Thompson, John, illus. 2002. 80p. (J). pap. 6.99 (978-0-590-43028-9(9)) Scholastic, Inc.

McKissack, Patricia C. & McKissack, Fredrick L., Jr. Let My People Go: Bible Stories Told by a Freeman of Color. Ransome, James E., illus. 1998. 144p. (YA). (gr. 4-7). 21.99 (978-0-689-80856-2(9) , Atheneum/Anne Schwartz Bks.) Simon & Schuster Children's Publishing.

McKissack, Patricia C. & McKissack, Fredrick L. Messy Bessey & the Birthday Overnight. Regan, Dana, illus. 1998. (Rookie Readers Ser.). 32p. (J). (gr. 1-2). 19.50 (978-0-516-20828-2(4) , Children's Pr.) Scholastic Library Publishing.

—Messy Bessey's Garden. Regan, Dana, illus. rev. ed. 2002. (Rookie Reader Espanol Ser.). 32p. (J). (gr. k-2). pap. 4.95 (978-0-516-27386-0(8) , Children's Pr.) Scholastic Library Publishing.

—Messy Bessey's Garden Level C. Regan, Dana, illus. rev. ed. 2002. (Rookie Readers Ser.). 32p. (J). (gr. 1-2). 19.50 (978-0-516-22491-6(3) , Children's Pr.) Scholastic Library Publishing.

—Miami Jackson Makes the Play. Chesworth, Michael, illus. 2004. (Road to Reading Ser.). 96p. (J). (gr. k-3). pap. 3.99 (978-0-307-26505-0(6) , Random Hse. Bks. for Young Readers) Random Hse. Children's Bks.

—Miami Jackson Sees It Through. Chesworth, Michael, illus. 2004. (Road to Reading Ser.). 96p. (J). (gr. 2-4). pap. 3.99 (978-0-307-26513-5(7) , Random Hse. Bks. for Young Readers) Random Hse. Children's Bks.

—Miami Makes the Play. Chesworth, Michael, illus. 2004. 92p. (J). (gr. 4-7). lib. bdg. 11.19 (978-0-606-32802-9(5)) Tandem Library Bks.

McKissack, Patricia C. & Moss, Onawumi Jean. Precious & the Boo Hag. Brooker, Kyrsten, illus. 2005. 40p. (J). (ps-3). 17.99 (978-0-689-85194-0(4) , Atheneum/Anne Schwartz Bks.) Simon & Schuster Children's Publishing.

McKissack, Patricia C. & Pinkney, Jerry. Goin' Someplace Special. 2001. (Illus.). 40p. (J). (ps-3). 16.99 (978-0-689-81885-1(8) , Atheneum/Anne Schwartz Bks.) Simon & Schuster Children's Publishing.

McKissack, Patricia C. & Potter, Giselle. The Honest-to-Goodness Truth. 2003. (Illus.). 40p. (J). (ps-3). pap. 7.99 (978-0-689-85395-1(5) , Aladdin) Simon & Schuster Children's Publishing.

McKissack, Patricia C., et al. Miami Jackson Gets It Straight. 2004. (Road to Reading Ser.). (Illus.). 96p. (J). (gr. k-3). pap. 3.99 (978-0-307-26501-2(3) , Random Hse. Bks. for Young Readers) Random Hse. Children's Bks.

Mead, Alice. Junebug & the Reverend. 2002. (Illus.). (J). 13.40 (978-0-7587-6518-5(5)) Book Wholesalers, Inc.

—Junebug & the Reverend. 2000. (J). (ps-7). 186p. per. 13.00 (978-0-613-21831-3(0)); (Illus.). 11.64 (978-0-606-18785-5(5)) Tandem Library Bks.

—Junebug in Trouble. 2003. (Illus.). 144p. (J). (gr. 4-7). pap. 5.50 (978-0-440-41937-2(9) , Yearling) Random Hse. Children's Bks.

Mead, Alice & Weber James, Alice. Junebug in Trouble. 2002. 144p. (J). (gr. 4-7). 16.00 (978-0-374-33969-2(4) , Farrar, Straus & Giroux (BYR)) Farrar, Straus & Giroux.

Medearis, Angela Shelf. Dancing with the Indians. Byrd, Samuel, illus. 2000. pap. 18.95 incl. audio compact disk (978-1-59519-248-6(4)); pap. 39.95 incl. audio compact disk (978-1-59519-249-3(2)); (J). (gr. 1-6). 24.95 incl. audio (978-0-87499-333-2(4)); (J). (gr. 1-6). pap. 16.95 incl. audio (978-0-87499-332-5(6)) Live Oak Media.

—Dancing with the Indians, Grades 1-6. Byrd, Samuel, illus. unabr. ed. 2000. (J). pap., tchr. ed. 37.95 incl. audio (978-0-87499-334-9(2)) Live Oak Media.

—Lights Out! Tadgell, Nicole, illus. 2004. 32p. (J). lib. bdg. 15.00 (*978-1-4242-0221-8(3))* Fitzgerald Bks.

—Singing for Dr. King. Wright and Hu, Cornelius Van and Ying-Hwa, illus. 2004. 32p. (J). lib. bdg. 15.00 (*978-1-4242-0237-9(X))* Fitzgerald Bks.

Medearis, Angela Shelf. Snug in Mama's Arms. Sandford, John, illus. 2004. 32p. (J). 14.95 (978-1-57768-430-5(3) , Gingham Dog Pr.) School Specialty Publishing.

Medearis, Michael & Medearis, Angela Shelf. Daisy & the Doll. Johnson, Larry, illus. 2000. (Family Heritage Ser.). 32p. (J). (gr. 1-5). 14.95 (978-0-916718-15-2(8)) Vermont Folklife Ctr.

Medina, Tony. Christmas Makes Me Think. Cox, Chandra, illus. 2001. 32p. (J). (gr. 1-7). (978-1-58430-024-3(8)) Lee & Low Bks., Inc.

Mendez, Phil. The Black Snowman. Byard, Carole M., illus. 2005. 48p. (J). (ps-3). pap. 5.99 (978-0-439-76993-8(0) , Scholastic Paperbacks) Scholastic, Inc.

Meyer, Carolyn. Jubilee Journey. 2007. (Illus.). 288p. (YA). pap. 6.95 (978-0-15-205845-6(1) , Harcourt Paperbacks) Harcourt Children's Bks.

—White Lilacs. 2007. (Illus.). 256p. (YA). pap. 6.95 (978-0-15-205851-7(6) , Harcourt Paperbacks) Harcourt Children's Bks.

Michaelson, Richard. Across the Alley. Lewis, E. B., illus. 2006. 32p. (J). (ps-3). 16.99 (978-0-399-23970-0(7) , Putnam Juvenile) Penguin Group (USA) Inc.

Michelson, Richard. Happy Feet: The Savoy Ballroom Lindy Hoppers & Me. Lewis, E. B., illus. 2005. 32p. (J). (ps-ps). 16.00 (978-0-15-205057-3(4)) Harcourt Children's Bks.

Miller, Mitzi & Millner, Denene. Hotlanta #1. 2008. 288p. (J). 8.99 (*978-0-545-00308-7(3)* , Scholastic Paperbacks) Scholastic, Inc.

Miller, William. The Bus Ride. Ward, John, illus. 32p. (YA). (gr. k up). 1998. 15.95 (978-1-880000-60-1(1)); 2001. reprint ed. 6.95 (978-1-58430-026-7(4)) Lee & Low Bks., Inc.

—The Bus Ride. 2001. (J). 13.75 (978-0-606-21094-2(6)) Tandem Library Bks.

—Joe Louis, My Champion. Pate, Rodney, tr. Pate, Rodney, illus. 2004. 32p. (J). 16.95 (978-1-58430-161-5(9)) Lee & Low Bks., Inc.

—Night Golf. Lucas, Cedric, illus. 32p. 2002. (YA). pap. 6.95 (978-1-58430-056-4(6)); 1999. (J). (gr. 1-4). 15.95 (978-1-880000-79-3(2)) Lee & Low Bks., Inc.

—The Piano. Keeter, Susan, illus. 32p. 2005. (gr. 1-4). 7.95 (978-1-58430-242-1(9)); 2000. (J). (ps up). 15.95 (978-1-880000-98-4(9)) Lee & Low Bks., Inc.

—Rent Party Jazz. Riley-Webb, Charlotte, illus. 2001. 32p. (J). (gr. 1-5). 16.95 (978-1-58430-025-0(6)) Lee & Low Bks., Inc.

—Richard Wright & the Library Card. Christie, Gregory R., illus. 1999. 32p. (J). (gr. k up). 6.95 (978-1-880000-88-5(1)) Lee & Low Bks., Inc.

—Richard Wright y el Carne de Biblioteca. Christie, Gregory R., illus. 2003. (SPA.). (J). 32p. 16.95 (978-1-58430-180-6(5)); pap. 6.95 (978-1-58430-181-3(3)) Lee & Low Bks., Inc.

Mills, Charles. Stranger in the Shadows. 1998. (Shadow Creek Ranch Ser.: Vol. 11). 151p. (Orig.). (J). (gr. 4-7). pap. 5.99 (978-0-8280-1316-1(0)) Review & Herald Publishing Assn.

Mills, Eva. Simon & the Aliens. 1999. (gr. 3-6). lib. bdg. 12.60 (978-0-613-30734-5(8)) Tandem Library Bks.

Milord, Sonya. In One Day. Noland Anderson, illus. l.t. ed. 2002. 33p. (J). bds. 14.95 (978-0-9723826-1-8(5)) Tajiri Ventures LLC.

Mitchell, Margaree King. Uncle Jed's Barber Shop. Ransome, James E., illus. 2002. (J). 15.53 (978-0-7587-0402-3(X)) Book Wholesalers, Inc.

—Uncle Jed's Barber Shop. 1998. (J). pap. 5.99 (978-0-87628-331-8(8)) Ctr. for Applied Research in Education, The.

Moore, Johnny Ray. But Still, We Dream. 1999. (Illus.). 36p. pap. 7.95 (978-1-58521-006-0(4)) Books for Black Children, Inc.

—Talking Tyrone Said It. 1999. (Illus.). 60p. pap. 6.95 (978-1-58521-007-7(2)) Books for Black Children, Inc.

Moore, Shahari. It's Good Sunday. Waddington, Nicole, illus. 2003. (J). (978-0-9743394-0-5(7)) More Pr.

Moore, Stephanie Perry. Problem Solved: Perry Skky Jr. Series #3. 2007. 208p. pap. 9.95 (*978-0-7582-1874-2(5)* , Dafina) Kensington Publishing Corp.

—Saved Race, Vol. 3. 2001. (Payton Skky Ser.). 160p. (YA). (gr. 7-13). pap. 6.99 (978-0-8024-4238-3(2)) Moody Pubs.

—Saved Race. 2001. (gr. 7-12). lib. bdg. 15.30 (978-0-613-88831-8(6)) Tandem Library Bks.

—Sweet Honesty. 2005. (Carmen Browne Ser.: No. 2). 160p. (YA). (gr. 7-12). pap. 5.99 (978-0-8024-8168-9(X)) Moody Pubs.

—True Friends. 2005. (Carmen Browne Ser.). 128p. (YA). pap. 5.99 (978-0-8024-8172-6(8)) Moody Pubs.

Moses, Shelia P. The Baptism. 2007. 144p. (YA). (gr. 7 up). 15.99 (978-1-4169-0671-1(1) , McElderry, Margaret K.) Simon & Schuster Children's Publishing.

—I, Dred Scott: A Fictional Slave Narrative Based on the Life & Legal Precedent of Dred Scott. Christensen, Bonnie, illus. 2005. 112p. (YA). (gr. 7 up). 16.95 (978-0-689-85975-5(9) , McElderry, Margaret K.) Simon & Schuster Children's Publishing.

—The Legend of Buddy Bush. unabr. ed. 2005. (J). (gr. 3-7). 55.70 incl. audio (978-1-4193-3575-4(8) , 42043) Recorded Bks., LLC.

—The Legend of Buddy Bush. (Illus.). 224p. 2005. (YA). pap. 5.99 (978-1-4169-0716-9(5) , Simon Pulse); 2003. (J). 15.95 (978-0-689-85839-0(6) , McElderry, Margaret K.) Simon & Schuster Children's Publishing.

—The Legend of Buddy Bush. l.t. ed. 2005. 179p. 22.95 (978-0-7862-7311-9(9)) Thorndike Pr.

—The Return of Buddy Bush. 2008. 176p. (YA). pap. 5.99 (*978-1-4169-3925-2(3)* , Simon Pulse); 2005. (Illus.). 160p. (J). 15.95 (978-0-689-87431-4(6) , McElderry, Margaret K.) Simon & Schuster Children's Publishing.

—Sallie Gal & the Wall-a-Kee Man. Daly, Niki, illus. 2007. 160p. (J). (gr. 2-5). pap. 15.99 (*978-0-439-90890-0(6))* Scholastic, Inc.

Mosley, Walter. 47. 2006. 240p. (J). (gr. 7-17). reprint ed. pap. 7.99 (978-0-316-01635-3(7)) Little Brown & Co.

Moss, Thylias. I Want to Be. 1998. (978-0-606-13511-5(1)) Tandem Library Bks.

Mowry, Jess. Babylon Boyz. Gore, Leonid, illus. 1999. 192p. (YA). (gr. 8-12). mass mkt. 10.95 (978-0-689-82592-7(7) , 076714008007, Simon Pulse) Simon & Schuster Children's Publishing.

—Babylon Boyz. 1999. (J). (978-0-606-16318-7(2)) Tandem Library Bks.

Murphy, Rita. Black Angels. 2002. 176p. (J). (gr. 4). pap. 4.99 (978-0-440-22934-6(0) , Yearling) Random Hse. Children's Bks.

—Black Angels. 2002. (gr. 3-6). lib. bdg. 13.00 (978-0-613-57701-4(9)) Tandem Library Bks.

Myers, Christopher A. Fly! Myers, Christopher A., illus. 2001. (Illus.). 32p. (ps-17). 16.49 (978-0-7868-2373-4(9) , Jump at the Sun) Hyperion Bks. for Children.

Myers, Walter Dean. Autobiography of My Dead Brother. Myers, Christopher, illus. 2006. 224p. (J). pap. 6.99 (978-0-06-058293-7(6) , Amistad) HarperCollins Pubs.

—Autobiography of My Dead Brother. Myers, Christopher, illus. 2005. 224p. (J). 15.99 (978-0-06-058291-3(X)); lib. bdg. 16.89 (978-0-06-058292-0(8)) HarperCollins Pubs. (Amistad).

—The Beast. 2005. 192p. (YA). (gr. 7-12). 6.99 (978-0-439-36842-1(1) , Scholastic Paperbacks) Scholastic, Inc.

—Crystal. 2002. 208p. (YA). (gr. 7 up). reprint ed. pap. 6.50 (978-0-06-447312-5(0) , Harper Trophy) HarperCollins Pubs.

—Crystal. 2001. (gr. 5-8). lib. bdg. 14.10 (978-0-613-59802-6(4)) Tandem Library Bks.

—The Dream Bearer. 192p. (J). (gr. 5 up). 2003. 15.99 (978-0-06-029521-9(X)); 2004. reprint ed. pap. 5.99 (978-0-06-447289-0(2)) HarperCollins Pubs. (Amistad).

—The Dream Bearer. l.t. ed. 2003. 207p. (J). 25.95 (978-0-7862-5923-6(X)) Thorndike Pr.

—Fallen Angels. 2002. (Illus.). (J). 13.19 (978-0-7587-0353-8(8)) Book Wholesalers, Inc.

—Fallen Angels. 2003. (Illus.). 320p. (YA). (gr. 7-12). pap. 5.99 (978-0-590-40943-8(3) , Scholastic Paperbacks) Scholastic, Inc.

—Game. 2008. 240p. (J). 16.99 (*978-0-06-058294-4(4));* lib. bdg. 17.89 (*978-0-06-058295-1(2))* HarperCollins Pubs. (HarperTeen).

—The Glory Field. 1999. 420p. (J). 15.60 (978-0-03-054616-7(8)) Holt, Rinehart & Winston.

—Handbook for Boys: A Novel. (Amistad Ser.). (J). (gr. 5 up). 2003. 224p. pap. 6.99 (978-0-06-440930-8(9)); 2002. (Illus.). 192p. 16.99 (978-0-06-029146-4(X)) HarperCollins Pubs.

—Handbook for Boys: A Novel. 2003. (gr. 5-8). lib. bdg. 14.15 (978-0-613-65786-0(1)) Tandem Library Bks.

—Harlem Summer. (Illus.). (J). 2008. 304p. 17.99 (*978-0-439-91624-0(0));* 2007. 176p. (gr. 7 up). pap. 16.99 (978-0-439-36843-8(X)) Scholastic, Inc. (Scholastic Pr.).

—The Journal of Biddy Owens: The Negro Leagues, Birmingham, Alabama 1948. 2001. (978-0-606-22807-7(1)) Tandem Library Bks.

—The Journal of Joshua Loper: A Black Cowboy: The Chisholm Trail, 1871. 1999. (My Name Is America Ser.). (Illus.). 160p. (J). (gr. 4-8). pap. 10.95 (978-0-590-02691-8(7)) Scholastic, Inc.

—Monster. Myers, Christopher A., illus. 1999. (Amistad Ser.). 288p. (J). (gr. 7 up). 16.99 (978-0-06-028077-2(8)) HarperCollins Pubs.

—Monster. Myers, Christopher, illus. (Newbery Honor Roll Ser.). (J). 1999. 288p. (gr. 7 up). lib. bdg. 17.89 (978-0-06-028078-9(6)); 2001. 304p. reprint ed. pap. 7.99 (978-0-06-440731-1(4) , Amistad) HarperCollins Pubs.

—Motown & Didi: A Love Story. 2002. (Illus.). (J). 13.40 (978-0-7587-0384-2(8)) Book Wholesalers, Inc.

—The Mouse Rap. 3rd ed. (J). pap. 3.95 (978-0-13-800087-5(5)) Prentice Hall (Schl. Div.).

—The Righteous Revenge of Artemis Bonner. 2003. (J). (gr. 5 up). 22.25 (978-0-8446-7250-2(5)) Smith, Peter Pub., Inc.

—Slam! 1998. (Point Signature Ser.). 272p. (YA). (gr. 7-12). 5.99 (978-0-590-48668-2(3) , Scholastic Paperbacks) Scholastic, Inc.

—Street Love. (J). 2007. 160p. pap. 7.99 (*978-0-06-440732-8(2));* 2006. 144p. 15.99 (978-0-06-028079-6(4)); 2006. 144p. (gr. 8 up). lib. bdg. 16.89 (978-0-06-028080-2(8)) HarperCollins Pubs. (Amistad).

—145th Street: Short Stories. 160p. (YA). (gr. 7 up). 2001. pap. 5.99 (978-0-440-22916-2(2) , Laurel Leaf); 2000. 15.99 (978-0-385-32137-2(6) , Delacorte Bks. for Young Readers) Random Hse. Children's Bks.

—145th Street: Short Stories. 2001. (978-0-606-22414-7(9)) Tandem Library Bks.

Myers, Walter Dean. 145th Street: Short Stories. 2007. 160p. (YA). (gr. 7). lib. bdg. 18.99 (*978-0-385-90538-1(6)* , Delacorte Bks. for Young Readers) Random Hse. Children's Bks.

Myers, Walter Dean & Myers, Walter Dean. Slam! 1998. 266p. (YA). (gr. 7-12). lib. bdg. 14.15 (978-0-613-12111-8(2)) Tandem Library Bks.

—145th Street: Short Stories. 2001. 151p. (YA). (gr. 7-12). per. 13.55 (978-0-613-36855-1(X)) Tandem Library Bks.

Nash, Alissa. Markita. 2003. (Illus.). 35p. (J). (gr. k-3). pap. 7.95 (978-0-913543-39-9(X)) African American Images.

Neasi, Barbara J. Escucheme. Wummer, Amy, illus. (Rookie Reader Espanol Ser.). (J). (gr. k-2). 2002. pap. 4.95 (978-0-516-26314-4(5)); 2001. (SPA.). 32p. 19.50 (978-0-516-22358-2(5)) Scholastic Library Publishing. (Children's Pr.).

—Escucheme. 2001. (SPA.). (gr. k-3). lib. bdg. 12.95 (978-0-613-54203-6(7)) Tandem Library Bks.

—Listen to Me. Wummer, Amy, illus. 2nd rev. ed. 2001. (Rookie Reader Espanol Ser.). 32p. (J). (gr. k-2). pap. 4.95 (978-0-516-25970-3(9) , Children's Pr.) Scholastic Library Publishing.

—Listen to Me. 2001. (gr. k-3). lib. bdg. 12.95 (978-0-613-46085-9(5)) Tandem Library Bks.

Nelson, Vaunda Micheaux. Almost to Freedom. Bootman, Colin, illus. 2003. (Carolrhoda Picture Books Ser.). 40p. (J). (gr. 1-5). 15.95 (978-1-57505-342-4(X)) Lerner Publishing Group.

—Beyond Mayfield. 1999. 1p. (J). (gr. 5-9). 15.99 (978-0-399-23355-5(5) , Putnam Juvenile) Penguin Group (USA) Inc.

—Mayfield Crossing. 2002. 96p. (J). pap. 5.99 (978-0-698-11930-7(4) , Putnam Juvenile) Penguin Group (USA) Inc.

Netzarel, Orly. Yellow, Yellow-Brown, Yellow-Brown & Black. 2001. 160p. pap. 11.95 (978-0-595-18742-3(0) , Writers Club Pr.) iUniverse, Inc.

Neufeld, John. Edgar Allan. 2007. 136p. (gr. 5-9). per. 11.95 (*978-0-595-45039-8(3)* , Backinprint.com) iUniverse, Inc.

Nikola-Lisa, W. Summer Sun Risin' Tate, Don, illus. 32p. (J). (ps-ps). 2005. pap. 7.95 (978-1-58430-252-0(6)); 2002. 16.95 (978-1-58430-034-2(5)) Lee & Low Bks., Inc.

A B

Nobody Knows (Africans) 76p. (YA). (gr. 6-12). pap. 9.95 (978-0-8224-3683-6(3)) Globe Fearon Educational Publishing.

Nolan, Han. A Summer of Kings. 2006. (Illus.). 352p. (YA). 17.00 (978-0-15-205108-2(2)) Harcourt Children's Bks.

—A Summer of Kings. 2006. 334p. (J). (978-1-4156-7340-9(3)) Harcourt Trade Pubs.

Nolen, Jerdine. Big Jabe. Nelson, Kadir A., illus. 32p. (J). (gr. 1 up). 2004. pap. 6.99 (978-0-06-054061-6(3) , Amistad); 2000. 16.89 (978-0-688-13663-5(X)) HarperCollins Pubs.

—Big Jabe. 2004. (gr. k-3). lib. bdg. 15.30 (978-0-613-71462-4(8)) Tandem Library Bks.

—In My Momma's Kitchen. 2001. (Illus.). (J). 12.75 (978-0-606-21246-5(9)) Tandem Library Bks.

Nolen, Jerdine. Thunder Rose. Nelson, Kadir, illus. 2007. 32p. (J). pap. 7.00 (***978-0-15-206006-0(5)*** , Voyager Bks./Libros Viajeros) Harcourt Children's Bks.

Olswanger, Anna. Sweet Potato Pudding. 1999. (Illus.). 60p. pap. 6.95 (978-1-58521-008-4(0)) Books for Black Children, Inc.

Oseye, Ebele. Hold That Thought! You Too Can Be a Simpleton. Thomas, Cecilio, illus. 2000. 30p. (YA). pap. 5.00 (978-1-929454-05-1(8) , 917 863-6528) Eneke Pubns.

O'Shea, Robbie. I'm Brown & My Sister Isn't. Ambre, Matthew, illus. 2002. 20p. (J). (ps-5). pap. 13.95 (978-0-9718034-0-4(4) , 9718034) RKO Enterprises.

Owens, Tom. Free to Learn. Pollema-Cahill, Phyllis, illus. 2000. (Cover-to-Cover Bks.). (J). 55p. pap. (978-0-7891-5164-3(2)); 56p. (gr. 1-4). lib. bdg. 16.95 (978-0-7807-9314-9(5)) Perfection Learning Corp.

Owens, Vivian W. I Met a Great Lady: Ivy Meets Mary McLeod Bethune. Maxwell, Carolyn, ed. Watson, Richard J., illus. unabr. ed. 1998. 80p. (J). (gr. 4-11). pap. 8.95 (978-0-9623839-5-3(3)) Eschar Pubns.

—I Met a Great Man: John Meets Dr. Carver of Tuskegee. Owens, April, ed. Watson, Richard J., illus. unabr. ed. 1998. 64p. (J). (gr. 4-10). pap. 8.95 (978-0-9623839-6-0(1)) Eschar Pubns.

Pace, Lorenzo. Jalani & the Lock. 2001. (Jalani & the Lock Ser.). (Illus.). 24p. (J). lib. bdg. 23.95 (978-0-8239-9700-8(6) , PowerKids Pr.) Rosen Publishing Group, Inc., The.

Parker, Toni Trent. Sienna's Scrapbook: Our African American Heritage Trip. Genovese, Janell, illus. 2005. 64p. (J). 15.95 (978-0-8118-4300-3(9)) Chronicle Bks. LLC.

—Snowflake Kisses & Gingerbread Smiles. Anderson, Earl, illus. 2002. 16p. (J). pap. 6.95 (978-0-439-33872-1(7) , Cartwheel Bks.) Scholastic, Inc.

—Sweets & Treats. Anderson, Earl, illus. 2002. 16p. (J). pap. 6.95 (978-0-439-33871-4(9) , Cartwheel Bks.) Scholastic, Inc.

Paterson, Katherine. Jip, His Story. 2005. 192p. (YA). (gr. 5-9). pap. 5.99 (978-0-14-240411-9(X) , Puffin) Penguin Group (USA) Inc.

Patrick, Denise Lewis. Ma Dear's Old Green House. Sadler, Sonia Lynn, illus. 2004. (J). (gr. k-3). 16.95 (978-0-940975-55-2(6) , Sankofa Bks.) Just Us Bks., Inc.

Paulsen, Gary. The Legend of Bass Reeves. 2006. 160p. (YA). (gr. 7). 15.95 (978-0-385-74661-8(X) , Lamb, Wendy) Random Hse. Children's Bks.

—Sarny. 1999. 192p. (YA). (gr. 7-12). mass mkt. 5.99 (978-0-440-21973-6(6) , Laurel Leaf) Random Hse. Children's Bks.

—Sarny. 1999. (gr. 7-12). lib. bdg. 13.55 (978-0-613-19444-0(6)) Tandem Library Bks.

—Sarny: A Life Remembered. 1999. (978-0-606-16454-2(5)) Tandem Library Bks.

Pearsall, Shelley. Trouble Don't Last. 256p. (gr. 4-8). 2002. (Illus.). 14.95 (978-0-375-81490-7(6) , Knopf Bks. for Young Readers); 2002. (Illus.). lib. bdg. 16.99 (978-0-375-91490-4(0) , Knopf Bks. for Young Readers); 2003. (J). reprint ed. pap. 5.99 (978-0-440-41811-5(9) , Yearling) Random Hse. Children's Bks.

—Trouble Don't Last. 2003. (gr. 3-6). lib. bdg. 13.55 (978-0-613-85706-2(2)) Tandem Library Bks.

Pegram, Laura. Daughter's Day Blues. 2002. (gr. k-3). lib. bdg. 15.30 (978-0-613-49468-7(7)) Tandem Library Bks.

Per, Sharon Mills. Double Dutch. 2004. (gr. 5-8). lib. bdg. 13.00 (978-0-613-88160-9(5)) Tandem Library Bks.

Piercy, Patricia A. The Great Encounter: A Special Meeting Before Columbus. Wilkerson, Napoleon, illus. 2003. 41p. (J). (gr. 2-5). pap. 6.95 (978-0-913543-26-9(8)) African American Images.

Pinkney, Andrea Davis. Boycott Blues. 2008. (J). (***978-0-06-082118-0(3)); (*978-0-06-082119-7(1))*** HarperCollins Pubs. (Greenwillow Bks.).

—Fishing Day. Evans, Shane W., illus. 2003. 32p. (gr. k-4). 15.99 (978-0-7868-0766-6(0)); 16.49 (978-0-7868-2614-8(2) , Jump at the Sun) Hyperion Bks. for Children.

—Peggony-Po: A Whale of a Tale. Pinkney, Brian, illus. 2006. 32p. (ps-2). 16.99 (978-0-7868-1958-4(8) , Jump at the Sun) Hyperion Bks. for Children.

—Raven in a Dove House. 1999. (978-0-606-17789-4(2)) Tandem Library Bks.

—Silent Thunder. 2001. 224p. (gr. 3-7). pap. 5.99 (978-0-7868-1569-2(8) , Jump at the Sun) Hyperion Bks. for Children.

—Silent Thunder: A Civil War Story. 2001. (J). (978-0-606-21434-6(8)); (gr. 5-8). lib. bdg. 14.15 (978-0-613-62425-1(4)) Tandem Library Bks.

Pinkney, Brian. The Adventures of Sparrowboy. Pinkney, Brian, illus. 2002. (Illus.). (J). 14.47 (978-0-7587-1906-5(X)) Book Wholesalers, Inc.

—The Adventures of Sparrowboy. Pinkney, Brian, illus. 2000. (Illus.). 40p. (J). (ps-3). 7.99 (978-0-689-83534-6(5) , Aladdin) Simon & Schuster Children's Publishing.

—Adventures of Sparrowboy. 2000. (gr. k-3). lib. bdg. 14.15 (978-0-613-28396-0(1)) Tandem Library Bks.

—Jojo's Flying Sidekick. Pinkney, Brian, illus. 1998. (Illus.). 32p. (J). (gr. k-3). pap. 6.99 (978-0-689-82192-9(1) , Aladdin) Simon & Schuster Children's Publishing.

—Max Found Two Sticks. Pinkney, Brian, illus. 2002. (Illus.). (J). 15.53 (978-0-7587-3106-7(X)) Book Wholesalers, Inc.

—Max Found Two Sticks. Pinkney, Brian, illus. 2nd ed. 2005. (Stories to Go! Ser.). (Illus.). 40p. (J). 4.99 (978-1-4169-0310-9(0) , Aladdin) Simon & Schuster Children's Publishing.

Pinkney, Gloria Jean. Back Home. 1999. (J). 13.79 (978-0-606-16773-4(0)); lib. bdg. 15.30 (978-0-613-18238-6(3)) Tandem Library Bks.

Pinkney, Sandra. Read & Rise. Pinkney, Myles, illus. 2006. 40p. (J). (ps-3). pap. 15.99 (978-0-439-30929-5(8) , Cartwheel Bks.) Scholastic, Inc.

Pinkney, Sandra L. Shades of Black: A Celebration of Our Children. Pinkney, Myles, illus. 2006. 24p. (J). bds. 6.99 (978-0-439-80251-2(2) , Cartwheel Bks.) Scholastic, Inc.

—Shades of Black: A Celebration of Our Children. Pinkney, Myles C., illus. 2000. 40p. (J). (ps-3). pap. 15.95 (978-0-439-14892-4(8)) Scholastic, Inc.

—Shades of Black: A Celebration of Our Children. Pinkney, Myles C., photos by. 2000. (Illus.). 32p. (J). (ps-2). pap. 5.99 (978-0-439-14893-1(6)) Scholastic, Inc.

Polacco, Patricia. Mrs. Katz & Tush. Polacco, Patricia, illus. 2002. (Illus.). (J). 14.79 (978-0-7587-3191-3(4)) Book Wholesalers, Inc.

Porter, Connie. Addy's Short Story Collection. Dellosso, Gabriella & Graef, Renee, illus. 2006. 248p. (J). 12.95 (***978-1-59369-122-6(X))*** American Girl Publishing, Inc.

Porter, Connie Rose. All-Bright Court. 2000. (Illus.). 240p. pap. 12.00 (978-0-618-05679-8(3) , Mariner Bks.) Houghton Mifflin Co. Trade & Reference Div.

—All-Bright Court. 2000. (gr. 7-12). lib. bdg. 21.10 (978-0-613-27703-7(1)) Tandem Library Bks.

Poryes, Michael & Sherman, Susan. Dueling Divas. 2005. (That's So Raven Ser.: Vol. 8). (Illus.). 137p. (J). (***978-1-4156-0366-6(9))*** Disney Pr.

—Psyched. 2005. (That's So Raven Ser.: Vol. 10). (Illus.). 136p. (J). (***978-1-4156-2557-6(3))*** Disney Pr.

—Showtime! 2005. (That's So Raven Ser.: Vol. 9). (Illus.). 134p. (J). (***978-1-4156-1643-7(4))*** Disney Pr.

Poryes, Michael, et al. Family Affair. 2005. (Illus.). 128p. (J). (***978-1-4155-6887-3(1))*** Disney Pr.

Price, Hope Lynne. These Hands. Collier, Bryan, illus. rev. ed. 2007. 24p. (ps-1). pap. 6.99 (***978-1-4231-0633-3(4)*** , Jump at the Sun) Hyperion Bks. for Children.

Pride, Felicia, et al. Hallway Diaries: How to Be down Double Act the Summer She Learned to Dance. 2007. 400p. pap. 9.99 (***978-0-373-83084-8(X))*** Harlequin Enterprises, Ltd. CAN. *Dist:* Simon & Schuster, Inc.

Pugliano-Martin, Carol. John Henry: An AMER Tall Tale. 2006. 42.00 (***978-1-4108-6170-2(8))*** Benchmark Education Co.

Quattlebaum, Mary. Jackson Jones & Mission Greentop. 2005. 112p. (gr. 3-7). 5.50 (978-0-440-41957-0(3) , Yearling) Random Hse. Children's Bks.

—Jackson Jones & the Curse of the Outlaw Rose. 2006. 112p. (J). (gr. 3-7). 14.95 (978-0-385-73349-6(6)); lib. bdg. 16.99 (978-0-385-90365-3(0)) Random Hse. Children's Bks. (Delacorte Bks. for Young Readers).

Rabin, Staton. Black Powder. 2005. 256p. (J). (gr. 6-9). 16.95 (978-0-689-86876-4(6) , McElderry, Margaret K.) Simon & Schuster Children's Publishing.

Rahaman, Vashanti. Read for Me, Mama. McElrath-Eslick, Lori, illus. 2003. 32p. (J). (gr. 2-4). 15.95 (978-1-56397-313-0(8)) Boyds Mills Pr.

Rand, Edward A. The Knights of the White Shield: Up-the-Ladder Club Series Round One Play. 2007. 166p. pap. 11.99 (***978-1-4264-8273-1(6));*** 184p. pap. 14.99 (***978-1-4264-8310-3(4))*** BiblioBazaar.

Ransom, Candice. Rescue on the Outer Banks. Ritz, Karen, illus. 2002. 48p. (J). (gr. 1-3). lib. bdg. 14.10 (978-0-613-46163-4(0)) Tandem Library Bks.

Ransom, Candice F. Rescue on the Outer Banks. Ritz, Karen, illus. 2002. (On My Own History Ser.). 48p. (J). (gr. 1-3). lib. bdg. 23.93 (978-0-87614-460-2(1) , Carolrhoda Bks.) Lerner Publishing Group.

Raschka, Chris. Yo ! Yes? 2004. (J). (ps-5). 24.95 incl. audio (978-1-55592-066-1(7)); pap. 14.95 incl. audio (978-1-55592-067-8(5) , QPRA566) Weston Woods Studios, Inc.

—Yo! Yes? 2007. 32p. (J). pap. 6.99 (978-0-439-92185-5(6)) Scholastic, Inc.

Raven, Margot Theis. Circle Unbroken. Lewis, E. B., illus. 2004. 48p. (J). 16.00 (978-0-374-31289-3(3) , Farrar, Straus & Giroux (BYR)) Farrar, Straus & Giroux.

—Circle Unbroken. Lewis, E.B., illus. 2007. 48p. (J). pap. 6.99 (***978-0-312-37603-1(0))*** Square Fish.

Rees, Douglas. Lightning Time. 1999. (J). (978-0-606-19069-5(4)) Tandem Library Bks.

Reese, Della. God Inside of Me. Buchanan, Yvonne, illus. 2005. 30p. (J). (gr. 4-8). reprint ed. 16.00 (978-0-7567-9366-1(1)) DIANE Publishing Co.

—God Inside of Me. Buchanan, Yvonne, illus. 1999. 32p. (J). lib. bdg. 16.49 (978-0-7868-2395-6(X) , Jump at the Sun) Hyperion Bks. for Children.

Regan, Dana, illus. Messy Bessey. 2002. (Messy Bessey Ser.). (J). 12.83 (978-0-7587-7183-4(5)) Book Wholesalers, Inc.

Reid, Robin. Big Storm. 2002. (gr. k-3). lib. bdg. 11.25 (978-0-613-50410-2(0)) Tandem Library Bks.

Reynolds, Aaron. Metal Man. Hoppe, Paul, illus. 2008. (J). (***978-1-58089-150-9(0))*** Charlesbridge Publishing, Inc.

Rhone, Alexus D. Premature Pleasures. 2001. 224p. (YA). (gr. 6 up). 16.95 (978-0-9708688-0-0(4)) Unshackled Publishing.

Richardson, Charisse. The Real Slam Dunk (SE) 2005. 80p. (J). pap. 3.99 (978-0-14-240442-3(X) , Puffin) Penguin Group (USA) Inc.

Riggio, Anita. Secret Signs: An Escape Through the Underground Railroad. Riggio, Anita, illus. 2003. (Illus.). 32p. (J). (gr. k-3). 15.95 (978-1-56397-555-4(6)) Boyds Mills Pr.

Rinaldi, Ann. Come Juneteenth. 2007. (Great Episodes Ser.). (Illus.). 256p. (YA). 17.00 (978-0-15-205947-7(4)) Harcourt Children's Bks.

—The Education of Mary: A Little Miss of Color, 1832. 2000. 256p. (gr. 5-9). 15.99 (978-0-7868-0532-7(3) , Jump at the Sun) Hyperion Bks. for Children.

—The Education of Mary: A Little Miss of Color, 1832. 2005. 176p. (J). pap. (978-0-7868-1377-3(6)) Hyperion Pr.

—Hang a Thousand Trees with Ribbons: The Story of Phillis Wheatley. 2005. (Great Episodes Ser.). 352p. (YA). pap. 6.95 (978-0-15-205393-2(X) , Gulliver Bks.) Harcourt Children's Bks.

—Taking Liberty: The Story of Oney Judge, George Washington's Runaway Slave. Dudash, C. Michael, illus. 2004. 272p. (YA). mass mkt. 5.99 (978-0-689-85188-9(X) , Simon Pulse) Simon & Schuster Children's Publishing.

—Taking Liberty: The Story of Oney Judge, George Washington's Runaway Slave. 2002. 272p. (YA). (gr. 7 up). 16.95 (978-0-689-85187-2(1)) Simon & Schuster Children's Publishing.

—Taking Liberty: The Story of Oney Judge, George Washington's Runaway Slave. 2004. (gr. 7-12). lib. bdg. 14.15 (978-0-613-73369-4(X)) Tandem Library Bks.

Ringgold, Faith. Cassie's Word Quilt. 2004. (Illus.). 32p. (J). (ps-1). pap. 6.99 (978-0-553-11233-7(3) , Dragonfly Bks.) Random Hse. Children's Bks.

—Cassie's Word Quilt. Ringgold, Faith, illus. 2002. (Illus.). 32p. (J). (gr. k-ps). 13.95 (978-0-375-81200-2(8)); lib. bdg. 15.99 (978-0-375-91200-9(2)) Random Hse. Children's Bks. (Knopf Bks. for Young Readers).

—The Invisible Princess. 2001. 13.79 (978-0-606-20729-4(5)) Tandem Library Bks.

—Tar Beach. Ringgold, Faith, illus. 2002. (Illus.). (J). 14.79 (978-0-7587-5352-6(7)) Book Wholesalers, Inc.

Robbins, Jacqui. The New Girl ... & Me. Phelan, Matt, illus. 2006. 32p. (J). (ps-2). 16.95 (978-0-689-86468-1(X) , Atheneum) Simon & Schuster Children's Publishing.

Robinet, Harriette Gillem. Children of the Fire. 2001. (gr. 3-6). lib. bdg. 13.00 (978-0-613-33685-7(2)) Tandem Library Bks.

—Forty Acres & Maybe a Mule. 2000. (YA). (gr. 3 up). pap. 52.00 incl. audio (978-0-7887-4332-0(5) , 41127) Recorded Bks., LLC.

—Forty Acres & Maybe a Mule. Nickens, Bessie, illus. 1998. (Jean Karl Ser.). 144p. (J). (gr. 3-7). 17.99 (978-0-689-82078-6(X) , Atheneum) Simon & Schuster Children's Publishing.

—Forty Acres & Maybe a Mule. 2000. 11.64 (978-0-606-17824-2(4)); (gr. 3-6). lib. bdg. 13.00 (978-0-613-22986-9(X)) Tandem Library Bks.

—Twelve Travelers, Twenty Horses. 208p. (J). 2005. pap. 4.99 (978-0-689-87607-3(6) , Aladdin); 2003. (Illus.). 16.95 (978-0-689-84561-1(8) , Atheneum) Simon & Schuster Children's Publishing.

—Walking to the Bus-Rider Blues. 2002. (gr. 3-6). lib. bdg. 13.00 (978-0-613-57932-2(1)) Tandem Library Bks.

Robinet, Harriette Gillem & Minor, Wendell. Forty Acres & Maybe a Mule. 2000. (Jean Karl Ser.). 144p. (J). (gr. 3-7). reprint ed. pap. 4.99 (978-0-689-83317-5(2) , Aladdin) Simon & Schuster Children's Publishing.

Robinson, Sharon. Safe at Home. 160p. (J). 2007. (gr. 4-7). pap. 4.99 (***978-0-439-67198-9(1)*** , Scholastic Paperbacks); 2006. pap. 16.99 (978-0-439-67197-2(3) , Scholastic) Scholastic, Inc.

—Slam Dunk! 2007. 160p. (J). (gr. 4-7). pap. 16.99 (***978-0-439-67199-6(X)*** , Scholastic Pr.) Scholastic, Inc.

Roddy, Lee. Risking the Dream. 2000. (Between Two Flags Ser.: Vol. 6). (Illus.). 176p. (J). (gr. 6-9). pap. 5.99 (978-0-7642-2030-2(6)) Bethany Hse. Pubs.

Rodman, Mary Ann. Yankee Girl. 2004. (Illus.). 224p. (J). 17.00 (978-0-374-38661-0(7) , Farrar, Straus & Giroux (BYR)) Farrar, Straus & Giroux.

Rogers, Karen M. Mano Sobre Mano. Alvarado, Ana María, tr. Taylor, Piper, illus. 2000. (Think-Kids Book Collection).Tr. of Hand over Hand. (SPA.). 16p. (J). pap. 2.95 (978-1-58237-053-8(2)) Creative Thinkers, Inc.

Romain, Trevor. Jemma's Journey. Lopez, Pat, illus. 2003. 32p. (YA). (gr. k-2). 15.95 (978-1-56397-937-8(3)) Boyds Mills Pr.

Rosales, Melodye. 'Twas the Night B'Fore Christmas: An African-American Version. Rosales, Melodye, illus. 2002. (Illus.). (J). 22.40 (978-0-7587-3878-3(1)) Book Wholesalers, Inc.

Ross, Andrea. To Touch the Sun. Davenport, May, ed. l.t. ed. 2000. 195p. (YA). (gr. 9-12). pap. 15.95 (978-0-943864-99-0(2)) Davenport, May Pubs.

Roth, Philip. The Human Stain. 2001. (gr. 7-12). lib. bdg. 23.45 (978-0-613-45775-0(7)) Tandem Library Bks.

Rountree, Wendy. Lost Soul. 2003. 87p. (J). pap. 14.95 (978-1-59129-975-2(6)) PublishAmerica, Inc.

Rubright, Lynn. Mama's Window. Smith, Duane, illus. 2005. 89p. (J). 16.95 (978-1-57480-160-6(0)) Lee & Low Bks., Inc.

Rue, Nancy N. The Ally. 1998. (Christian Heritage Ser.). 192p. (J). (gr. 3-7). pap. (978-1-56179-561-1(5)) Focus on the Family Publishing.

—Do I Have to Paint You a Picture. 1998. (gr. 7-12). lib. bdg. 15.25 (978-0-613-88736-6(0)) Tandem Library Bks.

—The Misfit. 1998. (Christian Heritage Ser.). 192p. (J). (gr. 3-7). pap. (978-1-56179-560-4(7)) Focus on the Family Publishing.

—The Stunt. 1999. (Christian Heritage Ser.). 208p. (J). (gr. 3-7). pap. 5.99 (978-1-56179-833-9(9)) Bethany Hse. Pubs.

Russell, Barbara Timberlake. Maggie's Amerikay. Burke, Jim, illus. 2006. 40p. (J). 17.00 (978-0-374-34722-2(0) , Farrar, Straus & Giroux (BYR)) Farrar, Straus & Giroux.

Rust, Ann O'Connell. Torry Island. Rust, Allen F., ed. 2002. (Nonie of the Everglades Ser.: Vol. II). 94p. (J). (gr. 4-7). pap. 7.95 (978-1-883203-06-1(6)) Amaro Bks.

Rutberg, Donald Paul. Running Through Kenya. 1999. (Illus.). 40p. (J). (gr. 3-8). pap. 8.95 (978-1-58521-011-4(0)) Books for Black Children, Inc.

Sachar, Louis. Small Steps. (YA). 2008. 288p. (gr. 7). pap. 8.99 (***978-0-385-73315-1(1));*** 2006. 272p. (gr. 5). 16.95 (978-0-385-73314-4(3)); 2006. 272p. (gr. 7). lib. bdg. 19.99 (978-0-385-90333-2(2)) Random Hse. Children's Bks. (Delacorte Bks. for Young Readers).

—Small Steps. rev. l.t. ed. 2006. 339p. 23.95 (978-0-7862-8297-5(5)) Thorndike Pr.

Samton, Sheila W. Amazing Aunt Agatha. 2000. (Metro Reading Program Ser.). (J). (gr. k). 7.98 (978-1-58120-963-1(0)); 45.95 (978-1-58830-015-7(3)) Metropolitan Teaching & Learning Co.

San Francisco Shake-Up, 6 Packs. (Greetings Ser.: Vol. 3). (gr. 3-5). 31.00 (978-0-7635-2075-5(6)) Rigby Education.

Sanders, Scott Russell. A Place Called Freedom. 2001. (J). (978-0-606-20854-3(2)) Tandem Library Bks.

Sargent, Dave & Sargent, Pat. Nubbin: (Linebacked Apricot Dun) Freedom, 30, 43. Lenoir, Jane, illus. 2003. (Saddle Up Ser.: Vol. 43). 42p. (J). pap. 6.95 (978-1-56763-704-5(3)); lib. bdg. 22.60 (978-1-56763-703-8(5)) Ozark Publishing.

Sarratt, Carla. Freshman Focus Carter G Woodson High Sc. 2006. 292p. pap. 14.95 (***978-1-4327-0109-3(6))*** Outskirts Press, Inc.

Sawyer, Kem Knapp. Freedom Calls: Journey of a Slave Girl. 2001. v, 181p. (J). (gr. 3-6). lib. bdg. 17.95 (978-1-57249-206-6(6) , White Mane Kids) White Mane Publishing Co., Inc.

Schertle, Alice. Down the Road. Lewis, Earl, illus. 2000. 40p. (J). (gr. k-3). pap. 7.00 (978-0-15-202471-0(9) , Harcourt Paperbacks) Harcourt Children's Bks.

—Down the Road. Lewis, E. B., illus. 2000. (J). (ps-17). lib. bdg. 14.15 (978-0-613-29935-0(3)) Tandem Library Bks.

—Down the Road. 2000. 12.80 (978-0-606-20324-1(9)) Tandem Library Bks.

Schlabach, Janet. Riverboat Runaways. 1999. (Illus.). 138p. (J). (gr. 4-8). pap. 15.95 (978-0-936389-75-2(3)) Tudor Pubs., Inc.

Scholastic, Inc. Staff & Barnes, Derrick D. Low-Down Bad-Day Blues. Boyd, Aaron, illus. 2004. (Just for You! Ser.). 32p. (gr. k-1). pap. 3.99 (978-0-439-56867-8(6) , Teaching Resources) Scholastic, Inc.

Scholastic, Inc. Staff & Bermiss, Aamir Lee. Just for You; I Hate to Be Sick. Wilson-Max, Ken, illus. 2004. (Just for You! Ser.). 32p. (gr. k-3). pap. 3.99 (978-0-439-56877-7(3) , Teaching Resources) Scholastic, Inc.

Scholastic, Inc. Staff & Black, Sonia. Just for You! Jumping the Broom. 2004. (Just for You! Ser.). (Illus.). 32p. pap. 3.99 (978-0-439-56878-4(1) , Teaching Resources) Scholastic, Inc.

—Mommy's Bed. 2004. (Just for You! Ser.). (Illus.). 32p. pap. 3.99 (978-0-439-56857-9(9) , Teaching Resources) Scholastic, Inc.

Scholastic, Inc. Staff & Boyd, Dee. Only the Stars. Rich, Anna, illus. 2004. (Just for You! Ser.). 32p. pap. 3.99 (978-0-439-56862-3(5) , Teaching Resources) Scholastic, Inc.

Scholastic, Inc. Staff & Brooks, Regina. Just for You! Never Finished, Never Done! Borgella, Marjorie, illus. 2004. (Just for You! Ser.). 32p. pap. 3.99 (978-0-439-56863-0(3) , Teaching Resources) Scholastic, Inc.

Scholastic, Inc. Staff & Ford, Bernette G. Don't Hit Me! Grier, Gary, illus. 2004. (Just for You! Ser.). 32p. (gr. k-1). pap. 3.99 (978-0-439-56860-9(9) , Teaching Resources) Scholastic, Inc.

Scholastic, Inc. Staff & Ford, Juwanda G. Shop Talk. Hoston, Jim, illus. 2004. (Just for You! Ser.). 32p. (gr. k-3). pap. 3.99 (978-0-439-56873-9(0) , Teaching Resources) Scholastic, Inc.

Scholastic, Inc. Staff & Giovanni, Nikki. The Girls in the Circle. Johnson, Cathy Ann, illus. 2004. (Just for You! Ser.). 32p. pap. 3.99 (978-0-439-56861-6(7) , Teaching Resources) Scholastic, Inc.

Scholastic, Inc. Staff & Grimes, Nikki. Day with Daddy. Tadgell, Nicole, illus. 2004. (Just for You! Ser.). 32p. pap. 3.99 (978-0-439-56850-0(1) , Teaching Resources) Scholastic, Inc.

Scholastic, Inc. Staff & Hooks, Gwendolyn. Three's a Crowd. Walker, Sylvia, illus. 2004. (Just for You! Ser.). 32p. (gr. k-3). pap. 3.99 (978-0-439-56865-4(X) , Teaching Resources) Scholastic, Inc.

Scholastic, Inc. Staff & Hudson, Cheryl. Just for You! What Do You Know? Snow! Walker, Sylvia, illus. 2004. (Just for You! Ser.). 32p. pap. 3.99 (978-0-439-56851-7(X) , Teaching Resources) Scholastic, Inc.

Scholastic, Inc. Staff & Hudson, Wade. The Two Tyrones. Page, Mark, illus. 2004. (Just for You! Ser.). 32p. (gr. k-3). pap. 3.99 (978-0-439-56866-1(8) , Teaching Resources) Scholastic, Inc.

Scholastic, Inc. Staff & Medearis, Angela Shelf. Singing for Dr. King. Van Wright, Cornelius & Hu, Ying-Hwa, illus. 2004. (Just for You! Ser.). 32p. (gr. k-3). pap. 3.99 (978-0-439-56855-5(2) , Teaching Resources) Scholastic, Inc.

Scholastic, Inc. Staff & Taylor-Butler, Christine. Just for You! No Boys Allowed! Page, Mark, illus. 2004. (Just for You! Ser.). 32p. pap. 3.99 (978-0-439-56856-2(0) , Teaching Resources) Scholastic, Inc.

—Mom Like No Other. Devard, Nancy, illus. 2004. (Just for You! Ser.). 32p. pap. 3.99 (978-0-439-56853-1(6) , Teaching Resources) Scholastic, Inc.

Scholastic, Inc. Staff, et al. Lights Out! Tadgell, Nicole, illus. 2004. (Just for You! Ser.). 32p. (J). (gr. k-1). pap. 3.99 (978-0-439-56868-5(4) , Teaching Resources) Scholastic, Inc.

Schotter, Roni & Dorling Kindersley Publishing Staff. F Is for Freedom. Mordan, C. B., illus. 2000. 96p. (J). (gr. 2-5). 15.99 (978-0-7894-2641-3(2)) Dorling Kindersley Publishing, Inc.

Schraff, Ann. Until We Meet Again. 2007. (Bluford Ser.: No. 7). 160p. (J). pap. 3.99 (***978-0-439-90488-9(9)** , Scholastic Paperbacks) Scholastic, Inc.

Schraff, Anne. Freedom Knows No Color. 2000. 118p. (J). pap. (978-0-7891-5136-0(7)); (gr. 5-12). lib. bdg. 13.95 (978-0-7807-9270-8(X)) Perfection Learning Corp.

—Lost & Found. Langan, Paul, ed. 2002. (Bluford Ser.: 1). 133p. (J). mass mkt. 4.95 (978-0-944210-02-4(3)) Townsend Pr.

Schunk, Laurel. Black & Secret Midnight. 1998. 238p. (gr. 6-8). 24.99 (978-0-9661879-0-8(3) , SKP98-41) St Kitts Pr.

Scillian, Devin. Pappy's Handkerchief. Ellison, Chris, illus. rev. ed. 2007. (Tales of Young Americans Ser.). 40p. (J). (gr. 3-7). 17.95 (***978-1-58536-316-2(2)**) Sleeping Bear Pr.

Scruggs, Afi. Jump Rope Magic. Diaz, David, illus. 2000. 40p. (J). (ps-4). pap. 16.95 (978-0-590-69327-1(1) , Blue Sky Pr., The) Scholastic, Inc.

Serfozo, Mary. What's What? a Guessing Game. 2000. (gr. k-3). lib. bdg. 15.30 (978-0-613-22614-1(3)) Tandem Library Bks.

Sewell, Earl. Keysha's Drama. 2007. 256p. pap. 9.99 (***978-0-373-83079-4(3)**) Harlequin Enterprises, Ltd. CAN. *Dist:* Simon & Schuster, Inc.

Shahan, Sherry. Together for Kwanzaa. 2000. (Pictureback Ser.). (978-0-606-18504-2(6)) Tandem Library Bks.

Shaik, Fatima. Melitte. 2000. (978-0-606-18432-8(5)) Tandem Library Bks.

Sharing Turf. 2004. (Illus.). (YA). mass mkt. 19.95 (978-0-9753663-0-1(0)) Ballad Productions.

Shaw, Marilyn Bishop. Solomon. 2006. 203p. (J). 14.95 (978-1-56164-349-3(1)) Pineapple Pr., Inc.

Shelton, Rick. Hoggle's Christmas. Gates, Donald, illus. 2007. 80p. (J). pap. 11.95 (***978-1-60306-026-4(X)**) NewSouth, Inc.

Sibley, Linda. David Joins the California Gold Rush. 2004. 96p. (***978-0-7891-6002-7(1)**) Perfection Learning Corp.

Siegelson, Kim L. Escape South. Jackson, Shelley, illus. 2004. (Road to Reading Ser.). 80p. (J). (gr. k-3). pap. 3.99 (978-0-307-26504-3(8) , Random Hse. Bks. for Young Readers) Random Hse. Children's Bks.

—Escape South. 2000. (J). 10.79 (978-0-606-18931-6(9)) Tandem Library Bks.

—In the Time of the Drums. Pinkney, Brian, illus. 1999. (Jump at the Sun Bks.). 32p. (gr. 1-4). 15.99 (978-0-7868-0436-8(X)) Hyperion Bks. for Children.

Simon, Charnan. I Like to Win! Handelman, Dorothy, photos by. 1999. (Real Kids Readers Ser.). (Illus.). 32p. (J). (gr. k-1). pap. 4.99 (978-0-7613-2087-6(3) , Millbrook Pr.) Lerner Publishing Group.

—I Like to Win! 1999. (ps-2). lib. bdg. 13.00 (978-0-613-18157-0(3)) Tandem Library Bks.

Singletary, Mabel Elizabeth. Something to Jump About! 2008. 150p. pap. 5.99 (***978-0-8024-2252-1(7)**) Moody Pubs.

Sion Charnan. ¡Me gusta ganar! (I Like to Win!) 2007. (Lecturas para niños de verdad - Nivel 1 (Real Kids Readers - Level 1) Ser.). (J). pap. 5.95 (***978-0-8225-7801-7(8)** , Ediciones Lerner) Lerner Publishing Group.

Sitomer, Alan Lawrence. Hip-Hop High School. 2006. 368p. (J). (978-0-7868-3831-8(0) , Jump at the Sun) Hyperion Bks. for Children.

—The Hoopster. 2006. 224p. (gr. 7-17). pap. 5.99 (978-0-7868-4910-9(X) , Jump at the Sun) Hyperion Bks. for Children.

—The Hoopster: Read-Along/Homework Pack. unabr. ed. 2005. (YA). 65.74 incl. audio (978-1-4025-7027-8(9) , 41853) Recorded Bks., LLC.

Smalls-Hector, Irene. Because You're Lucky. Hays, Michael, illus. 2004. 48p. (J). (ps-ps). lib. bdg. 13.19 (978-0-606-30471-9(1)) Tandem Library Bks.

—I Can't Take a Bath. Boyd, Aaron, illus. 2004. (Just for You! Ser.). 32p. (J). pap. 3.99 (978-0-439-56852-4(8)) Scholastic, Inc.

Smalls, Irene. Irene & the Big, Fine Nickel. Geter, Tyrone, illus. 2nd ed. 2003. 32p. (J). (ps-3). pap. 5.99 (978-0-316-69832-0(6)) Little, Brown Bks. for Young Readers.

—Irene & the Big, Fine Nickel. 2003. (gr. k-3). lib. bdg. 7.20 (978-0-613-71768-7(6)) Tandem Library Bks.

—My Nana & Me. Johnson, Cathy Ann, illus. 2005. 24p. (J). (ps-3). 15.99 (978-0-316-16821-2(1)) Little Brown & Co.

—A Strawbeater's Thanksgiving. Rosales, Meodye, illus. 1998. 32p. (J). (gr. 2-5). 15.95 (978-0-316-79866-2(5)) Little Brown & Co.

Smith, Grant Callie. Janie's Freedom: African-Americans in the Aftermath of the Civil War. 2006. 144p. (J). pap. 4.97 (978-1-59789-086-1(3)) Barbour Publishing, Inc.

Smith, Patricia. Janna & the Kings. Boyd, Aaron, illus. 2003. 32p. (J). 16.95 (978-1-58430-088-5(4)) Lee & Low Bks., Inc.

Smith, Sherri L. Sparrow. 2008. 192p. (YA). (gr. 7). mass mkt. 6.50 (***978-0-440-23945-1(1)** , Laurel Leaf) Random Hse. Children's Bks.

Smothers, Ethel Footman. Down in the Piney Woods. 2004. 128p. (J). pap. 7.00 (978-0-8028-5248-9(3)) Eerdmans, William B. Publishing Co.

—Down in the Piney Woods. 2003. (gr. 3-6). lib. bdg. 15.30 (978-0-613-75341-8(0)) Tandem Library Bks.

—The Hard-Times Jar. Holyfield, John, illus. 2003. 32p. (J). 16.00 (978-0-374-32852-8(8) , Farrar, Straus & Giroux (BYR)) Farrar, Straus & Giroux.

—Moriah's Pond. 2004. 96p. (J). pap. 7.00 (978-0-8028-5249-6(1)) Eerdmans, William B. Publishing Co.

—Moriah's Pond. 2003. (gr. 3-6). lib. bdg. 15.30 (978-0-613-67247-4(X)) Tandem Library Bks.

The Snowy Day. 2001. (J). pap., wbk. ed. (978-1-56137-476-2(8)) Novel Units, Inc.

The Snowy Day. 2004. 29.95 incl. cd-rom (978-1-55592-853-7(6)) Weston Woods Studios, Inc.

Southgate, Martha. Another Way to Dance. 1998. (978-0-606-12878-0(6)) Tandem Library Bks.

—Fall of Rome. 2003. (gr. 7-12). lib. bdg. 21.10 (978-0-613-62902-7(7)) Tandem Library Bks.

Spruill, Ed & Spruill, Sonya. Jordan's Hair. Peringer, Stephen Mercer, illus. 2005. 16p. (J). 8.00 (978-0-8170-1484-1(5)) Judson Pr.

Staples, Suzanne Fisher. Dangerous Skies. 1998. 12.64 (978-0-606-13312-8(7)) Tandem Library Bks.

Stauffacher, Sue. Bessie Smith & the Night Riders. Holyfield, John, illus. 2006. 32p. (J). (ps-3). 16.99 (978-0-399-24237-3(6) , Putnam Juvenile) Penguin Group (USA) Inc.

Stephens, Torrance. A Matter of Attention. 2003. 129p. (YA). pap. 11.95 (978-0-7414-1505-9(4)) Infinity Publishing.

Steptoe, Javaka. The Jones Family Express. Steptoe, Javaka, illus. 2005. (Illus.). 40p. (J). 7.95 (978-1-58430-262-9(3)) Lee & Low Bks., Inc.

—The Jones Family Express. 2003. (Illus.). 40p. (J). (ps-4). 17.95 (978-1-58430-047-2(7)) Lee & Low Bks., Inc.

Steptoe, John L. Creativity. Lewis, Earl, illus. 2003. 32p. (J). (gr. k-3). pap. 5.95 (978-0-618-31677-9(9) , Clarion Bks.) Houghton Mifflin Co. Trade & Reference Div.

Stowe, Harriet Beecher. Uncle Tom's Cabin. 2002. (gr. 3-6). lib. bdg. 14.15 (978-0-613-63239-3(7)) Tandem Library Bks.

Strickland, Brad. The Wrath of the Grinning Ghost. 2001. (Illus.). (J). (978-0-606-21537-4(9)) Tandem Library Bks.

Strickland, Michael R. Haircuts at Sleepy Sam's. Holliday, Keaf, illus. 2003. 32p. (J). (gr. 2-4). 15.95 (978-1-56397-562-2(9)) Boyds Mills Pr.

Stroud, Bettye. The Patchwork Path: A Quilt Map to Freedom. Bennett, Erin Susanne, illus. 2005. 32p. (J). (gr. k-3). 16.99 (978-0-7636-2423-1(3)) Candlewick Pr.

Stroud, Bettye & Lucas, Cedric, illus. The Leaving. 2001. 32p. (J). (gr. 1-4). 15.95 (978-0-7614-5067-2(X) , Cavendish Children's Bks.) Cavendish, Marshall Corp.

Stuchner, Joan Betty. Josephine's Dream. Walther, Chantelle, illus. 2008. 32p. 16.95 (***978-1-934393-04-8(5)**) Silverleaf Pr.

Suen, Anastasia. Loose Tooth. 2003. (gr. k-3). lib. bdg. 11.80 (978-0-613-67459-1(6)) Tandem Library Bks.

—The Loose Tooth. Eitzen, Allan, illus. 2003. (Easy-to-Read Ser.). 32p. (J). (gr. k-2). pap. 3.99 (978-0-14-250064-4(X) , Puffin) Penguin Group (USA) Inc.

Sullivan, Jaqueline Levering. Annie's War. 2007. 190p. (J). (gr. 3-7). 15.00 (***978-0-8028-5325-7(0)** , Eerdmans Bks For Young Readers) Eerdmans, William B. Publishing Co.

Switzer-Clarke, Eileen. Blossom: A Girl's Adventures in Revolutionary Rockland. Carney, Barbara J., illus. 1998. 108p. (J). (gr. 3-6). pap. 8.00 (978-0-911183-44-3(2)) Historical Society of Rockland County, The.

Tarpley, Natasha Anastasia. Bippity Bop Barbershop. Lewis, E. B., illus. 2002. 32p. (J). (ps-3). 16.99 (978-0-316-52284-7(8)) Little, Brown Bks. for Young Readers.

—Destiny's Gift. Burrowes, Adjoa J., tr. Burrowes, Adjoa J., illus. 2004. 32p. (J). 16.95 (978-1-58430-156-1(2)) Lee & Low Bks., Inc.

—I Love My Hair! Lewis, E. B., illus. 1998. 32p. (J). (ps-3). 16.99 (978-0-316-52275-5(9)) Little Brown & Co.

—I Love My Hair! Lewis, E. B., illus. (J). (ps-k). 2003. 11p. bds. 6.99 (978-0-316-52558-9(8)); 2001. 32p. pap. 6.99 (978-0-316-52375-2(5)) Little, Brown Bks. for Young Readers.

Tarpley, Natasha Anastasia, ed. & illus. I Love My Hair! Tarpley, Natasha Anastasia, illus. 2001. 12.75 (978-0-606-22561-8(7)) Tandem Library Bks.

Tate, Eleanora E. Celeste's Harlem Renaissance. 2007. 288p. (J). (gr. 3-7). 15.99 (978-0-316-52394-3(1)) Little Brown & Co.

—The Minstrel's Melody. 2001. (American Girl Collection). (Illus.). (J). (978-0-606-21331-8(7)) Tandem Library Bks.

Taulbert, Clifton L. Little Cliff & the Porch People. Kane, Cindy, ed. Lewis, Earl, illus. 1999. 32p. (J). (ps-3). 16.99 (978-0-8037-2174-6(9) , Dial) Penguin Group (USA) Inc.

Taylor, Ann & HarperCollins Staff. Baby Dance. Van Heerden, Marjorie, illus. 1999. (Growing Tree Ser.). 16p. (J). (ps up). 6.99 (978-0-694-01206-0(8) , Harper Festival) HarperCollins Pubs.

Taylor-Butler, Christine. A Mom Like No Other. Devard, Nancy, illus. 2004. 32p. (J). lib. bdg. 15.00 (***978-1-4242-0227-0(2)**) Fitzgerald Bks.

Taylor, Debbie. Sweet Music in Harlem. Morrison, Frank, tr. Morrison, Frank, illus. 2004. 32p. (J). 16.95 (978-1-58430-165-3(1)) Lee & Low Bks., Inc.

Taylor, Mildred D. The Friendship. Ginsberg, Max, illus. 1998. 56p. (gr. 2-6). pap. 4.99 (978-0-14-038964-7(4) , Puffin) Penguin Group (USA) Inc.

—The Friendship. 1998. 11.79 (978-0-606-12938-1(3)) Tandem Library Bks.

—The Gold Cadillac. Hays, Michael & Ginsberg, Max, illus. 1998. 48p. (YA). (gr. 2-6). pap. 4.99 (978-0-14-038963-0(6) , Puffin) Penguin Group (USA) Inc.

—The Gold Cadillac. 1998. 11.79 (978-0-606-13433-0(6)) Tandem Library Bks.

—The Land. 2003. 400p. (YA). pap. 6.99 (978-0-14-250146-7(8) , Puffin) Penguin Group (USA) Inc.

—The Land. Ginsburg, Max, illus. 2001. 392p. (J). (gr. 7 up). 17.99 (978-0-8037-1950-7(7) , Dial) Penguin Group (USA) Inc.

—Lloro por la Tierra. 2000. (gr. 5-8). lib. bdg. 19.90 (978-0-613-70978-1(0)) Tandem Library Bks.

—Mississippi Bridge. 2002. (J). 12.87 (978-0-7587-9586-1(6)) Book Wholesalers, Inc.

—Mississippi Bridge. Ginsburg, Max, illus. 2000. 64p. (J). (gr. 4-7). pap. 4.99 (978-0-14-130817-3(6) , Puffin) Penguin Group (USA) Inc.

—Mississippi Bridge. 2002. (J). (gr. 2-6). 21.00 (978-0-8446-7213-7(0)) Smith, Peter Pub., Inc.

—Mississippi Bridge. Ginsburg, Max, illus. 2000. 62p. (J). (ps-7). lib. bdg. 13.00 (978-0-8335-9262-0(9)) Tandem Library Bks.

—Mississippi Bridge. 2000. (978-0-606-18434-2(1)) Tandem Library Bks.

—Roll of Thunder, Hear My Cry. 2002. (Illus.). (J). 14.04 (978-0-7587-0209-8(4)) Book Wholesalers, Inc.

—Roll of Thunder, Hear My Cry. 2004. 276p. (gr. 4-8). reprint ed. pap. 10.00 (978-0-7567-7955-9(3)) DIANE Publishing Co.

—Roll of Thunder, Hear My Cry. l.t. ed. 2000. (LRS Large Print Cornerstone Ser.). 348p. (YA). (gr. 5-12). lib. bdg. 32.95 (978-1-58118-057-2(8) , 23471) LRS.

—Roll of Thunder, Hear My Cry. 1999. (Masterpiece Series Access Editions). xvii, 205p. (J). pap. 10.95 (978-0-8219-1985-9(7) , 35335) Paradigm Publishing, Inc.

—Roll of Thunder, Hear My Cry. Pinkney, Jerry, illus. 25th anniv. ed. 2001. 296p. (J). (gr. 5 up). 17.99 (978-0-8037-2647-5(3) , Dial) Penguin Group (USA) Inc.

—Roll of Thunder, Hear My Cry. 1999. 60p. (J). (gr. 6-8). stu. ed., ring bd. 12.99 (978-1-58609-152-1(2)) Progeny Pr.

—Roll of Thunder, Hear My Cry. unabr. ed. 2004. 276p. (J). (gr. 5-9). pap. 48.00 incl. audio (978-0-8072-0678-2(4) , Listening Library) Random Hse. Audio Publishing Group.

—Roll of Thunder, Hear My Cry. 1998. (J). (gr. 5). pap. 3.95 (978-0-439-04476-9(6)) Scholastic, Inc.

—The Well: David's Story. 1998. 96p. (J). (gr. 4-7). pap. 5.99 (978-0-14-038642-4(4) , Puffin) Penguin Group (USA) Inc.

Teenage Bluez: Series 2, 2. 2006. 200p. (YA). pap. 10.99 (978-0-9741394-8-7(3)) Power Play Media.

Thomas, Jacquelin. Simply Divine. 2006. 288p. (YA). pap. 9.95 (978-1-4165-2718-3(4) , Pocket) Simon & Schuster.

Thomas, Joyce Carol. I Have Heard of a Land. Cooper, Floyd, illus. 2000. (Trophy Picture Bk.). 32p. (J). (gr. k-3). pap. 6.99 (978-0-06-443617-5(9) , Harper Trophy) HarperCollins Pubs.

—I Have Heard of a Land. 1998. (Illus.). 32p. (J). (gr. 2-6). 15.95 (978-0-06-023477-5(6) , Cotler, Joanna Books) HarperCollins Pubs.

—I Have Heard of a Land. Cooper, Floyd, illus. 1998. 32p. (J). (gr. 3 up). lib. bdg. 14.89 (978-0-06-023478-2(4) , Cotler, Joanna Books) HarperCollins Pubs.

—Marked by Fire. rev. ed. 2007. 192p. (YA). (gr. 8-17). 15.99 (***978-1-4231-0143-7(X)**); pap. 7.99 (***978-1-4231-0144-4(8)**) Hyperion Bks. for Children. (Jump at the Sun).

Thomas, Joyce Carol. You Are My Perfect Baby. Bennett, Nneka, photos by. 1999. (Joanna Cotler Bks.). (Illus.). 14p. (J). (ps up). 5.95 (978-0-694-01096-7(0) , Harper Festival) HarperCollins Pubs.

Thomassie, Tynia. Mimi's Tutu. Gilchrist, Jan Spivey, illus. 2002. 32p. (J). (gr. k-2). pap. 5.99 (978-0-590-44021-9(7) , Scholastic Pr.) Scholastic, Inc.

—Mimi's Tutu. 2001. (978-0-606-22267-9(7)) Tandem Library Bks.

TJ & the Mysterious Stranger. 2004. (J). bds. 16.95 (978-0-9710487-2-0(X)) Highlights of Chicago Pr.

Townley, Roderick. Sky. 2004. (Illus.). 272p. (J). 16.95 (978-0-689-85712-6(8) , Atheneum/Richard Jackson Bks.) Simon & Schuster Children's Publishing.

Trice, Linda. Kenya's Word. Johnson, Pamela, illus. 32p. (J). 2006. pap. 6.95 (978-1-57091-888-9(0)); 2005. 16.95 (978-1-57091-887-2(2)) Charlesbridge Publishing, Inc.

Turner-Denstaedt, Melanie. Grandma's Good Hat. Morrison, Frank, illus. 2008. (J). (978-0-374-32794-1(7)) Farrar, Straus & Giroux.

Turner, Morrie. Super Sistahs: Featuring the Accomplishments of African-American Women. 2005. (Illus.). 112p. pap. 14.95 (978-0-9656739-5-2(2)) BYE Publishing Services.

Turtleback Books, creator. Evvy's Civil War. 2004. 209p. (YA). (gr. 8-12). per. 13.64 (978-0-606-30114-5(3)) Tandem Library Bks.

Underwood, Jamilah. Today's Rain, Tomorrow's Sunshine. 2003. 104p. (YA). pap. 10.00 (978-0-9727201-4-4(6)) Blessed Beginnings Publishing.

van Diepen, Allison. Street Pharm. 2006. 304p. (YA). (gr. 8 up). pap. 6.99 (978-1-4169-1154-8(5) , Simon Pulse) Simon & Schuster Children's Publishing.

Van Steenwyk, Elizabeth. My Name Is York. Farnsworth, Bill, illus. 2000. 32p. (J). (ps-3). 7.95 (978-0-87358-758-7(8) , Rising Moon Bks. for Young Readers) Northland Publishing.

Vander Zee, Ruth. Mississippi Morning. Cooper, Floyd, illus. 2004. 32p. (J). 16.00 (978-0-8028-5211-3(4)) Eerdmans, William B. Publishing Co.

Vanoosting, James. Walking Mary. 2005. 144p. (J). (gr. 7 up). lib. bdg. 16.89 (978-0-06-028472-5(2)) HarperCollins Pubs.

Vaughan, Marcia. The Secret to Freedom. Johnson, Larry, illus. 32p. (J). 2001. (gr. 1-4). 16.95 (978-1-58430-021-2(3)); 2nd ed. 2005. (ps-ps). pap. 7.95 (978-1-58430-251-3(8)) Lee & Low Bks., Inc.

—Up the Learning Tree. Blanks, Derek, illus. 2003. 32p. (J). 16.96 (978-1-58430-049-6(3)) Lee & Low Bks., Inc.

Velasquez, Gloria. Ankiza. 2000. (Roosevelt High School Ser.). 152p. (J). (gr. 2 up). pap. 9.95 (978-1-55885-309-6(X)); (gr. 8-12). pap. 16.95 (978-1-55885-308-9(1)) Arte Publico Pr. (Piñata Books).

—Ankiza. 2000. (gr. 7-12). lib. bdg. 18.75 (978-0-613-59377-9(4)) Tandem Library Bks.

Velasquez, Gloria. Tyrone's Betrayal. 144p. (J). pap. 9.95 (978-1-55885-465-9(7) , Piñata Books) Arte Publico Pr.

Vision, David & Vision, Mutiya Sahar. Missing You. Alcantara, Ignacio, illus. 2005. 40p. (J). mass mkt. 17.00 (978-0-9659538-6-3(6)) Soul Vision Works Publishing.

Vision, David & Vision, Mutiya Sahar, illus. Daddy Loves His Baby Girl. 2005. 32p. (J). 16.00 (978-0-9659538-7-0(4)) Soul Vision Works Publishing.

Volponi, Paul. Black & White. 2005. 192p. (YA). (gr. 7). 15.99 (978-0-670-06006-1(2) , Viking Adult) Penguin Group (USA) Inc.

—Rooftop. (gr. 7). 2007. 224p. (J). pap. 6.99 (978-0-14-240844-5(1) , Puffin); 2006. 208p. (YA). 15.99 (978-0-670-06069-6(0) , Viking Adult) Penguin Group (USA) Inc.

—Rucker Park Setup. 2007. 208p. (J). 15.99 (978-0-670-06130-3(1) , Viking Juvenile) Penguin Group (USA) Inc.

Wagner, Jane. J. T. 125p. (J). (gr. 3-5). pap. 3.00 (978-0-8072-1403-9(5) , Listening Library) Random Hse. Audio Publishing Group.

Wahl, Jan. Candy Shop. Wong, Nicole, illus. 2005. 32p. (J). (ps-ps). pap. 6.95 (978-1-57091-668-7(3)) Charlesbridge Publishing, Inc.

Walter, Mildred Pitts. Alec's Primer. Johnson, Larry, illus. 2005. (Family Heritage Ser.). 36p. (J). 15.95 (978-0-916718-20-6(4)) Vermont Folklife Ctr.

—Justin & the Best Biscuits in the World. Stock, Catherine, illus. 2002. (J). 13.40 (978-0-7587-0371-2(6)) Book Wholesalers, Inc.

—Justin & the Best Biscuits in the World. 1999. (Illus.). 128p. (J). (gr. 3-5). pap. 4.99 (978-0-679-89448-3(9)) Knopf, Alfred A. Inc.

—Suitcase. Flavin, Teresa, illus. 1999. 112p. (J). (gr. 3 up). 16.99 (978-0-688-16547-5(8)) HarperCollins Pubs.

Walvoord, Linda. Rosetta, Rosetts, Sit by Me! Velasquez, Eric, illus. 2004. 80p. (J). 14.95 (978-0-7614-5171-6(4)) Cavendish, Marshall Corp.

Watson, Kim. Just Like Dad. 2001. (Little Bill Books for Beginning Readers Ser.). (Illus.). (J). 12.79 (978-0-606-21276-2(0)) Tandem Library Bks.

—A Trip to the Hospital. 2001. (Little Bill Books for Beginning Readers Ser.). (Illus.). (J). (978-0-606-21300-4(7)) Tandem Library Bks.

—Trip to the Hospital. 2001. (gr. k-3). lib. bdg. 11.25 (978-0-613-35705-0(1)) Tandem Library Bks.

Watson, Pat. Slam! Durst, Shirley J., ed. 2000. (YA). 9.95 (978-1-58130-640-8(7)); 11.95 (978-1-58130-641-5(5)) Novel Units, Inc.

Watts, Jeri Hanel. Keepers. Marshall, Felicia, illus. 2000. 32p. (gr. k up). (YA). 15.95 (978-1-880000-58-8(X)); (J). 6.95 (978-1-58430-013-7(2)) Lee & Low Bks., Inc.

—Keepers. 2000. (J). (978-0-606-19832-5(6)) Tandem Library Bks.

Weatherford, Carole Boston. Champions on the Bench: The Cannon Street YMCA All-Stars. Jenkins, Leonard, illus. 2007. 32p. (J). (gr. 1-4). 16.99 (978-0-8037-2987-2(1) , Dial) Penguin Group (USA) Inc.

—Dear Mr. Rosenwald. Christie, Gregory, illus. 2006. 32p. (J). (gr. 2-5). pap. 16.99 (978-0-439-49522-6(9) , Scholastic Pr.) Scholastic, Inc.

—Freedom on the Menu: The Greensboro Sit-Ins. Lagarrigue, Jerome Lagarrigue, illus. 2007. 32p. (J). (ps). pap. 5.99 (***978-0-14-240894-0(8)** , Puffin) Penguin Group (USA) Inc.

—Freedom on the Menu: The Greensboro Sit-Ins. Lagarrigue, Jerome, illus. 2004. 32p. (J). (gr. 1). 16.99 (978-0-8037-2860-8(3) , Dial) Penguin Group (USA) Inc.

Wenberg, Michael. Elizabeth's Song. Van Wright, Cornelius, illus. 2003. 32p. (J). (gr. 3 up). lib. bdg. 24.67 (978-0-8368-3572-4(7)) Stevens, Gareth Inc.

Wesley, Valerie Wilson. How to (Almost) Ruin Your School Play. Roos, Maryn, illus. 2005. 105p. (J). (978-1-4155-7357-0(3) , Jump at the Sun) Hyperion Bks. for Children.

—How to Almost Ruin Your School Play. 2005. (Illus.). 105p. (J). lib. bdg. 15.00 (***978-1-4242-0645-2(6)**) Fitzgerald Bks.

—How to Fish for Trouble. Roos, Maryn, illus. 2004. 89p. (J). lib. bdg. 15.00 (***978-1-4242-0643-8(X)**) Fitzgerald Bks.

—How to Fish for Trouble. Roos, Maryn, illus. 2nd rev. ed. 2004. (Willimena Rules! Ser.: Bk. 2). 96p. (gr. 2-5). pap. 3.99 (978-0-7868-1807-5(7)) Hyperion Bks. for Children.

—How to Lose Your Cookie Money. Roos, Maryn, illus. 2004. 105p. (J). lib. bdg. 15.00 (***978-1-4242-0644-5(8)**) Fitzgerald Bks.

—Willimena, Bk. 2. 2002. 368p. (J). 12.99 (978-0-7868-0466-5(1)) Hyperion Bks. for Children.

Wesley, Valerie Wilson. Willimena Rules!: How to Have the Best Kwanzaa Ever - Book #7. 7th rev. ed. 2007. (Illus.). 96p. (J). (gr. 2-7). pap. 3.99 (***978-1-4231-0037-9(9)** , Jump at the Sun) Hyperion Bks. for Children.

Wheels of Danger. 64p. (YA). (gr. 9-12). pap. 9.50 (978-0-8359-1086-6(5)) Globe Fearon Educational Publishing.

Whitehouse, Elizabeth. Black Boys. 2005. (J). pap. 5.95 (978-1-933031-93-4(X)) Whitehouse Publishing.

Whitmore, Arvella. Trapped Between the Lash & the Gun. 2001. (YA). (978-0-606-21604-3(9)) Tandem Library Bks.

—Trapped Between the Lash & the Gun: A Boy's Journey. 2001. 184p. (YA). (gr. 7-12). lib. bdg. 14.15 (978-0-613-33734-2(4)) Tandem Library Bks.

Whittenberg, Allison. Life Is Fine. 2008. 192p. (YA). (gr. 7). 15.99 (***978-0-385-73480-6(8)***, Delacorte Bks. for Young Readers) Random Hse. Children's Bks.

Whittenberg, Allison. Sweet Thang. 160p. (J). (gr. 3-7). 2007. pap. 5.99 (978-0-440-42086-6(5), Yearling); 2006. 15.95 (978-0-385-73292-5(9), Delacorte Bks. for Young Readers); 2006. lib. bdg. 17.99 (978-0-385-90313-4(8), Delacorte Bks. for Young Readers) Random Hse. Children's Bks.

Williams-Garcia, Rita. Fast Talk on a Slow Track. 1998. 192p. (J). (gr. 7-12). pap. 6.99 (978-0-14-130231-7(3), Puffin) Penguin Group (USA) Inc.

—Like Sisters on the Homefront. 1998. 176p. (J). (gr. 7-12). pap. 5.99 (978-0-14-038561-8(4), Puffin) Penguin Group (USA) Inc.

—No Laughter Here. 144p. (J). (gr. 7 up). 2007. pap. 6.99 (978-0-06-440992-6(9), Amistad); 2004. 15.99 (978-0-688-16247-4(9)); 2004. lib. bdg. 16.89 (978-0-688-16248-1(7)) HarperCollins Pubs.

Williams, Lori Aurelia. Broken China. (YA). (gr. 7 up). 2005. 272p. 16.95 (978-0-689-86878-8(2), Simon & Schuster Children's Publishing); 2006. 336p. reprint ed. mass mkt. 5.99 (978-1-4169-1618-5(0), Simon Pulse) Simon & Schuster Children's Publishing.

—Shayla's Double Brown Baby Blues. 2003. (Illus.). 304p. (YA). pap. 7.99 (978-0-689-85670-9(9), Simon Pulse) Simon & Schuster Children's Publishing.

—Shayla's Double Brown Baby Blues. 2003. 300p. (gr. 7-12). lib. bdg. 16.45 (978-0-613-61815-1(7)) Tandem Library Bks.

—When Kambia Elaine Flew in from Neptune. unabr. ed. 2004. 246p. (J). (gr. 7 up). pap. 50.00 incl. audio (978-0-8072-8851-1(9), Listening Library) Random Hse. Audio Publishing Group.

—When Kambia Elaine Flew in from Neptune. Louth, Jack, illus. 2001. 256p. (YA). pap. 10.00 (978-0-689-84593-2(6), Simon Pulse) Simon & Schuster Children's Publishing.

—When Kambia Elaine Flew in from Neptune. 2002. (978-0-606-22109-2(3)); 2001. (gr. 7-12). lib. bdg. 18.80 (978-0-613-73307-6(X)) Tandem Library Bks.

Williams, Sherley Anne. Working Cotton. Byard, Carole, illus. 2002. (J). 14.04 (978-0-7587-0168-8(3)) Book Wholesalers, Inc.

Winston, Sherri. Acting: A Novel. 2004. 256p. (YA). 15.95 (978-0-7614-5173-0(0)) Cavendish, Marshall Corp.

Wisehart, Randall. A Winding Road to Freedom. 1999. 184p. (J). (gr. 5-8). pap. 13.00 (978-0-944350-47-8(X)) Friends United Pr.

Woodruff, Elvira. Dear Austin: Letters from the Underground Railroad. 2000. (gr. 5-8). lib. bdg. 13.00 (978-0-613-28463-9(1)) Tandem Library Bks.

Woods, Brenda. Emako Blue. 128p. (YA). 2005. (gr. 6). pap. 5.99 (978-0-14-240418-8(7), Puffin); 2004. (gr. 5-12). 15.99 (978-0-399-24006-5(3), Putnam Juvenile) Penguin Group (USA) Inc.

—My Name Is Sally Little Song. 192p. (J). 2007. (gr. 2). 5.99 (***978-0-14-240943-5(X)***, Puffin); 2006. (gr. 3-6). 15.99 (978-0-399-24312-7(7), Putnam Juvenile) Penguin Group (USA) Inc.

Woods, Brenda. The Red Rose Box. 2002. 160p. (YA). (gr. 4-6). 16.99 (978-0-399-23702-7(X), Putnam Juvenile) Penguin Group (USA) Inc.

—The Red Rose Box. 2003. (gr. 5-8). lib. bdg. 14.15 (978-0-613-87822-7(1)) Tandem Library Bks.

Woodson, Jacqueline. After Tupac & D Foster. 2008. 160p. (YA). (gr. 5). 15.99 (***978-0-399-24654-8(1)***, Putnam Juvenile) Penguin Group (USA) Inc.

—Behind You. 128p. (YA). 2006. (gr. 7). pap. 5.99 (978-0-14-240390-7(3), Puffin); 2004. (gr. 5-12). 15.99 (978-0-399-23988-5(X), Putnam Juvenile) Penguin Group (USA) Inc.

—Between Madison & Palmetto. 2002. 128p. (J). pap. 5.99 (978-0-698-11958-1(4)); (YA). 16.99 (978-0-399-23757-7(7)) Penguin Group (USA) Inc. (Putnam Juvenile).

—Between Madison & Palmetto. 2002. (gr. 5-8). lib. bdg. 14.15 (978-0-613-50092-0(X)) Tandem Library Bks.

—Coming on Home Soon. Lewis, Earl, illus. 2004. 32p. (J). (ps). 16.99 (978-0-399-23748-5(8), Putnam Juvenile) Penguin Group (USA) Inc.

—The Dear One. 2004. 144p. (YA). pap. 6.99 (978-0-14-250190-0(5), Puffin) Penguin Group (USA) Inc.

—Feathers. 2007. 128p. (J). (gr. 3-7). 15.99 (978-0-399-23989-2(8), Putnam Juvenile) Penguin Group (USA) Inc.

—From the Notebooks of Melanin Sun. 2003. 160p. (J). (gr. 7 up). pap. 5.99 (978-0-590-45881-8(7), Scholastic Paperbacks) Scholastic, Inc.

—The House You Pass on the Way. 2003. 112p. (YA). reprint ed. pap. 5.99 (978-0-14-250191-7(3), Puffin); (gr. 5). 16.99 (978-0-399-23969-4(3), Putnam Juvenile) Penguin Group (USA) Inc.

—The House You Pass on the Way. 1999. (J). (978-0-606-16085-8(X)) Tandem Library Bks.

—The House You Pass on the Way. l.t. ed. 2004. 109p. (J). 22.95 (978-0-7862-6428-5(4)) Thorndike Pr.

—Hush. 192p. (gr. 5). 2006. (J). pap. 5.99 (978-0-14-240600-7(7), Puffin); 2002. (YA). 15.99 (978-0-399-23114-8(5), Putnam Juvenile) Penguin Group (USA) Inc.

—Hush. 2003. (gr. 5-8). lib. bdg. 14.15 (978-0-613-67332-7(8)) Tandem Library Bks.

—If You Come Softly. (gr. 5). 2006. 192p. (YA). pap. 5.99 (978-0-14-240601-4(5), Puffin); 1998. 1p. (J). 16.99 (978-0-399-23112-4(9), Putnam Juvenile) Penguin Group (USA) Inc.

—If You Come Softly. 2000. 12.64 (978-0-606-17863-1(5)) Tandem Library Bks.

—Last Summer with Maizon. 2002. 112p. (J). 17.99 (978-0-399-23755-3(0)); (Illus.). (gr. 3-7). pap. 5.99 (978-0-698-11929-1(0)) Penguin Group (USA) Inc. (Putnam Juvenile).

—Last Summer with Maizon. 2002. (gr. 3-6). lib. bdg. 13.00 (978-0-613-45286-1(0)) Tandem Library Bks.

—Maizon at Blue Hill. 2002. 160p. (J). pap. 5.99 (978-0-698-11957-4(6)); 144p. (YA). 16.99 (978-0-399-23756-0(9)) Penguin Group (USA) Inc. (Putnam Juvenile).

—Maizon at Blue Hill. 2002. (gr. 3-6). lib. bdg. 14.15 (978-0-613-50098-2(9)) Tandem Library Bks.

—Our Gracie Aunt. Muth, Jon J., illus. 2002. 32p. (J). lib. bdg. 16.49 (978-0-7868-2532-5(4)); 15.99 (978-0-7868-0620-1(6)) Hyperion Bks. for Children.

—Show Way. Talbott, Hudson, illus. 2005. 48p. (J). (ps). 16.99 (978-0-399-23749-2(6), Putnam Juvenile) Penguin Group (USA) Inc.

—Visiting Day. Ransome, James E., illus. 2002. 32p. (J). (ps-3). pap. 15.95 (978-0-590-40005-3(3), Scholastic Pr.) Scholastic, Inc.

—We Had a Picnic This Sunday Past. Greenseid, Diane, illus. 1998. 32p. (ps-3). 14.95 (978-0-7868-0242-5(1)) Hyperion Bks. for Children.

Woodson, Jacqueline & Ransome, James E. Visiting Day. 2001. (Illus.). (J). pap. (978-0-590-55262-2(7)) Scholastic, Inc.

Wright, Bil. When the Black Girl Sings. 2008. 272p. (YA). (gr. 7 up). 16.99 (***978-1-4169-3995-5(4)***, Simon & Schuster Children's Publishing) Simon & Schuster Children's Publishing.

Wright, Bill. Sunday You Learn to Box. 2000. (gr. 7-12). lib. bdg. 21.10 (978-0-613-33972-8(X)) Tandem Library Bks.

Wright, Sue. Blind Man's Bluff. 2005. (Davey & Goliath Ser.). (Illus.). 32p. (J). (ps-ps). pap. 3.50 (978-0-439-75830-7(0), Scholastic Paperbacks) Scholastic, Inc.

Wyeth, Sharon Dennis. Flying Free: Corey's Underground Railroad Diary. 2002. (My America Ser.: Bk. 2). (Illus.). 112p. (J). (gr. 2-5). pap. 10.95 (978-0-439-24443-5(9), Scholastic Pr.) Scholastic, Inc.

—Freedom's Wings: Corey's Underground Railroad Diary, Bk. 1. 2002. (My America Ser.). (Illus.). 112p. (J). (gr. 4-7). 4.99 (978-0-439-36907-7(X), Scholastic Pr.) Scholastic, Inc.

—Freedom's Wings: Corey's Underground Railroad Diary. 2002. (gr. 3-6). lib. bdg. 13.00 (978-0-613-53813-8(7)); 2001. (J). (gr. 4-7). (978-0-606-22804-6(7)) Tandem Library Bks.

—Message in the Sky Bk. 3: Corey's Underground Railroad Diary. 2003. (My America Ser.). 112p. (J). pap. 10.95 (978-0-439-37057-8(4), Scholastic Pr.) Scholastic, Inc.

—A Piece of Heaven. 2002. (gr. 5-8). lib. bdg. 13.00 (978-0-613-64761-8(0)) Tandem Library Bks.

—Something Beautiful. Soentpiet, Chris K., illus. 1998. 32p. (J). (gr. 2-4). 16.95 (978-0-385-32239-3(9), Doubleday Bks. for Young Readers) Random Hse. Children's Bks.

Yarbrough, Camille. Tamika & the Wisdom Rings. 2004. (J). pap. 5.95 (978-0-940975-67-5(X), Sankofa Bks.) Just Us Bks., Inc.

Yarbrough, Elizabeth. Which Way, Michael? Ragsdale, Cathy, illus. 2001. 44p. (J). (gr. 1-6). lib. bdg. 14.95 (978-0-9705727-8-3(6)) Coastal Publishing Carolina, Inc.

Youngblood, Shay. Black Girl in Paris. 2001. (Illus.). (J). (978-0-606-20571-9(3)) Tandem Library Bks.

AFRICAN AMERICANS—HISTORY

An Account of Afro-American in Weir Kansas 1868-1988. 1999. (YA). pap. 24.95 (978-0-9703275-1-2(X)) Tolson, Norma Y.

African American Heritage Pictures, Puzzles, & Word Games. 2004. (YA). per. 16.00 (978-0-9758586-0-8(2)) Jenkins-Simmons, Glenda.

African American History. 2004. (Illus.). lib. bdg. 7.95 (978-0-8225-4418-0(0)); lib. bdg. 7.95 (978-0-8225-4422-7(9)) Lerner Publishing Group.

African American History. 2003. (Eye on History Ser.). 32p. (gr. 5-12). 5.99 (978-1-56822-448-0(6), IF2660) School Specialty Publishing.

African-American Primary, 2 vol., set, Vol. 2. 2nd ed. 2001. 62.50 (978-0-06-001319-6(2)) HarperCollins Pubs.

Africans in America: America's Journey Through Slavery. 2004. (gr. 7 up). tchr. ed. 19.95 incl. VHS, cd-rom (978-1-57807-195-1(X), WG665) WGBH Boston Video.

Altman, Susan. Encyclopedia of African-American Heritage. 2nd ed. 2000. (Illus.). 368p. (YA). (gr. 6-12). 45.00 (978-0-8160-4125-1(3)) Facts On File, Inc.

—Extraordinary African-Americans. 2nd rev. ed. 2002. (Extraordinary People Ser.). (Illus.). (YA). (gr. 6 up). pap. 16.95 (978-0-516-25962-8(8), Children's Pr.) Scholastic Library Publishing.

American Mosaic: African-American Contributions. (Illus.). (gr. 6-12). lib. bdg. (978-0-7910-8057-3(9), Chelsea Hse.) Facts On File, Inc.

Aretha, David. Selma & the Voting Rights ACT. 2007. (J). (***978-1-59935-056-1(4)***) Reynolds, Morgan Inc.

Ball, Lynda Anne. Kwanzaa Teddy, The Curious Bear. Johnson, Larry, illus. 2001. (Adventures of KT). 32p. (J). (ps-2). per. 6.95 (978-1-889383-11-8(2)) Angel Pubns.

Banfield, Susan. The Fifteenth Amendment: African-American Men's Right to Vote. 1998. (Constitution Ser.). (Illus.). 128p. (YA). (gr. 6-12). lib. bdg. 26.60 (978-0-7660-1033-8(3)) Enslow Pubs., Inc.

Barr, Gary. Slavery in the Civil War Era. 2004. (Illus.). 56p. (J). pap. 8.95 (978-1-4034-4578-0(8)); lib. bdg. (978-1-4034-4570-4(2)) Heinemann Library.

Beckner, Chrisanne. 100 African Americans Who Changed History. 2005. (People Who Changed History Ser.). (Illus.). 112p. (J). lib. bdg. 30.00 (978-0-8368-5767-2(4), World Almanac Library) Stevens, Gareth Inc.

Bernard-Nollins, Sonya M. Here I Stand: A Musical History of African Americans in Battle Creek, Michigan. 2003. (Illus.). (YA). pap. 15.00 (978-0-9741611-0-5(1)) Fortitude Graphic Design & Printing.

Bolden, Tonya. Rock of Ages. Christie, Gregory R., illus. 2003. 32p. (J). (gr. k-3). pap. 6.99 (978-0-440-41800-9(3), Dragonfly Bks.) Random Hse. Children's Bks.

—Tell All the Children Our Story: Memories & Mementos of Being Young & Black in America. 2002. (Illus.). 128p. (J). (gr. 5-17). 24.95 (978-0-8109-4496-1(0)) Abrams, Harry N., Inc.

Branham, LaTonya, compiled by & des. CultureSeek: Connecting to African & African American History. Branham, LaTonya, des. 2006. (YA). per. 8.00 (978-0-9787296-0-8(9)) BabyStar Productions.

Buffalo Soldiers & the Western Frontier Vol. 2: Individual Title Six-Packs. (On Deck Ser.: Vol. 2). 24p. (gr. 4-5). 35.00 (978-0-7578-5805-5(8)) Rigby Education.

Byers, Ann. African-American History from Emancipation to Today: Rising above the Ashes of Slavery. 2004. (Slavery in American History Ser.). (Illus.). 128p. (YA). lib. bdg. 26.60 (978-0-7660-2153-2(X)) Enslow Pubs., Inc.

Celebrating African American History. 96p. (gr. 5-8). 13.99 (978-0-7682-0627-2(8), GA13084) School Specialty Publishing.

Clare, John D. The Black Peoples of America. 2001. (Illus.). 48p. pap. 23.50 (***978-0-340-79033-5(4)***, Hodder Murray) Hodder Education GBR. *Dist:* Trans-Atlantic Pubns., Inc.

Clark, Carolyn. Little Rock Nine. 2002. (Illus.). 16p. (J). (978-0-439-35188-1(X)) Scholastic, Inc.

Collier, Christopher & Collier, James Lincoln. Reconstruction & the Rise of Jim Crow: 1864-1896. 1999. (Drama of American History Ser.). (Illus.). 96p. (YA). (gr. 5-9). lib. bdg. 31.36 (978-0-7614-0819-2(3), Benchmark Bks.) Cavendish, Marshall Corp.

Common. Mirror & Me. West, Lorraine, illus. 2005. 40p. (J). pap. 9.95 (978-0-9768674-0-1(0)) Hip Hop Schl. House.

Corrick, James. The Civil War & Emancipation. 2007. (Lucent Library of Black History Ser.). (Illus.). 128p. (J). (gr. 7-10). 28.70 (***978-1-4205-0008-0(2)***, Lucent Bks.) Thomson Gale.

Davis, Ella D. Black History Coloring Book Series. 1999. (Illus.). 20p. (J). (ps-4). pap. 1.95 (978-1-888185-58-4(9)) Davis Publishing Co.

—Black History Picture Book Series. 1999. (Illus.). 20p. (J). (ps-4). pap. 3.95 (978-1-888185-59-1(7)) Davis Publishing Co.

Davis, Julia A. African American History for Today's Students. 2001. (Illus.). 218p. (YA). (gr. 5-12). 30.00 (978-0-9631110-4-3(3)) Epps-Alford Publishing.

Deitch, JoAnne Weisman, ed. Northern Migration & the Harlem Renaissance. 2001. (Researching American History Ser.). (Illus.). 56p. (J). pap. 7.95 (978-1-57960-068-6(9)) History Compass, LLC.

Diouf, Sylviane A. Growing up in Slavery. 2001. (Growing Up in... Ser.). (Illus.). 96p. (J). (gr. 5-8). lib. bdg. 25.90 (978-0-7613-1763-0(5), Millbrook Pr.) Lerner Publishing Group.

Drama of African-American History, 5 bks., Set. Incl. Africa : A Look Back. Haskins, James & Benson, Kathleen. lib. bdg. 34.21 (978-0-7614-2148-1(3)); Civil War. Jordan, Anne Devereaux & Schomp, Virginia. lib. bdg. 34.21 (978-0-7614-2179-5(3)); Reconstruction ERA. Stroud, Bettye & Schomp, Virginia. lib. bdg. 34.21 (978-0-7614-2181-8(5)); Slave Trade & the Middle Passage. Sharp, S. Pearl & Schomp, Virginia. lib. bdg. 34.21 (978-0-7614-2176-4(9)); Slavery & Resistance. Jordan, Anne Devereaux & Schomp, Virginia. lib. bdg. 34.21 (978-0-7614-2178-8(5)); (Illus.). 80p. (J). 2006. 2007. Set lib. bdg. 171.07 (***978-0-7614-2174-0(2)***, Benchmark Bks.) Cavendish, Marshall Corp.

Ellis, Barbara C. & Feder, Chris Welles. Brain Quest Black History. rev. ed. 2005. (Illus.). 148p. (J). 10.95 (978-0-7611-3996-6(6), 13996) Workman Publishing Co., Inc.

Exploring the World of Thomas Day, 2 cds. 2002. (J). cd-rom 59.95 (978-0-9726129-0-6(4)) New Hope Pubns., LLC.

Fandel, Jennifer. Martin Luther King, Jr. 2005. (Genius Ser.). (Illus.). 48p. (gr. 5-9). 21.95 (978-1-58341-329-6(4), Creative Education) Creative Co., The.

Featonby, Douglas & Whittock, Martyn. The Black Peoples of America. 2001. (Illus.). 48p. pap. 23.50 (***978-0-340-79034-2(2)***, Hodder Murray) Hodder Education GBR. *Dist:* Trans-Atlantic Pubns., Inc.

Feinstein, Stephen. Lee sobre Martin Luther King, Jr./Read about Martin Luther King, Jr. 2006. (I Like Biographies! Bilingual Ser.). (ENG & SPA., Illus.). 24p. (J). (gr. 1-3). lib. bdg. 21.26 (978-0-7660-2745-9(7), Enslow Elementary) Enslow Pubs., Inc.

Fiorelli, June Estep. Fannie Lou Hamer: A Voice for Freedom. 2004. (Avisson Young Adult Ser.). (Illus.). 117p. (J). pap. 19.95 (978-1-888105-62-9(3)) Avisson Pr., Inc.

Flanagan, Alice K. The Buffalo Soldiers. 2004. (We the People Ser.). (Illus.). 48p. (J). 22.60 (978-0-7565-0833-3(9)) Compass Point Bks.

Flanagan, Timothy. Reconstruction: A Primary Source History of the Struggle to Unite the North & South after the Civil War. 2005. (Illus.). 64p. (J). (gr. 5-8). lib. bdg. 29.25 (978-1-4042-0177-4(7)) Rosen Publishing Group, Inc., The.

Ford, Carin T. Lincoln, Slavery, & the Emancipation Proclamation. 2004. (Civil War Library Ser.). (Illus.). 48p. (J). lib. bdg. 23.93 (978-0-7660-2252-2(8)) Enslow Pubs., Inc.

Gaines, Ann Graham. The Harlem Renaissance in American History. 2002. (In American History Ser.). (Illus.). 112p. (J). (gr. 5-12). lib. bdg. 26.60 (978-0-7660-1458-9(4)) Enslow Pubs., Inc.

Giovanni, Nikki. On My Journey Now: Looking at African-American History Through the Spirituals. 2007. (Illus.). 128p. (J). (gr. 6-9). 18.99 (978-0-7636-2885-7(9)) Candlewick Pr.

Glaser, Jason. The Buffalo Soldiers & the American West. Smith, Tod & Barnett, Charles, illus. 2005. (Graphic Library). 32p. (J). (gr. 3-7). lib. bdg. 25.26 (978-0-7368-4966-1(1)) Capstone Pr., Inc.

Green, Jen. The Africans. 2000. 15.75 (978-0-606-22825-1(X)) Tandem Library Bks.

—Africans. 2000. (gr. 3-6). lib. bdg. 17.60 (978-0-613-27697-9(3)) Tandem Library Bks.

Greene, Meg. Into the Land of Freedom: African Americans in Reconstruction. 2004. (People's History Ser.). (Illus.). 96p. (J). lib. bdg. 29.27 (978-0-8225-4690-0(6)) Lerner Publishing Group.

Halpern, Monica. The Great Migration: African Americans Move to the North, 1915-1930. 2002. (Seeds of Change in American History Ser.). (Illus.). 40p. (J). (978-0-7922-8677-6(4)) National Geographic Society.

—Moving North: African Americans & the Great Migration 1915 - 1930. 2005. (Crossroads America Ser.). (Illus.). 40p. (gr. k-3). (J). 12.95 (978-0-7922-8278-5(7)); 21.90 (978-0-7922-8358-4(9)) National Geographic Society. (National Geographic Children's Bks.).

Hansen, Joyce. "Bury Me Not in a Land of Slaves" African-Americans in the Time of Reconstruction. 2000. (Single Titles Social Studies Ser.). (Illus.). 160p. (YA). (gr. 8-12). pap. 8.95 (978-0-531-16463-1(2), Watts, Franklin) Scholastic Library Publishing.

—Bury Me Not in a Land of Slaves: African-Americans in the Time of Reconstruction. 2000. (J). 15.60 (978-0-606-19779-3(6)) Tandem Library Bks.

—Bury Me Not in the Land of Slaves: African-Americans in the Time of Reconstruction. 2000. (Single Titles Ser.). (Illus.). 160p. (YA). (gr. 8-12). 24.00 (978-0-531-11539-8(9), Watts, Franklin) Scholastic Library Publishing.

Hansen, Joyce & McGowan, Gary. Freedom Roads: Searching for the Underground Railroad. Ransome, James E., illus. 2003. (Marcato Book Ser.). 166p. (J). (gr. 5-9). 18.95 (978-0-8126-2673-5(7)) Cricket Bks.

Hardy, P. Stephen & Hardy, Sheila Jackson. Extraordinary People of the Civil Rights Movement. 2006. (Extraordinary People Ser.). (Illus.). 288p. (YA). (gr. 9 up). (978-0-516-25461-6(8)) Children's Pr., Ltd.

Harkrader, Lisa. Reconstruction & Aftermath of the Civil War: A MyReportLinks. com Book. 2004. (American Civil War Ser.). (Illus.). 48p. (J). lib. bdg. 25.26 (978-0-7660-5265-9(6), MyReportLinks.com Bks.) Enslow Pubs., Inc.

Haskins, James. Bound for America: The Forced Migration of Africans to the New World. Cooper, Floyd, illus. 1999. 48p. (J). (gr. 6 up). 17.89 (978-0-688-10259-3(X)) HarperCollins Pubs.

Haskins, James & Benson, Kathleen. Africa: A Look Back. 2006. (Drama of African-American History Ser.). (Illus.). 80p. (J). lib. bdg. 34.21 (978-0-7614-2148-1(3), Benchmark Bks.) Cavendish, Marshall Corp.

—Out of the Darkness: The Story of Blacks Moving North, 1890-1940. 2000. (Great Journeys Ser.). (Illus.). 112p. (J). (gr. 5 up). lib. bdg. 32.79 (978-0-7614-0970-0(X), Benchmark Bks.) Cavendish, Marshall Corp.

Hine. The African-American Odyssey (to 1877), Vol. 1. 2nd ed. 2000. pap., suppl. ed. 21.33 (978-0-13-086298-3(3), Prentice Hall) Prentice Hall PTR.

Hine, Darlene Clark. The African-American Odyssey (since 1865), Vol. 2. Ball, Alan, ed. 2nd ed. 2000. 160p. pap., suppl. ed. 21.33 (978-0-13-086290-7(8), Prentice Hall) Prentice Hall PTR.

Hoobler, Dorothy & Hoobler, Thomas. The African American Family Album. 1998. (American Family Albums Ser.). (Illus.). 128p. (YA). reprint ed. pap. 17.95 (978-0-19-512419-4(7)) Oxford Univ. Pr., Inc.

Horton, James Oliver. Landmarks of African American History. 2005. (American Landmarks Ser.). (Illus.). 208p. (YA). 30.00 (978-0-19-514118-4(0)) Oxford Univ. Pr., Inc.

Hudson, Wade. More Than 200 Years of Extraordinary Writing by African Americans. Qualls, Sean, illus. 2004. (Powerful Words Ser.). 192p. (J). (gr. 4-7). pap. 19.95 (978-0-439-40969-8(1)) Scholastic, Inc.

Jordan, Anne Devereaux & Schomp, Virginia. The Civil War. 2006. (Drama of African-American History Ser.). (Illus.). 80p. (J). lib. bdg. 34.21 (978-0-7614-2179-5(3), Benchmark Bks.) Cavendish, Marshall Corp.

—Slavery & Resistance. 2006. (Drama of African-American History Ser.). (Illus.). 80p. (J). lib. bdg. 34.21 (978-0-7614-2178-8(5), Benchmark Bks.) Cavendish, Marshall Corp.

Jordan, Denise. Juneteenth Day. 2003. (Holiday Histories Ser.). (Illus.). 32p. (J). pap. 112.60 (978-1-4034-4253-6(3)); lib. bdg. 22.79 (978-1-4034-3505-7(7)) Heinemann Library.

Kallen, Stuart A. Black History, Set. Incl. Civil Rights Movement. (gr. 3-8). lib. bdg. 25.65 (978-1-57765-466-7(8)); Civil War & Reconstruction. (gr. 3-8). lib. bdg. 25.65 (978-1-57765-469-8(2)); Days of Slavery. (gr. 3-8). lib. bdg. 25.65 (978-1-57765-470-4(6)); Harlem Renaissance. (gr. 3-8). lib. bdg. 25.65 (978-1-57765-468-1(4)); Kingdoms of Africa. (gr. 4-8). lib. bdg. 25.65 (978-1-57765-465-0(X)); Striving into 2000. (gr. 3-8). lib. bdg. 25.65 (978-1-57765-467-4(6)); 48p. (J). 2001. (Illus.). 2001. Set lib. bdg. 153.90 (978-1-57765-297-7(5), ABDO & Daughters) ABDO Publishing Co.

—The Civil War & Reconstruction. 2001. (Black History Ser.). (Illus.). 48p. (J). (gr. 3-8). lib. bdg. 25.65 (978-1-57765-469-8(2), ABDO & Daughters) ABDO Publishing Co.

—A History of Free Blacks in America. 2005. (Lucent Library of Black History). (Illus.). 112p. (YA). (gr. 7-10). lib. bdg. 32.45 (978-1-59018-776-0(8) , Lucent Bks.) Thomson Gale.

—Marcus Garvey & the Back to Africa Movement. 2006. (Lucent Library of Black History). (Illus.). 112p. (J). (gr. 7-10). 32.45 (978-1-59018-838-5(1) , Lucent Bks.) Thomson Gale.

—Striving into 2000. 2001. (Black History Ser.). (Illus.). 48p. (J). (gr. 3-8). lib. bdg. 25.65 (978-1-57765-467-4(6) , ABDO & Daughters) ABDO Publishing Co.

—A Travel Guide to Harlem Renaissance. 2003. (J). 29.95 (978-1-59018-358-8(4) , Lucent Bks.) Thomson Gale.

Kalman, Bobbie. Slave Family. 2003. (ps-2). lib. bdg. 17.60 (978-0-613-52908-2(1)) Tandem Library Bks.

Kishel, Ann-Marie. Rosa Parks: Una Vida de Valentía. 2006. (Libros para Avanzar Ser.). (ENG & SPA.). 32p. (J). lib. bdg. 22.60 (978-0-8225-6239-9(1)) Lerner Publishing Group.

Kleinman, Joseph & Kurtis-Kleinman, Eileen. Life on an African Slave Ship. 2000. (Way People Live Ser.). (Illus.). 112p. (J). (gr. 7-10). 28.70 (978-1-56006-653-8(9) , LML00902-178007, Lucent Bks.) Thomson Gale.

Kunjufu, Jawanza. Lessons from History, Advanced Edition: A Celebration in Blackness. 2003. (Illus.). 108p. (J). (gr. 6-12). pap. 9.95 (978-0-913543-06-1(3)) African American Images.

—Lessons from History, Elementary Edition: A Celebration in Blackness. 2003. 108p. (J). (gr. 1-5). 19.95 (978-0-913543-05-4(5)) African American Images.

—Lessons from History, Jr.-Sr. High Edition: A Celebration in Blackness. 2003. (Illus.). 108p. (J). (gr. 6-12). 19.95 (978-0-913543-07-8(1)) African American Images.

Kunjufu, Jawanza & Prescott, Folami. Eighth Grade: Self-Esteem Through Culture Leads to Academic Excellence. 2003. (SETCLAE Ser.). 60p. (J). pap. 9.95 (978-0-913543-93-1(4)) African American Images.

—High School: Self-Esteem Through Culture Leads to Academic Excellence. 2003. (SETCLAE Ser.). 60p. (J). pap. 9.95 (978-0-913543-94-8(2)) African American Images.

—Kindergarten: Self-Esteem Through Culture Leads to Academic Excellence. 2003. (SETCLAE Ser.). 60p. (J). pap. 9.95 (978-0-913543-85-6(3)) African American Images.

—SETCLAE, Fifth Grade: Self-Esteem Through Culture Leads to Academic Excellence. 2003. (SETCLAE Ser.). 60p. (J). pap. 9.95 (978-0-913543-90-0(X)) African American Images.

—SETCLAE, First Grade: Self-Esteem Through Culture Leads to Academic Excellence. 2003. (SETCLAE Ser.). 60p. (J). pap. 9.95 (978-0-913543-86-3(1)) African American Images.

—SETCLAE, Fourth Grade: Self-Esteem Through Culture Leads to Academic Excellence. 2003. (SETCLAE Ser.). 60p. (J). pap. 9.95 (978-0-913543-89-4(6)) African American Images.

—SETCLAE, Second Grade: Self-Esteem Through Culture Leads to Academic Excellence. 2003. (SETCLAE Ser.). 60p. (J). pap. 9.95 (978-0-913543-87-0(X)) African American Images.

—SETCLAE, Seventh Grade: Self-Esteem Through Culture Leads to Academic Excellence. 2003. (SETCLAE Ser.). 60p. (J). pap. 9.95 (978-0-913543-92-4(6)) African American Images.

—SETCLAE, Sixth Grade: Self-Esteem Through Culture Leads to Academic Excellence. 2003. (SETCLAE Ser.). 60p. (J). pap. 9.95 (978-0-913543-91-7(8)) African American Images.

—SETCLAE, Third Grade: Self-Esteem Through Culture Leads to Academic Excellence. 2003. (SETCLAE Ser.). 60p. (J). pap. 9.95 (978-0-913543-88-7(8)) African American Images.

Landau, Elaine. The Abolitionist Movement. 2004. (Cornerstones of Freedom Ser.). (Illus.). 48p. (J). 26.00 (978-0-516-24202-6(4) , Children's Pr.) Scholastic Library Publishing.

Lanier, Shannon & Feldman, Jane. Jefferson's Children: The Story of One American Family. 2004. (Illus.). 144p. (J). (gr. 4-8). reprint ed. 20.00 (978-0-7567-7418-9(7)) DIANE Publishing Co.

—Jefferson's Children: The Story of One American Family. Feldman, Jane, photos by. 2002. 160p. (gr. 5). pap. 16.95 (978-0-375-82168-4(6) , Random Hse. Bks. for Young Readers) Random Hse. Children's Bks.

—Jefferson's Children: The Story of One American Family. Feldman, Jane, photos by. 2002. (Illus.). 160p. (J). (ps-7). lib. bdg. 24.55 (978-0-613-57230-9(0)) Tandem Library Bks.

Lee, Spike & Lee, Tonya Lewis. Please, Baby, Please. Nelson, Kadir, illus. 2006. 32p. (J). reprint ed. pap. 6.99 (978-0-689-83457-8(8) , Aladdin) Simon & Schuster Children's Publishing.

Leeper, Angela. Juneteenth: A Day to Celebrate Freedom from Slavery. 2004. (Finding Out about Holidays Ser.). (Illus.). 48p. (J). (gr. 3-5). lib. bdg. 23.93 (978-0-7660-2206-5(4)) Enslow Pubs., Inc.

Lester, Julius. To Be a Slave. Feelings, Tom, illus. 30th anniv. ed. 2000. 176p. (J). (gr. 5-9). pap. 6.99 (978-0-14-131001-5(4) , Puffin) Penguin Group (USA) Inc.

—To Be a Slave. 2000. (gr. 5-8). lib. bdg. 15.30 (978-0-613-33732-8(8)) Tandem Library Bks.

Levine, Ellen. Freedom's Children: Young Civil Rights Activists Tell Their Own Stories. 2000. (Illus.). 1p. (J). (gr. 5-9). pap. 7.99 (978-0-698-11870-6(7) , Putnam Juvenile) Penguin Group (USA) Inc.

The Library of African American Arts & Culture, 8 vols., Set. Incl. African American Kitchen : Food for Body & Soul. Erdosh, George. lib. bdg. 26.50 (978-0-8239-1850-8(5) , AAKITC); African-American Quilting : The Warmth of Tradition. Wilson, Sule Greg C. lib. bdg. 26.50 (978-0-8239-1854-6(8) , AAQUCR); Blues : Its Birth & Growth. Elmer, Howard. lib. bdg. 26.50 (978-0-8239-1853-9(X) , AABLUE); Capoeira : A Martial Art & a Cultural Tradition. Atwood, Jane E. lib. bdg. 26.50 (978-0-8239-1859-1(9) , AACAPO); Jam! The Story of Jazz Music. Lee, Jeanne. lib. bdg. 26.50 (978-0-8239-1852-2(1) , AAJAZZ); Jazz Tap : From African Drums to American Feet. Johnson, Anne E. lib. bdg. 26.50 (978-0-8239-1856-0(4) , AAJATA); Kwanzaa! Africa Lives in a New World Festival. Wilson, Sule Greg C. lib. bdg. 26.50 (978-0-8239-1857-7(2) , AAKWAN); Rap & Hip Hop : The Voice of a Generation. Ayazi-Hashjin, Sherry. lib. bdg. 26.50 (978-0-8239-1855-3(6) , AARAHI); (Illus.). 64p. (YA). (gr. 7-12). 1999. Set lib. bdg. 212.00 (978-2-8239-9932-7(9) , AAARCU) Rosen Publishing Group, Inc., The.

Lilly, Melinda. St. Augustine. 2003. (Rourke Discovery Library). (Illus.). 24p. (gr. 1-4). 14.95 (978-1-58952-368-5(7)) Rourke Publishing, LLC.

Linney, Susan. Martin Luther King, Jr: With a Discussion of Responsibility. 2004. (Values in Action Ser.). (J). (978-1-59203-069-9(6)) Learning Challenge, Inc.

McKissack, Patricia C. & McKissack, Fredrick L. Black Hands, White Sails: The Story of African-American Whalers. 1999. (Illus.). 192p. (J). (gr. 3-8). pap. 17.95 (978-0-590-48313-1(7)) Scholastic, Inc.

—End of Slavery in the United States. Dillon, Leo & Dillon, Dianne, illus. 2003. (Days of Jubilee Ser.). 144p. (J). (gr. 3-7). pap. 18.95 (978-0-590-10764-8(X) , Scholastic Pr.) Scholastic, Inc.

McNeese, Tim. The Rise & Fall of American Slavery: Freedom Denied, Freedom Gained. 2004. (Slavery in American History Ser.). (Illus.). 128p. (J). lib. bdg. 26.60 (978-0-7660-2156-3(4)) Enslow Pubs., Inc.

Medearis, Angela Shelf & Bryant, Michael. Our People. 2002. (Illus.). 32p. (J). (gr. k-4). 14.95 (978-1-57768-440-4(0) , Gingham Dog Pr.) School Specialty Publishing.

Media Projects, Inc., Staff. Student Almanac of African American History: From Reconstruction to Today, 1877 to the Present, 2 vols., Vol. 2. 2003. (Middle School Reference Ser.). (Illus.). (J). (978-0-313-32598-4(7)) Greenwood Publishing Group, Inc.

—Student Almanac of African American History: From Slavery to Freedom, 1492-1876, 2 vols., Vol. 1. 2003. (Middle School Reference Ser.). (Illus.). (J). 80.00 (978-0-313-32597-7(9)) Greenwood Publishing Group, Inc.

Media Projects, Inc., Staff, contrib. by. Student's Almanac of African American History, 2 vols. 2003. (Middle School Reference Ser.). (Illus.). 144p. (J). (gr. 6-8). 86.95 (978-0-313-32596-0(0) , MS2596, Middle School Reference) Greenwood Publishing Group, Inc.

Miles, Johnnie H. Almanac of African American Heritage. 2001. (gr. 7-12). lib. bdg. 24.95 (978-0-613-64946-9(X)) Tandem Library Bks.

Murphy, Nora & Murphy-Gnatz, Mary, contrib. by. Meet African Americans in Minnesota: Telling Our Own Stories. 2000. (Illus.). 88p. (J). (gr. 3-7). pap. 12.95 (978-0-87351-380-7(0) , 380-0, Borealis Bk.) Minnesota Historical Society Pr.

Myers, Walter Dean. Now Is Your Time! The African-American Struggle for Freedom. 2002. (J). 21.91 (978-0-7587-0388-0(0)) Book Wholesalers, Inc.

O'Connell, Kim A. Slavery, Emancipation, & the Civil War: A MyReportLinks. com Book. 2004. (American Civil War Ser.). (Illus.). 48p. (J). lib. bdg. 25.26 (978-0-7660-5190-4(0) , MyReportLinks.com Bks.) Enslow Pubs., Inc.

Olson, Kay Melchisedech. Africans in America, 1665-1865. 2002. (Blue Earth Books). (Illus.). 32p. (J). (gr. 4). lib. bdg. 22.60 (978-0-7368-1204-7(0) , Bridgestone Bks.) Capstone Pr., Inc.

Perrin, Pat, ed. Slavery. 2000. (Researching American History Ser.). (Illus.). 56p. (J). (978-1-57960-062-4(X)) History Compass, LLC.

Pierce, Alan. The Montgomery Bus Boycott. 2005. (American Moments Ser.). (Illus.). 48p. (J). (gr. 4-8). lib. bdg. 25.65 (978-1-59197-935-7(8)) ABDO Publishing Co.

Plowden, Martha Ward. Famous Firsts of Black Women. Jones, Ronald, illus. 2nd ed. 2002. 176p. (J). (gr. 5-9). pap. 18.95 (978-1-56554-197-9(9)) Pelican Publishing Co., Inc.

Rappaport, Doreen. Free at Last! Stories & Songs of Emancipation. Evans, Shane W., illus. 2006. 64p. (J). (gr. 4-7). pap. 7.99 (978-0-7636-3147-5(7)) Candlewick Pr.

Robertson, Theda Robinson. Journey to a Free Land: The Story of Nicodemus, the First All Black Town West of the Mississippi. 2006. (Illus.). (J). (978-0-9705721-6-5(6)) Written Images, Inc.

Ruth, Annie. I Can Read. Ruth, Annie, illus. l.t. ed. 2005. (Illus.). 32p. (J). 9.95 (978-0-9656306-7-2(6)) Ruth, A. Creations.

Salzman, Jack. African-American Culture & History, 4 vols. 2000. (Illus.). xix, 1082p. (J). (978-0-02-865535-2(4) , Macmillan Reference USA) Thomson Gale.

Salzman, Jack, ed. African-American Culture & History, 4 vols. 2000. (Illus.). xix, 1082p. (J). (978-0-02-865533-8(8)) Macmillan Reference USA.

—African-American Culture & History, 4 vols. 2000. (Illus.). xix, 1082p. (J). (978-0-02-865532-1(X)); (978-0-02-865534-5(6)) Thomson Gale. (Macmillan Reference USA).

Sanders, Nancy. A Kid's Guide to African American History: More Than 70 Activities. 2001. (Illus.). (J). (978-0-606-20751-5(1)) Tandem Library Bks.

Sanders, Nancy I. Kid's Guide to African American History. 2000. (gr. 3-6). lib. bdg. 24.55 (978-0-613-90267-0(X)) Tandem Library Bks.

Sanders, Nancy I. A Kid's Guide to African American History: More than 70 Activities. 2nd ed. 2007. (Kid's Guide Ser.). 256p. (J). pap. 14.95 (**978-1-55652-653-4(9)**) Chicago Review Pr., Inc.

Schaefer, Adam. The Harlem Renaissance. 2003. (20th Century Perspectives Ser.). 48p. pap. 7.95 (978-1-4034-3858-4(7)) Heinemann Library.

Schleichert, Elizabeth. The Thirteenth Amendment: Ending Slavery. 1998. (Constitution Ser.). (Illus.). 128p. (YA). (gr. 6-12). lib. bdg. 26.60 (978-0-89490-923-8(1)) Enslow Pubs., Inc.

Shallop, Laura. Celebrating Our Heritage: African-American History. 2001. (Celebrating Our Heritage Ser.). 48p. (J). (gr. 2-3). pap. 6.99 (978-0-7424-0080-1(8) , IF2820); (gr. 4-6). pap. 6.99 (978-0-7424-0081-8(6) , IF2821) School Specialty Publishing.

Sharp, Anne Wallace. A Dream Deferred: the Jim Crow Era. 2005. (Lucent Library of Black History). (Illus.). 112p. (YA). (gr. 7-10). lib. bdg. 32.45 (978-1-59018-700-5(8) , Lucent Bks.) Thomson Gale.

Sinnott, Susan. Welcome to Addy's World, 1864: Growing up During America's Civil War. 1999. (American Girls Collection). (Illus.). 64p. (J). (gr. 2 up). 16.95 (978-1-56247-771-4(4)) American Girl Publishing, Inc.

Sioux, Tracee. African American Migration. 2004. (Primary Sources of Immigration & Migration in America Ser.). (Illus.). 24p. (J). lib. bdg. 19.95 (978-0-8239-6827-5(8)); lib. bdg. (978-0-8239-8953-9(4)) Rosen Publishing Group, Inc., The. (PowerKids Pr.).

Sirimarco, Elizabeth. The Time of Slavery. 2006. (American Voices Ser.). (Illus.). xxiii, 114p. (J). lib. bdg. 37.07 (978-0-7614-2169-6(6) , Benchmark Bks.) Cavendish, Marshall Corp.

Slavery DBA. 2002. spiral bd. 16.95 (978-1-56004-128-3(5)) Social Studies Schl. Service.

Slavery in America. 2004. (Historical Reader Ser.). (Illus.). 240p. (gr. 6-12). 13.32 (978-0-618-04822-9(7) , 2-00154) McDougal Littell Inc.

Steele, Christy & Graves, Kerry, eds. A Free Black Girl Before the Civil War: The Diary of Charlotte Forten, 1854. 1999. (Diaries, Letters & Memoirs Ser.). 32p. (J). (gr. 2-7). pap. 21.00 (978-0-516-21339-2(3) , Children's Pr.) Scholastic Library Publishing.

Stefoff, Rebecca. The Civil War & Reconstruction 1863-1877. 2002. (North American Historical Atlases Ser.). (Illus.). 48p. (J). 27.07 (978-0-7614-1347-9(2) , Benchmark Bks.) Cavendish, Marshall Corp.

Sterling, Kristin. Mary McLeod Bethune: A Life of Resourcefulness. 2008. (Pull Ahead Books-Biographies Ser.). (J). lib. bdg. 22.60 (**978-0-8225-8588-6(X)** , Lerner Pubns.) Lerner Publishing Group.

Stewart, Gail B. Fighting for Freedom: Blacks in the American Military. 2006. (Illus.). 112p. (J). (gr. 7-10). 32.45 (978-1-59018-952-8(3) , Lucent Bks.) Thomson Gale.

Stimpson, Bea. Black People of the Americas. 2001. (Illus.). 48p. (J). pap. 19.95 (978-0-7487-6013-8(X)) Nelson Thornes Ltd. GBR. *Dist:* Trans-Atlantic Pubns., Inc.

Stroud, Bettye & Schomp, Virginia. The Reconstruction ERA. 2006. (Drama of African-American History Ser.). (Illus.). 80p. (J). lib. bdg. 34.21 (978-0-7614-2181-8(5) , Benchmark Bks.) Cavendish, Marshall Corp.

Swain, Gwenyth. Civil Rights Pioneer: A Story about Mary Church Terrell. Beier, Ellen, illus. 64p. (J). pap. 6.95 (978-0-8225-4170-7(X)); 1999. (gr. 4-8). lib. bdg. 22.60 (978-1-57505-355-4(1)) Lerner Publishing Group.

—Civil Rights Pioneer: A Story about Mary Church Terrell. 1999. (gr. 3-6). lib. bdg. 15.25 (978-0-613-68325-8(0)) Tandem Library Bks.

Thomson Gale Staff. Civil Rights Movement. 2002. (gr. 7-12). lib. bdg. 33.25 (978-0-613-73614-5(1)) Tandem Library Bks.

Thornton, Jeremy. Immigration & the Slave Trade: Africans Come to America (1607-1830) 2004. (Primary Sources of Immigration & Migration in America Ser.). (Illus.). 24p. (J). lib. bdg. 19.95 (978-0-8239-6829-9(4) , PowerKids Pr.) Rosen Publishing Group, Inc., The.

—Immigration & the Slave Trade: Africans Come to America, 1607-1830. 2004. (Primary Sources of Immigration & Migration in America Ser.). (Illus.). 24p. (J). lib. bdg. (978-0-8239-8955-3(0) , PowerKids Pr.) Rosen Publishing Group, Inc., The.

Turck, Mary. Civil Rights Movement for Kids: A History with 21 Activities. 2000. (For Kids Ser.). (Illus.). 208p. (J). (gr. 4-8). pap. 14.95 (978-1-55652-370-0(X)) Chicago Review Pr., Inc.

Turner, Morrie. Explore Black History with Wee Pals. 1998. (Illus.). 64p. (J). (gr. 1-7). pap. 5.95 (978-0-940975-79-8(3) , Sankofa Bks.) Just Us Bks., Inc.

Upchurch, Thomas Adams. The Encyclopedia of African-American Civil Rights: From Emancipation to the Twenty-First Century, 2 vols., Vol. 1. Lowery, Charles D. & Marszalek, John F., eds. 2nd ed. 2003. (Illus.). xxviii, 920p. lib. bdg. 175.00 (978-0-313-32766-7(1)) Greenwood Publishing Group, Inc.

Uschan, Michael V. Forty Years of Medical Racism: The Tuskegee Experiments. 2005. (American Secrets & Scandals Ser.). (Illus.). 112p. (J). (gr. 7-10). lib. bdg. 32.45 (978-1-59018-486-8(6) , Lucent Bks.) Thomson Gale.

—Lynching & Murder in the Deep South. 2006. (Lucent Library of Black History). 112p. (YA). (gr. 8 up). lib. bdg. 32.45 (978-1-59018-845-3(4) , Lucent Bks.) Thomson Gale.

—Reconstruction. 2007. (Lucent Library of Black History Ser.). (Illus.). 128p. (gr. 7-10). 28.70 (**978-1-4205-0009-7(0)** , Lucent Bks.) Thomson Gale.

Uschan, Michael V. The Scottsboro Case. 2004. (Landmark Events in American History Ser.). (Illus.). 48p. (J). (gr. 5 up). pap. 11.95 (978-0-8368-5416-9(0)); lib. bdg. 30.00 (978-0-8368-5388-9(1)) Stevens, Gareth Inc. (World Almanac Library).

Vaughn, Wally G. & Davis, Mattie Campbell, eds. The Selma Campaign, 1963-1965: The Decisive Battle of the Civil Rights Movement. 2006. 261p. pap. 19.95 (978-0-912469-44-7(7)) Majority Pr., Inc., The.

Veciana-Suarez, Ana. Flight to Freedom. 2004. (First Person Fiction Ser.). (SPA.). 240p. (J). (gr. 7 up). pap. 4.99 (978-0-439-66358-8(X) , Scholastic Paperbacks) Scholastic, Inc.

—Flight to Freedom. 2004. 215p. (YA). (gr. 8-12). lib. bdg. 15.30 (978-0-613-72054-0(7)) Tandem Library Bks.

Walsh, Frank. The Montgomery Bus Boycott. 2003. (Landmark Events in American History Ser.). (Illus.). 48p. (J). (gr. 5 up). pap. 14.95 (978-0-8368-5403-9(9)); lib. bdg. 30.00 (978-0-8368-5375-9(X)) Stevens, Gareth Inc. (World Almanac Library).

We the People - Exploration & Colonization, 7 bks. Incl. African-Americans in the Colonies. Williams, Jean Kinney. 2002. lib. bdg. 22.60 (978-0-7565-0303-1(5)); California Missions. Heinrichs, Ann. 2002. lib. bdg. 22.60 (978-0-7565-0208-9(X)); French & Indian War. Santella, Andrew. 2004. lib. bdg. 22.60 (978-0-7565-0613-1(1)); Jamestown Colony. January, Brendan. 2000. lib. bdg. 22.60 (978-0-7565-0043-6(5)); Plymouth Colony. Santella, Andrew. 2000. lib. bdg. 22.60 (978-0-7565-0046-7(X)); Thirteen Colonies. Nobleman, Marc Tyler. 2002. lib. bdg. 22.60 (978-0-7565-0211-9(X)); Williamsburg. Alter, Judy. 2002. lib. bdg. 22.60 (978-0-7565-0300-0(0)); 48p. (J). (gr. 4 up). (Illus.). Set lib. bdg. 158.20 (978-0-7565-0775-6(8)) Compass Point Bks.

Williams, Jean Kinney. African-Americans in the Colonies. 2002. (We the People Ser.). (Illus.). 48p. (J). (gr. 4 up). lib. bdg. 22.60 (978-0-7565-0303-1(5)) Compass Point Bks.

Wills, Ora, ed. Images in Black: A Pictorial History of Black Pensacola. 2004. (Illus.). 224p. 30.00 (978-0-9659142-6-0(7)) Univ. of West Florida Foundation, Inc.

Wirkner, Linda. Learning about the Settlement of the Americas, with Graphic Organizers. 2005. (Graphic Organizers in Social Studies). (J). 19.95 (978-1-4042-2814-6(4) , PowerKids Pr.) Rosen Publishing Group, Inc., The.

Wistrand, Carolyn Nur. Beauty in Black Performance: Plays for African American Youth. 2006. (Illus.). (YA). 151p. (978-1-59221-379-5(0)); 158p. pap. (978-1-59221-380-1(4)) Africa World Pr.

Worth, Richard. Africans in America. 2004. (Immigration to the United States Ser.). (Illus.). 96p. (J). (gr. 4-9). 35.00 (978-0-8160-5691-0(9)) Facts On File, Inc.

Worth, Richard. Harlem Renaissance: An Explosion of African-American Culture. 2008. (J). (**978-0-7660-2907-1(7)**) Enslow Pubs., Inc.

AFRICAN AMERICANS—HISTORY—FICTION

Armistead, John. The Return of Gabriel. 2002. (gr. 5-8). lib. bdg. 15.25 (978-0-613-79202-8(5)) Tandem Library Bks.

Asim, Jabari. The Road to Freedom. 2004. 131p. (J). lib. bdg. 16.92 (**978-1-4242-0765-7(7)**) Fitzgerald Bks.

Carney-Nunes, Charisse. Nappy. Williams, Ann Marie, illus. 2006. 24p. (J). 14.99 (978-0-9748142-1-6(0)) Nunes Productions, LLC.

Craft, Jerry. Mama's Boyz: Home Schoolin' Because Learning Shouldn't Stop at 3 O'clock!, 2. 2007. (Illus.). 112p. (YA). per. 9.95 (**978-0-9796132-0-3(5)**) Mama's Boyz, Inc.

Dean, Jeffrey J. & Dean, Debra A. The Amazing Adventures of Abiola, Vol. 3. Ferguson, Dwayne, illus. l.t. ed. 1999. (Selected Children's Multicultural Stories). 32p. (J). (gr. 4-6). lib. bdg. 12.95 (978-1-56674-225-2(0)) Forest Hse. Publishing Co., Inc.

Draper, Sharon M. Copper Sun. 2006. 320p. (YA). (gr. 8 up). 16.95 (978-0-689-82181-3(6) , Atheneum) Simon & Schuster Children's Publishing.

Fenner, Carol. Running & Dancing. Kindert, Jennifer, illus. 2004. 200p. (J). 18.95 (978-0-9726290-1-0(7)) Blue Pheonix Bks.

Grimes, Nikki. Talkin' about Bessie: The Story of Aviator Elizabeth Coleman. Lewis, Earl B & Moser, B., illus. 2002. 48p. (J). pap. 16.95 (978-0-439-35243-7(6) , Orchard Bks.) Scholastic, Inc.

Iturralde, Edna. Y Su Corazon Escapo para Convertirse en Pajaro. Gonzalez, Santiago, illus. (SPA.). 177p. (J). (gr. 8-12). pap. 10.95 (978-9978-07-331-5(0)) Santillana USA Publishing Co., Inc.

Kay, Alan. Breaking the Rules. 2007. (Young Heroes of History: 7). (J). pap. 7.95 (**978-1-57249-389-6(5)** , White Mane Kids) White Mane Publishing Co., Inc.

Lester, Julius. Day of Tears. 2007. 192p. (gr. 7 up). pap. 7.99 (**978-1-4231-0409-4(9)** , Jump at the Sun) Hyperion Bks. for Children.

Literature Connections English: Jubilee. 2004. (gr. 6-12). (978-0-395-83362-9(0) , 2-70785) McDougal Littell Inc.

Literature Connections English: Roll of Thunder, Hear My Cry. 2004. (gr. 6-12). (978-0-395-77530-1(2) , 2-80099) McDougal Littell Inc.

McKissack, Patricia C. A Picture of Freedom: The Diary of Clotee, a Slave Girl, Belmont Plantation, Virginia, 1859. 1999. (Dear America Ser.). (J). 9.95 (978-0-439-15599-1(1)) Scholastic, Inc.

McNaught, Maria. Grandma's Ashanti Cloth. 2003. 24p. (J). pap. 8.95 (978-0-913543-83-2(7)) African American Images.

Monjo, F. N. La Osa Menor: Una Historia del Ferrocarril Subterraneo. Mlawer, Teresa, tr. Brenner, Fred, illus. 2001. (SPA.). (J). (gr. 3-10). pap. 6.95 (978-1-880507-90-2(0) , LC7973); ring bd. 15.95 (978-1-880507-91-9(9) , LC7976) Lectorum Pubns., Inc.

—La Osa Menor: Una Historia del Ferrocarril Subterraneo. 2001. (978-0-606-21286-1(8)) Tandem Library Bks.

Mosley, Walter. 47. 2005. 240p. (YA). (gr. 7-17). 16.99 (978-0-316-11035-8(3)) Little Brown & Co.

Paterson, Katherine. Jip, His Story. 1998. (Puffin Novel Ser.). 208p. (J). (gr. 5-9). pap. 6.99 (978-0-14-038674-5(2) , Puffin) Penguin Group (USA) Inc.

Perez, L. King. Remember As You Pass Me By. 2007. 224p. (J). (gr. 4-8). 16.95 (***978-1-57131-677-6(9)***) Milkweed Editions.

—Remember as You Pass Me By. 2007. 184p. (J). (gr. 2-7). per. 6.95 (***978-1-57131-678-3(7)***) Milkweed Editions.

Rubright, Lynn. Mama's Window. 2005. (Illus.). 144p. (J). (gr. 4-8). 16.95 (978-1-58430-160-8(0)) Lee & Low Bks., Inc.

Sawyer, Kem Knapp. Freedom Calls: Journey of a Slave Girl. 2001. v, 181p. (J). (gr. 3-6). lib. bdg. 17.95 (978-1-57249-206-6(6) , White Mane Kids) White Mane Publishing Co., Inc.

Wall, Patricia Q. Child Out of Place: A Story for New England. Ronnquist, Debby, illus. 2003. 116p. (J). (gr. 6-9). pap. 12.00 (978-0-9742185-0-2(2)) Fall Rose Bks.

AFRICAN AMERICANS IN ART

Duggleby, John. Story Painter: The Life of Jacob Lawrence. 1998. (Illus.). 64p. (J). (gr. 1-7). 16.95 (978-0-8118-2082-0(3)) Chronicle Bks. LLC.

Gnojewski, Carol. African-American Crafts Kids Can Do! 2006. (Multicultural Crafts Kids Can Do! Ser.). (Illus.). 32p. (J). lib. bdg. 22.60 (978-0-7660-2457-1(1) , Enslow Elementary) Enslow Pubs., Inc.

Lester, Julius. From Slave Ship to Freedom Road. Brown, Rod, illus. 1999. 40p. (J). (gr. 5-8). pap. 6.99 (978-0-14-056669-7(4) , Puffin) Penguin Group (USA) Inc.

—From Slave Ship to Freedom Road. Brown, Rod, illus. 1999. 40p. (J). (gr. k-8). lib. bdg. 15.30 (978-0-613-22990-6(8)) Tandem Library Bks.

AFRICAN AMERICANS IN BUSINESS

see African Americans—Employment

AFRICAN AMERICANS—MUSIC

Cooper, Michael L. Slave Spirituals & the Jubilee Singers. 2001. (Illus.). 96p. (J). (gr. 5-9). tchr. ed. 16.00 (978-0-395-97829-0(7) , Clarion Bks.) Houghton Mifflin Co. Trade & Reference Div.

Haskins, James. Black Music in America: A History Through Its People. 2000. (Illus.). 200p. (J). pap. 12.95 (978-1-56649-133-4(9)) Welcome Rain Pubs.

Higginsen, V. & Johnson, H. A Harlem Century. 2000. (J). 20.00 (978-0-517-70949-8(X) , Random Hse. Bks. for Young Readers) Random Hse. Children's Bks.

Igus, Toyomi. I See the Rhythm. Wood, Michele, illus. 1998. 32p. (J). (gr. 1 up). 16.95 (978-0-89239-151-6(0)) Children's Bk. Pr.

Igus, Toyomi & Wood, Michele. I See the Rhythm. 2005. (Illus.). 32p. (J). pap. 7.95 (978-0-89239-212-4(6)) Children's Bk. Pr.

Wood, Michele, illus. I See the Rhythm. 1998. (J). (gr. 2-4). pap. 21.27 (978-0-516-21191-6(9) , Children's Pr.) Scholastic Library Publishing.

Woog, Adam. From Ragtime to Hip-Hop: A Century of Black American Music. 2006. (Lucent Library of Black History). (Illus.). 112p. (J). (gr. 7-10). 32.45 (978-1-59018-978-8(7) , 1256817, Lucent Bks.) Thomson Gale.

AFRICAN AMERICANS—POETRY

Greenfield, Eloise. Honey, I Love. Gilchrist, Jan Spivey, illus. anniv. ed. 2003. 32p. (J). (ps-k). 16.99 (978-0-06-009123-1(1)); lib. bdg. 17.89 (978-0-06-009124-8(X)) HarperCollins Pubs.

Grimes, Nikki. A Dime a Dozen. Angelo, illus. 1998. 56p. (YA). (gr. 7-12). 17.99 (978-0-8037-2227-9(3) , Dial) Penguin Group (USA) Inc.

Little, Lessie Jones. Children of Long Ago: Poems. Gilchrist, Jan Spivey, illus. 2000. 32p. (J). (ps up). 15.95 (978-1-58430-008-3(6)); 6.95 (978-1-58430-009-0(4)) Lee & Low Bks., Inc.

—Children of Long Ago: Poems. 2000. (Illus.). (J). (978-0-606-18246-1(2)) Tandem Library Bks.

Myers, Walter Dean. Blues Journey. Myers, Christopher, illus. 48p. (YA). pap. 8.95 (***978-0-8234-2079-7(5)***) Holiday Hse., Inc.

Smith Turner, Jennifer. Lost & Found: Rhyming Verse Honoring African American Heroes. 4th ed. 2006. per. 22.00 (***978-0-9790817-0-5(X)***) Smith & Assocs.

AFRICAN AMERICANS—POLITICS AND GOVERNMENT

Booker, Christopher B. African-Americans & the Presidency: A History of Broken Promises. 2000. (Single Titles Ser.). (Illus.). 192p. (YA). (gr. 9-12). 24.00 (978-0-531-11882-5(7) , Watts, Franklin) Scholastic Library Publishing.

Kitto, John. An Illustrated History of the Holy Bible: Being a Connected Account of the Remarkable Events & Distinguished Characters Contained in the Old & New Testaments, & in Jewish History During the Four Hundred Years Intervening Between the Time of Malachi & the Birth of Christ, Including Also the Life of Christ & His Apostles. 2006. (Illus.). (YA). cd-rom (978-1-892824-00-4(0)) AFCHRON.

Sharpten, Al. African-American Civil Rights Activists: Black Panthers. 2000. (My Ancestors—My Heroes Ser.: Vol. 39). (J). (gr. 3-4). (978-1-893091-38-2(4)) Parker Publishing Co.

AFRICAN AMERICANS—SEGREGATION

Collier, Christopher & Collier, James Lincoln. Reconstruction & the Rise of Jim Crow: 1864-1896. 1999. (Drama of American History Ser.). (Illus.). 96p. (YA). (gr. 5-9). lib. bdg. 31.36 (978-0-7614-0819-2(3) , Benchmark Bks.) Cavendish, Marshall Corp.

George, Charles. Life under the Jim Crow Laws. 1999. (Way People Live Ser.). (Illus.). 96p. (YA). (gr. 7-10). 27.45 (978-1-56006-499-2(4) , LML00902-177862, Lucent Bks.) Thomson Gale.

Sharp, Anne Wallace. A Dream Deferred: the Jim Crow Era. 2005. (Lucent Library of Black History). (Illus.). 112p. (YA). (gr. 7-10). lib. bdg. 32.45 (978-1-59018-700-5(8) , Lucent Bks.) Thomson Gale.

AFRICAN AMERICANS—SEGREGATION—FICTION

McKissack, Patricia C. & Pinkney, Jerry. Goin' Someplace Special. 2001. (Illus.). 40p. (J). (ps-3). 16.99 (978-0-689-81885-1(8) , Atheneum/Anne Schwartz Bks.) Simon & Schuster Children's Publishing.

Wiles, Deborah. Freedom Summer. Lagarrigue, Jerome, illus. 32p. (J). (ps-3). 2001. 16.95 (978-0-689-83016-7(5) , Atheneum/Anne Schwartz Bks.); 2005. reprint ed. 6.99 (978-0-689-87829-9(X) , Aladdin) Simon & Schuster Children's Publishing.

AFRICAN AMERICANS—SOCIAL CONDITIONS

see also African Americans—Suffrage

Cartlidge, Cherese. Reparations for Slavery. 2007. (Lucent Library of Black History Ser.). (Illus.). 128p. (J). (gr. 7-10). 28.70 (***978-1-59018-868-2(3)*** , Lucent Bks.) Thomson Gale.

Clare, John D. The Black Peoples of America. 2001. (Illus.). 48p. pap. 23.50 (***978-0-340-79033-5(4)*** , Hodder Murray) Hodder Education GBR. *Dist:* Trans-Atlantic Pubns., Inc.

Davis, Anthony C. & Jackson, Jeffrey. Yo, Little Brother: Basic Rules of Survival for Young African-American Males. 1998. 145p. (gr. 4-7). pap. 14.95 (978-0-913543-58-0(6)) African American Images.

Dawson, George. Life Is So Good. 2001. (gr. 7-12). lib. bdg. 23.45 (978-0-613-36465-2(1)) Tandem Library Bks.

Deiters, Erika & Deiters, Jim. The African Community in America. 2003. (J). pap. (978-1-58417-095-2(6)); lib. bdg. (978-1-58417-032-7(8)) Lake Street Pubs.

Dray, Philip. Daughter of Freedom: The Life & Times of Ida B. Wells. Alcorn, Stephen, illus. 2007. (J). (***978-1-56145-417-4(6)***) Peachtree Pubs., Ltd.

Featonby, Douglas & Whittock, Martyn. The Black Peoples of America. 2001. (Illus.). 48p. pap. 23.50 (***978-0-340-79034-2(2)*** , Hodder Murray) Hodder Education GBR. *Dist:* Trans-Atlantic Pubns., Inc.

Greene, Meg. Into the Land of Freedom: African Americans in Reconstruction. 2004. (People's History Ser.). (Illus.). 96p. (J). lib. bdg. 29.27 (978-0-8225-4690-0(6)) Lerner Publishing Group.

Halpern, Monica. Moving North: African Americans & the Great Migration 1915 - 1930. 2005. (Crossroads America Ser.). (Illus.). 40p. (gr. k-3). (J). 12.95 (978-0-7922-8278-5(7)); 21.90 (978-0-7922-8358-4(9)) National Geographic Society. (National Geographic Children's Bks.).

Hansen, Joyce. Bury Me Not in a Land of Slaves: African-Americans in the Time of Reconstruction. 2000. (J). 15.60 (978-0-606-19779-3(6)) Tandem Library Bks.

Haskins, James & Benson, Kathleen. Building a New Land: African Americans in Colonial America. Ransome, James E., illus. 2001. (Amistad Ser.). 48p. (J). (gr. 2-5). 17.89 (978-0-06-029361-1(6)); 17.95 (978-0-688-10266-1(2)) HarperCollins Pubs.

—Out of the Darkness: The Story of Blacks Moving North, 1890-1940. 2000. (Great Journeys Ser.). (Illus.). 112p. (J). (gr. 5 up). lib. bdg. 32.79 (978-0-7614-0970-0(X) , Benchmark Bks.) Cavendish, Marshall Corp.

Holliday, Laurel. Dreaming in Color, Living in Black & White. 2000. (gr. 3-6). lib. bdg. 13.00 (978-0-613-21468-1(4)) Tandem Library Bks.

—Dreaming in Color Living in Black & White: Our Own Stories of Growing up Black in America. 2000. (J). 12.15 (978-0-606-19494-5(0)) Tandem Library Bks.

Kallen, Stuart A. A History of Free Blacks in America. 2005. (Lucent Library of Black History). (Illus.). 112p. (YA). (gr. 7-10). lib. bdg. 32.45 (978-1-59018-776-0(8) , Lucent Bks.) Thomson Gale.

—Striving into 2000. 2001. (Black History Ser.). (Illus.). 48p. (J). (gr. 3-8). lib. bdg. 25.65 (978-1-57765-467-4(6) , ABDO & Daughters) ABDO Publishing Co.

Kunjufu, Jawanza & Prescott, Folami. Eighth Grade: Self-Esteem Through Culture Leads to Academic Excellence. 2003. (SETCLAE Ser.). 60p. (J). pap. 9.95 (978-0-913543-93-1(4)) African American Images.

—High School: Self-Esteem Through Culture Leads to Academic Excellence. 2003. (SETCLAE Ser.). 60p. (J). pap. 9.95 (978-0-913543-94-8(2)) African American Images.

—Kindergarten: Self-Esteem Through Culture Leads to Academic Excellence. 2003. (SETCLAE Ser.). 60p. (J). pap. 9.95 (978-0-913543-85-6(3)) African American Images.

—SETCLAE, Fifth Grade: Self-Esteem Through Culture Leads to Academic Excellence. 2003. (SETCLAE Ser.). 60p. (J). pap. 9.95 (978-0-913543-90-0(X)) African American Images.

—SETCLAE, First Grade: Self-Esteem Through Culture Leads to Academic Excellence. 2003. (SETCLAE Ser.). 60p. (J). pap. 9.95 (978-0-913543-86-3(1)) African American Images.

—SETCLAE, Fourth Grade: Self-Esteem Through Culture Leads to Academic Excellence. 2003. (SETCLAE Ser.). 60p. (J). pap. 9.95 (978-0-913543-89-4(6)) African American Images.

—SETCLAE, Second Grade: Self-Esteem Through Culture Leads to Academic Excellence. 2003. (SETCLAE Ser.). 60p. (J). pap. 9.95 (978-0-913543-87-0(X)) African American Images.

—SETCLAE, Seventh Grade: Self-Esteem Through Culture Leads to Academic Excellence. 2003. (SETCLAE Ser.). 60p. (J). pap. 9.95 (978-0-913543-92-4(6)) African American Images.

—SETCLAE, Sixth Grade: Self-Esteem Through Culture Leads to Academic Excellence. 2003. (SETCLAE Ser.). 60p. (J). pap. 9.95 (978-0-913543-91-7(8)) African American Images.

—SETCLAE, Third Grade: Self-Esteem Through Culture Leads to Academic Excellence. 2003. (SETCLAE Ser.). 60p. (J). pap. 9.95 (978-0-913543-88-7(8)) African American Images.

Myers, Walter Dean. The Harlem Hellfighters: When Pride Met Courage. 2006. (Illus.). 160p. (J). 17.99 (978-0-06-001136-9(X) , Amistad) HarperCollins Pubs.

Myers, Walter Dean & Miles, Bill. The Harlem Hellfighters: When Pride Met Courage. 2006. (Illus.). 160p. (J). lib. bdg. 18.89 (978-0-06-001137-6(8) , Amistad) HarperCollins Pubs.

Neri, Greg. Yummy: The Last Days of a Southside Shorty. DuBurke, Randy, illus. 2007. (J). (978-1-58430-266-7(6)); pap. (978-1-58430-267-4(4)) Lee & Low Bks., Inc.

Nutter, Jeanne D. Growing up Black in New Castle County, Delaware. 2001. (Black America Ser.). (Illus.). 128p. (gr. 5 up). pap. 18.99 (978-0-7385-0622-7(2)) Arcadia Publishing.

Sioux, Tracee. African American Migration. 2004. (Primary Sources of Immigration & Migration in America Ser.). (Illus.). 24p. (J). lib. bdg. 19.95 (978-0-8239-6827-5(8)); lib. bdg. (978-0-8239-8953-9(4)) Rosen Publishing Group, Inc., The. (PowerKids Pr.).

Tackach, James. Early Black Reformers. 2003. (gr. 7-12). lib. bdg. 33.25 (978-0-613-73930-6(2)) Tandem Library Bks.

—Early Black Reformers. 2003. (History Firsthand Ser.). (Illus.). (YA). 224p. pap. 24.95 (978-0-7377-1598-9(7)); 202p. lib. bdg. 36.20 (978-0-7377-1597-2(9)) Thomson Gale. (Greenhaven Pr., Inc.).

AFRICAN AMERICANS—SOCIAL LIFE AND CUSTOMS

Bolden, Tonya. Maritcha: A Nineteenth-Century American Girl. 2005. (Illus.). 48p. (J). (gr. k-4). 17.95 (978-0-8109-5045-0(6)) Abrams, Harry N. , Inc.

Branham, LaTonya, compiled by & des. CultureSeek: Connecting to African & African American History. Branham, LaTonya, des. 2006. (YA). per. 8.00 (978-0-9787296-0-8(9)) BabyStar Productions.

Chocolate, Deborah M. Newton. My First Kwanzaa Book. 1999. (978-0-606-18580-6(1)); lib. bdg. 14.15 (978-0-613-22048-4(X)) Tandem Library Bks.

Doering, Amanda. Kwanzaa. 2006. (First Facts Ser.). (Illus.). 24p. (J). (978-0-7368-5390-3(1)) Capstone Pr., Inc.

Freeman, Dorothy Rhodes & MacMillan, Dianne M. Kwanzaa. rev. ed. 2008. (Best Holiday Books Ser.). (Illus.). 48p. (J). (gr. 3-4). lib. bdg. 23.93 (***978-0-7660-3042-8(3)***) Enslow Pubs., Inc.

Gillis, Jennifer Blizin & Jordan, Denise M. Kwanzaa. 2002. (Fiestas Con Velas (Candle Time) Ser.). (SPA.). 24p. (J). (ps-1). lib. bdg. 18.50 (978-1-58810-783-1(3)); (Illus.). pap. 5.25 (978-1-58810-830-2(9) , 91591) Heinemann Library.

Jordan, Denise M. Juneteenth. 2003. (Holiday Histories Ser.). 32p. pap. 6.95 (978-1-4034-3690-0(8)) Heinemann Library.

—Kwanzaa. 2002. (Candle Time Ser.). 24p. (J). (ps-1). pap. 5.25 (978-1-58810-737-4(X)); (Illus.). lib. bdg. 18.50 (978-1-58810-528-8(8)) Heinemann Library.

Korantema, Jwajiku. I'm African & Proud. 2005. (Illus.). 24p. (J). 19.95 (978-1-933285-27-6(3)) Brown Bks. Publishing Group.

Levy, Janey. Juneteenth: Celebrating the End of Slavery. 2003. (Reading Room Collection). (Illus.). 24p. (J). lib. bdg. 18.75 (978-0-8239-3711-0(9)) Rosen Publishing Group, Inc., The.

Moore, Stephanie Perry. Staying Pure. 2000. (gr. 7-12). lib. bdg. 15.30 (978-0-613-90878-8(3)) Tandem Library Bks.

Nelson, Michael. Juneteenth. Schroder, Marc, illus. 2006. (On My Own Holidays Ser.). 48p. (J). pap. 5.95 (978-0-8225-5974-0(9) , First Avenue Editions) Lerner Publishing Group.

Nelson, Vaunda Micheaux & Nelson, Drew. Juneteenth. Schroder, Mark, illus. 2006. (On My Own Holidays Ser.). 48p. (J). 25.26 (978-1-57505-876-4(6)) Lerner Publishing Group.

Nobleman, Marc Tyler. Kwanzaa. 2004. (Let's See Ser.). (Illus.). 24p. (J). (gr. 1 up). lib. bdg. 19.93 (978-0-7565-0647-6(6)) Compass Point Bks.

Preszler, June. Juneteenth: Jubilee for Freedom. 2007. (First Facts Ser.). (Illus.). 24p. (J). 21.26 (978-0-7368-6396-4(6) , 1258818) Capstone Pr., Inc.

Rau, Dana. Kwanzaa. 2000. (gr. 3-6). lib. bdg. 15.25 (978-0-613-51658-7(3)) Tandem Library Bks.

Rosinsky, Natalie M. Juneteenth. 2004. (Let's See Ser.). (Illus.). 24p. (J). (gr. 1). lib. bdg. 19.93 (978-0-7565-0770-1(7)) Compass Point Bks.

Seven Candles for Kwanzaa. 2004. 29.95 incl. cd-rom (978-1-55592-739-4(4)); pap. 18.95 incl. audio compact disk (978-1-55592-746-2(7)); pap. 38.75 incl. audio compact disk (978-1-55592-753-0(X)); pap. 32.75 incl. audio (978-1-55592-307-5(0)); pap. 14.95 incl. audio (978-1-55592-046-3(2)) Weston Woods Studios, Inc.

Tokunbo, Dimitrea. The Sound of Kwanzaa. Cohen, Lisa, illus. 2008. (J). (***978-0-545-01865-4(X)*** , Scholastic Pr.) Scholastic, Inc.

Trueit, Trudi Strain. Kwanzaa. 2006. (Rookie Read-About Holidays Ser.). (Illus.). 31p. (J). 20.50 (978-0-531-12458-1(4) , Children's Pr.) Scholastic Library Publishing.

Walter, Mildred Pitts. Kwanzaa: A Family Affair. 2000. (Illus.). 95p. (YA). reprint ed. 17.00 (978-0-7881-6956-4(4)) DIANE Publishing Co.

Weber, Valerie & Jackson, Jeraldine. Food in Grandma's Day. 1999. (In Grandma's Day Ser.). (Illus.). 32p. (J). (gr. 2-4). lib. bdg. 21.27 (978-1-57505-328-8(4) , Carolrhoda Bks.) Lerner Publishing Group.

Williams, Nancy. A Kwanzaa Celebration: Pop-up Book. Sabuda, Robert, illus. 2004. 14p. (J). reprint ed. 13.00 (978-0-7567-8229-0(5)) DIANE Publishing Co.

Winchester, Faith. African American Holidays. 1999. (Ethnic Holidays Ser.). (Illus.). 24p. (J). (gr. 2-3). lib. bdg. 18.60 (978-1-56065-456-8(2) , Bridgestone Bks.) Capstone Pr., Inc.

Worth, Richard. Harlem Renaissance: An Explosion of African-American Culture. 2008. (J). (***978-0-7660-2907-1(7)***) Enslow Pubs., Inc.

AFRICAN AMERICANS—SOUTHERN STATES

Dumas, Bianca. Robert Moses. 2003. (African-American Biographies Ser.). (Illus.). 64p. (J). lib. bdg. 28.56 (978-0-7398-7031-0(9)) Raintree.

—Robert Parris Moses. 2003. (African-American Biographies Ser.). (Illus.). 64p. (J). (ps-7). pap. 9.50 (978-1-4109-0319-8(2)) Raintree.

Haskins, Jim. The Geography of Hope: Black Exodus from the South after Reconstruction. 1999. (Single Titles Ser.: up). (Illus.). 144p. (gr. 7 up). lib. bdg. 31.90 (978-0-7613-0323-7(5) , Millbrook Pr.) Lerner Publishing Group.

Igus, Toyomi, ed. Going Back Home: An Artist Returns to the South. Wood, Michele, illus. 2004. 32p. (J). (gr. 1 up). pap. 7.95 (978-0-89239-197-4(9)) Children's Bk. Pr.

Katz, William Loren. Breaking the Chains: African-American Slave Resistance, Class Set. unabr. ed. 1998. (YA). 155.80 incl. audio (978-0-7887-2556-2(4) , 46726) Recorded Bks., LLC.

—Breaking the Chains Homework Set: African-American Slave Resistance. unabr. ed. 1998. (YA). 53.25 incl. audio (978-0-7887-2252-3(2) , 40736) Recorded Bks., LLC.

Simms, Patsy Ford. Harriet's Freedom Train. 2000. (J). stu. ed. 12.50 (978-0-7692-9377-6(8)); tchr. ed. 24.95 (978-0-7692-9376-9(X)) Alfred Publishing Co., Inc. (Warner Bros. Pubns.).

AFRICAN AMERICANS—SUFFRAGE

Aretha, David. Freedom Summer. 2007. (J). (***978-1-59935-059-2(9)***) Reynolds, Morgan Inc.

—Selma & the Voting Rights ACT. 2007. (J). (***978-1-59935-056-1(4)***) Reynolds, Morgan Inc.

Banfield, Susan. The Fifteenth Amendment: African-American Men's Right to Vote. 1998. (Constitution Ser.). (Illus.). 128p. (YA). (gr. 6-12). lib. bdg. 26.60 (978-0-7660-1033-8(3)) Enslow Pubs., Inc.

Bjornlund, Lydia D. Women of the Suffrage Movement. 2003. (Women in History Ser.). (Illus.). 112p. (J). 32.45 (978-1-59018-173-7(5) , Lucent Bks.) Thomson Gale.

AFRICAN AMERICANS—WEST (U.S.)

Buffalo Soldiers & the Western Frontier Vol. 2: Individual Title Six-Packs. (On Deck Ser.: Vol. 2). 24p. (gr. 4-5). 35.00 (978-0-7578-5805-5(8)) Rigby Education.

Dickinson, Malcolm. Bill Pickett's Great Adventures: The Rodeo King's Legend Lives On. 2002. (Illus.). 100p. 10.95 (978-1-57168-737-1(8)) Eakin Pr.

Glaser, Jason. The Buffalo Soldiers & the American West. Smith, Tod & Barnett, Charles, illus. 2005. (Graphic Library). 32p. (J). (gr. 3-7). lib. bdg. 25.26 (978-0-7368-4966-1(1)) Capstone Pr., Inc.

Haskins, Jim. The Geography of Hope: Black Exodus from the South after Reconstruction. 1999. (Single Titles Ser.: up). (Illus.). 144p. (gr. 7 up). lib. bdg. 31.90 (978-0-7613-0323-7(5) , Millbrook Pr.) Lerner Publishing Group.

McGowen, Tom. African-Americans in the Old West. 1999. (Cornerstones of Freedom Ser.). (Illus.). 32p. (J). (gr. 4-6). pap. 5.95 (978-0-516-26348-9(X) , Children's Pr.) Scholastic Library Publishing.

Raabe, Emily. Buffalo Soldiers & the Western Frontier. 2003. (Reading Power Ser.). (Illus.). 24p. (J). lib. bdg. 17.25 (978-0-8239-6495-6(7) , PowerKids Pr.) Rosen Publishing Group, Inc., The.

Randolph, Ryan P. Black Cowboys. 2003. (Library of the Westward Expansion). (Illus.). 24p. (J). lib. bdg. 19.95 (978-0-8239-6294-5(6)) Rosen Publishing Group, Inc., The.

Unseld, Teresa S. Portfolios: African-Americans of the Old West. Dana, Bev et al, eds. Unseld, Teresa S., illus. Date not set. (Illus.). 80p. (J). (gr. 4-8). pap. 24.95 (978-1-57232-360-5(4) , 31331) Seymour, Dale Pubns.

AFRICAN LANGUAGES

African Languages & Cultural Beliefs. 2000. (My Ancestors—My Heroes Ser.: Vol. 3). (J). (gr. 3-4). (978-1-893091-02-3(3)) Parker Publishing Co.

Martivo, Kyalo. Herufi Zetu: African Traditional Writing Systems: Traditional Graphic Arts As Writing Systems. Leoni, Diana, illus. 1st ed. 1999. 100p. (J). (gr. 5-8). pap. 8.95 (978-0-9642831-2-1(3)) Amenta Bks.

National Curriculum Development Centre Staff. Ateso Pupil. 2004. Bk. 1. pap., pupil's gde. ed. (978-0-521-78928-8(1)); Bk. 2. pap., pupil's gde. ed. (978-0-521-78929-5(X)); Bk. 3. pap., pupil's gde. ed. (978-0-521-78930-1(3)); Bk. 4. pap., pupil's gde. ed. (978-0-521-78931-8(1)) Cambridge Univ. Pr.

—Luganda. 2004. Bk. 1. pap., pupil's gde. ed. (978-0-521-78932-5(X)); Bk. 2. pap., pupil's gde. ed. (978-0-521-78933-2(8)); Bk. 4. pap., pupil's gde. ed. (978-0-521-78935-6(4)) Cambridge Univ. Pr.

—Luganda Pupil, Bk. 5. 2004. pap., pupil's gde. ed. (978-0-521-78934-9(6)) Cambridge Univ. Pr.

—Runyankore-Rukiga. 2004. Bk. 1. pap., pupil's gde. ed. (978-0-521-78924-0(9)); Bk. 2. pap., pupil's gde. ed. (978-0-521-78925-7(7)); Bk. 3. pap., pupil's gde. ed. (978-0-521-78926-4(5)); Bk. 4. pap., pupil's gde. ed. (978-0-521-78927-1(3)) Cambridge Univ. Pr.

—Uganda Mother Tongue: Primary 1. 2004. pap., tchr. ed. (978-0-521-78940-0(0)) Cambridge Univ. Pr.

—Uganda Mother Tongue: Primary 2. 2004. pap., tchr. ed. (978-0-521-78941-7(9)) Cambridge Univ. Pr.

—Uganda Mother Tongue: Primary 4. 2004. pap., tchr. ed. (978-0-521-78943-1(5)) Cambridge Univ. Pr.

Welcome to Africa, Swahili & English: Fun & Adventure, a Swahili/English Multicultural Book. 2004. (J). per. 9.95 (978-0-9742688-1-1(X)) Ndegwa, Catherine W.

Wilson-Max, Ken. Furaha Means Happy! A Book of Swahili Words. 2000. (J). (978-0-606-19448-8(7)) Tandem Library Bks.

AFRO-AMERICAN ACTORS

see African American Actors

AFRO-AMERICAN ART

see African American Art

AFRO-AMERICAN ARTISTS

see African American Artists

AFRO-AMERICAN ATHLETES

see African American Athletes

AFRO-AMERICAN AUTHORS

see African American Authors

AFRO-AMERICAN COOKERY

see African American Cookery

AFRO-AMERICAN FOLKLORE

see African Americans—Folklore

AFRO-AMERICAN LITERATURE (ENGLISH)

see American Literature—African American Authors

AFRO-AMERICAN MUSIC

see African Americans—Music

AFRO-AMERICAN MUSICIANS

see African American Musicians

AFRO-AMERICAN POETRY (ENGLISH)

see American Poetry—African American Authors

AFRO-AMERICAN SCIENTISTS

see African American Scientists

AFRO-AMERICAN SOLDIERS

see African American Soldiers

AFRO-AMERICAN SONGS

see African Americans—Music

AFRO-AMERICAN SPIRITUALS

see Spirituals (Songs)

AFRO-AMERICANS

see African Americans

AFTERLIFE

see Future Life

AGED

see Older People

AGGREGATES (MATHEMATICS)

see Set Theory

AGRICULTURAL BANKS

see Banks and Banking

AGRICULTURAL BOTANY

see Botany, Economic

AGRICULTURAL LABORERS

see also Migrant Labor; Peasantry

Atkin, S. Beth. Voices from the Fields: Children of Migrant Farm Workers Tell Their Stories. 2000. (gr. 5-8). lib. bdg. 21.95 (978-0-613-27432-6(6)) Tandem Library Bks.

Ebon Research Systems Staff. Dare to Be... A Hero Vol. 3: Cesar Chavez. l.t. ed. 2003. Tr. of Atrevete Ser... Un Heroe Cesar Chavez. (ENG & SPA., Illus.). 16p. (J). 3.99 (978-0-9648313-6-0(8)) Ebon Research Systems Publishing, LLC.

Feinstein, Stephen. Lee sobre César Chavez/Read about Cesar Chavez. 2006. (I Like Biographies! Bilingual Ser.). (ENG & SPA., Illus.). 24p. (J). (gr. 1-3). lib. bdg. 21.26 (978-0-7660-2744-2(9) , Enslow Elementary) Enslow Pubs., Inc.

Gotsch, Patrice. Cesar Chavez: Changing Lives. Arreola, Gil, illus. 2005. 19p. (J). pap. ***978-1-55501-780-4(0)*** Dallard & Tighe Pubs.

Guzman, Lila & Guzman, Rick. César Chavez: Fighting for Fairness. 2006. (Famous Latinos Ser.). (Illus.). 32p. (J). lib. bdg. 22.60 (978-0-7660-2370-3(2) , Enslow Elementary) Enslow Pubs., Inc.

Herrera, Juan Felipe. Calling the Doves. 2001. Tr. of El Canto De Las Palomos. (SPA.). (gr. 3-6). lib. bdg. 16.40 (978-0-613-34098-4(1)) Tandem Library Bks.

Jiménez, Francisco. Breaking Through: A Migrant Child's Journey from the Fields. 2001. (Illus.). 208p. (YA). (gr. 7 up). tchr. ed. 16.00 (978-0-618-01173-5(0)) Houghton Mifflin Co. Trade & Reference Div.

Libal, Joyce. Migrant Youth: Falling Between the Cracks. 2007. (Youth in Rural North America Ser.). (J). (978-1-4222-0020-9(5)); (978-1-4222-0011-7(6)) Mason Crest Pubs.

Tello, Jerry. Let's Read About— César Chavez. Marchesi, Stephen, illus. 2004. (Scholastic First Biographies Ser.). (J). pap. (978-0-439-68051-6(4)) Scholastic, Inc.

Thompson, E. L. Cesar Chavez, with Profiles of Terence V. Powderly & Dolores Huerta. 2006. (Biographical Connections Ser.). (Illus.). 112p. (J). (978-0-7166-1827-0(3)) World Bk., Inc.

AGRICULTURAL MACHINERY

Auch, Alison. Garden Tools. 2003. (Spyglass Books). (Illus.). 24p. (J). (gr. 1 up). lib. bdg. 18.60 (978-0-7565-0448-9(1)) Compass Point Bks.

Bryant, Raymond. On the Farm. 2004. (Funtime Rhymes Ser.). (Illus.). 10p. (J). bds. 4.95 (978-0-7641-5715-8(9)) Barron's Educational Series, Inc.

Chronicle Books Staff, contrib. by. Big Farm Machines. 2002. (Illus.). 24p. (J). bds. 6.95 (978-0-8118-3565-7(0)) Chronicle Bks. LLC.

Cox, Steven M. Big Machines in the Farm. (Illus.). 24p. (J). pap. 7.95 (978-0-14-056209-5(5)) Penguin Group (USA) Inc.

Doeden, Matt. Combines. 2006. (Pebble Plus: Mighty Machines Ser.). (J). (978-0-7368-4265-5(9)) Capstone Pr., Inc.

—Cultivators. 2006. (Pebble Plus: Mighty Machines Ser.). (J). (978-0-7368-4266-2(7)) Capstone Pr., Inc.

—Farm Tractors. 2007. 24p. (J). (978-0-7368-6721-4(X) , Pebble Bks.) Capstone Pr., Inc.

—Planters. 2006. (Pebble Plus: Mighty Machines Ser.). (J). (978-0-7368-4267-9(5)) Capstone Pr., Inc.

Dorling Kindersley Publishing Staff. Fire Truck. 2006. (Machines at Work Ser.). 32p. (J). pap. 6.99 (978-0-7566-1908-4(4)) Dorling Kindersley Publishing, Inc.

Gillis, Jennifer Blizin. Farm Machines. 2004. (Let's See Ser.). (Illus.). 24p. (J). (gr. 1 up). lib. bdg. 19.93 (978-0-7565-0672-8(7)) Compass Point Bks.

Kilby, Don. In the Country. Kilby, Don, illus. 2006. (Illus.). 24p. (978-1-55337-985-0(3)) Kids Can Pr., Ltd.

—In the Country. 2005. (Wheels at Work Ser.). (Illus.). 24p. (J). (ps-2). (978-1-55337-472-5(X)) Kids Can Pr., Ltd.

Knopf, Susan. Welcome to Merriweather Farm. Walstead, Curt, illus. 2005. 10p. (J). pap. 11.95 (978-0-7624-2342-2(0) , Running Pr. Kids) Running Pr. Bk. Pubs.

North, Dawn. Pull-Alongs: Digger. 2007. 12p. (ps). per. 6.95 (978-1-84610-446-6(7)) Make Believe Ideas GBR. *Dist:* Ingram Pub. Services.

Peterson, Cris. Fantastic Farm Machines. 2006. (Illus.). 32p. (J). 17.95 (978-1-59078-271-2(2)) Boyds Mills Pr.

Rogers, Hal. Plows. 2000. (Machines at Work Ser.). (Illus.). 24p. (J). (ps-3). 21.36 (978-1-56766-755-4(4)) Child's World, Inc.

Rogers, Hal. Tractors. 2008. (Machines at Work Ser.). 24p. (J). 22.79 ***(978-1-59296-959-3(3))*** Child's World, Inc.

Running Press Staff & Newberger, Devra. Busy Days in Deerfield Valley. Wakelin, Bob, illus. 2005. 10p. (J). pap. 11.95 (978-0-7624-2343-9(9) , Running Pr.) Running Pr. Bk. Pubs.

Sloan, Peter. Machines on the Farm. 1999. (gr. k-3). lib. bdg. 11.80 (978-0-613-30576-1(0)) Tandem Library Bks.

Stone, Lynn M. Farm Machinery. 2002. (Life on the Farm Ser.). (Illus.). 24p. (J). (gr. 1-4). 14.95 (978-1-58952-093-6(9)) Rourke Publishing, LLC.

Sutcliffe, Jane. John Deere. 2007. (History Maker Biographies Ser.). (J). 26.60 (978-0-8225-6579-6(X) , Lerner Pubns.) Lerner Publishing Group.

AGRICULTURAL PRODUCTS

see Farm Produce

AGRICULTURAL TOOLS

see Agricultural Machinery

AGRICULTURE

see also Botany, Economic; Dairying; Domestic Animals; Farms; Forests and Forestry; Fruit Culture; Gardening; Land Use; Livestock; Organiculture; Soils

also names of agricultural products e.g. Corn; etc.; and headings beginning with the words Agricultural and Farm

Ag E. Bear on Agriculture. 2001. (Illus.). 32p. 6.95 (978-0-9727833-4-7(2)) Really Big Coloring Bks., Inc.

Baines, John. Food for Life. 2006. (Sustainable Futures Ser.). (Illus.). 48p. (J). (978-1-58340-978-7(5) , 1262622) Smart Apple Media.

Barnett, Michelle Noble, et al. Theme Pockets - June: Amazon Rainforest; Artists; Farmers Feed Us. Evans, Marilyn, ed. Larsen, Jo, illus. 1999. (Making Books with Pockets). 96p. (J). pap., tchr. ed. 12.99 (978-1-55799-703-6(9) , EMC 589) Evan-Moor Educational Pubs.

Bial, Raymond. The Farms: Building America. 2002. (Building America Ser.). (Illus.). 56p. (J). (gr. 4-7). lib. bdg. 27.07 (978-0-7614-1332-5(4) , Benchmark Bks.) Cavendish, Marshall Corp.

Bodden, Valerie. A Farming Town. 2007. (J). (978-1-58341-513-9(0) , Creative Education) Creative Co., The.

Bowdish, Lynea. George Washington Carver. 2004. (Rookie Biographies Ser.). (Illus.). 31p. (J). 20.50 (978-0-516-23610-0(5) , Children's Pr.) Scholastic Library Publishing.

Brighter Vision Publishing Staff. About the Farm. 1998. (My Discovery Bks.). (ps). 32p. (J). pap. 3.99 (978-1-55254-001-5(4)); pap. 7.95 incl. audio (978-1-55254-033-6(2)) Brighter Vision Pubns.

—Things That Grow. 1998. (Learning Adventures Preschool Ser.). 32p. (J). (ps-k). pap. 2.25 (978-1-55254-007-7(3) , BV12003) Brighter Vision Pubns.

Canizares, Susan & Waugh, Betsey. On a Farm. 2000. (Scholastic Placebook Ser.). (Illus.). (J). pap. (978-0-439-15371-3(9)) Scholastic, Inc.

Casper, Julie Kerr. Agriculture: The Food We Grow & Animals We Raise. 2007. (Natural Resources Ser.). (Illus.). 224p. (J). (gr. 6-12). 39.50 (978-0-8160-6352-9(4) , Chelsea Hse.) Facts On File, Inc.

Chalmers, Michelle. Passages: A Journal for Growing Home. 1999. (Illus.). 151p. (YA). (gr. 7 up). 15.00 (978-0-9637696-4-0(2)) Growing Home.

Cipriano, Jeri S. Harvest Time. (Social Studies). (Illus.). (J). 2004. 16p. lib. bdg. 15.93 (978-0-7368-2926-7(1) , Yellow Umbrella Bks.); 2003. 17p. pap. (978-0-7368-2885-7(0)) Capstone Pr., Inc.

Connelly, Garrett. Construcao Do Tanques Do Ferrocimento. 2nd ed. 2004. (SPA & FRE., Illus.). 80p. per. 22.50 (978-0-9748016-5-0(8)) ferrocement.com.

—Construccion de Tanques de Ferrocemento: Segunda Edicion. 2nd ed. 2004. Tr. of Construcao do Tanques do Ferrocimento. (SPA., Illus.). 80p. per. 22.50 (978-0-9748016-2-9(3)) ferrocement.com.

Coster, Patience. Farming & Industry. Aldous, Kate & Farmer, Andrew, illus. 1998. (Step-by-Step Geography Ser.). 32p. (J). (gr. 1-3). 18.50 (978-0-516-20354-6(1) , Children's Pr.) Scholastic Library Publishing.

Council for Agricultural Science and Technology Staff, contrib. by. Boundless Science for Bountiful Agriculture: Winning Student Essays, 2003. 2003. viii, 55p. (J). (978-1-887383-24-0(7)) Council for Agricultural Science & Technology (CAST).

DK Publishing Staff. Harvest. 2007. 14p. (J). (ps-k). pap. 5.99 (978-0-7566-2978-6(0)) Dorling Kindersley Publishing, Inc.

Flanagan, Alice K. Farmers. 2002. (Community Workers Ser.). (Illus.). 32p. (J). (gr. 1 up). lib. bdg. 21.26 (978-0-7565-0305-5(1)) Compass Point Bks.

Flour: Level M, 6 vols. (Wonder Worldtm Ser.). 16p. 34.95 (978-0-7802-1998-4(8)) Wright Group, The.

Food & Nutrition. 2004. (Atlases of the Earth & Its Resources Ser.). (Illus.). 80p. (J). (gr. 5 up). lib. bdg. 34.00 (978-0-8368-5617-0(1) , World Almanac Library) Stevens, Gareth Inc.

Gillis, Jennifer Blizin. Farms Long Ago. 2004. (Let's See Ser.). (Illus.). 24p. (J). (gr. 1 up). lib. bdg. 19.93 (978-0-7565-0671-1(9)) Compass Point Bks.

—Unusual Farms. 2004. (Let's See Ser.). (Illus.). 24p. (J). (gr. 1 up). lib. bdg. 19.93 (978-0-7565-0668-1(9)) Compass Point Bks.

Gilpin, Daniel. Food & Clothing. 2004. (History of Invention Ser.). (Illus.). 96p. (YA). (gr. 6-12). 35.00 (978-0-8160-5441-1(X)) Facts On File, Inc.

Gordon, Sharon. At Home on the Farm. 2005. (Bookworms Ser.). (ENG & SPA., Illus.). 32p. (J). (gr. 3-7). lib. bdg. (978-0-7614-1958-7(6) , Benchmark Bks.) Cavendish, Marshall Corp.

—At Home on the Farm (Mi Casa en la Granja) 2006. (Bookworms Ser.). (ENG & SPA., Illus.). 32p. (J). lib. bdg. 22.79 (978-0-7614-2454-3(7)) Cavendish, Marshall Corp.

—Mi Casa en la Granja. 2006. (Bookworms Ser.). (SPA & ENG., Illus.). 32p. (J). lib. bdg. 22.79 (978-0-7614-2375-1(3)) Cavendish, Marshall Corp.

Green, Jen. Feeding the People. 2004. (J). lib. bdg. (978-1-59389-138-1(5)) Chrysalis Education.

Halley, Ned B. & Dorling Kindersley Publishing Staff. Farm. 2000. (Eyewitness Bks.). (Illus.). 64p. (J). (gr. 4-7). lib. bdg. 19.99 (978-0-7894-6615-0(5)) Dorling Kindersley Publishing, Inc.

Halvorsen, Lisa. George Washington Carver: Innovator in Agriculture. 2002. (Giants of Science Ser.). (Illus.). 64p. (J). 26.20 (978-1-56711-657-1(4) , Blackbirch Pr., Inc.) Thomson Gale.

Hansen, Dianne. Agriculture. 2005. (Yesterday & Today Ser.). (Illus.). 32p. (J). (ps-7). lib. bdg. 23.70 (978-1-56711-827-8(5) , Blackbirch Pr., Inc.) Thomson Gale.

Harcourt School Publishers Staff. Stone Age Farmers Level D: Library Edition. 2001. (Collections Ser.). (Illus.). (J). 5.90 (978-0-15-314442-4(4)) Harcourt Schl. Pubs.

Haywood, John. Farming & Trade: Work, Trade & Farming Through the Ages. 2003. (How We Lived Ser.). (Illus.). 64p. (gr. 3-7). pap. 7.99 (978-1-84215-813-5(9) , Southwater) Anness Publishing GBR. *Dist:* National Bk. Network.

Herren, Ray V. Exploring Agriscience. 2nd rev. ed. 2000. (Illus.). 544p. (C). 133.95 (978-0-7668-1674-9(5)) Thomson Delmar Learning.

Hoena, B. A. The Farm. 2004. (Pebble Plus, Let's Visit Ser.). (Illus.). 24p. (J). 17.26 (978-0-7368-2390-6(5)) Capstone Pr., Inc.

Hoena, B. A. & Saunders-Smith, Gail. Farm ABC: An Alphabet Book. 2005. (A+ Alphabet Books). 32p. (J). 22.60 (978-0-7368-3664-7(0)) Capstone Pr., Inc.

Holt, Rinehart and Winston Staff. Environmental Science Chptr. 15: Food & Agriculture. 4th ed. Date not set. pap. 11.20 (978-0-03-068076-2(X)) Holt, Rinehart & Winston.

J. G. Ferguson Publishing Company Staff, contrib. by. Careers in Focus: Agriculture. 2nd rev. ed. 2006. 192p. (J). (gr. 6-12). 22.95 (978-0-8160-6585-1(3) , Ferguson Publishing Co.) Facts On File, Inc.

Keen, Jared, ed. The Future of Farming: Understanding Global Issues. 2002. (Understanding Global Issues Ser.). (Illus.). 56p. (J). (gr. 10-12). lib. bdg. 19.95 (978-1-58340-170-5(9)) Smart Apple Media.

Kidd, J. S. & Kidd, Renee A. Agricultural Versus Environmental Science: A Green Revolution. 2005. (Science & Society Ser.). 224p. (YA). (gr. 6-12). 35.00 (978-0-8160-5608-8(0)) Facts On File, Inc.

Konrad, Donna. How the Cornstalks Got Their Ears. Konrad, Donna, illus. 1999. (Illus.). 16p. (J). (gr. k-2). pap. 4.99 (978-1-893181-21-2(9) , Lagesse Stevens) Martell Publishing Co.

Kroll, Mary, et al. Fields of Genes: Making Sense of Biotechnology in Agriculture. Hoff, Mary, ed. Morales, Elizabeth, illus. 1999. 96p. (YA). pap. 30.00 (978-0-7881-7569-5(6)) DIANE Publishing Co.

Lascaro, Rita. Down on the Farm. 2003. (Green Light Readers Level 1 Ser.). (Illus.). 24p. (J). 11.95 (978-0-15-204815-0(4)); pap. 3.95 (978-0-15-204855-6(3)) Harcourt Children's Bks. (Green Light Readers).

—Down on the Farm. 2003. (ps-2). lib. bdg. 11.80 (978-0-613-64490-7(5)) Tandem Library Bks.

Long, Cathryn J. The Agricultural Revolution. 2004. (World History Ser.). (Illus.). 112p. (J). (gr. 7-10). 32.45 (978-1-59018-180-5(8) , Lucent Bks.) Thomson Gale.

Love, Ann. Farming. 2002. (gr. 3-6). lib. bdg. 14.10 (978-0-613-84969-2(8)) Tandem Library Bks.

Love, Ann & Drake, Jane. Farming. Cupples, Pat, illus. 2002. (America at Work Ser.). 32p. (J). (gr. k-3). (978-1-55337-421-3(5)) Kids Can Pr., Ltd.

MacDonald, Fiona. Work, Trade & Farming. 2001. (Through the Ages Ser.). (Illus.). 64p. (gr. 3-7). 12.95 (978-0-7548-0817-6(3)) Anness Publishing GBR. *Dist:* National Bk. Network.

Mayer, Cassie. Farming. 2007. (J). ***(978-1-4034-9401-6(0))***; pap. ***(978-1-4034-9410-8(X))*** Heinemann Library.

McArthur, Debra. The Dust Bowl & the Depression in American History. 2002. (In American History Ser.). (Illus.). 128p. (J). (gr. 5-12). lib. bdg. 26.60 (978-0-7660-1838-9(5)) Enslow Pubs., Inc.

Ottenheimer-Maquet, L. World Agriculture. Gibson, Sarah et al, trs. 1998. (Creative Discoveries Ser.). Orig. Title: Our Food. (Illus.). 75p. (J). (gr. 2-9). lib. bdg. 23.95 (978-0-88682-952-0(6) , Creative Education) Creative Co., The.

Paulsen, Gary. The Tortilla Factory. Paulsen, Ruth Wright, illus. 1998. 32p. (J). (ps-ps). pap. 7.00 (978-0-15-201698-2(8) , Harcourt Paperbacks) Harcourt Children's Bks.

Peterson, Cris. Harvest Year. Upitis, Alvis, photos by. 2003. (Illus.). 32p. (J). (gr. k-2). 19.95 (978-1-56397-571-4(8)) Boyds Mills Pr.

Ready, Dee. Granjeros y Granjeras. Schon, Isabel, ed. Ferrer, Martín Luis Guzman, tr. from ENG. 1998. (Servidores Comunitarios Ser.). (SPA., Illus.). 24p. (J). (gr. 1-2). lib. bdg. 18.60 (978-1-56065-798-9(7) , Bridgestone Bks.) Capstone Pr., Inc.

Roza, Greg. America's Transition from Agriculture to Industry: Drawing Inferences & Conclusions. 2005. (Critical Thinking in American History Ser.). (Illus.). 48p. (YA). (gr. 5-8). lib. bdg. 25.25 (978-1-4042-0410-2(5)) Rosen Publishing Group, Inc., The.

Rubin, Alan. This Farm. 2006. (Illus.). (J). 16p. (978-0-7368-5986-8(1)); (ENG & SPA., 18p. (978-0-7368-6022-2(3)) Yellow Umbrella Pr.

Ryan, Pam Muñoz. How Do You Raise a Raisin? Brown, Craig, illus. 2004. 32p. (J). 16.95 (978-1-57091-397-6(8)) Charlesbridge Publishing, Inc.

—How Do You Raise a Raisin? Brown, Craig McFarland, illus. 2004. 32p. (J). pap. 6.95 (978-1-57091-398-3(6)) Charlesbridge Publishing, Inc.

Saunders-Smith, Gail. Fall Harvest. 1998. (J). pap. 13.25 (978-0-516-21247-0(8) , Children's Pr.) Scholastic Library Publishing.

—From Blossom to Fruit. 1998. (J). pap. 13.25 (978-0-516-21244-9(3) , Children's Pr.) Scholastic Library Publishing.

—Picking Apples. 1998. (J). pap. 13.25 (978-0-516-21245-6(1) , Children's Pr.) Scholastic Library Publishing.

Schaefer, Lola M. Helpers in Our Community: We Need Dentists; We Need Doctors; We Need Farmers; We Need Fire Fighters; We Need Mail Carriers; We Need Nurses; We Need Police Officers; We Need Veterinarians, 8 bks. Saunders-Smith, Gail, ed. 2000. (Illus.). (J). (gr. k-1). lib. bdg. 116.80 (978-0-7368-0451-6(X) , Pebble Bks.) Capstone Pr., Inc.

—We Need Farmers. Saunders-Smith, Gail, ed. 1999. (Helpers in Our Community Ser.). (Illus.). 24p. (J). (gr. k-1). lib. bdg. 15.93 (978-0-7368-0390-8(4) , Pebble Bks.) Capstone Pr., Inc.

Shuter, Jane. Food & Farming. 1999. (Ancient Egypt Ser.). 32p. (J). (gr. 3-5). lib. bdg. 22.79 (978-1-57572-730-1(7)) Heinemann Library.

Sieling, Peter. Growing up on a Farm: Responsibilities & Issues. 2007. (Youth in Rural North America Ser.). (J). (978-1-4222-0012-4(4)) Mason Crest Pubs.

Smith, Andrea Claire Harte. The Effects of Farming. 2004. (Earth's Changing Landscape Ser.). (Illus.). 45p. (J). lib. bdg. 28.50 (978-1-58340-475-1(9)) Smart Apple Media.

Snyder, Inez. Harvesttime: Set, 6 Bks. 2004. 87.00 (978-0-516-23721-3(7) , Children's Pr.) Scholastic Library Publishing.

—Tomatoes. 2004. (Harvesttime Ser.). (J). 18.00 (978-0-516-27594-9(1)); pap. 4.95 (978-0-516-25914-7(8)) Scholastic Library Publishing. (Children's Pr.).

—Wheat. 2004. (Harvesttime Ser.). (Illus.). 24p. (J). 18.00 (978-0-516-27596-3(8)); pap. 4.95 (978-0-516-25915-4(6)) Scholastic Library Publishing. (Children's Pr.).

Stone, Lynn M. Cultivos de la Granja. Sarfatti, Esther & de la Vega, Eida, trs. 2001. (Vida en la Granja Ser.).Tr. of Farm Crops. (SPA., Illus.). 24p. (J). (gr. 1-3). lib. bdg. 19.27 (978-1-58952-183-4(8) , RK7241) Rourke Publishing, LLC.

—Edificios de la Granja. Sarfatti, Esther & de la Vega, Eida, trs. 2001. (La Vida en la Granja Ser.).Tr. of Farm Buildings. (SPA., Illus.). 24p. (J). (gr. 1-4). lib. bdg. 19.27 (978-1-58952-182-7(X)) Rourke Publishing, LLC.

—Maquinaria de la Granja. Sarfatti, Esther & de la Vega, Eida, trs. 2001. (Vida en la Granja Ser.).Tr. of Farm Machinery. (SPA., Illus.). 24p. (J). (gr. 1-3). lib. bdg. 19.27 (978-1-58952-184-1(6) , RK3916) Rourke Publishing, LLC.

This Farm. 2006. (Yellow Umbrella Social Studies). 8,16p. (J). 6.50 (978-0-7368-1717-2(4)) Red Brick Learning.

Tlock, Andrew. We Are Happy Farmers. 1999. (Illus.). (J). pap. 12.95 (978-1-57717-125-6(X)) New Line Bks.

Walpole, Brenda. Feeding the World. 2007. (Illus.). 32p. (J). ***(978-1-59771-064-0(4))*** Sea-To-Sea Pubns.

Waters, Jennifer. Harvest Time. 2002. (Spyglass Books). (Illus.). 24p. (J). (gr. 1 up). 18.60 (978-0-7565-0239-3(X)) Compass Point Bks.

We Need Farmers, 6 vols. (gr. k-2). 28.95 (978-0-7368-8600-0(1)) Red Brick Learning.

Welvaert, Scott R. Follow That Crop: From the Farmer's Field to Our Grocery Store. 2003. (From Here to There Ser.). (J). (978-1-58417-194-2(4)); pap. (978-1-58417-195-9(2)) Lake Street Pubs.

Witherick, Michael. Farming, Food & Famine. 2001. (Epics Ser.). (Illus.). 104p. (YA). (gr. 11 up). pap. 26.50 (978-0-7487-5819-7(4)) Nelson Thornes Ltd. GBR. *Dist:* Trans-Atlantic Pubns., Inc.

Wolfman, Judy. Life on a Crop Farm. Winston, David Lorenz, photos by. 2005. (Life on a Farm Ser.). (Illus.). 48p. (gr. 2-5). lib. bdg. 23.93 (978-1-57505-518-3(X)) Lerner Publishing Group.

Woods, Michael & Woods, Mary B. Ancient Agriculture: From Foraging to Farming. 1999. (Ancient Technology Ser.). (Illus.). 96p. (gr. 6-12). 25.26 (978-0-8225-2995-8(5)) Lerner Publishing Group.

AGRICULTURE—BIOGRAPHY

African-American Farmers. 2000. (My Ancestors—My Heroes Ser.: Vol. 34). (J). (gr. 3-4). (978-1-893091-33-7(3)) Parker Publishing Co.

Carter, Andy. George Washington Carver. 2000. (gr. 3-6). lib. bdg. 14.10 (978-0-613-79176-2(2)) Tandem Library Bks.

Carter, Andy, et al. George Washington Carver. Paladino, Lance, illus. (On My Own Biographies Ser.). 48p. (J). (gr. 1-3). 2003. 5.95 (978-1-57505-458-2(2)); 2000. lib. bdg. 23.93 (978-1-57505-427-8(2) , Carolrhoda Bks.) Lerner Publishing Group.

Krensky, Stephen. Man for All Seasons. 2008. 32p. (J). (gr. k-4). lib. bdg. 17.89 (978-0-06-027886-1(2)) HarperCollins Pubs.

—Man for All Seasons. Clay, Wil, illus. 2008. 32p. (J). (gr. k-4). 16.99 (978-0-06-027885-4(4)) HarperCollins Pubs.

AGRICULTURE—FICTION

Dodds, Siobhan & Bentley, Dawn. The Noisy Farm. 1999. (Picture Puzzle Board Bks.). (Illus.). 12p. (J). bds. (978-1-58117-031-3(9) , Intervisual/Piggy Toes) Dalmatian Pr.

Good Job, Rob! 2006. 16p. (J). pap. 1.99 (978-0-7847-1693-9(5) , 02995) Standard Publishing.

Howard-Parham, Pam. This Is Farmer Greg. Coates, Jennifer, illus. l.t. ed. 2005. (Hrl Board Book Ser.). (ps-k). pap. 10.95 (978-1-57332-305-5(5)) HighReach Learning, Inc.

Jennings, Sharon, et al. Franklin's Pumpkin. Southern, Shelley et al, illus. 2005. (Kids Can Read Ser.). 32p. (J). (gr. 1-2). (978-1-55337-496-1(7)); (978-1-55337-495-4(9)) Kids Can Pr., Ltd.

Jimenez, Francisco. Senderos Fronterizos. 2002. (SPA.). (gr. 7-12). lib. bdg. 15.25 (978-0-613-60784-1(8)) Tandem Library Bks.

Kalz, Jill. Farmer Cap. Erkocak, Sahin, illus. 2007. (Pfeffernut County Ser.). 26p. (J). (gr. k-2). lib. bdg. 23.93 ***(978-1-4048-3139-1(8))*** Picture Window Bks.

Logsdon, Gene. The Man Who Created Paradise: A Fable. 2001. (Illus.). 68p. 20.00 (978-0-8214-1407-1(0)) Ohio Univ. Pr.

Meunier, Brian & Edgerton, Perky. Bravo, Tavo! 2007. (Illus.). 32p. (J). (gr. k-3). 16.99 (978-0-525-47478-4(1) , Dutton Juvenile) Penguin Group (USA) Inc.

Morpurgo, Michael. Farm Boy. 2007. (Illus.). 76p. (J). pap. 16.99 ***(978-1-84365-090-4(8))*** Anova Bks. GBR. *Dist:* Independent Pubs. Group.

Nechaer, Michelle W. The Hungry Farmer, Vol. 4417. Kuppersteín, Joel, ed. Allen, Joy, illus. 1998. (Learn to Read Social Studies). 16p. (J). (ps-2). pap. 2.75 (978-1-57471-340-4(X) , 4417) Creative Teaching Pr., Inc.

Pelletier, Andrew T. The Toy Farmer. Nash, Scott, illus. 2007. 32p. (J). (ps). 16.99 (978-0-525-47649-8(0) , Dutton Juvenile) Penguin Group (USA) Inc.

Pienkowski, Jan, illus. Jan Pienkowski's Farm. 1998. (Animal Action Pops Ser.). 10p. (J). (gr. 2 up). 4.95 (978-1-58117-021-4(1) , Intervisual/Piggy Toes) Dalmatian Pr.

Sandburg, Carl. The Huckabuck Family & How They Raised: Popcorn in Nebraska & Quit & Came Back. Small, David, illus. 2006. 30p. (J). (gr. k-4). reprint ed. 16.00 ***(978-1-4223-5854-2(2))*** DIANE Publishing Co.

Say, Allen. Music for Alice. 2004. (Illus.). 32p. (J). (gr. k-3). tchr. ed. 17.00 (978-0-618-31118-7(1) , Walter Lorraine) Houghton Mifflin Co. Trade & Reference Div.

Shi, Sharon. Mr. Scotts Magical Farm. Hernandez, Alaena, illus. rev. ed. 2000. 24p. (J). mass mkt. 4.99 (978-0-9678636-7-2(8) , B008, Tattootles Bks.) Tattoo Manufacturing.

Stevens, Jan Romero. Carlos & the Cornfield. 1999. Tr. of Carlos y la Milpa de Maiz. (SPA & ENG., Illus.). 32p. (J). (gr. k-3). 7.95 (978-0-87358-735-8(9) , Rising Moon Bks. for Young Readers) Northland Publishing.

Switzer, Vern. Lucy the Cantaloupe. Connally, Perry L., Sr., illus. 2005. 32p. (J). 15.95 ***(978-0-9753542-1-6(3))*** Rural Farm Productions.

—Puffy the Watermelon. Listokin, David & Connally, Perry L., Sr., illus. 2004. 24p. (J). 15.95 ***(978-0-9753542-0-9(5))*** Rural Farm Productions.

Takhar, Jodi. The Farmer's Helper. Takhar, Jodi & Jones, Paul, illus. 15p. (J). (ps-3). 19.95 (978-1-886000-00-1(X)) Takhar's, Jodi Spilt Milk Collection.

Ward, Nick. Farmer George & the Fieldmice. 2001. (Illus.). 32p. (J). (ps-k). pap. 8.99 (978-1-86205-413-4(4) , Pavilion Bks., Ltd.) Anova Bks. GBR. *Dist:* Independent Pubs. Group.

—Farmer George & the Lost Chick. 2001. (Illus.). 32p. (J). (ps-k). pap. 8.99 (978-1-86205-412-7(6) , Pavilion Bks., Ltd.) Anova Bks. GBR. *Dist:* Trafalgar Square Publishing.

Wilder, Laura Ingalls. Sugar Snow. Graef, Renee & Ettlinger, Doris, illus. 1998. (My First Little House Bks.). 40p. (J). (ps-3). 12.89 (978-0-06-025933-4(7)) HarperCollins Pubs.

Winfield, Arthur M. The Rover Boys on the Farm. 2006. pap. 27.95 ***(978-1-4254-9148-2(0))*** Kessinger Publishing, LLC.

AGRICULTURE—VOCATIONAL GUIDANCE

Olesky, Walter. Choosing a Career in Agriculture. 2005. (World of Work Ser.). (Illus.). 64p. (YA). (gr. 7-12). lib. bdg. 25.25 (978-0-8239-3332-7(6)) Rosen Publishing Group, Inc., The.

AGRONOMY

see Agriculture

AGUE

see Malaria

AHAB, CAPTAIN (FICTITIOUS CHARACTER)—FICTION

Capdevila, Roser. Moby Dick. 2002. (Cuentos Fantasticos de las Tres Mellizas Coleccion: Vol. 1). (SPA.). (J). (gr. k-2). pap. 5.95 (978-1-930332-38-6(6) , LC6629) Lectorum Pubns., Inc.

Dalmatian Press Staff, adapted by. Moby Dick. 2002. (Spot the Classics Ser.). (Illus.). 180p. (J). (gr. k-5). 4.99 (978-1-57759-547-2(5)) Dalmatian Pr.

—Moby Dick. (J). 9.95 (978-1-56156-308-1(0)) Kidsbooks, Inc.

Hagerty, Carol, ed. Moby Dick. 1998. (Classics Ser.: Set II). 77p. (YA). (gr. 5-12). pap. 7.95 (978-1-56254-258-0(3) , SP2583) Saddleback Educational Publishing.

Melville, Herman. Cities of the Fantastic: Brusel. Eisner, Will, illus. 2003. (Cities of the Fantastic Ser.). 120p. 19.95 (978-1-56163-291-6(0)) NBM Publishing Co.

—Moby Dick. 2002. (Great Illustrated Classics Ser.). (Illus.). 240p. (J). (gr. 3-8). 21.35 (978-1-57765-695-1(4) , ABDO & Daughters) ABDO Publishing Co.

—Moby Dick. Giordano, Dick, illus. 2002. 48p. (J). (gr. 5). tchr. ed. 16.00 (978-0-618-26571-8(6)) Houghton Mifflin Co. Trade & Reference Div.

—Moby Dick. 2000. (Coleccion "Clasicos Juveniles" Ser.). (SPA.). 228p. (YA). pap. 12.95 (978-0-595-13218-8(9)) iUniverse, Inc.

—Moby Dick. 2003. (Illus.). 32p. 7.95 (978-1-56163-294-7(5)) NBM Publishing Co.

—Moby Dick. Eisner, Will, illus. 2003. 32p. (gr. 4-7). 15.95 (978-1-56163-293-0(7)) NBM Publishing Co.

—Moby Dick. Nino, Alex, illus. 2nd ed. 1998. (Illustrated Classic Book Ser.). 61p. (J). (gr. 3 up). reprint ed. pap. 4.95 (978-1-56767-235-0(3)) Educational Insights, Inc.

—Moby Dick. adapted ed. (YA). (gr. 5-12). pap. 8.50 (978-0-8359-0225-0(0)) Globe Fearon Educational Publishing.

—Moby Dick. 2nd ed. 2003. (Historias de Siempre Ser.). (SPA., Illus.). 92p. (J). (gr. 5-8). pap. 9.95 (978-84-204-5732-1(9)) Santillana USA Publishing Co., Inc.

—Moby Dick, Grades 5-12. adapted ed. pap., tchr. ed. 4.95 (978-0-8359-0123-9(8)) Globe Fearon Educational Publishing.

—Moby Dick, or the Whale. 2005. (J). Pt. 1. pap. 9.95 (978-1-4105-0263-6(5)); Pt. 1. cd-rom (978-1-4105-0265-0(1)); Pt. 2. pap. 9.95 (978-1-4105-0267-4(8)); Pt. 2. cd-rom (978-1-4105-0269-8(4)) Johnston, Don Inc.

Melville, Herman & Huth, Michael. Moby Dick. 2004. (GER., Illus.). 92p. (978-3-921743-52-2(4)) Maximilian-Gesellschaft e. V.

Melville, Herman & Schwartz, Lew Sayre. Moby Dick. Giordano, Dick, illus. 2002. 48p. (J). pap. 6.95 (978-0-618-26572-5(4)) Houghton Mifflin Co. Trade & Reference Div.

Melville, Herman, et al. Moby Dick. (Classics Illustrated Ser.). (Illus.). 52p. (YA). pap. 4.95 (978-1-57209-003-3(0)) Classics International Entertainment, Inc.

Scott, James, adapted by. Moby Dick: Reproducible Teaching Unit. 2001. 110p. (YA). (gr. 7-12). tchr. ed., ring bd. 29.50 (978-1-58049-283-6(5) , TU169) Prestwick Hse., Inc.

AIDS (DISEASE)

AIDS & Other STDs. 2001. (YA). (gr. 6-12). pap. 11.50 (978-0-8359-0766-8(X)) Globe Fearon Educational Publishing.

Arnold, Lynda. My Mommy Has AIDS: Angels of Love: Celebrating Diversity & Adoption. Monahan, Ellen M. & Rosemont School of the Holy Child Staff, illus. 1998. 32p. (J). (gr. k-5). 18.95 (978-1-892073-01-3(3)) Dream Publishing.

Bajah, S. T. & Oroge, S. Adenike. AIDS: The Wicked Disease. 2002. 37p. pap. (978-978-2951-47-2(1)) CSS Bookshops, Ltd., Agency & Publishing Div.

Balkwill, Fran & Rolph, Mic. Staying Alive: Fighting HIV/AIDS. 2002. (Illus.). 30p. (J). pap. 8.95 (978-0-87969-651-1(6)) Cold Spring Harbor Laboratory Pr.

Balkwill, Frances R. & Rolph, Mic. You, Me & HIV: With Knowledge, We Have Hope! 2004. (J). pap. (978-0-87969-718-1(0)) Cold Spring Harbor Laboratory Pr.

Bardhan-Quallen, Sudipta. AIDS. 2004. (Illus.). 112p. (J). (gr. 7-10). 32.45 (978-1-59018-404-2(1)) Thomson Gale.

Begun, Abbey M., et al, eds. AIDS. 5th rev. ed. 1998. (Information Plus Reference Ser.). (Illus.). 120p. (YA). (gr. 9-12). pap. 32.00 (978-1-57302-072-5(9)) Thomson Gale.

Blake, Jeanne. Risky Times: How to Be AIDS-Smart & Stay Healthy. 1999. (Illus.). 196p. (gr. 8 up). pap. 5.95 (978-0-89480-656-8(4) , 1656) Workman Publishing Co., Inc.

Boldt, Mark. Awareness Is Doing Something. l.t. ed. 1998. (U-Do Book Ser.). (Illus.). 32p. (J). (gr. k-8). pap. (978-0-9662556-2-1(3) , U-DO 03) Boldt.Entertainment.

Brimner, Larry Dane. The Names Project: The AIDS Quilt. 2000. (Cornerstones of Freedom Ser.). (Illus.). 32p. (J). (gr. 4-6). pap. 5.95 (978-0-516-26517-9(2) , Children's Pr.) Scholastic Library Publishing.

—The Names Project: The AIDS Quilt. 1999. (gr. 3-6). lib. bdg. 14.10 (978-0-613-52153-6(6)) Tandem Library Bks.

Check, William A. AIDS. rev. ed. (Illus.). 128p. (YA). (gr. 7 up). 1999. 16.00 (978-0-7910-4885-6(3)); 1998. lib. bdg. 19.95 (978-0-7910-0054-0(0)) Facts On File, Inc. (Chelsea Hse.).

Choosing the Best Path. 3rd ed. 2004. (978-0-9724890-2-7(9)) Choosing The Best Publishing.

Connolly, Sean. AIDS. 2002. (Just the Facts Ser.). (Illus.). 56p. (J). (gr. 6-8). lib. bdg. 25.64 (978-1-58810-677-3(2)) Heinemann Library.

Draimin, Barbara Hermie. Everything You Need to Know about AIDS & HIV. 2001. (Need to Know Library). (Illus.). 64p. (YA). (gr. 4-6). lib. bdg. 25.25 (978-0-8239-3314-3(8) , NTAIHI) Rosen Publishing Group, Inc., The.

Ellis, Deborah. Our Stories, Our Songs: African Children Talk About AIDS. 2005. (Illus.). 112p. (YA). (978-1-55041-913-9(7)) Fitzhenry & Whiteside, Ltd.

Gedatus, Gustav Mark. HIV & AIDS. 1999. (Perspectives on Disease & Illness Ser.). (Illus.). 64p. (J). (gr. 4-6). lib. bdg. 23.93 (978-0-7368-0281-9(9) , LifeMatters Bks.) Capstone Pr., Inc.

Great Expectations: Death & Resurrection, HIV & AIDS. 2000. (Connect Ser.: Vol. 7). (YA). 20.00 (978-0-687-72148-1(2)) Abingdon Pr.

Harris, H. Robie. Its Perfectly Normal: Changing Bodies, Growing up, Sex, & Sexual Health. Emberley, Michael, illus. 10th anniv. ed. 2004. 96p. (J). (gr. 5 up). 22.99 (978-0-7636-2610-5(4)) Candlewick Pr.

Harris, Robie H. Es Alucinante! Emberley, Michael, illus. 2000. Tr. of It's So Amazing!. (J). (CAT.). 80p. (gr. k-2). pap. 17.95 (978-84-95040-33-6(6)); (SPA.). 84p. (gr. 3-5). 17.95 (978-84-95040-32-9(8) , RR4476) Serres, Ediciones, S. L. ESP. *Dist:* Lectorum Pubns., Inc.

—Its Perfectly Normal: A Book about Changing Bodies, Growing Up, Sex, & Sexual Health. Emberley, Michael, illus. 10th anniv. ed. 2004. 96p. (gr. 5 up). pap. 10.99 (978-0-7636-2433-0(0)) Candlewick Pr.

Hinds, Maurene J. Fighting the AIDS & HIV Epidemic: A Global Battle. 2007. (Issues in Focus Today Ser.). (Illus.). 104p. (J). (gr. 6). lib. bdg. 31.93 ***(978-0-7660-2683-4(3))*** Enslow Pubs., Inc.

Holt, Rinehart and Winston Staff. A Lifetime of Health Chptr. 21: HIV & AIDS. 4th ed. Date not set. pap. 11.20 (978-0-03-068116-5(2)) Holt, Rinehart & Winston.

Houle, Michelle M. AIDS in the 21st Century: What You Should Know. 2003. (Issues in Focus Ser.). (Illus.). 112p. (J). (gr. 6-12). lib. bdg. 26.60 (978-0-7660-1690-3(0)) Enslow Pubs., Inc.

Howard, Helen. Living with AIDS: Mary's Story. 2005. (Children in Crisis Ser.). (Illus.). 48p. (YA). (gr. 10-12). lib. bdg. 30.00 (978-0-8368-5962-1(6) , World Almanac Library) Stevens, Gareth Inc.

Johanson, Paula. HIV & AIDS. 2006. (Coping in a Changing World Ser.). 112p. (YA). (gr. 7-12). lib. bdg. 31.95 (978-1-4042-0948-0(4)) Rosen Publishing Group, Inc., The.

Kuklin, Susan. Fighting Back: What Some People Are Doing about AIDS. 2001. (Illus.). 112p. (YA). (gr. 8-12). pap. 9.95 (978-0-595-16961-0(9)) iUniverse, Inc.

Majure, Janet. AIDS. 1998. (Diseases & People Ser.). (Illus.). 128p. (YA). (gr. 6-12). lib. bdg. 20.95 (978-0-7660-1182-3(8)) Enslow Pubs., Inc.

McGraw-Hill Staff. Teen Health Course 3, Modules, HIV/AIDS. 5th ed. 2002. (Three-Level Middle School Health Ser.). (gr. 8 up). 15.32 (978-0-07-826213-5(5) , 9780078262135) Glencoe/McGraw-Hill.

McIntosh, Kenneth & Walker, Ida. Youth with HIV/AIDS: Living with the Diagnosis. 2008. (J). ***(978-1-4222-0146-6(5))*** Mason Crest Pubs.

McPhee, Andrew T. AIDS. 2001. (Watts Library). (Illus.). 64p. (J). (gr. 5-7). pap. 8.95 (978-0-531-16528-7(0) , Watts, Franklin) Scholastic Library Publishing.

—AIDS. 2000. 15.75 (978-0-606-20537-5(3)) Tandem Library Bks.

Nakaya, Andrea C. AIDS. 2005. (Introducing Issues with Opposing Viewpoints Ser.). (Illus.). 144p. (YA). (gr. 8-12). lib. bdg. 33.70 (978-0-7377-3218-4(0) , Greenhaven Pr., Inc.) Thomson Gale.

Packer, Kenneth L. HIV Infection: The Facts You Need to Know. 1998. (Venture Ser.). (Illus.). 160p. (J). (gr. 7-12). 25.00 (978-0-531-11333-2(7) , Watts, Franklin) Scholastic Library Publishing.

Reed, Jennifer. The AIDS Epidemic: Disaster & Survival. 2005. (Deadly Disasters Ser.). (Illus.). 48p. (J). lib. bdg. 23.93 (978-0-7660-2382-6(6)) Enslow Pubs., Inc.

Ringbom, Antonia & Wiklund, Alison. The Hiding Hyena. 2nd ed. 2007. (YA). ***(978-0-9789617-1-8(4))*** H.B.P., Inc.

Roleff, Tamara L. AIDS. 3rd ed. 2002. (Opposing Viewpoints Ser.). (Illus.). 200p. (YA). (gr. 10-12). pap. 24.95 (978-0-7377-1135-6(3) , Greenhaven Pr., Inc.) Thomson Gale.

Routh, Kristina. AIDS. 2005. (21st Century Issues Ser.). (Illus.). 48p. (J). 30.00 (978-0-8368-5641-5(4)); pap. ***(978-0-8368-5658-3(9)*** , World Almanac Library) Stevens, Gareth Inc.

Shire, Amy. Everything You Need to Know about Being HIV-Positive. rev. ed. 1999. (Need to Know Library). (Illus.). 64p. (YA). (gr. 7-12). lib. bdg. 25.25 (978-0-8239-3077-7(7) , NTHIPO) Rosen Publishing Group, Inc., The.

Silverstein, Alvin, et al. AIDS: An All-About Guide for Young Adults. 1999. (Issues in Focus Ser.). (Illus.). 160p. (YA). (gr. 6-12). lib. bdg. 20.95 (978-0-89490-716-6(6)) Enslow Pubs., Inc.

Silverstein, Alvin, et al. The AIDS Update. 2007. (Disease Update Ser.). (Illus.). 128p. (J). (gr. 5 up). lib. bdg. 31.93 ***(978-0-7660-2746-6(5))*** Enslow Pubs., Inc.

Storad, Conrad J. Inside AIDS: HIV Attacks the Immune System. 1998. (Discovery! Ser.). (Illus.). 120p. (gr. 5-12). lib. bdg. 27.93 (978-0-8225-2857-9(6)) Lerner Publishing Group.

Sudipta Bardhan-Quallen. AIDS. 2005. (Understanding Diseases & Disorders Ser.). (Illus.). 48p. (J). (gr. 4-8). 26.20 (978-0-7377-2638-1(5) , Kidhaven) Thomson Gale.

Taylor, Barbara. Everything You Need to Know about AIDS. Rosen, Ruth C., ed. rev. ed. 1998. (Need to Know Library). (Illus.). 64p. (J). (gr. 4-6). lib. bdg. 25.25 (978-0-8239-2833-0(0) , NTAIDS) Rosen Publishing Group, Inc., The.

Whelan. AIDS. 2001. (Health Issues Ser.). (Illus.). 64p. (YA). (gr. 6-8). lib. bdg. 28.54 (978-0-7398-4771-8(6)) Raintree.

Wolf, Bernard. HIV Positive. 2000. (Illus.). (J). pap. 4.99 (978-0-14-130304-8(2) , Puffin) Penguin Group (USA) Inc.

Woods, Samuel G. Enfermedades de Transmision Sexual. 2002. (Todo lo Que Necesitas Saber Ser.). (ENG & SPA., Illus.). 64p. (YA). lib. bdg. 26.50 (978-0-8239-3580-2(9)) Rosen Publishing Group, Inc., The.

Yount, Lisa. The Discovery of the AIDS Virus. 2002. (At Issue in History Ser.). (Illus.). 128p. (YA). (gr. 7-10). pap. 23.70 (978-0-7377-1353-4(4)); lib. bdg. 27.45 (978-0-7377-1352-7(6)) Thomson Gale. (Greenhaven Pr., Inc.).

—Discovery of the AIDS Virus. 2003. (gr. 7-12). lib. bdg. 28.90 (978-0-613-57555-9(2)) Tandem Library Bks.

AIDS (DISEASE)—FICTION

Carlson, Melody. Notes from a Spinning Planet—Papua, New Guinea. 2007. (Notes from a Spinning Planet Ser.). 240p. (YA). pap. 12.99 (978-1-4000-7145-6(3) , WaterBrook Pr.) WaterBrook Pr.

Chinodya, Shimmer. Tale of Tamari. 2003. (Illus.). 56p. pap. 12.95 (978-1-77922-026-4(X)) Weaver Pr. ZWE. *Dist:* Michigan State Univ. Pr.

Dow, Unity. Far & Beyon' 2002. 208p. (YA). (gr. 7 up). pap. 11.95 (978-1-879960-64-0(8)) Aunt Lute Bks.

Ellis, Deborah. The Heaven Shop. 2004. 186p. (978-1-55041-908-5(0)); 192p. (J). (gr. 6-9). pap. (978-1-55041-907-8(2)) Fitzhenry & Whiteside, Ltd.

Kramer, Berri, photos by & text. Mbali: A story from South Africa. Kramer, Berri, text. 2nd ed. 2006. (J). per. ***(978-0-9706901-1-1(8))*** Rotaplast Pr.

Loyie, Larry & Brissenden, Constance. The Gathering Tree. Holmlund, Heather D., illus. 2006. 48p. (J). bds. 18.95 (978-1-894778-28-2(6)) Theytus Bks., Ltd. CAN. *Dist:* Orca Bk. Pubs. USA.

Ng, Leandro, illus. Passage 2: HIV/AIDS — First Love. 2005. (1 World Manga Ser.: Vol. 2). 40p. pap. 3.99 (978-0-8213-6406-2(5)) World Bank Pubns.

Ray-Ray's Dream. 2002. 28p. (J). lib. bdg. 14.95 (978-0-9702601-2-3(1)) Lovegifts Publishing.

Simoen, Jan. What about Anna? Nieuwenhuizen, John, tr. from DUT. 2002. (Illus.). 264p. (YA). (gr. 7 up). 16.95 (978-0-8027-8808-5(4)) Walker & Co.

The Smartest Thing. 2004. (YA). (978-0-9762904-8-3(0)) Layne Morgan Media, Inc.

AIDS (DISEASE)—PATIENTS

Bush, Jenna. Ana's Story: A Journey of Hope. Baxter, Mia, illus. 2007. (YA). (gr. 9 up). 304p. 18.99 ***(978-0-06-137908-6(5))***; 290p. lib. bdg. 19.89 ***(978-0-06-137910-9(7))*** HarperCollins Pubs.

—Ana's Story (Spanish Edition) La Historia de Ana. Baxter, Mia, illus. 2007. 304p. (J). 18.99 ***(978-0-06-144861-4(3)*** , Rayo) HarperCollins Pubs.

Winick, Judd. Pedro & Me: Friendship, Loss & What I Learned. rev. ed. 2000. (Illus.). 192p. (YA). (gr. 9 up). pap. 16.00 (978-0-8050-6403-2(6) , Holt, Henry & Co. Bks. For Young Readers) Holt, Henry & Co.

AIR

Here are entered works treating of air as an element and of its chemical and physical properties. Works treating of the body of air surrounding the earth are entered under Atmosphere.

see also Aerodynamics; Atmosphere

Air. (Jump Ser.). (Illus.). 32p. (J). (gr. 2-7). pap. (978-1-882210-26-8(3)) Action Publishing, Inc.

Air. 2001. (Physical Science Ser.). (J). (gr. k-12). vinyl bd. 4.95 (978-1-58845-111-8(9)) School Specialty Publishing.

Air & Bubbles. 2005. 48p. (J). per. 6.99 (978-1-59441-201-1(4) , CD-104109) Carson-Dellosa Publishing Co., Inc.

Ardley, Neil & Challoner, Jack. Air. 2000. (J). (gr. 4-6). 11.00 (978-0-8172-9796-1(0)) Steck-Vaughn.

Branley, Franklyn M. Air Is All Around You. O'Brien, John, illus. 2006. (Let's-Read-and-Find-Out Science Ser.). 40p. (J). (gr. k-2). 15.99 (978-0-06-059413-8(6)); pap. 5.99 (978-0-06-059415-2(2) , Harper Trophy) HarperCollins Pubs.

Cooper, Sharon Katz. Using Air. Cooper, Sharon Katz, illus. 2007. (Illus.). 24p. (J). ***(978-1-4034-9323-1(5))*** Heinemann.

—Using Air. 2007. (Exploring Earth's Resources Ser.). (Illus.). 24p. (J). (ps-1). lib. bdg. 21.36 ***(978-1-4034-9315-6(4))*** Heinemann.

Dann, Sarah. The Science of Air. 2000. (Living Science Ser.). (Illus.). 32p. (J). (gr. 2 up). lib. bdg. 24.67 (978-0-8368-2569-5(1)) Stevens, Gareth Inc.

Davis, Barbara J. Air & Weather. 2006. (J). pap. ***(978-0-8368-7871-4(X))*** Stevens, Gareth Inc.

Dorion, Christiane. Earth's Garbage Crisis. 2006. (J). pap. ***(978-0-8368-7760-1(8)*** , World Almanac Library) Stevens, Gareth Inc.

Douglas, Vincent & School Specialty Publishing Staff. Air & Water Science Kit. 2004. (Science Kits Ser.). (Illus.). 52p. (J). pap. 16.95 (978-1-58845-613-7(5) , Brighter Child) School Specialty Publishing.

Evans, David & Williams, Claudette. Air & Flying. (Let's Explore Science Ser.). (Illus.). (J). 12.95 (978-0-590-74943-5(9)) Scholastic, Inc.

Flynn, James J. Air. 2003. (Matter & Materials Ser.). (J). pap. (978-1-58417-169-0(3)); lib. bdg. (978-1-58417-163-8(4)) Lake Street Pubs.

Frisch, Aaron. Air. 2001. (Elements Ser.). (Illus.). 24p. (J). 21.35 (978-1-58340-073-9(7)) Smart Apple Media.

Golden Books Staff. Air Power! 2007. (Color Plus Tattoos Ser.). (Illus.). 32p. (J). (gr. k-4). pap. 3.99 (978-0-375-84142-2(3) , Golden Bks.) Random Hse. Children's Bks.

Graham, Ian. Air: A Resource Our World Depends On. 2004. (J). pap. 7.50 (978-1-4034-5622-9(4)); lib. bdg. 24.22 (978-1-4034-5614-4(3)) Heinemann Library.

Hidalgo, Maria. Air. 2002. (Let's Investigate Ser.). (Illus.). 32p. (J). lib. bdg. (978-1-58341-231-2(X) , Creative Education) Creative Co., The.

Holt, Rinehart and Winston Staff. Environmental Science Chptr. 12: Air. 4th ed. Date not set. pap. 11.20 (978-0-03-068072-4(7)) Holt, Rinehart & Winston.

Jennings, Terry. Aire (Air) (SPA.). 32p. (J). 6.95 (978-84-348-1743-2(8)) SM Ediciones ESP. *Dist:* AIMS International Bks., Inc.

Katz Cooper, Sharon. Usar el Aire. 2007. (SPA & ENG.). (J). (***978-1-4329-0239-1(3)**); pap. (***978-1-4329-0247-6(4)***) Heinemann Library.

Korb, Rena B. Awesome Air. Reibeling, Brandon, illus. 2007. (Science Rocks Ser.). 32p. (J). (ps-4). lib. bdg. 27.07 (***978-1-60270-036-9(2)*** , Looking Glass Library) Magic Wagon.

Lauw, Darlene. Air. 2003. (gr. 3-6). lib. bdg. 16.40 (978-0-613-52800-9(X)) Tandem Library Bks.

Lauw, Darlene & Puay, Lim Cheng. Air. 2002. (Science Alive! Ser.). (Illus.). 32p. (J). (gr. 4-5). pap. (978-0-7787-0612-0(5)); lib. bdg. (978-0-7787-0566-6(8)) Crabtree Publishing Co.

Madgwick, Wendy. Up in the Air. 1998. (Science Starters Ser.). (Illus.). 32p. (J). (gr. k-4). lib. bdg. 25.70 (978-0-8172-5325-7(4)) Raintree.

Manutoli, Sophie, et al. Ella (Air) Sims, John, illus. 1998. (ESK.). 20p. (J). (gr. k-3). pap. 8.00 (978-1-58084-049-1(3)) Lower Kuskokwim Schl. District.

Meacham, Nancy. Air: Science Discovery Activity Book. Zuman, John & Barra, Nancy, eds. Deming, Linda, illus. 2002. (Sunflower/Girasol Ser.). 20p. (J). 5.00 (978-1-58332-012-9(1)) Intercultural Center for Research in Education (I N C R E).

Meiani, Antonella. Air. 2003. (Experimenting with Science Ser.). (Illus.). 40p. (J). (gr. 4-8). lib. bdg. 23.93 (978-0-8225-0082-7(5)) Lerner Publishing Group.

Murphy, Brian. Air. 2004. (Experiment with Ser.). (SPA., Illus.). 32p. (J). (gr. 2-5). pap. 5.95 (978-1-58728-113-6(9)); 32p. (gr. 2-5). 9.95 (978-1-58728-244-7(5)); 48p. (J). (gr. 3-6). pap. 14.95 incl. cd-rom (978-1-58728-454-0(5)) T&N Children's Publishing. (Two Can Publishing).

—Experimenta Con el Aire. 2004. (Experiment with Ser.).Tr. of Experiment With Air. (SPA., Illus.). 32p. (gr. 2-5). 9.95 (978-1-58728-435-9(9) , Creative Publishing International) Quayside.

Parker, Steve. The Science of Air: Projects & Experiments on Air & Flight. 2005. (Tabletop Scientist Ser.). (Illus.). 32p. (J). (gr. 4-7). lib. bdg. 27.79 (978-1-4034-7280-9(7)); (ps-6). pap. 7.95 (978-1-4034-7287-8(4)) Heinemann Library.

Parker, Victoria. Air. 2006. (Illus.). 24p. (J). (978-1-4034-7882-5(1)); pap. (978-1-4034-7888-7(0)) Steck-Vaughn.

Pluckrose, Henry. Air. 2001. (Let's Explore Ser.). (Illus.). 32p. (J). (gr. 1 up). lib. bdg. 23.33 (978-0-8368-2957-0(3)) Stevens, Gareth Inc.

Pluckrose, Henry Arthur. Air. 2006. (Illus.). 32p. (J). (978-1-59771-033-6(4)) Sea-To-Sea Pubns.

Richards, Jon. Air & Flight. 2008. (J). lib. bdg. (***978-1-4042-3907-4(3)***) Rosen Publishing Group, Inc., The.

Roca, Nuria. Aprendamos sobre los 4 Elementos: The 4 Elements (Spanish Edition) Curto, Rosa M., illus. 2006. (Let's Learn About Ser.). (SPA.). 36p. (J). pap. 6.99 (978-0-7641-3315-2(2)) Barron's Educational Series, Inc.

—Let's Learn about the 4 Elements. Curto, Rosa M., illus. 2006. (Let's Learn About Ser.). 36p. (J). pap. 6.99 (978-0-7641-3314-5(4)) Barron's Educational Series, Inc.

Simon, Seymour. Let's Try It Out in the Air. 2003. (gr. k-3). lib. bdg. 15.30 (978-0-613-67150-7(3)) Tandem Library Bks.

Spilsbury, Richard. Air & Water Pressure. 2006. (Fantastic Forces Ser.). (Illus.). 32p. (J). (978-1-4034-8170-2(9)); pap. (978-1-4034-8175-7(X)) Heinemann Library.

Stewart, Melissa. Air Is Everywhere. 2004. (Investigate Science Ser.). 32p. (J). (gr. 1 up). lib. bdg. 21.26 (978-0-7565-0638-4(7)) Compass Point Bks.

Stille, Darlene R. Air: Outside, Inside, & All Around. Boyd, Sheree, illus. 2004. (Amazing Science Ser.). 24p. (C). (gr. k-4). 22.60 (978-1-4048-0248-3(7)) Picture Window Bks.

Taylor-Butler, Christine. Tiny Life in the Air. (J). 2006. 32p. (gr. 1-2). pap. 4.95 (978-0-516-25476-0(6)); 2005. (Illus.). 31p. (ps-ps). 20.50 (978-0-516-25273-5(9)) Scholastic Library Publishing. (Children's Pr.).

AIR—POLLUTION

Acid Rain. (Our Planet in Peril Ser.). 24p. (YA). 7.95 (978-0-7368-3294-6(7)) Capstone Pr., Inc.

Bellamy, Rufus. Clean Air. 2005. (Action for the Environment Ser.). (Illus.). 32p. (J). (gr. 4-7). lib. bdg. 27.10 (978-1-58340-594-9(1) , 1247273) Smart Apple Media.

Capstone Press Editors. Our Planet in Peril, 4 bks. Incl. Acid Rain. lib. bdg. 22.60 (978-0-7368-1360-0(8)); Global Warming. lib. bdg. 22.60 (978-0-7368-1361-7(6)); Nuclear Waste. lib. bdg. 22.60 (978-0-7368-1362-4(4)); Oil Spills. lib. bdg. 22.60 (978-0-7368-1363-1(2)); 48p. (J). (gr. 3-4). 2002. (Illus.). 2002. Set lib. bdg. 90.40 (978-0-7368-1364-8(0) , Bridgestone Bks.) Capstone Pr., Inc.

Chapman, Matthew & Bowden, Rob. Air Pollution: Our Impact on the Planet. 2002. (Twenty-First Century Debates Ser.). (Illus.). 64p. (YA). (gr. 6-8). lib. bdg. 19.99 (978-0-7398-4874-6(7)) Raintree.

Costain, Meredith. Clean Air. 2000. (gr. k-3). lib. bdg. 11.80 (978-0-613-30324-8(5)) Tandem Library Bks.

Dalgleish, Sharon. Cleaning the Air. 2002. (Our World - Our Future Ser.). (Illus.). 32p. (gr. 4-8). 28.00 (978-0-7910-7019-2(0) , Chelsea Hse.) Facts On File, Inc.

Donald, Rhonda Lucas. Air Pollution. 2001. (gr. 3-6). lib. bdg. 15.25 (978-0-613-51609-9(5)) Tandem Library Bks.

Graham, Ian. Air: A Resource Our World Depends On. 2004. (J). pap. 7.50 (978-1-4034-5622-9(4)); lib. bdg. 24.22 (978-1-4034-5614-4(3)) Heinemann Library.

Green, Jen. Reducing Air Pollution. 2005. (Improving Our Environment Ser.). (Illus.). 32p. (J). lib. bdg. 24.67 (978-0-8368-4428-3(9)) Stevens, Gareth Inc.

Harlow, Rosie. Pollution & Waste: Environmental Facts & Experiments. 2002. (Young Discoverers Ser.). (Illus.). 32p. (J). (gr. k-3). 7.95 (978-0-7534-5505-0(6) , Kingfisher) Houghton Mifflin Co. Trade & Reference Div.

—Pollution & Waste: Environmental Facts & Experiments. 2002. (gr. k-3). lib. bdg. 16.40 (978-0-613-90577-0(6)) Tandem Library Bks.

Hudak, Heather C. Air Pollution. 2006. (Science Matters Ser.). (J). (978-1-59036-415-4(5)); pap. (978-1-59036-421-5(X)) Weigl Pubs., Inc.

Kidd, J. S. & Kidd, Renee A. Air Pollution: Problems & Solutions. 2nd rev. ed. 2005. (Science & Society Ser.). 208p. (gr. 6-12). 35.00 (978-0-8160-5605-7(6)) Facts On File, Inc.

Llewellyn, Claire. Fight Air Pollution. 2005. (Illus.). 32p. (YA). (gr. 1 up). lib. bdg. 27.10 (978-1-932333-21-5(5)) Chrysalis Education.

Roleff, Tamara L., ed. Pollution. 2000. (Opposing Viewpoints Ser.). (Illus.). 244p. (YA). (gr. 10-12). pap. 21.20 (978-0-7377-0134-0(X) , Greenhaven Pr., Inc.) Thomson Gale.

Trapp, Clayton. Polluted Air. 2004. (Green Alert Ser.). (Illus.). 48p. (J). lib. bdg. 28.56 (978-0-7398-7011-2(4)) Raintree.

Walker, Jane. Atmosphere in Danger. 2004. (J). lib. bdg. 27.10 (978-1-932799-12-5(5)) Stargazer Bks.

AIR CARGO

see Aeronautics, Commercial

AIR CUSHION VEHICLES

see Ground Effect Machines

AIR FREIGHT

see Aeronautics, Commercial

AIR HOSTESSES

see Flight Attendants

AIR PILOTS

see also Astronauts; Women in Aeronautics

Abraham, Philip. Amelia Earhart. 2002. (Wel-Real People Ser.). (Illus.). 24p. (J). (ps-2). 18.00 (978-0-516-23952-1(X)); pap. 4.95 (978-0-516-23600-1(8)) Scholastic Library Publishing. (Children's Pr.).

—Amelia Earhart. 2002. (gr. k-3). lib. bdg. 12.95 (978-0-613-58823-2(1)) Tandem Library Bks.

Anderson, Jameson. Amelia Earhart: Legendary Aviator. Whigham, Rod & Barnett, Charles, illus. 2007. (Graphic Library). 32p. (J). 25.26 (978-0-7368-6496-1(2)); pap. (***978-0-7368-7532-5(8)***) Capstone Pr., Inc.

Asso, B. & Rideau, J. Biggles Recounts: The Falklands War. Spear, Luke, tr. Chauvin, D. & Uderzo, M., illus. 2007. 48p. pap. 9.99 (***978-1-905460-22-9(8)***) CineBook GBR. *Dist:* Biblio Distribution.

Bennett, Leonie. A Day with an Airplane Pilot. 2006. (I Love Reading Ser.). (Illus.). 24p. (J). lib. bdg. 19.96 (978-1-59716-147-3(0)) Bearport Publishing Co., Inc.

Bledsoe, Karen E. Daredevils of the Air: Thrilling Tales of Pioneer Aviators. 2003. (Avisson Young Adult Ser.). (Illus.). 155p. (J). pap. 19.95 (978-1-888105-58-2(5)) Avisson Pr., Inc.

Braun, Eric. Bessie Coleman. 2006. (Illus.). 24p. (J). 15.93 (978-0-7368-4229-7(2) , Pebble Bks.) Capstone Pr., Inc.

Brooks, Philip. The Tuskegee Airmen. 2004. (Illus.). 48p. (J). (gr. 4 up). lib. bdg. 22.60 (978-0-7565-0683-4(2)) Compass Point Bks.

Brown, Jonatha A. Amelia Earhart. 2005. (People to Know Ser.). (Illus.). 24p. (J). pap. (978-0-8368-4472-6(6)); (YA). lib. bdg. 19.33 (978-0-8368-4465-8(3) , Weekly Reader Early Learning Library) Stevens, Gareth Inc.

Burke, John. Sterling Point Books: Amelia Earhart: Flying Solo. 2007. (Sterling Point Bks.). (Illus.). 208p. (J). 12.95 (978-1-4027-4520-1(6)); pap. 6.95 (978-1-4027-4140-1(5)) Sterling Publishing Co., Inc.

Burleigh, Robert. Amelia Earhart: Free in the Skies. Wylie, Bill, illus. 2003. (American Heroes Ser.). 48p. (J). 16.00 (978-0-15-202498-7(0) , Silver Whistle) Harcourt Trade Pubs.

—Amelia Earhart: Free in the Skies. 2003. (gr. 3-6). lib. bdg. 14.10 (978-0-613-70522-6(X)) Tandem Library Bks.

—Amelia Earhart Free in the Skies. Wylie, Bill, illus. 2003. (American Heroes Ser.). 48p. (J). pap. 5.95 (978-0-15-216810-0(9) , Silver Whistle) Harcourt Trade Pubs.

Canizares, Susan & Chanko, Pamela. Up, up, & Away: The Story of Amelia Earhart. 1999. (ps-2). lib. bdg. 10.10 (978-0-613-22557-1(0)) Tandem Library Bks.

The Chocolate Flier: Individual Title Six-Packs. (Action Packs Ser.). 104p. (gr. 3-5). 44.00 (978-0-7635-3304-5(1)) Rigby Education.

Compass Point Books, contrib. by. Pilots. (Community Workers Ser.). 24p. (J). pap. 7.95 (978-0-7565-1195-1(X)) Compass Point Bks.

Cooper, Sharon Katz. Whose Vehicle Is This? A Look at Vehicles Workers Drive—Fast, Loud, & Bright. Muehlenhardt, Amy Bailey, illus. 2006. (Whose Is It? Ser.). 24p. (J). (ps-2). 22.60 (978-1-4048-1603-9(8) , 1253206) Picture Window Bks.

Cummins, Julie. Tom Boy of the Air: Daredevil Pilot Blanche Stuart Scott. 2006. (Illus.). 80p. (J). (gr. 4-8). reprint ed. 17.00 (978-1-4223-5510-7(1)) DIANE Publishing Co.

—Tomboy of the Air: Daredevil Pilot Blanche Stuart Scott. 2001. (Illus.). 80p. (J). (gr. 3-6). lib. bdg. 17.89 (978-0-06-029243-0(1)) HarperCollins Pubs.

Davis, Anita P. & Hall, Ed Y. Harriet Quimby - America's First Lady of the Air: A Biography for Intermediate Readers. 1998. (Aviation History Ser.: Vol. 5). (Illus.). 96p. (YA). (gr. 5-12). lib. bdg. 10.95 (978-1-885354-06-8(1)) Honoribus Pr., The.

Davis, Lucile. Charles Lindbergh. 1999. (Photo-Illustrated Biographies Ser.). (Illus.). 24p. (J). (gr. 2-3). lib. bdg. 18.60 (978-0-7368-0204-8(5) , Bridgestone Bks.) Capstone Pr., Inc.

DeMallie, H. R. Behind Enemy Lines: A Young Pilot's Story. 2007. (Sterling Point Bks.). (Illus.). 192p. (J). (gr. 6-9). pap. 6.95 (978-1-4027-4137-1(5)) Sterling Publishing Co., Inc.

DeMolay, Jack. The Bermuda Triangle: The Disappearance of Flight 19. 2007. (Graphic Mysteries Ser.). (J). (978-1-4042-2347-9(9)); pap. (978-1-4042-2157-4(3)); (gr. 2-6). lib. bdg. 21.25 (978-1-4042-3404-8(7)) Rosen Publishing Group, Inc., The. (PowerKids Pr.).

Devillier, Christy. Amelia Earhart. 2001. (First Biographies Ser.). (Illus.). 32p. (J). (gr. k-4). lib. bdg. 22.78 (978-1-57765-596-1(6) , Buddy Bks.) ABDO Publishing Co.

Famous Flyers. (Illus.). (gr. 6-12). lib. bdg. (978-0-7910-8058-0(7)); 2005. 112p. pap. 180.00 (978-0-7910-7211-0(8)) Facts On File, Inc. (Chelsea Hse.).

Feinstein, Stephen. Read about Amelia Earhart. 2006. (I Like Biographies! Ser.). (Illus.). 24p. (J). lib. bdg. 21.26 (978-0-7660-2582-0(9) , Enslow Elementary) Enslow Pubs., Inc.

Flanagan, Alice K. Flying an Agricultural Plane with Mr. Miller. Flanagan, Romie, illus. 1999. (Our Neighborhood Ser.). 32p. (J). (gr. 1-2). 20.00 (978-0-516-21132-9(3) , Children's Pr.) Scholastic Library Publishing.

—Flying an Agricultural Plane with Mr. Miller. 1999. (gr. k-3). lib. bdg. 15.25 (978-0-613-54488-7(9)) Tandem Library Bks.

Fleischman, John. Black & White Airmen: Their True History. 2007. (Illus.). 160p. (J). (gr. 5 up). 20.00 (978-0-618-56297-8(4)) Houghton Mifflin Co.

Ford, Carin T. Amelia Earhart: Meet the Pilot. 2002. (Meeting Famous People Ser.). (Illus.). 32p. (J). (gr. 1-4). lib. bdg. 22.60 (978-0-7660-2003-0(7)) Enslow Pubs., Inc.

Gaffney, Timothy R. Air Show Pilots & Airplanes. 2001. (Aircraft Ser.). (Illus.). 48p. (YA). (gr. 4-10). lib. bdg. 23.93 (978-0-7660-1570-8(X)) Enslow Pubs., Inc.

Gordon, Janet & Merkur, Janet. Livewire Real Lives Sir Charles Kingsford Smith. 1999. (Livewire Real Lives Ser.). 32p. (gr. 6-9). pap. 6.00 (978-0-521-77637-0(6)) Cambridge Univ. Pr.

Graves, Jeseca, illus. Bessie Coleman: The Story of an Aviation Pioneer. 2007. 24p. (J). (***978-0-9745294-1-7(9)***) San Diego County Regional Airport Authority.

Grimes, Nikki. Talkin' 'Bout Bess: The Story of Aviator Bessie Coleman. Lewis, Ted G., illus. (J). 2002. (978-0-531-30069-5(2)); 1998. lib. bdg. (978-0-531-33069-2(9)) Scholastic, Inc. (Orchard Bks.).

Hansen, Ole Steen. The Wright Brothers & Other Pioneers of Flight. 2003. (Story of Flight Ser.). (Illus.). 32p. (J). (gr. 4). pap. (978-0-7787-1216-9(8)); lib. bdg. (978-0-7787-1200-8(1)) Crabtree Publishing Co.

Harkins, Susan Sales. Breaking the Sound Barrier: The Story of Chuck Yeager. 2005. (Monumental Milestones Ser.). (Illus.). 48p. (YA). (ps-7). lib. bdg. (978-1-58415-398-6(9) , 1244924) Mitchell Lane Pubs., Inc.

Hart, Phillip S. Bessie Coleman. 2005. (Just the Facts Biographies Ser.). (Illus.). 112p. (J). (gr. 6-12). 27.93 (978-0-8225-2469-4(4)) Lerner Publishing Group.

Harvey, Al. I Want to Be a Pilot. 1999. (978-0-606-17484-8(2)) Tandem Library Bks.

Haugen, Brenda. Amelia Earhart: Legendary Aviator. 2006. (J). (978-0-7565-1880-6(6)) Compass Point Bks.

Holden, Henry M. American Women of Flight: Pilots & Pioneers. 2003. (Collective Biographies Ser.). (Illus.). 112p. (J). (gr. 6-12). lib. bdg. 26.60 (978-0-7660-2005-4(3)) Enslow Pubs., Inc.

Homan, Lynn M. & Reilly, Thomas. Women Who Fly. Shepherd, Rosalie M., illus. 2004. 104p. (J). pap. 14.95 (978-1-58980-160-8(1)) Pelican Publishing Co., Inc.

Hopkins, Ellen H. Storming the Skies: The Story of Katherine & Marjorie Stinson: Pioneer Women Aviators. 2003. (Avisson Young Adult Ser.). (Illus.). 75p. (J). pap. 18.95 (978-1-888105-56-8(9)) Avisson Pr., Inc.

Howe, Jane Moore. Amelia Earhart: Young Air Pioneer. Underdown, Harold, ed. Morrison, Cathy, illus. 2nd rev. ed. 2000. (Young Patriots Ser.). 111p. (J). (gr. 5 up). 15.95 (978-1-882859-02-3(2)) Patria Pr., Inc.

Jaffe, Elizabeth Dana. Pilots. 2001. (Community Workers Ser.). (Illus.). 32p. (J). (gr. 1 up). lib. bdg. 21.26 (978-0-7565-0065-8(6)) Compass Point Bks.

Jerome, Kate Boehm. Who Was Amelia Earhart? Cain, David & Harrison, Nancy, illus. 2002. (Who Was...? Ser.). 112p. (J). mass mkt. 4.99 (978-0-448-42856-7(3) , Grosset & Dunlap) Penguin Group (USA) Inc.

—Who Was Amelia Earhart? 2002. (gr. 3-6). lib. bdg. 13.00 (978-0-613-61667-6(7)) Tandem Library Bks.

The Knights of Avalon: Seaplanes of Catalina Island. 2004. 207p. per. 22.00 (978-0-9749426-0-5(X)) Horizon Line Pr.

Koestler-Grack, Rachel A. Eddie Rickenbacker. 2003. (Famous Flyers Ser.). (Illus.). 112p. (gr. 6-12). 30.00 (978-0-7910-7215-8(0) , Chelsea Hse.) Facts On File, Inc.

—Spirit of St. Louis. 2005. (American Moments Ser.). (Illus.). 48p. (J). (gr. 4-8). lib. bdg. 25.65 (978-1-59197-940-1(4)) ABDO Publishing Co.

Koopmans, Andy. Charles Lindbergh. 2002. (Importance of Ser.). (Illus.). 112p. (J). (gr. 7-10). 32.45 (978-1-59018-245-1(6) , Lucent Bks.) Thomson Gale.

Kramer, Sydelle A. Night Flight: Charles Lindbergh's Incredible Adventure. 2002. (gr. k-3). lib. bdg. 11.80 (978-0-613-43635-9(0)) Tandem Library Bks.

Lakin, Patricia, et al. Amelia Earhart: More Than a Flier. 2003. (Ready-to-Read Stories of Famous Americans Ser.). (Illus.). 48p. (J). pap. 3.99 (978-0-689-85575-7(3) , Aladdin) Simon & Schuster Children's Publishing.

Langley, Wanda. Women of the Wind: Early Women Aviators. 2006. (Women Adventurers Ser.). (Illus.). 160p. (J). lib. bdg. 26.95 (978-1-931798-81-5(8)) Reynolds, Morgan Inc.

Leavitt, Amie. Amelia Earhart. 2007. (What's So Great About... ? Ser.). (J). lib. bdg. 25.70 (***978-1-58415-576-8(0)***) Mitchell Lane Pubs., Inc.

Lenski, Lois. The Little Airplane. Lenski, Lois, illus. 2003. (Illus.). 56p. (J). (ps-1). lib. bdg. 13.99 (978-0-375-91079-1(4)); reprint ed. 11.95 (978-0-375-81079-4(X)) Random Hse. Children's Bks. (Random Hse. Bks. for Young Readers).

Liebman, Dan. I Want to Be a Pilot. 8th ed. 1999. (I Want to Be Ser.). (Illus.). 24p. (J). (ps-2). pap. 3.99 (978-1-55209-434-1(0)) Firefly Bks., Ltd.

—Je veux etre Pilote. Lior, Tsipora, tr. from ENG. 2006. (Je veux Etre Ser.).Tr. of I Want to Be A Pilot. (FRE., Illus.). 24p. (J). (ps-2). pap. 5.95 (978-1-55407-106-7(2)) Firefly Bks., Ltd.

—Quiero ser Piloto. 2003. (Quiero Ser.). (SPA., Illus.). 24p. (J). (ps-2). pap. 5.99 (978-1-55297-745-3(5)) Firefly Bks., Ltd.

—Quiero Ser Piloto. 2003. Tr. of I Want to Be a Pilot. (SPA.). (gr. k-3). lib. bdg. 14.15 (978-0-613-78624-9(6)) Tandem Library Bks.

Lindbergh, Charles A., Jr. The Spirit of St Louis. 2003. 562p. pap. 29.00 (978-0-7581-3991-7(8)) Textbook Pubs.

Lucia, Raatma. Charles Lindbergh: Pilot. 2000. (Career Biographies Ser.). (Illus.). 128p. (J). (gr. 6-12). 25.00 (978-0-89434-340-7(8) , F401, Ferguson Publishing Co.) Facts On File, Inc.

Martin, Michael. Chuck Yeager. 2003. (Importance of Ser.). (Illus.). 112p. (J). 32.45 (978-1-59018-284-0(7) , Lucent Bks.) Thomson Gale.

Mattern, Joanne. Pilotos. 2004. (Trabajo en Grupo Ser.). (SPA & ENG., Illus.). 24p. (J). (gr. 3-6). lib. bdg. 17.25 (978-0-8239-6840-4(5) , Buenas Letra) Rosen Publishing Group, Inc., The.

Maurer, Richard. The Wright Sister: Katharine Wright & Her Famous Brothers. rev. ed. 2003. (Illus.). 128p. (J). (gr. 5-9). 19.95 (978-0-7613-1546-9(2)) Roaring Brook Pr.

McLeese, Don. Amelia Earhart. 2003. (Discover the Life of an American Legend Ser.). (gr. 2-5). 14.95 (978-1-58952-301-2(6)) Rourke Publishing, LLC.

Meachum, Virginia. Charles Lindbergh: American Hero of Flight. 2002. (People to Know Ser.). (Illus.). 128p. (YA). (gr. 6-12). lib. bdg. 26.60 (978-0-7660-1535-7(1)) Enslow Pubs., Inc.

Micklos, John. Unsolved: What Really Happened to Amelia Earhart? 2006. (Prime Ser.). (Illus.). 128p. (J). (gr. 5 up). lib. bdg. 33.27 (978-0-7660-2365-9(6)) Enslow Pubs., Inc.

Minden, Cecilia & Minden-Zins, Mary. Pilots. 2006. (Neighborhood Helpers Ser.). (Illus.). 32p. (J). (gr. k-4). 22.79 (978-1-59296-567-0(9)) Child's World, Inc.

Morris, Neil. Air Pioneers. (Illus.). 48p. (YA). (gr. 5 up). lib. bdg. 29.95 (978-1-932333-81-7(9)) Chrysalis Education.

Mortensen, Lori. Amelia Earhart: Female Pioneer in Flight. McGuire, Robert, illus. 2007. (J). lib. bdg. (***978-1-4048-3728-7(0)***) Picture Window Bks.

Moss, Marissa. Brave Harriet: The First Woman to Fly the English Channel. Payne, C. F., illus. 2001. 32p. (J). (gr. 1-4). 17.00 (978-0-15-202380-5(1) , Silver Whistle) Harcourt Trade Pubs.

Nathan, Amy. Yankee Doodle Gals: Women Pilots of World War II. 2001. (Illus.). 96p. (J). (gr. 3-7). 21.00 (978-0-7922-8216-7(7) , National Geographic Children's Bks.) National Geographic Society.

Osborn. Born to Fly. 2003. (gr. 5-8). lib. bdg. 13.55 (978-0-613-84567-0(6)) Tandem Library Bks.

Osborn, Shane & McConnell, Malcolm. Born to Fly: The Heroic Story of Downed U. S. Navy Pilot Lt. Shane Osborn. 2003. 192p. (gr. 5). 5.99 (978-0-440-23796-9(3) , Yearling) Random Hse. Children's Bks.

—Born to Fly: The Heroic Story of Downed U. S. Navy Pilot Lt. Shane Osborn. l.t. ed. 2002. 403p. 29.45 (978-0-7862-4101-9(2)) Thomson Gale.

Patrick, Jean L. S. & Sutcliffe, Jane. Amelia Earhart. 2002. (History Maker Bios Ser.). (Illus.). 48p. (J). pap. 6.95 (978-0-8225-1561-6(X)) Lerner Publishing Group.

Petrick, Neila Skinner. Katherine Stinson Otero, High Flyer. Wallace, Daggi, illus. 2006. 32p. (J). 15.95 (978-1-58980-368-8(X)) Pelican Publishing Co., Inc.

Pflueger, Lynda. Amelia Earhart: Legend of Flight. 2003. (Historical American Biographies Ser.). (Illus.). 128p. (J). lib. bdg. 26.60 (978-0-7660-1976-8(4)) Enslow Pubs., Inc.

Plantz, Connie. Bessie Coleman: First Black Woman Pilot. 2001. (African-American Biographies Ser.). (Illus.). 128p. (J). (gr. 6-12). lib. bdg. 26.60 (978-0-7660-1545-6(9)) Enslow Pubs., Inc.

Provensen, Alice. The Glorious Flight: Across the Channel with Louis Bleriot. Provensen, Alice, illus. 2002. (Illus.). (J). 14.04 (978-0-7587-0049-0(0)) Book Wholesalers, Inc.

Purcell, Martha Sias. Pioneer Pilots & Flying Aces of World War I. 2003. (Reading Essentials in Social Studies). (Illus.). 48p. (J). (978-0-7891-5881-9(7)) Perfection Learning Corp.

Raatma, Lucia. Amelia Earhart. 2001. (Trailblazers of the Modern World Ser.). (Illus.). 48p. (J). (gr. 5 up). pap. 14.95 (978-0-8368-5223-3(0)) ; lib. bdg. 30.00 (978-0-8368-5063-5(7)) Stevens, Gareth Inc. (World Almanac Library).

Rauf, Don & Vescia, Monique. Virtual Apprentice: Airline Pilot. 2007. (Virtual Apprentice Ser.). 64p. (J). (gr. 6-12). 29.95 (***978-0-8160-6755-8(4)*** , Ferguson Publishing Co.) Facts On File, Inc.

Raum, Elizabeth. Eileen Collins. 2005. (American Lives Ser.). (Illus.). 32p. (J). (978-1-4034-6943-4(1)) ; pap. (978-1-4034-6950-2(4)) Heinemann Library.

Raven, Margot Theis. Mercedes & the Chocolate Pilot: A True Story of the Berlin Airlift & the Candy That Dropped from the Sky. van Frankenhuyzen, Gijsbert, illus. 2002. 48p. (J). (gr. k-5). 17.95 (978-1-58536-069-7(4)) Sleeping Bear Pr.

Reyburn, Susan. Women Who Dare: Amelia Earhart. 2006. (Illus.). 64p. 12.95 (978-0-7649-3545-9(3) , A111) Pomegranate Communications, Inc.

Rice, Earle. Claire Chennault: Flying Tigers. 2003. (gr. 5-8). lib. bdg. 18.75 (978-0-613-65196-7(0)) Tandem Library Bks.

Rinaldo, Denise. Amelia Earhart: With a Discussion of Courage. 2004. (Values in Action Ser.). (J). (978-1-59203-068-2(8)) Learning Challenge, Inc.

Robbins, Trina. Bessie Coleman: Daring Stunt Pilot. Steacy, Ken, illus. 2007. (Graphic Library). 32p. (J). (gr. 3-5). lib. bdg. 25.26 (978-0-7368-6851-8(8)) ; pap. 7.95 (***978-0-7368-7903-3(X)***) Capstone Pr., Inc.

Rosenbaum, Robert. Aviators: American Profiles. 2000. (Illus.). 122p. (YA). (gr. 7-9). reprint ed. 17.00 (978-0-7881-6932-8(7)) DIANE Publishing Co.

Rosenthal, Marilyn S. & Freeman, Daniel. Amelia Earhart. 1999. (Photo-Illustrated Biographies Ser.). (Illus.). 24p. (J). (gr. 2-3). lib. bdg. 18.60 (978-0-7368-0203-1(7) , Bridgestone Bks.) Capstone Pr., Inc.

Roza, Greg. Famous Flights: Understanding & Using Variables. 2006. (Math for the Real World Ser.). (Illus.). 32p. (J). pap. (978-1-4042-6087-0(0)) ; lib. bdg. (978-1-4042-3367-6(9)) Rosen Publishing Group, Inc., The.

Sabin, Francene & Mattern, Joanne. Amelia Earhart: Adventure in the Sky. Dugan, Karen, illus. 2006. 50p. (J). pap. (***978-0-439-66041-9(6)***) Scholastic, Inc.

Schaefer, Lola M. Amelia Earhart. Saunders-Smith, Gail, ed. 2002. (First Biographies Ser.). (Illus.). 24p. (J). (gr. k-1). lib. bdg. 15.93 (978-0-7368-1433-1(7) , Pebble Bks.) Capstone Pr., Inc.

Schomp, Virginia. If You Were a Pilot. 2000. (If You Were A... Ser.). (Illus.). 32p. (J). (gr. 2-4). lib. bdg. 22.79 (978-0-7614-0919-9(X) , Benchmark Bks.) Cavendish, Marshall Corp.

Sisson, Kathryn Cleven. Eddie Rickenbacker: Boy Pilot & Racer, 6 vols. Underdown, Harold, ed. Morrison, Cathy, illus. rev. ed. 2003. (Young Patriots Ser.: Vol. 6). 120p. (J). 15.91 (978-1-882859-12-2(X)) Patria Pr., Inc.

—Eddie Rickenbacker: Boy Pilot & Racer, 6 vols. Morrison, Cathy, illus. rev. ed. 2003. (Young Patriots Ser.: Vol. 6). 120p. (J). pap. 9.95 (978-1-882859-13-9(8)) Patria Pr., Inc.

—Eddie Rickenbacker: Boy Pilot & Racer. 2003. (gr. 3-6). lib. bdg. 18.75 (978-0-613-80168-3(7)) Tandem Library Bks.

Smith, A. G. Pete, the Pilot: With 20 Stickers. 2001. (Illus.). 4p. (J). pap. 1.50 (978-0-486-41632-8(1)) Dover Pubns., Inc.

Sofer, Barbara. Ilan Ramon: Israel's Space Hero. 2003. (Illus.). 64p. (J). (gr. 3-6). 16.95 (978-1-58013-115-5(8)) ; pap. (978-1-58013-116-2(6)) Kar-Ben Publishing.

Speregen, Devra Newberger. Ilan Ramon: Jewish Star. 2004. (Illus.). 120p. pap. 9.95 (978-0-8276-0769-9(5)) Jewish Pubn. Society.

Stone, Tanya. Amelia Earhart. 2007. (Biography Ser.). 128p. (J). (gr. 3-8). pap. 4.99 (978-0-7566-2552-8(1)) ; (Illus.). 14.99 (978-0-7566-2553-5(X)) Dorling Kindersley Publishing, Inc.

Sutcliffe, Jane. Amelia Earhart. 2003. (History Maker Bios Ser.). (Illus.). 48p. (J). (gr. 3-5). lib. bdg. 26.60 (978-0-8225-0396-5(4)) Lerner Publishing Group.

Szabo, Corinne. Sky Pioneer: A Photobiography of Amelia Earhart. 2007. (Illus.). 64p. (J). (gr. 5). 7.95 (978-1-4263-0044-8(1) , National Geographic Children's Bks.) National Geographic Society.

Wagner, Heather Lehr. Amelia Earhart. 2003. (Famous Flyers Ser.). (Illus.). 112p. (gr. 6-12). 30.00 (978-0-7910-7213-4(4)) ; pap. 30.00 (978-0-7910-7498-5(6)) Facts On File, Inc. (Chelsea Hse.).

—Amelia Earhart. 2003. (gr. 5-8). lib. bdg. 18.75 (978-0-613-65152-3(9)) Tandem Library Bks.

Walker, Sally M. Bessie Coleman: Daring to Fly. Porter, Janice Lee, illus. 2005. (On My Own Biographies Ser.). 48p. (gr. 2-5). lib. bdg. 23.93 (978-0-87614-919-5(0)) Lerner Publishing Group.

Watson, Marilyn Myrick. Frank Luke, the Arizona Balloon Buster. 2007. (***978-0-9790826-3-4(3) ; 978-0-9790826-4-1(1)***) Acacia Publishing, Inc.

Williams, Colleen Madonna Flood. Chuck Yeager. 2006. (Illus.). 106p. (J). (gr. 4-8). reprint ed. 20.00 (978-1-4223-5543-5(8)) DIANE Publishing Co.

—Chuck Yeager. 2003. (Famous Flyers Ser.). (Illus.). 112p. (gr. 6-12). 30.00 (978-0-7910-7216-5(9)) ; pap. 30.00 (978-0-7910-7500-5(1)) Facts On File, Inc. (Chelsea Hse.).

—Chuck Yeager. 2003. (gr. 5-8). lib. bdg. 18.75 (978-0-613-65195-0(2)) Tandem Library Bks.

Winegarten, Debra L. Katherine Stinson: The Flying Schoolgirl. 2004. (Illus.). 133p. (gr. 4-7). 26.95 (978-1-57168-459-2(X)) Eakin Pr.

AIR POLLUTION

see Air—Pollution

AIR RAIDS—PROTECTIVE MEASURES

see Aeronautics, Military

AIR STEWARDESSES

see Flight Attendants

AIR TRAFFIC CONTROL

Gish, Melissa. An Airport. 2003. 24p. (J). lib. bdg. 21.35 (978-1-58340-322-8(1)) Smart Apple Media.

Winne, Joanne. A Day with Air Traffic Controllers. 2001. (Welcome Bks.). (Illus.). 24p. (J). (ps-2). pap. 4.95 (978-0-516-23064-1(6)) ; 17.00 (978-0-516-23139-6(1)) Scholastic Library Publishing. (Children's Pr.).

—Day with Air Traffic Controllers. 2001. (gr. k-3). lib. bdg. 12.95 (978-0-613-58764-8(2)) Tandem Library Bks.

AIR TRANSPORT

see Aeronautics, Commercial

AIR WARFARE

see Aeronautics, Military; Airplanes, Military

see names of wars with the subdivision Aerial Operations, e.g. World War, 1939-1945—Aerial Operations; etc.

AIRCRAFT ACCIDENTS

see also Survival after Airplane Accidents, Shipwrecks, etc.

Bingham, Jane. The Hindenburg 1937: A Huge Airship Is Destroyed by Fire. 2006. (When Disaster Struck Ser.). (Illus.). 56p. (J). (978-1-4109-2281-6(2)) Steck-Vaughn.

Byers, Ann. The Crash of the Concorde: When Disaster Strikes! 2005. (When Disaster Strikes! Ser.). (Illus.). 48p. (YA). (gr. 5-8). lib. bdg. 23.95 (978-0-8239-3673-1(2)) Rosen Publishing Group, Inc., The.

Cole, Michael D. TWA Flight 800: Explosion in Midair. 1999. (American Disasters Ser.). (Illus.). 48p. (YA). (gr. 4-10). lib. bdg. 23.93 (978-0-7660-1217-2(4)) Enslow Pubs., Inc.

Deady, Kathleen W. The Hindenburg: The Fiery Crash of a German Airship. 2002. (Disaster! Ser.). (Illus.). 32p. (J). (gr. 3-4). lib. bdg. 21.26 (978-0-7368-1321-1(7) , Capstone High-Interest Bks.) Capstone Pr., Inc.

DeAngelis, Gina. Hindenburg. 2000. (Great Disasters Ser.). (Illus.). 112p. (J). (gr. 5 up). 30.00 (978-0-7910-5272-3(9) , Chelsea Hse.) Facts On File, Inc.

DeMolay, Jack. The Bermuda Triangle: The Disappearance of Flight 19. 2007. (Graphic Mysteries Ser.). (J). (978-1-4042-2347-9(9)) ; pap. (978-1-4042-2157-4(3)) ; (gr. 2-6). lib. bdg. 21.25 (978-1-4042-3404-8(7)) Rosen Publishing Group, Inc., The. (PowerKids Pr.).

Doeden, Matt. The Hindenburg Disaster. Erwin, Steve et al, illus. 2006. 32p. (J). 25.26 (978-0-7368-5481-8(9)) Capstone Pr., Inc.

Dokey, Cameron. Hindenburg, 1937. 1999. (Illus.). (J). 11.64 (978-0-606-18373-4(6)) Tandem Library Bks.

Feigenbaum, Aaron. The Hindenburg Disaster. 2007. (Code Red Ser.). (Illus.). 32p. (J). lib. bdg. 25.27 (978-1-59716-361-3(9)) Bearport Publishing Co., Inc.

Flight 901. 2001. (YA). (gr. 6-12). pap. incl. audio (978-0-8224-3286-9(2)) Globe Fearon Educational Publishing.

Friedrich, Belinda. The Explosion of TWA Flight 800. 2001. (Great Disasters, Reforms & Ramifications Ser.). (Illus.). 112p. (YA). (gr. 8-10). 30.00 (978-0-7910-6325-5(9) , Chelsea Hse.) Facts On File, Inc.

Hamilton, Sue L. Air & Sea Mysteries. 2007. (Unsolved Mysteries Ser.). 32p. (J). (gr. 4-8). lib. bdg. 25.65 (***978-1-59928-837-6(0)*** , ABDO & Daughters) ABDO Publishing Co.

Hasday, Judy L. The Apollo 13 Mission: Overcoming Adversity. 2006. (Illus.). 120p. (J). (gr. 4-8). reprint ed. 25.00 (978-1-4223-5546-6(2)) DIANE Publishing Co.

Holden, Henry M. The Tragedy of the Space Shuttle Challenger: A MyReportLinks. com Book. 2004. (Space Flight Adventures & Disasters Ser.). (Illus.). 48p. (J). lib. bdg. 25.26 (978-0-7660-5165-2(X) , MyReportLinks.com Bks.) Enslow Pubs., Inc.

Innes, Brian. Ghosts of Flight 401. 1999. (Unsolved Mysteries Ser.). (Illus.). 48p. (J). (gr. 3-7). lib. bdg. 25.69 (978-0-8172-5475-9(7)) Raintree.

—The Ghosts of Flight 401. 1998. (Unsolved Mysteries Ser.). (Illus.). 48p. (J). (gr. 3-7). pap. 8.05 (978-0-8172-4272-5(4)) Steck-Vaughn.

Koestler-Grack, Rachel A. Space Shuttle Columbia Disaster. 2005. (American Moments Ser.). (Illus.). 48p. (J). (gr. 4-8). lib. bdg. 25.65 (978-1-59197-659-2(6) , ABDO & Daughters) ABDO Publishing Co.

Landau, Elaine. Air Crashes. 1999. (Watts Library). (Illus.). 64p. (YA). (gr. 5-7). 25.50 (978-0-531-20346-0(8) , Watts, Franklin) Scholastic Library Publishing.

—Air Crashes. 2000. (Illus.). 63p. (J). (gr. 5-7). lib. bdg. 17.60 (978-0-613-29389-1(4)) Tandem Library Bks.

Laws, Gordon D. & Laws, Lauren M. Airplane Crashes. 2003. (Manmade Disasters Ser.). (Illus.). 112p. (J). 29.95 (978-1-59018-054-9(2) , Lucent Bks.) Thomson Gale.

Leroe, Ellen. Disaster! Three Real-Life Stories of Survival. 2000. (gr. 5-8). lib. bdg. 14.15 (978-0-613-36304-4(3)) Tandem Library Bks.

Nobleman, Marc Tyler. The Hindenburg. 2005. (We the People Ser.). (Illus.). 48p. (J). (gr. 4-6). 23.93 (978-0-7565-1266-8(2) , 1244100) Compass Point Bks.

O'Brien, Patrick. The Hindenburg. Date not set. (J). pap. 6.95 (978-0-8050-7264-8(0) , Holt, Henry & Co. Bks. For Young Readers) Holt, Henry & Co.

Osborn, Shane & McConnell, Malcolm. Born to Fly: The Heroic Story of Downed U. S. Navy Pilot Lt. Shane Osborn. 2003. 192p. (gr. 5). 5.99 (978-0-440-23796-9(3) , Yearling) Random Hse. Children's Bks.

—Born to Fly: The Heroic Story of Downed U. S. Navy Pilot Lt. Shane Osborn. l.t. ed. 2002. 403p. 29.45 (978-0-7862-4101-9(2)) Thomson Gale.

Schafer, Christopher. The Space Shuttle Columbia Explosion. 2004. (American Moments Ser.). (J). (978-1-59197-288-4(4)) ABDO Publishing Co.

Sherrow, Victoria. The Hindenburg Disaster: Doomed Airship. 2002. (American Disasters Ser.). (Illus.). 48p. (J). (gr. 4-10). lib. bdg. 23.93 (978-0-7660-1554-8(8)) Enslow Pubs., Inc.

Sofer, Barbara. Ilan Ramon: Israel's Space Hero. 2003. (Illus.). 64p. (J). (gr. 3-6). 16.95 (978-1-58013-115-5(8)) ; pap. (978-1-58013-116-2(6)) Kar-Ben Publishing.

Spalding, Frank. Plane Crash: True Stories of Survival. 2006. (Survivor Stories Ser.). (Illus.). 48p. (J). (gr. 5-8). lib. bdg. 26.50 (978-1-4042-0999-2(9) , 1267009) Rosen Publishing Group, Inc., The.

Weil, Ann. Air Disasters. 2003. (Illus.). 64p. (YA). per. 3.95 (978-1-56254-650-2(3) , SP6503) Saddleback Educational Publishing.

Werther, Scott P. Alive! Airplane Crash in the Andes Mountains. 2003. (Survivor Ser.). (Illus.). 48p. (J). 24.00 (978-0-516-24329-0(2) , Children's Pr.) Scholastic Library Publishing.

—Alive! Airplane Crash in the Andes Mountains. 2003. (gr. 7-12). lib. bdg. 15.25 (978-0-613-67864-3(8)) Tandem Library Bks.

Woods, Michael & Woods, Mary B. Air Disasters. 2008. (Disasters up Close Ser.). (J). lib. bdg. 27.93 (978-0-8225-6772-1(5) , Lerner Pubns.) Lerner Publishing Group.

Woodson, Frank. The Last Flight of 007. Taylor, Marjorie, illus. 1999. (Take Ten Ser.). 46p. (YA). (gr. 4 up). pap. 3.95 (978-1-58659-025-3(1)) Artesian Pr.

AIRCRAFT CARRIERS

Aircraft Carriers, 6, Pack. (On Deck Ser.). 24p. (gr. 4-5). 35.00 (978-0-7578-1058-9(6)) Rigby Education.

Amato, William. Aircraft Carriers. 2002. (Reading Power Ser.). (Illus.). 24p. (J). (gr. 2). lib. bdg. 17.25 (978-0-8239-6012-5(9) , PowerKids Pr.) Rosen Publishing Group, Inc., The.

—Portaaviones. 2004. (Vehiculos de Alta Tecnologia Ser.). (SPA & ENG., Illus.). 24p. (J). (gr. 3-6). lib. bdg. 17.25 (978-0-8239-6883-1(9) , Buenas Letra) Rosen Publishing Group, Inc., The.

Beyer, Mark. Aircraft Carriers: Inside & Out. Calvetti, Leonello & Cecchi, Lorenzo, illus. 2006. 47p. (J). (gr. 4-8). 19.00 (978-1-4223-5550-3(0)) DIANE Publishing Co.

—Aircraft Carriers: Inside & Out. 2005. (Technology Ser.). (Illus.). 48p. (YA). (gr. 4-8). lib. bdg. 26.50 (978-0-8239-6111-5(7)) Rosen Publishing Group, Inc., The.

Braulick, Carrie A. U.S. Navy Aircraft Carriers. 2006. (Blazers—Military Vehicles Ser.). (Illus.). 32p. (J). (978-0-7368-5470-2(3)) Capstone Pr., Inc.

Doeden, Matt. Aircraft Carriers. (Mighty MacHines Ser.). 24p. (J). pap. 6.95 (978-0-7368-5136-7(4)) Capstone Pr., Inc.

—Aircraft Carriers. (Pull Ahead Books). 32p. (J). (ps). 2006. (Illus.). 22.60 (978-0-8225-2666-7(2)); 2005. pap. 5.95 (978-0-8225-2872-2(X)) Lerner Publishing Group. (Lerner Pubns.).

Doyle, Kevin. Aircraft Carriers. 2004. (Military Hardware in Action Ser.). (Illus.). 48p. (J). (gr. 4-9). lib. bdg. 25.26 (978-0-8225-4702-0(3)) Lerner Publishing Group.

Green, Michael. Supercarriers. 2001. (Land & Sea Ser.). (Illus.). 48p. (J). (gr. 3-4). lib. bdg. 21.26 (978-0-7368-0760-9(8) , Capstone High-Interest Bks.) Capstone Pr., Inc.

Green, Michael & Green, Gladys. Aircraft Carriers: The Nimitz Class. 2004. (War Machines Ser.). (Illus.). 32p. (J). lib. bdg. 22.60 (978-0-7368-2720-1(X)) Capstone Pr., Inc.

Patton, Geoff. Giants of the Sea. 2005. (X-Zone Ser.). (Illus.). 30p. (gr. 4-8). 23.00 (978-0-7910-8978-1(9)) Facts On File, Inc.

Portaaviones: Individual Title Six-Packs. (On Deck en Espanol Ser.).Tr. of Aircraft Carriers. (SPA.). 24p. (gr. 4-5). 35.00 (978-0-7578-6433-9(3)) Rigby Education.

Roza, Greg. The Incredible Story of Aircraft Carriers. 2004. (Kid's Guide to Incredible Technology Ser.). (Illus.). 24p. (J). lib. bdg. 19.95 (978-0-8239-6714-8(X) , PowerKids Pr.) Rosen Publishing Group, Inc., The.

Stone, Lynn M. Aircraft Carriers. 2006. (Fighting Forces Ser.). (Illus.). 32p. (gr. 4-8). 19.95 (978-1-59515-459-0(0) , 1244401) Rourke Publishing, LLC.

Strazzabosco, John. Aircraft Carriers, Supplies for a City at Sea: Multiplying Multidigit Numbers with Regrouping. 2004. (PowerMath Ser.). (Illus.). 32p. (J). lib. bdg. 22.50 (978-0-8239-8995-9(X) , PowerKids Pr.) Rosen Publishing Group, Inc., The.

—Aircraft Carriers, Supplies for a City at Sea: Multiplying Multidigit Numbers with Renaming. 2004. (PowerMath Ser.). (Illus.). 32p. (J). lib. bdg. (978-0-8239-8919-5(4) , PowerKids Pr.) Rosen Publishing Group, Inc., The.

Tripp, Will. Water Adventures. 2005. (Real Deal Ser.). (Illus.). 32p. (J). pap. (978-0-7608-9636-5(4)) Sundance/Newbridge Educational Publishing.

AIRLINE CRASHES

see Aircraft Accidents

AIRLINES—HOSTESSES

see Flight Attendants

AIRPLANE ACCIDENTS

see Aircraft Accidents

AIRPLANE CARRIERS

see Aircraft Carriers

AIRPLANE CRASHES

see Aircraft Accidents

AIRPLANES

see also Aeronautics; Gliders (Aeronautics)

also types of airplanes, e.g. Bombers; Vertically Rising Airplanes; etc.

Adams, Colleen. Planes Go Places: Learning the Sound of PL. (PowerPhonics Ser.). (Illus.). (J). 2002. 24p. (gr. 1). lib. bdg. 18.50 (978-0-8239-5951-8(1)); 2001. 23p. pap. 26.40 (978-0-8239-8296-7(3)) Rosen Publishing Group, Inc., The. (PowerKids Pr.).

Aircraft, 14 bks., Set. Incl. Air Force Aircraft. Holden, Henry M. (J). 2001. lib. bdg. 23.93 (978-0-7660-1714-6(1)) ; Air Show Pilots & Airplanes. Gaffney, Timothy R. (YA). 2001. lib. bdg. 23.93 (978-0-7660-1570-8(X)) ; Amazing Agricultural Aircraft. Gaffney, Timothy R. (J). 2001. lib. bdg. 23.93 (978-0-7660-1608-8(0)) ; Black Hawk Helicopter. Holden, Henry M. (J). 2002. lib. bdg. 23.93 (978-0-7660-1568-5(8)) ; Hurricane Hunters. Gaffney, Timothy R. (YA). 2001. lib. bdg. 23.93 (978-0-7660-1569-2(6)) ; Stealth Fighters & Bombers. Berliner, Don. (YA). 2001. lib. bdg. 23.93 (978-0-7660-1567-8(X)) ; 48p. (gr. 4-10). (Illus.). Set lib. bdg. 227.40 (978-0-7660-1799-3(0)) Enslow Pubs., Inc.

The Airplane, 6 vols. (gr. 2-5). 36.95 (978-0-7368-4612-7(3)) Red Brick Learning.

Airplane Adventures, 6 vols. (gr. 4 up). 39.95 (978-0-7368-9282-7(6)) Red Brick Learning.

Airplanes. 2005. (Transportation Ser.). (YA). (gr. k-3). (978-1-56065-969-3(6) , Pebble Bks.) Capstone Pr., Inc.

Ardagh, Philip. Up in the Air. (Mighty Machines Ser.). (Illus.). 32p. lib. bdg. 24.25 (978-1-931983-03-7(8)) Chrysalis Education.

Armentrout, David & Armentrout, Patricia, trs. Planes. 2003. (Transportation Ser.). (Illus.). 24p. (J). 20.64 (978-1-58952-670-9(8)) Rourke Publishing, LLC.

Ashley, Susan. Going by Plane. 2003. (Going Places Ser.). (Illus.). 24p. (YA). (gr. 2 up). lib. bdg. 19.33 (978-0-8368-3731-5(2) , Weekly Reader Early Learning Library) Stevens, Gareth Inc.

—Por Avion. 2003. (Weekly Reader Early Learning Library). (SPA., Illus.). 24p. (J). (gr. 2 up). pap. 5.95 (978-0-8368-3841-1(6) , Weekly Reader Early Learning Library) Stevens, Gareth Inc.

—Por Avion. Coffey, Colleen & Carrillo, Consuelo, trs. 2003. (Weekly Reader Early Learning Library). (SPA., Illus.). 24p. (J). (gr. 2 up). lib. bdg. 19.33 (978-0-8368-3736-0(3) , Weekly Reader Early Learning Library) Stevens, Gareth Inc.

Aylmore, Angela. I Like Planes. 2007. (J). pap. (978-1-4034-9285-2(9)) ; (Illus.). 24p. (978-1-4034-9267-8(0)) ; (Illus.). 24p. (***978-1-4034-9276-0(X)***) Heinemann Library.

B-29 Superfortress Pilot's Manual Collection. 2005. (YA). cd-rom 69.95 (978-0-9742781-6-2(5)) Rhode, Steve Inc.

Baggette, Susan K. Jonathan Goes to the Airport. Moriarty, William J., photos by. 1998. (Jonathan Adventures Ser.). (Illus.). 16p. (J). (ps-k). bds. 5.95 (978-0-9660172-6-7(9)) Brookfield Reader, Inc., The.

Barton, Byron. Planes. Barton, Byron, illus. 1998. (Illus.). 34p. (J). (ps up). bds. 6.99 (978-0-694-01166-7(5)) HarperCollins Pubs.

Baum, Brian. Super Jumbo Jets: Inside & Out. 2002. (Technology Ser.). (Illus.). 48p. (YA). (ps-3). lib. bdg. 26.50 (978-0-8239-6112-2(5) , PowerKids Pr.) Rosen Publishing Group, Inc., The.

Baysura, Kelly. Cargo Planes. 2001. (Flying Machines Ser.). (Illus.). 24p. (J). (gr. 1-4). lib. bdg. 20.64 (978-1-58952-003-5(3)) Rourke Publishing, LLC.

—First Flight. 2001. (Flying Machines Ser.). (Illus.). 24p. (J). (gr. 1-4). lib. bdg. 20.64 (978-1-58952-001-1(7)) Rourke Publishing, LLC.

—Jet Airliners. 2001. (Flying Machines Ser.). (Illus.). 24p. (J). (gr. 1-4). lib. bdg. 20.64 (978-1-58952-005-9(X)) Rourke Publishing, LLC.

Bender, Lionel. Airplanes & Helicopters. 2006. (J). (978-1-59389-261-6(6)) Chrysalis Education.

Berger, Melvin & Berger, Gilda. Can You Fly High, Wright Brothers? 2007. (Scholastic Science Super Giants Ser.: Vol. 1). 48p. (J). pap. 4.99 (978-0-439-83378-3(7)) Scholastic, Inc.

—How Do Airplanes Fly? A Book about Airplanes. Babb, Paul, illus. 1998. (Discovery Readers Ser.). 48p. (J). (gr. 4-7). lib. bdg. 17.55 (978-0-7910-5064-4(5) , Chelsea Hse.) Facts On File, Inc.

Beyer, Mark. Aviones Del Pasado. 2004. (Transporte Ayer y Hoy Ser.). (SPA & ENG., Illus.). 24p. (J). (gr. 3-6). lib. bdg. 17.25 (978-0-8239-6905-0(3) , Buenas Letra) Rosen Publishing Group, Inc., The.

—Planes of the Past. 2002. (Reading Power Ser.). (Illus.). 24p. (J). (gr. 1). lib. bdg. 17.25 (978-0-8239-5984-6(8) , PowerKids Pr.) Rosen Publishing Group, Inc., The.

BHB International Staff. Airplanes. 1998. (Our World in Pictures Ser.). (J). (ps-3). (978-2-215-06168-7(5)) Editions Fleurus.

Biesty, Stephen. Look Inside Cross-Sections: Planes. (Illus.). 32p. (J). mass mkt. 8.99 (978-0-590-24341-4(1)) Scholastic, Inc.

Bingham, Caroline. Airplane. 2003. (Machines at Work Ser.). (Illus.). 32p. (J). 8.99 (978-0-7894-9222-7(9)) Dorling Kindersley Publishing, Inc.

Bingham, Caroline & Millard, Anne. The Big Book of Airplanes. 2001. (Illus.). 32p. (J). (ps-3). 14.99 (978-0-7894-6521-4(3)) Dorling Kindersley Publishing, Inc.

Birtles, Philip. ABC Boeing 747-400. 2000. (Illus.). 96p. (J). pap. 14.95 (978-1-882663-51-4(9)) Plymouth Toy & Book.

Britton, Tamara L. Air Force. 2005. (Symbols, Landmarks & Monuments Ser.). (Illus.). 32p. (J). (gr. k-6). lib. bdg. 22.78 (978-1-59197-520-5(4) , Checkerboard Library) ABDO Publishing Co.

Bryant, Raymond. Up in the Sky. 2003. (Funtime Rhymes Ser.). (Illus.). 10p. (J). bds. 4.95 (978-0-7641-2657-4(1)) Barron's Educational Series, Inc.

Burch, Lynda S. Wicky Wacky Things that Go! Airplanes 1. Roberts, MarySue, photos by. 2004. (Illus.). 28p. (J). E-Book 9.95 incl. cd-rom (978-1-933090-07-8(3)) Guardian Angel Publishing, Inc.

Butterfield, Moira. Airplanes. 1999. (Supreme Machines Ser.). (Illus.). 48p. (J). (gr. 3-7). 14.95 (978-0-7641-5194-1(0)) Barron's Educational Series, Inc.

Cain, Bill & Hama, Larry. Unmanned Aerial Vehicles. 2007. (High-Tech Military Weapons Ser.). (Illus.). 48p. (J). pap. (978-0-531-18711-1(X)) Children's Pr., Ltd.

—Unmanned Aerial Vehicles. 2006. (High-Tech Military Weapons Ser.). (Illus.). 48p. (J). (978-0-531-12095-8(3) , Children's Pr.) Scholastic Library Publishing.

Castor, Hariet. Planes & Helicopters. rev. ed. 2005. 32p. (J). pap. 6.95 (978-0-7945-0841-8(3) , Usborne) EDC Publishing.

Catala, Ellen. Up, up, & Away. 2005. (Yellow Umbrella Ser.). (Illus.). 16p. (J). (978-0-7368-5265-4(4)); (978-0-7368-5301-9(4)) Capstone Pr., Inc.

Chant, Christopher. Civil Aircraft. 1999. (World's Greatest Aircraft Ser.). (Illus.). 64p. (J). (gr. 5 up). 12.95 (978-0-7910-5421-5(7) , Chelsea Hse.) Facts On File, Inc.

—Specialized Aircraft. 1999. (World's Greatest Aircraft Ser.). (Illus.). 64p. (J). (gr. 5 up). 21.95 (978-0-7910-5422-2(5) , Chelsea Hse.) Facts On File, Inc.

Civardi, Anne. Going on a Plane. Cartwright, Stephen, illus. rev. ed. 2005. 16p. (J). pap. 4.99 (978-0-7945-1005-3(1) , Usborne) EDC Publishing.

Clemson, Wendy, et al. Fly a Jumbo Jet. 2004. (Mathworks!). (Illus.). 31p. (J). lib. bdg. 24.67 (978-0-8368-4212-8(X)) Stevens, Gareth Inc.

Collicutt, Paul. This Plane. Collicutt, Paul, illus. 2002. (Illus.). 32p. (J). (ps-1). pap. 5.95 (978-0-374-47517-8(2) , Sunburst) Farrar, Straus & Giroux.

—This Plane. 2002. (Illus.). 24p. (ps). lib. bdg. 13.15 (978-0-606-25524-0(9)) Tandem Library Bks.

Court, Rob. How to Draw Airplanes. 2007. (Doodle Bks.). 32p. (J). 21.36 (***978-1-59296-803-9(1)***) Child's World, Inc.

Dahl, Michael. Roll, Slope, & Slide: A Book about Inclined Planes. Shea, Denise, illus. 2006. (Amazing Science Ser.). 24p. (J). (gr. k-4). 22.60 (978-1-4048-1304-5(7)) Picture Window Bks.

David, Jack. Predator Drones. 2007. (Torque: Military Machines Ser.). (Illus.). 24p. (J). (gr. 3-7). lib. bdg. 20.00 (***978-0-531-18473-8(0)*** , Children's Pr.) Scholastic Library Publishing.

David West. Jet Plane. 2006. (Illus.). 32p. (J). pap. (978-1-4109-2563-3(3)) Steck-Vaughn.

Davies, Gill. Trains, Boats & Planes. Guile, Gill, illus. 2005. 20p. (J). (gr. k-4). reprint ed. 20.00 (978-0-7567-8703-5(3)) DIANE Publishing Co.

DiSpezio, Michael Anthony. Flying Things: Simple Experiments in the Science of Flight. 2000. (Illus.). 77p. (J). (gr. k-12). 12.95 (978-1-57232-864-8(9)) Seymour, Dale Pubns.

Doeden, Matt. Aircraft Carriers. 2005. (Pebble Plus: Mighty Machines Ser.). (Illus.). 24p. (J). 19.93 (978-0-7368-3656-2(X)) Capstone Pr., Inc.

Dorling Kindersley Publishing Staff. Airplane. (Machines at Work Ser.). (J). 2006. 32p. pap. 6.99 (978-0-7566-1788-2(X)); 2004. 16p. pap. 3.99 (978-0-7566-0226-0(2)) Dorling Kindersley Publishing, Inc.

—What's Inside Planes? 1999. (978-0-606-17819-8(8)) Tandem Library Bks.

Draw 50 Airplanes, Aircraft & Spacecraft. 2002. (Draw 50 Ser.). (Illus.). (J). 17.60 (978-0-7587-4700-6(4)) Book Wholesalers, Inc.

Dubowski, Mark. Superfast Planes. 2005. (Ultimate Speed Ser.). (Illus.). 32p. (J). lib. bdg. 25.27 (978-1-59716-082-7(2)) Bearport Publishing Co., Inc.

Eden, Paul E. Weird & Wonderful Aircraft. 2006. (Aircraft of the World Ser.). (Illus.). 32p. (J). lib. bdg. (978-0-8368-6906-4(0)) Stevens, Gareth Inc.

Faber, Harold. The Airplane. 2005. (Great Inventions Ser.). (Illus.). 128p. (J). (gr. 3-7). lib. bdg. (978-0-7614-1876-4(8) , Benchmark Bks.) Cavendish, Marshall Corp.

Farndon, John. Flight. 2001. (Science Experiments Ser.). (Illus.). 32p. (J). (gr. 3-5). lib. bdg. 25.64 (978-0-7614-1342-4(1) , Benchmark Bks.) Cavendish, Marshall Corp.

A Fifty Year Affair: Living with Light Planes. Lt. ed. 2004. (Illus.). 208p. (YA). pap. 18.95 (978-0-9746564-0-3(2)) Julson, D. K.

Flight Sets: 1 Each of 3 Big Books. (Sunshinetm Science Ser.). (gr. 1-2). 111.50 (978-0-7802-2816-0(2)) Wright Group, The.

Flight Sets: 1 Each of 3 Student Books. (Sunshinetm Science Ser.). (gr. 1-2). 20.95 (978-0-7802-2817-7(0)) Wright Group, The.

Fraterrigo, Elizabeth. Beyond Kitty Hawk: Inventing Flight at Huffman Prairie Flying Field. 2002. (Illus.). 44p. (YA). 4.95 (978-1-888213-98-0(1)) Eastern National.

French, Cathy. Haz un avion de papel & Make a Paper Airplane. 2005. spiral bd. 66.00 (***978-1-4108-5631-9(3)***) Benchmark Education Co.

Gaffney, Timothy R. Air Show Pilots & Airplanes. 2001. (Aircraft Ser.). (Illus.). 48p. (YA). (gr. 4-10). lib. bdg. 23.93 (978-0-7660-1570-8(X)) Enslow Pubs., Inc.

—Amazing Agricultural Aircraft. 2001. (Aircraft Ser.). (Illus.). 48p. (J). (gr. 4-10). lib. bdg. 23.93 (978-0-7660-1608-8(0)) Enslow Pubs., Inc.

—Hurricane Hunters. 2001. (Aircraft Ser.). (Illus.). 48p. (YA). (gr. 4-10). lib. bdg. 23.93 (978-0-7660-1569-2(6)) Enslow Pubs., Inc.

Graham, Ian. Aircraft. 1999. (Built for Speed Ser.). (Illus.). 32p. (J). (gr. 3-7). lib. bdg. 25.69 (978-0-8172-4220-6(1)) Raintree.

—Aircraft. 2006. (Mighty Machines Ser.). (J). (978-1-58340-918-3(1)) Smart Apple Media.

—Flight. 2001. (Single Subject References Ser.). (Illus.). 64p. (J). (gr. 4-8). tchr. ed. 16.95 (978-0-7534-5326-1(6) , Kingfisher) Houghton Mifflin Co. Trade & Reference Div.

—In the Air: Machines at Work. 2007. (QEB Machines at Work Ser.). (J). lib. bdg. 19.95 (978-1-59566-315-3(0)) QEB Publishing Inc.

—Planes, Rockets & Other Flying Machines. 2000. (Fast Forward Ser.). (Illus.). 32p. (J). (gr. 4-8). pap. 9.95 (978-0-531-16444-0(6) , Watts, Franklin) Scholastic Library Publishing.

—Planes, Rockets & Other Flying Machines. 2000. (gr. 3-6). lib. bdg. 18.75 (978-0-613-34898-0(2)) Tandem Library Bks.

—Planes, Rockets, & Other Flying Machines. Hewetson, Nicholas, illus. 2000. (Fast Forward Ser.). 32p. (J). (gr. 4-8). 29.00 (978-0-531-11878-8(9) , Watts, Franklin) Scholastic Library Publishing.

Grant, Donald. El Avion. (Coleccion Mundo Maravilloso). (SPA., Illus.). 40p. (J). (gr. 2-4). 13.56 (978-84-348-3536-8(3) , AV9291) SM Ediciones ESP. *Dist:* Lectorum Pubns., Inc.

Greenfield Educational Center Staff. Small Airplane. 2000. (I Can Read Ser.: Bk. 3). (CHI & ENG., Illus.). 8p. (J). pap. 2.99 (978-962-563-070-0(8)); pap. 24.99 (978-962-563-136-3(4)) Greenfield Enterprises, Ltd. HKG. *Dist:* Cheng & Tsui Co.

—Small Airplane: Simplified Edition. 2000. (I Can Read Ser.: Bk. 3). (CHI & ENG., Illus.). 8p. (J). pap. 2.99 (978-962-563-208-7(5)) Greenfield Enterprises, Ltd. HKG. *Dist:* Cheng & Tsui Co.

Grist, Julie. Flying: Just Plane Fun. 2006. (Illus.). 24p. (J). pap. 8.95 (978-0-9725750-2-7(2)) Spoonbender Bks.

—Flying: Just Plane Fun. Grist, Julie, illus. 2003. (Illus.). 24p. (J). (gr. 1-7). 17.95 (978-0-9725750-0-3(6)) Spoonbender Bks.

Gunston, Bill. Aero-Mania! 2003. (Vehicle-Mania! Ser.). (Illus.). 32p. (J). (gr. 2 up). lib. bdg. 23.33 (978-0-8368-3780-3(0)) Stevens, Gareth Inc.

Hansen, Ole Steen. Weird & Wonderful Aircraft. 2003. (Story of Flight Ser.). (Illus.). 32p. (J). (gr. 4). pap. (978-0-7787-1226-8(5)); lib. bdg. (978-0-7787-1210-7(9)) Crabtree Publishing Co.

Hanson, Anders. Let's Go by Airplane. 2007. (Let's Go! Ser.). (ENG., Illus.). 24p. (J). (ps-3). lib. bdg. 19.93 (***978-1-59928-893-2(1)*** , SandCastle) ABDO Publishing Co.

Hartelius, Margaret A. Zoom! The Complete Paper Airplane Kit. Hartelius, Margaret A. & Eagle, Cameron, illus. ed. 2003. (Trend Friends Ser.). 64p. (J). (ps-4). pap. 8.99 (978-0-448-43174-1(2) , Grosset & Dunlap) Penguin Group (USA) Inc.

Hewitt, Sally. Planes. 2006. (Illus.). 24p. (YA). (gr. 1 up). lib. bdg. 22.80 (978-1-931983-54-9(2)) Chrysalis Education.

High Flying: Level P, 6 vols., Vol. 3. (Explorers Ser.). 32p. (gr. 3-6). 44.95 (978-0-7699-0619-5(2)) Shortland Pubns. (U. S. A.) Inc.

Hill, Lee Sullivan. Get Around in Air & Space. 1999. (Get Around Bks.). (Illus.). 32p. (J). (gr. k-3). lib. bdg. 14.60 (978-1-57505-310-3(1) , Carolrhoda Bks.) Lerner Publishing Group.

Hofer, Charles. Airplanes. 2008. (J). lib. bdg. (***978-1-4042-4173-2(6)*** , PowerKids Pr.) Rosen Publishing Group, Inc., The.

Holden, Henry M. Air Force Aircraft. 2001. (Aircraft Ser.). (Illus.). 48p. (J). (gr. 4-10). lib. bdg. 23.93 (978-0-7660-1714-6(1)) Enslow Pubs., Inc.

Holzer, David. Make & Play Airplanes. Galvani, Maureen, illus. 2005. 48p. (J). (ps-3). (978-1-84510-549-5(4)) Top That! Publishing PLC.

Hosley, Maria. Airplanes. 2007. (Illus.). 24p. (J). 21.35 (***978-1-59679-799-4(1)***) ABDO Publishing Co.

How Airplanes Fly: 6 Each of 1 Student Book, 6 vols. (Sunshinetm Science Ser.). 24p. (gr. 1-2). 41.95 (978-0-7802-2716-3(6)) Wright Group, The.

How Airplanes Fly: Big Book. (Sunshinetm Science Ser.). 24p. (gr. 1-2). 37.50 (978-0-7802-2792-7(1)) Wright Group, The.

How Do Airplanes Fly? (Discovery Readers Ser.). 48p. (J). pap. 3.95 (978-0-8249-5317-1(7) , Ideals Children's Bks.) Ideals Pubns.

Howatson, Ian & Quigley, Sebastian, illus. The World of Flight. 2001. (Inside Look Ser.). 48p. (J). (gr. 4 up). lib. bdg. 26.00 (978-0-8368-2903-7(4)) Stevens, Gareth Inc.

January, Brendan. Air Force One. 2004. (Cornerstones of Freedom Ser.). (Illus.). 48p. (J). 26.00 (978-0-516-24236-1(9) , Children's Pr.) Scholastic Library Publishing.

Jefferis. Jets. 2004. (Mean Machines Ser.). (Illus.). 64p. (J). pap. 8.95 (978-1-4109-0829-2(1)) Harcourt Schl. Pubs.

—Jets 6-Pack. 2004. (Illus.). (J). pap. 48.35 (978-1-4109-0834-6(8)) Harcourt Schl. Pubs.

Jefferis, David. Planes. 2007. (J). (***978-1-59920-042-2(2)***) Smart Apple Media.

Jefferis, David & Dorling Kindersley Publishing Staff. Aircraft. 2nd ed. 2004. (Pocket Guides Ser.). (Illus.). 128p. (J). pap. 6.99 (978-0-7566-0205-5(X)) Dorling Kindersley Publishing, Inc.

Jeffries. Jets. 2003. (Monster Machines Ser.). (Illus.). 32p. (J). pap. 7.95 (978-1-4109-0056-2(8)) Raintree.

Kids Can Press Staff, Press Can, ed. This Is Daniel Cook on a Plane. 2006. (Illus.). 24p. (J). (978-1-55453-081-6(4)) Kids Can Pr., Ltd.

—This Is Daniel Cook on A Plane. 2006. (Illus.). 24p. (J). (978-1-55453-082-3(2)) Kids Can Pr., Ltd.

Kirk, Ellen. My Plane Book. 2006. 16p. (J). 5.99 (978-0-06-089941-7(7)) HarperCollins Pubs.

Leoni, Cristiana. A History of Aircraft. 2005. (Moving People, Things, & Ideas Ser.). (Illus.). 48p. (J). (ps-7). lib. bdg. 24.95 (978-1-4103-0659-3(3) , Blackbirch Pr., Inc.) Thomson Gale.

Lindeen, Mary. Airplanes. 2007. (Illus.). 24p. (J). lib. bdg. 16.95 (978-1-60014-058-7(0)) Bellwether Media.

—Airplanes. 2007. (Blastoff! Readers Ser.). 24p. (J). (gr. k-2). 18.50 (***978-0-531-17556-9(1)*** , Children's Pr.) Scholastic Library Publishing.

Loewen, Nancy. Airplanes. 2003. 24p. (J). lib. bdg. 21.35 (978-1-58340-321-1(3)) Smart Apple Media.

Loves, June. Airplanes. 2001. (Database Transportation Ser.). (Illus.). 32p. (J). (gr. 4 up). 22.95 (978-0-7910-6587-7(1) , 010501); (YA). (gr. 5 up). 22.95 (978-0-7910-6560-0(X) , 010301) Facts On File, Inc. (Chelsea Hse.).

—Database Transportation, 6 bks. Incl. Airplanes. 22.95 (978-0-7910-6587-7(1) , 010501); Bicycles & Motorcycles. 22.95 (978-0-7910-6591-4(X) , 010502); Cars. 22.95 (978-0-7910-6589-1(8) , 010503); Ships. 22.95 (978-0-7910-6590-7(1) , 010504); Spacecraft. 22.95 (978-0-7910-6588-4(X) , 010505); Trains. 22.95 (978-0-7910-6586-0(3) , 010506); (J). (gr. 4 up). 2001. (Illus.). 32p. 2005. Set pap. 137.70 (978-0-7910-6585-3(5) , 010500S, Chelsea Hse.) Facts On File, Inc.

Mandel, Peter. Planes at the Airport. Miller, Edward, illus. 2004. 8p. (J). pap. 6.99 (978-0-439-56416-8(6)) Scholastic, Inc.

Masters, Nancy Robinson. The Airplane. 2005. (Inventions That Shaped the World Ser.). (Illus.). 80p. (J). (gr. 5-8). pap. 9.95 (978-0-531-16733-5(X) , Watts, Franklin) Scholastic Library Publishing.

Mayer, Cassie. By Plane. 2006. (Illus.). 24p. (J). (978-1-4034-8390-4(6)); pap. (978-1-4034-8397-3(3)) Heinemann Library.

—En Avion. 2006. (Illus.). 24p. (J). (978-1-4034-8631-8(X)); pap. (978-1-4034-8638-7(7)) Heinemann Library.

McKee, Karen & Griffin, Georgene. Airplanes. 2001. (How to Draw Ser.). (Illus.). 32p. (J). (gr. 2-5). lib. bdg. 25.27 (978-1-58952-151-3(X)) Rourke Publishing, LLC.

Mellet, Peter, et al, trs. All about Aircraft & Flight. 2004. (All About...Ser.). (Illus.). 64p. pap. 7.99 (978-1-84215-892-0(9) , Southwater) Anness Publishing GBR. *Dist:* National Bk. Network.

Micro Planes. 2004. (Whizz Kits Ser.). (Illus.). 48p. (J). (978-1-84229-946-3(8)) Top That! Publishing PLC.

Miller, Edward, illus. Airplanes. 1999. (Sticker Stories Ser.). 20p. (J). (ps-1). pap. 4.99 (978-0-448-41963-3(7) , Grosset & Dunlap) Penguin Group (USA) Inc.

Mitton, Tony. Amazing Airplanes. Parker, Ant, illus. (Amazing Machines Ser.). 24p. (J). (ps-k). 2005. pap., pap. 3.95 (978-0-7534-5915-7(9)); 2002. tchr. ed. 9.95 (978-0-7534-5403-9(3)) Houghton Mifflin Co. Trade & Reference Div. (Kingfisher).

Molzahn, Arlene Bourgeois. Airplanes. 2003. (Transportation & Communication Ser.). (Illus.). 48p. (J). (gr. 1-4). lib. bdg. 23.93 (978-0-7660-2026-9(6)) Enslow Pubs., Inc.

Morris, Mark. Jets. 2004. (Mean Machines Ser.). (Illus.). 64p. (J). (gr. 6-8). lib. bdg. 32.79 (978-1-4109-0555-0(1)) Raintree.

Morris, Neil. Planes. (Past & Present Ser.). (Illus.). 32p. lib. bdg. 24.25 (978-1-931983-35-8(6)) Chrysalis Education.

Morse, Jenifer Corr. Planes. 2001. (Speed! Ser.). (Illus.). 24p. (J). (gr. 3-6). 21.20 (978-1-56711-466-9(0) , Blackbirch Pr., Inc.) Thomson Gale.

Mott, Professor. Flight: First Vehicles. Lenehan, Mary & Weber, Rich, illus. 8p. (J). (ps-3). 14.99 (978-1-890647-36-0(5)) RC2 Corp.

Mravec, James. You Can Draw Planes, Trains & Boats. 2005. (Illus.). 96p. spiral bd. (978-0-7853-8303-1(4) , 3460900) Publications International, Ltd.

Nahum, Andrew & Dorling Kindersley Publishing Staff. Flying Machine. 2004. (Eyewitness Books). (Illus.). 72p. (J). lib. bdg. 19.99 (978-0-7566-0679-4(9)) Dorling Kindersley Publishing, Inc.

Nelson, Robin. From Metal to Airplane. 2004. (Start to Finish Ser.). (J). 18.60 (978-0-8225-1388-9(9) , Lerner Pubns.); pap. 4.95 (978-0-8225-2145-7(8)) Lerner Publishing Group.

Oxlade, Chris. Airplanes: Uncovering Technology. 2006. (Uncovering Ser.). (Illus.). 52p. (J). (gr. 3-12). 16.95 (978-1-55407-134-0(8)) Firefly Bks., Ltd.

—Plane. (Take It Apart Ser.). (Illus.). 32p. (J). (gr. 4-6). lib. bdg. 24.25 (978-1-930643-95-6(0)) Chrysalis Education.

—Planes. (Transportation Around the World Ser.). 32p. pap. 6.95 (978-1-4034-4134-8(0)); 2000. (Illus.). (J). lib. bdg. 21.36 (978-1-57572-303-7(4)) Heinemann Library.

P-47B, P-47C & P-47D Airplanes - Erection & Maintenance Instructions. 2005. (YA). cd-rom 29.95 (978-0-9742781-9-3(X)) Rhode, Steve Inc.

Pallotta, Jerry & Stillwell, Fred. The Airplane Alphabet Book. Bolster, Rob, illus. 2004. 32p. (YA). pap. 6.95 (978-0-88106-906-8(X)) Charlesbridge Publishing, Inc.

Parker, Steve. The Inside & Out Guide to Speed Machines. 2006. (Illus.). 32p. (J). (978-1-4034-9089-6(9)); pap. (978-1-4034-9096-4(1)) Heinemann Library.

Parsont, Meg. Seaplane. Curti, Anna, illus. 1999. (Go Bks.). 12p. (ps). 5.95 (978-0-7892-0546-9(7)) Abbeville Pr., Inc.

Pascoe, Elaine, ed. World's Largest Building. 2003. (Super Structures of the World Ser.). (Illus.). 48p. (J). 24.95 (978-1-56711-871-1(2)); 11.20 (978-1-4103-0187-1(7)) Thomson Gale. (Blackbirch Pr., Inc.).

Patchett, F. Planes. 2004. (Beginners Ser.). (Illus.). 32p. (J). (gr. 1 up). pap. 4.95 (978-0-7945-0319-2(5) , Usborne); lib. bdg. 12.95 (978-1-58086-484-8(8)) EDC Publishing.

Petruccio, Steven James. Airport Stickers Picture. 1998. (Illus.). (J). 4.95 (978-0-486-40587-2(7)) Dover Pubns., Inc.

Pipe, Jim. Planes. 2006. (Illus.). 24p. (J). (978-1-59604-118-9(8)) Stargazer Bks.

Planes of the Past: Individual Title Six-Packs. (On Deck Ser.). 24p. (gr. 4-5). 35.00 (978-0-7578-1049-7(7)) Rigby Education.

Priddy Books Staff & Priddy, Roger. Happy Baby: Things That Go. 2004. (Illus.). 28p. (J). bds. 8.95 (978-0-312-49198-7(0) , Priddy Bks.) St. Martin's Pr.

Provensen, Alice. The Glorious Flight: Across the Channel with Louis Bleriot. Provensen, Alice, illus. 2002. (Illus.). (J). 14.04 (978-0-7587-0049-0(0)) Book Wholesalers, Inc.

Radabaugh, Melinda Beth. First Time Series, 11 bks., Set. 2003. (First Time Ser.). (Illus.). (J). lib. bdg. 203.50 (978-1-4034-3871-3(4)) Heinemann Library.

—Going on an Airplane. 2003. (First Time Ser.). (Illus.). 24p. (J). pap. 5.50 (978-1-4034-3881-2(1)) Heinemann Library.

Rare B-17 Flying Fortress Document & Photo Collection. 2004. (YA). cd-rom 89.95 (978-0-9742781-4-8(9)) Rhode, Steve Inc.

Raymer, Daniel P. Dan Raymer's Simplified Aircraft Design for Homebuilders. 2002. (Illus.). 143p. pap. 49.95 (978-0-9722397-0-7(7)) Conceptual Research Corp.

Red Bird Press Staff. Flying Machines. 2004. (Mission Xtreme 3D Ser.). 18p. (J). pap. 5.95 (978-1-902626-63-5(X)) Red Bird Publishing GBR. *Dist:* Weatherhill, Inc.

—High Flyers. 2004. (Build Your Own Ser.). 20p. (J). pap. 5.95 (978-1-902626-69-7(9)) Red Bird Publishing GBR. *Dist:* Weatherhill, Inc.

Roberts, Cynthia. Airplanes. 2007. (Machines at Work Ser.). 24p. (J). 22.79 (978-1-59296-825-1(2)) Child's World, Inc.

Robinson Masters, Nancy. The Airplane, 80 vols. 2004. (Inventions That Shaped the World Ser.). (Illus.). 8p. (J). 30.50 (978-0-531-12360-7(X) , Watts, Franklin) Scholastic Library Publishing.

Robinson Masters, Nancy. Airplanes. 2008. (J). lib. bdg. 25.26 (***978-1-60279-119-0(8)***) Cherry Lake Publishing.

Rogers, Hal. Airplanes. 2001. (Machines at Work Ser.). (Illus.). 24p. (J). (ps-3). 21.36 (978-1-56766-962-6(X)) Child's World, Inc.

Sandler, Martin W. Flying over the USA: Airplanes in American Life. 2006. (Illus.). 61p. (J). (gr. 4-8). reprint ed. 20.00 (978-1-4223-5623-4(X)) DIANE Publishing Co.

Santella, Andrew. Air Force One. 2003. (Illus.). 48p. (gr. 4 up). (J). pap. 8.95 (978-0-7613-1926-9(3)); (Women at War Ser.: up). lib. bdg. 24.90 (978-0-7613-2617-5(0)) Lerner Publishing Group. (Millbrook Pr.).

—Air Force One. 2003. (gr. 5-8). lib. bdg. 17.60 (978-0-613-58954-3(8)) Tandem Library Bks.

Saunders-Smith, Gail. Airplanes. 1998. (J). pap. 13.25 (978-0-516-21229-6(X) , Children's Pr.) Scholastic Library Publishing.

Schaefer, Lola M. Aircraft. 2003. (Wheels, Wings, & Water Ser.). (Illus.). 24p. (J). (ps-1). lib. bdg. 18.50 (978-1-4034-0884-6(X)); pap. (978-1-4034-3616-0(9)) Heinemann Library.

—Airplanes. 2000. (Transportation Library). (Illus.). 24p. (J). (gr. 1-2). lib. bdg. 18.60 (978-0-7368-0358-8(0) , Bridgestone Bks.) Capstone Pr., Inc.

—Maquinas de Vuelo. 2003. (Ruedas, Alas y Agua Ser.). (SPA.). 24p. (J). pap. 5.25 (978-1-4034-3528-6(6)) Heinemann Library.

—Maquinas de Vuelo. 2003. (Ruedas, Alas y Agua Ser.). (SPA & ENG., Illus.). 24p. (J). (ps-1). lib. bdg. 18.50 (978-1-4034-0921-8(8)) Heinemann Library.

Schmidt, Norman. Best Ever Paper Airplanes. 2007. (Illus.). 96p. (J). pap. 7.95 (978-1-895569-83-4(4)) Tamos Bks., Inc. CAN. *Dist:* Sterling Publishing Co., Inc.

Scholastic, Inc. Staff. Micro Planes. 2002. (Fun Pack Ser.). (Illus.). 16p. (J). pap. 5.99 (978-0-439-35818-7(3) , Tangerine Pr.) Scholastic, Inc.

Scholastic, Inc. Staff. Mr. Magorium's Paper Airplane Designs. 2007. (Mr. Magorium's Wonder Emporium Ser.). 48p. (J). pap. 4.99 (***978-0-439-91251-8(2)***) Scholastic, Inc.

Simon, Seymour. Aeronaves Asombrosos. 2006. 32p. (J). pap. 3.95 (978-0-8118-5472-6(8)) Chronicle Bks. LLC.

—Amazing Aircraft, Vol. 2. 2002. (SeeMore Readers Ser.). (Illus.). 32p. (J). (gr. 1-3). pap. 3.95 (978-1-58717-180-2(5) , SeaStar Bks.) Chronicle Bks. LLC.

—SeeMore Aeronaves Asombrosos. 2006. (SPA.). 32p. (J). 14.50 (978-0-8118-5471-9(X)) Chronicle Bks. LLC.

Sinclair, Julie. The Airplane. 2003. (Fact Finders Ser.). (Illus.). 32p. (J). lib. bdg. 22.60 (978-0-7368-2213-8(5)) Capstone Pr., Inc.

Sloan, Peter. Flying Machines. 1999. (gr. k-3). lib. bdg. 11.80 (978-0-613-30412-2(8)) Tandem Library Bks.

—Making a Plane. 1999. (gr. k-3). lib. bdg. 11.80 (978-0-613-30584-6(1)) Tandem Library Bks.

Steers, Billy. The Little Book of Planes. Steers, Billy, illus. 1999. (Jellybean Bks.). (Illus.). 24p. (J). (ps-k). lib. bdg. 7.99 (978-0-375-90219-2(8) , Random Hse. Bks. for Young Readers) Random Hse. Children's Bks.

Stickland, Paul. Planes. 2004. (By Air, Sea, & Land Ser.). (Illus.). 24p. (J). pap. 3.99 (978-0-7696-3375-6(7) , Waterbird Bks.) School Specialty Publishing.

—Planes. Stickland, Paul, illus. 1998. (On the Move Ser.). (Illus.). 16p. (J). (ps up). lib. bdg. 19.93 (978-0-8368-2153-6(X)) Stevens, Gareth Inc.

Stille, Darlene R. Airplanes. 2001. (Transportation Ser.). (Illus.). 32p. (J). (gr. 1 up). lib. bdg. 19.93 (978-0-7565-0146-4(6)) Compass Point Bks.

Stillinger, Doug. Aviones de Papel. 2005. (SPA., Illus.). 56p. (J). spiral bd. 19.95 (978-987-1078-44-8(7)) Klutz Latino MEX. *Dist:* Independent Pubs. Group.

Strickland, Paul. On the Move: Boats; Cars; Planes; Trains, 4 bks. Strickland, Paul, illus. 2002. (Illus.). (J). (ps up). pap. (978-0-8368-3333-1(3) , Weekly Reader Early Learning Library) Stevens, Gareth Inc.

Suen, Anastasia. Air Show. Mariniello, Cecco, illus. 2006. 30p. (J). (gr. k-4). reprint ed. 16.00 (978-1-4223-5669-2(8)) DIANE Publishing Co.

Sweetman, Bill. Stealth Bombers: The B-2 Spirits. 2001. (War Planes Ser.). (Illus.). 32p. (J). (gr. 3-4). lib. bdg. 21.26 (978-0-7368-0791-3(8) , Capstone High-Interest Bks.) Capstone Pr., Inc.

Tallarico, Tony. A-Maze-Ing Airplanes. 2002. (Illus.). 96p. (J). (978-1-58865-081-8(2)) Kidsbooks, Inc.

Tatge, Cathy. Airplanes. 2007. (J). (978-1-58341-525-2(4) , Creative Education) Creative Co., The.

Tiner, John Hudson. Airplanes. (Illus.). 32p. 2004. pap. 8.95 (978-0-89812-387-6(9) , Creative Paperbacks); 2003. (J). lib. bdg. 18.95 (978-1-58341-258-9(1) , Creative Education) Creative Co., The.

Top That Publishing Staff, ed. Aircraft. 2005. (Illus.). 24p. (978-1-84510-537-2(0)) Top That! Publishing PLC.

—Ultimate Micro Fliers. 2005. 48p. (978-1-84510-659-1(8)) Top That! Publishing PLC.

Tuxworth, Nicola & Lorenz Editors. Flying Machines. 2002. (Let's Look at Board Bks.). (Illus.). 20p. (ps-3). 5.95 (978-0-7548-1031-5(3) , Lorenz Bks.) Anness Publishing GBR. *Dist:* National Bk. Network.

Walker, Pam. Plane Rides. 2000. (Welcome Bks.). (Illus.). 24p. (J). (ps-2). pap. 4.95 (978-0-516-23027-6(1)); 18.00 (978-0-516-23102-0(2)) Scholastic Library Publishing. (Children's Pr.).

Walker, Sally M. & Feldmann, Roseann. Planos Inclinados. 2005. (Libros de Física para Madrugadores (Early Bird Physics) Ser.). (SPA & ENG., Illus.). 48p. (J). (gr. 3-7). lib. bdg. 25.26 (978-0-8225-2970-5(X) , Ediciones Lerner) Lerner Publishing Group.

Wallace, Lane E. Wild Blue Wonders: Exploring the Magic of Flight. 2001. (Illus.). 164p. (J). per. 19.95 (978-1-58932-002-4(6)) EAA (Experimental Aircraft Assn.).

Wars, Beck. Big Wings. Crowson, Andrew, illus. 2005. 8p. (J). (gr. 4-8). reprint ed. 13.00 (978-0-7567-9254-1(1)) DIANE Publishing Co.

Weitzman, David. Jenny: The Airplane That Taught America to Fly. Weitzman, David, illus. 2006. (Illus.). 27p. (J). (gr. k-4). reprint ed. 19.00 (978-1-4223-5582-4(9)) DIANE Publishing Co.

Weitzman, David L. Jenny: The Airplane That Taught America to Fly. Weitzman, David L., illus. rev. ed. 2002. (Illus.). 40p. (J). (gr. 1-4). 17.95 (978-0-7613-1547-6(0)) Roaring Brook Pr.

West, David. Plane. 2006. (Why Things Don't Work Ser.). (Illus.). 32p. (J). (gr. 4-6). lib. bdg. 29.29 (978-1-4109-2556-5(0)) Raintree.

Whitecap Books Staff. Planes. 2000. (Investigate Ser.). (Illus.). 64p. (J). (gr. 1-7). pap. 3.95 (978-1-55285-068-8(4)) Whitecap Bks., Ltd. CAN. *Dist:* Firefly Bks., Ltd.

Williams, Zachary. How Do Airplanes Fly? 2002. (Reading Room Collection). (Illus.). 24p. (J). pap. (978-0-8239-8160-1(6)); lib. bdg. 18.75 (978-0-8239-3723-3(2)) Rosen Publishing Group, Inc., The.

Willis, Shirley. Dime por Que Tienen Alas los Aviones. (Los Estupendos Whiz Kids, Spanish Edition Ser.). (SPA., Illus.). 32p. (J). 2000. (gr. 1-3). pap. 5.95 (978-0-531-15998-9(1) , OD30032); 1999. (gr. 2-4). 20.00 (978-0-531-11848-1(7) , OD30033) Scholastic Library Publishing. (Watts, Franklin).

—Dime por Que Tienen Alas los Aviones. 2000. (Estupendos Ser.). (J). 12.75 (978-0-606-20151-3(3)) Tandem Library Bks.

Winchester, Jim. Civil Aircraft. 2006. (Aircraft of the World Ser.). (Illus.). 32p. (J). lib. bdg. (978-0-8368-6903-3(6)) Stevens, Gareth Inc.

Woodward, Kay & Woodward, Andrew. Aircraft. 2005. (Technology All Around Us Ser.). (Illus.). 32p. (J). (gr. 4-7). lib. bdg. 27.10 (978-1-58340-724-0(3)) Smart Apple Media.

AIRPLANES—ACCIDENTS

see Aircraft Accidents

AIRPLANES—FICTION

Adair, Amy. Jay Jay's Special Delivery. 2003. (Illus.). (J). 15.98 (978-0-7853-8625-4(4)) Publications International, Ltd.

Afetian, "Uncle Ted". The Adventures of Midas & the Little Red Airplane. 2005. (Illus.). 32p. (J). 16.95i (978-0-9752749-0-3(2)) Snyder-Winston Pr.

Appleton, Victor. Tom Swift & His Airship. 2004. (Tom Swift Original Ser.: No. 3). 216p. (J). (ps-3). 17.95 (978-1-55709-177-2(3)) Applewood Bks.

—Tom Swift & His Airship. 2000. (Tom Swift Original Ser.: Vol. No. 3). 118p. (gr. 3-7). 19.95 (978-1-57646-359-8(1)); 118p. (gr. 3-7). pap. 7.95 (978-1-57646-203-4(X)); 186p. pap. 12.99 (978-1-57646-360-4(5)) Quiet Vision Publishing.

Bachand, Stephen. Patch in I Want to Be a Pilot. Bachand, Stephen, illus. 1999. (Booktime Buddies Ser.). (Illus.). (J). (ps-2). 5.00 (978-1-928972-00-6(4)) Critter Pubns.

Baggette, Susan K. Jonathan Goes to the Airport. Moriarty, William J., photos by. 1998. (Jonathan Adventures Ser.). (Illus.). 16p. (J). (ps-k). bds. 5.95 (978-0-9660172-6-7(9)) Brookfield Reader, Inc., The.

Baker, Kane. Bobby the Bush Pilot. Swain, Alison Campbell, illus. 2003. (J). pap. (978-1-932046-02-1(X)) Pastime Pr.

Bardwell, Harrison. Roberta's Flying Courage. 2003. 248p. (J). pap. 13.95 (978-1-55753-335-7(0)) Purdue Univ. Pr.

Bartholomew, Carl R. Plane Phenomenon: The Pawnshop Mysteries. 2006. (Illus.). 44p. (J). pap. 9.95 (978-1-933255-24-8(2)) DNA Pr.

Barton, Byron. Planes Lap Edition. Barton, Byron, illus. 2006. 34p. (J). 12.99 (978-0-06-115015-9(0) , Harper Festival) HarperCollins Pubs.

Beach, Charles Amory. Air Service Boys over the Atlantic. rev. ed. 2006. 180p. 26.95 (978-1-4218-1718-7(7)); pap. 11.95 (978-1-4218-1818-4(3)) 1st World Publishing, Inc. (1st World Library - Literary Society).

Bentley, Dawn. Shapes. Rivoli Group Staff, illus. 2000. (Jay Jay the Jet Plane's Peek-a-Boo Board Bks.). 12p. (J). (ps-k). bds. 6.95 (978-1-58117-101-3(3) , Intervisual/Piggy Toes) Dalmatian Pr.

Billy & Baxter at the Airport, 4 vols. 2005. (Illus.). 24p. (J). (ps-7). 8.95 (978-1-58087-100-6(3)) Stampley, C.D. Enterprises, Inc.

Blake, Jocelyn. Mama Is on an Airplane. Blake, Jocelyn, illus. ed. 2006. (Illus.). (J). per. 9.99 (***978-0-9790572-0-5(5)***) Kreativ Kaos.

Bond, Michael. Paddington Takes the Air. Fortnum, Peggy, illus. 2003. 144p. (J). (gr. 4-6). 15.00 (978-0-618-33141-3(7)) Houghton Mifflin Co. Trade & Reference Div.

Brisco, Dianna. The Day Marcus Flew. 2007. (J). per. 9.99 (***978-1-60247-024-8(3)***) Tate Publishing & Enterprises, L.L.C.

Bruna, Dick. Miffy Goes Flying. 1998. (Miffy Ser.). (Illus.). 28p. (J). (ps-k). pap. 4.95 (978-1-56836-221-2(8)) Kodansha America, Inc.

Catran, Ken. Dawn Hawk. 96p. pap. (978-0-7344-0468-8(9) , Lothian Bks.) Hachette Livre Australia.

Craine, E. J. Airplane Boys at Belize. 2003. 224p. (J). pap. 13.95 (978-1-55753-323-4(7)) Purdue Univ. Pr.

—Airplane Boys at Cap Rock. 2002. 248p. (J). pap. 13.95 (978-1-55753-317-3(2)) Purdue Univ. Pr.

—Airplane Boys at Platinum River. 2003. 200p. (J). pap. 13.95 (978-1-55753-320-3(2)) Purdue Univ. Pr.

—Airplane Boys Discover the Secrets of Cuzco. 2003. 246p. (J). pap. 13.95 (978-1-55753-318-0(0)) Purdue Univ. Pr.

—Airplane Boys Flying to Amy-Ran Fastness. 2003. 245p. (J). pap. 13.95 (978-1-55753-319-7(9)) Purdue Univ. Pr.

—Airplane Boys in the Black Woods. 2003. 209p. (J). pap. 13.95 (978-1-55753-322-7(9)) Purdue Univ. Pr.

—Airplane Boys on the Border Line. 2003. 246p. (J). pap. 13.95 (978-1-55753-316-6(4)) Purdue Univ. Pr.

—Airplane Boys with the Revolutionists in Bolivia. 2003. 201p. (J). pap. 13.95 (978-1-55753-321-0(0)) Purdue Univ. Pr.

Cunliffe, John. Postman Pat Makes an Aeroplane. (Illus.). 20p. (J). pap. (978-0-340-73716-3(6) , Hodder & Stoughton) Hodder General Publishing Division.

Cussler, Clive. The Adventures of Vin Fiz. Farnsworth, William, illus. 2006. 144p. (J). (gr. 3). 15.99 (978-0-399-24474-2(3) , Philomel) Penguin Group (USA) Inc.

Daval, Josie. The Wright Twist. 2006. (Illus.). 151p. (J). (978-1-933197-19-7(6)) Orange Frazer Pr.

de Saint-Exupery, Antoine. The Little Prince. l.t. ed. 2005. 100p. pap. 10.95 (978-0-7862-7539-7(1)) Thorndike Pr.

Duble, Kathleen Benner. Bravo Zulu, Samantha! 2007. 144p. (J). (gr. 4-7). 14.95 (***978-1-56145-401-3(X)*** , Peachtree Junior) Peachtree Pubs., Ltd.

Eastman, Peter Anthony. Fred & Ted Like to Fly. 2007. (Beginner Books(R) Ser.). (Illus.). 48p. (J). (gr. k-3). 8.99 (978-0-375-84064-7(8)); lib. bdg. 12.99 (978-0-375-94064-4(2)) Random Hse. Children's Bks. (Random Hse. Bks. for Young Readers).

Fardell, John. Flight of the Silver Turtle. 2006. 212p. (J). (gr. 3). 15.99 (978-0-399-24382-0(8) , Putnam Juvenile) Penguin Group (USA) Inc.

Feldman, Thea. Things That Go. 2006. 3p. 5.99 (978-1-932915-31-0(1)) Sandvik Publishing.

Fienberg, Anna. Minton Goes Flying. Gamble, Kim, illus. 2001. (Minton Ser.). 32p. (J). (ps-1). mass mkt. 6.95 (978-1-86448-593-6(0)) Allen & Unwin AUS. *Dist:* Independent Pubs. Group.

Floca, Brian. Five Trucks. 2001. (978-0-606-22360-7(6)) Tandem Library Bks.

Gordon, David. The Ugly Truckling. Gordon, David, illus. 2004. (Illus.). 32p. (J). (ps-2). lib. bdg. 16.89 (978-0-06-054601-4(8) , Geringer, Laura Book) HarperCollins Pubs.

Gordon, David & Downs, Mike. Noisy Airplane Ride. 2005. (Illus.). 32p. (J). 6.95 (978-1-58246-157-1(0) , Tricycle Pr.) Ten Speed Pr.

Gutman, Anne & Hallensleben, Georg. Lisa's Airplane Trip. Schulman, Janet, ed. 2001. (Illus.). 32p. (J). (ps-1). 9.95 (978-0-375-81114-2(1) , Knopf Bks. for Young Readers) Random Hse. Children's Bks.

Guy, Ginger Foglesong. My Grandma/Mi Abuelita. Escriva, Vivi, illus. 2007. Tr. of Mi Abuela. (ENG & SPA.). 24p. (J). (ps-2). 15.99 (978-0-06-079098-1(9)); lib. bdg. 16.89 (978-0-06-079099-8(7)) HarperCollins Pubs. (Harper Festival).

Hall, Henry R. The Little Airplane. l.t. ed. 2002. (Illus.). 36p. per. 9.95 (978-0-9723309-9-2(2)) Thornton Publishing.

Harcourt School Publishers Staff. Coast to Coast Level D: Library Edition. 2001. (Collections Ser.). (Illus.). pap. 13.20 (978-0-15-314434-9(3)) Harcourt Schl. Pubs.

Harman, Chuck. Lost City. 2000. (Adventures of Artie the Airplane & His Friends Ser.). (Illus.). 40p. (J). (ps-6). pap. 6.95 (978-1-891736-10-0(8)) Studio Five/Fourteen.

Henry, Heather French. Flying Away. Henry, Heather French, illus. 2004. (Claire's Everyday Adventures Ser.). (Illus.). 32p. (gr. k-4). (J). pap. 8.95 (978-0-9706341-8-4(8) , 1231610); 15.95 (978-0-9706341-4-6(5) , 1231610) Cubbie Blue Publishing.

—Volando. 2007. (Claire's Everyday Adventures Ser Ser.). (SPA., Illus.). 32p. (gr. k-4). pap. 9.95 (978-1-932824-04-9(9)) Cubbie Blue Publishing.

Henry, Panya A. Francis' Fear of Flying. 2006. (ENG.). 40p. per. 24.95 (***978-1-4259-3162-9(6)***) AuthorHouse.

Horvath, Polly. The Corps of the Bare-Boned Plane. 2007. 272p. (J). (gr. 7 up). 17.00 (***978-0-374-31553-5(1)*** , Farrar, Straus & Giroux (BYR)) Farrar, Straus & Giroux.

Hubbell, Patricia. Airplanes: Soaring! Diving! Turning! Halsey, Megan & Addy, Sean, illus. 2008. (J). (***978-0-7614-5388-8(1)***) Cavendish, Marshall Corp.

Hughes, Walker. Sea to Shining Sea with Sticker. 2003. (gr. 3-6). lib. bdg. 11.80 (978-0-613-72162-2(4)) Tandem Library Bks.

I Miss You a Whole Lot Story Book. 2004. (Jay Jay the Jet Plane Ser.). (Illus.). 24p. (J). (ps-2). 7.99 (978-0-8499-7949-1(8)) Nelson, Thomas Inc.

Ichikawa, Satomi. Come Fly with Me. Ichikawa, Satomi, illus. 2008. 40p. (J). (ps). 15.99 (***978-0-399-24679-1(7)*** , Philomel) Penguin Group (USA) Inc.

Ingram, W. J. Evelyn. Saint Crispin & Other Quaint Conceits. 2005. pap. 24.95 (978-1-4179-6255-6(0)) Kessinger Publishing, LLC.

James, Mark S. Christopher's Little Airplane Coloring & Activity Fun Book. Smelcer, Harold, illus. 2001. 48p. (J). 3.95 (978-0-9676960-1-0(1)) Chelonian Pr, Inc.

Johns, W. E. Biggles & the Missing Millionaire. 2001. iii, 148p. pap. (978-0-7551-0713-1(6)) House of Stratus, Inc.

—Biggles & the Pirate Treasure & Other Stories. 2001. 167p. pap. (978-0-7551-0714-8(4)) House of Stratus, Inc.

—Biggles Breaks the Silence. 2001. 156p. pap. (978-0-7551-0716-2(0)) House of Stratus, Inc.

—Biggles Flies to Work. 2001. 141p. pap. (978-0-7551-0717-9(9)) House of Stratus, Inc.

—Biggles Gets His Men. 2001. 166p. pap. (978-0-7551-0820-6(5)) House of Stratus, Inc.

—Biggles of the Interpol. 2000. 193p. pap. (978-0-7551-0720-9(9)) House of Stratus, Inc.

—Biggles of the Special Air Police. 2001. 184p. pap. (978-0-7551-0721-6(7)) House of Stratus, Inc.

—Biggles Sorts It Out. 2001. ii, 158p. pap. (978-0-7551-0727-8(6)) House of Stratus, Inc.

—Biggles Takes a Holiday. 2001. (Illus.). 204p. pap. (978-0-7551-0730-8(6)) House of Stratus, Inc.

Jopling, John Perry & Jopling, Hazel Joan. John, the Airport Kid: A Magical Adventure. 2007. (YA). per. (***978-0-9778070-4-8(5)***) SilverBear.

Kalep, Elvy. Air Babies. 2003. (Illus.). 24p. (ps-k). pap. 9.95 (978-1-55709-391-2(1)) Applewood Bks.

Kalz, Jill. Flying with Oliver. Mahan, Ben, illus. 2006. (Read-It! Readers Ser.). 24p. (J). (ps-3). 18.60 (978-1-4048-1583-4(X)) Picture Window Bks.

Kinerk, Robert. Clorinda Takes Flight. Kellogg, Steven, illus. 2007. 40p. (J). (ps-3). 16.99 (978-0-689-86864-1(2) , Simon & Schuster/Paula Wiseman Bks.) Simon & Schuster Children's Publishing.

LeapFrog Staff & Partnership Staff, compiled by. Jay Jay the Jet Plane: U.K. 2003. (J). spiral bd. 8.99 (978-1-58605-072-6(9)) LeapFrog Enterprises, Inc.

Lewis, H. B. Winnie Mae. 2001. (Illus.). 40p. (J). (gr. 3). pap. 8.95 (978-0-89812-013-4(6) , Creative Paperbacks) Creative Co., The.

Lewis, Sinclair & Graham, Tom. Hike & the Aeroplane. Pastore, Stephen, ed. Price, Richard, illus. unabr. ed. 1999. 250p. (YA). (gr. 5 up). 45.00 (978-1-893173-06-4(2)) YaleBooks.

McCarty, Peter. Moon Plane. 2006. (Illus.). 40p. (J). 16.95 (978-0-8050-7943-2(2)) Holt, Henry & Co.

Mikaelsen, Ben. Sparrow Hawk Red. 1999. 192p. pap. 5.99 (978-0-7868-1002-4(5)) Hyperion Pr.

Mills, Charles. Wings over Oshkosh. 2005. (Honors Club Story Ser.: Vol. 5). 127p. (J). (978-0-8163-2089-9(6)) Pacific Pr. Publishing Assn.

Mitzo Thompson, Kim. Things That Go, 2 Packs. 2006. (Read & Sing along Board Books with CDs Ser.). 36p. (J). bds. 14.98 (978-0-7696-4595-7(X)) School Specialty Publishing.

Moyer, Bess. Gypsies of the Air. 2004. reprint ed. pap. 19.95 (978-1-4179-9112-9(7)) Kessinger Publishing, LLC.

Newcomb, Ambrose. Flying the Coast Skyways or Jack Ralston. 2005. pap. 26.95 (978-1-4179-8975-1(0)) Kessinger Publishing, LLC.

Noonan, Julia. Going to the Corner. Noonan, Julia, illus. 2000. (Puppy & Me Ser.). (Illus.). 20p. (J). (ps-1). pap. 6.99 (978-0-439-17323-0(X)) Scholastic, Inc.

North, Bill. The Disappearing Airplane. 2001. 108p. pap. 9.95 (978-0-595-18789-8(7) , Writers Club Pr.) iUniverse, Inc.

Once upon a Time- Fantasy Flight. 2005. (J). bds. (978-1-4194-0095-7(9)) Paradise Pr., Inc.

Ondra, Winona Hollar. Yellow Bird. Kennedy, John H., illus. unabr. ed. 2002. 52p. (Orig.). pap. 10.00 (978-0-9655858-1-1(6)) Boyden Publishing.

Paulson, Gary. Hatchet. unabr. ed. 2004. 195p. (J). (gr. 5-9). pap. 36.00 incl. audio (978-0-8072-8319-6(3) , YA161SP, Listening Library) Random Hse. Audio Publishing Group.

Porchlight Entertainment, creator. Our Favorite Places: Peg Puzzle Book. 2003. (Jay Jay the Jet Plane Ser.). 8p. (J). pap. 10.99 (978-1-4003-0330-4(3)) Nelson, Thomas Inc.

Reid, Charles. Chasing the Arrow: Charles Reid. 2006. 144p. (J). pap., tchr. ed. 6.95 (978-0-88878-439-1(2) , Sandcastle Bks.) Dundurn Group, The CAN. *Dist:* Univ. of Toronto Pr.

Rigsby, Annelle & Raffa, Edwina. Race to Kitty Hawk. 2003. (Adventures in America Ser.). (Illus.). 84p. (J). 14.95 (978-1-893110-33-5(8)) Silver Moon Pr.

Rivoli Group Staff, illus. Hide & Seek Opposites. 2000. (Jay Jay the Jet Plane's Peek-a-Boo Board Bks.). 12p. (J). (ps-k). bds. 6.95 (978-1-58117-100-6(5) , Intervisual/Piggy Toes) Dalmatian Pr.

—Number Fun in Tarrytown. 2000. (Jay Jay the Jet Plane's Ready, Set, Let's Learn! Bks.). 10p. (J). (ps-k). 6.95 (978-1-58117-099-3(8) , Intervisual/Piggy Toes) Dalmatian Pr.

—Tarrytown's Rainbow of Colors. 2000. (Jay Jay the Jet Plane's Ready, Set, Let's Learn! Bks.). 10p. (J). (ps-k). 6.95 (978-1-58117-098-6(X) , Intervisual/Piggy Toes) Dalmatian Pr.

Rockwood, Roy. Through the Air to the North Pole or the. 2006. 33.99 (***978-1-4280-2972-9(9)***) IndyPublish.com.

Samson, Don. Teenage Aviation Stories. 2005. reprint ed. pap. 26.95 (978-1-4191-1624-7(X)) Kessinger Publishing, LLC.

Scarry, Richard & Scarry, Huck. Richard Scarry's A Day at the Airport. 2001. (Pictureback Ser.). (Illus.). 24p. (J). (gr. k-3). pap. 3.99 (978-0-375-81202-6(4) , Random Hse. Bks. for Young Readers) Random Hse. Children's Bks.

Seidler, Tor. The Silent Spillbills. 1998. 224p. (J). (gr. 3-7). 14.95 (978-0-06-205180-6(6)); 14.89 (978-0-06-205181-3(4)) HarperCollins Pubs.

Sherwood, Ben. The Man Who Ate The 747. 2002. 258p. (gr. 7-12). per. 14.75 (978-0-613-49504-2(7)) Tandem Library Bks.

Simon, Charnan. To Grandmother's House We Go. Gallagher-Cole, Mernie, illus. 2007. (Rookie Reader Ser.). 31p. (J). pap. (***978-0-531-12491-8(6)***) Children's Pr., Ltd.

Singh-Kaw, Praveena. Go Back from Where You Came. 2004. (Illus.). 16p. (J). pap. 14.95 (978-1-932373-78-3(0)) Cedar Hill Publishing.

Snell, Roy F. Wings for Victory. 2005. pap. 26.95 (978-1-4191-6999-1(8)) Kessinger Publishing, LLC.

Snuffy Goes to School Story Book. 2004. (Jay Jay the Jet Plane Ser.). (Illus.). 24p. (J). (ps-2). 7.99 (978-0-8499-7760-2(6)) Nelson, Thomas Inc.

Solo Flyer, 6 Packs. 16p. (gr. 2 up). 35.00 (978-0-7635-9375-9(3)) Rigby Education.

Spanyol, Jessica. Come on, Bugs! Let's Have Some Fun! Spanyol, Jessica, illus. 2006. (Illus.). 32p. (J). (gr. k-k). 15.99 (978-0-7636-3055-3(1)) Candlewick Pr.

Sykes, Harold S. The Beacon of Airport Seven. 2004. reprint ed. pap. 15.95 (978-1-4191-5375-4(7)); pap. 1.99 (978-1-4192-5375-1(1)) Kessinger Publishing, LLC.

Uncle Ted. Midas & the Little Red Airplane. Young, Eddie, illus. 2000. 28p. (J). per. 15.95 (978-0-9672540-0-5(0)) Midas Entertainment, Inc.

Van Straaten, Harmen. TIM & the FLYING MACHINE. 2008. 28p. 12.95 (***978-1-60136-003-8(7)***) Mars Media Pubs.

Walker, Peter. The Magic Airplane. 2006. (ENG.). 160p. per. 12.95 (***978-1-59526-416-9(7)***) Media Creations, Inc.

White, Howard. The Airplane Ride. Guzek, Greta, illus. unabr. ed. 2006. 32p. (J). bds. 14.95 (***978-0-88971-224-9(7)***) Harbour Publishing Co., Ltd. CAN. *Dist:* Graphic Arts Ctr. Publishing Co.

Wings. 2001. stu. ed., wbk. ed. (978-1-56137-787-9(2)) Novel Units, Inc.

Woodbury, Mary. Flight of the Tiger Moth. 2007. 224p. (YA). (gr. 7 up). 9.95 (***978-1-55050-364-7(2)***) Coteau Bks. CAN. *Dist:* Fitzhenry & Whiteside, Ltd.

Woodson, Frank. Last Flight of Zero Zero Seven. 2000. (gr. 5-8). lib. bdg. 11.80 (978-0-613-51217-6(0)) Tandem Library Bks.

AIRPLANES—FLIGHT TESTING

see Airplanes—Testing

AIRPLANES, JET PROPELLED

see Jet Planes

AIRPLANES, MILITARY

see also types of military airplanes, e.g. Bombers

Aircraft, 14 bks., Set. Incl. Air Force Aircraft. Holden, Henry M. (J). 2001. lib. bdg. 23.93 (978-0-7660-1714-6(1)); Air Show Pilots & Airplanes. Gaffney, Timothy R. (YA). 2001. lib. bdg. 23.93 (978-0-7660-1570-8(X)); Amazing Agricultural Aircraft. Gaffney, Timothy R. (J). 2001. lib. bdg. 23.93 (978-0-7660-1608-8(0)); Black Hawk Helicopter. Holden, Henry M. (J). 2002. lib. bdg. 23.93 (978-0-7660-1568-5(8)); Hurricane Hunters. Gaffney, Timothy R. (YA). 2001. lib. bdg. 23.93 (978-0-7660-1569-2(6)); Stealth Fighters & Bombers. Berliner, Don. (YA). 2001. lib. bdg. 23.93 (978-0-7660-1567-8(X)); 48p. (gr. 4-10). (Illus.). Set lib. bdg. 227.40 (978-0-7660-1799-3(0)) Enslow Pubs., Inc.

Anderson, Jameson. Fighter Pilot. 2006. (Illus.). 32p. (J). pap. (978-1-4109-2501-5(3)) Steck-Vaughn.

Baysura, Kelly. Military Planes. 2001. (Flying Machines Ser.). (Illus.). 24p. (J). (gr. 1-4). lib. bdg. 20.64 (978-1-58952-006-6(8)) Rourke Publishing, LLC.

Berliner, Don. Stealth Fighters & Bombers. 2001. (Aircraft Ser.). (Illus.). 48p. (YA). (gr. 4-10). lib. bdg. 23.93 (978-0-7660-1567-8(X)) Enslow Pubs., Inc.

Bledsoe, Glen & Bledsoe, Karen. The World's Fastest Helicopters. 2002. (Built for Speed Ser.). (Illus.). 48p. (J). (gr. 3-4). lib. bdg. 21.26 (978-0-7368-1059-3(5) , Capstone High-Interest Bks.) Capstone Pr., Inc.

Built for Speed: World's Fastest Boats; Cars; Helicopters; Military Airplanes; Superbikes; Trains; Trucks; Wildest Roller Coasters, 8 bks. (Illus.). (J). (gr. 3-4). lib. bdg. 170.08 (978-0-7368-1081-4(1) , Capstone High-Interest Bks.) Capstone Pr., Inc.

Burgan, Michael. The World's Fastest Military Airplanes. 2000. (Built for Speed Ser.). (Illus.). 48p. (J). (gr. 3-4). lib. bdg. 21.26 (978-0-7368-0568-1(0) , Capstone High-Interest Bks.) Capstone Pr., Inc.

Chant, Christopher. Military Aircraft. 1999. (World's Greatest Aircraft Ser.). (Illus.). 62p. (J). (gr. 5 up). 24.15 (978-0-7910-5420-8(9) , Chelsea Hse.) Facts On File, Inc.

—Specialized Aircraft. 1999. (World's Greatest Aircraft Ser.). (Illus.). 64p. (J). (gr. 5 up). 21.95 (978-0-7910-5422-2(5) , Chelsea Hse.) Facts On File, Inc.

Cornish, Geoff. Battleground Support. 2004. (Military Hardware in Action Ser.). (Illus.). 48p. (J). (gr. 4-9). lib. bdg. 25.26 (978-0-8225-4708-2(2)) Lerner Publishing Group.

Cross-Sections. 2005. (Illus.). (J). (gr. 3-4). lib. bdg. 135.60 (978-0-7368-5256-2(5)) Capstone Pr., Inc.

Dartford, Mark. Bombers. 2004. (Military Hardware in Action Ser.). (Illus.). 48p. (J). (gr. 4-9). lib. bdg. 25.26 (978-0-8225-4705-1(8)) Lerner Publishing Group.

—Fighter Planes. 2004. (Military Hardware in Action Ser.). (Illus.). 48p. (J). (gr. 4-9). lib. bdg. 25.26 (978-0-8225-4706-8(6)) Lerner Publishing Group.

David, Jack. F-16 Fighting Falcons. 2007. (Illus.). 24p. (J). lib. bdg. 19.95 (978-1-60014-104-1(8)) Bellwether Media.

—Predator Drones. 2007. (Illus.). 24p. (J). lib. bdg. 19.95 (978-1-60014-105-8(6)) Bellwether Media.

—U-2 Planes. 2007. (Illus.). 24p. (J). lib. bdg. 19.95 (978-1-60014-106-5(4)) Bellwether Media.

—U-2 Planes. 2007. (Torque: Military Machines Ser.). (Illus.). 24p. (J). (gr. 3-7). lib. bdg. 20.00 (***978-0-531-18474-5(9)*** , Children's Pr.) Scholastic Library Publishing.

Dean, Francis H. The Curtiss X-Planes: Curtiss-Wright's VTOL Effort 1958-1965. 2001. (Schiffer Military History Ser.). (Illus.). 176p. (gr. 10-13). 49.95 (978-0-7643-1434-6(3)) Schiffer Publishing, Ltd.

Dowswell. Military Aircraft. 2004. (Mean Machines Ser.). (Illus.). (J). 64p. pap. 8.95 (978-1-4109-1196-4(9)); pap. 48.30 (978-1-4109-1201-5(9)) Harcourt Schl. Pubs.

Dowswell, Paul. Military Aircraft. 2004. (Mean Machines Ser.). (Illus.). 64p. (J). 32.79 (978-1-4109-1081-3(4)) Harcourt Schl. Pubs.

Fitzpatrick, Kevin J. Flying Gunship: The AC-130 Spectre. 2000. (High Interest Bks.). (Illus.). 48p. (YA). (gr. 7-12). pap. 6.95 (978-0-516-23539-4(7) , Children's Pr.) Scholastic Library Publishing.

—Flying Gunship: The AC-130 Spectre. 2000. (gr. 7-12). lib. bdg. 15.25 (978-0-613-58696-2(4)) Tandem Library Bks.

Graham, Ian. Attack Fighters. 2003. (Designed for Success Ser.). 32p. pap. 7.50 (978-1-4034-3356-5(9)); (Illus.). (J). 24.22 (978-1-4034-0769-6(X)) Heinemann Library.

—Military Planes: Model Maker. 2006. (Illus.). 48p. (J). (gr. 4-8). reprint ed. 13.00 (978-1-4223-5180-2(7)) DIANE Publishing Co.

—Warplanes. 2005. (World's Greatest Ser.). (Illus.). 32p. (J). (978-1-4109-2089-8(5)); pap. (978-1-4109-2096-6(8)) Steck-Vaughn.

Green, Michael & Green, Gladys. Air Superiority Fighters: F/A-22 Raptors. 2003. (War Planes Ser.). (Illus.). 32p. (J). lib. bdg. 22.60 (978-0-7368-2148-3(1) , Capstone High/Low Bks.) Capstone Pr., Inc.

—Carrier-Based Strike Fighters: The F-14 Tomcat. 2003. (War Planes Ser.). (Illus.). 32p. (J). lib. bdg. 22.60 (978-0-7368-2149-0(X) , Capstone High/Low Bks.) Capstone Pr., Inc.

—Remotely Piloted Aircraft: The Predators. 2004. (War Machines Ser.). (Illus.). 32p. (J). 16.95 (978-0-7368-2417-0(0)) Capstone Pr., Inc.

—Stealth Attack Fighters: The F-117A Nighthawks. 2003. (War Planes Ser.). (Illus.). 32p. (J). (gr. 3-4). lib. bdg. 21.26 (978-0-7368-1510-9(4) , Capstone High-Interest Bks.) Capstone Pr., Inc.

—Tactical Fighters: The F-15 Eagles. 2003. (War Planes Ser.). (Illus.). 32p. (J). (gr. 3-4). lib. bdg. 21.26 (978-0-7368-1511-6(2) , Capstone High-Interest Bks.) Capstone Pr., Inc.

Gunston, Bill. Aero-Mania! 2003. (Vehicle-Mania! Ser.). (Illus.). 32p. (J). (gr. 2 up). lib. bdg. 23.33 (978-0-8368-3780-3(0)) Stevens, Gareth Inc.

Hamilton, John. Aircraft of World War I. 2004. (World War I Ser.). (Illus.). 32p. (J). (gr. 4-8). lib. bdg. 24.21 (978-1-57765-912-9(0)) ABDO Publishing Co.

Hansen, Ole Steen. The A-10 Thunderbolt. 2006. (Illus.). 32p. (J). (978-0-7368-5251-7(4) , 1244013) Capstone Pr., Inc.

—Air Combat. 2003. (Story of Flight Ser.). (Illus.). 32p. (J). (gr. 4). lib. bdg. (978-0-7787-1206-0(0)) Crabtree Publishing Co.

—The EA-6B Prowler. 2006. (Illus.). 32p. (J). (978-0-7368-5252-4(2) , 1244014) Capstone Pr., Inc.

—Military Aircraft of World War One. 2003. (gr. 3-6). lib. bdg. 17.60 (978-0-613-59087-7(2)) Tandem Library Bks.

—Military Aircraft of World War Two. 2003. (gr. 3-6). lib. bdg. 17.60 (978-0-613-59088-4(0)) Tandem Library Bks.

—Military Aircraft of WWII. 2003. (Story of Flight Ser.). (Illus.). 32p. (J). (gr. 4). pap. (978-0-7787-1219-0(2)); lib. bdg. (978-0-7787-1203-9(6)) Crabtree Publishing Co.

—Modern Military Aircraft. 2003. (Story of Flight Ser.). (Illus.). 32p. (J). (gr. 4). pap. (978-0-7787-1220-6(6)); lib. bdg. (978-0-7787-1204-6(4)) Crabtree Publishing Co.

—Modern Military Aircraft. 2003. (gr. 3-6). lib. bdg. 17.60 (978-0-613-59090-7(2)) Tandem Library Bks.

Holden, Henry M. Navy Combat Aircraft & Pilots. 2002. (Aircraft Ser.). (Illus.). 48p. (J). (gr. 4-10). lib. bdg. 23.93 (978-0-7660-1716-0(8)) Enslow Pubs., Inc.

Holder, Bill. Lockheed SR-71 Blackbird. 2002. (Illus.). 80p. (gr. 10-13). pap. 19.95 (978-0-7643-1467-4(X)) Schiffer Publishing, Ltd.

Hopkins, Ellen H. U. S. Air Force Fighting Vehicles. 2003. (Heinemann Know It Ser.). (Illus.). 48p. (J). pap. 7.95 (978-1-4034-0447-3(X)) Heinemann Library.

Littlejohn, Randy. Air Warfare of the Future. 2005. (Library of Future Weaponry). (Illus.). 64p. (J). (978-1-4042-0523-9(3)) Rosen Publishing Group, Inc., The.

Loves, June. Military Aircraft. 2001. (Flight Ser.). (Illus.). 32p. (J). (gr. 5 up). 22.95 (978-0-7910-6559-4(6) , 010305, Chelsea Hse.) Facts On File, Inc.

Myhra, David. Gotha P 60. 2001. (Schiffer Military History Book Ser.). (Illus.). 120p. (gr. 10-13). pap. 19.95 (978-0-7643-1399-8(1)) Schiffer Publishing, Ltd.

—The Horten HO 9/HO 229: Retrospective. 2002. (Illus.). 224p. (gr. 10-13). 49.95 (978-0-7643-1666-1(4)) Schiffer Publishing, Ltd.

Osborn, Shane & McConnell, Malcolm. Born to Fly: The Heroic Story of Downed U. S. Navy Pilot Lt. Shane Osborn. 2003. 192p. (gr. 5). 5.99 (978-0-440-23796-9(3) , Yearling) Random Hse. Children's Bks.

—Born to Fly: The Heroic Story of Downed U. S. Navy Pilot Lt. Shane Osborn. l.t. ed. 2002. 403p. 29.45 (978-0-7862-4101-9(2)) Thomson Gale.

Santella, Andrew. Air Force One. 2003. (gr. 5-8). lib. bdg. 17.60 (978-0-613-58954-3(8)) Tandem Library Bks.

Sautter, Aaron. How to Draw Crazy Fighter Planes. Whigham, Rod, illus. 2008. (J). (***978-1-4296-1298-2(3)***) Capstone Pr., Inc.

Seidman, David. F/A-18C Hornet. 2005. (U. S. Warplanes Ser.). (Illus.). 48p. (YA). (gr. 5-8). lib. bdg. 26.50 (978-0-8239-3874-2(3)) Rosen Publishing Group, Inc., The.

Sweetman, Bill. High-Altitude Spy Planes: The U-2s. 2001. (War Planes Ser.). (Illus.). 32p. (J). (gr. 3-4). lib. bdg. 17.01 (978-0-7368-0790-6(X) , Capstone High-Interest Bks.) Capstone Pr., Inc.

—Radar Jammers: The EA-6B Prowlers. 2002. (War Planes Ser.). (Illus.). 32p. (J). (gr. 3-4). lib. bdg. 21.26 (978-0-7368-1069-2(2) , Capstone High-Interest Bks.) Capstone Pr., Inc.

—Strike Fighters: The F/A-18E/F Super Hornets. 2002. (War Planes Ser.). (Illus.). 32p. (J). (gr. 3-4). lib. bdg. 21.26 (978-0-7368-1070-8(6) , Capstone High-Interest Bks.) Capstone Pr., Inc.

—Supersonic Fighters: The F-16 Fighting Falcons. 2001. (War Planes Ser.). (Illus.). 32p. (J). (gr. 3-4). lib. bdg. 17.01 (978-0-7368-0792-0(6) , Capstone High-Interest Bks.) Capstone Pr., Inc.

US Warplanes. 2005. (Illus.). (gr. 5-8). lib. bdg. 159.00 (978-0-8239-4057-8(8)) Rosen Publishing Group, Inc., The.

War Planes. (Illus.). (J). (gr. 3-4). lib. bdg. 361.60 (978-0-7368-2334-0(4)) Capstone Pr., Inc.

The World's Fastest Military Airplanes, 6 vols. (gr. 4 up). 39.95 (978-0-7368-8945-2(0)) Red Brick Learning.

AIRPLANES—MODELS

Botermans, Jack & Bookman International B.V. Staff. Fantastic Paper Airplanes. 2004. (Illus.). 96p. (J). pap. 7.95 (978-1-4027-1149-7(2)) Sterling Publishing Co., Inc.

Collins, Francis. The Boys' Book of Model Aeroplanes: How to Build & Fly Them: with the Story of the Evolution of the Flying Machine. 2004. (Illus.). 308p. (YA). per. 16.95 (978-0-9758914-3-8(X)) Gustav's Library.

—The Second Boys' Book of Model Aeroplanes. 2004. (Illus.). 262p. per. 16.95 (978-0-9758914-4-5(8)) Gustav's Library.

Elliot, Adam, illus. Night Fighter: The Ultimate Book of Paper Airplanes. 2005. 80p. (J). pap. 14.95 (978-0-7641-3153-0(2)) Barron's Educational Series, Inc.

Kinmont, Ritchie. Every Kid Needs Things That Fly. Casey, Robert, photos by. 2005. (Illus.). 136p. (J). 14.95 (978-1-58685-509-3(3) , 1241179) Gibbs Smith, Publisher.

Rudy, Lisa Jo. Micro Spies: Spy Planes the Size of a Bird! 2007. (24/7: Science Behind the Scenes: Spy Files Ser.). 64p. (YA). (gr. 5 up). pap. 7.95 (***978-0-531-17535-4(9)***); (gr. 8-12). 26.00 (978-0-531-12083-5(X)) Scholastic Library Publishing. (Watts, Franklin).

Stunt Planes. 2004. (Fantastic Fliers Ser.). (Illus.). 48p. (J). pap. (978-1-84229-726-1(0)) Top That! Publishing PLC.

Supercool Fliers. 2004. (Fantastic Fliers Ser.). (Illus.). 48p. (J). pap. (978-1-84229-729-2(5)) Top That! Publishing PLC.

AIRPLANES, NAVAL

see Airplanes, Military

AIRPLANES—OPERATION

see Airplanes—Piloting

AIRPLANES—PILOTING

Anderson, Jameson. Fighter Pilot. 2006. (Illus.). 32p. (J). (978-1-4109-2496-4(3)); pap. (978-1-4109-2501-5(3)) Steck-Vaughn.

Bennett, Leonie. A Day with an Airplane Pilot. 2006. (I Love Reading Ser.). (Illus.). 24p. (J). lib. bdg. 19.96 (978-1-59716-147-3(0)) Bearport Publishing Co., Inc.

Clemson, Wendy, et al. Fly a Jumbo Jet. 2004. (Mathworks!). (Illus.). 31p. (J). lib. bdg. 24.67 (978-0-8368-4212-8(X)) Stevens, Gareth Inc.

Firefly, Books, ed. I Want to Be a Pilot. 1999. (gr. k-3). lib. bdg. 11.80 (978-0-613-25644-5(1)) Tandem Library Bks.

Godkin, Celia. Flying Lessons. 1999. (First Flight Ser.). 31p. (J). (978-1-55041-401-1(1)); pap. (978-1-55041-399-1(6)) Fitzhenry & Whiteside, Ltd.

Mattern, Joanne. Pilots. 2002. (Reading Power Ser.). (Illus.). 24p. (J). lib. bdg. 17.25 (978-0-8239-5979-2(1) , PowerKids Pr.) Rosen Publishing Group, Inc., The.

Minden, Cecilia & Minden-Zins, Mary. Pilots. 2006. (Neighborhood Helpers Ser.). (Illus.). 32p. (J). (gr. k-4). 22.79 (978-1-59296-567-0(9)) Child's World, Inc.

Parks, Peggy J. Fighter Pilot. 2005. (Exploring Careers Ser.). (Illus.). 48p. (J). (gr. 4-8). lib. bdg. 26.20 (978-0-7377-3079-1(X) , Kidhaven) Thomson Gale.

Pilot's Flight Operating Instructions for P-47B, P-47C, P-47D & P-47G Airplanes. 2005. (YA). cd-rom 29.95 (978-0-9742781-8-6(1)) Rhode, Steve Inc.

Rauf, Don & Vescia, Monique. Virtual Apprentice: Airline Pilot. 2007. (Virtual Apprentice Ser.). 64p. (J). (gr. 6-12). 29.95 (***978-0-8160-6755-8(4)*** , Ferguson Publishing Co.) Facts On File, Inc.

Savage, Jeff. Stunt Planes. 2003. (Wild Rides! Ser.). (Illus.). 32p. (J). (gr. 3-4). lib. bdg. 21.26 (978-0-7368-1519-2(8) , Capstone High-Interest Bks.) Capstone Pr., Inc.

Tetrick, Byron. Choosing a Career as a Pilot. 2005. (World of Work Ser.). (Illus.). 64p. (YA). (gr. 7-12). lib. bdg. 25.25 (978-0-8239-3571-0(X)) Rosen Publishing Group, Inc., The.

AIRPLANES—PILOTS

see Air Pilots

AIRPLANES—TESTING

Bitetto, Marco A. V., ed. Test Pilot Stories. braille ed. 2000. (J). (978-1-58578-073-0(1)) Institute of Cybernetics Research, Inc.

AIRPORTS

The Airport 2 packs: Individual Title. (Chiquilibros Ser.). (ps-1). 12.00 (978-0-7635-8537-2(8)) Rigby Education.

Baggette, Susan K. Jonathan Goes to the Airport. Moriarty, William J., photos by. 1998. (Jonathan Adventures Ser.). (Illus.). 16p. (J). (ps-k). bds. 5.95 (978-0-9660172-6-7(9)) Brookfield Reader, Inc., The.

Broyles, Matthew. U.S. Air Marshals. 2006. (Extreme Careers Ser.). (Illus.). 64p. (J). (gr. 5-8). lib. bdg. 26.50 (978-1-4042-0942-8(5)) Rosen Publishing Group, Inc., The.

Canizares, Susan. Where Does It Park? 1999. (J). pap. 2.50 (978-0-439-04583-4(5)) Scholastic, Inc.

Canizares, Susan & Weber, Arianne. Airport. 2000. (Illus.). (J). pap. (978-0-439-15374-4(3)) Scholastic, Inc.

Gish, Melissa. An Airport. 2003. 24p. (J). lib. bdg. 21.35 (978-1-58340-322-8(1)) Smart Apple Media.

Harcourt School Publishers Staff. Working at the Airport Below Level. 3rd ed. 2002. (Trophies Reading Program Ser.). (Illus.). pap. 5.10 (978-0-15-323066-0(5)) Harcourt Schl. Pubs.

Hill, Mary. Signs at the Airport. 2003. (Signs in My World Ser.). (Illus.). 24p. (J). 18.00 (978-0-516-24272-9(5)); pap. 4.95 (978-0-516-24364-1(0)) Scholastic Library Publishing. (Children's Pr.).

—Signs at the Airport. 2003. (gr. k-3). lib. bdg. 12.95 (978-0-613-59720-3(6)) Tandem Library Bks.

Malam, John. Airport: Explore the Building Room by Room. 1999. (Building Works Ser.). (Illus.). 32p. (YA). (gr. 3 up). lib. bdg. 16.95 (978-0-87226-586-8(2) , 65862B, Bedrick, Peter Bks.) School Specialty Publishing.

Mandel, Peter. Planes at the Airport. Miller, Edward, illus. 2004. 8p. (J). pap. 6.99 (978-0-439-56416-8(6)) Scholastic, Inc.

Mellentin, Kath. Let's Build an Airport. 1998. (J). (gr. k-4). (978-1-84089-026-6(6) , Zero to Ten, Limited) Evans Publishing Group.

Murphy, Patricia J. The Airport. 2004. (Visit To Ser.). (Illus.). 24p. (J). lib. bdg. 19.93 (978-0-7368-2578-8(9) , Pebble Bks.) Capstone Pr., Inc.

Radabaugh, Melinda Beth. First Time Series, 11 bks., Set. 2003. (First Time Ser.). (Illus.). (J). lib. bdg. 203.50 (978-1-4034-3871-3(4)) Heinemann Library.

—Going on an Airplane. 2003. (First Time Ser.). (Illus.). 24p. (J). pap. 5.50 (978-1-4034-3881-2(1)) Heinemann Library.

Ready for School: Individual Title Six-Packs. (gr. 1-2). 22.00 (978-0-7635-9188-5(2)) Rigby Education.

Sarver, Amy. Science at the Airport. 2004. (Illus.). 24p. (J). pap. (978-0-7922-4568-1(7)) National Geographic Society.

Schaefer, Lola M. Airport. 2000. (Who Works Here? Ser.). (Illus.). 32p. (J). (gr. 1-3). lib. bdg. 21.36 (978-1-57572-515-4(0)) Heinemann Library.

Smith, A. G. Little Airport Sticker Activity Book. 2001. (Illus.). 4p. (J). (ps-3). pap. 1.50 (978-0-486-41272-6(5)) Dover Pubns., Inc.

Souter, Janet. Air Marshal & Careers in Transportation Security. 2006. (Homeland Security & Counterterrorism Careers Ser.). (Illus.). 128p. (J). lib. bdg. 31.93 (978-0-7660-2647-6(7)) Enslow Pubs., Inc.

Waugh, John C. Kansai International Airport: Airport in the Sea. 2004. (High Interest Bks.). (Illus.). 48p. (J). (gr. 7-12). pap. 6.95 (978-0-516-25909-3(1) , Children's Pr.) Scholastic Library Publishing.

Wawrychuk, Carol & McSweeney, Cherie. Airport: Active Learning about Transportation. Chalk, Philip, illus. 1999. (Hands-On Units Ser.). 48p. (J). (ps-1). pap. 7.95 (978-1-57612-075-0(9) , MM2089) Monday Morning Bks., Inc.

Wright, John. The U. S. Transportation Security Administration. 2003. (Rescue & Prevention Ser.). (Illus.). 96p. (J). (gr. 7 up). lib. bdg. 22.95 (978-1-59084-412-0(2)) Mason Crest Pubs.

AIRSHIPS

see also Aeronautics; Balloons

Baysura, Kelly. Blimps. 2001. (Flying Machines Ser.). (Illus.). 24p. (J). (gr. 1-4). lib. bdg. 20.64 (978-1-58952-002-8(5)) Rourke Publishing, LLC.

Biello, David. Portaaviones: Por Dentro y por Fuera. 2002. (Tecnología Ser.). (SPA.). 48p. (YA). lib. bdg. 26.50 (978-0-8239-6153-5(2) , Buenas Letra) Rosen Publishing Group, Inc., The.

Bingham, Jane. The Hindenburg 1937: A Huge Airship Is Destroyed by Fire. 2006. (When Disaster Struck Ser.). (Illus.). 56p. (J). (978-1-4109-2281-6(2)) Steck-Vaughn.

Deady, Kathleen W. The Hindenburg: The Fiery Crash of a German Airship. 2002. (Disaster! Ser.). (Illus.). 32p. (J). (gr. 3-4). lib. bdg. 21.26 (978-0-7368-1321-1(7) , Capstone High-Interest Bks.) Capstone Pr., Inc.

DeAngelis, Gina. Hindenburg. 2000. (Great Disasters Ser.). (Illus.). 112p. (J). (gr. 5 up). 30.00 (978-0-7910-5272-3(9) , Chelsea Hse.) Facts On File, Inc.

Doeden, Matt. The Hindenburg Disaster. Erwin, Steve et al, illus. 2006. 32p. (J). 25.26 (978-0-7368-5481-8(9)) Capstone Pr., Inc.

Dokey, Cameron. Hindenburg, 1937. 1999. (Illus.). (J). 11.64 (978-0-606-18373-4(6)) Tandem Library Bks.

Donkin, Andrew. Zeppelin: The Age of the Airship. 2000. (Readers Ser.). (Illus.). 48p. (J). (gr. 2-3). pap. 3.99 (978-0-7894-5715-8(6)) Dorling Kindersley Publishing, Inc.

—Zeppelin: The Age of the Airship. 2000. (gr. k-3). lib. bdg. 11.80 (978-0-613-33282-8(2)) Tandem Library Bks.

Donkin, Andrew & Dorling Kindersley Publishing Staff. Zeppelin: The Age of the Airship. 2000. (Readers Ser.). (Illus.). 48p. (J). (ps-3). 14.99 (978-0-7894-5714-1(8)) Dorling Kindersley Publishing, Inc.

Dykema, Owen Wood & Dykema, Owen W., eds. Warbird History Part II: Fighter, Attack & Support Aircraft of WWII. 2003. 190p. per. 7.00 (978-0-9701538-1-4(3)) Dykema Publishing Co.

Feigenbaum, Aaron. The Hindenburg Disaster. 2007. (Code Red Ser.). (Illus.). 32p. (J). lib. bdg. 25.27 (978-1-59716-361-3(9)) Bearport Publishing Co., Inc.

Icanberry, Mark & Mount, Arthur. Picnic on a Cloud. 1999. (Look, Learn & Do Ser.). (Illus.). 48p. (J). (gr. 3-5). 14.95 (978-1-893327-00-9(0)) Look, Learn & Do Pubns.

Loves, June. Balloons, Kites, Airships & Gliders. 2001. (Flight Ser.). (Illus.). (J). (gr. 5 up). 27.00 (978-0-7910-6563-1(4) , 010302, Chelsea Hse.) Facts On File, Inc.

Nobleman, Marc Tyler. The Hindenburg. 2005. (We the People Ser.). (Illus.). 48p. (J). (gr. 4-6). 23.93 (978-0-7565-1266-8(2) , 1244100) Compass Point Bks.

O'Brien, Patrick. The Hindenburg. Date not set. (J). pap. 6.95 (978-0-8050-7264-8(0) , Holt, Henry & Co. Bks. For Young Readers) Holt, Henry & Co.

Sherrow, Victoria. The Hindenburg Disaster: Doomed Airship. 2002. (American Disasters Ser.). (Illus.). 48p. (J). (gr. 4-10). lib. bdg. 23.93 (978-0-7660-1554-8(8)) Enslow Pubs., Inc.

AKHENATEN, KING OF EGYPT, 1388-1358 B.C.

Jaime, Valencia Villa. Akhenaton. 2005. 132p. pap. (978-958-30-1981-4(X)) Panamericana Editorial.

ALABAMA

Ashby, Ruth. Rosa Parks: Freedom Rider. 2008. (Sterling Biographies Ser.). (Illus.). 128p. (J). pap. 5.95 (***978-1-4027-4865-3(5)***) Sterling Publishing Co., Inc.

Bailey, Tom. Sam Dale: Alabama Frontiersman. 2001. (Alabama Roots Biography Ser.). (Illus.). 107p. (J). (978-1-878561-82-4(0)) Seacoast Publishing, Inc.

Bower, Donette, et al. Alabama: Its History & Geography. 2000. (Illus.). ix, 470p. (J). (978-1-56733-975-8(1)) Clairmont Pr., Inc.

Brown, Dottie. Alabama. 2nd rev. ed. (Hello U. S. A. Ser.). (Illus.). 84p. (J). (gr. 3-6). 2002. lib. bdg. 25.26 (978-0-8225-4067-0(3)); 2003. pap. 6.95 (978-0-8225-4143-1(2)) Lerner Publishing Group.

—Alabama. 2001. (gr. 3-6). lib. bdg. 15.25 (978-0-613-81321-1(9)) Tandem Library Bks.

Brown, Vanessa. Alabama. (Bilingual Library of the United States of America). (J). 2006. lib. bdg. (978-1-4042-3142-9(0) , PowerKids Pr.); 2005. (ENG & SPA., Illus.). 32p. lib. bdg. 22.50 (978-1-4042-3065-1(3) , Buenas Letra) Rosen Publishing Group, Inc., The.

Broyles, Angela. Heart of Dixie Alabama History. 2002. (Illus.). 251p. spiral bd. 49.95 (978-0-9719946-4-5(1)) Bluewater Pubns.

Crane, Carol. Y Is for Yellowhammer: An Alabama Alphabet. Burn, Ted, illus. 2003. 40p. (J). 17.95 (978-1-58536-118-2(6)) Sleeping Bear Pr.

Crewe, Sabrina & Uschan, Michael V. The Scottsboro Case. 2004. (Events That Shaped America Ser.). (Illus.). 32p. (J). lib. bdg. 24.67 (978-0-8368-3407-9(0)) Stevens, Gareth Inc.

Dennis, Jep & Dennis, Bill. It Really Was a Lovely Village: Auburn, Alabama. 2002. (Illus.). 244p. (YA). (gr. 11 up). pap. 16.95 (978-0-9632180-9-4(3)) Chinaberry Hse.

Feeney, Kathy. Alabama. 2002. (From Sea to Shining Sea Ser.: 2). (Illus.). 80p. (J). (gr. 3-5). 30.50 (978-0-516-22314-8(3) , Children's Pr.) Scholastic Library Publishing.

Fradin, Dennis Brindell. Alabama. 1998. (From Sea to Shining Sea Ser.). (Illus.). 64p. (J). (gr. 3-5). pap. 7.95 (978-0-516-26291-8(2) , Children's Pr.) Scholastic Library Publishing.

Hart, Joyce. Alabama. 2006. (It's My State! Ser.). 80p. (J). lib. bdg. 29.93 (978-0-7614-1925-9(X) , Benchmark Bks.) Cavendish, Marshall Corp.

Heinrichs, Ann. Alabama. 2005. (Welcome to the USA Ser.). 40p. (J). (gr. 1-5). 27.07 (978-1-59296-370-6(6)) Child's World, Inc.

—Alabama. 2003. (This Land Is Your Land Ser.). (Illus.). 48p. (J). (gr. 3 up). lib. bdg. 22.60 (978-0-7565-0332-1(9)) Compass Point Bks.

—California. 2005. (Welcome to the USA Ser.). 40p. (J). (gr. 1-5). 27.07 (978-1-59296-283-9(1)) Child's World, Inc.

Johnston, Lissa Jones. Alabama. 2006. (Portraits of the States Ser.). (Illus.). 32p. (J). pap. (978-0-8368-4678-2(8)); lib. bdg. 23.33 (978-0-8368-4659-1(1)) Stevens, Gareth Inc.

Kjelle, Marylou Morano. Alabama: A MyReportLinks. Com Book. 2003. (States Ser.). (Illus.). 48p. (J). lib. bdg. 25.26 (978-0-7660-5151-5(X) , MyReportLinks.com Bks.) Enslow Pubs., Inc.

Kummer, Patricia K. Alabama. rev. ed. 2002. (One Nation Ser.). (Illus.). 48p. (J). (gr. 3-4). lib. bdg. 22.60 (978-0-7368-1225-2(3) , Bridgestone Bks.) Capstone Pr., Inc.

Leber, Holli. Alabama. 2004. (Rookie Read-About Geography Ser.). (Illus.). 31p. (J). 20.50 (978-0-516-22719-1(X) , Children's Pr.) Scholastic Library Publishing.

Marsh, Carole. Alabama Current Events Projects: 30 Cool, Activities, Crafts, Experiments & More for Kids to Do to Learn about Your State! 2003. (Alabama Experience Ser.). 32p. (gr. k-8). pap. 5.95 (978-0-635-02020-8(3) , Marsh, Carole Bks.) Gallopade International.

A
B

—The Alabama Experience Pocket Guide. 2001. (Carole Marsh Alabama Bks.). (Illus.). 96p. (J). (gr. 3-8). pap. 6.95 (978-0-7933-9905-5(X)) Gallopade International.

—Alabama Geography Projects: 30 Cool, Activities, Crafts, Experiments & More for Kids to Do to Learn about Your State! 2003. (Alabama Experience Ser.). 32p. (gr. k-5). pap. 5.95 (978-0-635-01820-5(9) , Marsh, Carole Bks.) Gallopade International.

—Alabama Government Projects: 30 Cool, Activities, Crafts, Experiments & More for Kids to Do to Learn about Your State! 2003. (Alabama Experience Ser.). 32p. (gr. k-5). pap. 5.95 (978-0-635-01920-2(5) , Marsh, Carole Bks.) Gallopade International.

—Alabama History Projects: 30 Cool, Activities, Crafts, Experiments & More for Kids to Do to Learn about Your State! 2003. (Alabama Experience Ser.). 32p. (gr. k-5). pap. 5.95 (978-0-635-01770-3(9) , Marsh, Carole Bks.) Gallopade International.

—Alabama Jeopardy! Answers & Questions about Our State! 2001. (Carole Marsh Alabama Bks.). (Illus.). 32p. (J). (gr. 3-8). pap. 7.95 (978-0-7933-9789-1(8)) Gallopade International.

—Alabama Jography. 2001. (Carole Marsh Alabama Bks.). (Illus.). 32p. (J). (gr. 3-8). pap. 7.95 (978-0-7933-9818-8(5)) Gallopade International.

—Alabama Millionaire. 2001. (GameBook Ser.). 32p. (J). (gr. 3-8). pap., act. bk. ed. 9.95 (978-0-635-00018-7(0)) Gallopade International.

—Alabama Survivor: Game Book. 2001. (Carole Marsh Alabama Bks.). 32p. (J). (gr. 3-8). pap., act. bk. ed. 9.95 (978-0-635-00522-9(0)) Gallopade International.

—Alabama Symbols & Facts Projects: 30 Cool, Activities, Crafts, Experiments & More for Kids to Do to Learn about Your State! 2003. (Alabama Experience Ser.). 32p. (gr. k-5). pap. 5.95 (978-0-635-01869-4(1) , Marsh, Carole Bks.) Gallopade International.

—My First Book about Alabama. 2001. (Carole Marsh Alabama Bks.). (Illus.). 32p. (J). (gr. k-4). pap. 7.95 (978-0-7933-9876-8(2)) Gallopade International.

—My First Pocket Guide Alabama. 2000. (Alabama Experience! Ser.). (Illus.). 96p. (J). (gr. 3-8). 12.95 (978-0-635-01291-3(X)) Gallopade International.

—The Survivor: A Class Challenge. 2001. (Alabama Experience! Ser.). lib. bdg. 29.95 (978-0-635-00647-9(2)) Gallopade International.

—Who Wants to Be an Alabama Millionaire? 2001. (Carole Marsh Alabama Bks.). lib. bdg. 29.95 (978-0-635-00019-4(9)) Gallopade International.

Martin, Michael A. Alabama: The Heart of Dixie. 2002. (World Almanac Library of the States). (Illus.). 48p. (J). (gr. 5 up). pap. 14.95 (978-0-8368-5297-4(4)); lib. bdg. 30.00 (978-0-8368-5127-4(7)) Stevens, Gareth Inc. (World Almanac Library).

Mayer, Robert H. When the Children Marched: The Birmingham Civil Rights Movement. 2008. (Prime Ser.). (Illus.). 160p. (J). (gr. 5 up). lib. bdg. 34.60 (***978-0-7660-2930-9(1)**) Enslow Pubs., Inc.

McAuliffe, Emily. Alabama: Facts & Symbols. 1999. (Illus.). 24p. (J). (gr. k-3). pap. 15.00 (978-0-531-12000-2(7) , Watts, Franklin) Scholastic Library Publishing.

—Alabama Facts & Symbols. (States & Their Symbols Ser.). 24p. (J). 2000. (Illus.). (gr. 2-3). lib. bdg. 18.60 (978-0-7368-0374-8(2) , Bridgestone Bks.); 2003. lib. bdg. 19.93 (978-0-7368-2231-2(3)) Capstone Pr., Inc.

Morris, Ann. Grandma Lois Remembers: An African-American Family Story. Linenthal, Peter, illus. 2002. (What Was It Like, Grandma? Ser.). 32p. (gr. k-3). lib. bdg. 22.90 (978-0-7613-2316-7(3) , Millbrook Pr.) Lerner Publishing Group.

Murray, Julie. Alabama. 2005. (Buddy Book Ser.). (Illus.). 32p. (J). (gr. k-4). lib. bdg. 22.78 (978-1-59197-660-8(X) , Buddy Bks.) ABDO Publishing Co.

Norrell, Robert J. The Alabama Journey: State History & Geography. 1998. (Illus.). 299p. (J). (gr. 4). 39.95 (978-1-882700-02-8(3)) Yellowhammer Co.

Parker, Janice. A Guide to Alabama. 2001. (American States Ser.). (Illus.). 32p. (J). lib. bdg. 16.95 (978-1-930954-23-6(9)); per. 7.95 (978-1-930954-66-3(2)) Weigl Pubs., Inc.

Pierce, Alan. The Montgomery Bus Boycott. 2005. (American Moments Ser.). (Illus.). 48p. (J). (gr. 4-8). lib. bdg. 25.65 (978-1-59197-935-7(8)) ABDO Publishing Co.

Ross, Margie Dover. Emma Sansom: Confederate Heroine. 2001. (Alabama Roots Biography Ser.). (Illus.). 104p. (J). (978-1-878561-83-1(9)) Seacoast Publishing, Inc.

Shofner, Shawndra. Alabama. 2008. (J). (***978-1-58341-626-6(9)** , Creative Education) Creative Co., The.

Somervill, Barbara A. Alabama. 2007. (America the Beautiful, Third Ser.). 144p. (J). 38.00 (***978-0-531-18556-8(7)** , Children's Pr.) Scholastic Library Publishing.

Sosal. Alabama. 2000. (Switched on Schoolhouse Ser.). (Illus.). (YA). (gr. 7-12). pap. 24.95 incl. cd-rom (978-0-7403-0253-4(1) , SOSAL) Alpha Omega Pubns., Inc.

Stephens, Elise Hopkins. Historic Huntsville: A City of New Beginninngs. 2002. (Illus.). 230p. 32.95 (978-1-892724-31-1(6)) American Historical Pr.

Vaughn, Wally G. & Davis, Mattie Campbell, eds. The Selma Campaign, 1963-1965: The Decisive Battle of the Civil Rights Movement. 2006. 261p. pap. 19.95 (978-0-912469-44-7(7)) Majority Pr., Inc., The.

Welsbacher, Anne. Alabama. 2003. (Land of Liberty Ser.). (Illus.). 64p. (J). (gr. 3-4). lib. bdg. 23.93 (978-0-7368-1569-7(4) , Bridgestone Bks.) Capstone Pr., Inc.

Wilson, Martin. Uniquely Alabama. 2003. (State Studies). (Illus.). 48p. (J). pap. 8.50 (978-1-4034-4500-1(1)); lib. bdg. 27.07 (978-1-4034-4485-1(4)) Heinemann Library.

ALABAMA—FICTION

Armistead, John. The $66 Summer. 2000. (978-0-606-21752-1(5)) Tandem Library Bks.

—The $66 Summer: A Novel of the Segregated South. 2nd ed. 2006. (Milkweed Prize for Children's Literature Ser.). 240p. (J). reprint ed. pap. 6.95 (978-1-57131-663-9(9)) Milkweed Editions.

Brown, Virginia Pounds. Gold Disc of Coosa: A Young Adult Historical Novel. 2003. (gr. 7-12). lib. bdg. 17.60 (978-0-613-79797-9(3)) Tandem Library Bks.

Butler, Darren J. The Secret of Crybaby Hollow. 2004. (YA). mass mkt. 6.99 (***978-0-9753367-5-5(4)**) Onstage Publishing, LLC.

Collier, Kristi. Jericho Walls. 2007. 224p. (YA). pap. 7.95 (***978-0-8050-8184-8(4)** , Holt, Henry & Co. Bks. For Young Readers) Holt, Henry & Co.

Curtis, Christopher Paul. The Watsons Go to Birmingham - 1963. 1998. 15p. pap., stu. ed., tchr.'s training gde. ed. 15.95 (978-1-58303-068-4(9)) Pathways Publishing.

—The Watsons Go to Birmingham - 1963. 210p. (YA). (gr. 5 up). pap. 5.50 (978-0-8072-8336-3(3)); 2004. (J). (gr. 4 up). pap. 38.00 incl. audio (978-0-8072-8335-6(5) , YA166SP) Random Hse. Audio Publishing Group. (Listening Library).

—The Watsons Go to Birmingham - 1963. 2000. 224p. (YA). (gr. 5-7). pap. 6.50 (978-0-440-22800-4(X) , Laurel Leaf) Random Hse. Children's Bks.

Davis, Ossie. Just Like Martin. (J). 2002. 176p. 15.99 (978-0-7868-0812-0(8)); 2001. pap. (978-0-7868-1642-2(2)) Hyperion Bks. for Children. (Jump at the Sun).

Devoto, Pat Cunningham. My Last Days As Roy Rogers. 2000. (gr. 7-12). lib. bdg. 23.40 (978-0-613-27988-8(3)) Tandem Library Bks.

Dunagan, Ted. A Yellow Watermelon. 2007. 256p. (J). 23.95 (***978-1-58838-197-2(8)** , Junebug Bks.) NewSouth, Inc.

Grizzle-Moon, Ivy. Selma. 2001. (J). pap. 8.00 (978-0-8059-5015-1(X)) Dorrance Publishing Co., Inc.

Hanna, James Milton, Sr. Once upon a Time in the South. l.t. ed. 2004. (Illus.). 235p. per. 12.95 (978-1-930052-15-4(4)) Cherokee Bks.

Harris, Rita & Long, Paul. The 19 Cats of Alabama. 2004. 35p. pap. 17.95 (978-1-4137-3006-7(X)) PublishAmerica, Inc.

Hermes, Patricia. Summer Secrets. 2004. (Illus.). 144p. (YA). 15.95 (978-0-7614-5074-0(2)) Cavendish, Marshall Corp.

Hopkins, Nicolia. What was Grandma Doing? eVision, ed. Wiggins, Margaret W., illus. 2007. (J). per. 9.99 (***978-0-9768579-8-3(7)**) eVision, LLC.

Jackson, Dave & Jackson, Neta. The Forty-Acre Swindle: George Washington Carver. McLaughlin, Catherine R., illus. 2000. (Trailblazer Bks.: Vol. 31). 144p. (J). (gr. 3-7). pap. 6.99 (978-0-7642-2264-1(3)) Bethany Hse. Pubs.

Johnson, Angela. Bird. 2006. 144p. (YA). (gr. 5). reprint ed. pap. 5.99 (978-0-14-240544-4(2) , Puffin) Penguin Group (USA) Inc.

Key, Watt. Alabama Moon. 2006. 304p. (J). 16.00 (978-0-374-30184-2(0)) Farrar, Straus & Giroux.

Klise, Kate. Deliver Us from Normal: Read-Along/Homework Pack. unabr. ed. 2005. (YA). (gr. 5-8). 65.70 incl. audio (978-1-4193-3619-5(3) , 42050) Recorded Bks., LLC.

Les Becquets, Diane. The Stones of Mourning Creek. 2005. 306p. (YA). (gr. 7). reprint ed. pap. 6.95 (978-0-7614-5238-6(9)) Cavendish, Marshall Corp.

—The Stones of Mourning Creek. 2001. (Illus.). 320p. (J). (gr. 7 up). 16.95 (978-1-58837-004-4(6)) Winslow Pr.

Lyon, George Ella. Sonny's House of Spies. 2004. (Illus.). 304p. (J). 16.95 (978-0-689-85168-1(5) , Atheneum/Richard Jackson Bks.) Simon & Schuster Children's Publishing.

McKissack, Pat. Stitchin' & Pullin' A Gee's Bend Quilt. Cabrera, Cozbi S., illus. 2007. (J). (***978-0-375-83163-8(0)**); lib. bdg. (***978-0-375-93163-5(5)**) Random Hse., Inc.

McKissack, Patricia C. Ma Dear's Aprons. 2000. (Illus.). (J). (978-0-606-17928-7(3)) Tandem Library Bks.

McKissack, Patricia C. & Cooper, Floyd. Ma Dear's Aprons. 2000. (Illus.). 32p. (J). (ps-3). reprint ed. pap. 7.99 (978-0-689-83262-8(1) , Aladdin) Simon & Schuster Children's Publishing.

Medearis, Angela Shelf. Singing for Dr. King. Wright and Hu, Cornelius Van and Ying-Hwa, illus. 2004. 32p. (J). lib. bdg. 15.00 (***978-1-4242-0237-9(X)**) Fitzgerald Bks.

Miller, J. P. Over the River & Through the Woods: A Journey with Harriet Tubman. 2004. 74p. pap. 14.95 (978-1-4137-1604-7(0)) PublishAmerica, Inc.

Miller, Sarah Elizabeth. Miss Spitfire: Reaching Helen Keller. 2007. 240p. (J). (gr. 5-9). 16.99 (978-1-4169-2542-2(2)) Simon & Schuster Children's Publishing.

Nelson, R. A. Breathe My Name. 2007. 288p. (J). (gr. 7). 16.99 (***978-1-59514-094-4(8)** , Razorbill) Penguin Group (USA) Inc.

Nolan, Han. Send Me down a Miracle. 2003. 276p. (YA). pap. 6.95 (978-0-15-204680-4(1)) Harcourt Children's Bks.

—Send Me down a Miracle. 2003. (gr. 7-12). lib. bdg. 15.25 (978-0-613-59926-9(8)) Tandem Library Bks.

Pinkney, Andrea Davis. Boycott Blues. 2008. (J). (***978-0-06-082118-0(3)**); (***978-0-06-082119-7(1)**) HarperCollins Pubs. (Greenwillow Bks.).

Ray, Delia. Singing Hands. 2006. (Illus.). 224p. (J). (gr. 5-9). 16.00 (978-0-618-65762-9(2) , Clarion Bks.) Houghton Mifflin Co. Trade & Reference Div.

Scholastic, Inc. Staff & Medearis, Angela Shelf. Singing for Dr. King. Van Wright, Cornelius & Hu, Ying-Hwa, illus. 2004. (Just for You! Ser.). 32p. (gr. k-3). pap. 3.99 (978-0-439-56855-5(2) , Teaching Resources) Scholastic, Inc.

Schraff, Anne. Strawberry Autumn. 1999. (Passages Ser.). (Illus.). 135p. (J). (gr. 5-12). lib. bdg. 13.95 (978-0-7807-8985-2(7)) Perfection Learning Corp.

Sorrells, Walter. Fake ID. 2005. (Hunted Ser.: 1). 192p. (YA). (gr. 6). 12.99 (978-0-525-47514-9(1) , Dutton Juvenile) Penguin Group (USA) Inc.

—Fake ID: A Mystery. 2007. (Hunted Ser.). 336p. (YA). (gr. 7 up). pap. 6.99 (978-0-14-240762-2(3) , Puffin) Penguin Group (USA) Inc.

Thompson, Shannon Raines. Mad about Miller. Stone, Kathrine Thompson, ed. Shehan, Terece, illus. 2006. 24p. (YA). 12.95 (978-1-59971-853-8(7)) Aardvark Global Publishing.

—Nuts about Neal. Stone, Kathrine Thompson, ed. Shehan, Terece, illus. 2006. 24p. (YA). 12.95 (978-1-59971-852-1(9)) Aardvark Global Publishing.

Wallin, Luke. The Redneck Poacher's Son. 2001. 260p. (YA). pap. 17.95 (978-0-595-19244-1(0)) iUniverse, Inc.

Warner, Gertrude Chandler. Mystery of the Midnight Dog. 2001. (gr. 3-6). lib. bdg. 11.80 (978-0-613-35789-0(2)) Tandem Library Bks.

—The Mystery of the Midnight Dog, Vol. 81. 2004. (Boxcar Children Ser.: No. 81). (Illus.). 122p. (J). (gr. 2-7). pap. 4.50 (978-0-8075-5476-0(6)) Whitman, Albert & Co.

ALADDIN (FICTITIOUS CHARACTER)—FICTION

Aladdin: Here Comes a Parade. unabr. ed. (My First Read Along Ser.). (Illus.). (J). 7.99 incl. audio (978-1-55723-748-4(4)) Walt Disney Records.

Aladino. 2001. Tr. of Aladdin. (978-84-305-7555-8(3)) Lectorum Pubns., Inc.

Baker, Darrell, illus. Aladdin. 2004. (Little Golden Book Ser.). 24p. (J). (gr. k-k). 2.99 (978-0-7364-2259-8(5) , Golden/Disney) Random Hse. Children's Bks.

Daynes, Katie. Aladdin & His Magical Lamp. 2004. (Young Reading Ser.: Vol. 1). 48p. (J). (gr. 2 up). pap. 5.95 (978-0-7945-0582-0(1)); lib. bdg. 13.95 (978-1-58086-559-3(3) , Usborne) EDC Publishing.

Deighton, Jo, adapted by. Scheherezade Presents. (Scheherezade Presents Ser.: No. 1). (Illus.). 48p. (J). pap. (978-1-85964-091-3(5)); pap. (978-1-85964-100-2(8)); pap. (978-1-85964-092-0(3)); pap. (978-1-85964-093-7(1)); pap. (978-1-85964-094-4(X)); pap. (978-1-85964-095-1(8)); pap. (978-1-85964-096-8(6)); pap. (978-1-85964-097-5(4)); pap. (978-1-85964-098-2(2)); pap. (978-1-85964-099-9(0)) Garnet Publishing, Ltd. (Ithaca Pr.).

Disney Book Club Staff. Aladdin & the Wonderful Lamp. 1999. (J). lib. bdg. (978-0-394-93937-7(9) , Random Hse. Bks. for Young Readers) Random Hse. Children's Bks.

Disney Staff. Aladdin. (FRE.). 96p. (J). (gr. k-5). pap. 9.95 (978-0-7859-8852-6(1)) French & European Pubns., Inc.

Fairy Tale- Aladdin. 2005. (J). bds. (978-1-4194-0037-7(1)) Paradise Pr., Inc.

Landes, William-Alan. Aladdin n' His Magic Lamp. rev. ed. 2003. (Wondrawhopper Ser.). 51p. (J). (gr. 3-12). pap. 6.00 (978-0-88734-102-1(0)) Players Pr., Inc.

Mouse Works Staff. Aladdin - Peter Pan, 2. 75th anniv. ed. 1998. (Illus.). (ps-3). 9.99 (978-0-7364-0086-2(9)) Mouse Works.

Nassar, Nabil A. A. Aladdin in Genie Land. 2006. pap. 8.95 (978-0-533-15165-3(1)) Vantage Pr., Inc.

Smith, Philip, ed. Listen & Read Aladdin & Other Favorite Arabian Nights Stories. 1998. (gr. 3-6). pap. 7.95 (978-0-486-40108-9(1)) Dover Pubns., Inc.

Stempleski. Aladdin & the Magic Lamp. Date not set. (Illus.). 23p. pap. 72.95 (978-0-582-03043-5(9)) Addison-Wesley Longman, Ltd. GBR. *Dist:* Trans-Atlantic Pubns., Inc.

Vallverdu, Josep. Aladdin & the Magic Lamp. Montserrat, Pep, illus. 2006. (ENG & SPA.). 32p. (J). 14.95 (978-0-8118-5061-2(7)); pap. 6.95 (978-0-8118-5062-9(5)) Chronicle Bks. LLC.

Wells, H. G. The War of the Worlds. Gorey, Edward, illus. 2005. (New York Review Books Classics). 260p. pap. 16.95 (978-1-59017-158-5(6) , NYRB Classics) New York Review of Bks., Inc., The.

—The War of the Worlds. 2005. (Aladdin Classics Ser.). 336p. (J). pap. 4.99 (978-1-4169-0368-0(2) , Aladdin) Simon & Schuster Children's Publishing.

ALAMO (SAN ANTONIO, TEX.)

Allen, Charles F. David Crockett: Scout, Small Boy, Pilgrim, Mountaineer, Soldier, Bear-Hunter, & Congressman, Defender of the Alamo. (Illus.). 308p. reprint ed. lib. bdg. 98.00 (978-0-7222-4856-0(3)) Library Reprints, Inc.

—David Crockett, Scout: Small Boy, Pilgrim, Mountaineer, Soldier, Bear-Hunter & Congressman: Defender of the Alamo. McKernan, Frank, illus. 2000. (J). (978-0-89526-228-8(2)) Regnery Publishing, Inc., An Eagle Publishing Co.

Barr, Amelia E. Remember the Alamo. l.t. ed. 1999. (Large Print Heritage Ser.). 385p. (J). (gr. 7-12). lib. bdg. 34.95 (978-1-58118-044-2(6) , 22513) LRS.

Britton, Tamara L. The Alamo. 2005. (Symbols, Landmarks, & Monuments Set Ii Ser.). (Illus.). 32p. (J). (gr. k-6). lib. bdg. 22.78 (978-1-59197-518-2(2)) ABDO Publishing Co.

Burgan, Michael. The Alamo. 2001. (We the People Ser.). (Illus.). 48p. (J). (gr. 4 up). lib. bdg. 22.60 (978-0-7565-0097-9(4)) Compass Point Bks.

Coleman, Wim & Perrin, Pat. The Alamo: A MyReportLinks.com Book. 2005. (Virtual Field Trips Ser.). (Illus.). 48p. (J). (gr. 4-10). lib. bdg. 25.26 (978-0-7660-5221-5(4) , MyReportLinks.com Bks.) Enslow Pubs., Inc.

Copeland, Peter F. The Story of the Alamo. 2005. (Illus.). 32p. (J). (gr. 3). pap. 3.95 (978-0-486-44459-8(7)) Dover Pubns., Inc.

Doeden, Matt. La Batalla del Alamo. Lilley, Jessica S., tr. Barnett, Charles, III & Miller, Phil, illus. 2006. (Historia Grafica en Espanol Ser.). (SPA.). 32p. (J). lib. bdg. 18.95 (978-0-7368-6056-7(8)) Capstone Pr., Inc.

—The Battle of the Alamo. (Graphic History Ser.). 32p. (YA). pap. 7.95 (978-0-7368-5242-5(5)) Capstone Pr., Inc.

—The Battle of the Alamo. Barnett, Charles, illus. 2005. (Graphic Library). 32p. (J). 22.60 (978-0-7368-3832-0(5)) Capstone Pr., Inc.

Edmondson, J. R. Jim Bowie: Frontier Legend, Alamo Hero. 2005. (Library of American Lives & Times). (Illus.). 112p. (YA). (gr. 4-8). lib. bdg. 31.95 (978-0-8239-5734-7(9)) Rosen Publishing Group, Inc., The.

Feeney, Kathy. Davy Crockett. 2002. (Photo-Illustrated Biographies Ser.). (Illus.). 24p. (J). (gr. 2-3). lib. bdg. 18.60 (978-0-7368-1110-1(9) , Bridgestone Bks.) Capstone Pr., Inc.

Fradin, Dennis B. The Alamo. 2006. (Turning Points in U. S. History Ser.). (Illus.). 48p. (J). (gr. 3-6). lib. bdg. 29.93 (978-0-7614-2127-6(0) , Benchmark Bks.) Cavendish, Marshall Corp.

Garland, Sherry. Voices of the Alamo. Himler, Ronald, illus. 2004. 40p. (J). pap. 15.95 (978-1-58980-222-3(5)) Pelican Publishing Co., Inc.

Gunderson, Cory Gideon. The Battle of the Alamo. 2005. (American Moments Ser.). (Illus.). 48p. (J). (gr. 4-8). lib. bdg. 25.65 (978-1-59197-278-5(7)) ABDO Publishing Co.

Hargrove, Julia. The Alamo. Mitchell, Judy, ed. Mohrman, Gary, illus. 2001. (Historic Monuments Ser.). 48p. (J). (gr. 4-8). pap. 6.95 (978-1-57310-281-0(4)) Teaching & Learning Co.

Harlowe, Jerry. Monitors: The Men, Machines & Mystique. Thomas Publications Staff, ed. 2001. (Illus.). 111p. (J). pap. 17.95 (978-1-57747-056-4(7)) Thomas Pubns.

Isaacs, Sally Senzell. Life at the Alamo. 2003. (Picture the Past Ser.). (Illus.). 32p. (J). (gr. 2-4). lib. bdg. (978-1-58810-695-7(0)); pap. 7.50 (978-1-4034-0523-4(9)) Heinemann Library.

Love, D. Anne. I Remember the Alamo. 2001. (J). 11.15 (978-0-606-21245-8(0)) Tandem Library Bks.

Marcovitz, Hal. The Alamo. 2002. (American Symbols & Their Meanings Ser.). (Illus.). 48p. (YA). (gr. 4 up). lib. bdg. (978-1-59084-037-5(2)) Mason Crest Pubs.

McGowen, Tom. The Alamo. (Cornerstones of Freedomtrade;, Second Ser.). 48p. (J). (gr. 4-6). 2007. pap. 5.95 (***978-0-531-18684-8(9)**); 2003. (Illus.). 26.00 (978-0-516-24208-8(3)) Scholastic Library Publishing. (Children's Pr.).

McNeese, Tim. Alamo. 2003. (Sieges That Changed the World Ser.). (Illus.). 112p. (gr. 6-12). 30.00 (978-0-7910-7101-4(4) , Chelsea Hse.) Facts On File, Inc.

—The Alamo. 2003. (Sieges That Changed the World Ser.). (Illus.). 112p. (gr. 6-12). pap. 13.25 (978-0-7910-7529-6(X) , Chelsea Hse.) Facts On File, Inc.

Nelson, Kristin L. The Alamo. 2004. (Pull Ahead Bks.). (Illus.). 32p. (J). (gr. k-3). lib. bdg. 22.60 (978-0-8225-3599-7(8)) Lerner Publishing Group.

O'Hern, Kerri & Riehecky, Janet. The Battle of the Alamo. 2006. (Graphic Histories Ser.). (Illus.). (J). pap. (978-0-8368-6253-9(8)); 32p. lib. bdg. 26.00 (978-0-8368-6201-0(5)) Stevens, Gareth Inc. (World Almanac Library).

Riehecky, Janet. The Siege of the Alamo. 2002. (Landmark Events in American History Ser.). (Illus.). 48p. (J). (gr. 5 up). pap. 14.60 (978-0-8368-5356-8(3)); lib. bdg. 30.00 (978-0-8368-5342-1(3)) Stevens, Gareth Inc. (World Almanac Library).

Ruffin, Frances E. The Alamo. 2006. (Illus.). 24p. (J). pap. (978-0-8368-6414-4(X)); lib. bdg. 19.33 (978-0-8368-6407-6(7)) Stevens, Gareth Inc.

Schaefer, Ted & Schaefer, Lola M. The Alamo. 2005. (Symbols of Freedom Ser.). (Illus.). 32p. (J). pap. (978-1-4034-6671-6(8)); lib. bdg. 25.36 (978-1-4034-6662-4(9)) Heinemann Library.

Sipe, Antoinette Leonard. The Alamo. 2004. (American Forts & Their Strategic Importance Ser.). (J). (978-1-59084-708-4(3)) Mason Crest Pubs.

Stewart, Mark. The Alamo: February 23-March 6, 1836. 2004. (American Battlefields Ser.). (Illus.). 32p. (J). 14.95 (978-1-59270-026-4(8)) Enchanted Lion Bks., LLC.

Walker, Paul Robert. Remember the Alamo: Texians, Tejanos, & Mexicans Tell Their Stories. 2007. (National Geographic Children's Books Ser.). (Illus.). 64p. (J). (gr. 4-8). 17.95 (978-1-4263-0010-3(7) , National Geographic Children's Bks.) National Geographic Society.

Weber, Valerie J. & Riehecky, Janet. The Siege of the Alamo. 2002. (Events That Shaped America Ser.). (Illus.). 32p. (J). (gr. 3 up). lib. bdg. 24.67 (978-0-8368-3226-6(4)) Stevens, Gareth Inc.

Wilson, Mike. The Alamo. 2002. (History of the Old West Ser.). (Illus.). 64p. (J). (gr. 5 up). lib. bdg. (978-1-59084-062-7(3)) Mason Crest Pubs.

ALAMO (SAN ANTONIO, TEX.)—FICTION

Barr, Amelia M. Remember the Alamo. 2005. 156p. pap. (978-1-84637-856-0(7)) Echo Library.

Cuate, Melodie A. Journey to the Alamo. 2006. 144p. (J). 17.95 (978-0-89672-592-8(8)) Texas Tech Univ. Pr.

Garland, Sherry. In the Shadow of the Alamo. 2001. (Great Episodes Ser.). 288p. (YA). (gr. 5-8). 18.00 (978-0-15-201744-6(5) , Gulliver Bks.) Harcourt Children's Bks.

Love, D. Anne. I Remember the Alamo. 1999. 156p. (J). (gr. 3-7). tchr. ed. 15.95 (978-0-8234-1426-0(4)) Holiday Hse., Inc.

Marsh, Carole. The Mystery of the Alamo Ghost. 2003. (Carole Marsh Mysteries Ser.). 160p. (J). (gr. 2-8). 14.95 (978-0-635-01654-6(0)); pap. 5.95 (978-0-635-01652-2(4)) Gallopade International.

—Mystery of the Alamo Ghost. 2003. (gr. 3-6). lib. bdg. 14.10 (978-0-613-73038-9(0)) Tandem Library Bks.

Rice, James. Victor Lopez at the Alamo. 2001. (Illus.). 128p. (J). (gr. 3-7). pap. 12.95 (978-1-56554-866-4(3)) Pelican Publishing Co., Inc.

Rogers, Lisa Waller. Angel of the Alamo. Thigpen, Gwen, illus. 2000. 48p. (J). (gr. 3-8). 18.95 (978-0-87443-125-4(5) , 125-5); pap. 8.95 (978-0-87443-126-1(3) , 126-3) Benson, W. S. & Co., Inc.

—Remember the Alamo! The Runaway Scrape Diary of Belle Wood. 2003. (Lone Star Journals: Bk. 3). 208p. (J). 15.95 (978-0-89672-497-6(2)) Texas Tech Univ. Pr.

Sibley, Linda & Marks, Dea. David Takes Part in the Battle of the Alamo. 2004. (Cover-To-Cover Books). (Illus.). 84p. (J). pap. ***978-0-7891-6044-7(7))** Perfection Learning Corp.

ALASKA

Bic, Alexander D. Alexander's Alaskan Adventure: From the Travel Journal of a Fifth-Grader. Johnson, Kurt E., ed. 2002. (Illus.). 51p. (J). (gr. 3-7). pap. 12.95 (978-1-888308-13-6(3)) J&S Publishing Co., Inc.

Bjorklund, Ruth. Alaska. 2004. (It's My State! Ser.). (Illus.). 80p. (J). 27.07 (978-0-7614-1823-8(7)) Cavendish, Marshall Corp.

Bowermaster, Jon. Aleutian Adventure: Kayaking in the Birthplace of the Winds. Tessman, Barry, photos by. 2001. (Illus.). 64p. (J). (gr. 7-7). 17.95 (978-0-7922-7999-0(9) , National Geographic Children's Bks.) National Geographic Society.

Burts, Janet M. Alaskan Safari. Tietz, Kathryn S., illus. 2001. 32p. (J). (ps-2). 10.95 (978-1-930020-00-9(7)) A J B Productions.

Chamberlin-Calamar, Pat. Alaska's 12 Days of Summer. Cartwright, Shannon, illus. 2003. (PAWS IV Ser.). 32p. (J). pap. 9.95 (978-1-57061-341-8(9)); 16.95 (978-1-57061-340-1(0)) Sasquatch Bks.

—Alaska's 12 Days of Summer. 2003. (gr. k-3). lib. bdg. 18.75 (978-0-613-79151-9(7)) Tandem Library Bks.

Conover, Ted. In My Grandfather's Footsteps. 1999. (YA). (gr. 6 up). 17.95 (978-0-679-88588-7(9) , Knopf Bks. for Young Readers) Random Hse. Children's Bks.

Corwin, Jeff. Into Wild Alaska. Pascoe, Elaine, ed. 2003. (Jeff Corwin Experience Ser.). (Illus.). 48p. (J). 24.95 (978-1-4103-0059-1(5)); 11.20 (978-1-4103-0180-2(X)) Thomson Gale. (Blackbirch Pr., Inc.).

Crane, Carol. L Is for Last Frontier: An Alaska Alphabet. Monroe, Michael Glenn, illus. 2002. 40p. (J). (ps-5). 17.95 (978-1-58536-020-8(1)) Sleeping Bear Pr.

Dils, Tracey E. The Exxon Valdez. 2001. (Great Disasters, Reforms & Ramifications Ser.). (Illus.). 112p. (J). (gr. 4-7). 30.00 (978-0-7910-5784-1(4) , Chelsea Hse.) Facts On File, Inc.

Dubois, Muriel L. Alaska Facts & Symbols. (States & Their Symbols Ser.). 24p. (J). 2000. (Illus.). (gr. 2-3). lib. bdg. 13.95 (978-0-7368-0522-3(2) , Bridgestone Bks.); 2003. lib. bdg. 19.93 (978-0-7368-2232-9(1)) Capstone Pr., Inc.

Feinstein, Stephen. Alaska: A MyReportLinks.com Book. 2003. (States Ser.). (Illus.). 48p. (J). (gr. 4-10). lib. bdg. 25.26 (978-0-7660-5025-9(4) , MyReportLinks.com Bks.) Enslow Pubs., Inc.

—The Pacific States. 2006. (Regions of the USA Ser.). (Illus.). 56p. (J). (978-1-4109-2310-3(X)); pap. (978-1-4109-2318-9(5)) Steck-Vaughn.

Flowers, Pam. Alone Across the Arctic: One Woman's Epic Journey by Dog Team. 2001. (gr. 5-8). lib. bdg. 25.70 (978-0-613-59797-5(4)) Tandem Library Bks.

Flowers, Pam & Dixon, Ann. Alone Across the Arctic: One Woman's Epic Journey by Dog Team. 2005. (Illus.). 120p. (gr. 5-10). 22.95 (978-0-88240-547-6(0)) Graphic Arts Ctr. Publishing Co.

Gill, Shelley. Alaska. Endres, Patrick J., photos by. 2007. (Illus.). 32p. (J). (gr. 4-7). 16.95 (978-0-88106-292-2(8)); pap. 6.95 (978-0-88106-293-9(6)) Charlesbridge Publishing, Inc.

Heinrichs, Ann. Alaska. 2005. (Welcome to the USA Ser.). 40p. (J). (gr. 1-5). 27.07 (978-1-59296-371-3(4)) Child's World, Inc.

—Alaska. 2003. (This Land Is Your Land Ser.). (Illus.). 48p. (J). (gr. 3 up). lib. bdg. 22.60 (978-0-7565-0337-6(X)) Compass Point Bks.

Henry, Judy. Uniquely Alaska. 2004. (Heinemann State Studies). (Illus.). 48p. (J). 31.36 (978-1-4034-4642-8(3)); pap. 9.00 (978-1-4034-4711-1(X)) Heinemann Library.

Heuer, Karsten, photos by. Being Caribou: Five Months on Foot with a Caribou Herd. 2007. (Illus.). 48p. (J). (gr. 7 up). 17.95 ***978-0-8027-9565-6(X))** Walker & Co.

Heuer, Karsten & Wood, Ted. Being Caribou: Five Months on Foot with a Caribou Herd. 2007. (Illus.). 48p. (J). 18.85 ***978-0-8027-9566-3(8))** Walker & Co.

Hoshino, Michio. Hoshino's Alaska. 2007. (Illus.). 160p. pap. 24.95 (978-0-8118-5651-5(8)) Chronicle Bks. LLC.

Johnston, Joyce. Alaska. 2nd exp. rev. ed. (Hello U. S. A. Ser.). (Illus.). 84p. (J). (gr. 3-6). 2002. lib. bdg. 25.26 (978-0-8225-4051-9(7)); 2003. pap. 6.95 (978-0-8225-4157-8(2)) Lerner Publishing Group.

—Alaska. 2001. (gr. 3-6). lib. bdg. 15.25 (978-0-613-81866-7(0)) Tandem Library Bks.

Kummer, Patricia K. Alaska. rev. ed. 2002. (One Nation Ser.). (Illus.). 48p. (J). (gr. 3-4). lib. bdg. 22.60 (978-0-7368-1226-9(1) , Bridgestone Bks.) Capstone Pr., Inc.

Leacock, Elspeth. Exxon Valdez Oil Spill. 2005. (Environmental Disasters Ser.). (Illus.). 112p. (J). (gr. 6-12). 35.00 (978-0-8160-5754-2(0)) Facts On File, Inc.

Levinson, Nancy Smiler. If You Lived in the Alaska Territory. 1998. (Illus.). 80p. (J). (gr. 2-5). pap. 5.99 (978-0-590-74429-6(5)) Scholastic, Inc.

Marsh, Carole. Alaska Classic Christmas Trivia. 2002. (Carole Marsh Alaska Bks.). (Illus.). 32p. pap. 6.95 (978-0-635-01371-2(1) , 13711, Marsh, Carole Bks.); lib. bdg. 21.95 (978-0-635-01372-9(X) , 1372X) Gallopade International.

—Alaska Current Events Projects: 30 Cool, Activities, Crafts, Experiments & More for Kids to Do to Learn about Your State! 2003. (Alaska Experience Ser.). 32p. (gr. k-5). pap. 5.95 (978-0-635-02021-5(1) , Marsh, Carole Bks.) Gallopade International.

—The Alaska Experience Pocket Guide. 2001. (Carole Marsh Alaska Bks.). (Illus.). 96p. (J). (gr. 3-8). pap. 6.95 (978-0-7933-9906-2(8)) Gallopade International.

—Alaska Geography Projects: 30 Cool, Activities, Crafts, Experiments & More for Kids to Do to Learn about Your State! 2003. (Alaska Experience Ser.). 32p. (gr. k-5). pap. 5.95 (978-0-635-01821-2(7) , Marsh, Carole Bks.) Gallopade International.

—Alaska Government Projects: 30 Cool, Activities, Crafts, Experiments & More for Kids to Do to Learn about Your State! 2003. (Alaska Experience Ser.). 32p. (gr. k-5). pap. 5.95 (978-0-635-01921-9(3) , Marsh, Carole Bks.) Gallopade International.

—Alaska Jeopardy! Answers & Questions about Our State! 2001. (Carole Marsh Alaska Bks.). (Illus.). 32p. (J). (gr. 3-8). pap. 7.95 (978-0-7933-9790-7(1)) Gallopade International.

—Alaska "Jography" A Fun Run Thru Our State! 2001. (Carole Marsh Alaska Bks.). (Illus.). 32p. (J). (gr. 3-8). pap. 7.95 (978-0-7933-9819-5(3)) Gallopade International.

—Alaska Millionaire: Game Book. 2001. (Carole Marsh Alaska Bks.). (Illus.). 32p. (J). (gr. 3-8). pap., act. bk. ed. 9.95 (978-0-635-00020-0(2)) Gallopade International.

—Alaska People Projects: 30 Cool, Activities, Crafts, Experiments & More for Kids to Do to Learn about Your State! 2003. (Alaska Experience Ser.). 32p. (gr. k-5). pap. 5.95 (978-0-635-01971-4(X) , Marsh, Carole Bks.) Gallopade International.

—Alaska Survivor: Game Book. 2001. (Carole Marsh Alaska Bks.). (Illus.). 32p. (J). (gr. 3-8). pap. 9.95 (978-0-635-00523-6(9)) Gallopade International.

—Alaska Symbols & Facts Projects: 30 Cool, Activities, Crafts, Experiments & More for Kids to Do to Learn about Your State! 2003. (Alaska Experience Ser.). 32p. (gr. k-5). pap. 5.95 (978-0-635-01870-0(5) , Marsh, Carole Bks.) Gallopade International.

—The Big Alaska Reproducible. 2001. (Carole Marsh Alaska Bks.). (Illus.). 96p. (J). (gr. 2-6). pap., act. bk. ed. 9.95 (978-0-7933-9935-2(1)) Gallopade International.

—My First Book about Alaska. 2001. 32p. (J). (gr. k-4). pap. 7.95 (978-0-7933-9877-5(0)) Gallopade International.

—My First Pocket Guide Alaska. 2000. (Alaska Experience! Ser.). (Illus.). 96p. (J). (gr. 3-8). 12.95 (978-0-635-01292-0(8) , 12928) Gallopade International.

—The Survivor: A Class Challenge. 2001. (Alaska Experience! Ser.). lib. bdg. 29.95 (978-0-635-00648-6(0)) Gallopade International.

—Who Wants to Be an Alaska Millionaire? 2001. (Carole Marsh Alaska Bks.). lib. bdg. 29.95 (978-0-635-00021-7(0)) Gallopade International.

Miller, Debbie S. Big Alaska: Journey Across America's Most Amazing State. Van Zyle, Jon, illus. 2006. 40p. (J). 18.85 (978-0-8027-8070-6(9)); 17.95 (978-0-8027-8069-0(5)) Walker & Co.

—A Caribou Journey. 2000. (Illus.). (J). (978-0-606-18255-3(1)) Tandem Library Bks.

Morgan, Marilyn. Alaska Alphabet CD-ROM. 2007. cd-rom 29.95 ***978-1-878051-56-1(3))** Circumpolar Pr.

Muir, John. Stickeen. Buell, Carl Dennis, illus. Date not set. 94p. (J). 16.95 (978-0-8488-2803-5(8)) Amereon LTD.

Murray, Julie. Alaska. 2005. (Buddy Book Ser.). (Illus.). 32p. (J). (gr. k-4). lib. bdg. 22.78 (978-1-59197-661-5(8) , Buddy Bks.) ABDO Publishing Co.

Niebergall, Jane S. The Alaska Report. O'Meara, Jan, ed. rev. ed. 1999. (Illus.). 76p. (gr. 4 up). 7.95 (978-1-878051-46-2(6)) Circumpolar Pr.

Niz, Xavier. Alaska. 2003. (Land of Liberty Ser.). (Illus.). 64p. (J). (gr. 3-4). lib. bdg. 23.93 (978-0-7368-1570-3(8) , Bridgestone Bks.) Capstone Pr., Inc.

Obregon, Jose M. Alaska. 2005. (Bilingual Library of the United States of America: Set 1). (ENG & SPA., Illus.). 32p. (J). (ps-k). lib. bdg. 22.50 (978-1-4042-3066-8(1) , Buenas Letra) Rosen Publishing Group, Inc., The.

Obregon, José María. Alaska. 2006. (Bilingual Library of the United States of America). (SPA.). (J). lib. bdg. (978-1-4042-3143-6(9) , PowerKids Pr.) Rosen Publishing Group, Inc., The.

Ogintz, Eileen & Yemma, Reggie. The Kid's Guide to Cruising Alaska. 2004. (Kid's Guides). (Illus.). 112p. (J). pap. 8.95 (978-0-7627-3077-3(3) , Falcon) Globe Pequot Pr., The.

Orr, Tamra. Alaska. 2007. (America the Beautiful, Third Ser.). 144p. (J). spiral bd. 38.00 ***978-0-531-18569-8(9)** , Children's Pr.) Scholastic Library Publishing.

Papademetriou, Dorrie. North Star: St. Herman of Alaska. 2000. (Illus.). 32p. (J). 17.00 (978-0-88141-223-9(6)) St. Vladimir's Seminary Pr.

Peterson, Sheryl. Alaska. 2008. (J). ***978-1-58341-627-3(7)** , Creative Education) Creative Co., The.

Rabinovitch, Leon & Carson, Steven, illus. Alaska Zoo Activity & Guide Book. 1999. 68p. (J). pap. 6.00 (978-1-57833-120-8(X)) Todd Communications.

Richter, Bernard. Touch & Feel Alaskas Animals. 2003. (Illus.). 12p. bds. 9.95 (978-1-931353-13-7(1)) Saddle Pal Creations, Inc.

Richter, Bernd & Richter, Susan. Come along & Ride the Alaska Train. 2001. (Illus.). 48p. 14.95 (978-1-931353-03-8(4)); (gr. 1). 9.95 (978-1-931353-02-1(6)) Saddle Pal Creations, Inc.

Richter, Bernd C. When Grandma Visited Alaska She. . . 1999. 48p. 14.95 (978-0-9663495-7-3(1)) Saddle Pal Creations, Inc.

Richter, Bernd C. & Richter, Susan E. Do Alaskans Live in Igloos? Show Me Your Alaska Home. Richter, Bernd C., illus. 1999. (Illus.). 32p. (ps-6). 9.95 (978-0-9663495-2-8(0)) Saddle Pal Creations, Inc.

—How Alaska Got Its Flag. 2000. (Illus.). 32p. (gr. 1-4). 9.95 (978-0-9663495-4-2(7)) Saddle Pal Creations, Inc.

—Uncover Alaska's Wonders. Richter, Bernd C., illus. 1999. 24p. (ps-1). 10.95 (978-0-9663495-3-5(9)) Saddle Pal Creations, Inc.

—When Grandma Visited Alaska She. . . Richter, Bernd C., illus. 1999. (Illus.). 48p. (ps-6). 9.95 (978-0-9663495-1-1(2)) Saddle Pal Creations, Inc.

Riddles, Libby. Storm Run: The Story of the First Woman to Win the Iditarod Sled Dog Race. Cartwright, Shannon, illus. (PAWS IV Ser.). 48p. (J). 2003. 16.95 (978-1-57061-298-5(6)); 2002. pap. 9.95 (978-1-57061-293-0(5)) Sasquatch Bks.

Seder, Isaac. Alaska: The Last Frontier. 2003. (World Almanac Library of the States). (Illus.). 48p. (J). (gr. 5 up). pap. 14.95 (978-0-8368-5318-6(0)); lib. bdg. 30.00 (978-0-8368-5147-2(1)) Stevens, Gareth Inc. (World Almanac Library).

Somervill, Barbara A. Alaska. 2002. (From Sea to Shining Sea Ser.: 2). (Illus.). 80p. (J). (gr. 3-5). 30.50 (978-0-516-22318-6(6) , Children's Pr.) Scholastic Library Publishing.

Sosak. Alaska. 2000. (Switched on Schoolhouse Ser.). (Illus.). (YA). (gr. 7-12). pap. 24.95 incl. cd-rom (978-0-7403-0254-1(X) , SOSAK) Alpha Omega Pubns., Inc.

Staub, Frank. Children of the Tlingit. 1998. (World's Children Ser.). (Illus.). 56p. (J). (gr. 3-6). lib. bdg. (978-1-57505-333-2(0) , Carolrhoda Bks.) Lerner Publishing Group.

Stefoff, Rebecca. Alaska. 2nd ed. 2006. (Celebrate the States Ser.). (J). lib. bdg. 39.93 (978-0-7614-2153-5(X) , Benchmark Bks.) Cavendish, Marshall Corp.

Strudwick, Leslie. A Guide to Alaska. 2001. (American States Ser.). 32p. (J). (Illus.). (gr. 4-7). lib. bdg. 16.95 (978-1-930954-75-5(1)); per. 7.95 (978-1-930954-46-5(8)) Weigl Pubs., Inc.

Thomas, William. Alaska. 2006. (Portraits of the States Ser.). (J). pap. (978-0-8368-4714-7(8)); lib. bdg. (978-0-8368-4697-3(4)) Stevens, Gareth Inc.

The Trail to the Iditarod Trail. 2003. (Illus.). 166p. per. 24.95 (978-0-9741254-0-4(7) , Dynagraphix) Elliott, Jane.

Von Ammon, Helen. Alaska Llama - Far North Hero. Mauterer, Erin Marie, illus. 1998. 37p. (YA). (gr. 7 up). pap. 12.95 (978-0-9647756-7-1(0)) Doodlebug Bks.

Webb, Sophie. Looking for Seabirds: Journal from an Alaskan Voyage. 2004. (Illus.). 48p. (J). (gr. 5 up). tchr. ed. 16.00 (978-0-618-21235-4(3)) Houghton Mifflin Co. Trade & Reference Div.

Weber, Jen Funk. Clueless in Alaska: An Activity Book Filled with Puzzles, Fun Facts, Games, & Jokes. Weber, Mike, photos by. 2006. (Illus.). 48p. (J). pap., act. bk. ed. 12.95 (978-1-57061-441-5(5)) Sasquatch Bks.

Winner, Cherie. Life in the Tundra. 2003. (Ecosystems in Action Ser.). (Illus.). 72p. (J). (gr. 6-12). lib. bdg. 26.60 (978-0-8225-4686-3(8)) Lerner Publishing Group.

Wong, Su Tien. Alaska. 2004. (Rookie Read-About Geography Ser.). (Illus.). 31p. (J). 20.50 (978-0-516-22724-5(6) , Children's Pr.) Scholastic Library Publishing.

Wood, Ted. Iditarod Dream: Dusty & His Sled Dogs Compete in Alaska's Jr. Iditarod. 2002. (gr. 3-6). lib. bdg. 17.60 (978-0-613-57306-1(4)) Tandem Library Bks.

—Iditarod Dream: Dusty & His Sled Dogs Compete in Alaska's Jr. Iditarod. 2002. (Illus.). 48p. (J). (gr. 3-6). pap. 8.95 (978-0-8027-7535-1(7)) Walker & Co.

Young, Ian. The Iditarod: The Last Great Race. 2002. (High Five Reading Ser.). (Illus.). 48p. (J). (gr. 3-4). lib. bdg. 22.60 (978-0-7368-9545-3(0) , Capstone High-Interest Bks.); pap. (978-0-7368-9523-1(X)) Capstone Pr., Inc.

ALASKA—ANNEXATION TO THE UNITED STATES

Fremon, David K. The Alaska Purchase in American History. 1999. (In American History Ser.). (Illus.). 128p. (YA). (gr. 5-12). lib. bdg. 26.60 (978-0-7660-1138-0(0)) Enslow Pubs., Inc.

Kent, Zachary. William Seward: The Mastermind of the Alaska Purchase. 2001. (Historical American Biographies Ser.). (Illus.). 128p. (J). (gr. 6-12). lib. bdg. 26.60 (978-0-7660-1391-9(X)) Enslow Pubs., Inc.

Whitcraft, Melissa. Seward's Folly. 2002. (Cornerstones of Freedom). (Illus.). 48p. (J). (gr. 4-6). 26.00 (978-0-516-22525-8(1) , Children's Pr.) Scholastic Library Publishing.

ALASKA—FICTION

AaronG, Driftin'. Claude Henry, the Iditarod Mouse: The Adventures Begin. 2007. 108p. (J). per. 9.95 ***978-0-595-44990-3(5))** iUniverse, Inc.

Amato, Carol A. On the Trail of the Grizzly, Vol. 9. O'Brien, Patrick & Wenzel, David, illus. 1998. (Young Reader Ser.: No. 9). 48p. (J). (gr. 3-6). lib. bdg. 13.45 (978-1-56674-240-5(4)) Forest Hse. Publishing Co., Inc.

Andrew, Tommy. Neqsulartukut. Swope, Dean, illus. 1998. Tr. of We Fish. (ESK.). 8p. (J). (gr. k-3). pap. 6.00 (978-1-58084-032-3(9)) Lower Kuskokwim Schl. District.

Appleton, Victor. Tom Swift in the Caves of Ice or the Wre. 2006. pap. ***978-1-4065-0915-1(9))** Dodo Pr.

Bauer, Marion Dane. A Bear Named Trouble. 2005. 128p. (J). (gr. 3-5). 14.00 (978-0-618-51738-1(3) , Clarion Bks.) Houghton Mifflin Co. Trade & Reference Div.

—A Bear Named Trouble. 2006. 128p. (J). (gr. 4-7). pap. 5.99 (978-0-440-42132-0(2) , Yearling) Random Hse. Children's Bks.

Blake, Robert J. Togo. Blake, Robert J., illus. 2002. (Illus.). 48p. (J). 16.99 (978-0-399-23381-4(4) , Philomel) Penguin Group (USA) Inc.

Bodett, Tom. Norman Tuttle on the Last Frontier. 208p. (YA). (gr. 7). 2006. mass mkt. 5.99 (978-0-553-49493-8(7) , Laurel Leaf); 2004. 15.95 (978-0-679-89031-7(9) , Knopf Bks. for Young Readers) Random Hse. Children's Bks.

—Norman Tuttle on the Last Frontier: A Novel in Stories. 2004. 208p. (J). (gr. 7). lib. bdg. 17.99 (978-0-679-99031-4(3) , Knopf Bks. for Young Readers) Random Hse. Children's Bks.

—Williwaw! 2000. 208p. (YA). (gr. 5-8). pap. 5.99 (978-0-375-80687-2(3) , Yearling) Random Hse. Children's Bks.

—Williwaw! 2000. (J). (978-0-606-19440-2(1)) Tandem Library Bks.

Brin, Susannah. Climb. 2000. (gr. 5-8). lib. bdg. 11.80 (978-0-613-51205-3(7)) Tandem Library Bks.

Clay, Margaret. Double Identity. 2007. 276p. (YA). pap. 12.95 ***978-0-9792328-6-2(4))** Helm Publishing.

Clements, Becky. A Picnic with Friends: Alaska Adventure Bears. 2003. (Alaska Adventure Bears Ser.). 16p. pap. 9.95 (978-1-888125-87-0(X)) Publication Consultants.

Cosgrove, Stephen. Gnome from Nome. James, Robin, illus. 2003. (Serendipity Bks.). 32p. (J). (gr. k-3). pap. 4.99 (978-0-8431-0585-8(2) , Price Stern Sloan) Penguin Group (USA) Inc.

—Gnome from Nome. 2003. (gr. k-3). lib. bdg. 13.00 (978-0-613-70763-3(X)) Tandem Library Bks.

Dalmatian Press Staff, adapted by. The Call of the Wild. 2002. (Spot the Classics Ser.). (Illus.). 182p. (J). (gr. k-5). 4.99 (978-1-57759-545-8(9)) Dalmatian Pr.

Dillingham, Mike. Rivers Book Two: Through the Eyes of a Blind Sled Dog. 2003. 13.95 (978-1-59433-004-9(2)) Publication Consultants.

Dunevant, Darlene J. An A+ Alaskan Adventure. 2002. 110p. pap. 9.95 (978-0-595-22991-8(3) , Writers Club Pr.) iUniverse, Inc.

Dwyer, Mindy. The Salmon Princess: An Alaska Cinderella Story. 2004. (Illus.). 32p. (J). pap. 9.95 (978-1-57061-355-5(9)) Sasquatch Bks.

Forbush, Kyle. The Sourdoughs' Five Children. Forbush, Lisa, illus. 2004. (J). bds. 6.95 (978-1-57833-258-8(3)) Todd Communications.

—Who Is Alaska's Favorite Bear? Forbush, Lisa, illus. 2003. (J). bds. 6.95 (978-1-57833-211-3(7)) Todd Communications.

Frost, Helen. Diamond Willow. 2008. 128p. (J). 16.00 ***978-0-374-31776-8(3))** Farrar, Straus & Giroux.

George, Jean Craighead. The Julie Trilogy. 1999. (Julie of the Wolves Ser.). (Illus.). (J). (gr. 5 up). pap. 17.97 (978-0-06-449350-5(4)) HarperCollins Pubs.

Giles, Gail. Right Behind You. 2007. 304p. (YA). (gr. 10 up). 15.99 ***978-0-316-16636-2(7))** Little, Brown Bks. for Young Readers.

Gill, Shelley. Sitka Rose. Cartwright, Shannon, illus. 2005. (J). 16.95 (978-1-57091-353-2(6)); 32p. pap. 7.95 (978-1-57091-364-8(1)) Charlesbridge Publishing, Inc.

Golding, Theresa Martin & Easley, Mary Ann. I Am the Ice Worm. 2004. (Illus.). 128p. (YA). (gr. 4-6). pap. 9.95 (978-1-59078-281-1(X)) Boyds Mills Pr.

Green, John. Looking for Alaska. 2006. 256p. (YA). (gr. 8). pap. 7.99 (978-0-14-240251-1(6) , Puffin) Penguin Group (USA) Inc.

Guenther, James. Turnagain, Ptarmigan! Where Did You Go? A Story about the Alaska State Bird. Cartwright, Shannon, illus. 2003. (J). (ps-2). lib. bdg. 17.60 (978-0-613-79147-2(9)) Tandem Library Bks.

Harcourt School Publishers Staff. Adventure in Alaska: Take-Home Book. 2001. (Collections Ser.). (Illus.). (J). pap. 1.90 (978-0-15-319520-4(7)) Harcourt Schl. Pubs.

—Adventure in Alaska Below Level. 3rd ed. 2002. (Trophies Reading Program Ser.). (Illus.). pap. 5.10 (978-0-15-323318-0(4)) Harcourt Schl. Pubs.

—Aventura en Alaska: Take-Home Book. 2001. (Vamos Ser.). (SPA., Illus.). (J). pap. 2.80 (978-0-15-319952-3(0)) Harcourt Schl. Pubs.

—Better Than Gold On Level. 3rd ed. 2002. (Trophies Reading Program Ser.). (Illus.). pap. 5.10 (978-0-15-323167-4(X)) Harcourt Schl. Pubs.

Harrison, Jack M. Alaskan Tails of the Trail: A Collection of Short Stories. 2003. 124p. (J). pap. 11.99 (978-1-57921-606-1(4)) Pleasant Word.

Harter, Lois. Where's the Boss. 2005. 32p. 9.95 (978-1-888125-63-4(2)) Publication Consultants.

Henry, Sue. Deadfall: An Alaska Mystery. 1999. (gr. 7-12). lib. bdg. 15.30 (978-0-613-29223-8(5)) Tandem Library Bks.

Higgins, Kitty. Mushing in Alaska. 2005. 40.00 ***978-1-4108-4228-2(2))** Benchmark Education Co.

Hill, Kirkpatrick. Dancing at the Odinochka. 2005. (Illus.). 272p. (J). (ps-9). 15.95 (978-0-689-87388-1(3) , McElderry, Margaret K.) Simon & Schuster Children's Publishing.

—The Year of Miss Agnes. 2002. 128p. (J). (ps-7). mass mkt. 4.99 (978-0-689-85124-7(3) , Aladdin) Simon & Schuster Children's Publishing.

—The Year of Miss Agnes. Knorr, Peter, illus. 2000. 128p. (J). (gr. 3-7). 16.00 (978-0-689-82933-8(7) , McElderry, Margaret K.) Simon & Schuster Children's Publishing.

—The Year of Miss Agnes. 2002. (gr. 3-6). lib. bdg. 13.00 (978-0-613-53884-8(6)) Tandem Library Bks.

Hobbs, Will. Leaving Protection. 192p. (J). (gr. 5 up). 2005. pap. 5.99 (978-0-380-73312-5(9) , Harper Trophy); 2004. 15.99 (978-0-688-17475-0(2)) HarperCollins Pubs.

Hobbs, William. Down the Yukon. 2001. (Illus.). 208p. (J). (gr. 5 up). 17.99 (978-0-688-17472-9(8)) HarperCollins Pubs.

—Jason's Gold. (Illus.). 240p. (J). (gr. 6 up). 2000. pap. 5.99 (978-0-380-72914-2(8)); 1999. 16.99 (978-0-688-15093-8(4)) HarperCollins Pubs.

—Wild Man Island. 192p. (J). (gr. 5 up). 2003. pap. 5.99 (978-0-380-73310-1(2) , Harper Trophy); 2002. (Illus.). lib. bdg. 16.89 (978-0-06-029810-4(3)) HarperCollins Pubs.

—Wild Man Island. 2003. (gr. 5-8). lib. bdg. 14.15 (978-0-613-61741-3(X)) Tandem Library Bks.

Horner, Polly. Polly & the North Star. (Illus.). pap. 11.00 (978-1-84255-281-0(3)); 2003. 32p. 19.99 (978-1-84255-085-4(3)) Orion Children's Bks. GBR. *Dist:* Trafalgar Square Publishing.

Johannes, Avril & Branham, Jan. Bunny an Alaskan Hare. 2006. 32p. 7.95 (978-0-9749360-3-1(0)) Icicle Falls Publishing Co.

Johns, Elizabeth, illus. The Sleeping Lady. 2005. 32p. 8.95 (978-0-88240-495-0(4)) Graphic Arts Ctr. Publishing Co.

Kerr, Mike. Mike & a Lynx Named Kitty. Vitt, Karren, illus. 2nd rev. ed. 2006. 112p. per. 13.50 (*978-1-931195-36-2(6)) KiwE Publishing, Ltd.

Kittredge, Frances. Neeluk: An Eskimo Boy in the Days of the Whaling Ships. Rock, Howard, illus. 2005. 88p. (J). (gr. 3-7). 18.95 (978-0-88240-545-2(4)) Graphic Arts Ctr. Publishing Co.

—Neeluk: An Eskimo Boy in the Days of the Whaling Ships. 2001. (gr. 3-6). lib. bdg. 21.05 (978-0-613-55638-5(0)) Tandem Library Bks.

Kondak, Margarida. The Wild Horses of Summer Bay. Kondak, Mary, illus. l.t. ed. 2002. 31p. 9.95 (978-1-890692-06-3(9)) Wizard Works.

Lion, Melissa. Upstream. 160p. (YA). (gr. 7). 2006. pap. 8.95 (978-0-375-83954-2(2)); 2005. 15.95 (978-0-385-74643-4(1)) Random Hse. Children's Bks. (Lamb, Wendy).

Listen to Alaskas Animals. 2006. 10.95 (978-1-931353-25-0(5)) Saddle Pal Creations, Inc.

London, Jack. The Call of the Wild. 2002. 11.49 (978-0-7587-7808-6(2)) Book Wholesalers, Inc.

—The Call of the Wild. Minor, Wendell, illus. 1999. (Scribner Illustrated Classics Ser.). 128p. (YA). (gr. 4-7). 24.00 (978-0-689-81836-3(X) , Atheneum) Simon & Schuster Children's Publishing.

—White Fang. (J). 9.95 (978-1-56156-306-7(4)) Kidsbooks, Inc.

London, Jack & Access Matrix Staff. The Call of the Wild. adapted ed. (YA). (gr. 5-12). 8.50 (978-0-8359-0040-9(1)) Globe Fearon Educational Publishing.

Magdanz, James. Go Home, River. Widom, Dianne, illus. 2002. 32p. (ps up). 8.95 (978-0-88240-568-1(3)) Graphic Arts Ctr. Publishing Co.

McPherson, Missie & O'Neill, Elizabeth. Alfred Visits Alaska. 2006. (Illus.). 24p. (J). pap. 12.00 (978-0-9771836-3-0(7)) Funny Bone Bks.

Meissner, Amy, illus. Seldovia Sam & Wildfire Escape. 2005. (Misadventures of Seldovia Sam Ser.: Bk. 3). 64p. (J). (ps-ps). pap. 6.95 (978-0-88240-601-5(9)) Graphic Arts Ctr. Publishing Co.

Mikaelsen, Ben. Touching Spirit Bear. 2001. 256p. (J). (gr. 5 up). 16.99 (978-0-380-97744-4(3)) HarperCollins Pubs.

—Touching Spirit Bear. l.t. ed. 2004. 305p. pap. 10.95 (978-0-7862-6351-6(2)) Thorndike Pr.

Miller, Heather. Lost in Alaska: A Texas Girl & an Aleut Boy. 2001. (J). pap. 9.95 (978-0-89992-149-5(3)) Council for Indian Education.

Morris, Jennifer. Come, Llamas. 2006. 208p. (gr. 3-7). 5.99 (978-0-440-42024-8(5) , Yearling) Random Hse. Children's Bks.

Muir, John. Stikeen: An Adventure with a Dog & a Glacier. 2003. (gr. k-3). lib. bdg. 12.95 (978-0-613-88678-9(X)) Tandem Library Bks.

Murphy, Claire Rudolf. Free Radical. 2002. 208p. (YA). (gr. 7). 15.00 (978-0-618-11134-3(4) , Clarion Bks.) Houghton Mifflin Co. Trade & Reference Div.

—Gold Rush Winter. 2002. (gr. 3-6). lib. bdg. 11.80 (978-0-613-50201-6(9)) Tandem Library Bks.

—To the Summit. 1998. 208p. pap. 3.99 (978-0-380-79537-6(X)) HarperCollins Pubs.

Murphy, Claire Rudolf & Golden Books Staff. Gold Rush Winter. 2002. (Road to Reading Ser.). (Illus.). 48p. (J). (gr. 2-4). pap. 3.99 (978-0-307-26413-8(0) , Random Hse. Bks. for Young Readers) Random Hse. Children's Bks.

Nolting, Anne Carse. Pythagoras Eagle & the Music of the Spheres. 2003. 172p. (YA). 23.95 (978-1-878044-94-5(X)) Mayhaven Publishing.

Orenstein, Denise Gosliner. Unseen Companion. 368p. (J). 2003. 15.99 (978-0-06-052056-4(6)); 2003. lib. bdg. 16.89 (978-0-06-052057-1(4)); 2005. reprint ed. pap. 7.99 (978-0-06-052058-8(2) , HarperTeen) HarperCollins Pubs.

Papish, Ramiel. The Little Fox. 2006. (J). (978-1-889963-87-7(9)) Univ. of Alaska Pr.

Paulsen, Gary. Zero to Sixty: The Motorcycle Journey of a Lifetime. 1999. (gr. 7-12). lib. bdg. 21.10 (978-0-613-16042-1(8)) Tandem Library Bks.

Peterson, Sara Budinger. Alice Meets Inupiat Eskimos. 2000. (Illus.). 68p. 11.95 (978-0-9665282-1-3(2)) Saranjon Publishing.

—The Journey of Perm. Kaufman, Mary Bee, illus. 2004. 96p. pap. 11.95 (978-0-9665282-3-7(9)) Saranjon Publishing.

Peterson, Tracie. Ashes & Ice. 2001. (gr. 5-8). lib. bdg. 22.25 (978-0-613-55565-4(1)) Tandem Library Bks.

Pockets Learning Staff. Samantha's Alaska Adventure. 1998. (Illus.). 2p. (J). (ps-1). 15.00 (978-1-888074-90-1(6)) Pockets of Learning.

Poulsen, David A. The Book of Vampire. 4th rev. ed. 2007. (Salt & Pepper Chronicles). 160p. (gr. 3-7). pap. 6.95 (*978-1-55263-805-7(7)) Key Porter Bks. CAN. *Dist:* Perseus Distribution.

Repp, Gloria. Charlie. 2002. (Illus.). 147p. (J). (gr. 4-7). 7.49 (978-1-57924-817-8(9)) Jones, Bob Univ. Pr.

—Mik-Shrok. 1998. 133p. (J). (gr. 4-7). pap. 7.49 (978-1-57924-069-1(0) , 113902) Jones, Bob Univ. Pr.

—Zebra 77. Schuppert, David, illus. 2002. (Adventures of an Arctic Missionary Ser.). 156p. (J). (gr. 4-7). 7.49 (978-1-57924-930-4(2)) Jones, Bob Univ. Pr.

Richter, Bernd & Richter, Susan. Cruising Alaska's Inside Passage. 2003. 56p. 9.95 (978-1-931353-09-0(3)) Saddle Pal Creations, Inc.

—Goodnight Alaska - Goodnight Little Bear. 2002. 14p. bds. 6.95 (978-1-931353-06-9(9)) Saddle Pal Creations, Inc.

—The Twelve Days of Christmas in Alaska. 2002. 14p. bds. 9.95 (978-1-931353-08-3(5)) Saddle Pal Creations, Inc.

Richter, Bernd C. When Grandma & Grandpa Visited Alaska They. . . 1999. 48p. 14.95 (978-0-9663495-6-6(3)) Saddle Pal Creations, Inc.

Richter, Bernd C. & Richter, Susan E. When Grandma & Grandpa Visited Alaska They. . . Richter, Bernd C., illus. 1998. (Illus.). 48p. (ps-6). pap. 9.95 (978-0-9663495-0-4(4)) Saddle Pal Creations, Inc.

Robinet, Harriette Gillem. Walking to the Bus-Rider Blues. 2002. (gr. 3-6). lib. bdg. 13.00 (978-0-613-57932-2(1)) Tandem Library Bks.

Rogers, Jean. Goodbye, My Island. Munoz, Rie, illus. 2005. 96p. (gr. 2 up). pap. 9.95 (978-0-88240-538-4(1)) Graphic Arts Ctr. Publishing Co.

—Goodbye, My Island. 2001. (gr. 3-6). lib. bdg. 18.75 (978-0-613-77288-4(1)) Tandem Library Bks.

Sargent, Daina. Alaska: Be Brave, 4. Lenoir, Jane, illus. l.t. ed. 2004. (Double Trouble Ser.: 4). 48p. (J). pap. 9.95 (978-1-59381-121-1(7)); lib. bdg. 22.60 (978-1-59381-120-4(9)) Ozark Publishing.

Senshu, Noriko. Sonny's Dream. Senshu, Noriko, illus. 2001. (Illus.). 40p. (J). (ps up). 16.95 (978-1-57174-215-5(8)) Hampton Roads Publishing Co., Inc.

Simmons, Lynn Sheffield. Bo, the Famous Retriever. Hampton, Lin, illus. 2004. 128p. (YA). (gr. 3-6). pap. 10.95 (978-1-58980-217-9(9)) Pelican Publishing Co., Inc.

Smelcer, John. The Trap. 2006. 176p. (YA). (gr. 4-7). 15.95 (978-0-8050-7939-5(4)) Holt, Henry & Co.

—The Trap. 2007. 192p. (YA). pap. 7.99 (*978-0-312-37755-7(X)) Square Fish.

Smith, Sherri L. Lucy the Giant. l.t. ed. 2002. 236p. 23.95 (978-0-7862-4751-6(7)) Thorndike Pr.

Stevens, Beverly. This Dog Team Lives in the House. 2005. (J). pap. 9.95 (*978-1-57833-317-2(2)) Todd Communications.

Stine, R. L. El Abominable Hombre de las Nieves en Pasadena. 2004. (Goosebumps Ser.). (SPA.). 144p. (J). (gr. 4-7). 4.99 (978-0-439-67055-5(1) , Scholastic en Espanol) Scholastic, Inc.

Thorpe, Kiki. Follow the Lemming. 2001. (gr. k-3). lib. bdg. 11.80 (978-0-613-35513-1(X)) Tandem Library Bks.

Trout, Richard E. Czar of Alaska: The Cross of Charlemagne. 2005. 248p. (J). (gr. 5-8). 15.95 (978-1-58980-328-2(0)) Pelican Publishing Co., Inc.

Upton, Joe. Runaways on the Inside Passage. 2005. (Illus.). 304p. (gr. 5 up). 17.95 (978-0-88240-564-3(0)); pap. 9.95 (978-0-88240-565-0(9)) Graphic Arts Ctr. Publishing Co.

Vanasse, Deb. Under Alaska's Midnight Sun. Trammell, Jeremiah, illus. 2005. 32p. (J). (ps-ps). 15.95 (978-1-57061-451-4(2)); pap., pap. 10.95 (978-1-57061-422-4(9)) Sasquatch Bks.

Warbelow, Willy Lou & Warbelow-Tack, Cyndie, illus. The Guffinys Too. 1999. 104p. (J). (gr. 2-6). 19.95 (978-0-9618314-4-8(8)) Warbelow, Willy Lou.

Warner, Gertrude Chandler. The Mystery of the Black Raven. 1999. (Boxcar Children Special Ser.: No. 12). (Illus.). (J). (gr. 2-5). (978-0-606-18770-1(7)) Tandem Library Bks.

—Mystery of the Black Raven. 1999. (gr. 3-6). lib. bdg. 11.80 (978-0-613-16286-9(2)) Tandem Library Bks.

Warner, Gertrude Chandler, creator. The Mystery of the Black Raven, Vol. 12. 1999. (Boxcar Children Special Ser.: No. 12). (Illus.). 144p. (J). (gr. 2-5). 14.95 (978-0-8075-2988-1(5)); pap. 3.95 (978-0-8075-2989-8(3)) Whitman, Albert & Co.

Way, Daniel. Planet Hulk Prelude. 2006. (Illus.). 144p. pap. 13.99 (978-0-7851-1953-1(1)) Marvel Enterprises, Inc.

Weaver, Jenny. Following the Raven. 2003. 113p. (YA). (gr. 5-8). pap. 14.95 (978-1-878044-91-4(5)) Mayhaven Publishing.

Whelan, Gloria. Silver. Marchesi, Stephen, illus. 2004. (Stepping Stone Bks.). 64p. (J). (gr. 1-4). pap. 3.99 (978-0-394-89611-3(4) , Random Hse. Bks. for Young Readers) Random Hse. Children's Bks.

Winfield, Arthur M. Rover Boys in Alaska or Lost in the Fiel. 2006. pap. 30.95 (*978-1-4286-4107-5(6)) Kessinger Publishing, LLC.

Wood, Beverley & Wood, Chris. Jack's Knife. 2006. (Sirius Mystery Ser.). 288p. (J). pap. 7.95 (978-1-55192-709-1(8)) Raincoast Bk. Distribution CAN. *Dist:* Perseus Distribution.

Wood, Beverley. DogStar. rev. ed. 2004. (Sirius Mystery Ser.). 320p. (J). pap. 7.95 (978-1-55192-638-4(5)) Raincoast Bk. Distribution CAN. *Dist:* Perseus Distribution.

Yanuchi, Lori. Running with the Big Dogs: A Sled Dog Puppy Grows up in Denali National Park, Alaska. Brown, Wendy, illus. 1999. 32p. (J). 8.95 (978-0-9670177-0-9(X)) Ridge Rock Pr.

ALASKA—HISTORY

Beech, Linda Ward. The Exxon Valdez's Deadly Oil Spill. 2007. (Code Red Ser.). (Illus.). 32p. (J). (gr. 3-7). lib. bdg. 25.27 (978-1-59716-366-8(X)) Bearport Publishing Co., Inc.

Carpenter, Chad. Tundra Alaska Coloring Book. (J). pap. 3.00 (978-1-878100-32-0(7)) Todd Communications.

Dunlap, Julie & Lorbiecki, Marybeth. John Muir & the Stickeen: An Icy Adventure with a No Good Dog. Farnsworth, Bill, illus. 2004. 32p. (gr. k-3). 16.95 (978-1-55971-903-2(6) , NorthWord Bks. for Young Readers) T&N Children's Publishing.

Forbush, Kyle & Forbush, Kyle. A Is for Alaska - an ABC Book. Forbush, Lisa, illus. 2004. (J). bds. 6.95 (978-1-57833-287-8(7)) Todd Communications.

Fremon, David K. The Alaska Purchase in American History. 1999. (In American History Ser.). (Illus.). 128p. (YA). (gr. 5-12). lib. bdg. 26.60 (978-0-7660-1138-0(0)) Enslow Pubs., Inc.

Harcourt School Publishers Staff. A Race Across Alaska: Take-Home Book. 1999. (Collections Ser.). (Illus.). (J). pap. 1.90 (978-0-15-317295-3(9)) Harcourt Schl. Pubs.

—Traveling Around Alaska On Level. 3rd ed. 2002. (Trophies Reading Program Ser.). (Illus.). pap. 5.10 (978-0-15-323348-7(6)) Harcourt Schl. Pubs.

Jones, Charlotte Foltz. Yukon Gold: The Story of the Klondike Gold Rush. 1998. (Illus.). 112p. (J). (gr. 4-7). tchr. ed. 18.95 (978-0-8234-1403-1(5)) Holiday Hse., Inc.

Kimmel, Elizabeth Cody. Balto & the Great Race. 2004. (Stepping Stone Bks.). (Illus.). 112p. (J). (gr. k-3). lib. bdg. 11.99 (978-0-679-99198-4(0) , Random Hse. Bks. for Young Readers) Random Hse. Children's Bks.

—Balto & the Great Race. Koerber, Nora, illus. 1999. (Stepping Stone Bks.). 112p. (J). (gr. k-3). pap. 3.99 (978-0-679-89198-7(6) , Random Hse. Bks. for Young Readers) Random Hse. Children's Bks.

—Balto & the Great Race. 1999. (Step into Reading Ser.). 10.64 (978-0-606-17522-7(9)) Tandem Library Bks.

King, Elaine. Alaskan Honeymoon Adventure. 2004. per. (978-0-9758654-0-8(4)) Adventure Pr.

Levinson, Nancy Smiler. If You Lived in the Alaska Territory. 1998. (Illus.). 80p. (J). (gr. 2-5). pap. 5.99 (978-0-590-74449-2(6)) Scholastic, Inc.

Marsh, Carole. Alaska History Projects: 30 Cool, Activities, Crafts, Experiments & More for Kids to Do to Learn about Your State! 2003. (Alaska Experience Ser.). 32p. (gr. k-5). pap. 5.95 (978-0-635-01771-0(7) , Marsh, Carole Bks.) Gallopade International.

Marsh, Kenneth L. A River Between Us: The Upper Susitna River Valley of Alaska, a Historical Story Collection. 2nd ed. 2002. (Illus.). 268p. per. 19.95 (978-0-9718302-0-2(7) , 001) Trapper Creek Museum Sluice Box Productions.

Maxwell, Noel. Kid's Alaska; Workbook of Alaska & its History. 2005. 60p. (gr. 6 up). 12.95 (978-0-9745187-0-1(0)) Good Roots Publishing.

Miller, Debbie S. The Great Serum Race. Van Zyle, Jon, illus. 2006. 40p. (J). pap. 8.95 (978-0-8027-7723-2(6)) Walker & Co.

Mossy Moose Alaska: Coloring & Activity Book. (J). pap. 5.00 (978-0-9677477-2-9(4)) "Grandma's Hope Notes".

Olson, Marie. Tlingit Coloring Book. 24p. (J). pap. 6.00 (978-1-57833-051-5(3)) Todd Communications.

Olson, Robert. Alaska - Hints of Paradise: Photographs & Essays by Robert Olson. Olson, Robert, photos by. 2004. 160p. 39.95 (978-0-9749570-0-5(3)) Visions Of Nature.

Parker, Lewis K. Russian Colonies in the Americas. 2003. (Reading Power Ser.). (Illus.). 24p. (J). lib. bdg. 17.25 (978-0-8239-6470-3(1) , PowerKids Pr.) Rosen Publishing Group, Inc., The.

Sherrow, Victoria. The Exxon Valdez: Tragic Oil Spill. 1998. (American Disasters Ser.). (Illus.). 48p. (YA). (gr. 4-10). lib. bdg. 23.93 (978-0-7660-1058-1(9)) Enslow Pubs., Inc.

Standiford, Natalie. Bravest Dog Ever: Story of Balto. Cook, Donald, illus. 2003. (Step into Reading Ser.: Step 3). 48p. (J). (gr. 1-3). lib. bdg. 11.99 (978-0-394-99695-0(X) , Random Hse. Bks. for Young Readers) Random Hse. Children's Bks.

Stone, Lynn M. Sea Otter. 2003. (Animals in U.S. History Ser.). (Illus.). 24p. (J). 25.64 (978-1-58952-701-0(1)) Rourke Publishing, LLC.

Whitcraft, Melissa. Seward's Folly. 2002. (Cornerstones of Freedom). (Illus.). 48p. (J). (gr. 4-6). 26.00 (978-0-516-22525-8(1) , Children's Pr.) Scholastic Library Publishing.

Wong, Su Tien. Alaska. 2004. (Rookie Read-About Geography Ser.). 32p. (J). (gr. 1-2). pap. 5.95 (978-0-516-27938-1(6) , Children's Pr.) Scholastic Library Publishing.

ALASKA PURCHASE, 1867

see Alaska—Annexation to the United States

ALBERTA

Johnson, Allen L. Willmore Horseback Adventure: Adventures with Grandchildren, 2004. (Illus.). 190p. 15.00 (978-1-880675-08-3(0)) Creative Enterprises.

Laws, Gordon D. & Laws, Lauren M. Alberta. 2002. (Exploring Canada Ser.). (Illus.). 104p. (J). 29.95 (978-1-59018-045-7(3) , Lucent Bks.) Thomson Gale.

Yates, Sarah. Alberta. 2nd rev. ed. (Hello Canada Ser.). 72p. (J). pap. (978-1-55041-766-1(5)) Fitzhenry & Whiteside, Ltd.

—Alberta. 1998. (Hello Canada Ser.). (Illus.). (J). (gr. 3-6). pap. 6.95 (978-0-8225-9796-4(9)) Lerner Publishing Group.

Yates, Susan. Alberta. 1999. (Hello Canada Ser.). (J). pap. (978-1-55041-273-4(6)) Fitzhenry & Whiteside, Ltd.

ALBERTA—FICTION

Clay, Ian. Coyote Lake. 2007. 104p. per. 9.95 (*978-0-595-44590-5(X)) iUniverse, Inc.

Cook, Gerri. Christmas in the Badlands. 2003. (Dinosaur Soup Ser.). (Illus.). 120p. (YA). (gr. 3-5). pap. 9.95 (978-1-895836-94-3(8)) River Bks. CAN. *Dist:* Fitzhenry & Whiteside, Ltd.

—A Penny for Albert. 2005. (Illus.). 64p. (J). 9.95 (978-1-895836-93-6(X)) River Bks. CAN. *Dist:* Fitzhenry & Whiteside, Ltd.

Draper, Penny. Terror at Turtle Mountain. 2006. (Illus.). 196p. (J). (gr. 4-7). pap. (*978-1-55050-343-2(X)) Coteau Bks.

Guest, Jacqueline. Rink Rivals. 2001. (Sports Stories Ser.). 104p. (gr. 3-8). (J). (*978-1-55028-745-5(1)); 7.95 (978-1-55028-744-8(3)) Lorimer, James & Co., Ltd., Pubs. CAN. *Dist:* Casemate Pubs. & Bk. Distributors, LLC.

Heidbreder, Robe. Drumheller Dinosaur Dance. Slavin, Bill, illus. 2006. 32p. (978-1-55337-982-9(9)) Kids Can Pr., Ltd.

Holubitsky, Katherine. The Mountain That Walked. 2005. 224p. (J). (gr. 5-8). pap. 7.95 (978-1-55143-376-9(1)); lib. bdg. 16.95 (978-1-55143-392-9(3)) Orca Bk. Pubs. USA.

Lottridge, Celia Barker. Ticket to Curlew. 2007. 144p. (J). pap. 7.95 (*978-0-88899-843-9(0)) Groundwood Bks. CAN. *Dist:* Perseus Distribution.

Lottridge, Celia Barker & Gerber, Mary Jane. Wings to Fly. 1999. (Illus.). 216p. (J). (gr. 3-7). pap. 5.95 (978-0-88899-346-5(3) , Libros Tigrillo) Groundwood Bks. CAN. *Dist:* Perseus Distribution.

Oke, Janette. Drums of Change: The Story of Running Fawn. 2003. (Classics for Girls Ser.). (Illus.). 176p. (J). 9.99 (978-0-7642-2714-1(9)) Bethany Hse. Pubs.

Saunders, Susan. Kate's Secret Plan. 1998. (Treasured Horses Ser.: Vol. 6). (J). (gr. 3-7). pap. 3.99 (978-0-590-31658-3(3)) Scholastic, Inc.

—Kate's Secret Plan. Rabinowitz, Sandy & Keiffer, Christa, illus. l.t. ed. 1999. (Treasured Horses Collection). 128p. (J). (gr. 4 up). lib. bdg. 23.33 (978-0-8368-2278-6(1)) Stevens, Gareth Inc.

—Kate's Secret Plan, 6. 1998. (Treasured Horses Ser.). (J). (978-0-606-13866-6(8)) Tandem Library Bks.

Truckey, Don. The Adventures of Caraway Kim— Southpaw. 2005. 192p. pap. 8.95 (978-1-894345-90-3(8)) Thistledown Pr., Ltd. CAN. *Dist:* Literary Pr. Group of Canada.

Woodson, Marion. Dinosaur Fever. 2007. 168p. (YA). pap. 11.99 (*978-1-55002-690-0(9) , Sandcastle Bks.) Dundurn Group, The CAN. *Dist:* Univ. of Toronto Pr.

ALCINDOR, LEW, 1947-

see Abdul-Jabbar, Kareem, 1947-

ALCOHOLICS

see Alcoholism

ALCOHOLISM

Amos, Janine. Jon Drinks Alcohol. 2002. (Body Matters Ser.). (Illus.). 32p. (YA). 19.99 (978-1-84234-106-3(5) , Cherrytree Books) Evans Publishing Group GBR. *Dist:* Independent Pubs. Group.

Aretha, David. On the Rocks: Teens & Alcohol. 2006. (Illus.). 144p. (J). (gr. 9-12). 30.50 (978-0-531-16792-2(5) , Watts, Franklin) Scholastic Library Publishing.

Benton, John. New Hope Series, 10 bks., Set. 2004p. (J). (gr. 3-12). 35.00 (978-0-9635411-1-6(0)) Benton, John Bks.

Bichler, Christine. Teen Drinking. 1999. (Drug Abuse Prevention Library). (Illus.). 64p. (YA). (gr. 7-12). lib. bdg. 25.25 (978-0-8239-2830-9(6) , DRTEDR) Rosen Publishing Group, Inc., The.

Biggers, Jeff. Chemical Dependency & the Dysfunctional Family. rev. ed. 1998. (Drug Abuse Prevention Library). (Illus.). 64p. (YA). (gr. 7-12). lib. bdg. 17.95 (978-0-8239-2749-4(0) , DRDYFA) Rosen Publishing Group, Inc., The.

Bingham, Jane. Alcohol. 2005. (What's the Deal? Ser.). (Illus.). 56p. (J). (gr. 3-7). lib. bdg. (978-1-4034-7020-1(0)) Heinemann Library.

Carson-DeWitt, Rosalyn, ed. Drugs, Alcohol, & Tobacco: Learning about Addictive Behavior, 3 vols. 2002. (Illus.). (J). Vol. 1. (978-0-02-865757-8(8)); Vol. 2. (978-0-02-865758-5(6)); Vol. 3. (978-0-02-865759-2(4)) Thomson Gale. (Macmillan Reference USA).

Chiu, Christina. Teen Guide to Staying Sober. 1998. (Drug Abuse Prevention Library). 64p. (J). (gr. 7-12). pap. 6.95 (978-1-56838-249-4(9)) Hazelden Publishing & Educational Services.

Clayton, Lawrence. Alcohol Drug Dangers. (Drug Dangers Ser.). (Illus.). 64p. (YA). (gr. 4-10). 2000. pap. 13.26 (978-0-7660-1735-1(4)); 1999. lib. bdg. 27.93 (978-0-7660-1159-5(3)) Enslow Pubs., Inc.

—Barbiturates & Other Depressants. rev. ed. 2005. (Drug Abuse Prevention Library). (Illus.). 64p. (YA). (gr. 7-12). lib. bdg. 25.25 (978-0-8239-3442-3(X)) Rosen Publishing Group, Inc., The.

Connolly, Sean. Alcohol. 2006. (Straight Talking Ser.). (J). (978-1-58340-923-7(8)) Smart Apple Media.

Constant. Alcohol. 2004. (Teen Issues Ser.). (J). 28.56 (978-1-4109-0609-0(4)); (Illus.). pap. 8.95 (978-1-4109-0880-3(1)) Harcourt Schl. Pubs.

—Alcohol 6-Pack. 2004. (Teen Issues Ser.). (Illus.). (YA). pap. 48.30 (978-1-4109-0887-2(9)) Harcourt Schl. Pubs.

Cross, David B., ed. Book of Stories & Study Guide. 2nd exp. ed. 2005. 116p. (YA). per. 4.95 (978-0-9759988-1-6(1)) Working Words & Graphics.

Deboo, Ana. Alcohol. 2007. (J). (*978-1-4034-9737-6(0)); pap. (*978-1-4034-9742-0(7)) Heinemann Library.

Derkins, Susie. Barbiturates & Your Central Nervous System: The Incredibly Disgusting Story. 2005. (Incredibly Disgusting Drugs Ser.). (Illus.). 48p. (YA). (gr. 5-8). lib. bdg. 25.25 (978-0-8239-3388-4(1)) Rosen Publishing Group, Inc., The.

DiConsiglio, John. True Confessions: Real stories about drinking & Drugs. 2008. (Scholastic Choices Ser.). 112p. (J). pap. 8.95 (*978-0-531-14773-3(8) , Watts, Franklin) Scholastic Library Publishing.

Diou, Suzanne & Caldwell, Lois. 12 Stepping Stones: For Young Children of Alcoholics & Other Addictive-Drug Users. Cavazos, Hector Dionicio, illus. 1999. 104p. (J). (gr. k-10). pap. 14.95 (978-1-57543-077-5(0)) MAR*CO Products, Inc.

Drug & Alcohol Prevention. (J). (gr. 2-3). 3.80 (978-0-8374-1262-7(5) , 211); (gr. 3). 3.80 (978-0-8374-0120-1(8) , 212); (gr. 4). 3.80 (978-0-8374-0121-8(6) , 213); (gr. 5-6). 5.95 (978-0-8374-1266-5(8) , 267); (gr. 7-9). 3.80 (978-0-8374-0080-8(5) , 411) Weekly Reader Corp.

Dudley, William. Alcohol: An Opposing Viewpoints Guide. 2005. (Writing the Critical Essay Ser.). (Illus.). 96p. (YA). (gr. 10-13). lib. bdg. 29.95 (978-0-7377-3192-7(3) , Greenhaven Pr., Inc.) Thomson Gale.

Esherick, Joan. Dying for Acceptance: A Teen's Guide to Drug- & Alcohol-Related Health Issues. 2005. (Science of Health Ser.). (Illus.). 128p. (J). lib. bdg. 24.95 (978-1-59084-847-0(0)) Mason Crest Pubs.

Fatal Decision, Grade 8. (YA). pap., tchr. ed. 195.00 incl. VHS (978-0-8068-0614-3(1)) AIMS Multimedia.

Ferry, Charles. Binge II: Recovery: Eight Steps to Sobriety & a Better You. 2nd rev. ed. 1999. 130p. (J). pap. 12.00 (978-0-9632799-8-9(X)) Daisy Hill Pr. International.

Gaissert, Anna Jean. C. O. A. - Counceling Children of Alcoholics/Addicts: A Support Group for Children Ages 10-15. Miele, Bob, illus. 2000. 24p. (YA). (gr. 5-11). pap. 5.95 (978-1-57543-081-2(9)) MAR*CO Products, Inc.

Gottfried, Ted. The Facts about Alcohol. 2004. (Illus.). 111p. (J). 37.07 (978-0-7614-1805-4(9) , Benchmark Bks.) Cavendish, Marshall Corp.

Graves, Bonnie. Alcohol Use & Abuse. 2000. (Perspectives on Physical Health Ser.). (Illus.). 64p. (J). (gr. 4-6). lib. bdg. 23.93 (978-0-7368-0415-8(3) , LifeMatters Bks.) Capstone Pr., Inc.

Green, Carl R. Alcohol: A Myreportlinks. com Book. 2005. (Drugs Ser.). (Illus.). 48p. (J). (ps-10). lib. bdg. 25.26 (978-0-7660-5282-6(6) , MyReportLinks.com Bks.) Enslow Pubs., Inc.

Hanan, Jessica. When Someone You Love Is Addicted. 1999. (Drug Abuse Prevention Library). (Illus.). 64p. (YA). (gr. 7-12). 25.25 (978-0-8239-2831-6(4) , DRSOLO) Rosen Publishing Group, Inc., The.

Harvey, John H. Alcohol. 2001. (Teen Decisions Ser.). (Illus.). 144p. (YA). (gr. 10 up). lib. bdg. 36.20 (978-0-7377-0490-7(X) , Greenhaven Pr., Inc.) Thomson Gale.

Haughton, Emma. Alcohol. 1999. (Talking Points Ser.). (Illus.). 64p. (YA). (gr. 4-7). lib. bdg. 27.12 (978-0-8172-5318-9(1)) Raintree.

Holt, Rinehart and Winston Staff. Decisions for Health Blue, Chptr. 15: Alcohol. 4th ed. 2004. pap. 11.20 (978-0-03-068049-6(2)) Holt, Rinehart & Winston.

—Decisions for Health Green Chptr. 14: Tobacco & Alcohol. 4th ed. 2004. pap. 11.20 (978-0-03-068036-6(0)) Holt, Rinehart & Winston.

—Decisions for Health Red Chptr. 12: Teens & Alcohol. 4th ed. 2004. pap. 11.20 (978-0-03-068038-0(7)) Holt, Rinehart & Winston.

Huard, Donald V. Teen-Agers: What Will Cigarettes, Booze & Drugs Do for/to You? 1998. 50p. (J). (gr. 7-12). mass mkt. 3.95 (978-0-9661606-1-1(4)) Huard Pubns.

Jaffe, Steven L., ed. How to Say No. 1999. (Junior Drug Awareness Ser.). (Illus.). 80p. (J). (gr. 4-8). 27.50 (978-0-7910-5202-0(8) , Chelsea Hse.) Facts On File, Inc.

Jaffe, Steven L. & McCaffrey, Barry R., eds. Alcohol. 1999. (Junior Drug Awareness Ser.). (Illus.). 80p. (J). (gr. 4-8). 27.50 (978-0-7910-5174-0(9) , Chelsea Hse.) Facts On File, Inc.

Johnson, Julie. Why Do People Drink Alcohol? Sloan, Frank, ed. 2001. (Exploring Tough Issues Ser.). (Illus.). 48p. (J). (gr. 4-7). lib. bdg. 25.69 (978-0-7398-3235-6(2)) Raintree.

Kaplan, Sheldon A. Cold Turkey Before You Become One! Stop Smoking, Drinking, Gambling & or Abusing Drugs. Resseguie, Douglas, ed. deluxe ed. 1999. (YA). 5.95 (978-0-9677993-1-5(7)) Kaplan, Sheldon A. & Assocs,.

Kidsdom: An Alcohol Prevention Curriculum. 2005. (J). 119.95 (978-1-55548-059-2(4)) Human Relations Media.

Kulp, Liz & Kulp, Jodee. The Best I Can Be: Living with Fetal Alcohol Syndrome-Effects. 2000. (Illus.). 96p. (YA). (gr. 6 up). 12.95 (978-0-9637072-3-9(X)) Better Endings New Beginnings.

Lamb, Kirsten. Alcohol. 2002. (Health Issues Ser.). (Illus.). 64p. (YA). (gr. 6-8). lib. bdg. 28.54 (978-0-7398-4772-5(4)) Raintree.

Landau, Elaine. Alcohol. 2003. (Watts Library). 64p. (J). (gr. 5-7). pap. 8.95 (978-0-531-16665-9(1) , Watts, Franklin) Scholastic Library Publishing.

—Alcohol. 2003. (gr. 5-8). lib. bdg. 17.60 (978-0-613-67594-9(0)) Tandem Library Bks.

Lauri S. Friedman. Drunk Driving. 2007. (Writing the Critical Essay Ser.). 128p. (gr. 6-10). 29.95 (978-0-7377-3581-9(3) , Greenhaven Pr., Inc.) Thomson Gale.

Levete, Sarah. Alcohol. 2006. (Let's Talk about Ser.). (Illus.). 32p. (J). (gr. 3-5). lib. bdg. 27.10 (978-1-59604-086-1(6)) Stargazer Bks.

Lynette, Rachel. The Real Deal: Alcohol Hardback. 2007. (Illus.). 32p. (J). (***978-0-431-90728-4(5)***) Heinemann Library.

—The Real Deal: Alcohol Paperback. 2007. (Illus.). 32p. (J). (***978-0-431-90735-2(8)***) Heinemann Library.

Macaulay, John. Alcoholism. 2007. (Illus.). 244p. (gr. 10-12). 24.95 (978-0-7377-2473-8(0)); pap. 36.20 (978-0-7377-2472-1(2)) Thomson Gale. (Greenhaven Pr., Inc.).

MacGowan, Shane & O'Callaghan, Deirdre. Hide That Can: A Photographic Diary of the Men of Arlington House. 2002. (Illus.). 192p. 39.95 (978-0-9542079-8-4(X)) Trolley GBR. *Dist:* D.A.P./Distributed Art Pubs.

Mainheimer, Ann. Alcohol. 2006. (History of Drugs Ser.). (Illus.). 224p. (gr. 10-12). 36.20 (978-0-7377-2841-5(8) , Greenhaven Pr., Inc.) Thomson Gale.

Marcom Group Ltd, prod. Under the Influence Win Lb. (YA). cd-rom 222.50 (978-0-7365-4347-7(3)) Films Media Group.

Marcovitz, Hal. Drugs & Alcohol. 2006. (Gallup Major Trends & Events Ser.). (Illus.). 112p. (J). (gr. 7 up). lib. bdg. (978-1-59084-963-7(9)) Mason Crest Pubs.

McClellan, Marilyn. The Big Deal about Alcohol: What Teens Need to Know about Drinking. 2004. (Issues in Focus Ser.). (Illus.). 128p. (J). lib. bdg. 26.60 (978-0-7660-2163-1(7)) Enslow Pubs., Inc.

McGraw-Hill Staff. Teen Health Course 2, Modules, Tobacco, Alcohol, & Other Drugs. 5th ed. 2002. (Three-Level Middle School Health Ser.). (C). (gr. 7 up). 15.32 (978-0-07-826183-1(X) , 9780078261831) Glencoe/ McGraw-Hill.

McGuire, Paula. Alcohol. 1998. (Preteen Pressures Ser.). (Illus.). 48p. (J). (gr. 4-8). lib. bdg. 25.69 (978-0-8172-5026-3(3)) Raintree.

McIntosh, Kenneth & Livingston, Phyllis. Youth with Alcohol & Drug Addiction: Escape from Bondage. 2008. (J). (978-1-4222-0143-5(0)) Mason Crest Pubs.

Miller, Andrew. Alcohol & Your Liver: The Incredibly Disgusting Story. 2005. (Incredibly Disgusting Drugs Ser.). (Illus.). 48p. (YA). (gr. 5-8). lib. bdg. 25.25 (978-0-8239-3254-2(0) , DDALLI) Rosen Publishing Group, Inc., The.

Mintzer, Richard. Alcohol = Busted! 2005. (Busted! Ser.). (Illus.). 104p. (J). (gr. 6-12). lib. bdg. 31.93 (978-0-7660-2552-3(7)) Enslow Pubs., Inc.

Monroe, Judy. Alcohol. 2001. (Drug Library). (Illus.). 128p. (YA). (gr. 6-12). pap. 13.26 (978-0-7660-1916-4(0)) Enslow Pubs., Inc.

Nadelson, Carol C. & Reinburg, Claire E., eds. Drowning Our Sorrows: Psychological Effects of Alcohol Abuse. 1999. (Encyclopedia of Psychological Disorders Ser.). (Illus.). 88p. (YA). (gr. 7 up). 35.00 (978-0-7910-4954-9(X) , Chelsea Hse.) Facts On File, Inc.

Nakaya, Andrea C. Alcohol. 2007. (Opposing Viewpoints Ser.). (Illus.). 240p. (gr. 10-12). 36.20 (***978-0-7377-3733-2(6)***); pap. 24.95 (***978-0-7377-3734-9(4)***) Thomson Gale. (Greenhaven Pr., Inc.).

—Alcohol: Compact Research Series. 2007. (ENG.). (YA). lib. bdg. (***978-1-60152-007-4(7)***) ReferencePoint Pr., Inc.

O'Neill, Eugene. Long Day's Journey into Night. 2002. (gr. 7-12). lib. bdg. 22.20 (978-0-613-58331-2(0)) Tandem Library Bks.

Parks, Peggy J. Driving under the Influence. 2007. (J). (***978-1-60217-013-1(4)***) Erickson Pr.

Powell, Jillian. Alcohol. 2005. (It's Your Health Ser.). (Illus.). 45p. (J). (gr. 6-9). lib. bdg. 29.95 (978-1-58340-590-1(9)) Smart Apple Media.

Richards, Pamela. Alcohol. 2000. (Just the Facts Ser.). (Illus.). 56p. (YA). (gr. 6-8). lib. bdg. 24.22 (978-1-57572-253-5(4)) Heinemann Library.

Ruiz, Ruth Anne. Everything You Need to Know about the Dangers of Binge Drinking. 2001. (Need to Know Library). (Illus.). 64p. (YA). (gr. 4-6). lib. bdg. 25.25 (978-0-8239-3289-4(3) , NTBIDR) Rosen Publishing Group, Inc., The.

Sanders, Pete & Myers, Steve. Drinking Alcohol. 2005. (Choices & Decisions Ser.). (Illus.). 32p. (J). (gr. 4-7). lib. bdg. 27.10 (978-1-59604-074-8(2)) Stargazer Bks.

Shannon, Joyce Brennfleck, ed. Alcohol Information for Teens: Health Tips about Alcohol & Alcoholism. 2004. (Teen Health Ser.). 370p. (J). (978-0-7808-0741-9(3)) Omnigraphics, Inc.

Sheen, Barbara. Teen Alcoholism. 2003. (Illus.). 112p. 29.95 (978-1-59018-501-8(3) , Lucent Bks.) Thomson Gale.

Snyder, Gail. Teens & Alcohol. 2004. (Gallup Youth Survey, Major Issues & Trends Ser.). (Illus.). 112,128p. (J). (gr. 7-9). lib. bdg. 22.95 (978-1-59084-723-7(7)) Mason Crest Pubs.

Stewart, Gail B. Fetal Alcohol Syndrome. 2004. (Illus.). 112p. (YA). (gr. 7-12). lib. bdg. 32.45 (978-1-59018-591-9(9) , Lucent Bks.) Thomson Gale.

Stewart, Jan. Stars How Drugs & Alcohol Affect Us. 2004. (Illus.). 32p. (J). pap. 9.95 (978-0-89793-314-8(1)) Hunter Hse., Inc.

Taylor, Barbara. Everything You Need to Know about Alcohol. rev. ed. 1999. (Need to Know Library). (Illus.). 64p. (YA). (gr. 7-12). lib. bdg. 25.25 (978-0-8239-2952-8(3) , NTALCO) Rosen Publishing Group, Inc., The.

Tubbs, Janet. Alcoholism, Set. 2000. (Spud Packs Ser.). 16p. (J). pap. 19.95 (978-1-881185-08-6(7)) Arcadia Pr.

Wilson, Mike. Drunk Driving. 2006. 244p. (J). 33.70 (978-0-7377-3621-2(6) , Greenhaven Pr., Inc.) Thomson Gale.

Wybmy, Shella. Alcoholism. 2007. (Diseases & Disorders Ser.). (Illus.). 128p. (gr. 7-10). 31.20 (***978-1-59018-996-2(5)*** , Lucent Bks.) Thomson Gale.

ALCOHOLISM—FICTION

Bauer, Cat. Harley, Like a Person. 2007. 288p. (gr. 9). (J). pap. 8.99 (978-0-375-83735-7(3)); (YA). 15.99 (978-0-375-93735-4(8)) Random Hse. Children's Bks. (Knopf Bks. for Young Readers).

—Harley, Like a Person. 2000. (Illus.). (J). 13.60 (978-0-606-20690-7(6)) Tandem Library Bks.

—Harley, Like a Person. 2000. (Illus.). 248p. (J). (gr. 7 up). pap. 5.95 (978-1-58837-005-1(4)) Winslow Pr.

Bauer, Joan. Rules of the Road. 208p. (gr. 7). 2005. (YA). pap. 7.99 (978-0-14-240425-6(X) , Puffin); 1998. (J). 16.99 (978-0-399-23140-7(4) , Putnam Juvenile) Penguin Group (USA) Inc.

—Rules of the Road. 2000. (YA). (978-0-606-20252-7(8)); 201p. (gr. 7-12). lib. bdg. 13.64 (978-0-606-20370-8(2)) Tandem Library Bks.

Bo, Ben. Skullcrack. 2003. 168p. (J). pap. 6.95 (978-0-8225-3311-5(1)); (gr. 9-12). 14.95 (978-0-8225-3308-5(1)) Lerner Publishing Group.

—Skullcrack. 2000. (gr. 5-8). lib. bdg. 15.25 (978-0-613-58938-3(6)) Tandem Library Bks.

Brooks, Kevin. Martyn Pig. 240p. (J). 2003. pap. 6.99 (978-0-439-50752-3(9)); 2002. (gr. 5 up). pap. 16.95 (978-0-439-29595-6(5) , Chicken Hse., The) Scholastic, Inc.

—Martyn Pig. 2003. (gr. 7-12). lib. bdg. 15.30 (978-0-613-64813-4(7)) Tandem Library Bks.

Buffie, Margaret. Out of Focus. 2006. 240p. (978-1-55337-956-0(X)); (978-1-55337-955-3(1)) Kids Can Pr., Ltd.

Carlson, Melody. Burnt Orange: Color Me Wasted. 2005. 207p. (YA). pap. 12.99 (978-1-57683-533-3(2)) NavPress Publishing Group.

Carter, Alden R. Up Country. 2004. 256p. (J). (gr. 5). pap. 6.99 (978-0-14-240243-6(5) , Puffin) Penguin Group (USA) Inc.

Coburn, Jake. LoveSick. 2005. 240p. (YA). (gr. 8-12). 16.99 (978-0-525-47383-1(1) , Dutton Juvenile) Penguin Group (USA) Inc.

Cormier, Robert. We All Fall Down. 2002. 21.50 (978-0-8446-7217-5(3)) Smith, Peter Pub., Inc.

Davis, Deborah. Not Like You. 2007. 272p. (YA). (gr. 7 up). 16.00 (***978-0-618-72093-4(6)*** , Clarion Bks.) Houghton Mifflin Co. Trade & Reference Div.

Dean, Carolee. Comfort. (J). (gr. 7 up). 2004. 256p. pap. 6.99 (978-0-618-43912-6(9) , Graphia); 2002. 240p. 15.00 (978-0-618-13846-3(3)) Houghton Mifflin Co. Trade & Reference Div.

Deuker, Carl. Runner. 224p. (YA). (gr. 7). 2007. pap. 7.99 (***978-0-618-73505-1(4)*** , Graphia); 2005. 16.00 (978-0-618-54298-7(1)) Houghton Mifflin Co. Trade & Reference Div.

Ehrenhaft, Daniel. The After Life. 2006. 272p. (YA). (gr. 9-12). pap. 8.99 (978-1-59514-080-7(8) , Razorbill) Penguin Group (USA) Inc.

Emmy's Question. 2007. (J). 16.99 (***978-0-9790395-2-2(5)***) Morningtide Pr.

Fogelin, Adrian. The Sorta Sisters. 2007. 240p. (J). (gr. 3-7). 14.95 (***978-1-56145-424-2(9)*** , Peachtree Junior) Peachtree Pubs., Ltd.

Fox, Paula. The Moonlight Man. 2003. (Illus.). 176p. (J). pap. 5.99 (978-0-689-85886-4(8) , Aladdin) Simon & Schuster Children's Publishing.

—The Moonlight Man. 2003. (gr. 5-8). lib. bdg. 13.00 (978-0-613-66425-7(6)) Tandem Library Bks.

Friend, Natasha. Lush. 192p. (J). 2007. (gr. 7 up). pap. 6.99 (***978-0-439-85347-7(8)***); 2006. pap. 16.99 (978-0-439-85346-0(X)) Scholastic, Inc. (Scholastic Paperbacks).

Frye, Tom. Scratchin' on the Eight Ball. 2000. 240p. (YA). pap. 12.95 (978-0-595-12971-3(4) , Writer's Showcase Pr.) iUniverse, Inc.

Gantos, Jack. Joey Pigza Loses Control. braille ed. 2003. (J). (gr. 2). spiral bd. (978-0-616-15268-3(X)) Canadian National Institute for the Blind/Institut National Canadien pour les Aveugles.

—Joey Pigza Loses Control. 2000. (Joey Pigza Ser.). 208p. (J). (gr. 4-7). 16.00 (978-0-374-39989-4(1) , Farrar, Straus & Giroux (BYR)) Farrar, Straus & Giroux.

—Joey Pigza Loses Control. 2002. 208p. (J). (gr. 5 up). pap. 5.99 (978-0-06-441022-9(6) , Harper Trophy) HarperCollins Pubs.

—Joey Pigza Loses Control. unabr. ed. 2004. 195p. (J). (gr. 5-9). pap. 36.00 incl. audio (978-0-8072-8726-2(1) , LyA 248 SP, Listening Library) Random Hse. Audio Publishing Group.

—Joey Pigza Loses Control. 2002. (gr. 5-8). lib. bdg. 14.15 (978-0-613-49677-3(9)) Tandem Library Bks.

—Joey Pigza Loses Control. l.t. ed. 2001. 196p. (J). 22.95 (978-0-7862-3425-7(3)) Thorndike Pr.

Garfinkle, Debra. The Band: Trading Guys: Trading Guys. 2007. 256p. (YA). (gr. 12). pap. 9.99 (***978-0-425-21513-5(X)*** , Berkley Trade) Penguin Group (USA) Inc.

Garsee, Jeannine. Before, after, & Somebody in Between. 2007. 352p. (YA). (gr. 9 up). 16.95 (***978-1-59990 022-3(X)***) Bloomsbury Publishing.

Grande-Tabor, Nancy Maria. Las Botellas Se Rompen. 1999. Tr. of Bottle Is Broken. (SPA., Illus.). 13.75 (978-0-606-17689-7(6)) Tandem Library Bks.

Haley, Gail E. My father's Beast. Haley, Gail E., illus. 2006. (Illus.). 32p. (J). (978-1-933251-35-6(2)) Parkway Pubs., Inc.

Hogan, Mary. The Serious Kiss. 2005. 256p. (J). pap. 7.99 (978-0-06-072208-1(8) , Harper Trophy); (YA). (gr. 7 up). 16.99 (978-0-06-072206-7(1)) HarperCollins Pubs.

Hopkins, Ellen. Burned. 2007. 544p. (YA). pap. 9.99 (***978-1-4169-0355-0(0)*** , Simon Pulse) Simon & Schuster Children's Publishing.

Irgens, Barbara E. Finding the Way. 2001. 187p. (YA). pap. 14.95 (978-1-930580-06-0(1) , Luminary Media Group) Pine Orchard, Inc.

—Finding the Way. 2001. (gr. 7-12). lib. bdg. 24.55 (978-0-613-80418-9(X)) Tandem Library Bks.

Jenkins, A. M. Breaking Boxes. 2000. (978-0-606-17834-1(1)) Tandem Library Bks.

Johnson, Kathleen Jeffrie. Dumb Love. 2005. 176p. (YA). (gr. 7-17). 16.95 (978-1-59643-062-4(1)) Roaring Brook Pr.

Johnson, Maureen G. The Key to the Golden Firebird. 2005. 304p. (YA). reprint ed. pap. 7.99 (978-0-06-054140-8(7) , Harper Trophy) HarperCollins Pubs.

Keizer, Garret. God of Beer. 256p. (J). 2003. pap. 6.99 (978-0-06-447276-0(0)); 2002. (gr. 8 up). 15.95 (978-0-06-029456-4(6)) HarperCollins Pubs.

—God of Beer. 2003. (gr. 7-12). lib. bdg. 15.30 (978-0-613-71500-3(4)) Tandem Library Bks.

Koja, Kathe. The Blue Mirror. 2006. 128p. (YA). (gr. 8). pap. 6.99 (978-0-14-240693-9(7) , Puffin) Penguin Group (USA) Inc.

—The Blue Mirror. l.t. ed. 2004. 134p. 21.95 (978-0-7862-6960-0(X) , Large Print Pr.) Thorndike Pr.

Lawton, Wendy. Flip Flop. 2004. (Real Tv - Real Transformations Series (Take 2) Ser.). 208p. (J). pap. 10.99 (978-0-8024-5414-0(3)) Moody Pubs.

Luddy, Karon. Spelldown: The Big-Time Dreams of a Small-Town Word Whiz. 2007. 224p. (YA). 15.99 (978-1-4169-1610-9(5)) Simon & Schuster Children's Publishing.

Lynch, Chris. Inexcusable. 2005. (Illus.). 176p. (YA). (gr. 7 up). 16.95 (978-0-689-84789-9(0) , Atheneum) Simon & Schuster Children's Publishing.

MacCready, Robin. Buried. 2006. 208p. (YA). (gr. 9). 16.99 (978-0-525-47724-2(1) , Dutton Juvenile) Penguin Group (USA) Inc.

Mangum, Kay Lynn. When the Bough Breaks. 2007. 352p. (YA). pap. 15.95 (***978-1-59038-748-1(1)***) Deseret Bk. Co.

Martinez, Victor. El Loro en el Horno. 2001. (SPA.). (gr. 7-12). lib. bdg. 19.90 (978-0-613-80733-3(2)) Tandem Library Bks.

—Parrot in the Oven: Mi Vida. Scott, Steve, illus. rev. ed. 1998. 240p. (J). (gr. 7 up). pap. 5.99 (978-0-06-447186-2(1) , Harper Trophy) HarperCollins Pubs.

—Parrot in the Oven: Mi Vida. 1998. (978-0-606-13695-2(9)) Tandem Library Bks.

The Misadventures of Wags & Freckles. (J). 4.00 (978-1-56230-043-2(1)) Syndistar, Inc.

Murray, Jaye. Bottled Up. 2004. 224p. (YA). (gr. 6-12). reprint ed. pap. 6.99 (978-0-14-240240-5(0) , Puffin) Penguin Group (USA) Inc.

—Bottled Up. 2004. 220p. (J). (gr. 2-13). lib. bdg. 13.04 (978-0-606-32733-6(9)) Tandem Library Bks.

Pearson, Mary E. A Room on Lorelei Street. rev. ed. 2005. 272p. (YA). 16.95 (978-0-8050-7667-7(0)) Holt, Henry & Co.

Plum-Ucci, Carol. What Happened to Lani Garver. (YA). 2002. 328p. (gr. 9 up). 17.00 (978-0-15-216813-1(3)); 2004. 336p. reprint ed. pap. 6.95 (978-0-15-205088-7(4) , Harcourt Paperbacks) Harcourt Children's Bks.

Quarles, Heather. A Door Near Here. 2000. 11.64 (978-0-606-17796-2(5)) Tandem Library Bks.

—Door near Here. 2000. (gr. 7-12). lib. bdg. 13.00 (978-0-613-22981-4(9)) Tandem Library Bks.

—A Door Near Here. 2000. (Illus.). 240p. (YA). (gr. 7 up). pap. 5.50 (978-0-440-22761-8(5) , Laurel Leaf) Random Hse. Children's Bks.

Ratcliffe, Jane. The Free Fall. rev. ed. 2001. (Illus.). 192p. (YA). (gr. 9-12). 16.95 (978-0-8050-6667-8(5) , Holt, Henry & Co. Bks. For Young Readers) Holt, Henry & Co.

Roberts, Willo Davis. Buddy Is a Stupid Name for a Girl. Cipolla, Karen, illus. 2002. 224p. (J). pap. 5.99 (978-0-689-85164-3(2) , Aladdin) Simon & Schuster Children's Publishing.

—Buddy Is a Stupid Name for a Girl. 2001. (Illus.). 224p. (J). (gr. 3-7). 16.00 (978-0-689-81670-3(7) , Atheneum) Simon & Schuster Children's Publishing.

Rottman, S. L. Stetson. 2002. 224p. (J). (gr. 9 up). 16.99 (978-0-670-03542-7(4) , Viking Juvenile) Penguin Group (USA) Inc.

Saksena, Kate. Hang on in There, Shelley. 2003. 219p. (J). 16.95 (978-1-58234-822-3(7) , Bloomsbury Children) Bloomsbury Publishing.

Samuels, Gertrude. Yours, Brett. 2000. 180p. (YA). (gr. 4-7). pap. 13.95 (978-0-595-00806-3(2)) iUniverse, Inc.

Sanchez, Alex. Rainbow Boys. (YA). 2003. 272p. 8.99 (978-0-689-85770-6(5) , Simon Pulse); 2001. 256p. (gr. 9 up). 17.00 (978-0-689-84100-2(0)) Simon & Schuster Children's Publishing.

—Rainbow Boys. 2003. (gr. 7-12). lib. bdg. 16.45 (978-0-613-66434-9(5)) Tandem Library Bks.

Smith, Stephen D. & Caldwell, Lise. High Hurdles. 2006. 128p. (J). pap. 5.99 (978-0-7847-1439-3(8) , 42144) Standard Publishing.

Stoehr, Shelley. Crosses. 2003. (gr. 7-12). lib. bdg. 23.40 (978-0-613-86660-6(6)) Tandem Library Bks.

—Crosses. 2003. 161p. (YA). pap. 13.95 (978-0-595-26952-5(4) , Backinprint.com) iUniverse, Inc.

Tabor, Nancy. Bottles Break. 1999. (Illus.). 32p. (J). (ps-3). 15.95 (978-0-88106-317-2(7)); pap. 6.95 (978-0-88106-318-9(5)) Charlesbridge Publishing, Inc.

Tiddle, Deanna Hessedal. Hold on, Jessica, Don't Let Go. 2001. (gr. 3-6). lib. bdg. 28.00 (978-0-613-74714-1(3)) Tandem Library Bks.

Tony's Sobering Lesson. (J). 39.50 (978-1-56230-075-3(X)) Syndistar, Inc.

Velasquez, Gloria. Tyrone's Betrayal. 144p. (J). pap. 9.95 (978-1-55885-465-9(7) , Piñata Books) Arte Publico Pr.

Wilhelm, Doug. Raising the Shades. l.t. ed. 2005. 182p. 20.95 (978-0-7862-7812-1(9) , Large Print Pr.) Thorndike Pr.

Williams, Laura E. The Spider's Web. Magnus, Erica, illus. 1999. 150p. (J). (gr. 3-8). pap. 6.95 (978-1-57131-622-6(1)) Milkweed Editions.

—Spider's Web. 1999. (J). (978-0-606-19036-7(8)) Tandem Library Bks.

Williams, Laura Ellen. The Spider's Web. Magnus, Erica, illus. 1999. 134p. (J). (ps-8). per. 15.25 (978-0-613-23977-6(6)) Tandem Library Bks.

Woodson, Jacqueline. The Dear One. 2004. 144p. (YA). pap. 6.99 (978-0-14-250190-0(5) , Puffin) Penguin Group (USA) Inc.

Woodworth, Chris. When Ratboy Lived Next Door. 2005. (Illus.). 192p. (J). 16.00 (978-0-374-34677-5(1) , Farrar, Straus & Giroux (BYR)) Farrar, Straus & Giroux.

Wright, Julie. My Not-So-Fairytale Life. 2005. 256p. (YA). pap. 15.95 (978-1-59038-476-3(8)) Deseret Bk. Co.

Zitelman, Jem. Ventures Tested: One Teenager's Story . . . to Happiness. 2000. viii, 206p. (J). 24.95 (978-1-891612-00-8(X) , 9701); pap. 15.95 (978-1-891612-01-5(8) , 9701); lib. bdg. 24.95 (978-1-891612-02-2(6) , 9701) Celjon Bks.

ALCOTT, LOUISA MAY, 1832-1888

Alcott, Louisa May. The Girlhood Diary of Louisa May Alcott, 1843-1846: Writings of a Young Author. Graves, Kerry A., ed. 2000. (Blue Earth Books). (Illus.). 32p. (J). (gr. 3-4). lib. bdg. 22.60 (978-0-7368-0599-5(0) , Bridgestone Bks.) Capstone Pr., Inc.

Aller, Susan Bivin. Beyond Little Women: A Story about Louisa May Alcott. Wang, Qi Z., illus. 2004. (Creative Minds Biography Ser.). 64p. (J). (gr. 4-8). lib. bdg. 22.60 (978-1-57505-602-9(X)) Lerner Publishing Group.

Ditchfield, Christin. Louisa May Alcott: Author of Little Women. 2005. (Great Life Stories Ser.). (Illus.). 111p. (J). (gr. 6-8). 30.50 (978-0-531-12403-1(7) , Watts, Franklin) Scholastic Library Publishing.

Gormley, Beatrice. Louisa May Alcott: Young Novelist. 1999. 219p. lib. bdg. 12.04 (978-0-606-16303-3(4)); (gr. 3-6). lib. bdg. 13.00 (978-0-613-15890-9(3)) Tandem Library Bks.

Gormley, Beatrice, et al. Louisa May Alcott: Young Novelist. Henderson, Meryl, illus. 1999. (Childhood of Famous Americans Ser.). 224p. (J). (gr. 3-7). pap. 5.99 (978-0-689-82025-0(9) , 076714004993, Aladdin) Simon & Schuster Children's Publishing.

Meigs, Cornelia. Invincible Louisa. 2005. 216p. (J). (gr. 4-7). 21.50 (978-0-8446-7268-7(8) , 3584) Smith, Peter Pub., Inc.

Ruth, Amy. Louisa May Alcott: American Storyteller. 1998. (Biography Ser.). (Illus.). 128p. (YA). (gr. 6-12). lib. bdg. 27.93 (978-0-8225-4938-3(7) , Lerner Pubns.) Lerner Publishing Group.

Silverthorne, Elizabeth. Louisa May Alcott. 2002. (Who Wrote That? Ser.). (Illus.). 112p. (gr. 6-12). 30.00 (978-0-7910-6721-5(1) , Chelsea Hse.) Facts On File, Inc.

Warrick, Karen Clemens. Louisa May Alcott: Author of "Little Women" 2000. (Historical American Biographies Ser.). (Illus.). 128p. (YA). (gr. 6-12). lib. bdg. 26.60 (978-0-7660-1254-7(9)) Enslow Pubs., Inc.

ALCOTT, LOUISA MAY, 1832-1888—FICTION

Frederick, Heather Vogel. The Mother-Daughter Book Club. 2007. 256p. (J). (gr. 4-7). 15.99 (978-0-689-86412-4(4)) Simon & Schuster Children's Publishing.

ALEUTS

Ansary, Mir Tamim. Arctic Peoples. (Native Americans Ser.). (Illus.). 32p. (J). 2002. (gr. 1-4). pap. 7.50 (978-1-58810-450-2(8) , 91169); 1999. (gr. 2-4). lib. bdg. 21.36 (978-1-57572-920-6(2)) Heinemann Library.

Papademetriou, Dorrie. North Star: St. Herman of Alaska. 2000. (Illus.). 32p. (J). 17.00 (978-0-88141-223-9(6)) St. Vladimir's Seminary Pr.

ALEUTS—FICTION

Hesse, Karen. Aleutian Sparrow. Zerbetz, Evon, illus. 2003. 160p. (J). (gr. 5-9). 16.95 (978-0-689-86189-5(3) , McElderry, Margaret K.) Simon & Schuster Children's Publishing.

—Aleutian Sparrow. McGillivray, Kim & Zerbetz, Evon, illus. 2005. 160p. (J). reprint ed. pap. 5.99 (978-1-4169-0327-7(5) , Aladdin) Simon & Schuster Children's Publishing.

Stites, Clara. Katya of Fort Ross. 2001. (Illus.). 80p. (J). pap. 8.95 (978-1-56474-379-4(9)) Fithian Pr.

ALEXANDER, THE GREAT, 356-323 B.C.

Abbott, Jacob. Alexander the Great. 2004. (Illus.). (J). pap. 9.99 (978-1-887159-97-5(5)) Preston-Speed Pubns.

Adams, Simon. Alexander: The Boy Soldier Who Conquered the World. 2005. (World History Biographies Ser.). (Illus.). 64p. (J). (gr. 3-7). 27.90 (978-0-7922-3661-0(0)); 17.95 (978-0-7922-3660-3(2)) National Geographic Society. (National Geographic Children's Bks.).

Bankston, John. The Life & Times of Alexander the Great. (Biography from Ancient Civilizations Ser.). (Illus.). 48p. (J). 2005. (gr. 4-8). lib. bdg. 29.95 (978-1-58415-283-5(4)); 2004. lib. bdg. (978-1-58415-235-4(4)) Mitchell Lane Pubs., Inc.

Behnke, Alison. The Conquests of Alexander the Great. 2007. (Pivotal Moments in History Ser.). 160p. (YA). (gr. 9-12). lib. bdg. 38.60 (978-0-8225-5920-7(X) , Twenty-First Century Bks.) Lerner Publishing Group.

Bingham, Jane. Alexander the Great. 2005. (Famous Lives Gift Books Ser.). 64p. (J). 8.95 (978-0-7945-0869-2(3) , Usborne) EDC Publishing.

Burgan, Michael. Alexander the Great: World Conqueror. 2006. (J). (978-0-7565-1872-1(5)) Compass Point Bks.

Caper, William. Alexander the Great. 2005. (Navigators Ser.). (J). pap. 44.00 (***978-1-4108-5116-1(8))** Benchmark Education Co.

Chrisp, Peter, contrib. by. Alexander the Great. 2000. (Illus.). 48p. (YA). 14.95 (978-0-7894-6109-4(9)) Dorling Kindersley Publishing, Inc.

Crompton, Samuel Willard. Alexander the Great. 2003. (Ancient World Leaders Ser.). (Illus.). 112p. (gr. 6-12). (J). 30.00 (978-0-7910-7219-6(3)); pap. 30.00 (978-0-7910-7493-0(5)) Facts On File, Inc. (Chelsea Hse.).

Ganeri, Anita. Alexander the Great: The Life of a King & Conqueror. 2005. (Graphic Nonfiction Ser.). (Illus.). 48p. (J). lib. bdg. 26.50 (978-1-4042-0238-2(2) , 1241094) Rosen Publishing Group, Inc., The.

Greenblatt, Miriam. Alexander the Great & Ancient Greece. 1999. (Rulers & Their Times Ser.). (Illus.). 80p. (YA). (gr. 6 up). lib. bdg. 29.93 (978-0-7614-0913-7(0) , Benchmark Bks.) Cavendish, Marshall Corp.

Gunther, John. Sterling Point Books: Alexander the Great. 2007. (Sterling Point Bks.). (Illus.). 176p. (J). 12.95 (978-1-4027-4519-5(2)); pap. 6.95 (978-1-4027-4139-5(1)) Sterling Publishing Co., Inc.

MacDonald, Fiona. World Time O/Alexander Great. 2000. (World in the Time of... Ser.). (Illus.). 48p. (J). (gr. 4-7). 22.95 (978-0-7910-6029-2(2) , Chelsea Hse.) Facts On File, Inc.

McGowen, Tom. Alexander the Great: Conqueror of the Ancient World. 2006. (Rulers of the Ancient World Ser.). (Illus.). 160p. (J). lib. bdg. 27.93 (978-0-7660-2560-8(8)) Enslow Pubs., Inc.

Morley, Jacqueline. You Wouldn't Want to Be in Alexander the Great's Army! Miles You'd Rather Not March. Antram, David, illus. 2005. (You Wouldn't Want to... Ser.). 32p. (J). (gr. 2-5). 28.50 (978-0-531-12410-9(X)); pap. 9.95 (978-0-531-12390-4(1)) Scholastic Library Publishing. (Watts, Franklin).

Nardo, Don. Philip II & Alexander the Great Unify Greece in World History. 2000. (In World History Ser.). (Illus.). 112p. (J). (gr. 5-12). lib. bdg. 26.60 (978-0-7660-1399-5(5)) Enslow Pubs., Inc.

Pancella, Peggy. Alexander the Great. 2003. (Historical Biographies Ser.). (Illus.). 32p. (J). pap. 7.50 (978-1-4034-3707-5(6)); lib. bdg. 22.79 (978-1-4034-3699-3(1)) Heinemann Library.

Saunders, Nicholas. The Life of Alexander the Great. 2006. (Stories from History Ser.). 48p. (J). 14.95 (978-0-7696-4713-5(8)); pap. 6.95 (978-0-7696-4694-7(8)) School Specialty Publishing.

Shecter, Vicky Alvear. Alexander the Great Rocks the World. Naughton, Terry, illus. 2006. 128p. (J). (gr. 6 up). 18.95 (978-1-58196-045-7(X)) Darby Creek Publishing.

Slavicek, Louise Chipley. Alexander the Great. 2005. (Heroes & Villains Ser.). (Illus.). 112p. (J). (ps-7). lib. bdg. 29.95 (978-1-59018-595-7(1) , Lucent Bks.) Thomson Gale.

Viorst, Judith. Alexander Series, 2 bks., Set. 2000. (Illus.). (J). (gr. 1-6). pap. 30.95 incl. audio (978-0-87499-478-0(0)) Live Oak Media.

ALEXANDER, THE GREAT, 356-323 B.C.—FICTION

Johnson, Vargie. Alexander the Great the All-Powerful: What Made Them Famous? 2006. 156p. (J). per. 15.00 (978-1-931195-93-5(5)) KiwE Publishing, Ltd.

Roberts, Katherine. I Am the Great Horse. 2006. (Illus.). 416p. (YA). pap. 16.99 (978-0-439-82163-6(0) , Chicken Hse., The) Scholastic, Inc.

ALEXANDRA, EMPRESS, CONSORT OF NICHOLAS II, EMPEROR OF RUSSIA, 1872-1918

Massie, Robert K. Nicholas & Alexandra. 2000. (gr. 7-12). lib. bdg. 28.05 (978-0-613-37162-9(3)) Tandem Library Bks.

ALFRED, KING OF ENGLAND, 849-899

Abbott, Jacob. King Alfred of England. 2006. pap. (***978-1-4068-0240-5(9))** Echo Library.

—King Alfred of England, Makers of Histor. 2006. pap. (***978-1-4065-0359-3(2))** Dodo Pr.

ALFRED, KING OF ENGLAND, 849-899—FICTION

Cross, Gillian. Down with the Dirty Danes. (Illus.). 61p. (J). pap. 7.99 (978-0-00-675534-0(8) , HarperSport) HarperCollins Pubs. Ltd. GBR. *Dist:* Trafalgar Square Publishing.

Tingle, Rebecca. The Edge on the Sword. 2003. (Sailing Mystery Ser.). 288p. (YA). (gr. 8-12). pap. 6.99 (978-0-14-250058-3(5) , Puffin) Penguin Group (USA) Inc.

ALGAE

Cerullo, Mary M. Sea Soup: Phytoplankton. Curtsinger, Bill, photos by. 2005. (Illus.). 40p. (J). (gr. 3-7). 16.95 (978-0-88448-208-6(1)) Tilbury Hse. Pubs.

Deep Sea Invasion. 2004. (NOVA Ser.). (gr. 4 up). 19.95 (978-1-57807-980-3(2) , WG36733) WGBH Boston Video.

Douglas, Lloyd G. Kelp. 2005. (Ocean Life Ser.). (Illus.). 24p. (J). (ps-2). pap. 4.95 (978-0-516-23742-8(X)); 18.00 (978-0-516-25029-8(9)) Scholastic Library Publishing. (Children's Pr.).

Murphy. Seaweed Soup. 2003. (J). pap., tchr. ed. (978-0-7398-6546-0(3)); (Illus.). pap. (978-0-7398-6790-7(3)) Steck-Vaughn.

Zabludoff, Marc. The Protoctist Kingdom. 2005. (Family Trees Ser.). (Illus.). 95p. (J). (gr. 3-7). lib. bdg. 32.79 (978-0-7614-1818-4(0) , Benchmark Bks.) Cavendish, Marshall Corp.

ALGEBRA

see also Number Theory; Probabilities

Accelerated Math Learning Cards - Algebra I. 2004. 199.00 (978-1-59455-121-5(9)) Renaissance Learning, Inc.

Accelerated Math West Virginia State Tagged Algebra I Library. 2004. cd-rom 1199.00 (978-1-59455-113-0(8)) Renaissance Learning, Inc.

Accelerated Math West Virginia State Tagged Algebra II Library. 2004. cd-rom 1199.00 (978-1-59455-114-7(6)) Renaissance Learning, Inc.

Accelerated Math West Virginia State Tagged Pre-Calculus Library. 2004. cd-rom 1199.00 (978-1-59455-116-1(2)) Renaissance Learning, Inc.

Ace Academics & Burchard, Elizabeth R., eds. Algebra 1: A Whole Course in a Box! 2007. (Exambusters Ser.). 384p. (gr. 7 up). 12.95 (978-1-881374-92-3(0) , Exambusters) Ace Academics, Inc.

Algebra: Structure & Method. 2000. (gr. 8-10). stu. ed. (978-0-395-97722-4(3) , 2-13326); Bk. 1. (978-0-618-04898-4(7) , 2-12587); Bk. 1. (978-0-618-04899-1(5) , 2-12588) McDougal Littell Inc.

Algebra 1. 2004. (gr. 6-12). stu. ed., wbk. ed. (978-0-618-02060-7(8) , 2-60322); stu. ed., wbk. ed. (978-0-618-02062-1(4) , 2-60324); stu. ed., wbk. ed. (978-0-618-02063-8(2) , 2-60325) McDougal Littell Inc.

Algebra 1: Concepts & Skills. 2004. (gr. 6-12). stu. ed. (978-0-618-05051-2(5) , 2-60405); wbk. ed. (978-0-618-07865-3(7) , 2-61257); wbk. ed. (978-0-618-07867-7(3) , 2-61259); wbk. ed. (978-0-618-07869-1(X) , 2-61261); Vol. 1. stu. ed. (978-0-618-10646-2(4) , 2-61311); Vol. 2. stu. ed. (978-0-618-10648-6(0) , 2-61313) McDougal Littell Inc.

Algebra 1: Explorations & Applications. 2001. (gr. 8-10). (978-0-395-88322-8(9) , 2-77638); (978-0-618-02194-9(9) , 2-61152); (978-0-618-02195-6(7) , 2-61153); tchr. ed. (978-0-395-93163-9(0) , 2-99440); wbk. ed. (978-0-395-93787-7(6) , 2-78791) McDougal Littell Inc.

Algebra 1 Syllabus & Tests. 3rd ed. 1999. 10p. (YA). (gr. 8-9). ring bd., suppl. ed. 2.50 (978-1-57896-077-4(0) , 1002, Hewitt Homeschooling Resources) Hewitt Research Foundation, Inc.

Algebra 1/2 Syllabus & Tests. 1999. 10p. (YA). (gr. 7-8). ring bd. 2.50 (978-1-57896-070-5(3) , 1735, Hewitt Homeschooling Resources) Hewitt Research Foundation, Inc.

Algebra 2. 2004. (gr. 6-12). stu. ed. 76.52 (978-0-395-93778-5(7) , 2-77962); stu. ed. (978-0-618-02031-7(4) , 2-99720); stu. ed., wbk. ed. (978-0-618-02033-1(0) , 2-99744); stu. ed., wbk. ed. (978-0-618-02034-8(9) , 2-99745) McDougal Littell Inc.

Algebra 2: Explorations & Applications. 2003. (gr. 10-12). tchr. ed. (978-0-395-93164-6(9) , 2-99441); wbk. ed. (978-0-395-93789-1(2) , 2-78793) McDougal Littell Inc.

Algebra 2: Explorations & Applications: Computer Test & Practice Generator with User's Guide for Macintosh(r) & Windows(r) 2003. (gr. 10-12). incl. cd-rom (978-0-395-87896-5(9) , 2-77563) McDougal Littell Inc.

Algebra 2: Explorations & Applications: Study Guide Answer Key. 2003. (gr. 10-12). (978-0-395-76966-9(3) , 2-12811) McDougal Littell Inc.

Algebra 2 Syllabus & Tests. 1999. 10p. (YA). (gr. 10). ring bd. 2.50 (978-1-57896-061-3(4) , 1003, Hewitt Homeschooling Resources) Hewitt Research Foundation, Inc.

Algebra & Trigonometry: Complete Solutions Guide. 6th ed. 2004. (gr. 11-12). (978-0-618-31785-1(6) , 3-32723) McDougal Littell Inc.

Algebra & Trigonometry: Learning Tools. 6th ed. 2004. (gr. 11-12). stu. ed. incl. cd-rom (978-0-618-31794-3(5) , 3-32732) McDougal Littell Inc.

Algebra & Trigonometry: Test Item File. 6th ed. 2004. (gr. 11-12). (978-0-618-31786-8(4) , 3-32724) McDougal Littell Inc.

Algebra & Trigonometry: A Graphing Approach: Complete Solutions Guide. 3rd ed. 2001. (gr. 11-12). (978-0-618-07303-0(5) , 3-32224) McDougal Littell Inc.

Algebra & Trigonometry Vol. 2: Structure & Method. 2000. (gr. 10-12). tchr. ed. (978-0-395-97726-2(6) , 2-13330); stu. ed. (978-0-395-97725-5(8) , 2-13329) McDougal Littell Inc.

Algebra I Set (CA Version) 2002. stu. ed., per. (978-1-930804-36-4(9)) Carnegie Learning.

Algebra I Set (CA Version) Spanish Student Consumable. 2002. per. (978-1-930804-40-1(7)) Carnegie Learning.

Algebra I Set (CA Version) Spanish Student Edition. 2002. per. (978-1-930804-39-5(3)) Carnegie Learning.

Algebra I Set (CA Version) Student Consumable. 2002. per. (978-1-930804-37-1(7)) Carnegie Learning.

Algebra I Student Consumable. 2002. per. (978-1-930804-04-3(0)) Carnegie Learning.

Algebra I Student Consumable Assignment. 2002. per. (978-1-930804-05-0(9)) Carnegie Learning.

Algebra I Student Edition. 2002. per. (978-1-930804-02-9(4)) Carnegie Learning.

Algebra II. 2002. stu. ed., per. (978-1-930804-14-2(8)) Carnegie Learning.

Algebra II Student Consumable. 2002. per. (978-1-930804-44-9(X)) Carnegie Learning.

Algebra Tiles Workbook. 2002. (J). pap. 7.95 (978-1-56911-049-2(2)) Learning Resources, Inc.

Algebraic Foundations - Third Edition. 2000. pap., stu. ed. (978-1-57290-033-2(4)) National Training Network, Inc.

Algebraic Thinking - Part II - Fourth Edition, Vol. 2. 2000. pap., stu. ed. (978-1-57290-037-0(7)) National Training Network, Inc.

Algebraic Thinking Algebra I Supplement. 2005. (978-1-57290-068-4(7)) National Training Network, Inc.

Algebraic Thinking Part I Third Edition, Vol. 1. 2000. pap., stu. ed. (978-1-57290-035-6(0)) National Training Network, Inc.

Analysis I: Grundlagen: Zahlenfolgen und Reelle Funktionen. (Duden Abiturhilfen Ser.). (GER.). 112p. (YA). (gr. 11). (978-3-411-70122-3(6)) Bibliographisches Institut & F. A. Brockhaus AG DEU. *Dist:* International Bk. Import Service, Inc.

Aufmann. Aufmann Algebra: Beginning & Intermediate Plus Study & Solutions Manual Plus Eduspace Two. 2004. (YA). pap., pap. 117.96 (978-0-618-53460-9(1) , 389574) Houghton Mifflin College Div.

—Aufmann, Applied College Algebra Plus Eduspace 1. 2003. (YA). pap. 99.56 (978-0-618-55560-4(9) , 395079) Houghton Mifflin College Div.

—Aufmann College Algebra Plus Study Guide/solutions Manual Plus Math Space Cd Fifth Edition. 5th ed. 2004. (YA). pap. 124.76 incl. cd-rom (978-0-618-50780-1(9) , 389164) Houghton Mifflin College Div.

—Aufmann Essentials College Algebra Plus Dvd. 2005. (YA). 109.96 (978-0-618-72259-4(9) , 397219) Houghton Mifflin College Div.

—Aufmann Essentials College Algebra Plus Smarthinking. 2005. (YA). pap. 109.96 (978-0-618-72260-0(2) , 397220) Houghton Mifflin College Div.

—Aufmann Essentials College Algebra Plus Student Solutions Manual. 2005. (YA). pap. 103.16 (978-0-618-72258-7(0) , 397218) Houghton Mifflin College Div.

—Aufmann Intermediate Algebra Paperback Plus Mathspace Cd. 7th ed. 2005. (YA). pap., pap. 126.76 incl. cd-rom (978-0-618-72267-9(X) , 397221) Houghton Mifflin College Div.

—Aufmann Intermediate Algebra Paperback Plus Mathspace Cd Plus Dvd Seventh Edition. 7th ed. 2005. (YA). pap. 126.76 incl. cd-rom (978-0-618-72268-6(8) , 397222) Houghton Mifflin College Div.

—Aufmann Introductory Algebra Paperback Plus Mathspace Cd Plus Dvd Seventh Edition. 7th ed. 2005. (YA). pap. 126.76 incl. cd-rom (978-0-618-72271-6(8) , 397224) Houghton Mifflin College Div.

—Aufmann Introductory Algebra Paperback Plus Mathspace Cd Seventh Edition Plus Smarthinking. 7th ed. 2005. (YA). pap., pap. 126.76 incl. cd-rom (978-0-618-72269-3(6) , 397223) Houghton Mifflin College Div.

—College Algebra with Eduspace. 5th ed. 2004. (YA). pap., pap. 124.76 (978-0-618-51753-4(7) , 389282) Houghton Mifflin College Div.

—Intermediate Algebra: With HM Cubed & Eduspace. 6th ed. 2004. (YA). pap. 127.56 incl. cd-rom (978-0-618-52946-9(2) , 389451) Houghton Mifflin College Div.

—Student Solutions Manual: Used with ... Aufmann-Beginning Algebra with Applications. 6th ed. 2003. (YA). stu. ed. 45.56 (978-0-618-30607-7(2) , 301493) Houghton Mifflin College Div.

—Student Solutions Manual: Used with ... Aufmann-Exploring Introductory & Intermediate Algebra: A Graphing Approach. 2003. (YA). stu. ed. 44.76 (978-0-618-15689-4(5) , 301533) Houghton Mifflin College Div.

—Student Study Guide: Used with ... Aufmann-College Algebra. 5th ed. 2004. (YA). stu. ed. 49.16 (978-0-618-38672-7(6) , 302382) Houghton Mifflin College Div.

Aufmann, Richard N., et al. Exploring Elementary & Intermediate Algebra: A Graphing Approach. 2003. (Illus.). 845p. (YA). 124.76 (978-0-618-15686-3(0) , 301530) Houghton Mifflin College Div.

Barcharts, Inc. Staff, ed. Algebra 2. 2005. (Quick Study Academic Ser.). (YA). pap. 5.95 (978-1-57222-922-8(5)) Barcharts, Inc.

Barclay, Judith M. Solving Algebra Word Problems. 2004. (Illus.). 208p. (C). pap. 22.95 (978-0-534-49573-2(7)) Brooks/Cole.

Basic Algebra. 2000. (gr. 8-11). (978-0-618-02197-0(3) , 2-61154); (978-0-618-02198-7(1) , 2-61155); stu. ed. (978-0-395-98002-6(X) , 2-07214) McDougal Littell Inc.

Basic Algebra: Resource Book. 2000. (gr. 8-11). (978-0-395-41191-9(2) , 2-07203) McDougal Littell Inc.

Beck, Ray, et al. Practicing Basic Skills in Algebra. 2004. (One-Minute Fluency Builders Ser.). 248p. per. (978-1-59318-005-8(5) , 234ALG) Sopris West Educational Services.

Benchmark Education Staff, compiled by. Algebra. 2005. spiral bd. 105.00 (***978-1-4108-3883-4(8));** spiral bd. 55.00 (***978-1-4108-3884-1(6));** spiral bd. 245.00 (***978-1-4108-3891-9(9));** spiral bd. 215.00 (***978-1-4108-3892-6(7));** spiral bd. 255.00 (***978-1-4108-3899-5(4));** spiral bd. 105.00 (***978-1-4108-3900-8(1));** spiral bd. 35.00 (***978-1-4108-3913-8(3));** spiral bd. 440.00 (***978-1-4108-4510-8(9));** spiral bd. 365.00 (***978-1-4108-5449-0(3));** spiral bd. 295.00 (***978-1-4108-5450-6(7));** spiral bd. 375.00 (***978-1-4108-5860-3(X));** spiral bd. 255.00 (***978-1-4108-5861-0(8))** Benchmark Education Co.

BJU Staff. Algebra 1 Student Text Grd 9. 2004. 32.00 (978-1-57924-325-8(8)) Jones, Bob Univ. Pr.

Blitzer, Robert F. Precalculus. 2003. (Homework Booklets Ser.). 72p. (YA). (gr. 8 up). pap. 2.99 (978-1-56822-418-3(4) , Instructional Fair) Schaffer, Frank Pubns.

Blitzer, Robert F. & Bentley, Wayne J. Precalculus. 1999. (100+ Seriestm Ser.). 128p. (YA). (gr. 9-12). pap. 12.99 (978-1-56822-488-6(5) , IF8768) School Specialty Publishing.

Bradsby, Larry, et al. Algebra 1 Rescue! Student Book: Chapters 1-6. 2003. 190p. (YA). per. (978-1-57035-935-4(0) , 169ALG) Sopris West Educational Services.

—Algebra 1 Rescue! Student Book: Chapters 7-12. 2003. 192p. (YA). per. (978-1-57035-936-1(9) , 169ALG) Sopris West Educational Services.

Britt, Murray, et al. Equations & Algebraic Expressions. 2001. (Algebra Makes Sense Ser.: Bk. 1). 48p. (YA). (gr. 6-10). pap., stu. ed. 16.50 (978-0-7690-2840-8(3)) Seymour, Dale Pubns.

Carson-Dellosa Publishing Staff. Jumpstarters for Pre-Algebra Ages 6 + 2005. 48p. (J). pap. (978-1-58037-303-6(8)) Carson-Dellosa Publishing Co., Inc.

Christopher Lee Publications Staff. Einstein's Algebra 1 Made Easy. 2002. (Einstein's... Made Easy Flippers Ser.). (Illus.). 50p. pap. 7.95 (978-1-59125-159-0(1)) Penton Overseas, Inc.

—Einstein's Algebra 2 Made Easy. 2002. (Einstein's... Made Easy Flippers Ser.). pap. 7.95 (978-1-59125-135-4(4)); (Illus.). pap. 7.95 (978-1-59125-160-6(5)) Penton Overseas, Inc.

CMSP Projects Staff. Prealgebra. rev. ed. (Illus.). 101p. (YA). reprint ed. pap. (978-0-942851-00-7(5)) CMSP Projects.

Cognitive Technologies Corporation Staff. Algebra World. 1998. (J). (gr. 6 up). 79.95 incl. cd-rom (978-1-57204-476-0(4) , CD00023); 224.95 incl. cd-rom (978-1-57204-477-7(2) , CD00024) Global Energy.

Cognitive Tutor (R) Algebra I. 2002. tchr. ed., per. (978-1-930804-90-6(3)); stu. ed., per. (978-1-930804-91-3(1)) Carnegie Learning.

Cognitive Tutor (R) Algebra I Software Edition. 2002. per. (978-1-930804-92-0(X)) Carnegie Learning.

Concentrate on! Algebra I. 2003. (J). spiral bd. 15.95 (978-1-58123-336-0(1)) Larson Learning, Inc.

Dana, Marcia. Elementary Algebra. 2005. (Four-Blocks Ser.). 128p. (J). pap. (978-1-59441-192-2(1) , CD-104105); pap. (978-1-59441-194-6(8) , CD-104106) Carson-Dellosa Publishing Co., Inc.

—Elementary Algebra Grades 3-4. 2005. 128p. (J). pap. (978-1-59441-193-9(X)) Carson-Dellosa Publishing Co., Inc.

Dankberg, Tracy. Algebra: Grades 5-8. 2003. (Skill Builders Ser.). 80p. (gr. 5-8). 2.95 (978-1-932210-10-1(5)) Rainbow Bridge Publishing.

Davis, Karen Lyn. Coolmath Algebra, Pt. 2. 2007. (YA). per. 19.95 ***(978-0-9791628-1-7(5))*** Coolmath.com, Inc.

—Coolmath Algebra Part 1. 2007. (YA). per. 19.95 ***(978-0-9791628-0-0(7))*** Coolmath.com, Inc.

Denholm, Richard A. Elementary Algebra. 2002. (Basic Skills Ser.). 48p. (J). (gr. k-1). pap. 5.99 (978-0-7424-0236-2(3) , IF5215); (gr. 2-3). pap. 5.99 (978-0-7424-0237-9(1) , IF5216); (gr. 4-5). pap. 5.99 (978-0-7424-0238-6(X) , IF5217) School Specialty Publishing.

Douglas, Vincent & School Specialty Publishing Staff. The Complete Book of Algebra & Geometry. 2005. (Complete Book Ser.). (Illus.). 352p. (J). pap. 14.95 (978-0-7696-4330-4(2) , American Education Publishing) School Specialty Publishing.

Downey, Tika. How the Arabs Invented Algebra: The History of the Concept of Variables. 2004. (Powermath Ser.). (Illus.). 32p. (J). lib. bdg. (978-0-8239-8879-2(1)); lib. bdg. 22.50 (978-0-8239-8986-7(0)) Rosen Publishing Group, Inc., The. (PowerKids Pr.).

Draper, Catheryne. The Algebra Game Linear Equations. 1999. (Algebra Game Ser.). (Illus.). 142p. (J). tchr. ed. 25.00 (978-1-929362-05-9(6) , AGL010) Math Studio, The.

Dressler, Isidore. Algebra I. 2nd ed. 2005. Orig. Title: Algebra One Review Guide. (YA). pap. (978-1-56765-575-9(0) , R27P) AMSCO Schl. Pubns., Inc.

Ebs Trust, prod. Concepts in Abstract Algebra: Group Theory. (Concepts in Abstract Algebra: Group Theory Ser.). (YA). cd-rom 269.95 (978-0-7365-4752-9(5)) Films Media Group.

Encyclopaedia Britannica Publishers, Inc. Staff. Math in Context: Algebra Rules! 6th ed. 2005. pap. 10.60 (978-0-03-038574-2(1)) Harcourt Schl. Pubs.

FFA Skill Builders Year 1 Year 2: Version 3. 0. 2002. (gr. 6-12). 7.00 (978-1-931287-34-0(1) , M0-341) CPM Educational Program.

Flip over Math: Algebraic Thinking. 2004. (J). spiral bd. 14.95 (978-1-56911-539-8(7)) Learning Resources, Inc.

Foundations for Algebra Year 1: Version 3. 0. 2002. (gr. 6-12). 42.00 (978-1-931287-03-6(1) , M0-031) CPM Educational Program.

Foundations for Algebra Year 2: Version 3. 0. 2002. (gr. 6-12). 42.00 (978-1-931287-09-8(0) , M0-090) CPM Educational Program.

Four-Pan Algebra Balance: Modeling Integers & Equations. 2000. (J). pap. 9.95 (978-1-56911-054-6(9)) Learning Resources, Inc.

Gateways to Algebra & Geometry, an Integrated Approach: Multi-Language Glossary. 2003. (gr. 11-12). (978-0-618-10650-9(2) , 2-61315) McDougal Littell Inc.

Great Source Education Group Staff. Algebra to Go: A Mathematics Handbook. 2000. (YA). (gr. 8 up). 25.33 (978-0-669-47152-6(6) , 047152); pap. 21.00 (978-0-669-47151-9(8) , 047151) Great Source Education Group, Inc.

Greenes, Carole, et al. Hot Math Topics: Algebraic Reasoning. 2003. 64p. (J). (gr. 5). 16.95 (978-0-7690-0839-4(9)) Seymour, Dale Pubns.

Hall, Basia, et al. Algebra I Assessments. 2002. (Illus.). 462p. per. 40.00 (978-0-9707948-5-7(1)) Dana, Charles A. Ctr., Univ. of Texas at Austin.

Hamilton, Said. Mastering Algebra: Intermediate Level. Eblen, Pat, ed. 1998. 590p. (YA). (gr. 9 up). pap. 49.95 (978-0-9649954-2-0(5)) Hamilton Assocs.

Harcourt Brace Staff. Astro Algebra: Grades 6-8 Net Version Software Package. 99th ed. 2003. (Mighty Mathun Ser.). (gr. 6-8). cd-rom 851.80 (978-0-15-313212-4(4)) Harcourt Schl. Pubs.

Harnadek, Anita. Algebra I Word Problems: Foolproof Problem-Solving Strategies, Instruction & Guided Practice. 2003. (YA). pap. 32.99 (978-0-89455-799-6(8)) Critical Thinking Bks. & Software.

—Algebra II Word Problems: Foolproof Problem-Solving Strategies, Instruction & Guided Practice. 2003. (YA). pap. 32.99 (978-0-89455-800-9(5)) Critical Thinking Bks. & Software.

Holt, Rinehart and Winston Staff. Algebra: Data Analysis: Test Preparation - Maryland Edition. 3rd ed. 2003. (YA). pap. 12.20 (978-0-03-070221-1(6)) Holt, Rinehart & Winston.

—Algebra 1. (SPA., 3rd ed. 2003. Illus.). stu. ed. 69.60 (978-0-03-074346-7(X)); 4th ed. 2004. 69.60 (978-0-03-070042-2(6)) Holt, Rinehart & Winston.

—Algebra 2: Practice Workbooks - Set of 5. 2001. (YA). pap., wbk. ed. 1.60 (978-0-03-066153-2(6)) Holt, Rinehart & Winston.

—Algebra 2 - 2001: Transparencies wth Answer Key. 2000. trans. 227.26 (978-0-03-064689-8(8)) Holt, Rinehart & Winston.

—Making Sense of Numbers. 2001. pap. 31.93 (978-0-03-064284-5(1)) Holt, Rinehart & Winston.

—Making Sense of Numbers: Answer Key. 2001. pap. 13.86 (978-0-03-064286-9(8)) Holt, Rinehart & Winston.

—Pre-Algebra: Are You Ready: Intervention. 4th ed. Date not set. pap. 74.40 (978-0-03-070803-9(6)) Holt, Rinehart & Winston.

—Pre-Algebra: Chapter Resources. 4th ed. Date not set. pap. 367.00 (978-0-03-070828-2(1)) Holt, Rinehart & Winston.

—Pre-Algebra: Homework & Practice Workbook Answer Key. 4th ed. Date not set. pap., wbk. ed. 11.00 (978-0-03-069701-2(8)) Holt, Rinehart & Winston.

—Pre-Algebra: Interactive Problem Solving with Answer Key. 4th ed. 2003. pap. 30.53 (978-0-03-069702-9(6)) Holt, Rinehart & Winston.

—Pre-Algebra: Interactive Study Guide with Answer Key. 4th ed. 2003. pap., stu. ed. 13.20 (978-0-03-069703-6(4)) Holt, Rinehart & Winston.

—Pre-Algebra: Interactive Study Guide Workbook. 4th ed. 2003. pap., wbk. ed. 10.06 (978-0-03-069714-2(X)) Holt, Rinehart & Winston.

—Pre-Algebra: Math: Reading, Writing & Content Areas. 4th ed. 2003. pap. 30.45 (978-0-03-069801-9(4)) Holt, Rinehart & Winston.

—Pre-Algebra: Multilingual Glossary. 4th ed. Date not set. pap. 26.00 (978-0-03-070804-6(4)) Holt, Rinehart & Winston.

—Pre-Algebra: Readiness Activities with Answer Key. 4th ed. 2003. pap. 13.20 (978-0-03-069803-3(0)) Holt, Rinehart & Winston.

—Pre-Algebra: Standard Test Preparation. 4th ed. Date not set. pap., wbk. ed. 8.40 (978-0-03-070801-5(X)) Holt, Rinehart & Winston.

—Pre-Algebra: Standard Test Preparation with Answer Key. 4th ed. Date not set. pap., wbk. ed. 12.60 (978-0-03-070802-2(8)) Holt, Rinehart & Winston.

—Pre-Algebra: Success for English Language Learners. 4th ed. 2003. pap. 80.66 (978-0-03-069859-0(6)) Holt, Rinehart & Winston.

—Pre-Algebra Chptr. 2: Resource Book with Answer Key. 4th ed. 2003. pap. 38.86 (978-0-03-069681-7(X)) Holt, Rinehart & Winston.

—Pre-Algebra Chptr. 9: Resource Book with Answer Key. 4th ed. 2003. pap. 38.86 (978-0-03-069689-3(5)) Holt, Rinehart & Winston.

—Pre-Algebra Chptr. 10: Resource Book with Answer Key. 4th ed. 2003. pap. 38.86 (978-0-03-069691-6(7)) Holt, Rinehart & Winston.

—Pre-Algebra Chptr. 11: Resource Book with Answer Key. 4th ed. 2003. pap. 38.86 (978-0-03-069692-3(5)) Holt, Rinehart & Winston.

—Pre-Algebra Chptr. 12: Resource Book with Answer Key. 4th ed. 2003. pap. 38.86 (978-0-03-069693-0(3)) Holt, Rinehart & Winston.

—Pre-Algebra Chptr. 13: Resource Book with Answer Key. 3rd ed. 2003. pap. 38.86 (978-0-03-069694-7(1)) Holt, Rinehart & Winston.

—Pre-Algebra Chptr. 14: Resource Book with Answer Key. 4th ed. 2003. pap. 38.86 (978-0-03-069696-1(8)) Holt, Rinehart & Winston.

—Pre-Algebra Know-It Notebook. 4th ed. 2004. pap. 13.93 (978-0-03-038014-3(6)) Holt, Rinehart & Winston.

—Standard Test Practice Workbook: South Carolina Edition - Algebra. 3rd ed. 2003. pap. 13.26 (978-0-03-069033-4(1)) Holt, Rinehart & Winston.

Hostetler, Robert & Larson, Ron. Precalculus. 6th ed. 2003. 781p. (YA). stu. ed. 144.36 incl. cd-rom (978-0-618-38653-6(X) , 332757) Houghton Mifflin College Div.

Hushin, Iftikhar. Exploring Algebra with Creative Designs. 2002. ii, 114p. (YA). (gr. 7-12). pap. 19.95 (978-0-9718640-0-9(4)) Inaz Enterprises.

Ideals Publications Inc. Staff & Goodnow, Judy. Begin Algebra Thinking. 1999. 64p. (J). (gr. 5-6). pap. 8.99 (978-1-56451-096-9(4) , ID7271) School Specialty Publishing.

Ideals Publications Inc. Staff, et al. Begin Algebra Thinking. 1999. 64p. (J). (gr. 3-4). pap. 8.99 (978-1-56451-095-2(6) , ID7270) School Specialty Publishing.

In Step with the Standards - Algebra Concepts. 2005. (J). spiral bd. 15.95 (978-1-58123-380-3(9)) Larson Learning, Inc.

Instructional Fair. Algebraic Reasoning. 2002. (Mathematical Mind Ser.). (Illus.). 48p. (J). (gr. 5-8). pap. 6.99 (978-0-7424-0264-5(9) , IF2909) School Specialty Publishing.

Integrating Grade 10 TAKS Algebra I Objectives into Geometry, A Graphing Calculator Approach - Student Approach. 2005. (Region IV ESC Resources for Mathematics Ser.). pap. (978-1-932797-69-5(6)) Region IV Education Service Ctr.

Interactive Mathematics - College Algebra: Personal Academic Notebook. rev. ed. 1999. 690p. (YA). (gr. 6 up). pap. 68.50 (978-1-928962-03-8(3) , MP-504-010) Academic Systems Corp.

Interactive Mathematics - Elementary Algebra: Personal Academic Notebook. rev. ed. Date not set. (Illus.). 492p. (YA). (gr. 6 up). pap. 68.50 (978-1-928962-01-4(7) , MP-502-010) Academic Systems Corp.

Interactive Mathematics - Intermediate Algebra: Personal Academic Notebook. rev. ed. 1999. (Illus.). 1550p. (YA). (gr. 6 up). pap. 68.50 (978-1-928962-02-1(5) , MP-503-010) Academic Systems Corp.

Jahnke, Stephen B. Algebra, 2 vols. rev. ed. 2000. (Straight Forward Advanced Math Ser.). (YA). Bk. 1. (Illus.). 83p. pap. 9.95 (978-1-930820-04-3(6)); Bk. 2. 101p. pap. 9.95 (978-1-930820-05-0(4)) Garlic Pr.

The Journey of Al & Gebra to the Land of Algebra PPT. 2006. (YA). cd-rom 20.00 ***(978-1-929229-72-7(0))*** aha! Process, Inc.

Karapetian, Marjam. Bilingual Content Dictionary: English to Spanish. 2004. (SPA & ENG., Illus.). 4.95 (978-0-9764829-1-8(6)) WizdomInc.

Kopp, Jaine. Algebraic Reasoning: Professor Arbegla Introduces Variables & Functions. 2003. (Great Explorations in Math & Science Ser.). (Illus.). 148p. (Orig.). (J). (gr. 3-5). pap. 18.00 (978-0-924886-70-6(6) , GEMS) Univ. of California, Berkeley, Lawrence Hall of Science.

Lane County Mathematics Project Staff. Problem Solving in Mathematics. (YA). (gr. 9). pap. 27.95 (978-0-86651-186-5(5) , DSO1412) Globe Fearon Educational Publishing.

Larson. Algebra & Trigonometry A Graphing Approach 4th Edition Plus Smarthinking. 4th ed. 2004. (YA). pap. 151.16 (978-0-618-52382-5(0) , 389381) Houghton Mifflin College Div.

—Algebra & Trigonometry A Graphing Approach Eduspace Ebook Fourth Edition. 4th ed. 2005. (YA). pap. 27.56 (978-0-618-72511-3(3) , 333023) Houghton Mifflin College Div.

—Algebra for College Students Eduspace Ebook. 2005. (YA). pap. 27.56 (978-0-618-72514-4(8) , 332419) Houghton Mifflin College Div.

—College Algebra: Used with ... Larson-College Algebra: A Graphing Approach. 4th ed. 2004. (YA). 42.36 (978-0-618-39452-4(4) , 333018) Houghton Mifflin College Div.

—College Algebra: Concepts & Models Student Study Guide: Used with ... Larson-Precalculus with Limits: A Graphing Approach. 3rd ed. 2000. (YA). (gr. 11-12). stu. ed. 49.56 (978-0-618-07410-5(4) , 332282) Houghton Mifflin College Div.

—Precalculus: Used with ... Larson-Precalculus. 5th ed. 2000. (YA). (gr. 11-12). stu. ed. 49.56 (978-0-618-07271-2(3) , 330443) Houghton Mifflin College Div.

—Precalculus Interactive 2.0. 5th ed. 2001. (YA). cd-rom 61.56 (978-0-618-07276-7(4) , 330448) Houghton Mifflin College Div.

—Precalculus with Limits: A Graphing Approach 3rd Edition Plus Learning CD 6th Edition. 3rd ed. 2003. (YA). (gr. 11-12). 144.36 incl. cd-rom (978-0-618-39802-7(3) , 386344) Houghton Mifflin College Div.

—Precalculus with Limits: A Graphing Approach Plus Eduspace/Blackboard. 4th ed. 2004. (YA). pap. 144.36 (978-0-618-52373-3(1) , 389380) Houghton Mifflin College Div.

—Student Success Organizer: Used with ... Larson-Algebra & Trigonometry. 6th ed. 2003. (YA). (gr. 11-12). stu. ed. 8.36 (978-0-618-31787-5(2) , 332725) Houghton Mifflin College Div.

—Student Success Organizer: Used with ... Larson-Precalculus. 6th ed. 2003. (YA). (gr. 11-12). stu. ed. 8.36 (978-0-618-31440-9(7) , 332746) Houghton Mifflin College Div.

—Study & Solutions Guide: Used with ... Larson-Algebra & Trigonometry. 6th ed. 2003. (YA). (gr. 11-12). stu. ed. 49.56 (978-0-618-31784-4(8) , 332722) Houghton Mifflin College Div.

—Study & Solutions Guide: Used with ... Larson-Algebra & Trigonometry: A Graphing Approach. 4th ed. 2004. (YA). stu. ed. 49.56 (978-0-618-39457-9(5) , 333027) Houghton Mifflin College Div.

—Study & Solutions Guide: Used with ... Larson-College Algebra: A Graphing Approach. 4th ed. 2004. (YA). stu. ed. 49.56 (978-0-618-39443-2(5) , 333012) Houghton Mifflin College Div.

—Study & Solutions Guide: Used with ... Larson-Precalculus. 6th ed. 2003. (YA). (gr. 11-12). stu. ed. 49.56 (978-0-618-31437-9(7) , 332743) Houghton Mifflin College Div.

—Study & Solutions Guide: Used with ... Larson-Precalculus: A Graphing Approach. 4th ed. 2004. (YA). stu. ed. 49.56 (978-0-618-39468-5(0) , 333032) Houghton Mifflin College Div.

—Study & Solutions Guide: Used with ... Larson-Precalculus with Limits: A Graphing Approach. 4th ed. 2004. (YA). 49.56 (978-0-618-39481-4(8) , 333053) Houghton Mifflin College Div.

Larson, Roland E. Passport to Algebra & Geometry: (c)2004. l.t. ed. 2004. (YA). (gr. 6-9). stu. ed. (978-0-618-37422-9(1) , 2-05530) McDougal Littell Inc.

Larson, Ron. McDougal Littell Geometry. l.t. ed. 2004. (YA). (gr. 8-12). stu. ed. 77.64 (978-0-618-25022-6(0) , 2-06012) McDougal Littell Inc.

Larson, Ron & Hostetler, Robert. Algebra & Trigonometry: Text with Learning Tools. 6th ed. 2003. 885p. (YA). (gr. 11-12). 144.36 incl. cd-rom (978-0-618-38650-5(5) , 332735) Houghton Mifflin College Div.

—Interactive Algebra & Trigonometry 3.0. 6th ed. 2003. (YA). cd-rom 59.96 (978-0-618-37586-8(4) , 332733) Houghton Mifflin College Div.

Larson, Ron, et al. Precalculus: A Graphing Approach. 4th ed. 2004. 832p. (YA). 144.36 (978-0-618-39466-1(4) , 333030) Houghton Mifflin College Div.

—Precalculus Functions & Graphs: A Graphing Approach. 4th ed. 2004. 704p. (YA). 144.36 (978-0-618-39476-0(1) , 333045) Houghton Mifflin College Div.

—Precalculus with Limits: A Graphing Approach. 4th ed. 2004. 796p. (YA). 144.36 (978-0-618-39478-4(8) , 333050) Houghton Mifflin College Div.

Lassiter, Karen. Algebra Core Skills. 2001. pap. (978-0-7398-4895-1(X)) Steck-Vaughn.

Lawler, Graham. Algebra: Basic Algebra Explained. 2005. (Illus.). 174p. (C). pap. 29.50 (978-1-84285-068-8(7)) Studymates Ltd. GBR. *Dist:* Trans-Atlantic Pubns., Inc.

Lawrence, Ann & Hennessy, Charlie. Lessons for Algebraic Thinking, Grades 6-8. 2002. (Lessons for Algebraic Thinking Ser.). (Illus.). 280p. (gr. 3-5). pap. 29.95 (978-0-941355-49-0(7)) Math Solutions Pubns.

Lawrence, David P. Skill & Practice Masters in Algebra Using the Ti-84. 2004. 50p. pap. 14.95 net. (978-1-58108-050-6(6)) Pencil Point Pr., Inc.

—Ti-84 Easy Warm Ups in Algebra One. 2004. 32p. pap. 14.95 net. (978-1-58108-049-0(2) , 1-58108-049-2) Pencil Point Pr., Inc.

Lay, Steven & Lay, Clark. Prelude to Algebra. 2007. 338p. 60.00 ***(978-0-9793087-0-3(4))*** Cross Product Pubns.

Lineare Algebra und Analytische Geometrie I: Leistungskurs. (Duden Abiturhilfen Ser.). (GER.). 96p. (YA). (gr. 12-13). (978-3-411-04601-0(5)) Bibliographisches Institut & F. A. Brockhaus AG DEU. *Dist:* International Bk. Import Service, Inc.

Lineare Algebra und Analytische Geometrie II: Leistungskurs. (Duden Abiturhilfen Ser.). (GER.). 96p. (YA). (gr. 12-13). (978-3-411-04631-7(7)) Bibliographisches Institut & F. A. Brockhaus AG DEU. *Dist:* International Bk. Import Service, Inc.

Long, Lynette. Algebra Sin Dolor: Painless Algebra. Morehouse, Hank, illus. 2002. (Painless Ser.). (ENG & SPA.). 304p. pap. 12.99 (978-0-7641-2145-6(6)) Barron's Educational Series, Inc.

Low, Yvonne. Kyoodoz Pre-Algebra Maven. 2007. (Illus.). 200p. (YA). per. 16.50 ***(978-0-9771172-2-2(7))*** Kyoodoz.

Math 1: Version 6. 1, 2 vols. 2nd ed. 2002. (gr. 6-12). stu. ed. 25.00 (978-1-885145-72-7(1) , M1-721) CPM Educational Program.

Math Forum Staff. Dr. Math Explains Algebra: Learning Algebra Is Easy! Just Ask Dr. Math! 2003. (Illus.). 192p. pap. 14.95 (978-0-471-22555-3(X) , Wiley) Wiley, John & Sons, Inc.

Mathematical Models with Applications: Algebra II Alignment Student Handbook. 2003. per. (978-1-932524-01-7(0)) Region IV Education Service Ctr.

Mathematics: Structure & Method. 2004. (gr. 6-12). cd-rom (978-0-618-01300-5(8) , 2-99708) McDougal Littell Inc.

McDougal Littell Algebra 1: Data Analysis Sourcebook. 2002. (gr. 8-12). (978-0-618-37044-3(7) , 2-06530) McDougal Littell Inc.

McDougal Littell Algebra 1: EEdition. 2004. (gr. 6-12). cd-rom (978-0-618-43977-5(3) , 2-05846) McDougal Littell Inc.

McDougal Littell Algebra 1: Exercises in Spanish. 2004. (gr. 6-12). (978-0-618-37048-1(X) , 2-06532) McDougal Littell Inc.

McDougal Littell Algebra 1: Explorations & Projects Book. 2004. (gr. 6-12). (978-0-618-25223-7(1) , 2-61392) McDougal Littell Inc.

McDougal Littell Algebra 1: Functions Sourcebook. 2004. (gr. 6-12). (978-0-618-39081-6(2) , K-51303) McDougal Littell Inc.

McDougal Littell Algebra 1: Notetaking Guide, PE. 2004. (gr. 6-12). (978-0-618-41021-7(X) , 2-05710) McDougal Littell Inc.

McDougal Littell Algebra 1: Personal Student Tutor. 2004. (gr. 6-12). cd-rom (978-0-618-35333-0(X) , 2-91224); cd-rom (978-0-618-39631-3(4) , 2-05623); cd-rom (978-0-618-38108-1(2) , 2-05537) McDougal Littell Inc.

McDougal Littell Algebra 1: Pupil's Edition. 2004. (gr. 6-12). (978-0-618-25018-9(2) , 2-06008) McDougal Littell Inc.

McDougal Littell Algebra 2: EEdition. 2004. (gr. 6-12). cd-rom (978-0-618-43978-2(1) , 2-05467) McDougal Littell Inc.

McDougal Littell Algebra 2: Exercises in Spanish. 2004. (gr. 6-12). (978-0-618-37050-4(1) , 2-06534) McDougal Littell Inc.

McDougal Littell Algebra 2: Personal Student Tutor. 2004. (gr. 6-12). cd-rom (978-0-618-35340-8(2) , 2-91231); cd-rom (978-0-618-39639-9(X) , 2-05626); cd-rom (978-0-618-38109-8(0) , 2-05538) McDougal Littell Inc.

McDougal Littell Algebra 2: Pupil's Edition (c) 2004. 2004. (gr. 6-12). (978-0-618-25020-2(4) , 2-06010) McDougal Littell Inc.

McDougal Littell Geometry: Notetaking Guide, PE. 2004. (gr. 6-12). (978-0-618-41023-1(6) , 2-05712) McDougal Littell Inc.

McGraw-Hill Staff. Algebra 1. 2002. stu. ed. 82.64 incl. cd-rom (978-0-07-829058-9(9) , 9780078290589) Glencoe/McGraw-Hill.

—Algebra 1: Integration. 2000. (C). 86.64 (978-0-07-822894-0(8) , 9780078228940) Glencoe/McGraw-Hill.

—Algebra 1, Spanish. 2002. (SPA.). (C). stu. ed. 82.64 (978-0-07-829399-3(5) , 9780078293993) Glencoe/McGraw-Hill.

—Algebra Prerequisite Skills: Remediation & Intervention. 2002. (C). (gr. 6-12). pap., stu. ed., wbk. ed. 10.64 (978-0-07-827759-7(0) , 9780078277597) Glencoe/McGraw-Hill.

—Contemporary Precalculus Through Applications. 1999. stu. ed. 78.64 (978-1-57039-775-2(9) , 9781570397752) Glencoe/McGraw-Hill.

—Glencoe Algebra: Concepts & Applications, . 2nd ed. 2003. 866p. (gr. 9-12). stu. ed. 79.96 (978-0-07-845771-5(8) , 9780078457715) Glencoe/McGraw-Hill.

—Glencoe Algebra Vol. 1: Concepts & Applications. 2003. (C). (gr. 6-12). stu. ed. 62.64 (978-0-07-860855-1(4) , 9780078608551) Glencoe/McGraw-Hill.

—Glencoe Algebra Vol. 2: Concepts & Applications. 2003. (gr. 6-12). stu. ed. 62.64 (978-0-07-860775-2(2) , 9780078607752) Glencoe/McGraw-Hill.

—Glencoe Algebra 1. 2005. stu. ed. 82.64 (978-0-07-865113-7(1) , 9780078651137) Glencoe/McGraw-Hill.

—Glencoe Algebra 2. 2004. (C). stu. ed. 87.96 (978-0-07-865609-5(5) , 9780078656095) Glencoe/McGraw-Hill.

—IMPACT Mathematics: Algebra & More, Course 3, StudentWorks. 2005. cd-rom 89.32 (978-0-07-861317-3(5) , 9780078613173) Glencoe/McGraw-Hill.

—IMPACT Mathematics: Algebra & More for the Middle Grades, Course 1. 2nd ed. 2001. (C). stu. ed. 73.32 (978-1-57039-850-6(X) , 9781570398506) Glencoe/McGraw-Hill.

—Interactive Student Edition CD-ROM. 2006. (C). cd-rom 77.96 (978-0-07-875710-5(X) , 9780078757105) Glencoe/McGraw-Hill.

McKeague. Ssm Elementary Algebra. 7th ed. 2003. (C). pap. 34.95 (978-0-534-42311-7(6)) Brooks/Cole.

—Ssm Intermediate Algebra. 7th ed. 2003. (C). pap. 36.95 (978-0-534-42291-2(8)) Brooks/Cole.

Meader, Pam & Storer, Judy. Algebra. 2000. 120p. (YA). (gr. 9-12). tchr. ed. 20.99 (978-0-8251-3862-1(0) , 0-38620) Walch Publishing.

Mitchell, Robert. Pre-Algebra. 2001. (Jamestown's Number Power Ser.). pap., stu. ed. 17.32 (978-0-8092-2283-4(3) , 9780809222834) Jamestown.

Murdock, Jerald, et al. Discovering Algebra Preliminary Edition: An Investigative Approach. 2000. (YA). (gr. 8-10). Vol. 1. 422p. stu. ed. 14.95 (978-1-55953-338-6(2) , MN53338); Vol. 2. 402p. stu. ed., per. 14.95 (978-1-55953-421-5(4) , MN53421) Key Curriculum Pr.

Nathan, Kris. Kris's Key - Math & Pre-Algebra Concepts. 2004. pap. 8.95 (978-0-9755341-0-6(6) , 20) Abccurate Business Ventures.

Neill, Hugh & Payne, Sarah. Starting Advanced Mathematics: The Essential Foundation. 2002. (Illus.). 128p. pap. 12.00 (978-0-521-89356-5(9)) Cambridge Univ. Pr.

Osofsky, Jill. Algebra at School. 2003. (It's Everyplace You Are! Ser.). 48p. (J). (gr. 2-2). pap. 6.99 (978-0-7682-2547-1(7) , FS99005); (Illus.). (gr. 1-1). pap. 6.99 (978-0-7682-2540-2(X) , FS99004) Schaffer, Frank Pubns. (Schaffer, Frank).

—Algebra at School, Grade K. 2003. (It's Everyplace You Are! Ser.). (Illus.). 48p. (J). (gr. k-k). pap. 6.99 (978-0-7682-2510-5(8) , FS99003, Schaffer, Frank) Schaffer, Frank Pubns.

Passaporte a las Algebra y a la Geometria. 2004. Tr. of Passport to Algebra & Geometry. (SPA.). (gr. 6-12). (978-0-395-91854-8(5) , 2-80510) McDougal Littell Inc.

Passport to Algebra & Geometry. 2004. (gr. 6-12). stu. ed. (978-0-618-18596-2(8) , 2-05508); stu. ed. (978-0-395-87988-7(4) , 2-77610) McDougal Littell Inc.

Passport to Algebra & Geometry: Answer Masters. 2004. (gr. 6-12). (978-0-395-89679-2(7) , 2-77751) McDougal Littell Inc.

Passport to Algebra & Geometry: Complete Solutions Manual. 2004. (gr. 6-12). (978-0-395-89681-5(9) , 2-77753) McDougal Littell Inc.

Passport to Algebra & Geometry: Daily Cumulative Review. 2004. (gr. 6-12). (978-0-395-89674-7(6) , 2-77746) McDougal Littell Inc.

Passport to Algebra & Geometry: Enrichment Copymasters. 2004. (gr. 6-12). (978-0-395-89678-5(9) , 2-77750) McDougal Littell Inc.

Passport to Algebra & Geometry: Math Log. 2004. (gr. 6-12). (978-0-395-89676-1(2) , 2-77748) McDougal Littell Inc.

Passport to Algebra & Geometry: Practice Workbook. 2004. (gr. 6-12). (SPA.). (978-0-395-90160-1(X) , 2-77865); stu. ed., wbk. ed. (978-0-395-89670-9(3) , 2-77742) McDougal Littell Inc.

Passport to Algebra & Geometry: Problem of the Day. 2004. (gr. 6-12). (978-0-395-89677-8(0) , 2-77749) McDougal Littell Inc.

Passport to Algebra & Geometry: Reteaching Copymasters. 2004. (gr. 6-12). (978-0-395-89669-3(X) , 2-77741) McDougal Littell Inc.

Passport to Algebra & Geometry: Warm-up Exercises. 2004. (gr. 6-12). (978-0-395-89680-8(0) , 2-77752) McDougal Littell Inc.

Penton Overseas, Inc. Staff. Einstein's Algebra 1 Made Easy. 2002. (Einstein's... Made Easy Flippers Ser.). pap. 7.95 (978-1-59125-134-7(6)) Penton Overseas, Inc.

—Einstein's Pre Algebra Made Easy Flippers. 2002. (Einstein's... Made Easy Flippers Ser.). (Illus.). 50p. (J). pap. 7.95 (978-1-59125-162-0(1)) Penton Overseas, Inc.

Potter, Kevin. Frugal Bear's Algebra Boot Camp. 2004. (YA). per. (978-0-9678694-5-2(5) , FrugalBear.com) Frugal Bear Communications.

Pre-Algebra. 2000. (Kelley Wingate Ser.). 80p. (YA). (gr. 7-10). pap. 9.99 (978-0-88724-602-9(8)) Carson-Dellosa Publishing Co., Inc.

Pre-Algebra. 2003. (Algebra Ser.). 128p. (YA). (gr. 5-8). pap. 12.99 (978-1-56822-064-2(2)) School Specialty Publishing.

Precalculus. 5th ed. 2001. (gr. 11-12). (978-0-618-07272-9(1) , 3-30444); (978-0-618-07273-6(X) , 3-30445); cd-rom (978-0-618-07277-4(2) , 3-30448) McDougal Littell Inc.

Precalculus: Complete Solutions Guide. 6th ed. 2004. (gr. 11-12). (978-0-618-31438-6(5) , 3-32744) McDougal Littell Inc.

Precalculus: HM MathSpace Technology Package. 3rd ed. 2004. (gr. 6-12). tchr. ed. (978-0-618-35699-7(1) , 3-02981) McDougal Littell Inc.

Precalculus with Limits: a Graphing Approach: Complete Solutions Guide. 3rd ed. 2001. (gr. 11-12). (978-0-618-07412-9(0) , 3-32284) McDougal Littell Inc.

Precalculus with Limits: a Graphing Approach: Learning Tools. 6th ed. 2004. (gr. 11-12). stu. ed. incl. cd-rom (978-0-618-31447-8(4) , 3-32754) McDougal Littell Inc.

Quantitative Literacy. 2002. tchr. ed., per. (978-1-930804-46-3(6)); stu. ed., per. (978-1-930804-45-6(8)) Carnegie Learning.

Rappaport, Josh. Algebra Survival Kit: A Conversational Guide for the Thoroughly Befuddled. Blakemore, Sally, illus. unabr. ed. 1998. 520p. (YA). (gr. 8-12). pap. 22.95 (978-0-9659113-5-1(7)) Singing Turtle Pr.

Real World Algebra: Understanding the Power of Mathematics. 2001. 310p. per. 24.95 (978-0-9679915-2-8(8)) Hickory Grove Pr.

Reeves, Brian & Robinson, Craig. Pre-Calculus Student Activities Book. Matthews, Douglas L., ed. 2003. (Illus.). stu. ed., per., wbk. ed. (978-1-931680-24-0(8) , Expert Systems for Teachers) Teaching Point, Inc.

Robinson, C. L. MATH1on1 Algebra Foundation. 2006. (YA). per. 9.99 (978-0-9786767-5-9(0)) Robinson, Consuelo.

Rock, Nathaniel. Math for Everyone Algebra I. 2007. pap. 99.99 (***978-1-59980-002-8(0)***) Nathaniel Max Rock.

—Math for Everyone Algebra Ii. 2007. pap. 99.99 (***978-1-59980-004-2(7)***) Nathaniel Max Rock.

Rock, Nathaniel Max. Standards-Driven Power Algebra I (Textbook & Classroom Supplement) A Hands-on Standards-Driven Study Guide on How to Understand & Retain Algebra I. 2nd ed. 2005. (Illus.). 412p. per. 99.99 (978-0-9749392-0-9(X)) Nathaniel Max Rock.

Roza, Greg. Famous Flights: Understanding & Using Variables. 2006. (Math for the Real World Ser.). (Illus.). 32p. (J). pap. (978-1-4042-6087-0(0)); lib. bdg. (978-1-4042-3367-6(9)) Rosen Publishing Group, Inc., The.

—Inside the Human Body: Using Scientific & Exponential Notation. 2006. (Math for the Real World Ser.). (Illus.). 32p. (J). pap. (978-1-4042-6077-1(3)); lib. bdg. (978-1-4042-3362-1(8)) Rosen Publishing Group, Inc., The.

Sadler, Robert. Pre-Calculus. 1999. (Illus.). 128p. (YA). (gr. 5). pap. 11.95 (978-1-58037-093-6(4)) Twain, Mark Media, Inc. Pubs.

Sandall, B. & Olson, M. Algebra Practice Book Grades 7+ 2006. 128p. (J). pap. (978-1-58037-325-8(9)) Carson-Dellosa Publishing Co., Inc.

Saxon Algebra 1/2 Answer Key & Test. 2004. 18.00 (978-0-01-205182-5(9)) Saxon Pubs., Inc.

Saxon Algebra 1/2 Home Study Kit. 2004. 60.25 (978-0-01-204722-4(8)) Saxon Pubs., Inc.

School Specialty Publishing. Introductory Algebra Gr 5. 2005. (Math 2 Master Ser.). 32p. (J). pap. 3.99 (978-0-7696-3925-3(9) , Brighter Child) School Specialty Publishing.

—Introductory Algebra, Grade 5. 2006. (Skills for Scholars Ser.). 80p. (C). pap. 4.99 (***978-0-7696-4975-7(0)*** , Schaffer, Frank) Schaffer, Frank Pubns.

—Step-by-Step Homework Booklets: Algebra. 2003. (Homework Booklets Ser.). 80p. (C). pap. 2.99 (978-0-7682-2626-3(0) , IFG99144) School Specialty Publishing.

—Step-by-Step Homework Booklets: Data Analysis. 2003. (Homework Booklets Ser.). 80p. (C). pap. 2.99 (978-0-7682-2627-0(9) , IFG99145) School Specialty Publishing.

Schultz. Algebra 2. 2001. 76.86 (978-0-03-052223-9(4)); 1999. 111.13 (978-0-03-052224-6(2)) Holt, Rinehart & Winston.

Shea. Algebra. 2001. (Working with Numbers Ser.). (C). pap. 15.80 (978-0-7398-3543-2(2)) Steck-Vaughn.

Simpson, Jeff. Access to Algebra, Vol. 2. Simpson, Marilyn, ed. 2006. (Count, Notice, & Remember Ser.: 514). ring bd. 100.00 (978-1-888976-35-9(7) , 514); ring bd. 100.00 (978-1-888976-36-6(5) , 514) Mastery Learning Systems.

Ssm Algebra F/Coll Stdts. 7th ed. 2004. (C). pap. 41.95 (978-0-534-46390-8(8)) Brooks/Cole.

Ssm Contmp Coll Alg/Trig. 2nd ed. 2004. (C). pap. 39.95 (978-0-534-46792-0(X)) Brooks/Cole.

Ssm Precalc: Func/Graphs. 10th ed. 2005. (C). pap. 37.95 (978-0-534-99995-7(6)) Brooks/Cole.

Steck-Vaughn Staff. Algebra. rev. ed. 2001. (J). pap., tchr. ed. (978-0-7398-4411-3(3)) Steck-Vaughn.

—Core Skills Math - Algebra. 2004. (Illus.). pap. (978-0-7398-8539-0(1)) Steck-Vaughn.

—Math: Number Operations, Algebra. 2002. (Illus.). pap. (978-0-7398-5428-0(3)) Steck-Vaughn.

—Middle School Pre-Algebra. 1999. (Illus.). (J). pap. 7.99 (978-0-7398-1302-7(1)) Steck-Vaughn.

—Pre-Algebra Patterns in Math. 2002. (Illus.). (J). (gr. 5). pap. (978-0-7398-5451-8(8)); (gr. 6). pap. (978-0-7398-5452-5(6)) Steck-Vaughn.

—Strength in Numbers: Algebra. 2002. (J). pap., tchr. ed. (978-0-7398-6256-8(1)); pap., tchr. ed. (978-0-7398-6257-5(X)) Steck-Vaughn.

—Strength in Numbers: Algebra L. 2002. pap. 15.27 (978-0-7398-6251-3(0)); (J). pap. 15.27 (978-0-7398-6250-6(2)) Steck-Vaughn.

—Top Line Math: Algebra. 2005. pap. 5.49 (978-1-4190-0372-1(0)) Steck-Vaughn.

—Top Line Math 10-Pack: Algebra. 2005. pap. 54.95 (978-1-4190-0393-6(3)) Harcourt Schl. Pubs.

Sterling, Mary Jane. Algebra II. 2004. (Illus.). 368p. pap. 14.99 (978-0-7645-4135-3(8) , Cliff Notes) Wiley, John & Sons, Inc.

Thomas, Margaret. Pre-Algebra. 2001. (Mathematical Mind Ser.). (Illus.). 48p. (J). (gr. 6-8). pap. 6.99 (978-0-7424-0085-6(9) , IF2905) School Specialty Publishing.

Todd, Deborah. Facts on File Algebra Handbook. (Science Handbook Ser.). (Illus.). 176p. (J). (gr. 9-12). pap. 17.95 (978-0-8160-6228-7(5)) Facts On File, Inc.

Using Cuisenaire Rods: Patterns & Algebra. 2002. (J). pap. 7.95 (978-1-56911-741-5(1)) Learning Resources, Inc.

Using Equations to Solve Problems Student: RUA Using Equations to Solve Problems Student. 2005. 70p. per. 7.50 (978-1-932976-76-2(0)) National Ctr. on Education & The Economy.

Webber, Berryl & Barnes, Terry. How to Dazzle at Algebra. 2004. (Illus.). 48p. pap. 30.00 (978-1-903853-12-2(5)) Brilliant Pubns. GBR. *Dist:* Parkwest Pubns., Inc.

Wiebe, et al. Multiplication the Algebra Way. Cordel, Betty, ed. Richmond, Brenda, illus. 2001. 159p. (J). pap. 18.95 (978-1-881431-93-0(2) , 1319) AIMS Education Foundation.

Wiebe, Arthur, et al. Looking at Lines: Interesting Objects & Linear Functions. Cordel, Betty, ed. Richmond, Brenda, illus. 2001. 210p. (YA). pap. 18.95 (978-1-881431-91-6(6)) AIMS Education Foundation.

Wingard-Nelson, Rebecca. Algebra I & Algebra II. 2004. (Math Success Ser.). (Illus.). 64p. (J). lib. bdg. 22.60 (978-0-7660-2566-0(7)) Enslow Pubs., Inc.

—Problem Solving & Word Problems. 2004. (Math Success Ser.). (Illus.). 64p. (J). lib. bdg. 22.60 (978-0-7660-2565-3(9)) Enslow Pubs., Inc.

Woods, Michael. Factoring. 2005. 28p. 8.84 (978-1-4116-6014-4(5)) Lulu.com.

ALGERIA

DiPiazza, Francesca. Algeria in Pictures. 2007. lib. bdg. (***978-0-8225-7144-5(7)***) Twenty First Century Bks.

Habeeb, William Mark. Algeria. 2004. (J). lib. bdg. 30.00 (978-0-8368-3114-6(4)) Stevens, Gareth Inc.

Hintz, Martin. Algeria. 2006. (Enchantment of the World, Second Ser.). (Illus.). 144p. (J). (gr. 5-9). 36.00 (978-0-516-24855-4(3) , Children's Pr.) Scholastic Library Publishing.

Kagda, Falaq & Latif, Zawiah Abdul. Algeria. 2nd ed. 2007. (Cultures of the World Ser.). 144p. (J). lib. bdg. 39.93 (***978-0-7614-2085-9(1)*** , Benchmark Bks.) Cavendish, Marshall Corp.

Ling, Chin Oi. Welcome to Algeria: Chin Oi Ling. 2005. (Welcome to My Country Ser.). (Illus.). 48p. (J). lib. bdg. 26.00 (978-0-8368-3132-0(2)) Stevens, Gareth Inc.

Morrow, James. Algeria. 2003. (Modern Middle East Nations & Their Strategic Place in the World Ser.). (Illus.). 112,128p. (YA). (gr. 7 up). lib. bdg. (978-1-59084-516-5(1)) Mason Crest Pubs.

Zurlo, Tony. Algeria. 2005. (Modern Nations of the World Ser.). (Illus.). 112p. (YA). (gr. 7-10). lib. bdg. 29.95 (978-1-59018-622-0(2) , Lucent Bks.) Thomson Gale.

ALGERIA—FICTION

Fequiere, Marie A. Devil Rain & the Bearded Child of the Desert. 2007. (J). pap. 8.00 (***978-0-8059-7366-2(4)***) Dorrance Publishing Co., Inc.

ALI, MUHAMMAD, 1942-

Ali, Maryum. I Shook up the World: The Incredible Life of Muhammad Ali. Johnson, Patrick, illus. 2004. 32p. (J). 16.95 (978-1-58270-090-8(7)) Beyond Words Publishing, Inc.

—I Shook up the World: The Incredible Life of Muhammad Ali. Johnson, Patrick, illus. 2004. 32p. (J). (gr. 3 up). lib. bdg. 24.67 (978-0-8368-4098-8(4)) Stevens, Gareth Inc.

Bolden, Tonya. The Champ. Christie, R. Gregory, illus. 2004. 40p. (J). (gr. k-3). 17.95 (978-0-375-82401-2(4) , Knopf Bks. for Young Readers) Random Hse. Children's Bks.

—The Champ: The Story of Muhamad Ali. Gregory Christie, R. Gregory, illus. 2007. 40p. (J). (gr. k-3). pap. 6.99 (***978-0-440-41782-8(1)*** , Dragonfly Bks.) Random Hse. Children's Bks.

Bolden, Tonya. The Champ: The Story of Muhammad Ali. Christie, R. Gregory, illus. 2004. 40p. (J). (gr. k-3). 19.99 (978-0-375-92401-9(9) , Knopf Bks. for Young Readers) Random Hse. Children's Bks.

Brown, Jonatha A. Muhammad Ali. (People We Should Know Ser.). 24p. (J). 2006. pap. 5.95 (978-0-8368-4764-2(4)); 2006. lib. bdg. 19.33 (978-0-8368-4757-4(1)); 2005. (Illus.). pap. (978-0-8368-4750-5(4)); 2005. (Illus.). lib. bdg. 19.33 (978-0-8368-4743-7(1)) Stevens, Gareth Inc.

Buckley, James. Muhammad Ali. 2004. (Trailblazers of the Modern World Ser.). (Illus.). 48p. (J). (gr. 5 up). pap. 11.95 (978-0-8368-5256-1(7)); lib. bdg. 30.00 (978-0-8368-5096-3(3)) Stevens, Gareth Inc. (World Almanac Library).

Burgan, Michael. Muhammad Ali: American Champion. Bascle, Brian, illus. 2008. (J). (***978-1-4296-0153-5(1)***) Capstone Pr., Inc.

Christopher, Matt. Muhammed Ali. 2005. (Illus.). 113p. (J). (ps-7). per. 11.64 (978-0-606-33451-8(3)) Tandem Library Bks.

Drohan, Michele Ingber. Learning about Strength of Character from the Life of Muhammad Ali. 1999. (Character Building Book Ser.). (Illus.). 24p. (J). (gr. 3). lib. bdg. 18.75 (978-0-8239-5347-9(5) , PowerKids Pr.) Rosen Publishing Group, Inc., The.

Feinstein, Stephen. Muhammad Ali. 2007. (African-American Heroes Ser.). (Illus.). 24p. (J). (gr. 1-3). lib. bdg. 21.26 (978-0-7660-2763-3(5) , Enslow Elementary) Enslow Pubs., Inc.

Ford, Carin T. Muhammad Ali: I Am the Greatest. 2006. (African-American Biography Library). (Illus.). 128p. (J). lib. bdg. 31.93 (978-0-7660-2460-1(1)) Enslow Pubs., Inc.

Garrett, Leslie. Story of Muhammad Ali. 2002. (gr. k-3). lib. bdg. 11.80 (978-0-613-45625-8(4)) Tandem Library Bks.

Garrett, Leslie & Dorling Kindersley Publishing Staff. The Story of Muhammad Ali. 2002. (Readers Ser.). (Illus.). 48p. (J). (gr. 1-4). 12.99 (978-0-7894-8516-8(8)); Vol. 4. pap. 3.99 (978-0-7894-8517-5(6)) Dorling Kindersley Publishing, Inc.

Golus, Carrie. Muhammad Ali. 2006. (Sports Heroes & Legends Ser.). (Illus.). 110p. (J). 27.93 (978-0-8225-5960-3(9) , Lerner Pubns.) Lerner Publishing Group.

Haskins, James. Champion: The Story of Muhammad Ali. Velasquez, Eric, illus. 2001. (J). (gr. 1-5). 18.85 (978-0-8027-8785-9(1)) Walker & Co.

Healy, Nick. Muhammad Ali. 2005. (Genius Ser.). (Illus.). 48p. (gr. 5-9). 21.95 (978-1-58341-333-3(2) , Creative Education) Creative Co., The.

Hook, Jason. Muhammad Ali: The Greatest. 2001. (Famous Lives Ser.). (Illus.). 48p. (J). (gr. 3-7). lib. bdg. 27.12 (978-0-8172-5717-0(9)) Raintree.

Jordan, Denise M. Muhammad Ali: Meet the Champion. 2003. (Meeting Famous People Ser.). (Illus.). 32p. (J). lib. bdg. 22.60 (978-0-7660-2272-0(2)) Enslow Pubs., Inc.

Kent, Daniel T. Muhammad Ali & Laila Ali. 2004. (Famous Families Ser.). (Illus.). 48p. (J). lib. bdg. 25.25 (978-1-4042-0261-0(7)) Rosen Publishing Group, Inc., The.

Lewis, Jon E. Muhammad Ali. 1999. (Life & Times of Ser.). (Illus.). 48p. (YA). (gr. 5 up). 12.95 (978-0-7910-4641-8(9) , Chelsea Hse.) Facts On File, Inc.

Myers, Walter Dean. The Greatest: Muhammad Ali. 2001. (Greatest Ser.). (Illus.). 192p. (J). (gr. 7 up). pap. 4.99 (978-0-590-54343-9(1) , Scholastic Paperbacks) Scholastic, Inc.

—Greatest: Muhammad Ali. 2001. (gr. 5-8). lib. bdg. 13.00 (978-0-613-49432-8(6)) Tandem Library Bks.

—The Greatest: Muhammed Ali. 2001. 11.64 (978-0-606-22250-1(2)) Tandem Library Bks.

—Muhammad Ali Biography. Date not set. 40p. (J). (gr. k-3). 15.99 (978-0-06-029131-0(1)); 16.89 (978-0-06-029132-7(X)); pap. 5.99 (978-0-06-443718-9(3)) HarperCollins Pubs.

Rummel, Jack. Muhammad Ali. (Black Americans of Achievement Ser.). (Illus.). 112p. (J). (gr. 6-12). 2005. pap. 13.25 (978-0-7910-8330-7(6)); 2004. 30.00 (978-0-7910-8156-3(7)) Facts On File, Inc. (Chelsea Hse.).

Savage, Jeff. Muhammad Ali: The Greatest. 2006. (Fact Finders Ser.). (Illus.). 32p. (J). 22.60 (978-0-7368-6422-0(9)) Capstone Pr., Inc.

Schulman, Arlene. Muhammad Ali. (Just the Facts Biographies Ser.). (Illus.). (J). (gr. 6-12). 2005. 112p. 27.93 (978-0-8225-2448-9(1)); 2003. 128p. pap. 7.95 (978-0-8225-9693-6(8) , Lerner Pubns.) Lerner Publishing Group.

Shone, Rob. Muhammad Ali: The Life of a Boxing Hero. Spender, Nik, illus. 2006. 48p. (J). (978-1-4042-0918-3(2)); pap. (978-1-4042-0919-0(0)) Rosen Publishing Group, Inc., The.

—Muhammed Ali: The Life of a Boxing Hero. Spender, Nick, illus. 2006. (Graphic Biographies Ser.). 48p. (J). (gr. 3-8). lib. bdg. 29.95 (978-1-4042-0856-8(9)) Rosen Publishing Group, Inc., The.

Smith, Charles R. Twelve Rounds to Glory: The Story of Muhammad Ali. Collier, Bryan, illus. 2007. 80p. (J). (gr. 5). 19.99 (***978-0-7636-1692-2(3)***) Candlewick Pr.

Stout, Glenn & Christopher, Matt. Muhammad Ali: Legends in Sports. 2005. (Matt Christopher Legends of Sports Ser.). (Illus.). 128p. (J). (gr. 5-8). pap. 4.99 (978-0-316-10843-0(X)) Little Brown & Co.

Streissguth, Thomas. Clay V. United States & How Muhammad Ali Fought the Draft: Debating Supreme Court Decisions. 2006. (Debating Supreme Court Decisions Ser.). (Illus.). 112p. (J). lib. bdg. 26.60 (978-0-7660-2393-2(1)) Enslow Pubs., Inc.

Tessitore, John. Muhammad Ali: The World's Champion. 1999. (Single Titles-Biography Ser.). (Illus.). 144p. (YA). (gr. 8-12). pap. 9.95 (978-0-531-15927-9(2) , Watts, Franklin) Scholastic Library Publishing.

Wilmore, Kathy. Muhammad Ali: With a Discussion of Honesty. 2003. (Values in Action Ser.). (J). (978-1-59203-065-1(3)) Learning Challenge, Inc.

Winter, Jonah. Muhammad Ali: Champion of the World. Roca, Francois, illus. 2008. 40p. (J). (ps-3). 16.99 (978-0-375-83622-0(5)) Random Hse. Children's Bks.

—Muhammad Ali: Champion of the World. Roca, Francois, illus. 2006. (J). (978-0-375-87787-6(6) , Schwartz & Wade Bks.) Random Hse. Children's Bks.

Winter, Jonah. Muhammad Ali: Champion of the World. Roca, Francois, illus. 2008. 40p. (J). (ps-3). lib. bdg. 19.99 (***978-0-375-93787-3(0)*** , Schwartz & Wade Bks.) Random Hse. Children's Bks.

ALICE (FICTITIOUS CHARACTER : CARROLL)—FICTION

Alice in Wonderland. 2003. (J). 12.99 (978-0-7868-3476-1(5)) Disney Pr.

Alice in Wonderland. 2003. (Illus.). 288p. (J). 9.98 (978-1-4054-1674-0(2)) Parragon, Inc.

Brown, Michele. New Tales from Alice's Wonderland: Alice & the Curious Stick. Martyr, Paula, illus. 1999. 24p. (J). pap. 7.99 (978-0-233-99534-2(X)) Andre Deutsch GBR. *Dist:* Independent Pubs. Group.

—New Tales From Alice's Wonderland: Collection One. 2000. (Illus.). 96p. (J). pap. 13.99 (978-0-233-99610-3(9)) Andre Deutsch GBR. *Dist:* Independent Pubs. Group.

—New Tales from Alice's Wonderland: Dinah Plays Hide & Seek. Martyr, Paula, illus. 24p. (J). pap. 7.99 (978-0-233-99535-9(8)) Andre Deutsch GBR. *Dist:* Trafalgar Square Publishing.

—New Tales from Alice's Wonderland: The March Hare's Big Secret. Martyr, Paula, illus. 1999. 24p. (J). pap. 7.99 (978-0-233-99537-3(4)) Andre Deutsch GBR. *Dist:* Independent Pubs. Group.

But I Knew Better: Individual Title, 6 pack. (gr. k-1). 23.00 (978-0-7635-9033-8(9)) Rigby Education.

Carroll, Lewis, pseud. Alice. 2004. 112p. (J). pap. 8.95 (978-0-9716338-3-4(5)) About Comics.

—Alice im Wunderland. 1999. Tr. of Alice in Wonderland. (GER., Illus.). (J). (ps up). 12.95 (978-3-499-20733-4(8)) Rowohlt Taschenbuch Verlag GmbH DEU. *Dist:* Distribooks, Inc.

—Alice in Wonderland. 2007. 228p. 12.99 (***978-1-58726-532-7(X)***) Ann Arbor Media Group, LLC.

—Alice in Wonderland. Tenniel, John, illus. 2007. 204p. 24.95 (***978-1-58218-791-4(6)***); per. 14.95 (***978-1-58218-790-7(8)***) Digital Scanning, Inc.

—Alice in Wonderland. Zwerger, Lisbeth, illus. 2007. 103p. (J). (ps). 24.99 (***978-0-698-40052-8(6)*** , Minedition) Penguin Group (USA) Inc.

—Alice in Wonderland. 2004. (Illus.). 96p. (J). 9.99 (978-0-517-22362-8(7) , Gramercy) Random Hse. Value Publishing.

—Alice in Wonderland Jigsaw Book. Tenniel, John, illus. 1999. 16p. (J). 19.99 (978-0-333-76291-2(6)) Macmillan Publishers Ltd. GBR. *Dist:* Independent Pubs. Group.

—Alice Through the Looking-Glass. Oxenbury, Helen, illus. 2005. 208p. (J). (gr. 3-7). 24.99 (978-0-7636-2892-5(1)) Candlewick Pr.

—Alice's Adventures in Wonderland. 2004. 124p. pap. 10.95 (978-1-59540-442-8(2) , 1st World Library - Literary Society) 1st World Publishing, Inc.

—Alice's Adventures in Wonderland. Date not set. (J). lib. bdg. 16.95 (978-0-8488-1262-1(X)) Amereon LTD.

—Alice's Adventures in Wonderland. Tenniel, John, illus. Date not set. 248p. (YA). 14.95 (978-1-884807-19-0(4)) Blushing Rose Publishing.

—Alice's Adventures in Wonderland. Oxenbury, Helen, illus. 2003. 208p. (J). (gr. 3). pap. 12.99 (978-0-7636-2049-3(1)) Candlewick Pr.

—Alice's Adventures in Wonderland. Carruth, Jane, ed. Cloke, Rene, illus. 2000. 93p. (J). (gr. 4-6). reprint ed. 25.00 (978-0-7881-9229-6(9)) DIANE Publishing Co.

—Alice's Adventures in Wonderland. 1998. (Illus.). 192p. (J). (gr. 3-5). pap. 3.99 (978-0-87406-864-1(9) , Silver Elm Classic) Darby Creek Publishing.

—Alice's Adventures in Wonderland. Noble, Marty, illus. 1998. (Dover Children's Thrift Classics Ser.). 80p. (J). pap. 1.00 (978-0-486-40345-8(9)) Dover Pubns., Inc.

—Alice's Adventures in Wonderland. unabr. ed. 2001. (Dover Juvenile Classics Ser.). (Illus.). 160p. (J). (gr. 4-7). pap. 3.00 (978-0-486-41658-8(5)) Dover Pubns., Inc.

—Alice's Adventures in Wonderland. Steadman, Ralph, illus. 2006. 128p. pap. 19.95 (978-1-55407-203-3(4)) Firefly Bks., Ltd.

—Alice's Adventures in Wonderland, Vol. 1. Ewing, Carolyn, illus. 1999. (Selected Classic Fairy Tales Ser.). 20p. (J). (gr. k-7). lib. bdg. 13.95 (978-1-56674-220-7(X)) Forest Hse. Publishing Co., Inc.

—Alice's Adventures in Wonderland. Date not set. 192p. (YA). (gr. 3 up). mass mkt. 8.99 (978-0-06-440929-2(5)); (Illus.). 176p. (J). 14.95 (978-0-06-095770-4(0)) HarperCollins Pubs.

—Alice's Adventures in Wonderland, Level 2. 2nd abr. ed. 2000. (Bookworms Ser.). (Illus.). 64p. 6.50 (978-0-19-422964-7(5)) Oxford Univ. Pr., Inc.

—Alice's Adventures in Wonderland, Level 2. 2001. (Illus.). 48p. (C). pap. 9.00 (978-0-582-42123-3(3)) Pearson ESL.

—Alice's Adventures in Wonderland. rev. ed. 2002. (Illus.). 160p. (J). (gr. 2). pap. 3.99 (978-0-439-29149-1(6)) Scholastic, Inc.

—Alice's Adventures in Wonderland. 2000. (Aladdin Classics Ser.). (Illus.). 176p. (J). (gr. 3-7). pap. 3.99 (978-0-689-83375-5(X) , Aladdin) Simon & Schuster Children's Publishing.

—Alice's Adventures in Wonderland. Ghiuselev, Iassen, illus. 2003. 120p. 29.95 (978-1-894965-00-2(0)) Simply Read Bks. CAN. *Dist:* Perseus Distribution.

—Alice's Adventures in Wonderland. McKowen, Scott, illus. 2005. (Unabridged Classics Ser.). 136p. (J). (gr. 5-9). 9.95 (978-1-4027-2502-9(7)) Sterling Publishing Co., Inc.

—Alice's Adventures in Wonderland. Oxenbury, Helen, illus. 2003. 207p. (J). (gr. 4-7). per. 22.25 (978-0-613-60270-9(6)) Tandem Library Bks.

—Alice's Adventures in Wonderland. (gr. 3-6). 2001. lib. bdg. 11.80 (978-0-613-66612-1(7)); 2000. lib. bdg. 11.80 (978-0-613-63173-0(0)) Tandem Library Bks.

—Alice's Adventures in Wonderland. (Children's Classics). (ENG., Illus.). 2001. 272p. (J). pap. (978-1-85326-118-3(1)); 1998. 288p. pap. (978-1-85326-002-5(9) , 0029WW) Wordsworth Editions, Ltd.

—Alice's Adventures in Wonderland / Through the Looking Glass & What Alice Found There. Bachelier, Anne, illus. 2005. (J). per. (978-0-9769071-1-4(9)); (978-0-9728620-8-0(0)); (978-0-9769071-0-7(0)); im. lthr. (978-0-9728620-9-7(9)) CFM.

—Alice's Adventures under Ground. Deitch, Kim, illus. 2000. (Cottage Classics). 88p. (YA). (gr. 3-12). 29.95 (978-1-892847-00-3(0)) Word Play Pubns.

—Alicia en el Pais de las Maravillas. (SPA.). pap. 11.95 (978-84-95311-04-7(6)) Mestas, Jorge A. Ediciones Escolares La Escuela Nueva y Alinorma, S.L. ESP. *Dist:* Distribooks, Inc.

—Alicia en el Pais de las Maravillas. 2000. (Coleccion "Clasicos Juveniles" Ser.). (SPA.). 156p. pap. 10.95 (978-0-595-13544-8(7)) iUniverse, Inc.

—Alicia en el Pais de las Maravillas,Fantasmagoria, y un cuento Enredado. 2004. (Clasicos Seleccion Ser.). (SPA.). 304p. 6.95 (978-84-8403-409-4(7)) Edimat Libros, S. A. ESP. *Dist:* Independent Pubs. Group.

—Las Aventuras de Alicia. (Coleccion Clasicos de la Juventud). (SPA., Illus.). 240p. (J). 12.95 (978-84-7189-060-3(7) , ORT308) Ortells, Alfredo Editorial S.L. ESP. *Dist:* Continental Bk. Co., Inc.

—The Best of Lewis Carroll. Tenniel, John & Holiday, Henry, illus. 2001. 480p. (gr. 4-7). pap. 7.99 (978-0-7858-1326-2(8)) Book Sales, Inc.

—Through the Looking Glass. Date not set. 176p. (J). 19.95 (978-0-8488-2629-1(9)) Amereon LTD.

—Through the Looking Glass: And What Alice Found There. 1999. (Thrift Edition Ser.). 128p. (gr. 6). pap. 2.00 (978-0-486-40878-1(7)) Dover Pubns., Inc.

—Through the LookingGlass. l.t. ed. 2006. 176p. pap. (978-1-84637-329-9(8)) Echo Library.

—A Traves del Espejo. 2002. (Clover Ser.). (SPA., Illus.). 204p. (YA). 11.50 (978-84-392-8028-6(9) , EV5540) Lectorum Pubns., Inc.

Carroll, Lewis, pseud & Baker, Kyle. Through the Looking Glass. (Classics Illustrated Ser.). (Illus.). 52p. (YA). pap. 4.95 (978-1-57209-002-6(2)) Classics International Entertainment, Inc.

Carroll, Lewis, pseud & Bloom, Harold. Alice's Adventures in Wonderland. 2006. (Bloom's Modern Critical Interpretations Ser.). 256p. (gr. 9). 45.00 (978-0-7910-8586-8(4) , Chelsea Hse.) Facts On File, Inc.

Carroll, Lewis, pseud & Jay, Alison. Alice's Adventures in Wonderland. 2006. (Illus.). 224p. (J). (gr. 2). 25.99 (978-0-8037-2940-7(5) , Dial) Penguin Group (USA) Inc.

Carroll, Lewis, pseud & Kipling, Rudyard. Alice's Adventures in Wonderland. 2003. (J). cd-rom (978-0-9724995-2-1(0)) Alcazar AudioWorks.

Carroll, Lewis, pseud & Sabuda, Robert. Alice's Adventures in Wonderland. 2003. (Classic Collectible Pop-Up Ser.). (Illus.). 12p. (J). 26.99 (978-0-689-84743-1(2) , Little Simon) Simon & Schuster Children's Publishing.

Carroll, Lewis, pseud, et al. Alice's Adventures in Wonderland. 2002. (Illus.). 208p. (J). 19.95 (978-1-58717-152-9(X) , SeaStar Bks.) Chronicle Bks. LLC.

Carter, R. J. Alices Journey Beyond Moon. Wright, Lucy, illus. 2004. 98p. (978-1-903889-76-3(6)) Telos Publishing, Ltd. GBR. *Dist:* Fitzhenry & Whiteside, Ltd.

Dalmatian Press Staff. Disney Alice in Wonderland. 2006. 72p. (J). 9.99 (978-1-4037-2185-3(8)) Dalmatian Pr.

Gauthier, Gilles. La Petite Lili Est un Genie. Deromer, Pierre-André, illus. 2004. (Premier Roman Ser.). (FRE.). 64p. (J). (gr. 1-4). pap. (978-2-89021-686-0(1)) Diffusion du livre Mirabel.

Gorham, C. J. Alice's Adventures in Wonderland. 2007. (ENG.). 76p. per. 87.99 (*978-1-4280-7448-4(1)) Indy-Publish.com.

Hildebrandt, Greg. Magical Storybook Treasury. 2006. (Illus.). 184p. 14.98 (978-0-7624-2837-3(6) , Running Pr.) Running Pr. Bk. Pubs.

Landes, William-Alan. Alice n' Wonderland. 2003. (Wondrawhopper Ser.). 32p. (Orig.). (YA). (gr. 3 up). pap. 6.00 (978-0-88734-112-0(8)) Players Pr., Inc.

Maconie, Robin. Alice & Her Fabulous Teeth! Fruisen, Catherine Myler, illus. 2004. 32p. (J). per. (978-1-893974-21-0(9) , Design Pr. Bks.) Savannah College of Art & Design.

Mouse Works Staff. Alice in Wonderland. 2002. (Classic Storybook Ser.). (J). 7.99 (978-1-57082-976-5(4)) Mouse Works.

Noble, Marty. Alice in Wonderland Sticker Activity Book. 1998. 4p. (J). pap. 1.50 (978-0-486-40314-4(9)) Dover Pubns., Inc.

Peabody, Richard. Alice Redux: New Stories of Alice, Lewis, & Wonderland. 2006. (Illus.). xvi, 319p. pap. (*978-0-931181-22-1(4)) Paycock Pr.

Seibold, J. Otto & Carroll, Lewis. Alice's Adventures in Wonderland. Seibold, J. Otto, illus. 2003. (Illus.). 6p. (J). (gr. k-3). bds. 19.95 (978-0-439-41184-4(X) , Orchard Bks.) Scholastic, Inc.

Through the Looking Glass. (Read-Along Ser.). (YA). pap., stu. ed. 34.95 incl. audio (978-0-88432-971-8(2) , S23946) Norton, Jeffrey Pubs., Inc.

Titlebaum, Ellen. Alice in Wonderland Read Aloud: Storybook. 2000. 64p. (J). 6.99 (978-0-7364-1051-9(1)) Hyperion Bks. for Children.

ALIENS

Here are entered works on persons who are not citizens of the country in which they reside.

see also Citizenship; Emigration and Immigration; Illegal Aliens

Anderson, Kirsten. From Zeus to Aliens. 2003. (Illus.). 60p. (978-0-7398-5177-7(2)) Steck-Vaughn.

Atkin, S. Beth. Voices from the Fields: Children of Migrant Farm Workers Tell Their Stories. 2000. (gr. 5-8). lib. bdg. 21.95 (978-0-613-27432-6(6)) Tandem Library Bks.

Nesbitt, Ken. The Aliens Have Landed at Our School. Lucas, Margeaux, illus. 2006. 87p. (J). pap. 9.95 (978-0-689-04864-7(5)) Meadowbrook Pr.

Parks, Peggy J. Aliens. 2006. (Illus.). 48p. (J). (gr. 4-8). 26.20 (978-0-7377-3518-5(X) , Kidhaven) Thomson Gale.

Sioux, Tracee. Immigrants, Migration, & the Industrial Revolution. 2004. (Primary Sources of Immigration & Migration in America Ser.). (Illus.). 24p. (J). lib. bdg. 19.95 (978-0-8239-6826-8(X) , PowerKids Pr.) Rosen Publishing Group, Inc., The.

Steck-Vaughn Staff. From Zeus to Aliens. 2002. (Illus.). pap. 41.60 incl. audio compact disk (978-0-7398-6982-6(5)) Steck-Vaughn.

Teichmann, Iris. Immigration & the Law. 2006. (Understanding Immigration Ser.). (Illus.). 44p. (J). (gr. 5-8). lib. bdg. 31.35 (978-1-58340-970-1(X)) Smart Apple Media.

ALIENS—FICTION

Schrecengost, Maity. Tasso of Tarpon Springs. Stock, Rose, illus. 1998. 118p. (J). (gr. 3-6). pap. 5.95 (978-0-929895-24-6(X) , Hoot Owl Bks.) Maupin Hse. Publishing.

Slade, Arthur. The Invasion of the IQ Snatchers. 2007. (Arthur Slade's Canadian Chills Ser.: No. 3). 120p. (YA). (gr. 4 up). 6.95 (*978-1-55050-361-6(8)) Coteau Bks. CAN. *Dist:* Fitzhenry & Whiteside, Ltd.

Thomas, Lynne N. Sneak Force: Mission 1 the Legend. 2003. 148p. pap. 9.95 (*978-1-932303-18-6(9) , Lumina Pr.) Media Creations, Inc.

Weaver, K. C. For the Sake of the Children. 2007. 75p. 14.95 (*978-1-4241-0647-9(8)) PublishAmerica, Inc.

ALIENS (EXTRATERRESTRIALS)

see Extraterrestrial Beings; Life on Other Planets

ALIENS, ILLEGAL

see Illegal Aliens

ALL FOOLS' DAY

see April Fools' Day

ALL HALLOWS' EVE

see Halloween

ALLEGORIES

see also Fables; Parables

Canfield, Andrea. Sassy the Seahag. Hallinan, Susan, illus. 2003. Orig. Title: Sassy the Seahag. (J). per. (978-0-9721327-3-2(2)) Eight Dog Publishing.

Hill, Karen. Owen's Walk. Thompson, Carol, illus. 2006. 32p. (J). 14.99 (978-1-4003-0694-7(9)) Nelson, Thomas Inc.

ALLEN, ETHAN, 1738-1789

Aronson, Virginia. Ethan Allen: Revolutioinary Hero. 2001. (gr. 5-8). lib. bdg. 17.60 (978-0-613-32518-9(4)) Tandem Library Bks.

—Ethan Allen: Revolutionary Hero. 2000. (Revolutionary War Leaders Ser.). (Illus.). 80p. (J). (gr. 4-7). pap. 27.50 (978-0-7910-6132-9(9)); (gr. 8-12). 27.50 (978-0-7910-5974-6(X)) Facts On File, Inc. (Chelsea Hse.).

Haugen, Brenda & Santella, Andrew. Ethan Allen: Green Mountain Rebel. 2004. (Signature Lives Ser.). (Illus.). 112p. (J). 30.60 (978-0-7565-0824-1(X) , 1240131) Compass Point Bks.

Price Hossell, Karen. Ethan Allen. 2004. (American War Biographies Ser.). (J). lib. bdg. 29.93 (978-1-4034-5077-7(3)); (Illus.). pap. 8.50 (978-1-4034-5084-5(6)) Heinemann Library.

Raabe, Emily. Ethan Allen: The Green Mountain Boys & Vermont's Path to Statehood. 2005. (Library of American Lives & Times). (Illus.). 112p. (J). (gr. 4-8). lib. bdg. 31.95 (978-0-8239-5722-4(5)) Rosen Publishing Group, Inc., The.

Stein, R. Conrad. Ethan Allen & the Green Mountain Boys. 2003. (Cornerstones of Freedom). (Illus.). 48p. (J). (gr. 4-6). 26.00 (978-0-516-24206-4(7) , Children's Pr.) Scholastic Library Publishing.

ALLEN, ETHAN, 1738-1789—FICTION

Gauthier, Gail. The Hero of Ticonderoga. 2002. 240p. (J). (gr. 5-9). pap. 6.99 (978-0-698-11968-0(1) , Putnam Juvenile) Penguin Group (USA) Inc.

ALLERGY

Baldwin, Carol. Allergies. 2003. (Health Matters Ser.). (Illus.). 32p. (J). lib. bdg. 24.22 (978-1-4034-0247-9(7)) Heinemann Library.

Bellenir, Karen, ed. Allergy Information for Teens: Health Tips about Allergic Reactions Such As Anaphylaxis, Respiratory Problems, & Rashes; Including Facts about Identifying & Managing Allergies to Food, Pollen, Mold, Animals, Chemicals, Drugs, & Other Substances. 2005. (Teen Health Ser.). (Illus.). xiii, 410p. (YA). lib. bdg. 65.00 (978-0-7808-0799-0(5)) Omnigraphics, Inc.

A Day at the Playground. 2004. (J). pap. 12.95 (*978-1-59526-606-4(2)) Media Creations, Inc.

Edelson, Edward. Allergies. 1999. (Twenty-First Century Health & Wellness Ser.). (Illus.). 96p. (YA). (gr. 7 up). 36.00 (978-0-7910-5523-6(X) , Chelsea Hse.) Facts On File, Inc.

Edwards, Nicola. My Friend Has Allergies. 2004. (J). lib. bdg. 27.10 (978-1-59389-169-5(5)) Chrysalis Education.

Ford, Jean. Breathe Easy! A Teen's Guide to Allergies & Asthma. 2004. (Science of Health Ser.). (Illus.). 128p. (J). (978-1-59084-842-5(X)) Mason Crest Pubs.

Gordon, Sharon. Allergies. 2003. (Rookie Read-About Health Ser.). (Illus.). (J). (gr. k-2). 31p. pap. 5.95 (978-0-516-27394-5(9)); 32p. 20.50 (978-0-516-22581-4(2)) Scholastic Library Publishing. (Children's Pr.).

—Allergies. 2003. (gr. k-3). lib. bdg. 14.10 (978-0-613-67865-0(6)) Tandem Library Bks.

Gordon, Sherri Mabry. Peanut Butter, Milk, & Other Deadly Threats: What You Should Know about Food Allergies. 2006. (Issues in Focus Today). (Illus.). 104p. (J). lib. bdg. 31.93 (978-0-7660-2529-5(2)) Enslow Pubs., Inc.

Hicks, Terry Allan. Allergies. 2005. (Health Alert Ser.). (Illus.). 64p. (J). (978-0-7614-1918-1(7) , Benchmark Bks.) Cavendish, Marshall Corp.

Johnson, Rebecca L. Daring Cell Defenders. Desrocher, Jack & Fairman, Jennifer E., illus. 2007. (Microquests Ser.). 48p. (J). (gr. 3-5). lib. bdg. 29.27 (*978-0-8225-7140-7(4) , Millbrook Pr.) Lerner Publishing Group.

Latta, Sara L. Allergies. 1998. (Diseases & People Ser.). (Illus.). 128p. (YA). (gr. 6-12). lib. bdg. 20.95 (978-0-7660-1048-2(1)) Enslow Pubs., Inc.

Lennard-Brown, Sarah. Allergies. 2003. (Health Issues Ser.). (Illus.). 64p. (J). lib. bdg. 28.56 (978-0-7398-6421-0(1)) Raintree.

Lerner, Carol. Plants that Make You Sniffle & Sneeze. 2004. (Illus.). 32p. (J). (gr. k-4). reprint ed. 15.00 (978-0-7567-8288-7(0)) DIANE Publishing Co.

Monroe, Judy. Allergies. 2001. (Perspectives on Disease & Illness Ser.). (Illus.). 64p. (J). (gr. 4-6). lib. bdg. 23.93 (978-0-7368-0752-4(7) , LifeMatters Bks.) Capstone Pr., Inc.

Moragne, Wendy. Allergies. 1999. (Medical Library). (Illus.). 128p. (gr. 7 up). lib. bdg. 26.90 (978-0-7613-1359-5(1) , Twenty-First Century Bks.) Lerner Publishing Group.

Parker, Steve. Allergies. 2003. (Just the Facts Ser.). (Illus.). 56p. (J). lib. bdg. (978-1-4034-4598-8(2)) Heinemann Library.

Pascoe, Elaine, ed. Out of Control: Brain Function & Immune Reactions. 2003. (Body Story Ser.). (Illus.). 48p. (J). 24.95 (978-1-4103-0063-8(3)); pap. 11.20 (978-1-4103-0184-0(2)) Thomson Gale. (Blackbirch Pr., Inc.).

Powell, Jillian. Aneil has a Food Allergy. 2004. (Like Me Like You Ser.). (Illus.). 32p. (gr. 2-4). 23.00 (978-0-7910-8182-2(6) , Chelsea Hse.) Facts On File, Inc.

Rogers, Robyn. No Lobster, Please! A Story of a Child with a Severe Seafood Allergy. 2003. (Illus.). 30p. (J). 19.95 (978-0-9726408-0-0(0)) Heartsome Publishing.

Royston, Angela. Allergies. 2004. (Illus.). 32p. (J). lib. bdg. (978-1-4034-4820-0(5)) Heinemann Library.

—Why Do My Eyes Itch? And Other Questions about Allergies. 2003. (Body Matters Ser.). (Illus.). 32p. (J). (gr. 3-5). lib. bdg. 24.22 (978-1-4034-0207-3(8)); pap. 7.50 (978-1-4034-0462-6(3)) Heinemann Library.

Schwartz, Robert H. & Deane, Peter M. G. Coping with Allergies. 1999. (Coping Ser.). (Illus.). 128-192p. (YA). (gr. 7-12). lib. bdg. 26.50 (978-0-8239-2511-7(0) , COALLE) Rosen Publishing Group, Inc., The.

Silverstein, Alvin. Allergies. 1999. (gr. 3-6). lib. bdg. 15.25 (978-0-613-30926-4(X)) Tandem Library Bks.

Silverstein, Alvin, et al. Allergies. 1999. (My Health Ser.). (Illus.). 48p. (J). (gr. 3-5). 25.50 (978-0-531-11581-7(X) , Watts, Franklin) Scholastic Library Publishing.

Taylor-Butler, Christine. Food Allergies. 2007. (True Book-trade;: Health & the Human Body Ser.). 48p. (J). spiral bd. 26.00 (*978-0-531-16858-5(1) , Children's Pr.) Scholastic Library Publishing.

Weiner, Ellen. Taking Food Allergies to School. Gosselin, Kim, ed. Freedman, Moss, illus. 1999. (Special Kids in School Ser.: Vol. 5). 32p. (J). (gr. k-5). pap. 11.95 (978-1-891383-05-2(1)) JayJo Bks., LLC.

Weitzman, Elizabeth. Let's Talk about Having Allergies. 1998. (Conflict Resolution Library). (Illus.). 24p. (J). (gr. k-4). pap. 6.95 (978-1-56838-273-9(1)) Hazelden Publishing & Educational Services.

ALLEYS

see Streets

ALLIGATORS

Alligator Alley. (Sails Literacy Ser.). 24p. (gr. 1 up). 27.00 (978-0-7635-5928-1(8)); Pack. 57.00 (978-0-7578-3203-1(2)) Rigby Education.

Alligator Alley: 6 Small Books. (Sails Literacy Ser.). 24p. (gr. 1 up). 25.00 (978-0-7578-3179-9(6)) Rigby Education.

The American Alligator. (Wildlife of North America Ser.). 48p. (YA). 7.95 (978-0-7368-8480-8(7)) Capstone Pr., Inc.

Behler, John L. & Behler, Deborah A. Alligators & Crocodiles. rev. ed. 1998. (WorldLife Library). (Illus.). 72p. (gr. 5 up). pap. 17.95 (978-0-89658-370-2(8)) Voyageur Pr., Inc.

Berger, Melvin. Snap! A Book about Alligators & Crocodiles. 2001. (gr. k-3). lib. bdg. 11.80 (978-0-613-63564-6(7)) Tandem Library Bks.

Berger, Melvin & Berger, Gilda. Snap! A Book about Alligators & Crocodiles. 2002. (Hello Reader! Science Ser.). (Illus.). 40p. (J). pap. 3.99 (978-0-439-31746-7(0) , Cartwheel Bks.) Scholastic, Inc.

Bredeson, Carmen. Fun Facts about Alligators! 2007. (I Like Reptiles & Amphibians! Ser.). (Illus.). 24p. (J). (gr. 1-3). lib. bdg. 21.26 (*978-0-7660-2786-2(4) , Enslow Elementary) Enslow Pubs., Inc.

Clarke, Ginjer. Baby Alligator. Twinem, Neecy, illus. 2000. (All Aboard Reading Ser.). 48p. (J). (gr. 1-3). pap. 3.99 (978-0-448-42095-0(3) , Grosset & Dunlap) Penguin Group (USA) Inc.

—Baby Alligator. 2000. (gr. k-3). lib. bdg. 11.80 (978-0-613-24274-5(2)); (Illus.). (J). (978-0-606-18463-2(5)) Tandem Library Bks.

Crocodiles & Alligators. 2005. (J). per. 4.99 (978-1-933581-23-1(9)) Byeway Bks.

Dennard, Deborah. Alligators & Crocodiles. Dewey, Jennifer Owings, illus. 2004. (Our Wild World Ser.). 48p. (J). (gr. 2-5). ring bd. 10.95 (978-1-55971-860-8(9)); pap. 7.95 (978-1-55971-859-2(5)) T&N Children's Publishing. (NorthWord Bks. for Young Readers).

Dingwall, Laima, et al. Woodchucks. 1999. (Getting to Know ... Nature's Children Ser.). (Illus.). 47p. (J). (978-0-7172-8844-1(7) , Grolier) Scholastic Library Publishing.

Fairweather, Gari D. Alligators & Other Crocodilians, Vol. 1. World Book, Inc. Staff, ed. 2001. (World Book's Animals of the World Ser.: Set 2). (Illus.). 64p. (J). (978-0-7166-1218-6(6)) World Bk., Inc.

Feeney, Kathy. Those Amazing Alligators. Weaver, Steve, illus. 2006. 55p. (J). 14.95 (978-1-56164-359-2(9)); pap. 8.95 (978-1-56164-356-1(4)) Pineapple Pr., Inc.

Feigenbaum, Aaron. American Alligators: Freshwater Survivors. 2008. (America's Animal Comebacks Ser.). (J). lib. bdg. 25.27 (*978-1-59716-503-7(4)) Bearport Publishing Co., Inc.

Fitzgerald, Patrick J. Croc & Alligator Attacks. 2000. (gr. 7-12). lib. bdg. 15.25 (978-0-613-52016-4(5)) Tandem Library Bks.

—Croc & Gator Attacks. 2000. (High Interest Bks.). (Illus.). 48p. (YA). (gr. 7-12). pap. 6.95 (978-0-516-23514-1(1) , Children's Pr.) Scholastic Library Publishing.

Francis, Dorothy Brenner. The American Alligator. 2001. (Animal Adventures Ser.). (Illus.). (J). 54p. pap. (978-0-7891-5302-9(5)); 56p. (gr. 1-4). lib. bdg. 16.95 (978-0-7807-9646-1(2)) Perfection Learning Corp.

Garver, Lorie. Alligators. 2003. (Animals Attack Ser.). (Illus.). 48p. (J). 23.70 (978-0-7377-1524-8(3) , Greenhaven Pr., Inc.) Thomson Gale.

George, Jean Craighead. Autumn Moon. 2003. (J). (gr. 3-7). 20.75 (978-0-8446-7241-0(6)) Smith, Peter Pub., Inc.

—Autumn Moon. 2001. (gr. 3-6). lib. bdg. 14.10 (978-0-613-50407-2(0)) Tandem Library Bks.

Gray, Susan H. American Alligator. 2008. (J). lib. bdg. 25.26 (*978-1-60279-035-3(3)) Cherry Lake Publishing.

Harcourt School Publishers Staff. Alligators in the Everglades On Level. 3rd ed. 2002. (Trophies Reading Program Ser.). (Illus.). pap. 5.10 (978-0-15-323351-7(6)) Harcourt Schl. Pubs.

Holden, Henry M. The American Alligator: A MyReportLinks. Com Book. 2003. (Endangered & Threatened Animals Ser.). (Illus.). 48p. (J). lib. bdg. 25.26 (978-0-7660-5117-1(X) , MyReportLinks.com Bks.) Enslow Pubs., Inc.

Johnson, Jinny. Alligator. Rosewarne, Graham, illus. 2006. 32p. (J). (978-1-58340-902-2(5)) Smart Apple Media.

Kendell, Patricia. Alligators. 2003. (In the Wild Ser.). (Illus.). 32p. (J). lib. bdg. 25.70 (978-0-7398-5495-2(X)) Raintree.

Kulling, Monica. Alligators: Life in the Wild. Roper, Marty, illus. 1999. (Road to Reading Ser.). (978-0-307-26307-0(X)) Whitman Publishing LLC.

Landau, Elaine. Alligators & Crocodiles: Hunters of the Night. 2007. (Animals after Dark Ser.). (Illus.). 32p. (J). (gr. 2-4). lib. bdg. 22.60 (*978-0-7660-2771-8(6) , Enslow Elementary) Enslow Pubs., Inc.

Landau, Elaine. Fearsome Alligators. 2003. (Fearsome, Scary, & Creepy Animals Ser.). (Illus.). 48p. (J). (gr. 1-4). lib. bdg. 23.93 (978-0-7660-2060-3(6)) Enslow Pubs., Inc.

Legg, Gerald. Alligators & Crocodiles. Bergin, Mark, illus. 2002. (Scary Creatures Ser.). (J). (gr. 2-4). pap. 6.95 (978-0-531-14848-8(3)) ; 32p. pap. 22.50 (978-0-531-14670-5(7)) Scholastic Library Publishing. (Watts, Franklin).

—Alligators & Crocodiles. 2002. (gr. 3-6). lib. bdg. 15.25 (978-0-613-53901-2(X)) Tandem Library Bks.

Morgan, Sally. Alligators & Crocodiles. 2006. (QEB Animal Lives Ser.). (Illus.). 32p. (J). lib. bdg. 19.95 (978-1-59566-205-7(7)) QEB Publishing Inc.

Munoz, William. Waiting Alligators. (Pull Ahead Bks.). (Illus.). 32p. (J). (gr. k-2). 2003. pap. 5.95 (978-0-8225-3621-5(8)); 1999. lib. bdg. 22.60 (978-0-8225-3615-4(3) , Lerner Pubns.) Lerner Publishing Group.

—Waiting Alligators. 1999. (gr. k-3). lib. bdg. 14.10 (978-0-613-27440-1(7)) Tandem Library Bks.

Murray, Julie. Alligators. 2002. (Buddy Book Ser.). (Illus.). 24p. (J). (gr. k-4). lib. bdg. 21.35 (978-1-57765-716-3(0)) ABDO Publishing Co.

Otfinoski, Steven. Alligators. 2008. (J). (***978-0-7614-2930-2(1)***) Cavendish, Marshall Bks., Ltd.

Pohl, Kathleen. Alligators. 2007. (J). pap. (***978-0-8368-8224-7(5)***); 24p. lib. bdg. 19.93 (***978-0-8368-8217-9(2)***) Stevens, Gareth Inc. (Weekly Reader Early Learning Library).

—Alligators: Caimanes. 2007. (SPA & ENG.). (J). pap. (***978-0-8368-8238-4(5)*** , Weekly Reader Early Learning Library) Stevens, Gareth Inc.

—Alligators/Caimanes. 2007. (Animals I See at the Zoo/ Animales que Veo en el Zoologico Ser.). (SPA & ENG.). 24p. (J). (gr. k-2). lib. bdg. 19.93 (***978-0-8368-8231-5(8)*** , Weekly Reader Early Learning Library) Stevens, Gareth Inc.

Potts, Steve. The American Alligator, 6 vols. (gr. 4 up). 39.95 (978-0-7368-8492-1(0)) Red Brick Learning.

Rockwell, Anne F. Alligators. 2000. (Let's-Read-and-Find-Out Science Ser.). (Illus.). 40p. (J). (gr. k-4). lib. bdg. 15.89 (978-0-06-028531-9(1)) HarperCollins Pubs.

—Who Lives in an Alligator Hole? Rockwell, Lizzy, illus. 2006. (Let's-Read-and-Find-Out Science Ser.). 40p. (J). (gr. k-4). 15.99 (978-0-06-028530-2(3)); pap. 4.99 (978-0-06-445200-7(X) , Harper Trophy) HarperCollins Pubs.

Rockwell, Anne F. & Rockwell, Lizzy, illus. Who Lives in an Alligator Hole? 2006. (Let's-Read-and-Find-Out Science Ser.). 33p. (J). (***978-1-4156-8321-7(2)*** , Collins) HarperCollins Pubs. Ltd.

Royston, Angela. Alligators & Crocodiles. 2003. (Amazing Animals Ser.). (Illus.). 24p. (J). lib. bdg. 21.35 (978-1-58340-225-2(X)) Weigl Pubs., Inc.

Shea, Therese. Crocodiles & Alligators. 2006. (Illus.). 24p. (J). lib. bdg. 24.77 (978-1-4042-3523-6(X) , PowerKids Pr.) Rosen Publishing Group, Inc., The.

Simon, Seymour. Crocodiles & Alligators. 2001. (Illus.). 32p. (J). (gr. k up). pap. 6.99 (978-0-06-443829-2(5) , Harper Trophy) HarperCollins Pubs.

—Crocodiles & Alligators. Simon, Seymour, illus. 1999. (Illus.). 32p. (J). (gr. k-3). 16.89 (978-0-06-027474-0(3)) HarperCollins Pubs.

—Crocodiles & Alligators. 2001. (ps-ps). (Illus.). (J). lib. bdg. 15.25 (978-0-613-44201-5(6)); 13.79 (978-0-606-22283-9(9)) Tandem Library Bks.

Spilsbury, Louise & Spilsbury, Richard. The Alligator. 2004. (Animals under Threat Ser.). (Illus.). 48p. (J). pap. 8.50 (978-1-4034-5431-7(0)) Heinemann Library.

—American Alligator. 2004. (Animals under Threat Ser.). (Illus.). 48p. (J). lib. bdg. (978-1-4034-4857-6(4)) Heinemann Library.

Stone, Tanya Lee. Crocodilians. 2003. (Wild Wild World Ser.). (Illus.). 24p. (J). 22.45 (978-1-4103-0037-9(4) , Blackbirch Pr., Inc.) Thomson Gale.

Swanson, Diane. Alligators & Crocodiles. 2004. (Welcome to the World of Animals Ser.). (Illus.). 32p. (J). (gr. 3 up). lib. bdg. 23.33 (978-0-8368-4021-6(6)) Stevens, Gareth Inc.

—Welcome to the World of Alligators & Crocodiles. 2002. (Welcome to the World Ser.). (Illus.). 32p. (J). (ps-2). pap. 5.95 (978-1-55285-355-9(1)) Whitecap Bks., Ltd. CAN. *Dist:* Firefly Bks., Ltd.

Thomas, Isabel. Alligator vs. Crocodile. 2006. (Illus.). 32p. (J). pap. (978-1-4109-2402-5(5)); lib. bdg. (978-1-4109-2395-0(9)) Steck-Vaughn.

Trueit, Trudi Strain. Alligators & Crocodiles. 2003. (True Bks.). (gr. 3-5). pap. 6.95 (978-0-516-29353-0(2)); (Illus.). 48p. (J). 25.00 (978-0-516-22653-8(3)) Scholastic Library Publishing. (Children's Pr.).

—Alligators & Crocodiles. 2003. (Illus.). 47p. (J). (gr. 4-7). lib. bdg. 15.25 (978-0-613-67950-3(4)) Tandem Library Bks.

Twine, Alice. Alligators. 2008. (J). lib. bdg. (***978-1-4042-4146-6(9)*** , PowerKids Pr.) Rosen Publishing Group, Inc., The.

Wexo, John Bonnett. Alligators & Crocodiles. (Zoobooks Ser.). (Illus.). 24p. (J). (gr. 1-6). 2001. 15.95 (978-1-888153-35-4(0)); 2003. 10.95 (978-1-932396-03-4(9) , Zoo Bks.) Wildlife Education, Ltd.

Whitehouse, Patricia. Alligator. 2003. (Zoo Animals Ser.). (Illus.). 24p. (J). (ps-1). lib. bdg. 17.08 (978-1-58810-903-3(8)); pap. 5.25 (978-1-4034-0642-2(1)) Heinemann Library.

—El Caiman. 2003. (Animales del Zoologico (Zoo Animals) Ser.).Tr. of Alligator. (SPA., Illus.). 24p. (ps-1). (J). lib. bdg. 17.08 (978-1-4034-0402-2(X)); pap. 5.25 (978-1-4034-0650-7(2)) Heinemann Library.

Wildlife Education, Ltd. Staff & Wexo, John Bonnett. Alligators & Crocodiles. Hoopes, Barbara, illus. 2000. (Zoobooks Ser.). 18p. (Orig.). (YA). (gr. 5 up). pap. 2.95 (978-0-937934-25-8(9)) Wildlife Education, Ltd.

Woodward, John. Crocodiles & Alligators. 1999. (Endangered! Ser.). (Illus.). 32p. (J). (gr. 3-5). lib. bdg. 25.64 (978-0-7614-0322-7(1) , Benchmark Bks.) Cavendish, Marshall Corp.

ALLIGATORS—FICTION

Accorsi, William. Apple, Apple, Alligator: A Picture-Puzzle Book. 2000. (Illus.). 20p. (J). (ps). bds. 14.95 (978-0-7611-1787-2(3)) Workman Publishing Co., Inc.

Alligators All Around. 2004. (J). 24.95 incl. audio (978-0-7882-0568-2(4)); pap. 14.95 incl. audio (978-0-7882-0633-7(8)) Weston Woods Studios, Inc.

Amoss, Berthe. The Cajun Gingerbread Boy. 1999. (J). 13.95 (978-0-922589-66-1(6)) More Than a Card, Inc.

Armstrong, Cindy. Boudreaux & His Buddies. 2006. 98p. pap. 14.95 (978-1-4241-3906-4(6)) PublishAmerica, Inc.

Asch, Frank. Monsieur Saguette & His Baguette. Asch, Frank, illus. 2006. (Illus.). 32p. 6.95 (978-1-55337-978-2(0)) Kids Can Pr., Ltd. CAN. *Dist:* Wybel Marketing Group.

Baker, Keith. Lucky Days with Mr. & Mrs. Green. (Mr. & Mrs. Green Ser.). (Illus.). 72p. (J). 2006. pap. 5.95 (978-0-15-205604-9(1) , Harcourt Paperbacks); 2005. 16.00 (978-0-15-216500-0(2) , Gulliver Bks.) Harcourt Children's Bks.

—Lucky Days with Mr. & Mrs. Green. 2007. (Mr. & Mrs. Green Ser.). 72p. (J). (gr. 2-4). 27.07 (***978-1-59961-300-0(X)***) Spotlight.

—Meet Mr. & Mrs. Green. 2004. (Easy Reader Ser.). (Illus.). 72p. (J). pap. 5.95 (978-0-15-204955-3(X) , Harcourt Paperbacks) Harcourt Children's Bks.

—Meet Mr. & Mrs. Green. 2007. (Mr. & Mrs. Green Ser.). 72p. (J). (gr. 2-4). 27.07 (***978-1-59961-301-7(8)***) Spotlight.

—Meet Mr. & Mrs. Green. 2004. (ps-ps). (Illus.). 72p. (J). lib. bdg. 13.15 (978-0-606-30391-0(X)); lib. bdg. 14.10 (978-0-613-71636-9(1)) Tandem Library Bks.

—More Mr. & Mrs. Green. (Mr. & Mrs. Green Ser.). (Illus.). 68p. (J). 2005. pap. 5.95 (978-0-15-205246-1(1) , Harcourt Paperbacks); 2004. 16.00 (978-0-15-216494-2(4)) Harcourt Children's Bks.

—More Mr. & Mrs. Green. 2007. (Mr. & Mrs. Green Ser.). 72p. (J). (gr. 2-4). 27.07 (***978-1-59961-302-4(6)***) Spotlight.

—On the Go with Mr. & Mrs. Green. 2007. (Mr. & Mrs. Green Ser.). (Illus.). 72p. (J). pap. 5.95 (978-0-15-205867-8(2) , Harcourt Paperbacks) Harcourt Children's Bks.

—On the Go with Mr. & Mrs. Green. 2006. (Mr. & Mrs. Green Ser.). (Illus.). 72p. (J). 16.00 (978-0-15-205762-6(5)) Harcourt Trade Pubs.

—On the Go with Mr. & Mrs. Green. 2007. (Mr. & Mrs. Green Ser.). 72p. (J). (gr. 2-4). 27.07 (***978-1-59961-303-1(4)***) Spotlight.

—Sometimes. 2003. (Green Light Readers Level 1 Ser.). (Illus.). 24p. (J). 11.95 (978-0-15-204807-5(3)); pap. 3.95 (978-0-15-204847-1(2)) Harcourt Children's Bks. (Green Light Readers).

—Sometimes. 1999. (Green Light Readers Ser.). (978-0-606-16510-5(X)); lib. bdg. 11.80 (978-0-613-64597-3(9)) Tandem Library Bks.

—Sometimes/Algunas Veces. Campoy, F. Isabel & Ada, Alma Flor, trs. from ENG. 2007. (Green Light Readers Level 1 Ser.). (ENG & SPA., Illus.). 28p. (J). 12.95 (978-0-15-205959-0(8)); pap. 3.95 (978-0-15-205961-3(X)) Harcourt Trade Pubs.

Beard, Darleen Bailey. The Flimflam Man. 2003. (gr. 3-6). lib. bdg. 14.10 (978-0-613-71860-8(7)) Tandem Library Bks.

Beckenstein, Cara. The True Story of Federico Fish & Ana Alligator. Tanchak, Diane, illus. 2003. 32p. 11.95 (978-0-9726699-0-0(6)) Laughing Gull Pr.

Bergman, Mara. Snip Snap! What's That? Maland, Nick, illus. 2005. 32p. (J). (ps-17). 16.99 (978-0-06-077754-8(0)) HarperCollins Pubs.

Blanchard, Patricia & Suhr, Joanne. Old Bumpy Alligator. Wolff, Jason, illus. 2000. (Books for Young Learners). 16p. (J). pap. 5.00 (978-1-57274-275-8(5)) Owen, Richard C. Pubs., Inc.

Bryan, Sean. A Girl & Her Gator. Murphy, Tom, illus. rev. ed. 2006. 36p. (J). (ps-1). 14.99 (978-1-55970-798-5(4)) Arcade Publishing, Inc.

Calmenson, Stephanie. Rockin' Reptiles. 1998. (Gator Girls Ser.). (978-0-606-13416-3(6)) Tandem Library Bks.

Calmenson, Stephanie & Cole, Joanna. Rockin' Reptiles. Munsinger, Lynn, illus. 1998. 80p. (J). pap. 5.95 (978-0-688-15633-6(9)) HarperCollins Pubs.

Carter, Joey. The Great Airboat Ride! A Cantor Kids! Book. 2006. 72p. pap. 9.95 (978-1-59800-523-3(5)) Outskirts Press, Inc.

Cecil, Randy. Gator. Cecil, Randy, illus. 2007. (Illus.). 40p. (J). (ps-k). 15.99 (978-0-7636-2952-6(9)) Candlewick Pr.

Chapin, Tom & reader. Mama Don't Allow. Chapin, Tom, reader. 2001. (Live Oak Readalong Ser.). (Illus.). (J). (ps-4). pap. 16.95 incl. audio (978-0-87499-743-9(7)) Live Oak Media.

Christelow, Eileen. Jerome Camps Out. 2002. (Illus.). 32p. (J). (gr. k-3). 5.95 (978-0-618-19467-4(3) , Clarion Bks.) Houghton Mifflin Co. Trade & Reference Div.

—Jerome Camps Out. Christelow, Eileen, illus. 1998. (Illus.). 32p. (J). (gr. k-3). tchr. ed. 16.00 (978-0-395-75831-1(9) , Clarion Bks.) Houghton Mifflin Co. Trade & Reference Div.

—Jerome Camps Out. 2002. (gr. k-3). lib. bdg. 14.10 (978-0-613-72915-4(3)) Tandem Library Bks.

Cole, Joanna. Get Well, Gators! 2000. (gr. 1-4). pap. 4.95 (978-0-688-17641-9(0)) HarperCollins Pubs.

Cole, Joanna & Calmenson, Stephanie. Gator Halloween. Munsinger, Lynn, illus. 1999. (Gator Girls Ser.: Vol. 3). 64p. (J). (gr. 1-4). 14.89 (978-0-688-14785-3(2)) HarperCollins Pubs.

Conlon, Mara, adapted by. Bill Hatches an Egg. 2005. (Sitting Ducks Ser.). (J). (978-0-8431-1343-3(X) , Price Stern Sloan) Penguin Group (USA) Inc.

Cronin, Susan L. Gidget Goes Away. 2006. 54p. pap. 12.95 (978-1-4137-9878-4(0)) PublishAmerica, Inc.

Doucet, Sharon Arms. Alligator Sue. Wilsdorf, Anne, illus. 2003. 40p. (J). 17.00 (978-0-374-30218-4(9) , Farrar, Straus & Giroux (BYR)) Farrar, Straus & Giroux.

Federspiel, Jurg. Alligator Mike. Rappo, Petra, illus. 2007. 32p. (J). (ps-3). 15.95 (978-0-7358-2124-8(0)) North-South Bks., Inc.

Fleming, Candace. Gator Gumbo: A Spicy-Hot Tale. Lambert, Sally Anne, illus. 2004. 32p. (J). (gr. k-3). 16.00 (978-0-374-38050-2(3) , Farrar, Straus & Giroux (BYR)) Farrar, Straus & Giroux.

Forney, Melissa. Oonawassee Summer: Something is Lurking Beneath the Surface... Scott, Gregg, illus. 2000. 126p. (J). (gr. 4-8). pap. 14.95 (978-1-928961-04-8(5)) Barker Creek Publishing, Inc.

Foust, Cindy G. Austin Alligator: I'll See You Guys Later. Revoir, Joyce, illus. 2003. (J). 12.95 (978-0-9749220-0-3(5)) Alpha-kidZ.

Fox, Mem & Rodunsky, Vladimir. Where the Giant Sleeps. 2007. (Illus.). 32p. (J). (gr. k-2). 16.00 (978-0-15-206092-3(8)) Harcourt Trade Pubs.

Garrett, Ann. El Guardian del Pantano. Chandler, Karen, illus. 2001. (SPA.). 40p. (J). (gr. 3-5). 8.95 (978-1-890515-28-7(0) , TK30971) Turtle Bks.

—El Guardian del Pantano. Gutiérrez, Guillermo, tr. Chandler, Karen, illus. 1998. (SPA.). 40p. (J). (gr. 3-5). 16.95 (978-1-890515-13-3(2) , TK2991) Turtle Bks.

—Keeper of the Swamp. 1999. (gr. 3-6). lib. bdg. 17.60 (978-0-613-50211-5(6)) Tandem Library Bks.

—Keeper of the Swamp. Chandler, Karen, illus. 40p. (J). 2001. (ps-3). pap. 8.95 (978-1-890515-27-0(2)); 1998. (SPA.). (gr. 1-4). 16.95 (978-1-890515-12-6(4)) Turtle Bks.

George, Jean Craighead. The Missing 'Gator of Gumbo Limbo. 1999. (J). 9.95 (978-1-56137-700-8(7)) Novel Units, Inc.

Geringswald, Rita T. The Adventures of Ali Alligator. 2007. (Illus.). 33p. (J). 6.95 (***978-0-9797566-1-0(8)***) R & D Publishing of Lakeland, Florida.

Grader, Argentina. Alli Gator's Tail of Golf. Vickery, Shea, illus. 1999. 28p. (J). pap. 7.95 (978-0-9670529-1-5(2)) Argentina Pubns.

Gralley, Jean. Very Boring Alligator. rev. ed. 2001. (Illus.). 32p. (J). (ps-3). 15.95 (978-0-8050-6328-8(5) , Holt, Henry & Co. Bks. For Young Readers) Holt, Henry & Co.

Harcourt School Publishers Staff. The Alamo Across Texas: Library Book. 1999. (Collections Ser.). (Illus.). pap. 14.90 (978-0-15-313409-8(7)) Harcourt Schl. Pubs.

—Justin's Alligator On Level. 3rd ed. 2002. (Trophies Reading Program Ser.). (Illus.). pap. 5.10 (978-0-15-323088-2(6)) Harcourt Schl. Pubs.

—Sometimes Little Book. 3rd ed. 2002. (Trophies Reading Program Ser.). (Illus.). (J). pap. 10.20 (978-0-15-329348-1(9)) Harcourt Schl. Pubs.

—There's an Alligater: Library Book. 1999. (Collections Ser.). (Illus.). pap. 14.90 (978-0-15-313408-1(9)) Harcourt Schl. Pubs.

Harper, Charise Mericle. The Invisible Mistakecase. 2005. (Illus.). 32p. (J). (gr. k-3). 16.00 (978-0-618-44885-2(3)) Houghton Mifflin Co. Trade & Reference Div.

How the Gator's Snout Grew Out. Date not set. 5.95 (978-0-89868-359-2(9)) ARO Publishing Co.

Hoy, Marian A. Sissy the Alligator. Waters, Rose, tr. Frandsen, Breanna, illus. 2001. Tr. of Sissy la Lagarto. (SPA & ENG.). (J). (ps-2). pap. 12.95 incl. cd-rom (978-0-9706943-0-0(X)) Hoy, Marian A.

Hurd, Thacher. Mama Don't Allow. Hurd, Thacher, illus. 2001. (Illus.). pap. 33.95 incl. audio (978-0-87499-745-3(3)); pap. 35.95 incl. audio compact disk (978-1-59112-605-8(3)); (J). pap. 18.95 incl. audio compact disk (978-1-59112-135-0(3)) Live Oak Media.

Is There an Alligator at Kaipapa'u? / Aia Ka 'Alakeka Ma Kaipapa'u? The Ho'ulu Hou Project: Stories Told by Us. 2004. (J). per. (978-0-9760892-1-6(1)) Na Kamalei Koolauloa Early Education Program.

Jewell, Nancy. Alligator Wedding. Date not set. (J). 15.95 (978-0-8050-6819-1(8) , Holt, Henry & Co. Bks. For Young Readers) Holt, Henry & Co.

Koury, Jen. Allie Gator - A Good Helper. Torgerson, Dell & Reyner, Mark, eds. Koury, Jen, illus. 1999. (John Deere Kids Toybook Ser.). (Illus.). 10p. (J). (ps up). mass mkt. (978-1-887327-27-5(4)) Ertl Co., Inc.

Larsen, Alison. Thomas the Turtle. 2006. (Illus.). 21p. (J). per. 14.95 (978-1-60002-097-1(6) , 3961, Airleaf Publishing) Airleaf Publishing & Bookselling.

Lee, Dennis. Alligator Pie. Newfeld, Frank, illus. rev. ed. 2001. 64p. (J). 22.95 (978-1-55263-338-0(1)) Key Porter Bks. CAN. *Dist:* Firefly Bks., Ltd.

Leland, Debbie. The Firegator. 2002. (Illus.). 24p. (J). 14.95 (978-0-9667086-2-2(8)) Wildflower Run.

Lionni, Leo. An Extraordinary Egg. Lionni, Leo, illus. 1998. (Illus.). 32p. (J). (gr. k-ps). pap. 6.99 (978-0-679-89385-1(7) , Dragonfly Bks.) Random Hse. Children's Bks.

Marvin's Egg: Early Level Satellite Individual Title Six-Packs. (Sails Literacy Ser.). 16p. (gr. 1-2). 27.00 (978-0-7578-3155-3(9)) Rigby Education.

Mayer, Mercer. There's an Alligator under My Bed. Mayer, Mercer, illus. 2002. (Illus.). (J). 24.43 (978-0-7587-3784-7(X)) Book Wholesalers, Inc.

McAllister, Angela. Just Like Sisters. Fatus, Sophie, illus. 2006. 32p. (J). (ps-3). 15.95 (978-1-4169-0643-8(6) , Atheneum/Anne Schwartz Bks.) Simon & Schuster Children's Publishing.

McCarthy, Bobette. See You Later, Alligator. McCarthy, Bobette, illus. 1999. (Illus.). 30p. (J). (ps-1). reprint ed. 15.00 (978-0-7881-6645-7(X)) DIANE Publishing Co.

McClellan, E. P. Roar of the 'Gator. Lenoir, Jane, illus. 2001. 36p. (J). (gr. 1-6). lib. bdg. 14.95 (978-0-9705727-3-8(5)) Coastal Publishing Carolina, Inc.

McLaughlin, Julie. Hungry Mr. Gator. McKay, Ann Marie, illus. 2002. 32p. (J). (gr. k-2). pap. (978-0-615-12335-6(X)) JAM Publishers.

—Hungry Mr. Gator. McKay, Ann Marie, illus. 2005. (J). 15.99 (978-0-933101-24-1(4)) Legacy Pubns.

Minarik, Else Holmelund. No Fighting, No Biting! Sendak, Maurice, illus. 2004. 63p. (J). (gr. k-4). reprint ed. pap. 17.00 (978-0-7567-7235-2(4)) DIANE Publishing Co.

Moon, Nicola. Alligator Tales & Crocodile Cakes. Ellis, Andy, illus. 2005. (I Am Reading Ser.). 48p. (J). (gr. k-3). pap., pap. 3.95 (978-0-7534-5853-2(5) , Kingfisher) Houghton Mifflin Co. Trade & Reference Div.

Morris, Jennifer E. May I Please Have a Cookie? Morris, Jennifer E., illus. 2005. (Scholastic Reader Ser.). (Illus.). 32p. (J). (ps-3). pap. 3.99 (978-0-439-73819-4(9) , Cartwheel Bks.) Scholastic, Inc.

Mozelle, Shirley. Zack's Alligator Goes to School. Watts, James, illus. 1998. (I Can Read Bks.). 64p. (J). (gr. k-3). pap. 3.99 (978-0-06-444248-0(9)) HarperCollins Pubs.

—Zack's Alligator Goes to School. 1998. (I Can Read Bks.). (J). (gr. 1-3). (978-0-606-13942-7(7)) Tandem Library Bks.

Mrs O'Malley in Alligator Alley: 3-in-1 Package. (Sails Literacy Ser.). 24p. (gr. 1 up). 57.00 (978-0-7578-3209-3(1)) Rigby Education.

Mrs O'Malley in Alligator Alley: 6 Small Books. (Sails Literacy Ser.). 24p. (gr. 1 up). 25.00 (978-0-7578-3185-0(0)) Rigby Education.

Mrs O'Malley in Alligator Alley: Big Book Only. (Sails Literacy Ser.). 24p. (gr. 1 up). 27.00 (978-0-7635-5932-8(6)) Rigby Education.

Munsch, Robert. Alligator Baby. ed. 2004. (Illus.). (J). (gr. k-3). spiral bd. (978-0-616-01730-2(8)); spiral bd. (978-0-616-01731-9(6)) Canadian National Institute for the Blind/Institut National Canadien pour les Aveugles.

—Alligator Baby. Martchenko, Michael, illus. 2002. 32p. (J). pap. 4.99 (978-0-439-38849-8(X)) Scholastic, Inc.

—Alligator Baby. 1998. (Illus.). (J). pap. 3.99 (978-0-590-34195-0(2) , Cartwheel Bks.) Scholastic, Inc.

—Alligator Baby. Martchenko, Michael, illus. 1998. 32p. (J). (ps-3). pap. 4.99 (978-0-590-88594-2(4) , Cartwheel Bks.) Scholastic, Inc.

—Alligator Baby. 1998. 10.79 (978-0-606-13117-9(5)) Tandem Library Bks.

—Un Bebe Alligator? ed. 2004. Tr. of Alligator Baby. (FRE., Illus.). (J). (gr. k-3). spiral bd. (978-0-616-01839-2(8)) Canadian National Institute for the Blind/Institut National Canadien pour les Aveugles.

Nanette. The Black Alligator. 2004. (Life on Granny's Farm Ser.). (J). 12.95 (978-0-9741269-3-7(4)) St. Bernard Publishing, LLC.

Nesci, Andrea Lynn & Nesci, Jim. Bubba: A True Story about an Amazing Alligator. Kostelyk, Jason, illus. l.t. ed. 2003. 24p. (J). pap. 12.50 (978-0-9713197-6-9(6)) ECO Herpetological Pub. & Dist.

Nickl, Peter. Crocodile, Crocodile. Cutler, Ebbitt, tr. Schroeder, Binette, illus. 2000. Orig. Title: Krokodil, Krokodil. 32p. (J). (gr. k-5). pap. 7.95 (978-0-940793-32-3(6) , Crocodile Bks.) Interlink Publishing Group, Inc.

Olson, Mary. An Alligator Ate My Brother. Lyon, Tammie Speer, illus. 2003. 32p. (J). (gr. k-2). 15.95 (978-1-56397-803-6(2)) Boyds Mills Pr.

Palatini, Margie. No Biting, Louise. Reinhart, Matthew, illus. 2007. 32p. (J). (ps-2). 16.99 (978-0-06-052627-6(0)); lib. bdg. 17.89 (978-0-06-052628-3(9)) HarperCollins Pubs. (Tegen, Katherine Bks).

Random House Staff, ed. Alligator King. 1998. (J). 3.25 (978-0-679-89412-4(8)); lib. bdg. 8.99 (978-0-679-99412-1(2)) Random Hse. Children's Bks. (Random Hse. Bks. for Young Readers).

Reneaux, J. J. Why Alligator Hates Dog: A Cajun Folktale. 2001. (ps-2). lib. bdg. 15.25 (978-0-613-49793-0(7)) Tandem Library Bks.

Rice, James. Gaston Goes to Mardi Gras. 2nd ed. 1999. (Illus.). 32p. (ps-3). 15.95 (978-1-56554-286-0(X)) Pelican Publishing Co., Inc.

—Gaston the Green-Nosed Alligator. Rice, James, illus. 2nd ed. 1998. (Illus.). 32p. (ps up). 15.95 (978-1-56554-285-3(1)) Pelican Publishing Co., Inc.

Rovetch, L. Bob. Hot Dog & Bob & the Exceptionally Eggy Attack of the Game Gators. Whamond, Dave, illus. 2007. 96p. (J). pap. 4.95 (978-0-8118-5604-1(6)) Chronicle Bks. LLC.

Rovetch, Lissa. Hot Dog & Bob & the Exceptionally Eggy Attack of the Game Gators. Whamond, Dave, illus. 2007. 96p. (J). 15.50 (978-0-8118-5603-4(8)) Chronicle Bks. LLC.

Sargent, Dave & Sargent, Pat. I Can Read, Too/Puedo Leer, Tambien, 10. Robinson, Laura, illus. 2003. (Puedo Leer Ser.). 24p. (J). Vol. 1. (SPA.). pap. 6.95 (978-1-56763-944-5(5)); Vol. 1. (SPA.). lib. bdg. 19.95 (978-1-56763-943-8(7)); Vol. 2. (SPA.). pap. 6.95 (978-1-56763-946-9(1)); Vol. 2. (SPA.). lib. bdg. 19.95 (978-1-56763-945-2(3)); Vol. 3. (SPA.). pap. 6.95 (978-1-56763-948-3(8)); Vol. 3. (SPA.). lib. bdg. 19.95 (978-1-56763-947-6(X)); Vol. 4. (SPA.). pap. 6.95 (978-1-56763-950-6(X)); Vol. 4. (SPA.). lib. bdg. 19.95 (978-1-56763-949-0(6)); Vol. 5. (SPA.). pap. 6.95 (978-1-56763-952-0(6)); Vol. 5. (SPA.). lib. bdg. 19.95 (978-1-56763-951-3(8)); Vol. 6. (SPA.). pap. 6.95 (978-1-56763-954-4(2)); Vol. 6. (SPA.). lib. bdg. 19.95 (978-1-56763-953-7(4)); Vol. 7. (SPA.). pap. 6.95 (978-1-56763-956-8(9)); Vol. 7. lib. bdg. 19.95 (978-1-56763-955-1(0)); Vol. 8. (SPA.). pap. 6.95 (978-1-56763-958-2(5)); Vol. 8. (SPA.). lib. bdg. 19.95 (978-1-56763-957-5(7)); Vol. 9. (SPA.). pap. 6.95

(978-1-56763-960-5(7)); Vol. 9. (SPA.). lib. bdg. 19.95 (978-1-56763-959-9(3)); Vol. 10. (SPA.). pap. 6.95 (978-1-56763-962-9(3)); Vol. 10. (SPA.). lib. bdg. 19.95 (978-1-56763-961-2(5)) Ozark Publishing.

Schnetzler, Pattie L. Fast 'n Snappy. Manning, Jane K., tr. Manning, Jane K., illus. 2004. (Carolrhoda Picture Books Ser.). 32p. (J). (gr. k-3). 16.95 (978-1-57505-539-8(2)) Lerner Publishing Group.

Shaffert, Charles. Googus, the Toothless Alligator. Stringer, Margaret, illus. l.t. ed. 2003. 30p. (J). per. 7.95 (978-1-932338-27-0(6)) Lifevest Publishing, Inc.

Shaffert, Charles F. Googus to the Rescue. Stringer, Margaret, illus. l.t. ed. 2005. 31p. (J). per. 10.00 (978-1-59879-043-6(9)) Lifevest Publishing, Inc.

Smeeton, Miles. Alligator Tales (& Crocodiles Too) 1998. (Illus.). (J). pap. (978-1-896209-17-3(3)) Bayeux Arts, Inc.

Spaht-Gill, Janie. Gator's Out, Said the Trout. Reese, Bob, illus. (J). (gr. k-2). 5.95 (978-0-89868-305-9(X)) ARO Publishing Co.

—Gator's Out, Said the Trout. 1998. (ps-3). pap. 4.95 (978-0-89868-369-1(6)) ARO Publishing Co.

Stark, Paula Allene. Abraham the Alligator. 2007. 32p. (J). 14.99 (***978-1-60247-099-6(5)***) Tate Publishing & Enterprises, L.L.C.

Tate, Suzanne. Izzie Lizzie Alligator: A Tale of a Big Lizard. Melvin, James, illus. 1999. (Suzanne Tate's Nature Ser.: Vol. 21). 32p. (J). (ps-4). pap. 4.95 (978-1-878405-23-4(3)) Nags Head Art, Inc.

Viviani, Luisa. There Is Something Special Inside of Me. 2004. 25p. pap. 14.95 (978-1-4137-2372-4(1)) PublishAmerica, Inc.

Walton, Rick. Suddenly, Alligator! An Adverbial Tale. Bradshaw, Jim, illus. 2001. 32p. (J). 15.95 (978-1-58685-313-6(9)) Gibbs Smith, Publisher.

Warren, Sandra & Pfleger, Deborah Bel. Arlie the Alligator. Thomas, Deborah, illus. 2000. 48p. (J). 23.90 incl. audio compact disk (978-1-880175-16-3(9)) Arlie Enterprises.

Wilsdon, Christina. An Alligator Adventure in Florida. Mayo, Frank, illus. 2006. 26p. (J). 7.99 (978-1-59939-010-9(8) , Reader's Digest Young Families, Inc.) Reader's Digest Children's Publishing, Inc.

Wilson, Karma & Rankin, Joan. A Frog in the Bog. 2007. 32p. (J). pap. 6.99 (978-1-4169-2727-3(1) , Aladdin) Simon & Schuster Children's Publishing.

Ziefert, Harriet. Egad Alligator! McKie, Todd, illus. 2002. 40p. (J). (gr. k-3). 16.00 (978-0-618-14171-5(5) , Walter Lorraine) Houghton Mifflin Co. Trade & Reference Div.

ALLOYS

see also Metallurgy

Gray, Leon. Zinc. 2005. (Elements Ser.). (Illus.). 32p. (J). (gr. 3-7). lib. bdg. (978-0-7614-1922-8(5) , Benchmark Bks.) Cavendish, Marshall Corp.

ALLUSIONS

Fandel, Jennifer. Puns, Allusions, & Other Word Secrets: Understanding Poetry. 2005. (Illus.). 48p. (gr. 5-9). 21.95 (978-1-58341-341-8(3) , Creative Education) Creative Co., The.

ALMANACS

see also Calendars; Yearbooks

Almanac, Old Farmer's. The Old Farmer's Almanac for Kids. Stillman, Janice, ed. rev. ed. 2005. (Illus.). 224p. (gr. 4-6). pap. 9.95 (978-1-57198-358-9(9)) Yankee Publishing, Inc.

Brunner, Borgna. Time Almanac 2001. 2000. (gr. 7-12). lib. bdg. 19.95 (978-0-613-33647-5(X)) Tandem Library Bks.

Georgian, Bay & Kops, Deborah. Scholastic Kid's Almanac: Facts, Figures, & Stats. rev. ed. 2004. (Illus.). 352p. (J). pap. 12.95 (978-0-439-56078-8(0) , Scholastic Reference) Scholastic, Inc.

Greenfeld, Barbara C. & Weinstein, Robert A. The Kids College Almanac: A First Look at College. 3rd ed. 2005. (Illus.). 352p. (J). pap. 16.95 (978-1-59357-104-7(6) , J1046, JIST Works) JIST Publishing.

Hopkins, Lee Bennett. Days to Celebrate: A Full Year of Poetry, People, Holidays, History, Fascinating Facts, & More. Alcorn, Stephen, illus. 2005. 112p. (J). (gr. 1-5). 17.99 (978-0-06-000765-2(6)); lib. bdg. 18.89 (978-0-06-000766-9(4)) HarperCollins Pubs.

Howes, Kelly King & Baker, Lawrence W. Almanac, Reconstruction Era. 2004. (Reconstruction ERA Reference Library). (Illus.). xxxvii, 228p. (J). lib. bdg. 67.00 (978-0-7876-9217-9(4) , UXL) Thomson Gale.

Howes, Kelly King & Carnagie, Julie. The Roaring Twenties Almanac & Primary Sources. 2005. (Illus.). liv, 286p. (J). 67.00 (978-1-4144-0212-3(0) , UXL) Thomson Gale.

Israel, Elaine. The World Almanac for Kids 1999. 1998. (Illus.). 320p. (J). (gr. 3-6). 8.95 (978-0-88687-826-9(8)); 16.95 (978-0-88687-827-6(6)) World Almanac Bks.

—The World Almanac for Kids 2001. 2000. (Illus.). 336p. (J). (gr. 4-7). pap. 10.95 (978-0-88687-857-3(8)) World Almanac Bks.

—The World Almanac for Kids 2002. 2001. (Illus.). (J). (978-0-606-21580-0(8)) Tandem Library Bks.

—World Almanac for Kids 2002. 2000. (gr. 3-6). lib. bdg. 21.05 (978-0-613-50091-3(1)) Tandem Library Bks.

—The World Almanac for Kids 2002. rev. ed. 2001. (Illus.). 336p. (J). (gr. 4-7). pap. 11.95 (978-0-88687-868-9(3)) World Almanac Bks.

Media Projects, Inc., Staff. Almanac of Asian American History, 2 vols. 2004. (Illus.). 144p. (J). (gr. 6-8). stu. ed. 83.95 (978-0-313-32602-8(9) , MS2602, Greenwood Pr.) Greenwood Publishing Group, Inc.

Media Projects, Inc., Staff, contrib. by. Student Almanac of Hispanic American History, 2 vols. 2003. (Illus.). (J). (978-0-313-32606-6(1)); 80.00 (978-0-313-32607-3(X)) Greenwood Publishing Group, Inc. (Greenwood Pr.).

—Student's Almanac of African American History, 2 vols. 2003. (Middle School Reference Ser.). (Illus.). 144p. (J). (gr. 6-8). 86.95 (978-0-313-32596-0(0) , MS2596, Middle School Reference) Greenwood Publishing Group, Inc.

—Students Almanac of Asian American History, 2 vols. 2003. (Illus.). (J). (978-0-313-32603-5(7)); (978-0-313-32604-2(5)) Greenwood Publishing Group, Inc. (Greenwood Pr.).

Miles, Johnnie H. Almanac of African American Heritage. 2001. (gr. 7-12). lib. bdg. 24.95 (978-0-613-64946-9(X)) Tandem Library Bks.

Pendergast, Tom & Pendergast, Sara. Almanac, Sixties in America. 2004. (U-X-L the Sixties in America Reference Library). (Illus.). xxxviii, 229p. (J). lib. bdg. 67.00 (978-0-7876-9246-9(8) , UXL) Thomson Gale.

—The Sixties in America, 3 vols. 2004. 600p. 181.00 (978-0-7876-9249-0(2) , UXL) Thomson Gale.

Porras, Carlos & D'Andrea, Patricia, trs. World Almanac Biblioteca de los Estados, 6 bks. Incl. California. Ingram, Scott. lib. bdg. 30.00 (978-0-8368-5542-5(6)); Florida. Chui, Patricia. lib. bdg. 30.00 (978-0-8368-5543-2(4)); Illinois. Feeley, Kathleen. lib. bdg. 30.00 (978-0-8368-5544-9(2)); Nueva Jersey. Holtz, Eric Siegfried. lib. bdg. 30.00 (978-0-8368-5545-6(0)); Nueva York. Ball, Jackie & Behrens, Kristen. lib. bdg. 30.00 (978-0-8368-5546-3(9)); Texas. Barenblat, Rachel. lib. bdg. 30.00 (978-0-8368-5547-0(7)); 48p. (J). (gr. 5 up). (SPA., Illus.). 2003. Set lib. bdg. 175.60 (978-0-8368-5541-8(8) , World Almanac Library) Stevens, Gareth Inc.

Saari, Peggy. Colonial America: Almanac, 2 vols. 2000. (U-X-L Colonial America Reference Library). (Illus.). lxv, 409p. (J). pap. (978-0-7876-3765-1(3)) Thomson Gale.

Siegel, Alice & McLoone, Margo. The Blackbirch Kid's Almanac of Geography. 2005. (Illus.). 336p. (J). (gr. 4-8). reprint ed. 27.00 (978-0-7567-7338-0(5)) DIANE Publishing Co.

Time for Kids Editors. Almanac 2005. rev. ed. 2004. (Time for Kids Ser.). (Illus.). 360p. (J). pap., pap. 11.99 (978-1-931933-67-4(7)) Time, Inc. Home Entertainment.

—Almanac 2006. Rowen, Beth & Slepian, Curtis, eds. rev. ed. 2005. (Time for Kids Ser.). (Illus.). 360p. (J). (ps-7). 19.95 (978-1-932994-06-3(8)) Time, Inc. Home Entertainment.

—Time for Kids: Almanac 2004 with Fact Monster. Slepian, Curtis & Rowen, Beth, eds. 2003. 360p. (YA). (gr. 8). pap. (978-1-929049-97-4(8)) Hachette Bk. Group.

Time for Kids Editors. Time for Kids: Almanac 2008. rev. ed. 2007. (Illus.). 256p. (J). (gr. 2-8). pap. 12.99 (***978-1-933821-84-9(1)***) Time, Inc. Home Entertainment.

Time-Life Books Editors. Time 1999 Almanac: The Ultimate Worldwide Fact & Information Source. 1999. (Time Almanac Ser.). (YA). (gr. 7). 27.50 (978-1-883013-51-6(8)) Time, Inc. Home Entertainment.

Willard, Nancy. Cracked Corn & Snow Ice Cream: A Family Almanac. Dyer, Jane, illus. 2005. 56p. (YA). (gr. 4-8). 18.00 (978-0-7567-8835-3(8)) DIANE Publishing Co.

World Almanac Editors. The World Almanac for Kids 2000. 1999. (World Almanac for Kids Ser.). (J). (gr. 4-7). 336p. 18.95 (978-0-88687-841-2(1)); (Illus.). 320p. pap. 10.95 (978-0-88687-840-5(3)) World Almanac Bks.

—The World Almanac for Kids 2004. 2003. pap. 17.95 (978-0-88687-908-2(6)) World Almanac Bks.

—The World Almanac for Kids 2004. Seabrooke, Kevin, ed. rev. ed. 2003. (Illus.). 336p. (J). (gr. 2-9). pap. 11.95 (978-0-88687-902-0(7)) World Almanac Bks.

—World Almanac for Kids 2004 Event Kit. 2003. (J). pap. (978-0-88687-907-5(8)) World Almanac Bks.

—The World Almanac for Kids 2005. 2004. (Illus.). 336p. (J). pap. 12.95 (978-0-88687-929-7(9)) World Almanac Bks.

—World Almanac for Kids 2005: Canadian Edition. 2004. (J). pap. 18.95 (978-0-88687-933-4(7)) World Almanac Bks.

—The World Almanac for Kids 2007. Kashner, Zoe, ed. 2006. (World Almanac for Kids Ser.). (Illus.). 352p. pap. 12.99 (978-0-88687-983-9(3)) World Almanac Bks.

World Almanac Editors, ed. & illus. The World Almanac for Kids 2005. World Almanac Editors, illus. 2004. 336p. (J). 21.95 (978-0-88687-930-3(2)) World Almanac Bks.

World Almanac for Kids 2003. 2002. (gr. 3-6). lib. bdg. 21.05 (978-0-613-53787-2(4)) Tandem Library Bks.

World Almanac for Kids Editors. The Little World Almanac: Big Facts for Young Readers. Kashner, Zoe, ed. 2007. (World Almanac for Kids Ser.). 96p. pap. 11.99 (***978-1-60057-012-4(7)***) World Almanac Bks.

—The World Almanac for Kids 2008. Kashner, Zoe, ed. 2007. (World Almanac for Kids Ser.). 352p. (J). 21.99 (***978-1-60057-060-5(7)***); (gr. 3-8). pap. 12.99 (***978-1-60057-059-9(3)***) World Almanac Bks.

World Almanac for Kids Editors & Kashner, Zoe. The Little World Almanac: Big Facts for Young Readers. 2007. (World Almanac for Kids Ser.). 96p. (J). 19.99 (978-1-60057-013-1(5)) World Almanac Bks.

World Almanac Kids 2004 Carton Stuffer. 2003. pap. (978-0-88687-928-0(0)) World Almanac Bks.

World Almanac Library of the States, 52 bks. Incl. Alabama : The Heart of Dixie. Martin, Michael A. 2002. pap. 14.95 (978-0-8368-5297-4(4)); Alaska : The Last Frontier. Seder, Isaac. 2003. pap. 14.95 (978-0-8368-5318-6(0)); Arizona : The Grand Canyon State. Martin, Michael A. 2002. pap. 14.95 (978-0-8368-5298-1(2)); Arkansas : The Natural State. Bailer, Darice. 2002. pap. 14.95 (978-0-8368-5299-8(0)); California : The Golden State. Ingram, Scott. 2002. pap. 14.95 (978-0-8368-5282-0(6)); Colorado : The Centennial State. Elias, Megan. 2002. pap. 14.95 (978-0-8368-5300-1(8)); Connecticut : The Constitution State. Bailer, Darice. 2002. pap. 14.95 (978-0-8368-5301-8(6)); Delaware : The First State. Fontes, Justine & Fontes, Ron. 2003. pap. 14.95 (978-0-8368-5319-3(9)); Florida : The Sunshine State. Chui, Patricia. 2002. pap. 14.95 (978-0-8368-5283-7(4)); Georgia : Empire State of the South. Holtz, Eric Siegfried. 2002. pap. 14.95 (978-0-8368-5302-5(4)); Hawaii : The Aloha State. Doak, Robin S. 2003. pap. 14.95 (978-0-8368-5320-9(2)); Idaho : The Gem State. Edwards, Karen. 2003. pap. 14.95 (978-0-8368-5321-6(0)); Illinois : The Prairie State. Feeley, Kathleen. 2002. pap. 14.95 (978-0-8368-5284-4(2)); Indiana : The Hoosier State. Brunelle, Lynn. 2002. pap. 14.95 (978-0-8368-5285-1(0)); Iowa : The Hawkeye State. Martin, Michael A. 2002. pap. 14.95 (978-0-8368-5303-2(2)); Kansas : The Sunflower State. Ingram, W. Scott. 2002. pap. 14.95 (978-0-8368-5304-9(0)); Kentucky : The Blue Grass State. Ingram, Scott. 2002. pap. 14.95 (978-0-8368-5305-6(9)); Louisiana : The Pelican State. Gildart, Leslie S. 2002. pap. 14.95 (978-0-8368-5306-3(7)); Maine : The Pine Tree State. Craig, Janet. 2003. pap. 14.95 (978-0-8368-5322-3(9)); Maryland : The Old Line State. Martin, Michael A. 2002. pap. 14.95 (978-0-8368-5307-0(5)); Massachusetts : The Bay State. Barenblat, Rachel. 2002. pap. 14.95 (978-0-8368-5286-8(9)); Michigan : The Wolverine State. Barenblat, Rachel. 2002. pap. 14.95 (978-0-8368-5287-5(7)); Mississippi : The Magnolia State. Figueroa, Acton. 2003. pap. 14.95 (978-0-8368-5323-0(7)); Missouri : The Show Me State. Ingram, W. Scott. 2002. pap. 14.95 (978-0-8368-5309-4(1)); Montana : The Treasure State. Hirschmann, Kris. 2003. pap. 14.95 (978-0-8368-5324-7(5)); Nebraska : The Cornhusker State. Flocker, Michael. 2002. pap. 14.95 (978-0-8368-5310-0(5)); Nevada : The Silver State. Deford, Debra. 2003. pap. 14.95 (978-0-8368-5325-4(3)); New Hampshire : The Granite State. Mattern, Joanne. 2003. pap. 14.95 (978-0-8368-5326-1(1)); New Jersey : The Garden State. Holtz, Eric Siegfried. 2002. pap. 14.95 (978-0-8368-5311-7(3)); New Mexico : Land of Enchantment. Burgan, Michael. 2003. pap. 14.95 (978-0-8368-5327-8(X)); New York : The Empire State. Ball, Jacqueline A. 2002. pap. 14.95 (978-0-8368-5288-2(5)); North Carolina : The Tar Heel State. Rafle, Sarah. 2002. pap. 14.95 (978-0-8368-5289-9(3)); North Dakota : The Peace Garden State. Fontes, Justine & Fontes, Ron. 2003. pap. 14.95 (978-0-8368-5328-5(8)); Ohio : The Buckeye State. Martin, Michael A. 2002. pap. 14.95 (978-0-8368-5290-5(7)); Oklahoma : The Sooner State. Martin, Michael A. 2002. pap. 14.95 (978-0-8368-5312-4(1)); Oregon : The Beaver State. Ingram, Scott. 2002. pap. 14.95 (978-0-8368-5313-1(X)); Pennsylvania : The Keystone State. Ingram, Scott. 2002. pap. 14.95 (978-0-8368-5291-2(5)); Puerto Rico & Other Outlying Territories. Burgan, Michael. 2003. pap. 14.95 (978-0-8368-5329-2(6)); Rhode Island : The Ocean State. Mattern, Joanne. 2003. pap. 14.95 (978-0-8368-5330-8(X)); South Carolina : The Palmetto State. Volkwein, Ann. 2002. pap. 14.95 (978-0-8368-5314-8(8)); South Dakota : The Mount Rushmore State. Hirschmann, Kris. 2003. pap. 14.95 (978-0-8368-5331-5(8)); Tennessee : The Volunteer State. Peck, Barbara. 2002. pap. 14.95 (978-0-8368-5315-5(6)); Texas : The Lone Star State. Barenblat, Rachel. 2002. pap. 14.95 (978-0-8368-5292-9(3)); Utah : The Beehive State. Hirschmann, Kris. 2003. pap. 14.95 (978-0-8368-5332-2(6)); Vermont : The Green Mountain State. Flocker, Michael. 2002. pap. 14.95 (978-0-8368-5316-2(4)); Virginia : The Old Dominion. Pollack, Pamela. 2002. pap. 14.95 (978-0-8368-5293-6(1)); Washington : The Evergreen State. Barenblat, Rachel. 2002. pap. 14.95 (978-0-8368-5294-3(X)); Washington, D. C. Figueroa, Acton. 2003. pap. 14.95 (978-0-8368-5333-9(4)); West Virginia : The Mountain State. Fontes, Justine & Fontes, Ron. 2003. pap. 14.95 (978-0-8368-5334-6(2)); Wisconsin : The Badger State. Barenblat, Rachel. 2002. pap. 14.95 (978-0-8368-5295-0(8)); Wyoming : The Equality State. Fontes, Justine & Fontes, Ron. 2003. pap. 14.95 (978-0-8368-5335-3(0)); 48p. (J). (gr. 5 up). (Illus.). 2002. Set pap. 777.40 (978-0-8368-5168-7(4)); Set lib. bdg. 1560.00 (978-0-8368-5473-2(X)) Stevens, Gareth Inc. (World Almanac Library).

World Almanac Library of the States: Alaska; Delaware; Hawaii; Idaho; Maine; Mississippi; Montana; Nevada; New Hampshire; New Mexico; North Dakota; Puerto Rico & Other Outlying Areas; Rhode Island; South Dakota; Utah; Washington, D.C.; West Virginia; Wyoming, 18 bks. 2002. (Illus.). (J). (gr. 5 up). lib. bdg. 526.68 (978-0-8368-5167-0(6)); pap. 269.10 (978-0-8368-5317-9(2)) Stevens, Gareth Inc. (World Almanac Library).

World Almanac Library of the States New Releases: Alabama, Arizona, Arkansas, Colorado, Connecticut, Georgia, Iowa, Kansas, Kentucky, Louisiana, Maryland, Minnesota, Nebraska, New Jersey, Oklahoma, Oregon, South Carolina, Tennessee, Vermont, 20 bks. 2002. (Illus.). (J). (gr. 5 up). lib. bdg. 532.00 (978-0-8368-5166-3(8) , World Almanac Library) Stevens, Gareth Inc.

ALPHABET

see also Writing

Above the Chalkboard Alphabet: Manuscript. 1999. (gr. k-3). 10.95 (978-0-673-36027-4(X) , Scott Foresman) Addison-Wesley Educational Pubs., Inc.

Active Minds, 6 bks. (Illus.). (J). (ps-3). lib. bdg. 71.70 (978-1-56674-926-8(3)) Forest Hse. Publishing Co., Inc.

Ada, Alma Flor. Gathering the Sun: An Alphabet in Spanish & English. (ENG & SPA.). (J). (gr. k-2). 12.95 net. (978-1-58186-202-7(4) , DSP8805) Del Sol Publishing.

—Gathering the Sun: An Alphabet in Spanish & English. Silva, Simon, illus. 2001. (ENG & SPA.). 40p. (J). pap. 6.99 (978-0-688-17067-7(6) , Harper Trophy) HarperCollins Pubs.

—Gathering the Sun: An Alphabet in Spanish & English. 2001. (SPA.). (gr. k-3). lib. bdg. 15.30 (978-0-613-44389-0(6)) Tandem Library Bks.

AG Publishers Editors. Letter Art. 2002. (American Girl Library). (Illus.). 60p. (J). (gr. 3). 7.95 (978-1-58485-636-8(X)) American Girl Publishing, Inc.

Agnon, Shmuel Yosef. Agnon's Alef Bet: Poems. Friend, Robert, tr. from HEB. Zeldich, Arieh, illus. 1998. 72p. 19.95 (978-0-8276-0599-2(4)) Jewish Pubn. Society.

Aigner-Clark, Julie. My First Book of Letters. 2007. (J). (ps-17). bds. 9.99 (***978-1-4231-0204-5(5)***) Baby Einstein Co., LLC, The.

Allen, Susan & Lindaman, Jane. Read Anything Good Lately? Enright, Vicky, illus. 2003. 32p. 22.90 (978-0-7613-2322-8(8)); (J). 14.95 (978-0-7613-1889-7(5)) Lerner Publishing Group. (Millbrook Pr.).

Alphabet. 2004. (J). ring bd. 29.95 (978-1-56911-525-1(7)) Learning Resources, Inc.

Alphabet ABC: Which Little Monsters Can You See? 2002. (J). 7.98 (978-0-7525-7936-8(3)) Parragon, Inc.

Alphabet & Phonics. 2004. (Skill Builders for Young Learners Ser.). (Illus.). 96p. 11.99 (978-0-7439-3687-3(6)) Teacher Created Materials, Inc.

Alphabet Block Collections: Wildlife Series. 2001. (SPA.). (J). 10.00 (978-0-9722647-4-7(4)) BNDC.

Alphabet, Colors, & Numbers. . . 2000. (Kelley Wingate Ser.). 80p. (J). (ps-k). pap. 9.99 (978-0-88724-591-6(9)) Carson-Dellosa Publishing Co., Inc.

An Alphabet of Animal Signs. 2002. (Beginning Sign Language Ser.). bds. 6.95 (978-1-930820-08-1(9)) Garlic Pr.

Alphabet Sack Puppets. 2004. (J). ring bd. (978-0-9749844-0-7(X)) Sunshine Publishing.

Alphabet Sack Puppets: Colored Edition. 2004. (J). ring bd. (978-0-9749844-1-4(8)) Sunshine Publishing.

Alphabet Soundtracks. 2003. (YA). (ps up). pap. 15.99 (978-0-7424-1538-6(4)) School Specialty Publishing.

Alphabet Zoo. (J). Date not set. (Illus.). bds. 9.98 (978-0-7525-9888-8(0)); 2002. 32p. 4.98 (978-0-7525-7879-8(0)) Parragon, Inc.

Alvarez, Lourdes M. Alphabet. Brooks, David, illus. 2005. (My First Book Ser.). 9p. (J). (ps-17). bds. 3.95 (978-1-933050-08-9(X)) Sweetwater Pr.

—Mi Primer Libro Alfabeto. Brooks, David, illus. 2005. (Mi primer libro Ser.). (SPA.). 9p. (J). (ps-ps). bds. 3.95 (978-1-933050-02-7(0)) Sweetwater Pr.

Amazing ABCs And 123s. 2005. 128p. (J). per. 19.99 (978-1-59441-189-2(1) , DJ-604009) Carson-Dellosa Publishing Co., Inc.

American Education Publishing Staff. I Can Write Letters. 2001. (Illus.). 64p. (J). pap. 2.99 (978-1-56189-591-5(1) , 31199, American Education Publishing) School Specialty Publishing.

Archambault, John & Martin, Bill. Chicka Chicka ABC Magnet Book. Ehlert, Lois, illus. 2002. 22p. (J). (ps-3). 15.95 (978-0-689-85026-4(3) , Little Simon) Simon & Schuster Children's Publishing.

Arnold, Clareen. Alphabet Ages 3-6. 2003. (Skill Builders Ser.). 80p. 2.95 (978-1-887923-24-8(1)) Rainbow Bridge Publishing.

Ashanti to Zulu. 2004. (J). pap. 14.95 incl. audio (978-0-7882-0674-0(5)) Weston Woods Studios, Inc.

Ashanti to Zulu: African Traditions. 2004. (J). 24.95 incl. audio (978-1-56008-159-3(7)) Weston Woods Studios, Inc.

Astroword: Module 10-Vowel Digraphs & Diphthongs (1-3) 2003. 55.50 net. (978-0-7652-0587-2(4)); 166.95 net. (978-0-7652-0831-6(8)) Modern Curriculum Pr.

Astroword: Module 11-R-Controlled Vowels (1-3) 2003. 55.50 net. (978-0-7652-0588-9(2)) Modern Curriculum Pr.

Astroword: Module 12-Base Words & Endings (2-6) 2003. 55.50 net. (978-0-7652-0589-6(0)) Modern Curriculum Pr.

Astroword: Module 13-Compound Words (2-6) 2003. 55.50 net. (978-0-7652-0590-2(4)) Modern Curriculum Pr.

Astroword: Module 3-Short Vowels A, I (1-2) 2003. 55.50 net. (978-0-7652-0579-7(3)) Modern Curriculum Pr.

Astroword: Module 4-Short Vowels I, O (1-2) 2003. 55.50 net. (978-0-7652-0580 3(7)) Modern Curriculum Pr.

Astroword: Module 5-Short Vowels E, U (1-2) 2003. 55.50 net. (978-0-7652-0581-0(5)) Modern Curriculum Pr.

Astroword: Module 6-Consonant Blends & Digraphs (1-2) 2003. 55.50 net. (978-0-7652-0582-7(3)); 166.95 net. (978-0-7652-0825-5(3)) Modern Curriculum Pr.

Astroword: Module 7-Long Vowels A, I (1-3) 2003. 55.50 net. (978-0-7652-0583-4(1)); 166.95 net. (978-0-7652-0826-2(1)) Modern Curriculum Pr.

Astroword: Module 8-Long Vowels I, O (1-3) 2003. 55.50 net. (978-0-7652-0585-8(8)); 166.95 net. (978-0-7652-0828-6(8)) Modern Curriculum Pr.

Astroword: Module 9-Long Vowels E, U (1-3) 2003. 55.50 net. (978-0-7652-0586-5(6)); 166.95 net. (978-0-7652-0829-3(6)) Modern Curriculum Pr.

Aylesworth, Jim. Naughty Little Monkeys. Cole, Henry, illus. 2006. 32p. (J). reprint ed. pap. 6.99 (978-0-14-240562-8(0) , Puffin) Penguin Group (USA) Inc.

Azarian, Mary. A Gardener's Alphabet. 2005. (Illus.). 32p. (J). (gr. k-3). reprint ed. 5.95 (978-0-618-54881-1(5)) Houghton Mifflin Co. Trade & Reference Div.

Baby's First ABC Book. 2004. 10p. (J). bds. 4.99 (978-1-85854-923-1(X)) Brimax Books Ltd. GBR. *Dist:* Byeway Bks.

Baker, Alan. Black & White Rabbit's ABC. 1999. (ps-2). lib. bdg. 11.80 (978-0-613-88635-2(6)) Tandem Library Bks.

Baker, Leslie A. The Animal ABC. rev. ed. 2003. (Illus.). 40p. (J). 15.95 (978-0-8050-6746-0(9) , Holt, Henry & Co. Bks. For Young Readers) Holt, Henry & Co.

Baldus, Patrick. Amazing Alphabet Maze Book. Baldus, Patrick, illus. 2002. (Illus.). 64p. (J). pap. 5.99 (978-0-8431-4915-9(9) , Price Stern Sloan) Penguin Group (USA) Inc.

Bates, John, et al. My First Buddhist Alphabet. 2004. (Illus.). 32p. (J). (978-0-915678-79-2(9)) World Tribune Pr.

Beckes, Shirley V., illus. Dialing Alphabet. 2002. (Dial Bks.). 10p. (J). (ps-k). bds. 10.95 (978-1-57145-522-2(1) , Silver Dolphin Bks.) Advantage Pubs. Group.

Bellefontaine, Kim. ABC of America. Gurth, Per-Henrik, tr. Gurth, Per-Henrik, illus. 2004. 32p. (J). (ps-k). (978-1-55337-645-3(5)) Kids Can Pr., Ltd.

—ABC of Canada. Gurth, Per-Henrik, illus. 2004. 32p. (J). (ps-1). (978-1-55337-685-9(4)) Kids Can Pr., Ltd.

—ABC of Canada. Gurth, Per-Henrik, illus. 2002. 30p. (J). (ps-1). (978-1-55337-340-7(5)) Kids Can Pr., Ltd.

Berge, Ann. Russia ABCs: A Book about the People & Places of Russia. Yesh, Jeff, illus. 2004. (Country ABCs Ser.). 32p. (J). (gr. k-5). 23.93 (978-1-4048-0284-1(3)) Picture Window Bks.

Bible A-Z Learning the Alphabe. 2003. 64p. (C). pap. 7.99 (978-0-7647-0964-7(X)) School Specialty Publishing.

Birnbaumi, Ricki Korey. Alphabet Jingles. 2005. (Illus.). 26p. (J). 15.95 (978-0-9706094-2-7(6)) Effective Literacy Methods.

Blends, Set. l.t. ed. Incl. Ch : See It Say It Hear It. Scheunemann, Pam. lib. bdg. 19.93 (978-1-57765-409-4(9)); Sh : See It Say It Hear It. Molter, Carey. lib. bdg. 19.93 (978-1-57765-412-4(9)); St : See It Say It Hear It. Scheunemann, Pam. lib. bdg. 19.93 (978-1-57765-407-0(2)); Th : See It Say It Hear It. Scheunemann, Pam. lib. bdg. 19.93 (978-1-57765-408-7(0)); Tr : See It Say It Hear It. Molter, Carey. lib. bdg. 19.93 (978-1-57765-411-7(0)); Wh : See It Say It Hear It. Molter, Carey. lib. bdg. 19.93 (978-1-57765-410-0(2)); 24p. (J). (ps-3). 2000. (Illus.). 2000. Set lib. bdg. 119.58 (978-1-57765-286-1(X) , SandCastle) ABDO Publishing Co.

Bluedorn, Harvey. A Greek Alphabetarion: A Primer for Teaching How to Read, Write & Pronounce Ancient & Biblical Greek. 5th ed. 2004. (ENG & GEC.). 158p. pap. 25.00 incl. cd-rom (978-0-9743616-9-7(0)) Trivium Pursuit.

Body, Wendy. Azlo's ABC. 2006. (J). lib. bdg. 15.95 (978-1-59566-222-4(7)) QEB Publishing Inc.

Bonder, Dianna. An Accidental Alphabet. 2003. (Illus.). 32p. (J). (978-1-55285-394-8(2)) Whitecap Bks., Ltd.

—Accidental Alphabet. Bonder, Dianna, illus. 2nd ed. 2004. (Illus.). 32p. (J). (ps-2). pap. 8.95 (978-1-55285-596-6(1)) Whitecap Bks., Ltd. CAN. *Dist:* Firefly Bks., Ltd.

Book Company Staff. Alphabet Flash Cards. 2004. (Novelty Bks.). (Illus.). 16p. (J). (gr. 3-5). bds. (978-1-74047-473-3(2)) Book Co. Publishing Pty, Ltd., The.

—Lift & Learn ABC. 2005. (Lift & Learn Ser.). (Illus.). 8p. (J). (gr. 3-5). bds. 10.95 (978-1-74047-460-3(0)) Book Co. Publishing Pty, Ltd., The AUS. *Dist:* Penton Overseas, Inc.

Brindise, Susan. Look, Write & Remember Letter-Formation Practice Pages: 52 Reproducible, Hands-On Lessons That Really Help All Children Visualize, Write & Learn Each Letter of the Alphabet. 2002. 128p. pap., tchr. ed. 16.95 (978-0-439-26586-7(X)) Scholastic, Inc.

Browne, Philippa-Alys. African Animals ABC. Browne, Philippa-Alys, illus. 2001. (Illus.). 32p. (J). (ps-2). pap. 7.99 (978-1-84148-319-1(2)) Barefoot Bks., Inc.

Bruce, Lisa. Amazing Alphabets. Gliori, Debi, illus. 2003. 24p. (J). pap. 9.95 (978-0-7112-2129-1(4)) Lincoln, Frances Ltd. GBR. *Dist:* Transition Vendor.

Bruce, Lisa & Gliori, Debi. Amazing Alphabets. 2004. (Illus.). 24p. (J). pap. 9.95 (978-1-84507-272-8(3)) Lincoln, Frances Ltd. GBR. *Dist:* Perseus Distribution.

Bryant-Mole, Karen. Mortimer Plays I-Spy. Mukhida, Zul, illus. 2000. (Mortimer's Fun with Words Ser.). 24p. (J). (ps up). lib. bdg. 22.00 (978-0-8368-2749-1(X)) Stevens, Gareth Inc.

—Mortimer's ABC's. Mukhida, Zul, illus. 2000. (Mortimer's Fun with Words Ser.). 24p. (J). (ps up). lib. bdg. 22.00 (978-0-8368-2750-7(3)) Stevens, Gareth Inc.

Buckley, James, Jr. & Dorling Kindersley Publishing Staff. Baseball ABC. 2001. (Illus.). 24p. (J). (ps-k). bds. 6.99 (978-0-7894-7338-7(0)) Dorling Kindersley Publishing, Inc.

Burke, Mary McManus. A, My Name Is Andrew. Guevara, Linda L., ed. Ingemanson, Donna, illus. 2003. 40p. (J). (gr. k-5). 16.95 (978-0-9710278-5-5(4)) All About Kids Publishing.

Burnard, Damon. I Spy in the Jungle. Cairns, Julia, illus. 2001. 28p. (J). (ps-k). bds. 6.95 (978-0-8118-2987-8(1)) Chronicle Bks. LLC.

Cameron, Eileen. G Is for Garden State: A New Jersey Alphabet. Ettlinger, Doris, illus. 2004. 40p. (J). 17.95 (978-1-58536-152-6(6)) Sleeping Bear Pr.

A Can of Gas: Consonant g: Level A, 6 vols. (Wright Skills Ser.). 12p. (gr. k-3). 17.95 (978-0-322-03111-1(7)) Wright Group, The.

Candlewick Books Staff, Books. I Spy ABC. 2003. (gr. k-3). lib. bdg. 11.80 (978-0-613-74746-2(1)) Tandem Library Bks.

Capital & Lower Case Letters. 2002. (Home Workbooks Ser.). 64p. pap. 2.49 (978-0-88724-713-2(X) , CD-4515) Carson-Dellosa Publishing Co., Inc.

Capital Letters, Set. l.t. ed. Incl. Cities. Scheunemann, Pam. lib. bdg. 19.93 (978-1-57765-610-4(5)); Days. Scheunemann, Pam. lib. bdg. 19.93 (978-1-57765-611-1(3)); Months. Rondeau, Amanda. lib. bdg. 19.93 (978-1-57765-612-8(1)); Names. Scheunemann, Pam. lib. bdg. 19.93 (978-1-57765-608-1(3)); Places. Scheunemann, Pam. lib. bdg. 19.93 (978-1-57765-609-8(1)); States. Scheunemann, Pam. lib. bdg. 19.93 (978-1-57765-613-5(X)); 24p. (J). (ps-3). 2001. (Illus.). 2001. Set lib. bdg. 119.58 (978-1-57765-514-5(1) , SandCastle) ABDO Publishing Co.

Carlson, Nancy. ABC I Like Me! 1999. (gr. k-3). lib. bdg. 15.30 (978-0-613-14500-8(3)) Tandem Library Bks.

Cave, Kathryn. W Is for World: A Round-the-World ABC. 2004. (World Alphabets Ser.). (Illus.). 36p. (J). pap. 7.95 (978-1-84507-314-5(2)) Lincoln, Frances Ltd. GBR. *Dist:* Perseus Distribution.

—W Is for World: Around the World ABC. 1999. (J). (978-0-382-42113-6(2)); (978-0-382-42114-3(0)) Silver Pr. Co.

—W Is for World Big Book: A Round-the-World ABC. Oxfam, illus. 2004. 32p. (J). pap. (978-1-84507-026-7(7)) Lincoln, Frances Ltd.

Chaley, Dimitry, illus. Marty the Martian Learns ABC. 2005. 24p. (J). bds. 6.99 (978-0-9747387-1-0(9)) EKADOO Publishing Group.

Chatfield, Steve, et al. Animaly ABC. Duncheskie, Joan, illus. 1998. iii, 42p. (J). (ps-6). pap. 19.95 (978-0-9663505-0-0(2)) Bubba Bear Publishing, Inc.

Cheney, Lynne. A Is for Abigail: An Almanac of Amazing American Women. Glasser, Robin Preiss, illus. 2003. 48p. (J). 16.95 (978-0-689-85819-2(1)) Simon & Schuster Children's Publishing.

Chorao, Kay. D Is for Drums: A Colonial Williamsburg A. B. C. 2004. (J). 16.95 (978-0-87935-197-7(7)) Colonial Williamsburg Foundation.

Clark, Judy. I Spy Disney: An ABC Book. 2020. 32p. (J). 13.49 (978-0-7868-5069-3(8)) Disney Pr.

Clarke, Jacqueline. Shoe Box Learning Centers: Alphabet. 2006. 80p. pap. 12.99 (978-0-439-53792-6(4) , Teaching Resources) Scholastic, Inc.

Cline-Ransome, Lesa. Quilt Alphabet. Ransome, James E., illus. 2005. 48p. (J). (gr. k-3). pap. 6.95 (978-0-8234-1765-0(4)) Holiday Hse., Inc.

Coerr, Eleanor. S Is for Silver: A Nevada Alphabet. Park, Darcie, illus. 2004. (State Ser.). 40p. (J). 17.95 (978-1-58536-117-5(8)) Sleeping Bear Pr.

Collard, Sneed B., III. B Is for Big Sky Country: A Montana Alphabet. Yardley, Joanna, illus. 2003. 40p. (J). 17.95 (978-1-58536-098-7(8)) Sleeping Bear Pr.

Color, Cut, Paste, & Trace: Alphabet Letters. (ps-k). 2.99 (978-0-7424-0168-6(5) , IF0401) School Specialty Publishing.

Consonant Digraphs. (Modified Basic Skills Ser.). 48p. (gr. k-4). 5.99 (978-0-7424-0276-8(2) , LL80030) School Specialty Publishing.

Conway, Ian. A Preschoolers Guide to Writing ABC's. 2006. 29p. 7.99 (978-1-4116-6846-1(4)) Lulu.com.

Copycats. 2001. (ps-2). lib. bdg. 9.80 (978-0-613-32425-0(0)) Tandem Library Bks.

Crane, Carol. F Is for First State: A Delaware Alphabet. Traynor, Elizabeth, illus. 2005. (State Ser.). 40p. (J). (ps-3). 17.95 (978-1-58536-154-0(2)) Sleeping Bear Pr.

—L Is for Lonestar: A Texas Alphabet. Stacy, Alan, illus. 2001. 40p. (J). 17.95 (978-1-58536-019-2(8)) Sleeping Bear Pr.

—P Is for Pilgrim: A Thanksgiving Alphabet. Urban, Helle, illus. 2003. 40p. (J). 14.95 (978-1-58536-134-2(8)) Sleeping Bear Pr.

—S Is for Sunshine: A Florida Alphabet. Monroe, Michael Glenn, illus. 2000. 40p. (J). (ps-3). 16.95 (978-1-58536-012-3(0)) Sleeping Bear Pr.

—Y Is for Yellowhammer: An Alabama Alphabet. Burn, Ted, illus. 2003. 40p. (J). 17.95 (978-1-58536-118-2(6)) Sleeping Bear Pr.

Crawford, Laura. The Pilgrims' Thanksgiving from A to Z. Hierstein, Judith, illus. 2005. 32p. (J). (ps-k). pap. 7.95 (978-1-58980-238-4(1)) Pelican Publishing Co., Inc.

Crazy Miss Majsey's Alphabet Pets: Level N, 6 vols. 128p. (gr. 2-3). 49.95 (978-0-7699-1018-5(1)) Shortland Pubns. (U. S. A.) Inc.

Dahl, Michael. Alphabet Soup: A Book of Riddles about Letters. Reibeling, Brandon, illus. 2004. (Read-It! Joke Books). 24p. (C). (gr. k-3). 18.60 (978-1-4048-0228-5(2)) Picture Window Bks.

Dalmatian Press Staff. Alphabet. rev. ed. 1999. (Tools Ser.). (Illus.). 32p. (J). (gr. k-1). pap. 2.29 (978-1-57759-141-2(0)) Dalmatian Pr.

—Lowercase Alphabet. 1999. (Tools Ser.). (Illus.). 32p. (J). (ps up). pap. 2.29 (978-1-57759-143-6(7)) Dalmatian Pr.

—Play ABC with Me: Happy Tale. 2005. (Illus.). 24p. (J). bds. 2.99 (978-1-4037-1269-1(7)) Dalmatian Pr.

—Uppercase Alphabet. (Precious Moments Workbooks Ser.). (Illus.). (J). (ps-3). 1998. 34p. pap. 2.99 (978-1-57759-113-9(5)); 1999. 32p. pap. 2.29 (978-1-57759-142-9(9)) Dalmatian Pr.

D'Andrea, Deborah. Picture Me Letters A,B,C. 2002. (Learning Basics Ser.). 10p. (J). (ps up). bds. 4.99 (978-1-57151-556-8(9)) Playhouse Publishing.

Dartez, Cecilia Casrill. L Is for Louisiana. 2002. (Illus.). 32p. (J). (gr. k-3). pap. 7.95 (978-1-58980-022-9(2)) Pelican Publishing Co., Inc.

—L Is for Louisiana. 2002. (gr. k-3). lib. bdg. 16.40 (978-0-613-71062-6(2)) Tandem Library Bks.

Davis, Rebecca. ABC Fun. Blair, Bill, ed. Cagley, Diana, illus. l.t. ed. 2002. 62p. (J). (gr. k-3). spiral bd. 9.00 (978-0-9720881-0-7(5)) His Hands, Inc.

—Vowels & Other Strange Letters. Blair, Bill, ed. Yancey, Joshua Lee, illus. 2002. 25p. (J). (gr. 6-8). spiral bd. 7.00 (978-0-9720881-1-4(3) , B002) His Hands, Inc.

de Brunhoff, Laurent. Babar's ABC. 2001. (Babar Ser.). (Illus.). 38p. (J). (ps-3). 17.95 (978-0-8109-5707-7(8)) Abrams, Harry N. , Inc.

Demarest, Chris L. Alpha Bravo Charlie: The Military Alphabet. Demarest, Chris L., illus. 2005. (Illus.). 40p. (J). 16.95 (978-0-689-86928-0(2) , McElderry, Margaret K.) Simon & Schuster Children's Publishing.

—Firefighters A to Z. Demarest, Chris L., illus. (Illus.). (J). 2003. 32p. 6.99 (978-0-689-85999-1(6) , Aladdin); 2000. 40p. 17.99 (978-0-689-83798-2(4) , McElderry, Margaret K.) Simon & Schuster Children's Publishing.

Derico, Laura. God Says I Am: What God Tells Us about Himself in the Bible from A to Z. McLouglin, Wayne, illus. 2002. (Heritage Builders Ser.). 32p. 15.99 (978-0-7847-1378-5(2)) Standard Publishing.

Dick & Jane. Short Vowels. 2005. (Dick & Jane Ser.). 32p. (J). (ps-2). pap. 3.99 (978-0-448-43649-4(3) , Grosset & Dunlap) Penguin Group (USA) Inc.

Dinosaur Alphabet Dinosaur Alphabet. bds. (978-1-58394-099-0(5)) North Atlantic Bks.

DK Publishing Staff. Pop-Up Animal ABC. 2007. (DK Toys & Games Ser.). (Illus.). (J). (ps-1). 12.99 (978-0-7566-2588-7(2)) Dorling Kindersley Publishing, Inc.

Domeniconi, David. G Is for Golden: A California Alphabet. Carroll, Pam, illus. 2002. 40p. (J). (ps-5). 17.95 (978-1-58536-045-1(7)) Sleeping Bear Pr.

—M Is for Majestic: A National Parks Alphabet. Carroll, Pam, illus. 2003. 40p. (J). 17.95 (978-1-58536-138-0(0)) Sleeping Bear Pr.

Dorling Kindersley Publishing Staff. The ABC. 2000. (Touch & Feel Ser.). (Illus.). 12p. (J). (ps). bds. 6.99 (978-0-7894-5219-1(7)) Dorling Kindersley Publishing, Inc.

Dorling Kindersley Publishing Staff, contrib. by. C Is for Cat: A Touch-and-Say ABC Book. 2002. (DK Ladybird Ser.). 16p. (J). bds. 6.95 (978-0-7894-8471-0(4)) Dorling Kindersley Publishing, Inc.

Dot-to-Dot Alphabet (Gr. K-1) 2003. (J). (978-1-58232-067-0(5)) Bryan Hse. Pubs., Inc.

Doudna, Kelly. Aa: See It Say It Hear It. l.t. ed. 2000. (Alphabet Ser.). (Illus.). 24p. (J). (ps-3). lib. bdg. 19.93 (978-1-57765-394-3(7) , SandCastle) ABDO Publishing Co.

—The Alphabet - Set I. l.t. ed. Incl. Aa : See It Say It Hear It. lib. bdg. 19.93 (978-1-57765-394-3(7)); Bb : See It Say It Hear It. lib. bdg. 19.93 (978-1-57765-395-0(5)); Cc : See It Say It Hear It. lib. bdg. 19.93 (978-1-57765-396-7(3)); Dd : See It Say It Hear It. lib. bdg. 19.93 (978-1-57765-397-4(1)); Ee : See It Say It Hear It. lib. bdg. 19.93 (978-1-57765-398-1(X)); Ff : See It Say It Hear It. lib. bdg. 19.93 (978-1-57765-399-8(8)); Gg : See It Say It Hear It. lib. bdg. 19.93 (978-1-57765-400-1(5)); Hh : See It Say It Hear It. lib. bdg. 19.93 (978-1-57765-401-8(3)); Ii : See It Say It Hear It. lib. bdg. 19.93 (978-1-57765-402-5(1)); Jj : See It Say It Hear It. lib. bdg. 19.93 (978-1-57765-403-2(X)); Kk : See It Say It Hear It. lib. bdg. 19.93 (978-1-57765-404-9(8)); Ll : See It Say It Hear It. lib. bdg. 19.93 (978-1-57765-405-6(6)); Mm : See It Say It Hear It. lib. bdg. 19.93 (978-1-57765-406-3(4)); 24p. (J). (ps-k). 2000. (Illus.). 2000. Set lib. bdg. 259.09 (978-1-57765-285-4(1) , SandCastle) ABDO Publishing Co.

—Cc: See It Say It Hear It. l.t. ed. 2000. (Alphabet Ser.). (Illus.). 24p. (J). (ps-3). lib. bdg. 19.93 (978-1-57765-396-7(3) , SandCastle) ABDO Publishing Co.

—Dd: See It Say It Hear It. l.t. ed. 2000. (Alphabet Ser.). (Illus.). 24p. (J). (ps-3). lib. bdg. 19.93 (978-1-57765-397-4(1) , SandCastle) ABDO Publishing Co.

—Ee: See It Say It Hear It. l.t. ed. 2000. (Alphabet Ser.). (Illus.). 24p. (J). (ps-3). lib. bdg. 19.93 (978-1-57765-398-1(X) , SandCastle) ABDO Publishing Co.

—Ff: See It Say It Hear It. l.t. ed. 2000. (Alphabet Ser.). (Illus.). 24p. (J). (ps-3). lib. bdg. 19.93 (978-1-57765-399-8(8) , SandCastle) ABDO Publishing Co.

—Gg: See It Say It Hear It. l.t. ed. 2000. (Alphabet Ser.). (Illus.). 24p. (J). (ps-3). lib. bdg. 19.93 (978-1-57765-400-1(5) , SandCastle) ABDO Publishing Co.

—Hh: See It Say It Hear It. l.t. ed. 2000. (Alphabet Ser.). (Illus.). 24p. (J). (ps-3). lib. bdg. 19.93 (978-1-57765-401-8(3) , SandCastle) ABDO Publishing Co.

—Ii: See It Say It Hear It. l.t. ed. 2000. (Alphabet Ser.). (Illus.). 24p. (J). (ps-3). lib. bdg. 19.93 (978-1-57765-402-5(1) , SandCastle) ABDO Publishing Co.

—Jj: See It Say It Hear It. l.t. ed. 2000. (Alphabet Ser.). (Illus.). 24p. (J). (ps-3). lib. bdg. 19.93 (978-1-57765-403-2(X) , SandCastle) ABDO Publishing Co.

—Kk: See It Say It Hear It. 2000. (Alphabet Ser.). (Illus.). 24p. (J). (ps-3). lib. bdg. 19.93 (978-1-57765-404-9(8) , SandCastle) ABDO Publishing Co.

—Ll: See It Say It Hear It. l.t. ed. 2000. (Alphabet Ser.). (Illus.). 24p. (J). (ps-3). lib. bdg. 19.93 (978-1-57765-405-6(6) , SandCastle) ABDO Publishing Co.

—Nn: See It Say It Hear It. l.t. ed. 2001. (Alphabet Ser.). (Illus.). 24p. (J). (ps-3). lib. bdg. 19.93 (978-1-57765-434-6(X) , SandCastle) ABDO Publishing Co.

—Pp: See It Say It Hear It. l.t. ed. 2001. (Alphabet Ser.). (Illus.). 24p. (J). (ps-3). lib. bdg. 19.93 (978-1-57765-436-0(6) , SandCastle) ABDO Publishing Co.

—Qq: See It Say It Hear It. l.t. ed. 2001. (Alphabet Ser.). (Illus.). 24p. (J). (ps-3). lib. bdg. 19.93 (978-1-57765-437-7(4) , SandCastle) ABDO Publishing Co.

—Rr: See It Say It Hear It. l.t. ed. 2001. (Alphabet Ser.). (Illus.). 24p. (J). (ps-3). lib. bdg. 19.93 (978-1-57765-438-4(2) , SandCastle) ABDO Publishing Co.

—Ss: See It Say It Hear It. l.t. ed. 2001. (Alphabet Ser.). (Illus.). 24p. (J). (ps-3). lib. bdg. 19.93 (978-1-57765-439-1(0) , SandCastle) ABDO Publishing Co.

—Tt: See It Say It Hear It. l.t. ed. 2001. (Alphabet Ser.). (Illus.). 24p. (J). (ps-3). lib. bdg. 19.93 (978-1-57765-440-7(4) , SandCastle) ABDO Publishing Co.

—Uu: See It Say It Hear It. l.t. ed. 2001. (Alphabet Ser.). (Illus.). 24p. (J). (ps-3). lib. bdg. 19.93 (978-1-57765-441-4(2) , SandCastle) ABDO Publishing Co.

—Vv: See It Say It Hear It. l.t. ed. 2001. (Alphabet Ser.). (Illus.). 24p. (J). (ps-3). lib. bdg. 19.93 (978-1-57765-442-1(0) , SandCastle) ABDO Publishing Co.

—Ww: See It Say It Hear It. l.t. ed. 2001. (Alphabet Ser.). (Illus.). 24p. (J). (ps-3). lib. bdg. 19.93 (978-1-57765-443-8(9) , SandCastle) ABDO Publishing Co.

—Xx: See It Say It Hear It. l.t. ed. 2001. (Alphabet Ser.). (Illus.). 24p. (J). (ps-3). lib. bdg. 19.93 (978-1-57765-444-5(7) , SandCastle) ABDO Publishing Co.

—Yy: See It Say It Hear It. l.t. ed. 2001. (Alphabet Ser.). (Illus.). 24p. (J). (ps-3). lib. bdg. 19.93 (978-1-57765-445-2(5) , SandCastle) ABDO Publishing Co.

Douglas, Vincent & School Specialty Publishing Staff. Alphabet Dot-to-Dot. 2003. (Homework Helpers Ser.). (Illus.). 32p. (J). (gr. k-1). pap. 2.99 (978-0-7696-2946-9(6) , American Education Publishing) School Specialty Publishing.

—Alphabet Puzzles. 2003. (Homework Helpers Ser.). (Illus.). 32p. (J). (gr. k-1). pap. 2.99 (978-0-7696-2948-3(2) , American Education Publishing) School Specialty Publishing.

—My Little Library of ABCs, 12 bks. 2001. (My Little Library). (Illus.). 120p. (J). (ps-k). bds. 12.95 (978-1-58845-233-7(6)) School Specialty Publishing.

—Practice the Alphabet. 2002. (Edu-Slates Ser.). (Illus.). 1p. (J). 2.99 (978-1-57768-997-3(6) , Brighter Child) School Specialty Publishing.

A Dress for Fran: R-Family Blends: Level B, 6 vols. (Wright Skills Ser.). 16p. (gr. k-3). 17.95 (978-0-322-01460-2(3)) Wright Group, The.

Duncan Edwards, Pamela. O Is for Old Dominion: A Virginia Alphabet. Howell, Troy, illus. 2004. (State Ser.). 40p. (J). 17.95 (978-1-58536-161-8(5)) Sleeping Bear Pr.

Ehlert, Lois. Eating the Alphabet: Fruits & Vegetables from A to Z Lap-Sized Board Book. 2006. (Illus.). 28p. (J). bds. 10.95 (978-0-15-205688-9(2) , Red Wagon Bks.) Harcourt Children's Bks.

Elissa, Grodin. N Is for Nutmeg: A Connecticut Alphabet. Brookfield, Maureen, illus. 2003. 40p. (J). 17.95 (978-1-58536-124-3(0)) Sleeping Bear Pr.

Elkins, Stephen. The Memory Bible: The Sure-Fire, Fun Way to Learn 52 Bible Verses. Semple, David, illus. 2003. 224p. (J). (ps-3). 25.99 incl. audio compact disk (978-1-59145-063-4(2)) Nelson, Thomas Inc.

Ernst, Lisa Campbell. The Letters Are Lost. 1999. (Illus.). (J). (ps-ps). lib. bdg. 14.15 (978-0-613-14920-4(3)) Tandem Library Bks.

—The Turn-Around, Upside-down Alphabet Book. Ernst, Lisa Campbell, illus. 2004. (Illus.). 32p. (J). 15.95 (978-0-689-85685-3(7)) Simon & Schuster Children's Publishing.

Erwin, Vicki B. "C" Is for Canada. Thurman, Mark, illus. 2000. (Alpha Flight Bks.). 60p. (J). (ps-3). 17.95 (978-1-892920-30-0(1)) GHB Publishers, LLC.

Esparza, Thomas, Jr., prod. Esther's Playhouse, Disk A. 2004. (Illus.). (J). cd-rom (978-1-879817-42-5(X) , Children) Star Light Pr.

Eubank, Patti Reeder, tr. ABCs of Halloween. 2003. (Illus.). 40p. (J). (ps-k). 8.95 (978-0-8249-5467-3(X)) Ideals Pubns.

Fans: Consonant f: Level A, 6 vols. (Wright Skills Ser.). 12p. (gr. k-3). 17.95 (978-0-322-03107-4(9)) Wright Group, The.

Farmer, Bonnie. ABC Letters in the Library. McLeod, Chum, illus. 2004. 32p. (J). 15.95 (978-1-894222-87-7(3)) Lobster Pr. CAN. *Dist:* Univ. of Toronto Pr.

Farmer Fred's Sticker Book: ABC. 2002. 16p. pap. 3.98 (978-0-7525-8346-4(8)) Parragon, Inc.

Faulkenberry, Lauren. What Do Animals Do on the Weekend? Adventures from A to Z. Faulkenberry, Lauren, illus. 2002. (Illus.). 64p. (gr. k-3). 17.95 (978-0-9708972-4-4(3)) Novello Festival Pr.

Fay & Kay by the Bay: Long a Digraphs: Level B, 6 vols. (Wright Skills Ser.). 16p. (gr. k-3). 26.50 (978-0-322-01478-7(6)) Wright Group, The.

Fifi Ferret's Flute. 2001. (ps-2). lib. bdg. 9.80 (978-0-613-32550-9(8)) Tandem Library Bks.

Fine, Jil. Writing in Ancient India. 2003. (Writing in the Ancient World Ser.). (Illus.). 24p. (J). lib. bdg. 17.25 (978-0-8239-6508-3(2) , PowerKids Pr.) Rosen Publishing Group, Inc., The.

—Writing in Ancient Phoenicia. 2003. (Writing in the Ancient World Ser.). (Illus.). 24p. (J). lib. bdg. 17.25 (978-0-8239-6507-6(4) , PowerKids Pr.) Rosen Publishing Group, Inc., The.

First Steps: Abc. 2002. (First Steps Reading Ser.). 48p. (J). pap. 2.95 (978-0-7894-8481-9(1)) Dorling Kindersley Publishing, Inc.

Fisher, Jeff & Gaga. Pass the Celery, Ellery! 2000. (Illus.). 48p. (J). (gr. 2-7). 14.95 (978-1-58479-031-0(8)) Stewart, Tabori & Chang.

Fitch, Sheree. Peek-a-Little Boo. Watson, Laura, illus. 2005. 32p. (J). (ps-2). 17.95 (978-1-55143-342-4(7)) Orca Bk. Pubs. USA.

Flanagan, Alice K. Cats: The Sound of Short A. 1999. (Wonder Books Phonics: Vowels Ser.). (Illus.). 24p. (J). (ps-3). 21.36 (978-1-56766-691-5(4)) Child's World, Inc.

Focus on Prephonics Kits: Focus on Prephonics Complete Kit. (Wright Skillstm Ser.). 397.50 (978-0-322-01636-1(3)) Wright Group, The.

Focus on Prephonics Kits: Focus on Prephonics Core Kit. (Wright Skillstm Ser.). 312.50 (978-0-322-01637-8(1)) Wright Group, The.

Focus on Prephonics Write-on Rhyme Charts Kit. (gr. k-3). 158.50 (978-0-322-01638-5(X)) Wright Group, The.

Forbush, Kyle & Forbush, Kyle. A Is for Alaska - an ABC Book. Forbush, Lisa, illus. 2004. (J). bds. 6.95 (978-1-57833-287-8(7)) Todd Communications.

Foster James, Helen. E Is for Enchantment: A New Mexico Alphabet. Twinem, Neecy, illus. 2004. (State Ser.). 40p. (J). 17.95 (978-1-58536-153-3(4) , 1235984) Sleeping Bear Pr.

French, Karen. Dr. Frenchy's Pet Training from a to Z: A Fun, Colorful, Stimulating Alphabet Pattern Book. 2003. (J). per. 9.95 (978-1-888125-07-8(1)) Publication Consultants.

Furlong Reynolds, Cynthia. H Is for Hoosier: An Indiana Alphabet. Langton, Bruce, illus. 2001. 40p. (J). 17.95 (978-1-58536-041-3(4)) Sleeping Bear Pr.

Ga'g, Wanda. ABC Bunny. 2004. (Illus.). 40p. 14.95 (978-0-8166-4416-2(0)) Univ. of Minnesota Pr.

Gagliano, Eugene. C Is for Cowboy: A Wyoming Alphabet. Guy, Susan, illus. 2003. 40p. (J). 17.95 (978-1-58536-097-0(X)) Sleeping Bear Pr.

Garnett, Sammie & Pallotta, Jerry. U.S. Navy Alphabet Book. Bolster, Rob, illus. 2005. 32p. (J). 17.95 (978-1-57091-586-4(5)) Charlesbridge Publishing, Inc.

Gaydos, Nora. Snack Attack, Level 2. Sams, B. B., illus. 2004. (Now I'm Reading! Ser.). 128p. (J). (ps-2). 16.99 (978-1-58476-264-5(0)) Innovative Kids.

Gerstein, Mordicai. The Absolutely Awful Alphabet. Gerstein, Mordicai, illus. 2001. (Illus.). 32p. (J). (ps-2). pap. 6.00 (978-0-15-216343-3(3) , Voyager Bks./Libros Viajeros) Harcourt Children's Bks.

—The Absolutely Awful Alphabet. 2001. 12.80 (978-0-606-22606-6(0)); lib. bdg. 14.15 (978-0-613-44543-6(0)) Tandem Library Bks.

Ghigna, Charles. The Alphabet Parade. Woods, Patti, illus. 2002. 32p. (J). 17.95 (978-1-880216-74-3(4)) River City Publishing.

Gifford, Myrna. Alphabet Letters: A Read-and-Sing Book. Cooper, Frances, illus. 2002. 12p. (J). 9.95 (978-0-9720763-1-9(X) , RAS01) Action Factor, Inc.

—Little Partners: A Read-and-Sing Book. Cooper, Frances, illus. 2002. 12p. (J). 9.95 (978-0-9720763-2-6(8)) Action Factor, Inc.

Gillis, Jennifer Blizin. You & Me ABC. 2003. (You & Me Ser.). (Illus.). 24p. (J). lib. bdg. 18.50 (978-1-4034-2510-2(8)) Heinemann Library.

Godsey, Kallen & Calitri, Susan, trs. Learn about Alphabet. Godsey, Kallen & Calitri, Susan, illus. 2001. (My Wipe-Off Book Ser.). (Illus.). 10.98 (978-0-7853-4402-5(0)) Publications International, Ltd.

Golden Books Staff. Alphabet Zoo. 2005. (Illus.). 2p. (J). (ps-2). 4.99 (978-0-375-83181-2(9) , Golden Bks.) Random Hse. Children's Bks.

Gorilla, Be Good! 2001. (ps-2). lib. bdg. 9.80 (978-0-613-32610-0(5)) Tandem Library Bks.

Gowan, Barb. G Is for Grand Canyon: An Arizona Alphabet. Larson, Katherine, illus. 2002. 40p. (J). 17.95 (978-1-58536-068-0(6)) Sleeping Bear Pr.

Grodin, Elissa. D Is for Democracy: An American Citizen's Alphabet. Juhusz, Victor, illus. 2004. 40p. (J). 16.95 (978-1-58536-234-9(4)) Sleeping Bear Pr.

Grose, Crystal. Eat & Drink Your ABCs. 2005. 57p. (J). pap. 15.64 (978-1-4116-0098-0(3)) Lulu.com.

A Grosset & Dunlap. 2005. (Dick & Jane Ser.). 32p. (J). (ps-1). pap., wbk. ed. 3.99 (978-0-448-43843-6(7) , Grosset & Dunlap) Penguin Group (USA) Inc.

Group/McGraw-Hill, Wright. The Wright Skills: Level A Sets - 1 Each of 40 Titles (includes Short Vowels) (gr. k-3). (978-0-322-03873-8(1)) Wright Group, The.

—The Wright Skills: Level A Sets - 6 Each of 40 Titles (includes Short Vowels) (gr. k-3). 730.50 (978-0-322-03874-5(X)) Wright Group, The.

—The Wright Skills: Level A Sets - Short Vowels only: 1 Each of 19 Titles. (gr. k-3). 56.95 (978-0-322-06473-7(2)) Wright Group, The.

—The Wright Skills: Level A Sets - Short Vowels only: 6 Each of 19 Titles. (gr. k-3). 122.95 (978-0-322-06474-4(0)) Wright Group, The.

—The Wright Skills: Level B Sets - 1 Each of 40 Titles (includes long Vowels) (gr. k-3). 143.95 (978-0-322-03878-3(2)) Wright Group, The.

—The Wright Skills: Level B Sets - 6 Each of 40 Titles (includes long Vowels) (gr. k-3). 860.50 (978-0-322-03880-6(4)) Wright Group, The.

Grover, Max. The Accidental Zucchini: An Unexpected Alphabet. (gr. k-3). lib. bdg. 8.15 (978-0-613-03580-4(1)) Tandem Library Bks.

Grundon, Holly & Novelli, Joan. Smartpads ABCs: 40 Fun Games to Help Kids Master the Alphabet. 2005. 48p. pap. 7.99 (978-0-439-72075-5(3) , Teaching Resources) Scholastic, Inc.

Hall, Eve D. Dontay's Alphabet Book of Color. Hale, J. P., illus. 2004. 46p. (J). per. 13.00 (978-0-9758899-1-6(5)) Imagine Publishing.

Hall, Rebecca. A Is for Arches: A Utah Alphabet. Larson, Katherine, illus. 2003. 40p. (J). 17.95 (978-1-58536-096-3(1)) Sleeping Bear Pr.

Hands on Alphabet Skills (Gr. K-1) 2003. (J). (978-1-58232-114-1(0)) Bryan Hse. Pubs., Inc.

Harcourt School Publishers Staff. A to Zoom: Letters & Sounds. 1999. (Collections Ser.). (Illus.). (gr. k-1). 8.60 (978-0-15-314980-1(9)) Harcourt Schl. Pubs.

—Alphabet Construction. 3rd ed. 2003. (Trophies Reading Program Ser.). (ps). pap. 58.00 (978-0-15-340894-6(4)) Harcourt Schl. Pubs.

—Where Did You Learn the ABCs? Advanced Level. 3rd ed. 2002. (Trophies Reading Program Ser.). (Illus.). pap. 5.10 (978-0-15-323483-5(0)) Harcourt Schl. Pubs.

Harper, Marrisa and Normita. ABC Book. 2005. 58p. 8.19 (978-1-4116-2660-7(5)) Lulu.com.

Harris, Sue. ABC: A Busy Fingers Book. Chrystall, Claire, illus. 2003. 10p. (J). bds. 10.95 (978-1-57145-936-7(7) , Silver Dolphin Bks.) Advantage Pubs. Group.

Harte, May. ABCs in My House. 2004. (Look-And-Learn Books). (Illus.). (J). lib. bdg. 7.95 (978-1-4042-2824-5(1) , PowerKids Pr.) Rosen Publishing Group, Inc., The.

Haugen, Brenda. Canada ABCs: A Book about the People & Places of Canada. Shaw, David, illus. 2004. (Country ABCs Ser.). 32p. (J). (gr. k-5). 23.93 (978-1-4048-0285-8(1)) Picture Window Bks.

Hausmann, Gisela. Obvious Letters: The Alphabet Every Child Will Remember. 2nd ed. 2004. (Illus.). 60p. (J). cd-rom 18.00 (978-0-9664217-1-2(X)) Educ-Easy Bks.

Hays, Anna Jane. Happy Alphabet! A Phonics Reader. Mathieu, Joe, illus. 2002. (Early Step into Reading Ser.: Vol. 1). 32p. (J). (ps-1). pap. 3.99 (978-0-375-81230-9(X) , Random Hse. Bks. for Young Readers) Random Hse. Children's Bks.

Herzog, Brad. H Is for Home Run: A Baseball Alphabet. Rose, Melanie, illus. 2004. 40p. (J). 16.95 (978-1-58536-219-6(0)) Sleeping Bear Pr.

Hidden Pictures Alphabet (Gr. K-1) 2003. (J). (978-1-58232-062-5(4)) Bryan Hse. Pubs., Inc.

Hiemen, Sara. Germany ABCs: A Book about the People & Places of Germany. Miller, Jason, illus. 2004. (Country ABCs Ser.). 32p. (gr. k-5). 23.93 (978-1-4048-0020-5(4)) Picture Window Bks.

—Japan ABCs: A Book about the People & Places of Japan. Ouren, Todd, illus. 2004. (Country ABCs Ser.). 32p. (gr. k-5). 23.93 (978-1-4048-0021-2(2)) Picture Window Bks.

—Kenya ABCs: A Book about the People & Places of Kenya. Avila, Antonio, illus. 2004. (Country ABCs Ser.). 32p. (J). (gr. k-5). 23.93 (978-1-4048-0022-9(0)) Picture Window Bks.

Higashi/Glaser Design Inc. Staff. What Will I Be A to Z? 2005. (Hello Kitty Ser.). (Illus.). 28p. (J). (ps-k). bds. 6.95 (978-0-8109-5850-0(3)) Abrams, Harry N. , Inc.

Hoena, B. A. A Desert ABCs: An Alphabet Book. 2004. (A+ Alphabet Books). (Illus.). 17p. (J). 22.60 (978-0-7368-2605-1(X) , Aplus Bks.) Capstone Pr., Inc.

—Dogs ABC: An Alphabet Book. 2004. (A+ Alphabet Books). (Illus.). 32p. (J). lib. bdg. 22.60 (978-0-7368-2606-8(8) , Aplus Bks.) Capstone Pr., Inc.

—Toys ABC: An Alphabet Book. 2004. (A+ Alphabet Books). (Illus.). 17p. (J). 22.60 (978-0-7368-2609-9(2) , Aplus Bks.) Capstone Pr., Inc.

Hoffman, Joan. ABC Dot-to-Dot. Carmona, Lisa, ed. Boyer, Robin, illus. 2001. (Get Ready! Wkbks.). 32p. (J). pap., wbk. ed. 2.49 (978-0-88743-446-4(0) , 02070) School Zone Publishing Co.

Hot Off the Press Staff. Alphabet Tiles. 2003. 24p. pap. 8.99 (978-1-56231-841-3(1)) Hot off the Pr.

—Alphabet Tiles #2. 2003. 24p. pap. 8.99 (978-1-56231-897-0(7)) Hot off the Pr.

Howell, Theresa. A Is for Airplane, A es para Avion. Brooks, David, illus. 2003. (SPA & ENG.). 28p. (J). bds. 6.95 (978-0-87358-831-7(2) , Rising Moon Bks. for Young Readers) Northland Publishing.

Howell, Will C. Zooflakes ABC. 2002. (Illus.). 32p. (J). 16.85 (978-0-8027-8827-6(0)) Walker & Co.

Ideals Editors Staff. Baby Looney Tunes Alphabet. 2005. (Illus.). 26p. (J). bds. 7.95 (978-0-8249-6574-7(4)) Ideals Pubns.

I'm Learning My ABCs. 2004. (Flash Card + Music CD Learning Kits Ser.). 20p. 18.99 (978-1-894677-60-8(9)) Kidzup Productions.

Is Nan In? Consonant n: Level A, 6 vols. (Wright Skills Ser.). 12p. (gr. k-3). 17.95 (978-0-322-03106-7(0)) Wright Group, The.

Jackson, Woody. A Cow's Alfalfa-Bet. 2003. (Illus.). 32p. (J). (gr. k-ps). tchr. ed. 15.00 (978-0-618-16599-5(1)) Houghton Mifflin Co. Trade & Reference Div.

Jirankova-Limbrick, Martha. Artful Alphabet. 2003. (Illus.). 72p. (J). 16.99 (978-0-7636-2187-2(0)) Candlewick Pr.

Jocelyn, Marthe. ABC x 3: English, Espanol, Francais. Slaughter, Tom, illus. 2005. (ENG, SPA & FRE.). 32p. (J). (gr. k-k). 12.95 (978-0-88776-707-4(9)) Tundra Bks., Inc./Livres Toundra, Inc. CAN. *Dist:* Random Hse., Inc.

Johnson, Stephen. Alphabet City. 1999. (gr. k-3). lib. bdg. 15.30 (978-0-613-22966-1(5)) Tandem Library Bks.

Jordan, Denise. You & Me ABC. 2003. (Heinemann Read & Learn Ser.). (Illus.). 24p. (J). pap. 5.25 (978-1-4034-2512-6(4)) Heinemann Library.

Kalman, Bobbie. ABCs of Animals. 2007. (Illus.). 32p. (J). ***(978-0-7787-3410-9(2))*** Crabtree Publishing Co.

—ABCs of Habitats. 2007. (Illus.). 32p. (J). ***(978-0-7787-3411-6(0))*** Crabtree Publishing Co.

—ABCs of Plants. 2007. (Illus.). 32p. (J). ***(978-0-7787-3413-0(7))*** Crabtree Publishing Co.

—Christmas Long Ago from A to Z. 1999. (AlphaBasiCs Ser.). (Illus.). 32p. (J). (gr. 2-3). lib. bdg. (978-0-86505-385-4(5)) Crabtree Publishing Co.

—Everyday Structures from a to Z. 2000. (gr. 3-6). lib. bdg. 16.40 (978-0-613-21505-3(2)) Tandem Library Bks.

—Mexico from A to Z. 1999. (Illus.). (J). (gr. k-3). lib. bdg. 16.40 (978-0-613-11864-4(2)) Tandem Library Bks.

—Santa Claus from A to Z. 1999. (AlphaBasiCs Ser.). (Illus.). 32p. (J). (gr. 2-3). pap. (978-0-86505-419-6(3)); lib. bdg. (978-0-86505-389-2(8)) Crabtree Publishing Co.

—Santa Claus from A to Z. 2000. (gr. 3-6). lib. bdg. 16.40 (978-0-613-22328-7(4)) Tandem Library Bks.

—School from A to Z. 1999. (gr. 3-6). lib. bdg. 16.40 (978-0-613-19531-7(0)) Tandem Library Bks.

—United States from a to Z. 1999. (gr. k-3). lib. bdg. 16.40 (978-0-613-12228-3(3)) Tandem Library Bks.

—What Is a Community? from a to Z. 2000. (gr. 3-6). lib. bdg. 16.40 (978-0-613-22603-5(8)) Tandem Library Bks.

Kane, Kristen. K Is for Keystone: A Pennsylvania Alphabet. Knorr, Laura, illus. 2003. 40p. (J). 17.95 (978-1-58536-104-5(6)) Sleeping Bear Pr.

Kappely, Sarah. Happy Baby ABC. rev. ed. 2003. (Priddy Bicknell Big Ideas for Little People Ser.). (Illus.). 28p. (J). bds. 5.95 (978-0-312-49169-7(7) , Priddy Bks.) St. Martin's Pr.

Kent, Lorna, illus. Baby's First ABC Book. 2004. 12p. (J). bds. 7.99 (978-1-85854-659-9(1)) Brimax Books Ltd. GBR. *Dist:* Byeway Bks.

Kern, Donna. The Kern Alphabet Book. 1998. (Illus.). 32p. (ps-2). pap. 10.00 (978-1-57281-099-0(8) , CBK908) U. S. Games Systems, Inc.

Kids Can Press Staff, Press Can. Alphabet Mazes. 2004. (Kids Can Learn with Franklin Ser.). (Illus.). 32p. (J). (gr. k-3). (978-1-55337-592-0(0)) Kids Can Pr., Ltd.

Kidzup Productions Staff. ABC Theater. 2003. (Interactive Learning Kits Ser.). (Illus.). 24p. (J). (gr. k-2). 13.99 incl. audio (978-1-894281-00-3(4)) Kidzup Productions.

The Kitty: Long Vowels e, y, CVCe & Final y Patterns: Level B, 6 vols. (Wright Skills Ser.). 16p. (gr. k-3). 17.95 (978-0-322-03130-2(3)) Wright Group, The.

Klein, Frederick C. For the Love of the Cubs: An A to Z Primer for Cubs Fans of All Ages. Anderson, Mark, illus. 2003. 36p. (J). 16.95 (978-1-57243-545-2(3)) Triumph Bks.

Klein, Fredrick C. For the Love of the Yankees: An A-to-Z Primer for Yankees Fans of All Ages. Anderson, Mark, illus. 2003. 48p. (J). 19.95 (978-1-57243-579-7(8)) Triumph Bks.

Klingel, Cynthia Fitterer. Quack! The Sound of Q. 1999. (Wonder Books Phonics: Consonants Ser.). (Illus.). 24p. (J). (ps-3). 21.36 (978-1-56766-724-0(4)) Child's World, Inc.

Klingel, Cynthia Fitterer & Ballard, Peg. Fun! The Sound of Short U. 1999. (Wonder Books Phonics: Vowels Ser.). (Illus.). 24p. (J). (ps-3). 21.36 (978-1-56766-725-7(2)) Child's World, Inc.

Klingel, Cynthia Fitterer & Noyed, Robert B. The Amazing Letter F. 2003. (Alphaphonics Ser.). (Illus.). 24p. (J). (ps-2). 21.36 (978-1-59296-096-5(0)) Child's World, Inc.

—The Amazing Letter L. 2003. (Alphaphonics Ser.). (Illus.). 24p. (J). (ps-2). 21.36 (978-1-59296-102-3(9)) Child's World, Inc.

—The Amazing Letter N. 2003. (Alphaphonics Ser.). (Illus.). 24p. (J). (ps-2). 21.36 (978-1-59296-104-7(5)) Child's World, Inc.

—The Amazing Letter O. 2003. (Alphaphonics Ser.). (Illus.). 24p. (J). (ps-2). 21.36 (978-1-59296-105-4(3)) Child's World, Inc.

—The Amazing Letter T. 2003. (Alphaphonics Ser.). (Illus.). 24p. (J). (ps-2). 21.36 (978-1-59296-110-8(X)) Child's World, Inc.

—Anna & the Letter A. 2003. (Alphaphonics Ser.). (Illus.). 24p. (J). (ps-2). 21.36 (978-1-59296-091-0(X)) Child's World, Inc.

—Bernard, Me & the Letter B. 2003. (Alphaphonics Ser.). (Illus.). 24p. (J). (ps-2). 21.36 (978-1-59296-092-7(8)) Child's World, Inc.

—Carmen & the Letter C. 2003. (Alphaphonics Ser.). (Illus.). 24p. (J). (ps-2). 21.36 (978-1-59296-093-4(6)) Child's World, Inc.

—Cute! The Sound of Long U. 1999. (Wonder Books Phonics: Vowels Ser.). (Illus.). 24p. (J). (ps-3). 21.36 (978-1-56766-734-9(1)) Child's World, Inc.

—Daisy, My Dad & the Letter D. 2003. (Alphaphonics Ser.). (Illus.). 24p. (J). (ps-2). 21.36 (978-1-59296-094-1(4)) Child's World, Inc.

—Ezra & the Letter E. 2003. (Alphaphonics Ser.). (Illus.). 24p. (J). (ps-2). 21.36 (978-1-59296-095-8(2)) Child's World, Inc.

—Grandma, Grandpa, & the Letter G. 2003. (Alphaphonics Ser.). (Illus.). 24p. (J). (ps-2). 21.36 (978-1-59296-097-2(9)) Child's World, Inc.

—Helen at Home & the Letter H. 2003. (Alphaphonics Ser.). (Illus.). 24p. (J). (ps-2). 21.36 (978-1-59296-098-9(7)) Child's World, Inc.

—Imagination & the Letter I. 2003. (Alphaphonics Ser.). (Illus.). 24p. (J). (ps-2). 21.36 (978-1-59296-099-6(5)) Child's World, Inc.

—Josef's Journal & the Letter J. 2003. (Alphaphonics Ser.). (Illus.). 24p. (J). (ps-2). 21.36 (978-1-59296-100-9(2)) Child's World, Inc.

—Kaya's Kindergarten & the Letter K. 2003. (Alphaphonics Ser.). (Illus.). 24p. (J). (ps-2). 21.36 (978-1-59296-101-6(0)) Child's World, Inc.

—Muhammad's Monday & the Letter M. 2003. (Alphaphonics Ser.). (Illus.). 24p. (J). (ps-2). 21.36 (978-1-59296-103-0(7)) Child's World, Inc.

—Pablo, His Papa, & the Letter P. 2003. (Alphaphonics Ser.). (Illus.). 24p. (J). (ps-2). 21.36 (978-1-59296-106-1(1)) Child's World, Inc.

—Quentin's Quiz & the Letter Q. 2003. (Alphaphonics Ser.). (Illus.). 24p. (J). (ps-2). 21.36 (978-1-59296-107-8(X)) Child's World, Inc.

—Raquel & the Letter R. 2003. (Alphaphonics Ser.). (Illus.). 24p. (J). (ps-2). 21.36 (978-1-59296-108-5(8)) Child's World, Inc.

—Sabina at School & the Letter S. 2003. (Alphaphonics Ser.). (Illus.). 24p. (J). (ps-2). 21.36 (978-1-59296-109-2(6)) Child's World, Inc.

—Uncle Russ & the Letter U. 2003. (Alphaphonics Ser.). (Illus.). 24p. (J). (ps-2). 21.36 (978-1-59296-111-5(8)) Child's World, Inc.

—Victoria's Vacation & the Letter V. 2003. (Alphaphonics Ser.). (Illus.). 24p. (J). (ps-2). 21.36 (978-1-59296-112-2(6)) Child's World, Inc.

—Walter in the Woods & the Letter W. 2003. (Alphaphonics Ser.). (Illus.). 24p. (J). (ps-2). 21.36 (978-1-59296-113-9(4)) Child's World, Inc.

—Xavier & the Letter X. 2003. (Alphaphonics Ser.). (Illus.). 24p. (J). (ps-2). 21.36 (978-1-59296-114-6(2)) Child's World, Inc.

—Yesterday & the Letter Y. 2003. (Alphaphonics Ser.). (Illus.). 24p. (J). (ps-2). 21.36 (978-1-59296-115-3(0)) Child's World, Inc.

—Zlata, Me, & the Letter Z. 2003. (Alphaphonics Ser.). (Illus.). 24p. (J). (ps-2). 21.36 (978-1-59296-116-0(9)) Child's World, Inc.

Klutz Press Staff, ed. Magnetic A to Z. 2005. (Chicken Socks Ser.). (Illus.). 12p. (J). 12.95 (978-1-59174-359-0(1)) Klutz.

Knox, Barbara. ABC under the Sea: An Ocean Life Alphabet Book. 2003. (A+ Alphabet Books). (Illus.). 32p. (J). (gr. k-1). lib. bdg. 22.60 (978-0-7368-1684-7(4) , Aplus Bks.) Capstone Pr., Inc.

Korman, Susan. P Is for Philadelphia. 2005. (Illus.). 64p. 16.95 (978-1-59213-107-5(7)) Temple Univ. Pr.

Lakeshore Learning Materials Staff, contrib. by. Alphabet Write & Wipe Practice Book, 10 vols., Set. 2000. (J). pap. 75.00 (978-1-929255-15-3(2)) Lakeshore Learning Materials.

Langley, Judy. God's World & Me from A to Z. Coker, Carla, illus. 2004. 32p. (ps). 8.99 (978-1-56309-367-8(7)) New Hope Pubs.

Latza, Jodi Holley & Latza, Greg, photos by. South Dakota: An Alphabetical Scrapbook. 2000. (Illus.). (J). 11.95 (978-0-9673485-2-0(8)) PeopleScapes.

Laun D'Nealian Alphabet: Capital Letters. 1999. 13.45 (978-0-673-28591-1(X)) Addison-Wesley Educational Pubs., Inc.

Laun D'Nealian Alphabet: Lower-case Letters. 1999. 13.45 (978-0-673-28590-4(1)) Addison-Wesley Educational Pubs., Inc.

Law, Felicia. Alphabet: A First ABC Book. Knight, Paula, illus. (Patchwork First Poem Bks.). 24p. (J). (ps). 8.95 (978-1-904668-87-9(9)) Mercury Bks. Ltd. GBR. *Dist:* International Publishers Marketing.

LD COACH. TEH Learns to Read: Beginning Words & Written Characters, Volume One. 2004. (Illus.). 40p. (J). 34.95 (978-0-9745938-1-4(8)) LD Coach, LLC.

LeapFrog Staff. Imagination Desk Alphabet Activities. 2003. (Illus.). (978-1-59319-024-8(7)) LeapFrog Enterprises, Inc.

LeapFrog Staff, compiled by. Alphabet Adventures. 2002. (J). (ps-2). spiral bd. 14.99 (978-1-58605-738-1(3)) LeapFrog Enterprises, Inc.

—Leap's Friends from A to Z. 2002. (J). (ps-2). 14.95 (978-1-58605-908-8(4) , LeapFrog Schl. Hse.) LeapFrog Enterprises, Inc.

—Let's Learn Letters. 2002. (YA). (ps up). spiral bd. 9.99 (978-1-58605-819-7(3)) LeapFrog Enterprises, Inc.

Lear, Edward. A Was Once an Apple Pie. MacDonald, Suse, illus. 2005. 32p. (J). (ps-ps). pap. 12.99 (978-0-439-66056-3(4) , Orchard Bks.) Scholastic, Inc.

Learn about ABCs. 1998. (Illus.). 8p. (J). bds. 4.99 (978-1-929174-03-4(9)) Oshkosh B'Gosh, Inc.

Learn the Alphabet Wall Chart. 2004. (Wall Charts Ser.). (J). 4.99 (978-1-85997-290-8(X)) Byeway Bks.

Learning Wrap-Ups Early Child. 2004. 29.99 (978-0-943343-18-1(6)) Learning Wrap-Ups.

Leber, Nancy Jolson. (2) Word Workout. 2007. (Clear & Simple Ser.). 64p. (J). pap. 4.99 (978-0-448-44437-6(2) , Grosset & Dunlap) Penguin Group (USA) Inc.

Leonard, Barry, ed. & illus. Alphabet Connections: English-Spanish: 26 Picture Cards. Leonard, Barry, illus. 2004. 26p. (J). (gr. k-4). reprint ed. (978-0-7567-7825-5(5)) DIANE Publishing Co.

Leopold, Niki Clark. K Is for Kitten. Jeffers, Susan, illus. 2002. 32p. (J). 15.99 (978-0-399-23563-4(9) , Putnam Juvenile) Penguin Group (USA) Inc.

Letter Clusters Big Book, 6 vols. 32p. (gr. k-3). 38.50 (978-0-7802-7194-4(7)) Wright Group, The.

Letters & Their Sounds. 2002. (Home Workbooks Ser.). 64p. pap. 2.49 (978-0-88724-725-5(3) , CD-4527) Carson-Dellosa Publishing Co., Inc.

Levels A-F Letter Cards. 1999. (Metro Reading Ser.). (J). (gr. 1-2). 39.95 (978-1-58120-185-7(0)); 26.95 (978-1-58120-186-4(9)) Metropolitan Teaching & Learning Co.

Litchfield, Jo, illus. First Picture Abc. 2005. (First Picture Board Books Ser.). 16p. (J). 11.95 (978-0-7945-0907-1(X) , Usborne) EDC Publishing.

Lluch, Alex A. I Like to Learn: Alphabet, Numbers, Colors, & Opposites. 2008. 19.95 ***(978-1-887169-95-0(4))*** Wedding Solutions Publishing, Inc.

Lobel, Anita. Animal Antics: A to Z. Lobel, Anita, illus. 2005. (Illus.). 32p. (J). 15.99 (978-0-06-051814-1(6)); lib. bdg. 16.89 (978-0-06-051815-8(4)) HarperCollins Pubs.

Long Vowels & Inflections Big Book: Level C, set. (Sing-along Songs Ser.). (ps-2). 48.46 incl. audio compact disk (978-0-7362-0421-7(0)) Hampton-Brown Bks.

Luebs Shepherd, Rajean. C Is for Cornhusker: A Nebraska Alphabet. Appleoff, Sandy, illus. 2004. (State Ser.). 40p. (J). 17.95 (978-1-58536-147-2(X)) Sleeping Bear Pr.

Lundeen, Connie R. Alpha-Pets: A to Z. Lundeen, Bob, illus. 1998. 32p. (J). (gr. k-1). pap. 12.95 (978-1-880090-72-5(4) , Weasel Bks.) Galde Pr., Inc.

MacDonald, Ross. Achoo! Bang! Crash! The Noisy Alphabet. MacDonald, Ross, illus. rev. ed. 2003. (Illus.). 32p. (J). (ps-3). 23.90 (978-0-7613-2900-8(5)) Roaring Brook Pr.

MacDonald, Suse. Alphabatics. MacDonald, Suse, illus. 2005. (Stories to Go! Ser.). 56p. (J). 4.99 (978-1-4169-0305-5(4) , Aladdin) Simon & Schuster Children's Publishing.

Martin, Bill, Jr. & Archambault, John. Chicka Chicka Boom Boom. Ehlert, Lois, illus. 2000. 40p. (J). (ps-3). pap. 7.99 (978-0-689-83568-1(X) , Aladdin) Simon & Schuster Children's Publishing.

Martinsen, Bente & Pedersen, Solveig. Sing with Me ABC. 2001. 68p. (J). pap., tchr. ed., wbk. ed 16.95 incl. audio compact disk (978-1-928595-03-8(0)) Citron Bay Pr.

—Workbook Sing with Me ABC. 2001. 32p. (J). pap., wbk. ed. 3.95 (978-1-928595-04-5(9)) Citron Bay Pr.

Marzollo, Jean. I Spy Little Letters. Wick, Walter, illus. 2000. (I Spy Bks.). 26p. (J). (ps). bds. 6.99 (978-0-439-11496-7(9) , Cartwheel Bks.) Scholastic, Inc.

Maurer, Tracy. A to Z of All of Me. 2002. (A to Z Ser.). (Illus.). 48p. (gr. k-2). 20.95 (978-1-58952-059-2(9)) Rourke Publishing, LLC.

— A to Z of Friends & Family. 2002. (A to Z Ser.). (Illus.). 48p. (gr. k-2). 20.95 (978-1-58952-060-8(2)) Rourke Publishing, LLC.

— A to Z of Helping Hands. 2002. (A to Z Ser.). (Illus.). 48p. (gr. k-2). 20.95 (978-1-58952-061-5(0)) Rourke Publishing, LLC.

— A to Z of Ps & Qs. 2002. (A to Z Ser.). (Illus.). 48p. (gr. k-2). 20.95 (978-1-58952-062-2(9)) Rourke Publishing, LLC.

—Autumn. 2006. (to Z Ser.). (Illus.). 32p. (gr. k-2). 20.95 (978-1-58952-196-4(X)) Rourke Publishing, LLC.

—Spring. 2006. (to Z Ser.). (Illus.). 32p. (gr. k-2). 20.95 (978-1-58952-197-1(8)) Rourke Publishing, LLC.

McGrath, Barbara Barbieri. I Love Words. 2004. (Illus.). 32p. (J). 16.95 (978-1-57091-567-3(9)); pap. 6.95 (978-1-57091-568-0(7)) Charlesbridge Publishing, Inc.

Mein Erstes Lexikon A-Z. 3rd ed. 2005. (GER., Illus.). 104p. (J). (ps-3). pap. 27.75 (978-3-411-05453-4(0)) Langenscheidt Pubs Inc.

Melmed, Laura Krauss. Capital! Washington D. C. from A to Z. Lessac, Frane, illus. 2003. 48p. (J). (gr. 1 up). 16.99 (978-0-688-17561-0(9)); lib. bdg. 16.89 (978-0-688-17562-7(7)) HarperCollins Pubs.

—New York, New York! The Big Apple from A to Z. Lessac, Frane, illus. 2005. 48p. (J). (ps-ps). lib. bdg. 17.89 (978-0-06-054876-6(2)) HarperCollins Pubs.

Menendez, Shirley. B Is for Blue Crab: A Maryland Alphabet. Stutzman, Laura, illus. 2004. (State Ser.). 40p. (J). 17.95 (978-1-58536-160-1(7)) Sleeping Bear Pr.

Metropolitan Museum of Art Staff. Museum ABC Nesting Blocks. 2004. (Illus.). (J). (ps-1). 19.99 (978-0-316-73608-4(2)) Little, Brown Bks. for Young Readers.

Miles, L. Copio las Letras. 2004. (Farmyard Tales Ser.).Tr. of Letters to Copy. (SPA., Illus.). 16p. (J). (ps up). pap. 6.95 (978-0-7460-4531-2(X)) EDC Publishing.

Milne, A. A. Slide & Seek Alphabet: A Sliding Window Book. 1999. (Illus.). 8p. (J). bds. 10.99 (978-0-7868-3240-8(1)) Disney Pr.

Miranda, Anne. Alphabet Fiesta. 2001. (ENG & SPA., Illus.). 56p. (J). (ps-3). 12.95 (978-1-890515-30-0(2)) Turtle Bks.

—Alphabet Fiesta: An English/Spanish Alphabet Story. 2001. (ENG & SPA., Illus.). 56p. (J). (ps-3). 18.95 (978-1-890515-29-4(9)) Turtle Bks.

Mitter, Matt. ABC. 2000. (Talking Pages Deluxe Ser.). (Illus.). (J). 12.95 (978-1-58224-133-3(3)) Futech Interactive Products, Inc.

Moncure, Jane Belk. My "e" Sound Box. King, Colin, illus. 2000. (New Sound Box Library). 32p. (J). (ps-3). 22.79 (978-1-56766-771-4(6)) Child's World, Inc.

—My "f" Sound Box. King, Colin, illus. 2000. (New Sound Box Library). 32p. (J). (ps-3). 22.79 (978-1-56766-772-1(4)) Child's World, Inc.

—My "h" Sound Box. King, Colin, illus. 2000. (New Sound Box Library). 32p. (J). (ps-3). 22.79 (978-1-56766-774-5(0)) Child's World, Inc.

—My "k" Sound Box. King, Colin, illus. 2000. (New Sound Box Library). 32p. (J). (ps-3). 22.79 (978-1-56766-777-6(5)) Child's World, Inc.

—My "l" Sound Box. King, Colin, illus. 2000. (New Sound Box Library). 32p. (J). (ps-3). 22.79 (978-1-56766-778-3(3)) Child's World, Inc.

—My "m" Sound Box. King, Colin, illus. 2000. (New Sound Box Library). 32p. (J). (ps-3). 22.79 (978-1-56766-779-0(1)) Child's World, Inc.

—My "o" Sound Box. King, Colin, illus. 2000. (New Sound Box Library). 32p. (J). (ps-3). 22.79 (978-1-56766-781-3(3)) Child's World, Inc.

—My "q" Sound Box. King, Colin, illus. 2000. (New Sound Box Library). 32p. (J). (ps-3). 22.79 (978-1-56766-783-7(X)) Child's World, Inc.

—My "r" Sound Box. King, Colin, illus. 2000. (New Sound Box Library). 32p. (J). (ps-3). 22.79 (978-1-56766-784-4(8)) Child's World, Inc.

—My Sound Parade. King, Colin, illus. 2000. (New Sound Box Library). 32p. (J). (ps-3). 22.79 (978-1-56766-766-0(X)) Child's World, Inc.

—My "u" Sound Box. King, Colin, illus. 2000. (New Sound Box Library). 32p. (J). (ps-3). 22.79 (978-1-56766-787-5(2)) Child's World, Inc.

Munari, Bruno. Bruno Munari's ABC. 2003. (J). 60.00 (978-0-8118-4119-1(7)) Chronicle Bks. LLC.

My Abc. 32p. (gr. k-3). 38.50 (978-0-7802-4191-6(6)) Wright Group, The.

My Abc Student Book: 6 Each of 1 Student Book, 6 vols. 32p. (gr. k-3). 31.95 (978-0-7802-9032-7(1)) Wright Group, The.

My ABC's. 1998. (Fisher-Price Bubble-Bath Bks.). (Illus.). 6p. (J). (ps). vinyl bd. (978-0-7666-0145-1(5) , Honey Bear Bks.) Modern Publishing.

Newfield, Frank. Creatures: An Alphabet for Adults & Worldly Children. 1999. (Illus.). 32p. (YA). (gr. 5 up). pap. (978-0-88899-333-5(1) , Libros Tigrillo) Groundwood Bks. CAN. *Dist:* Transition Vendor.

Nichol, Barbara. The City ABC Book. Milich, Zorin, photos by. unabr. ed. 2003. (Illus.). 32p. (J). (ps-k). (978-1-55074-942-7(0)) Kids Can Pr., Ltd.

Nicholson, Sue & Ward, Beck, eds. Alphabet. Giraffe, Red, illus. 2002. (My First Write & Wipe Ser.). 26p. (J). (ps-k). 14.95 (978-1-57145-724-0(0) , Silver Dolphin Bks.) Advantage Pubs. Group.

No, not Yet: Consonants k, v, y; Short Vowel e word families: Level A, 6 vols. (Wright Skills Ser.). 12p. (gr. k-3). 17.95 (978-0-322-01455-8(7)) Wright Group, The.

Noah's Ark Abc: My Wipe-off Book. 2003. spiral bd. (978-0-7853-8571-4(1)) Publications International, Ltd.

Novick, Mary. Alphabet. Harlin, Sybel, illus. 2002. (Double Delight Ser.). 24p. (J). (ps-k). 9.95 (978-1-57145-779-0(8) , Silver Dolphin Bks.) Advantage Pubs. Group.

Oetting, Judy. "M" Is for Missouri's Rocks & Minerals. Dorenkamp, Michelle, illus. 2000. (Alpha Flight Bks.). 60p. (J). (ps-3). 17.95 (978-1-892920-29-4(8)) GHB Publishers, LLC.

O'Kane, George & Weikert, Dana, illus. Baldwin's Colorful Campus Tour - Boston College A-Z. 2004. (J). 9.99 (978-1-933069-00-5(7)) Odd Duck Ink, Inc.

Olsen, Jan Z. My Printing Book. Olsen, Jan Z., illus. 7th ed. 2003. (ENG, SPA & FRE., Illus.). 84p. (J). stu. ed. 5.95 (978-1-891627-01-9(5)) Handwriting Without Tears, Inc.

Ong, Christina. Little Engine That Could ABC Time. 2000. (ps-2). lib. bdg. 11.25 (978-0-613-26024-4(4)) Tandem Library Bks.

Onish, Liane. Reading Skills Card Games: ABC's. 2004. (Reading Skills Card Games Ser.). 48p. pap. 10.99 (978-0-439-46599-1(0) , Teaching Resources) Scholastic, Inc.

—Reading Skills Card Games: Long & Short Vowels. 2004. (Reading Skills Card Games Ser.). 48p. pap. 10.99 (978-0-439-46597-7(4) , Teaching Resources) Scholastic, Inc.

Open Court Staff. Breaking Code Cursive Alphabet. (J). pap. (978-0-87548-599-7(5) , 1210) Open Court Publishing Co.

Pallotta, Jerry. The Beetle Alphabet Book. Biedrzycki, David, illus. 2004. 32p. (J). 16.95 (978-1-57091-551-2(2)) Charlesbridge Publishing, Inc.

—The Beetle Alphabet Book. Biedrzycki, David, tr. Biedrzycki, David, illus. 2004. 32p. (J). pap. 7.95 (978-1-57091-552-9(0)) Charlesbridge Publishing, Inc.

—Beetle Alphabet Book. 2004. (gr. k-3). lib. bdg. 16.40 (978-0-613-88752-6(2)) Tandem Library Bks.

—The Skull Alphabet Book. Masiello, Ralph, illus. 2004. 32p. (YA). 16.95 (978-0-88106-914-3(0)); pap. 7.95 (978-0-88106-915-0(9)) Charlesbridge Publishing, Inc.

Pallotta, Jerry & Stillwell, Fred. The Airplane Alphabet Book. Bolster, Rob, illus. 2004. 32p. (YA). pap. 6.95 (978-0-88106-906-8(X)) Charlesbridge Publishing, Inc.

Pandell, Karen. Animal Action ABC. Sheehan, Nancy, illus. Wolfe, Art & Sheehan, Nancy, photos by. 2003. 32p. (J). (ps-1). 12.95 (978-1-929766-92-5(0)) Handprint Bks.

Paré, Roger. Alphabet. Lantier, Patricia, tr. from FRE. Paré, Roger, illus. 2001. (Smart Start Ser.). (Illus.). 24p. (J). (ps up). lib. bdg. 22.00 (978-0-8368-2843-6(7)) Stevens, Gareth Inc.

—L' Alphabet. (Livres-jeux Ser.). (FRE., Illus.). (J). (ps). 2004. 12p. pap. (978-2-89021-655-6(1)); 2003. 24p. pap. (978-2-89021-224-4(6)) Diffusion du livre Mirabel.

Parker, Laurie. Louisiana Alphabet, 3 vols. Parker, Laurie, illus. 2001. (State Alphabet Ser.). (Illus.). 32p. 15.95 (978-1-893062-31-3(7)) Quail Ridge Pr., Inc.

—Texas Alphabet, 3 vols., Vol. 2. 2000. (State Alphabet Ser.: Vol. 2). (Illus.). 32p. (J). (ps-3). 15.95 (978-1-893062-17-7(1)) Quail Ridge Pr., Inc.

Pfister, Marcus. Rainbow Fish A, B, C. Pfister, Marcus, illus. 2002. (Rainbow Fish Ser.). (Illus.). 20p. (J). (ps). 9.95 (978-0-7358-1714-2(6)) North-South Bks., Inc.

Phillips, Lavearne. Consonant Blends & Digraphs Coloring Book. Phillips, Lavearne, illus. 1999. 16p. (J). (gr. 1-3). pap. 4.00 (978-1-930058-03-3(9)) Phillips, Lavearne Products.

Phillips, Vivian A. The Biblical Alphabets Book. Date not set. (Illus.). 32p. (Orig.). (J). pap. (978-1-888413-01-4(8)) Seasoning Quilting (Arts & Crafts).

Pierce, Patricia A. & Langton, Bruce, trs. H Is for Hawkeye: An Iowa Alphabet. Langton, Bruce, illus. 2003. (Illus.). 40p. (J). 17.95 (978-1-58536-114-4(3)) Sleeping Bear Pr.

Pinto, Sara. The Alphabet Room. Pinto, Sara, illus. 2003. (Illus.). 56p. (J). 16.95 (978-1-58234-841-4(3) , Bloomsbury Children) Bloomsbury Publishing.

Pomaska, Anna. Animal Alphabet Follow the Dots. 2002. (Dover Little Activity Bks.). (Illus.). 64p. (J). pap. 1.50 (978-0-486-42101-8(5)) Dover Pubns., Inc.

—Little ABC Coloring Book. 1998. (Illus.). 64p. (J). (ps-2). pap. 1.50 (978-0-486-25156-1(X)) Dover Pubns., Inc.

Pomeroy, Diana. Wildflower ABC. 2001. (gr. k-3). lib. bdg. 14.15 (978-0-613-35479-0(6)) Tandem Library Bks.

Practice & Learn the Alphabet. 2004. (Alphabet Ser.). (Illus.). 224p. 17.99 (978-0-7439-3616-3(7)) Teacher Created Materials, Inc.

Preis, Donna, illus. & photos by. Alphabet. Preis, Donna, photos by. Siede, George, photos by. 2005. (Active Minds Ser.). (J). pap. (978-1-4127-6035-5(6)) Publications International, Ltd.

Priddy Books Staff & Priddy, Roger. Play & Learn ABC: Easy Learning Fun, for the Very Young. rev. ed. 2004. (Play & Learn Ser.). (Illus.). 10p. (J). bds. 8.95 (978-0-312-49395-0(9) , Priddy Bks.) St. Martin's Pr.

Priddy, Roger. Baby Hugs Shaker - ABC. rev. ed. 2005. (Illus.). 22p. (J). bds. 5.95 (978-0-312-49634-0(6) , Priddy Bks.) St. Martin's Pr.

—My Little Word Book: Mi Libro Pequeño de Palabras. 2005. (ENG & SPA., Illus.). 28p. (J). (ps-ps). bds. 9.95 (978-0-312-49462-9(9) , Priddy Bks.) St. Martin's Pr.

Prieto, Anita C. P Is for Pelican: A Louisiana Alphabet. Knorr, Laura, illus. 2004. 40p. (J). 17.95 (978-1-58536-137-3(2)) Sleeping Bear Pr.

Primm III, E. Russell & Petelinsek, Kathleen. At School/en la Escuela. 2006. (Talking Hands Ser.). (ENG & SPA., Illus.). 24p. (J). (ps). 21.36 (978-1-59296-450-5(8)) Child's World, Inc.

Publications International Staff, contrib. by. Noah's Ark ABC. 2001. (My Wipe-Off Book Ser.). (Illus.). (J). (978-0-7853-5101-6(9)) Publications International, Ltd.

Radabaugh, Melinda Beth. First Time ABC. 2003. (First Time Ser.). (Illus.). 24p. (J). pap. 5.25 (978-1-4034-3883-6(8)); lib. bdg. 18.50 (978-1-4034-3868-3(4)) Heinemann Library.

Raintree Steck-Vaughn Staff. Consonant Blends: Level A, Set 3. 1998. (J). pap. 46.00 (978-0-8172-5697-5(0)) Steck-Vaughn.

Random House Disney Staff. ABC, 123. 2005. (Super Color Plus Poster Ser.). (Illus.). 64p. (J). (ps-2). pap. 3.99 (978-0-375-83057-0(X) , Golden/Disney) Random Hse. Children's Bks.

Raven, Margot Theis. M Is for Mayflower: A Massachusetts Alphabet. Brett, Jeannie, illus. 2002. 40p. (J). 17.95 (978-1-58536-072-7(4)) Sleeping Bear Pr.

Reading Rods Alphabet Books. 2003. (J). pap. 24.95 (978-1-56911-120-8(0)) Learning Resources, Inc.

Really Big Coloring Books Staff. ABC 123 Learn My Letters & Numbers. l.t. ed. 2003. Orig. Title: 123-ABC Learn My Letters & Numbers. (Illus.). 321p. (J). (978-0-9729753-1-5(4)) Really Big Coloring Bks., Inc.

Realtime Associates and Mazer Corporation Staff & LeapFrog Staff, compiled by. Complex Vowels ai, ay. 2002. (J). (gr. k-1). 66.75 (978-1-58605-283-6(7) , LeapFrog Schl. Hse.) LeapFrog Enterprises, Inc.

—Complex Vowels ee, ea. 2002. (J). (gr. k-1). 66.75 (978-1-58605-284-3(5) , LeapFrog Schl. Hse.) LeapFrog Enterprises, Inc.

—Complex Vowels oa. 2002. (J). (gr. k-1). 66.75 (978-1-58605-286-7(1) , LeapFrog Schl. Hse.) LeapFrog Enterprises, Inc.

—Complex Vowels oi, oy. 2002. (J). (gr. k-1). 66.75 (978-1-58605-285-0(3) , LeapFrog Schl. Hse.) LeapFrog Enterprises, Inc.

—Diagraph sh. 2002. (J). (gr. k-1). 66.75 (978-1-58605-280-5(2)) LeapFrog Enterprises, Inc.

—Digraph th. 2002. (J). (gr. k-1). 2002.00 (978-1-58605-281-2(0) , LeapFrog Schl. Hse.) LeapFrog Enterprises, Inc.

—Digraphs ch, wh. 2002. (J). (gr. k-1). 66.75 (978-1-58605-282-9(9) , LeapFrog Schl. Hse.) LeapFrog Enterprises, Inc.

—Know the Letters of the Alphabet. 2002. (J). (gr. 2). 66.75 (978-1-58605-314-7(0) , LeapFrog Schl. Hse.) LeapFrog Enterprises, Inc.

—Long i as _ie or _y. 2002. (J). (gr. k-1). 66.75 (978-1-58605-279-9(9) , LeapFrog Schl. Hse.) LeapFrog Enterprises, Inc.

—Long i (i_e) 2002. (J). (gr. k-1). 66.75 (978-1-58605-276-8(4) , LeapFrog Schl. Hse.) LeapFrog Enterprises, Inc.

—Long u. 2002. (J). (gr. k-1). 66.75 (978-1-58605-278-2(0) , LeapFrog Schl. Hse.) LeapFrog Enterprises, Inc.

—Phonics Diagraphs ch, wh. 2002. 66.75 (978-1-58605-255-3(1)) LeapFrog Enterprises, Inc.

—Short A. 2002. (J). (gr. k-1). 66.75 (978-1-58605-263-8(2) , LeapFrog Schl. Hse.) LeapFrog Enterprises, Inc.

—Short e. 2002. (J). (gr. k-1). 66.75 (978-1-58605-266-9(7) , LeapFrog Schl. Hse.) LeapFrog Enterprises, Inc.

—Short i. 2002. (J). (gr. k-1). 66.75 (978-1-58605-264-5(0)) LeapFrog Enterprises, Inc.

—Short O. 2002. (J). (gr. k-1). 66.75 (978-1-58605-265-2(9) , LeapFrog Schl. Hse.) LeapFrog Enterprises, Inc.

—Short u. 2002. (J). (gr. k-1). 66.75 (978-1-58605-267-6(5) , LeapFrog Schl. Hse.) LeapFrog Enterprises, Inc.

Riehle, Mary Ann McCabe. M Is for Mountain State: A West Virginia Alphabet. Bryant, Laura J., illus. 2004. (State Ser.). 40p. (J). 17.95 (978-1-58536-151-9(8)) Sleeping Bear Pr.

Ritchie, Fern J. Alphabet Toys: Illuminated Alphabet: A Child's First Book. Ritchie, Fern J., illus. 2002. 26p. (J). 29.95 (978-0-939656-64-6(7)) Ritchie Unlimited Pubns.

Robb, Don. Ox, House, Stick: The History of Our Alphabet. Smith, Anne, illus. 2007. 48p. (J). (gr. 3-6). 16.95 (978-1-57091-609-0(8)) Charlesbridge Publishing, Inc.

Roberson, Bobby. Lillie Boy Willie Thompson. 2006. 178p. pap. 8.57 (978-1-4116-2271-5(5)) Lulu.com.

Rosie Rabbit's Radish. 2001. (ps-2). lib. bdg. 9.80 (978-0-613-33000-8(5)) Tandem Library Bks.

Ross, Kathy. Kathy Ross Crafts Letter Shapes. Barger, Jan, illus. 2002. (Crafts from Kathy Ross Ser.). 64p. (ps-1). lib. bdg. 24.90 (978-0-7613-2103-3(9) , Millbrook Pr.) Lerner Publishing Group.

—Kathy Ross Crafts Letter Sounds. Barger, Jan, illus. 2002. (Crafts from Kathy Ross Ser.). 64p. (ps-1). lib. bdg. 24.90 (978-0-7613-2102-6(0) , Millbrook Pr.) Lerner Publishing Group.

—Letter Shapes. Barger, Jan, illus. 2002. (Crafts from Kathy Ross Ser.). 64p. (J). (gr. k-2). pap. 8.95 (978-0-7613-1490-5(3) , Millbrook Pr.) Lerner Publishing Group.

—Letter Sounds. Barger, Jan, illus. 2002. (Crafts from Kathy Ross Ser.). 64p. (J). (gr. k-2). pap. 8.95 (978-0-7613-1491-2(1) , Millbrook Pr.) Lerner Publishing Group.

Rudisill, J. J., et al, illus. Wimzie's Alphabet. 1999. (Wimzie's House Bks.). 32p. (J). pap. 2.99 (978-0-88724-513-8(7) , CD-4854) Carson-Dellosa Publishing Co., Inc.

Ruttle, Kate & Budgell, Gill. Cambridge Alphabet Books: American English Edition. 2000. (Cambridge Reading Ser.). (Illus.). 8p. pap. 72.00 (978-0-521-79790-0(X)) Cambridge Univ. Pr.

Ryan, Susan Jane. Florida A to Z. Tornatore, Carol, illus. 2003. 64p. (J). 19.95 (978-1-56164-249-6(5)) Pineapple Pr., Inc.

Saffer, Barbara. ABC Science Riddles. Johnson, Jennifer, illus. 2004. (ABC Riddles Ser.). 32p. (J). (ps-3). (978-0-939217-55-7(4)) Peel Productions, Inc.

Salisbury, Kent. Alpha Zoo: Have Fun with Your Animal Friends from A to Z. 1998. (Illus.). 13p. (J). (ps-k). 6.99 (978-0-7681-0082-2(8) , McClanahan Bk.) Learning Horizons, Inc.

Salzmann, Mary Elizabeth. Angling to Zorbing: Sports from A to Z. 2007. (Let's See A to Z Ser.). (Illus.). 32p. (J). (ps-3). lib. bdg. 25.65 (***978-1-59928-881-9(8)*** , Super SandCastle) ABDO Publishing Co.

Sanders, Nancy I. Adventures with Letters. 1998. (Archy's Activity Bks.). (Illus.). 16p. (J). (ps-2). pap. 3.99 (978-0-570-05080-3(4)) Concordia Publishing Hse.

Santillo, LuAnn. A Sights & Sounds - Level, 36 vols. Santillo, LuAnn, ed. 2003. (Half-Pint Kids Readers Ser.). (Illus.). 7p. (J). (ps-1). pap. 39.99 (978-1-59256-126-1(8)) Half-Pint Kids, Inc.

Schaefer, Lola M. It's My Body ABC. 2003. (It's My Body Ser.). (Illus.). 24p. (J). (ps-1). lib. bdg. 18.50 (978-1-4034-0894-5(7)); pap. 5.25 (978-1-4034-3481-4(6)) Heinemann Library.

—Ooey-Gooey Animals ABC. 2002. (Ooey-Gooey Animals Ser.). (Illus.). 24p. (J). (ps-1). pap. 5.25 (978-1-58810-719-0(1) , 91371) Heinemann Library.

—Tiny Spiny Animals ABC. 2003. (Heinemann Read & Learn Ser.). (Illus.). 24p. (J). pap. 5.25 (978-1-4034-3509-5(X)); lib. bdg. 18.50 (978-1-4034-3246-9(5)) Heinemann Library.

Schafer, Kevin. Penguins ABC. 2002. (Penguins Ser.). (Illus.). 32p. (ps up). 14.95 (978-1-55971-831-8(5) , NorthWord Bks. for Young Readers) T&N Children's Publishing.

Schnur, Steven. Winter: An Alphabet Acrostic. Evans, Leslie, illus. 2002. 32p. (J). (ps-k). tchr. ed. 15.00 (978-0-618-02374-5(7) , Clarion Bks.) Houghton Mifflin Co. Trade & Reference Div.

School Specialty Publishing. 101 Activities: Circle Time Ideas. 2004. 80p. (J). pap. 10.99 (978-1-57029-486-0(0) , WPH99028, Totline Pubns.) Schaffer, Frank Pubns.

School Zone Interactive Staff. Flash Action Software Go Fish / Old Maid. 2005. (J). cd-rom 12.99 (978-1-58947-830-5(4)) School Zone Publishing Co.

School Zone Publishing Company Staff. ABC Dot-to-Dot Bilingual: Get Ready! 2004. 64p. (J). pap. 3.79 (978-1-58947-972-2(6)) School Zone Publishing Co.

—Alphabet Fun A Wipe-off Book: Hours of Reusable Fun! rev. ed. 2005. 26p. (J). (gr. k-1). pap. 3.79 (978-1-58947-781-0(2)) School Zone Publishing Co.

—Lowercase Alphabet. 2000. (Whimsy Workbooks Ser.). (Illus.). 32p. (J). (ps-1). pap., wbk. ed. 2.49 (978-0-88743-467-9(3)) School Zone Publishing Co.

—Lowercase Alphabet Bilingual: Get Ready! 2004. 64p. (J). pap. 3.79 (978-1-58947-970-8(X)) School Zone Publishing Co.

—Preschool Basics. 2002. (Illus.). 128p. (J). (ps). pap., wbk. ed. 7.99 (978-1-58947-002-6(8) , 02453) School Zone Publishing Co.

—Uppercase Alphabet. 2000. (Whimsy Workbooks Ser.). (Illus.). 32p. (J). (ps-1). pap., wbk. ed. 2.49 (978-0-88743-466-2(5)) School Zone Publishing Co.

—Whimsy Readiness. 2001. (Flash Cards Whimsy Ser.). 56p. (J). 2.79 (978-0-88743-671-0(4) , 04062) School Zone Publishing Co.

School Zone Staff. Alphabet. 2004. 56p. (J). 2.79 (978-1-58947-981-4(5)) School Zone Publishing Co.

—Alphbate Match. rev. ed. 2005. 56p. (J). 2.79 (978-1-58947-477-2(5)) School Zone Publishing Co.

—Go Fish. rev. ed. 2004. 56p. (J). 2.79 (978-1-58947-991-3(2)) School Zone Publishing Co.

Schrager, Howard. LMNOP: And All the Letters A to Z. Bischof, Bruce, illus. 1999. (J). (gr. k-4). 16.95 (978-0-9644846-0-3(9)) LemonTree Pr.

Schroeder, Holly. China ABCs: A Book about the People & Places of China. Yesh, Jeff, illus. 2004. (Country ABCs Ser.). 32p. (J). (gr. k-5). 23.93 (978-1-4048-0180-6(4)) Picture Window Bks.

—Israel ABCs: A Book about the People & Places of Israel. Wolf, Claudia, illus. 2004. (Country ABCs Ser.). 32p. (J). (gr. k-5). 23.93 (978-1-4048-0179-0(0)) Picture Window Bks.

—New Zealand ABCs: A Book about the People & Places of New Zealand. Wolf, Claudia, illus. 2004. (Country ABCs Ser.). 32p. (J). (gr. k-5). 23.93 (978-1-4048-0178-3(2) , 1229507) Picture Window Bks.

—The United States ABCs: A Book about the People & Places of the United States. Yesh, Jeff, illus. 2004. (Country ABCs Ser.). 32p. (J). (gr. k-5). 23.93 (978-1-4048-0181-3(2) , 1229509) Picture Window Bks.

Schumacher, Bev. Letters Aa to Zz. 2005. (J). bds. (978-0-9741549-9-2(7)) Learning Props.

Scillian, Devin. P Is for Passport: A World Alphabet. 2003. (Illus.). 56p. (J). 19.95 (978-1-58536-157-1(7)) Sleeping Bear Pr.

—S Is for Sooner: An Oklahoma Alphabet. Doner, Kim, illus. 2003. 40p. (J). 17.95 (978-1-58536-062-8(7)) Sleeping Bear Pr.

Scott, Karen. Endangered Species & Friends in the U. S. A. Seamans, Amanda, illus. unabr. ed. Date not set. (J). (ps-6). 16.95 (978-1-889667-00-3(5)) Second Ark Pubns.

Seeger, Laura Vaccaro. The Hidden Alphabet. Seeger, Laura Vaccaro, illus. rev. ed. 2003. (Single Titles Ser.). (Illus.). 32p. (J). (ps-1). 17.95 (978-0-7613-1941-2(7)) Roaring Brook Pr.

Serensits, Jaime F. M. Alphabet Train Coloring Book. Serensits, Jaime F. M., illus. 2001. 32p. (J). pap. 5.00 (978-1-931477-01-7(9)) Railroad Pr., The.

Severe, Doreese. ABC's See What They Say. alt. ed. 2006. (J). spiral bd. (***978-1-890566-06-7(3)***) See abc's LC.

—Beginning See ABC'S Package. 2006. (J). per. (***978-1-890566-00-5(4)***) See abc's LC.

Seymour, Gloria, told to. ABC Sing-along. 2004. (J). pap. 8.00 (978-0-8059-6473-8(8)) Dorrance Publishing Co., Inc.

Shaw, Eve. Grandmother's Alphabet: Grandma Can Be Anything from A to Z. Shaw, Eve, illus. 2001. (Illus.). 32p. (J). (ps-2). pap. 14.95 (978-0-439-19995-7(6)) Scholastic, Inc.

Sheldon, Ken. Sing along & Learn: The Alphabet Kit. 2006. 32p. (J). 9.99 (978-0-439-80497-4(3) , Teaching Resources) Scholastic, Inc.

Shonberg, Marcia. B Is for Buckeye: An Ohio Alphabet. Langton, Bruce, illus. 2000. 40p. (J). (ps-3). 16.95 (978-1-58536-004-8(X)) Sleeping Bear Pr.

Short Vowels Set: Level B. (Sing-along Songs Ser.). (ps-2). 48.46 incl. audio compact disk (978-0-7362-0420-0(2)) Hampton-Brown Bks.

Shoulders, Michael. N Is for Natural State: An Arkansas Alphabet. Anderson, Rick, illus. 2003. 40p. (J). 17.95 (978-1-58536-067-3(8)) Sleeping Bear Pr.

—V Is for Volunteer: A Tennessee Alphabet. Langton, Bruce, illus. 2001. 40p. (J). 17.95 (978-1-58536-033-8(3)) Sleeping Bear Pr.

Shulman, Mark. AA Is for Aardvark. Petrosino, Tamara, illus. 2005. 32p. (J). 14.95 (978-1-4027-2871-6(9)) Sterling Publishing Co., Inc.

Siede Preis Photography (Firm) Staff & Brian Warling Photography (Firm) Staff, contrib. by. Alphabet. 2003. (Active Minds Ser.). (Illus.). (J). (978-0-7853-7828-0(6)) Publications International, Ltd.

Smith, Lynn & Faust Kalscheur, Jann. ABC's Naturally: A Child's Guide to the Alphabet Through Nature. Faust Kalscheur, Jann, photos by. 2003. (Illus.). (J). 16.95 (978-1-931599-27-6(0) , Trails Bks.) Big Earth Publishing.

Smith, Roland & Smith, Marie. E Is for Evergreen: A Washington State Alphabet. Holt Ayriss, Linda, illus. 2004. (State Ser.). 40p. (J). 17.95 (978-1-58536-143-4(7)) Sleeping Bear Pr.

Sounding Out the Alphabet. 2004. (J). cd-rom, audio compact disk 9.95 (978-1-930006-62-1(4) , Reading Co., The) Rhoades & Assocs.

Spencer, Carolyn. Alphabet Sea. Harris, David, photos by. 1999. (Illus.). 31p. (J). (ps-3). 14.95 (978-1-893561-00-7(3)) Tortuga Bks.

Spirin, Gennady. A Apple Pie. Spirin, Gennady, illus. 2005. (Illus.). 32p. (J). (ps-1). 16.99 (978-0-399-23981-6(2) , Philomel) Penguin Group (USA) Inc.

Steck-Vaughn Staff. At-Home Workbooks: The Alphabet. 2004. (Illus.). pap., wbk. ed. (978-0-7398-8528-4(6)) Steck-Vaughn.

—Big Box/Yum Yum Yum. 1999. (Take Me Home Ser.). (Illus.). (J). pap. (978-0-7398-2794-9(4)) Steck-Vaughn.

—Fire Racer/Jake's Fine Mess. 1999. (Take Me Home Ser.). (Illus.). (J). pap. (978-0-7398-2795-6(2)) Steck-Vaughn.

—The Pan Man. 1998. (Illus.). (J). pap. (978-0-8172-5626-5(1)) Steck-Vaughn.

—Phonics Readers Plus Aa. 1998. (Illus.). (J). pap. (978-0-8172-5600-5(8)) Steck-Vaughn.

—Phonics Readers Plus Bb. 1998. (Illus.). pap. (978-0-8172-5601-2(6)) Steck-Vaughn.

—Phonics Readers Plus Cc. 1998. (Illus.). pap. (978-0-8172-5602-9(4)) Steck-Vaughn.

—Phonics Readers Plus Dd. 1998. (Illus.). pap. (978-0-8172-5603-6(2)) Steck-Vaughn.

—Phonics Readers Plus Ee. 1998. (Illus.). pap. (978-0-8172-5604-3(0)) Steck-Vaughn.

—Phonics Readers Plus Ff. 1998. (Illus.). pap. (978-0-8172-5605-0(9)) Steck-Vaughn.

—Phonics Readers Plus Gg. 1998. (Illus.). pap. (978-0-8172-5606-7(7)) Steck-Vaughn.

—Phonics Readers Plus Hh. 1998. (Illus.). pap. (978-0-8172-5607-4(5)) Steck-Vaughn.

—Phonics Readers Plus Ii. 1998. (Illus.). pap. (978-0-8172-5608-1(3)) Steck-Vaughn.

—Phonics Readers Plus Jj. 1998. (Illus.). pap. (978-0-8172-5609-8(1)) Steck-Vaughn.

—Phonics Readers Plus Kk. 1998. (Illus.). pap. (978-0-8172-5610-4(5)) Steck-Vaughn.

—Phonics Readers Plus Ll. 1998. (Illus.). pap. (978-0-8172-5611-1(3)) Steck-Vaughn.

—Phonics Readers Plus Mm. 1998. (Illus.). pap. (978-0-8172-5612-8(1)) Steck-Vaughn.

—Phonics Readers Plus Nn. 1998. (Illus.). pap. (978-0-8172-5613-5(X)) Steck-Vaughn.

—Phonics Readers Plus Oo. 1998. (Illus.). pap. (978-0-8172-5614-2(8)) Steck-Vaughn.

—Phonics Readers Plus Pp. 1998. (Illus.). (J). pap. (978-0-8172-5615-9(6)) Steck-Vaughn.

—Phonics Readers Plus Qq. 1998. (Illus.). pap. (978-0-8172-5616-6(4)) Steck-Vaughn.

—Phonics Readers Plus Rr. 1998. (Illus.). pap. (978-0-8172-5617-3(2)) Steck-Vaughn.

—Phonics Readers Plus Ss. 1998. (Illus.). pap. (978-0-8172-5618-0(0)) Steck-Vaughn.

—Phonics Readers Plus Tt. 1998. (Illus.). pap. (978-0-8172-5619-7(9)) Steck-Vaughn.

—Phonics Readers Plus Uu. 1998. (Illus.). (J). pap. (978-0-8172-5620-3(2)) Steck-Vaughn.

—Phonics Readers Plus Vv. 1998. (Illus.). pap. (978-0-8172-5621-0(0)) Steck-Vaughn.

—Phonics Readers Plus Ww. 1998. (Illus.). pap. (978-0-8172-5622-7(9)) Steck-Vaughn.

—Phonics Readers Plus Yy. 1998. (Illus.). pap. (978-0-8172-5624-1(5)) Steck-Vaughn.

—Phonics Readers Plus Zz. 1998. (Illus.). pap. (978-0-8172-5625-8(3)) Steck-Vaughn.

Strother, Ruth. W Is for Woof: A Dog Alphabet. Frankenhuyzen, Gijsbert van, illus. 2008. (J). ***978-1-58536-343-8(X))** Sleeping Bear Pr.

Sunshine Tool Box: Alphabet Books. (gr. k-3). 73.50 (978-0-7802-4559-4(8)); 127.50 (978-0-7802-6760-2(5)) Wright Group, The.

Tabletop Pocket Chart Alphabet Photo Cards. 2004. (J). 8.95 (978-1-56911-199-4(5)) Learning Resources, Inc.

Tam on Sam: Consonants m, s, t; Short Vowel a; -am, -at word families: Level A, 6 vols. (Wright Skills Ser.). 12p. (gr. k-3). 17.95 (978-0-322-01445-9(X)) Wright Group, The.

Targo Publishing Staff. Alphabet 1 Travel Pad. 1999. (My Art Ser.). pap. 2.50 (978-1-894307-09-3(7)) Sterling Publishing.

Thornhill, Jan. The Wildlife ABC & 123: A Nature Alphabet & Counting Book. 2004. (Illus.). 64p. (J). 16.95 (978-1-897066-09-6(0)) Maple Tree Pr. CAN. *Dist:* Perseus Distribution.

Tobias, Tobi. A World of Words: An ABC of Quotations. Malone, Peter, illus. 1998. 48p. (J). (ps-3). 16.00 (978-0-688-12129-7(2)) HarperCollins Pubs.

Tobias, Tobi, ed. A World of Words: An ABC of Quotations. Malone, Peter, illus. 2004. 40p. (J). (gr. k-4). reprint ed. 16.00 (978-0-7567-8303-7(8)) DIANE Publishing Co.

Tobias, Tobi & Malone, Peter. A World of Words: An ABC of Quotations. 1998. (Illus.). 40p. (J). (ps-3). 15.89 (978-0-688-12130-3(6)) HarperCollins Pubs.

Todd, Traci. C Is for Caboose: Riding the Rails from A to Z. 2007. (Illus.). 40p. (J). (ps-3). 14.95 (978-0-8118-5643-0(7)) Chronicle Bks. LLC.

Top That Publishing Staff, ed. Magnetic Play & Learn ABC. 2005. (Illus.). 12p. (978-1-84510-727-7(6)) Top That! Publishing PLC.

Tropical ABC's. 2004. (J). 12.95 (978-0-9763907-0-1(1)) Ola's Hanalei LTD.

Tunes for June: Long Vowel u: Level B, 6 vols. (Wright Skills Ser.). 16p. (gr. k-3). 17.95 (978-0-322-01468-8(9)) Wright Group, The.

Turrell, Linda. Mastering Capitals Student Activities Book: Mastering Language Arts Series. Matthews, Douglas L., ed. 2003. (Illus.). stu. ed., wbk. ed. (978-1-931680-71-4(X) , Expert Systems for Teachers) Teaching Point, Inc.

Ulmer, Michael. H Is for Horse: An Eqestrian Alphabet. van-Frankenhuyze, Gijsbert, illus. rev. ed. 2004. 40p. (J). 17.95 (978-1-58536-213-4(1)) Sleeping Bear Pr.

Ulmer, Mike. M Is for Maple: A Canadian Alphabet. Rose, Melanie, illus. 2001. 40p. (J). (ps-3). 19.95 (978-1-58536-051-2(1)) Sleeping Bear Pr.

—M Is for Maple: A Canadian Alphabet. Rose-Popp, Melanie, illus. rev. ed. 2004. 48p. (J). pap. 10.95 (978-1-58536-235-6(2)) Sleeping Bear Pr.

Unidad 1 Superlibro: un dia con el ABC. 2001. (McGraw-Hill. Lectura Ser.). (ENG & SPA.). (gr. k up). (978-0-02-186023-4(8)) Macmillan/McGraw-Hill Schl. Div.

University Games Staff. I Have. 2007. 32p. (J). (978-1-57528-888-8(5)) University Games.

Vassar, Michael. Learning the Alphabet Can Be Easy A-Z. 2003. (Illus.). 27p. (J). (ps up). 12.95 (978-0-9741043-1-7(0)) Mike-Mike Distribution.

Vidrine, Beverly Barras. Halloween Alphabet. Lyne, Alison Davis, illus. 2004. 32p. (J). pap. 7.95 (978-1-58980-242-1(X)) Pelican Publishing Co., Inc.

Vitali, Daniela, illus. Play with My Animals ABCs. 2003. 16p. (J). bds. 5.99 (978-1-931722-34-6(X) , Sixth Avenue Bks.) Grand Central Publishing.

Walling, Sandy Seeley, illus. & text. ABC's at the Zoo! The Fun Way to Teach Your Child the Relationship between Upper Case & Lower Case Letters, Walling, Sandy Seeley, text. l.t. ed. 2004. 36p. (J). per. 7.95 (978-0-9741940-1-1(8)) Abernathy Hse. Publishing.

Ward, Allison, ed. Storytime from A to Z. 2005. 112p. 14.95 (978-1-56234-639-3(3) , Mailbox Bks., The) Education Ctr., Inc.

Wargin, Kathy-Jo. B Is for Badger: A Wisconsin Alphabet. Graef, Renee, illus. 2004. 40p. (J). 17.95 (978-1-58536-135-9(6)) Sleeping Bear Pr.

—L Is for Lincoln: An Illinois Alphabet. van Frankenhuyzen, Gijsbert, illus. 40p. (J). 2004. pap. 7.95 (978-1-58536-250-9(6)); 2000. 16.95 (978-1-58536-016-1(3)) Sleeping Bear Pr.

—M Is for Melody: A Music Alphabet. Larson, Katherine, illus. 2004. 40p. (J). 16.95 (978-1-58536-215-8(8)) Sleeping Bear Pr.

Weber, Lou, ed. Fisher Price ABC Stencil Fun. 2005. (Illus.). 22p. (J). spiral bd., bds. 10.98 (978-1-4127-3448-6(7) , 7247900) Publications International, Ltd.

—Sesame Street 123 Learning Cards. 2005. 26p. (J). 10.98 (978-1-4127-3198-0(4) , 7235000) Publications International, Ltd.

—Sesame Street ABC Learning Cards. 2005. 26p. (J). 10.98 (978-1-4127-3197-3(6) , 7235100) Publications International, Ltd.

Wells, Rosemary. Letters & Sounds, Bk. 1. Wells, Rosemary, illus. 2001. (Get Set for Kindergarten Ser.). (Illus.). 24p. (J). (ps-3). pap. 5.99 (978-0-14-056805-9(0) , Puffin) Penguin Group (USA) Inc.

Welykochy, Dawn. C Is for Chinook: An Alberta Alphabet. Bennett, Lorna, illus. rev. ed. 2004. (Province Ser.). 40p. (J). 17.95 (978-1-58536-223-3(9)) Sleeping Bear Pr.

What Is That? 2002. (Interactive Book of Words). (J). 14.95 (978-1-74047-201-2(2)) Book Co. Publishing Pty, Ltd., The AUS. *Dist:* Penton Overseas, Inc.

When Tilly Turtle Came to Tea. 2001. (ps-2). lib. bdg. 9.80 (978-0-613-33239-2(3)) Tandem Library Bks.

Whitehouse, Patricia. Food ABC. 2002. 24p. (J). (ps-1). pap. 5.25 (978-1-58810-748-0(5) , 91416); (Illus.). lib. bdg. 18.50 (978-1-58810-540-0(7)) Heinemann Library.

—Plant ABC. 2002. (Plants Ser.). (Illus.). 24p. (J). (ps-1). pap. 5.25 (978-1-58810-733-6(7) , 91405); lib. bdg. 17.08 (978-1-58810-522-6(9)) Heinemann Library.

—Seasons A B C. 2002. (Seasons Ser.). (Illus.). 24p. (J). pap. 5.25 (978-1-4034-0539-5(5)) Heinemann Library.

—Seasons ABC. 2003. (Seasons Ser.). (Illus.). 24p. (J). (ps-1). lib. bdg. 17.08 (978-1-58810-895-1(3)) Heinemann Library.

—What's Awake ABC. 2003. (Heinemann Read & Learn Ser.). 24p. (ps-1). (Illus.). (J), lib. bdg. 17.08 (978-1-58810-884-5(8)); pap. 5.25 (978-1-4034-0632-3(4)) Heinemann Library.

—What's Awake ABC. 2002. (ps-2). lib. bdg. 13.30 (978-0-613-89120-2(1)) Tandem Library Bks.

Whitney, Gleaves & Whitney, Louise. B Is for Buckaroo: A Cowboy Alphabet. Guy, Sue, illus. rev. ed. 2003. 40p. (J). 17.95 (978-1-58536-139-7(9)) Sleeping Bear Pr.

Whitney, Louise Doak. C Is for Centennial: A Colorado Alphabet. Urban, Helle, illus. 2002. 40p. (J). 17.95 (978-1-58536-058-1(9)) Sleeping Bear Pr.

Wildsmith, Rebecca. The Alphabet Chest: A Collection of 26 Three-Dimensional Surprises! Wildsmith, Rebecca, illus. 1998. (Illus.). (J). (ps-3). 19.95 (978-1-888443-83-7(9) , Intervisual/Piggy Toes) Dalmatian Pr.

Wimbrey, Crystal M. Alphascripts: The ABCs of the Bible. Mozley, Peggy, illus. 2007. (J). 14.95 ***978-1-933285-63-4(X))** Brown Bks. Publishing Group.

Wolf, Jackie. Campbell's Alphabet Soup Book. 2002. (Illus.). 10p. (J). bds. 5.99 (978-1-57151-639-8(5)) Playhouse Publishing.

Wood, Audrey. Alphabet Adventure. Wood, Audrey, illus. 2002. (Illus.). (J). 25.06 (978-0-7587-8819-1(3)) Book Wholesalers, Inc.

—Alphabet Adventure. Wood, Bruce Robert, illus. 2001. 40p. (J). (ps-1). pap. 15.95 (978-0-439-08069-9(X) , Blue Sky Pr., The) Scholastic, Inc.

Worm's Wagon. 2001. (ps-2). lib. bdg. 9.80 (978-0-613-33267-5(9)) Tandem Library Bks.

The Wright Skills: Level B Sets - Long vowels only: 1 Each of 6 Titles. (gr. k-3). 17.95 (978-0-322-01934-8(6)) Wright Group, The.

The Wright Skills: Level B Sets - Long vowels only: 6 Each of 6 Titles. (gr. k-3). 109.50 (978-0-322-01935-5(4)) Wright Group, The.

The Wright Skills: Level C Sets - 1 Each of 16 Titles. (gr. k-3). 69.95 (978-0-322-00734-5(8)) Wright Group, The.

The Wright Skills: Level C Sets - 6 Each of 16 Titles. (gr. k-3). 322.95 (978-0-322-00813-7(1)) Wright Group, The.

Xylophone for X-Ray Fish. 2001. (ps-2). lib. bdg. 9.80 (978-0-613-33269-9(5)) Tandem Library Bks.

Yak Who Yelled Yuck. 2001. (ps-2). lib. bdg. 9.80 (978-0-613-33271-2(7)) Tandem Library Bks.

Young, Judy. S Is for Show Me: A Missouri Alphabet. Young, Ross B., illus. 2004. 40p. (J). pap. 7.95 (978-1-58536-248-6(4)) Sleeping Bear Pr.

—S Is for Show Me: A Missouri Alphabet. Young, Ross, illus. 2001. 40p. (J). 17.95 (978-1-58536-026-0(0)) Sleeping Bear Pr.

YoYo Books. ABC: Mini Baby's First Library. 2005. 42p. bds. 4.95 (978-90-5843-806-5(6)) YoYo Bks. BEL. *Dist:* National Bk. Network.

Zack the Lazy Zebra. 2001. (ps-2). lib. bdg. 9.80 (978-0-613-33280-4(6)) Tandem Library Bks.

1st & 2nd Grade Excelerator, 2 CDs. 2002. cd-rom 9.99 (978-1-59150-012-4(5)) TOPICS Entertainment.

ALPHABET BOOKS

Here are entered A B C books.

A+ Books - Alphabet: Birds A to Z; Bugs A to Z; My ABCs, 3 bks. 2000. (A+ Alphabet Books). (Illus.). (J). (ps-2). lib. bdg. 63.78 (978-0-7368-7046-7(6) , Pebble Bks.) Capstone Pr., Inc.

ABC: Fun to Learn. 1999. (Illus.). 32p. (ps-2). 1.99 (978-1-58279-007-7(8) , 94) Trident Pr. International.

ABC AnyBody Can: The Geeatest Alphabet Book in the World. 2002. 14.95 (978-0-9717570-0-4(3)) Parents Choice Pr.

ABC Atlantic City: An Alphabet Book, Travel Guide & Souvenir for Kids! 2006. (J). 8.95 (978-0-9760047-1-4(2)) Rosenberger, Matthew.

ABC Book: Interactive Playbook. 1998. (Illus.). 10p. (J). (ps-6). 19.99 (978-1-890647-06-3(3)) RC2 Corp.

ABC Learning Wall Chart. 2004. (Wall Charts Ser.). (J). 4.99 (978-1-85997-302-8(7)) Byeway Bks.

ABC Order (Gr. 1-2) 2003. (J). (978-1-58232-041-0(1)) Bryan Hse. Pubs., Inc.

ABCs. 2002. (Puppy Steps Ser.). (Illus.). 10p. (J). (ps-1). bds. 3.99 (978-1-57759-660-8(9)) Dalmatian Pr.

El Abecedario. 2007. (Sesame Street Ser.). (SPA & ENG.). 50p. (J). 2.95 ***978-1-59545-062-3(9))** Learning Horizons, Inc.

Aboff, Marcie. Guatemala ABCs: A Book about the People & Places of Guatemala. Trover, Zachary, illus. 2006. (Country ABCs Ser.). 32p. (J). (gr. k-5). 23.93 (978-1-4048-1570-4(8)) Picture Window Bks.

—India ABCs: A Book about the People & Places of India. Moore, Frances, illus. 2006. (Country ABCs Ser.). 32p. (J). (gr. k-5). 23.93 (978-1-4048-1571-1(6)) Picture Window Bks.

Abrams, Harry N. Campbell Kids Alphabet Soup: An ABC Book. 2004. (Illus.). 40p. (J). (ps-1). 10.95 (978-0-8109-5041-2(3)) Abrams, Harry N., Inc.

Abrams, Pam. Now I Eat My ABCs. Wolf, Bruce, illus. 2004. 14p. (J). (ps up). bds. 7.99 (978-0-439-64942-1(0) , Cartwheel Bks.) Scholastic, Inc.

Adventures of Abby Alligator. 2001. (ps-2). lib. bdg. 9.80 (978-0-613-32244-7(4)) Tandem Library Bks.

Agbabian, Alidz. Ayp for Soup: A Bilingual Armenian Alphabet Book. Sarkissian, Anahid, illus. 2000. (ARM, ENG & FRE.). 56p. (J). (gr. 2). pap. 15.00 (978-0-9655507-4-1(5)) Dziludzar.

Agee, Jon. Z Goes Home. 2003. (Illus.). 32p. (J). (ps-17). (978-0-7868-1987-4(1)) Hyperion Bks. for Children.

Aigner-Clark, Julie. Alphabooks, 26 vols. Zaidi, Nadeem, illus. 2005. (Baby Einstein Ser.). 156p. (ps-17). 14.99 (978-0-7868-1907-2(3)) Disney Pr.

Akmon, Nancy C. & Akmon, Roni, eds. Christmas ABC: Story/Stickerbook. 1999. (Illus.). 28p. (J). 10.95 (978-1-884807-42-8(9) , EC742) Blushing Rose Publishing.

Albers, Everett C. Lewis & Clark Animal ABC Book: As Told By Seaman the Dog. Eslinger, Kimberly, illus. l.t. ed. 2001. 32p. (J). pap. 3.95 (978-0-9674002-3-5(6)) United Printing.

Alberti, Theresa Jarosz. Vietnam ABCs: A Book about the People & Places of Vietnam. Blanks, Natascha Alex, illus. 2006. (Country ABCs Ser.). 32p. (J). (gr. k-5). lib. bdg. 25.26 (978-1-4048-2251-1(8)) Picture Window Bks.

Alda, Arlene. Arlene Alda's A B C. 2004. (Illus.). 32p. (J). 6.95 (978-1-58246-073-4(6) , Tricycle Pr.) Ten Speed Pr.

Alfavitario: A Greek Alphabet Book for Children. 2006. (Illus.). 114p. 15.00 (978-960-86960-2-0(X)) American Schl. of Classical Studies at Athens.

Allen, Margaret. The ABC Bags (Double F, I & S), Bk. 8. Kupperstein, Joel, ed. Jarrett, Michael, photos by. 1999. (Dr. Maggie's Phonics Readers Ser.). (Illus.). 15p. (J). (gr. k-3). pap., stu. ed. 2.99 (978-1-57471-583-5(6) , 2908) Creative Teaching Pr., Inc.

Allen, Susan & Lindaman, Jane. Read Anything Good Lately? Enright, Vicky, illus. 2006. 32p. (J). (gr. k-2). pap. 6.95 (978-0-8225-6470-6(X) , First Avenue Editions) Lerner Publishing Group.

Allio, Mark R. R Is for Rhode Island Red: A Rhode Island Alphabet. Begin, Mary Jane, illus. 2005. (Discover America State by State Ser.). 40p. (J). (gr. k-5). 17.95 (978-1-58536-149-6(6)) Sleeping Bear Pr.

Allred, Sylvester. The ForestAlphabet: Encyclopedia. Iverson, Diane, illus. unabr. ed. 2005. (Naturencyclopedia Ser.). 48p. (J). pap. 24.95 (978-0-88045-155-0(6)) Stemmer Hse. Pubs., Inc.

Aloha Bear's ABC Workbook. 2000. (J). 5.99 (978-0-89610-432-7(X)) Island Heritage Publishing.

Alpers, Jody. T Is for Tortilla: A Southwestern Alphabet Book. Johnson, Celeste, illus. 2005. (J). ***978-1-929115-14-3(8))** Azro Pr., Inc.

Alpha Touch Letters: Cursive. 1999. (gr. 2-4). 45.83 (978-0-673-28563-8(4) , Scott Foresman) Addison-Wesley Educational Pubs., Inc.

Alpha Touch Letters: Manuscript. 1999. (gr. 1-3). 45.83 (978-0-673-28562-1(6) , Scott Foresman) Addison-Wesley Educational Pubs., Inc.

Alphabet. (Active Minds(R) Ser.). (J). 22p. spiral bd., bds. (978-0-7853-8610-0(6) , 7188200); 12p. bds. (978-1-4127-0538-7(X) , 3970601) Publications International, Ltd.

Alphabet. 2004. (In Celebration Coloring & Activity Book Ser.). 32p. (J). pap. 1.99 (978-0-7647-1020-9(6) , In Celebration) Schaffer, Frank Pubns.

Alphabet & Phonemic Awareness Activity Cards (OCR) 2004. (J). 14.95 (978-1-56911-192-5(8)) Learning Resources, Inc.

Alphabet Animals. 2002. (Home Workbooks Ser.). 64p. pap. 2.49 (978-0-88724-711-8(3) , CD-4513) Carson-Dellosa Publishing Co., Inc.

Alphabet Blackline Projects. 2005. 83p. (J). spiral bd. 14.99 (978-1-59441-468-8(8) , K04019) Carson-Dellosa Publishing Co., Inc.

Alphabet Book. 2006. (YA). per. (978-1-59872-350-2(2)) Instantpublisher.com.

Alphabet Book Classroom Library Set. 2004. (J). pap. 139.95 (978-1-56911-190-1(1)) Learning Resources, Inc.

Alphabet Books. 2005. (Illus.). (J). (gr. k-1). lib. bdg. 429.40 (978-0-7368-3672-2(1)) Capstone Pr., Inc.

Alphabet Books. 2005. (J). (978-1-59564-988-1(3)) Steps To Literacy, LLC.

Alphabet Books, 3 bks. Incl. ABC under the Sea : An Ocean Life Alphabet Book. Knox, Barbara. 32p. 2003. lib. bdg. 22.60 (978-0-7368-1684-7(4)); African Animals ABC : An Alphabet Safari. Schuette, Sarah L. 17p. 2003. 22.60 (978-0-7368-1679-3(8)); Alphabet Salad : Fruits & Vegetables from A to Z. Schuette, Sarah L. 17p. 2003. 22.60 (978-0-7368-1683-0(6)); Animal Babies ABC : An Alphabet of Animal Offspring. Knox, Barbara. 17p. 2003. 22.60 (978-0-7368-1680-9(1)); Birds A to Z. DeGezelle, Terri. 17p. 2000. 22.60 (978-0-7368-7038-2(5)); Bugs A to Z. DeGezelle, Terri, contrib. by. 32p. 2000. lib. bdg. 22.60 (978-0-7368-7036-8(9)); My ABC's. Curry, Don L. 17p. 2000. 22.60 (978-0-7368-7040-5(7)); (J). (gr. k-1). (Illus.). 2002. Set lib. bdg. 158.20 (978-0-7368-1682-3(8) , Aplus Bks.) Capstone Pr., Inc.

Alphabet Booster. 2005. (J). per. 0.00 (978-1-59441-504-3(8) , C04036) Carson-Dellosa Publishing Co., Inc.

Alphabet Day. 2000. (Pooh Learning Ser.). (J). (ps-3). pap. 6.98 incl. audio (978-0-7634-0472-7(1)) Walt Disney Records.

Alphabet Dot-to-Dot. 2001. (Illus.). 32p. (J). pap. 1.59 (978-1-55254-230-9(0)) Brighter Vision Pubns.

Alphabet Dot-to-Dot. 2004. (Play & Learn Pads Ser.). 48p. (J). 3.99 (978-1-85997-717-0(0)) Byeway Bks.

Alphabet Fun Kit. 2006. (J). pap. ***978-1-57332-389-5(6))** HighReach Learning, Inc.

Alphabet (Gr. K-1) 2003. (J). (978-1-58232-029-8(2)) Bryan Hse. Pubs., Inc.

Alphabet Recognition (Gr. K-1) 2003. (J). (978-1-58232-036-6(5)) Bryan Hse. Pubs., Inc.

Alphabet Sorting Box. (ps-12). 22.40 (978-0-7362-1095-9(4)) Hampton-Brown Bks.

Alphabet Sounds & Pictures. 2002. (Home Workbooks Ser.). 64p. pap. 2.49 (978-0-88724-712-5(1) , CD-4514) Carson-Dellosa Publishing Co., Inc.

Alphasnaps & Snapphonics: Snapphonics Big Book: The Big & Little Alphabet Book. 2003. 46.95 (978-0-673-60205-3(2)) Celebration Pr.

Altema, Ginette B. Children of the Future Alphabet Book. 2000. (Illus.). 26p. (J). (ps-1). pap. 8.99 (978-1-928540-00-7(7)) Smart Kids of the Future Publishing.

Alvarez, Juan. Jose Rabbit's Southwest Adventures: An ABC Coloring Book with Spanish Words. Alvarez, Juan, illus. 2004. (Illus.). 32p. (Orig.). (ps-3). pap. 3.95 (978-1-878610-00-3(7)) Red Crane Bks., Inc.

American Education Publishing Staff. Alphabet. 2000. (Beginners Bible Ser.). (J). pap., wbk. ed. 14.95 (978-1-56189-617-2(9) , American Education Publishing) School Specialty Publishing.

American Education Publishing Staff & Douglas, Vincent. The Alphabet: Kindergarten. 2001. (Illus.). 32p. (C). pap. 2.99 (978-1-56189-624-0(1) , 31320-324, American Education Publishing) School Specialty Publishing.

Amery, H. & Cartwright, S. Alphabet Lotto. 2004. (Encyclopedia of World Religions Ser.). (Illus.). (J). 12.95 (978-0-7945-0314-7(4) , Usborne) EDC Publishing.

Amft, Robert. Peter's ABC Book: Peter Learns about Animals, Birds, Fishes, & Insects. 2006. (Illus.). 56p. pap. 12.00 (978-0-945323-08-2(5)) WhiteWalls, Inc.

Anders, Isabel. Easter ABCs. Rasche, Shelly, illus. 2004. (ENG.). 32p. (J). tchr. ed. 7.99 (978-0-570-07020-7(1) , 56-2040) Concordia Publishing Hse.

Anderson, Rodney P. The Invisible ABCs: Exploring the World of Microbes. 2006. (Illus.). 64p. (J). 19.95 (978-1-55581-386-4(0)) ASM Pr.

Andreae, Giles. K Is for Kissing a Cool Kangaroo. Parker-Rees, Guy, illus. 2003. 32p. (J). pap. 15.95 (978-0-439-53126-9(8) , Orchard Bks.) Scholastic, Inc.

Animal ABCs. 2003. (Wipe-Off Activity Bks.). 16p. (J). (gr. 2). 3.79 (978-1-58792-047-9(6)) Trend Enterprises, Inc.

Animal Alphabet. (J). pap. 6.95 incl. audio (978-0-86545-096-7(X)) Spizzirri Pr., Inc.

Anjou, Colette. Olga's Cats: An ABC Book. Linville, S. Olga, illus. 2005. 28p. (J). (ps-3). per. 15.95 (978-0-9748933-5-8(8)) E & E Publishing.

Appleford, Annie. M Is for Mitten: A Michigan Alphabet. Monroe, Michael G., illus. 1999. 40p. (J). (ps-3). 16.95 (978-1-886947-73-3(2)) Sleeping Bear Pr.

Archambault, John & Martin, Bill, Jr. Chicka Chicka ABC: Board Book & Rattle. Ehlert, Lois, illus. 2005. 16p. (J). bds. 9.99 (978-0-689-87820-6(6) , Little Simon) Simon & Schuster Children's Publishing.

Arcure, Suzanne. Little Angels. 2002. 36p. pap. 9.95 (978-0-7414-0791-7(4)) Infinity Publishing.

Armstrong, Moses K. Orthodox Christian Alphabet Coloring Book. Date not set. 35p. (J). (gr. k-3). pap. 5.00 (978-1-879038-45-5(5) , 9013) Synaxis Pr.

Artell, Mike. Awesome Alphabets. 2nd ed. 2004. 88p. pap. (978-1-59647-030-9(5)) Good Year Bks.

Astroword: Module 11-r-Controlled Vowels (1-3) 2003. 158.95 net. (978-0-7652-0832-3(6)) Modern Curriculum Pr.

Atkins, Tonya Smith. The ABC's of Clemson: (For Tigers of All Ages!) Lowe, Todd, illus. 2001. (Collegiate ABC Bks.). 32p. (J). (gr. k-8). lib. bdg. 18.95 (978-1-885354-96-9(7)) Honoribus Pr., The.

Avenues PreK Level: Plastic Magnetic Letters. (ps-12). 28.38 (978-0-7362-0344-9(3)) Hampton-Brown Bks.

Awdry, Wilbert V. Thomas & Friends ABC Wipe-Off Sound Activity Book. 2002. (Illus.). 16p. (J). spiral bd., bds. 12.98 (978-0-7853-6397-2(1) , 7160400) Publications International, Ltd.

Aylesworth, Jim. Old Black Fly. 2002. (Illus.). (J). 15.49 (978-0-7587-3302-3(X)) Book Wholesalers, Inc.

Azarian, Mary. A Farmer's Alphabet. (Illus.). (J). (ps-1). pap. 14.95 (978-0-9673268-8-7(5)) Learning Fasten-Ations, Inc.

Bagley, Val. My Gospel ABCs. 2004. 9.95 (978-1-57734-669-2(6)); cd-rom 5.98 (978-1-57734-762-0(5)) Covenant Communications, Inc.

Bahan, Ben & Dannis, Joe. My ABC Signs of Animal Friends. Pearson, Patricia, illus. 2003. 32p. (J). pap. 8.95 (978-0-915035-31-1(6) , 4201) DawnSignPress.

Bailer, Darice. ABC Animals: A Bedtime Story. Moffatt, Judith, illus. 2005. 60p. (J). 10.95 (978-0-689-86729-3(8) , Little Simon) Simon & Schuster Children's Publishing.

Baker, Alan. Black & White Rabbit's ABC. Baker, Alan, illus. 2002. (Illus.). (J). 11.87 (978-0-7587-4101-1(4)) Book Wholesalers, Inc.

—Black & White Rabbit's ABC. 1999. (Little Rabbit Bks.). (Illus.). 24p. (J). (gr. k-ps). 4.95 (978-0-7534-5253-0(7) , Kingfisher) Houghton Mifflin Co. Trade & Reference Div.

Ballard, Peg. Chad Checks: The Sound of CH. 1999. (Wonder Books Phonics: Consonant Digraphs Ser.). (Illus.). 24p. (J). (ps-3). 21.36 (978-1-56766-727-1(9)) Child's World, Inc.

Bar-El, Dan. Alphabetter. Ross, Graham, illus. 2006. 32p. 17.95 (978-1-55143-439-1(3)) Orca Bk. Pubs. USA.

Barbaresi, Nina. The Little Animal ABC Coloring Book. 80th ed. 1998. (Stickers Ser.). (Illus.). 64p. (J). (ps-2). pap. 1.50 (978-0-486-25834-8(3)) Dover Pubns., Inc.

—Spanish Alphabet Coloring Book. 1998. (Illus.). 32p. (J). (gr. k-3). pap. 3.95 (978-0-486-27249-8(4)) Dover Pubns., Inc.

Barber, Shirley, illus. The Fairies Alphabet Puzzle Tray: With Five 6-Piece Jigsaw Puzzles. 2004. 10p. (J). (978-1-74124-437-3(4)) Five Mile Pr. Pty Ltd. The.

Barker, Cicely Mary. Flower Fairies Library: A Flower Fairy Alphabet. 2007. 16.99 (***978-0-7232-5975-6(5)***) Penguin Group (USA) Inc.

Barnes, Cheryl Shaw, et al. Washington, DC, ABCs: An Alphabet Book about Our Nations Capital. Golembe, Carla, illus. 2001. 32p. (J). (978-1-893622-06-7(1) , VSP Bks.) Vacation Spot Publishing.

Batson, Mary. Mary's Alphabet Garden. Batson, Mary, illus. 2001. (Illus.). 56p. (J). (ps-2). pap. 10.95 (978-0-9702880-0-4(X)) Sun R.A.Y.S., LLC.

Bauer, Christina. The ABCs of Hidden Heroines. 2007. 280p. (J). 16.99 (978-1-59092-367-2(7) , Orchard Academy Pr.) Windstorm Creative.

Beall, Pamela Conn & Nipp, Susan Hagen. Wee Sing & Learn ABC. 2005. (Wee Sing & Learn Ser.). 20p. (J). (ps). 9.99 (978-0-8431-1661-8(7) , Price Stern Sloan) Penguin Group (USA) Inc.

—Wee Sing & Learn ABC. Pongmee, Yudthana, illus. 2001. (Reading Railroad Bks.). 32p. (J). (ps-k). pap. 3.49 (978-0-448-42590-0(4) , Grosset & Dunlap) Penguin Group (USA) Inc.

Bean, Eric. The ABC's of Parade. Senesi, Susan, illus. 2000. 32p. (YA). (ps up). pap. 10.00 (978-1-56167-509-8(1)) American Literary Pr.

Beccia, Carlyn. Who Put the "B" in Ballyhoo? The Most Amazing, Bizarre, & Celebrated Circus Performers. 2007. (Illus.). 32p. (J). (ps-k). 16.00 (978-0-618-71718-7(8)) Houghton Mifflin Co. Trade & Reference Div.

Beccia, Carlyn. Who Put the B in the Ballyhoo? 2007. (Illus.). (J). (***978-1-4287-3570-5(4)***) Houghton Mifflin Co.

Behrens, Janice. Let's Make Letters: ABC Kids. 2007. (Let's Find Out Early Learning Bks.). (Illus.). 32p. (J). (ps-k). 18.00 (***978-0-531-14867-9(X)*** , Children's Pr.) Scholastic Library Publishing.

Bennett, Andrea T. & Kessler, James H. Apples, Bubbles, & Crystals: Your Science ABCs. Sarecky, Melody, illus. 2004. (J). (978-0-8412-3944-9(4)) American Chemical Society.

Berger, Samantha. Fifi Ferret's Flute: Letter F. 2001. (Illus.). 16p. (ps-1). pap. 2.25 (978-0-439-16529-7(6)) Scholastic, Inc.

—Hide-and-Seek Hippo: Letter H. 2001. (Alpha Tales Ser.). (Illus.). 16p. (ps-1). pap. 2.25 (978-0-439-16531-0(8)) Scholastic, Inc.

—Worm's Wagon: Letter W. 2001. (Alpha Tales Ser.). (Illus.). 16p. (ps-1). pap. 2.25 (978-0-439-16546-4(6)) Scholastic, Inc.

Bernthal, Mark S. & Scholastic, Inc. Staff. Barney's ABC Animals! Baker, Darrell, illus. 1999. (Barney Ser.). 32p. (J). (ps-k). pap. 3.50 (978-1-57064-453-5(5)) Scholastic, Inc.

Bess Press Staff, creator. From Aloha to Zippy's: A Keiki Alphabet Book. 2007. (Illus.). 32p. (J). pap. 14.95 (***978-1-57306-255-8(3)***) Bess Pr., Inc.

Bianchi, Mike & Novak, Marisol. Gator Alphabet ABC. Marlette, Andy, illus. 2004. 32p. (J). (ps-k). 6.95 (978-1-58261-403-8(2)) Sports Publishing, LLC.

Biskup, Agnieszka. Awesome Animals ABC. Brooks, David, illus. 2005. (J). (978-1-58987-095-6(6)) Kindermusik International.

Blackstone, Stella. Alligator Alphabet. Bauer, Stephanie, illus. 2005. 48p. (J). (ps-k). 16.99 (978-1-84148-494-5(6)) Barefoot Bks., Inc.

—Cleo's Alphabet Book. Mockford, Caroline, illus. 32p. (J). 2004. pap. 5.99 (978-1-84148-165-4(3)); 2003. 15.99 (978-1-84148-008-4(8)) Barefoot Bks., Inc.

Blood, Danielle, ed. Around the World Cursive Alphabet Set: 26 Ready-to-Display Letter Cards with Fabulous Photos of Extraordinary Natural Wonders, Ancient Sites, Architecture, & More. 2006. pap. 9.99 (978-0-439-54257-9(X) , Teaching Resources) Scholastic, Inc.

Blue Lantern Studio, creator. The Green Tiger's Illustrated ABC. 2006. (Illus.). 72p. (J). (ps-3). 24.95 (978-1-59583-041-8(3) , Green Tiger Pr.) Laughing Elephant.

Bodleian Library & F. Warne and Co. Staff. Father Christmas ABC. 2005. (Illus.). 24p. 11.99 (978-1-85124-325-9(9)) Bodleian Library GBR. *Dist:* Chicago Distribution Ctr.

Bond, Mary. T Is for Twins: An ABC Book. 2002. (Illus.). 32p. (J). (ps-1). 15.95 (978-1-887137-34-8(3)) Source Bk. Pubns.

Bond, Susan. Ride with Me Through ABC. Lemke, Horst, illus. 32p. (J). (ps). 14.95 (978-0-87592-043-6(8)) Scroll Pr., Inc.

Bowen, Betsy. Antler, Bear, Canoe: A Northwoods Alphabet. Bowen, Betsy, illus. 2002. (Illus.). 40p. (J). (gr. k-3). 6.95 (978-0-618-22638-2(9)); tchr. ed. 16.00 (978-0-618-20864-7(X)) Houghton Mifflin Co. Trade & Reference Div.

—Antler, Bear, Canoe: A Northwoods Alphabet Year. 2002. (gr. k-3). lib. bdg. 14.10 (978-0-613-89005-2(1)) Tandem Library Bks.

Bowman-Kruhm, Mary. N Is for New York. Harris, Phyllis, illus. 2001. (Alpha Flight Books Ser.). 60p. (J). (ps-3). 17.95 (978-1-892920-44-7(1)) GHB Publishers, LLC.

Brainy Baby Quad Book. 2005. (Brainy Baby Ser.). 40p. (J). bds. 10.39 (978-1-59394-240-3(0)) Bendon Publishing International.

Branson, Dave. The Monster Encyclopedia. Bartimole, Tom, illus. 1998. 40p. (J). (gr. k-3). 16.95 (978-1-880851-35-7(0)) Greene Bark Pr., Inc.

Bratcher, Jeryl L. A-b-c bible Book. 2006. (ENG.). 32p. per. 15.99 (***978-1-4208-8505-7(7)***) AuthorHouse.

Braybrooks, Ann. Mickey's ABC. 2005. 32p. (J). (978-0-7868-3088-6(3)) Disney Pr.

Breaking the Code Cursive Alphabet. (J). pap. (978-0-87548-954-4(0) , 8512) Open Court Publishing Co.

Briggs-Ward, Barbara. Snarly Sally's Garden of ABC. (Illus.). 32p. 14.95 (978-1-890621-30-8(7)) Landauer Corp.

Brighter Vision Publishing Staff. Alphabet - Pre-K. 2000. (Primary Skills Ser.). (Illus.). (J). (ps-3). pap. 2.25 (978-1-55254-174-6(6)) Brighter Vision Pubns.

—Alphabet Activities Activity Book. 2000. (Illus.). 32p. (J). pap. 1.39 (978-1-55254-151-7(7)) Brighter Vision Pubns.

—Wipe Away Halloween-Alpha. 2000. (Illus.). (J). (ps-3). pap. 2.95 (978-1-55254-183-8(5)) Brighter Vision Pubns.

Bringhurst, Nancy J. A Is for Alligator. Stark, Mindy C., illus. 2004. 32p. (J). 17.95 (978-1-883991-96-8(X)) White Cloud Pr.

Bronson, Linda. The Circus Alphabet. rev. ed. 2001. (Illus.). 40p. (J). (ps-1). 15.95 (978-0-8050-6294-6(7) , Holt, Henry & Co. Bks. For Young Readers) Holt, Henry & Co.

Brown. Sleepy ABC. Date not set. 32p. (J). (ps-2). pap. 4.99 (978-0-06-443370-9(6)) HarperCollins Pubs.

Brown, Robert S. & Carey, Susan. My Alphabet Letter Books, Aa to Zz. 2000. (Illus.). 160p. (J). (ps-3). pap., stu. ed. 3.95 (978-0-13-014808-7(3)) Prentice Hall PTR.

Browning, Kurt. A Is for Axel: An Ice Skating Alphabet. Rose, Melanie, illus. rev. ed. 2006. 40p. (J). 17.95 (978-1-58536-280-6(8)) Sleeping Bear Pr.

Bruchac, Joseph. Many Nations. Goetzl, Robert F., illus. 2004. 32p. (J). pap. 5.99 (978-0-439-63590-5(X)) Scholastic, Inc.

—Many Nations: An Alphabet of Native America. Goetzl, Robert F., illus. 2004. 32p. (J). (ps-ps). lib. bdg. 12.79 (978-0-606-30986-8(1)) Tandem Library Bks.

Bruel, Nick. Bad Kitty. Bruel, Nick, illus. 2005. (Illus.). 40p. (J). (ps-3). 15.95 (978-1-59643-069-3(9)) Roaring Brook Pr.

Bruel, Nick. Poor Puppy. 2007. (Illus.). 40p. (J). (ps up). 16.95 (***978-1-59643-270-3(5)***) Roaring Brook Pr.

Bryan-Hunt, Jan, illus. A Is for Angel: A Christmas Alphabet & Activity Book. 2005. 32p. pap., act. bk. ed. 10.99 (978-0-8066-5121-7(0)) Augsburg Fortress, Pubs.

Bullard, Lisa. Not Enough Beds. Oeltjenbruns, Joni, illus. 2004. (Carolrhoda Picture Books Ser.). 32p. (J). (ps-3). pap. 6.95 (978-1-57505-797-2(2)) Lerner Publishing Group.

—Not Enough Beds! A Christmas Alphabet Book. Oeltjenbruns, Joni, illus. 2004. (Picture Bks.). 32p. (J). (ps-3). 15.95 (978-1-57505-356-1(X) , Carolrhoda Bks.) Lerner Publishing Group.

—Not Enough Beds: A Christmas Alphabet Book. Oeltjenbruns, Joni, illus. 2004. 26p. (J). (ps-ps). lib. bdg. 13.75 (978-0-606-30541-9(6)) Tandem Library Bks.

Bulloch, Ivan & James, Diane. Learn with Me ABC. Pangbourne, Daniel, photos by. 2007. (J). pap. (***978-1-58728-599-8(1)*** , Two Can Publishing) T&N Children's Publishing.

Bunnell, Deb T. My First French ABC Picture Coloring Book. 2000. (FRE & ENG., Illus.). 32p. (J). pap. 3.50 (978-0-486-41039-5(0)) Dover Pubns., Inc.

—My First Spanish ABC Picture Coloring Book. 1998. (Illus.). 32p. (J). (gr. k-5). pap. 2.95 (978-0-486-40358-8(0)) Dover Pubns., Inc.

Bunting, Eve. Girls A to Z. Bloom, Suzanne, illus. 2003. 32p. (J). (gr. k-2). 15.95 (978-1-56397-147-1(X)) Boyds Mills Pr.

Bunting, Jane. My First ABC. (Illus.). (J). (ps). pap. 15.95 (978-0-590-24127-4(3)) Scholastic, Inc.

Burch, Marilyn Myers, et al. A B C Stationery. 2003. 32p. pap. 8.95 (978-0-439-51754-6(0) , Teaching Resources) Scholastic, Inc.

Burkhalter, Mary L. Active Children's Literature: Alphabet Story, Colors, Mister Prince. 1998. (Illus.). 50p. (J). (gr. k-4). pap. 20.00 (978-0-934284-09-7(1)) Jolean Publishing Co.

Burningham, John. Letters. Burningham, John, illus. 2003. (Illus.). 24p. (J). (ps-k). bds. 5.99 (978-0-7636-2046-2(7)) Candlewick Pr.

Burris, Andrea M. & Schad, Anna M. A Dog Lover's Alphabet Book. Burris, Andrea M., illus. 2007. 32p. (J). 14.95 (***978-0-9743294-1-3(X)***) A & D Bks.

Burris, Andrea M. & Schad, Anna M. The Kitty Cat Alphabet Book. Burris, Andrea M., illus. 2004. (Illus.). 33p. (J). 14.95 (978-0-9743294-0-6(1)) A & D Bks.

Bustard, Ned. The Alphabet Quest. Bustard, Ned et al, illus. 2000. per. 3.00 (978-1-930710-51-1(8)) Veritas Pr., Inc.

Butler, Darnell. ABC's of People in the Bible. 2006. (Illus.). 56p. (J). pap. 28.95 (978-1-59299-163-1(7)) Inkwater Pr.

Butler, Dori Hillestad. F Is for Firefighting. Dieterichs, Shelley, illus. 2001. (Alpha Flight Book Ser.). 60p. (J). (ps-3). 17.95 (978-1-892920-20-1(4)) GHB Publishers, LLC.

Cabat, Erni. Erni Cabat's Magical ABC: Animals Around the Farm. Date not set. (Illus.). 64p. (Orig.). (J). (ps-2). 23.00 (978-0-943173-73-3(6)) Cabat Studio Pubns.

Cahoon, Heather. Word Play ABC. Cahoon, Heather, illus. 1999. (Illus.). 32p. (J). (ps-3). 15.95 (978-0-8027-8683-8(9)); lib. bdg. 16.85 (978-0-8027-8684-5(7)) Walker & Co.

Caldwell, Mary B. A Is for Adobe. 1998. (Illus.). 60p. (J). (gr. k-3). 17.00 (978-0-944551-35-6(1)) Book Pubs. of El Paso.

Campos, Maria de Fatima. B Is for Brazil. 2004. (World Alphabets Ser.). (Illus.). 32p. (J). pap. 7.95 (978-1-84507-316-9(9)) Lincoln, Frances Ltd. GBR. *Dist:* Perseus Distribution.

Campos, Maria de Fatima, contrib. by. B Is for Brazil. 1999. (J). (978-0-382-42116-7(7)) Cobblestone Publishing Co.

Carder, Ken & Laroy, Sue. Songs That Teach Alphabet & Counting. 2006. (Songs That Teach Ser.). 72p. (J). pap. 14.95 (978-0-7696-6459-0(8) , American Education Publishing) School Specialty Publishing.

Carle, Eric. Eric Carle's ABC. 2007. (World of Eric Carle Ser.). 16p. (J). 5.99 (978-0-448-44564-9(6) , Grosset & Dunlap) Penguin Group (USA) Inc.

Carlson, Nancy. ABC I Like Me. 1999. (Illus.). 32p. (J). (ps-k). pap. 6.99 (978-0-14-056485-3(3) , Puffin) Penguin Group (USA) Inc.

—ABC I Like Me. 1999. (J). 13.79 (978-0-606-16771-0(4)) Tandem Library Bks.

Carolan. B Is for Beach: An Alphabet Book. 2005. (Illus.). 64p. (J). 16.95 (978-0-9715333-1-8(8)) Banana Patch Pr.

Carter, David A. Alpha Bugs: A Pop-Up Alphabet. Carter, David A., illus. ed. 2006. (Illus.). 28p. (J). (ps-2). 11.95 (978-1-4169-0973-6(7) , Little Simon) Simon & Schuster Children's Publishing.

Cartwright, Stephen. Abc Floor. Cartwright, Stephen, illus. 2006. 16p. (J). bds. 15.99 (978-0-7945-1367-2(0) , Usborne) EDC Publishing.

Catalanotto, Peter. Matthew A. B. C. Catalanotto, Peter, illus. (Illus.). 32p. (J). (ps-2). 2002. 15.95 (978-0-689-84582-6(0) , Atheneum/Richard Jackson Bks.); 2005. reprint ed. pap., pap. 6.99 (978-1-4169-0330-7(5) , Aladdin) Simon & Schuster Children's Publishing.

Caterpillar Inc. Staff, contrib. by. C Is for Construction: Big Trucks & Diggers from A to Z. 2003. (Illus.). 32p. (J). 12.95 (978-0-8118-4028-6(X)) Chronicle Bks. LLC.

Celia, Shannon Casey. ABC's of the Sea. Bates, Carla, illus. 2002. 32p. (J). (gr. k-2). 14.95 (978-0-9718825-1-5(7)); pap. 7.95 (978-0-9718825-0-8(9)) Seashop Pr.

Chamorro Alphabet. 2004. (Illus.). 56p. 4.95 (978-1-57306-213-8(8)) Bess Pr., Inc.

Chang, Maria & Sevaly, Karen. Lace-up Cards Alphabet & Numbers. 2007. (In or Out Ser.). 256p. 9.99 (***978-0-439-91222-4(2)*** , Teaching Resources) Scholastic, Inc.

Chapman, Todd & Judge, Lita. D Is for Dinosaur: A Prehistoric Alphabet. Judge, Lita, illus. 2007. (General Alphabet Ser.). 48p. (J). 17.95 (***978-1-58536-242-4(5)***) Sleeping Bear Pr.

Charlesworth, Liza. The Enormous Elephant Show: Letter E. 2001. (Illus.). 16p. (ps-1). pap. 2.25 (978-0-439-16528-0(8)) Scholastic, Inc.

—Olive the Octopus's Day of Juggling: Letter O. 2001. (Alpha Tales Ser.). (Illus.). 16p. (ps-1). pap. 2.25 (978-0-439-16538-9(5)) Scholastic, Inc.

—A Xylophone for X-Ray Fish: Letter X. 2001. (Alpha Tales Ser.). (Illus.). 16p. (ps-1). pap. 2.25 (978-0-439-16547-1(4)) Scholastic, Inc.

Chatfield, Steve, et al. Animaly ABC. Duncheskie, Joan, illus. 1998. iii, 42p. (J). (ps-6). pap. 19.95 (978-0-9663505-0-0(2)) Bubba Bear Publishing, Inc.

Cheney, Lynne. America: A Patriotic Primer. Glasser, Robin Preiss, illus. 2002. 40p. (J). 16.95 (978-0-689-85192-6(8)) Simon & Schuster Children's Publishing.

—A Is for Abigail: An Almanac of Amazing American Women. Glasser, Robin Preiss, illus. 2003. 48p. (J). 16.95 (978-0-689-85819-2(1)) Simon & Schuster Children's Publishing.

Cheney, Martha C. Alphabet. Kaminski, Karol, illus. 1998. (Gifted & Talented Ser.). 312p. (J). (ps-k). pap., wbk. ed. 5.95 (978-1-56565-839-4(6) , 08396W) Lowell Hse. Juvenile.

Chesworth, Michael. Alphaboat. Chesworth, Michael D., illus. 2002. 32p. (J). 16.00 (978-0-374-30244-3(8) , Farrar, Straus & Giroux (BYR)) Farrar, Straus & Giroux.

Children's Psychiatric Center Staff. All-Aboard Children's Picture-Alphabet Book. 2001. (Illus.). 100p. (J). (ps-3). 25.00 (978-0-9705111-0-2(8)) Children's Psychiatric Ctr., Inc., The.

Chin, Foo Swee. Zeet. Chin, Foo Swee, illus. 2003. 32p. (Orig.). pap. 2.95 (978-0-943151-75-5(9)) Slave Labor Bks.

Chin-Lee, Cynthia, et al. A Is for the Americas. 1999. (Illus.). 32p. (J). (gr. k-4). 16.99 (978-0-531-33194-1(6) , Orchard Bks.) Scholastic, Inc.

Chorao, Kay. D Is for Drums: A Colonial Williamsburg ABC. 2004. (Illus.). 32p. (J). (ps-1). 16.95 (978-0-8109-4927-0(X)) Abrams, Harry N., Inc.

—D Is for Drums: A Colonial Williamsburg ABC. Chorao, Kay, illus. 2006. (Illus.). 30p. (J). (gr. k-4). reprint ed. 17.00 (978-1-4223-5240-3(4)) DIANE Publishing Co.

Chuukese Alphabet. 2004. (Illus.). 56p. 4.95 (978-1-57306-222-0(7)) Bess Pr., Inc.

Ciminera, Siobhan. Find Your Heartsong: Happy Feet. 2006. 16p. (J). (ps-1). 4.99 (978-0-8431-2092-9(4) , Price Stern Sloan) Penguin Group (USA) Inc.

Clark, Anita. Bible Rhymes from A to Z. 2006. 142p. (J). per. 11.95 (978-1-59886-123-5(9)) Tate Publishing & Enterprises, L.L.C.

Clark, Judy. I Spy Disney: An ABC Book. 2020. (Illus.). 32p. (J). 12.99 (978-0-7868-3185-2(5)) Disney Pr.

Cleary, Beverly. The Hullabaloo ABC. 2000. pap. (978-0-688-17715-7(8)) HarperCollins Pubs.

—The Hullabaloo ABC. Rand, Ted, illus. rev. ed. 1998. 40p. (J). (ps-3). 16.99 (978-0-688-15182-9(5)) HarperCollins Pubs.

Clement, Janet. The Jewish Alphabet. Rodriguez, Albert G., illus. 2006. 32p. (J). 15.95 (978-1-58980-414-2(7)) Pelican Publishing Co., Inc.

Clingan, Mary. Let's Learn Letters. 1999. (J). (ps-3). (978-1-929343-03-4(5)) Stretching Charts, Inc.

Cobb, Deborah B., illus. Bible Verse ABC's with the Cobblekids. 2001. vii, 64p. (J). (ps-1). 18.95 (978-0-9709793-0-8(4)) Lollipop Publishing, LLC.

Coburn, Claudia. Did the Aardvarks Say "No Ark"? Hoard, Angela, illus. 2004. 32p. (J). (978-0-9759343-1-9(7)) Purfect Promises.

Cohn, Tricia L. Beobi & the Magic Coloring Book ABC First Words. 2003. (J). (978-0-9743847-0-2(4)) Cohn, Tricia.

Collison, Cathy. An Out of This World Alphabet. rev. ed. 2007. 40p. pap. 7.95 (***978-1-58536-335-3(9)***) Sleeping Bear Pr.

Collison, Cathy & Campbell, Janis. G Is for Galaxy: An Out of This World Alphabet. Stacy, Alan, illus. 2005. (World/Country Alphabet Ser.). 40p. (J). (gr. k-5). 16.95 (978-1-58536-255-4(7)) Sleeping Bear Pr.

Color All About: A Giant Coloring Book about the Alphabet: the Alphabet. 2004. (SPA & ENG., Illus.). 36p. (J). (978-1-59949-000-7(5)) Food Marketing Consultants, Inc.

Compestine, Ying Chang. D Is for Dragon Dance. Xuan, Yong-Sheng, illus. 32p. (J). (ps-3). 17.95 (978-0-8234-1887-9(1)) Holiday Hse., Inc.

Connelly, Neil O. Alphabet. Thornburgh, Rebecca, illus. 10p. (J). (ps). bds. 3.95 (978-1-58989-004-6(3)) Thurman Hse., LLC.

Cooper, Sharon Katz. Costa Rica ABCs: A Book about the People & Places of Costa Rica. Eitzen, Allan, illus. 2006. (Country ABCs Ser.). 32p. (J). (gr. k-5). lib. bdg. 25.26 (***978-1-4048-2249-8(6)***) Picture Window Bks.

—France ABCs: A Book about the People & Places of France. Previn, Stacey, illus. 2006. (Country ABCs Ser.). 32p. (J). (gr. k-5). 23.93 (978-1-4048-1568-1(6)) Picture Window Bks.

—Italy ABCs: A Book about the People & Places of Italy. Eitzen, Allan, illus. 2006. (Country ABCs Ser.). 32p. (J). (gr. k-5). 23.93 (978-1-4048-1569-8(4)) Picture Window Bks.

Cooper, Sharon Katz. Venezuela ABCs: A Book about the People & Places of Venezuela. Previn, Stacey, illus. 2006. (Country ABCs Ser.). 32p. (J). (gr. k-5). lib. bdg. 25.26 (*978-1-4048-2250-4(X)) Picture Window Bks.

Cooper, Terry, ed. Alphatales: A to Z Letter Formation Practice Pages:Fun-Filled Reproducible Practice Pages That Help Young Learners Recognize & Print Every Letter of the Alphabet. 2002. (Illus.). 64p. (ps-1). pap. 10.95 (978-0-439-33151-7(X)) Scholastic, Inc.

—Alphatales Alphabet Set: 26 A to Z Jumbo Letter Cards to Display on Your Wall or Bulletin Board. 2002. (ps-3). pap. 7.95 (978-0-439-33152-4(8)) Scholastic, Inc.

—Learning the Alphabet. 2006. (Kindergarten Ser.). 48p. pap. 5.99 (978-0-439-81936-7(9) , Teaching Resources) Scholastic, Inc.

Cordero, Flor de Maria. M Is for Mexico. 2008. (World Alphabets Ser.). (Illus.). 32p. (J). 16.95 (*978-1-84507-593-4(5)) Lincoln, Frances Ltd. GBR. *Dist:* Perseus Distribution.

Cormack, Malcolm. Tigers & Sails & ABC Tales. 2003. (Illus.). 64p. 14.95 (978-0-917046-65-0(X)) Virginia Museum of Fine Arts.

Cosby, Eileen Tucker. A Is for Adopted. Strange, Norma S., illus. 2000. 56p. (J). (ps-5). 14.95 (978-0-9676385-0-8(X) , 1001) Swak Pak, LLC.

Cousins, Lucy. Maisy's Amazing Big Book of Words. Cousins, Lucy, illus. 2007. (Maisy Ser.). (Illus.). 64p. (J). (ps-k). 14.99 (978-0-7636-0794-4(0)) Candlewick Pr.

Crane, Carol. Discover Florida, 2 bks. Monroe, Michael Glenn & Monroe Donovan, Jane, illus. 2003. 40p. (J). 27.95 (978-1-58536-226-4(3)) Sleeping Bear Pr.

—Discover Texas, 2 bks. Stacy, Alan, illus. 2003. 40p. (J). 27.95 (978-1-58536-227-1(1)) Sleeping Bear Pr.

—L Is for Last Frontier: An Alaska Alphabet. Monroe, Michael Glenn, illus. 2002. 40p. (J). (ps-5). 17.95 (978-1-58536-020-8(1)) Sleeping Bear Pr.

—P Is for Palmetto: A South Carolina Alphabet. Whyte, Mary, illus. 2002. 40p. (J). 17.95 (978-1-58536-047-5(3)) Sleeping Bear Pr.

—P Is for Pilgrim: A Thanksgiving Alphabet. rev. ed. 2007. (Holiday Ser.). 40p. pap. 7.95 (*978-1-58536-353-7(7)) Sleeping Bear Pr.

Crane, Carol. T Is for Tar Heel: A North Carolina Alphabet. Palmer, Gary, illus. 2003. 40p. (J). 17.95 (978-1-58536-082-6(1)) Sleeping Bear Pr.

Cronin, Doreen. Click, Clack, Quackity-Quack: An Alphabetical Adventure. 2006. (J). (ps-3). 22.78 (978-1-59961-089-4(2)) Spotlight.

Curry, Don L. Counting My ABCs. 1999. (Illus.). 32p. (J). pap. (978-0-7368-7051-1(2)) Capstone Pr., Inc.

—My ABC's. (A+ Alphabet Books). (Illus.). (J). (gr. k-1). 2000. 17p. 22.60 (978-0-7368-7040-5(7) , Aplus Bks.); 1999. 32p. pap. (978-0-7368-7048-1(2)) Capstone Pr., Inc.

—Willie's Word World. Stromoski, Rick, illus. 2005. (Rookie Reader Skill Set Ser.). 31p. (J). (gr. k-2). pap. 4.95 (978-0-516-25288-9(7) , Children's Pr.) Scholastic Library Publishing.

Cyr, Lynne G. Drako's ABC Adventures as an Iguana. ed. 2006. (Illus.). 37p. (J). spiral bd. 21.95 (978-0-9774543-0-3(4)) Cyr Design Publishing.

Dahl, Michael. Wild Animals ABC: An Alphabet Book. 2004. (A+ Alphabet Books). (Illus.). 32p. (J). lib. bdg. 22.60 (978-0-7368-2608-2(4) , Aplus Bks.) Capstone Pr., Inc.

Dahl, Roald. D Is for Dahl: A Gloriumptious A-Z Guide to the World of Roald Dahl. Blake, Quentin, illus. 2005. 160p. (J). (gr. k). 15.99 (978-0-670-06023-8(2) , Viking Juvenile) Penguin Group (USA) Inc.

Daleo, Morgan Simone. A Spirited Alphabet: From A to Z. Riccio, Frank, illus. 1999. 32p. (J). (ps). 14.95 (978-1-57174-148-6(8)) Hampton Roads Publishing Co., Inc.

Dalmatian Press Staff. Mickey's Alphbet BK. 2006. 32p. pap. 11.99 (978-1-4037-2188-4(2)) Dalmatian Pr.

—My Little Book of ABCs. 2002. (Illus.). 24p. (J). (gr. k-5). pap. 2.99 (978-1-57759-366-9(9)) Dalmatian Pr.

—Precious Moments Lowercase Alphabet. 1999. (Precious Moments Ser.). (Illus.). 32p. (J). (ps-3). pap., wbk. ed. 2.99 (978-1-57759-208-2(5)) Dalmatian Pr.

Dalmatian Press Staff, ed. Zoophabet ABC: Board Book with Blocks Gift Set. rev. ed. 2007. 10p. 10.99 (*978-1-4037-2955-2(7)) Dalmatian Pr.

D'Amelio, Dennis P. All Aboard the Alphabet Train. D'Amelio, Dennis P., illus. 1998. (Right Track Bks.: Vol. 3). (Illus.). (J). (ps). pap. (978-1-891528-61-3(0)) Telescopic Pr.

Dance Alpha. 2007. 17.95 (*978-1-58536-312-4(X)) Sleeping Bear Pr.

D'Andrea, Deborah. Picture Me Learning Letters A, B, C. Ayers, Michael B., illus. rev. ed. 2000. (Picture Me Ser.). 10p. (J). (ps-1). bds. 4.99 (978-1-57151-582-7(8)) Playhouse Publishing.

Darling, Kathy. ABC Cats. Darling, Tara, photos by. 1998. (Illus.). 32p. (J). (ps-3). 15.95 (978-0-8027-8666-1(9)); lib. bdg. 16.85 (978-0-8027-8667-8(7)) Walker & Co.

Daste, Larry. Alphabet Search: Activity & Coloring Book. 2007. 48p. (J). pap. 4.95 (*978-0-486-46196-0(3)) Dover Pubns., Inc.

David C. Cook. ABC's. 2003. (My Jesus Pocket Bks.). (Illus.). 32p. (J). (gr. 5-3). pap., pap. 8.90 (978-1-55513-091-6(7) , 1555130917) Cook, David C. Publishing Co.

Davidow, Shelley. The Wise Enchanter: A Journey Through the Alphabet. Kurzyca, Krystyna Emilia, illus. 2005. 159p. (J). (gr. 3-7). pap. 17.95 (978-0-88010-562-0(3)) SteinerBooks, Inc.

Davis, Guy. Barney's ABC, 123 & More. McKee, Darren, illus. 1999. (Barney Ser.). 14p. (J). (ps-k). bds. 9.99 (978-1-57064-243-2(5)) Scholastic, Inc.

Davis, Rebecca. ABC Fun. Blair, Bill, ed. Cagley, Diana, illus. l.t. ed. 2002. 62p. (J). (gr. k-3). spiral bd. 9.00 (978-0-9720881-0-7(5)) His Hands, Inc.

—Vowels & Other Strange Letters. Blair, Bill, ed. Yancey, Joshua Lee, illus. 2002. 25p. (J). (gr. 6-8). spiral bd. 7.00 (978-0-9720881-1-4(3) , B002) His Hands, Inc.

DeGezelle, Terri. Birds A to Z. 2000. (A+ Alphabet Books). (Illus.). 17p. (J). (gr. k-1). 22.60 (978-0-7368-7038-2(5) , Aplus Bks.) Capstone Pr., Inc.

del Sur, Duendes. ABC: A Book about Letter. 2003. (Care Bears Ser.). (Illus.). 8p. (J). bds. 5.99 (978-0-439-51804-8(0)) Scholastic, Inc.

Del'Homme, Melissa. Letter Recognition Workbook: Uppercase & Lowercase Letters. McMahon, Kelly, illus. 2000. (Tutor Books: Helping Your Child Learn & Succeed). 160p. (YA). (ps up). pap. 12.95 (978-0-7373-0455-8(3) , 04553W, Roxbury Park Juvenile) Lowell Hse. Juvenile.

Demarest, Chris L. Firefighters A to Z. 2003. (gr. k-3). lib. bdg. 15.30 (978-0-613-66404-2(3)) Tandem Library Bks.

Demarest, Chris L. & Mayer, Bill. All Aboard! A Traveling Alphabet. 2008. 32p. (J). 17.99 (*978-0-689-85249-7(5) , McElderry, Margaret K.) Simon & Schuster Children's Publishing.

Demeo, Kristen. Sounds Like This ... 2007. (J). per. 7.95 (*978-1-59872-819-4(9)) Instantpublisher.com.

Diaz-Cubero, Jose H. Practicas de Ortografia: 5 Grado. (SPA & ENG.). (J). (gr. 5). 9.95 (978-84-357-0125-9(5) , CPR92) Ediciones y Distribuciones Codice, S.A. ESP. *Dist:* Continental Bk. Co., Inc.

Diaz, James & Gerth, Melanie. My First Jumbo Book of Letters. 2003. (My First Jumbo Book Ser.). (Illus.). 10p. (J). pap. 9.95 (978-0-439-44325-8(3) , Cartwheel Bks.) Scholastic, Inc.

Diehl, David. Sports A to Z. 2007. (Illus.). 28p. (J). (gr. 1). bds. 5.95 (*978-1-60059-113-6(2)) Lark Bks.

DiTerlizzi, Tony. G Is for One Gzonk! DiTerlizzi, Tony, illus. 2006. 27p. (J). 12.99 (978-1-4169-4115-6(0) , Simon Scribbles) Simon & Schuster Children's Publishing.

—G Is for One Gzonk! An Alpha-Number-Bet Book. DiTerlizzi, Tony, illus. 2006. (Illus.). 80p. (J). (ps-2). 16.95 (978-0-689-85290-9(8)) Simon & Schuster Children's Publishing.

DK Publishing. A b C. 2008. 16p. (J). (ps-k). 4.99 (*978-0-7566-3815-3(1)) Dorling Kindersley Publishing, Inc.

—Water Magic Letters ABC. 2007. 16p. (J). bds. 7.99 (*978-0-7566-3452-0(0)) Dorling Kindersley Publishing, Inc.

DK Publishing Staff. Baby ABC. 1998. (Soft-to-Touch Bks.). (Illus.). 16p. (J). (ps-k). bds. 4.99 (978-0-7894-3648-1(5)) Dorling Kindersley Publishing, Inc.

—Hide & Seek ABC. 2007. 12p. (J). (ps-1). 3.99 (978-0-7566-2920-5(9)) Dorling Kindersley Publishing, Inc.

—Magic Alphabet. 2007. 24p. (J). (ps-1). ring bd. 12.99 (978-0-7566-2933-5(0)) Dorling Kindersley Publishing, Inc.

—My 1st Wipe Clean: Letters. 2007. 26p. (J). (ps-1). bds. 9.99 (978-0-7566-3028-7(2)) Dorling Kindersley Publishing, Inc.

—Pull & Learn. 2007. 70p. (J). (ps-1). 9.99 (978-0-7566-2923-6(3)) Dorling Kindersley Publishing, Inc.

Dodd, Emma. Dog's ABC: A Silly Story about the Alphabet. Dodd, Emma, illus. 2002. (Illus.). 32p. (J). 14.99 (978-0-525-46837-0(4) , Dutton Juvenile) Penguin Group (USA) Inc.

Dodd, Marion. Mystic by the A,B, Sea. Dodd, Marion, illus. 2006. (J). 17.95 (978-0-9773725-2-2(9)) Flat Hammock Pr.

Dodds, James. Alphabet of Boats. 2002. (Illus.). 32p. 9.95 (978-0-939510-72-6(3) , 1017229) Mystic Seaport Museum Stores, Inc.

Doering, Amanda. Cats ABC: An Alphabet Book. 2004. (A+ Alphabet Books). (Illus.). 17p. (J). 22.60 (978-0-7368-2604-4(1) , Aplus Bks.) Capstone Pr., Inc.

Dog Artlist Collection Staff. The Dog: From Arf! Arf! to Zzzzzz. Dog Artlist Collection Staff, illus. 2005. (Illus.). 32p. (J). (ps up). bds. 6.99 (978-0-06-077181-2(X) , Harper Festival) HarperCollins Pubs.

—The Dog from Arf! Arf! to Zzzzzz. 2007. (Illus.). 40p. (J). (ps-3). pap. 6.99 (*978-0-06-059859-4(X) , Harper Trophy) HarperCollins Pubs.

—The Dog from Arf! Arf! to Zzzzzz. Dog Artlist Collection Staff, illus. 2004. (Illus.). 40p. (J). 14.99 (978-0-06-059857-0(3)) HarperCollins Pubs.

Dolphin, Colleen. Armadillos to Zorillas: Animals from A to Z. 2007. (Let's See A to Z Ser.). (ENG., Illus.). 32p. (J). (ps-3). lib. bdg. 25.65 (*978-1-59928-883-3(4) , Super SandCastle) ABDO Publishing Co.

Domeniconi, David. A National Parks Alphabet. 2007. 40p. pap. 7.95 (*978-1-58536-333-9(2)) Sleeping Bear Pr.

Dora the Explorer Lowercase ABC's. 2006. (J). pap. 2.95 (*978-1-58610-990-5(1)) Learning Horizons, Inc.

Dorfman, Gladys E. The Little Pelican Alphabet Book. 1999. (Illus.). (J). (ps-2). 14.95 (978-0-9671111-1-7(0)) Hannah Mae Enterprises, Inc.

Dorling Kindersley Publishing Staff. ABC Play Book. 2003. (My First Bks.). (Illus.). 80p. (J). 12.99 (978-0-7894-9848-9(0)) Dorling Kindersley Publishing, Inc.

—Alphabet. 2000. (All Aboard Bks.). (Illus.). 22p. (J). (ps-k). 6.95 (978-0-7894-5327-3(4) , D K Ink) Dorling Kindersley Publishing, Inc.

—Farm ABC. 2006. (Illus.). 12p. (J). (ps-1). 8.99 (978-0-7566-2331-9(6)) Dorling Kindersley Publishing, Inc.

—My First ABC. 2003. (My First Sticker Board Books). (Illus.). 12p. (J). pap. 6.99 (978-0-7894-9247-0(4)) Dorling Kindersley Publishing, Inc.

Dot-to-Dot Numbers & Alphabet Booster. 2005. (J). per. 0.00 (978-1-59441-502-9(1) , C04034) Carson-Dellosa Publishing Co., Inc.

Doudna, Kelly. The Alphabet - Set II. l.t. ed. Incl. Nn : See It Say It Hear It. lib. bdg. 19.93 (978-1-57765-434-6(X)); Oo : See It Say It Hear It. lib. bdg. 19.93 (978-1-57765-435-3(8)); Pp : See It Say It Hear It. lib. bdg. 19.93 (978-1-57765-436-0(6)); Qq : See It Say It Hear It. lib. bdg. 19.93 (978-1-57765-437-7(4)); Rr : See It Say It Hear It. lib. bdg. 19.93 (978-1-57765-438-4(2)); Ss : See It Say It Hear It. lib. bdg. 19.93 (978-1-57765-439-1(0)); Tt : See It Say It Hear It. lib. bdg. 19.93 (978-1-57765-440-7(4)); Uu : See It Say It Hear It. lib. bdg. 19.93 (978-1-57765-441-4(2)); Vv : See It Say It Hear It. lib. bdg. 19.93 (978-1-57765-442-1(0)); Ww : See It Say It Hear It. lib. bdg. 19.93 (978-1-57765-443-8(9)); Xx : See It Say It Hear It. lib. bdg. 19.93 (978-1-57765-444-5(7)); Yy : See It Say It Hear It. lib. bdg. 19.93 (978-1-57765-445-2(5)); Zz : See It Say It Hear It. lib. bdg. 19.93 (978-1-57765-446-9(3)); 24p. (J). (ps-3). 2001. (Illus.). 2000. Set lib. bdg. 259.09 (978-1-57765-296-0(7) , SandCastle) ABDO Publishing Co.

—Emma & Eddie. 2005. (First Sounds Ser.). (Illus.). 23p. (J). pap. (978-1-59679-145-9(4)); 19.93 (978-1-59679-144-2(6)) ABDO Publishing Co.

—Mm: See It Say It Hear It. l.t. ed. 2000. (Alphabet Ser.). (Illus.). 24p. (J). (ps-k). lib. bdg. 19.93 (978-1-57765-406-3(4) , SandCastle) ABDO Publishing Co.

Douglas, Julie. M Is for Michigan. Dorenkamp, Michelle, illus. 2001. (Alpha Flight Books Ser.). 60p. (J). (ps-3). 17.95 (978-1-892920-43-0(3)) GHB Publishers, LLC.

Douglas, Lisa Jo. Active Animals A Thru Z. 2007. (J). per. 13.99 (*978-1-59879-311-6(X)) Lifevest Publishing, Inc.

Douglas, Vincent & School Specialty Publishing Staff. Alphabet, Colors, & Shapes. 2004. (My Little Heavenly Helpers Ser.). (Illus.). 64p. (J). (ps-k). pap. 3.99 (978-0-7696-3649-8(7) , Brighter Child) School Specialty Publishing.

—Alphabet Hidden Pictures. 2003. (Homework Helpers Ser.). (Illus.). 32p. (J). (gr. k-1). pap. 2.99 (978-0-7696-2947-6(4) , American Education Publishing) School Specialty Publishing.

—Learning Letters: Preschool. 2001. (Starburst Spectrum Workbook Ser.). (Illus.). 150p. (C). pap. 8.95 (978-1-57768-329-2(3) , American Education Publishing) School Specialty Publishing.

—My Little Showcase of the ABCs. 2005. (My Little Showcase Ser.). (Illus.). 100p. (J). bds. 14.95 (978-1-58845-647-2(1) , Brighter Child) School Specialty Publishing.

—Sounds & Letters. 2004. (Kindergarten Bound Ser.). (Illus.). 80p. (J). (ps up). pap. 5.95 (978-0-7696-3438-8(9) , American Education Publishing) School Specialty Publishing.

Doyle, Charlotte. The Bouncing, Dancing, Galloping ABC. Gorton, Julia, illus. 2006. 32p. (J). (ps-1). 10.99 (978-0-399-23778-2(X) , Putnam Juvenile) Penguin Group (USA) Inc.

Drake, Aaron & Drake, Jennifer. A-B-C & 1-2-3 Travel Coloring Book. 2007. (Illus.). 80p. (J). 4.99 (978-1-56251-799-1(6)) AAA.

Dugan, Joanne. ABC NYC: A Book about Seeing New York City. 2005. (Illus.). 56p. (J). (ps-1). 15.95 (978-0-8109-5854-8(6)) Abrams, Harry N. , Inc.

DuTemple, Lesley A. R Is for Raccoon. 2007. 32p. pap. 11.95 (*978-1-892384-42-3(6)) Avery Color Studios, Inc.

Dwyer, Mindy. The Northern Lights A to Z. 2007. (Illus.). 32p. (J). (gr. k-3). pap. 10.95 (978-1-57061-515-3(2)) Sasquatch Bks.

Dyslexia Institute Staff, ed. An ABC Picture Gallery: An ABC of Contemporary Illustrators. Benson, Patrick et al, illus. 1999. 64p. pap. 14.99 (978-0-434-80472-6(X) , Butterworth-Heinemann) Elsevier Science & Technology Bks.

Edwards, Ann & Goldberg, Karen. Bumpy Books. 2006. (J). spiral bd. (978-0-9778736-0-9(9)) Bumpy Bks Inc.

Edwards, Pamela Duncan. The Wacky Wedding: A Book of Alphabet Antics. 2005. 32p. (J). pap. (978-0-7868-1172-4(2)) Hyperion Bks. for Children.

—The Wacky Wedding: A Book of Alphabet Antics. Cole, Henry, illus. 1999. 32p. (ps-2). 14.99 (978-0-7868-0308-8(8)) Hyperion Bks. for Children.

Edwards, Richard & Hendra, Sue. Amazing Animal Alphabet: With Fantastic Flaps. 1999. (Illus.). 32p. (J). (ps-k). pap. 14.95 (978-0-531-30123-4(0) , Orchard Bks.) Scholastic, Inc.

Edwards, Wallace. Alphabeasts. Edwards, Wallace, illus. 2002. (Illus.). 32p. (J). (gr. k-3). (978-1-55337-386-5(3)) Kids Can Pr., Ltd.

Ehlert, Lois. Eating the Alphabet: Fruits & Vegetables from A to Z. Ehlert, Lois, illus. 2002. (Illus.). (J). 14.79 (978-0-7587-2434-2(9)) Book Wholesalers, Inc.

—Eating the Alphabet: Fruits & Vegetables from A to Z, Vol. 5. 2000. (Illus.). (J). pap. 28.50 (978-0-8172-8060-4(X)) Steck-Vaughn.

Eichenberg, Fritz. Ape in a Cape: An Alphabet of Odd Animals. Eichenberg, Fritz, illus. 2002. (Illus.). (J). 14.04 (978-0-7587-0092-6(X)) Book Wholesalers, Inc.

Einhorn, Kama. I Can Write My ABCs. 2001. 64p. pap. 10.95 (978-0-439-22846-6(8)) Scholastic, Inc.

Eisele, Beat, et al. My ABC Storybook. 2001. 80p. (C). pap. 22.67 (978-0-13-017587-8(0)) Pearson ESL.

Ellis, Belinda. Giant See-a-Shape My Giant ABC Book. 2005. (Giant See a Shape Ser.). (Illus.). 52p. (ps-k). bds. 9.95 (978-1-905051-92-2(1)) Make Believe Ideas GBR. *Dist:* Ingram Pub. Services.

—Touch & Learn: Fairy Tale ABC. 2006. (Illus.). 12p. (J). (ps). per. 12.95 (978-1-84610-090-1(9)) Make Believe Ideas GBR. *Dist:* Ingram Pub. Services.

Ellis, Rowland-Grey & Kentor, Teddy. The Scariest Alphabet Book. 2002. (Illus.). 152p. 6.95 (978-1-57168-717-3(3)) Eakin Pr.

Engelbreit, Mary. Mary Engelbreit's A Merry Little Christmas: Celebrate from A to Z. Engelbreit, Mary, illus. 2006. (Illus.). 40p. (J). pap. lib. bdg. 17.89 (978-0-06-074159-4(7)) HarperCollins Pubs.

—Mary Engelbreit's a Merry Little Christmas: Celebrate from A to Z. Engelbreit, Mary, illus. 2006. (Illus.). 40p. (J). 16.99 (978-0-06-074158-7(9)) HarperCollins Pubs.

English Alphabet. 2004. (Illus.). 56p. (J). 4.95 (978-1-57306-219-0(7)) Bess Pr., Inc.

Enormous Elephant Show. 2001. (ps-2). lib. bdg. 9.80 (978-0-613-32505-9(2)) Tandem Library Bks.

Ernst, Lisa Campbell. The Letters Are Lost. Ernst, Lisa Campbell, illus. 1999. 32p. (J). (ps-1). pap. 5.99 (978-0-14-055663-6(X) , Puffin) Penguin Group (USA) Inc.

Falls, C. B. & Glassman, Peter. ABC Book. Falls, C. B., illus. 1998. (Books of Wonder). (Illus.). 40p. (J). (ps-3). 15.00 (978-0-688-14712-9(7)) HarperCollins Pubs.

Famke Zonneveld Staff. Waldorf Alphabet Book. 2005. (Illus.). 54p. (J). (ps-7). pap. 12.95 (978-0-88010-559-0(3) , Bell Pond Bks.) SteinerBooks, Inc.

Farmer, Bonnie. ABC Letters in the Library. McLeod, Chum, illus. 2005. 32p. (J). (ps-2). pap. 6.95 (978-1-897073-19-3(4)) Lobster Pr. CAN. *Dist:* Univ. of Toronto Pr.

Feldman, Heather. The Nicest Newt: Letter N. 2001. (Alpha Tales Ser.). (Illus.). 16p. (ps-1). pap. 2.25 (978-0-439-16537-2(7)) Scholastic, Inc.

—The Quiet Quail: Letter Q. 2001. (Alpha Tales Ser.). (Illus.). 16p. (ps-1). pap. 2.25 (978-0-439-16540-2(7)) Scholastic, Inc.

—Umbrella Bird's Umbrella: Letter U. 2001. (Alpha Tales Ser.). (Illus.). 16p, (ps-1). pap. 2.25 (978-0-439-16544-0(X)) Scholastic, Inc.

Ferarro, Bonita. Alphabet & Letters: Preschool. 2003. (Brighter Child Workbooks Ser.). (Illus.). 24p. (J). (ps). pap. 2.25 (978-1-56189-059-0(6) , American Education Publishing) School Specialty Publishing.

Fields, Kim. Alphabet: Cards, Games & Activities. 2006. 176p. pap. 21.99 (978-1-4206-8008-9(0)) Austin & Company, Inc.

Finale, Frank. A Gull's Story: A Tale of Learning about Life, the Shore & the ABCs. Valente, George C., ed. Moore, Margie, illus. 2007. 36p. (J). 22.00 (978-0-9632906-3-2(0)) Jersey Shore Pubns.

Fisher, Valorie. Ellsworth's Extraordinary Electric Ears & Other Amazing Alphabet Anecdotes. Fisher, Valorie, illus. 2003. (Illus.). 40p. (J). (gr. k-3). 16.95 (978-0-689-85030-1(1) , Atheneum) Simon & Schuster Children's Publishing.

Fitka, Alice N. Kuvyallrem Aperyarai. Fitka, Alice N. & Shantz, Joy, illus. 1998. Tr. of Fishing Words. (ESK.). 16p. (J). (gr. k-3). pap. 6.00 (978-1-58084-035-4(3)) Lower Kuskokwim Schl. District.

Fleming, Maria. The Adventures of Abby the Alligator: Letter A. 2001. (Illus.). 16p. (ps-1). pap. 2.25 (978-0-439-16524-2(5)) Scholastic, Inc.

—Alpha Tales. 2001. (J). pap., tchr. ed. 12.95 (978-0-439-16523-5(7)) Scholastic, Inc.

—Copycats: Letter C. 2001. (Illus.). 16p. (ps-1). pap. 2.25 (978-0-439-16526-6(1)) Scholastic, Inc.

—Gorilla, Be Good! Letter G. 2001. (Illus.). 16p. (ps-1). pap. 2.25 (978-0-439-16530-3(X)) Scholastic, Inc.

Floca, Brian. The Racecar Alphabet. Floca, Brian, illus. 2003. (Illus.). 40p. (J). 17.99 (978-0-689-85091-2(3) , Atheneum/Richard Jackson Bks.) Simon & Schuster Children's Publishing.

Foam Magnetic Letters in Spanish. (ps-12). 26.20 (978-0-7362-1530-5(1)) Hampton-Brown Bks.

Folsom, Michael & Elting, Mary. Q Is for Duck: An Alphabet Guessing Game. Kent, Jack, illus. 2005. 64p. (J). (ps-k). 16.00 (978-0-618-57389-9(5)); pap., pap. 6.95 (978-0-618-57412-4(3)) Houghton Mifflin Co. Trade & Reference Div. (Clarion Bks.).

Forte, Imogene. Ready to Learn Alphabet & Beginning Sounds. 2003. (Illus.). 64p. per. 7.95 (978-0-86530-597-7(8)) Incentive Pubns., Inc.

Franco, Betsy. Guess-Me Poems & Puzzles: Alphabet. 2003. (Guess-me Poems & Puzzles Ser.). (Illus.). 64p. pap. 11.95 (978-0-439-38529-9(6) , Teaching Resources) Scholastic, Inc.

Freeman, Don. Corduroy's ABC Felt Read & Play. McCue, Lisa, illus. 2007. 10p. (J). (ps). pap. 16.99 (*978-0-670-06197-6(2) , Viking Juvenile) Penguin Group (USA) Inc.

Fremont, Victoria. A Is for Astronaut. 1999. (J). pap. 1.00 (978-0-486-40554-4(0)) Dover Pubns., Inc.

French, Vivian. I Spy ABC. Holmes, Sally, illus. 1999. (Read & Share Ser.). 24p. (J). (ps). pap. 3.99 (978-0-7636-0865-1(3)) Candlewick Pr.

Fried, Miriam. My Jelly Bean Book. 2005. (Illus.). (J). (978-1-57400-049-8(7)) Data Trace Publishing, Co.

Fuertes, Gloria. Abecedario - Don Hillario (Don Hillario's Alphabet) (SPA.). 40p. (J). 10.50 (978-84-305-7195-6(7)) Susaeta Ediciones, S.A. ESP. *Dist:* AIMS International Bks., Inc.

—Aurora, Brigida y Carlos. 2001. Tr. of Aurora, Brigida, & Carlos. (SPA.). 32p. (J). (ps-k). 10.95 (978-84-264-3717-4(6)) Lectorum Pubns., Inc.

Furlong Reynolds, Cynthia. L Is for Lobster: A Maine Alphabet. Brett, Jeannie, illus. 2001. 40p. (J). (ps-3). 17.95 (978-1-58536-024-6(4)) Sleeping Bear Pr.

Gagnon, Lauren. An Exeter Alphabet: Learning about Exeter from a to Z. 2005. (J). per. (978-1-933002-05-7(0)) PublishingWorks.

Gaiman, Neil. Dangerous Alphabet. Grimly, Gris, illus. 2008. 32p. (J). 17.99 (*978-0-06-078333-4(8)); lib. bdg. 18.89 (*978-0-06-078334-1(6)) HarperCollins Pubs.

Galvin, Laura Gates. Alphabet of Ocean Animals. 2007. (Illus.). 40p. 15.95 (*978-1-59249-690-7(3)) Soundprints.

—Princess ABCs. 2004. (Illus.). 36p. (J). bds. 12.99 incl. audio compact disk (978-1-59069-412-1(0) , 1A107) Studio Mouse LLC.

—Winnie the Pooh Take-with-Me Alphabet. 2006. 36p. 12.99 (978-1-59069-480-0(5)) Studio Mouse LLC.

A
B

Gant, Robert, illus. My Big Box of Letters. gif. ed. 2005. 64p. (J). cd-rom 24.95 (978-1-57791-193-7(8)) Brighter Minds Children's Publishing.

Garfield, Valerie. Detective Dog & the Disappearing Donuts: Letter D. 2001. (Illus.). 16p. (ps-1). pap. 2.25 (978-0-439-16527-3(X)) Scholastic, Inc.

—Monday's Miserable Monday: Letter M. 2001. (Alpha Tales Ser.). (Illus.). 16p. (J). (ps-1). pap. 2.25 (978-0-439-16536-5(9)) Scholastic, Inc.

Garnett, Sammie & Pallotta, Jerry. U.S. Navy Alphabet Book. Bolster, Rob, illus. 2005. 32p. (J). 17.95 (978-1-57091-586-4(5)) Charlesbridge Publishing, Inc.

Garnett, Sammie, et al. U.S. Navy Alphabet Book. 2005. (Illus.). 32p. (J). pap. 7.95 (978-1-57091-587-1(3)) Charlesbridge Publishing, Inc.

Gaydos, Nora. All about the ABC's. Sams, B. B., illus. 2006. (Now I'm Reading! Ser.). 112p. (J). (ps-1). 16.99 (978-1-58476-410-6(4) , IKIDS) Innovative Kids.

Gelber, Lisa & Roberts, Jody. P Is for Peanut: A Photographic ABC. 2007. (Getty Trust Publications: J. Paul Getty Museum Ser.). (Illus.). 58p. 9.95 (***978-0-89236-878-5(0)***) Getty Pubns.

George, Pamela & Brown, Walter M. The North Carolina Alphabet. 2005. 60p. (J). (978-0-932112-50-7(1)) Carolina Wren Pr.

Gillis, Jennifer Blizin. Candle Time ABC. 2002. (Candle Time Ser.). (Illus.). 24p. (J). (ps-1). lib. bdg. 18.50 (978-1-58810-532-5(6)) Heinemann Library.

Gillis, Jennifer Blizin & Jordan, Denise M. Candle Time ABC. 2002. (Candle Time Ser.). (Illus.). 24p. (J). (ps-1). pap. 5.25 (978-1-58810-741-1(8) , 91383) Heinemann Library.

Giordano, Jean. Alphabet for Young Eckists. Epps, SArah, illus. 2nd ed. 2007. (J). pap. (***978-1-57043-245-3(7)***) Eckankar.

Girnis, Meg. ABC for You & Me. Green, Shirley Leamon, photos by. 2000. (Concept Book Ser.). (Illus.). 32p. (J). (ps-2). 15.95 (978-0-8075-0101-6(8)) Whitman, Albert & Co.

Glaser, Byron & Higashi, Sandra. The Zolo A-B-Z: An Alphabet Book. Glaser, Byron & Higashi, Sandra, illus. 2003. (Illus.). 44p. (J). (ps-1). 15.95 (978-0-8109-4260-8(7)) Abrams, Harry N. , Inc.

Glover, Maria Robinson. Who Do I Want to Be? Contemporary Black Women from A to Z. Glover, Maria Robinson, illus. 2006. (J). 16.95 (978-0-9787940-0-2(1)) Hot-Comb Pr.

Golden Books Staff. Alphabet Skills. 2000. (Step Ahead Ser.). (Illus.). 64p. (J). (gr. k). pap. 3.99 (978-0-307-03664-3(2) , 03664, Golden Bks.) Random Hse. Children's Bks.

—Count along with Thomas. 2000. (Thomas the Tank Engine Ser.). (J). (ps-3). bds. 12.99 (978-0-307-71308-7(3) , Golden Bks.) Random Hse., Inc.

—Fun with Letters. 2000. (Disney Ser.). (Illus.). 48p. (J). (ps-k). pap. 2.99 (978-0-307-20130-0(9) , 20130, Golden Bks.) Random Hse. Children's Bks.

—Pat the Bunny Alphabet Book. LV Studio Staff, illus. 2006. (Pat the Bunny Ser.). 30p. (J). (gr. k-ps). 10.95 (978-0-375-83550-6(4) , Golden Bks.) Random Hse. Children's Bks.

Goldman, Todd Harris. The Zoo I Drew. 2008. (J). (***978-0-375-85201-5(8)); (978-0-375-95201-2(2)***) Random Hse., Inc.

Goldsberry, U'ilani. A Is for Aloha: A Hawaii Alphabet. Yee, Tammy, illus. 2005. (Discover America State by State Ser.). 40p. (J). (gr. k-5). 17.95 (978-1-58536-146-5(1)) Sleeping Bear Pr.

Good, Phyllis Pellman. Plain Pig's ABC's: A Day on Plain Pig's Amish Farm. Benner, Cheryl A., illus. 1998. 24p. (J). (ps-1). 14.95 (978-1-56148-251-1(X)) Good Bks.

Goosby, Michelle. EZ Reading from A to Z. 2001. 108p. (J). pap. 13.00 (978-0-8059-4834-9(1)) Dorrance Publishing Co., Inc.

Gordon, Bob. Wipe Clean ABC. 2007. (Illus.). 12p. (J). (ps-3). bds. 10.99 (***978-1-84610-432-9(7)***) Make Believe Ideas GBR. *Dist:* Ingram Pub. Services.

Gorman, Lovenia. A Is for Algonquin: An Ontario Alphabet. Rose, Melanie, illus. rev. ed. 2005. (World/Country Alphabet Ser.). 40p. (J). (gr. k-5). 17.95 (978-1-58536-263-9(8)) Sleeping Bear Pr.

Grassby, Donna. A Seaside Alphabet. Tooke, Susan, illus. 2000. 32p. (J). (gr. 1-3). 19.95 (978-0-88776-516-2(5)) Tundra Bks., Inc./Livres Toundra, Inc. CAN. *Dist:* Random Hse., Inc.

Greene, Carol. "C" Is for California. Gorenkamp, Michelle, illus. 2000. (Alpha Flight Bks.). 60p. (J). (ps-3). 17.95 (978-1-892920-27-0(1)) GHB Publishers, LLC.

—"M" Is for Missouri. Dorenkamp, Michelle, illus. 2000. (Alpha Flight Bks.). 60p. (J). (ps-3). 17.95 (978-1-892920-26-3(3)) GHB Publishers, LLC.

Grishaver, Joel Lurie, et al. Marilyn Price & Friends Present the Alphabet from Alef to Bet. Price, Marilyn, photos by. 1998. (HEB., Illus.). 96p. (J). (gr. k-3). pap. 9.95 (978-0-933873-99-5(9)) Torah Aura Productions.

Gritz, Ona. Tangerines & Tea, My Grandparents & Me: An Alphabet Book. Heo, Yumi, illus. 2005. 32p. (J). (ps-3). 15.95 (978-0-8109-5871-5(6) , Abrams Bks. for Young Readers) Abrams, Harry N. , Inc.

Gritz, Ona, et al. Rolling Stone 1,000 Covers: A History of the Most Influential Magazine in Pop Culture. Heo, Yumi, illus. 2006. 568p. 35.00 (978-0-8109-5865-4(1)) Abrams, Harry N. , Inc.

Grobler, Piet. Little Bird's ABC. Grobler, Piet, illus. 2005. (Illus.). 52p. (J). (ps-3). 8.95 (978-1-932425-52-9(7) , Lemniscaat) Boyds Mills Pr.

Grodin, Elissa. A Citizen's Alphabet. 2007. 40p. pap. 7.95 (***978-1-58536-328-5(6)***) Sleeping Bear Pr.

Grossman, Bill. My Little Sister Hugged an Ape. Hawkes, Kevin, illus. 2004. 40p. (J). (gr. k-3). 16.95 (978-0-517-80017-1(9)); lib. bdg. 18.99 (978-0-517-80018-8(7)) Random Hse. Children's Bks. (Knopf Bks. for Young Readers).

Group/McGraw-Hill, Wright. Sign Language Alphabet Cards. (Professional Resources Ser.). 19.50 (978-0-7802-4383-5(8)) Wright Group, The.

Gruelle, Johnny. Raggedy Ann's Alphabet Book. Gruelle, Johnny, illus. 2004. reprint ed. pap. 15.95 (978-1-4179-1691-7(5)) Kessinger Publishing, LLC.

Guy, Pauline & Pierre-Louis, Jerry. Alphabet Rocks: Happy Kids Rock. 2006. 26p. (J). 12.99 (***978-0-9769364-0-4(2)***) Golden Eagle Publishing Hse., Inc.

Hall, Francie. Appalachian ABCs. Oehm, Kent, illus. 2nd ed. 1998. 56p. (J). (ps-3). 16.95 (978-1-57072-087-1(8)) Overmountain Pr.

Hall, Pamela. ELEMENOPEE, the Day l, M, N, O & P Left the Abc's. Williamson, James, illus. 2005. 16p. (J). 12.95 (978-1-58117-209-6(5) , Intervisual/Piggy Toes) Dalmatian Pr.

Hallinan, P. K. ABC I Love You. 2003. (Illus.). 26p. (J). bds. 7.95 (978-0-8249-5458-1(0)) Ideals Pubns.

Hanson, Anders. Elephants Are Not Little! (Illus.). 23p. (J). (ps-3). 2006. 19.93 (978-1-59679-370-5(8) , Sand-Castle); 2005. pap. (978-1-59679-371-2(6)) ABDO Publishing Co.

—Liz & Len. 2005. (First Sounds Ser.). (Illus.). 23p. (J). pap. (978-1-59679-173-2(X)) ABDO Publishing Co.

—Meg & Mark. 2005. (First Sounds Ser.). (Illus.). 23p. (J). pap. (978-1-59679-175-6(6)); lib. bdg. 19.93 (978-1-59679-174-9(8)) ABDO Publishing Co.

—Nan & Nick. 2005. (First Sounds Ser.). (Illus.). 23p. (J). pap. (978-1-59679-177-0(2)); lib. bdg. 19.93 (978-1-59679-176-3(4)) ABDO Publishing Co.

—Olga & Olaf. 2005. (First Sounds Ser.). (Illus.). 23p. pap. (978-1-59679-179-4(9)); (J). lib. bdg. 19.93 (978-1-59679-178-7(0)) ABDO Publishing Co.

—Olive & Oscar. 2005. (First Sounds Ser.). (Illus.). 23p. pap. (978-1-59679-181-7(0)); (J). lib. bdg. 19.93 (978-1-59679-180-0(2)) ABDO Publishing Co.

—Pam & Pete. 2005. (First Sounds Ser.). (Illus.). 23p. (J). pap. (978-1-59679-183-1(7)); lib. bdg. 19.93 (978-1-59679-182-4(9)) ABDO Publishing Co.

—Quinn & Quenton. 2005. (First Sounds Ser.). (Illus.). 23p. (J). pap. (978-1-59679-185-5(3)); lib. bdg. 19.93 (978-1-59679-184-8(5)) ABDO Publishing Co.

—Ruth & Rob. 2005. (First Sounds Ser.). 23p. (J). pap. (978-1-59679-187-9(X)); lib. bdg. 19.93 (978-1-59679-186-2(1)) ABDO Publishing Co.

—Sara & Sam. 2005. (First Sounds Ser.). (Illus.). 23p. (J). pap. (978-1-59679-189-3(6)); lib. bdg. 19.93 (978-1-59679-188-6(8)) ABDO Publishing Co.

—Sharon & Shawn. 2005. (First Sounds Ser.). (Illus.). 23p. (J). (ps-3). lib. bdg. 19.93 (978-1-59679-190-9(X)) ABDO Publishing Co.

Hanwell, Kent. The Musical Letters, 3 bks., Set. 2000. (Orig.). (J). pap. 19.95 (978-0-9699149-3-8(8)) Hanwell Production CAN. *Dist:* Hushion Hse. Publishing, Ltd.

Harcourt School Publishers Staff. Alphabet Book, Bk. 2. 3rd ed. 2002. (Trophies Reading Program Ser.). (Illus.). pap. 50.00 (978-0-15-329266-8(0)) Harcourt Schl. Pubs.

—Alphabet Book Collection. 3rd ed. 2002. (Trophies Reading Program Ser.). (Illus.). (gr. k-6). pap. 128.70 (978-0-15-329256-9(3)) Harcourt Schl. Pubs.

—The Edible Pyramid: Library Edition. 1999. (Collections Ser.). (Illus.). (J). 4.70 (978-0-15-314348-9(7)) Harcourt Schl. Pubs.

—From Anne to Zach: Little Book. 2000. (Collections Ser.). (Illus.). (J). pap. 10.20 (978-0-15-314508-7(0)) Harcourt Schl. Pubs.

Harder Tangvald, Christine. God's ABCs... For Me! 1999. (for Me! Bks.). (Illus.). 16p. (J). (ps). pap. 4.99 (978-0-7642-2282-5(1)) Bethany Hse. Pubs.

—Whoo! Moo! Cock-a-Doodle-Doo! Conteh-Morgan, Jane, illus. 2000. 24p. (J). (ps-k). bds. 7.99 (978-0-570-07096-2(1)) Concordia Publishing Hse.

Harley, Avis. Leap into Poetry: More ABCs of Poetry. Harley, Avis, illus. 2003. (Illus.). 48p. (J). (gr. 2-4). 19.95 (978-1-56397-673-5(0)) Boyds Mills Pr.

Harris, Marie. G Is for Granite: A New Hampshire Alphabet. Holman, Karen, illus. 2002. 40p. (J). 17.95 (978-1-58536-083-3(X)) Sleeping Bear Pr.

The Hat Alphabet Book. 2000. 66p. pap. 22.95 (978-0-9701944-0-4(4)) Aiglet Pr.

Hathersmith, June. From Akebu to Zapotec: A Book of Bibleless Peoples. Roder, Alice, illus. 2002. 31p. (J). pap. (978-0-938978-28-2(4)) Wycliffe Bible Translators.

Hayashi, Leslie Ann. A Fishy Alphabet in Hawaii. Bishop, Kathleen Wong, illus. 2007. (J). (***978-1-56647-830-4(8)***) Mutual Publishing LLC.

Hayes, Larry E. My Name Starts with J. Anderson, Airlie, illus. 2004. (My Name Starts With Ser.). 31p. (J). 12.95 (978-0-9725292-2-8(5)) Inspire Pubns.

—My Name Starts with M. Anderson, Airlie, illus. Hayes, Larry E., photos by. 2004. (My Name Starts With Ser.). 32p. (J). 12.95 (978-0-9725292-3-5(3) , 1) Inspire Pubns.

—My Name Starts with S. Anderson, Airlie, illus. Hayes, Larry E., photos by. 2003. (My Name Starts With Ser.). 32p. 10.95 (978-0-9725292-1-1(7)) Inspire Pubns.

Hayes, Larry E. & Anderson, Airlie. My Name Starts with A. 2002. (My Name Starts With Ser.). (Illus.). 32p. 10.95 (978-0-9725292-0-4(9)) Inspire Pubns.

Heck, Cathy. Zoophabet 123: Board Book with Plush Toy. rev. ed. 2007. 10p. bds. 12.99 (***978-1-4037-2553-0(5)***) Dalmatian Pr.

Heck, Cathy, illus. Zoophabet Abc. 2006. 20p. bds. 5.99 (978-1-4037-1989-8(6)) Dalmatian Pr.

Heiman, Sarah. Country ABCs: Australia ABCs; Egypt ABCs; Germany ABCs; Japan ABCs; Kenya ABCs; Mexico ABCs, 6 bks. 2003. (Illus.). (J). (gr. k-5). lib. bdg. 135.60 (978-1-4048-0072-4(7)) Picture Window Bks.

Heller, Ruth. Merriam-Webster's Alphabet Book. Heller, Ruth, illus. 2005. (Illus.). 32p. (J). (gr. k). 12.95 (978-0-87779-023-5(X) , MER-23) Merriam-Webster, Inc.

Helman, Andrea. O Is for Orca: An Alphabet Book. Wolfe, Art, illus. Wolfe, Art, photos by. 2003. 32p. (J). pap., pap. 10.95 (978-1-57061-392-0(3)) Sasquatch Bks.

Herrington, Nancy. An Alphabet Adventure with Rose. Herrington, Nancy, illus. 2002. (Laughing & Learning Ser.: Vol. 1). (Illus.). 26p. (J). pap. 6.95 (978-0-9711299-0-0(8)) Herrington, Nancy Publishing.

Hershenhorn, Esther. I Is for Illinois. Havekost, Rebecca, illus. 2001. (Alpha Flight Bks.). 60p. (J). (ps-3). 17.95 (978-1-892920-41-6(7)) GHB Publishers, LLC.

Herzog, Brad. A Football Alphabet. 2007. 40p. pap. 7.95 (***978-1-58536-337-7(5)***) Sleeping Bear Pr.

—K Is for Kick: A Soccer Alphabet. Rose, Melanie, illus. rev. ed. 2003. 40p. (J). 16.95 (978-1-58536-130-4(5)) Sleeping Bear Pr.

—P Is for Putt: A Golf Alphabet. Langton, Bruce, illus. 2005. 40p. (J). 16.95 (978-1-58536-252-3(2)) Sleeping Bear Pr.

—R Is for Race: A Stock Car Alphabet. Bready, Jane Gilltrap, illus. 2006. 40p. (J). (gr. k-5). 16.95 (978-1-58536-272-1(7)) Sleeping Bear Pr.

—A Soccer Alphabet. rev. ed. 2007. 40p. pap. 7.95 (***978-1-58536-339-1(1)***) Sleeping Bear Pr.

Herzog, Brad. T Is for Touchdown: A Football Alphabet. Stacy, Alan, illus. 2004. 40p. (J). 16.95 (978-1-58536-233-2(6)) Sleeping Bear Pr.

Herzog, Joyce. Exploring the Alphabet: Student Activity Book. Sinclair, Angie & Sinclair, Dan, eds. 2005. (J). spiral bd. 15.00 (***978-1-887225-42-7(0)***) JoyceHerzog-.com, Inc.

—LetterMaster: Comic Book. 2004. (J). 6.00 (***978-1-887225-17-5(X)***) JoyceHerzog.com, Inc.

Heshka, Ryan. Ryan Heshka's ABC Spookshow. 2007. (Illus.). 58p. (gr. k up). 12.95 (***978-1-894965-68-2(X)***) Simply Read Bks. CAN. *Dist:* Perseus Distribution.

Hide & Seek ABC. 2007. (Illus.). 10p. bds. 14.95 (***978-1-59125-795-0(6)***, Penton Kids) Penton Overseas, Inc.

Higgins, Maxwell. Bubble Bear: Letter B. 2001. (Illus.). 16p. (ps-1). pap. 2.25 (978-0-439-16525-9(3)) Scholastic, Inc.

—Vera Viper's Valentine: Letter V. 2001. (Alpha Tales Ser.). (Illus.). 16p. (ps-1). pap. 2.25 (978-0-439-16545-7(8)) Scholastic, Inc.

Highlights for Children Editorial Staff & Boyds Mills Press Staff. The Timbertoes ABC Alphabet Book. Hunt, Judith, illus. 2003. 32p. (J). (ps up). 7.95 (978-1-56397-604-9(8)) Boyds Mills Pr.

Hines Weaver, Dorothy. California A to Z. Wacker, Kay, illus. 1999. 32p. (J). (ps-1). 6.95 (978-0-87358-682-5(4) , Rising Moon Bks. for Young Readers) Northland Publishing.

—California A to Z. 1999. (J). 13.75 (978-0-606-17023-9(5)) Tandem Library Bks.

Hinkler Books. Slide & Learn ABC. rev. ed. 2005. (Illus.). 12p. (J). (gr. 3-6). 7.95 (978-1-74157-602-3(4)) Hinkler Bks. Pty, Ltd. AUS. *Dist:* Penton Overseas, Inc.

Ho, Jane. ABC Alphabet Book, No. 1. 29p. (J). (ps). 20.00 (978-0-9619126-0-4(X)) Ho's, Jane Children Bks.

Hobbie, Holly. Puddle's ABC. Hobbie, Holly, illus. 2000. (Toot & Puddle Ser.: Bk. 4). (Illus.). 48p. (J). (ps-1). 14.95 (978-0-316-36593-2(9)) Little Brown & Co.

Hoena, B. A. Toys ABC: An Alphabet Book. 2004. (A+ Alphabet Books). (Illus.). 17p. (J). 22.60 (978-0-7368-2609-9(2) , Aplus Bks.) Capstone Pr., Inc.

—Weather ABC: An Alphabet Book. 2005. (A+ Alphabet Books). (Illus.). 32p. (J). 22.60 (978-0-7368-3666-1(7)); 22.60 (978-0-7368-3667-8(5)) Capstone Pr., Inc.

Hoffman, Joan. Alphabet Fun. 2006. 64p. (J). (ps-k). pap. 7.99 (***978-1-58947-746-9(4)***) School Zone Publishing Co.

Holliday, Patricia. A Is for Anjelina: an Introduction to ABC's And 123's. 2005. 29p. (J). 12.26 (978-1-4116-4471-7(9)) Lulu.com.

Holmes, Stephen. Alphabet Zoo. (J). 2003. bds. 5.98 (978-0-7525-8922-0(9)); 2002. 32p. 7.98 (978-0-7525-3999-7(X)) Parragon, Inc.

Hop, L. L. C. Hooked on Pre-K: ABCs. 2006. 64p. 3.79 (978-1-931020-62-6(0)) HOP, LLC.

HOP, LLC. Hooked on ABCs Super Activity Kit. 2006. (J). (ps). 9.99 (978-1-933863-16-0(1)) HOP, LLC.

Hopkins, Lee Bennett. Alphathoughts: Alphabet Poems from A to Z. Baggetta, Marla, illus. 2003. 32p. (J). (gr. k-2). 15.95 (978-1-56397-979-8(9)) Boyds Mills Pr.

Hopkins, Mary R. Animal Alphabet: On the Land, in the Sky or Sea, Meet God's Creatures from a to Z. Francisco, Wendy, illus. 2003. 32p. (ps-1). 12.99 (978-0-89107-968-2(8)) Crossway Bks.

Horne, Jane. ABC: First Concepts. 2007. (Busy Baby Ser.). (Illus.). 12p. (ps-k). per., bds. 6.95 (***978-1-84610-467-1(X)***) Make Believe Ideas GBR. *Dist:* Ingram Pub. Services.

Hosta, Dar. I Love the Alphabet. 2004. (J). 16.95 (978-0-9721967-1-0(4)) Brown Dog Bks.

Houghton Mifflin Company Editors. Curious George Discovery Day. 2007. (Illus.). 14p. (J). (gr. k-ps). bds. 13.95 (***978-0-618-73761-1(8)***) Houghton Mifflin Co. Trade & Reference Div.

Howland, Naomi. ABCDrive! A Car Trip Alphabet. 2000. (Illus.). 32p. (J). (gr. k-3). 5.95 (978-0-618-04034-6(X) , Clarion Bks.) Houghton Mifflin Co. Trade & Reference Div.

Hudson, Cheryl Willis. Afro-Bets A, B, C Book. Hudson, Cheryl Willis, illus. 2002. (Afro-Bets Ser.). (Illus.). 24p. (J). (ps-1). pap. 3.50 (978-0-439-42917-7(X) , Cartwheel Bks.) Scholastic, Inc.

—Afro-Bets A B C Book. rev. ed. 1999. (Illus.). 24p. (J). (ps-1). pap. 3.95 (978-0-940975-88-0(2)) Just Us Bks., Inc.

Hughes, Shirley. Alfie's ABC. Hughes, Shirley, illus. 1998. (Illus.). 32p. (J). (ps-k). 16.00 (978-0-688-16126-2(X)) HarperCollins Pubs.

Hughes, Shirley. Alfie's Alphabet. 2007. (Illus.). 32p. (J). pap. 8.95 (***978-0-09-940902-1(X)***, Red Fox) Random Hse. Children's Bks. GBR. *Dist:* Independent Pubs. Group.

—Alfie's Alphabet. Hughes, Shirley, illus. 1999. (Illus.). 30p. (J). 6.99 (978-1-58048-084-0(5)) Sandvik Publishing.

—Alfie's Alphabet. 2007. (Illus.). 32p. (J). bds. 7.95 (***978-0-370-32348-0(3)***) Transworld Publishers Ltd. GBR. *Dist:* Independent Pubs. Group.

Hull, Bunny. Alphabet Affirmations. Saint-James, Synthia, illus. 2000. (ps-3). pap. 10.95 incl. audio (978-0-9673762-3-3(8) , BH103PKG) BrassHeart Music.

Hummingbird, Sandy & Hummingbird, Jesse. Powwow ABC Coloring Book. 2000. (Illus.). 28p. (ps-3). 4.95 (978-1-57067-096-1(X)) Book Publishing Co., The.

Hyperion Staff. First Signing ABC. 2007. 64p. (J). (ps-3). 16.99 (978-1-4231-0248-9(7)) Hyperion Pr.

I Can Print A to Z (Modern) 2000. (Wipe-Off Activity Bks.). (Illus.). 16p. (J). (ps-1). wbk. ed. 3.79 (978-1-889319-79-7(1)) Trend Enterprises, Inc.

I Love to Read (Spanish) 2007. (Illus.). bds. 15.95 (***978-1-59572-064-1(2)***) Star Bright Bks., Inc.

Iguana on Ice. 2001. (ps-2). lib. bdg. 9.80 (978-0-613-32677-3(6)) Tandem Library Bks.

Ikids. My Giant ABC Bath Book. Hine, Eileen, illus. 2005. (Soft Shapes Numbers Ser.). 2p. (J). (ps-17). 14.99 (978-1-58476-356-7(6)) Innovative Kids.

Inkpen, Mick. A to Z: An Alphabet Adventure. 2001. (Kipper Ser.). (Illus.). 64p. (J). (ps-2). 16.95 (978-0-15-202594-6(4) , Red Wagon Bks.) Harcourt Children's Bks.

—Kipper's A to Z: An Alphabet Adventure. 2005. (Kipper Ser.). (Illus.). 64p. (J). (ps-ps). pap. 7.00 (978-0-15-205441-0(3) , Red Wagon Bks.) Harcourt Children's Bks.

Insera, Rose & Insera, Rose. Alphabet. Insera, Rose, illus. 2005. (Illus.). 15p. (J). (gr. 3-6). 8.95 (978-1-74157-267-4(3)) Hinkler Bks. Pty, Ltd. AUS. *Dist:* Penton Overseas, Inc.

A Is for Algonquin: Ont Alpha. 2005. 8.95 (***978-1-58536-297-4(2)***) Sleeping Bear Pr.

Isadora, Rachel. ABC Pop! Isadora, Rachel, illus. 2002. (Illus.). (J). 22.72 (978-0-7587-1898-3(5)) Book Wholesalers, Inc.

—ABC Pop! 2001. (Illus.). (J). (978-0-606-21013-3(X)) Tandem Library Bks.

—On Your Toes: A Ballet ABC. Isadora, Rachel, illus. 2003. (Illus.). 40p. (J). 17.99 (978-0-06-050238-6(X)) Harper-Collins Pubs.

Island Style Alphabet. 2000. (J). 12.99 (978-0-89610-442-6(7)); 12.99 (978-0-89610-454-9(0)) Island Heritage Publishing.

Island Style Alphabets: Color & Activity Book. 2000. (J). 5.99 (978-0-89610-453-2(2)) Island Heritage Publishing.

Jackaman, Philippa. ABC Kaleidoscope Book. Walsh, Mike, illus. 16p. (J). bds. (978-1-84322-126-5(8)) Alligator Bks. Ltd.

James, Diane. Letters. 2001. (Crafty Ideas Ser.). (J). (gr. 2-7). 9.95 (978-1-58728-264-5(X)); pap. 5.95 (978-1-58728-123-5(6)) T&N Children's Publishing. (Two Can Publishing).

James, Helen Foster. S Is for S'mores: A Camping Alphabet. Judge, Lita, illus. rev. ed. 2007. 40p. (J). 17.95 (***978-1-58536-302-5(2)***) Sleeping Bear Pr.

Jarboe, Tracy & Sadler, Stefani. Cut, Paste & Write ABC Activity Pages: 26 Lessons That Use Art & Alliterative Poetry to Build Phonemic Awareness, Teach Letter Sounds, & Help Children Really Learn the Alphabet. 2006. 80p. pap. 12.99 (978-0-439-57630-7(X) , Teaching Resources) Scholastic, Inc.

Jarrie, Martin, illus. ABC USA. 2005. 32p. 14.95 (978-1-4027-1619-5(2)) Sterling Publishing Co., Inc.

Jarvis, Dennis R. Alphabet World Tour. Jarvis, Dennis R., illus. 1999. (Illus.). 8p. (J). (gr. k-6). mass mkt. 6.95 (978-0-9670826-0-8(9)) Jarvis, Dennis R.

Jay, Alison. ABC: A Child's First Alphabet Book. Jay, Alison, illus. 2005. 32p. (J). (ps). bds. 8.99 (978-0-525-47524-8(9) , Dutton Juvenile) Penguin Group (USA) Inc.

Johnson, Bob. The Squatland Chronicles: Book 5 - the Dreaded Swamp of the Bubble Dragon. 2005. (Illus.). 56p. (J). per. 11.00 (978-1-59453-853-7(0) , Airleaf Publishing) Airleaf Publishing & Bookselling.

Johnson, Crockett. Harold's ABC. Johnson, Crockett, illus. 2002. (Illus.). (J). 14.43 (978-0-7587-2696-4(1)) Book Wholesalers, Inc.

Johnson, Odette & Johnson, Bruce. Apples, Alligators & Also Alphabets. (Illus.). 26p. (978-1-55005-077-6(X)) Fitzhenry & Whiteside, Ltd.

Johnson, Russ & Johnson, Annie. My Florida Alphabet. 2007. (Illus.). 63p. (J). 14.95 (***978-1-56164-392-9(0)***) Pineapple Pr., Inc.

Johnson, Stephen T. Alphabet City. Johnson, Stephen T., illus. 2002. (Illus.). (J). 14.04 (978-0-7587-0088-9(1)) Book Wholesalers, Inc.

—Alphabet City. 1999. (Illus.). 32p. (J). (ps-3). pap. 6.99 (978-0-14-055904-0(3) , Puffin) Penguin Group (USA) Inc.

—Alphabet City. 1999. (J). 13.79 (978-0-606-17258-5(0)) Tandem Library Bks.

Jordan, Denise M. Circus Clown ABC. 2002. (Circus Ser.). 24p. (J). (ps-1). pap. 5.25 (978-1-58810-754-1(X)); (Illus.). lib. bdg. 18.50 (978-1-58810-546-2(6)) Heinemann Library.

Joyce, Susan. ABC Nature Riddles. DuBosque, Doug, illus. 2004. (ABC Riddles Ser.). 32p. (J). (ps-k). (978-0-939217-53-3(8)) Peel Productions, Inc.

Kalman, Bobbie. The ABCs of Animals. 2007. (ABCs of the Natural World Ser.). (Illus.). 32p. (J). (gr. 1-5). pap. ***978-0-7787-3430-7(7))** Crabtree Publishing Co.

—The ABCs of Habitats. 2007. 32p. (J). (gr. 6-10). pap. ***978-0-7787-3431-4(5))** Crabtree Publishing Co.

—The ABCs of Oceans. 2007. (ABCs of the Natural World Ser.). (Illus.). 32p. (J). (gr. 1-5). pap. ***978-0-7787-3432-1(3))** Crabtree Publishing Co.

—The ABCs of Plants. 2007. 32p. (J). (gr. 6-10). pap. ***978-0-7787-3433-8(1))** Crabtree Publishing Co.

—Christmas Long Ago from A to Z. 1999. (AlphaBasiCs Ser.). (Illus.). 32p. (J). (gr. 2-3). pap. (978-0-86505-415-8(0)); lib. bdg. (978-0-86505-385-4(5)) Crabtree Publishing Co.

—School from A to Z. 1999. (AlphaBasiCs Ser.). (Illus.). 32p. (J). (gr. 1-2). pap. (978-0-86505-418-9(5)) Crabtree Publishing Co.

Kalman, Bobbie & Crossingham, John. The Earth from A to Z. 1999. (AlphaBasiCs Ser.). (Illus.). 32p. (J). (gr. 2-3). lib. bdg. (978-0-86505-383-0(9)) Crabtree Publishing Co.

Kalman, Maira. What Pete Ate from a to Z. 2003. (gr. k-3). lib. bdg. 15.30 (978-0-613-86703-0(3)) Tandem Library Bks.

—What Pete Ate from A-Z. 2003. (Illus.). 48p. (J). pap. 6.99 (978-0-14-250159-7(X) , Puffin) Penguin Group (USA) Inc.

—What Pete Ate from A-Z. Kalman, Maira, illus. 2001. (Illus.). 40p. (J). (ps-4). 15.99 (978-0-399-23362-3(8) , Putnam Juvenile) Penguin Group (USA) Inc.

Kangeroo Kazoo. 2001. (ps-2). lib. bdg. 9.80 (978-0-613-32735-0(7)) Tandem Library Bks.

Katie. The Sunday Alphabet of Animals. 1998. (Illus.). 112p. (J). (ps-3). 10.00 (978-1-57683-089-5(6)) NavPress Publishing Group.

Kelley, Gary. T is for Toscana. 2003. (Illus.). 40p. 17.95 (978-1-56846-177-9(1) , Creative Editions) Creative Co., The.

Kerns, Thelma. Flea Market Fleas From A to Z. Owens, Bryant, illus. 1998. 32p. (J). (ps-3). 9.95 (978-1-57072-085-7(1)) Overmountain Pr.

Kidzup Productions Staff. ABC Theater. 2000. (Interactive Learning Kits Ser.). (Illus.). 24p. (J). (gr. k-2). pap. 8.99 incl. audio (978-1-894281-45-4(4)) Kidzup Entertainment CAN. *Dist:* Penton Overseas, Inc.

Kinast, Susan. Play from A to Z. 2006. (J). lib. bdg. 19.95 ***978-1-933732-11-4(3)** , Bear Hug Bks.) MidAmerica Publishing Co.

Kirk, David. Miss Spider's ABC. Kirk, David, illus. 1998. (Miss Spider Ser.). (Illus.). 32p. (J). (ps-2). pap. 16.95 (978-0-590-28279-6(4)) Scholastic, Inc.

—Miss Spider's ABC: New Board Book Edition. Kirk, David, illus. 2000. (Miss Spider Ser.). (Illus.). 32p. (J). (ps-2). bds. 8.95 (978-0-439-13747-8(0) , Scholastic Reference) Scholastic, Inc.

Kissick, Elizabeth Beal. Singing the ABC's Through KC. 2000. (Illus.). 32p. (J). (ps-3). pap. 19.95 (978-1-58597-052-0(2)) Leathers Publishing.

Kline, Trish & Donev, Mary. The Busy Preschooler's Guide to Learning. 2007. (Illus.). 128p. (J). per. 60.00 ***978-1-934307-17-5(3))** Ghost Hunter Productions.

—Celebration of Letters A & B: Busy Preschoolers. 2007. (Illus.). 16p. (J). per. 20.00 ***978-1-934307-04-5(1))** Ghost Hunter Productions.

—Celebration of Letters C & D: Busy Preschoolers. 2007. (Illus.). 16p. (J). per. 20.00 ***978-1-934307-05-2(X))** Ghost Hunter Productions.

—Celebration of Letters E & F: Busy Preschoolers. 2007. (Illus.). 16p. (J). per. 20.00 ***978-1-934307-06-9(8))** Ghost Hunter Productions.

—Celebration of Letters G & H: Busy Preschoolers. 2007. (Illus.). 16p. (J). per. 20.00 ***978-1-934307-07-6(6))** Ghost Hunter Productions.

—Celebration of Letters I & J: Busy Preschoolers. 2007. (Illus.). 16p. (J). per. 20.00 ***978-1-934307-08-3(4))** Ghost Hunter Productions.

—Celebration of Letters K & L: Busy Preschoolers. 2007. (Illus.). 16p. (J). per. 20.00 ***978-1-934307-09-0(2))** Ghost Hunter Productions.

—Celebration of Letters M & N: Busy Preschoolers. 2007. (Illus.). 16p. (J). per. 20.00 ***978-1-934307-10-6(6))** Ghost Hunter Productions.

—Celebration of Letters O & Q: Busy Preschoolers. 2007. (Illus.). 16p. (J). per. 20.00 ***978-1-934307-11-3(4))** Ghost Hunter Productions.

—Celebration of Letters P & R: Busy Preschoolers. 2007. (Illus.). 16p. (J). per. 20.00 ***978-1-934307-12-0(2))** Ghost Hunter Productions.

—Celebration of Letters S & T: Busy Preschoolers. 2007. (Illus.). 16p. (J). per. 20.00 ***978-1-934307-13-7(0))** Ghost Hunter Productions.

—Celebration of Letters U & V: Busy Preschoolers. 2007. (Illus.). 16p. (J). per. 20.00 ***978-1-934307-14-4(9))** Ghost Hunter Productions.

—Celebration of Letters W & X: Busy Preschoolers. 2007. (Illus.). 16p. (J). per. 20.00 ***978-1-934307-15-1(7))** Ghost Hunter Productions.

—Celebration of Letters Y & Z: Busy Preschoolers. 2007. (Illus.). 16p. (J). per. 20.00 ***978-1-934307-16-8(5))** Ghost Hunter Productions.

Klingel, Cynthia Fitterer & Noyed, Robert B. Smiles: The Sound of Long I. 1999. (Wonder Books Phonics: Vowels Ser.). (Illus.). 24p. (J). (ps-3). 21.36 (978-1-56766-732-5(5)) Child's World, Inc.

Knox, Barbara. Animal Babies ABC: An Alphabet of Animal Offspring. 2003. (A+ Alphabet Books). (Illus.). 17p. (J). (gr. k-1). 22.60 (978-0-7368-1680-9(1) , Aplus Bks.) Capstone Pr., Inc.

Knudsen, Natalie S. A Child's Garden of Flowers. Graham, Margaret Ann Baker, ed. Case, Teena Martin, illus. 2001. 64p. (J). lib. bdg. 9.95 (978-0-9710093-0-1(9)) Reiman Gardens.

koenigsberg, Phyllis & Winkler, Ziporah, creators. Color My Alef Bet. 2004. (J). (978-965-90462-5-6(1)) Mazo Pubs.

Kontis, Alethea. AlphaOops! The Day Z Went First. Kolar, Bob, illus. 2006. 56p. (J). (ps-3). 16.99 (978-0-7636-2728-7(3)) Candlewick Pr.

Kosraean Alphabet. 2004. (Illus.). 48p. 4.95 (978-1-57306-217-6(0)) Bess Pr., Inc.

Kratter, Paul. The Living Rain Forest: An Animal Alphabet. Kratter, Paul, illus. (Illus.). (J). 2006. 32p. pap. 8.95 (978-1-57091-465-2(6)); 2004. 64p. 17.95 (978-1-57091-603-8(9)) Charlesbridge Publishing, Inc.

Krause, Bill & Waner. From Abe to Zach. 3.99 (978-0-87162-636-3(5)) Warner Pr. Pubs.

Krull, Kathleen. M Is for Music. Innerst, Stacy, illus. 2003. 56p. (J). (ps-3). 17.00 (978-0-15-201438-4(1)) Harcourt Children's Bks.

Kumon Publishing, creator. ABCs Uppercase Write & Wipe! 2006. 32p. (J). 9.95 (978-1-933241-10-4(1)) Kumon Publishing North America, Inc.

Kumon Publishing Staff, ed. My Book of Alphabet Games. 2007. 80p. pap. 6.95 ***978-1-933241-36-4(5))** Kumon Publishing North America, Inc.

Kwas, Susan Estelle. ABC Block Books, 26 bks., Set. Kwas, Susan Estelle, illus. 1999. (Illus.). 8p. (J). (ps). bds. 24.95 (978-0-8118-2474-3(8)) Chronicle Bks. LLC.

Ladybird Books Staff. ABC, Vol. 1. 1998. (First Steps Ser.). (Illus.). 24p. (J). pap. 1.99 (978-0-7214-2606-8(9) , Dutton Juvenile) Penguin Group (USA) Inc.

Lakeshore Learning Materials, contrib. by. Read-along Alphabet Chants: Big Book. 2007. (J). pap. 19.95 ***978-1-59746-013-2(3))** Lakeshore Learning Materials.

—Read-along Alphabet Chants: Student Books. 2007. (J). pap. 16.95 ***978-1-59746-012-5(5))** Lakeshore Learning Materials.

—Spanish Alphabet Big Book. 2006. (SPA.). (J). pap. 19.95 ***978-1-59746-000-2(1))** Lakeshore Learning Materials.

Lamb, Stacey & Bowman, Crystal. My ABC Bible/My ABC Prayers. Lamb, Stacey, illus. 2001. (Illus.). 112p. (J). 9.99 (978-0-310-70160-6(0)) Zonderkidz.

Lamb Who Loved to Laugh. 2001. (ps-2). lib. bdg. 9.80 (978-0-613-32754-1(3)) Tandem Library Bks.

Landoll Inc. Staff. Letters Workbook. 2000. (Beginners Bible Ser.). (J). pap. 14.95 (978-1-56189-620-2(9) , American Education Publishing) School Specialty Publishing.

Larousse Color ABC y 123 (Amarillo), Vol. 1. 2003. (SPA., Illus.). 6p. (J). 2.98 (978-970-22-0163-2(2)) Larousse, Ediciones, S. A. de C. V. MEX. *Dist:* Giron Bks.

Lauria, David C. The Alphabet God's Way. Lauria, David C., illus. 1999. (Illus.). 56p. (J). (ps-6). pap. 12.00 (978-0-9676600-0-4(9)) Lauria, David C.

Lauture, Denize. Running the Road to ABC. Ruffins, Reynold, illus. 2000. 32p. (J). (gr. k-3). reprint ed. 6.99 (978-0-689-83165-2(X) , Aladdin) Simon & Schuster Children's Publishing.

—Running the Road to ABC. 2000. (gr. k-3). lib. bdg. 15.30 (978-0-613-23027-8(2)) Tandem Library Bks.

Layne, Steven & Layne, Deborah. A School Alphabet. 2007. 7.95 ***978-1-58536-331-5(6))** Sleeping Bear Pr.

Layne, Steven L. & Layne, Deborah Dover. P Is for Princess: A Royal Alphabet. Papp, Robert & Papp, Lisa, illus. rev. ed. 2007. 40p. (J). 17.95 ***978-1-58536-306-3(5))** Sleeping Bear Pr.

Leap Frog Leaping Letters Wipe off Mat. 2006. (J). 3.95 ***978-1-59545-088-3(2))** Learning Horizons, Inc.

LeapFrog Staff, compiled by. More Chores. 2001. (J). (ps-2). spiral bd. 14.95 (978-1-58605-064-1(8)) LeapFrog Enterprises, Inc.

—My First LeapPad: Richard Scarry ABC. 2001. (J). (ps-2). spiral bd. 12.99 (978-1-58605-217-1(9)) LeapFrog Enterprises, Inc.

LeapFrog Upper & Lowercase Letters. 2007. (J). 4.99 ***978-1-59545-134-7(X))** Learning Horizons, Inc.

Learn the Alphabet. 2004. (Alphabet & Counting Ser.). 12p. (J). bds. 5.99 (978-1-85997-809-2(6)) Byeway Bks.

Learn to Write: ABC. (Disney Princess Ser.). (Illus.). 20p. (J). bds. (978-2-7643-0216-3(9)) Phidal Publishing, Inc./ Editions Phidal, Inc.

Learn with Dick & Jane: Letters. 2004. (Dick & Jane Ser.). (Illus.). 32p. (J). (ps-1). pap. 3.99 (978-0-448-43549-7(7) , Grosset & Dunlap) Penguin Group (USA) Inc.

Learning Company Books Staff, ed. Reader Rabbit: ABC Order. 2003. (Illus.). 32p. (J). pap., wbk. ed. 3.99 (978-0-7630-7644-3(9)) Learning Co. Bks.

—Reader Rabbit: Alphabet. 2003. (Illus.). 32p. (J). pap., wbk. ed. 3.99 (978-0-7630-7577-4(9)) Learning Co. Bks.

—Reader Rabbit Fun with ABC's. 2004. (Illus.). 32p. (J). pap. 4.99 (978-0-7630-7737-2(2)) Learning Co. Bks.

Learning Lowercase Letters. 2003. (Kermit the Frog & Friends Ser.). (Illus.). 16p. (J). (ps-k). pap., act. bk. ed. 4.99 (978-1-57768-715-3(9)) School Specialty Publishing.

Leber, Nancy Jolson. (Pre-K) Pre-K Practice. 2007. (Clear & Simple Ser.). 64p. (J). pap. 4.99 (978-0-448-44434-5(8) , Grosset & Dunlap) Penguin Group (USA) Inc.

Leber, Nancy Jolson & Onish, Liane B. Letter Locker: Letters Aa-Zz. 2006. (Clear & Simple Workbooks Ser.). 64p. (J). (gr. k-k). 4.99 (978-0-448-44307-2(4) , Grosset & Dunlap) Penguin Group (USA) Inc.

Leman, Nora. The Alpha Building Crew. Hartmann, April, illus. 2005. (J). (978-1-58987-110-6(3)) Kindermusik International.

Lennon, Mary I. Mind Your P's & Q's: Your B's, D's & S's Too! Cruzen, Kenneth W., illus. 1998. 32p. (Orig.). (J). (gr. k-3). mass mkt. 6.25 (978-0-9658531-0-1(1)) Acrospire Bk. Pubs.

Lester, Mike. A Is for Salad. Lester, Mike, illus. 2002. 40p. (J). (ps-3). pap. 5.99 (978-0-698-11926-0(6) , Putnam Juvenile) Penguin Group (USA) Inc.

—Is for Salad. 2002. (gr. k-3). lib. bdg. 14.15 (978-0-613-85667-6(8)) Tandem Library Bks.

Lester, Vivian & Luhrs, Jeannece Jackson. Alphabet Alive Lesson Plans Books. 78p. (J). pap. 9.95 (978-1-929785-03-2(8)) Connexions Unlimited.

Letter Fun Wipe-Off Book. 2001. (Illus.). 16p. (J). (gr. k-2). mass mkt. 3.79 (978-1-889319-97-1(X)) Trend Enterprises, Inc.

Letters & Numbers. 2004. 12.99 incl. audio compact disk (978-1-57583-300-2(X)) Twin Sisters Productions, LLC.

Letters/Numbers, 4 bks., Set. Incl. Let's Add to Ten, Again & Again! Miller, Amanda. Michael, Joan J., illus. Levin, James, photos by. lib. bdg. 18.00 (978-0-531-14869-3(6)); Let's Count Critters, 1-20. Madden, Caolan. Vangsgard, Amy, illus. lib. bdg. 18.00 (978-0-531-14870-9(X)); Let's Have Fun with Alphabet Riddles. Madden, Caolan. 18.00 ***978-0-531-14868-6(8));** Let's Make Letters : ABC Kids. Behrens, Janice. 18.00 ***978-0-531-14867-9(X));** (Illus.). 32p. (J). (ps-k). (Let's Find Out Early Learning Bks.). 2007. 72.00 ***978-0-531-17599-6(5)** , Children's Pr.) Scholastic Library Publishing.

Leuck, Laura. Jeepers Creepers: A Monstrous ABC. Parkins, David, illus. 2003. 32p. (J). 15.95 (978-0-8118-3509-1(X) , 53408263) Chronicle Bks. LLC.

Lewison, Wendy Cheyette. Kangaroo Kazoo: Letter K. 2001. (Alpha Tales Ser.). (Illus.). 16p. (ps-1). pap. 2.25 (978-0-439-16534-1(2)) Scholastic, Inc.

—Rosey Rabbit's Radish: Letter R. 2001. (Alpha Tales Ser.). (Illus.). 16p. (ps-1). pap. 2.25 (978-0-439-16541-9(5)) Scholastic, Inc.

—Zack the Lazy Zebra: Letter Z. 2001. (Alpha Tales Ser.). (Illus.). 16p. (ps-1). pap. 2.25 (978-0-439-16549-5(0)) Scholastic, Inc.

Lisa LeLeu, 6th. Alphie's Alphabet Act. 2007. (Lisa Leleu Puppet Show Books Ser.: 6). (J). ***978-0-9770299-0-7(5)** , W12348) LeLeu, Lisa Studios! Inc.

Litchfield, Jo. First Abc. Litchfield, Jo, illus. 2007. 22p. (J). bds. 14.99 (978-0-7945-1435-8(9) , Usborne) EDC Publishing.

Lloyd, Sue & Wernham, Sara. Finger Phonics, 7 vols., Vol. 4, Bk. 4. 2001. (Jolly Phonics Ser.: BIG BOOK 4). (Illus.). 16p. (J). 13.95 (978-1-870946-90-2(1) , JL901) Jolly Learning, Ltd. GBR. *Dist:* American International Distribution Corp.

—Finger Phonics Big Book 1: S, a, t, i, p, N, 7 vols. 2001. (Jolly Phonics Ser.: BIG BOOK 1). (Illus.). 16p. (J). 13.95 (978-1-870946-87-2(1) , JL871) Jolly Learning, Ltd. GBR. *Dist:* American International Distribution Corp.

—Finger Phonics Big Book 2: C, k, e, h, r, m, D, 7 vols. 2001. (Jolly Phonics Ser.: BIG BOOK 2). (Illus.). 16p. (J). 13.95 (978-1-870946-88-9(X) , JL88X) Jolly Learning, Ltd. GBR. *Dist:* American International Distribution Corp.

—Finger Phonics Big Book 3: G, o, u, l, f, B, 7 vols. 2001. (Jolly Phonics Ser.: BIG BOOK 3). (Illus.). 16p. (J). 13.95 (978-1-870946-89-6(8) , JL898) Jolly Learning, Ltd. GBR. *Dist:* American International Distribution Corp.

—Finger Phonics Big Book 5: Z, W, Ng, V, Oo ,Oo, 7 vols. 2001. (Jolly Phonics Ser.: BIG BOOK 5). (Illus.). 16p. (J). 13.95 (978-1-870946-91-9(X) , JL91X) Jolly Learning, Ltd. GBR. *Dist:* American International Distribution Corp.

—Finger Phonics Big Book 6: Y, X, Ch, Sh, Th, Th, 7 vols. 2001. (Jolly Phonics Ser.: BIG BOOK 6). (Illus.). 16p. (J). 13.95 (978-1-870946-92-6(8) , JL928) Jolly Learning, Ltd. GBR. *Dist:* American International Distribution Corp.

—Finger Phonics Big Book 7: Qu, Ou, Oi, Ue, Er, Ar, 7 vols. 2001. (Jolly Phonics Ser.: BIG BOOK 7). (Illus.). 16p. (J). 13.95 (978-1-870946-93-3(6) , JL936) Jolly Learning, Ltd. GBR. *Dist:* American International Distribution Corp.

Lohnes, Marilyn. F for Fiddlehead: Nb Alpha. Tooke, Susan, illus. rev. ed. 2007. (Provincial Alphabet Ser.). 40p. (J). 18.95 ***978-1-58536-318-6(9))** Sleeping Bear Pr.

London, Jonathan & Moore, Margie. Do Your ABCs, Little Brown Bear. 2007. 32p. (J). pap. 5.99 (978-0-14-240713-4(5) , Puffin) Penguin Group (USA) Inc.

Lou Weber Staff, ed. Alphabet Wipe off Learning Board. 2004. 6p. (J). spiral bd., bds. 7.98 (978-0-7853-9994-0(1) , 7212200) Publications International, Ltd.

Love, Mary A. The ABC's & Symbols. Flournoy, L. Diana, illus. 1998. 32p. (J). pap. 4.50 (978-1-929548-01-9(X)) Love's Creative Resources.

Love, Maryann Cusimano. Alphaducks. 2007. (Lucky Ducks Ser.). 14p. (J). (ps-k). pap. 6.99 (978-0-8431-2495-8(4) , Price Stern Sloan) Penguin Group (USA) Inc.

Lowery, Linda. Trick or Treat, It's Halloween! 2000. (gr. k-3). lib. bdg. 10.95 (978-0-613-27266-7(8)) Tandem Library Bks.

Lucado, Max. ABC's. 2004. (Buginnings Ser.). (Illus.). 24p. (J). 9.99 (978-1-4003-0420-2(2)) Nelson, Thomas Inc.

Lund, Evelyn. It Happened on Alphabet Street. 2003. (Illus.). 32p. (J). pap. 12.95 (978-1-878044-50-1(8) , Wild Rose) Mayhaven Publishing.

Lundeen, Connie R. Alpha-Pets: A to Z. Lundeen, Bob, illus. 1998. 32p. (J). (gr. k-1). pap. 12.95 (978-1-880090-72-5(4) , Weasel Bks.) Galde Pr., Inc.

Lundell, Margo. Disney Babies A to Z. 1998. (Disney Ser.). (Illus.). 14p. (J). (ps-k). bds. 3.99 (978-0-307-12317-6(0) , 12317, Golden Bks.) Random Hse. Children's Bks.

Lynch, Wayne. Arctic Alphabet: Exploring the North from A to Z. Lynch, Wayne, photos by. 2006. (Illus.). 32p. (J). (gr. k-4). reprint ed. 20.00 (978-1-4223-5190-1(4)) DIANE Publishing Co.

—Arctic Alphabet: Exploring the North from A to Z. Lynch, Wayne, photos by. 1999. (Illus.). 32p. (J). (gr. k-5). pap. 6.95 (978-1-55209-334-4(4)) Firefly Bks., Ltd.

—Arctic Alphabet: Exploring the North from A to Z. 1999. (Illus.). 32p. (J). (gr. k-5). lib. bdg. 19.95 (978-1-55209-336-8(0)) Firefly Bks., Ltd.

—Arctic Alphabet: Exploring the North from A to Z. 1999. (gr. 3-6). lib. bdg. 15.25 (978-0-613-35065-5(0)) Tandem Library Bks.

MacDonald, Suse. Alphabatics. MacDonald, Suse, illus. 2002. (Illus.). (J). 15.49 (978-0-7587-0087-2(3)) Book Wholesalers, Inc.

—Alphabatics. 1998. (J). pap. 6.95 (978-0-87628-366-0(0)) Ctr. for Applied Research in Education, The.

Maclean, K. Pigs over Denver. 2001. (978-0-9652998-4-8(8)) On the Spot! Bks.

Magnetic Alphabet Tiles & Magnetic Lapboard: Magnetic Alphabet Tiles (130 Letters) (ps-12). 8.36 (978-0-7362-1097-3(0)) Hampton-Brown Bks.

Magnetic Alphabet Tiles & Magnetic Lapboard: Magnetic Lapboard 12 9. (ps-12). 8.74 (978-0-7362-0850-5(X)) Hampton-Brown Bks.

Main, Judith Lang. A Is for Altar, B Is for Bible. 2003. (Illus.). 65p. (J). 10.00 (978-1-56854-458-8(8) , Catechesis of the Good Shepherd) Liturgy Training Pubns.

Major, Kevin. Eh? to Zed: A Canadian Abecedarium. ed. 2004. (Illus.). (J). (ps-3). spiral bd. (978-0-616-11119-2(3)); spiral bd. (978-0-616-11120-8(7)) Canadian National Institute for the Blind/Institut National Canadien pour les Aveugles.

—Eh? to Zed: A Canadian Abecedarium. Daniel, Alan, illus. 2001. (Northern Lights Books for Children Ser.). 32p. (J). (ps-3). (978-0-88995-222-5(1)) Red Deer Pr.

—Eh? to Zed: A Canadian Abecedarium. Daniel, Alan, illus. 2004. (Northern Lights Books for Children). 32p. (J). pap. 9.95 (978-0-88995-272-0(8)) Red Deer Pr. CAN. *Dist:* Fitzhenry & Whiteside, Ltd.

Makeeff, Cyndi Sue. Inky Winky Spider ABC's. Riley, Kevin, illus. 2006. 32p. (J). pap. 7.99 (978-0-9778310-0-5(0)) New Vision Ent.

Marino, Gianna. Zoopa: An Animal Alphabet. 2005. (Illus.). 36p. (J). (ps-2). 14.95 (978-0-8118-4789-6(6)) Chronicle Bks. LLC.

Markes, Julie. Sidewalk ABC. Markes, Jennifer, illus. 2001. 24p. (J). (ps-k). 8.95 (978-0-694-01455-2(9) , Harper Festival) HarperCollins Pubs.

Marshallese Alphabet. 2004. (Illus.). 56p. 4.95 (978-1-57306-221-3(9)) Bess Pr., Inc.

Martin, Bill, Jr. Chicka Chicka Boom Boom. 2000. (Illus.). (J). 13.79 (978-0-606-18798-5(7)) Tandem Library Bks.

Martin, Bill, Jr. & Archambault, John. Chicka Chicka ABC. 1998. (J). 4.95 (978-0-87628-352-3(0)) Ctr. for Applied Research in Education, The.

—Chicka Chicka Boom Boom. Ehlert, Lois, illus. 2006. 40p. (J). pap. 9.99 incl. audio compact disk (978-1-4169-2718-1(2) , Little Simon) Simon & Schuster Children's Publishing.

Martin, Mary J. From Anne to Zach. Grejniec, Michael, illus. 2003. 32p. (J). (gr. k-2). 16.95 (978-1-56397-573-8(4)) Boyds Mills Pr.

Martin, Steve & Chast, Roz. The Alphabet from A to Y, with Bonus Letter Z! 2007. (Illus.). 64p. (J). 17.95 ***978-0-385-51662-4(2));** lib. bdg. 17.95 ***978-0-385-52377-6(7))** Doubleday Publishing. (Flying Dolphin Pr.).

Marzollo, Jean. I Spy Little Learning Box: I Spy Little Book; I Spy Little Letters; I Spy Little Numbers, 3 bks. Wick, Walter, illus. Wick, Walter, photos by. 2003. (I Spy Ser.). 78p. (J). 19.95 (978-0-439-45537-4(5) , Cartwheel Bks.) Scholastic, Inc.

Mazxzeo, J. L. Xavia's X Book (BL) el libro X de Xavia (PB), 24 vols. 2007. (My Letter Library Ser.: 24). (SPA.). (J). pap. 9.95 ***978-1-59646-558-9(1))** Dingles & Co.

Mazzeo, J. L. Aimee's A Book, 1. 2007. (My Letter Library Ser.: 1). (Illus.). 32p. (J). lib. bdg. 22.60 ***978-1-59646-416-2(X))** Dingles & Co.

—Aimee's A Book (PB), 1. 2007. (My Letter Library Ser.: 1). (J). pap. 9.95 ***978-1-59646-417-9(8))** Dingles & Co.

—Bebe's B Book, 26 vols. 2007. (My Letter Library Ser.: 2). (J). pap. 9.95 ***978-1-59646-423-0(2));** 32p. lib. bdg. 22.60 ***978-1-59646-422-3(4))** Dingles & Co.

—Bebe¿s B Book (BL) el libro B de Bebé, 2 vols. 2007. (My Letter Library Ser.: 2). (SPA.). (J). lib. bdg. 22.60 ***978-1-59646-425-4(9))** Dingles & Co.

—Bebe¿s B Book (BL) el libro B de Bebé (PB), 2 vols. 2007. (My Letter Library Ser.: 2). (SPA.). (J). pap. 9.95 ***978-1-59646-426-1(7))** Dingles & Co.

—Cassie's C Book. 2007. (My Letter Library Ser.: 3). (J). lib. bdg. 22.60 ***978-1-59646-428-5(3))** Dingles & Co.

—Cassie's C Book (PB), 3 vols. 2007. (My Letter Library Ser.: 3). (J). pap. 9.95 ***978-1-59646-429-2(1))** Dingles & Co.

—Delia's D Book. 2007. (My Letter Library Ser.: 4). (J). lib. bdg. 22.60 ***978-1-59646-434-6(8))** Dingles & Co.

—Delia¿s D Book (BL) el libro D de Delia, 4 vols. 2007. (My Letter Library Ser.: 4). (SPA.). (J). lib. bdg. 22.60 ***978-1-59646-437-7(2))** Dingles & Co.

—Delia¿s D Book (BL) el libro D de Delia (PB), 4 vols. 2007. (My Letter Library Ser.: 4). (SPA.). (J). pap. 9.95 ***978-1-59646-438-4(0))** Dingles & Co.

—Delia's D Book (PB), 4 vols. 2007. (My Letter Library Ser.: 4). (J). pap. 9.95 ***978-1-59646-435-3(6))** Dingles & Co.

—Emma's E Book, 5 vols. 2007. (My Letter Library Ser.: 5). (J). lib. bdg. 22.60 ***978-1-59646-440-7(2))** Dingles & Co.

A B

—Emma¿s E Book (BL) el libro E de Emma, 5 vols. 2007. (My Letter Library Ser.: 5). (J). lib. bdg. 22.60 (*978-1-59646-443-8(7)) Dingles & Co.

—Emma¿s E Book (BL) el libro E de Emma (PB), 5 vols. 2007. (My Letter Library Ser.: 5). (SPA.). (J). pap. 9.95 (*978-1-59646-444-5(5)) Dingles & Co.

—Emma's E Book (PB), 5 vols. 2007. (My Letter Library Ser.: 5). (J). pap. 9.95 (*978-1-59646-441-4(0)) Dingles & Co.

—Faye's F Book, 6 vols. 2007. (My Letter Library Ser.: 6). (J). lib. bdg. 22.60 (*978-1-59646-446-9(1)) Dingles & Co.

—Faye¿s F Book (BL) el libro F de Faye, 5 vols. 2007. (My Letter Library Ser.: 6). (SPA.). (J). lib. bdg. 22.60 (*978-1-59646-449-0(6)) Dingles & Co.

—Faye's F Book (BL) el libro F de Faye (PB), 6 vols. 2007. (My Letter Library Ser.: 6). (SPA.). (J). pap. 9.95 (*978-1-59646-450-6(X)) Dingles & Co.

—Faye's F Book (PB), 6 vols. 2007. (My Letter Library Ser.: 6). (J). pap. 9.95 (*978-1-59646-447-6(X)) Dingles & Co.

—George's G Book, 7 vols. 2007. (My Letter Library Ser.: 7). (J). lib. bdg. 22.60 (*978-1-59646-452-0(6)) Dingles & Co.

—George's G Book (BL) el libro G de George, 7 vols. 2007. (My Letter Library Ser.: 7). (J). lib. bdg. 22.60 (*978-1-59646-455-1(0)) Dingles & Co.

—George's G Book (BL) el libro G de George (PB), 7 vols. 2007. (My Letter Library Ser.: 7). (SPA.). (J). pap. 9.95 (*978-1-59646-456-8(9)) Dingles & Co.

—George's G Book (PB), 7 vols. 2007. (My Letter Library Ser.: 7). (J). pap. 9.95 (*978-1-59646-453-7(4)) Dingles & Co.

—Henry's H Book, 8 vols. 2007. (My Letter Library Ser.: 8). (Illus.). (J). lib. bdg. 22.60 (*978-1-59646-458-2(5)) Dingles & Co.

—Henry's H Book (BL) el libro H de Henry, 8 vols. 2007. (My Letter Library Ser.: 8). (J). lib. bdg. 22.60 (*978-1-59646-461-2(5)) Dingles & Co.

—Henry's H Book (BL) el libro H de Henry (PB), 8 vols. 2007. (My Letter Library Ser.: 8). (SPA.). (J). pap. 9.95 (*978-1-59646-462-9(3)) Dingles & Co.

—Henry's H Book (PB), 8 vols. 2007. (My Letter Library Ser.: 8). (J). pap. 9.95 (*978-1-59646-459-9(3)) Dingles & Co.

—Izzy's I Book, 9 vols. 2007. (My Letter Library Ser.: 9). (J). lib. bdg. 22.60 (*978-1-59646-464-3(X)) Dingles & Co.

—Izzy's I Book (BL) el libro I de Izzy, 9 vols. 2007. (My Letter Library Ser.: 9). (SPA.). (J). lib. bdg. 22.60 (*978-1-59646-467-4(4)) Dingles & Co.

—Izzy's I Book (BL) el libro I de Izzy (PB), 9 vols. 2007. (My Letter Library Ser.: 9). (SPA.). (J). pap. 9.95 (*978-1-59646-468-1(2)) Dingles & Co.

—Izzy's I Book (PB), 9 vols. 2007. (My Letter Library Ser.: 9). (J). pap. 9.95 (*978-1-59646-465-0(8)) Dingles & Co.

—Jade's J Book, 10 vols. 2007. (My Letter Library Ser.: 10). (J). lib. bdg. 22.60 (*978-1-59646-470-4(4)) Dingles & Co.

—Jade's J Book (BL) el libro J de Jade, 10 vols. 2007. (My Letter Library Ser.: 10). (SPA.). (J). lib. bdg. 22.60 (*978-1-59646-473-5(9)) Dingles & Co.

—Jade's J Book (BL) el libro J de Jade (PB), 10 vols. 2007. (My Letter Library Ser.: 10). (SPA.). (J). pap. 9.95 (*978-1-59646-474-2(7)) Dingles & Co.

—Jade's J Book (PB), 10 vols. 2007. (My Letter Library Ser.: 10). (J). pap. 9.95 (*978-1-59646-471-1(2)) Dingles & Co.

—Kelsey's K Book, 11 vols. 2007. (My Letter Library Ser.: 11). (J). lib. bdg. 22.60 (*978-1-59646-476-6(3)) Dingles & Co.

—Kelsey's K Book (BL) el libro K de Kelsey, 11 vols. 2007. (My Letter Library Ser.: 11). (SPA.). (J). lib. bdg. 22.60 (*978-1-59646-479-7(8)) Dingles & Co.

—Kelsey's K Book (BL) el libro K de Kelsey (PB), 11 vols. 2007. (My Letter Library Ser.: 11). (SPA.). (J). pap. 9.95 (*978-1-59646-480-3(1)) Dingles & Co.

—Kelsey's K Book (PB), 11 vols. 2007. (My Letter Library Ser.: 11). (J). pap. 9.95 (*978-1-59646-477-3(1)) Dingles & Co.

—Logan's L Book, 12 vols. 2007. (My Letter Library Ser.: 12). (J). lib. bdg. 22.60 (*978-1-59646-482-7(8)) Dingles & Co.

—Logan's L Book (BL) el libro L de Logan, 12 vols. 2007. (My Letter Library Ser.: 12). (SPA.). (J). lib. bdg. 22.60 (*978-1-59646-485-8(2)) Dingles & Co.

—Logan's L Book (BL) el libro L de Logan (PB), 12 vols. 2007. (My Letter Library Ser.: 12). (SPA.). (J). pap. 9.95 (*978-1-59646-486-5(0)) Dingles & Co.

—Logan's L Book (PB), 12 vols. 2007. (My Letter Library Ser.: 12). (J). pap. 9.95 (*978-1-59646-483-4(6)) Dingles & Co.

—Mia's M Book, 13 vols. 2007. (My Letter Library Ser.: 13). (J). lib. bdg. 22.60 (*978-1-59646-488-9(7)) Dingles & Co.

—Mia's M Book (BL) el libro M de Mia, 13 vols. 2007. (My Letter Library Ser.: 13). (SPA.). (J). lib. bdg. 22.60 (*978-1-59646-491-9(7)) Dingles & Co.

—Mia's M Book (BL) el libro M de Mia (PB), 13 vols. 2007. (My Letter Library Ser.: 13). (SPA.). (J). pap. 9.95 (*978-1-59646-492-6(5)) Dingles & Co.

—Mia's M Book (PB), 13 vols. 2007. (My Letter Library Ser.: 13). (J). pap. 9.95 (*978-1-59646-489-6(5)) Dingles & Co.

—Nate's N Book, 14 vols. 2007. (My Letter Library Ser.: 14). (J). lib. bdg. 22.60 (*978-1-59646-494-0(1)) Dingles & Co.

—Nate's N Book (BL) el libro N de Nate, 14 vols. 2007. (My Letter Library Ser.: 14). (SPA.). (J). lib. bdg. 22.60 (*978-1-59646-497-1(6)) Dingles & Co.

—Nate's N Book (BL) el libro N de Nate (PB), 14 vols. 2007. (My Letter Library Ser.: 14). (SPA.). (J). pap. 9.95 (*978-1-59646-498-8(4)) Dingles & Co.

—Nate's N Book (PB), 14 vols. 2007. (My Letter Library Ser.: 14). (J). pap. 9.95 (*978-1-59646-495-7(X)) Dingles & Co.

—Owen's O Book, 15 vols. 2007. (My Letter Library Ser.: 15). (J). lib. bdg. 22.60 (*978-1-59646-500-8(X)) Dingles & Co.

—Owen's O Book (BL) el libro O de Owen, 15 vols. 2007. (My Letter Library Ser.: 15). (SPA.). (J). lib. bdg. 22.60 (*978-1-59646-503-9(4)) Dingles & Co.

—Owen's O Book (BL) el libro O de Owen (PB), 15 vols. 2007. (My Letter Library Ser.: 15). (SPA.). (J). pap. 9.95 (*978-1-59646-504-6(2)) Dingles & Co.

—Owen's O Book (PB), 15 vols. 2007. (My Letter Library Ser.: 15). (J). pap. 9.95 (*978-1-59646-501-5(8)) Dingles & Co.

—Perer's P Book, 16 vols. 2007. (My Letter Library Ser.: 16). (J). lib. bdg. 22.60 (*978-1-59646-506-0(9)) Dingles & Co.

—Peter's P Book (BL) el libro P de Peter, 16 vols. 2007. (My Letter Library Ser.: 16). (SPA.). (J). lib. bdg. 22.60 (*978-1-59646-509-1(3)) Dingles & Co.

—Peter's P Book (BL) el libro P de Peter (PB), 16 vols. 2007. (My Letter Library Ser.: 16). (SPA.). (J). pap. 9.95 (*978-1-59646-510-7(7)) Dingles & Co.

—Peter's P Book (PB), 16 vols. 2007. (My Letter Library Ser.: 16). (J). pap. 9.95 (*978-1-59646-507-7(7)) Dingles & Co.

—Quinn's Q Book, 17 vols. 2007. (My Letter Library Ser.: 17). (J). lib. bdg. 22.60 (*978-1-59646-512-1(3)) Dingles & Co.

—Quinn's Q Book (BL) el libro Q de Quinn, 17 vols. 2007. (My Letter Library Ser.: 17). (SPA.). (J). lib. bdg. 22.60 (*978-1-59646-515-2(8)) Dingles & Co.

—Quinn's Q Book (BL) el libro Q de Quinn (PB), 17 vols. 2007. (My Letter Library Ser.: 17). (SPA.). (J). pap. 9.95 (*978-1-59646-516-9(6)) Dingles & Co.

—Quinn's Q Book (PB), 17 vols. 2007. (My Letter Library Ser.: 17). (J). lib. bdg. 9.95 (*978-1-59646-513-8(1)) Dingles & Co.

—Rosie's R Book, 18 vols. 2007. (My Letter Library Ser.: 18). (J). lib. bdg. 22.60 (*978-1-59646-518-3(2)) Dingles & Co.

—Rosie's R Book (BL) el libro R de Rosie, 18 vols. 2007. (My Letter Library Ser.: 18). (SPA.). (J). lib. bdg. 22.60 (*978-1-59646-521-3(2)) Dingles & Co.

—Rosie's R Book (BL) el libro R de Rosie (PB), 18 vols. 2007. (My Letter Library Ser.: 18). (SPA.). (J). pap. 9.95 (*978-1-59646-522-0(0)) Dingles & Co.

—Rosie's R Book (PB), 18 vols. 2007. (My Letter Library Ser.: 18). (J). pap. 9.95 (*978-1-59646-519-0(0)) Dingles & Co.

—Sofie's S Book, 19 vols. 2007. (My Letter Library Ser.: 19). (J). lib. bdg. 22.60 (*978-1-59646-524-4(7)) Dingles & Co.

—Sofie's S Book (BL) el libro S de Sofie, 19 vols. 2007. (My Letter Library Ser.: 19). (SPA.). (J). lib. bdg. 22.60 (*978-1-59646-527-5(1)) Dingles & Co.

—Sofie's S Book (BL) el libro S de Sofie (PB), 19 vols. 2007. (My Letter Library Ser.: 19). (SPA.). (J). pap. 9.95 (*978-1-59646-528-2(X)) Dingles & Co.

—Sofie's S Book (PB), 19 vols. 2007. (My Letter Library Ser.: 19). (J). pap. 9.95 (*978-1-59646-525-1(5)) Dingles & Co.

—Tad's T Book, 20 vols. 2007. (My Letter Library Ser.: 20). (J). lib. bdg. 22.60 (*978-1-59646-530-5(1)) Dingles & Co.

—Tad's T Book (BL) el libro T de Tad, 20 vols. 2007. (My Letter Library Ser.: 20). (SPA.). (J). lib. bdg. 22.60 (*978-1-59646-533-6(6)) Dingles & Co.

—Tad's T Book (BL) el libro T de Tad (PB), 20 vols. 2007. (My Letter Library Ser.: 20). (SPA.). (J). pap. 9.95 (*978-1-59646-534-3(4)) Dingles & Co.

—Tad's T Book (PB), 20 vols. 2007. (My Letter Library Ser.: 20). (J). pap. 9.95 (*978-1-59646-531-2(X)) Dingles & Co.

—Uri's U Book, 21 vols. 2007. (My Letter Library Ser.: 21). (Illus.). (J). lib. bdg. 22.60 (*978-1-59646-536-7(0)) Dingles & Co.

—Uri's U Book (BL) el libro U de Uri, 21 vols. 2007. (My Letter Library Ser.: 21). (SPA.). (J). lib. bdg. 22.60 (*978-1-59646-539-8(5)) Dingles & Co.

—Uri's U Book (BL) el libro U de Uri (PB), 21 vols. 2007. (My Letter Library Ser.: 21). (SPA.). (J). pap. 9.95 (*978-1-59646-540-4(9)) Dingles & Co.

—Uri's U Book (PB), 21 vols. 2007. (My Letter Library Ser.: 21). (Illus.). (J). pap. 9.95 (*978-1-59646-537-4(9)) Dingles & Co.

—Vera's V Book, 22 vols. 2007. (My Letter Library Ser.: 22). (J). lib. bdg. 22.60 (*978-1-59646-542-8(5)) Dingles & Co.

—Vera's V Book (BL) el libro V de Vera, 22 vols. 2007. (My Letter Library Ser.: 22). (SPA.). (J). lib. bdg. 22.60 (*978-1-59646-545-9(X)) Dingles & Co.

—Vera's V Book (BL) el libro V de Vera (PB), 22 vols. 2007. (My Letter Library Ser.: 22). (SPA.). (J). pap. 9.95 (*978-1-59646-546-6(8)) Dingles & Co.

—Vera's V Book (PB), 22 vols. 2007. (My Letter Library Ser.: 22). (J). pap. 9.95 (*978-1-59646-543-5(3)) Dingles & Co.

—Will's W Book, 23 vols. 2007. (My Letter Library Ser.: 23). (J). lib. bdg. 22.60 (*978-1-59646-548-0(4)) Dingles & Co.

—Will's W Book (BL) el libro W de Will, 23 vols. 2007. (My Letter Library Ser.: 23). (SPA.). (J). lib. bdg. 22.60 (*978-1-59646-551-0(4)) Dingles & Co.

—Will's W Book (BL) el libro W de Will (PB), 23 vols. 2007. (My Letter Library Ser.: 23). (SPA.). (J). pap. 9.95 (*978-1-59646-552-7(2)) Dingles & Co.

—Will's W Book (PB), 23 vols. 2007. (My Letter Library Ser.: 23). (J). pap. 9.95 (*978-1-59646-549-7(2)) Dingles & Co.

—Xavia's X Book, 24 vols. 2007. (My Letter Library Ser.: 24). (J). lib. bdg. 22.60 (*978-1-59646-554-1(9)) Dingles & Co.

—Xavia's X Book (BL) el libro X de Xavia, 24 vols. 2007. (My Letter Library Ser.: 24). (SPA.). (J). lib. bdg. 22.60 (*978-1-59646-557-2(3)) Dingles & Co.

—Xavia's X Book (PB), 24 vols. 2007. (My Letter Library Ser.: 24). (J). pap. 9.95 (*978-1-59646-555-8(7)) Dingles & Co.

—Yola's Y Book, 25 vols. 2007. (My Letter Library Ser.: 25). (Illus.). (J). lib. bdg. 22.60 (*978-1-59646-560-2(3)) Dingles & Co.

—Yola's Y Book (BL) el libro Y de Yola, 25 vols. 2007. (My Letter Library Ser.: 25). (SPA.). (J). lib. bdg. 22.60 (*978-1-59646-563-3(8)) Dingles & Co.

—Yola's Y Book (BL) el libro Y de Yola (PB), 25 vols. 2007. (My Letter Library Ser.: 25). (SPA.). (J). pap. 9.95 (*978-1-59646-564-0(6)) Dingles & Co.

—Yola's Y Book (PB), 25 vols. 2007. (My Letter Library Ser.: 25). (Illus.). (J). pap. 9.95 (*978-1-59646-561-9(1)) Dingles & Co.

—Zach's Z Book. 2007. (My Letter Library Ser.: 26). (J). lib. bdg. 22.60 (*978-1-59646-566-4(2)) Dingles & Co.

—Zach's Z Book (PB), 26 vols. 2007. (My Letter Library Ser.: 26). (J). pap. 9.95 (*978-1-59646-567-1(0)) Dingles & Co.

McAtee, Rick. Alphabetland the Beginning. Hammons, Barbara, illus. 2005. 48p. (J). 12.95 (978-0-9762030-0-1(6)) Turning a New Page.

—Alphabetland the Story of R. Hammons, Barbara, illus. ed. 2005. (J). 14.95 (978-0-9762030-1-8(4) , 1000) Turning a New Page.

McDonnell, Flora. Flora McDonnell's ABC Book. McDonnell, Flora, illus. 2001. (Illus.). 36p. (J). (gr. k-ps). bds. 6.99 (978-0-7636-1399-0(1)) Candlewick Pr.

McFarland-Johnson, Jeffrey. The Perfect ABC Songbook. Corel Gallery Magic 200,000 Staff, illus. 1998. 55p. (J). (ps-1). spiral bd. 24.95 incl. audio compact disk (978-1-892397-03-4(X)); spiral bd. 19.95 incl. audio (978-1-892397-04-1(8)) JohnSong Music.

McFarland-Johnson, Jeffrey, ed. The Perfect ABC Songbook. Corel Gallery Magic 200,000 Staff, illus. 1998. 55p. (J). (ps-1). spiral bd. 10.00 (978-1-892397-00-3(5)) JohnSong Music.

McGehee, Claudia. A Tallgrass Prairie Alphabet. McGehee, Claudia, illus. 2004. (Bur Oak Book Ser.). (Illus.). 32p. (J). 17.95 (978-0-87745-897-5(9)) Univ. of Iowa Pr.

McGraw-Hill Staff. Everything for Letters & Numbers. 2003. (Early Learning Ser.). (Illus.). 320p. (J). (gr. 1-2). pap. 7.95 (978-0-7696-2189-0(9) , Learning Materials) School Specialty Publishing.

McGraw-Hill Staff & School Specialty Publishing Staff. Alphabet: Dot-to-Dot. 2001. (Homework Helpers Ser.). (Illus.). 56p. (J). (gr. k-1). pap., act. bk. ed. 2.99 (978-0-7682-0673-9(1) , FS109002, Schaffer, Frank) Schaffer, Frank Pubns.

—Alphabet: Hidden Pictures. 2001. (Homework Helpers Activity Bks.). (Illus.). 56p. (J). (gr. k-1). pap., act. bk. ed. 2.99 (978-0-7682-0674-6(X) , FS109003, Schaffer, Frank) Schaffer, Frank Pubns.

Mckinsey, Michelle. Weird O. 2006. (J). 15.99 (978-0-9788092-0-1(3)) McGab Publishing.

McLeod, Bob. SuperHero ABC. McLeod, Bob, illus. 2006. (Illus.). 40p. (J). (ps-1). 16.99 (978-0-06-074514-1(2)) HarperCollins Pubs.

McLimans, David. Gone Wild: An Endangered Animal Alphabet. 2006. (Illus.). 40p. (J). (gr. 3 up). 17.85 (978-0-8027-9564-9(1)); 16.95 (978-0-8027-9563-2(3)) Walker & Co.

McNaught, Harry, illus. ABC & 1,2,3: A Sesame Street Treasury of Words & Numbers. 1998. (Sesame Street Ser.). 80p. (J). (gr. k-ps). 9.99 (978-0-375-80042-9(5) , Random Hse. Bks. for Young Readers) Random Hse. Children's Bks.

McTaggart, Stephen & McTaggart, Debra. ABC Talking Book Adventures. Nord, Mary, illus. (Talking Book Adventures Ser.). 12p. (J). (ps up). 16.95 (978-0-9627001-2-5(6)) Futech Educational Products, Inc.

Medley, Steven P. Antelope, Bison, Cougar: A National Park Wildlife Alphabet Book. San Souci, Robert D., illus. 2001. (J). (ps-5). 14.95 (978-1-930238-03-9(7)) Yosemite Assn.

Melmed, Laura & Melmed, Laura Krauss. New York, New York City: The Big Apple from A to Z. Lessac, Frané & Lessac, Frane, illus. 2005. 48p. (J). (ps-ps). 16.99 (978-0-06-054874-2(6)) HarperCollins Pubs.

Metaxas, Eric. A to Z: The Prince of Egypt. 1998. (Prince of Egypt Ser.). (Illus.). 32p. (J). (ps-1). 9.99 (978-0-8499-5850-2(4)) Nelson, Thomas Inc.

Michaels, Pat. W Is for Wind: A Weather Alphabet. Rose, Melanie, illus. rev. ed. 2005. 40p. (J). 16.95 (978-1-58536-237-0(9)) Sleeping Bear Pr.

Michaels, Pat. A Weather Alphabet. rev. ed. 2007. 40p. pap. 7.95 (*978-1-58536-330-8(8)) Sleeping Bear Pr.

Milich, Zoran. The City ABC Book. 2003. (Illus.). 32p. (J). (ps-k). (978-1-55074-948-9(X)) Kids Can Pr., Ltd.

—City ABC Book. 2003. (gr. k-3). lib. bdg. 14.10 (978-0-613-87158-7(8)) Tandem Library Bks.

Millard, Anne. Baby's Little Library. 2001. (Illus.). 1p. (J). 9.99 (978-0-7894-6798-0(4)) Dorling Kindersley Publishing, Inc.

Miller, Karen. Alphabet Adventures. 2001. (Illus.). 64p. (ps-1). 9.99 (978-0-570-05271-5(8)) Concordia Publishing Hse.

Mills, Liz, ed. My First Alphabet. 2006. (Leapfrog Ser.). (Illus.). 12p. (J). pap. 9.99 (978-0-439-85095-7(9) , Cartwheel Bks.) Scholastic, Inc.

Milne, A. A. Winnie the Pooh's ABC Sign Language Edition. Shepard, Ernest H., illus. 2001. 32p. (J). (ps-1). 10.99 (978-0-525-46714-4(9) , Dutton Juvenile) Penguin Group (USA) Inc.

Minor, Wendell. Yankee Doodle America: The Spirit of 1776 from A to Z. 2006. (Illus.). 48p. (J). (ps). 16.99 (978-0-399-24003-4(9) , Putnam Juvenile) Penguin Group (USA) Inc.

Mischel, Jenny Ann. Animal Alphabet. Bell-Myers, Darcy, illus. 2006. (J). bds. (978-0-9769239-0-9(4)) Perfect 4 Preschool.

Mitchell, Cynthia. A Big & Beastly Alphabet. 2006. pap. (*978-1-84401-716-4(8)) Athena Pr.

Mitter, Matt. ABC: Alphabet Rhyme. Cushman, Doug & Banta, Susan, illus. 2004. (Rhyme Time Learning Ser.). 16p. (J). (gr. 1 up). lib. bdg. 20.67 (978-0-8368-4095-7(X)) Stevens, Gareth Inc.

Mitzo Hilderbrand, Karen & Mitzo Thompson, Kim. A Is for Alligator. 2005. (Read & Sing along Board Books with CDs Ser.). (Illus.). 18p. (J). (ps-k). bds., bds. 7.49 incl. audio compact disk (978-0-7696-4455-4(4)) School Specialty Publishing.

Mitzo Thompson, Kim. Alphabet & Counting, 2 Packs. 2006. (Read & Sing along Board Books with CDs Ser.). 36p. (J). bds. 14.98 (978-0-7696-4592-6(5)) School Specialty Publishing.

Mitzo Thompson, Kim & Mitzo Hilderbrand, Karen. ABC Nursery Rhymes. Holm, Sharon, illus. 2008. (Sing-A-Story Ser.). 16p. (J). bds. 10.95 (978-0-7696-4905-4(X)) School Specialty Publishing.

Moak, Allan. A Big City ABC. rev. ed. 2002. (Illus.). 32p. (J). (ps up). 16.95 (978-0-88776-587-2(4)) Tundra Bks., Inc./Livres Toundra, Inc. CAN. *Dist:* Random Hse., Inc.

Mock, Jean. The Amazing Animal ABC Book. Martin, Joyce, illus. 2005. (J). (978-0-9767210-1-7(5)) JM2 Publishing Co.

—The Amazing Animal ABC Book (big Format) 2005. (J). (978-0-9767210-0-0(7)) JM2 Publishing Co.

—The Amazing Animal ABC Book the Study Guide. Martin, Joyce, illus. 2005. (978-0-9767210-2-4(3)) JM2 Publishing Co.

Molter, Carey. Ng: See It Say It Hear It. l.t. ed. 2001. (More Blends Ser.). (Illus.). 24p. (J). (ps-3). lib. bdg. 19.93 (978-1-57765-450-6(1) , SandCastle) ABDO Publishing Co.

Moncure, Jane Belk. My "a" Sound Box. King, Colin, illus. 2000. (New Sound Box Library). 32p. (J). (ps-3). 22.79 (978-1-56766-767-7(8)) Child's World, Inc.

—My "c" Sound Box. King, Colin, illus. 2000. (New Sound Box Library). 32p. (J). (ps-3). 22.79 (978-1-56766-769-1(4)) Child's World, Inc.

—My "d" Sound Box. King, Colin, illus. 2000. (New Sound Box Library). 32p. (J). (ps-3). 22.79 (978-1-56766-770-7(8)) Child's World, Inc.

—My "g" Sound Box. King, Colin, illus. 2000. (New Sound Box Library). 32p. (J). (ps-3). 22.79 (978-1-56766-773-8(2)) Child's World, Inc.

—My "i" Sound Box. King, Colin, illus. 2000. (New Sound Box Library). 32p. (J). (ps-3). 22.79 (978-1-56766-775-2(9)) Child's World, Inc.

—My "j" Sound Box. King, Colin, illus. 2000. (New Sound Box Library). 32p. (J). (ps-3). 22.79 (978-1-56766-776-9(7)) Child's World, Inc.

—My "n" Sound Box. King, Colin, illus. 2000. (New Sound Box Library). 32p. (J). (ps-3). 22.79 (978-1-56766-780-6(5)) Child's World, Inc.

—My "p" Sound Box. King, Colin, illus. 2000. (New Sound Box Library). 32p. (J). (ps-3). 22.79 (978-1-56766-782-0(1)) Child's World, Inc.

—My "s" Sound Box. King, Colin, illus. 2000. (New Sound Box Library). 32p. (J). (ps-3). 22.79 (978-1-56766-785-1(6)) Child's World, Inc.

—My "t" Sound Box. King, Colin, illus. 2000. (New Sound Box Library). 32p. (J). (ps-3). 22.79 (978-1-56766-786-8(4)) Child's World, Inc.

—My "v" Sound Box. King, Colin, illus. 2000. (New Sound Box Library). 32p. (J). (ps-3). 22.79 (978-1-56766-788-2(0)) Child's World, Inc.

—My "w" Sound Box. King, Colin, illus. 2000. (New Sound Box Library). 32p. (J). (ps-3). 22.79 (978-1-56766-789-9(9)) Child's World, Inc.

—My "xyz" Sound Box. King, Colin, illus. 2000. (New Sound Box Library). 32p. (J). (ps-3). 22.79 (978-1-56766-790-5(2)) Child's World, Inc.

Monreal, Violeta. Sos Se Necesita Sonrisa. 2004. (Coleccion Pictogramas Pictograms Ser.). (SPA.). 36p. (J). 8.50 (978-84-241-8101-7(8)) Everest de Ediciones y Distribucion, S.L. ESP. *Dist:* Continental Bk. Co., Inc., Lectorum Pubns., Inc.

Moody-Luther, Jacqueline. Stop that noise - word World. 2007. 12p. (J). 12.95 (*978-1-59764-296-5(7)) New Line Bks.

Moore, Helen H. Jaguar's Jamboree: Letter J. 2001. (Alpha Tales Ser.). (Illus.). 16p. (ps-1). pap. 2.25 (978-0-439-16533-4(4)) Scholastic, Inc.

—The Pigs Picnic: Letter P. 2001. (Alpha Tales Ser.). (Illus.). 16p. (ps-1). pap. 2.25 (978-0-439-16539-6(3)) Scholastic, Inc.

Moore, Sheila. Abadaba Alphabet: Learning Letter Sounds. Holsinger, Carol, illus. 2006. (J). (*978-0-9789473-0-9(4)) Abadaba Reading LLC.

More Blends, Set. l.t. ed. Incl. Ck : See It Say It Hear It. Molter, Carey. lib. bdg. 19.93 (978-1-57765-447-6(1) , SandCastle); Dr : See It Say It Hear It. Scheunemann, Pam. lib. bdg. 19.93 (978-1-57765-448-3(X)); Ght : See It Say It Hear It. Scheunemann, Pam. lib. bdg. 19.93 (978-1-57765-449-0(8) , SandCastle); Ng : See It Say It Hear It. Molter, Carey. lib. bdg. 19.93 (978-1-57765-450-6(1) , SandCastle); Ph : See It Say It Hear It. Molter, Carey. lib. bdg. 19.93 (978-1-57765-451-

3(X) , SandCastle); Sl : See It Say It Hear It. Scheunemann, Pam. lib. bdg. 19.93 (978-1-57765-452-0(8) , SandCastle); 24p. (J). (ps-3). (Illus.). 2001. Set lib. bdg. 119.58 (978-1-57765-298-4(3) , SandCastle) ABDO Publishing Co.

Morgan, Marilyn. Alaska Alphabet CD-ROM. 2007. cd-rom 29.95 ***978-1-878051-56-1(3))** Circumpolar Pr.

Morganstern, Mimi. The Good Food ABC Book. Bergier, Barbara, illus. unabr. ed. 2000. vi, 28p. (J). (ps-3). per. 5.95 (978-0-9700522-1-6(9)) Morganstern, Mimi.

—The Good Food ABC-Read-Along with Mimi: A Fun Nutritional Headstart Pack. Bergier, Barbara, illus. 2000. (J). (ps-3). per. 8.99 incl. audio (978-0-9700522-2-3(7)) Morganstern, Mimi.

Most, Bernard. ABC T-Rex. (Illus.). 32p. (J). 2004. pap. 6.00 (978-0-15-205028-3(0) , Voyager Bks./Libros Viajeros); 2000. 14.00 (978-0-15-202007-1(1)) Harcourt Children's Bks.

—ABC T-Rex. 2004. (ps-2). lib. bdg. 14.15 (978-0-613-83875-7(0)) Tandem Library Bks.

Mouse Works Staff. Learn & Grow Carry Along. 1999. (J). 9.99 (978-0-7364-0181-4(4)) Mouse Works.

Muench-Williams, Heather, ed. Alphabet Fun for Little Ones: Activities for Preschoolers. 2005. (J). pap. (978-1-57332-379-6(9)) HighReach Learning, Inc.

Munari, Bruno. Bruno Munari's ABC. 6th ed. 2006. (Illus.). 48p. (J). 15.95 (978-0-8118-5463-4(9)) Chronicle Bks. LLC.

Murphy, Cary. Meeko the Monkey's A-Z Animal Band. Victoria, Arody, illus. 2006. 32p. (J). (978-0-9778546-0-8(4)) Lucky Dog Publishing.

Murphy, Chuck, intro. Animal Babies A to Z. 2007. 8p. 16.95 ***978-1-58117-652-0(X)** , Intervisual/Piggy Toes) Dalmatian Pr.

Murphy, Liz. ABC Doctor: Staying Healty from A to Z. 2007. (Illus.). 40p. (J). (ps-1). 15.95 (978-1-59354-593-2(2)) Blue Apple Bks.

Murray, Margaret Cox. A-Z Children of Maine. 1999. (Illus.). 15p. (J). (ps-5). pap. 6.95 (978-0-9665140-1-8(7)) Rainbow Pr.

My First A B C. Date not set. (Illus.). (J). bds. 5.98 (978-0-7525-7984-9(3)) Parragon, Inc.

My First Book of Lowercase Letters. 2004. (Illus.). 80p. (J). per. 6.95 (978-4-7743-0706-0(8)) Kumon Publishing North America, Inc.

My First Book of Uppercase Letters. 2004. (Illus.). 80p. (J). per. 6.95 (978-4-7743-0705-3(X)) Kumon Publishing North America, Inc.

My Little Book of ABC's. 2002. (Puppy Tales Ser.). (Illus.). 24p. (J). (gr. k-3). 1.49 (978-1-57759-269-3(7)) Dalmatian Pr.

My TakeAlong Li, ed. Alphabet. 2007. (My Take-along Library). 120p. (J). (ps). bds. 14.95 ***978-0-7696-5519-2(X))** School Specialty Publishing.

Myers, Samantha Ann. ABC's & 123's of the Great Outdoors. 2006. (ENG.). 28p. per. 13.99 ***978-1-4259-6659-1(4))** AuthorHouse.

Namm, Diane. Gags & Giggles from A to Z. Becker, Wayne, illus. 2008. (Laugh-A-Long Readers Ser.). 32p. (J). pap. 3.95 ***978-1-4027-5000-7(5))** Sterling Publishing Co., Inc.

Napier, Matt. Hat Tricks Count. Rose, Melanie, illus. rev. ed. 2005. (Sports Alphabet Ser.). 40p. (J). (gr. k-5). 16.95 (978-1-58536-163-2(1)) Sleeping Bear Pr.

—Z Is for Zamboni: A Hockey Alphabet. Rose, Melanie, illus. rev. ed. (J). 2006. 38p. bds. 7.99 (978-1-58536-303-2(0)); 2002. 40p. 19.95 (978-1-58536-065-9(1)) Sleeping Bear Pr.

Napier, Matt & Rose, Melanie. Z Is for Zamboni: A Hockey Alphabet. Rose, Melanie, illus. rev. ed. 2003. 38p. pap. 8.95 (978-1-58536-238-7(7)) Sleeping Bear Pr.

Nelson, Beth. Alphabet Flash Cards. Nelson, Beth, illus. 2004. (Illus.). 26p. 14.95 (978-0-8118-4394-2(7)) Chronicle Bks. LLC.

Nelson, Trish. My Name Is A: Meeting the Letters of the Alphabet. Nelson, Nancy, illus. 1999. 32p. (J). (ps-1). pap. 6.95 (978-0-9673943-0-5(9)) Nelson Building Block Bks.

Newgarden, Mark & Cash, Megan Montague. Bow-Wow attracts Opposites. 2008. (Illus.). 18p. (J). bds. 4.95 ***978-0-15-205847-0(8)** , Red Wagon Bks.) Harcourt Children's Bks.

Newman-D'Amico, Fran. Alphabet Mazes. 2006. 32p. (J). pap. 2.95 (978-0-486-44894-7(0)) Dover Pubns., Inc.

Nguyen, An Mai. Let's Learn the Vietnamese Alphabet. 2006. (VIE & ENG., Illus.). (J). bds. 6.95 (978-0-9776482-0-7(6)) Viet Baby, LLC.

Nicest Newt. 2001. (ps-2). lib. bdg. 9.80 (978-0-613-32886-9(8)) Tandem Library Bks.

Nichol, Barbara. Trunks All Aboard: An Elephant ABC. Van Horne, William C., illus. 2001. 24p. (J). (gr. 1-3). 14.95 (978-0-88776-536-0(X)) Tundra Bks., Inc./Livres Toundra, Inc. CAN. *Dist:* Random Hse., Inc.

Nickelodeon Staff. Nick Jr. ABC Block Books, 26 vols., Set. 2003. (Illus.). 8p. (J). bds. 24.95 (978-0-8118-4012-5(3)) Chronicle Bks. LLC.

Nickle, John. Alphabet Explosion! An Astounding, Bedazzling Counting Book. Nickle, John, illus. 2006. (Illus.). 40p. (J). (ps-3). lib. bdg. 18.99 (978-0-375-93598-5(3) , Schwartz & Wade Bks.) Random Hse. Children's Bks.

—Alphabet Explosion! Search & Count from Alien to Zebra. Nickle, John, illus. 2006. (Illus.). 40p. (J). (ps-3). 16.95 (978-0-375-83598-8(9) , Schwartz & Wade Bks.) Random Hse. Children's Bks.

Nogueras, Paola. ABC de Puerto Rico. 2006. (SPA.). (J). (gr. k-1). 12.00 (978-0-9721888-2-1(7) , GP33485) Gabriel Pr.

Norelli, Sallianne. The Opposite Obstacle Course. Wetzel, Rick, illus. 2002. (Read-To-Me Ser.). 25p. (J). (978-0-7665-1215-3(0)) Abrams, Harry N. , Inc.

Novelli, Joan. Irresistible ABC's: 50 Easy, Fun, Multi-Sensory Activities to Help All Kids Explore & Learn the Alphabet. 2000. (Little Learners Ser.). (Illus.). 48p. pap. 8.95 (978-0-590-04930-6(5)) Scholastic, Inc.

November, Deborah. Elmo's ABC Book. Nicklaus, Carol, illus. 2007. (Big Bird's Favorites Brd Bks.). 24p. (J). (gr. k). bds. 4.99 ***978-0-375-84037-1(0)** , Random Hse. Bks. for Young Readers) Random Hse. Children's Bks.

Novit, Renee Z. Alphabet Aa to Zz. R. Z. Novit Graphic Design Staff, illus. (Kidz & Katz Educational Learning Book Ser.). 16p. (J). (ps). pap. 7.95 (978-1-883371-00-5(7)) Kidz & Katz Publishing Co.

O'Keefe, Susan Heyboer. Hungry Monster ABC: An Alphabet Book. Munsinger, Lynn, illus. 2007. 32p. (J). (ps-1). 12.99 (978-0-316-15574-8(8)) Little Brown & Co.

Olivares, Katie Lydon. ABC Book of Shadows. l.t. ed. 2005. (Illus.). 30p. (J). bds. 9.99 (978-0-9768573-0-3(8)) Itty Bitty Witch Works.

Ong, Cristina & Piper, Watty. The Little Engine That Could ABC. 1999. (Wee Pudgy Board Bks.). (Illus.). 20p. (J). (ps-k). 1.99 (978-0-448-41970-1(X) , Grosset & Dunlap) Penguin Group (USA) Inc.

Open Court Staff. Breaking Code Manuscript Alphabet. (J). pap. (978-0-87548-955-1(9) , 8514) Open Court Publishing Co.

Outside Your Back Door. 2004. (J). bds. 12.00 net. (978-0-9747081-0-2(0)) Cohen, Deanna Moreau.

Palauan Alphabet. 2004. (Illus.). 40p. 4.95 (978-1-57306-216-9(2)) Bess Pr., Inc.

Pallotta, Jerry. The Boat Alphabet Book. Biedrzycki, David, illus. 1998. 32p. (J). (ps-3). 16.95 (978-0-88106-910-5(8)) Charlesbridge Publishing, Inc.

—Boat Alphabet Book. 2003. (gr. k-3). lib. bdg. 16.40 (978-0-613-90104-8(5)) Tandem Library Bks.

—The Construction Alphabet Book. Bolster, Rob, illus. 2006. (Jerry Pallotta's Alphabet Bks.). 32p. (J). (gr. 4). 16.95 (978-1-57091-437-9(0)); (ps-4). pap. 7.95 (978-1-57091-438-6(9)) Charlesbridge Publishing, Inc.

—The Icky Bug Alphabet Book. Masiello, Ralph, illus. 2004. 28p. (J). (ps-3). bds. 6.95 (978-1-57091-439-3(7)) Charlesbridge Publishing, Inc.

—The Icky Bug Alphabet Book. Masiello, Ralph, photos by. (Illus.). 32p. (J). (ps-1). 10.95 (978-0-933341-95-1(4)); pap. 4.95 (978-0-933341-66-1(0)) Quinlan Pr.

—The Jet Alphabet Book. Bolster, Rob, illus. 32p. (J). (ps-3). 2004. pap. 7.95 (978-0-88106-917-4(5)); 1999. 16.95 (978-0-88106-916-7(7)) Charlesbridge Publishing, Inc.

—The Jet Alphabet Book. 1999. (gr. k-3). lib. bdg. 16.40 (978-0-613-65271-1(1)) Tandem Library Bks.

—Skull Alphabet Book. 2002. (gr. 3-6). lib. bdg. 16.40 (978-0-613-61387-3(2)) Tandem Library Bks.

Pandell, Karen. Animal Action ABC. 2000. 32p. (J). pap. (978-0-14-055885-2(3) , Puffin) Penguin Group (USA) Inc.

Paratore, Coleen. 26 Big Things Small Hands Do. Reed, Mike, illus. 2004. 32p. (J). (ps up). 16.95 (978-1-57542-166-7(6)) Free Spirit Publishing, Inc.

Paré, Roger. The Annick ABC. Paré, Roger, illus. 2003. (Annikins Press Ser.: Vol. 6). (Illus.). 12p. (J). (ps-2). pap. 0.99 (978-0-920303-78-8(1)) Annick Pr., Ltd. CAN. *Dist:* Firefly Bks., Ltd.

Pastel, JoAnne & Fitzsimmons, Kakie. Bur Bur's TM Boating ABC's: Learn the Most Amazing Things with the ABC's of Boating! 2007. (J). ***978-0-9777121-2-0(5))** Interface Publishing.

Paterson Chappell, Ruth. All 'Bout Charleston. Wroth, Dean, illus. 1998. 54p. (J). 14.95 (978-0-87844-144-0(1)) Sandlapper Publishing Co., Inc.

Paulson, Tim. Rainforest ABC. Spirin, Ilya, illus. 2001. (J). (978-1-890817-44-2(9)) Winslow Pr.

Pearson, Debora. Alphabeep! A Zipping, Zooming ABC. Miller, Edward, illus. 36p. (J). (ps-1). 6.95 ***978-0-8234-2076-6(0))** Holiday Hse., Inc.

Pearson, Kim. Animal ABC. Pearson, Kim, illus. 1999. (Illus.). v, 54p. (J). (ps). pap. 4.95 (978-1-881849-01-8(5)) Primary Sources.

Pelham, David. A Is for Animals: An ABC Pop-Up. Pelham, David, illus. 10th anniv. ed. 2001. (Illus.). 14p. (J). 18.99 (978-0-689-84706-6(8) , Little Simon) Simon & Schuster Children's Publishing.

Pelletier, David L. The Graphic Alphabet. Pelletier, David L., illus. 2002. (Illus.). (J). 27.19 (978-0-7587-0112-1(8)) Book Wholesalers, Inc.

Penguin Books Staff, ed. My Alphabet Book. (Early Readers Ser.: No. S8711-5). (Illus.). 24p. (J). (ps-2). 3.95 (978-0-7214-5145-9(4) , Dutton Juvenile) Penguin Group (USA) Inc.

Perrett, Lisa, illus. Princess ABC. 2004. 12p. (J). bds. 4.95 (978-1-4027-1488-7(2)) Sterling Publishing Co., Inc.

Perry, Gayle. Alphabet, Grades K-2. Friedman, Susan, ed. Yuh, Catherine, illus. 1999. (Primary Theme Ser.). 32p. pap., tchr. ed. 7.99 (978-1-57471-541-5(0) , 2428) Creative Teaching Pr., Inc.

Phillips, Lori. Carolinian Alphabet. 2004. (Illus.). 80p. (J). 4.95 (978-1-57306-220-6(0)) Bess Pr., Inc.

—Hawaiian Alphabet. 2004. (Illus.). 32p. (J). 4.95 (978-1-57306-218-3(9)) Bess Pr., Inc.

—Pohnpeian Alphabet. 2004. (Illus.). 40p. (J). 4.95 (978-1-57306-215-2(4)) Bess Pr., Inc.

—Samoan Alphabet. 2004. (Illus.). 40p. (J). 4.95 (978-1-57306-214-5(6)) Bess Pr., Inc.

Phillips, Sarah. First Words. 2006. (Shiny, Touchy, Smelly Ser.). (Illus.). 12p. (ps-k). bds. 7.95 (978-1-84610-087-1(9)) Make Believe Ideas GBR. *Dist:* Ingram Pub. Services.

—Lift & Learn ABC. Snaith, Andy, photos by. 2006. (Illus.). 24p. (ps). per., bds. 5.95 (978-1-84610-029-1(1)) Make Believe Ideas GBR. *Dist:* Ingram Pub. Services.

—Magnet Matching: ABC. 2006. (Illus.). 12p. (J). (gr. k-2). 14.95 (978-1-84610-121-2(2)) Make Believe Ideas GBR. *Dist:* Ingram Pub. Services.

—Touch & Learn: ABC. 2007. (Touch & Learn (Make Believe Ideas) Ser.). (Illus.). 12p. (ps). per., bds. 6.95 (978-1-84610-461-9(0)) Make Believe Ideas GBR. *Dist:* Ingram Pub. Services.

—Touch & Learn ABC. 2005. (Illus.). 12p. (J). (ps-1). per., bds. 12.95 (978-1-905051-75-5(1)) Make Believe Ideas GBR. *Dist:* Ingram Pub. Services.

Phillips, Sarah. Trace, Stick & Learn Wipe Clean ABC Activity Book. 2007. (Trace, Stick & Learn Ser.). (Illus.). 12p. (J). (ps-3). pap. 4.99 ***978-1-84610-430-5(0))** Make Believe Ideas GBR. *Dist:* Ingram Pub. Services.

Pierce, Jill. Little Tex's ABC'S. Colina, Charmaine, illus. 2000. 24p. (ps-k). 6.95 (978-0-87719-359-3(2)) Lone Star Bks.

Piggy Toes Press Staff & Borlasca, Hector. The Alphabet Song. 2006. 12.95 (978-1-58117-444-1(6) , Intervisual/Piggy Toes) Dalmatian Pr.

Pig's Picnic. 2001. (ps-2). lib. bdg. 9.80 (978-0-613-32947-7(3)) Tandem Library Bks.

Pike, Katy. Funny Photo Alphabet. Jurevicius, Luke, photos by. 2006. (Funny Photo Alphabet Ser.). (Illus.). 32p. (J). lib. bdg. (978-0-8225-6076-0(3) , Lerner Pubns.) Lerner Publishing Group.

Pilobolus. The Human Alphabet: Pilobolus. Kane, John, photos by. 2003. (Illus.). 40p. (J). (978-1-58717-225-0(9)); lib. bdg. (978-1-58717-226-7(7)) Chronicle Bks. LLC. (SeaStar Bks.).

—The Human Alphabet: Pilobolus. Kane, John, photos by. 2005. (Illus.). 32p. (J). (gr. k-4). 16.95 (978-1-59643-066-2(4)) Roaring Brook Pr.

Piper, Watty. The Little Engine That Could ABC Time. Ong, Cristina, illus. 2000. (Reading Railroad Bks.). 32p. (J). (ps-3). pap. 3.99 (978-0-448-42166-7(6) , Grosset & Dunlap) Penguin Group (USA) Inc.

Pirog, Kristen T. An Army ABC Book. Pierce, Julie A., illus. 2007. 32p. (J). per. 14.99 ***978-1-59879-324-6(1))** Lifevest Publishing, Inc.

—A Marine ABC Book. Pierce, Julie A., illus. l.t. ed. 2006. 32p. (J). per. 16.99 ***978-1-59879-221-8(0))** Lifevest Publishing, Inc.

Plante, Charles. A French Alphabet Book Of 1814: For Alfred Bourdier de Beauregard, Created by his uncle Arnaud at the Chateau Debeaumoont de Beauregard. 2007. (Illus.). 114p. 24.95 ***978-0-8478-3010-7(1))** Rizzoli International Pubns., Inc.

Play & Learn Fo, ed. Alphabet. 2007. (Play & Learn Foam Puzzle Bks.). 10p. (J). bds. 16.95 ***978-0-7696-5359-4(6)** , Brighter Child) School Specialty Publishing.

Polacco, Patricia. G Is for Goat. Gauch, Patricia Lee, ed. Polacco, Patricia, illus. 2003. (Illus.). 32p. (J). (ps-1). 16.99 (978-0-399-24018-8(7) , Philomel) Penguin Group (USA) Inc.

—G Is for Goat. Polacco, Patricia, illus. 32p. (J). 2007. 6.99 (978-0-399-24530-5(8) , Philomel); 2006. (Illus.). reprint ed. pap. 6.99 (978-0-14-240550-5(7) , Puffin) Penguin Group (USA) Inc.

Pomaska, Anna. Holiday Alphabet Follow-the-Dots. 2003. (Dover Little Activity Bks.). (Illus.). 64p. (J). (ps-5). pap. 1.50 (978-0-486-42749-2(8)) Dover Pubns., Inc.

Pomeroy, Diana. Wildflower ABC: An Alphabet of Potato Prints. Pomeroy, Diana, illus. 2001. (Illus.). 32p. (J). (ps). pap. 6.00 (978-0-15-202455-0(7) , Harcourt Paperbacks) Harcourt Children's Bks.

—Wildflower ABC: An Alphabet of Potato Prints. 2001. (Illus.). (J). (978-0-606-20992-2(1)) Tandem Library Bks.

Porter, Matthew. ABC. 2006. (Illus.). 28p. (J). bds. 8.95 (978-1-894965-38-5(8)) Simply Read Bks. CAN. *Dist:* Perseus Distribution.

Potter, Beatrix. Peter Rabbit's Hide & Seek. 2004. (Potter Ser.). (Illus.). 16p. (J). 12.99 (978-0-7232-5351-8(X) , Warne) Penguin Group (USA) Inc.

Powell, Consie. A Bold Carnivore: An Alphabet of Predators. 2007. (J). ***978-0-9766264-8-0(9)** ; pap. ***978-0-9766264-9-7(7))** Raven Productions, Inc.

—A Bold Carnivore: An Alphabet of Predators. Powell, Consie, illus. 2000. (Illus.). 32p. (ps-1). pap. 7.95 (978-1-57098-143-2(4)) Rinehart, Roberts Pubs.

Practice Pals Bilingual Practice Book: Cursive Letters. 2006. (ENG & FRE., Illus.). 16p. (J). (gr. k-2). spiral bd. (978-1-930355-54-5(8)) Greenbrier/Scentex.

Practice Pals Bilingual Practice Book: Manuscript Letters. 2006. (ENG & FRE., Illus.). 16p. (J). (ps-1). spiral bd. (978-1-930355-56-9(4)) Greenbrier/Scentex.

Pratt-Serafini, Kristin Joy. A Swim Through the Sea. Pratt-Serafini, Kristin Joy, illus. 2006. (Illus.). 26p. (J). bds. 7.95 (978-1-58469-080-1(1)) Dawn Pubns.

Pratt-Serafini, Kristin Joy. A Walk in the Rainforest. Pratt-Serafini, Kristin Joy, illus. 2007. (Illus.). 26p. (J). (ps-ps). bds. 7.95 ***978-1-58469-088-7(7))** Dawn Pubns.

Preece, Mary Ellen Goble. The ABC Cousins & Fun from A to Z. 2007. (J). per. 12.00 ***978-1-60458-005-1(4))** Instantpublisher.com.

Priddy Books Staff & Priddy, Roger. Dinosaur ABC. l.t. rev. ed. 2004. (Illus.). 32p. (J). bds. 9.95 (978-0-312-49254-0(5) , Priddy Bks.) St. Martin's Pr.

—Happy Baby: ABC. 2004. (Illus.). 28p. (J). bds. 8.95 (978-0-312-49192-5(1) , Priddy Bks.) St. Martin's Pr.

Priddy, Roger. Early Learning Pack - Letters. 2007. 52p. (J). 14.95 ***978-0-312-49966-2(3)** , Priddy Bks.) St. Martin's Pr.

—Happy Baby. rev. ed. 2001. (Baby Shakers Ser.). (Illus.). 24p. (J). bds. 5.95 (978-0-312-49021-8(6) , Priddy Bks.) St. Martin's Pr.

—Soft-to-Touch Slipcase 2: Colors,123,Abc. 2004. 84p. (J). bds. 22.95 (978-0-312-49423-0(8) , Priddy Bks.) St. Martin's Pr.

—Wipe Clean: Learn to Write Your Letters 26 Wipe-Clean Pages of Letter-Writing Fun. rev. ed. 2004. (Wipe Clean Ser.). (Illus.). 28p. (J). 8.95 (978-0-312-49251-9(0) , Priddy Bks.) St. Martin's Pr.

—Wipe Clean Flash Cards - ABC. 2006. (Wipe Clean Ser.). 30p. (J). bds. 9.95 (978-0-312-49816-0(0) , Priddy Bks.) St. Martin's Pr.

Priest, Jerry and Beverly. ABC Memory Verse Program. 2003. (Illus.). 60p. (J). spiral bd. 15.95 (978-0-9743871-0-9(X)) Priest, Gerald L.

Prieto, Anita C. B Is for Bookworm: A Library Alphabet. Graef, Renee, illus. 2005. (National Alphabet Bks.). 40p. (J). (gr. k-5). 16.95 (978-1-58536-145-8(3)) Sleeping Bear Pr.

Prieto, Anita C. A Library Alphabet. 2007. 40p. pap. 7.95 ***978-1-58536-326-1(X))** Sleeping Bear Pr.

Pringle, Cindy & Pringle, Kirby. Happy Tails: Earl & Pearl on the Farm. l.t. ed. 2006. (Illus.). 32p. (J). 16.95 (978-0-9777126-0-1(5)) Dogtown Artworks.

Pugliano-Martin, Carol. Iguana on Ice: Letter I. 2001. (Alpha Tales Ser.). (Illus.). 16p. (ps-1). pap. 2.25 (978-0-439-16532-7(6)) Scholastic, Inc.

—The Lamb Who Loved to Laugh: Letter L. 2001. (Alpha Tales Ser.). (Illus.). 16p. (ps-1). pap. 2.25 (978-0-439-16535-8(0)) Scholastic, Inc.

—When Tilly Turtle Came to Tea: Letter T. 2001. (Alpha Tales Ser.). (Illus.). 16p. (ps-1). pap. 2.25 (978-0-439-16543-3(1)) Scholastic, Inc.

—The Yak Who Yelled Yuck: Letter Y. 2001. (Alpha Tales Ser.). (Illus.). 16p. (ps-1). pap. 2.25 (978-0-439-16548-8(2)) Scholastic, Inc.

Quadrillion Media Staff. Let's Learn ABC. 1999. (J). pap. 1.99 (978-1-84100-285-9(2)) Quadrillion Media LLC.

—Let's Learn ABC: Sticker Books. 1999. (J). pap. 3.99 (978-1-84100-296-5(8)) Quadrillion Media LLC.

Quiet Quail. 2001. (ps-2). lib. bdg. 9.80 (978-0-613-32975-0(9)) Tandem Library Bks.

Rabe, Tish. Lots of Letters: From A to Z. Atteberry, Kevan, illus. 2006. 54p. (J). (ps-1). 15.99 (978-1-58476-481-6(3) , IKIDS) Innovative Kids.

Raczka, Bob. 3-D ABC: A Sculptural Alphabet. 2006. (Bob Raczka's Art Adventures Ser.). (Illus.). 32p. (J). (gr. k-3). lib. bdg. 23.93 (978-0-7613-9456-3(7) , Millbrook Pr.) Lerner Publishing Group.

Raintree Steck-Vaughn Staff, contrib. by. Eating the Alphabet. 2000. (J). (ps-3). pap. 22.00 (978-0-8172-9785-5(5)) Steck-Vaughn.

Ramey, Kathy. The Animal Alphabet. 2007. (J). pap. 12.95 ***978-1-931334-96-9(X))** Pieces of Learning.

Rayner, Shoo. Noah's ABC. (Illus.). 32p. (J). pap. 9.95 (978-0-14-054360-5(0)) Penguin Bks., Ltd. GBR. *Dist:* Trafalgar Square Publishing.

Reynolds, Eleanor D. LetterFun ABC Book. 1999. (Illus.). 32p. (J). pap. 5.95 (978-0-9660157-1-3(1)) FunStuff Productions, Inc.

Rhein, Elaine M. Do You Noah Your ABC's? 1999. (Illus.). 28p. (J). (ps-3). pap. 8.98 (978-0-9676333-0-5(3)) Jubilation Creation, Inc.

Rigby Education Staff. Animals: A Is for Animal. (Pebble Soup Explorations Ser.). 16p. (ps up). 5.00 (978-0-7635-7047-7(8)) Rigby Education.

Ring, Laura. The First Christmas: An ABC Book. Caldwell, Lise, ed. Cottrell, Kelly, illus. 1999. (Happy Day Bks.). 24p. (J). (ps-2). pap. 2.49 (978-0-7847-1087-6(2) , 04283, Bean Sprouts) Standard Publishing.

Robb, Don. Ox, House, Stick: The History of Our Alphabet. Smith, Anne, illus. 2007. 48p. (J). (gr. 3-6). pap. 7.95 ***978-1-57091-610-6(1))** Charlesbridge Publishing, Inc.

Roberts, G. Gregory. S Is for Spirit Bear: A British Columbia Alphabet. Doucet, Bob, illus. rev. ed. 2006. 40p. (J). 18.95 (978-1-58536-291-2(3)) Sleeping Bear Pr.

Robins, Harry S. Dinosaur Alphabet. 2006. (Illus.). 80p. (J). (978-1-58394-167-6(3) , Frog Ltd.) North Atlantic Bks.

Robinson, Alise. U, F & O... Where Did They Go? An Alphabet Book. 2005. (Illus.). 16p. (J). per. 6.95 (978-1-58117-395-6(4) , Intervisual/Piggy Toes) Dalmatian Pr.

Rogalski, Mark. Tickets to Ride: An Alphabetic Amusement. 2006. (Illus.). 64p. (J). 15.95 (978-0-7624-2782-6(5) , Running Pr. Kids) Running Pr. Bk. Pubs.

Root, Evelyn E. How to Learn the Alphabet the Pictured Sound Symbol Way: Speak & Spell with Alphabet Letters. Fieber, Frances S., illus. Root, Donald Y., photos by. 2000. 48p. (J). (ps-3). 15.95 (978-0-9654548-4-1(3)) Donalyn Bks.

Rosa-Mendoza, Gladys. The Alphabet. Cifuentes, Carolina, ed. Noiset, Michele, illus. 2004. (English-Spanish Foundations Ser.).Tr. of El Alfabeto. (ENG & SPA.). 32p. (J). bds. 6.95 (978-0-9679748-0-4(1)) Me+Mi Publishing.

Rosario, Sherwin, illus. Meet the Letters. 2005. 26p. (J). 9.99 (978-0-9767008-0-7(8)) KRO Publishing.

Rose, Deborah Lee. Into the A, B, Sea: An Ocean Alphabet Book. Jenkins, Steve, illus. 2000. 40p. (J). (ps-3). 16.99 (978-0-439-09696-6(0)) Scholastic, Inc.

Rose, Deborah Lee & Jenkins, Steve. Into the A, B, Sea. 2000. (Illus.). (J). (978-0-439-09697-3(9)) Scholastic, Inc.

Rosen, Michael. Alphabet Poem. Tullet, Herve, illus. 2004. 40p. (J). 15.95 (978-1-84059-393-8(8)) Milet Publishing.

Ross, Andrea. Chester Earth Ant (Alphabets & Numbers/Insects) Ross, Andrea, illus. 1999. (Chester Earth Ant Ser.). (Illus.). 26p. (J). (gr. k-3). pap. 9.95 (978-1-887683-35-7(6)) Storybook Pr. & Productions.

Rossi, Michelle. Letters & sounds in Loveland. 2005. 28p. (J). 6.95 (978-1-4116-3185-4(4)) Lulu.com.

Ruurs, Margriet. A Pacific Alphabet. Bonder, Dianna, illus. 2004. 32p. (J). (ps-2). 16.95 (978-1-55285-264-4(4)); pap. 8.95 (978-1-55285-521-8(X)) Whitecap Bks., Ltd. CAN. *Dist:* Firefly Bks., Ltd.

A
B

Sabuda, Robert. Christmas. 2006. (Illus.). 18p. (J). pap. 12.99 (978-0-439-84568-7(8) , Orchard Bks.) Scholastic, Inc.

—The Christmas Alphabet. 10th anniv. deluxe ed. 2004. (Illus.). 16p. (J). pap. 22.95 (978-0-439-67256-6(2) , Orchard Bks.) Scholastic, Inc.

Salisbury, Kent. Alpha Zoo: Have Fun with Your Animal Friends from A to Z. 1998. (Illus.). 13p. (J). (ps-k). 6.99 (978-0-7681-0082-2(8) , McClanahan Bk.) Learning Horizons, Inc.

Salonen, Roxane B. P Is for Peace Garden: A North Dakota Alphabet. Yardley, Joanna, illus. 2005. (Discover America State by State Ser.). 40p. (J). (ps-7). 17.95 (978-1-58536-142-7(9)) Sleeping Bear Pr.

Salzmann, Mary Elizabeth. Amy & Abe. 2005. (First Sounds Ser.). (Illus.). 23p. (J). pap. (978-1-59679-125-1(X)) ABDO Publishing Co.

—Ann & Alan. 2005. (First Sounds Ser.). (Illus.). 23p. (J). pap. (978-1-59679-127-5(6)); 19.93 (978-1-59679-126-8(8)) ABDO Publishing Co.

—Bess & Bill. 2005. (First Sounds Ser.). (Illus.). 23p. (J). pap. (978-1-59679-217-3(5)); 19.93 (978-1-59679-216-6(7)) ABDO Publishing Co.

—Blair & Blaine. 2005. (First Sounds Ser.). (Illus.). 23p. (J). pap. (978-1-59679-129-9(2)); 19.93 (978-1-59679-128-2(4)) ABDO Publishing Co.

—Brandi & Brent. 2005. (First Sounds Ser.). (Illus.). 23p. (J). pap. (978-1-59679-131-2(4)); 19.93 (978-1-59679-130-5(6)) ABDO Publishing Co.

—Cassie & Carl. 2005. (First Sounds Ser.). (Illus.). 23p. (J). pap. (978-1-59679-133-6(0)); 19.93 (978-1-59679-132-9(2)) ABDO Publishing Co.

—Chelsey & Chad. 2005. (First Sounds Ser.). 23p. (J). pap. (978-1-59679-135-0(7)); 19.93 (978-1-59679-134-3(9)) ABDO Publishing Co.

—Cindy & Cecil. 2005. (First Sounds Ser.). (Illus.). 23p. (J). pap. (978-1-59679-137-4(3)); 19.93 (978-1-59679-136-7(5)) ABDO Publishing Co.

—Cristy & Craig. 2005. (First Sounds Ser.). (Illus.). 23p. (J). pap. (978-1-59679-139-8(X)); 19.93 (978-1-59679-138-1(1)) ABDO Publishing Co.

—Deb & Dan. 2005. (First Sounds Ser.). (Illus.). 23p. (J). pap. (978-1-59679-141-1(1)); 19.93 (978-1-59679-140-4(3)) ABDO Publishing Co.

—Drew & Drake. 2005. (First Sounds Ser.). (Illus.). 23p. (J). pap. (978-1-59679-143-5(8)); 19.93 (978-1-59679-142-8(X)) ABDO Publishing Co.

—Ou: See It Say It Hear It. 2001. (Vowel Blends Ser.). (Illus.). 24p. (J). (ps-3). lib. bdg. 19.93 (978-1-57765-458-2(7) , SandCastle) ABDO Publishing Co.

Sandage, Charley. Big Bear's Arkansas ABCs Big Book. 2005. (J). pap. (*978-0-9794044-1-2(X)) Archeological Assessments, Inc.

Sanders, Nancy I. D Is for Drinking Gourd: An African American Alphabet. Lewis, Earl B, illus. 2007. (General Alphabet Ser.). 40p. (J). (gr. 1-7). 17.95 (*978-1-58536-293-6(X)) Sleeping Bear Pr.

Sandhaus, Ellen. 26 of the Most Interesting Letters in the Alphabet: 26 de las letras mas intersantes del alfabeto. Blanco, Osvaldo J., tr. Sandhaus, Ellen, illus. unabr. ed. 1999. (SPA & ENG., Illus.). 28p. (J). (gr. k-4). pap. 4.95 (978-1-893266-02-5(8)) Sandhaus, Paul Assocs., Inc.

Sandved, Kjell B. The Butterfly Alphabet. 1999. (Illus.). 64p. (J). (ps-3). pap. 5.99 (978-0-439-07947-1(0)) Scholastic, Inc.

—The Butterfly Alphabet. 1999. (J). (978-0-606-16930-1(X)) Tandem Library Bks.

Sayles, Alayne. Alphie & the Alphabets: A Fun Way to Learn to Read. Platt, Greg, illus. 2005. 44p. (J). spiral bd. 79.95 incl. audio compact disk (978-0-9767506-0-4(0)) Reading Studio Pr.

Schaefer, Lola M. Alpha-Butts: An Alphabet Book about Animal Rumps. Manning, Jane K., illus. 2008. 32p. (J). lib. bdg. 17.89 (*978-0-06-088394-2(4) , Greenwillow Bks.) HarperCollins Pubs.

—Musty-Crusty Animals ABC. 2002. (Musty-Crusty Animals Ser.). (Illus.). 24p. (J). (ps-1). pap. 5.25 (978-1-58810-727-5(2) , 91380); lib. bdg. 17.08 (978-1-58810-518-9(0)) Heinemann Library.

—Wheels, Wings & Water. 2003. (Wheels, Wings, & Water Ser.). (Illus.). 24p. (J). pap. (978-1-4034-3625-2(8)) Heinemann Library.

—Wheels, Wings, & Water ABC. 2003. (Wheels, Wings, & Water Ser.). (Illus.). 24p. (J). lib. bdg. 18.50 (978-1-4034-0887-7(4)) Heinemann Library.

—Wheels, Wings & Water ABC. 2003. (gr. k-3). lib. bdg. 13.30 (978-0-613-67441-6(3)) Tandem Library Bks.

Schaefer, Lola M. & Miller, Heather Lynn. Alpha-Butts: An Alphabet Book about Animal Rumps. Manning, Jane K., illus. 2008. 32p. (J). 16.99 (*978-0-06-088393-5(6) , Greenwillow Bks.) HarperCollins Pubs.

Schafer, Kevin. Penguins ABC. 2004. (Penguins Ser.). (Illus.). 28p. (J). (ps up). bds. 6.95 (978-1-55971-905-6(2) , NorthWord Bks. for Young Readers) T&N Children's Publishing.

Schnur, Steven. Spring: An Alphabet Acrostic. Evans, Leslie, illus. 1999. 32p. (J). (gr. k-3). tchr. ed. 15.00 (978-0-395-82269-2(6) , Clarion Bks.) Houghton Mifflin Co. Trade & Reference Div.

Scholastic, Inc. Staff. Abc Quilt Trimmer. 2002. (Scholastic Trimmers Ser.). lthr. 3.50 (978-0-439-40270-5(0) , Teaching Resources) Scholastic, Inc.

—Alpha Tales Learning Library. 2001. (Alpha Tales Ser.). (Illus.). 26p. (ps-1). pap. 64.95 (978-0-439-16521-1(0)) Scholastic, Inc.

—Barney: Let's Play & Pretend. Harris, Annmarie, ed. 2005. 400p. (J). pap. 5.99 (978-0-439-78926-4(5)) Scholastic, Inc.

—Cursive Alphabet. 2005. 5.99 (*978-0-439-73280-2(8) , Teaching Resources) Scholastic, Inc.

—Manusctipt Alphabet. 2005. 5.99 (*978-0-439-73277-2(8) , Teaching Resources) Scholastic, Inc.

—Modern Manu Alphabet. 2005. 5.99 (*978-0-439-73278-9(6) , Teaching Resources) Scholastic, Inc.

Scholastic, Inc. Staff. 26 Interactive Alphabet Wheels. 2000. (Illus.). (J). 26.95 (978-0-439-15542-7(8)) Scholastic, Inc.

Scholastic, Inc. Staff, et al. America from A to Z: Cursive Alphabet Set. 2003. (America from A to Z Alphabet Set Ser.). (Illus.). pap. 9.95 (978-0-439-45334-9(8) , Teaching Resources) Scholastic, Inc.

Schonberg, Marcia. Discover Ohio, 2 bks. Langton, Bruce, illus. 2003. 40p. (J). 27.95 (978-1-58536-225-7(5)) Sleeping Bear Pr.

—I Is for Idea: An Inventions Alphabet. Radzinski, Kandy, illus. 2005. (National Alphabet Bks.). 48p. (J). (gr. k-5). 16.95 (978-1-58536-257-8(3)) Sleeping Bear Pr.

School Specialty Publishing. The Alphabet. 2004. (On-File Ser.). 4p. (J). (gr. k-k). ring bd. 4.99 (978-0-7424-2848-5(6) , Instructional Fair) Schaffer, Frank Pubns.

—Alphabet. 2006. (Brighter Child Flash Cards Ser.). 54p. (J). 2.99 (978-0-7696-4679-4(4) , Brighter Child) School Specialty Publishing.

—Alphabet / el Alfabeto. 2006. (Brighter Child Flash Cards Ser.). 54p. (J). 2.99 (978-0-7696-4759-3(6) , Brighter Child) School Specialty Publishing.

—The Animal Alphabet. 2004. (On-File Ser.). 4p. (J). (gr. k-k). ring bd. 4.99 (978-0-7424-2849-2(4) , Instructional Fair) Schaffer, Frank Pubns.

—Easy Alphabet, Colors, Numbers & Shapes. 2001. (Phonics Flash Cards Ser.). 104p. (C). 6.99 (978-0-86734-411-0(3) , Schaffer, Frank) Schaffer, Frank Pubns.

—Easy Consonants. 2001. (Phonics Flash Cards Ser.). 104p. (C). 6.99 (978-0-86734-409-7(1) , Schaffer, Frank) Schaffer, Frank Pubns.

—Handwriting, Cursive. 2006. (Skills for Scholars Ser.). 80p. (C). pap. 4.99 (*978-0-7696-4926-9(2) , Schaffer, Frank) Schaffer, Frank Pubns.

—Handwriting, Printing. 2006. (Skills for Scholars Ser.). 80p. (C). pap. 4.99 (*978-0-7696-4925-2(4) , Schaffer, Frank) Schaffer, Frank Pubns.

—Learn about the Alphabet. 2005. (Learn about Coloring Bks.). 32p. (J). (ps-3). pap. 1.99 (978-0-7696-4156-0(3) , Brighter Child) School Specialty Publishing.

—Learning Letters, Preschool. 2006. (Skills for Scholars Ser.). 80p. (C). pap. 4.99 (*978-0-7696-5019-7(8) , Schaffer, Frank) Schaffer, Frank Pubns.

—Letras del Alfabeto. 2006. (Aprendamos Ser.). 64p. (J). pap. 3.99 (978-0-7696-4322-9(1) , Brighter Child) School Specialty Publishing.

—Starter Skills Learning Letters. 2007. (English-Espanol Starter Skills Ser.). 80p. (C). pap. 8.99 (*978-0-7682-3409-1(3) , Schaffer, Frank) Schaffer, Frank Pubns.

School Specialty Publishing. Wipe-Away Books: Alphabet Dot-to-Dot. 2001. (Illus.). 16p. (J). (ps). pap. 3.99 (978-0-7682-0067-6(9)) School Specialty Publishing.

School Zone Publishing Co. Alphabet Bingo Game. rev. ed. 2006. (J). (ps-k). 5.99 (*978-1-58947-494-9(5)) School Zone Publishing Co.

School Zone Publishing Company Staff. Alphabet. 2000. (Flash Cards Spanish Ser.). (SPA., Illus.). 56p. (J). 2.89 (978-0-88743-619-2(6) , 04041) School Zone Publishing Co.

—Alphabet: Flash Cards. rev. ed. 1999. (Flash Cards Ser.). (Illus.). 56p. (J). 2.79 (978-0-938256-86-1(6) , 04001) School Zone Publishing Co.

—Alphabet Express. 1998. (Illus.). (J). (gr. k-1). ring bd., lab manual ed., tchr.'s training gde. ed. 149.99 incl. audio compact disk (978-0-88743-584-3(X)); ring bd., tchr.'s training gde. ed. 49.99 incl. audio compact disk (978-0-88743-583-6(1) , 08500); ring bd., tchr.'s training gde. ed. 360.00 incl. audio compact disk (978-0-88743-640-6(4)) School Zone Publishing Co.

—Alphabet Sticker Workbook. 1999. (Alphabet Sticker Workbook Ser.: Vol. 2750). (Illus.). 16p. (J). (gr. k-2). pap. 3.59 (978-0-88743-118-0(6) , 02750) School Zone Publishing Co.

—Christmas ABCs: An Alphabet Book. 1999. (Board Books Ser.). (Illus.). 18p. (J). (ps-3). bds. 4.99 (978-0-88743-601-7(3) , 06602) School Zone Publishing Co.

—UpperCase Alphabet Bilingual: Get Ready! 2004. 64p. (J). pap. 3.79 (978-1-58947-969-2(6)) School Zone Publishing Co.

—Whimsy Alphabet. 2001. (Flash Cards Whimsy Ser.). 36p. (J). 2.79 (978-0-88743-472-3(X) , 04064) School Zone Publishing Co.

Schuette, Sarah L. African Animals ABC: An Alphabet Safari. 2003. (A+ Alphabet Books). (Illus.). 17p. (J). (gr. k-1). 22.60 (978-0-7368-1679-3(8) , Aplus Bks.) Capstone Pr., Inc.

—An Alphabet Salad: Fruits & Vegetables from A to Z. 2003. (A+ Alphabet Books). (Illus.). 17p. (J). (gr. k-1). 22.60 (978-0-7368-1683-0(6) , Aplus Bks.) Capstone Pr., Inc.

Schwaeber, Barbie Heit. Alphabet of Bears. Nelson, Will, illus. 2007. 40p. 15.95 (*978-1-59249-689-1(X)) Soundprints.

Schwartz, David M. G Is for Googol: A Math Alphabet Book. Moss, Marissa, illus. 2004. 57p. (J). (gr. 4-7). tchr. ed. 15.95 (978-1-883672-58-4(9) , Tricycle Pr.) Ten Speed Pr.

—Q Is for Quark: A Science Alphabet Book. Doner, Kim, illus. 2004. 64p. (YA). (gr. 4-8). tchr. ed. 15.95 (978-1-58246-021-5(3) , Tricycle Pr.) Ten Speed Pr.

—Q Is for Quark, Grades 4-8: A Science Alphabet Book. Doner, Kim, illus. 2001. 64p. tchr. ed. 2.95 (978-1-58246-049-9(3) , Tricycle Pr.) Ten Speed Pr.

Scillian, Devin. A Is for America: An American Alphabet. Carroll, Pam, illus. 2001. 56p. (J). (ps-3). 22.95 (978-1-58536-015-4(5)) Sleeping Bear Pr.

—H Is for Honor: A Military Family Alphabet. Juhasz, Victor, illus. 2006. 40p. (J). 17.95 (978-1-58536-292-9(1)) Sleeping Bear Pr.

Scillian, Devin & Scillian, Corey. S Is for Sunflower: A Kansas Alphabet. Bowles, Doug, illus. 2004. (State Ser.). 40p. (J). 17.95 (978-1-58536-061-1(9) , 1235980) Sleeping Bear Pr.

Segal, Robin. ABC in Chicago. 2007. 32p. (J). 12.95 (*978-0-9719697-8-0(7)) Murray Hill Bks., LLC.

—ABC in Washington, DC. 2007. (J). 12.95 (*978-0-9719697-7-3(9)) Murray Hill Bks., LLC.

Segal, Robin, ed. ABC in NYC. 2006. (Illus.). 32p. (J). 12.95 (978-0-9719697-6-6(0)) Murray Hill Bks., LLC.

Sehmi, Amritpal Kaur, et al, eds. Punjabi Letters Board Book. Sehmi, Amritpal Kaur, tr. Sarch, Gagan Kaur, illus. Gray, Kerry Lynn, photos by. 2002. (PAN.). 50p. (J). bds. 12.95 (978-0-9709736-1-0(6)) Small People Publishing.

Seidman, David. Brazil ABCs: A Book about the People & Places of Brazil. Thompson, Jeffrey, illus. 2006. (Country ABCs Ser.). 32p. (J). (gr. k-5). lib. bdg. 25.26 (*978-1-4048-2248-1(8)) Picture Window Bks.

Sellers, Paul. Little 'b' 2000. (Illus.). 12p. (J). 3.99 (978-0-552-52873-3(0)) Transworld Publishers Ltd. GBR. *Dist:* Trafalgar Square Publishing.

—Little 'm' 2000. (Illus.). 12p. (J). 3.99 (978-0-552-52884-9(6)) Transworld Publishers Ltd. GBR. *Dist:* Trafalgar Square Publishing.

—Little 'p' 2000. (Illus.). 12p. (J). 3.99 (978-0-552-52887-0(0)) Transworld Publishers Ltd. GBR. *Dist:* Trafalgar Square Publishing.

—Little 'x' 2000. (Illus.). 12p. (J). 3.99 (978-0-552-52895-5(1)) Transworld Publishers Ltd. GBR. *Dist:* Trafalgar Square Publishing.

—Little 'z' 2000. (Illus.). 12p. (J). 3.99 (978-0-552-52897-9(8)) Transworld Publishers Ltd. GBR. *Dist:* Trafalgar Square Publishing.

Sempere, Vicky. ABC. 2001. (SPA.). (J). pap. 8.95 (978-980-257-028-7(1)) Ekare, Ediciones VEN. *Dist:* Lectorum Pubns., Inc.

Sesame Street ABC. 2005. (J). 2.95 (*978-1-58610-978-3(2)) Learning Horizons, Inc.

Sesame Street Learn about ABCs. 1999. (J). 11.99 (978-0-679-89428-5(4) , Random Hse. Bks. for Young Readers) Random Hse. Children's Bks.

Sesame Street Learn about Letters with Cookie Monster: Ages 2 To 4. 2005. (Illus.). 48p. (J). (ps-ps). 3.95 (978-1-58610-864-9(6) , 73000) Learning Horizons, Inc.

Sesame Street Storybook COLL 2. 2007. 10.99 (*978-1-4037-3614-7(6)) Dalmatian Pr.

Sesame's: A Giant Coloring Book that Introduces Kids to the Alphabet: the ABCs of Sesame Street. 2006. (J). 6.99 (978-1-59949-498-2(1)) Food Marketing Consultants, Inc.

Seuss, Dr. Hooper Humperdink... ? Not Him! Stevenson, James & Nash, Scott, illus. (Bright & Early Bks.). 48p. (J). (gr. k-1). 2006. 8.99 (978-0-679-88129-2(8)); 1999. lib. bdg. 12.99 (978-0-679-98129-9(2)) Random Hse. Children's Bks. (Random Hse. Bks. for Young Readers).

Shannon, George. Tomorrow's Alphabet. Crews, Donald, illus. 1999. 56p. (J). (ps-3). pap. 6.99 (978-0-688-16424-9(2) , Harper Trophy) HarperCollins Pubs.

—Tomorrow's Alphabet. 1999. (978-0-606-16755-0(2)); lib. bdg. 15.30 (978-0-613-18196-9(4)) Tandem Library Bks.

Sharpe, Jesse. Pictures Poetry & ABCs: my alphabet Learning Book. 2005. 69p. spiral bd. 9.95 (978-1-4116-2461-0(0)) Lulu.com.

Sheldon. Not Just Another Alphabet Book. (J). 15.95 (978-0-8118-4329-4(7)) Chronicle Bks. LLC.

Sheldon, Ken. Sing along & Learn the Alphabet. 1999. (Illus.). 32p. (J). pap. 9.95 (978-0-590-98337-2(7)) Scholastic, Inc.

Shindler, Ramon & Graniczewski, Wojciech. Found Alphabet. Andrzejewska, Anita & Pilichowski-Ragno, Andrzej, illus. 2005. 32p. (J). (gr. k-3). 16.00 (978-0-618-44232-4(4)) Houghton Mifflin Co. Trade & Reference Div.

Shoulders, Michael. The ABC Book of American Homes. Brannen, Sarah, illus. 2008. (J). (*978-1-57091-565-9(2)) Charlesbridge Publishing, Inc.

—Discover Tennessee: Count on Us; V is for Volunteer, 2 bks. Langton, Bruce, illus. 2003. 40p. (J). 27.95 (978-1-58536-228-8(X)) Sleeping Bear Pr.

—M Is for Magnolia: A Mississippi Alphabet. Anderson, Rick, illus. 2003. 40p. (J). 17.95 (978-1-58536-129-8(1)) Sleeping Bear Pr.

Shoulders, Michael & Shoulders, Debbie. D Is for Drum: A Native American Alphabet. Toddy, Irving, illus. rev. ed. 2006. 40p. (J). (gr. k-5). 16.95 (978-1-58536-274-5(3)) Sleeping Bear Pr.

Shulman, Mark. A Is for Zebra. Petrosino, Tamara, illus. 2006. 32p. (J). 14.95 (978-1-4027-3494-6(8)) Sterling Publishing Co., Inc.

Silence, illus. A Is for Artist: An Alphabet. Doran, Ella, photos by. 2005. 56p. (J). (ps-1). 19.95 (978-1-85437-556-8(3)) Tate Gallery Publishing, Ltd. GBR. *Dist:* Hachette Bk. Group.

The Silly Sheepdog: Alphabet Book - First 100 Words, 3 bks., 3 discs, Set. 2004. (Make Reading Fun! Ser.: Module 2). (SPA.). (J). (ps-k). 49.95 (978-1-58086-179-3(2)) EDC Publishing.

Sing & Learn, ed. Alphabet. 2007. (Sing & Learn Padded Board Bks.). 53p. (J). bds. 16.95 (*978-0-7696-5419-5(3)) School Specialty Publishing.

Skirving, Janet. P Is for Puffin: A Newfoundland & Labrador Alphabet. Archibald, Odell, illus. rev. ed. 2006. 40p. (J). 18.95 (978-1-58536-287-5(5)) Sleeping Bear Pr.

Sklar, Dorothy J. Seal's Silly Sandwich: Letter S. 2001. (Alpha Tales Ser.). (Illus.). 16p. (ps-1). pap. 2.25 (978-0-439-16542-6(3)) Scholastic, Inc.

Slater, Teddy. ABC Sing-along. Chauncy Guida, Lisa, illus. 2006. 24p. (J). pap. 12.99 (978-0-439-85357-6(5) , Cartwheel Bks.) Scholastic, Inc.

Sloan, Susan M. Adventuring Through the Abc's with Your Favorite Beanie Babies. 1998. 27p. (J). pap. 9.95 (978-0-9668566-0-6(0)) Universe of Imagination Pubns.

Smith, Marie & Smith, Roland. B Is for Beaver: An Oregon Alphabet. Roydon, Michael, illus. 2003. 40p. (J). 17.95 (978-1-58536-071-0(6)) Sleeping Bear Pr.

Smith, Roland. Z Is for Zookeeper: A Zoo Alphabet. Cole, Henry, illus. 2005. 40p. (J). 16.95 (978-1-58536-158-8(5)) Sleeping Bear Pr.

Smith, Roland. A Zoo Alphabet. rev. ed. 2007. 40p. pap. 7.95 (*978-1-58536-329-2(4)) Sleeping Bear Pr.

Snow, Todd & Snow, Peggy. Feelings to Share from A to Z. Hartman, Carrie, illus. 2007. 32p. (J). per. 8.95 (*978-1-934277-00-3(2)) Marn Green Publishing, Inc.

So, Sungwan. C Is for China. So, Sungwan, photos by. 2004. (World Alphabets Ser.). (Illus.). 32p. (J). pap. 7.95 (978-1-84507-318-3(5)) Lincoln, Frances Ltd. GBR. *Dist:* Perseus Distribution.

Sobel, June. B Is for Bulldozer: A Construction ABC. Iwai, Melissa, illus. 2003. 32p. (J). 16.00 (978-0-15-202250-1(3)) Harcourt Children's Bks.

—B Is for Bulldozer: A Construction ABC. Iwai, Melissa, illus. 2006. 32p. (J). pap. 6.00 (978-0-15-205774-9(9) , Voyager Bks./Libros Viajeros) Harcourt Children's Bks.

Soffer, Ruth. Birds Alphabet: Coloring Book. 2005. (Illus.). 32p. (J). (ps-ps). pap. 3.95 (978-0-486-44035-4(4)) Dover Pubns., Inc.

—Garden Flowers Alphabet Coloring Book. 2004. (Dover Coloring Bks.). (Illus.). 32p. (J). pap. 3.95 (978-0-486-43595-4(4)) Dover Pubns., Inc.

Soffer, Ruth. Nature Alphabet Coloring Book. 2006. 96p. pap. 7.95 (*978-0-486-45921-9(7)) Dover Pubns., Inc.

Somme, Kate. Very Active Alphabet & Other Alphabet Rhymes. Coco, Yoko, illus. 2006. 32p. pap. 8.95 (978-0-7145-3304-9(1)) Consortium Bk. Sales & Distribution.

Sonday, Arlene. The Sonday System - Let's Play Learn: Alphabet Book. Breckman, Cindy, ed. l.t. ed. 2004. (Illus.). 53p. (J). per. (978-1-891602-11-5(X)) Winsor Learning, Inc.

Soundprints. Pooh's First Concepts Pack. rev. ed. (First Concepts Ser.). (Illus.). 36p. (J). 12.99 incl. cd-rom (978-1-59069-363-6(9) , 1A502) Studio Mouse LLC.

Sounds & Letters, Level A. 2000. (Let's Read Literacy Center Ser.). (Illus.). (gr. k-3). 205.88 (978-0-7362-1088-1(1)) Hampton-Brown Bks.

Sounds & Letters. 2003. (Full-Color Literacy Activities Ser.). (Illus.). 176p. (J). (ps-1). 19.99 (978-0-7439-3235-6(8)) Teacher Created Materials, Inc.

Spinelli, Patti. Alphabet Book with Mackenzie & Emma. Spinelli, Patti, illus. 2003. (Illus.). 32p. (Orig.). (J). (gr. k-4). pap. 11.95 (978-1-892066-00-8(9)) Nicolin Fields Publishing, Inc.

Spooner, Joe. N Is for Nostril—and Other Alphabet Silliness. 2007. (Illus.). 32p. (J). 14.95 (*978-0-9794771-1-9(5)) Arnica Publishing, Inc.

Spray, Michelle. My ABCs: An ABC Book for Any Age. Pasternack, Susan, ed. Martines, Donna, illus. l.t. ed. 2006. 64p. (J). per. 8.95 (978-0-9714160-4-8(4)) Bk. Shelf.

Sprick, Marilyn, et al. Write Well Big Book of Alphabet Poems. 2000. (Write Well Curriculum Ser.). (Illus.). 36p. (J). (gr. 1-3). pap., stu. ed. (978-1-57035-315-4(8) , 193POEM) Sopris West Educational Services.

Springett, Martin, illus. Jousting with Jesters: An ABC for the Younger Dragon. 2006. 32p. (J). 17.95 (978-1-55143-327-1(3)) Orca Bk. Pubs. USA.

Stamper, Judith Bauer & Blevins, Wiley. Monster Town Fair. Evans, Nate, illus. 1998. (Hello Reader! Ser.). 160p. (J). (gr. 1-2). pap. 3.99 (978-0-590-76268-7(0)) Scholastic, Inc.

Steck-Vaughn Staff. What Can We Make Together. 2000. pap. (978-0-7398-4484-7(9)) Steck-Vaughn.

Steig, William. Cdb! Steig, William, illus. 2005. (Stories to Go! Ser.). 48p. (J). 4.99 (978-1-4169-0306-2(2) , Aladdin) Simon & Schuster Children's Publishing.

Steiner, Stan, et al. P Is for Potato: An Idaho Alphabet. Stack, Jocelyn, illus. 2005. (Discover America State by State Ser.). 40p. (J). 17.95 (978-1-58536-155-7(0)) Sleeping Bear Pr.

Sterling Publishing Company Staff. Learning to Write with Benjamin the Bear: Wipe & Clean Book. 1998. (Balloon Ser.). (Illus.). 14p. (J). (ps-1). pap. 5.95 (978-0-8069-3824-0(2)) Sterling Publishing Co., Inc.

Stevens, Christian. An Animal Alphabet. 2002. (Illus.). 112p. (J). (gr. k-3). pap. 5.95 (978-0-86327-878-5(7)) Interlink Publishing Group, Inc.

Stewart, Shannon. Alphabad: Mischievous ABCs. Petricic, Dusan, illus. 2007. 32p. (J). (ps-3). 12.95 (*978-1-4236-0147-0(5)) Gibbs Smith, Publisher.

Stinga, Jennifer. Aprende las Letras Con Cookie Monster. 2007. (Sesame Street Ser.). (SPA & ENG.). 48p. (J). pap., wbk. ed. 3.95 (*978-1-59545-072-2(6)) Learning Horizons, Inc.

Stone, Tanya Lee. B Is for Bunny: A Springtime Alphabet Book. Rama, Sue, illus. 2006. 24p. (J). (ps-1). pap. 4.99 (978-0-8431-1826-1(1) , Price Stern Sloan) Penguin Group (USA) Inc.

—D Is for Dreidel: A Hanukkah Alphabet Book. Apperley, Dawn, illus. 2002. 24p. (J). (gr. k-2). pap. 4.99 (978-0-8431-4576-2(5) , Price Stern Sloan) Penguin Group (USA) Inc.

Stuart, Neil & Stuart, Catherine. My ABC Suitcase. 2004. (Illus.). 3p. (J). bds. 13.95 (978-1-59354-047-0(7)) Handprint Bks.

Studio Mouse. Disney Marie: A Is for Adorable: A Fabulous Alphabet: Zip & Carry Book & Cd. rev. ed. 2007. 36p. 12.99 (*978-1-59069-569-2(0)) Studio Mouse LLC.

—Disney Princess Take-with-Me Alphabet: Zip & Carry Book & CD. rev. ed. 2007. 36p. 12.99 (***978-1-59069-570-8(4)***) Studio Mouse LLC.

—Princess ABC's & 123's. rev. ed. 2007. (Disney Princess Ser.). 24p. 4.99 (***978-1-59069-560-9(7)***) Studio Mouse LLC.

Stull, Elizabeth Crosby. Alphabet Animals Activities Kit: Over 150 Ready-to-Use Activity Sheets for Reinforcing Letter-Sound Relationships. 1999. (Illus.). 324p. (J). (gr. k-3). pap. 24.95 (978-0-13-040106-9(4) , Addison Wesley) Benjamin-Cummings Publishing Co.

Stutson, Caroline. On the River ABC. Crum, Anna-Maria, illus. 2000. 32p. (gr. k-3). 12.95 (978-1-879373-46-4(7)) Rinehart, Roberts Pubs.

—Prairie Primer: A to Z. Lamb, Susan Condie, illus. 2006. 29p. (J). (ps-2). reprint ed. 16.00 (978-1-4223-5585-5(3)) DIANE Publishing Co.

—Prairie Primer A to Z. 1999. (978-0-606-16783-3(8)) Tandem Library Bks.

Style Guide Staff, illus. Alphabet Power. 2005. (Blue's Clues Ser.: Vol. 18). 24p. (J). pap. 3.99 (978-1-4169-0709-1(2) , Simon Spotlight/Nickelodeon) Simon & Schuster Children's Publishing.

Sunshine Alphabet Book. (gr. k-3). 13.95 (978-0-7802-6169-3(0)) Wright Group, The.

Szekeres, Cyndy. Wilbur Bunny's Funny Friends A to Z. Szekeres, Cyndy, illus. 2000. (Illus.). 15p. (J). (ps). bds. 6.99 (978-0-439-17327-8(2)) Scholastic, Inc.

Tapahonso, Luci. Navajo ABC: A Dine Alphabet Book. 1999. (978-0-606-16321-7(2)) Tandem Library Bks.

Taylor, Damon. Bible Characters A to Z. 2002. (Child Sockology Ser.). 60p. (J). 9.99 (978-0-8254-3851-6(9)) Kregel Pubns.

Taylor, Maxwell. Fun with Letters. Mshindu, illus. Date not set. (Fun with Ser.: Vol. 3). (J). (ps-1). pap. 3.95 (978-1-881316-42-8(4)) A & B Distributors & Pubs. Group.

Teach-Me-Bears Learn Letters. 2003. (J). per. (978-1-884907-63-0(6)) Paradise Pr., Inc.

Thistlethwaite, Diane, ed. My First Lift-the-Flap ABC Book. 2001. (My First Word Books). (Illus.). 12p. (J). (ps-k). bds. 9.99 (978-0-7894-7413-1(1)) Dorling Kindersley Publishing, Inc.

Thompson, Karen & Mitzo Thompson, Kim. Alphabet: Songs That Teach Alpabet. 2006. (Sing along Activity Books with CDs Ser.). (Illus.). 32p. (J). pap. 4.99 (978-0-7696-4572-8(0)) School Specialty Publishing.

A to Z with Noah. ed. 2006. (J). bds. (978-0-9771117-3-2(3)) JMG Studio.

Top That!, ed. Alphabet Farm. Parry, Jo, illus. 2007. 10p. (J). (ps). 8.99 (***978-1-84666-272-0(9)*** , Tide Mill Pr.) Top That! Publishing PLC GBR. *Dist:* Random Hse., Inc.

Torres, Melissa, ed. Schol Hands on Learning ABCs. 2004. (Scholastic Hands-on Learning Ser.). (Illus.). 13p. (J). 9.95 (978-0-439-63898-2(4) , Cartwheel Bks.) Scholastic, Inc.

Touch, Trace & Write Lowercase. 2005. (J). pap. (***978-1-60015-001-2(2)***) Steps To Literacy, LLC.

Touch, Trace & Write Uppercase. 2005. (J). pap. (***978-1-60015-000-5(4)***) Steps To Literacy, LLC.

Trago Publishing Staff. The Alphabet 1 Painting Pad. 1999. (My Art Ser.: Vol. 1). 26p. (J). (ps-3). pap. 7.95 (978-0-9683883-0-3(2)) Sterling Publishing Co., Inc.

—The Alphabet 1 Travel Kit. 1999. (My Art Ser.). 35p. (J). (ps-3). pap. 4.95 (978-0-9683883-2-7(9)) Sterling Publishing Co., Inc.

Transparent Letter Tiles. (ps-12). 21.95 (978-0-7362-1289-2(2)) Hampton-Brown Bks.

Travers, P. L. Mary Poppins from A to Z. Shepard, Mary, illus. 2006. 64p. (J). 14.00 (978-0-15-205834-0(6)) Harcourt Children's Bks.

Tudor, Tasha. A Is for Annabelle: A Doll's Alphabet. Tudor, Tasha, illus. 2001. (Illus.). 64p. (J). 16.99 (978-0-689-82845-4(4)) Simon & Schuster Children's Publishing.

—A Is for Annabelle: A Doll's Alphabet. Tudor, Tasha, illus. 2004. (Illus.). 64p. (J). reprint ed. pap. 6.99 (978-0-689-86996-9(7) , Aladdin) Simon & Schuster Children's Publishing.

Twin Sisters Productions Staff, prod. Alphabet & Counting: Songs That Teach. 2005. (J). per. 12.99 (978-1-57583-819-9(2)) Twin Sisters Productions, LLC.

—Preschool: Songs That Teach. 2005. (J). per. (978-1-57583-817-5(6)) Twin Sisters Productions, LLC.

Twist, Clint. Endangered Animals A-Z. 2004. (Illus.). 64p. (J). 26.20 (978-1-4103-0488-9(4)) Thomson Gale.

Twin Sisters Productions, prod. Phonics: Songs That Teach. 2005. (J). per. 12.99 (978-1-57583-820-5(6)) Twin Sisters Productions, LLC.

Ulmer, Michael. A Basketball Alphabet. rev. ed. 2007. 40p. pap. 7.95 (***978-1-58536-338-4(3)***) Sleeping Bear Pr.

—An Equestrain Alphabet. van Frankenhuyzen, Gijsbert, illus. rev. ed. 2007. 40p. pap. 7.95 (***978-1-58536-334-6(0)***) Sleeping Bear Pr.

Ulmer, Michael. J Is for Jump Shot: A Basketball Alphabet. Braught, Mark, illus. 2005. (Sports Alphabet Ser.). 40p. (J). (gr. k-5). 16.95 (978-1-58536-229-5(8)) Sleeping Bear Pr.

Ulmer, Mike. M Is for Maple: A Canadian Alphabet. rev. ed. 2007. (Board Ser.). 36p. bds. 7.99 (***978-1-58536-345-2(6)***) Sleeping Bear Pr.

Ulmer, Wendy K. A Isnt for Fox: The Isnt Alpha. Knorr, Laura, illus. rev. ed. 2007. (General Alphabet Ser.). 32p. (J). 16.95 (***978-1-58536-319-3(7)***) Sleeping Bear Pr.

Vera Viper's Valentine. 2001. (ps-2). lib. bdg. 9.80 (978-0-613-33181-4(8)) Tandem Library Bks.

Vidrine, Beverly. Thanksgiving Day Alphabet. 2006. (Illus.). 32p. (J). pap. 7.95 (978-1-58980-338-1(8)) Pelican Publishing Co., Inc.

Vidrine, Beverly Barras. Easter Day Alphabet. Lyne, Alison Davis, illus. 2003. 32p. (J). (gr. k-3). pap. 7.95 (978-1-58980-076-2(1)) Pelican Publishing Co., Inc.

—Halloween Alphabet. Lyne, Alison Davis, illus. 2004. 32p. (J). pap. 7.95 (978-1-58980-242-1(X)) Pelican Publishing Co., Inc.

Vischer, Phil. Bob & Larry's ABC's: A Veggiecational Book about Letters! 1999. (Veggiecational Ser.). (Illus.). 12p. (J). (ps-3). 8.99 (978-0-8499-5986-8(1)) Nelson, Thomas Inc.

—The Veggiecational Book: A Book about Numbers, Colors, Shapes & Letters! 1998. (Veggiecational Ser.: Vol. 7). (Illus.). 128p. (J). (ps-2). 19.99 (978-0-8499-5865-6(2)) Nelson, Thomas Inc.

Wade, Mary D. M Is for Massachusetts. Roader, Virginia, illus. 2001. (Alpha Flight Books Ser.). 60p. (J). (ps-3). 17.95 (978-1-892920-42-3(5)) GHB Publishers, LLC.

Wade, Mary Dodson. "T" Is for Texas. Roeder, Virginia M., illus. 2000. (Alpha Flight Bks.). 60p. (J). (ps-3). 17.95 (978-1-892920-28-7(X)) GHB Publishers, LLC.

Walker, Susan, ed. Literacy for Little Learners Alphabet Songs & Rhymes. 2004. 80p. 12.95 (978-1-56234-604-1(0) , Mailbox Bks., The) Education Ctr., Inc.

—Literacy for Little Learners Sounds & Letters. 2004. 80p. 12.95 (978-1-56234-606-5(7) , Mailbox Bks., The) Education Ctr., Inc.

Wallace, Nancy Elizabeth. Alphabet House. Wallace, Nancy Elizabeth, illus. 2005. (Illus.). 32p. (J). (ps-2). per. 16.95 (978-0-7614-5192-1(7)) Cavendish, Marshall Corp.

Walling, Sandy Seeley, illus. & text. ABC's at the Zoo! The Fun Way to Teach Your Child the Relationship between Upper Case & Lower Case Letters, Walling, Sandy Seeley, text. l.t. ed. 2004. 36p. (J). per. 7.95 (978-0-9741940-1-1(8)) Abernathy Hse. Publishing.

Walton, Rick. So Many Bunnies: A Bedtime ABC & Counting Book. Miglio, Paige, illus. 32p. (J). (ps-3). 2002. pap. 5.95 (978-0-06-443751-6(5) , Harper Trophy); 2000. 6.99 (978-0-688-17364-7(0) , Harper Festival) HarperCollins Pubs.

—So Many Bunnies: A Bedtime ABC & Counting Book. 1998. (Illus.). 32p. (J). (ps-1). 15.89 (978-0-688-13657-4(5)) HarperCollins Pubs.

—So Many Bunnies: A Bedtime ABC & Counting Book. Miglio, Paige, illus. 1998. 32p. (J). (ps-3). 17.99 (978-0-688-13656-7(7)) HarperCollins Pubs.

Wargin, Kathy-Jo. A Music Alphabet. rev. ed. 2007. 40p. pap. 7.95 (***978-1-58536-332-2(4)***) Sleeping Bear Pr.

—P Is for Pumpkin. Pang, Ariel Ya-Wen, illus. 2008. (J). (978-0-310-71180-3(0)) Zonderkidz.

—V Is for Viking: A Minnesota Alphabet. Latham, Karen & Latham, Rebecca, illus. 2003. 40p. (J). 17.95 (978-1-58536-125-0(9)) Sleeping Bear Pr.

Warnes, Tim. Little Tiger's Funtime ABC. 2001. (J). 8.95 (978-1-58925-659-0(X) , tiger tales) ME Media LLC.

Waters, Kim. Enchanted Tales: An ABC Fantasy. l.t. ed. 1999. (Illus.). 56p. (J). (gr. k-4). 15.95 (978-1-886069-08-4(5)) Mandala Publishing.

Watt, Melanie. The Alphabet with Wild Animals. 2005. (Learning with Animals Board Bks.). (Illus.). 30p. (J). (gr. k up). (978-1-55337-829-7(6)) Kids Can Pr., Ltd.

Watts, Sean. Silly Milly's ABCs. 2002. 32p. (J). 4.95 (978-0-9720424-5-1(8) , Jacob & Victoria) Brown Bag Bks, Inc.

Weber, Lou, ed. Alphabet. (J). 2005. 46p. 4.98 (978-1-4127-3460-8(6) , 7261600); 2004. 1p. 7.98 (978-1-4127-3298-7(0) , 5542000) Publications International, Ltd.

Weill, Cynthia & Basseches, K. B. ABeCedarios: Mexican Folk Art ABCs in Spanish & English. Jiménez, Moisés & Jiménez, Armando, illus. 2007. (SPA & ENG.). 32p. (J). (ps up). 14.95 (***978-1-933693-13-2(4)***) Cinco Puntos Pr.

Wells, Carolyn. Christmas Alphabet. 1999. (Illus.). 32p. (ps up). 20.00 (978-1-883211-22-6(0) , Darling & Co.) Laughing Elephant.

Wells, Rosemary. Letters & Sounds. 2001. (ps-2). lib. bdg. 14.15 (978-0-613-31413-8(1)); (Illus.). (J). (978-0-606-20764-5(3)) Tandem Library Bks.

—Max's ABC. 2006. (Illus.). 32p. (J). (ps). 15.99 (978-0-670-06074-0(7) , Viking Juvenile) Penguin Group (USA) Inc.

Westley, Joan. Learning with Letter Tiles: A Guide to Hands-On Phonics. 1999. 80p. (J). (gr. k-3). pap. 14.95 (978-1-893791-01-5(7)) Primary Concepts/Concepts to Go.

Wethered, Peggy & Edgett, Ken. Touchdown Mars! An ABC Adventure. Chesworth, Michael, illus. 2000. 1p. (J). (ps-3). 15.99 (978-0-399-23214-5(1) , Putnam Juvenile) Penguin Group (USA) Inc.

Whelan, Barbara. Always Be Children for Jesus. 2006. pap. 11.99 (***978-1-4259-6879-3(1)***) AuthorHouse.

Whitney, Gleaves & Whitney, Louise. A Cowboy Alphabet. 2007. 40p. pap. 7.95 (***978-1-58536-336-0(7)***) Sleeping Bear Pr.

Wigington, Patti. Pirate's Alphabet. Umscheid, Kit, illus. 2006. 32p. 15.95 (978-0-9766805-8-1(0) , Moo Pr.) Keene Publishing.

Wilbur, Helen L. Z is for Zeus. rev. ed. 2008. (General Alphabet Ser.). 40p. 17.95 (***978-1-58536-341-4(3)***) Sleeping Bear Pr.

Wildman, Dale. Do You Know the Way to Find an A? A Rhyming ABC Book. Sisung, Peter, illus. 2006. 24p. (J). per. 2.99 (978-1-59958-002-9(0)) Journey Stone Creations, LLC.

Wildsmith, Brian. Brian Wildsmith ABC. Fiol, Maria A., tr. Wildsmith, Brian, illus. 1998. (SPA., Illus.). 32p. (J). (ps). bds. 6.95 (978-1-887734-16-5(3)) Star Bright Bks., Inc.

—Brian Wildsmith's Amazing Animal Alphabet Book. Wildsmith, Brian, illus. (Illus.). 32p. (J). 2008. 16.95 (***978-1-59572-104-4(5)***); 2007. pap. 8.95 (***978-1-59572-111-2(8)***) Star Bright Bks., Inc.

Wildsmith, Brian. Cuantos Animales Hay? Fiol, María A., tr. Wildsmith, Brian, illus. 1998. (SPA., Illus.). 16p. (J). (ps). bds. 4.95 (978-1-887734-17-2(1)) Star Bright Bks., Inc.

Wildsmith, Rebecca. The Alphabet Chest: A Collection of 26 Three-Dimensional Surprises! Wildsmith, Rebecca, illus. 1998. (Illus.). (J). (ps-3). 19.95 (978-1-888443-83-7(9) , Intervisual/Piggy Toes) Dalmatian Pr.

Willenken, Roberta. Learn-the-Alphabet Arts & Crafts: Easy Letter-by-Letter Arts & Crafts Projects That Turn into Beautiful Take-Home ABC Books. (Joyful Learning Ser.). 128p. 2001. pap., tchr. ed. 14.95 (978-0-439-40809-7(1) , Teaching Resources); 2000. pap. 14.95 (978-0-439-16354-5(4)) Scholastic, Inc.

Williams, Connie M. Around the Alphabet Vol. 1: A New Way to Look at Letters. 1999. (Illus.). 64p. (J). (ps). 18.95 (978-1-892092-00-7(X)) Major for Minors Publishing Co.

Williams, Jean & Somerville, Louisa. Coming Top: Alphabet & First Words Sticker Books. 2007. (Illus.). 32p. pap. 4.99 (978-0-7548-1683-6(4)); pap. 4.99 (978-0-7548-1685-0(0)); pap. 4.99 (978-0-7548-1684-3(2)); pap. 4.99 (978-0-7548-1686-7(9)) Anness Publishing GBR. (Lorenz Bks.). *Dist:* National Bk. Network.

Williams, Laura E. ABC Kids. Williams, Laura E., illus. 2003. (Illus.). 32p. (J). (ps-1). 6.99 (978-0-399-24001-0(2) , Philomel) Penguin Group (USA) Inc.

Williamson, Chet. Pennsylvania Dutch Alphabet. Stacy, Alan Fearl, illus. 2007. 32p. (J). (gr. k-3). 15.95 (***978-1-58980-496-8(1)***) Pelican Publishing Co., Inc.

Wilner, Isabel. B Is for Bethlehem: A Christmas Alphabet. Kleven, Elisa, illus. 2004. 24p. (J). (ps). bds. 8.99 (978-0-525-47323-7(8) , Dutton Juvenile) Penguin Group (USA) Inc.

Winter, Jeanette. Calavera Abecedario: A Day of the Dead Alphabet Book. 2004. (Illus.). 48p. (J). 16.00 (978-0-15-205110-5(4)) Harcourt Children's Bks.

Wipe Clean ABC Workbook. 2001. (J). pap. 5.99 (978-0-89610-411-2(7)) Island Heritage Publishing.

Witty Bit World Book: Letters A-E & Music CD. 2005. (J). 19.95 (978-0-9770548-1-7(0)) Witty Bit World, Inc.

Witty Bit World Book: Letters F-J & Music CD. 2005. (J). 19.95 (978-0-9770548-2-4(9)) Witty Bit World, Inc.

Witty Bit World Book: Letters K-O & Music CD. 2005. (J). 1995.00 (978-0-9770548-3-1(7)) Witty Bit World, Inc.

Witty Bit World Book: Letters P-T & Music CD. 2005. (J). 19.95 (978-0-9770548-4-8(5)) Witty Bit World, Inc.

Witty Bit World Book: Letters U-Z & Music CD. 2005. (J). 19.95 (978-0-9770548-5-5(3)) Witty Bit World, Inc.

Witty Bit World Complete Alphabet & Music Collection. 2005. (J). 79.95 (978-0-9770548-0-0(2)) Witty Bit World, Inc.

Witty One Restickable Framed ABC Book. 2003. per. (978-1-932435-07-8(7)); per. (978-1-932435-01-6(8)) Cardinal Brands, Inc.

Wojtowycz, David. Animal ABC. Wojtowycz, David, illus. 2000. (Illus.). 32p. (J). (ps-k). 14.95 (978-1-86233-107-5(3)) Sterling Publishing Co., Inc.

Wolff, Ashley. Miss Bindergarten Plans a Circus with Kindergarten. Slate, Joseph & Wolff, Ashley, illus. 2002. 40p. (J). 16.99 (978-0-525-46884-4(6) , Dutton Juvenile) Penguin Group (USA) Inc.

Wood, Jakki. Animal Parade: A Wildlife Alphabet. 1999. (Illus.). 27p. (J). (ps). pap. (978-0-7112-0777-6(1)) Lincoln, Frances Ltd. GBR. *Dist:* Transition Vendor.

The World of Eric Carle My Alphabet Activity Kit. 2007. (J). 16.99 (***978-0-9794445-0-0(0)***) Loew-Cornell, Inc.

Wormell, Christopher. New Alphabet of Animals. 2006. (Illus.). 26p. (J). pap. 6.95 (978-0-7624-2729-1(9) , Running Pr. Kids) Running Pr. Bk. Pubs.

—The New Alphabet of Animals, Vol. 5. 2004. (Illus.). 64p. reprint ed. pap. 7.95 (978-0-7624-1847-3(8) , Running Pr. Kids) Running Pr. Bk. Pubs.

Yates, Irene. My ABC Dictionary. Fisher, Chris, illus. 2001. 64p. (J). (ps-k). 11.95 (978-0-7641-5433-1(8)) Barron's Educational Series, Inc.

Yolen, Jane. All in the Woodland Early: An ABC Book. Zalben, Jane Breskin, illus. 2003. 32p. (J). (gr. k-2). pap. 9.95 (978-1-56397-645-2(5)) Boyds Mills Pr.

Yoon, Salina. My Shimmery Alphabet Book. Yoon, Salina, illus. 2002. (My Shimmery Board Book Ser.). (Illus.). 10p. (J). (ps up). bds. 8.95 (978-1-58117-037-5(8) , Intervisual/Piggy Toes) Dalmatian Pr.

Yorinks, Arthur. The Alphabet Atlas. Yorinks, Adrienne, illus. 1999. 64p. (J). (ps-3). 19.95 (978-1-890817-14-5(7)) Winslow Pr.

Young, Judy. R Is for Rhyme: A Poetry Alphabet. Juhasz, Victor, illus. rev. ed. 2006. 48p. (J). (gr. k-5). 17.95 (978-1-58536-240-0(9)) Sleeping Bear Pr.

Zarick, Nicole, ed. My First ABC Board Book. 2004. (Illus.). 36p. (J). bds. 5.99 (978-0-7894-9900-4(2)) Dorling Kindersley Publishing, Inc.

Ziefert, Harriet. Me! Me! ABC. Von Bergen, Ingri, illus. 2006. 40p. (J). 15.95 (978-1-59354-146-0(5)) Blue Apple Bks.

Zocchi, Judith Mazzeo. Uri's "U" Book. Revutsky, Helen Ross, illus. 2007. (J). (***978-1-59646-538-1(7)***) Dingles & Co.

—Yola's "Y" Book. Revutsky, Helen Ross, illus. 2007. (J). (***978-1-59646-562-6(X)***) Dingles & Co.

Zocchi, Judith Mazzeo, et al. Zach's "Z" Book: El Libro "Z" de Zach. Revutsky, Helen Ross, illus. 2005. (SPA & ENG.). (J). (***978-1-59646-571-8(9)***) Dingles & Co.

Zolty, Howard. Mountain View A through Z. A Colorful Reader for Children of All Ages. 2006. 28p. 14.99 (978-1-4116-5708-3(X)) Lulu.com.

Zschock, Martha Day. Journey Around Maine from A to Z. Zschock, Martha Day, illus. 2007. (J). 17.95 (***978-1-933212-31-9(4)***) Commonwealth Editions.

ALPS

Maynard, Charles W. The Alps. 2004. (Great Mountain Ranges of the World Ser.). (Illus.). 24p. (J). lib. bdg. 21.25 (978-0-8239-6697-4(6) , PowerKids Pr.) Rosen Publishing Group, Inc., The.

Pyers, Greg. Mountain Explorer. 2004. (Habitat Explorer Ser.). (Illus.). 32p. (J). (ps). lib. bdg. 25.70 (978-1-4109-0509-3(8)) Raintree.

Somervill, Barbara A. The Awesome Alps. 2004. (Geography of the World Ser.). 32p. (J). (gr. 2-6). 27.07 (978-1-59296-330-0(7)) Child's World, Inc.

ALPS—FICTION

Dagg, Stephanie. Escape the Avalanche. 1999. 95p. (J). (gr. 4-8). per. (978-1-902586-49-6(2)) Mentor Bks.

Horowitz, Anthony. Point Blank. (Alex Rider Ser.: Bk. 2). 2006. 304p. (J). (gr. 7). pap. 7.99 (978-0-14-240612-0(0) , Puffin); 2002. 208p. (YA). (gr. 5 up). 17.99 (978-0-399-23621-1(X) , Philomel) Penguin Group (USA) Inc.

Spyri, Johanna. Heidi Book & Charm. 2000. (Charming Classics). (J). (gr. 3-7). pap. 6.99 (978-0-694-01453-8(2) , Harper Festival) HarperCollins Pubs.

ALTITUDE, INFLUENCE OF

see Human Beings—Effect of Environment on

ALUMINUM

Farndon, John. Aluminum. 2000. (Elements Ser.). (Illus.). 32p. (J). (gr. 3-5). lib. bdg. 25.64 (978-0-7614-0947-2(5) , Benchmark Bks.) Cavendish, Marshall Corp.

Saunders, N. Aluminum & the Elements of Group 13. 2003. (Periodic Table Ser.). (Illus.). 64p. (J). lib. bdg. (978-1-4034-1661-2(3)) Heinemann Library.

Tocci, Salvatore. Aluminum. (True Bks.). (Illus.). (J). (gr. 3-5). 2005. 47p. pap. 6.95 (978-0-516-25568-2(1)); 2004. 48p. 25.00 (978-0-516-23692-6(X)) Scholastic Library Publishing. (Children's Pr.).

Walker, Kate. Aluminum. 2004. (Recycle, Reduce, Reuse, Rethink Ser.). (J). lib. bdg. 27.10 (978-1-58340-559-8(3)) Smart Apple Media.

ALZHEIMER'S DISEASE

Altman, Linda Jacobs. Alzheimer's Disease. 2000. (Diseases & Disorders Ser.). (Illus.). 120p. (YA). (gr. 6-9). 32.45 (978-1-56006-695-8(4) , GML12001-178047, Lucent Bks.) Thomson Gale.

Bell, Sherry M. Visiting Mom: An Unexpected Gift: a Guide for Visiting Elders with Alzheimer's. 2000. 160p. (gr. 5 up). pap. (978-0-9677081-0-2(9)) Elder Pr., Inc.

Brill, Marlene Targ. Alzheimer's Disease. 2004. (Illus.). 64p. (J). 28.50 (978-0-7614-1799-6(0) , Benchmark Bks.) Cavendish, Marshall Corp.

Gold, Susan Dudley. Alzheimer's Disease. rev. ed. 2000. (Health Watch Ser.). (Illus.). 48p. (YA). (gr. 4-10). lib. bdg. 23.93 (978-0-7660-1650-7(1)) Enslow Pubs., Inc.

Gosselin, Kim. Allie Learns about Alzheimer's Disease: A Family Story about Love, Patience, & Acceptance. Dineen, Tom, illus. 2001. (Special Family & Friends: Vol. 1). 32p. (J). pap. 14.95 (978-1-891383-15-1(9)) JayJo Bks., LLC.

Landau, Elaine. Alzheimer's Disease: A Forgotten Life. 2005. (Illus.). 112p. (YA). (gr. 9-13). 26.00 (978-0-531-16755-7(0) , Watts, Franklin) Scholastic Library Publishing.

Mayo Clinic on Alzheimer's Disease: Practical Answers on Memory Loss, Aging, Research, Treatment & Caregiving. (Illus.). 178,248p. (YA). (gr. 8 up). lib. bdg. (978-1-59084-542-4(0)) Mason Crest Pubs.

McGuigan, Jim. Alzheimer's Disease. 2004. (Just the Facts Ser.). (Illus.). 56p. (J). lib. bdg. 27.07 (978-1-4034-5143-9(5)) Heinemann Library.

Mobley, Tracy. I Remember When. l.t. ed. 2006. (ENG., Illus.). 34p. (J). per. 7.95 (978-1-933300-04-7(3)) Wandering Sage Bookstore & More, LLC.

Nadelson, Carol C. Life Out of Focus: Alzheimer's Disease & Dementia. 1999. (Encyclopedia of Psychological Disorders Ser.). (Illus.). 88p. (gr. 7-12). 35.00 (978-0-7910-4896-2(9) , Chelsea Hse.) Facts On File, Inc.

Schnurbush, Barbara. Striped Shirts & Flowered Pants: A Story about Alzheimer's Disease for Young Children. Pillo, Cary, illus. 2006. 32p. (J). (ps-3). 14.95 (978-1-59147-475-3(2)); pap. 8.95 (978-1-59147-476-0(0)) American Psychological Assn. (Magination Pr.).

Tubbs, Janet. Alzheimer's Disease. 2000. 16p. (J). pap. 19.95 (978-1-881185-09-3(5)) Arcadia Pr.

Webber, Barbara. Alzheimer's Disease. 2004. (Understanding Diseases & Disorders Ser.). (J). (gr. 4-7). 26.20 (978-0-7377-2165-2(0) , Greenhaven Pr., Inc.) Thomson Gale.

Weitzman, Elizabeth. Let's Talk about When Someone You Love Has Alzheimer's Disease. 1998. (PowerKids Ser.). 24p. (J). (gr. k-3). reprint ed. pap. 6.95 (978-1-56838-224-1(3)) Hazelden Publishing & Educational Services.

Willett, Edward. Alzheimer's Disease. 2002. (Diseases & People Ser.). (Illus.). 112p. (YA). (gr. 6-12). lib. bdg. 26.60 (978-0-7660-1596-8(3)) Enslow Pubs., Inc.

ALZHEIMER'S DISEASE—FICTION

Abeele, Veronique van den. Still My Grandma. Dubois, Claude K., illus. 2007. 28p. (J). (ps-3). 16.00 (***978-0-8028-5323-3(4)*** , Eerdmans Bks For Young Readers) Eerdmans, William B. Publishing Co.

Altman, Linda Jacobs. Singin' with Momma Lou. Johnson, Larry, illus. 2002. 32p. (J). (gr. 1-5). 16.95 (978-1-58430-040-3(X)) Lee & Low Bks., Inc.

Bauer, Marion Dane. An Early Winter. 1999. (Illus.). 128p. (J). (gr. 5-9). tchr. ed. 15.00 (978-0-395-90372-8(6) , Clarion Bks.) Houghton Mifflin Co. Trade & Reference Div.

—An Early Winter. 2000. (YA). pap. 42.00 incl. audio (978-0-7887-4328-3(7) , 41123) Recorded Bks., LLC.

—An Early Winter. 2001. (J). 11.15 (978-0-606-20643-3(4)) Tandem Library Bks.

Bell, Ossie S. When Grandma Is Not Grandma: Alzheimer's Steals Family's Treasures. 2006. 51p. pap. 12.95 (978-1-4241-2920-1(6)) PublishAmerica, Inc.

Broome, Errol. The Judas Donkey. Thompson, Sharon, illus. 2003. 144p. pap. 13.50 (978-1-920731-18-2(0)) Fremantle Pr. AUS. *Dist:* International Specialized Bk. Services.

Glass, Sue. Remember Me?/¿Te acuerdas de Mí? Alzheimer's Through the Eyes of a Child/la enfermedad de Alzheimer a través de los ojos de un Niño. de la Vega, Eida, tr. Yunker, W., illus. 2003. Tr. of ¿Te acuerdas de mí? la enfermedad de Alzheimer a través de los ojos de un Niño. (SPA & ENG.). 32p. (J). (gr. 4-6). 16.95 (978-0-9720192-5-5(1) , 626999) Raven Tree Pr.

MacKall, Dandi Daley. Horse Whispers in the Air, Vol. 3. 2000. (Horsefeathers Ser.: Vol. 3). 192p. (YA). (gr. 7-11). 5.99 (978-0-570-07008-5(2)) Concordia Publishing Hse.

—Horse Whispers in the Air. 2000. (gr. 7-12). lib. bdg. 14.15 (978-0-613-72831-7(9)) Tandem Library Bks.

McDonald, Diane. Treasure Chest. Halicky, Sandi, illus. 2002. 34p. (J). spiral bd. 12.95 (978-0-9721681-0-6(9)) McDonald, Diane.

McIntyre, Connie. Flowers for Grandpa Dan: A Gentle Story to Help Children Understand Alzheimer's Disease. McIntyre, Louise, illus. 2004. 20p. (J). 12.95 (978-0-9677685-5-7(1)); lib. bdg. 17.95 (978-0-9677685-6-4(X)) McIntyre, Connie. (Thumbprint Pr.).

Moore, Isabel. Daughter. 1999. (gr. 5-8). lib. bdg. 15.25 (978-0-613-33886-8(3)) Tandem Library Bks.

Newbery, Linda. Sisterland. 2004. 384p. (J). (gr. 7). 15.95 (978-0-385-75026-4(9) , Fickling, David Bks.) Random Hse. Children's Bks.

Park, Barbara. The Graduation of Jake Moon. Colin, Paul, illus. 2000. 128p. (J). (gr. 4-6). 15.00 (978-0-689-83912-2(X) , Atheneum/Anne Schwartz Bks.) Simon & Schuster Children's Publishing.

—The Graduation of Jake Moon. 2002. (gr. 3-6). lib. bdg. 13.00 (978-0-613-54234-0(7)) Tandem Library Bks.

Scacco, Linda. Always My Grandpa: A Story for Children about Alzheimer's Disease. Wong, Nicole, illus. 2005. 48p. (J). (gr. 1-3). 14.95 (978-1-59147-311-4(X)); pap. 8.95 (978-1-59147-312-1(8)) American Psychological Assn. (Magination Pr.).

Schwartz, Noa. Old Timers: The One That Got Away. Vipond, Erica, illus. 1998. (J). pap. 5.95 (978-0-9683303-1-9(2)) Tumbleweed Pr.

Shawver, Margaret. What's Wrong with Grandma? A Family's Experience with Alzheimer's. Bagby, Jeffrey K., illus. 2004. 62p. pap. 16.00 (978-1-59102-174-2(X)) Prometheus Bks., Pubs.

Stang, Debra L. Visiting Grandma. 2003. 136p. (YA). pap. 12.95 (978-1-59113-322-3(X)) Booklocker.com, Inc.

Swallow, Pamela Curtis. It Only Looks Easy. rev. ed. 2003. 176p. (J). (gr. 3-7). 15.95 (978-0-7613-1790-6(2)) Roaring Brook Pr.

Thurston, Dorie. Thank-You for the Thistle. Hawkins, Mecca, illus. 2001. 36p. (J). (ps-3). pap. 9.95 (978-0-9703326-0-8(2)) Dorie Bks.

Williams, Dell. If I Forget, You Remember. 1999. (J). 11.64 (978-0-606-16171-8(6)) Tandem Library Bks.

Willner-Pardo, Gina. Figuring Out Frances. 1999. (Illus.). 144p. (J). (gr. 4-6). tchr. ed. 14.00 (978-0-395-91510-3(4) , Clarion Bks.) Houghton Mifflin Co. Trade & Reference Div.

AMAZON RIVER

Castner, James L. Layers of Life: Deep in the Amazon. 2001. (Deep in the Amazon Ser.). (Illus.). 32p. (J). (gr. 5 up). lib. bdg. 28.50 (978-0-7614-1130-7(5) , Benchmark Bks.) Cavendish, Marshall Corp.

—Partners & Rivals: Deep in the Amazon. 2001. (Deep in the Amazon Ser.). 32p. (J). (gr. 5 up). lib. bdg. 28.50 (978-0-7614-1131-4(3) , Benchmark Bks.) Cavendish, Marshall Corp.

—Rainforest Researchers: Deep in the Amazon. 2001. (Deep in the Amazon Ser.). (Illus.). 32p. (J). (gr. 5 up). lib. bdg. 27.07 (978-0-7614-1129-1(1) , Benchmark Bks.) Cavendish, Marshall Corp.

—River Life: Deep in the Amazon. 2002. (Deep in the Amazon Ser.). (Illus.). 32p. (J). (gr. 5 up). lib. bdg. 28.50 (978-0-7614-1127-7(5) , Benchmark Bks.) Cavendish, Marshall Corp.

Chapman, Simon. Explorers Wanted! In the Jungle. 2005. (Illus.). 128p. (J). (gr. 5-8). pap. 5.99 (978-0-316-15539-7(X)) Little Brown & Co.

Cheshire, Gerald. Nature Unfolds the Tropical Rainforest. 2001. (Nature Unfolds Ser.). (Illus.). 40p. (J). (gr. 4). lib. bdg. (978-0-7787-0308-2(8)); pap. (978-0-7787-0320-4(7)) Crabtree Publishing Co.

Fitzpatrick, Anne. Amazon River. 2004. (Natural Wonders of the World Ser.). (Illus.). 32p. (J). lib. bdg. 27.10 (978-1-58341-322-7(7) , Creative Education) Creative Co., The.

Furnweger, Karen. Amazon Rising Floods of Fun Coloring & Activity Book. Smith, Sally, illus. 2000. 16p. (J). (ps-8). pap. 2.75 (978-0-9701035-2-9(2)) Shedd Aquarium Society.

Graf, Mike. The Amazon River. 2004. (Fact Finders Ser.). (Illus.). 32p. (J). 22.60 (978-0-7368-2482-8(0)) Capstone Pr., Inc.

Hollander, Malika. Brazil - The Land. 2003. (Lands, Peoples & Cultures Ser.). (Illus.). 32p. (J). (gr. 2-9). (978-0-7787-9338-0(9)); pap. (978-0-7787-9706-7(6)) Crabtree Publishing Co.

Kallen, Stuart A. Life in the Amazon Rain Forest. 1999. (Way People Live Ser.). (Illus.). 96p. (YA). (gr. 7-10). 27.45 (978-1-56006-387-2(4) , LML00902-177770, Lucent Bks.) Thomson Gale.

Kozar, Richard. Theodore Roosevelt & the Exploration of the Amazon Basin. 2000. (Explorers of the New World Ser.). (Illus.). (J). 63p. (gr. 4-7). pap. 25.00 (978-0-7910-6164-0(7)); 64p. 25.00 (978-0-7910-5954-8(5)) Facts On File, Inc. (Chelsea Hse.).

—Theodore Roosevelt & the Exploration of the Amazon Basin. 2001. (gr. 3-6). lib. bdg. 17.60 (978-0-613-33134-0(6)) Tandem Library Bks.

Lourie, Peter. Amazon: A Young Reader's Look at the Last Frontier. 2003. (River Ser.). (Illus.). 48p. (YA). (gr. 4-6). pap. 11.95 (978-1-56397-712-1(5)) Boyds Mills Pr.

McAlarney, Kathryn, et al. Amazon Connections: The People, the Forest & the River. McAlarney, Kathryn, illus. 2002. (Illus.). 56p. (J). (gr. 3-5). pap. 12.00 (978-0-9701035-4-3(9)) Shedd Aquarium Society.

Meister, Cari. Amazon River. 2002. (Rivers & Lakes Ser.). (Illus.). 24p. (J). (gr. k-6). lib. bdg. 21.35 (978-1-57765-101-7(4) , Checkerboard Library) ABDO Publishing Co.

Montgomery, Sy. Encantado: Pink Dolphin of the Amazon. Taylor-Snow, Dianne, photos by. 2002. (Illus.). 80p. (J). (gr. 4-6). 18.00 (978-0-618-13103-7(5)) Houghton Mifflin Co. Trade & Reference Div.

Parker, Edward. The Amazon. 2003. (Great Rivers of the World Ser.). (Illus.). 48p. (gr. 5 up). (J). pap. 14.95 (978-0-8368-5449-7(7)); (YA). lib. bdg. 30.00 (978-0-8368-5442-8(X)) Stevens, Gareth Inc. (World Almanac Library).

Pyers, Greg. Rain Forest Explorer. 2004. (Habitat Explorer Ser.). (Illus.). 32p. (J). (ps-ps). lib. bdg. 25.70 (978-1-4109-0511-6(X)) Raintree.

Ryan, Marla. Into Wild Amazonia. 2004. (Jeff Corwin Experience Ser.). (Illus.). 48p. (J). 11.20 (978-1-4103-0252-6(0) , Blackbirch Pr., Inc.) Thomson Gale.

Schulte, Mary. The Amazon River. 2006. 32p. (gr. 1-2). (YA). pap. 5.95 (978-0-516-29700-2(7)); (Illus.). (J). 20.50 (978-0-516-25031-1(0)) Scholastic Library Publishing. (Children's Pr.).

Scoones, Simon. The Amazon. 2003. (River Journey Ser.). (Illus.). 48p. lib. bdg. 28.56 (978-0-7398-6069-4(0)) Raintree.

Simon, Charnan. The Mysterious Amazon. 2004. (Geography of the World Ser.). (Illus.). 32p. (J). (gr. 2-6). 27.07 (978-1-59296-336-2(6)) Child's World, Inc.

Telford, Carole & Theodorou, Rod. Up a Rainforest Tree. 1998. (Amazing Journeys Ser.). (Illus.). 32p. (J). (gr. 2-4). lib. bdg. 22.79 (978-1-57572-156-9(2)) Heinemann Library.

Zuravicky, Orli. The Amazon & the Sahara: Using Double Line Graphs & Double Bar Graphs. 2004. (PowerMath Ser.). (Illus.). 32p. (J). lib. bdg. (978-0-8239-8868-6(6)); lib. bdg. 22.50 (978-0-8239-8981-2(X)) Rosen Publishing Group, Inc., The. (PowerKids Pr.).

AMAZON RIVER—FICTION

Abelove, Joan. Go & Come Back. 2000. (Illus.). 192p. (J). (gr. 7-12). pap. 5.99 (978-0-14-130694-0(7) , Puffin) Penguin Group (USA) Inc.

—Go & Come Back. 2000. (gr. 7-12). lib. bdg. 14.15 (978-0-613-28498-1(4)); (Illus.). (J). (978-0-606-18406-9(6)) Tandem Library Bks.

Allen, Nancy Kelly. On the Banks of the Amazon/en las orillas del Amazonas. de la Vega, Eida, tr. Driessen, Elizabeth, illus. 2004. Tr. of En las orillas del Amazonas. (SPA & ENG.). 32p. (J). (gr. 4-6). 16.95 (978-0-9720192-7-9(8) , 626999) Raven Tree Pr.

Allende, Isabel. City of the Beasts. 2005. Tr. of Ciudad de las Bestias. 464p. (J). (gr. 7-17). pap. 7.99 (978-0-06-077645-9(5) , Rayo) HarperCollins Pubs.

—City of the Beasts. Peden, Margaret Sayers, tr. from SPA. 2002. Tr. of Ciudad de las Bestias. 416p. (J). (gr. 5 up). 19.99 (978-0-06-050918-7(X)) HarperCollins Pubs.

—City of the Beasts. l.t. ed. 2002. Tr. of Ciudad de las Bestias. 400p. (J). (gr. 5). pap. 19.99 (978-0-06-051195-1(8)) HarperCollins Pubs.

—City of the Beasts. Peden, Margaret Sayers, tr. from SPA. 2004. Tr. of Ciudad de las Bestias. 432p. (J). (gr. 5 up). reprint ed. pap. 7.99 (978-0-06-053503-2(2)) HarperCollins Pubs.

—City of the Beasts. 2004. Tr. of Ciudad de las Bestias. (gr. 5-8). lib. bdg. 16.45 (978-0-613-71427-3(X)) Tandem Library Bks.

—La Ciudad de las Bestias. 2002. (SPA., Illus.). 416p. 19.95 (978-0-06-051031-2(5) , Rayo) HarperCollins Pubs.

Blake, Richard R. A Dolphin's Tale. Blake, Rachelle & Seratte, Rachel, illus. 2001. (J). per. 9.97 (978-0-9670242-3-3(4)) Thornton Publishing.

Cherry, Lynne. The Great Kapok Tree: A Tale of the Amazon Rain Forest. Cherry, Lynne, illus. 2002. (Illus.). (J). 14.04 (978-0-7587-2651-3(1)) Book Wholesalers, Inc.

—The Great Kapok Tree: A Tale of the Amazon Rain Forest. 2000. (Illus.). 40p. (YA). (ps-3). pap. 7.00 (978-0-15-202614-1(2) , Voyager Bks./Libros Viajeros) Harcourt Children's Bks.

Cherry, Lynne & Plotkin, Mark J. The Shaman's Apprentice: A Tale of the Amazon Rain Forest. Cherry, Lynne, illus. 1998. (Illus.). 40p. (J). 16.00 (978-0-15-201281-6(8)) Harcourt Children's Bks.

Gates, Phil. Terror on the Amazon. 2000. (gr. k-3). lib. bdg. 11.80 (978-0-613-33130-2(3)) Tandem Library Bks.

—Terror on the Amazon: The Quest for el Dorado. Martin, Linda, ed. 2000. (Readers Ser.). (Illus.). 48p. (J). (gr. 2-3). pap. 3.99 (978-0-7894-6638-9(4)) Dorling Kindersley Publishing, Inc.

Gates, Phil & Dorling Kindersley Publishing Staff. Terror on the Amazon: The Quest for el Dorado. 2000. (Eyewitness Readers). (Illus.). 48p. (J). (gr. 2-3). 12.95 (978-0-7894-6639-6(2)) Dorling Kindersley Publishing, Inc.

Gleitzman, Morris. Toad Away. 2006. 208p. (J). (gr. 3-7). 14.95 (978-0-375-82766-2(8)); lib. bdg. 16.99 (978-0-375-92766-9(2)) Random Hse. Children's Bks. (Random Hse. Bks. for Young Readers).

Grote, Rich. Megan & the Borealis Butterfly. 1999. (Magic Attic Club Ser.). (J). lib. bdg. (978-0-606-16953-0(9)) Tandem Library Bks.

Hanson, Ed. Amazon Adventure. 2003. (Barclay Family Adventure Ser.: Bk. 1). 64p. (J). (gr. k-6). per. 3.95 (978-1-56254-550-5(7) , SP 5507) Saddleback Educational Publishing.

Hussey, Charmian. The Valley of Secrets. Crump, Christopher, illus. 400p. 2006. (J). pap. 9.99 (978-1-4169-0015-3(2) , Simon Pulse); 2005. (YA). 17.95 (978-0-689-87862-6(1)) Simon & Schuster Children's Publishing.

Ibbotson, Eva. Journey to the River Sea. Hawkes, Kevin, illus. 2002. 336p. (J). (gr. 4-8). 17.99 (978-0-525-46739-7(4) , Dutton Juvenile) Penguin Group (USA) Inc.

—Journey to the River Sea. 2003. (gr. 3-6). lib. bdg. 14.15 (978-0-613-86704-7(1)) Tandem Library Bks.

Marsh, Carole. The Mystery in the Amazon Rainforest. 2007. 144p. (gr. 3-5). 14.95 (***978-0-635-06212-3(7)***) Gallopade International.

—The Mystery in the Amazon Rainforest: South America. 2007. (Around the World in 80 Mysteries (Paperback) Ser.). (Illus.). 131p. (J). (gr. 3-5). per. 5.95 (***978-0-635-06208-6(9)***) Gallopade International.

Montgomery, R. A. Lost on the Amazon. 2006. (Choose Your Own Adventure Ser.: No. 9). (Illus.). 144p. (J). mass mkt. 5.99 (978-1-933390-09-3(3) , CHCL09) Chooseco LLC.

Nesbitt, Kris. My Amazon River Day. Lines, Edward, Jr., photos by. 2000. (Illus.). 48p. (J). (gr. 3-8). 23.95 (978-0-9701035-0-5(6)) Shedd Aquarium Society.

Place, Francois. A Voyage of Discovery Vol. 1: From the Land of the Amazons to the Indigo Isles. 2001. (Illus.). 144p. (YA). (gr. 3 up). 22.99 (978-1-86205-213-0(1) , Pavilion Bks., Ltd.) Anova Bks. GBR. *Dist:* Trafalgar Square Publishing.

Shua, Ana Maria. Expedicion al Amazonas. 2002. (SPA.). (gr. 3-6). lib. bdg. 15.25 (978-0-613-88201-9(6)) Tandem Library Bks.

Stilton, Geronimo. The Temple of the Ruby of Fire. Wolf, Matt, illus. 2004. (Geronimo Stilton Ser.: No. 14). 109p. (J). lib. bdg. 10.00 (***978-1-4242-0283-6(3)***) Fitzgerald Bks.

—The Temple of the Ruby of Fire. 2004. (Geronimo Stilton Ser.: No. 14). (Illus.). 106p. (J). (gr. 2-5). lib. bdg. 13.94 (978-0-606-33277-4(4)) Tandem Library Bks.

Zindel, Paul. Night of the Bat. 144p. (gr. 5-9). 2003. pap. 5.99 (978-0-7868-1226-4(5)); 2001. 15.99 (978-0-7868-0340-8(1)) Hyperion Bks. for Children.

Zoehfeld, Kathleen Weidner. Amazon Fever. Bogan, Paulette, illus. 2006. (Road to Reading Ser.). 48p. (J). (gr. 1-4). 11.99 (978-0-307-46407-1(5)); pap. 3.99 (978-0-307-26407-7(6)) Random Hse. Children's Bks. (Random Hse. Bks. for Young Readers).

AMAZON VALLEY

Castner, James L. Native Peoples: Deep in the Amazon. 2001. (Deep in the Amazon Ser.). (Illus.). 32p. (J). (gr. 5 up). lib. bdg. 28.50 (978-0-7614-1128-4(3) , Benchmark Bks.) Cavendish, Marshall Corp.

AMBASSADORS

see Diplomats

AMELIA-BEDELIA (FICTITIOUS CHARACTER)—FICTION

Amelia Bedelia. 2002. (Amelia Bedelia Ser.). (Illus.). (J). 11.91 (978-0-7587-5973-3(8)) Book Wholesalers, Inc.

Amelia Bedelia. 2005. (J). (978-1-59564-833-4(X)) Steps To Literacy, LLC.

Amelia Bedelia & the Baby. 2002. (Amelia Bedelia Ser.). (Illus.). (J). 12.34 (978-0-7587-0422-1(4)) Book Wholesalers, Inc.

Amelia Bedelia & the Surprise Shower. 2002. (Amelia Bedelia Ser.). (Illus.). (J). 12.34 (978-0-7587-5974-0(6)) Book Wholesalers, Inc.

Amelia Bedelia Goes Camping. 2002. (Amelia Bedelia Ser.). (Illus.). (J). 12.34 (978-0-7587-0423-8(2)) Book Wholesalers, Inc.

Amelia Bedelia Helps Out. 2002. (Amelia Bedelia Ser.). (Illus.). (J). 12.34 (978-0-7587-0424-5(0)) Book Wholesalers, Inc.

Bravo, Amelia Bedelia! 2002. (Amelia Bedelia Ser.). (Illus.). (J). 11.87 (978-0-7587-8899-3(1)) Book Wholesalers, Inc.

Come Back, Amelia Bedelia. 2002. (Amelia Bedelia Ser.). (Illus.). (J). 12.34 (978-0-7587-6057-9(4)) Book Wholesalers, Inc.

De Uribe, Maria L. Senorita Amelia (Miss Amelia) (SPA.). 24p. (J). 16.95 (978-84-233-1245-0(3)) Ediciones Destino ESP. *Dist:* AIMS International Bks., Inc.

Moss, Marissa. Amelia's Must-Keep Resolutions for the Best Year Ever! Moss, Marissa, illus. 2006. (Amelia's Notebooks). 40p. (J). 9.95 (978-1-4169-3361-8(1) , Simon & Schuster/Paula Wiseman Bks.) Simon & Schuster Children's Publishing.

Parish, Herman. Amelia Bedelia 4 Mayor. Sweat, Lynn, illus. (I Can Read Bks.). (J). 2001. 64p. (gr. k-2). pap. 3.99 (978-0-06-444309-8(4) , Harper Trophy); 1999. 48p. (gr. 1 up). 15.99 (978-0-688-16721-9(7)) HarperCollins Pubs.

—Amelia Bedelia 4 Mayor. 1999. (I Can Read Bks.). (Illus.). (J). 10.79 (978-0-606-21026-3(1)) Tandem Library Bks.

—Amelia Bedelia Bookworm. Sweat, Lynn, illus. 2005. (I Can Read Bks.). 64p. (J). pap. 3.99 (978-0-06-051892-9(8) , Harper Trophy) HarperCollins Pubs.

—Amelia Bedelia Goes Back to School. Sweat, Lynn, illus. 2004. 20p. (J). pap. 6.99 (978-0-06-051873-8(1) , Harper Festival) HarperCollins Pubs.

—Amelia Bedelia, Rocket Scientist? Sweat, Lynn, illus. (I Can Read Bks.). 64p. (J). 2007. pap. 3.99 (978-0-06-051889-9(8) , Harper Trophy); 2005. (gr. 1 up). 15.99 (978-0-06-051887-5(1)); 2005. (gr. 1 up). lib. bdg. 16.89 (978-0-06-051888-2(X)) HarperCollins Pubs.

—Amelia Bedelia's Masterpiece. Sweat, Lynn, illus. 2007. 64p. (J). 15.99 (978-0-06-084355-7(1)); lib. bdg. 16.89 (978-0-06-084356-4(X)) HarperCollins Pubs.

—Be My Valentine, Amelia Bedelia. Sweat, Lynn, illus. 2004. 20p. (J). (gr. 1 up). pap. 6.99 (978-0-06-051886-8(3) , Harper Festival) HarperCollins Pubs.

—Bravo, Amelia Bedelia!, Vol. 2. Sweat, Lynn, illus. 2002. (I Can Read Bks.). 48p. (J). pap. 3.99 (978-0-06-444318-0(3) , Harper Trophy) HarperCollins Pubs.

—Calling Doctor Amelia Bedelia. Sweat, Lynn, illus. (I Can Read Bks.). 64p. (J). 2004. (gr. k-3). pap. 3.99 (978-0-06-008780-7(3) , Harper Trophy); 2002. (gr. 1-2). 15.99 (978-0-06-001421-6(0)); 2002. (gr. 1-2). lib. bdg. 17.89 (978-0-06-001422-3(9)) HarperCollins Pubs.

—Good Driving, Amelia Bedelia. Sweat, Lynn, illus. 2002. (I Can Read Bks.). 48p. (J). (gr. 1-3). pap. 3.99 (978-0-06-008092-1(2) , Harper Trophy) HarperCollins Pubs.

—Good Driving, Amelia Bedelia. 2002. (gr. k-3). lib. bdg. 11.80 (978-0-613-66230-7(X)) Tandem Library Bks.

—Happy Haunting, Amelia Bedelia. Sweat, Lynn, illus. (I Can Read Bks.). 64p. (J). 2006. pap. 3.99 (978-0-06-051895-0(2) , Harper Trophy); 2004. 15.99 (978-0-06-051893-6(6)); 2004. lib. bdg. 16.89 (978-0-06-051894-3(4)) HarperCollins Pubs.

Parish, Peggy. Amelia Bedelia. Siebel, Fritz, illus. 1999. (I Can Read Bks.). 64p. (J). (ps-3). 16.99 (978-0-694-01296-1(3) , Harper Festival) HarperCollins Pubs.

—Amelia Bedelia. Thomas, Barbara Siebel & Siebel, Fritz, illus. 2000. (Coleccion Ya Se Leer). (SPA.). (J). (gr. 1-3). 15.95 (978-1-880507-76-6(5) , LC0355); pap. 6.99 (978-1-880507-75-9(7) , LC0360) Lectorum Pubns., Inc.

—Amelia Bedelia. Siebel, Fritz, illus. 1999. (J). (gr. 1-3). 9.95 (978-1-56137-023-8(1)) Novel Units, Inc.

—Amelia Bedelia. 2001. (SPA., Illus.). (J). 13.75 (978-0-606-21546-6(8)) Tandem Library Bks.

—Amelia Bedelia. Siebel, Fritz, illus. 1999. (I Can Read Bks.). (J). (gr. 1-3). 11.50 (978-0-88103-916-0(0)) Tandem Library Bks.

—Amelia Bedelia 4 Mayor. 1999. (gr. k-3). lib. bdg. 11.80 (978-0-613-68400-2(1)) Tandem Library Bks.

—Amelia Bedelia 40th Anniversary Collection: Amelia Bedelia; Play Ball, Amelia Bedelia; Amelia Bedelia & the Surprise Shower. 40th anniv. ed. 2003. (I Can Read Bks.). (Illus.). (J). (gr. k-3). pap. 11.99 (978-0-06-054238-2(1)) HarperCollins Pubs.

—Amelia Bedelia & the Baby. Sweat, Lynn, illus. 2004. (I Can Read Bks.). 64p. (J). (gr. k-3). pap. 3.99 (978-0-06-051105-0(2) , Harper Trophy) HarperCollins Pubs.

—Amelia Bedelia Goes Camping. Sweat, Lynn, illus. 2003. (I Can Read Bks.). 64p. (J). (ps-ps). pap. 3.99 (978-0-06-051106-7(0) , Harper Trophy) HarperCollins Pubs.

—Amelia Bedelia Goes Camping. 2003. (gr. k-3). lib. bdg. 11.80 (978-0-613-62664-4(8)) Tandem Library Bks.

—Amelia Bedelia Helps Out. Sweat, Lynn, illus. 2005. 64p. (J). (ps-ps). lib. bdg. 11.19 (978-0-606-33266-8(9)) Tandem Library Bks.

—Amelia Bedelia's Family Album. Sweat, Lynn, illus. 2003. (I Can Read Bks.). 48p. (J). (gr. k-3). pap. 3.99 (978-0-06-051116-6(8) , Harper Trophy) HarperCollins Pubs.

—Amelia Bedelia's Family Album. 2003. (gr. k-3). lib. bdg. 11.80 (978-0-613-62129-8(8)) Tandem Library Bks.

—Good Work, Amelia Bedelia. Sweat, Lynn, illus. 2003. (I Can Read Bks.). 64p. (J). (gr. k-3). pap. 3.99 (978-0-06-051115-9(X)) HarperCollins Pubs.

—Good Work, Amelia Bedelia. 2003. (gr. k-3). lib. bdg. 11.80 (978-0-613-68343-2(9)) Tandem Library Bks.

—Thank You, Amelia Bedelia. 1999. (I Can Read Bks.). (J). (gr. 1-3). 11.55 (978-0-88103-910-8(1)) Tandem Library Bks.

Parish, Peggy & Brookes, Diane. A Novel Study for Grade One & Two Based on Amelia Bedelia & the Surprise Shower Novel Study, 25 vols. 1998. (J). pap., tchr. ed. (978-0-9683234-4-1(8)) Raven Rock Publishing.

Teach Us, Amelia Bedelia. 2002. (Amelia Bedelia Ser.). (Illus.). (J). 11.91 (978-0-7587-1726-9(1)) Book Wholesalers, Inc.

Thank You, Amelia Bedelia. 2002. (Amelia Bedelia Ser.). (J). 12.34 (978-0-7587-6292-4(5)) Book Wholesalers, Inc.

AMENHETEP 4TH, KING OF EGYPT, 1388-1358 B.C.

see Akhenaten, King of Egypt, 1388-1358 B.C.

AMERICA

see also Central America; Latin America; North America; South America

Benchmark Education Staff, compiled by. Social Studies Theme: Civilizations of the Americas. 2005. spiral bd. 115.00 (***978-1-4108-5323-3(3)***) Benchmark Education Co.

Green, et al. Encyclopedia of Ancient Americas. 2000. (Illus.). 256p. (J). (gr. 3-7). (978-1-84215-186-0(X) , Southwater) Anness Publishing.

Isaacs, Sally Senzell. America in the Time of Columbus: Earliest Times to 1590. 1999. (America in the Time of... Ser.). (Illus.). 48p. (J). (gr. 4-7). pap. 8.50 (978-1-57572-933-6(4)) Heinemann Library.

Jackson, Margaret, ed. Listen America, Kids Speak Out. 2000. 238p. (YA). pap. 12.95 (978-0-9704231-0-8(1)) Creative Expressions of America.

Learning Wrap-Ups All About. 2004. 7.99 (978-0-943343-20-4(8)) Learning Wrap-Ups.

Rappaport, Doreen. In the Promised Land: Lives of Jewish Americans. Van Wright, Cornelius, illus. 2005. 32p. (J). (gr. k-4). lib. bdg. 16.89 (978-0-06-059395-7(4)) HarperCollins Pubs.

Reef, Catherine. Africans in American: The Spread of People & Culture. 1998. (Library of African-American History). (Illus.). 144p. (J). (gr. 7-12). 25.00 (978-0-8160-3772-8(8)) Facts On File, Inc.

Thoennes Keller, Kristin. The Slave Trade in Early America. 2004. (Let Freedom Ring Ser.). (Illus.). 48p. (J). 17.95 (978-0-7368-2465-1(0) , Bridgestone Bks.) Capstone Pr., Inc.

AMERICA—ANTIQUITIES

Benson, Sonia & Baker, Deborah J. Early Civilizations in the, 2 vols. 2005. (Early Civilizations in the Americas Reference Library). (Illus.). xli, 551p. (J). 120.00 (978-0-7876-9252-0(2) , UXL) Thomson Gale.

Innes, Brian. Native American Monuments. 1999. (Unsolved Mysteries Ser.). (Illus.). 48p. (YA). (gr. 3 up). lib. bdg. 25.69 (978-0-8172-5482-7(X)) Raintree.

Long, Cathryn J. Ancient America. 2002. (World History Ser.). (Illus.). 112p. (YA). (gr. 8-11). 32.45 (978-1-56006-889-1(2) , LML00902-178210, Lucent Bks.) Thomson Gale.

MacDonald, Fiona, et al. Ancient Americas: Explore the Aztec, Maya, Inca, North American Indian & Arctic World. 2003. (Illustrated History Encyclopedia Ser.). (Illus.). 264p. (gr. 3-7). pap. 19.99 (978-0-7548-1204-3(9) , Lorenz Bks.) Anness Publishing GBR. *Dist:* National Bk. Network.

Sattler, Helen Roney. The Earliest Americans. Zallinger, Jean Day, illus. 2001. 128p. (J). (gr. 4-6). pap. 8.95 (978-0-618-11146-6(8) , Clarion Bks.) Houghton Mifflin Co. Trade & Reference Div.

AMERICA—DISCOVERY AND EXPLORATION

see also Explorers; Northwest Passage

Aaseng, Nathan. You Are the Explorer. 2000. (Great Decisions Ser.). (Illus.). 160p. (gr. 5 up). lib. bdg. 19.95 (978-1-881508-55-7(2)) Oliver Pr., Inc.

Abnett, Dan. Christopher Columbus & the Voyage of 1492. Q2A, illus. 2007. (Jr. Graphic Biographies Ser.). 24p. (J). (978-1-4042-2333-2(9)); pap. (978-1-4042-2143-7(3)); (gr. 2-6). lib. bdg. 21.25 (978-1-4042-3390-4(3)) Rosen Publishing Group, Inc., The. (PowerKids Pr.).

Aller, Susan Bivin. Christopher Columbus. 2003. (History Maker Bios Ser.). (Illus.). 48p. (J). (gr. 3-5). lib. bdg. 26.60 (978-0-8225-0398-9(0)) Lerner Publishing Group.

Alter, Judy. Christopher Columbus: Explorer. 2002. (Spirit of America: Our People Ser.). (Illus.). 32p. (J). (gr. 2-6). 27.07 (978-1-56766-161-3(0)) Child's World, Inc.

Anderson, Dale. Westward Expansion. 2000. (Making of America Ser.). (Illus.). 96p. (J). (gr. 4-7). lib. bdg. 28.54 (978-0-8172-5705-7(5)) Raintree.

Ansary, Mir Tamim. Columbus Day. (J). 2006. (Illus.). 32p. (***978-1-4034-8883-1(5)***); 2002. (Illus.). 32p. pap. 6.95 (978-1-58810-430-4(3) , 91158); 1999. (Illus.). 32p. lib. bdg. 21.36 (978-1-57572-702-8(1)); 1998. lib. bdg. 19.92 (978-0-01-575702-1(1)) Heinemann Library.

Art, Suzanne Strauss. Ancient Times: The Story of the First Americans. Art, Suzanne Strauss, illus. 1999. (Illus.). 178p. (YA). (gr. 5-8). pap. 14.95 (978-0-9656557-7-4(6)) Pemblewick Pr.

Asikinak, Bill. North America. 2000. (Exploration Into... Ser.). (Illus.). 48p. (J). (gr. 4-7). 25.00 (978-0-7910-6025-4(X) , Chelsea Hse.) Facts On File, Inc.

Aykroyd, Clarissa. Exploration of the California Coast. 2002. (Exploration & Discovery Ser.). (Illus.). 64p. (J). (gr. 5 up). lib. bdg. (978-1-59084-043-6(7)) Mason Crest Pubs.

Bedesky, Baron. Sir Walter Raleigh: Founding the Virginia Colony. 2006. (In the Footsteps of Explorers Ser.). (Illus.). 32p. (J). (gr. 3-9). (978-0-7787-2424-7(7) , 1253445) Crabtree Publishing Co.

Bell, Robin. My Adventure Discovering America. 2007. 44p. (J). 8.99 (978-1-59092-415-0(0) , Orchard Academy Pr.) Windstorm Creative.

Benchmark Education Staff. Spain Explores the Americas. 2005. 2.00 (***978-1-4108-4645-7(8)***) Benchmark Education Co.

Benge, Janet Hazel & Benge, Geoffrey Francis. Meriwether Lewis: Off the Edge of the Map. 2001. 232p. pap. 8.99 (978 1-883002-80-0(X)) Emerald Bks.

Bennett, William J. Our Country's Founders: Book of Advice for Young People Adapted From Our Sacred Honor. 2001. (Illus.). 320p. (YA). (gr. 7-12). pap. 11.99 (978-0-689-84469-0(7) , Simon Pulse) Simon & Schuster Children's Publishing.

—Our Country's Founders: Words of Advice from the Founders in Stories, Letters, Poems & Speeches. 1998. 17.00 (978-0-8054-1600-8(5)) B&H Publishing Grp.

Bergen, Lara Rice. The Travels of Sieur de la Salle. 1999. (Explorers & Exploration Ser.). (Illus.). 48p. (J). (gr. 4-7). lib. bdg. 22.83 (978-0-7398-1495-6(8)) Raintree.

Binns, Tristan Boyer. Louis Jolliet. 2002. (Groundbreakers Ser.). (Illus.). 48p. (J). (gr. 5-7). lib. bdg. 27.07 (978-1-58810-597-4(0)) Heinemann Library.

Blue, Rose. Exploring the Americas, 4 bks., Set. 2003. pap. 32.20 (978-1-4109-0145-3(9)) Raintree.

Blue, Rose & Naden, Corinne J. Exploring Central America, Mexico, & the Caribbean. 2003. (Illus.). 64p. lib. bdg. 28.56 (978-0-7398-4952-1(2)) Raintree.

—Exploring Northeastern America. 2003. (Illus.). 64p. (J). lib. bdg. 28.56 (978-0-7398-4948-4(4)) Raintree.

—Exploring South America. 2003. (Illus.). 64p. (J). pap. 9.50 (978-1-4109-0335-8(4)) Raintree.

—Exploring the Southwestern United States. 2003. (Illus.). 64p. (J). pap. 9.50 (978-1-4109-0336-5(2)) Raintree.

Brown, Janet Hubbard. Hernando de Soto: And His Expeditions Across the Americas. Goetzmann, William H., ed. 2005. (Explorers of New Lands Ser.). (Illus.). 138p. (J). (gr. 4-8). lib. bdg. 30.00 (978-0-7910-8610-0(0) , Chelsea Hse.) Facts On File, Inc.

Burgan, Michael. Leif Eriksson. 2002. (Groundbreakers Ser.). (Illus.). 48p. (J). (gr. 5-7). lib. bdg. 27.07 (978-1-58810-596-7(2)) Heinemann Library.

Burgan, Michael & Overmyer-Velazquez, Mark. The Spanish Conquest of America: Prehistory - 1775. 2006. (Latino American History Ser.). (Illus.). 112p. (J). (gr. 5-8). 35.00 (978-0-8160-6440-3(7) , Chelsea Hse.) Facts On File, Inc.

Calvert, Patricia. Zebulon Pike: Lost in the Rockies. 2003. (Great Explorations Ser.). (J). (978-0-7614-1740-8(0)); 29.93 (978-0-7614-1612-8(9)) Cavendish, Marshall Corp. (Benchmark Bks.).

Capstone Press. Christopher Columbus: Famous Explorer. 2007. (Graphic Library). (Illus.). 32p. (J). (***978-0-7368-6853-2(4)*** , 1264941) Capstone Pr., Inc.

Champion, Neil. John Cabot. (Groundbreakers Ser.). (Illus.). 48p. (J). (gr. 5-7). 2002. pap. 8.50 (978-1-58810-370-3(6) , 91095); 2001. lib. bdg. 25.64 (978-1-58810-046-7(4)) Heinemann Library.

Chin-Lee, Cynthia. A Es para Decir Americas. 1999. (978-0-606-17568-5(7)) Tandem Library Bks.

Chin-Lee, Cynthia & De la Pena, Terri. A Es para Decir America's. Sanchez, Enrique O., illus. 1999. (SPA.). 32p. (J). (gr. k-4). pap. 6.95 (978-0-531-07134-2(0) , Orchard Bks.) Scholastic, Inc.

Chippendale, Neil. Sir Walter Raleigh & the Search for El Dorado. 2001. (Explorers of New Worlds Ser.). (Illus.). 63p. (J). 31.00 (978-0-7910-6434-4(4) , Chelsea Hse.) Facts On File, Inc.

Chrisp, Peter. Christopher Columbus. 2006. (DK Discoveries Ser.). 48p. (J). pap. 6.99 (978-0-7566-1965-7(3)) Dorling Kindersley Publishing, Inc.

—Christopher Columbus: Admiral of the Ocean Sea. Parsons, Jayne, ed. Dennis, Peter, illus. 2001. (DK Discoveries Ser.). 48p. (J). 14.95 (978-0-7894-7936-5(2)) Dorling Kindersley Publishing, Inc.

Christopher Columbus, 6 vols. (gr. k-2). 28.95 (978-0-7368-9369-5(5)) Red Brick Learning.

Collier, James Lincoln. Christopher Columbus: To the New World. 2006. (Great Explorations Ser.). (Illus.). 80p. (J). lib. bdg. 32.79 (978-0-7614-2221-1(8) , Benchmark Bks.) Cavendish, Marshall Corp.

Conquistadors: Hernan Cortes; Francisco Pizarro; Inca Rebellion, 3 cass.; set. 2003. (YA). (gr. 7-12). tchr. ed. 129.95 (978-1-58738-433-2(7)) Discovery Communications.

Cook, Diane. Pathfinders of the American Frontier. 2002. (Exploration & Discovery Ser.). (Illus.). 64p. (YA). (gr. 5 up). lib. bdg. (978-1-59084-045-0(3)) Mason Crest Pubs.

Cox, Caroline & Albala, Ken. Opening up North America, 1497-1800. 2005. (Discovery & Exploration (John S. Bowman & Maurice Isserman Are General Editors of the Set.) Ser.). (Illus.). 208p. (J). (gr. 6-12). 40.00 (978-0-8160-5261-5(1)) Facts On File, Inc.

Craats, Rennay. Columbus Day. 2004. (American Holidays Ser.). (Illus.). 24p. (J). pap. 6.95 (978-1-59036-164-1(4)); lib. bdg. 15.95 (978-1-59036-106-1(7)) Weigl Pubs., Inc.

—Exploration of North America. (Great Journeys Ser.). (Illus.). 32p. (J). 2005. pap. 7.95 (978-1-59036-258-7(6)); 2004. lib. bdg. 26.00 (978-1-59036-206-8(3)) Weigl Pubs., Inc.

Crisfield, Deborah. The Travels of Francisco de Coronado. 1999. (Explorers & Exploration Ser.). (Illus.). 48p. (J). (gr. 4-7). lib. bdg. 22.83 (978-0-7398-1493-2(1)) Raintree.

Currie, Stephen. Expeditions in the Americas: 1492-1700. 2004. (National Geographic Reading Expeditions Ser.). (Illus.). 32p. (J). pap. (978-0-7922-4544-5(X)) National Geographic Society.

Davenport, John. Juan Ponce de Leon: And His Lands of Discovery. Goetzmann, William H., ed. 2005. (Explorers of New Lands Ser.). (Illus.). 142p. (J). (ps-8). lib. bdg. 30.00 (978-0-7910-8607-0(0) , Chelsea Hse.) Facts On File, Inc.

DeAngelis, Gina. Francisco Pizarro & the Conquest of the Inca. 2000. (Explorers of the New World Ser.). (Illus.). 63p. (J). (gr. 8-12). 31.00 (978-0-7910-5951-7(0)); (gr. 4-7). pap. 25.00 (978-0-7910-6161-9(2)) Facts On File, Inc. (Chelsea Hse.).

DeLucenayLeon, George. Explorers of the Americas Before Columbus. 1999. (Illus.). 64p. (J). (gr. 5-7). 17.00 (978-0-7881-6846-8(0)) DIANE Publishing Co.

Ditchfield, Christin. The Lewis & Clark Expedition. 2006. 48p. (YA). (gr. 3-5). pap. 6.95 (978-0-516-25222-3(4) , Children's Pr.) Scholastic Library Publishing.

Donaldson-Forbes, Jeff. Amerigo Vespucci. 2002. (Famous Explorers Ser.). (Illus.). 24p. (J). (gr. 3). lib. bdg. 18.75 (978-0-8239-5833-7(7) , PowerKids Pr.) Rosen Publishing Group, Inc., The.

—Jacques Marquette & Louis Jolliet. 2002. (Famous Explorers Ser.). (Illus.). 24p. (J). (gr. 3). lib. bdg. 18.75 (978-0-8239-5835-1(3) , PowerKids Pr.) Rosen Publishing Group, Inc., The.

Drake, Samuel Adams. The Making of the Great West 1512-1883. 2001. 350p. (YA). reprint ed. (978-1-58218-439-5(9)); pap. (978-1-58218-438-8(0)) Digital Scanning, Inc.

Duran, Gloria. Maria de Estrada: Gypsy Conquistadora. 1999. (Discoveries Ser.). 227p. (YA). (gr. 7 up). pap. 14.95 (978-1-891270-01-7(X)) Latin American Literary Review Pr.

Eagen, Rachel. Ponce de Léon: Exploring Florida & Puerto Rico. 2005. (In the Footsteps of Explorers Ser.). (Illus.). 32p. (J). (gr. 3-9). pap. (978-0-7787-2448-3(4)) Crabtree Publishing Co.

Englar, Mary. Sieur de la Salle. 2004. (Fact Finders Ser.). (Illus.). 32p. (J). lib. bdg. 22.60 (978-0-7368-2666-2(1)) Capstone Pr., Inc.

Exploring the Americas, 8 vols. 2003. (Illus.). (978-0-7398-4958-3(1)); (978-0-7398-4957-6(3)); Set. (Illus.). pap. 68.40 (978-1-4109-0708-0(2)) Raintree.

Faber, Harold, et al. La Salle: Down the Mississippi. 2002. (Great Explorations Ser.). (Illus.). 80p. (J). (gr. 4 up). lib. bdg. 29.93 (978-0-7614-1239-7(5) , Benchmark Bks.) Cavendish, Marshall Corp.

Freedman, Russell. Who Was First? Discovering the Americas. 2007. (Illus.). 96p. (J). (gr. 4-7). 19.00 (***978-0-618-66391-0(6)*** , Clarion Bks.) Houghton Mifflin Co. Trade & Reference Div.

Gaines, Ann Graham. Hernando de Soto & the Spanish Search for Gold in World History. 2002. (In World History Ser.). (Illus.). 112p. (YA). (gr. 5-12). lib. bdg. 26.60 (978-0-7660-1821-1(0)) Enslow Pubs., Inc.

Gallagher, Jim. Hernando de Soto & the Exploration of Florida. 1999. (Explorers of the New World Ser.). (Illus.). 63p. (J). (gr. 4 up). 31.00 (978-0-7910-5512-0(4) , Chelsea Hse.) Facts On File, Inc.

—Viking Explorers. 2000. (Explorers of the New World Ser.). (Illus.). (J). 63p. (gr. 4-7). pap. 8.95 (978-0-7910-6165-7(5)); 64p. (gr. 8-12). 25.00 (978-0-7910-5955-5(3)) Facts On File, Inc. (Chelsea Hse.).

Ganeri, Anita. The Story of Columbus, Vol. 2. Ling, Mary, ed. 2001. (Readers Ser.). (Illus.). 32p. (J). (gr. 5-3). pap. 3.99 (978-0-7894-7878-8(1)) Dorling Kindersley Publishing, Inc.

Ganeri, Anita & Dorling Kindersley Publishing Staff. The Story of Columbus. 2001. (Readers Ser.). (Illus.). 32p. (J). (gr. 1-3). 14.99 (978-0-7894-7877-1(3)) Dorling Kindersley Publishing, Inc.

Glaser, Jason. Leif Eriksson. 2004. (Fact Finders Ser.). (Illus.). 32p. (J). lib. bdg. 22.60 (978-0-7368-2664-8(5)) Capstone Pr., Inc.

—Lewis & Clark. 2004. (Fact Finders Ser.). (Illus.). 32p. (J). lib. bdg. 22.60 (978-0-7368-2665-5(3)) Capstone Pr., Inc.

Gleason, Carrie. Henry Hudson: Seeking the Northwest Passage. 2005. (In the Footsteps of Explorers Ser.). (Illus.). 32p. (J). (ps-9). (978-0-7787-2408-7(5)); pap. (978-0-7787-2444-5(1)) Crabtree Publishing Co.

Goodman, Joan Elizabeth. Beyond the Sea of Ice: The Voyages of Henry Hudson. Rangel, Fernando, illus. 1999. (Great Explorers Ser.: Vol. 1). 48p. (J). (gr. k-12). 19.95 (978-0-9650493-8-2(8)) Mikaya Pr.

Graf, Mike & McFarren, Kathleen. History Pockets: Explorers of North America. McClain, Lynn, illus. 2003. (History Pockets Ser.). 96p. (J). (gr. 4-6). suppl. ed. 12.99 (978-1-55799-905-4(8) , EMC 3708) Evan-Moor Educational Pubs.

Green, Tamara. Juan Ponce de Leon. (Great Explorers Ser.). (Illus.). 48p. (J). (gr. 5 up). 2002. pap. 14.60 (978-0-8368-5178-6(1)); 2001. lib. bdg. 30.00 (978-0-8368-5018-5(1)) Stevens, Gareth Inc. (World Almanac Library).

Hakim, Joy. A History of US Bk. 1: The First Americans. 3rd rev. ed. (History of US Ser.). (Illus.). 192p. 2006. 19.95 (978-0-19-518230-9(8)); 2005. 19.95 (978-0-19-518894-3(2)) Oxford Univ. Pr., Inc.

Hakim, Joy. A History of US Vol. 1: The First Americans. rev. ed. 2007. (History of US Ser.). 192p. pap. 15.95 (***978-0-19-532715-1(2)***) Oxford Univ. Pr., Inc.

Harkins, Susan and William. The Life & Times of Father Jacques Marquette. 2007. (Profiles in American History Ser.). (J). lib. bdg. (***978-1-58415-528-7(0)***) Mitchell Lane Pubs., Inc.

Harmon, Daniel E. The Early French Explorers of North America. 2002. (Exploration & Discovery Ser.). (Illus.). 64p. (YA). (gr. 5 up). lib. bdg. (978-1-59084-044-3(5)) Mason Crest Pubs.

—Jacques Cartier & the Exploration of Canada. 2000. (Explorers of the New World Ser.). (Illus.). (J). 63p. (gr. 4-7). pap. 25.00 (978-0-7910-6168-8(X)); 64p. (gr. 8-12). 25.00 (978-0-7910-5958-6(8)) Facts On File, Inc. (Chelsea Hse.).

—Jacques Cartier & the Exploration of Canada. 2001. (gr. 3-6). lib. bdg. 17.60 (978-0-613-32700-8(4)) Tandem Library Bks.

—Jolliet & Marquette: Explorers of the Mississippi River. 2001. (Explorers of New Worlds Ser.). (Illus.). (J). 63p. pap. 25.00 (978-0-7910-6427-6(1)); 64p. 25.00 (978-0-7910-6426-9(3)) Facts On File, Inc. (Chelsea Hse.).

—Jolliet & Marquette: Explorers of the Mississippi River. 2001. (Illus.). 63p. (J). (gr. 4-7). lib. bdg. 17.60 (978-0-613-65434-0(X)) Tandem Library Bks.

—LaSalle & the Exploration of the Mississippi. 2000. (Explorers of the New World Ser.). (Illus.). (J). 63p. (gr. 4-7). pap. 25.00 (978-0-7910-6162-6(0)); 64p. (gr. 8-12). 25.00 (978-0-7910-5952-4(9)) Facts On File, Inc. (Chelsea Hse.).

Hart, Avery & Mantell, Paul. Who Really Discovered America? Unraveling the Mystery & Solving the Puzzle. Kline, Michael P., illus. 2000. (Kaleidoscope Kids Bks.). 96p. (J). (gr. 2-8). pap. 12.95 (978-1-885593-46-7(5) , Williamson Bks.) Ideals Pubns.

Harvey, Dan. The English Colonization of North America. 2002. (Exploration & Discovery Ser.). (Illus.). 64p. (J). (gr. 4-7). lib. bdg. (978-1-59084-051-1(8)) Mason Crest Pubs.

Haskins, Jim. Against All Opposition: Black Explorers in America. 2003. (gr. 5-8). lib. bdg. 17.60 (978-0-613-91054-5(0)) Tandem Library Bks.

—Against All Opposition: Black Explorers in America. 2003. 96p. (J). pap. 8.95 (978-0-8027-7672-3(8)) Walker & Co.

Higgins, Nadia. Columbus & the Age of Explorers. 2007. (Illus.). 48p. (J). (978-1-60044-119-6(X)) Rourke Publishing, LLC.

Hoogenboom, Lynn. Amerigo Vespucci: A Primary Source Biography. 2006. (Illus.). 24p. (J). lib. bdg. (978-1-4042-3037-8(8) , PowerKids Pr.) Rosen Publishing Group, Inc., The.

—Christopher Columbus: A Primary Source Biography. 2006. (Illus.). 24p. (J). lib. bdg. (978-1-4042-3036-1(X) , PowerKids Pr.) Rosen Publishing Group, Inc., The.

—Francisco Pizarro: A Primary Source Biography. 2006. (J). lib. bdg. (978-1-4042-3038-5(6) , PowerKids Pr.) Rosen Publishing Group, Inc., The.

—Juan Ponce de Leon: A Primary Source Biography. 2006. (Illus.). 24p. (J). lib. bdg. (978-1-4042-3040-8(8) , PowerKids Pr.) Rosen Publishing Group, Inc., The.

—Sir Francis Drake: A Primary Source Portrait. 2006. (J). lib. bdg. (978-1-4042-3035-4(1) , PowerKids Pr.) Rosen Publishing Group, Inc., The.

Hopkins, Andrea. Vikings: The Norse Discovery of America. 2011. (Viking Library). (Illus.). 24p. (J). (gr. 3). lib. bdg. 19.50 (978-0-8239-5817-7(5) , PowerKids Pr.) Rosen Publishing Group, Inc., The.

Hurwicz, Claude. Henry Hudson. 2001. (Famous Explorers Ser.). (Illus.). 24p. (J). (gr. 3). lib. bdg. 18.75 (978-0-8239-5561-9(3) , PowerKids Pr.) Rosen Publishing Group, Inc., The.

—Juan Ponce de Leon. 2001. (Famous Explorers Ser.). (Illus.). 24p. (J). (gr. 3). lib. bdg. 18.75 (978-0-8239-5563-3(X) , PowerKids Pr.) Rosen Publishing Group, Inc., The.

Isserman, Maurice. Across America: The Lewis & Clark Expedition. 2004. (Discovery & Exploration Ser.). (Illus.). 192p. (J). (gr. 6-12). 40.00 (978-0-8160-5256-1(5)) Facts On File, Inc.

—Exploring North America, 1800-1900. 2005. (Discovery & Exploration Ser.). (Illus.). 208p. (J). (gr. 6-12). 40.00 (978-0-8160-5263-9(8)) Facts On File, Inc.

January, Brendan. Explorers of North America. 2000. (gr. 3-6). lib. bdg. 15.25 (978-0-613-51644-0(3)) Tandem Library Bks.

Johnston, Charles H. Famous Discoverers & Explorers of Amer. 2006. pap. 38.95 (***978-1-4254-9677-7(6)***) Kessinger Publishing, LLC.

Johnston, Lissa J. & Nunez Cabeza de Vaca, Alvar. Crossing a Continent: The Incredible Journey of Cabeza de Vaca. 2005. 82p. (J). pap. 9.95 (978-1-57168-183-6(3) , Eakin Pr.) Eakin Pr.

Jones, Charlotte Foltz. Westward Ho! Eleven Explorers of the American West. 2005. (Illus.). 240p. (J). (gr. 4-6). tchr. ed. 22.95 (978-0-8234-1586-1(4)) Holiday Hse., Inc.

Jordan, Shirley. Explorers to the New World: Moments in History. 2000. (Cover-to-Cover Bks.). (Illus.). 64p. (J). pap. (978-0-7891-5125-4(1)); (gr. 4-7). lib. bdg. 17.95 (978-0-7807-9269-2(6)) Perfection Learning Corp.

Kachurek, Sandra J. Francisco Pizarro: Explorer of South America. 2004. (Explorers! Ser.). (Illus.). 48p. (J). lib. bdg. 23.93 (978-0-7660-2178-5(5)) Enslow Pubs., Inc.

Kimmel, Elizabeth Cody. Before Columbus: The Leif Eriksson Expedition. 2004. 112p. (J). (gr. 3-5). pap. 5.99 (978-0-375-82307-7(7) , Random Hse. Bks. for Young Readers) Random Hse. Children's Bks.

—Before Columbus: The Leif Eriksson Expedition: A True Adventure. 2003. (Landmark Books Ser.). (Illus.). 112p. (J). (gr. 4). lib. bdg. 16.99 (978-0-375-91347-1(5) , Random Hse. Bks. for Young Readers) Random Hse. Children's Bks.

Kline, Trish. Christopher Columbus. 2001. (Discover the Life of an Explorer Ser.). (Illus.). 24p. (J). (gr. 1-4). lib. bdg. 20.64 (978-1-58952-066-0(1)) Rourke Publishing, LLC.

—Francisco Coronado. 2002. (ENG & SPA.). (J). lib. bdg. 19.27 (978-1-58952-428-6(4)) Rourke Publishing, LLC.

—Ponce de Leon. 2001. (Discover the Life of an Explorer Ser.). (Illus.). 24p. (J). (gr. 1-4). lib. bdg. 20.64 (978-1-58952-068-4(8)) Rourke Publishing, LLC.

—Robert la Salle. 2002. (Discover the Life of an Explorer Ser.). (Illus.). 24p. (gr. 2-5). 14.95 (978-1-58952-069-1(6)) Rourke Publishing, LLC.

—Samuel de Champlain. 2001. (Illus.). 24p. (J). (gr. 1-4). lib. bdg. 20.64 (978-1-58952-070-7(X)) Rourke Publishing, LLC.

Kling, Andrew A. Life on a New World Voyage. 2004. (Way People Live Ser.). (J). (gr. 7-10). 29.95 (978-1-59018-163-8(8) , Lucent Bks.) Thomson Gale.

Knudsen, Shannon. Leif Eriksson. Oldroyd, Mark, illus. 2005. (On My Own Biography Ser.). 48p. (J). (gr. 3-7). pap. 5.95 (978-1-57505-828-3(6)); (ps-7). 25.26 (978-1-57505-649-4(6) , Carolrhoda Bks.) Lerner Publishing Group.

Kudlinski, Kathleen. Christopher Columbus: Young Explorer. 2005. 199p. (J). lib. bdg. 18.46 (***978-1-4242-1727-4(X)***) Fitzgerald Bks.

Lackey, Jennifer D. B. Jacques Cartier: Exploring the St. Lawrence River. 2006. (In the Footsteps of Explorers Ser.). (Illus.). 32p. (J). (gr. 3-9). pap. (978-0-7787-2466-7(2)); lib. bdg. (978-0-7787-2430-8(1)) Crabtree Publishing Co.

Lambert, Lorene. Who in the World Was the Forgotten Explorer? The Story of Amerigo Vespucci. Mickle, Jed, illus. 2005. 56p. (J). (gr. 2 up). pap. 9.50 (978-0-9728603-8-3(X)) Peace Hill Pr.

Landau, Elaine. Columbus Day: Celebrating a Famous Explorer. 2001. (Finding Out about Holidays Ser.). (Illus.). 48p. (J). (gr. 1-4). lib. bdg. 23.93 (978-0-7660-1573-9(4)) Enslow Pubs., Inc.

Larkin, Tanya. Christopher Columbus. 2001. (Famous Explorers Ser.). (Illus.). 24p. (J). (gr. 3). lib. bdg. 18.75 (978-0-8239-5554-1(0) , PowerKids Pr.) Rosen Publishing Group, Inc., The.

—Sir Francis Drake. 2001. (Famous Explorers Ser.). (Illus.). 24p. (J). (gr. 3). lib. bdg. 18.75 (978-0-8239-5556-5(7) , PowerKids Pr.) Rosen Publishing Group, Inc., The.

Lassieur, Allison. Lords of the Sea: The Vikings Explore the North Atlantic. Barnett, Charles, III & Frenz, Ron, illus. 2005. (Graphic Library). 32p. (J). (gr. 3-7). lib. bdg. 25.26 (978-0-7368-4974-6(2)) Capstone Pr., Inc.

Leavitt, Amie. Christopher Columbus. 2007. (What's So Great About... ? Ser.). (J). lib. bdg. 25.70 (***978-1-58415-578-2(7)***) Mitchell Lane Pubs., Inc.

Levy, Elizabeth. Are We There Yet? The Europeans Meet the Americans. 2002. (America's Horrible Histories Ser.: No. 3). 160p. (J). 12.95 (978-0-439-30350-7(8) , Scholastic Paperbacks) Scholastic, Inc.

MacDonald, Fiona. You Wouldn't Want to Sail with Christopher Columbus! Uncharted Waters You'd Rather Not Cross. Antram, David, illus. 2004. (You Wouldn't Want to Ser.). 32p. (J). (gr. 2-5). pap. 9.95 (978-0-531-16060-2(2) , Watts, Franklin) Scholastic Library Publishing.

MacDonald, Fiona, et al. You Wouldn't Want to Sail with Christopher Columbus! Uncharted Waters You'd Rather Not Cross. 2004. (You Wouldn't Want To Ser.). (J). 28.50 (978-0-531-12355-3(3) , Watts, Franklin) Scholastic Library Publishing.

MacGregor, Cynthia. Kids During the Age of Exploration. 1999. (Kids Throughout History Ser.). (Illus.). 24p. (J). (gr. 3). lib. bdg. 18.75 (978-0-8239-5257-1(6) , PowerKids Pr.) Rosen Publishing Group, Inc., The.

Manning, Ruth. Henry Hudson. (Groundbreakers Ser.). 48p. (J). (gr. 5-7). 2002. pap. 8.50 (978-1-58810-342-0(0) , 91093); 2000. (Illus.). lib. bdg. 25.64 (978-1-57572-370-9(0)) Heinemann Library.

—Henry Hudson. 2001. (gr. 5-8). lib. bdg. 17.05 (978-0-613-86815-0(3)) Tandem Library Bks.

—Hernando de Soto. 2000. (Groundbreakers Ser.). (Illus.). 48p. (J). (gr. 5-7). lib. bdg. 25.64 (978-1-57572-388-4(3)) Heinemann Library.

—Juan Ponce de Leon. 2000. (Groundbreakers Ser.). (Illus.). 48p. (J). (gr. 5-7). lib. bdg. 25.64 (978-1-57572-376-1(X)) Heinemann Library.

Marcovitz, Hal. Coronado to Escalate: Francisco Coronado & the Exploration of the American Southwest. 1999. (Explorers of the New World Ser.). (Illus.). 64p. (J). (gr. 4 up). 31.00 (978-0-7910-5515-1(9) , Chelsea Hse.) Facts On File, Inc.

—Vasco Nuanez de Balboa & the Discovery of the South Sea. 2001. (Explorers of New Worlds Ser.). (Illus.). (J). 63p. pap. 25.00 (978-0-7910-6429-0(8)); 64p. 25.00 (978-0-7910-6428-3(X)) Facts On File, Inc. (Chelsea Hse.).

Marzollo, Jean. In 1492. (J). (gr. 1-3). pap. (978-0-590-44414-9(X) , SO3017) Scholastic, Inc.

Mattern, Joanne. Celebrate Columbus Day. 2006. (Celebrate Holidays Ser.). (Illus.). 104p. (J). lib. bdg. 31.93 (978-0-7660-2580-6(2)) Enslow Pubs., Inc.

—The Travels of John & Sebastian Cabot. 1999. (Explorers & Exploration Ser.). (Illus.). 48p. (J). (gr. 4-7). lib. bdg. 22.83 (978-0-7398-1492-5(3)) Raintree.

—The Travels of Samuel de Champlain. 1999. (Explorers & Exploration Ser.). (Illus.). 48p. (J). (gr. 4-7). lib. bdg. 22.83 (978-0-7398-1494-9(X)) Raintree.

McCormick, Lisa Wade. Christopher Columbus. 2005. (Scholastic News Nonfiction Readers Ser.). (Illus.). 24p. (J). (gr. 1-2). 19.00 (978-0-516-24938-4(X) , Children's Pr.) Scholastic Library Publishing.

—Lewis & Clark. 2006. 32p. (YA). (gr. 1-2). pap. 4.95 (978-0-516-21443-6(8) , Children's Pr.) Scholastic Library Publishing.

McIntosh, Kenneth. First Encounters Between Spain & the Americas: Two Worlds Meet. 2005. (Illus.). 112p. (J). (ps-7). lib. bdg. (978-1-59084-925-5(6)) Mason Crest Pubs.

McKain, Mark. The Spanish Exploration of South America. 2002. (Exploration & Discovery Ser.). (Illus.). 64p. (J). (gr. 5 up). lib. bdg. (978-1-59084-047-4(X)) Mason Crest Pubs.

McNeese, Tim. Christopher Columbus & the Discovery of the Americas. Goetzmann, William H., ed. 2005. (Explorers of New Lands Ser.). (Illus.). 166p. (J). (gr. 4-8). lib. bdg. 30.00 (978-0-7910-8613-1(5) , Chelsea Hse.) Facts On File, Inc.

Meter, Larry Van. Yerba Buena. 2007. (Colonial Settlements in America Ser.). 104p. (J). (gr. 5-8). 30.00 (*978-0-7910-9338-2(7) , Chelsea Hse.) Facts On File, Inc.

Mir Tamim Ansary. Columbus Day. 2nd ed. 2006. (Illus.). 32p. (J). pap. (*978-1-4034-8896-1(7)) Heinemann Library.

Mitchell, Mark. Raising la Belle. Mitchell, Mark, illus. (Professor Wigglestix & the Weather Ser.). (Illus.). 112p. 10.95 (978-1-57168-703-6(3)) Eakin Pr.

Molzahn, Arlene Bourgeois. Henry Hudson: Explorer of the Hudson River. 2003. (Explorers! Ser.). (Illus.). 48p. (J). lib. bdg. 23.93 (978-0-7660-2070-2(3)) Enslow Pubs., Inc.

—Ponce de Leon: Explorer of Florida. 2003. (Explorers! Ser.). (Illus.). 48p. (J). lib. bdg. 23.93 (978-0-7660-2071-9(1)) Enslow Pubs., Inc.

Morganelli, Adrianna. Christopher Columbus: Sailing to a New World. 2005. (In the Footsteps of Explorers Ser.). (Illus.). 32p. (J). (ps-9). (978-0-7787-2409-4(3)); pap. (978-0-7787-2445-2(X)) Crabtree Publishing Co.

—Samuel de Champlain: From New France to Cape Cod. 2005. (In the Footsteps of Explorers Ser.). (Illus.). 32p. (J). (gr. 3-9). (978-0-7787-2414-8(X)); pap. (978-0-7787-2450-6(6)) Crabtree Publishing Co.

Mountjoy, Shane. Francisco Coronado & the Seven Cities of Gold. Goetzmann, William H., ed. 2005. (Explorers of New Lands Ser.). (Illus.). 142p. (J). (gr. 4-8). lib. bdg. 30.00 (978-0-7910-8631-5(3) , Chelsea Hse.) Facts On File, Inc.

Murphy, Claire Rudolf. I Am Sacagawea, I Am York: Our Journey West with Lewis & Clark. Bond, Higgins, illus. 2005. 32p. (J). (gr. 3-5). 17.85 (978-0-8027-8921-1(8)); 16.95 (978-0-8027-8919-8(6)) Walker & Co.

Murray, Julie. Columbus Day. 2005. (Holidays Ser.). (Illus.). 24p. (J). (gr. k-4). lib. bdg. 21.35 (978-1-59197-587-8(5)) ABDO Publishing Co.

National Geographic Society Staff. Experiences in the Grand Canyon. 1999. (Cultural & Geographical Exploration Ser.). (Illus.). x, 107p. (J). (gr. 7-12). 21.95 (978-0-7910-5442-0(X) , Chelsea Hse.) Facts On File, Inc.

Nelson, Sharlene P. & Nelson, Ted W. Jedediah Smith. 2004. (Watts Library). (Illus.). 64p. (J). 25.50 (978-0-531-12287-7(5) , Watts, Franklin) Scholastic Library Publishing.

Nextext Staff, contrib. by. The Ancient Americas: 30,000 B.C.-A.D.1600. 2004. (Stories in History Ser.). (Illus.). 192p. (gr. 6-12). tchr. ed. (978-0-618-25525-2(7) , 2-00331); stu. ed. (978-0-618-22210-0(3) , 2-00315) McDougal Littell Inc.

Nicholson, Sue. Aztecs & Incas: A Guide to the Pre-Colonized Americas in 1504. 2000. (Sightseers Ser.). (Illus.). 32p. (J). (gr. 3-5). tchr. ed. 8.95 (978-0-7534-5236-3(7) , Kingfisher) Houghton Mifflin Co. Trade & Reference Div.

Nobleman, Marc Tyler. Juan Ponce de Leon. 2004. (Fact Finders Ser.). (Illus.). 32p. (J). lib. bdg. 22.60 (978-0-7368-2667-9(X)) Capstone Pr., Inc.

O'Donnell, Kerri. Explorers in North America: Solving Addition & Subtraction Problems Using Timelines. 2004. (PowerMath Ser.). (Illus.). 32p. (J). lib. bdg. (978-0-8239-8898-3(8)); lib. bdg. 22.50 (978-0-8239-8987-4(9)) Rosen Publishing Group, Inc., The. (PowerKids Pr.).

O'Neal, Bill. Long Before the Pilgrims: The First Thanksgiving, el Paso del Norte, 1598. Martinez, Lynn O'Neal, tr. Morgan, Polsky, illus. 2000. (ENG & SPA.). 48p. (J). 15.95 (978-1-57168-448-6(4)) Eakin Pr.

Otfinoski, Steven. Francisco Coronado: In Search of the Seven Cities of Gold. 2002. (Great Explorations Ser.). (Illus.). 76p. (J). 29.93 (978-0-7614-1484-1(3) , Benchmark Bks.) Cavendish, Marshall Corp.

—Henry Hudson: In Search of the Northwest Passage. 2007. (Great Explorations Ser.). (Illus.). 80p. (J). lib. bdg. 32.79 (*978-0-7614-2225-9(0) , Benchmark Bks.) Cavendish, Marshall Corp.

—Juan Ponce de Leon: Discoverer of Florida. 2003. (Great Explorations Ser.). (J). (978-0-7614-1741-5(9)); 29.93 (978-0-7614-1610-4(2)) Cavendish, Marshall Corp. (Benchmark Bks.).

—Vasco Nunez de Balboa: Explorer of the Pacific. 2004. (Great Explorations Ser.). (Illus.). 79p. (J). 29.93 (978-0-7614-1609-8(9) , Benchmark Bks.) Cavendish, Marshall Corp.

Owens, Ann-Maureen & Yealland, Jane. The Kids Book of Canadian Exploration. Mantha, John, illus. 2004. (Kids Books Of ... Ser.). 56p. (J). (gr. 3-7). (978-1-55337-353-7(7)) Kids Can Pr., Ltd.

Petrie, Kristin. Christopher Columbus. 2004. (Explorers Set I Ser.). (Illus.). 32p. (J). (gr. k-6). lib. bdg. 22.78 (978-1-59197-595-3(6)) ABDO Publishing Co.

—Daniel Boone. 2004. (Explorers Set I Ser.). (J). (gr. k-6). lib. bdg. 22.78 (978-1-59197-592-2(1)) ABDO Publishing Co.

—Francisco Vasquez de Coronado. 2004. (Explorers Set I Ser.). (J). (gr. k-6). lib. bdg. 22.78 (978-1-59197-597-7(2)) ABDO Publishing Co.

—Henry Hudson. 2007. (Illus.). 32p. (J). 22.78 (978-1-59679-741-3(X)) ABDO Publishing Co.

—Hernando de Soto. 2004. (Explorers Set I Ser.). (J). (gr. k-6). lib. bdg. 22.78 (978-1-59197-600-4(6)) ABDO Publishing Co.

—Jacques Cartier. 2004. (Explorers Set I Ser.). (Illus.). 32p. (J). (gr. k-6). lib. bdg. 22.78 (978-1-59197-594-6(8)) ABDO Publishing Co.

—John Cabot. 2004. (Explorers Set I Ser.). (J). (gr. k-6). lib. bdg. 22.78 (978-1-59197-593-9(X)) ABDO Publishing Co.

—Juan Ponce de Leon. 2007. (Illus.). 32p. (J). 22.78 (978-1-59679-742-0(8)) ABDO Publishing Co.

—Marquette & Jolliet. 2007. (Illus.). 32p. (J). 22.78 (978-1-59679-745-1(2)) ABDO Publishing Co.

—La Salle. 2007. (Illus.). 32p. (J). 22.78 (978-1-59679-750-5(9)) ABDO Publishing Co.

—Sir Francis Drake. 2004. (Explorers Ser.). (Illus.). 32p. (J). (gr. k-6). lib. bdg. 22.78 (978-1-59197-601-1(4) , Checkerboard Library) ABDO Publishing Co.

—Vasco Nuñez de Balboa. 2007. (Illus.). 32p. (J). 22.78 (978-1-59679-740-6(1)) ABDO Publishing Co.

Powell, John Wesley. The Diary of John Wesley Powell: Exploring the Grand Canyon. Roop, Connie & Roop, Peter, eds. 2000. (In My Own Words Ser.). (Illus.). 96p. (J). (gr. 5 up). lib. bdg. 24.21 (978-0-7614-1013-3(9) , Benchmark Bks.) Cavendish, Marshall Corp.

Price Hossell, Karen. Francisco Coronado. 2002. (Groundbreakers Ser.). (Illus.). 48p. (J). pap. 8.50 (978-1-4034-0478-7(X)) Heinemann Library.

Raintree IL Staff. Connections: Exploring the Americas. 2003. (Illus.). pap. 5.95 (978-1-4109-0796-7(1)) Raintree.

—Connections: Landscapes & People. 2003. (Illus.). pap. 5.95 (978-1-4109-0801-8(1)) Raintree.

—Connections: Microhabitats. 2003. (Illus.). pap. 5.95 (978-1-4109-0804-9(6)) Raintree.

Ransom, Candice. Daniel Boone. 2006. (History Maker Bios Ser.). (Illus.). 48p. (J). (gr. 3-7). 26.60 (978-0-8225-2941-5(6) , Lerner Pubns.) Lerner Publishing Group.

Reid, Struan. Christopher Columbus. 2002. (Groundbreakers Ser.). 48p. (J). (gr. 5-7). (Illus.). lib. bdg. 27.07 (978-1-58810-593-6(8)); pap. 8.50 (978-1-58810-986-6(0) , 91601) Heinemann Library.

Rossi, Ann. Native American & Europeans 1492-1700: Cultures Collide. 2004. (Crossroads America Ser.). (Illus.). 40p. (J). (gr. 5-9). 21.90 (978-0-7922-7198-7(X) , National Geographic Children's Bks.) National Geographic Society.

Russian Colonies in the Americas, 6 Packs. (On Deck Ser.: Vol. 2). 24p. (gr. 4-5). 35.00 (978-0-7578-5803-1(1)) Rigby Education.

Safari. 2003. (J). per. (978-1-57657-957-2(3)) Paradise Pr., Inc.

Sanders, Walter. England Explores the Americas. 2005. 42.00 (*978-1-4108-4611-2(3)) Benchmark Education Co.

—Spain Explores the Americas. 2005. 39.00 (*978-1-4108-4597-9(4)) Benchmark Education Co.

Santella, Andrew. Henry Hudson. 2001. (gr. 3-6). lib. bdg. 17.60 (978-0-613-51651-8(6)) Tandem Library Bks.

—Sieur de La Salle. 2002. (Groundbreakers Ser.). (Illus.). 48p. (J). (gr. 5-7). lib. bdg. 27.07 (978-1-58810-598-1(9)) Heinemann Library.

Schaefer, Lola M. Christopher Columbus. Saunders-Smith, Gail, ed. 2002. (First Biographies Ser.). (Illus.). 24p. (J). (gr. k-1). lib. bdg. 15.93 (978-0-7368-1173-6(7) , Pebble Bks.) Capstone Pr., Inc.

—Christopher Columbus. 2005. (First Biographies Ser.). 24p. (YA). (gr. k-3). pap. (978-0-7368-9368-8(7) , Pebble Bks.) Capstone Pr., Inc.

Schaefer, Ted. Exploring the Americas. 2006. (Making a New Nation Ser.). (Illus.). 48p. (J). (978-1-4034-7826-9(0)); pap. (978-1-4034-7833-7(3)) Heinemann Library.

Shafer, Susan. Ponce de Leon & the Fountain of Youth. 2005. 40.00 (*978-1-4108-4231-2(2)) Benchmark Education Co.

Shardlow, Tom & Wysotski, Chrissie. Mapping the Wilderness: The Story of David Thompson. 2006. (Illus.). 72p. (J). 16.95 (978-0-929141-85-5(7)) Napoleon Publishing/ Rendezvous Pr. CAN. *Dist:* AtlasBooks Distribution.

Shields, Charles J. Let's Discover Central America, 8 vols., Set. Henderson, James D., ed. 2002. (Illus.). 64p. (YA). (gr. 5 up). lib. bdg. (978-1-59084-091-7(7)) Mason Crest Pubs.

—Panama. 2002. (Let's Discover Central America Ser.). (Illus.). 64p. (YA). (gr. 5 up). lib. bdg. (978-1-59084-098-6(4)) Mason Crest Pubs.

Smith, Tom. Discovery of the Americas, 1492-1800. Bowman, John S. & Isserman, Maurice, eds. 2005. (Discovery & Exploration Ser.). (Illus.). 224p. (J). (gr. 6-12). 40.00 (978-0-8160-5262-2(X)) Facts On File, Inc.

Souza, Dorothy M. John C. Fremont. 2004. (Watts Library). (Illus.). 64p. (J). 25.50 (978-0-531-12288-4(3) , Watts, Franklin) Scholastic Library Publishing.

—John Wesley Powell. 2004. (Watts Library). (Illus.). 64p. (J). 25.50 (978-0-531-12289-1(1) , Watts, Franklin) Scholastic Library Publishing.

Stanley, George Edward. The European Settlement of North America (1492-1754) 2005. (Illus.). 48p. (J). pap. (978-0-8368-5833-4(6)); lib. bdg. 30.00 (978-0-8368-5824-2(7)) Stevens, Gareth Inc. (World Almanac Library).

Stefoff, Rebecca. Exploration & Settlement. 2007. (Colonial Life Ser.). (Illus.). 96p. (gr. 6 up). 37.95 (*978-0-7656-8108-9(0)) Sharpe, M.E. Inc.

Stefoff, Rebecca. Exploring the New World. 2000. (North American Historical Atlases Ser.). (Illus.). 48p. (J). (gr. 4-8). lib. bdg. 27.07 (978-0-7614-1056-0(2) , Benchmark Bks.) Cavendish, Marshall Corp.

Stein, R. Conrad. The Conquistadors: Building a Spanish Empire in the Americas. 2004. (Proud Heritage: the Hispanic Library Ser.). 40p. (J). (gr. 3-7). 28.50 (978-1-59296-144-3(4)) Child's World, Inc.

Steins, Richard. Exploration & Settlement. 2000. (Making of America Ser.). (Illus.). 96p. (J). (gr. 4-7). lib. bdg. 28.54 (978-0-8172-5700-2(4)) Raintree.

Sundel, Al. Christopher Columbus & the Age of Exploration in World History. 2002. (In World History Ser.). (Illus.). 128p. (YA). (gr. 5-12). lib. bdg. 26.60 (978-0-7660-1820-4(2)) Enslow Pubs., Inc.

Sutcliffe, Jane. Juan Ponce de Leon. 2006. (History Maker Bios Ser.). (Illus.). 48p. (J). (gr. 3-7). 26.60 (978-0-8225-2944-6(0) , Lerner Pubns.) Lerner Publishing Group.

Taylor-Butler, Christine. Explorers of North America. (True Booktrade;: American History Ser.). 48p. (J). 2008. pap. 6.95 (*978-0-531-14782-5(7)); 2007. (Illus.). (gr. 3-5). lib. bdg. 26.00 (*978-0-531-12632-5(3)) Scholastic Library Publishing. (Children's Pr.).

Thompson, Linda. The First Settlements. 2006. (Expansion of America II Ser.). (Illus.). 48p. (gr. 4-8). 20.95 (978-1-59515-511-5(2)) Rourke Publishing, LLC.

—Los Españoles en América. 2005. (ENG & SPA., Illus.). 48p. (J). (978-1-59515-657-0(7)) Rourke Publishing, LLC.

—Los Primeros Asentamientos. 2005. (ENG & SPA., Illus.). 48p. (J). (978-1-59515-660-0(7)) Rourke Publishing, LLC.

Thompson, William & Thompson, Dorcas. The Spanish Exploration of Florida. 2002. (Exploration & Discovery Ser.). (Illus.). 64p. (YA). (gr. 5 up). lib. bdg. (978-1-59084-053-5(4)) Mason Crest Pubs.

Warrick, Karen Clemens. The Perilous Search for the Fabled Northwest Passage in American History. 2004. (In American History Ser.). (Illus.). 128p. (J). lib. bdg. 26.60 (978-0-7660-2148-8(3)) Enslow Pubs., Inc.

Webster, Christine. The Lewis & Clark Expedition. 2007. (Cornerstones of Freedomtrade;, Second Ser.). 48p. (J). pap. 5.95 (*978-0-531-18689-3(X) , Children's Pr.) Scholastic Library Publishing.

Weinberger, Kimberly. Let's Read about Christopher Columbus. Van Wright, Cornelius & Hu, Ying-Hwa, illus. 2001. (Scholastic First Biographies Ser.). (J). (978-0-439-29546-8(7)) Scholastic, Inc.

West, David & Gaff, Jackie. Christopher Columbus: The Life of a Master Navigator & Explorer. 2005. (Illus.). 48p. (J). (gr. 4-6). lib. bdg. 26.50 (978-1-4042-0243-6(9)) Rosen Publishing Group, Inc., The.

Where Do You Think You're Going, Christopher Columbus? 2004. 24.95 incl. audio (978-1-56008-218-7(6)); pap. 14.95 incl. audio (978-1-56008-225-5(9)); pap. 32.75 incl. audio (978-1-55592-355-6(0)) Weston Woods Studios, Inc.

Whiting, Jim. Francisco Vasquez de Coronado. 2002. (Latinos in American History). (Illus.). 56p. (gr. 4-8). lib. bdg. 29.95 (978-1-58415-146-3(3)) Mitchell Lane Pubs., Inc.

—Juan Ponce de Leon. 2002. (Latinos in American History). (Illus.). 56p. (gr. 4-8). lib. bdg. 29.95 (978-1-58415-149-4(8)) Mitchell Lane Pubs., Inc.

—The Life & Times of Hernando Cortes. 2006. (Profiles in American History Ser.). (Illus.). 48p. (J). (gr. 4-8). lib. bdg. 29.95 (978-1-58415-449-5(7)) Mitchell Lane Pubs., Inc.

Wilson, Leonore. The Spanish Exploration of the Southwest. 2002. (Exploration & Discovery Ser.). (Illus.). 64p. (YA). (gr. 5 up). lib. bdg. (978-1-59084-055-9(0)) Mason Crest Pubs.

Wirkner, Linda. Learning about the Settlement of the Americas, with Graphic Organizers. 2005. (Graphic Organizers in Social Studies). (J). 19.95 (978-1-4042-2814-6(4) , PowerKids Pr.) Rosen Publishing Group, Inc., The.

Wittmann, Kelly. The European Rediscovery of America. 2002. (Exploration & Discovery Ser.). (Illus.). 64p. (J). (gr. 5 up). lib. bdg. (978-1-59084-052-8(6)) Mason Crest Pubs.

Worth, Richard. Ponce de Leon & the Age of Spanish Exploration in World History. 2003. (In World History Ser.). (Illus.). 112p. (J). (gr. 5-12). lib. bdg. 26.60 (978-0-7660-1940-9(3)) Enslow Pubs., Inc.

Zronik, John Paul. Sieur de La Salle: New World Adventurer. 2005. (In the Footsteps of Explorers Ser.). (Illus.). 32p. (J). (gr. 3-9). (978-0-7787-2413-1(1)) Crabtree Publishing Co.

AMERICA—DISCOVERY AND EXPLORATION—FICTION

Campbell, Donna. Pale as the Moon. Davis, Debi, illus. 1999. (Carolina Young People Ser.). 104p. (J). (gr. 4-8). pap. 10.95 (978-1-928556-02-2(7)) Coastal Carolina Pr.

Chibbaro, Julie. Redemption. 2004. (Illus.). 272p. (YA). 17.99 (978-0-689-85736-2(5) , Atheneum) Simon & Schuster Children's Publishing.

Danticat, Edwidge. Anacaona: Golden Flower, Haiti 1490. 2005. (Royal Diaries). (Illus.). 192p. (J). pap. 10.95 (978-0-439-49906-4(2)) Scholastic, Inc.

Dorris, Michael. Guests. 1999. 128p. (gr. 4-17). pap. 4.99 (978-0-7868-1356-8(3)) Hyperion Pr.

—Morning Girl. rev. ed. 1999. 80p. (gr. 4-17). pap. 4.99 (978-0-7868-1358-2(X)) Hyperion Pr.

—Morning Girl. 2005. 80p. (J). (gr. 3 up). 20.50 (978-0-8446-7272-4(6) , 3587) Smith, Peter Pub., Inc.

Duble, Kathleen Benner. Quest. 2008. 256p. (J). 15.99 (*978-1-4169-3386-1(7) , McElderry, Margaret K.) Simon & Schuster Children's Publishing.

Fritz, Jean. Brendan the Navigator: A History Mystery about the Discovery of America. 1999. 32p. (J). (gr. 1-6). pap. 6.99 (978-0-698-11759-4(X) , Putnam Juvenile) Penguin Group (USA) Inc.

Garfield, Henry. The Lost Voyage of John Cabot. 2004. (Illus.). 320p. (YA). 16.95 (978-0-689-85173-5(1) , Atheneum/Richard Jackson Bks.) Simon & Schuster Children's Publishing.

Mattern, Joanne. Leif Eriksson: Viking Explorer. 2004. (Explorers! Ser.). (Illus.). 48p. (J). lib. bdg. 23.93 (978-0-7660-2146-4(7)) Enslow Pubs., Inc.

O'Dell, Scott. The King's Fifth. 2002. (Illus.). (J). 24.36 (978-0-7587-0284-5(1)) Book Wholesalers, Inc.

Piercy, Patricia A. The Great Encounter: A Special Meeting Before Columbus. Wilkerson, Napoleon, illus. 2003. 41p. (J). (gr. 2-5). pap. 6.95 (978-0-913543-26-9(8)) African American Images.

Rocca, Al. Explorer Courage: The First Voyage of Christopher Columbus. l.t. ed. 2006. (Illus.). 72p. (J). per. 4.95 (*978-0-9643378-1-7(9)) Renown Publishing Co.

Stainer, M. L. The Lyon's Crown. Melvin, James, illus. 2000. (Lyon Saga Ser.: No. 5). 165p. (J). (gr. 5-9). lib. bdg. 9.95 (978-1-893337-03-9(0)); pap. 6.95 (978-1-893337-04-6(9)) Chicken Soup Pr., Inc.

—The Lyon's Throne. Melvin, James, illus. 1999. (Lyon Saga Ser.: Bk. 4). 153p. (YA). (gr. 5-9). pap. 6.95 (978-1-893337-02-2(2)) Chicken Soup Pr., Inc.

Whittier, Mary Ann. Tales from 1492. (YA). (gr. 7 up). lib. bdg. 19.99 (978-0-89824-981-1(3)) Royal Fireworks Publishing Co.

AMERICAN ABORIGINES

see Indians of North America; Indians of South America

AMERICAN ARTISTS

see Artists, American

AMERICAN AUTHORS

see Authors, American

AMERICAN BISON

Here are entered works on the American buffalo. Works on buffaloes of the eastern hemisphere are entered under Buffaloes.

The American Bison. (Wildlife of North America Ser.). 48p. (YA). 7.95 (978-0-7368-8481-5(5)) Capstone Pr., Inc.

Bruchac, Joseph. Buffalo Song. Farnsworth, Bill, illus. 2008. (J). Lee & Low Bks., Inc.

Kite, L. Patricia. Watching Bison in North America. 2006. (Illus.). 32p. (J). (978-1-4034-7232-8(7)); pap. (978-1-4034-7245-8(9)) Heinemann Library.

Koestler-Grack, Rachel A. The Sioux: Nomadic Buffalo Hunters. 2003. (America's First Peoples Ser.). (Illus.). 32p. (J). (gr. 2-3). lib. bdg. 23.93 (978-0-7368-1540-6(6) , Bridgestone Bks.) Capstone Pr., Inc.

Marrin, Albert. Saving the Buffalo. 2006. (Illus.). 128p. (J). (gr. 5-7). pap. 18.99 (978-0-439-71854-7(6)) Scholastic, Inc.

Patent, Dorothy Hinshaw. The Buffalo & the Indians: A Shared Destiny. Munoz, William, photos by. 2006. (Illus.). 96p. (J). (gr. 4-6). 18.00 (978-0-618-48570-3(8) , Clarion Bks.) Houghton Mifflin Co. Trade & Reference Div.

Perry, Phyllis J. Buffalo. 2005. (Animals Animals Ser.). (Illus.). 48p. (J). (gr. 3-7). lib. bdg. (978-0-7614-1866-5(0) , Benchmark Bks.) Cavendish, Marshall Corp.

Picton, Harold. Buffalo: Natural History & Conservation. rev. ed. 2005. (WorldLife Library). (Illus.). 72p. (gr. 3-7). pap., pap. 17.95 (978-0-89658-727-4(4)) Voyageur Pr., Inc.

Randolph, Ryan P. Following the Great Herds: The Plains Indians & the American Buffalo. 2003. (Library of the Westward Expansion). (Illus.). 24p. (J). lib. bdg. 19.95 (978-0-8239-6296-9(2) , PowerKids Pr.) Rosen Publishing Group, Inc., The.

Somervill, Barbara A. American Bison. 2008. (J). lib. bdg. 25.26 (*978-1-60279-031-5(0)) Cherry Lake Publishing.

Stone, Lynn M. Bison. 2003. (Animals in U.S. History Ser.). (Illus.). 24p. (J). 25.64 (978-1-58952-698-3(8)) Rourke Publishing, LLC.

Swanson, Diane. Buffalo Sunrise: The Story of a North American Giant. 2nd rev. ed. 2007. (Illus.). 58p. (J). (gr. 5-12). pap. 12.95 (*978-1-55285-858-5(8) , Walrus Bks.) Whitecap Bks., Ltd. CAN. *Dist:* Firefly Bks., Ltd.

AMERICAN CIVIL WAR

see United States—History—Civil War, 1861-1865

AMERICAN CIVILIZATION

see Civilization, American; United States—Civilization

AMERICAN COLONIES

see United States—History—Colonial Period, ca. 1600-1775

AMERICAN DRAMA—COLLECTIONS

Marx, Pamela. Practical Plays. 2nd rev. ed. 2007. 176p. (Orig.). pap. 17.95 (*978-1-59647-196-2(4)) Good Year Bks.

AMERICAN DRAMA—HISTORY AND CRITICISM

Blair, Cathy. About 100 Years of American Musical Theatre in about 100 Minutes: Ten Short Units Covering Broadway Shows from 1900-2000 (CD Enclosed) 2006. (J). 29.95 (978-0-89328-244-8(8)) Heritage Music Pr.

The Crucible. 1998. 36p. (YA). 11.95 (978-1-56137-364-2(8) , NU3648SP) Novel Units, Inc.

Hermann, Spring. A Student's Guide to Tennessee Williams. 2007. (Understanding Literature Ser.). (Illus.). 160p. (YA). (gr. 6). lib. bdg. 27.93 (*978-0-7660-2706-0(6)) Enslow Pubs., Inc.

Literature Connections English: The Crucible. 2004. (gr. 6-12). (978-0-395-77551-6(5) , 2-80120) McDougal Littell Inc.

AMERICAN ESSAYS—COLLECTIONS

Why Is Your Best Friend Your Best Friend. 2006. (YA). per. 16.95 (*978-0-9661256-7-2(3)) Youth Communication - New York Center.

AMERICAN FICTION—HISTORY AND CRITICISM

Bloom, Harold. Stephen King. 2002. (Bloom's BioCritiques Ser.). (Illus.). 112p. (gr. 9-13). 35.00 (978-0-7910-6178-7(7) , 000859, Chelsea Hse.) Facts On File, Inc.

—Toni Morrison's Beloved. 2004. (gr. 7-12). lib. bdg. 18.75 (978-0-613-70825-8(3)) Tandem Library Bks.

Bloom, Harold, ed. American Women Fiction Writers, 1900-1960. 1999. (Women Writers of English & Their Works Ser.: Vol. 3). 200p. (YA). (gr. 4-7). 34.95 (978-0-7910-4652-4(4)); (gr. 9 up). pap. 16.95 (978-0-7910-4653-1(2)) Facts On File, Inc. (Chelsea Hse.).

—Miss Lonelyhearts. 2005. (Bloom's Modern Critical Interpretations Ser.). (Illus.). 144-176p. (gr. 9-13). 45.00 (978-0-7910-8123-5(0) , Chelsea Hse.) Facts On File, Inc.

—Moby-Dick - Herman Melville. 2nd rev. ed. 2007. (Bloom's Modern Critical Interpretations Ser.). 256p. (YA). (gr. 9 up). 45.00 (978-0-7910-9363-4(8) , Chelsea Hse.) Facts On File, Inc.

—Stephen King. 1999. (Bloom's Modern Critical Views Ser.). 300p. (YA). (gr. 8-12). 52.00 (978-0-7910-4780-4(6) , Chelsea Hse.) Facts On File, Inc.

—To Kill a Mockingbird - Harper Lee. 2006. (Bloom's Modern Critical Interpretations Ser.). 216p. (YA). (gr. 9 up). 45.00 (978-0-7910-9308-5(5) , Chelsea Hse.) Facts On File, Inc.

Bloom, Harold, ed. & intro. Edith Wharton's The Age of Innocence. Bloom, Harold, intro. 1999. (Bloom's Notes Ser.). (Illus.). 90p. (YA). (gr. 8-12). 32.00 (978-0-7910-4515-2(3) , Chelsea Hse.) Facts On File, Inc.

—William Faulkner's The Sound & the Fury. Bloom, Harold, intro. 1999. (Bloom's Notes Ser.). 90p. (YA). (gr. 8-12). lib. bdg. 21.95 (978-0-7910-4519-0(6) , Chelsea Hse.) Facts On File, Inc.

The Catcher in the Rye. 1998. 44p. (YA). 11.95 (978-1-56137-450-2(4) , NU4504SP) Novel Units, Inc.

Clausen, Andrew. Charlotte's Web. 2000. 58p. (J). (gr. 4-6). stu. ed., ring bd. 12.99 (978-1-58609-169-9(7)) Progeny Pr.

Cliffs Notes Staff. The Giver. 1999. (CliffsNotes Ser.). (J). pap. (978-0-8220-0530-8(1) , Cliff Notes) Wiley, John & Sons, Inc.

Gehres, Eleanor M. Best American Novels of the Twentieth Century Still Readable Today. 2001. (gr. 7-12). lib. bdg. 24.55 (978-0-613-54978-3(3)) Tandem Library Bks.

Hemingway, Ernest. The Old Man & the Sea. Bloom, Harold, ed. 1999. (Modern Critical Interpretations Ser.). 150p. (YA). 45.00 (978-0-7910-4778-1(4) , Chelsea Hse.) Facts On File, Inc.

Lee, Harper. To Kill a Mockingbird. Bloom, Harold, ed. 1999. (Modern Critical Interpretations Ser.). 176p. (YA). (gr. 8-12). 52.00 (978-0-7910-4779-8(2) , Chelsea Hse.) Facts On File, Inc.

Levine, Gloria. Johnny Tremain. 1999. 44p. (YA). stu. ed., wbk. ed. 11.95 (978-1-56137-530-1(6)) Novel Units, Inc.

McArthur, Debra. A Student's Guide to Edgar Allan Poe. 2006. (Understanding Literature Ser.). (Illus.). 160p. (J). lib. bdg. 27.93 (978-0-7660-2437-3(7)) Enslow Pubs., Inc.

Pathways Publishing Staff. Go Ask Alice. 1998. (Assessment Packs Ser.). 15p. (YA). (gr. 9-12). pap., tchr.'s training gde. ed. 15.95 (978-1-58303-044-8(1)) Pathways Publishing.

Tackach, James. Uncle Tom's Cabin: Indictment of Slavery. 2000. (Words That Changed History Ser.). (Illus.). 128p. (YA). (gr. 4-12). lib. bdg. 27.45 (978-1-56006-591-3(5) , LML00902-177946, Lucent Bks.) Thomson Gale.

Troy, Anne. Johnny Tremain. 1999. 44p. (J). 9.95 (978-1-56137-127-3(0)) Novel Units, Inc.

AMERICAN FURNITURE

see Furniture, American

AMERICAN INDIANS

see Indians; Indians of North America; Indians of South America

AMERICAN LITERATURE

Bookbuilders Staff. Colonialism & the Revolutionary Period. 2005. (Background to American Literature Ser.). 96p. (gr. 6-12). 30.00 (978-0-8160-5667-5(6)) Facts On File, Inc.

—Contemporary American Literature. 2005. (Background to American Literature Ser.). (Illus.). 96p. (gr. 6-12). 30.00 (978-0-8160-5671-2(4)) Facts On File, Inc.

Center for Learning Network Staff. American Literature 1. 2000. (English Ser.). 262p. (YA). tchr. ed., spiral bd. 39.95 (978-1-56077-638-3(2)) Ctr. for Learning, The.

Dandelion & Other Stories: Individual Title, 6 packs. (Story Steps Ser.). (gr. k-2). 48.00 (978-0-7635-9838-9(0)) Rigby Education.

Decades of American History Set. 2005. (Decades of American History Ser.). (gr. 4-9). 350.00 (978-0-8160-6489-2(X)) Facts On File, Inc.

DeSpain, Pleasant. Sweet Land of Story: Thirty-Six American Tales to Tell. Bell, Donald-, illus. 2000. 176p. (J). (gr. 3-7). lib. bdg. 22.20 (978-0-613-35886-6(4)) Tandem Library Bks.

Hunter, Julia, et al. A Puppy. Sparck, Carole C., illus. l.t. ed. 2000. 8p. (J). (gr. k-3). pap. 6.00 (978-1-58084-206-8(2)) Lower Kuskokwim Schl. District.

—A Puppy (Cup'ik) Sparck, Carole C., illus. l.t. ed. 2000. (ESK.). 8p. (J). (gr. k-3). pap. 6.00 (978-1-58084-208-2(9)) Lower Kuskokwim Schl. District.

—Qimugkauyar' Sparck, Carole C., illus. l.t. ed. 2000. Tr. of Puppy. (ESK.). 8p. (J). (gr. k-3). pap. 6.00 (978-1-58084-207-5(0)) Lower Kuskokwim Schl. District.

Keeley, Jennifer. I Am the Cheese. 2000. (Understanding Great Literature Ser.). (Illus.). 112p. (J). (gr. 8-11). lib. bdg. 29.95 (978-1-56006-678-1(4) , Lucent Bks.) Thomson Gale.

Lauter. Anthology of American Literature Volume E Fifth Edition Plus Barton Contemporary Handbook of Literary Terms Second Edition. 5th ed. 2005. (YA). pap., pap. 50.76 (978-0-618-72319-5(6) , 397266) Houghton Mifflin College Div.

Martz, Sandra, ed. When I Am an Old Woman I Shall Wear Purple: Petite Version. 2nd gif. rev. ed. 2006. (Illus.). 64p. (C). pap. 47.70 (978-1-57601-093-8(7) , Papier-Mache Pr.) Moyer Bell.

Prentice-Hall Staff, contrib. by. Authors in Depth. 2000. (Prentice Hall Literature Library). (Illus.). iv, 212p. (J). 8.97 (978-0-13-050401-2(7)) Prentice Hall PTR.

Stahl, R. James, ed. Merlyn's Pen Vol. II: Fiction, Essays & Poems by America's Teens. (Illus.). 100p. (YA). (gr. 6-12). 1999. pap. 29.00 (978-1-886427-49-5(6)); 1998. pap. 29.00 (978-1-886427-48-8(8)) Merlyn's Pen, Inc.

AMERICAN LITERATURE—AFRICAN AMERICAN AUTHORS

see also African American Authors

Brezina, Corona. Sojourner Truth's "Ain't I a Woman?" Speech: A Primary Source Investigation. 2004. (Great Historic Debates & Speeches Ser.). (Illus.). 64p. (J). lib. bdg. 29.95 (978-1-4042-0154-5(8)) Rosen Publishing Group, Inc., The.

Golphin, Vincent F. A. African-American Stories. Johnson, Cathy & Patterson, John, illus. 2003. (My First Treasury Ser.). 40p. (J). bds. 7.98 (978-0-7853-8779-4(X) , 7191300) Publications International, Ltd.

Harkins, Pamela & Corrin, William J., compiled by. African-American Writers. 2004. (Literary Reader Ser.). (Illus.). 240p. (gr. 6-12). (978-0-618-04813-7(8) , 2-00145) McDougal Littell Inc.

Kuehner, Karen, compiled by. The Harlem Renaissance. 2004. (Literary Reader Ser.). (Illus.). 176p. (gr. 6-12). 14.64 (978-0-618-04815-1(4) , 2-00147) McDougal Littell Inc.

Levine, Gloria. Native Son. 1999. 44p. (YA). 11.95 (978-1-56137-624-7(8)) Novel Units, Inc.

Native Son. 1999. (YA). 9.95 (978-1-56137-623-0(X)) Novel Units, Inc.

Price, Hope Lynne. The Jump at the Sun Treasury: An African American Picture Book Collection. Collier, Bryan, illus. 2004. 205p. (J). (gr. 4-8). reprint ed. 17.00 (978-0-7567-7328-1(8)) DIANE Publishing Co.

Samuels, Wilfred D. Encyclopedia of African-American Literature. 2007. (Encyclopedia of Multi-Cultural Literature Ser.). 624p. (gr. 9). 75.00 (978-0-8160-5073-4(2)) Facts On File, Inc.

Scott, James. I Know Why the Caged Bird Sings: A Student Response Journal. 2001. 28p. (YA). (gr. 7-12). wbk. ed. 19.95 (978-1-58049-919-4(8) , RJ11) Prestwick Hse., Inc.

Sullivan, Charles. Children of Promise: African-American Literature & Art for Young People. 2002. (Illus.). 126p. 12.98 (978-0-8109-8221-5(8)) Abrams, Harry N. , Inc.

AMERICAN LITERATURE—BIOGRAPHY

see Authors, American

AMERICAN LITERATURE—COLLECTIONS

Appalachian Writers. 1999. (J). (gr. 9-12). (978-0-13-009974-7(0)) Prentice Hall (Schl. Div.).

Brown, Margaret Wise. Mouse of My Heart. Krupinski, Loretta, illus. 2001. 192p. (ps-3). 20.49 (978-0-7868-2546-2(4)) Hyperion Bks. for Children.

—Mouse of My Heart: Picture Book. Krupinski, Loretta, illus. 2001. 192p. (ps-3). 19.99 (978-0-7868-0628-7(1)) Hyperion Bks. for Children.

Carlson, Lori M., ed. Barrio Streets, Carnival Dreams: Three Generations of Latino Artistry. 1998. (Illus.). 127p. (YA). (gr. 7-12). 16.00 (978-0-7881-5782-0(5)) DIANE Publishing Co.

Center for Learning Network Staff. Honors American Literature 2: World War I to the Present. 3rd rev. ed. 2001. (English Ser.). 260p. (YA). (gr. 10-12). tchr. ed., spiral bd. 39.95 (978-1-56077-641-3(2)) Ctr. for Learning, The.

The Collector's Anthology. (Illus.). 48.50 (978-0-8359-0100-0(9)) Globe Fearon Educational Publishing.

Dureke, Chidinma & Dureke, Angel. Arts, Poems & Stories of the Heart. 2003. (Illus.). 70p. (YA). pap. 9.95 (978-0-9701144-8-8(6)) Jahs Publishing Group.

Gilman, Charlotte Perkins. The Yellow Wallpaper & Other Writings. 2000. (gr. 7-12). lib. bdg. 16.40 (978-0-613-50143-9(8)) Tandem Library Bks.

Haynes, David & Landsman, Julie, eds. Welcome to Your Life: Writings for the Heart of Young America. tchr. ed. 4.95 (978-1-57131-291-4(9)) Milkweed Editions.

Heron, Ann, ed. Two Teenagers in Twenty: Writings by Gay & Lesbian Youth. 192p. (ps up). reprint ed. pap. 13.95 (978-1-55583-282-7(2)) Alyson Pubns.

Locker, Thomas. Home: A Journey Through America. 2000. (Illus.). 32p. (J). (gr. 2-5). pap. 7.00 (978-0-15-202452-9(2) , Voyager Bks./Libros Viajeros) Harcourt Children's Bks.

—Home: A Journey Through America. 1998. (Illus.). 32p. (J). (gr. 1-5). 16.00 (978-0-15-201473-5(X) , Silver Whistle) Harcourt Trade Pubs.

—Home: A Journey Through America. 2000. (978-0-606-20325-8(7)); (gr. 3-6). lib. bdg. 14.15 (978-0-613-30476-4(4)) Tandem Library Bks.

McGraw-Hill Staff. Glencoe Literature: The Reader's Choice, Grade 11, American Literature. 1999. (gr. 12-13). stu. ed. 97.32 (978-0-02-635423-3(3) , 9780026354233) Glencoe/McGraw-Hill.

Meyer, John & Meyer, Stephanie. More Voices, More Visions. 2nd ed. 2001. (Teen Ink Ser.: Vol. 2). (Illus.). 300p. (YA). (gr. 9 up). pap. 12.95 (978-1-55874-913-9(6)) Health Communications, Inc.

Meyer, John, et al. Our Voices, Our Visions: Today's Teenagers Sharing Thoughts on Friends, Family, Fitting In, Challenges, Loss, Memories, Love, Heroes. 2000. (Teen Ink Ser.). (Illus.). 300p. (YA). (gr. 9 up). pap. 12.95 (978-1-55874-816-3(4)) Health Communications, Inc.

Meyer, Stephanie H. Teen Ink: Friends & Family. 2001. (gr. 7-12). lib. bdg. 22.20 (978-0-613-90259-5(9)) Tandem Library Bks.

—Teen Ink Love & Relation. 2002. (gr. 7-12). lib. bdg. 22.20 (978-0-613-88764-9(6)) Tandem Library Bks.

Murray, John A., ed. American Nature Writing 2003, Vol. 1. 2003. 224p. (gr. 4). pap. 17.95 (978-1-55591-353-3(9)) Fulcrum Publishing.

Ortiz Cofer, Judith, ed. Riding Low Through Streets of Gold: Latino Literature for Young Adults. 192p. (YA). pap. 14.95 (978-1-55885-380-5(4) , Piñata Books) Arte Publico Pr.

Scieszka, Jon. Guys Write for Guys Read: Boys' Favorite Authors Write about Being Boys. 2005. (Illus.). 272p. (J). (gr. 6-12). 16.99 (978-0-670-06007-8(0) , Viking Juvenile) Penguin Group (USA) Inc.

Scieszka, Jon, ed. Guys Write for Guys Read: Boys' Favorite Authors Write about Being Boys. 2005. (Illus.). 272p. (gr. 6-12). pap. 10.99 (978-0-670-06027-6(5) , Viking Juvenile) Penguin Group (USA) Inc.

St. Antoine, Sara, ed. The South Atlantic Coast & Piedmont: A Literary Field Guide. Nicholson, Trudy, illus. 2006. (Stories from Where We Live Ser.). 256p. (J). pap. 10.95 (978-1-57131-664-6(7)) Milkweed Editions.

Zilboorg, Caroline. American Prose & Poetry in the 20th Century. 2000. (Cambridge Contexts in Literature Ser.). (Illus.). 128p. (gr. 9-12). pap. 16.00 (978-0-521-66390-8(3)) Cambridge Univ. Pr.

AMERICAN LITERATURE—HISTORY AND CRITICISM

American Literature, 6 vols., Set. 2004. (Illus.). (YA). (gr. 9 up). stu. ed., wbk. ed. 38.95 (978-0-7403-0134-6(9) , EL9415, Lifepac) Alpha Omega Pubns., Inc.

American Literature. 2004. (gr. 11 up). stu. ed. (978-0-618-17047-0(2) , 2-71098) McDougal Littell Inc.

Bernard, Catherine. Understanding to Kill a Mockingbird. 2003. (Understanding Great Literature Ser.). (Illus.). 112p. (J). 29.95 (978-1-56006-860-0(4) , Lucent Bks.) Thomson Gale.

Bloom, Harold, ed. Women Memoirists. 1999. (Women Writers of English & Their Works Ser.: Vol. 2). 200p. (YA). (gr. 8-12). pap. 18.65 (978-0-7910-4655-5(9)); pap. 34.95 (978-0-7910-4654-8(0)) Facts On File, Inc. (Chelsea Hse.).

Bloom, Harold, ed. & tr. The House on Mango Street. Bloom, Harold, tr. 2003. (Bloom's Guides Ser.). (Illus.). 80p. (gr. 9-13). 30.00 (978-0-7910-7565-4(6) , Chelsea Hse.) Facts On File, Inc.

Bloom, Harold, intro. Arthur Miller's the Crucible. 2004. (Bloom's Guides Ser.). (Illus.). 80p. (YA). (gr. 9-13). 30.00 (978-0-7910-7876-1(0) , Chelsea Hse.) Facts On File, Inc.

—David Guterson's Snow Falling on Cedars. 2004. (Bloom's Guides Ser.). (Illus.). 80p. (YA). (gr. 9-13). 30.00 (978-0-7910-7877-8(9) , Chelsea Hse.) Facts On File, Inc.

—Huck Finn. 2004. (Bloom's Major Literary Characters Ser.). (Illus.). 180p. (gr. 9-13). 40.00 (978-0-7910-7883-9(3) , Chelsea Hse.) Facts On File, Inc.

—Nick Adams. 2004. (Bloom's Major Literary Characters Ser.). (Illus.). 180p. (gr. 9-13). 40.00 (978-0-7910-7885-3(X) , Chelsea Hse.) Facts On File, Inc.

Bookbuilders Staff. American Modernism. 2005. (Background to American Literature Ser.). (Illus.). 96p. (gr. 6-12). 30.00 (978-0-8160-5670-5(6)) Facts On File, Inc.

—Backgrounds to American Literature Set. 2005. (Background to American Literature Ser.). (gr. 6-12). 150.00 (978-0-8160-5672-9(2)) Facts On File, Inc.

—Realism & Regionalism. 2005. (Background to American Literature Ser.). (Illus.). 96p. (gr. 6-12). 30.00 (978-0-8160-5669-9(2)) Facts On File, Inc.

—Romanticism & Transcendentalism. 2005. (Background to American Literature Ser.). (Illus.). 96p. (gr. 6-12). 30.00 (978-0-8160-5668-2(4)) Facts On File, Inc.

Collins, Carolyn Strom & Eriksson, Christina Wyss. Inside the Secret Garden: A Treasury of Crafts, Recipes, & Activities. Tudor, Tasha, illus. 2004. 130p. (J). (gr. 2-8). reprint ed. 25.00 (978-0-7567-7630-5(9)) DIANE Publishing Co.

Dreibrodt, Stacie Champlin. Little Women. 2000. (YA). 9.95 (978-1-58130-630-9(X)); 11.95 (978-1-58130-631-6(8)) Novel Units, Inc.

Dunkleberger, Amy. A Student's Guide to Arthur Miller. 2005. (Understanding Literature Ser.). (Illus.). 160p. (YA). (gr. 7-13). lib. bdg. 27.93 (978-0-7660-2432-8(6)) Enslow Pubs., Inc.

Eriksson, Christina Wyss & Collins, Carolyn Strom. Inside the Secret Garden: A Treasury of Crafts, Recipes, & Activities. Collier, Mary & Tudor, Tasha, illus. 2002. 136p. (J). (gr. 3 up). 24.99 (978-0-06-027922-6(2)) HarperCollins Pubs.

Glassman, Peter. Oz: The Hundredth Anniversary Celebration. 2000. (J). lib. bdg. 19.89 (978-0-06-029219-5(9)) HarperCollins Pubs.

Green, Phyllis A. The Castle in the Attic. 1999. 40p. (J). 9.95 (978-1-56137-371-0(0)) Novel Units, Inc.

—Frog & Toad Are Friends; Frog & Toad Together; Frog & Toad All Year. 1999. 36p. (J). (gr. 1-2). 9.95 (978-1-56137-207-2(2)) Novel Units, Inc.

—Harriet the Spy. 1999. 32p. (J). 9.95 (978-1-56137-349-9(4)) Novel Units, Inc.

Holt, Rinehart and Winston Staff. Elements of Literature: Family Involvement Activities. 5th ed. 2003. (SPA & ENG., Illus.). pap. 38.80 (978-0-03-073854-8(7)) Holt, Rinehart & Winston.

—Elements of Literature: Supporting Instructions. 5th ed. 2003. (SPA.). pap. 29.20 (978-0-03-073824-1(5)); pap. 29.20 (978-0-03-073826-5(1)); (Illus.). pap. 29.20 (978-0-03-073823-4(7)) Holt, Rinehart & Winston.

—Elements of Literature, Grade 6: Holt Reader. 4th ed. 2003. pap., tchr. ed. 23.20 (978-0-03-068398-5(X)) Holt, Rinehart & Winston.

—Elements of Literature, Grade 7: Holt Reader. 5th ed. 2003. pap., tchr. ed. 23.20 (978-0-03-068399-2(8)) Holt, Rinehart & Winston.

—Elements of Literature, Grade 8: Holt Reader. 5th ed. 2003. pap., tchr. ed. 23.20 (978-0-03-068401-2(3)) Holt, Rinehart & Winston.

Ishizuka, Kathy. John Grisham: Best-Selling Author. 2003. (People to Know Ser.). (Illus.). 112p. (J). lib. bdg. 26.60 (978-0-7660-2102-0(5)) Enslow Pubs., Inc.

Jamieson, Jean. The Egypt Game. 1999. 44p. (J). 11.95 (978-1-56137-824-1(0)) Novel Units, Inc.

Kuehner, Karen, compiled by. The Harlem Renaissance. 2004. (Literary Reader Ser.). (Illus.). 176p. (gr. 6-12). 14.64 (978-0-618-04815-1(4) , 2-00147) McDougal Littell Inc.

Loewen, Nancy. Jack London. 1998. (Notebooks Ser.). 48p. 17.95 (978-1-56846-157-1(7) , Creative Education) Creative Co., The.

Ludwig, Elisa. Judy Blume. 2003. (Who Wrote That? Ser.). (Illus.). 112p. (gr. 6-12). 30.00 (978-0-7910-7619-4(9) , Chelsea Hse.) Facts On File, Inc.

Madison, Bob. American Horror Writers. 2001. (Collective Biographies Ser.). (Illus.). 104p. (YA). (gr. 6-12). lib. bdg. 26.60 (978-0-7660-1379-7(0)) Enslow Pubs., Inc.

Peterson, Nancy. Elsie & Me: A Reading Comprehension Guide to Elsie Dinsmore. 2001. ix, 79p. (J). pap. 6.95 (978-1-58182-202-1(2)) Cumberland Hse. Publishing.

Rozakis, Laurie. Where the Red Fern Grows. 2003. (Bookfiles Ser.). 64p. (J). pap. 4.99 (978-0-439-46375-1(0)) Scholastic, Inc.

Sanderson, Jeannette & Lowry, Lois. Giver. 2003. (Bookfiles Ser.). 64p. (J). pap. 4.99 (978-0-439-46356-0(4)) Scholastic, Inc.

Shields, Charles J. Amy Tan. 2001. (Women of Achievement Ser.). (Illus.). 116p. (J). pap. 30.00 (978-0-7910-5890-9(5)); 112p. (YA). (gr. 5 up). 30.00 (978-0-7910-5889-3(1)) Facts On File, Inc. (Chelsea Hse.).

Smith, Christopher. American Realism. 2000. (gr. 7-12). lib. bdg. 33.25 (978-0-613-64245-3(7)) Tandem Library Bks.

—American Realism. 2000. (Literary Movements & Genres Ser.). (Illus.). 208p. (YA). (gr. 10 up). pap. 24.95 (978-0-7377-0323-8(7) , Greenhaven Pr., Inc.) Thomson Gale.

Smith, Robert Kimmel. Chocolate Fever. Novel Units, Inc. Staff, ed. 1999. (J). 11.95 (978-1-56137-703-9(1)) Novel Units, Inc.

Stobaugh, James. American Literature Student. 2005. (Broadman & Holman Literature Ser.). 368p. stu. ed. 24.99 (978-0-8054-5900-5(6)) B&H Publishing Grp.

Troy, Anne. Chocolate Fever. 1999. 32p. (J). 9.95 (978-1-56137-176-1(9)) Novel Units, Inc.

A B

Vescia, Monique & Sachar, Louis. A Reading Guide to Holes by Louis Sachar. 2003. (Bookfiles Ser.). 64p. (J). pap. 4.99 (978-0-439-46336-2(X) , Scholastic Reference) Scholastic, Inc.

Welsch, Gabe. Philip Roth. 2003. (Bloom's Modern Critical Views Ser.). (Illus.). 200p. (gr. 9-13). 45.00 (978-0-7910-7446-6(3) , Chelsea Hse.) Facts On File, Inc.

Welsch, Gabriel. Of Mice & Men. 2006. (Bloom's Guides Ser.). 136p. 30.00 (978-0-7910-8581-3(3) , Chelsea Hse.) Facts On File, Inc.

Wilkinson, Brenda. African American Women Writers. Haskins, Jim, ed. 1999. (Black Stars Ser.). (Illus.). 176p. (gr. 5-9). 22.95 (978-0-471-17580-3(3) , Wiley) Wiley, John & Sons, Inc.

AMERICAN MUSEUM OF NATURAL HISTORY

Wynne, Patricia J. Exploring the American Museum of Natural History: A Children's Guide with Pictures to Color. 2004. (Illus.). 32p. (J). pap. 4.95 (978-0-486-43714-9(0)) Dover Pubns., Inc.

AMERICAN MUSIC

see Music, American

AMERICAN MUSICIANS

see Musicians, American

AMERICAN NATIONAL RED CROSS

Anderson, Dale. Elizabeth Dole. 2004. (Women in Politics Ser.). (Illus.). 120p. 30.00 (978-0-7910-7733-7(0) , Chelsea Hse.) Facts On File, Inc.

Devillier, Christy. Clara Barton. 2004. (First Biographies Set Iv Ser.). (Illus.). 32p. (J). (gr. k-4). lib. bdg. 22.78 (978-1-59197-511-3(5)) ABDO Publishing Co.

Ditchfield, Christin. Clara Barton: Founder of the American Red Cross. 2004. (Great Life Stories Ser.). (Illus.). 111p. (J). 30.50 (978-0-531-12276-1(X) , Watts, Franklin) Scholastic Library Publishing.

Lakin, Patricia. Clara Barton: Spirit of the American Red Cross. Sullivan, Simon, illus. 2004. (Ready-to-Read Stories of Famous Americans Ser.). 48p. (J). pap. 3.99 (978-0-689-86513-8(9) , Aladdin) Simon & Schuster Children's Publishing.

Nardo, Don. Clara Barton: "Face Danger, but Never Fear It" 2008. (Americans-the Spirit of a Nation Ser.). 128p. (J). (gr. 5 up). lib. bdg. 31.93 (***978-0-7660-3024-4(5)***) Enslow Pubs., Inc.

Rau, Dana Meachen. Elizabeth Dole: Public Servant & Senator. 2005. (J). (978-0-7565-1583-6(1)) Compass Point Bks.

Somervill, Barbara A. Clara Barton: Founder of the American Red Cross. (Illus.). 112p. (J). 2007. pap. (***978-0-7565-2199-8(8)***); 2006. (978-0-7565-1888-2(1)) Compass Point Bks.

Suen, Anastasia. The Red Cross. 2002. (Reading Power Ser.). (Illus.). 24p. (J). (gr. 2). lib. bdg. 17.25 (978-0-8239-6003-3(X) , PowerKids Pr.) Rosen Publishing Group, Inc., The.

AMERICAN PAINTERS

see Painters—United States

AMERICAN POETRY

Ackerman, Diane. The Senses of Animals. 2000. (J). 14.95 (978-0-375-80400-7(5)); lib. bdg. 16.99 (978-0-375-90400-4(X)) Knopf, Alfred A. Inc.

—The Senses of Animals. 2002. lib. bdg. 17.99 (978-0-517-70918-4(X)) Random Hse., Inc.

Adinolfi, JoAnn, illus. Valentine Hearts: Holiday Poetry. 2005. 32p. (J). lib. bdg. 13.85 (***978-1-4242-0510-3(7)***) Fitzgerald Bks.

Adoff, Jamie Levi. Song Shoots Out of My Mouth: A Celebration of Music. French, Martin, illus. 2002. 48p. (J). 17.99 (978-0-525-46949-0(4) , Dutton Juvenile) Penguin Group (USA) Inc.

Altman, Susan. Ancient Egypt. 2001. (gr. 3-6). lib. bdg. 18.75 (978-0-613-53909-8(5)) Tandem Library Bks.

—Ancient Rome. 2001. (gr. 3-6). lib. bdg. 18.75 (978-0-613-53911-1(7)) Tandem Library Bks.

Altman, Susan & Lechner, Susan. Ancient Africa. Perrone, Donna, illus. (Modern Rhymes about Ancient Times Ser.). 48p. (J). (gr. 3-5). 2002. pap. 9.95 (978-0-516-27371-6(X)); 2001. 30.00 (978-0-516-21151-0(X)) Scholastic Library Publishing. (Children's Pr.).

—Ancient Africa. Perrone, Donna, illus. 2002. 48p. (J). (gr. 4-7). lib. bdg. 18.75 (978-0-613-53908-1(7)) Tandem Library Bks.

—Ancient Egypt. Appleoff, Sandy, illus. 2001. (Modern Rhymes about Ancient Times Ser.). 48p. (J). (gr. 3-5). 30.00 (978-0-516-21149-7(8) , Children's Pr.) Scholastic Library Publishing.

—Ancient Greece: Modern Rhymes about Ancient Times. Schilling, Deborah, illus. 2001. (Modern Rhymes about Ancient Times Ser.). 48p. (J). (gr. 3-5). 30.00 (978-0-516-21150-3(1) , Children's Pr.) Scholastic Library Publishing.

—Ancient Rome. Hughes, Susan, illus. 2001. (Modern Rhymes about Ancient Times Ser.). 48p. (J). (gr. 3-5). 30.00 (978-0-516-21148-0(X) , Children's Pr.) Scholastic Library Publishing.

Anaya, Rudolfo A. An Elegy on the Death of Cesar Chavez: A Poem. Enriquez, Gaspar, illus. 2000. 32p. (J). (gr. 4-7). 16.95 (978-0-938317-51-7(2)) Cinco Puntos Pr.

Andreae, Giles. Christopher Crocodile's Jungly Jingles. Wojtowycz, David, illus. 2001. 10p. (J). (ps-k). bds. 5.95 (978-1-58925-650-7(6) , tiger tales) ME Media LLC.

—Larry Lion's Rumbly Rhymes. Wojtowycz, David, illus. 2001. (J). (ps-k). bds. 5.95 (978-1-58925-651-4(4) , tiger tales) ME Media LLC.

—Olive Octopus's Deep Sea Ditties. Wojtowycz, David, illus. 2001. (J). (ps-k). bds. 5.95 (978-1-58925-652-1(2) , tiger tales) ME Media LLC.

—Sidney Shark's Seaside Shanties. Wojtowycz, David, illus. 2001. 10p. (J). (ps-k). bds. 5.95 (978-1-58925-653-8(0) , tiger tales) ME Media LLC.

Andreae, Giles & Wojtowycz, David. Christopher Crocodile's Jungly Jingles. Andreae, Giles & Wojtowycz, David, illus. 2000. (Illus.). (J). (ps-k). bds. 6.95 (978-1-888444-67-4(3)) Little Tiger Pr.

—Larry Lion's Rumbly Rhymes. Andreae, Giles & Wojtowycz, David, illus. 2000. (Illus.). (J). (ps-k). bds. 6.95 (978-1-888444-68-1(1)) Little Tiger Pr.

—Olive Octopus's Deep Sea Ditties. Andreae, Giles & Wojtowycz, David, illus. 2000. (Illus.). (J). (ps-k). bds. 6.95 (978-1-888444-69-8(X)) Little Tiger Pr.

—Sidney Shark's Seaside Shanties. Andreae, Giles & Wojtowycz, David, illus. 2000. (Illus.). 8p. (J). (ps-k). bds. 6.95 (978-1-888444-70-4(3)) Little Tiger Pr.

Anglund, Joan Walsh. Babies Are a Bit of Heaven. Anglund, Joan Walsh, illus. 2002. (Illus.). 32p. (J). 9.95 (978-0-689-83988-7(X)) Simon & Schuster Children's Publishing.

Appelt, Kathi. I See the Moon. Jenkins, Debra Reid, illus. 2004. 24p. (J). (ps-2). 15.00 (978-0-8028-5118-5(5)); pap. 8.00 (978-0-8028-5226-7(2)) Eerdmans, William B. Publishing Co.

—Poems from Homeroom: A Writer's Place to Start. rev. ed. 2002. 128p. (YA). (gr. 7-12). 16.95 (978-0-8050-6978-5(X) , Holt, Henry & Co. Bks. For Young Readers) Holt, Henry & Co.

Aylesworth, Jim, et al. The Burger & the Hot Dog. 2001. (Illus.). 32p. (J). (gr. k-3). 17.99 (978-0-689-83897-2(2) , Atheneum) Simon & Schuster Children's Publishing.

Bagert, Brod. Giant Children. Arnold, Tedd, illus. 2002. 32p. (J). (gr. k-3). 16.99 (978-0-8037-2556-0(6) , Dial) Penguin Group (USA) Inc.

Barsotti, Joan B. The Little Green Frog & Other Poems. Mathis, Carol, illus. 1999. (Apple Hill Ser.). 32p. (J). (gr. k-5). pap. 6.95 (978-0-9642112-5-4(4)) Barsotti Bks.

Bates, Katharine Lee. America the Beautiful. Minor, Wendell & Howell, Troy, illus. 2003. 32p. (J). (ps). 16.99 (978-0-399-23885-7(9) , Putnam Juvenile) Penguin Group (USA) Inc.

—America the Beautiful. Waldman, Neil, illus. 2002. 32p. (J). (ps-3). 6.99 (978-0-689-85245-9(2) , Aladdin) Simon & Schuster Children's Publishing.

Bauer, Marion Dane. Love Song for a Baby. Andreasen, Dan, illus. 2002. 32p. (J). 16.99 (978-0-689-82268-1(5)) Simon & Schuster Children's Publishing.

Behn, Harry. Halloween. Couch, Greg, illus. 2003. 32p. (J). 15.95 (978-0-7358-1609-1(3)) North-South Bks., Inc.

Benet, Rosemary & Benet, Stephen Vincent. Johnny Appleseed. Schindler, S. D., illus. 2001. 40p. (J). (ps-3). 16.95 (978-0-689-82975-8(2) , McElderry, Margaret K.) Simon & Schuster Children's Publishing.

Booth, Philip. Crossing. Ibatoulline, Bagram, illus. 2002. (J). 24.36 (978-0-7587-9755-1(9)) Book Wholesalers, Inc.

—Crossing. Ibatoulline, Bagram, illus. 2004. 40p. (J). (gr. k-4). reprint ed. pap. 6.99 (978-0-7636-2434-7(9)) Candlewick Pr.

Borden, Louise. America Is... Schuett, Stacey, illus. 2002. 40p. (J). (gr. k-3). 17.95 (978-0-689-83900-9(6) , McElderry, Margaret K.) Simon & Schuster Children's Publishing.

Bowman, Crystal. If Peas Could Taste Like Candy: And Other Funny Poems for Kids. Jeffery, Lynn, illus. 1998. 128p. (J). 12.99 (978-0-310-21950-7(7)) Zonderkidz.

Brown, Calef. Dutch Sneakers & Flea Keepers: 14 More Stories. 2000. (Illus.). 32p. (J). (gr. k-3). tchr. ed. 16.00 (978-0-618-05183-0(X)) Houghton Mifflin Co. Trade & Reference Div.

—Flamingos on the Roof: Poems & Paintings. 2006. (Illus.). 64p. (J). (gr. 4-6). 16.00 (978-0-618-56298-5(2)) Houghton Mifflin Co.

—Polka-Bats & Octopus Slacks: 14 Stories. 1998. (Illus.). 32p. (J). (gr. k-3). 16.00 (978-0-395-85403-7(2)) Houghton Mifflin Co. Trade & Reference Div.

Brown, Margaret Wise. Give Yourself to the Rain. Weidner, Teri, illus. 2002. 32p. (J). (gr. k-3). 16.95 (978-0-689-83344-1(X) , McElderry, Margaret K.) Simon & Schuster Children's Publishing.

—I Like Stars. 2002. (Illus.). (J). 11.91 (978-0-7587-1324-7(X)) Book Wholesalers, Inc.

—I Like Stars. Paley, Joan, illus. (Step into Reading Ser.). 32p. (J). (ps-k). 2004. lib. bdg. 11.99 (978-0-375-99994-9(9)); 1998. pap. 3.99 (978-0-307-26105-2(0) , 26105) Random Hse. Children's Bks. (Random Hse. Bks. for Young Readers).

—I Like Stars. 1998. (gr. k-3). lib. bdg. 11.80 (978-0-613-81156-9(9)) Tandem Library Bks.

—Love Songs of the Little Bear. Jeffers, Susan, illus. 2001. 32p. (ps-1). 16.49 (978-0-7868-2445-8(X)) Hyperion Bks. for Children.

—Nibble Nibble. Minor, Wendell, illus. 2007. 32p. (J). (ps-3). 16.99 (978-0-06-059208-0(7)) HarperCollins Pubs.

Brown, Michael R. Susquehanna. 2003. 80p. per. 12.00 (978-0-9633092-3-5(4)) Ragged Sky Pr.

Bruchac, Joseph. The Earth under Sky Bear's Feet: Native American Poems of the Land. Locker, Thomas, illus. 1998. 32p. (J). (gr. k-3). pap. 6.99 (978-0-698-11647-4(X) , Putnam Juvenile) Penguin Group (USA) Inc.

Bunting, Eve. Sing a Song of Piglets: A Calendar in Verse. McCully, Emily Arnold, illus. 2002. 32p. (J). (gr. k-3). tchr. ed. 16.00 (978-0-618-01137-4(X) , Clarion Bks.) Houghton Mifflin Co. Trade & Reference Div.

—Who Was Born This Special Day? 2003. (ps-2). lib. bdg. 15.30 (978-0-613-88998-8(3)) Tandem Library Bks.

Burg, Brad. Outside the Lines. Gibbon, Rebecca, illus. 2002. 32p. (J). 15.99 (978-0-399-23446-0(2) , Putnam Juvenile) Penguin Group (USA) Inc.

Burleigh, Robert. Goal. Johnson, Stephen T., illus. 2001. 32p. (J). (gr. 1-4). 16.00 (978-0-15-201789-7(5) , Silver Whistle) Harcourt Trade Pubs.

—Hoops. Johnson, Stephen T., illus. 2001. 32p. (J). (gr. k-3). pap. 6.00 (978-0-15-216380-8(8) , Voyager Bks./Libros Viajeros) Harcourt Children's Bks.

—Hoops. 2001. (gr. k-3). lib. bdg. 14.15 (978-0-613-83779-8(7)) Tandem Library Bks.

Burton, Michael H. In the Light of a Child: A Journey Through the 52 Weeks of the Year in Both Hemispheres for Children & for the Child in Each Human Being. 1998. 64p. pap. 14.95 (978-0-88010-450-0(3)) Steiner-Books, Inc.

Bush, Timothy. Ferocious Girls, Steamroller Boys & Other Poems in Between. 2000. (Illus.). 64p. (J). (gr. 1-4). 17.99 (978-0-531-33250-4(0) , Orchard Bks.) Scholastic, Inc.

Calmenson, Stephanie. Good for You! Toddler Rhymes for Toddler Times. Sweet, Melissa, illus. 2001. 64p. (J). (ps up). 17.99 (978-0-688-17737-9(9)) HarperCollins Pubs.

—Welcome, Baby! Baby Rhymes for Baby Times. Sweet, Melissa, illus. 2002. 64p. (J). (ps up). 16.99 (978-0-688-17736-2(0)) HarperCollins Pubs.

Cameron, Eileen. Canyon. Collier, Michael, illus. Collier, Michael, photos by. 2002. 32p. (J). (gr. 1-3). 16.95 (978-1-931414-03-6(3)) Mikaya Pr.

Carlson, Lori Marie. Red Hot Salsa: Bilingual Poems on Being Young & Latino in the United States. rev. ed. 2005. (ENG & SPA.). 160p. (YA). bds. 15.95 (978-0-8050-7616-5(6)) Holt, Henry & Co.

Carlstrom, Nancy White. Glory. Jenkins, Debra Reid, illus. 2004. 32p. (J). (ps-3). 17.00 (978-0-8028-5143-7(6)) Eerdmans, William B. Publishing Co.

Carpenter, Stephen, illus. If Kids Ruled the School: More Kids' Favorite Funny School Poems. 2004. 73p. (J). (978-0-88166-468-3(5)) Meadowbrook Pr.

—Mary Had a Little Jam, & Other Silly Rhymes. 2004. 32p. (J). (978-0-88166-470-6(7)) Meadowbrook Pr.

—My Dog Ate My Homework. 2003. 96p. (J). 15.00 (978-0-689-02770-3(2)) Meadowbrook Pr.

Chan, Jennifer L. Why Does a B Look Like a D? Date not set. (J). (978-1-879965-06-5(2)) Polychrome Publishing Corp.

Child, Lydia Marie. Over the River & Through the Wood. Catrow, David, illus. rev. ed. 1999. 32p. (J). (ps-3). pap. 7.95 (978-0-8050-6311-0(0) , Holt, Henry & Co. Bks. For Young Readers) Holt, Henry & Co.

—Over the River & Through the Wood. Manson, Christopher, illus. 1998. 32p. (J). (ps-3). pap. 6.95 (978-1-55858-959-9(7)) North-South Bks., Inc.

Chorao, Kay. The Baby's Playtime Book. Chorao, Kay, illus. 2006. (Illus.). 40p. (J). (ps). 16.99 (978-0-525-47576-7(1) , Dutton Juvenile) Penguin Group (USA) Inc.

—Jumpety-Bumpety-Hop: A Parade of Animal Poems. 2000. (Illus.). (J). (978-0-606-18415-1(5)) Tandem Library Bks.

Clarke, Gillian. The Kingfisher Book of Scary Poems. Todd, Justin, illus. 2003. 72p. (J). (gr. 3-5). pap. 9.95 (978-0-7534-5647-7(8) , Kingfisher) Houghton Mifflin Co. Trade & Reference Div.

Cleary, Brian P. Rainbow Soup: Adventures in Poetry. Layton, Neal, tr. Layton, Neal, illus. 2004. 88p. (J). (gr. 3-6). 16.95 (978-1-57505-597-8(X)) Lerner Publishing Group.

—Rhyme & Punishment: Adventures in Wordplay. Sandy, J. P., illus. 2006. 48p. (J). 15.95 (978-1-57505-849-8(9) , Millbrook Pr.) Lerner Publishing Group.

Cline-Ransome, Lesa. Quilt Alphabet. Ransome, James E., illus. 2005. 48p. (J). (gr. k-3). pap. 6.95 (978-0-8234-1765-0(4)) Holiday Hse., Inc.

Clinton, Catherine. I, Too, Sing America: Three Centuries of African American Poetry. Alcorn, Stephen, illus. 1998. 128p. (J). (gr. 4-6). tchr. ed. 22.00 (978-0-395-89599-3(5)) Houghton Mifflin Co. Trade & Reference Div.

—A Poem of Her Own: Voices of American Women Yesterday & Today. Alcorn, Stephen, illus. 2003. 80p. (J). (gr. 7-17). 17.95 (978-0-8109-4240-0(2)) Abrams, Harry N. , Inc.

cummings, e e. The Little Tree. Raschka, Chris, illus. 2001. 32p. (J). 16.49 (978-0-7868-2629-2(0)) Hyperion Bks. for Children.

Curtis, Chara M. Fun Is a Feeling. Aldrich, Cynthia, illus. 1998. 32p. (ps up). 15.95 (978-0-935699-13-5(9)) Illumination Arts Publishing Co., Inc.

Cyrus, Kurt. Hotel Deep: Light Verse from Dark Water. 2005. (Illus.). 40p. (J). 16.00 (978-0-15-216771-4(4)) Harcourt Trade Pubs.

Dakos, Kalli. The Goof Who Invented Homework: And Other School Poems. 1999. 80p. (J). (gr. 2). 5.99 (978-0-14-038694-3(7) , Puffin) Penguin Group (USA) Inc.

Danielsen, Brian. Zoloco: The Yippee-Yahoo, Boo-Hoo, Koo-Koo Book about Feelings. Glaser, Byron & Higashi, Sandra, illus. 2002. (J). (978-0-8109-1019-5(5)) Abrams, Harry N. , Inc.

Decker, Marjorie Ainsborough. The Christian Mother Goose Book of Nursery Rhymes. Gibb, Sarah, illus. 2001. (Christian Mother Goose Ser.). 64p. (J). (ps-k). 9.99 (978-0-448-42511-5(4) , Grosset & Dunlap) Penguin Group (USA) Inc.

Di Pasquale, Emanuel P. Cartwheel to the Moon: My Sicilian Childhood. Thompson, Kathryn Dyble, illus. 2003. 64p. (J). (gr. 3-7). 16.95 (978-0-8126-2679-7(6)) Cricket Bks.

Diggory & Terence. Encyclopedia of the New York School of Poets. 2008. (Literary Movements Ser.). 400p. (gr. 9). 75.00 (***978-0-8160-5743-6(5)***) Facts On File, Inc.

Dilenschneider, Geoffrey. Between Two Junes Is a Forest: A Journal. 2004. 288p. (gr. 7 up). 20.00 (978-1-893224-83-4(X) , New Millennium Pr.) New Millennium Entertainment.

Disch, Tom. A Child's Garden of Grammar. 2002. (Illus.). 96p. pap. 14.95 (978-0-472-08911-6(0) , 08911) Univ. of Michigan Pr.

Dotlich, Rebecca Kai. Lemonade Sun: And Other Summer Poems. Gilchrist, Jan Spivey, illus. 2003. 32p. (J). (gr. k-2). pap. 9.95 (978-1-56397-944-6(6)) Boyds Mills Pr.

—Lemonade Sun: And Other Summer Poems. 2001. (gr. k-3). lib. bdg. 17.60 (978-0-613-78919-6(9)) Tandem Library Bks.

Dubois, Tevon. A Child on the Island: The Ageless Wisdom of a Ten-Year-Old. 2002. 64p. per. 9.95 (978-1-931105-05-7(7)) Opal Creek Pr., LLC.

Dunbar, Polly, illus. Here's a Little Poem: A Very First Book of Poetry. 2007. 112p. (J). (ps-k). 21.99 (978-0-7636-3141-3(8)) Candlewick Pr.

Dunster, Mark. Buzzer: Poems from Hollywood. 2001. 11p. (YA). pap. 5.00 (978-0-7949-0569-9(2)) Linden Pubs.

—A Flow of Words: Poems from Hollywood. 2001. 11p. (YA). pap. 5.00 (978-0-7949-0567-5(6)) Linden Pubs.

—Objectivities: Poems from Hollywood. 2001. 11p. (YA). pap. 5.00 (978-0-7949-0568-2(4)) Linden Pubs.

—Twitches: Poems from Hollywood. 2001. 11p. (YA). pap. 5.00 (978-0-7949-0565-1(X)) Linden Pubs.

Ehrmann, Max. Desiderata: Words to Live By. Tauss, Marc, illus. 2003. (Desiderata Ser.). 48p. (J). pap. 15.95 (978-0-439-37293-0(3) , Scholastic Pr.) Scholastic, Inc.

Esbensen, Barbara Juster. The Night Rainbow. Davie, Helen K., illus. 2000. 32p. (J). (gr. 2-6). 17.99 (978-0-531-33244-3(6) , Orchard Bks.) Scholastic, Inc.

—Swing Around the Sun. Chee, Cheng-Khee et al, illus. 2003. 48p. (J). 16.95 (978-0-87614-143-4(2) , Carolrhoda Bks.) Lerner Publishing Group.

Ewald, Wendy. The Best Part of Me: Children Talk about Their Bodies in Pictures & Words. Ewald, Wendy, illus. 2002. (Illus.). 32p. (ps-3). 16.99 (978-0-316-70306-2(0) , Tingley, Megan Bks.) Little, Brown Bks. for Young Readers.

Fearnley, Jan & Andreae, Giles. Rumble in the Jungle. Wojtowycz, David, illus. 2001. 28p. (J). (ps-k). tchr. ed. 16.95 (978-1-58925-005-5(2) , tiger tales) ME Media LLC.

Feelings, Tom. Soul Looks Back in Wonder. 1999. (Illus.). 40p. (J). (ps-ps). pap., pap. 7.99 (978-0-14-056501-0(9) , Puffin) Penguin Group (USA) Inc.

—Soul Looks Back in Wonder. 1999. (978-0-606-15992-0(4)) Tandem Library Bks.

—Soul Looks Back in Wonder. Feelings, Tom, illus. 1999. (Illus.). (J). (ps-ps). lib. bdg. 16.45 (978-0-613-12128-6(7)) Tandem Library Bks.

Field, Eugene. Wynken, Blynken, & Nod. 1998. (gr. k-3). lib. bdg. 15.25 (978-0-613-81232-0(8)) Tandem Library Bks.

Fleischman, Paul. Big Talk: Poems for Four Voices. Giacobbe, Beppe, illus. 2000. 48p. (J). (gr. 5-9). 18.99 (978-0-7636-0636-7(7)) Candlewick Pr.

Fletcher, Ralph J. Grandpa Never Lies. Stevenson, Harvey, illus. 2000. 32p. (J). (gr. k-3). tchr. ed. 16.00 (978-0-395-79770-9(5) , Clarion Bks.) Houghton Mifflin Co. Trade & Reference Div.

—Have You Been to the Beach Lately? Poems. Sperling, Andrea, photos by. 2001. (Illus.). 48p. (J). (gr. 3-7). pap. 15.95 (978-0-531-30330-6(6) , Orchard Bks.) Scholastic, Inc.

—Relatively Speaking: Poems about Family. Krudop, Walter L., illus. 1999. 48p. (J). (ps-3). 15.99 (978-0-531-33141-5(5)); (gr. 2-4). pap. 14.95 (978-0-531-30141-8(9)) Scholastic, Inc. (Orchard Bks.).

Florian, Douglas. Autumnblings. Florian, Douglas, illus. 2003. (Illus.). 48p. (J). 15.99 (978-0-06-009278-8(5)); lib. bdg. 16.89 (978-0-06-009279-5(3)) HarperCollins Pubs.

—Bow Wow Meow Meow: It's Rhyming Cats & Dogs. 2003. (Illus.). 56p. (J). (gr. k-5). 17.00 (978-0-15-216395-2(6)) Harcourt Children's Bks.

—Handsprings: Poems & Paintings. Florian, Douglas, illus. 2006. (Illus.). 48p. (J). 15.99 (978-0-06-009280-1(7)) HarperCollins Pubs.

—Insectlopedia. 1998. (Illus.). 56p. (J). (gr. k-5). 16.00 (978-0-15-201306-6(7)) Harcourt Children's Bks.

—Laugh-eteria. 2008. (Illus.). 160p. (J). pap. 8.00 (***978-0-15-206148-7(7)*** , Harcourt Paperbacks) Harcourt Children's Bks.

—Lizards, Frogs, & Polliwogs. 2001. (Illus.). 56p. (J). (gr. k-5). 16.00 (978-0-15-202591-5(X)) Harcourt Children's Bks.

—Omnibeasts: Animal Poems & Paintings. 2004. (Illus.). 96p. (J). 18.00 (978-0-15-205038-2(8)) Harcourt Children's Bks.

—Summersaults. Florian, Douglas, illus. 2002. (Illus.). 48p. (J). (gr. k up). 16.99 (978-0-06-029267-6(9)); lib. bdg. 17.89 (978-0-06-029268-3(7)) HarperCollins Pubs.

—Zoo's Who: Poems & Paintings. 2005. (Illus.). 56p. (J). (gr. k-5). 17.00 (978-0-15-204639-2(9)) Harcourt Children's Bks.

Franco, Betsy. Counting Caterpillars..., 1 vol. 1998. 64p. pap. 9.95 (978-0-590-64210-1(3)) Scholastic, Inc.

—Counting Our Way to the 100th Day! 100 Poems & 100 Pictures to Celebrate the 100th Day of School. Salerno, Steven, illus. 2004. 48p. (J). 15.95 (978-0-689-84793-6(9) , McElderry, Margaret K.) Simon & Schuster Children's Publishing.

Franco, Betsy & Salerno, Steven. Mathematickles! 2003. (Illus.). 40p. (J). (gr. k-5). 17.95 (978-0-689-84357-0(7) , McElderry, Margaret K.) Simon & Schuster Children's Publishing.

Frost, Robert. Birches. Young, Ed, illus. rev. ed. 2002. 32p. (J). (gr. 1-5). pap. 7.95 (978-0-8050-7230-3(6) , Holt, Henry & Co. Bks. For Young Readers) Holt, Henry & Co.

Frost, Robert & Berry, S. L. Robert Frost. 2003. (Voices of Poetry Ser.). (J). (978-1-58341-282-4(4) , Creative Education) Creative Co., The.

Gage, Amy Glaser & McIntyre, Connie. Upside Downside Inside Out: Poems about Being a Kid. Gage, Amy Glaser & McIntyre, Connie, illus. 2nd rev. ed. 2003. (Illus.). 49p. (J). per. 9.95 (978-0-9677685-4-0(3) , Thumbprint Pr.) McIntyre, Connie.

Galdone, Paul. Over in the Meadow. 1998. (J). pap. 5.95 (978-0-87628-986-0(3)) Ctr. for Applied Research in Education, The.

George, Kristine O'Connell. Book! Smith, Maggie, illus. 2001. 32p. (J). (gr. k-ps). tchr. ed. 9.95 (978-0-395-98287-7(1) , Clarion Bks.) Houghton Mifflin Co. Trade & Reference Div.

—Fold Me a Poem. Stringer, Lauren, illus. 2005. 56p. (J). 16.00 (978-0-15-202501-4(4)) Harcourt Trade Pubs.

—Little Dog & Duncan. Otani, June, illus. 2002. 40p. (J). (gr. k-3). 14.00 (978-0-618-11758-1(X) , Clarion Bks.) Houghton Mifflin Co. Trade & Reference Div.

—Little Dog Poems. Otani, June, illus. 1999. 40p. (J). (gr. k-3). tchr. ed. 13.00 (978-0-395-82266-1(1) , Clarion Bks.) Houghton Mifflin Co. Trade & Reference Div.

—Old Elm Speaks: Tree Poems. Kiesler, Kate A., illus. 1998. 48p. (J). (gr. k-3). tchr. ed. 16.00 (978-0-395-87611-4(7) , Clarion Bks.) Houghton Mifflin Co. Trade & Reference Div.

—Swimming Upstream: Middle School Poems. Tilley, Debbie, illus. 2002. 80p. (J). (gr. 4-6). tchr. ed. 14.00 (978-0-618-15250-6(4) , Clarion Bks.) Houghton Mifflin Co. Trade & Reference Div.

—Toasting Marshmallows: Camping Poems. Kiesler, Kate A., illus. 2001. 52p. (J). (gr. k-3). tchr. ed. 15.00 (978-0-618-04597-6(X) , Clarion Bks.) Houghton Mifflin Co. Trade & Reference Div.

Geraty, Virginia Mixson. Gullah Night Before Christmas. Rice, James, illus. 1998. (Night Before Christmas Ser.). 32p. (J). (ps-3). 15.95 (978-1-56554-330-0(0)) Pelican Publishing Co., Inc.

Ghigna, Debra & Ghigna, Charles. Christmas Is Coming! Young, Mary O'Keefe, illus. 2000. 32p. (J). (ps-3). 15.95 (978-0-88106-113-0(1)) Charlesbridge Publishing, Inc.

Giovanni, Nikki. Ego-Tripping & Other Poems for Young People. Ford, George, illus. 2nd rev. ed. 2003. 76p. (J). (gr. 5-11). pap. 10.95 (978-1-55652-189-8(8) , Hill, Lawrence Bks.) Chicago Review Pr., Inc.

Glenn, Mel. Who Killed Mr. Chippendale? A Mystery in Poems. 1999. 112p. (J). (gr. 5-9). pap. 5.99 (978-0-14-038513-7(4) , Puffin) Penguin Group (USA) Inc.

—Who Killed Mr. Chippendale? A Mystery in Poems. 1999. (978-0-606-16842-7(7)) Tandem Library Bks.

Godwin, Laura. Prayers from the Barnyard. 2000. (Illus.). 40p. (J). (ps-2). 15.49 (978-0-7868-2302-4(X)) Disney Pr.

Graham, Joan Bransfield. Flicker Flash. Davis, Nancy, illus. 1999. 32p. (J). (gr. k-3). tchr. ed. 16.00 (978-0-395-90501-2(X)) Houghton Mifflin Co. Trade & Reference Div.

—Flicker Flash. Davis, Nancy, illus. 2003. 32p. (J). (gr. k-3). pap. 6.95 (978-0-618-31102-6(5)) Houghton Mifflin Co. Trade & Reference Div.

Grandits, John. Technically, It's Not My Fault: Concrete Poems. 2004. (Illus.). 48p. (J). (gr. 5-8). tchr. ed. 15.00 (978-0-618-42833-5(X)); pap. 5.95 (978-0-618-50361-2(7)) Houghton Mifflin Co. Trade & Reference Div. (Clarion Bks.).

Greenberg, David. Don't Forget Your Etiquette! The Essential Guide to Misbehavior. Westcott, Nadine Bernard, illus. 2006. 40p. (J). 16.00 (978-0-374-34990-5(8) , Farrar, Straus & Giroux (BYR)) Farrar, Straus & Giroux.

Greenberg, David T. The Book of Boys (for Girls) & the Book of Girls (for Boys) Allen, Joy, illus. 2005. 32p. (J). (ps-1). 15.99 (978-0-316-36210-8(7)) Little Brown & Co.

Greenfield, Eloise. For the Love of the Game: Michael Jordan & Me. Gilchrist, Jan Spivey, illus. 1999. (Trophy Picture Bk.). 32p. (J). (ps-3). pap. 6.99 (978-0-06-443555-0(5) , Harper Trophy) HarperCollins Pubs.

—For the Love of the Game: Michael Jordan & Me. 1999. (gr. k-3). lib. bdg. 15.30 (978-0-613-17800-6(9)) Tandem Library Bks.

—I Can Draw a Weeposaur & Other Dinosaurs. Spivey-Gilchrist, Jan, illus. 2001. 32p. (J). (gr. k-3). lib. bdg. 14.89 (978-0-688-17635-8(6)) HarperCollins Pubs.

—In the Land of Words: New & Selected Poems. Gilchrist, Jan Spivey, illus. 2004. 48p. (J). (ps-3). 16.99 (978-0-06-028993-5(7)) HarperCollins Pubs.

Grimes, Brittney. Poetry for a Child - By a Child. l.t. ed. 1998. (Illus.). 40p. (J). pap. (978-1-889732-12-1(5) , Key-A-Teese Production) Word For Word Publishing Co.

Grimes, Nikki. A Dime a Dozen. Angelo, illus. 1998. 56p. (YA). (gr. 7-12). 17.99 (978-0-8037-2227-9(3) , Dial) Penguin Group (USA) Inc.

—Hopscotch Love: A Family Treasury of Love Poems. Rosales, Melodye Benson, illus. 1999. 40p. (J). (gr. 3 up). 17.99 (978-0-688-15667-1(3)) HarperCollins Pubs.

—Is It Far to Zanzibar. Parms, Clifford Alexander, illus. 2000. 32p. (J). (gr. 1-4). 15.89 (978-0-688-13158-6(1)) HarperCollins Pubs.

—Is It Far to Zanzibar? Poems about Tanzania. Parms, Clifford Alexander, illus. 2000. 32p. (J). (gr. 1 up). 15.95 (978-0-688-13157-9(3)) HarperCollins Pubs.

—A Pocketful of Poems. Steptoe, Javaka, illus. 2001. (J). 15.00. 32p. tchr. ed. 15.00 (978-0-395-93868-3(6)) Houghton Mifflin Co. Trade & Reference Div. (Clarion Bks.).

—Shoe Magic. Widener, Terry, illus. 2000. 30p. (J). pap. 16.95 (978-0-531-30286-6(5)); 17.99 (978-0-531-33286-3(1)) Scholastic, Inc. (Orchard Bks.).

—Shoe Magic. Widener, Terry, illus. 2001. (J). 16.00 (978-0-689-82480-7(7) , Simon & Schuster Children's Publishing) Simon & Schuster Children's Publishing.

—Stepping Out with Grandma Mac. Angelo, illus. 2001. 38p. (J). lib. bdg. (978-0-531-33320-4(5) , Orchard Bks.) Scholastic, Inc.

—Stepping Out with Grandma Mac. 2001. (J). per. 15.00 (978-0-689-82275-9(8) , Simon & Schuster Children's Publishing) Simon & Schuster Children's Publishing.

—Tai Chi Morning: Snapshots of China. Young, Ed, illus. 2004. 64p. (J). 15.95 (978-0-8126-2707-7(5)) Cricket Bks.

—What Is Goodbye? Colon, Raul, illus. 2004. 64p. (gr. 3-7). 15.99 (978-0-7868-0778-9(4) , Jump at the Sun) Hyperion Bks. for Children.

—What Is Goodbye? Poems on Grief. 2005. (Illus.). (J). lib. bdg. (978-0-7868-2623-0(1) , Jump at the Sun) Hyperion Bks. for Children.

Grossman, Bill. Timothy Tunny Swallowed a Bunny. Hawkes, Kevin, illus. 2001. 32p. (J). (ps-2). 14.95 (978-0-06-028010-9(7)); 14.89 (978-0-06-028758-0(6)) HarperCollins Pubs. (Geringer, Laura Book).

—Timothy Tunny Swallowed a Bunny. 2003. (gr. k-3). lib. bdg. 15.30 (978-0-613-60115-3(7)) Tandem Library Bks.

Grover, Lorie Ann. Loose Threads. 2002. 304p. (J). (gr. 4-7). 16.95 (978-0-689-84419-5(0) , McElderry, Margaret K.) Simon & Schuster Children's Publishing.

Gunning, Monica. America, My New Home. Condon, Ken, illus. 2004. 32p. (J). (gr. 2-4). 16.95 (978-1-59078-057-2(4)) Boyds Mills Pr.

Gutmann, Bessie P., et al. My Goodnight Book. 2000. (Illus.). 48p. (J). (ps-3). 14.95 (978-1-884807-51-0(8) , EC 751) Blushing Rose Publishing.

Hall, Donald, ed. The Oxford Illustrated Book of American Children's Poems. 1999. (Illus.). 96p. (YA). (gr. 2-6). 19.95 (978-0-19-512373-9(5)) Oxford Univ. Pr., Inc.

Halstead, Virginia, illus. Spectacular Science: A Book of Poems. 2002. 40p. (J). (gr. k up). 6.99 (978-0-689-85120-9(0) , Aladdin) Simon & Schuster Children's Publishing.

Harrison, David L. Farmer's Garden: Rhymes for Two Voices. Johnson-Petrov, Arden, illus. 2001. 32p. (J). (ps-k). 15.95 (978-1-56397-776-3(1)) Boyds Mills Pr.

Herrera, Juan Felipe. Laughing Out Loud, I Fly: Poems in English & Spanish. Barbour, Karen, illus. 1998. (ENG & SPA.). 48p. (J). (gr. 7-12). 15.99 (978-0-06-027604-1(5) , Cotler, Joanna Books) HarperCollins Pubs.

High, Linda Oatman. A Humble Life: Plain Poems. Farnsworth, Bill, illus. 2004. 40p. (J). (gr. 10 up). 17.00 (978-0-8028-5207-6(6)) Eerdmans, William B. Publishing Co.

Hillert, Margaret. Come Play with Me. (J). 4.95 (978-0-87895-629-6(8)) Modern Curriculum Pr.

Ho, Minfong. Hush! A Thai Lullaby. Meade, Holly, illus. 2000. (ps-ps). lib. bdg. 15.30 (978-0-613-72622-1(7)) Tandem Library Bks.

Hoberman, Mary Ann. You Read to Me, I'll Read to You: Very Short Mother Goose Tales to Read Together. Emberley, Michael, illus. 3rd ed. 2005. 32p. (J). (ps-3). 16.99 (978-0-316-14431-5(2)) Little Brown & Co.

Holbrook, Sara. By Definition: Poems of Feelings. Mattern, Scott, illus. 2003. 48p. (J). (gr. 4-6). 15.95 (978-1-59078-060-2(4)); pap. 8.95 (978-1-59078-085-5(X)) Boyds Mills Pr.

Hollander, John, ed. American Poetry. Comport, Sally Wern, illus. 2004. (Poetry for Young People Ser.). 48p. (J). 14.95 (978-1-4027-0517-5(4)) Sterling Publishing Co., Inc.

Hooper, Mary. The Remarkable Life & Times of Eliza Rose. McGough, Roger, ed. 2006. 336p. (YA). 16.95 (978-1-58234-854-4(5)) Bloomsbury Publishing.

Hopkins, Lee Bennett. Good Books, Good Times! 2000. (gr. k-3). lib. bdg. 15.25 (978-0-613-21617-3(2)) Tandem Library Bks.

—Lives: Poems about Famous Americans. Staub, Leslie, illus. 1999. 40p. (J). (gr. 3-6). lib. bdg. 17.89 (978-0-06-027768-0(8)); 16.99 (978-0-06-027767-3(X)) HarperCollins Pubs.

—Mother Goose Through the Seasons. Fehlau, Dagmar et al, illus. 2005. (Lee Bennett Hopkins Mother Goose Ser.). (YA). (ps-1). 76.50 (978-0-8215-0480-2(0)); suppl. ed. 57.00 (978-0-8215-0484-0(3)) Sadlier, William H. Inc.

—Mother Goose Through the Seasons: Theme 3. Fehlau, Dagmar et al, illus. l.t. ed. 1999. (Sadlier Phonics Reading Program). 16p. (YA). (ps-1). 29.85 (978-0-8215-0482-6(7)) Sadlier, William H. Inc.

—Oh, No! Where Are My Pants? And Other Disasters: Poems. Erlbruch, Wolf, illus. 2005. 32p. (J). (gr. k-4). 15.99 (978-0-688-17860-4(X)); lib. bdg. 16.89 (978-0-688-17861-1(8)) HarperCollins Pubs.

—A Pet for Me: Poems. Manning, Jane, illus. (I Can Read Bks.). 48p. (J). (gr. k-3). 2004. pap. 3.99 (978-0-06-443716-5(7) , Harper Trophy); 2003. 15.99 (978-0-06-029111-2(7)) HarperCollins Pubs.

—Spectacular Science: A Book of Poems. 2002. (gr. k-3). lib. bdg. 15.30 (978-0-613-45108-6(2)) Tandem Library Bks.

—Sports! Sports! Sports! A Poetry Collection. Floca, Brian, illus. 1999. (I Can Read Bks.: Vol. 2). 48p. (J). (gr. k-3). 15.89 (978-0-06-027801-4(3)) HarperCollins Pubs.

—Valentine Hearts: Holiday Poetry. Adinolfi, JoAnn, illus. 2004. (I Can Read Bks.). 32p. (J). (gr. k-3). 15.99 (978-0-06-008057-0(4)); lib. bdg. 16.89 (978-0-06-008058-7(2)) HarperCollins Pubs.

Horton, Joan. Halloween Hoots & Howls. Adinolfi, JoAnn, illus. 2008. 32p. (J). pap. 6.99 (***978-0-312-38016-8(X)**) Square Fish.

Hovey, Kate. Voices of the Trojan War. Gore, Leonid, tr. Gore, Leonid, illus. 2004. 128p. (YA). 17.95 (978-0-689-85768-3(3) , McElderry, Margaret K.) Simon & Schuster Children's Publishing.

Hubbell, Patricia. Black Earth, Gold Sun: Poems. DePalma, Mary Newell, illus. 2001. 32p. (J). (gr. 1-4). 15.95 (978-0-7614-5090-0(4) , Cavendish Children's Bks.) Cavendish, Marshall Corp.

—Boo! Halloween Poems & Limericks. Spackman, Jeff, illus. 40p. 2005. (YA). pap. 5.95 (978-0-7614-5151-8(X)); 1998. (J). 15.95 (978-0-7614-5023-8(8) , Cavendish Children's Bks.) Cavendish, Marshall Corp.

—Earthmates: Poems. Cassels, Jean, illus. 2000. 32p. (J). (gr. k-3). 15.95 (978-0-7614-5062-7(9) , Cavendish Children's Bks.) Cavendish, Marshall Corp.

Hubbell, Patricia & Flavin, Teresa. City Kids: Poems. 2001. (Illus.). 32p. (J). (ps-3). 15.95 (978-0-7614-5079-5(3) , Cavendish Children's Bks.) Cavendish, Marshall Corp.

Hudson, Beverly J. Bees to Baleens: The Rhyme & the Rhythm of Living Things. Hammons, Marjorie, ed. Hudson, Beverly J., illus. Hudson, Delise L., photos by. 2001. (Illus.). 32p. (J). (ps-3). lib. bdg. 16.95 (978-0-9658040-5-9(4) , 40-5-4) Talents From God.

Janeczko, Paul B. Stone Bench in an Empty Park. Silberman, Henri, illus. 2000. 40p. (J). (gr. 4-7). pap. 15.95 (978-0-531-30259-0(8) , Orchard Bks.) Scholastic, Inc.

Janeczko, Paul B., ed. A Poke in the I: A Collection of Concrete Poems. Raschka, Chris, illus. 2001. 48p. (J). (gr. 1-5). 17.99 (978-0-7636-0661-9(8)) Candlewick Pr.

—A Poke in the I: A Collection of Concrete Poems. Raschka, Chris, illus. 2005. 48p. (J). (gr. 1-5). reprint ed. pap. 7.99 (978-0-7636-2376-0(8)) Candlewick Pr.

Jensen, Evelyn O. Farmer Brown. Jensen, Jill J., illus. 2000. 28p. (J). pap. 7.50 (978-0-9644772-1-6(1)) Triple J Productions.

Johnson, Angela. Other Side: Shorter Poems. 1998. 64p. (YA). (gr. 5-9). lib. bdg. 16.99 (978-0-531-33114-9(8) , Orchard Bks.) Scholastic, Inc.

—Other Side: Shorter Poems. 2000. (gr. 5-8). lib. bdg. 15.25 (978-0-613-72623-8(5)); (978-0-606-18335-2(3)) Tandem Library Bks.

—The Other Side: Shorter Poems. 1998. 64p. (YA). (gr. 5-9). pap. 15.95 (978-0-531-30114-2(1) , Orchard Bks.) Scholastic, Inc.

Johnston, Tony. The Ancestors Are Singing. Barbour, Karen, illus. 2003. 64p. (J). 16.00 (978-0-374-30347-1(9) , Farrar, Straus & Giroux (BYR)) Farrar, Straus & Giroux.

Jules, Jacqueline. Clap & Count! Action Rhymes for the Jewish Year. Springer, Sally, illus. 2000. 56p. (J). (ps-1). 17.95 (978-1-58013-067-7(4)) Kar-Ben Publishing.

Katz, Bobbi. A Rumpus of Rhymes: A Book of Noisy Poems. Kwas, Susan Estelle, illus. 2001. 32p. (J). (gr. 1-4). 15.99 (978-0-525-46718-2(1) , Dutton Juvenile) Penguin Group (USA) Inc.

—We the People: Poems. Crews, Nina, illus. 2000. 112p. (J). (gr. 3 up). 17.99 (978-0-688-16531-4(1)) HarperCollins Pubs.

Katz, Susan. Mrs. Brown on Exhibit: And Other Museum Poems. Alley, R. W., illus. 2002. 40p. (J). (gr. 1-5). 16.95 (978-0-689-82970-3(1)) Simon & Schuster Children's Publishing.

—A Revolutionary Field Trip: Poems of Colonial America. Alley, R. W., illus. 2004. 40p. (J). 16.95 (978-0-689-84004-3(7)) Simon & Schuster Children's Publishing.

King, Suzette. Chasing Rainbows: Poetry for Young Adults. 2002. 95p. (YA). (gr. 6-12). pap. 9.95 (978-0-9712217-3-4(1)) Adventure Bks., Inc.

Kirk, Daniel F. Dogs Rule! Kirk, Daniel F., illus. 2003. (Illus.). 56p. (ps-3). 18.99 incl. cd-rom (978-0-7868-1949-2(9) , Disney Editions) Disney Pr.

Knowlton, Laurie Lazzaro. God Be in My Heart: Poems & Prayers for Children. 2003. (Illus.). 24p. (J). (ps up). 11.95 (978-1-56397-646-9(3)) Boyds Mills Pr.

Koontz, Dean. The Paper Doorway: Funny Verse & Nothing Worse. Parks, Phil, illus. 2001. 160p. (J). (gr. 5 up). 17.95 (978-0-06-029488-5(4)) HarperCollins Pubs.

Kumin, Maxine. Mites to Mastodons: A Book of Animal Poems. Zagarenski, Pamela, illus. 2006. 32p. (J). (gr. k-3). 16.00 (978-0-618-50753-5(1)) Houghton Mifflin Co.

Kuskin, Karla. Moon, Have You Met My Mother? Ruzzier, Sergio, illus. 2003. 336p. (J). (gr. k up). 16.99 (978-0-06-027173-2(6) , Geringer, Laura Book) HarperCollins Pubs.

—The Sky Is Always in the Sky. Dervaux, Isabelle, illus. 1998. 48p. (J). (ps-2). 15.89 (978-0-06-027084-1(5) , Geringer, Laura Book) HarperCollins Pubs.

Lanksy, Bruce. Rolling in the Aisles: A Collection of Laugh-Out-Loud Poems. Carpenter, Stephen, illus. 2004. 116p. (J). (978-0-88166-473-7(1)) Meadowbrook Pr.

Lansky, Bruce. Happy Birthday to Me! Lindstrom, Jack, illus. 1998. 27p. (J). 8.95 (978-0-88166-305-1(0)) Meadowbrook Pr.

—If Pigs Could Fly. Carpenter, Stephen, illus. 2000. xii, 83p. (J). pap. (978-0-88166-379-2(4)) Meadowbrook Pr.

—My Dog Ate My Homework! A Collection of Funny Poems. Carpenter, Stephen, illus. 2nd ed. 2001. 83p. (J). (978-0-88166-406-5(5)) Meadowbrook Pr.

Lansky, Bruce, ed. A Bad Case of the Giggles. Carpenter, Stephen, illus. 2008. 126p. (J). pap. 9.95 (***978-1-4169-5197-1(0)**) Meadowbrook Pr.

Lewis, J. Patrick. Doodle Dandies: Poems That Take Shape. Desimini, Lisa, illus. (J). 2002. 40p. 7.99 (978-0-689-84889-6(7) , Aladdin); 1998. 32p. 17.95 (978-0-689-81075-6(X) , Atheneum/Anne Schwartz Bks.) Simon & Schuster Children's Publishing.

—Doodle Dandies: Poems That Take Shape. 2002. (gr. 3-6). lib. bdg. 15.30 (978-0-613-45030-0(2)) Tandem Library Bks.

—Freedom Like Sunlight: Praisesongs for Black Americans. Thompson, John, illus. 2000. 40p. (gr. 4 up). 17.95 (978-1-56846-163-2(1) , Creative Editions) Creative Co., The.

—Freedom Like Sunlight: Praisesongs for Black Americans. 2003. (gr. 3-6). lib. bdg. 16.40 (978-0-613-77490-1(6)) Tandem Library Bks.

—Galileo's Universe. Curry, Tim, illus. 2005. (Creative Editions Ser.). 18p. (J). (gr. 4-7). 17.95 (978-1-56846-183-0(6)) Creative Co., The.

—Please Bury Me in the Library. Stone, Kyle M., illus. 2005. 32p. (J). 16.00 (978-0-15-216387-7(5) , Gulliver Bks.) Harcourt Children's Bks.

—Swan Song. Wormell, Christopher, illus. 2003. 32p. 16.95 (978-1-56846-175-5(5) , Creative Editions) Creative Co., The.

—World of Wonders: Geographic Travels in Verse & Rhyme. Jay, Alison, illus. 2002. 40p. (J). (gr. 4-6). 16.99 (978-0-8037-2579-9(5) , Dial) Penguin Group (USA) Inc.

Lewis, J. Patrick & Cooke, Jim, trs. Heroes & She-Roes: Poems of Amazing & Everyday Heroes. Cooke, Jim, illus. 2005. (Illus.). 40p. (J). (gr. k). 16.99 (978-0-8037-2925-4(1) , Dial) Penguin Group (USA) Inc.

Lewis, J. Patrick & Remkiewicz, Frank. Scien-Trickery: Riddles in Science. 2004. (Illus.). 32p. (J). 16.00 (978-0-15-216681-6(5) , Silver Whistle) Harcourt Trade Pubs.

Lewis, L. W. Why Do Flies Eat Doggy Poop? And Other Poems. Clary, Charles, illus. 2001. 128p. (J). kivar 14.95 (978-0-9711572-0-0(0)) Red Pumpkin Pr.

London, Jonathan. Park Beat: Rhymin' Through the Seasons. 2001. (Illus.). 32p. (J). (ps-3). 15.89 (978-0-688-13995-7(7)) HarperCollins Pubs.

—Sun Dance, Water Dance. Couch, Greg, illus. 2001. 40p. (J). (ps-3). 15.99 (978-0-525-46682-6(7) , Dutton Juvenile) Penguin Group (USA) Inc.

—Who Bop. Cole, Henry, illus. 2000. 32p. (J). (ps-1). 14.95 (978-0-06-027917-2(6)) HarperCollins Pubs.

Longfellow, Henry Wadsworth. Henry Wadsworth Longfellow. Schoonmaker, Frances, ed. Wallace, Chad, illus. 1998. (Poetry for Young People Ser.). 48p. (gr. 4-7). 14.95 (978-0-8069-9417-8(7)) Sterling Publishing Co., Inc.

Longfellow, Henry Wadsworth & Remington, Frederic. The Song of Hiawatha. 2004. (Nonpareil Book Ser.). (Illus.). 288p. pap. 14.95 (978-1-56792-258-5(9)); 23.95 (978-1-56792-273-8(2)) Godine, David R. Pub.

Lowe, Judith. Animals at the Zoo, on the Loose Too. 2001. (Illus.). (J). (978-1-56492-349-3(5)) Laredo Publishing Co., Inc.

Mannis, Celeste Davidson. One Leaf Rides the Wind. Hartung, Susan Kathleen, illus. 2005. 32p. (J). pap. 6.99 (978-0-14-240195-8(1) , Puffin) Penguin Group (USA) Inc.

Mannis, Celeste Davidson & Hartung, Susan Kathleen. One Leaf Rides the Wind: Counting in a Japanese Garden. Mannis, Celeste Davidson, illus. 2002. (Illus.). 40p. (J). (gr. k-3). 15.99 (978-0-670-03525-0(4) , Viking Juvenile) Penguin Group (USA) Inc.

Martin, Peggy-Lou. Songs, Seas, & Green Peas: Poems for Anywhere. 2000. (Poetry Parade Ser.). (Illus.). 32p. (J). 21.36 (978-1-57572-400-3(6)) Heinemann Library.

Meltzer, Milton. Walt Whitman: A Biography. 2002. (Single Titles Ser.). (Illus.). 160p. (gr. 7 up). lib. bdg. 31.90 (978-0-7613-2272-6(8) , Twenty-First Century Bks.) Lerner Publishing Group.

Merriam, Eve. Ten Rosy Roses. Horton, Julia, illus. 1999. 32p. (J). (ps-1). 14.95 (978-0-06-027887-8(0)) HarperCollins Pubs.

Millay, Edna St. Vincent. Edna St. Vincent Millay. Schoonmaker, Frances, ed. Bryce, Mike, illus. 1999. (Poetry for Young People Ser.). 48p. (gr. 3-7). 14.95 (978-0-8069-5928-3(2)) Sterling Publishing Co., Inc.

Miller, Kate. Poems in Black & White. 2007. (Illus.). 32p. (J). (gr. 1). 17.95 (978-1-59078-412-9(X)) Boyds Mills Pr.

Mills, Donald. The Night Before Christmas. Moore, Clement C., ed. Moore, Clement C., illus. 2000. 32p. (J). (ps-3). 7.95 (978-0-8249-4186-4(1)) Ideals Pubns.

Moeller Masel, Christy A. Eerie Little Bedtime Stories. 2001. (Madame M Presents Ser.: Vol. 2). (Illus.). 128p. (J). per. 18.95 (978-0-9704159-1-2(5)) Creepy Little Productions.

Monks, Julie, illus. Soft Hay Will Catch You. 2004. 128p. (J). (gr. 4-6). 17.95 (978-0-689-83460-8(8)) Simon & Schuster Children's Publishing.

Moore, Clement C. The Night Before Christmas. abr. ed. 2004. (Wee Books for Wee Folks). (Illus.). 64p. (J). (ps-3). 6.95 (978-1-55709-410-0(1)) Applewood Bks.

—The Night Before Christmas. Whatley, Bruce, illus. (J). (ps up). 2004. 32p. 6.99 (978-0-06-073917-1(7) , Harper Festival); 1999. 40p. 16.99 (978-0-06-026608-0(2)) HarperCollins Pubs.

—The Night Before Christmas. de Paola, Tomie, illus. abr. ed. 32p. (J). (gr. k-3). 6.95 (978-0-8234-0417-9(X)) Holiday Hse., Inc.

—The Night Before Christmas. Moore, Clement C., ed. Tudor, Tasha, illus. 1999. 32p. (J). (ps-17). 16.99 (978-0-316-85579-2(0)) Little Brown & Co.

—The Night Before Christmas. Moore, Clement C., ed. Tudor, Tasha & Sanderson, Ruth, illus. 2002. 32p. (J). (ps-17). pap. 6.99 (978-0-316-83271-7(5)) Little, Brown Bks. for Young Readers.

—The Night Before Christmas. Catusanu, Mircea, illus. 2001. (Little Golden Book Ser.). 24p. (J). (gr. k-k). 2.99 (978-0-307-96003-0(X) , Golden Bks.) Random Hse. Children's Bks.

—The Night Before Christmas. abr. ed. 1998. (Miniature Editionstm Ser.). (Illus.). 112p. (ps up). 4.95 (978-0-7624-0352-3(7) , Running Pr. Minature Editions) Running Pr. Bk. Pubs.

—The Night Before Christmas. Tudor, Tasha, illus. 2000. 64p. (J). (ps up). pap. 7.99 (978-0-689-83932-0(4) , Aladdin) Simon & Schuster Children's Publishing.

—The Night Before Christmas: A Trim-a-Tree Story. l.t. ed. 1999. (Illus.). 16p. (J). (ps-3). 6.99 (978-1-57866-076-6(9) , Galahad Bks.) BBS Publishing Corp.

—The Night Before Christmas: Pull the Tabs! Change the Pictures! 2003. (Magic Windows Ser.). (Illus.). 10p. (gr. k-3). pap. 12.95 (978-0-7624-1573-1(8) , Running Pr. Kids) Running Pr. Bk. Pubs.

—The Night Before Christmas: The Classic Edition. Birmingham, Christian, illus. abr. ed. 2005. (Children's Illustrated Classics Ser.). 48p. (ps-3). 9.98 (978-1-56138-476-1(3) , Running Pr. Kids) Running Pr. Bk. Pubs.

Moore, Clement C., ed. & illus. The Night Before Christmas. Moore, Clement C., illus. 1999. 40p. (J). (ps-3). 16.89 (978-0-06-028380-3(7)) HarperCollins Pubs.

—The Night Before Christmas. Moore, Clement C., illus. Porfirio, Guy, illus. 2004. 20p. (J). 9.95 (978-0-8249-6553-2(1)) Ideals Pubns.

—The Night Before Christmas. Moore, Clement C., illus. Finster, Howard, illus. 1998. 26p. reprint ed. 14.95 (978-1-56352-533-9(X)) Longstreet Pr., Inc.

—The Night Before Christmas. Moore, Clement C., illus. Rice, James, illus. 2000. 32p. (J). (ps-3). reprint ed. 15.95 (978-0-88289-755-4(1)) Pelican Publishing Co., Inc.

—The Night Before Christmas. Moore, Clement C., illus. Gorsline, Douglas, illus. 32p. (J). Random Hse. Children's Bks.

—The Night Before Christmas. Moore, Clement C., illus. Lobel, Anita, illus. 2003. 32p. (J). 8.95 (978-0-375-82414-2(6) , Knopf Bks. for Young Readers) Random Hse. Children's Bks.

—The Night Before Christmas. Moore, Clement C., illus. Cartwright, Sharon, illus. 1999. (Jellybean Bks.). 24p. (J). (ps-k). lib. bdg. 7.99 (978-0-375-90147-8(7) , Random Hse. Bks. for Young Readers) Random Hse. Children's Bks.

—The Night Before Christmas. Moore, Clement C., illus. Birmingham, Christian, photos by. 1999. 60p. (J). (ps-1). pap. 12.98 (978-1-58048-065-9(9)) Sandvik Publishing.

—The Night Before Christmas. Moore, Clement C., illus. Brett, Jan, illus. 2001. (J). 27.95 incl. audio (978-0-8045-6859-3(6)) Spoken Arts, Inc.

—The Night Before Christmas. Moore, Clement C., illus. 2000. (gr. 3-6). lib. bdg. 15.30 (978-0-613-31526-5(X)); lib. bdg. 15.30 (978-0-613-32892-0(2)) Tandem Library Bks.

—The Night Before Christmas. Moore, Clement C., illus. Lobel, Anita, illus. 2000. (J). (978-0-606-19773-1(7)) Tandem Library Bks.

Moore, Clement C. & Jaramillo, Raquel. The Night Before Christmas. 2001. (Illus.). 40p. (J). (ps up). 18.95 (978-0-689-84053-1(5) , Atheneum/Anne Schwartz Bks.) Simon & Schuster Children's Publishing.

Moore, Clement C., et al. The Night Before Christmas: A Classic Illustrated Edition. 1998. (Illus.). 44p. (J). (ps up). 16.95 (978-0-8118-1712-7(1)) Chronicle Bks. LLC.

Mora, Pat. This Big Sky. Jenkins, Steve, illus. 1999. (J). pap. 3.95 (978-0-590-37121-6(5)) Scholastic, Inc.

Myers, Walter Dean. Harlem: A Poem. 2002. (J). 26.13 (978-0-7587-0115-2(2)) Book Wholesalers, Inc.

—Here in Harlem: Poems in Many Voices. 2004. (Illus.). 96p. (YA). (gr. 7 up). tchr. ed. 16.95 (978-0-8234-1853-4(7)) Holiday Hse., Inc.

Nesbitt, Kenn. The Aliens Have Landed! Poems. 2001. (Illus.). 87p. (J). (978-0-88166-396-9(4)) Meadowbrook Pr.

Nikola-Lisa, W. Bein' with You This Way. Bryant, Michael, illus. 2002. (J). 14.66 (978-0-7587-2067-2(X)) Book Wholesalers, Inc.

—Bein' with You This Way. 2001. (Live Oak Readalong Ser.). (Illus.). (J). pap. 18.95 incl. audio compact disk (978-1-59112-400-9(X)) Live Oak Media.

Norman, Lissette. My Feet Are Laughing. Morrison, Frank, illus. 2006. 32p. (J). 16.00 (978-0-374-35096-3(5)) Farrar, Straus & Giroux.

Nye, Naomi Shihab. Come with Me: Poems for a Journey. Yaccarino, Dan, illus. 2000. 40p. (J). (gr. k-3). 16.99 (978-0-688-15946-7(X)) HarperCollins Pubs.

—A Maze Me: Poems for Girls. Maher, Terre, illus. 2005. 128p. (YA). (gr. 7 up). 16.99 (978-0-06-058189-3(1)); lib. bdg. 17.89 (978-0-06-058190-9(5)) HarperCollins Pubs.

One from the Willow. 2003. (Illus.). 99p. (J). bds. 17.95 (978-1-929416-67-7(9)) Magner Publishing & American Binding & Publishing.

O'Neill, Mary L. The Sound of Day: The Sound of Night. Jabar, Cynthia, illus. 1999. (J). (978-0-7894-2567-6(X)) Dorling Kindersley Publishing, Inc.

Paraskevas, Betty. Junior Kroll. 2000. (978-0-606-20329-6(X)) Tandem Library Bks.

Pearson, Susan. Squeal & Squawk: Barnyard Talk. Slonim, David, tr. Slonim, David, illus. 2004. 32p. (J). 16.95 (978-0-7614-5160-0(9)) Cavendish, Marshall Corp.

Perry, Andrea J. Here's What You Do When You Can't Find Your Shoe. Snow, Alan, illus. 2003. 40p. (J). (gr. k-3). 16.95 (978-0-689-83067-9(X) , Atheneum) Simon & Schuster Children's Publishing.

Peters, Lisa Westberg. Earthshake: Poems from the Ground Up. Felstead, Cathie, illus. 2003. 32p. (J). (gr. 1-6). lib. bdg. 17.89 (978-0-06-029266-9(0)) HarperCollins Pubs.

Pinz, Shelley. Holly, Bear & Coty, & the Very First Angel of Christmas. (Illus.). 18p. (J). pap. 12.95 incl. cd-rom (978-0-9700251-3-5(0)) Pinz, Shelley Music.

Poe, Edgar Allan. The Raven. Price, Ryan, illus. 2006. (Visions in Poetry). 48p. (YA). (gr. 7 up). (978-1-55337-473-2(8)) Kids Can Pr., Ltd.

—The Raven, the & Other Poems. 2002. (Scholastic Classic Ser.). 80p. (J). pap. 3.99 (978-0-439-22406-2(3)) Scholastic, Inc.

Polisar, Barry Louis. A Little Less Noise. Clark, David, illus. 2001. (Rainbow Morning Music Picture Bks.). 32p. (J). (gr. k-7). 14.95 (978-0-938663-23-2(2)) Rainbow Morning Music Alternatives.

Pomerantz, Charlotte. Thunderboom! Poems for Everybody. Shepperson, Rob, illus. 2006. 48p. (J). 17.95 (978-1-932425-40-6(3) , Lemniscaat) Boyds Mills Pr.

Posner, Tina. In Your Face: Poems about Real Life. 2002. (Read 180 Ser.). (Illus.). 63p. (J). (978-0-439-12351-8(8)) Scholastic, Inc.

Powell, Consie. Amazing Apples. Powell, Consie, illus. 2003. (Illus.). 32p. (J). (gr. k-4). 15.95 (978-0-8075-0399-7(1)) Whitman, Albert & Co.

Prelutsky, Jack. Awful Ogre's Awful Day. Zelinsky, Paul O., illus. 40p. (J). (gr. 1 up). 2001. 15.99 (978-0-688-07778-5(1)); 2001. lib. bdg. 16.89 (978-0-688-07779-2(X)); 2005. reprint ed. pap. 6.99 (978-0-06-077459-2(2) , Harper Trophy) HarperCollins Pubs.

—The Dragons Are Singing Tonight. Sis, Peter, illus. 1998. 40p. (J). (ps-3). pap. 6.99 (978-0-688-16162-0(6) , Harper Trophy) HarperCollins Pubs.

—If Not for the Cat. Rand, Ted, illus. 2004. 40p. (J). 16.99 (978-0-06-059677-4(5)); lib. bdg. 17.89 (978-0-06-059678-1(3)) HarperCollins Pubs.

—It's Thanksgiving. Hafner, Marylin, illus. 2007. (I Can Read Bks.). 48p. (J). (ps-3). 15.99 (978-0-06-053710-4(8) , Greenwillow Bks.) HarperCollins Pubs.

—What a Day It Was at School! Cushman, Doug, illus. 2006. 40p. (J). 16.99 (978-0-06-082335-1(6)) HarperCollins Pubs.

Proimos, James. If I Were in Charge the Rules Would Be Different! 2002. (Illus.). 80p. (J). (gr. k up). pap. 16.95 (978-0-439-20864-2(5) , Scholastic Pr.) Scholastic, Inc.

Rogasky, Barbara. Winter Poems, Vol. 1. Hyman, Trina Schart & Cooper, Martha, illus. 1999. 40p. (J). (gr. 2-6). pap. 5.99 (978-0-590-42873-6(X)) Scholastic, Inc.

Rose, Deborah Lee. The Twelve Days of Kindergarten: A Counting Book. Armstrong-Ellis, Carey, illus. 2003. 30p. (J). (ps-1). 14.95 (978-0-8109-4512-8(6)) Abrams, Harry N. , Inc.

Ross, Mandy. Animal Lullabies. Nagy, Krisztina, tr. Nagy, Krisztina, illus. 2003. 32p. (J). 14.99 (978-0-85953-052-1(3)); 7.99 (978-0-85953-116-0(3)) Child's Play-International.

Rosten, Norman. A City Is. Filan, Patricia Rosten, ed. Filan, Patricia Rosten & Greenberg, Melanie Hope, trs. Greenberg, Melanie Hope, illus. rev. ed. 2004. 32p. (J). 16.95 (978-0-8050-6793-4(0) , Holt, Henry & Co. Bks. For Young Readers) Holt, Henry & Co.

Rowden, Justine. Paint Me a Poem: Poems Paired with Glorious Museum Paintings. 2005. (Illus.). 32p. (J). (gr. 1-4). 16.95 (978-1-59078-289-7(5) , Wordsong) Boyds Mills Pr.

Sabuda, Robert & Moore, Clement C. The Night Before Christmas. 2002. (Illus.). 12p. (J). 26.99 (978-0-689-83899-6(9) , Little Simon) Simon & Schuster Children's Publishing.

Sandburg, Carl. From Daybreak to Good Night: Poems for Children. Smith-Ary, Lynn, illus. 2001. 24p. (J). (gr. k-3). pap. 7.95 (978-1-55037-680-7(2)); lib. bdg. 19.95 (978-1-55037-681-4(0)) Annick Pr., Ltd. CAN. *Dist:* Firefly Bks., Ltd.

Santore, Charles & Carryl, Charles Edward. The Camel's Lament. 2004. (Illus.). 32p. (J). (ps-1). 16.95 (978-0-375-81426-6(4) , Random Hse. Bks. for Young Readers) Random Hse. Children's Bks.

Scanlon, Elizabeth Garton. A Sock Is a Pocket for Your Toes: A Pocket Book. Glasser, Robin Preiss, illus. 2004. 32p. (J). (ps-2). 15.99 (978-0-06-029526-4(0)) HarperCollins Pubs.

Schuler, Karen A. Poetry Patterns. Hamilton, Jeannie, illus. 1998. 32p. (J). (gr. 3-7). pap. 9.95 (978-1-889590-01-1(0)) Cherubic Pr.

Schwartz, Alvin. And the Green Grass Grew All Around: Folk Poetry from Everyone. Truesdell, Sue, illus. 1999. 208p. (J). (gr. 3-7). pap. 10.95 (978-0-06-446214-3(5) , Harper Trophy) HarperCollins Pubs.

—And the Green Grass Grew All Around: Folk Poetry from Everyone. 1999. (J). (978-0-606-16704-8(8)) Tandem Library Bks.

Schwartz, Betty Ann, ed. My Kingdom for a Horse. Berenzy, Alix, illus. rev. ed. 2001. 48p. (J). (gr. 3-7). 17.95 (978-0-8050-6212-0(2) , Holt, Henry & Co. Bks. For Young Readers) Holt, Henry & Co.

Serio, John N., ed. Wallace Stevens. Steele, Robert Gantt, illus. 2004. (Poetry for Young People Ser.). 48p. (J). 14.95 (978-1-4027-0925-8(0)) Sterling Publishing Co., Inc.

Shange, Ntozake. Ellington Was Not a Street. Nelson, Kadir A., illus. 2004. 40p. (J). (gr. k-6). 17.99 (978-0-689-82884-3(5)) Simon & Schuster Children's Publishing.

—Ellington Was Not a Street. Nelson, Kadir, illus. 2005. (J). 24.95 incl. audio (978-0-439-77576-2(0) , WHRA672); 29.95 incl. audio compact disk (978-0-439-77582-3(5) , WHCD672) Weston Woods Studios, Inc.

Shapiro, Karen Jo. Because I Could Not Stop My Bike: And Other Poems. Faulkner, Matt, illus. 2004. 32p. (J). (gr. 2-7). 15.95 (978-1-58089-035-9(0)) Charlesbridge Publishing, Inc.

Sherman, Erica. The Mists of Eden: Nature's Last Paradise. Thatch, Nancy R., ed. Sherman, Erica, illus. 1998. (Books for Students by Students). (Illus.). 29p. (J). (ps-3). lib. bdg. 15.95 (978-0-933849-69-3(9)) Landmark Editions, Inc.

Shields, Carol Diggory. American History, Fresh Squeezed! 41 Thirst-for-Knowledge-Quenching Poems. Thompson, Richard, illus. 2002. 64p. (J). 14.95 (978-1-929766-62-8(9)) Handprint Bks.

—Brainjuice: English, Fresh Squeezed! 2004. (Illus.). 64p. (J). 14.95 (978-1-59354-053-1(1)) Handprint Bks.

Sidman, Joyce. Eureka! Poems about Inventors. Chavez, K. Bennett, illus. 2002. (Techies Ser.). 48p. (J). (gr. 5-8). lib. bdg. 24.90 (978-0-7613-1665-7(5) , Millbrook Pr.) Lerner Publishing Group.

—Meow Ruff: A Story in Concrete Poetry. Berg, Michelle, illus. 2006. 32p. (J). (gr. k-3). 16.00 (978-0-618-44894-4(2)) Houghton Mifflin Co.

—Song of the Water Boatman: And Other Pond Poems. Prange, Beckie, illus. 2005. 32p. (J). (gr. k-3). 16.00 (978-0-618-13547-9(2)) Houghton Mifflin Co. Trade & Reference Div.

Sierra, Judy. Good Night, Dinosaurs. Chess, Victoria, illus. 2002. 32p. (J). (gr. k-3). pap. 5.95 (978-0-618-19600-5(5) , Clarion Bks.) Houghton Mifflin Co. Trade & Reference Div.

—Good Night, Dinosaurs. 2002. (gr. k-3). lib. bdg. 14.10 (978-0-613-60677-6(9)) Tandem Library Bks.

—There's a Zoo in Room 22. Saltzberg, Barney, illus. 40p. (J). 2004. pap. 6.00 (978-0-15-205020-7(5) , Voyager Bks./Libros Viajeros); 2000. 16.00 (978-0-15-202033-0(0) , Gulliver Bks.) Harcourt Children's Bks.

Silberman, Henri, photos by. Stone Beach in an Empty Park. 2000. (Illus.). 40p. (J). (gr. 4-7). 16.99 (978-0-531-33259-7(4) , Orchard Bks.) Scholastic, Inc.

Silverstein, Shel. Where the Sidewalk Ends: Poems & Drawings. anniv. ed. 2000. (Illus.). 176p. (J). (gr. 4-7). 22.99 incl. audio compact disk (978-0-06-029169-3(9)) HarperCollins Pubs.

—Where the Sidewalk Ends: Poems & Drawings. Silverstein, Shel, illus. 30th anniv. ed. 2004. (Illus.). 192p. (J). (gr. 4 up). 18.99 (978-0-06-057234-1(5)) HarperCollins Pubs.

Singer, Marilyn. Central Heating: Poems about Fire & Warmth. So, Meilo, illus. 2005. 48p. (J). (gr. 3-7). 15.95 (978-0-375-82912-3(1) , Knopf Bks. for Young Readers) Random Hse. Children's Bks.

—Fireflies at Midnight. Robbins, Ken, illus. 2003. 32p. (J). (ps-4). 16.95 (978-0-689-82492-0(0) , Atheneum) Simon & Schuster Children's Publishing.

—Footprints on the Roof: Poems about the Earth. So, Meilo, illus. 2002. 48p. (gr. 3-7). 14.95 (978-0-375-81094-7(3)); lib. bdg. 16.99 (978-0-375-91094-4(8)) Random Hse. Children's Bks. (Knopf Bks. for Young Readers).

—How to Cross a Pond: Poems about Water. So, Meilo, illus. 2003. 48p. (J). (gr. 3-7). lib. bdg. 16.99 (978-0-375-92376-0(4) , Knopf Bks. for Young Readers) Random Hse. Children's Bks.

Sklansky, Amy E. From the Doghouse: Poems to Chew On. Firehammer, Karla et al, illus. rev. ed. 2002. 48p. (J). (gr. 1-4). 17.95 (978-0-8050-6673-9(X) , Holt, Henry & Co. Bks. For Young Readers) Holt, Henry & Co.

—Skeleton Bones & Goblin Groans: Poems for Halloween. Dismukes, Karen, illus. rev. ed. 2004. 32p. (J). 16.95 (978-0-8050-7046-0(X) , Holt, Henry & Co. Bks. For Young Readers) Holt, Henry & Co.

Smith, Charles R., Jr. Short Takes Vol. 3: Fast-Break Basketball Poetry. Brooks, Donna, ed. 2001. (Illus.). 32p. (J). (gr. 4-10). 17.99 (978-0-525-46454-9(9) , Dutton Juvenile) Penguin Group (USA) Inc.

Soto, Gary. Fearless Fernie: Hanging Out with Fernie & Me. Dunnick, Regan, illus. 2002. 64p. (J). (gr. 4-6). 14.99 (978-0-399-23615-0(5) , Putnam Juvenile) Penguin Group (USA) Inc.

—Worlds Apart: Traveling with Fernie & Me: Poems. Clarke, Greg, illus. 2005. 64p. (J). 14.99 (978-0-399-24218-2(X) , Putnam Juvenile) Penguin Group (USA) Inc.

Soto, Gary, et al. Wachale! Poems & Prose about Growing up Latino in America. Stevens, Ilan, ed. 2001. 160p. (J). (gr. 6 up). 16.95 (978-0-8126-4750-1(5)) Cricket Bks.

Spinelli, Eileen. Feathers: Poems about Birds. McCue, Lisa, illus. rev. ed. 2004. 40p. (J). 16.95 (978-0-8050-6713-2(2) , Holt, Henry & Co. Bks. For Young Readers) Holt, Henry & Co.

—Polar Bear, Arctic Hare: Poems of the Frozen North. Fernandes, Eugenie, illus. 2007. 32p. (J). (ps-3). (978-1-59078-344-3(1)) Boyds Mills Pr.

—Song for the Whooping Crane. Warnick, Elsa, illus. 2004. 32p. (J). (gr. 3-6). 16.00 (978-0-8028-5172-7(X)) Eerdmans, William B. Publishing Co.

—Tea Party Today: Poems to Sip & Savor. Dugan, Karen M., illus. 2003. 32p. (J). (gr. 2-4). 15.95 (978-1-56397-662-9(5)) Boyds Mills Pr.

Stevenson, James. Candy Corn: Poems. Stevenson, James, illus. 1999. (Illus.). 56p. (J). (gr. 3 up). 16.99 (978-0-688-15837-8(4)) HarperCollins Pubs.

—Corn Chowder: Poems. Stevenson, James, illus. 2003. (Illus.). 48p. (J). (gr. 3 up). 16.99 (978-0-06-053059-4(6)) HarperCollins Pubs.

—Corn-Fed: Poems. 2002. (Illus.). 48p. (J). (gr. 3 up). 15.95 (978-0-06-000597-9(1)) HarperCollins Pubs.

—Popcorn: Poems. 1998. (Illus.). 64p. (J). (gr. 3 up). 16.99 (978-0-688-15261-1(9)) HarperCollins Pubs.

Stevenson, Robert Louis. Robert Louis Stevenson: Selected Poems. 1999. (gr. 7-12). lib. bdg. 18.75 (978-0-613-64319-1(4)) Tandem Library Bks.

Still, James. An Appalachian Mother Goose. Johnson, Paul Brett, illus. 1998. 64p. (ps-3). 16.95 (978-0-8131-2092-8(6)) Univ. Pr. of Kentucky.

Stockland, Patricia M., tr. The Free & the Brave: A Collection of Poems about the United States. 2004. (Poet's Toolbox Ser.). (Illus.). 32p. (J). (gr. 3 up). 22.60 (978-0-7565-0563-9(1)) Compass Point Bks.

—Fur, Fangs, & Footprints: A Collection of Animal Poems. 2004. (Poet's Toolbox Ser.). (Illus.). 32p. (J). (gr. 3 up). 22.60 (978-0-7565-0562-2(3)) Compass Point Bks.

—Recess, Rhyme, & Reason: A Collection of Poems about School. 2004. (Poet's Toolbox Ser.). (Illus.). 32p. (J). (gr. 3 up). 22.60 (978-0-7565-0564-6(X)) Compass Point Bks.

Stortz, Diane M. Jesus Loves You: A Read-the-Pictures Book. Ebert, Len, illus. 2002. (Heritage Builders Ser.). 32p. (J). 10.99 (978-0-7847-1364-8(2)) Standard Publishing.

Strand, Mark & Boland, Eavan. The Making of a Poem: A Norton Anthology of Poetic Forms. 2001. 448p. (YA). 27.50 (978-0-393-04916-9(7)) Norton, W. W. & Co., Inc.

Sturges, Philemon. Down to the Sea in Ships. Laroche, Giles, illus. 2005. 32p. (J). (ps-3). 16.99 (978-0-399-23464-4(0) , Putnam Juvenile) Penguin Group (USA) Inc.

—She'll Be Comin' 'Round the Mountain. Wolff, Ashley, illus. 2004. 32p. (J). (ps-3). 15.99 (978-0-316-82256-5(6)) Little Brown & Co.

Swados, Elizabeth. Hey You! C'mere! A Poetry Slam. Cepeda, Joe, illus. 2002. (J). 47p. pap. 4.95 (978-0-439-09258-6(2)); 48p. (gr. 2-5). pap. 16.95 (978-0-439-09257-9(4)) Scholastic, Inc. (Levine, Arthur A. Bks.).

Swain, Holly, illus. The Kingfisher Book of Family Poems. 2003. (Kingfisher Book of Ser.). 224p. (J). (gr. 3-5). tchr. ed. 18.95 (978-0-7534-5557-9(9) , Kingfisher) Houghton Mifflin Co. Trade & Reference Div.

Sweeney, Jacqueline, ed. Poems about Anger by America's Children. 2002. (Kids Express Ser.). (Illus.). 32p. (J). 25.64 (978-0-7614-1508-4(4) , Benchmark Bks.) Cavendish, Marshall Corp.

—Poems about Family by America's Children. 2002. (Kids Express Ser.). (Illus.). 32p. (J). 25.64 (978-0-7614-1507-7(6) , Benchmark Bks.) Cavendish, Marshall Corp.

—Poems about Friends by America's Children. 2002. (Kids Express Ser.). (Illus.). 32p. (J). 25.64 (978-0-7614-1506-0(8) , Benchmark Bks.) Cavendish, Marshall Corp.

—Poems about Myself by America's Children. 2002. (Kids Express Ser.). (Illus.). 32p. (J). 25.64 (978-0-7614-1504-6(1) , Benchmark Bks.) Cavendish, Marshall Corp.

—Poems about School by America's Children. 2002. (Kids Express Ser.). (Illus.). 32p. (J). 25.64 (978-0-7614-1505-3(X) , Benchmark Bks.) Cavendish, Marshall Corp.

Tamblyn, Amber. Free Stallion: Poems. 2005. 96p. (YA). (gr. 10 up). 14.95 (978-1-4169-0259-1(7)) Simon & Schuster Children's Publishing.

Thayer, Ernest Lawrence. Casey at the Bat: A Ballad of the Republic, Sung in the Year 1888. Payne, C. F., illus. 2002. 40p. (J). (gr. 1-5). (978-1-890817-67-1(8)) Winslow Pr.

—Casey at the Bat: A Ballad of the Republic Sung in the Year 1888. Payne, C. F., illus. 2003. 40p. (J). 16.95 (978-0-689-85494-1(3)) Simon & Schuster Children's Publishing.

Thayer, Ernest Lawrence & Bing, Christopher H. Casey at the Bat: A Ballad of the Republic Sung in the Year 1888. 2000. (Illus.). 32p. (J). (gr. 3-7). 17.95 (978-1-929766-00-0(9)) Handprint Bks.

Thomas, Joyce Carol. Cherish Me. Bennett, Nneka, illus. 1998. (Growing Tree Ser.). 24p. (J). (ps up). 9.95 (978-0-694-01097-4(9) , Harper Festival) HarperCollins Pubs.

—Crowning Glory. Joysmith, Brenda, illus. 2002. 32p. (J). (ps-3). 15.95 (978-0-06-023473-7(3) , Cotler, Joanna Books) HarperCollins Pubs.

—A Mother's Heart, A Daughter's Love: Poems for Us to Share. 2001. (Ageless Bks.). (Illus.). 64p. (YA). 14.89 (978-0-06-029650-6(X) , Cotler, Joanna Books) HarperCollins Pubs.

Trapani, Iza. Twinkle, Twinkle, Little Star. Trapani, Iza, illus. 1998. (Illus.). 26p. (J). (ps-k). bds. 6.95 (978-1-58089-015-1(6)) Charlesbridge Publishing, Inc.

Troupe, Quincy. Little Stevie Wonder. Cohen, Lisa, illus. 2005. 32p. (J). (gr. k-3). 18.00 (978-0-618-34060-6(2)) Houghton Mifflin Co. Trade & Reference Div.

Turner, Ann Warren. Learning to Swim: A Memoir. 2003. (Learning to Swim Ser.). 128p. (J). pap. 3.99 (978-0-439-52831-3(3)) Scholastic, Inc.

—A Lion's Hunger: Poems of First Love. Jimenez, Maria, illus. 1999. 48p. (YA). (gr. 7-12). 15.95 (978-0-7614-5035-1(1) , Cavendish Children's Bks.) Cavendish, Marshall Corp.

Under the Dorag: A Collection of Poems for Teenagers. 2000. (Illus.). 43p. (YA). (gr. 8-12). per. 10.00 (978-0-9704470-0-5(0)) Siedon Pubns.

Updike, John. A Child's Calendar. Hyman, Trina Schart, illus. 1999. (Caldecott Honor Book Ser.). (J). (gr. k-3). 32p. 6.95 (978-0-8234-1766-7(2)); 36p. tchr. ed. 16.95 (978-0-8234-1445-1(0)) Holiday Hse., Inc.

Vecchione, Patrice. The Body Eclectic: An Anthology of Poems. rev. ed. 2002. 224p. (YA). (gr. 8-12). 16.95 (978-0-8050-6935-8(6) , Holt, Henry & Co. Bks. For Young Readers) Holt, Henry & Co.

Wadsworth, Olive A. Over in the Meadow: A Counting Rhyme. Vojtech, Anna, illus. 2002. (Cheshire Studio Bk.). 32p. (J). (ps-3). 15.95 (978-0-7358-1596-4(8)) North-South Bks., Inc.

Wallace, Nancy Elizabeth. The Sun, the Moon, & the Stars. Wallace, Nancy Elizabeth, illus. 2003. (Illus.). 40p. (J). (gr. k-3). tchr. ed. 12.00 (978-0-618-26353-0(5)) Houghton Mifflin Co. Trade & Reference Div.

Warren-Turner, Ann. Secrets from the Dollhouse. Colon, Raul, illus. 2000. 32p. (J). (gr. k-3). 15.95 (978-0-06-024564-1(6)); 15.89 (978-0-06-024567-2(0)) HarperCollins Pubs.

Watson, Clyde. Father Fox's Christmas Rhymes. Watson, Wendy, illus. 2003. 40p. (J). 16.00 (978-0-374-37576-8(3) , Farrar, Straus & Giroux (BYR)) Farrar, Straus & Giroux.

—Father Fox's Pennyrhymes. 2001. (Illus.). 64p. (J). 15.89 (978-0-06-029502-8(3)) HarperCollins Pubs.

—Father Fox's Pennyrhymes. Watson, Wendy, illus. 2001. 64p. (J). 15.95 (978-0-06-029501-5(5)) HarperCollins Pubs.

Weatherford, Carole Boston. Remember the Bridge: Poems of a People. 2002. (Illus.). 56p. (J). 17.99 (978-0-399-23726-3(7) , Philomel) Penguin Group (USA) Inc.

Wheeler, Lisa. Sailor Moo Cow at Sea. Goembel, Ponder, illus. 2002. 32p. (J). (ps-2). 16.95 (978-0-689-84219-1(8) , Atheneum/Richard Jackson Bks.) Simon & Schuster Children's Publishing.

—Wool Gathering: A Sheep Family Reunion. Ansley, Frank, illus. 2001. 32p. (J). (ps-1). 16.95 (978-0-689-84369-3(0) , Atheneum/Richard Jackson Bks.) Simon & Schuster Children's Publishing.

Whipple, Laura. If the Shoe Fits: Voices from Cinderella. Beingessner, Laura, illus. 2002. 80p. (J). (gr. 4-6). 18.99 (978-0-689-84070-8(5) , McElderry, Margaret K.) Simon & Schuster Children's Publishing.

Whitehead, Jenny. Lunch Box Mail & Other Poems. 2007. (Illus.). 48p. (J). pap. 7.95 ***(978-0-8050-8204-3(2)** , Holt, Henry & Co. Bks. For Young Readers) Holt, Henry & Co.

Whitman, Walt. I Hear America Singing. Sabuda, Robert, illus. 2004. 30p. (J). (gr. k-4). reprint ed. 15.00 (978-0-7567-8097-5(7)) DIANE Publishing Co.

Wilbur, Richard. The Disappearing Alphabet. Diaz, David, illus. 2001. 32p. (J). (ps up). pap. 6.00 (978-0-15-216362-4(X) , Voyager Bks./Libros Viajeros) Harcourt Children's Bks.

Willard, Nancy. Step Lightly: Poems for the Journey. 1998. (Illus.). 112p. (J). (gr. 5-9). pap. 12.00 (978-0-15-202052-1(7) , Harcourt Paperbacks) Harcourt Children's Bks.

Williams, Vera B. Amber Was Brave, Essie Was Smart: The Story of Amber & Essie, Told Here in Poems & Pictures. Williams, Vera B., illus. 2003. (Illus.). (J). (gr. k-3). 28.95 incl. audio compact disk (978-1-59112-339-2(9)); 25.95 incl. audio (978-1-59112-186-2(8)) Live Oak Media.

—Amber Was Brave, Essie Was Smart: The Story of Amber & Essie, Told Here in Poems & Pictures. 2004. (gr. 3-6). lib. bdg. 15.30 (978-0-613-85740-6(2)) Tandem Library Bks.

Wilson, Karma. Bear Hugs: Romantically Ridiculous Animal Rhymes. Watts, Suzanne, illus. 2004. 32p. (J). 14.95 (978-0-689-85763-8(2) , McElderry, Margaret K.) Simon & Schuster Children's Publishing.

Wing, Natasha. The Night Before Easter. 1999. (gr. k-3). lib. bdg. 11.25 (978-0-613-72420-3(8)) Tandem Library Bks.

Winnick, Karen B. A Year Goes Round: Poems for the Months. Winnick, Karen B., illus. 2003. (Illus.). 32p. (J). (gr. k-2). 15.95 (978-1-56397-898-2(9)) Boyds Mills Pr.

Wolf, Allan. The Blood-Hungry Spleen: And Other Poems about Our Parts. Clarke, Greg, illus. 2003. 56p. (J). (gr. 3). 17.99 (978-0-7636-1565-9(X)) Candlewick Pr.

Wong, Janet S. Behind the Wheel. Wong, Janet S., photos by. 1999. (Illus.). 48p. (YA). (gr. 7-12). 15.95 (978-0-689-82531-6(5) , McElderry, Margaret K.) Simon & Schuster Children's Publishing.

—You Have to Write. Flavin, Teresa, illus. 2002. 40p. (J). (gr. 4 up). 17.00 (978-0-689-83409-7(8) , McElderry, Margaret K.) Simon & Schuster Children's Publishing.

Wong, Janet S. & Paschkis, Julie. Knock on Wood: Poems about Superstitions. 2003. (Illus.). 40p. (J). (gr. 2-5). 17.95 (978-0-689-85512-2(5) , McElderry, Margaret K.) Simon & Schuster Children's Publishing.

Woodson, Jacqueline. Locomotion. 2003. 112p. (J). (gr. 4-6). 15.99 (978-0-399-23115-5(3) , Putnam Juvenile) Penguin Group (USA) Inc.

Worth, Valerie. Peacock & Other Poems. Babbitt, Natalie, illus. 2002. 48p. (J). (gr. 2-6). 15.00 (978-0-374-35766-5(8) , Farrar, Straus & Giroux (BYR)) Farrar, Straus & Giroux.

Yarcho, Al. Eye'm Sew Kunfuzed. Stoff, Michael, illus. 2001. (J). 9.95 (978-1-882203-72-7(0)) Orange Frazer Pr.

Yolen, Jane. Fine Feathered Friends: Poems for Young People to Perform. Stemple, Jason, illus. Stemple, Jason, photos by. 2004. 32p. (J). (gr. 4-6). 17.95 (978-1-59078-193-7(7)) Boyds Mills Pr.

Yolen, Jane & Yolen-Stemple, Heidi Elizabet. Dear Mother, Dear Daughter: Poems for Young People. Ashby, Gil, illus. 2003. 40p. (YA). (gr. 4-6). 15.95 (978-1-56397-886-9(5)) Boyds Mills Pr.

Zolotow, Charlotte. Seasons: A Book of Poems. Blegvad, Erik, illus. 2002. (I Can Read Bks.). 64p. (J). (gr. k-3). 14.95 (978-0-06-026698-1(8)) HarperCollins Pubs.

AMERICAN POETRY—AFRICAN AMERICAN AUTHORS

Adoff, Arnold, ed. I Am the Darker Brother: An Anthology of Modern Poems by Negro Americans. 1998. (Illus.). (J). pap. 4.99 (978-0-87628-443-8(8)) Ctr. for Applied Research in Education, The.

Almustafa, Kahlil. Grandma's Soup. 2001. 96p. (J). per. 11.95 (978-0-9671082-4-7(1) , Division of Words) Black Alchemist Pr., Inc.

Bolden, Tonya. Rock of Ages. Christie, Gregory R., illus. 2003. 32p. (J). (gr. k-3). pap. 6.99 (978-0-440-41800-9(3) , Dragonfly Bks.) Random Hse. Children's Bks.

Brooks, Gwendolyn. Bronzeville Boys & Girls. Ringgold, Faith, illus. 2007. 48p. (J). (gr. 2-5). 16.99 (978-0-06-029505-9(8) , Amistad) HarperCollins Pubs.

Bryan, Ashley. Ashley Bryan's ABC of African American Poetry. Bryan, Ashley, illus. 2001. (Illus.). 32p. (J). (ps-3). 7.99 (978-0-689-84045-6(4) , Aladdin) Simon & Schuster Children's Publishing.

—Ashley Bryan's ABC of African American Poetry. 2001. (gr. k-3). lib. bdg. 15.30 (978-0-613-33666-6(6)) Tandem Library Bks.

Feelings, Tom. Soul Looks Back in Wonder. 1999. (Illus.). 40p. (J). (ps-ps). pap., pap. 7.99 (978-0-14-056501-0(9) , Puffin) Penguin Group (USA) Inc.

—Soul Looks Back in Wonder. 1999. (978-0-606-15992-0(4)) Tandem Library Bks.

—Soul Looks Back in Wonder. Feelings, Tom, illus. 1999. (Illus.). (J). (ps-ps). lib. bdg. 16.45 (978-0-613-12128-6(7)) Tandem Library Bks.

Greenfield, Eloise. Honey, I Love. Gilchrist, Jan Spivey, illus. anniv. ed. 2003. 32p. (J). (ps-k). 16.99 (978-0-06-009123-1(1)); lib. bdg. 17.89 (978-0-06-009124-8(X)) HarperCollins Pubs.

Little, Lessie Jones. Children of Long Ago: Poems. Gilchrist, Jan Spivey, illus. 2000. 32p. (J). (ps up). 15.95 (978-1-58430-008-3(6)); 6.95 (978-1-58430-009-0(4)) Lee & Low Bks., Inc.

—Children of Long Ago: Poems. 2000. (Illus.). (J). (978-0-606-18246-1(2)) Tandem Library Bks.

Marsalis, Wynton. Jazz A-B-Z: An A to Z Collection of Jazz Portraits. Rogers, Paul, illus. 2005. 76p. (J). (gr. 4-7). 24.99 (978-0-7636-2135-3(8)) Candlewick Pr.

McGill, Alice. In the Hollow of Your Hand: Slave Lullabies. Cummings, Michael, illus. 2000. 40p. (J). (gr. k-3). 18.00 (978-0-618-10445-1(3)); tchr. ed. 18.00 (978-0-395-85755-7(4)) Houghton Mifflin Co. Trade & Reference Div.

Myers, Walter Dean. Harlem: A Poem. 2002. (J). 26.13 (978-0-7587-0115-2(2)) Book Wholesalers, Inc.

—Here in Harlem: Poems in Many Voices. 2004. (Illus.). 96p. (YA). (gr. 7 up). tchr. ed. 16.95 (978-0-8234-1853-4(7)) Holiday Hse., Inc.

Nelson, Marilyn. A Wreath for Emmett Till. Lardy, Philippe, illus. 2005. 48p. (J). (gr. 7). 17.00 (978-0-618-39752-5(3)) Houghton Mifflin Co. Trade & Reference Div.

Shange, Ntozake. Ellington Was Not a Street. Nelson, Kadir A., illus. 2004. 40p. (J). (gr. k-6). 17.99 (978-0-689-82884-3(5)) Simon & Schuster Children's Publishing.

—Ellington Was Not a Street. Nelson, Kadir, illus. 2005. (J). 24.95 incl. audio (978-0-439-77576-2(0) , WHRA672); 29.95 incl. audio compact disk (978-0-439-77582-3(5) , WHCD672) Weston Woods Studios, Inc.

AMERICAN POETRY—COLLECTIONS

Antarctic Antics. 2004. (J). 24.95 incl. audio (978-1-55592-058-6(6)); pap. 18.95 incl. audio compact disk (978-1-55592-122-4(1)); pap. 18.95 incl. audio compact disk (978-1-55592-615-1(0)); pap. 38.75 incl. audio compact disk (978-1-55592-616-8(9)); pap. 32.75 incl. audio (978-1-55592-614-4(2)); pap. 14.95 incl. audio (978-1-55592-613-7(4)) Weston Woods Studios, Inc.

Authors. Poems Teachers Ask for. 2006. 99.99 ***(978-1-4280-4939-0(8))**; pap. 93.99 ***(978-1-4280-4905-5(3))*** IndyPublish.com.

Barner, Bob. To Everything. 2004. (Illus.). 38p. (J). pap. 6.95 (978-0-8118-4456-7(0)) Chronicle Bks. LLC.

Baxter, Jennifer. Turned Inside Out. 2003. (YA). per. 10.00 (978-0-9741294-3-3(7)) Main St Publishing, Inc.

Carpenter, Stephen, illus. If Kids Ruled the School: More Kids' Favorite Funny School Poems. 2004. 73p. (J). (978-0-88166-468-3(5)) Meadowbrook Pr.

Celebrate! Young Poets Speak Out - Appalachia Spring 2006. 2006. (YA). 21.95 (978-1-60050-039-8(0)) Creative Communication.

Celebrate! Young Poets Speak Out - California Spring 2006. 2006. (YA). 21.95 (978-1-60050-057-2(9)) Creative Communication.

Celebrate! Young Poets Speak Out - Canada Spring 2006. 2006. (YA). 21.95 (978-1-60050-037-4(4)) Creative Communication.

Celebrate! Young Poets Speak Out - Illinois/Indiana Spring 2006. 2006. (YA). 21.95 (978-1-60050-043-5(9)) Creative Communication.

Celebrate! Young Poets Speak Out - Michigan Spring 2006. 2006. (YA). 21.95 (978-1-60050-048-0(X)) Creative Communication.

Celebrate! Young Poets Speak Out - Midwest Spring 2006. 2006. (YA). 21.95 (978-1-60050-045-9(5)) Creative Communication.

Celebrate! Young Poets Speak Out - New Jersey Spring 2006. 2006. (YA). 21.95 (978-1-60050-033-6(1)) Creative Communication.

Celebrate! Young Poets Speak Out - New York Spring 2006. 2006. (YA). 21.95 (978-1-60050-031-2(5)) Creative Communication.

Celebrate! Young Poets Speak Out - Northeast Spring 2006. 2006. (YA). 21.95 (978-1-60050-028-2(5)) Creative Communication.

Celebrate! Young Poets Speak Out - Pennsylvania Spring 2006. 2006. (YA). 21.95 (978-1-60050-032-9(3)) Creative Communication.

Celebrate! Young Poets Speak Out - Rocky Mountain Spring 2006. 2006. (YA). 21.95 (978-1-60050-053-4(6)) Creative Communication.

Celebrate! Young Poets Speak Out - South Spring 2006. 2006. (YA). 21.95 (978-1-60050-038-1(2)) Creative Communication.

Celebrate! Young Poets Speak Out - Texas Spring 2006. 2006. (YA). 21.95 (978-1-60050-055-8(2)) Creative Communication.

Celebrate! Young Poets Speak Out - West Spring 2006. 2006. (YA). 21.95 (978-1-60050-052-7(8)) Creative Communication.

Celebrate! Young Poets Speak Out - Wisconsin/Minnesota Spring 2006. 2006. (YA). 21.95 (978-1-60050-047-3(1)) Creative Communication.

Celebrate! Young Poets Speak Out -Heartland Spring 2006. 2006. (YA). 21.95 (978-1-60050-041-1(2)) Creative Communication.

Celebrating Poetry ¿ East Spring 2006. 2006. (J). 21.95 (978-1-60050-034-3(X)) Creative Communication.

Celebrating Poetry ¿ Midwest Spring 2006. 2006. (J). 21.95 (978-1-60050-050-3(1)) Creative Communication.

Celebrating Poetry ¿ Spring 2006. 2006. (J). 21.95 (978-1-60050-035-0(8)) Creative Communication.

Celebrating Poetry ¿ West Spring 2006. 2006. (J). 21.95 (978-1-60050-058-9(7)) Creative Communication.

A Celebration of Young Poets - California Spring 2006. 2006. (J). 21.95 (978-1-60050-056-5(0)) Creative Communication.

A Celebration of Young Poets - Canada Spring 2006. 2006. (J). 21.95 (978-1-60050-025-1(0)) Creative Communication.

A Celebration of Young Poets - Heartland Spring 2006. 2006. (J). 21.95 (978-1-60050-040-4(4)) Creative Communication.

A Celebration of Young Poets - Illinois/Indiana Spring 2006. 2006. (J). 21.95 (978-1-60050-042-8(0)) Creative Communication.

A Celebration of Young Poets - Midwest Spring 2006. 2006. (J). 21.95 (978-1-60050-044-2(7)) Creative Communication.

A Celebration of Young Poets - New Jersey Spring 2006. 2006. (J). 21.95 (978-978-160-050-0(0)) Creative Communication.

A Celebration of Young Poets - New York Spring 2006. 2006. (J). 21.95 (978-1-60050-029-9(3)) Creative Communication.

A Celebration of Young Poets - Northeast Spring 2006. 2006. (J). 21.95 (978-1-60050-026-8(9)) Creative Communication.

A Celebration of Young Poets - Ohio Spring 2006. 2006. (J). 21.95 (978-1-60050-049-7(8)) Creative Communication.

A Celebration of Young Poets - Pennsylvania Spring 2006. 2006. (J). 21.95 (978-1-60050-030-5(7)) Creative Communication.

A Celebration of Young Poets - South Spring 2006. 2006. (J). 21.95 (978-1-60050-036-7(6)) Creative Communication.

A Celebration of Young Poets - Texas Spring 2006. 2006. (J). 21.95 (978-1-60050-054-1(4)) Creative Communication.

A Celebration of Young Poets - West Spring 2006. 2006. (J). 21.95 (978-1-60050-051-0(X)) Creative Communication.

A Celebration of Young Poets - Wisconsin/Michigan Spring 2006. 2006. (J). 21.95 (978-1-60050-046-6(3)) Creative Communication.

A Celebration of Young Poets ¿ New Jersey Spring 2006. 2006. (J). 21.95 (978-1-60050-027-5(7)) Creative Communication.

Chow, Symon. Daydreams & Night Dreams: An Anthology of Poems & Photographs. 2002. (J). pap. (978-1-59034-479-8(0)) Mondo Publishing.

Cole, Joanna & Calmenson, Stephanie. Yours till Banana Splits: 201 Autograph Rhymes. Tiegreen, Alan, illus. 2004. 64p. (J). (gr. 6-8). reprint ed. pap. 7.00 (978-0-7567-7349-6(0)) DIANE Publishing Co.

Coulson, Joseph, et al, eds. Modern American Poetry. 2002. xii, 511p. (YA). 19.95 (978-1-880323-88-5(5)) Great Bks. Foundation.

Feldman, Thea. First Foil Poetry Love, 2 vols. Berg, Michelle, illus. 2005. (First Foil Poetry Haikus Ser.). 10p. (J). 6.95 (978-1-58117-189-1(7) , Intervisual/Piggy Toes) Dalmatian Pr.

Fields, Terri. After the Death of Anna Gonzales. rev. ed. 2002. 112p. (YA). (gr. 7-12). 16.95 (978-0-8050-7127-6(X) , Holt, Henry & Co. Bks. For Young Readers) Holt, Henry & Co.

Glaser, Michael, ed. Weavings: A Maryland Anthology for Young People. Comitz, Cindy, illus. abr. ed. 2000. 145p. (J). (gr. k-12). pap. 12.00 (978-0-938572-28-2(8)) Bunny & The Crocodile Pr., The.

Greenberg, Jan. Heart to Heart: New Poems Inspired by Twentieth-Century American Art. 2001. (Illus.). 80p. (gr. 5-9). 19.95 (978-0-8109-4386-5(7)) Abrams, Harry N. , Inc.

Grimes, Nikki. My Man Blue: Poems. Sherry, Toby, ed. Lagarrigue, Jerome, illus. 1999. 32p. (J). (ps-3). pap. 16.99 (978-0-8037-2326-9(1) , Dial) Penguin Group (USA) Inc.

Grimes, Nikki, frwd. Dreams by Day, Dreams by Night: An Anthology of Poems & Photographs. 2002. (Illus.). 32p. (J). 15.95 (978-1-59034-390-6(5)) Mondo Publishing.

Harrison, Michael. The Oxford Treasury of Classic Poems. 2nd rev. ed. 2004. (Illus.). 160p. (YA). 19.95 (978-0-19-276289-4(3)) Oxford Univ. Pr., Inc.

Hoberman, Mary Ann. Fathers, Mothers, Sisters, Brothers: A Collection of Family Poems. Hafner, Marylin, illus. 2001. 32p. (J). (ps-3). pap. 6.99 (978-0-316-36251-1(4)) Little, Brown Bks. for Young Readers.

Hopkins, Lee Bennett. Hanukkah Lights: Holiday Poetry. Hall, Melanie, illus. 2004. (I Can Read Bks.). (J). (gr. k-3). 15.99 (978-0-06-008051-8(5)); 32p. lib. bdg. 16.89 (978-0-06-008052-5(3)) HarperCollins Pubs.

—Lives: Poems about Famous Americans. Staub, Leslie, illus. 1999. 40p. (J). (gr. 3-6). lib. bdg. 17.89 (978-0-06-027768-0(8)); 16.99 (978-0-06-027767-3(X)) HarperCollins Pubs.

Janeczko, Paul B. Dirty Laundry Pile: Poems in Different Voices. Sweet, Melissa, illus. 2001. 40p. (J). (ps-5). lib. bdg. 16.89 (978-0-688-16252-8(5)) HarperCollins Pubs.

Janeczko, Paul B., compiled by. Seeing the Blue Between: Advice & Inspiration for Young Poets. 2002. (Illus.). 144p. (J). (gr. 4-8). 18.99 (978-0-7636-0881-1(5)) Candlewick Pr.

Katz, Bobbi. Pocket Poems. Hafner, Marylin, illus. 2004. 32p. (J). (gr. k). 15.99 (978-0-525-47172-1(3) , Dutton Juvenile) Penguin Group (USA) Inc.

Kennedy, X. J. & Dorothy. Knock at a Star: A Child's Introduction to Poetry. rev. ed. 1999. (gr. 3-6). lib. bdg. 19.60 (978-0-8085-9332-4(3)) Tandem Library Bks.

Kiesler, Kate A., compiled by. Wings on the Wind: Bird Poems. 2002. (Illus.). 40p. (J). (gr. k-3). 14.00 (978-0-618-13333-8(X) , Clarion Bks.) Houghton Mifflin Co. Trade & Reference Div.

Lansky, Bruce. Miles of Smiles: Kids Pick the Funniest Poems. Carpenter, Stephen, illus. 1998. xi, 115p. (J). (gr. 3-7). 16.00 (978-0-88166-313-6(1)) Meadow Brook Pubns.

Lewis, J. Patrick. Swan Song. Wormell, Christopher, illus. 2005. 32p. (J). reprint ed. 17.00 (978-0-7567-8662-5(2)) DIANE Publishing Co.

Lewis, J. Patrick & Dotlich, Rebecca Kai. Castles: Old Stone Poems. Burr, Dan, illus. 2006. 48p. (YA). (gr. 5-9). 18.95 (978-1-59078-380-1(8)) Boyds Mills Pr.

Malone, Peter, illus. The Drowsy Hours: Poems for Bedtime. 2002. 40p. (J). (ps up). 16.89 (978-0-06-029421-2(3)) HarperCollins Pubs.

Martin, Peggy-Lou. Wishes, Wings, & Other Things: Poems for Anytime. 2000. (Poetry Parade Ser.). (Illus.). 32p. (J). 21.36 (978-1-57572-399-0(9)) Heinemann Library.

McGough, Roger. The Kingfisher Book of Funny Poems. Holden, Caroline, illus. 2002. 256p. (J). (gr. 3-5). tchr. ed. 18.95 (978-0-7534-5480-0(7) , Kingfisher) Houghton Mifflin Co. Trade & Reference Div.

Medina, Tony. Love to Langston. Christie, Gregory R., illus. 2002. 40p. (J). (gr. 1 up). 16.95 (978-1-58430-041-0(8)) Lee & Low Bks., Inc.

Memories of Christmas in West Tennessee: Short Stories & Poems from Area Writers. 2nd ed. 2002. per. 10.00 (978-0-9710470-8-2(1) , 400, MSP) Main St Publishing, Inc.

Moncus, Shane. Multiverse: By Shane Moncus - A Texas Street Poet. Galloway, Annette, ed. Moncus, Steve, illus. l.t. ed. 2001. (Multiverse). 72p. (C). per. 6.95 (978-0-9666676-8-4(9)) Main St Publishing, Inc.

Nye, Naomi Shihab. Is This Forever, or What? Poems & Paintings from Texas. 2004. (Illus.). 176p. (J). (gr. 5 up). 24.99 (978-0-06-051178-4(8)) HarperCollins Pubs.

Philip, Neil. Hot Potato: Mealtime Rhymes. Henley, Claire, tr. Henley, Claire, illus. 2004. 32p. (J). (ps-k). tchr. ed. 16.00 (978-0-618-31554-3(3) , Clarion Bks.) Houghton Mifflin Co. Trade & Reference Div.

Rachel, T. Cole. Bend, Don't Shatter: Poets on the Beginning of Desire. Costello, Rita, ed. 2004. 120p. pap. 7.95 (978-1-932360-17-2(4)) Penguin Group (USA) Inc.

Rivers, Ruth, illus. This Amazing World: Poems & Prayers about Everything under the Sun. 2002. 48p. (J). (gr. 1-7). 16.00 (978-1-56148-363-1(X)) Good Bks.

Roche, Judith, ed. The Bottom of Heaven: Artwork & Poetry of the Remann Hall Women's Project. 2003. (J). per. 19.95 (978-0-9726649-0-5(4)) Museum of Glass.

Ross, H. K., ed. Great Story Poems: Collection. rev. ed. 2000. 160p. (YA). (gr. 5-12). pap. 12.95 (978-0-87460-385-9(4)) Lion Bks.

Smith, Charles R., Jr. Perfect Harmony: A Musical Journey with the Boy's Choir of Harlem: Poems & Photographs by Charles Smith. 2002. (Illus.). 32p. (J). lib. bdg. (978-0-7868-2608-7(8) , Jump at the Sun) Hyperion Bks. for Children.

Steptoe, Javaka, illus. In Daddy's Arms I Am Tall: African Americans Celebrating Fathers. 2000. 32p. (J). 15.95 (978-1-880000-31-1(8)) Lee & Low Bks., Inc.

Stevenson, Robert Louis. Leaves from a Child's Garden of Verses. Green, Donna, illus. 2004. 77p. (J). (gr. k-4). reprint ed. 22.00 (978-0-7567-8293-1(7)) DIANE Publishing Co.

Stuart-Clark, Christopher. One Hundred Years of Poetry for Children. 2000. (Illus.). (J). (978-0-606-20831-4(3)) Tandem Library Bks.

Tobias, Tobi. A World of Words: An ABC of Quotations. Malone, Peter, illus. 1998. 48p. (J). (ps-3). 16.00 (978-0-688-12129-7(2)) HarperCollins Pubs.

Tobias, Tobi, ed. A World of Words: An ABC of Quotations. Malone, Peter, illus. 2004. 40p. (J). (gr. k-4). reprint ed. 16.00 (978-0-7567-8303-7(8)) DIANE Publishing Co.

Tobias, Tobi & Malone, Peter. A World of Words: An ABC of Quotations. 1998. (Illus.). 40p. (J). (ps-3). 15.89 (978-0-688-12130-3(6)) HarperCollins Pubs.

Todd, Mark, ed. The Pain Tree: And Other Teenage Angst-Ridden Poetry. 2000. (Illus.). 64p. (YA). (gr. 7-12). pap. 6.95 (978 0-618-04758-1(1)) Houghton Mifflin Co. Trade & Reference Div.

Tripp, Wallace. Rose's Are Red, Violet's Are Blue: And Other Silly Poems. Tripp, Wallace, illus. 1999. (Illus.). 32p. (YA). (gr. 2-5). 15.95 (978-0-316-85440-5(9)) Little Brown & Co.

Vecchione, Patrice, ed. Whisper & Shout: Poems to Memorize. 2002. (Illus.). 64p. (J). (gr. 4-7). 16.95 (978-0-8126-2656-8(7)) Cricket Bks.

Williamson, Melanie, illus. Drift upon a Dream: Poems for Sleepy Babies. 2004. 32p. (J). 16.95 (978-1-57091-577-2(6)); pap. 6.95 (978-1-57091-578-9(4)) Charlesbridge Publishing, Inc.

AMERICAN SOCIETY FOR THE PREVENTION OF CRUELTY TO ANIMALS

Miller-Schroeder, Patricia. The ASPCA. 2002. (International Organizations Ser.). (Illus.). 32p. (J). lib. bdg. 16.95 (978-1-59036-024-8(9)) Weigl Pubs., Inc.

Suen, Anastasia. The American Society for the Prevention of Cruelty to Animals (ASPCA) 2002. (Reading Power Ser.). (Illus.). 24p. (J). (gr. k-3). lib. bdg. 17.25 (978-0-8239-6004-0(8) , PowerKids Pr.) Rosen Publishing Group, Inc., The.

AMERICAN WIT AND HUMOR

Bathroom Readers' Institute Staff. Uncle John's Bathroom Reader for Kids Only, Vol. 1. 2002. (Bathroom Readers Institute Ser.). (Illus.). 324p. (J). (gr. 3-7). pap. 12.95 (978-1-57145-867-4(0)) Advantage Pubs. Group.

—Uncle John's Book of Fun. 2004. (Illus.). 320p. pap. 12.95 (978-1-59223-259-8(0) , Portable Pr.) Advantage Pubs. Group.

—Uncle John's Unstoppable Bathroom Reader. 2003. (Bathroom Reader Ser.). (Illus.). 522p. pap. 16.95 (978-1-59223-116-4(0) , Portable Pr.) Advantage Pubs. Group.

Graham, Joan Claire. Minnesota Memories 3. 2003. (Illus.). 192p. pap. 13.95 (978-0-9711971-2-1(1)) Megyeri, Graham Bks.

Hample, Stuart E. Silly Book. 2004. (Illus.). 32p. (J). 15.99 (978-0-7636-2256-5(7)) Candlewick Pr.

Joke Book. 2002. (Illus.). 48p. (J). pap. 2.99 (978-0-689-86191-8(5) , Simon Spotlight/Nickelodeon) Simon & Schuster Children's Publishing.

Keller, Charles. The Little Giant Book of Giggles. 2003. (Little Giant Bks.). (Illus.). 352p. (J). pap. 6.95 (978-1-4027-0287-7(6)) Sterling Publishing Co., Inc.

Leno, Jay. How to Be the Funniest Kid in the Whole Wide World: Side-Splitting, Gut-Busting, Snort-Milk-Out-Your-Nose Jokes. Whitehead, S. B., illus. 2005. 144p. (J). 12.95 (978-1-4169-0631-5(2)) Simon & Schuster Children's Publishing.

Linz, Kathi. Chickens May Not Cross Road: And Other Crazy (But True) Laws. Griego, Tony, illus. 2007. 32p. (J). 6.95 (***978-0-618-80905-9(8))** Houghton Mifflin Co. Trade & Reference Div.

Nolan, Michael. American Humor. 2001. (gr. 7-12). lib. bdg. 34.70 (978-0-613-64243-9(0)) Tandem Library Bks.

Parr, Todd. Underwear Do's & Don'ts. 2004. (Illus.). 24p. (J). (ps-ps). bds. 6.99 (978-0-316-90806-1(1)) Little, Brown Bks. for Young Readers.

Price, Roger & Stern, Leonard. Mad Libs Worst Case Scenario Survival Handbook. 2003. (Mad Libs Ser.). (Illus.). 48p. (J). pap. 3.99 (978-0-8431-0298-7(5) , Price Stern Sloan) Penguin Group (USA) Inc.

Puzzle House Staff. Jokes. Teviotdale, Stuart, illus. 2001. 128p. (J). (gr. 3-8). pap. 7.95 (978-0-439-22009-5(2)) Scholastic, Inc.

Rosenbloom, Joseph. Giggles, Gags & Groaners. Hoffman, Sanford, illus. 2005. 96p. pap. 4.95 (978-1-4027-1755-0(5)) Sterling Publishing Co., Inc.

—Jokes. Hoffman, Sanford, illus. 2007. 360p. (J). pap. 6.95 (***978-1-4027-4973-5(2))** Sterling Publishing Co., Inc.

Rosenbloom, Joseph. The Little Giant Book of Jokes. Hoffman, Sanford, illus. 2003. 352p. (J). (gr. 4-7). pap. 6.95 (978-0-8069-6101-9(5)) Sterling Publishing Co., Inc.

Rowinski, Kate. Cats in the Dark. Bishop, Bonnie, illus. 1998. 32p. (J). (ps-3). 14.95 (978-0-89272-427-7(7)) Down East Bks.

Russell, James. Fabulous America: Romantic Comedy Screenplay. 2001. 108p. (YA). pap. 12.95 (978-0-916367-33-6(9)) Russell, James.

Sassoon, Tanya. Parent Training Kit. 2003. 36p. pap. 8.95 (978-1-58234-335-8(7)) Bloomsbury Publishing.

Scholastic, Inc. Staff & Usual Gang of Idiots Staff. Mad Student Survival Guide for Those Bored of Education. Mad Magazine Editors, ed. 2003. (Mad Magazine Ser.). (Illus.). 64p. (J). pap. 3.99 (978-0-439-38201-4(7)) Scholastic, Inc.

Schultz, Sam. Animal Antics: The Beast Jokes Ever! 2004. (Make Me Laugh! Ser.). (Illus.). 32p. (J). (gr. k-3). lib. bdg. 19.93 (978-1-57505-640-1(2)) Lerner Publishing Group.

—Animal Antics: The Beast Jokes Ever! 2004. (gr. k-3). lib. bdg. 12.95 (978-0-613-79287-5(4)) Tandem Library Bks.

Schulz, Charles M. Security Is a Thumb & a Blanket. 2006. (Peanuts Ser.). (Illus.). 72p. 5.95 (978-1-933662-09-1(3)) Cider Mill Pr. Bk. Pubs. LLC.

Seed, David. Talk about Good Grades, Vol. 6. Brewer, Mary, illus. 1998. 120p. (J). (gr. 7 up). 20.00 (978-1-892082-05-3(5)) Marion Street Pr.

Snicket, Lemony, pseud. Horseradish: Bitter Truths You Can't Avoid. Tucker, Mark, illus. 2007. 176p. (J). (gr. 5 up). 12.99 (***978-0-06-124006-5(0))** HarperCollins Pubs.

St. George, Judith. So You Want to Be President? Small, David, illus. rev. ed. 2004. 56p. (J). (gr. 3). 17.99 (978-0-399-24317-2(8) , Philomel) Penguin Group (USA) Inc.

Tait, Chris. Ridiculous Knock-Knocks. Zahnd, Mark, illus. 2002. 96p. (J). (gr. 1-4). pap. 4.95 (978-0-8069-7689-1(6)) Sterling Publishing Co., Inc.

—Ridiculous Knock-Knocks. 2002. (gr. k-3). lib. bdg. 12.95 (978-0-613-75613-6(4)) Tandem Library Bks.

Ungerer, Tomi. I Am Papa Snap & These Are My Favorite No Such Stories. Ungerer, Tomi, illus. 1999. (Illus.). 32p. (J). (ps-3). reprint ed. 17.95 (978-1-57098-279-8(1)) Rinehart, Roberts Pubs.

Weiner, Andy J. & Whipple, Rick. The Legacy of John Cyclone. 2000. (Publish-a-Book Ser.). (Illus.). 24p. (J). (ps-3). 7.95 (978-0-7398-2370-5(1)) Steck-Vaughn.

Wilson, Gahan & Bierce, Ambrose. The Devil's Dictionary & Other Works. (Classics Illustrated Ser.). (Illus.). 52p. (YA). pap. 4.95 (978-1-57209-018-7(9)) Classics International Entertainment, Inc.

Yoe, Craig. Thanksgiving Jokes & Riddles. Yoe, Craig, illus. 2003. (Holiday Ha Ha's Ser.). (Illus.). 128p. (J). (gr. 3). pap. 4.99 (978-0-8431-0273-4(X) , Price Stern Sloan) Penguin Group (USA) Inc.

AMERICAN WIT AND HUMOR, PICTORIAL

Agee, Jon. Who Ordered the Jumbo Shrimp? 2002. (gr. 3-6). lib. bdg. 17.60 (978-0-613-53880-0(3)) Tandem Library Bks.

—Why Did the Chicken Cross the Road? Arnold, Tedd et al, illus. 2006. 40p. (J). (ps-4). 16.99 (978-0-8037-3094-6(2) , Dial) Penguin Group (USA) Inc.

Barrett, Judi. Animals Should Definitely Not Act Like People. Barrett, Ron, illus. 2000. (J). pap. 19.97 incl. audio (978-0-7366-9222-9(3)) Books on Tape, Inc.

—Animals Should Definitely Not Act Like People. Barrett, Ron, illus. pap. 35.95 incl. audio compact disk (978-1-59112-827-4(7)); (J). pap. 33.95 incl. audio (978-0-87499-232-8(X)) Live Oak Media.

—Animals Should Definitely Not Wear Clothing. Barrett, Ron, illus. 2002. (J). 14.47 (978-0-7587-1951-5(5)) Book Wholesalers, Inc.

—Animals Should Definitely Not Wear Clothing. Barrett, Ron, illus. 2000. 32p. pap. 19.97 incl. audio (978-0-7366-9197-0(9)) Books on Tape, Inc.

—Animals Should Definitely Not Wear Clothing. 2005. (Illus.). (J). pap. 18.95 incl. audio compact disk (978-1-59112-690-4(8)) Live Oak Media.

Lichtenheld, Tom. What Are You So Grumpy About? Lichtenheld, Tom, illus. 2003. (Illus.). 32p. (J). (ps-17). 15.99 (978-0-316-59236-9(6)) Little, Brown Bks. for Young Readers.

Ocker, Karen, illus. George W. Bush Coloring Book. 2005. 24p. pap. 8.95 (978-1-891053-94-8(9)) Garrett County Pr.

AMERICANISMS

O'Reilly, Gillian. Slangalicious: Where We Got That Crazy Lingo. Johnston, Krista, illus. 2004. 88p. (J). (gr. 5). pap. 12.95 (978-1-55037-764-4(7)) Annick Pr., Ltd. CAN. *Dist:* Firefly Bks., Ltd.

O'Reilly, Gillina. Slangalicious: Where We Got That Crazy Lingo. Johnston, Krista, illus. 2004. 88p. (J). (gr. 5). 24.95 (978-1-55037-765-1(5)) Annick Pr., Ltd. CAN. *Dist:* Firefly Bks., Ltd.

Sikorski, Lorna D. The Consonant Variations of American English, 4th ed. 2004. (Mastering Effective English Communication Ser.). (Illus.). 119p. spiral bd. 99.95 incl. audio compact disk (978-1-883574-08-6(0) , 5311) LDS & Assocs., LLC.

AMERICANS—EUROPE—FICTION

Gopnik, Adam. The King in the Window. 2005. (Illus.). 416p. (gr. 5-17). 19.95 (978-0-7868-1862-4(X)) Hyperion Bks. for Children.

—The King in the Window. Rayyan, Omar, illus. 2006. 416p. (gr. 5-17). reprint ed. pap. 9.99 (978-0-7868-3894-3(9)) Miramax Bks.

King, Donna. Kick Off. 2007. 168p. (J). (gr. 3-5). pap. 5.95 (***978-0-7534-6082-5(3)** , Kingfisher) Houghton Mifflin Co. Trade & Reference Div.

Sheldon, Dyan. I Conquer Britain. 2007. (Illus.). 208p. (YA). (gr. 7). 15.99 (***978-0-7636-3300-4(3))** Candlewick Pr.

AMISH

Ammon, Richard. An Amish Year. Patrick, Pamela, illus. 2007. 36p. (J). (ps-3). pap. 10.95 (***978-1-59078-465-5(0))** Boyds Mills Pr.

George, Charles. What Makes Me Amish? 2005. (What Makes Me A— ? Ser.). (Illus.). 48p. (J). (gr. 4-8). lib. bdg. 26.20 (978-0-7377-3081-4(1) , Greenhaven Pr., Inc.) Thomson Gale.

Hunter, David. Teen Life among the Amish & Other Alternative Communities: Choosing a Lifestyle. 2008. (Youth in Rural North America Ser.). (J). (978-1-4222-0017-9(5)) Mason Crest Pubs.

Therrien, Patricia. Amish & Mennonite Cooking. 2005. (American Regional Cooking Library). (Illus.). 72p. (J). lib. bdg. 20.95 (978-1-59084-612-4(5)); lib. bdg. 299.25 (978-1-59084-609-4(5)) Mason Crest Pubs.

Wagner, Katherine. Life in an Amish Community. 2001. (Way People Live Ser.). (Illus.). 112p. (J). (gr. 7-10). 28.70 (978-1-56006-654-5(7) , LML00902-178008, Lucent Bks.) Thomson Gale.

AMISH—FICTION

Beiler, Edna. Mattie Mae. Graber, Esther Rose, illus. 2nd ed. 2000. 112p. (J). (ps-4). pap. 6.99 (978-0-8361-9141-7(2)) Herald Pr.

Bender, Carrie. Birch Hollow Schoolmarm. 1999. (gr. 7-12). lib. bdg. 17.60 (978-0-613-81313-6(8)) Tandem Library Bks.

—Hemlock Hill Hideaway. 2000. (Whispering Brook Ser.: Bk. 4). (Illus.). 168p. (J). (gr. 4-8). pap. 8.99 (978-0-8361-9128-8(5)) Herald Pr.

—Hemlock Hill Hideaway: Whispering Brook Series #4. 2007. (Illus.). 168p. pap. 8.99 (***978-1-60126-022-2(9))** Masthof Pr.

—Summerville Days. 2001. (Whispering Brook Ser.). (Illus.). 183p. (J). 25.95 (978-0-7862-3081-5(9) , Five Star) Thomson Gale.

—Summerville Days: Whispering Brook Series #2. 2007. (Illus.). 224p. pap. 8.99 (***978-1-60126-023-9(7))** Masthof Pr.

Bender, Carrie. Timber Lane Cove. 2003. (Whispering Brook Ser.: Bk. 6). 144p. (YA). pap. 8.99 (978-0-8361-9202-5(8)) Herald Pr.

Borntrager, Mary Christner. Andy. l.t. ed. 2002. 161p. 25.95 (978-0-7862-4029-6(6)) Thomson Gale.

—Daniel. l.t. ed. 2000. (Christian Fiction Ser.). 191p. 23.95 (978-0-7862-2859-1(8)) Thorndike Pr.

—Ellie. l.t. ed. 2001. (Christian Fiction Ser.). 208p. 23.95 (978-0-7862-3383-0(4)) Thorndike Pr.

—Mandy Bk. 9: Ellie's People. l.t. ed. 2002. (Christian Fiction Ser.). 25.95 (978-0-7862-4539-0(5)) Thorndike Pr.

—Polly. l.t. ed. 2002. 165p. (J). 25.95 (978-0-7862-4030-2(X)) Thomson Gale.

—Rachel. l.t. ed. 2001. (Thorndike Press Large Print Christian Fiction Ser.). 175p. (J). 23.95 (978-0-7862-3595-7(0)) Thorndike Pr.

—Rebecca. l.t. ed. 2001. (Thorndike Christian Fiction Ser.). 245p. 24.95 (978-0-7862-3252-9(8)) Thorndike Pr.

—Sarah. l.t. ed. 2002. (Christian Fiction Ser.). 177p. 25.95 (978-0-7862-4526-0(3)) Thorndike Pr.

Clinton, Cathryn. Simeon's Fire. 128p. (J). 2007. (gr. 3-7). pap. 5.99 (978-0-7636-3294-6(5)); 2005. (gr. 5-9). 15.99 (978-0-7636-2707-2(0)) Candlewick Pr.

De Angeli, Marguerite. Henner's Lydia. 1998. (Illus.). 74p. (YA). (ps-3). 15.99 (978-0-8361-9093-9(9)) Herald Pr.

Good, Merle. Reuben & the Blizzard. Moss, P. Buckley, illus. 2003. (Reuben Ser.). 32p. (J). (gr. k-3). 7.95 (978-1-56148-375-4(3)) Good Bks.

—Reuben & the Fire. Moss, P. Buckley, illus. 2003. (Bestselling Children's Book Ser.). 32p. (J). 7.95 (978-1-56148-388-4(5)) Good Bks.

—Reuben & the Fire. 2003. (gr. k-3). lib. bdg. 16.40 (978-0-613-84738-4(5)) Tandem Library Bks.

Heitzmann, Kristen. Chestnut Ridge Acres. 2001. 220p. (J). 25.95 (978-0-7862-3415-8(6) , Five Star) Thomson Gale.

Hershberger, Noah. Salamonie Farm. Koehler, Chris, illus. 1998. 240p. pap. 12.95 (978-1-879863-53-8(7)) Goosefoot Acres Pr.

The Journey. 2003. 170p. (YA). per. 10.95 (978-0-9713292-8-7(1)) Aim Higher Bks.

Kjellberg, B. Abe: A Farm Boy. 2006. (J). per. (978-0-912868-07-3(4)) Kjellberg, Inc.

—Apple Acres: The Farm. 2006. (J). per. 7.95 (***978-0-912868-10-3(4))** Kjellberg, Inc.

—Courtnee: A Farm Girl. 2005. (Illus.). 84p. (J). per. 7.95 (978-0-912868-06-6(6)) Kjellberg, Inc.

—Sandy: A City Girl. 2005. (Illus.). 94p. (J). per. 7.95 (978-0-912868-08-0(2) , 8080) Kjellberg, Inc.

Lewis, Beverly. Just Like Mama. Bladholm, Cheri, illus. 2002. 32p. (J). 14.99 (978-0-7642-2507-9(3)) Bethany Hse. Pubs.

—October Song: Lancaster County Is Cloaked in Autumn Splendor, & a Reunion Is in the Air. 2001. (gr. 5-8). lib. bdg. 22.25 (978-0-613-55643-9(7)) Tandem Library Bks.

Mitchell, Barbara. Down Buttermilk Lane. Sandford, John, illus. 2003. 32p. (YA). (gr. k-2). pap. 9.95 (978-1-59078-089-3(2)) Boyds Mills Pr.

Munro, Sandie. Karlee's Other Family. 2006. 84p. pap. 8.95 (***978-1-60126-000-0(8))** Masthof Pr.

Stewart, Sarah. The Journey. Small, David, illus. 40p. (J). 2001. (gr. 2-6). 16.00 (978-0-374-33905-0(8)); 2006. reprint ed. pap. 6.95 (978-0-374-40010-1(5)) Farrar, Straus & Giroux. (Farrar, Straus & Giroux (BYR)).

—The Journey. Smalls, David, illus. pap. 16.95 incl. audio (978-0-87499-922-8(7)); pap. incl. audio (978-0-87499-924-2(3)); pap. 18.95 incl. audio compact disk (978-1-59112-344-6(5)); pap. incl. audio compact disk (978-1-59112-556-3(1)) Live Oak Media.

—The Journey. 2002. (Illus.). (J). 28.95 incl. audio compact disk (978-1-59112-345-3(3)); 25.95 incl. audio (978-0-87499-923-5(5)) Live Oak Media.

AMISTAD (SCHOONER)

Freedman, Suzanne. United States vs. Amistad: Rebellion on a Slave Ship. 2000. (Landmark Supreme Court Cases Ser.). (Illus.). 112p. (J). (gr. 6-12). lib. bdg. 26.60 (978-0-7660-1337-7(5)) Enslow Pubs., Inc.

Gold, Susan Dudley. United States v. Amistad: Slave Ship Mutiny. 2006. (Supreme Court Milestones Ser.). (Illus.). 144p. (J). lib. bdg. 39.93 (978-0-7614-2143-6(2) , Benchmark Bks.) Cavendish, Marshall Corp.

McKissack, Patricia C. Amistad: Station Stop 3. Stanley, Sanna, illus. 2005. (All Aboard Reading Ser.). 48p. (J). (gr. 2-4). pap. 3.99 (978-0-448-43900-6(X) , Grosset & Dunlap) Penguin Group (USA) Inc.

Worth, Richard. Cinque of the Amistad & the Slave Trade in World History. 2001. (In World History Ser.). (Illus.). 112p. (J). (gr. 5-12). lib. bdg. 26.60 (978-0-7660-1460-2(6)) Enslow Pubs., Inc.

AMNESIA—FICTION

Bayle, B. J. Perilous Passage. 2007. 176p. (YA). pap. 11.99 (***978-1-55002-689-4(5)** , Sandcastle Bks.) Dundurn Group, The CAN. *Dist:* Univ. of Toronto Pr.

Buffie, Margaret. The Dark Garden. 2001. (Margaret Buffie Ser.). 240p. (YA). (gr. 13 up). (978-1-55337-091-8(0)) Kids Can Pr., Ltd.

Clement-Davies, David. Fell. 2007. 542p. (YA). (gr. 7-17). 19.95 (***978-0-8109-1185-7(X))** Abrams, Harry N. , Inc.

Fisk, Pauline. The Secret of Sabrina Fludde. 2002. 250p. (J). (gr. 5 up). 15.95 (978-1-58234-754-7(9) , Bloomsbury Children) Bloomsbury Publishing.

Grimes, Martha. Biting the Moon. 2000. (gr. 7-12). lib. bdg. 22.25 (978-0-613-34018-2(3)) Tandem Library Bks.

Holland, Julia. Nothing to Remember. 1998. 136p. pap. 14.95 (978-0-7022-3062-2(6)) Univ. of Queensland Pr. AUS. *Dist:* International Specialized Bk. Services.

Keaney, Brian. Jacob's Ladder. 2007. (Illus.). 224p. (J). (gr. 5-9). 15.99 (978-0-7636-3071-3(3)) Candlewick Pr.

Kleyla, Mary Pat. Identity Unknown. 2003. (gr. 7-12). lib. bdg. 22.20 (978-0-613-83502-2(6)) Tandem Library Bks.

—Identity Unknown. 2003. 154p. (YA). 22.95 (978-0-595-65812-1(1)); pap. 12.95 (978-0-595-28473-3(6)) iUniverse, Inc.

MacKall, Dandi Daley. Sierra's Story. 2004. (Degrees of Betrayal Ser.). 336p. (YA). pap. 9.99 (978-0-8423-8726-2(9)) Tyndale Hse. Pubs.

Maselli, Christopher P. N. In Pursuit of the Enemy. 1998. (Commander Kellie & the Superkids' Early Adventures Ser.). (J). pap. (978-1-57562-218-7(1)) Copeland, Kenneth Pubns.

Mendes, Valerie. Coming of Age. 2004. 224p. (YA). pap. 8.99 (978-0-689-83772-2(0)) Simon & Schuster, Ltd. GBR. *Dist:* Independent Pubs. Group.

Schatzer, Jeffrey L. Bump on Santa's Noggin. 2006. (Illus.). 32p. (J). 18.95 (978-1-58726-289-0(4) , Mitten Pr.) Ann Arbor Media Group, LLC.

Weatherly, Lee. Kat Got Your Tongue. 2007. 208p. (YA). (gr. 7-9). lib. bdg. 18.99 (978-0-385-75122-3(2)); 15.99 (978-0-385-75117-9(6)) Random Hse. Children's Bks. (Fickling, David Bks.).

Zevin, Gabrielle. Memoirs of a Teenage Amnesiac. 2007. 288p. (YA). (gr. 9 up). 17.00 (***978-0-374-34946-2(0)** , Farrar, Straus & Giroux (BYR)) Farrar, Straus & Giroux.

AMPHIBIANS

see also names of amphibians, e.g. Frogs; Salamanders; etc.

Amphibians & Reptiles. 2005. (World of Animals Ser.: Vols. 41-50). (J). 499.00 (978-0-7172-5916-8(1)) Scholastic Library Publishing.

Baquedano, Elizabeth & Clarke, Barry. Anfibios. 2004. (Dk Eyewitness Books Ser.). (SPA.). 64p. (J). 15.99 (978-0-7566-0414-1(1)) Dorling Kindersley Publishing, Inc.

Barnes, Julia, et al. 101 Facts about Terrarium Pets. 2002. (One Hundred One Facts about Pets Ser.). (Illus.). 32p. (J). (gr. 3 up). lib. bdg. 23.33 (978-0-8368-3021-7(0)) Stevens, Gareth Inc.

Basic Domestic Reptiles & Amphibians. 2005. 64p. pap. 192.50 (978-0-7910-8062-7(5) , Chelsea Hse.) Facts On File, Inc.

Berkowitz, Henry. Amphibians & Reptiles. Lampert, Erv, ed. rev. ed. 1999. (Educational Coloring Bks.). (Illus.). 32p. (J). (gr. 1-4). reprint ed. pap. 3.95 (978-0-932855-49-7(0)) Winner Enterprises.

Bulletpoints Reptiles & Amphibians. 2005. (Illus.). (J). per. 4.99 (978-1-933581-05-7(0)) Byeway Bks.

Bumstead, Pat & Worsley, Norman H. Canadian Skin & Scales. 2003. (Illus.). 168p. (YA). (gr. 5-6). pap. (978-0-9689278-1-6(5)) Simply Wild Pubns., Inc.

Cassie, Brian. Amphibians. 1999. (National Audubon Society First Field Guides). (Illus.). 160p. (YA). (gr. 3-7). pap. 17.95 (978-0-590-63982-8(X)); pap. 8.95 (978-0-590-64008-4(9)) Scholastic, Inc. (Scholastic Reference).

Cassie, Bruce. National Audubon Society First Field Guide: Amphibians. 1999. (978-0-606-18581-3(X)) Tandem Library Bks.

Chelsea House Publishing Staff. Reptile & Amphibian, 9 vols., Set. 1998. 161.55 (978-0-7910-5076-7(9) , Chelsea Hse.) Facts On File, Inc.

Clarke, Barry. Anfibios. 2004. (DK Guides Ser.).Tr. of Amphibian. 64p. (J). lib. bdg. 19.99 (978-0-7566-0415-8(X)) Dorling Kindersley Publishing, Inc.

Clarke, Barry & Buller, Laura. Amphibian. Brightling, Geoff & Greenaway, Frank, photos by. 2005. (Dk eyewitness Bks.). (Illus.). 72p. (J). (gr. 4-7). 15.99 (978-0-7566-1380-8(9)); lib. bdg. 19.99 (978-0-7566-1381-5(7)) Dorling Kindersley Publishing, Inc.

Crump, Marty. Amphibians Reptiles & Their Conservation. 2002. (Illus.). 136p. (J). (gr. 8-12). 25.00 (978-0-208-02511-1(1)) Shoe String Pr., Inc.

Dalgleish, Sharon. Reptiles & Amphibians. 2002. (Junior Adventure Ser.). (Illus.). 32p. (J). (gr. 3 up). lib. bdg. (978-1-59084-196-9(4)) Mason Crest Pubs.

—Reptiles & Amphibians. Cavaluzzo, Laura & McEwen, Rebecca, eds. 1999. (Explorers Ser.). (Illus.). 32p. (J). (978-0-7699-0490-0(4)) Shortland Pubns. (U. S. A.) Inc.

Fisher, Diana. Reptiles & Amphibians: Step by Step Intsructions for 29 Reptiles & Amphibians. 2006. (Draw & Color Ser.). (Illus.). 40p. (J). pap. 4.95 (978-1-56010-994-5(7)) Foster, Walter Publishing, Inc.

Gareth Stevens Publishing Staff, contrib. by. Fish & Amphibians. 2002. (Discovery Channel School Science Ser.). (Illus.). 32p. (J). (gr. 5 up). lib. bdg. 24.67 (978-0-8368-3212-9(4)) Stevens, Gareth Inc.

Gilpin, Daniel. Tree Frogs, Mud Puppies & Other Amphibians. 2005. (Animal Kingdom Classification Ser.). (Illus.). 48p. (J). (gr. 4-6). 26.20 (978-0-7565-1249-1(2)) Compass Point Bks.

Grambo, Rebecca L., et al. Animal Kingdom. 2000. (Eyes on Nature Ser.). (Illus.). 109p. (J). (978-1-56156-882-6(1)) Kidsbooks, Inc.

Hall, Julie. Reptiles & Amphibians: Grades 2 & 3. (Illus.). (J). pap., wbk. ed. 4.99 (978-0-88743-964-3(0)) School Zone Publishing Co.

Harvey, Bev. Amphibians. 2002. (Chelsea Clubhouse Science Exploration Ser.). (Illus.). 32p. (gr. k-2). 23.00 (978-0-7910-6983-7(4) , Chelsea Hse.) Facts On File, Inc.

Holt, Rinehart and Winston Staff. Holt Science & Technology Chapter 16: Life Science: Fishes, Amphibians, & Reptiles. 5th ed. 2004. (Illus.). pap. 12.86 (978-0-03-030221-3(8)) Holt, Rinehart & Winston.

—Holt Science & Technology Chptr. 9: Fishes & Amphibians: Chapter Resources - Tennessee Edition. 3rd ed. 2003. (YA). pap. 11.40 (978-0-03-069139-3(7)) Holt, Rinehart & Winston.

Hudak, Heather C. Reptiles & Amphibians. 2004. (Animal Facts Ser.). (Illus.). 24p. (J). lib. bdg. 24.45 (978-1-59036-204-4(7)) Weigl Pubs., Inc.

Kalman, Bobbie. Les Amphibiens. 2001. (FRE.). 32p. (J). pap. (978-2-920660-75-5(6)) Crabtree Publishing Co.

—Frogs & Other Amphibians. 2005. (What Kind of Animal Is It? Ser.). (Illus.). 32p. (J). (978-978-077-872-9(1)); (978-0-7787-2159-8(0)); pap. (978-0-7787-2217-5(1)) Crabtree Publishing Co.

—Ranas y otros Anfibios. 2007. (SPA.). 32p. (J). (gr. 1-2). (***978-0-7787-8837-9(7)**); pap. (***978-0-7787-8873-7(3))** Crabtree Publishing Co.

Kalman, Bobbie. What Is an Amphibian? 2000. (Science of Living Things Ser.). (978-0-606-18074-0(5)); (gr. 3-6). lib. bdg. 14.10 (978-0-613-22607-3(0)) Tandem Library Bks.

Kalman, Bobbie & Langille, Jacqueline. Qué Son los Anfibios? 2005. (Ciencia de los Seres Vivos Ser.). (SPA., Illus.). 32p. (J). (gr. 3-4). pap. (978-0-7787-8807-2(5)); (978-0-7787-8761-7(3)) Crabtree Publishing Co.

—What Is an Amphibian? 1999. (Science of Living Things Ser.). (Illus.). 32p. (J). (gr. 2-3). pap. (978-0-86505-952-8(7)); (978-0-86505-934-4(9)) Crabtree Publishing Co.

Kidd, Nina. Reptiles & Amphibians. Kidd, Nina, illus. 1998. (Draw Science Ser.). (Illus.). 64p. (J). (gr. 3-7). pap. 7.95 (978-1-56565-936-0(8) , 09368W) Lowell Hse. Juvenile.

Little & Large Sticker Activity - Reptiles & Amphibians. 2006. (J). 3.99 (978-1-933581-35-4(2)) Byeway Bks.

Mattern, Joanne. Reptiles & Amphibians. 2002. (Reading Room Collection). (Illus.). 24p. (J). (978-0-8239-8241-7(6)); lib. bdg. 18.75 (978-0-8239-3746-2(1)) Rosen Publishing Group, Inc., The.

Mattison, Christopher, et al. Reptiles & Amphibians. 2006. (Facts at Your Fingertips Ser.). (Illus.). 64p. (J). (***978-1-933834-04-7(8))** Brown Bear Books.

McLaurin, Thad, ed. Investigating Science - Amphibians & Reptiles. 2000. 48p. 9.95 (978-1-56234-365-1(3) , Mailbox Bks., The) Education Ctr., Inc.

Merker, Gerold & Mulks, Mitchell. Alterna: The Gray Banded Kingsnake. 2005. (Illus.). 64p. 19.95 (978-0-9760770-1-5(9)) LM Digital.

Mertz, Leslie A., et al. Grzimek's Student Animal Life Resource, 3 vols. 2005. (Illus.). (J). (978-0-7876-9408-1(8)); (978-0-7876-9409-8(6)); (978-0-7876-9410-4(X)) Thomson Gale. (UXL).

—Grzimek's Student Animal Life Resource: Amphibians, 3 vols. 2005. (Grzimek's Student Animal Life Resource Ser.). (Illus.). 600p. (J). 181.00 (978-0-7876-9407-4(X) , UXL) Thomson Gale.

Miller, Sara Swan. Amazing Amphibians. 2001. (Library Ser.). (Illus.). 64p. (J). (gr. 5-7). 25.50 (978-0-531-11793-4(6) , Watts, Franklin) Scholastic Library Publishing.

—Amazing Amphibians. 2001. (gr. 3-6). lib. bdg. 17.60 (978-0-613-37263-3(8)) Tandem Library Bks.

Miller-Schroeder, Patricia. Scales, Slime & Salamanders: The Science of Reptiles & Amphibians. 1999. (Science @ Work Ser.). (Illus.). 48p. (J). (gr. 4-6). lib. bdg. 27.12 (978-0-7398-0141-3(4)) Raintree.

Morgan, Sally. Amphibians. 2004. (Illus.). 48p. (J). 25.70 (978-1-4109-1046-2(6)); pap. 9.50 (978-1-4109-1342-5(2)) Harcourt Schl. Pubs.

—Frogs & Other Amphibians. 2001. (Illus.). 32p. (J). lib. bdg. 24.25 (978-1-930643-45-1(4)) Chrysalis Education.

Murray, Peter. Amphibians. 2004. (Science Around Us Ser.). 32p. (J). (gr. 2-6). 27.07 (978-1-59296-271-6(8)) Child's World, Inc.

O'Hare, Ted. Amphibians. 2006. (What Is an Animal Ser.). (Illus.). 24p. (gr. 1-4). 14.95 (978-1-59515-415-6(9)) Rourke Publishing, LLC.

Ohare, Ted. Amphibians. 2005. 24p. pap. 5.45 (978-1-59515-729-4(8)) Rourke Publishing, LLC.

O'Reilly, Wenda. GO FISH WILDLIFE REPTILES & AMPHIBIANS. 2007. n/ap. pap. 119.40 (***978-1-59960-018-5(8)***) Birdcage Pr.

Pettifor, Bonnie. Reptiles & Amphibians. 1999. (Gifted & Talented Ser.). (Illus.). 64p. (J). (gr. 1-3). pap. 5.95 (978-0-7373-0208-0(9)) Lowell Hse.

Phillips, Dee. Reptiles & Amphibians. 2006. (Blue Zoo Guides Ser.). (Illus.). 96p. 18.95 (978-1-58728-561-5(4) , Two Can Publishing) T&N Children's Publishing.

Pyers, Greg. Why Am I an Amphibian? 2005. (Illus.). 32p. (J). (gr. 3-5). lib. bdg. 27.50 (978-1-4109-2018-8(6)); (gr. 6-8). pap. 7.85 (978-1-4109-2025-6(9)) Steck-Vaughn.

Raintree Steck-Vaughn Staff. Encyclopedia of Reptiles & Amphibians. 2nd ed. 1999. (Encyclopedias of Animals Ser.). (Illus.). 240p. (J). (gr. 4-7). lib. bdg. 47.95 (978-0-7398-0685-2(8)) Raintree.

—Las Ranas. 1999. (Coleccion en Parejas). (SPA.). (J). pap., stu. ed. 21.50 (978-0-7398-0823-8(0)) Steck-Vaughn.

Reptiles & Amphibians. 2003. (Science Card Games Ser.). (gr. 1-3). 9.99 (978-0-7682-1992-0(2) , J53020) School Specialty Publishing.

Reptiles & Amphibians: Level P, 6 vols., Vol. 3. (Explorers Ser.). 32p. (gr. 3-6). 44.95 (978-0-7699-0614-0(1)) Shortland Pubns. (U. S. A.) Inc.

Richardson, Adele D. Amphibians. 2004. (First Facts Ser.). (Illus.). 24p. (J). lib. bdg. 21.26 (978-0-7368-2620-4(3)) Capstone Pr., Inc.

Royston, Angela. Amphibians. (Illus.). 32p. (YA). (gr. 2 up). lib. bdg. 27.10 (978-1-932333-33-6(9)) Chrysalis Education.

Rundquist, Eric M. Reptile & Amphibian Parasites. 1999. (Basic Domestic Reptile & Amphibian Library). (Illus.). 64p. (YA). (gr. 4-7). lib. bdg. 19.75 (978-0-7910-5080-4(7) , Chelsea Hse.) Facts On File, Inc.

Savage, Stephen. Amphibians. 1999. (What's the Difference? Ser.). (Illus.). 32p. (J). (gr. 2-4). lib. bdg. 25.69 (978-0-7398-1359-1(5)) Raintree.

—Amphibians. 2000. (What's the Difference? Ser.). (Illus.). 32p. (J). (ps-3). pap. 9.95 (978-0-7398-2038-4(9)) Steck-Vaughn.

Schaefer, Lola M. El Lagarto Cornudo. Abello, Patricia, tr. 2004. (SPA., Illus.). 12p. (J). 12.95 (978-1-4034-4300-7(9)) Heinemann Library.

—El Lagarto Cornudo. 2003. (SPA.). 24p. pap. 5.25 (978-1-4034-4306-9(8)) Heinemann Library.

—What Is an Amphibian? Saunders-Smith, Gail, ed. 2001. (Animal Kingdom Ser.). (Illus.). 24p. (J). (gr. k-1). lib. bdg. 14.60 (978-0-7368-0863-7(9) , Pebble Bks.) Capstone Pr., Inc.

—What Is an Amphibian?, 6 vols. (gr. k-2). 28.95 (978-0-7368-9113-4(7)) Red Brick Learning.

School Zone Publishing Company Staff. Reptiles & Amphibians. (Illus.). (J). 19.99 incl. audio compact disk (978-0-88743-978-0(0)) School Zone Publishing Co.

Schulte, Mary Knudson. Newts & Other Amphibians. 2005. (Scholastic News Nonfiction Readers Ser.). (Illus.). 24p. (J). (gr. 1-2). 19.00 (978-0-516-24934-6(7) , Children's Pr.) Scholastic Library Publishing.

Sill, Cathryn P. About Amphibians: A Guide for Children. Sill, John, illus. (J). 2004. 48p. (gr. 1-2). pap. 7.95 (978-1-56145-312-2(9)); 2001. 40p. (ps-4). 15.95 (978-1-56145-234-7(3)) Peachtree Pubs., Ltd.

Snedden, Robert. Amphibians. 2007. (J). (***978-1-59920-075-0(9)***) Smart Apple Media.

Solway, Andrew. Poison Frogs & Other Amphibians. 2006. (Illus.). 48p. (J). (978-1-4034-8225-9(X)); pap. (978-1-4034-8232-7(2)) Heinemann Library.

Spilsbury, Louise. Life Cycle of Amphibians. 2003. (gr. 3-6). lib. bdg. 15.90 (978-0-613-70782-4(6)) Tandem Library Bks.

Spilsbury, Louise & Spilsbury, Richard. Classifying Amphibians. 2003. (Classifying Living Things Ser.). (Illus.). 32p. (J). (gr. 3-5). lib. bdg. 24.22 (978-1-4034-0845-7(9)); pap. (978-1-4034-3343-5(7)) Heinemann Library.

—The Life Cycle of Amphibians. 2003. (From Egg to Adult Ser.). (J). lib. bdg. 24.22 (978-1-4034-0785-6(1)); 32p. pap. 7.50 (978-1-4034-3403-6(4)) Heinemann Library.

Spirn, Michele. Ripley's Cold-Blooded Creatures. 2004. (Illus.). 60p. (J). (978-0-439-63362-8(1)) Scholastic, Inc.

Stefoff, Rebecca. The Amphibian Class. 2007. (Family Trees Ser.). 96p. (J). lib. bdg. 32.79 (***978-0-7614-2692-9(2)*** , Benchmark Bks.) Cavendish, Marshall Corp.

Stewart, Melissa. Amphibians. 2001. (True Bks.). (Illus.). 48p. (J). (gr. 3-5). pap. 6.95 (978-0-516-25950-5(4) , Children's Pr.) Scholastic Library Publishing.

—Amphibians. 2001. (Illus.). 47p. (J). (ps-3). lib. bdg. 15.25 (978-0-613-53906-7(0)) Tandem Library Bks.

—Amphibians: Animals. 2001. (Animals Ser.). (Illus.). 48p. (J). (gr. 3-5). 25.00 (978-0-516-22037-6(3) , Children's Pr.) Scholastic Library Publishing.

Theodorou, Rod. Amphibians. 2007. (Illus.). 32p. (J). (***978-1-4034-9248-7(4)); (*978-1-4034-9241-8(7)***) Heinemann Library.

Townsend. Incredible Amphibians, 6 Pack. 2004. (Illus.). pap. 51.30 (978-1-4109-0858-2(5)) Harcourt Schl. Pubs.

Townsend, John. Incredible Amphibians. 2004. (J). pap. 9.50 (978-1-4109-0849-0(6)); (Illus.). 56p. lib. bdg. 31.36 (978-1-4109-0525-3(X)) Harcourt Schl. Pubs.

—Incredible Amphibians. 2005. (J). 56p. (978-1-4109-1719-5(3)); (978-1-4109-1710-2(X)) Steck-Vaughn.

Twist, Clint. Reptiles & Amphibians A-Z. 2005. (A-Z Ser.). (Illus.). 64p. (J). (gr. k-7). per. 26.20 (978-1-4103-0487-2(6) , Blackbirch Pr., Inc.) Thomson Gale.

—Reptiles & Amphibians Dictionary. 2005. (Illus.). 64p. (J). pap. (978-0-439-66828-6(X)) Scholastic, Inc.

What Is an Amphibian? 2005. (Animals, Animals, Animals Ser.). (YA). (gr. k-3). (978-0-7368-9092-2(0) , Pebble Bks.) Capstone Pr., Inc.

Wilkes, Sarah. Amphibians. 2006. (Illus.). 48p. (J). 30.00 (978-0-8368-6208-9(2)); (978-0-8368-6227-0(9)) Stevens, Gareth Inc. (World Almanac Library).

World Book, Inc. Staff, contrib. by. Amphibians & Reptiles of the United States & Canada. 2004. (World Book's Science & Nature Guides Ser.). (Illus.). 80p. (J). (978-0-7166-4209-1(3)) World Bk., Inc.

—Frogs & Other Amphibians. 2005. (World Book's Animals of the World Ser.). (Illus.). 64p. (J). (978-0-7166-1269-8(0)) World Bk., Inc.

AMPHIBIANS—FICTION

Leedy, Loreen. The Great Graph Contest. Leedy, Loreen, illus. (Illus.). 32p. (J). 2006. 6.95 (978-0-8234-2029-2(9)); 2005. 16.95 (978-0-8234-1710-0(7)) Holiday Hse., Inc.

Small, David. Eulalie & the Hopping Head. (Illus.). (J). 2005. pap. 16.95 incl. audio (978-1-59112-216-6(3)); 2005. pap. 18.95 incl. audio compact disk (978-1-59112-509-9(X)); 2003. 25.95 incl. audio (978-1-59112-217-3(1)) Live Oak Media.

There's a Toad in the Hole - English/ Spanish Bilingual Translation: A Big Fat Toad in the Hole. 2005. (J). cd-rom 13.95 (978-1-59649-304-9(6)) Whispering Pine Pr., Inc.

There's a Toad in the Hole - English/French Bilingual Translation: A Big Fat TOad in the Hole. 2005. (J). cd-rom 13.95 (978-1-59649-301-8(1)) Whispering Pine Pr., Inc.

There's a Toad in the Hole - English/Spanish Bilingual Translation: A Big Fat Toad in the Hole. 2005. (J). per. 15.95 (978-1-59649-303-2(8)) Whispering Pine Pr., Inc.

There's a Toad in the Hole: A Big Fat Toad in the Hole. 2005. (J). spiral bd. 15.95 (978-1-59649-299-8(6)); per. 15.95 (978-1-59649-298-1(8)); cd-rom 13.95 (978-1-59649-300-1(3)) Whispering Pine Pr., Inc.

AMUNDSEN, ROALD, 1872-1928

Broderick, Enid. Roald Amundsen. (Great Explorers Ser.). (Illus.). 48p. (J). (gr. 5 up). 2002. pap. 14.60 (978-0-8368-5171-7(4)); 2001. lib. bdg. 30.00 (978-0-8368-5011-6(4)) Stevens, Gareth Inc. (World Almanac Library).

Gogerly, Liz. Amundsen & Scott's Race to the South Pole. 2007. (J). (***978-1-4034-9761-1(3)***) Heinemann Library.

Harcourt School Publishers Staff. Antarctica Below Level: The Race for the South Pole. 3rd ed. 2002. (Trophies Reading Program Ser.). (Illus.). pap. 5.10 (978-0-15-323409-5(1)) Harcourt Schl. Pubs.

Karner, Julie. Roald Amundsen: The Conquest of the South Pole. 2006. (In the Footsteps of Explorers Ser.). (Illus.). 32p. (J). (gr. 3-9). pap. (978-0-7787-2468-1(9)); lib. bdg. (978-0-7787-2432-2(8)) Crabtree Publishing Co.

McNeil, Niki, et al. HOCPP 1102 Roald Amundsen. 2006. spiral bd. 18.50 (***978-1-60308-102-3(X)***) In the Hands of a Child.

Pipe, Jim. The Race to the South Pole. 2006. (Stories from History Ser.). 48p. (J). 14.95 (***978-0-7696-4722-7(7)***); pap. 6.95 (***978-0-7696-4702-9(2)***) School Specialty Publishing.

Thompson, Gare. Roald Amundsen & Robert Scott Race to the South Pole. 2007. (History Chapters Ser.). 48p. (J). (gr. 1-4). lib. bdg. 17.90 (***978-1-4263-0187-2(1)*** , National Geographic Children's Bks.) National Geographic Society.

AMUNDSEN SCOTT SOUTH POLE STATION (ANTARCTICA)

Hao, K. T. & Fulla, Monserrat. Scott y Amundsen: La Conquista del Polo Sur. Ingpen, Robert, illus. 2006. Tr. of Scott & Amundsen, The Conquest of the South Pole. (SPA.). (J). (gr. 6-8). 9.60 (978-84-316-7172-3(6) , W32815) Vicens-Vives, Editorial, S.A. ESP. *Dist:* Lectorum Pubns., Inc.

AMUSEMENT PARKS—FICTION

Adams, Diane. Zoom! Luthardt, Kevin, illus. 2005. 32p. (J). 15.95 (978-1-56145-332-0(3)) Peachtree Pubs., Ltd.

Anderson, M. T. Me, All Alone, at the End of the World. Hawkes, Kevin, illus. 2005. 40p. (J). (gr. 1-5). 16.99 (978-0-7636-1586-4(2)) Candlewick Pr.

Arena, Felice & Kettle, Phil. Wet World. Vane, Mitch, illus. 2004. (J). pap. (978-1-59336-356-7(7)) Mondo Publishing.

Auerbach, Annie. No Parent's Day. 2001. (gr. k-3). lib. bdg. 11.25 (978-0-613-43945-9(7)) Tandem Library Bks.

Cecil, Randy. Gator. Cecil, Randy, illus. 2007. (Illus.). 40p. (J). (ps-k). 15.99 (978-0-7636-2952-6(9)) Candlewick Pr.

Corlett, William. The Tunnel Behind the Waterfall. 2001. (gr. 7-12). lib. bdg. 13.00 (978-0-613-74172-9(2)) Tandem Library Bks.

Demeritt, Mary Anne. The Twilight Ride of the Pink Fairy. Daniel, Ellen, illus. 2006. (J). 17.95 (***978-1-58597-410-8(2)***) Leathers Publishing.

Dixon, Franklin W. Thrill Ride. 2005. 154p. (J). lib. bdg. 16.92 (***978-1-4242-0386-4(4)***) Fitzgerald Bks.

—Thrill Ride. 2005. (Illus.). 154p. (J). (978-1-4156-0585-1(8) , Aladdin) Simon & Schuster Children's Publishing.

Ewart, Franzeska G. Sita Snake Queen of Speed. 2008. (Illus.). 96p. (J). 15.95 (***978-1-84507-779-2(2)***); pap. 7.95 (***978-1-84507-748-8(2)***) Lincoln, Frances Ltd. GBR. *Dist:* Perseus Distribution.

Fontes, Justine. Cheerios Action Park Adventure. 2005. (Picture Clue Math Reader Ser.). (Illus.). 28p. (J). pap. (***978-0-439-70343-7(3)***) Scholastic, Inc.

Horse, Harry. Little Rabbit Lost. 2005. (Illus.). 32p. (J). (ps). per. 9.95 (978-1-56145-345-0(5) , Peachtree Junior) Peachtree Pubs., Ltd.

Jack Stanley. The Coaster Cats Go to the Amusement Park. Breuer, Paul, illus. 2006. 19p. (J). pap. 5.99 (***978-0-9776284-0-7(X)***) Forbes Literary Ltd. Inc.

Kalz, Jill. Tuckerbean at Waggle World. 2007. (Illus.). 32p. (J). (***978-1-4048-3389-0(7)***) Picture Window Bks.

—Tuckerbean at Waggle World. Mahan, Ben, illus. 2006. 32p. (J). lib. bdg. (***978-1-4048-3388-3(9)***) Picture Window Bks.

Lerangis, Peter. Whoa! Amusement Park Gone Wild! Talbot, Jim, illus. 2003. (Abracadabra Ser.: No. 7). 112p. (J). pap. 3.99 (978-0-439-38938-9(0) , Scholastic Paperbacks) Scholastic, Inc.

McCann, Jesse Leon. Scooby-Doo & the Weird Water Park. 2000. (gr. k-3). lib. bdg. 11.25 (978-0-613-26855-4(5)) Tandem Library Bks.

McMullan, Kate. Pearl & Wagner: Three Secrets. Alley, R. W., illus. 2004. (Easy-to-Read, Dial Ser.). 48p. (J). (gr. 2). 14.99 (978-0-8037-2574-4(4) , Dial) Penguin Group (USA) Inc.

Moloney, James. Scream World: Prepare for the Ride of Your Life! 2007. 72p. (J). pap. 3.95 (***978-0-7624-2926-4(7)*** , Running Pr. Kids) Running Pr. Bk. Pubs.

Morgan, Ruth. Behind You! Glyn, Chris, tr. Glyn, Chris, illus. 2003. 48p. pap. 11.95 (978-1-84323-269-8(3)) Beekman Bks., Inc.

—Funfair of Fear. Glynn, Chris, illus. 2002. 45p. pap. 11.95 (978-1-84323-121-9(2)) Beekman Bks., Inc.

Ogilvy, Ian. Measle & the Dragodon. 2006. 352p. (J). pap. 6.99 (978-0-06-058690-4(7) , Harper Trophy) HarperCollins Pubs.

Oldfield, Jenny. Wilde Party. 2004. (Wilde Family Ser.: Vol. 6). (Illus.). pap. (978-0-340-87323-6(X) , Hodder Children's Books) Hodder Children's Division.

—Wilde Ride. 2004. (Wilde Family Ser.: Vol. 5). (Illus.). pap. (978-0-340-87322-9(1) , Hodder Children's Books) Hodder Children's Division.

Perez, Monica & Saric, Lazar. Curious George Roller Coaster. 2007. (Illus.). 24p. (J). (ps-k). pap. 3.99 (***978-0-618-80040-7(9)***) Houghton Mifflin Co.

Powell, Jillian. Roller Coaster. Savage, Paul, illus. 2008. (Keystone Books). (J). pap. (***978-1-59889-902-3(3)***); 33p. (YA). (gr. 5-9). lib. bdg. 21.26 (***978-1-59889-850-7(7)***) Stone Arch Bks.

Remkiewicz, Frank, illus. Horrible Harry & the Drop of Doom. 2002. (Horrible Harry Ser.). (J). 11.49 (978-0-7587-0589-1(1)) Book Wholesalers, Inc.

Romano, Ray. Raymie, Dickie, & the Bean: Why I Love & Hate My Brothers. Locke, Gary, illus. 2007. 30p. (J). 18.00 (***978-1-4223-6806-0(8)***) DIANE Publishing Co.

Shudo, Takeshi. Art of Pokemon, the Movie: Mewtwo Strikes Back! 1999. (gr. 3-6). lib. bdg. 17.60 (978-0-613-22684-4(4)) Tandem Library Bks.

Smith, Michael & Smith, Debbie. Where's Whitney? 2000. 32p. 12.99 (978-0-310-20717-7(7)) Zondervan.

Stine, R. L. One Day at HorrorLand. 2003. (gr. 5-8). lib. bdg. 13.00 (978-0-613-70771-8(0)) Tandem Library Bks.

—Revenge of the Living Dummy. 2008. (Goosebumps Horrorland Ser.). 144p. (J). 5.99 (***978-0-439-91869-5(3)*** , Scholastic Paperbacks) Scholastic, Inc.

Stine, R. L. Terror Trips. 2007. (Goosebumps Graphix Ser.). 144p. (J). pap. 16.99 (978-0-439-85777-2(5)); (Illus.). pap. 8.99 (978-0-439-85780-2(5)) Scholastic, Inc. (Graphix).

Stine, R.L. Creep from the Deep. 2008. (Goosebumps Horrorland Ser.). 160p. (J). 5.99 (***978-0-439-91870-1(7)*** , Scholastic Paperbacks) Scholastic, Inc.

Taylor, Donna. Dream Come True. 2000. (gr. k-3). lib. bdg. 11.25 (978-0-613-31140-3(X)) Tandem Library Bks.

Tym, Kate. We Love the Seaside. 2007. (J). lib. bdg. 16.95 (***978-1-59566-369-6(X)***) QEB Publishing Inc.

Wilsdon, Christina. An Amusement Park Mystery in Ohio. Ebert, Len, illus. 2006. 26p. (J). 7.99 (978-1-59939-013-0(2) , Reader's Digest Young Families, Inc.) Reader's Digest Children's Publishing, Inc.

Ziefert, Harriet. Fun Land Fun! Kido, Yukiko, illus. 2006. (I'm Going to Read Ser.). 32p. (J). (ps-1). pap. 3.95 (978-1-4027-3416-8(6)) Sterling Publishing Co., Inc.

AMUSEMENTS

see also Charades; Circus; Concerts; Dance; Entertaining; Fortune-Telling; Games; Hobbies; Magic; Mathematical Recreations; Play; Puzzles; Recreation; Riddles; Scientific Recreations; Sports; Theater; Toys; Ventriloquism

Adam, Winky. Bugs. 2000. (Dover Little Activity Bks.). (Illus.). 64p. (J). pap., act. bk. ed. 1.50 (978-0-486-40969-6(4)) Dover Pubns., Inc.

—Flowers Follow-the-Dots. 1999. (Dover Little Activity Bks.). 64p. (J). pap. 1.50 (978-0-486-40732-6(2)) Dover Pubns., Inc.

—Little Egyptian Mazes. 1999. (Dover Little Activity Bks.). 64p. (J). (ps-3). pap. 1.50 (978-0-486-40733-3(0)) Dover Pubns., Inc.

Adams, Pam. Meet Mrs. Honey Doll. 1999. (J). (ps-3). 16.99 (978-0-85953-824-4(9)) Child's Play-International.

Aihara, Kazunori, illus. Let's Find Pokemon, Vol. 3. 2000. (Pokemon Ser.). 34p. (ps-3). 11.95 (978-1-56931-503-3(5)) Viz Media.

Albregts, Lisa & Cape, Elizabeth. Best Friends: Tons of Crazy, Cool Things to Do with Your Girlfriends. 1998. (Illus.). 152p. (J). (gr. 3-7). pap. 12.95 (978-1-55652-326-7(2)) Chicago Review Pr., Inc.

American Girl Editorial Staff. Pages & Pockets: Four Mini Books for Secrets & Stuff. Higgins, Anne Keegan, illus. 2004. (Americangirl Library(R) Ser.). 96p. (J). (gr. 3 up). 12.95 (978-1-58485-873-7(7)) American Girl Publishing, Inc.

American Heritage Dictionary Editors, ed. What Can I Do When it Rains? Zagarenski, Pamela, illus. 2004. (Good Beginnings Ser.). 4p. (J). (ps-k). bds. 3.95 (978-0-618-43170-0(5)) Houghton Mifflin Co. Trade & Reference Div.

—What Can I Do When it Rains? / Qué Puedo Hacer Cuando llueve? Zagarenski, Pamela, illus. 2004. (Good Beginnings Ser.). (SPA & ENG.). 4p. (J). (gr. k-ps). bds. 3.95 (978-0-618-44376-5(2)) Houghton Mifflin Co. Trade & Reference Div.

Anderson, Jon. Bad Guys Beware! Steck, Jim, illus. 2004. (Story Cards Ser.). 6p. (J). (gr. 1-17). bds. 9.99 (978-1-58476-271-3(3)) Innovative Kids.

Anderson, Maxine. Great Civil War Projects You Can Build Yourself. 2005. (Build It Yourself Ser.). (Illus.). 144p. (J). (ps-17). pap. 14.95 (978-0-9749344-1-9(0)) Nomad Pr.

Angel's Christmas Party Activity Fun. 2003. (Christmas Activity Bks.). (Illus.). 128p. (J). 3.98 (978-0-7525-6499-9(4)) Parragon, Inc.

Appelt, Kathi. Incredible Me! Date not set. 32p. (J). (ps-1). pap. 5.99 (978-0-06-443609-0(8)) HarperCollins Pubs.

—Incredible Me! Karas, G. Brian, illus. 2003. 32p. (J). (ps-1). lib. bdg. 16.89 (978-0-06-028623-1(7)) HarperCollins Pubs.

August/September: Full Color Monthly Activities for Grades 1-3. 2000. (Monthly Bks.). (Illus.). 64p. (J). (gr. 1-3). pap. 12.95 (978-0-88724-548-0(X) , CD-2090) Carson-Dellosa Publishing Co., Inc.

Avis, Ed. The Lobster Kids' Guide to Exploring Chicago. Battuz, Christine, illus. 2001. (Lobster Kids' City Explorers Ser.). 237p. (J). (ps-3). pap. 12.95 (978-1-894222-40-2(7)) Lobster Pr. CAN. *Dist:* Univ. of Toronto Pr.

Baillie, Marilyn & Ripley, Catherine, eds. The Anti-Boredom Book: 133 Completely Unboring Things to Do! 2000. (Illus.). 128p. (J). (gr. k-4). pap. 12.95 (978-1-895688-99-3(X) , Owl Bks.) Maple Tree Pr. CAN. *Dist:* Firefly Bks., Ltd.

Balloon Books Staff. I Can Draw. 2003. (Illus.). 18p. (J). pap., wbk. ed. 3.95 (978-1-4027-0494-9(1) , Balloon Bks.) Sterling Publishing Co., Inc.

—I Can Write. 2003. (Playful Learning Sticker Workbooks Ser.). (Illus.). 18p. (J). pap. 3.95 (978-1-4027-0496-3(8) , Balloon Bks.) Sterling Publishing Co., Inc.

—Sticker Workbook: I Can Trace. 2003. (Illus.). 18p. (J). pap. 3.95 (978-1-4027-0495-6(X) , Balloon Bks.) Sterling Publishing Co., Inc.

Bany-Winters, Lisa. Funny Bones: Comedy Games & Activities for Kids. 2002. (Illus.). 176p. (J). (gr. 4-7). pap. 14.95 (978-1-55652-444-8(7)) Chicago Review Pr., Inc.

Barbaresi, Nina. Clown Faces Stickers. 1998. (Illus.). 4p. (J). (ps-3). pap. 1.50 (978-0-486-27248-1(6)) Dover Pubns., Inc.

Bassachs, Anna G., et al. Tiny Hands: Autumn. 1998. (Tiny Hands Ser.). (Illus.). 48p. (J). (ps-k). pap. 7.95 (978-0-7641-0740-5(2)) Barron's Educational Series, Inc.

Beard, Daniel Carter. The American Boy's Handy Book: Turn-of-the-Century Classic of Crafts & Activities. 2003. (Dover Value Editions Ser.). (Illus.). 464p. (J). pap. 9.95 (978-0-486-43138-3(X)) Dover Pubns., Inc.

Beaton, Clare. Halloween Fun. 2004. (Fun Activity Ser.). (Illus.). 24p. (J). pap., act. bk. ed. 4.95 (978-0-7641-2750-2(0)) Barron's Educational Series, Inc.

Bender, Lionel. Tiger. 2005. (Illus.). 32p. (J). 18.95 (978-1-59389-193-0(8)) Chrysalis Education.

Benjamin's Super Sticker Book. 1998. (Illus.). 12p. (J). (ps-k). pap. 4.95 (978-0-8069-3766-3(1)) Sterling Publishing Co., Inc.

Beylon, Cathy. Doctor's Office Sticker Activity Book. 2000. (Dover Little Activity Bks.). (Illus.). 4p. (J). pap. 1.50 (978-0-486-40982-5(1)) Dover Pubns., Inc.

—Kids Cuts: Sticker Activity Book. 2003. (Dover Little Activity Bks.). (Illus.). 4p. (J). act. bk. ed. 1.50 (978-0-486-43011-9(1)) Dover Pubns., Inc.

—Learning Signs with 34 Stickers. 1999. (Illus.). (J). pap. 4.50 (978-0-486-40816-3(7)) Dover Pubns., Inc.

—Little Cars Stickers. 2000. (Illus.). 4p. (J). pap. 1.50 (978-0-486-40975-7(9)) Dover Pubns., Inc.

A B

—Little Mermaid Sticker Activity Book. 2001. (Illus.). 4p. (J). pap. 1.50 (978-0-486-41270-2(9)) Dover Pubns., Inc.

—Picnic Fun Sticker Activity Book. 2004. (Dover Little Activity Bks.). (Illus.). 4p. (J). 1.50 (978-0-486-43013-3(8)) Dover Pubns., Inc.

Bidder, Jane. Inventions We Use for Information & Entertainment. 2006. (Illus.). 32p. (J). lib. bdg. (978-0-8368-6899-9(4)) Stevens, Gareth Inc.

Big Fun! Date not set. (Furby Coloring & Activity Book Ser.). (Illus.). 96p. (J). pap. (978-0-7666-0412-4(8), Honey Bear Bks.) Modern Publishing.

Big Fun Learning Workbook. 2003. (Bumper Gold Stars Ser.). (Illus.). 256p. (J). 9.98 (978-1-4054-1717-4(X)); 9.98 (978-1-4054-1718-1(8)) Parragon, Inc.

Birmingham, Maria, et al. 365 Outdoor Activities. Kennedy, Anne, illus. 2000. 240p. (978-0-7853-3898-7(5), 3651500) Publications International, Ltd.

Biz Buzz Activity Set. 1998. (Illus.). 10p. (YA). stu. ed. 25.00 (978-1-893215-02-3(4)) Independent Means, Inc.

Blair, Beth & Ericsson, Jennifer. The Everything Kids' Halloween Puzzle. 2005. (Illus.). 144p. (J). pap., act. bk. ed. 6.95 (978-1-58062-959-1(8)) Adams Media Corp.

Blakey, Nancy. Go Outside! Over 130 Activities for Outdoor Adventures. 2002. (gr. 3-6). lib. bdg. 23.40 (978-0-613-56912-5(1)) Tandem Library Bks.

—Go Outside! Over 130 Activities for Outdoor Adventures. Doering, Dane Dean, illus. Doering, Dane Dean, photos by. 2004. 144p. (J). (gr. 3-6). 14.95 (978-1-58246-064-2(7) , Tricycle Pr.) Ten Speed Pr.

Bland, Celia. Arts & Entertainment. 1999. (Eyes on America Ser.). (Illus.). 29p. (J). pap. (978-1-56156-711-9(6)) Kidsbooks, Inc.

Borst, Donna & Mitchell, Judy, eds. The Best of Holidays & Seasonal Celebrations, PreK-K, Issues 5-8. 2000. (Illus.). 320p. (J). pap., tchr. ed. 24.95 (978-1-57310-235-3(0)) Teaching & Learning Co.

Bowdish, Lynea. The Carousel Ride. Bowdish, Lynea & Girouard, Patrick, illus. 1998. (Rookie Readers Ser.). 32p. (J). (gr. 1-2). 19.50 (978-0-516-20967-8(1) , Children's Pr.) Scholastic Library Publishing.

Bower, Bugs. Cartoons & Christmas Tunes. 2004. (Illus.). 68p. (J). 9.95 incl. audio compact disk (978-0-8256-2785-9(0) , NM10097) Music Sales Corp.

Boys Town Press Staff. Time to Enrich: Activity Kit. 2004. (Illus.). 134p. (gr. k-6). pap., spiral bd. 99.95 (978-1-889322-50-6(4) , 45-502); 187p. (gr. 7-12). pap., spiral bd. 99.95 (978-1-889322-51-3(2) , 45-503) Boys Town Pr.

Bree, Loris Theovin & Bree, Marlin. Kid's Squish Book: Slimy, Squishy, Sticky Things to Do That Should Only Be Done When Wearing Your Oldest Clothes. 2nd ed. 2002. (Illus.). 112p. (J). (ps-7). pap. 8.95 (978-1-892147-07-3(6)) Marlor Pr., Inc.

Brian, Sarah Jane. Brainiac's Secret Agent: Fun Activities for Spies of All Ages. 2005. (Activity Journal Ser.). 128p. act. bk. ed. 12.99 (978-0-88088-446-4(0)) Peter Pauper Pr. Inc.

Brighter Vision Publishing Staff. About Nursery Rhymes Activity Book. 2000. (My Discovery Bks.). (Illus.). 20p. (J). (ps). pap. 2.95 (978-1-55254-206-4(8)) Brighter Vision Pubns.

—Fun in the City & Country. 2000. (Learning Adventures Grade 1 Ser.). (Illus.). (J). (gr. 1-2). pap. 2.25 (978-1-55254-064-0(2)) Brighter Vision Pubns.

—Springtime. 2000. (Illus.). 32p. (J). (ps-1). pap. 1.59 (978-1-55254-077-0(4)) Brighter Vision Pubns.

—Zoo. 2000. (Learning Adventures Grade 1 Ser.). (Illus.). (J). (gr. 1-2). pap. 2.25 (978-1-55254-063-3(4)) Brighter Vision Pubns.

British Museum Staff & Wilson. Vikings. 1999. (Illus.). 16p. (gr. 4-7). pap. 5.95 (978-0-7141-2174-1(6)) Brimfield Pubns.

Bronston, Barri. The Lobster Kids' Guide to Exploring New Orleans. Fischer, Alison, ed. Battuz, Christine, illus. 2002. (Lobster Kids' City Explorers Ser.). 256p. (J). (ps-3). pap. 14.95 (978-1-894222-51-8(2)) Lobster Pr. CAN. *Dist:* Univ. of Toronto Pr.

Brown, Marc. Scared Silly! A Book for the Brave. 2000. (J). (978-0-606-19842-4(3)) Tandem Library Bks.

—Scared Silly! A Halloween Book for the Brave. Brown, Marc, illus. 2000. (Illus.). 64p. (J). (ps-5). 7.95 (978-0-316-10372-5(1)) Little Brown & Co.

Bruce, Linda. Entertainment Technology. 2006. (How Does It Work? Ser.). (Illus.). 32p. (J). (978-1-58340-792-9(8)) Smart Apple Media.

Buddy & Belle's Winter Fun. 1998. (Wipe-Off Activity Bks.). (Illus.). 16p. (J). (ps-1). wbk. ed. 3.79 (978-1-889319-25-4(2)) Trend Enterprises, Inc.

Bull, Jane. The Vacation Activity Book. 2007. 48p. (J). (gr. 1-3). 12.99 (978-0-7566-2942-7(X)) Dorling Kindersley Publishing, Inc.

Burgan, Michael. The World's Wildest Roller Coasters. 2000. (Built for Speed Ser.). (Illus.). 48p. (J). (gr. 3-4). lib. bdg. 21.26 (978-0-7368-0571-1(0) , Capstone High-Interest Bks.) Capstone Pr., Inc.

Burke, Jennifer S. Rainy Days. 2000. (Illus.). 24p. (J). (gr. 4-7). lib. bdg. 12.95 (978-0-613-50492-8(5)) Tandem Library Bks.

—Sunny Days. 2000. (gr. k-3). lib. bdg. 12.95 (978-0-613-62223-3(5)) Tandem Library Bks.

Burnett, Frances Hodgson. The Secret Garden Paper Dolls. adapted ed. 1998. (Illus.). 24p. (J). (ps-3). 7.95 (978-0-694-00969-5(5)) HarperCollins Pubs.

Burns, Marilyn. Brown Paper School Book: Or How to Solve a Problem Twice Your Size. 2006. 128p. (J). pap. 12.99 (978-0-316-05974-9(9)) Little Brown & Co.

Burton, Marilee Robin, et al. 365 after School Activities. Ulrich, George, illus. 2001. 240p. (J). lib. bdg. 24.95 (978-1-56674-294-8(3)) Forest Hse. Publishing Co., Inc.

Bussard, Paula. Come to a Critter County Party: Children Critter County Activity Book - Discover How You Can Honor Jesus. Kenney, Cindy, ed. Maurice, Dan, illus. 1999. (Celebrate Jesus! Ser.). 64p. (J). 7.00 (978-1-57849-176-6(2)) Mainstay Church Resources.

Button, Beth & Mitchell, Judy, eds. The Best of Holidays & Seasonal Celebrations: Kid Space - School Yard Learning Adventures. 2000. (Illus.). 128p. (J). (ps-3). pap., tchr. ed. 13.95 (978-1-57310-261-2(X)) Teaching & Learning Co.

Byrd, Sandra. Stuff 2 Do: A-to-Z Activities for Girls Like You. 2003. (Girls Like You Ser.). (Illus.). 160p. (J). pap. 8.99 (978-0-7642-2753-0(X)) Bethany Hse. Pubs.

Carlson, Nancy. Harriet & the Roller Coaster. Carlson, Nancy, illus. unabr. ed. (Illus.). (J). (gr. k-3). 24.95 incl. audio (978-0-941078-56-6(6)); pap. 15.95 incl. audio (978-0-941078-54-2(X)); pap., tchr. ed. 31.95 incl. audio (978-0-941078-55-9(8)) Live Oak Media.

Castaldo, Nancy F. Winter Day Play! Activities, Crafts, & Games for Indoors & Out. 2001. (Illus.). 176p. (J). pap. 13.95 (978-1-55652-381-6(5)) Chicago Review Pr., Inc.

Chapman, Vera. Quest for Camelot Kayley in Camelot Jewel Sticker Book. 1998. (Quest for Camelot Ser.). (Illus.). 16p. (J). (ps-3). pap. 5.99 (978-0-590-02436-5(1)) Scholastic, Inc.

Chicken Run with Book & Poster & Crayons & Paint Brush. 2000. (J). (ps-3). pap. (978-0-7696-1680-3(1) , American Education Publishing) School Specialty Publishing.

Cole, David & Trees Cole, Mary Lee. San Francisco. 2001. (Lobster Kids' City Explorers Ser.). 249p. (J). (ps-3). pap. 12.95 (978-1-894222-28-0(8)) Lobster Pr. CAN. *Dist:* Univ. of Toronto Pr.

Coll, Shane. The Hulk Bk. 3: Action Scenes Book with Stickers. Mangiat, Jeff, illus. 2003. (Hulk Ser.). 16p. (J). (ps-2). pap. 3.99 (978-0-06-051901-8(0)) HarperCollins Pubs.

Collings, Julie. Utterly Elegant Tea Parties: For Dolls, Daddies, & Other Guests. 2005. (Illus.). 22p. (J). (ps-3). pap. 12.95 (978-1-59174-092-6(4)) Klutz.

Cousins, Lucy. Maisy's Pirate Treasure Hunt. Cousins, Lucy, illus. 2004. (Maisy Ser.). (Illus.). 12p. (J). (gr. k-k). bds. 10.99 (978-0-7636-2469-9(1)) Candlewick Pr.

—Maisy's Twinkly Crinkly Fun Book. Cousins, Lucy, illus. 2004. (Maisy Ser.). (Illus.). 12p. (J). (gr. k-ps). 10.99 (978-0-7636-2273-2(7)) Candlewick Pr.

Cullen, Ruth. Brainiac's Giant Book of Gross Outs. 2005. (Activity Journal Ser.). 128p. 14.99 (978-0-88088-448-8(7)) Peter Pauper Pr. Inc.

Dagel, Carol K. The Gift of Time Coupon Booklet for Children. 2000. (Illus.). 32p. (J). (ps-3). pap. 9.95 (978-0-9704578-0-6(4)) Image & Vision Builders, Inc.

Dalmatian Press Staff. Beginning Sounds. rev. ed. 1999. (Tools Ser.). (Illus.). 32p. (J). (ps up). pap. 2.29 (978-1-57759-192-4(5)) Dalmatian Pr.

Daniel in the Lion's Den. Date not set. (J). stu. ed., act. bk. ed. 1.49 (978-0-88271-233-8(0) , 1749) Regina Pr., Malhame & Co.

Danziger, Paula. Amber Brown Scrap Book. Ross, Tony, illus. 2006. 24p. (J). (gr. 2). pap. 7.99 (978-0-14-240620-5(1) , Puffin) Penguin Group (USA) Inc.

de Jongh, Tim & Vandyck, William. How to Have the Best Holiday Ever. Rowe, Alan, illus. 96p. pap. 7.99 (978-0-340-66730-9(3) , Coronet) Hodder General Publishing Division GBR. *Dist:* Trafalgar Square Publishing.

December: Full Color Monthly Activities for Grades 1-3. 2000. (Monthly Bks.). (Illus.). 96p. (gr. 1-3). pap. 12.99 (978-0-88724-551-0(X) , CD-2093) Carson-Dellosa Publishing Co., Inc.

Digimon Victory. 1999. (Digimon Sticker Activity Bks.). (Illus.). 25p. (J). (ps-2). pap. (978-0-7666-0571-8(X)) Modern Publishing.

Disney Staff. One-of-a-Kind Family. 2003. (Illus.). (J). pap. 2.99 (978-0-7364-2172-0(6) , RH/Disney) Random Hse. Children's Bks.

Dorling Kindersley Publishing Staff. Playtime. 1999. (Bath Bks.). (Illus.). 10p. (J). (ps-k). 6.99 (978-0-7894-4324-3(4)) Dorling Kindersley Publishing, Inc.

—Speedy Machines. 2005. (J). bds. 6.99 (978-0-7566-1109-5(1)) Dorling Kindersley Publishing, Inc.

—Springtime. 2005. (Dk Picture Stickers Ser.). 16p. (J). pap. 3.99 (978-0-7566-0845-3(7)) Dorling Kindersley Publishing, Inc.

—Villains of the DC Universe. 2005. (Ultimate sticker Bks.). 16p. (J). pap. 6.99 (978-0-7566-1123-1(7)) Dorling Kindersley Publishing, Inc.

Dorling Kindersley Publishing Staff, ed. Shark Tale. 2004. (Ultimate Sticker Bks.). (Illus.). 16p. (J). pap. 6.99 (978-0-7566-0553-7(9)) Dorling Kindersley Publishing, Inc.

Douglas, Vincent. Daily Learning Drills: Grade 1. 2003. (Daily Learning Drills Ser.). (Illus.). 416p. (J). (gr. 1-1). pap. 10.95 (978-0-7696-3091-5(X) , American Education Publishing) School Specialty Publishing.

—Daily Learning Drills: Grade 2. 2003. (Daily Learning Drills Ser.). (Illus.). 416p. (J). (gr. 2). pap. 10.95 (978-0-7696-3092-2(8) , American Education Publishing) School Specialty Publishing.

—Daily Learning Drills: Grade 3. 2003. (Daily Learning Drills Ser.). (Illus.). 416p. (J). (gr. 3-3). pap. 10.95 (978-0-7696-3093-9(6) , American Education Publishing) School Specialty Publishing.

—Daily Learning Drills: Grade K. 2003. (Daily Learning Drills Ser.). (Illus.). 416p. (J). (gr. k-k). pap. 10.95 (978-0-7696-3090-8(1) , American Education Publishing) School Specialty Publishing.

Douglas, Vincent & School Specialty Publishing Staff. Play Throughout the Year. 2004. (Playful Learning Ser.). (Illus.). 128p. (J). (gr. k-k). pap. 10.95 (978-0-7696-3302-2(1) , American Education Publishing) School Specialty Publishing.

—Puzzles, Games, & Word Searches. 2003. (Homework Helpers Ser.). (Illus.). 32p. (J). (gr. 2-2). pap. 2.99 (978-0-7696-2926-1(1) , American Education Publishing) School Specialty Publishing.

—Summer Link Reading, Grades 1-2. 2004. (Summer Link Ser.). (Illus.). 96p. (J). (ps-6). pap. 6.95 (978-0-7696-3321-3(8) , American Education Publishing) School Specialty Publishing.

—Summer Link Reading, Grades 2-3. 2004. (Summer Link Ser.). (Illus.). 96p. (J). (ps-6). pap. 6.95 (978-0-7696-3322-0(6) , American Education Publishing) School Specialty Publishing.

—Summer Link Reading, Kindergarten-Grade 1. 2004. (Summer Link Ser.). (Illus.). 96p. (J). (ps-6). pap. 6.95 (978-0-7696-3320-6(X) , American Education Publishing) School Specialty Publishing.

—Summer Link Reading, Preschool-Kindergarten. 2004. (Summer Link Ser.). (Illus.). 96p. (J). (ps-6). pap. 6.95 (978-0-7696-3319-0(6) , American Education Publishing) School Specialty Publishing.

Dover Staff. Jewish Fun Books, 10 bks. 2000. (Illus.). (J). pap. 10.00 (978-0-486-41188-0(5)) Dover Pubns., Inc.

Dower, Laura. Road Trippin' Back-Seat Shrek-Tivity Book. Henderson, Bill, illus. 2004. (Shrek 2 Ser.). 64p. (J). act. bk. ed. 14.99 (978-0-439-64134-0(9) , Tangerine Pr.) Scholastic, Inc.

Drake, Jane & Love, Ann. The Kids Winter Handbook. Collins, Heather, illus. (Fun for All Seasons Ser.). 128p. (J). (gr. 4-6). 2004. (978-1-55074-969-4(2)); 2001. (978-1-55337-033-8(3)) Kids Can Pr., Ltd.

—My Vacation Place: A Memory Book. Collins, Heather, illus. 2001. 128p. (YA). (gr. 1 up). pap. (978-1-55074-971-7(4)) Kids Can Pr., Ltd.

Durant, Alan. Spot the Ball. 2003. (Illus.). 88p. (J). pap. 6.99 (978-0-330-35129-4(X) , Pan) Pan Macmillan GBR. *Dist:* Trafalgar Square Publishing.

Educational Publishing Concept Staff. Party Time, Critter County Activity Center: Children's CD-ROM. 1999. (Celebrate Jesus! 2000 50-Day Spiritual Adventure Ser.). (J). (ps-2). cd-rom 15.00 (978-1-57849-177-3(0)) Mainstay Church Resources.

El Dorado Activity Book Kit. 2000. (J). (ps-3). pap. (978-0-7696-1670-4(4) , American Education Publishing) School Specialty Publishing.

El Dorado Sticker Storybook. 2000. 20p. (J). (ps-3). pap. 3.29 (978-0-7696-1671-1(2) , American Education Publishing) School Specialty Publishing.

Elliott, Lynne. Children & Games in the Middle Ages. 2004. (Medieval World Ser.). (Illus.). 32p. (J). (978-0-7787-1349-4(0)); pap. (978-0-7787-1381-4(4)) Crabtree Publishing Co.

Enright, Dominique & MacDonald, Guy. The Boys' Book: How to Be the Best at Everything. Catlow, Niki, illus. 2007. (Boys' Book Ser.). 128p. (J). (gr. 4-7). 9.99 (***978-0-545-01628-5(2)*** , Scholastic Pr.) Scholastic, Inc.

Foley, Cate. Weekend Fun, 6 bks., Set. 2004. (Illus.). 24p. (J). (ps-2). 87.00 (978-0-516-22998-0(2) , Children's Pr.) Scholastic Library Publishing.

Folmer, A. P. Fabulous Rainy Day Fun Book. (FRE., Illus.). (Orig.). (J). pap. 7.99 (978-0-590-74412-6(7)) Scholastic, Inc.

Foster, Juliana. The Girls' Book: How to Be the Best at Everything. Enright, Amanda, illus. 2007. (Girls' Book Ser.). 128p. (J). (gr. 4-7). 9.99 (***978-0-545-01629-2(0)*** , Scholastic Pr.) Scholastic, Inc.

Foxx, Kylie. Pajama Parties: Wacky Charades. Ledesma, Sophie, illus. 2001. 16p. tchr. ed. 7.95 (978-0-7611-2357-6(1) , 12357) Workman Publishing Co., Inc.

Fredricks, Faye, et al. Busy Day Activities & Bulletins for Kids. 2000. (ReproBooks Ser.). (Illus.). 112p. (J). (gr. k-8). pap. 8.99 (978-0-8010-4449-6(9)) Baker Bks.

Fremont, Victoria & Lavash, Ted. Word & Picture Rebus Fun. 1999. (Dover Little Activity Bks.). 64p. (J). pap. 1.50 (978-0-486-40734-0(9)) Dover Pubns., Inc.

Gaspas, Dianne. Eastern Woodlands Sticker Picture. 1999. (Illus.). (J). pap. 5.95 (978-0-486-40817-0(5)) Dover Pubns., Inc.

Gaydos, Nora. Let's Play!, Level 4. Sams, B. B., illus. 2004. (Now I'm Reading! Ser.: Vol. 1). 128p. (J). (ps-2). 16.99 (978-1-58476-246-1(2)) Innovative Kids.

Gilpin, Rebecca. Fairy Things to Make & Do Kid Kit. McCafferty, Jan, illus. 2004. (Kid Kits Ser.). 32p. (J). 15.99 (978-1-58086-727-6(8)); 15.99 (978-1-58086-731-3(6)) EDC Publishing. (Usborne).

Givens, David. For the Kids: A Family-Friendly Guide to Outings & Activities. 2003. (Illus.). 220p. (YA). pap. 20.95 (978-1-904148-27-2(1)) Liffey Pr., The IRL. *Dist:* Dufour Editions, Inc.

Go! Exercise with the Teletubbies. 2002. (J). pap. 7.98 incl. audio (978-0-7379-0170-2(5) , 76716) Rhino Entertainment Co, A Warner Music Group Co.

Golden Books Staff. Fun & Fancy. Disney Productions Staff, illus. 2004. 12p. (J). (ps-2). pap. 3.99 (978-0-7364-2233-8(1) , Golden/Disney) Random Hse. Children's Bks.

—Monster Bash! Hall, Susan T., illus. 2004. 32p. (J). (ps-2). pap. 4.99 (978-0-375-82814-0(1) , Golden Bks.) Random Hse. Children's Bks.

—Mulan II Lesson Number One: A Hero's Journey. Rodriguez, Angel, illus. 2005. 64p. (J). (ps-2). pap. 2.99 (978-0-7364-2235-2(8) , Golden/Disney) Random Hse. Children's Bks.

—On the Go! 2000. (Illus.). 128p. (J). (ps-2). pap. 0.99 (978-0-307-44330-4(2) , Golden Bks.) Random Hse. Children's Bks.

—Surprise Disguise! Baker, Darrell, illus. 2004. 32p. (J). (ps-2). pap. 2.99 (978-0-375-82792-1(7) , Golden Bks.) Random Hse. Children's Bks.

Goldstein, Doris. Imagination Collaboration. Shupe, Bobbi, illus. 1998. 16p. (J). (ps-k). pap. 5.95 (978-0-9655442-6-9(5)) Business Word, The.

Golosi, Rosanne. Best Friends Forever! Martini, Angela, illus. 2005. 64p. (J). (***978-0-439-80072-3(2)***) Scholastic, Inc.

Gordon, Lynn. 52 Christmas Activities. Johnson, Karen, illus. 2004. 52p. 6.95 (978-0-8118-4123-8(5)) Chronicle Bks. LLC.

Green, Yuko. Anastasia from Russia Sticker Paper Doll. 1998. (Dover Little Activity Bks.). (Illus.). 4p. (J). (gr. k-5). pap. 1.50 (978-0-486-40514-8(1)) Dover Pubns., Inc.

Greene, Lisa A. Toy Cars Stickers. 1998. (Shiny Stickers Ser.). (Illus.). 4p. (J). (gr. k-3). pap. 1.50 (978-0-486-27692-2(9)) Dover Pubns., Inc.

Grossnickle, Anna H. What Can You Do in the Snow? Kliros, Thea, illus. 1999. 10p. (J). (ps-k). pap. 5.95 (978-0-688-16078-4(6)) HarperCollins Pubs.

—What Can You Do in the Wind? Kliros, Thea, illus. 1999. 10p. (J). (ps-k). pap. 5.95 (978-0-688-16079-1(4)) HarperCollins Pubs.

Hailsip, Chrissy & Fulton, Nancy. Month-by-Month Artic Carry-Over Fun. Hart, Chuck & Turner, Christopher, illus. 1999. 165p. (J). (ps-6). spiral bd. 31.95 (978-1-58650-079-5(1) , BK-277) Super Duper Pubns.

Hantman, Clea. Hey, Day! 2001. 74.75 (978-0-06-000169-8(0)) HarperCollins Pubs.

Harder Tangvald, Christine. So Big Activity Book. Regan, Dana, illus. 2001. 32p. (J). (ps-k). pap. 9.99 (978-0-570-07110-5(0)) Concordia Publishing Hse.

—So Smart. 2001. (Illus.). 32p. (J). (ps-k). pap., act. bk. ed. 9.99 (978-0-570-07111-2(9)) Concordia Publishing Hse.

Hays, Anna Jane. Ready, Set, Preschool! Stories, Poems & Picture Games with an Educational Guide for Parents. Kelley, True, illus. 2005. 40p. (J). (ps-1). 16.95 (978-0-375-82519-4(3) , Knopf Bks. for Young Readers) Random Hse. Children's Bks.

Hedderwick, Mairi. Katie Morag's Rainy Day Book. 2000. (Illus.). 32p. (J). (gr. k-2). 17.95 (978-0-370-32550-7(8)) Random Hse. GBR. *Dist:* Trafalgar Square Publishing.

Henley, Karyn. Sunlight & Starry Night. 2000. (Tails Activity Bks.). (Illus.). (J). pap. 7.99 (978-0-8054-2286-3(2)) B&H Publishing Grp.

Herman, Debbie & Koffsky, Ann D. Beyond Turkey: A Thankgiving Feast of Fun, Facts, & Activities. 2005. (Let's Celebrate Ser.). (Illus.). 48p. (J). pap. 8.99 (978-0-7641-3063-2(3)) Barron's Educational Series, Inc.

Heston, Lauren. Water Baby: A First Fun Book of Water Skills. 1999. (Illus.). 48p. (J). 16.95 (978-1-902618-51-7(3)) Element Children's Bks.

Highlights for Children Editorial Staff, compiled by. The Third Jumbo Book of Hidden Pictures, Vol. 3. 2003. (Illus.). 96p. (J). (gr. 6-9). pap. 6.95 (978-1-56397-276-8(X)) Boyds Mills Pr.

Hines, Anna Grossnickle. Assorted What Can You Do in the Sun & Rain. 1999. (J). pap. 11.90 (978-0-688-17170-4(2)) HarperCollins Pubs.

—What Can You Do in the Sun? Kliros, Thea, illus. 1999. 10p. (J). (ps-k). pap. 6.95 (978-0-688-16080-7(8)) HarperCollins Pubs.

Holabird, Katharine. My First Activity Book. Craig, Helen, illus. 2007. 32p. (J). 9.99 (978-0-448-44550-2(6) , Grosset & Dunlap) Penguin Group (USA) Inc.

Horne, Richard & Szirtes, Helen. 101 Things to Do Before You're Old & Boring. 2006. (Illus.). 224p. (YA). (gr. 7 up). pap. 9.95 (978-0-8027-7745-4(7)) Walker & Co.

Hurley, Jo. Secret Spy Super Ear. Baumann, Marty, illus. 2003. 32p. (J). pap. 8.99 (978-0-439-52484-1(9) , Tangerine Pr.) Scholastic, Inc.

Hyde, Andrew. Experience the Point: Unofficial Guidebook to Cedar Point. 2nd ed. 2003. 87p. (YA). pap. 10.95 (978-0-7414-1499-1(6)) Infinity Publishing.

Imagineers Books Staff, ed. Imagineering Field Guide to Disney's Animal Kingdom at Walt Disney World. 2007. 128p. (ps-17). pap. 9.95 (***978-1-4231-0320-2(3)*** , Disney Editions) Disney Pr.

Jenkins, Sandra. My Play & Learn Book. (Illus.). (J). (ps). pap. 19.99 (978-0-590-24537-1(6)) Scholastic, Inc.

Jolly Jungle. Date not set. (Sticker Shapes Ser.). (Illus.). 16p. (J). 2.98 (978-0-7525-8140-8(6)) Parragon, Inc.

The Journey's of Paul. Date not set. (J). stu. ed., act. bk. ed. 1.49 (978-0-88271-232-1(2) , 1748) Regina Pr., Malhame & Co.

Jumbo Activity. Date not set. (Illus.). 256p. (J). 5.98 (978-1-4054-0698-7(4)) Parragon, Inc.

June/July: Full Color Monthly Activities for Grades 1-3. 2000. (Monthly Bks.). (Illus.). 64p. (J). (gr. 1-3). pap. 12.95 (978-0-88724-557-2(9) , CD-2099) Carson-Dellosa Publishing Co., Inc.

Jungle Fun. 2003. 32p. 12.98 (978-1-4054-2004-4(9)) Parragon, Inc.

Kawai, Ritsuko. Hamtaro Pop-Up Playset. Kawai, Ritsuko, illus. 2003. (Hamtaro Ser.). (Illus.). 20p. (YA). pap. 16.95 (978-1-56931-846-1(8)) Viz Media.

Kemp, Marion, et al. All Together. Barnes-Murphy, Rowan, illus. Date not set. (Whizz Bang Bumper Bk.). 63p. (J). 129.15 (978-0-582-18259-2(X)) Addison-Wesley Longman, Ltd. GBR. *Dist:* Trans-Atlantic Pubns., Inc.

Kilby, Janice Eaton, et al. The Book of Wizard Craft: In Which the Apprentice Finds Spells, Potions, Fantastic Tales & 50 Enchanting Things to Make. Burnett, Lindy, illus. deluxe ed. 2001. 144p. (J). (gr. 4-6). 7.95 (978-1-57990-206-3(5)) Lark Bks.

Klein, Nancy C. Healing Images for Children Activity Book: For Days When Quiet Activities Are Best. Holden, Matthew, illus. 2001. 90p. (J). (gr. k-7). pap. 12.95 (978-0-9636027-4-9(8)) Inner Coaching.

Klimt, Gustav. Klimt 16 Art Stickers. 1999. (Illus.). 4p. pap. 1.50 (978-0-486-40831-6(0)) Dover Pubns., Inc.

Klutz Editors. Amazing Lacing. 2005. (Chicken Socks Ser.). (Illus.). 22p. (J). (ps-7). 9.95 (978-1-59174-356-9(7)) Klutz.

Klutz Press Staff. The Amazing Booka-Ma-Thing for the Backseat: Thousands of Miles Worth of Hands-On Games & Activities. 1998. (Illus.). 20p. (J). (gr. 4-7). spiral bd. 16.95 (978-1-57054-169-8(8)) Klutz.

Klutz Press Staff, ed. Klutz Googly Eyes: Making Funny Faces. 2003. (Illus.). 40p. (J). spiral bd. 6.95 (978-1-59174-256-2(0)) Klutz.

—The Only Coloring, Puzzle, Game, Dot-to-Dot Activity Book: You'll Ever Need! 2002. (Illus.). 120p. (J). (gr. 4-7). spiral bd., act. bk. ed. 21.95 (978-1-57054-767-6(X)) Klutz.

Kranz, Linda. My Nature Book: A Journal & Activity Book for Kids. Garrow, Linda & McGee, John F., illus. 2004. 128p. (YA). (gr. 1-6). pap. 12.95 (978-1-55971-893-6(5) , NorthWord Bks. for Young Readers) T&N Children's Publishing.

Kubistal, Lester. Kaleidoscopic Design Coloring Book. 1999. 32p. (J). pap. 3.95 (978-0-486-40566-7(4)) Dover Pubns., Inc.

Kuffner, Trish. Preschooler's Busy Book: 365 Creaative Games & ActivitiesTo Occupy 2-6 Yr Olds: 365 Creaative Games & ActivitiesTo Occupy 2-6 Yr Olds. 1998. (Illus.). 406p. pap. 9.95 (978-0-671-31633-4(8)) Meadowbrook Pr.

Lacome, Susie. The Big Shiny Sparkly Activity Book. 2003. (Illus.). 10p. (J). pap., act. bk. ed. 9.98 (978-0-7624-1647-9(5) , Courage Bks.) Running Pr. Bk. Pubs.

Ladybird Books Staff. Games We Like. 2nd ed. (Key Words Readers Ser.: A Series, No. 641-9a). (Illus.). 56p. (J). (ps-5). 3.50 (978-0-7214-0555-1(X) , Dutton Juvenile) Penguin Group (USA) Inc.

LaFontaine, Bruce. Construction Trucks Stickers. 2000. (Illus.). 4p. (J). (ps-5). 1.50 (978-0-486-40973-3(2)) Dover Pubns., Inc.

Lakeshore Learning Materials Staff, contrib. by. Take Home Learning Packs Level 2, 16 vols., Set. 2000. (J). pap. 295.00 (978-1-929255-14-6(4)) Lakeshore Learning Materials.

—Take Home Learning Packs Set, 2 vols., Set. 2000. (J). pap. 550.00 (978-1-929255-12-2(8)) Lakeshore Learning Materials.

Lane, Sheila Mary & Kemp, Marion. Start Here. Birch, Linda, illus. Date not set. (Whizz Bang Bumper Bk.). 64p. (J). pap. 129.15 (978-0-582-19331-4(1)) Addison-Wesley Longman, Ltd. GBR. *Dist:* Trans-Atlantic Pubns., Inc.

Lapin, Gloria. Fun Times: Little Books to Make & Read with Other. 1999. (J). (ps-3). pap. 2.95 (978-1-55254-019-0(7)) Brighter Vision Pubns.

Lawder, Ursula. For Baby. Lawder, Ursula, illus. 1999. (Illus.). (J). bds. 14.95 (978-0-9703905-0-9(5)) Lawder, Ursula.

Learning Everywhere. 2001. (Learning Everywhere Ser.). (Illus.). 96p. (J). (ps-k). pap. 9.95 (978-1-55254-229-3(7)) Brighter Vision Pubns.

Liebman, Dan. Mini-Book Fun Pack 2, 9 bks., Vol. 2. 2002. (I Want to Be Ser.). (Illus.). 24p. (J). (ps-2). pap. 4.99 (978-1-55297-582-4(7)) Firefly Bks., Ltd.

Lithgow, John. Boredom Blasters: Rainy Day Fun Edition. 2005. (Illus.). 64p. (YA). pap. 14.95 (978-0-7624-2212-8(2) , Running Pr. Kids) Running Pr. Bk. Pubs.

—Boredom Blasters: Travel Edition. 2005. (Illus.). 64p. 14.95 (978-0-7624-2213-5(0) , Running Pr. Kids) Running Pr. Bk. Pubs.

Lorenz Books Staff. Dressing Up. 2000. (Sticker Fun Ser.). (Illus.). 16p. (ps-k). pap. 5.00 (978-0-7548-0542-7(5)) Anness Publishing GBR. *Dist:* National Bk. Network.

—Party. 2000. (Sticker Fun Ser.). (Illus.). 16p. (ps-k). pap. 5.00 (978-0-7548-0538-0(7) , Lorenz Bks.) Anness Publishing GBR. *Dist:* National Bk. Network.

Macaulay, David. Shortcut. Macaulay, David, illus. 1999. (Illus.). 64p. (J). (gr. 4-6). pap. 8.95 (978-0-618-00607-6(9) , Walter Lorraine) Houghton Mifflin Co. Trade & Reference Div.

Macaulay, David & Macaulay, David. Shortcut. 1999. (Illus.). (J). (gr. 3-7). lib. bdg. 16.40 (978-0-613-28064-8(4)) Tandem Library Bks.

Madruga, Dina Jo. The Lobster Kids' Guide to Exploring San Diego. Fischer, Alison, ed. 2002. (Lobster Kids' City Explorers Ser.). (Illus.). 256p. (J). (ps-3). pap. 14.95 (978-1-894222-52-5(0)) Lobster Pr. CAN. *Dist:* Univ. of Toronto Pr.

Maizels, Jennie. Things to Do Book. Maizels, Jennie, illus. 2007. (Illus.). 20p. (J). (gr. k-3). 15.99 (978-0-7636-3371-4(2)) Candlewick Pr.

Marsh, Carole. The Budding Genius Book of Reproducible Activities on Latin, Chess, Bridge, Shakespeare, Physics & More for Pre-Schoolers, Kindergartens & Early Elementary Students. 2001. (Here & Now Series!). (Illus.). 48p. (J). (gr. k-6). pap. 7.95 (978-0-635-00265-5(5)) Gallopade International.

Marshall, Peter, et al. Sounding Forth the Trumpet Children's Activity Book: Ages 5-8. 2001. (Illus.). 72p. pap. 10.99 (978-0-8007-5774-8(2) , Spire) Revell.

Martin, Sam. The Curious Boy's Book of Adventure: 100 Hijinks & Escapades. 2007. 160p. (J). (gr. 5). pap. 15.00 (***978-1-59514-206-1(1)***) Penguin Group (USA) Inc.

Maryknoll World Productions Staff. Children of the Earth: Maryknoll Coloring & Activity Book. Pallaton, Karen E., illus. 1999. 24p. (J). (gr. 3-6). 2.00 (978-0-941395-10-6(3)) Maryknoll World Productions.

Marzollo, Jean. I Spy Fantasy. Wick, Walter, photos by. (I Spy Bks.). (FRE., Illus.). (J). (ps-3). pap. 16.99 (978-0-590-24340-7(3)) Scholastic, Inc.

Mattox, Wendy Ann. Babysitting Activities: Fun with Kids of All Ages. 2007. (Snap Books). (Illus.). 32p. (J). 25.26 (978-0-7368-6461-9(X)) Capstone Pr., Inc.

Mayer, Becker. The Happy Birthday Game: Make Each Child's Birthday Extra Special While Building Important Math Skills. 2001. -p. (ps-3). pap. 12.95 (978-0-439-22253-2(2)) Scholastic, Inc.

Mc Cleary, Donece M. Children's Liturgical Calendar. 2005. (Illus.). 16p. pap., act. bk. ed. 4.95 (978-0-8091-6725-8(5) , 6725-5) Paulist Pr.

McCullagh, Sheila K. & Myers, Lois. Galapagos. Date not set. (Whizz Bang Bumper Bk.). (Illus.). 32p. (J). pap. 129.15 (978-0-582-19338-3(9)) Addison-Wesley Longman, Ltd. GBR. *Dist:* Trans-Atlantic Pubns., Inc.

McGillian, Jamie Kyle. Sleepover Party! Games & Giggles for a Fun Night. 2007. (Illus.). 96p. (J). (gr. 3-5). 14.95 (***978-1-4027-2978-2(2)***) Sterling Publishing Co., Inc.

Miller, Ray. Beat the Clock Sports. Crabtree, Andrew, illus. 1999. 24p. (J). pap. 6.95 (978-1-58295-014-3(8) , Beehive Bk.) Pace Products, Inc.

Miller, Raymond. U. S. Stamps: Collect All 50 States. Janikowski, Dan, illus. 2003. (U. S. Stamps Ser.). 40p. (J). pap. 8.99 (978-0-439-52072-0(X) , Tangerine Pr.) Scholastic, Inc.

Mitchell, Judy & Borst, Donna, eds. The Best of Holidays & Seasonal Celebrations, Grades 1-3, Issues 18-21. 2000. (Illus.). 320p. (J). pap., tchr. ed. 24.95 (978-1-57310-228-5(8)) Teaching & Learning Co.

Morin, Virginia K. Fun to Grow On: Engaging Play Activities for Kids, Teachers, Parents & Grandparents. Sokoloff, David, illus. 2nd rev. ed. 1999. (J). (ps-6). pap. 12.95 (978-1-890374-01-3(6)) Magnolia Street Pubs.

Moss, Marissa. Dr. Amelia's Boredom Survival Guide: First Aid for Rainy Days, Boring Errands, Waiting Rooms, Whatever! 1999. (Amelia's Notebooks). (J). (gr. 3-5). (978-0-606-17408-4(7)) Tandem Library Bks.

Mulcahy, Lisa, et al. Bye Bye Boredom! The Girl's Life Big Book of Fun. 2003. (Illus.). 124p. (J). (978-0-439-44976-2(6)) Scholastic, Inc.

My Big Creepy Sticker. 2003. (Illus.). 48p. (J). 5.98 (978-1-4054-1218-6(6)) Parragon, Inc.

My Big Spooky Sticker Activity Book. 2003. (Illus.). 48p. (J). 5.98 (978-1-4054-1219-3(4)) Parragon, Inc.

My Pocket Dot to Dot Boat. 2003. (Illus.). 192p. (J). 1.49 (978-1-4054-0884-4(7)) Parragon, Inc.

Negus, Jacque. You Are My Sunshine: Sing, Dance & Read with Me. 2000. 13p. (J). (ps-k). pap., act. bk. ed. 12.95 incl. audio compact disk (978-1-931127-02-8(6) , 986-018) Kindermusik International.

Newman-D'Amico, Fran. Travel Fun. 2004. (Illus.). 64p. (J). (ps-3). pap., act. bk. ed. 1.50 (978-0-486-43532-9(6)) Dover Pubns., Inc.

Newman, Fred. Mouthsounds: How to Whistle, Pop, Boing & Honk for All Occasions...and Then Some. 2004. (Illus.). 160p. pap. 13.95 (978-0-7611-3422-0(0) , 13422) Workman Publishing Co., Inc.

Newman, Marjorie. Ideas for a Windy Day. 1999. (Ideas Activity Bks.). (Illus.). 12p. (J). (ps-3). pap. 5.99 (978-0-89051-245-6(0)) Master Bks.

—Ideas with Water. 1999. (Ideas Activity Bks.). (Illus.). 12p. (J). (ps-3). pap. 5.99 (978-0-89051-246-3(9)) Master Bks.

Niederman, Derrick, et al. The Secret Clubhouse Game Book. 2004. (Illus.). 128p. (J). pap. 4.95 (978-1-4027-1107-7(7)) Sterling Publishing Co., Inc.

Noble, Marty. Merry Christmas Sticker Activity Book. 2000. (Dover Little Activity Bks.). (Illus.). 4p. (J). (ps-5). 1.50 (978-0-486-40986-3(4)) Dover Pubns., Inc.

—Nutcracker Sticker Paper Doll. 1998. (Dover Little Activity Bks.). (Illus.). 4p. (J). (ps-5). 1.50 (978-0-486-40516-2(8)) Dover Pubns., Inc.

November: Full Color Monthly Activities for Grades 1-3. 2000. (Monthly Bks.). (Illus.). 96p. (gr. 1-3). pap. 12.99 (978-0-88724-550-3(1) , CD-2092) Carson-Dellosa Publishing Co., Inc.

October: Full Color Monthly Activities for Grades 1-3. 2000. (Monthly Bks.). (Illus.). 96p. (gr. 1-3). pap. 12.99 (978-0-88724-549-7(8) , CD-2091) Carson-Dellosa Publishing Co., Inc.

O'Hare, Jeffrey A. Halloween Book of Fun: Puzzles, Games, Jokes, Ideas, & More. 2003. (Illus.). 64p. (YA). (gr. 2-7). pap. 7.95 (978-1-56397-959-0(4)) Boyds Mills Pr.

Oliver, Don. My Fun Time: With Billy & Harold. l.t. ed. 2002. (Illus.). 24p. (J). 14.95 (978-1-930002-46-3(7)) I & L Publishing.

On the Go Travel Pack. 2000. (J). (ps up). pap. 7.95 (978-1-55254-123-4(1)) Brighter Vision Pubns.

Outdoor Fun. 2001. (Stick'n Learn Stories Ser.). (Illus.). 96p. (J). (ps-3). pap. 6.95 (978-1-55254-233-0(5)) Brighter Vision Pubns.

Parks, Peggy J. Entertainment. 2005. (Yesterday & Today Ser.). (Illus.). 32p. (J). (ps-7). lib. bdg. 23.70 (978-1-56711-830-8(5) , Blackbirch Pr., Inc.) Thomson Gale.

Party Fun. (Illus.). 24p. (J). (gr. 2 up). lib. bdg. 12.95 (978-0-88110-458-5(2)) EDC Publishing.

Petruccio, Steven James. Airport Stickers Picture. 1998. (Illus.). (J). 4.95 (978-0-486-40587-2(7)) Dover Pubns., Inc.

Pickett, Beth Kneeland. 50 Nifty Super Things to Do After School. Angeloch, Eric, illus. 2nd ed. 1998. (Fifty Nifty Super Ser.). 80p. (J). (gr. 4-7). pap. 6.95 (978-1-56565-686-4(5) , 06865W) Lowell Hse. Juvenile.

Pilkey, Dav. Ricky Ricotta's Mighty Robot. 2006. (Ricky Ricotta Ser.). 96p. (J). pap. 3.99 (978-0-439-82601-3(2) , Blue Sky Pr., The) Scholastic, Inc.

Popular Mechanics Press Editors. How to Make Cool Gadgets for Your Room. Rodrigues, Teco, illus. 2001. (Popular Mechanics for Kids Ser.). 64p. (J). (gr. 4-7). pap. 8.95 (978-0-688-17727-0(1) , Harper Trophy) HarperCollins Pubs.

Precious Moments: Ultimate Activity Book. 2002. (Illus.). 128p. (J). (ps-7). pap. 4.97 (978-1-57759-525-0(4)) Dalmatian Pr.

Priddy, Roger. First Concepts ABC: Sticker Activity. rev. ed. 2003. (Illus.). 12p. (J). 5.95 (978-0-312-49143-7(3) , Priddy Bks.) St. Martin's Pr.

—First Learning Shapes: Sticker Activity Shapes. rev. ed. 2003. (Illus.). 20p. (J). 5.95 (978-0-312-49159-8(X) , Priddy Bks.) St. Martin's Pr.

—My Giant Sticker Activity Book. rev. ed. 2004. (Illus.). 72p. (J). pap. 12.95 (978-0-312-49099-7(2) , Priddy Bks.) St. Martin's Pr.

Pringle, Betsy, ed. Nascar Micro Cars. 2003. (Illus.). 16p. (J). 6.99 (978-0-439-55280-6(X) , Tangerine Pr.) Scholastic, Inc.

Purton, Michael. I Can Make Music: Simple-to-Make & Fun-to-Play Musical Instruments for Young C. 2000. (gr. k-3). lib. bdg. 16.40 (978-0-613-74514-7(0)) Tandem Library Bks.

Puzzles Sparkly Sticker Book. Date not set. (Illus.). 16p. (J). 3.98 (978-1-4054-0995-7(9)) Parragon, Inc.

Rasmussen, Greta & Rasmussen, Ted. Gotta Think! An Entertaining Assortment of Thinking Activities. 2000. (Illus.). 112p. (J). (gr. 2-6). pap. 12.95 (978-0-936110-23-3(6)) Tin Man Pr.

Rau, Dana Meachen. Toys, Games, & Fun in American History. 2006. (Illus.). 24p. (J). pap. (978-0-8368-7216-3(9)); lib. bdg. (978-0-8368-7209-5(6)) Stevens, Gareth Inc.

Rauchwerger, Lisa. Chocolate Chip Challah. Rauchwerger, Lisa, illus. 2004. (Illus.). (J). (gr. k-3). pap., act. bk. ed. 9.95 (978-0-8074-0736-3(4) , 104035) URJ Pr.

Rinella, Heidi Knapp. The Lobster Kids' Guide to Exploring Las Vegas. 2001. (Lobster Kids' City Explorers Ser.). (Illus.). 225p. (J). (ps-3). pap. 12.95 (978-1-894222-29-7(6)) Lobster Pr. CAN. *Dist:* Univ. of Toronto Pr.

Rogers, Kathy. Color & Learn - Ancient Rome. Adams, Elizabeth, illus. 1999. 32p. (J). (gr. 2-6). pap., wbk. ed. 3.99 (978-1-56472-210-2(4) , EP210) Edupress, Inc.

Roman, Beverly D. Let's Make a Move! A Creative Visualization Activity Book for Children. Bickel, Dalene, ed. Cadieux, Michael J., illus. 2nd ed. 2000. 32p. (J). (gr. k-7). pap. 8.45 (978-1-888891-26-3(2)) BR Anchor Publishing.

Romeo, Joe & Barnett, LaQuela. Road Trip Survival Kit. Phillips, Karen, illus. 1999. 24p. (J). (ps-2). spiral bd. 9.99 (978-1-929140-00-8(2)) Music, Inc.

Rosenthal, Lisa. A Dog's Best Friend: An Activity Book for Kids & Their Dogs. Matthews, Bonnie, illus. 1999. 176p. (J). (gr. 1-7). pap. 12.95 (978-1-55652-362-5(9)) Chicago Review Pr., Inc.

Ross, Stewart. Ancient Greece Entertainment. Hook, Adam, illus. 2006. (Changing Times Ser.). 32p. (J). (gr. 5-6). 27.93 (978-0-7565-2086-1(X)) Compass Point Bks.

Rowe, John. Amazing Animal Hide & Seek. 2003. (Illus.). 32p. (J). 12.95 (978-0-7641-5667-0(5)) Barron's Educational Series, Inc.

Rudisill, J. J., et al, illus. Get in Shape, Jonas! 1999. (Wimzie's House Bks.). 24p. (J). pap. 3.99 (978-0-88724-517-6(X) , CD-4841) Carson-Dellosa Publishing Co., Inc.

Running Press Staff & Lithgow, John. Boredom Blasters: Halloween Edition. 2005. (LithgowPalooza Ser.: No. 3). (Illus.). 64p. (J). pap. 14.95 (978-0-7624-2232-6(7) , Running Pr. Kids) Running Pr. Bk. Pubs.

Saint-Exupery, Antoine De. The Little Prince Book of Fun & Adventure. Bent, Lucinda, tr. from FRE. 2006. (Illus.). 64p. (J). 18.95 (978-0-15-205705-3(6) , Red Wagon Bks.) Harcourt Children's Bks.

Savage, Jeff. Thrill Rides! All about Roller Coasters. 2006. 48p. (J). pap. (978-1-59336-727-5(9)) Mondo Publishing.

Sawyer, Dawn. Too Big (Clifford Color & Activity) Yee, Josie & Garcia, Segundo, illus. 2004. (Clifford Ser.). 80p. (J). pap. 2.99 (978-0-439-55668-2(6)) Scholastic, Inc.

Scarry, Richard. Richard Scarry's Best Rainy Day Book Ever. Scarry, Richard, illus. 2004. (Illus.). 144p. (J). (ps-3). pap. 9.99 (978-0-375-82927-7(X) , Golden Bks.) Random Hse. Children's Bks.

Schaefer, A. R. Roller Coasters. 2004. (Wild Rides! Ser.). (Illus.). 32p. (J). lib. bdg. 22.60 (978-0-7368-2726-3(9)) Capstone Pr., Inc.

Scholastic, Inc. Staff. Ultimate Godzilla Tattoo Book. 1998. (Godzilla Ser.). (J). pap. 4.98 (978-0-590-02452-5(3)) Scholastic, Inc.

Scholastic, Inc. Staff, et al. Secret Spy. Im, Angela, ed. 2003. (Fun Pack Ser.). 48p. (J). pap. 7.99 (978-0-439-45145-1(0) , Tangerine Pr.) Scholastic, Inc.

Scratch & Sketch Funny Faces. 2005. (Activity Journal Ser.). (Illus.). 60p. (J). 12.99 (978-0-88088-487-7(8)) Peter Pauper Pr. Inc.

Scream Machines: All about Roller Coasters. 2005. (Book Treks Ser.). (J). 37.95 (978-0-7652-3244-1(8)) Celebration Pr.

Sheep. Date not set. (Old MacDonald Stickers Ser.). (Illus.). 16p. (J). 5.98 (978-0-7525-9969-4(0)) Parragon, Inc.

Siomades, Lorianne. Look What You Can Make with Boxes: Over 90 Pictured Crafts & Dozens of Other Ideas. 2003. (Illus.). 48p. (YA). (gr. k-7). pap. 5.95 (978-1-56397-704-6(4)) Boyds Mills Pr.

Sklansky, Amy E. Zoom Fun Outside. 2000. (Zoom Ser.). (Illus.). 62p. (J). (gr. 1-7). pap. 7.95 (978-0-316-95278-1(8)) Little Brown & Co.

—ZoomDos You Can Do: 50+ Cool Things You Can Craft, Bake, & Build. 2000. (gr. 3-6). lib. bdg. 16.15 (978-0-613-27679-5(5)) Tandem Library Bks.

—ZoomFun with Friends: 50+ Great Games, Parties, Recipes, Jokes & More from the Hit PBS TV Show. 1999. (Illus.). 64p. (J). (gr. 1-7). pap. 7.95 (978-0-316-95275-0(3)) Little Brown & Co.

—ZoomZingers: 50+ Amazing Activities from the Hit PBS TV Show. 1999. (Illus.). 64p. (J). (gr. 1-7). pap. 7.95 (978-0-316-95261-3(3)) Little Brown & Co.

Smith, A. G. King Tut Stickers. 2000. (Illus.). 4p. (J). pap. 1.50 (978-0-486-40980-1(5)) Dover Pubns., Inc.

Smith, Becky Cardon & Smith, Shane W. The LDS Children's Activity Book: Independence to Nauvoo. Smith, Shane W., illus. 2002. (Illus.). (J). pap. 4.99 (978-0-9720782-0-7(7)) LDS Family Travels.

Smith, Keri. Tear up This Book! The Sticker, Stencil, Stationery, Games, Crafts, Doodle, & Journal Book for Girls! 2005. (American Girl Library). (Illus.). 96p. (J). pap. 9.95 (978-1-58485-977-2(6) , American Girl) American Girl Publishing, Inc.

Southwater Staff. The Ultimate Activity Book. 2000. (Illus.). 256p. (ps-3). pap. 19.95 (978-1-84215-280-5(7) , Southwater) Anness Publishing GBR. *Dist:* National Bk. Network.

Stacy, Lori Moore. It's My Party: How to Throw a Great Bash for Any Occasion. 2000. (All about You Ser.). 144p. (J). (gr. 4-7). pap. 4.50 (978-0-439-16137-4(1)) Scholastic, Inc.

Steadman, Barbara. Create Your Own Farm Stickers: With Full-Color Background & 32 Pressure-Sensitive Stickers. 1998. (Illus.). (J). (gr. k-3). pap. 5.95 (978-0-486-27775-2(5)) Dover Pubns., Inc.

Stillerman, Robbie. Amusement Park Stickers. 2004. (Stickers Ser.). (Illus.). 8p. (J). (ps-5). pap. 1.50 (978-0-486-43305-9(6)) Dover Pubns., Inc.

—Joe the Sports Boy. 1998. (Illus.). 4p. (J). pap. 1.50 (978-0-486-40520-9(6)) Dover Pubns., Inc.

—Pretty Faces Sticker. 2001. (Illus.). 4p. (J). pap., act. bk. ed. 1.50 (978-0-486-41629-8(1)) Dover Pubns., Inc.

—Princess the Pony Sticker Activity Book. 2003. (Dover Little Activity Bks.). (Illus.). 4p. (J). (ps-3). pap. 1.50 (978-0-486-43012-6(X)) Dover Pubns., Inc.

Stone, Lynn M. Roller Coasters. 2001. (How are They Built? Ser.). (Illus.). 48p. (J). (gr. 4-8). lib. bdg. 29.93 (978-1-58952-134-6(X)) Rourke Publishing, LLC.

Sussman, Ellen. Cooking with Kids. Mitchell, Judy, ed. 2000. (Illus.). 128p. (J). (ps-3). pap., tchr. ed. 13.95 (978-1-57310-260-5(1)) Teaching & Learning Co.

Tait, Chris. How to Be a Kid. Paillot, Jim, illus. 2003. 96p. (J). pap. 6.95 (978-0-8069-8503-9(8)) Sterling Publishing Co., Inc.

Taylor, Jody, selected by. Hidden Pictures 2003-2004: With Picture & Word Clues. 2003. (Hidden Pictures Ser.). (Illus.). 48p. (J). (gr. 6-9). Vol. 1. pap. 4.95 (978-1-59078-030-5(2)); Vol. 2. pap. 4.95 (978-1-59078-031-2(0)); Vol. 3. pap. 4.95 (978-1-59078-032-9(9)); Vol. 4. pap. 4.95 (978-1-59078-033-6(7)) Boyds Mills Pr.

Taylor, Sherril W. Pick 'n Stick, Bk. 1. Drolet, Cindy, ed. Imaginart Staff, illus. 2000. 171p. (J). spiral bd. 32.50 (978-1-883315-52-8(2)) Imaginart International, Inc.

Tefford, Lisa. Minute Mania: People & Places. 2003. (Illus.). 96p. (J). pap. 7.99 (978-0-439-51917-5(9) , Tangerine Pr.) Scholastic, Inc.

Teitelbaum, Michael. Iron Eagle. 2003. (G. I. Joe Ser.). 16p. (J). pap. 4.99 (978-0-439-45542-8(1) , Scholastic Paperbacks) Scholastic, Inc.

—Iron Eagle. 2003. (gr. k-3). lib. bdg. 13.00 (978-0-613-72171-4(3)) Tandem Library Bks.

TerKeurst, Lysa. The Sweetest Story Ever Told Activity Kit. Sparks, Michal, illus. 2003. 14.99 (978-0-8024-7093-5(9)) Moody Pubs.

Things to Make & Do. (J). Date not set. 64p. 5.98 (978-1-4054-0412-9(4)); Date not set. 48p. pap. 4.98 (978-0-7525-8411-9(1)); 2003. (Illus.). 64p. 12.98 (978-1-4054-1220-9(8)) Parragon, Inc.

Thomas, Keith A. Cross-Lengua Coloring Book for Kids. Thomas, Keith A., illus. l.t. ed. 2004. (ENG & SPA., Illus.). 22p. (J). (gr. 3 up). pap. (978-0-9617451-2-7(6)) KALEXT Productions, LLC.

Thomas, Lyn. Ha! Ha! Ha! 1,000+ Jokes, Riddles, Facts, & More. Eastman, Dianne, illus. 2004. 128p. (J). pap. 9.95 (978-1-897066-12-6(0)) Maple Tree Pr. CAN. *Dist:* Perseus Distribution.

Thrills & Spills, Bk. 3/2. (J). (gr. 3). 34.40 (978-0-673-72656-8(8) , Scott Foresman) Addison Wesley Schl.

Today's Superstars: Entertainment, 6 bks., Set. Incl. Jessica Simpson. Mitchell, Susan K. (J). lib. bdg. 23.93 (***978-0-8368-8201-8(6)***); Jim Carrey. Stone, Amy. (J). lib. bdg. 23.93 (***978-0-8368-8197-4(4)***); Kenny Chesney. Thomas, William. (YA). lib. bdg. 23.93 (***978-0-8368-8198-1(2)***); Olsen Twins. Gorman, Jacqueline Laks. (YA). lib. bdg. 23.93 (***978-0-8368-8199-8(0)***); Tyra Banks. Mitchell, Susan K. (YA). lib. bdg. 23.93 (***978-0-8368-8196-7(6)***); 32p. (gr. 5 up). 2007. 2007. Set lib. bdg. 143.58 (***978-0-8368-8195-0(8)***); Set lib. bdg. 143.58 (***978-0-8368-8120-2(6)***) Stevens, Gareth Inc.

Travis-Bildahl, Sandra. The Boat Book of Fun Vol. 1: An Activity Book for Nautical Kids. 2000. (Illus.). 100p. (J). pap. (978-1-878797-16-2(6)) Weems & Plath, Inc.

Treasure Chest. 2003. (J). per. (978-1-57657-978-7(6)) Paradise Pr., Inc.

A Treasury for One Year Olds. Date not set. 96p. (J). 7.98 (978-1-4054-0021-3(8)) Parragon, Inc.

A Treasury for Two Year Olds. Date not set. (Illus.). 96p. (J). 7.98 (978-1-4054-0022-0(6)) Parragon, Inc.

Trumbauer, Lisa. Our Favorite Things to Do. 2000. (Yellow Umbrella Books). (Illus.). 16p. (J). (gr. 1). lib. bdg. 14.60 (978-0-7368-0739-5(X) , Pebble Bks.) Capstone Pr., Inc.

Tulip, Jenny. At Home. 2000. (Illus.). 16p. (ps-k). pap. 5.00 (978-0-7548-0131-3(4)) Anness Publishing, Inc.

Veranos, Sandi. David's Friend. Mclean, Mina, illus. 2003. (Pencil Fun Bks.: Vol. 10). 16p. (J). (ps-3). pap. 9.90 (978-1-55513-117-3(4) , 1555131174) Cook, David C. Publishing Co.

Warshaw, Hallie & Brown, Julie. Get Out! Outdoor Activities Kids Can Enjoy Anywhere (Except Indoors) 2003. (Illus.). 128p. pap. 9.95 (978-1-4027-0169-6(1)) Sterling Publishing Co., Inc.

Weekly Reader Early Learning Library (Firm) Staff, contrib. by. Things I Play With. 2006. (Things in My World Ser.). (Illus.). 16p. (J). pap. (978-0-8368-6818-0(8)); lib. bdg. (978-0-8368-6811-1(0)) Stevens, Gareth Inc.

A
B

A B

Where's Henry? (J). 21.95 (978-0-8136-4327-4(9)); pap. 13.15 (978-0-8136-4326-7(0)) Modern Curriculum Pr.

Wilcox, Charlotte. Games & Leisure in Colonial America. 2004. (Everyday Life Long Ago Ser.). (J). (978-0-7368-2162-9(7) , Blue Earth Bks.) Capstone Pr., Inc.

The Wild Thornberrys with Book & Poster & Crayons & Paint Brush. 2000. (J). (ps-3). pap. (978-0-7696-1976-7(2) , American Education Publishing) School Specialty Publishing.

Williams, Colleen Madonna Flood. My Adventure at the Water Park. 2007. 44p. (J). 8.99 (978-1-59092-579-9(3) , Orchard Academy Pr.) Windstorm Creative.

Wilmes, Liz & Wilmes, Dick. Felt Board Fun: For Everyday & Holidays. Dane, Donna, illus. 2004. 244p. (J). pap. 16.95 (978-0-943452-02-9(3)) Building Blocks, LLC.

Wilson, Deirdre. The Lobster Kids' Guide to Exploring Boston. 2001. (Lobster Kids' City Explorers Ser.). (Illus.). 235p. (J). (ps-3). pap. 12.95 (978-1-894222-41-9(5)) Lobster Pr. CAN. *Dist:* Univ. of Toronto Pr.

Wingate, P. I Can Waddle, Wriggle, Wave. O'Neil, Rachel, illus. 2004. (My Carry-Around Action Bks.). 16p. (J). bds. 3.95 (978-0-7641-5734-9(5)) Barron's Educational Series, Inc.

—I Can Woof, Quack, Moo. O'Neil, Rachel, illus. 2004. (My Carry-Around Action Bks.). 16p. (J). bds. 3.95 (978-0-7641-5735-6(3)) Barron's Educational Series, Inc.

Winters, Kas. Fall Fun for Families. 2000. (Illus.). 80p. (J). (ps-7). pap. 7.00 (978-1-892225-01-6(8)) Winmark Communications.

Yates, Vicki. Having Fun. 2007. (J). ***(978-1-4034-9832-8(6)***); pap. ***(978-1-4034-9840-3(7))*** Heinemann Library.

50 Great Americans Sticker Book. 1998. (Active Learning Bks.). (Illus.). 64p. (J). (gr. 1-7). pap. 6.95 (978-0-7681-0024-2(0) , McClanahan Bk.) Learning Horizons, Inc.

100s of Fun Things to Make & Do. Date not set. 256p. (J). 12.98 (978-1-4054-0452-5(3)) Parragon, Inc.

365 Things to Make & Do. Date not set. (Illus.). 256p. (J). 12.98 (978-1-4054-0023-7(4)) Parragon, Inc.

ANALYSIS (CHEMISTRY)

see Chemistry, Analytic

ANALYSIS, MICROSCOPIC

see Microscopy

ANALYTICAL CHEMISTRY

see Chemistry, Analytic

ANALYTICAL GEOMETRY

see Geometry, Analytic

ANATOMY

Here are entered general treatises and works on human anatomy. General works on animal anatomy are entered under Anatomy, Comparative.

see also Anatomy, Comparative; Bones; Nervous System; Physiology; Plant Anatomy

also subjects with the subdivision Anatomy, e.g. Birds—Anatomy; Botany—Anatomy; etc.; and names of organs and regions of the body, e.g. Heart

Allison, Linda. Blood & Guts. 2006. 128p. (J). pap. 12.99 (978-0-316-05972-5(2)) Little Brown & Co.

Andrews, Barbara. The Nervous & Digestive Systems. 2006. pap. 42.00 ***(978-1-4108-6512-0(6))*** Benchmark Education Co.

Apel, Melanie Ann. Let's Talk about When You Have to Have Your Appendix Out. 2002. (Let's Talk Library). (Illus.). 24p. (J). lib. bdg. 18.75 (978-0-8239-5865-8(5) , PowerKids Pr.) Rosen Publishing Group, Inc., The.

Baggaley, Ann & Page, Martyn, eds. Human Body. 2001. (Illus.). 448p. (gr. 12). pap. 18.00 (978-0-7894-7988-4(5)) Dorling Kindersley Publishing, Inc.

Bailey, Jill. Life in the Human Body. 2003. (gr. k-3). lib. bdg. 15.90 (978-0-613-78245-6(3)) Tandem Library Bks.

Ballard, Carol. How Do We Move? 1998. (How Your Body Works Ser.). (Illus.). 32p. (J). (ps-3). lib. bdg. 25.70 (978-0-8172-4741-6(6)) Raintree.

Barron's Educational Editorial Staff. Human Body in Action. 1999. (Bravo Ser.). (Illus.). 123p. (J). (gr. 6 up). pap. 8.95 (978-0-7641-0950-8(2)) Barron's Educational Series, Inc.

—Understanding the Human Body. 1998. (Megascope Ser.). (Illus.). 64p. (J). (gr. 4-7). 6.95 (978-0-7641-5093-7(6)) Barron's Educational Series, Inc.

Barron's Educational Editorial Staff & Roca, Nuria. Tu Cuerpo, de la Cabeza a Los Pies: Your Body, from Head to Toe, Spanish Edition. Curto, Rosa Maria, illus. 2000. (SPA.). 36p. (J). (gr. k-1). pap. 6.95 (978-0-7641-1519-6(7)) Barron's Educational Series, Inc.

Bauer, Marion Dane. Toes, Ears, & Nose! Katz, Karen, illus. 2003. (Lift-the-Flap Bks.). 16p. (J). (ps-3). 6.99 (978-0-689-84712-7(2) , Little Simon) Simon & Schuster Children's Publishing.

BHB International Staff. Human Body. 1998. (Our World in Pictures Ser.). (J). (978-2-215-06164-9(2)) Editions Fleurus.

Bingham, Caroline. Human Body. 2003. (Eye Wonder Ser.). (Illus.). 48p. (J). (gr. k). 9.99 (978-0-7894-9044-5(7)) Dorling Kindersley Publishing, Inc.

Body. (Make it Work Ser.). 42p. (J). (gr. 4-8). pap. (978-1-882210-42-8(5)) Action Publishing, Inc.

The Body. (J). (gr. k-1). (978-84-342-2399-8(6) , PR30569) Parramon Ediciones S.A. ESP. *Dist:* Lectorum Pubns., Inc.

Bones & Hearts & Other Parts. 2002. (Illus.). 48p. (J). 2.99 (978-0-88724-801-6(2) , WG 3030) Carson-Dellosa Publishing Co., Inc.

Boynton, Sandra. The Going to Bed Book. Boynton, Sandra, illus. 2004. 14p. (J). 9.99 (978-0-689-87028-6(0) , Little Simon) Simon & Schuster Children's Publishing.

Bozzo, Linda. Amazing Beaks. 2008. (J). lib. bdg. ***(978-1-4042-4169-5(8)*** , PowerKids Pr.) Rosen Publishing Group, Inc., The.

Brighter Vision Publishing Staff. My Body. 1998. (Learning Adventures Preschool Ser.). 32p. (J). (ps-k). pap. 2.25 (978-1-55254-005-3(7) , BV12001) Brighter Vision Pubns.

Bronner, Rivka D. Human Anatomy: The Inside Story Student Study Guide. Bronner, Abraham J., illus. 1998. 128p. (J). (gr. 7-10). pap., stu. ed. 10.00 (978-0-9660684-2-9(4)) Bronner, Rivka D.

Bruno, Stephen. The Human Body. 2002. (Nature's Record-Breakers Ser.). (Illus.). 32p. (J). (gr. 3 up). lib. bdg. 23.33 (978-0-8368-2905-1(0)) Stevens, Gareth Inc.

Bullard, Lisa. Smooth & Rough. 2006. (A+ Books). (Illus.). 32p. (J). (978-0-7368-4277-8(2)) Capstone Pr., Inc.

Center for Learning Network Staff. Demian/the Illustrated Man: Curriculum Unit — Novel Series — Grades 9-12. 2001. (Novel Ser.). 87p. (YA). tchr. ed., spiral bd. 19.95 (978-1-56077-661-1(7)) Ctr. for Learning, The.

Challoner, Jack. Human Wonders. 1998. (Detective Files Ser.). (Illus.). 32p. (J). (gr. 3-7). 19.95 (978-1-57145-324-2(5) , Silver Dolphin Bks.) Advantage Pubs. Group.

Collins, Katie. Anatomy Academy: Respiration, Circulation & Digestion, Vol. 2. 2005. 64p. 11.95 (978-1-59363-050-8(6)) Prufrock Pr.

—Anatomy Academy Bk. 1: Cells, Muscles & Bones. 2005. 64p. 11.95 (978-1-59363-049-2(2)) Prufrock Pr.

—Anatomy Academy Bk. 3: Nervous System, Senses & Glands. 2005. 64p. 11.95 (978-1-59363-051-5(4)) Prufrock Pr.

Cooper, Sharon Katz. Major Organs: Sustaining Life. 2006. (Illus.). 48p. (J). (978-0-7565-1959-9(4) , 1265926) Compass Point Bks.

Coster-Longman, Christina. The Human Body. Stalio, Ivan, illus. 2001. (Blow Up! Junior Science Ser.). 48p. (J). (gr. 2-5). pap. (978-0-439-98702-8(4)) Scholastic, Inc.

Coupe, Robert. The Human Body. 2002. (Junior Adventure Ser.). (Illus.). 32p. (J). (gr. 3 up). lib. bdg. (978-1-59084-172-3(7)) Mason Crest Pubs.

Cuerpo Humano. 2003. (Fun Non-Fiction Ser.). (SPA.). (J). (978-970-690-135-4(3)) Planeta Mexicana Editorial S. A. de C. V.

Cumbaa, Stephen. The Bones Book & Skeleton. 2nd ed. 2006. (Illus.). 64p. (J). 16.95 (978-0-7611-4218-8(5)) Workman Publishing Co., Inc.

Dahl, Michael. Do Frogs Have Fur? A Book about Animal Coats & Coverings. Yesh, Jeff, illus. 2004. (Animals All Around Ser.). 24p. (J). (gr. k-2). 22.60 (978-1-4048-0292-6(4)) Picture Window Bks.

—Do Whales Have Wings? A Book about Animal Bodies. D'Antonio, Sandra, illus. 2004. (Animals All Around Ser.). 24p. (C). (gr. k-2). 22.60 (978-1-4048-0103-5(0)) Picture Window Bks.

Dixon, Malcolm & Smith, Karen. The Body. 1998. (Young Scientists Ser.). (Illus.). 32p. (J). (ps-3). lib. bdg. 16.95 (978-1-887068-69-7(4)) Smart Apple Media.

DK Publishing Staff. Busy Little Bodies. 2005. 16p. (J). bds. 7.99 (978-0-7566-1122-4(9)) Dorling Kindersley Publishing, Inc.

Dolphin, Colleen. Armpits to Zits: The Body from A to Z. Craig, Diane, ed. 2007. (Let's See A to Z Ser.). (ENG., Illus.). 32p. (J). (ps-3). lib. bdg. 25.65 ***(978-1-59928-884-0(2)*** , Super SandCastle) ABDO Publishing Co.

Dorling Kindersley Publishing Staff. Human Body. 2002. (Eye Wonder Ser.). (Illus.). 48p. (J). (gr. k-3). lib. bdg. 17.99 (978-0-7894-9045-2(5)) Dorling Kindersley Publishing, Inc.

—Mi Primer Libro del Cuerpo/My First Body Board Book. 2005. (SPA.). 36p. (J). (ps-3). bds. 5.99 (978-0-7566-1501-7(1)) Dorling Kindersley Publishing, Inc.

Douglas, Lloyd G. My Hands. 2004. (Wel-My Body Ser.). (Illus.). 24p. (J). 18.00 (978-0-516-24059-6(5) , Children's Pr.) Scholastic Library Publishing.

—My Mouth. 2004. (Wel-My Body Ser.). (J). 18.00 (978-0-516-24061-9(7) , Children's Pr.) Scholastic Library Publishing.

—My Nose. 2004. (Wel-My Body Ser.). (J). 18.00 (978-0-516-24063-3(3) , Children's Pr.) Scholastic Library Publishing.

Farndon, John. The Human Body. 2001. (Science Experiments Ser.). (Illus.). 32p. (J). (gr. 3-5). lib. bdg. 25.64 (978-0-7614-1339-4(1) , Benchmark Bks.) Cavendish, Marshall Corp.

—The Human Body. 2001. (Science Fact Files Ser.). (Illus.). 48p. (J). (gr. 4-7). lib. bdg. 27.12 (978-0-7398-1013-2(8)) Raintree.

Fernandez, Vivian. Body Design. Morrow, Michelle, illus. 1998. 16p. (J). 6.95 (978-1-880592-98-4(3) , Beehive Bk.) Pace Products, Inc.

Fowler, Allan. Arms & Legs & Other Limbs. 1999. (Rookie Read-About Science Ser.). (Illus.). 32p. (J). (gr. 1-2). pap. 4.95 (978-0-516-26478-3(8) , Children's Pr.) Scholastic Library Publishing.

—Arms & Legs & Other Limbs. 1999. (gr. k-3). lib. bdg. 12.95 (978-0-613-53932-6(X)) Tandem Library Bks.

—Knowing about Noses. 1999. (Rookie Read-About Science Ser.). (Illus.). 32p. (J). (gr. 1-2). pap. 4.95 (978-0-516-26480-6(X) , Children's Pr.) Scholastic Library Publishing.

—Knowing about Noses. 1999. (gr. k-3). lib. bdg. 12.95 (978-0-613-54601-0(6)) Tandem Library Bks.

Fredericks, Anthony D. Your Amazing, Fantastic, Incredible Body. 2002. (J). (978-0-531-11699-9(9) , Watts, Franklin) Scholastic Library Publishing.

Fromm, Jim, prod. Continuity of Life Mac Labpak. (YA). cd-rom 322.50 (978-0-7365-4364-4(3)) Films Media Group.

—Continuity of Life Win Lb. (YA). cd-rom 322.50 (978-0-7365-4365-1(1)) Films Media Group.

Frost, Helen. The Skeletal System. Saunders-Smith, Gail, ed. 2000. (Human Body Systems Ser.). (Illus.). 24p. (J). (gr. k-1). lib. bdg. 15.93 (978-0-7368-0653-4(9) , Pebble Bks.) Capstone Pr., Inc.

Fullick, Ann. Body Systems & Health. 2005. (Life Science In-Depth Ser.). (Illus.). 64p. (978-1-4034-7519-0(9)); pap. (978-1-4034-7527-5(X)) Heinemann Library.

—The Human Body. 2003. (Science Topics Ser.). (Illus.). 32p. (YA). (gr. 6-8). lib. bdg. 24.22 (978-1-57572-769-1(2)) Heinemann Library.

Futech Interactive Products Staff. Learning the Body. deluxe ed. 1999. (Look, Listen & Learn Ser.). (Illus.). (ps-3). 14.95 (978-1-58224-006-0(X)) Futech Interactive Products, Inc.

Ganeri, Anita. Animals. 2006. (Inside & Out Guides Ser.). (Illus.). 32p. (J). (978-1-4034-9084-1(8)); pap. (978-1-4034-9091-9(0)) Heinemann Library.

—The Body. 1998. (Find Out about Ser.). (Illus.). 24p. (J). (ps-3). (978-0-563-35543-4(3)) BBC Worldwide.

Gareth Stevens Publishing Staff, contrib. by. Major Systems of the Body. 2002. (Twenty-First Century Science Ser.). (Illus.). 64p. (J). (gr. 5 up). lib. bdg. 32.67 (978-0-8368-5007-9(6) , World Almanac Library) Stevens, Gareth Inc.

Gerwitz, Felice, creator. Creation Anatomy: Experiments, Games, Activities & Puzzles: Hands-on Experiment & Activity Pack. 2000. 73p. (J). pap. 12.95 (978-1-931941-01-3(7)) Media Angels, Inc.

—Creation Astronomy: Experiments, Games, Activities & Puzzles: Hands-on Experiment & Activity Pack! 2000. 63p. (J). pap. 12.95 (978-1-931941-02-0(5)) Media Angels, Inc.

Goode, Katherine. Mouth. 2000. (Bodyworks Ser.). (Illus.). 32p. (J). (gr. 3-6). 23.70 (978-1-56711-494-2(6) , Blackbirch Pr., Inc.) Thomson Gale.

Hall, Katy, pseud. Esqueletos! Esqueletos! Todo Acerca de los Huesos. Billin-Frye, Paige, illus. (SPA.). (J). pap. 3.16 net. (978-0-590-46873-2(1) , SO30501, Scholastic en Espanol) Scholastic, Inc.

Haslam, Andrew. Body. 2004. (Make It Work! Science Ser.). (Illus.). 48p. (gr. 3-6). (J). pap. 6.95 (978-1-58728-350-5(6)); 12.95 (978-1-58728-370-3(0)) T&N Children's Publishing. (Two Can Publishing).

Henry-Biabaud, Chantal. The Human Body. 1998. (Creative Discoveries Ser.). Orig. Title: Our Body. (Illus.). 75p. (J). (gr. 2-9). lib. bdg. 23.95 (978-0-88682-951-3(8) , Creative Education) Creative Co., The.

Hewitt, Sally. You & Your Body. 1999. (It's Science! Ser.). (Illus.). 32p. (J). (gr. k-3). 23.50 (978-0-516-21182-4(X) , Children's Pr.) Scholastic Library Publishing.

Hixson, Bryce. Anatomy Academy. Hixson, Bryce, illus. 2003. (Illus.). (J). per. 14.95 (978-1-931801-03-4(7)) Loose In The Lab.

Human Anatomy-Flip Chart. 2003. (J). (gr. k-12). spiral bd. 14.95 (978-1-58845-178-1(X)) School Specialty Publishing.

The Human Body. 2003. (Science Card Games Ser.). (gr. 2-4). 9.99 (978-0-7682-1993-7(0) , J53021) School Specialty Publishing.

The Human Body. 2002. (Super Science Activities Ser.). 48p. (J). (gr. 2-5). 7.99 (978-0-7439-3662-0(0) , 3662) Teacher Created Materials, Inc.

Jefferis, David. Human Body. 2002. (Young Library). (Illus.). 32p. (J). lib. bdg. 25.69 (978-0-7398-6322-0(3)) Raintree.

Johnson, Rebecca L. Ultra-Organized Cell Systems. Desrocher, Jack, illus. 2007. (Microquests Ser.). 48p. (J). (gr. 3-5). lib. bdg. 29.27 ***(978-0-8225-7138-4(2)*** , Millbrook Pr.) Lerner Publishing Group.

Kauffman, Dorothy. How the Earth Gets Its Shape. 2005. (Content Area Readers Ser.). 4.95 (978-0-19-430956-1(8)) Oxford Univ. Pr., Inc.

—Inside the Human Body. 2005. (Content Area Readers Ser.). 24p. 4.95 (978-0-19-430953-0(3)) Oxford Univ. Pr., Inc.

Leake, Diyan. Tails. 2007. (J). ***(978-1-4329-0002-1(1)***; pap. ***(978-1-4329-0007-6(2))*** Heinemann Library.

LeVert, Suzanne. The Lungs. 2001. (Kaleidoscope Ser.). (Illus.). 48p. (J). (gr. 3 up). lib. bdg. 25.64 (978-0-7614-1307-3(3) , Benchmark Bks.) Cavendish, Marshall Corp.

Liflander, Pamela. Gray's Anatomy. 2011. (Start Exploring Ser.). (Illus.). 16p. (J). pap. 19.95 (978-0-7624-1590-8(8)) Running Pr. Bk. Pubs.

Llamas, Andreu. The Human Body, 4 bks. Rizo, Luis, illus. Incl. Digestion & Reproduction. lib. bdg. 24.67 (978-0-8368-2111-6(4)); Muscles & Bones. lib. bdg. 24.67 (978-0-8368-2112-3(2)); Nervous System. lib. bdg. 24.67 (978-0-8368-2113-0(0)); Respiration & Circulation. lib. bdg. 24.67 (978-0-8368-2110-9(6)); 32p. (J). (gr. 5 up). (Illus.). 1998. Set lib. bdg. 98.68 (978-0-8368-2109-3(2)) Stevens, Gareth Inc.

—Muscles & Bones. Rizo, Luis, illus. 1998. (Human Body Ser.). 32p. (J). (gr. 5 up). lib. bdg. 24.67 (978-0-8368-2112-3(2)) Stevens, Gareth Inc.

—The Nervous System. Rizo, Luis, illus. 1998. (Human Body Ser.). 32p. (J). (gr. 5 up). lib. bdg. 24.67 (978-0-8368-2113-0(0)) Stevens, Gareth Inc.

—Respiration & Circulation. Rizo, Luis, illus. 1998. (Human Body Ser.). 32p. (J). (gr. 5 up). lib. bdg. 24.67 (978-0-8368-2110-9(6)) Stevens, Gareth Inc.

Llewellyn, Claire. How Bodies Work. 2006. (Illus.). 24p. (J). (978-1-59771-023-7(7)) Sea-To-Sea Pubns.

Lobb, Janice. Bump! Thump! How Do We Jump? Experiments in the Kitchen. Savage, Ann & Utton, Peter, illus. 2002. (At Home with Science Ser.). 32p. (J). pap. 5.95 (978-0-7534-5461-9(0) , Kingfisher) Houghton Mifflin Co. Trade & Reference Div.

Lombardo, Michelle. The OrganWise Guys - Basic Training for Better Health Vol. 2, 2 vols. Herron, Mark, illus. 1998. 35p. (J). (gr. 2-5). (978-0-9648438-3-7(8)) Wellness, Inc.

Mammals; Dinosaurs; Human Body, 3 vols., Set. 2001. 192p. (J). 25.95 (978-0-7525-5456-3(5)) Parragon, Inc.

Maurer, Tracy. A to Z of All of Me. 2002. (A to Z Ser.). (Illus.). 48p. (gr. k-2). 20.95 (978-1-58952-059-2(9)) Rourke Publishing, LLC.

Maynard, Christopher & Martin, Terry. Why Do We Laugh? Questions Children Ask about the Human Body. (Why Bks.). (Illus.). 24p. (J). pap. 10.99 (978-0-590-24955-3(X)) Scholastic, Inc.

Maynard, Christopher, et al. How Your Body Works. 2004. (Knowledge Masters Plus Ser.). (Illus.). 32p. (YA). pap. incl. cd-rom (978-1-903954-44-7(4)) Chrysalis Children's Bks.

McCormick, Rosie. Our Bodies & Art Activities. 2002. (Arty Facts Ser.). (Illus.). 48p. (J). (gr. 3-4). pap. (978-0-7787-1145-2(5)); lib. bdg. (978-0-7787-1117-9(X)) Crabtree Publishing Co.

—Our Bodies & Art Activities. 2002. (gr. 3-6). lib. bdg. 17.60 (978-0-613-52891-7(3)) Tandem Library Bks.

McCourt, Lisa, et al. What's Inside My Body? 2000. (Brain Builders Ser.). (Illus.). 48p. (J). (gr. k-3). pap. 7.95 (978-0-7373-0463-3(4) , 04634W, Roxbury Park Juvenile) Lowell Hse. Juvenile.

McCoy, Kathy & Wibbelsman, Charles. The Teenage Body Book. rev. ed. 1999. (Illus.). 1p. (J). (gr. 7-12). pap. 18.95 (978-0-399-52535-3(1) , Perigee Trade) Penguin Group (USA) Inc.

Micklethwait, Lucy. I Spy Two Eyes: Numbers in Art. 1998. (Illus.). 48p. (J). (ps-3). pap. 10.99 (978-0-688-16158-3(8) , Harper Trophy) HarperCollins Pubs.

Mitchell, Melanie S. Mouths. 2003. (First Step Nonfiction Ser.). (Illus.). 8p. (J). pap. 3.95 (978-0-8225-3913-1(6) , Lerner Pubns.) Lerner Publishing Group.

Moor, Jo Ellen. How Your Body Works. Evans, Marilyn, ed. Larsen, Jo, illus. 1998. (ScienceWorks for Kids Ser.: Vol. 4). 80p. (J). (gr. 1-3). pap., tchr. ed. 9.95 (978-1-55799-685-5(7) , EMC 856) Evan-Moor Educational Pubs.

—The Human Body: Grades 1-3. Evans, Marilyn, ed. Larsen, Jo, illus. 1998. (Science Picture Cards Ser.: Vol. 1). 24p. (J). pap., tchr. ed. 12.95 (978-1-55799-692-3(X) , 863) Evan-Moor Educational Pubs.

Moore, Jo Ellen. Learning about My Body. Larsen, Jo et al, illus. 2000. (ScienceWorks for Kids Ser.). 80p. (J). (gr. k-1). pap. 9.95 (978-1-55799-773-9(X) , EMC 869) Evan-Moor Educational Pubs.

Movement. (Jump Ser.). (Illus.). 32p. (J). (gr. 2-7). pap. (978-1-882210-24-4(7)) Action Publishing, Inc.

Nagel, Rob. Body by Design: From the Digestive to the Skeleton, 2 vols. 1999. xxxix, 342p. (J). (978-0-7876-3898-6(6)) Thomson Gale.

National Geographic Society Staff. Incredible Voyage: Exploring the Human Body. 1998. (Illus.). 352p. (YA). (gr. 7 up). 35.00 (978-0-7922-7148-2(3) , National Geographic) National Geographic Society.

Nayer, Judy. Human Body. Brown, Robert, illus. rev. ed. 1998. (At Your Fingertips Ser.). 5p. (J). (ps-3). 6.95 (978-0-7681-0065-5(8) , McClanahan Bk.) Learning Horizons, Inc.

Nichols, Catherine. If You Had a Tail. 2001. (We Can Read about Nature! Ser.). (Illus.). 32p. (J). (gr. 1-2). lib. bdg. 21.36 (978-0-7614-1251-9(4) , Benchmark Bks.) Cavendish, Marshall Corp.

O'Brien-Palmer, Michelle. Watch Me Grow: Fun Ways to Learn about Cells, Bones, Muscles, Joints. Lee, Fran, illus. 1999. 144p. (J). (gr. k-4). pap. 14.95 (978-1-55652-367-0(X)) Chicago Review Pr., Inc.

Oleksy, Walter. The Head & Neck: Learning How We Use Our Muscles. 2002. (3-D Library of the Human Body). (Illus.). 48p. (YA). (gr. 5-8). lib. bdg. 26.50 (978-0-8239-3531-4(0) , Rosen Central) Rosen Publishing Group, Inc., The.

Omoto, Garrett, illus. Tutu Books- A set of three Books w/ CD. 2006. (ENG & HAW.). (YA). (978-1-933835-04-4(4)) Partners in Development.

Parker, Steve. Atlas Visual del Cuerpo Humano. (Coleccion Atlas Visual). (SPA., Illus.). 64p. (YA). (gr. 5-8). (978-84-216-2056-4(8) , BU5680) Bruño, Editorial ESP. *Dist:* Lectorum Pubns., Inc.

—How the Body Works: 100 Ways Parents & Kids Can Share the Miracles of the Human Body. 1999. (How It Works Ser.). (Illus.). 192p. (gr. 12-9). pap. 16.95 (978-0-7621-0236-5(5)) Reader's Digest Assn., Inc., The.

Pelham, David & Miller, Jonathan. Human Body. 2000. (Illus.). 12p. (YA). (gr. 3 up). 16.95 (978-1-58117-092-4(0) , Intervisual/Piggy Toes) Dalmatian Pr.

Penguin Books Staff, ed. Your Body. (Information Activity Ser.). 24p. (J). 3.50 (978-0-7214-3441-4(X) , Dutton Juvenile) Penguin Group (USA) Inc.

Rabe, Tish. Inside Your Outside! All about the Human Body. Ruiz, Aristides, illus. 2003. (Cat in the Hat's Learning Library). 48p. (J). (gr. k-3). 8.99 (978-0-375-81100-5(1) , Random Hse. Bks. for Young Readers) Random Hse. Children's Bks.

—Inside Your Outsides. Ruiz, Aristides, illus. 2003. (Cat in the Hat's Learning Library). 48p. (J). (gr. k-3). lib. bdg. 11.99 (978-0-375-91100-2(6) , Random Hse. Bks. for Young Readers) Random Hse. Children's Bks.

Random House Staff. Head, Shoulders, Nose & Toes. 2001. (Play It Smart Workbks.). (J). pap. 2.99 (978-0-375-80461-8(7) , Random Hse. Bks. for Young Readers) Random Hse. Children's Bks.

Ring, Susan. Gross Anatomy. Snow, Alan, illus. 2002. (Crash Course Ser.). 68p. (J). (gr. 2-17). spiral bd. 16.99 (978-1-58476-136-5(9)) Innovative Kids.

Roca, Nuria. Tu Cuerpo de la Cabeza a los Pies. 2000. Tr. of Your Body from Head to Toe. (Illus.). (J). (978-0-606-20957-1(3)) Tandem Library Bks.

Rotner, Shelley & Calcagnino, Stephen. The Body Book. 2000. (Illus.). 32p. (J). (ps-1). pap. 15.95 (978-0-531-30256-9(3) , Orchard Bks.) Scholastic, Inc.

Royston, Angela. Why Does My Body Smell? 2003. (Body Matters Ser.). (Illus.). 32p. pap. 7.50 (978-1-4034-0463-3(1)) Heinemann Library.

Scaly Things: Level N, 6 vols. (Explorers Ser.). 32p. (gr. 3-6). 44.95 (978-0-7699-0594-5(3)) Shortland Pubns. (U. S. A.) Inc.

Schaefer, Lola M. Arms, Elbows, Hands, & Fingers. 2003. (It's My Body Ser.). (Illus.). 24p. (J). (ps-1). lib. bdg. 18.50 (978-1-4034-0889-1(0)); pap. 5.75 (978-1-4034-3478-4(6)) Heinemann Library.

—Hair. 2003. (It's My Body Ser.). (Illus.). 24p. (J). (ps-1). lib. bdg. 18.50 (978-1-4034-0893-8(9)); pap. 5.25 (978-1-4034-3480-7(8)) Heinemann.

—My Head. 2003. (It's My Body Ser.). (Illus.). 24p. (J). (ps-1). lib. bdg. 18.50 (978-1-4034-0891-4(2)); pap. 5.25 (978-1-4034-3483-8(2)) Heinemann Library.

—My Neck & Shoulders. 2003. (It's My Body Ser.). (Illus.). 24p. (J). (ps-1). lib. bdg. 18.50 (978-1-4034-0892-1(0)); pap. 5.25 (978-1-4034-3484-5(0)) Heinemann Library.

Scholastic, Inc. Staff & Fleming, Maria. Human Body Riddle Book: Colorful & Engaging Books on Favorite Thematic Topics for Guided & Independent Reading. 2000. (Super Science Readers Ser.). (Illus.). 16p. pap. 10.95 (978-0-439-16778-9(7)) Scholastic, Inc.

Schumacher, Bev, creator. Body Parts. 2005. (J). ***(978-0-9768706-0-9(6))*** Learning Props.

Seidlitz, Lauri. The Science of the Human Body. 1999. (Living Science Ser.). (Illus.). 32p. (J). (gr. 2 up). lib. bdg. 24.67 (978-0-8368-2570-1(5)) Stevens, Gareth Inc.

Sherman, Josepha. The Upper Limbs: Learning about How We Use Our Arms, Elbows, Forearms, & Hands. 2002. (3-D Library of the Human Body). (Illus.). 48p. (YA). (gr. 5-8). lib. bdg. 26.50 (978-0-8239-3537-6(X) , Rosen Central) Rosen Publishing Group, Inc., The.

Sideri, Simona. Feet. Noble, Sheilagh, tr. Noble, Sheilagh, illus. 2004. (J). lib. bdg. (978-1-58340-492-8(9)) Smart Apple Media.

—Hands. Noble, Sheilagh, tr. Noble, Sheilagh, illus. 2004. (J). lib. bdg. (978-1-58340-493-5(7)) Smart Apple Media.

—Mouths. Noble, Sheilagh, tr. Noble, Sheilagh, illus. 2004. (J). lib. bdg. (978-1-58340-494-2(5)) Smart Apple Media.

Silver, Donald M. & Wynne, Patricia J. Easy Make & Learn Projects - The Human Body: Easy How-To's for Making 20 Models, Manipulations & Mini Books That Would Teach the Kids about the Incredible Human Body. 2000. (Illus.). 80p. (J). (gr. 2-4). pap. 15.99 (978-0-439-04087-7(6)) Scholastic, Inc.

Simon, P. My Body. 1998. (Images Ser.). (Illus.). 136p. (ps-3). pap. 9.95 (978-2-215-06191-5(X)) Continental Enterprises Group, Inc. (CEG).

Snedden, Robert. Animals: Multicelled Life. 2003. (Cells & Life Ser.). (Illus.). 48p. (gr. 6-8). (J). lib. bdg. 27.86 (978-1-58810-671-1(3)); (YA). pap. 8.50 (978-1-58810-933-0(X)) Heinemann Library.

Stone, Lynn M. Beaks & Bills. 2007. (Illus.). 24p. (J). (978-1-60044-169-1(6)) Rourke Publishing, LLC.

Tuxworth, Nicola. A First Book about Bodies. 1999. (Look & Learn Ser.). (Illus.). 24p. (J). (gr. 1 up). lib. bdg. 22.00 (978-0-8368-2286-1(2)) Stevens, Gareth Inc.

von Mackensen, Manfred, et al. Uprightness, Weight, & Balance: Human Biology in Grade Eight. Mitchell, David S., ed. Allgoewer, Claudia, tr. 2004. (YA). per. 12.00 (978-1-888365-53-5(6)) Assn. of Waldorf Schls. of North America Pubns. (AWSNA).

Vriesenga, Daryl. The Human Body. 1999. (100+ Seriestm Ser.). 128p. (J). (gr. 5-8). pap. 12.99 (978-0-88012-827-8(5) , IF8754) School Specialty Publishing.

Walker, Richard. The Kingfisher First Human Body Encyclopedia. 1999. (Kingfisher First Reference Ser.). (Illus.). 112p. (J). (gr. k-3). tchr. ed. 16.95 (978-0-7534-5177-9(8) , Kingfisher) Houghton Mifflin Co. Trade & Reference Div.

—The Little Encyclopedia of the Human Body. 2001. (Kingfisher Little Encyclopedias Ser.). (Illus.). 112p. (J). (gr. k-3). pap. 11.95 (978-0-7534-5423-7(8) , Kingfisher) Houghton Mifflin Co. Trade & Reference Div.

—Under the Microscope: The Human Body, 8 vols., Set. 1998. (Illus.). (YA). (gr. 2 up). lib. bdg. 235.00 (978-0-7172-9265-3(7) , Grolier) Scholastic Library Publishing.

Ward, Pat & Ward, Barb. Your Body & How It Works. 1999. (Illus.). 128p. (YA). (gr. 5). pap. 11.95 (978-1-58037-111-7(6)) Twain, Mark Media, Inc. Pubs.

Waters, Jennifer. All Kinds of People: What Makes Us Different. 2002. (Spyglass Books). (Illus.). 24p. (J). (gr. 1 up). lib. bdg. 18.60 (978-0-7565-0377-2(9)) Compass Point Bks.

Weinroth, Elissa Dosik, et al. The Human Body. 2000. (ScienceWorks for Kids Ser.). (Illus.). 80p. (J). (gr. 4-6). per. 9.99 (978-1-55799-833-0(7) , EMC 877) Evan-Moor Educational Pubs.

Weston, Steve, illus. The World of Animal Life. 2001. (Inside Look Ser.). 48p. (J). (gr. 4 up). lib. bdg. 26.00 (978-0-8368-2902-0(6)) Stevens, Gareth Inc.

Wilkes, Angela. The Human Body. 2001. (Question Time Ser.). (Illus.). 32p. (J). (gr. k-3). tchr. ed. 11.95 (978-0-7534-5341-4(X) , Kingfisher) Houghton Mifflin Co. Trade & Reference Div.

—My Body, 4 vols., Set. 1999. (Ladders Ser.). (Illus.). 32p. (J). (gr. k-3). (978-0-7166-7709-3(1)) World Bk., Inc.

Woodward, John. What Lives on Your Body? 2006. (Illus.). 48p. (J). lib. bdg. ***(978-0-8368-7861-5(2))*** Stevens, Gareth Inc.

Wright, Rachel. Mi Asombroso Cuerpo. 2004. (Discovery Guides Ser.).Tr. of My Amazing Body. (SPA., Illus.). 32p. (gr. 2-5). (J). pap. 6.95 (978-1-58728-705-3(6)); 11.95 (978-1-58728-648-3(3)) T&N Children's Publishing. (Two Can Publishing).

Yagyu, Genichiro. Breasts. Stinehecum, Amanda M., tr. from JPN. 2004. (My Body Science Ser.). Orig. Title: The Story of Breasts. (Illus.). 28p. (J). (gr. k-3). 12.95 (978-0-916291-88-4(X)) Kane/Miller Bk. Pubs., Inc.

Ylvisaker, Anne. Your Lungs. 2002. (Bridgestone Science Library). (Illus.). 24p. (J). (gr. 1-2). lib. bdg. 18.60 (978-0-7368-1149-1(4) , Bridgestone Bks.) Capstone Pr., Inc.

ANATOMY, ARTISTIC

see also Figure Drawing

Anatomy for the Artist. 2003. (Essential Art Ser.). (Illus.). 160p. 9.98 (978-0-7525-8668-7(8)) Parragon, Inc.

ANATOMY, COMPARATIVE

see also Human Beings—Origin

Blackbirch Press Staff, creator. Biters. 2005. (Planet's Most Extreme Ser.). (Illus.). 48p. (J). (ps-7). lib. bdg. 24.95 (978-1-4103-0389-9(6) , Blackbirch Pr., Inc.) Thomson Gale.

Chessen, Betsey. Sharks: Tiburones. 2002. (Science Emergent Readers Ser.). (Illus.). (J). pap. (978-0-439-41162-2(9)) Scholastic, Inc.

Cho, Shinta. Gas We Pass: The Story of Farts. 2001. (gr. k-3). lib. bdg. 15.25 (978-0-613-68588-7(1)) Tandem Library Bks.

Fowler, Allan. Arms & Legs & Other Limbs. 1999. (Rookie Read-About Science Ser.). (Illus.). 32p. (J). (gr. 1-2). 19.50 (978-0-516-20809-1(8) , Children's Pr.) Scholastic Library Publishing.

—How Animals See Things. 1999. (Rookie Read-About Science Ser.). (Illus.). 32p. (J). (gr. 1-2). pap. 4.95 (978-0-516-26416-5(8) , Children's Pr.) Scholastic Library Publishing.

—How Animals See Things. 1999. (Illus.). 31p. (J). (gr. 1-2). lib. bdg. 12.95 (978-0-613-37388-3(X)) Tandem Library Bks.

Legg, Gerald. The X-Ray Picture Book of Incredible Creatures. Salariya, David & Scrace, Carolyn, illus. 2004. 48p. (J). (gr. 4-8). pap. 9.00 (978-0-7567-7406-6(3)) DIANE Publishing Co.

Manning, Mick & Granstrom, Brita. My Body, Your Body. 1998. (Wonderwise Ser.). (Illus.). 32p. (J). (gr. k-3). pap. 6.95 (978-0-531-15324-6(X) , Watts, Franklin) Scholastic Library Publishing.

Miles, Elizabeth. Tails. 2003. (Animal Parts Ser.). (Illus.). 32p. pap. 6.95 (978-1-4034-0431-2(3)) Heinemann Library.

—Wings, Fins & Flippers. 2002. (Heinemann First Library). (Illus.). 32p. (J). (gr. k-2). pap. 6.95 (978-1-4034-0432-9(1)) Heinemann Library.

Obligado, Lilian. Nose to Toes. 1999. (gr. k-3). lib. bdg. 10.95 (978-0-613-22110-8(9)) Tandem Library Bks.

Pallotta, Jerry. The Skull Alphabet Book. Masiello, Ralph, illus. 2004. 32p. (YA). 16.95 (978-0-88106-914-3(0)); pap. 7.95 (978-0-88106-915-0(9)) Charlesbridge Publishing, Inc.

Sideri, Simona. Let's Look at Mouths. Noble, Sheilagh, illus. 2003. (Let's Look at Ser.). 24p. (J). (978-1-84089-147-8(5) , Zero to Ten, Limited) Evans Publishing Group.

Swanson, Diane. Noses That Plow & Poke. 2003. (Up Close Ser.). (Illus.). 32p. (J). 5.95 (978-1-55054-733-7(X)) Sterling Publishing Co., Inc.

—Teeth That Stab & Grind. 2003. (Up Close Ser.). (Illus.). 32p. (J). (gr. 2-4). 9.95 (978-1-55054-768-9(2)) Sterling Publishing Co., Inc.

—Up Close Headgear That Hides & Plays. 2001. (Up Close Ser.). (Illus.). 32p. (J). (ps-3). 9.95 (978-1-55054-819-8(0)) Sterling Publishing Co., Inc.

Swanson, Diane & Cowles, Rose. Noses That Plow & Poke. 2000. (Up Close Ser.). (Illus.). 32p. (gr. k-2). 9.95 (978-1-55054-715-3(1)) Sterling Publishing Co., Inc.

Whittaker, Nicola. Creature Features, 4 bks. Incl. Feet. lib. bdg. 23.33 (978-0-8368-3163-4(2)); Hair. lib. bdg. 23.33 (978-0-8368-3164-1(0)); Noses. lib. bdg. 23.33 (978-0-8368-3165-8(9).); Tails. lib. bdg. 23.33 (978-0-8368-3166-5(7)); 32p. (J). (ps up). 2002. (Illus.). 2002. Set lib. bdg. 93.32 (978-0-8368-3162-7(4)) Stevens, Gareth Inc.

Woodward, John. Body Parts. 2005. (Planet's Most Extreme Ser.). (J). (gr. 3-7). 24.95 (978-1-4103-0395-0(0) , Blackbirch Pr., Inc.) Thomson Gale.

Yagyu, Genichiro. The Holes in Your Nose. Yagyu, Genichiro, illus. 2005. (Illus.). 28p. (J). pap. 6.95 (978-1-929132-82-9(4)) Kane/Miller Bk. Pubs., Inc.

ANATOMY, DENTAL

see Teeth

ANCIENT ART

see Art, Ancient

ANCIENT CIVILIZATION

see Civilization, Ancient

ANCIENT HISTORY

see History, Ancient

ANDERSEN, H. C. (HANS CHRISTIAN), 1805-1875

Bloom, Harold. Hans Christian Andersen. 2004. (Bloom's Modern Critical Views Ser.). (Illus.). 300p. (YA). (gr. 9-13). 45.00 (978-0-7910-8129-7(X) , Chelsea Hse.) Facts On File, Inc.

Brust, Beth Wagner. The Amazing Paper Cuttings of Hans Christian Andersen. Seng, Terry & Andersen, Hans Christian, illus. 2003. 80p. (J). (gr. 5-6). pap. 9.95 (978-0-618-31109-5(2)) Houghton Mifflin Co. Trade & Reference Div.

Carew-Miller, Anna. Hans Christian Andersen: Denmark's Famous Author. 2002. (Great Names Ser.). (Illus.). 32p. (J). (gr. 3 up). lib. bdg. 19.95 (978-1-59084-160-0(3)) Mason Crest Pubs.

Fradin, Dennis B. Tell Us a Tale, Hans! The Life of Hans Christian Andersen. Buhler, Cynthia von, illus. 2006. (J). (978-1-59336-681-0(7)); pap. (978-1-59336-682-7(5)) Mondo Publishing.

Frank, Jeffrey & Frank, Diana, trs. from DAN. The Stories of Hans Christian Andersen: A New Translation from the Danish. Frolich, Lorenz & Pederson, Vilhelm, illus. 2003. 304p. tchr. ed. 30.00 (978-0-618-22456-2(4)) Houghton Mifflin Co. Trade & Reference Div.

Hesse, Karen. The Young Hans Christian Andersen. Blegvad, Erik, illus. 2005. 48p. (J). (gr. 2-5). pap. 16.99 (978-0-439-67990-9(7)) Scholastic, Inc.

Varmer, Hjordis. Hans Christian Andersen: His Fairy Tale Life. Nunnally, Tiina, tr. from DAN. Brogger, Lilian, illus. 2005. 112p. (J). (gr. 5). 19.95 (978-0-88899-690-9(X)) Groundwood Bks. CAN. *Dist:* Perseus Distribution.

—Hans Christian Andersen: His Fairy Tale Life. Brogger, Lilian, illus. 2007. 112p. (J). pap. 12.95 (978-0-88899-798-2(1)) Groundwood Bks. CAN. *Dist:* Perseus Distribution.

Yolen, Jane. The Perfect Wizard: Hans Christian Andersen. Nolan, Dennis, illus. 2005. 32p. (J). (gr. 1). 16.99 (978-0-525-46955-1(9) , Dutton Juvenile) Penguin Group (USA) Inc.

ANDERSON, EINSTEIN (FICTITIOUS CHARACTER)—FICTION

Simon, Seymour. The Gigantic Ants & Other Cases. 1998. (Einstein Anderson, Science Detective Ser.). (Illus.). (J). (gr. 3-6). pap. 3.99 (978-0-380-72657-8(2)) HarperCollins Pubs.

—The Halloween Horror & Other Cases, Bk. 2. Schindler, S. D., illus. 1998. (Einstein Anderson, Science Detective Ser.). (J). (gr. 3-6). pap. 3.99 (978-0-380-72656-1(4)) HarperCollins Pubs.

—The Howling Dog & Other Cases. 1998. (Einstein Anderson, Science Detective Ser.). (Illus.). (J). (gr. 3-6). pap. 3.99 (978-0-380-72655-4(6)) HarperCollins Pubs.

—The Howling Dog & Other Cases. 2000. (Einstein Anderson, Science Detective Ser.). (J). (gr. 3-6). pap. 32.00 incl. audio (978-0-7887-4457-0(7) , 41148) Recorded Bks., LLC.

—The Invisible Man & Other Cases. (Einstein Anderson, Science Detective Ser.: Vol. 7). 96p. (J). (gr. 3-7). 1999. pap. 3.99 (978-0-380-72661-5(0) , Harper Trophy); 1998. (Illus.). 14.95 (978-0-688-14447-0(0)) HarperCollins Pubs.

—The Invisible Man & Other Cases. 1999. (Einstein Anderson, Science Detective Ser.). (J). (gr. 3-6). (978-0-606-16358-3(1)) Tandem Library Bks.

—The Mysterious Lights & Other Cases. Schindler, S. D., illus. (Einstein Anderson, Science Detective Ser.). 96p. (J). (gr. 3-6). 1999. pap. 3.99 (978-0-380-72660-8(2)); 1998. 14.95 (978-0-688-14445-6(4)) HarperCollins Pubs.

—The Mysterious Lights & Other Cases. 1999. (Einstein Anderson, Science Detective Ser.). (J). (gr. 3-6). (978-0-606-16354-5(9)) Tandem Library Bks.

—The On-Line Spaceman & Other Cases. 1998. (Einstein Anderson, Science Detective Ser.). (Illus.). 96p. (J). (gr. 3-6). reprint ed. pap. 3.99 (978-0-380-72662-2(9)) HarperCollins Pubs.

—The On-Line Spaceman & Other Cases. 1998. (Einstein Anderson, Science Detective Ser.). (J). (gr. 3-6). (978-0-606-13352-4(6)) Tandem Library Bks.

—The Time Machine & Other Cases. Schindler, S. D., illus. 1999. (Einstein Anderson, Science Detective Ser.). (J). (gr. 3-6). pap. 3.99 (978-0-380-72658-5(0)) HarperCollins Pubs.

—The Time Machine & Other Cases. 1999. (Einstein Anderson, Science Detective Ser.). (J). (gr. 3-6). (978-0-606-16005-6(1)) Tandem Library Bks.

—The Wings of Darkness & Other Cases, Bk. 5. Schindler, S. D., illus. 1999. (Einstein Anderson, Science Detective Ser.). 80p. (J). (gr. 3-6). pap. 3.99 (978-0-380-72659-2(9) , Harper Trophy) HarperCollins Pubs.

—The Wings of Darkness & Other Cases. 1999. (Einstein Anderson, Science Detective Ser.). (J). (gr. 3-6). (978-0-606-16341-5(7)) Tandem Library Bks.

ANDERSON, ELIZABETH (GARRETT), 1836-1917

Klobuchar, Lisa. Elizabeth Blackwell: With Profiles of Elizabeth Garrett Anderson & Susan la Flesche Picotte. 2006. (Biographical Connections Ser.). (Illus.). 112p. (978-0-7166-1826-3(5)) World Bk., Inc.

ANDERSON, MARIAN, 1897-1993

Freedman, Russell. The Voice That Challenged a Nation: Marian Anderson & the Struggle for Equal Rights. 2004. (Illus.). 128p. (J). (gr. 4-6). tchr. ed. 18.00 (978-0-618-15976-5(2) , Clarion Bks.) Houghton Mifflin Co. Trade & Reference Div.

Hopkinson, Deborah. Sweet Land of Liberty. Jenkins, Leonard, illus. 2007. 32p. (J). (gr. 1-5). 16.95 (978-1-56145-395-5(1) , Peachtree Junior) Peachtree Pubs., Ltd.

Jones, Victoria Garrett. Marian Anderson: A Voice Uplifted. 2008. (Sterling Biographies Ser.). (Illus.). 128p. (J). pap. 5.95 ***(978-1-4027-4239-2(8))*** Sterling Publishing Co., Inc.

Kramer, Candice. Eleanor Roosevelt & Marian Anderson. 2005. 40.00 ***(978-1-4108-4537-5(0))*** Benchmark Education Co.

Livorse, Kay. Let Freedom Sing. Copeland, Greg, illus. 2002. 16p. (J). (978-0-439-35159-1(6)) Scholastic, Inc.

McKissack, Patricia C. & McKissack, Fredrick L. Marian Anderson: A Great Singer. rev. ed. 2001. (Great African Americans Ser.). (Illus.). 32p. (J). (gr. 1-4). lib. bdg. 18.60 (978-0-7660-1676-7(5)) Enslow Pubs., Inc.

Ryan, Pam Muñoz. When Marian Sang: The True Recital of Marian Anderson. Selznick, Brian, illus. pap. 16.95 incl. audio (978-1-59112-943-1(5)); pap. incl. audio (978-1-59112-945-5(1)); pap. 18.95 incl. audio compact disk (978-1-59112-947-9(8)); pap. incl. audio compact disk (978-1-59112-949-3(4)); 2004. (J). 25.95 incl. audio (978-1-59112-944-8(3)); 2004. (J). 28.95 incl. audio compact disk (978-1-59112-948-6(6)) Live Oak Media.

—When Marian Sang: The True Recital of Marian Anderson. Selznick, Brian, illus. 2002. 40p. (J). (gr. 1-5). pap. 16.95 (978-0-439-26967-4(9) , Scholastic Pr.) Scholastic, Inc.

Sutcliffe, Jane. Marian Anderson. 2008. (History Maker Biographies Ser.). (J). lib. bdg. 26.60 ***(978-0-8225-7170-4(6)*** , Lerner Pubns.) Lerner Publishing Group.

ANDES MOUNTAINS

Maynard, Charles W. The Andes. 2004. (Great Mountain Ranges of the World Ser.). (Illus.). 24p. (J). lib. bdg. 21.25 (978-0-8239-6696-7(8) , PowerKids Pr.) Rosen Publishing Group, Inc., The.

Somervill, Barbara A. The Land of the Andes. 2004. (Geography of the World Ser.). 32p. (J). (gr. 2-6). 27.07 (978-1-59296-331-7(5)) Child's World, Inc.

ANDES MOUNTAINS—FICTION

Garcia-Huidobro, Beatriz. Misterio en el Campamento. 2002. (J). (978-956-240-348-1(3)) Arrayan Editores S.A.

Silvano, Wendi. Just One More. Gamboa, Ricardo, illus. 2007. 36p. (J). reprint ed. pap. 14.95 (978-0-9744446-5-9(0)) All About Kids Publishing.

ANDREW, APOSTLE, SAINT

Rock, Lois & Piper, Sophie. Saint Andrew of Scotland. 2005. (Illus.). 24p. (J). pap. 7.50 (978-0-7459-4808-9(1) , Lion) Lion Hudson plc GBR. *Dist:* Independent Pubs. Group.

ANDREWS, ROY CHAPMAN, 1884-1960

Bausum, Ann. Dragon Bones & Dinosaur Eggs: A Photo-Biography of Explorer Roy Chapman Andrews. 2000. (Illus.). 64p. (J). (gr. 3-7). 17.95 (978-0-7922-7123-9(8) , National Geographic Children's Bks.) National Geographic Society.

Hartzog, Brooke. The First Dinosaur Eggs & Roy Chapman Andrews. 1999. (Dinosaurs & Their Discoverers Ser.). (Illus.). 24p. (J). (gr. k-4). lib. bdg. 18.75 (978-0-8239-5329-5(7) , PowerKids Pr.) Rosen Publishing Group, Inc., The.

ANECDOTES

Crowest, Frederick J. A Book of Musical Anecdote, 2 vols., set. 2001. (YA). reprint ed. 250.00 (978-0-7222-5235-2(8)) Library Reprints, Inc.

Tait, Chris. How to Be a Kid. Paillot, Jim, illus. 2003. 96p. (J). pap. 6.95 (978-0-8069-8503-9(8)) Sterling Publishing Co., Inc.

ANESTHETICS—HISTORY

Lace, William. Anesthetics. 2004. (Great Medical Discoveries Ser.). (Illus.). 112p. (J). 29.95 (978-1-56006-924-9(4)) Thomson Gale.

ANGEL (FICTITIOUS CHARACTER)—FICTION

Ciencin, Scott. Vengance. 2002. (gr. 7-12). lib. bdg. 14.15 (978-0-613-63240-9(0)) Tandem Library Bks.

Debrandt, Don. Shakedown. 2000. (Angel Ser.: No. 5). 320p. (YA). (gr. 7 up). pap. 5.99 (978-0-7434-0696-3(6) , Simon Pulse) Simon & Schuster Children's Publishing.

—Shakedown. 2000. (gr. 7-12). lib. bdg. 14.15 (978-0-613-63231-7(1)) Tandem Library Bks.

Holder, Nancy. The Angel Chronicles. (Buffy the Vampire Slayer Ser.: No. 6). (Illus.). (YA). (gr. 7 up). Vol. 1. 1998. 224p. pap. 5.99 (978-0-671-02133-7(8)); Vol. 3. 1999. 192p. pap. 5.99 (978-0-671-02631-8(3)) Simon & Schuster Children's Publishing. (Simon Pulse).

—Heat. 2005. (Buffy/Angel Crossover Ser.). 464p. (YA). pap. 6.99 (978-0-689-86906-8(1) , Simon Spotlight Entertainment) Simon & Schuster.

—Not Forgotten. 2000. (Angel Ser.: No. 2). 256p. (YA). (gr. 7 up). pap. 5.99 (978-0-671-04145-8(2) , Simon Pulse) Simon & Schuster Children's Publishing.

—Not Forgotten. 2000. (gr. 7-12). lib. bdg. 14.15 (978-0-613-28001-3(6)) Tandem Library Bks.

Marriotte, Jeff. Door to Alternity. 2001. (gr. 7-12). lib. bdg. 15.30 (978-0-613-63279-9(6)) Tandem Library Bks.

ANGELINA BALLERINA (FICTITIOUS CHARACTER)—FICTION

Craig, Helen, illus. Angelina's Halloween. 2007. 32p. (J). ***(978-0-670-91162-2(3)*** , Viking Juvenile) Penguin Group (USA) Inc.

Holabird, Katharine. Angelina in the Wings. Craig, Helen, illus. 2006. (Angelina Ballerina Ser.). 24p. (J). (ps-1). 3.99 (978-0-448-44471-0(2) , Grosset & Dunlap) Penguin Group (USA) Inc.

—Dance of the Sunbeams. Craig, Helen, illus. 2006. (Angelina Ballerina Ser.). 24p. (J). (ps-1). 4.99 (978-0-448-44020-0(2) , Grosset & Dunlap) Penguin Group (USA) Inc.

—A Really-Truly Special Day! Craig, Helen, illus. 2006. (Angelina Ballerina Ser.). 32p. (J). (ps-k). 4.99 (978-0-448-44333-1(3) , Grosset & Dunlap) Penguin Group (USA) Inc.

—The Silver Locket. Craig, Helen, illus. 2006. (Angelina Ballerina Ser.). 24p. (J). (ps-1). 3.99 (978-0-448-44472-7(0) , Grosset & Dunlap) Penguin Group (USA) Inc.

—Two Mice in a Boat. 2002. (gr. k-3). lib. bdg. 11.25 (978-0-613-88472-3(8)) Tandem Library Bks.

Weber, Lou. Angelina Ballerina Interactive Play a Sound. 2005. 24p. (J). 15.98 (978-1-4127-3559-9(9) , 7229701) Publications International, Ltd.

—Angelina Ballerina Little Music Note Play a Song. 2005. 12p. 9.98 (978-1-4127-3563-6(7)) Publications International, Ltd.

ANGELS

Bostrom, Kathleen Long & Kucharik, Elena. Are Angels Real? 2001. (Little Blessings Ser.). (Illus.). 80p. (J). (ps-k). 9.99 (978-0-8423-3959-9(0)) Tyndale Hse. Pubs.

Cooper, Diana. Angel Cards for Children. 2004. (Illus.). 33p. (J). pap. 15.99 (978-1-84409-027-3(2)) Findhorn Pr. GBR. *Dist:* Independent Pubs. Group.

Dittmer, Cherie Pless. Angel! Angel! 2004. (Illus.). 24p. (J). (ps-k). bds. 6.99 (978-0-7586-0687-7(7)) Concordia Publishing Hse.

Ellis, Gwen. Christmas Angels: Read & Share. 2007. 32p. (J). 12.99 (***978-1-4003-0854-5(2)***) Nelson, Thomas Inc.

Freed, Shirley Ann & Moon, Louise. Angels Care for Me. Morelan, Bill, ed. Harrell, Rob, illus. l.t. ed. 2002. 8p. (J). (ps-k). pap. 3.99 (978-1-58938-005-9(3)) Concerned Communications.

God's Angels: Our Friends. 2005. (Illus.). 48p. (J). pap. 15.00 (978-1-893757-42-4(0) , 42-0) Needer, E.T. Publishing.

Halpin, D. My Guardian Angel Col/Act Bk. 24p. pap. 1.25 (978-0-8198-4825-3(5) , 332-216) Pauline Bks. & Media.

Hennessey, Geri. Children's Encounters with Angels. 2006. (ENG.). 28p. per. 12.49 (***978-1-4259-7725-2(1)***) AuthorHouse.

Hunt, Marigold. A Book of Angels: Stories of Angels from the Bible. 2005. (Illus.). v, 167p. (J). pap. 13.95 (978-1-933184-00-5(0)) Sophia Institute Pr.

Klutz Press Staff. Make Your Own Itty-Bitty Angels. 2005. (Illus.). 32p. (J). (gr. 3 up). spiral bd. 9.95 (978-1-59174-275-3(7)) Klutz.

Lane, Leena. Angels among Us. Baboni, Elena, illus. 2007. 30p. (J). (gr. k-5). 17.00 (***978-0-8028-5321-9(8)*** , Eerdmans Bks For Young Readers) Eerdmans, William B. Publishing Co.

Libby, Larry & Gauthier, Corbert. Angels, Angels Everywhere. Gauthier, Corbert, illus. 2003. (Illus.). 40p. (J). (gr. k-3). 12.99 (978-0-310-70342-6(5)) Zonderkidz.

Llewellyn, Claire. Saints & Angels. (Illus.). 64p. (J). 2003. (gr. 5-9). tchr. ed. 16.95 (978-0-7534-5588-3(9)); 2006. (gr. 4-6). 8.95 (978-0-7534-5906-5(X)) Houghton Mifflin Co. Trade & Reference Div. (Kingfisher).

Lynette, Rachel. Angels. 2006. (Mysterious Encounters Ser.). 48p. (J). (gr. 4-8). 26.20 (978-0-7377-3607-6(0) , Kidhaven) Thomson Gale.

Noble, Marty. Invisible Angels Magic Picture Book. 1998. (Illus.). 16p. (J). pap. 1.50 (978-0-486-40330-4(0)) Dover Pubns., Inc.

O'Brien, Joan. Littlest Angels Stickers. 2003. (Dover Little Activity Bks.). (Illus.). 4p. (J). (ps-5). pap. 1.50 (978-0-486-43007-2(3)) Dover Pubns., Inc.

Osborne, Rick & Strauss, Ed. Bible Angels & Demons. 2004. (2:52 Ser.). (Illus.). 112p. (J). pap. 7.99 (978-0-310-70775-2(7)) Zonderkidz.

Ruth, Annie. Little Angels Coloring & Activity Book: The Special Gift. Ruth, Annie, illus. l.t. ed. 1999. (Illus.). 24p. (J). (gr. k-3). 3.50 (978-0-9656306-2-7(5)) Ruth, A. Creations.

Stevens, Joyce Ann. From the Heart. 2001. (Illus.). 284p. per. 20.00 (978-0-9708645-1-2(5)) Divine Power Publishing.

Stone, Elaine Murphy & Rayburn, Cathy. Angels in the Bible. Sabatte, Frank, illus. 2006. 88p. (J). pap. 7.95 (978-0-8091-6729-6(8) , 6729-8) Paulist Pr.

Strong, Cynda. Where Do Angels Sleep? Denos, Julia, illus. 2007. 32p. (J). (ps-3). 14.99 (***978-0-7586-1298-4(2)***) Concordia Publishing Hse.

Virtue, Doreen & Tracy, Kristina. Thank You, Angels. Keeler, Patricia, illus. 2007. 32p. (ps-3). 15.95 (***978-1-4019-1846-0(8)***) Hay Hse., Inc.

ANGELS—FICTION

Adams, Denise H. Annabelle's Angels. 2007. (J). per. 11.99 (***978-1-59879-386-4(1)***) Lifevest Publishing, Inc.

Al-Chokhachy, Elissa. The Angel with the Golden Glow: A Family's Journey Through Loss & Healing. Graf, Ulrike, illus. 2001. 32p. (J). (ps up). 15.95 (978-1-893356-00-9(0) , Penny Bear Publishing) Penny Bear Co., Inc., The.

Almond, David. Skellig. 2001. (Illus.). 208p. (gr. 5). mass mkt. 6.50 (978-0-440-22908-7(1) , Laurel Leaf) Random Hse. Children's Bks.

—Skellig. Wojtyla, Karen, ed. 2000. (Illus.). 192p. (gr. 5-7). 6.50 (978-0-440-41602-9(7) , Yearling) Random Hse. Children's Bks.

—Skellig. 1999. 192p. (gr. 5 up). 16.95 (978-0-385-32653-7(X) , Delacorte Bks. for Young Readers) Random Hse. Children's Bks.

—Skellig. 2001. (gr. 5-8). lib. bdg. 14.15 (978-0-613-84565-6(X)); 2000. (J). (978-0-606-19192-0(5)); 2000. (gr. 5-8). lib. bdg. 13.00 (978-0-613-28330-4(9)) Tandem Library Bks.

Angel in Heavy Shoes. 2000. (Katie Rose/Stacy Belford Ser.). (YA). (gr. 5-9). per. 12.95 (978-1-930009-14-1(3)) Image Cascade Publishing.

An Angel on My Shoulder. 2000. (Illus.). 32p. (YA). (gr. 3-12). lib. bdg. 8.95 (978-1-893595-04-0(8)) Four Seasons Bks., Inc.

Anjelae, Samara. My Guardian Angel. Ferguson, Martha-Elizabeth, illus. 2002. (Wonder Window Ser.). 32p. (J). 16.95 (978-0-9634910-7-7(5) , BelleTress Bks.) Red Wheel/Weiser.

Arena, Umberto J. The Angel & the Greedy Kid. 2006. 25p. (J). pap. 7.95 (978-0-533-15387-9(5)) Vantage Pr., Inc.

Arrigan, Mary & Mclure, Gillian. Mario's Angels: A Story about the Artist Giotto. 2006. (Illus.). 32p. (J). 15.95 (978-1-84507-404-3(1)) Lincoln, Frances Ltd. GBR. *Dist:* Perseus Distribution.

Avi. The Christmas Rat. 2002. (gr. 3-6). lib. bdg. 13.00 (978-0-613-88162-3(1)) Tandem Library Bks.

Bankow, Henriette. Alfie's Angels: Big Book English Only. Garson, Sarah, illus. 2004. 30p. (J). (978-1-84444-119-8(9)) Mantra Publishing, Ltd.

Barkow, Henriette. Alfie's Angels. 2004. (Illus.). 32p. (J). (TAM, CZE, VIE, SPA & GUJ.). (978-1-85269-957-4(4)); (TAM, CZE, VIE, SPA & GUJ., pap. (978-1-85269-908-6(6)); (TAM, CZE, VIE, SPA & GUJ., pap. (978-1-85269-913-0(2)); (TAM, CZE, VIE, SPA & GUJ., pap. (978-1-85269-918-5(3)); (TAM, CZE, VIE, SPA & GUJ., pap. (978-1-85269-923-9(X)); (TAM, CZE, VIE, SPA & GUJ., pap. (978-1-85269-928-4(0)); (CZE, TAM, VIE, SPA & GUJ., pap. (978-1-85269-933-8(7)); (TAM, CZE, VIE, SPA & GUJ., pap. (978-1-85269-938-3(8)); (TAM, CZE, VIE, SPA & GUJ., pap. (978-1-85269-943-7(4)); (TAM, CZE, VIE, SPA & GUJ., pap. (978-1-85269-947-5(7)); (TAM, CZE, VIE, SPA & GUJ., pap. (978-1-85269-903-1(5)); (TAM, CZE, VIE, SPA & GUJ., pap. (978-1-85269-952-9(3)); (TAM, CZE, SPA, VIE & GUJ., pap. (978-1-85269-948-2(5)); (TAM, CZE, VIE, SPA & GUJ., pap. (978-1-85269-962-8(0)); (TAM, CZE, VIE, SPA & GUJ., pap. (978-1-85269-967-3(1)); (TAM, CZE, VIE, SPA & GUJ., pap. (978-1-85269-972-7(8)); (TAM, CZE, VIE, SPA & GUJ., pap. (978-1-85269-977-2(9)); (TAM, CZE, VIE, SPA & GUJ., pap. (978-1-85269-982-6(5)); (TAM, CZE, VIE, SPA & GUJ., pap. (978-1-85269-987-1(6)); (TAM, CZE, VIE, SPA & GUJ., pap. (978-1-85269-992-5(2)); (TAM, CZE, VIE, SPA & GUJ., pap. (978-1-85269-997-0(3)) Mantra Publishing, Ltd.

Bates, Sheree. Megan's One Wish. 2006. 124p. (YA). pap. 12.99 (978-1-4141-0555-0(X)) Pleasant Word.

Bauer, Marion Dane. The Blue Ghost. 2005. (Illus.). 96p. (J). (gr. 3-7). 11.95 (978-0-375-83179-9(7)); lib. bdg. 13.99 (978-0-375-93179-6(1)) Random Hse. Children's Bks. (Random Hse. Bks. for Young Readers).

Bennett, Ruth. Where Angels Wait. l.t. ed. 2004. (Dales Large Print Ser.). (Illus.). 288p. (J). 23.99 (978-1-84262-334-3(6)) Magna Large Print Bks. GBR. *Dist:* Ulverscroft Large Print Bks., Ltd.

Berkeley, Jon. The Palace of Laughter: The Wednesday Tales No. 1. Dorman, Brandon, illus. (J). 2007. 464p. (gr. 3-7). pap. 7.99 (***978-0-06-075509-6(1)*** , Harper Trophy); 2006. 448p. lib. bdg. 17.89 (978-0-06-075508-9(3) , Julie Andrews Collection) HarperCollins Pubs.

—The Tiger's Egg. Dorman, Brandon, illus. 2007. 416p. (J). (gr. 3-7). lib. bdg. 17.89 (***978-0-06-075511-9(3)***); (Wednesday Tales Ser.: No. 2). 16.99 (***978-0-06-075510-2(5)***) HarperCollins Pubs. (Julie Andrews Collection).

Berrios, Frank. My Guardian Angel. 2005. (Illus.). 10p. (J). (gr. k-ps). bds. 4.99 (978-0-375-83381-6(1) , Golden Bks.) Random Hse. Children's Bks.

Bethany: Adventures of the Mighty Mustard Seed. 2004. Orig. Title: Bethany in Beulah Land. (J). mass mkt. 12.95 (978-0-9745440-0-7(0)) McKatlib Pr.

Blacker, Terence. The Angel Factory. (Illus.). 224p. 2003. (J). (gr. k-17). pap. 5.99 (978-0-689-86413-1(2) , Aladdin); 2002. (YA). (gr. 6-9). 16.95 (978-0-689-85171-1(5)) Simon & Schuster Children's Publishing.

Blanco, Alberto. Angel's Kite (La Estrella de Angel) Bellm, Dan, tr. Morales, Rodolfo, illus. 1998. (ENG & SPA.). 32p. (J). (gr. 1-4). pap. 7.95 (978-0-89239-156-1(1)) Children's Bk. Pr.

Bock, Suzanne, illus. In the Beginning: Angels with Attitudes. 2004. 32p. (J). 12.99 (978-0-9758709-0-7(4) , 11412) Journey Stone Creations, LLC.

—Meet the Angels. l.t. ed. 2004. 10p. (J). bds. 12.99 (978-0-9758709-4-5(7) , 13401) Journey Stone Creations, LLC.

Boggs, Patdee. Island of Angels. 2006. 55p. pap. 12.95 (***978-1-4241-3758-9(6)***) PublishAmerica, Inc.

Bornstein, Laurie. Angel Cloud. 2003. pap. 9.00 (978-0-8059-6083-9(X)) Dorrance Publishing Co., Inc.

Brouwer, Sigmund. The Angel & the Cross. 2005. (Guardian Angel Ser.). 168p. (gr. 3-7). pap. 7.99 (978-0-7369-0296-0(1)) Harvest Hse. Pubs.

—The Angel & the Ring: A Supernatural Adventure. 2005. (Guardian Angel Ser.). 165p. (J). (ps-7). pap. 7.99 (978-0-7369-0294-6(5)) Harvest Hse. Pubs.

—The Angel & the Sword: A Supernatural Adventure. 2005. (Guardian Angel Ser.). 172p. (J). (ps-7). pap. 7.99 (978-0-7369-0293-9(7)) Harvest Hse. Pubs.

Buffie, Margaret. Angels Turn Their Backs. (Margaret Buffie Ser.). 240p. (YA). (gr. 13 up). 1998. (978-1-55074-415-6(1)); 2001. (978-1-55337-098-7(8)) Kids Can Pr., Ltd.

—Angels Turn Their Backs. 2001. (gr. 7-12). lib. bdg. 15.25 (978-0-613-87660-5(1)) Tandem Library Bks.

Carabine, Sue. An Angel's Night Before Christmas. Kawasaki, Shauna Mooney, illus. 2001. 60p. 5.95 (978-1-58685-087-6(3)); 2nd gif. ed. 5.95 (978-1-58685-122-4(5)) Gibbs Smith, Publisher.

Causton, Linda. Lester's Rainy Lake Pony. l.t. ed. 2004. (Illus.). 32p. (J). 12.00 (978-1-930374-09-6(7)) DeForest Pr.

Chandler, Elizabeth. Kissed by an Angel: The Power of Love Soulmates. collector's ed. 1998. (Kissed by an Angel Ser.). 704p. (YA). (gr. 8-12). pap. 7.99 (978-0-671-02346-1(2) , Simon Pulse) Simon & Schuster Children's Publishing.

Chase, et al. Angel in a Gum Tree. (Illus.). 32p. pap. 13.95 (978-1-86368-222-0(8)) Fremantle Pr. AUS. *Dist:* International Specialized Bk. Services.

Chass, Vikentia. The Visiting Angels. 1999. 16p. (J). (gr. k-6). pap. 8.00 (978-0-8059-4713-7(2)) Dorrance Publishing Co., Inc.

The Childlren's Book of Angels. 2005. (J). pap. (978-0-9769166-6-6(5)) Living Life Publishing Co.

The Children's Book of Angels. 2005. (J). per. (978-0-9769166-5-9(7)) Living Life Publishing Co.

Clark, Debbie. Amberleigh's Christmas Angel: An Adolescent's Story of Love, Loss, & Renewed Hope for the Future. 2004. 48p. pap. 12.95 (978-1-4137-4528-3(8)) PublishAmerica, Inc.

Clay, Judith L. Mansfield. "ABE" the Chumsy Angel. (Illus.). 18p. (J). (ps-k). pap. 8.95 (978-0-9707428-0-3(0)) Mansfield, J. Hse. Publishing Co.

Clements, Andrew. Bright Christmas: An Angel Remembers. Kiesler, Kate A., illus. 2000. 32p. (J). (gr. k-3). 6.95 (978-0-618-05153-3(8) , Clarion Bks.) Houghton Mifflin Co. Trade & Reference Div.

—Bright Christmas: An Angel Remembers. 2000. (gr. k-3). lib. bdg. 14.10 (978-0-613-31024-6(1)) Tandem Library Bks.

Cleofas-Moore, Ramona. The Runaway Angels. 2005. 86p. pap. 14.95 (978-1-4137-7710-9(4)) PublishAmerica, Inc.

Collins, H. Elizabeth. To Sleep with the Angels. Kuusisto, Judy, illus. 1999. 32p. (ps-3). 15.95 (978-0-935699-16-6(3)) Illumination Arts Publishing Co., Inc.

Cowden, Christine. Mystical Christmas with Angels in Disguise: No Reward Needed. 2005. 48p. pap. 12.95 (978-1-4137-6759-9(1)) PublishAmerica, Inc.

Cowen, Fletcher. Baby Angels. 2005. (Illus.). 16p. (J). (gr. k-ps). bds. 6.99 (978-0-7636-2896-3(4)) Candlewick Pr.

Craft, Mahlon. Christmas Moon. Craft, K. Y., illus. 2003. 32p. (J). 15.95 (978-1-58717-056-0(6)); lib. bdg. (978-1-58717-057-7(4)) Chronicle Bks. LLC. (SeaStar Bks.).

Crosse, Joanna. A Child's Book of Angels. Whelan, Olwyn, illus. 2000. 64p. (J). (gr. 1-4). 19.99 (978-1-84148-082-4(7)) Barefoot Bks., Inc.

Cyr, Joe. Shawn the Hopping Christmas Tree. Cyr, Diane, ed. Henry, Diane, illus. l.t. ed. 2001. 32p. 5.95 (978-0-9713768-0-9(8)) Cyr, Joe.

—Two Tales of That Very First Christmas: An Angel Named Etoile & the Straw Girl, Owen, Ramon E., illus. l.t. ed. 2002. 24p. 5.95 (978-0-9713768-1-6(6)) Cyr, Joe.

Dalton, Annie. Angels Unlimited: Losing the Plot. l.t. ed. 2005. 164p. (J). pap. (978-1-4056-6047-1(3)) BBC Audio.

—The Heavenly Collection. 2008. 400p. (J). pap. 19.95 (***978-0-00-723307-6(8)***) HarperCollins Pubs. Ltd. GBR. *Dist:* Independent Pubs. Group.

—Losing the Plot. 2002. (Angels Unlimited Ser.: Vol. 2). (Illus.). 160p. (J). (ps-3). pap. 4.99 (978-0-06-008816-3(8)) HarperCollins Pubs.

—Mel Beeby, Agent Angel - Flying High. 2008. 144p. (J). pap. 6.95 (***978-0-00-720473-1(6)***) HarperCollins Pubs. Ltd. GBR. *Dist:* Independent Pubs. Group.

—Mel Beeby, Agent Angel - Losing the Plot. 2008. 160p. (J). pap. 6.95 (***978-0-00-720472-4(8)***) HarperCollins Pubs. Ltd. GBR. *Dist:* Independent Pubs. Group.

—Mel Beeby, Agent Angel - Winging It. 2008. 144p. pap. 6.95 (***978-0-00-720471-7(X)***) HarperCollins Pubs. Ltd. GBR. *Dist:* Independent Pubs. Group.

Dalton, Annie. Winging It. 2002. (Angels Unlimited Ser.: Vol. 1). (Illus.). 144p. (J). (ps-3). pap. 4.99 (978-0-06-008815-6(X)) HarperCollins Pubs.

Davis, Christine. For Every Dog an Angel. 2nd ed. 2004. (Illus.). 32p. (J). 9.95 (978-0-9659225-2-4(9)) Lighthearted Press Inc.

de Paola, Tomie. Pascual & the Kitchen Angels. de Paola, Tomie, illus. 2006. (Illus.). 32p. (J). pap. 5.99 (978-0-14-240536-9(1) , Puffin) Penguin Group (USA) Inc.

—Pascual & the Kitchen Angels. 2004. (Illus.). 32p. (J). (ps-3). 16.99 (978-0-399-24214-4(7) , Putnam Juvenile) Penguin Group (USA) Inc.

Dean Wafstet, Cindi. Wings of Light. 2005. 31p. 15.00 (978-1-4116-5567-6(2)) Lulu.com.

Delton, Judy. Back Yard Angel. Weber, Jill, illus. 1999. 128p. (J). (gr. 4-6). pap. 5.95 (978-0-395-96060-8(6)) Houghton Mifflin Co. Trade & Reference Div.

DePaola, Tomie. Angels, Angels Everywhere. DePaola, Tomie, illus. 2005. (Illus.). 28p. (J). (ps-3). 14.99 (978-0-399-24370-7(4) , Putnam Juvenile) Penguin Group (USA) Inc.

Doggett, Sue. Advent Angels: A Host of Stories, Crafts, Puzzles & Things to Do for the Days of Advent. Blake, Francis, illus. 1999. 64p. (J). pap. (978-1-84101-099-1(5) , Barnabas) Bible Reading Fellowship.

Dollin, Laura. Christmas Angel. Beardshaw, Rosalind, illus. 2003. 12p. (J). (gr. k-k). bds. 5.99 (978-0-7636-2142-1(0)) Candlewick Pr.

Doman, Regina. Angel in the Waters. Hatke, Ben, illus. 2004. 48p. (J). (ps-3). pap. 6.95 (978-1-928832-81-2(4)) Sophia Institute Pr.

Doman, Regina. Mi Angelito en las aquas. 2006. (SPA.). 46p. pap. 6.95 (***978-1-933184-22-7(1)***) Sophia Institute Pr.

Donna, Gelsinger, ed. In My Father's Garden. 2007. 10p. pap. 6.99 (***978-1-4037-3625-3(1)*** , Spirit Pr.) Dalmatian Pr.

Doran-Smith, Eileen J. The Cloud Painter, Vol. 2. Smith, Douglas M., ed. 2000. (Illus.). 32p. (J). (ps-3). 14.99 (978-1-929489-64-0(1)) Platinum Medallion Children's Bks.

Duhon, Katherine. The Christmas Angel. 2006. pap. 7.95 (978-0-533-15381-7(6)) Vantage Pr., Inc.

Durgin, Doranna. Impressions. 2003. (gr. 7-12). lib. bdg. 14.15 (978-0-613-61777-2(0)) Tandem Library Bks.

Dyer, Heather. The GIRL with the BROKEN WIND. 2007. 160p. (J). pap. 4.99 (***978-0-439-74828-5(3)*** , Scholastic Paperbacks) Scholastic, Inc.

Dyer, Heather. The Girl with the Broken Wing. Bailey, Peter, illus. 2005. 160p. (J). pap. 15.99 (978-0-439-74827-8(5) , Chicken Hse., The) Scholastic, Inc.

Eachus, Jennifer. Angel: A Tale of Wonder. Eachus, Jennifer, illus. 2005. (Illus.). 32p. (J). (ps-3). 10.99 (978-0-7636-2953-3(7)) Candlewick Pr.

Elliott, Dorothy. Little Angel Third Class - below Stairs. 2007. 92p. per. (***978-1-84685-562-7(4)*** , Exposure Publishing) Meadow Bks.

Eubanks, Sandra. Carina the Angel. 2005. 17.00 (978-0-8059-9793-4(8)) Dorrance Publishing Co., Inc.

Evangel - the Smallest Angel. 2006. (J). (***978-0-9790210-0-8(6)***) Evening Star Enterprise, Inc.

Eyuboglu, Melisa, illus. Angel in a Bubble. Eyuboglu, Melisa, . 2007. 28p. (J). 10.95 (***978-1-933090-48-1(0)***) Guardian Angel Publishing, Inc.

Falzon, Adrienne. What Is an Angel? Salzberg, Helen M., illus. 2004. 27p. pap. 14.95 (978-1-4137-4461-3(3)) PublishAmerica, Inc.

Feliciano, Luis. The Adventures of the Three Angels. 2005. (J). pap. 8.00 (978-0-8059-6676-3(5)) Dorrance Publishing Co., Inc.

Fisher, Coleen. When I Was With the Angels. 1998. 12.95 (978-0-9652894-7-4(8)) GA Publishing.

Fox, Sabrina. Who Can Help Me Sleep? Rothan, Ann, illus. 2004. 32p. (ps-3). 16.95 (978-1-885394-36-1(5)) Amber Lotus Publishing.

Gaither, Gloria & Hranilovich, Barbara. My Father's Angels. Hranilovich, Barbara, illus. 1999. (Illus.). 32p. (J). (ps-3). 14.99 (978-0-310-23104-2(3)) Zonderkidz.

Gossett, Dean L. The Hair Angel. 2006. (ENG.). 32p. per. 15.99 (***978-1-4259-7677-4(8)***) AuthorHouse.

Grant, Eleanor. Ministering Angels. 2003. 32p. (J). pap. 9.00 (978-0-8059-5611-5(5)) Dorrance Publishing Co., Inc.

Greenfield, Eloise. Guardian Angel. 1999. 32p. (J). pap. 5.99 (978-0-7868-1305-6(9)) Hyperion Pr.

Greenlee, Don. This Countryboy Guardian Was Heaven Sent. 2007. (Illus.). 114p. (YA). per. 14.95 net. (***978-0-9795574-0-8(2)***) Country Boy Publishing Co.

Guest, Charlotte. Peredur the Son of Evrawc. 2004. reprint ed. pap. 15.95 (978-1-4191-4086-0(8)); pap. 1.99 (978-1-4192-4086-7(2)) Kessinger Publishing, LLC.

Hamel, William T. Sam Whitton & the Angels' Prophecy. 2006. 283p. pap. 16.95 (978-0-9759818-7-0(0) , 349-020) High-Pitched Hum Inc.

Hardgrove, Micheal. The Ogre & the Angel: To Go & Tell Somebody. Hardgrove, J. Franklin, ed. Hardgrove, Micheal, illus. 1998. (Illus.). 32p. (J). (ps-6). pap. 12.95 (978-0-9660797-2-2(8) , OAA) Twinke Publishing, Inc.

Harper, Stephan J. One Christmas Story. Steuerwald, Joy, illus. 2003. 32p. (J). lib. bdg. 16.95 (978-0-9741800-0-7(9)) Inspire Press, Inc.

Hawkins, Jimmy. It's a Wonderful Life for Kids! Jones, Douglas B., illus. 2006. 40p. (J). (gr. k). 16.99 (978-0-525-47767-9(5) , Dutton Juvenile) Penguin Group (USA) Inc.

Hees, Miriam. From Heaven to Earth - Angel Eyes. Kinneman, D. Michael, illus. 2002. 128p. (J). (gr. 3-7). pap. 5.95 (978-0-9718348-3-5(0)) Blooming Tree Pr.

Hendry, Diana. Harvey Angel y la Nina Fantasma. Alban, Rafael Segovia, tr. Morin, Mauricio Gomez, illus. 2003. (la Orilla Del Viento Ser.). (SPA.). 166p. (J). reprint ed. pap. 4.99 (978-968-16-6723-8(9)) Fondo de Cultura Economica USA.

Hesse, Karen & Hesse, Hermann. A Time for Angels. rev. ed. 2000. 288p. (gr. 5-9). 16.99 (978-0-7868-0621-8(4)); 17.49 (978-0-7868-2534-9(0)) Hyperion Pr.

Holburn, Sandra. The Angel & the Bear. 2006. (ENG.). 28p. per. 15.30 (***978-1-4259-4994-5(0)***) AuthorHouse.

Hood, Karen Jean Matsko. Angels, Angels, Way up High: A Read Aloud Picture Book. 2003. 24.95 (978-1-930948-81-5(6)) Whispering Pine Pr., Inc.

—Angels, Angels Way up High Daily Journal. 2003. pap. 24.95 (978-1-930948-10-5(7)) Whispering Pine Pr., Inc.

—Angels, Angels Way up High Read Aloud Picture Book. 2003. pap. 24.95 (978-1-930948-09-9(3)) Whispering Pine Pr., Inc.

Hopkinson, Deborah. A Band of Angels: A Story Inspired by the Jubilee Singers. Colon, Raul, illus. 2002. 40p. (J). (gr. 1-4). 7.99 (978-0-689-84887-2(0) , Aladdin) Simon & Schuster Children's Publishing.

Horman, John. The Angel Band: a Christmas Musical Based on Luke 2:1-20: Bulletins. (gr. 2-6). 15.00 (978-0-687-08660-3(4)) Abingdon Pr.

Horner, Susan. The Mission: An Angel's Most Important Assignment. Allen, Joe, illus. 2006. pap. 10.99 (978-1-59317-148-3(X)) Warner Pr. Pubs.

Hunt, Laurel E. Angel Pawprints. 2002. (Illus.). (J). pap. (978-0-7868-8491-9(6)) Disney Pr.

I Can Share. 2004. (J). per. (978-1-57657-392-1(3)) Paradise Pr., Inc.

I Have Feelings. 2004. (J). per. (978-1-57657-393-8(1)) Paradise Pr., Inc.

I Like You. 2004. (J). per. (978-1-57657-394-5(X)) Paradise Pr., Inc.

Itty-Bitty/The Mission/Easter Storybook 1-6. 2006. pap. 11.99 (978-1-59317-152-0(8)) Warner Pr. Pubs.

Jacques, Brian. The Angel's Command. Elliot, David & Schoenherr, Ian, illus. 2005. (Castaways of the Flying Dutchman Ser.: No. 2). 384p. (J). (gr. 5-9). pap. 7.99 (978-0-14-240285-6(0) , Puffin) Penguin Group (USA) Inc.

—The Angel's Command. Elliot, David, illus. 2003. (Castaways of the Flying Dutchman Ser.: No. 2). 384p. (J). (gr. 5-6). 23.99 (978-0-399-23999-1(5) , Philomel) Penguin Group (USA) Inc.

—Castaways of the Flying Dutchman. Schoenherr, Ian, illus. 2001. (Castaways of the Flying Dutchman Ser.: No. 1). 1p. (J). (gr. 4-7). 23.99 (978-0-399-23601-3(5) , Philomel) Penguin Group (USA) Inc.

Jenkins, Barbie. The Legend of Christmas Kiss. 2005. 32p. 13.99 (978-1-4165-3382-5(6) , Howard Bks.) Simon & Schuster.

Johnson, Marsha Deveaux. Power Angels on Assignment: Cinnamon Comes to Earth. 2003. (Illus.). 48p. (J). lib. bdg. 14.95 (978-1-59094-022-8(9) , 1590940229) Jawbone Publishing Corp.

Jones, H. Lena. Trapped on Planet Liska. 2006. 180p. pap. 19.95 (978-1-4241-0989-0(2)) PublishAmerica, Inc.

Julian, B. T. Mirror Me This. 2006. 172p. per. 12.95 (978-1-59886-056-6(9)) Tate Publishing & Enterprises, L.L.C.

Kanan. Galaxy Angel Party, Vol. 2. 2005. (Galaxy Angel Ser.). Orig. Title: Galaxy Angel Anthology. (Illus.). 208p. pap. 9.99 (978-1-932480-27-6(7) , Broccoli Bks. Deluxe) Broccoli International USA, Inc.

Kishiro, Yukito. Battle Angle Alita Vol. 7: Last Order. 2006. (Battle Angel Alita Last Order Ser.). 208p. (YA). pap. 9.99 (978-1-4215-0433-9(2)) Viz Media.

Knights, Harry B. Angel's Star. 2006. (J). lib. bdg. 20.00 (978-0-9632248-8-0(3)) Synergetic Pubns., Inc.

Knott, Anthony & Kneen, Maggie. An Angel Came to Nazareth. Kneen, Maggie, illus. 2005. (Illus.). 24p. (J). (ps-3). 15.95 (978-0-8118-4798-8(5)) Chronicle Bks. LLC.

Koda-Callan, Elizabeth. The Tiny Angel. 2004. (Illus.). 48p. (J). 9.95 (978-0-7611-3638-5(X) , 13638) Workman Publishing Co., Inc.

Koshkin, Alexander, illus. The Angel & the Donkey. 2004. 40p. (J). (ps-ps). lib. bdg. 13.15 (978-0-606-30510-5(6)) Tandem Library Bks.

LaMothe, Karin Elaine. The Angels' Lullaby. 2003. (Illus.). 8p. (J). pap. 9.95 (978-0-9728763-0-8(8)) LaMothe, Karin.

Lane, Nickel. The Ferret Crusaders: Quest of the Wish A Pod. 2nd ed. 2004. 73p. (J). per. 8.49 (978-1-4116-0459-9(8)) Lulu.com.

Lee, Quinlan B. Christmas Angel. 2006. (Clifford's Puppy Days Ser.). (Illus.). 24p. (J). pap. 3.99 (978-0-439-75533-7(6)) Scholastic, Inc.

Leeson, Christine. Snow Angel. Chapman, Jane, illus. 2007. 32p. (J). (ps-2). 15.95 ***978-1-58925-068-0(0)** , tiger tales) ME Media LLC.

Lester, Julius. Why Heaven Is Far Away. Cepeda, Joe, illus. 2002. 40p. (J). (gr. 1-3). pap. 16.95 (978-0-439-17871-6(1) , Scholastic Pr.) Scholastic, Inc.

Lewandowski, Frrich. Babci's Angel. Delisle, Kathryn H., illus. 1998. 20p. (J). (gr. 2-3). 9.50 (978-0-9646439-5-6(2)) Ambassador Bks., Inc.

The Littlest Angel. 2002. (Illus.). 24p. (J). (gr. k-3). 6.95 (978-0-8249-4224-3(8)) Ideals Pubns.

Lockhart, Linda J. A Little Angel Dressed in Red. 2006. (J). pap. 8.00 (978-0-8059-6923-8(3)) Dorrance Publishing Co., Inc.

Lucado, Max. Alabaster's Song. Garland, Michael, illus. 2005. 20p. (J). (ps-3). bds., bds. 15.99 (978-1-4003-0697-8(3)) Nelson, Thomas Inc.

—Alabaster's Song: Christmas Through the Eyes of an Angel. 2004. (Max Lucado Ser.). 32p. 19.99 incl. DVD (978-1-4003-0180-5(7)) Nelson, Thomas Inc.

Maggio, Viqui, illus. Absolutely Angels: Poems for Children & Other Believers. 2003. 32p. (J). (gr. 4-6). 14.95 (978-1-56397-708-4(7)) Boyds Mills Pr.

Magnier, Thierry & Hallenleben, Georg. Babel y el Angel. (CAT., Illus.). 40p. (J). 14.95 (978-84-8488-051-6(6)) Serres, Ediciones, S. L. ESP. *Dist:* Lectorum Pubns., Inc.

Malanga, Tara & O'Keefe, Susan Heyboer. Sleepy Angel's First Bedtime Story. 2000. (Illus.). 32p. (ps-2). 9.95 (978-0-8091-6670-1(4) , 6670-4) Paulist Pr.

Mark, Deana. Little Angel Stories Volume One. 2004. (Illus.). 35p. (J). pap. 14.95 (978-1-932373-88-2(8)) Cedar Hill Publishing.

Marks, Graham. How It Works: Everyone Gets the Angel They Deserve. 224p. (J). pap. 12.99 (978-0-7475-7015-8(9)) Bloomsbury Publishing Plc GBR. *Dist:* Trafalgar Square Publishing.

Marsh, Carole. The Mystery of the Missing Angel. 2006. 96p. (gr. 2-4). 14.95 ***978-0-635-06232-1(1)**); 14.95 ***978-0-635-06230-7(5)**); pap. 4.99 ***978-0-635-06229-1(1)**) Gallopade International.

Matsuura, Richard & Matsuura, Ruth. Angels Masquerading on Earth. Chao, Linus, illus. (J). 7.95 (978-1-887916-07-3(5)) Orchid Isle Publishing Co.

Matthews, Andrew & Birmingham, Christian. Tod & the Clock Angel. 1999. (Illus.). 32p. (J). (gr. k-4). pap. 8.99 (978-0-7112-1357-9(7)) Lincoln, Frances Ltd. GBR. *Dist:* Antique Collectors' Club.

Mayer, Mercer. The Rocking Horse Angel. 2000. (Illus.). 48p. (J). (gr. 1-5). 17.95 (978-0-7614-5072-6(6) , Cavendish Children's Bks.) Cavendish, Marshall Corp.

McBride, Earvin, Jr. Angel on My Shoulders. unabr. ed. 2002. (Illus.). 24p. (gr. 7-12). (978-1-892511-14-0(2)) MacBride, E. J. Pubn., Inc.

McDaniel, Lurlene. Angel of Mercy. 2001. (Mercy Trilogy). 224p. (YA). (gr. 7). pap. 5.50 (978-0-553-57083-0(8) , Laurel Leaf) Random Hse. Children's Bks.

McDonald, Jill. Angel Book & Purse. 2006. (J). bds. 5.99 (978-0-439-82733-1(7) , Cartwheel Bks.) Scholastic, Inc.

McGee, Marni. While Angels Watch. Macnaughton, Tina, illus. 2006. 26p. (J). (ps-2). 16.00 (978-1-56148-513-0(6)) Good Bks.

McNish, Cliff. Angel. 2008. (Exceptional Reading & Language Arts Titles for Upper Grades Ser.). (J). 16.95 ***978-0-8225-8900-6(1)** , Carolrhoda Bks.) Lerner Publishing Group.

Messer, Celeste M. Angel Experiment J134 Bk #1. 2004. (Adventures of Andi O'Malley Ser.). (Illus.). 82-92p. (J). (gr. 4-7). 4.95 (978-0-9702171-0-3(2)) AshleyAlan Enterprises.

—The Broken Wing: The Adventures of Andi O'Malley. Hoeffner, Deb, illus. 2004. (Adventures of Andi O'Malley Ser.). 82-92p. (J). (gr. 4-7). 4.95 (978-0-9702171-1-0(0)) AshleyAlan Enterprises.

—The Circle of Light. 2004. (Adventures of Andi O'Malley Ser.). (Illus.). 82-92p. (J). (gr. 4-7). 4.95 (978-0-9702171-2-7(9)) AshleyAlan Enterprises.

—The Gift. 2004. (Adventures of Andi O'Malley Ser.). (Illus.). 82-92p. (J). (gr. 4-7). 4.95 (978-0-9702171-3-4(7)) AshleyAlan Enterprises.

—Three Miracles. 2004. (Adventures of Andi O'Malley Ser.). (Illus.). 82-92p. (J). (gr. 4-7). 4.95 (978-0-9702171-4-1(5)) AshleyAlan Enterprises.

Miller, Jessel. Angels in the Vineyards. Gamble, Carolynne, ed. Miller, Jessel, illus. 2001. 36p. (J). (ps-7). 18.95 (978-0-9660381-6-3(9)) Jessel Gallery.

Mims, Melanie. Not All Angels Have Wings. Floyd, John, Jr., illus. 2005. (J). pap. 6.95 ***978-0-9752860-6-7(4)*** OurRainbow Pr., LLC.

Morehead, Ruth J. Waiting for Christmas. Morehead, Ruth J., illus. 1999. (Jellybean Bks.). (Illus.). 24p. (J). (ps-k). lib. bdg. 7.99 (978-0-375-90102-7(7) , Random Hse. Bks. for Young Readers) Random Hse. Children's Bks.

Morpurgo, Michael. On Angel Wings. 2007. 48p. 8.99 ***978-0-7636-3466-7(2)*** Candlewick Pr.

Moulton, Mark Kimball. Everyday Angels. Winget, Susan, illus. 2003. 32p. (J). 14.95 (978-0-8249-5479-6(3)) Ideals Pubns.

—Everyday Angels. Winget, Susan, illus. 3rd ed. 2000. 32p. (J). (gr. k-3). 18.00 (978-0-7412-0737-1(0)) Lang Graphics, Ltd.

Murphy, Rita. Black Angels. 2002. 176p. (J). (gr. 4). pap. 4.99 (978-0-440-22934-6(0) , Yearling) Random Hse. Children's Bks.

—Black Angels. 2002. (gr. 3-6). lib. bdg. 13.00 (978-0-613-57701-4(9)) Tandem Library Bks.

Napoli, Donna Jo. April Flowers. Ben-Ami, Doren & Klementz-Harte, Lauren, illus. 2000. (Angelwings Ser.: No. 7). 80p. (J). (gr. 2-5). pap. 7.95 (978-0-689-83207-9(9) , Aladdin) Simon & Schuster Children's Publishing.

—April Flowers. 2000. (Angelwings Ser.: No. 7). (Illus.). (J). 10.79 (978-0-606-17910-2(0)) Tandem Library Bks.

—Friends Everywhere. 1999. (Angelwings Ser.: No. 1). (Illus.). (J). 10.79 (978-0-606-17904-1(6)) Tandem Library Bks.

—Give & Take. Ben-Ami, Doren & Klementz-Harte, Lauren, illus. 2000. (Angelwings Ser.: No. 5). 96p. (J). (gr. 2-5). pap. 7.95 (978-0-689-83205-5(2) , Aladdin) Simon & Schuster Children's Publishing.

—Give & Take. 2000. (Angelwings Ser.: No. 5). (Illus.). (J). 10.79 (978-0-606-17908-9(9)) Tandem Library Bks.

—Hang in There. 2001. (Angelwings Ser.: No. 16). 80p. (J). (gr. 4-7). pap. 7.95 (978-0-689-83973-3(1) , Aladdin) Simon & Schuster Children's Publishing.

—Hang in There. 2001. (Angelwings Ser.: No. 16). (gr. 3-6). lib. bdg. 11.80 (978-0-613-31285-1(6)) Tandem Library Bks.

—Happy Holidays. Ben-Ami, Doron, illus. 2000. (Angelwings Ser.: No. 14). 80p. (J). (gr. 2-5). pap. 7.95 (978-0-689-83977-1(4) , Simon Pulse) Simon & Schuster Children's Publishing.

—Happy Holidays. 2000. (Angelwings Ser.: No. 14). (Illus.). (J). 10.79 (978-0-606-21613-5(8)) Tandem Library Bks.

—Know-It-All. Klementz-Harte, Lauren, illus. 2000. (Angelwings Ser.: No. 11). 96p. (J). (gr. 4-7). pap. 7.95 (978-0-689-83572-8(8) , Aladdin) Simon & Schuster Children's Publishing.

—Know-It-All. 2000. (Angelwings Ser.: No. 11). (Illus.). (J). (978-0-606-20385-2(0)) Tandem Library Bks.

—Left Out. Ben-Ami, Doron, illus. 2000. (Angelwings Ser.: No. 13). 80p. (J). (gr. 2-5). pap. 7.95 (978-0-689-83971-9(5) , Aladdin) Simon & Schuster Children's Publishing.

—Left Out. 2000. (Angelwings Ser.: No. 13). (Illus.). (J). (978-0-606-21906-8(4)) Tandem Library Bks.

—Lies & Lemons. 2000. (Angelwings Ser.: No. 9). 96p. (J). (gr. 4-7). pap. 7.95 (978-0-689-83209-3(5) , Aladdin) Simon & Schuster Children's Publishing.

—Lies & Lemons. 2000. (Angelwings Ser.: No. 9). (Illus.). (J). (978-0-606-20387-6(7)) Tandem Library Bks.

—New Voices. 2000. (Angelwings Ser.: No. 12). (gr. 3-6). lib. bdg. 11.80 (978-0-613-26372-6(3)) Tandem Library Bks.

—No Fair! Ben-Ami, Doren & Klementz-Harte, Lauren, illus. 2000. (Angelwings Ser.: No. 6). 96p. (J). (gr. 2-5). pap. 7.95 (978-0-689-83206-2(0) , Aladdin) Simon & Schuster Children's Publishing.

—No Fair! 2000. (Angelwings Ser.: No. 6). (Illus.). (J). (978-0-606-17909-6(7)) Tandem Library Bks.

—On Her Own. 1999. (Angelwings Ser.: No. 3). Orig. Title: Room to Grow. (Illus.). 96p. (J). (gr. 2-5). pap. 7.95 (978-0-689-82985-7(X) , Aladdin) Simon & Schuster Children's Publishing.

—On Her Own. 1999. (Angelwings Ser.: No. 3). Orig. Title: Room to Grow. (Illus.). (J). (978-0-606-17906-5(2)) Tandem Library Bks.

—One Leap Forward. 1999. (Angelwings Ser.: No. 4). (Illus.). 96p. (J). (gr. 2-5). pap. 7.95 (978-0-689-82986-4(8) , Aladdin) Simon & Schuster Children's Publishing.

—One Leap Forward. 1999. (Angelwings Ser.: No. 4). (Illus.). (J). (978-0-606-17907-2(0)) Tandem Library Bks.

—Partners. 2001. (Angelwings Ser.: No. 15). 80p. (J). (gr. 2-5). pap. 7.95 (978-0-689-83972-6(3) , Aladdin) Simon & Schuster Children's Publishing.

—Playing Games. Ben-Ami, Doren & Klementz-Harte, Lauren, illus. 2000. (Angelwings Ser.: No. 8). 80p. (J). (gr. 2-5). mass mkt. 7.95 (978-0-689-83208-6(7) , Aladdin) Simon & Schuster Children's Publishing.

—Playing Games. 2000. (Angelwings Ser.: No. 8). (Illus.). (J). (978-0-606-20386-9(9)) Tandem Library Bks.

—Running Away. 2000. (Angelwings Ser.: No. 10). 96p. (J). (gr. 2-6). pap. 7.95 (978-0-689-83210-9(9) , Aladdin) Simon & Schuster Children's Publishing.

—Running Away. 2000. (Angelwings Ser.: No. 10). (Illus.). (J). (978-0-606-20384-5(2)) Tandem Library Bks.

Napoli, Donna Jo & Ben-Ami, Doron. Friends Everywhere. Klementz-Harte, Lauren, illus. 1999. (Angelwings Ser.: No. 1). 96p. (J). (gr. 2-5). pap. 7.95 (978-0-689-82694-8(X) , Aladdin) Simon & Schuster Children's Publishing.

Nieto, Nancy. My Angel & Me. Nieto, Gina L., illus. 2003. 19p. (J). (978-1-932046-04-5(6)) Pastime Pr.

Nishimori, Hiroyuki. Cheeky Angel, Vol. 8. 2005. (Cheeky Angel Ser.). 192p. (YA). pap. 9.99 (978-1-59116-979-6(8)) Viz Media.

—Cheeky Angel, Vol. 13. Nishimori, Hiroyuki, illus. 2006. (Cheeky Angel Ser.). 208p. (YA). pap. 9.99 (978-1-4215-0447-6(2)) Viz Media.

—Cheeky Angel, Vol. 14. 2006. (Cheeky Angel Ser.). 208p. (YA). pap. 9.99 (978-1-4215-0448-3(0)) Viz Media.

Nora, David, Jr. Happy Balloon to You. 2005. 9.00 (978-0-8059-9870-2(5)) Dorrance Publishing Co., Inc.

O'Reilly, Orla Marie. Angels for Little People. 2006. (Illus.). 36p. pap. 11.95 (978-1-85390-908-5(4)) Veritas Pubns. IRL. *Dist:* STL Distribution North America.

Otto, Gina. Cassandra's Angel. Joost, Trudy, illus. 2001. 32p. (ps-3). 15.95 (978-0-935699-20-3(1)) Illumination Arts Publishing Co., Inc.

Pancheri, Jan. The Little Angel. 2000. (Illus.). 32p. (J). (gr. 2-4). pap. 9.99 (978-0-09-926442-2(0)) Random Hse. GBR. *Dist:* Trafalgar Square Publishing.

Patsakos, Julienne. Angel, Angel Where are You? 2004. 20p. pap. 14.95 (978-1-4137-3350-1(6)) PublishAmerica, Inc.

Pickard, W. Raymond. When an Angel Cries: (but I Don't Want to Be an Angel) 2006. 67p. pap. 14.95 (978-1-4241-0243-3(X)) PublishAmerica, Inc.

Powell, Inez. Sparkle, My Angel. 2003. (Illus.). 30p. per. 8.95 (978-1-932344-24-0(1) , Profitable Publishing) Thornton Publishing.

Pyle, Howard. The Garden Behind the Moon. 2002. (gr. 3-6). lib. bdg. 14.15 (978-0-613-57052-7(9)) Tandem Library Bks.

Quarles, Jean Marie. Not Quite Angels of Iciclelap. 2004. 204p. 14.00 (978-1-58961-093-4(8)) PageFree Publishing, Inc.

Raven, Margot Theis. Angels in the Dust. 1999. (J). (978-0-606-16871-7(0)) Tandem Library Bks.

Rich, Beatrice. Vanessa & the Angel. Rich, Beatrice, illus. 2002. (Illus.). 40p. (J). (ps-3). 14.95 (978-0-9672215-0-2(1)) Bridge Hse. Publishing, Inc.

Richardson, Beverly J. Timbs. Where do Angels Come From? 2006. (Illus.). 44p. pap. 14.95 (978-1-59800-650-6(9)) Outskirts Press, Inc.

Riley, Christine. Chester's Field, O'Brien, Laurel, illus. 2004. 296p. (J). per. 17.50 (978-0-9740683-6-7(5)) Authors & Artists Publishers of New York, Inc.

—Chester's Field. 2002. 103p. per. 10.00 (978-0-9724680-3-9(X)) Lifevest Publishing, Inc.

Ring, Laura. What Do Angels Do? Caldwell, Lise, ed. Burris, Priscilla, illus. 1999. (Happy Day Bks.). 24p. (J). (ps-2). 2.49 (978-0-7847-1045-6(7) , 04275, Bean Sprouts) Standard Publishing.

Roesti, Delores. Mareena Maree Mulligan & the Flying Wheel Chair: Book 1: School Days. 2007. 81p. pap. 9.95 ***978-0-7414-4048-8(2)*** Infinity Publishing.

Rose, Lynda J. Assignment Earth. 2008. 160p. (J). pap. 8.95 ***978-0-7459-6063-0(4)*** Lion Hudson plc GBR. *Dist:* Independent Pubs. Group.

Royce Conant, Jan. Children of Light. Royce Conant, Jan, illus. 2005. (J). per. 20.00 (978-0-9740683-7-4(3) , Ithaca Pr.) Authors & Artists Publishers of New York, Inc.

Rozek, Kathy. Rudy & the Magical Twin Balloons. 2002. 32p. (J). 15.95 (978-0-9720871-0-0(9)) Brookline Mermac Pubs.

Ruiz, Joseph J. Angel on Daniel's Shoulder. 2004. (SPA & ENG., Illus.). 108p. (J). pap. 12.95 (978-0-86534-402-0(7)) Sunstone Pr.

Saunders, Ray. Ballerina, the dancing Angel. Mitchell, Francis et al, eds. Guerra, Nuri, illus. Mills, Marilyn & Dambergs, Nikoljas, photos by. 2001. 34p. (J). lib. bdg. (978-1-895814-13-2(8) , NWP124) New World Publishing.

Scheer, Ruth D. The Mouse & the Angel. 2003. (J). lib. bdg. 15.95 (978-0-9671761-3-0(1)) Scheer Delight Publishing.

Schmidt, John. Two Stories for Children: Betty Blooper Is Super! & Hands Holding Heaven. Heflin, David et al, trs. Beckner, Joni & King, Rachael, illus. 1999. (ENG & SPA.). 42p. (J). (ps-3). pap. 9.00 (978-1-891774-09-6(3)) Path Publishing, Inc.

Schwartz, Virginia Frances. Send One Angel Down. 2000. 176p. (J). (gr. 7 up). tchr. ed. 16.95 (978-0-8234-1484-0(1)) Holiday Hse., Inc.

—Send One Angel Down. 2003. (YA). 22.95 (978-0-7862-4800-1(9)) Thorndike Pr.

Scott, Margaret Ashton & Goldstein, R. David. A Heavenly Hallo: Introducing Archer Angel & Bea Cherub. Scarnati, Gilbert Bruce F., ed. Kankanian, Armen, illus. 2nd rev. ed. 1999. (Angels in Our Midst Ser.). 50p. (J). (gr. k-2). pap. 5.99 (978-1-892801-00-5(0)) AABC Angels, Inc.

Seuffert, Marie. Tiny Red's Trip to Earth. Palmer, Frances, illus. 2002. 32p. (J). (ps-1). 12.95 (978-0-9639838-7-9(3)) Little Treasure Pubns., Inc.

Sigal, Maxine Handelman. Shabbat Angels. Rothenberg, Joani, illus. 2003. (gr. k-3). 13.95 (978-0-8074-0865-0(4) , 164051) URJ Pr.

Skevington, Andrea. The Little Christmas Tree. Hussey, Lorna, illus. 2002. 32p. (J). (gr. k-2). pap. 8.99 (978-0-7459-4588-0(0) , Lion) Lion Hudson plc GBR. *Dist:* Independent Pubs. Group.

Snyder, Tim & Snyder, Lesley. Painting Rainbows with Angels. Graham, Debbie, illus. 2002. (Graham Cracker Kids Adventure Ser.). 28p. (J). 12.99 (978-0-9716475-0-3(X)) Graham Cracker Kids.

Springer, Nancy. Sky Rider. 2000. 128p. (J). (gr. 7 up). pap. 4.95 (978-0-380-79565-9(5) , Harper Trophy) HarperCollins Pubs.

Stinnett, Leia A. The Other Me. Date not set. (Little Angel Bks.). (Illus.). (J). (gr. k-8). pap. (978-1-880737-18-7(3)) Crystal Journeys Publishing.

Sunkuli, O. Hero & the Dream. 2004. (Illus.). 24p. 13.95 (978-9966-25-161-9(8)) Heinemann Kenya, Limited (East African Educational Publishers Ltd E.A.E.P.) KEN. *Dist:* Michigan State Univ. Pr.

Swenson, Jadean Moon. Deanie's Story. Hudgins, Paul, illus. 2002. (J). pap. 14.95 (978-0-934955-48-5(4)) Watercress Pr.

Tan, Amy H. My Mommy's an Angel! Tan, Mariam, illus. l.t. ed. 2002. (Angel Ser.). 20p. (J). 18.95 incl. audio compact disk (978-0-9717299-0-2(5)) JeaMei Publishing.

Tazewell, Charles. The Littlest Angel. lthr. 29.95 (978-0-8249-5333-1(9)) Ideals Pubns.

—The Littlest Angel. Rasmussen, Wendy, illus. 2007. 32p. pap. 3.99 ***978-0-8249-5549-6(8)*** , Ideals Children's Bks.) Ideals Pubns.

—The Littlest Angel. Porfirio, Guy, illus. 2004. 32p. (J). 16.95 (978-0-8249-5473-4(4)) Ideals Pubns.

—The Littlest Angel. Thornburgh, Rebecca McKillip, illus. 2002. (J). (978-0-8249-4232-8(9) , Candy Cane Pr.) Ideals Pubns.

—The Littlest Angel. Lanino, Deborah, illus. 1998. (Modern Rhymes about Ancient Times Ser.). 32p. (YA). (ps up). 29.00 (978-0-516-20433-8(5) , Children's Pr.) Scholastic Library Publishing.

—The Littlest Angel. 1998. pap. 7.95 (978-0-516-26192-8(4) , Children's Pr.) Scholastic Library Publishing.

—The Littlest Uninvited One. Tribble, Gail, illus. 2001. (J). (ps-3). 16.95 (978-0-8249-5404-8(1) , Ideals Children's Bks.) Ideals Pubns.

Telles, Cecilia R. & Heinerke, Kristina. Soar with the Angels. 2004. pap. 14.95 (978-1-889743-30-1(5)) Robbie Dean Pr.

Tiller, Steve. Connected at the Heart. Tecosky, Kathryn, ed. Cremeans, Robert, illus. 2001. (Adventures with Little Angels Ser.). 32p. (J). (ps-3). per. 7.95 (978-0-9704597-3-2(4)) MichaelsMind LLC.

—Connected at the Heart. Cremeans, Robert, illus. 2001. (Adventures with Little Angels Ser.). 36p. (J). (ps-3). 14.95 (978-0-9704597-2-5(6)) MichaelsMind LLC.

Townsend, John. The Omen & the Ghost. Cunningham, Kelley, illus. 2007. (J). 80p. ***978-1-59889-353-3(X)***); 71p. pap. ***978-1-59889-448-6(X)*** Stone Arch Bks.

Trudel, Sylvain. L' Ange de Monsieur Chose. 1999. (Premier Roman Ser.). (Illus.). 64p. (J). (gr. 2-5). pap. (978-2-89021-347-0(1)) Diffusion du livre Mirabel.

Trujillo, Elizabeth Guerin. Meet Annie Angel. 2005. pap. 7.95 (978-0-533-14653-6(4)) Vantage Pr., Inc.

Turner, Ann Warren. Angel Hide & Seek. Ehlert, Lois, illus. 1998. 48p. (J). (gr. k-5). 14.95 (978-0-06-027085-8(3)) HarperCollins Pubs.

Tyrrell, Melissa. Busy Little Angels: A Little Foil Book. 1998. (Merry Little Foil Bks.). (Illus.). 10p. (J). (ps up). 2.95 (978-1-58117-009-2(2) , Intervisual/Piggy Toes) Dalmatian Pr.

Van Scoyoc, Pam. Angel Wings. Telage, Susenne, illus. l.t. ed. 1998. 32p. (J). (ps-3). lib. bdg. 16.95 (978-0-9663629-1-6(8)) By Grace Enterprises.

Voll, Donna G. Tell Me, Could a Bad Thing Happen to Me? Voll, Donna G. & Voll, Dudley J., eds. 2002. (Illus.). 26p. (J). (ps-3). 12.95 (978-0-9726662-0-6(6)) Golden Words Publishing.

Von Dornheim, Curt H. The Children's Angel Clock. Date not set. (Illus.). 64p. (YA). (gr. 5 up). 12.95 (978-0-89404-225-6(4)) Aztex Corp.

Wangerin, Walter, Jr. Probity Jones & the Fear Not Angel. Ladwig, Tim, illus. 2005. 32p. (J). (gr. 1-4). 16.95 (978-1-55725-457-3(5)) Paraclete Pr., Inc.

Warfel, Elizabeth Stuart. The Blue Pearls. Giarrusso, Veronique, illus. 2001. 32p. (J). (gr. k-4). 16.99 (978-1-902283-78-4(3)) Barefoot Bks., Inc.

Watson, Pat. Fallen Angels. Durst, Shirley J., ed. 2000. (YA). 9.95 (978-1-58130-636-1(9)); 11.95 (978-1-58130-637-8(7)) Novel Units, Inc.

Watt, Fiona. Sparkly Christmas Angel. 2007. (Luxury Touchy-Feely Board Bks). 10p. (J). bds. 15.99 ***978-0-7945-1477-8(4)*** , Usborne) EDC Publishing.

Westerfield, Jane R. The Secret of the Angels. Daniels, David, illus. Hall, David, photos by. 1999. 52p. (J). (gr. 1-3). pap. 19.95 (978-1-928772-00-2(5)) Keepsafe, Inc.

Weyand, Judy L. Patchwork Angel. Kirkpatrick, Nancy, illus. 2000. 36p. (J). (ps-6). 19.95 (978-1-930712-01-0(4)) In Unexpected Ways.

Whitedove, Michelle. My Invisible Friends: Guardian Angels. Poynter, Linda, illus. l.t. ed. 2005. 33p. (J). (ps-3). 18.95 (978-0-9714908-4-0(8)) Whitedove Pr.

Wilhelm, Hans. Christmas Angel. 2006. (Illus.). 32p. (J). pap. 8.99 (978-0-439-86397-1(X)) Scholastic, Inc.

Wilhelm, Hans. The Christmas Angel. 2007. 32p. (J). (ps-k). pap. 3.99 ***978-0-545-00853-2(0)*** Scholastic, Inc.

Williams, Rachel. Alex & the Archangel. Konopka, Jan, illus. 2005. (ENG.). 56p. pap. ***978-1-84401-614-3(5)*** Athena Pr.

Williams, Sam. Snowy Magic. Williams, Sam, illus. 2002. (Angel & Elf Ser.). (Illus.). 32p. (J). (ps-3). 9.99 (978-0-06-029652-0(6) , Harper Festival) HarperCollins Pubs.

Wilson, Agy. From Heaven to Earth - Angel on My Shoulder. Wilson, Agy, illus. 2004. (From Heaven to Earth Ser.). (Illus.). 150p. (J). (gr. 2-7). pap. 5.95 (978-0-9718348-1-1(4)) Blooming Tree Pr.

Wilson, Michelle L. Nash Happy from Cloud 9: The Unassigned Mission. 2007. 24p. (J). pap. 8.99 ***978-1-59886-979-8(5)*** Tate Publishing & Enterprises, L.L.C.

Yamashita, Satsuki, et al, eds. Aquarian Age - Juvenile Orion Illustration Book: Realm of Light. Yamashita, Satsuki, tr. Gokurakuin, Sakurako et al, illus. 2006. (Aquarian Age - Juvenile Orion Ser.). 96p. 19.99 (978-1-59741-108-0(6) , Broccoli Bks.) Broccoli International USA, Inc.

A B

Yates, Dan. An Angel in the Family: A Novel. 1999. (Illus.). 188 p. pap. 12.95 (978-1-57734-282-3(8) , 01113461) Covenant Communications, Inc.

—An Angel's Christmas. 1999. (J). pap. 3.95 (978-1-57734-544-2(4) , 01114379) Covenant Communications, Inc.

Yuki, Kaori. Angel Sancturary, Vol. 15. 2006. (Angel Sanctuary Ser.). 208p. (YA). pap. 9.99 (978-1-4215-0521-3(5)) Viz Media.

Zahn, Timothy. Angelmass. 2002. (gr. 7-12). lib. bdg. 16.45 (978-0-613-67052-4(3)) Tandem Library Bks.

Zuhdi, Darla L. Tale of a Christmas Angel. 2000. (Cat Detectives Present Ser.: Vol. 1). (Illus.). 92p. (J). (gr. 2-7). pap. 5.99 (978-0-9706062-0-4(6)) Aloha Publications.

ANGINA PECTORIS

see Heart—Diseases

ANGLING

see Fishing

ANGLO-SAXONS

McNeil, Niki, et al. HOCPP 1097 Anglo-Saxons. 2006. spiral bd. 24.50 (***978-1-60308-097-2(X)***) In the Hands of a Child.

Sharman, Margaret. Anglo-Saxons. 2003. (Illus.). 32p. (YA). pap. 12.99 (978-0-237-52571-2(2) , Evans Brothers, Limited) Evans Publishing Group GBR. *Dist:* Independent Pubs. Group.

Whistler, W. Charles. Wulfric the Weapon Thane (a Story of the. 2006. 34.99 (***978-1-4280-1745-0(3)***) IndyPublish-.com.

ANGLO-SAXONS—FICTION

Cadnum, Michael. Raven of the Waves. 2004. 208p. (J). (gr. 7 up). pap. 5.99 (978-0-439-62661-3(7)); 2001. 224p. (YA). (gr. 9 up). pap. 17.95 (978-0-531-30334-4(9) , Orchard Bks.) Scholastic, Inc.

Farmer, Nancy. The Sea of Trolls. 2006. 480p. (J). (gr. 5-9). reprint ed. pap. 9.99 (978-0-689-86746-0(8) , Simon Pulse) Simon & Schuster Children's Publishing.

Priestley, Chris. Redwulf's Curse. 2008. (Illus.). 272p. (YA). pap. 9.95 (***978-0-552-55483-1(9)***) Transworld Publishers Ltd. GBR. *Dist:* Independent Pubs. Group.

Tingle, Rebecca. The Edge on the Sword. (Sailing Mystery Ser.). 2003. 288p. (YA). (gr. 8-12). pap. 6.99 (978-0-14-250058-3(5) , Puffin); 2001. (Illus.). 1p. (J). (gr. 7 up). 18.99 (978-0-399-23580-1(9) , Putnam Juvenile) Penguin Group (USA) Inc.

—Far Traveler. (gr. 4). 2006. 240p. (J). pap. 6.99 (978-0-14-240630-4(9) , Puffin); 2005. (Illus.). 10p. (YA). 18.99 (978-0-399-23890-1(5) , Putnam Juvenile) Penguin Group (USA) Inc.

ANIMAL BABIES

see Animals—Infancy

ANIMAL BEHAVIOR

see Animals—Habits and Behavior

ANIMAL COMMUNICATION

Animals Communicating. (Animal Behavior Ser.). 24p. (J). 6.95 (978-0-7368-5164-0(X)) Capstone Pr., Inc.

Banks, Martin. How Monkeys "Talk" 1998. (Nature's Mysteries Ser.). (Illus.). 32p. (J). (gr. 3-5). lib. bdg. 22.79 (978-0-7614-0858-1(4) , Benchmark Bks.) Cavendish, Marshall Corp.

Chinery, Michael. Amazing Animals: How Animals Communicate. 2005. (Illus.). 64p. pap. 8.99 (978-1-84476-180-7(0) , Southwater) Anness Publishing GBR. *Dist:* National Bk. Network.

—How Animals Communicate: Wild Animal Planet. 2003. (Illus.). 64p. 14.99 (978-0-7548-1086-5(0) , Lorenz Bks.) Anness Publishing GBR. *Dist:* National Bk. Network.

Communicating. 2001. (Animal Marvels Ser.). (Illus.). 32p. (J). (gr. 3 up). lib. bdg. 24.67 (978-0-8368-2930-3(1)) Stevens, Gareth Inc.

de Paola, Tomie & Shapiro, Arnold. Mice Squeak, We Speak. 2002. (Illus.). 32p. (J). (ps-1). pap. 6.99 (978-0-399-23798-0(4) , Putnam Juvenile) Penguin Group (USA) Inc.

Dudzinski, Kathleen. Meeting Dolphins. 2000. (Illus.). 64p. (J). (gr. 3-7). 17.95 (978-0-7922-7129-1(7) , National Geographic Children's Bks.) National Geographic Society.

Ehrlich, Fred. Does a Seal Smile? 2006. (Illus.). 32p. 13.50 (978-1-59354-168-2(6)); (J). pap. 5.95 (978-1-59354-169-9(4)) Blue Apple Bks.

Feely, Jenny. Animal Communication. 2001. (gr. k-3). lib. bdg. 11.65 (978-0-613-33326-9(8)) Tandem Library Bks.

Ganeri, Anita. Animal Communication. 2004. (Nature Files Ser.). (Illus.). 32p. (J). (gr. 4-8). 28.00 (978-0-7910-8214-0(8) , Chelsea Hse.) Facts On File, Inc.

Gates, Phil. Animal Communication: South African Edition. 1999. (Cambridge Reading Routes Ser.). (Illus.). pap. 5.50 (978-0-521-77889-3(1)) Cambridge Univ. Pr.

Gravelle, Karen. Animal Talk. 2000. (Illus.). 132p. (gr. 4-7). pap. 9.95 (978-0-595-15647-4(9) , Backinprint.com) iUniverse, Inc.

Harcourt School Publishers Staff. Do Animals Talk? Advanced Level. 3rd ed. 2002. (Trophies Reading Program Ser.). (Illus.). pap. 5.10 (978-0-15-323293-0(5)) Harcourt Schl. Pubs.

Hoff, Mary. Communication. 2002. (Illus.). 32p. (J). lib. bdg. (978-1-58341-238-1(7) , Creative Education) Creative Co., The.

Jenkins, Steve. Slap, Squeak & Scatter: How Animals Communicate. 2001. (Illus.). 32p. (J). (gr. k-3). tchr. ed. 16.00 (978-0-618-03376-8(9)) Houghton Mifflin Co. Trade & Reference Div.

Kaner, Etta. Animal Talk: How Animals Communicate Through Sight, Sound & Smell. Douglas, Greg, illus. unabr. ed. 2004. (Animal Behavior Ser.). 40p. (J). (gr. 4-6). (978-1-55074-984-7(6)); (978-1-55074-982-3(X)) Kids Can Pr., Ltd.

Nichols, Catherine. Animal Talk. 2001. (We Can Read about Nature! Ser.). (Illus.). 32p. (J). (gr. 1-2). lib. bdg. 21.36 (978-0-7614-1253-3(0) , Benchmark Bks.) Cavendish, Marshall Corp.

Niz, Xavier. Animals Communicating. 2004. (First Facts Ser.). (Illus.). 24p. (J). lib. bdg. 21.26 (978-0-7368-2626-6(2)) Capstone Pr., Inc.

Preszler, June. Why Do Birds Sing? A Book about Animal Communication. 2007. (First Facts Ser.). (Illus.). 24p. (J). (978-0-7368-6756-6(2) , 1264908) Capstone Pr., Inc.

Robson, Pam. Body Language. 1998. (Hello Out There! Ser.). (Illus.). 32p. (J). (gr. 2-5). pap. 6.95 (978-0-531-15349-9(5) , Watts, Franklin) Scholastic Library Publishing.

Schlein, Miriam. Hello, Hello! Kirk, Daniel, illus. 2002. 32p. (J). (ps-3). 16.95 (978-0-689-83435-6(7)) Simon & Schuster Children's Publishing.

Stonehouse, Bernard & Bertram, Esther. The Truth about Animal Communication. Francis, John, illus. 2003. (Animals Exposed! Ser.). 48p. (J). 11.99 (978-0-439-54329-3(0)) Scholastic, Inc.

Tatham, Betty. How Animals Communicate. 2004. (Watts Library). (Illus.). 64p. (J). (gr. 5-7). pap. 8.95 (978-0-531-16214-9(1)); 25.50 (978-0-531-12167-2(4)) Scholastic Library Publishing. (Watts, Franklin).

ANIMAL DRAWING

see Animal Painting and Illustration

ANIMAL HOMES

see Animals—Habitations

ANIMAL-HUMAN RELATIONSHIPS

see Human-animal Relationships

ANIMAL INDUSTRY

see Domestic Animals; Livestock

ANIMAL INTELLIGENCE

see also Animals—Habits and Behavior; Psychology, Comparative

Driscoll, Laura. Do Dolphins Really Smile? Station Stop 2. Wald, Christina, illus. 2006. (All Aboard Science Reader Ser.). 48p. (J). (gr. 1-3). pap. 3.99 (978-0-448-44341-6(4) , Grosset & Dunlap) Penguin Group (USA) Inc.

Ingram, Scott. Dolphins. 2006. (Smart Animals! Ser.). (Illus.). 32p. (J). lib. bdg. 25.27 (978-1-59716-161-9(6)) Bearport Publishing Co., Inc.

Lunis, Natalie. Crows. 2006. (Smart Animals! Ser.). (Illus.). 32p. (J). lib. bdg. 25.27 (978-1-59716-160-2(8)) Bearport Publishing Co., Inc.

Mason, Paul. Nature's Tricks. 2007. (J). (***978-1-4109-2970-9(1)***); pap. (***978-1-4109-2991-4(4)***) Steck-Vaughn.

Nichols, Catherine. Animal Masterminds: A Chapter Book. 2003. (True Tales Ser.). (Illus.). 48p. (J). 22.50 (978-0-516-22913-3(3) , Children's Pr.) Scholastic Library Publishing.

Searl, Duncan. Elephants. 2006. (Smart Animals! Ser.). (Illus.). 32p. (J). lib. bdg. 25.27 (978-1-59716-162-6(4)) Bearport Publishing Co., Inc.

—Pigs. 2006. (Smart Animals! Ser.). (Illus.). 32p. (J). lib. bdg. 25.27 (978-1-59716-164-0(0)) Bearport Publishing Co., Inc.

Spirn, Michele. Octopuses. 2006. (Smart Animals! Ser.). (Illus.). 32p. (J). (gr. 3-7). lib. bdg. 25.27 (978-1-59716-250-0(7)) Bearport Publishing Co., Inc.

ANIMAL KINGDOM

see Zoology

ANIMAL LANGUAGE

see Animal Communication

ANIMAL LIGHT

see Bioluminescence

ANIMAL LORE

see Animals, Mythical; Natural History

ANIMAL MIGRATION

see Animals—Migration

ANIMAL PAINTING AND ILLUSTRATION

see also Animals in Art; Photography of Animals

Davies, Jacqueline. The Boy Who Drew Birds: A Story of John James Audubon. Sweet, Melissa, illus. 2004. 32p. (J). (gr. k-3). tchr. ed. 16.00 (978-0-618-24343-3(7)) Houghton Mifflin Co. Trade & Reference Div.

Dorling Kindersley Publishing Staff. I Can Draw Dinosaurs. 2006. (I can Draw Ser.). (Illus.). 48p. (J). pap. 7.99 (978-0-7566-2106-3(2)) Dorling Kindersley Publishing, Inc.

Green, John. Big Book of Horses to Color. 2006. 160p. (J). pap. 7.95 (978-0-486-45178-7(X)) Dover Pubns., Inc.

—Horse Scenes to Paint or Color. 2006. 48p. (J). pap. 4.95 (978-0-486-45209-8(3)) Dover Pubns., Inc.

Heller, Elaine. Thinker Doodles Half 'n Half Animals A1: Think, Draw, & Color. 2005. (J). pap. 7.99 (978-0-89455-867-2(6)) Critical Thinking Bks. & Software.

—Thinker Doodles Half 'n Half Animals B1: Think, Draw, & Color. 2005. (J). pap. 7.99 (978-0-89455-868-9(4)) Critical Thinking Bks. & Software.

Holub, Joan. Magical Creatures. 2003. (ps-2). lib. bdg. 14.15 (978-0-613-81295-5(6)) Tandem Library Bks.

Hood, Karen Jean Matsko. Icelandic Horse Activity & Coloring Book: Eductional Book Series. 2nd braille ed. 2006. spiral bd. 49.95 (978-1-59649-546-3(4)) Whispering Pine Pr., Inc.

Huancai, Yang, et al. Drawing Fun: Animals. Liu, Xuemei & Henderson, Ann, eds. Noad, Sarah, tr. from CHI. (Illus.). 55p. (978-90-806752-1-6(0)) Merry Star Pr.

Leroux-Hugon, Helene. I Can Draw Animals!, 4 bks. Leroux-Hugon, Helene, illus. Incl. I Can Draw Country Animals. lib. bdg. 24.67 (978-0-8368-2838-2(0)); I Can Draw Forest Animals. lib. bdg. 24.67 (978-0-8368-2839-9(9)); I Can Draw Polar Animals. lib. bdg. 24.67 (978-0-8368-2840-5(2)); I Can Draw Wild Animals. lib. bdg. 24.67 (978-0-8368-2841-2(0)); 40p. (J). (gr. 1 up). 2001. (Illus.). Set lib. bdg. 74.10 (978-0-8368-2837-5(2)) Stevens, Gareth Inc.

—I Can Draw Country Animals. Leroux-Hugon, Helene, illus. 2001. (I Can Draw Animals! Ser.). (Illus.). 40p. (J). (gr. 1 up). lib. bdg. 24.67 (978-0-8368-2838-2(0)) Stevens, Gareth Inc.

—I Can Draw Forest Animals. Leroux-Hugon, Helene, illus. 2001. (I Can Draw Animals! Ser.). (Illus.). 40p. (J). (gr. 1 up). lib. bdg. 24.67 (978-0-8368-2839-9(9)) Stevens, Gareth Inc.

—I Can Draw Polar Animals. Leroux-Hugon, Helene, illus. 2001. (I Can Draw Animals! Ser.). (Illus.). 40p. (J). (gr. 1 up). lib. bdg. 24.67 (978-0-8368-2840-5(2)) Stevens, Gareth Inc.

—I Can Draw Wild Animals. Leroux-Hugon, Helene, illus. 2001. (I Can Draw Animals! Ser.). (Illus.). 40p. (J). (gr. 1 up). lib. bdg. 24.67 (978-0-8368-2841-2(0)) Stevens, Gareth Inc.

Levy, Barbara Soloff. How to Draw Farm Animals. 2006. (Illus.). 32p. (J). pap. 2.95 (978-0-486-45168-8(2)) Dover Pubns., Inc.

—How to Draw Forest Animals. 2006. 32p. (J). pap. 2.95 (978-0-486-45231-9(X)) Dover Pubns., Inc.

Makowski, Robin. Cats Drawing Made Fun. 2005. 32p. pap. 6.45 (978-1-59515-782-9(4)) Rourke Publishing, LLC.

—Dogs Drawing Made Fun. 2005. 32p. pap. 6.45 (978-1-59515-783-6(2)) Rourke Publishing, LLC.

—Marine Mammals Drawing Made Fun. 2005. 32p. pap. 6.45 (978-1-59515-786-7(7)) Rourke Publishing, LLC.

—Reptiles Drawing Made Fun. 2005. 32p. pap. 6.45 (978-1-59515-787-4(5)) Rourke Publishing, LLC.

Murawski, Laura. How to Draw Horses. 2001. (Kid's Guide to Drawing Ser.). (Illus.). 24p. (J). (gr. 3). lib. bdg. 21.25 (978-0-8239-5552-7(4) , PowerKids Pr.) Rosen Publishing Group, Inc., The.

Pratt, Leonie & Stowell, Louie. Ht Draw Animals. 2006. 32p. (J). pap. 8.99 (978-0-7945-1241-5(0) , Usborne) EDC Publishing.

ANIMAL PHOTOGRAPHY

see Photography of Animals

ANIMAL PHYSIOLOGY

see Zoology

ANIMAL PRODUCTS

see Dairy Products

see names of special products, e.g. Hides and Skins; Ivory; etc

ANIMAL PSYCHOLOGY

see Animal Intelligence; Psychology, Comparative

ANIMAL WELFARE

see Animals—Treatment

ANIMALS

see also Desert Animals; Domestic Animals; Forest Animals; Fresh-Water Animals; Fur-Bearing Animals; Geographical Distribution of Animals and Plants; Human-animal Relationships; Marine Animals; Natural History; Pets; Zoology; Zoos

also names of orders and classes of the animal kingdom (e.g. Birds; Insects; etc.); and names of animals, e.g. Dogs; Bears; etc.

The ABC of Animals. (Illus.). 44p. 9.95 (978-1-55285-421-1(3) , Walrus Bks.) Whitecap Bks., Ltd. CAN. *Dist:* Graphic Arts Ctr. Publishing Co.

Ablow, Gail. A Horse in the House & Other Strange but True Animal Stories. Osborn, Kathy, illus. 2007. 40p. (J). (gr. 1-4). 17.99 (***978-0-7636-2838-3(7)***) Candlewick Pr.

Acredolo, Linda & Goodwin, Susan. Animals. 2007. 12p. bds. 12.99 (***978-0-8249-6718-5(6)*** , Ideals Children's Bks.) Ideals Pubns.

Acredolo, Linda & Goodwyn, Susan. Baby Signs for Animals. Gentieu, Penny, illus. 2003. 24p. (J). (ps up). 6.99 (978-0-06-009075-3(8) , Harper Entertainment) HarperCollins Pubs.

Acredolo, Linda & Goodwyn, Susan. I Can Sign! Animals. Brazillion Pictures Inc, illus. 2007. 12p. 9.99 (***978-0-8249-6709-3(7)***) Ideals Pubns.

Ada, Alma Flor. Quien Nacera Aqui? (Libros para Contar Ser.).Tr. of Who's Hatching Here?. (SPA., Illus.). 24p. (J). (gr. k-3). pap. 6.95 (978-1-58105-198-8(0)) Santillana USA Publishing Co., Inc.

—Quien Nacera Aqui? 2000. Tr. of Who's Hatching Here?. (SPA.). (gr. k-3). lib. bdg. 15.25 (978-0-613-79382-7(X)) Tandem Library Bks.

—Who's Hatching Here? Escriva, Vivi, illus. (Stories for the Telling Ser.). Orig. Title: Quien Nacera Aqui?. (SPA & ENG.). 24p. (J). (gr. k-3). pap. 6.95 (978-1-58105-232-9(4)) Santillana USA Publishing Co., Inc.

Adam, Winky. African Animals Stickers. 2001. (Illus.). 4p. (J). pap. 1.50 (978-0-486-41263-4(6)) Dover Pubns., Inc.

Adding Arctic Animals Math, 6 vols. (gr. k-2). 28.95 (978-0-7368-2990-8(3) , Yellow Umbrella Bks.) Capstone Pr., Inc.

Aigner-Clark, Julie. Animal Discovery Cards: Beautiful Nature Photographs & Animals Facts to Delight Your Tots. 2003. (Baby Einstein Ser.). 29p. (ps-17). 9.99 (978-1-892309-80-8(7)) Hyperion Bks. for Children.

Alderton, David. Animals of the World. 2nd ed. 2003. (Pockets Ser.). (Illus.). 512p. (gr. 3). pap. 12.99 (978-0-7894-9603-4(8)) Dorling Kindersley Publishing, Inc.

Alexander, Florence & Alexander, Stanley. Come with Me & See... Animals of the World. 2003. (Illus.). 32p. 9.99 (978-0-915960-60-6(5)) Ebon Research Systems Publishing, LLC.

Alexander, Florence, et al. Come with Me & See... A Total Eclipse in Africa. Alexander, Florence et al, illus. 2003. (ENG & SPA.). 40p. (J). 3.99 (978-0-915960-50-7(8)) Ebon Research Systems Publishing, LLC.

All About Animals, 4 Vols., Set. 2005. 38p. (J). pap. 112.00 (978-0-7910-8775-6(1) , Chelsea Hse.) Facts On File, Inc.

Allegators to Zebras. 2002. 128p. (J). (gr. k-4). pap. 17.88 (978-1-889369-46-4(2)) Teaching Ink, Inc.

Allen, Francesca, illus. Wild Animals. 2005. 10p. (J). 4.95 (978-0-7945-0858-6(8) , Usborne) EDC Publishing.

Allen, Julia & Iggulden, Margaret. Animal Rights. 2005. (Your Environment Ser.). (Illus.). 32p. (J). (978-1-59604-062-5(9)) Stargazer Bks.

Allen, Nancy Kelly. Whose Food Is This: A Look at What Animals Eat - Seeds, Bugs, & Nuts. Alderman, Derrick & Shea, Denise, illus. 2004. (Whose Is It? Ser.). 24p. (C). (gr. k-2). 22.60 (978-1-4048-0607-8(5)) Picture Window Bks.

—Whose Sound Is This? A Look at Animal Noises - Chirps, Clicks, & Hoots. Alderman, Derrick & Shea, Denise, illus. 2004. (Whose Is It? Ser.). 24p. (C). (gr. k-2). 22.60 (978-1-4048-0610-8(5)) Picture Window Bks.

Allen, Vicky, contrib. by. It's a Wild Life! Living with Animals. 2000. (Illus.). 128p. (YA). (gr. 4-7). pap. 4.95 (978-1-902618-87-6(4)) Element Children's Bks.

Allman, Toney. Life in a Cave. 2004. (Ecosystems Ser.). (Illus.). 48p. (J). (gr. 4-7). 26.20 (978-0-7377-3014-2(5) , Greenhaven Pr., Inc.) Thomson Gale.

Aloian, Molly. Habitats Subterraneos. 2007. (SPA.). 32p. (J). (gr. 1-2). (***978-0-7787-8331-2(6)***) Crabtree Publishing Co.

Aloian, Molly & Kalman, Bobbie. Habitats Subterraneos. rev. ed. 2007. (SPA.). 32p. (J). (gr. 1-2). pap. (***978-0-7787-8355-8(3)***) Crabtree Publishing Co.

—Many Kind Animals. 2005. (Illus.). 32p. pap. incl. audio compact disk (978-0-7787-7597-3(6)) Crabtree Publishing Co.

—Many Kinds of Animals. 2005. (What Kind of Animal Is It? Ser.). (Illus.). 32p. (J). (978-0-7787-2156-7(6)); pap. (978-0-7787-2214-4(7)) Crabtree Publishing Co.

—Muchos Tipos de Animales. 2005. (SPA., Illus.). 32p. (J). (978-0-7787-8832-4(6)) Crabtree Publishing Co.

—Muchos Tipos de Animales: Many Kinds of Animals. 2006. (SPA., Illus.). 32p. pap. (978-0-7787-8868-3(7)) Crabtree Publishing Co.

Alphabet Animals. 2002. (Home Workbooks Ser.). 64p. pap. 2.49 (978-0-88724-711-8(3) , CD-4513) Carson-Dellosa Publishing Co., Inc.

An Alphabet of Animal Signs. 2002. (Beginning Sign Language Ser.). bds. 6.95 (978-1-930820-08-1(9)) Garlic Pr.

Alvarez, Lourdes M. Animales. Brooks, David, illus. 2005. (Mi primer libro Ser.). (SPA.). 9p. (J). (ps-ps). bds. 3.95 (978-1-933050-04-1(7)) Sweetwater Pr.

—Formas. Brooks, David, illus. 2005. (Mi primer libro Ser.). (SPA.). 9p. (J). (ps-ps). bds. 3.95 (978-1-933050-05-8(5)) Sweetwater Pr.

—Mi Primer Libro Cosas. Brooks, David, illus. 2005. (Mi primer libro Ser.). (SPA.). 9p. (J). (ps-ps). bds. 3.95 (978-1-933050-03-4(9)) Sweetwater Pr.

Amato, Carol A. Backyard Pets: Activities for Exploring Wildlife Close to Home. 2002. (gr. 3-6). lib. bdg. 22.20 (978-0-613-61361-3(9)) Tandem Library Bks.

—Backyard Pets: Activities for Exploring Wildlife Close to Home. Noll, Cheryl Kirk, illus. 2002. 128p. (gr. 3-7). pap. 12.95 (978-0-471-41693-7(2) , Wiley) Wiley, John & Sons, Inc.

Amazing Animals. Date not set. (Illus.). 12p. (J). 3.98 (978-1-4054-0496-9(5)) Parragon, Inc.

Amazing Blue Animals, Vol. 2. 2005. (Early Library). (YA). (ps-3). 23.94 (978-0-8215-8948-9(2)) Sadlier, William H. Inc.

Amazing Eggs: Individual Title Six-Packs. (Discovery World Ser.). 16p. (gr. 1-2). 28.00 (978-0-7635-8455-9(X)) Rigby Education.

American Education Publishing Staff & School Specialty Publishing Staff. Animals. 2001. (Brighter Child Fact Card Ser.). (Illus.). 54p. (J). (gr. 3-5). 2.99 (978-1-56189-687-5(X) , 31383, American Education Publishing) School Specialty Publishing.

Amos, Janine. Animals. 2004. (Picture Reference Ser.). (SPA., Illus.). 48p. (gr. 3-6). (J). pap. 7.95 (978-1-58728-658-2(0)); 13.95 (978-1-58728-650-6(5)) T&N Children's Publishing. (Two Can Publishing).

Anastasio, Dina & Herndon, Ryan. Guinness World Records Wild Lives. 2006. (Illus.). 103p. (J). pap. 4.99 (978-0-439-74585-7(3)) Scholastic, Inc.

Anderson, Jill, ed. Let's Go on Safari!/Vamos de Safari! Utton, Peter, illus. 2005. (ENG & SPA.). 20p. (J). (ps-k). bds. 6.95 (978-1-58728-522-6(3) , Two Can Publishing) T&N Children's Publishing.

—Let's Visit the Jungle! !Vamos a la Selva!, 5. Holmes, Steve, illus. 2005. (ENG & SPA.). 20p. (J). (gr. 3-7). bds. 6.95 (978-1-58728-523-3(1) , Two Can Publishing) T&N Children's Publishing.

Anderson, Melissa & Elrazky, Sumaiyah. Animals A-Z in Arabic - an Arabic / English Easy Reader. 2004. (ARA.). 23p. (J). per. 17.95 (978-1-4116-0752-1(X)) Lulu.com.

Animal ABCs. 2003. (Wipe-Off Activity Bks.). 16p. (J). (gr. 2). 3.79 (978-1-58792-047-9(6)) Trend Enterprises, Inc.

Animal Adventures/Aventuras De Animales. 2005. 64p. (J). pap. 3.99 (978-0-9762071-3-9(3)) Big City Publishing.

Animal Classifying Cards: Grasslands. 2004. (J). 9.95 (978-1-56911-537-4(0)) Learning Resources, Inc.

Animal Clues: 6 Small Books. (gr. k-1). 35.00 (978-0-7635-6226-7(2)) Rigby Education.

Animal Faces. 16p. (J). 1.89 (978-0-7847-1020-3(1)) Standard Publishing.

Animal Facts, 4 vols., Set. 2005. (Illus.). 24p. (gr. 2-4). pap. 92.00 (978-0-7910-7279-0(7) , Chelsea Hse.) Facts On File, Inc.

Animal Families. gif. ed. (Illus.). (J). (ps-k). 6.95 (978-1-55254-259-0(9) , BV50002) Brighter Vision Pubns.

Animal Fun House, 4 bks. 2002. (J). bds. 7.98 (978-0-7525-8730-1(7)) Parragon, Inc.

Animal Habitats Bingo. 2003. (Science Card Games Ser.). (gr. 3-4). 9.99 (978-0-7682-1980-7(9) , J53008) School Specialty Publishing.

The Animal Kingdom. 2005. (Animals, Animals, Animals Ser.). (YA). (gr. k-3). 178.20 (978-0-7368-4207-5(1) , Pebble Bks.) Capstone Pr., Inc.

The Animal Kingdom, Set. (gr. k-2). 172.95 (978-0-7368-9121-9(8)) Red Brick Learning.

Animal Kingdom Classification. 2006. 48p. (J). (gr. 4-6). 319.20 (978-0-7565-1696-3(X)) Compass Point Bks.

Animal Kingdom Classification Series, 7 bks., Set. 2005. (J). (gr. 4-8). 186.20 (978-0-7565-1390-0(1)) Compass Point Bks.

Animal Kingdom-Flip Chart. 2001. 10p. (J). (gr. k up). spiral bd., tchr.'s training gde. ed. 12.95 (978-1-58845-179-8(8)) School Specialty Publishing.

The Animal Kingdom Series, 8 bks., Set 1. 2004. pap. 68.40 (978-1-4109-1358-6(9)) Harcourt Schl. Pubs.

Animal Legs 6 Packs: Individual Title. (Discovery World Ser.). 12p. (gr. k-1). 28.00 (978-0-7635-8449-8(5)) Rigby Education.

Animal Life Cycles. 2004. (Illus.). lib. bdg. 7.95 (978-0-8225-4757-0(0)); Set. 2006. (J). 20.95 (***978-0-8225-4754-9(6)***) Lerner Publishing Group.

Animal Opposites. 2002. (Illus.). (J). pap. 3.74 (978-0-7398-5857-8(2)) Steck-Vaughn.

Animal Patterns Math, 6 vols. (gr. k-2). 28.95 (978-0-7368-2991-5(1) , Yellow Umbrella Bks.) Capstone Pr., Inc.

Animal Predators. 2005. (Animal Predators Ser.). (J). (gr. 3-6). pap., tchr. ed. 7.95 (978-0-8225-4044-1(4)) Lerner Publishing Group.

Animal Shapes, 6 vols., Pack. (Rigby Focus Ser.). 16p. (gr. 1 up). 30.00 (978-0-7578-5542-9(3)) Rigby Education.

Animal Shapes: Individual Title Six-Packs. (Rigby Focus Ser.). 16p. (gr. 1 up). 28.00 (978-0-7578-5310-4(2)) Rigby Education.

Animal Signs: Flip Charts. (J). spiral bd. 15.95 (978-1-930820-37-1(2)) Garlic Pr.

Animal Soundtracks. 2003. (YA). (ps up). pap. 15.99 (978-0-7424-1528-7(7)) School Specialty Publishing.

Animal Stickers. 2004. (Art Rom Create Your Own... Ser.). (Illus.). 24p. (J). pap. incl. audio compact disk (978-1-84229-736-0(8)) Top That! Publishing PLC.

Animal Tracks: Level C, 6 vols. (Wonder Worldtm Ser.). 16p. 24.95 (978-0-7802-1211-4(8)) Wright Group, The.

Animal Treasury. 2001. 190p. (J). 19.95 (978-0-7525-3835-8(7)) Parragon, Inc.

Animal Wonders, 12 bks. Incl. Wonder of Bats. Bauman, Amy & Lundberg, Kathryn T. 2000. lib. bdg. 26.00 (978-0-8368-2660-9(4)); Wonder of Beavers. Bauman, Amy & Corrigan, Patricia. 2000. lib. bdg. 26.00 (978-0-8368-2661-6(2)); Wonder of Butterflies. Bauman, Amy & Norsgaard, E. Jaediker. 2000. lib. bdg. 26.00 (978-0-8368-2662-3(0)); Wonder of Cheetahs. Lantier-Sampon, Patricia & MacPherson, Winnie. McGee, John F., illus. 2001. lib. bdg. 26.00 (978-0-8368-2763-7(5)); Wonder of Elephants. Lantier-Sampon, Patricia & Fredericks, Anthony D. McGee, John F., illus. 2001. lib. bdg. 26.00 (978-0-8368-2764-4(3)); Wonder of Foxes. Lantier-Sampon, Patricia & Schuler, Judy. McGee, John F., illus. 2001. lib. bdg. 26.00 (978-0-8368-2765-1(1)); Wonder of Kangaroos. Lantier-Sampon, Patricia & Lehne, Judith Logan. McGee, John F., illus. 2001. lib. bdg. 26.00 (978-0-8368-2766-8(X)); Wonder of Koalas. Lantier-Sampon, Patricia & Feeney, Kathy. McGee, John F., illus. 2001. lib. bdg. 26.00 (978-0-8368-2767-5(8)); Wonder of Manatees. Bauman, Amy & Corrigan, Patricia. 2000. lib. bdg. 26.00 (978-0-8368-2663-0(9)); Wonder of Owls. Bauman, Amy & Niemuth, Neal D. 2000. lib. bdg. 26.00 (978-0-8368-2664-7(7)); Wonder of Pandas. Lantier-Sampon, Patricia & Feeney, Kathy. McGee, John F., illus. 2001. lib. bdg. 26.00 (978-0-8368-2768-2(6)); Wonder of Sharks. Bauman, Amy & Corrigan, Patricia. 2000. lib. bdg. 26.00 (978-0-8368-2665-4(5)); 48p. (J). (gr. 1 up). (Illus.). Set lib. bdg. 312.00 (978-0-8368-2864-1(X)) Stevens, Gareth Inc.

Animales. 2005. 101p. (J). spiral bd. 14.99 (978-1-59441-457-2(2) , K04008) Carson-Dellosa Publishing Co., Inc.

Animales: Individual Title Six Packs. (Chiquilibros Ser.). (SPA.). (gr. k-1). 23.00 (978-0-7635-8607-2(2)) Rigby Education.

Animales, animales, animales Interactive Packages: Animales grandes y Peqenos. (Pebble Soup Exploraciones Ser.). (SPA.). (ps up). 52.00 (978-0-7578-5261-9(0)) Rigby Education.

Animales, animales, animales Interactive Packages: Donde viven los Animales. (Pebble Soup Exploraciones Ser.). (SPA.). (ps up). 52.00 (978-0-7578-5260-2(2)) Rigby Education.

Animales Con Escamas, 6 vols. (Explorers. Exploradores Nonfiction Sets Ser.). (SPA.). 32p. (gr. 3-6). 44.95 (978-0-7699-0630-0(3)) Shortland Pubns. (U. S. A.) Inc.

Los animales: Cuaderno de Evaluacion: Unit 4: Los Animales (Animals) 2000. (McGraw-Hill Ciencias Ser.). (ENG & SPA.). (gr. 4 up). (978-0-02-278663-2(5)) Macmillan/McGraw-Hill Schl. Div.

Los Animales Cuentan 365 Historias. 2003. (SPA., Illus.). (J). 14.50 (978-970-22-0445-9(3)) Larousse, Ediciones, S. A. de C. V. MEX. *Dist:* Giron Bks.

Animales de la Granja. 2005. (Collection Abre Tus Ojos, Collection Eye Openers Ser.).Tr. of Barnyard Animals. (SPA.). (J). (gr. k-2). 6.95 (978-950-11-0901-6(1)) Sigmar ARG. *Dist:* Iaconi, Mariuccia Bk. Imports.

Animales de noche, animales de Dia 16: Leveled Books. 2001. (McGraw-Hill. Lectura Ser.). (ENG & SPA.). (gr. 2 up). (978-0-02-188065-2(4)) Macmillan/McGraw-Hill Schl. Div.

Animales Del Zoologico. 2005. (Collection Abre Tus Ojos, Collection Eye Openers Ser.).Tr. of Zoo Animals. (SPA.). (J). (gr. k-2). 6.95 (978-950-11-0898-9(8)) Sigmar ARG. *Dist:* Iaconi, Mariuccia Bk. Imports.

Animales Peligrosos, 6 vols., Vol. 3. (Explorers. Exploradores Nonfiction Sets Ser.). (SPA.). (gr. 3-6). (978-0-7699-0649-2(4)) Shortland Pubns. (U. S. A.) Inc.

Los animales: Recursos para el maestro con clave de Respuestas: Unit 4: Los Animales (Animals) 2000. (McGraw-Hill Ciencias Ser.). (ENG & SPA.). (gr. 4 up). (978-0-02-278703-5(8)) Macmillan/McGraw-Hill Schl. Div.

Animals. (Active Minds(R) Ser.). 22p. (J). spiral bd., bds. (978-0-7853-8612-4(2) , 7188000) Publications International, Ltd.

Animals. (Reading for Every Child Ser.). 32p. 5.99 (978-1-57029-451-8(8) , WPH99007, Totline Pubns.) Schaffer, Frank Pubns.

Animals, 22 bks. Incl. Baboons. Holmes, Kevin J. 2000. lib. bdg. 18.60 (978-0-7368-0494-3(3)); Bats. Holmes, Kevin J. 1997. lib. bdg. 18.60 (978-1-56065-602-9(6)); Bears. Holmes, Kevin J. 1998. lib. bdg. 18.60 (978-1-56065-741-5(3)); Bees. Holmes, Kevin J. 1998. 18.60 (978-1-56065-742-2(1)); Butterflies. Holmes, Kevin J. 1998. lib. bdg. 18.60 (978-1-56065-743-9(X)); Dolphins. Holmes, Kevin J. 1997. lib. bdg. 18.60 (978-1-56065-574-9(7)); Earthworms. Holmes, Kevin J. 1998. 18.60 (978-1-56065-744-6(8)); Elephants. Holmes, Kevin J. 2000. lib. bdg. 18.60 (978-0-7368-0495-0(1)); Frogs. Holmes, Kevin J. 1998. lib. bdg. 18.60 (978-1-56065-745-3(6)); Hyenas. Holmes, Kevin J. 1998. lib. bdg. 18.60 (978-0-7368-0064-8(6)); Lions. Holmes, Kevin J. 1998. lib. bdg. 18.60 (978-0-7368-0065-5(4)); Meerkats. Weaver, Robyn. 1998. lib. bdg. 18.60 (978-0-7368-0066-2(2)); Mice. Holmes, Kevin J. 1997. lib. bdg. 18.60 (978-1-56065-604-3(2)); Owls. Holmes, Kevin J. 1997. lib. bdg. 18.60 (978-1-56065-603-6(4)); Penguins. Holmes, Kevin J. 1997. lib. bdg. 18.60 (978-1-56065-573-2(9)); Rhinos. Holmes, Kevin J. 2000. 18.60 (978-0-7368-0496-7(X)); Sharks. Holmes, Kevin J. 1997. 18.60 (978-1-56065-600-5(X)); Snails. Holmes, Kevin J. 1998. 18.60 (978-1-56065-746-0(4)); Spiders. Holmes, Kevin J. 1997. lib. bdg. 18.60 (978-1-56065-605-0(0)); Warthogs. Holmes, Kevin J. 1998. lib. bdg. 18.60 (978-0-7368-0067-9(0)); Whales. Holmes, Kevin J. 1997. lib. bdg. 18.60 (978-1-56065-601-2(8)); Zebras. Holmes, Kevin J. 2000. lib. bdg. 18.60 (978-0-7368-0497-4(8)); 24p. (J). (gr. 2-3). (Illus.). Set lib. bdg. 409.20 (978-0-7368-0554-4(0) , Bridgestone Bks.) Capstone Pr., Inc.

Animals. 2003. (Busy Blocks Ser.). 8p. pap. 1.95 (978-0-7624-1945-6(8)) Running Pr. Bk. Pubs.

Animals: Fun to Learn. 1999. (Illus.). 32p. (ps-3). 1.99 (978-1-58279-009-1(4) , 95) Trident Pr. International.

Animals: Individual Title-Six Packs. (Chiquilibros Ser.). (gr. k-1). 23.00 (978-0-7635-0428-1(9)) Rigby Education.

Animals: KinderFacts Individual Title Six-Packs. (Kinderstarters Ser.). 8p. (ps-1). 21.00 (978-0-7635-8739-0(7)) Rigby Education.

Animals: Lift-a-Flap Fun. 2000. (Active Minds Ser.). (Illus.). 12p. (J). bds. 7.98 (978-0-7853-4256-4(7) , 3998500) Publications International, Ltd.

Animals: Resource Guide. 2006. 24.95 (978-1-59679-977-6(3) , Checkerboard Library) ABDO Publishing Co.

Animals ABC's. 2001. (Early Learning Ser.). (J). (gr. k-12). vinyl bd. 4.95 (978-1-58845-058-6(9)) School Specialty Publishing.

Animals All Around. 2000. (Illus.). 18p. (J). (ps). (978-1-57584-810-5(4)) Reader's Digest Children's Publishing, Inc.

Animals & Their Sounds. 2004. (J). per. 15.99 (978-0-9759122-2-5(4)) Golden Eagle Publishing Hse., Inc.

Animals Animals, 6 bks., Group 6. Incl. Buffalo. Perry, Phyllis J. lib. bdg. (978-0-7614-1866-5(0)); Jellyfish. King, David C. lib. bdg. (978-0-7614-1867-2(9)); Kangaroos. Jango-Cohen, Judith. lib. bdg. (978-0-7614-1869-6(5)); Moose. Estigarribia, Diana. lib. bdg. (978-0-7614-1870-2(9)); Porcupines. Jango-Cohen, Judith. lib. bdg. (978-0-7614-1868-9(7)); Zebras. Noble-Goodman, Katherine. lib. bdg. (978-0-7614-1871-9(7)); (Illus.). 48p. (J). (gr. 3-7). 2005. (978-0-7614-1865-8(2)); Set lib. bdg. 171.00 (***978-0-7614-2523-6(3)***) Cavendish, Marshall Corp. (Benchmark Bks.).

Animals Animals - Group 1, 6 bks., Set. Incl. Bears. Schwabacher, Martin. lib. bdg. 25.64 (978-0-7614-1169-7(0) , Benchmark Bks.); Chimpanzees. Greenberg, Daniel A. lib. bdg. 25.64 (978-0-7614-1165-9(8) , Benchmark Bks.); Elephants. Schwabacher, Martin. lib. bdg. 25.64 (978-0-7614-1168-0(2) , Benchmark Bks.); Lions. Schafer, Susan. lib. bdg. 25.64 (978-0-7614-1166-6(6) , Benchmark Bks.); Tigers. Schafer, Susan. lib. bdg. 25.64 (978-0-7614-1170-3(4)); Whales. Greenberg, Daniel A. lib. bdg. 25.64 (978-0-7614-1167-3(4) , Benchmark Bks.); 48p. (J). (gr. 3-5). 2000. (Illus.). 2001. Set lib. bdg. 153.86 (978-0-7614-1164-2(X) , Benchmark Bks.) Cavendish, Marshall Corp.

Animals Animals: Group 5, 5 Bks, Set. 2004. (J). 153.86 (978-0-7614-1748-4(6)) Cavendish, Marshall Corp.

Animals, Animals, Animals Interactive Packages: Animals Big & Little. (Pebble Soup Explorations Ser.). (ps up). 52.00 (978-0-7578-5237-4(8)) Rigby Education.

Animals, Animals, Animals Interactive Packages: Where Animals Live. (Pebble Soup Explorations Ser.). (ps up). 52.00 (978-0-7578-5236-7(X)) Rigby Education.

Animals Animals Group 7, 6 bks., Set. Incl. Anteaters. Rebman, Renee C. lib. bdg. 28.50 (978-0-7614-2234-1(X)); Bees. Jango-Cohen, Judith. lib. bdg. 28.50 (978-0-7614-2235-8(8)); Eagles. Noblemen, Marc Tyler. lib. bdg. 28.50 (978-0-7614-2236-5(6)); Foxes. Nobleman, Marc Tyler. lib. bdg. 28.50 (978-0-7614-2237-2(4)); Hippopotamuses. Jango-Cohen, Judith. lib. bdg. 28.50 (978-0-7614-2238-9(2)); Turtles & Tortoises. Rebman, Renee C. lib. bdg. 28.50 (978-0-7614-2239-6(0)); (Illus.). 48p. (J). 2006. 2006. Set lib. bdg. 171.00 (***978-0-7614-2233-4(1)*** , Benchmark Bks.) Cavendish, Marshall Corp.

Animals Animals Series - Group 3, 6 bks., Set. 153.86 (978-0-7614-1442-1(8) , Benchmark Bks.) Cavendish, Marshall Corp.

Animals at Work: Individual Title Six-Packs. (gr. k-1). 23.00 (978-0-7635-9060-4(6)) Rigby Education.

Animals Building Homes. (Animal Behavior Ser.). 24p. (J). 6.95 (978-0-7368-5161-9(5)) Capstone Pr., Inc.

Animals Classroom Library. (gr. k-2). lib. bdg. 90.95 (978-0-7368-7135-8(7)); (gr. 2-5). lib. bdg. 104.95 (978-0-7368-7090-0(3)) Red Brick Learning.

Animals Complete Unit. (gr. k-2). 519.95 (978-0-7368-7145-7(4)); (gr. 2-5). 597.95 (978-0-7368-7091-7(1)) Red Brick Learning.

Animals Extremes. (C). 135.60 (978-1-4048-1001-3(3)) Picture Window Bks.

Animals Far & Wide. (Magnets on the Move Ser.). 8p. (J). bds. (978-2-7643-0102-9(2)) Phidal Publishing, Inc./Editions Phidal, Inc.

Animals Finding Food. (Animal Behavior Ser.). 24p. (J). 6.95 (978-0-7368-5160-2(7)) Capstone Pr., Inc.

Animals (Gr. 1-2) 2003. (J). (978-1-58232-073-1(X)) Bryan Hse. Pubs., Inc.

Animals I - PowerPhonics Skill Set I, 6 bks. Incl. Ant : Learning the Short A Sound. Chapman, Joan. lib. bdg. 18.50 (978-0-8239-5916-7(3)); I Have a Horse : Learning the H Sound. Sarkisian, Kevin. lib. bdg. 18.50 (978-0-8239-5906-8(6)); Just Bugs : Learning the Short U Sound. Jones, Jeff. lib. bdg. 18.50 (978-0-8239-5911-2(2)); Little Pigs, Big Pigs : Learning the Short I Sound. Braidich, Shelby. lib. bdg. 18.50 (978-0-8239-5904-4(X)); Pet Pals : Learning the P Sound. Chapman, Joan. lib. bdg. 18.50 (978-0-8239-5915-0(5)); Tiger Talk : Learning the T Sound. Moore, Sharon. lib. bdg. 18.50 (978-0-8239-5914-3(7)); 24p. (J). (gr. 1). 2002. (Illus.). 2001. Set lib. bdg. 108.00 (978-0-8239-7201-2(1) , PowerKids Pr.) Rosen Publishing Group, Inc., The.

Animals II - PowePhonics Skill Set II, 6 bks. Incl. Chicks & Chickens : Learning the CH Sound. Barnes, J. Lou. lib. bdg. 18.50 (978-0-8239-5923-5(6)); Giant Giraffes : Learning the Soft G Sound. Leigh, Autumn. lib. bdg. 18.50 (978-0-8239-5919-8(8)); Huge Animals : Learning the Long U Sound. Vastola, Pam. lib. bdg. 18.50 (978-0-8239-5931-0(7)); Sharks : Learning the SH Sound. Wood, Ira. lib. bdg. 18.50 (978-0-8239-5921-1(X)); What a Whale! Learning the WH Sound. Battistoni, Ilse. lib. bdg. 18.50 (978-0-8239-5929-7(5)); Wild Wolf : Learning the W Sound. Tanner, Susan. lib. bdg. 18.50 (978-0-8239-5927-3(9)); 24p. (J). (gr. 1). 2002. (Illus.). 2001. Set lib. bdg. 108.00 (978-0-8239-7205-0(4) , PowerKids Pr.) Rosen Publishing Group, Inc., The.

Animals II Classroom Library. (gr. k-2). lib. bdg. 54.95 (978-0-7368-9127-1(7)) Red Brick Learning.

Animals II Complete Unit. (gr. k-2). 311.95 (978-0-7368-9128-8(5)) Red Brick Learning.

Animals in Action. 1999. (Illus.). 88p. (J). (ps-2). 14.95 (978-0-8094-4869-2(6)) Time-Life, Inc.

Animals Life Cycles, Set. (gr. k-2). 114.95 (978-0-7368-9041-0(6)) Red Brick Learning.

Animals Live Everywhere. (Early Intervention Levels Ser.). 28.38 (978-0-7362-0412-5(1)) Hampton-Brown Bks.

Animals Long Ago: Fourth Grade Newcomer Books. (On Our Way to English Ser.). (gr. 4 up). 34.50 (978-0-7578-7260-0(3)) Rigby Education.

Animals Near & Far. 1998. (Reading Counts Ser.). (Illus.). (J). pap. 514.82 incl. cd-rom (978-0-7398-0952-5(0)) Raintree.

Animals of North America, 10 vols., set. 2002. (Zoobooks). (Illus.). (J). (gr. k-7). pap. 24.75 (978-1-888153-67-5(9)) Wildlife Education, Ltd.

Animals of the Rain Forest, 30 bks. 2002. (978-0-7398-5376-4(7)) Raintree.

Animals of the Rain Forest: Includes: Anteaters, Boa Constrictors, Ocelots, Orangutans, Tarantulas, Tree Frogs, 6 bks., Set. 2001. (Illus.). (J). (gr. 4-7). lib. bdg. 136.98 (978-0-7398-3558-6(0)) Raintree.

Animals of the Rain Forest Collection 3. 2002. (Illus.). (J). pap. (978-0-7398-6027-4(5)) Steck-Vaughn.

Animals of the Rain Forest Set: Includes: Anacondas, Ants, Caimans, Jaguars, Piranhas, Toucans, 6 bks., Set. 2001. (Illus.). (J). (gr. 4-7). lib. bdg. 136.98 (978-0-7398-3103-8(8)) Raintree.

Animals of the Rainforest. 2001. (Illus.). (J). Set 1. pap. (978-0-7398-3363-6(4)); Set 2. pap. (978-0-7398-4670-4(1)); Set 3. pap. (978-0-7398-4932-3(8)) Steck-Vaughn.

Animals of the World. (Look, Find & Learn Ser.). (Illus.). 32p. (J). per. (978-1-4127-1045-9(6) , 7233800) Publications International, Ltd.

Animals of the World, Sets 1 & 2. 2001. (J). (gr. 1-6). 238.00 (978-0-7166-1222-3(4)) World Bk., Inc.

Animals on the Go! (Flip Flap Fun Book Ser.). (Illus.). 10p. (J). bds. (978-2-7643-0041-1(7)) Phidal Publishing, Inc./Editions Phidal, Inc.

Animals Raising Offspring. (Animal Behavior Ser.). 24p. (J). 6.95 (978-0-7368-5162-6(3)) Capstone Pr., Inc.

Animals Set 1: Cats, Dogs & Other Pets. 2005. (J). spiral bd. 23.40 (978-0-9770248-7-2(3)) Sidedoor Publishing LLC.

Animals Staying Safe. (Animal Behavior Ser.). 24p. (J). 6.95 (978-0-7368-5165-7(8)) Capstone Pr., Inc.

Animals You Will Never Forget. 2002. (Illus.). (J). pap. 6.25 (978-0-7398-6160-8(3)) Steck-Vaughn.

AnimalWays, 5 bks., Group 5. Incl. Butterflies. Schlaepfer, Gloria G. (gr. 3-7). lib. bdg. (978-0-7614-1745-3(1)); Hawks. Warhol, Tom. (gr. 4-7). lib. bdg. (978-0-7614-1744-6(3)); Lions. Stefoff, Rebecca. (gr. 3-7). lib. bdg. (978-0-7614-1746-0(X)); Penguins. Stefoff, Rebecca. (gr. 3-7). lib. bdg. (978-0-7614-1743-9(5)); Spiders. Zabludoff, Marc. (gr. 3-7). lib. bdg. (978-0-7614-1747-7(8)); (Illus.). 112p. (J). 2005. (978-0-7614-1742-2(7) , Benchmark Bks.) Cavendish, Marshall Corp.

AnimalWays - Group 3. 156.79 (978-0-7614-1388-2(X) , Benchmark Bks.) Cavendish, Marshall Corp.

Animaux de la Savane. 16.95 (978-2-03-553030-1(X)) Librairie Larousse FRA. *Dist:* Distribooks, Inc.

Aprende sobre los animales: Cuaderno de Actividades: Unit 3: Aprende sobre los animales (All about Animals) 2000. (McGraw-Hill Ciencias Ser.). (ENG & SPA.). (gr. k up). (978-0-02-278992-3(8)) Macmillan/McGraw-Hill Schl. Div.

Arnold, Caroline. Did You Hear That? 2001. (gr. 3-6). lib. bdg. 15.25 (978-0-613-51242-8(1)) Tandem Library Bks.

—Did You Hear That? Animals with Super Hearing. 2001. (978-0-606-22634-9(6)) Tandem Library Bks.

—Mealtime for Zoo Animals. 1999. (Zoo Animals Ser.). (Illus.). 32p. (J). (ps-2). 9.95 (978-1-57505-389-9(6) , Carolrhoda Bks.) Lerner Publishing Group.

—Mealtime for Zoo Animals. Hewett, Richard, illus. 1999. (Zoo Animals Ser.). 32p. (J). (ps-2). lib. bdg. 21.27 (978-1-57505-286-1(5) , Carolrhoda Bks.) Lerner Publishing Group.

—Playtime for Zoo Animals. 1999. (Zoo Animals Ser.). (Illus.). 32p. (J). (ps-2). pap. 9.95 (978-1-57505-391-2(8) , Carolrhoda Bks.) Lerner Publishing Group.

—Playtime for Zoo Animals. Hewett, Richard, illus. 1999. (Zoo Animals Ser.). 32p. (J). (ps-2). lib. bdg. 21.27 (978-1-57505-287-8(3) , Carolrhoda Bks.) Lerner Publishing Group.

Arnold, Katya R. Let's Find It! My First Nature Guide. Arnold, Katya R., illus. 2002. (Illus.). 32p. (J). (gr. k-3). tchr. ed. 16.95 (978-0-8234-1539-7(2)) Holiday Hse., Inc.

Arnold, Nick. Esa Repelente Naturaleza. 2003. (Coleccion Esa Horrible Cienca). (SPA., Illus.). 158p. (YA). (978-84-272-2053-9(7) , ML8314) Molino, Editorial ESP. *Dist:* Lectorum Pubns., Inc.

Aronin, Miriam. Black-footed Ferrets: Back from the Brink. 2008. (J). lib. bdg. 25.27 (***978-1-59716-506-8(9)***) Bearport Publishing Co., Inc.

Art with Animals! (Learning Ser.). 22p. (J). bds. (978-2-7643-0164-7(2)) Phidal Publishing, Inc./Editions Phidal, Inc.

Artell, Mike. Backyard Bloodsuckers: Questions, Facts & Tongue Twisters about Creepy Crawlers. 2004. (Illus.). 80p. pap. (978-0-673-59248-4(0)) Good Year Bks.

Auch, Alison. Tame & Wild. 2002. (Spyglass Books). (Illus.). 24p. (J). (gr. 1 up). lib. bdg. 18.60 (978-0-7565-0226-3(8)) Compass Point Bks.

Baby Animal Giant Sticker Shapes. 2002. (Sticker Shapes Ser.). 16p. (J). pap. 5.98 (978-0-7525-7925-2(8)) Parragon, Inc.

Baby's First Animal Book. 2004. 10p. (J). bds. 4.99 (978-1-85854-921-7(3)) Brimax Books Ltd. GBR. *Dist:* Byeway Bks.

Baddiel, Ivor. Fantastic Creatures. 1999. (Mysterious World Ser.). (Illus.). 30p. (J). (gr. 5-9). pap. 6.95 (978-0-7641-1153-2(1)) Barron's Educational Series, Inc.

Bailey, Jacqui. Amazing Animal Facts: A Visual Guide to the World's Most Incredible Creatures. 2003. (Illus.). 64p. (J). pap. 12.99 (978-0-7894-9870-0(7)) Dorling Kindersley Publishing, Inc.

Bailey, Jill. Life in a Garbage Dump. 2003. (Microhabitats Ser.). (Illus.). 32p. (J). pap. 7.50 (978-1-4109-0348-8(6)) Raintree.

Bair, Diane. Wildlife Watching, 8 bks. Incl. Bat Watching. Wright, Pamela. lib. bdg. 21.26 (978-0-7368-0318-2(1)); Bear Watching. lib. bdg. 21.26 (978-0-7368-0319-9(X)); Butterfly Watching. lib. bdg. 21.26 (978-0-7368-0320-5(3)); Deer Watching. Wright, Pamela. lib. bdg. 21.26 (978-0-7368-0321-2(1)); Eagle Watching. lib. bdg. 21.26 (978-0-7368-0322-9(X)); Sea Turtle Watching. Wright, Pamela. lib. bdg. 21.26 (978-0-7368-0323-6(8)); Tide Pool Life Watching. lib. bdg. 21.26 (978-0-7368-0324-3(6)); Whale Watching. lib. bdg. 21.26 (978-0-7368-0325-0(4)); 48p. (J). (gr. 3-4). 1999. (Illus.). Set lib. bdg. 170.08 (978-0-7368-0442-4(0) , Capstone High-Interest Bks.) Capstone Pr., Inc.

Baker, Charles F., ed. Wild Animals. 2005. (Illus.). 32p. (J). 17.95 (978-0-8126-7928-1(8)) Cobblestone Publishing Co.

Baker, Leslie A. The Animal ABC. rev. ed. 2003. (Illus.). 40p. (J). 15.95 (978-0-8050-6746-0(9) , Holt, Henry & Co. Bks. For Young Readers) Holt, Henry & Co.

Baker, Lucy. Las Selvas. 2004. (Ecologia Ser.). (SPA., Illus.). 32p. (gr. 3-6). 12.95 (978-1-58728-299-7(2) , Two Can Publishing) T&N Children's Publishing.

—Las Selvas. 2000. (Illus.). (J). (978-0-606-20972-4(7)) Tandem Library Bks.

Balliet, Gay. Touched by All Creatures: Doctoring Animals in the Pennsylvania Dutch Country. 1999. (Illus.). 368p. 25.95 (978-0-88282-169-6(5)) New Horizon Pr. Pubs., Inc.

Balloon Books Staff, ed. Wild Animals Board Book. 2003. (Animal Bring-Along Bks.). (Illus.). 32p. (J). bds. 5.95 (978-0-8069-8965-5(3)) Sterling Publishing Co., Inc.

Bampton, Bob, illus. Animals in the Wild. 2004. (Look & Learn about Ser.). 18p. (J). bds. 5.99 (978-1-85854-351-2(7)) Brimax Books Ltd. GBR. *Dist:* Byeway Bks.

A B

Bankroff, Georgene. A Compilation of Classy Animal Names. 2002. 174p. (YA). pap. 11.95 (978-0-595-20674-2(3) , Writers Club Pr.) iUniverse, Inc.

Baptista, Lynne Hardie & Rosenthal, Mark. Discover Animal Life. Robare, Lorie, illus. 2005. (Discover Ser.). 48p. (J). 7.98 (978-0-7853-6108-4(1) , 3049302) Publications International, Ltd.

Barbaresi, Nina. Animal Firefighters Stickers. 2004. (Stickers Ser.). (Illus.). 4p. (J). pap. 1.50 (978-0-486-43451-3(6)) Dover Pubns., Inc.

Barbey, Dorine. Animals Around Us. Gibson, Sarah et al, trs. 1998. (Creative Discoveries Ser.). (Illus.). 75p. (J). (gr. 2-8). lib. bdg. 23.95 (978-0-88682-943-8(7) , Creative Education) Creative Co., The.

Barnes, Julia. 101 Facts about Predators, 6 bks. Incl. 101 Facts about Eagles. lib. bdg. 23.33 (978-0-8368-4036-0(4)); 101 Facts about Lions. lib. bdg. 23.33 (978-0-8368-4037-7(2)); 101 Facts about Polar Bears. lib. bdg. 23.33 (978-0-8368-4038-4(0)); 101 Facts about Sharks. lib. bdg. 23.33 (978-0-8368-4039-1(9)); 101 Facts about Snakes. lib. bdg. 23.33 (978-0-8368-4040-7(2)); 101 Facts about Tigers. lib. bdg. 23.33 (978-0-8368-4041-4(0)); 32p. (J). (gr. 3 up). (Illus.). 2004. Set lib. bdg. 139.98 (978-0-8368-4035-3(6)) Stevens, Gareth Inc.

Barnes, Trevor, as told by. The Kingfisher Children's Illustrated Bible. ed. 2005. 256p. (J). (gr. 4-6). 14.95 (978-0-7534-5905-8(1) , Kingfisher) Houghton Mifflin Co. Trade & Reference Div.

Barnett, Michelle Noble, et al. Theme Pockets - April: Easter; Animals That Lay Eggs; Celebrate Earth Day. Evans, Marilyn, ed. Larsen, Jo, illus. 1999. (Making Books with Pockets). 96p. (J). pap., tchr. ed. 12.99 (978-1-55799-701-2(2) , EMC 587) Evan-Moor Educational Pubs.

Barnhill, Kelly Regan. Animals with No Eyes: Cave Adaptation. 2008. (J). (*978-1-4296-1262-3(2) , Fact Finders) Capstone Pr., Inc.

Barraclough, Sue. Animals in the Wild. 2005. (Raintree Sprouts Ser.). (Illus.). 24p. (J). (978-1-4109-1896-3(3)); pap. (978-1-4109-1901-4(3)) Steck-Vaughn.

—Animals That Work. 2005. (J). pap. (978-1-4109-1902-1(1)); (Illus.). 24p. (gr. 3-5). lib. bdg. 21.36 (978-1-4109-1897-0(1)) Steck-Vaughn.

Barret & Allen. El Lynx. 2002. (Gatos Salvajes Serie).Tr. of Wild Cats: The Lynx. (SPA.). 24p. (J). (gr. 3-5). 22.45 (978-1-4103-0011-9(0) , Blackbirch Pr., Inc.) Thomson Gale.

—El Puma. 2002. (Gatos Salvajes Serie).Tr. of Wild Cats: The Cougar. (SPA.). 24p. (J). (gr. 3-5). 22.45 (978-1-4103-0012-6(9) , Blackbirch Pr., Inc.) Thomson Gale.

Barrett, Judi. Los Animales No Deven Actuar Como la Gente. (SPA., Illus.). (J). (gr. k-1). pap. (978-950-515-807-2(6) , FL5250) De La Flor ARG. *Dist:* Lectorum Pubns., Inc.

—Animals Should Definitely Not Act Like People. Barrett, Ron, illus. 2000. (J). pap. 19.97 incl. audio (978-0-7366-9222-9(3)) Books on Tape, Inc.

—Animals Should Definitely Not Act Like People. Barrett, Ron, illus. pap. 35.95 incl. audio compact disk (978-1-59112-827-4(7)); (J). pap. 33.95 incl. audio (978-0-87499-232-8(X)) Live Oak Media.

—Animals Should Definitely Not Wear Clothing. Barrett, Ron, illus. 2002. (J). 14.47 (978-0-7587-1951-5(5)) Book Wholesalers, Inc.

—Animals Should Definitely Not Wear Clothing. Barrett, Ron, illus. 2000. (J). pap. 19.97 incl. audio (978-0-7366-9197-0(9)) Books on Tape, Inc.

—Animals Should Definitely Not Wear Clothing. 2005. (Illus.). (J). pap. 18.95 incl. audio compact disk (978-1-59112-690-4(8)) Live Oak Media.

Base, Graeme. The Water Hole. Base, Graeme, illus. 2004. 32p. (J). reprint ed. pap. 8.99 (978-0-14-240197-2(8) , Puffin) Penguin Group (USA) Inc.

Bateman, Donna M. Deep in the Swamp. Lies, Brian, illus. 2007. 32p. (J). (ps-1). 15.95 (978-1-57091-596-3(2)); pap. 6.95 (*978-1-57091-597-0(0)) Charlesbridge Publishing, Inc.

Bateman, Helen & Denshire, Jayne. Of the Grasslands. 2005. (Illus.). 32p. (J). (gr. 4-7). lib. bdg. 27.10 (978-1-58340-765-3(0)) Smart Apple Media.

—Of the Mountains & Polar Regions. 2005. (Illus.). 32p. (J). (gr. 4-7). lib. bdg. 27.10 (978-1-58340-767-7(7)) Smart Apple Media.

Batten, Mary. Aliens from Earth: When Animals & Plants Invade Other Ecosystems. Doyle, Beverly, illus. 2003. 32p. (J). 15.95 (978-1-56145-236-1(X)) Peachtree Pubs., Ltd.

Be a Plant Scientist: Level L, 6 vols. (Take-Twostm Ser.). 16p. 36.95 (978-0-322-03403-7(5)) Wright Group, The.

Beach, Stewart. Good Morning-Sun's Up. Sugita, Yataka, illus. 32p. (J). (ps-3). 13.95 (978-0-87592-021-4(7)) Scroll Pr., Inc.

Beaton, Clare. Animals Count Dominoes. gif. ed. (J). 14.99 (978-0-7353-1811-3(5)) Galison.

—Two-in-One Animal Puzzle. (J). 9.99 (978-0-7353-0597-7(8)) Galison.

Beaton, Clare, illus. Animals: Los Animales. l.t. ed. 1998. (English-Spanish Bilingual First Bks.). (ENG & SPA.). 24p. (J). (ps up). lib. bdg. 14.45 (978-1-56674-247-4(1)) Forest Hse. Publishing Co., Inc.

—Wild Animals: English-Spanish. 2002. (Bilingual First Bks.). (ENG & SPA.). 24p. (J). pap. 4.95 (978-0-7641-2213-2(4)) Barron's Educational Series, Inc.

Beattie, Laura C. Discover African Wildlife: Activity Book. Plazek, Caroline, illus. 2008. 24p. pap., stu. ed. 2.95 (*978-0-911239-38-6(3)) Rinehart, Roberts Pubs.

Los Bebes Animales y Sus Mamas.Tr. of Animal Babies & Their Moms. (SPA.). (J). 2.50 (978-970-607-744-8(8)) Larousse, Ediciones, S. A. de C. V. MEX. *Dist:* Continental Bk. Co., Inc.

Beckes, Shirley V., illus. Dialing Animals. 2002. (Dial Bks.). 10p. (J). (ps-k). bds. 10.95 (978-1-57145-521-5(3) , Silver Dolphin Bks.) Advantage Pubs. Group.

Bedford, David. Toes. Worthington, Leonie, illus. 2007. 16p. (J). (ps-k). 9.95 (*978-1-921049-64-4(2)) Little Hare Bks. AUS. *Dist:* Independent Pubs. Group.

Beeke, Tiphanie. Wake up Baby Bear! A First Book about Opposites. 2001. (Illus.). 16p. (J). (978-1-86233-138-9(3) , Gullane Children's Bks.) Pinwheel.

Behm, Barbara J. Animal Opposites, 4 bks. Incl. Daytime & Nighttime Animals. Camm, Martin, illus. lib. bdg. 20.67 (978-0-8368-2459-9(8)); Prickly & Soft Animals. Twinney, Dick. lib. bdg. 20.67 (978-0-8368-2460-5(1)); Quick & Slow Animals. Camm, Martin, illus. lib. bdg. 20.67 (978-0-8368-2461-2(X)); Sleepy & Busy Animals. lib. bdg. 20.67 (978-0-8368-2462-9(8)); (J). (ps up). 1999. (Illus.). 24p. 1999. Set lib. bdg. 82.68 (978-0-8368-2458-2(X)) Stevens, Gareth Inc.

—Daytime & Nighttime Animals. Camm, Martin, illus. 1999. (Animal Opposites Ser.). 24p. (J). (ps up). lib. bdg. 20.67 (978-0-8368-2459-9(8)) Stevens, Gareth Inc.

—Prickly & Soft Animals. Twinney, Dick et al, illus. 1999. (Animal Opposites Ser.). 24p. (J). (ps up). lib. bdg. 20.67 (978-0-8368-2460-5(1)) Stevens, Gareth Inc.

—Quick & Slow Animals. Camm, Martin, illus. 1999. (Animal Opposites Ser.). 24p. (J). (ps up). lib. bdg. 20.67 (978-0-8368-2461-2(X)) Stevens, Gareth Inc.

—Sleepy & Busy Animals. 1999. (Animal Opposites Ser.). (Illus.). 24p. (J). (ps up). lib. bdg. 20.67 (978-0-8368-2462-9(8)) Stevens, Gareth Inc.

Benchmark Education Staff, compiled by. Animal Adaptation. 2006. spiral bd. 219.00 (*978-1-4108-7057-5(X)) Benchmark Education Co.

—Plants & Animals. 2006. spiral bd. 159.00 (*978-1-4108-7063-6(4)); spiral bd. 165.00 (*978-1-4108-7083-4(9)); spiral bd. 159.00 (*978-1-4108-7137-4(1)) Benchmark Education Co.

Berendes, Mary. Animals/Los Animales. 2007. (WordBooks/Libros de Palabras Ser.). (SPA & ENG.). 24p. (J). 19.93 (*978-1-59296-795-7(7)) Child's World, Inc.

Berge, Claire. Whose Shadow Is This? A Look at Animal Shapes - Round, Long, & Pointy. Alderman, Derrick & Shea, Denise, illus. 2004. (Whose Is It? Ser.). 24p. (C). (gr. k-2). 22.60 (978-1-4048-0609-2(1)) Picture Window Bks.

Berger, Melvin & Berger, Gilda. Animales Polares en Peligro: Polar Animals in Danger. 2006. (SPA & ENG., Illus.). (J). (*978-0-439-87987-3(6)) Scholastic, Inc.

—Do Tarantulas Have Teeth? Questions & Answers about Poisonous Creatures. Effler, Jim, illus. 2000. (Question & Answer Ser.). 48p. (J). (gr. 2-4). pap. 5.95 (978-0-439-14877-1(4) , Scholastic Reference); (gr. 4-7). pap. 14.95 (978-0-439-09578-5(6)) Scholastic, Inc.

—Life in the Rainforest: Plants, Animals, & People. Brittingham, Geoffrey H., illus. 1999. (Discovery Readers Ser.). 48p. (YA). (ps up). lib. bdg. 15.95 (978-0-7910-5068-2(8) , Chelsea Hse.) Facts On File, Inc.

—Penguins Swim but Don't Get Wet: And Other Amazing Facts about Polar Animals. 2004. (Speedy Facts Ser.). (Illus.). 48p. (J). (978-0-439-32783-1(0)) Scholastic, Inc.

Berger, Melvin, et al. Do Tarantulas Have Teeth? Questions & Answers about Poisonous Creatures. 1999. (Question & Answer Ser.). (J). 4.99 (978-0-439-09579-2(4)) Scholastic, Inc.

—What Do Animals Do in Winter? How Animals Survive the Cold. Harrison, Susan J., illus. 1999. (Discovery Readers Ser.). 48p. (J). (ps-3). lib. bdg. 17.55 (978-0-7910-5070-5(X) , Chelsea Hse.) Facts On File, Inc.

Bernhard, Durga. Earth, Sky, Wet, Dry: A Book of Opposites. Bernhard, Durga, illus. 2000. (Illus.). 40p. (J). (gr. k-4). 17.99 (978-0-531-33213-9(6) , Orchard Bks.) Scholastic, Inc.

Bernstein, Robin. Terrible, Terrible! A Folktale Retold. Kawasaki, Shauna Mooney, illus. 1998. 32p. (J). (ps-5). 15.95 (978-1-58013-016-5(X)); pap. 6.95 (978-1-58013-017-2(8)) Kar-Ben Publishing.

Bertolucci, Cristiano, et al. Past & Present. Cucchiariani, Fer, illus. 2003. (Contrasts Ser.). 32p. (J). (gr. 1-4). 14.95 (978-1-57768-525-8(3) , Waterbird Bks.) School Specialty Publishing.

Betancourt, Jeanne. Ten True Animal Rescues. 1998. 80p. (J). (gr. 2-5). pap. 3.99 (978-0-590-68117-9(6)) Scholastic, Inc.

Bevan, Finn. Fabulous Beasts. Mayo, Diana, illus. 1998. (Landscapes of Legend Ser.). 32p. (J). (gr. 4-8). pap. 6.95 (978-0-516-26298-7(X) , Children's Pr.) Scholastic Library Publishing.

Bickel, Karla. The Animals' Debate. Bickel, Karla, illus. l.t. ed. 2004. (Illus.). 16p. (J). (ps-6). pap. 5.00 (978-1-891452-16-1(9) , 10) Heart Arbor Bks.

Bicknell, Joanna. My Animal Book. 2005. (Shimmer & Shine Books Ser.). 12p. (ps-k). per., bds. 5.95 (978-1-905051-28-1(X)) Make Believe Ideas GBR. *Dist:* Ingram Pub. Services.

—Wild Animals. 2001. (Softies Ser.). (Illus.). 12p. (ps-k). per., bds. 6.95 (978-1-84610-083-3(6)) Make Believe Ideas GBR. *Dist:* Ingram Pub. Services.

Big & Little: KinderWords Individual Title Six-Packs. (Kinderstarters Ser.). 8p. (ps-1). 21.00 (978-0-7635-8700-0(1)) Rigby Education.

Big Box of Board Books: The Giant Panda; The African Elephant; The Koala & The Mountain Gorilla, 4 bks., Set. 2002. (Animal's Around the World Mini Bks.). (Illus.). (J). bds. (978-1-59069-080-2(X) , ZS1001) Studio Mouse LLC.

Big or Small? 2006. (Yellow Umbrella Math Ser.). 8,16p. (J). 6.50 (978-0-7368-1692-2(5)) Red Brick Learning.

Bilgrami, Shaheen. Safari Animal Adventure. Kees, Chantal & Shields, Chris, illus. 2003. (Magic Color Bks.). 12p. (J). (gr. k-2). 9.95 (978-1-4027-0822-0(X)) Sterling Publishing Co., Inc.

Billings, Henry & Billings, Melissa. Angry Animals. 1998. (Wild Side Ser.). (Illus.). 114p. (YA). (gr. 6-12). 13.00 (978-0-89061-801-1(1) , R0801-1E) Jamestown.

Bingham, Jane. Great Prehistoric Search. 2004. (Great Searches Ser.). 32p. (J). lib. bdg. 16.95 (978-1-58086-641-5(7) , Usborne) EDC Publishing.

—Great Prehistoric Search. Jackson, Ian, illus. 2004. (Great Searches Ser.). 32p. (J). pap. 8.95 (978-0-7945-0663-6(1) , Usborne) EDC Publishing.

Bishop, Nic. The Secrets of Animal Flight. 2007. (Illus.). 32p. (J). (gr. k-3). pap. 6.95 (*978-0-618-80904-2(X)) Houghton Mifflin Co. Trade & Reference Div.

Bishop, Nic, illus. The Backyard Detective: Critters up Close. 2002. (Backyard Detective Ser.). 48p. (J). (gr. 3-6). pap. 16.95 (978-0-439-17478-7(3) , Scholastic Pr.) Scholastic, Inc.

Biskup, Agnieszka. Awesome Animals ABC. Brooks, David, illus. 2005. (J). (978-1-58987-095-6(6)) Kindermusik International.

Black, Jessica L. What Do the Animals Say? Board Book & Felt Puppet Set. Coates, Jennifer, illus. 2005. (J). bds. (978-1-57332-360-4(8)) HighReach Learning, Inc.

Black, Sonia. Animal Mysteries: A Chapter Book. 2006. (True Tales Ser.). (Illus.). 48p. (J). (gr. 2-4). pap. 4.95 (978-0-516-25456-2(1) , Children's Pr.) Scholastic Library Publishing.

Black, Sonia W. Animal Mysteries: A Chapter Book. 2005. (True Tales Ser.). (Illus.). 48p. (J). (ps-ps). 22.50 (978-0-516-25187-5(2) , Children's Pr.) Scholastic Library Publishing.

Blackbirch Press Staff, creator. Horrors. 2005. (Planet's Most Extreme Ser.). (Illus.). 48p. (J). (ps-7). lib. bdg. 24.95 (978-1-4103-0385-1(3) , Blackbirch Pr., Inc.) Thomson Gale.

Blackstone, Stella. Counting Cockatoos. Bauer, Stephanie, illus. 2006. 32p. (J). 16.99 (978-1-905236-31-2(X)) Barefoot Bks., Inc.

Blair, Beth & Ericsson, Jennifer. Everything Kids' Animal Puzzles. 2005. (Illus.). 144p. (J). pap., act. bk. ed. 6.95 (978-1-59337-305-4(8)) Adams Media Corp.

Blair, Beth L. Jumbo Animal Puzzle & Activity Book: Enter the Wild Kingdom of Mind-Bending Fun! 2006. 384p. pap. 8.95 (978-1-59869-046-0(9)) Adams Media Corp.

Blashfield, Jean F. Animal Life. 2007. (J). pap. (*978-0-8368-8445-6(0)); 48p. (gr. 5-8). lib. bdg. 26.60 (*978-0-8368-8436-4(1)) Stevens, Gareth Inc.

Blevins, Wiley. Can You See It? 2003. (Compass Point Phonics Readers Ser.). (Illus.). 16p. (J). (gr. 1 up). 13.26 (978-0-7565-0506-6(2)) Compass Point Bks.

Boardworks Learning Centers: Amazing Animals. 2006. (J). bds. (978-0-9755252-3-4(9)) Evergreen Pr. of Brainerd, LLC.

Bogue, Gary. Raccoon Next Door: And Other Creatures of the Urban Wilderness. Todd, Chuck, illus. 2003. 196p. pap. 16.95 (978-1-890771-71-3(6)) Heyday Bks.

Bolchazy, Marie Carducci. How Many Animals? Quot Animalia? Stock, Kristie, illus. 2002. (I Am Reading Latin Ser.). (LAT & ENG.). 64p. (J). 12.00 (978-0-86516-540-3(8)) Bolchazy-Carducci Pubs.

Book Company Staff. Lift & Learn Animals. 2004. (Novelty Bks.). (Illus.). 10p. (J). (gr. 3-5). bds. 7.95 (978-1-74047-555-6(0)) Book Co. Publishing Pty, Ltd., The AUS. *Dist:* Penton Overseas, Inc.

—Time for Mother Earth. Schimmel, Schim, illus. 2002. (Sparkle Bks.). 16p. (J). bds. 14.95 (978-1-74047-188-6(1)) Book Co. Publishing Pty, Ltd., The AUS. *Dist:* Penton Overseas, Inc.

Books Are Fun 8 Title Animal Lives Set. 2006. (J). mass mkt. (978-1-59566-305-4(3)) QEB Publishing Inc.

Books Are Fun Exclusive Animal Lives 4 Set. 2005. lib. bdg. (978-1-59566-166-1(2)) QEB Publishing Inc.

Boos, Andre, illus. Hi! Read, Stick & Learn about Animals. Little Bears are Brown. 2004. 20p. (J). pap. 6.99 (978-1-59496-003-1(8)) Teora USA LLC.

—Hi! Read, Stick & Learn about Animals. Little rabbits have Fur. 2004. 20p. (J). pap. 6.99 (978-1-59496-002-4(X)) Teora USA LLC.

Boothroyd, Jennifer. Animals & the Environment. 2008. (First Step Nonfiction - Ecology Ser.). (J). lib. bdg. 18.60 (*978-0-8225-8602-9(9) , Lerner Pubns.) Lerner Publishing Group.

—In a Cave. 2006. (First Step Nonfiction Ser.). (Illus.). 8p. (J). pap. (978-0-8225-5662-6(6) , Lerner Pubns.) Lerner Publishing Group.

—Under the Ground. 2006. (First Step Nonfiction Ser.). (Illus.). 8p. (J). pap. (978-0-8225-5661-9(8) , Lerner Pubns.) Lerner Publishing Group.

Boring, Mel. Rabbits, Squirrels & Chipmunks. Garrow, Linda, illus. 2004. (Take-Along Guide Ser.). 48p. (J). (gr. 2-5). pap. 7.95 (978-1-55971-579-9(0) , NorthWord Bks. for Young Readers) T&N Children's Publishing.

Boring, Mel, et al. More Fun with Nature. Garrow, Linda & McGee, John F., illus. 2004. (Big Books Ser.). 224p. (J). (gr. 2-5). ring bd. 16.95 (978-1-55971-795-3(5) , NorthWord Bks. for Young Readers) T&N Children's Publishing.

Brainy Baby Animals. 2004. (978-1-59394-234-2(6)) Bendon Publishing International.

Bramwell, Martyn J. World Wildlife: The Complete Guide to the Animals of Our World. 1999. (J). (978-1-84100-263-7(1)) Quadrillion Publishing.

Bredeson, Carmen. Boa Constrictors up Close. 2006. (Zoom in on Animals! Ser.). (Illus.). 24p. (J). lib. bdg. 21.26 (978-0-7660-2498-4(9) , Enslow Elementary) Enslow Pubs., Inc.

Brett, Jane. Animal Noises in the Jungle. 1999. (Illus.). 10p. (J). 2.95 (978-1-57717-097-6(0)) New Line Bks.

—Animal Noises on the Farm. 1999. (Illus.). 10p. (J). 2.95 (978-1-57717-096-9(2)) New Line Bks.

Brett, Jessica. Animals on the Go. Cowdrey, Richard, illus. 2003. 18p. (J). (ps-3). lib. bdg. 11.80 (978-0-613-63248-5(6)) Tandem Library Bks.

—Animals on the Go. 2000. (Green Light Readers Ser.). (Illus.). (J). (978-0-606-18167-9(9)) Tandem Library Bks.

—Animals on the Go. Cowdrey, Richard, illus. 2003. (Green Light Readers Level 2 Ser.). 24p. (J). 11.95 (978-0-15-204867-9(7)); pap. 3.95 (978-0-15-204827-3(8)) Harcourt Children's Bks. (Green Light Readers).

Brian Wildsmith's Box of Books. 2004. (Illus.). (J). 24.95 (978-1-59572-016-0(2)) Star Bright Bks., Inc.

Bright & Beautiful. (J). (gr. 6). 43.50 (978-0-673-72659-9(2) , Scott Foresman) Addison Wesley Schl.

Bright, Michael, et al. Nature's Predators. 2003. (Illustrated Encyclopedia Ser.). (Illus.). 264p. pap. 19.99 (978-0-7548-1249-4(9)) Anness Publishing GBR. *Dist:* National Bk. Network.

Brim, Warren & Eglitis, Anna. Creatures of the Rainforest: Two Artists Explore Djabugay Country. Brim, Warren & Eglitis, Anna, illus. 2005. (Illus.). 60p. (J). 24.50 (978-1-875641-99-4(8)) Magabala Bks. AUS. *Dist:* International Specialized Bk. Services.

Brischke, D. Wake Up Zoo. 2005. 28p. (J). pap. (978-0-9752878-9-7(3)) Dream-Catcher Pubns.

Brocklehurst, Ruth. Animal Sticker Atlas. Turnbull, Stephanie, ed. 2004. (Sticker Atlas Ser.). (Illus.). 24p. (J). pap. 8.95 (978-0-7945-0670-4(4) , Usborne) EDC Publishing.

—1001 Animals to Spot. 2004. (1001 Things to Spot Ser.). (SPA., Illus.). 32p. (J). lib. bdg. 14.95 (978-1-58086-424-4(4)); pap. 6.95 (978-0-7945-0149-5(4) , Usborne) EDC Publishing.

Brown, Jonatha A. Animal Tails. 2006. (Illus.). 24p. (J). pap. (978-0-8368-6868-5(4)); lib. bdg. (978-0-8368-6863-0(3)) Stevens, Gareth Inc.

Browne, Philippa-Alys. "Bushbaby blinks" (African Animals ABC) (Illus.). 14.99 (978-1-84148-756-4(2)) Barefoot Bks., Inc.

—"Giraffe dozes" (African Animals ABC) (Illus.). 14.99 (978-1-84148-758-8(9)) Barefoot Bks., Inc.

—"Hippo sleeps" (African Animals ABC) (Illus.). 14.99 (978-1-84148-754-0(6)) Barefoot Bks., Inc.

Browne, Sylvia & Dufresne, Chris. Animals on the Other Side. McElwee, Jo, illus. l.t. ed. 2005. 32p. (J). 16.95 (978-0-9717843-4-5(5)) Angel Bea Publishing.

Brunelle, Lynn. My Blue Zoo. Shorten, Chris, photos by. 1999. (Gymboree Book Ser.). (Illus.). 20p. (J). reprint ed. 4.95 (978-1-892374-13-4(7)) Weldon Owen, Inc.

Bullard, Lisa. Animal Opposites. 2005. (Illus.). (J). (gr. k-1). lib. bdg. 135.60 (978-0-7368-4409-3(0)) Capstone Pr., Inc.

—Fast & Slow: An Animal Opposites Books. Saunders-Smith, Gail, ed. 2005. (Illus.). 32p. (J). (ps-7). 22.60 (978-0-7368-4274-7(8)) Capstone Pr., Inc.

—Long & Short: An Animal Opposites Book. Saunders-Smith, Gail, ed. 2005. (Illus.). 32p. (J). (ps-7). 22.60 (978-0-7368-4275-4(6)) Capstone Pr., Inc.

—Loud & Quiet: An Animal Opposites Book. Saunders-Smith, Gail, ed. 2005. (A+ Books). (Illus.). 32p. (J). (ps-7). lib. bdg. 22.60 (978-0-7368-4276-1(4)) Capstone Pr., Inc.

Bulloch, Ivan & James, Diane. Brinca y Salta! 2004. (Me Toca a Mi Ser.).Tr. of Let's Hop & Skip!. (SPA., Illus.). 12p. (J). (ps-k). bds. 6.95 (978-1-58728-496-0(0) , Two Can Publishing) T&N Children's Publishing.

—Las Cosas Que Mas Nos Gustan! 2004. (Me Toca a Mi Ser.). (SPA., Illus.). 12p. (J). (ps-k). bds. 6.95 (978-1-58728-499-1(5) , Two Can Publishing) T&N Children's Publishing.

—Es Hora de Despertar! 2004. (Me Toca a Mi Ser.). (SPA., Illus.). 12p. (J). (ps-k). bds. 6.95 (978-1-58728-497-7(9) , Two Can Publishing) T&N Children's Publishing.

—Suena Sabroso! 2004. (Me Toca a Mi Ser.). (SPA., Illus.). 12p. (J). (ps-k). bds. 6.95 (978-1-58728-498-4(7) , Two Can Publishing) T&N Children's Publishing.

—Tomate, Lechuga, Cuchara y Tenedor. 2004. (Me Toca a Mi Ser.). (SPA., Illus.). 12p. (J). (ps-k). bds. 6.95 (978-1-58728-492-2(8) , Two Can Publishing) T&N Children's Publishing.

Burgess, Thornton W. The Burgess Animal Book for Children. (J). 28.95 (978-0-8488-0716-0(2)) Amereon LTD.

—The Burgess Animal Book for Children. 2002. (Illus.). 384p. (YA). pap. (978-1-931839-59-4(X)) Ross & Perry, Inc.

—Burgess Animal Book for Children. 2005. 304p. pap. 14.95 (978-1-59540-696-5(4) , 1st World Library - Literary Society) 1st World Publishing, Inc.

Burnie, David. The Concise Animal Encyclopedia. 2003. (Concise Encyclopedias Ser.). (Illus.). 320p. (J). (gr. 4-8). bds. 14.95 (978-0-7534-5590-6(0) , Kingfisher) Houghton Mifflin Co. Trade & Reference Div.

Burns, Diane L. Horsing Around: Jokes to Make Ewe Smile. Gable, Brian, illus. 2005. (Make Me Laugh! Ser.). 32p. (J). (gr. k-3). lib. bdg. 19.93 (978-1-57505-662-3(3)) Lerner Publishing Group.

Burr, Debora. In the Wild. (Animal Families Board Bks.). (Illus.). (J). bds. 4.00 net. (978-1-56021-389-5(2)) W.J. Fantasy, Inc.

Burton, Margie, et al. Animal Coverings. Evento, Susan, ed. 1998. (Early Connections Ser.). 16p. (J). (gr. k-2). pap. 4.25 (978-1-892393-65-4(4)) Benchmark Education Co.

Butler, John. Whose Nose & Toes? 2004. (Illus.). 20p. (J). (ps-ps). 10.99 (978-0-670-05904-1(8) , Viking Juvenile) Penguin Group (USA) Inc.

Butterfield, Moira. Animals in Cold Places. 1999. (Looking at...Ser.). (Illus.). 32p. (J). (gr. k-3). pap. 5.95 (978-0-7398-0714-9(5)) Steck-Vaughn.

—Animals in Hot Places. 1999. (Looking at...Ser.). (Illus.). 32p. (J). (gr. 1-4). lib. bdg. 24.26 (978-0-7398-0112-3(0)) Raintree.

—Animals in Hot Places. 1999. (Looking at...Ser.). (Illus.). 32p. (J). (gr. k-3). pap. 5.95 (978-0-7398-0715-6(3)) Steck-Vaughn.

—Animals on Plains & Prairies. 1999. (Looking at...Ser.). (Illus.). 32p. (J). (gr. 1-4). lib. bdg. 24.26 (978-0-7398-0109-3(0)) Raintree.

—Looking At..., 6 bks., Set. Incl. Animals in Cold Places. (Illus.). lib. bdg. 24.26 (978-0-7398-0111-6(2)); Animals in Hot Places. (Illus.). lib. bdg. 24.26 (978-0-7398-0112-3(0)); Animals in Rivers & Lakes. (Illus.). lib. bdg. 24.26 (978-0-7398-0108-6(2)); Animals in the Oceans. lib. bdg. 24.26 (978-0-7398-0107-9(4)); Animals in Trees. (Illus.). lib. bdg. 24.26 (978-0-7398-0110-9(4)); Animals on Plains & Prairies. (Illus.). lib. bdg. 24.26 (978-0-7398-0109-3(0)); 32p. (J). (gr. 1-4). (Looking at...Ser.). (Illus.). 1999. Set lib. bdg. 145.56 (978-0-7398-0113-0(9)) Raintree.

—Wild Animals. 2006. (Illus.). 24p. (YA). (gr. 1 up). lib. bdg. 22.80 (978-1-931983-60-0(7)) Chrysalis Education.

Butz, Christopher. Tundra Animals. 2002. (Animals of the Biomes Ser.). (Illus.). 48p. (J). lib. bdg. 25.70 (978-0-7398-5691-8(X)) Raintree.

—Tundra Animals. 2002. (Animals of the Biomes Ser.). (Illus.). 48p. (J). pap. (978-0-7398-6410-4(6)) Steck-Vaughn.

Cabat, Erni. Erni Cabat's Magical ABC: Animals Around the Farm. Date not set. (Illus.). 64p. (Orig.). (J). (ps-2). 23.00 (978-0-943173-73-3(6)) Cabat Studio Pubns.

Campbell, Rod. Wild Animals. (Pop-Up Paperback Bk.). (Illus.). 16p. (J). (ps-k). pap. (978-1-56021-356-7(6) , 207) W.J. Fantasy, Inc.

Campeones Del Mundo Animal Series, 6 bks., Set. 2003. (Campeones Del Mundo Animal Ser.). (SPA & ENG., Illus.). (J). lib. bdg. 103.50 (978-0-8239-6912-8(6) , Buenas Letra) Rosen Publishing Group, Inc., The.

Capogna, Vera Vullo. Did You Ever Wonder about Things You Find in the Woods? 2000. (Did You Ever Wonder? Ser.). (Illus.). 32p. (J). (gr. k-3). lib. bdg. 22.79 (978-0-7614-0852-9(5) , Benchmark Bks.) Cavendish, Marshall Corp.

—Did You Ever Wonder about Things You Find in Your Backyard? 1999. (Did You Ever Wonder? Ser.). (Illus.). 32p. (J). (gr. k-3). lib. bdg. 22.79 (978-0-7614-0855-0(X) , Benchmark Bks.) Cavendish, Marshall Corp.

Carle, Eric. Does a Kangaroo Have a Mother, Too? 2008. (SPA., Illus.). 32p. (J). 6.99 ***(978-0-06-001111-6(4)*** , Rayo) HarperCollins Pubs.

—Does a Kangaroo Have a Mother, Too? Carle, Eric, illus. (Illus.). (J). (ps-1). 2002. 28p. bds. 7.99 (978-0-694-01456-9(7) , Harper Festival); 2000. 32p. 16.99 (978-0-06-028768-9(3)) HarperCollins Pubs.

—Does a Kangaroo Have a Mother, Too? 2005. (Illus.). 32p. (J). (ps-1). reprint ed. pap. 6.99 (978-0-06-443642-7(X)) HarperCollins Pubs.

—My Very First Book of Animal Sounds. Carle, Eric, illus. 2007. 20p. (J). (ps-k). bds. 5.99 (978-0-399-24648-7(7) , Philomel) Penguin Group (USA) Inc.

Carlson, Melody. God Made Them All. Banek, Yvette Santiago, illus. 2000. (God Is Here Ser.). 20p. (ps-k). 9.99 (978-1-58134-159-1(8) , Crossway Bibles) Crossway Bks.

Carmi, Rebecca. Expedition down Under. 2002. (Magic School Bus Chapter Bks.: No. 10). (Illus.). 96p. (J). pap. 4.99 (978-0-439-20424-8(0) , Scholastic Paperbacks) Scholastic, Inc.

—Expedition down Under. 2001. (gr. 3-6). lib. bdg. 11.80 (978-0-613-50686-1(3)) Tandem Library Bks.

Carroll, Michael W., et al, illus. Animals of the World. 2005. (J). 7.99 (978-0-310-70582-6(7)) Zonderkidz.

Carroll, Michael W., et al. Fish, Bugs & Birds, Vol. 4. 2005. (God's Creation Ser.). 40p. (J). 7.99 (978-0-310-70581-9(9)) Zonderkidz.

Carson, Mary Kay. The Creepist, Scariest, Weirdest Creatures Ever! 2002. (Illus.). 60p. (J). (978-1-58865-080-1(4)) Kidsbooks, Inc.

Cartwright, Stephen. Animal Noises. 2004. (Usborne Farmyard Tales Ser.). (Illus.). 10p. (J). (ps-k). 4.99 (978-0-7460-4104-8(7)) EDC Publishing.

—Noisy Animals Board Bk. Cartwright, Stephen, illus. 2007. 12p. (J). bds. 18.99 (978-0-7945-1551-5(7) , Usborne) EDC Publishing.

Casado, Dami & Casado, Alicia. Los Ruidos Del Bosque. 2005. (SPA.). 12p. 7.99 (978-84-272-8292-6(3)) Molino, Editorial ESP. *Dist:* Santillana USA Publishing Co., Inc.

—Ruidos de la Selva. 2005. (SPA.). 12p. 7.99 (978-84-272-8294-0(X)) Molino, Editorial ESP. *Dist:* Santillana USA Publishing Co., Inc.

Cassie, Brian. Say It Again. Mooney, David A., illus. 2000. 32p. (J). (ps-3). 16.95 (978-0-88106-341-7(X)); pap. 6.95 (978-0-88106-342-4(8)) Charlesbridge Publishing, Inc.

—Say It Again. 2000. (978-0-606-18029-0(X)); lib. bdg. 15.25 (978-0-613-28310-6(4)) Tandem Library Bks.

Casterline, L. C. Natural-Born Killers: A Chapter Book. 2004. (True Tales Ser.). (Illus.). 48p. (J). 22.50 (978-0-516-23725-1(X) , Children's Pr.) Scholastic Library Publishing.

Casterline, Linda. Natural-Born Killers: A Chapter Book. 2005. (True Tales Ser.). (Illus.). 48p. (J). (gr. 2-4). pap. 4.95 (978-0-516-24687-1(9) , Children's Pr.) Scholastic Library Publishing.

—Rare Animals. 2004. (True Tales Ser.). (J). (gr. 2-4). pap. 4.95 (978-0-516-24607-9(0) , Children's Pr.) Scholastic Library Publishing.

Cerfolli, Fulvio. Adapting to the Environment. Stalio, Ivan, illus. 1999. (Everyday Life of Animals Ser.). 64p. (J). (gr. 4-6). 19.98 (978-0-8172-4196-4(5)) Raintree.

—The Animal Atlas. Cantucci, Alessandro & Morandi, Andrea, illus. 1998. (Everyday Life of Animals Ser.). 64p. (J). 19.99 (978-0-7451-5296-7(1) , Cherrytree Books) Evans Publishing Group GBR. *Dist:* Independent Pubs. Group.

Chaffey, Samantha, illus. Who Lives Here? 2006. 8p. (J). bds. 8.99 (978-0-7641-5997-8(6)) Barron's Educational Series, Inc.

Chamberlin-Calamar, Pat. Alaska's 12 Days of Summer. Cartwright, Shannon, illus. 2003. (PAWS IV Ser.). 32p. (J). pap. 9.95 (978-1-57061-341-8(9)); 16.95 (978-1-57061-340-1(0)) Sasquatch Bks.

—Alaska's 12 Days of Summer. 2003. (gr. k-3). lib. bdg. 18.75 (978-0-613-79151-9(7)) Tandem Library Bks.

Chapman, Cindy. Baby Animals. 2003. (Compass Point Phonics Readers Ser.). (Illus.). 16p. (J). (gr. 1 up). 13.26 (978-0-7565-0504-2(6)) Compass Point Bks.

—On a Farm. 2003. (Compass Point Phonics Readers Ser.). (Illus.). 16p. (J). (gr. 1 up). 13.26 (978-0-7565-0516-5(X)) Compass Point Bks.

Chatterjee, Debjani, et al. Tiger Time. 2007. (I-read Ser.). (Illus.). 40p. pap. ***(978-0-521-70478-6(2))*** Cambridge Univ. Pr.

Chatterton, Martin. Nutty World of Animals. (Illus.). 96p. (J). 7.95 (978-0-14-038988-3(1)) Penguin Bks., Ltd. GBR. *Dist:* Trafalgar Square Publishing.

Chen, Tony, et al, illus. Animals Showing Off. 2004. 14p. (J). (gr. k-4). reprint ed. 16.00 (978-0-7567-7640-4(6)) DIANE Publishing Co.

Cheney, Martha C. Animals Workbook for Preschoolers. Kaminski, Karol, illus. 1999. (Gifted & Talented Ser.). 48p. (J). (ps-k). pap., wbk. ed. 5.95 (978-0-7373-0137-3(6)) Lowell Hse.

Cherry Lake Publishing, compiled by. Road to Recovery. 2008. lib. bdg. ***(978-1-60279-106-0(6))*** Cherry Lake Publishing.

Children's Nature Library: Animals, Animals, Animals. (Illus.). (J). (gr. k-4). lib. bdg. 104.65 (978-1-56674-930-5(1)) Forest Hse. Publishing Co., Inc.

Chinery, Michael. Amazing Animals. 2004. (Wild Animal Planet Ser.). (Illus.). 64p. 14.99 (978-0-7548-1254-8(5)) Anness Publishing GBR. *Dist:* National Bk. Network.

—Animal Planet: Illustrated Wildlife Encyclopedia. 2004. (Illustrated Wildlife Encyclopedia Ser.). (Illus.). 256p. pap. 24.99 (978-1-84215-850-0(3) , Southwater) Anness Publishing GBR. *Dist:* National Bk. Network.

—Animales Salvajes. (Enciclopedias Everest Internacional Ser.). (SPA., Illus.). 320p. (J). (gr. 3-5). (978-84-241-9399-7(7) , EV1502) Everest de Ediciones y Distribucion, S.L. ESP. *Dist:* Lectorum Pubns., Inc.

—How Animals Work. 2003. (Wild Animal Planet Ser.). (Illus.). 64p. (gr. 3-7). 14.99 (978-0-7548-1155-8(7)) Anness Publishing GBR. *Dist:* National Bk. Network.

—Hunt for Food, 90 vols. 2005. (Illus.). 64p. pap. 8.99 (978-1-84476-060-2(X) , Southwater) Anness Publishing GBR. *Dist:* National Bk. Network.

—Life in the Wild: Animal Survival. 2005. (Illus.). 512p. 45.00 (978-0-7548-1475-7(0) , Lorenz Bks.) Anness Publishing GBR. *Dist:* National Bk. Network.

—Living in the Wild. 2003. (Illustrated Wildlife Encyclopedia... Ser.). (Illus.). 256p. pap. 24.99 (978-1-84215-725-1(6)) Anness Publishing, Inc.

—Poisoners & Pretenders. 2000. (Secrets of the Rainforest Ser.). (Illus.). 32p. (J). (gr. 3-4). pap. (978-0-7787-0229-0(4)); lib. bdg. (978-0-7787-0219-1(7)) Crabtree Publishing Co.

—Poisoners & Pretenders. 2000. (gr. 3-6). lib. bdg. 16.40 (978-0-613-28024-2(5)) Tandem Library Bks.

Christie, Peter. Naturally Wild Musicians: The Wondrous World of Animal Song. 2007. (Illus.). 56p. (J). (gr. 3-6). pap. 8.95 ***(978-1-55451-097-9(X)***); lib. bdg. 19.95 ***(978-1-55451-098-6(8))*** Annick Pr., Ltd. CAN. *Dist:* Firefly Bks., Ltd.

Christopher, Garrett. Look at These Animals: A Content Area Reader-science. 2005. (Sadlier Phonics Reading Program). (Illus.). 16p. (YA). (ps-2). 25.20 (978-0-8215-7812-4(X)) Sadlier, William H. Inc.

Ciovacco, Justine. Meerkats. 2007. (J). ***(978-1-59939-129-8(5)*** , Reader's Digest Young Families, Inc.) Reader's Digest Children's Publishing, Inc.

Clarke, Ginjer L. Fake Out! Animals That Play Tricks. Mueller, Pete, illus. 2007. (All Aboard Science Reader Ser.). 48p. (J). (gr. 1-3). pap. 3.99 ***(978-0-448-44656-1(1)*** , Grosset & Dunlap) Penguin Group (USA) Inc.

Clarke, Ginjer L. Freak Out! Animals Beyond Your Wildest Imagination All Aboard Science Reader Station Stop 2. Mueller, Peter, illus. 2006. (All Aboard Science Reader Ser.). 48p. (J). (gr. 1-3). pap. 3.99 (978-0-448-44308-9(2) , Grosset & Dunlap) Penguin Group (USA) Inc.

Clarke, Penny. Big Cats. Bergin, Mark, illus. 2002. (Scary Creatures Ser.). (J). (gr. 2-4). pap. 6.95 (978-0-531-14849-5(1)); 32p. pap. 22.50 (978-0-531-14668-2(5)) Scholastic Library Publishing. (Watts, Franklin).

—Scary Creatures of the Arctic! (Scary Creatures Ser.). 32p. (J). 2008. pap. 8.95 ***(978-0-531-21008-6(1)*** , Watts, Franklin); 2007. spiral bd. 26.00 ***(978-0-531-20449-8(9)*** , Children's Pr.) Scholastic Library Publishing.

—Scary Creatures of the Rain Forest! (Scary Creatures Ser.). 32p. (J). 2008. pap. 8.95 ***(978-0-531-21010-9(3)*** , Watts, Franklin); 2007. spiral bd. 26.00 ***(978-0-531-20544-0(4)*** , Children's Pr.) Scholastic Library Publishing.

Clarke, Phillip & Khan, Sarah. Facts & Records - Internet Linked: Combined Volume. 2004. (Facts & Lists Internet-Linked Ser.). 256p. (J). pap. 12.95 (978-0-7945-0679-7(8) , Usborne) EDC Publishing.

Claybourne, Anna. Can You Tell a Skink from a Salamander? 2005. (Illus.). 32p. (J). (978-1-4109-1967-0(6)); (978-1-4109-1936-6(6)) Steck-Vaughn.

Clyne, Margaret. Animals Together. 2001. (gr. k-3). lib. bdg. 11.65 (978-0-613-33327-6(5)) Tandem Library Bks.

Coldiron, Deborah. Coral. 2007. (Underwater World Ser.). (Illus.). 32p. (J). (gr. k-4). lib. bdg. 24.21 ***(978-1-59928-811-6(7)*** , Buddy Bks.) ABDO Publishing Co.

Cole & Leeson. El Jaguar y el Leopardo. 2002. (Gatos Salvajes del Mundo Serie).Tr. of Wild Cats Of The World: The Jaguar And The Leopard. (SPA.). 24p. (J). (gr. 3-5). 24.94 (978-1-4103-0005-8(6) , Blackbirch Pr., Inc.) Thomson Gale.

Cole, Joanna. Gets Cold Feet: A Book about Warm- And Cold-Blooded Animals. 2002. (Magic School Bus Ser.). (J). 11.45 (978-0-7587-6955-8(5)) Book Wholesalers, Inc.

—The Magic School Bus Explores the World of Animals. 2000. (Magic School Bus Ser.). (J). (gr. 1-4). (978-0-606-20063-9(0)) Tandem Library Bks.

Cole, Joanna & West, Tracey. Gets Cold Feet: A Book about Warm- And Cold-Blooded Animals. 1998. (Magic School Bus Ser.). (Illus.). (J). (gr. 1-4). (978-0-606-13589-4(8)) Tandem Library Bks.

Cole, Joanna & White, Nancy. Explores the World of Animals. Spiers, John, illus. 2001. (Magic School Bus Ser.). 32p. (J). (gr. 5). pap. 5.99 (978-0-439-22678-3(3)) Scholastic, Inc.

Colella, O. Animales de la Selva (Jungle Animals) 2005. (Collection Abre Tus Ojos, Collection Eye Openers Ser.). (SPA.). (J). (gr. k-2). 6.95 (978-950-11-0900-9(3)) Sigmar ARG. *Dist:* AIMS International Bks., Inc., Iaconi, Mariuccia Bk. Imports.

Collard, Sneed B., III. Animal Dazzlers: The Role of Brilliant Colors in Nature. 1999. (First Bks.). (Illus.). 64p. (J). (gr. 5-7). pap. 6.95 (978-0-531-15918-7(3) , Watts, Franklin) Scholastic Library Publishing.

—In the Wild. 2005. (Science Adventures Ser.). (Illus.). 44p. (J). (gr. 4-7). lib. bdg. 28.50 (978-0-7614-1955-6(1) , Benchmark Bks.) Cavendish, Marshall Corp.

—One Night in the Coral Sea. Brickman, Robin, illus. 2005. 32p. (J). (ps-7). 15.95 (978-1-57091-389-1(7)) Charlesbridge Publishing, Inc.

—Smart Survivors. 2004. (It's Nature! Ser.). (Illus.). 32p. (J). (gr. 3-6). pap. 7.95 (978-1-55971-750-2(5) , Creative Publishing International) Quayside.

Collard, Sneed B. Wings. Brickman, Robin, illus. 2008. (J). ***(978-1-57091-611-3(X))*** Charlesbridge Publishing, Inc.

Communicating with Animals. 2005. (Book Treks Ser.). (J). 37.95 (978-0-7652-3247-2(2)) Celebration Pr.

¿Como Hablan los Animales? (Coleccion Primeros Pasos en la Ciencia). (SPA., Illus.). (J). (gr. 1-3). pap. (978-950-724-220-5(1) , LMA8224) Lumen ARG. *Dist:* Lectorum Pubns., Inc.

Complete Set. (Animals & Their Young Ser.). (gr. 1-3). 279.02 (978-0-7565-0214-0(4)); (gr. 2-4). 271.20 (978-0-7565-0708-4(1)) Compass Point Bks.

Cooper, Jason. Antlers & Horns. 2007. (Let's Look at Animals Ser.). (Illus.). 24p. (J). (gr. k-2). lib. bdg. 21.35 (978-1-60044-168-4(8)) Rourke Publishing, LLC.

—Hooves & Claws. 2007. (Let's Look at Animals Ser.). (Illus.). 24p. (J). (gr. k-2). lib. bdg. 21.35 (978-1-60044-173-8(4)) Rourke Publishing, LLC.

Cooper, Wade & Page, Nick. Polar Animals. 2007. (Scholastic Reader Level 1 Ser.). 32p. (J). pap. 3.99 ***(978-0-545-00718-4(6)*** , Cartwheel Bks.) Scholastic, Inc.

Corbett, Pie. Animals. 2005. (Illus.). 24p. (J). (gr. 1 up). lib. bdg. 22.80 (978-1-59389-206-7(3)) Chrysalis Education.

Corwin, Jeff. Into Wild Indonesia. 2004. (Jeff Corwin Experience Ser.). (Illus.). 48p. (J). 24.95 (978-1-4103-0243-4(1) , Blackbirch Pr., Inc.) Thomson Gale.

Corwin, Jeff & Woodward, John. Extreme Encounters. 2004. (Jeff Corwin Experience Ser.). (Illus.). 48p. (J). 11.20 (978-1-4103-0229-8(6)); (gr. 4-7). 24.95 (978-1-4103-0228-1(8)) Thomson Gale. (Blackbirch Pr., Inc.).

Costain, Meredith. City Animals. 2000. (gr. k-3). lib. bdg. 11.80 (978-0-613-30321-7(0)) Tandem Library Bks.

—Desert Life. 2000. (gr. k-3). lib. bdg. 11.80 (978-0-613-30354-5(7)) Tandem Library Bks.

—Rainforests. 2000. (gr. k-3). lib. bdg. 11.80 (978-0-613-30693-5(7)) Tandem Library Bks.

Counting with Animals. 2007. (Illus.). 10p. bds. 14.95 ***(978-1-59125-794-3(8)*** , Penton Kids) Penton Overseas, Inc.

Coupe, Robert. Dangerous Animals. 2002. (Junior Adventure Ser.). (Illus.). 32p. (J). (gr. 3 up). lib. bdg. (978-1-59084-186-0(7)) Mason Crest Pubs.

—Incredible Creatures. 2002. (Junior Adventure Ser.). (Illus.). 32p. (J). (gr. 3 up). lib. bdg. (978-1-59084-165-5(4)) Mason Crest Pubs.

—Incredible Creatures. 1999. (Explorers Ser.). (Illus.). 32p. (J). (978-0-7699-0466-5(1)) Shortland Pubns. (U. S. A.) Inc.

Cox, Rosamund Kidman. Wild Animals. 2004. (Spotter's Guides). (Illus.). 64p. (J). pap. 5.95 (978-0-7945-0037-5(4) , Usborne) EDC Publishing.

—Wild Animals. 2001. (gr. k-3). lib. bdg. 14.10 (978-0-613-90682-1(9)) Tandem Library Bks.

Creative Publishing international Editors. Amazing Animals. 2004. (It's Nature! Ser.). (Illus.). 160p. (YA). (gr. 3-6). ring bd. 16.95 (978-1-55971-752-6(1) , NorthWord Bks. for Young Readers) T&N Children's Publishing.

Creative Publishing international Editors, et al. Prairie Animals. 2004. (Our Wild World Ser.). (Illus.). 192p. (J). (gr. 2-5). ring bd. 16.95 (978-1-55971-895-0(1) , NorthWord Bks. for Young Readers) T&N Children's Publishing.

Creature's Corner. (Super Sticker Book Ser.). (Illus.). 64p. (J). pap. (978-2-7643-0129-6(4)) Phidal Publishing, Inc./Editions Phidal, Inc.

Creatures of the Night: Individual Title Six-Packs. (Rigby Focus Ser.). 24p. (gr. 2 up). 28.00 (978-0-7578-5353-1(6)); 30.00 (978-0-7578-5583-2(0)) Rigby Education.

Criaturas Increibles, 6 vols. (Explorers. Exploradores Nonfiction Sets Ser.). (SPA.). 32p. (gr. 3-6). 44.95 (978-0-7699-0625-6(7)) Shortland Pubns. (U. S. A.) Inc.

Cricket Magazine Group. Oink-Oink & Other Animal Sounds. Conteh-Morgan, Jane, illus. 2007. 20p. (J). bds. 7.95 (978-0-8126-7934-2(2)) Cricket Bks.

Critter Chronicles. 2007. 512.40 (978-1-59928-428-6(6) , SandCastle) ABDO Publishing Co.

Critters. 2007. (J). lib. bdg. 9.95 ***(978-0-9768706-6-1(5))*** Learning Props.

Critters & Bugs of the Tropical Rainforest. 2003. (J). spiral bd. 12.95 (978-1-931334-33-4(1)) Pieces of Learning.

Crozon, Alain & Lanchais, Aurelie. What Am I? 1998. (Illus.). 14p. (J). (ps). 7.95 (978-0-8118-2102-5(1)) Chronicle Bks. LLC.

—Who Am I? 1998. (Illus.). 14p. (J). (ps). 7.95 (978-0-8118-2103-2(X)) Chronicle Bks. LLC.

Currie-McGhee, L. K. Animal Rights. 2004. (Lucent Overview Ser.). (Illus.). 112p. (J). (gr. 7-10). 29.95 (978-1-56006-548-7(6) , Lucent Bks.) Thomson Gale.

Curry, Don L. What Hatches? 2000. (Yellow Umbrella Books). (Illus.). 16p. (J). (gr. 1). lib. bdg. 14.60 (978-0-7368-0721-0(7) , Pebble Bks.) Capstone Pr., Inc.

Curry, Vickie. Best Friends on the Mccurry Farm: Buster & Gomez. 2004. 29p. pap. 14.95 (978-1-4137-1827-0(2)) PublishAmerica, Inc.

Czajkowski, Alexandre C. Amazing Creatures. 2000. (Creative Discoveries Ser.). Orig. Title: The Animal World. (Illus.). 80p. (J). (gr. 4 up). lib. bdg. 25.30 (978-0-88682-945-2(3) , Creative Education) Creative Co., The.

Dahl, Michael. Animals All Around, 12 bks. Incl. Do Bears Buzz? A Book about Animal Noise. D'Antonio, Sandra, illus. (C). 22.60 (978-1-4048-0100-4(6)); Do Bees Make Butter? A Book about the Things Animals Make. Ouren, Todd, illus. (J). 22.60 (978-1-4048-0288-9(6)); Do Cows Eat Cake? A Book about What Animals Eat. D'Antonio, Sandra, illus. (C). 22.60 (978-1-4048-0101-1(4)); Do Dogs Make Dessert? A Book about How Animals Help Humans. Yesh, Jeff, illus. (J). 22.60 (978-1-4048-0289-6(4)); Do Ducks Live in the Desert? A Book about Where Animals Live. Haberstroh, Anne, illus. (J). 22.60 (978-1-4048-0290-2(8) , 1229500); Do Frogs Have Fur? A Book about Animal Coats & Coverings. Yesh, Jeff, illus. (J). 22.60 (978-1-4048-0292-6(4)); Do Goldfish Gallop? A Book about Animal Movement. D'Antonio, Sandra, illus. (C). 22.60 (978-1-4048-0105-9(7)); Do Parrots Have Pillows? A Book about Where Animals Sleep. D'Antonio, Sandra, illus. (C). 22.60 (978-1-4048-0104-2(9)); Do Penguins Have Puppies? A Book about Animal Babies. D'Antonio, Sandra, illus. (C). 22.60 (978-1-4048-0102-8(2)); Do Salamanders Spit? A Book about How Animals Protect Themselves. Ayers, Franklin, illus. (J). 22.60 (978-1-4048-0291-9(6) , 1229502); Do Squirrels Swarm? A Book about Animal Groups. Ayers, Franklin, illus. (J). 22.60 (978-1-4048-0287-2(8) , 1229503); Do Whales Have Wings? A Book about Animal Bodies. D'Antonio, Sandra, illus. (C). 22.60 (978-1-4048-0103-5(0)); 24p. (gr. k-2). 2004. 2003. 271.20 (978-1-4048-0286-5(X)) Picture Window Bks.

—Animals All Around: Do Bears Buzz?; Do Cows Eat Cake?; Do Goldfish Gallop?; Do Parrots Have Pillows; Do Penguins Have Puppies?; Do Whales Have Wings?, 6 bks. D'Antonio, Sandra, illus. 2003. (J). (ps-2). lib. bdg. 127.56 (978-1-4048-0099-1(9)) Picture Window Bks.

—Deep, Deeper, Deepest: Animals That Go to Great Depths. Jensen, Brian, illus. 2005. (Animal Extremes Ser.). 24p. (J). (ps). lib. bdg. 22.60 (978-1-4048-1015-0(3)) Picture Window Bks.

—Do Cows Eat Cake? A Book about What Animals Eat. D'Antonio, Sandra, illus. 2004. (Animals All Around Ser.). 24p. (C). (gr. k-2). 22.60 (978-1-4048-0101-1(4)) Picture Window Bks.

—Do Dogs Make Dessert? A Book about How Animals Help Humans. Yesh, Jeff, illus. 2004. (Animals All Around Ser.). 24p. (J). (gr. k-2). 22.60 (978-1-4048-0289-6(4)) Picture Window Bks.

—Do Ducks Live in the Desert? A Book about Where Animals Live. Haberstroh, Anne, illus. 2004. (Animals All Around Ser.). 24p. (J). (gr. k-2). 22.60 (978-1-4048-0290-2(8) , 1229500) Picture Window Bks.

—Do Goldfish Gallop? A Book about Animal Movement. D'Antonio, Sandra, illus. 2004. (Animals All Around Ser.). 24p. (C). (gr. k-2). 22.60 (978-1-4048-0105-9(7)) Picture Window Bks.

—Do Salamanders Spit? A Book about How Animals Protect Themselves. Ayers, Franklin, illus. 2004. (Animals All Around Ser.). 24p. (J). (gr. k-2). 22.60 (978-1-4048-0291-9(6) , 1229502) Picture Window Bks.

—Fast, Faster, Fastest: Animals That Move at Great Speeds. Jensen, Brian, illus. 2005. (Animal Extremes Ser.). 24p. (J). (ps-7). lib. bdg. 22.60 (978-1-4048-1172-0(9)) Picture Window Bks.

—High, Higher, Highest: Animals That Go to Great Heights. Jensen, Brian, illus. 2005. (Animal Extremes Ser.). 24p. (J). (ps). lib. bdg. 22.60 (978-1-4048-1016-7(1)) Picture Window Bks.

—Old, Older, Oldest: Animals That Live Long Lives. Jensen, Brian, illus. 2005. (Animal Extremes Ser.). 24p. (J). (ps). lib. bdg. 22.60 (978-1-4048-1173-7(7)) Picture Window Bks.

Dalgleish, Sharon. Scaly Things. 2002. (Junior Adventure Ser.). (Illus.). 32p. (J). (gr. 3 up). lib. bdg. (978-1-59084-169-3(7)) Mason Crest Pubs.

Dalmatian Press Staff. Animals with Shaped Crayons: Book to Color Play Set. 2003. 64p. (J). pap. 4.99 (978-1-4037-0327-9(2)) Dalmatian Pr.

—Barnyard Friends: Little Pups. 2002. (Little Pups Board Bks.). (Illus.). 20p. (J). bds. 2.99 (978-1-57759-632-5(3)) Dalmatian Pr.

Dalmatian Press Staff. My Spanish Book of Animals: Mi libro de los animales en espanol e Ingles. rev. ed. 2007. 12p. 7.99 ***(978-1-4037-3054-1(7))*** Dalmatian Pr.

D'Amico, Fran Newman. Animal Dot to Dot. 2000. (Illus.). 32p. (J). pap. 2.95 (978-0-486-41312-9(8)) Dover Pubns., Inc.

Dangerous Animals, 4 bks. Incl. Black Widow Spiders. McAuliffe, Bill. lib. bdg. 21.26 (978-1-56065-619-7(0)); Killer Bees. Hines, Marcia. lib. bdg. 21.26 (978-1-56065-618-0(2)); Piranhas. McAuliffe, Emily. lib. bdg. 21.26 (978-1-56065-620-3(4)); Tarantulas. McAuliffe, Emily. lib. bdg. 21.26 (978-1-56065-621-0(2)); 48p. (J). (gr. 3-4). 1998. (Illus.). Set lib. bdg. 85.04 (978-0-7368-0459-2(5) , Capstone High-Interest Bks.) Capstone Pr., Inc.

Dangerous Animals: Level P, 6 vols., Vol. 3. (Explorers Ser.). 32p. (gr. 3-6). 44.95 (978-0-7699-0613-3(3)) Shortland Pubns. (U. S. A.) Inc.

D'Aulaire, Ingri & D'Aulaire, Edgar Parin. D'Aulaire's Book of Animals. 2007. (New York Review Children's Collection). (Illus.). 30p. (J). (gr. k-1). 16.95 (*978-1-59017-226-1(4) , NYR Children's Collection) New York Review of Bks., Inc., The.

Davidson, Susanna & Unwin, Mike. The Usborne World of Animals. Montgomery, Lee & Jackson, Ian, illus. 2005. 128p. (J). pap. (*978-0-439-86321-6(X)) Scholastic, Inc.

Davidson, Susanna & Unwin, Mike. World of Animals. 2005. 128p. (J). 19.95 (978-0-7945-0926-2(6) , Usborne) EDC Publishing.

Davies, Valerie. Amazing Animals. Tomblin, Gill, illus. 2006. (Wildlife!). 28p. (J). (gr. 3-8). 17.95 (978-0-7696-4822-4(3)) School Specialty Publishing.

—Killer Creatures. Tomblin, Gill, illus. 2006. (Wildfire!). 28p. (J). (gr. 3-8). 17.95 (978-0-7696-4825-5(8)) School Specialty Publishing.

Davis, Katie. Quien Salta? 2000. Tr. of Who Hops?. (SPA., Illus.). 76p. (J). 17.95 (978-84-261-3133-1(6)) Juventud, Editorial ESP. *Dist:* Distribooks, Inc., Lectorum Pubns., Inc.

Davis, Lee. Feeding Time. 2001. (gr. k-3). lib. bdg. 11.80 (978-0-613-35116-4(9)); (Illus.). (J). 10.75 (978-0-606-20657-0(4)) Tandem Library Bks.

—The Lifesize Animal Opposites Book. (Illus.). 32p. (J). pap. 16.95 (978-0-590-24372-8(1)) Scholastic, Inc.

Davis, Rebecca Fjelland. Counting down with Polar Animals. 2007. (Illus.). 32p. (J). 23.93 (978-0-7368-6374-2(5)) Capstone Pr., Inc.

A de Animales: Big Book. (Pebble Soup Exploraciones Ser.). (SPA.). 16p. (ps up). 31.00 (978-0-7578-1681-9(9)) Rigby Education.

A de Animales: Small Book. (Pebble Soup Exploraciones Ser.). (SPA.). 16p. (ps up). 5.00 (978-0-7578-1721-2(1)) Rigby Education.

de Lambilly-Bresson, Elisabeth. Animals in Polar Regions. 2007. (Animal Show & Tell Ser.). 16p. (J). (ps-2). lib. bdg. 17.27 (*978-0-8368-8203-2(2)) Stevens, Gareth Inc.

—Animals of the Mountains. 2007. (Animal Show & Tell Ser.). 16p. (J). (ps-2). lib. bdg. 17.27 (*978-0-8368-8207-0(5)) Stevens, Gareth Inc.

de Paola, Tomie. Fin M'Coul: The Giant of Knockmany Hill. (Ala Notable Book Ser.). (Illus.). 32p. (J). (gr. k-3). 6.95 (978-0-8234-0385-1(8)) Holiday Hse., Inc.

del Moral, Susana & Zaidi, Nadeem. Baby Einstein: Donde Viven? Baby Einstein: Animal Match, Spanish-Language Edition. 2006. (Illus.). 8p. (J). bds. 9.95 (*978-970-718-395-7(0) , Silver Dolphin en Español) Advanced Marketing, S. de R. L. de C. V. MEX. *Dist:* Perseus Distribution.

Dell, Pamela. How Animals Move. 2004. (Animal Behavior Ser.). (Illus.). 24p. (J). lib. bdg. 21.26 (978-0-7368-2628-0(9)) Capstone Pr., Inc.

Dena, Anael. My Animals. Eho, Jerome, illus. 2002. (Stroller Bks.). 12p. (J). 5.99 (978-0-7641-5495-9(8)) Barron's Educational Series, Inc.

DePrisco, Dorothea. Animal Explorers: A Walk in the Jungle. 2007. (Animal Explorers Ser.). (Illus.). 14p. (J). bds. 12.95 (978-1-59223-560-5(3) , Silver Dolphin Bks.) Advantage Pubs. Group.

—Safari Adventure. 2007. (Animal Explorers Ser.). (Illus.). 14p. bds. 12.95 (978-1-59223-474-5(7) , Silver Dolphin Bks.) Advantage Pubs. Group.

Los Desiertos. (Coleccion Planeta Vivo).Tr. of Deserts. (SPA.). (J). (gr. 5-8). 12.00 (978-84-342-1947-2(6)) Parramon Ediciones S.A. ESP. *Dist:* Distribuidora Norma, Inc., Lectorum Pubns., Inc.

Devaney, Sherri. Oddities. 2005. (Planet's Most Extreme Ser.). (Illus.). 48p. (J). (gr. 3-7). 24.95 (978-1-4103-0402-5(7) , Blackbirch Pr., Inc.) Thomson Gale.

Dewire, Bob. My Guide to America's Animals & Plants. Sullivan, Beth, illus. 2000. 48p. (J). (gr. 1-2). pap. 2.50 (978-1-56762-126-6(0)) Modern Learning Pr.

Diagram Group, contrib. by. On the Land. 2004. (Life on Earth Ser.). (Illus.). 112p. (J). (gr. 4-9). 35.00 (978-0-8160-5047-5(3)) Facts On File, Inc.

Diehl, Judy. What's the Difference? 10 Animal Look-Alikes. 2003. (gr. k-3). lib. bdg. 15.25 (978-0-613-78360-6(3)) Tandem Library Bks.

Diehl, Judy & Plumb, David. What's the Difference? 10 Animal Look-Alikes. van Kampen, Vlasta, illus. 2000. 24p. (J). (gr. k-3). pap. 6.95 (978-1-55037-564-0(4)); lib. bdg. 19.95 (978-1-55037-565-7(2)) Annick Pr., Ltd. CAN. *Dist:* Firefly Bks., Ltd.

Dijs, Carla. Truck Two: On Safari in North America, South America, Europe B, Asia, 4. 1999. (Illus.). 12p. (J). (ps-3). 12.99 (978-0-85953-831-2(1)) Child's Play-International.

Discovery Channel School Science Set 1: The Plant & Animal Kingdom, 10 bks. (Illus.). (J). (gr. 5 up). lib. bdg. 246.70 (978-0-8368-3209-9(4)) Stevens, Gareth Inc.

Discovery Channel Staff. Animal Planet the Most Extreme Animals. Gerstein, Sherry & Packard, Mary, eds. 2007. (Animal Planet Extreme Animals Ser.). 80p. 15.95 (*978-0-7879-8662-9(3) , Jossey-Bass) Wiley, John & Sons, Inc.

Discovery Channel Staff & Jossey-Bass Publishers Staff. Animal Planet the Most Extreme Predators. Packard, Mary, ed. 2007. (Animal Planet Extreme Animals Ser.). 80p. 15.95 (*978-0-7879-8664-3(X) , Jossey-Bass) Wiley, John & Sons, Inc.

Disney Staff. Let's Discover Animals Playtime Learning Box: With Winnie the Pooh & Friends. 2004. (Illus.). 128p. (ps-1). 19.99 (978-0-7868-0934-9(5) , Disney Editions) Disney Pr.

Dixon, Dougal. Ankylosaurus & Other Mountain Dinosaurs. Field, James & Weston, Steve, illus. 2004. (Dinosaur Find Ser.). 24p. (C). (gr. k-3). 22.60 (978-1-4048-0670-2(9)) Picture Window Bks.

—Deltadromeus & Other Shoreline Dinosaurs. Field, James & Weston, Steve, illus. 2004. (Dinosaur Find Ser.). 24p. (C). (gr. k-3). 22.60 (978-1-4048-0669-6(5)) Picture Window Bks.

—Plateosaurus & Other Desert Dinosaurs. Field, James & Weston, Steve, illus. 2004. (Dinosaur Find Ser.). 24p. (C). (gr. k-3). 22.60 (978-1-4048-0667-2(9)) Picture Window Bks.

—Stegosaurus & Other Plains Dinosaurs. Field, James & Weston, Steve, illus. 2004. (Dinosaur Find Ser.). 24p. (C). (gr. k-3). 22.60 (978-1-4048-0668-9(7)) Picture Window Bks.

DK Publishing. Animals. 2008. 14p. (J). (ps-k). bds. 5.99 (*978-0-7566-3468-1(7)) Dorling Kindersley Publishing, Inc.

—Noisy Animals. 2008. 10p. (J). (ps-k). 6.99 (*978-0-7566-3854-2(2)) Dorling Kindersley Publishing, Inc.

—Pop-up Animals: Pop-up. 2008. 10p. (J). 8.99 (*978-0-7566-3453-7(9)) Dorling Kindersley Publishing, Inc.

—Wild Animals. 2008. 10p. (J). (ps-k). 6.99 (*978-0-7566-3853-5(4)) Dorling Kindersley Publishing, Inc.

DK Publishing Staff. Amazing Animals Q & A: Everything You Never Knew about the Animal Kingdom. 2007. 64p. (J). 12.99 (978-0-7566-2914-4(4)) Dorling Kindersley Publishing, Inc.

—Animals. 2007. 26p. (J). (ps-1). bds. 9.99 (978-0-7566-3029-4(0)) Dorling Kindersley Publishing, Inc.

—Animals: My First Activity Box. 2007. (My First Bks.). (J). (ps-1). 19.99 (978-0-7566-3023-2(1)) Dorling Kindersley Publishing, Inc.

—Pop-Up Animal ABC. 2007. (DK Toys & Games Ser.). (Illus.). (J). (ps-1). 12.99 (978-0-7566-2588-7(2)) Dorling Kindersley Publishing, Inc.

Doeden, Matt. Real-Life Dragons. 2008. (J). (*978-1-4296-1296-8(7)) Capstone Pr., Inc.

Doeden, Matt. The World's Fastest Animals. 2007. (Edge Books, the World's Top Tens). (Illus.). 32p. (J). 23.93 (978-0-7368-6436-7(9)) Capstone Pr., Inc.

Doherty, Gillian. 1001 Animales Que Buscar. 2003. Tr. of 1001 Animals to Spot. (SPA.). (ps-2). lib. bdg. 15.25 (978-0-613-86948-5(6)) Tandem Library Bks.

—1001 Animales que Buscar. 2004. (Facts & Lists Internet-Linked Ser.). Orig. Title: 1001 Animals to Spot. (SPA.). 64p. (J). lib. bdg. 14.95 (978-1-58086-493-0(7)) EDC Publishing.

—1001 Animals, Farm, Town & Long Ago. 2004. (1001 Things to Spot Ser.). 132p. (J). pap. 12.95 (978-0-7945-0352-9(7)); lib. bdg. 20.95 (978-1-58086-496-1(1)) EDC Publishing.

—1001 Animals to Spot. 2002. (ps-2). lib. bdg. 15.25 (978-0-613-75324-1(0)) Tandem Library Bks.

Dolphin, Colleen. Armadillos to Zorillas: Animals from A to Z. 2007. (Let's See A to Z Ser.). (ENG., Illus.). 32p. (J), (ps-3). lib. bdg. 25.65 (*978-1-59928-883-3(4) , Super SandCastle) ABDO Publishing Co.

Doner, Kim & Martin, Chryssee. On a Road in Africa. Doner, Kim, illus. 2007. (J). (*978-1-58246-230-1(5) , Tricycle Pr.) Ten Speed Pr.

Donovan, Sandy. Iguanas. 2002. (Animals of the Rain Forest Ser.). (Illus.). 32p. (YA). lib. bdg. 22.83 (978-0-7398-5372-6(4)) Raintree.

Doolittle, Bev. Reading the Wild. Maclay, Elise, illus. 2001. 31p. (J). (gr. 1-5). tchr. ed. 16.95 (978-0-86713-061-4(X)) Greenwich Workshop Pr.

Dorling Kindersley Publishing Staff. Animal Hide & Seek. 2006. (Dk Readers Ser.). (Illus.). 32p. (J). 14.99 (978-0-7566-1962-6(9)); (gr. 5). pap. 3.99 (978-0-7566-1961-9(0)) Dorling Kindersley Publishing, Inc.

—Animals. (Let's Look Ser.). (Illus.). (J). 2006. 36p. bds. 4.99 (978-0-7566-1751-6(0)); 2005. 12p. bds. 6.99 (978-0-7566-1378-5(7)); 2005. 14p. bds. 4.99 (978-0-7566-0985-6(2)) Dorling Kindersley Publishing, Inc.

—Animals. 2004. (Illus.). lib. bdg. 7.95 (978-0-8225-3624-6(2)) Lerner Publishing Group.

—Animals. 2003. (J). per. (978-1-884907-46-3(6)); per. (978-1-884907-42-5(3)) Paradise Pr., Inc.

—Animals. (Questions & Answers Ser.). (J). Date not set. (Illus.). 176p. 7.98 (978-0-7525-9623-5(3)); Date not set. (Illus.). 40p. 3.98 (978-1-4054-0176-0(1)); Date not set. (Illus.). bds. 5.98 (978-0-7525-8558-1(4)); 2002. 32p. 7.95 (978-0-7525-9552-8(0)) Parragon, Inc.

—Animals. (J). (gr. k-1). (978-84-342-2417-9(8) , PR30571) Parramon Ediciones S.A. ESP. *Dist:* Lectorum Pubns., Inc.

—Animals Like Us. 2005. 80p. (J). 19.99 (978-0-7566-1008-1(7)) Dorling Kindersley Publishing, Inc.

—Baby Animals Library. 2006. (Touch & Feel Ser.). 36p. (J). bds. 19.99 (978-0-7566-2029-5(5)) Dorling Kindersley Publishing, Inc.

—Barbie Mi Primer Libro de Pegatinas Sobre Animales/ My First Animals Sticker Book. 2005. (Barbie sticker Bks.). (Illus.). 16p. (J). (ps-ps). bds. 6.99 (978-0-7566-1111-8(3)) Dorling Kindersley Publishing, Inc.

—Cave Life. 2000. (978-0-606-17799-3(X)) Tandem Library Bks.

—e.Encyclopedia Animal. 2005. 376p. (J). 29.99 (978-0-7566-1131-6(8)) Dorling Kindersley Publishing, Inc.

—Encyclopedia of Animals. 2006. 376p. (J). (gr. 8). pap. 19.99 (978-0-7566-1972-5(6)) Dorling Kindersley Publishing, Inc.

—Fluffy, Snuggly, Cuddly Baby Animals. 2006. (Touchables Ser.). (Illus.). 14p. (J). bds. 8.99 (978-0-7566-2022-6(8)) Dorling Kindersley Publishing, Inc.

—My First Spanish Animal Book. 2002. (Illus.). 36p. (J). (ps-1). bds. 6.99 (978-0-7894-8590-8(7)) Dorling Kindersley Publishing, Inc.

—My First Touch & Feel Picture Cards: Animals. 2005. (Baby Genius Ser.). 16p. (J). pap. 9.99 (978-0-7566-1515-4(1)) Dorling Kindersley Publishing, Inc.

—Reino Animal/Wild Animals. 2005. (TOUCH & FEEL Ser.). 12p. (J). bds. 6.99 (978-0-7566-1199-6(7)) Dorling Kindersley Publishing, Inc.

Dorling Kindersley Publishing Staff, ed. Animales de la Granja. 2004. (Soft-to-Touch Books Ser.). 20p. (J). bds. 4.99 (978-0-7566-0624-4(1)) Dorling Kindersley Publishing, Inc.

—Los Animales Salvajes. 2004. (Soft-to-Touch Books Ser.).Tr. of Wild Animals. 20p. (J). bds. 4.99 (978-0-7566-0623-7(3)) Dorling Kindersley Publishing, Inc.

—El Mundo Marino. 2004. (Dk Readers Ser.). (SPA.). 32p. (J). 12.99 (978-0-7566-0637-4(3)) Dorling Kindersley Publishing, Inc.

—My First Animal Play Book. 2004. (Illus.). 62p. (J). 12.99 (978-0-7566-0762-3(0)) Dorling Kindersley Publishing, Inc.

Dossenbach, Hans D. Beware We Are Poisonous! How Animals Defend Themselves. 1998. (Illus.). 40p. (J). (gr. 4-6). 23.70 (978-1-56711-215-3(3) , Blackbirch Pr., Inc.) Thomson Gale.

Dot-to-Dots, Mazes & More: Baby Animals. (gr. k-1). 2.99 (978-0-7424-0172-3(3) , IF0405) School Specialty Publishing.

Douche, Charles. Meet 100 Animals. Balloon Books Staff, ed. 2003. (Animal Bring-Along Bks.). (Illus.). 96p. (J). (ps-1). 4.95 (978-0-8069-8060-7(5) , Balloon Bks.) Sterling Publishing Co., Inc.

Douglas, Lisa Jo. Active Animals A Thru Z. 2007. (J). per. 13.99 (*978-1-59879-311-6(X)) Lifevest Publishing, Inc.

Douglass, Jo & Graham, Neville. Happy Baby Animals. rev. ed. 2002. (Priddy Bicknell Big Ideas for Little People Ser.). (Illus.). 28p. (J). bds. 5.95 (978-0-312-49061-4(5) , Priddy Bks.) St. Martin's Pr.

Doward, Jan S. Grandpa's Furry & Feathered Friends: Meet Stubbytail, Hop-Hops, & All Other Birds & Animals at Grandpa's Place. 2003. (Illus.). 95p. (J). pap. 7.99 (978-0-8163-1952-7(9)) Pacific Pr. Publishing Assn.

Downs, Michael. Pig Giggles & Rabbit Rhymes: A Book of Animal Riddles. Sheldon, David, illus. 2002. 32p. (J). (ps-3). 13.95 (978-0-8118-3114-7(0)) Chronicle Bks. LLC.

Dowswell, P. Little Book of Animals - Internet Linked. rev. ed. 2007. (Miniature Editions Ser.). 64p. (J). 6.99 (*978-0-7945-1872-1(9) , Usborne) EDC Publishing.

Dr. Kind Answers Kids' Questions about Animals. 3rd ed. 2001. 64p. (J). 2.50 (978-0-941246-09-5(4)) National Assn. for Humane & Environmental Education.

Drew, David. Fins & Feathers. Harradine, Dona, tr. Falla, Dominique, illus. 1999. (Hello! Lote Ser.). (IND.). 17p. (J). pap. 5.99 (978-0-7339-0877-4(2)) Pearson Education Australia AUS. *Dist:* Cheng & Tsui Co.

—Fins & Feathers. Batt, Deleece, tr. Falla, Dominique, illus. 1999. (Hello! Lote Ser.). (JPN.). 17p. (J). pap. 5.99 (978-0-7339-0892-7(6)) Pearson Education Australia AUS. *Dist:* Cheng & Tsui Co.

Dublin, Robin, ed. Alaska Wildlife Curriculum. 2001st ed. 2001. (Illus.). 1017p. (gr. k-12). 39.95 incl. cd-rom (978-1-890692-12-4(3)) Wizard Works.

Dubovoy, Silvia. Caparazones. 2002. (SPA.). (gr. k-3). lib. bdg. 15.25 (978-0-613-64343-6(7)) Tandem Library Bks.

—Colas. 2002. (SPA.). (gr. k-3). lib. bdg. 15.25 (978-0-613-64345-0(3)) Tandem Library Bks.

—Dientes. 2002. (SPA.). (gr. k-3). lib. bdg. 15.25 (978-0-613-64348-1(8)) Tandem Library Bks.

—Picos. 2002. (SPA.). (gr. k-3). lib. bdg. 15.25 (978-0-613-64576-8(6)) Tandem Library Bks.

Duey, Kathleen. Animal Book. 2000. (J). (978-0-06-028293-6(2)) HarperCollins Pubs.

Dunn, Phoebe, illus. Guess Who I Am... gif. ed. 2005. 5p. (J). (ps). per. 7.99 (978-1-57791-175-3(X)) Brighter Minds Children's Publishing.

Eason, Cassandra & Sterling/Balloon Staff. My Favorite Animals. 1998. (Animal Bring-Along Bks.). (Illus.). 16p. (J). (ps-k). 5.95 (978-0-8069-0384-2(8) , Balloon Bks.) Sterling Publishing Co., Inc.

Eckart, Edana. Animals of the World, 6 Bks, Set. 2005. (J). (ps-2). 96.00 (978-0-516-25217-9(8) , Children's Pr.) Scholastic Library Publishing.

Eder, Tamara & Sheldon, Ian. Animal Tracks of Nevada & the Great Basin, Vol. 1. Ross, Gary, illus. rev. ed. 2002. (Animal Tracks Ser.). 176p. (gr. 4-6). pap. 6.95 (978-1-55105-339-4(X)) Lone Pine Publishing USA.

—Animal Tracks of New Jersey, Vol. 1. Bodegom, Volker, ed. rev. ed. 2002. (Animal Tracks Ser.). (Illus.). 144p. (gr. 4-6). pap. 6.95 (978-1-55105-341-7(1)) Lone Pine Publishing USA.

Ehrlich, Fred. Does a Camel Cook? Early Experiences. Bolam, Emily, illus. 2007. 32p. (J). 13.50 (978-1-59354-588-8(6)) Handprint Bks.

—Does a Camel Cook? Early Experiences. Bolam, Emily, illus. 2007. 28p. pap. 5.95 (978-1-59354-595-6(9)) Blue Apple Bks.

—Does a Panda Go to School? Bolam, Emily, illus. 2003. (Early Experiences Ser.). 32p. 10.95 (978-1-59354-017-3(5)) Blue Apple Bks.

Elementary Science Animals Series, Set. 2003. (Illus.). (J). 799.68 (978-1-4109-0138-5(6)) Raintree.

Elgar, Rebecca. Is That an Elephant over There? (Illus.). 10p. (J). (ps-k). bds. 7.99 (978-0-590-24917-1(7)) Scholastic, Inc.

Elliott, Leslie. World's Wildest Animals. 2001. (gr. 3-6). lib. bdg. 18.75 (978-0-613-75647-1(9)) Tandem Library Bks.

Elwood, Ann, et al. Animal Champions, Vol. 2. 2000. (Zoobooks Ser.). 24p. (J). (gr. 1-7). 15.95 (978-0-937934-98-2(4)) Wildlife Education, Ltd.

An Encyclopedia of Animals: Fourth Grade Guided Comprehension Level M. (On Our Way to English Ser.). (gr. 4 up). 34.50 (978-0-7578-7158-0(5)) Rigby Education.

Encyclopedia Prehistorica Set. 2006. (J). 55.98 (*978-0-7636-3507-7(3)) Candlewick Pr.

English, June. Let's Talk Tails. Regan, Dana, illus. 2004. 14p. (J). (gr. k-4). reprint ed. 4.00 (978-0-7567-7832-3(8)) DIANE Publishing Co.

Equipo Staff. Animales. (Coleccion Mundo Maravilloso). (SPA.). 48p. (J). (gr. 3-5). (978-84-348-4431-5(1)) SM Ediciones.

—El Dodo Desaparecio. 2003. (Enciclopedia Me Pregunto Por Que). (SPA., Illus.). 124p. (J). (gr. 3-5). (978-84-241-1963-8(0) , EV6618) Everest de Ediciones y Distribucion, S.L. ESP. *Dist:* Lectorum Pubns., Inc.

Escaping Danger. 2001. (Animal Marvels Ser.). (Illus.). 32p. (J). (gr. 3 up). lib. bdg. 24.67 (978-0-8368-2931-0(X)) Stevens, Gareth Inc.

Exiting & Unusual Animals: Includes: Birds of Prey; Land Predators; Night Creatures; When Dinosaurs Ruled the Earth, 4 bks., Set. (Remarkable World Ser.). (Illus.). (J). (gr. 4-7). lib. bdg. 75.92 (978-0-8172-5153-6(7)) Raintree.

Exotic Animals, 13 vols., set. 2002. (Zoobooks). (Illus.). (J). (gr. k-7). pap. 23.28 (978-1-888153-66-8(0)) Wildlife Education, Ltd.

Fabiny, Sarah. Rainforest Animal Adventure. Kees, Chantal & Shields, Chris, illus. 2003. (Magic Color Bks.). 12p. (J). (gr. k-2). 9.95 (978-1-4027-0823-7(8)) Sterling Publishing Co., Inc.

Facklam, Margery. Bugs for Lunch. 1999. (J). 13.75 (978-0-606-16409-2(X)) Tandem Library Bks.

—What Does the Crow Know? The Mysteries of Animal Intelligence. Johnson, Pamela, illus. 2001. 48p. (J). (gr. 3-6). pap. 6.95 (978-1-57805-075-8(8)) Gibbs Smith, Publisher.

Facts on File, Inc. Staff, ed. Invasive Species Set, 5 Vols. 2007. (Invasive Species Ser.). 10+p. (J). (gr. 6-12). 150.00 (978-0-7910-9455-6(3) , Chelsea Hse.) Facts On File, Inc.

Fajerman, Deborah. Baa for Beginners. 2005. (Illus.). 32p. (J). pap. 5.95 (978-0-7641-3095-3(1)) Barron's Educational Series, Inc.

Family Trees, 5 bks., Set. Incl. Flowering Plant Division. Stefoff, Rebecca. 92p. (gr. 3-7). lib. bdg. (978-0-7614-1817-7(2)); Insect Class. Zabludoff, Marc. 96p. (gr. 3-7). lib. bdg. 29.93 (978-0-7614-1819-1(9)); Primate Order. Stefoff, Rebecca. 93p. (gr. 3-7). lib. bdg. 32.79 (978-0-7614-1816-0(4)); Protoctist Kingdom. Zabludoff, Marc. 95p. (gr. 3-7). lib. bdg. 32.79 (978-0-7614-1818-4(0)); Reptile Class. Zabludoff, Marc. 95p. (gr. 4-7). lib. bdg. 32.79 (978-0-7614-1820-7(2)); (Illus.). (J). 2005. (978-0-7614-1815-3(6) , Benchmark Bks.) Cavendish, Marshall Corp.

Famous Animals: Individual Title, 6 pack. (Action Packs Ser.). 104p. (gr. 3-5). 44.00 (978-0-7635-8409-2(6)) Rigby Education.

Farm Animal Sounds. 2000. (Illus.). (J). lib. bdg. 3.21 (978-0-7398-4479-3(2)) Steck-Vaughn.

Farndon, John. Little Animal Encyclopedia. 2001. (gr. k-3). lib. bdg. 21.05 (978-0-613-88860-8(X)) Tandem Library Bks.

—1000 Things You Should Know about Wild Animals. 2002. (1000 Things You Should Know about Ser.). (Illus.). 64p. (YA). (gr. 5 up). lib. bdg. (978-1-59084-473-1(4)) Mason Crest Pubs.

Farndon, John & Kirkwood, Jon, texts. The Little Animal Encyclopedia. 2001. (Kingfisher Little Encyclopedias Ser.). (Illus.). 160p. (J). (gr. k-3). pap. 11.95 (978-0-7534-5422-0(X) , Kingfisher) Houghton Mifflin Co. Trade & Reference Div.

Farran, Christopher. Animals To The Rescue! True Stories of Animal Heroes. 2000. (Illus.). (J). (978-0-606-21754-5(1)) Tandem Library Bks.

Fecher, Sarah, et al. Wild Animals, 4 vols., Set. 1999. (Ladders Ser.). (Illus.). 32p. (J). (gr. k-3). (978-0-7166-7707-9(5)) World Bk., Inc.

Fechert, Sarah & Kespert, Deborah, contrib. by. Animales Salvajes: Wild Animals. 2004. (Ladders—Spanish Ser.). (SPA., Illus.). 32p. (J). pap. 9.95 (978-1-58728-445-8(6)); 12.95 (978-1-58728-164-8(3)) T&N Children's Publishing. (Two Can Publishing).

Feely, Jenny. Animal Skeletons. 1999. (ps-2). lib. bdg. 11.80 (978-0-613-19334-4(2)) Tandem Library Bks.

—Staying Alive. 2000. (gr. k-3). lib. bdg. 11.65 (978-0-613-33442-6(6)) Tandem Library Bks.

Fenichel, Marilyn P. Lulu the Potbellied Pig & Other True Animal Hero Stories. 2002. (J). (978-0-9707768-8-4(8)) Moonstone Pr.

Ferguson, Richard. On Safari. 2007. (Illus.). 14p. (J). (gr. k-3). 12.99 (978-0-7566-2537-5(8)) Dorling Kindersley Publishing, Inc.

Ferrari, Marco. The Search for Food. Stalio, Ivan, illus. 1998. (Everyday Life of Animals Ser.). 64p. (YA). (gr. 4-6). lib. bdg. 19.98 (978-0-8172-4195-7(7)) Raintree.

Fiedler, Julie. Pit Bulls. 2006. (Illus.). 24p. (J). lib. bdg. (978-1-4042-3117-7(X) , PowerKids Pr.) Rosen Publishing Group, Inc., The.

Filipowich, Bob. Splashtime Book of Animals. 2000. (God's Creation Ser.). (Illus.). (J). pap. 4.99 (978-0-310-98093-3(3)) Zonderkidz.

First Reports-Animals Complete Set. (First Reports-Animals Ser.). (Illus.). (gr. 2-4). 180.80 (978-0-7565-0704-6(9)) Compass Point Bks.

Fishy Tales. 12p. (J). (978-2-7643-0193-7(6)) Phidal Publishing, Inc./Editions Phidal, Inc.

Fleisher, Paul. Life Cycles of a Dozen Diverse Creatures. 1998. (Single Titles Ser.: 6). (Illus.). 80p. (gr. 3-7). pap. 9.95 (978-0-7613-0349-7(9) , Millbrook Pr.) Lerner Publishing Group.

Fleming, Denise. Count! Fleming, Denise, illus. 2002. (Illus.). (J). 15.49 (978-0-7587-2282-9(6)) Book Wholesalers, Inc.

Fleming, Sally. Rapid Runners. Underwood, Kay Povelite, illus. 2004. (It's Nature! Ser.). 32p. (J). (gr. 3-6). pap. 7.95 (978-1-55971-789-2(0) , NorthWord Bks. for Young Readers) T&N Children's Publishing.

—Rapid Runners. 2001. (gr. 3-6). lib. bdg. 16.40 (978-0-613-55886-0(3)) Tandem Library Bks.

Florida's Colorful Critters. 2002. (Illus.). (J). pap. 2.95 (978-0-8200-1102-8(9)) Great Outdoors Publishing Co.

Follen, Eliza Lee. What the Animals Do & Say. 2004. reprint ed. pap. 15.95 (978-1-4191-9359-0(7)) Kessinger Publishing, LLC.

Fontanel, Beatrice. Monsters: The World's Most Incredible Animals. 2000. (Monsters-the World's Most Incredible Animals Ser.). (Illus.). 92p. (J). (gr. 3-8). 19.95 (978-0-87226-605-6(2) , 66052B, Bedrick, Peter Bks.) School Specialty Publishing.

Foran, Jill. Herbivores. 2004. (Nature's Food Chain Ser.). (Illus.). 24p. (J). lib. bdg. 19.95 (978-1-59036-240-2(3)) Weigl Pubs., Inc.

Forbush, Kyle. Alaska's Wild Animals Coloring Book. Forbush, Lisa, illus. 2003. (J). 3.95 (978-1-57833-232-8(X)) Todd Communications.

Las Formas (Touch & Feel Shapes) 2000. (SPA., Illus.). 10p. (J). (ps). pap. (978-950-11-1418-8(X)) Sigmar.

Foster, Walter, ed. Drawing Animals. Fisher, Diana, illus. 2005. 32p. (J). pap. 12.95 (978-1-56010-937-2(8)) Foster, Walter Publishing, Inc.

—Wild Animals: Step by Step Instructions for 26 Captivating Creatures. Fisher, Diana, illus. 2005. (Draw & Color Ser.). 40p. pap. 4.95 (978-1-56010-864-1(9)) Foster, Walter Publishing, Inc.

Fowler, Allan. Horns & Antlers. 1998. (Rookie Read-About Science Ser.). (Illus.). 32p. (J). (gr. 1-2). pap. 4.95 (978-0-516-26364-9(1) , Children's Pr.) Scholastic Library Publishing.

—How Animals See Things. 1999. (Rookie Read-About Science Ser.). (Illus.). 32p. (J). (gr. 1-2). pap. 4.95 (978-0-516-26416-5(8) , Children's Pr.) Scholastic Library Publishing.

—How Animals See Things. 1999. (Illus.). 31p. (J). (gr. 1-2). lib. bdg. 12.95 (978-0-613-37388-3(X)) Tandem Library Bks.

—Mammals of Long Ago. 2001. (Rookie Read-About Science Ser.). (Illus.). 32p. (J). (gr. 1-2). pap. 4.95 (978-0-516-27090-6(7) , Children's Pr.) Scholastic Library Publishing.

—Mammals of Long Ago. 2001. (Illus.). 31p. (J). (ps-3). lib. bdg. 12.95 (978-0-613-54609-6(1)) Tandem Library Bks.

Fowler, Allan & Rau, Dana. Telling Tails. 1998. (Rookie Read-About Science Ser.). (Illus.). 32p. (J). (gr. 1-2). pap. 4.95 (978-0-516-26368-7(4) , Children's Pr.) Scholastic Library Publishing.

Franco, Betsy. Amazing Animals. Reisch, Jesse, illus. 2002. (Rookie Reader Skill Set Ser.). 32p. (J). (gr. k-2). pap. 4.95 (978-0-516-27385-3(X) , Children's Pr.) Scholastic Library Publishing.

—Amazing Animals. 2002. (gr. k-3). lib. bdg. 12.95 (978-0-613-53902-9(8)) Tandem Library Bks.

Frank, Marjorie Slavick, et al. Science Instant Readers Bk. 3: Animal Homes. 1999. (Harcourt Science Ser.). (gr. 1 up). pap. 15.50 (978-0-15-316201-5(5)) Harcourt Schl. Pubs.

—Science Instant Readers Bk. 4: Do Animals Live in Plants? 1999. (Harcourt Science Ser.). (gr. 1 up). pap. 15.50 (978-0-15-316202-2(3)) Harcourt Schl. Pubs.

Fraser, Mary Ann. Where Are the Night Animals? Fraser, Mary Ann, illus. 1999. (Let's-Read-and-Find-Out Science Ser.). (Illus.). 32p. (J). (ps-1). 15.89 (978-0-06-027718-5(1)); pap. 5.99 (978-0-06-445176-5(3) , Harper Trophy) HarperCollins Pubs.

—Where Are the Night Animals? 1999. (Let's-Read-and-Find-Out Ser.). (978-0-606-16683-6(1)) Tandem Library Bks.

—Where Are the Night Animals? Fraser, Mary Ann, illus. 1999. (Illus.). 29p. (J). (ps-ps). lib. bdg. 12.95 (978-0-613-12270-2(4)) Tandem Library Bks.

—Where Are the Night Animals. Fraser, Mary Ann, illus. 1999. (Let's-Read-&-Find-Out Science Bks.). (Illus.). 32p. (J). (ps-1). 15.95 (978-0-06-027717-8(3)) HarperCollins Pubs.

Fredericks, Anthony D. Near One Cattail: Turtles, Logs, & Leaping Frogs. DiRubbio, Jennifer, illus. 2005. (Sharing Nature with Children Book Ser.). 32p. (J). 16.95 (978-1-58469-070-2(4)); pap. 7.95 (978-1-58469-071-9(2)) Dawn Pubns.

—Under One Rock: Bugs, Slugs, & Other Ughs. DiRubbio, Jennifer, illus. 2004. (Sharing Nature with Children Book Ser.). 32p. (J). 16.95 (978-1-58469-028-3(3)); pap. 7.95 (978-1-58469-027-6(5)) Dawn Pubns.

—Under One Rock: Bugs, Slugs, & Other Ughs. 2001. (gr. 3-6). lib. bdg. 16.40 (978-0-613-49784-8(8)) Tandem Library Bks.

—Weird Walkers. 2004. (It's Nature! Ser.). (Illus.). 32p. (J). (gr. 3-6). pap. 7.95 (978-1-55971-630-7(4) , Creative Publishing International) Quayside.

—Weird Walkers. 2000. (gr. 3-6). lib. bdg. 16.40 (978-0-613-27488-3(1)) Tandem Library Bks.

Fredericks, Anthony D. & Collard, Sneed B., III. Amazing Animals: Nature's Most Incredible Creatures! 2000. (Illus.). 160p. (J). pap. (978-1-55971-753-3(X) , NorthWord Bks. for Young Readers) T&N Children's Publishing.

Freed, Shirley Ann & Moon, Louise. Adam Named the Animals. Morelan, Bill, ed. Butler, Steven, illus. l.t. ed. 2002. 8p. (J). (ps-k). pap. 3.99 (978-1-58938-000-4(2)) Concerned Communications.

Freeman, Marcia S. Animal Lives. 2005. (Rourke Discovery Library). (Illus.). 24p. (gr. 1-4). 14.95 (978-1-59515-121-6(4)) Rourke Publishing, LLC.

Fremont, Victoria & Beylon, Cathy. Animal Crossword Puzzles. 1998. (Illus.). 64p. (J). pap. 1.50 (978-0-486-40302-1(5)) Dover Pubns., Inc.

French, Vivian. Swallow Journey. Littlewood, Karin, illus. 2001. (Fantastic Journeys Ser.). 32p. (J). 15.95 (978-1-84089-215-4(3) , Zero to Ten, Limited) Evans Publishing Group GBR. *Dist:* Independent Pubs. Group.

La Fresa. (Coleccion Ciclos Vitales). (SPA., Illus.). (J). (gr. 3-5). pap. (978-84-236-2653-3(9) , ED4700) Edebé ESP. *Dist:* Lectorum Pubns., Inc.

Fridell, Ron & Royston, Angela. Life Cycle of a... Series: An In-Depth Look at Some Familiar Plants & Animals, 16 bks., Set. (Illus.). (J). (gr. k-2). lib. bdg. 341.76 (978-1-58810-186-0(X)) Heinemann Library.

Fridell, Ron & Walsh, Patricia. Life Cycle of a... Series: An In-Depth Look at Some Familiar Plants & Animals, 4 bks., Set 4. 2001. (Illus.). 32p. (J). (gr. k-2). lib. bdg. 85.44 (978-1-58810-022-1(7)) Heinemann Library.

Friedman, Sharon. Grin & Bear It: Zoo Jokes to Make You Roar. Gable, Brian, illus. 2005. (Make Me Laugh! Ser.). 32p. (J). (gr. k-3). lib. bdg. 19.93 (978-1-57505-660-9(7)) Lerner Publishing Group.

Frizado, Orlando. Dots & Spots. 2002. (Illus.). 13p. (J). (978-0-439-40381-8(2)) Scholastic, Inc.

Frydenborg, Kay. Animal Therapist. 2005. (Weird Careers in Science Ser.). (Illus.). 82p. (J). (gr. 4-8). lib. bdg. 25.00 (978-0-7910-8704-6(2) , Chelsea Hse.) Facts On File, Inc.

Fuertes, Gloria. El Gran Libro de los Animales. 2003. (SPA.). 168p. 17.56 (978-84-305-8755-1(1) , SU3119) Susaeta Ediciones, S.A. ESP. *Dist:* Lectorum Pubns., Inc.

Fullick, Ann. Variation & Classification. 2005. (Life Science In-Depth Ser.). (Illus.). 64p. (J). (978-1-4034-7524-4(5)); pap. (978-1-4034-7532-9(6)) Heinemann Library.

Fur, Feathers, or Skin: Early Level Satellite Individual Title Six-Packs. (Sails Literacy Ser.). 16p. (gr. 1-2). 27.00 (978-0-7578-3165-2(6)) Rigby Education.

Galko, Francine. Animals in Their Habitats, 11 vols., Set. 2003. (Illus.). (J). (gr. k-2). lib. bdg. 250.69 (978-1-58810-608-7(X)) Heinemann Library.

—Mountain Animals. 2003. (Animals in Their Habitats Ser.). (Illus.). 32p. (J). (gr. k-2). lib. bdg. 21.36 (978-1-4034-0180-9(2)); pap. 6.95 (978-1-4034-0437-4(2)) Heinemann Library.

—Mountain Animals. 2003. (gr. k-3). lib. bdg. 14.75 (978-0-613-45799-6(4)) Tandem Library Bks.

—Rainforest Animals. 2003. (Animals in Their Habitats Ser.). (Illus.). 32p. (J). pap. 6.95 (978-1-4034-0439-8(9)) Heinemann Library.

—River Animals. 2003. (Animals in Their Habitats Ser.). (Illus.). 32p. (J). pap. 6.95 (978-1-4034-0440-4(2)) Heinemann Library.

—River Animals. 2003. (gr. k-3). lib. bdg. 14.75 (978-0-613-45818-4(4)) Tandem Library Bks.

—Seashore Animals. 2003. (Animals in Their Habitats Ser.). (Illus.). 32p. (J). pap. 6.95 (978-1-4034-0442-8(9)) Heinemann Library.

Ganeri, Anita. Animal Groupings. 2004. (Nature Files Ser.). (Illus.). 32p. (J). (gr. 4-8). 28.00 (978-0-7910-8216-4(4) , Chelsea Hse.) Facts On File, Inc.

—Animal Life Cycles. 2005. (Nature's Patterns Ser.). (Illus.). 32p. (J). (978-1-4109-1317-3(1)); lib. bdg. 16.95 (978-1-4034-5894-0(4)) Heinemann Library.

—Animals. 2006. (Inside & Out Guides Ser.). (Illus.). 32p. (J). (978-1-4034-9084-1(8)); pap. (978-1-4034-9091-9(0)) Heinemann Library.

—Creatures That Glow. 1999. (Weird & Wonderful! Ser.). (Illus.). 30p. (YA). (gr. 3 up). pap. 7.99 (978-0-7681-0183-6(2) , 57002, McClanahan Bk.) Learning Horizons, Inc.

—Prickly & Poisonous: The Deadly Defenses of Nature's Strangest Animals & Plants. 1999. (Weird & Wonderful! Ser.). (Illus.). 45p. (YA). (gr. 3 up). pap. 7.99 (978-0-7681-0185-0(9) , 57005, McClanahan Bk.) Learning Horizons, Inc.

Garcia, Gloria. Los Animales. (SPA.). 8p. 9.95 (978-84-272-7272-9(3)) Molino, Editorial ESP. *Dist:* Distribooks, Inc.

Gareth Stevens Publishing Staff, contrib. by. All about Wild Animals, 10 bks. Incl. Chimpanzees. lib. bdg. 23.33 (978-0-8368-4171-8(9)); Dolphins. lib. bdg. 23.33 (978-0-8368-4115-2(8)); Giraffes. lib. bdg. 23.33 (978-0-8368-4116-9(6)); Hippos. lib. bdg. 23.33 (978-0-8368-4118-3(2)); Kangaroos. lib. bdg. 23.33 (978-0-8368-4119-0(0)); Pandas. lib. bdg. 23.33 (978-0-8368-4121-3(2)); Parrots. lib. bdg. 23.33 (978-0-8368-4122-0(0)); Spiders. lib. bdg. 23.33 (978-0-8368-4172-5(7)); Turtles. lib. bdg. 23.33 (978-0-8368-4123-7(9)); Wolves. lib. bdg. 23.33 (978-0-8368-4124-4(7)); 32p. (J). (gr. 2 up). (Illus.). 2004. Set lib. bdg. 226.00 (978-0-8368-4114-5(X)) Stevens, Gareth Inc.

Garris, Norma. Fun with Animal Friends. 1999. (Illus.). 48p. (J). (ps-2). 2.99 (978-0-7847-0759-3(6) , 22049, Bean Sprouts) Standard Publishing.

Geltrich, Brigitta, ed. In the Love of Animals. Baldwin, Christopher, illus. Date not set. (Animals Ser.). 96p. (J). pap. 6.00 (978-0-936945-64-4(8)) Creative with Words Pubns.

Gentle, Victor & Perry, Janet. Plagues. 2001. (Natural Disasters Ser.). (Illus.). 24p. (J). (gr. 2 up). lib. bdg. 22.00 (978-0-8368-2835-1(6)) Stevens, Gareth Inc.

George, Jean Craighead. Incredible Animal Adventures. 1999. Orig. Title: Animals who Have Won Our Hearts. (J). 11.05 (978-0-606-17464-0(8)); (gr. 3-6). lib. bdg. 12.10 (978-0-613-22875-6(8)) Tandem Library Bks.

—Rhino Romp. 1998. (J). 12.45 (978-0-7868-3209-5(6)) Hyperion Pr.

—Winter Moon. 2001. (gr. 3-6). lib. bdg. 14.10 (978-0-613-50525-3(5)) Tandem Library Bks.

Giant Sticker Book: Animal World. 2002. 48p. pap. 5.98 (978-0-7525-8194-1(5)) Parragon, Inc.

Gibbons, Gail. Gail Gibbons' Creatures Great & Small Series, 5 bks. Gibbons, Gail, illus. 2000. (Illus.). (J). (gr. 1-6). pap. 76.95 incl. audio (978-0-87499-579-4(5)) Live Oak Media.

Gildart, Bert. Bighorn Sheep: Mountain Monarchs. 1999. (J). (978-0-606-19764-9(8)) Tandem Library Bks.

Gillis, Jennifer Blizin. Hamsters. 2004. (Heinemann Read & Learn Ser.). (Illus.). 24p. (J). 18.50 (978-1-4034-5054-8(4)); pap. 5.75 (978-1-4034-6022-6(1)) Heinemann Library.

Gilpin, Daniel. Life-Size Killer Creatures. 2006. (Life-Size Ser.). (Illus.). 28p. (J). 9.95 (978-1-4027-2701-6(1)) Sterling Publishing Co., Inc.

Godown, Jan Annino. Florida's Famous Animals: True Stories of Sunset Sam the Dolphin, Snooty the Manatee, Big Guy the Panther, & Others. 2008. (Illus.). 128p. pap. 9.95 (***978-0-7627-4136-6(8)***) Globe Pequot Pr., The.

Golden Books Staff. Animal Sounds. Battaglia, Aurelius, illus. 2005. (Golden Sturdy Book Ser.). 24p. (J). (gr. k-k). 5.99 (978-0-375-83278-9(5) , Golden Bks.) Random Hse. Children's Bks.

Goldman, Phyllis, ed. Monkeyshines on What's up down There: Exploring the World Underground. 2003. (Illus.). 122p. (YA). per. 32.95 (978-1-888325-23-2(2)) Allosaurus Pubs.

Goodman, Susan E. Animal Rescue: The Best Job There Is. 2001. (Ready-to-Read Ser.). (Illus.). (J). 10.79 (978-0-606-20548-1(9)) Tandem Library Bks.

Gordon, Bob. Moo-riel & Friends. 2007. (Illus.). 16p. (ps-k). per., bds. 6.95 (***978-1-84610-472-5(6)***) Make Believe Ideas GBR. *Dist:* Ingram Pub. Services.

Gottlieb. Land Animals. 2004. (Illus.). (J). pap. 15.60 incl. cd-rom (978-0-7398-9177-3(4)) Steck-Vaughn.

Graham, Anna. Deadly Creatures. 2005. (Top Tens Ser.). (Illus.). 32p. (J). (gr. 3-7). lib. bdg. 25.27 (978-1-59716-064-3(4)) Bearport Publishing Co., Inc.

—Fierce Predators. 2005. (Top Tens Ser.). (Illus.). 32p. (J). (gr. 3-7). lib. bdg. 25.27 (978-1-59716-068-1(7)) Bearport Publishing Co., Inc.

Grambo, Rebecca L. Claws & Jaws. 2002. (Amazing Animals Ser.). (Illus.). 32p. (gr. 2-5). 18.95 (978-1-58952-142-1(0)) Rourke Publishing, LLC.

—Defenses. 2002. (Amazing Animals Ser.). (Illus.). 32p. (gr. 2-5). 18.95 (978-1-58952-144-5(7)) Rourke Publishing, LLC.

—Eyes. 2002. (Amazing Animals Ser.). (Illus.). 32p. (gr. 2-5). 18.95 (978-1-58952-145-2(5)) Rourke Publishing, LLC.

—Hunters. 2002. (Amazing Animals Ser.). (Illus.). 32p. (gr. 2-5). 18.95 (978-1-58952-147-6(1)) Rourke Publishing, LLC.

Graziano, Claudia. Meerkat's Safari. 2007. (Illus.). 36p. 15.99 (***978-0-9778072-0-8(7)***) Meerkat's Adventures Bks.

Green, Jen. Big Cats & Wild Dogs: Explore the Incredible World & Lions, Tigers, Cheetahs, Leopards, Wolves, Hyenas, Dingos & Other Hunting Dogs. 2005. (Illus.). 128p. pap. 17.99 (978-1-84476-131-9(2) , Southwater) Anness Publishing GBR. *Dist:* National Bk. Network.

—In a Backyard. 2002. (Small Worlds Ser.). (Illus.). 32p. (J). (gr. 3-4). pap. (978-0-7787-0155-2(7)); lib. bdg. (978-0-7787-0141-5(7)) Crabtree Publishing Co.

—In a Backyard. 2002. (gr. 3-6). lib. bdg. 17.60 (978-0-613-52960-0(X)) Tandem Library Bks.

Greenaway, Theresa. Animals: Foldout Book. 2005. (Illus.). 12p. (J). (gr. k-4). reprint ed. 10.00 (978-0-7567-8778-3(5)) DIANE Publishing Co.

—The Secret World Of..., 6 bks., Set. Incl. Ants. lib. bdg. 27.12 (978-0-7398-3511-1(4)); Crabs. lib. bdg. 27.12 (978-0-7398-3506-7(8)); Snakes. lib. bdg. 27.12 (978-0-7398-3510-4(6)); Spiders. lib. bdg. 27.12 (978-0-7398-3509-8(2)); Whales. lib. bdg. 27.12 (978-0-7398-3508-1(4)); Wolves, Wild Dogs & Foxes. lib. bdg. 27.12 (978-0-7398-3507-4(6)); 48p. (J). (gr. 4-7). 2001. (Illus.). 2000. Set lib. bdg. 162.72 (978-0-7398-3512-8(2)) Raintree.

Greive, Bradley Trevor & Easton, Samantha. Querida Mama' (Dear Mom Spanish) Gracias por Todo. 2007. 80p. 9.95 (978-0-7407-6543-8(4)) Andrews McMeel Publishing.

Grolier (Firm) Staff, contrib. by. Amazing Animals of the the World 3. 2006. (978-0-7172-6179-6(4)); (978-0-7172-6180-2(8)); (978-0-7172-6181-9(6)); (978-0-7172-6182-6(4)); (978-0-7172-6183-3(2)); (978-0-7172-6184-0(0)); (978-0-7172-6185-7(9)); (978-0-7172-6186-4(7)); (978-0-7172-6187-1(5)); (978-0-7172-6188-8(3)); (978-0-7172-6189-5(1)) Grolier, Ltd.

Grolier Educational (Firm) Staff, contrib. by. Nature's Children. 2007. (J). (***978-0-7172-8079-7(9)***) Grolier, Ltd.

Grolier Educational Staff. Nature's Children, 21 vols., Set VII. 2001. (Nature's Children Ser.). (Illus.). 1008p. (J). 289.00 (978-0-7172-5531-3(X) , Grolier) Scholastic Library Publishing.

Grolier Educational Staff, contrib. by. Amazing Animals of the the World 2, 10 vols. 2005. (Illus.). (J). 179.00 (978-0-7172-6112-3(3)); (978-0-7172-6113-0(1)); (978-0-7172-6114-7(X)); (978-0-7172-6115-4(8)); (978-0-7172-6116-1(6)); (978-0-7172-6117-8(4)); (978-0-7172-6118-5(2)); (978-0-7172-6119-2(0)); (978-0-7172-6120-8(4)); (978-0-7172-6121-5(2)); (978-0-7172-6122-2(0)) Scholastic Library Publishing. (Grolier).

Group/McGraw-Hill, Wright. Amazing under Water Animals: Magazine Anthology: Level 4, 6 vols. (Comprehension Strand Ser.). (gr. 4-8). 54.00 (978-0-322-09852-7(1)) Wright Group, The.

—Animal Advocates, 6 vols. (Wildcats Ser.). 32p. (gr. 2-8). (978-0-322-05861-3(9)) Wright Group, The.

—Las Crias de Los Animales, 6 vols. (First Explorers. Primeros Exploradores Nonfiction Sets Ser.). (SPA.). (gr. 1-2). 29.95 (978-0-7699-1467-1(5)) Shortland Pubns. (U. S. A.) Inc.

—Donde Viven Algunos Animales, 6 vols. (First Explorers. Primeros Exploradores Nonfiction Sets Ser.). (SPA.). (gr. 1-2). 29.95 (978-0-7699-1472-5(1)) Shortland Pubns. (U. S. A.) Inc.

—Lights Out! 6 Each of 1 Anthology, 6 vols. (Wildcats Ser.). 32p. (gr. 2-8). (978-0-322-05858-3(9)) Wright Group, The.

—Take-Twos Animals: Early Fluency - Complete Kit, Vol. 4. (gr. 2 up). 420.50 (978-0-322-09175-7(6)) Wright Group, The.

—Take-Twos Animals Vol. 4: Early Fluency - Student Book Set - 1 Each of 12 Titles. (gr. 2 up). 69.95 (978-0-322-09303-4(1)) Wright Group, The.

Guidoux, Valerie. Hidden Animals. Caillou, Pierre & Eydoux, Anne, illus. 2006. (Explore Your World Ser.). (ENG & FRE.). 28p. (J). (ps-1). 15.95 (978-1-55407-008-4(2)) Firefly Bks., Ltd.

Guile, Gill, illus. In My Garden. 20p. (J). (978-1-932209-38-9(7)) Bendon Publishing International.

Gulberson, Brenda. Exotic Species: Invaders in Paradise. 1999. (Single Titles Ser.). (Illus.). 80p. (gr. 5-8). lib. bdg. 24.90 (978-0-7613-1319-9(2) , Millbrook Pr.) Lerner Publishing Group.

Gunzi, Christiane. Big & Wild. 2006. (Feels Real Bks.). (Illus.). 10p. (J). bds. 4.99 (978-0-7641-5946-6(1)) Barron's Educational Series, Inc.

—In the Jungle. 2006. (Feels Real Bks.). (Illus.). 10p. (J). bds. 4.99 (978-0-7641-5949-7(6)) Barron's Educational Series, Inc.

Gunzi, Christiane & Greenaway, Theresa. Animals Foldout Book. 2002. (Foldout Bks.). (Illus.). 6p. (J). (gr. 3-7). 9.95 (978-1-57145-755-4(0) , Silver Dolphin Bks.) Advantage Pubs. Group.

Haddon, Jean. It's a Beautiful Day! Enright, Vicky, tr. Enright, Vicky, illus. 2004. (Silly Millies Ser.). 32p. (J). lib. bdg. (978-0-7613-2834-6(3) , Millbrook Pr.) Lerner Publishing Group.

Halfmann, Janet. Life in the Sea. 2000. (Lifeviews Ser.). (Illus.). 32p. (J). (gr. 5-7). lib. bdg. (978-1-58341-074-5(0) , Creative Education) Creative Co., The.

—Life under a Stone. 2000. (Lifeviews Ser.). (Illus.). 32p. (J). (978-1-58341-075-2(9) , Creative Education) Creative Co., The.

Hall, Kirsten. Animals & Their Senses. 24p. (YA). 96.65 (978-0-8368-4801-4(2)); 96.65 (978-0-8368-4813-7(6)) Stevens, Gareth Inc.

Hall, Peg. Whose Ears Are These? A Look at Animal Ears - Short, Flat, & Floppy. Landmark, Ken, illus. 2004. (Whose Is It? Ser.). 24p. (C). (gr. k-2). 22.60 (978-1-4048-0004-5(2)) Picture Window Bks.

—Whose Eyes Are These? A Look at Animal Eyes - Big, Round, & Narrow. Landmark, Ken, illus. 2004. (Whose Is It? Ser.). 24p. (C). (gr. k-2). 22.60 (978-1-4048-0005-2(0)) Picture Window Bks.

—Whose Feet Are These? A Look at Hooves, Paws, & Claws. Landmark, Ken, illus. 2004. (Whose Is It? Ser.). 24p. (C). (gr. k-2). 22.60 (978-1-4048-0006-9(9)) Picture Window Bks.

—Whose Legs Are These? A Look at Animal Legs - Kicking, Running, & Hopping. Landmark, Ken, illus. 2004. (Whose Is It? Ser.). 24p. (C). (gr. k-2). 22.60 (978-1-4048-0007-6(7)) Picture Window Bks.

—Whose Nose Is This? A Look at Beaks, Snouts, & Trunks. Landmark, Ken, illus. 2004. (Whose Is It? Ser.). 24p. (C). (gr. k-2). 22.60 (978-1-4048-0009-0(3)) Picture Window Bks.

—Whose Tail Is This? A Look at Tails - Swishing, Wiggling, & Rattling. Landmark, Ken, illus. 2004. (Whose Is It? Ser.). 24p. (C). (gr. k-2). 22.60 (978-1-4048-0011-3(5)) Picture Window Bks.

Halls, Kelly Milner. Albino Animals. 2004. (Junior Library Guild Selection Ser.). (Illus.). 72p. (J). (gr. 4 up). 18.95 (978-1-58196-012-9(3)); pap. 8.95 (978-1-58196-019-8(0)) Darby Creek Publishing.

Hamilton, Sue L. Nature on the Rampage. 2007. (ENG., Illus.). 32p. (YA). lib. bdg. 24.21 (***978-1-59928-773-7(0)*** , ABDO & Daughters) ABDO Publishing Co.

Hamilton, Tisha. Animals of Asia. 2005. (Navigators Ser.). (J). pap. 42.00 (***978-1-4108-5075-1(7)***) Benchmark Education Co.

Hammerslough, Jane. Wild in the U S A. 2003. (gr. 3-6). lib. bdg. 11.80 (978-0-613-72115-8(2)) Tandem Library Bks.

Hammersmith, Craig. Kerplunk! 2002. (Spyglass Books). (Illus.). 24p. (J). (gr. 1 up). lib. bdg. 18.60 (978-0-7565-0236-2(5)) Compass Point Bks.

Hands on Crafts for Kids Staff. What Do You Say? 2002. (Illus.). 12p. (J). bds. 3.95 (978-1-4027-0177-1(2) , Balloon Bks.) Sterling Publishing Co., Inc.

Hansen, Rosanna. Animal Rescuers. 2004. (True Tales Ser.). (J). (gr. 2-4). pap. 4.95 (978-0-516-24602-4(X) , Children's Pr.) Scholastic Library Publishing.

—Caring Animals. 2004. (True Tales Ser.). (J). (gr. 2-4). pap. 4.95 (978-0-516-24603-1(8) , Children's Pr.) Scholastic Library Publishing.

—Caring Animals: A Chapter Book. 2003. (True Tales Ser.). (Illus.). 48p. (J). 22.50 (978-0-516-22912-6(5) , Children's Pr.) Scholastic Library Publishing.

Harcourt School Publishers Staff. Amigos los Animales: Take-Home Book. 1999. (Vamos Ser.). (SPA., Illus.). (J). pap. 2.50 (978-0-15-318821-3(9)) Harcourt Schl. Pubs.

—Animal Adventures: Practice Book. 3rd ed. 2001. (Trophies Reading Program Ser.). (Illus.). (J). pap. 1.80 (978-0-15-325088-0(7)) Harcourt Schl. Pubs.

—Animal Adventures: Practice Book: Florida Edition. 3rd ed. 2002. (Trophies Reading Program Ser.). (Illus.). (J). pap. 2.00 (978-0-15-326603-4(1)) Harcourt Schl. Pubs.

—Animal Adventures: Theme Book. 1999. (Collections Ser.). (Illus.). (J). pap. 3.00 (978-0-15-314024-2(0)) Harcourt Schl. Pubs.

—Animal Families: Practice Book. 3rd ed. 2001. (Trophies Reading Program Ser.). (Illus.). (J). pap. 1.80 (978-0-15-325086-6(0)) Harcourt Schl. Pubs.

—Animal Families: Practice Book: California Edition. 3rd ed. 2002. (Trophies Reading Program Ser.). (Illus.). (J). pap. 2.00 (978-0-15-326628-7(7)) Harcourt Schl. Pubs.

—Animal Families: Practice Book: Florida Edition. 3rd ed. 2002. (Trophies Reading Program Ser.). (Illus.). (J). pap. 2.00 (978-0-15-326601-0(5)) Harcourt Schl. Pubs.

—Animal Families: Theme Book. 1999. (Collections Ser.). (J). pap. 3.00 (978-0-15-314022-8(4)) Harcourt Schl. Pubs.

—Animals I Like: Theme Book. 1999. (Collections Ser.). (Illus.). (J). pap. 3.00 (978-0-15-314017-4(8)) Harcourt Schl. Pubs.

—Animals in Plants: Science Reader. 1999. (SPA., Illus.). (J). pap. 3.70 (978-0-15-316107-0(8)) Harcourt Schl. Pubs.

—Animals of the Frozen South On Level. 3rd ed. 2002. (Trophies Reading Program Ser.). (Illus.). pap. 5.10 (978-0-15-323439-2(3)) Harcourt Schl. Pubs.

—Critters in the Urban Wilderness Below Level. 3rd ed. 2002. (Trophies Reading Program Ser.). (Illus.). (gr. 4). pap. 5.10 (978-0-15-323233-6(1)) Harcourt Schl. Pubs.

—Does a Kangaroo Have a Mother Too? Little Book. 3rd ed. 2002. (Trophies Reading Program Ser.). (Illus.). (J). pap. 10.20 (978-0-15-325450-5(5)) Harcourt Schl. Pubs.

—From Head to Toe Little Book. 3rd ed. 2002. (Trophies Reading Program Ser.). (Illus.). (J). pap. 10.20 (978-0-15-329355-9(1)) Harcourt Schl. Pubs.

—Harcourt Science: Animals Reader. 1999. (Illus.). pap. 2.90 (978-0-15-314842-2(X)) Harcourt Schl. Pubs.

—Hiding to Survive On Level. 3rd ed. 2002. (Trophies Reading Program Ser.). (Illus.). pap. 5.10 (978-0-15-323279-4(X)) Harcourt Schl. Pubs.

—Look at the Pond. 3rd ed. 2002. (Trophies English Language Learners Ser.). (Illus.). (J). pap. 3.20 (978-0-15-327571-5(5)) Harcourt Schl. Pubs.

—Looking for Animals Below Level. 3rd ed. 2002. (Trophies Reading Program Ser.). (Illus.). (gr. 2). pap. 5.10 (978-0-15-323041-7(X)) Harcourt Schl. Pubs.

—Meow, Hiss, Purr: Take-Home Book. 1999. (Signatures Ser.). (Illus.). (J). (gr. 3). pap. 1.90 (978-0-15-313886-7(6)) Harcourt Schl. Pubs.

—Mice Squeak, We Speak: Little Book. 2000. (Collections Ser.). (Illus.). (J). pap. 10.20 (978-0-15-314495-0(5)) Harcourt Schl. Pubs.

—Moo Moo Brown Cow: Little Book. 2000. (Collections Ser.). (Illus.). (J). pap. 10.20 (978-0-15-314507-0(2)) Harcourt Schl. Pubs.

—The Most Advanced Level. 3rd ed. 2002. (Trophies Reading Program Ser.). (Illus.). pap. 5.10 (978-0-15-323303-6(6)) Harcourt Schl. Pubs.

—Small Animal, Big Animal. 3rd ed. 2002. (Trophies English Language Learners Ser.). (Illus.). (J). pap. 3.20 (978-0-15-327568-5(5)) Harcourt Schl. Pubs.

—Staying Warm Below Level. 3rd ed. 2002. (Trophies Reading Program Ser.). (Illus.). pap. 5.10 (978-0-15-323060-8(6)) Harcourt Schl. Pubs.

—What Has a Beak? 3rd ed. 2002. (Illus.). (J). pap. 3.20 (978-0-15-327579-1(0)) Harcourt Schl. Pubs.

—Where Does the Brown Bear Go? Little Book. 3rd ed. 2002. (Trophies Reading Program Ser.). (Illus.). (J). pap. 10.20 (978-0-15-329352-8(7)) Harcourt Schl. Pubs.

—Where the Animals Live. 3rd ed. 2002. (Trophies English Language Learners Ser.). (Illus.). pap. 5.10 (978-0-15-327707-8(6)) Harcourt Schl. Pubs.

—Wild Animals: Take-Home Book. 1999. (Signatures Ser.). (Illus.). (J). pap. 1.70 (978-0-15-313843-0(2)) Harcourt Schl. Pubs.

Hare, Tony. Animal Life, 3 vols., Set. 2002. 300p. (J). (gr. 4-8). 120.00 (978-0-8160-4744-4(8)) Facts On File, Inc.

Harper, Kathryn & Mitton, Tony. Animal Antics. 2007. (Illus.). 48p. pap. *(*978-0-521-70471-7(5))* Cambridge Univ. Pr.

Harris, Monica. My First Book of Animals. 2005. (My First Ser.). (Illus.). 128p. 7.98 (978-0-7853-8372-7(7) , 7183700) Publications International, Ltd.

Harris, Nicholas. Animals of the World. 2006. (First Library of Knowledge). 32p. (J). (gr. 2-4). 23.70 (978-1-4103-0348-6(9) , Blackbirch Pr., Inc.) Thomson Gale.

Harter, Debbie. Cha-Cha-Cha en la Selva. 2003. (SPA.). (gr. k-3). lib. bdg. 18.80 (978-0-613-67257-3(7)) Tandem Library Bks.

Hartley, Karen, et al. Senses in Living Things. 2000. (Senses Ser.). (Illus.). 32p. (J). 21.95 (978-1-58810-134-1(7)) Heinemann Library.

Hartman, Bob. The Generous Rabbit: And Other Animal Stories. Hudson, Brett, illus. 2004. 64p. (J). pap. 8.99 (978-0-7459-4697-9(6) , Lion) Lion Hudson plc GBR. *Dist:* Independent Pubs. Group.

—Why Dogs Chase Cats. Hudson, Brett, illus. 2004. 64p. (J). pap. 8.99 (978-0-7459-4696-2(8) , Lion) Lion Hudson plc GBR. *Dist:* Independent Pubs. Group.

Harvey, Bev. Animal Kingdom, 6 vols., Set. 2005. (Illus.). 32p. (gr. 2-4). pap. 138.00 (978-0-7910-7056-7(5) , Chelsea Hse.) Facts On File, Inc.

Harvey, Bob. The African Bush. Elliot, Rebecca, illus. 2006. (Get Inside... Ser.). 48p. pap. 18.95 (978-1-904668-96-1(8)) Mercury Bks. Ltd. GBR. *Dist:* International Publishers Marketing.

The Haunted Drive-Thru. 2001. (Illus.). 12p. (J). bds. 7.99 (978-0-307-10149-5(5) , 10149, Golden Bks.) Random Hse. Children's Bks.

Haus, Robyn. Create a Year-Round Wildlife Habitat: For Urban & Suburban Small Spaces. 2004. (Quick Starts for Kids! Ser.). (Illus.). 64p. (J). pap. 8.95 (978-1-885593-97-9(X) , Williamson Bks.) Ideals Pubns.

Helbrough, Emma. 1001 Bugs to Spot. 32p. (J). lib. bdg. 14.95 (978-1-58086-808-2(8) , Usborne) EDC Publishing.

—1001 Bugs to Spot. Gower, Teri, illus. 2005. 32p. (J). pap. 6.95 (978-0-7945-1000-8(0) , Usborne) EDC Publishing.

Heller, Ruth. Animals Born Alive & Well. 1999. (Ruth Heller's World of Nature Ser.). (Illus.). 48p. (J). (ps-3). pap. 7.99 (978-0-698-11777-8(8) , Putnam Juvenile) Penguin Group (USA) Inc.

—Animals Born Alive & Well. (FRE., Illus.). (J). 6.99 (978-0-590-73030-3(4)) Scholastic, Inc.

—Animals Born Alive & Well. 1999. (gr. k-3). lib. bdg. 16.45 (978-0-7857-0023-4(4)) Tandem Library Bks.

—How to Hide a Crocodile: And Other Reptiles. unabr. ed. 2001. (How to Hide Ser.). (Illus.). (J). (gr. k-3). pap. 14.45 incl. audio Spoken Arts, Inc.

—How to Hide a Polar Bear: And Other Mammals. unabr. ed. 2001. (How to Hide Ser.). (Illus.). (J). (gr. k-3). pap. 14.45 incl. audio (978-0-8045-6569-1(4) , 6569) Spoken Arts, Inc.

—Nous Ne Sommes Pas Nes/Oeuf! l.t. ed. (FRE., Illus.). (J). bds. 29.99 (978-0-590-73029-7(0)) Scholastic, Inc.

Helmer, Marilyn. Critter Riddles. Parker, Eric, illus. 2004. (Kids Can Read Ser.). 32p. (J). (gr. k-3). (978-1-55337-411-4(8)); (978-1-55337-445-9(2)) Kids Can Pr., Ltd.

—Critter Riddles. 2003. (gr. k-3). lib. bdg. 11.80 (978-0-613-84968-5(X)) Tandem Library Bks.

Hemminger, Marcia. World Animals Early Learner Photo Fun Activities. Rogers, Kathy, ed. 2001. (Early Learner Photo Fun Activities Ser.). (Illus.). 8p. (J). (ps-1). pap. 6.95 (978-1-56472-380-2(1)) Edupress, Inc.

Hess, Nina. Whose Feet? Kanzler, John, tr. Kanzler, John, illus. 2004. (Step into Reading Ser.). 32p. (J). (ps-2). pap. 3.99 (978-0-375-82623-8(8) , Random Hse. Bks. for Young Readers) Random Hse. Children's Bks.

—Whose Feet? 2004. (ps-2). lib. bdg. 11.80 (978-0-613-86693-4(2)) Tandem Library Bks.

Hess, Paul. Animal Worlds. 2006. (Animal Verse Ser.). (Illus.). 96p. (J). pap. 10.95 (978-1-84089-408-0(3) , Zero to Ten, Limited) Evans Publishing Group GBR. *Dist:* Independent Pubs. Group.

—Polar Animals. 2001. (Animals Ser.). (Illus.). 24p. (J). (ps-k). bds. 5.95 (978-1-84089-167-6(X) , Zero to Ten, Limited) Evans Publishing Group GBR. *Dist:* Independent Pubs. Group.

—Polar Animals. 2002. (ps-2). lib. bdg. 15.25 (978-0-613-79938-6(0)) Tandem Library Bks.

—Rainforest Animals. 2001. (Animals Ser.). (Illus.). 24p. (J). (ps-k). bds. (978-1-84089-166-9(1) , Zero to Ten, Limited) Evans Publishing Group.

—Safari Animals. 2001. (Animals Ser.). (Illus.). 24p. (J). (ps-k). bds. (978-1-84089-165-2(3) , Zero to Ten, Limited) Evans Publishing Group.

Hess, Paul, illus. Animal Worlds, 4 bks. Incl. African Animals. Macken, JoAnn Early. lib. bdg. 20.67 (978-0-8368-3038-5(5)); Farm Animals. Macken, JoAnn Early, text. lib. bdg. 20.67 (978-0-8368-3039-2(3)); Polar Animals. Macken, JoAnn Early. lib. bdg. 20.67 (978-0-8368-3040-8(7)); Rain Forest Animals. Macken, JoAnn Early. lib. bdg. 20.67 (978-0-8368-3041-5(5)); 24p. (J). (ps up). (Illus.). 2002. Set lib. bdg. 82.68 (978-0-8368-3037-8(7)) Stevens, Gareth Inc.

—Polar Animals. 2002. (Animal Verse Ser.). 24p. (J). pap. 6.95 (978-1-84089-173-7(4) , Zero to Ten, Limited) Evans Publishing Group GBR. *Dist:* Independent Pubs. Group.

—Rainforest Animals. (Animals Ser.). 2003. 24p. (J). pap. (978-1-84089-172-0(6)); 1998. (YA). (978-1-84089-008-2(8) , 868230) Evans Publishing Group. (Zero to Ten, Limited).

—Safari Animals. 1998. (Animal Worlds Ser.). (J). (ps). (978-1-84089-007-5(X) , 868232, Zero to Ten, Limited) Evans Publishing Group.

—Safari Animals. 2002. (Animals Ser.). 24p. (J). pap. 6.95 (978-1-84089-171-3(8) , Zero to Ten, Limited) Evans Publishing Group GBR. *Dist:* Independent Pubs. Group.

Hewitt, Sally. All Kinds of Animals. 1998. (It's Science! Ser.). (Illus.). 32p. (J). (gr. k-3). 23.50 (978-0-516-21175-6(7) , Children's Pr.) Scholastic Library Publishing.

—Animal Kingdom: Ants to Whales. 2005. (Science Starters Ser.). (Illus.). 32p. (J). (gr. 1-4). lib. bdg. 27.10 (978-1-59604-009-0(2)) Stargazer Bks.

Hibbert, Adam. Freshwater Pond. 1999. (gr. 3-6). lib. bdg. 17.60 (978-0-613-19513-3(2)) Tandem Library Bks.

Hickman, Pamela. Animals & Their Mates: How Animals Attract, Fight for & Protect Each Other. Stephens, Pat, illus. 2005. (Animal Behavior Ser.). 40p. (YA). (gr. 2-6). (978-1-55337-546-3(7)); (978-1-55337-545-6(9)) Kids Can Pr., Ltd.

—Animals Eating: How Animals Chomp, Chew, Slurp & Swallow. 2001. (Illus.). (J). (978-0-606-21033-1(4)) Tandem Library Bks.

—Animals Eating: How Animals Chomp, Chew, Slurp, & Swallow. 2001. (gr. 3-6). lib. bdg. 14.10 (978-0-613-81249-8(2)) Tandem Library Bks.

—Animals Eating: How Animals Chomp, Chew, Slurp & Swallow. Stephens, Pat, illus. unabr. ed. 2004. (Animal Behavior Ser.). 40p. (J). (gr. 4-6). (978-1-55074-579-5(4)); (978-1-55074-577-1(8)) Kids Can Pr., Ltd.

—Animals in Motion: How Animals Swim, Jump, Slither & Glide. Stephens, Pat, illus. unabr. ed. 2004. (Animal Behavior Ser.). 40p. (J). (gr. 4-6). (978-1-55074-575-7(1)); (978-1-55074-573-3(5)) Kids Can Pr., Ltd.

—Animals in Motion: How Animals Swim, Jump, Slither & Glide. Stephens, Pat, illus. 2000. 40p. (J). (ps-ps). lib. bdg. 14.10 (978-0-613-24200-4(9)) Tandem Library Bks.

—Animals in Motion: How Animals Swim, Jump, Slither & Glide. 2000. (Illus.). (J). (978-0-606-18223-2(3)) Tandem Library Bks.

Hide to Survive, 6 Packs. (gr. k-1). 23.00 (978-0-7635-8857-1(1)) Rigby Education.

Highlights Editors. Animal Rebus Run: A Magnetic Story Maker. Highlights Artists Staff, illus. 2007. 16p. 16.99 (978-0-8249-1501-8(1) , Ideals Children's Bks.) Ideals Pubns.

Hil, Mcgraw. Gr 4 Animals Sci Pe. 2000. (McGraw-Hill Science Ser.). (gr. 4 up). (978-0-02-278218-4(4)) Macmillan/McGraw-Hill Schl. Div.

—Sciasmtbk Animals. 2000. (McGraw-Hill Science Ser.). (gr. 4 up). (978-0-02-277758-6(X)) Macmillan/McGraw-Hill Schl. Div.

—Trfpaswak Animals. 2000. (McGraw-Hill Science Ser.). (gr. 4 up). (978-0-02-277639-8(7)) Macmillan/McGraw-Hill Schl. Div.

Hile, Kevin. Animal Rights. 2004. (Point/Counterpoint Ser.). (Illus.). 120p. (gr. 9-13). 32.95 (978-0-7910-7922-5(8) , Chelsea Hse.) Facts On File, Inc.

Hillard, Leith. A Giraffe for France. Blackall, Sophie, illus. 2000. 42p. (J). 13.95 (978-0-949284-41-9(6)) Watermark Pr., The AUS. *Dist:* Antique Collectors' Club.

Himmelman, John. Frog in a Bog. 2004. (Illus.). 32p. (J). pap. 6.95 (978-1-57091-518-5(0)) Charlesbridge Publishing, Inc.

—Mouse in a Meadow. Himmelman, John, illus. 2005. (Illus.). 32p. (J). 15.95 (978-1-57091-520-8(2)); pap. 6.95 (978-1-57091-521-5(0)) Charlesbridge Publishing, Inc.

Hirschi, Ron. Lions, Tigers, & Bears: Why Are Big Predators So Rare? Mangelsen, Thomas D., photos by. 2007. (Illus.). 32p. (J). (gr. 2-5). 16.95 *(*978-1-59078-435-8(9))* Boyds Mills Pr.

Hirschmann, Kris. Glow-in-the-Dark Animals. 2001. (Planet Reader Ser.). (Illus.). (J). (978-0-606-21214-4(0)) Tandem Library Bks.

—Manatees. 2005. (Creatures of the Sea Ser.). (Illus.). 48p. (J). (ps-8). lib. bdg. 26.20 (978-0-7377-3008-1(0) , Greenhaven Pr., Inc.) Thomson Gale.

—Moray Eels. 2002. (Creatures of the Sea Ser.). (Illus.). 48p. (J). (gr. 3-5). 23.70 (978-0-7377-0985-8(5) , Kidhaven) Thomson Gale.

—Oh Baby! Amazing Baby Animals. 2003. (Illus.). 32p. (J). pap. 5.99 (978-0-439-41918-5(2)) Scholastic, Inc.

Hodge, Deborah. Polar Animals. Stephens, Pat, illus. 2008. 24p. pap. *(*978-1-55453-044-1(X))* Kids Can Pr., Ltd.

Hodge, Judith. Animal Hospital. 1999. (gr. k-3). lib. bdg. 11.80 (978-0-613-17084-0(9)) Tandem Library Bks.

Hoff, Mary. Metamorphosis. 2003. (World of Wonder Ser.). (Illus.). 32p. (J). lib. bdg. (978-1-58341-268-8(9) , Creative Education) Creative Co., The.

Holder, Greg, ed. God's Animals. 1998. (Baby Board Bks.). (Illus.). 6p. (J). (ps). bds. 3.99 (978-0-7847-0840-8(1) , 03480, Bean Sprouts) Standard Publishing.

Holmes, Kevin J. Animals Series, 8 bks., Set. (J). pap. 110.00 (978-1-56065-671-5(9) , Bridgestone Bks.) Capstone Pr., Inc.

—Warthogs. 1998. (Animals Ser.). (Illus.). 24p. (J). (gr. 2-3). lib. bdg. 18.60 (978-0-7368-0067-9(0) , Bridgestone Bks.) Capstone Pr., Inc.

Holt, Rinehart and Winston Staff. Animals: Item Listing, Group B. 2nd ed. 2001. (Holt Science & Technology Ser.). pap. 11.26 (978-0-03-065509-8(9)) Holt, Rinehart & Winston.

—Animals Science Kit: Non-Consumable Edition, Module B. 2nd ed. 2002. (Holt Science & Technology Ser.). pap. 527.40 (978-0-03-067613-0(4)) Harcourt Schl. Pubs.

Holub, Joan. Animals. 2002. (gr. k-3). lib. bdg. 14.15 (978-0-613-81292-4(1)) Tandem Library Bks.

Home in a Tree. (J). pap. 13.15 (978-0-8136-4256-7(6)) Modern Curriculum Pr.

HOP, LLC. Hooked on Animals in the Wild Super Activity Kit. 2006. (J). (ps). 9.99 (978-1-933863-17-7(X)) HOP, LLC.

—Super Activity 3-pack - Hooked on Animals. 2006. (J). (ps). 24.99 (978-1-933863-97-9(8)) HOP, LLC.

Hopkins, Mary R. Animal Alphabet: On the Land, in the Sky or Sea, Meet God's Creatures from a to Z. Francisco, Wendy, illus. 2003. 32p. (ps-1). 12.99 (978-0-89107-968-2(8)) Crossway Bks.

Hoppner, Gabi. Fun with Animals. 2004. (What A Series of Fun! Ser.). (Illus.). 10p. (J). bds. 3.99 (978-1-59384-052-5(7)) Parklane Publishing.

Horstman, Lisa. The Troublesome Cub. Horstman, Lisa, illus. 2001. (Illus.). 32p. pap. 6.50 (978-0-937207-32-1(2)) Great Smoky Mountains Natural History Assn.

—The Troublesome Cub in the Great Smoky Mountains. 2001. 32p. (J). (ps-3). pap. 6.50 (978-0-937207-31-4(4)) Great Smoky Mountains Natural History Assn.

Houghton, Sarah. Bloodsuckers: Bats, Bugs, & Other Bloodthirsty Creatures. 2003. (High Five Reading Ser.). (Illus.). (J). 64p. lib. bdg. 22.60 (978-0-7368-2789-8(7)); 48p. pap. 23.93 (978-0-7368-2834-5(6)) Capstone Pr., Inc.

—Bloodsuckers: Bats, Bugs, & Other Bloodthirsty Creatures, 6 vols. (gr. 4 up). 49.95 (978-0-7368-2844-4(3) , High Five) Red Brick Learning.

How Animals Hide: Level G, 6 vols. (Wonder Worldtm Ser.). 16p. 29.95 (978-0-7802-4581-5(4)) Wright Group, The.

How Animals Move. (Animal Behavior Ser.). 24p. (J). 6.95 (978-0-7368-5166-4(6)) Capstone Pr., Inc.

How Animals Move: Individual Title Six-Packs. (Discovery World Ser.). 24p. (gr. 1-2). 33.00 (978-0-7635-8473-3(8)) Rigby Education.

Huang, Chungliang Al. The Chinese Book of Animal Powers. 1999. (Illus.). 32p. (YA). (gr. 3-7). 16.89 (978-0-06-027729-1(7)); 16.95 (978-0-06-027728-4(9)) HarperCollins Pubs. (Cotler, Joanna Books).

Hudak, Heather C. Carnivores. 2004. (Nature's Food Chain Ser.). (Illus.). 24p. (J). lib. bdg. (978-1-59036-238-9(1)) Weigl Pubs., Inc.

—Omnivores. 2004. (Nature's Food Chain Ser.). (Illus.). 24p. (J). lib. bdg. (978-1-59036-241-9(1)) Weigl Pubs., Inc.

Hughes. Creepy Creatures, 4 vols., Set 1. 2003. (Illus.). 74.24 (978-1-4109-0621-2(3)); (J). pap. 19.80 (978-1-4109-0647-2(7)) Raintree.

Hunter, Anne. What's in the Meadow? 2000. (Illus.). 32p. (J). (gr. k-3). tchr. ed. 4.95 (978-0-618-01512-2(4)) Houghton Mifflin Co. Trade & Reference Div.

Hunter, Tom. Critters for Kids: A North American Wildlife Activity Book. 2004. 80p. (J). pap., act. bk. ed. 7.95 (978-1-895811-69-8(4)) Heritage Hse. Publishing Co., Ltd. CAN. *Dist:* Midpoint Trade Bks., Inc.

Hurwitz, Jane. In Animal Care, Choosing a Vet. 2005. (World of Work Ser.). (Illus.). 64p. (YA). (gr. 7-12). lib. bdg. 25.25 (978-0-8239-3356-3(3)) Rosen Publishing Group, Inc., The.

Hyenas, 6 vols. (gr. 2-5). 36.95 (978-0-7368-8414-3(9)) Red Brick Learning.

I Love Animals: My Little Box of Books, 4 bks. 2002. 40p. (J). bds. 15.95 (978-0-7525-8653-3(X)) Parragon, Inc.

Iegg, Gerard. Minibeasts. 2006. (Illus.). 24p. (YA). (gr. 1 up). lib. bdg. 22.80 (978-1-931983-59-4(3)) Chrysalis Education.

Imbriaco, Alison. The Otter: A MyReportLinks. com Book. 2005. (Endangered & Threatened Animals Ser.). (Illus.). 48p. (J). lib. bdg. 25.26 (978-0-7660-5067-9(X) , MyReportLinks.com Bks.) Enslow Pubs., Inc.

In Danger, 6 Packs. (gr. k-1). 23.00 (978-0-7635-8841-0(5)) Rigby Education.

In the Wild Series, 12 bks., Set. 2003. (Illus.). 308.40 (978-0-7398-5502-7(6)) Raintree.

Incredible Creatures: Level N, 6 vols. (Explorers Ser.). 32p. (gr. 3-6). 44.95 (978-0-7699-0589-1(7)) Shortland Pubns. (U. S. A.) Inc.

Insera, Rose. Animals. Insera, Rose, illus. 2005. (Illus.). (J). (gr. 3-6). 8.95 (978-1-74157-268-1(1)) Hinkler Bks. Pty, Ltd. AUS. *Dist:* Penton Overseas, Inc.

Into Wild Indonesia. 2004. 11.20 (978-1-4103-0244-1(X) , Blackbirch Pr., Inc.) Thomson Gale.

Into Wild Nepal. 2004. 11.20 (978-1-4103-0238-0(5) , Blackbirch Pr., Inc.) Thomson Gale.

It's Amazing: It's Amazing Package. 2003. 125.95 (978-0-673-61613-5(4)) Celebration Pr.

Jackson, Abby. Donde? 2005. Tr. of Where?. (SPA., Illus.). 16p. (J). (gr. k-1). lib. bdg. 15.93 (978-0-7368-4133-7(4)) Capstone Pr., Inc.

Jackson, Tom. The World Encyclopedia of Animals. 2004. (Illus.). 256p. 35.00 (978-0-7548-1347-7(9) , Lorenz Bks.) Anness Publishing GBR. *Dist:* National Bk. Network.

Jacobs, Daniel. Patrones en los Animales. 2005. Tr. of Animal Patterns. (SPA., Illus.). 16p. (J). (gr. k-1). lib. bdg. 15.93 (978-0-7368-4148-1(2)) Capstone Pr., Inc.

Jacobs, Lee. Unique Animals of Alaska. 2004. (Illus.). 24p. (J). (gr. 3-5). 22.45 (978-1-4103-0088-1(9) , Blackbirch Pr., Inc.) Thomson Gale.

—Unique Animals of Hawaii. 2004. (Illus.). 24p. (J). (gr. 3-5). 22.45 (978-1-4103-0087-4(0) , Blackbirch Pr., Inc.) Thomson Gale.

—Unique Animals of the Midwest. 2004. (Illus.). 24p. (J). (gr. 3-5). 22.45 (978-1-56711-965-7(4) , Blackbirch Pr., Inc.) Thomson Gale.

—Unique Animals of the Pacific Coast. 2004. (Illus.). 24p. (J). (gr. 3-5). 22.45 (978-1-56711-967-1(0) , Blackbirch Pr., Inc.) Thomson Gale.

—Unique Animals of the Southeast. 2004. (Illus.). 24p. (J). (gr. 3-5). 22.45 (978-1-56711-969-5(7) , Blackbirch Pr., Inc.) Thomson Gale.

Jaeger, Pamela. Fiona No No. 2005. 32p. (J). 8.95 (978-0-9704876-4-3(9)) First Mom's Club, The.

Jakab, Cheryl. The Animal Life Cycle. 2007. (J). *(*978-1-59920-148-1(8))* Smart Apple Media.

James, Diana. Animal Homes. 2000. (gr. 3-6). lib. bdg. 14.10 (978-0-613-43296-2(7)) Tandem Library Bks.

James, Diane. On the Farm. 2004. (My First Look at Animals Ser.). (SPA., Illus.). 24p. (ps-2). 9.95 (978-1-58728-855-5(9) , Two Can Publishing) T&N Children's Publishing.

James, Diane, et al. En Safari. 2004. (Descubre los Animales Ser.).Tr. of On Safari. (SPA., Illus.). 24p. (ps-2). 9.95 (978-1-58728-399-4(9) , Two Can Publishing) T&N Children's Publishing.

Jarrell, Pamela R. Animals I Know: Cuddle Book. Van Wagner, Holly, illus. 2002. 8p. (J). (ps-1). bds. 10.95 (978-1-57332-224-9(5)) HighReach Learning, Inc.

Jefferis, David. Animal Kingdom. 2002. (Young Library). (Illus.). 32p. (J). lib. bdg. 25.69 (978-0-7398-6321-3(5)) Raintree.

Jenkins, Steve. Actual Size. 2004. (Illus.). 28p. (J). (gr. k-3). tchr. ed. 16.00 (978-0-618-37594-3(5)) Houghton Mifflin Co. Trade & Reference Div.

—Biggest, Strongest, Fastest. Jenkins, Steve, illus. 2002. (Illus.). (J). 13.77 (978-0-7587-2106-8(4)) Book Wholesalers, Inc.

Jenkins, Steve & Page, Robin. What Do You Do with a Tail Like This? 2003. (Illus.). 32p. (J). (gr. k-3). 15.00 (978-0-618-25628-0(8)) Houghton Mifflin Co. Trade & Reference Div.

Jenny, Christine. Animal Friends from Around the World. 2004. 32p. (J). pap. 2.95 (978-0-486-43325-7(0)) Dover Pubns., Inc.

Jesus Loves Me: A Soft-Edges Photo Frame Book. 2000. (Baby Blessings Ser.). (Illus.). 10p. (ps-k). bds. 9.99 (978-0-7847-1135-4(6) , 04315) Standard Publishing.

Jeunesse, Gallimard. Animals on the Move. De Hugo, Pierre, illus. 2002. (Look-It-Up Ser.: No. 6). 14p. (J). bds. 4.95 (978-0-439-29723-3(0) , Cartwheel Bks.) Scholastic, Inc.

Jeunesse, Gallimard & Grant, Donald. Animals at Home. 2002. (Look-It-Up Ser.). (Illus.). 14p. (J). bds. 4.95 (978-0-439-35590-2(7) , Cartwheel Bks.) Scholastic, Inc.

Jeunesse, Gallimard, et al. What Do Animals Eat? 2002. (Look-It-Up Ser.). (Illus.). 14p. (J). bds. 4.95 (978-0-439-35591-9(5) , Cartwheel Bks.) Scholastic, Inc.

Jocelyn, Marthe. Eats. Slaughter, Tom, illus. 2007. 24p. (J). (ps-k). 15.95 ***(978-0-88776-820-0(2))*** Tundra Bks., Inc./Livres Toundra, Inc. CAN. *Dist:* Random Hse., Inc.

Johnson-Farris, Nancy. Critters & Bugs of the Great Sonoran Desert. 2003. (J). spiral bd. 12.95 (978-1-931334-32-7(3)) Pieces of Learning.

Johnson, Jinny. Tyrannosaurus & Other Mighty Hunters. 2007. (J). ***(*978-1-59920-063-7(5))*** Smart Apple Media.

Johnson, Jinny & Humphries, Tudor. How Fast Is a Cheetah? (Illus.). (J). pap. 18.99 (978-0-590-24630-9(5)) Scholastic, Inc.

Jordan, Denise M. Animales de Circo. 2002. (SPA.). 24p. (ps-1). pap. 5.25 (978-1-58810-844-9(9) , 91569); lib. bdg. 17.08 (978-1-58810-797-8(3)) Heinemann Library.

Judson, Karen. Animal Testing. 2005. (Open for Debate Ser.). (Illus.). 144p. (J). (978-0-7614-1882-5(2) , Benchmark Bks.) Cavendish, Marshall Corp.

Julivers, Maria Angels. Las Serpientes. 1998. (SPA.). (gr. 3-6). lib. bdg. 16.80 (978-0-613-89372-5(7)) Tandem Library Bks.

Jungle Animals. Date not set. (Question & Answers of the Natural World Ser.). 32p. 4.98 (978-0-7525-4319-2(9)) Parragon, Inc.

Kalman, Bobbie. The ABCs of Animals. 2007. (ABCs of the Natural World Ser.). (Illus.). 32p. (J). (gr. 1-5). pap. ***(*978-0-7787-3430-7(7))*** Crabtree Publishing Co.

—ABCs of Animals. 2007. (Illus.). 32p. (J). ***(*978-0-7787-3410-9(2))*** Crabtree Publishing Co.

—L' Adaptation Au Milieu. 2002. (FRE., Illus.). 32p. (J). pap. (978-2-920660-91-5(8)) Crabtree Publishing Co.

—Animal Families. 2007. (Introducing Living Things Ser.). (Illus.). 24p. (J). (gr. 1-4). pap. ***(*978-0-7787-3250-1(9))*** Crabtree Publishing Co.

—Animal Life Cycles: Growing & Changing. 2006. (Nature's Changes Ser.). (Illus.). 32p. (J). (gr. k-6). pap. (978-0-7787-2312-7(7)); (978-0-7787-2278-6(3)) Crabtree Publishing Co.

—Animals Grow & Change. 2007. (Introducing Living Things Ser.). (Illus.). 24p. (J). (gr. 1-4). pap. ***(*978-0-7787-3251-8(7))*** Crabtree Publishing Co.

—El Ciclo de Vida de la Rana. 2005. (Serie Ciclos de Vida Ser.). (SPA., Illus.). 32p. (J). (978-0-7787-8663-4(3)) Crabtree Publishing Co.

—Ciclos de vida de los Animales: Crecimiento y Cambios. 2006. (SPA., Illus.). 32p. (J). (gr. 3). pap. (978-0-7787-8389-3(8)) Crabtree Publishing Co.

—Le Cycle de Vie. 2001. (FRE., Illus.). 31p. (J). pap. (978-2-920660-73-1(X)) Crabtree Publishing Co.

—How Do Animals Adapt? 2000. (gr. 3-6). lib. bdg. 14.10 (978-0-613-27882-9(8)) Tandem Library Bks.

—Living Things in My Back Yard. 2007. (Introducing Living Things Ser.). (Illus.). 24p. (J). (gr. 1-4). pap. ***(*978-0-7787-3255-6(X))*** Crabtree Publishing Co.

—Metamorphosis: Changing Bodies. 2005. (Nature's Changes Ser.). (Illus.). 32p. (J). (978-0-7787-2273-1(2)) Crabtree Publishing Co.

—Metamorphosis: Changing Bodies. 2005. (Nature's Changes Ser.). (Illus.). 32p. (J). (ps-k). pap. (978-0-7787-2307-3(0)) Crabtree Publishing Co.

—Polar Oceans. 2003. (gr. 3-6). lib. bdg. 15.25 (978-0-613-59135-5(6)) Tandem Library Bks.

—Qué Es el Reino Animal? 2005. (Ciencia de los Seres Vivos Ser.). (SPA., Illus.). 32p. (J). (978-0-7787-8757-0(5)) Crabtree Publishing Co.

—Que Es el Reino Animal? 2005. (Ciencia de los Seres Vivos Ser.). (SPA., Illus.). 32p. (J). (ps). pap. (978-0-7787-8803-4(2)) Crabtree Publishing Co.

—Que Son los Biomas? 2005. (Ciencia de los Seres Vivos Ser.). (SPA., Illus.). 32p. (J). (ps). pap. (978-0-7787-8801-0(6)) Crabtree Publishing Co.

—Le Regne des Animaux. 2005. (FRE., Illus.). 32p. (J). pap. (978-2-89579-025-9(6)) Crabtree Publishing Co.

—What Is a Carnivore? 2007. (Big Science Ideas Ser.). (Illus.). 32p. (J). (gr. 1-4). lib. bdg. ***(*978-0-7787-3274-7(6)); pap. (*978-0-7787-3294-5(0))*** Crabtree Publishing Co.

—What Is a Herbivore? 2007. (Big Science Ideas Ser.). (Illus.). 32p. (J). (gr. 1-4). lib. bdg. ***(*978-0-7787-3275-4(4)); pap. (*978-0-7787-3295-2(9))*** Crabtree Publishing Co.

—What Is an Omnivore? 2007. (Big Science Ideas Ser.). (Illus.). 32p. (J). (gr. 1-4). lib. bdg. ***(*978-0-7787-3276-1(2)); pap. (*978-0-7787-3296-9(7))*** Crabtree Publishing Co.

Kalman, Bobbie. What Is the Animal Kingdom? 1999. (Science of Living Things Ser.). (Illus.). 32p. (J). (gr. 2-3). (978-0-86505-877-4(6)); pap. (978-0-86505-889-7(X)) Crabtree Publishing Co.

Kalman, Bobbie & Aloian, Molly. Polar Oceans. 2003. (Living Ocean Ser.). (Illus.). 32p. (J). (gr. 2-9). (978-0-7787-1297-8(4)); pap. (978-0-7787-1319-7(9)) Crabtree Publishing Co.

Kalman, Bobbie & Langille, Jacqueline. How Do Animals Adapt? 2000. (Science of Living Things Ser.). (Illus.). 32p. (J). (gr. 2-3). (978-0-86505-980-1(2)); pap. (978-0-86505-957-3(8)) Crabtree Publishing Co.

—Que Son las Redes y Cadenas Alimentarias. 2005. (Ciencia de los Seres Vivos Ser.). (SPA., Illus.). 32p. (J). pap. (978-0-7787-8802-7(4)) Crabtree Publishing Co.

Kalman, Bobbie & Larin, Alison. Les Poissons. rev. ed. 2007. (FRE., Illus.). 32p. (J). (gr. 2-3). pap. ***(*978-2-89579-126-3(0))*** Editions Banjo.

Kalman, Bobbie & Smithyman, Kathryn. El Ciclo de Vida de la Rana. Rouse, Bonna, illus. 2005. (Serie Ciclos de Vida Ser.). (SPA.). 32p. (J). (ps-ps). pap. (978-0-7787-8709-9(5)) Crabtree Publishing Co.

Kalman, Bobbie & Walker, Niki. Como se adaptan los Animales? 2006. (SPA., Illus.). 32p. (gr. 2-3). pap. (978-0-7787-8813-3(X)) Crabtree Publishing Co.

Kaner, Etta. How Animals Defend Themselves. Stephens, Pat, illus. 2006. 32p. (978-1-55337-905-8(5)); (978-1-55337-904-1(7)) Kids Can Pr., Ltd.

Katie. The Sunday Alphabet of Animals. 1998. (Illus.). 112p. (J). (ps-3). 10.00 (978-1-57683-089-5(6)) NavPress Publishing Group.

Katschka, Gustav. Mr. Cue's Zoo: Phonics & Cued Speech. Katschka, Gustav, illus. 1998. (Illus.). 53p. (J). (gr. k-5). spiral bd. 30.00 (978-1-892917-05-8(X)) Cued Speech for Integrated Communication, Inc.

Kavanagh, James. African Wildlife: An Introduction to Familiar Species. Leung, Raymond, illus. 2001. (Pocket Traveller Ser.). 12p. pap. 5.95 (978-1-58355-032-8(1)) Waterford Pr., Ltd.

—British Columbia Wildlife. Leung, Raymond, illus. 1999. (Pocket Naturalist Ser.). (J). 5.95 (978-1-58355-044-1(5)) Waterford Pr., Ltd.

—California Trees & Wildflowers: An Introduction to Familiar Species. Leung, Raymond, illus. 2001. (Pocket Naturalist Ser.). 12p. pap. 5.95 (978-1-58355-071-7(2)) Waterford Pr., Ltd.

Kavanagh, Shannon & Davie, Rob. Safari Jeff & Shannon Visit Africa. 2004. (Great Green Adventure Ser.). (Illus.). 46p. 14.95 incl. audio compact disk (978-0-9734409-0-4(2)) Croctalk Publishing CAN. *Dist:* Hushion Hse. Publishing, Ltd.

Keating, Brian. Amazing Animal Adventures Around the World. 2005. (Illus.). 48p. (J). (gr. k-7). pap. 12.95 (978-1-894856-22-5(8)) Fifth Hse. Pubs. CAN. *Dist:* Fitzhenry & Whiteside, Ltd.

—Amazing Animal Adventures at the Poles, Vol. 2. 2005. (Illus.). 48p. (J). 16.95 (978-1-894856-53-9(8)); pap. 12.95 (978-1-894856-54-6(6)) Fifth Hse. Pubs. CAN. *Dist:* Fitzhenry & Whiteside, Ltd.

—Going Wild: Amazing Animal Adventures Around the World. 2004. (Illus.). 48p. 16.95 (978-1-894856-50-8(3)) Fifth Hse. Pubs. CAN. *Dist:* Fitzhenry & Whiteside, Ltd.

Kee, Lisa Morris. Whose Mouth Is This? A Look at Bills, Suckers & Tubes. Landmark, Ken, illus. 2004. (Whose Is It? Ser.). 24p. (C). (gr. k-2). 22.60 (978-1-4048-0008-3(5)) Picture Window Bks.

Keeping Warm. 2006. (Yellow Umbrella Science Ser.). 8,16p. (J). 6.50 (978-0-7368-1711-0(5)) Red Brick Learning.

Kenah, Katharine. Amazing Journeys: Level 2. 2006. (Extreme Readers Ser.). (Illus.). 32p. (J). (gr. k-1). pap. 3.95 (978-0-7696-4337-3(X)) School Specialty Publishing.

—Animals Day & Night Animales D. 2005. (English-Spanish Extreme Readers Ser.). 32p. (J). pap. 3.95 (978-0-7696-3809-6(0) , Waterbird Bks.) School Specialty Publishing.

—Big Beasts: Level 1. 2006. (Extreme Readers Ser.). (Illus.). 32p. (J). (gr. k-k). pap. 3.95 (978-0-7696-4335-9(3)) School Specialty Publishing.

—Hidden Critters. 2004. (Extreme Readers Ser.). (Illus.). 32p. (J). (gr. k-1). pap. 3.95 (978-0-7696-3181-3(9)) School Specialty Publishing.

—Predator Attack! 2004. (Extreme Readers Ser.). (Illus.). 32p. (J). (gr. 1-2). pap. 3.95 (978-0-7696-3176-9(2)) School Specialty Publishing.

—Predator Attack el Predador At. 2005. (English-Spanish Extreme Readers Ser.). 32p. (J). pap. 3.95 (978-0-7696-3811-9(2) , Waterbird Bks.) School Specialty Publishing.

—Tiny Terrors. 2004. (Extreme Readers Ser.). (Illus.). 32p. (J). (gr. k-1). pap. 3.95 (978-0-7696-3179-0(7)) School Specialty Publishing.

Kendell, Patricia. Wwf (World Watch (Chicago, Ill.) 2004. (World Watch Ser.). 48p. (YA). (gr. 6-8). lib. bdg. 27.14 (978-0-7398-6615-3(X)) Raintree.

Kennedy, Pamela & Kennedy, Douglas. My Big Book of 5-Minute Devotions. Wummer, Amy, illus. 2007. 96p. (J). (ps-3). pap. 12.99 ***(*978-0-8249-5556-4(0)*** , Ideals Children's Bks.) Ideals Pubns.

Kennst du Das? Die Tiere. (Duden Ser.). (GER., Illus.). 16p. (J). (978-3-411-70441-5(1)) Bibliographisches Institut & F. A. Brockhaus AG DEU. *Dist:* International Bk. Import Service, Inc.

Kent, Lorna, illus. Baby's First Animal Book. 2004. 12p. (J). bds. 7.99 (978-1-85854-884-5(5)) Brimax Books Ltd. GBR. *Dist:* Byeway Bks.

Khan, S. Amazing Animal Facts & Lists. 2004. (Facts & Lists Internet-Linked Ser.). 64p. (J). lib. bdg. 15.95 (978-1-58086-577-7(1)); pap. 7.95 (978-0-7945-0543-1(0)) EDC Publishing.

Khanduri, K. The Usborne Book of World Wildlife. 2004. (World Wildlife Ser.). 128p. (J). lib. bdg. 26.95 (978-1-58086-034-5(6) , Usborne) EDC Publishing.

Kidslabel Staff. Spot 7 Animals. 2007. (Illus.). 40p. (J). (gr. k-2). 12.95 (978-0-8118-5722-2(0)) Chronicle Bks. LLC.

Kimble, Evan & Kimble, Lael. Baby Animals Dot-to-Dot. Geeson, Andrew & Riley, Terry, illus. 2003. 80p. (J). pap. 5.95 (978-1-4027-0415-4(1)) Sterling Publishing Co., Inc.

Kind News Book of Critter Views. 2nd ed. 2001. 62p. (J). 2.50 (978-0-941246-08-8(6)) National Assn. for Humane & Environmental Education.

Kinsner, Kathy. Animales en los extremos & Animals at the Extremes. 2005. spiral bd. 84.00 ***(*978-1-4108-5694-4(1))*** Benchmark Education Co.

Kinsner, Kathy. Animals at the Extremes. 2004. (Navigators Ser.). (J). pap. 42.00 (978-1-4108-0425-9(9)) Benchmark Education Co.

Klingel, Cynthia Fitterer & Noyed, Robert B. Underground. 2001. (Wonder Books Level 2: Habitats Ser.). (Illus.). 24p. (J). (ps-3). 22.79 (978-1-56766-975-6(1)) Child's World, Inc.

Knight, K. R. Zoo Friends: Cuddly Pups Board Book. 2003. (Cuddly Pups Board Bks.). (Illus.). 20p. (J). 4.99 (978-1-4037-0188-6(1)) Dalmatian Pr.

Knight, Tim. Fantastic Feeders. 2003. (Amazing Nature Ser.). (Illus.). 32p. (J). pap. 6.95 (978-1-4034-3256-8(2)); (gr. 2-4). lib. bdg. 24.22 (978-1-4034-1146-4(8)) Heinemann Library.

—Handmade Cards. 2003. (Step-by-Step Ser.). 32p. (J). pap. 7.95 (978-1-4034-0717-7(7)) Heinemann Library.

—Powerful Predators. 2003. (Amazing Nature Ser.). (Illus.). 32p. (J). lib. bdg. 24.22 (978-1-4034-1147-1(6)); pap. 6.95 (978-1-4034-3261-2(9)) Heinemann Library.

Knowlton, Laurie Lazzaro. African Giants. Tusan, Stan, illus. Prebeg, Rick, photos by. 2005. (J). (978-1-933248-08-0(4)) World Quest Learning.

—Come on Down. Brown, Kevin, illus. 2005. (J). (978-1-933248-07-3(6)) World Quest Learning.

Koler-Matznick, Janice. The Dingo. 2002. (Library of Wolves & Wild Dogs). (Illus.). 24p. (J). (gr. 2-4). lib. bdg. 18.75 (978-0-8239-5768-2(3) , PowerKids Pr.) Rosen Publishing Group, Inc., The.

Koonts, Robin. How Is A Moose Like A Goose. 2002. 2. 32p. (J). (gr. 1-3). pap. 4.99 (978-0-7613-1784-5(8) , Millbrook Pr.) Lerner Publishing Group.

Koopmans, Andy. Chupacabra. 2007. (Monsters Ser.). 48p. (J). (gr. 4-8). 23.70 (978-0-7377-3162-0(1) , Greenhaven Pr., Inc.) Thomson Gale.

Kras, Sara Louise. Animal Giants! What Kids Really Want to Know about Giant Animals. 2005. (Kids' Faqs Ser.). (Illus.). 64p. (978-1-55971-923-0(0)); (J). pap. (978-1-55971-924-7(9)) T&N Children's Publishing. (NorthWord Bks. for Young Readers).

Kratter, Paul. The Living Rain Forest: An Animal Alphabet. Kratter, Paul, illus. 2004. (Illus.). 64p. (J). 17.95 (978-1-57091-603-8(9)) Charlesbridge Publishing, Inc.

Krebs, Laurie. Nos Fuimos Todos de Safari: Una Aventura de Numeros Por Tanzania. Cairns, Julia, illus. 2005. (SPA & ESP.). 30p. (ps-ps). pap. 6.99 (978-1-905236-08-4(5)) Barefoot Bks., Inc.

Kroll, Virginia. Let There Be Llamas! Lombardo, Irina, illus. 2006. 31p. (J). pap. 11.95 (978-0-8198-4519-1(1)) Pauline Bks. & Media.

Kudlinski, Kathleen V. The Sunset Switch. Burnett, Lindy, illus. 2005. (Picture Book Ser.). 32p. (978-1-55971-916-2(8) , Two Can Publishing) T&N Children's Publishing.

Kwas, Susan Estelle. Learning Block Books: Shapes, Animals, Colors, Numbers, 26 vols. 2001. (Illus.). -1p. (J). bds. 24.95 (978-0-8118-3278-6(3)) Chronicle Bks. LLC.

La Jars, David. My Animal Friends. rev. ed. 2004. (Talk Together Ser.). (Illus.). (ps-k). 24p. (J). pap. 5.95 (978-1-58728-017-7(5)); 22p. 9.95 (978-1-58728-013-9(2)) T&N Children's Publishing. (Two Can Publishing).

Labella, Susan. Salamanders & Other Animals with Amazing Tails. 2005. (Scholastic News Nonfiction Readers Ser.). (Illus.). 24p. (J). (gr. 1-2). 19.00 (978-0-516-24929-2(0) , Children's Pr.) Scholastic Library Publishing.

Lacome, Susie. The Big Shiny Sparkly Book of Animals. 2004. (Illus.). 10p. (J). pap. 9.98 (978-0-7624-2004-9(9) , Courage Bks.) Running Pr. Bk. Pubs.

Lalley, Kristine. How Many Legs? 2006. (Rosen Publishing Group's Reading Room Collection). (Illus.). 16p. (J). lib. bdg. (978-1-4042-3336-2(9) , PowerKids Pr.) Rosen Publishing Group, Inc., The.

Lambert, Angela, illus. Animals. 2006. (All Change! Ser.). 10p. (J). (ps). 6.99 (978-1-904550-16-7(9)) Child's Play-International.

Lambert, David, et al. Super Little Giant Book of Weird Animal Facts. 2005. (Illus.). 288p. (J). (gr. 1-4). pap. 6.95 (978-1-4027-2596-8(5) , 1249629) Sterling Publishing Co., Inc.

Lambilly-Bresson, Elisabeth de. Animals in the Field. 2006. (Illus.). 14p. (J). lib. bdg. ***(*978-0-8368-7831-8(0))*** Stevens, Gareth Inc.

—Animals in the Garden. 2006. (Illus.). 14p. (J). lib. bdg. ***(*978-0-8368-7832-5(9))*** Stevens, Gareth Inc.

—Unusual Animals. 2006. (Illus.). 14p. (J). lib. bdg. ***(*978-0-8368-7836-3(1))*** Stevens, Gareth Inc.

Landstrom, Lee Ann & Shragg, Karen. Nature's Yucky! Gross Stuff That Helps Nature Work, Vol. 1. Bergum, Constance Rummel, illus. rev. ed. 48p. (J). (gr. k-5). pap. 10.00 (978-0-87842-474-0(1) , 338) Mountain Pr. Publishing Co., Inc.

Larousse Mexico Staff, ed. Los Animales de la Sabana. 2005. (Mi Pequena Enciclopedia Ser.). (SPA.). 38p. (ps-k). pap. 3.95 (978-970-22-0859-4(9)) Larousse, Ediciones, S. A. de C. V. MEX. *Dist:* Houghton Mifflin Co. Trade & Reference Div.

Laroy, Sue & Carder, Ken. Kindergarten: Songs That Teach Kindergarten. 2005. (Sing along Activity Books with CDs Ser.). (Illus.). 32p. (J). pap. 4.99 (978-0-7696-4453-0(8)) School Specialty Publishing.

Laskey, Elizabeth. Giant & Teeny. 2004. (Heinemann Infosearch Ser.). (Illus.). 32p. (J). pap. 7.50 (978-1-4034-4962-7(7)); lib. bdg. (978-1-4034-4957-3(0)) Heinemann Library.

—Gross & Gory. 2004. (Heinemann Infosearch Ser.). (Illus.). 32p. (J). pap. 7.50 (978-1-4034-4964-1(3)); lib. bdg. (978-1-4034-4959-7(7)) Heinemann Library.

—Speedy & Slow. 2004. (Heinemann Infosearch Ser.). (Illus.). 32p. (J). pap. 7.50 (978-1-4034-4963-4(5)); lib. bdg. (978-1-4034-4958-0(9)) Heinemann Library.

—Weird & Wonderful. 2004. (Heinemann Infosearch Ser.). (Illus.). 32p. (J). pap. 7.50 (978-1-4034-4965-8(1)); lib. bdg. (978-1-4034-4960-3(0)) Heinemann Library.

A B

Lazier, Christine. Exotic Wildlife. Royston, Angela et al, trs. 1998. (Creative Discoveries Ser.). Orig. Title: Animals of the Wild. (Illus.). 75p. (J). (gr. 2-8). lib. bdg. 23.95 (978-0-88682-956-8(9) , Creative Education) Creative Co., The.

Le Jars, David. Mes Amis, Les Animaux. 2000. (Talk Together Ser.). (FRE., Illus.). 24p. (J). (ps-k). pap. 5.95 (978-1-58728-185-3(6) , Two Can Publishing) T&N Children's Publishing.

—Mis Amigos, los Animales. 2004. (Hablemos Ser.).Tr. of My Friends, the Animals. (SPA., Illus.). 22p. (ps-k). 9.95 (978-1-58728-946-0(6) , Two Can Publishing) T&N Children's Publishing.

LeapFrog Staff, compiled by. Animals: (Blue Book) 2002. (J). (ps-2). 19.95 (978-1-58605-696-4(4)) LeapFrog Enterprises, Inc.

—Animals: (Green Book) 2002. (J). (ps-2). 19.95 (978-1-58605-694-0(8)) LeapFrog Enterprises, Inc.

—Animals: (Orange Book) 2002. (J). (ps-2). 19.95 (978-1-58605-695-7(6)) LeapFrog Enterprises, Inc.

—Animals: (Purple Book) 2002. (J). (ps-2). 19.95 (978-1-58605-693-3(X)) LeapFrog Enterprises, Inc.

Learn about Animals. 1998. (Illus.). 8p. (J). bds. 4.99 (978-1-929174-04-1(7)) Oshkosh B'Gosh, Inc.

Learning Horizons, creator. Treasury of Animals & Nature. 2005. (Illus.). 287p. (J). (ps-ps). 9.99 (978-1-58610-784-0(4)) Learning Horizons, Inc.

Leber, Nancy. Rain Forest Animals. 2003. (Compass Point Phonics Readers Ser.). (Illus.). 16p. (J). (gr. 1 up). 13.26 (978-0-7565-0523-3(2)) Compass Point Bks.

—What Plants & Animals Need. 2003. (Compass Point Phonics Readers Ser.). (Illus.). 16p. (J). (gr. 1 up). 13.26 (978-0-7565-0529-5(1)) Compass Point Bks.

Leber, Nancy J. Ants to Zebras: Silly Animal Jokes & Riddles. Griego, Tony, illus. 2000. (Scholastic At-Home Phonics Reading Program Ser.: Vol. 53). 24p. (J). (978-0-590-68848-2(0)) Scholastic, Inc.

Lee, Evelyn. Big Box of Animals Around the World. Kratter, Paul, illus. 2002. (Big Box of Board Books). 10p. (J). 14.95 (978-1-59069-179-3(2) , Silver Dolphin Bks.) Advantage Pubs. Group.

Lee Follen, Eliza. What the Animals Do & Say. 2004. reprint ed. pap. 1.99 (978-1-4192-9359-7(1)) Kessinger Publishing, LLC.

Lee, Frances. Too Many Animals. 1999. (ps-2). lib. bdg. 11.80 (978-0-613-19475-4(6)) Tandem Library Bks.

Legg, Gerald. The X-Ray Picture Book of Incredible Creatures. Salariya, David & Scrace, Carolyn, illus. 2004. 48p. (J). (gr. 4-8). pap. 9.00 (978-0-7567-7406-6(3)) DIANE Publishing Co.

Legs: Big Book: Level C. 8p. 20.95 (978-0-322-00343-9(1)) Wright Group, The.

Legs: Individual Title Six-Packs. (Literatura 2000 Ser.). (gr. 1-2). 28.00 (978-0-7635-0094-8(1)) Rigby Education.

Legs: Level C, 6 vols. 8p. 24.95 (978-0-7802-9120-1(4)) Wright Group, The.

Leonard, Marcia. Animal Talk. Handelman, Dorothy, photos by. 2000. (Hanna Bks.). (Illus.). 24p. (J). (ps-k). 7.95 (978-0-694-01363-0(3)) HarperCollins Pubs.

Lerner Publishing Group Staff. Animal Predators: Classroom Set. 2005. (Illus.). (J). (gr. 3-6). 54.95 (978-0-8225-5487-5(9)) Lerner Publishing Group.

—Animal Predators: Complete Set. Incl. Animal Predators. pap., tchr. ed. 7.95 (978-0-8225-4044-1(4)); Animal Predators : Classroom Set. (Illus.). 54.95 (978-0-8225-5487-5(9)); Crocodiles. (Illus.). 40p. pap. 46.95 (978-0-8225-5493-6(3)); Great White Sharks. (Illus.). 40p. pap. 46.95 (978-0-8225-5488-2(7)); Killer Whales. (Illus.). 40p. pap. 46.95 (978-0-8225-5492-9(5)); Lions. (Illus.). 40p. pap. 46.95 (978-0-8225-5491-2(7)); Owls. (Illus.). 40p. pap. 46.95 (978-0-8225-5490-5(9)); Polar Bears. (Illus.). 40p. pap. 46.95 (978-0-8225-5489-9(5)); Wolves. (Illus.). 40p. pap. 46.95 (978-0-8225-5494-3(1)); (J). (gr. 3-6). 2005. 327.95 (978-0-8225-3885-1(7)) Lerner Publishing Group.

Leslie, Amanda. Cu-cu Quien Es? 2002. (SPA & ENG., Illus.). 20p. 11.95 (978-84-7864-526-8(8)) Combel Editorial, S.A. ESP. *Dist:* Independent Pubs. Group.

—Toc-Toc, Quien Es? 2002. Tr. of Knock, Knock, Who's There?. (SPA & ENG., Illus.). 20p. (ps). 11.95 (978-84-7864-611-1(6)) Combel Editorial, S.A. ESP. *Dist:* Independent Pubs. Group.

Lesser, Carolyn. Spots: Counting Creatures from Sky to Sea. Regan, Laura, illus. 1999. 32p. (YA). (ps-3). 16.00 (978-0-15-200666-2(4)) Harcourt Children's Bks.

The Letter Bb: What Animals Do, 6 vols. (gr. k-2). 17.50 (978-0-7368-4101-6(6)) Red Brick Learning.

The Letter Kk: Animals, 6 vols. (gr. k-2). 17.50 (978-0-7368-4110-8(5)) Red Brick Learning.

Levine, Stuart P. My Baby Animal Book. 2007. 16p. (J). 5.99 (978-0-06-089948-6(4)) HarperCollins Pubs.

Levy, Barbara Soloff. Who's Who in the Zoo? Dot-to-Dot Fun. 2007. (Pictorial Archive Ser.). (Illus.). 30p. (J). (ps-3). per. 3.95 ***(*978-0-486-46181-6(5))*** Dover Pubns., Inc.

Levy, Barbara Soloff. You Can Draw Animals. 2003. (Dover Super Value Editions Ser.). (Illus.). 128p. (J). pap. 7.95 (978-0-486-42899-4(0)) Dover Pubns., Inc.

Levy, Duncan. Happy about Animals: An 8-Year Old's View on Sharing the Earth. 2007. 60p. (J). 21.95 (***978-1-60005-019-0(0)***) Happy About.

Levy, Janey. What Lives on a Prairie? 2003. (Reading Room Collection). (Illus.). 24p. (J). lib. bdg. 18.75 (978-0-8239-3701-1(1)) Rosen Publishing Group, Inc., The.

Lewis, Anthony, illus. My First Animal Signs. 2006. 14p. bds. 6.99 (978-1-904550-76-1(2)) Child's Play-International.

Lewis, Brenda Ralph. Prehistoric Creatures in the Sea & Sky. 2006. (Nature's Monsters Ser.). (Illus.). 32p. (J). lib. bdg. (978-0-8368-6845-6(5)) Stevens, Gareth Inc.

Lindeen, Carol. Life in a Stream. 2003. (Pebble Plus: Living in a Biome Ser.). (Illus.). 24p. (J). lib. bdg. 17.26 (978-0-7368-2103-2(1) , Pebble Bks.) Capstone Pr., Inc.

—Life in a Wetland. 2003. (Pebble Plus: Living in a Biome Ser.). (Illus.). 24p. (J). lib. bdg. 17.26 (978-0-7368-2104-9(X)) Capstone Pr., Inc.

Lindeen, Carol K. Life in a Desert, Vol. 3. 2005. (Earth & Outer Space Ser.). 24p. (YA). (gr. k-3). pap. (978-0-7368-3399-8(4) , Pebble Bks.) Capstone Pr., Inc.

—Velociraptor. 2006. (Pebble Plus—Dinosaurs & Prehistoric Animals Ser.). (Illus.). 24p. (J). (978-0-7368-4258-7(6)) Capstone Pr., Inc.

Linden, Joanne. Shih Tzus. 2007. (Illus.). 24p. (J). 15.93 (978-0-7368-6328-5(1)) Capstone Pr., Inc.

Litchfield, Jo. Animals. 2004. (First Words Board Bks.). (SPA., Illus.). 10p. (J). (ps up). bds. 4.95 (978-0-7460-4093-5(8)) EDC Publishing.

Lithgow, John & Blackaby, Susan. Classifying Creatures: Level 4. 2007. (Lithgow Palooza Readers Ser.). (Illus.). 32p. (J). (gr. 2-3). pap. 3.95 (978-0-7696-4244-4(6)) School Specialty Publishing.

Little & Large Sticker Activity - Big Animals. 2006. (J). 3.99 (978-1-933581-30-9(1)) Byeway Bks.

Llewellyn, Claire. Ask Dr. K. Fisher about Animals. Sheppard, Kate, illus. 2007. (Ask Dr. K. Fisher about... Ser.). 32p. (J). (gr. k-3). 10.95 (978-0-7534-6043-6(2) , Kingfisher) Houghton Mifflin Co. Trade & Reference Div.

—City Animals. 2005. (Illus.). 24p. (YA). (gr. 1 up). lib. bdg. 22.80 (978-1-932889-31-4(0)) Sea-To-Sea Pubns.

—Going for a Ride American English Edition. 2000. (Cambridge Reading Ser.). (Illus.). pap. 5.00 (978-0-521-79908-9(2)) Cambridge Univ. Pr.

Lloyd, Sam. Whose Tail? 2005. (Illus.). 14p. (J). (ps). 5.95 (978-1-56148-454-6(7)) Good Bks.

Lock, David. Animals at Home. 2007. (Dk Readers Ser.). 32p. (J). (gr. k-2). 14.99 (***978-0-7566-3141-3(6)***) Dorling Kindersley Publishing, Inc.

Long, Matthew & Long, Thomas. Any Bear Can Wear Glasses: The Spectacled Bear & other Curious Creatures. Long, Sylvia, illus. 2005. 24p. (J). (gr. k-4). reprint ed. 17.00 (978-0-7567-9763-8(2)) DIANE Publishing Co.

Longnecker, Theresa. Who Grows Up Here?, 6 bks. Carpenter, Melissa, illus. Incl. Who Grows Up in the Desert? A Book about Desert Animals & Their Offspring. 21.26 (978-1-4048-0024-3(7)); Who Grows Up in the Forest? A Book about Forest Animals & Their Offspring. 21.26 (978-1-4048-0025-0(5)); Who Grows Up in the Ocean? A Book about Ocean Animals & Their Offspring. 21.26 (978-1-4048-0026-7(3)); Who Grows Up in the Rain Forest? A Book about Rain Forest Animals & Their Offspring. 21.26 (978-1-4048-0027-4(1)); Who Grows Up in the Snow? A Book about Snow Animals & Their Offspring. 21.26 (978-1-4048-0028-1(X)); Who Grows Up on the Farm? A Book about Farm Animals & Their Offspring. 21.26 (978-1-4048-0029-8(8)); (C). (gr. k-4). 2004. (Illus.). 24p. 2002. 127.56 (978-1-4048-0073-1(5)) Picture Window Bks.

Loomis, Jennifer A. Wildlife in the Rocky Mountains. Loomis, Jennifer A., photos by. unabr. ed. 2005. (Illus.). 100p. (J). 24.95 (978-0-88045-159-8(9)) Stemmer Hse. Pubs., Inc.

Lorenz Books Staff, ed. Animal Friends: A First Word & Picture Book. 2000. (Point & Say Bks.). (Illus.). 96p. (ps-k). 9.95 (978-1-85967-800-8(9)) Anness Publishing GBR. *Dist:* National Bk. Network.

Lorenz Books Staff & Tuxworth, Nicola. Wild Animals. 1999. (Very First Picture Bks.). (Illus.). 12p. (ps). bds. 4.95 (978-0-7548-0382-9(1) , Lorenz Bks.) Anness Publishing GBR. *Dist:* National Bk. Network.

Lorimer, Janet. Beasts. 2004. (Illus.). 32p. (YA). 2.95 (978-1-56254-738-7(0) , SP7380) Saddleback Educational Publishing.

Loves, June. Flying Animals. 2001. (Flight Ser.). (Illus.). 32p. (J). (gr. 5 up). 22.95 (978-0-7910-6561-7(8) , 010303, Chelsea Hse.) Facts On File, Inc.

Lunde, Darrin. Meet the Meerkat. Wynne, Patricia J., illus. 2007. 28p. (J). (ps-1). pap. 6.95 (***978-1-58089-154-7(3)***) Charlesbridge Publishing, Inc.

Lynch, Wayne. Arctic. Lynch, Wayne, photos by. 2007. (Our Wild World Ecosystems Ser.). (Illus.). 64p. (J). (gr. 3-7). 16.95 (978-1-55971-960-5(5)); pap. 8.95 (978-1-55971-961-2(3)) T&N Children's Publishing. (NorthWord Bks. for Young Readers).

—Name That Animal!, 6 bks. Lynch, Wayne, photos by. Incl. Whose Baby Is This? lib. bdg. 23.33 (978-0-8368-3638-7(3)); Whose Bottom Is This? lib. bdg. 23.33 (978-0-8368-3639-4(1)); Whose Feet Are These? lib. bdg. 23.33 (978-0-8368-3640-0(5)); Whose House Is This? lib. bdg. 23.33 (978-0-8368-3641-7(3)); Whose Nose Is This? lib. bdg. 23.33 (978-0-8368-3642-4(1)); Whose Teeth Are These? lib. bdg. 23.33 (978-0-8368-3643-1(X)); 32p. (J). (gr. 1 up). 2003. (Illus.). 2002. Set lib. bdg. 139.98 (978-0-8368-3637-0(5)) Stevens, Gareth Inc.

—Whose Bottom Is This? Lynch, Wayne, photos by. 2003. (Name That Animal! Ser.). (Illus.). 32p. (J). (gr. 1 up). lib. bdg. 23.33 (978-0-8368-3639-4(1)) Stevens, Gareth Inc.

—Whose Bottom Is This? 2000. (Whose? Animal Ser.). (Illus.). 32p. (J). (ps-2). pap. 6.95 (978-1-55285-073-2(0)) Whitecap Bks., Ltd. CAN. *Dist:* Firefly Bks., Ltd.

—Whose Nose Is This? Lynch, Wayne, photos by. 2003. (Name That Animal! Ser.). (Illus.). 32p. (J). (gr. 1 up). lib. bdg. 23.33 (978-0-8368-3642-4(1)) Stevens, Gareth Inc.

—Whose Nose Is This? 2001. (gr. k-3). lib. bdg. 15.25 (978-0-613-78509-9(6)) Tandem Library Bks.

—Whose Nose Is This? (Whose? Animal Ser.). (Illus.). 32p. (J). (ps-2). 2001. pap. 6.95 (978-1-55285-174-6(5)); 2000. pap. 6.95 (978-1-55285-021-3(8)) Whitecap Bks., Ltd. CAN. *Dist:* Firefly Bks., Ltd., Graphic Arts Ctr. Publishing Co.

—Whose Teeth Are These? Lynch, Wayne, photos by. 2003. (Name That Animal! Ser.). (Illus.). 32p. (J). (gr. 1 up). lib. bdg. 23.33 (978-0-8368-3643-1(X)) Stevens, Gareth Inc.

—Whose Teeth Are These? 2001. (gr. k-3). lib. bdg. 15.25 (978-0-613-87567-7(2)) Tandem Library Bks.

—Whose Teeth Are These? 2001. (Whose? Animal Ser.). (Illus.). 32p. (J). (ps-2). pap. 6.95 (978-1-55285-204-0(0)) Whitecap Bks., Ltd. CAN. *Dist:* Firefly Bks., Ltd.

Lyons, Eric. God Made Animals. 2005. (Illus.). 32p. (J). pap. 3.00 (978-0-932859-70-9(4)) Apologetics Pr., Inc.

Macken, JoAnn Early. Animals I See at the Zoo, 12 bks. Incl. Bears. lib. bdg. 19.33 (978-0-8368-3266-2(3)); Camels. lib. bdg. 19.33 (978-0-8368-3267-9(1)); Elephants. lib. bdg. 19.33 (978-0-8368-3268-6(X)); Giraffes. lib. bdg. 19.33 (978-0-8368-3269-3(8)); Hippos. lib. bdg. 19.33 (978-0-8368-3270-9(1)); Lions. lib. bdg. 19.33 (978-0-8368-3271-6(X)); Monkeys. lib. bdg. 19.33 (978-0-8368-3272-3(8)); Penguins. lib. bdg. 19.33 (978-0-8368-3273-0(6)); Sea Lions. lib. bdg. 19.33 (978-0-8368-3274-7(4)); Snakes. lib. bdg. 19.33 (978-0-8368-3275-4(2)); Tigers. lib. bdg. 19.33 (978-0-8368-3276-1(0)); Zebras. lib. bdg. 19.33 (978-0-8368-3277-8(9)); 24p. (J). (ps up). (Weekly Reader Early Learning Library). (Illus.). 2002. Set lib. bdg. 231.96 (978-0-8368-3265-5(5)); pap. (978-0-8368-3278-5(7)) Stevens, Gareth Inc. (Weekly Reader Early Learning Library).

—Rivers. 2005. (Illus.). 24p. (J). pap. (978-0-8368-4893-9(4)); lib. bdg. 19.33 (978-0-8368-4886-1(1)) Stevens, Gareth Inc.

—Rivers/Ríos. 2005. (ENG & SPA., Illus.). 24p. (J). (ps-17). lib. bdg. 19.33 (978-0-8368-6031-3(4)) Stevens, Gareth Inc.

Maclay, Elise. Reading the Wild. Doolittle, Bev, illus. 2005. 32p. (J). (gr. k-4). reprint ed. 17.00 (978-0-7567-9649-5(0)) DIANE Publishing Co.

Macmillan, contrib. by. Animals in Danger. 1999. (Illus.). 12p. (J). bds. 9.99 (978-0-333-76266-0(5)) Macmillan Publishers Ltd. GBR. *Dist:* Trafalgar Square Publishing.

Malam, John. Scary Creatures of the Night! (Scary Creatures Ser.). 32p. (J). 2008. pap. 8.95 (***978-0-531-21009-3(X)*** , Watts, Franklin); 2007. spiral bd. 26.00 (***978-0-531-20424-5(3)*** , Children's Pr.) Scholastic Library Publishing.

El Manzano. (Coleccion Ciclos Vitales). (SPA., Illus.). (J). (gr. 3-5). pap. 7.96 (978-84-236-2659-5(8) , ED4704) Edebé ESP. *Dist:* Lectorum Pubns., Inc.

La Mariposa y la Oruga. (Coleccion Ciclos Vitales). (SPA., Illus.). (J). (gr. 3-5). pap. 7.96 (978-84-236-2663-2(6) , ED4702) Edebé ESP. *Dist:* Lectorum Pubns., Inc.

La Mariquita. (Coleccion Ciclos Vitales). (SPA., Illus.). (J). (gr. 3-5). pap. 7.96 (978-84-236-2661-8(X) , ED4701) Edebé ESP. *Dist:* Lectorum Pubns., Inc.

Markle, Sandra. Animal Scavengers, 6 bks., Set. Incl. Army Ants. 40p. 25.26 (978-0-8225-3196-8(8)); Hyenas. 39p. 25.26 (978-0-8225-3194-4(1)); Jackals. 40p. 25.26 (978-0-8225-3197-5(6)); Tasmanian Devils. 40p. 25.26 (978-0-8225-3199-9(2)); Vultures. 39p. 25.26 (978-0-8225-3195-1(X)); Wolverines. 39p. 25.26 (978-0-8225-3198-2(4)); (Illus.). (J). (gr. 3-7). 2005. Set lib. bdg. 151.56 (978-0-8225-3210-1(7) , Lerner Pubns.) Lerner Publishing Group.

—Los Demonios de Tasmania (Tasmanian Devils) 2007. (Animales carroñeros (Animal Scavengers) Ser.). (SPA.). 40p. (J). (gr. 3-6). pap. 7.95 (***978-0-8225-7737-9(2)***); lib. bdg. 25.26 (***978-0-8225-7733-1(X)***) Lerner Publishing Group. (Ediciones Lerner).

—Jackals. 2006. (Illus.). 39p. (J). pap. 7.95 (978-0-8225-3469-3(X) , First Avenue Editions) Lerner Publishing Group.

—Predators. Bosson, Jo-Ellen C., tr. Bosson, Jo-Ellen C., illus. 2003. 48p. (J). pap. (978-0-439-35615-2(6)) Scholastic, Inc.

Marla Felkins Ryan. Predators. 2005. (Planet's Most Extreme Ser.). (Illus.). 48p. (J). (gr. 3-7). 24.95 (978-1-4103-0396-7(9) , Blackbirch Pr., Inc.) Thomson Gale.

Marshall Cavendish Corporation Staff, contrib. by. Wildlife & Plants, 20 Vols., Set. 3rd ed. 2007. (Illus.). 1280p. (J). (gr. 4-8). lib. bdg. 514.21 (***978-0-7614-7693-1(8)***) Cavendish, Marshall Corp.

Marsico, Katie. A Kangaroo Joey Grows Up. 2007. (Scholastic News Nonfiction Readers Ser.). (Illus.). 24p. (J). (gr. 1-2). 19.00 (978-0-531-17476-0(X) , Children's Pr.) Scholastic Library Publishing.

Mason, Adrienne. Skunks. Ogle, Nancy Gray, illus. 2006. (Kids Can Press Wildlife Ser.). 32p. 6.95 (978-1-55337-734-4(6)) Kids Can Pr., Ltd. CAN. *Dist:* Wybel Marketing Group.

Mason, Cherie. Everybody's Somebody's Lunch. Moore, Gustav, illus. 1998. 40p. (J). (gr. 3-6). 16.95 (978-0-88448-198-0(0)) Tilbury Hse. Pubs.

Mason, Paul. Nature's Armour & Defences. 2007. (J). (***978-1-4109-2965-5(5)***); pap. (***978-1-4109-2986-0(8)***) Steck-Vaughn.

Mason, Paul. The World's Most Dangerous Animals. 2006. (Illus.). 32p. (J): (978-1-4109-2480-3(7)); pap. (978-1-4109-2485-8(8)) Steck-Vaughn.

Masson, Jeffrey Moussaieff. Altruistic Armadillos, Zenlike Zebras: A Menagerie of 100 Favorite Animals. 2006. (Illus.). 448p. 27.95 (978-0-345-47881-8(9) , Ballantine Bks.) Random House Publishing Group.

Matero, Robert. Animals Asleep. 2000. (Illus.). 80p. (gr. 3-6). lib. bdg. (978-0-7613-1652-7(3) , Millbrook Pr.) Lerner Publishing Group.

Mattern, Joanne. Animals of the Savanna. 2002. (Reading Room Collection). (Illus.). 24p. (J). lib. bdg. 18.75 (978-0-8239-3751-6(8)) Rosen Publishing Group, Inc., The.

—Animals of the Tropical Rain Forest. 2006. (Rosen Publishing Group's Reading Room Collection). (Illus.). 16p. (J). lib. bdg. (978-1-4042-3341-6(5) , PowerKids Pr.) Rosen Publishing Group, Inc., The.

—Crazy Creatures of the World. 2001. (Cover-to-Cover Bks.). (Illus.). (J). 55p. pap. (978-0-7891-5446-0(3)); 56p. (gr. 1-4). lib. bdg. 16.95 (978-0-7569-0105-9(7)) Perfection Learning Corp.

—The Outrageous Animal Record Book. 2001. (Cover-to-Cover Chapter Bks.). (Illus.). 56p. (J). pap. (978-0-7891-5410-1(2)); (gr. 1-4). lib. bdg. 16.95 (978-0-7569-0074-8(3)) Perfection Learning Corp.

—What Grassland Animals Eat. 2006. (Nature's Food Chains Ser.). (Illus.). 24p. (J). (gr. 1-2). pap. 5.95 (978-0-8368-6879-1(X)); lib. bdg. 19.93 (978-0-8368-6872-2(2)) Stevens, Gareth Inc.

—What Grassland Animals Eat: Qué Comen Los Animales de Las Praderas? 2006. (ENG & SPA., Illus.). 24p. (J). pap. (978-0-8368-7380-1(7)); lib. bdg. (978-0-8368-7373-3(4)) Stevens, Gareth Inc. (Weekly Reader Early Learning Library).

—What Polar Animals Eat. 2006. (Nature's Food Chains Ser.). (Illus.). 24p. (J). (gr. 1-2). pap. 5.95 (978-0-8368-6880-7(3)); lib. bdg. 19.93 (978-0-8368-6873-9(0)) Stevens, Gareth Inc.

—What Polar Animals Eat: Qué Comen Los Animales de Los Polos? 2006. (ENG & SPA., Illus.). 24p. (J). pap. (978-0-8368-7381-8(5)); lib. bdg. (978-0-8368-7374-0(2)) Stevens, Gareth Inc. (Weekly Reader Early Learning Library).

—What River Animals Eat. 2006. (Nature's Food Chains Ser.). (Illus.). 24p. (J). (gr. 1-2). pap. 5.95 (978-0-8368-6881-4(1)); lib. bdg. 19.93 (978-0-8368-6874-6(9)) Stevens, Gareth Inc.

Mattern, Joanne & Herndon, Ryan, compiled by. Guinness World Records. 2005. (Illus.). 47p. pap. (***978-0-439-71568-3(7)***) Scholastic, Inc.

Matthews, Derek, illus. Animales de la Selva. 2005. (Escucha y Aprende Ser.). (SPA.). 10p. (J). (ps-7). 12.95 (978-970-718-298-1(9) , Silver Dolphin en Español) Advanced Marketing, S. de R. L. de C. V. MEX. *Dist:* Perseus Distribution.

—Escucha y Aprende: Animales de la Granja. 2005. (Escucha y Aprende Ser.). (SPA.). 10p. (J). (ps-7). 12.95 (978-970-718-300-1(4) , Silver Dolphin en Español) Advanced Marketing, S. de R. L. de C. V. MEX. *Dist:* Perseus Distribution.

Matthews, Rupert. Gone Forever, 6 bks., Set. 2003. (Illus.). (J). (gr. k-2). 136.74 (978-1-4034-0794-8(0)) Heinemann Library.

May, Suellen. Invasive Terrestrial Animals. 2006. (Invasive Species Ser.). (Illus.). 112p. (J). (gr. 6-12). 30.00 (978-0-7910-9127-2(9) , Chelsea Hse.) Facts On File, Inc.

Mayer, Mercer & Kassirer, Sue. Sleeping Beauty. Mayer, Mercer & S. I. International Staff, illus. 2003. (Little Critter Ser.). 16p. (J). (gr. k-k). 2.99 (978-0-307-10602-5(0) , 10602, Golden Bks.) Random Hse. Children's Bks.

Maze, Stephanie. Momentos de Paz en el Reino Animal: Los Animales y Sus Hogares. (Coleccion Momentos en el Reino Animal). (SPA., Illus.). 32p. (J). (gr. k-3). 15.00 (978-0-9707768-4-6(5) , MST31406) Moonstone Pr.

—Momentos Divertidos en el Reino Animal: Los Animales y Sus Amigos. (SPA., Illus.). 32p. (J). (gr. k-3). 15.00 (978-0-9707768-5-3(3) , MST31407) Moonstone Pr.

McAlpine, Margaret. Working with Animals. 2004. (Illus.). 64p. (J). lib. bdg. 26.00 (978-0-8368-4240-1(5)) Stevens, Gareth Inc.

McCourt, Lisa. The Long & Short of It. Nathan, Cheryl, illus. 1999. (J). (978-0-606-16872-4(9)) Tandem Library Bks.

McDowell, Barbara. Animals. 2004. (Illus.). 24p. (J). act. bk. ed. 3.99 (978-1-85997-696-8(4)) Byeway Bks.

McGee, John F., illus. Animal Magic for Kids, 6 bks. Incl. Cheetah Magic for Kids. MacPherson, Winnie. lib. bdg. 26.00 (978-0-8368-2631-9(0)); Elephant Magic for Kids. Fredericks, Anthony D. lib. bdg. 26.00 (978-0-8368-2632-6(9)); Fox Magic for Kids. Schuler, Judy. lib. bdg. 26.00 (978-0-8368-2633-3(7)); Kangaroo Magic for Kids. Lehne, Judith Logan. lib. bdg. 26.00 (978-0-8368-2634-0(5)); Koala Magic for Kids. Feeney, Kathy. lib. bdg. 26.00 (978-0-8368-2635-7(3)); Panda Magic for Kids. Feeny, Kathy. lib. bdg. 26.00 (978-0-8368-2636-4(1)); 48p. (J). (gr. 3 up). 1999. (Illus.). Set lib. bdg. 156.00 (978-0-8368-2655-5(8)) Stevens, Gareth Inc.

McGehee, Claudia. A Tallgrass Prairie Alphabet. McGehee, Claudia, illus. 2004. (Bur Oak Book Ser.). (Illus.). 32p. (J). 17.95 (978-0-87745-897-5(9)) Univ. of Iowa Pr.

McGraw-Hill Staff. Glencoe Science: Animal Diversity. 2nd ed. 2004. stu. ed. 20.64 (978-0-07-861740-9(5) , 9780078617409) Glencoe/McGraw-Hill.

McGuinness, Rik. Cloze Encounters Vol. 1: Animals, 3 vols. 2000. 48p. pap. 6.95 (978-1-58324-044-1(6) , World Teachers Pr.) Didax Educational Resources, Inc.

McKendry, Sam. Are You Ticklish? Bilingual Edition. 2006. 12p. 10.95 (978-1-58117-472-4(1) , Intervisual/Piggy Toes) Dalmatian Pr.

McKissack, Fredrick, Jr. & McKissack, Lisa Beringer. Counting in the Grasslands. 2008. (J). (***978-0-7660-2991-0(3)***) Enslow Pubs., Inc.

—Counting in the Tiaga. 2008. (J). (***978-0-7660-2995-8(6)***) Enslow Pubs., Inc.

—Counting in the Tundra. 2008. (Counting in the Biomes Ser.). 32p. (J). (gr. 1-3). lib. bdg. 22.60 (***978-0-7660-2989-7(1)***) Enslow Pubs., Inc.

—Counting in the Wetlands. 2008. (J). (***978-0-7660-2993-4(X)***) Enslow Pubs., Inc.

McLaren, Chris. Rats, Bags, & Frogs of London. 2004. (Illus.). 96p. 8.99 (978-1-904153-05-4(4)) Watling St., Ltd. GBR. *Dist:* Trafalgar Square Publishing.

McLeod, Beatrice. Courtship. McLeod, Beatrice, illus. 2000. (Nature Undercover Ser.). (Illus.). 40p. (J). (gr. 5-8). 23.70 (978-1-56711-503-1(9) , Blackbirch Pr., Inc.) Thomson Gale.

—Growing Up. 2000. (Nature Undercover Ser.). (Illus.). 40p. (J). (gr. 5-8). 23.70 (978-1-56711-501-7(2) , Blackbirch Pr., Inc.) Thomson Gale.

Medley, Steven P. Antelope, Bison, Cougar: A National Park Wildlife Alphabet Book. San Souci, Robert D., illus. 2001. (J). (ps-5). 14.95 (978-1-930238-03-9(7)) Yosemite Assn.

Meerkats, 6 vols. (gr. 2-5). 36.95 (978-0-7368-8416-7(5)) Red Brick Learning.

Menon, Sujatha. Mountain Creatures. 2008. (J). lib. bdg. (***978-1-4042-3877-0(8)*** , PowerKids Pr.) Rosen Publishing Group, Inc., The.

—Safari Creatures. 2007. (J). lib. bdg. (***978-1-4042-3894-7(8)*** , PowerKids Pr.) Rosen Publishing Group, Inc., The.

Meredith, S. Night Animals. 2004. (Beginners Ser.). 32p. (J). (gr. 1 up). lib. bdg. 12.95 (978-1-58086-510-4(0)) EDC Publishing.

Metrobooks Staff. Funny Faces: A Spinning Ball Book. 2000. (Illus.). 8p. (J). (ps-k). 9.99 (978-1-58663-103-1(9)) Friedman, Michael Publishing Group, Inc.

—Spots & Stripes: A Baby Soft Book. 2000. (Illus.). 8p. (J). (ps-k). 8.99 (978-1-58663-105-5(5)) Friedman, Michael Publishing Group, Inc.

Michels, Dia L. Look What I See! Where Can I Be?, 3 vols. 2001. (Look What I See! Where Can I Be? Ser.). (Illus.). (J). 39.95 (978-1-930775-37-4(7)) Platypus Media, L.L.C.

Milbourne, Anna. In the Nest. 2005. (First Discovery Ser.). 24p. (J). 9.95 (978-0-7945-0735-0(2) , Usborne) EDC Publishing.

Miles, Elizabeth. Animal Parts, 10 vols., Set. 2003. (Illus.). (J). (gr. k-2). lib. bdg. 227.90 (978-1-58810-761-9(2)) Heinemann Library.

—Fur & Feathers. 2003. (Animal Parts Ser.). (Illus.). 32p. (J). (gr. k-2). lib. bdg. 21.36 (978-1-4034-0016-1(4)) Heinemann Library.

—Fur & Feathers. 2003. (gr. k-3). lib. bdg. 15.25 (978-0-613-45760-6(9)) Tandem Library Bks.

—Legs & Feet. 2003. (Animal Parts Ser.). (Illus.). 32p. (J). (gr. k-2). lib. bdg. 21.36 (978-1-4034-0017-8(2)); pap. 6.95 (978-1-4034-0426-8(7)) Heinemann Library.

—Legs & Feet. 2003. (gr. k-3). lib. bdg. 15.25 (978-0-613-45789-7(7)) Tandem Library Bks.

—Paws & Claws. 2003. (Animal Parts Ser.). (Illus.). 32p. (J). (gr. k-2). lib. bdg. 21.36 (978-1-4034-0020-8(2)) Heinemann Library.

—Paws & Claws. 2003. (gr. k-3). lib. bdg. 14.75 (978-0-613-45810-8(9)) Tandem Library Bks.

—Tails. 2003. (Animal Parts Ser.). (Illus.). 32p. (J). (gr. k-2). lib. bdg. 21.36 (978-1-4034-0022-2(9)) Heinemann Library.

—Wings, Fins, & Flippers. 2003. (Animal Parts Ser.). (Illus.). 32p. (J). (gr. k-2). lib. bdg. 21.36 (978-1-4034-0023-9(7)) Heinemann Library.

—Wings, Fins, & Flippers. 2003. (gr. k-3). lib. bdg. 14.75 (978-0-613-45857-3(5)) Tandem Library Bks.

Miles, Elizabeth & Wright, David. Animals Masks. 2001. (Big Book of... Ser.). (Illus.). 24p. (J). pap. 9.95 (978-1-901323-15-3(3)) Orpheus Bks., Ltd. GBR. *Dist:* CPG Publishing, Inc.

Miles Kelly Staff. Animals. 2003. (Info Bank Ser.). (Illus.). 96p. (J). 7.95 (978-1-84236-153-5(8)) Miles Kelly Publishing, Ltd. GBR. *Dist:* Independent Pubs. Group.

—Animals: Flip Quiz. 2003. (Flip Quiz Ser.). (Illus.). 38p. (J). spiral bd. 5.95 (978-1-84236-078-1(7)); spiral bd. 5.95 (978-1-84236-076-7(0)); spiral bd. 5.95 (978-1-84236-079-8(5)); spiral bd. 5.95 (978-1-84236-077-4(9)) Miles Kelly Publishing, Ltd. GBR. *Dist:* Independent Pubs. Group.

Miller, Connie Colwell. Manatees. 2005. (Illus.). 24p. (J). (ps-7). lib. bdg. 21.26 (978-0-7368-4311-9(6)) Capstone Pr., Inc.

Miller, Gary. Staying Alive. 2005. (Real Deal-Red Plus Ser.). (Illus.). 32p. (gr. 4-8). 19.00 (978-0-7910-8896-8(0)) Facts On File, Inc.

Miller, J. Tiburones. 2004. (Discovery Program Ser.).Tr. of Sharks. (SPA., Illus.). 64p. (J). (gr. 3 up). lib. bdg. 16.95 (978-1-58086-348-3(5)) EDC Publishing.

Miller, Jonathan S. & Turnbull, Stephanie. Los Felinos. 2005. (SPA., Illus.). 48p. (J). pap. 8.95 (978-0-7460-5070-5(4) , Usborne) EDC Publishing.

Miller, Sara Swan. Cows. 2001. (True Bks.). (Illus.). 48p. (J). (gr. 3-5). pap. 6.95 (978-0-516-27181-1(4) , Children's Pr.) Scholastic Library Publishing.

Miller-Schroeder, Patricia, tr. Orangutans. 2003. (Untamed World Ser.). (Illus.). 64p. (J). lib. bdg. 28.56 (978-0-7398-6845-4(4)) Raintree.

Misterios de Oceano. (Coleccion Ventana Transparente). (SPA., Illus.). (J). (gr. 3-5). (978-950-11-1247-4(0) , SG5233) Sigmar ARG. *Dist:* Lectorum Pubns., Inc.

Mitchell, Judy, ed. Big & Little Animals. Bojas, Mary Galan, illus. 2001. (Pictures to Color Ser.). 32p. (J). (ps-k). pap. 4.95 (978-1-57310-263-6(6)) Teaching & Learning Co.

Mitchell, Melanie S. Ears. 2003. (First Step Nonfiction Ser.). (Illus.). 8p. (J). pap. 3.95 (978-0-8225-3910-0(1) , Lerner Pubns.) Lerner Publishing Group.

Mitton, Jacqueline. Zoo in the Sky: A Book of Animal Constellations. Balit, Christina, illus. 2006. 32p. (J). (gr. 1-4). pap. 7.95 (978-0-7922-5935-0(1) , National Geographic Children's Bks.) National Geographic Society.

Molter, Carey. Zoo Animals, Set. l.t. ed. Incl. Bears. lib. bdg. 19.93 (978-1-57765-558-9(3)); Dolphins. lib. bdg. 19.93 (978-1-57765-559-6(1)); Elephants. lib. bdg. 19.93 (978-1-57765-560-2(5)); Monkeys. lib. bdg. 19.93 (978-1-57765-561-9(3)); Penguins. lib. bdg. 19.93 (978-1-57765-562-6(1)); Zebras. lib. bdg. 19.93 (978-1-57765-563-3(X)); 24p. (J). (ps-3). 2001. (Illus.). 2001. Set lib. bdg. 119.58 (978-1-57765-505-3(2) , SandCastle) ABDO Publishing Co.

Mon Premier Larousse: Le Dictionnaire des 4-7 Ans. 2000. Tr. of My First Larousse: Dictionary for Ages 4-7. (FRE., Illus.). 264p. (J). pap. 54.95 (978-2-03-653009-6(5)) Librairie Larousse FRA. *Dist:* Distribooks, Inc.

Mondello, Cindy, ed. Investigating Science - Animals. 2000. 48p. 9.95 (978-1-56234-410-8(2) , Mailbox Bks., The) Education Ctr., Inc.

Monreal, Violeta. Que Animal Es? 2004. Tr. of What Animal Is It?. (SPA., Illus.). (J). pap. 8.50 (978-84-241-8100-0(X)) Everest de Ediciones y Distribucion, S.L. ESP. *Dist:* Lectorum Pubns., Inc.

Monstruos Gigantes. 2005. (Jeff Corwin Experience Ser.). (ENG & SPA., Illus.). 48p. (J). (ps-7). lib. bdg. 24.95 (978-1-4103-0675-3(5) , Blackbirch Pr., Inc.) Thomson Gale.

Moor, Jo Ellen. Animals with Backbones. Evans, Marilyn, ed. Davis, Cindy, illus. 1998. (ScienceWorks for Kids Ser.: Vol. 2). 80p. (J). (gr. 1-3). pap., tchr. ed. 9.95 (978-1-55799-683-1(0) , EMC 854) Evan-Moor Educational Pubs.

—Animals Without Backbones. Evans, Marilyn, ed. Davis, Cindy, illus. 1998. (ScienceWorks for Kids Ser.: Vol. 3). 80p. (J). (gr. 1-3). pap., tchr. ed. 9.95 (978-1-55799-684-8(9) , EMC 855) Evan-Moor Educational Pubs.

Moore, Heidi, et al. Animal Groups, 8 bks., Set 2. 2004. (J). (gr. 3-5). lib. bdg. 216.57 (978-1-4034-4695-4(4)) Heinemann Library.

Moore, Jo Ellen. Learning about Animals. Kopp, Kathy & Smith, Phillip, illus. 2000. (ScienceWorks for Kids Ser.). 80p. (J). (gr. k-1). pap., tchr. ed. 9.95 (978-1-55799-771-5(3) , EMC 867) Evan-Moor Educational Pubs.

Mora, Pat. Listen to the Desert. Mora, Francisco X., illus. 2001. Tr. of Oye Al Desierto. (SPA & ENG.). 32p. (J). (gr. k-3). reprint ed. pap. 6.95 (978-0-618-11144-2(1) , Clarion Bks.) Houghton Mifflin Co. Trade & Reference Div.

Morgan, Sally. Animals & Their World. 2002. (Young Discoverers Ser.). (Illus.). 32p. (J). (gr. k-3). pap. 7.95 (978-0-7534-5498-5(X) , Kingfisher) Houghton Mifflin Co. Trade & Reference Div.

—Cities, 1 vols. 2001. (World Book Ecology Ser.). (Illus.). 32p. (J). (978-0-7166-5228-1(5)) World Bk., Inc.

—In the Ground & Other Landscapes. 2006. (Hidden Habitats Ser.). (J). (978-1-59389-281-4(0)) Chrysalis Education.

—Lions, 6 vols. 2005. (QEB Animal Lives Ser.). (Illus.). 32p. (J). (gr. 4-7). lib. bdg. 18.95 (978-1-59566-117-3(4)) QEB Publishing Inc.

Moriuchi, Mique, intro. Mix-and-Match Animals. 2007. 5p. bds. 10.95 (*978-1-58117-603-2(1) , Intervisual/Piggy Toes) Dalmatian Pr.

Morog, Joyce Jo. Boots A Fireside Critter: A Fireside Critter. 2004. (Illus.). 32p. (J). (978-0-9753248-0-6(2)) Fireside Critters.

Moses, Brian. Munching, Crunching, Sniffing & Snooping. 1999. (Eyewitness Readers). (Illus.). 32p. (J). (ps-3). pap. 3.99 (978-0-7894-4752-4(5)) Dorling Kindersley Publishing, Inc.

—Munching, Crunching, Sniffing, & Snooping. 1999. (gr. k-3). lib. bdg. 11.80 (978-0-613-22043-9(9)) Tandem Library Bks.

Moses, Brian & Dorling Kindersley Publishing Staff. Munching, Crunching, Sniffing & Snooping. 1999. (Eyewitness Readers). (Illus.). 32p. (J). (ps-3). 14.99 (978-0-7894-4753-1(3)) Dorling Kindersley Publishing, Inc.

Mostue, Trude. Wild about Animals: A Book of Beastly Behaviour. (Illus.). 108p. (J). (gr. 4-6). 24.95 (978-0-233-99684-4(2)) Andre Deutsch GBR. *Dist:* Trafalgar Square Publishing.

Mudpuppy Press Staff. Baby Animal Block Puzzle. 2005. (J). 12.99 (978-0-7353-0174-0(3)) Galison.

Mullin, Rita T. Animalogy; Weird & Wacky Animal Facts. 1998. (Animal Planet Ser.). (J). (978-0-606-13133-9(7)) Tandem Library Bks.

El Mundo Salvaje de los Animales: Amigos y Enemigos: Leveled Books. 2000. (McGraw-Hill Ciencias Ser.). (ENG & SPA.). (gr. 4 up). (978-0-02-279659-4(2)) Macmillan/McGraw-Hill Schl. Div.

Munnerlyn, Cindy, ed. Investigating Science - Animals. 2003. 48p. 9.95 (978-1-56234-567-9(2) , Mailbox Bks., The) Education Ctr., Inc.

Murphy, Patricia J. Why Do Some Animals Shed. 2004. (Library of Why Ser.). (Illus.). 24p. (J). lib. bdg. 18.75 (978-0-8239-6237-2(7)) Rosen Publishing Group, Inc., The.

Murray, Julie. Animal Kingdom, Set II. 2005. (Animal Kingdom Set Ii Ser.). (J). (gr. k-4). lib. bdg. 854.00 (978-1-59197-300-3(7) , Buddy Bks.) ABDO Publishing Co.

Musty-Crusty Animals, 8 bks., Set. 2002. (J). (ps-1). lib. bdg. 148.00 (978-1-58810-474-8(5)) Heinemann Library.

My First BK Of: Animals. 2007. 12p. pap. 7.99 (*978-1-4037-3059-6(8)) Dalmatian Pr.

My Little Animals. 2000. (J). 84.00 (978-0-7641-7371-4(5)) Barron's Educational Series, Inc.

My Little Box of Animals. Date not set. (Illus.). (J). bds. 6.98 (978-1-4054-0810-3(3)) Parragon, Inc.

My World of Animals.Tr. of Yo y los animales. (ENG & SPA., Illus.). (J). (gr. 1-2). 96.00 (978-1-4042-7533-1(9) , Buenas Letra) Rosen Publishing Group, Inc., The.

Myers, Jack. On the Trail of the Komodo Dragon: And Other Explorations of Science in Action. Rice, John, illus. 2004. 64p. (YA). (gr. 4-6). 17.95 (978-1-56397-761-9(3)) Boyds Mills Pr.

Myers, Jack. The Puzzle of the Platypus: And Other Explorations of Science in Action. Rice, John, illus. 2008. (J). (*978-1-59078-556-0(8)) Boyds Mills Pr.

Myers, Janet Nuzum. Critter Jokes & Riddles. Clegg, Dave, illus. 2007. 96p. (J). pap. 4.95 (*978-1-4027-3865-4(X)) Sterling Publishing Co., Inc.

Nathan, Emma. Animales. 2002. (Abre los Ojos y Aprende Serie).Tr. of Eyeopeners: Animals. (SPA.). 24p. (J). (-3). 24.94 (978-1-4103-0018-8(8) , Blackbirch Pr., Inc.) Thomson Gale.

—Animals. 2002. (Eyeopeners Ser.). (Illus.). 24p. (J). 22.45 (978-1-56711-595-6(0) , Blackbirch Pr., Inc.) Thomson Gale.

Nature's Children, 21 vols. rev. ed. (J). (gr. 3-8). Set 1. 2007. (Illus.). lib. bdg. 339.00 (*978-0-7172-8080-3(2)); Set 2. 2007. lib. bdg. 339.00 (*978-0-7172-8081-0(0)); Set 3. 2008. lib. bdg. 339.00 (*978-0-7172-8082-7(9)) Scholastic Library Publishing. (Grolier).

Navarro, Laura. Flores para Lucía, la Murciélaga. Sebastian, Juan, illus. 2001. Tr. of Flowers for Lucia, the Bat. (SPA & ENG.). 47p. (J). (ps-5). pap. 8.95 (978-0-292-75575-8(9)) Univ. of Texas Pr.

Nayer, Judy. Zoo Animals. Brown, Robert & Harris, Greg, illus. 1998. (At Your Fingertips Ser.). 5p. (J). (ps-3). 6.95 (978-0-7681-0066-2(6) , McClanahan Bk.) Learning Horizons, Inc.

Nelson, Angela, creator. Lang-O-Learn: Animal Cards. 2001. (SPA, FRE, GER, ITA & RUS.). (J). 12.95 (978-0-9668008-3-8(4)) Stages Learning Materials.

Nelson, Esther & Hirsch, Davida. Riggeldy Jiggeldy Joggeldy Jam: Can You Guess Who I Am? Ellis, Libby, illus. 2003. (J). bds. 5.95 (978-0-7607-3278-6(7)) Barnes & Noble, Inc.

—Riggeldy Jiggeldy Joggeldy Roo: Can You Guess What I Do? Ellis, Libby, illus. 2003. (J). bds. 5.95 (978-0-7607-3279-3(5)) Barnes & Noble, Inc.

Nelson, Mary Beth, tr. & illus. Elmo's World: Animals! Nelson, Mary Beth, illus. Barrett, John E., illus. Barrett, John E., photos by. 2001. (Elmo's World Ser.). 12p. (J). (gr. k-ps). bds. 4.99 (978-0-375-81336-8(5) , Random Hse. Bks. for Young Readers) Random Hse. Children's Bks.

Newman-D'Amico, Fran. Animal Spot-the-Differences. 2007. 64p. (J). pap. 1.50 (*978-0-486-45649-2(8)) Dover Pubns., Inc.

Newson, Joyce E. Animals. Davico, Francesco et al, illus. 2000. (Nature's Record-Breakers Ser.). 32p. (J). (gr. 3 up). lib. bdg. 23.33 (978-0-8368-2473-5(3)) Stevens, Gareth Inc.

Nguyen, An Mai. Let's Learn Animals in Vietnamese. 2006. (VIE & ENG., Illus.). (J). bds. 6.95 (978-0-9776482-3-8(0)) Viet Baby, LLC.

Nicholaus, Bret & Lowrie, Paul. KidChat Gone Wild! 202 Creative Questions to Unleash the Imagination. 2007. (KidChat Ser.). (Illus.). 128p. (J). (gr. 3 up). pap. 6.99 (*978-1-59643-316-8(7)) Roaring Brook Pr.

Nichols, Catherine. Animal Masterminds. 2004. (True Tales Ser.). (J). (gr. 2-4). pap. 4.95 (978-0-516-24601-7(1) , Children's Pr.) Scholastic Library Publishing.

Nick Jr. Staff, ed. Nick Jr's. Diego's Animal Adventures. 2007. (Watch Me Draw Ser.). (Illus.). 24p. (J). pap. 5.95 (978-1-56010-892-4(4)) Foster, Walter Publishing, Inc.

El Nido del Pajaro. (Coleccion Ciclos Vitales). (SPA., Illus.). (J). (gr. 3-5). pap. 7.96 (978-84-236-2651-9(2) , ED4699) Edebé ESP. *Dist:* Lectorum Pubns., Inc.

Nilsen, Anna. Let's Swim & Dive. Axworthy, Anni, illus. 2001. (Animal Antics Ser.). 24p. (J). (ps up). lib. bdg. 22.00 (978-0-8368-2913-6(1)) Stevens, Gareth Inc.

Nilsen, Anna & Axworthy, Anni. Let's All Dig & Burrow! 1998. (Animals on the Move Ser.). 24p. (J). (ps-k). 10.95 (978-1-84089-003-7(7) , Zero to Ten, Limited) Evans Publishing Group GBR. *Dist:* Independent Pubs. Group.

Noah's Ark Abc: My Wipe-off Book. 2003. spiral bd. (978-0-7853-8571-4(1)) Publications International, Ltd.

Noble, Marty. Invisible Rain Forest Animals Magic Picture Book. 1999. (Illus.). 16p. (J). pap. 1.50 (978-0-486-40766-1(7)) Dover Pubns., Inc.

The Noises Animals Make. Date not set. 5.95 (978-0-89868-313-4(0)) ARO Publishing Co.

Nolan, Joy. Animals of North America. 2005. (Navigators Ser.). (J). pap. 42.00 (*978-1-4108-5076-8(5)) Benchmark Education Co.

Norby, Lisa. Animals of Africa. 2005. (Navigators Ser.). (J). pap. 42.00 (*978-1-4108-5077-5(3)) Benchmark Education Co.

Northey, Neil W. Wild Creatures in Winter. 1998. (Illus.). 188p. (J). (gr. 4-7). pap. 6.95 (978-1-881545-86-6(5)) A B Publishing.

Northwest Film Center, prod. Alien Invaders: INVAS Workbook. (YA). (978-0-7365-4404-7(6)) Films Media Group.

NorthWord Books for Young Readers Editors, ed. Forest Babies. 2003. (Animal Babies Ser.). (Illus.). 22p. (J). (ps up). bds. 5.95 (978-1-55971-874-5(9) , NorthWord Bks. for Young Readers) T&N Children's Publishing.

Los Numeros (Touch & Feel 1, 2, 3) 2000. (SPA., Illus.). 10p. (J). (ps). pap. (978-950-11-1420-1(1)) Sigmar.

Obligado, Lilian. Nose to Toes. 1999. (gr. k-3). lib. bdg. 10.95 (978-0-613-22110-8(9)) Tandem Library Bks.

O'Brady, Terry. Count the Animals. 2002. (Windows on Literacy Ser.). (Illus.). 10p. (J). (978-0-7922-8484-0(4)) National Geographic Society.

Los Oceanos.Tr. of Oceans. (SPA.). (J). (gr. 5-8). 12.00 (978-84-342-1949-6(2)) Parramon Ediciones S.A. ESP. *Dist:* Distribuidora Norma, Inc., Lectorum Pubns., Inc.

O'Connell, Lisa B. C. Miracle Max... Missing in Maryland!, Vol. 1. O'Connell, Lisa B. C., illus. 2000. (Illus.). 88p. (J). (gr. 2-7). per. 15.95 (978-1-56167-642-2(X) , Shooting Star Edition) American Literary Pr.

O'Hare, Jeff. Beastly Behaviors: Find the Baffling Bonds Between Amazing Animals. Nadel, Marc, illus. 2003. 32p. (YA). (gr. 2-9). pap. 8.95 (978-1-56397-988-0(8)) Boyds Mills Pr.

—Searchin' Safari: Looking for Camouflaged Creatures. Hadel, Marc, illus. 2003. 32p. (YA). (gr. 2-7). pap. 7.95 (978-1-56397-817-3(2)) Boyds Mills Pr.

Ohare, Ted. Anfibios. 2005. (Que Es un Animal? Biblioteca del Descubrimiento Ser.).Tr. of Amphibian. (SPA.). 24p. pap. 5.45 (978-1-59515-685-3(2)) Rourke Publishing, LLC.

O'Hare, Ted. Animals of the Rain Forest. 2005. (Rain Forest Today Discovery Library Ser.). (Illus.). 24p. (gr. 1-4). 14.95 (978-1-59515-152-0(4)) Rourke Publishing, LLC.

Ohare, Ted. Mamiferos. 2005. (Que Es un Animal? Biblioteca del Descubrimiento Ser.). (SPA.). 24p. pap. 5.45 (978-1-59515-690-7(9)) Rourke Publishing, LLC.

O'Hare, Ted. Rain Forest at Night. 2005. (Rain Forest Today Discovery Library). 24p. (gr. 1-4). 5.45 (978-1-59515-303-6(9)); (Illus.). 14.95 (978-1-59515-155-1(9)) Rourke Publishing, LLC.

Oliver, Narelle. Twilight Hunt. Oliver, Narelle, illus. 2007. (Illus.). 40p. (J). 16.95 (*978-1-59572-107-5(X)) Star Bright Bks., Inc.

Olson, Nathan. Animal Patterns. 2007. (Finding Patterns Ser.). 32p. (J). (Illus.). 7.95 (*978-0-7368-7846-3(7)); 23.93 (978-0-7368-6728-3(7)) Capstone Pr., Inc. (Pebble Bks.).

One, Two, Three, Four: KinderWords Individual Title Six-Packs. (Kinderstarters Ser.). 8p. (ps-1). 21.00 (978-0-7635-8705-5(2)) Rigby Education.

O'Neil, Sarah. Predators. 2000. (gr. k-3). lib. bdg. 11.80 (978-0-613-29723-3(7)) Tandem Library Bks.

Ooey-Gooey Animals, 8 bks., Set. 2002. (J). (ps-1). 148.00 (978-1-58810-461-8(3)) Heinemann Library.

Orenstein, Ronald. New Animal Discoveries. 2000. (Illus.). 64p. (J). (gr. 3-7). 16.95 (978-1-55263-152-2(4)) Key Porter Bks. CAN. *Dist:* Firefly Bks., Ltd.

—New Animal Discoveries. 2001. (Worlds Beyond Ser.). (Illus.). 64p. (gr. 4-8). lib. bdg. 24.90 (978-0-7613-2274-0(4) , Millbrook Pr.) Lerner Publishing Group.

Osborne, Rick, et al. Creepy Creatures & Bizarre Beasts from the Bible. Carpenter, Anthony, illus. 2004. (2:52 Ser.). 128p. (J). pap. 7.99 (978-0-310-70654-0(8)) Zonderkidz.

Packard, Mary. Talented Animals. 2004. (True Tales Ser.). (J). (gr. 2-4). pap. 4.95 (978-0-516-24609-3(7) , Children's Pr.) Scholastic Library Publishing.

Packed with Poison! Deadly Animal Defenses. 2007. (J). pap. 5.95 (*978-0-8225-6448-5(3) , First Avenue Editions) Lerner Publishing Group.

Page, Nick & Cooper, Wade. Night Creatures. 2007. (Scholastic Reader Level 2 Ser.). 32p. (J). (ps-3). pap. 3.99 (*978-0-545-00719-1(4) , Cartwheel Bks.) Scholastic, Inc.

Page, Robin & Jenkins, Steve. Animals in Flight. Jenkins, Steve, illus. (Illus.). 32p. (J). (gr. k-3). 2005. pap. 5.95 (978-0-618-54882-8(3)); 2001. tchr. ed. 16.00 (978-0-618-12351-3(2)) Houghton Mifflin Co. Trade & Reference Div.

Paige, Joy. Record-Breaking Animals, 6 bks. Incl. Blue Whale : World's Largest Mammal. lib. bdg. 17.25 (978-0-8239-5962-4(7)); Cheetah : World's Fastest Land Animal. lib. bdg. 17.25 (978-0-8239-5959-4(7)); Giraffe : World's Tallest Animal. lib. bdg. 17.25 (978-0-8239-5964-8(3)); Hummingbird : World's Smallest Bird. lib. bdg. 17.25 (978-0-8239-5960-0(0)); Sloth : The World's Slowest Mammal. lib. bdg. 17.25 (978-0-8239-5961-7(9)); Stick Insect : World's Longest Insect. lib. bdg. 17.25 (978-0-8239-5963-1(5)); 24p. (J). (gr. 1). 2002. (Illus.). Set lib. bdg. 96.00 (978-0-8239-7119-0(8) , PowerKids Pr.) Rosen Publishing Group, Inc., The.

Paine, Penelope C. Gift of Love. Maeno, Itoko, illus. 2006. 24p. per. 5.95 (978-0-7909-7443-9(6)) Paper Posie.

El Paisaje. (Coleccion Planeta Vivo).Tr. of Topography. (SPA.). (YA). (gr. 5-8). 10.36 (978-84-342-1948-9(4)) Parramon Ediciones S.A. ESP. *Dist:* Lectorum Pubns., Inc.

Pajaros. 2005. (Collection Abre Tus Ojos, Collection Eye Openers Ser.).Tr. of Birds. (SPA.). (J). (gr. k-2). 6.95 (978-950-11-0965-8(8)) Sigmar ARG. *Dist:* Iaconi, Mariuccia Bk. Imports.

Pandell, Karen. Animal Action ABC. Sheehan, Nancy, illus. Wolfe, Art & Sheehan, Nancy, photos by. 2003. 32p. (J). (ps-1). 12.95 (978-1-929766-92-5(0)) Handprint Bks.

—Animal Action ABC. 2000. 32p. (J). pap. (978-0-14-055885-2(3) , Puffin) Penguin Group (USA) Inc.

Park, Linda Sue. Mung-Mung! Bigda, Diane, illus. 2004. (J). pap. 9.95 (978-1-57091-487-4(7)); 36p. 9.95 (978-1-57091-486-7(9)) Charlesbridge Publishing, Inc.

Parker. Fantastic Animal Features. 1999. (Illus.). pap. 6.20 (978-0-7398-0861-0(3)) Steck-Vaughn.

Parker, Andy. Mekanimals: Clockwork Safari, Spanish-Language Edition. 2005. (Mekanimals Ser.). (SPA., Illus.). 8p. (J). bds. 12.95 (978-970-718-322-3(5) , Silver Dolphin en Español) Advanced Marketing, S. de R. L. de C. V. MEX. *Dist:* Perseus Distribution.

Parker, Heather. Fantastic Animal Features. 1999. (Illus.). 32p. (gr. 2-4). pap. 5.95 (978-0-7398-1479-6(6)) Steck-Vaughn.

Parker, Steve & Dewan, Ted. Inside the Whale & Other Animals. (Illus.). (J). 18.95 (978-0-590-73869-9(0)) Scholastic, Inc.

Parker, Victoria. Food. 2006. (Heinemann Read & Learn Ser.). (Illus.). 24p. (J). pap. (978-1-4034-7890-0(2)); lib. bdg. (978-1-4034-7884-9(8)) Steck-Vaughn.

Party Animals: Individual Title Six-Packs. (Story Steps Ser.). (gr. k-2). 32.00 (978-0-7635-9820-4(8)) Rigby Education.

Pascoe, Elaine. Animals Are Poisonous. Kuhn, Dwight, photos by. 2002. (Springboards into Science Ser.). (Illus.). 24p. (J). (gr. 1 up). lib. bdg. 20.67 (978-0-8368-3002-6(4)) Stevens, Gareth Inc.

—Animals Grow New Parts. Kuhn, Dwight, photos by. 2002. (Springboards into Science Ser.). (Illus.). 24p. (J). (gr. 1 up). lib. bdg. 20.67 (978-0-8368-3003-3(2)) Stevens, Gareth Inc.

—Animals Prepare for Winter. Kuhn, Dwight, photos by. 2002. (Springboards into Science Ser.). (Illus.). 24p. (J). (gr. 1 up). lib. bdg. 20.67 (978-0-8368-3006-4(7)) Stevens, Gareth Inc.

—The Ecosystem of an Apple Tree. 2003. (Library of Small Ecosystems Ser.). (Illus.). 24p. (J). lib. bdg. 21.25 (978-0-8239-6304-1(7) , PowerKids Pr.) Rosen Publishing Group, Inc., The.

—How & Why Animals Are Poisonous. Kupperstein, Joel, ed. Kuhn, Dwight, photos by. 2000. (How & Why Ser.). (Illus.). 16p. (J). (gr. 1-3). pap. 2.99 (978-1-57471-666-5(2) , 2973) Creative Teaching Pr., Inc.

—How & Why Animals Grow New Parts. Kupperstein, Joel, ed. Kuhn, Dwight, photos by. 2000. (How & Why Ser.). (Illus.). 16p. (J). (gr. 1-3). pap. 2.99 (978-1-57471-663-4(8) , 2970) Creative Teaching Pr., Inc.

—How & Why Animals Prepare for Winter. Kupperstein, Joel, ed. Kuhn, Dwight, photos by. 2000. (How & Why Ser.). (Illus.). 16p. (J). (gr. 1-3). pap. 2.99 (978-1-57471-664-1(6) , 2971) Creative Teaching Pr., Inc.

Pasternak, Ceel & Thornburg, Linda. Cool Careers for Girls with Animals. 1999. (Cool Careers for Girls Ser.). 145p. pap. 12.95 (978-1-57023-105-6(2)) Impact Pubns.

Pat Them Gently w/ Plush. 2007. 14.95 (*978-1-58117-626-1(0) , Intervisual/Piggy Toes) Dalmatian Pr.

La Patata. (Coleccion Ciclos Vitales). (SPA., Illus.). pap. 7.96 (978-84-236-2657-1(1) , ED4698) Edebé ESP. *Dist:* Lectorum Pubns., Inc.

Patkau, Karen. Creatures Great & Small. 2006. (Illus.). 32p. (J). (gr. 1-4). 17.95 (978-0-88776-754-8(0) , Random Hse. Bks. for Young Readers) Random Hse. Children's Bks.

Patkau, Karen. Creatures Yesterday & Today. 2008. (Illus.). 32p. 18.95 (*978-0-88776-833-0(4)) Tundra Bks., Inc./Livres Toundra, Inc. CAN. *Dist:* Random Hse. of Canada, Ltd.

Patrick, B. & Schotz, Leo D. Is That Funny? 2006. 32p. (J). 15.95 (978-0-9741319-6-2(2)) 4N Publishing LLC.

Paul, Tessa. In the Jungle. 1998. (Animal Trackers Ser.). (Illus.). 32p. (J). (gr. 2-3). pap. (978-0-86505-599-5(8)); lib. bdg. (978-0-86505-591-9(2)) Crabtree Publishing Co.

Pearce, Mallory. Celtic Animals Stained Glass Coloring Book. 1998. (Illus.). 16p. (J). pap. 5.95 (978-0-486-40572-8(9)) Dover Pubns., Inc.

Pearce, Querida L. Animals. Fraser, Mary Ann, illus. 1999. (Science Crosswords Ser.). 48p. (J). (gr. 3-7). pap. 4.95 (978-0-7373-0169-4(4) , 01694W) McGraw-Hill/Contemporary.

Pearcy, Alice & Brocklehurst, Ruth. Animal Jigsaw Atlas. Edwards, Linda, illus. 2005. 14p. (J). (ps-7). per. 14.95 (978-0-7945-1144-9(9) , Usborne) EDC Publishing.

Pearson, Deborah. Animachines. Hilb, Nora, illus. 2003. 24p. (J). (gr. k-ps). pap. 5.95 (978-1-55037-796-5(5)); lib. bdg. 17.95 (978-1-55037-797-2(3)) Annick Pr., Ltd. CAN. *Dist:* Firefly Bks., Ltd.

Pebble Books: Animals, Animals, Animals. 2005. (YA). (gr. k-3). 683.10 (978-0-7368-4221-1(7) , Pebble Bks.) Capstone Pr., Inc.

Pelham, David. A Is for Animals: An ABC Pop-Up. Pelham, David, illus. 10th anniv. ed. 2001. (Illus.). 14p. (J). 18.99 (978-0-689-84706-6(8) , Little Simon) Simon & Schuster Children's Publishing.

Penguin Books Staff, ed. Animals. (Learners Ser.). (Illus.). 48p. (J). 3.50 (978-0-7214-1705-9(1) , Dutton Juvenile) Penguin Group (USA) Inc.

Penny, Malcolm. Hidden Hibernators. 2003. (Amazing Nature Ser.). (Illus.). 32p. (J). pap. (978-1-4034-5400-3(0)) Heinemann Library.

—Life under a Stone. 2003. (Illus.). 32p. (J). pap. (978-1-4109-0352-5(4)); lib. bdg. 24.28 (978-0-7398-6806-5(3)) Raintree.

Pequena Historia de Mi Gatito, Conejito, Perrito. 2003. (SPA.). 3.98 (978-968-855-202-5(X)) Suromex, Ediciones, S.A. MEX. *Dist:* Giron Bks.

Perkins, Wendy. Animal Feathers. 2007. (Pebble Plus Ser.). (Illus.). 24p. (J). 19.93 (978-0-7368-6350-6(8)) Capstone Pr., Inc.

—Animals Building Homes. 2004. (First Facts Ser.). (Illus.). 24p. (J). 15.95 (978-0-7368-2508-5(8)) Capstone Pr., Inc.

—Let's Look at Animal Bottoms. 2007. (Pebble Plus Ser.). (Illus.). 24p. (J). (978-0-7368-6715-3(5) , 1264881) Capstone Pr., Inc.

—Let's Look at Animal Legs. 2007. (J). (978-0-7368-6717-7(1)) Capstone Pr., Inc.

—Let's Look at Animal Tails. 2007. (J). (978-0-7368-6718-4(X)) Capstone Pr., Inc.

—Let's Look at Animal Wings. 2007. (J). (978-0-7368-6716-0(3)) Capstone Pr., Inc.

A B

Perry, Kate. Animal Movement. 2004. (Nature Files Ser.). (Illus.). 32p. (J). (gr. 4-8). 28.00 (978-0-7910-8218-8(0) , Chelsea Hse.) Facts On File, Inc.

Perry, Phyllis J. Animals under the Ground. 2001. (gr. 3-6). lib. bdg. 17.60 (978-0-613-52243-4(5)) Tandem Library Bks.

Petty, Kate. Gerbil. 2005. (Illus.). 24p. (J). (gr. 2-5). lib. bdg. 22.80 (978-1-59604-030-4(0)) Stargazer Bks.

—Hamster. 2005. (Illus.). 24p. (J). (gr. 2-5). lib. bdg. 22.80 (978-1-59604-028-1(9)) Stargazer Bks.

Peyrols, Sylvaine. La Historia de la Vida: Los Animales. (SPA., Illus.). 64p. (J). (gr. 3-5). (978-84-261-3149-2(2) , JV30157) Juventud, Editorial ESP. *Dist:* Lectorum Pubns., Inc.

Pfeffer, Wendy. High Mountains. 2002. (Living on the Edge Ser.). (Illus.). 39p. (J). 25.64 (978-0-7614-1441-4(X) , Benchmark Bks.) Cavendish, Marshall Corp.

Pfister, Marcus. El Pez Arco Iris y la Ballena Azul. 2001. Orig. Title: Regenbogenfisch und Grosser Blauer Wal. (SPA., Illus.). 14p. (J). (ps-k). bds. 9.95 (978-0-7358-1431-8(7)) North-South Bks., Inc.

Pfloog, Jan. Monkey Book. 1999. (ps-2). lib. bdg. 11.00 (978-0-613-87570-7(2)) Tandem Library Bks.

Phillips, Dee. Find It in the Park. 2006. (Illus.). 24p. (J). 22.00 (978-0-8368-6301-7(1)) Stevens, Gareth Inc.

Phillips, Sara. Animals. 2003. (Illus.). 8p. (J). pap. 4.95 (978-0-7624-1650-9(5)) Running Pr. Bk. Pubs.

Phillips, Sarah. Wipe Clean: Animals. 2007. (Trace, Stick & Learn Ser.). (Illus.). 12p. (J). (ps-3). pap. 4.99 ***(978-1-84610-429-9(7))*** Make Believe Ideas GBR. *Dist:* Ingram Pub. Services.

Pichette, Marise & Rousseau, Serge. Show & Tell Animals. 2000. (Illus.). 12p. (J). bds. (978-2-922148-80-0(7)) Presses aventure/Adventure Pr.

Pickering, Fran. The Illustrated Encyclopedia of Animals in Nature & Myth. 2003. (Illus.). 144p. (YA). (978-1-903954-53-9(3)) Chrysalis Children's Bks.

Pierson, Clara Dillingham. Among the Forest People (Yesterday's Classics) 2005. (Illus.). 148p. (J). per. 8.95 (978-1-59915-018-5(2)) Yesterday's Classics.

—Among the Meadow People (Yesterday's Classics) 2005. (Illus.). 136p. (J). per. 8.95 (978-1-59915-019-2(0)) Yesterday's Classics.

—Among the Night People (Yesterday's Classics) 2005. (Illus.). 164p. (J). per. 8.95 (978-1-59915-020-8(4)) Yesterday's Classics.

—Among the Pond People (Yesterday's Classics) 2005. (Illus.). 160p. (J). per. 8.95 (978-1-59915-021-5(2)) Yesterday's Classics.

Pierson, Dillingham Clara. Among the Farmyard People. 2007. (ENG.). 116p. 40.99 ***(978-1-4280-7240-4(3) ;*** per. 34.99 ***(978-1-4280-7265-7(9))*** IndyPublish.com.

Pingry, Patricia A. & Zoo, San Diego, eds. My Big Book of Wild Animals. 2007. 224p. (J). (gr. k-2). pap. 19.99 (978-0-8249-5543-4(9) , Ideals Children's Bks.) Ideals Pubns.

Pipe, Jim. Animal Bodies: Paws, Tails, & Whiskers. 2005. (Science Starters Ser.). (Illus.). 32p. (J). (gr. 1-4). lib. bdg. 27.10 (978-1-59604-012-0(2)) Stargazer Bks.

—Minibeasts. 2007. (J). ***(978-1-59604-131-8(5))*** Stargazer Bks.

—Noisy Animals. 2007. (J). ***(978-1-59604-160-8(9))*** Stargazer Bks.

Pisos, Cecilia. El Baul de los Animales: Un Libro Sobre Opuestos. Perica, illus. (Coleccion el Baul Ser.). (SPA.). 10p. (J). (gr. k-1). (978-950-46-1156-1(7)) Santillana USA Publishing Co., Inc.

Pitts, Kieren. Hitchers & Thieves. 2003. (Parasites & Partners Ser.). (Illus.). 32p. (J). pap. 7.50 (978-1-4109-0356-3(7)); lib. bdg. (978-0-7398-6989-5(2)) Raintree.

—Hitchers & Thieves. 2003. (gr. 5-8). lib. bdg. 15.90 (978-0-613-78249-4(6)) Tandem Library Bks.

Play & Learn Fo, ed. Wild Animals. 2007. (Play & Learn Foam Puzzle Bks.). 10p. (J). bds. 16.95 ***(978-0-7696-5399-0(5)*** , Brighter Child) School Specialty Publishing.

Pollock, Steve. Deadly Creatures. 1999. (Illus.). 24p. (J). (gr. 5-9). reprint ed. 14.00 (978-0-7881-6479-8(1)) DIANE Publishing Co.

Pomaska, Anna. Animal Alphabet Follow the Dots. 2002. (Dover Little Activity Bks.). (Illus.). 64p. (J). pap. 1.50 (978-0-486-42101-8(5)) Dover Pubns., Inc.

Pomerance, Diane. Animal Companions: In Our Hearts, Our Lives, & Our World. Mier, Vanessa, illus. 2004. (YA). per. 9.95 (978-0-9708500-3-4(4)) Polaire Pubns.

Poole, Susie. God Loves the Jungle Animals. 2004. (Illus.). 18p. (J). 6.99 (978-0-310-70866-7(4)) Zonderkidz.

Potter, Beatrix. Peter Rabbit Giant Shaped Board Book. abr. ed. 2001. (Illus.). 10p. (J). (ps-k). bds. 7.99 (978-0-7232-4682-4(3) , Warne) Penguin Group (USA) Inc.

Pountney, Beth. Wacky Wild Animals. 2007. (Touchy Feely Ser.). (Illus.). 12p. (ps). per., bds. 5.95 (978-1-84610-456-5(4)) Make Believe Ideas GBR. *Dist:* Ingram Pub. Services.

Powell, Consie. A Bold Carnivore: An Alphabet of Predators. 2007. (J). pap. ***(978-0-9766264-9-7(7))*** Raven Productions, Inc.

—A Bold Carnivore: An Alphabet of Predators. Powell, Consie, illus. 2000. (Illus.). 32p. (ps-1). pap. 7.95 (978-1-57098-143-2(4)) Rinehart, Roberts Pubs.

Powell, Richard J. Who's Peeking at You? from the Pond. Clark, Debbie, illus. 2006. (Who's Peeking? Bks.). 12p. (J). bds. 4.99 (978-0-7641-5994-7(1)) Barron's Educational Series, Inc.

—Who's Peeking at You? in the Pet Store. Clark, Debbie, illus. 2006. (Who's Peeking Bks.). 12p. (J). bds. 4.99 (978-0-7641-5996-1(8)) Barron's Educational Series, Inc.

PowerPhonics Skill Set I: Includes Animals I, Self I & Growing Things, 18 bks. (Illus.). (J). (gr. 1). lib. bdg. 324.00 (978-0-8239-7204-3(6) , PowerKids Pr.) Rosen Publishing Group, Inc., The.

Prap, Lila. Why? Prap, Lila, illus. 2007. Orig. Title: Zakaj?. (Illus.). (J). pap. 3.99 (978-1-933605-33-3(2) , 05333) Kane/Miller Bk. Pubs., Inc.

Pratt, Kristin Joy. Salamander Rain: A Lake & Pond Journal. 2000. (gr. 3-6). lib. bdg. 16.40 (978-0-613-49355-0(9)) Tandem Library Bks.

Pratt-Serafini, Kristin Joy. Salamander Rain: A Lake & Pond Journal. 2004. (Sharing Nature with Children Book Ser.). (Illus.). 32p. (YA). (gr. 4-7). 16.95 (978-1-58469-018-4(6)) Dawn Pubns.

Pratt-Serafini, Kristin Joy & Pratt, Kristin Joy. Salamander Rain: A Lake & Pond Journal. 2004. (Sharing Nature with Children Book Ser.). (Illus.). 32p. (YA). (gr. 4-7). pap. 7.95 (978-1-58469-017-7(8)) Dawn Pubns.

Predators in the Wild, 8 bks. Incl. Anacondas. Welsbacher, Anne. 48p. (gr. 3-4). 2001. lib. bdg. 21.26 (978-0-7368-0785-2(3)); Cougars. Welsbacher, Anne. 32p. (gr. 3-4). 2002. lib. bdg. 21.26 (978-0-7368-1316-7(0)); Crocodiles. Welsbacher, Anne. 32p. (gr. 3-4). 2002. lib. bdg. 21.26 (978-0-7368-1315-0(2)); Great White Sharks. Deady, Kathleen W. 48p. (gr. 3-4). 2001. lib. bdg. 21.26 (978-0-7368-0786-9(1)); Grizzly Bears. Deady, Kathleen W. 32p. (gr. 3-4). 2002. lib. bdg. 21.26 (978-0-7368-1063-0(3)); Hawks. Deady, Kathleen W. 32p. (gr. 3-4). 2002. lib. bdg. 21.26 (978-0-7368-1064-7(1)); Killer Whales. Welsbacher, Anne. 32p. (gr. 2-3). 2002. lib. bdg. 21.26 (978-0-7368-1065-4(X)); Komodo Dragons. Welsbacher, Anne. 32p. (gr. 3-4). 2002. lib. bdg. 21.26 (978-0-7368-1066-1(8)); Rattlesnakes. Richardson, Adele D. 32p. (gr. 3-4). 2002. lib. bdg. 21.26 (978-0-7368-1317-4(9)); Scorpions. Richardson, Adele D. 32p. (gr. 3-4). 2002. lib. bdg. 21.26 (978-0-7368-1318-1(7)); Vampire Bats. Welsbacher, Anne. 48p. (gr. 3-4). 2001. lib. bdg. 21.26 (978-0-7368-0787-6(X)); Wolves. Welsbacher, Anne. 48p. (gr. 3-4). 2001. lib. bdg. 21.26 (978-0-7368-0788-3(8)); (J). (Illus.), Set lib. bdg. 255.12 (978-0-7368-1319-8(5) , Capstone High-Interest Bks.) Capstone Pr., Inc.

Presnall, Judith Janda. Rodeo Animals. 2003. (Animals with Jobs Ser.). (Illus.). 48p. (J). 26.20 (978-0-7377-2052-5(2) , Greenhaven Pr., Inc.) Thomson Gale.

Price, Nick, illus. Animal Legends. 2004. (Young Reading Series One Ser.). 48p. (J). (gr. 2 up). pap. 5.95 (978-0-7945-0408-3(6) , Usborne) EDC Publishing.

—Magical Animals. 2004. (Young Reading Series One Ser.). 48p. (J). (gr. 2 up). pap. 5.95 (978-0-7945-0454-0(X) , Usborne) EDC Publishing.

Priddy Books Staff. Animals. rev. ed. 2004. (Bright Baby Ser.). (Illus.). 26p. (J). bds. 4.95 (978-0-312-49248-9(0) , Priddy Bks.) St. Martin's Pr.

—Wipe Clean: Learn to Draw Animals 26 Wipe-Clean Pages of Early Learning Fun. rev. ed. 2004. (Wipe Clean Ser.). (Illus.). 28p. (J). bds. 8.95 (978-0-312-49401-8(7) , Priddy Bks.) St. Martin's Pr.

Priddy Books Staff & Priddy, Roger. Happy Baby: Animals. 2004. (Illus.). 28p. (J). bds. 8.95 (978-0-312-49195-6(6) , Priddy Bks.) St. Martin's Pr.

—Soft to Touch: Wild, Scary, Cute or Cuddly, We Love Them All! rev. ed. 2004. (Illus.). 20p. (J). bds. 8.95 (978-0-312-49391-2(6) , Priddy Bks.) St. Martin's Pr.

Priddy, Roger. Animals. 2005. (Sticker Activity Fun Workbooks). (J). (Illus.). 48p. pap. 3.47 (978-0-312-49660-9(5)); 12p. bds. 0.97 (978-0-312-49610-4(9)) St. Martin's Pr. (Priddy Bks.).

—Baby Gund Animals. 2005. (Illus.). 20p. (J). bds. 5.95 (978-0-312-49513-8(7) , Priddy Bks.) St. Martin's Pr.

—Bilingual Sticker Flash Cards Animals. 2006. 30p. (J). 5.95 (978-0-312-49793-4(8) , Priddy Bks.) St. Martin's Pr.

—Bright Baby Board Book Animals. 2007. (J). bds. 4.95 ***(978-0-312-49774-3(1)*** , Priddy Bks.) St. Martin's Pr.

—Bright Baby Soft-to-Touch Large: Words, Animals, Colors. 2005. (J). 22.95 (978-0-312-49555-8(2) , Priddy Bks.) St. Martin's Pr.

—Bright Baby Touch & Feel at the Zoo. 2006. (Bright Baby Ser.). (Illus.). 10p. (J). bds. 4.95 (978-0-312-49857-3(8) , Priddy Bks.) St. Martin's Pr.

—Cloth Shaker Teether Animals. rev. ed. 2006. 10p. (J). 6.95 (978-0-312-49669-2(9) , Priddy Bks.) St. Martin's Pr.

—Dilly Duck. 2007. 6p. (J). bds., act. bk. ed. 9.95 (978-0-312-49907-5(8) , Priddy Bks.) St. Martin's Pr.

—First 100 Animals. rev. ed. 2006. (Illus.). 14p. (J). bds. 8.95 (978-0-312-49676-0(1) , Priddy Bks.) St. Martin's Pr.

—I Love Animals Sticker Book. 2007. 20p. (J). pap. 3.95 ***(978-0-312-49962-4(0)*** , Priddy Bks.) St. Martin's Pr.

—Jungle Picture Pops. 2005. (Illus.). 14p. (J). (ps-ps). 12.95 (978-0-312-49449-0(1) , Priddy Bks.) St. Martin's Pr.

—My Big Animal Book. rev. ed. 2002. (Illus.). 12p. (J). bds. 5.95 (978-0-312-49083-6(6) , Priddy Bks.) St. Martin's Pr.

—My Little Animal Book. 2006. 28p. (J). bds. 10.95 (978-0-312-49731-6(8)); (Illus.). bds., bds. 9.95 (978-0-312-49807-8(1)) St. Martin's Pr. (Priddy Bks.).

—Slide & Find - Animals. 2007. 10p. (J). bds. 6.95 (978-0-312-49908-2(6) , Priddy Bks.) St. Martin's Pr.

—Soft-to-Touch Slipcase 1: Things,Words & Animals. 2004. 84p. (J). bds. 22.95 (978-0-312-49422-3(X) , Priddy Bks.) St. Martin's Pr.

—Sticker Flash Animals. 2006. 30p. (J). bds. 5.95 (978-0-312-49828-3(4) , Priddy Bks.) St. Martin's Pr.

—3 in 1: My Big Animal,World,Dinosaur. 2005. (J). bds. 16.95 (978-0-312-49562-6(5) , Priddy Bks.) St. Martin's Pr.

—3 In 1: Who Lives in the Wild, Farm, House. 2005. (J). bds. 16.95 (978-0-312-49564-0(1) , Priddy Bks.) St. Martin's Pr.

Primm & Petelinsek. Animals/Animales. 2004. (Talking Hands, Listening Eyes Ser.). (ENG & SPA., Illus.). 24p. (J). (ps-3). 21.36 (978-1-59296-018-7(9)) Child's World, Inc.

Pringle, Laurence P. Strange Animals, New to Science. 2002. (Illus.). 112p. (J). (gr. 3-7). 16.95 (978-0-7614-5083-2(1) , Cavendish Children's Bks.) Cavendish, Marshall Corp.

Publications International Staff, contrib. by. Noah's Ark ABC. 2001. (My Wipe-Off Book Ser.). (Illus.). (J). (978-0-7853-5101-6(9)) Publications International, Ltd.

Pupeza, Lori K. Wildlife Gardens. 2002. (Gardening Ser.). (Illus.). 32p. (J). (gr. k-6). lib. bdg. 22.78 (978-1-57765-032-4(8) , Checkerboard Library) ABDO Publishing Co.

Pye, Claire. Wild World of the Future. 2003. (gr. 3-6). lib. bdg. 24.55 (978-0-613-78618-8(1)) Tandem Library Bks.

Pyers, Greg. Pill Bugs up Close. 2005. (Minibeasts up Close Ser.). (Illus.). 32p. (J). (ps-1). pap. 7.85 (978-1-4109-1538-2(7)) Harcourt Schl. Pubs.

—Pill Bugs up Close. 2005. (Minibeasts up Close Ser.). (Illus.). 32p. (J). (978-1-4109-1531-3(X)) Steck-Vaughn.

Quadrillion Media Staff. Nature & Animals. 1999. (Start Me Up Ser.). (J). pap. 3.95 (978-1-58185-101-4(4)) Quadrillion Media LLC.

—Wild Animals. 2000. (Start Me Up Ser.: Vol. 12). (Illus.). (J). 12.95 (978-1-58185-016-1(6)) Quadrillion Media LLC.

Radtke, Becky. Invisible Forest Animals Magic Picture Book. 2004. (Illus.). 16p. (J). pap. 1.50 (978-0-486-43721-7(3)) Dover Pubns., Inc.

Rahmlow, Robert C. Nature's Store. 2007. 80p. (J). 8.99 ***(978-1-59886-987-3(6))*** Tate Publishing & Enterprises, L.L.C.

Rain Forest Animals Set B, 6 vols. (Phonics Readers Ser.). (gr. k-2). 17.50 (978-0-7368-3198-7(3)) Red Brick Learning.

Raintree Steck-Vaughn Staff. Animals-Elementary: Arkansas Edition, 39 bks., Set. 2003. (Illus.). (J). 992.48 (978-1-4109-0141-5(6)) Raintree.

—Animals II: Arkansas Edition, 54 bks., Set. 2003. (J). 1445.40 (978-1-4109-0143-9(2)) Raintree.

—Biomes Animals: Arkansas Edition, 36 bks., Set. 2003. (Illus.). 1062.48 (978-1-4109-0142-2(4)) Harcourt Schl. Pubs.

—Day in the Sun. 2000. (Read All about It Ser.). (Illus.). (J). pap. 4.95 (978-0-8114-3766-0(3)) Steck-Vaughn.

—It's Snowing. 2000. (Read All about It Ser.). (Illus.). (J). (gr. k-3). pap. 4.95 (978-0-8114-3767-7(1)) Steck-Vaughn.

—You & Me. 2000. (Read All about It Ser.). (Illus.). (J). pap. 4.95 (978-0-8114-3768-4(X)) Steck-Vaughn.

Ramey, Kathy. The Animal Alphabet. 2007. (J). pap. 12.95 ***(*978-1-931334-96-9(X))*** Pieces of Learning.

Random House Staff. Animals. 2001. (Play It Smart Workbks.). 32p. (J). pap. 2.99 (978-0-375-80463-2(3) , Random Hse. Bks. for Young Readers) Random Hse. Children's Bks.

Rau, Dana Meachen. Veterinarian. 2007. (Jobs in Town Ser.). 24p. (J). lib. bdg. 22.79 ***(*978-0-7614-2622-6(1)*** , Benchmark Bks.) Cavendish, Marshall Corp.

Rauen, Amy. Counting at the Zoo. 2007. (J). pap. ***(*978-0-8368-8478-4(7));*** 24p. (gr. 1-3). lib. bdg. 19.93 ***(*978-0-8368-8469-2(8))*** Stevens, Gareth Inc. (Weekly Reader Early Learning Library).

Reader dsm-3 plant&animal population Ea. 2004. (J). (978-1-59242-524-2(0)) Delta Education, LLC.

Ready Set Learn Staff. Peeps Animals & Nature. 2005. (Illus.). 24p. (J). (ps-2). bds. 15.99 (978-1-59249-519-1(2) , 1C301) Soundprints.

Reed, Janet. Animal Patterns. 2003. (Yellow Umbrella Books for Early Readers). (Illus.). 17p. (J). 15.93 (978-0-7368-2914-4(8)); pap. (978-0-7368-2873-4(7)) Yellow Umbrella Pr.

Regan, Dana, illus. Old MacDonald Had a Farm. 2006. (Sing-A-Story Ser.). 16p. (J). bds. 10.95 (978-0-7696-4913-9(0)) School Specialty Publishing.

Rehnberg, Peter, photos by. Critters & Kids: Clip Art for the Classroom. 2000. (Illus.). 64p. (J). pap. 12.95 (978-1-877673-41-2(2) , CR-BWK03) Cottonwood Pr., Inc.

Reinhart, Matthew & Sabuda, Robert. Mega-Beasts. Reinhart, Matthew & Sabuda, Robert, illus. 2007. (Encyclopedia Prehistorica Ser.). (Illus.). 12p. (J). (gr. k up). 27.99 (978-0-7636-2230-5(3)) Candlewick Pr.

Renne. Animal Trails & Tracks. Taurel, Alison, tr. from DUT. Renne, illus. 2000. (Animals Up Close Ser.). (Illus.). 38p. (J). (gr. 3 up). lib. bdg. 24.67 (978-0-8368-2713-2(9)) Stevens, Gareth Inc.

—Animals Up Close, 6 bks. Renne, illus. Incl. Animal Males & Females. Taurel, Alison, tr. from DUT. lib. bdg. 24.67 (978-0-8368-2712-5(0)); Animal Trails & Tracks. Taurel, Alison, tr. from DUT. lib. bdg. 24.67 (978-0-8368-2713-2(9)); Animals & Their Eggs. Taurel, Alison, tr. from DUT. lib. bdg. 24.67 (978-0-8368-2714-9(7)); Animals That Live in Water. lib. bdg. 24.67 (978-0-8368-2715-6(5)); Why Animals Have Tails. lib. bdg. 24.67 (978-0-8368-2716-3(3)); Young Animals & Their Parents. lib. bdg. 24.67 (978-0-8368-2717-0(1)); 38p. (J). (gr. 3 up). 2000. (Illus.). 2000. Set lib. bdg. 148.02 (978-0-8368-2711-8(2)) Stevens, Gareth Inc.

El rescate de los Animales 6: Leveled Books. 2001. (McGraw-Hill. Lectura Ser.). (ENG & SPA.). (gr. 4 up). (978-0-02-188206-9(1)) Macmillan/McGraw-Hill Schl. Div.

Rey, H. A. Feed the Animals. rev. ed. 1998. (Illus.). 22p. (J). (gr. k-ps). pap. 5.95 (978-0-395-90693-4(8)) Houghton Mifflin Co. Trade & Reference Div.

Rey, H. A. & Rey, Margret. Curious George's First Words at the Aquarium, 4 vols. 2006. (Illus.). 12p. (J). (ps-k). bds. 3.95 (978-0-618-55458-4(0)) Houghton Mifflin Co.

—Curious George's First Words at the Circus, 4 vols. 2006. (Illus.). 12p. (J). (ps-k). bds. 3.95 (978-0-618-55457-7(2)) Houghton Mifflin Co.

—Curious George's First Words at the Farm, 4 vols. 2006. (Illus.). 12p. (J). (ps-k). bds. 3.95 (978-0-618-55455-3(6)) Houghton Mifflin Co.

—Curious George's First Words at the Zoo, 4 vols. 2006. (Illus.). 12p. (J). (ps-k). bds. 3.95 (978-0-618-55456-0(4)) Houghton Mifflin Co.

Reyes, Blanca Matilde. Wild Animals. 2006. (Illus.). 16p. (J). act. bk. ed. 0.75 (978-1-933984-01-8(5)) Two Lands.

Rice, David L. & Calvert, Trudy L. Do Animals Have Feelings Too? 2004. (Circle of Destiny Ser.). (Illus.). 32p. (YA). (gr. 4-5). pap. 7.95 (978-1-58469-004-7(6)); (ps-7). 16.95 (978-1-58469-003-0(8)) Dawn Pubns.

Richter, Bernard. Touch & Feel Alaskas Animals. 2003. (Illus.). 12p. bds. 9.95 (978-1-931353-13-7(1)) Saddle Pal Creations, Inc.

Richter, Bernd & Richter, Susan. Alaska Animals - Where Do They Go at 40 Below? 2001. 32p. 14.95 (978-1-931353-01-4(8)); 9.95 (978-1-931353-00-7(X)) Saddle Pal Creations, Inc.

Rigby. Write on Wipe off Handwriting: Manuscript. 2001. (Illus.). pap. (978-0-7635-7344-7(2)) Steck-Vaughn.

Rigby Education Staff. A Is for Animals. (Pebble Soup Explorations Ser.). (Illus.). 16p. (ps up). 31.00 (978-0-7635-6466-7(4) , 764664C99) Rigby Education.

—Animals: A Is For Animal. (Pebble Soup Explorations Ser.). 16p. (ps up). 5.00 (978-0-7635-7047-7(8)) Rigby Education.

—At the Big & Small Zoo. (Illus.). (J). suppl. ed. 20.00 (978-0-7635-6469-8(9) , 764699C99) Rigby Education.

—Bugs on the Menu. (Sails Literacy Ser.). (Illus.). 16p. (gr. 2-3). 27.00 (978-0-7635-9954-6(9) , 699549C99) Rigby Education.

—Discovery World Yel Animl Leg. (Discovery World Ser.). (Illus.). 12p. (gr. k-1). 23.00 (978-0-7635-2696-2(7)) Rigby Education.

—Helping Out. (Sails Literacy Ser.). (Illus.). 16p. (gr. 1-2). 27.00 (978-0-7635-9899-0(2) , 698992C99) Rigby Education.

—The Hiders. (Sails Literacy Ser.). (Illus.). 16p. (gr. 2-3). 27.00 (978-0-7635-9957-7(3) , 699573C99) Rigby Education.

—Hold on Tight. (Sails Literacy Ser.). (Illus.). 16p. (gr. k-1). 27.00 (978-0-7635-9861-7(5)) Rigby Education.

—In the Jungle River. (Sails Literacy Ser.). (Illus.). 16p. (gr. 1-2). 27.00 (978-0-7635-9921-8(2) , 699212C99) Rigby Education.

—Peekaboo. (Illus.). 8p. (J). bds. 3.95 (978-0-7635-6464-3(8) , 764648C99) Rigby Education.

—Spikes, Scales & Armor. (Sails Literacy Ser.). (Illus.). 16p. (gr. 1-2). 27.00 (978-0-7635-9919-5(0) , 699190C99) Rigby Education.

—Stomachs. (Sails Literacy Ser.). (Illus.). 16p. (gr. 2-3). 27.00 (978-0-7635-9960-7(3) , 699603C99) Rigby Education.

—Stripes & Spots. (Sails Literacy Ser.). (Illus.). 16p. (gr. k-1). 27.00 (978-0-7635-9862-4(3) , 698623C99) Rigby Education.

—That's Us. (Sails Literacy Ser.). (Illus.). 16p. (gr. 1-2). 27.00 (978-0-7635-9918-8(2) , 699182C99) Rigby Education.

—Under the Ground. (Sails Literacy Ser.). (Illus.). 16p. (gr. k-1). 27.00 (978-0-7635-9866-2(6) , 698666C99) Rigby Education.

—Using a Tail. (Sails Literacy Ser.). (Illus.). 16p. (gr. 2-3). 27.00 (978-0-7635-9950-8(6) , 699506C99) Rigby Education.

Riha, Susanne. Animal Journeys: Life Cycles & Migrations. Riha, Susanne, illus. 1999. (Animals in the Wild Ser.). (Illus.). 32p. (J). (gr. 3-6). 22.45 (978-1-56711-426-3(1) , Blackbirch Pr., Inc.) Thomson Gale.

—Animals & the Seasons: The Cycle of Nature. Riha, Susanne, illus. 2000. (Animals in the Wild Ser.). (Illus.). 32p. (J). (gr. 3-6). 22.45 (978-1-56711-429-4(6) , Blackbirch Pr., Inc.) Thomson Gale.

Riley, Peter D. Animals. Moller, Ray, photos by. 2003. (Everyday Science Ser.). (Illus.). 32p. (J). (gr. 1 up). lib. bdg. 23.33 (978-0-8368-3713-1(4)) Stevens, Gareth Inc.

—Movement. Moller, Ray, photos by. 2003. (Everyday Science Ser.). (Illus.). 32p. (J). (gr. 1 up). lib. bdg. 23.33 (978-0-8368-3717-9(7)) Stevens, Gareth Inc.

Rinaldo, Luana & Sladen, Louisa. Jungle Animals. 2004. (Magic Color Bks.). (Illus.). 10p. (J). 3.95 (978-1-4027-1208-1(1)) Sterling Publishing Co., Inc.

Ring, Susan. Where? 2003. (Yellow Umbrella Books). (Illus.). 16p. (J). (gr. 1). lib. bdg. 14.60 (978-0-7368-2016-5(7) , Pebble Bks.) Capstone Pr., Inc.

—Where? 2003. (Math Ser.). (J). (978-0-7368-1700-4(X)) Yellow Umbrella Pr.

Rivera, Sheila. Wetland. 2005. (First Step Nonfiction Ser.). (Illus.). 23p. (J). (ps-7). 18.60 (978-0-8225-2598-1(4) , Lerner Pubns.) Lerner Publishing Group.

Roachford, Deirdre. Rights for Animals? 2005. (Illus.). 32p. (J). (gr. 5-9). lib. bdg. 27.10 (978-1-932889-55-0(8)) Sea-To-Sea Pubns.

Roberts, G. D. Charles. Kindred of the Wild. 2001. 164p. pap. 19.95 ***(*978-1-55096-599-5(9))*** Exile Editions, Ltd. CAN. *Dist:* Independent Pubs. Group.

Robertson, Matthew. Aranas. 2002. (SPA.). 64p. (978-970-651-635-0(2) , 1610) Editorial Oceano De Mexico, S.A. DE C.V.

Robinson, Anthony. Animals in the Jungle: American English Edition. 2000. (Cambridge Reading Ser.). (Illus.). pap. 5.00 (978-0-521-79904-1(X)) Cambridge Univ. Pr.

—Animals in the Jungle Pack of 6 American English Edition. 2000. (Cambridge Reading Ser.). (Illus.). 8p. pap. 28.00 (978-0-521-79905-8(8)) Cambridge Univ. Pr.

Robinson, Claire. In the Wild. 1999. (Illus.). 24p. (J). (gr. 1-6). pap. 119.52 (978-1-57572-131-6(7)) Heinemann Library.

Robleda, Margarita. Quien Soy? Adivinanzas Animales. Gurovich, Natalia, illus. 2003. (SPA.). 32p. (J). 12.95 (978-970-690-805-6(6)) Planeta Mexicana Editorial S. A. de C. V. MEX. *Dist:* Lectorum Pubns., Inc.

Robson, Gary D. Who Pooped in the Black Hills? Rath, Robert, illus. 2006. (J). (978-1-56037-387-2(3)) Farcountry Pr.

—Who Pooped in the Park? Rath, Robert, illus. 2006. 48p. (J). (978-1-56037-339-1(3)); pap. (***978-1-56037-338-4(5)***) Farcountry Pr.

—Who Pooped in the Park: Yellowstone. 2004. (Illus.). 48p. (J). pap. 9.95 (978-1-56037-273-8(7)) Farcountry Pr.

—Who Pooped in the Park? Red Rock Canyon National Conservation Area. Rath, Robert, illus. 2005. 48p. (J). pap. 9.95 (978-1-56037-371-1(7)) Farcountry Pr.

—Who Pooped in the Sonoran Desert? Scat & Tracks for Kids. Rath, Robert, illus. 2006. 48p. (J). (978-1-56037-349-0(0)) Farcountry Pr.

Robson, Gary D. & Rath, Robert. Who Pooped in the Park? 2006. (Illus.). 48p. (J). 9.95 (978-1-56037-327-8(X)) Farcountry Pr.

Rohr, Ian. Biggest, Highest, Fastest. 2005. 32p. (J). lib. bdg. 13.95 (978-0-7608-6689-4(9)) Sundance/Newbridge Educational Publishing.

—Predators. 2006. (Real Deal - Yellow Ser.). (Illus.). 32p. (gr. 4-8). 19.00 (978-0-7910-9063-3(9)) Facts On File, Inc.

Rohrer, Martha. Animals, Animals, Animals. 2004. (Illus.). 32p. (ps-5). 1.70 (978-0-7399-2348-1(X) , 2950) Rod & Staff Pubs., Inc.

Romero, Libby. Characteristics of Animals. 2006. pap. 39.00 (***978-1-4108-6481-9(2)***) Benchmark Education Co.

—Discover Animals. 2006. pap. 39.00 (***978-1-4108-6484-0(7)***) Benchmark Education Co.

Rose, Elizabeth. Animal Adaptations. 2006. (Life Science Library). (Illus.). 24p. (J). 21.25 (978-1-4042-2817-7(9) , PowerKids Pr.) Rosen Publishing Group, Inc., The.

Rosenberg, Pam. Underground. 2007. (Icky, Sticky, Gross-Out Bks.). 24p. (J). (gr. 2-6). 22.79 (***978-1-59296-900-5(3)***) Child's World, Inc.

—Yuck! Icky, Sticky, Gross Stuff in Your Garden. 2007. (Icky, Sticky, Gross-Out Bks.). 24p. (J). (gr. 2-6). 22.79 (***978-1-59296-896-1(1)***) Child's World, Inc.

Rosewarne, Graham, et al, illus. Discover the Amazing World of Animals. 87p. (J). (978-1-902272-27-6(7)) Tucker Slingsby, Ltd.

Ross, Odette. Counting. 2007. (Wordless Board Bks.). (Illus.). 12p. (J). (ps). bds. 5.95 (***978-1-894965-91-0(4)***) Simply Read Bks. CAN. *Dist:* Perseus Distribution.

Rothaus, Don & Stevens, Kathryn. Afghanistan. 2003. (Countries: Faces & Places Ser.). (Illus.). 32p. (J). (gr. 1-5). 25.64 (978-1-56766-181-1(5)) Child's World, Inc.

Royston. Jungle Animals Eye Openers. 1998. (J). 8.99 (978-0-87628-471-1(3)) Simon & Schuster.

Royston, Angela. Life Cycle of a... Series: An In-Depth Look at Some Familiar Plants & Animals, 4 bks., Set 3. 2000. (Illus.). 32p. (J). (gr. k-2). lib. bdg. 85.44 (978-1-57572-407-2(3)) Heinemann Library.

—LifeCycles of... Series, 5 bks., Set. Abello, Patricia, tr. 2003. (Illus.). (J). lib. bdg. 79.75 (978-1-4034-3036-6(5)) Heinemann Library.

Runnells, Treesha. Forest Friends: A Fold-Out Fun Book. Runnells, Treesha, illus. 2005. (Fold-Out Fun Ser.). (Illus.). 10p. (J). 4.95 (978-1-58117-275-1(3) , Intervisual/Piggy Toes) Dalmatian Pr.

—Safari Friends: Fold-Out Fun. Runnells, Treesha, illus. 2005. (Fold-Out Fun Ser.). (Illus.). 10p. (J). 4.95 (978-1-58117-276-8(1) , Intervisual/Piggy Toes) Dalmatian Pr.

Ruth, Brocklehurst. Atlas con Pegatinas los Animales - Internet Referenced. 2006. (Illus.). 24p. (J). pap. 8.99 (978-0-7460-6649-2(X) , Usborne) EDC Publishing.

Ruurs, Margriet. In My Backyard. Broda, Ron, illus. 2007. 32p. (J). (ps-3). 18.95 (978-0-88776-775-3(3)) Tundra Bks., Inc./Livres Toundra, Inc. CAN. *Dist:* Random Hse., Inc.

Ryan, Marla. Into Wild Amazonia. 2004. (Jeff Corwin Experience Ser.). (Illus.). 48p. (J). (gr. 4-7). 24.95 (978-1-4103-0251-9(2) , Blackbirch Pr., Inc.) Thomson Gale.

Ryan, Marla Felkins & Corwin, Jeff. Into Wild Thailand. 2004. (Jeff Corwin Experience Ser.). (Illus.). 48p. (J). 11.20 (978-1-4103-0254-0(7)); (gr. 4-7). 24.95 (978-1-4103-0253-3(9)) Thomson Gale. (Blackbirch Pr., Inc.).

Sabuda, Robert & Reinhart, Matthew. Encyclopedia Prehistorica Mega-Beasts. Sabuda, Robert & Reinhart, Matthew, illus. ed. 2007. (Sabuda Encyclopedias Ser.). (Illus.). 12p. (J). (gr. k). 250.00 (***978-0-7636-3204-5(X)***) Candlewick Pr.

Sacks, Janet, et al. Animals & Art Activities. 2002. (Arty Facts Ser.). (Illus.). 48p. (J). (gr. 3-4). pap. (978-0-7787-1136-0(6)); lib. bdg. (978-0-7787-1108-7(0)) Crabtree Publishing Co.

Saez Castan, Javier & Murugarren, Miguel. Animalario Universal. (Los Especials de A la Orilla Del Viento Ser.).Tr. of Universal Animalary. 40p. (J). (SPA.). (978-968-16-7048-1(5)); (CAT.). (978-968-16-7049-8(3)) Fondo de Cultura Economica USA.

Salane, Jeffrey, ed. All about Animals Wipe-off. 2007. (Leapfrog Ser.). 10p. (J). bds. 7.99 (978-0-439-89229-2(5) , Cartwheel Bks.) Scholastic, Inc.

Salas, Laura Purdie. Do Pelicans Sip Nectar? A Book about How Animals Eat. Ouren, Todd, illus. 2006. (Animals All Around Ser.). (J). 23.93 (978-1-4048-2233-7(X)) Picture Window Bks.

—Does an Elephant Fit in Your Hand? A Book about Animal Sizes. Yesh, Jeff, illus. 2006. (Animals All Around Ser.). (J). 23.93 (978-1-4048-2235-1(6)) Picture Window Bks.

Salzmann, Mary Elizabeth. What Has a Tail? 2007. (Creature Features Ser.). (ENG., Illus.). 24p. (J). (ps-3). lib. bdg. 24.21 (***978-1-59928-874-1(5)*** , Super SandCastle) ABDO Publishing Co.

—What Has Claws? 2007. (Creature Features Ser.). (ENG., Illus.). 24p. (J). (ps-3). lib. bdg. 24.21 (***978-1-59928-865-9(6)*** , Super SandCastle) ABDO Publishing Co.

—What Has Fur? 2007. (Creature Features Ser.). (ENG., Illus.). 24p. (J). (ps-3). lib. bdg. 24.21 (***978-1-59928-866-6(4)*** , Super SandCastle) ABDO Publishing Co.

—What Has Hooves? 2007. (Creature Features Ser.). (ENG., Illus.). 24p. (J). (ps-3). lib. bdg. 24.21 (***978-1-59928-867-3(2)*** , Super SandCastle) ABDO Publishing Co.

—What Has Webbed Feet? 2007. (Creature Features Ser.). (ENG., Illus.). 24p. (J). (ps-3). lib. bdg. 24.21 (***978-1-59928-875-8(3)*** , Super SandCastle) ABDO Publishing Co.

San Diego Zoo Staff. Animal ABC's San Diego Zoo. 2004. (Illus.). 20p. (J). 7.95 (978-0-8249-6551-8(5)) Ideals Pubns.

Sanchez, Richard. Animales (Animals) (SPA.). (J). 4.95 (978-84-243-2173-4(1)) Publicaciones Fher, S.A. ESP. *Dist:* AIMS International Bks., Inc.

Sargent, Daina. Colors & the Number 2, 11. Lenoir, Jane, illus. 2004. (Learn to Read Ser.: 11). 24p. (J). pap. 9.95 (978-1-59381-033-7(4)) Ozark Publishing.

Sargent, Dave & Sargent, Pat. I Can Read, Too. Robinson, Laura, illus. 2002. (Learn to Read Ser.). 24p. (J). Bk. 3. lib. bdg. 19.95 (978-1-56763-581-2(4)); Bk. 9. lib. bdg. 19.95 (978-1-56763-593-5(8)) Ozark Publishing.

Saunders, Dave & Michelson, Richard. Ten Times Better. Baskin, Leonard, illus. 2000. 40p. (J). (ps-3). 17.95 (978-0-7614-5070-2(X) , Cavendish Children's Bks.) Cavendish, Marshall Corp.

Saunders-Smith, Gail. Animals: Life Cycles, 4 vols., Set. 1998. (J). pap. 53.00 (978-0-516-29776-7(7) , Children's Pr.) Scholastic Library Publishing.

—Animals: Life Cycles, 4 bks. Incl. Butterflies. lib. bdg. 14.60 (978-1-56065-485-8(6)); Chickens. lib. bdg. 14.60 (978-1-56065-483-4(X)); Frogs. lib. bdg. 14.60 (978-1-56065-484-1(8)); Koalas. lib. bdg. 14.60 (978-1-56065-486-5(4)); 24p. (J). (gr. k-1). 1997. (Illus.). Set lib. bdg. 58.40 (978-1-56065-674-6(3) , Pebble Bks.) Capstone Pr., Inc.

Savage, Andrea. On Safari. 2005. (X-Zone Ser.). (Illus.). 30p. (gr. 4-8). 23.00 (978-0-7910-8991-0(6)) Facts On File, Inc.

Savage, Stephen. Animals of the Rain Forest. 1999. (Animals by Habitat Ser.). (Illus.). 32p. (J). (gr. 2-5). pap. 7.95 (978-0-7398-0116-1(3)) Steck-Vaughn.

—What's the Difference?, 6 bks., Set. Incl. Amphibians. lib. bdg. 25.69 (978-0-7398-1359-1(5)); Birds. lib. bdg. 25.69 (978-0-7398-1356-0(0)); Fish. lib. bdg. 25.69 (978-0-7398-1357-7(9)); Insects. lib. bdg. 25.69 (978-0-7398-1355-3(2)); Mammals. lib. bdg. 25.69 (978-0-7398-1354-6(4)); Reptiles. lib. bdg. 25.69 (978-0-7398-1358-4(7)); 32p. (J). (gr. 2-4). (Illus.). 1999. Set lib. bdg. 154.14 (978-0-7398-1360-7(9)) Raintree.

Schaefer, Lola M. Alpha-Butts: An Alphabet Book about Animal Rumps. Manning, Jane K., illus. 2008. 32p. (J). lib. bdg. 17.89 (***978-0-06-088394-2(4)*** , Greenwillow Bks.) HarperCollins Pubs.

—The Animal Kingdom, 6 bks. Saunders-Smith, Gail, ed. Incl. What Is a Bird? lib. bdg. 14.60 (978-0-7368-0864-4(7)); What Is a Fish? lib. bdg. 14.60 (978-0-7368-0865-1(5)); What Is a Mammal? lib. bdg. 14.60 (978-0-7368-0867-5(1)); What Is a Reptile? lib. bdg. 14.60 (978-0-7368-0868-2(X)); What Is an Amphibian? lib. bdg. 14.60 (978-0-7368-0863-7(9)); What Is an Insect? lib. bdg. 14.60 (978-0-7368-0866-8(3)); 24p. (J). (gr. k-1). 2001. (Illus.). Set lib. bdg. 87.60 (978-0-7368-0889-7(2) , Pebble Bks.) Capstone Pr., Inc.

—Animales Acorazados, 7 bks., Set. Cano, Patricia, tr. Tr. of Musty-Crusty Animals. (SPA., (J). 2003. Illus.). pap. 33.10 (978-1-4034-1601-8(X)); 2002. 90.65 (978-1-58810-775-6(2)) Heinemann Library.

—Animales Acorazados 123. 2002. (Animales Acorazados (Musty-Crusty Animals) Ser.). (SPA.). 24p. (J). (ps-1). lib. bdg. 18.50 (978-1-58810-859-3(7)); (Illus.). pap. 5.25 (978-1-58810-821-0(X) , 91556) Heinemann Library.

—Animales Espinosos 123. 2003. (SPA., Illus.). 24p. pap. 5.25 (978-1-4034-4309-0(2)) Heinemann Library.

—Animales Resbalosos, 8 bks., Set. Cano, Patricia, tr. 2002. Tr. of Ooey-Gooey Animals. (SPA.). (J). (ps-1). lib. bdg. 90.65 (978-1-58810-770-1(1)) Heinemann Library.

—Animales Resbalosos 123. 2002. (Animales Resbalosos (Ooey-Gooey Animals) Ser.). (SPA.). 24p. (J). (ps-1). lib. bdg. 18.50 (978-1-58810-769-5(8)); (Illus.). pap. 5.25 (978-1-58810-813-5(9)) Heinemann Library.

—El Equidna. 2003. (SPA.). 24p. pap. 5.25 (978-1-4034-4305-2(X)) Heinemann Library.

—El Erizo de Mar. Abello, Patricia, tr. 2004. (SPA., Illus.). 12p. (J). 12.95 (978-1-4034-4302-1(5)) Heinemann Library.

—El Erizo de Mar. 2003. (SPA.). 24p. pap. 5.25 (978-1-4034-4308-3(4)) Heinemann Library.

—La Lombriz de Tierra. 2002. (Animales Resbalosos (Ooey-Gooey Animals) Ser.). (SPA.). 24p. (J). (ps-1). lib. bdg. 18.50 (978-1-58810-764-0(7)); (Illus.). pap. 5.25 (978-1-58810-808-1(2) , 91518) Heinemann Library.

—La Salamandra. 2002. (Animales Resbalosos (Ooey-Gooey Animals) Ser.). (SPA.). 24p. (J). (ps-1). lib. bdg. 18.50 (978-1-58810-767-1(1)); (Illus.). pap. 5.25 (978-1-58810-811-1(2) , 91520) Heinemann Library.

—Tiny Spiny Animals ABC. 2003. (Heinemann Read & Learn Ser.). (Illus.). 24p. (J). pap. 5.25 (978-1-4034-3509-5(X)); lib. bdg. 18.50 (978-1-4034-3246-9(5)) Heinemann Library.

Schaefer, Lola M. & Miller, Heather Lynn. Alpha-Butts: An Alphabet Book about Animal Rumps. Manning, Jane K., illus. 2008. 32p. (J). 16.99 (***978-0-06-088393-5(6)*** , Greenwillow Bks.) HarperCollins Pubs.

Schieber, Jennifer. Animals in Motion. ed. 2004. (Shared Connections Ser.). (J). pap. 27.00 (978-1-4108-1630-6(3)); pap., instr.'s gde. ed. 27.00 (978-1-4108-1606-1(0)) Benchmark Education Co.

Schiller, Pam. Critter Pals. 2006. (NOODLEBUG Activities for Hands-on Learning Ser.). 32p. (J). pap. 4.99 (978-0-7696-4236-9(5)) School Specialty Publishing.

Schimmel, Schim & Book Company Staff. Playful Planet. Schimmel, Schim, illus. 2002. (Pop-up Bks.). (Illus.). 14p. (J). (978-1-74047-182-4(2)) Book Co. Publishing Pty, Ltd., The.

Schlein, Miriam. What the Dinosaurs Saw: Animals Living Then & Now. 1998. (Hello Reader! Science Ser.). (J). (978-0-606-13903-8(6)) Tandem Library Bks.

Scholastic Clubs US Animal Kingdom Pack #2: Animal Lives. 2006. (J). 44.75 (978-1-59566-324-5(X)) QEB Publishing Inc.

Scholastic Clubs US Animal Kingdom Pack #3: Animal Lives. 2007. (J). 44.75 (978-1-59566-327-6(4)) QEB Publishing Inc.

Scholastic, Inc. Staff. Animal Fun Sticker Book. 2005. 12.99 (***978-0-439-72570-5(4)*** , Teaching Resources) Scholastic, Inc.

—Night Creatures. 2007. (Scholastic First Discovery Ser.). 24p. (J). (ps-k). pap. 5.99 (***978-0-545-00145-8(5)*** , Scholastic Reference) Scholastic, Inc.

Scholastic, Inc. Staff. Rain Forest Animals. 1998. (Pocket Charts Ser.). (J). 7.95 (978-0-590-04246-8(7)) Scholastic, Inc.

School Specialty Publishing. The Animal Alphabet. 2004. (On-File Ser.). 4p. (J). (gr. k-k). ring bd. 4.99 (978-0-7424-2849-2(4) , Instructional Fair) Schaffer, Frank Pubns.

—Animal Classification. 2004. (On-File Ser.). 4p. (J). (gr. 3-5). ring bd. 4.99 (978-0-7424-2886-7(9) , Instructional Fair) Schaffer, Frank Pubns.

School Zone Publishing Company Staff. Animal Match. 2000. (Game Cards Ser.). 56p. (J). 2.89 (978-0-88743-215-6(8) , 05038) School Zone Publishing Co.

School Zone Staff. Animals of All Kinds. 2004. (J). 2.79 (978-1-58947-989-0(0)); 12.99 (978-1-58947-473-4(2) , 03604) School Zone Publishing Co.

Schwartz, David M. Animal Eyes. Kuhn, Dwight, photos by. 1999. (Springboards into Science Ser.). (Illus.). 24p. (J). (gr. 1 up). lib. bdg. 20.67 (978-0-8368-2423-0(7)) Stevens, Gareth Inc.

—Animal Feathers & Fur. Kuhn, Dwight, photos by. 1999. (Springboards into Science Ser.). (Illus.). 24p. (J). (gr. 1 up). lib. bdg. 20.67 (978-0-8368-2424-7(5)) Stevens, Gareth Inc.

—Animal Mouths. Kuhn, Dwight, photos by. 1999. (Springboards into Science Ser.). (Illus.). 24p. (J). (gr. 1 up). lib. bdg. 20.67 (978-0-8368-2425-4(3)) Stevens, Gareth Inc.

—Animal Tails. Kuhn, Dwight, photos by. 1999. (Springboards into Science Ser.). (Illus.). 24p. (J). (gr. 1 up). lib. bdg. 20.67 (978-0-8368-2426-1(1)) Stevens, Gareth Inc.

—At the Zoo. Kuhn, Dwight, photos by. 1998. (Springboards into Science Ser.). (Illus.). 24p. (J). (gr. 1 up). lib. bdg. 19.93 (978-0-8368-2225-0(0)) Stevens, Gareth Inc.

—Exploring Habitats. Kuhn, Dwight, photos by. 2000. (Habitats Ser.). (Illus.). 80 p. (J). (gr. 1-3). pap., instr.'s gde. ed. 9.99 (978-1-57471-367-1(1) , 3096) Creative Teaching Pr., Inc.

—In a Tree. Kuhn, Dwight, photos by. 1999. (Springboards into Science Ser.). (Illus.). 24p. (J). (gr. 1 up). lib. bdg. 20.67 (978-0-8368-2245-8(5)) Stevens, Gareth Inc.

—In the Meadow. Kuhn, Dwight, photos by. 1998. (Springboards into Science Ser.). (Illus.). 24p. (J). (gr. 1 up). lib. bdg. 20.67 (978-0-8368-2223-6(4)) Stevens, Gareth Inc.

—In the Park. Kuhn, Dwight, photos by. (Habitats Ser.). (Illus.). 16p. (J). (gr. 1-3). pap. 2.99 (978-1-57471-214-8(4) , 3006) Creative Teaching Pr., Inc.

—In the Park. Kuhn, Dwight, photos by. 1999. (Springboards into Science Ser.). (Illus.). 24p. (J). (gr. 1 up). lib. bdg. 20.67 (978-0-8368-2243-4(9)) Stevens, Gareth Inc.

—Underfoot. Kuhn, Dwight, photos by. 1999. (Springboards into Science Ser.). (Illus.). 24p. (J). (gr. 1 up). lib. bdg. 20.67 (978-0-8368-2246-5(3)) Stevens, Gareth Inc.

Schwartz, David M. & Schy, Yael. Where in the Wild? Camouflaged Creatures Concealed & Revealed. Kuhn, Dwight, photos by. 2007. (Illus.). 44p. (J). (ps-3). 15.95 (***978-1-58246-207-3(0)*** , Tricycle Pr.) Ten Speed Pr.

Schwarzkopf, Chet. Heart of the Wild: Animal Stories of the California Redwood Coast. Trimm, Wayne, illus. 2004. (Classic Ser.). 286p. (gr. 5 up). pap. 17.95 (978-0-87004-407-6(9)) Caxton Pr.

Science & Technology for Children's Books, Animal Studies Set, 8 vols. 2004. (Illus.). 64p. (J). (978-1-933008-12-7(1)) National Science Resources Ctr.

Sebastiani, Laura, creator. Penny & Drew's Penciltips: Animal Alliteration. 2006. 80p. (J). 4.95 (978-0-9766793-1-8(0)) ThoughtRockets, Inc.

The Secret World Of..., 20 bks., Sets 1-3. 2003. (J). 571.20 (978-1-4109-0704-2(X)) Raintree.

Seidensticker, John & Lumpkin, Susan. Predators/John Saeidensticker & Susan Lumpkin. 2008. (Insiders Ser.). 64p. (J). 16.99 (***978-1-4169-3863-7(X)*** , Simon & Schuster Children's Publishing) Simon & Schuster Children's Publishing.

Seidlitz, Lauri. Animals. 2007. (J). (***978-1-59036-701-8(4)***); (***978-1-59036-702-5(2)***) Weigl Pubs., Inc.

Seidlitz, Lauri. The Science of Animals. 1999. (Living Science Ser.). (Illus.). 32p. (J). (gr. 2 up). lib. bdg. 24.67 (978-0-8368-2464-3(4)) Stevens, Gareth Inc.

Selsam, Millicent Ellis. Big Tracks, Little Tracks: Following Animal Prints. Donnelly, Marlene Hill, illus. 1999. 31p. (J). (ps-ps). lib. bdg. 14.15 (978-0-613-11333-5(0)) Tandem Library Bks.

Sen, Benita. Polar Creatures. 2008. (J). lib. bdg. (***978-1-4042-3892-3(1)*** , PowerKids Pr.) Rosen Publishing Group, Inc., The.

—Rainforest Creatures. 2007. (J). lib. bdg. (***978-1-4042-3893-0(X)*** , PowerKids Pr.) Rosen Publishing Group, Inc., The.

Seto, Alex. What do you See? 2006. 14p. pap. 6.95 (978-0-9734496-4-8(0)) ADVAN Pr., Inc. CAN. *Dist:* Biblio Distribution.

Seton, Ernest Thompson. The Trail of the Sandhill Stag. Seton, Ernest Thompson, illus. 2007. (Illus.). 94p. (YA). pap. 16.95 (***978-1-60355-055-0(0)***) Juniper Grove.

Seton, Ernest Thompson, et al. Books about Animals. 2004. cd-rom 25.00 (978-0-931968-83-9(6)) B & R Samizdat Express.

Seuling, Barbara. Cows Sweat Through Their Noses: And Other Freaky Facts about Animal Habits, Characteristics, & Homes. Skeens, Matthew, illus. 2007. (J). lib. bdg. (***978-1-4048-3749-2(3)***) Picture Window Bks.

Sevaly, Karen, ed. Hands on Learning: Animal Dominoes. 2006. 12.99 (978-0-439-82405-7(2) , Teaching Resources) Scholastic, Inc.

Shalev, Zahavit & Dorling Kindersley Publishing Staff. Water Hole. 2005. (Dk 24 Hours Ser.). (Illus.). 48p. (J). 12.99 (978-0-7566-1126-2(1)) Dorling Kindersley Publishing, Inc.

Shattil, Wendy & Rozinski, Bob, photos by. On the Trail of Colorado Critters: Wildlife Watching for Kids. 2000. (Illus.). 96p. (J). (gr. 4-7). 14.95 (978-1-56579-350-7(1) , A195) Westcliffe Pubs.

Shaw, Marjorie B. & Elwood, Ann. Sharing the World with Animals. 2000. (Zoobooks Ser.). 24p. (J). (gr. 1-7). 15.95 (978-1-888153-02-6(4)) Wildlife Education, Ltd.

Sheehan, Thomas F. Pequenos Vecinos: Little Neighbors. 2006. (Rourke Discovery Library). (SPA., Illus.). 24p. (J). (978-1-59515-664-8(X)) Rourke Publishing, LLC.

Sheikh-Miller, J. & Turnbull, S. Big Cats. 2004. (Discovery Program Ser.). (Illus.). 48p. (J). pap. 8.99 (978-0-7945-0143-3(5) , Usborne) EDC Publishing.

Sheldon, Ian & Eder, Tamara. Animal Tracks of Missouri & Arkansas, Vol. 1. Ross, Gary, illus. rev. ed. 2002. (Animal Tracks Ser.). 144p. (J). (gr. 4-6). pap. 6.95 (978-1-55105-317-2(9)) Lone Pine Publishing USA.

—Animal Tracks of the Carolinas, Vol. 1. rev. ed. 2002. (Animal Tracks Ser.). (Illus.). 144p. (gr. 4). pap. 6.95 (978-1-55105-328-8(4)) Lone Pine Publishing USA.

Sherman, Janice. Colorful Critters. 2007. (ENG., Illus.). 10p. (J). pap. 4.99 (***978-0-9797139-2-7(7)***) Jan's Looks & Bks.

—Colorful Critters Color Match Coloring Book. 2007. (ENG., Illus.). 10p. (J). pap. 1.99 (***978-0-9797139-3-4(5)***) Jan's Looks & Bks.

—Counting Critters. 2007. (ENG., Illus.). 10p. (J). pap. 4.99 (***978-0-9797139-1-0(9)***) Jan's Looks & Bks.

—Critter Zoo. 2007. (ENG., Illus.). 10p. (J). pap. 4.99 (***978-0-9797139-8-9(6)***) Jan's Looks & Bks.

—Critters A-Z. 2007. (ENG., Illus.). 26p. (J). pap. 5.99 (***978-0-9797139-0-3(0)***) Jan's Looks & Bks.

—Ocean Critters. 2007. (ENG., Illus.). 13p. (J). pap. 4.99 (***978-0-9797139-9-6(4)***) Jan's Looks & Bks.

—Rainforest Critters. 2007. (ENG., Illus.). 10p. (J). pap. 4.99 (***978-0-9797139-4-1(3)***) Jan's Looks & Bks.

—Where Critters Live. 2007. (ENG., Illus.). 10p. (J). pap. 4.99 (***978-0-9797139-7-2(8)***) Jan's Looks & Bks.

Shi, Sharon. Animals at the Zoo. Neilson, Shannon, illus. rev. ed. 2000. 23p. (J). (ps-2). pap. 4.99 (978-0-9678636-4-1(3) , B005, Tattootles Bks.) Tattoo Manufacturing.

Shirley, Gayle C. Amazing Animals of Colorado: Incredible True Stories. 2005. (Four-Legged Legends Ser.). (Illus.). 144p. pap. 9.95 (978-0-7627-3854-0(5) , Falcon) Globe Pequot Pr., The.

Shirley, Gayle C. & Falcon Publishing Staff. Amazing Animals of Montana: Incredible True Stories. 2005. (Four-Legged Legends Ser.). (Illus.). 80p. (gr. 4-7). pap. 9.95 (978-0-7627-3855-7(3) , Falcon) Globe Pequot Pr., The.

—Amazing Animals of Oregon: Incredible True Stories. 2005. (Four-Legged Legends Ser.). (Illus.). 80p. (gr. 4-7). pap. 9.95 (978-0-7627-3856-4(1) , Falcon) Globe Pequot Pr., The.

Sideri, Simona. Eyes. Noble, Sheilagh, tr. Noble, Sheilagh, illus. 2004. (J). lib. bdg. (978-1-58340-495-9(3)) Smart Apple Media.

—Feet. Noble, Sheilagh, tr. Noble, Sheilagh, illus. 2004. (J). lib. bdg. (978-1-58340-492-8(9)) Smart Apple Media.

—Hands. Noble, Sheilagh, tr. Noble, Sheilagh, illus. 2004. (J). lib. bdg. (978-1-58340-493-5(7)) Smart Apple Media.

Silbering, Shelly. Killer Science: Nature's Dealiest Predators. Domm, Jeffrey C., illus. Mays, Buddy, photos by. 1999. (Killer Science! Ser.). 101p. (J). (gr. 3-7). pap. 9.95 (978-0-7373-0124-3(4) , 01244W) McGraw-Hill/Contemporary.

Silver Dolphin en Español Editors. Disney Learning: Animales: Disney Learning: Animals, Spanish-Language Edition. 2006. (Illus.). 20p. (J). 3.99 (***978-970-718-431-2(0)*** , Silver Dolphin en Español) Advanced Marketing, S. de R. L. de C. V. MEX. *Dist:* Perseus Distribution.

Silverstein, Alvin & Silverstein, Virginia B. Nature's Champions: The Biggest, the Fastest, the Best. Zallinger, Jean, tr. Zallinger, Jean, illus. 2003. 64p. (J). (gr. 5-8). pap. 5.95 (978-0-486-42888-8(5)) Dover Pubns., Inc.

A
B

Simon, Seymour. Animals Nobody Loves. 2001. (Illus.). 46p. (J). (ps-3). 16.50 (978-1-58717-080-5(9) , SeaStar Bks.) Chronicle Bks. LLC.

—Creepy Creatures. 2006. (Illus.). 24p. (J). ***(978-0-439-77703-2(8))*** Scholastic, Inc.

Simon, Seymour. They Walk the Earth. 2000. (Illus.). 40p. (J). (ps-3). lib. bdg. 27.12 (978-0-7398-2196-1(2)) Raintree.

Singer, Marilyn. Animales a Tu Alrededor. Zaidi, Nadeem, illus. 2004. (Baby Einstein Ser.). (SPA.). 16p. (J). bds. 5.95 (978-970-718-152-6(4) , Silver Dolphin en Español) Advanced Marketing, S. de R. L. de C. V. MEX. *Dist:* Perseus Distribution.

—Neighborhood Animals. Zaidi, Nadeem, illus. 2001. (Baby Einstein Ser.). 16p. (J). (ps-ps). 5.99 (978-0-7868-0806-9(3)) Hyperion Bks. for Children.

Sirret, Dawn. Winking, Blinking, Wiggling, & Waggling. 2000. (Eyewitness Readers Ser.). (978-0-606-18121-1(0)) ; lib. bdg. 11.80 (978-0-613-27596-5(9)) Tandem Library Bks.

Skwarck, Skip, ed. Tails: An Interactive Book. 2006. (Illus.). 18p. (ps-3). reprint ed. 13.00 (978-1-4223-5439-1(3)) DIANE Publishing Co.

Sladen, Louisa. Baby Animals. Rinaldo, Luana, illus. 2005. (Magic Color Bks.). 10p. (J). 3.95 (978-1-4027-2054-3(8) , Sterling/Pinwheel) Sterling Publishing Co., Inc.

Slater, Patrick. Australian Kangaroos & Wallabies. 2002. (Nature Kids Ser.). (Illus.). 52p. (J). (gr. 3 up). lib. bdg. (978-1-59084-217-1(0)) Mason Crest Pubs.

—Australian Rainforest Animals. 2002. (Nature Kids Ser.). (Illus.). 52p. (J). (gr. 3 up). lib. bdg. (978-1-59084-213-3(8)) Mason Crest Pubs.

Smart Animals. 2006. (Smart Animals! Ser.). (J). lib. bdg. 143.76 (978-1-59716-200-5(0)) Bearport Publishing Co., Inc.

Smith, Alastair. Animales Nocturnos. Butler, John, illus. 2004. (SPA.). 16p. (J). 8.95 (978-0-7460-4524-4(7) , Usborne) EDC Publishing.

—Nighttime Lift-the-flap. Butler, John, illus. 2005. 16p. (J). (gr. 1 up). 11.95 (978-0-7945-0967-5(3) , Usborne) EDC Publishing.

Smith, Naniloa. The Children Are Happy Activity Book with Animals from the Southwest. 2003. (J). 11.00 (978-0-9744005-0-1(5)) In the Desert.

Smith, Tim. Buck Wilder's Animal Wisdom. Herrick, Mark, illus. 2006. 32p. (J). (978-1-934133-02-6(7)) Mackinac Island Pr., Inc.

Snakes, crocodiles & Reptiles. 2007. 24p. pap. 2.99 ***(978-1-4037-3435-8(6))*** Dalmatian Pr.

Snap! Snap! 2002. 10p. (J). 9.95 (978-0-7525-5580-5(4)) Parragon, Inc.

Snedden, Robert. Northern Forests. 2003. (Illus.). 32p. (J). lib. bdg. (978-1-58340-385-3(X)) Smart Apple Media.

—Tropical Grasslands. 2004. (Illus.). 32p. (J). lib. bdg. (978-1-58340-386-0(8)) Smart Apple Media.

The Sneeze: Early Level Satellite Individual Title Six-Packs. (Sails Literacy Ser.). 16p. (gr. 1-2). 27.00 (978-0-7578-2911-6(2)) Rigby Education.

Snyder, Margaret. World of Animals. deluxe ed. 1999. (Talking Pages Ser.). (Illus.). (ps-3). 12.95 (978-1-58224-012-1(4)) Futech Interactive Products, Inc.

Soens, Chris. Animal Friends. 2002. pap. 9.00 (978-0-8059-5592-7(5)) Dorrance Publishing Co., Inc.

Soffer, Ruth. Amazing Animals Coloring Book. 2002. (Illus.). 48p. (J). pap. 3.95 (978-0-486-42061-5(2)) Dover Pubns., Inc.

—Australian Wildlife Coloring Book. 2006. 32p. (J). pap. 3.95 (978-0-486-45167-1(4)) Dover Pubns., Inc.

Solway, Andrew. Killer Carnivores. 2005. (Illus.). 48p. (J). (978-1-4034-6567-2(3)); pap. (978-1-4034-6573-3(8)) Heinemann Library.

—Killer Fish. 2004. (J). 29.93 (978-1-4034-5768-4(9)); pap. 8.50 (978-1-4034-5774-5(3)) Heinemann Library.

Somervill, Barbara A. Animal Survivors of the Wetlands. 2004. (Watts Library). (Illus.). 64p. (J). 25.50 (978-0-531-12203-7(4) , Watts, Franklin) Scholastic Library Publishing.

Southwater Staff. Wild Animals: Look & Learn. 2000. (Look & Learn Ser.). (Illus.). 32p. (ps). 7.95 (978-1-84215-166-2(5) , Southwater) Anness Publishing GBR. *Dist:* National Bk. Network.

Souza, D.M. Look What Tails Can Do. 2007. (Look What Animals Can Do Ser.). (Illus.). 48p. (J). 22.60 (978-0-7613-9458-7(3) , Lerner Pubns.) Lerner Publishing Group.

—Packed with Poison! Deadly Animal Defenses. Harris, Jack, illus. 2006. (On My Own Science Ser.). 48p. (J). (gr. 2-4). lib. bdg. 25.26 (978-1-57505-877-1(4) , Millbrook Pr.) Lerner Publishing Group.

Sovak, Jan. African Animals Notebook. 1999. (Illus.). 64p. (J). pap. 1.00 (978-0-486-40544-5(3)) Dover Pubns., Inc.

—African Animals Sticker Activity Book. 1999. (Dover Little Activity Bks.). (Illus.). 4p. (J). (ps-3). pap. 1.50 (978-0-486-40749-4(7)) Dover Pubns., Inc.

—Learning about Swamp Animals. 2003. (Learning about Ser.). (Illus.). 16p. (J). (gr. 3-5). pap. 1.50 (978-0-486-43025-6(1)) Dover Pubns., Inc.

Spada, Ada. Fangs, Claws & Talons: Animal Predators. Lark Books Staff, ed. 2007. (Illus.). 48p. (J). (gr. 1). 9.95 ***(978-1-60059-150-1(7))*** Lark Bks.

Spafford, Suzy. Witzy's Book of Words. 2001. (Little Suzy's Zoo Ser.). 12p. (J). (ps-1). bds. 9.99 (978-1-58668-054-1(4)) Lyrick Studios.

Spilsbury, Richard & Spilsbury, Louise. Animal Groups Series, 6 bks., Set. 2003. (Illus.). (J). (978-1-4034-0747-4(9)) Heinemann Library.

Spooky Animals, 5 vols., set. 2002. (Zoobooks). (Illus.). (J). (gr. k-7). pap. 12.50 (978-1-888153-71-2(7)) Wildlife Education, Ltd.

Spots & Stripes. (Rosen Real Readers Big Bookstm Ser.). 8p. (J). (gr. k-1). 27.95 (978-1-4042-6209-6(1)) Rosen Publishing Group, Inc., The.

Squire, Ann O. Animal Homes. 2001. (gr. 3-6). lib. bdg. 15.25 (978-0-613-51612-9(5)) Tandem Library Bks.

—Animals, 6 bks., Set. 2005. (J). 144.00 (978-0-516-25215-5(1) , Children's Pr.) Scholastic Library Publishing.

—Animals of the Sea & Shore. 2001. (gr. 3-6). lib. bdg. 15.25 (978-0-613-51613-6(3)) Tandem Library Bks.

—The Secret Lives of Animals: A Chapter Book. (True Tales Ser.). (Illus.). 48p. (J). 2006. (gr. 2-4). pap. 4.95 (978-0-516-25457-9(X)); 2005. (ps-ps). 22.50 (978-0-516-25189-9(9)) Scholastic Library Publishing. (Children's Pr.).

St. Pierre, Stephanie. In the Wild: Facts about Favorite Animals, 6 bks., Set 2. 2001. (Illus.). 24p. (J). (gr. k-2). lib. bdg. 128.16 (978-1-58810-021-4(9)) Heinemann Library.

Stanley, Mandy. Quack! Quack! 1999. (Illus.). 12p. (J). 4.99 (978-0-7214-2734-8(0) , Dutton Juvenile) Penguin Group (USA) Inc.

—What Do You Say? Stanley, Mandy, illus. 2003. (Illus.). 24p. (J). bds. 8.99 (978-0-689-85404-0(8) , Little Simon) Simon & Schuster Children's Publishing.

Staub, Frank. The Signs Animals Leave. 2002. (Watts Library). (Illus.). 64p. (J). (gr. 5-7). pap. 8.95 (978-0-531-16575-1(2) , Watts, Franklin) Scholastic Library Publishing.

Steck-Vaughn Staff. Animal Eyes. 2003. pap. 4.10 (978-0-7398-7638-1(4)) Steck-Vaughn.

—Animals Around the World Big Book. 2002. (Illus.). pap. (978-0-7398-5895-0(5)) Steck-Vaughn.

—Animals of the Rainforest. 2001. Set 1. pap., tchr. ed. (978-0-7398-3362-9(6)); Set 2. (Illus.). (J). pap., tchr. ed. (978-0-7398-4143-3(2)); Set 3. (Illus.). pap., tchr. ed. (978-0-7398-4931-6(X)) Steck-Vaughn.

—Counting Baby Animals Big Book. 2002. (Illus.). (J). pap. (978-0-7398-5897-4(1)) Steck-Vaughn.

—Creepy Creatures. 2003. pap. 4.10 (978-0-7398-7629-9(5)) Steck-Vaughn.

Steele, Christy. Grassland Animals. 2002. (Animals of the Biomes Ser.). (Illus.). 48p. (J). lib. bdg. 24.26 (978-0-7398-5688-8(X)) Raintree.

—Grassland Animals. 2003. (Animals of the Biomes Ser.). (Illus.). 48p. (J). pap. 6.95 (978-0-7398-6408-1(4)) Steck-Vaughn.

Stephens, Catherine. Classification Clues. 2004. (National Geographic Reading Expeditions Ser.). (Illus.). 32p. (J). pap. (978-0-7922-4576-6(8)) National Geographic Society.

—Life Cycles. 2004. (National Geographic Reading Expeditions Ser.). (Illus.). 32p. (J). pap. (978-0-7922-4579-7(2)) National Geographic Society.

Stephens, Edna Cucksey & Farstvedt, Diane Norberg. Looking at Animals with Mr. Etch a Sketch. George, Tim, illus. 2002. 32p. (J). pap. 9.95 (978-0-9712692-1-7(1)) EDCO Publishing, Inc.

Stephens, R. David. My Animal Friends. Shoemaker, Kathryn, illus. 2002. 32p. (J). (978-1-896580-03-6(3)) Tradewind Bks.

Stephens, William R. Finding Food in the Wild. 2003. (Extreme Animals Ser.). (J). pap. (978-1-58417-247-5(9)); lib. bdg. (978-1-58417-246-8(0)) Lake Street Pubs.

Sterling Publishing Company Staff & Sterling/Balloon. Cute Animals. 1999. (Balloon Ser.). (Illus.). 6p. (ps-k). 2.95 (978-0-8069-1921-8(3)) Sterling Publishing Co., Inc.

Sterling Publishing Company Staff & Ward, Adam. Endangered Animals. 2004. (Pocket Factfiles Ser.). (Illus.). 256p. (J). 4.98 (978-1-4027-1850-2(0)) Sterling Publishing Co., Inc.

Sterling/Balloon. Wild Animals. 1998. (Peek-a-Boo Bks.). (Illus.). 20p. (J). bds. 3.95 (978-0-8069-3761-8(0) , Balloon Bks.) Sterling Publishing Co., Inc.

Stevens, Kathryn. Night Creatures. 2007. (Boys Rock! Ser.). 32p. (J). (gr. 1-5). 24.21 ***(978-1-59296-855-8(4))*** Child's World, Inc.

Stewart, Melissa. Animals All Around. 2004. (Investigate Science Ser.). (Illus.). 32p. (J). (gr. 1 up). lib. bdg. 21.26 (978-0-7565-0594-3(1)) Compass Point Bks.

Stickland, Paul. Animals. Stickland, Paul, illus. 1998. (Working Ser.). (Illus.). 16p. (J). (ps up). lib. bdg. 19.93 (978-0-8368-2156-7(4)) Stevens, Gareth Inc.

—Working, 4 bks. Stickland, Paul, illus. Incl. Animals. lib. bdg. 19.93 (978-0-8368-2156-7(4)); People. lib. bdg. 19.93 (978-0-8368-2157-4(2)); Places. lib. bdg. 19.93 (978-0-8368-2158-1(0)); Tools. lib. bdg. 19.93 (978-0-8368-2159-8(9)); 16p. (J). (ps up). 1998. (Illus.). Set lib. bdg. 79.73 (978-0-8368-2155-0(6)) Stevens, Gareth Inc.

Stockland, Patricia M. Pointy, Long, or Round: A Book about Animal Shapes. Ouren, Todd, illus. 2005. (Animal Wise Ser.). 24p. (J). (gr. k-2). 22.60 (978-1-4048-0935-2(X)) Picture Window Bks.

—Swing, Slither, or Swim: A Book about Animal Movements. Ouren, Todd, illus. 2005. (Animal Wise Ser.). 24p. (C). (gr. k-2). 22.60 (978-1-4048-0933-8(3)) Picture Window Bks.

Stone, Lynn M. Animales de la Granja. Sarfatti, Esther & de la Vega, Eida, trs. 2001. (Vida en la Granja Ser.).Tr. of Farm Animals. (SPA., Illus.). 24p. (J). (gr. 1-3). lib. bdg. 19.27 (978-1-58952-181-0(1)) Rourke Publishing, LLC.

—Border Collies. 2007. (Illus.). 24p. (J). (978-1-60044-237-7(4)) Rourke Publishing, LLC.

—Feathers & Fur. 2007. (Illus.). 24p. (J). (978-1-60044-171-4(8)) Rourke Publishing, LLC.

—How Do Animals Use Their Ears? 2008. (J). ***(978-1-60044-503-3(9))*** Rourke Publishing, LLC.

—How Do Animals Use Their Voices & Sound? 2008. (J). ***(978-1-60044-507-1(1))*** Rourke Publishing, LLC.

—How Do Animals Use Their Wings? 2008. (J). ***(978-1-60044-508-8(X))*** Rourke Publishing, LLC.

—Miniature Schnauzers. 2007. (J). (978-1-60044-236-0(6)) Rourke Publishing, LLC.

—Pugs. 2007. (Illus.). 24p. (J). (978-1-60044-242-1(0)) Rourke Publishing, LLC.

—Yorkshire Terriers. 2005. (Eye to Eye with Dogs Ser.). (Illus.). 24p. (gr. 2-5). 17.95 (978-1-59515-163-6(X)) Rourke Publishing, LLC.

Stone, Tanya Lee. Unique Animals of the Islands. 2005. (Regional Wild America Ser.). (Illus.). 24p. (J). (gr. 3-5). 22.45 (978-1-4103-0446-9(9) , Blackbirch Pr., Inc.) Thomson Gale.

—Unique Animals of the Mountains & Prairies. 2005. (Regional Wild America Ser.). (Illus.). 24p. (J). (gr. 3-5). 22.45 (978-1-4103-0445-2(0) , Blackbirch Pr., Inc.) Thomson Gale.

—Unique Animals of the Northeast. 2005. (Regional Wild America Ser.). (Illus.). 24p. (J). (gr. 3-5). 22.45 (978-1-56711-966-4(2) , Blackbirch Pr., Inc.) Thomson Gale.

—Unique Animals of the South. 2005. (Regional Wild America Ser.). (Illus.). 24p. (J). (ps-7). lib. bdg. 22.45 (978-1-56711-968-8(9) , Blackbirch Pr., Inc.) Thomson Gale.

—Unique Animals of the Southwest. 2005. (Regional Wild America Ser.). (Illus.). 24p. (J). (gr. 3-5). 22.45 (978-1-56711-970-1(0) , Blackbirch Pr., Inc.) Thomson Gale.

Stonehouse, Bernard. Animal Watch, 6 vols., Set. Camm, Martin & Orr, Richard, illus. 2001. 48p. (gr. 4-9). pap. 101.70 (978-0-8160-4745-1(6)) Facts On File, Inc.

—Defenders. Francis, John, illus. 2000. 48p. (J). pap. (978-0-439-15347-8(6)) Scholastic, Inc.

—Predators. Francis, John, illus. 1999. (J). pap. (978-0-439-09590-7(5)) Scholastic, Inc.

Storey Publishing Staff, creator. The Petting Farm Poster Book. 2005. (Illus.). 64p. pap. 9.95 (978-1-58017-597-5(X)) Storey Publishing, LLC.

Stout, Frankie. Nature's Best Jumpers. 2008. (J). lib. bdg. ***(978-1-4042-4155-8(8)*** , PowerKids Pr.) Rosen Publishing Group, Inc., The.

—Nature's Deadliest Animals. 2008. (J). lib. bdg. ***(978-1-4042-4159-6(0)*** , PowerKids Pr.) Rosen Publishing Group, Inc., The.

—Nature's Fastest Animals. 2008. (J). lib. bdg. ***(978-1-4042-4156-5(6)*** , PowerKids Pr.) Rosen Publishing Group, Inc., The.

—Nature's Nastiest Biters. 2008. (J). lib. bdg. ***(978-1-4042-4157-2(4)*** , PowerKids Pr.) Rosen Publishing Group, Inc., The.

—Nature's Strongest Animals. 2008. (J). lib. bdg. ***(978-1-4042-4158-9(2)*** , PowerKids Pr.) Rosen Publishing Group, Inc., The.

Strain, Connie Rae. Perfect Imperfections: For Animal lovers of all Ages, collector's ed. 2003. (Illus.). 257p. (YA). 27.95 (978-0-9741321-0-5(1)) Isle of Dogs Publishing, Co.

Suen, Anastasia. Asociacion Para la Prevencion de la Crueldad de los Animales, (ASPCA) 2004. (Organizaciones de Ayuda Ser.). (SPA & ENG., Illus.). 24p. (J). (gr. 3-6). lib. bdg. 17.25 (978-0-8239-6861-9(8) , Buenas Letra) Rosen Publishing Group, Inc., The.

Sumando Animales del Artico Math, 6 vols.Tr. of Adding Arctic Animals Math. (SPA.). (gr. k-2). 28.95 (978-0-7368-3026-3(X) , Yellow Umbrella Bks.) Capstone Pr., Inc.

Superlibro de Aprende sobre los Animales: Unit 3: Aprende sobre los animales (All about Animals) 2000. (McGraw-Hill Ciencias Ser.). (ENG & SPA.). (gr. k up). (978-0-02-277159-1(X)) Macmillan/McGraw-Hill Schl. Div.

Surviving. 2001. (Animal Marvels Ser.). (Illus.). 32p. (J). (gr. 3 up). lib. bdg. 24.67 (978-0-8368-2933-4(6)) Stevens, Gareth Inc.

Swan, Erin Pembrey. Land Predators Around the World. 2001. (Animals in Order Ser.). (Illus.). 48p. (J). (gr. 4-6). 26.50 (978-0-531-11627-2(1) , Watts, Franklin) Scholastic Library Publishing.

—Land Predators of North America. 1999. (Animals in Order Ser.). (Illus.). 48p. (J). (gr. 4-6). pap. 6.95 (978-0-531-15945-3(0)) Scholastic Library Publishing.

—Land Predators of North America. 1999. (gr. 3-6). lib. bdg. 15.25 (978-0-613-36459-1(7)) Tandem Library Bks.

Swanson, Diane. Animals Can Be So Playful. (Illus.). 22p. (J). (978-1-55041-328-1(7)) Fitzhenry & Whiteside, Ltd.

—Animals Can Be So Playful. 2002. (Illus.). 21p. (J). pap. (978-1-55054-904-1(9)) Greystone Bks., Ltd.

—Animals Can Be So Playful. Cowles, Rose, illus. 2002. (Animals Can Be So... Ser.). 24p. (J). 10.95 (978-1-55054-900-3(6) , Greystone Bks.) Douglas & McIntyre, Ltd. CAN. *Dist:* Sterling Publishing Co., Inc.

—Animals Can Be So Speedy. Cowles, Rose, illus. 2002. (Animals Can Be So... Ser.). 24p. (J). 5.95 (978-1-55054-856-3(5) , Greystone Bks.) Douglas & McIntyre, Ltd. CAN. *Dist:* Sterling Publishing Co., Inc.

—Animals Can Be So Speedy. 2001. (Animals Can Be So... Ser.). (Illus.). 24p. (J). 10.95 (978-1-55054-827-3(1) , Greystone Bks.) Douglas & McIntyre, Ltd. CAN. *Dist:* Sterling Publishing Co., Inc.

—Animals Can Be So Speedy. (Illus.). 22p. (J). (978-1-55041-334-2(1)); pap. (978-1-55041-336-6(8)) Fitzhenry & Whiteside, Ltd.

—A Crash of Rhinos, A Party of Jays: The Wacky Ways We Name Animal Groups. Spencer, Mariko Ando, illus. 2006. 24p. (J). (gr. k-2). pap. 8.95 (978-1-55451-047-4(3)); lib. bdg. 19.95 (978-1-55451-048-1(1)) Annick Pr., Ltd. CAN. *Dist:* Firefly Bks., Ltd.

—Feet That Suck & Feed. 2003. (Up Close Ser.). (Illus.). 32p. (J). (gr. k-2). 5.95 (978-1-55054-769-6(0)) Douglas & McIntyre, Ltd. CAN. *Dist:* Transition Vendor.

—Feet That Suck & Feed. 2003. (Up Close Ser.). (Illus.). 32p. (J). (gr. k-2). 9.95 (978-1-55054-767-2(4)) Sterling Publishing Co., Inc.

—Teeth That Stab & Grind. 2003. (Up Close Ser.). (Illus.). 32p. (J). (gr. 2-4). 5.95 (978-1-55054-770-2(4)) Douglas & McIntyre, Ltd. CAN. *Dist:* Transition Vendor.

—Welcome to the World of Animals, 23 bks. Incl. Alligators & Crocodiles. 2004. lib. bdg. 23.33 (978-0-8368-4021-6(6)); Bats. 2003. lib. bdg. 23.33 (978-0-8368-3559-5(X)); Bears. 1998. lib. bdg. 23.33 (978-0-8368-2213-7(7)); Beavers. 2003. lib. bdg. 23.33 (978-0-8368-3560-1(3)); Coyotes. 2002. lib. bdg. 23.33 (978-0-8368-3313-3(9)); Eagles. 2003. lib. bdg. 23.33 (978-0-8368-3561-8(1)); Elephants. 2004. lib. bdg. 23.33 (978-0-8368-3562-5(X)); Foxes. 2003. lib. bdg. 23.33 (978-0-8368-4022-3(4)); Frogs & Toads. 2004. lib. bdg. 23.33 (978-0-8368-4023-0(2)); Hummingbirds. 2004. lib. bdg. 23.33 (978-0-8368-4024-7(0)); Octopuses. 2002. lib. bdg. 23.33 (978-0-8368-3314-0(7)); Owls. 1998. lib. bdg. 23.33 (978-0-8368-2215-1(3)); Penguins. 2004. lib. bdg. 23.33 (978-0-8368-4025-4(9)); Porcupines. 2002. lib. bdg. 23.33 (978-0-8368-3315-7(5)); Rabbits & Hares. 2002. lib. bdg. 23.33 (978-0-8368-3316-4(3)); Sharks. 2003. lib. bdg. 23.33 (978-0-8368-3563-2(8)); Skunks. 2002. lib. bdg. 23.33 (978-0-8368-3317-1(1)); Snakes. 2002. lib. bdg. 23.33 (978-0-8368-3318-8(X)); Squirrels. 2003. lib. bdg. 23.33 (978-0-8368-3564-9(6)); Whales. 1998. lib. bdg. 23.33 (978-0-8368-2216-8(1)); Wild Cats. 1998. lib. bdg. 23.33 (978-0-8368-2217-5(X)); Wild Horses. 2004. lib. bdg. 23.33 (978-0-8368-4026-1(7)); Wolves. 1998. lib. bdg. 23.33 (978-0-8368-2218-2(8)); 32p. (J). (gr. 3 up). (Illus.). Set lib. bdg. 419.94 (978-0-8368-4170-1(0)) Stevens, Gareth Inc.

—Welcome to the World of Animals New Releases: Alligators & Crocodiles; Elephants; Frogs & Toads; Hummingbirds; Penguins; Wild Horses, 6 bks. 2004. (Illus.). (J). (gr. 3 up). lib. bdg. 135.60 (978-0-8368-4020-9(8)) Stevens, Gareth Inc.

Sweeney, Alyse. Nonfiction Read & Write Booklets: Animals & Habitats: 10 Interactive Reproducible Booklets That Help Students Build Content Knowledge & Reading Comprehension Skills. 2007. 48p. pap. 10.99 (978-0-439-56760-2(2) , Teaching Resources) Scholastic, Inc.

Swinburne, Stephen R. Boxing Rabbits, Bellowing Alligators: Courtship Poems from the Animal World. 2002. (All about Animals Ser.). (Illus.). 32p. (gr. 2-4). lib. bdg. 23.90 (978-0-7613-2556-7(5) , Millbrook Pr.) Lerner Publishing Group.

Targo Publishing Staff. Zoo Animal Travel Pad. 1999. (My Art Ser.). 35p. (J). (ps-3). pap. (978-1-894307-11-6(9)) Sterling Publishing.

Tatham, Betty. How Animals Shed Their Skin. 2002. (Watts Library). (Illus.). 64p. (J). (gr. 5-7). pap. 25.50 (978-0-531-12042-2(2) , Watts, Franklin) Scholastic Library Publishing.

Taylor, B. Fascinating Animal Facts. 2006. (Illus.). 512p. 39.99 (978-0-7548-1595-2(1) , Lorenz Bks.) Anness Publishing GBR. *Dist:* National Bk. Network.

Taylor, Barbara. Animal Encyclopedia. Parsons, Jayne, ed. 2000. (Dorling Kindersley Ser.). (Illus.). 376p. (J). (gr. 3-7). 29.99 (978-0-7894-6499-6(3)) Dorling Kindersley Publishing, Inc.

—Animal Giants. 2004. (Kingfisher Knowledge Ser.). (Illus.). 64p. (J). (gr. 4-8). 12.95 (978-0-7534-5770-2(9) , Kingfisher) Houghton Mifflin Co. Trade & Reference Div.

—Mega & Micro. 2001. (Weird & Wonderful Ser.). (Illus.). 24p. (J). (gr. 1-5). 9.95 (978-0-87226-659-9(1) , Bedrick, Peter Bks.) School Specialty Publishing.

—Urban Wildlife Habitats. 2006. (Exploring Habitats Ser.). (Illus.). 36p. (J). lib. bdg. (978-0-8368-7259-0(2)) Stevens, Gareth Inc.

—Zooming & Creeping. Greenaway, Frank, photos by. 2001. (Weird & Wonderful Ser.). (Illus.). 24p. (J). (gr. 1-5). 9.95 (978-0-87226-657-5(5) , Bedrick, Peter Bks.) School Specialty Publishing.

Taylor, Barbara & Revkin, Andrew. Animal Giants. 2007. (Kingfisher Knowledge Ser.). (Illus.). 64p. (J). pap. 8.95 ***(978-0-7534-6157-0(9)*** , Kingfisher) Houghton Mifflin Co. Trade & Reference Div.

Taylor, Bonnie Highsmith. Amos: An American Badger. 2001. (Animal Adventures Ser.). (Illus.). (J). 54p. pap. (978-0-7891-5238-1(X)); 56p. (gr. 1-4). lib. bdg. 16.95 (978-0-7807-9648-5(9)) Perfection Learning Corp.

—Callie: A Great Gray Owl. 2000. (Cover-to-Cover Chapter Bks.). (Illus.). 56p. (J). (gr. 1-4). lib. bdg. 16.95 (978-0-7807-9652-2(7)) Perfection Learning Corp.

Taylor, J. David. Florida Manatees. 2003. (Untamed World Ser.). (Illus.). 64p. (J). lib. bdg. 28.56 (978-0-7398-6844-7(6)) Raintree.

Teeth Sets: 1 Each of 3 Big Books. (Sunshinetm Science Ser.). (gr. 1-2). 111.50 (978-0-7802-1449-1(8)) Wright Group, The.

Telford & Theodorou, Rod. Up a Rainforest Tree. 2002. (Amazing Journeys Ser.). (Illus.). 32p. (J). (gr. 2-6). pap. 7.50 (978-1-58810-304-8(8) , 91074) Heinemann Library.

Teora, ed. Amazing Animal Puzzle Stickers BK 1. 2004. (Illus.). 8p. pap. 5.99 (978-1-59496-063-5(1)) Teora USA LLC.

—Amazing Animal Puzzle Stickers BK 2, Vol. 2. 2004. (Illus.). 8p. pap. 5.99 (978-1-59496-064-2(X)) Teora USA LLC.

—Amazing Animal Puzzle Stickers BK 3, Vol. 3. 2004. (Illus.). 8p. pap. 5.99 (978-1-59496-065-9(8)) Teora USA LLC.

—Lets Get to Know the Animals. 2004. (Illus.). 32p. pap. 9.95 (978-1-59496-081-9(X)) Teora USA LLC.

Theodorou, Rod. Amphibians. 2007. (Illus.). 32p. (J). ***(978-1-4034-9248-7(4)); (978-1-4034-9241-8(7))*** Heinemann Library.

—Animal Babies, 6 bks., Set. Incl. Amphibians. (gr. k-2). lib. bdg. 21.36 (978-1-57572-950-3(4)); Birds. (gr. 1-3). lib. bdg. 21.36 (978-1-57572-881-0(8)); Fish. (gr. 1-3). lib. bdg. 21.36 (978-1-57572-882-7(6)); Insects. (gr. 1-3). lib. bdg. 21.36 (978-1-57572-880-3(X)); Mammals. (gr. 1-3). lib. bdg. 21.36 (978-1-57572-883-4(4)); Reptiles. (gr. 1-3). lib. bdg. 21.36 (978-1-57572-884-1(2)); (J). 1999. (Illus.). 32p. 1999. Set lib. bdg. 128.16 (978-1-57572-885-8(0)) Heinemann Library.

—Animals in Danger: Accelerated Reader, 6 bks., Set 2. Incl. Cheetah. lib. bdg. 21.36 (978-1-57572-269-6(0)); Gray Bat. lib. bdg. 21.36 (978-1-57572-270-2(4)); Koala. lib. bdg. 21.36 (978-1-57572-271-9(2)); Leatherback Sea Turtle. lib. bdg. 21.36 (978-1-57572-272-6(0)); Polar Bear. lib. bdg. 21.36 (978-1-57572-273-3(9)); Whooping Crane. lib. bdg. 21.36 (978-1-57572-274-0(7)); 32p. (J). (gr. k-2). 2001. (Illus.). 2001. Set lib. bdg. 128.16 (978-1-57572-298-6(4)) Heinemann Library.

They All Ran Away: Individual Title Six-Pack Pouch - Level C. (Lighthouse Ser.). 12p. (gr. k-1). 24.00 (978-0-7578-0828-9(X)) Rigby Education.

Thompson, Gare. Science Chapters: Serengeti Journey: On Safari in Africa. 2006. (National Geographic Science Chapters Ser.). (Illus.). 48p. (gr. 1-4). 17.90 (978-0-7922-5952-7(1) , National Geographic Children's Bks.) National Geographic Society.

Those Tricky Animals, 6 Packs. (Literatura 2000 Ser.). (gr. 2-3). 33.00 (978-0-7635-0211-9(1)) Rigby Education.

Tiger Tales, Inc., creator. Savanna Animals. 2006. (Illus.). 24p. (J). bds. 7.95 (978-1-58925-798-6(7) , tiger tales) ME Media LLC.

Tildes, Phyllis L. Animals Brightly Colored. Tildes, Phyllis L., illus. 1998. (Illus.). 32p. (J). (ps-3). pap. 6.95 (978-0-88106-978-5(7)) Charlesbridge Publishing, Inc.

—Animals in Camouflage. Tildes, Phyllis L., illus. 2000. (Illus.). 32p. (J). (ps-3). pap. 6.95 (978-0-88106-134-5(4)) Charlesbridge Publishing, Inc.

—Animals in Camouflage. 2000. (gr. k-3). lib. bdg. 15.25 (978-0-613-28275-8(2)); (Illus.). (J). 14.75 (978-0-606-18021-4(4)) Tandem Library Bks.

Tildes, Phyllis Limbacher. Eye Guess: A Foldout Guessing Game. 2005. (Illus.). 36p. (J). (ps-ps). per. 9.95 (978-1-57091-650-2(0)) Charlesbridge Publishing, Inc.

Tiny-Spiny, Ooey-Gooey, Musty-Crusty Animals Package, 22 bks. 2004. (978-1-4034-6153-7(8)) Heinemann Library.

Toft, Kim Michelle. The World That We Want. Toft, Kim Michelle, illus. 2005. (Illus.). 32p. (J). pap. 17.95 (978-0-7022-3482-8(6)) Univ. of Queensland Pr. AUS. *Dist:* International Specialized Bk. Services.

Toms, Kate. Animal Tails. 2006. (Illus.). 12p. (ps-k). per., bds. 5.95 (978-1-84610-098-7(4)) Make Believe Ideas GBR. *Dist:* Ingram Pub. Services.

Top 10s. 2005. (Top 10's Ser.). (J). lib. bdg. 143.76 (978-1-59716-092-6(X)) Bearport Publishing Co., Inc.

Top That Publishing Staff. What Am I. 2006. 10p. (978-1-84666-101-3(3)) Top That! Publishing PLC.

Top That Publishing Staff, ed. Animal Fun. 2006. (Illus.). 16p. (978-1-84666-012-2(2)) Top That! Publishing PLC.

—Animals. 2005. (Illus.). 12p. (978-1-84510-728-4(4)) Top That! Publishing PLC.

—Arctic Animals. 2005. (Illus.). 24p. (978-1-84510-533-4(8)) Top That! Publishing PLC.

Townsend. Incredible Creatures, 8 vols., Set. 2004. pap. 68.40 (978-1-4109-0857-5(7)) Raintree.

Townsend, Emily Rose. Polar Animals, 4 bks. Incl. Arctic Foxes. lib. bdg. 15.93 (978-0-7368-2356-2(5)); Penguins. Saunders-Smith, Gail, ed. lib. bdg. 15.93 (978-0-7368-2357-9(3)); Polar Bears. Saunders-Smith, Gail, ed. lib. bdg. 15.93 (978-0-7368-2358-6(1)); Seals. lib. bdg. 15.93 (978-0-7368-2359-3(X)); 24p. (J). (gr. k-1). 2004. (Illus.). 2004. Set lib. bdg. 63.72 (978-0-7368-2532-0(0) , Pebble Bks.) Capstone Pr., Inc.

Travis, Joelle & Figueras, Ligaya, eds. Los Animales y los Verbos. Hazan, Maurice, illus. 2003. (SPA.). 89p. (J). per. 20.00 (978-1-932770-16-2(X) , SWLB1) Symtalk, Inc.

Treasury of Animals & Nature Volume II. 2006. (J). pap. 9.99 (***978-1-59545-014-2(9)***) Learning Horizons, Inc.

Tripp, Penny. Animal Rights. (Illus.). 64p. (YA). (gr. 5 up). lib. bdg. 29.95 (978-1-931983-80-8(1)) Chrysalis Education.

Trueba, Jose Luis. Descubre... Los Animales. Cortes, Osvaldo, illus. 2004. (Ser. Descubre). 96p. (J). (gr. 3-5). pap. 18.95 (978-970-29-0510-3(9)) Santillana USA Publishing Co., Inc.

Trumbauer, Lisa. Animal Ears. 2000. (Yellow Umbrella Books). (Illus.). 16p. (J). (gr. 1). lib. bdg. 14.60 (978-0-7368-0723-4(3) , Pebble Bks.) Capstone Pr., Inc.

—Animal Giants. 2006. 16p. (J). (gr. k-2). 15.93 (978-0-7368-5862-5(8) , Yellow Umbrella Bks.) Capstone Pr., Inc.

Trunks, Humps, & Tails: Individual Title Six-Packs. (Sails Literacy Ser.). (gr. 1-2). 36.00 (978-0-7578-6731-6(6)) Rigby Education.

Turner, F. Bernadette. Faith of Little Creatures. (J). (gr. 1-3). pap. 5.00 (978-0-8315-0138-9(3)) Speller, Robert & Sons, Pubs., Inc.

Tuxworth, Nicola. Wild Animals: A Very First Picture Book. 1999. (Pictures & Words Ser.). (Illus.). 24p. (J). (ps up). lib. bdg. 22.00 (978-0-8368-2274-8(9)) Stevens, Gareth Inc.

Tuxworth, Nicola & Lorenz Editors. Animals. 2001. (Let's Look at... Ser.). (Illus.). 20p. 5.95 (978-0-7548-0946-3(3)) Anness Publishing GBR. *Dist:* National Bk. Network.

Twinem, Neecy. Hungry Beasties. 2006. (Illus.). 12p. (J). bds. 6.95 (978-1-55971-944-5(3) , 1259986, NorthWord Bks. for Young Readers) T&N Children's Publishing.

—In the Ocean. Twinem, Neecy, illus. 1998. (Animal Clues Ser.). (Illus.). 10p. (J). (ps-k). bds. 4.95 (978-0-88106-944-0(2)) Charlesbridge Publishing, Inc.

—Noisy Beasties. 2007. (Little Beasties Ser.). (Illus.). 12p. (J). (ps). bds. 6.95 (978-1-55971-959-9(1) , NorthWord Bks. for Young Readers) T&N Children's Publishing.

Twist, Clint. Scaly Creatures. 2005. (Animal Touch Ser.). (Illus.). 32p. (J). 12.95 (978-0-7696-4154-6(7) , Waterbird Bks.) School Specialty Publishing.

—Slimy Creatures. 2005. (Animal Touch Ser.). (Illus.). 32p. (J). (ps-ps). 12.95 (978-0-7696-4155-3(5) , Waterbird Bks.) School Specialty Publishing.

Two-Can Publishing Ltd. Staff, contrib. by. Wild Animals. 2004. (Interfact Play & Discover Ser.). (Illus.). 48p. (J). (ps-2). 14.95 incl. cd-rom (978-1-58728-628-5(9) , Two Can Publishing) T&N Children's Publishing.

Tye, Laurie. The Animal in Me: Is Very Plain to See. Mangelsen, Thomas D., photos by. 2005. (Illus.). 32p. (J). (ps-7). 15.95 (978-1-55868-864-3(1)); pap. 8.95 (978-1-55868-898-8(6)) Graphic Arts Ctr. Publishing Co. (West Winds Pr.).

Untamed World, 24 vols. 2003. (Illus.). 685.44 (978-1-4109-0467-6(9)) Raintree.

Untamed World: Classroom/Library Edition. 1999. (Illus.). (J). pap. (978-0-7398-1826-8(0)) Steck-Vaughn.

Up Close, 6 bks., Set. Incl. Dinosaurs. Amery, Heather. lib. bdg. 23.95 (***978-1-4042-3759-9(3));*** Micro Bugs. Harrison, Paul. lib. bdg. 23.95 (***978-1-4042-3760-5(7));*** Mummies. Fleury, Kevin. lib. bdg. 23.95 (***978-1-4042-3761-2(5));*** Reptiles. Harrison, Paul. lib. bdg. 23.95 (***978-1-4042-3763-6(1));*** Sharks. Gibbons, Lynn & Coode, Chris. lib. bdg. 23.95 (***978-1-4042-3762-9(3));*** Snakes. Harrison, Paul. lib. bdg. 23.95 (***978-1-4042-3764-3(X));*** (Illus.). 24p. (J). (gr. 3-5). 2007. 2007. Set lib. bdg. 143.70 (***978-1-4042-3765-0(8)*** , PowerKids Pr.) Rosen Publishing Group, Inc., The.

Urton, Andrea. Animals. 2001. (Illus.). 48p. (J). (gr. 3-7). pap. 8.95 (978-0-7373-0536-4(3)) Lowell Hse. Juvenile.

—Bugs & Animals. 2001. (Stick'n Learn Stories Ser.). (Illus.). 96p. (J). (gr. 3-7). pap. 6.95 (978-1-55254-235-4(1)) Brighter Vision Pubns.

Ury, Allen B. Dangerous Encounters: Grizzly Real-Life Animal Attacks. 1999. (Cinco Sentides del Mundo Animal Ser.: Vol. 1). (Illus.). 96p. (J). (gr. 3-7). pap. 5.95 (978-0-7373-0042-0(6) , 00426W) McGraw-Hill/Contemporary.

Usborne Publishing Staff, ed. Los Animales del Mundo. 2004. Tr. of Great Animal Search. (SPA., Illus.). 48p. (J). (ps-3). lib. bdg. 17.95 (978-1-58086-228-8(4)) EDC Publishing.

Using Leaves: Early Level Satellite Individual Title Six-Packs. (Sails Literacy Ser.). 16p. (gr. 1-2). 27.00 (978-0-7578-3164-5(8)) Rigby Education.

Valat, Pierre-Marie. Animal Faces. 2007. 32p. (J). pap. 12.95 (***978-1-59354-196-5(1)***) Handprint Bks.

Valer, Frantisek, illus. The Buffalo & the Boat: Thathanka na Wata. 2004. (DAK, ENG & SIO.). 18p. (J). 9.95 (978-0-9761082-3-8(2)) Lakota Language Consortium, Inc.

—Prairie Dog Goes to School: Pispíza wan Wayawa Iyaye. 2004. (DAK, ENG & SIO.). 24p. (J). 9.95 (978-0-9761082-4-5(0)) Lakota Language Consortium, Inc.

Van Eerbeek, Ton. The World of Baby Animals: An Early Encyclopedia for Beginning Readers. Balloon Books Staff, ed. 2001. (Animal Bring-Along Bks.). (Illus.). 24p. (J). (gr. k-1). 4.95 (978-0-8069-8058-4(3) , Balloon Bks.) Sterling Publishing Co., Inc.

—The World of Wild Animals: An Early Encyclopedia for Beginning Readers. Balloon Books Staff, ed. 2003. (Animal Bring-Along Bks.). (Illus.). 24p. (J). (ps-1). 4.95 (978-0-8069-8452-0(X) , 019720, Balloon Bks.) Sterling Publishing Co., Inc.

Vander Klipp, Michael A. God Made Animals. 1999. (God Made Bks.). (Illus.). 12p. (J). (ps). 2.99 (978-0-310-97860-2(2)) Zonderkidz.

VanVoorst, Jennifer. Rapido y mas Rapido. 2005. Tr. of Fast & Faster!. (SPA., Illus.). 16p. (J). (gr. 1 up). lib. bdg. 15.93 (978-0-7368-4135-1(0)) Capstone Pr., Inc.

Vecchione, Glen. The Little Giant Book of Animal Facts. Harris, Joel Chandler & Harris, Sharon, illus. 2004. 352p. (J). pap. 6.95 (978-1-4027-0785-8(1)) Sterling Publishing Co., Inc.

Videau, Valerie. Animals of the Cold. Latyk, Olivier & Eydoux, Anne, illus. 2006. (Explore Your World Ser.). 28p. (J). (ps-1). 15.95 (978-1-55407-002-2(3)) Firefly Bks., Ltd.

Vogel, Elizabeth. Big Cats, 6 bks. Incl. Cheetahs. lib. bdg. 16.00 (978-0-8239-6023-1(4)); Jaguars. lib. bdg. 16.00 (978-0-8239-6024-8(2)); Leopards. lib. bdg. 16.00 (978-0-8239-6019-4(6)); Lions. lib. bdg. 16.00 (978-0-8239-6021-7(8)); Pumas. lib. bdg. 16.00 (978-0-8239-6022-4(6)); Tigers. lib. bdg. 16.00 (978-0-8239-6020-0(X)); 24p. (J). (gr. 1). 2002. (Illus.). Set lib. bdg. 88.50 (978-0-8239-7112-1(0) , PowerKids Pr.) Rosen Publishing Group, Inc., The.

Volke, Gordon. Born Free Animal Predators. 2005. (Illus.). 24p. (J). (978-1-84510-626-3(1)) Top That! Publishing PLC.

Votaw, Carol J. Good Morning, Little Polar Bear. Banta, Susan, illus. 2005. 32p. (J). 15.95 (978-1-55971-932-2(X) , NorthWord Bks. for Young Readers) T&N Children's Publishing.

Votaw, Carol J. Waking up down Under. Banta, Susan, illus. 2007. 32p. (J). (***978-1-55971-976-6(1)*** , NorthWord Bks. for Young Readers) T&N Children's Publishing.

Vrato, Elizabeth & Mann, Holly. Animals. 2003. (Magic Window Bks.). (Illus.). 8p. (J). pap. 4.95 (978-0-7624-1649-3(1) , Running Pr. Kids) Running Pr. Bk. Pubs.

Wadsworth, Ginger. River Discoveries. Kratter, Paul, illus. 2002. (J). pap. 6.95 (978-1-57091-419-5(2)); (gr. 1-4). 16.95 (978-1-57091-418-8(4)) Charlesbridge Publishing, Inc.

—River Discoveries. 2002. (gr. k-3). lib. bdg. 15.25 (978-0-613-62645-3(1)) Tandem Library Bks.

Wadsworth, Pamela. Golwg Gyntaf Ar Bethau Byw. 2005. (WEL., Illus.). 24p. pap. (978-1-85596-250-7(0)) Dref Wen.

—Golwg Gyntaf Ar Wahanol Blanhigion Ac Anifeiliaid. 2005. (WEL., Illus.). 24p. pap. (978-1-85596-254-5(3)) Dref Wen.

—Gwahanol Blanhigion Ac Anifeiliaid. 2005. (WEL., Illus.). 24p. pap. (978-1-85596-223-1(3)) Dref Wen.

—Rhagor Am Bethau Byw Ar Waith. 2005. (WEL., Illus.). 24p. pap. (978-1-85596-234-7(9)) Dref Wen.

—Rhagor Am Wahanol Blanhigion Ac Anifeiliaid. 2005. (WEL., Illus.). 24p. pap. (978-1-85596-224-8(1)) Dref Wen.

Waldherr, Kris. Sacred Animals. 2001. (Illus.). 48p. (J). (gr. 5 up). 16.95 (978-0-688-16379-2(3)); 16.89 (978-0-688-16380-8(7)) HarperCollins Pubs.

A Walk in the Woods with Poppy. 2004. per. 11.95 (978-1-58961-314-0(7)) PageFree Publishing, Inc.

Walker, Colin, et al. Los Pajaros Son Animales. (Coleccion Conceptos de Ciencia en Big Books). (SPA., Illus.). (J). (gr. k-3). 12.00 (978-0-8136-6751-5(8) , MD7208) Modern Curriculum Pr.

—Los Peces Son Animales. (Coleccion Conceptos de Ciencia en Big Books). (SPA., Illus.). (J). (gr. k-3). 12.00 net. (978-0-8136-6750-8(X) , MD7213) Modern Curriculum Pr.

Walker, Niki & Kalman, Bobbie. Les Animaux en Mouvement. 2003. (FRE., Illus.). 32p. (J). pap. (978-2-89579-004-4(3)) Crabtree Publishing Co.

Wallace, Bruce. Wild Animals. 2005. (Touch & Sparkle Ser.). (Illus.). 12p. (ps-k). per., bds. 5.95 (978-1-905051-00-7(X)) Make Believe Ideas GBR. *Dist:* Ingram Pub. Services.

Wallace, Bruce & Make Believe Ideas Staff. Baby Animals. 2005. (Touch & Sparkle Ser.). (Illus.). 12p. (ps-k). bds. 5.95 (978-1-905051-03-8(4)) Make Believe Ideas GBR. *Dist:* Ingram Pub. Services.

Wallace, Marianne D. America's Mountains: Guide to Plants & Animals. Wallace, Marianne D., illus. 1999. (America's EcoSystem Ser.: Vol. 2). (Illus.). 48p. (gr. 4-6). pap. 11.95 (978-1-55591-383-0(0)) Fulcrum Publishing.

—America's Mountains: Guide to Plants & Animals. 1999. (gr. 3-6). lib. bdg. 26.85 (978-0-613-87961-3(9)) Tandem Library Bks.

—America's Seashores: Guide to Plants & Animals. 2005. (Illus.). 46p. (J). (ps-7). pap. 11.95 (978-1-55591-483-7(7) , 1250708) Fulcrum Publishing.

Walsh, Kieran. Animal Math. 2005. (Math & My World Ser.). (Illus.). 48p. (gr. 4-6). 20.95 (978-1-59515-491-0(4)) Rourke Publishing, LLC.

Walsh, Melanie. Do Donkeys Dance? Walsh, Melanie, illus. (Illus.). (J). (gr. k-ps). 2002. 14p. bds. 5.95 (978-0-618-15046-5(3)); 2000. 40p. tchr. ed. 15.00 (978-0-618-00330-3(4)) Houghton Mifflin Co. Trade & Reference Div.

—Do Pigs Have Stripes? Walsh, Melanie, illus. 2002. (Illus.). (J). 22.45 (978-0-7587-2393-2(8)) Book Wholesalers, Inc.

—Wild Animals. Walsh, Melanie, illus. 2002. (Tiny Teether Ser.). (Illus.). 14p. (J). (gr. k-ps). bds. 4.99 (978-0-7636-1809-4(8)) Candlewick Pr.

Walsh, Molly. 50 Animal Mothers & Babies. 1999. (High Q Books Ser.). (Illus.). 48p. (ps-3). 5.99 (978-0-7681-0137-9(9) , McClanahan Bk.) Learning Horizons, Inc.

Ward, Beck & Nicholson, Sue, eds. Animals. Giraffe, Red, illus. 2002. (My First Write & Wipe Ser.). 26p. (J). (ps-k). 14.95 (978-1-57145-725-7(9) , Silver Dolphin Bks.) Advantage Pubs. Group.

Ward, Jennifer. Forest Bright, Forest Night. Henterly, Jamichael, illus. 2005. (Sharing Nature with Children Book Ser.). 32p. (J). (gr. k-3). 16.95 (978-1-58469-066-5(6)); pap. 8.95 (978-1-58469-067-2(4)) Dawn Pubns.

Ward, Kristin. Oceans. 2000. (PowerKids Readers Ser.). (Illus.). 24p. (J). (gr. 1). lib. bdg. 16.00 (978-0-8239-5532-9(X) , PKNAOC, PowerKids Pr.) Rosen Publishing Group, Inc., The.

Warnau, Genevieve. The Encyclopedia of Animals: A Compact Guide to the Animal Kingdom. 2004. (Illus.). 304p. (J). pap. (978-1-59496-035-2(6)) Teora USA LLC.

Warthogs. (Animals Ser.). 32p. (J). 6.95 (978-0-7368-8412-9(2)) Capstone Pr., Inc.

Warty, illus. Find the Differences. 2003. 48p. (J). (gr. 2-4). pap. 3.95 (978-0-8069-8959-4(9) , Balloon Bks.) Sterling Publishing Co., Inc.

Watanabe, Kaori, illus. Sweet Dreams. 2003. (My First Taggies Book Ser.). 8p. (J). 12.95 (978-0-439-53771-1(1) , Cartwheel Bks.) Scholastic, Inc.

Waters, Jo. A Walk in the Park. 2006. (Raintree Sprouts Ser.). (Illus.). 24p. (J). (978-1-4109-2291-5(X)); pap. (978-1-4109-2296-0(0)) Steck-Vaughn.

Watt, Melanie. The Alphabet with Wild Animals. 2005. (Learning with Animals Board Bks.). (Illus.). 30p. (J). (gr. k up). (978-1-55337-829-7(6)) Kids Can Pr., Ltd.

—Colors. 2005. (Learning with Animals Board Bks.). (Illus.). 24p. (J). (gr. k up). (978-1-55337-830-3(X)) Kids Can Pr., Ltd.

—Numbers. 2005. (Learning with Animals Board Bks.). (Illus.). 24p. (J). (gr. k up). (978-1-55337-831-0(8)) Kids Can Pr., Ltd.

—Opposites. 2005. (Learning with Animals Board Bks.). (Illus.). 24p. (J). (gr. k up). (978-1-55337-832-7(6)) Kids Can Pr., Ltd.

—Shapes. 2005. (Learning with Animals Board Bks.). (Illus.). 24p. (J). (gr. k up). (978-1-55337-833-4(4)) Kids Can Pr., Ltd.

Watts, Barrie. El Hamster. (Coleccion Ciclos Vitales). (SPA., Illus.). 32p. (J). (gr. 3-5). (978-84-236-2665-6(2) , ED4704) Edebé ESP. *Dist:* Lectorum Pubns., Inc.

Watts, Claire. Mascotas. 2004. (Descubre los Animales Ser.).Tr. of Pets. (SPA., Illus.). 20p. (ps-2). 9.95 (978-1-58728-488-5(X) , Two Can Publishing) T&N Children's Publishing.

Watts, Claire & Nicholson, Robert. Amazing Animals. 2000. (Info Adventure Ser.). (Illus.). 32p. (J). (gr. 3-6). pap. 3.95 (978-1-58728-100-6(7) , Two Can Publishing) T&N Children's Publishing.

—Dangerous Animals. 2000. (Info Adventure Ser.). (Illus.). 32p. (J). (gr. 3-6). pap. 3.95 (978-1-58728-103-7(1) , Two Can Publishing) T&N Children's Publishing.

Watts Library: Animals. 2004. 96.00 (978-0-531-12425-3(8) , Watts, Franklin) Scholastic Library Publishing.

We Can Read! Series, 4 bks., Set. 85.43 (978-0-7614-1509-1(2) , Benchmark Bks.) Cavendish, Marshall Corp.

Weaver, Robyn. Meerkats. 1998. (Animals Ser.). (Illus.). 24p. (J). (gr. 2-3). lib. bdg. 18.60 (978-0-7368-0066-2(2) , Bridgestone Bks.) Capstone Pr., Inc.

Webb, Steve. Tanka Tanka Skunk! 2004. (Illus.). 32p. (J). 15.95 (978-0-439-57844-8(2) , Orchard Bks.) Scholastic, Inc.

Weber, Belinda. Animal Disguises. (Science Kids Ser.). (Illus.). 48p. (J). 2007. pap. 6.95 (***978-0-7534-6162-4(5));*** 2004. 9.95 (978-0-7534-5772-6(5)) Houghton Mifflin Co. Trade & Reference Div. (Kingfisher).

Weber, Lou, ed. Animals Lace & Learn. 2004. 16p. (J). spiral bd., bds. 9.98 (978-1-4127-3154-6(2) , 7232400) Publications International, Ltd.

—Tummy Time Animal Babies. 2004. 8p. 6.98 (978-1-4127-3063-1(5)) Publications International, Ltd.

Weekly Reader Early Learning Library (Firm) Staff, contrib. by. Things at the Park. 2006. (Things in My World Ser.). (Illus.). 16p. (J). pap. (978-0-8368-6816-6(1)); lib. bdg. (978-0-8368-6809-8(9)) Stevens, Gareth Inc.

—Things at the Park: Las Cosas Del Parque. 2006. (ENG & SPA., Illus.). 16p. (J). pap. (978-0-8368-7228-6(2) , Weekly Reader Early Learning Library) Stevens, Gareth Inc.

—Things at the Park (Las Cosas del Parque) 2006. (ENG & SPA., Illus.). 16p. (J). lib. bdg. 17.27 (978-0-8368-7221-7(5) , Weekly Reader Early Learning Library) Stevens, Gareth Inc.

Weird Wildlife, 5 bks., Set 1. 2003. (Illus.). (J). pap. 40.30 (978-1-4109-0151-4(3)) Raintree.

West, Tracey. Gets Cold Feet: A Book about Warm- And Cold-Blooded Animals. Ruiz, Art, illus. 1998. (Magic School Bus Ser.). 32p. (J). (gr. 1-4). pap. 3.50 (978-0-590-39724-7(9)) Scholastic, Inc.

Weston, Steve, illus. The World of Animal Life. 2001. (Inside Look Ser.). 48p. (J). (gr. 4 up). lib. bdg. 26.00 (978-0-8368-2902-0(6)) Stevens, Gareth Inc.

Wexo, John Bonnett. Animal Champions. Wildlife Education, Ltd. Staff, ed. 2001. (Zoobooks Ser.). (Illus.). 24p. (J). 15.95 (978-0-937934-73-9(9)) Wildlife Education, Ltd.

—Endangered Animals. 2001. (Zoobooks Ser.). (Illus.). 24p. (J). (gr. 1-6). 15.95 (978-1-888153-39-2(3)) Wildlife Education, Ltd.

—Night Animals. 2001. (Zoobooks Ser.). 24p. (J). (gr. 1-7). 15.95 (978-0-937934-99-9(2)) Wildlife Education, Ltd.

What Can Fly?, 6 Packs. (Literatura 2000 Ser.). (gr. k-1). 28.00 (978-0-7635-0073-3(9)) Rigby Education.

What Do Animals Do in Winter? (Discovery Readers Ser.). 48p. (J). pap. 3.95 (978-0-8249-5314-0(2) , Ideals Children's Bks.) Ideals Pubns.

What's That Sound? (Peek A Boo Pockets Ser.). (Illus.). 12p. (J). bds. (978-2-89393-877-6(9)) Phidal Publishing, Inc./Editions Phidal, Inc.

Whitehouse, Patricia. Animal Camouflage, 5 bks., Set. 2003. (Illus.). (J). (gr. k-2). lib. bdg. 113.95 (978-1-58810-848-7(1)) Heinemann Library.

—Que Puede Correr? Abello, Patricia, tr. 2004. (SPA.). 24p. (J). 12.95 (978-1-4034-4387-8(4)) Heinemann Library.

—Quien Esta Despierto? 1 2 3. 2003. (Que Esta Despierto? (What's Awake?) Ser.). (SPA.). 24p. (J). (ps-1). lib. bdg. 17.08 (978-1-4034-0399-5(6)) Heinemann.

—What Can... ? Series, 6 bks., Set. 2004. (978-1-4034-4371-7(8)) Heinemann Library.

—What Can Jump? 2003. (Illus.). 24p. (J). lib. bdg. 18.50 (978-1-4034-4366-3(1)) Heinemann Library.

—What Can Jump? 2003. (ps-2). lib. bdg. 28.65 (978-0-613-84306-5(1)) Tandem Library Bks.

Whittaker, Andrea. All-Star Animals: Pets who'd rather play than Stay. 2004. (YA). 3.99 (978-1-930623-35-4(6)) Sports Illustrated For Kids.

Who Grows up in the Snow? (Who Grows up Here? Ser.). 24p. (J). 7.95 (978-1-4048-0210-0(X)) Picture Window Bks.

Who's Hiding Inside? Animals. 2005. (Who's Hiding Inside Ser.). 12p. (J). bds. 7.95 (978-1-58117-306-2(7) , Intervisual/Piggy Toes) Dalmatian Pr.

Whos Who at the Zoo. 2004. pap. 9.99 (978-0-307-14272-6(8)) Random Hse., Inc.

Whose Ears Are These? (Whose Is It? Ser.). 24p. (J). 7.95 (978-1-4048-0213-1(4)) Picture Window Bks.

Whose Eyes Are These? (Whose Is It? Ser.). 24p. (J). 7.95 (978-1-4048-0214-8(2)) Picture Window Bks.

Whose Feet Are These? (Whose Is It? Ser.). 24p. (J). 7.95 (978-1-4048-0324-4(6)) Picture Window Bks.

Whose Is It?, 14 bks. Incl. Whose Ears Are These? A Look at Animal Ears - Short, Flat, & Floppy. Hall, Peg. Landmark, Ken, illus. 22.60 (978-1-4048-0004-5(2)); Whose Eyes Are These? A Look at Animal Eyes - Big, Round, & Narrow. Hall, Peg. Landmark, Ken, illus. 22.60 (978-1-4048-0005-2(0)); Whose Feet Are These? A Look at Hooves, Paws, & Claws. Hall, Peg. Landmark, Ken, illus. 22.60 (978-1-4048-0006-9(9)); Whose Food Is This : A Look at What Animals Eat - Seeds, Bugs, & Nuts. Allen, Nancy Kelly. Alderman, Derrick & Shea, Denise, illus. 22.60 (978-1-4048-0607-8(5)); Whose House Is This? A Look at Animal Homes - Webs, Nests, & Shells. Gregoire, Elizabeth. Alderman,

Derrick & Shea, Denise, illus. 22.60 (978-1-4048-0608-5(3)); Whose Legs Are These? A Look at Animal Legs - Kicking, Running, & Hopping. Hall, Peg. Landmark, Ken, illus. 22.60 (978-1-4048-0007-6(7)); Whose Mouth Is This? A Look at Bills, Suckers & Tubes. Kee, Lisa Morris. Landmark, Ken, illus. 22.60 (978-1-4048-0008-3(5)); Whose Nose Is This? A Look at Beaks, Snouts, & Trunks. Hall, Peg. Landmark, Ken, illus. 22.60 (978-1-4048-0009-0(3)); Whose Shadow Is This? A Look at Animal Shapes - Round, Long, & Pointy. Berge, Claire. Alderman, Derrick & Shea, Denise, illus. 22.60 (978-1-4048-0609-2(1)); Whose Skin Is This? A Look at Skin - Scaly, Furry & Prickly. Kee, Lisa Morris. Landmark, Ken, illus. 22.60 (978-1-4048-0010-6(7)); Whose Sound Is This? A Look at Animal Noises - Chirps, Clicks, & Hoots. Allen, Nancy Kelly. Alderman, Derrick & Shea, Denise, illus. 22.60 (978-1-4048-0610-8(5)); Whose Spots Are These? A Look at Animal Markings - Round, Bright, & Big. Wohlrabe, Sarah C. Alderman, Derrick & Shea, Denise, illus. 22.60 (978-1-4048-0611-5(3)); Whose Tail Is This? A Look at Tails - Swishing, Wiggling, & Rattling. Hall, Peg. Landmark, Ken, illus. 22.60 (978-1-4048-0011-3(5)); Whose Work Is This? A Look at Things Animals Make - Pearls, Silk, & Honey. Allen, Nancy Kelly. Alderman, Derrick & Shea, Denise, illus. 22.60 (978-1-4048-0612-2(1)); 24p. (C). (gr. k-2). 2004. 316.40 (978-1-4048-0633-7(4)) Picture Window Bks.

Whose Legs Are These? (Whose Is It? Ser.). 24p. (J). 7.95 (978-1-4048-0325-1(4)) Picture Window Bks.

Whose Mouth Is This? (Whose Is It? Ser.). 24p. (J). 7.95 (978-1-4048-0326-8(2)) Picture Window Bks.

Whose Nose Is This? (Whose Is It? Ser.). 24p. (J). 7.95 (978-1-4048-0327-5(0)) Picture Window Bks.

Whose Skin Is This? (Whose Is It? Ser.). 24p. (J). 7.95 (978-1-4048-0328-2(9)) Picture Window Bks.

Whose Tail Is This? (Whose Is It? Ser.). 24p. (J). 7.95 (978-1-4048-0329-9(7)) Picture Window Bks.

Whyman, Kathryn. The Animal Kingdom: A Guide to Vertebrate Classification & Biodiversity. 1999. (Classification Ser.). (Illus.). 48p. (J). (gr. 6-8). lib. bdg. 27.12 (978-0-8172-5885-6(X)) Raintree.

Wickings, Ruth. In the Pond. 2007. (World at Your Feet Ser.). (Illus.). 10p. (J). 9.95 (978-1-84560-026-6(6)) Mercury Bks. Ltd. GBR. *Dist:* International Publishers Marketing.

—Make & Meet Wild Animals. 2006. (Make & Meet Kits Ser.). (Illus.). 24p. 8.95 (978-1-84560-028-0(2)) Mercury Bks. Ltd. GBR. *Dist:* International Publishers Marketing.

Wiebe, Trina. Lizards Don't Wear Lip Gloss. Pavanel, Jane & Sarrazin, Marisol, illus. 2004. (Abby & Tess Pet-Sitters Ser.: Vol. 2). 96p. (J). pap. 5.95 (978-1-894222-11-2(3)) Lobster Pr. CAN. *Dist:* Univ. of Toronto Pr.

—Lizards Don't Wear Lip Gloss. 2000. (gr. 3-6). lib. bdg. 14.10 (978-0-613-62559-3(5)) Tandem Library Bks.

A Wild Animal. 2005. (J). (978-1-58453-312-2(9)) Pioneer Valley Educational Pr., Inc.

Wild Animals. (First Facts about Ser.). 24p. (J). (gr. 3-7). pap. (978-1-882210-18-3(2)) Action Publishing, Inc.

Wild Animals. (C). 143.58 (978-1-4048-1517-9(1)) Picture Window Bks.

Wild Animals. 2007. (My First Sticker Encyclopedia Ser.). (Illus.). 18p. (J). pap. 5.95 (***978-1-59496-141-0(7)***) Teora USA LLC.

Wild Animals Action. 2002. 12p. (J). pap. 3.98 (978-0-7525-8041-8(8)) Parragon, Inc.

Wild, Anne S. Wildlife Pop-Ups: A Collection of 3-D Greetings Cards on Wildlife Themes to Cut Out & Make. 2004. (Illus.). 36p. (J). 12.00 (978-1-899618-48-4(1)) Tarquin Pubns. GBR. *Dist:* Parkwest Pubns., Inc.

A Wild Time! Individual Title Six-Packs. (Bookweb Ser.). 32p. (gr. 6 up). 34.00 (978-0-7578-0904-0(9)) Rigby Education.

The Wild World of Animals, 22 bks. Incl. Baboons : Life in the Troop. Richardson, Adele D. 2001. lib. bdg. 18.60 (978-0-7368-0961-0(9)); Bears : Paws, Claws & Jaws. Schaefer, Lola M. 2001. lib. bdg. 18.60 (978-0-7368-0823-1(X)); Beavers : Big-Toothed Builders. Sullivan, Jody. 2002. lib. bdg. 18.60 (978-0-7368-1392-1(6)); Butterflies : Pollinators & Nectar-Sippers. Schaefer, Lola M. 2001. lib. bdg. 18.60 (978-0-7368-0824-8(8)); Cheetahs : Spotted Speedsters. Sullivan, Jody. 2002. lib. bdg. 18.60 (978-0-7368-1393-8(4)); Deer : Graceful Grazers. Sullivan, Jody. 2002. lib. bdg. 18.60 (978-0-7368-1394-5(2)); Dolphins : Fins, Flippers & Flukes. Schaefer, Lola M. 2001. lib. bdg. 18.60 (978-0-7368-0825-5(6)); Eagles : Birds of Prey. Richardson, Adele D. 2002. lib. bdg. 18.60 (978-0-7368-1136-1(2)); Earthworms : Underground Burrowers. Schaefer, Lola M. 2001. lib. bdg. 18.60 (978-0-7368-0826-2(4)); Elephants : Trunks & Tusks. Richardson, Adele D. 2001. lib. bdg. 18.60 (978-0-7368-0962-7(7)); Foxes : Clever Hunters. Olien, Becky. 2002. lib. bdg. 18.60 (978-0-7368-1137-8(0)); Frogs : Leaping Amphibians. Schaefer, Lola M. 2001. lib. bdg. 18.60 (978-0-7368-0827-9(2)); Giraffes : Long-Necked Leaf-Eaters. Schaefer, Lola M. 2001. lib. bdg. 18.60 (978-0-7368-0965-8(1)); Groundhogs : Woodchucks, Marmots, & Whistle Pigs. Richardson, Adele D. 2002. lib. bdg. 18.60 (978-0-7368-1397-6(7)); Hyenas : Hunters & Scavengers. Richardson, Adele D. 2001. lib. bdg. 18.60 (978-0-7368-0963-4(5)); Leopards : Spotted Hunters. Schaefer, Lola M. 2001. lib. bdg. 18.60 (978-0-7368-0966-5(X)); Lions : Life in the Pride. Richardson, Adele D. 2001. lib. bdg. 18.60 (978-0-7368-0964-1(3)); Manatees : Peaceful Plant-Eaters. Richardson, Adele D. 2002. lib. bdg. 18.60 (978-0-7368-1395-2(0)); Owls : Flat-Faced Flyers. Richardson, Adele D. 2002. lib. bdg. 18.60 (978-0-7368-1396-9(9)); Rhinos : Horn-Faced Chargers. Schaefer, Lola M. 2001. lib. bdg. 18.60 (978-0-7368-0967-2(8)); Sharks : Hunters of the Deep. Richardson, Adele D. 2001. lib. bdg. 18.60 (978-0-7368-0828-6(0)); Snakes : Cold-Blooded Crawlers. Olien, Becky. 2002. lib. bdg. 18.60 (978-0-7368-1138-5(9)); Spiders : Spinners & Trappers. Richardson, Adele D. 2001. lib. bdg. 18.60 (978-0-7368-0829-3(9)); Squirrels : Furry Scurriers. Olien, Becky. 2002. lib. bdg. 18.60 (978-0-7368-1139-2(7)); Tigers : Striped Stalkers. Richardson, Adele D. 2002. lib. bdg. 18.60 (978-0-7368-1140-8(0)); Whales : Giants of the Deep. Richardson, Adele D. 2002. lib. bdg. 18.60 (978-0-7368-1141-5(9)); Wolves : Life in the Pack. Richardson, Adele D. 2001. lib. bdg. 18.60 (978-0-7368-0830-9(2)); Zebras : Striped Grass-Grazers. Schaefer, Lola M. 2001. lib. bdg. 18.60 (978-0-7368-0968-9(6)); 24p. (J). (gr. 1-2). (Illus.). Set lib. bdg. 520.80 (978-0-7368-1398-3(5) , Bridgestone Bks.) Capstone Pr., Inc.

Wild World of Animals. (Illus.). (J). (gr. 2-3). lib. bdg. 680.32 (978-0-7368-2749-2(8)) Capstone Pr., Inc.

Wildlife & Plants of the World, 17 vols., Set. rev. exp. ed. 1999. (Illus.). 1,000p. (gr. 4-8). 471.36 (978-0-7614-7099-1(9) , Cavendish, Marshall Reference Bks.) Cavendish, Marshall Corp.

Wildlife Coloring Book. 2004. (Illus.). 24p. (J). pap. 4.95 (978-0-88839-599-3(X)) Hancock Hse. Pubs., Ltd. CAN. *Dist:* Hancock Hse. Pubs.

Wildlife Education, Ltd. Staff. Rhinos. Woods, Michael et al, illus. 2000. (Zoobooks Ser.). 18p. (Orig.). (J). (gr. 1-8). pap. 2.95 (978-0-937934-29-6(1)) Wildlife Education, Ltd.

Wildlife Education, Ltd. Staff, contrib. by. Amazing Animals, Set. 2002. (All about Animals Ser.). (Illus.). (J). (gr. k-6). 16.95 incl. VHS (978-1-888153-89-7(X)) Wildlife Education, Ltd.

—Spanish Hardcover Set, 12 vols. 2003. (Zoobooks Ser.). (SPA., Illus.). 24p. (J). (gr. k-6). 191.40 (978-1-932396-06-5(3)) Wildlife Education, Ltd.

Wildlife Education, Ltd. Staff & Wexo, John Bonnett. Animal Wonders. Stuart, Walter, illus. 2001. (Zoobooks Ser.). 24p. (J). 15.95 (978-0-937934-74-6(7)) Wildlife Education, Ltd.

Wildlife Education, Ltd. Staff, et al. Animal Champions Two. 1999. (Zoobooks Ser.). (Illus.). 18p. (Orig.). (J). pap. 2.95 (978-0-937934-64-7(X)) Wildlife Education, Ltd.

Wildlife of North America Classroom Library. (gr. 4 up). lib. bdg. 74.95 (978-0-7368-7092-4(X)) Red Brick Learning.

Wildlife of North America Complete Unit. (gr. 4 up). 430.95 (978-0-7368-7093-1(8)) Red Brick Learning.

Wildlife Safari Africa, Swahili & English: Who's Who in the African Jungle & Savanna, a Swahili/English Multicultural Book. 2004. (J). per. 9.95 (978-0-9742688-2-8(8)) Ndegwa, Catherine W.

Wildlife Watching: Level R, 6 vols. (Wonder Worldtm Ser.). 48p. 44.95 (978-0-7802-7076-3(2)) Wright Group, The.

Wildlife Wonders. (Britannica Learning Library). (Illus.). (gr. 2-5). 14.95 (978-1-59339-015-0(7) , 049909-EN-REF) Encyclopaedia Britannica, Inc.

Wildsmith, Brian. Brian Wildsmith ABC. Fiol, Maria A., tr. Wildsmith, Brian, illus. 1998. (SPA., Illus.). 32p. (J). (ps). bds. 6.95 (978-1-887734-16-5(3)) Star Bright Bks., Inc.

—Brian Wildsmith's Amazing Animal Alphabet Book. Wildsmith, Brian, illus. (Illus.). 32p. (J). 2008. 16.95 (***978-1-59572-104-4(5)***); 2007. pap. 8.95 (***978-1-59572-111-2(8)***) Star Bright Bks., Inc.

—Brian Wildsmith's Animals to Count (Portugese) Wildsmith, Brian, illus. 2003. (POR., Illus.). 16p. (J). bds. 4.95 (978-1-932065-15-2(6) , 17187849112) Star Bright Bks., Inc.

—Cuantos Animales Hay? Fiol, Maria A., tr. Wildsmith, Brian, illus. 1998. (SPA., Illus.). 16p. (J). (ps). bds. 4.95 (978-1-887734-17-2(1)) Star Bright Bks., Inc.

—Los Colores de los Animales. 2005. (SPA & ENG., Illus.). 16p. (J). (ps-ps). per. 5.95 (978-1-59572-023-8(5)) Star Bright Bks., Inc.

—Los Colores de los Animales. Wildsmith, Brian, illus. 2001. (SPA., Illus.). 16p. (J). (ps-k). bds. 4.95 (978-1-887734-51-6(1)) Star Bright Bks., Inc.

Wildsmith, Brian, illus. Brian Wildsmith's Animal Colors (Arabic) 2004. (ARA.). 16p. (J). bds. 4.95 (978-1-932065-44-2(X) , 718-784-9112) Star Bright Bks., Inc.

—Brian Wildsmith's Animal Colors (Korean) 2003. (KOR.). 16p. (J). bds. 4.95 (978-1-932065-28-2(8) , 1-718-784-9112) Star Bright Bks., Inc.

—Brian Wildsmith's Animal Colors (Navajo) 2004. (NAV.). 16p. (J). bds. 4.95 (978-1-932065-34-3(2) , 718-784-9112) Star Bright Bks., Inc.

—Brian Wildsmith's Animal Colors (Portugese) 2003. (POR.). 16p. (J). bds. 4.95 (978-1-932065-27-5(X) , 1-718-784-9112) Star Bright Bks., Inc.

—Brian Wildsmith's Animal Colors (Simplified Chinese) 2004. (CHI.). 16p. (J). bds. 4.95 (978-1-932065-52-7(0) , 7187849112) Star Bright Bks., Inc.

—Brian Wildsmith's Animal Colors (Tagalog) 2003. (TAG.). 16p. (J). bds. 4.95 (978-1-932065-30-5(X) , 1-718-784-9112) Star Bright Bks., Inc.

—Brian Wildsmith's Animal Colors (Traditional Chinese) 2004. (CHI.). 16p. (J). bds. 4.95 (978-1-932065-53-4(9)) Star Bright Bks., Inc.

—Brian Wildsmith's Animal Colors (Vietnamese) 2004. (VIE.). 16p. (J). bds. 4.95 (978-1-932065-51-0(2)) Star Bright Bks., Inc.

—Brian Wildsmith's Animals to Count (Farsi) 2004. (PER.). 16p. (J). bds. 4.95 (978-1-932065-43-5(1)) Star Bright Bks., Inc.

—Brian Wildsmith's Animals to Count (Korean) 2003. (KOR.). 16p. (J). bds. 4.95 (978-1-932065-13-8(X) , 1718-784-9112) Star Bright Bks., Inc.

—Brian Wildsmith's Animals to Count (Simplified Chinese) 2003. (CHI.). 16p. (J). bds. 4.95 (978-1-932065-17-6(2) , 1718-784-9112) Star Bright Bks., Inc.

—Brian Wildsmith's Animals to Count (Tagalog) 2003. (TAG.). 16p. (J). bds. 4.95 (978-1-932065-31-2(8) , 1-718-784-9112) Star Bright Bks., Inc.

—Brian Wildsmith's Animals to Count (Traditional Chinese) 2003. (CHI.). 16p. (J). bds. 4.95 (978-1-932065-18-3(0) , 1-718-784-9112) Star Bright Bks., Inc.

—Brian Wildsmith's Animals to Count (Vietnamese) 2003. (VIE.). 16p. (J). bds. 4.95 (978-1-932065-16-9(4) , 17187849112) Star Bright Bks., Inc.

Wildsmith, Brian & Ayiilaa, Naaltsoos. Brian Wildsmith's Animals to Count (Navajo) 2004. Tr. of Animals to Count. (NAV., Illus.). 16p. (J). bds. 4.95 (978-1-932065-25-1(3)) Star Bright Bks., Inc.

Wiley, Paula. Groove with the Animals. 2003. 29p. spiral bd. 14.59 (978-1-4116-0160-4(2)) Lulu.com.

Wilkes, Angela. Animales de la Selva Tropical. 2004. (Ladders Ser.).Tr. of Rain Forest Animals. (SPA., Illus.). 32p. (ps-3). 12.95 (978-1-58728-406-9(5) , Two Can Publishing) T&N Children's Publishing.

—Dangerous Creatures. (Kingfisher Knowledge Ser.). (Illus.). 64p. (J). (gr. 4-6). 2007. pap. 8.95 (***978-0-7534-6120-4(X)***); 2003. tchr. ed., bds. 12.95 (978-0-7534-5622-4(2)) Houghton Mifflin Co. Trade & Reference Div. (Kingfisher).

—Rain Forest Animals. 2000. (ps-2). lib. bdg. 15.25 (978-0-613-43496-6(X)) Tandem Library Bks.

—Rain Forest Animals. 2000. (Ladders Ser.). (Illus.). 32p. (J). (gr. k-3). (978-0-7166-7703-1(2)) World Bk., Inc.

—Wild Animals. rev. ed. 2004. (Ladders Ser.). (Illus.). (ps-3). 32p. (J). pap. 6.95 (978-1-58728-616-2(5)); 30p. 12.95 (978-1-58728-608-7(4)) T&N Children's Publishing. (Two Can Publishing).

Wilkes, Angela & Webster, Belinda. Rain Forest Animals. Holmes, Steve, illus. rev. ed. 2004. (Ladders Ser.). 32p. (J). (ps-3). pap. 6.95 (978-1-58728-618-6(1) , Two Can Publishing) T&N Children's Publishing.

Windham, Ryder. What You Don't Know about Animals. 2002. 144p. (J). (gr. 3-7). pap. 4.50 (978-0-439-22533-5(7) , Scholastic Paperbacks) Scholastic, Inc.

Windsor, Jo. Animals Can Change: Emergent Level Satellite Individual Title Six-Packs. (Sails Literacy Ser.). (gr. k-1). 27.00 (978-0-7578-7943-2(8)) Rigby Education.

—Animals in the Grasslands: Emergent Level Satellite Individual Title Six-Packs. (Sails Literacy Ser.). (gr. k-1). 27.00 (978-0-7578-7942-5(X)) Rigby Education.

—Animals in the Mountains: Emergent Level Satellite Individual Title Six-Packs. (Sails Literacy Ser.). (gr. k-1). 27.00 (978-0-7578-7941-8(1)) Rigby Education.

—Good Ideas for People: Early Level Satellite Individual Title Six-Packs. (Sails Literacy Ser.). 16p. (gr. 1-2). 27.00 (978-0-7578-2930-7(9)) Rigby Education.

—Horns: Early Level Satellite Individual Title Six-Packs. (Sails Literacy Ser.). 16p. (gr. 1-2). 27.00 (978-0-7578-2915-4(5)) Rigby Education.

Winkler, Peter. Animal Adaptations. 2004. (National Geographic Reading Expeditions Ser.). (Illus.). 32p. (J). pap. (978-0-7922-4577-3(6)) National Geographic Society.

Winner, Cherie. Animal Minis! What Kids Really Want to Know about Tiny Animals. 2006. (Kids' Faqs Ser.). (Illus.). 64p. (J). 7.95 (978-1-55971-934-6(6)); 10.95 (978-1-55971-933-9(8)) T&N Children's Publishing. (NorthWord Bks. for Young Readers).

Winsten, Martha R. Awesome Elijah. 2007. (Illus.). 32p. (J). 14.95 (***978-1-57258-476-1(9)***) TEACH Services, Inc.

Winter, Jeanette. Beatrix: Various Episodes from the Life of Beatrix Potter. Winter, Jeanette, illus. 2003. (Illus.). 64p. (J). (gr. k-3). 15.00 (978-0-374-30655-7(9) , Farrar, Straus & Giroux (BYR)) Farrar, Straus & Giroux.

Winter Survival: Individual Title Six-Packs. (Action Packs Ser.). 104p. (gr. 3-5). 44.00 (978-0-7635-8400-9(2)) Rigby Education.

Wiskur, Darrell. Great Creatures. 2002. (Take a Trip on the Silver Ship Ser.). (Illus.). (J). 6.99 (978-0-89051-380-4(5)) Master Bks.

The Wolf, 6 vols. (gr. 4 up). 39.95 (978-0-7368-8503-4(X)) Red Brick Learning.

Wolf, Ema. Que Animales! 2002. (SPA.). 56p. (J). pap. 19.95 (978-1-4000-0065-4(3)) Random Hse., Inc.

Woodward, John. Clever Camouflage. 2005. (Amazing Nature Ser.). (Illus.). 32p. (J). (ps-7). pap. 7.50 (978-1-4034-5399-0(3)) Heinemann Library.

—Lovers. 2005. (Planet's Most Extreme Ser.). (Illus.). 48p. (J). (gr. 3-7). 24.95 (978-1-4103-0388-2(8) , Blackbirch Pr., Inc.) Thomson Gale.

—Perfect Partners. 2003. (Amazing Nature Ser.). (Illus.). 32p. (J). pap. 7.50 (978-1-4034-5404-1(3)) Heinemann Library.

—Venom. 2005. (Planet's Most Extreme Ser.). (Illus.). 48p. (J). (gr. 3-7). 24.95 (978-1-4103-0392-9(6) , Blackbirch Pr., Inc.) Thomson Gale.

—What Lives in the Garden? 2006. lib. bdg. (***978-0-8368-7859-2(0)***) Stevens, Gareth Inc.

—What Lives under the Carpet? 2006. (Illus.). 48p. (J). lib. bdg. (***978-0-8368-7862-2(0)***) Stevens, Gareth Inc.

Woodward, Kay. Animal Rights. 2004. (21st Century Issues Ser.). (J). pap. 11.95 (978-0-8368-5659-0(7)); lib. bdg. 30.00 (978-0-8368-5642-2(2)) Stevens, Gareth Inc. (World Almanac Library).

World Book, Inc. Staff. World Book's Animals of the World. 2002. 24&25p. 347.00 (978-0-7166-1234-6(8) , 200270); (J). 238.00 (978-0-7166-1248-3(8)) World Bk., Inc.

World Book, Inc Staff, contrib. by. Rain Forest Animals. 2007. (J). (***978-0-7166-7729-1(6)***) World Bk., Inc.

—Resources & Cumulative Index. 2005. (World Book's Science & Nature Guides Ser.). 80p. (J). (978-0-7166-4216-9(6)) World Bk., Inc.

World Book, Inc Staff, contrib. by. Wild Animals. 2007. (J). (***978-0-7166-7733-8(4)***) World Bk., Inc.

World Book, Inc. Staff, ed. Friends in the Wild. 1998. (How & Why Bookshelf Ser.). 224p. (J). (gr. 2-6). 23.00 (978-0-7166-0698-7(4) , 4107) World Bk., Inc.

—World Book's Animals of the World: Set 1, 10 vols. 1999. (World Book's Animals of the World Ser.: Set 1). (Illus.). 640p. (J). (gr. 1-4). (978-0-7166-1200-1(3) , 20100) World Bk., Inc.

World Book's Animals of the World. 2005. 569.00 (978-0-7166-1284-1(4) , 60107); 2000. 640p. (gr. 2-8). 189.00 (978-0-7166-1273-5(9) , 20185) World Bk., Inc.

World Book's Animals of the World Set 2, 10 vols. 2005. (gr. 2-8). 189.00 (978-0-7166-1249-0(6) , 20125) World Bk., Inc.

World of Animals. 2003. (Illus.). 256p. (J). 12.98 (978-1-4054-1704-4(8)) Parragon, Inc.

A World of Animals Set D, 6 vols. (Phonics Readers Ser.). (gr. k-2). 28.95 (978-0-7368-4059-0(1)) Red Brick Learning.

The World of Eric Carle My Animals Activity Kit. 2007. (J). 16.99 (***978-0-9794445-4-8(3)***) Loew-Cornell, Inc.

Wormell, Christopher. Number of Animals. 2003. (gr. k-3). lib. bdg. 16.40 (978-0-613-77491-8(4)) Tandem Library Bks.

Wright, Betty Ren. Pet Detectives. 1999. (978-0-606-18668-1(9)) Tandem Library Bks.

Wright, Russell G. Survive? Investigations in Animal Diversity. (Event-Based Science Ser.). (gr. 5-9). 38p. pap., tchr.'s training gde. ed. 25.95 incl. VHS (978-0-7690-2353-3(3)); 66p. (YA). pap., stu. ed. 11.50 (978-0-7690-2352-6(5)) Seymour, Dale Pubns.

Xuan, Yong-Sheng, illus. The Rooster's Antlers: A Story of the Chinese Zodiac. 1999. 32p. (J). (gr. k-3). tchr. ed. 16.95 (978-0-8234-1385-0(3)) Holiday Hse., Inc.

Yaccarino, Dan. Unlovable. rev. ed. 2002. (Illus.). 32p. (J). (ps-1). 16.95 (978-0-8050-6321-9(8) , Holt, Henry & Co. Bks. For Young Readers) Holt, Henry & Co.

Yaks: Early Level Satellite, 6 Packs. (Sails Literacy Ser.). 16p. (gr. 1-2). 27.00 (978-0-7578-6520-6(8)) Rigby Education.

Yoon, Salina, illus. Peek-a-Boo Farm Animals. 2005. (Peek-a-Boo Guess Who Book Ser.: Vol. 2). 10p. (J). 7.95 (978-1-58117-158-7(7) , Intervisual/Piggy Toes) Dalmatian Pr.

—Peek-a-Boo Wild Animals. 2005. (Peek-a-Boo Guess Who Book Ser.: Vol. 1). 10p. (J). (ps-k). 7.95 (978-1-58117-157-0(9) , Intervisual/Piggy Toes) Dalmatian Pr.

Young, Caroline. Great Animal Search. rev. ed. 2006. 48p. (J). pap. 8.99 (978-0-7945-1028-2(0) , Usborne) EDC Publishing.

Young, Dianne. A World of Difference. 1999. (Which-Is-Which Bks.). (Illus.). 32p. (J). (gr. k-2). pap. 6.95 (978-1-55110-955-8(7)) Whitecap Bks., Ltd. CAN. *Dist:* Graphic Arts Ctr. Publishing Co.

—World of Difference: A Which Is Which Book. 1999. (978-0-606-18761-9(8)) Tandem Library Bks.

Yoyo Books. Animals: Mini Baby's First Library. 2005. 42p. bds. 4.95 (978-90-5843-805-8(8)) YoYo Bks. BEL. *Dist:* National Bk. Network.

Yoyo Books Staff. Animals Around Me: Animal Jigsaw Fun. 2004. 12p. bds. 9.95 (978-90-5843-550-7(4)) YoYo Bks. BEL. *Dist:* National Bk. Network.

—Baby Animals: Animal Jigsaw Fun. 2004. 12p. bds. 9.95 (978-90-5843-551-4(2)) YoYo Bks. BEL. *Dist:* National Bk. Network.

—Wild Animals: Animal Jigsaw Fun. 2004. 12p. bds. 9.95 (978-90-5843-552-1(0)) YoYo Bks. BEL. *Dist:* National Bk. Network.

Zarick, Nicole, ed. My First Touch & Feel Baby Animals. 2004. (Illus.). 36p. (J). bds. 5.99 (978-0-7894-9901-1(0)) Dorling Kindersley Publishing, Inc.

Ziegler, Mark. Critter Jitters: A Book of Animal Jokes. Haberstroh, Anne, illus. 2005. (Read-It! Readers Ser.). 24p. (C). (gr. 1-3). 18.60 (978-1-4048-0967-3(8)) Picture Window Bks.

Zimmermann, Dottie, creator. Interactive Sing-along Big Books Old MacDonald. 2007. (J). spiral bd. 12.95 (***978-1-58650-722-0(2)***) Super Duper Pubns.

Zoehfeld, Kathleen Weidner. What's That Grrr? Lift the Flap. 2001. 16p. (J). 5.99 (978-0-7364-1006-9(6)) Little Brown & Co.

Zollman, Pam. Animal Life Cycles. 2006. 144p. (J). (gr. 1-2). pap. 8.95 (978-0-516-24555-3(4) , Children's Pr.) Scholastic Library Publishing.

Zoo Animals. (Puzzle Shapes Ser.). 10p. (J). bds. (978-2-89393-788-5(8)) Phidal Publishing, Inc./Editions Phidal, Inc.

Zoobooks, 56 bks., Set. Incl. Alligators & Crocodiles. Wexo, John Bonnett. 24p. (gr. 3-12). lib. bdg. 19.95 (978-0-88682-220-0(3)); Animal Champions. Wexo, John Bonnett. 32p. (gr. 1-4). lib. bdg. 19.95 (978-0-88682-409-9(5)); Animal Champions 2. Shaw, Marjorie B. & Elwood, Ann. 24p. (gr. 1-4). lib. bdg. 19.95 (978-0-88682-774-8(4)); Animal Wonders. Wexo, John Bonnett. 32p. (gr. 1-4). lib. bdg. 14.95 (978-0-88682-407-5(9)); Apes. Wexo, John Bonnett. 24p. (gr. 2-12). lib. bdg. 19.95 (978-0-88682-265-1(3)); Baby Animals. Wexo, John Bonnett. 24p. (gr. 1-4). lib. bdg. 19.95 (978-0-88682-270-5(X)); Baby Animals 2. Elwood, Ann. 32p. (gr. 1-4). lib. bdg. 19.95 (978-0-88682-418-1(4)); Bats. Wood, Linda C. & Rink, Deane. 24p. (gr. 2-12). lib. bdg. 19.95 (978-0-88682-337-5(4)); Bears. Wexo, John Bonnett. 24p. (gr. 3-12). lib. bdg. 19.95 (978-0-88682-221-7(1)); Big Cats. Wexo, John Bonnett. 24p. (gr. 2-12). lib. bdg. 19.95 (978-0-88682-264-4(5)); Birds of Prey. Wexo, John Bonnett. 24p. (gr. 2-12). lib. bdg. 19.95 (978-0-88682-332-0(3)); Butterflies. Brust, Beth Wagner. 32p. (gr. 3-12). lib. bdg. 19.95 (978-0-88682-421-1(4)); Camels. Wexo, John Bonnett. 32p. (gr. 2-12). lib. bdg. 19.95 (978-0-88682-222-4(X)); Cheetahs. Wood, Linda C. & Jenson, Cynthia L. 32p. (gr. 2-12). lib. bdg. 19.95 (978-0-88682-417-4(6)); Chimpanzees & Bonobos. Elwood, Ann.

24p. (gr. 2-12). lib. bdg. 19.95 (978-0-88682-340-5(4)); Deer Family. Biel, Timothy Levi. 24p. (gr. 2-12). lib. bdg. 19.95 (978-0-88682-775-5(2)); Dinosaurs. Wexo, John Bonnett. 24p. (gr. 2-12). lib. bdg. 19.95 (978-0-88682-223-1(8)); Dolphins & Porpoises. Brust, Beth Wagner. 24p. (gr. 2-12). lib. bdg. 19.95 (978-0-88682-339-9(0)); Ducks, Geese & Swans. Wexo, John Bonnett. 24p. (gr. 3-12). lib. bdg. 19.95 (978-0-88682-224-8(6)); Eagles. Richardson, Adele D. 24p. (gr. 2-12). lib. bdg. 19.95 (978-0-88682-225-5(4)); Elephants. Wexo, John Bonnett. 24p. (gr. 2-12). lib. bdg. 19.95 (978-0-88682-226-2(2)); Endangered Animals. Wexo, John Bonnett. 24p. (gr. 2-12). lib. bdg. 19.95 (978-0-88682-269-6(6)); Giant Pandas. Wexo, John Bonnett. 24p. (gr. 2-12). lib. bdg. 19.95 (978-0-88682-228-6(9)); Giraffes. Wexo, John Bonnett. 24p. (gr. 2-12). lib. bdg. 19.95 (978-0-88682-334-4(X)); Gorillas. Wexo, John Bonnett. 32p. (gr. 2-12). lib. bdg. 19.95 (978-0-88682-423-5(0)); Hippos. Brust, Beth Wagner. 32p. (gr. 2-12). lib. bdg. 19.95 (978-0-88682-424-2(9)); Hummingbirds. Biel, Timothy Levi. 24p. (gr. 2-12). lib. bdg. 19.95 (978-0-88682-336-8(6)); Insects. Wexo, John Bonnett. 24p. (gr. 2-12). lib. bdg. 19.95 (978-0-88682-335-1(8)); Insects 2. Wexo, John Bonnett. 24p. (gr. 2-12). lib. bdg. 19.95 (978-0-88682-776-2(0)); Kangaroos. Brust, Beth Wagner. 32p. (gr. 2-12). lib. bdg. 19.95 (978-0-88682-425-9(7)); Koalas. Wexo, John Bonnett. 24p. (gr. 2-12). lib. bdg. 19.95 (978-0-88682-227-9(0)); Lions. Elwood, Ann & Estrada, Jackie. 32p. (gr. 2-12). lib. bdg. 19.95 (978-0-88682-422-8(2)); Little Cats. Wexo, John Bonnett. 32p. (gr. 2-12). lib. bdg. 19.95 (978-0-88682-413-6(3)); Night Animals. Wexo, John Bonnett. 24p. (gr. 2-12). lib. bdg. 19.95 (978-0-88682-777-9(9)); Old World Monkeys. Elwood, Ann. 32p. (gr. 3-12). lib. bdg. 19.95 (978-0-88682-419-8(2)); Orangutans. Wexo, John Bonnett. 32p. (gr. 2-12). lib. bdg. 19.95 (978-0-88682-412-9(5)); Ostriches, Emus, Rheas, Kiwis & Cassowaries. Elwood, Ann. 24p. (gr. 2-12). lib. bdg. 19.95 (978-0-88682-338-2(2)); Owls. Biel, Timothy Levi. 24p. (gr. 3-12). lib. bdg. 19.95 (978-0-88682-268-2(8)); Parrots. Wexo, John Bonnett. 32p. (gr. 2-12). lib. bdg. 19.95 (978-0-88682-408-2(7)); Penguins. Wexo, John Bonnett. 24p. (gr. 2-12). lib. bdg. 19.95 (978-0-88682-263-7(7)); Polar Bears. Biel, Timothy Levi. 32p. (gr. 2-12). lib. bdg. 19.95 (978-0-88682-414-3(1)); Rattlesnakes. Brust, Beth Wagner & Dorn, Bob. 32p. (gr. 2-12). lib. bdg. 19.95 (978-0-88682-426-6(5)); Rhinos. Wexo, John Bonnett. 24p. (gr. 2-12). lib. bdg. 19.95 (978-0-88682-333-7(1)); Sea Birds. Brust, Beth Wagner. 32p. (gr. 2-12). lib. bdg. 19.95 (978-0-88682-416-7(8)); Sea Otters. Brust, Beth Wagner. 32p. (gr. 2-12). lib. bdg. 19.95 (978-0-88682-415-0(X)), Seals, Sea Lions & Walruses. Wexo, John Bonnett. 24p. (gr. 2-12). lib. bdg. 19.95 (978-0-88682-271-2(8)); Sharing the World with Animals. Shaw, Marjorie B. & Elwood, Ann. 24p. (gr. 1-4). lib. bdg. 19.95 (978-0-88682-778-6(7)); Sharks. Wexo, John Bonnett. 24p. (gr. 2-12). lib. bdg. 19.95 (978-0-88682-229-3(7)); Skunks & Their Relatives. Biel, Timothy Levi. 24p. (gr. 2-12). lib. bdg. 19.95 (978-0-88682-779-3(5)); Snakes. Wexo, John Bonnett. 24p. (gr. 2-12). lib. bdg. 19.95 (978-0-88682-331-3(5)); Spiders. Biel, Timothy Levi. 32p. (gr. 2-12). lib. bdg. 19.95 (978-0-88682-410-5(9)); Tigers. Biel, Timothy Levi. 24p. (gr. 2-12). lib. bdg. 19.95 (978-0-88682-266-8(1)); Turtles. Biel, Timothy Levi. 32p. (gr. 2-12). lib. bdg. 19.95 (978-0-88682-411-2(7)); Whales. Wexo, John Bonnett. 24p. (gr. 2-12). lib. bdg. 19.95 (978-0-88682-272-9(6)); Wild Dogs. Biel, Timothy Levi. 24p. (gr. 2-12). lib. bdg. 19.95 (978-0-88682-780-9(9)); Wild Horses. Wexo, John Bonnett. 24p. (gr. 2-12). lib. bdg. 19.95 (978-0-88682-781-6(7)); Wolves. Wexo, John Bonnett. 24p. (gr. 2-12). lib. bdg. 19.95 (978-0-88682-267-5(X)); Zebras. Wood, Linda C. 32p. (gr. 2-12). lib. bdg. 19.95 (978-0-88682-420-4(6)); (YA). 1995. (Illus.). 1157.10 (978-0-88682-238-5(6) , Creative Education) Creative Co., The.

Zoobooks Set, 58 vols., set. 2002. (Zoobooks Ser.). (Illus.). (J). (gr. k-7). pap. 135.58 (978-1-888153-65-1(2)) Wildlife Education, Ltd.

Zumbusch, Amelie von. Safari Animals, 6 bks., Set. Incl. Cheetahs. lib. bdg. 21.25 (978-1-4042-3614-1(7) , 1260066); Elephants. lib. bdg. 21.25 (978-1-4042-3616-5(3)); Giraffes. lib. bdg. 21.25 (978-1-4042-3615-8(5)); Hippos. lib. bdg. 21.25 (978-1-4042-3617-2(1)); Lions. lib. bdg. 21.25 (978-1-4042-3612-7(0)); Zebras. lib. bdg. 21.25 (978-1-4042-3613-4(9) , 1266071); (Illus.). 24p. (J). (gr. k-3). 2007. , PowerKids Pr. 2007. Set lib. bdg. 127.50 (978-1-4042-3597-7(3)) Rosen Publishing Group, Inc., The.

Zuravicky, Orli. Amazing Animals: Multiplying Multidigit Numbers by a One-Digit Number with Renaming. 2004. (PowerMath Ser.). (Illus.). 24p. (J). lib. bdg. (978-0-8239-8861-7(9)); lib. bdg. 21.25 (978-0-8239-8964-5(X)) Rosen Publishing Group, Inc., The. (PowerKids Pr.).

ANIMALS—ANATOMY

see Anatomy, Comparative

ANIMALS, AQUATIC

see Fresh-Water Animals; Marine Animals

ANIMALS—COLOR

Los Colores (Touch & Feel - Animal Colours) 2000. (SPA., Illus.). 10p. (J). (ps). pap. (978-950-11-1419-5(8)) Sigmar.

Les Couleurs des Animaux. 2005. (FRE & ENG., Illus.). 16p. (J). (ps). per. 5.95 (978-1-59572-031-3(6)) Star Bright Bks., Inc.

Grambo, Rebecca L. Colors. 2002. (Amazing Animals Ser.). (Illus.). 32p. (gr. 2-5). 18.95 (978-1-58952-143-8(9)) Rourke Publishing, LLC.

Jenkins, Steve. Living Color. 2007. (Illus.). 32p. (J). (gr. 3-5). 17.00 (***978-0-618-70897-0(9)***) Houghton Mifflin Co. Trade & Reference Div.

Lambilly, Elisabeth de. Colorful Animals. 2006. (Illus.). 14p. (J). (***978-0-8368-8159-2(1)***) Stevens, Gareth Inc.

Maze, Stephanie, ed. Beautiful Moments in the Wild: Animals & Their Colors. (Moments in the Wild Ser.). (Illus.). (J). 2006. 36p. pap. 8.00 (978-0-9769542-5-5(7)); 2002. 32p. 15.00 (978-0-9707768-7-7(X)) Moonstone Pr.

—Momentos hermosos en el reino Animal: Los animales y sus Colores. 2006. (Momentos en el reino Animal Ser.). (SPA., Illus.). 36p. (J). pap. 8.00 (978-0-9769542-7-9(3)) Moonstone Pr.

Momentos Hermosos en el Veino Animal: Los Animales y Sus Colores. 2002. (Momentos en el Reino Animal Ser.: Vol. 4). (ENG & SPA., Illus.). 32p. (J). (ps-1). 15.00 (978-0-9707768-6-0(1)) Moonstone Pr.

Patent, Dorothy Hinshaw. Bold & Bright, Black & White Animals. Jubb, Kendahl Jan, illus. 1998. 32p. (J). (gr. k-3). 15.95 (978-0-8027-8672-2(3)); lib. bdg. 16.85 (978-0-8027-8673-9(1)) Walker & Co.

Petty, Kate. Animal Camouflage & Defense. 2004. (Nature Files Ser.). (Illus.). 32p. (J). (gr. 4-8). 28.00 (978-0-7910-8213-3(X) , Chelsea Hse.) Facts On File, Inc.

Salzmann, Mary Elizabeth. What Has Spots? 2007. (Creature Features Ser.). (ENG., Illus.). 24p. (J). (ps-3). lib. bdg. 24.21 (***978-1-59928-872-7(9)*** , Super SandCastle) ABDO Publishing Co.

—What Has Stripes? 2007. (Creature Features Ser.). (ENG., Illus.). 24p. (J). (ps-3). lib. bdg. 24.21 (***978-1-59928-873-4(7)*** , Super SandCastle) ABDO Publishing Co.

Shattil, Wendy & Rozinski, Bob, photos by. On the Trail of Colorado Critters: Wildlife Watching for Kids. 2000. (Illus.). 96p. (J). (gr. 4-7). 14.95 (978-1-56579-350-7(1) , A195) Westcliffe Pubs.

Stockland, Patricia M. Red Eyes or Blue Feathers: A Book about Animal Colors. Ouren, Todd, illus. 2005. (Animal Wise Ser.). 24p. (C). (gr. k-2). 22.60 (978-1-4048-0931-4(7)) Picture Window Bks.

Tildes, Phyllis L. Animals Brightly Colored. Tildes, Phyllis L., illus. 1998. (Illus.). 32p. (J). (ps-3). pap. 6.95 (978-0-88106-978-5(7)) Charlesbridge Publishing, Inc.

Whitehouse, Patricia, tr. Hiding in a Desert. 2003. (Heinemann First Library). (Illus.). 32p. (J). pap. 6.50 (978-1-4034-3186-8(8)) Heinemann Library.

ANIMALS, CRUELTY TO

see Animals—Treatment

ANIMALS—DICTIONARIES

Amos, Janine. Scholastic First Encyclopedia: Animals & Nature. 2000. (978-0-606-18598-1(4)) Tandem Library Bks.

Animal Kingdom, Set. 2002. (J). (gr. k-4). lib. bdg. 854.00 (978-1-57765-531-2(1)) ABDO Publishing Co.

Arlon, Penelope & Dorling Kindersley Publishing Staff. First Animal Encyclopedia. 2004. (Dk First Reference Ser.). (Illus.). 160p. (J). 15.99 (978-0-7566-0227-7(0)) Dorling Kindersley Publishing, Inc.

Armentrout, David & Armentrout, Patricia. Animals. 2003. (50 Words about Ser.). (Illus.). 32p. (gr. 2-4). 19.95 (978-1-58952-341-8(5)) Rourke Publishing, LLC.

—Dinosaurs. 2003. (50 Words about Ser.). (Illus.). 32p. (gr. 2-4). 19.95 (978-1-58952-342-5(3)) Rourke Publishing, LLC.

Brooks, Felicity, ed. First Encyclopedia of Animals. 2000. (First Encyclopedia Ser.). (Illus.). 64p. (J). (ps-3). pap. 9.95 (978-0-7460-2839-1(3)) EDC Publishing.

Burnie, David. The Kingfisher Illustrated Animal Encyclopedia. 2000. (Kingfisher Encyclopedias Ser.). (Illus.). 320p. (J). (gr. 5-8). tchr. ed. 27.95 (978-0-7534-5283-7(9) , Kingfisher) Houghton Mifflin Co. Trade & Reference Div.

Butterfield, Moira. Who Am I?, 4 vols., Set. Incl. Cow. lib. bdg. 16.95 (978-1-929298-89-1(7)); Horse. lib. bdg. 16.95 (978-1-929298-90-7(0)); Pig. lib. bdg. 16.95 (978-1-929298-91-4(9)); Rooster. lib. bdg. 16.95 (978-1-929298-92-1(7)); (Illus.). 32p. (J). (ps-1). 2000. Set lib. bdg. 67.80 (978-1-929298-93-8(5)) Chrysalis Education.

Capstone Press Staff. Bridgestone Animals, 18 bks. 1998. (J). (gr. 1-5). pap. (978-0-516-29798-9(8) , Children's Pr.) Scholastic Library Publishing.

Chinery, Michael. Animals in the Wild, 24 vols. 2005. (Illustrated Wildlife Encyclopedia Ser.). (Illus.). 264p. pap. -19.99 (978-0-7548-1441-2(6) , Lorenz Bks.) Anness Publishing GBR. *Dist:* National Bk. Network.

Chinery, Michael, ed. Collier's Illustrated Encyclopedia of Animals: From Aardvark to Zorille - & 2000 Other Animals. 2000. (Illus.). 365p. (YA). reprint ed. 40.00 (978-0-7881-9457-3(7)) DIANE Publishing Co.

Daniels, Lucy. Animal Ark: Animals in the Ark. l.t. ed. 2001. 200p. (J). 16.95 (978-0-7540-6159-5(0) , Galaxy Children's Large Print) BBC Audiobooks America.

Dorling Kindersley Publishing Staff. My Little Encyclopedia of Animals. 2006. 160p. (J). 8.99 (978-0-7566-2540-5(8)) Dorling Kindersley Publishing, Inc.

—Visual Encyclopedia of Animals. 3rd ed. 2005. (Illus.). 512p. (J). pap. 12.99 (978-0-7566-0701-2(9)) Dorling Kindersley Publishing, Inc.

Dowswell, Paul. First Encyclopedia of Animals. (First Encyclopedias Ser.). (Illus.). 64p. (J). 2004. (SPA.). (gr. 3 up). pap. 9.95 (978-0-7945-0215-7(6) , Usborne); 2004. (SPA., (gr. 3 up). lib. bdg. 17.95 (978-1-58086-426-8(0)); 2000. (ps-3). lib. bdg. 17.95 (978-1-58086-275-2(6)) EDC Publishing.

—Little Encyclopedia of Animals. 2005. (Illus.). 64p. (J). (ps-ps). 6.95 (978-0-7945-1093-0(0) , Usborne) EDC Publishing.

Dowswell, Paul, ed. First Encyclopedia of Animals. 2000. (First Encyclopedia Ser.). (Illus.). 64p. (YA). (ps-3). pap. 9.95 (978-0-7460-3400-2(8)) EDC Publishing.

Farndon, John & Kirkwood, Jon. Kingfisher First Encyclopedia of Animals. 2005. (Illus.). 144p. (J). (978-1-4156-2475-3(5) , Kingfisher) Houghton Mifflin Co. Trade & Reference Div.

Grolier Incorporated Staff, contrib. by. Amazing Animals of the World. 2007. (J). (***978-0-7172-6226-7(X)); (978-0-7172-6227-4(8)); (978-0-7172-6228-1(6)); (978-0-7172-6229-8(4)); (978-0-7172-6230-4(8)); (978-0-7172-6231-1(6)); (978-0-7172-6232-8(4)); (978-0-7172-6233-5(2)); (978-0-7172-6234-2(0)); (978-0-7172-6235-9(9))*** Grolier, Ltd.

—Amazing Animals of the World, 10 vols., Set 1. rev. ed. 2007. (J). (gr. 3-9). lib. bdg. 199.00 (***978-0-7172-6225-0(1)*** , Grolier) Scholastic Library Publishing.

Howell, Laura & Rogers, Kirsteen. Animal World. 2004. (Internet-Linked Library of Science). 64p. (J). pap. 9.95 (978-0-7945-0083-2(8) , Usborne); lib. bdg. 17.95 (978-1-58086-372-8(8)) EDC Publishing.

Kingfisher Editors, ed. Kingfisher First Encyclopedia of Animals. 2005. (Kingfisher First Reference Ser.). (Illus.). 144p. (J). (gr. k-3). pap., pap. 10.95 (978-0-7534-5922-5(1) , Kingfisher) Houghton Mifflin Co. Trade & Reference Div.

Kirkwood, Jon & Farndon, John. The Kingfisher First Animal Encyclopedia. 1998. (Kingfisher First Reference Ser.). (Illus.). 160p. (J). (gr. k-3). tchr. ed. 16.95 (978-0-7534-5135-9(2) , Kingfisher) Houghton Mifflin Co. Trade & Reference Div.

Klevansky, Rhonda, et al. The Illustrated Wildlife Encyclopedia: Big Mammals. 2001. (Illus.). 256p. pap. 19.95 (978-1-84215-526-4(1) , Southwater) Anness Publishing GBR. *Dist:* National Bk. Network.

Larousse Mexico Staff, ed. Mi Primer Larousse de Animales. 2006. (Mi Primer Larousse Ser.). (Illus.). 160p. (gr. k-3). 19.95 (978-970-22-1086-3(0)) Larousse, Ediciones, S. A. de C. V. MEX. *Dist:* Houghton Mifflin Co. Trade & Reference Div.

Larousse Staff. The Peter Bedricks Young Peoples Encyclopedia: Plants & Animals. 2000. (Peter Bedrick Young People's Encyclopedia Ser.). (Illus.). 103p. (J). (gr. 5-9). 24.95 (978-0-87226-623-0(0) , 66230B, Bedrick, Peter Bks.) School Specialty Publishing.

Moore, Donald. Wonderful World of Animals. 2006. (Illus.). 128p. (gr. 1-4). 12.99 (978-0-7868-4961-1(4)) Disney Pr.

National Geographic Society Staff, et al. Encyclopedia of Animals. 2006. (Illus.). 192p. (YA). (gr. 3 up). 24.95 (978-0-7922-5936-7(X)); lib. bdg. 38.90 (978-0-7922-5937-4(8)) National Geographic Society. (National Geographic Children's Bks.).

Pet Dictionary: An a to Z of Animal Companions. 2005. (Illus.). 64p. (J). pap. (***978-0-439-75459-0(3)***) Scholastic, Inc.

Phillips, Sarah. My 2 in 1 Animal Picture Dictionary. 2007. (Illus.). 64p. (J). (gr. k-2). 6.95 (978-1-84610-465-7(3)) Make Believe Ideas GBR. *Dist:* Ingram Pub. Services.

Pringle, Laurence P. Scholastic Encyclopedia of Animals. Wu, Norbert, illus. 2001. 128p. (gr. 3-6). pap. 19.95 (978-0-590-52253-3(1) , Scholastic Reference) Scholastic, Inc.

Raintree Steck-Vaughn Staff. Encyclopedias of Animals, 2 bks., Set. 2nd ed. Incl. Encyclopedia of Birds. pap. 68.50 (978-0-7398-0684-5(X)); Encyclopedia of Fishes. lib. bdg. 47.95 (978-0-7398-0683-8(1)); Encyclopedia of Mammals. pap. 68.50 (978-0-7398-0682-1(3)); Encyclopedia of Reptiles & Amphibians. lib. bdg. 47.95 (978-0-7398-0685-2(8)); 240p. (J). (gr. 4-7). 1999. (Illus.). 1998. Set pap. 137.00 (978-0-7398-0686-9(6)) Raintree.

Taplin, Sam. Little Encyclopedia of Dinosaurs. 2005. (Illus.). 64p. (J). (ps-ps). 6.95 (978-0-7945-1087-9(6) , Usborne) EDC Publishing.

Taylor & Kerrod, Robin. Encyclopedia of Elephants, Big Cats, Bears & Whales. 2000. (Illus.). 256p. (J). 29.95 (978-1-84215-071-9(5) , Southwater) Anness Publishing GBR. *Dist:* Hachette Bk. Group.

Taylor, Barbara. Animal Encyclopedia. Parsons, Jayne, ed. 2000. (Dorling Kindersley Ser.). (Illus.). 376p. (J). (gr. 3-7). 29.99 (978-0-7894-6499-6(3)) Dorling Kindersley Publishing, Inc.

Wild Wild World. (Illus.). (J). Date not set. 48p. 5.98 (978-1-4054-0208-8(3)); 2003. 256p. 12.98 (978-1-4054-1541-5(X)) Parragon, Inc.

Young, Carol. Los Animales del Mundo. 2004. Tr. of Great Animal Search. (SPA., Illus.). 48p. (J). (ps-3). pap. 9.95 (978-0-7460-3656-3(6)) EDC Publishing.

ANIMALS—DISEASES

see Veterinary Medicine

ANIMALS, DOMESTIC

see Domestic Animals

ANIMALS, EXTINCT

see Extinct Animals

ANIMALS—FICTION

see also Fables

Aardema, Verna. Por Que Zumban los Mosquitos en los Oidos de la Gente. Blanco, Osvaldo, tr. 1998. (SPA., Illus.). 32p. (J). (ps-3). 18.99 (978-0-8037-2298-9(2) , VK7503, Dial) Penguin Group (USA) Inc.

Aber, Linda Williams. Who's Got Spots? Fiammenghi, Gioia, illus. 2000. (Math Matters Ser.). 32p. (J). (ps-3). pap. 4.95 (978-1-57565-099-9(1)) Kane Pr., The.

—Who's Got Spots? Fiammenghi, Gioia, illus. 2000. 32p. (J). (ps-3). lib. bdg. 12.95 (978-0-613-39375-1(9)) Tandem Library Bks.

—Who's Got Spots? 2000. (Math Matters Ser.). (J). (978-0-606-20184-1(X)) Tandem Library Bks.

Abernathy, Francis E. How the Critters Created Texas. Sargent, Ben, illus. 2nd rev. ed. 1998. 46p. (J). (gr. 1-6). lib. bdg. 14.95 (978-0-936650-14-2(1)) Temple, Ellen C. Publishing, Inc.

Abernathy, Mary. Tales of the Black Jack Forest. 2002. per. (978-1-930493-61-2(4)) Athena Pr.

Aboff, Marcie. Alex & Marty Run Wild. 2005. (Madagascar Ser.). 32p. (J). pap. 3.99 (978-0-439-69631-9(3)) Scholastic, Inc.

Aboff, Marcie, ed. Animals with Attitude. 2006. (Over the Hedge Ser.: No. 1). (Illus.). 48p. (J). pap. 3.99 (978-0-439-80147-8(8)) Scholastic, Inc.

Absolutely Not! Individual Title Six-Packs. (Story Steps Ser.). (gr. k-2). 29.00 (978-0-7635-9613-2(2)) Rigby Education.

Ackerman, Tova. Group Soup. Gorbachev, Valeri, illus. (Orig.). pap. 6.95 (978-0-9720183-0-2(1)) Puppetry in Practice.

Ada, Alma Flor. Cuentos para Todo el Ano Cuaderno de Actividades. 2001. (SPA.). (J). (gr. k-3). pap. 10.95 (978-1-58105-241-1(3)) Santillana USA Publishing Co., Inc.

—Dear Peter Rabbit. Tryon, Leslie, illus. 2006. (Stories to Go! Ser.).Tr. of Dear Peter Rabbit. 32p. (J). pap. 4.99 (978-1-4169-1233-0(9) , Aladdin) Simon & Schuster Children's Publishing.

—One More Friend. Fatus, Sophie, illus. 2007. 24p. (J). (***978-0-15-206278-1(5)***); pap. (***978-0-15-206284-2(X)***) Harcourt Trade Pubs.

Ada, Alma Flor. Stories the Year 'Round. 2001. (J). (gr. k-3). pap., tchr.'s training gde. ed. 43.95 (978-1-58105-238-1(3)) Santillana USA Publishing Co., Inc.

Ada, Alma Flor & Campay, F. Isabel, contrib. by. Ojos del Jaguar. (Literature Collection of Puertas Al Sol Ser.). (SPA.). 48p. (J). (gr. k-6). pap. 13.95 (978-1-58105-799-7(7)) Santillana USA Publishing Co., Inc.

Ada, Alma Flor & Campoy, F. Isabel. El Nuevo Hogar de los Siete Cabritos. Escriva, Viví, illus. (Gateway to the Sun Ser.). (SPA.). 32p. (J). (gr. k-6). pap. 13.95 (978-1-58105-755-3(5)) Santillana USA Publishing Co., Inc.

—Ratoncito Perez, Cartero. Escriva, Sandra Lopez, illus. (Gateway to the Sun Ser.). (SPA.). 32p. (J). (gr. k-6). pap. 13.95 (978-1-58105-757-7(1)) Santillana USA Publishing Co., Inc.

—Uno, Dos, Tres, Dime Quien Es! Escriva, Viví, illus. (Gateway to the Sun Ser.). (SPA.). 32p. (J). (gr. k-6). pap. 13.95 (978-1-58105-810-9(1)) Santillana USA Publishing Co., Inc.

Adams, Mark Wayne. Miss Mary's Missing Book Bag. Adams, Mark Wayne, illus. l.t. ed. 2004. (Illus.). (J). (gr. k-6). pap. 8.95 (978-1-59616-000-2(4)) Caballo Bks.

Adams, Michelle Medlock. The Sparrow's Easter Song. Eldridge, Marion, illus. 2003. 32p. (J). 14.95 (978-0-8249-5470-3(X)) Ideals Pubns.

Adlerman, Daniel. Africa Calling, Nighttime Falling. Adlerman, Kim, illus. 2001. 32p. (J). (ps-2). pap. 6.95 (978-1-58089-025-0(3)) Charlesbridge Publishing, Inc.

Adlerman, Daniel, ed. Africa Calling, Nighttime Falling. 2001. (J). 13.75 (978-0-606-20533-7(0)) Tandem Library Bks.

Aesop & Perrault, Charles. Animal Fables, 4 bks., Set. Roederer, Charlotte et al, illus. 2007. (Classic Fairy Tales Ser.). 112p. (J). (ps-3). 19.95 (***978-0-7892-0951-1(9)***) Abbeville Pr., Inc.

Agard, John & Paul, Korky. Brer Rabbit & the Great Tug-O-War. 1998. (Illus.). 32p. (J). (ps-2). 13.95 (978-0-7641-5077-7(4)) Barron's Educational Series, Inc.

Ahlberg, Allan. Chicken, Chips & Peas, Vol. 1. (Illus.). 32p. (J). pap. 9.95 (978-0-14-056397-9(0)) Penguin Group (USA) Inc.

—The Improbable Cat. Bailey, Peter, illus. 2004. 128p. (gr. 5). 9.95 (978-0-385-73186-7(8) , Delacorte Bks. for Young Readers) Random Hse. Children's Bks.

—Slow Dog Falling. (Illus.). 32p. (J). pap. 9.95 (978-0-14-056398-6(9)) Penguin Group (USA) Inc.

Ahmed, Said Salah. The Lion's Share/Qayb Libaax: A Somali Folktale. Dupre, Kelly, illus. 2006. 32p. (J). (ps-3). pap. 7.95 (***978-1-931016-13-1(5)***) Minnesota Humanities Commission.

Aigner-Clark, Julie. Animal Match. Zaidi, Nadeem, illus. 2005. (Baby Einstein Ser.). 8p. (J). (ps-17). bds. 7.99 (978-0-7868-5532-2(0)) Baby Einstein Co., LLC, The.

—Baby Einstein: Rain-forest Discoveries, Spanish-Language Edition. Zaidi, Nadeem, illus. 2005. (Baby Einstein: Libros de Carton Ser.). (SPA.). 10p. (J). bds. 9.95 (978-970-718-306-3(3) , Silver Dolphin en Español) Advanced Marketing, S. de R. L. de C. V. MEX. *Dist:* Perseus Distribution.

—Jane's Animal Expedition. Zaidi, Nadeem, illus. 2002. (Baby Einstein Ser.). 16p. (J). bds. 6.99 (978-0-7868-0841-0(1)) Hyperion Bks. for Children.

Aigner-Clark, Julie & Godwin, Parke. Baby Noah - World Animals. Zaidi, Nadeem, illus. 2005. (Baby Einstein Ser.). 16p. (ps-17). 5.99 (978-0-7868-5476-9(6)) Hyperion Bks. for Children.

Aiken, Joan. Fog Hounds, Wind Cat, Sea Mice. 2nd ed. 2002. (Illus.). 94p. (J). pap. (978-0-340-68131-2(4) , Hodder Children's Books) Hodder Children's Division.

Aikins, Dave, illus. Race to the Tower of Power. 2005. (Backyardigans Ser.: Vol. 1). 24p. (J). pap. 3.99 (978-1-4169-0799-2(8) , Simon Spotlight/Nickelodeon) Simon & Schuster Children's Publishing.

Albee, Sarah. Max Can Fix That. Schick, Joel, illus. 2006. (Step-By-Step Readers Ser.). (J). pap. (978-1-59939-055-0(8) , Reader's Digest Young Families, Inc.) Reader's Digest Children's Publishing, Inc.

Albers, Everett C. Lewis & Clark Animal ABC Book: As Told By Seaman the Dog. Eslinger, Kimberly, illus. l.t. ed. 2001. 32p. (J). pap. 3.95 (978-0-9674002-3-5(6)) United Printing.

Alborough, Jez. Cuddly Dudley. Alborough, Jez, illus. 2002. (J). 13.83 (978-1-4046-0155-0(4)) Book Wholesalers, Inc.

—Duck in the Truck. Alborough, Jez, illus. 2008. (Illus.). 32p. (J). pap. 7.95 (***978-1-933605-76-0(6)***) Kane/Miller Bk. Pubs., Inc.

A B

Alborough, Jez. Fix-It Duck. Alborough, Jez, illus. 2002. (Illus.). 40p. (J). (ps-1). 16.99 (978-0-06-000699-0(4)) HarperCollins Pubs.

Alcamo, John. A Musical Mystery. 2004. 62p. pap. 12.95 (978-1-4137-3457-7(X)) PublishAmerica, Inc.

Alcantara, Ricardo. Perro y Gato. Gusti, illus. 2001. (SPA.). 32p. (J). (ps-2). (978-84-246-3903-7(0) , GL3147) La Galera, S.A. Editorial ESP. *Dist:* Lectorum Pubns., Inc.

Alex, Ben. Fables of Spiritual Wisdom: From Around the World. Imhoff, Ruth, illus. 1998. 70p. 16.95 (978-87-7247-532-5(3)) Scandinavia Publishing Hse. DNK. *Dist:* National Bk. Network.

Alexander, Lee. Arnie Hackett. Hooper, Kevin T., illus. l.t. ed. 2002. 127p. (J). pap. 8.95 (978-0-9714782-5-1(2)) Crossroads Pr.

Alexander, Marge. Adventures at the Grandparents' House. 2001. 96p. 9.99 (978-1-58169-064-4(9) , Evergreen Pr.) Genesis Communications, Inc.

Allan-Meyer, Kathleen. Little Bear's Big Adventure. Garvin, Elaine, illus. 1998. 32p. (J). (ps-1). pap. 6.49 (978-1-57924-060-8(7)) Jones, Bob Univ. Pr.

Allen, Jonathan. I'm Not Cute. 2006. (Illus.). 32p. (ps-k). 14.99 (978-0-7868-3720-5(9)) Hyperion Pr.

Allen, Margaret. Cat & Dog at the Circus. 1999. (ps-2). lib. bdg. 10.65 (978-0-613-34110-3(4)) Tandem Library Bks.

—Splish, Splash. 1999. (ps-2). lib. bdg. 10.65 (978-0-613-34489-0(8)) Tandem Library Bks.

Allen, Teresa R. Laura, the Bichon Frise: My New Home. 2004. 31p. pap. 17.95 (978-1-4137-3525-3(8)) PublishAmerica, Inc.

Allevato, Diane. Sausage Patty. 1998. (J). per. 3.99 (978-0-9644062-1-6(7)) Animal Place.

Alvin, John & Alvin, Andrea, illus. Simba's Pride. 1998. (Classic Storybook Ser.). 96p. (J). (ps-3). 7.99 (978-1-57082-876-8(8)) Mouse Works.

Amery, H. Where's Woolly? Cartwright, Stephen, illus. 2004. (Treasury of Farmyard Tales Ser.). 16p. (J). (gr. 1 up). pap. 7.95 (978-0-7945-0405-2(1)) EDC Publishing.

Amery, Heather. El Cerdito Chancho. Cartwright, Stephen, illus. 2004. (Titles in Spanish Ser.). (SPA.). 10p. (J). bds. 3.99 (978-0-7460-6105-3(6) , Usborne) EDC Publishing.

—Where's Woolly? Cartwright, Stephen, illus. 1998. (Farmyard Tales Ser.). 16p. (J). (ps-2). pap. 7.95 (978-0-7460-3012-7(6)); lib. bdg. 15.95 (978-1-58086-127-4(X)) EDC Publishing.

Amma, Jill. The Indaba Tree Odyssey: An African Tale. 2006. 360p. pap. 18.95 (978-0-7414-3172-1(6)) Infinity Publishing.

Anastas, Margaret. Mommy's Best Kisses. Winter, Susan, illus. 32p. (J). (ps-1). 2003. 15.99 (978-0-06-623601-8(0)); 2000. reprint ed. pap. 6.99 (978-0-06-443839-1(2)) HarperCollins Pubs.

Anaya, Hector. Cuenta, Cuenta. Moreno, Sergio, illus. 2nd rev. ed. 2004. (Castillo de la Lectura Verde Ser.). (SPA.). 184p. (J). pap. 7.95 (978-970-20-0135-5(8)) Castillo, Ediciones, S. A. de C. V. MEX. *Dist:* Macmillan.

Anaya, Rudolfo A. Roadrunner's Dance. Diaz, David, illus. 2000. 32p. (gr. k-4). 16.49 (978-0-7868-2209-6(0)) Disney Pr.

—Roadrunner's Dance. Diaz, David, illus. 2000. 32p. (gr. k-4). 15.99 (978-0-7868-0254-8(5)) Hyperion Bks. for Children.

Andersen, Hans Christian. The Racers: A Tale about Fairness. Goodell, Jon, illus. 2007. (J). (***978-1-59939-090-1(6)*** , Reader's Digest Young Families, Inc.) Reader's Digest Children's Publishing, Inc.

Andersen, Hans Christian & White, Mus. For Sure! for Sure! Czernecki, Stefan, illus. 2004. 32p. 16.95 (978-0-87483-742-1(1)) August Hse. Pubs., Inc.

Anderson, Airlie. A Very Furry Flap Book. 2004. (Illus.). 10p. (J). bds. 5.95 (978-1-58925-701-6(4) , tiger tales) ME Media LLC.

Anderson, Airlie, illus. A Very Patchy Flap Book. 2004. 10p. (J). bds. 5.95 (978-1-58925-702-3(2) , tiger tales) ME Media LLC.

—A Very Stripy Flap Book. 2004. 10p. (J). bds. 5.95 (978-1-58925-704-7(9) , tiger tales) ME Media LLC.

Anderson, Doug. Too Big to Dance. Anderson, Sara, illus. 2004. 32p. (J). 15.95 (978-1-59354-046-3(9)) Handprint Bks.

Anderson, Jane. Anansi the Spider & the Sky King: A Tale from Africa. 2006. 23.00 (***978-1-4108-6175-7(9)***) Benchmark Education Co.

Anderson, Janet. Going Through the Gate. 2000. (Illus.). (J). (978-0-606-18407-6(4)) Tandem Library Bks.

Anderson, Lena. Tick-Tock. 1998. (J). (978-0-385-32554-7(1) , Doubleday Bks. for Young Readers) Random Hse. Children's Bks.

Andrews, Julie. The Little Grey Men: A Story for the Young in Heart. Watkins-Pitchford, Denys, illus. 2004. 304p. (J). 17.89 (978-0-06-055449-1(5) , Julie Andrews Collection) HarperCollins Pubs.

Andrews, Julie & "BB". The Little Grey Men: A Story for the Young in Heart. Watkins-Pitchford, Denys, illus. ed. 2004. 304p. (J). 17.99 (978-0-06-055448-4(7) , Julie Andrews Collection) HarperCollins Pubs.

Angers, Michelle. The Animal Garden. 2004. 31p. pap. 17.95 (978-1-4137-5270-0(5)) PublishAmerica, Inc.

The Animal Band 6 Packs: Individual Title. 32p. (gr. 2 up). 37.00 (978-0-7635-9223-3(4)) Rigby Education.

Animal Farm. 1999. (YA). 11.95 (978-1-56137-306-2(0)) Novel Units, Inc.

Animal Friends Squeaky. 2005. (J). bds. (978-1-4194-0094-0(0)) Paradise Pr., Inc.

Animal Friends Squeaky - Cat. 2005. (J). bds. (978-1-4194-0092-6(4)) Paradise Pr., Inc.

Animal Parade. (J). 26.20 (978-0-8136-8441-3(2)); 1998. pap. (978-0-8136-8306-5(8)) Modern Curriculum Pr.

The Animal Parade. (J). 59.50 (978-0-8136-8002-6(6)) Modern Curriculum Pr.

Animal Race. 2004. (J). (978-1-932570-25-0(X)) Literacy Footprints Inc.

Animal Tales: Bunnies, Cats & Daring Ducks. 2002. (Animal Tales Ser.). 96p. (J). pap. 6.95 (978-0-7894-8492-5(7)) Dorling Kindersley Publishing, Inc.

Animal Tales: Frogs, Mice & Wiggly Worms. 2002. 96p. (J). pap. 6.95 (978-0-7894-8494-9(3)) Dorling Kindersley Publishing, Inc.

Animal Tales: Hippos, Chimps & Creepy Crocodiles. 2002. (Animal Tales Ser.). 96p. (J). pap. 6.95 (978-0-7894-8493-2(5)) Dorling Kindersley Publishing, Inc.

Animal Tales: Lions, Tigers, & Big, Bad Bears. 2002. (Animal Tales Ser.). 96p. (J). pap. 6.95 (978-0-7894-8491-8(9)) Dorling Kindersley Publishing, Inc.

Animal Walk. 2005. (J). (978-1-58453-300-9(5)) Pioneer Valley Educational Pr., Inc.

The Animals, 6 vols., Pack. (Sails Literacy Ser.). 16p. (gr. k up). 27.00 (978-0-7635-4398-3(5)) Rigby Education.

Animals at Play (English), 5 bks. vols., Set. 2000. (J). (978-1-58805-102-8(1)) DS-Max USA, Inc.

Animals at School. 2001. (J). (978-1-58453-135-7(5)) Pioneer Valley Educational Pr., Inc.

The Animals Went to Bed: Individual Title-Six Packs. (Chiquilibros Ser.). (gr. k-1). 23.00 (978-0-7635-0457-1(2)) Rigby Education.

Animaniacs in Thingamagigging. (Look & Find Bks.). (Illus.). 24p. (J). (ps-1). 14.98 (978-0-7853-1623-7(X) , PI15) Publications International, Ltd.

Antonelli, Gina. Who Is Porky? Antonelli, Gina, illus. 2002. (Illus.). 44p. (Orig.). (J). 10.99 (978-1-886383-02-9(2) , Little Blue Works) Windstorm Creative.

—Who Is Welby? Antonelli, Gina, illus. 2002. (Illus.). 44p. (J). 10.99 (978-1-886383-41-8(3) , Little Blue Works) Windstorm Creative.

Anza, Ana Luisa. El Misterio de la Casa Chueca (y el Bulto Color Mugre) Escobar, Antonio Rocha, illus. rev. ed. 2006. (Castillo de la Lectura Naranja Ser.). (SPA.). 120p. (J). pap. 7.95 (978-970-20-0200-0(1)) Castillo, Ediciones, S. A. de C. V. MEX. *Dist:* Macmillan.

Aoki, Hisako. Santa's Favorite Story: Santa Tells the Story of the First Christmas. Gantschev, Ivan, illus. 2007. 28p. (J). (ps-3). 9.99 (***978-1-4169-5029-5(X)***) Simon & Schuster Children's Publishing.

Apperley, Dawn. Crash Bang, Thud! 2002. (Illus.). 25p. (J). (978-0-340-78800-4(3) , Hodder & Stoughton) Hodder General Publishing Division.

—Crash Bang, Thud! 2002. (Illus.). 32p. (J). pap. 9.99 (978-0-340-78801-1(1) , Hodder & Stoughton) Hodder General Publishing Division GBR. *Dist:* Trafalgar Square Publishing.

—Good Night, Sleep Tight, Little Bunnies. Apperley, Dawn, illus. 2002. (Illus.). 32p. (J). (ps-k). pap. 9.95 (978-0-439-22525-0(6) , Cartwheel Bks.) Scholastic, Inc.

Apperley, Dawn, illus. Santa Claus Will Come Tonight. 2002. 24p. (J). (ps-1). pap. 6.95 (978-0-439-40449-5(5) , Cartwheel Bks.) Scholastic, Inc.

Araki, Mie. Perfect Tail. 2004. (Illus.). 32p. (J). 14.95 (978-0-8118-4266-2(5)) Chronicle Bks. LLC.

Arias, Carlos Ballesteros. The Magic Forest. 2006. (J). pap. 8.00 (***978-0-8059-7022-7(3)***) Dorrance Publishing Co., Inc.

Aristizabal, Nora. The Wonderful Jungle / la selva Maravillosa. 2005. 44p. pap. (978-958-30-1966-1(6)) Panamericana Editorial.

Armstrong, Alan W. Whittington. 2006. (Illus.). 208p. (J). (gr. 3-7). pap. 6.50 (978-0-375-82865-2(6) , Yearling) Random Hse. Children's Bks.

Armstrong, Helen. Road to Somewhere. Horse, Harry, illus. 2005. 96p. (J). pap. 9.99 (978-1-84255-052-6(7)) Dolphin Paperbacks GBR. *Dist:* Trafalgar Square Publishing.

—The Road to Somewhere. Horse, Harry, illus. l.t. ed. 2005. (J). pap. (978-0-7540-7827-2(2) , CLP 417) BBC Audio.

Armstrong, Luanne. Jeannie & the Gentle Giants. 2005. (Illus.). 152p. (J). (gr. 3-7). pap., tchr. ed. 8.95 (978-0-921870-91-3(4)) Ronsdale Pr. CAN. *Dist:* General Distribution Services, Inc., Literary Pr. Group of Canada.

Arnold, Katya R., illus. & retold by. Me Too! Two Small Stories about Small Animals. Arnold, Katya R., retold by. 2000. 32p. (J). (gr. k-3). tchr. ed. 15.95 (978-0-8234-1483-3(3)) Holiday Hse., Inc.

Arnosky, Jim. Armadillo's Orange. Arnosky, Jim, illus. 2003. (Illus.). 32p. (J). (ps-3). 15.99 (978-0-399-23412-5(8) , Putnam Juvenile) Penguin Group (USA) Inc.

—Rabbits & Raindrops. Arnosky, Jim, illus. 2001. (Illus.). 32p. (J). (ps-k). pap. 5.99 (978-0-698-11815-7(4) , Putnam Juvenile) Penguin Group (USA) Inc.

—Rabbits & Raindrops. 2000. (gr. k-3). lib. bdg. 14.15 (978-0-613-36004-3(4)) Tandem Library Bks.

Aroner, Miriam. Clink, Clank, Clunk. Catalano, Dominic, illus. 2006. 32p. (J). 15.95 (978-1-59078-270-5(4)) Boyds Mills Pr.

Artifact Group. The Mighty Egg Sitters. 2008. (Backyardigans Ser.). 24p. (J). pap. 3.99 (***978-1-4169-5039-4(7)*** , Simon Spotlight/Nickelodeon) Simon & Schuster Children's Publishing.

Artifact Group. Riding the Range. 2006. (Backyardigans Ser.). (Illus.). 24p. (J). pap. 3.99 (978-1-4169-1304-7(1) , Simon Spotlight/Nickelodeon) Simon & Schuster Children's Publishing.

Arturo y la Carrera por la Lectura. 2004. Tr. of Arthur & the Race to Read. (SPA., Illus.). (J). pap. 4.95 (978-1-930332-60-7(2)) Lectorum Pubns., Inc.

Ashley, Joanne. Life at the Lake. 2005. 48p. pap. 12.95 (978-1-4137-6248-8(4)) PublishAmerica, Inc.

Ashman, Linda. Can You Make a Piggy Giggle? Cole, Henry, illus. 2002. 32p. (J). 12.99 (978-0-525-46881-3(1) , Dutton Juvenile) Penguin Group (USA) Inc.

—Castles, Caves, & Honeycombs. Stringer, Lauren, illus. 2001. 32p. (J). (ps-k). 17.00 (978-0-15-202211-2(2)) Harcourt Children's Bks.

Asquith, Ros & Childs, Sam. Baby's Shoe. 2005. (Illus.). 32p. (J). (ps-7). pap., pap. 9.99 (978-0-09-945107-5(7) , Red Fox) Random Hse. Children's Bks. GBR. *Dist:* Trafalgar Square Publishing.

Aston, Dianna Hutts. Bless This Mouse: A Soft-to-Touch Book. 2004. (Illus.). 24p. (J). 14.95 (978-1-59354-050-0(7)) Handprint Bks.

Atkins, Jill. Toad Swims for his Life! Mostyn, David, illus. 2004. 24p. (J). lib. bdg. 22.65 (***978-1-59646-712-5(6)***) Dingles & Co.

Atlas, Ron. Ten Pigs Fiddling. Flint, Stacie, illus. 2nd rev. ed. 2006. 32p. (J). 17.95 (978-0-9630243-3-6(7)) Amberwood Pr.

Auch, Mary Jane. Chickerella. Auch, Herm and Mary Jane, illus. 2006. 32p. 6.95 (978-0-8234-2015-5(9)) Holiday Hse., Inc.

Augarde, Steve. Big Nose, Small Nose. 2004. (Silly Monsters Ser.). (Illus.). 8p. (J). 5.95 (978-0-7696-3337-4(4) , Gingham Dog Pr.) School Specialty Publishing.

Ausbun, Nellie M. Skip & Meow. 2001. 22p. (J). per. 8.95 (978-0-7414-0613-2(6)) Infinity Publishing.

Austen, Jane. Puppy Love. Jennings, Patti, illus. 2001. (Animal Snuggles Ser.). 8p. (J). bds. 7.95 (978-0-8069-8095-9(8)) Sterling Publishing Co., Inc.

Austin, Margot & McPhail, David M. A Friend for Growl Bear Board Book. 1999. (Illus.). 32p. (J). (ps-k). 6.95 (978-0-694-01257-2(2) , Harper Festival) HarperCollins Pubs.

Avi. Avi Mid Grade 2. 2008. 208p. (J). 16.99 (***978-0-06-000015-8(5)***); lib. bdg. 17.89 (***978-0-06-000016-5(3)***) HarperCollins Pubs.

—Ereth's Birthday. Floca, Brian, illus. 2000. (Tales from Dimwood Forest Ser.). 192p. (J). (gr. 4-7). 17.99 (978-0-380-97734-5(6)) HarperCollins Pubs.

—The Good Dog. 2003. 256p. mass mkt. 5.99 (978-0-689-83825-5(5) , Aladdin) Simon & Schuster Children's Publishing.

—The Good Dog. l.t. ed. 2003. 176p. (J). 23.95 (978-0-7862-5600-6(1)) Thorndike Pr.

—The Mayor of Central Park. Floca, Brian, illus. 2003. 208p. (J). (gr. 3-6). 15.99 (978-0-06-000682-2(X)); lib. bdg. 16.89 (978-0-06-051556-0(2)) HarperCollins Pubs.

—Poppy & Rye. Floca, Brian, illus. (Poppy Bks.). (J). (gr. 3-7). 1999. 240p. pap. 5.99 (978-0-380-79717-2(8) , Harper Trophy); 1998. 192p. 16.99 (978-0-380-97638-6(2)) HarperCollins Pubs.

—Poppy & Rye, unabr. ed. 2000. (J). (gr. 8). pap., stu. ed. 50.24 incl. audio (978-0-7887-3185-3(8) , 40920E5) Recorded Bks., LLC.

—Poppy & Rye. Floca, Brian, illus. 1999. 182p. (J). (ps-7). per. 14.15 (978-0-613-17447-3(X)) Tandem Library Bks.

—Poppy & Rye. 1999. (978-0-606-16352-1(2)) Tandem Library Bks.

—Poppy's Return. Floca, Brian, illus. (Poppy Stories Ser.). (J). 2006. 256p. pap. 5.99 (978-0-06-000014-1(7) , Harper Trophy); 2005. 240p. lib. bdg. 16.89 (978-0-06-000013-4(9)) HarperCollins Pubs.

Avignone, June. A Peek into the Secret Little Ones of Turtle Back Island. My Wolf Dog, illus. 2004. 40p. (J). pap. (978-0-9654628-2-2(X)) Mill Street Forward, The.

Awdry, W. Thomas & the Hide & Seek Animals. Bell, Owain, illus. 2007. (Thomas & Friends Ser.). 24p. (J). (ps-1). pap. 5.99 (***978-0-375-84173-6(3)*** , Random Hse. Bks. for Young Readers) Random Hse. Children's Bks.

Awdry, Wilbert V. Cow On the Line Book & CD. 2005. (Illus.). 24p. (J). (ps-2). 9.95 (978-0-375-83499-8(0) , Random Hse. Bks. for Young Readers) Random Hse. Children's Bks.

—Engines & Animals. Yee, Josie, illus. 2005. (Thomas & Friends Ser.). 12p. (J). (gr. k-k). bds. 4.99 (978-0-375-83162-1(2) , Random Hse. Bks. for Young Readers) Random Hse. Children's Bks.

Axelrod. Pigs Will Be Pigs. 1998. (J). pap. 5.99 (978-0-87628-989-1(8)) Simon & Schuster.

Babaian, Haig S. Bruce & Lucky: Trouble at the SPCA. Omoto, Larry, illus. 2001. 20p. (J). (gr. 1-3). pap. 4.95 (978-0-9712284-1-2(8)) Bruce & Lucky Story Bks.

—Bruce & Lucky Story. Omoto, Larry, illus. 2000. 20p. (J). (gr. 1-3). pap. 4.95 (978-0-9712284-0-5(X)) Bruce & Lucky Story Bks.

Baby Animal Songs: Take along Songs. 2004. (Illus.). 16p. (J). bds. incl. audio compact disk (978-1-4127-0399-4(9) , 7218900) Publications International, Ltd.

Baby Looney Tunes Visit a Haunted House. 2005. (Baby Looney Tunes Ser.). (Illus.). 14p. (J). (ps-3). bds. 9.95 (978-0-8249-6609-6(0)) Ideals Pubns.

Bachman, Kathy. Silent Raiders. 2005. 60p. pap. 12.95 (978-1-4137-5802-3(9)) PublishAmerica, Inc.

Baglio, Ben M. Bunny Bonanza. Howard, Paul, illus. 2001. (Animal Ark Pets Ser.: Vol. 15). 128p. (J). (gr. 2-5). pap. 3.99 (978-0-439-23024-7(1)) Scholastic, Inc.

—Cat in the Crypt. Baum, Ann, illus. 2002. (Animal Ark Hauntings Ser.: No. 2). 144p. (J). pap. 3.99 (978-0-439-34407-4(7)) Scholastic, Inc.

—Cub in the Cupboard. 1999. (Animal Ark Ser.: No. 8). 160p. (J). (gr. 3-5). pap. 3.99 (978-0-590-18755-8(4) , Scholastic Paperbacks) Scholastic, Inc.

—Ferret Fun. 2000. (Animal Ark Pets Ser.: Vol. 14). (Illus.). 144p. (J). (gr. 2-5). pap. 3.99 (978-0-439-23023-0(3)) Scholastic, Inc.

—Goat in the Garden. McNicholas, Shelagh, illus. 1998. (Animal Ark Ser.: No. 4). (J). (gr. 3-5). 10.64 (978-0-606-13132-2(9)) Tandem Library Bks.

—Hamster in the Holly. Baum, Ann & Gregory, Jenny, illus. 2004. (Animal Ark Ser.: No. 35). 144p. (J). (gr. 2-5). 3.99 (978-0-439-44893-2(X) , Scholastic Paperbacks) Scholastic, Inc.

—Kitten in the Cold. McNicholas, Shelagh, illus. 1999. (Animal Ark Ser.). 144p. (J). (gr. 3-5). pap. 3.99 (978-0-439-09698-0(7)) Scholastic, Inc.

—The Kitten That Won First Prize & Other Animal Stories. Gregory, Jenny, illus. 2000. (Animal Ark Special Ser.: No. 1). 160p. (J). (gr. 4-7). pap. 3.99 (978-0-439-09703-1(7)) Scholastic, Inc.

—Kittens in the Kitchen. McNicholas, Shelagh, illus. 1998. (Animal Ark Ser.: No. 1). (J). (gr. 3-5). (978-0-606-13129-2(9)) Tandem Library Bks.

—Lamb in the Laundry. McNicholas, Shelagh, illus. 1999. (Animal Ark Ser.: No. 12). (J). (gr. 3-5). (978-0-606-19928-5(4)) Tandem Library Bks.

—Owl in the Office. 1999. (Animal Ark Ser.: No. 11). (J). (gr. 3-5). (978-0-606-19934-6(9)) Tandem Library Bks.

—Pets' Party. Howard, Paul, illus. 2001. (Animal Ark Ser.: No. 17). 128p. (J). (gr. 6). 3.99 (978-0-439-23026-1(8)) Scholastic, Inc.

—Piglet in a Playpen. 1999. (Animal Ark Ser.: No. 9). (J). (gr. 3-5). (978-0-606-19935-3(7)) Tandem Library Bks.

—Pony on the Porch. McNicholas, Shelagh, illus. 1998. (Animal Ark Ser.: No. 2). (J). (gr. 3-5). (978-0-606-13130-8(2)) Tandem Library Bks.

—Shetland in the Shed. Gregory, Jenny, illus. 2001. (Animal Ark Ser.: No. 20). 144p. (J). (gr. 3-5). 3.99 (978-0-439-23019-3(5)) Scholastic, Inc.

Baicker, Karen & Williams, Sam. Wake-Ity Wake! 2004. (Illus.). 5p. (J). bds. 6.95 (978-1-59354-036-4(1)) Handprint Bks.

Baiker, Karen. Barnyard Friends. (Felt Read-and-Play Ser.). (Illus.). 14p. (J). 17.95 (978-1-59354-052-4(3)) Handprint Bks.

Bailey, Arthur Scott. Sleepy Time Tales the Tale of Fatty Coon. 2004. reprint ed. pap. 15.95 (978-1-4191-4779-1(X)); pap. 1.99 (978-1-4192-4779-8(4)) Kessinger Publishing, LLC.

—The Tale of Benny Badger. 2005. reprint ed. pap. 20.95 (978-1-4179-0197-5(7)) Kessinger Publishing, LLC.

—The Tale of Peter Mink. 2005. pap. 20.95 (978-0-7661-9699-5(2)) Kessinger Publishing, LLC.

Bajaj, Varsha. How Many Kisses Do You Want Tonight? Bates, Ivan, illus. 2004. 28p. (J). (ps-3). 15.99 (978-0-316-82381-4(3)) Little, Brown Bks. for Young Readers.

Baker, Elliott, adapted by. The Adventures of Doctor Dolittle. 2002. 104p. (YA). pap. 6.95 (978-1-58342-113-0(0) , A03) Dramatic Publishing Co.

Baker, Harriet Li. Book I: Boyduck Goose: His Life & Times. 2004. pap. 9.00 (978-0-8059-6541-4(6)) Dorrance Publishing Co., Inc.

Baker, Keith. Hickory Dickory Dock. 2007. (Illus.). 32p. (J). (ps-2). 16.00 (978-0-15-205818-0(4)) Harcourt Trade Pubs.

Baker, Liza. Harold & the Purple Crayon: Animals, Animals, Animals! 2002. (gr. k-3). lib. bdg. 11.80 (978-0-613-62516-6(1)) Tandem Library Bks.

Baldry, Cherith. The Emerald Throne. Wyatt, David, illus. 2003. (J). 144p. 15.95 (978-1-59034-584-9(3)); 141p. pap. (978-1-59034-585-6(1)) Mondo Publishing.

—The Lake of Darkness. Wyatt, David, illus. 2004. 144p. (J). 15.95 (978-1-59034-586-3(X)); pap. (978-1-59034-587-0(8)) Mondo Publishing.

—The Silver Horn. 2002. (Eaglesmount Ser.). (Illus.). 132p. (J). (gr. 3-6). 15.95 (978-1-59034-475-0(8)) Mondo Publishing.

—The Silver Horn. Wyatt, David, illus. 2002. 141p. (J). pap. 15.95 (978-1-59034-490-3(1)) Mondo Publishing.

Ballantyne, R. M. Hunting the Lions. 2004. reprint ed. pap. 15.95 (978-1-4191-2501-0(X)); pap. 1.99 (978-1-4192-2501-7(4)) Kessinger Publishing, LLC.

Balloon Books Staff, ed. Small Cat, Smaller Cat. 2003. (Animal Bring-Along Bks.). (Illus.). 16p. (J). bds. 3.50 (978-0-8069-8066-9(4) , Balloon Bks.) Sterling Publishing Co., Inc.

—A Visit to the Farm: Sticker Story Time. 2003. (Sticker Bks.). (Illus.). 16p. (J). (ps-1). pap. 4.95 (978-0-8069-2260-7(5) , Balloon Bks.) Sterling Publishing Co., Inc.

Banana-Tail. 2003. lib. bdg. 13.95 (978-0-9727681-0-8(6)) Active Media Publishing, LLC.

Bang-Campbell, Monika. Little Rat Sets Sail. Bang, Molly Garrett, illus. (Little Rat Ser.). 48p. (J). 2003. pap. 5.95 (978-0-15-204769-6(7) , Harcourt Paperbacks); 2002. (gr. 1-3). 14.00 (978-0-15-216297-9(6)) Harcourt Children's Bks.

—Little Rat Sets Sail. 2003. (gr. k-3). lib. bdg. 14.10 (978-0-613-70519-6(X)) Tandem Library Bks.

Banks, Kate. Baboon. Hallensleben, Georg, illus. 2004. 24p. (J). (ps-ps). lib. bdg. 13.75 (978-0-606-30284-5(0)) Tandem Library Bks.

—The Bird, the Monkey, & the Snake in the Jungle. Bogacki, Tomek, illus. 2003. 32p. (J). pap. 6.95 (978-0-374-40658-5(8) , Sunburst) Farrar, Straus & Giroux.

—El Pajaro, el Mono y la Serpiente en la Selva. Bogacki, Tomek, illus. (SPA.). 24p. (J). (gr. k-2). (978-84-261-3129-4(8) , JV2823) Juventud, Editorial ESP. *Dist:* Lectorum Pubns., Inc.

Banks, Lynne Reid. I, Houdini: The Autobiography of a Self-Educated Hamster. Riley, Terry, illus. 2003. 128p. (J). (gr. 4-7). pap. 5.50 (978-0-440-41924-2(7) , Yearling) Random Hse. Children's Bks.

—Tiger, Tiger. 2005. 208p. (gr. 7-12). (J). 15.95 (978-0-385-73240-6(6)); (YA). lib. bdg. 17.99 (978-0-385-90264-9(6)) Random Hse. Children's Bks. (Delacorte Bks. for Young Readers).

Barad, Alexis. Eyes, Ears, Toes! Discovering Me! 2008. (Fisher-Price Ser.). 16p. (J). 4.99 (***978-0-06-144769-3(2)*** , Harper Festival) HarperCollins Pubs.

Barberis, France. Would You Like a Parrot? Barberis, Franco, illus. 32p. (J). (ps). 16.95 (978-0-87592-060-3(8)) Scroll Pr., Inc.

Barham, Olivia. Summer Picnic. Kaminski, Karol, illus. 2002. (Chubby Puppies Ser.: Vol. 2). 32p. (J). (ps-3). pap. 3.50 (978-0-439-35586-5(9)) Scholastic, Inc.

Barile, Colleen. A Super Day for Sailing. Van Patter, Bruce, illus. 2002. (Read-To-Me Ser.). 25p. (J). (978-0-7665-1219-1(3)) Abrams, Harry N. , Inc.

Barkan, Joanne & Gevry, Claudine. Little Cricket's Song. 2007. 10p. (J). bds. 6.99 (978-0-7944-1282-1(3)) Reader's Digest Assn., Inc., The.

Barkow, Henriette & Johnson, Richard, illus. Don't Cry, Sly! Ne Pleure Pas Sly! 2004. (TAM, CZE, VIE, SPA & GUJ.). 23p. (J). pap. (978-1-85269-654-2(0)) Mantra Publishing, Ltd.

Barnes, Laura T. Ernest & Elston. Camburn, Carol A., illus. 2005. (Ernest Ser.). 32p. (J). (ps). 15.95 (978-0-9674681-6-7(7)) Barnesyard Bks.

Barnum, P. T. Dick Broadhead: A Story of Perilous Adve. 2006. pap. 30.95 ***(*978-1-4286-1959-3(3))*** Kessinger Publishing, LLC.

—Jack in the Jungle: A Tale of Land & S. 2006. pap. 33.95 ***(*978-1-4286-0764-4(1))*** Kessinger Publishing, LLC.

Barnum, Richard. Mappo the Merry Monkey Illustrated Editi. 2006. (Illus.). pap. ***(*978-1-4065-0920-5(5))*** Dodo Pr.

Barrett George, Lindsay. In the Snow, Who's Been Here? 1999. (J). (978-0-606-17395-7(1)) Tandem Library Bks.

Barrett, Judi. Animals Should Definitely Not Wear Clothing: Los Animales No Se Visten. Davis, J., tr. Barrett, Ron, illus. unabr. ed. 1999. (ENG & SPA.). (J). (gr. 1-3). pap. 33.95 incl. audio (978-0-87499-564-0(7)) Live Oak Media.

—Never Take a Giraffe to the Movies & Other Things Not to Do. Nickle, John, illus. 2008. 34p. (J). 16.99 (978-1-4169-0724-4(6)) Simon & Schuster Children's Publishing.

Bartlett, T. C. Tuba Lessons. Felix, Monique, illus. 2004. 32p. pap. 9.95 (978-0-89812-522-1(7) , Creative Paperbacks) Creative Co., The.

Barton, Byron. La Gallinita Roja. 2004. (SPA.). 40p. (J). 14.99 (978-84-8470-077-7(1)) Corimbo, Editorial S.L. ESP. *Dist:* Lectorum Pubns., Inc.

Barwood, Lee. Klassic Koalas: Ancient Aboriginal Tales in New Retellings. 2007. (Illus.). 64p. (J). pap. 28.99 ***(*978-0-9764698-1-0(2))*** Koala Jo Publishing.

Base, Graeme. The Water Hole. Base, Graeme, illus. 2001. (Illus.). 32p. (J). (gr. 2-7). 18.95 (978-0-8109-4568-5(1)) Abrams, Harry N. , Inc.

Basora, Bettye. Pride's Pride. 2003. 32p. (J). pap. 9.00 (978-0-8059-5833-1(9)) Dorrance Publishing Co., Inc.

Bates, Ivan. All by Myself. Bates, Ivan, illus. 2000. (Illus.). 32p. (J). (ps-2). 14.95 (978-0-06-028585-2(0)) HarperCollins Pubs.

—All by Myself. 1999. 32p. (J). (ps-2). pap. 4.95 (978-0-06-443608-3(X)) HarperCollins Pubs.

Battleson, Mariella. Her Name Was Emaline. 2005. 60p. (J). pap. 25.99 (978-1-4141-0364-8(6)) Pleasant Word.

Bauer, Elizabeth. The Happy Forest: Animal Adventures in the Forest. Bauer, Elizabeth, illus. l.t. ed. 2001. 130p. (J). per. incl. cd-rom (978-0-9630409-7-8(9)) Galaxy Publishing Hse.

Bauer, Marion Dane. If Frogs Made the Weather. Donohue, Dorothy, illus. 2005. 32p. (J). 16.95 (978-0-8234-1622-6(4)) Holiday Hse., Inc.

—My Mother Is Mine. Elwell, Peter, illus. 40p. (J). (ps-k). 2001. 13.00 (978-0-689-82267-4(7)); 2004. reprint ed. pap. 6.99 (978-0-689-86695-1(X) , Aladdin) Simon & Schuster Children's Publishing.

—My Mother Is Mine. 2004. (ps-2). lib. bdg. 14.15 (978-0-613-88067-1(6)) Tandem Library Bks.

Bauer, Marion Dane & Wu, Leslie. The Very Best Daddy of All. 2007. 40p. (J). pap. 6.99 (978-1-4169-2736-5(0) , Aladdin) Simon & Schuster Children's Publishing.

Baumann, Kurt. Joachim. (SPA.). 32p. (YA). (gr. 5-8). (978-84-264-3551-4(3) , LM1740) Editorial Lumen ESP. *Dist:* Lectorum Pubns., Inc.

Baumgart, Klaus. Lenny & Tweek. 2002. (Illus.). (J). 31p. pap. (978-1-59034-387-6(5)) ; 32p. 15.95 (978-1-59034-197-1(X)) Mondo Publishing.

Baxter, Nicola. Old MacDonald's: Barnyard Tales. Davis, Caroline, illus. 256p. (J). (978-0-7525-8771-4(4)) Parragon Bk. Service Ltd.

Baynes, Pauline, illus. The Elephant's Ball. 2007. 32p. (J). 17.00 (978-0-8028-5316-5(1) , Eerdmans Bks For Young Readers) Eerdmans, William B. Publishing Co.

Beall, Pamela Conn & Nipp, Susan Hagen. Wee Sing & Pretend. 2006. (Wee Sing Ser.). 60p. (J). (ps-2). 9.99 (978-0-8431-2099-8(1) , Price Stern Sloan) Penguin Group (USA) Inc.

Beames, Margaret. Night Cat. Hitchcock, Sue, illus. 2003. 40p. (J). (gr. k-2). pap. 15.95 (978-0-439-38576-3(8) , Orchard Bks.) Scholastic, Inc.

The Bean Bag that Mom Made: 6 Small Books. (gr. k-3). 24.00 (978-0-7635-6241-0(6)) Rigby Education.

Bears & Ducklings. 2002. (Three Minute Tales Ser.). 64p. (J). 12.98 (978-0-7525-5468-6(9)) Parragon, Inc.

Beaton, Clare. One Moose, Twenty Mice. 1999. (Barefoot Beginner Ser.). (Illus.). 32p. (J). (ps-k). 14.95 (978-1-902283-37-1(6)) Barefoot Bks., Inc.

—There's a Cow in the Cabbage Patch. 2001. 32p. (J). pap. 5.99 (978-1-84148-335-1(4)) Barefoot Bks., Inc.

Beaumont, Karen. Move Over, Rover! Dyer, Jane, illus. 2006. (J). ***(*978-1-4287-0246-2(6))*** Harcourt Trade Pubs.

—Who Ate All the Cookie Dough? Yelchin, Eugene, illus. 2008. 32p. (J). 16.95 ***(*978-0-8050-8267-8(0))*** Holt, Henry & Co.

Bechtold, Lisze. Buster: The Very Shy Dog. 1999. (gr. 3-6). lib. bdg. 14.10 (978-0-613-35495-0(8)) ; (Illus.). (J). 12.75 (978-0-606-21095-9(4)) Tandem Library Bks.

Beck, Ana. Elliot Bakes a Cake. 1999. (gr. k-3). lib. bdg. 14.10 (978-0-613-33361-0(6)) Tandem Library Bks.

—Elliot Digs for Treasure. 2001. (ps-2). lib. bdg. 14.10 (978-0-613-53183-2(3)) Tandem Library Bks.

Beck, Andrea. Elliot Digs for Treasure. Beck, Andrea, illus. 2004. (Elliot Moose Ser.). (Illus.). 32p. (J). (gr. k-3). (978-1-55074-806-2(8)) ; (978-1-55074-808-6(4)) Kids Can Pr., Ltd.

Beckhorn, Susan. In the Morning of the World: Six Woodland Why Stories. Beckhorn, Susan, illus. 2000. (Illus.). 48p. (gr. 4-7). 15.95 (978-0-89272-503-8(6)) Down East Bks.

Becquer, Gustavo Adolfo. La Corza Blanca Level 2. 1998. (SPA.). (gr. 7-12). lib. bdg. 14.10 (978-0-613-80722-7(7)) Tandem Library Bks.

Bedard, Michael. Sitting Ducks. 2001. (J). (978-0-606-22064-4(X)) ; (gr. 3-6). lib. bdg. 15.30 (978-0-613-45548-0(7)) Tandem Library Bks.

Bedford, David & Worthington, Leonie. Who's Laughing. 2007. (Illus.). 16p. (J). (ps-k). 9.95 ***(*978-1-921049-40-8(5))*** Little Hare Bks. AUS. *Dist:* Independent Pubs. Group.

Bedore, Bernie. Mythical Mufferaw. (Illus.). 96p. (J). pap. 10.95 (978-1-55082-087-4(7)) Quarry Pr. CAN. *Dist:* LPC/InBook.

Begin, Mary Jane. Willow Buds #1. 2008. 40p. 14.99 ***(*978-0-316-01352-9(8))*** Little Brown & Co.

Beifuss, John. Armadillo Ray. Turley, Peggy, illus. 1998. 32p. (J). (ps-1). pap. 6.95 (978-0-8118-2135-3(8)) Chronicle Bks. LLC.

—Armadillo Ray: Anish Edition. Turley, Peggy, illus. 1998. (SPA.). 32p. (J). (ps-2). 15.95 (978-0-8118-2277-0(X) , CHR8868) Chronicle Bks. LLC.

Beinstein, Phoebe. Baby Animals! Roper, Robert, illus. 2003. (Dora the Explorer Ser.). 14p. (J). bds. 5.99 (978-0-689-85017-2(4) , Simon Spotlight/Nickelodeon) Simon & Schuster Children's Publishing.

Bell, Debora. Lyssa Lamb. Ronda, Gilger, illus. 2005. 32p. (J). 4.95 (978-0-9768465-0-5(0)) Frontier Pr.

Bellamy, Marian Meredith. Goldie & Androcles—A Fable for the 21st Century. Bellamy, Marian Meredith, illus. 2005. (Illus.). 91p. (YA). per. 20.00 (978-0-9765341-0-5(X)) Meredith Group Ltd., The.

Bender, Carrie, compiled by. Betty Girl & Other Animal Stories. 2004. pap. 7.95 (978-1-930353-96-1(0)) Masthof Pr.

Benjamin, A. H. Little Mouse & the Big Red Apple. Williamson, Gwyneth, illus. 2001. 32p. (J). pap. 5.95 (978-1-58925-358-2(2) , tiger tales) ME Media LLC.

Benjamin & Tulip. 2004. (J). 24.95 incl. audio (978-1-56008-037-4(X)) ; pap. 14.95 incl. audio (978-1-56008-038-1(8)) Weston Woods Studios, Inc.

Benjamin, Cynthia. Footprints in the Sand. 1999. (Hello Reader! Ser.). (J). 10.79 (978-0-606-16655-3(6)) Tandem Library Bks.

Bennett, Dean. Everybody Needs a Hideaway. 2004. (Illus.). 32p. 15.95 (978-0-89272-645-5(8)) Down East Bks.

—Finding a Friend in the Forest: A True Story. 2005. (Illus.). 15.95 (978-0-89272-662-2(8)) Down East Bks.

Bennett, Maureen A. The Wolf & the Whitetail. Bennett, Exlus S., illus. 1999. 72p. (YA). (gr. 7-12). pap. 5.95 (978-1-929914-00-5(8) , Ruf-Fur Pubns) Megaverse City Studios.

Bennett, Steven. The Adventures of Super Dad: Colossal Encounters (Book #1) 2005. 98p. pap. 10.49 (978-1-4116-5947-6(3)) Lulu.com.

Bentley, Dawn. Buzz-Buzz, Busy Bees: An Animal Sounds Book. Cahoon, Heather, illus. 2004. 24p. (J). 10.95 (978-0-689-86848-1(0) , Little Simon) Simon & Schuster Children's Publishing.

—Saber-Tooth Trap. (Smithsonian's Prehistoric Pals Ser.). (Illus.). 36p. (J). (ps-2). 2.95 (978-1-59249-456-9(0) , S2456); 9.95 (978-1-59249-457-6(9) , PS2456); 14.95 incl. cd-rom (978-1-59249-453-8(6) , H2406) Soundprints.

—Saber-Tooth Trap. Reavely, Trevor, illus. 2005. (Smithsonian's Prehistoric Pals Ser.). 358p. (J). (ps-ps). pap. 6.95 (978-1-59249-454-5(4) , S2406) Soundprints.

—Velociraptor: Small & Speedy. Carr, Karen, illus. 2005. (Smithsonian's Prehistoric Pals Ser.). 36p. (J). (ps-2). 9.95 (978-1-59249-164-3(2) , PS2452) Soundprints.

—Woolly Mammoth in Trouble. Carr, Karen, illus. 2005. (Smithsonian's Prehistoric Pals Ser.). (J). (ps-2). 36p. 14.95 incl. cd-rom (978-1-59249-364-7(5) , H2404); 32p. 2.95 (978-1-59249-367-8(X) , S2454); 36p. 6.95 (978-1-59249-365-4(3) , S2404) Soundprints.

Berends, Polly Berrien. I Heard, Said the Bird. Sneed, Brad, illus. 1998. (Picture Puffin Ser.). 32p. (J). (ps-1). pap. 6.99 (978-0-14-056426-6(8) , Puffin) Penguin Group (USA) Inc.

Berenstain, Stan & Berenstain, Jan. The Runamuck Dog Show. 2001. (Berenstain Bears Ser.). (Illus.). (J). (gr. k-3). 10.79 (978-0-606-21059-1(8)) Tandem Library Bks.

Bergen, Lara. Telling Time with Diego. Maher, Alex, illus. 2007. (Go, Diego, Go! Ser.). 14p. (J). bds. 7.99 ***(*978-1-4169-3369-4(7)*** , Simon Spotlight/Nickelodeon) Simon & Schuster Children's Publishing.

Berger, Barbara Helen. Animalia: Thirteen Small Tales. 1999. (gr. 3-6). lib. bdg. 16.40 (978-0-613-56184-6(8)) Tandem Library Bks.

Berkowitz, Henry. Rosie, the Manatee: A Storyteller Coloring Book. Berkowitz, Henry, illus. 2002. 32p. (J). (gr. k-3). pap. 4.95 (978-0-932855-69-5(5)) Winner Enterprises.

Berleman, Sean & Salyards, Jeffrey. Camera Contest. Saunders, Zina, illus. 2004. 14p. (J). bds. (978-0-7853-9955-1(0) , 7210000) Publications International, Ltd.

Bernal, Mitchell. Skelanimals: Dead Animals Need Love Too. Bernal, Mitchell, illus. l.t. ed. 2005. (Illus.). 22p. (J). per. 12.95 (978-0-9766621-0-5(8) , 818 554-8965) Kreations.

Bernthal, Mark S. & Scholastic, Inc. Staff. Barney's ABC Animals! Baker, Darrell, illus. 1999. (Barney Ser.). 32p. (J). (ps-k). pap. 3.50 (978-1-57064-453-5(5)) Scholastic, Inc.

Berry, Virginia B. Iggie's Big Adventure. King, Garry W., illus. ed. 2002. 20p. (J). (gr. k-6). pap. 5.00 (978-0-9726091-0-4(5)) Berry Enterprises.

Betancourt, Jeanne. Lost & Found Pony. Bachem, Paul, illus. 2001. (Pony Pals Ser.: Vol. 29). 96p. (J). (gr. 2-5). pap. 3.99 (978-0-439-16572-3(5)) Scholastic, Inc.

Between the Lions for QVC Only, 6 vols. 2003. (Between the Lions Presents the Vowels Ser.). (J). lib. bdg. 30.00 incl. VHS (978-1-59375-029-9(3)) WGBH Boston Video.

Bidoli, Katie. Karate Adventures of Kisho, Hana, & Nobu: Karate Is for Everyone! 2006. (Illus.). 16p. (J). 10.00 ***(*978-1-60243-029-7(2))*** Keen's Martial Arts Academy.

The Big, Bad Cook: Individual Title Six-Packs. (Literatura 2000 Ser.). (gr. 2-3). 33.00 (978-0-7635-0252-2(9)) Rigby Education.

Big Book of Backyard Adventures. 2007. (Backyardigans Ser.). 192p. (J). 10.99 ***(*978-1-4169-3842-2(7)*** , Simon Spotlight/Nickelodeon) Simon & Schuster Children's Publishing.

Big Egg, Little Egg. 1999. (Chunky Roly-Poly Book Ser.). (Illus.). 16p. (J). 3.50 (978-1-57082-990-1(X)) Mouse Works.

Bilgrami, Shaheen. Icy Antics. Chambers, Sally & Ratie, Patricia, illus. 2003. (Curious Creatures Bks.). 12p. (J). bds. 12.95 (978-1-4027-0820-6(3) , Sterling/Pinwheel) Sterling Publishing Co., Inc.

Bill's Baby: 6 Small Books. (gr. k-3). 24.00 (978-0-7635-6242-7(4)) Rigby Education.

Bird, Sheila & Bird, Sheila M. Dr. Witch's Animal Hospital. Parrish, Emma, illus. 2007. (I Am Reading Ser.). 48p. (J). (ps-3). pap. 3.95 ***(*978-0-7534-5977-5(9)*** , Kingfisher) Houghton Mifflin Co. Trade & Reference Div.

Birney, Betty. Oh, Bother! Someone Won't Share. Stevenson, Nancy, illus. 2000. (Oh, Bother! Ser.). 24p. (J). (ps-3). pap. 3.29 (978-0-307-12766-2(4) , 12766, Golden Bks.) Random Hse. Children's Bks.

Birrer, Cynthia & Birrer, Bill, illus. The Confused Zebra. 1999. (J). 16.95 (978-0-86543-795-1(5)) Africa World Pr.

Bishop, Brett & Olson, Laura. Clayton's Path. Eagle, Mona, illus. 2001. 40p. (J). (gr. k-6). pap. 12.95 (978-0-9700035-3-9(6)) Apogee Publishing.

Bjerkvold, Belinda & Kipling, Rudyard. The Jungle Book. Larrea, Miguel & Andrada, Javier, illus. 2006. (J). lib. bdg. ***(*978-0-8368-7663-5(6))*** Stevens, Gareth Inc.

Bjorkman, Steve. Good Night, Little One. Bjorkman, Steve, illus. 1999. (Illus.). 40p. (J). (ps-3). 9.99 (978-1-57856-275-6(9) , WaterBrook Pr.) WaterBrook Pr.

Black, Michael Ian. Chicken Cheeks. Hawkes, Kevin, illus. 2008. (J). ***(*978-1-4169-4864-3(3)*** , Simon & Schuster Children's Publishing) Simon & Schuster Children's Publishing.

Blackstone, Stella. Alligator Alphabet. Bauer, Stephanie, illus. 2005. 48p. (J). (ps-k). 16.99 (978-1-84148-494-5(6)) Barefoot Bks., Inc.

—The Animal Boogie. Harter, Debbie, illus. 2002. 32p. (gr. k-2). pap. 9.99 (978-1-84148-915-5(8)) Barefoot Bks., Inc.

—A Dragon on the Doorstep. Harter, Debbie, illus. 2005. 32p. (J). (ps-1). 15.99 (978-1-84148-227-9(7)) Barefoot Bks., Inc.

—Hay una Vaca Entre las Coles. Beaton, Clare, illus. 2003. (SPA.). 32p. (J). (gr. k-2). 6.99 (978-1-84148-965-0(4)) Barefoot Bks., Inc.

—How Big Is a Pig? Beaton, Clare, illus. 24p. (J). (gr. k-2). 2002. bds. 6.99 (978-1-84148-959-9(X)); 2000. 14.99 (978-1-84148-077-0(0)) Barefoot Bks., Inc.

—Storytime: First Tales for Sharing. Wilson, Anne, illus. 2005. 96p. (J). (ps-3). 19.99 (978-1-84148-345-0(1)) Barefoot Bks., Inc.

—There's a Cow in the Cabbage Patch. Beaton, Clare, illus. 2001. 32p. (J). (ps). 14.99 (978-1-84148-333-7(8)) Barefoot Bks., Inc.

—Walking Through the Jungle. Harter, Debbie, illus. 2004. 32p. (J). 9.99 (978-1-84148-182-1(3)) Barefoot Bks., Inc.

—Who Are You? Harter, Debbie, illus. 2003. 24p. (J). (gr. k-2). bds. 6.99 (978-1-84148-609-3(4)) Barefoot Bks., Inc.

—Who Are You, Baby Kangaroo? Beaton, Clare, illus. 2004. 32p. (J). 14.99 (978-1-84148-217-0(X)) Barefoot Bks., Inc.

Blade, Adam. Beast Quest #5 Arcta the Ice Beast. 2007. 80p. pap. 4.99 ***(*978-0-439-02457-0(9)*** , Scholastic Paperbacks) Scholastic, Inc.

Blair, Eric. Los Musicos de Bremen: Version del Cuento de los Hermanos Grimm. Dickson, Bill, illus. 2006. (Read-It! Readers en Espanol Ser.).Tr. of Bremen Town Musicians: A Retelling of the Grimm's Fairy Tale. (SPA.). 32p. (J). (ps-3). 19.95 (978-1-4048-1628-2(3)) Picture Window Bks.

Blake, Quentin. Fantastic Daisy Artichoke. 2001. (Illus.). 32p. (J). (ps-1). pap. 11.99 (978-0-09-940006-6(5)) Random Hse. GBR. *Dist:* Trafalgar Square Publishing.

Blazin' Hot: Coloring/Activity Book (English) 2005. (Illus.). (J). (978-0-9770455-0-1(1)) Educational Adventures.

Blazin' Hot: Picture Book (English) 8x8. 2006. (J). (978-1-933934-29-7(8)) Educational Adventures.

Blazin' Hot Picture Book (English) 2005. (Illus.). (J). (978-0-9765953-9-7(7)) Educational Adventures.

Blishen, Edward & Blishen, Nancy. The Kingfisher Treasury of Stories for Four Year Olds. Dinan, Carolyn, illus. 2005. (Kingfisher Treasury of Stories Ser.). 160p. (J). (gr. k-3). pap. 5.95 (978-0-7534-5891-4(8) , Kingfisher) Houghton Mifflin Co. Trade & Reference Div.

Bloom, Becky. Mr. Cuckoo. Bloom, Becky, illus. 1998. (Illus.). 32p. (J). (gr. k-4). 15.95 (978-1-57255-626-3(9)) Mondo Publishing.

—Wolf. Biet, Pascal, illus. 2001. (J). 26.90 incl. audio (978-0-8045-6864-7(2)) Spoken Arts, Inc.

Bloxam, Frances. Little Tom Turkey. Sollers, Jim, illus. 2005. 32p. 15.95 (978-0-89272-671-4(7)) Down East Bks.

BlueWolf, James Don. Speaking for Fire. Greenlee, Carolyn Wing, illus. 2003. 44p. (J). (gr. 2-7). 14.95 (978-1-887400-31-2(1)) Earthen Vessel Production, Inc.

Blume, Judy. The One in the Middle Is the Green Kangaroo. Trivas, Irene, illus. 2002. (J). 13.83 (978-0-7587-0726-0(6)) Book Wholesalers, Inc.

—The One in the Middle Is the Green Kangaroo. 39p. (J). (gr. k-3). pap. 3.99 (978-0-8072-1337-7(3) , Listening Library) Random Hse. Audio Publishing Group.

Blumenthal, Bliss & Alarcon, Claudia. Wiley's Way: El Camino de Wiley. Gonzalez, Ricky & Gonzalez, Crysol, illus. 2004. (ENG & SPA.). 112p. pap. 9.95 (978-0-292-70615-6(4)) Univ. of Texas Pr.

Blyton, Enid. Mr Twiddle in Trouble Again. 2000. (Enid Blyton's Happy Days Ser.). (Illus.). 95p. (J). (ps-3). pap. 7.99 (978-0-7475-4355-8(0)) Bloomsbury Publishing Plc GBR. *Dist:* Trafalgar Square Publishing.

The Boat, 6 pack. (Sails Literacy Ser.). 16p. (gr. k up). 27.00 (978-0-7635-4424-9(8)) Rigby Education.

Bode, Mark & McCormick, Carlo. The Lizard of Oz. 2004. (Illus.). 64p. 12.95 (978-1-56097-595-3(4)) Fantagraphics Bks.

Bolam, Emily, illus. Chunky Safari. 2001. 14p. (J). 4.95 (978-0-7641-7446-9(0)) Barron's Educational Series, Inc.

—I'm Going to Read (Level 2): Fooba Wooba John. 2006. (I'm Going to Read Ser.). 32p. (J). pap. 3.95 (978-1-4027-3420-5(4)) Sterling Publishing Co., Inc.

Boniface, William. The Treasure Hunter. Harris, Jim, illus. 1998. 32p. (J). 15.99 (978-0-939251-97-1(3)) Accord Publishing, Ltd.

Bonnell, Kris. Look Who's at the Zoo. 2005. (J). 3.75 (978-1-933727-07-3(1)) Reading Reading Bks., LLC.

—We Like the Beach. 2007. (J). 3.95 ***(*978-1-933727-55-4(1))*** Reading Reading Bks., LLC.

—The White, White Snow. 2007. (J). 3.95 ***(*978-1-933727-44-8(6))*** Reading Reading Bks., LLC.

—Who Has a Hump? 2007. (J). 3.95 ***(*978-1-933727-58-5(6))*** Reading Reading Bks., LLC.

Bonning, Tony. Another Fine Mess. Hobson, Sally, illus. 1998. 32p. (J). (ps-2). 14.95 (978-1-888444-43-8(6)) Little Tiger Pr.

Bonning, Tony & Hobson, Sally. Another Fine Mess. 2001. (Illus.). 32p. (J). 5.95 (978-1-58925-356-8(6) , tiger tales) ME Media LLC.

Book Company Staff. Animal Friends. 2003. (Sparkle Bks.). (Illus.). (J). bds. 14.95 (978-1-74047-322-4(1)) Book Co. Publishing Pty, Ltd., The AUS. *Dist:* Penton Overseas, Inc.

—Funky Farm. Morrison, Geoff, illus. 2007. 10p. (J). (gr. 3-5). 8.95 ***(*978-1-74047-883-0(5)*** , Penton Kids) Penton Overseas, Inc.

Book Company Staff. Our Precious World Stationery Set. Schimmel, Schim, illus. 2003. (Stationery Ser.). (J). pap. 15.95 (978-1-74047-215-9(2)) Book Co. Publishing Pty, Ltd., The AUS. *Dist:* Penton Overseas, Inc.

Borgo, Lacy Finn. Big Mama's Baby. Cote, Nancy, illus. 2007. (J). (gr. k-2). 15.95 ***(*978-1-59078-187-6(2))*** Boyds Mills Pr.

Borlenghi, Patricia. Chaucer the Cat & the Animal Pilgrims. 2001. (Illus.). 77p. (J). pap. 16.99 (978-0-7475-4790-7(4)) Bloomsbury Publishing Plc GBR. *Dist:* Independent Pubs. Group.

—Chaucer the Cat & the Animal Pilgrims. Greenfield, Giles, illus. 2001. 77p. (J). (gr. 3-6). 22.99 (978-0-7475-4491-3(3)) Bloomsbury Publishing Plc GBR. *Dist:* Trafalgar Square Publishing.

Bornstein, Ruth. Brave Bunny. Bornstein, Ruth, illus. 2003. (Illus.). 32p. (J). 9.95 (978-1-58685-282-5(5)) Gibbs Smith, Publisher.

Bosse, Malcolm. Tusk & Stone. 2004. 256p. (YA). reprint ed. pap. 8.95 (978-1-886910-74-4(X) , Lemniscaat) Boyds Mills Pr.

Bourgeois, Paulette. El Diente de Franklin. 2001. (SPA.). (gr. k-3). lib. bdg. 14.10 (978-0-613-35932-0(1)) Tandem Library Bks.

—Franklin & Harriet. Clark, Brenda, illus. 2001. (J). (978-0-439-26424-2(3)) Scholastic, Inc.

—Franklin & Harriet. 2001. (Franklin Ser.). (Illus.). (J). 11.30 (978-0-606-20664-8(7)) Tandem Library Bks.

—Franklin & the Tooth Fairy. Clark, Brenda, illus. 2002. (Franklin Ser.). 12.40 (978-1-4046-0311-0(5)) Book Wholesalers, Inc.

—Franklin Plants a Tree. 2001. (Franklin Ser.). (Illus.). (J). 11.30 (978-0-606-21196-3(9)) Tandem Library Bks.

Bousman, Cindy. Watch Me! Sing, Dance & Read with Me, Read-Along with Big Book. 2000. 12p. (J). (ps-3). pap. 14.95 incl. audio (978-1-931127-40-0(9) , 986-014); pap. 29.95 incl. audio compact disk (978-1-931127-42-4(5) , 986-015) Kindermusik International.

—Watch Me! Sing, Dance & Read with Me, Read-Along with Small Book. 2000. 12p. (J). (ps-3). pap. 9.95 incl. audio (978-1-931127-41-7(7) , 986-013) Kindermusik International.

Bowdish, Lynea. One Glad Man. Sorra, Kristin, illus. 1999. (Rookie Readers Ser.). 32p. (J). (gr. 1-2). 19.50 (978-0-516-21595-2(7) , Children's Pr.) Scholastic Library Publishing.

—One Glad Man. Sorra, Kristin, illus. 2000. 31p. (J). (ps-3). lib. bdg. 12.95 (978-0-613-54628-7(8)) Tandem Library Bks.

—Preguntas Tontitas. Doty, Eldon C., illus. 2002. (Rookie Reader Espanol Ser.). (SPA.). (J). (gr. k-2). pap. 4.95 (978-0-516-26319-9(6) , Children's Pr.) Scholastic Library Publishing.

—Silly Questions Level C. Doty, Eldon C., illus. 2001. (Rookie Readers Ser.). 32p. (J). (gr. 1-2). 19.50 (978-0-516-22230-1(9) , Children's Pr.) Scholastic Library Publishing.

Bowen. Maren's Nest. Date not set. 48p. (J). pap. 6.99 (978-0-06-440790-8(X)) HarperCollins Pubs.

Bowen, Gary. The Mare's Nest. Kimble, Warren, illus. 2001. 48p. (J). (gr. 1-5). 17.95 (978-0-06-028408-4(0)); (gr. 3-6). 17.89 (978-0-06-028407-7(2)) HarperCollins Pubs.

The Boy Who Cried Wolf: Individual Title Six-Packs. 32p. (gr. 2 up). 37.00 (978-0-7635-9218-9(8)) Rigby Education.

Boyle, Bob. Hugo & the Mysterious Red String. 2007. (J). (978-0-375-83423-3(0)); lib. bdg. (978-0-375-93423-0(5)) Random Hse., Inc.

Boynton, Sandra. A to Z. 2001. (Illus.). (J). bds. 4.99 (978-0-689-83624-4(4) , Simon & Schuster Children's Publishing) Simon & Schuster Children's Publishing.

—Azul el Sombrero, Verde el Sombrero. Boynton, Sandra, illus. 2003. Tr. of Blue Hat, Green Hat. (SPA., Illus.). 14p. (J). bds. 5.99 (978-0-689-86304-2(7) , Libros Para Ninos) Simon & Schuster Children's Publishing.

—Barnyard Dance! Boynton, Sandra, illus. 1999. (Illus.). 24p. (J). (ps-k). bds. 6.95 (978-1-56305-442-6(6) , 3442) Workman Publishing Co., Inc.

—Bath Time. 2007. (Illus.). 10p. (J). 7.95 (***978-0-7611-4708-4(X)***) Workman Publishing Co., Inc.

—Big Box of Boynton: Barnyard Dance! Pajama Time! Oh My Oh My Oh Dinosaurs! Boynton, Sandra, illus. 2005. (Illus.). 24p. (J). (ps-k). bds. 18.95 (978-0-7611-3989-8(3) , 13989) Workman Publishing Co., Inc.

—Blue Hat, Green Hat. 2001. (Illus.). 8p. (J). bds. 4.99 (978-0-689-83625-1(2) , Simon & Schuster Children's Publishing) Simon & Schuster Children's Publishing.

—But Not the Hippopotamus. 2001. (Illus.). (J). bds. 4.99 (978-0-689-83626-8(0) , Simon & Schuster Children's Publishing) Simon & Schuster Children's Publishing.

—Fuzzy Fuzzy Fuzzy! A Touch, Skritch, & Tickle Book. Boynton, Sandra, illus. 2003. (Illus.). 12p. (J). bds. 12.95 (978-0-689-86363-9(2) , Little Simon) Simon & Schuster Children's Publishing.

—The Going to Bed Book. Boynton, Sandra, illus. 2006. 14p. (J). 12.95 (978-1-4169-2794-5(8) , Little Simon) Simon & Schuster Children's Publishing.

—Hey! Wake Up! ed. 2004. (Illus.). (J). (ps up). spiral bd., bds. (978-0-616-14611-8(6)) Canadian National Institute for the Blind/Institut National Canadien pour les Aveugles.

—Hey! Wake Up! 2000. (Illus.). 24p. (J). (ps). bds. 6.95 (978-0-7611-1976-0(0) , 11976) Workman Publishing Co., Inc.

—Moo, Baa, La La La! braille ed. 2004. (J). (gr. 1). spiral bd., bds. (978-0-616-03082-0(7)) Canadian National Institute for the Blind/Institut National Canadien pour les Aveugles.

—Moo, Baa, La La La! Boynton, Sandra, illus. 2004. (Illus.). 16p. (J). 9.99 (978-0-689-87027-9(2) , Little Simon) Simon & Schuster Children's Publishing.

—Muu. Beee. ¡Asi Fue! Boynton, Sandra, illus. 2003. (SPA., Illus.). 14p. (J). bds. 5.99 (978-0-689-86302-8(0) , Libros Para Ninos) Simon & Schuster Children's Publishing.

—Opuestos. Ziegler, Argentina Palacios, tr. Boynton, Sandra, illus. 2004. Tr. of Opposites. (SPA., Illus.). 16p. (J). bds. 5.99 (978-0-689-86978-5(9) , Libros Para Ninos) Simon & Schuster Children's Publishing.

Boynton, Sandra. Sandra Boynton's Moo, Baa, la la La! Book & Rattle. Boynton, Sandra, illus. 2009. 16p. (J). bds. 16.99 (***978-1-4169-5035-6(4)*** , Little Simon) Simon & Schuster Children's Publishing.

Brady, Irene. Wild Babies: A Canyon Sketchbook. Brady, Irene, illus. 1998. (Illus.). iix, 53p. (J). reprint ed. per. 7.95 (978-0-915965-03-8(8)) Nature Works Press.

The Brain's Grand Plan, Bk. 1. 1999. (McGraw-Hill Junior Academic Ser.). (Illus.). 16p. (J). (gr. 2). pap. 2.99 (978-1-57768-512-8(1)) School Specialty Publishing.

Brandon, Anthony G. Moving Day. Yee, Wong Herbert, illus. 2005. (Green Light Readers Level 2 Ser.). 32p. (J). (ps-ps). 12.95 (978-0-15-205646-9(7)); pap. 3.95 (978-0-15-205652-0(1)) Harcourt Trade Pubs.

Braun, Sebastien. I Love My Mommy. Braun, Sebastien, illus. 2004. (Illus.). 32p. (J). (ps-2). 15.99 (978-0-06-054310-5(8)) HarperCollins Pubs.

Bray, Jeannine D. Pop Pop: What Do Armadillos Eat? Kenyatta, Imani, ed. Mitchell, Denise B., illus. 1998. 56p. (J). (gr. k-6). 13.95 (978-1-886580-87-9(1)) Pinnacle-Syatt Pubns.

Braybrooks, Ann. Hunny, Funny, Sunny Day. 1999. (Disney Ser.). 24p. (ps-3). pap. 3.29 (978-0-307-13148-5(3) , Golden Bks.) Random Hse. Children's Bks.

Brenner, Barbara. Too Many Mice. Cymerman, John E., illus. 1998. (Bank Street Reader Collection). 48p. (J). (gr. 1-3). lib. bdg. 22.60 (978-0-8368-1771-3(0)) Stevens, Gareth Inc.

Brenner, Emily. On the First Day of Grade School. Whatley, Bruce, illus. 2004. 32p. (J). (ps-1). 15.99 (978-0-06-028013-0(1)); lib. bdg. 16.89 (978-0-06-051041-1(2)) HarperCollins Pubs.

Brett, Jan. Annie & the Wild Animals. 2006. (Illus.). 17p. (J). (gr. k-3). bds. 7.95 (978-0-618-74786-3(9)) Houghton Mifflin Co. Trade & Reference Div.

—Armadillo Rodeo. Brett, Jan, illus. 2004. (Illus.). 32p. (J). (ps-1). pap. 6.99 (978-0-14-240125-5(0) , Puffin) Penguin Group (USA) Inc.

—Jan Brett's Little Library: The Mitten, the Hat, Gingerbread Baby. Brett, Jan, illus. 2003. (Illus.). 36p. (J). (ps). lthr. 23.99 (978-0-399-24183-3(3) , Putnam Juvenile) Penguin Group (USA) Inc.

—The Mitten. Brett, Jan, illus. 2002. (Illus.). (J). 23.64 (978-0-7587-3151-7(5)) Book Wholesalers, Inc.

—The Mitten. 2001. (J). (gr. k-3). 27.95 incl. audio (978-0-8045-6862-3(6) , 6862) Spoken Arts, Inc.

—On Noah's Ark. 2003. (Illus.). 32p. (J). (ps-3). 16.99 (978-0-399-24028-7(4) , Putnam Juvenile) Penguin Group (USA) Inc.

—El Sombrero. (Buenas Noches Coleccion).Tr. of Hat. (SPA.). (J). 7.95 (978-958-04-4169-4(3)) Norma S.A. COL. *Dist:* Distribuidora Norma, Inc., Lectorum Pubns., Inc.

—The Umbrella. 2004. (Illus.). 32p. (J). (ps-3). 16.99 (978-0-399-24215-1(5) , Putnam Juvenile) Penguin Group (USA) Inc.

—The Umbrella. 2005. (Illus.). (J). (gr. k-3). 27.95 incl. audio (978-0-8045-6931-6(2) , SAC6931); 29.95 incl. audio compact disk (978-0-8045-4126-8(4) , SACD4126) Spoken Arts, Inc.

Brian Wildsmith's Wild Animals. 2004. (J). pap. 14.95 incl. audio (978-1-56008-168-5(6)) Weston Woods Studios, Inc.

Bricker, Sherry A. Simon & Salina: The Journey Has Begun. 2006. 108p. pap. 16.95 (978-1-4241-1283-8(4)) PublishAmerica, Inc.

Bridges, Margaret Park. Edna Elephant. Bynum, Janie, illus. 2002. (Brand New Readers Ser.). 32p. (J). (ps-2). pap. 5.99 (978-0-7636-1556-7(0)) Candlewick Pr.

Brightwood, Laura, illus. Mousanga Bira Mousa. Brightwood, Laura, . 2006. (J). (978-0-9789871-1-4(X)) 3-C Institute for Social Development.

Brilliant Beginnings Staff. Furry Friends & Merry Melodies Follow-Along Picture Book. 1999. (Illus.). (978-0-9665815-9-1(8)) Brilliant Beginnings, LLC.

Brimner, Larry Dane. Bigger & Smaller. Girouard, Patrick, illus. 2005. (Magic Door to Learning Ser.). 24p. (J). (ps-3). 21.36 (978-1-59296-532-8(6)) Child's World, Inc.

Brook, Jasmine. Top to Tail Bear. 1998. (Illus.). 12p. (J). (ps). 7.95 (978-0-7641-5072-2(3)) Barron's Educational Series, Inc.

Brooker, Belinda. Mundarda. Brooker, Belinda, illus. (Illus.). 32p. 18.95 (978-1-875560-18-9(1)) Univ. of Western Australia Pr. AUS. *Dist:* International Specialized Bk. Services.

Brooks, Alan. Frogs Jump: A Counting Book. Kellogg, Steven, illus. 1999. 48p. (J). (ps-1). pap. 6.99 (978-0-590-45529-9(X)) Scholastic, Inc.

—Frogs Jump: A Counting Book. 1999. (J). lib. bdg. (978-0-606-17058-1(8)) Tandem Library Bks.

Brooks, Stephen. Creatures of the Night. Wilson, Rodger, illus. 2005. 32p. (J). 19.95 (978-0-9769017-1-6(4)) Purple Sky Publishing.

Brooks, Walter R. Freddy & Simon the Dictator. 2003. 220p. (J). (gr. 4-7). 23.95 (978-1-58567-359-9(5)) Overlook Pr., The.

Broutin & Stehr. Baldomero Va A la Escuela. (SPA.). 26p. (978-84-95150-47-9(6)) Corimbo, Editorial S.L.

Brown, Janet Allison. Choo! Choo! A Squeak Me Book. Pirie, Janie, illus. 2005. 12p. (J). bds. 5.95 (978-0-7641-5825-4(2)) Barron's Educational Series, Inc.

Brown, Jo. Where's My Mommy? Brown, Jo, illus. 2006. (Illus.). 18p. (J). bds. 6.95 (978-1-58925-795-5(2) , tiger tales) ME Media LLC.

—Where's My Mommy? 2004. (Illus.). 32p. (J). tchr. ed. 14.95 (978-1-58925-019-2(2) , tiger tales) ME Media LLC.

Brown, Ken, illus. What's the Time, Grandma Wolf? 2001. 32p. (J). (ps-1). 15.95 (978-1-56145-250-7(5) , Q33285) Peachtree Pubs., Ltd.

Brown, Lisa. How to Be. Brown, Lisa, illus. 2006. (Illus.). 32p. (J). 15.99 (978-0-06-054635-9(2)); lib. bdg. 16.89 (978-0-06-054636-6(0)) HarperCollins Pubs.

Brown, Marc. Arthur & the 1,001 Dads. Brown, Marc, illus. 28th ed. 2003. (Arthur Chapter Bks. : Bk. 28). (Illus.). 64p. (J). (gr. 1-4). 14.95 (978-0-316-12516-1(4)); pap. 4.25 (978-0-316-12280-1(7)) Little, Brown Bks. for Young Readers.

—Arthur & the 1,001 Dads. 2003. (Arthur Chapter Bks.: Bk. 28). (Illus.). 57p. (J). (ps). lib. bdg. 12.10 (978-0-613-58311-4(6)) Tandem Library Bks.

—Arthur & the Bad-Luck Brain. 30th ed. 2003. (Arthur Chapter Bks.: Bk. 30). (Illus.). 64p. (J). (gr. 2-4). pap. 4.25 (978-0-316-12377-8(3)) Little Brown & Co.

—Arthur & the Bad-Luck Brain. 30th ed. 2003. (Arthur Chapter Bks. : Bk. 30). (Illus.). 64p. (J). (gr. 2-4). 14.95 (978-0-316-12650-2(0)) Little, Brown Bks. for Young Readers.

—Arthur & the Best Coach Ever. Brown, Marc, illus. 4th ed. 2001. (Arthur Good Sports Ser.: Bk. 4). (Illus.). 64p. (J). (gr. 2-4). 13.95 (978-0-316-11965-8(2)); pap. 4.25 (978-0-316-12117-0(7)) Little, Brown Bks. for Young Readers.

—Arthur & the Best Coach Ever. 2001. (Arthur Good Sports Ser.: Bk. 4). (gr. 3-6). lib. bdg. 11.80 (978-0-613-35627-5(6)); (Illus.). (J). 10.75 (978-0-606-21910-5(2)) Tandem Library Bks.

—Arthur & the Double Dare. 2002. (Arthur Chapter Bks.: Bk. 25). (Illus.). (J). 11.70 (978-0-7587-9423-9(1)) Book Wholesalers, Inc.

—Arthur & the Double Dare. Brown, Marc, illus. 2002. (Arthur Chapter Bks. : Bk. 25). (Illus.). 64p. (J). (gr. 2-4). 13.95 (978-0-316-12264-1(5)); pap. 4.25 (978-0-316-12087-6(1)) Little, Brown Bks. for Young Readers.

—Arthur & the Double Dare. 2002. (Arthur Chapter Bks.: Bk. 25). (gr. k-3). lib. bdg. 12.10 (978-0-613-50586-4(7)) Tandem Library Bks.

—Arthur & the Goalie Ghost. Brown, Marc, illus. 5th ed. 2001. (Arthur Good Sports Ser.: Bk. 5). (Illus.). 64p. (J). (gr. 2-4). 14.95 (978-0-316-12042-5(1)); pap. 3.95 (978-0-316-12146-0(0)) Little, Brown Bks. for Young Readers.

—Arthur & the Goalie Ghost. 2001. (Arthur Good Sports Ser.). (gr. k-3). lib. bdg. 11.80 (978-0-613-44164-3(8)); (Illus.). (J). 10.75 (978-0-606-22027-9(5)) Tandem Library Bks.

—Arthur & the Nerves of Steal. 2004. (Arthur Chapter Bks. : Bk. 32). (Illus.). 64p. (J). (gr. 2-4). 14.99 (978-0-316-12895-7(3)); pap. 4.25 (978-0-316-12618-2(7)) Little, Brown Bks. for Young Readers. (Tingley, Megan Bks.).

—Arthur & the New Kid. 2004. (Arthur Ser.). (Illus.). 24p. (J). (gr. k-3). pap. 3.99 (978-0-375-81381-8(0)); lib. bdg. 11.99 (978-0-375-91381-5(5)) Random Hse. Children's Bks. (Random Hse. Bks. for Young Readers).

—Arthur & the Pen-Pal Playoff. 2002. (Arthur Good Sports Ser.: Bk. 6). (Illus.). (J). 11.70 (978-0-7587-6863-6(X)) Book Wholesalers, Inc.

—Arthur & the Pen-Pal Playoff. Brown, Marc, illus. 6th ed. 2001. (Arthur Good Sports Ser.: Bk. 6). (Illus.). 64p. (J). (gr. 2-4). 14.95 (978-0-316-12054-8(5)); pap. 4.25 (978-0-316-12170-5(3)) Little, Brown Bks. for Young Readers.

—Arthur & the Pen-Pal Playoff. 2001. (Arthur Good Sports Ser.: Bk. 6). (ps-3). (Illus.). 55p. (J). lib. bdg. 12.10 (978-0-613-44165-0(6)); 11.05 (978-0-606-22556-4(0)) Tandem Library Bks.

—Arthur & the Poetry Contest. Brown, Marc, illus. 18th ed. 1999. (Arthur Chapter Bks.: Bk. 18). (Illus.). 64p. (J). (gr. 2-4). pap. 4.25 (978-0-316-12295-5(5)) Little, Brown Bks. for Young Readers.

—Arthur & the Popularity Test. (Arthur Chapter Bks. : Bk. 12). (J). 1999. (gr. 3-6). pap. 3.95 (978-0-316-11999-3(7)); 12th ed. 1998. (Illus.). 64p. (gr. 2-4). pap. 4.25 (978-0-316-11545-2(2)) Little, Brown Bks. for Young Readers.

—Arthur & the Popularity Test. (Arthur Chapter Bks.: Bk. 12). 58p. (J). (gr. 3-6). pap. 3.95 (978-0-8072-1308-7(X)); 2004. (gr. 2-4). pap. 17.00 incl. audio (978-0-8072-0413-9(7) , FTR204SP) Random Hse. Audio Publishing Group. (Listening Library).

—Arthur & the Race to Read. 2001. (Arthur Good Sports Ser.: Bk. 1). (Illus.). (J). (ps). 58p. lib. bdg. 12.10 (978-0-613-35628-2(4)); 11.05 (978-0-606-21041-6(5)) Tandem Library Bks.

—Arthur & the Recess Rookie. 2001. (Arthur Good Sports Ser.: Bk. 3). (Illus.). 64p. (J). (gr. 2-4). 13.95 (978-0-316-11916-0(4)); 3rd ed. pap. 4.25 (978-0-316-12105-7(3)) Little, Brown Bks. for Young Readers.

—Arthur & the Recess Rookie. 2001. (Arthur Good Sports Ser.: Bk. 3). (gr. 3-6). lib. bdg. 11.80 (978-0-613-35629-9(2)); (Illus.). (J). 10.75 (978-0-606-21909-9(9)) Tandem Library Bks.

—Arthur & the Seventh-Inning Stretcher. Brown, Marc, illus. 2nd ed. 2001. (Arthur Good Sports Ser.: Bk. 2). (Illus.). 64p. (J). (gr. 2-4). 13.95 (978-0-316-11861-3(3)) Little, Brown Bks. for Young Readers.

—Arthur Jumps into Fall. 2006. (Illus.). 24p. (J). (ps-1). mass mkt. 3.99 (978-0-316-05775-2(4)) Little Brown & Co.

—Arthur Lost & Found. ed. 2004. (Arthur Adventure Ser.). (J). (gr. k-3). spiral bd. (978-0-616-11102-4(9)) Canadian National Institute for the Blind/Institut National Canadien pour les Aveugles.

—Arthur Lost & Found. Brown, Marc, illus. 1998. (Arthur Adventure Ser.). (Illus.). 32p. (J). (ps-3). 15.95 (978-0-316-10912-3(6)) Little, Brown Bks. for Young Readers.

—Arthur Lost & Found. 2000. (Arthur Adventure Ser.). (J). (gr. k-3). 12.75 (978-0-606-19835-6(0)) Tandem Library Bks.

—Arthur to the Rescue. 13th ed. 2006. (Illus.). 24p. (J). (ps-1). mass mkt. 3.99 (978-0-316-05773-8(8)) Little Brown & Co.

—Arthur's Birthday. Brown, Marc, illus. 2005. (Arthur Adventure Ser.). (Illus.). 32p. (J). (ps-3). pap., pap. 10.99 incl. audio compact disk (978-0-316-05957-2(9)) Little Brown & Co.

—Arthur's Birthday. ed. 1998. (Arthur Adventure Ser.). (J). pap. 5.95 (978-0-316-10573-6(2)) Little Brown & Co.

—Arthur's Birthday Surprise. 2004. (Arthur's 8 x 8 Bks.). (Illus.). 24p. (J). (ps-1). pap. 3.99 (978-0-316-73379-3(2)) Little, Brown Bks. for Young Readers.

—Arthur's Classroom Fib. 2007. (Illus.). 24p. (J). (gr. 1-3). pap. 3.99 (978-0-375-82975-8(X)); lib. bdg. 11.99 (978-0-375-92975-5(4)) Random Hse. Children's Bks. (Random Hse. Bks. for Young Readers).

—Arthur's Family Treasury: Three Arthur Adventures in One Volume. Brown, Marc, illus. 2000. (Illus.). 112p. (J). (ps-3). 18.95 (978-0-316-12147-7(9)) Little Brown & Co.

—Arthur's Fire Drill. Brown, Marc, illus. 2000. (Arthur Ser.). (Illus.). 24p. (J). (gr. k-3). pap. 3.99 (978-0-679-88476-7(9)); lib. bdg. 11.99 (978-0-679-98476-4(3)) Random Hse. Children's Bks. (Random Hse. Bks. for Young Readers).

—Arthur's Fire Drill. 2000. (Arthur Ser.). (ps-2). lib. bdg. 11.80 (978-0-613-46251-8(3)) Tandem Library Bks.

—Arthur's First Kiss. Brown, Marc, illus. 2001. (Arthur Ser.). (Illus.). 24p. (J). (gr. k-3). lib. bdg. 11.99 (978-0-375-90602-2(9) , Random Hse. Bks. for Young Readers) Random Hse. Children's Bks.

—Arthur's First Sleepover. Brown, Marc, illus. 2002. (Arthur Adventure Ser.). (Illus.). (J). 13.15 (978-0-7587-1982-9(5)) Book Wholesalers, Inc.

—Arthur's First Sleepover. Brown, Marc, illus. 2005. (Arthur Adventure Ser.). 32p. (J). (ps-1). pap. 10.99 (978-0-316-05956-5(0)) Little Brown & Co.

—Arthur's First Sleepover. Brown, Marc, illus. 1999. (Arthur Adventure Ser.). (Illus.). 30p. (J). (ps-k). bds. 5.95 (978-0-316-10560-6(0)) Little, Brown Bks. for Young Readers.

—Arthur's First Sleepover. 1998. (Arthur Adventure Ser.). (J). (gr. k-3). pap. 5.95 (978-0-316-11974-0(1)); 32p. 9.95 (978-0-316-11948-1(2)) Little, Brown Bks. for Young Readers.

—Arthur's Heart Mix-Up. 2004. (Arthur's 8 x 8 Bks.). (Illus.). 24p. (J). (ps-1). pap. 3.99 (978-0-316-73381-6(4)) Little Brown & Co.

—Arthur's Jelly Beans. 2004. (Arthur's 8 x 8 Bks.). (Illus.). 24p. (J). (ps-1). pap. 3.99 (978-0-316-73382-3(2)) Little Brown & Co.

—Arthur's Jelly Beans. 2004. (Arthur's 8 x 8 Bks.). (ps-2). lib. bdg. 11.80 (978-0-613-71774-8(0)) Tandem Library Bks.

—Arthur's Lost Ducklin, 18 vols., Vol. 18. 2001. (Illus.). 28p. (J). 3.79 (978-1-57973-124-3(4)) Advance Pubs. LLC.

—Arthur's New Puppy. Brown, Marc, illus. 2005. (Arthur Adventure Ser.). 32p. (J). (ps-1). pap. 10.99 (978-0-316-05955-8(2)) Little Brown & Co.

—Arthur's Nose. Brown, Marc, illus. 25th rev. anniv. ed. 2005. (Arthur Adventure Ser.). (Illus.). 30p. (J). reprint ed. 16.00 (978-0-7567-9715-7(2)) DIANE Publishing Co.

—Arthur's Nose. Brown, Marc, illus. 25th ltd. anniv. ed. 2001. (Arthur Adventure Ser.). (Illus.). 40p. (J). (ps-3). pap. 15.95 (978-0-316-11884-2(2)) Little, Brown Bks. for Young Readers.

—Arthur's off to School. 2004. (Arthur's 8 x 8 Bks.). (Illus.). 24p. (J). (ps-1). pap. 3.99 (978-0-316-73378-6(4)) Little, Brown Bks. for Young Readers.

—Arthur's off to School. 2004. (Arthur's 8 x 8 Bks.). (ps-2). lib. bdg. 11.80 (978-0-613-71773-1(2)) Tandem Library Bks.

—Arthur's Teacher Moves In. Brown, Marc, illus. 2000. (Arthur Adventure Ser.). (Illus.). 32p. (J). (ps-3). 15.95 (978-0-316-11979-5(2)) Little, Brown Bks. for Young Readers.

—Arthur's Teacher Moves In. 2000. (Arthur Adventure Ser.). (J). (gr. k-3). 15.95 (978-0-316-11856-9(7)) Little, Brown Bks. for Young Readers.

—Arthur's Tooth. Brown, Marc, illus. 2005. (Arthur Adventure Ser.). 32p. (J). (gr. 1-3). pap. 10.99 (978-0-316-05960-2(9)) Little Brown & Co.

—Arthur's Underwear: An Arthur Adventure. Brown, Marc, illus. 1999. (Arthur Adventure Ser.). (Illus.). 32p. (J). (ps-3). 15.95 (978-0-316-11012-9(4)) Little, Brown Bks. for Young Readers.

—Arturo Escribe un Cuento. 2001. (SPA.). (gr. k-3). lib. bdg. 15.25 (978-0-613-35899-6(6)); (Illus.). (J). 13.75 (978-0-606-21043-0(1)) Tandem Library Bks.

—Arturo Visita la Casa Blanca. Sarfatti, Esther, tr. from ENG. 2001. (SPA., Illus.). (J). (gr. k-2). pap. 6.95 (978-1-930332-11-9(4) , LC30189) Lectorum Pubns., Inc.

—Arturo Visita la Casa Blanca. 2001. (SPA.). lib. bdg. 15.25 (978-0-613-64341-2(0)) Tandem Library Bks.

—Arturo y el Dia de Accion de Gracias. 2000. (Arthur Adventure Ser.). (SPA., Illus.). (J). (gr. k-2). pap. 6.95 (978-1-880507-79-7(X) , LC7610) Lectorum Pubns., Inc.

—Arturo y el Dia de Accion de Gracias. 2000. (J). 13.75 (978-0-606-20186-5(6)) Tandem Library Bks.

—Buster Baxter, Cat Saver. 2000. (Arthur Chapter Bks. : Bk. 19). (J). (gr. 3-6). pap. 3.95 (978-0-316-11817-0(6)) Little, Brown Bks. for Young Readers.

—Buster Baxter, Cat Saver. Brown, Marc, illus. 19th ed. 2000. (Arthur Chapter Bks. : Bk. 19). (Illus.). 64p. (J). (gr. 2-4). 13.95 (978-0-316-12111-8(8)); pap. 3.95 (978-0-316-12220-7(3)) Little, Brown Bks. for Young Readers.

—Buster Baxter, Cat Saver. (Arthur Chapter Bks.: Bk. 19). 2000. (gr. k-3). lib. bdg. 11.80 (978-0-613-21268-7(1)); 1999. (Illus.). (J). (gr. 3-6). 10.75 (978-0-606-18250-8(0)) Tandem Library Bks.

—Buster's Activity Book. 2004. (Postcards from Buster Ser.). (Illus.). 32p. (J). (gr. 1-4). act. bk. ed. 7.99 (978-0-316-00076-5(0)) Little, Brown Bks. for Young Readers.

—El Cachorrito de Arturo. 1999. (Arthur Adventure Ser.).Tr. of Arthur's New Puppy. (SPA., Illus.). (J). (gr. k-2). pap. 6.95 (978-1-880507-59-9(5) , LC0400) Lectorum Pubns., Inc.

—El Cachorrito de Arturo. 1999. Tr. of Arthur's New Puppy. (SPA.). (gr. k-3). lib. bdg. 15.25 (978-0-613-86349-0(6)) Tandem Library Bks.

—Cumpleanos de Arturo. 2000. (SPA.). (gr. k-3). lib. bdg. 15.25 (978-0-613-28287-1(6)) Tandem Library Bks.

—El Cumpleaños de Arturo. Sarfatti, Esther, tr. from ENG. 2000. (Arthur Adventure Ser.). (SPA., Illus.). (J). (ps-3). pap. 6.95 (978-1-880507-78-0(1) , LC7609) Lectorum Pubns., Inc.

—D. W. All Wet. Brown, Marc, illus. 2002. (D. W. Ser.). (Illus.). (J). 13.15 (978-0-7587-2325-3(3)) Book Wholesalers, Inc.

—D. W. Flips! Brown, Marc, illus. 2002. (D. W. Ser.). (Illus.). (J). 13.15 (978-0-7587-2326-0(1)) Book Wholesalers, Inc.

—D. W. Thinks Big. Brown, Marc, illus. 2002. (D. W. Ser.). (Illus.). (J). 13.15 (978-0-7587-2329-1(6)) Book Wholesalers, Inc.

—D. W.'s Lost Blankie. Brown, Marc, illus. 1998. (D. W. Ser.). (Illus.). 32p. (J). (ps-1). 13.95 (978-0-316-10914-7(2)) Little, Brown Bks. for Young Readers.

—Francine, Believe It or Not! ed. 1999. (Arthur Chapter Bks. : Bk. 14). (J). (gr. 3-6). pap. 3.95 (978-0-316-10463-0(9)) Little, Brown Bks. for Young Readers.

—Francine the Superstar. Brown, Marc, illus. 22nd ed. 2000. (Arthur Chapter Bks. : Bk. 22). (Illus.). 64p. (J). (gr. 2-4). 13.95 (978-0-316-12227-6(0)) Little, Brown Bks. for Young Readers.

—Francine the Superstar. Krensky, Stephen, tr. Brown, Marc, illus. 22nd ed. 2000. (Arthur Chapter Bks. : Bk. 22). (Illus.). 64p. (J). (gr. 2-4). pap. 4.25 (978-0-316-12250-4(5)) Little, Brown Bks. for Young Readers.

—Francine the Superstar. 2000. (Arthur Chapter Bks.: Bk. 22). (Illus.). (J). 57p. (ps). lib. bdg. 11.80 (978-0-613-25249-2(7)); (gr. 3-6). 10.75 (978-0-606-18253-9(5)) Tandem Library Bks.

—Los Vacaciones de Arturo. 1999. (Arthur Adventure Ser.). (SPA., Illus.). (J). (ps-3). pap. 6.95 (978-1-880507-60-5(9) , LC0364) Lectorum Pubns., Inc.

—La Visita del Señor Rataquemada. Sarfatti, Esther, tr. from ENG. 2003. (SPA.). (J). (gr. k-2). pap. 6.95 (978-1-930332-41-6(6)) Lectorum Pubns., Inc.

Brown, Marc, illus. Arthur & the Goalie Ghost. 2002. (Arthur Good Sports Ser.: Bk. 5). (J). 11.45 (978-0-7587-6862-9(1)) Book Wholesalers, Inc.

Brown, Marc & Sarfatti, Esther. Arturo y la Navidad. 2004. (SPA.). (J). pap. 6.95 (978-1-930332-48-5(3)) Lectorum Pubns., Inc.

Brown, Margaret. Bumble Bugs & Elephants: A Big & Little Book. Hurd, Clement, illus. 2006. 32p. (J). 14.99 (978-0-06-074512-7(6)); lib. bdg. 15.89 (978-0-06-074513-4(4)) HarperCollins Pubs.

Brown, Margaret Wise. The Dirty Little Boy. Salerno, Steven, illus. 2005. 32p. (J). (ps-1). pap. 5.95 (978-0-7614-5180-8(3)) Cavendish, Marshall Corp.

—The Dirty Little Boy. Salerno, Steven, illus. 2001. 40p. (J). (ps-3). 16.95 (978-1-890817-52-7(X)) Winslow Pr.

—Little Fur Family. 2002. (Illus.). (J). 25.04 (978-0-7587-3002-2(0)) Book Wholesalers, Inc.

—Little Fur Family. Williams, Garth, illus. deluxe ed. 2003. 32p. (J). (ps-1). 12.99 (978-0-06-051898-1(7) , Harper Festival) HarperCollins Pubs.

—Where Have You Been? Dillon, Leo & Dillon, Diane, illus. 2004. 32p. (J). (ps-1). 16.99 (978-0-06-028378-0(5)) HarperCollins Pubs.

Brown, Margaret Wise & Andreasen, Dan. Sailor Boy Jig. 2002. (Illus.). 32p. (J). (ps-k). 16.00 (978-0-689-83348-9(2) , McElderry, Margaret K.) Simon & Schuster Children's Publishing.

Brown, Maureen. The Adventures of Pinky Pig & Friends. 2001. (Illus.). 53p. (J). 14.95 (978-1-85776-598-4(2)) Book Guild, Ltd. GBR. *Dist:* Trans-Atlantic Pubns., Inc.

Brown, Pamela. Barnyard Buddies II. Hutchins, Annie H., illus. 2004. 90p. (J). pap. 16.00 (978-1-928589-21-1(9)) Gival Pr., LLC.

Brown, Peter. Chowder. 2006. (Illus.). 32p. (J). (ps-1). 15.99 (978-0-316-01180-8(0)) Little Brown & Co.

Brown, Ruth. The Old Tree: An Environmental Fable. Brown, Ruth, illus. 2007. (Illus.). 32p. (J). (ps-3). 16.99 (***978-0-7636-3461-2(1)***) Candlewick Pr.

Browne, Anthony. La Feria de Los Animales. 2002. (SPA.). 10p. 9.99 (978-968-16-6548-7(1)) Fondo de Cultura Economica USA.

Browne, Anthony, illus. Anthony Browne Presents the Animal Fair: A Spectacular Pop-up. 2004. 12p. (J). (gr. k-4). reprint ed. 15.00 (978-0-7567-8005-0(5)) DIANE Publishing Co.

Bruchac, Joseph & Bruchac, James. Raccoon's Last Race: A Traditional Abenaki Story. Aruego, Jose & Dewey, Ariane, illus. 2004. 32p. (J). (ps). 16.99 (978-0-8037-2977-3(4) , Dial) Penguin Group (USA) Inc.

Bruel, Nick. Boing! Bruel, Nick, illus. rev. ed. 2004. (Illus.). 32p. (J). 15.95 (978-1-59643-002-0(8)) Roaring Brook Pr.

Bruna, Dick. Hide & See. 2004. (Illus.). 12p. 6.99 (978-1-59226-042-3(X)) Big Tent Entertainment, Inc.

—Let's Learn: Animals. 2004. (Illus.). 24p. pap. 4.99 (978-1-59226-167-3(1)) Big Tent Entertainment, Inc.

—Let's Learn: Boris in the Forest. 2004. (Illus.). 24p. pap. 4.99 (978-1-59226-174-1(4)) Big Tent Entertainment, Inc.

—Let's Learn: Miffy Looks Around. 2004. (Illus.). 24p. pap. 4.99 (978-1-59226-173-4(6)) Big Tent Entertainment, Inc.

—Let's Learn: Miffy's Adventure. 2004. (Illus.). 24p. pap. 4.99 (978-1-59226-171-0(X)) Big Tent Entertainment, Inc.

—Let's Learn: Miffy's Day. 2004. (Illus.). 24p. pap. 4.99 (978-1-59226-170-3(1)) Big Tent Entertainment, Inc.

—Let's Learn: School Time. 2004. (Illus.). 24p. pap. 4.99 (978-1-59226-172-7(8)) Big Tent Entertainment, Inc.

—Let's Learn: Seasons of the Year. 2004. (Illus.). 24p. pap. 4.99 (978-1-59226-168-0(X)) Big Tent Entertainment, Inc.

—Let's Learn: The Great Outdoors. 2004. (Illus.). 24p. pap. 4.99 (978-1-59226-169-7(8)) Big Tent Entertainment, Inc.

—Miffy. 2004. (Illus.). 24p. (J). 7.99 (978-1-59226-022-5(5)) Big Tent Entertainment, Inc.

—Miffy & Friends: Blue-Green Coloring Book. 2004. (Illus.). 48p. pap. 5.99 (978-1-59226-096-6(9)) Big Tent Entertainment, Inc.

—Miffy & Friends: Yellow-Red Coloring Book. 2004. (Illus.). 48p. pap. 5.99 (978-1-59226-098-0(5)) Big Tent Entertainment, Inc.

—Miffy Dances. 2004. 24p. 7.99 (978-1-59226-024-9(1)); (Illus.). pap. 4.99 (978-1-59226-010-2(1)) Big Tent Entertainment, Inc.

—Miffy Says, I Love You! 2004. (Illus.). 12p. bds. 5.99 (978-1-59226-187-1(6)) Big Tent Entertainment, Inc.

The Bull & the Tramp. 2005. (J). (978-0-9746600-1-1(9)) Scott, Josephine.

Bulow, Wayde. Mystical Land: Short Stories for Children. 2001. 112p. pap. 9.95 (978-0-595-18550-4(9) , Writers Club Pr.) iUniverse, Inc.

Bumpus, Gloria. Violee: Legend of Where the Crow's Foot Grows. 2004. 48p. pap. 12.95 (978-1-4137-4983-0(6)) PublishAmerica, Inc.

Bunting, Eve. The Baby Shower. Love, Judy, illus. 2007. 28p. (J). (ps-1). 15.95 (978-1-58089-139-4(X)) Charlesbridge Publishing, Inc.

—Dear Wish Fairy. Bjhorkman, Steve, illus. 2000. (Hello Reader! Ser.). (J). (978-0-439-20634-1(0)) Scholastic, Inc.

—Riding the Tiger. Frampton, David, illus. 2001. 32p. (J). (gr. 4-6). tchr. ed. 16.00 (978-0-395-79731-0(4) , Clarion Bks.) Houghton Mifflin Co. Trade & Reference Div.

—We Were There: A Nativity Story. Minor, Wendell, illus. 2001. 32p. (J). (gr. k-3). tchr. ed. 16.00 (978-0-395-82265-4(3) , Clarion Bks.) Houghton Mifflin Co. Trade & Reference Div.

—The Wedding. Trapani, Iza, illus. 32p. (J). (ps). 2005. pap. 6.95 (978-1-58089-118-9(7)); 2004. 15.95 (978-1-58089-040-3(7)) Charlesbridge Publishing, Inc.

Burg, Sara Emmanuelle. One More Egg. 2005. (Illus.). 32p. (J). (ps up). 16.50 (978-0-7358-2002-9(3)) North-South Bks., Inc.

Burgess, Janice. Here Come the Backyardigans! Hunt, Gary, illus. 2005. (Backyardigans Ser.). 16p. (J). 9.99 (978-1-4169-0629-2(0) , Simon Spotlight/Nickelodeon) Simon & Schuster Children's Publishing.

Burgess, Thornton W. The Adventures of Bob White. (J). 18.95 (978-0-88411-776-6(6)) Amereon LTD.

—The Adventures of Grandfather Frog. (J). (gr. 5-6). 18.95 (978-0-88411-777-3(4)) Amereon LTD.

—The Adventures of Happy Jack. 2004. (Dover Children's Thrift Classics Ser.). (Illus.). 128p. (J). (gr. 3-6). pap. 2.00 (978-0-486-43321-9(8)) Dover Pubns., Inc.

—The Adventures of Jerry Muskrat. (J). (gr. 5-6). 18.95 (978-0-88411-782-7(0)) Amereon LTD.

—The Adventures of Jerry Muskrat. 2004. reprint ed. pap. 15.95 (978-1-4191-5151-4(7)); pap. 1.99 (978-1-4192-5151-1(1)) Kessinger Publishing, LLC.

—The Adventures of Johnny Chuck. 2004. reprint ed. pap. 15.95 (978-1-4191-5154-5(1)); pap. 1.99 (978-1-4192-5154-2(6)) Kessinger Publishing, LLC.

—The Adventures of Mr. Mocker. (J). 18.95 (978-0-8488-0378-0(7)) Amereon LTD.

—The Adventures of Ol' Mistah Buzzard. (J). (gr. 5-6). 18.95 (978-0-88411-784-1(7)) Amereon LTD.

—The Adventures of Ol' Mistah Buzzard. 2005. reprint ed. pap. 22.95 (978-1-4179-2352-6(0)) Kessinger Publishing, LLC.

—The Adventures of Old Man Coyote. (J). (gr. 5-6). 18.95 (978-0-88411-781-0(2)) Amereon LTD.

—The Adventures of Old Mr. Toad. (J). (gr. 5-6). 18.95 (978-0-88411-785-8(5)) Amereon LTD.

—The Adventures of Old Mr. Toad. 1998. (Illus.). 80p. (J). (gr. 3-6). pap. 1.50 (978-0-486-40385-4(8)) Dover Pubns., Inc.

—Adventures of Poor Mrs. Quack. 2004. reprint ed. pap. 15.95 (978-1-4191-5160-6(6)); pap. 1.99 (978-1-4192-5160-3(0)) Kessinger Publishing, LLC.

—The Adventures of Prickly Porky. (J). (gr. 5-6). 18.95 (978-0-88411-783-4(9)) Amereon LTD.

—The Adventures of Reddy Fox. 2005. 84p. pap. 10.95 (978-1-59540-695-8(6) , 1st World Library - Literary Society) 1st World Publishing, Inc.

—The Adventures of Unc' Billy Possum. Cady, Harrison & Stewart, Pat Ronson, trs. Cady, Harrison & Stewart, Pat Ronson, illus. 2003. (Dover Children's Thrift Classics Ser.). 90p. (J). pap. 1.50 (978-0-486-43031-7(6)) Dover Pubns., Inc.

—Big Book of Animal Stories. 2001. (Illus.). 208p. (J). (gr. 4-7). pap. 7.95 (978-0-486-41980-0(0)) Dover Pubns., Inc.

—Blacky the Crow. Cady, Harrison, illus. 1998. 80p. (J). pap. 2.00 (978-0-486-40550-6(8)) Dover Pubns., Inc.

—Bowser the Hound. 2003. (Dover Children's Thrift Classics Ser.). (Illus.). 96p. (J). (gr. 3-6). pap. 1.50 (978-0-486-42847-5(8)) Dover Pubns., Inc.

—Bowser the Hound. 2004. reprint ed. pap. 24.95 (978-1-4179-2323-6(7)) Kessinger Publishing, LLC.

—The Burgess Animal Book for Children. 2004. 288p. pap. 7.95 (978-0-486-43745-3(0)) Dover Pubns., Inc.

—The Burgess Seashore Book for Children. Southwick, W. H. & Sutton, George Miksch, illus. 2005. 288p. (gr. 4-7). pap. 9.95 (978-0-486-44253-2(5)) Dover Pubns., Inc.

—Buster Bear's Twins. 1999. (Dover Children's Thrift Classics Ser.). 80p. (J). (gr. 3-6). pap. 1.50 (978-0-486-40790-6(X)) Dover Pubns., Inc.

—Dear Old Briar Patch. (J). 18.95 (978-0-8488-0402-2(3)) Amereon LTD.

—Happy Jack. (J). 19.95 (978-0-8488-0389-6(2)) Amereon LTD.

—Lightfoot the Deer. Cady, Harrison, illus. 1998. (Dover Children's Thrift Classics Ser.). 96p. (J). (gr. 3-6). pap. 2.00 (978-0-486-40100-3(6)) Dover Pubns., Inc.

—Longlegs the Heron. (J). 19.95 (978-0-8488-0400-8(7)) Amereon LTD.

—Mother West Wind's Animal Friends. Kerr, George, tr. Kerr, George & Stewart, Pat Ronson, illus. 2003. (Dover Children's Thrift Classics Ser.). 80p. (J). pap. 1.50 (978-0-486-43030-0(8)) Dover Pubns., Inc.

—Mother West Wind's Neighbors. Kerr, George & Stewart, Pat, illus. 2003. (Dover Children's Thrift Classics Ser.). 96p. (J). (gr. 3-6). pap. 1.50 (978-0-486-42846-8(X)) Dover Pubns., Inc.

—Mrs. Peter Rabbit. 2004. reprint ed. pap. 15.95 (978-1-4191-3581-1(3)); pap. 1.99 (978-1-4192-3581-8(8)) Kessinger Publishing, LLC.

—The National Review Treasury of Classic Bedtime Stories. Cady, Harrison, illus. 2004. 368p. (J). 29.95 (978-0-9627841-8-7(4)) ISI Bks.

—Old Granny Fox. 2004. (ENG.). 94.99 (***978-1-4142-8186-5(2)***) IndyPublish.com.

—Old Granny Fox. 2004. reprint ed. pap. 15.95 (978-1-4191-3801-0(4)); pap. 1.99 (978-1-4192-3801-7(9)) Kessinger Publishing, LLC.

—Old Mother West Wind. Hague, Michael, illus. rev. ed. 2003. 96p. (J). (gr. 1 up). 18.95 (978-0-8050-7238-9(1) , Holt, Henry & Co. Bks. For Young Readers) Holt, Henry & Co.

—Old Mother West Wind's Animal Friends. 2000. (J). lib. bdg. 21.95 (978-0-88411-779-7(0) , Aeonian Pr.) Amereon LTD.

—Old Mother West Wind's Children. (J). 18.95 (978-0-8488-0386-5(8)) Amereon LTD.

—Old Mother West Wind's "Where" Stories. (J). 18.95 (978-0-8488-0388-9(4)) Amereon LTD.

—Whitefoot the Wood Mouse. 2006. (Dover Children's Thrift Classics Ser.). 112p. (J). pap. 2.00 (978-0-486-44944-9(0)) Dover Pubns., Inc.

Burgess, W. Thornton. Adventures of Jerry Muskrat. 2006. pap. 87.99 (***978-1-4280-3662-8(8)***) IndyPublish.com.

—Adventures of Paddy Beaver. 2007. pap. 33.99 (***978-1-4280-5109-6(0)***) IndyPublish.com.

—Bowser the Hound. 2006. 77.99 (***978-1-4280-3737-3(3))***; pap. 70.99 (***978-1-4280-3759-5(4)***) IndyPublish.com.

Burkhart, Christina. Surf Sammy's New Computer: A Surf Sammy & Friends Computer Adventure. 1999. (Surf Sammy & Friends Computer Adventure Ser.). (Illus.). 32p. (J). (ps-k). 14.95 (978-0-9662025-0-2(3)) Roof Publishing Co.

Burnford, Sheila. The Incredible Journey. (J). (gr. 6-8). 18.95 (978-0-88411-099-6(0)) Amereon LTD.

—The Incredible Journey. unabr. ed. 2004. 145p. (J). (gr. 5-9). pap. 29.00 incl. audio (978-0-8072-8322-6(3) , YA162SP, Listening Library) Random Hse. Audio Publishing Group.

Burns, Kate. Blink Like an Owl! 1998. (Lift-the-Flap Bk.). (Illus.). 10p. 6.95 (978-1-899607-41-9(2)) Sterling Publishing Co., Inc.

—Waddle Like a Duck! 1998. (Lift-the-Flap Bk.). (Illus.). 10p. (J). 6.95 (978-1-899607-42-6(0)) Sterling Publishing Co., Inc.

Burns, Laura. A Fine State of Affairs, No. 3. 2006. (Darcy's Wild Life Ser.: Bk. 3). 176p. (J). (gr. 4-7). pap. 4.99 (978-0-448-44260-0(4) , Grosset & Dunlap) Penguin Group (USA) Inc.

Burns, Laura J. Go West, Darcy! 2006. (Darcy's Wild Life Ser.: Bk. 6). 160p. (J). (***978-1-4156-8867-0(2)*** , Grosset & Dunlap) Penguin Group (USA) Inc.

Busby, Ailie. As Big As a Pig. 2001. (Storyboards Ser.). (Illus.). 16p. (J). bds. 5.95 (978-0-7641-5383-9(8)) Barron's Educational Series, Inc.

Bush, John & Geraghty, Paul. The Bungle in the Jungle. (Illus.). 32p. (J). 17.95 (978-0-09-174056-6(8)) Random Hse. GBR. *Dist:* Trafalgar Square Publishing.

Butler, John. Can You Cuddle Like a Koala? Butler, John, illus. (Illus.). (J). 2005. 20p. bds. 6.95 (978-1-56145-347-4(1)); 2003. 32p. 15.95 (978-1-56145-298-9(X)) Peachtree Pubs., Ltd.

—Can You Growl Like a Bear? Butler, John, illus. 2007. (Illus.). 40p. (J). (ps-1). pap. 15.95 (***978-1-56145-396-2(X)*** , Peachtree Junior) Peachtree Pubs., Ltd.

Butler, John. Ten in the Meadow. 2006. (Illus.). 32p. (J). 15.95 (978-1-56145-372-6(2)) Peachtree Pubs., Ltd.

Butler, John, illus. If You See a Kitten. 2003. 24p. (J). 13.95 (978-1-56145-108-1(8)) Peachtree Pubs., Ltd.

Butler, Kristi T. A Big Surprise. Paparone, Pamela, illus. 2005. (Green Light Readers Level 1 Ser.). 24p. (J). (ps-ps). 12.95 (978-0-15-205142-6(2)); pap. 3.95 (978-0-15-205141-9(4)) Harcourt Trade Pubs.

Butler, Kristi T. Big Surprise. Paparone, Pamela, illus. 2005. 24p. (J). lib. bdg. 10.00 (***978-1-4242-0175-4(6)***) Fitzgerald Bks.

Butler, M. Christina. One Snowy Night. Macnaughton, Tina, illus. 2007. 26p. (J). (ps). bds. 8.95 (***978-1-56148-591-8(8)***) Good Bks.

—One Winter's Day. Macnaughton, Tina, illus. 2006. 28p. (J). 16.00 (978-1-56148-532-1(2)) Good Bks.

—A Star So Bright: A Christmas Tale. Pedler, Caroline, illus. 2006. 21p. (J). (ps-2). 14.95 (978-1-56148-536-9(5)) Good Bks.

Butler, Mary Nyegard. Fantasy Marsh. Butler, Mary Nyegard, illus. 2000. (Illus.). 27p. (J). (ps-2). per. 6.95 (978-0-9701497-0-1(0)) Bay Tree Enterprises.

—Palmetto Who?, 4 vols. Butler, Mary Nyegard, illus. 2001. (Illus.). 27p. (J). (ps-3). per. 7.95 (978-0-9701497-9-4(4)) Bay Tree Enterprises.

Butterfield, Moira. Do Frogs Fly? Canals, Sonia, illus. 2007. (Animal Flappers Bks.). 16p. (J). (gr. k-k). 7.99 (978-0-7641-6027-1(3)) Barron's Educational Series, Inc.

—Do Lions Like Lettuce? Canals, Sonia, illus. 2007. (Animal Flappers Bks.). 16p. (J). (gr. k-k). 7.99 (978-0-7641-6026-4(5)) Barron's Educational Series, Inc.

—Peek-a-Boo! 2007. 10p. (J). pap. 6.99 (978-0-439-87521-9(8) , Cartwheel Bks.) Scholastic, Inc.

Butterworth, Nick. After the Storm. 2003. (Illus.). 32p. (J). pap. 11.00 (978-0-00-715515-6(8) , HarperSport) HarperCollins Pubs. Ltd. GBR. *Dist:* Independent Pubs. Group.

—One Snowy Night. Butterworth, Nick, illus. (Percy the Park Keeper Ser.). (Illus.). 32p. (J). 2008. 12.95 (***978-0-00-726024-9(5));*** Set. 2007. 22.99 (***978-0-00-720068-9(4)***) HarperCollins Pubs. Ltd. GBR. *Dist:* Independent Pubs. Group.

—One Snowy Night: Hardback plus DVD. Butterworth, Nick, illus. 2007. (Illus.). 32p. (J). 24.00 (***978-0-00-725942-7(5)***) HarperCollins Pubs. Ltd. GBR. *Dist:* Independent Pubs. Group.

—Percy the Park Keeper Treasury. 2007. (Percy the Park Keeper Ser.). (Illus.). 240p. (J). 18.99 (***978-0-00-721137-1(6)***) HarperCollins Pubs. Ltd. GBR. *Dist:* Independent Pubs. Group.

—Percy's Bumpy Ride. 2003. (Illus.). 32p. (J). pap. 11.00 (978-0-00-715514-9(X) , HarperSport) HarperCollins Pubs. Ltd. GBR. *Dist:* Trafalgar Square Publishing.

—Percy's Bumpy Ride. 2000. (Illus.). 28p. (J). (978-1-58048-091-8(8)) Sandvik Publishing.

—The Secret Path. 2003. (Illus.). 32p. (J). pap. 11.00 (978-0-00-715518-7(2)) HarperCollins Pubs. Ltd. GBR. *Dist:* Trafalgar Square Publishing.

Buzzeo, Toni. Little Loon & Papa. Spengler, Margaret, tr. Spengler, Margaret, illus. 2004. 32p. (J). (ps). 16.99 (978-0-8037-2958-2(8) , Dial) Penguin Group (USA) Inc.

—Ready or Not, Dawdle Duckling. Spengler, Margaret, illus. 2005. 32p. (J). (ps). 15.99 (978-0-8037-2959-9(6) , Dial) Penguin Group (USA) Inc.

Byars, Betsy. Bingo Brown, Amante Gitano. 2003. (Survival Ser.). (SPA., Illus.). 168p. (J). (gr. 4-7). 10.95 (978-84-239-7158-9(9) , EC6469) Espasa Calpe, S.A. ESP. *Dist:* Planeta Publishing Corp.

—Me Tarzan. Cigliano, Bill, illus. 2000. 96p. (J). (ps-3). lib. bdg. 15.89 (978-0-06-028707-8(1)) HarperCollins Pubs.

—Me Tarzan. 2002. (gr. 3-6). lib. bdg. 13.00 (978-0-613-61917-2(X)) Tandem Library Bks.

Bye-bye, Katy, Vol. 3. 2005. (Emergent Library: Vol. 1). (YA). (ps-1). 23.94 (978-0-8215-8914-4(8)) Sadlier, William H. Inc.

Byrd, Cheryl. Aaron Glen & His Animal Friends. Long, Cristina, illus. 2001. 17p. per. (978-0-9718538-0-5(0)) Rainbow Star Publishing.

Caballero, Erica. Mount Mole. 2006. pap. 10.00 (***978-1-4257-2301-9(2)***) Xlibris Corp.

Cabrera, Jane. Kitty's Cuddles. Cabrera, Jane, illus. 2007. (Illus.). 26p. (J). (ps-k). 16.95 (***978-0-8234-2066-7(3)***) Holiday Hse., Inc.

Cabrera, Jane. Mommy, Carry Me Please! Cabrera, Jane, illus. 2005. (Illus.). 32p. (J). (ps-1). 16.95 (978-0-8234-1935-7(5)) Holiday Hse., Inc.

Cader, Michael. Kiss This Book. 2001. (Illus.). 5p. (J). (ps). bds. 7.95 (978-0-8118-2862-8(X)) Chronicle Bks. LLC.

Cain, Sheridan. Donde Dormiras Pequena Liebre? Percy, Sally, illus. (SPA.). (J). (gr. k-2). pap. 16.95 (978-84-488-0869-3(X) , BS3556) Beascoa, Ediciones S.A. ESP. *Dist:* Lectorum Pubns., Inc.

Caldwell, Lise. God's Animals on the Farm. Julien, Terry, illus. 1999. 28p. (J). (ps-2). pap. 3.49 (978-0-7847-1092-0(9) , 22076) Standard Publishing.

Calhoun, Terry. The Muggwapps. 2007. (J). pap. 8.00 (***978-0-8059-7223-8(4)***) Dorrance Publishing Co., Inc.

Calmenson, Stephanie. Birthday at the Panda Palace. Cushman, Doug, illus. 2007. 32p. (J). (ps-1). 15.99 (978-0-06-052663-4(7)); lib. bdg. 16.89 (978-0-06-052664-1(5)) HarperCollins Pubs.

Calmenson, Stephanie. Jazzmatazz! Degen, Bruce, illus. 2008. 32p. (J). 16.99 (***978-0-06-077289-5(1));*** lib. bdg. 17.89 (***978-0-06-077290-1(5)***) HarperCollins Pubs.

El Camaleon. (Coleccion Animalitos Exoticos). (SPA., Illus.). 16p. (J). 16.95 (978-84-7630-370-2(X) , SAN370) Libsa, Editorial S.A. ESP. *Dist:* Continental Bk. Co., Inc.

Camp, Lindsay. Keeping up with Cheetah. Newton, Jill, illus. 2004. (ENG, VIE, CHI & GUJ.). 28p. (J). (ps-2). (978-1-85269-150-9(6)) Mantra Publishing, Ltd.

—Keeping up with Cheetah. 2000. (GUJ, ENG, VIE & CHI., Illus.). 32p. (J). 15.50 (978-1-85269-313-8(4)) Mantra Publishing, Ltd. GBR. *Dist:* AIMS International Bks., Inc.

Campbell, Joanna. Derby Dreams. 2001. (Thoroughbred Ser.: No. 10). (Illus.). 176p. (gr. 4-7). mass mkt. 4.99 (978-0-06-106672-6(9) , Harper Entertainment) HarperCollins Pubs.

—Derby Dreams. 2001. (gr. 3-6). lib. bdg. 13.00 (978-0-613-67185-9(6)) Tandem Library Bks.

Campbell, Rod. Dear Santa. Campbell, Rod, illus. 2004. (Illus.). 16p. (J). bds. 7.99 (978-0-689-87415-4(4) , Little Simon) Simon & Schuster Children's Publishing.

—Dear Zoo: A Pop-up Book. 2004. (Illus.). (J). (ENG & CHI.). (978-1-84444-170-9(9)); (ENG & ARA., bds. (978-1-84444-168-6(7)); (ENG & BEN., 32p. bds. (978-1-84444-169-3(5)); (ENG & ALB., 32p. bds. (978-1-84444-167-9(9)); (ENG & CHI., 32p. bds. (978-1-84444-171-6(7)); (ENG & PER., 32p. bds. (978-1-84444-172-3(5)); (ENG & FRE., 32p. bds. (978-1-84444-173-0(3)); (ENG & GUJ., 32p. bds. (978-1-84444-174-7(1)); (ENG & HIN., 32p. bds. (978-1-84444-175-4(X)); (ENG & PAN., 32p. bds. (978-1-84444-176-1(8)); (POR & ENG., 32p. bds. (978-1-84444-177-8(6)); (RUS & ENG., 32p. bds. (978-1-84444-178-5(4)); (ENG & SPA., 32p. bds. (978-1-84444-179-2(2)); (ENG & SOM., bds. (978-1-84444-180-8(6)); (ENG & TUR., 32p. bds. (978-1-84444-181-5(4)); (ENG & URD., bds. (978-1-84444-182-2(2)); (ENG & VIE., 32p. bds. (978-1-84444-183-9(0)) Mantra Publishing, Ltd.

—Dear Zoo: A Pop-up Book. Campbell, Rod, illus. 2005. (Illus.). 20p. (J). 12.95 (978-0-689-87751-3(X) , Little Simon) Simon & Schuster Children's Publishing.

—I Won't Bite. 14p. (J). (gr. k-1). 11.96 (978-1-57227-076-3(4) , YL7476) Pan Asia Pubns. (USA), Inc.

Candlewick Books Staff, Books. Handa's Surprise. 2003. (gr. k-3). lib. bdg. 11.80 (978-0-613-74744-8(5)) Tandem Library Bks.

Candlewick Press Staff. Love & Kisses Ams Ed. 2002. (J). bds. 12.99 (978-0-7636-1823-0(3)) Candlewick Pr.

Canetti, Yanitzia, tr. Cha-Cha-Cha en la Selva (The Animal Boogie) Harter, Debbie, illus. 2003. (SPA.). 32p. (J). 6.99 (978-1-84148-265-1(X)) Barefoot Bks., Inc.

A
B

Cannon, Janell. Little Yau: A Fuzzhead Tale. 2002. (Illus.). 56p. (J). (gr. k-3). 16.00 (978-0-15-201791-0(7)) Harcourt Children's Bks.

—Pinduli. Cannon, Janell, illus. 2004. (Illus.). 48p. (J). 16.00 (978-0-15-204668-2(2)) Harcourt Children's Bks.

Capdevila i Valls, Roser. La Escuela Que Aventura Roser. 1999. (SPA.). 40p. 15.95 (978-84-261-3005-1(4)) Lectorum Pubns., Inc.

Caple, Kathy. Termite Trouble. Caple, Kathy, illus. 2005. (Brand New Readers Ser.). (Illus.). 48p. (J). (ps-2). 14.99 (978-0-7636-2572-6(8)) Candlewick Pr.

—Worm Gets a Job. Caple, Kathy, illus. 2004. (Illus.). 40p. (J). (gr. k-3). 15.99 (978-0-7636-1694-6(X)) Candlewick Pr.

—Wow, It's Worm! Caple, Kathy, illus. 2001. (Brand New Readers Ser.). (Illus.). 32p. (J). (ps-2). pap. 5.99 (978-0-7636-1153-8(0)) Candlewick Pr.

Capriola, Arlene & Swenson, Rigmor. Little Red Riding Hood. Mastry, Cherisse, ed. Burns, Kathy, illus. 1998. (Once upon a Time Ser.). (J). (gr. k-2). pap., wbk. ed. 12.95 incl. audio (978-1-57022-176-7(6)) ECS Learning Systems, Inc.

Capucilli, Alyssa Satin. Happy Birthday, Biscuit! Schories, Pat, illus. 1999. (Biscuit Ser.). 24p. (J). (ps-1). lib. bdg. 15.89 (978-0-06-028361-2(0)) HarperCollins Pubs.

—Hello, Biscuit! Schories, Pat, illus. 1998. (Biscuit Ser.). 24p. (J). (ps-1). 12.95 (978-0-06-028071-0(9)) HarperCollins Pubs.

Carey, Graham. The Tails Book. 2002. (Illus.). 132p. (J). reprint ed. 18.00 (978-1-930873-63-6(8)) Neumann Pr., The.

Carey, Janet Lee. The Beast of Noor. 2006. 512p. (J). 16.95 (978-0-689-87644-8(0)) Simon & Schuster Children's Publishing.

Carle, Eric. Hello Red Fox. (J). (gr. k-3). 2000. (Illus.). 26p. per. (978-0-689-83492-9(6)); 1998. per. (978-0-689-00581-7(4)) Simon & Schuster Children's Publishing. (Simon & Schuster Children's Publishing).

—Hello Red Fox. Carle, Eric & Beneduce, Ann, illus. 1998. 32p. (J). (ps-3). 19.95 (978-0-689-81775-5(4)) Simon & Schuster Children's Publishing.

—Hello, Red Fox. Carle, Eric, illus. 2001. (Illus.). 32p. (J). pap. 8.99 (978-0-689-84431-7(X) , Aladdin) Simon & Schuster Children's Publishing.

—The Mixed-up Chameleon. Carle, Eric, illus. 1998. (Illus.). 32p. (J). (ps up). 7.99 (978-0-694-01147-6(9) , Harper Festival) HarperCollins Pubs.

—"Slowly, Slowly, Slowly," Said the Sloth. Carle, Eric, illus. 2002. (Illus.). 32p. (J). (ps-1). 16.99 (978-0-399-23954-0(5) , Philomel) Penguin Group (USA) Inc.

—The Very Clumsy Click Beetle. Carle, Eric, illus. 1999. (Illus.). 32p. (J). (ps-3). 21.99 (978-0-399-23201-5(X) , Philomel) Penguin Group (USA) Inc.

—10 Little Rubber Ducks (Spanish Edition) 10 patitos de Goma. Carle, Eric, illus. 2007. (SPA.). 36p. (J). 19.99 (978-0-06-112623-9(3) , Rayo) HarperCollins Pubs.

Carling, Amelia Lau, illus. Alfombras de Aserr. 2005. (SPA.). 32p. (J). 16.95 (978-0-88899-624-4(1)) Groundwood Bks. CAN. *Dist:* Perseus Distribution.

Carlson, Nancy. I Don't Like to Read! Carlson, Nancy, illus. 2007. (Illus.). 32p. (J). (gr. k-2). 15.99 (978-0-670-06191-4(3) , Viking Juvenile) Penguin Group (USA) Inc.

—Louanne Pig in Witch Lady. 2006. (Illus.). 32p. (J). 15.95 (978-0-8225-6196-5(4) , Carolrhoda Bks.); pap. 6.95 (978-0-8225-6197-2(2) , First Avenue Editions) Lerner Publishing Group.

Carlson, Nancy L. Louanne Pig in the Talent Show. 2005. (Illus.). 32p. (J). (ps-ps). lib. bdg. 15.95 (978-1-57505-915-0(0)) Lerner Publishing Group.

Carlstrom, Nancy White. Glory. Jenkins, Debra Reid, illus. 2005. 32p. (J). pap. 8.50 (978-0-8028-5291-5(2)) Eerdmans, William B. Publishing Co.

Carman, Patrick. The Dark Hills Divide. 2005. (Land of Elyon Ser.: Bk. 1). (Illus.). 253p. (J). (978-0-439-75843-7(2) , Orchard Bks.) Scholastic, Inc.

—The Dark Hills Divide. l.t. ed. 2005. (Land of Elyon Ser.: Bk. 1). 356p. 23.95 (978-0-7862-7752-0(1) , Large Print Pr.) Thorndike Pr.

Carmichael, Bruce. The Little Path by Shadow Mountain. 2003. (J). per. 10.95 (978-1-58597-198-5(7)) Leathers Publishing.

Carmody, Isobelle. A Fox Called Sorrow. (Little Fur Ser.). (Illus.). (J). (gr. 1-7). 2008. 272p. 5.99 (978-0-375-83857-6(0)); 2007. 256p. 14.99 (978-0-375-83856-9(2) , Random Hse. Bks. for Young Readers); 2007. 256p. lib. bdg. 16.99 (978-0-375-93856-6(7) , Random Hse. Bks. for Young Readers) Random Hse. Children's Bks.

Carmody, Isobelle. A Mystery of Wolves: Little Fur #3. 2008. (J). pap. (*978-0-375-83859-0(7)); (Little Fur: 3). 12.99 (*978-0-375-83858-3(9)); (Little Fur: 3). lib. bdg. 15.99 (*978-0-375-93858-0(3)) Random Hse., Inc.

Carol, Light. Chickensing Story Book Board. Carol, Light, illus. 2003. (Illus.). 60p. (J). (978-0-9745803-0-2(9)) Little Big Tomes.

Carr, Roger. Lost in the Park. 2001. (gr. k-3). lib. bdg. 11.95 (978-0-613-33390-0(X)) Tandem Library Bks.

Carris, Joan Davenport. Welcome to the Bed & Biscuit. Jones, Noah Z., illus. 2006. 128p. (J). (gr. 1-5). 15.99 (978-0-7636-2151-3(X)) Candlewick Pr.

Carter, David A. Whoo? Whoo? Carter, David A., illus. 2007. (Illus.). 32p. (J). (ps-1). 12.99 (*978-1-4169-3816-3(8) , Little Simon) Simon & Schuster Children's Publishing.

Cartwright, Reg. What We Do. 2005. (Illus.). 32p. (J). (ps). 7.95 (978-0-8050-7671-4(9) , Holt, Henry & Co. Bks. For Young Readers) Holt, Henry & Co.

Casanova, Mary. One Dog Canoe. Goodrich, Carter, illus. 1999. (978-0-7894-2582-9(3)) Dorling Kindersley Publishing, Inc.

—One-Dog Canoe. Hoyt, Ard, illus. 2003. 32p. (J). (ps-1). 16.50 (978-0-374-35638-5(6) , Farrar, Straus & Giroux (BYR)) Farrar, Straus & Giroux.

Casey, Barbara. Two Dogs & a Tail. 2004. (Illus.). 30p. (J). 7.95 (978-1-932162-25-7(9)) Benoy Publishing.

Cassels, Jean. Br'er Rabbit Captured! A Dr. David Harleyson Adventure. Cassels, Jean, illus. 2007. (Illus.). 32p. (J). 18.85 (*978-0-8027-9557-1(9)); 17.95 (*978-0-8027-9556-4(0)) Walker & Co.

Cassels, Jean. The Mysterious Collection of Dr. David Harleyson. Cassels, Jean, illus. 2004. (Illus.). 32p. (J). 17.95 (978-0-8027-8916-7(1)) Walker & Co.

Cassidy, Sean. Good to Be Small. Cassidy, Sean, illus. 2002. (Illus.). 32p. (J). (ps-k). (978-1-55041-734-0(7)) Fitzhenry & Whiteside, Ltd.

Cast, John. All Change. 1999. (Let's Play Ser.). (Illus.). 24p. (J). (ps-3). pap. 3.99 (978-0-85953-569-4(X)) Child's Play-International.

—Animal Bluff. 1999. (Let's Play Ser.). (Illus.). 24p. (J). (ps-3). pap. 3.99 (978-0-85953-567-0(3)) Child's Play-International.

Catchpool, Michael. Where There's a Bear, There's Trouble. Cabban, Vanessa, illus. 2004. 32p. (J). pap. 6.95 (978-1-58925-389-6(2) , tiger tales) ME Media LLC.

Cave, Kathryn. Henry's Song. Hendra, Sue, illus. 2000. 32p. (J). (ps-3). 16.00 (978-0-8028-5198-7(3) , Eerdmans Bks For Young Readers) Eerdmans, William B. Publishing Co.

—Out for the Count: A Counting Adventure. Riddell, Chris, illus. 2006. 32p. pap. 7.95 (978-1-84507-539-2(0)) Lincoln, Frances Ltd. GBR. *Dist:* Perseus Distribution.

Cazet, Denys. Minnie & Moo: Will You Be My Valentine? Cazet, Denys, illus. 2002. (I Can Read Bks.). (Illus.). 48p. (J). (gr. k-3). 15.99 (978-0-06-623754-1(8)); lib. bdg. 16.89 (978-0-06-623755-8(6)) HarperCollins Pubs.

—Never Poke a Squid. Cazet, Denys, illus. 2000. (Illus.). 32p. (J). (ps-2). 17.99 (978-0-531-33279-5(9) , Watts, Franklin) Scholastic Library Publishing.

Cazet, Denys, reader. Minnie & Moo: Will You Be My Valentine? (Read-Alongs for Beginning Readers Ser.). (Illus.). (J). (ps-3). 2005. pap. 18.95 incl. audio compact disk (978-1-59112-893-3(1)); 2004. 25.95 incl. audio (978-1-59112-892-2(7)); 2004. pap. 31.95 incl. audio compact disk (978-1-59112-897-7(8)); 2004. pap. 29.95 incl. audio (978-1-59112-893-9(5)) Live Oak Media.

Cecil, Charles. Little Boy Bob's Animal Friends. 2007. 27p. pap. 7.95 (978-0-533-15489-0(8)) Vantage Pr., Inc.

Cendrars, Blaise. Petits Contes Negres pour les Enfants. (FRE.). (J). pap. 19.95 (978-2-07-051787-9(X)) Gallimard, Editions FRA. *Dist:* Distribooks, Inc.

Centeio, Tara Jaye. Mommy Loves Her Baby. Date not set. 32p. (J). (ps-1). pap. 5.99 (978-0-06-443715-8(9)) HarperCollins Pubs.

Chadwick, Robert. Vengeful Impulse. 2003. 70p. pap. 8.95 (978-0-595-27876-3(0)) iUniverse, Inc.

Chamberlain, Margaret. Please Don't Tease Tootsie. 2008. 32p. (J). (ps). 16.99 (*978-0-525-47982-6(1) , Dutton Juvenile) Penguin Group (USA) Inc.

Chambers, Melinda. We Are Whoooo We Are. Spiker, Sue Ann, illus. 2006. 32p. (J). 16.95 (978-0-929915-46-3(1)) Headline Bks., Inc.

Chanda, J-P. Ah-Choo! Piluso, Piero, illus. 2003. (Oswald Pre-School Ready-to-Read Ser.: Vol. 2). 24p. (J). pap. 3.99 (978-0-689-85853-6(1) , Simon Spotlight/ Nickelodeon) Simon & Schuster Children's Publishing.

Chapman, Lynn. When You're Not Looking. 2006. (Illus.). 10p. (J). bds. 12.95 (978-0-7696-4638-1(7) , Gingham Dog Pr.) School Specialty Publishing.

Chardiet, Jon. Parker Penguin & the Winter Games. Micucci, Charles, illus. 1999. (Read with Me Ser.). 32p. (J). (gr. k-2). pap. 3.25 (978-0-590-14925-9(3)) Scholastic, Inc.

Chase, Diana. Surf's Up. 1999. 200p. (J). pap. 12.95 (978-1-86368-250-3(3)) Fremantle Pr. AUS. *Dist:* International Specialized Bk. Services.

Chato & the Party Animals. 2004. 29.95 incl. audio compact disk (978-1-55592-703-5(3)); 24.95 incl. audio (978-1-55592-693-9(2)); pap. 14.95 incl. audio (978-1-55592-687-8(8)) Weston Woods Studios, Inc.

Cherrington, Janelle. Mystery at the Big Blue House. 2000. (gr. k-3). lib. bdg. 11.25 (978-0-613-26334-4(0)) Tandem Library Bks.

Cherrington, Janelle & Strader, P. Kevin. Mystery at the Big Blue House. Brannon, Tom, illus. 2000. (Bear in the Big Blue House Ser.). 24p. (J). pap. (978-0-7434-0843-1(8) , Simon & Schuster Children's Publishing) Simon & Schuster Children's Publishing.

Cherry, Lynne. The Armadillo from Amarillo. 1999. (Illus.). 40p. (J). pap. 7.00 (978-0-15-201955-6(3) , Harcourt Paperbacks) Harcourt Children's Bks.

—The Armadillo from Amarillo. 1999. (J). 12.80 (978-0-606-16507-5(X)) Tandem Library Bks.

Child, Lauren. I Am Not Sleepy & I Will Not Go to Bed. ed. 2004. (J). (gr. k-3). spiral bd. (978-0-616-11105-5(3)); spiral bd. (978-0-616-11104-8(5)) Canadian National Institute for the Blind/Institut National Canadien pour les Aveugles.

—I Am Not Sleepy & I Will Not Go to Bed. Child, Lauren, illus. 2001. (Illus.). 32p. (J). (ps-3). 16.99 (978-0-7636-1570-3(6)) Candlewick Pr.

Child, Lauren, illus. I Am Not Sleepy & I Will Not Go to Bed. 2005. (Charlie & Lola Ser.). 32p. (J). (ps-1). reprint ed. pap. 6.99 (978-0-7636-2970-0(7)) Candlewick Pr.

Chinery, Michael. Enciclopedia de los Animales Salvajes, 8 vols.Tr. of Wild World of Animals. (SPA.). 346p. (J). (gr. 3-5). 100.00 (978-84-241-2059-7(0)) Everest de Ediciones y Distribucion, S.L. ESP. *Dist:* Lectorum Pubns., Inc.

Chocolate, Debbi. Pigs Can Fly! The Adventures of Harriet Pig & Friends. Tryon, Leslie, illus. 2004. 64p. (J). 15.95 (978-0-8126-2706-0(7)) Cricket Bks.

The Chocolate Moose. 2007. (Illus.). 48p. (J). per. 13.00 (*978-0-9767189-5-6(2)) Better Day Publishing Co.

Christelow, Eileen. The Robbery at the Diamond Dog Diner. 1999. (Illus.). (J). (ps-2). lib. bdg. 15.25 (978-0-8335-2149-1(7)) Tandem Library Bks.

Christianders, Hans & Falloon, Jane. Thumbelina. Clark, Emma Chichester, illus. 2006. 38p. (J). (gr. k-4). reprint ed. 16.00 (978-1-4223-5373-8(7)) DIANE Publishing Co.

Christie, Jean. Thunder in the Jungle. Chambers, Sally, illus. 2002. (Curious Creatures Bks.). 12p. (J). (ps-k). bds. 12.95 (978-1-4027-0209-9(4)) Sterling Publishing Co., Inc.

Christmas Is Coming. 2003. (J). 6.99 (978-1-59384-012-9(8)) Parklane Publishing.

Chronicle Books LLC Staff. Animals Charles Darwin Saw. 2009. (J). 15.95 (978-0-8118-5049-0(8)) Chronicle Bks. LLC.

—Animals Marco Polo Saw. 2009. (J). 15.95 (978-0-8118-5051-3(X)) Chronicle Bks. LLC.

—Animals Robert Scott Saw. 2007. (J). pap. 6.95 (978-0-8118-4919-7(8)) Chronicle Bks. LLC.

—Classic Illustrated/Animal Stories. 2008. 144p. (J). 19.99 (978-0-8118-5769-7(7)) Chronicle Bks. LLC.

Church, Caroline Jayne. Woof's Playtime: Woof Touch-and-Feel. Church, Caroline Jayne, illus. 2007. (Illus.). 10p. (J). (ps). 5.95 (*978-0-8027-9621-9(4)) Walker & Co.

—Woof's Snacktime: Woof Touch-and-Feel. Church, Caroline Jayne, illus. 2007. (Illus.). 10p. (J). (ps). 5.95 (*978-0-8027-9622-6(2)) Walker & Co.

Churchill, Vicki. Sometimes I Like to Curl up in a Ball. Fuge, Charles, illus. 2001. 24p. (J). 12.95 (978-1-86233-253-9(3)) David & Charles Children's Bks. GBR. *Dist:* Sterling Publishing Co., Inc.

Churchill, Vicki & Fuge, Charles. Sometimes I Like to Curl up in a Ball. (Illus.). 24p. (J). 2003. bds. 5.95 (978-1-4027-0870-1(X)); 2001. 12.95 (978-0-8069-7943-4(7)) Sterling Publishing Co., Inc.

Clark, Brenda, illus. Franklin Goes to School. 2002. (Franklin Ser.). 12.40 (978-1-4046-0312-7(3)) Book Wholesalers, Inc.

—Franklin Is Bossy. 2002. (Franklin Ser.). 12.40 (978-1-4046-0316-5(6)) Book Wholesalers, Inc.

—Franklin Plays the Game. 2002. (Franklin Ser.). 12.40 (978-1-4046-0317-2(4)) Book Wholesalers, Inc.

—Franklin Rides a Bike. 2002. (Franklin Ser.). 12.40 (978-1-4046-0318-9(2)) Book Wholesalers, Inc.

—Franklin Wants a Pet. 2002. (Franklin Ser.). 12.40 (978-1-4046-0320-2(4)) Book Wholesalers, Inc.

—Franklin's Secret Club. 2002. (Franklin Ser.). (J). 12.40 (978-0-7587-2533-2(7)) Book Wholesalers, Inc.

—Hurry up, Franklin. 2002. (Franklin Ser.). (J). 12.40 (978-0-7587-4167-7(7)) Book Wholesalers, Inc.

Clark, Patricia Nikolina. Goodbye, Goose. Diez-Luckie, Cathy, illus. 2000. (Books for Young Learners). 16p. (J). pap. 5.00 (978-1-57274-261-1(5)) Owen, Richard C. Pubs., Inc.

Classic Tales: Based on the Originals by Beatrix Potter, 12 bks. (Illus.). (J). (gr. 2-4). lib. bdg. 143.40 (978-1-56674-923-7(9)) Forest Hse. Publishing Co., Inc.

The Classic Treasury of Aesop's Fables. 2007. (Illus.). 54p. (J). (ps-3). 7.98 (*978-0-7624-2876-2(7) , Courage Bks.) Running Pr. Bk. Pubs.

Clement-Davies, David. The Sight. 2007. 480p. (YA). (gr. 7 up). pap. 8.99 (978-0-14-240874-2(3) , Puffin) Penguin Group (USA) Inc.

Clement, Rod. Just Another Ordinary Day. 1998. (Illus.). 32p. (J). (ps-3). pap. 5.95 (978-0-06-443500-0(8)) HarperCollins Pubs.

Clementoni, Donna. Tony, Tony, Tony! Tails of an Italian Greyhound. 2002. 111p. (J). pap. 9.95 (978-0-595-21879-0(2) , Writers Club Pr.) iUniverse, Inc.

Clynes, Kate. Not Again, Red Riding Hood! Daykin, Louise, illus. 2004. 32p. (J). (TAM, CZE, VIE, SPA & GUJ.). (978-1-85269-904-8(3)); (TAM, CZE, VIE, SPA & GUJ.). (978-1-85269-909-3(4)); (TAM, CZE, VIE, SPA & GUJ.). (978-1-85269-914-7(0)); (TAM, CZE, VIE, SPA & GUJ.). (978-1-85269-919-2(1)); (TAM, CZE, VIE, SPA & GUJ.). (978-1-85269-924-6(8)); (TAM, CZE, VIE, SPA & GUJ.). (978-1-85269-929-1(9)); (TAM, CZE, VIE, SPA & GUJ.). (978-1-85269-934-5(5)); (TAM, CZE, VIE, SPA & GUJ.). (978-1-85269-939-0(6)); (CZE, TAM, VIE, SPA & GUJ.). (978-1-85269-944-4(2)); (TAM, CZE, VIE, SPA & GUJ.). (978-1-85269-949-9(3)); (TAM, CZE, VIE, SPA & GUJ.). (978-1-85269-953-6(1)); (TAM, CZE, VIE, SPA & GUJ.). (978-1-85269-954-3(X)); (TAM, CZE, VIE, SPA & GUJ.). (978-1-85269-958-1(2)); (TAM, CZE, SPA, VIE & GUJ.). (978-1-85269-959-8(0)); (TAM, CZE, VIE, SPA & GUJ.). (978-1-85269-968-0(X)); (TAM, CZE, VIE, SPA & GUJ.). (978-1-85269-973-4(6)); (TAM, CZE, VIE, SPA & GUJ.). (978-1-85269-978-9(7)); (TAM, CZE, VIE, SPA & GUJ.). (978-1-85269-983-3(3)); (TAM, CZE, VIE, SPA & GUJ.). (978-1-85269-988-8(4)); (TAM, CZE, VIE, SPA & GUJ.). (978-1-85269-993-2(0)); (TAM, CZE, VIE, SPA & GUJ.). (978-1-85269-998-7(1)) Mantra Publishing, Ltd.

Cneut, Carll. The Amazing Love Story of Mr. Morf: An Astonishing Circus Romance. Cneut, Carll, illus. 2003. (Illus.). 32p. (J). (gr. k-3). tchr. ed. 15.00 (978-0-618-33170-3(0) , Clarion Bks.) Houghton Mifflin Co. Trade & Reference Div.

Coates, Theresa. Imaginary Time of Life. 2007. 102p. pap. 10.95 (*978-0-7414-4067-9(9)) Infinity Publishing.

Cock, Nicole de. The Girl & the Elephant. 2004. (Illus.). 48p. (J). 15.95 (978-1-58246-133-5(3) , Tricycle Pr.) Ten Speed Pr.

Cocos, Deborah. Tale One of the Wignuts: The Golden Sprigget of Fritzwitz. 2007. (J). 19.99 (*978-1-60247-034-7(0)) Tate Publishing & Enterprises, L.L.C.

Coffey, Timothy. Christmas at the Top of the World. Coffey, Timothy, illus. 2003. (Illus.). 32p. (J). (ps-1). 16.95 (978-0-8075-5762-4(5)) Whitman, Albert & Co.

Cohen, Caron Lee. Digger Pig & the Turnip/Marranita Poco Rabo y el Nabo. Campoy, F. Isabel, tr. Denise, Christopher, illus. 2008. (Green Light Readers Level 2 Ser.). 28p. (J). pap. 3.95 (*978-0-15-206255-2(6) , Green Light Readers) Harcourt Children's Bks.

Cohn, Marvin. Tell Me A Story Gramps. 2007. 52p. pap. 12.95 (*978-1-4241-5075-5(2)) PublishAmerica, Inc.

Cole, Babette. Los Animales Me Aterrorizan. 2003. (Babette Cole Ser.). (SPA.). 28p. (J). (ps-3). 15.95 (978-84-233-3234-2(9)) Ediciones Destino ESP. *Dist:* Lectorum Pubns., Inc., Planeta Publishing Corp.

—Beware of the Vet. (Illus.). 40p. (J). (gr. k-6). 19.95 (978-0-241-10813-0(6) , Hamilton, Hamish) Penguin Bks., Ltd. GBR. *Dist:* Trafalgar Square Publishing.

Cole, Grace. Bill the Bull. Miller, Leila, illus. 1998. 18p. (J). (ps-1). pap. 4.99 (978-1-893181-07-6(3) , Lagesse Stevens) Martell Publishing Co.

—The Donkey's Thanksgiving. Miller, Leila, illus. 1998. 16p. (J). pap. 4.99 (978-1-893181-06-9(5) , Lagesse Stevens) Martell Publishing Co.

—The Donkey's Thanksgiving. Miller, Lelia, illus. 2002. (J). 4.95 (978-0-9712923-1-4(0)) Taylor-Dth Publishing.

Coles, Michael Joseph, et al. The Land of Caring Bou. Banks, Timothy, illus. 2006. (J). (978-0-87483-814-5(2)) August Hse. Pubs., Inc.

Coll, Ivar Da. El Senor Joser Tomillo. (SPA.). (J). bds. (978-958-04-4906-5(6)) Norma S.A. COL. *Dist:* Lectorum Pubns., Inc.

Collier, Kevin Scott. Tales from Kensington Forest. l.t. ed. 2006. (Illus.). 26p. (J). E-Book 5.00 incl. cd-rom (978-1-933090-26-9(X)) Guardian Angel Publishing, Inc.

Collins, Charles. Hover for a Day. Seltzer, Jerry, illus. 2006. (J). 19.95 (978-1-60131-004-0(8)) Big Tent Bks.

Collins, Suzanne. Gregor & the Code of Claw. 2007. (Underland Chronicles). 416p. (YA). (gr. 5-9). pap. 17.99 (*978-0-439-79143-4(X) , Scholastic Pr.) Scholastic, Inc.

—Gregor & the Curse of the Warmbloods. 368p. 2006. (J). pap. 6.99 (978-0-439-65624-5(9) , Scholastic Paperbacks); 2005. (Underland Chronicles: Bk. 3). pap. 16.95 (978-0-439-65623-8(0) , Scholastic Pr.) Scholastic, Inc.

—Gregor & the Curse of the Warmbloods. l.t. ed. 2006. 297p. (J). 23.95 (978-0-7862-8083-4(2)) Thorndike Pr.

—Gregor & the Marks of Secret. 352p. (J). 2007. pap. 6.99 (*978-0-439-79146-5(4) , Scholastic Paperbacks); Vol. 4. 2006. pap. 16.99 (978-0-439-79145-8(6) , Scholastic Pr.) Scholastic, Inc.

—Gregor & the Marks of Secret. rev. l.t. ed. 2007. (Underland Chronicles Ser.). 343p. (YA). 23.95 (*978-0-7862-9553-1(8)) Thorndike Pr.

Collins, Suzanne. Gregor & the Prophecy of Bane. (J). (gr. 3-6). 2005. (Underland Chronicles: Bk. 2). 304p. 6.99 (978-0-439-65076-2(3)); 2003. 320p. 16.95 (978-0-439-43536-9(6)) Scholastic, Inc.

—Gregor & the Prophecy of Bane. l.t. ed. 2006. 297p. 23.95 (978-0-7862-8084-1(0)) Thorndike Pr.

Collins, Terry. Rancid Little Christmas. 2000. (gr. 3-6). lib. bdg. 11.80 (978-0-613-31628-6(2)) Tandem Library Bks.

Combel Editorial Staff. Los Musicos de Bremen. 2004. (Caballo alado clasicos-Al Galope Ser.). (SPA., Illus.). 24p. 6.95 (978-84-7864-783-5(X)) Combel Editorial, S.A. ESP. *Dist:* Independent Pubs. Group.

Come & Play: Individual Title Six-Packs. (Story Steps Ser.). (gr. k-2). 29.00 (978-0-7635-9595-1(0)) Rigby Education.

Conly, Jane Leslie. The Rudest Alien on Earth. rev. ed. 2002. 272p. (J). (gr. 5-8). 16.95 (978-0-8050-6069-0(3) , Holt, Henry & Co. Bks. For Young Readers) Holt, Henry & Co.

Conover, Chris. The Lion's Share. Conover, Chris, illus. 2003. (Illus.). 40p. (J). pap. 6.95 (978-0-374-44481-5(1) , Sunburst) Farrar, Straus & Giroux.

Conversations on the Ark. 2003. (Illus.). 28p. (J). 14.95 (978-0-8249-5440-6(8)) Ideals Pubns.

Conway, David. The Most Important Gift of All. Littlewood, Karin, illus. 2006. 32p. (J). 15.95 (978-0-7696-4618-3(2) , Gingham Dog Pr.) School Specialty Publishing.

Cony, Frances. Old MacDonald Had a Farm. Smyth, Iain, illus. 2002. 12p. (J). (ps-k). bds. 10.95 (978-0-531-30129-6(X) , Orchard Bks.) Scholastic, Inc.

Cook, Gerri. Where the Buffalo Jump. Yu, Chao & Wang, Jue, illus. 2003. (Dinosaur Soup Ser.). 120p. (YA). (gr. 3-5). pap. 9.95 (978-1-895836-95-0(6)) River Bks. CAN. *Dist:* Fitzhenry & Whiteside, Ltd.

Cook, Jean Thor. Los Amiguitos' Fiesta. Wilson, Lincoln, ed. Shade, Judith Donoho, illus. l.t. ed. 2001. Tr. of Little Friends' Fiesta. (SPA.). 28p. (J). (ps-3). 17.00 (978-0-9708940-0-7(7)) Gently Worded Bks., LLC.

Cook, Sherry & Johnson, Terri. Jazzy Jet, 26 vols. Kuhn, Jesse, illus. l.t. ed. 2006. (Quirkles—Exploring Phonics through Science Ser.: 10). 32p. (J). 7.99 (978-1-933815-09-1(4) , Quirkles, The) Creative 3, LLC.

—Ollie Oxygen, 26 vols. Kuhn, Jesse, illus. l.t. ed. 2006. (Quirkles—Exploring Phonics through Science Ser.: 15). 32p. (J). 7.99 (978-1-933815-14-5(0) , Quirkles, The) Creative 3, LLC.

Cook, Sherry & Terri, Johnson. Yawning Yolanda, 26. l.t. ed. 2006. (Quirkles—Exploring Phonics through Science Ser.: 25). (Illus.). 32p. (J). 7.99 (978-1-933815-24-4(8) , Quirkles, The) Creative 3, LLC.

Cool by the Pool: Coloring/Activity Book. 2005. (Illus.). (J). (978-0-9770455-2-5(8)) Educational Adventures.

Cool by the Pool: Picture Book (English) 2005. (Illus.). 47p. (J). (978-0-9770455-3-2(6)) Educational Adventures.

Cooling, Wendy. Farmyard Tales from Far & Wide. Moran, Rosslyn, illus. 1998. (Barefoot Beginners Ser.). 48p. (J). (ps-2). 15.95 (978-1-901223-38-5(8)) Barefoot Bks., Inc.

Cooper, Helen. Donde Esta Tatty Ratty? Bourgeois, Elodie, tr. 2005. (SPA.). (J). (gr. k-2). 20.95 (978-84-261-3260-4(X)) Juventud, Editorial ESP. *Dist:* Iaconi, Mariuccia Bk. Imports.

—A Pipkin of Pepper. 2004. (Illus.). 32p. (J). (978-0-385-60007-1(0) , Doubleday) Transworld Publishers Ltd.

—Toy Tales. 2000. (gr. k-3). lib. bdg. 16.40 (978-0-613-30803-8(4)) Tandem Library Bks.

Cooper, Helen, et al. Pinsiaid o Bupur. 2005. (WEL., Illus.). 28p. (978-1-84512-022-1(1)) Cymdeithas Lyfrau Ceredigion.

Cooper, Melrose. "Pets!" Heo, Yumi, illus. rev. ed. 1998. 32p. (C). (ps-2). pap. 15.95 (978-0-8050-3893-4(0) , Holt, Henry & Co. Bks. For Young Readers) Holt, Henry & Co.

Corbett, Jim. The Second Illustrated Corbett. 2006. (Illus.). 220p. pap. 19.95 (978-0-19-568428-5(1)) Oxford Univ. Pr., Inc.

Corke, Estelle. Cheetah Tale. 2001. (Bendy Tales Ser.). 8p. (J). (ps). 4.95 (978-0-7641-5368-6(4)) Barron's Educational Series, Inc.

Cosgrove, Stephen. Leo the Lop. James, Robin, illus. ed. 2002. (Serendipity Bks.). 32p. (J). pap. 4.99 (978-0-8431-7723-7(3) , Price Stern Sloan) Penguin Group (USA) Inc.

—Leo the Lop. 2002. (gr. k-3). lib. bdg. 13.00 (978-0-613-64533-1(2)) Tandem Library Bks.

—Leo the Lop: Tail Two. James, Robin, illus. ed. 2002. (Serendipity Bks.). 32p. (J). pap. 4.99 (978-0-8431-7725-1(X) , Price Stern Sloan) Penguin Group (USA) Inc.

—Leo the Lop: Tail Two. 2002. (gr. k-3). lib. bdg. 13.00 (978-0-613-86128-1(0)) Tandem Library Bks.

—Squabbles. 2003. (gr. k-3). lib. bdg. 13.00 (978-0-613-64600-0(2)) Tandem Library Bks.

Cosgrove, Stephen & James, Robin. Leo the Lop: Tail Four. ed. 2002. (Serendipity Bks.). (Illus.). 32p. (J). pap. 4.99 (978-0-8431-7727-5(6) , Price Stern Sloan) Penguin Group (USA) Inc.

Costello, David. I Can Help. 2007. (J). (978-0-374-33526-7(5)) Farrar, Straus & Giroux.

Cote, Genevieve. With You Always, Little Monday. 2007. (Illus.). 32p. (J). (ps-2). 16.00 (978-0-15-205997-2(0)) Harcourt Children's Bks.

Coulman, Valerie. When Pigs Fly. Roge, illus. 2001. 32p. (J). (ps-1). (978-1-894222-36-5(9)) Lobster Pr.

Courtin, Thierry. Decouvre les animaux avec T. (FRE.). pap. (978-2-09-202274-0(1)) Editions Rouge et Or.

Cousins, Lucy. Jazzy in the Jungle. Cousins, Lucy, illus. 2002. (Illus.). 32p. (J). (gr. k-k). 14.99 (978-0-7636-1903-9(5)) Candlewick Pr.

—Maisy, Charley, & the Wobbly Tooth. Cousins, Lucy, illus. 2006. (Illus.). 32p. (J). (gr. k-k). 12.99 (978-0-7636-2904-5(9)) Candlewick Pr.

—Maisy Drives the Bus. 2000. (ps-2). lib. bdg. 11.00 (978-0-613-27961-1(1)) Tandem Library Bks.

—Maisy Goes Camping. Cousins, Lucy, illus. 2004. (Maisy Ser.). (Illus.). 32p. (J). (gr. k-k). 12.99 (978-0-7636-2369-2(5)) Candlewick Pr.

—Maisy Goes to the Hospital. 2007. (Maisy Ser.). (Illus.). 32p. (J). (ps-k). 12.99 (978-0-7636-3377-6(1)) Candlewick Pr.

—Maisy Goes to the Library. Cousins, Lucy, illus. 2005. (Illus.). 32p. (J). (gr. k-k). 12.99 (978-0-7636-2669-3(4)) Candlewick Pr.

—Maisy Likes Music. Cousins, Lucy, illus. 2002. (Maisy Ser.). (Illus.). 12p. (J). (ps-k). bds. 6.99 (978-0-7636-1915-2(9)) Candlewick Pr.

—Maisy Loves You. 2004. (Illus.). 10p. (J). (gr. k-k). bds. 4.99 (978-0-7636-2687-7(2)) Candlewick Pr.

—Maisy Loves You. Cousins, Lucy, illus. 2003. (Maisy Ser.). (Illus.). 10p. (J). (gr. k-k). bds. 5.99 (978-0-7636-2065-3(3)) Candlewick Pr.

—Maisy Loves You: Book & Toy Gift Set. 2004. (Illus.). 1p. (J). 12.99 (978-0-7636-2564-1(7)) Candlewick Pr.

—Maisy Se Va al Parque. 2000. Tr. of Maisy Goes to the Playground. (Illus.). 16p. (J). (ps-k). (CAT.). 16.95 (978-84-88061-48-5(X)); (SPA., 16.95 (978-84-88061-46-1(3) , RR7147) Serres, Ediciones, S. L. ESP. *Dist:* Lectorum Pubns., Inc.

—Maisy's Favorite Animals. Cousins, Lucy, illus. 2001. (Maisy Bks.). (Illus.). 22p. (J). (gr. k-k). bds. 3.99 (978-0-7636-1572-7(2)) Candlewick Pr.

—Maisy's Snowy Christmas Eve. Cousins, Lucy, illus. 2003. (Maisy Ser.). (Illus.). 32p. (J). (gr. k-k). 12.99 incl. audio compact disk (978-0-7636-2196-4(X)) Candlewick Pr.

—Pool. 1999. (gr. k-3). lib. bdg. 11.00 (978-0-613-22206-8(7)) Tandem Library Bks.

—Smile, Maisy! Cousins, Lucy, illus. 2004. (Maisy Ser.). (Illus.). 16p. (J). (gr. k-k). bds. 7.99 (978-0-7636-2368-5(7)) Candlewick Pr.

Coutu, Raymond & Jones, Dawn L. Poker & the Cupcake Chase. Graef, Renee, illus. 2001. (J). pap. (978-0-9712840-7-4(5)) Boyds Collection Ltd., The.

Cowan, Catherine. My Life with Wave. Buehner, Mark, illus. ed. 2004. (J). (gr. k-3). spiral bd. (978-0-616-11863-4(5)) Canadian National Institute for the Blind/Institut National Canadien pour les Aveugles.

Cowell, Cressida. What Shall We Do with the Boo-Hoo Baby? Godon, Ingrid, illus. (J). 2003. 12p. bds. 7.99 (978-0-439-44266-4(4)); 2000. 32p. 15.95 (978-0-439-15311-9(5)) Scholastic, Inc.

Cowell, Cressida & Godon, Ingrid, illus. What Shall We Do with the Boo-Hoo Baby? 2000. (J). pap. (978-0-439-15312-6(3)) Scholastic, Inc.

Cowley, Joy. The Hole in the Tub. 2002. (Shared Reading with Joy Ser.). (Illus.). (J). (gr. k-1). pap. 43.76 (978-0-322-09782-7(7)) Wright Group, The.

Cox, Joseph J. Grobar & the Mind Control Potion. Becker, Rebecca J., illus. 2005. 168p. (J). per. 9.95 (978-0-9764659-3-5(0)) Suckerfish Bks.

Cox, Phil Roxbee. Curly's Friends. Cartwright, Stephen, illus. rev. ed. 2005. 10p. (J). bds. 7.95 (978-0-7945-1180-7(5) , Usborne) EDC Publishing.

Coxe, Molly. Bookworm. 2000. (J). (978-0-606-18920-0(3)) Tandem Library Bks.

—Fox Trot. 1999. (Road to Reading Ser.). (J). lib. bdg. (978-0-03-074629-1(9) , Saunders) Elsevier - Health Sciences Division.

Coxon, Michele. Catch up, Little Cheetah: A Lift-the-Flap Book. Coxon, Michele, illus. 1999. (Illus.). 20p. (J). (ps-k). pap. 5.95 (978-1-887734-63-9(5)) Star Bright Bks., Inc.

Coyle, Carmela LaVigna. Do Princesses Count? Gordon, Mike & Gordon, Carl, illus. 2007. 26p. (J). bds. (978-0-87358-916-1(5) , Rising Moon Bks. for Young Readers) Northland Publishing.

Crandall, Sharon Olexa. Owlie & His Magic Music. Salzman, Yuri, illus. 2001. 24p. (J). pap. 14.95 incl. audio compact disk (978-0-9662378-7-0(0)); bds. 19.95 (978-0-9662378-3-2(8)) Astoria Productions.

Crawford, Ann Fears. Keechee: The Witch of the Woods. 2005. (J). (978-1-931823-21-0(9)) Halcyon Pr.

Crawford, Joanne. Bilby & the Bushfire. 2007. 28p. pap. 17.00 (***978-1-921248-30-6(0)***) Magabala Bks. AUS. *Dist:* International Specialized Bk. Services.

Crawford, Joanne. A Home for Bilby. Fielding, Grace, illus. 2004. 28p. (J). pap. 17.00 (978-1-875641-91-8(2)) Magabala Bks. AUS. *Dist:* International Specialized Bk. Services.

Crawford, Laura. In Arctic Waters. Hodson, Ben, illus. 2007. 32p. (J). pap. 8.95 (***978-1-934359-34-1(3)***) Sylvan Dell Pubng.

Crazy Animals. 2002. (Tap My Nose Ser.). (J). (ps-k). 4.98 (978-0-7525-8726-4(9)) Parragon, Inc.

Crimi, Carolyn. Don't Need Friends. Munsinger, Lynn, illus. 2001. 32p. (J). (ps-3). reprint ed. pap. 6.99 (978-0-440-41532-9(2) , Dragonfly Bks.) Random Hse. Children's Bks.

—Don't Need Friends. 2001. (gr. k-3). lib. bdg. 15.30 (978-0-613-33752-6(2)); (Illus.). (J). 13.79 (978-0-606-21156-7(X)) Tandem Library Bks.

Cronin, Doreen. Click, Clack, Quackity-Quack: An Alphabetical Adventure. Lewin, Betsy, illus. 2005. 24p. (J). 12.95 (978-0-689-87715-5(3) , Atheneum) Simon & Schuster Children's Publishing.

—Click, Clack, Quackity-Quack: An Alphabetical Adventure. 2006. (J). (ps-3). 22.78 (978-1-59961-089-4(2)) Spotlight.

—Click, Clack, Splish, Splash. 2006. (J). (ps-3). 22.78 (978-1-59961-090-0(6)) Spotlight.

—Click, Clack, Splish, Splash: A Counting Adventure. Lewin, Betsy, illus. 2006. 24p. (J). (ps-k). 12.95 (978-0-689-87716-2(1) , Atheneum) Simon & Schuster Children's Publishing.

—Wiggle. 2006. (J). (ps-3). 22.78 (978-1-59961-093-1(0)) Spotlight.

Croteau, Marie-Danielle. The Amazing Story of the Little Black Sheep. Cote, Genevieve, illus. 1999. 32p. (J). (ps up). pap. (978-1-894363-16-7(7)) Dominique & Friends.

Crowe, Ellie. The Littlest Paniolo. KaMille, Barbara, illus. 2000. (J). 8.99 (978-0-89610-426-6(5)) Island Heritage Publishing.

—The Littlest Paniolo. KaMille, Barbara, illus. 2nd rev. ed. 2000. 42p. (J). per. 12.99 (978-0-9712885-2-2(6)) Regent Music & Bk. Publishing.

Crowson, Andrew. Flip Flap Farm. 2003. (Illus.). 12p. bds. (978-1-85602-430-3(X)) Chrysalis Children's Bks.

Crozon, Alain & Lanchais, Aurelie. Wild Animals Who Am I? 2002. (Illus.). 14p. (J). 7.95 (978-0-8118-3321-9(6)) Chronicle Bks. LLC.

Cruickshank, Margrit. We're Going to Feed the Ducks. Reeve, Rosie, illus. 2004. 24p. (J). (gr. 1 up). lib. bdg. 23.33 (978-0-8368-4027-8(5)) Stevens, Gareth Inc.

Crummel, Susan Stevens. Shoe Town. 1999. (gr. k-3). lib. bdg. 11.80 (978-0-613-66029-7(3)) Tandem Library Bks.

—Ten-Gallon Bart. Donohue, Dorothy, illus. 2006. 32p. (J). 16.95 (978-0-7614-5246-1(X)) Cavendish, Marshall Corp.

Crummel, Susan Stevens & Stevens, Janet. Shoe Town. 2003. (Green Light Readers Level 2 Ser.). (Illus.). 32p. (J). 11.95 (978-0-15-204882-2(0)); pap. 3.95 (978-0-15-204842-6(1) , Green Light Readers) Harcourt Children's Bks.

Cuentos de Animales Fantasticos para Ninos (Fantastic Animal Tales for Children) (SPA., Illus.). 72p. (J). pap. 11.95 (978-968-494-014-7(9) , NOR609) Centro de Informacion y Desarrollo de la Comunicacion y la Literatura MEX. *Dist:* Continental Bk. Co., Inc.

Cuentos de Animales Fantasticos para Ninos (Fantastic Animal Tales for Children) (SPA.). 72p. (J). 9.95 (978-958-04-0960-1(9) , 103378519) Norma S.A. COL. *Dist:* Distribuidora Norma, Inc.

Cunliffe, John. Postman Pat & the Beast of Greendale, Bk. 12. (Animal Alert Ser.). (Illus.). 32p. (J). pap. 8.99 (978-0-340-71332-7(1) , Hodder & Stoughton) Hodder General Publishing Division GBR. *Dist:* Trafalgar Square Publishing.

Cunningham, Albert Benjamin. Animal Tales of the Rockies. 2003. (gr. 3-6). lib. bdg. 26.90 (978-0-613-74801-8(8)) Tandem Library Bks.

Curry, Don, ed. It's a Big Big World: Mapping the World Tree. 2007. 24p. (J). pap. 3.99 (***978-0-696-23546-7(3)***) Meredith Bks.

—It's a Big Big World: Where's Wartz? 2007. 22p. (J). 15.95 (***978-0-696-23545-0(5)***) Meredith Bks.

—It's a Big Big World: World Tree Day. 2007. 24p. (J). pap. 3.99 (***978-0-696-23547-4(1)***) Meredith Bks.

Curtis, Mary. Little Stinky Gets Ready for School. 2006. 24p. (J). per. 11.99 (***978-1-59886-586-8(2)***) Tate Publishing & Enterprises, L.L.C.

Curtis, Susan. Baa Baa Bedtime. Samuel, Janet, illus. 2007. 24p. (J). 14.99 (978-1-4169-3836-1(2) , Little Simon) Simon & Schuster Children's Publishing.

Cushman, Doug. Mystery at the Club Sandwich. 2004. (Illus.). 32p. (J). (gr. k-3). tchr. ed. 15.00 (978-0-618-41969-2(1) , Clarion Bks.) Houghton Mifflin Co. Trade & Reference Div.

Cutting, David A., illus. Tasha's Tea Party: A Lift-the-Flap Board Book. 2006. (Backyardigans Ser.). 12p. (J). 5.99 (978-1-4169-1363-4(7) , Simon Spotlight/Nickelodeon) Simon & Schuster Children's Publishing.

Cuyler, Margery. Biggest, Best Snowman. Hillenbrand, Will, illus. 2004. (Bookshelf Ser.). 32p. (J). (gr. k-ps). pap. 5.99 (978-0-439-66940-5(5) , Scholastic Paperbacks) Scholastic, Inc.

—Biggest, Best Snowman, Library Edition. 2007. (J). 18.95 (***978-0-545-01780-0(7)***) Scholastic, Inc.

—Biggest Best Snowman, The (Readalong) 2007. (J). 9.95 (***978-0-545-01484-7(0)***) Scholastic, Inc.

—Bookshelf: Biggest, Best Snowman. Hillenbrand, Will, illus. 1998. (J). (ps-2). pap. 15.95 (978-0-590-13493-4(0)) Scholastic, Inc.

—Groundhog Stays up Late. Cassels, Jean, illus. 2005. 32p. (J). (ps-2). 16.95 (978-0-8027-8939-6(0)) Walker & Co.

—Please Play Safe! Penguin's Guide to Playground Safety. Hillenbrand, Will, illus. 2006. 32p. (J). pap. 15.99 (978-0-439-52832-0(1) , Scholastic Pr.) Scholastic, Inc.

—Please Say Please! Penguin's Guide to Manners. Hillenbrand, Will, illus. 2005. (J). (***978-0-439-67874-2(9)***) Scholastic, Inc.

—Please Say Please! Penguin's Guide to Manners. Hillenbrand, Will, tr. Hillenbrand, Will, illus. 2004. 32p. (J). pap. 15.95 (978-0-590-29224-5(2)) Scholastic, Inc.

—Road Signs: A Harey Race with a Tortoise. Haskamp, Steven, illus. 2000. 40p. (J). (ps-1). 15.95 (978-1-890817-23-7(6)) Winslow Pr.

Cuyler, Margery & Hillenbrand, Will. Bookshelf: Biggest, Best Snowman. 1998. (Illus.). 32p. (J). (ps-2). pap. 15.95 (978-0-590-13922-9(3)) Scholastic, Inc.

D C Thomson Staff, ed. Animals & You Annual 2004. 2003. (Illus.). 128p. (J). 9.95 (978-0-85116-840-1(X)) Thomson, D.C. & Co., Ltd. GBR. *Dist:* APG Sales and Fulfillment.

Dahl, Roald. Agu Trot. Blake, Quentin, illus. 2003. (SPA.). 64p. (J). (gr. 3-5). pap. 9.95 (978-84-204-4436-9(7)) Santillana USA Publishing Co., Inc.

—La Jirafa, el Pelicano y el Mono. Blake, Quentin, illus. 2003. (SPA.). 67p. (J). (gr. 3-5). pap. 10.95 (978-968-19-0756-3(6)) Santillana USA Publishing Co., Inc.

Daigneault, Sylvie. Bruno Falls Asleep. 2000. (Bruno Book Ser.). (Illus.). 32p. (J). (ps-2). 16.00 (978-0-00-224557-9(4)) HarperCollins Pubs.

Daisy, April. The Crazy 8 Diner. 2004. (Illus.). 28p. (J). per. 7.95 (978-1-59466-023-8(9) , Little Ones) Port Town Publishing.

Dakin, Glenn. Disney Animals Essential Guide. 2006. (Illus.). 48p. (J). 12.99 (978-0-7566-2006-6(6)) Dorling Kindersley Publishing, Inc.

—Finding Nemo: The Essential Guide. 2003. (Illus.). 48p. (J). (gr. k-3). 12.99 (978-0-7894-9244-9(X)) Dorling Kindersley Publishing, Inc.

Dale, Jenny. Forever Sam. Reid, Mick, illus. 2003. 104p. (J). (978-0-439-33801-1(8)) Scholastic, Inc.

—Superdog! Reid, Mick & Rowe, Michael, trs. Reid, Mick, illus. 2003. 110p. (J). (978-0-439-38921-1(6)) Scholastic, Inc.

Dale, Jenny & Reid, Mick. Puppy School. 2002. (Puppy Patrol Ser.: No. 14). 112p. (J). per. 3.99 (978-0-439-21815-3(2)) Scholastic, Inc.

Dalmatian Press Staff. Bow Wow Peep. 2006. 24p. (J). 12.99 (978-1-4037-2351-2(6)) Dalmatian Pr.

—Disney Animal Friends Treasury. 2006. 162p. bds. 10.99 (978-1-4037-2193-8(9)) Dalmatian Pr.

—Jungle BK. 2007. 5p. 9.99 (***978-1-4037-3605-5(7)***) Dalmatian Pr.

—Little Bunny: Little Pups. 2002. (Little Pups Board Bks.). (Illus.). 20p. (J). bds. 2.99 (978-1-57759-631-8(5)) Dalmatian Pr.

—Looney Tunes: Your Favorite Looney Tunes: Storybook Collection. (Looney Tunes Ser.). (Illus.). 217p. (J). 10.99 (978-1-4037-0524-2(0)) Dalmatian Pr.

Dalmatian Press Staff. Sesame Street Rise & Shine. 2007. 24p. pap. 3.50 (***978-1-4037-3233-0(7)***) Dalmatian Pr.

Dalmatian Press Staff, adapted by. The Call of the Wild. 2002. (Spot the Classics Ser.). (Illus.). 182p. (J). (gr. k-5). 4.99 (978-1-57759-545-8(9)) Dalmatian Pr.

Daly, Niki. Welcome to Zanzibar Road. 2006. (Illus.). 40p. (J). (gr. k-3). 16.00 (978-0-618-64926-6(3) , Clarion Bks.) Houghton Mifflin Co. Trade & Reference Div.

Daly, Niki, illus. A Family for Old Mill Farm. 2007. 32p. (J). (gr. k-3). 16.00 (978-0-618-42846-5(1) , Clarion Bks.) Houghton Mifflin Co. Trade & Reference Div.

D'Amico, Carmela. Ella Sets the Stage. D'Amico, Steven, illus. 2006. 41p. (J). pap. 16.99 (978-0-439-83153-6(9) , Levine, Arthur A. Bks.) Scholastic, Inc.

D'Amico, Carmela & D'Amico, Steven. Ella Sets Sail. 2008. (J). (***978-0-439-83156-7(3)***); pap. (***978-0-439-83155-0(5)***) Scholastic, Inc. (Levine, Arthur A. Bks.).

Damjan, Mischa. The Clown Said No. ed. 2004. (Illus.). (J). (gr. k-3). spiral bd. (978-0-616-14569-2(1)) Canadian National Institute for the Blind/Institut National Canadien pour les Aveugles.

—The Clown Said No. Casty, Gian, illus. 2007. 32p. (J). 17.99 (***978-0-698-40063-4(1)***, Minedition) Penguin Group (USA) Inc.

Damschroder, Scott. Pinky's Rainy Day: Pinky Padooka takes a trip to Imaginationville. Faust, Laurie, illus. 2004. 36p. (J). lib. bdg. 19.95 (978-0-9754728-0-4(1)) MidAmerica Publishing Co.

D'Andrea, Deborah. Picture Me Counting 1,2,3. Ayers, Michael B., illus. rev. ed. 2000. (Picture Me Ser.). 10p. (J). (ps-1). bds. 4.99 (978-1-57151-581-0(X)) Playhouse Publishing.

Daniel, Claire. The Chick That Wouldn't Hatch. Ernst, Lisa Campbell, illus. 2003. (Green Light Readers Level 2 Ser.). 24p. (J). 11.95 (978-0-15-204871-6(5)); pap. 3.95 (978-0-15-204831-0(6)) Harcourt Children's Bks. (Green Light Readers).

—Chick That Wouldn't Hatch. 1999. (gr. k-3). lib. bdg. 11.80 (978-0-613-63269-0(9)) Tandem Library Bks.

Daniels, Lucy. Kitten Crowd. Howard, Paul, illus. 1999. (Animal Ark Pets Ser.: No. 2). 128p. (J). (gr. 3-6). pap. 3.99 (978-0-439-05159-0(2)) Scholastic, Inc.

Dann, Colin. Animals of Farthing Wood. 2007. (Illus.). 302p. (J). (gr. 4-6). pap. 9.99 (***978-1-4052-2552-6(1)***) Egmont Bks., Ltd. GBR. *Dist:* Independent Pubs. Group.

Dann, Colin. Farthing Wood Collection 3, Vol. 3. 2001. (Illus.). 528p. (J). pap. 11.99 (978-0-09-941724-8(3)) Random Hse. GBR. *Dist:* Independent Pubs. Group.

Dann, Penny, illus. The Animals' Bedtime Storybook. 2000. 224p. (J). (978-1-85881-804-7(4)) Orion Children's Bks.

Danneberg, Julie. Que Nervios! El Primer Dia De Escuela. Mlawer, Teresa, tr. Love, Judy, illus. 2006. (J). 16.95 (978-1-58089-147-9(0)) Charlesbridge Publishing, Inc.

Darden, Floyd. Drumdee makes a Drum. 2007. 15.95 (***978-1-59526-711-5(5)***) Media Creations, Inc.

Dasilva, Kiko. Moncho y la Mancha. 2004. (SPA.). 40p. (J). 15.99 (978-84-8464-078-3(7)) Kalandraka Editora, S.L. ESP. *Dist:* Lectorum Pubns., Inc.

David C. Cook. Li'l Critters. 2003. (My Jesus Pocket Bks.). (Illus.). 32p. (J). (gr. 5-3). pap., pap. 8.90 (978-1-55513-098-5(4) , 1555130984) Cook, David C. Publishing Co.

David, Erica. There Goes the Neighborhood. 2006. (Over the Hedge Ser.). (Illus.). 32p. (J). pap. 3.99 (978-0-439-80143-0(5)) Scholastic, Inc.

Davidson, Andrew, illus. Animal Stories. 2003. (Red Hot Reads Ser.). 224p. (J). (gr. 4-8). pap. 6.95 (978-0-7534-5673-6(7) , Kingfisher) Houghton Mifflin Co. Trade & Reference Div.

Davies, Caroline & Martin, Sharon. Chwarae Cuddio. 2005. (WEL., Illus.). 12p. (978-1-86101-080-3(X)) Acen Limited.

—Y Frech Goch. 2005. (WEL., Illus.). 12p. (978-1-86101-079-7(6)) Acen Limited.

Davis, Caroline, illus. One, Two, Who's Who? 2002. 20p. (J). 5.95 (978-1-58925-685-9(9) , tiger tales) ME Media LLC.

—Swish, Swish, Who's This? 2002. 20p. (J). 5.95 (978-1-58925-686-6(7) , tiger tales) ME Media LLC.

Davis, Guy. Witzy Wonders. Spafford, Suzy, illus. 2001. 18p. (J). (ps-3). bds. 5.99 (978-1-58668-057-2(9)) Lyrick Studios.

—Witzy's Colors. Spafford, Suzy, illus. 2001. (Little Suzy's Zoo Ser.). 12p. (J). (ps-k). pap. 5.99 (978-1-58668-055-8(2)) Lyrick Studios.

Davis, Kate. Whose Back Is Bumpy? Filipowich, Bob, illus. 2000. (Textured Soft Shapes Ser.). 8p. (J). (ps-ps). 10.99 (978-1-58476-040-5(0)) Innovative Kids.

Davis, Katie. Party Animals. 2002. (Illus.). 40p. (J). (gr. k-k). 15.00 (978-0-15-216675-5(0)) Harcourt Children's Bks.

—Who Hoots? Davis, Katie, illus. 2004. (Illus.). 32p. (ps-ps). lib. bdg. 13.20 (978-0-606-30393-4(6)) Tandem Library Bks.

—Who Hops? 2002. (Illus.). 34p. (J). bds. 5.95 (978-0-15-216608-3(4) , Red Wagon Bks.) Harcourt Children's Bks.

—Who Hops? Davis, Katie, illus. (Illus.). (J). (ps-1). 2001. 36p. pap. 6.00 (978-0-15-216412-6(X) , Voyager Bks./Libros Viajeros); 1998. 40p. 15.00 (978-0-15-201839-9(5)) Harcourt Children's Bks.

—Who Hops? 2001. (978-0-606-22598-4(6)) Tandem Library Bks.

—Who Hops?/Quien Salta? Campoy, F. Isabel, tr. from ENG. 2006. (ENG & SPA., Illus.). 34p. (J). bds. 10.95 (978-0-15-205889-0(3)) Harcourt Trade Pubs.

Davis, Tim. More Tales from Dust River Gulch. 2002. (Tales from Dust River Gulch Ser.). (Illus.). 108p. (J). (gr. 4-7). 7.49 (978-1-57924-855-0(1)) Jones, Bob Univ. Pr.

Day, Alexandra. The Flight of a Dove. 2004. (Illus.). 32p. (J). 16.00 (978-0-374-39952-8(2) , Farrar, Straus & Giroux (BYR)) Farrar, Straus & Giroux.

De Anda, Diane. Immortal Rooster & Other Stories. 1999. (gr. 3-6). lib. bdg. 18.75 (978-0-613-88762-5(X)) Tandem Library Bks.

De Beaumont, Leprince. La Belle et la Bete.Tr. of Beauty & the Beast. (FRE.). (J). pap. 14.95 (978-2-07-052101-2(X)) Gallimard, Editions FRA. *Dist:* Distribooks, Inc.

De la Garza, Phyllis. Camels West. 1999. (YA). (gr. 6 up). 9.99 (978-0-88092-443-6(8)) Royal Fireworks Publishing Co.

de Paola, Tomie. Four Friends at Christmas. de Paola, Tomie, illus. 2002. (Illus.). 32p. (J). 14.95 (978-0-689-85282-4(7)) Simon & Schuster Children's Publishing.

—Four Friends in Autumn. 2004. (Illus.). 32p. (J). 14.95 (978-0-689-85980-9(5)) Simon & Schuster Children's Publishing.

—Four Friends in Summer. de Paola, Tomie, illus. 2003. (Illus.). 32p. (J). reprint ed. 14.95 (978-0-689-85693-8(8)) Simon & Schuster Children's Publishing.

De Regniers, Beatrice Schenk. May I Bring A Friend? Montresor, Beni, illus. 2002. (J). 14.47 (978-0-7587-0057-5(1)) Book Wholesalers, Inc.

A B

—What Did You Put in Your Pocket? Date not set. 32p. (J). (ps-1). pap. 5.95 (978-0-06-443700-4(0)) HarperCollins Pubs.

—What Did You Put in Your Pocket? Grejniec, Michael, illus. 2003. 40p. (J). (ps-1). 16.99 (978-0-06-029028-3(5)) HarperCollins Pubs.

de Rosson, Francisco. Lo Que Pasa es Que el Rinoceronte es Sordo. (SPA.). (J). pap. (978-980-01-0474-3(7)) Monte Avila Editores Latinoamericana CA VEN. *Dist:* Lectorum Pubns., Inc.

—Lo Que Pasa es Que el Rinoceronte es Sordo. Saldivia, Meylin, illus. (SPA.). (J). pap. (978-980-01-0879-6(3)) Monte Avila Editores Latinoamericana CA VEN. *Dist:* Lectorum Pubns., Inc.

De Valdenebro, Eladio. Tono y los Animales Cautivos. (SPA.). (J). 8.95 (978-958-04-6021-3(3)) Norma S.A. COL. *Dist:* Distribuidora Norma, Inc.

Dean, Richard B. The Bear & the Ox. 2005. 28p. (YA). pap. 8.95 (978-0-7414-2855-4(5)) Infinity Publishing.

DeBoer, Rondi. God Must Really Love... Opposites. Haskamp, Steve, illus. 2007. 14p. (J). (ps). 6.99 ***(978-1-4169-3357-1(3)***, Little Simon Inspirations) Simon & Schuster Children's Publishing.

Décary, Marie. Adam's Tropical Adventure. Cummins, Sarah, tr. from FRE. Beshwaty, Steve, illus. 2005. (First Novel Ser.). 64p. (gr. 2-5). ***(978-0-88780-687-2(2));*** (J). 4.95 (978-0-88780-686-5(4)) Formac Publishing Co., Ltd. CAN. *Dist:* Casemate Pubs. & Bk. Distributors, LLC.

Dee. Everglades Encounter. 2006. pap. 10.74 ***(978-1-4259-5358-4(1))*** AuthorHouse.

Deen, Ron. Annabelle Rides Her Bike on an Iowa Farm. 2005. (J). 6.95 (978-1-57166-261-3(8)) Quixote Pr.

deGroat, Diane. Brand-New Pencils, Brand-New Books. deGroat, Diane, illus. 2007. 32p. (J). (ps-3). pap. 6.99 ***(978-0-06-072616-4(4)***, Harper Trophy) HarperCollins Pubs.

deGroat, Diane. Jingle Bells, Homework Smells. deGroat, Diane, illus. 2003. 32p. (J). (ps-3). pap. 6.99 (978-0-688-17545-0(7)) HarperCollins Pubs.

—Jingle Bells, Homework Smells. 2000. (gr. k-3). lib. bdg. 14.15 (978-0-613-68435-4(4)) Tandem Library Bks.

Delessert, Etienne. Big & Bad. 2008. 32p. (J). (gr. 3-5). 17.00 ***(978-0-618-88934-1(5))*** Houghton Mifflin Co.

Delessert, Etienne. Yok-Yok, 12 bks., Set. Delessert, Etienne, illus. Incl. At Home. lib. bdg. 14.60 (978-0-88682-646-8(2) , 97934-098); Best Friends. lib. bdg. 14.60 (978-0-88682-639-0(X) , 97927-098); For the Birds. lib. bdg. 14.60 (978-0-88682-638-3(1) , 97926-098); Moonlight. lib. bdg. 14.60 (978-0-88682-648-2(9) , 97936-098); Nonsense. lib. bdg. 14.60 (978-0-88682-641-3(1) , 97929-098); Nuts! lib. bdg. 14.60 (978-0-88682-644-4(6) , 97932-098); Surprises. lib. bdg. 14.60 (978-0-88682-643-7(8) , 97931-098); Weird? lib. bdg. 14.60 (978-0-88682-645-1(4) , 97933-098); What a Circus! lib. bdg. 14.95 (978-0-88682-640-6(3) , 97928-098); 32p. (J). (gr. 1-5). 1993. (Illus.). lib. bdg. (978-0-88682-637-6(3) , Creative Education) Creative Co., The.

Delonas, Sean & Delonas, Ryan. Scuttle's Big Wish. 2006. (Illus.). 40p. (J). 16.95 (978-0-06-072645-4(8) , Regan-Books) HarperCollins Pubs.

Denega, Danielle. I Love You Even If. 2007. 12p. 10.95 ***(978-1-58117-557-8(4))*** Dalmatian Pr.

Dennis, Murray Marjorie. Dont Wake up Bear. Wittmann, Patricia, illus. 2006. 32p. 5.99 (978-0-7614-5330-7(X)) Cavendish, Marshall Corp.

Denslow, Sharon Phillips. In the Snow. Tafuri, Nancy, illus. 2005. 40p. (J). 15.99 (978-0-06-059683-5(X)); lib. bdg. 16.89 (978-0-06-059684-2(8)) HarperCollins Pubs.

DePrisco, Dorothea. What Will I Become? A Changing Picture Book. Lunsford, Annie, illus. 2002. (Learning Pictures Ser.). 10p. (ps). 7.95 (978-1-58117-160-0(9) , Intervisual/Piggy Toes) Dalmatian Pr.

—Who Lives Here? A Changing Picture Book. Lunsford, Annie, illus. 2002. (Learning Pictures Ser.). 10p. (J). (ps). 7.95 (978-1-58117-159-4(5) , Intervisual/Piggy Toes) Dalmatian Pr.

DePrisco, Dorothea & Barnard, Lucy. Lullaby & Good Night. 2006. 12.95 (978-1-58117-450-2(0) , Intervisual/Piggy Toes) Dalmatian Pr.

Derrick, Patricia. Mr Walrus & the Old School Bus. 2007. 32p. 18.95 (978-1-933818-13-9(1)) Animalations.

Deru, Myriam, illus. Little Mouse. 2001. (Little Pebbles Ser.). 32p. (J). (ps-3). 6.95 (978-0-7892-0692-3(7)) Abbeville Pr., Inc.

deRubertis, Barbara. Bouncy Mouse. Cockrille, Eva V., illus. 1998. (Let's Read Together Ser.). 32p. (J). (ps-3). pap. 4.95 (978-1-57565-043-2(6)) Kane Pr., The.

El desfile de Animales, 6 Pack. (Literatura 2000 Ser.). (SPA.). (ps-1). 28.00 (978-0-7635-1190-6(0)) Rigby Education.

Dever, Sean M. The Adventures of Parsley Dumpling. 1999. (J). pap. 4.99 (978-0-9658180-5-6(5)) Fox Bks.

Devernois, Elsa. Una Vez Mas. Gay, Michel, illus. (SPA.). 32p. (J). 7.16 (978-84-95150-32-5(8)) Corimbo, Editorial S.L. ESP. *Dist:* Lectorum Pubns., Inc.

Devlin, Wende. How Fletcher Was Hatched: 30th Anniversary Edition. Devlin, Harry, illus. 30th anniv. ed. 1998. 48p. (J). (ps-3). 14.00 (978-1-892657-00-8(7)) Town Bk. Pr. The.

Dewey, Jennifer Owings. Family Ties: Raising Wild Babies. 1998. (Accelerated Reader Bks.). (Illus.). 80p. (J). (gr. 3-7). 15.95 (978-0-7614-5037-5(8) , Cavendish Children's Bks.) Cavendish, Marshall Corp.

Di Maggio, Joyce. Give Me My Tail Back Because... I'm Cold. 2000. (Illus.). 24p. (J). (ps-1). pap. 4.95 (978-1-928970-12-5(5)) GWR Pr.

Díaz, Katacha. Badger at Sandy Ridge Road. Kest, Kristin, illus. 2005. (Smithsonian's Backyard Ser.). 32p. (J). (ps-2). 15.95 (978-1-59249-420-0(X) , B5028); 4.95 (978-1-59249-421-7(8) , B5078); pap. 6.95 (978-1-59249-422-4(6) , S5028) Soundprints.

Diaz, Katacha. Badger at Sandy Ridge Road. Kest, Kristin, illus. 2005. (Smith Sonian's Backyard Ser.). 32p. (J). (gr. 2-2). pap. 8.95 (978-1-59249-423-1(4) , SC5028) Soundprints.

DiCamillo, Kate. Great Joy. Ibatoulline, Bagram, illus. 2007. 32p. (J). (ps-3). 16.99 ***(978-0-7636-2920-5(0))*** Candlewick Pr.

DiCamillo, Kate. The Tiger Rising. 2002. (gr. 5-8). lib. bdg. 14.15 (978-0-613-66924-5(X)) Tandem Library Bks.

Dickinson, Peter. Po's Story. Jakesevic, Nenad, illus. 1999. (Peter Dickinson's The Kin Ser.). 1p. (J). (gr. 5-9). pap. 3.99 (978-0-448-41711-0(1) , Grosset & Dunlap) Penguin Group (USA) Inc.

Dinner: Individual Title Six-Packs. (Sails Literacy Ser.). 16p. (gr. k up). 27.00 (978-0-7635-4445-4(0)) Rigby Education.

Dipucchio, Kelly. What's the Magic Word? Winborn, Marsha, illus. 2005. 32p. (J). (ps-1). 15.99 (978-0-06-000578-8(5)) HarperCollins Pubs.

Disney Co. Disney Animals Storybook. rev. ed. 2005. (Illus.). 128p. (J). (gr. 4-12). 14.95 incl. audio compact disk (978-1-74121-922-7(1)) Hinkler Bks. Pty, Ltd. AUS. *Dist:* Penton Overseas, Inc.

Disney Press Staff. Classics Scrapbook. 2007. 14p. (J). (ps-3). 12.99 ***(978-1-4231-0273-1(8))*** Disney Pr.

Disney Press Staff. Disney Friendship Stories. Disney Storybook Artists Staff, illus. 2006. 304p. (ps-17). 15.99 (978-1-4231-0087-4(5)) Disney Pr.

Disney Staff. Give It Your All. 2000. (Lessons from the Hundred-Acre Woods: Vol. 10). (Illus.). 32p. (J). (ps-3). 3.49 (978-1-57973-096-3(5)) Advance Pubs. LLC.

—I'm Really Sorry. 2000. (Lessons from the Hundred-Acre Woods: Vol. 6). (Illus.). 32p. (J). (ps-4). 3.49 (978-1-57973-092-5(2)) Advance Pubs. LLC.

—Listen Up, Tigger. 2000. (Lessons from the Hundred-Acre Woods: Vol. 9). (Illus.). 32p. (J). (ps-4). 3.49 (978-1-57973-095-6(7)) Advance Pubs. LLC.

—Rox & Rouky. (FRE.). 96p. (J). (gr. k-5). pap. 9.95 (978-0-7859-8851-9(3)) French & European Pubns., Inc.

—Use Your Words! 2000. (Lessons from the Hundred-Acre Woods: Vol. 18). (Illus.). 32p. (J). (ps-3). 3.49 (978-1-57973-104-5(X)) Advance Pubs. LLC.

DiTerlizzi, Tony. G Is for One Gzonk! An Alpha-Number-Bet Book. DiTerlizzi, Tony, illus. 2006. 80p. (J). (ps-2). (Illus.). 16.95 (978-0-689-85290-9(8)); 150.00 (978-1-4169-2471-5(X)) Simon & Schuster Children's Publishing.

Dixon, Andy. Dragon Quest. Brooks, Felicity, ed. Harris, Nick, illus. rev. ed. 2005. 32p. (J). (ps-7). pap. 7.99 (978-0-7945-1098-5(1) , Usborne) EDC Publishing.

Dixon, Ann. Blueberry Shoe. 1999. (gr. k-3). lib. bdg. 17.60 (978-0-613-24058-1(8)) Tandem Library Bks.

DK Publishing Staff. Backyardigans: The Essential Guide. 2007. (Illus.). 48p. (J). 8.99 (978-0-7566-2703-4(6)) Dorling Kindersley Publishing, Inc.

Dobbie, Geraldine, illus. Town Mouse. 1999. (Patchwork Mice Ser.). 10p. (J). bds. 5.95 (978-1-57717-110-2(1)) New Line Bks.

Dobrin, Arthur. Love Your Neighbor: Stories of Values & Virtues. Rogers, Jacqueline, illus. 1999. 64p. (J). (ps-3). pap. 16.95 (978-0-590-04410-3(9)) Scholastic, Inc.

Dodd, Emma. Yellow, Blue, & Bunny, Too! A Changing Picture Book of Colors. Dodd, Emma, illus. 2004. (Illus.). 16p. (J). (gr. k-3). reprint ed. 12.00 (978-0-7567-7267-3(2)) DIANE Publishing Co.

Dodd, Lynley. A Dragon in a Wagon. Dodd, Lynley, illus. 2000. (Gold Star First Readers Ser.). (Illus.). 32p. (J). (gr. 1 up). lib. bdg. 22.00 (978-0-8368-2687-6(6)) Stevens, Gareth Inc.

—Find Me a Tiger. Dodd, Lynley, illus. 2001. (Gold Star First Readers Ser.). (Illus.). 32p. (J). (gr. 1 up). lib. bdg. 22.00 (978-0-8368-2781-1(3)) Stevens, Gareth Inc.

—Hairy Maclary's Rumpus at the Vet. Dodd, Lynley, illus. 2000. (Gold Star First Readers Ser.). (Illus.). 32p. (J). (gr. 1 up). lib. bdg. 21.26 (978-0-8368-2691-3(4)) Stevens, Gareth Inc.

—Hairy Maclary's Rumpus at the Vet. 2005. (Illus.). 32p. (J). 5.95 (978-1-58246-094-9(9) , Tricycle Pr.) Ten Speed Pr.

—Wake up, Bear. Dodd, Lynley, illus. 2001. (Gold Star First Readers Ser.). (Illus.). 32p. (J). (gr. 1 up). lib. bdg. 22.00 (978-0-8368-2786-6(4)) Stevens, Gareth Inc.

Donahue, Michael. The Fire That Saved the Forest. Grove, Diane O., illus. 2002. 32p. (ps-3). 24.95 (978-1-57098-420-4(4)); pap. 9.95 (978-1-57098-421-1(2)) Rinehart, Roberts Pubs.

Donaldson, Julia. Follow the Swallow. Ursell, Martin, illus. 2001. (Blue Bananas Ser.). 48p. (J). (gr. 1-2). (978-0-7787-0842-1(X)); pap. (978-0-7787-0888-9(8)) Crabtree Publishing Co.

—Follow the Swallow. 2002. (gr. k-3). lib. bdg. 12.95 (978-0-613-52844-3(1)) Tandem Library Bks.

—El Grufalo. Scheffler, Axel, illus. 2003. (SPA.). 32p. (J). (gr. k-2). 7.96 (978-84-233-3145-1(8) , DS4478) Ediciones Destino ESP. *Dist:* Lectorum Pubns., Inc.

—The Gruffalo. 2006. 32p. (J). pap. 5.99 (978-0-14-240387-7(3) , Puffin) Penguin Group (USA) Inc.

—The Gruffalo's Child. Scheffler, Axel, illus. 2005. 32p. (J). (ps). 16.99 (978-0-8037-3009-0(8) , Dial) Penguin Group (USA) Inc.

—Room on the Broom. Scheffler, Axel, illus. 32p. (J). (gr. k-3). 2003. pap. 6.99 (978-0-14-250112-2(3) , Puffin); 2001. 16.99 (978-0-8037-2657-4(0) , Dial) Penguin Group (USA) Inc.

—Room on the Broom. 2003. (gr. k-3). lib. bdg. 15.30 (978-0-613-83001-0(6)) Tandem Library Bks.

—The Spiffiest Giant in Town. Scheffler, Axel, illus. 2005. 32p. (J). reprint ed. pap. 5.99 (978-0-14-240275-7(3) , Puffin) Penguin Group (USA) Inc.

Donohue, Dorothy. Veggie Soup. 40p. (J). (ps-1). 2002. pap. 6.95 (978-1-58837-020-4(8)); 2000. (Illus.). 16.95 (978-1-890817-21-3(X)) Winslow Pr.

Dora & Diego's Adventures! 2007. (Dora the Explorer Ser.). 80p. (J). 6.99 ***(978-1-4169-3532-2(0)***, Simon Spotlight/Nickelodeon) Simon & Schuster Children's Publishing.

Doray, Malika. One More Wednesday. Freeman, Suzanne, tr. Doray, Malika, illus. 2001. (Illus.). 32p. (J). (ps up). 15.89 (978-0-06-029590-5(2)) HarperCollins Pubs.

Dorling Kindersley Publishing Staff. Animal Sticker. 2002. (Illus.). 16p. (J). pap. 6.99 (978-0-7894-8875-6(2)) Dorling Kindersley Publishing, Inc.

—Disney Animals. 2006. (Ultimate Sticker Bks.). 16p. (J). pap. 6.99 (978-0-7566-2003-5(1)) Dorling Kindersley Publishing, Inc.

—Wild Animals. 2001. (Soft-to-Touch Bk.). (Illus.). 18p. (J). (ps-3). bds. 4.95 (978-0-7894-7402-5(6)) Dorling Kindersley Publishing, Inc.

Dorling Kindersley Publishing Staff, contrib. by. Love & Kisses. 2005. (Glitter Stickers Ser.). (Illus.). 16p. (J). (ps-3). pap. 6.99 (978-0-7566-1413-3(9)) Dorling Kindersley Publishing, Inc.

Dorman, Clive. Okomi: The New Baby. 2001. (ps-2). lib. bdg. 12.95 (978-0-613-79611-8(X)) Tandem Library Bks.

Dowling, James. Animal Ark Bk. 1: In the Beginning. Dowling, Brenda, ed. Ileana & Broderick, Michael, illus. 2nd l.t. ed. 1998. 48p. (J). (gr. 3-5). 19.95 (978-1-57087-381-2(X)) Professional Pr.

Down on Piggy Farm. 2005. (J). bds. 12.95 (978-0-9764114-2-0(3)) Little People Bks.

Down, Reg. The Magic Knot: And other Tangles. 2007. (Illus.). 100p. (J). per. 14.95 ***(978-0-9794452-0-0(5))*** Lightly Pr.

Downard, Barry. Flash Harry Hare & Tom Tortoise. Downard, Barry, illus. 2008. 40p. (J). 15.99 ***(978-1-4169-2509-5(0)***, Simon & Schuster Children's Publishing) Simon & Schuster Children's Publishing.

Downey, Lynn. The Flea's Sneeze. Firehammer, Karla, illus. rev. ed. 2000. 32p. (J). (ps-1). 17.95 (978-0-8050-6103-1(7) , Holt, Henry & Co. Bks. For Young Readers) Holt, Henry & Co.

—Matilda's Humdinger. Bowers, Tim, illus. 2006. 40p. (J). (gr. k-4). 15.95 (978-0-375-82403-6(0)); lib. bdg. 17.99 (978-0-375-92403-3(5)) Random Hse. Children's Bks. (Knopf Bks. for Young Readers).

Downing, Johnette & Kadair, Deborah Ousley. Down in Louisiana. 2007. 32p. (J). 15.95 (978-1-58980-451-7(1)) Pelican Publishing Co., Inc.

Drescher, Henrik. Hubert the Pudge: A Vegetarian Tale. Drescher, Henrik, illus. 2006. (Illus.). 40p. (J). (ps-3). 16.99 (978-0-7636-1992-3(2)) Candlewick Pr.

Driscoll, Laura. Diego's Animal Friends. Maher, Alex, illus. 2006. (Go, Diego, Go! Ser.). 12p. (J). bds. 6.99 (978-1-4169-1791-5(8) , Simon Spotlight/Nickelodeon) Simon & Schuster Children's Publishing.

Dube, Jasmine & Paré, Roger. Elvis Aime Danser. 2001. (Elvis Ser.). (FRE., Illus.). 24p. (YA). (ps up). pap. (978-2-89021-462-0(1)) Diffusion du livre Mirabel.

Dubovoy, Silvia. La Noche de los Calamares. Peinador, Angeles, illus. 2004. (SPA.). 32p. (J). 14.99 (978-84-241-7946-5(3)) Everest de Ediciones y Distribucion, S.L. ESP. *Dist:* Lectorum Pubns., Inc.

Dubowski, Cathy East. Mulan. 1998. (Junior Novelization Ser.). (Illus.). 96p. (J). (gr. 3-7). pap. 3.95 (978-0-7868-4222-3(9)) Disney Pr.

—Wild Thornberrys Movie. 2002. (gr. 3-6). lib. bdg. 13.00 (978-0-613-58171-4(7)) Tandem Library Bks.

Dubowski, Mark, illus. Stone Soup. 1998. (Domino Readers Ser.). 24p. (J). (ps-1). 5.95 (978-1-887734-22-6(8)) Star Bright Bks., Inc.

Dufresne, Didier. Solamente un Poco de Gripe. Vinent, Julia, tr. Modere, Armelle, illus. 2004. (SPA.). 32p. (J). 14.99 (978-84-8470-123-1(9)) Corimbo, Editorial S.L. ESP. *Dist:* Lectorum Pubns., Inc.

Duggleby, Sue & Duggleby, Ross. Storycards Narrative. (Illus.). 108p. (978-0-86388-549-5(7) , 003-5294) Speechmark Publishing Ltd.

Duhon, Joe. The T-graben: Discovery & Exploration of the Mammalian Graben. Loren, illus. 2002. 189p. (YA). pap. 14.95 (978-1-58736-109-8(4) , Starbound Bks.) Wheatmark.

Dumortier, Marjorie. Zoe & her Zany Animals. 2006. (Illus.). 32p. (J). 14.99 (978-0-7145-3306-3(8)) Boyars, Marion Pubs., Inc.

Dunn, Carolyn. A Pie Went By. 32p. (J). (ps-1). Date not set. pap. 4.99 (978-0-06-443649-6(7)); 2000. (Illus.). 14.95 (978-0-06-028807-5(8)) HarperCollins Pubs.

Dunn, Connie. Stories from under the Wisdom Tree. 2002. (Illus.). 179p. (J). pap. 20.00 (978-1-890641-06-1(5)) No Stress Pr.

Dunn, Opal & Gale, Cathy. El Gato Leo Comes to Play! A First Spanish Story. 2004. (ENG & SPA., Illus.). 24p. (J). 7.95 (978-1-84507-336-7(3)) Lincoln, Frances Ltd. GBR. *Dist:* Perseus Distribution.

Dunnick, Regan. Sweet Dreams Douglas. Dunnick, Regan, illus. 2002. (Illus.). (J). (ps-2). 16.95 (978-0-9632421-3-6(X)) Junior League of Houston, Inc.

Dunrea, Olivier. Bear Noel. Dunrea, Olivier, illus. (Illus.). 32p. (J). 2006. pap. 5.95 (978-0-374-40001-9(6)); 2000. 16.00 (978-0-374-39990-0(5)) Farrar, Straus & Giroux. (Farrar, Straus & Giroux (BYR)).

Dupasquier, Philippe. 1 2 3 Follow Me. 2002. (Illus.). 20p. (J). (gr. k-k). bds. 6.99 (978-0-7636-1797-4(0)) Candlewick Pr.

Durant, Alan. Always & Forever. Gliori, Debi, tr. Gliori, Debi, illus. 2004. 32p. (J). 16.00 (978-0-15-216636-6(X)) Harcourt Children's Bks.

—Brown Bear Gets in Shape. Hudson, Annabel, illus. 2004. (I Am Reading Ser.). 48p. (J). (gr. 1-3). pap. 3.95 (978-0-7534-5797-9(0) , Kingfisher) Houghton Mifflin Co. Trade & Reference Div.

Duroux, Mary. The Rain Flower. Briggs, Karen, illus. 2005. 48p. (J). pap. 13.45 (978-0-85575-467-9(2)) Aboriginal Studies Pr. AUS. *Dist:* International Specialized Bk. Services.

DuTemple, Lesley A. One Little Balsam Fir: A Northwoods Counting Book. Robinson, Susan, illus. 2006. (J). ***(978-1-892384-37-9(X))*** Avery Color Studios, Inc.

Dutton, Sandra. Dear Miss Perfect: A Beast's Guide to Proper Behavior. 2007. (Illus.). 48p. (J). (gr. k-3). 16.00 (978-0-618-67717-7(8)) Houghton Mifflin Co.

Dwyer, Mindy. Sweet Dreams, Polar Bear. 2005. (Illus.). 32p. (J). 15.95 (978-0-88240-554-4(3)); pap. 8.95 (978-0-88240-555-1(1)) Graphic Arts Ctr. Publishing Co.

Dyer, Jane. Animal Crackers: Bedtime. 1998. (Illus.). 16p. (J). (ps). bds. 5.95 (978-0-316-19660-4(6)) Little Brown & Co.

Dyer, Sarah. Clementine & Mungo. 2004. (Illus.). 32p. (J). (ps-3). 16.95 (978-1-58234-883-4(9) , Bloomsbury Children) Bloomsbury Publishing.

East, Jacqueline. Ed the Pup Ed's New Baby Sister. 1999. (Ed the Pup Ser.). (ps-3). (978-1-894155-67-0(X)) Cethial & Bossche Co.

—Ed the Pup I Can't. 1999. (Ed the Pup Ser.). (J). (ps-3). (978-1-894155-66-3(1)) Cethial & Bossche Co.

Eberhart, Nancy. The Adventures of Granny: Granny Goes to the Zoo. 2007. (J). pap. 10.99 ***(978-1-59879-372-7(1));*** per. 13.99 ***(978-1-59879-373-4(X))*** Lifevest Publishing, Inc.

Edwards, Frank B. Nightgown Countdown. 1999. (New Reader Ser.). (Illus.). (J). (978-0-606-22035-4(6)) Tandem Library Bks.

—Peek-a-Boo at the Zoo. Bianchi, John, illus. 1999. (New Reader Ser.). 24p. (J). (ps-1). pap. 4.95 (978-1-894323-06-2(8)) Pokeweed Pr. CAN. *Dist:* Fitzhenry & Whiteside, Ltd.

—Snug As a Big Red Bug. Bianchi, John, illus. 1999. (New Reader Ser.). 24p. (J). (ps-1). lib. bdg. 14.95 (978-1-894323-01-7(7)) Pokeweed Pr. CAN. *Dist:* Fitzhenry & Whiteside, Ltd.

—Snug As a Big Red Bug. 1999. (gr. k-3). lib. bdg. 12.95 (978-0-613-37045-5(7)) Tandem Library Bks.

Edwards, Frank B. & Bianchi, John. New at the Zoo. 2001. (New Reader Ser.). (Illus.). 24p. (J). (ps-k). lib. bdg. 14.95 (978-1-894323-29-1(7)); pap. 4.95 (978-1-894323-26-0(2)) Pokeweed Pr. CAN. *Dist:* Fitzhenry & Whiteside, Ltd.

—Nightgown Countdown. 1999. (New Reader Ser.). (Illus.). 24p. (J). (ps-1). pap. 4.95 (978-1-894323-04-8(1)); lib. bdg. 14.95 (978-1-894323-05-5(X)) Pokeweed Pr. CAN. *Dist:* Fitzhenry & Whiteside, Ltd.

—Snug As a Big Red Bug. 1999. (New Reader Ser.). (Illus.). 24p. (J). (ps-1). pap. 4.95 (978-1-894323-00-0(9)) Pokeweed Pr. CAN. *Dist:* Fitzhenry & Whiteside, Ltd.

—The Zookeeper's Sleepers. 1999. (New Reader Ser.). (Illus.). 24p. (J). (ps-1). pap. (978-1-894323-07-9(6)) Pokeweed Pr.

Edwards, Pamela Duncan. Ms. Bitsy Bat's Kindergarten. Cole, Henry, illus. 2005. (J). ***(978-1-4156-2782-2(7))*** Hyperion Bks. for Children.

—Some Smug Slug. Cole, Henry, illus. 1998. 32p. (J). (ps-4). pap. 6.99 (978-0-06-443502-4(4) , Harper Trophy) HarperCollins Pubs.

—The Wacky Wedding: A Book of Alphabet Antics. 2005. 32p. (J). pap. (978-0-7868-1172-4(2)) Hyperion Bks. for Children.

—The Wacky Wedding: A Book of Alphabet Antics. Cole, Henry, illus. 1999. 32p. (ps-2). 14.99 (978-0-7868-0308-8(8)) Hyperion Bks. for Children.

—The Worrywarts. Cole, Henry, illus. 32p. (J). (ps-1). 2003. pap. 6.99 (978-0-06-443516-1(4)); 1999. 15.95 (978-0-06-028150-2(2)) HarperCollins Pubs.

—The Worrywarts. (gr. k-3). 2003. lib. bdg. 14.15 (978-0-613-61836-6(X)); 1999. (Illus.). (J). (978-0-606-22071-2(2)) Tandem Library Bks.

Edwards, Pamela Duncan & Cole, Henry. Bravo, Livingstone Mouse! 2000. (Illus.). 32p. (gr. k-4). 16.49 (978-0-7868-2247-8(3)) Hyperion Bks. for Children.

Edwards, Pat. What's That? 1999. (gr. k-3). lib. bdg. 10.95 (978-0-613-30867-0(0)) Tandem Library Bks.

Edwards, Richard. The Forest Child. Malone, Peter, illus. 2004. 28p. (J). reprint ed. (978-0-7567-7850-7(6)) DIANE Publishing Co.

Egan, Tim. The Blunder of the Rogues. Egan, Tim, illus. (Illus.). 32p. (J). (gr. k-3). 2002. pap. 5.95 (978-0-618-25075-2(1)); 1999. tchr. ed. 15.00 (978-0-395-91007-8(2)) Houghton Mifflin Co. Trade & Reference Div.

—Blunder of the Rogues. 2002. (gr. k-3). lib. bdg. 14.10 (978-0-613-91048-4(6)) Tandem Library Bks.

Ehlert, Lois. Oodles of Animals. 2008. (J). ***(978-0-15-206274-3(2))*** Harcourt Trade Pubs.

Ehrlich, Fred. Does a Yak Get a Haircut? 2006. (Illus.). 28p. pap. 5.95 (978-1-59354-158-3(9)) Blue Apple Bks.

Eirug Wyn. Powdwr Rhech! 2005. (WEL.). 64p. pap. (978-0-86243-571-4(4)) Y Lolfa.

Eisch, Beverly. In the Woods. Eisch, Lisa & Grabner, Mike, illus. 2002. 12p. (J). pap. 5.00 (978-0-9724517-0-3(6)) Eisch, Beverly.

Elliott, David. And Here's to You! Cecil, Randy, illus. 2004. 32p. (J). (ps-2). 15.99 (978-0-7636-1427-0(0)) Candlewick Pr.

Ellis, Brian. The Web at Dragonfly Pond. Maydak, Michael S., illus. 2006. (Sharing Nature with Children Book Ser.). 32p. (J). 16.95 (978-1-58469-078-8(X)); pap. 8.95 (978-1-58469-079-5(8)) Dawn Pubns.

Ellis, Libby. Say Moo! A Speak-and-Play Book. Castillon, Carly, illus. 2001. (Stories to Share Ser.). 10p. (J). (ps-k). act. bk. ed. 11.95 (978-1-58117-140-2(4) , Intervisual/Piggy Toes) Dalmatian Pr.

Ells, Marcia Louise. Glips, Snodagers & Wallywogs. Ells, Marcia Louise, illus. l.t. ed. 2006. (Illus.). 44p. (J). 6.99 (978-0-9777359-0-7(7)) Marcia's Menagerie.

Elya, Susan Middleton. Eight Animals Bake a Cake. Chapman, Lee, illus. 2002. (ENG & SPA.). 32p. (J). (ps-3). 15.99 (978-0-399-23468-2(3) , Putnam Juvenile) Penguin Group (USA) Inc.

—Eight Animals on the Town. Chapman, Lee, illus. (SPA.). (J). 2002. 32p. pap. 6.99 (978-0-698-11961-1(4)); 2000. 1p. 15.99 (978-0-399-23437-8(3)) Penguin Group (USA) Inc. (Putnam Juvenile).

—Eight Animals on the Town. 2002. (gr. k-3). lib. bdg. 15.30 (978-0-613-73480-6(7)) Tandem Library Bks.

Emberley, Rebecca. My Animals/Mis Animales. Emberley, Rebecca, illus. 2002. (SPA & ENG., Illus.). 10p. (J). (ps-ps). bds. 6.99 (978-0-316-17343-8(6)) Little, Brown Bks. for Young Readers.

—My Shapes, My Colors, My Numbers, My Animals. 2005. (J). bds. 24.92 (978-0-316-05781-3(9)) Little Brown & Co.

Emerson, Carl. Old Oak & the Summer Playground. Doerrfeld, Cori, illus. 2007. (J). (978-1-4048-2626-7(2)) Picture Window Bks.

Emmett, Jonathan. Diamond in the Snow. Cabban, Vanessa, illus. 2006. 32p. (J). (ps-1). 15.99 (978-0-7636-3117-8(5)) Candlewick Pr.

—I Love You Always & Forever. Howarth, Daniel, illus. 2007. 32p. (J). (ps-3). pap. 14.99 (978-0-439-91654-7(2)) Scholastic, Inc.

—A Mouse in the Marmalade. Church, Caroline, illus. 2002. (J). tchr. ed. 14.95 (978-1-58925-687-3(5) , tiger tales) ME Media LLC.

—No Place Like Home. Cabban, Venessa, illus. 2005. 32p. (J). (ps-1). 15.99 (978-0-7636-2554-2(X)) Candlewick Pr.

—Ruby in Her Own Time. 2007. 32p. (J). pap. 5.99 (978-0-439-86278-3(7)) Scholastic, Inc.

—Through the Heart of the Jungle. Gomez, Elena, illus. 2003. 32p. (J). tchr. ed. 15.95 (978-1-58925-029-1(X)); pap. 5.95 (978-1-58925-380-3(9)) ME Media LLC. (tiger tales).

—Through the Heart of the Jungle. 2003. (gr. k-3). lib. bdg. 14.10 (978-0-613-85249-4(4)) Tandem Library Bks.

—A Turtle in the Toilet. Jayne Church, Caroline, illus. 2002. 16p. (J). tchr. ed. 14.95 (978-1-58925-688-0(3) , tiger tales) ME Media LLC.

Ende, Michael. El Osito de Peluche y Otros Animales. Oberdiek, Berhard, illus. (SPA.). 32p. (J). (gr. k-3). 2001. 6.95 (978-84-241-3359-7(5) , EV1154); 2000. 12.95 (978-84-241-3350-4(1) , EV1156) Everest de Ediciones y Distribucion, S.L. ESP. *Dist:* Lectorum Pubns., Inc.

Endredy, James. The Journey of Tunuri & the Blue Deer: A Huichol Indian Story. Hernandez de la Cruz, Maria & Cruz Lopez, Casimiro de la, trs. Hernandez de la Cruz, Maria & Cruz Lopez, Casimiro de la, illus. 2003. 32p. 15.95 (978-1-59143-016-2(X)) Bear & Co.

England-Lord, Susan. The Adventures of Andrew: Breezy's Day Out. 2004. 23p. pap. 14.95 (978-1-4137-3285-6(2)) PublishAmerica, Inc.

Engle, Janice. Rainbows Stories & Poetry for Children. 2004. 277p. (J). pap. 15.08 (978-1-4116-8612-0(8)) Lulu.com.

Ensor, Barbara. Thumbelina: Tiny Little Runaway Bride. 2008. (J). (***978-0-375-83960-3(7)); (*978-0-375-93960-0(1))** Random Hse. Children's Bks. (Schwartz & Wade Bks.).

Epelbaum, Anna V. & Wayne D. Pickette. About Animals & Others. 2003. (J). per. 17.95 (978-0-9747418-2-6(5)) Management Services.

Epner, Paul. Herbert Hilligan & His Magical Adventure. Kuon, Vuthy & Nguyen, Duke, illus. 2003. 32p. (J). 15.95 (978-0-9743335-0-2(6)) Imaginative Publishing, Ltd.

Equidna. (Coleccion Animalitos Exoticos). (SPA., Illus.). 166p. (J). 16.95 (978-84-7630-368-9(8) , SAN688) Libsa, Editorial S.A. ESP. *Dist:* Continental Bk. Co., Inc.

Erdrich, Lise. Bears Make Rock Soup: And Other Stories. Fifield, Lisa, illus. 2002. 32p. (J). (gr. 1 up). 16.95 (978-0-89239-172-1(3)) Children's Bk. Pr.

Erickson, Gina Clegg & Foster, Kelli C. The Pancake Day. Gifford, Kerri, illus. 2004. 30p. (J). (ps-ps). lib. bdg. 11.30 (978-0-606-30082-7(1)) Tandem Library Bks.

Ering, Timothy Basil. The Story of Frog Belly Rat Bone. Ering, Timothy Basil, illus. 2008. (Illus.). 48p. (J). (ps-2). pap. 6.99 (***978-0-7636-2611-2(2))** Candlewick Pr.

Ermine on His Own. 2002. (Wild Heritage Collection Mini Bks.). (Illus.). 32p. (J). (978-1-59069-239-4(X) , H3010) Studio Mouse LLC.

Ernst, Lisa Campbell. Wake up, It's Spring! Ernst, Lisa Campbell, illus. 2004. (Illus.). 40p. (J). (ps-3). 16.99 (978-0-06-008985-6(7)) HarperCollins Pubs.

—Wake Up, It's Spring! Ernst, Lisa Campbell, illus. 2004. (Illus.). 40p. (J). (ps-3). lib. bdg. 17.89 (978-0-06-008986-3(5)) HarperCollins Pubs.

Ets, Marie Hall. Just Me. Ets, Marie Hall, illus. unabr. ed. (Illus.). (J). (gr. k-3). pap., stu. ed. 33.95 (978-0-941078-74-0(4)); pap. 15.95 incl. audio (978-0-941078-73-3(6)) Live Oak Media.

Eubank, Patricia Reeder. Do I Belong with You? Eubank, Patricia Reeder, illus. 2002. (Illus.). 32p. (J). (ps-3). 9.95 (978-1-59093-074-8(6) , Eager Minds Pr.) Warehousing & Fulfillment Specialists, LLC (WFS, LLC).

Eubank, Patti Reeder, illus. Just Where You Belong. 2004. 32p. (J). 8.95 (978-0-8249-5481-9(5)) Ideals Pubns.

Evangelista, Susan. Tommy's New Shell, 2nd in series. Coke, Sherrie, illus. 2005. 24p. (J). bds. 19.95 (978-0-9769602-0-1(6)) Evangelista, Susan.

Evans, Alwyn. Old MacDonald's Farm: A Three-Dimensional Playset with Sound! Bell, Owen, illus. 2001. (J). (ps-k). act. bk. ed. 16.95 (978-1-58117-145-7(5) , Intervisual/Piggy Toes) Dalmatian Pr.

Exactly Like Me. 2003. (J). per. 8.95 (978-0-9746151-0-3(2)) Alta Retreat Ctr.

Eyuboglu, Melisa, illus. Angel in a Bubble. Eyuboglu, Melisa, . 2007. 28p. (J). 10.95 (***978-1-933090-48-1(0))** Guardian Angel Publishing, Inc.

Fair Ideal Instructional Staff. What Matches with Sammy Spider. 1999. (Lost-N-Found Book Ser.). (Illus.). (J). 7.95 (978-1-56451-294-9(0) , Ideal School Supply) Schaffer, Frank Pubns.

—What's Different with Freddy Frog, Vol. 1. 1999. (Lost-N-Found Book Ser.). (Illus.). (J). 7.95 (978-1-56451-293-2(2) , Ideal School Supply) Schaffer, Frank Pubns.

Falcon, Marilyn Perez. Cui-Cui-Cuidado! Animales al Volante. Repiso, Elena, illus. 2002. (SPA.). 32p. (J). pap. (978-980-257-269-4(1)) Ekare, Ediciones.

Falconer, Ian. Olivia Helps with Christmas (W. T.) Mawhinney, Art, illus. 2007. 32p. (J). 5.99 (***978-1-4169-5387-6(6)** , Simon Scribbles) Simon & Schuster Children's Publishing.

Fallon, Karla. Rainforest Moon. 2005. 102p. pap. 9.98 (978-1-4116-3776-4(3)) Lulu.com.

Falwell, Cathryn. Scoot! 2008. 32p. (J). 16.99 (***978-0-06-128882-1(9));** lib. bdg. 17.89 (***978-0-06-128883-8(7))** HarperCollins Pubs. (Greenwillow Bks.).

Farber, Erica. Golden Eagle. Mayer, Mercer, illus. 2006. (Critter Kids Adventure Ser.). 32p. (J). (gr. 2-5). pap. 4.95 (978-0-7696-4764-7(2) , Gingham Dog Pr.) School Specialty Publishing.

—Octopus Island. Mayer, Mercer, illus. 2006. (Critter Kids Adventure Ser.). 32p. (J). (gr. 2-5). pap. 4.95 (978-0-7696-4766-1(9) , Gingham Dog Pr.) School Specialty Publishing.

—The Swamp Thing. Mayer, Mercer, illus. 2006. (Critter Kids Adventure Ser.). 32p. (J). (gr. 2-5). pap. 4.95 (978-0-7696-4762-3(6) , Gingham Dog Pr.) School Specialty Publishing.

Farber, Norma. How the Hibernators Came to Bethlehem. Cooney, Barbara, illus. 2006. 32p. (J). 9.95 (978-0-8027-9610-3(9)) Walker & Co.

Farley, Terri. Kidnapped Colt. 2005. (Phantom Stallion Ser.: No. 15). (Illus.). 224p. (J). (gr. 5 up). pap. 4.99 (978-0-06-058316-3(9)) HarperCollins Pubs.

—The Wildest Heart, Vol. 16. 2005. (Phantom Stallion Ser.: No. 16). 208p. (gr. 5 up). pap. 4.99 (978-0-06-058317-0(7)) HarperCollins Pubs.

Farm Animal Board Books 800654, 7. 2005. (J). bds. (978-1-59794-006-1(2)) Environments, Inc.

Farmer Fred's: Noisy Animals. 2002. bds. 3.98 (978-0-7525-8175-0(9)) Parragon, Inc.

Farmer, Karen, ed. If I Could Be Anything What Would I Be. 2007. 12p. pap. 8.95 (***978-1-59125-914-5(2))** Penton Overseas, Inc.

Fast/Spy Staff. The Cobra. 2001. 32p. (YA). (gr. 6-12). pap. (978-0-8224-6535-5(3)) Globe Fearon Educational Publishing.

Fatus, Sophie, illus. A Hen, a Chick & a String Guitar. 2005. 32p. (J). 17.99 incl. audio compact disk (978-1-84148-796-0(1)) Barefoot Bks., Inc.

Faulkenberry, Lauren. What Do Animals Do on the Weekend? Adventures from A to Z. Faulkenberry, Lauren, illus. 2002. (Illus.). 64p. (gr. k-3). 17.95 (978-0-9708972-4-4(3)) Novello Festival Pr.

Faulkner, Keith. The Giraffe Who Cock-a-Doodle-Doo'd. Lambert, Jonathan, illus. 2002. 16p. (J). (ps-1). 13.99 (978-0-8037-2739-7(9) , Dial) Penguin Group (USA) Inc.

—The Mixed-Up Tooth Fairy. Lambert, Jonathan, illus. 2002. 8p. (J). (ps-1). pap. 9.95 (978-0-439-35609-1(1) , Cartwheel Bks.) Scholastic, Inc.

Favorite Animals Book Set 800892, 3 vols. 2005. (J). (978-1-59794-067-2(1)) Environments, Inc.

Fearnley, Jan. Little Robin's Christmas. Fearnley, Jan, illus. 2002. 32p. (J). 5.95 (978-1-58925-371-1(X) , tiger tales) ME Media LLC.

—Mr. Wolf & the Enormous Turnip. 2005. (Illus.). 40p. (Orig.). (J). (ps-ps). pap. 9.99 (978-1-4052-1580-0(1)) Egmont Bks., Ltd. GBR. *Dist:* Trafalgar Square Publishing.

Feiffer, Jules. A Room with a Zoo. Feiffer, Jules, illus. 2007. (Illus.). 182p. (J). (gr. 2-7). per. 7.99 (***978-0-7868-3703-8(9))** Hyperion Bks. for Children.

Ferguson, Sarah. Little Red. Williams, Sam, illus. 2006. 40p. (J). 6.99 (978-1-4169-1853-0(1) , Aladdin) Simon & Schuster Children's Publishing.

Ferri, Francesca, illus. Cucu-Tras: Peek-a-Boo, Spanish Edition. 2007. 10p. (J). 7.99 (978-0-7641-6039-4(7)) Barron's Educational Series, Inc.

—Cucu-Tras de la Selva: Peek-a-Boo Jungle, Spanish Edition. 2007. 10p. (J). 7.99 (978-0-7641-6040-0(0)) Barron's Educational Series, Inc.

—Peek-a-Boo Jungle. 2006. 10p. (J). 7.99 (978-0-7641-5940-4(2)) Barron's Educational Series, Inc.

—Pets. 2003. (My First Animals Ser.). 8p. (J). pap. 9.95 (978-0-7641-2599-7(0)) Barron's Educational Series, Inc.

—Safari Animals. 2003. (My First Animals Ser.). 8p. (J). pap. 9.95 (978-0-7641-2598-0(2)) Barron's Educational Series, Inc.

Fifi Ferret's Flute. 2001. (ps-2). lib. bdg. 9.80 (978-0-613-32550-9(8)) Tandem Library Bks.

Figueroa, Rafael Olivares. Que Animal Es? (SPA.). (J). pap. 7.16 (978-980-01-1012-6(7)) Monte Avila Editores Latinoamericana CA VEN. *Dist:* Lectorum Pubns., Inc.

Figuerola, Maite. Las Estaciones del Ano. 2003. (Disney Collection). (SPA.). 32p. (J). 5.95 (978-84-670-0300-0(6)) Espasa Calpe, S.A. ESP. *Dist:* Planeta Publishing Corp.

Finklea, Ernest. Little One. 2006. (Illus.). 32p. (J). 12.99 (978-1-57921-849-2(0)) WinePress Publishing.

Finklea, Michael. Good Natured Nina the Nervous Gnat. Sissel, Vickie, illus. 1998. (C). pap. (978-1-56763-434-1(6)); (J). (978-1-56763-433-4(8)) Ozark Publishing.

Finn, Isobel. The Very Lazy Ladybug. Tickle, Jack, illus. 2000. (J). (ps-3). 11.96 (978-1-888444-66-7(5)) Little Tiger Pr.

—The Very Lazy Ladybug. Tickle, Jack, illus. (J). 2005. 16p. bds. 6.95 (978-1-58925-758-0(8)); 2001. 28p. tchr. ed. 15.95 (978-1-58925-007-9(9)) ME Media LLC. (tiger tales).

Finn, Isobel & Tickle, Jack. The Very Lazy Ladybug. 2003. (Illus.). (J). 16p. tchr. ed. 15.95 (978-1-58925-714-6(6)); 32p. pap. 6.95 (978-1-58925-379-7(5)) ME Media LLC. (tiger tales).

Fiorello, Frank. Pumpkinville. Fiorello, Frank, illus. 2001. 40p. (J). pap. 7.95 (978-0-9708400-0-4(4)); lib. bdg. 12.95 (978-0-9708400-1-1(2)) Pumpkin Patch Publishing.

First Animal Stories. 2000. (J). bds. 19.95 (978-0-7525-6555-2(9)) Parragon, Inc.

Fisher, Judy. The Alpha & Omega Series. 2007. pap. 14.99 (***978-1-59886-841-8(1))** Tate Publishing & Enterprises, L.L.C.

Fisscher, Tiny. RUBY & the LION. 2008. 48p. 11.95 (***978-1-60136-014-4(2))** Mars Media Pubs.

Fite, Mary G. Annie's Friends: A Collection of Animal Stories. 1998. (Illus.). 80p. (J). (gr. 3-6). pap. 4.99 (978-1-57502-748-7(8) , PO2079) Morris Publishing.

Fitzkee, Jeremy. One, Two, Three, Me. Budde, Nadia, illus. 2006. 24p. (J). (ps). 8.99 (978-0-670-06124-2(7) , Viking Adult) Penguin Group (USA) Inc.

Fitzpatrick, Marie-Louise. I'm a Tiger, Too! Fitzpatrick, Marie-Louise, illus. 2002. (Illus.). 6.95 (978-0-86327-871-6(X)) Interlink Publishing Group, Inc.

Fitzsimmons, Robin C. Bop, Bop at the Bunny Hop. Sasaki, Ellen Joy, illus. 2002. (Word Family Tales Ser.). 16p. (ps-2). pap. 2.95 (978-0-439-26261-3(5)) Scholastic, Inc.

Flack, Marjorie. Ask Mr. Bear. Flack, Marjorie, illus. 2002. (Illus.). (J). 14.47 (978-0-7587-1995-9(7)) Book Wholesalers, Inc.

Fleagle, Gail S. Juega con la Pelota! Romo, Alberto, tr. Henry, Marilyn, illus. 1998. (Books for Young Learners).Tr. of Play Ball!. (SPA.). 8p. (J). (gr. k-2). pap. 5.00 (978-1-57274-206-2(2) , A2870) Owen, Richard C. Pubs., Inc.

Fleischman, Paul. The Animal Hedge. Ibatoulline, Bagram, illus. 2003. 48p. (J). (gr. 1-5). 16.99 (978-0-7636-1606-9(0)) Candlewick Pr.

Fleischman, Sid. A Carnival of Animals. Hafner, Marylin, illus. 2000. 48p. (J). (gr. 2 up). 15.89 (978-0-688-16949-7(X)) HarperCollins Pubs.

Fleming, Candace. Gator Gumbo: A Spicy-Hot Tale. Lambert, Sally Anne, illus. 2004. 32p. (J). (gr. k-3). 16.00 (978-0-374-38050-2(3) , Farrar, Straus & Giroux (BYR)) Farrar, Straus & Giroux.

Fleming, Denise. Barnyard Banter. Fleming, Denise, illus. 2002. (Illus.). (J). 15.49 (978-0-7587-2039-9(4)) Book Wholesalers, Inc.

—Barnyard Banter. Fleming, Denise, illus. rev. ed. 2001. (Illus.). 30p. (J). (ps-k). bds. 6.95 (978-0-8050-6594-7(6) , Holt, Henry & Co. Bks. For Young Readers) Holt, Henry & Co.

—In the Small, Small Pond. Fleming, Denise, illus. 2002. (Illus.). (J). 15.49 (978-0-7587-0119-0(5)) Book Wholesalers, Inc.

—In the Small, Small Pond. 2007. (Illus.). 32p. (J). pap. 22.95 (***978-0-8050-8117-6(8)** , Holt, Henry & Co. Bks. For Young Readers) Holt, Henry & Co.

—In the Small, Small Pond. Fleming, Denise, illus. rev. ed. 1998. (Illus.). 32p. (J). (ps-1). pap. 7.95 (978-0-8050-5983-0(0) , Holt, Henry & Co. Bks. For Young Readers) Holt, Henry & Co.

—In the Tall, Tall Grass. Fleming, Denise, illus. 2002. (Illus.). (J). 15.49 (978-0-7587-2843-2(3)) Book Wholesalers, Inc.

Flemming, Paul. Toby Toucan & His Noisy Beak: Includes Toy. Goode, Jon, illus. 1998. (Snappy Head Books Ser.: Vol. 2). 12p. (J). (ps-k). bds. 4.99 (978-1-57584-172-4(X) , Reader's Digest Children's Bks.) Reader's Digest Children's Publishing, Inc.

Florczak, Robert. Yikes!!! Florczak, Robert, illus. 2003. (Illus.). 32p. (J). pap. 15.95 (978-0-590-05043-2(5) , Blue Sky Pr., The) Scholastic, Inc.

Floss, Laura, et al. Double-Talk. Style Guide Staff & YOE! Studio Staff, illus. 2007. (Baby Looney Tunes Ser.). 400p. (J). 5.99 (978-1-4169-3510-0(X) , Simon Scribbles) Simon & Schuster Children's Publishing.

Fogle, Llynda & Gonzalez, Althea. A Friendship Place. 2005. (ENG & SPA., Illus.). (J). (978-0-9760282-6-0(3)) RAPC - Sparkle & Shine Project.

Follen, Eliza Lee. What the Animals Do & Say. 2006. pap. (***978-1-4250-3428-3(4))** Assistedreadingbooks.com Inc.

Folsom, Michael & Elting, Mary. Q Is for Duck: An Alphabet Guessing Game. Kent, Jack, illus. 2005. 64p. (J). (ps-k). 16.00 (978-0-618-57389-9(5)); pap., pap. 6.95 (978-0-618-57412-4(3)) Houghton Mifflin Co. Trade & Reference Div. (Clarion Bks.).

Fontenot, Mary Alice. Clovis Crawfish & Echo Gecko. Buckner, Julie Dupre, illus. 2003. 32p. (J). 15.95 (978-1-56554-708-7(X)) Pelican Publishing Co., Inc.

—Clovis Crawfish & Raoul Raccoon. Landry, Cat, illus. 1999. (Clovis Crawfish Ser.). 32p. (J). (gr. k-3). 15.95 (978-1-56554-369-0(6)) Pelican Publishing Co., Inc.

—Clovis Crawfish & Silvie Sulphur. Buckner, Julie Dupre, illus. 2004. (ENG & FRE.). 32p. (J). pap. 15.95 (978-1-56554-864-0(7)) Pelican Publishing Co., Inc.

—Clovis Ecrevisse et Batiste Bete Puante. 1999. (FRE., Illus.). 32p. (J). (gr. k-3). 16.95 (978-1-56554-430-7(7)) Pelican Publishing Co., Inc.

Fontenot, Mary Alice & Landry, Julie Fontenot. Clovis Crawfish & the Twin Sister. 2007. 32p. (J). 15.95 (***978-1-58980-467-8(8))** Pelican Publishing Co., Inc.

Fontes, Justine. Mulan: Mushu's Story. 1998. (Disney Chapters Ser.). (Illus.). 64p. (J). (gr. 2-4). pap. 3.95 (978-0-7868-4225-4(3)) Disney Pr.

Forbes, Robert. Beastly Feasts! A Mischievous Menagerie in Rhyme. Searle, Ronald, illus. 2007. 96p. (gr. k-5). 19.95 (***978-1-58567-929-4(1))** Overlook Pr., The.

Ford, Brent. Disney's Mulan. Clarke, Judie & Tilley, Scott, illus. 1998. 48p. (J). (ps-3). 10.95 (978-0-7868-3172-2(3)) Disney Pr.

Ford, Carolyn. The Paper Bag. Diez-Luckie, Cathy, illus. 2005. 8p. (J). pap. 5.00 (978-1-57274-756-2(0) , 2494, Bks. for Young Learners) Owen, Richard C. Pubs., Inc.

Foreman, Michael. Hello World. Foreman, Michael, illus. 2003. (Illus.). 48p. (J). (ps). 16.99 (978-0-7636-2112-4(9)) Candlewick Pr.

—Hola, Mundo. 2004. (SPA., Illus.). 28p. (J). 19.99 (978-84-88342-41-6(1)) S.A. Kokinos ESP. *Dist:* Lectorum Pubns., Inc.

—Norman's Ark. Foreman, Michael, illus. 2006. (Illus.). 32p. (J). pap. 6.95 (978-1-58925-401-5(5) , tiger tales) ME Media LLC.

Forest, Heather. Stone Soup. 2000. (gr. 3-6). lib. bdg. 15.25 (978-0-613-54363-7(7)) Tandem Library Bks.

Foster, Kelli C. & Erickson, Gina Clegg. Whiptail of Blackshale Trail. Gifford, Kerri, illus. 2004. 18p. (J). (gr. k-3). lib. bdg. 11.15 (978-0-606-30085-8(6)) Tandem Library Bks.

Foster, Kimberly. A Dolphin up a Tree. 2002. (Illus.). 24p. (J). per. 16.99 (978-0-9664624-3-2(2)) Telos Pubns.

Fowler, Susi Gregg. Albertina, the Animals & Me. 2000. (Illus.). 96p. (YA). (gr. 5 up). 14.89 (978-0-06-029160-0(5)) HarperCollins Pubs.

—Albertina, the Animals, & Me. 2000. (Illus.). 96p. (J). (gr. 2 up). 14.95 (978-0-688-17127-8(3)) HarperCollins Pubs.

Fox, Mem. Hunwick's Egg. Lofts, Pamela, tr. Lofts, Pamela, illus. 2005. 32p. (J). 16.00 (978-0-15-216318-1(2)) Harcourt Children's Bks.

—Time for Bed. Dyer, Jane, illus. 2005. 28p. (J). bds. 10.95 (978-0-15-205349-9(2) , Red Wagon Bks.) Harcourt Children's Bks.

—Wombat Divine. 2002. (Illus.). (J). 13.19 (978-0-7587-4046-5(8)) Book Wholesalers, Inc.

—Wombat Divine. Argent, Kerry, illus. 1999. 32p. (J). (ps-3). pap. 6.00 (978-0-15-202096-5(9) , Harcourt Paperbacks) Harcourt Children's Bks.

—Wombat Divine. 1999. (gr. k-3). lib. bdg. 14.15 (978-0-613-22962-3(2)) Tandem Library Bks.

—Zoo-Looking. Love, Judith DuFour & Whitman, Candace, illus. 2001. (J). (ps-2). pap. 6.00 (978-1-57255-011-7(2)) Mondo Publishing.

France, Anthony. From Me to You. Beeke, Tiphanie, illus. 2003. 32p. (J). (ps-2). 15.99 (978-0-7636-2255-8(9)) Candlewick Pr.

Franke, Kristina & Leberer, Sigrid. The Bunny Kindergarten. 2004. (Illus.). 32p. (J). 10.99 (978-1-59384-039-6(X)) Parklane Publishing.

Franklin's Easter: A Sticker Activity Book. 2004. (Franklin Sticker & Activity Bks.). (Illus.). 16p. (J). (gr. k-3). (978-1-55337-690-3(0)) Kids Can Pr., Ltd.

Fraser, Mary Ann. I. Q. Goes to the Library. Fraser, Mary Ann, illus. 2005. (Illus.). 32p. (J). (ps-3). pap. 6.95 (978-0-8027-7727-0(9)) Walker & Co.

Fraser, W. A. The Outcasts. 2005. reprint ed. pap. 21.95 (978-1-4179-5533-6(3)) Kessinger Publishing, LLC.

Frazier, Craig. There Is a Monkey in My Drawers! 2003. (Illus.). 24p. (J). (ps-k). 14.95 (978-1-932026-10-8(X)) Graphis, U S , Inc.

Frederick, Susan. Miss Callie Lallie's Mouse Tales. Walter, J., illus. 2006. 48p. pap. 12.95 (978-1-4241-1431-3(4)) PublishAmerica, Inc.

Free Wheelin' Coloring/Activity Book (English) 2005. (Illus.). (J). (978-0-9770455-7-0(9)) Educational Adventures.

Freedman, Claire. New Kid in Town. Stephenson, Kristina, illus. 2006. 28p. (J). 16.00 (978-1-56148-547-5(0)) Good Bks.

—One Magical Day. Macnaughton, Tina, illus. 2007. 28p. (J). (ps-1). 16.95 (***978-1-56148-567-3(5))** Good Bks.

Freedman, Claire. Where's Your Smile, Crocodile? Julian, Sean, illus. 2001. 32p. (J). (ps-k). 16.95 (978-1-56145-251-4(3)) Peachtree Pubs., Ltd.

Freeman, Don. Earl the Squirrel. 2007. 48p. (J). (gr. k up). pap. 6.99 (***978-0-14-240893-3(X)** , Puffin) Penguin Group (USA) Inc.

—Favorite Author Collection: Don Freeman, 6 bks., Set. unabr. ed. 1999. (Illus.). (J). (ps-3). pap. 106.95 incl. audio (978-0-87499-483-4(7)) Live Oak Media.

Freeman, Don. Quiet! There's a Canary in the Library. Freeman, Don, illus. 2007. 48p. (J). (ps). 15.99 (***978-0-670-06230-0(8)** , Viking Juvenile) Penguin Group (USA) Inc.

Freeman, Tor. Hooray, I'm Five Today! Freeman, Tor, illus. 2004. (Illus.). 32p. (J). (gr. k-k). 16.99 (978-0-7636-2452-1(7)) Candlewick Pr.

French, Vivian. Henny Penny. Windham, Sophie, illus. 2006. 32p. (J). 16.95 (978-1-58234-706-6(9) , Bloomsbury Children) Bloomsbury Publishing.

Freschet, Gina. Up & at 'Em with Winnie & Ernst. 2005. (Winnie & Ernst Ser.). (Illus.). 48p. (J). 15.00 (978-0-374-38446-3(0) , Farrar, Straus & Giroux (BYR)) Farrar, Straus & Giroux.

—Winnie & Ernst. Freschet, Gina, illus. 2003. (Winnie & Ernst Ser.). (Illus.). 48p. (J). 15.00 (978-0-374-38452-4(5) , Farrar, Straus & Giroux (BYR)) Farrar, Straus & Giroux.

Friedman, Mel. Kitten Castle. 2001. (gr. k-3). lib. bdg. 12.95 (978-0-613-39335-5(X)); (Illus.). (J). (978-0-606-20753-9(8)) Tandem Library Bks.

Friend, R. Down on Friendly Acres Set 1: Books #1-4, 4. 2007. (Illus.). (J). (***978-0-9743627-8-6(6)***) Sunflower Seeds Pr.

Fries, Claudia. A Pig Is Moving In! Fries, Claudia, illus. 2000. (Illus.). 32p. (J). (ps-2). 16.99 (978-0-531-33307-5(8)); pap. 15.95 (978-0-531-30307-8(1)) Scholastic, Inc. (Orchard Bks.).

Froeb, Lori & Brown, Jo. Zoo! A Big Fold-Out Counting Book. 2007. 10p. (J). (ps-k). bds. 12.99 (***978-0-7944-1361-3(7)***) Reader's Digest Assn., Inc., The.

Froese, Dorothy Cheever. Captain Rhino's Progress: An Allegory of the Workplace. 2003. (Illus.). 32p. pap. 9.00 (978-1-890437-86-2(7)) Western Reflections Publishing Co.

Fry, Sonali. My Finest Friends. G Studios, illus. 2007. (Land of Milk & Honey Ser.). 14p. (J). 8.99 (978-1-4169-2765-5(4) , Little Simon Inspirations) Simon & Schuster Children's Publishing.

Fuchs, Menucha. Who Will Be King of the Jungle? Rappaport, Aviva, tr. 2002. (HEB., Illus.). 32p. (J). 9.95 (978-1-880582-81-7(3) , KOJH) Judaica Pr., Inc., The.

Fuertes, Gloria. Cuentos de Humor: Un Pulpo en un Garaje. 2003. (SPA.). 128p. 15.16 (978-84-305-7987-7(7) , SU5205) Susaeta Ediciones, S.A. ESP. *Dist:* Lectorum Pubns., Inc.

Fuge, Charles. I Know a Rhino. 2003. (Illus.). 32p. (J). bds. 5.95 (978-1-4027-0861-9(0)) Sterling Publishing Co., Inc.

—I Know a Rhino. Fuge, Charles, illus. 2002. (Illus.). 32p. (J). (ps-1). 12.95 (978-1-4027-0137-5(3)) Sterling Publishing Co., Inc.

Full, Dennis, photos by. Barney's Favorite Farm Animals. 2001. (Barney Ser.). (Illus.). 10p. (J). (ps-k). bds. 3.99 (978-1-58668-129-6(X)) Scholastic, Inc.

Furgang, Kathy. Unlucky Stanley. ed. 2003. (Early Connections Ser.). (J). pap. 33.00 (978-1-4108-1357-2(6)) Benchmark Education Co.

The Furry Friends. 2005. (J). per. (978-0-9664783-2-7(0)) Jacqueline Beverly Hills.

Gaber, Susan, illus. The Little Red Hen: An Old Fable. 2006. 32p. (J). 16.95 (978-0-87483-795-7(2)) August Hse. Pubs., Inc.

Gable, Paul. Love Flute. 2001. (J). (gr. k-3). pap. 16.95 incl. audio. pap. 16.95 incl. audio (978-0-8045-6843-2(X) , 6843) Spoken Arts, Inc.

Gagne, Michel. Insanely Twisted Rabbits. 2001. (Illus.). 32p. 14.95 (978-0-9666404-4-1(6)) Gagne International Pr.

Gaines, Isabel. Be Quiet, Pooh! 1999. (Winnie the Pooh First Readers Ser.: Vol. 18). (Illus.). 37p. (J). (gr. k-3). pap. 3.99 (978-0-7868-4318-3(7)) Disney Pr.

—Happy Birthday, Eeyore! 1998. (Winnie the Pooh First Readers Ser.). (Illus.). 48p. (J). (ps-3). pap. 3.95 (978-0-7868-4183-7(4)) Disney Pr.

—Pooh's Christmas Gifts. 1999. (Winnie the Pooh First Readers Ser.). (Illus.). 37p. (J). (gr. k-3). pap. 3.99 (978-0-7868-4315-2(2)) Disney Pr.

—Pooh's Halloween Parade. Wenzel, Paul, illus. 1999. (Winnie the Pooh First Readers Ser.: Vol. 15). 37p. (J). (gr. k-3). pap. 3.99 (978-0-7868-4314-5(4)) Disney Pr.

—Pooh's Leaf Pile. Sharon, Gayle, illus. 1999. (Winnie the Pooh First Readers Ser.: Vol. 16). 37p. (J). (gr. k-3). pap. 3.99 (978-0-7868-4316-9(0)) Disney Pr.

—Pooh's Leaf Pile Book Club: Special Sales Edition. 1999. 40p. (J). pap. 3.99 (978-0-7868-4387-9(X)) Disney Pr.

—Pooh's Scavenger Hunt. Yee, Josie, illus. 1999. (Winnie the Pooh First Readers Ser.: Vol. 19). 37p. (J). (gr. k-3). pap. 3.99 (978-0-7868-4317-6(9)) Disney Pr.

Gaines, Simon Ludvigsen. Good Night, Sleep Tight. 2007. (Little Scholastic Ser.). (Illus.). 24p. (J). (ps). bds. 9.99 (***978-0-439-86726-9(6)*** , Cartwheel Bks.) Scholastic, Inc.

Galdone, Joanna C. The Tailypo: A Ghost Story. Galdone, Paul, illus. 1999. (J). (ps-ps). lib. bdg. 15.25 (978-0-8085-3422-8(X)) Tandem Library Bks.

Galvin, Laura Gates. Orang Utan's Playtime. Cohen, Jessie, photos by. 1999. (Let's Go to the Zoo! Ser.: Vol. 2). (Illus.). 16p. (J). (ps-k). bds. 5.95 (978-1-56899-796-4(5) , B9002) Soundprints.

Gamble, Isobel. Quien Hay? 2003. (SPA.). 228p. (978-84-488-1080-1(5) , BS30459) Beascoa, Ediciones S.A. ESP. *Dist:* Lectorum Pubns., Inc.

Gambrell, Linda B. & Dorling Kindersley Publishing Staff. Garden Friends. 2003. (Readers Ser.). (Illus.). (J). 32p. 12.99 (978-0-7894-9993-6(2)); 1p. pap. 3.99 (978-0-7894-9991-2(6)) Dorling Kindersley Publishing, Inc.

Gannett, Ruth Stiles. My Father's Dragon: Books 1 & 2: #1 My Father's Dragon #2 Elmer & the Dragon. Gannett, Ruth Chrisman, illus. 2002. (J). 14.47 (978-0-7587-0296-8(5)) Book Wholesalers, Inc.

Gansle, Sherry. Oops, a Curious Horse Big Book. Light, Carol, illus. 2003. 56p. (J). (978-0-9745803-6-4(8)) Little Big Tomes.

—Oops, a Curious Horse Little Book. Light, Carol, illus. 2003. 52p. (J). (978-0-9745803-7-1(6)) Little Big Tomes.

—Oops, a Curious Horse Story Book Reader. Light, Carol, illus. 2003. 58p. (J). (978-0-9745803-5-7(X)) Little Big Tomes.

Gardiner, Lindsey. Here Come Poppy & Max. Gardiner, Lindsey, illus. 2000. (Illus.). 24p. (J). (ps-1). 12.95 (978-0-316-60346-1(5)) Little Brown & Co.

Gardner, Hugh. Tales from the Marble Mountain. 2005. pap. 26.95 (978-1-4191-1589-9(8)) Kessinger Publishing, LLC.

Garelick, May. Where Does the Butterfly Go When It Rains? Wilton, Nicholas, illus. 2001. (J). (gr. 1-6). pap. 6.00 (978-1-57255-162-6(3)) Mondo Publishing.

—Where Does the Butterfly Go When It Rains? 2001. (978-0-606-22653-0(2)) Tandem Library Bks.

—Who Likes It Hot? O'Brien, John, illus. 1998. 32p. (J). (gr. 2-6). 15.95 (978-1-57255-553-2(X)) Mondo Publishing.

Garfield, Valerie. So Big! Yaccarino, Dan, illus. 2001. (Playtime Rhymes Ser.). 12p. (J). (ps up). pap. 7.99 (978-0-694-01509-2(1) , Harper Festival) HarperCollins Pubs.

Garis, Howard Roger. Uncle Wiggily & the Littletails. Date not set. 192p. (J). 20.95 (978-0-8488-2279-8(X)) Amereon LTD.

Garland, Michael. Last Night at the Zoo. Garland, Michael, illus. 2003. (Illus.). 32p. (J). (gr. k-2). pap. 8.95 (978-1-59078-167-8(8)) Boyds Mills Pr.

—Last Night at the Zoo. 2001. (Illus.). 32p. (J). (gr. k-2). 15.95 (978-1-56397-759-6(1)) Boyds Mills Pr.

—Last Night at the Zoo. 2003. (gr. k-3). lib. bdg. 17.60 (978-0-613-79885-3(6)) Tandem Library Bks.

Garside, Alice H. The Ant & the Duck, Set 2. l.t. ed. 1999. (Illus.). 29p. (Orig.). (J). (gr. k-6). reprint ed. pap. 2.50 (978-1-893688-05-6(4)) Carroll Schl., The.

Garwood, Ben. Animals in Heaven. 2004. 217p. (J). per. 11.95 (978-0-9714086-2-3(9)) Tarbutton Pr.

El Gato y los Pajaros: Individual Title Six-Packs. (Coleccion Pm Ser.).Tr. of Kitty & the birds. (SPA.). 16p. (gr. 1 up). 26.00 (978-0-7578-2959-8(7)) Rigby Education.

Gauthier, Lance C., text. The One-Eared Mouse of Pasture Hill. 2003. 55p. (J). per. 6.95 (978-1-884540-70-7(8)) Haley's.

Gay, Michel. El Cochecito. 2003. (SPA.). 68p. (978-84-8470-084-5(4)) Corimbo, Editorial S.L.

Gedovius, Juan. From the Vine. Gedovius, Juan, illus. (Illus.). 24p. (J). (gr. k-6). 14.95 (978-968-19-1053-2(2)) Santillana USA Publishing Co., Inc.

Geiger, Lorraine Lynch. A Wild & Woolly Night. Vargo, Sharon, illus. 2007. (J). (***978-1-891795-25-1(2)***) RGU Group, The.

George, Jean Craighead. Morning, Noon, & Night. Minor, Wendell, illus. 1999. 32p. (J). (ps-3). 16.99 (978-0-06-023628-1(0)); lib. bdg. 17.89 (978-0-06-023629-8(9)) HarperCollins Pubs.

George, Lindsay Barrett. The Secret. George, Lindsay Barrett, illus. 2005. (Illus.). 32p. (J). 15.99 (978-0-06-029598-1(8)); 16.89 (978-0-06-029600-1(3)) HarperCollins Pubs.

Geraghty, Paul. The Hoppameleon. 2001. (Illus.). 28p. (J). (ps-2). 13.95 (978-0-7641-5406-5(0)) Barron's Educational Series, Inc.

Gerritsen, Paula. Nuts. 2006. 32p. (J). 15.95 (978-1-932425-66-6(7) , Lemniscaat) Boyds Mills Pr.

Gershator, Phillis. When It Starts to Snow. Matje, Martin, illus. rev. ed. 2001. 32p. (J). (ps-2). pap. 7.95 (978-0-8050-6765-1(5) , Holt, Henry & Co. Bks. For Young Readers) Holt, Henry & Co.

—When It Starts to Snow. 2001. (ps-2). lib. bdg. 15.25 (978-0-613-51425-5(4)) Tandem Library Bks.

Gershenson, Harold P. Freddy Flamingo & the Kindertown Five. Mills, Christopher, illus. 2005. 27p. (J). (978-1-58987-070-3(0)) Kindermusik International.

—Noodles from Scratch. Mills, Christopher, illus. 2006. (J). (978-1-58987-007-9(7)) Kindermusik International.

Gervais, Ricky. Flanimals. Steen, Rob, illus. 2004. 64p. (J). (978-0-571-22077-9(0)) Faber & Faber, Ltd.

Gerver, Jane E. The Big Red Sled. Burris, Priscilla, illus. 2001. (Hello Reader! Ser.). 32p. (J). (ps-1). 3.99 (978-0-439-20434-7(8) , Cartwheel Bks.) Scholastic, Inc.

—The Big Red Sled. Burris, Priscilla, illus. 2001. (J). (ps-3). lib. bdg. 11.80 (978-0-613-43797-4(7)) Tandem Library Bks.

—The Big Red Sled. 2001. 10.79 (978-0-606-22227-3(8)) Tandem Library Bks.

Geste, Mal, et al. Zoo Room. Gelsthorpe, Loraine & Rex, Sue, eds. 2002. (Illus.). 32p. (J). pap. 14.95 (978-1-86368-339-5(9)) Fremantle Pr. AUS. *Dist:* International Specialized Bk. Services.

Ghigna, Charles. The Alphabet Parade. Woods, Patti, illus. 2002. 32p. (J). 17.95 (978-1-880216-74-3(4)) River City Publishing.

Ghosh, Premola, illus. Ten Timeless Tales. 2005. 38p. (J). (***978-81-89013-35-6(1)***) Zubaan.

Giancamilli, Vanessa. Platypus Creek. Thivierge, Claude, illus. 2005. (Soundprints' Amazing Animal Adventures! Ser.). (J). (ps-2). 36p. 19.95 incl. audio (978-1-59249-355-5(6) , BC7109); 36p. 8.95 incl. audio (978-1-59249-356-2(4) , SC7109); 32p. 9.95 (978-1-59249-357-9(2) , PS7159); 36p. 15.95 (978-1-59249-352-4(1) , B7109); 36p. pap. 6.95 (978-1-59249-353-1(X) , S7109) Soundprints.

—Platypus Creek: Micro Book. Thivierge, Claude, illus. 2005. (Amazing Animal Adventures Ser.). 32p. (J). (ps-2). 2.95 (978-1-59249-354-8(8) , S7159) Soundprints.

Gikow, Louise. Over the Hedge: The Movie Novel. 2006. (Over the Hedge Ser.). (Illus.). 168p. (J). pap. 4.99 (978-0-439-80141-6(9)) Scholastic, Inc.

Gilkey, Gail. No More Garbage. Gilkey, Gail, ed. Kittell DiOrio, Kathy, illus. 2003. 32p. (J). (gr. k-2). lib. bdg. 14.95 (978-0-9662983-4-5(9)) Windy Hill Pr.

Gilson, Jamie. It Goes Eeeeeeeeeeeee! deGroat, Diane, illus. 2001. 80p. (J). (gr. 4-6). pap. 4.95 (978-0-618-05155-7(4) , Clarion Bks.) Houghton Mifflin Co. Trade & Reference Div.

The Gingerbread Fudd. 1999. (McGraw-Hill Junior Academic Ser.). (Illus.). 16p. (J). (gr. k-2). pap. 3.99 (978-1-57768-214-1(9)) School Specialty Publishing.

Given, Cate. Cartwheeling. Hill-Peterson, Jodi, illus. 2006. (J). (***978-0-9790057-1-8(X)***) Paws In the Sand Publishing.

Glass, Julie. Counting Sheep. 2000. (Illus.). (J). 11.99 (978-0-375-90658-9(4)); 32p. pap. 3.99 Random Hse. Children's Bks.

—Counting Sheep. Wohnoutka, Mike, illus. 2000. (Step into Reading Ser.). (J). 10.79 (978-0-606-19890-5(3)) Tandem Library Bks.

Glynn, Gower. Stories Told in the Wigwam. 2006. pap. 24.95 (***978-1-4254-9966-2(X)***) Kessinger Publishing, LLC.

Godwin, Laura. Forest: Level 2. 2000. (Illus.). (J). (gr. 1-3). (978-0-606-18690-2(5)) Tandem Library Bks.

—Little White Dog. 2000. (ps-2). lib. bdg. 14.15 (978-0-613-31428-2(X)) Tandem Library Bks.

—The Little White Dog. Yaccarino, Dan, illus. 2000. 32p. (ps-k). pap. 5.99 (978-0-7868-1515-9(9)) Disney Pr.

Godwin, Parke. Disney's Main Street Storybook Collection. 2003. (Illus.). 320p. (J). 15.99 (978-0-7868-3431-0(5)) Disney Pr.

Golden Books Staff. Animal House. Saunders, Zina, illus. 2004. (Blue's Clues Ser.). 32p. (J). (ps-2). pap. 3.99 (978-0-375-82744-0(7) , Golden Bks.) Random Hse. Children's Bks.

—Animal Magic. 2007. (Paint Box Book Ser.). (Illus.). 48p. (J). (ps-2). 3.99 (***978-0-375-84466-9(X)*** , Golden Bks.) Random Hse. Children's Bks.

—Animal Tales. 2007. (Little Golden Book Treasury Ser.). (Illus.). 224p. (J). (ps-k). 10.99 (978-0-375-84178-1(4) , Golden Bks.) Random Hse. Children's Bks.

—Baby Farm Animals. Williams, Garth, illus. 2006. (Little Golden Treasures Ser.). 26p. (J). (gr. k-ps). bds. 4.99 (978-0-375-83686-2(1) , Golden Bks.) Random Hse. Children's Bks.

—Farm Tales. 2005. (Little Golden Book Ser.). (Illus.). 320p. (J). 14.95 (978-0-375-83190-4(8) , Golden Bks.) Random Hse. Children's Bks.

—Little Golden Book Collection: Animal Tales. 2004. (Illus.). 320p. (J). (gr. k-k). 14.95 (978-0-375-83128-7(2) , Golden Bks.) Random Hse. Children's Bks.

—Little Golden Book Favorites, No. 1. 2007. (Little Golden Book Ser.). (Illus.). 80p. (J). (gr. k-k). 5.99 (***978-0-375-84215-3(2)*** , Golden Bks.) Random Hse. Children's Bks.

—Little Golden Book Favorites by Richard Scarry. 2008. (Little Golden Book Ser.). (Illus.). 72p. (J). 5.99 (***978-0-375-84580-2(1)*** , Golden Bks.) Random Hse., Inc.

—Once upon a Time. Hall, Susan T., illus. 2004. 32p. (J). (ps-2). 3.99 (978-0-375-83063-1(4) , Golden Bks.) Random Hse. Children's Bks.

—Red Tractor. 2006. (Illus.). 20p. (J). (ps-2). bds. 6.99 (978-0-375-83490-5(7) , Golden Bks.) Random Hse. Children's Bks.

—A Tale of Tails. Williams, Garth, illus. 2008. (Little Golden Treasures Ser.). 26p. (J). (gr. k-k). bds. 4.99 (***978-0-375-83360-1(9)*** , Golden Bks.) Random Hse., Inc.

—65 Years of Little Golden Books. 2007. (Little Golden Book Ser.). (Illus.). 24p. (J). (gr. k-k). 17.94 (***978-0-375-84225-2(X)*** , Golden Bks.) Random Hse. Children's Bks.

Goldie & the Fawn. 2005. (J). (978-1-58453-310-8(2)) Pioneer Valley Educational Pr., Inc.

Goldman-Rubin, Susan. Andy Warhol's Colors. 2007. (Illus.). 26p. (J). bds. 6.95 (978-0-8118-5721-5(2)) Chronicle Bks. LLC.

Goldstone, Bruce. The Beastly Feast. Lent, Blair, illus. 2001. 32p. (J). (ps-1). pap. 7.95 (978-0-8050-6709-5(4) , Holt, Henry & Co. Bks. For Young Readers) Holt, Henry & Co.

—The Beastly Feast. 2001. 13.75 (978-0-606-22584-7(6)) Tandem Library Bks.

—Beastly Feast. 2001. (ps-2). lib. bdg. 15.25 (978-0-613-75496-5(4)) Tandem Library Bks.

Gollub, Matthew. Gobble, Quack, Moon. Love, Judy, illus. 2002. 32p. (J). (ps-3). 18.95 incl. audio compact disk (978-1-889910-20-8(1)) Tortuga Pr.

Gomez Ojea, Carmen. El Ave Que No Sabe Cantar. 2004. (SPA., Illus.). 72p. (YA). 9.99 (978-84-241-8555-8(2)) Everest de Ediciones y Distribucion, S.L. ESP. *Dist:* Lectorum Pubns., Inc.

Gomi, Taro. Everyone Poops. Stinchecum, Amanda M., tr. 2004. (My Body Science Ser.). (Illus.). 28p. (J). (ps). pap. 6.95 (978-1-929132-14-0(X)) Kane/Miller Bk. Pubs., Inc.

—Everyone Poops. 2001. (gr. k-3). lib. bdg. 15.25 (978-0-613-68572-6(5)) Tandem Library Bks.

—My Friends. 2006. (ENG & SPA., Illus.). 40p. (J). pap. 6.95 (978-0-8118-5204-3(0)) Chronicle Bks. LLC.

Gondek, Heather. Who's in the Jungle? Lift-the-Flap 'n' Learn. Gilvan-Cartwright, Chris, illus. 2005. (Fun with Animals Ser.). 10p. (J). 9.95 (978-1-58117-075-7(0) , Intervisual/Piggy Toes) Dalmatian Pr.

Good-Night Owl. 2004. (J). 24.95 incl. audio (978-1-56008-206-4(2)) Weston Woods Studios, Inc.

Goodman, Susan E. What Do You Do... at the Farm? 2002. 2. (Illus.). 32p. (J). (gr. k-2). pap. 4.99 (978-0-7613-1786-9(4) , Millbrook Pr.) Lerner Publishing Group.

—What Do You Do... at the Zoo? 2002. 2. (Illus.). 32p. (J). (gr. k-2). pap. 4.99 (978-0-7613-1787-6(2) , Millbrook Pr.) Lerner Publishing Group.

Gorbachev, Valeri. Chicken Chickens Go to School. Gorbachev, Valeri, illus. 2003. (Illus.). (J). (ps-1). 28p. 15.95 (978-0-7358-1600-8(X)); 32p. 16.50 (978-0-7358-1767-8(7)) North-South Bks., Inc.

—Un Dia de lluvia. Puerta, Cristina, tr. 2003. (SPA.). 40p. (J). 8.95 (978-958-04-7074-8(X)) Norma S.A. COL. *Dist:* Distribuidora Norma, Inc., Lectorum Pubns., Inc.

—Peter's Picture. 2003. (ps-2). lib. bdg. 15.25 (978-0-613-73549-0(8)) Tandem Library Bks.

—Red Red Red. Gorbachev, Valeri, illus. 2007. 40p. (J). (ps-3). 16.99 (978-0-399-24628-9(2) , Philomel) Penguin Group (USA) Inc.

—Whose Hat Is It? Gorbachev, Valeri, illus. (My First I Can Read Bks.). (Illus.). 32p. (J). (ps up). 2005. pap. 3.99 (978-0-06-053436-3(2) , Harper Trophy); 2004. 14.99 (978-0-06-053434-9(6)); 2004. lib. bdg. 15.89 (978-0-06-053435-6(4)) HarperCollins Pubs.

Gordon, Beth. Wish upon a Star: Whimsical Rhymes to Read & Sing. G Studios, illus. 2007. (Land of Milk & Honey Ser.). 30p. (J). bds. 10.99 (978-1-4169-3654-1(8) , Little Simon Inspirations) Simon & Schuster Children's Publishing.

Gordon, Maria & Gordon, Mike, illus. Cats Can't Count, 4 vols. 2000. (Kids Corner Literacy Stories: Vol. 4). (J). (978-0-7608-4270-6(1)) Sundance/Newbridge Educational Publishing.

—Dogs Can't Read, 4 vols. 2000. (Kids Corner Literacy Stories: Vol. 1). (J). (978-0-7608-4271-3(X)) Sundance/Newbridge Educational Publishing.

—Mice Can't Write, 4 vols. 2000. (Kids Corner Literacy Stories: Vol. 2). (J). (978-0-7608-4272-0(8)) Sundance/Newbridge Educational Publishing.

—Spiders Can't Spell, 4 vols. 2000. (Kids Corner Literacy Stories: Vol. 3). (J). (978-0-7608-4273-7(6)) Sundance/Newbridge Educational Publishing.

Goscinny, René. Nicholas on Vacation. Bell, Anthea, tr. from FRE. Sempé, Jean-Jacques, illus. rev. ed. 2006. 132p. (gr. 2-5). 19.95 (978-0-7148-4678-1(3)) Phaidon Pr., Inc.

Goscinny, René & Sempé, Jean-Jacques. Nicholas Again. Bell, Anthea, tr. from FRE. rev. ed. 2006. (Illus.). 120p. 19.95 (978-0-7148-4564-7(7)) Phaidon Pr., Inc.

Gosline, Andrea Alban. Ten Little Wishes: A Baby Animal Counting Book. Bossi, Lisa Burnett, illus. 2007. 40p. (J). (ps-k). 15.99 (978-0-06-053410-3(9)); lib. bdg. 16.89 (978-0-06-053411-0(7)) HarperCollins Pubs.

Got, Yves. Sweet Dreams, Sam. 2000. (Illus.). 14p. (J). (ps). 9.95 (978-0-8118-2985-4(5)) Chronicle Bks. LLC.

Graff, Nancy Price. Taking Wing. Minor, Wendell, illus. 2005. 224p. (YA). (gr. 5-9). 15.00 (978-0-618-53591-0(8) , Clarion Bks.) Houghton Mifflin Co. Trade & Reference Div.

Graham, Bob. Benny: An Adventure Story. Graham, Bob, illus. 2003. (Illus.). 32p. (J). (ps-2). pap. 6.99 (978-0-7636-1703-5(2)) Candlewick Pr.

—Tales from the Waterhole. Graham, Bob, illus. 2004. (Illus.). 64p. (J). (ps-3). 16.99 (978-0-7636-2324-1(5)) Candlewick Pr.

Graham, John. I Love You, Mouse. dePaola, Tomie, illus. 2008. 32p. (J). (ps-k). 16.99 (***978-0-399-25079-8(4)*** , Putnam Juvenile) Penguin Group (USA) Inc.

Grahame, Kenneth. Classic Starts: the Wind in the Willows. Akib, Jamel, illus. 2007. (Classic Starts Ser.). 160p. (J). 4.95 (978-1-4027-3696-4(7)) Sterling Publishing Co., Inc.

—The Classic Tale of the Wind in the Willows. Daily, Don, illus. rev. ed. 2001. 56p. (J). (gr. 4-7). 9.98 (978-0-7624-0999-0(1) , Courage Bks.) Running Pr. Bk. Pubs.

—Mr. Toad, Vol. 2. Johnson, Joe, tr. from FRE. 2003. (Wind in the Willows Ser.: Vol. 2). (Illus.). 32p. (gr. 4-7). 15.95 (978-1-56163-218-3(X)) NBM Publishing Co.

—The Open Road by Kenneth Grahame. Iosa, Ann, illus. 2003. 32p. (J). (978-0-7607-3215-1(9)) Barnes & Noble, Inc.

—El Viento en los Sauces. 2001. (SPA.). 229p. (YA). 12.95 (978-84-261-5577-1(4)) Juventud, Editorial ESP. *Dist:* AIMS International Bks., Inc.

—El Viento en los Sauces. 2002. (Clover Ser.). (SPA., Illus.). 208p. (YA). 11.50 (978-84-392-8012-5(2) , EV2974) Lectorum Pubns., Inc.

—El Viento en los Sauces. (SPA.). 192p. (J). I. 9.50 (978-84-372-1882-3(9)); II. 9.50 (978-84-372-1883-0(7)) Santillana USA Publishing Co., Inc.

—The Wind in the Willows. 224p. 2005. 27.95 (978-1-4218-0646-4(0)); 2004. pap. 12.95 (978-1-59540-046-8(X)) 1st World Publishing, Inc. (1st World Library - Literary Society).

—The Wind in the Willows. Tomei, Lorna, illus. 2002. (Great Illustrated Classics Ser.). 240p. (J). (gr. 3-8). 21.35 (978-1-57765-808-5(6) , ABDO & Daughters) ABDO Publishing Co.

—The Wind in the Willows. Percy, Graham, illus. 1999. (Abbeville Classics Ser.). 192p. (J). 12.95 (978-0-7892-0559-9(9)); pap. 7.95 (978-0-7892-0549-0(1)) Abbeville Pr., Inc. (Abbeville Kids).

—The Wind in the Willows. 2006. (ENG.). 168p. per. 13.95 (***978-1-59818-946-9(8)***); 24.95 (***978-1-59818-378-8(8)***) Aegypan.

—The Wind in the Willows. 2003. (J). cd-rom (978-0-9724995-4-5(7)) Alcazar AudioWorks.

—The Wind in the Willows. Moss, Joanne, illus. 253p. (J). (gr. 5-6). reprint ed. lib. bdg. 22.95 (978-0-88411-877-0(0)) Amereon LTD.

—The Wind in the Willows. Perry, Graham, illus. 2000. 192p. (J). pap. 8.95 (978-1-85793-914-9(X) , Pavilion Bks., Ltd.) Anova Bks. GBR. *Dist:* Trafalgar Square Publishing.

—The Wind in the Willows. Moore, Inga, illus. (J). 2003. 184p. 19.99 (978-0-7636-2242-8(7)); 2000. 180p. 4.50 (978-0-7445-7553-8(2)) Candlewick Pr.

—The Wind in the Willows. (Great Classics for Children Ser.). 192p. (J). (Illus.). 5.99 (978-1-4037-0600-3(X)); 2003. 4.99 (978-1-57759-567-0(X)) Dalmatian Pr.

—The Wind in the Willows. 2005. 96p. per. 5.95 (978-1-4209-2239-4(4)) Digireads.com.

—The Wind in the Willows. (Dover Large Print Classics Ser.). 2002. 288p. pap. 12.95 (978-0-486-42467-5(7)); 1999. (Illus.). 176p. (J). (gr. 4-7). pap. 3.00 (978-0-486-40785-2(3)) Dover Pubns., Inc.

—The Wind in the Willows. Kliros, Thea, illus. abr. ed. 1998. (Dover Children's Thrift Classics Ser.). 96p. (J). pap. 1.00 (978-0-486-28600-6(2)) Dover Pubns., Inc.

—The Wind in the Willows. Exams Unlimited, Inc. Staff, ed. 2001. 174p. (C). reprint ed. cd-rom 5.60 (978-1-59132-022-7(4)) Exams Unlimited, Inc.

—The Wind in the Willows. Hague, Michael, illus. rev. ed. 2003. 224p. (J). (gr. 1 up). 26.95 (978-0-8050-7237-2(3) , Holt, Henry & Co. Bks. For Young Readers) Holt, Henry & Co.

—The Wind in the Willows. Barnhart, Nancy, illus. 2004. reprint ed. pap. 33.95 (978-1-4179-1206-3(5)) Kessinger Publishing, LLC.

—The Wind in the Willows. l.t. ed. 2000. (LRS Large Print Heritage Ser.). 271p. (J). (gr. 3-8). lib. bdg. 29.95 (978-1-58118-066-4(7) , 23661) LRS.

—The Wind in the Willows, Level 2. 2001. (Illus.). 48p. (C). pap. 9.00 (978-0-582-42660-3(X)) Longman Publishing Group.

—The Wind in the Willows. 1998. (Twelve-Point Ser.). 185p. reprint ed. lib. bdg. 24.00 (978-1-58287-080-9(2)) North Bks.

—The Wind in the Willows. Green, Peter, ed. 1999. (Oxford World's Classics Ser.). 192p. 11.95 (978-0-19-283515-4(7)) Oxford Univ. Pr., Inc.

—The Wind in the Willows. 240p. (gr. 12). 2006. pap. 5.95 (978-0-451-53014-1(4) , Signet Classics); 2005. (YA). 12.00 (978-0-14-303909-9(1) , Penguin Classics) Penguin Group (USA) Inc.

—The Wind in the Willows. 1999. (Aladdin Classics Ser.). (Illus.). 304p. (J). (gr. 4-7). pap. 4.99 (978-0-689-83140-9(4) , Aladdin) Simon & Schuster Children's Publishing.

—The Wind in the Willows. 1999. (978-0-606-17323-0(4)) Tandem Library Bks.

—The Wind in the Willows. l.t. ed. 2005. 334p. 20.95 (978-0-7862-7489-5(1)) Thorndike Pr.

—The Wind in the Willows. Hanft, Joshua, ed. (Great Illustrated Classics Ser.: Vol. 39). (Illus.). 240p. (J). (gr. 3-6). 9.95 (978-0-86611-990-0(6)) Waldman Publishing Corp.

—The Wind in the Willows. 1998. (Children's Classics). (ENG., Illus.). 192p. (YA). (ps up). pap. (978-1-85326-122-0(X) , 122XWW); (J). (gr. 4-7). pap. (978-1-85326-017-9(7) , 0177WW) Wordsworth Editions, Ltd.

—The Wind in the Willows: #1 the Riverbank. 2007. (Easy Reader Classics Ser.). 32p. (J). (ps-3). 21.35 (***978-1-59961-340-6(9)***) Spotlight.

—The Wind in the Willows: With Charm. 2003. (Charming Classics). (Illus.). 256p. (J). pap. 6.99 (978-0-06-053723-4(X) , Harper Festival) HarperCollins Pubs.

—The Wind in the Willows Vol. 3: The Gates of Dawn. Johnson, Joe, tr. Plessix, Michel, illus. 2003. 32p. (gr. 4-7). 15.95 (978-1-56163-245-9(7)) NBM Publishing Co.

—The Wind in the Willows Vol. 3: The Wild Wood. Iosa, Ann, illus. 2007. (Easy Reader Classics Ser.). 32p. (J). pap. 3.95 (978-1-4027-3295-9(3)) Sterling Publishing Co., Inc.

—The Wind in the Willows Vol. 4: Home Sweet Home. Iosa, Ann, illus. 2007. (Easy Reader Classics Ser.). 32p. (J). pap. 3.95 (978-1-4027-3296-6(1)) Sterling Publishing Co., Inc.

Grahame, Kenneth & Basset, Jennifer. The Wind in the Willows, Level 3. 2nd abr. ed. 2000. (Bookworms Ser.). (Illus.). 74p. 6.50 (978-0-19-423022-3(8)) Oxford Univ. Pr., Inc.

Grant, Robert. Jack in the Bush or A Summer on a Salmon River. 2005. pap. 33.95 (978-1-4179-5573-2(2)) Kessinger Publishing, LLC.

Gray, Kes. The Get Well Soon Book. 2000. (Single Titles Ser.: 1). (Illus.). 32p. (J). (ps-3). (978-0-7613-1435-6(0) , Millbrook Pr.) Lerner Publishing Group.

—The Get Well Soon Book: Good Wishes for Bad Times. McQuillan, Mary, illus. 2000. 32p. (J). (ps-1). lib. bdg. 22.90 (978-0-7613-1922-1(0) , Millbrook Pr.) Lerner Publishing Group.

—Our Twitchy. McQuillan, Mary, illus. rev. ed. 2003. 32p. (J). 15.95 (978-0-8050-7451-3(6) , Holt, Henry & Co. Bks. For Young Readers) Holt, Henry & Co.

Gray, Rita. Nonna's Porch. Widener, Terry, illus. 2004. 40p. (ps-2). 15.99 (978-0-7868-1613-2(9)) Hyperion Bks. for Children.

Graziani, Maria. The Adventures of Valeria Veterinarian: Las Aventuras de Valeria Veterinaria, 1. Elejalde, Eliana, illus. l.t. ed. 2004. (SPA.). 23p. (J). 7.00 (978-0-9762361-0-8(9)) Ed. Acespanish S.A.C.- Lima, Peru.

The Great Paua Mystery: Kyss Series. 2003. (J). mass mkt. (978-1-932233-69-8(5)) Aurora Libris Corp.

The Great Redwall Feast. 2002. (Redwall Ser.). (Illus.). (J). 25.47 (978-0-7587-2657-5(0)) Book Wholesalers, Inc.

Greathouse, Rebecca. Katie & Riley's Magical Adventures: Journey to the Amazon. 2006. 48p. pap. 12.95 (***978-1-4241-5341-1(7)***) PublishAmerica, Inc.

Greaves, Nick. When Bat Was a Bird: And Other Animal Tales from Africa. du Plessis, David, illus. 2005. 144p. pap. 12.95 (978-1-86872-998-2(2)) Struik Pubs. ZAF. *Dist:* International Publishers Marketing.

Greenburg, Dan. Attack of the Giant Octopus. Fischer, Scott M., illus. 2007. (Secrets of Dripping Fang Ser.: Bk. 6). 160p. (J). 9.95 (978-0-15-206041-1(3)) Harcourt Children's Bks.

—Claws. 2006. 208p. (YA). (gr. 5). 15.95 (978-0-375-83410-3(9).); lib. bdg. 17.99 (978-0-375-93410-0(3)) Random Hse. Children's Bks. (Random Hse. Bks. for Young Readers).

Greenburg, J. C. In the Desert. Gerardi, Jan, illus. 2008. (Andrew Lost: 17). 96p. (J). (***978-0-375-84667-0(0)***) Random Hse., Inc.

Greene, Rhonda. Santa's Stuck. Cole, Henry, illus. 2006. 32p. (J). (ps). pap. 5.99 (978-0-14-240686-1(4) , Puffin) Penguin Group (USA) Inc.

Greene, Rhonda Gowler. Barnyard Song. Bender, Robert, illus. 2002. (J). 22.98 (978-0-7587-2041-2(6)) Book Wholesalers, Inc.

—Barnyard Song. 2001. (Illus.). (J). 12.79 (978-0-606-20561-0(6)) Tandem Library Bks.

—Santa's Stuck. Cole, Henry, illus. 2004. 32p. (J). (ps). 16.99 (978-0-525-47292-6(4) , Dutton Juvenile) Penguin Group (USA) Inc.

Greenstein, Elaine, contrib. by. One Little Lamb. 2004. (Illus.). 32p. (J). 10.99 (978-0-670-03683-7(8) , Viking Juvenile) Penguin Group (USA) Inc.

Gregorich, Barbara. Waltur Buys a Pig in a Poke & Other Stories. Sorra, Kristin, illus. 2006. 64p. (J). (gr. 3-5). 15.00 (978-0-618-47306-9(8)) Houghton Mifflin Co.

Greive, Bradley Trevor. Every Day Is Christmas. 2007. 120p. 9.95 (***978-0-7407-6860-6(3)***) Andrews McMeel Publishing.

Grejniec, Michael. A Que Sabe la Luna? 2002. (SPA., Illus.). 28p. (J). (gr. k-1). (978-84-95123-61-9(4) , KA4094) Kalandraka Editora, S.L. ESP. *Dist:* Lectorum Pubns., Inc.

Griessman, Annette. Like a Hundred Drums. Monks, Julie, illus. 2006. 32p. (J). (gr. k-3). 15.00 (978-0-618-55878-0(0)) Houghton Mifflin Co.

Griffith, Helen V. How Many Candles? Lamut, Sonja, illus. 1999. 24p. (J). (gr. k-3). 16.00 (978-0-688-16258-0(4)); (gr. 7 up). 15.89 (978-0-688-16259-7(2)) HarperCollins Pubs.

Griffiths, Andy. The Cat on the Mat Is Flat. Denton, Terry, illus. 2007. 176p. (J). (ps-3). 9.95 (***978-0-312-36787-9(2)***) Feiwel & Friends.

Grimsdell, Jeremy. Bushbaby Night. 2006. 32p. pap. 17.95 (978-1-77009-056-9(8)) Jacana Media ZAF. *Dist:* Independent Pubs. Group.

Grindley, Sally. Little Sibu: An Orangutan Tale. Butler, John, illus. 1999. 32p. (J). (ps-3). 15.95 (978-1-56145-196-8(7) , 51967) Peachtree Pubs., Ltd.

—Reve de Glace et Patins Blancs. Duchesne, Christiane, tr. from ENG. Hieta, Heli, illus. (FRE.). 28p. (J). pap. 6.95 (***978-2-922435-06-1(7)***) Editions Homard CAN. *Dist:* Univ. of Toronto Pr.

—Silly Goose & Dizzy Duck & the Colorful Day. Reynolds, Adrian, illus. 2001. (Toddlers Ser.). 24p. (J). (ps). pap. 5.95 (978-0-7894-7860-3(9) , D K Ink) Dorling Kindersley Publishing, Inc.

—What Are Friends For? Dann, Penny, illus. 1998. 32p. (J). (ps-k). tchr. ed. 15.95 (978-0-7534-5108-3(5) , Kingfisher) Houghton Mifflin Co. Trade & Reference Div.

—What Will I Do Without You? Dann, Penny, illus. 2001. 32p. (J). (ps-k). 6.95 (978-0-7534-5411-4(4) , Kingfisher) Houghton Mifflin Co. Trade & Reference Div.

—What Will I Do Without You? Dann, Penny, illus. 2001. (J). (ps-3). lib. bdg. 15.25 (978-0-613-88863-9(4)) Tandem Library Bks.

Griner, Jack. Creature or Critter? Chase, Linda, illus. 2005. 107p. (J). per. 12.95 (978-1-59879-064-1(1)) Lifevest Publishing, Inc.

Grobler, Piet. Hey, Frog! 1998. (Illus.). 32p. (J). (ps-k). 15.95 (978-1-886910-84-3(7) , Lemniscaat) Boyds Mills Pr.

Grooms, Molly. We Are Horses. 2005. 40p. bds. 12.95 (978-90-5843-814-0(7)) YoYo Bks. BEL. *Dist:* National Bk. Network.

Grosgebauer, Clare Ham. Snickerdoodle's Star-Spangled Fourth of July! Rissing, Karen, illus. 4th ed. 2005. 36p. 12.99 (978-0-9741888-6-7(7)) Small Wonders Enterprises.

Group/McGraw-Hill, Wright. Animal Mysteries, 6 vols. (Wildcats Ser.). 32p. (gr. 2-8). (978-0-322-05859-0(7)) Wright Group, The.

Gruelle, Johnny. Raggedy Ann's Wishing Pebble. Gruelle, Johnny, illus. 2004. reprint ed. pap. 15.95 (978-1-4179-0709-0(6)) Kessinger Publishing, LLC.

—Raggedy Ann's Wishing Pebble. Palmer, Jan, illus. 2002. (My First Raggedy Ann Ser.). 40p. (J). (ps-2). pap. 6.99 (978-0-689-85117-9(0) , Aladdin) Simon & Schuster Children's Publishing.

—Raggedy Ann's Wishing Pebble. 2002. (ps-2). lib. bdg. 15.30 (978-0-613-90193-2(2)) Tandem Library Bks.

Guarino, Deborah. Is Your Mama a Llama? Kellogg, Steven, illus. unabr. ed. 2006. (J). 9.95 (978-0-439-87588-2(9)) Scholastic, Inc.

—Is Your Mama A Llama Read along Library. 2006. (J). 18.95 (978-0-439-87594-3(3)) Scholastic, Inc.

Guenther, James. Turnagain, Ptarmigan! Where Did You Go? A Story about the Alaska State Bird. Cartwright, Shannon, illus. 2003. (J). (ps-2). lib. bdg. 17.60 (978-0-613-79147-2(9)) Tandem Library Bks.

Gugler, Laurel Dee. There's a Billy Goat in the Garden. Beaton, Clare, illus. 2003. 32p. (J). (ps-2). 14.99 (978-1-84148-089-3(4)) Barefoot Bks., Inc.

Gunson, Christopher. Animal Surprise. 2003. (Illus.). 32p. (J). 19.99 (978-0-385-60223-5(5) , Doubleday); pap. 11.95 (978-0-552-54741-3(7) , Corgi) Transworld Publishers Ltd. GBR. *Dist:* Trafalgar Square Publishing, Independent Pubs. Group.

Gunzi, Christiane. Colorful Animals. 2007. (Feels Real Ser.). 10p. (J). bds. 4.99 (978-0-7641-6025-7(7)) Barron's Educational Series, Inc.

—Furry Kittens. 2005. (Feels Real Bks.). (Illus.). 10p. (J). bds. 4.95 (978-0-7641-5854-4(6)) Barron's Educational Series, Inc.

Gupta, Ranu. Campfires & Creepy Calls. (J). 2006. per. (978-1-933449-42-5(X)); 2005. (Illus.). 26p. per. 16.95 (978-0-9761289-1-5(8)) Nightengale Pr.

Gustafson, Scott. Alphabet Soup: A Feast of Letters. Gustafson, Scott, illus. 2003. (Illus.). 48p. (J). (ps-3). tchr. ed. 15.95 (978-0-86713-025-6(3) , 88071) Greenwich Workshop Pr.

—Animal Orchestra: A Counting Book. Gustafson, Scott, illus. 2003. (Illus.). 32p. (J). (ps-k). 14.95 (978-0-86713-030-0(X) , 88070) Greenwich Workshop Pr.

Gutman, Anne. Penelope in the Winter. Hallensleben, Georg, illus. 2005. 12p. (J). (ps-k). pap. 9.99 (978-0-439-67360-0(7) , Cartwheel Bks.) Scholastic, Inc.

Gutman, Anne & Hallensleben, Georg. Daddy Cuddles. 2005. (Illus.). 14p. (J). bds. 5.95 (978-0-8118-4674-5(1)) Chronicle Bks. LLC.

—Mommy Loves. 2005. (Illus.). 14p. (J). bds. 5.95 (978-0-8118-4616-5(4)) Chronicle Bks. LLC.

Haas, Jessie. Shaper. 2002. 192p. (J). (gr. 5 up). 16.99 (978-0-06-000170-4(4)) HarperCollins Pubs.

Hader, Berta H. The Big Snow. Hader, Berta H., illus. 2002. (Illus.). (J). 15.49 (978-0-7587-0041-4(5)) Book Wholesalers, Inc.

Hader, Berta H. & Hader, Elmer. The Big Snow. Hader, Berta H. & Hader, Elmer, illus. 3rd ed. 2005. (Stories to Go! Ser.). (Illus.). 48p. (J). 4.99 (978-0-689-87826-8(5) , Aladdin) Simon & Schuster Children's Publishing.

Hadley, Caroline. Woodside or Look Listen & Learn. 2007. pap. 87.99 (***978-1-4280-5242-0(9)***) IndyPublish.com.

—Woodside; or, Look, Listen & Learn. 2007. (ENG., Illus.). 80p. per. (***978-1-4065-1557-2(4)***) Dodo Pr.

Hale, Bruce. The Big Nap. Hale, Bruce, illus. (Chet Gecko Mystery Ser.: No. 4). (Illus.). (J). 2002. 132p. (ps-7). pap. 4.95 (978-0-15-202479-6(4) , Harcourt Paperbacks); 2001. 128p. (gr. 3-7). 15.00 (978-0-15-202521-2(9)) Harcourt Children's Bks.

—The Big Nap: From the Tattered Casebook of Chet Gecko, Private Eye. 2002. (Chet Gecko Mystery Ser.: No. 4). (J). (gr. 3-6). lib. bdg. 12.95 (978-0-613-50549-9(2)) Tandem Library Bks.

—The Hamster of the Baskervilles: A Chet Gecko Mystery. (Chet Gecko Mystery Ser.: No. 5). (Illus.). (J). 2003. 144p. (gr. 3-7). pap. 4.95 (978-0-15-202509-0(X) , Harcourt Paperbacks); 2002. 132p. (gr. 4-7). 14.00 (978-0-15-202503-8(0)) Harcourt Children's Bks.

—Hiss Me Deadly: A Chet Gecko Mystery. Hale, Bruce, illus. 2007. (Chet Gecko Mystery Ser.: No. 13). (Illus.). 144p. (J). (gr. 3-7). 15.00 (***978-0-15-205482-3(0)***) Harcourt Children's Bks.

—The Malted Falcon: A Chet Gecko Mystery. (Chet Gecko Mystery Ser.: No. 7). (Illus.). (J). (gr. 3-7). 2004. 132p. pap. 4.95 (978-0-15-216712-7(9) , Harcourt Paperbacks); 2003. 128p. 14.00 (978-0-15-216706-6(4)) Harcourt Children's Bks.

—The Malted Falcon: A Chet Gecko Mystery. 2004. (Chet Gecko Mystery Ser.: No. 7). (J). (gr. 3-6). lib. bdg. 12.95 (978-0-613-71645-1(0)) Tandem Library Bks.

—Murder, My Tweet: A Chet Gecko Mystery. 2004. (Illus.). 117p. (J). (gr. 3-7). per. 12.00 (978-0-606-33413-6(0)) Tandem Library Bks.

—The Possum Always Rings Twice: A Chet Gecko Mystery. Hale, Bruce, illus. 2007. (Chet Gecko Mystery Ser.: No. 11). (Illus.). 144p. (J). (gr. 3-7). pap. 4.95 (978-0-15-205233-1(X) , Harcourt Paperbacks) Harcourt Children's Bks.

—The Possum Always Rings Twice: A Chet Gecko Mystery. 2006. (Chet Gecko Mystery Ser.: No. 11). (Illus.). 128p. (J). (gr. 3-7). 14.00 (978-0-15-205075-7(2)) Harcourt Children's Bks.

—Trouble Is My Beeswax: A Chet Gecko Mystery. 2004. (Chet Gecko Mystery Ser.: No. 8). (Illus.). 132p. (J). (gr. 3-6). pap. 4.95 (978-0-15-216724-0(2) , Harcourt Paperbacks) Harcourt Children's Bks.

—Trouble Is My Beeswax: A Chet Gecko Mystery. Weinman, Brad, illus. 2003. (Chet Gecko Mystery Ser.: No. 8). 128p. (J). (gr. 3-6). 14.00 (978-0-15-216718-9(8)) Harcourt Children's Bks.

—Trouble Is My Beeswax: A Chet Gecko Mystery. 2004. (Chet Gecko Mystery Ser.: No. 8). (J). (gr. 3-6). lib. bdg. 12.95 (978-0-613-71557-7(8)) Tandem Library Bks.

Hale, Rachael. Furry Friends. rev. ed. 2007. (Paw Pals Ser.). 20p. (J). (ps-ps). bds. 6.99 (***978-0-316-11319-9(0)***) Little, Brown Bks. for Young Readers.

—Love Tails. rev. ed. 2007. (Paw Pals Ser.). 20p. (J). (ps-ps). bds. 6.99 (***978-0-316-11321-2(2)***) Little, Brown Bks. for Young Readers.

Hall, Amanda, illus. The Barefoot Book of Animal Tales. 2004. 80p. (J). pap. 12.99 (978-1-84148-547-8(0)) Barefoot Bks., Inc.

Hall, August. Song & Juniper. Hall, August, illus. ed. 2005. 32p. (J). 17.95 (978-0-9771990-0-6(2)) Big Kid Bks.

Hall, Kirsten. Slider's Pet: All about Nature. Luedecke, Bev, illus. (Beastieville Ser.). (J). (gr. k-1). 2005. 32p. pap. 3.95 (978-0-516-25522-4(3)); 2004. 19.50 (978-0-516-22898-3(6)) Scholastic Library Publishing. (Children's Pr.).

Hall, Susan', illus. Agent Secret. 2007. (Backyardigans Ser.). 24p. (J). pap. 3.99 (***978-1-4169-3823-1(0)*** , Simon Spotlight/Nickelodeon) Simon & Schuster Children's Publishing.

Hamilton, Leo. Leo Hamilton Presents: The Mighty Hill. Larkin, Jessica, illus. l.t. ed. 2002. 40p. (J). (gr. 1-9). pap. 9.99 (978-0-9671660-5-6(5)) Story Place, The.

—Leo Hamilton's Odd Collection of Animal & Insect Stories. Larkin, Jessica, illus. l.t. ed. (p. (ps-5). Vol. I. 2000. 36p. pap. 7.99 (978-0-9671660-0-1(4)); Vol. II. 2000. 40p. pap. 8.99 (978-0-9671660-1-8(2)); Vol. III. 2002. 24p. pap. 8.99 (978-0-9671660-3-2(9)) Story Place, The.

Hamilton, Richard & Williams, Sophy. Polly's Picnic. 2003. (Illus.). 32p. (J). (ps-2). 16.95 (978-1-58234-819-3(7) , Bloomsbury Children) Bloomsbury Publishing.

Hammerslough, Jane. Langur Monkey's Day. Buelt, Laura, illus. 2005. (Wild Reading Adventures! Ser.). (J). (ps-2). 32p. 2.95 (978-1-59249-143-8(X) , S7156); 36p. 9.95 (978-1-59249-144-5(8) , PS7156); 32p. 19.95 incl. audio (978-1-59249-221-3(5) , BC7106) Soundprints.

—Langur Monkey's Day. Buelt, Laura, tr. Buelt, Laura, illus. 2005. (Wild Reading Adventures! Ser.). 36p. (J). (ps-2). 15.95 (978-1-59249-141-4(3) , B7106); pap. 6.95 (978-1-59249-142-1(1) , S7106) Soundprints.

Hanken, Sandra. Sky Castle. Bergsma, Jody Lynn, illus. 1998. 32p. (ps-3). 15.95 (978-0-935699-14-2(7)) Illumination Arts Publishing Co., Inc.

Hansen, Brooks. Caesar's Antlers. Hansen, Brooks, illus. 2001. (Illus.). 224p. (J). pap. 6.95 (978-0-374-41072-8(0) , Sunburst) Farrar, Straus & Giroux.

Hanson, Anders. Iguana Mama. Nobens, C. A., illus. (Fact & Fiction Ser.). 24p. (J). 2007. 21.35 (978-1-59928-444-6(8)); 2006. (978-1-59928-445-3(6)) ABDO Publishing Co.

Hao, K. T. Little Stone Buddha. Ferri, Giuliano, illus. 2005. 32p. (J). 16.85 (978-1-933327-05-1(7)); 15.95 (978-1-933327-01-3(4)) Purple Bear Bks., Inc.

Happily Ever After Agency. Hoodwinked! The True Story of Little Red Riding Hood. 2005. 32p. (J). (gr. 1-6). pap. 9.95 (978-1-57178-188-8(9)) Council Oak Bks.

—Hoodwinked: The True Story of Red Riding Hood. 2005. 32p. (J). (gr. 1-6). 14.95 (978-1-57178-174-1(9)) Council Oak Bks.

Happy Animals. 2002. (978-0-9720825-2-5(2)) Toy Box Pr., The.

Harbin, P. L. Mr. Packmouse Builds a House. 2004. 50p. pap. 12.95 (978-1-4137-2535-3(X)) PublishAmerica, Inc.

Harcourt School Publishers Staff. The Bremen Town Band Advanced Level. 3rd ed. 2002. (Trophies Reading Program Ser.). (Illus.). pap. 5.10 (978-0-15-323298-5(6)) Harcourt Schl. Pubs.

—The Caterpillar & the Cave Advanced Level. 3rd ed. 2002. (Trophies Reading Program Ser.). (Illus.). pap. 5.10 (978-0-15-323106-3(8)) Harcourt Schl. Pubs.

—Criaturas en Urbana: Take-Home Book. 2001. (Vamos Ser.). (SPA., Illus.). (J). pap. 2.80 (978-0-15-319938-7(5)) Harcourt Schl. Pubs.

—Critter in the Urban Wilderness: Take-Home Book. 2001. (Collections Ser.). (Illus.). (J). pap. 1.90 (978-0-15-319495-5(2)) Harcourt Schl. Pubs.

—Critters: Take-Home Book. 1999. (Signatures Ser.). (Illus.). (J). pap. 1.70 (978-0-15-314548-3(X)) Harcourt Schl. Pubs.

—Follow Me: Below Level. 3rd ed. 2002. (Trophies Reading Program Ser.). (Illus.). (J). pap. 3.20 (978-0-15-322954-1(3)) Harcourt Schl. Pubs.

—The Graceful Bull & Other Stories Below Level. 3rd ed. 2002. (Trophies Reading Program Ser.). (Illus.). pap. 5.10 (978-0-15-323334-0(6)) Harcourt Schl. Pubs.

—Hiding Places: Take-Home Book. 1999. (Collections Ser.). (Illus.). (J). pap. 1.90 (978-0-15-317222-9(3)) Harcourt Schl. Pubs.

—Just Around the Corner Advanced Level. 3rd ed. 2002. (Trophies Reading Program Ser.). (Illus.). pap. 5.10 (978-0-15-323034-9(7)) Harcourt Schl. Pubs.

—Leap Like a Frog. 3rd ed. 2002. (Trophies English Language Learners Ser.). (Illus.). pap. 5.10 (978-0-15-327643-9(6)) Harcourt Schl. Pubs.

—The Little Red Hen: Library Book. 1999. (Collections Ser.). (Illus.). pap. 14.90 (978-0-15-313414-2(3)) Harcourt Schl. Pubs.

—Lonely No More Below Level. 3rd ed. 2002. (Trophies Reading Program Ser.). (Illus.). (gr. 5). pap. 5.10 (978-0-15-323311-1(7)) Harcourt Schl. Pubs.

—Looking for Clues Advanced Level. 3rd ed. 2002. (Trophies Reading Program Ser.). (Illus.). pap. 5.10 (978-0-15-323036-3(3)) Harcourt Schl. Pubs.

—On a Raft: On Level. 3rd ed. 2002. (Trophies Reading Program Ser.). (Illus.). (J). pap. 3.20 (978-0-15-322976-3(4)) Harcourt Schl. Pubs.

—Rick Is Sick Advanced Level. 3rd ed. 2002. (Trophies Reading Program Ser.). (Illus.). (J). pap. 3.70 (978-0-15-323010-3(X)) Harcourt Schl. Pubs.

—Tall Tales, Big Numbers Below Level. 3rd ed. 2002. (Trophies Reading Program Ser.). (Illus.). pap. 5.10 (978-0-15-323248-0(X)) Harcourt Schl. Pubs.

—Three Fables Below Level. 3rd ed. 2002. (Trophies Reading Program Ser.). (Illus.). pap. 5.10 (978-0-15-323145-2(9)) Harcourt Schl. Pubs.

—Trofeos Advanced Level: Aqui, Hay el Pista. 3rd ed. 2002. (SPA., Illus.). pap. 6.80 (978-0-15-323947-2(6)) Harcourt Schl. Pubs.

—Trofeos Below Level: Sigueme, Niki! 3rd ed. 2002. (SPA., Illus.). (J). pap. 3.50 (978-0-15-323865-9(8)) Harcourt Schl. Pubs.

—Trofeos On Level: A Trabajar. 3rd ed. 2002. (SPA., Illus.). pap. 5.50 (978-0-15-323898-7(4)) Harcourt Schl. Pubs.

—Trofeos On Level: Melaza y Cereza. 3rd ed. 2002. (SPA., Illus.). pap. 5.50 (978-0-15-323897-0(6)) Harcourt Schl. Pubs.

—Walking Thru the Jungle: Little Book. 2000. (Collections Ser.). (Illus.). (J). pap. 10.20 (978-0-15-314502-5(1)) Harcourt Schl. Pubs.

—Warthogs in the Kitchen. 3rd ed. 2002. (Trophies Reading Program Ser.). (Illus.). pap. 52.60 (978-0-15-325443-7(2)) Harcourt Schl. Pubs.

—Warthogs in the Kitchen Little Book. 3rd ed. 2002. (Trophies Reading Program Ser.). (Illus.). (J). pap. 10.20 (978-0-15-325448-2(3)) Harcourt Schl. Pubs.

—Working Hard 5-Pack, On Level. 3rd ed. 2002. (Trophies Reading Program Ser.). (Illus.). (gr. 1). pap. 20.10 (978-0-15-326837-3(9)) Harcourt Schl. Pubs.

—The World Next Door: Take-Home Book. 1999. (Collections Ser.). (Illus.). (J). pap. 1.90 (978-0-15-317305-9(X)) Harcourt Schl. Pubs.

—500 Isabels On Level. 3rd ed. 2002. (Trophies Reading Program Ser.). (Illus.). pap. 5.10 (978-0-15-323072-1(X)) Harcourt Schl. Pubs.

Harder Tangvald, Christine. Whoo! Moo! Cock-a-Doodle-Doo! Conteh-Morgan, Jane, illus. 2000. 24p. (J). (ps-k). bds. 7.99 (978-0-570-07096-2(1)) Concordia Publishing Hse.

Hardy, Robert. Todd & the TimbaThump. 2001. 20p. pap. 25.00 (978-0-9656945-6-8(9)) LHA Bks.

Harley, Bill. Bear's All-Night Party. Ferreira, Melissa, illus. 2001. 32p. (J). (ps-2). 15.95 (978-0-87483-572-4(0)) August Hse. Pubs., Inc.

—Sitting down to Eat. 2000. (ps-2). lib. bdg. 15.25 (978-0-613-86915-7(X)) Tandem Library Bks.

Harlin, Kathy. Maverick. 2004. 79p. pap. 14.95 (978-1-4137-2395-3(0)) PublishAmerica, Inc.

Harlow, Patty F. Rock with Rodney & Party with Perky to Preserve Wildlife. 2006. (Illus.). 108p. (J). per. 16.95 (978-1-60002-002-5(X) , 3583, Airleaf Publishing) Airleaf Publishing & Bookselling.

Harper, Isabelle. Our New Puppy. 2001. (Illus.). (J). (978-0-606-21370-7(8)) Tandem Library Bks.

Harper, Jo. I Could Eat You Up! Chorao, Kay, illus. 2007. 32p. (J). (ps-k). 16.95 (978-0-8234-1733-9(6)) Holiday Hse., Inc.

HarperCollins Staff. Friends Furever. 2002. (Ice Age Ser.). (Illus.). 6p. (ps). 6.99 (978-0-06-621437-5(8) , Harper Entertainment) HarperCollins Pubs.

—Join the Herd! A Pull-Tab, Lift-the-Flap, & Pop-Up Book. 2002. (Ice Age Ser.). (Illus.). 10p. (ps). 9.99 (978-0-06-621438-2(6)) HarperCollins Pubs.

Harrington, Janice N. The Chicken-Chasing Queen of Lamar County. Jackson, Shelley, illus. 2007. 40p. (J). (ps-3). 16.00 (978-0-374-31251-0(6) , Farrar, Straus & Giroux (BYR)) Farrar, Straus & Giroux.

Harris, Joel Chandle. Told by Uncle Remus: New Stories of the. 2006. (Illus.). pap. 31.95 (***978-1-4254-9964-8(3)***) Kessinger Publishing, LLC.

Harris, Joel Chandler. Uncle Remus His Songs & His Sayings. 2006. (Illus.). (YA). cd-rom (978-1-892824-57-8(4)) AFCHRON.

Harris, Robie H. Maybe a Bear Ate It! Emberley, Michael, illus. 2008. (Jewel Fairies Ser.). 40p. (J). pap. 15.99 (***978-0-439-92961-5(X)*** , Orchard Bks.) Scholastic, Inc.

Harris, Sue. The Little Seal. Boey, Stephanie, illus. 2007. 28p. (J). (ps). pap. 15.99 (***978-0-525-47839-3(6)*** , Dutton Juvenile) Penguin Group (USA) Inc.

Harrison, David L. Animals' Song. 2003. (ps-2). lib. bdg. 17.60 (978-0-613-59274-1(3)) Tandem Library Bks.

Harrison, J. The Adventurous Journey of Willowby Went. 2005. 350p. pap. 24.95 (978-1-4137-7249-4(8)) PublishAmerica, Inc.

Harry the Great Blue Heron. 2000. (Illus.). 18p. (J). pap. 12.00 (978-0-9667192-2-2(0)) Holman, Doris Anne.

Harshman, Terry Webb. Bessie's Bed. Vargo, Sharon Hawkins, illus. 2003. (Silly Millies Ser.). 32p. lib. bdg. 17.90 (978-0-7613-2742-4(8) , Millbrook Pr.) Lerner Publishing Group.

Hart, Alison. Shadow Horse. 2001. 272p. (J). (gr. 5-8). mass mkt. 4.99 (978-0-375-80263-8(0) , Random Hse. Bks. for Young Readers) Random Hse. Children's Bks.

—Shadow Horse. 2001. (gr. 5-8). lib. bdg. 13.00 (978-0-613-85134-3(X)); (J). (978-0-606-20905-2(0)) Tandem Library Bks.

Hart, Sue. Tales of the Full Moon. Harvey, Chris, illus. 2006. 96p. (J). pap. 16.95 (978-1-55591-582-7(5) , 800.992.2908) Fulcrum Publishing.

Harter, Debbie. The Animal Boogie. Blackstone, Stella, illus. 2005. 32p. (J). (ps-1). 14.99 (978-1-84148-094-7(0)) Barefoot Bks., Inc.

—The Animal Boogie. Harter, Debbie, illus. 32p. pap. 6.99 (978-1-84148-996-4(4)) Barefoot Bks., Inc.

—The Animal Boogie. 2005. (Illus.). (J). pap. (***978-1-905236-49-7(2)***) Barefoot Bks., Inc.

—Cha-Cha-Cha en la Selva (The Animal Boogie) Harter, Debbie, illus. 2003. (SPA., Illus.). 32p. (J). pap. 9.99 (978-1-84148-913-1(1)) Barefoot Bks., Inc.

—Walking Through the Jungle. 2001. (Illus.). 32p. (J). (ps-k). pap. 5.95 (978-0-531-07185-4(5) , Orchard Bks.) Scholastic, Inc.

Harter, Debbie, illus. De Paseo por la Selva (Walking through the Jungle) 2002. (SPA & ENG.). 32p. (J). (gr. k-2). 9.99 incl. audio compact disk (978-1-84148-912-4(3)) Barefoot Bks., Inc.

—Walking Through the Jungle. 2004. 30p. (J). (ps). pap. 6.99 (978-1-84148-548-5(9)) Barefoot Bks., Inc.

—Walking Through the Jungle. 2004. 30p. (J). (TAM, CZE, VIE, SPA & GUJ.). (978-1-85269-811-9(X)); (TAM, CZE, VIE, SPA & GUJ.). (978-1-85269-816-4(0)); (TAM, CZE, VIE, SPA & GUJ.). (978-1-85269-821-8(7)); (TAM, CZE, VIE, SPA & GUJ.). (978-1-85269-826-3(8)); (TAM, CZE, VIE, SPA & GUJ.). (978-1-85269-831-7(4)); (TAM, CZE, VIE, SPA & GUJ.). (978-1-85269-841-6(1)); (TAM, CZE, VIE, SPA & GUJ.). (978-1-85269-846-1(2)); (TAM, CZE, VIE, SPA & GUJ.). (978-1-85269-807-2(1)); (TAM, CZE, VIE, SPA & GUJ.). (978-1-85269-851-5(9)); (TAM, CZE, VIE, SPA & GUJ.). (978-1-85269-861-4(6)); (TAM, CZE, VIE, SPA & GUJ.). (978-1-85269-866-9(7)); (TAM, CZE, VIE, SPA & GUJ.). (978-1-85269-871-3(3)); (CZE, TAM, VIE, SPA & GUJ.). (978-1-85269-876-8(4)); (TAM, CZE, VIE, SPA & GUJ.). (978-1-85269-881-2(0)); (TAM, CZE, VIE, SPA & GUJ.). (978-1-85269-886-7(1)); (TAM, CZE, SPA, VIE & GUJ.). (978-1-85269-891-1(8)); (TAM, CZE, VIE, SPA & GUJ.). (978-1-85269-856-0(X)) Mantra Publishing, Ltd.

Harter, Debbie, tr. & illus. Walking Through the Jungle: Duke Ecur Neper Xhungel. Harter, Debbie, illus. 2004. (TAM, CZE, VIE, SPA & GUJ.). 30p. (J). (978-1-85269-806-5(3)) Mantra Publishing, Ltd.

—Walking Through the Jungle: Marchant a Travers la Jungle. Harter, Debbie, illus. 2004. (TAM, CZE, VIE, SPA & GUJ.). 30p. (J). (978-1-85269-836-2(5)) Mantra Publishing, Ltd.

Hartman, Bob. The Lion Storyteller Bedtime Book. Poole, Susie, illus. 2003. 120p. (J). (gr. k-4). pap. 13.99 (978-0-7459-4654-2(2) , Lion) Lion Hudson plc GBR. *Dist:* Independent Pubs. Group.

—The Lion Storyteller Bedtime Book. 1998. (Illus.). 120p. (J). (ps-2). pap. 17.99 (978-0-7459-3626-0(1) , Lion) Lion Hudson plc GBR. *Dist:* Trafalgar Square Publishing.

—The Lion Storyteller Book of Animal Tales. Poole, Susie, illus. 2003. 120p. (J). pap. 13.95 (978-0-7459-4838-6(3) , Lion) Lion Hudson plc GBR. *Dist:* Trafalgar Square Publishing.

Hartman, Bob & Poole, Susie. The Lion Storyteller Book of Animal Tales: Stories Old & New Especially for Reading Aloud. 2003. (Illus.). 120p. (J). pap. 19.99 (978-0-7459-4581-1(3) , Lion) Lion Hudson plc GBR. *Dist:* Trafalgar Square Publishing.

Harvey, Damian. Make Way for the Queen! Brown, Jo, illus. 2005. (Reading Corner Ser.). 24p. (J). (gr. k-3). lib. bdg. 22.80 (978-1-59771-012-1(1)) Sea-To-Sea Pubns.

Hash, Bill. Jahmon's Adventure Home. 2007. (J). per. 10.99 (***978-1-59886-790-9(3)***) Tate Publishing & Enterprises, L.L.C.

Hassett, Ann & Hassett, John. Mouse in the House. 2007. (Illus.). 32p. (J). (gr. k-3). 6.95 (***978-0-618-84064-9(8)*** , Walter Lorraine) Houghton Mifflin Co. Trade & Reference Div.

Hassett, John & Hassett, Ann. Mouse in the House. 2004. (Illus.). 32p. (J). (gr. k-3). tchr. ed. 15.00 (978-0-618-35317-0(8) , Walter Lorraine) Houghton Mifflin Co. Trade & Reference Div.

Hausman, Sid. Cactus Critter Bash. Hausman, Sid, illus. 2007. (Illus.). 32p. (J). 21.95 (***978-1-929115-15-0(6)***) Azro Pr., Inc.

Have You Seen a Javelina? Individual Title Six-Packs. (Literatura 2000 Ser.). (gr. 2-3). 33.00 (978-0-7635-0201-0(4)) Rigby Education.

Hawkins, Al. April Is Born: Adventures of a New Quarter Horse Filly. Erickson, Terri, illus. l.t. ed. 2004. 24p. (J). pap. 9.50 (978-0-9640056-5-5(4)) Arrowhead Publishing.

Hawkins, Colin. Mr Wolf's Week. 2004. (Illus.). 32p. (J). pap. 9.99 (978-1-4052-0683-9(7)) Egmont Bks., Ltd. GBR. *Dist:* Trafalgar Square Publishing.

—Mr. Wolf's Week: Mini Pop-Up. 2005. (Illus.). 12p. (J). pap. 8.99 (978-1-4052-0708-9(6)) Egmont Bks., Ltd. GBR. *Dist:* Trafalgar Square Publishing.

—What's the Time,Mr. Wolf? Mini Pop-Up. 2005. (Illus.). 14p. (J). bds. 8.99 (978-1-4052-0707-2(8)) Egmont Bks., Ltd. GBR. *Dist:* Trafalgar Square Publishing.

Hawkins, Colin & Hawkins, Jacqui. Here's a Happy Elephant. 2004. (Illus.). 8p. (J). 3.95 (978-1-56148-442-3(3)) Good Bks.

—Here's a Happy Kitten. 2004. (Illus.). 8p. (J). 3.95 (978-1-56148-440-9(7)) Good Bks.

—Here's a Happy Pig. 2004. (Illus.). 8p. (J). 3.95 (978-1-56148-441-6(5)) Good Bks.

—Here's a Happy Puppy. 2004. (Illus.). 8p. (J). 3.95 (978-1-56148-439-3(3)) Good Bks.

—Mr. Wolf's Nursery Time. 2005. (Illus.). (J). (ps-ps). 31p. pap. 9.99 (978-1-4052-1975-4(0)); 32p. 20.00 (978-1-4052-1101-7(6)) Egmont Bks., Ltd. GBR. *Dist:* Trafalgar Square Publishing, Independent Pubs. Group.

Hayashi, Leslie Ann. Fables Beneath the Rainbow. Bishop, Kathleen Wong, illus. 2005. 32p. (J). 14.95 (978-1-56647-741-3(7) , 477417) Mutual Publishing LLC.

Hayes, Ladene. The Continuing Saga of Rikki Tikki Tavi. 2007. 20p. (J). per. 10.99 (***978-1-59886-786-2(5)***) Tate Publishing & Enterprises, L.L.C.

Hays, Anna Jane. The Pup Speaks Up: A Phonics Reader. Petrone, Valeria, illus. 2003. (Early Step into Reading Ser.). 32p. (J). (ps-1). pap. 3.99 (978-0-375-81232-3(6) , Random Hse. Bks. for Young Readers) Random Hse. Children's Bks.

Hayward, Linda. It Takes Three. Koontz, Robin Michal, illus. 2003. (Silly Millies Ser.: 3). 32p. lib. bdg. 17.90 (978-0-7613-2902-2(1) , Millbrook Pr.) Lerner Publishing Group.

Hazen, Barbara Shook. Where Do Bears Sleep? Van Royen, Mary Morgan, illus. 1998. (Growing Tree Ser.). 24p. (J). (ps up). 9.95 (978-0-694-01037-0(5) , Harper Festival) HarperCollins Pubs.

Heale, Jay. African Animal Tales. 2004. (Illus.). 96p. 10.00 (978-1-86872-704-9(1)) Struik Pubs. ZAF. *Dist:* Continental Enterprises Group, Inc. (CEG).

Heap, Sue. Four Friends Together. Heap, Sue, illus. 2003. (Illus.). 32p. (J). (ps). 15.99 (978-0-7636-2111-7(0)) Candlewick Pr.

Heatwole, Marsha. Jambo, Watoto! Hello, Children! 1998. (Illus.). 32p. (J). (ps-k). 15.95 (978-0-9642712-3-4(0)) Creative Art Pr.

Heck, Cathy. Little Pond. 2007. 10p. bds. 5.99 (***978-1-4037-3303-0(1)***) Dalmatian Pr.

Hedrick, Helen Groves. Sis & the Singing Hens. 2001. (Illus.). 32p. (J). pap. 8.00 (978-0-87012-664-2(4)) McClain Printing Co.

Hegarty, Sue. Barnaby & Thor. Shaw, Alice, illus. 2002. (J). 16.95 (978-0-939549-53-5(0)) ZON International Publishing Co.

Heger, Jennifer Sy & Sykes, Christine. I'm Nocturnal, How about You? 2007. 44p. (J). pap. 10.99 (978-1-59092-064-0(3) , Orchard Academy Pr.) Windstorm Creative.

Heide, Florence Parry & Clief, Sylvia Van. That's What Friends Are For. Meade, Holly, illus. 2007. 40p. (J). (ps-3). pap. 6.99 (978-0-7636-2646-4(5)) Candlewick Pr.

Heine, Helme. Abenteurer. pap. 14.95 (978-3-257-25106-7(8)) Diogenes Verlag AG CHE. *Dist:* Distribooks, Inc.

Heins, Edward, illus. Horses. 2001. (Nature Sticker Stories Ser.). 20p. (J). (ps-3). pap. 4.99 (978-0-448-42195-7(X) , Grosset & Dunlap) Penguin Group (USA) Inc.

Helft, Claude. Dulces Suenos, Teddy! (SPA.). 28p. (J). (978-84-488-0684-2(0)) Beascoa, Ediciones S.A. ESP. *Dist:* Lectorum Pubns., Inc.

Heller, Sarah. Disney Animal Friends Storybook & Music Player. 2006. (Music Player Storybook Ser.). 40p. (J). bds. 24.99 (978-0-7944-1165-7(7)) Reader's Digest Assn., Inc., The.

Heller, Sarah E. Disney Animal Friends Movie Theater Storybook & Projector. Disney Art Archives Staff, illus. 2003. (Movie Theater Storybooks & Movie Projectortm Ser.). 48p. (J). 24.99 incl. audio compact disk (978-0-7944-0122-1(8) , Reader's Digest Children's Bks.) Reader's Digest Children's Publishing, Inc.

Hello Goodbye, 6 Pack. (Literatura 2000 Ser.). (gr. k-1). 28.00 (978-0-7635-0056-6(9)) Rigby Education.

Helmer, Marilyn. Mr. McGratt & the Ornery Cat. Gourbault, Martine, illus. unabr. ed. 2002. 32p. (J). (gr. k-3). (978-1-55337-162-5(3)) Kids Can Pr., Ltd.

—Three Tales of Three. Jackson, Chris, illus. 2004. (Once-upon-a-Time Ser.). 32p. (J). (gr. k-3). (978-1-55074-759-1(2)) Kids Can Pr., Ltd.

Hendricks, Robert V. A Snout Full of Honey: Includes Audio Cassette, Coloring Pad & Crayons. Hendricks, Lu, illus. 1998. 20p. (J). (gr. k-4). pap. 12.50 incl. audio (978-0-9662994-0-3(X)) Adventure Meadow.

Henkes, Kevin. A Good Day. Henkes, Kevin, illus. 2007. (Illus.). 32p. (ps-1). 16.99 (978-0-06-114018-1(X) , Greenwillow Bks.); lib. bdg. 17.89 (978-0-06-114019-8(8)) HarperCollins Pubs.

—Oh! Dronzek, Laura, illus. 1999. 24p. (J). (ps-k). 16.99 (978-0-688-17053-0(6)) HarperCollins Pubs.

Hereford, L. F. Gerry the Grape. Skardarasy, Doreen L., illus. 2005. (J). pap. (978-0-9728969-9-3(6)) Acorn Publishing.

Herfurtner, Rudolf. Cumpleanos con Animales. 2002. Tr. of Birthday with Animals. (SPA.). 118p. (gr. 3-4). 3.99 (978-968-16-4266-2(X)) Fondo de Cultura Economica USA.

Hergé. Tintín: Descubro Los Animales. 2004. (SPA.). 24p. 19.95 (978-1-59497-065-8(3)) Public Square Bks.

Herlihy, Matt & Clarke, Nzingha, selected by. Sweet Fancy Moses: Book 2. 2005. per. (978-0-9767048-0-5(3)) Literary License, Inc.

Herriot, James. James Herriot's Treasury of Inspirational Stories for Children: Warm & Joyful Tales by the Author of All Creatures Great & Small. Brown, Ruth & Barrett, Peter, illus. 2005. 260p. (gr. 4-7). per. 14.95 (978-0-312-34972-1(6) , St. Martin's Griffin) St. Martin's Pr.

Hest, Amy. You Can Do It, Sam. Jeram, Anita, illus. 2007. (Sam Bks.). 32p. (J). (ps). pap. 4.99 (***978-0-7636-3688-3(6)***) Candlewick Pr.

Heurtelou, Maude. Makso. Louissaint, Louis, illus. (CRP.). 24p. (J). (gr. k-2). pap. 8.50 (978-1-58432-005-0(2)) Educa Vision.

—Tipoul. Louissaint, Louis, illus. 1999. (Big Book Ser.).Tr. of Four Friends. (CRP.). 20p. (J). (gr. 3-5). 19.50 (978-1-58432-061-6(3)); pap. 8.50 (978-1-58432-008-1(7)) Educa Vision.

Hibbeler, Stephen Paul. A Wonderful, Magical World. 2006. 48p. pap. 12.95 (978-1-4241-2631-6(2)) PublishAmerica, Inc.

Higgenson, Hadley. Keeker & the Sneaky Pony, Bk. 1. Andersen, Maja, illus. 2006. (Sneaky Pony Ser.: Bk. 1). 47p. (J). 15.50 (978-0-8118-4052-1(2)) Chronicle Bks. LLC.

Higginson, Sheila Sweeny. Donald's Christmas Gift. rev. ed. 2007. 24p. (ps-1). pap. 3.99 (***978-1-4231-0745-3(4)***) Disney Pr.

Hilgendorf, L. B. Orville Oak & Friends. Dow, S. B., illus. 2005. 24p. bds. 11.95 (***978-1-58275-149-8(8)***) Black Forest Pr.

Hill, Eric. Hello, Spot! Hill, Eric, illus. 2004. (Illus.). 5p. (J). (ps-1). 8.99 (978-0-399-24282-3(1) , Putnam Juvenile) Penguin Group (USA) Inc.

—Spot's Birthday Party. Hill, Eric, illus. 2003. (Illus.). 24p. (J). pap. 6.99 (978-0-14-250125-2(5) , Puffin) Penguin Group (USA) Inc.

—Spot's Birthday Party. 2003. (gr. k-3). lib. bdg. 15.30 (978-0-613-87829-6(9)) Tandem Library Bks.

—Spot's Halloween. Hill, Eric, illus. 2003. (Spot Ser.). (Illus.). 10p. (J). (ps-1). bds. 5.99 (978-0-399-24185-7(X) , Putnam Juvenile) Penguin Group (USA) Inc.

—Where's Spot? Hill, Eric, illus. 2003. (Illus.). (J). (ps-1). (SPA.). 22p. bds. 7.99 (978-0-399-24046-1(2) , 53517281, Putnam Juvenile); 24p. pap. 7.99 (978-0-14-250126-9(3) , Puffin) Penguin Group (USA) Inc.

Hill, Karen. The Something Wonderful: A Christmas Story. Reagan, Susan, illus. 2005. 36p. (J). (ps-3). pap. 15.99 (978-1-58134-732-6(4) , Crossway Bibles) Crossway Bks.

Hill, Laban Carrick. Casa Azul: An Encounter with Frida Kahlo. 2005. (Art Encounters Ser.). (Illus.). 160p. (YA). 15.95 (978-0-8230-0411-9(2)) Watson-Guptill Pubns., Inc.

Hill, Susan. Ruby Bakes a Cake. Moore, Margie, illus. (I Can Read Bks.). 32p. (J). (gr. k-3). 2005. pap. 3.99 (978-0-06-008977-1(6) , Harper Trophy); 2004. 15.99 (978-0-06-008975-7(X)); 2004. lib. bdg. 16.89 (978-0-06-008976-4(8)) HarperCollins Pubs.

—Ruby Bakes a Cake. Moore, Margie, illus. 2004. 32p. (J). lib. bdg. 13.85 (***978-1-4242-0476-2(3)***) Fitzgerald Bks.

Hill, Susan. Ruby Paints a Picture. Moore, Margie, illus. 2005. (I Can Read Bks.). 32p. (J). (ps-ps). 15.99 (978-0-06-008978-8(4)) HarperCollins Pubs.

Hillenbrand, Jane. What a Treasure! Hillenbrand, Will, illus. 24p. (J). (ps-1). pap. 6.95 (***978-0-8234-2077-3(9)***) Holiday Hse., Inc.

Hillerman, Tony. Buster Mesquite's Cowboy Band. Franklin, Ernest, illus. 2001. 32p. (J). 19.95 (978-0-914001-11-9(6)) Sidewinder Publishing LLC.

Hillerman, Tony. Buster Mesquite's Cowboy Band (Reprint) 2006. (J). lib. bdg. 14.95 (***978-0-914001-12-6(4)***) Sidewinder Publishing LLC.

Hillert, Margaret. Four Good Friends: The Bremen Town Musicians Retold. Stasiak, Krystyna, illus. rev. exp. ed. 2007. (Beginning to Read Ser.). 32p. (J). lib. bdg. (978-1-59953-047-5(3)) Norwood Hse. Pr.

—The Purple Pussycat. Stasiak, Krystyna, illus. rev. exp. ed. 2007. (Beginning to Read Ser.). 32p. (J). lib. bdg. (978-1-59953-044-4(9)) Norwood Hse. Pr.

Hills, Tad. My Fuzzy Safari Babies: A Book to Touch & Feel. Hills, Tad, illus. 2001. (My Fuzzy Friends Board Bks.). (Illus.). 12p. (J). bds. 6.99 (978-0-689-84164-4(7) , Little Simon) Simon & Schuster Children's Publishing.

Himmelman, John. The Animal Rescue Club. Himmelman, John, illus. 1999. (I Can Read Chapter Bks.). (Illus.). 48p. (J). (ps-3). pap. 5.99 (978-0-06-444224-4(1) , Harper Trophy) HarperCollins Pubs.

—The Animal Rescue Club. 1999. (I Can Read Chapter Bks.). (J). (gr. 3-4). (978-0-606-16694-2(7)) Tandem Library Bks.

Hincher, Theresa B. Baldy the Balloon. 2005. 16p. (J). (ps). per. 13.95 (978-0-933767-06-5(4)) Pex Publishing Co.

Hindley, Judy. Sleepy Places. Freeman, Tor, illus. 2006. 32p. (J). (ps-1). 15.99 (978-0-7636-2983-0(9)) Candlewick Pr.

—Ten Bright Eyes. Bartlett, Alison, illus. 1998. 32p. (J). (ps-3). 14.95 (978-1-56145-173-9(8)) Peachtree Pubs., Ltd.

Hippely, Hilary Horder. Adventure on Klickitat Island. Upton, Barbara, illus. 2000. (J). (ps-ps). lib. bdg. 15.30 (978-0-613-24092-5(8)) Tandem Library Bks.

Hiscock, Karen, illus. Baby Animals. 1998. (Find & Fit Ser.). 10p. (J). (ps-k). bds. 14.95 (978-1-57145-358-7(X) , Silver Dolphin Bks.) Advantage Pubs. Group.

Hiskey, Iris. I Like a Bath. Sandford, John B., illus. 2000. 13p. (J). (ps-1). 9.95 (978-0-694-01073-8(1)) HarperCollins Pubs.

Ho, Minfong. Peek! A Thai Hide-and-Seek. Ho, Minfong & Meade, Holly, illus. 2004. 40p. (J). (ps-1). 16.99 (978-0-7636-2041-7(6)) Candlewick Pr.

Hoban, Russell. The Mouse & His Child. Small, David, illus. 2001. 256p. (J). pap. 16.95 (978-0-439-09826-7(2) , Levine, Arthur A. Bks.) Scholastic, Inc.

Hoban, Tana. I Wonder. 2003. (Green Light Readers Level 2 Ser.). (Illus.). 24p. (J). 11.95 (978-0-15-204875-4(8)); pap. 3.95 (978-0-15-204835-8(9)) Harcourt Children's Bks. (Green Light Readers).

—I Wonder. 1999. (gr. k-3). lib. bdg. 11.80 (978-0-613-64525-6(1)); (Illus.). (J). (978-0-606-18179-2(2)) Tandem Library Bks.

Hobbie, Holly. I'll Be Home for Christmas, Set. gif. ed. 2004. (Toot & Puddle Ser.). (Illus.). 32p. (J). (ps-3). 19.99 (978-0-316-73586-5(8)) Little, Brown Bks. for Young Readers.

—Toot & Puddle, 3 vols., Box Set. Hobbie, Holly, illus. 2003. (Illus.). 32p. (J). (ps-1). 11.99 (978-0-316-14564-0(5)) Little, Brown Bks. for Young Readers.

Hobbs, William. Far North: Class Set. unabr. ed. 1998. (YA). (gr. 7). 114.70 incl. audio (978-0-7887-2563-0(7) , 46733) Recorded Bks., LLC.

—Far North: Homework Set. unabr. ed. 1998. (J). pap. 57.24 incl. audio (978-0-7887-2565-4(3) , 40801) Recorded Bks., LLC.

Hoberman, Mary Ann. A House Is a House for Me. Fraser, Betty, illus. 2000. (J). pap. 19.97 incl. audio (978-0-7366-9199-4(5)) Books on Tape, Inc.

—Sing-along Stories 3: Mary Had a Little Lamb, Yankee Doodle, Bill Grogan's Goat, 3 vols. Westcott, Nadine Bernard, illus. 3rd ed. 2005. (Sing-Along Stories Ser.). 33p. (J). (ps-k). 14.99 (978-0-316-01139-6(8) , Tingley, Megan Bks.) Little, Brown Bks. for Young Readers.

Hobnob the Troll: Set B Individual Title Six-Packs. (gr. k-3). 29.00 (978-0-7635-0539-4(0)) Rigby Education.

Hobson, Sally, illus. All Aboard! 2000. 24p. (J). (978-1-86233-079-5(4) , Gullane Children's Bks.) Pinwheel.

Hodgson, Mona Gansberg. Bedtime in the Southwest. Graef, Renee, illus. 2004. 32p. 14.95 (978-0-87358-871-3(1) , Rising Moon Bks. for Young Readers) Northland Publishing.

—Desert Critter Friends Set, 12 vols. (Desert Critter Friends Ser.). (J). 54.99 (978-0-7586-0007-3(0)) Concordia Publishing Hse.

—Smelly Tales. Sharp, Chris, illus. 1998. (Desert Critter Friends Ser.: Vol. 4). 48p. (J). (ps-2). 4.99 (978-0-570-05071-1(5) , 56-1895) Concordia Publishing Hse.

—Smelly Tales. 1998. (ps-2). lib. bdg. 13.00 (978-0-613-72807-2(6)) Tandem Library Bks.

—Sour Snacks. Sharp, Chris, illus. 1998. (Desert Critter Friends Ser.: Vol. 3). 48p. (J). (ps-2). 4.99 (978-0-570-05070-4(7) , 56-1894) Concordia Publishing Hse.

—Sour Snacks. 1998. (ps-2). lib. bdg. 13.00 (978-0-613-72806-5(8)) Tandem Library Bks.

Hoeye, Michael. No Time Like Show Time. 2007. 304p. (J). pap. 7.99 (***978-0-14-240982-4(0)*** , Puffin) Penguin Group (USA) Inc.

—No Time Like Show Time: A Hermux Tantamoq Adventure. 2004. (Illus.). 288p. (J). (ps). 14.99 (978-0-399-23880-2(8) , Putnam Juvenile) Penguin Group (USA) Inc.

—No Time Like Showtime. 2006. (Illus.). 288p. (YA). (gr. 7). pap. 7.99 (978-0-14-240563-5(9) , Puffin) Penguin Group (USA) Inc.

—The Sands of Time. (J). 2007. 304p. (gr. 1). pap. 7.99 (*978-0-14-240983-1(9), Puffin); 2002. (Hermux Tantamoq Adventure Ser.: Bk. 2). (Illus.). 288p. (gr. 5-8). 14.99 (978-0-399-23879-6(4), Putnam Juvenile) Penguin Group (USA) Inc.

—The Sands of Time. 2001. (Hermux Tantamoq Adventure Ser.: Bk. 2). (Illus.). 300p. (YA). (gr. 5-8). pap. 12.95 (978-0-9675111-2-2(7)) Terfle Bks.

—The Sands of Time: A Hermux Tantamoq AdventureTM. 2004. 288p. (J). (gr. 5-9). pap. 40.00 incl. audio (978-1-4000-9016-7(4), Listening Library) Random Hse. Audio Publishing Group.

—The Sands of Time: A New Hermux Tantamoq Adventure. 2003. 288p. pap. 6.99 (978-0-14-250176-4(X), Puffin) Penguin Group (USA) Inc.

—Time Stops for No Mouse. 272p. 2007. (J). pap. 7.99 (*978-0-14-240984-8(7)); 2003. (Hermux Tantamoq Adventure Ser.: Bk. 1). (Illus.). (YA). (gr. 5-8). pap. 7.99 (978-0-698-11991-8(6)) Penguin Group (USA) Inc. (Puffin).

—Time Stops for No Mouse. 2003. (Illus.). 250p. (J). (ps-7). per. 16.45 (978-0-613-62122-9(0)) Tandem Library Bks.

—Time Stops for No Mouse. 2000. (Hermux Tantamoq Adventure Ser.: Bk. 1). (Illus.). 288p. (YA). (gr. 5-8). pap. 12.95 (978-0-9675111-1-5(9)) Terfle Bks.

—Time Stops for No Mouse: A Hermux Tantamoq Adventure. 2002. (Hermux Tantamoq Adventure Ser.: Bk. 1). (Illus.). 288p. (J). (gr. 5-8). 14.99 (978-0-399-23878-9(6), Putnam Juvenile) Penguin Group (USA) Inc.

Hoffman, Alice & Martin, Wolfe. Moondog. Heo, Yumi, illus. 2004. (J). pap. (978-0-439-09862-5(9)); 32p. pap. 16.95 (978-0-439-09861-8(0)) Scholastic, Inc.

Hoffman, Mary. Parables & Miracles of Jesus. Morris, Jackie, illus. 2007. 64p. (J). 19.95 (*978-1-84507-786-0(5)) Lincoln, Frances Ltd. GBR. *Dist:* Perseus Distribution.

Hogan, Mary. Let's Play with Winnie the Pooh. 1999. (Disney's Winnie the Pooh Ser.). (Illus.). 10p. (J). (ps-3). 9.99 (978-0-7364-0185-2(7)) Mouse Works.

Holabird, Katharine. A Year with Angelina. Craig, Helen, illus. 2007. 72p. (J). 9.99 (*978-0-448-44689-9(8), Grosset & Dunlap) Penguin Group (USA) Inc.

Holabird, Katherine, contrib. by. Angelina at the Palace. 2005. (Angelina Ballerina Ser.). 32p. (J). 12.99 (978-0-670-06048-1(8), Viking Juvenile) Penguin Group (USA) Inc.

Holbert, Lesley Lyford. Susie. 2001. (Illus.). 22p. (J). 13.90 (978-0-7541-1522-9(4)) Minerva Pr. GBR. *Dist:* Unity Distribution.

Holbrook, Florence. Why the Crocodile Has a Wide Mouth: And Other Nature Myths. 2004. (Illus.). 128p. pap. 5.95 (978-0-486-43649-4(7)) Dover Pubns., Inc.

The Hole: Individual Title Six-Packs. (Sails Literacy Ser.). 16p. (gr. k up). 27.00 (978-0-7635-4418-8(3)) Rigby Education.

Holland, Elizabeth, compiled by. Awesome Animal Stories. 2007. (Super Shorts Ser.). 160p. (J). pap. 6.95 (*978-0-7534-6071-9(8), Kingfisher) Houghton Mifflin Co. Trade & Reference Div.

Holm, Jennifer L. & Holm, Matthew. Our Hero. 2005. (Babymouse Ser.). (Illus.). 96p. (J). (gr. 2-5). pap. 5.95 (978-0-375-83230-7(0)); lib. bdg. 12.99 (978-0-375-93230-4(5)) Random Hse. Children's Bks. (Random Hse. Bks. for Young Readers).

—Queen of the World! 2005. (Babymouse Ser.). (Illus.). 96p. (J). (gr. 2-5). pap. 5.95 (978-0-375-83229-1(7)); lib. bdg. 12.99 (978-0-375-93229-8(1)) Random Hse. Children's Bks. (Random Hse. Bks. for Young Readers).

Holub, Joan. Marvelous Moms. Holub, Joan, illus. 2006. (Sparkle 'n' Shimmer Ser.). (Illus.). 14p. (J). 5.99 (978-1-4169-0622-3(3), Little Simon) Simon & Schuster Children's Publishing.

Homero & Martín, Jean. Cuentos y Leyendas de la Ilíada. Campos, Paz, tr. 2nd ed. 2003. (Fables & Legends Ser.). (SPA., Illus.). 116p. (J). 9.95 (978-84-239-6349-2(7)) Espasa Calpe, S.A. ESP. *Dist:* Planeta Publishing Corp.

The Honey Tree, 6 Packs. (Literatura 2000 Ser.). (gr. 2-3). 33.00 (978-0-7635-0262-1(6)) Rigby Education.

Honigsberg, Peter Jan. Armful of Memories. Morse, Tony, illus. 2004. 32p. 17.95 (978-1-57143-089-2(X)) RDR Bks.

Hood, Thomas. Before I Go to Sleep. Begin, Mary Jane, illus. 1999. 32p. (J). (ps-k). 15.95 (978-0-688-12424-3(0)) HarperCollins Pubs.

Hooks, William H. Little Poss & Horrible Hound. Newsom, Carol, illus. 1998. (Bank Street Reader Collection). 48p. (J). (gr. 2-4). lib. bdg. 22.60 (978-0-8368-1773-7(7)) Stevens, Gareth Inc.

Hooper, Meredith. Animals in the Ark. 2nd rev. ed. 2000. (Cambridge Reading Ser.). (Illus.). 10p. pap. 5.00 (978-0-521-78585-3(5)) Cambridge Univ. Pr.

—Animals in the Ark American English Edition. 2000. (Cambridge Reading Ser.). pap. 5.00 (978-0-521-79910-2(4)) Cambridge Univ. Pr.

Hoover, Helen. Great Wolf & the Good Woodsman. Bowen, Betsy, illus. 2005. (Fesler-Lampert Minnesota Heritage Book Ser.). 40p. (J). 14.95 (978-0-8166-4445-2(4)) Univ. of Minnesota Pr.

Hop to It, Minty! Individual Chapter Book Title Six-Packs. Vol. 28. 32p. (gr. 4 up). 44.00 (978-0-7578-0601-8(5)) Rigby Education.

Hopkins, Lee Bennett. Mother Goose & Her Animal Friends: Theme 2. Fehlau, Dagmar et al, illus. l.t. ed. 1999. (Sadlier Phonics Reading Program). 16p. (YA). (ps-2). 29.85 (978-0-8215-0472-7(X)) Sadlier, William H. Inc.

Horacek, Petr. When the Moon Smiled. 2004. (Illus.). 32p. (J). (ps-k). 14.99 (978-0-7636-2209-1(5)) Candlewick Pr.

Hord, Donald. Shortcut & Friends Australian Outback. 2006. pap. 12.99 (*978-1-4259-6355-2(2)) AuthorHouse.

Horn, Peter. The Best Father of All. James, J. Alison, tr. from GER. Kadmon, Cristina, illus. 2003. 32p. (J). (ps-1). 15.95 (978-0-7358-1679-4(4)) North-South Bks., Inc.

Horner, Polly. Polly & the North Star. (Illus.). pap. 11.00 (978-1-84255-281-0(3)); 2003. 32p. 19.99 (978-1-84255-085-4(3)) Orion Children's Bks. GBR. *Dist:* Trafalgar Square Publishing.

Hornik, Laurie Miller. Zoo School. Tilley, Debbie, illus. 2004. 144p. (J). (gr. 3-5). tchr. ed. 16.00 (978-0-618-34204-4(4), Clarion Bks.) Houghton Mifflin Co. Trade & Reference Div.

Horton, Michael. Original Animals. 2003. (J). per. 13.95 (978-0-943864-49-5(6)) Davenport, May Pubs.

Horwood, William. The Willows & Beyond. Benson, Patrick, illus. rev. ed. 1999. 304p. (gr. 4-7). pap. 12.95 (978-0-312-24497-2(5), St. Martin's Griffin) St. Martin's Pr.

Howard, Jane R. When I'm Sleepy. 2000. (ps-2). lib. bdg. 14.15 (978-0-613-31909-6(5)) Tandem Library Bks.

Howe, Deborah & Howe, James. A Rabbit-Tale of Mystery. unabr. ed. 2004. (Bunnicula Ser.). 98p. (J). (gr. 3-7). pap. 29.00 incl. audio (978-0-8072-8204-5(9), YYA139SP, Listening Library) Random Hse. Audio Publishing Group.

Howe, James. The Celery Stalks at Midnight. unabr. ed. 2004. (Bunnicula Ser.). 111p. (J). (gr. 3-7). pap. 29.00 incl. audio (978-0-8072-8357-8(6), YA173SP, Listening Library) Random Hse. Audio Publishing Group.

—Creepy-Crawly Birthday. Mack, Jeff, illus. 2007. (Bunnicula & Friends Ser.). 48p. (J). 16.99 (978-0-689-85728-7(4), Atheneum) Simon & Schuster Children's Publishing.

—Nighty-Nightmare. unabr. ed. 2004. (Bunnicula Ser.). 128p. (J). (gr. 3-7). pap. 29.00 incl. audio (978-0-8072-8397-4(5), YA201SP, Listening Library) Random Hse. Audio Publishing Group.

Howe, James & Howe, Deborah. Bunnicula: A Rabbit-Tale of Mystery. Daniel, Alan, illus. 25th anniv. ed. 2004. 112p. (J). 16.95 (978-0-689-86775-0(1), Atheneum) Simon & Schuster Children's Publishing.

Howe, James & Howe, James. La Posada del Aullido. 2000. (la Orilla Del Viento Ser.). (SPA., Illus.). 155p. (J). (ps-ps). pap. 6.99 (978-968-16-6038-3(2), 123) Fondo de Cultura Economica USA.

Howell, Theresa. I Don't See Any Bears. Do You? Jones, Larry, illus. 2004. 12p. (J). bds. 7.95 (978-0-87358-862-1(2), Rising Moon Bks. for Young Readers) Northland Publishing.

Howes, Jim. Rosa & Fredo. Forss, Ian, illus. 1999. (Supa Doopers Ser.). 56p. (J). (978-0-7608-1922-7(X)) Sundance/Newbridge Educational Publishing.

Hubbard, Coleen. One Golden Year. 1999. (Dog Tales Ser.). (Illus.). 128p. (J). (gr. 3-7). pap. 4.50 (978-0-590-18975-0(1)) Scholastic, Inc.

Hubery, Julia. A Friend for All Seasons. Matsuoka, Mei, illus. 2007. 32p. (J). (ps-2). 15.99 (*978-1-4169-2685-6(2)) Simon & Schuster Children's Publishing.

Hubner, Franz. Moaning Morris. Kessler, Mario, illus. 2004. 32p. (J). pap. (978-81-87649-93-9(3)) Katha.

Huck, Charlotte S. The Black Bull of Norroway: A Scottish Tale. Lobel, Anita, illus. 2001. 40p. (J). (gr. 1 up). 15.89 (978-0-688-16901-5(5)) HarperCollins Pubs.

Hudson, Charlotte & Gormley, Greg. Monkey Words. 2003. (Illus.). 32p. 19.99 (978-0-370-32636-8(9)) Random Hse. GBR. *Dist:* Independent Pubs. Group.

Hudson, Wade. Robo's Favorite Places. 1998. (Afro-Bets Ser.). (Illus.). 32p. (J). (ps-2). 5.95 (978-0-940975-85-9(8), Sankofa Bks.) Just Us Bks., Inc.

Hughes, Dawn Marie. Oakley Farm Friends. 2006. 83p. pap. 14.95 (978-1-4241-2094-9(2)) PublishAmerica, Inc.

Hughes, Marghanita. Toffee at Home on the Farm. (Illus.). 20p. 13.95 (978-1-899827-50-3(1)) Scottish Children's Pr. GBR. *Dist:* Wilson & Assocs.

—Toffee Goes Camping. (Illus.). 20p. 13.95 (978-1-899827-51-0(X)) Scottish Children's Pr. GBR. *Dist:* Wilson & Assocs.

Hughes, Ted. How the Whale Became: And Other Stories. Morris, Jackie, illus. 2000. 94p. (J). (ps-3). pap. 25.00 (978-0-531-30303-0(9), Orchard Bks.) Scholastic, Inc.

Hunter, Anne. Possum & the Peeper. 2000. (Illus.). 32p. (J). (gr. k-3). pap. 6.95 (978-0-618-07030-5(3)) Houghton Mifflin Co. Trade & Reference Div.

—Possum & the Peeper. 2000. (J). (978-0-606-19427-3(4)) Tandem Library Bks.

Hunter, Erin. Into the Wild. 2004. (Warriors Ser.: Bk. 1). 288p. (J). (gr. 5 up). pap. 6.99 (978-0-06-052550-7(9)) HarperCollins Pubs.

—Moonrise. 2005. (Warriors Ser.: Bk. 2). (Illus.). 304p. (J). (gr. 5 up). lib. bdg. 17.89 (978-0-06-074453-3(7)) HarperCollins Pubs.

Hunting Mowgli. 2001. 48p. (J). per. 4.95 (978-1-931319-49-2(9)) Max Media, Inc.

Hurd, Edith Thacher. Johnny Lion's Bad Day. Hurd, Clement, illus. 2001. (I Can Read Bks.). (J). 10.79 (978-0-606-20744-7(9)) Tandem Library Bks.

Hurwitz, Andy Bl. On Road. 2007. 16p. (J). bds. 7.99 (*978-0-8431-2208-4(0), Price Stern Sloan) Penguin Group (USA) Inc.

Hurwitz, Johanna. Pee Wee & Plush. Brewster, Patience, illus. 2004. (Park Pals Adventure Ser.). 144p. (J). (ps-k). pap. 4.95 (978-1-58717-243-4(7), SeaStar Bks.) Chronicle Bks. LLC.

Huskins, Suzanne Hallier, illus. No Matter What! 2004. (J). (978-1-887905-93-0(6)) Parkway Pubs., Inc.

Hutchins, Pat. Good Night, Owl! Hutchins, Pat, illus. 2002. (Illus.). (J). 15.53 (978-0-7587-2620-9(1)) Book Wholesalers, Inc.

—The Surprise Party. Hutchins, Pat, illus. 2002. (Illus.). (J). 14.47 (978-0-7587-3736-6(X)) Book Wholesalers, Inc.

Huxley, Aldous. The Crows of Pearblossom. (J). 15.95 (978-0-89190-167-9(1)) Amereon LTD.

I Am a Bee: Individual Title, 6 Packs. (Sails Literacy Ser.). 16p. (gr. k up). 27.00 (978-0-7635-4411-9(6)) Rigby Education.

I Can Say- Animals. 2005. (J). bds. (978-1-4194-0035-3(5)) Paradise Pr., Inc.

Ibbotson, Eva. The Beasts of Clawstone Castle. Hawkes, Kevin, illus. (J). 2007. 256p. (gr. 3 up). 6.99 (*978-0-14-240931-2(6), Puffin); 2006. 192p. (gr. 5). 16.99 (978-0-525-47719-8(5), Dutton Juvenile) Penguin Group (USA) Inc.

Ibbotson, Eva. Not Just a Witch. Hawkes, Kevin, illus. 2004. 192p. (gr. 3). pap. 5.99 (978-0-14-240232-0(X), Puffin) Penguin Group (USA) Inc.

Ichikawa, Satomi. En Busca de Tesoros. (SPA., Illus.). 40p. (J). (gr. k-2). (978-84-95150-33-2(6), COR0428) Corimbo, Editorial S.L. ESP. *Dist:* Lectorum Pubns., Inc.

—En Busca De Tesoros. (SPA.). 40p. (978-84-95150-43-1(3)) Corimbo, Editorial S.L.

Ikwuakor, Ugochukwu. Inside the Animal Kingdom. 2005. pap. 7.95 (978-0-533-14881-3(2)) Vantage Pr., Inc.

The Imaginary Zoo. 2007. (J). 16.95 (978-0-9789880-0-5(0)) Wild About Learning, Inc.

In My Bed: Individual Title, 6 Packs. (Literatura 2000 Ser.). (gr. k-1). 28.00 (978-0-7635-0007-8(0)) Rigby Education.

In My Room: Individual Title Six-Packs. (Literatura 2000 Ser.). (gr. k-1). 28.00 (978-0-7635-0032-0(1)) Rigby Education.

Inches, Alison. Castaways! 2006. (Illus.). 24p. (J). lib. bdg. 9.00 (*978-1-4242-0950-7(1)) Fitzgerald Bks.

Inkpen, Mick. A to Z: An Alphabet Adventure. 2001. (Kipper Ser.). (Illus.). 64p. (J). (ps-2). 16.95 (978-0-15-202594-6(4), Red Wagon Bks.) Harcourt Children's Bks.

—Bokobikes. 2006. (Blue Nose Island Ser.: Bk. 3). (Illus.). (J). (ps). 34p. audio compact disk 11.95 (978-1-84456-240-4(9), Hodder & Stoughton); No. 3. 32p. pap. 9.99 (978-0-340-89354-8(0)) Hodder General Publishing Division GBR. *Dist:* Trafalgar Square Publishing.

—Great Pet Sale. 1999. (Illus.). 16p. (J). (ps-1). pap. 14.95 (978-0-531-30130-2(3), Orchard Bks.) Scholastic, Inc.

—Picnic. Inkpen, Mick, illus. 2002. (Kipper Ser.). (Illus.). (J). 12.30 (978-0-7587-6469-0(3)) Book Wholesalers, Inc.

—Rocket. 2001. (gr. k-3). lib. bdg. 12.95 (978-0-613-53550-2(2)) Tandem Library Bks.

—Skates. 2001. (gr. k-3). lib. bdg. 12.95 (978-0-613-51326-5(6)) Tandem Library Bks.

Innovative Kids Staff. Bunny Jumps. Filipowich, Bob, illus. ed. 2000. (Mini Soft Shapes Ser.). 8p. (J). (ps-ps). 6.99 (978-1-58476-037-5(0)) Innovative Kids.

—Ducky Swims. Filipowich, Bob, illus. ed. 2000. (Mini Soft Shapes Ser.). 8p. (J). (ps-ps). 6.99 (978-1-58476-038-2(9)) Innovative Kids.

—Goodnight, Baby. Larranaga, Ana, illus. 2006. 12p. (J). (ps-ps). bds. 8.99 (978-1-58476-482-3(1), IKIDS) Innovative Kids.

Inns, Christopher. Cuddle Me! 2005. (Mirror, Mirror Ser.). (Illus.). 12p. (J). (ps-k). bds. 5.95 (978-0-7534-5846-4(2), Kingfisher) Houghton Mifflin Co. Trade & Reference Div.

Inteli, Nancy. Farm Faces. 2008. 10p. (J). (ps-k). bds. 8.99 (*978-0-618-91959-8(7)) Houghton Mifflin Co. Trade & Reference Div.

Interiano, Jeffrey. Critters of Forest City. 2006. pap. 10.00 (*978-1-4257-1721-6(7)) Xlibris Corp.

Ipcar, Dahlov. My Wonderful Christmas Tree. 1999. 28p. (J). (ps-3). 9.95 (978-0-89272-475-8(7)) Down East Bks.

Irbinskas, Heather. Pauly the Adventurous Pallid Bat. Anthis, Brian, illus. Tuttle, Merlin D., photos by. 2003. 32p. (J). pap. 7.95 (978-1-58369-032-1(8)) Western National Parks Assn.

Irvin-Marston, Hope. My Little Book of Whitetails. Magdalena-Brown, Maria, illus. 2004. 32p. (J). pap. 7.95 (978-0-89317-050-9(X), WW-050X, Windward Publishing) Finney Co., Inc.

Is That Funny? 2004. (J). per. 15.95 (978-0-9741319-2-4(X)) 4N Publishing LLC.

Isaacs, Anne & Bannerman, Helen. Pancakes for Supper! Teague, Mark, illus. 2006. 40p. (J). (gr. k-3). pap. 15.99 (978-0-439-64483-9(6), Scholastic Pr.) Scholastic, Inc.

Island, Fiona. Wishbone's Magic Garden. 2006. 120p. pap. (*978-1-84401-733-1(8)) Athena Pr.

It Could Be Worse: Individual Title, 6 Packs. (gr. k-1). 23.00 (978-0-7635-8832-8(6)) Rigby Education.

Jackson, Kathryn. The Animals' Merry Christmas. Scarry, Richard, illus. 2005. 72p. (J). (gr. k-k). 14.95 (978-0-375-83341-0(2)); lib. bdg. 16.99 (978-0-375-93341-7(7)) Random Hse. Children's Bks. (Golden Bks.).

Jacobson, Jennifer Richard. Moon Sandwich Mom. Huang, Benrei, illus. 2004. 24p. (J). (ps-1). pap. 6.95 (978-0-8075-4072-5(2)) Whitman, Albert & Co.

Jacques, Brian. Badgers. Baker, Chris, illus. 2002. (YA). 8.99 (978-0-399-23852-9(2), Philomel) Penguin Group (USA) Inc.

—Friend & Foe. 2000. (Redwall Ser.). (Illus.). 16p. (J). (gr. 4-7). 8.99 (978-0-399-23589-4(2), Philomel) Penguin Group (USA) Inc.

—The Great Redwall Feast. Denise, Christopher, illus. 2000. (Redwall Ser.). 64p. (J). (gr. 4-8). pap. 6.99 (978-0-698-11876-8(6), Putnam Juvenile) Penguin Group (USA) Inc.

—The Great Redwall Feast. Denise, Christopher, illus. 2000. (Redwall Ser.). 64p. (J). (ps-3). lib. bdg. 13.79 (978-0-606-20360-9(5)); lib. bdg. 15.30 (978-0-613-29968-8(X)) Tandem Library Bks.

—The Great Redwall Feast. 2000. (Redwall Ser.). (J). (gr. 4-8). (978-0-606-20236-7(6)) Tandem Library Bks.

—High Rhulain. (Redwall Ser.). 2008. 352p. (YA). (gr. 7). 8.99 (*978-0-14-240938-1(3), Puffin); 2007. 336p. mass mkt. 7.99 (978-0-441-01436-1(4), Ace Bks.) Penguin Group (USA) Inc.

—The Legend of Luke. 2005. (Redwall Ser.). (Illus.). 384p. (YA). (gr. k-3). pap. 7.99 (978-0-14-250109-2(3), Puffin) Penguin Group (USA) Inc.

—The Legend of Luke. Baker, Chris, illus. (Redwall Ser.). (gr. 4-8). 2000. 384p. (J). 23.99 (978-0-399-23490-3(X), Philomel); 2001. 368p. reprint ed. mass mkt. 7.99 (978-0-441-00773-8(2), Ace Bks.) Penguin Group (USA) Inc.

—The Legend of Luke. 2001. (J). (978-0-606-20880-2(1)) Tandem Library Bks.

—Loamhedge. Elliot, David, illus. 2003. (Redwall Ser.). 432p. (YA). (gr. 3-6). 23.99 (978-0-399-23724-9(0), Philomel) Penguin Group (USA) Inc.

—The Long Patrol. Curless, Allan, illus. 1998. (Redwall Ser.). 352p. (J). (gr. 4-8). 23.99 (978-0-399-23165-0(X), Philomel) Penguin Group (USA) Inc.

—The Long Patrol. 1999. (Redwall Ser.). (J). (gr. 4-8). (978-0-606-15882-4(0)); (gr. 5-8). lib. bdg. 15.30 (978-0-613-13199-5(1)) Tandem Library Bks.

—Lord Brocktree. 2002. (Redwall Ser.). 15.23 (978-1-4046-1587-8(3)) Book Wholesalers, Inc.

—Lord Brocktree. Fangorn, illus. 2005. (Redwall Ser.). 384p. (YA). (gr. 7). pap. 7.99 (978-0-14-250110-8(7), Puffin) Penguin Group (USA) Inc.

—Lord Brocktree. 2000. (Redwall Ser.). (Illus.). 384p. (J). (gr. 4-8). 23.99 (978-0-399-23590-0(6), Philomel) Penguin Group (USA) Inc.

—Lord Brocktree. 2001. (Redwall Ser.). (gr. 5-8). lib. bdg. 15.30 (978-0-613-44230-5(X)) Tandem Library Bks.

—Mariel of Redwall. Chalk, Gary, illus. 2003. (Redwall Ser.). 400p. (YA). (gr. 5). pap. 8.99 (978-0-14-230239-2(2), Puffin) Penguin Group (USA) Inc.

—Mariel of Redwall. 2000. (Redwall Ser.). (Illus.). 384p. (gr. 4-8). mass mkt. 7.99 (978-0-441-00694-6(9), Ace Bks.) Penguin Group (USA) Inc.

—Mariel of Redwall. 2003. (Redwall Ser.). (gr. 5-8). lib. bdg. 16.45 (978-0-613-59976-4(4)) Tandem Library Bks.

—Marlfox. Baker, Chris, illus. 1998. (Redwall Ser.). 400p. (J). (gr. 4-8). 22.99 (978-0-399-23307-4(5), Philomel) Penguin Group (USA) Inc.

—Marlfox. 2005. (Redwall Ser.). 400p. (J). (gr. 5). reprint ed. pap. 8.99 (978-0-14-250108-5(5)) Penguin Group (USA) Inc.

—Marlfox. 2000. (Redwall Ser.). (gr. 5-8). lib. bdg. 15.30 (978-0-613-23017-9(5)) Tandem Library Bks.

—Martin the Warrior. Chalk, Gary, illus. 2004. (Redwall Ser.). 376p. (YA). 8.99 (978-0-14-240055-5(6), Puffin) Penguin Group (USA) Inc.

—Martin the Warrior. 2004. (Redwall Ser.). (gr. 3-6). lib. bdg. 16.45 (978-0-613-71583-6(7)) Tandem Library Bks.

—Mattimeo. Chalk, Gary, illus. 2003. (Redwall Ser.). 448p. (J). pap. 8.99 (978-0-14-230240-8(6), Puffin) Penguin Group (USA) Inc.

—Mattimeo. 1999. (Redwall Ser.). (Illus.). 448p. (gr. 4-8). mass mkt. 7.99 (978-0-441-00610-6(8), Ace Bks.) Penguin Group (USA) Inc.

—Mattimeo. (Redwall Ser.). (gr. 5-8). 2003. lib. bdg. 16.45 (978-0-613-64193-7(0)); 1999. lib. bdg. 15.30 (978-0-8335-8134-1(1)) Tandem Library Bks.

—Mossflower. (Redwall Ser.). (Illus.). 2002. 432p. pap. 8.99 (978-0-14-230238-5(4), Puffin); 1998. 384p. (gr. 4-8). reprint ed. mass mkt. 7.99 (978-0-441-00576-5(4), Ace Bks.) Penguin Group (USA) Inc.

—Mossflower. 2002. (Redwall Ser.). (gr. 3-6). lib. bdg. 16.45 (978-0-613-71582-9(9)) Tandem Library Bks.

—Pearls of Lutra. 1998. (Redwall Ser.). (Illus.). 368p. (gr. 4-8). mass mkt. 7.99 (978-0-441-00508-6(X), Ace Bks.) Penguin Group (USA) Inc.

—Pearls of Lutra. 1998. (Redwall Ser.). (J). (gr. 4-8). (978-0-606-13015-8(2)) Tandem Library Bks.

—Rakkety Tam. 2005. (Redwall Ser.). 384p. (gr. 12). mass mkt. 7.99 (978-0-441-01318-0(X), Ace Bks.) Penguin Group (USA) Inc.

—Rakkety Tam. Elliot, David, illus. 2004. (Redwall Ser.). 432p. (YA). (gr. 4-6). 23.99 (978-0-399-23725-6(9), Philomel) Penguin Group (USA) Inc.

—Redwall. 2002. (Redwall Ser.). (Illus.). 352p. (J). pap. 8.99 (978-0-14-230237-8(6), Puffin) Penguin Group (USA) Inc.

—Redwall. Howell, Troy, illus. 2000. (Redwall Ser.). 352p. (J). (gr. 4-8). pap. 12.99 (978-0-399-23629-7(5), Philomel) Penguin Group (USA) Inc.

—Redwall. 10th anniv. ed. 1998. (Redwall Ser.). (Illus.). 352p. (gr. 4-8). mass mkt. 7.99 (978-0-441-00548-2(9), Ace Bks.) Penguin Group (USA) Inc.

—Redwall. (Redwall Ser.). 2002. (gr. 3-6). lib. bdg. 16.45 (978-0-613-71581-2(0)); 2000. (gr. 3-6). lib. bdg. 22.25 (978-0-613-89563-7(0)); 1998. (J). (gr. 4-8). (978-0-606-13734-8(3)) Tandem Library Bks.

—Redwall. Chalk, Gary, illus. l.t. ed. 2002. (Redwall Ser.). (J). 25.95 (978-0-7862-3858-3(5)) Thomson Gale.

—Redwall Map & Riddle Book: Includes the Redwall Riddler! Baker, Chris & Curless, Allan, illus. 1998. (Redwall Ser.). (J). (gr. 4-8). 9.99 (978-0-399-23248-0(6), Philomel) Penguin Group (USA) Inc.

—A Redwall Winter's Tale. Denise, Christopher, illus. (Redwall Ser.). (J). 2004. 72p. (gr. 6). pap. 7.99 (978-0-14-240198-9(6), Puffin); 2001. 80p. (gr. 4-8). 18.99 (978-0-399-23346-3(6), Philomel) Penguin Group (USA) Inc.

—Salamandastron. Chalk, Gary, illus. 2003. (Redwall Ser.). 400p. (YA). pap. 8.99 (978-0-14-250152-8(2), Puffin) Penguin Group (USA) Inc.

—Salamandastron. 2003. (Redwall Ser.). (gr. 5-8). lib. bdg. 16.45 (978-0-613-71576-8(4)) Tandem Library Bks.

A B

—Seven Strange & Ghostly Tales. 1999. (Illus.). 144p. (J). (gr. 4-7). pap. 5.99 (978-0-698-11808-9(1) , Putnam Juvenile) Penguin Group (USA) Inc.

—The Taggerung. Standley, Peter, illus. (Redwall Ser.). 448p. 2003. pap. 8.99 (978-0-14-250154-2(9) , Puffin); 2001. (J). (gr. 3-6). 23.99 (978-0-399-23720-1(8) , Philomel) Penguin Group (USA) Inc.

—The Taggerung. 2002. (Redwall Ser.). (Illus.). 416p. reprint ed. mass mkt. 7.99 (978-0-441-00968-8(9) , Ace Bks.) Penguin Group (USA) Inc.

—The Taggerung. 2001. (Redwall Ser.). (Illus.). 384p. (J). (978-0-09-176928-4(0) , Hutchinson) Random Hse.

—The Taggerung. Standley, Peter, illus. l.t. ed. 2002. (Redwall Ser). 683p. (J). 25.95 (978-0-7862-4014-2(8)) Thomson Gale.

—The Tale of Urso Brunov: Little Father of All Bears. Natchev, Alexi, illus. 2003. 45p. (J). (ps-3). 16.99 (978-0-399-23762-1(3) , Philomel) Penguin Group (USA) Inc.

—Triss. Elliot, David, illus. 2002. (Redwall Ser.). 432p. (YA). 23.99 (978-0-399-23723-2(2) , Philomel) Penguin Group (USA) Inc.

—Triss. l.t. ed. 2004. (Redwall Ser.). 596p. (J). 23.95 (978-0-7862-6207-6(9)) Thorndike Pr.

Jaekel, Susan, illus. The Tortoise & the Hare: A Tale about Determination. 2006. (J). 6.99 (978-1-59939-015-4(9)) Reader's Digest Young Families, Inc.

Jaffrey, Madhur. Robi Dobi: The Marvellous Adventures of an Indian Elephant. Hall, Amanda, illus. 2001. 64p. (YA). (gr. 1 up). pap. 13.00 (978-1-86205-160-7(7) , Pavilion Bks., Ltd.) Anova Bks. GBR. Dist: Trafalgar Square Publishing.

Jahn-Clough, Lisa. On the Hill. 2004. (Illus.). 32p. (J). (gr. k-3). tchr. ed. 15.00 (978-0-618-40741-5(3) , Walter Lorraine) Houghton Mifflin Co. Trade & Reference Div.

Jahn, Jazmine. Sneakers. 2006. (ENG.). 32p. per. 19.99 (*978-1-4259-3098-1(0)) AuthorHouse.

James, Andrea. Adventures at Ja-Mar Farms: Pup-Pup, Padluck & PIG Take a Walk in the Wet Woods. 2005. 47p. pap. 19.95 (978-1-4137-3437-9(5)) PublishAmerica, Inc.

James, Catherine. The Sad Little House. Collier, Kevin Scott, illus. l.t. ed. 2006. 28p. (J). E-Book 9.95 incl. cd-rom (978-1-933090-18-4(9)) Guardian Angel Publishing, Inc.

Jango-Cohen, Judith. Digging Armadillos. 1999. (Pull Ahead Bks.). (Illus.). 32p. (gr. k-3). lib. bdg. 22.60 (978-0-8225-3625-3(0)) Lerner Publishing Group.

Janisch, H. & Holland, C. Heave Ho! 2006. (Illus.). 32p. (J). 16.95 (978-0-7358-2091-3(0)) North-South Bks., Inc.

Janovitz, Marilyn. Look Out Bird. 2007. (Illus.). 32p. (J). 9.95 (978-0-7358-2078-4(3)) North-South Bks., Inc.

Jarman, Julia. Big Red Tub. Reynolds, Adrian, illus. 2004. (Clifford Big Red Reader Ser.). 32p. (J). pap. 14.95 (978-0-439-67232-0(5) , Orchard Bks.) Scholastic, Inc.

—Flying Friends. Parker-Rees, Guy, illus. 2002. 48p. (J). (978-0-439-47138-1(9)) Scholastic, Inc.

Jarrell, Pamela R. Animals, Animals. Crowell, Knox, illus. l.t. ed. 2000. (CB Ser.). 7p. (J). (ps-1). pap. 10.95 (978-1-57332-162-4(1)) HighReach Learning, Inc.

Jarrett, Clare. Best Picnic Ever. Jarrett, Clare, illus. 2004. (Illus.). 32p. (J). (gr. k-k). 16.99 (978-0-7636-2370-8(9)) Candlewick Pr.

Jarvis, Robin. The Final Reckoning. 2003. (Deptford Mice Ser.). (Illus.). 304p. (YA). pap. 6.95 (978-1-58717-244-1(5) , SeaStar Bks.) Chronicle Bks. LLC.

—Thomas. 2006. 400p. (J). 17.95 (978-0-8118-5412-2(4)) Chronicle Bks. LLC.

Jenkins, Emily. Plonk, Plonk, Plonk! A Bea & Haha Book. Bogacki, Tomek, illus. 2006. (Bea & Haha Board Bks.). 14p. (J). 5.95 (978-0-374-30585-7(4) , Farrar, Straus & Giroux (BYR)) Farrar, Straus & Giroux.

—Up, Up, Up! Bogacki, Tomek, illus. 2006. (Bea & Haha Board Bks.). 14p. (J). 5.95 (978-0-374-30584-0(6) , Farrar, Straus & Giroux (BYR)) Farrar, Straus & Giroux.

Jenkins, Gloria. Storm: The Peace Maker. 2006. (J). pap. 8.00 (*978-0-8059-7116-3(5)) Dorrance Publishing Co., Inc.

Jennings, Dwayne G. The Strawberry Skunk. Jennings, Daren G., illus. 2000. 16p. (J). (gr. k-7). (978-0-9678111-0-9(4)) Strawberry Laine LLC.

Jennings, Patrick. The Beastly Arms. 2001. 320p. (J). (gr. 5-9). pap. 16.95 (978-0-439-16589-1(X)) Scholastic, Inc.

Jennings, Richard W. Ferret Island. 2007. 192p. (J). (gr. 4-6). 16.00 (*978-0-618-80632-4(6) , Walter Lorraine) Houghton Mifflin Co. Trade & Reference Div.

Jennings, Richard W. My Life of Crime. 2002. 160p. (J). (gr. 4-6). tchr. ed. 15.00 (978-0-618-21433-4(X) , Walter Lorraine) Houghton Mifflin Co. Trade & Reference Div.

Jennings, Sharon. Franklin's Trading Cards. Jeffrey, Sean et al, illus. 2003. 32p. (J). (978-0-439-41816-4(X)) Scholastic, Inc.

Jennings, Sharon, et al. Franklin's Trading Cards. Southern, Shelley & Jeffrey, Sean, illus. 2004. (Kids Can Read Ser.). 32p. (J). (gr. k-3). (978-1-55337-464-0(9)); (978-1-55337-463-3(0)) Kids Can Pr., Ltd.

Jimenez, Angeles. Vecinos. Prestifilippo, Pablo, illus. 2002. (Libros para Soñar Ser.). (SPA.). 36p. 15.95 (978-84-8464-141-4(4)) Kalandraka Editora, S.L. ESP. Dist: Lectorum Pubns., Inc.

Jippes, Daan, et al. Walt Disney's Comics & Stories, Vol. 666. 2006. 64p. pap. 6.95 (978-1-888472-19-6(7)) Gemstone Publishing, Inc.

Joachimowski, Paula L. Swamp Band Lullaby. 2007. (J). per. 12.99 (*978-1-59879-211-9(3)) Lifevest Publishing, Inc.

Johnson, D. B. Henry Works. 2004. (Illus.). 32p. (J). (gr. k-3). tchr. ed. 15.00 (978-0-618-42003-2(7)) Houghton Mifflin Co. Trade & Reference Div.

Johnson, Gillian. Ma Soeur Bibi. Duchesne, Christiane, tr. from ENG. 2001. (FRE & SPA., Illus.). 32p. (J). (ps-k). 16.95 (978-0-88776-566-7(1) , Livres Toundra) Tundra Bks., Inc./Livres Toundra, Inc. CAN. Dist: Random Hse., Inc.

Johnson, Judith C. Poppel's Place. Moriarity, Aaron Joel, illus. 2002. 32p. (J). (ps-4). 16.95 (978-0-9724193-1-4(4)) Poppel Pr.

Johnson, Margaret A. Berber: A Lamb's Tale. Johnson, Margaret A., illus. 1999. (Illus.). 62p. (J). (gr. k-3). 15.95 (978-0-9663170-0-8(9)) WaterOak Publishing.

Johnson, Pauletta Cox. Come under the Mushroom. 2004. 30p. (J). per. 7.95 (978-1-932496-23-9(8)) Penman Publishing, Inc.

Johnson, Rebecca. Animal Storybooks. 165.36 (978-0-8368-5968-3(5)) Stevens, Gareth Inc.

Johnston, Tony. Desert Song. Young, Ed, illus. 2000. 32p. (J). (gr. k-4). reprint ed. 16.95 (978-0-87156-491-7(2)) Gibbs Smith, Publisher.

—Gopher up Your Sleeve. Park, Trip, illus. 2001. 32p. (J). (ps-3). 15.95 (978-0-87358-794-5(4) , Rising Moon Bks. for Young Readers) Northland Publishing.

Jolin, Dominique. Little Red Washington. Perkes, Carolyn, tr. from FRE. Jolin, Dominique, illus. 2001. (Bee-Bop Bks.). (Illus.). 24p. (J). bds. (978-1-894363-70-9(1)) Dominique & Friends.

—Peek-a-Boo, Deecee! Perkes, Carolyn, tr. from FRE. Jolin, Dominique, illus. 2001. (Deecee Ser.). (Illus.). 14p. (J). bds. (978-1-894363-53-2(1)) Dominique & Friends.

—Super Washington. Perkes, Carolyn, tr. from FRE. Jolin, Dominique, illus. 2001. (Bee-Bop Bks.). (Illus.). 24p. (J). bds. (978-1-894363-71-6(X)) Dominique & Friends.

Jones, Allan Frewin. Meerkat in Trouble. Kennaway, Adrienne, illus. 2002. 32p. (J). 13.95 (978-1-899248-52-0(8)); 5.95 (978-1-899248-47-6(1)) Happy Cat Bks. GBR. Dist: Star Bright Bks., Inc.

—Meerkat in Trouble. Kennaway, Adrienne, illus. 1998. 32p. (J). (ps-k). pap. 14.95 (978-1-887734-55-4(4)); pap. 5.95 (978-1-887734-61-5(9)) Star Bright Bks., Inc.

Jones, Carol. What's the Time, Mr. Wolf? 1999. (Illus.). 32p. (J). (gr. k-3). 15.00 (978-0-395-95800-1(8) , Walter Lorraine) Houghton Mifflin Co. Trade & Reference Div.

Jones-Hughes, Karen, illus. Munch, Munch! Who's There? 2002. (Mini Movers Ser.). 14p. (J). bds. 3.99 (978-0-7641-5570-3(9)) Barron's Educational Series, Inc.

Jones, Karen, illus. Bang, Bang! Who's There? 2002. (Mini Movers Ser.). 14p. (J). bds. 3.99 (978-0-7641-5571-0(7)) Barron's Educational Series, Inc.

—Tap,Tap! Who's There? 2002. (Mini Movers Ser.). 14p. (J). bds. 2.95 (978-0-7641-5568-0(7)) Barron's Educational Series, Inc.

Jones, Lara. Fun at the Park. Jones, Lara, illus. 2003. (Lola & Binky Bks.). (Illus.). 8p. (J). bds. 5.95 (978-0-7641-5689-2(6)) Barron's Educational Series, Inc.

—Fun at the Zoo. Jones, Lara, illus. 2003. (Lola & Binky Bks.). (Illus.). 8p. (J). bds. 5.95 (978-0-7641-5686-1(1)) Barron's Educational Series, Inc.

Jones, Marguerite A. Strangers. 1998. (Illus.). 16p. (J). (gr. k-3). pap. 7.00 (978-0-8059-4531-7(8)) Dorrance Publishing Co., Inc.

Jones, Maurice. Welcome Home Little Bear. Currey, Anna, illus. 1998. 28p. (J). (ps-1). 13.95 (978-0-7641-5081-4(2)) Barron's Educational Series, Inc.

Jones, Sherryl. WELCOME to GOD's ACRE Room for No More Sherryl Jones. 2006. 24p. 15.01 (978-1-4116-8100-2(2)) Lulu.com.

Jones, Sylvie. Who's in the Tub? Constantin, Pascale, illus. 2007. 38p. (ps-3). 15.95 (*978-1-59354-612-0(2)) Handprint Bks.

Jones, Terry, prod. Mr. Toad's Wild Ride. 1999. (Illus.). 64p. (J). (gr. 3-7). pap. 4.95 (978-0-7868-4100-4(1)) Disney Pr.

Jones, Terry & Newman, Nanette. Bedtime Stories. Foreman, Michael, illus. 2007. 192p. (J). pap. 16.99 (*978-1-84458-477-2(1)) Anova Bks. GBR. Dist: Independent Pubs. Group.

Jordan, Sandra. The Pond Book. 1999. (J). (978-0-7894-2565-2(3)) Dorling Kindersley Publishing, Inc.

Jordan's Zoo: Individual Title, 6 packs. (ps-2). 27.00 (978-0-7635-9456-5(3)) Rigby Education.

Journey to see the King. 2006. (J). (*978-0-9791168-0-3(5)) Lighthouse Bk. Publishing.

Julian, Russell. Lost Calf. 2005. (Farm Board Book Ser.). (Illus.). 12p. (J). pap. 9.99 (978-1-4052-1029-4(X)) Egmont Bks., Ltd. GBR. Dist: Trafalgar Square Publishing.

Jumbo & Tempo, the Food Bandit. 2004. (J). per. 15.99 (978-0-9759122-1-8(6)) Golden Eagle Publishing Hse., Inc.

Jungle BK. 2007. 18p. bds. 11.99 (*978-1-4037-3606-2(5)) Dalmatian Pr.

Jungle Books, 8 bks. 2002. (J). bds. (978-0-7853-8075-7(2) , 7181000) Publications International, Ltd.

Jurassic News: Individual Title Six-Packs. (Bookweb Ser.). 32p. (gr. 6 up). 34.00 (978-0-7578-0891-3(3)) Rigby Education.

Jusayu, Miguel Angel. Ni Era Vaca, Ni Era Caballo. Doppert, Monika, illus. 1999. (SPA.). 48p. (J). (gr. 3-5). pap. 8.50 (978-980-257-212-0(8)) Ekare, Ediciones VEN. Dist: Lectorum Pubns., Inc.

—Ni Era Vaca, Ni Era Caballo. 1999. (Illus.). (J). (978-0-606-21668-5(5)) Tandem Library Bks.

Kadair, Deborah Ousley. There Was an Ol' Cajun. Kadair, Deborah Ousley, illus. 2002. (Illus.). 32p. (J). (gr. k-3). 15.95 (978-1-56554-917-3(1)) Pelican Publishing Co., Inc.

Kalas, Sybille. The Goose Family Book. 2000. (Illus.). (J). (978-0-606-18320-8(5)) Tandem Library Bks.

Kamau, G. How Porcupine Got His Spines. 2004. (Illus.). 22p. 13.95 (978-9966-25-168-8(5)) Heinemann Kenya, Limited (East African Educational Publishers Ltd E.A.E.P.) KEN. Dist: Michigan State Univ. Pr.

—Why Beetles Roll Cowdung. 2004. 18p. 13.95 (978-9966-25-167-1(7)) Heinemann Kenya, Limited (East African Educational Publishers Ltd E.A.E.P.) KEN. Dist: Michigan State Univ. Pr.

Kaminsky, Jeff & Atwater, Martha. Bunny. 2002. (Stickamajigs Ser.: Vol. 4). (Illus.). 8p. (ps-1). 5.99 (978-0-7868-0713-0(X)) Hyperion Bks. for Children.

Kanemaki, Tomoco. Kingdom Hearts: Darkness Within. Disney Press Staff, ed. Amano, Shiro, illus. 2nd rev. ed. 2008. 224p. (J). (gr. 4-7). pap. 5.99 (*978-1-4231-0396-7(3)) Disney Pr.

—Kingdom Hearts: The First Door. Disney Press Staff, ed. Amano, Shiro, illus. 2008. 224p. (J). (gr. 4-7). pap. 5.99 (*978-1-4231-0395-0(5)) Disney Pr.

Kangira, Jairos. Creatures Great & Small: A Collection of Short Stories. 2005. vi, 114p. (*978-0-86922-786-2(6)) Mambo Pr.

Karim, Roberta. This Is a Hospital, Not a Zoo! 2002. (gr. k-3). lib. bdg. 14.10 (978-0-613-72912-3(9)) Tandem Library Bks.

Kaska, Keiko. Cuando el Elefante Camina. 2001. (SPA.). (J). (ps-3). pap. 7.95 (978-958-04-1425-4(4) , NR6444) Norma S.A. COL. Dist: Distribuidora Norma, Inc., Lectorum Pubns., Inc.

Kasser, Carol. Broccoliosaur Stories. 2007. pap. 26.49 (*978-1-4259-7933-1(5)) AuthorHouse.

Kasza, Keiko. Badger's Fancy Meal. Kasza, Keiko, illus. 2007. (Illus.). 32p. (J). (gr. k-2). 16.99 (978-0-399-24603-6(7) , Putnam Juvenile) Penguin Group (USA) Inc.

—El Estofado del Lobo. (Buenas Noches Coleccion). (SPA.). (J). 8.95 (978-958-04-1427-8(0) , NR6443) Norma S.A. COL. Dist: Distribuidora Norma, Inc., Lectorum Pubns., Inc.

Kathan, Christine. La Oracion de Ashford. Maval Publishing Inc. Staff, illus. 2001. Tr. of Ashford's Prayer. (SPA.). 32p. (J). (gr. k-3). pap. 7.50 (978-1-59134-013-3(6)); pap. 7.50 (978-1-884083-65-5(X)) Maval Publishing Inc.

Katschke, Judy. The Great Escape. 2006. (Ice Age 2 Ser.). 64p. (J). (SPA.). pap. 4.99 (978-0-06-112222-4(X)); (Illus.). pap. 4.99 (978-0-06-083972-7(4)) HarperCollins Pubs.

Katsoris, Nick. Loukoumi. 2006. 30p. (J). (ps-3). 15.95 (978-0-9705100-1-3(2)) Katsoris, Nicholas C.

Kaufmann, Nancy. Bye, Bye! Spetter, Jung-Hee, illus. 2004. 32p. (J). (ps-1). 14.95 (978-1-886910-95-9(2) , Lemniscaat) Boyds Mills Pr.

Kay, Elizabeth. The Jinx on the Divide. 2007. 384p. (J). pap. 6.99 (*978-0-439-72456-2(2)) Scholastic, Inc.

Keats, Ezra Jack. Over in the Meadow. Keats, Ezra Jack, illus. 2002. (Illus.). (J). 13.83 (978-0-7587-3351-1(8)) Book Wholesalers, Inc.

—Over in the Meadow. Keats, Ezra Jack, illus. 1999. (Illus.). 32p. (J). (gr. 1-6). pap. 6.99 (978-0-14-056508-9(6) , Puffin) Penguin Group (USA) Inc.

—Over in the Meadow. 1999. (ps-2). lib. bdg. 15.30 (978-0-7857-0709-7(3)) Tandem Library Bks.

Kehret, Peg. Cages. 2001. 160p. (J). (gr. 4-7). reprint ed. pap. 4.99 (978-0-14-131230-9(0) , Puffin) Penguin Group (USA) Inc.

Keller, Holly. Help! A Story of Friendship. Keller, Holly, illus. 2007. (Illus.). 32p. (J). (ps-3). 16.99 (*978-0-06-123913-7(5)); lib. bdg. 17.89 (*978-0-06-123914-4(3)) HarperCollins Pubs. (Greenwillow Bks.).

Keller, Holly. That's Mine, Horace. Keller, Holly, illus. 2000. (Illus.). 24p. (J). (ps up). 16.99 (978-0-688-17159-9(1)) HarperCollins Pubs.

Kellogg, Steven. Chicken Little. Kellogg, Steven, illus. 2002. (Illus.). (J). 14.43 (978-0-7587-2223-2(0)) Book Wholesalers, Inc.

—Pinkerton & Friends: A Steven Kellogg Treasury. 2004. (Illus.). 336p. (J). (ps). 30.00 (978-0-8037-2979-7(0) , Dial) Penguin Group (USA) Inc.

—Pinkerton, Behave! Kellogg, Steven, illus. 2002. (Illus.). (J). 14.04 (978-1-4046-0250-2(X)) Book Wholesalers, Inc.

—Pinkerton, Behave! Kellogg, Steven, illus. 2002. (Illus.). 32p. (J). 17.99 (978-0-8037-2722-9(4) , Dial); pap. 6.99 (978-0-14-230007-7(1) , Puffin) Penguin Group (USA) Inc.

—Prehistoric Pinkerton. Kellogg, Steven, illus. 2002. (Illus.). 32p. (J). pap. 6.99 (978-0-14-230008-4(X) , Puffin) Penguin Group (USA) Inc.

—A Rose for Pinkerton. Kellogg, Steven, illus. 2002. (Illus.). (J). 14.04 (978-0-7587-3531-7(6)) Book Wholesalers, Inc.

—A Rose for Pinkerton. Kellogg, Steven, illus. 2002. (Illus.). 32p. (J). 16.99 (978-0-8037-2723-6(2) , Dial); pap. 6.99 (978-0-14-230009-1(8) , Puffin) Penguin Group (USA) Inc.

—Tallyho, Pinkerton! Kellogg, Steven, illus. 2002. (Illus.). 14.04 (978-1-4046-0249-6(6)) Book Wholesalers, Inc.

—Tallyho, Pinkerton! Kellogg, Steven, illus. 2002. (Illus.). 32p. (J). 16.99 (978-0-8037-2724-3(0) , Dial); pap. 6.99 (978-0-14-230010-7(1) , Puffin) Penguin Group (USA) Inc.

Kelly, Everett. Tiny Tom. 2007. 56p. (J). per. 15.95 (*978-1-58939-983-9(8)) Virtualbookworm.com Publishing, Inc.

Kendall, Diane & Marsh, Merle. Carousel Kids. York, Susanne, photos by. 2004. (J). (978-0-9762385-0-8(0)) Houston Zoo, Inc.

Kennaway, Adrienne. Bushbaby. 2002. (Illus.). 32p. (J). pap. 5.95 (978-1-899248-57-5(9)) Happy Cat Bks. GBR. Dist: Star Bright Bks., Inc.

Kern, Noris. I Love You with All My Heart. 2002. (Illus.). 26p. (J). bds. 6.95 (978-0-8118-3622-7(3)) Chronicle Bks. LLC.

Kerr, Judith. Mog & the Granny. (Illus.). 32p. (J). pap. 9.99 (978-0-00-664592-4(5)) HarperCollins Pubs. Ltd. GBR. Dist: Trafalgar Square Publishing.

—Mog & the Vet. (Illus.). 32p. (J). 19.99 (978-0-00-198211-6(7)) HarperCollins Pubs. Ltd. GBR. Dist: Trafalgar Square Publishing.

Kessler, Leonard. Kick, Pass, & Run. Kessler, Leonard, illus. 2002. (Illus.). (J). 12.34 (978-0-7587-6173-6(2)) Book Wholesalers, Inc.

Ketteman, Helen. Armadillo Tattletale. Graves, Keith, illus. 2000. 32p. (J). (gr. k-5). pap. 15.95 (978-0-590-99723-2(8)) Scholastic, Inc.

Kido, Yukiko. Flip-a-Word. 2006. 32p. pap. 5.95 (978-1-59354-179-8(1)) Blue Apple Bks.

—Snake Cake. 2006. 32p. 12.95 (978-1-59354-176-7(7)) Blue Apple Bks.

Kids Discovery Staff. Animal Sticker Adventures. 2001. (Illus.). mass mkt. 12.95 (978-0-525-46813-4(7) , Dutton Juvenile) Penguin Group (USA) Inc.

—More Animal Sticker Adventures. 2001. (Illus.). mass mkt. 12.95 (978-0-525-46814-1(5) , Dutton Juvenile) Penguin Group (USA) Inc.

Kilpatrick, Irene. Meet Tyrone! A Hand-Puppet Cloth Book. McGee, Warner, illus. 2007. (Backyardigans Ser.). 6p. (J). 10.99 (978-1-4169-3515-5(0) , Simon Spotlight/ Nickelodeon) Simon & Schuster Children's Publishing.

Kindersley, Dorling. Go Diego Go Essential Gd. 2008. 48p. 8.99 (*978-0-7566-3501-5(2)) Dorling Kindersley Publishing, Inc.

King-Smith, Dick. More Animal Stories. (Illus.). 128p. (J). 24.95 (978-0-670-88218-2(6)) Penguin Group (USA) Inc.

—Mysterious Miss Slade. Kronheimer, Ann, illus. 2002. 128p. (gr. 3-5). 4.99 (978-0-440-41674-6(4) , Yearling) Random Hse. Children's Bks.

—Mysterious Miss Slade. 2002. (gr. 3-6). lib. bdg. 13.00 (978-0-613-88331-3(4)) Tandem Library Bks.

—Saddlebottom. Bartelt, Robert, illus. l.t. ed. 2002. 152p. (J). 16.95 (978-0-7540-7817-3(5) , Galaxy Children's Large Print) BBC Audiobooks America.

—Sophie's Snail. 1999. (Sophie Bks.). (978-0-606-16402-3(2)) Tandem Library Bks.

—The Stray. 1998. (Illus.). 144p. (gr. 3-5). 5.50 (978-0-679-89101-7(3) , Yearling) Random Hse. Children's Bks.

—The Stray. 1998. (J). (978-0-606-13821-5(8)) Tandem Library Bks.

King, Thomas. Coyote Sings to the Moon. Wales, Johnny, illus. 2002. 40p. (YA). (gr. 1-3). 15.95 (978-1-55868-642-7(8) , West Winds Pr.) Graphic Arts Ctr. Publishing Co.

King, Thomas. Coyote Sings to the Moon. Wales, Johnny, illus. 2008. 36p. pap. 9.95 (*978-1-55263-868-2(5)) Key Porter Bks. CAN. Dist: Perseus Distribution.

Kingfisher Editors, ed. What a Hoot! Over 150 Hilarious Animal Jokes. Chatterton, Martin, illus. 2005. (Sidesplitters Ser.). 64p. (J). (gr. 3-5). pap. 3.95 (978-0-7534-5892-1(6) , Kingfisher) Houghton Mifflin Co. Trade & Reference Div.

Kipling, Rudyard. The Elephant's Child. 1999. (Illus.). 36p. (J). (ps-5). 7.99 (978-0-85953-674-5(2)) Child's Play-International.

—How the Leopard Got His Spots. Lohstoeter, Lori, illus. 2006. (J). (gr. 2-6). 25.65 (978-1-59679-344-6(9)) Spotlight.

—The Jungle Book. Pablo Marcos Studio Staff, illus. 2002. (Great Illustrated Classics Ser.).Tr. of 192. 240p. (J). (gr. 3-8). 21.35 (978-1-57765-812-2(4) , ABDO & Daughters) ABDO Publishing Co.

—The Jungle Book. Alexander, Gregory, illus. 2003. (Chrysalis Children's Classics Ser.).Tr. of 192. 159p. (YA). pap. (978-1-84365-038-6(X)) Chrysalis Children's Bks.

—The Jungle Book. 2001. Tr. of 192. 168p. 8.95 (978-1-84232-943-6(X)) House of Stratus, Inc. GBR. Dist: Midpoint Trade Bks., Inc.

—The Jungle Book. Daily, Don, illus. 2003. Tr. of 192. 56p. (J). 9.98 (978-0-7624-1495-6(2) , Courage Bks.) Running Pr. Bk. Pubs.

—The Jungle Book. 2001. (Saddleback Classics).Tr. of 192. (Illus.). (J). 13.75 (978-0-606-21558-9(1)) Tandem Library Bks.

—Jungle Book. 2007. 192p. (J). 19.95 (*978-0-9545103-9-8(9)) Palazzo Editions, Ltd. GBR. Dist: Independent Pubs. Group.

—The Jungle Book. Corvino, Lucy, illus. 2008. (Classic Starts Ser.). 160p. (J). 5.95 (*978-1-4027-4576-8(1)) Sterling Publishing Co., Inc.

—The Jungle Book: #1 Rikki-Tikki-Tavi Moves In. 2007. (Easy Reader Classics Ser.). 32p. (J). (ps-3). 21.35 (*978-1-59961-336-9(0)) Spotlight.

—The Jungle Book: Mowgli's Story. Bayley, Nicola, illus. unabr. ed. 2005. 160p. (J). (gr. 4-7). 19.99 (978-0-7636-2317-3(2)) Candlewick Pr.

—The Jungle Book by Rudyard Kipling: Digital Classics. 2002. cd-rom 5.00 (978-1-931457-07-1(7)) Stargate Electronic Library, Inc.

—The Jungle Books. (Borders Classics Ser.). 276p. 7.95 (978-1-58726-165-7(0)) Ann Arbor Media Group, LLC.

—The Jungle Books. 2004. (Barnes & Noble Classics Ser.). (Illus.). 432p. pap. 5.95 (978-1-59308-109-6(X)) Barnes & Noble, Inc.

—The Jungle Books. 2005. 336p. (gr. 12). pap. 4.95 (978-0-451-52975-6(8) , Signet Classics) Penguin Group (USA) Inc.

—Just So Stories. 2003. (Illus.). 224p. (J). (gr. 2-9). 7.99 (978-0-517-26655-7(5) , Gramercy) Random Hse. Value Publishing.

—Just So Stories. Kipling, Rudyard, illus. 2002. (Aladdin Classics Ser.). 208p. (J). pap. 4.99 (978-0-689-85125-4(1) , Aladdin) Simon & Schuster Children's Publishing.

—Just So Stories Set: For Little Children. Salter, Safaya, illus. 2003. (Chrysalis Children's Classics Ser.). 125p. (YA). pap. (978-1-84365-036-2(3)) Chrysalis Children's Bks.

—Just So Stories Set: For Little Children. 2001. (Dover Juvenile Classics Ser.). (Illus.). 112p. (J). (gr. 4-7). pap. 2.50 (978-0-486-41722-6(0)) Dover Pubns., Inc.

—Just So Stories Set: For Little Children. 2003. (Illus.). 146p. 8.95 (978-1-84232-944-3(8)) House of Stratus, Inc. GBR. *Dist:* Midpoint Trade Bks., Inc.

—Just So Stories Set: For Little Children. Date not set. (Illus.). 192p. (YA). (gr. 3 up). reprint ed. 7.95 (978-1-56852-137-4(5) , Konecky & Konecky) Konecky, William S. Assocs., Inc.

—Just So Stories Set: For Little Children. 100th anniv. ed. 2002. (Illus.). 160p. mass mkt. 4.95 (978-0-451-52836-0(0) , Signet Classics) Penguin Group (USA) Inc.

—Just So Stories Set: For Little Children. 2002. (gr. 3-6). lib. bdg. 11.80 (978-0-613-63205-8(2)); (gr. 5-8). lib. bdg. 12.95 (978-0-613-52417-9(9)) Tandem Library Bks.

—Just So Stories Set: For Little Children. 1998. (Children's Classics). (ENG., Illus.). 144p. (J). pap. (978-1-85326-102-2(5) , 1025WW) Wordsworth Editions, Ltd.

—El Libro de la Selva. 2003. (Timeless Classics Ser.). (SPA., Illus.). 176p. (J). (gr. 5-8). 12.95 (978-84-372-2230-1(3)) Altea, Ediciones, S.A. - Grupo Santillana ESP. *Dist:* Santillana USA Publishing Co., Inc.

—El Libro de la Selva. 2002. (Clover Ser.). (SPA., Illus.). 240p. (YA). 13.95 (978-84-392-8046-0(7) , EV4895) Gaviota Ediciones ESP. *Dist:* Lectorum Pubns., Inc.

—El Libro de la Selva. (J). 7.95 (978-84-95311-11-5(9)) Mestas, Jorge A. Ediciones Escolares La Escuela Nueva y Alinorma, S.L. ESP. *Dist:* Continental Bk. Co., Inc.

—El Libro de la Selva. (SPA.). (J). 8.00 (978-958-04-7110-3(X)) Norma S.A. COL. *Dist:* Distribuidora Norma, Inc.

—Precisamente Asi. Dominguez, Angel, illus. 2000. (SPA.). 228p. (J). (gr. 4-6). (978-84-261-3073-0(9) , JV8627) Juventud, Editorial ESP. *Dist:* Lectorum Pubns., Inc.

—Rikki-Tikki-Tavi. Pinkney, Jerry, illus. 2004. 48p. (J). (ps-3). reprint ed. pap. 6.99 (978-0-06-058785-7(7) , Harper Trophy) HarperCollins Pubs.

—Rudyard Kipling's Just So Stories. Sis, Peter, illus. 2004. 128p. (J). (ps up). 22.99 (978-0-7636-2629-7(5)) Candlewick Pr.

—The Second Jungle Book. 1998. (Children's Library). 288p. (J). (ps-3). pap. 3.95 (978-1-85326-143-5(2) , 1432WW) Wordsworth Editions, Ltd. GBR. *Dist:* Combined Publishing.

Kipling, Rudyard & Busch, Jeffrey. The Jungle Books. (Classics Illustrated Ser.). (Illus.). 52p. (YA). pap. 4.95 (978-1-57209-022-4(7)) Classics International Entertainment, Inc.

Kipling, Rudyard & Solari, María J. El Libro de la Selva. Puerta, Carlos, tr. Puerta, Carlos, illus. (SPA.). 92p. (J). (gr. 5-8). pap. 12.95 (978-84-204-5766-6(3)) Santillana USA Publishing Co., Inc.

Kirschner, Tanja. Bottoms. 2005. (Illus.). 24p. (YA). (ps-17). per. 3.99 (978-0-7358-2026-5(0)) North-South Bks., Inc.

Kirwan, Debra Giampapa. Oh, Please Help Me Save the Tree! A Record-Your-Voice Book. Holodook, Joseph, illus. l.t. ed. 2002. (Adventures of Buford the Bull & Friends Ser.: Vol. 1). 16p. (J). 49.95 (978-0-9713153-7-2(X)) FunZone Co.

A Kiss for Little Bear. 2004. (J). 24.95 incl. audio (978-0-89719-885-1(9)); pap. 32.75 incl. audio (978-1-55592-252-8(X)); pap. 32.75 incl. audio (978-1-55592-253-5(8)); pap. 14.95 incl. audio (978-1-56008-059-6(0)) Weston Woods Studios, Inc.

Kiss, Kathrin. Que Hace un Cocodrilo por la Noche? Urberuaga, Emilio, illus. 2001. (SPA.). (J). (gr. k-3). (978-84-88342-18-8(7) , KK8906) S.A. Kokinos ESP. *Dist:* Lectorum Pubns., Inc.

Kisseloff, Jeff & Wells, Rosemary. Ruby's Tea for Two. 2003. (Max & Ruby Ser.). 12p. (J). bds. 5.99 (978-0-670-03652-3(8) , Puffin) Penguin Group (USA) Inc.

Klein, Abby. Ready, Freddy! McKinley, John, illus. 2004. (Ready, Freddy! Ser.: No. 3). 96p. (J). pap. 3.99 (978-0-439-55600-2(7) , Blue Sky Pr., The) Scholastic, Inc.

Kleven, Elisa. Sun Bread. 2004. (gr. k-3). lib. bdg. 15.30 (978-0-613-83005-8(9)) Tandem Library Bks.

Kline, Trish. Super Hero: KA Reader 1. 2007. (Illus.). 32p. (J). per. 20.00 (***978-0-9717234-2-9(7)***) Ghost Hunter Productions.

Knipe, Floyd P. Adventures in Cowface Caverns. Jackson, James K., illus. 1998. (Trackers Ser.: Bk. 2). 116p. (YA). (gr. 5 up). pap. 6.95 (978-1-930130-63-0(5)) Nature's Nest Bks.

Knisley, Eric. The Adventures of Furlington Mackelthwaite. 2005. 40p. pap. 19.95 (978-1-4116-4792-3(0)) Lulu-.com.

Knoche, Keith & Wood, Jeff. Buck to the Rescue. 20p. (gr. k-7). 2001. 14.99 (978-5-550-02994-7(4)); 2000. pap. 11.99 incl. audio (978-5-550-02995-4(2)) Faith Factory.

Knowles, Sheena. Edward the Emu. Clement, Rod, illus. 1998. 32p. (J). (ps-1). pap. 6.99 (978-0-06-443499-7(0)) HarperCollins Pubs.

—Edward the Emu. Clement, Rod, illus. 1998. 13.75 (978-0-606-11288-8(X)) Tandem Library Bks.

Kobert, Michael Gilead & Donato, Dona. Who Goes with That Nose? The Wild Adventures of Juicy Coppertoes. Fuller, Laurie, illus. 2005. 40p. (J). per. 9.95 (978-0-9770700-0-8(X)) Giggling Gorilla Productions, LLC.

Koehler, Mary, illus. The Children are Happy Story CD with Animals from the Southwest. 2003. (J). cd-rom 5.00 (978-0-9744005-1-8(3)) In the Desert.

Koller, Jackie French. Mole & Shrew Are Two. Reas, Anne, illus. 2000. (J). (978-0-606-19903-2(9)) Tandem Library Bks.

Konnikov, Svetlana. Grapette, the Runaway Who Rolled Away. Smishliaev, Anatoli, illus. 2007. (Grapette's Adventures Ser.). 32p. (J). 15.95 (***978-0-9791758-0-0(1)***) Aurora Pubs., Inc.

Koontz, Robin. Creepy Crawly Colors. Koontz, Robin, illus. 2006. (Illus.). 14p. (J). 10.95 (978-1-4169-0707-7(6) , Little Simon) Simon & Schuster Children's Publishing.

Koontz, Robin Michal. How Is a Moose Like a Goose? 2002. (Silly Millies Ser.). (Illus.). 32p. (gr. k-2). lib. bdg. 17.90 (978-0-7613-2669-4(3) , Millbrook Pr.) Lerner Publishing Group.

Koopmans, Loek. Frog, Bee & Snail Look for Snow. 2006. Orig. Title: Samen Op Zoek. (Illus.). 28p. (J). 15.95 (978-0-86315-559-8(6)) Floris Bks. GBR. *Dist:* Steiner-Books, Inc.

Koorang, Mundara. The Little Platypus & the Fire Spirit. 2005. (Illus.). 32p. (J). 24.95 (978-0-85575-494-5(X)) Aboriginal Studies Pr. AUS. *Dist:* International Specialized Bk. Services.

Koury, Jen. Big John on the Big Farm. Linden, Pat & Hilko, Steve, eds. Koury, Jen, illus. 1999. (Johnny Tractor Toybooks Ser.). (Illus.). 10p. (J). (ps-1). (978-1-887327-23-7(1)) Ertl Co., Inc.

Kraatz, David. La Cancion del Geco. Luengas, Mauricio, illus. (SPA.). 16p. (J). (gr. 3-5). pap. 11.95 (978-1-56014-579-0(X)) Santillana USA Publishing Co., Inc.

Kraus, Robert. Milton the Early Riser. Aruego, Jose & Dewey, Ariane, illus. 2006. (Stories to Go! Ser.). 32p. (J). pap. 4.99 (978-1-4169-1856-1(6) , Aladdin) Simon & Schuster Children's Publishing.

Kreischer, Elsie Karr. Bigger Than a Button. Brandenburg, Claire, illus. 2002. 28p. (J). 14.95 (978-0-9708940-4-5(X)) Gently Worded Bks., LLC.

Krensky, Stephen. Arthur & the Crunch Cereal Contest, Bk. 4. 1998. (Arthur Chapter Bks. : Bk. 4). (Illus.). 64p. (J). (gr. 2-4). pap. 4.25 (978-0-316-11553-7(3)) Little, Brown Bks. for Young Readers.

—Arthur & the Crunch Cereal Contest. 1998. (Arthur Chapter Bks.: Bk. 4). (J). (gr. 3-6). 11.05 (978-0-606-13150-6(7)) Tandem Library Bks.

—Arthur's Mystery Envelope. 1998. (Arthur Chapter Bks.: Bk. 1). (J). (gr. 3-6). 11.05 (978-0-606-13154-4(X)) Tandem Library Bks.

Krensky, Stephen. Noah's Bark. Rogé, illus. 2008. (J). lib. bdg. (***978-0-8225-7645-7(7)*** , Carolrhoda Bks.) Lerner Publishing Group.

Krings, Antoon. Dorita Mariquita. 2005. (Bichitos curiosos Ser.). (SPA., Illus.). 32p. (J). 5.95 (978-84-932442-8-6(7)) Blume ESP. *Dist:* Independent Pubs. Group.

Kroll, Virginia L. Equal Shmequal: A Math Adventure. O'Neill, Philomena, illus. 2005. (Math Adventures Ser.). 32p. (J). (ps). pap. 6.95 (978-1-57091-892-6(9)) Charlesbridge Publishing, Inc.

Kroll, Virginia L. & Jones, Dawn L. Bluffy's Mighty Mountain. Maydak, Michael S., illus. 2001. (J). (978-0-9712840-3-6(2)) Boyds Collection Ltd., The.

—Flurry's Frozen Tundra. Maydak, Michael S., illus. 2001. (J). (978-0-9712840-4-3(0)) Boyds Collection Ltd., The.

Kroll, Virginia L. & O'Neill, Philomena. Equal Shmequal: A Math Adventure. 2005. (Math Adventures Ser.). (Illus.). 32p. (J). (ps-ps). 16.95 (978-1-57091-891-9(0)) Charlesbridge Publishing, Inc.

Krulik, Nancy E. Disney's The Wind in the Willows. 1999. (Illus.). 96p. (J). 14.95 (978-0-7868-3117-3(0)) Disney Pr.

Kubler, Annie. Busy Builders. 1999. (Illus.). 44p. (ps-k). 4.99 (978-0-85953-882-4(6)) Child's Play International Ltd. GBR. *Dist:* Child's Play-International.

—Save Humpy. 1999. (Real Sound Bath Bks Ser.). (Illus.). 10p. (ps-k). pap. 9.99 (978-0-85953-611-0(4)) Child's Play International Ltd. GBR. *Dist:* Child's Play-International.

Kuhn, Bev. Wishes Are Horses & Beggars Can Fly. 2005. 195p. pap. 19.95 (978-1-4137-4952-6(6)) PublishAmerica, Inc.

Kulot-Frisch, Daniela. No Nos Pillaras! (SPA., Illus.). 120p. (J). (gr. k-2). 16.95 (978-84-261-3123-2(9) , JV2027) Juventud, Editorial ESP. *Dist:* Lectorum Pubns., Inc.

Kunhardt Davis, Edith. Pat the Pony. 2000. (Pat the Bunny Ser.). (Illus.). 8p. (J). (gr. k-ps). bds. 9.99 (978-0-307-12164-6(X) , Golden Bks.) Random Hse. Children's Bks.

Kuper, Peter. Theo & the Blue Note. Kuper, Peter, illus. 2006. (Illus.). 32p. (J). (ps). 15.99 (978-0-670-06137-2(9) , Viking Juvenile) Penguin Group (USA) Inc.

Kurtz, Jane & Kurtz, Christopher. Water Hole Waiting. Christiansen, Lee, illus. 2002. 32p. (J). (gr. 5 up). 16.99 (978-0-06-029850-0(2)); (gr. 7 up). lib. bdg. 18.89 (978-0-06-029851-7(0)) HarperCollins Pubs.

L. A. Goal Members, contrib. by. Disabled Fables: Aesop's Fables Retold & Illustrated by Artists with Developmental Disabilities. 2005. (Illus.). 52p. (J). (gr. 1 up). 19.95 (978-1-932065-97-8(0)) Star Bright Bks., Inc.

La Brack, Joy. Elmo's Animal Adventures. DiCiccio, Sue, illus. 2000. (Baby Fingers Ser.). 14p. (J). (gr. k-ps). bds. 4.99 (978-0-375-80331-4(9) , Random Hse. Bks. for Young Readers) Random Hse. Children's Bks.

Labatt, Mary. Franklin Stays Up. 2003. (gr. k-3). lib. bdg. 11.80 (978-0-613-87146-4(4)) Tandem Library Bks.

—Franklin's Trading Cards. 2003. (gr. k-3). lib. bdg. 11.80 (978-0-613-86543-2(X)) Tandem Library Bks.

Laden, Nina. El Dia Que Pigasso Conocio a Muutisse. 2000. (Illus.). (J). (gr. 4-7). (CAT.). 36p. 14.95 (978-84-95040-26-8(3)); 2nd ed. (SPA., 48p. 14.95 (978-84-95040-24-4(7) , RR6004) Serres, Ediciones, S. L. ESP. *Dist:* Lectorum Pubns., Inc., Lectorum Pubns., Inc., Libros Sin Fronteras.

—Who Loves You, Baby? 2007. (Illus.). 18p. (J). (ps). bds. 6.95 (978-0-8118-5724-6(7)) Chronicle Bks. LLC.

LaMarche, Jim. The Raft. LaMarche, Jim, illus. (Illus.). 40p. (J). (gr. 1 up). 2000. 16.99 (978-0-688-13977-3(9)); 2002. reprint ed. pap. 6.99 (978-0-06-443856-8(2) , Harper Trophy) HarperCollins Pubs.

Lamberti, B. J. Nelson Paige & the Treasure Trove. 2006. 174p. per. 12.95 (978-1-59886-193-8(X)) Tate Publishing & Enterprises, L.L.C.

Lammie, Karen J., illus. Baa! 2005. (On the Farm Ser.). 10p. (J). (ps-ps). bds. 4.95 (978-0-7641-5826-1(0)) Barron's Educational Series, Inc.

—Moo! 2005. (On the Farm Ser.). 10p. (J). (ps-ps). bds. 4.95 (978-0-7641-5827-8(9)) Barron's Educational Series, Inc.

—Oink! 2005. (On the Farm Ser.). 10p. (J). (ps-ps). bds. 4.95 (978-0-7641-5829-2(5)) Barron's Educational Series, Inc.

Landolf, Diane Wright. The Jungle Book. Rowe, John, illus. 2008. 112p. (J). (***978-0-375-84276-4(4)***); lib. bdg. (***978-0-375-94062-0(6)***) Random Hse., Inc.

Lane, Leonie. The Bushtails & other Stories. 2007. 228p. per. (***978-1-84685-592-4(6)*** , Exposure Publishing) Meadow Bks.

Lang, Andrew. Animal Story Book. 2002. (Illus.). 416p. (J). pap. 11.95 (978-0-486-42187-2(2)) Dover Pubns., Inc.

Lang, Andrew, ed. The Red Book of Animal Stories 1899. Ford, Henry J., illus. 2004. reprint ed. pap. 34.95 (978-1-4179-8249-3(7)) Kessinger Publishing, LLC.

Lasky, Kathryn. María Antonieta: Princesa de Versalles. 2002. (SPA., Illus.). 224p. (978-84-7888-776-7(8) , 1954) Emece Editores.

Law, Felicia. The Feathers. Philpott, Claire & Radford, Karen, illus. 2006. (J). (978-1-4048-2596-3(7)) Picture Window Bks.

—The Furry Caterpillar. Philpott, Claire & Radford, Karen, illus. 2006. (J). (978-1-4048-2599-4(1)) Picture Window Bks.

—Marvelous Meals. Evans, Nicola, illus. 2005. (Bamboo & Friends Ser.). 24p. (J). (ps-3). lib. bdg. 22.60 (978-1-4048-1285-7(7)) Picture Window Bks.

—The Moon. Evans, Nicola, illus. 2005. (Bamboo & Friends Ser.). 24p. (J). (ps-3). lib. bdg. 22.60 (978-1-4048-1282-6(2)) Picture Window Bks.

—The Mushroom Ring. Philpott, Claire & Radford, Karen, illus. 2007. (J). 23.93 (978-1-4048-2595-6(9)) Picture Window Bks.

—The Rainbow. Philpott, Claire & Radford, Karen, illus. 2007. (J). (978-1-4048-2598-7(3)) Picture Window Bks.

—The Rainy Day. Evans, Nicola, illus. 2005. (Bamboo & Friends Ser.). 24p. (J). (ps-3). lib. bdg. 22.60 (978-1-4048-1280-2(6)) Picture Window Bks.

—Rumble Meets Harry Hippo. Pak, Yoon Mi, illus. 2006. (Read-It! Readers Ser.). 32p. (J). (gr. 2-4). 18.60 (978-1-4048-1338-0(1)) Picture Window Bks.

—The Walk. Philpott, Claire & Radford, Karen, illus. 2007. (J). (978-1-4048-2594-9(0)) Picture Window Bks.

Lawrence, Peter. Little Red: The Wolf's Story. Nino, Alex, illus. 2001. (Twenty-First Century Grimms': Vol. 2). 94p. pap. 9.95 (978-1-930702-03-5(5) , Smart Kids Studio Productions) Literary Assocs. Pr.

Lawson, Julie. The Klondike Cat. Mombourquette, Paul, illus. 2002. 32p. (J). (gr. k-3). (978-1-55337-013-0(9)) Kids Can Pr., Ltd.

Lawson, Robert. Rabbit Hill. Lawson, Robert, illus. 2007. (Puffin Modern Classics Ser.). 128p. (J). (gr. 3). pap. 5.99 (978-0-14-240796-7(8) , Puffin) Penguin Group (USA) Inc.

Layton, Diane C. Hind's Feet on High Places. 1998. (Illus.). 128p. (J). (ps up). pap. 14.99 (978-0-7684-2021-0(0)) Destiny Image Pubs.

Le Jars, David. Mis Amigos, Los Animales. 2004. (Hablemos Ser.). (SPA., Illus.). 24p. (J). (ps-k). pap. 5.95 (978-1-58728-950-7(4) , Two Can Publishing) T&N Children's Publishing.

—Mis Amigos, Los Animales. 2000. (SPA., Illus.). (J). (978-0-606-20801-7(1)) Tandem Library Bks.

Leaf, Munro. Ferdinandus Taurus. 2000. (SPA.). (ps-2). lib. bdg. 25.70 (978-0-613-56367-3(0)) Tandem Library Bks.

—Noodle. Bemelmans, Ludwig, illus. 2006. 56p. (J). 15.99 (978-0-590-04310-6(2)); pap. 15.99 (978-0-590-04309-0(9)) Scholastic, Inc. (Levine, Arthur A. Bks.).

—The Story of Ferdinand. Lawson, Robert, illus. 2000. (Reading Railroad Bks.). 32p. (J). (ps-4). 3.99 (978-0-448-42190-2(9) , Grosset & Dunlap) Penguin Group (USA) Inc.

—The Story of Ferdinand. 2000. (gr. k-3). lib. bdg. 11.25 (978-0-613-30144-2(7)) Tandem Library Bks.

—The Story of Ferdinand Bilingual Pack. Lawson, Robert, illus. pap. incl. audio compact disk (978-1-59519-155-7(0)) Live Oak Media.

Leaf, Munro, et al. Ferdinandus Taurus. 2000. (Illus.). 80p. reprint ed. pap. 17.95 (978-1-56792-127-4(2)) Godine, David R. Pub.

Leaney, Cindy. What's Wrong Mrs. Wolf? Whitehouse, Patty, ed. King, Sue & Wilks, Peter, illus. 2004. (Friendly Phonics Ser.). 24p. (J). lib. bdg. 14.95 (978-1-59054-258-3(4)) Fitzgerald Bks.

Lears, Laurie. Nathan's Wish: A Story about Cerebral Palsy. Schuett, Stacey, illus. 2005. 32p. (J). (gr. 1-4). 15.95 (978-0-8075-7101-9(6)) Whitman, Albert & Co.

Lee, Chinlun. Good Dog, Paw! Lee, Chinlun, illus. 2004. (Illus.). 40p. (J). (ps-1). 15.99 (978-0-7636-2178-0(1)) Candlewick Pr.

Lee Follen, Eliza. Piccolissima. 2004. reprint ed. pap. 15.95 (978-1-4191-4149-2(X)); pap. 1.99 (978-1-4192-4149-9(4)) Kessinger Publishing, LLC.

Lee, Hector Viveros. I Had a Hippopotamus. 1999. (Metro Reading Program Ser.). (J). (gr. k). 29.95 (978-1-58120-109-3(5)) Metropolitan Teaching & Learning Co.

Lee, Nancy. Hoover's Funny Little Kids. 2005. (J). spiral bd. 8.95 (978-0-9748087-8-9(4)) Journey Pubns., LLC.

Lee, Quinlan B. Go, Diego, Go!, Set. 2007. (Go, Diego, Go! Ser.). (J). 12.99 (***978-0-439-91304-1(7)***) Scholastic, Inc.

Leese, Jennifer L. B. Two Spots Bakery. 2004. 41p. pap. 19.95 (978-1-4137-3207-8(0)) PublishAmerica, Inc.

Leeson, Christine. The Magic of Christmas. Hansen, Gaby, illus. 2001. 32p. (J). tchr. ed. 14.95 (978-1-58925-011-6(7) , tiger tales) ME Media LLC.

—Molly & the Storm. Hansen, Gaby, illus. 2003. 32p. (J). (gr. k-2). tchr. ed. 15.95 (978-1-58925-027-7(3) , tiger tales) ME Media LLC.

LeFleur, David, illus. Hide & Seek in the Jungle. 2007. 19p. (J). (ps-k). 16.99 (***978-1-58476-623-0(9)*** , IKIDS) Innovative Kids.

LeFrancois, Anabel. Poems & Stories for Our Children. 2005. (Illus.). 91p. (J). per. 11.95 (978-1-59453-896-4(4) , Airleaf Publishing) Airleaf Publishing & Bookselling.

Leland, Debbie. Daddy's Love. Rife, Ann Hollis, illus. ed. 2006. (J). 15.95 (978-0-9667086-4-6(4)) Wildflower Run.

LeMonde, Stephanie. Misty Forest. Fryba, Borivoj, illus. 2007. (YA). per. 14.95 (***978-1-934138-13-7(4)***) Bouncing Ball Bks., Inc.

Leon, Georgina Lazaro. El Mejor Es Mi Papa. 2003. (gr. k-3). lib. bdg. 14.10 (978-0-613-79286-8(6)) Tandem Library Bks.

Leonard, Barry, ed. Moo & Chew: 5 Fun Animal Pop-Ups. 2004. (Illus.). 10p. (J). (gr. k-3). reprint ed. 5.00 (978-0-7567-8153-8(1)) DIANE Publishing Co.

Leonard, Marie. Tibili: The Little Boy Who Didn't Want to Go to School. Prigent, Andree, illus. 2002. 36p. (J). (ps-2). 15.95 (978-1-929132-20-1(4)) Kane/Miller Bk. Pubs., Inc.

Leonhardt, Alice. The Mystery of the Missing Leopard. 1999. (Illus.). (J). pap. 5.65 (978-0-7398-0884-9(2)) Steck-Vaughn.

Lepp, Royden. Barnabas Helps a Friend. 2008. 32p. (J). pap. 3.99 (***978-0-310-71585-6(7)***) Zondervan.

—God Loves You Barnbas. 2008. 32p. (J). pap. 3.99 (***978-0-310-71587-0(3)***) Zondervan.

—Happy Birthday Barnabas. 2008. 32p. (J). pap. 3.99 (***978-0-310-71586-3(5)***) Zondervan.

Leslie, Amanda. Do Crocodiles Moo? 2000. (Illus.). 16p. (J). (ps). 5.95 (978-1-929766-08-6(4)) Handprint Bks.

—Do Crocodiles Moo? Two Lift-the-Flap Books. Leslie, Amanda, illus. 2000. (Illus.). 12p. (J). 5.99 (978-1-58048-087-1(X)) Sandvik Publishing.

—Flappy, Waggly, Wiggly. Leslie, Amanda, illus. 1999. (Illus.). (J). 9.99 (978-1-58048-089-5(6)) Sandvik Publishing.

—Who's That Scratching at My Door? A Peekaboo Riddle Book. 2001. (Illus.). 24p. (J). (ps-k). pap. 12.95 (978-1-929766-19-2(X)) Handprint Bks.

Lester, Helen. Batter up Wombat. Munsinger, Lynn, illus. 2006. 32p. (J). (***978-1-4287-0160-1(5)***) Houghton Mifflin Co.

—Batter up Wombat. Munsinger, Lynn M., illus. 2006. 32p. (J). (gr. k-3). 16.00 (978-0-618-73784-0(7) , Walter Lorraine) Houghton Mifflin Co. Trade & Reference Div.

—El Pinguino Taky. 2001. (Illus.). (J). 12.75 (978-0-606-20649-5(3)) Tandem Library Bks.

—Tacky in Trouble. Munsinger, Lynn M., illus. 2005. 32p. (J). (gr. k-3). 6.95 (978-0-618-38008-4(6) , Walter Lorraine) Houghton Mifflin Co. Trade & Reference Div.

Levert, Mireille. Les Nuits de Rose. braille ed. 2004. (FRE.). (J). (ps-k). spiral bd. (978-0-616-03073-8(8)) Canadian National Institute for the Blind/Institut National Canadien pour les Aveugles.

Levin, Betty. Creature Crossing. Smith, Joseph A., illus. 1999. 96p. (J). (gr. 3 up). 15.00 (978-0-688-16220-7(7)) HarperCollins Pubs.

Levin, Bridget. Rules of the Wild: An Unruly Book of Manners. Shepherd, Amanda, illus. 2004. 36p. (J). 14.95 (978-0-8118-4226-6(6)) Chronicle Bks LLC.

Levy, Constance & Nakata, Hiroe. The Story of Red Rubber Ball. 2004. (Illus.). 32p. (J). 16.00 (978-0-15-216589-5(4) , Silver Whistle) Harcourt Trade Pubs.

Lewis, C. S. L' Armoire Magique. Orig. Title: The Lion, the Witch & the Wardrobe. (FRE.). 188p. pap. 21.95 (978-2-07-054643-5(8)) Gallimard, Editions FRA. *Dist:* Distribooks, Inc.

—Le Cheval et Son Ecuyer. Morgaut, Philippe, tr. Baynes, Pauline, illus. 2005. (FRE.). 234p. (J). pap. 21.95 (978-2-07-054644-2(6)) Gallimard, Editions FRA. *Dist:* Distribooks, Inc.

—Le Neveu du Magicien. (FRE.). pap. 21.95 (978-2-07-054642-8(X)) Gallimard, Editions FRA. *Dist:* Distribooks, Inc.

—Le Prince Caspian. (FRE.). pap. 21.95 (978-2-07-054645-9(4)) Gallimard, Editions FRA. *Dist:* Distribooks, Inc.

Lewis, Edwina. Who Jumps? Parker, Ant, illus. 2003. (Who. . . Ser.). 16p. (YA). (978-1-85602-447-1(4)) Chrysalis Children's Bks.

—Who Plays? Parker, Ant, illus. 2003. (Who. . . Ser.). 16p. (J). (978-1-85602-469-3(5)) Chrysalis Children's Bks.

—Who Swims? Parker, Ant, illus. 2003. (Who. . . Ser.). 16p. (YA). (978-1-85602-448-8(2)) Chrysalis Children's Bks.

Lewis, J. Earth & Me, Our Family Tree: Nature's Creatures. 2002. (gr. k-3). lib. bdg. 16.40 (978-0-613-56752-7(8)) Tandem Library Bks.

Lewis, J. Patrick. Earth & Me, Our Family Tree: Nature's Creatures. Canyon, Christopher, illus. 2004. (Sharing Nature with Children Book Ser.). 36p. (J). (ps-5). 16.95 (978-1-58469-031-3(3)); pap. 7.95 (978-1-58469-030-6(5)) Dawn Pubns.

Lewis, Paul Owen. P Bear's New Year's Party: A Counting Book. 1999. (ps-2). lib. bdg. 15.25 (978-0-613-86794-8(7)) Tandem Library Bks.

Lewis, Sian. Josh in the Jungle. Roberts, Gill, illus. 2005. 32p. pap. 12.95 (978-1-84323-462-3(9)) Beekman Bks., Inc.

Lewis, Wendy A. Cheetah. Ross, Graham, illus. 2007. (Orca Echoes Ser.). 64p. (J). pap. (***978-1-55143-465-0(2)***) Orca Bk. Pubs.

Lewison, Wendy Cheyette. Billy the Bug's New Jug. Chambliss, Maxie, illus. 2002. (Word Family Tales Ser.). 16p. (ps-2). pap. 2.95 (978-0-439-26252-1(6)) Scholastic, Inc.

—Buzz Said the Bee. 1999. (Illus.). (J). (gr. k-3). lib. bdg. 11.80 (978-0-8335-8720-6(X)) Tandem Library Bks.

Lewman, David. Chuckle & Cringe: SpongeBob's Book of Embarrassing Stories. 2007. (SpongeBob SquarePants Ser.). 48p. (J). pap. 3.99 (***978-1-4169-4746-2(9)***, Simon Spotlight) Simon & Schuster Children's Publishing.

Lexau, Joan M. Crocodile & Hen: A Bakongo Folktale. Cushman, Doug, illus. 2003. (I Can Read Bks.). 48p. (J). (ps-1). pap. 4.99 (978-0-06-444263-3(2)) HarperCollins Pubs.

Li, Amanda. Charlotte's Web: The Radiant Guide. 2006. (Illus.). 48p. (J). 12.99 (978-0-7566-2063-9(5)) Dorling Kindersley Publishing, Inc.

Light, Carol. Chickensing Big Book. Light, Carol, illus. 2003. (Illus.). (J). (978-0-9745803-2-6(5)) Little Big Tomes.

—Chickensing Little Book. Light, Carol, illus. 2003. (Illus.). 108p. (J). (978-0-9745803-3-3(3)) Little Big Tomes.

—Chickensing Story Book Reader. Light, Carol, illus. 2003. (Illus.). 60p. (J). (978-0-9745803-1-9(7)) Little Big Tomes.

Light, Carol, illus. Oops, a Curious Horse Story Telling Board. 2003. (J). (978-0-9745803-4-0(1)) Little Big Tomes.

Lindbergh, Reeve. North Country Spring. Sivertson, Liz, illus. 2007. 32p. (J). (gr. k-3). 6.95 (***978-0-618-80906-6(6)***) Houghton Mifflin Co. Trade & Reference Div.

Lindenbaum, Pija. When Owen's Mom Breathed Fire. Dyssegaard, Elisabeth Kallick, tr. 2006. (Illus.). 32p. (J). 16.00 (978-91-29-66548-2(5)) R & S Bks. SWE. *Dist:* Macmillan.

Lindner, Brooke. Spotting Animals with Diego! Mawhinney, Art, illus. 2007. (Go, Diego, Go! Ser.). 12p. (J). 12.99 (***978-1-4169-3827-9(3)***, Simon Spotlight/Nickelodeon) Simon & Schuster Children's Publishing.

—Swing, Diego, Swing! Magic Eye (Beehive Illustration), illus. 2007. (Go, Diego, Go! Ser.). 12p. (J). bds. 12.99 (***978-1-4169-3563-6(0)***, Simon Spotlight/Nickelodeon) Simon & Schuster Children's Publishing.

Lindsay, George. In the Woods: Who's Been Here? 1999. (Illus.). (J). 13.75 (978-0-606-15588-5(0)) Tandem Library Bks.

Lindsay, Norman. The Magic Pudding. 2006. (Illus.). 144p. (J). pap. 7.95 (978-0-486-45281-4(6)) Dover Pubns., Inc.

—The Magic Pudding. 2006. 77.99 (***978-1-4280-3115-9(4)***); 2005. (ENG.). pap. 70.99 (***978-1-4219-2134-1(0)***) IndyPublish.com.

—The Magic Pudding. 2004. reprint ed. pap. 15.95 (978-1-4191-7119-2(4)); pap. 1.99 (978-1-4192-7119-9(9)) Kessinger Publishing, LLC.

—The Magic Pudding. Lindsay, Norman, illus. 2004. (New York Review Children's Collection). (Illus.). 184p. (J). (gr. 3-6). pap. 16.95 (978-1-59017-101-1(2), NYR Children's Collection) New York Review of Bks., Inc., The.

Linenthal, Peter. Look at the Animals! 2006. (Illus.). 18p. (J). (ps). pap. 6.99 (978-0-525-47582-8(6), Dutton Juvenile) Penguin Group (USA) Inc.

The Lion, the Witch, & the Wardrobe: Response Journal. 2003. 44p. (YA). (978-1-58049-975-0(9), RJ75) Prestwick Hse., Inc.

Lionni, Leo. Una Piedra Extraordinaria. 1999. (J). (978-0-606-21669-2(3)) Tandem Library Bks.

Lipara, Laura. Gramma Shares Her Faith: Cain & Abel. 2006. per. 7.95 (***978-0-9791757-1-8(2)***) Oak Manor Publishing, Inc.

Lisi, Branden. Count on the Farm. Lisi, Margaret, illus. 2006. (J). lib. bdg. 15.95 (978-0-9771472-0-5(7)) Count On Learning.

Lite, Lori. The Affirmation Web: A Believe in Yourself Adventure. Botelho, Helder, illus. 2003. 32p. (J). (gr. k-6). pap. 10.95 (978-1-886941-25-0(4), 0942) Specialty Pr., Inc.

Literature Connections English: Animal Farm. 2004. (gr. 6-12). (978-0-395-79677-1(6), 2-70297) McDougal Littell Inc.

Lithgow, John. The Carnival of the Animals. Kulikov, Boris, illus. 2004. 40p. (J). (ps-3). 17.95 (978-0-689-86721-7(2)) Simon & Schuster Children's Publishing.

Lithgow, John. Carnival of the Animals. Kulikov, Boris, illus. 2007. 40p. (J). (gr. k-5). pap. 7.99 (***978-0-689-87343-0(3)***, Aladdin) Simon & Schuster Children's Publishing.

Lithgow, John & Davis, Jack E. Marsupial Sue Presents the Runaway Pancake. 2005. (Illus.). 40p. (J). (ps-3). 17.95 (978-0-689-87847-3(8), Simon & Schuster Children's Publishing) Simon & Schuster Children's Publishing.

The Little Animals of Oaxaca: Lap Book. (Pebble Soup Explorations Ser.). 16p. (ps up). 21.00 (978-0-7578-1664-2(9)) Rigby Education.

The Little Animals of Oaxaca: Small Book. (Pebble Soup Explorations Ser.). 16p. (ps up). 5.00 (978-0-7578-1704-5(1)) Rigby Education.

Little Bunny. 2003. (Goodnight Mr. Moon Ser.). (Illus.). (J). bds. 2.98 (978-0-7525-4741-1(0)) Parragon, Inc.

Little Engine- Animal Friends. 2005. (J). (978-1-4194-0023-0(1)) Paradise Pr., Inc.

Little Farm down the Lane, Bk. III. 2005. pap. 10.99 (978-1-59781-702-8(3)) Xulon Pr., Inc.

Little, Jean. Birdie for Now. Benoit, Renne, illus. 2002. 160p. (J). (gr. 3-6). pap. 5.95 (978-1-55143-203-8(X)) Orca Bk. Pubs. USA.

—Pippin the Christmas Pig. Zimmermann, H. Werner, illus. 2004. 40p. (J). (ps-3). 16.95 (978-0-439-65062-5(3), Scholastic Pr.) Scholastic, Inc.

Little Softy, 4 bks., Set. alt. ed. 2002. (J). (978-1-931312-86-8(9)) SoftPlay, Inc.

The Llama Who Wished for Wings. 1999. (Illus.). 19p. (J). (ps-6). pap. 7.00 (978-0-9669355-0-9(0)) Chiappini, Lydia.

Lloyd, A. R. Kine. l.t. ed. 2005. (Ulverscroft Large Print Ser.). (Illus.). 384p. 32.50 (978-1-84395-554-2(7)) Ulverscroft Large Print Bks. GBR. *Dist:* Ulverscroft Large Print Bks., Ltd.

Lloyd, Jennifer. One Winter Night. Ray, Lynn, illus. 2006. 32p. 16.95 (978-1-894965-48-4(5)) Simply Read Bks. CAN. *Dist:* Perseus Distribution.

Lloyd-Jones, Sally. Old MacNoah Had an Ark. 2008. (HarperBlessings Ser.). (Illus.). 32p. (J). 17.89 (978-0-06-055718-8(4)) HarperCollins Pubs.

—Old MacNoah Had an Ark. Newton, Jill, illus. 2008. (HarperBlessings Ser.). 32p. (J). 16.99 (978-0-06-055717-1(6)) HarperCollins Pubs.

—Time to Say Goodnight. Chapman, Jane, illus. 2006. 32p. (J). 15.99 (978-0-06-054328-0(0)); lib. bdg. 16.89 (978-0-06-054329-7(9)) HarperCollins Pubs.

Lloyd, Stacy K. Friends & Letters. 2005. 36p. pap. 13.00 (978-1-4116-0900-6(X)) Lulu.com.

Lluch, Alex. Zoo Clues Animal Alphabet: Learn with Me the ABCs. 2005. (Illus.). 52p. bds. 7.95 (978-1-887169-49-3(0)) Wedding Solutions Publishing, Inc.

Lobel, Anita. The Boy Who Held Back the Sea. Lobel, Anita, illus. 2008. 32p. (J). 16.99 (***978-0-06-078765-3(1)***); lib. bdg. 17.89 (***978-0-06-078766-0(X)***) HarperCollins Pubs. (Greenwillow Bks.).

Lobel, Gillian. Fancy That! Geoghegan, Adrienne, illus. 2005. 32p. (J). (ps-7). 15.95 (978-1-84507-335-0(5)) Lincoln, Frances Ltd. GBR. *Dist:* Perseus Distribution.

Lobo, Cerdito, Pato y Oca (Wolf, Pig, Duck & Goose) (SPA.). 24p. (J). 4.95 (978-84-246-1606-9(5)) La Galera, S.A. Editorial ESP. *Dist:* AIMS International Bks., Inc.

Lock, Brian. There's a Hippo in My Bathtub. 2007. (ENG.). 76p. per. 14.95 (***978-1-4241-7331-0(0)***) PublishAmerica, Inc.

Lodge, Alison. Clever Chameleon. Lodge, Alison, illus. 2005. (Illus.). 24p. (J). 15.99 (978-1-84148-347-4(8)) Barefoot Bks., Inc.

Lodge, Jo. Pass the Parcel with Pig. 1998. (Illus.). 12p. (J). (ps-3). 5.95 (978-0-7641-5076-0(6)) Barron's Educational Series, Inc.

Lofting, Hugh. Animal Talk Bk. 1. Kanzler, John, illus. 2006. (Easy Reader Classics Ser.). 32p. (J). pap. 3.95 (978-1-4027-3291-1(0)) Sterling Publishing Co., Inc.

—The Story of Doctor Dolittle. 2005. 128p. pap. 10.95 (978-1-4218-0147-6(7), 1st World Library - Literary Society) 1st World Publishing, Inc.

—The Story of Doctor Dolittle. 2005. 96p. per. 4.95 (978-1-4209-2544-9(X)) Digireads.com.

—The Story of Doctor Dolittle. 2005. (Illus.). 96p. pap. 3.95 (978-0-486-43883-2(X)) Dover Pubns., Inc.

—The Story of Doctor Dolittle. Exams Unlimited, Inc. Staff, ed. 2001. 116p. (J). reprint ed. cd-rom 5.95 (978-1-885343-94-9(9)) Exams Unlimited, Inc.

—The Story of Doctor Dolittle. 2004. reprint ed. pap. 15.95 (978-1-4191-8383-6(4)); pap. 1.99 (978-1-4192-8383-3(9)) Kessinger Publishing, LLC.

—The Story of Doctor Dolittle: #1 Animal Talk. 2007. (Easy Reader Classics Ser.). 32p. (J). (ps-3). 21.35 (***978-1-59961-338-3(7)***) Spotlight.

—The Story of Doctor Dolittle: Being the History of His Peculiar Life at Home & Astonishing Adventures in Foreign Parts. Hague, Michael, illus. 2005. (Books of Wonder). 160p. (J). (ps-7). pap. 6.99 (978-0-06-077597-1(1), Harper Trophy) HarperCollins Pubs.

—The Story of Doctor Dolittle No. 3: Doctor Dolittle's Great Adventure. Kanzler, John, illus. 2007. (Easy Reader Classics Ser.). 32p. (J). pap. 3.95 (978-1-4027-4122-7(7)) Sterling Publishing Co., Inc.

—The Story of Doctor Dolittle No. 4: Doctor Dolittle's Magical Cure. Kanzler, John, illus. 2007. (Easy Reader Classics Ser.). 32p. (J). pap. 3.95 (978-1-4027-4123-4(5)) Sterling Publishing Co., Inc.

—Viages de Doctor Dolittle. 1999. (Espasa Juvenil Ser.: Vol. 94). Tr. of Voyages of Doctor Dolittle. (SPA., Illus.). 376p. (J). (gr. 4-7). 11.95 (978-84-239-7060-5(4)) Espasa Calpe, S.A. ESP. *Dist:* Planeta Publishing Corp.

—The Voyages of Doctor Dolittle. 2005. 340p. pap. 14.95 (978-1-4218-0148-3(5), 1st World Library - Literary Society) 1st World Publishing, Inc.

—The Voyages of Doctor Dolittle. Hague, Michael, illus. 2001. (Doctor Dolittle Ser.). 368p. (J). (gr. 4-6). 28.99 (978-0-688-14002-1(5)) HarperCollins Pubs.

—The Voyages of Doctor Dolittle. 2000. (Doctor Dolittle Ser.). (Illus.). 272p. (gr. 4-6). mass mkt. 4.95 (978-0-451-52769-1(0), Signet Classics) Penguin Group (USA) Inc.

—The Voyages of Doctor Dolittle. Lamut, Sonja, illus. 1998. (Doctor Dolittle Ser.). 288p. (J). (gr. 1-6). 16.99 (978-0-448-41863-6(0), Grosset & Dunlap) Penguin Group (USA) Inc.

—Voyages of Doctor Dolittle. 2006. 53.99 (***978-1-4280-2312-3(7)***) IndyPublish.com.

—Voyages of Doctor Dolittle. 2004. lib. bdg. 12.95 (978-0-613-90738-5(8)) Tandem Library Bks.

—The Voyages of Doctor Dolittle. Corvino, Lucy, illus. 2008. (Classic Starts Ser.). 160p. (J). 5.95 (***978-1-4027-4574-4(5)***) Sterling Publishing Co., Inc.

—Voyages of Doctor Dolittle. abr. ed. 2000. (gr. 3-6). lib. bdg. 14.15 (978-0-7857-5056-7(8)) Tandem Library Bks.

—Voyages of Dr Dolittle. 2000. (gr. 5-8). lib. bdg. 12.95 (978-0-613-27681-8(7)) Tandem Library Bks.

Lombardi, Kristine. Springtime on the Farm. 2006. (Illus.). 12p. (J). bds. 12.99 (978-0-7944-0947-0(4)) Reader's Digest Assn., Inc., The.

Lonczak, Heather Suzanne. Mookey the Monkey Gets over Being Teased. Ramsey, Marcy Dunn, illus. 2006. 32p. (J). (gr. k-2). 14.95 (978-1-59147-479-1(5)); pap. 8.95 (978-1-59147-480-7(9)) American Psychological Assn. (Magination Pr.).

London, Jack, ed. Call of the Wild Great Read. 2004. (Great Classics for Children Ser.). 128p. (J). 5.99 (978-1-4037-0983-7(1)) Dalmatian Pr.

London, Jonathan. Froggy Plays in the Band. Remkiewicz, Frank, illus. (Froggy Ser.). 32p. (J). 2004. pap. 5.99 (978-0-14-240051-7(3), Puffin); 2002. 15.99 (978-0-670-03532-8(7), Viking Juvenile) Penguin Group (USA) Inc.

—Froggy Plays Soccer. Remkiewicz, Frank, illus. 1999. 32p. (J). (ps-1). 15.99 (978-0-670-88257-1(7), Viking Juvenile) Penguin Group (USA) Inc.

—Froggy Plays T-Ball. Remkiewicz, Frank, illus. 2007. (Froggy Ser.). 32p. (J). (ps-1). 15.99 (978-0-670-06187-7(5), Viking Juvenile) Penguin Group (USA) Inc.

—Froggy's Best Christmas. Remkiewicz, Frank, illus. 32p. (J). 2002. pap. 5.99 (978-0-14-056735-9(6), Puffin); 2000. 15.99 (978-0-670-89220-4(3), Viking Juvenile) Penguin Group (USA) Inc.

—Froggy's Best Christmas. 2002. (gr. k-3). lib. bdg. 14.15 (978-0-613-83557-2(3)) Tandem Library Bks.

—What Newt Could Do for Turtle. 1998. (J). (978-0-606-13902-1(8)) Tandem Library Bks.

Long, Jonathan & Paul, Korky. The Wonky Donkey. 2000. (Illus.). 32p. (J). pap. 9.99 (978-0-09-926396-8(3)) Random Hse. GBR. *Dist:* Trafalgar Square Publishing.

Longstreet, Barbara, et al. Woodsey School Kids Thanksgiving Feast. 2004. 28p. pap. 14.95 (978-1-4137-1992-5(9)) PublishAmerica, Inc.

Look at the Animals: Individual Title, 6 Packs. (Sails Literacy Ser.). 16p. (gr. k up). 27.00 (978-0-7635-4423-2(X)) Rigby Education.

Looking for Lewis. 1999. (Books to Go Ser.). (J). pap. (978-0-8136-7879-5(X)) Modern Curriculum Pr.

Lopshire, Robert. Put Me in the Zoo. 2001. (Bright & Early Board Bks.). (Illus.). 24p. (J). (gr. k-ps). bds. 4.99 (978-0-375-81215-6(6), Random Hse. Bks. for Young Readers) Random Hse. Children's Bks.

Lorimer, Janet. Moby Dick. abr. ed. 1999. (gr. 7-12). lib. bdg. 15.25 (978-0-613-32841-8(8)) Tandem Library Bks.

Losordo, Stephen. Cow Moo Me. Conteh-Morgan, Jane, illus. 1998. (Growing Tree Ser.). 16p. (J). (ps up). 5.95 (978-0-694-01108-7(8), Harper Festival) HarperCollins Pubs.

Louise, Tina. When I Grow Up. Corwin, Oliver J., illus. 2007. 32p. (J). (ps-3). 15.95 (978-0-8109-3948-6(7), Abrams Bks. for Young Readers) Abrams, Harry N., Inc.

Loupy, Christophe. Hugs & Kisses. James, J. Alison, tr. from GER. Tharlet, Eve, illus. 2001. 36p. (J). (ps-k). 15.95 (978-0-7358-1484-4(8)) North-South Bks., Inc.

Lovejoy, Robert. The Golden Dog Book of Fairy Tales & Animals Stories. 2004. 140p. pap. 9.99 (978-0-919614-66-6(3)) Golden Dog Pr. CAN. *Dist:* Univ. of Toronto Pr.

Lubner, Susan. A Horse's Tale. Moore, Margie, illus. 2008. 32p. (J). 16.95 (***978-0-8109-9490-4(9)***, Abrams Bks. for Young Readers) Abrams, Harry N., Inc.

Lucado, Max. Hermie Flo the Lyin Fly. 2004. (SPA.). 14.99 (978-0-88113-807-8(X)) Grupo Nelson.

Lukas, Catherine. Race to the Tower of Power. 2007. 24p. (J). 21.35 (***978-1-59961-159-4(7)***) Spotlight.

Luksetich, John. Whose Coat? Kern, Patti, illus. 2002. (J). (gr. 1-2). trans. 14.95 (978-0-940411-02-9(4)) Imagine Nation Pr.

Lullaby Moon. 2003. (J). 14.99 (978-0-89610-495-2(8)) Island Heritage Publishing.

Lumry, Amanda & Hurwitz, Laura. Adventures of Riley: Mission to Madagascar. McIntyre, Sarah, illus. 2005. 36p. (gr. 2-3). 15.95 (978-0-9748411-2-0(9)) Eaglemont Pr.

Lund, Jillian. Have You Ever Seen A Jackalope? 2004. (Illus.). (J). 15.95 (978-1-891795-11-4(2)) RGU Group, The.

Lunge-Larsen, Lise. Noah's Mittens: How Noah Discovered Felt. Trueman, Matthew, illus. 2006. 32p. (J). (gr. k-3). 16.00 (978-0-618-32950-2(1)) Houghton Mifflin Co.

Luther, Jacqueline. Panda Bear Cub. Nelson, Will, illus. 2006. (Soundprints' Read-And-Discover Ser.). 32p. (J). pap. 3.95 (978-1-59249-585-6(0)) Soundprints.

Maccarone, Grace. "What Is That?" Said the Cat, Level 1. Scherer, Jeffrey, illus. 1998. (Hello Reader! Ser.). 32p. (J). (ps-1). pap. 3.99 (978-0-590-25945-3(8), Cartwheel Bks.) Scholastic, Inc.

—"What Is That?" Said the Cat. 1998. (J). (978-0-606-13900-7(1)) Tandem Library Bks.

Maccarone, Grace & Burns, Marilyn. It Was Halloween Night: A Scary Math Story - with Tangrams! Straub, Matthew, illus. 2001. (Hello Reader! Math Ser.). (J). (978-0-439-30471-9(7)) Scholastic, Inc.

MacDonald, Alan. Snarlyhissopus. Voce, Louise, illus. 2002. 32p. (J). pap. 5.95 (978-1-58925-370-4(1)); tchr. ed. 14.95 (978-1-58925-021-5(4)) ME Media LLC. (tiger tales).

—Snarlyhissopus. 2002. (ps-2). lib. bdg. 14.10 (978-0-613-53314-0(3)) Tandem Library Bks.

MacDonald, George. A Rough Shaking. 2006. 66.99 (***978-1-4280-3048-0(4)***) IndyPublish.com.

MacDonald, Margaret Read. Conejito: A Folktale from Panama. Valerio, Geraldo, illus. 2006. 32p. 16.95 (978-0-87483-779-7(0)) August Hse. Pubs., Inc.

MacDonald, Maryann. Princess Josie's Pets. Bluthenthal, Diana Cain, illus. 1998. (Hyperion Chapters Ser.). 64p. (J). (gr. 2-4). pap. 3.95 (978-0-7868-1134-2(X)) Disney Pr.

MacHado, Ana Maria. Delantal Que el Viento Lleva. (SPA.). pap. 12.95 (978-950-07-2220-9(8)) Editorial Sudamericana S.A. ARG. *Dist:* Distribooks, Inc.

—Pimienta en la Cebecita. (Torre de Papel Ser.). (SPA., Illus.). (J). 7.95 (978-958-04-5049-8(8), NR3067) Norma S.A. COL. *Dist:* Distribuidora Norma, Inc., Lectorum Pubns., Inc.

MacHale, D. J. The Merchant of Death. 2007. (Pendragon Ser.: Bk. 1). 384p. (J). 16.99 (978-1-4169-3625-1(4)) Simon & Schuster Children's Publishing.

Mack, David. The Shy Creatures. 2007. (Illus.). 48p. (J). (gr. k-2). 16.95 (***978-0-312-36794-7(5)***) Feiwel & Friends.

Mack, Lizzie. Catch a Ride to the Moon: Whimsical Rhymes to Read & Sing. G Studios, illus. 2007. (Land of Milk & Honey Ser.). 30p. (J). (ps). 10.99 (***978-1-4169-2764-8(6)***, Little Simon Inspirations) Simon & Schuster Children's Publishing.

Mack, Lizzie. Good Morning, Good Day. G Studios Staff, illus. 2007. (Land of Milk & Honey Ser.). 12p. (J). bds. 12.99 (978-1-4169-3650-3(5), Little Simon Inspirations) Simon & Schuster Children's Publishing.

Mack, Paulette. Cookout at Grandma's House: The Adventures of Mielle & Cheeky. 2006. (ENG., Illus.). 24p. per. 10.95 (***978-1-59800-998-9(2)***) Outskirts Press, Inc.

Mackall, Dandi Daley. A Gaggle of Geese & a Clutter of Cats. Hohn, David, illus. 2007. (Dandilion Rhymes Ser.). 32p. (J). (ps-3). 9.99 (***978-1-4000-7204-0(2)***, WaterBrook Pr.) WaterBrook Pr.

—Little Lost Donkey. Kucharik, Elena, illus. 2002. (I'm Not Afraid Ser.). 24p. (J). (ps-2). 6.99 (978-0-8499-7752-7(5)) Nelson, Thomas Inc.

—Merry Creature Christmas. 2006. 24p. (J). bds. 9.99 (978-1-4003-0823-1(2)) Nelson, Thomas Inc.

Mackay, J. A. Rockin' Roly Poly. 2005. (J). 9.95 (978-0-938423-14-0(2)) Eco Images.

MacLeod, Elizabeth. I Heard a Little Baa. Phillips, Louise, illus. 1998. 24p. (J). (ps-k). (978-1-55074-496-5(8)) Kids Can Pr., Ltd.

MacMillan, Ian C. Khala Maninge - the Little Elephant That Cried a Lot: An African Fable. MacMillan, Eric G., illus. 2nd ed. 2003. lib. bdg. 5.00 (978-0-9729698-0-2(2)) Maninge Mali.

Mad Dash. 2005. (J). 4.95 (978-1-59792-011-7(8)) F.A.S.T. Learning LLLC.

Maddox, Tony. Spike's Best Nest. 1998. (Illus.). 32p. (J). pap. 5.95 (978-0-7641-0548-7(5)) Barron's Educational Series, Inc.

Maguire, Gregory. Leaping Beauty: And Other Animal Fairy Tales. Demarest, Chris L., illus. (J). 2004. 208p. 15.99 (978-0-06-056417-9(2)); 2006. 224p. reprint ed. pap. 5.99 (978-0-06-056419-3(9), Harper Trophy) HarperCollins Pubs.

Maher, Alex, illus. Diego's Safari Rescue. 2007. (Go, Diego, Go! Ser.). 24p. (J). pap. 3.99 (***978-1-4169-3818-7(4)***, Simon Spotlight/Nickelodeon) Simon & Schuster Children's Publishing.

Mahoney, Daniel J. The Saturday Escape. 2002. (Illus.). 32p. (J). (gr. k-3). 14.00 (978-0-618-13326-0(7), Clarion Bks.) Houghton Mifflin Co. Trade & Reference Div.

Maltby, Ethel H. My Animal Story Book: A Treasury of Sunshine Stories for Children. Richardson, Frederick, illus. 2004. reprint ed. pap. 15.95 (978-1-4191-7300-4(6)) Kessinger Publishing, LLC.

Man-Kong, Mary. At the Farm: Create It All with Play-Doh Colors & Stencil. 2003. (Play-Doh Ser.). (Illus.). 12p. (J). 9.95 (978-0-7624-1562-5(2), Running Pr. Kids) Running Pr. Bk. Pubs.

Mangan, Anne. Little Teddy Left Behind. Moss, Joanne, illus. 2006. 26p. (J). 16.00 (978-1-56148-508-6(X)) Good Bks.

Manners, Richard. Girl Child Saturday: A Children's Fantasy. 2000. 152p. (J). (gr. 1-7). pap. 9.95 (978-0-595-12673-6(1)) iUniverse, Inc.

Margetson, Donald. The Unhappy Cow. 2004. 21p. pap. 14.95 (978-1-4137-1004-5(2)) PublishAmerica, Inc.

Marie, E. The Porcupine Connection: The Story of a Young Girl's Journey from Tragedy to Healing, with the Help of Her Forest Friends. 2004. 48p. pap. 19.95 (978-1-4137-3480-5(4)) PublishAmerica, Inc.

Markes, Julie. Good Thing You're Not an Octopus! Smith, Maggie, illus. 40p. (J). (ps-1). 2006. pap. 6.99 (978-0-06-443586-4(5), Harper Trophy); 2001. 15.99 (978-0-06-028465-7(X)) HarperCollins Pubs.

Markle, Sandra. Animals Robert Scott Saw. 2008. (J). 16.99 (978-0-8118-4918-0(X)) Chronicle Bks. LLC.

—The Fledglings. 2003. 144p. (YA). (gr. 4-6). pap. 9.95 (978-1-56397-696-4(X)) Boyds Mills Pr.

Marshall, James. Jorge y Marta en la Ciudad. 2001. (SPA., Illus.). 52p. (J). (ps-3). 978-84-239-2829-3(2), EC0827) Espasa Calpe, S.A. ESP. *Dist:* Lectorum Pubns., Inc.

—Taking Care of Carruthers. 2000. (J). (978-0-606-19365-8(0)) Tandem Library Bks.

—Willis. 2001. (Illus.). 48p. (J). (gr. k-3). tchr. ed. 15.00 (978-0-618-12441-1(1)) Houghton Mifflin Co. Trade & Reference Div.

—Wings: A Tale of Two Chickens. 2003. (Illus.). 32p. (J). (gr. k-3). 6.95 (978-0-618-31659-5(0)) Houghton Mifflin Co. Trade & Reference Div.

Martchenko, Michael. Ma, I'm a Farmer. Martchenko, Michael, illus. 2003. (Illus.). 32p. (J). (ps-2). pap. 5.95 (978-1-55037-696-8(9)) Annick Pr., Ltd. CAN. *Dist:* Firefly Bks., Ltd.

Martin, Ann M. Baby Animal Zoo. Tang, Charles, illus. 1998. (Kids in Ms. Colman's Class: No. 12). (J). (gr. 1-4). pap. 3.50 (978-0-590-06009-7(0) , Scholastic Paperbacks) Scholastic, Inc.

—A Dog's Life. 2005. 192p. (J). (gr. 4-7). pap. 16.99 (978-0-439-71559-1(8)) Scholastic, Inc.

Martin, Bill, Jr. Baby Bear, Baby Bear, What Do You See? Carle, Eric, illus. 2007. 32p. (J). (ps-3). 16.95 (*978-0-8050-8336-1(7)) , Holt, Henry & Co. Bks. For Young Readers) Holt, Henry & Co.

Martin, Bill, Jr. Brown Bear, Brown Bear, What Do You See? 2002. (Illus.). (J). 26.49 (978-0-7587-2157-0(9)) Book Wholesalers, Inc.

Martin, Bill. Oso Pardo, Oso Pardo, ¿Qué Ves Ahí? Mlawer, Teresa, tr. Carle, Eric, illus. rev. ed. 2002. (SPA.). 28p. (J). (ps-k). bds. 7.95 (978-0-8050-6901-3(1) , Holt, Henry & Co. Bks. For Young Readers) Holt, Henry & Co.

—Panda Bear, Panda Bear, What Do You See? Carle, Eric, illus. 2007. 32p. (J). 22.95 (*978-0-8050-8102-2(X)) , Holt, Henry & Co. Bks. For Young Readers) Holt, Henry & Co.

—Panda Bear, Panda Bear, What Do You See? Carlen, Eric, illus. 2006. 28p. (J). bds. 7.95 (978-0-8050-8078-0(3) , Holt, Henry & Co. Bks. For Young Readers) Holt, Henry & Co.

Martin, Bill & Carle, Eric. Brown Bear & Friends Board Book Gift Set. 2007. (Illus.). 26p. (J). (ps). bds. 23.95 (*978-0-8050-8273-9(5)) , Holt, Henry & Co. Bks. For Young Readers) Holt, Henry & Co.

Martin, David. We've All Got Bellybuttons! Cecil, Randy, illus. 2005. 32p. (J). (ps-1). 15.99 (978-0-7636-1775-2(X)) Candlewick Pr.

Martin, J. P. Uncle. Blake, Quentin, illus. 2007. 224p. (J). (gr. 3-7). 16.95 (978-1-59017-239-1(6) , NYR Children's Collection) New York Review of Bks., Inc., The.

Martin-Larranaga, Ana. Quacky & Hoppy. 2007. (Hide-and-Seek Pond Bath Bks.). (Illus.). 8p. (J). (ps). 12.99 (*978-0-7641-9377-4(5)) Barron's Educational Series, Inc.

Martin-Larranaga, Ana, illus. Squishy & Squirty. 2007. (Hide-and-Seek Pond Bath Bks.). 8p. (J). (ps). 12.99 (*978-0-7641-9378-1(3)) Barron's Educational Series, Inc.

Martin, Mary. Miss Lilly & the Hollyhock Garden. 2001. (Illus.). 48p. (J). 24.95 (978-1-58597-107-7(3)) Leathers Publishing.

Marzollo, Jean. I Spy Little Animals. Wick, Walter, photos by. 1998. (I Spy Bks.). (Illus.). 26p. (J). (ps). bds. 6.99 (978-0-590-11711-1(4) , Cartwheel Bks.) Scholastic, Inc.

—Shanna's Animal Riddles. Roos, Maryn, illus. 2004. (J). (ps-ps). lib. bdg. 10.79 (978-0-606-30551-8(3)) Tandem Library Bks.

—Ten Little Christmas Presents. 2008. (J). (*978-0-545-02791-5(8)) Scholastic, Inc.

Marzollo, Jean. What's the Matter with Mother Goose? Trivas, Irene, illus. 2000. 32p. (J). (ps-k). 14.95 (978-0-06-027276-0(7)) HarperCollins Pubs.

Marzollo, Jean, et al. What's the Matter with Mother Goose? Trivas, Irene, illus. 2000. 32p. (J). (ps-k). lib. bdg. 14.89 (978-0-06-027277-7(5)) HarperCollins Pubs.

Mason, Chad. Wake up, Bertha Bear! Wallace, Chad, illus. 2006. 32p. 15.95 (978-0-89272-655-4(5)) Down East Bks.

Mason, Cherie. Everybody's Somebody's Lunch. Moore, Gustav, illus. 1998. 40p. (J). (gr. 3-6). 16.95 (978-0-88448-198-0(0)) Tilbury Hse. Pubs.

Mason, Tom & Danko, Dan, adapted by. Barnyard: The Original Party Animals. 2006. (Barnyard Ser.). (Illus.). 128p. (J). pap. 4.99 (978-1-4169-0722-0(X) , Simon Spotlight) Simon & Schuster Children's Publishing.

Massey, Jane, illus. Animales de la Granja. (Coloca y Siente). (SPA.). 10p. (J). (gr. k-2). bds. (978-968-5308-67-0(5) , Silver Dolphin en Español) Advanced Marketing, S. de R. L. de C. V.

—Animales de la Selva. (Coloca y Siente). (SPA.). 10p. (J), (gr. k-2). bds. (978-968-5308-68-7(3) , Silver Dolphin en Español) Advanced Marketing, S. de R. L. de C. V.

Mathers, Petra. A Cake for Herbie. 2000. Orig. Title: A Poem for Lottie. (J). 15.00 (978-0-689-01506-9(2) , Atheneum) Simon & Schuster Children's Publishing.

Matteson, Rosemary. Tommy's Circle of Friends at Meadowview Farm. 2002. (Illus.) (J). (ps-5). 21.95 (978-1-881636-64-9(X)) Windsor Hse. Publishing Group, The.

Matthews, Derek. Snappy Sounds Circus. 2006. (Snappy Sounds Ser.). (Illus.). 10p. (J). 12.95 (978-1-59223-564-3(6) , Silver Dolphin Bks.) Advantage Pubs. Group.

Matthews, John & Matthews, Caitlin. Trick of the Tale: A Collection of Trickster Tales. Tomic, Tomislav, illus. 2007. 96p. (J). (gr. 5). 18.99 (*978-0-7636-3646-3(0)) Candlewick Pr.

Matthews, Tina. Out of the Egg. 2007. (Illus.). (J). (ps-k). 32p. 12.95 (978-0-618-73741-3(3)); (*978-1-4287-3693-1(X)) Houghton Mifflin Co.

Mawhinney, Art, illus. Eeyore's Cheerful Surprises. 2005. (*978-1-4127-3101-0(1)) Publications International, Ltd.

Maxwell-Hyslop, Miranda. Fish Go Woof! 2005. (Illus.). 36p. (J). (978-0-340-87338-0(8) , Hodder & Stoughton) Hodder General Publishing Division.

—Fish Go Woof! 2005. (Illus.). (J). pap. 9.99 (978-0-340-87339-7(6) , Hodder & Stoughton) Hodder General Publishing Division GBR. *Dist:* Trafalgar Square Publishing.

May, Jenny. Earth Adventures of Seedwin the Nix. 2000. 36p. (J). (ps-3). pap. (978-0-9684804-1-0(1)) Ogo Bks.

Maybarduk, Linda. James the Dancing Dog. Johnson, Gillian, illus. 2004. 24p. (J). (ps-3). 15.95 (978-0-88776-619-0(6)) Tundra Bks., Inc./Livres Toundra, Inc. CAN. *Dist:* Random Hse., Inc.

Mayer, Mercer. Ermine's New Home. 2002. (gr. k-3). lib. bdg. 25.70 (978-0-613-70874-6(1)) Tandem Library Bks.

—Goodnight, Little Critter. 2001. (gr. k-3). lib. bdg. 11.80 (978-0-613-67624-3(6)) Tandem Library Bks.

—Grandma, Grandpa, & Me. Mayer, Mercer, illus. 2007. (Little Critter Ser.). 24p. (J). pap. 3.99 (978-0-06-053951-1(8)) HarperCollins Pubs.

—Just a Snowy Day. Mayer, Mercer, illus. 2006. (Little Critter Ser.). 16p. (J). 8.99 (978-0-06-083880-5(9) , Harper Festival) HarperCollins Pubs.

—Just Going to the Dentist. Mayer, Mercer, illus. 1998. (Little Critter Ser.). (J). (ps-3). 10.09 (978-0-606-12374-7(1)) Tandem Library Bks.

—Just So Thankful. Mayer, Mercer, illus. 2006. (Little Critter Ser.). (Illus.). 24p. (J). pap. 3.99 (978-0-06-053950-4(X) , Harper Festival) HarperCollins Pubs.

—Little Critter's Read-It-Yourself Storybook. Mayer, Mercer, illus. 2000. (Little Critter Ser.). (Illus.). 192p. (J). (ps-2). 17.95 (978-0-307-16840-5(9) , 16840, Golden Bks.) Random Hse. Children's Bks.

—Little Critter's the Picnic. l.t. ed. 1999. (Early Childhood First Bks.: No. 1). (Illus.). 20p. (J). (gr. k-1). lib. bdg. 13.95 (978-1-56674-219-1(6)) Forest Hse. Publishing Co., Inc.

—Little Critter's the Trip. 1999. (Early Childhood First Bks.: No. 2). (Illus.). 20p. (J). (gr. k-1). lib. bdg. 13.95 (978-1-56674-254-2(4)) Forest Hse. Publishing Co., Inc.

—The Lost Dinosaur Bone. Mayer, Mercer, illus. 2007. (Little Critter Ser.). 24p. (J). (ps-2). pap. 3.99 (978-0-06-053952-8(6) , Harper Festival) HarperCollins Pubs.

—My Trip to the Hospital, No. 3. 2008. (Little Critter Ser.). (Illus.). 20p. (J). pap. 6.99 (*978-0-06-053969-6(0)) , Harper Festival) HarperCollins Pubs.

—My Trip to the Hospital, No. 5. Mayer, Mercer, illus. 2005. (Little Critter Ser.). (Illus.). 24p. (J). (ps-2). pap. 3.99 (978-0-06-053949-8(6) , Harper Festival) HarperCollins Pubs.

—New Kid in Town, Vol. 3. 2002. (Little Critter First Readers Ser.). (Illus.). 24p. (J). (gr. 1-2). pap. 3.95 (978-1-57768-829-7(5)) School Specialty Publishing.

—New Kid in Town. 2001. (gr. k-3). lib. bdg. 11.80 (978-0-613-67654-0(8)) Tandem Library Bks.

—No One Can Play. 2002. (Little Critter Ser.). (Illus.). 24p. (J). (ps-2). 10.95 (978-1-57768-608-8(X)) School Specialty Publishing.

—No One Can Play. 2000. (gr. k-3). lib. bdg. 11.80 (978-0-613-67656-4(4)) Tandem Library Bks.

—We Love You, Little Critter! 2003. (Little Critter First Readers Ser.). (Illus.). 24p. (J). (ps-k). pap. 3.95 (978-1-57768-587-6(3)) School Specialty Publishing.

—We Love You, Little Critter! 2004. lib. bdg. 11.80 (978-0-613-88740-3(9)) Tandem Library Bks.

—A Yummy Lunch. 2002. (Little Critter Ser.). (Illus.). 24p. (J). (ps-2). 10.95 (978-1-57768-627-9(6)) School Specialty Publishing.

Mayfield, Sue & Padua, Rochelle. I Can You Can Toucan! 2006. (Green Bananas Ser.). (Illus.). 48p. (J). pap. (978-0-7787-1048-6(3)) Crabtree Publishing Co.

Mayne, William. Fox Gate. (Illus.). 90p. pap. 7.99 (978-0-340-65571-9(2) , Hodder & Stoughton) Hodder General Publishing Division GBR. *Dist:* Trafalgar Square Publishing.

McAffee, Diane. Kaylee, Clean Your Room. Francis, Guy, illus. 1999. 24p. (J). (978-1-57008-688-5(5)) Scribbulations LLC.

McAllister, Angela. The Tortoise & the Hare: An Aesop's Fable. Heale, Jonathan, illus. 2004. 32p. (J). pap. 7.95 (978-1-84507-142-4(5)) Lincoln, Frances Ltd. GBR. *Dist:* Perseus Distribution.

McAllister, Angela & Fuge, Charles. Found You, Little Wombat! 2003. (Illus.). 24p. (J). 12.95 (978-1-4027-0708-7(8)) Sterling Publishing Co., Inc.

McAllister, M. I. Mistmantle Chronicles, the: Urchin & the Heartstone - Book #2. Rayyan, Omar, illus. 2nd rev. ed. 2007. 304p. (gr. 3-7). pap. 7.99 (*978-0-7868-5489-9(8)) Miramax Bks.

McAllister, M. I. Urchin of the Riding Stars. Rayyan, Omar, illus. 2006. (Mistmantle Chronicles Ser.: Bk. 1). 288p. (gr. 3-7). pap. 7.99 (978-0-7868-5487-5(1)) Hyperion Bks. for Children.

—Urchin of the Riding Stars. Ryann, Omar, illus. 2005. (Mistmantle Chronicles Ser.: Bk. 1). 288p. (gr. 3-7). 17.95 (978-0-7868-5486-8(3)) Miramax Bks.

McBratney, Sam. Guess How Much I Love You. 10th anniv. ed. 2003. (Illus.). 32p. (J). 19.99 (978-0-7636-2106-3(4)) Candlewick Pr.

—Just You & Me. Bates, Ivan, illus. 2000. 32p. (J). (gr. k-1). pap. 5.99 (978-0-7636-1078-4(X)) Candlewick Pr.

—Just You & Me. 2000. (J). (978-0-606-19318-4(9)); lib. bdg. 14.15 (978-0-613-28545-2(X)) Tandem Library Bks.

McCabe, Lauren A. How Many Spots Have I Got? Foulke, Nancy, illus. 2005. (J). 16.00 (978-1-893516-02-1(4)) Our Child Pr.

McCall, Francis & Keeler, Patricia A. A Huge Hog Is a Big Pig: A Rhyming Word Game. 2002. (Illus.). 32p. (J). (ps up). 16.99 (978-0-06-029765-7(4)); lib. bdg. 16.89 (978-0-06-029766-4(2)) HarperCollins Pubs.

McCann, Jesse Leon. The Case of the Hollywood Hound. Fantascope Staff, illus. 2001. (Ace Ventura Chapter Book Ser.: Vol. 4). 64p. (J). (gr. 1-4). pap. 3.99 (978-0-439-20862-8(9)) Scholastic, Inc.

McCartney, Paul & Ardagh, Philip. High in the Clouds. Dunbar, Geoff, illus. 2007. 93p. (J). 20.00 (*978-1-4223-6720-9(7)) DIANE Publishing Co.

McCourt, Lisa. I Love You, Stinky Face. Moore, Cyd, illus. (J). 2004. 32p. pap. 5.99 (978-0-439-63571-4(3)); 2004. 16p. bds. 6.99 (978-0-439-63572-1(1)); 2003. 32p. 5.99 (978-0-439-63469-4(5)) Scholastic, Inc.

McDonald, Jill. Hand Puppet Board Book (Vamos A Contar) Un Libro de Carton con Titeres. 2006. (Let's Count Ser.). 6p. (J). bds. 12.99 (978-0-439-85118-3(1) , Scholastic en Espanol) Scholastic, Inc.

McElligott, Walter Lee. A Blessed Bethlehem Birth: As told by Abraham & Anna Mousenstern. Collier, Kevin Scott, illus. 2006. 28p. (J). E-Book 5.00 incl. cd-rom (*978-1-933090-21-4(9)) Guardian Angel Publishing, Inc.

McGee, Marni. While Angels Watch. Macnaughton, Tina, illus. 2006. 26p. (J). (ps-2). 16.00 (978-1-56148-513-0(6)) Good Bks.

McGee, Warner, illus. Castaways! 2005. (Backyardigans Ser.). 24p. (J). pap. 3.99 (978-1-4169-0802-9(1) , Simon Spotlight/Nickelodeon) Simon & Schuster Children's Publishing.

McGillicuddy, Barbara. Adventures in the Kingdom of Mim: Buddie Saves the Day. 2006. (J). per. 13.95 (978-0-9774513-7-1(2)) Changing Lives Publishing.

McGinnis, Mark W. Buddhist Animal Wisdom Stories. 2004. (Illus.). 112p. 19.95 (978-0-8348-0551-4(0) , Weatherhill, Inc.) Shambhala Pubns., Inc.

McGraw-Hill Staff. If I Had a Gorilla. 2002. (gr. k-3). lib. bdg. 14.10 (978-0-613-84262-4(6)) Tandem Library Bks.

McGrew, Tom, et al. My Angel & Me. Byers, Brian & Byers, Eileen, illus. 2005. 22p. (J). (gr. 2-5). bds. 9.95 (978-1-59125-554-3(6)) Penton Overseas, Inc.

McIntyre, Dawn M. The Phantom Penguin. 2000. 108p. (J). pap. 9.95 (978-0-595-14293-4(1)) iUniverse, Inc.

McKay, Hilary. Zoo in the Attic. (Illus.). 80p. (J). mass mkt. 7.99 (978-0-340-72286-2(X) , Hodder & Stoughton) Hodder General Publishing Division GBR. *Dist:* Trafalgar Square Publishing.

McKay, Sindy. New Red Bed. 1999. (gr. k-3). lib. bdg. 11.80 (978-0-613-82080-6(0)) Tandem Library Bks.

McKee, David. Los Amigos de Elmer. 2000. (Coleccion "Elmer" Ser.). (SPA., Illus.). 16p. (J). (ps-7). per. (978-968-16-6066-6(8)) Fondo de Cultura Economica MEX. *Dist:* Lectorum Pubns., Inc.

—Los Amigos de Elmer. 2000. (Adventures of Elmer the Patchwork Elephant Ser.). (SPA., Illus.). 14p. (J). 9.95 (978-84-207-8102-0(9)) Grupo Anaya, S.A. ESP. *Dist:* Distribooks, Inc.

—Un Dia con Elmer. 2000. (Coleccion "Elmer" Ser.). (SPA., Illus.). 16p. (J). (ps-13). (978-968-16-6068-0(4)) Fondo de Cultura Economica MEX. *Dist:* Lectorum Pubns., Inc.

—Elmer & Friends Sticker Story Book. 2006. 16p. (J). (ps-k). pap., act. bk. ed. 6.99 (978-1-84270-535-3(0)) Andersen GBR. *Dist:* Independent Pubs. Group.

—Elmer & the Lost Teddy. McKee, David, illus. 2004. (Elmer Bks.). 32p. (J). 9.99 (978-0-06-075243-9(2)) HarperCollins Pubs.

McKendry, Sam. Imagine That. 2006. 12p. 9.95 (978-1-58117-484-7(5) , Intervisual/Piggy Toes) Dalmatian Pr.

McKenna, Mark, et al, illus. Banana Tail. 2003. 32p. (J). 12.95 (978-0-9727681-3-9(0)) Active Media Publishing, LLC.

McKeon, Kathryn. Mulan Saves the Day No. 18. Harchy, Atelier Philippe, illus. 1998. (Disney's First Readers. Level 1 Ser.). 22p. (J). (gr. 2-4). pap. 2.95 (978-0-7868-4246-9(6)) Disney Pr.

McKissack, Patricia C. Nettie Jo's Friends. 2002. (Illus.). (J). 15.74 (978-0-7587-3246-0(5)) Book Wholesalers, Inc.

McKissack, Patricia C. & McKissack, Pat. Where Crocodiles Have Wings. Barner, Bob, illus. 2005. 32p. (J). (ps-ps). 16.95 (978-0-8234-1748-3(4)) Holiday Hse., Inc.

McLaughlin, Diane & Tully, Lisa. The WhizAnt Who Isn't Coloring & Activity Book. 2003. (Illus.). 32p. (J). cd-rom 15.95 (978-0-9722249-1-8(2)) Bugeye Bks.

McMahon, Kara & Artful Doodlers Limited Staff. Diego's Animal Science Book. 2007. (Go, Diego, Go! Ser.). 16p. (J). pap. 6.99 (978-1-4169-4119-4(3) , Simon Spotlight/Nickelodeon) Simon & Schuster Children's Publishing.

McMahon, Kara & Random House Staff. Animal Alphabet. Moroney, Christopher, illus. 2005. 20p. (J). (gr. k-ps). bds. 7.99 (978-0-375-83228-4(9) , Random Hse. Bks. for Young Readers) Random Hse. Children's Bks.

McMullan, Kate & Lemaitre, Pascal. Supercat. 2002. (Illus.). 32p. (J). (ps). bds. 6.95 (978-0-7611-2644-7(9) , 12644) Workman Publishing Co., Inc.

McNeil, Florence. Sail Away. McPhail, David M., illus. 2001. (Young Reader Ser.). 32p. (J). (ps-2). 15.95 (978-1-55143-147-5(5)) Orca Bk. Pubs. USA.

McNicholas, Shelagh, illus. Puppies in the Pantry. 1998. (Animal Ark Ser.: No. 3). (J). (gr. 3-5). (978-0-606-13131-5(0)) Tandem Library Bks.

McOmber, Rachel B., ed. Bags... Bags (Animals) rev. ed. (Illus.). (J). (978-0-944991-97-8(1)) Swift Learning Resources.

MCP Staff. Goose Chase, Level 4, Bk. 20. (J). (ps-3). 24.50 (978-0-8136-2069-5(4)) Modern Curriculum Pr.

McPhail, David M. Big Pig & Little Pig. 2001. (Green Light Readers Ser.). (Illus.). (J). (978-0-606-21066-9(0)) Tandem Library Bks.

—Favorite Author Collection: David McPhail, 5 bks., Set. unabr. ed. 1999. (Illus.). (J). (ps-3). pap. 61.95 incl. audio (978-0-87499-594-7(9)) Live Oak Media.

—Puddle. 2000. (978-0-606-17841-9(4)); lib. bdg. 12.95 (978-0-613-30099-5(8)) Tandem Library Bks.

McQuinn, Austin. This Won't Take Long... 2003. (Mimi Mouse Book Ser.). (Illus.). 24p. (J). 9.95 (978-1-84089-181-2(5) , Zero to Ten, Limited) Evans Publishing Group GBR. *Dist:* Independent Pubs. Group.

Mead, David. Ark Angels: Play & Pray. Penton Overseas, Inc. Staff, ed. Currant, Gary, illus. 2006. 16p. (J). (gr. 3-8). bds. 9.95 (978-1-59125-746-2(8) , Penton Kids) Penton Overseas, Inc.

Meade, Holly. A Place to Sleep. 2001. (Illus.). 32p. (J). (ps-1). 15.95 (978-0-7614-5096-2(3) , Cavendish Children's Bks.) Cavendish, Marshall Corp.

Meddaugh, Susan. The Best Place. Meddaugh, Susan, illus. 1999. (Illus.). 32p. (J). (gr. k-3). tchr. ed. 15.00 (978-0-395-97994-5(3) , Walter Lorraine) Houghton Mifflin Co. Trade & Reference Div.

—The Best Place. 2004. (Illus.). 32p. (J). (gr. k-3). reprint ed. pap. 5.95 (978-0-618-44882-1(9) , Walter Lorraine) Houghton Mifflin Co. Trade & Reference Div.

Meeker, Clare Hodgson. Lootas, the Little Wave-Eater: An Orphaned Sea Otter's Story. Casson, C. J., photos by. 2002. (Illus.). 48p. (J). (gr. 1-5). pap. 12.95 (978-1-57061-164-3(5)) Sasquatch Bks.

Meeuwissen, Tony. Remarkable Animals. 2007. (Illus.). 24p. (J). spiral bd. 15.95 (978-1-84507-741-9(5)) Lincoln, Frances Ltd. GBR. *Dist:* Perseus Distribution.

Mejuto, Eva. La Casa de la Mosca Fosca. Mora, Sergio, illus. 2002. (Libros para Soñar Ser.). (SPA.). 28p. (J). (978-84-8464-143-8(0)) Kalandraka Editora, S.L.

Melling, David. The Tale of Jack Frost. 2003. (Illus.). 32p. (J). 14.95 (978-0-7641-5675-5(6)) Barron's Educational Series, Inc.

Melmed, Laura Krauss. I Love You as Much... Sorensen, Henri, illus. 1998. 11p. (J). (ps-2). bds. 7.99 (978-0-688-15978-8(8)) HarperCollins Pubs.

—I Love You As Much... Sorensen, Henri, illus. (J). (ps-2). 2005. 24p. pap. 5.99 (978-0-06-000202-2(6)); 2001. 22p. 12.99 (978-0-06-001011-9(8)) HarperCollins Pubs. (Harper Festival).

—I Love You As Much... 2001. (Illus.). 32p. (J). (ps up). pap. 6.95 (978-0-688-16806-3(X)) HarperCollins Pubs.

—I Love You As Much... Board Book & Picture Frame. 2003. (Illus.). 22p. (J). (ps-2). 12.99 (978-0-06-008659-6(9) , Harper Festival) HarperCollins Pubs.

Menchu, Rigoberta. The Honey Jar. Domi, illus. 2006. 56p. (J). 16.95 (978-0-88899-670-1(5)) Groundwood Bks. CAN. *Dist:* Perseus Distribution.

Menifield, Gloria. What's the Matter, Mr. Giraffe? 2003. (Illus.). 32p. (J). per. 14.95 (978-0-9716442-1-2(7)) Jackson Publishing.

Meomi. The Octonauts & the Only Lonely Monster. 2006. (Illus.). 36p. (J). (ps-3). 15.95 (978-1-59702-005-3(2)) Immedium.

Meomi (Firm) Staff, contrib. by. The Octonauts & the Sea of Shade. 2007. 36p. (J). (ps-3). 15.95 (*978-1-59702-010-7(9)) Immedium.

Mercer, Rita C. Earl the Squatchem. 2007. 9.00 (*978-0-8059-8823-9(8)) Dorrance Publishing Co., Inc.

Meredith Books Staff & Marshall, Paula, eds. Over the Hedge. 2006. (I Can Find It Ser.). 22p. (J). 7.99 (978-0-696-23068-4(2)) Meredith Bks.

—Over the Hedge: Deluxe Sound Storybook. 2006. 22p. (J). 15.95 (978-0-696-23066-0(6)) Meredith Bks.

—Over the Hedge Stencil Activity Book: With Stickers. 2006. 22p. (J). 9.95 (978-0-696-23067-7(4)) Meredith Bks.

Meredith-Markowitz, Susan. The Great Green Forest. ed. 2003. (Early Connections Ser.). (J). pap. 33.00 (978-1-4108-1373-2(8)) Benchmark Education Co.

Merz, Jennifer. Playground Day. 2007. 32p. 16.00 (*978-978-061-896-4(1) , Clarion Bks.) Houghton Mifflin Co. Trade & Reference Div.

Merz, Jennifer J. Playground Day! Merz, Jennifer J., illus. 2007. (Illus.). 32p. (J). (ps-1). 16.00 (*978-0-618-81696-5(8) , Clarion Bks.) Houghton Mifflin Co. Trade & Reference Div.

Meserve, Adria. No Room for Napoleon. 2006. (Illus.). 32p. (J). 16.00 (978-0-374-35536-4(3)) Farrar, Straus & Giroux.

Metzger, Steve. My Seeds Won't Grow! Wilhelm, Hans, illus. 2000. (Dinofours Ser.: No. 18). (J). (ps-1). (978-0-439-06329-6(9)) Scholastic, Inc.

Michels, Dia L. Look What I See! Where Can I Be? with My Animal Friends. Bowles, Michael J. N. & Bowles, Michael J. N., photos by. 2007. (Illus.). (J). pap. 9.95 (978 1 930775-08-4(3)) Platypus Media, L.L.C.

—Look What I See! Where Can I Be? with My Animal Friends. Bowles, Michael J. N., photos by. l.t. ed. 2002. (Look What I See! Where Can I Be? Ser.: Vol. 3). (Illus.). 32p. (J). 16.95 (978-1-930775-07-7(5)) Platypus Media, L.L.C.

Mikaelsen, Ben. Touching Spirit Bear. 256p. (J). (gr. 5 up). 2002. pap. 5.99 (978-0-380-80560-0(X)); 2001. 16.99 (978-0-380-97744-4(3)) HarperCollins Pubs.

—Touching Spirit Bear. unabr. ed. 2004. 256p. (J). (gr. 5-9). pap. 38.00 incl. audio (978-0-8072-0788-6(8) , LYA 312 SP, Listening Library) Random Hse. Audio Publishing Group.

—Touching Spirit Bear. 2002. (gr. 5-8). lib. bdg. 14.10 (978-0-613-55223-3(7)) Tandem Library Bks.

—Touching Spirit Bear. l.t. ed. 2004. 305p. 21.95 (978-0-7862-6228-1(1)) Thorndike Pr.

—Touching Spirit Bear (Rack) 2005. 320p. (J). (gr. 7 up). pap. 6.99 (978-0-06-073400-8(0) , Harper Trophy) HarperCollins Pubs.

Milbourne, Anna. In the Castle. Davies, Benji, illus. 2006. 24p. (J). 9.99 (978-0-7945-1243-9(7) , Usborne) EDC Publishing.

Miles, Ellen. Wind in the Willows. 2002. (gr. 3-6). lib. bdg. 11.80 (978-0-613-66682-4(8)) Tandem Library Bks.

—The Wind in the Willows. rev. ed. 2002. (Scholastic Junior Classics Ser.). (Illus.). 160p. (J). pap. 3.99 (978-0-439-22456-7(X) , Scholastic Paperbacks) Scholastic, Inc.

Miles, Ellen & Grahame, Kenneth. The Wind in the Willows. Smallman, Steve, illus. 2002. 147p. (J). (978-0-439-37531-3(2)) Scholastic, Inc.

Milgrim, David. See Santa Nap. Milgrim, David, illus. 2004. (Adventures of Otto Ser.). (Illus.). 32p. (J). 14.95 (978-0-689-85928-1(7) , Atheneum) Simon & Schuster Children's Publishing.

A B

Miller Cormier, Susan. Life on the Farm. 2007. (Illus.). 28p. (J). pap. (***978-1-4251-1913-3(1)***) Trafford Publishing.

Miller, Dorothy Anne. Stories to Read 'Round the Campfire. 2006. pap. 12.95 (978-1-4137-7554-9(3)) PublishAmerica, Inc.

Miller, Jonathan S. & Turnbull, Stephanie. Los Felinos. 2005. (SPA., Illus.). 48p. (J). pap. 8.95 (978-0-7460-5070-5(4) , Usborne) EDC Publishing.

Miller, Mike. Play in the Clouds: A Tomas the Tortoise Adventure. Miller, Mike, illus. 2003. 32p. (J). 15.95 (978-1-932173-22-2(6)) Stephens Pr. LLC.

Miller, Ruth. The Bear on the Bed. Slavin, Bill, illus. 32p. (J). (gr. k-3). 2004. (978-1-55337-687-3(0)); 2002. (978-1-55337-036-9(8)) Kids Can Pr., Ltd.

Miller, S. K., illus. & creator. Jesse's Color Field. Miller, S. K., creator. l.t. ed. 2002. 68p. (J). (gr. k-5). pap. 16.95 (978-0-9714636-0-8(3)) Treehouse Treasures Corp.

Mills, Liz, ed. Little Lamb: A Pull-the Tab Cloth Book. 2005. (Little Lamb Ser.). (J). 7.99 (978-0-439-71013-8(8) , Cartwheel Bks.) Scholastic, Inc.

Milne, A. A. Pooh Goes Visiting. 2002. (gr. k-3). lib. bdg. 11.80 (978-0-613-62567-8(6)) Tandem Library Bks.

Milter, Matt & Willson, Sarah. Sleepytime Farm. Calitri, Susan, illus. 1999. (Fisher-Price Move-Along Bead Bks.: Vol. 1). 12p. (J). (ps-3). bds. 7.99 (978-1-57584-258-5(0) , Reader's Digest Children's Bks.) Reader's Digest Children's Publishing, Inc.

Mimi Fufu's Backyard Zoo. 2001. 65p. (J). 14.95 (978-0-9709119-9-5(8)) Limpid Butterfly Productions, The.

Minne, Brigitte. The Best Bottom. Pottie, Marjolein, illus. 2006. 32p. pap. 5.95 (978-1-59687-387-2(6)) ibooks, Inc.

Minshull, Evelyn. Eaglet's World. Gabriel, Andrea, illus. 2002. 32p. (J). (ps-3). 16.95 (978-0-8075-8929-8(2)) Whitman, Albert & Co.

Miranda, Anne. Alphabet Fiesta. 2001. (ENG & SPA., Illus.). 56p. (J). (ps-3). 12.95 (978-1-890515-30-0(2)) Turtle Bks.

—Alphabet Fiesta: An English/Spanish Alphabet Story. 2001. (ENG & SPA., Illus.). 56p. (J). (ps-3). 18.95 (978-1-890515-29-4(9)) Turtle Bks.

Miranda, Twyla. Longfeather Ponds: A Chipmunk's Tale. 2006. 82p. pap. 14.95 (978-1-4241-1785-7(2)) PublishAmerica, Inc.

Miranda, Twyla T. Longfeather Ponds, A Bobcat's Tale. 2006. 160p. pap. 14.95 (978-1-59113-942-3(2)) Booklocker.com, Inc.

Mitchell, Adrian. Twice My Size. Pudles, Daniel, illus. 1999. (Fun Early Math Concepts Ser.). 32p. (ps-1). lib. bdg. 22.90 (978-0-7613-1423-3(7) , Millbrook Pr.) Lerner Publishing Group.

Mitchell, Cynthia. A Big & Beastly Alphabet. 2006. pap. (***978-1-84401-716-4(8)***) Athena Pr.

Mitchell, Marianne. Coo Coo Caroo. Henry, Marilyn, illus. 1999. (Books for Young Learners). 12p. (J). (gr. k-2). pap. 5.00 (978-1-57274-140-9(6) , 2845) Owen, Richard C. Pubs., Inc.

Mitchell, Melanie, illus. Good Morning, Good Night Bilingual: Buenos Dias! Buenas Noches! 2005. (ENG & SPA.). 12p. (J). 9.95 (978-1-58117-389-5(X) , Intervisual/Piggy Toes) Dalmatian Pr.

Mitchell, Susan K. Stone Pizza. Hayes, McNevin, illus. 2007. (J). (***978-1-891795-26-8(0)***) RGU Group, The.

Mitton, Tony. All Afloat on Noah's Boat! Parker-Rees, Guy, illus. 2007. 32p. (J). (ps-3). pap. 16.99 (978-0-439-87397-0(5) , Orchard Bks.) Scholastic, Inc.

—Dazzling Diggers. Parker, Ant, illus. 2000. (Amazing Machines Ser.). 24p. (J). (ps-k). pap. 3.95 (978-0-7534-5304-9(5) , Kingfisher) Houghton Mifflin Co. Trade & Reference Div.

—Dazzling Diggers. 2000. (ps-2). lib. bdg. 11.80 (978-0-613-51344-9(4)) Tandem Library Bks.

—Down by the Cool of the Pool. Parker-Rees, Guy, illus. 2002. 32p. (J). (ps-k). pap. 15.95 (978-0-439-30915-8(8) , Orchard Bks.) Scholastic, Inc.

—Tale of Tales. Bailey, Peter, illus. 2004. 112p. (J). (gr. k-7). 15.95 (978-0-385-75016-5(1) , Fickling, David Bks.) Random Hse. Children's Bks.

Mitzo Thompson, Kim. Early Learning, 2 Packs. 2006. (Read & Sing along Board Books with CDs Ser.). 36p. (J). bds. 14.98 (978-0-7696-4594-0(1)) School Specialty Publishing.

Miyazaki, Hayao. Miyazaki's Spirited Away. Miyazaki, Hayao, illus. 2002. (Spirited Away Ser.). (Illus.). 17.51 (978-1-4046-2807-6(X)); 17.51 (978-1-4046-2808-3(8)); 17.51 (978-1-4046-2809-0(6)); 17.51 (978-1-4046-2789-5(8)); 17.51 (978-1-4046-2587-7(9)) Book Wholesalers, Inc.

Mmm Very Nice: Individual Title Six-Packs. (gr. k-1). 23.00 (978-0-7635-8834-2(2)) Rigby Education.

Mock, Jean. The Amazing Animal ABC Book. Martin, Joyce, illus. 2005. (J). (978-0-9767210-1-7(5)) JM2 Publishing Co.

—The Amazing Animal ABC Book (big Format) 2005. (J). (978-0-9767210-0-0(7)) JM2 Publishing Co.

—The Amazing Animal ABC Book the Study Guide. Martin, Joyce, illus. 2005. (978-0-9767210-2-4(3)) JM2 Publishing Co.

Modesitt, Jeanne. Oh, What a Beautiful Day! Spowart, Robin, illus. 2008. (J). (***978-1-56397-409-0(6)***) Boyds Mills Pr.

Mola, Astrid & Khakdan, Wahed. The Good-Night Kiss. 2004. (Illus.). 32p. (J). 10.99 (978-1-59384-046-4(2)) Parklane Publishing.

Molnar, Gwen. Animal Rap & Far Out Fables. Weibe, Jeff, illus. 2000. 55p. (J). (gr. 2-5). pap. (978-0-88878-368-4(X) , Sandcastle Bks.) Dundurn Group, The.

Moncure, Jane Belk. My Sound Parade. King, Colin, illus. 2000. (New Sound Box Library). 32p. (J). (ps-3). 22.79 (978-1-56766-766-0(X)) Child's World, Inc.

Monk, Carol. The Walking Adventures of Ruthie & Coco. 2005. (Illus.). 29p. (J). pap. 12.95 (978-1-56167-881-5(3)) American Literary Pr.

Monkey's Miserable Monday. 2001. (ps-2). lib. bdg. 9.80 (978-0-613-32843-2(4)) Tandem Library Bks.

Monkman, Olga. Un Rey sin Corona. Sanchez, Javier G., illus. 2003. (SPA.). 39p. (J). (gr. k-3). pap. 7.95 (978-950-511-368-2(4)) Santillana USA Publishing Co., Inc.

Monroe, Colleen. A Wish to Be a Christmas Tree. Monroe, Michael Glenn, illus. 32p. (J). (ps-3). 2005. bds. 6.99 (978-1-58536-269-1(7)); 2000. 16.95 (978-1-58536-002-4(3)) Sleeping Bear Pr.

Montgomery, Rutherford G. Carcajou. Cram, L. D., illus. 2004. 300p. (gr. 4-7). pap. 17.95 (978-0-87004-403-8(6)) Caxton Pr.

—Yellow Eyes. 2004. (Classic Ser.). (Illus.). 358p. (gr. 4-7). pap. 15.95 (978-0-87004-417-5(6)) Caxton Pr.

Montgomery, Trego Frances. Billy Whiskers Adventures. 2006. 94.99 (***978-1-4280-5032-7(9)***); pap. 88.99 (***978-1-4280-5036-5(1)***) IndyPublish.com.

Moody-Luther, Jacqueline. Bear & the pizza tree - word World. 2007. 12p. (J). 12.95 (***978-1-59764-297-2(5)***) New Line Bks.

Mooney, Bel & Chamberlain, Margaret. Mr. Tubs Is Lost. 2006. (Blue Bananas Ser.). (Illus.). 46p. (J). (978-0-7787-0858-2(6)) Crabtree Publishing Co.

Moore, Billy. Cracker's Mule. 2002. 256p. 12.95 (978-1-58838-105-7(6)) NewSouth, Inc.

—Cracker's Mule. 2002. (gr. 7-12). lib. bdg. 22.20 (978-0-613-79796-2(5)) Tandem Library Bks.

Moore, Jim. The All Animal Band. Hall, Norris, illus. l.t. ed. 2004. 36p. (J). 16.00 (978-0-9752619-0-3(8)) Animal Band Productions, Inc., The.

Moost, Nele. It's All Mine! Or the Little Raven's Mischief. Rudolph, Annet, illus. 1999. 28p. (J). (ps-3). 14.95 (978-0-7892-0529-2(7)) Abbeville Pr., Inc.

Mora, Jo. Budgee Budgee Cottontail. Mora, Jo, illus. 2004. (Jo Mora Titles Ser.). (Illus.). 60p. (gr. 2 up). 15.00 (978-0-922029-23-5(7) , BK-30004) Stoecklein Publishing.

Mora, Pat. The Song of Francis & the Animals. Frampton, David, illus. 2005. 32p. (J). (ps-2). 16.00 (978-0-8028-5253-3(X)) Eerdmans, William B. Publishing Co.

Mora, Pat & Domi. La Carrera del Sapo y el Venado. 2004. (SPA., Illus.). 32p. (J). pap. 6.95 (978-0-88899-650-3(0)) Groundwood Bks. CAN. *Dist:* Perseus Distribution.

More about Animals Book Set 800940, 3 vols. 2005. (J). bds. (978-1-59794-098-6(4)) Environments, Inc.

Morgan, Michaela. Band of Friends. Price, Nick, illus. 2005. 24p. (J). lib. bdg. 22.65 (***978-1-59646-734-7(7)***) Dingles & Co.

Morgan, Nicola. Pride of Lions. 2000. (Illus.). 30p. (J). pap. (978-1-55041-077-8(6)) Fitzhenry & Whiteside, Ltd.

Morneau, Robert F. A Tale from Paleface Creek. Mau, Marjorie M., illus. 2001. 32p. (J). (ps-3). 9.95 (978-0-8091-6678-7(X) , 6678-x) Paulist Pr.

Morningforest, Chris & Raymond, Rebecca. The Adventures of Nate & Naomi. 2006. 36p. (J). pap. 15.43 (978-1-4116-9244-2(6)) Lulu.com.

Morpurgo, Michael. Animal Stories. 1999. (Red Hot Reads Ser.). (Illus.). 224p. (J). (gr. 4-8). tchr. ed. 14.95 (978-0-7534-5216-5(2) , Kingfisher) Houghton Mifflin Co. Trade & Reference Div.

—Jo-Jo the Melon Donkey. Kerins, Tony, illus. 2002. (Yellow Bananas Ser.). 48p. (J). (gr. 3-4). pap. (978-0-7787-0988-6(4)); lib. bdg. (978-0-7787-0942-8(6)) Crabtree Publishing Co.

—The Nine Lives of Montezuma. 2004. (Illus.). 120p. pap. 8.99 (978-1-4052-0189-6(4)) Egmont Bks., Ltd. GBR. *Dist:* Trafalgar Square Publishing.

—Toro! Toro! Foreman, Michael, illus. 2003. 128p. (J). 8.99 (978-0-00-710718-6(8) , HarperSport) HarperCollins Pubs. Ltd. GBR. *Dist:* Trafalgar Square Publishing.

Morpurgo, Michael, ed. More Muck & Magic. Blake, Quentin, illus. 2001. 148p. (J). pap. 8.99 (978-0-7497-4094-8(9)) Egmont Bks., Ltd. GBR. *Dist:* Independent Pubs. Group.

Morris, Gilbert. Dixie & Bandit. 1998. (Dixie Morris Animal Adventure Ser.: No. 6). (Illus.). 128p. (J). (gr. 4-7). pap. 5.99 (978-0-8024-3368-8(5)) Moody Pubs.

—Dixie & Champ. 1999. (Dixie Morris Animal Adventure Ser.: No. 7). (Illus.). 185p. (J). (gr. 4-7). pap. 5.99 (978-0-8024-3369-5(3)) Moody Pubs.

—Dixie & Sandy. 1998. (Dixie Morris Animal Adventure Ser.: No. 4). 128p. (Orig.). (J). (gr. 4-7). pap. 5.99 (978-0-8024-3366-4(9)) Moody Pubs.

Morrissey, Tricia. My Mom Is a Dragon: And My Dad Is a Boar. 2005. (Illus.). 32p. (J). (ps-3). 12.95 (978-0-9715940-5-0(8)) ThingsAsian Pr.

Morrow, Tara Jaye. Mommy Loves Her Baby/Daddy Loves His Baby. Beeke, Tiphanie, illus. 2003. 32p. (J). (ps-1). 15.99 (978-0-06-029077-1(3)); lib. bdg. 16.89 (978-0-06-029078-8(1)) HarperCollins Pubs.

Morton, Christine. Run Rabbit Run. Taylor, Eleanor, illus. 2002. 32p. pap. 10.99 (978-0-7475-5607-7(5)) Bloomsbury Publishing Plc GBR. *Dist:* Trafalgar Square Publishing.

Moser, Lisa. Sticky Burr: Adventures in Burrwood Forest. Gorbachev, Valeri, illus. 2007. (J). (***978-0-7636-3567-1(7)***) Candlewick Pr.

Moss, Miriam. Bad Hare Day. Chapman, Lynne, illus. 2003. 32p. (J). (gr. k-3). 15.95 (978-1-58234-785-1(9) , Bloomsbury Children) Bloomsbury Publishing.

—The Horse Girl. Cockroft, Jason, illus. 2004. 32p. (J). (978-0-7112-1876-5(5)) Lincoln, Frances Ltd. GBR. *Dist:* Transition Vendor.

—The Horse Girl. Cockroft, Jason, illus. 2004. 32p. (J). pap. 7.95 (978-1-84507-149-3(2)) Lincoln, Frances Ltd. GBR. *Dist:* Perseus Distribution.

—I'll Be Your Friend, Smudge! Chapman, Lynne, illus. 2002. 24p. (J). (ps-2). (978-1-86233-207-2(X) , Gullane Children's Bks.) Pinwheel.

Most, Bernard. The Cow That Went OINK. 2003. (Illus.). 40p. (J). pap. 6.00 (978-0-15-204763-4(8) , Voyager Bks./Libros Viajeros) Harcourt Children's Bks.

—La Vaca Que Decia Oink. Mlawer, Teresa, tr. (SPA., Illus.). (J). (gr. k-2). pap. 6.99 (978-1-880507-66-7(8) , LC4889) Lectorum Pubns., Inc.

—La Vaca Que Decia Oink. 2000. (Illus.). (J). (978-0-606-20757-7(0)) Tandem Library Bks.

Mother Goose & the Animal Friends: Take-Home Book. 2005. (Lee Bennett Hopkins Mother Goose Ser.). (YA). (ps-1). 13.50 (978-0-8215-0562-5(9)) Sadlier, William H. Inc.

Moulton, Mark Kimball. One Enchanted Evening. Crouch, Karen Hillard, illus. 2003. 32p. (J). 14.95 (978-0-8249-5480-2(7)) Ideals Pubns.

—One Enchanted Evening. Crouch, Karen Hillard, illus. 2000. 32p. (J). (gr. k-3). 18.00 (978-0-7412-0439-4(8)) Lang Graphics, Ltd.

Mouse Works Staff. La Bella y la Bestia. rev. ed. 1998. Tr. of Beauty & the Beast. (SPA., Illus.). 96p. (J). 7.99 (978-0-7364-0078-7(8)) Mouse Works.

—Blanca Nieves y los Enamos. 1998. (SPA., Illus.). 96p. (J). 7.99 (978-0-7364-0079-4(6)) Mouse Works.

—Butter's First Words. 1999. (P B & J Otter Noodle Stories Ser.). (Illus.). 16p. (J). (ps-k). 3.50 (978-0-7364-0184-5(9)) Mouse Works.

—The Jungle Book/Bambi, 2 vols. 75th anniv. ed. 1998. (978-0-7364-0090-9(7)) Mouse Works.

—Lion King. 1998. (Disney's the Lion King Simba's Pride Ser.). (Illus.). 24p. (J). (gr. k-3). 3.99 (978-1-57082-938-3(1)) Mouse Works.

—Mulan. 1998. (Classic Storybook Ser.). (Illus.). 96p. (J). (ps-4). 7.98 (978-1-57082-864-5(4)) Mouse Works.

—Night-Night, Roo! 1998. (Winnie the Pooh Ser.). (Illus.). 18p. (J). (ps-k). 3.99 (978-1-57082-984-0(5)) Mouse Works.

—Santa Minnie Friendly Tales. 1998. (J). 6.99 (978-1-57082-975-8(6)) Mouse Works.

Move Like Us!, 6 Packs. (gr. k-1). 23.00 (978-0-7635-9048-2(7)) Rigby Education.

Mueller, Richard. Zoonauts: The Secret of Animalville. Gosline, Sheldon, ed. Dal Chele, Egido Victor, illus. 2003. 210p. (J). 14.95 (978-0-9719496-6-9(2)) Shangri-La Pubns.

Mullen, Robert. Where Do Your Animals Live. 2005. 35p. 11.03 (978-1-4116-1670-7(7)) Lulu.com.

Mullican, Judy. My Forest Friends. Carroll, Ken, Jr., illus. l.t. ed. 2000. (Little Bks.). 8p. (J). (ps-1). pap. 10.95 (978-1-57332-172-3(9)); pap. 10.95 (978-1-57332-180-8(X)) HighReach Learning, Inc.

Murawski, Darlyne A. Animal Faces. 2005. (Illus.). 32p. (J). (ps-ps). 12.95 (978-1-4027-2295-0(8)) Sterling Publishing Co., Inc.

Murawski, Kevin, illus. Harold & the Purple Crayon: Animals, Animals, Animals! 2002. (Festival Reader Ser.). 32p. (J). (ps-2). pap. 3.99 (978-0-06-000177-3(1)) HarperCollins Pubs.

Murdocca, Sal. Tuttle's Shell. Murdocca, Sal, illus. 1999. (Illus.). 32p. (J). (gr. 1-5). 15.95 (978-1-57255-643-0(9)) Mondo Publishing.

Murphy, Barbara Beasley. Annie & the Animals. 2000. 112p. (gr. 4-7). pap. 9.95 (978-0-595-00443-0(1) , Backinprint.com) iUniverse, Inc.

Murphy, Cary. Meeko the Monkey's A-Z Animal Band. Victoria, Arody, illus. 2006. 32p. (J). (978-0-9778546-0-8(4)) Lucky Dog Publishing.

Murphy, Mary. I Kissed the Baby! Murphy, Mary, illus. 2003. (Illus.). 24p. (J). (gr. k-k). 14.99 (978-0-7636-2122-3(6)) Candlewick Pr.

Murphy, Mary. Panda Foo & the New Friend. Murphy, Mary, illus. 2007. (Illus.). 32p. (J). (ps-k). 15.99 (***978-0-7636-3405-6(0)***) Candlewick Pr.

Murphy, Mary Elizabeth. I Kissed the Baby! Murphy, Mary Elizabeth, illus. 2004. (Illus.). 24p. (J). (gr. k-ps). bds. 6.99 (978-0-7636-2443-9(8)) Candlewick Pr.

Murphy, Stuart J. Animals on Board. Alley, R. W., illus. 1998. (MathStart Ser.: Level 2). 40p. (J). (gr. 1 up). pap. 5.99 (978-0-06-446716-2(3) , Harper Trophy) HarperCollins Pubs.

—Animals on Board: Adding. Alley, R. W., illus. 1998. (MathStart Ser.). 40p. (J). (gr. 1 up). 15.89 (978-0-06-027443-6(3)) HarperCollins Pubs.

—Safari Park. Bjorkman, Steve, illus. 2001. (MathStart Ser.). 40p. (J). (gr. 2 up). pap. 5.99 (978-0-06-446245-7(5) , Harper Trophy) HarperCollins Pubs.

Murray, Andrew. The Very Sleepy Sloth. Tickle, Jack, tr. Tickle, Jack, illus. 2003. 32p. (J). tchr. ed. 15.95 (978-1-58925-033-8(8) , tiger tales) ME Media LLC.

Murray, Marjorie D. Don't Wake up the Bear! Wittmann, Patricia, illus. 2003. 32p. (J). 14.95 (978-0-7614-5107-5(2)) Cavendish, Marshall Corp.

Murray, Marjorie Dennis. Hippo Goes Bananas! O'Malley, Kevin, illus. 2006. 32p. (J). 14.95 (978-0-7614-5224-9(9)) Cavendish, Marshall Corp.

—The Stars Are Waiting. Rogers, Jacqueline, illus. 1998. (Accelerated Reader Bks.). 32p. (J). (ps-k). lib. bdg. 15.95 (978-0-7614-5024-5(6) , Cavendish Children's Bks.) Cavendish, Marshall Corp.

Musick, David. Jeremy Daniels & the Bambles: The Mystery in the Forest. 2002. 132p. (YA). pap. 11.95 (978-0-595-25402-6(0) , Writers Club Pr.) iUniverse, Inc.

Los Musicos de Bremen. 3rd ed. 2002. (Troquelados Clasicos Ser.). 16p. pap. 2.95 (978-84-7864-282-3(X)) Combel Editorial, S.A. ESP. *Dist:* Independent Pubs. Group.

Muth, Jon J. The Three Questions. Muth, Jon J., illus. 2002. (Illus.). 32p. (J). (gr. 1-4). pap. 16.99 (978-0-439-19996-4(4) , Scholastic Pr.) Scholastic, Inc.

My First Book of Bedtime Stories. 2003. (J). 8.99 (978-1-59384-013-6(6)) Parklane Publishing.

My Giant Animals of the World. 2001. (FRE.). (J). bds. (978-1-58805-146-2(3)) DS-Max USA, Inc.

My Little Softplay Cube Books. 2002. (J). (978-1-931312-69-1(9)) SoftPlay, Inc.

Mykowski, Michelle. Explore God's Forest. Ring, Laura, ed. Mykowski, Michelle, illus. 1999. (Shaped Paperback Bks.). (Illus.). 24p. (J). (ps-1). pap. 3.99 (978-0-7847-0900-9(9) , 03790, Bean Sprouts) Standard Publishing.

Nakamura, Katherine Riley. Song of Night: It's Time to Go to Bed. Riley, Linnea Asplind, illus. 2002. 40p. (J). (ps-3). pap. 15.95 (978-0-439-26678-9(5) , Blue Sky Pr., The) Scholastic, Inc.

Namm, Diane. Pick a Pet. Suarez, Maribel, tr. Suarez, Maribel, illus. 2004. (My First Reader Ser.). 31p. (J). 18.50 (978-0-516-24417-4(5) , Children's Pr.) Scholastic Library Publishing.

Navarro, Laura. Don Sabino, el Murciélago de la Ciudad: Don Sabino, the City Bat. Sebastian, Juan, illus. 2000. (ENG & SPA.). 45p. (J). (ps-3). pap. 8.95 (978-0-292-75569-7(4)) Univ. of Texas Pr.

Naylor, Phyllis Reynolds. Please Do Feed the Bears. Escriva, Ana Lopez, illus. 2002. 40p. (J). (ps-2). 16.00 (978-0-689-82561-3(7) , Atheneum) Simon & Schuster Children's Publishing.

—Shiloh. (SPA.). 146p. (YA). (gr. 5-8). (978-968-16-5805-2(1) , FC0086) Fondo de Cultura Economica MEX. *Dist:* Lectorum Pubns., Inc.

—Shiloh. l.t. ed. 2000. (Shiloh Ser.: No. 1). 155p. (J). (gr. 4-7). lib. bdg. 27.95 (978-1-58118-058-9(6) , 23472) LRS.

—Shiloh. 144p. (J). (Shiloh Ser.: No. 1). (gr. 4-7). pap. 4.99 (978-0-8072-8330-1(4)); No. 1. 2004. (gr. 3-7). pap. 29.00 incl. audio (978-0-8072-8329-5(0) , YA164SP) Random Hse. Audio Publishing Group. (Listening Library).

—Shiloh. Moser, Barry, illus. 2000. (Shiloh Ser.: No. 1). 144p. (J). (gr. 3-7). pap. 5.99 (978-0-689-83582-7(5) , Aladdin) Simon & Schuster Children's Publishing.

—Shiloh. movie tie-in ed. 2000. (Shiloh Ser.: No. 6). (Illus.). 144p. (J). (gr. 4-7). pap. 5.99 (978-0-689-83583-4(3) , Aladdin) Simon & Schuster Children's Publishing.

—Shiloh. 2000. (gr. 3-6). lib. bdg. 14.15 (978-0-613-73274-1(X)); (J). (978-0-606-19724-3(9)); (gr. 3-6). lib. bdg. 14.15 (978-0-613-30125-1(0)) Tandem Library Bks.

—Shiloh Trilogy. (J). 2000. 432p. (gr. 3-7). pap. 16.99 (978-0-689-01525-0(9) , Aladdin); 1998. (Shiloh Ser.: Nos. 1-3). (gr. 4-7). 35.00 (978-0-689-82327-5(4) , Atheneum) Simon & Schuster Children's Publishing.

Nazoa, Aquiles. El Libro de los Animales. (SPA.). (J). pap. 9.56 (978-980-01-0421-7(6)) Monte Avila Editores Latinoamericana CA VEN. *Dist:* Lectorum Pubns., Inc.

—El Perro, el Chivo y los Tigres. 2001. Tr. of Dog, Goat & the Tigers. (SPA., Illus.). 24p. (J). pap. 2.95 (978-980-257-057-7(5)) Ekare, Ediciones VEN. *Dist:* AIMS International Bks., Inc.

Ness, Berthetta. Originals: Short Stories for Children. 2007. (YA). pap. (***978-1-57579-351-1(2)***) Pine Hill Pr., Inc.

Nettrour, Nelani. Imagynairs of Jemmidar. Nettrour, Autumn, illus. 2003. 78p. pap. 11.95 (978-1-929381-99-9(9) , Third Millennium Publishing) Sci Fi-Arizona, Inc.

Newman, Lesléa. Skunk's Spring Surprise. Gorbachev, Valeri, illus. 2007. 44p. (J). 16.00 (978-0-15-205683-4(1)) Harcourt Trade Pubs.

Newman, Leslea. Where Is Bear? Gorbachev, Valeri, illus. 2004. 44p. (J). 16.00 (978-0-15-204936-2(3) , Gulliver Bks.) Harcourt Children's Bks.

Newman, Leslea & Gorbachev, Valeri. Where Is Bear? 2006. (Illus.). 44p. (J). pap. 6.00 (978-0-15-205918-7(0) , Voyager Bks./Libros Viajeros) Harcourt Children's Bks.

Newton, Jill. Peek-a-Boo, Papa! A Peek-under-the Flap Book. 2007. (Illus.). 20p. (ps). bds. 8.95 (***978-1-59354-626-7(2)***) Blue Apple Bks.

Newton, Jill & Roddie, Shen. Don't Chat to the Bus Driver. 2001. (Illus.). 32p. (J). (ps-k). pap. 10.95 (978-0-7475-5028-0(X)) Bloomsbury Publishing Plc GBR. *Dist:* Independent Pubs. Group.

Nicest Newt. 2001. (ps-2). lib. bdg. 9.80 (978-0-613-32886-9(8)) Tandem Library Bks.

Nicholson, Doris. Michael & His Animals. 2007. 19.00 (***978-0-8059-8859-8(9)***) Dorrance Publishing Co., Inc.

Nickerson, Margaret. Gathering Food. Nevak, Caroline, illus. l.t. ed. 1999. 8p. (J). (gr. k-3). pap. 14.50 (978-1-58084-060-6(4)) Lower Kuskokwim Schl. District.

—Katitchirugut Niqinik. Nevak, Caroline, illus. l.t. ed. 1999. Tr. of Gathering Food. (ESK.). 8p. (J). (gr. k-3). pap. 14.50 (978-1-58084-136-8(8)) Lower Kuskokwim Schl. District.

—Katitchiyuanni Niqinik. Nevak, Caroline, illus. l.t. ed. 1999. Tr. of Gathering Food. (ESK.). 8p. (J). (gr. k-3). pap. 14.50 (978-1-58084-126-9(0)) Lower Kuskokwim Schl. District.

—Neqengnaqler. Nevak, Caroline, illus. l.t. ed. 1999. Tr. of Gathering Food. (ESK.). 8p. (J). (gr. k-3). pap. 14.50 (978-1-58084-105-4(8)) Lower Kuskokwim Schl. District.

—Niginik Katittigaangapta. Nevak, Caroline, illus. l.t. ed. 1999. Tr. of Gathering Food. (ESK.). 8p. (J). (gr. k-3). pap. 14.50 (978-1-58084-133-7(3)) Lower Kuskokwim Schl. District.

—Quyurciyaraq Neqnek. Nevak, Caroline, illus. l.t. ed. 1999. Tr. of Gathering Food. (ESK.). 8p. (J). (gr. k-3). pap. 14.50 (978-1-58084-061-3(2)) Lower Kuskokwim Schl. District.

Night Beast. 2005. (J). 4.95 (978-1-59792-018-6(5)) F.A.S.T. Learning LLLC.

Night of the Cougar. 2005. (J). 4.95 (978-1-59792-014-8(2)) F.A.S.T. Learning LLLC.

Night Visitor. 2005. (J). 4.95 (978-1-59792-019-3(3)) F.A.S.T. Learning LLLC.

Nikola-Lisa, W. Can You Top That? Lee, Hector Viveros, illus. 2000. 32p. (J). (ps-2). 15.95 (978-1-880000-99-1(7)) Lee & Low Bks., Inc.

Niland, Deborah. Let's Play. Niland, Deborah, illus. 2007. (Illus.). 24p. (Orig.). (J). (ps). pap. 4.99 (***978-1-933605-47-0(2)***) Kane/Miller Bk. Pubs., Inc.

Nimh, Sonia & Shaw, Hannah. Ghaddar the ghould & other palestinian Tales. 2008. (Illus.). 96p. (J). 14.95 (***978-1-84507-771-6(7)***) Lincoln, Frances Ltd. GBR. *Dist:* Perseus Distribution.

Nimmo, Jenny. Pig on a Swing. Uff, Caroline, illus. 2004. 32p. mass mkt. (978-0-340-85242-2(9) , Hodder Children's Books) Hodder Children's Division.

—Pig on a Swing. Uff, Caroline, illus. 2003. (J). 16.99 (978-0-340-85241-5(0) , Hodder & Stoughton) Hodder General Publishing Division GBR. *Dist:* Trafalgar Square Publishing.

Nirgad, Lia. A Kiss for Lily. Aboulafia, Yossi, illus. 2006. 28p. (J). 12.95 (978-1-59692-163-4(3)) MacAdam/Cage Publishing, Inc.

Nishimura, Kae. I Am Dodo: Not a True Story. Nishimura, Kae, illus. 2005. (Illus.). 32p. (J). (ps-k). 15.00 (978-0-618-33614-2(1) , Clarion Bks.) Houghton Mifflin Co. Trade & Reference Div.

Nister, Ernest. Animal Tales. (Illus.). (J). (978-0-399-22392-1(4) , Philomel) Penguin Group (USA) Inc.

Nixon, Joan Lowery. Gus & Gertie & the Missing Pearl. deGroat, Diane, illus. 2000. 48p. (J). (ps-3). 15.50 (978-1-58717-023-2(X) , SeaStar Bks.) Chronicle Bks. LLC.

No Need for Words: Individual Title Six-Packs. (Rigby Infoquest Ser.). 24p. (gr. 3 up). 34.00 (978-0-7578-5772-0(8)) Rigby Education.

Noble, Mariagorretti. The Animal Kingdom in Confusion. 2003. pap. 19.00 (978-0-8059-5326-8(4)) Dorrance Publishing Co., Inc.

Nolen, Jerdine. Raising Dragons. Primavera, Elise, illus. 2002. (J). 21.70 (978-0-7587-3493-8(X)) Book Wholesalers, Inc.

—Raising Dragons. Primavera, Elise, illus. 40p. (J). 2002. (gr. 1-4). pap. 7.00 (978-0-15-216536-9(3) , Voyager Bks./Libros Viajeros); 1998. (ps-3). 16.00 (978-0-15-201288-5(5)) Harcourt Children's Bks.

—Raising Dragons. 2002. (ps-2). lib. bdg. 14.15 (978-0-613-53857-2(9)) Tandem Library Bks.

Noonen, Tom. Pelicans Belly Can. Fredericksen, Alison, illus. 1999. 38p. (J). (ps-3). 14.95 (978-1-893385-04-7(3)) Little Leaf Pr., Inc.

Nordin, Sofia. In the Wild! Lundin, Maria, tr. from SWE. (J). 2006. 120p. pap. 6.95 (978-0-88899-663-3(2)); 2005. 15.95 (978-0-88899-648-0(9)) Groundwood Bks. CAN. *Dist:* Perseus Distribution, Transition Vendor.

North Bedford, Annie. The Jolly Barnyard. Gergely, Tibor, illus. 2004. (Little Golden Book Ser.). 24p. (J). (gr. k-k). 2.99 (978-0-375-82842-3(7) , Golden Bks.) Random Hse. Children's Bks.

North, Merry. All Gone. Woolf, Julia, illus. 2005. (J). (***978-1-57151-753-1(7)***) Playhouse Publishing.

Numeroff, Laura Joffe. Chimps Don't Wear Glasses. Mathieu, Joe, illus. 2006. (Stories to Go! Ser.). 32p. (J). pap. 4.99 (978-1-4169-1859-2(0) , Aladdin) Simon & Schuster Children's Publishing.

—What Daddies Do Best. Munsinger, Lynn, illus. 2003. (Classic Board Bks.). 22p. (J). bds. 6.99 (978-0-689-85973-1(2) , Little Simon) Simon & Schuster Children's Publishing.

—What Grandmas Do Best What Grandpas Do Best. 2000. (Illus.). 36p. (J). (gr. k-3). per. 14.00 (978-0-689-83491-2(8) , Simon & Schuster Children's Publishing) Simon & Schuster Children's Publishing.

—What Grandmas Do Best What Grandpas Do Best. Munsinger, Lynn, illus. 2000. 40p. (J). (ps-3). 14.95 (978-0-689-80552-3(7)) Simon & Schuster Children's Publishing.

—What Grandpas Do Best. Munsinger, Lynn, illus. gif. ed. 2001. 24p. (J). 6.95 (978-0-689-84701-1(7)) Simon & Schuster Children's Publishing.

—What Mommies Do Best. Munsinger, Lynn, illus. abr. ed. 2003. (Classic Board Bks.). 22p. (J). bds. 6.99 (978-0-689-85659-4(8) , Little Simon) Simon & Schuster Children's Publishing.

—When Sheep Sleep. McPhail, David, illus. 2006. 24p. (J). (ps-3). 15.95 (978-0-8109-5469-4(9)) Abrams, Harry N., Inc.

Numeroff, Laura Joffe & Evans, Nate. The Jellybeans. 2008. 32p. (J). 15.95 (***978-0-8109-9352-5(X)*** , Abrams Bks. for Young Readers) Abrams, Harry N., Inc.

Numeroff, Laura Joffe & Munsinger, Lynn. What Aunts Do Best / What Uncles Do Best. 2004. (Illus.). 32p. (J). 14.95 (978-0-689-84825-4(0)) Simon & Schuster Children's Publishing.

—What Daddies Do Best. 2001. (Illus.). 24p. (J). (ps-3). 6.95 (978-0-689-84466-9(2)) Simon & Schuster Children's Publishing.

—What Grandmas Do Best. gif. ed. 2001. (Illus.). 24p. (J). 6.95 (978-0-689-84700-4(9)) Simon & Schuster Children's Publishing.

Nutkis, Phyllis. When the World Was Quiet. Argoff, Patti, illus. 2003. (J). pap. 9.95 (978-1-929628-14-8(5)) Hachai Publishing.

Nwapa-Ibuaka, Njideka. Tales from Animal Kingdom. l.t. unabr. ed. 2003. (Illus.). (gr. 2-5). 30p. pap. 7.95 (978-0-9661598-5-1(3)); 40p. pap. 7.95 (978-0-9661598-4-4(5)) Ekwike Bks. & Publishing.

Nygaard, Elizabeth. Snake Alley Band. 1999. (978-0-606-16731-4(5)) Tandem Library Bks.

O'Brien, Melanie & Runnells, Treesha. Pat Them Gently. 2006. (Illus.). 10p. (J). 8.95 (978-1-58117-462-5(4) , Intervisual/Piggy Toes) Dalmatian Pr.

Ocker, Christa Holder. A Crow Named Robin. 2006. (J). per. (***978-1-59872-712-8(5)***) Instantpublisher.com.

O'Donnell, Liam. Pepper Snowy Search. Diefendorf, Cathy, illus. 2005. (Pet Tales Ser.). 32p. (J). (ps-2). 9.95 (978-1-59249-363-0(7) , 1B028); 2.95 (978-1-59249-362-3(9) , 1B027) Soundprints.

Okamoto, Rod. Kingdom of Nu - TJ's Tale: TJ's Tale. Okamoto, Alan, illus. 2006. (J). per. 19.95 (978-0-9764116-0-4(1)) Nutrishare Publishing.

Oke, Janette. Animal Friends, 6. 2001. (J Okes Animal Friends Ser.). (J). Set. 432p. pap. 41.99 (978-0-7642-8796-1(6)); Vol. 7-12,Set. 464p. pap. 41.99 (978-0-7642-8857-9(1)) Bethany Hse. Pubs.

—This Little Pig. Munger, Nancy, illus. 2001. (Animal Friends Ser.: Vol. 4). 80p. (Orig.). (J). (ps-3). pap. 6.99 (978-0-7642-2448-5(4)) Bethany Hse. Pubs.

—Trouble in a Fur Coat. Munger, Nancy, illus. rev. ed. 2001. (Janette Oke's Animal Friends Ser.). 80p. (Orig.). (J). (gr. 1-5). pap. 6.99 (978-0-7642-2456-0(5)) Bethany Hse. Pubs.

Okrant, Mark. Judson's Island. 2006. per. 10.95 (***978-0-9791757-2-5(0)***) Oak Manor Publishing, Inc.

Olaleye, Isaac. Lake of the Big Snake: An African Rain Forest Adventure. Shepard, Claudia, illus. 2003. 32p. (J). (ps-3). 15.95 (978-1-56397-096-2(1)) Boyds Mills Pr.

Oldfield, J. Crash. (Animal Alert Ser.: No. 6). (Illus.). 140p. (J). pap. 8.99 (978-0-340-70869-9(7) , Hodder & Stoughton) Hodder General Publishing Division GBR. *Dist:* Trafalgar Square Publishing.

—Skin & Bone, Vol. 5. (Illus.). 138p. (J). pap. (978-0-340-70878-1(6) , Hodder & Stoughton) Hodder General Publishing Division.

Oliver & Company. (Read-Along Ser.). (J). 7.99 incl. audio (978-1-55723-024-9(2)) Walt Disney Records.

Olsen, Fran. Lili of St. Luke's: The Blessing of the Animals. Boggs, Buttons, illus. 2000. 20p. (J). pap. 8.95 (978-0-9702317-0-3(9) , 001LSL) Allure Pr.

One Special Christmas in Duckport. 2001. (Little Suzy's Zoo Ser.). (J). (ps-1). 12.99 (978-1-58668-230-9(X)) Lyrick Studios.

Oneal, Elizabeth. Alfred Visits Virginia. 2006. 24p. pap. 12.00 (***978-0-9771836-8-5(8)***) Funny Bone Bks.

O'Neil, Sarah. Sleeping Animals. 1999. (ps-2). lib. bdg. 11.80 (978-0-613-30739-0(9)) Tandem Library Bks.

Onishi, Saturo. Whos' Hiding? Onishi, Saturo, illus. 2007. (Illus.). 32p. (J). 14.95 (978-1-933605-24-1(3) , 05241) Kane/Miller Bk. Pubs., Inc.

Oppel, Kenneth. Emma's Emu. LaFave, Kim, illus. 1999. (First Flight Ser.). 64p. (YA). (gr. 3 up). pap. (978-1-55041-524-7(7)) Fitzhenry & Whiteside, Ltd.

Oram, Hiawyn. Badger's Bad Mood. Varley, Susan, illus. 1998. 32p. (J). (ps-3). pap. 15.95 (978-0-590-18920-0(4)) Scholastic, Inc.

—Counting Leopard's Spots & other Stories. Warnes, Tim, illus. 2005. 96p. (J). (gr. k-4). reprint ed. 17.00 (978-0-7567-9252-7(5)) DIANE Publishing Co.

—The Wrong Overcoat. Birchall, Mark, illus. 2000. (Picture Bks.). 32p. (J). (ps-3). lib. bdg. 15.95 (978-1-57505-453-7(1) , Carolrhoda Bks.) Lerner Publishing Group.

Orgel, Doris. The Bremen Town Musicians: And Other Animal Tales from Grimm. Kitchen, Bert, illus. rev. ed. 2004. 48p. (J). 18.95 (978-1-59643-010-5(9)) Roaring Brook Pr.

Orleans, Daniel Elliot. Snow Buddies. 2007. (Illus.). 14p. (ps). bds. 9.95 (***978-1-59354-605-2(X)***) Blue Apple Bks.

Orleans, Ilo. Animal Orchestra. Gergely, Tibor, illus. (Little Golden Treasures Ser.). (J). (gr. k-k). 2004. 26p. bds. 4.99 (978-0-375-82775-4(7)); 2001. 24p. 2.99 (978-0-307-98287-2(4)) Random Hse. Children's Bks. (Golden Bks.).

Ormerod, Jan. If You're Happy & You Know It! Gardiner, Lindsey, illus. 2003. 32p. (J). (ps-3). pap. 5.95 (978-1-932065-10-7(5)); 15.95 (978-1-932065-07-7(5)) Star Bright Bks., Inc.

—If You're Happy & You Know It! 2003. (gr. k-3). lib. bdg. 14.10 (978-0-613-80469-1(4)) Tandem Library Bks.

Ormerod, Jan & Gardiner, Lindsey. Doing the Animal Bop. 2005. 32p. (J). pap. 8.99 incl. audio compact disk (978-0-7641-7899-3(7)) Barron's Educational Series, Inc.

Orr, Wendy. Nim's Island. Millard, Kerry, illus. 2002. 128p. (gr. 3-7). 5.50 (978-0-440-41868-9(2) , Yearling) Random Hse. Children's Bks.

—Nim's Island. 2002. (gr. 3-6). lib. bdg. 13.00 (978-0-613-46203-7(3)) Tandem Library Bks.

Orwell, George. Animal Farm. 2002. 14.00 (978-0-7587-7843-7(0)) Book Wholesalers, Inc.

Orwell, George, et al. Animal Farm. 1999. (Literature Made Easy Ser.). (Illus.). 96p. pap. 6.99 (978-0-7641-0819-8(0)) Barron's Educational Series, Inc.

O'Ryan, Ellie. Geyser Blast! 2006. (I Can Read Bks.). (Illus.). 32p. (J). pap. 3.99 (978-0-06-083968-0(6) , Harper Trophy) HarperCollins Pubs.

—Join the Pack! 2006. (I Can Read Bks.). (Illus.). 32p. (J). pap. 3.99 (978-0-06-083970-3(8) , Harper Trophy) HarperCollins Pubs.

—Join the Pack: IVen con Nosotros! 2006. (I Can Read Bks.). (SPA.). 32p. (J). pap. 3.99 (978-0-06-111984-2(9) , Harper Trophy) HarperCollins Pubs.

O'Ryan, Ellie, adapted by. Ice Age 2: The Meltdown: Geyser Blast! 2006. (I Can Read Bks.). (Illus.). 31p. (J). (***978-1-4156-5153-7(1)***) HarperCollins Pubs.

—Ice Age 2: The Meltdown: Join the Pack! 2006. (I Can Read Bks.). (Illus.). 31p. (J). (***978-1-4156-5155-1(8)***) HarperCollins Pubs.

Osborne, Mary Pope. Dingoes at Dinnertime, Vol. 20. unabr. ed. 2004. (Magic Tree House Ser. : No. 20). 71p. (J). (gr. k-3). pap. 17.00 incl. audio (978-0-8072-0929-5(5) , S FTR 252 SP, Listening Library) Random Hse. Audio Publishing Group.

—Dingoes at Dinnertime. Murdocca, Sal, illus. 2000. (Magic Tree House Ser.: No. 20). 96p. (J). (gr. k-3). lib. bdg. 11.99 (978-0-679-99066-6(6)); pap. 3.99 (978-0-679-89066-9(1)) Random Hse. Children's Bks. (Random Hse. Bks. for Young Readers).

—Dingoes at Dinnertime. 2000. (Magic Tree House Ser. : No. 20). (J). (gr. k-3). lib. bdg. 11.80 (978-0-613-24836-5(8)); (Illus.). 10.79 (978-0-606-18491-5(0)) Tandem Library Bks.

—Un Tigre Dientes de Sable en el Ocaso. 2004. (Coleccion la Casa Del Arbol the Magic Tree House Ser.).Tr. of Sunset of the Sabretooth. (SPA., Illus.). (J). pap. 4.95 (978-1-930332-68-3(8)) Lectorum Pubns., Inc.

Osei-Agyemang, Andrew Nana. Before the Lion Became King. 2003. pap. 10.00 (978-0-8059-6183-6(6)) Dorrance Publishing Co., Inc.

—Before the Lion Became King: Law 202 the First Amendment Law of the Animal Kingdom. 2002. 32p. (J). pap. 10.00 (978-0-8059-5435-7(X)) Dorrance Publishing Co., Inc.

Osorio, Rick. The Great Adventure of Sally Rock & the Cretaceous Chicken. 2006. 65p. pap. 12.95 (978-1-4241-0971-5(X)) PublishAmerica, Inc.

Ottolenghi, Carol. Father Loves His Little One. Campanella, Marco, illus. 2006. (Tell Me a Story Ser.). 36p. (J). (gr. k-k). bds. 14.95 (978-0-7696-4813-2(4) , Gingham Dog Pr.) School Specialty Publishing.

—Grandparents Love Their Little Ones. Campanella, Marco, illus. 2006. (Tell Me a Story Ser.). 36p. (J). (gr. k-k). bds. 14.95 (978-0-7696-4815-6(0) , Gingham Dog Pr.) School Specialty Publishing.

—I Love You, My Little One! Campanella, Marco, illus. 2006. (Tell Me a Story Ser.). 36p. (J). (gr. k-k). bds. 14.95 (978-0-7696-4814-9(2) , Gingham Dog Pr.) School Specialty Publishing.

—Mother Loves Her Little One. Campanella, Marco, illus. 2006. (Tell Me a Story Ser.). 36p. (J). (gr. k-k). bds. 14.95 (978-0-7696-4812-5(6) , Gingham Dog Pr.) School Specialty Publishing.

Out on the Tundra. 2005. 14.95 (978-1-888125-96-2(9)) Publication Consultants.

Owens, Jim. New Allegory. 2006. (J). per. 12.00 (***978-0-9769132-4-5(0)***) Capri Publishing.

Owens, Mary Beth. Panda Whispers. 2007. (Illus.). 32p. (J). (ps-2). 16.99 (978-0-525-47171-4(5) , Dutton Juvenile) Penguin Group (USA) Inc.

Packard, Edward. You Are a Shark. 1999. (Illus.). 114p. mass mkt. (978-0-553-24963-7(0)) Random Hse., Inc.

Packard, Mary & Mitier, Matt. Same & Different: Comparison Rhymes. Banta, Susan & Cushman, Doug, illus. 2004. (Rhyme Time Learning Ser.). 16p. (J). (gr. 1 up). lib. bdg. 20.67 (978-0-8368-4097-1(6)) Stevens, Gareth Inc.

Packard, Mary & Mitter, Matt. Once upon a Rhyme: Story Rhymes. Banta, Susan & Cushman, Doug, illus. 2004. (Rhyme Time Learning Ser.). 16p. (J). (gr. 1 up). lib. bdg. 20.67 (978-0-8368-4096-4(8)) Stevens, Gareth Inc.

Pacovska, Kveta. Flying. Pacovska, Kveta, illus. 2005. Tr. of Turme. (Illus.). 39p. (J). reprint ed. 20.00 (978-0-7567-8532-1(4)) DIANE Publishing Co.

Paez, Enrique. La Olimpiada de los Animales. Alekos, illus. (SPA.). 48p. (J). (gr. k-2). (978-958-30-0792-7(7)) Panamericana Editorial COL. *Dist:* Lectorum Pubns., Inc.

Page, Josephine. Mommy Loves Her Bunny. Morgan, Mary, illus. 2003. 5p. (J). (ps). bds. 4.99 (978-0-439-44322-7(9) , Cartwheel Bks.) Scholastic, Inc.

Pagratis, Maggie & Pagratis, Illustrator Liliane, MaggieGrenier. Go Away Booboo! 2005. 29p. (J). 11.88 (978-1-4116-3689-7(9)) Lulu.com.

Palatini, Margie & Moser, Barry. Earthquack! 2002. (Illus.). 32p. (J). (ps-3). 15.95 (978-0-689-84280-1(5)) Simon & Schuster Children's Publishing.

Palmer, W. G. Awaiting Whisperland: The Calling of Galahad Green. 2007. 340p. 29.95 (***978-0-595-68248-5(0)***); per. 19.95 (***978-0-595-43560-9(2)***) iUniverse, Inc.

The Pamba & the Bink. Date not set. pap. 3.95 (978-0-89868-153-6(7)) ARO Publishing Co.

Papa's Spaghetti: Individual Title Six-Packs. (Literatura 2000 Ser.). (gr. 1-2). 28.00 (978-0-7635-0146-4(8)) Rigby Education.

Papineau, Lucie. Gilda the Giraffe & Leonardo the Lion Cub. Sarrazin, Marisol, illus. 2005. (Gilda the Giraffe Ser.). 32p. (J). (ps-3). lib. bdg. 22.60 (978-1-4048-1294-9(6)) Picture Window Bks.

—Gilda the Giraffe & Lucky the Leopard. Sarrazin, Marisol, illus. 2005. (Gilda the Giraffe Ser.). 32p. (J). 22.60 (978-1-4048-1295-6(4)) Picture Window Bks.

—Gilda the Giraffe & Marvin the Marmoset. Sarrazin, Marisol, illus. 2005. (Gilda the Giraffe Ser.). 32p. (J). (ps-3). lib. bdg. 22.60 (978-1-4048-1516-2(3)) Picture Window Bks.

—Gilda the Giraffe & Papaya the Panda. Sarrazin, Marisol, illus. 2005. (Gilda the Giraffe Ser.). 32p. (J). (ps-3). lib. bdg. 22.60 (978-1-4048-1293-2(8)) Picture Window Bks.

—Gilda the Giraffe & Pepin the Penguin. Sarrazin, Marisol, illus. 2005. (Gilda the Giraffe Ser.). 32p. (J). 22.60 (978-1-4048-1296-3(2)) Picture Window Bks.

—Gontrand et le Croissant des Cavernes. ed. 2004. (FRE., Illus.). (J). (gr. k-3). spiral bd. (978-0-616-11145-1(2)) Canadian National Institute for the Blind/Institut National Canadien pour les Aveugles.

—No Bananas for This Giraffe. Sarrazin, Marisol, illus. 2005. (Gilda the Giraffe Ser.). 32p. (J). 22.60 (978-1-4048-1292-5(X)) Picture Window Bks.

—No Spots for This Giraffe. Sarrazin, Marisol, illus. 2005. (Gilda the Giraffe Ser.). 32p. (J). 22.60 (978-1-4048-1291-8(1)) Picture Window Bks.

—Pas de Taches Pour une Girafe. ed. 2004. (FRE., Illus.). (J). (gr. k-3). spiral bd. (978-0-616-03075-2(4)) Canadian National Institute for the Blind/Institut National Canadien pour les Aveugles.

Papineau, Lucie & Fischman, Sheila. Marvin the Strange Little Marmoset. Sarrazin, Marisol, illus. 2001. 32p. (J). (ps up). pap. (978-1-894363-80-8(9)) Dominique & Friends.

Papineau, Lucie, et al. Leonardo the Lion Cub. 2000. (Adventures of Gilda Ser.). (Illus.). 29p. (J). (ps-3). pap. (978-1-894363-44-0(2)) Dominique & Friends.

Paraskevas, Betty. Peter Pepper's Pet Spectacular. Paraskevas, Michael, illus. 2007. 32p. (J). (gr. 2-6). pap. 14.95 (***978-1-60095-257-9(7)***) Carson-Dellosa Publishing Co., Inc.

Parent, Nancy. Barney's Zoo Friends. Yee, Josie, illus. 2001. (Barney Ser.). 12p. (J). (ps-1). bds. 9.99 (978-1-58668-233-0(4)) Scholastic, Inc.

—Friends Forever! A Witzy's World Storybook. Spafford, Suzy, illus. 2001. 14p. (J). (ps-3). 5.99 (978-1-58668-058-9(7)) Lyrick Studios.

—Jungle Colors. Hall, Susan, illus. 2005. (Backyardigans Ser.). 26p. (J). bds. 5.99 (978-1-4169-0797-8(1) , Simon Spotlight/Nickelodeon) Simon & Schuster Children's Publishing.

—Witzy to the Rescue! A Witzy's World Storybook. Spafford, Suzy, illus. 2001. 14p. (J). (ps-1). 5.99 (978-1-58668-059-6(5)) Lyrick Studios.

Parker, Andy, illus. Mekanimals Clockwork Safari. 2004. 8p. (J). bds. 12.95 (978-1-59223-145-4(4) , Silver Dolphin Bks.) Advantage Pubs. Group.

Parker, Jeff. King Liar. 2002. (Illus.). 64p. (J). per. 5.95 (978-1-59269-002-2(5)) Mcruffy Pr.

Parker, Kim. Counting in the Garden. 2005. (Illus.). 32p. (J). pap. 16.95 (978-0-439-69452-0(3) , Orchard Bks.) Scholastic, Inc.

Parr, Todd. Otto Goes to the Beach. 2003. (Illus.). 24p. (J). (ps-1). 9.95 (978-0-316-73870-5(0) , Tingley, Megan Bks.) Little, Brown Bks. for Young Readers.

Pascal, Francine. Trabajo del Equipo. Orig. Title: Team Work. (SPA.). 120p. (J). 6.95 (978-84-272-3797-1(9)) Molino, Editorial ESP. *Dist:* AIMS International Bks., Inc.

Pass, Erica. My Animal Friends: Storybook & Spotting Scope. 2007. (Nick Jr. Ser.). 32p. (YA). 24.99 (***978-0-7944-1319-4(6)***) Reader's Digest Assn., Inc., The.

Pati, Geeta. The Animals' Journey to the Moon. Dageforde, Linda, ed. 1999. (Illus.). 104p. (J). pap. 15.95 (978-1-886225-39-8(7) , 2000) Day of Grace Publishing Services.

Patten, Brian & Terry, Michael. Little Hotchpotch. 2001. (Illus.). 32p. pap. 10.99 (978-0-7475-5033-4(6)) Bloomsbury Publishing Plc GBR. *Dist:* Independent Pubs. Group.

Patten, William. Animal & Nature Stories Vol. 8: The Junior Classics. 2004. reprint ed. pap. 1.99 (978-1-4192-6805-2(8)) Kessinger Publishing, LLC.

Patten, William. Junior Classics Volume 8 Animal & Natu. 2006. 67.99 (***978-1-4280-3505-8(2)***); pap. 60.99 (***978-1-4280-3456-3(0)***) IndyPublish.com.

Patterson, Geoffrey. The Lion & the Gypsy. 2004. (Illus.). 32p. (J). pap. 7.95 (978-1-84507-140-0(9)) Lincoln, Frances Ltd. GBR. *Dist:* Perseus Distribution.

Paul, Ann Whitford. Count on Culebra. Long, Ethan, illus. 2008. (J). (***978-0-8234-2124-4(4)***) Holiday Hse., Inc.

—Manana, Iguana. Long, Ethan, tr. Long, Ethan, illus. 2005. 32p. (J). tchr. ed. 16.95 (978-0-8234-1808-4(1)) Holiday Hse., Inc.

Paul, Ann Whitford. Snail's Good Night. Litzinger, Rosanne, illus. 2008. (J). (***978-0-8234-1912-8(6)***) Holiday Hse., Inc.

Paul, Richard. Red Riding Hood Races the Big Bad Wolf. Clark, Eugene, illus. 1998. 40p. (J). (gr. k-2). 12.95 (978-0-9653238-1-9(1)) Twilight Pr.

Paz, Ramon. La Capa del Morrocoy. Keller, Cristina, illus. 2000. (SPA.). 36p. (J). (gr. 1-4). pap. 7.95 (978-980-257-070-6(2) , EK1451) Ekare, Ediciones VEN. *Dist:* Lectorum Pubns., Inc.

Pearson, Chris. Emma & Her Friends from Bluebell Wood. 2006. (ENG., Illus.). 76p. pap. (***978-1-84401-641-9(2)***) Athena Pr.

Pearson, Ridley. Kingdom Keepers: Disney after Dark. 2007. 336p. (gr. 5-17). pap. 8.99 (***978-1-4231-0545-9(1)*** , Disney Editions) Disney Pr.

Pearson, Tracey Campbell. Bob. Pearson, Tracey Campbell, illus. 2002. (Illus.). 32p. (J). (ps-1). 16.00 (978-0-374-39957-3(3) , Farrar, Straus & Giroux (BYR)) Farrar, Straus & Giroux.

—Bob. Pearson, Tracey Campbell, illus. 2006. (Illus.). 32p. (J). reprint ed. pap. 6.95 (978-0-374-40871-8(8)) Macmillan.

Peck, Jan. Way Far Away on a Wild Safari. Petrone, Valeria, illus. 2006. 32p. (J). (ps-1). 15.95 (978-1-4169-0072-6(1)) Simon & Schuster Children's Publishing.

—Way up High in a Tall Green Tree. Petrone, Valeria, illus. 2005. 32p. (J). (ps-ps). 15.95 (978-1-4169-0071-9(3)) Simon & Schuster Children's Publishing.

Peckham, Lori, ed. Guide's Greatest Animal Stories. 2006. 144p. (YA). pap. 10.99 (***978-0-8280-1944-6(4)***) Review & Herald Publishing Assn.

Pedersen, Janet. Millie in the Meadow. Pedersen, Janet, illus. 2003. (Illus.). 32p. (J). (ps-1). 14.99 (978-0-7636-1725-7(3)) Candlewick Pr.

Peek, Merle. ¡Dénse Vuelta!/Roll Over! 2008. (ENG & SPA., Illus.). 24p. (J). (gr. k-ps). bds. 5.95 (***978-0-618-89420-8(9)*** , Clarion Bks.) Houghton Mifflin Co. Trade & Reference Div.

Peirce-Bale, Mary. Wilma Wombat's Trek to Back of Beyond. 2006. (J). 9.90 (978-0-9773990-4-8(4)) Mother's Hse. Publishing.

Pelham, David. Trail: A Classic Collectible Pop-up. Pelham, David, illus. 2007. 12p. (J). (ps). 26.99 (***978-1-4169-4894-0(5)*** , Little Simon) Simon & Schuster Children's Publishing.

Pelizzari, Nora. Who Lives in the Rainforest? 2008. (Fisher-Price Ser.). 16p. (J). 6.99 (***978-0-06-144770-9(6)*** , Harper Festival) HarperCollins Pubs.
Pellant, Terry. The Real Valentine's Story. 2004. 27p. (J). pap. 14.95 (978-1-4137-2146-1(X)) PublishAmerica, Inc.
Pemberton, Bonnie. The Cat Master. 2007. 259p. (YA). (gr. 5-9). 16.99 (***978-0-7614-5340-6(7)***) Cavendish, Marshall Corp.
Penn, Audrey. Un Beso en Mi Mano. 2006. (SPA.). 32p. 16.95 (978-1-933718-01-9(3)) Tanglewood Pr.
—Feathers & Fur. 2000. (gr. k-3). lib. bdg. 17.60 (978-0-613-36345-7(0)) Tandem Library Bks.
—Feathers & Fur. Wyrick, Monica, illus. 2006. 32p. (J). pap. 7.99 (978-0-9749303-8-1(5)) Tanglewood Pr.
—A Kiss Goodbye. Gibson, Barbara Leonard, illus. 2007. 32p. (ps-3). 16.95 (***978-1-933718-04-0(8)***) Tanglewood Pr.
—A Kiss Goodbye. Gibson, Barbara, illus. 2007. 32p. 16.95 (***978-1-933718-03-3(X)***) Tanglewood Pr.
Penn, Audrey. A Pocket Full of Kisses. Gibson, Barbara Leonard, illus. 2004. (New Child & Family Press Titles Ser.). 32p. (ps-1). 16.95 (978-0-87868-894-4(3) , 8943, Child & Family Pr.) Child Welfare League of America, Inc.
—A Pocket Full of Kisses. Gibson, Barbara, illus. 2006. 32p. 16.95 (978-1-933718-02-6(1)) Tanglewood Pr.
Penner, Lucille Recht. Bears on the Brain. Adams, Lynn, illus. 2003. (Science Solves It! Ser.). 32p. (J). 4.99 (978-1-57565-121-7(1)) Kane Pr., The.
—Bears on the Brain. 2003. (gr. k-3). lib. bdg. 13.00 (978-0-613-79226-4(2)) Tandem Library Bks.
Perera, Hilda. Podria Ser Que una Vez. Delacre, Lulu, illus. (SPA.). 84p. (J). (gr. 3-5). 7.95 (978-84-241-3274-3(2) , EV0925) Everest de Ediciones y Distribucion, S.L. ESP. *Dist:* Lectorum Pubns., Inc.
Perkins, Larry B. Jake the Cow Hand. 2004. 27p. pap. 9.97 (978-1-4116-1344-7(9)) Lulu.com.
Perl, Erica S. Ninety-Three in My Family. Lester, Mike, illus. 2006. 32p. (J). (ps-3). 15.95 (978-0-8109-5760-2(4)) Abrams, Harry N. , Inc.
Perry, Phyllis J. Mr. Crumb's Secret. 2002. per. 16.95 (978-1-57950-080-1(3) , Upstart Bks.) Highsmith Inc.
Persun, Morgan R. No Pets Allowed. Banks, Timothy, illus. 1998. 32p. (J). (ps-1). pap. 5.49 (978-1-57924-077-6(1)) Jones, Bob Univ. Pr.
—No Pets Allowed. 1998. (gr. k-3). lib. bdg. 13.55 (978-0-613-81217-7(4)) Tandem Library Bks.
The Pet Parade: Individual Title Six-Packs. (Literatura 2000 Ser.). (ps-1). 28.00 (978-0-7635-0012-2(7)) Rigby Education.
Peter & the Wolf. 2004. (Illus.). (J). (978-1-84458-040-8(7)) Chrysalis Children's Bks.
Peters, Andrew Fusek. Animals Aboard! Coplestone, Jim, illus. 2007. 24p. (J). 16.95 (***978-1-84507-582-8(X)***) Lincoln, Frances Ltd. GBR. *Dist:* Perseus Distribution.
Pfister, Marcus. How Leo Learned to Be King. 1998. (Illus.). 32p. (J). (ps-3). 15.95 (978-1-55858-913-1(9)) North-South Bks., Inc.
—Just the Way You Are. Pfister, Marcus, illus. 2002. (Illus.). 32p. (J). (gr. k-3). 15.95 (978-0-7358-1615-2(8)) North-South Bks., Inc.
—Somos Como Somos. Almohar, Ariel, tr. Pfister, Marcus, illus. 2002. (SPA., Illus.). 32p. (J). (gr. k-3). 15.95 (978-0-7358-1654-1(9) , NS31596) North-South Bks., Inc.
Pfloog, Jan. The Zoo Book. Pfloog, Jan, illus. 1999. (Super Shape Bks.). (Illus.). 24p. (J). (gr. k-ps). bds. 3.99 (978-0-307-58118-1(7) , 10060, Golden Bks.) Random Hse. Children's Bks.
Picard, Anne M. Peace & Pancakes. 2006. 48p. bds. 25.00 (978-1-59298-149-6(6)) Beaver's Pond Pr., Inc.
Pienkowski, Jan. Jan Pienkowski's Sea. 1998. (Animal Action Pops Ser.). (Illus.). 10p. (J). (gr. 2 up). 4.95 (978-1-58117-019-1(X) , Intervisual/Piggy Toes) Dalmatian Pr.
Pienkowski, Jan, illus. Dinner Time. 2000. (Monsterpops Ser.). 12p. (J). (ps-3). 5.95 (978-1-58117-024-5(6) , Intervisual/Piggy Toes) Dalmatian Pr.
—Jan Pienkowski's Jungle. 1998. (Animal Action Pops Ser.). 10p. (J). (gr. 2 up). 4.95 (978-1-58117-020-7(3) , Intervisual/Piggy Toes) Dalmatian Pr.
—Monster Pops: Dinner Time; Oh My, a Fly!; Small Talk. 3 vols., Set. 2000. (J). (ps-3). 14.95 (978-1-58117-023-8(8) , Intervisual/Piggy Toes) Dalmatian Pr.
—Oh My, a Fly! 2000. (Monsterpops Ser.). 12p. (J). (ps-3). 5.95 (978-1-58117-026-9(2) , Intervisual/Piggy Toes) Dalmatian Pr.
—Small Talk. 2000. (Monsterpops Ser.). 12p. (J). (ps-3). 5.95 (978-1-58117-025-2(4) , Intervisual/Piggy Toes) Dalmatian Pr.
Pierce, Chonda & Pierce, David. Tales from the Manger. LeBarre, Matt, illus. 2004. 96p. (J). pap. 9.99 (978-0-310-70849-0(4)) Zonderkidz.
Pigni, Guido & Hermsen, Ronald. The Story of Giraffe. Pigni, Guido, illus. 2007. (Illus.). 32p. (J). (ps-2). 16.95 (978-1-932425-87-1(X) , Front Street) Boyds Mills Pr.
Pilgrim, Jane. The Complete Tales of Blackberry Farm. (Illus.). 254p. (J). 29.95 (978-1-84560-004-4(5)) Mercury Bks. Ltd. GBR. *Dist:* International Publishers Marketing.
Pilney, Dovie. Charlie, the Cocky Rooster. 2007. (ENG., Illus.). 28p. (J). per. 15.95 (***978-1-4327-0220-5(3)***) Outskirts Press, Inc.
Pinkney, Jerry. Rikki-Tikki-Tavi. 2004. (gr. k-3). lib. bdg. 15.30 (978-0-613-83560-2(3)) Tandem Library Bks.
Pinkney, Jerry, illus. Las Fabulas de Esopo. 2004. Tr. of Aesop's Fables. (SPA.). (J). pap. 10.99 (978-84-316-7164-8(5)) Vicens-Vives, Editorial, S.A. ESP. *Dist:* Lectorum Pubns., Inc.
Pinkwater, Daniel M. Mush's Jazz Adventure. 2002. (gr. 3-6). lib. bdg. 11.80 (978-0-613-57577-5(6)) Tandem Library Bks.
—Rainy Morning. Pinkwater, Jill, illus. 1999. (Pinkwater Ser.: Vol. 1). 32p. (J). (gr. k-3). 16.00 (978-0-689-81143-2(8) , Atheneum) Simon & Schuster Children's Publishing.
Pinwheel, ed. Sounds. 2001. (Bounce-Along Bks.). (Illus.). 12p. (J). bds. 4.95 (978-0-8069-8088-1(5)) Sterling Publishing Co., Inc.
—Wake Up, Sleepy Bear. 2001. (Changing Faces Ser.). (Illus.). 12p. (J). bds. 4.95 (978-0-8069-8092-8(3)) Sterling Publishing Co., Inc.
Pirotta, Saviour. Patrick Paints a Picture. West, Linzi, illus. 2007. 32p. (J). (ps-1). 16.95 (***978-1-84507-296-4(0)***) Lincoln, Frances Ltd. GBR. *Dist:* Perseus Distribution.
Pirotta, Saviour, ed. Aesops Fables. Johnson, Richard, illus. 2007. 80p. (J). 9.95 (***978-0-7534-6133-4(1)*** , Kingfisher) Houghton Mifflin Co. Trade & Reference Div.
Pitcher, Caroline. Are You Spring? 2000. (J). (978-0-606-20115-5(7)) Tandem Library Bks.
Pitman, Hinsdale Nor. A Chinese Wonder Book. 2006. 41.99 (***978-1-4280-4098-4(6)***); pap. 34.99 (***978-1-4280-4114-1(1)***) IndyPublish.com.
Pixton, Amy, creator. Creepy Crawlies. 2006. (J). (978-0-9779631-1-9(X)) TyBook.
Plante, Raymond & Favreau, Marie-Claude. Une Barbouillee Qui Avait Perdu Son Nez. 2000. (Itait une Fois Ser.). (FRE., Illus.). 24p. (YA). (ps up). pap. (978-2-89021-412-5(5)) Diffusion du livre Mirabel.
—Marilou Polaire Sur un Arbre Perchee. 2001. (Premier Roman Ser.). (FRE., Illus.). 64p. (J). pap. (978-2-89021-459-0(1)) Diffusion du livre Mirabel.
Pledger, Maurice. Pledger sounds of wild Nighttime. 2007. (Illus.). 16p. (J). 16.95 (***978-1-59223-471-4(2)*** , Silver Dolphin Bks.) Advantage Pubs. Group.
Pledger, Maurice, illus. Hiding in the Woods: A Maurice Pledger Nature Trails Book. 2004. 16p. (J). 12.95 (978-1-59223-151-5(9)) Advantage Pubs. Group.
Plume, Ilse. The Bremen-Town Musicians. 1998. (Illus.). 32p. (ps-3). reprint ed. pap. 6.99 (978-0-440-41456-8(3) , Dragonfly Bks.) Random Hse. Children's Bks.
Plush Book - Land Before Time (English) 2000. (J). (978-1-58805-103-5(X)) DS-Max USA, Inc.
Pochocki, Ethel. The Blessing of the Beasts. Moser, Barry, illus. 2007. 40p. (J). (gr. k up). 18.95 (978-1-55725-502-0(4)) Paraclete Pr., Inc.
Polak, Monique. No More Pranks. 2004. (Orca Soundings Ser.). 112p. (J). (gr. 7-12). pap. 7.95 (978-1-55143-315-8(X)) Orca Bk. Pubs. USA.
Polisar, Barry Louis. Peculiar Zoo. Clark, David, illus. 2003. (Rainbow Morning Music Picture Bks.). 32p. (J). 14.95 (978-0-938663-14-0(3)) Rainbow Morning Music Alternatives.
Popham, Karen. Ellie's Growl. (Illus.). 32p. (J). 2004. pap. 7.95 (978-1-84507-189-9(1)); 2001. pap. 8.99 (978-0-7112-1505-4(7)); 2000. 19.99 (978-0-7112-1504-7(9)) Lincoln, Frances Ltd. GBR. *Dist:* Perseus Distribution, Transition Vendor, Antique Collectors' Club.
Poploff, Michelle. The First Fangs-Giving. Basso, Bill, illus. 2001. 46p. (J). pap. (978-0-439-28913-9(0)) Scholastic, Inc.
Popper, Garry. High Noon in Didley Pidley. Forshaw, John, illus. 2004. (Bret the Vet Ser.). 40p. 7.00 (978-1-84161-013-9(5)) Ravette Publishing, Ltd. GBR. *Dist:* Parkwest Pubns., Inc.
Porter, Annaliese & Bancroft, Bronwyn. The Outback. 2005. (Illus.). 28p. (J). 20.95 (978-1-875641-86-4(6)) Magabala Bks. AUS. *Dist:* International Specialized Bk. Services.
Porter-Gaylord, Laurel. I Love My Daddy Because. Wolff, Ashley, illus. 2004. (SPA.). 24p. (J). bds. 6.99 (978-0-525-47251-3(7) , Dutton Juvenile) Penguin Group (USA) Inc.
—I Love My Mommy Because. Wolff, Ashley, illus. 2004. (SPA.). 24p. (J). bds. 6.99 (978-0-525-47248-3(7) , Dutton Juvenile) Penguin Group (USA) Inc.
—I Love My Mommy Because... Wolff, Ashley, illus. 2004. 24p. (J). (ps). bds. 6.99 (978-0-525-47247-6(9) , Dutton Juvenile) Penguin Group (USA) Inc.
Porter, Penny. Heartstrings & Tailtuggers. Savage, Marilu, illus. 1999. xvii, 310p. (J). 21.95 (978-1-893660-10-6(9) , 991101-P1) Ravenhawk Bks.
Potter, Beatrix. Beatrix Potter Favorite Tales: The Tales of Peter Rabbit & Jemimapuddle Duck Read along Book & CD. 2006. (Illus.). 64p. (J). 9.99 (978-0-7232-5879-7(1) , Warne) Penguin Group (USA) Inc.
—The Complete Tales of Peter Rabbit & Other Favorite Stories. 2001. (Courage Children's Ser.). (Illus.). 56p. (J). 9.98 (978-0-7624-1271-6(2) , Courage Bks.) Running Pr. Bk. Pubs.
—The Complete Tales of Peter Rabbit & Plush Toy Gift Set. 2002. (Courage Children's Ser.). (Illus.). 56p. (J). 19.98 (978-0-7624-1272-3(0)) Running Pr. Bk. Pubs.
—El Cuento de Dona Ratoncilla. Potter, Beatrix, tr. 1999. (Beatrix Potter Ser.). (SPA., Illus.). 60p. 6.95 (978-84-7444-541-1(8)) Debate, Editorial ESP. *Dist:* Libros Sin Fronteras.
—Peter Rabbit & Other Stories. unabr. ed. 2002. (J). pap. incl. audio compact disk (978-1-58472-304-2(1) , In Audio) Sound Room Pubs., Inc.
—Peter Rabbit Tales, 2 vols. 1999. (Potter Special Edition Ser.). (Illus.). 96p. (J). 13.25 (978-0-7232-4483-7(9) , Warne) Penguin Group (USA) Inc.
—Peter Rabbit's Touch & Feel Book. 1999. (Illus.). 12p. (J). (ps-3). 9.99 (978-0-7232-4518-6(5) , Warne) Penguin Group (USA) Inc.
—The Tale of Mr. Tod, Vol. 14. 2002. (Illus.). 88p. (J). 6.99 (978-0-7232-4783-8(8) , Warne) Penguin Group (USA) Inc.
—The Tale of Timmy Tiptoes. Potter, Beatrix, illus. 2002. (Illus.). (J). 15.23 (978-0-7587-3756-4(4)) Book Wholesalers, Inc.
—The Tale of Timmy Tiptoes. 2002. (Illus.). 64p. (J). 6.99 (978-0-7232-4781-4(1) , Warne) Penguin Group (USA) Inc.
—The Tale of Timmy Tiptoes. (Beatrix Potter Bookmark Board Book Ser.). (Illus.). 6p. (J). bds. 3.95 (978-1-58989-204-0(6)) Thurman Hse., LLC.
—Treasured Tales from Beatrix Potter. 2007. (Illus.). 128p. (J). 7.99 (978-0-7232-5860-5(0) , Warne) Penguin Group (USA) Inc.
—We Both Read-the Tales of Peter Rabbit & Benjamin Bunny. Potter, Beatrix, illus. 1998. (We Both Read Ser.). (Illus.). 44p. (J). (gr. 1-2). 7.99 (978-1-891327-01-8(1)) Treasure Bay, Inc.
Potter, Beatrix & Pomaska, Anna. Peter Rabbit & Friends, 10 bks., Set, incl. stickers. 1999. (Illus.). (J). pap. 10.00 (978-0-486-29463-6(3)) Dover Pubns., Inc.
Potter, Beatrix & Warne, Frederick. The Complete Adventures of Peter Rabbit. 2003. (Illus.). 80p. (J). (ps). 14.99 (978-0-7232-4734-0(X) , Warne) Penguin Group (USA) Inc.
Powell, Richard. Lucy Lamb. Rhodes, Katie, illus. 2004. (Fuzzy Friends Ser.). 8p. (J). 7.95 (978-1-58925-724-5(3) , tiger tales) ME Media LLC.
—Puppy's Tail. Davis, Carolina A., illus. 2003. (Animal Tails Ser.). 12p. (J). 3.95 (978-1-58925-674-3(3) , tiger tales) ME Media LLC.
—What's in the Box? Martín Larrañaga, Ana, illus. 2004. (Ana's Mini Movers Ser.). 12p. (J). 5.95 (978-1-58925-742-9(1) , tiger tales) ME Media LLC.
—What's in the Egg? Martín Larrañaga, Ana, illus. 2004. (Ana's Mini Movers Ser.). 14p. (J). 5.95 (978-1-58925-739-9(1) , tiger tales) ME Media LLC.
—Who Lives Here? Martín Larrañaga, Ana, illus. 2004. (Ana's Mini Movers Ser.). 14p. (J). 5.95 (978-1-58925-741-2(3) , tiger tales) ME Media LLC.
—Whose Hat Is That? Martín Larrañaga, Ana, illus. 2004. (Ana's Mini Movers Ser.). 12p. (J). 5.95 (978-1-58925-740-5(5) , tiger tales) ME Media LLC.
—Wiggle My Ears. Larranaga, Ana, illus. 2004. (Wrigglers Ser.). 8p. (J). bds. 5.95 (978-1-58925-692-7(1) , tiger tales) ME Media LLC.
Powell, Richard J. Flap My Wings. Martin-Laranaga, Ana, illus. 2003. 10p. (J). 5.95 (978-1-58925-690-3(5) , tiger tales) ME Media LLC.
—Wag My Tail. Martin-Larranaga, Ana, illus. 2003. 10p. (J). 5.95 (978-1-58925-691-0(3) , tiger tales) ME Media LLC.
Powers, Christine. Love Is a Rainbow. 1999. (Leap Frog Lift-A-Flap Ser.). (Illus.). (J). (978-0-7853-3370-8(3)) Publications International, Ltd.
Prap, Lila. Why? 2005. Orig. Title: Zakaj?. (Illus.). 32p. (J). (ps-ps). 14.95 (978-1-929132-80-5(8)) Kane/Miller Bk. Pubs., Inc.
Prater, John. The Big Dark. 2008. (Illus.). 32p. (J). pap. (***978-0-09-948752-4(7)*** , Red Fox) Random Hse. Children's Bks. GBR. *Dist:* Random Hse., Inc.
—Hide & Seek Big Book. 1999. (Cambridge Reading Ser.). (Illus.). 14p. pap. 16.95 (978-0-521-66702-9(X)) Cambridge Univ. Pr.
—On Top of the World. 1998. (Illus.). 32p. (J). (ps-2). 15.95 (978-1-57255-649-2(8)) Mondo Publishing.
Prather, Cathy. Miss Louise Ben & Animal Friends. Prather, Cathy, illus. 2000. Tr. of English. (Illus.). 136p. (J). (ps-6). 14.95 (978-0-9666959-0-8(9)) Prather, Cathy.
Prats, Joan de Déu. Un Topo en un Mar de Hierba. Caruncho, Isabel, illus. (SPA.). 31p. (978-84-236-5040-8(5)) Edebé ESP. *Dist:* Lectorum Pubns., Inc.
Price, Iain. Johnny the Pookie. 2005. 155p. (J). (978-1-905203-15-4(2)) Pen Pr. Pubs., Ltd.
Price, Mary Ellizabeth. Wallbaby Bumblebees. 2004. (Illus.). 40p. (J). per. 15.75 (978-0-9715402-2-4(5) , 410-707-6686) Barnhardt & Ashe Publishing, Inc.
Price, Mathew. Polo Tiene Una Amiga. (SPA.). pap. 7.95 (978-950-07-1980-3(0)) Editorial Sudamericana S.A. ARG. *Dist:* Distribooks, Inc.
Priddy Books Staff & Priddy, Roger. Fuzzy Bee & Friends. rev. ed. 2003. (Cloth Book Ser.). (Illus.). 14p. (J). 8.95 (978-0-312-49150-5(6) , Priddy Bks.) St. Martin's Pr.
Priddy, Roger. Animal World. 2007. 64p. (J). 14.95 (978-0-312-49702-6(4) , Priddy Bks.) St. Martin's Pr.
—Animals. 2006. (Wipe Clean Ser.). 12p. (J). bds., act. bk. ed. 3.47 (978-0-312-49811-5(X) , Priddy Bks.) St. Martin's Pr.
—Bright Baby Farm. 2006. 26p. (J). bds. 8.95 (978-0-312-49780-4(6) , Priddy Bks.) St. Martin's Pr.
—Bright Baby Kitten. 2006. 26p. (J). bds. 8.95 (978-0-312-49782-8(2) , Priddy Bks.) St. Martin's Pr.
Prince, April Jones. Valentine Friends. Schlossberg, Elisabeth, illus. 2007. 24p. (J). pap. 3.99 (978-0-439-79999-7(6)) Scholastic, Inc.
Prokofiev, Sergei. Sergei Prokofiev's Peter & the Wolf: With Fully-Orchestrated & Narrated CD. Malone, Peter, illus. 2004. 40p. (J). lib. bdg. 21.99 (978-0-375-92430-9(2) , Knopf Bks. for Young Readers) Random Hse. Children's Bks.
Prokofiev, Sergei & Malone, Peter. Sergei Prokofiev's Peter & the Wolf: With Fully-Orchestrated & Narrated CD. 2004. (Illus.). 40p. (J). 19.95 incl. audio compact disk (978-0-375-82430-2(8) , Knopf Bks. for Young Readers) Random Hse. Children's Bks.
Provensen, Alice & Provensen, Martin. Our Animal Friends at Maple Hill Farm. 2001. (Illus.). 64p. (J). 7.99 (978-0-689-84499-7(9) , Aladdin) Simon & Schuster Children's Publishing.
Provoost, Anne. In the Shadow of the Ark. Nieuwenhuizen, John, tr. from DUT. 2004. 384p. (J). pap. 17.95 (978-0-439-44234-3(6) , Levine, Arthur A. Bks.) Scholastic, Inc.
—Voyagers on the Ark. Nieuwenhuizen, John, tr. from DUT. 2004. 368p. (J). 4.99 (978-0-439-44235-0(4) , Levine, Arthur A. Bks.) Scholastic, Inc.
Prowl & Growl. 2002. 10p. (J). 9.95 (978-0-7525-5581-2(2)) Parragon, Inc.
Puffin Island. 2002. (Wild Heritage Collection Mini Bks.). (Illus.). 32p. (J). (978-1-59069-163-2(6) , H3007) Studio Mouse LLC.
Pugliano-Martin, Carol. The Great Big Giant Turnip. ed. 2003. (Early Connections Ser.). (J). pap. 35.00 (978-1-4108-1553-8(6)) Benchmark Education Co.
Puttock, Simon. Big Bad Wolf Is Good. Chapman, Lynne, illus. 2002. 32p. (J). (ps-2). 12.95 (978-0-8069-0027-8(X)) Sterling Publishing Co., Inc.
Puzzle Track Staff, ed. Great Train Ride. 2007. (Puzzle Track Ser.). 20p. (J). bds. 18.95 (***978-0-7696-5599-4(8)***) School Specialty Publishing.
Quadrillion Media Staff. Mr. Flips Visits the Animals. 1999. 5.95 (978-1-58185-217-2(7)) Quadrillion Media LLC.
Quest for a Moose: An Alaska Tale of Searching for an Animal that Doesn't Exist — until it Is Found. 2005. 12.95 (978-1-59433-019-3(0)) Publication Consultants.
Quiet Quail. 2001. (ps-2). lib. bdg. 9.80 (978-0-613-32975-0(9)) Tandem Library Bks.
Quiroga, Horacio. Cuentos de la Selva. 2nd ed. 2002. (Clover Ser.). (SPA., Illus.). 156p. (YA). 13.95 (978-84-392-8050-7(5) , EV4408) Lectorum Pubns., Inc.
Rabey, Katharine. Hare & the Big Green Lawn. MacDougall, Larry, illus. 2006. 32p. 15.95 (978-0-87358-889-8(4) , Rising Moon Bks. for Young Readers) Northland Publishing.
Raintree Steck-Vaughn Staff. The Amazing Animal Rescue Team. 1999. (J). pap. 35.60 (978-0-7398-0891-7(5)) Steck-Vaughn.
—Fantastic Animal Features. 1999. (J). pap. 35.60 (978-0-7398-0892-4(3)) Steck-Vaughn.
—Fossils Alive! 1999. (Illus.). (J). pap. 35.60 (978-0-7398-0895-5(8)) Steck-Vaughn.
—From Fish to Fossil: Level B. 2000. (Illus.). (J). pap. 4.95 (978-0-8114-3791-2(4)) Steck-Vaughn.
—Wild Cats. 1999. (Illus.). (J). pap. 35.60 (978-0-7398-0916-7(4)) Steck-Vaughn.
Raintree Steck-Vaughn Staff, contrib. by. The Napping House. 1999. (J). (ps-3). 16.00 (978-0-8172-9783-1(9)); pap. 22.00 (978-0-8172-9789-3(8)) Steck-Vaughn.
Ramage, Jan. Eyes in the Night. Peterson, Laura, illus. 2004. 32p. (J). 24.25 (978-1-920694-25-8(0)) Univ. of Western Australia Pr. AUS. *Dist:* International Specialized Bk. Services.
Ramanujam, Geeta. The Wise Monkey & Other Animal Stories. Guhathakurta, Ajanta, illus. 2002. 112p. (J). (978-0-14-333545-0(6) , Puffin) Penguin Group (USA) Inc.
Randall, Bob. Tracker Tjugingji. 2003. 32p. 22.50 incl. audio compact disk (978-1-86465-030-3(3)) IAD Pr. AUS. *Dist:* International Specialized Bk. Services.
Random House Disney Staff. The Jungle Book. 2003. (Little Golden Book Ser.). (Illus.). 24p. (J). 2.99 (978-0-7364-2096-9(7) , Golden/Disney) Random Hse. Children's Bks.
—Jungle Book II: Read-Aloud Storybook. Clarke, Judith & Tyminski, Lori, illus. 2003. (Read-Aloud Storybook Ser.). 72p. (J). (ps-3). 8.99 (978-0-7364-2084-6(3) , RH/Disney) Random Hse. Children's Bks.
Random House Staff. Super Friends: Flying High. 2008. (Step into Reading Ser.). 32p. (J). (ps-1). lib. bdg. 11.99 (***978-0-375-95208-1(X)*** , Random Hse. Bks. for Young Readers) Random Hse. Children's Bks.
Ranoia, Sharon Curry. The uninvited Houseguest. 2006. pap. 7.95 (978-0-533-15470-8(7)) Vantage Pr., Inc.
Rathmann, Peggy. Buenas Noches, Gorila. Mayobre, Maria Francisca, tr. from ENG. Rathmann, Peggy, illus. 2001. (SPA., Illus.). 36p. (J). 18.95 (978-980-257-265-6(9)) Ekare, Ediciones VEN. *Dist:* AIMS International Bks., Inc., Lectorum Pubns., Inc.
—Buenas Noches, Gorila. 2004. (SPA., Illus.). 34p. (J). (ps-k). bds. 7.99 (978-0-399-24300-4(3) , Putnam Juvenile) Penguin Group (USA) Inc.
—Good Night, Gorilla. Rathmann, Peggy, illus. 2000. (Picture Puffin Ser.). (SPA., Illus.). 40p. (J). (ps-1). reprint ed. pap. 5.99 (978-0-698-11649-8(6) , Putnam Juvenile) Penguin Group (USA) Inc.
—Good Night, Gorilla. 2000. (Illus.). (J). 12.79 (978-0-606-18837-1(1)) Tandem Library Bks.
Ratoff, Michael. Every Thing in an Empty Box, Vol. 3. Painter, Laurie, illus. l.t. ed. 2001. 168p. (J). lib. bdg. 24.00 (978-0-9627986-7-2(3)) Rebel Butterfly Pr.
Rau, Dana. Rise & Shine. 2007. 12p. 10.95 (***978-1-58117-559-2(0)***) Dalmatian Pr.
Raudenbush, Brenda. Brilly & the Boot. Meyers, Holly B., illus. 1998. 97p. (J). (gr. 4-6). pap. 9.95 (978-0-9661531-0-1(3)) Panola Publishing Co.
Ravishankar, Anushka & Rao, Sirish. One, Two, Tree! Bai, Durga, illus. 2004. 48p. 16.95 (978-81-86211-80-9(2)) Tara Publishing IND. *Dist:* Consortium Bk. Sales & Distribution.
Reader's Digest Editors. Party Animals: A Book of Counting. 2007. 10p. (J). bds. 7.99 (978-0-7944-1213-5(0)) Reader's Digest Assn., Inc., The.
—What Do You See? 2004. (Small Miracles Ser.: No. 4). 10p. (J). 6.99 (978-1-4003-0317-5(6)) Nelson, Thomas Inc.
Reader's Digest Staff. Disney's Little Einsteins Storybook & Viewer. 2007. (RD Innovative Book & Player Format Ser.). 40p. (J). 24.99 (***978-0-7944-1307-1(2)***) Reader's Digest Assn., Inc., The.
Reasoner, Charles. Who's There? Reasoner, Charles, illus. 2003. (Sliding Surprise Bks.). (Illus.). 12p. (J). (ps). bds. 7.99 (978-0-8431-0600-8(X) , Price Stern Sloan) Penguin Group (USA) Inc.
—Whose Mommy Is This? Reasoner, Charles, illus. 2002. (Sliding Surprise Bks.). (Illus.). 12p. (J). bds. 7.99 (978-0-8431-4579-3(X) , Price Stern Sloan) Penguin Group (USA) Inc.

Reed, Lynn Rowe. Thelonius Turkey Lives! 2005. (Illus.). 40p. (J). (gr. k-3). 15.95 (978-0-375-83126-3(6) , Knopf Bks. for Young Readers) Random Hse. Children's Bks.

—Thelonius Turkey Lives! On Felicia Ferguson's Farm. 2005. (Illus.). 40p. (J). (gr. k-3). lib. bdg. 17.99 (978-0-375-93126-0(0) , Knopf Bks. for Young Readers) Random Hse. Children's Bks.

Reetz, Kurt & Schure, Kimberley. Kasey & the Dream Forest: The First Dream. Voelker, Marty, illus. 2000. 24p. (J). (gr. 1-3). pap. (978-0-9701450-0-0(4)) Long Hill Productions, Inc.

Reetz, Kurt & Schure, Kimberly. Kasey & the Dream Forest: The First Dream. 2000. mass mkt. 8.95 incl. audio compact disk (978-1-931179-05-8(0)) Long Hill Productions, Inc.

Reeve, Penny. Find the Animals: God Made Something Beautiful. (Illus.). 16p. (J). pap. 3.99 (978-1-85792-774-0(5) , Christian Focus) Christian Focus Pubns. GBR. *Dist:* Riverside.

—Find the Animals: God Made Something Clever. (Illus.). 16p. (J). pap. 3.99 (978-1-85792-771-9(0) , Christian Focus) Christian Focus Pubns. GBR. *Dist:* Riverside.

—Find the Animals: God Made Something Quick. (Illus.). 16p. (J). pap. 3.99 (978-1-85792-773-3(7)) Christian Focus Pubns. GBR. *Dist:* Riverside.

—Find the Animals: God Made Something Strong. (Illus.). 16p. (J). pap. 3.99 (978-1-85792-772-6(9) , Christian Focus) Christian Focus Pubns. GBR. *Dist:* Riverside.

Reiche, Dietlof. Freddy to the Rescue. Cepeda, Joe, illus. 2006. (Golden Hamster Saga Ser.: Bk. 3). 240p. (J). pap. 4.99 (978-0-439-53158-0(6) , Scholastic Paperbacks) Scholastic, Inc.

—Freddy to the Rescue. Brownjohn, John, tr. from GER. Cepeda, Joe, illus. 2005. (Golden Hamster Saga: Bk. 3). 240p. (J). pap. 16.95 (978-0-439-53157-3(8)) Scholastic, Inc.

Reid, Carolyn. Busy in the Bushveld: South African Edition. 1998. (Cambridge Reading Routes Ser.). (Illus.). 16p. pap. 5.45 (978-0-521-63680-3(9)) Cambridge Univ. Pr.

Reider, Katja. Todo Empezo Con Caracol. 1999. (SPA.). (gr. k-3). lib. bdg. 15.25 (978-0-613-29109-5(3)) Tandem Library Bks.

Reider, Katja & Von Roehl, Angela. Todo Empezo Con Caracol. 1999. (978-0-606-17757-3(4)) Tandem Library Bks.

Reilly, Pauline. Brolga. Rolland, Will, illus. (Picture Roo Bks.). 32p. (J). pap. (978-0-86417-719-3(4) , Kangaroo Pr.) Simon & Schuster Australia.

Reitz, Ric. The Journey of Sir Douglas Fir: A Reader's Musical. Bell, Suzanne, ed. Brewer, David, illus. 1999. 48p. (J). (gr. 2-6). per. 19.95 (978-0-9670160-0-9(2) , Sir Fir Bks. & Music) Sir Fir Enterprises, LLC.

Remkiewicz, Frank, illus. Froggy Plays Soccer. 2002. (Froggy Ser.). (J). 13.19 (978-0-7587-5111-9(7)) Book Wholesalers, Inc.

—Froggy's Best Christmas. 2002. (Froggy Ser.). 13.19 (978-1-4046-1700-1(0)) Book Wholesalers, Inc.

Remolina, Tere. Un Cambio de Piel. Martinez, Enrique, illus. (Barril Sin Fondo Ser.). (SPA.). (J). (gr. 3-5). pap. (978-968-6465-20-4(0)) Casa de Estudios de Literatura y Talleres Artisticos Amaquemecan A.C. MEX. *Dist:* Lectorum Pubns., Inc.

Rex, Adam. Pssst! 2007. (Illus.). 40p. (J). (gr. k-3). 16.00 (978-0-15-205817-3(6)) Harcourt Trade Pubs.

—Tree-Ring Circus. 2006. (Illus.). 32p. (J). 16.00 (978-0-15-205363-5(8)) Harcourt Trade Pubs.

Rex, Michael. Dunk Skunk. Rex, Michael, illus. 2005. (Illus.). 32p. (J). 10.99 (978-0-399-24281-6(3) , Putnam Juvenile) Penguin Group (USA) Inc.

—Truck Duck. Rex, Michael, illus. (J). (ps-ps). 2008. 28p. bds. 6.99 (***978-0-399-25092-7(1)***); 2004. (Illus.). 34p. 9.99 (978-0-399-24009-6(8)) Penguin Group (USA) Inc. (Putnam Juvenile).

Rey, H. A. CG Puppies AMS Oversized Edition. 2005. (J). 12.99 (978-0-618-56451-4(9)) Houghton Mifflin Co. Trade & Reference Div.

Rey, H. A. & Rey, Margret. Billy's Picture. 2004. (Illus.). 24p. (J). (gr. k-3). 15.00 (978-0-618-49422-4(7)); pap. 5.95 (978-0-618-49420-0(0)) Houghton Mifflin Co. Trade & Reference Div.

—Brezel. 1999. (GER., Illus.). 36p. (J). pap. (978-3-257-00854-8(6)) Diogenes Verlag AG CHE. *Dist:* International Bk. Import Service, Inc.

—Curious George Feeds the Animals. 2005. (J). (gr. k-3). 9.95 (978-0-618-55520-8(X)) Houghton Mifflin Co. Trade & Reference Div.

Reynolds, Aaron. Buffalo Wings. Bogan, Paulette, illus. 2007. 32p. (J). 17.85 (***978-1-59990-139-8(0));*** 16.95 (***978-1-59990-062-9(9)***) Bloomsbury Publishing.

Reynolds, Cynthia Furlong. The Far Flung Adventures of Homer the Hummer. Catherine, McClung, illus. 2005. 32p. (J). (ps-3). 17.95 (978-1-58726-269-2(X)) Ann Arbor Media Group, LLC.

Reynolds, Yvonne. An Ox Tale. Muller, Eric, illus. 1998. 24p. (J). (gr. 2-5). pap. (978-0-9650824-1-9(5)) Lolot Pr.

Rhema, Dan. The Day the Animals Lost Their True Color. Adams, Blaine, illus. 2001. 32p. (J). (ps-6). 19.95 (978-0-9709615-0-1(2)) Brain Injury Assn. of Kentucky.

Ricchiuti, Paul B. Mr. Squirrel's Treasure/Ellen's Miracle Horse. Mashburn, Marcus, illus. 2002. 48p. (J). 6.99 (978-0-8280-1564-6(3) , 137-100) Review & Herald Publishing Assn.

Ricci, Christine. Dora's Picnic. Hall, Susan, illus. 2003. (Ready-to-Read Ser.: Vol. 1). 24p. (J). pap. 3.99 (978-0-689-85238-1(X) , Simon Spotlight/Nickelodeon) Simon & Schuster Children's Publishing.

—Dora's Picnic. 2003. (gr. k-3). lib. bdg. 11.80 (978-0-613-67079-1(5)) Tandem Library Bks.

—Follow Those Feet! Hall, Susan, illus. 2003. (Ready-to-Read Ser.: Vol. 2). 24p. (J). pap. 3.99 (978-0-689-85239-8(8) , Simon Spotlight/Nickelodeon) Simon & Schuster Children's Publishing.

—Follow Those Feet! 2003. (gr. k-3). lib. bdg. 11.80 (978-0-613-67087-6(6)) Tandem Library Bks.

—Meet the Animals! Aikins, Dave, illus. 2006. (Dora the Explorer Ser.). 16p. (J). 10.95 (978-1-4169-1819-6(1) , Simon Spotlight/Nickelodeon) Simon & Schuster Children's Publishing.

Rice, Joan W. The Winter Sleep: A Story of Hibernation. Slimp, Gwen H., illus. 2004. 48p. (J). (gr. k-3). (978-0-9755573-0-3(0)) Coastal Publishing, LLC.

Rice, Myrtle Alley. Friends of Fur & Feather. 2005. reprint ed. pap. 20.95 (978-1-4179-9023-8(6)) Kessinger Publishing, LLC.

Richards, Lucy. Little Farm. 2007. (Illus.). 10p. (J). bds. 4.99 (***978-1-84458-362-1(7)***) Anova Bks. GBR. *Dist:* Independent Pubs. Group.

Richards, Lucy, illus. Animal Antics (with Header Card) 2004. (Cuddly Cuffs Ser.: No. 5). 10p. (J). tchr. ed. 5.95 (978-1-58925-729-0(4) , tiger tales) ME Media LLC.

—Jumping Jungle (W/Hang Tag) 2004. (Cuddly Cuffs Ser.: No. 7). 12p. (J). tchr. ed. 5.95 (978-1-58925-727-6(8) , tiger tales) ME Media LLC.

—Jumping Jungle (W/Header Card) 2004. (Cuddly Cuffs Ser.: 7). 6p. (J). tchr. ed. 5.95 (978-1-58925-731-3(6) , tiger tales) ME Media LLC.

Richardson, Dick. The Oglin: A Hero's Journey Across Africa... Towards the Tomorrows. Feek, Cathy, illus. 2004. 417p. (J). 24.95 (978-0-9759440-3-5(7)) Savanna Pr.

Riddell, Chris. The Platypus & the Lucky Day. 2002. (Illus.). (J). 15.00 (978-0-15-204676-7(3)) Harcourt Trade Pubs.

Rigby Education Staff. Animal Advertisements. (Sails Literacy Ser.). (Illus.). 16p. (gr. 2-3). 27.00 (978-0-7635-9944-7(1) , 699441C99) Rigby Education.

—Animal Coats. (Sails Literacy Ser.). (Illus.). 16p. (gr. k-1). 27.00 (978-0-7635-9864-8(X) , 698649C99) Rigby Education.

—The Animal Show. (Sails Literacy Ser.). (Illus.). 16p. (gr. k-1). 27.00 (978-0-7635-9877-8(1) , 698771C99) Rigby Education.

—Animals of the Rainforest. (Sails Literacy Ser.). (Illus.). 16p. (gr. k-1). 27.00 (978-0-7635-9867-9(4) , 698674C99) Rigby Education.

—Animals Say... (Sails Literacy Ser.). (Illus.). 16p. (gr. 2-3). 27.00 (978-0-7635-9943-0(3) , 699433C99) Rigby Education.

—Animals That Build. (Sails Literacy Ser.). (Illus.). 16p. (gr. 1-2). 27.00 (978-0-7635-9897-6(6) , 698976C99) Rigby Education.

—Clean My Teeth. (Sails Literacy Ser.). (Illus.). 16p. (gr. k-1). 27.00 (978-0-7635-9882-2(8) , 698828C99) Rigby Education.

—Elephant & Mouse. (Sails Literacy Ser.). (Illus.). 16p. (gr. k-1). 27.00 (978-0-7635-9871-6(2) , 698712C99) Rigby Education.

—The Red Shoes. (Sails Literacy Ser.). (Illus.). 16p. (gr. 2-3). 27.00 (978-0-7635-9945-4(X) , 699459C99) Rigby Education.

Riggs-Mayfield, Nellie. A Collection of Short Stories for Children. 2006. (J). per. 19.95 (978-1-59872-640-4(4)) Instantpublisher.com.

Riley's Bow-Wow Blast. 2006. (J). per. 12.95 (978-0-9769058-0-6(9)) Boss Paws Publishing.

Rinck, Maranke. The Prince Child. Linden, Martijn van der, illus. 2004. (ENG & GER.). 32p. (J). 16.95 (978-1-932425-15-4(2) , Lemniscaat) Boyds Mills Pr.

Rinck, Maranke. The Sweetest Kiss. Van Der Linden, Martijn, illus. 2007. 32p. (J). 16.95 (***978-1-59078-519-5(3)***) Boyds Mills Pr.

Rioseco, Rosita & Ziliani, Monica. Animalfabeto. 1998. (SPA.). (J). (ps-k). pap. (978-956-13-1393-4(6)) Bello, Andres CHL. *Dist:* Lectorum Pubns., Inc.

Rip Squeak & His Friends. 2003. Tr. of Rip Squeak y Sus Amigos. (J). 16.95 (978-0-9672422-4-8(X)) Rip Squeak, Inc.

Ritchie, Alison. What Bear Likes Best! Kolanovic, Dubravka, illus. 2005. 28p. (J). 16.00 (978-1-56148-473-7(3)) Good Bks.

Ritchie, Joseph R. Peter Cottontail's Busy Day. Halverson, Lydia, illus. 2005. 16p. (J). bds. 9.95 (978-0-8249-6571-6(X)) Ideals Pubns.

—Peter Cottontail's Easter Egg Hunt. Thornburgh, Rebecca McKillip, illus. 2004. 12p. (J). (ps-k). bds. 9.95 (978-0-8249-6522-8(1)) Ideals Pubns.

—Peter Cottontail's Easter Surprise. Rasmussen, Wendy, illus. 2006. 18p. (J). bds. 9.95 (978-0-8249-6627-0(9) , Candy Cane Pr.) Ideals Pubns.

—Where's Santa? Halverson, Lydia, illus. 2006. 14p. (J). (ps). bds. 7.95 (978-0-8249-6673-7(2) , Candy Cane Pr.) Ideals Pubns.

Robbins, Beth. Tom & Ally Visit the Doctor: American Edition. Stuart, Jon, illus. 2001. (It's OK! Ser.). 24p. (J). (ps-k). pap. 3.95 (978-0-7894-7428-5(X) , D K Ink) Dorling Kindersley Publishing, Inc.

—Tom's First Day at School. Stuart, Jon, illus. 2001. (It's OK! Ser.). 24p. (J). (ps-k). pap. 3.95 (978-0-7894-7422-3(0) , D K Ink) Dorling Kindersley Publishing, Inc.

Robbins, Beth & Stuart, Jon. Tom's First Haircut. 2001. (It's OK! Ser.). (Illus.). 24p. (J). (ps-k). pap. 3.95 (978-0-7894-7424-7(7) , D K Ink) Dorling Kindersley Publishing, Inc.

Robbins, Sandra. No Balloons Today: A Zoo Story. Garzon, Alfredo, illus. 2001. 32p. (J). (ps-3). pap. 11.95 incl. audio (978-1-882601-29-5(7)); pap. 6.95 (978-1-882601-30-1(0)) See-More's Workshop.

Robby in the River: Individual Title Six-Pack Pouch - Level I. (Lighthouse Ser.). 16p. (gr. 1 up). 26.00 (978-0-7578-0854-8(9)) Rigby Education.

Roberts, Pauline J. Girls Crying. 2007. 9.00 (***978-0-8059-8863-5(7)***) Dorrance Publishing Co., Inc.

Roberts, Trina. The Lonley Little Birch. 2005. 9.00 (978-0-8059-8053-0(9)) Dorrance Publishing Co., Inc.

Robertson, Mark, illus. Kingfisher Treasury of Dragon Stories. 2005. (Kingfisher Treasury of Stories Ser.: Vol. 14). 160p. (J). (gr. k-3). pap. 5.95 (978-0-7534-5889-1(6) , Kingfisher) Houghton Mifflin Co. Trade & Reference Div.

Robertson, Susan, illus. Little Bunny. 2005. (Bedtime Babies Ser.). 8p. (J). (ps). per. 6.99 (978-1-57755-503-2(1)) Allied Publishing.

Robeson, K. S. A Home for Chloe. 2002. (Tales from Wind Creek Ser.: Bk. 1). 114p. (J). (gr. 3-6). per. 8.95 (978-0-9723530-0-7(3)) Falcor Bks.

Robinson, Anne. Tom Turkey. 2001. (J). cd-rom 9.95 (978-1-58338-357-5(3)) CrossroadsPub.com.

Robinson, Anthony. Animals in the Jungle. 2nd rev. ed. 2000. (Cambridge Reading Ser.). (Illus.). 10p. pap. 5.00 (978-0-521-78584-6(7)) Cambridge Univ. Pr.

Robinson, Connie. Porky & the Gasto. Robinson, Lori Clish, illus. l.t. ed. 2001. 30p. (J). (gr. k-3). pap. 7.95 (978-1-928632-55-9(6)) Writers Marketplace:Consulting, Critiquing & Publishing.

Rockwell, Anne F. Chip & the Karate Kick. Meisel, Paul, illus. 2004. (Good Sports Ser.). 40p. (J). (ps-1). lib. bdg. 15.89 (978-0-06-028446-6(3)) HarperCollins Pubs.

—Katie Catz Makes a Splash. Meisel, Paul, illus. 2003. (Good Sports Ser.). 40p. (J). (ps-1). 15.99 (978-0-06-028441-1(2)) HarperCollins Pubs.

—Katie Catz Swims at Last. Meisel, Paul, illus. 1999. 32p. (J). (ps-1). pap. 5.95 (978-0-06-446740-7(6)) HarperCollins Pubs.

—Morgan Plays Soccer. Meisel, Paul, illus. 1999. 32p. (J). (ps-1). pap. 5.95 (978-0-06-446739-1(2)) HarperCollins Pubs.

Rodgers, Frank. Mr. Croc's Silly Sock. 2006. (Read-It! Chapter Books). (J). 21.26 (978-1-4048-2730-1(7)) Picture Window Bks.

—Royal Roar. 2007. (Read-It! Chapter Books). (J). 21.26 (978-1-4048-2728-8(5)) Picture Window Bks.

—What Mr. Croc Forgets. 2006. (Read-It! Chapter Books). (J). 21.26 (978-1-4048-2731-8(5)) Picture Window Bks.

Rodrigues, Ann & Winch, John. What Little Rhino Sees. 2002. (J). 15.99 (978-0-7636-1396-9(7)) Candlewick Pr.

Rodriguez, Lucho. Abzoo. 2005. (SPA.). 36p. (J). 15.95 (978-980-6437-21-0(7)) Playco Editores, C.A.

Rogers, Alan. El Oso Verde. 2004. (Pequenos Gigantes Ser.).Tr. of Green Bear. (SPA., Illus.). 16p. (ps-k). (J). pap. 3.95 (978-1-58728-957-6(1)); 5.95 (978-1-58728-143-3(0)) T&N Children's Publishing. (Two Can Publishing).

—El Oso Verde. Rogers, Alan, illus. 2000. (Pequenos Gigantes Ser.).Tr. of Green Bear. (Illus.). 15p. (J). (ps-ps). lib. bdg. 10.75 (978-0-606-20836-9(4)) Tandem Library Bks.

Rogers, Jacqueline. Best Friends Sleep Over. 2000. (Illus.). 32p. (YA). (ps-4). pap. 5.99 (978-0-439-19994-0(8)) Scholastic, Inc.

Roitman, Tanya. Who Lives Here? Roitman, Tanya, illus. 2007. (Illus.). 32p. 12.95 (978-1-59354-599-4(1)) Blue Apple Bks.

Rojas, Emilio. Mitos, Leyendas, Cuentos, Fabulas, Apologos y Parabolas, 3 vols, Vol. 2. Rojas, Emilio, ed. Farshchian, Mahmoud et al, illus. Arcos, Bernardo & Alcaraz, Lorena, photos by. l.t. ed. 2001. (SPA.). 224p. (J). (gr. 2 up). per. 15.95 (978-0-9706814-3-0(7)) EDITER'S Publishing Hse.

—Mitos, Leyendas, Cuentos, Fabulas, Apologos y Parabolas, 3 vols., Vol. 3. Rojas, Emilio, ed. Rojas, Lauyumi Michelle et al, illus. Alcaraz, Lorena & Arcos, Bernardo, photos by. 2nd rev. l.t. ed. 2002. (SPA.). 224p. (YA). (gr. 4 up). reprint ed. per. 15.95 (978-0-9706814-0-9(2)) EDITER'S Publishing Hse.

—Mitos, Leyendas, Cuentos, Fabulas, Apologos y Parabolas I, 3 vols. Rojas, Emilio, ed. Gonzalez, Elva Nitzchiani et al, illus. Alcaraz, Lorena & Arcos, Bernardo, photos by. l.t. ed. 2001. (SPA.). 224p. (YA). per. 15.95 (978-0-9706814-4-7(5)) EDITER'S Publishing Hse.

Rojas, Emilio, ed. En Busca de Si Mismo: Apologos y Parabolas. Minguer, Edgar, illus. Alcaraz, Lorena & Arcos, Bernardo, photos by. l.t. ed. 2002. (SPA.). 168p. (YA). per. 15.95 (978-0-9706814-9-2(6)) EDITER'S Publishing Hse.

Roman, Kathy Blankley, illus. Dume's Roar. unabr. ed. 1998. 14p. (J). (ps-3). 14.95 (978-0-7737-3003-8(6)) Stoddart Kids CAN. *Dist:* Fitzhenry & Whiteside, Ltd.

Romay, Alexis. Diego Saves the Sloth! Mawhinney, Art, illus. 2007. (Go, Diego, Go! Ser.). 24p. (J). pap. 3.99 (978-1-4169-3470-7(7) , Simon Spotlight/Nickelodeon) Simon & Schuster Children's Publishing.

Rooney, M. A. Rudy the Rescue. 2005. 8p. 11.72 (978-1-4116-6057-1(9)) Lulu.com.

Root, Phyllis. Grandmother Winter. Krommes, Beth, illus. 32p. (J). (gr. k-3). 1999. tchr. ed. 16.00 (978-0-395-88399-0(7)); 2004. reprint ed. pap. 5.95 (978-0-618-49485-9(5)) Houghton Mifflin Co. Trade & Reference Div.

—Mouse Has Fun. Croft, James, illus. 2002. (Brand New Readers Ser.). 32p. (J). (ps-2). pap. 5.99 (978-0-7636-1358-7(4)) Candlewick Pr.

Rorby, Ginny. Hurt Go Happy. 2006. 272p. (J). 17.95 (978-0-7653-1442-0(8) , Starscape) Doherty, Tom Assocs., LLC.

Rosa-Mendoza, Gladys. Animals at the Farm/Animales de la Granja. Wolff, Jason, illus. 2004. (English-Spanish Foundations Ser.). (SPA & ENG.). 20p. (J). (ps). bds. 6.95 (978-1-931398-13-8(5)) Me+Mi Publishing.

Rose, Gerald. The Lion & the Mouse. 2002. (Illus.). 16p. pap. 0.40 (978-0-521-01515-8(4)) Cambridge Univ. Pr.

—The Lion & the Mouse ELT Edition. 2001. (Cambridge Storybooks Ser.). (Illus.). 16p. pap. 5.00 (978-0-521-00724-5(0)) Cambridge Univ. Pr.

—Millie's Big Surprise. 2004. (Illus.). 32p. (J). pap. 9.99 (978-1-84270-319-9(6)) Andersen GBR. *Dist:* Independent Pubs. Group.

—The Tortoise & the Hare. 2002. (Illus.). 16p. pap. 0.40 (978-0-521-01539-4(1)) Cambridge Univ. Pr.

Rosebush, Beatrice. What Would I Do if I Met a Moose? Cooke, Sean, illus. 1999. 24p. (J). pap. 8.00 (978-0-9678193-0-3(X)) Ebeemee Pubs.

Rosen, Michael. Ronquidos! Langley, Jonathan, illus. Tr. of Snore!. (SPA.). (J). (gr. 1-3). 8.95 (978-958-04-4646-0(6)) Norma S.A. COL. *Dist:* Distribuidora Norma, Inc., Lectorum Pubns., Inc.

Rosen, Michael & Langley, Jonathan. Ow. 2005. (Illus.). 32p. (J). pap. 9.99 (978-0-00-712443-5(0)) HarperCollins Pubs. Ltd. GBR. *Dist:* Trafalgar Square Publishing.

Ross, Diane. The Little Red Engine & the Rocket. Wood, Leslie, illus. 2005. (Little Red Engine Ser.). 32p. (J). pap. 8.99 (978-0-233-00146-3(8)) Andre Deutsch GBR. *Dist:* Independent Pubs. Group.

Ross, Eileen. The Halloween Showdown. Reed, Lynn R., illus. 1999. 32p. (J). (gr. k-3). tchr. ed. 15.95 (978-0-8234-1395-9(0)) Holiday Hse., Inc.

Ross, Mandy. Animal Lullabies. Kallai Nagy, Krisztina, illus. 2005. (J). pap. 9.99 incl. audio compact disk (978-1-904550-93-8(2)) Child's Play-International.

Ross, Thea. Molly Mole Loves to Garden. 2004. (Lift-the-Flap Surprise on Every Spread! Ser.). 12p. (J). 5.99 (978-1-59384-044-0(6)) Parklane Publishing.

Ross, Tony & Willis, Jeanne. Daft Bat. 2007. (Illus.). 32p. (J). (gr. k-2). 16.95 (***978-1-84270-476-9(1)***) Transworld Publishers Ltd. GBR. *Dist:* Independent Pubs. Group.

Rosseter, Patrick W. Grampa Pat's Little Animal Tales. 2005. 10.00 (978-0-8059-9797-2(0)) Dorrance Publishing Co., Inc.

Roth, Carol. Here Comes the Choo Choo! Cushman, Doug, illus. 2007. (J). (***978-0-15-205582-0(7)***) Harcourt Trade Pubs.

Roth, Carol. The Little School Bus. 2004. (Illus.). 32p. (J). (gr. k-1). pap. 6.95 (978-0-7358-1905-4(X)) North-South Bks., Inc.

—The Little School Bus. Paparone, Pamela, illus. 2002. 32p. (J). (ps-1). 14.95 (978-0-7358-1646-6(8)) North-South Bks., Inc.

Rouss, Sylvia. The Littlest Pair. Hannon, Holly, illus. 2005. 32p. (J). pap. 9.95 (978-1-930143-18-0(4) , Devora Publishing) Pitspopany Pr.

Rouss, Sylvia A. The Littlest Pair. Hannon, Holly, illus. 2005. 32p. (J). (ps-1). 14.95 (978-1-930143-17-3(6) , Devora Publishing) Pitspopany Pr.

Rovetch, Lissa. Frog Went A-Dancing. Berry, Holly, illus. 2006. (J). (978-1-58987-008-6(5)) Kindermusik International.

Rowe, Jeannette. YoYo's Animal Friends. Rowe, Jeannette, illus. 2002. (Illus.). 12p. (J). 3.95 (978-1-58925-681-1(6) , tiger tales) ME Media LLC.

Rowe, Kysha D. What Creatures Teach Us, 1. 2005. (Illus.). 112p. (J). per. (978-0-9769339-0-8(X)) Rowe, Kysha.

Rowlands, Avril. The Animals' Christmas: And Other Stories. 2003. (Illus.). 128p. (J). (gr. 2-5). pap. 7.99 (978-0-7459-3699-4(7) , Lion) Lion Hudson plc GBR. *Dist:* Independent Pubs. Group.

—Animals to the Rescue & Other Stories. 2002. (Illus.). 128p. (J). pap. 7.99 (978-0-7459-4764-8(6) , Lion) Lion Hudson plc GBR. *Dist:* Independent Pubs. Group.

—The Christmas Sheep: And Other Stories. Moran, Rosslyn, illus. 2001. 48p. (J). (ps-3). 16.00 (978-1-56148-336-5(2)) Good Bks.

Rowling, J. K. Les Animaux Fantastiques et Ou les Trouver. 2001. (FRE.). 96p. pap. 16.95 (978-0-320-04844-9(6)) French & European Pubns., Inc.

Rubel, William & Mandel, Gerry, eds. Animal Stories by Young Writers. 2004. 96p. (YA). (gr. 3-8). tchr. ed. 18.95 (978-1-58246-025-3(6) , Tricycle Pr.) Ten Speed Pr.

Ruben, Pamela J. Yenta the Chicken & Other Fowl Tales! Ruben, Anthony R., ed. 2004. (Illus.). 19p. (J). 12.95 (978-0-9764813-0-0(8)) Peppery Pr.

Ruben's Jungle. 2003. Tr. of Selva de Ruben. (SPA., Illus.). 26p. bds. 16.95 (978-0-9706953-1-4(4)) Globo Libros.

Rubin, Julian. The Orchid Grower. 2003. (J). 14.00 (978-1-894942-05-8(1)) Zumaya Pubns. LLC.

Ruelle, Karen Gray. The Thanksgiving Beast Feast. (Holiday House Readers Ser.). (Illus.). 32p. (J). (gr. k-3). pap. 4.95 (978-0-8234-1802-2(2)) Holiday Hse., Inc.

—The Thanksgiving Beast Feast Level 2: A Holiday House Reader. Ruelle, Karen Gray, illus. (Illus.). 32p. (J). (gr. k-3). tchr. ed. 15.95 (978-0-8234-1511-3(2)) Holiday Hse., Inc.

Ruffenach, Jessie, ed. Baby Learns about Animals. Thomas, Peter, tr. from NAV. Blacksheep, Beverly, illus. 2004. (ENG & NAV.). 16p. 7.95 (978-1-893354-49-4(0)) Salina Bookshelf.

Rugrats. 2007. (J). 128.10 (***978-1-59961-354-3(9)***) Spotlight.

Rumford, James. Calabash Cat. 2003. (ENG & ARA., Illus.). 32p. (J). (gr. k-3). 16.00 (978-0-618-22423-4(8)) Houghton Mifflin Co. Trade & Reference Div.

—Nine Animals & the Well. 2003. (Illus.). 32p. (J). (gr. k-3). tchr. ed. 16.00 (978-0-618-30915-3(2)) Houghton Mifflin Co. Trade & Reference Div.

The Runaway Engine & Other Stories: Individual Title Six-Pack. (Story Steps Ser.). (gr. k-2). 48.00 (978-0-7635-9803-7(8)) Rigby Education.

Russell, Natalie. Hamish the Highland Cow. 2003. (J). 7.99 (978-1-58234-818-6(9)) Bloomsbury Publishing.

Ryan, Margaret. Fuzzbuzz Takes a Tumble. Melling, David, illus. 2003. 44p. (J). (978-0-439-45587-9(1)) Scholastic, Inc.

—Kat McCrumble. 2004. (Kat Mccrumble Ser.). (Illus.). (J). pap. (978-0-340-87827-9(4) , Hodder Children's Books) Hodder Children's Division.

—Puffling in a Pickle. (Illus.). 64p. (J). 7.95 (978-0-14-037062-1(5)) Penguin Bks., Ltd. GBR. *Dist:* Trafalgar Square Publishing.

—Simply Kat McCrumble. 2005. (Kat Mccrumble Ser.). (J). pap. (978-0-340-88401-0(0) , Hodder Children's Books) Hodder Children's Division.

—Wild Kat Mccrumble. 2005. (Kat Mccrumble Ser.). 208p. (J). pap. (978-0-340-88402-7(9) , Hodder Children's Books) Hodder Children's Division.

Ryder, Joanne. Big Bear Ball. Kellogg, Steven, illus. 2002. 32p. (J). (ps-1). 15.95 (978-0-06-027955-4(9)) HarperCollins Pubs.

—Dance by the Light of the Moon. Francis, Guy, illus. 2007. 40p. (ps-1). 15.99 (978-0-7868-1820-4(4)) Hyperion Pr.

Rylant, Cynthia. The Case of the Baffled Bear. Karas, G. Brian, illus. 2004. (High-Rise Private Eyes Ser.: No. 7). 48p. (J). (gr. 1 up). 14.99 (978-0-06-053448-6(6)); lib. bdg. 16.89 (978-0-06-053449-3(4)) HarperCollins Pubs.

—The Case of the Climbing Cat. Karas, G. Brian, illus. 2000. (High-Rise Private Eyes Ser.: No. 2). 48p. (J). (gr. 1 up). 14.89 (978-0-688-16309-9(2)) HarperCollins Pubs.

—The Case of the Climbing Cat. Karas, G. Brian, illus. 2003. (High-Rise Private Eyes Ser.: No. 2). (J). (gr. k-3). 28.95 incl. audio compact disk (978-1-59112-611-9(8)); pap. 31.95 incl. audio compact disk (978-1-59112-612-6(6)) Live Oak Media.

—The Case of the Desperate Duck. Karas, G. Brian, illus. (High-Rise Private Eyes Ser.: No. 8). 48p. (J). (gr. k-3). 2006. pap. 3.99 (978-0-06-053453-0(2) , Harper Trophy); 2005. 14.99 (978-0-06-053451-6(6)); 2005. lib. bdg. 15.89 (978-0-06-053452-3(4)) HarperCollins Pubs.

—The Case of the Fidgety Fox. Karas, G. Brian, illus. 2003. (High-Rise Private Eyes Ser.: No. 6). 56p. (J). (gr. 1 up). 15.99 (978-0-06-009101-9(0)) HarperCollins Pubs.

—The Case of the Fidgety Fox. Karas, G. Brian, illus. unabr. ed. 2005. (High-Rise Private Eyes Ser.: No. 6). (J). (gr. k-4). 25.95 incl. audio (978-1-59519-405-3(3)); 28.95 incl. audio compact disk (978-1-59519-409-1(6)); pap. 18.95 incl. audio compact disk (978-1-59519-408-4(8)); pap. 16.95 incl. audio (978-1-59519-404-6(5)); Set. pap. 29.95 incl. audio (978-1-59519-406-0(1)); Set. pap. 31.95 incl. audio compact disk (978-1-59519-410-7(X)) Live Oak Media.

—The Case of the Missing Monkey. Karas, G. Brian, illus. 2000. (High-Rise Private Eyes Ser.: No. 1). 48p. (J). (gr. 1 up). 14.95 (978-0-688-16306-8(8)) HarperCollins Pubs.

—The Case of the Missing Monkey. Karas, G. Brian, illus. 2003. (High-Rise Private Eyes Ser.: No. 1). 28.95 incl. audio compact disk (978-1-59112-615-7(0)); pap. 31.95 incl. audio compact disk (978-1-59112-616-4(9)) Live Oak Media.

—The Case of the Puzzling Possum. Karas, G. Brian, illus. 2003. (High-Rise Private Eyes Ser.: No. 3). (J). (gr. k-3). 28.95 incl. audio compact disk (978-1-59112-619-5(3)); pap. 31.95 incl. audio compact disk (978-1-59112-620-1(7)) Live Oak Media.

—The Case of the Sleepy Sloth. 2004. (High-Rise Private Eyes Ser.: No. 5). (J). (gr. k-3). lib. bdg. 11.80 (978-0-613-85152-7(8)) Tandem Library Bks.

—The Case of the Troublesome Turtle. Karas, G. Brian, illus. 2003. (High-Rise Private Eyes Ser.: No. 4). (J). (gr. k-3). 25.95 incl. audio (978-1-59112-202-9(3)); 28.95 incl. audio compact disk (978-1-59112-623-2(1)); pap. 29.95 incl. audio (978-1-59112-203-6(1)); pap. 31.95 incl. audio compact disk (978-1-59112-624-9(X)); pap. 16.95 incl. audio (978-1-59112-201-2(5)) Live Oak Media.

—Gooseberry Park. 2007. (Illus.). 144p. (J). pap. 5.95 (***978-0-15-206159-3(2)*** , Harcourt Paperbacks) Harcourt Children's Bks.

—The Octopus. McDaniels, Preston, illus. 2005. (Lighthouse Family Ser.). 64p. (J). 15.99 (978-0-689-86246-5(6)) Simon & Schuster Children's Publishing.

—Poppleton Forever. Teague, Mark, illus. 2002. (Poppleton Ser.). (J). 11.91 (978-0-7587-1587-6(0)) Book Wholesalers, Inc.

—Poppleton Forever. Teague, Mark, illus. 1998. (Poppleton Ser.). 56p. (J). (gr. k-3). pap. 14.95 (978-0-590-84843-5(7) , Blue Sky Pr., The); pap. 3.99 (978-0-590-84844-2(5)) Scholastic, Inc.

—Poppleton Forever. 1998. (Poppleton Ser.). (J). (gr. k-3). (978-0-606-13718-8(1)) Tandem Library Bks.

—Poppleton Forever. Teague, Mark, illus. 1998. (Poppleton Ser.). 48p. (J). (ps). lib. bdg. 11.80 (978-0-613-11990-0(8)) Tandem Library Bks.

—Poppleton Has Fun. Teague, Mark, illus. 2002. (Poppleton Ser.). (J). 11.91 (978-0-7587-6242-9(9)) Book Wholesalers, Inc.

—Poppleton Has Fun. Teague, Mark, illus. 2000. (Poppleton Ser.). 56p. (J). (gr. k-3). pap. 15.95 (978-0-590-84839-8(9)) Scholastic, Inc.

—Poppleton in Fall. Teague, Mark, illus. 2002. (Poppleton Ser.). (J). 11.91 (978-0-7587-1588-3(9)) Book Wholesalers, Inc.

—Poppleton in Winter. Teague, Mark, illus. 2002. (Poppleton Ser.). (J). 11.91 (978-0-7587-6873-5(7)) Book Wholesalers, Inc.

—Puppies & Piggies. Bates, Ivan, illus. 2008. 32p. (J). 16.00 (978-0-15-202321-8(6)) Harcourt Trade Pubs.

—Thimbleberry Stories. Kneen, Maggie, illus. 2006. 64p. (J). reprint ed. pap. 7.00 (978-0-15-205645-2(9) , Harcourt Paperbacks) Harcourt Children's Bks.

—The Turtle. McDaniels, Preston, illus. 2005. (Lighthouse Family Ser.). 48p. (J). 14.95 (978-0-689-86244-1(X) , Simon & Schuster Children's Publishing) Simon & Schuster Children's Publishing.

—The Whale. McDaniels, Preston, illus. 2003. (Lighthouse Family Ser.). 64p. (J). 14.95 (978-0-689-84881-0(1)) Simon & Schuster Children's Publishing.

Saenz, Benjamin Alire. A Perfect Season for Dreaming. 2007. (SPA & ENG.). 32p. (J). 15.95 (***978-1-933693-01-9(0)***) Cinco Puntos Pr.

Safari Playset. 2007. 48p. pap. 3.99 (***978-1-4037-2202-7(1)***) Dalmatian Pr.

Safari Ride. 2000. (J). (978-1-58805-108-0(0)) DS-Max USA, Inc.

Sagar, Marie. Jimmy's Adventures: I'm Bored & Mr. Gray Bat. 2007. 20p. (J). 7.00 (***978-0-8059-7494-2(6)***) Dorrance Publishing Co., Inc.

Said, S. F. The Outlaw Varjak Paw. McKean, Dave, illus. 2006. 272p. (J). (gr. 3-7). 16.95 (978-0-385-75044-8(7) , Fickling, David Bks.) Random Hse. Children's Bks.

Sakade, Florence. Japanese Children's Favorite Stories, Bk. 1. Kurosaki, Yoshisuke, illus. 3rd rev. ed. 2003. 112p. (gr. 1-5). 19.95 (978-0-8048-3449-0(0)) Tuttle Publishing.

Salas, Macarena, ed. Disney Babies at the Farm / Los Bebes Disney en la Granja: A Book About Farm Words / Un Libro Sobre Palabras de la Granja. 2005. (SPA & ENG., Illus.). 6p. (J). bds. 3.99 (978-0-439-66359-5(8) , Scholastic) Scholastic, Inc.

Saltzberg, Barney. Animal Kisses. 2000. (Touch & Feel Bks.). (Illus.). 14p. (J). (ps-k). bds. 8.95 (978-0-15-202340-9(2) , Red Wagon Bks.) Harcourt Children's Bks.

—Besos de Animales. Campoy, F. Isabel & Ada, Alma Flor, trs. 2004. Tr. of Animal Kisses. (SPA., Illus.). 14p. (J). bds. 8.95 (978-0-15-205448-9(0) , Red Wagon Bks.) Harcourt Children's Bks.

—Noisy Kisses. 2004. (Illus.). 14p. (J). bds. 8.95 (978-0-15-204929-4(0) , Red Wagon Bks.) Harcourt Children's Bks.

—Peekaboo Kisses. 2002. (Touch & Feel Bks.). (Illus.). 14p. (J). bds. 8.95 (978-0-15-216541-3(X) , Red Wagon Bks.) Harcourt Children's Bks.

Sams, Carl R., II & Stoick, Jean. Stranger in the Woods: A Photographic Fantasy. 2002. (gr. 2-5). 12.95 (978-0-9671748-2-2(1)) Sams, II, Carl R. Photography, Inc.

—Stranger in the Woods: A Photographic Fantasy. Sams, Carl R., II & Stoick, Jean, photos by. 1999. (Illus.). 48p. (J). (gr. 2-4). pap. 19.95 (978-0-9671748-0-8(5)) Sams, II, Carl R. Photography, Inc.

—Stranger in the Woods: The Movie. 2002. (gr. k-3). 14.95 (978-0-9671748-1-5(3)) Sams, II, Carl R. Photography, Inc.

—Winter Friends. McDiarmid, Karen, ed. Sams, Carl R., II & Stoick, Jean, photos by. 2003. (Illus.). 12p. (J). bds. 7.95 (978-0-9671748-5-3(6)) Sams, II, Carl R. Photography, Inc.

Samton, Sheila W. Hurray for Rosa! 2001. (Brand New Readers Ser.). (Illus.). 1p. (J). (ps-2). pap. 5.99 (978-0-7636-1127-9(1)) Candlewick Pr.

Samuelson, Christine. Cat Kukupangqertat? Sparck, Amy, illus. 1998. Tr. of What Has Dots?. (ESK.). 12p. (J). (gr. k-3). pap. 6.00 (978-1-58084-036-1(1)) Lower Kuskokwim Schl. District.

Sanders, Jennifer. Tail Tales. 2005. 23p. 13.99 (978-1-4116-2914-1(0)) Lulu.com.

Santa Takes A Vacation. 2005. (J). 5.95 (978-0-9769321-4-7(8)) Steingart, Nathan Publishing.

Santillo, LuAnn. Barnyard Buddies, 6 vols. Santillo, LuAnn, ed. 2003. (Half-Pint Kids Readers Ser.). (Illus.). 42p. (J). (ps-1). pap. 6.99 (978-1-59256-063-9(6)) Half-Pint Kids, Inc.

—In the Meadow, 6 vols. Santillo, LuAnn, ed. 2003. (Half-Pint Kids Readers Ser.). (Illus.). 42p. (J). (ps-1). pap. 6.99 (978-1-59256-105-6(5)) Half-Pint Kids, Inc.

Sargent, Daina. Colors & the Number 10, 11. Lenoir, Jane, illus. 2004. (Learn to Read Ser.: 11). 24p. (J). pap. 9.95 (978-1-59381-049-8(0)); per. 9.95 (978-1-59381-527-1(1)) Ozark Publishing.

—Colors & the Number 1/Los Colores y el Numero 1, 11. Lenoir, Jane, illus. 2004. (Learn to Read Ser.: 11). (SPA & ENG.). 24p. (J). pap. 9.95 (978-1-59381-129-7(2)) Ozark Publishing.

—Colors & the Number 2, 11. Lenoir, Jane, illus. 2004. (Learn to Read Ser.: 11). 24p. (J). per. 9.95 (978-1-59381-529-5(8)) Ozark Publishing.

—Colors & the Number 2/Los Colores y el Numero 2, 11. Lenoir, Jane, illus. 2004. (Learn to Read Ser.: 11). Tr. of Los colores y el Numero 2. (SPA & ENG.). 24p. (J). pap. 9.95 (978-1-59381-131-0(4)); lib. bdg. 19.95 (978-1-59381-130-3(6)) Ozark Publishing.

—Colors & the Number 3, 11. Lenoir, Jane, illus. 2004. (Learn to Read Ser.: 11). 24p. (J). pap. 9.95 (978-1-59381-035-1(0)); pap. 9.95 (978-1-59381-530-1(1)) Ozark Publishing.

—Colors & the Number 3/Los Colores y el Numero 3, 11. Lenoir, Jane, illus. 2004. (Learn to Read Ser.: 11). Tr. of Los colores y el el Numero 3. (SPA & ENG.). 24p. (J). pap. 9.95 (978-1-59381-133-4(0)); lib. bdg. 19.95 (978-1-59381-132-7(2)) Ozark Publishing.

—Colors & the Number 4, 11. Lenoir, Jane, illus. 2004. (Learn to Read Ser.: 11). 24p. (J). per. 9.95 (978-1-59381-531-8(X)) Ozark Publishing.

—Colors & the Number 4/Los colores y el Numero 4, 11. Lenoir, Jane, illus. 2004. (Learn to Read Ser.: 11). Tr. of Los colores y el Numero 4. (SPA & ENG.). 24p. (J). pap. 9.95 (978-1-59381-135-8(7)); lib. bdg. 19.95 (978-1-59381-134-1(9)) Ozark Publishing.

—Colors & the Number 5, 11. Lenoir, Jane, illus. 2004. (Learn to Read Ser.: 11). 24p. (J). pap. 9.95 (978-1-59381-039-9(3)); per. 9.95 (978-1-59381-532-5(8)) Ozark Publishing.

—Colors & the Number 5/Los colores y el Numero 5, 11. Lenoir, Jane, illus. 2004. (Learn to Read Ser.: 11). Tr. of Los colores y el Numero 5. (SPA & ENG.). 24p. (J). pap. 9.95 (978-1-59381-137-2(3)); lib. bdg. 19.95 (978-1-59381-136-5(5)) Ozark Publishing.

—Colors & the Number 6, 11. Lenoir, Jane, illus. 2004. (Learn to Read Ser.: 11). 24p. (J). pap. 9.95 (978-1-59381-041-2(5)); per. 9.95 (978-1-59381-533-2(6)) Ozark Publishing.

—Colors & the Number 7, 11. Lenoir, Jane, illus. 2004. (Learn to Read Ser.: 11). 24p. (J). pap. 9.95 (978-1-59381-043-6(1)); per. 9.95 (978-1-59381-534-9(4)) Ozark Publishing.

—Colors & the Number 7/Los Colores y el Numero 7, 11. Lenoir, Jane, illus. 2004. (Learn to Read Ser.: 11). Tr. of Los colores y el Numero 7. (SPA & ENG.). 24p. (J). pap. 9.95 (978-1-59381-141-9(1)); lib. bdg. 19.95 (978-1-59381-140-2(3)) Ozark Publishing.

—Colors & the Number 8, 11. Lenoir, Jane, illus. 2004. (Learn to Read Ser.: 11). 24p. (J). pap. 9.95 (978-1-59381-045-0(8)) Ozark Publishing.

—Colors & the Number 8/Los Colores y el Numero 8, 11. Lenoir, Jane, illus. 2004. (Learn to Read Ser.: 11). Tr. of Los colores y el Numero 8. (SPA & ENG.). 24p. (J). pap. 9.95 (978-1-59381-143-3(8)); lib. bdg. 19.95 (978-1-59381-142-6(X)) Ozark Publishing.

—Colors & the Number 9, 11. Lenoir, Jane, illus. 2004. (Learn to Read Ser.: 11). 24p. (J). pap. 9.95 (978-1-59381-047-4(4)) Ozark Publishing.

—Colors & the Number 9/Los Colores y el Numero 9, 11. Lenoir, Jane, illus. 2004. (Learn to Read Ser.: 11). Tr. of Los colores y el Numero 9. (SPA & ENG.). 24p. (J). pap. 9.95 (978-1-59381-145-7(4)); lib. bdg. 19.95 (978-1-59381-144-0(6)) Ozark Publishing.

—Introduction to Colors & Niumbers, 11. Lenoir, Jane, illus. 2005. (Learn to Read Ser.: 11). 24p. (J). pap. 9.95 (978-1-59381-051-1(2)) Ozark Publishing.

—Introduction to Colors & Numbers, 11. Lenoir, Jane, illus. 2005. (Learn to Read Ser.: 11). 24p. (J). per. 9.95 (978-1-59381-528-8(X)) Ozark Publishing.

—Introduction to Colors & Numbers (BL) Introduccion a los colores y a los Numeros, 11. Lenoir, Jane, illus. 2004. (Learn to Read Ser.: 11). (SPA & ENG.). 24p. (J). lib. bdg. 19.95 (978-1-59381-148-8(9)) Ozark Publishing.

Sargent, Dave & Sargent, Pat. Annie Antelope: Don't Worry, 56 vols. Huff, Jeane, illus. 2001. (Animal Pride Ser.: 21). 36p. (J). lib. bdg. 19.95 (978-1-56763-358-0(7)) Ozark Publishing.

—Kenny Kangaroo: Fighting, 56 vols., 49. Lenoir, Jane, illus. 2001. (Animal Pride Ser.: Vol. 49). 36p. (J). lib. bdg. 19.95 (978-1-56763-539-3(3)) Ozark Publishing.

—Marty Mule: Stubborn Ole Mule!, 56 vols., 31. Huff, Jeane, illus. 2001. (Animal Pride Ser.: Vol. 31). 36p. (J). pap. 6.95 (978-1-56763-379-5(X)) Ozark Publishing.

—Robbie Razorback: Meanie! Meanie!, 56 vols., 35. Huff, Jeane, illus. 2001. (Animal Pride Ser.: 35). 36p. (J). lib. bdg. 19.95 (978-1-56763-386-3(2)) Ozark Publishing.

—Satan the Bull: I Don't Trust Anyoune!, 56 vols., 37. Huff, Jeane, illus. 2001. (Animal Pride Ser.: Vol. 37). 36p. (J). lib. bdg. 19.95 (978-1-56763-390-0(0)) Ozark Publishing.

Sargent, Dave, et al. Kenny Kangaroo: Fighting, 17, 49. 2000. (Animal Pride Ser.: 48). (Illus.). 42p. (J). pap. 6.95 (978-1-56763-540-9(7)) Ozark Publishing.

—Mattie Musk-Ox: Neatness, 17, 53. 2000. (Animal Pride Ser.: 53). (Illus.). 42p. (J). pap. 6.95 (978-1-56763-548-5(2)) Ozark Publishing.

Sargent, Pat. The Timber Wolf, 6. Lenoir, Jane, illus. 2003. (Barney the Bear Killer Ser.: Vol. 3). 123p. (J). 3. pap. 9.95 (978-1-56763-968-1(2)); Vol. 3. lib. bdg. 25.25 (978-1-56763-967-4(4)) Ozark Publishing.

Sargent, Pat L. The Cheetah, 6 vols, Vol. 6. Lenoir, Jane, illus. l.t. ed. 2004. (Barney the Bear Killer Ser.: No. 6). 146p. (YA). pap. 9.95 (978-1-56763-974-2(7)); lib. bdg. 25.25 (978-1-56763-973-5(9)) Ozark Publishing.

—The Grizzly, 8, Vol. 1. Lenoir, Jane, illus. l.t. ed. 2004. (Barney the Bear Killer Ser.: No. 1). 129p. (YA). lib. bdg. 25.25 (978-1-56763-963-6(1)) Ozark Publishing.

Sarrazin, Marisol & Homel, David. Peppy, Phlox & the Bath. 2000. (Illus.). 32p. (J). (gr. 1-4). pap. (978-1-894363-42-6(6)) Dominique & Friends.

Sato, Wakiko. Grandma Baba's Amazing Scarf!, Vol. 10. 2004. (Grandma Baba Ser.: Bk. 10). (Illus.). 28p. 12.95 (978-0-8048-3566-4(7)) Tuttle Publishing.

—Grandma Baba's Birthday Party, Vol. 4. 2004. (Grandma Baba Ser.). (Illus.). 32p. 10.95 (978-0-8048-3562-6(4)) Tuttle Publishing.

—Grandma Baba's Busy Night, Bk. 1. 2004. (Grandma Baba Ser.). (Illus.). 32p. 10.95 (978-0-8048-3559-6(4)) Tuttle Publishing.

Sauer, Cat. Flip Flop & Hoot. Jankowski, Dan, illus. l.t. ed. 2003. (Brown Bag Bedtime Bks.: 1). 35p. (YA). spiral bd. 16.95 (978-0-9704460-6-0(3)) Writer's Ink. Studios, Inc.

Saunders, Dave & Saunders, Julie. So Slow. 2001. (Illus.). 28p. (J). (gr. k-3). 15.95 (978-0-7614-5080-1(7) , Cavendish Children's Bks.) Cavendish, Marshall Corp.

Saunders, Susan. The Creature Double Feature. 1998. (Black Cat Club Ser.). (J). (978-0-606-13206-0(6)) Tandem Library Bks.

Saunders, Zina, illus. Say Please! A Book about Manners. 2006. (Backyardigans Ser.). 24p. (J). pap. 3.99 (978-1-4169-1386-3(6) , Simon Spotlight/Nickelodeon) Simon & Schuster Children's Publishing.

Sautel, Anne. Escale a Pékin! Brière, Marie-Josée, tr. from ENG. Stewart, Scott, illus. 2007. (FRE.). 96p. pap. (***978-2-922435-12-2(1)***) Lobster Pr.

Sax, Boria. Serpent & the Swan: The Animal Bride in Folklore & Literature. 1998. (Illus.). 268p. pap. 18.95 (978-0-939923-68-7(8)) McDonald & Woodward Publishing Co., The.

Saxon, Victoria. Tigger's Tall Tales: Chuncky Roly Poly Book. 1999. (Learn & Grow Ser.). (Illus.). 16p. (J). (ps-k). 3.50 (978-0-7364-0153-1(9)) Mouse Works.

Sayre, April Pulley. Dig, Wait, Listen: A Desert Toad's Tale. Bash, Barbara, illus. 2001. 32p. (J). (gr. 1 up). 15.99 (978-0-688-16614-4(8)) HarperCollins Pubs.

—Hush Little Puppy. Winter, Susan, illus. rev. ed. 2007. 32p. (J). (ps-k). 15.95 (978-0-8050-7102-3(4) , Holt, Henry & Co. Bks. For Young Readers) Holt, Henry & Co.

Scafuro, Lisa. Adventures at Cedar Hollow: Tigre Encounters the Great Horned Owl. 2005. (J). 18.00 (978-0-8059-6635-0(8)) Dorrance Publishing Co., Inc.

Scamell, Ragnhild. Ouch! Terry, Michael, illus. 2006. 26p. (J). 16.00 (978-1-56148-511-6(X)) Good Bks.

Scarry, Richard. The Best Mistake Ever! Scarry, Richard, illus. 2003. (Step into Reading Step 2 Bks.). (Illus.). 48p. (J). (ps-3). lib. bdg. 11.99 (978-0-394-96816-2(6) , Random Hse. Bks. for Young Readers) Random Hse. Children's Bks.

—The Best Mistake Ever! And Other Stories. Scarry, Richard, illus. 2002. (Illus.). (J). 11.91 (978-0-7587-0980-6(3)) Book Wholesalers, Inc.

—Cosas Que Nos Gustan.Tr. of Things We Love. (SPA., Illus.). (J). pap. 6.95 (978-950-04-1043-4(5)) Emecé Editores S.A. ARG. *Dist:* Planeta Publishing Corp.

—Cosas Que Nos Gustan. 2003. (Richard Scarry Ser.).Tr. of Things We Love. (SPA.). (J). pap. (978-970-690-848-3(X)) Planeta Mexicana Editorial S. A. de C. V.

—Richard Scarry's Animal Nursery Tales. 2006. (Illus.). 72p. (J). (ps-3). 14.95 (978-0-375-83791-3(4) , Golden Bks.) Random Hse. Children's Bks.

—Richard Scarry's Busiest Pop-up Ever! 2007. (Richard Scarry Ser.). 10p. (J). (ps-2). 19.99 (***978-0-375-84120-0(2)*** , Golden Bks.) Random Hse. Children's Bks.

—Richard Scarry's Father Cat's Christmas Tree. 2003. (Illus.). 24p. (J). (ps-2). pap. 3.25 (978-0-375-82556-9(8) , Golden Bks.) Random Hse. Children's Bks.

—Richard Scarry's Father Cat's Christmas Tree. 2003. (gr. k-3). lib. bdg. 10.95 (978-0-613-71907-0(7)) Tandem Library Bks.

—Richard Scarry's Pie Rats Ahoy. Scarry, Richard, illus. 2002. (Illus.). (J). 11.91 (978-0-7587-6251-1(8)) Book Wholesalers, Inc.

—Santa Needs Help! 2000. (J). (978-0-606-20036-3(3)) Tandem Library Bks.

—The Worst Helper Ever. Scarry, Richard, illus. 2004. 32p. (J). (ps-2). lib. bdg. 11.99 (978-0-375-99990-1(6) , Random Hse. Bks. for Young Readers) Random Hse. Children's Bks.

—The Worst Helper Ever. 1998. (Road to Reading Ser.). (Illus.). 32p. (J). (ps-2). pap. 3.99 (978-0-307-26100-7(X) , 26100, Random Hse. Bks. for Young Readers) Random Hse. Children's Bks.

Scarry, Richard & Golden Books Staff. Richard Scarry's Favorite Storybook Ever. 2003. (Picture Book Ser.). (Illus.). 72p. (J). (ps-3). 14.99 (978-0-375-82549-1(5) , Golden Bks.) Random Hse. Children's Bks.

Scelsa, Greg & Debney, John. Friends Forever. Faulkner, Stacey, ed. Mahan, Benton, illus. 2006. (J). pap. 2.99 (***978-1-59198-322-4(3)***) Creative Teaching Pr., Inc.

Schade, Susan. Baseball Camp on the Planet of the Eyeballs. Buller, Jon, illus. 1998. (Step into Reading Step 3 Bks.). (J). (gr. 2-3). (978-0-606-13950-2(8)) Tandem Library Bks.

—Cat at Bat. 2000. (gr. k-3). lib. bdg. 11.80 (978-0-613-27765-5(1)) Tandem Library Bks.

—Faradawn. Buller, Jon, illus. 2007. (Fog Mound Ser.: No. 2). 208p. (J). (gr. 3-7). 15.99 (978-0-689-87686-8(6)) Simon & Schuster Children's Publishing.

—Travels of Thelonious. Buller, Jon, illus. 2007. (Fog Mound Ser.: No. 1). 224p. (J). (gr. 3-7). pap. 7.99 (978-0-689-87685-1(8) , Simon & Schuster Children's Publishing) Simon & Schuster Children's Publishing.

Schade, Susan & Buller, Jon. Cat at Bat. 2000. (Road to Reading Ser.). (Illus.). 32p. (J). (ps-1). pap. 3.99 (978-0-307-26211-0(1) , Random Hse. Bks. for Young Readers) Random Hse. Children's Bks.

—Cat on the Mat. 1998. (Step into Reading Ser.: Vol. 2). (Illus.). 32p. (J). (ps-1). pap. 3.99 (978-0-307-26207-3(3) , Random Hse. Bks. for Young Readers) Random Hse. Children's Bks.

—The Travels of Thelonious. 2006. (Fog Mound Ser.: No. 1). (Illus.). 224p. (J). (gr. 3-7). 14.95 (978-0-689-87684-4(X)) Simon & Schuster Children's Publishing.

Schaefer, Carole Lexa. Cool Time Song. Morgan, Pierr, illus. 2005. 32p. (J). (ps-2). 15.99 (978-0-670-05928-7(5) , Viking Juvenile) Penguin Group (USA) Inc.

—Down in the Woods at Sleepytime. Cabban, Vanessa, illus. 2004. 24p. (J). (gr. k-ps). bds. 6.99 (978-0-7636-2566-5(3)) Candlewick Pr.

Schaefer, Lola M. Mittens. Hartung, Susan Kathleen, illus. 2006. (My First I Can Read Book Ser.). 32p. (J). 14.99 (978-0-06-054659-5(X)); lib. bdg. 15.89 (978-0-06-054660-1(3)) HarperCollins Pubs.

Schafer, Susan. Where's My Tail? Cushman, Doug, illus. 2005. 32p. (J). 16.95 (978-0-7614-5170-9(6)) Cavendish, Marshall Corp.

Schenberg. Kiki's Delivery. 1998. (J). pap. 3.95 (978-0-7868-4296-4(2)) Disney Pr.

Schieber, Jennifer. Burt's Counting Stew. ed. 2004. (Shared Connections Ser.). (J). pap. 27.00 (978-1-4108-1631-3(1)); pap., instr.'s gde. ed. 27.00 (978-1-4108-1607-8(9)) Benchmark Education Co.

—A contar con la sopa de Beto: Fiction-to-Fact Big Book. May, Gillie, illus. enl. ed. 2004. (SPA.). (J). pap. 26.00 (978-1-4108-2361-8(X) , 2361X) Benchmark Education Co.

Schiller, Pam. The Iguana in Lavender Socks. Nestor, Paul, illus. 2006. (Noodlebug Ser.). 16p. (J). 12.95 (978-0-7696-4275-8(6)) School Specialty Publishing.

Schindel, John. Busy Kitties. Franzen, Sean, photos by. 2004. (Illus.). 20p. (J). bds. 6.95 (978-1-58246-130-4(9) , Tricycle Pr.) Ten Speed Pr.

Schirado, William C. Creatures, Vol. 1. Assenzo, Teresa M., illus. 18th l.t. ed. 1998. 128p. (J). (gr. k-6). 21.95 (978-0-9660166-1-1(0)) TW Publishing.

Schkolnik, Saul. Cuentos Ecologicos. Cardemil, Carmen, illus. 2nd ed. 2003. Tr. of Ecological Tales. (SPA.). 54p. (J). (ps-7). pap. 7.50 (978-968-16-4757-5(2) , FC6400) Fondo de Cultura Economica MEX. *Dist:* Lectorum Pubns., Inc.

Schlaht, Kim. Ronnie's Rotten Recipes. Tijerina, Arnold G., 3rd, ed. Gregory, Chris, illus. 2006. 72p. (J). per. 18.95 (978-0-9777688-1-3(3)) TICO Publishing.

Schlegel, Paige. I Que Desorden! Schlegel, Paige, illus. 2001. Tr. of What a Mess. (SPA.). 32p. (J). (gr. k-8). pap. 7.50 (978-1-59134-014-0(4)) Maval Publishing, Inc.

Schmidt, Karen. Carl's Nose. 2006. (Illus.). 40p. (J). 16.00 (978-0-15-205049-8(3)) Harcourt Trade Pubs.

Schnurre, Wolfdietrich. La Princesa Viene a las Cuatro. Berner, Rotraut Susanne, illus. 2002. (Rosa y Manzana Ser.). (SPA.). 32p. (J). (gr. k-2). (978-84-89804-32-6(X) , LG30138) Loguez Ediciones ESP. *Dist:* Lectorum Pubns., Inc.

Schoberle, Cecile. Runaway Reptar! Ross, Sharon & Cardona, Jose Maria, illus. 1999. (Rugrats Ser.). 32p. (J). (ps-2). 5.99 (978-0-689-82524-8(2) , 076714005990, Simon Spotlight/Nickelodeon) Simon & Schuster Children's Publishing.

—Runaway Reptar! 1999. (gr. k-3). lib. bdg. 14.15 (978-0-613-15959-3(4)) Tandem Library Bks.

Scholastic, Inc. Staff. Bedtime Storybook Collection. 2007. (Sweet Dreams Ser.). 96p. (J). pap. 7.99 (***978-0-439-93403-9(6)*** , Cartwheel Bks.) Scholastic, Inc.

—Fluffy Bunny. Harper, Piers, illus. 2004. 32p. (J). 15.95 (978-0-439-57825-7(6) , Cartwheel Bks.) Scholastic, Inc.

—Hand Puppet Board Book (Un Libro de Carton Con Titeres) 2007. (Noah's Ark Ser.). 6p. (J). bds. 12.99 (***978-0-439-92274-6(7)*** , Scholastic en Espanol) Scholastic, Inc.

—Hello! Hello! Berg, Michelle, illus. 2004. 4p. (J). 12.95 (978-0-439-62158-8(5) , Cartwheel Bks.) Scholastic, Inc.

—I Love Animals. Amaral, Gayla, ed. McKee, Darren, illus. 2001. (Barney Ser.). 96p. (J). 2.99 (978-1-58668-131-9(1)) Scholastic, Inc.

Scholastic, Inc. Staff. Thumbelina/Pulgarcita. Andrada, Javier, illus. 2007. (Bilingual Tales Ser.). (ENG & SPA.). 24p. (J). pap. 3.99 (***978-0-439-87196-9(4)***) Scholastic, Inc.

Scholastic, Inc. Staff, contrib. by. Teacher's Pet: Clifford. 2002. (Illus.). 32p. (J). pap. 6.99 (978-0-439-36411-9(6)) Scholastic, Inc.

School Specialty Publishing. Learning Letters. 2004. (Kindergarten Standards Ser.). 144p. (C). pap. 16.99 (978-0-7682-2820-5(4) , FS99276) Schaffer, Frank Pubns.

Schuyer, Silvia. La Grimas/Cocodrilo. Bernalene, Poly, illus. 2001. Tr. of Crocodile Tears. (SPA.). 24p. (J). 12.50 (978-950-08-2570-2(8)) Atlantida ARG. *Dist:* AIMS International Bks., Inc.

Schwartz, Amy. A Beautiful Girl. Schwartz, Amy, illus. 2006. (Illus.). 32p. (J). 16.95 (978-1-59643-165-2(2)) Roaring Brook Pr.

Schwartz, Roslyn. The Mole Sisters & the Rainy Day. Schwartz, Roslyn, illus. 2001. (Mole Sisters Ser.). (Illus.). 32p. (J). (ps-k). lib. bdg. 14.95 (978-1-55037-611-1(X)) Annick Pr., Ltd. CAN. *Dist:* Firefly Bks., Ltd.

—Tales from Parc la Fontaine. Schwartz, Roslyn, illus. 2006. (Parc la Fontaine Ser.). (Illus.). 48p. (J). (ps-1). pap. 7.95 (978-1-55451-043-6(0)); lib. bdg. 19.95 (978-1-55451-044-3(9)) Annick Pr., Ltd. CAN. *Dist:* Firefly Bks., Ltd.

Schwartz, Tom. How Mother Nature Flowered the Fields. 2006. (Illus.). 120p. (J). per. 18.95 (978-1-57545-102-2(6) , Reagent Pr. Echo) Reagent Pr.

Scott, Carlton T. Grin's Message. Scott, Carlton T., illus. rev. ed. 1999. (Illus.). 32p. (J). (gr. k-3). reprint ed. 9.95 (978-0-9636652-7-0(8)) Ends of the Earth Books.com.

Scott, Nathan Kumar. The Sacred Banana Leaf. Raut, Radhashyam, illus. 2008. 32p. (J). (ps-2). 16.95 (***978-81-86211-28-1(4)***) Tara Publishing IND. *Dist:* Consortium Bk. Sales & Distribution.

Scraper, Katherine. Garden Lunch. 2006. (Early Explorers Ser.). (J). 30.00 (***978-1-4108-6027-9(2)***) Benchmark Education Co.

Scruton, Clive, illus. I Love You! 1999. (Leap Frog Lift-A-Flap Ser.). (J). (978-0-7853-3369-2(X)) Publications International, Ltd.

Sedgwick, Marcus & Andersen, Hans Christian. Emperor's New Clothes. Jay, Alison, illus. 2004. 32p. (J). 16.95 (978-0-8118-4569-4(9)) Chronicle Bks. LLC.

Seeley, Barbara J. The Red Squeaky Nose. Creamer, Jennifer, illus. 2001. 32p. (J). (ps-6). 11.95 (978-0-9704873-0-8(4)) Twynz Publishing.

Segal, John. Carrot Soup. Segal, John, illus. 2006. (Illus.). 32p. (J). (ps-1). 12.95 (978-0-689-87702-5(1) , McElderry, Margaret K.) Simon & Schuster Children's Publishing.

Segal, Lore. Why Mole Shouted & Other Stories. Ruzzier, Sergio, illus. 2004. 40p. (J). 16.00 (978-0-374-38417-3(7) , Farrar, Straus & Giroux (BYR)) Farrar, Straus & Giroux.

Segarra, Angelo M. Coca Finds a Shell. Segarra, Kirstie, ed. Segarra, Angelo M., illus. 2004. (Illus.). 24p. (J). 14.95 (978-0-9752664-0-3(3)) Segarra, Angelo.

Seltzer, Eric. Doodle Dog. Seltzer, Eric, illus. 2005. (Ready-to-Reads Ser.). (Illus.). 32p. (J). pap. 3.99 (978-0-689-85910-6(4) , Aladdin) Simon & Schuster Children's Publishing.

—Doodle Dog. 2005. (Ready-to-Reads Ser.). (Illus.). 32p. (J). lib. bdg. 11.89 (978-0-689-85913-7(9) , Aladdin Library) Simon & Schuster Children's Publishing.

Selway, Martina, illus. Clean Out the Fridge, Fred! 1999. (J). (978-0-7608-3199-1(8)) Sundance/Newbridge Educational Publishing.

—Fred Fixes a Faucet. 1999. (J). (978-0-7608-3193-9(9)) Sundance/Newbridge Educational Publishing.

—The Photograph. 1999. (J). (978-0-7608-3197-7(1)) Sundance/Newbridge Educational Publishing.

—Something Nasty! 1999. (J). (978-0-7608-3198-4(X)) Sundance/Newbridge Educational Publishing.

—What's That? 1999. (J). (978-0-7608-3195-3(5)) Sundance/Newbridge Educational Publishing.

Sendak, Maurice. Very Far Away. Sendak, Maurice, illus. 2005. (Sendak Reissues Ser.). 56p. 15.95 (978-0-06-029723-7(9)) HarperCollins Pubs.

Sensel, Joni. Bears Barge In. Bivins, Christopher, illus. 2003. 32p. (J). (ps up). 14.95 (978-0-9701195-0-6(X)) Dream Factory Bks.

Seppala, Ray. Willowrun Tales. 2006. (Illus.). 122p. (YA). per. 9.95 (978-1-933324-47-0(3)) Cedar Hill Publishing.

Serfozo, Mary. Big Bug Dug. Maccarone, Grace, ed. Scherer, Jeffrey, illus. 2003. 32p. (J). pap. 3.99 (978-0-439-59426-4(X)) Scholastic, Inc.

Seton, Ernest Thompson. Johnny Bear. 2004. reprint ed. pap. 15.95 (978-1-4191-2787-8(X)); pap. 1.99 (978-1-4192-2787-5(4)) Kessinger Publishing, LLC.

Seton, Ernest Thompson. Johnny Bear & Other Stories from Lives. 2006. 62.99 (***978-1-4280-3514-0(1));*** pap. 55.99 (***978-1-4280-3489-1(7)***) IndyPublish.com.

Seuling, Barbara. Robert Takes a Stand. Brewer, Paul, illus. 2004. (Robert Bks.). 120p. (J). 15.95 (978-0-8126-2712-1(1)) Cricket Bks.

Seuling, Barbara & Altshuler, Miriam. Whose House? Chorao, Kay, tr. Chorao, Kay, illus. 2004. 32p. (J). 16.00 (978-0-15-216347-1(6) , Gulliver Bks.) Harcourt Children's Bks.

Seuss, Dr. All Aboard the Circus McGurkus. 2004. (Illus.). 8p. (J). (gr. k-ps). bds. 6.99 (978-0-375-83011-2(1) , Random Hse. Bks. for Young Readers) Random Hse. Children's Bks.

—Gerald McBoing Boing Sound Book. 2003. (Illus.). 12p. (J). (ps). bds. 7.99 (978-0-375-82443-2(X) , Random Hse. Bks. for Young Readers) Random Hse. Children's Bks.

Sewell, Anna. Black Beauty. 2002. (Spot the Classics Ser.). (Illus.). 178p. (J). (gr. k-5). 4.99 (978-1-57759-544-1(0)) Dalmatian Pr.

—Black Beauty, Level 2. 2001. (Illus.). 48p. (C). pap. 9.00 (978-0-582-42121-9(7)) Pearson ESL.

Sexton, Brenda. Busy Bath. Maccarone, Grace, ed. 2006. (Illus.). 8p. (J). 8.99 (978-0-439-83652-4(2) , Cartwheel Bks.) Scholastic, Inc.

Seymour, Sylvia. The Animals' Side of the Story. Seymour, Sylvia, illus. 2001. (Illus.). 64p. (J). (gr. 3-6). pap. 14.95 (978-0-9651396-5-6(4)) StoryLoft Publishing.

Shah, Idries. The Clever Boy & the Terrible, Dangerous Animal. Santiago, Rose Mary, illus. 2005. 32p. (J). (ps-ps). pap. 6.99 (978-1-883536-51-0(0) , Hoopoe Bks.) ISHK.

—The Clever Boy & the Terrible, Dangerous Animal/el Muchachito Listo y el Terrible y Peligroso Animal. Wirkala, Rita, tr. Santiago, Rose Mary, illus. 2005. 32p. (J). (ps-ps). 18.00 (978-1-883536-39-8(1)); pap. 6.95 (978-1-883536-40-4(5)) ISHK. (Hoopoe Bks.).

Shah, Naseeruddin. The Blue Jackal - The Foolish Lion. 1998. (Karadi Tales Ser.). (Illus.). 24p. (YA). (gr. 1 up). 15.99 incl. audio (978-81-86838-00-6(7)) APG Sales and Fulfillment.

—The Crows & the Serpent - The Monkey & the Crocodile. 1998. (Karadi Tales Ser.). 24p. (YA). (gr. 1-4). 15.99 incl. audio (978-81-86838-04-4(X)) APG Sales and Fulfillment.

Shannon, David. Pato Va en Bici. 2005. (SPA.). 40p. (J). (gr. k-2). 17.99 (978-84-261-3270-3(7)) Juventud, Editorial ESP. *Dist:* Lectorum Pubns., Inc., Iaconi, Mariuccia Bk. Imports.

Shannon, George. Lizard's Guest. Aruego, Jose & Dewey, Ariane, illus. 2003. 32p. (J). 16.89 (978-0-06-009084-5(7)) HarperCollins Pubs.

—Wise Acres. Zemke, Deborah, illus. 2004. 40p. (J). 15.95 (978-1-59354-041-8(8)) Handprint Bks.

Shapiro, Arnold. Mice Squeak, We Speak. de Paola, Tomie, illus. 2000. 32p. (J). (ps-1). pap. 5.99 (978-0-698-11873-7(1) , Putnam Juvenile) Penguin Group (USA) Inc.

—Mice Squeak, We Speak. de Paola, Tomie, illus. 2000. (J). (978-0-606-20245-9(5)) Tandem Library Bks.

Sharkey, Niamh. Ravenous Beast. 2003. (Illus.). 32p. (J). (ps-1). 17.99 (978-0-7636-2182-7(X)) Candlewick Pr.

Sharp, Margery. The Turret. Williams, Garth, illus. 2006. 160p. (J). 15.99 (978-0-316-00059-8(0)) Little Brown & Co.

Shattuck, Louise. The Donkey & the Tree. Shattuck, Louise, illus. 1999. (Illus.). 32p. (J). (gr. k-2). 12.95 (978-1-880090-86-2(4) , Weasel Bks.) Galde Pr., Inc.

Shaw, Dana Alton, III. My Friend Zundel. 2006. per. (***978-0-9791091-0-2(8)***) Shaw, Dana.

Shaw, Greg. Meadow Friends. 2005. 50p. pap. 12.95 (978-1-4137-8081-9(4)) PublishAmerica, Inc.

Shaw, Victoria. The Ooch-Me-Noodle Bird. 2004. (Illus.). 28p. (J). pap. 19.95 (978-1-932373-73-8(X)) Cedar Hill Publishing.

Shea-Gass, Lucille. How Animals Sleep Vol. 1: In Africa. 2004. 48p. pap. 19.95 (978-1-4137-2039-6(0)) PublishAmerica, Inc.

Shepherd, Jodie. Safari Friends: Guess Who Safari Friends. 2006. (Guess Who? Ser.). (Illus.). 12p. (J). bds. 7.99 (978-0-7944-1142-8(8)) Reader's Digest Assn., Inc., The.

Shields, Carol Diggory. Homes. Junakovic, Svjetlan, illus. 2001. (Animagicals Ser.). 32p. (J). (ps-2). 9.95 (978-1-929766-27-7(0)) Handprint Bks.

—Patterns. Junakovic, Svjetlan, illus. 2001. (Animagicals Ser.). 32p. (J). (ps-1). bds. 9.95 (978-1-929766-15-4(7)) Handprint Bks.

—The Saturday Night at the Dinosaur Stomp. Nash, Scott, illus. 2002. 32p. (J). (ps-3). pap. 5.99 (978-0-7636-0696-1(0)) Candlewick Pr.

—Sports. Junakovic, Svjetlan, illus. 2001. (Animagicals Ser.). 32p. (J). 9.95 (978-1-929766-28-4(9)) Handprint Bks.

Shields, Carol Diggory & Junakovic, Svjetlan. On the Go. 2001. (Animagicals Ser.). (Illus.). 32p. (J). (ps-1). bds. 9.95 (978-1-929766-14-7(9)) Handprint Bks.

Shields, Carol Diggory, et al. Music. 2000. (Animagicals Ser.). (Illus.). 12p. (J). (ps-1). 9.95 (978-1-929766-05-5(X)) Handprint Bks.

Shipman, Gary, illus. Pakkins' Land: Tavitah, 4. 2003. (Pakkins' Land: 4). 128p. pap. 16.95 (978-0-9700241-4-5(2)) Pakkins Presents.

Shook, Babs. A House for Mouse, Level 1. Couri, Kathy, illus. 2000. (All-Star Readers Ser.). 32p. (J). (ps-1). pap. 3.99 (978-1-57584-383-4(8) , Reader's Digest Children's Bks.) Reader's Digest Children's Publishing, Inc.

Shook-Hazen, Barbara. House for Mouse. 2000. (ps-2). lib. bdg. 11.80 (978-0-613-25577-6(1)) Tandem Library Bks.

The Show: Individual Title Six-Packs. (Sails Literacy Ser.). 16p. (gr. k up). 27.00 (978-0-7635-4413-3(2)) Rigby Education.

Shreeve, Elizabeth. Hector Afloat. Levy, Pamela R., illus. 2004. (Ready-for-Chapters Ser.). 64p. (J). pap. 3.99 (978-0-689-86416-2(7) , Aladdin) Simon & Schuster Children's Publishing.

Shulman, Lisa. The Moon Might Be Milk. Hillenbrand, Will, illus. 2007. (J). (***978-1-4287-3291-9(8)*** , Dutton Juvenile) Penguin Group (USA) Inc.

Shulman, Mark. Amazing Animals. Harris, Jenny, illus. 2003. (Funny Fingers Ser.). 14p. (J). bds. 3.95 (978-1-4027-0703-2(7)) Sterling Publishing Co., Inc.

—Foxy Fox. Chambers, Sally, illus. 2004. 8p. (J). bds. 6.95 (978-1-58925-738-2(3) , tiger tales) ME Media LLC.

—Magic Fairy Forest. Wilburn, Kathy, illus. 2005. (Storytime Stickers Ser.). 16p. (J). pap. 4.95 (978-1-4027-1806-9(3)) Sterling Publishing Co., Inc.

—Some Sheep. Bartos, Joe & Nguyen, Vincent, illus. 2003. (Some Animals Ser.). 20p. (J). 5.95 (978-0-7641-5653-3(5)) Barron's Educational Series, Inc.

—El Zorro Astuto. Chambers, Sally, illus. 2004. (Todo cambia Ser.). (SPA.). 8p. 12.95 (978-84-7864-823-8(2)) Combel Editorial, S.A. ESP. *Dist:* Independent Pubs. Group.

Si, Artists. Peek-a-Boo in the Berry Patch. Si, Artists, illus. 2006. (Strawberry Shortcake Baby Ser.). (Illus.). 10p. (J). (ps-ps). bds. 5.99 (978-0-448-44351-5(1) , Grosset & Dunlap) Penguin Group (USA) Inc.

Siamon, Sharon. Fire Horse. 2002. (gr. 3-6). lib. bdg. 15.25 (978-0-613-78589-1(4)) Tandem Library Bks.

—Fire Horse. 2002. (Mustang Mountain Ser.). 144p. (J). (gr. 3-7). pap. 6.95 (978-1-55285-457-0(4)) Whitecap Bks., Ltd. CAN. *Dist:* Firefly Bks., Ltd.

—Night Horse. 2002. (Mustang Mountain Ser.: No. 3). 144p. (J). (gr. 3-7). pap. 6.95 (978-1-55285-363-4(2)) Whitecap Bks., Ltd. CAN. *Dist:* Firefly Bks., Ltd.

Silberberg, Alan. Pond Scum. 2007. 288p. (gr. 3-7). pap. 5.99 (978-0-7868-5635-0(1)) Hyperion Pr.

Silva Lee, Alfonso. Coqui y Sus Amigos: Los Animales de Puerto Rico. Hayskar, Bonnie J., ed. Silva Lee, Alfonso, photos by. 2000. Tr. of Coqui And His Friends: The Anima. (SPA & ENG., Illus.). 100p. (J). (gr. 3-6). pap. 12.95 (978-1-929165-03-2(X)) PANGAEA.

Silvano, Wendi. Counting Coconuts/Contando Cocos: A Counting Story in English & Spanish. Raven Tree Press Staff, ed. Granius, Marty, illus. 2004. Tr. of Contando Cocos. (SPA & ENG.). 32p. (J). (ps 3). 16.95 (978-0-9720192-6-2(X) , 626999) Raven Tree Pr.

Silver Dolphin en Español Editors. Disney Animales Cine en Casa. 2003. (Cine en casa Disney Ser.). (SPA., Illus.). 46p. (J). 24.95 (978-970-718-112-0(5) , Silver Dolphin en Español) Advanced Marketing, S. de R. L. de C. V. MEX. *Dist:* Perseus Distribution.

—Figuras Magicas: Disney Magical Magnets. 2005. (SPA., Illus.). 8p. (J). bds. 12.95 (978-970-718-242-4(3) , Silver Dolphin en Español) Advanced Marketing, S. de R. L. de C. V. MEX. *Dist:* Perseus Distribution.

Silver Dolphin en Español Staff. Musica en casa: Disney, cuentos de Animales: Music Player: Animal Friends. 2007. (Illus.). 38p. (J). 24.95 (***978-970-718-494-7(9)*** , Silver Dolphin en Español) Advanced Marketing, S. de R. L. de C. V. MEX. *Dist:* Perseus Distribution.

Silverhardt, Lauryn. Blue's Fall Day: A Lift-the-Flap Story. Kanemoto, Dan, illus. 2007. (Blue's Clues Ser.). 16p. (J). pap. 6.99 (***978-1-4169-3436-3(7)*** , Simon Spotlight/Nickelodeon) Simon & Schuster Children's Publishing.

Silverstein, Shel. Lafcadio, el Leon Que Devolvio el Disparo. 1998. (SPA., Illus.). 112p. (J). (gr. 3-5). (978-84-264-3663-4(3) , LM4642) Editorial Lumen ESP. *Dist:* Lectorum Pubns., Inc.

Simmons, Jane. Come along, Daisy! Simmons, Jane, illus. 2003. (Illus.). 32p. (J). (ps-1). pap. 6.99 (978-0-316-16878-6(5)) Little, Brown Bks. for Young Readers.

Simmons, Lynn Sheffield. Sugar Lump, the Orphan Calf. 2004. (Illus.). 50p. (YA). pap. 8.95 (978-1-58980-216-2(0)) Pelican Publishing Co., Inc.

Simmons, Monica. Aster Jungle: Furrdinand the Furrballer. Ward, Jon, illus. 1998. (Aster Planet Chronicles Ser.: Vol. 2). 32p. (J). (gr. k-4). 15.95 (978-0-9658128-3-2(9)) Long Wind Publishing.

Simon and Schuster Children's Staff & Barklem, Jill. Summer Story. Barklem, Jill, illus. 2000. (Brambly Hedge Ser.). (Illus.). 32p. (J). (ps-1). 9.95 (978-0-689-83059-4(9) , Atheneum) Simon & Schuster Children's Publishing.

Simson, Dana. Zooballie. 2003. (Sparkle Bks.). (J). bds. 10.95 (978-1-74047-207-4(1)) Book Co. Publishing Pty, Ltd., The AUS. *Dist:* Penton Overseas, Inc.

Singer, Marilyn. Good Day, Good Night. Goembel, Ponder, illus. 1998. (Accelerated Reader Bks.). 32p. (J). (ps-k). lib. bdg. 15.95 (978-0-7614-5018-4(1) , Cavendish Children's Bks.) Cavendish, Marshall Corp.

Sinnott, Bruce. A Special Place. 2005. (J). pap. 8.00 (978-0-8059-6678-7(1)) Dorrance Publishing Co., Inc.

Siomades, Lorianne. Cuckoo Can't Find You. Siomades, Lorianne, illus. 2003. (Illus.). 32p. (J). (ps up). 12.95 (978-1-56397-778-7(8)) Boyds Mills Pr.

—Kangaroo & Cricket. Siomades, Lorianne, illus. 2003. (Illus.). 32p. (J). (ps up). 12.95 (978-1-56397-780-0(X)) Boyds Mills Pr.

Sis, Peter. Madlenka's Dog. Sis, Peter, illus. 2002. (Illus.). 40p. (J). (ps-1). 17.00 (978-0-374-34699-7(2) , Farrar, Straus & Giroux (BYR)) Farrar, Straus & Giroux.

—Madlenka's dog. (Illus.). 19.95 (978-0-88899-462-2(1)) Groundwood Bks. CAN. *Dist:* Transition Vendor.

Skutch, Robert. Albie's Trip to the Jumble Jungle. Mathieu, Joe, illus. 2004. 32p. (J). 14.95 (978-1-58246-076-5(0) , Tricycle Pr.) Ten Speed Pr.

Slate, Joseph. Little Porcupine's Christmas. Bond, Felicia, illus. 2001. 32p. (J). (ps-1). 9.95 (978-0-06-029533-2(3) , Geringer, Laura Book) HarperCollins Pubs.

—Little Porcupine's Christmas. 2003. (gr. k-3). lib. bdg. 14.15 (978-0-613-68444-6(3)) Tandem Library Bks.

—Miss Bindergarten Celebrates the 100th Day of Kindergarten. 2002. (Miss Bindergarten Ser.). (Illus.). (YA). 15.53 (978-1-4046-2578-5(X)) Book Wholesalers, Inc.

—Miss Bindergarten Takes a Field Trip with Kindergarten. Wolff, Ashley, illus. (J). (ps up). 2004. 40p. pap. 6.99 (978-0-14-240139-2(0) , Puffin); 2001. 32p. 16.99 (978-0-525-46710-6(6) , Dutton Juvenile) Penguin Group (USA) Inc.

Sloat, Teri. This Is the House That Was Tidy & Neat. Alley, R. W., illus. rev. ed. 2005. 32p. (J). 16.95 (978-0-8050-6921-1(6) , Holt, Henry & Co. Bks. For Young Readers) Holt, Henry & Co.

Smath, Jerry. Once There Was a Christmas Tree. 2005. (Illus.). 40p. (J). (ps-3). pap. 10.99 (978-0-439-72499-9(6) , Cartwheel Bks.) Scholastic, Inc.

Smedley, Gord. Orca's Calling. Hammond, Gaye, illus. unabr. ed. 58p. (J). (978-0-920576-46-5(X)) Caitlin Pr., Inc.

Smee, Nicola. Clip-Clop. 2006. (Illus.). 32p. (J). (***978-1-905417-03-2(9)***) Boxer Bks., Ltd.

—Clip-Clop! 2006. (Illus.). 32p. (J). 12.95 (978-1-905417-09-4(8)) Boxer Bks., Ltd. GBR. *Dist:* Sterling Publishing Co., Inc.

—No Bed Without Ted. 2005. (Illus.). 24p. (J). (ps-ps). 14.95 (978-1-58234-963-3(0)) Bloomsbury Publishing.

Smith, Janice Lee. Wizard & Wart in Trouble. Meisel, Paul, illus. (I Can Read Bks.). 48p. (J). (ps-3). 2000. pap. 3.99 (978-0-06-444274-9(8)); 1998. 15.89 (978-0-06-027762-8(9)) HarperCollins Pubs.

—Wizard & Wart in Trouble. 2000. (I Can Read Bks.). (978-0-606-18731-2(6)) Tandem Library Bks.

Smith, Jeff. Bone: Out from Boneville. Smith, Jeff & Hamaker, Steve, illus. 2005. 138p. (J). (gr. 4-7). lib. bdg. 17.94 (978-0-606-33282-8(0)) Tandem Library Bks.

—Rock Jaw: Master of the Eastern Border. 2007. (Bone Ser.: No. 5). 128p. (J). pap. 9.99 (978-0-439-70636-0(X) , Graphix) Scholastic, Inc.

—Rock Jaw: Master of the Eastern Border. Smith, Jeff, illus. 2007. (Bone Ser.: No. 5). (Illus.). 128p. (J). (gr. 4-7). pap. 18.99 (978-0-439-70627-8(0) , Graphix) Scholastic, Inc.

Smith, Kathryn. Cheep! Cheep! Noisy Farmyard Fun. Bolton, Bill, illus. 2004. 10p. (J). bds. 5.95 (978-0-7641-5749-3(3)) Barron's Educational Series, Inc.

Smith, Laura R. & Fearis, J. S. Little Sir Echo. Faulkner, Stacey, ed. 2006. (J). pap. 2.99 (***978-1-59198-318-7(5)***) Creative Teaching Pr., Inc.

Smith, Laura Rountree. Snubby Nose & Tippy Toes. 2004. reprint ed. pap. 15.95 (978-1-4191-4792-0(7)); pap. 1.99 (978-1-4192-4792-7(1)) Kessinger Publishing, LLC.

Smith, Maggie Caldwell. Tommy Wilson, Junior Veterinarian: The Case of the Wounded Jack Rabbit. McHose, Jean, illus. 2005. 104p. (J). (gr. 3-6). pap. 7.95 (978-1-889159-14-0(X)) Magpie Pr., Pine Mtn Club, CA.

Smith, Naniloa. The Children are Happy CD with Animals from the Southwest. Smith, Naniloa, ed. 2004. (J). cd-rom 5.00 (978-0-9744005-2-5(1)) In the Desert.

Smith, Terrie. Little Paw 3. 1999. 112p. (J). pap. 9.95 (978-1-883847-35-7(4)) MU Pr.

Smith, Tim. Who Stole the Animal Poop? 2006. (Buck Wilder's Adventure Ser.). 60p. (J). pap. (978-1-934133-05-7(1)) Mackinac Island Pr., Inc.

Smith, Timothy R. The Owls Don't Give a Hoot. 2007. (Buck Wilder's Adventure Ser.: 4). (Illus.). 96p. (J). pap. 5.95 (***978-1-934133-11-8(6)***) Mackinac Island Pr., Inc.

Snappy Fun Slipcase. (Slipcase Ser.). (Illus.). (J). (ps-k). (978-1-57584-678-1(0)) Reader's Digest Children's Publishing, Inc.

Sockabasin, Allen. Thanks to the Animals. Raye, Rebekah, illus. 2005. 32p. (J). (ps-2). 16.95 (978-0-88448-270-3(7)) Tilbury Hse. Pubs.

Soleim, Heather. God's Incredible Creatures: The Gift of Sharing. Greisen, Steve, illus. ed. Hedgecock, Sean, illus. ed. 2005. 24p. (J). bds. 14.95 (978-0-9707422-9-2(0)) Reel Productions, LLC.

Sollinger, Emily. Diego's Arctic Adventure: A Book of Facts about Arctic Animals. Mawhinney, Art, illus. 2007. (Go, Diego, Go! Ser.). 16p. (J). pap. 6.99 (***978-1-4169-3822-4(2)*** , Simon Spotlight/Nickelodeon) Simon & Schuster Children's Publishing.

Sollinger, Emily. Meet Pablo! Saunders, Zina, illus. 2005. (Backyardigans Ser.). 10p. (J). 8.99 (978-1-4169-0923-1(0) , Simon Spotlight/Nickelodeon) Simon & Schuster Children's Publishing.

Solo Flite. 2005. 14.95 (978-1-888125-94-8(2)) Publication Consultants.

Solomon, Carl, Sr. Do Animals Believe in God? 2004. 7p. (J). pap. 10.99 (978-1-4116-1312-6(0)) Lulu.com.

Someday We'll Understand. 2006. (J). bds. 21.95 (***978-0-9745191-1-1(1)***) Lynn Tyner Mitchum & James Rogers.

Sommer, Carl. King of the Pond. 2003. (Another Sommer-Time Story Ser.). (Illus.). 48p. (J). (gr. k-4). lib. bdg. 23.95 incl. audio (978-1-57537-766-7(7)); (gr. k-4). lib. bdg. 23.95 incl. audio compact disk (978-1-57537-716-2(0)); (gr. 1-4). 16.95 incl. audio (978-1-57537-565-6(6)); (gr. 1-4). 16.95 incl. audio compact disk (978-1-57537-516-8(8)) Advance Publishing, Inc.

—King of the Pond. Budwine, Greg, illus. 2000. (Another Sommer-Time Story Ser.). 48p. (J). (gr. k-3). lib. bdg. 16.95 (978-1-57537-065-1(4)); 9.95 (978-1-57537-016-3(6)) Advance Publishing, Inc.

—Noise! Noise! Noise! 2003. (Another Sommer-Time Story Ser.). (Illus.). 48p. (J). (gr. 1-4). 16.95 incl. audio compact disk (978-1-57537-519-9(2)); 16.95 incl. audio (978-1-57537-568-7(0)) Advance Publishing, Inc.

—Noise! Noise! Noise! James, Kennon, illus. 2003. (J). 9.95 (978-1-57537-020-0(4)); lib. bdg. 16.95 (978-1-57537-069-9(7)) Advance Publishing, Inc.

—Noise! Noise! Noise! Read-along, 2003. (Another Sommer-Time Story Ser.). (Illus.). 48p. (J). lib. bdg. 23.95 incl. audio (978-1-57537-769-8(1)) Advance Publishing, Inc.

—The Sly Fox & the Chicks. 2003. (Another Sommer-Time Story Ser.). (Illus.). 48p. (J). 16.95 incl. audio compact disk (978-1-57537-504-5(4)); (gr. 1-4). 16.95 incl. audio (978-1-57537-553-3(2)) Advance Publishing, Inc.

—The Sly Fox & the Chicks. James, Kennon, illus. 2000. (Another Sommer-Time Story Ser.). 48p. (J). (gr. k-3). lib. bdg. 16.95 (978-1-57537-062-0(X)); 9.95 (978-1-57537-004-0(2)) Advance Publishing, Inc.

—You Move, You Lose. 2003. (Another Sommer-Time Story Ser.). (Illus.). 48p. (J). (gr. 1-4). 16.95 incl. audio compact disk (978-1-57537-505-2(2)); 16.95 incl. audio (978-1-57537-554-0(0)) Advance Publishing, Inc.

—You Move, You Lose. James, Kennon, illus. (Another Sommer-Time Story Ser.). 48p. (J). (gr. k-3). 2000. lib. bdg. 16.95 (978-1-57537-056-9(5)); 1999. 9.95 (978-1-57537-005-7(0)) Advance Publishing, Inc.

Sorrentino, Dawn. Rusty Visits the Zoo. 2006. (J). spiral bd. 15.00 (978-0-8059-7007-4(X)) Dorrance Publishing Co., Inc.

Soto, Gary. Chato & the Party Animals. Guevara, Susan, illus. 25.95 incl. audio (978-1-59112-460-3(3)); 28.95 incl. audio compact disk (978-1-59112-920-2(6)); pap. 37.95 incl. audio (978-1-59112-461-0(1)); pap. 39.95 incl. audio compact disk (978-1-59112-921-9(4)) Live Oak Media.

—Chato & the Party Animals. Guevara, Susan, illus. 32p. (J). (ps-3). 2000. (SPA.). 16.99 (978-0-399-23159-9(5) , Putnam Juvenile); 2004. reprint ed. pap. 6.99 (978-0-14-240032-6(7) , Puffin) Penguin Group (USA) Inc.

—Chato & the Party Animals. 2004. (gr. k-3). lib. bdg. 15.30 (978-0-613-89799-0(4)) Tandem Library Bks.

—Chato y los Amigos Pachangueros. Guevara, Susan, illus. 2004. Tr. of Chato & the Party Animals. (SPA.). 32p. (J). (gr. k-3). reprint ed. pap. 7.99 (978-0-14-240033-3(5) , Puffin) Penguin Group (USA) Inc.

Soule, Jean Conder. Never Tease a Weasel. Booth, George, illus. 2007. (Picture Book Ser.). 40p. (J). (ps-2). 15.99 (978-0-375-83420-2(6)); lib. bdg. 18.99 (978-0-375-93420-9(0)) Random Hse. Children's Bks. (Random Hse. Bks. for Young Readers).

Soundprints. Forest Adventures: Story-Time Treasury. 2005. (Smithsonian Institution Story-Time Treasures Ser.). (Illus.). 256p. (J). (ps-2). 14.95 (978-1-59069-227-1(6) , HT2001) Studio Mouse LLC.

Souza, Iza R. Andy, the Anteater. Lima, Gabriel S., tr. from POR. Lima, M., illus. 1999. 24p. (J). (gr. 2-7). pap. 3.25 (978-0-9662298-3-7(5)) Alba Bk. Co.

Sowach, Rick. Critters, Flitters & Spitters: 24 Amazing Ohio Animal Tales. 2003. (J). 19.95 (978-0-9762412-3-2(4)) Sowash, Rick Publishing Co.

Sowash, Rick. Critters, Flitters & Spitters: 24 Amazing Ohio Animal Tales. 2003. (J). pap. 11.95 (978-0-9762412-2-5(6)) Sowash, Rick Publishing Co.

Spafford, Suzy. Tales from Duckport: Helping Out Day Hooray. Spafford, Suzy, illus. 2003. (Tales from Duckport Ser.). (Illus.). 40p. (J). (gr. k-3). pap. 3.99 (978-0-439-38358-5(7)) Scholastic, Inc.

—Tales from Duckport: Stick Together! 2003. (Suzy's Zoo Ser.). (Illus.). 40p. (J). (gr. k-3). pap. 3.99 (978-0-439-38357-8(9)) Scholastic, Inc.

—Tales from Duckport: Stick Together! 2003. (gr. k-3). lib. bdg. 11.80 (978-0-613-63568-4(X)) Tandem Library Bks.

—Witzy Plays Hide & Seek. 2001. (Little Suzy's Zoo Ser.). (Illus.). 6p. (J). pap. 5.99 (978-0-439-34358-9(5)) Scholastic, Inc.

—Witzy's Backyard Easter Hunt. 2002. (Little Suzy's Zoo Ser.). (Illus.). 15p. (J). bds. 5.99 (978-0-439-36778-3(6)) Scholastic, Inc.

—Witzy's Book of Words. 2001. (Little Suzy's Zoo Ser.). (Illus.). 12p. (J). pap. 9.99 (978-0-439-34357-2(7)) Scholastic, Inc.

—Witzy's Shapes. 2002. (Little Suzy's Zoo Ser.). (Illus.). 12p. (J). bds. 4.99 (978-0-439-36632-8(1)) Scholastic, Inc.

Spaht-Gill, Janie. Gator's Out, Said the Trout. Reese, Bob, illus. (J). (gr. k-2). 5.95 (978-0-89868-305-9(X)) ARO Publishing Co.

Spanyol, Jessica. Little Neighbors of Sunnyside Street. Spanyol, Jessica, illus. 2007. 64p. (J). (ps-1). 16.99 (978-0-7636-2986-1(3)) Candlewick Pr.

The Sparkling Beauty. 2006. Orig. Title: Televisual Book. (J). 18.99 (978-0-9779672-0-9(4)) Karsonkina, Tatiana.

Speed, Bryan W. Little Bent Cedar. 2007. 24p. (J). 9.95 (***978-1-933255-38-5(2)***) DNA Pr.

Spelvin, Justin. Pirate Treasure. 2007. 24p. (J). 21.35 (***978-1-59961-158-7(9)***) Spotlight.

Spence, Rob & Spence, Amy. Clickety Clack. Spengler, Margaret, illus. 1999. 32p. (J). (ps-3). 15.99 (978-0-670-87946-5(0) , Viking Juvenile) Penguin Group (USA) Inc.

Spenceley, Annabel, illus. The Kingfisher Treasury of Animal Stories. 2003. (Kingfisher Treasury of Stories Ser.). 160p. (J). (gr. k-3). pap. 6.95 (978-0-7534-5629-3(X) , Kingfisher) Houghton Mifflin Co. Trade & Reference Div.

Spengler, Kenneth. Little Red Hen Gets Help. Spengler, Margaret, illus. 2007. (Green Light Readers Level 2 Ser.). 24p. (J). (gr. k-2). 12.95 (***978-0-15-206195-1(9)***); pap. 3.95 (***978-0-15-206189-0(4)***) Harcourt Children's Bks. (Green Light Readers).

Spinelli, Eileen & Parmenter, Wayne. When Christmas Came. Spinelli, Eileen & Parmenter, Wayne, illus. 2006. (Illus.). 32p. (J). (ps). bds. 16.95 (978-0-8249-5507-6(2) , Ideals Pr.) Ideals Pubns.

Spirit Bear. 2005. (978-0-9765358-1-2(5)) Strategic Dreamers, LLC.

Spohn, Kate. Turtle & Snake's Valentine's Day. 2003. (Viking Easy-To-Read Ser.). (Illus.). 32p. (J). (ps-3). 13.99 (978-0-670-03613-4(7) , Viking Juvenile) Penguin Group (USA) Inc.

Spurling, Margaret. Bilby Moon. Snell, Danny, illus. 2001. 32p. (J). (ps-4). 14.95 (978-1-929132-06-5(9)) Kane/Miller Bk. Pubs., Inc.

Spurr, Elizabeth. Two Bears Beneath the Stairs. Westcott, Nadine Bernard, illus. 2002. 16p. (J). (ps-1). 8.99 (978-0-689-84759-2(9) , Little Simon) Simon & Schuster Children's Publishing.

Squier, Emma-Lindsay. On Autumn Trails & Adventures in Captivity. 2004. reprint ed. pap. 26.95 (978-1-4179-2651-0(1)) Kessinger Publishing, LLC.

Stadler, John. Three Cheers for Hippo. Stadler, John, illus. 2006. (Illus.). 32p. (J). reprint ed. pap. (978-1-59572-046-7(4)) Star Bright Bks., Inc.

—What's So Scary? (Illus.). (J). (gr. k-4). 2001. 32p. pap. 16.95 (978-0-531-30301-6(2)); 2000. lib. bdg. 16.95 (978-0-531-33301-3(9)) Scholastic, Inc. (Orchard Bks.).

Staggs, Alvin DeWayne. Stories for Animal Lovers. 2000. 195p. (J). pap. 13.95 (978-0-7414-0553-1(9)) Infinity Publishing.

Stanley, Mandy. What Do You Do? Stanley, Mandy, illus. 2005. 24p. (J). bds. 8.99 (978-1-4169-0499-1(9) , Little Simon) Simon & Schuster Children's Publishing.

—Who Tickled Tilly? 2004. (Illus.). 32p. (J). (978-1-84458-047-7(4)) Chrysalis Children's Bks.

Stanley, Robin. Fun on the Farm. Julien, Terry, illus. 2006. (Happy Day Summer Titles Ser.). 16p. (J). pap. 1.99 (978-0-7847-1807-0(5) , 04189) Standard Publishing.

Staunton, Ted. Morgan Makes a Splash. Slavin, Bill, illus. 2004. (First Novel Ser.). 64p. (J). (gr. 1-5). 4.95 (978-0-88780-622-3(8)); (***978-0-88780-623-0(6)***) Formac Publishing Co., Ltd. CAN. *Dist:* Casemate Pubs. & Bk. Distributors, LLC.

Stead, Vince. Sammy, the Runaway Mastiff: Sammy Breaks Out of His Kennel. 2006. 102p. per. 8.95 (978-1-59824-314-7(4)) E-BookTime LLC.

Steck-Vaughn Staff. The Fox & the Crow. 1998. (Illus.). (J). pap. (978-0-8172-8700-9(0)) Steck-Vaughn.

—My Wild Wooly. 1999. (Illus.). pap. (978-0-8172-8705-4(1)) Steck-Vaughn.

—Old Stories New Stories: Goldilocks & the Three Bears. 1998. (Illus.). (J). pap. (978-0-8172-8637-8(3)) Steck-Vaughn.

—The Pan Man/Act Like a Cat. 1999. (Take Me Home Ser.). (Illus.). (J). pap. (978-0-7398-2672-0(7)) Steck-Vaughn.

Steele, Michael Anthony. It's a Zoo in Here! 2005. (Illus.). (J). (***978-0-439-78585-3(5)***) Scholastic, Inc.

Steig, William. Doctor De Soto. Steig, William, illus. 1998. (Illus.). pap. 39.95 incl. audio compact disk (978-1-59519-161-8(5)); (SPA., (J). pap. 18.95 incl. audio compact disk (978-1-59519-160-1(7)) Live Oak Media.

Steinberg, David. The Turkey Ball. Conrad, Liz, illus. 2005. 10p. (J). (ps-2). bds. 6.99 (978-0-8431-1456-0(8) , Price Stern Sloan) Penguin Group (USA) Inc.

Stenmark, Victoria. The Singing Chick. Cecil, Randy, illus. rev. ed. 1999. 32p. (J). (ps-1). 15.95 (978-0-8050-5255-8(0) , Holt, Henry & Co. Bks. For Young Readers) Holt, Henry & Co.

Stephens, Monique Z. The Incredible Mr. E! 2006. (I Can Read Bks.). 32p. (J). pap. 3.99 (978-0-06-084605-3(4) , Harper Trophy) HarperCollins Pubs.

—Meet the Characters. 2006. (I Can Read Bks.). 32p. (J). pap. 3.99 (978-0-06-084606-0(2) , Harper Trophy) HarperCollins Pubs.

Stephens, R.David. My Animal Friends. 2001. (Illus.). 32p. (J). 6.95 (978-1-896580-74-6(2)) Tradewind Bks. CAN. *Dist:* Orca Bk. Pubs. USA.

Stevens, Christian. An Animal Alphabet. 2002. (Illus.). 112p. (J). (gr. k-3). pap. 5.95 (978-0-86327-878-5(7)) Interlink Publishing Group, Inc.

Stevens, Janet. Cook-a-Doodle-Doo! Stevens, Janet, illus. 2002. (Illus.). (J). 22.55 (978-0-7587-2272-0(9)) Book Wholesalers, Inc.

Stevens, Janet & Crummel, Susan Stevens. Cook-a-Doodle-Doo! 2001. (J). (gr. k-3). 27.95 incl. audio (978-0-8045-6865-4(0) , 6865) Spoken Arts, Inc.

—Jackalope. Stevens, Janet, illus. 2003. (Illus.). 56p. (J). (gr. k-3). 17.00 (978-0-15-216736-3(6)) Harcourt Children's Bks.

Stevenson, James. Christmas at Mud Flat. 2000. (Illus.). 48p. (J). (gr. 1-3). 15.89 (978-0-688-17302-9(0)) HarperCollins Pubs.

—Don't Make Me Laugh. 2003. (ps-2). lib. bdg. 14.10 (978-0-613-59603-9(X)) Tandem Library Bks.

—Flying Feet: A Mud Flat Story. Stevenson, James, illus. 2004. (Illus.). 48p. (J). 15.99 (978-0-06-051975-9(4)) HarperCollins Pubs.

—Mud Flat April Fool. 1998. (Illus.). 48p. (J). (gr. k-3). 15.89 (978-0-688-15164-5(7)) HarperCollins Pubs.

—Mud Flat Mystery. 2003. (gr. k-3). lib. bdg. 12.10 (978-0-613-60093-4(2)) Tandem Library Bks.

—Mud Flat Spring. 1999. (Illus.). 40p. (J). (gr. k-3). 14.89 (978-0-688-15773-9(4)) HarperCollins Pubs.

Steward, Margaret. Tamsi: The Errant Lamb. 2005. (YA). per. 9.95 (978-1-59094-094-5(6)) Jawbone Publishing Corp. .

Stewart, Dianne. Zebra's Stripes & Other African Animal Tales. Pienaar, Kathy, illus. 2005. 144p. pap. 12.95 (978-1-86872-951-7(6)) Struik Pubs. ZAF. *Dist:* International Publishers Marketing.

Stewart, Paul. Dogbird & Other Mixed-up Tales. Ross, Tony, illus. 2006. 192p. (J). (gr. 1-2). 8.99 (978-0-552-55351-3(4) , Corgi) Transworld Publishers Ltd. GBR. *Dist:* Independent Pubs. Group.

—A Little Bit of Winter. Riddell, Chris, illus. 1999. 32p. (J). (ps-2). 14.95 (978-0-06-028278-3(9)) HarperCollins Pubs.

Stewart, Paul & Riddell, Chris. Little Bit of Winter. 2000. (Illus.). 32p. (J). pap. (978-0-86264-998-2(6)) Andersen GBR. *Dist:* Random Hse. of Canada, Ltd.

Stickland, Paul & Stickland, Henrietta. Dinosaur Roar! 2002. (Illus.). 32p. (J). (ps-2). pap. 6.99 (978-0-14-056808-0(5) , Puffin) Penguin Group (USA) Inc.

Stierle, Cynthia & Artful Doodlers Limited Staff. Diego's Egg Quest. 2007. (Go, Diego, Go! Ser.). 16p. (J). (ps-1). pap. 5.99 (978-1-4169-2751-8(4) , Simon Spotlight/Nickelodeon) Simon & Schuster Children's Publishing.

Stilton, Geronimo. Down & Out down under. 2007. (Geronimo Stilton Ser.: No. 29). (Illus.). 128p. (J). pap. 6.99 (978-0-439-84120-7(8) , Scholastic Paperbacks) Scholastic, Inc.

Stilton, Geronimo. I'm Too Fond of My Fur! Wolf, Matt, illus. 2004. (Geronimo Stilton Ser.: No. 4). 116p. (J). lib. bdg. 10.00 (***978-1-4242-0698-8(7)***) Fitzgerald Bks.

Stine, R. L. Creepy Creatures. 2006. (Goosebumps Ser.). (Illus.). 144p. (J). pap. 16.99 (978-0-439-84124-5(0)); pap. 8.99 (978-0-439-84125-2(9)) Scholastic, Inc. (Graphix).

—The Werewolf of Fever Swamp. 2003. (Goosebumps Ser.). 144p. pap. 4.99 (978-0-439-56848-7(X)) Scholastic, Inc.

Stockton, Frank Richard. RoundAbout Rambles in Lands of Fact and. 2006. pap. (***978-1-4068-3083-5(6)***) Echo Library.

Stoddart, Matthew, illus. Pirate Treasure. 2005. (Backyardigans Ser.). 24p. (J). pap. 3.99 (978-1-4169-0800-5(5) , Simon Spotlight/Nickelodeon) Simon & Schuster Children's Publishing.

Stohner, Anu. Santa's Littlest Helper Travels the World. Wilson, Henrike, illus. 2007. 32p. (J). (ps-3). 15.95 (***978-1-59990-187-9(0)*** , Bloomsbury Children) Bloomsbury Publishing.

Stohner, Anu & Wilson, Henrike. Brave Charlotte. Cole, Alyson, tr. from GER. 2005. (Illus.). 32p. (J). (ps-3). 16.95 (978-1-58234-690-8(9) , Bloomsbury Children) Bloomsbury Publishing.

Stone, Jeff. Monkey. 2006. (Five Ancestors Ser.: Bk. 1). 208p. (gr. 5). 5.99 (978-0-375-83074-7(X) , Yearling) Random Hse. Children's Bks.

Stonecipher, Philiip. Boudreau of de Bayou. Perez Sanchez, Delia, tr. from ENG. 1999. (SPA & ENG., Illus.). ii, 22p. (J). (gr. 2-3). 6.95 (978-0-943864-92-1(5)) Davenport, May Pubs.

Storad, Conrad J. Don't Call Me Pig! a Javelina Story. Neely, Beth, illus. 1999. 32p. (J). 6.95 (978-1-891795-01-5(5)) RGU Group, The.

Stowe, Dorothy Bye. Beary Bigger. Stowe, Dorothy Bye, illus. 2002. (Illus.). 32p. (J). (ps-2). (978-0-9704586-1-2(4)) Verse-a-Tale Pr.

Stowe, Harriet Beecher. Queer Little Folks. 2006. Tr. of 88. pap. (***978-1-4065-1076-8(9)***) Dodo Pr.

The Strange Shoe: Individual Title Six-Packs. 32p. (gr. 3 up). 37.00 (978-0-7635-9679-8(5)) Rigby Education.

Strauss, Kevin. Loon & Moon: And Other Animal Stories. Scheibe, Nancy, illus. 2005. 48p. (J). pap. 12.95 (978-0-9766264-3-5(8)) Raven Productions, Inc.

Stuart-Russell, C. Playtime with the Animals. 2007. 61p. pap. 12.95 (***978-1-4241-5473-9(1)***) PublishAmerica, Inc.

Sturges, Philemon. How Do You Make a Baby Smile? Strevens-Marzo, Bridget, illus. 2007. 24p. (J). (ps). 16.99 (***978-0-06-076072-4(9)***); lib. bdg. 17.89 (***978-0-06-076073-1(7)***) HarperCollins Pubs.

Sturges, Philemon. The Little Red Hen Makes a Pizza. 2002. 32p. (J). pap. 6.99 (978-0-14-230189-0(2) , Puffin) Penguin Group (USA) Inc.

Sturges, Philemon. The Little Red Hen (Makes a Pizza) 1999. (Illus.). 32p. (J). (ps-3). 15.99 (978-0-525-45953-8(7) , Dutton Juvenile) Penguin Group (USA) Inc.

Stutson, Caroline. Mama Loves You. Segal, John, illus. 2005. 32p. (J). pap. 6.99 (978-0-439-57842-4(6)) Scholastic, Inc.

Sugobono, Nahuel. Leyendas, Mitos, Cuentos y Otros Relatos Tobas. Huadi, illus. 2003. (SPA.). 86p. pap. 11.95 (978-987-550-296-3(0)) Longseller S.A. ARG. *Dist:* Bilingual Pubns. Co., The.

Sula, Sondra. Gorm & the Viking Birds: Ponies, Labs & Polarpogos. 2000. mass mkt. 4.50 (978-1-931179-28-7(X)) Long Hill Productions, Inc.

—Gorm & the Viking Birds: Ponies, Labs, & Polarpogos. 2000. mass mkt. 8.95 (978-1-931179-39-3(5)) Long Hill Productions, Inc.

Sullivan, Anne. The Adventures of Dino & Spike: Grandpa's Farm. 2006. (ENG.). 36p. per. 16.49 (***978-1-4259-3885-7(X)***) AuthorHouse.

Sullivan, William J. Taylor Rabbit & the Seeds of Success. 2001. 32p. (J). pap. 4.95 (978-0-9708066-1-1(2)) Painted Horse Pubns., Inc.

Sutherland, Paul H. Finding Utopia. Gibbons, Timothy M., illus. 2006. 48p. (J). bds. 20.00 (978-0-9661060-4-6(0)) Utopia Pr.

Sutherland, Tui. Meet Mo & Ella. 2001. (First Friends, First Readers Ser.). (Illus.). (J). (978-0-606-21323-3(6)) Tandem Library Bks.

Svendson, Elisabeth D. The Tale of Naughty Mac & Other Donkey Stories. (Illus.). 80p. (J). 17.95 (978-1-873580-14-1(2)) Whittet Bks., Ltd. GBR. *Dist:* Diamond Farm Bk. Pubs.

Swain, Cynthia. Sorting at the Nature Center. 2006. (Early Explorers Ser.). (J). 30.00 (***978-1-4108-6039-2(6)***) Benchmark Education Co.

Swanson, Bruce. Gray Wolf's Search. Peterson, Gary, illus. 2007. 24p. (J). (gr. 1-5). 14.95 (978-0-9779183-1-7(9)) Seventh Generation Design.

Swartz, Nancy Sohn. How Did the Animals Help God? Hall, Melanie, illus. 2004. 24p. (J). bds. 7.99 (978-1-59473-044-3(X)) SkyLight Paths Publishing.

Swartz, Neva. Tommy the Timid Turtle. Steinbauer, Larry, illus. 2004. 24p. (J). 19.95 (978-1-878044-75-4(3)) Mayhaven Publishing.

Sweeney, Jacqueline. Aloha! 2002. (We Can Read! Ser.). (Illus.). 32p. (J). 21.36 (978-0-7614-1510-7(6) , Benchmark Bks.) Cavendish, Marshall Corp.

—Freddy Bear. 2001. (We Can Read! Ser.). (Illus.). 32p. (J). (gr. 1-2). lib. bdg. 21.36 (978-0-7614-1121-5(6) , Benchmark Bks.) Cavendish, Marshall Corp.

—Hester. Hart, G. K. & Empey, Mark, illus. 1999. (We Can Read! Ser.). 32p. (J). (gr. 1-2). lib. bdg. 21.36 (978-0-7614-0923-6(8) , Benchmark Bks.) Cavendish, Marshall Corp.

—Homesick. Hart, G. K. & Empey, Mark, illus. 2000. (We Can Read! Ser.). 32p. (J). (gr. 1-2). lib. bdg. 21.36 (978-0-7614-1117-8(8) , Benchmark Bks.) Cavendish, Marshall Corp.

—Luau. Hart, G. K. & Hart, Vikki, illus. Hart, G. K. & Hart, Vikki, photos by. 2002. (We Can Read! Ser.). 32p. (J). 21.36 (978-0-7614-1513-8(0) , Benchmark Bks.) Cavendish, Marshall Corp.

—Molly's Store. Hart, G. K. & Empey, Mark, illus. 2000. (We Can Read! Ser.). 32p. (J). (gr. 1-2). lib. bdg. 21.36 (978-0-7614-1116-1(X) , Benchmark Bks.) Cavendish, Marshall Corp.

—Pond Monster. 2001. (We Can Read! Ser.). (Illus.). 32p. (J). (gr. 1-2). lib. bdg. 21.36 (978-0-7614-1123-9(2) , Benchmark Bks.) Cavendish, Marshall Corp.

—What about Bettie? Hart, G. K. & Empey, Mark, illus. 2000. (We Can Read! Ser.). 32p. (J). (gr. 1-2). lib. bdg. 21.36 (978-0-7614-1118-5(6) , Benchmark Bks.) Cavendish, Marshall Corp.

—Who Said Boo? Hart, G. K. & Empey, Mark, illus. 2000. (We Can Read! Ser.). 32p. (J). (gr. 1-2). lib. bdg. 21.36 (978-0-7614-0924-3(6) , Benchmark Bks.) Cavendish, Marshall Corp.

Sweetwater, Jesse, illus. Lunching & Munching. 2001. (J). 14.00 (978-0-689-81564-5(6) , Simon & Schuster Children's Publishing) Simon & Schuster Children's Publishing.

Swinburne, Stephen R. Water for One, Water for Everyone: A Counting Book of African Animals. Levine, Melinda, illus. 1998. (Fun Early Math Concepts Ser.). 32p. (ps-1). lib. bdg. 22.90 (978-0-7613-0269-8(7) , Millbrook Pr.) Lerner Publishing Group.

Sykes, Julie. Careful, Santa! Warnes, Tim, illus. 2002. 32p. (J). (ps-1). tchr. ed. 14.95 (978-1-58925-023-9(0) , tiger tales) ME Media LLC.

—Dora's Eggs. Chapman, Jane, illus. 2007. (J). bds. 6.95 (978-1-58925-801-3(0) , tiger tales) ME Media LLC.

—Little Tiger Goes to School. Warnes, Tim, illus. 1998. (Lift-The-Flap Book Ser.). 5p. (J). (ps-1). bds. 11.95 (978-1-888444-49-0(5)) Little Tiger Pr.

—Sleepover. 2001. (gr. k-3). lib. bdg. 11.25 (978-0-613-53562-5(6)) Tandem Library Bks.

Symes, Ruth. Harriet Dancing. Church, Caroline, illus. 2008. 32p. (J). 16.99 (***978-0-545-03204-9(0)*** , Chicken Hse., The) Scholastic, Inc.

Symes, Sally & Lavis, Steve. Who's Been Walking on My Floor? 2005. (Illus.). 24p. (J). 11.99 (978-0-7641-5904-6(6)) Barron's Educational Series, Inc.

Szekeres, Cyndy. Wilbur Bunny's Funny Friends A to Z. Szekeres, Cyndy, illus. 2000. (Illus.). 15p. (J). (ps). bds. 6.99 (978-0-439-17327-8(2)) Scholastic, Inc.

Taback, Simms. Can You Smile? 2007. (Illus.). 12p. (ps). bds. 8.95 (***978-1-59354-611-3(4)***) Blue Apple Bks.

—Do You Have a Tail? Taback, Simms, illus. 2007. (Illus.). 12p. (J). (ps). bds. 8.95 (978-1-59354-602-1(5)) Blue Apple Bks.

—Moo Baby Gift Set. 2007. 22.95 (***978-1-59354-630-4(0)***) Handprint Bks.

—Peekaboo Who? 2006. (Illus.). 14p. bds. 8.95 (978-1-59354-180-4(5)) Blue Apple Bks.

—Where Is My House? Bb. 2005. (Illus.). 6p. bds. 7.95 (978-1-59354-112-5(0)) Blue Apple Bks.

Tabby, Abigail. Baby Tickle Shakes: Book & Rattle Gift Set. Beeke, Tiphanie, illus. 2007. (Little Simon Baby Ser.). 16p. (J). bds. 9.99 (978-1-4169-1900-1(7) , Little Simon) Simon & Schuster Children's Publishing.

—Hokey Pokey Elmo. Brannon, Tom, illus. 2006. (Big Bird's Favorites Brd Bks.). 24p. (J). (gr. k). bds. 4.99 (978-0-375-83507-0(5) , Random Hse. Bks. for Young Readers) Random Hse. Children's Bks.

Tafuri, Nancy. The Busy Little Squirrel. Tafuri, Nancy, illus. 2007. 32p. (J). (ps-k). 15.99 (978-0-689-87341-6(7) , Simon & Schuster Children's Publishing) Simon & Schuster Children's Publishing.

—Counting to Christmas. 1998. (J). pap. (978-0-590-27144-8(X)) Scholastic, Inc.

—The Donkey's Christmas Song. Tafuri, Nancy, illus. 2002. (Illus.). 32p. (J). (ps-k). pap. 16.95 (978-0-439-27313-8(7) , Scholastic Pr.) Scholastic, Inc.

—The Donkey's Christmas Welcome. 2002. (Illus.). (J). pap. (978-0-439-27314-5(5)) Scholastic, Inc.

Tag, Hang. Animal Antics. Richards, Lucy, illus. 2004. (Cuddly Cuffs Ser.: No. 5). 12p. (J). tchr. ed. 5.95 (978-1-58925-725-2(1) , tiger tales) ME Media LLC.

Tagg, Christine. A Very Special Valentine. Kneen, Maggie, illus. 2003. (J). 15.95 (978-0-8118-4073-6(5)) Chronicle Bks. LLC.

Tal, Ronit. Animal Story Bk. 2: From Birth to 18 Months. 2000. (J). (978-965-7096-01-7(4)) A Different Story, Ltd.

—A Wild Story Bk. 3: Birth & Up. 2000. (J). (978-965-7096-02-4(2)) A Different Story, Ltd.

Tallarico, Tony. How Fire Came to the Indians. 2005. (Classics Illustrated Junior Ser.). 32p. 5.99 (978-1-894998-18-5(9)) Lake, Jack Productions, Inc. CAN. *Dist:* Hushion Hse. Publishing, Ltd.

Talley, Linda. Jackson's Plan. Chase, Andra, illus. 1998. (Key Concepts in Personal Development Ser.). 32p. (J). (gr. k-4). 17.95 (978-1-55942-104-1(5) , 7665) Marsh Media.

Tankard, Jeremy. Grumpy Bird. 2007. (Illus.). 32p. (J). (ps-k). pap. 12.99 (978-0-439-85147-3(5) , Scholastic Pr.) Scholastic, Inc.

Tarlow, Ellen. Pinwheel Days. Parker, Gretel, illus. 2007. 56p. (J). pap. 6.95 (978-1-59572-059-7(6)) Star Bright Bks., Inc.

Tashiro, Chisato. Chameleon's Colors. Martens, Marianne, tr. from GER. 2003. (Illus.). 32p. (J). 15.95 (978-0-7358-1887-3(8)) North-South Bks., Inc.

Taylor, Eleanor. Beep, Beep, Let's Go! 2005. (Illus.). 32p. (J). 15.95 (978-1-58234-973-2(8)) Bloomsbury Publishing.

Taylor, Jacqui. Baobab Is Big. 2005. (Illus.). 72p. 11.95 (978-1-86872-946-3(X)) Struik Pubs. ZAF. *Dist:* International Publishers Marketing.

Taylor, Sean. Small Bad Wolf. Lewis, Jan, illus. 2004. (I Am Reading Ser.). 48p. (J). (gr. k-3). pap. 3.95 (978-0-7534-5801-3(2) , Kingfisher) Houghton Mifflin Co. Trade & Reference Div.

Teckentrup, Britta. How Big Is the World? 2007. (Illus.). 40p. (J). (ps-1). 14.95 ***(978-1-905417-50-6(0))*** Boxer Bks., Ltd. GBR. *Dist:* Sterling Publishing Co., Inc.

Tench, U. M. & Tench, D. A. Cramberry & Friends. l.t. ed. 2003. (Illus.). 31p. (978-0-9686943-1-2(4)) Human Resources Projects.

Terry, Michael. Rhino's Horns. 2001. (Illus.). 32p. (J). (ps up). 19.99 (978-0-7475-5051-8(4)) Bloomsbury Publishing Plc GBR. *Dist:* Independent Pubs. Group.

—Rhinos Horns. 2003. (Illus.). (J). (978-1-58234-796-7(4) , Bloomsbury Children) Bloomsbury Publishing.

Tétro, Marc. My New Hat. 2005. (Illus.). (978-1-55278-543-0(2)) McArthur & Co. CAN. *Dist:* National Bk. Network.

Thanet, Octave, pseud. The Rowdy. 2004. reprint ed. pap. 15.95 (978-1-4191-8122-1(X)); pap. 1.99 (978-1-4192-8122-8(4)) Kessinger Publishing, LLC.

There's a Toad in the Hole - English/French Bilingual Translation: A Big Fat Toad in the Hole. 2005. (J). per. 15.95 (978-1-59649-302-5(X)) Whispering Pine Pr., Inc.

Thomas, Cameron. Shipwrecked on the Island of Skree. Krystoforski, Andrej, illus. 2004. (Jungle of Utt Ser.). 48p. (J). 16.95 (978-0-921800-01-9(0)) MGT Developments, Ltd. CAN. *Dist:* Independent Pubs. Group.

—The Utt Jungle Airline: The Jungle of Utt. Krystoforski, Andrej, illus. 2004. (Jungle of Utt Ser.). 48p. (J). 16.95 (978-0-921800-03-3(7)) MGT Developments, Ltd. CAN. *Dist:* Independent Pubs. Group.

Thomas, Jan. A Birthday for Cow! 2008. 40p. (J). 12.95 ***(978-0-15-206072-5(3))*** Harcourt Trade Pubs.

Thomas, Timothy. Buddy Manatee. 2nd l.t. ed. 2001. (Buddy Manatee). (Illus.). 48p. (J). per. 12.99 (978-0-9713573-0-3(7)) Thomas Expressions, Inc.

Thomas, Wes. Down the Crawfish Hole. Thomas, Wes, illus. 2004. (Illus.). 32p. (J). 15.95 (978-1-58980-163-9(6)) Pelican Publishing Co., Inc.

Thompson, Karen & Mitzo Thompson, Kim. At the Farm. 2006. (Read & Sing along Board Books with CDs Ser.). (Illus.). 18p. (J). bds. 7.49 (978-0-7696-4582-7(8)) School Specialty Publishing.

Thompson, Kate. Fourth World: Book One in the Missing Link Trilogy. 2006. 336p. (YA). pap. 7.95 (978-1-58234-897-1(9) , Bloomsbury Children) Bloomsbury Publishing.

—Midnight's Choice. unabr. ed. 2004. (Switchers Ser.: Vol. 2). 240p. (J). (gr. 5-9). pap. 38.00 incl. audio (978-0-8072-8769-9(5) , Listening Library) Random Hse. Audio Publishing Group.

—Midnight's Choice. 2000. (J). (978-0-606-20189-6(0)) Tandem Library Bks.

—Origins. 2007. (Missing Link Trilogy Ser.: Bk. 3). 320p. (YA). (gr. 7 up). 17.95 ***(978-1-58234-652-6(6)*** , Bloomsbury Children) Bloomsbury Publishing.

—Switchers. 220p. (J). (gr. 4-7). pap. 5.99 (978-0-8072-1553-1(8)) ; 2004. (Switchers Ser.: Vol. 1). (gr. 5-9). pap. 38.00 incl. audio (978-0-8072-8138-3(7) , YA115SP) Random Hse. Audio Publishing Group. (Listening Library).

—Switchers. 1999. (978-0-606-17387-2(0)); (gr. 5-8). lib. bdg. 14.15 (978-0-613-20224-4(4)) Tandem Library Bks.

—Wild Blood. 2002. 272p. (gr. 5-17). pap. 5.99 (978-0-7868-1422-0(5)) Hyperion Paperbacks for Children.

—Wild Blood. 2002. (gr. 3-6). lib. bdg. 14.15 (978-0-613-74970-1(7)) Tandem Library Bks.

Thompson, Kim Mitzo. Look at the Animals. 2006. (Dual Language Readers Ser.). (ENG & SPA.). 32p. (J). pap., pap. 4.99 (978-0-7696-4614-5(X)) School Specialty Publishing.

Thompson, Lauren. One Starry Night. (J). 2003. 6.99 (978-0-689-84215-3(5) , Aladdin); 2000. lib. bdg. 16.00 (978-0-689-82851-5(9) , Simon & Schuster Children's Publishing) Simon & Schuster Children's Publishing.

Thomson, Pat. Drat That Fat Cat! Busby, Ailie, illus. 2003. (J). (ps up). 40p. pap. 15.95 (978-0-439-47195-4(8)); (978-0-439-47196-1(6) , Levine, Arthur A. Bks.) Scholastic, Inc.

Thornhill, Jan. Folktails: Animal Legends from Around the World. Thornhill, Jan, illus. 2nd ed. 2006. (Illus.). 32p. 15.95 (978-1-897066-75-1(9)) Maple Tree Pr. CAN. *Dist:* Perseus Distribution.

Thorpe, Kiki. Ah-Choo! 2003. (ps-2). lib. bdg. 11.80 (978-0-613-73405-9(X)) Tandem Library Bks.

—Big Blue House Call. 2000. (gr. k-3). lib. bdg. 11.25 (978-0-613-21212-0(6)) Tandem Library Bks.

—Spring Has Sprung! 2000. (gr. k-3). lib. bdg. 11.25 (978-0-613-22429-1(9)) Tandem Library Bks.

Tibo, Gilles. Au Boulot les Animaux. ed. 2004. (FRE., Illus.). (J). (ps-k). spiral bd. (978-0-616-11146-8(0)) Canadian National Institute for the Blind/Institut National Canadien pour les Aveugles.

—Busy Critters. 2000. (Illus.). 32p. (J). (ps-3). pap. (978-1-894363-32-7(9)) Dominique & Friends.

—Noches de Papel. (Barril Sin Fondo Ser.). (SPA.). (J). (gr. 3-5). pap. (978-968-6465-32-7(4)) Casa de Estudios de Literatura y Talleres Artisticos Amaquemecan A.C. MEX. *Dist:* Lectorum Pubns., Inc.

—Les Quatre Saisons de Simon. 2006. (FRE., Illus.). 48p. (J). (ps-3). 17.95 (978-0-88776-794-4(X) , Livres Toundra) Tundra Bks., Inc./Livres Toundra, Inc. CAN. *Dist:* Random Hse., Inc.

Tich, Jan. Pope & Ba. 2006. (Adventures in Unusual Places Ser.). (Illus.). 28p. (J). 12.95 (978-9974-7925-8-6(4)) Hardenville SA URY. *Dist:* Independent Pubs. Group.

Tichenor, Richard. Tales from the Woods of Wisdom, Bk. 1. (J). 2000. 185p. pap. 16.95 (978-1-888725-37-7(0) , BeachHouse Bks.); 2001. 275p. per. 24.95 (978-1-888725-50-6(8) , MacroPrintBooks) Science & Humanities Pr.

Timmers, Leo. Happy with Me. 2002. (Illus.). 32p. (J). 16.95 (978-1-931290-08-1(3)) Tallfellow Pr.

—Who Is Driving? Timmers, Leo, illus. 2007. (Illus.). 32p. (J). (ps-k). 12.95 (978-1-59990-021-6(1) , Bloomsbury Children) Bloomsbury Publishing.

Tini Sisters Staff. Finny Finds Friends in the Forest: A Letter-Sound * Listen & Retell Adventure. Mauterer, Erin Marie, illus. 2002. (Letter-Sound Listen & Retell Adventure Ser.). (J). 18.95 incl. audio compact disk (978-0-9678459-3-7(9)) Atori Publishing, Inc.

Title in Development. 2002. (Wild Heritage Collection Mini Bks.). (Illus.). 32p. (978-1-59069-238-7(1) , H3009) Studio Mouse LLC.

Todd, Traci N. Wiggle, Waggle, Loop-De-Loo! Barner, Bob, illus. 2006. (J). (978-1-58987-009-3(3)) Kindermusik International.

Tolan, Stephanie S. Bartholomew's Blessing. Moore, Margie, illus. 2004. 32p. (J). (ps-3). lib. bdg. 16.89 (978-0-06-001198-7(X)) HarperCollins Pubs.

Toma, Al. Rainbow on the Tree of Life. 2005. (J). pap. 15.00 (978-0-8059-6607-7(2)) Dorrance Publishing Co., Inc.

Tomlinson, Jill. The Otter Who Wanted to Know. Howard, Paul, illus. 2005. 96p. (J). reprint ed. pap. 6.99 (978-1-4052-1082-9(6)) Egmont Bks., Ltd. GBR. *Dist:* Trafalgar Square Publishing.

Tompert, Ann & Chwast, Jacqueline. The Hungry Black Bag. 1999. (Illus.). 32p. (J). (gr. k-3). tchr. ed. 15.00 (978-0-395-89418-7(2) , Walter Lorraine) Houghton Mifflin Co. Trade & Reference Div.

Toms, Kate. Funny Faces Cloth Book: Jogger Dog. 2006. (Funny Faces (Make Believe Ideas) Ser.). (Illus.). 4p. (ps). 8.95 (978-1-84610-289-9(8)) Make Believe Ideas GBR. *Dist:* Ingram Pub. Services.

Torribio, Penelope. The Grass Is Green, a Farm Animal Musical: Includes Lyric Coloring Book. Ross, Suzanne, illus. 2000. 18p. (J). (ps-3). pap. 16.95 incl. cd-rom (978-0-9704516-1-3(X) , 002) One World Publishing.

Touchable Counting Books Tote. 2005. (J). 14.95 (978-1-58117-284-3(2) , Intervisual/Piggy Toes) Dalmatian Pr.

Touma, Patricia. Happy Times, the Adventures of Ish & Mish Vol. 1: Ish & Mish Go to the Circus. 2005. per. 7.00 (978-1-58396-873-4(3)) Blue Unicorn Edition, LLC.

ToyBox Innovations, creator. Deep in the Jungle. abr. ed. 2006. (Disney's Read along Collection). (J). (ps-3). pap. 14.99 incl. audio compact disk (978-0-7634-2182-3(0)) Walt Disney Records.

—Disney's Lilo & Stitch. 2006. (Disney's Read Along Ser.). (Illus.). 24p. (J). audio compact disk 7.99 (978-0-7634-2173-1(1)) Walt Disney Records.

(Translator), George Fyler Townsend. Aesops Fables EasyRead Edition. 2006. pap. ***(978-1-4250-3319-4(9))*** Assistedreadingbooks.com Inc.

—Aesops Fables EasyRead Large Edition. 2006. pap. ***(978-1-4250-4175-5(2))*** Assistedreadingbooks.com Inc.

Trevol, S. A. No quiero Banarme! Peris, Carme, illus. 2005. (Cucu Ser.). (SPA.). 16p. (J). 5.95 (978-84-7864-841-2(0)) Combel Editorial, S.A. ESP. *Dist:* Independent Pubs. Group.

—No quiero Comer! Rius, Maria, illus. 2005. (Cucu Ser.). (SPA.). 16p. (J). 5.95 (978-84-7864-839-9(9)) Combel Editorial, S.A. ESP. *Dist:* Independent Pubs. Group.

—No Quiero Dormir! Rius, Roser, illus. 2005. (Cucu Ser.). (SPA.). 16p. (J). 5.95 (978-84-7864-842-9(9)) Combel Editorial, S.A. ESP. *Dist:* Independent Pubs. Group.

—No quiero hacer pipi en el Orinal! Rius, Roser, illus. 2005. (Cucu Ser.). (SPA.). 16p. (J). 5.95 (978-84-7864-840-5(2)) Combel Editorial, S.A. ESP. *Dist:* Independent Pubs. Group.

Trewellard, J. M. Butterfingers. Beck, Ian, illus. 2007. 208p. (J). (gr. 3-7). 15.99 ***(978-0-385-75123-0(0));*** lib. bdg. 18.99 ***(978-0-385-75124-7(9))*** Random Hse. Children's Bks. (Fickling, David Bks.).

Trimble, Irene. Jungle Friends. 2003. (gr. k-3). lib. bdg. 11.80 (978-0-613-65128-8(6)) Tandem Library Bks.

Trondhein, Lewis. Harum Scarum: The Spiffy Adventures of McConey, Vol. 1. (Illus.). 48p. (gr. 10 up). pap. 10.95 (978-1-56097-288-4(2)) Fantagraphics Bks.

Troughton, Joanna. Monkey & the Water Dragon: A Folk Tale from China. (Illus.). 32p. (J). pap. 11.95 (978-0-14-038417-8(0)) Penguin Bks., Ltd. GBR. *Dist:* Trafalgar Square Publishing.

Trowbridge, Terri. Tulowly the Possum. McConkey, Barbara, illus. l.t. ed. 2005. 24p. (J). 9.95 (978-0-9766418-0-3(1)) Sidewalk Publishing.

Tryon, Leslie. Albert's Birthday. Tryon, Leslie, illus. 2002. (Illus.). 48p. (J). pap. 6.99 (978-0-689-85251-0(7) , Aladdin) Simon & Schuster Children's Publishing.

—Albert's Birthday. 2002. (gr. k-3). lib. bdg. 15.30 (978-0-613-88158-6(3)) Tandem Library Bks.

—Albert's Christmas. 2000. (J). (978-0-606-19247-7(6)) Tandem Library Bks.

Tsinajinnie, Veronica, et al. Johonaa'éí: Bringer of Dawn. Howard, Winston, illus. 2008. (ENG & NAV.). 32p. 17.95 (978-1-893354-54-8(7)) Salina Bookshelf.

Tsurumi, Yuki. Uncle Noah's Big Boat. Tsurumi, Yuki, illus. 1999. (Illus.). 26p. (J). (ps-1). 13.00 (978-0-8170-1336-3(9)) Judson Pr.

Tub Tales: The Farm. 2003. (Illus.). 10p. (J). 6.00 (978-0-9713507-3-1(6) , 844) Panline U.S.A., Inc.

Tub Tales: The Jungle. 2003. (Illus.). 10p. (J). 6.00 (978-0-9713507-2-4(8) , 843) Panline U.S.A., Inc.

Tuchman, Gail. Simba's Pouncing Lessons, Level 2. 1998. (Disney's First Readers Ser.: No. 14). (Illus.). 32p. (J). (gr. 1-3). pap. 2.95 (978-0-7868-4228-5(8)) Disney Pr.

Tudor, Tasha. Corgiville Christmas. 2004. (Corgiville Ser.: Bk. 3). (Illus.). 48p. (J). 15.95 (978-1-932425-00-0(4) , Lemniscaat) Boyds Mills Pr.

—Tale for Easter. 2004. lib. bdg. 14.15 (978-0-613-88066-4(8)) Tandem Library Bks.

Tukan, Jaytoe Anthony, Sr. Little Bernice Animal Book. Tukan, Jaytoe Anthony, Sr., illus. 2002. (J). per. 7.95 (978-0-9665909-3-7(7)) Kalawantis Publishing Services, Inc.

Tumbrello, Shannon. Freedom Forest. 2007. 17.00 ***(978-0-8059-8880-2(7))*** Dorrance Publishing Co., Inc.

Tunison, Dick. Marley & the Big Stone Castle. Carrel, Dolores W., illus. l.t. ed. 2001. 40p. (J). (gr. k-5). pap. 7.95 (978-0-9707015-0-3(0)) Emmaus Pr.

Twinem, Neecy. Baby Coyote Counts. 2004. (New Board Book Ser.).Tr. of Bebe Coyote cuenta. (Illus.). (J). 12p. bds. 5.95 (978-0-87358-852-2(5)); (ENG & SPA., bds. 5.95 (978-0-87358-868-3(1)) Northland Publishing. (Rising Moon Bks. for Young Readers).

—Baby Gecko's Colors. abr. ed. (New Board Book Ser.).Tr. of Los colores de Bebe Geco. (ENG & SPA.). bds. 5.95 (978-0-87358-867-6(3) , Rising Moon Bks. for Young Readers) Northland Publishing.

—Baby Snake's Shapes. 2004. (New Board Book Ser.).Tr. of Las formas de Bebe Serpiente. (ENG & SPA., Illus.). (J). bds. 5.95 (978-0-87358-866-9(5) , Rising Moon Bks. for Young Readers) Northland Publishing.

Tyler, Jenny & Cartwright, S. Animal Hide-and-Seek. rev. ed. 2004. (Treasury of Farmyard Tales Ser.). 10p. (J). 15.95 (978-0-7945-0513-4(9)) EDC Publishing.

Tyminski, Lori, illus. The Jungle Book 2. 2003. (J). 15.98 (978-0-7853-7968-3(1)) Publications International, Ltd.

Umansky, Kaye. Big Iggy. l.t. ed. 2005. (J). pap. (978-0-7540-7944-6(9)) BBC Audio.

—Donkey-Ride to Disaster. Fisher, Chris, illus. l.t. ed. 2005. 120p. (J). pap. (978-0-7540-6184-7(1) , CLP 378) BBC Audio.

—Donkey-Ride to Disaster. 2003. (J). pap. 24.95 incl. audio (978-0-7540-6246-2(5) , Galaxy Children's Large Print) BBC Audiobooks America.

—Sophie & the Wonderful Picture. Currey, Anna, illus. 2004. 30p. (J). 3.95 (978-1-56148-445-4(8)); 9.95 (978-1-56148-437-9(7)) Good Bks.

Umansky, Kaye & Currey, Anna, illus. Sophie & Abigail. 2004. 30p. (J). 3.95 (978-1-56148-444-7(X)); 9.95 (978-1-56148-434-8(2)) Good Bks.

Umina, Lisa M. Milo with a Halo. 2nd ed. 2003. (Illus.). 28p. (YA). per. 9.99 (978-0-9718350-1-6(2)) Halo Publishing International.

Uncle Markie. Pigletté & Bobo on Safari. 2003. (YA). ring bd. 9.95 (978-1-933129-16-7(6)) Studio 403.

Uncle Ted. Midas & the Little Red Airplane. Young, Eddie, illus. 2000. 28p. (J). per. 15.95 (978-0-9672540-0-5(0)) Midas Entertainment, Inc.

Under the Lilacs. 2005. (J). 19.95 (978-1-59808-649-2(9)); spiral bd. 19.95 (978-1-59808-648-5(0)); cd-rom 13.95 (978-1-59808-650-8(2)) Whispering Pine Pr., Inc.

Ungerer, Tomi. Crictor. (J). (ps-3). pap. 12.95 incl. audio Weston Woods Studios, Inc.

Urbanovic, Jackie. Duck Soup. 2008. 32p. (J). 17.89 ***(978-0-06-121442-4(6))*** HarperCollins Pubs.

—Duck Soup. Urbanovic, Jackie, illus. 2008. 32p. (J). 16.99 ***(978-0-06-121441-7(8))*** HarperCollins Pubs.

Ursu, Anne. The Shadow Thieves. Fortune, Eric, illus. 2007. (Cronus Chronicles Ser.). 432p. (J). (gr. 3-7). pap. 6.99 (978-1-4169-0588-2(X) , Aladdin) Simon & Schuster Children's Publishing.

Vaage, Carol. Bibi & the Bull. Graham, Georgia, illus. 2004. (Northern Lights Books for Children Ser.). 30p. (J). (gr. k-2). 6.95 (978-0-88995-178-5(0)) Red Deer Pr. CAN. *Dist:* Fitzhenry & Whiteside, Ltd.

Van Fleet, Matthew. Spotted Yellow Frogs: Fold-Out Fun with Patterns, Colors, 3-D Shapes, Animals. 1998. (Illus.). 24p. (J). (ps-k). 10.99 (978-0-8037-2350-4(4) , Dial) Penguin Group (USA) Inc.

—Tails. 2003. (Illus.). 20p. (J). 13.95 (978-0-15-216773-8(0) , Red Wagon Bks.) Harcourt Children's Bks.

van Holst Pellekaan, Karen. Coco Makes Music. De Backker, Vera, illus. 2000. (Coco the Koala Ser.). 29p. (J). (ps up). lib. bdg. 23.33 (978-0-8368-2730-9(9)) Stevens, Gareth Inc.

—Coco the Koala. De Backker, Vera, illus. 2000. (Coco the Koala Ser.). 29p. (J). (ps up). lib. bdg. 23.33 (978-0-8368-2729-3(5)) Stevens, Gareth Inc.

—Coco's Surprise. De Backker, Vera, illus. 2000. (Coco the Koala Ser.). 31p. (J). (ps up). lib. bdg. 23.33 (978-0-8368-2731-6(7)) Stevens, Gareth Inc.

Van Horn, William, et al. Walt Disney's Comics & Stories, Vol. 667. 2005. 64p. pap. 6.95 (978-1-888472-20-2(0)) Gemstone Publishing, Inc.

Van Laan, Nancy. Busy, Busy Moose. Rusch, Amy, illus. 2003. 48p. (J). (gr. k-3). tchr. ed. 15.00 (978-0-395-96091-2(6)) Houghton Mifflin Co. Trade & Reference Div.

—Busy, Busy Moose. Rusch, Amy, illus. 2007. 48p. (J). (gr. k-3). 6.95 ***(978-0-618-80907-3(4))*** Houghton Mifflin Co. Trade & Reference Div.

—Moose Tales. Rusch, Amy, illus. 1999. 48p. (J). (gr. k-3). tchr. ed. 15.00 (978-0-395-90863-1(9)) Houghton Mifflin Co. Trade & Reference Div.

—Moose Tales. 2004. (Illus.). (J). (978-0-606-21337-0(6)); 2001. lib. bdg. 14.10 (978-0-613-35539-1(3)) Tandem Library Bks.

—When Winter Comes: A Lullaby. Gaber, Susan, illus. 2000. 40p. (J). (ps-2). 16.95 (978-0-689-81778-6(9) , Atheneum/Anne Schwartz Bks.) Simon & Schuster Children's Publishing.

van Rossum, Heleen. Will You Carry Me? van Harmelen, Peter, illus. 2006. 28p. (J). pap. 3.99 (978-1-933605-22-7(7)) Kane/Miller Bk. Pubs., Inc.

Van Straaten, Harmen. For Me. 2008. 32p. (J). (ps). 16.95 ***(978-0-7358-2163-7(1))*** North-South Bks., Inc.

Vann, Robert Winter Owl. The Bull & the Peacock: And Other Animal Stories. 2003. (Illus.). 57p. (YA). 12.95 (978-0-9741828-0-3(X)) GO-LA-NV Pr.

Vaughan, Marcia. Kissing Coyotes. Spengler, Kenneth J., illus. 2002. 32p. (gr. 2-4). 15.95 (978-0-87358-814-0(2) , Rising Moon Bks. for Young Readers) Northland Publishing.

—Night Dancer: Mythical Piper of the Native American Southwest. Desimini, Lisa, illus. 2002. 32p. (J). (ps-2). pap. 16.95 (978-0-439-35248-2(7) , Orchard Bks.) Scholastic, Inc.

—The Treasure of Ghostwood Gully: A Southwest Mystery. Terry, Will, illus. 2004. 32p. (gr. k-4). 15.95 (978-0-87358-858-4(4) , Rising Moon Bks. for Young Readers) Northland Publishing.

Vazquez-Vigo, Carmen. La Fuerza de la Gacela. (Barco de Vapor). (SPA.). 64p. (J). (gr. 2-3). (978-84-348-2040-1(4)) SM Ediciones.

Veldkamp, Tjibbe. Little Monkey's Big Peeing Circus. de Boer, Kees, illus. 2006. 32p. (J). (ps-1). 12.95 (978-0-8109-3949-3(5) , Abrams Bks. for Young Readers) Abrams, Harry N., Inc.

Velthuijs, Max. Frog & the Stranger. ed. 2006. (Illus.). 32p. (J). 8.99 ***(978-1-84270-466-0(4))*** Andersen GBR. *Dist:* Independent Pubs. Group.

—Frog & the Stranger. Iqbal, Gulshan, tr. 2005. (Frog Ser.). (URD, ENG, VIE, CHI & BEN., Illus.). 32p. (J). 13.50 (978-1-84059-190-3(0)) Milet Publishing.

—Frog & the Stranger. 2000. (Frog Ser.). (Illus.). 32p. (J). (BEN, ENG, VIE, CHI & URD.). 13.50 (978-1-84059-187-3(0)); (VIE, ENG, CHI, BEN & URD., 13.50 (978-1-84059-191-0(9)); (ALB & ENG., 13.50 (978-1-84059-186-6(2)); (VIE, CHI, BEN, ENG & URD., 13.50 (978-1-84059-189-7(7)) Milet Publishing.

—Sapo y el Ancho Mundo. 1999. (Coleccion Sapo). (SPA., Illus.). 28p. (J). (ps-3). 14.99 (978-980-257-229-8(2) , KM2292) Ekare, Ediciones VEN. *Dist:* Kane/Miller Bk. Pubs., Inc., Lectorum Pubns., Inc.

Velthuijs, Max & Bell, Anthea. Frog in Love. Farrell, Kate, ed. rev. ed. 2005. (Illus.). 32p. (J). 5.99 (978-0-8050-7654-7(9) , Holt, Henry & Co. Bks. For Young Readers) Holt, Henry & Co.

Velvin, Ellen. Rataplan. 2004. reprint ed. pap. 20.95 (978-1-4191-4398-4(0)); pap. 1.99 (978-1-4192-4398-1(5)) Kessinger Publishing, LLC.

Velvin, F. Z. S. Rataplan, a Rogue Elephant & Other Sto. 2006. 62.99 ***(978-1-4280-1815-0(8))*** IndyPublish.com.

Vere, Ed. Everyones Hungry. Vere, Ed, illus. 2000. (Illus.). 12p. (J). (ps). bds. 6.95 (978-0-531-30299-6(7) , Orchard Bks.) Scholastic, Inc.

—Everyone's Noisy. 2003. (Illus.). 14p. (J). 8.99 (978-0-333-78040-4(X)) Macmillan Publishers Ltd. GBR. *Dist:* Trafalgar Square Publishing.

—Everyone's Noisy. 2001. (Illus.). 12p. (J). (ps). 6.95 (978-0-531-30335-1(7) , Orchard Bks.) Scholastic, Inc.

Verne, Jules. The Field of Ice: Part II of the Adventures of Captain Hatteras. 2006. 154p. pap. 11.99 (***978-1-4264-3591-1(6)**); 168p. pap. 12.99 (***978-1-4264-3642-0(4)***) BiblioBazaar.

Vestergaard, Hope. Hillside Lullaby. Moore, Margie, tr. Moore, Margie, illus. 2006. 32p. (J). (ps). 15.99 (978-0-525-47215-5(0) , Dutton Juvenile) Penguin Group (USA) Inc.

Visconti, Guido. One Night in a Stable. Cimatoribus, Alessandra, illus. 2004. 32p. (J). 16.00 (978-0-8028-5279-3(3)) Eerdmans, William B. Publishing Co.

—Wolf on a Leash. Vignoli, Daniella, illus. 2006. 23p. (J). lib. bdg. 23.33 (978-0-8368-6261-4(9)) Stevens, Gareth Inc.

Vitali, Daniela, illus. Play with My Animals ABCs. 2003. 16p. (J). bds. 5.99 (978-1-931722-34-6(X) , Sixth Avenue Bks.) Grand Central Publishing.

Viviani, Luisa. There Is Something Special Inside of Me. 2004. 25p. pap. 14.95 (978-1-4137-2372-4(1)) PublishAmerica, Inc.

Von Ammon, Helen. Alaskapaca. Mauterer, Erin Marie, illus. 2001. (J). 12.95 (978-0-9647756-9-5(7)) Doodlebug Bks.

von Konigslow, Andrea Wayne. Bing & Chutney. von Konigslow, Andrea Wayne, illus. 1999. (Bing & Chutney Adventures Ser.). (Illus.). 32p. (J). (gr. k-ps). lib. bdg. 16.95 (978-1-55037-609-8(8)) Annick Pr., Ltd. CAN. *Dist:* Firefly Bks., Ltd.

—Bing & Chutney. 1999. (ps-2). lib. bdg. 14.10 (978-0-613-53145-0(0)) Tandem Library Bks.

Vrombaut, An. Clarabella's Teeth. 2003. (Illus.). 32p. (J). (gr. k-3). 15.00 (978-0-618-33379-0(7) , Clarion Bks.) Houghton Mifflin Co. Trade & Reference Div.

Waber, Bernard. Bearsie Bear & the Surprise Sleepover Party. 2002. (Illus.). 40p. (J). (gr. k-3). pap. 4.95 (978-0-618-12541-8(8) , Walter Lorraine) Houghton Mifflin Co. Trade & Reference Div.

—Fast Food! Gulp! Gulp! 2005. (Illus.). 32p. (J). (gr. k-3). reprint ed. 5.95 (978-0-618-55561-1(7) , Walter Lorraine) Houghton Mifflin Co. Trade & Reference Div.

—Lyle at Christmas. Waber, Bernard, illus. 2002. (Lyle the Crocodile Ser.). (Illus.). (J). 23.40 (978-0-7587-3058-9(6)) Book Wholesalers, Inc.

—Lyle at Christmas. 2003. (Lyle the Crocodile Ser.). (Illus.). 48p. (J). (gr. k-3). pap. 5.95 (978-0-618-38002-2(7) , Walter Lorraine) Houghton Mifflin Co. Trade & Reference Div.

Waber, Bernard & Waber, Bernard. Lyle at Christmas. Waber, Bernard, illus. 2003. (Lyle the Crocodile Ser.). (Illus.). 48p. (J). (ps-3). lib. bdg. 14.10 (978-0-613-88087-9(0)) Tandem Library Bks.

Waddell, Martin. Good Job, Little Bear. Firth, Barbara, illus. 2002. (Little Bear Ser.). 32p. (J). (ps-1). pap. 5.99 (978-0-7636-1709-7(1)) Candlewick Pr.

—Good Job, Little Bear. 2002. (ps-2). lib. bdg. 14.15 (978-0-613-74781-3(X)) Tandem Library Bks.

—Room for a Little One: A Christmas Tale. Cockcroft, Jason, illus. 2004. 32p. (J). 15.95 (978-0-689-86841-2(3) , McElderry, Margaret K.) Simon & Schuster Children's Publishing.

—Room for a Little One: A Christmas Tale. Cockcroft, Jason, illus. 2006. 32p. (J). 9.95 (978-1-4169-2518-7(X) , McElderry, Margaret K.) Simon & Schuster Children's Publishing.

—Webster J. Duck. Parkins, David, illus. 2001. 32p. (J). (gr. k-ps). 13.99 (978-0-7636-1506-2(4)) Candlewick Pr.

Wagele, Elizabeth. Finding the Birthday Cake: Helping Children Raise Their Self-Esteem. Wagele, Elizabeth, illus. 2007. (Let's Talk Ser.). (Illus.). 48p. (J). pap. 8.95 (978-0-88282-277-8(2)) New Horizon Pr. Pubs., Inc.

Wagner, Jerri. Jako's Vacation. 2001. 58p. pap. 9.95 (978-0-7414-0704-7(3)) Infinity Publishing.

Waldren, Kathleen Cook. Roundup at the Palace. Daniel, Alan & Daniel, Lea, illus. 2006. 32p. 17.95 (978-0-88995-319-2(8)) Red Deer Pr. CAN. *Dist:* F & W Pubns., Inc.

Waldron, Kathleen Cook. Rough Day at Loon Lake. 2002. (ps-2). lib. bdg. 15.25 (978-0-613-57782-3(5)) Tandem Library Bks.

Walker, E. G. Mario & the Meerkat. Wilham, Nancy J., illus. 2002. 50p. (J). (gr. k-7). pap. 6.95 (978-0-9716071-3-2(3)) Walker, Esther.

Wallace, Bill & Wallace, Carol. Bub, Snow, & the Burly Bear Scare. Gurney, John Steven, illus. 2003. 128p. (J). pap. 4.99 (978-0-7434-0640-6(0) , Aladdin) Simon & Schuster Children's Publishing.

Wallace, John. Tiny Rabbit Goes to a Birthday Party. Wallace, John, illus. 2000. (Illus.). 32p. (J). (gr. k-3). 16.95 (978-0-8234-1489-5(2)) Holiday Hse., Inc.

Wallace, Karen. Bed for the Winter. 2000. (gr. k-3). lib. bdg. 11.80 (978-0-613-32318-5(1)) Tandem Library Bks.

Wallen, Ila. The Moon in My Room. Sauber, Robert, illus. 2002. (Willowbe Woods Campfire Stories Ser.: Bk. 1). 32p. (J). (ps-3). 16.95 (978-0-9710627-0-2(6)) Bent Willow Publishing.

Wally the Walleye. 2004. (J). lib. bdg. 14.95 (978-0-9725485-3-3(X)) Waterfall Ridge.

Walsh, Melanie. Tienen Raynas los Cerditos? Walsh, Melanie, illus. 2002. Tr. of Do Pigs Have Stripes?. (SPA., Illus.). 14p. (J). (gr. k-ps). bds. 5.95 (978-0-618-20319-2(2)) Houghton Mifflin Co. Trade & Reference Div.

—Trinan los Monos? Walsh, Melanie, illus. 2002. Tr. of Do Monkeys Tweet?. (SPA., Illus.). 14p. (J). (gr. k-ps). bds. 5.95 (978-0-618-20318-5(4)) Houghton Mifflin Co. Trade & Reference Div.

Walsh, Paton Jill. Pepi & the Secret Names. French, Fiona, illus. 2004. 32p. (J). pap. 8.95 (978-1-84507-351-0(7)) Lincoln, Frances Ltd. GBR. *Dist:* Perseus Distribution.

Walsh, Sheila. Will, God's Mighty Warrior. 2006. (Will, God's Mighty Warrior Ser.). (Illus.). 32p. (J). 12.99 (978-1-4003-0805-7(4)) Nelson, Thomas Inc.

Walt Disney's The Jungle Book. 2002. (J). spiral bd. (978-0-9720651-7-7(2)) Story Reader, Inc.

Walter, Debbie. Introducing Russell. Walter, Debbie, illus. 2007. (Illus.). 68p. (J). per. 6.95 (***978-0-9766315-2-1(0)***) Moose Run Productions.

Walters, Eric. Tiger Town. 2006. 168p. (YA). pap. 10.99 (***978-1-55002-631-3(3)*** , Sandcastle Bks.) Dundurn Group, The CAN. *Dist:* Univ. of Toronto Pr.

—Tiger Trap. 2007. 168p. (YA). pap. 11.99 (***978-1-55002-673-3(9)*** , Sandcastle Bks.) Dundurn Group, The CAN. *Dist:* Univ. of Toronto Pr.

Walther, Lou. Three Animal Stories: The Trouble with Cimmany, Bout a Butterful, Fleet Foot & Strange Light. Wiesner, Kelly, illus. 2000. 28p. (J). pap. 3.00 (978-0-9612672-3-0(2)) Walther, Lou.

Walton, Rick. Herd of Cows! Flock of Sheep! Olson, Julie Hansen, illus. 2002. 32p. (J). 15.95 (978-1-58685-153-8(5)) Gibbs Smith, Publisher.

Walton, Rick & Bardhan-Quallen, Sudipta. A Very Hairy Scary Story. Clark, David, illus. 2004. 32p. (J). (ps-3). 15.99 (978-0-399-23858-1(1) , Putnam Juvenile) Penguin Group (USA) Inc.

Wang, Margaret. I Love You Every Little Bit. 2006. 10p. 9.95 (978-1-58117-482-3(9) , Intervisual/Piggy Toes) Dalmatian Pr.

—Postcards from Kitty. Silver, Pattie, illus. 2005. 12p. (J). (ps-ps). per. 9.95 (978-1-58117-427-4(6) , Intervisual/Piggy Toes) Dalmatian Pr.

Ward, Helen. The Animals' Christmas Carol. 2001. (Picture Books for Holidays). (Illus.). 40p. lib. bdg. 24.90 (978-0-7613-2408-9(9) , Millbrook Pr.) Lerner Publishing Group.

—The Animals Christmas Carol. 2001. (Illus.). 40p. (J). 16.95 (978-0-7613-1496-7(2) , Millbrook Pr.) Lerner Publishing Group.

Ward, Jennifer. Because You Are My Baby. Long, Sylvia, illus. 2007. 32p. 15.95 (***978-0-87358-911-6(4)*** , Rising Moon Bks. for Young Readers) Northland Publishing.

—The Little Creek. 2005. (Illus.). (J). 7.95 (978-1-58369-057-4(3)) Western National Parks Assn.

—The Seed & the Giant Saguaro. Rangner, Mike, illus. 2003. 32p. (J). (gr. 4-8). 15.95 (978-0-87358-845-4(2) , Rising Moon Bks. for Young Readers) Northland Publishing.

Ward, Jo-Lynn M. The Mouse Without a House! 2003. pap. 6.95 (978-0-533-13928-6(7)) Vantage Pr., Inc.

Ward, Nick. Farmer George & the Snowstorm. 2002. (Illus.). 32p. 13.99 (978-1-86205-516-2(5) , Pavilion Bks., Ltd.) Anova Bks. GBR. *Dist:* Trafalgar Square Publishing.

—No Hay Quien Gane a un Leopardo! Rubies, Carlota, tr. Ward, Nick, illus. 2001. (SPA., Illus.). 32p. (J). (gr. k-3). (978-84-480-1668-5(8) , TM30405) Timun Mas, Editorial S.A. ESP. *Dist:* Lectorum Pubns., Inc.

Wardlaw, Lee. The Chair Where Bear Sits. Benfanti, Russell, illus. 2001. 56p. (J). (ps-2). 23.00 (978-1-890817-85-5(6)) Winslow Pr.

Wargin, Kathy-Jo. Minn from Minnesota. Holman, Karen Busch, illus. 2006. 141p. (J). 14.95 (978-1-58726-304-0(1) , Mitten Pr.) Ann Arbor Media Group, LLC.

Wargin, Kathy-Jo. Mitt & Minn at the Wisconsin Cheese Jamboree. Busch Holman, Karen, illus. 2007. 144p. (J). 14.95 (***978-1-58726-305-7(X)*** , Mitten Pr.) Ann Arbor Media Group, LLC.

Warnes, Tim. Can't You Sleep, Dotty? Warnes, Tim, illus. 2003. (Illus.). 32p. (J). pap. 5.95 (978-1-58925-376-6(0) , tiger tales) ME Media LLC.

—Can't You Sleep, Dotty? 2001. (Illus.). 28p. (J). tchr. ed. 14.95 (978-1-58925-010-9(9) , tiger tales) ME Media LLC.

—Can't You Sleep, Dotty? 2003. (ps-2). lib. bdg. 14.10 (978-0-613-84706-3(7)) Tandem Library Bks.

—Daddy Hug. Chapman, Jane, illus. 2008. 32p. (J). 16.99 (978-0-06-058950-9(7)) ; lib. bdg. 17.89 (978-0-06-058951-6(5)) HarperCollins Pubs.

—Happy Birthday, Dotty. Warnes, Tim, illus. 2003. (Illus.). 32p. (J). tchr. ed. 15.95 (978-1-58925-026-0(5) , tiger tales) ME Media LLC.

Warren, Adrian. Caminando a Orillas Del Rio. de la Vega, Eida, tr. Brown, Craig, illus. 2001. (Books for Young Learners).Tr. of Walking by the Rio. (SPA.). 16p. (J). (gr. k-2). pap. 5.00 (978-1-57274-439-4(1) , 2832) Owen, Richard C. Pubs., Inc.

Warrick, Karen Clemens. If I Had a Tail. Neidigh, Sherry, illus. 2001. 32p. (ps-k). 15.95 (978-0-87358-781-5(2) , Rising Moon Bks. for Young Readers) Northland Publishing.

—Who Needs That Nose? Neidigh, Sherry, tr. Neidigh, Sherry, illus. 2004. 32p. (J). (ps up). ring bd. 15.95 (978-1-55971-887-5(0) , NorthWord Bks. for Young Readers) T&N Children's Publishing.

Watanabe, Kaori & Grace, Will. Princess. 2005. 6p. (J). 12.99 (978-0-439-74891-9(7) , Cartwheel Bks.) Scholastic, Inc.

Watson, Dolores. The Country Life. 2004. 52p. (YA). pap. 9.95 (978-1-932373-04-2(7) , Cedar Hill Pr.) Cedar Hill Publishing.

Wattenberg, Jane, illus. & retold by. Henny-Penny. Wattenberg, Jane, retold by. 2001. (J). (gr. k-3). 26.90 incl. audio (978-0-8045-6877-7(4)) Spoken Arts, Inc.

Watts, Leslie Elizabeth. The Baabaasheep Quartet. 2005. (Illus.). 32p. (J). (978-1-55041-890-3(4)) Fitzhenry & Whiteside, Ltd.

Waucaush, Clair. Pokey's World. 2004. 72p. pap. 14.95 (978-1-4137-3923-7(7)) PublishAmerica, Inc.

Wax, Wendy. Animal Family Christmas. 2007. 10p. 14.95 (***978-1-58117-625-4(2)*** , Intervisual/Piggy Toes) Dalmatian Pr.

—Mission to Mars. 2007. 24p. (J). 21.35 (***978-1-59961-157-0(0)***) Spotlight.

—A Royal Valentine. Hall, Susan', illus. 2005. (Backyardigans Ser.). 24p. (J). pap. 3.99 (978-1-4169-0801-2(3) , Simon Spotlight/Nickelodeon) Simon & Schuster Children's Publishing.

—Secret Agents. 2007. 24p. (J). 21.35 (***978-1-59961-161-7(9)***) Spotlight.

—Valentine for Tommy. 2003. (gr. k-3). lib. bdg. 11.80 (978-0-613-57563-8(6)) Tandem Library Bks.

—What Do You Say? Please & Thank You. Dillard, Sarah, illus. 2005. (J). (978-1-58987-108-3(1)) Kindermusik International.

Wayne-von Konigslow, Andrea. Bing Finds Chutney. 2001. (ps-2). lib. bdg. 14.10 (978-0-613-53147-4(7)) Tandem Library Bks.

We Both Read-My Day Big Book: My Day Big Book Edition. 2006. (We Both Read Ser.). (J). pap. 29.95 (978-1-891327-93-3(3)) Treasure Bay, Inc.

Weale, David. The True Meaning of Crumbfest. McNevin, Dale, illus. 28p. pap. 5.95 (978-0-9698606-4-8(1)) Acorn Pr., The CAN. *Dist:* Goose Lane Editions.

Weare, Tim. I'm A Little Puppy: A Finger-Puppet Pal. 2002. (I'm A Little Ser.). (Illus.). 12p. (J). (ps-k). bds. 6.95 (978-0-439-40642-0(0) , Cartwheel Bks.) Scholastic, Inc.

Weaver, Katie McAllaster. Bill in a China Shop. Raglin, Tim, illus. 2005. 32p. (J). pap. 6.95 (978-1-58234-988-6(6) , Bloomsbury Children) Bloomsbury Publishing.

Weber, Lou, ed. Baby Animals Stories Musical Treasury. 2005. 40p. (J). bds. 12.98 (978-1-4127-3477-6(0) , 7259400) Publications International, Ltd.

Weeks, Sarah. Drip, Drop. Manning, Jane, illus. rev. ed. 2000. (I Can Read Bks.). 32p. (J). (gr. k-3). 14.95 (978-0-06-028523-4(0)) HarperCollins Pubs.

—Follow the Moon. Duranceau, Suzanne, illus. 2003. 32p. (J). (ps-2). 17.99 incl. audio compact disk (978-0-06-055744-7(3) , Geringer, Laura Book) HarperCollins Pubs.

—If I Were a Lion. Solomon, Heather M., illus. 40p. (J). (ps-2). 2007. pap. 6.99 (***978-1-4169-3837-8(0)*** , Aladdin); 2004. 16.99 (978-0-689-84836-0(6) , Atheneum) Simon & Schuster Children's Publishing.

Weeks, Sarah. Splish, Splash! Wolff, Ashley, illus. 1999. (My First I Can Read Bks.). 32p. (J). (ps up). 12.89 (978-0-06-027893-9(5)); 12.95 (978-0-06-027892-2(7)) HarperCollins Pubs.

Wehner, Adrienna. Elephants & Roses. 2003. (Illus.). (YA). (gr. 2 up). 22.00 (978-0-9653866-3-0(5)) Wehner, Adrienna.

Weigelt, U. & Kadmon, C. Hide, Easter Bunny, Hide! 2006. (Illus.). 32p. (J). 16.95 (978-0-7358-2054-8(6)) North-South Bks., Inc.

Weigelt, Udo. Bear's Last Journey. Kazeroid, Sibylle, tr. from GER. Kadmon, Cristina, illus. 2003. 32p. (J). (gr. k-3). 15.95 (978-0-7358-1799-9(5)) North-South Bks., Inc.

Weinstein, Ellen. Everywhere the Cow Says "Moo!" Andersson, Kenneth, illus. 2008. (J). (***978-1-59078-458-7(8)***) Boyds Mills Pr.

Weiss, Ellen. Fruit Salad: A Touch & Learn Book. Jourdan, Jason, illus. 2006. (PBS Kids(R) Ser.). 14p. (J). 6.95 (***978-1-57791-314-6(0)***) Brighter Minds Children's Publishing.

Weiss, Ellen. Safari Splash. Calitri, Susan, illus. 2003. (Fisher Price Move along Beads Ser.). 12p. (J). bds. 7.99 (978-0-7944-0212-9(7) , Reader's Digest Children's Bks.) Reader's Digest Children's Publishing, Inc.

Weiss, Jim, narrated by. Mole Music. 2001. (Illus.). (J). (ps-4). 25.95 incl. audio (978-0-87499-748-4(8) , 1124-LL1) Live Oak Media.

Welder-Dostal, Stacey Ann. Critter Lessons: Book 1. 2006. (ENG.). 28p. per. 19.99 (***978-1-4208-6691-9(5)***) AuthorHouse.

Weller, Frances Ward. The Day the Animals Came: A Story of Saint Francis Day. Long, Loren, illus. 2006. 35p. (J). (gr. k-4). reprint ed. 17.00 (978-1-4223-5396-7(6)) DIANE Publishing Co.

—The Day the Animals Came: A Story of Saint Francis Day. Long, Loren, illus. 2003. 48p. (J). (ps-4). 16.99 (978-0-399-23630-3(9) , 53247533, Philomel) Penguin Group (USA) Inc.

Welling, Peter J. Justin Potemkin & the 500-Mile Race. Welling, Peter J., illus. 2004. (Illus.). 32p. (J). pap. 15.95 (978-1-58980-149-3(0)) Pelican Publishing Co., Inc.

Wells, Robert E. Hay Algo Mas Grande Que una Ballena Azul? 1999. (SPA., Illus.). 32p. (J). (gr. k-3). 13.95 (978-84-261-3030-3(5) , JV7302) Juventud, Editorial ESP. *Dist:* Lectorum Pubns., Inc.

—Hay Algo Mas Pequeno Que Una Musarana? 1999. (SPA., Illus.). 32p. (J). (gr. k-3). 13.95 (978-84-261-3031-0(3) , JV7997) Juventud, Editorial ESP. *Dist:* Lectorum Pubns., Inc.

Wells, Rosemary. Be My Valentine. Wheeler, Jody & Nez, John, illus. 2001. (Yoko & Friends School Days Ser.: No. 5). 32p. (gr. k-2). 9.99 (978-0-7868-0724-6(5)) Hyperion Bks. for Children.

—Be My Valentine. 2001. (J). (978-0-606-22549-6(8)) Tandem Library Bks.

—Doris's Dinosaur. Wheeler, Jody & Nez, John, illus. 2001. (Yoko & Friends School Days Ser.: No. 4). 32p. (gr. k-2). 9.99 (978-0-7868-0726-0(1) , Volo) Hyperion Bks. for Children.

—Doris's Dinosaur. 2001. (J). 10.79 (978-0-606-22550-2(1)) Tandem Library Bks.

—Emily's First 100 Days of School. 2000. (Illus.). 64p. (J). (ps-1). 16.99 (978-0-7868-0507-5(2)) Hyperion Bks. for Children.

—Emily's First 100 Days of School. 2000. (Illus.). 64p. (ps-1). pap. 5.99 (978-0-7868-1354-4(7)) Hyperion Paperbacks for Children.

—Emily's First 100 Days of School. 2006. (Illus.). (J). (ps-4). 29.95 incl. audio compact disk (978-0-439-84900-5(4) , WHCD654); 24.95 incl. audio (978-0-439-84898-5(9) , WHRA654); pap. 14.95 incl. audio (978-0-439-84902-9(0) , WPRA654); pap. 18.95 incl. audio compact disk (978-0-439-84903-6(9) , WPCD654) Weston Woods Studios, Inc.

—The Germ Busters. Wheeler, Jody, illus. 2002. (Yoko & Friends School Days Ser.: Bk. 6). 32p. (gr. k-2). pap. 3.99 (978-0-7868-1534-0(5) , Volo) Hyperion Bks. for Children.

—The Germ Busters. (ps-2). 2002. lib. bdg. 11.80 (978-0-613-53188-7(4)); 2001. (J). 10.79 (978-0-606-22551-9(X)) Tandem Library Bks.

—Letters & Sounds. 2001. (ps-2). lib. bdg. 14.15 (978-0-613-31413-8(1)) Tandem Library Bks.

—Make New Friends. Wheeler, Jody, illus. 2003. 31p. (J). (ps-ps). lib. bdg. 11.80 (978-0-613-74980-0(4)) Tandem Library Bks.

—Mini McDuff & the Baby McDuff & Friends. 2001. 32p. (J). 9.99 (978-0-7868-0695-9(8)) Disney Pr.

—The School Play. Wheeler, Jody, illus. 2001. (Yoko & Friends School Days Ser.: No. 2). 32p. (gr. k-2). 9.99 (978-0-7868-0721-5(0)); pap. 3.99 (978-0-7868-1527-2(2)) Hyperion Bks. for Children. (Volo).

—The School Play. 2001. (J). (978-0-606-22547-2(1)) Tandem Library Bks.

—The Secret Birthday. Nez, John & Wheeler, Jody, illus. 2002. (Yoko & Friends School Days Ser.: No. 7). 32p. (gr. k-2). 9.99 (978-0-7868-0729-1(6)) Hyperion Bks. for Children.

—Timothy Goes to School. 2000. (Illus.). 32p. (J). (ps-3). pap. 5.99 (978-0-14-056742-7(9) , Puffin) Penguin Group (USA) Inc.

—Timothy Goes to School. 2000. (gr. k-3). lib. bdg. 14.15 (978-0-8085-3410-5(6)) Tandem Library Bks.

—Timothy's Tales from Hilltop School. Wells, Rosemary, illus. 2004. (Illus.). 64p. (J). (ps up). pap. 7.99 (978-0-14-240156-9(0) , Puffin) Penguin Group (USA) Inc.

Weninger, Brigitte. A Child Is a Child. Tharlet, Eve, illus. 2004. 32p. (J). (ps-3). 14.99 (978-0-698-40006-1(2) , Minedition) Penguin Group (USA) Inc.

—Davy's Christmas Gift. Tharlet, Eve, illus. 2003. 16p. (J). bds. 6.95 (978-0-7358-1754-8(5)) North-South Bks., Inc.

—Elf's Hat. 2002. (gr. k-3). lib. bdg. 15.25 (978-0-613-84073-6(9)) Tandem Library Bks.

Weninger, Brigitte. Good Night, Nori. Bishop, Kathryn, tr. from GER. Yonezu, Yusuke, illus. 2007. 32p. (J). (ps-2). 15.99 (***978-0-698-40065-8(8)*** , Minedition) Penguin Group (USA) Inc.

West, Colin. Moose & Mouse. 2004. (I Am Reading Ser.). (Illus.). 48p. (J). (gr. 1-3). pap. 3.95 (978-0-7534-5715-3(6) , Kingfisher) Houghton Mifflin Co. Trade & Reference Div.

West, Tracey. Double Trouble Dwarfs. 2006. (Pixie Tricks Ser.: No. 7). (Illus.). 96p. (J). (gr. 1-4). 3.99 (978-0-439-17983-6(1) , Scholastic Paperbacks) Scholastic, Inc.

—Double Trouble Dwarfs. 2000. (gr. 3-6). lib. bdg. 11.80 (978-0-613-32485-4(4)) Tandem Library Bks.

Westerlund, Kate. Sharing Christmas. Tharlet, Eve, illus. 2007. 32p. (J). (ps). 16.99 (***978-0-698-40074-0(7)*** , Minedition) Penguin Group (USA) Inc.

Weston, Martha. Dr. Clock-Sicle: A Holiday House Reader, Level 1. (Illus.). 32p. (J). (gr. k-3). tchr. ed. 14.95 (978-0-8234-1825-1(1)) Holiday Hse., Inc.

—Jack & Jill & Big Dog Bill. 2002. (ps-2). lib. bdg. 11.80 (978-0-613-86247-9(3)) Tandem Library Bks.

Whatley, Tom. James & Jessie (This Is Not A Mushy Romantic Novel) 2005. 70p. pap. 9.67 (978-1-4116-4370-3(4)) Lulu.com.

What's Wrong with Gilbert. 2005. (J). (978-1-58453-299-6(8)) Pioneer Valley Educational Pr., Inc.

Whayne, Susanne Santoro. Petropolis. Santoro, Christopher, illus. 2004. 40p. (J). 16.95 (978-1-59354-001-2(9)) Handprint Bks.

Wheeler, Lisa. Bubble Gum, Bubble Gum. Huliska-Beith, Laura & Harriet Kasak Portfolio Staff, illus. 2004. 32p. (J). (ps-3). 15.99 (978-0-316-98894-0(4)) Little Brown & Co.

—Where, Oh Where, Is Santa Claus? Bates, Ivan, illus. 2007. 32p. (J). (ps-2). 16.00 (978-0-15-216408-9(1)) Harcourt Trade Pubs.

Whippo, Walt. Little White Duck. Paley, Joan, illus. 2002. (J). 20.81 (978-0-7587-3019-0(5)) Book Wholesalers, Inc.

Whippo, Walt & Zaritzky, Bernard. Little White Duck. Paley, Joan, illus. 2005. 22p. (J). (ps-k). bds. 6.99 (978-0-316-73397-7(0)) Little, Brown Bks. for Young Readers.

White-Bowden, Susan. The Barn Cat, Sassy & a Guardian Angel: Heroic Animal Tales. 1998. (Illus.). 106p. (Orig.). (J). (gr. 4 up). pap. 6.95 (978-0-9633762-4-4(1) , Gateway Pr.) White-Bowden Assocs.

White, E. B. Charlotte's Web. Williams, Garth, illus. (Charming Classics). (J). 2005. 192p. pap. 7.99 (978-0-06-084594-0(5) , Harper Festival); 2006. 192p. mass mkt. 7.99 (978-0-06-122874-2(5) , Harper Trophy); Set. 2006. 50.99 (978-0-06-121501-8(5)); Set. 2006. pap. 19.99 (978-0-06-121502-5(3)) HarperCollins Pubs.

—La telarana de Carlota. Williams, Garth, illus. 2005. (SPA.). 224p. (J). pap. 7.99 (978-0-06-075740-3(X) , Rayo) HarperCollins Pubs.

—The Telarana of Carlota (La Telarana de Carlota) Williams, Garth, illus. 2005. (Charlotte's Web Ser.). (SPA.). 224p. (J). 16.99 (978-0-06-075739-7(6) , Rayo) HarperCollins Pubs.

White, Kathryn. The Nutty Nut Chase. Cabban, Vanessa, illus. 2005. 30p. (J). (ps-3). 16.00 (978-1-56148-446-1(6)) Good Bks.

—Snowshoe the Hare. Rivers, Ruth, illus. 2005. (Red Go Bananas Ser.). 43p. (J). lib. bdg. (978-0-7787-2677-7(0) , 1253648) Crabtree Publishing Co.

White, Marsha. Bear's New Classes. White, Marsha, illus. (Illus.). 16p. (J). 10.95 (978-1-58117-294-2(X) , Intervisual/Piggy Toes) Dalmatian Pr.

Whitehead, Peter, illus. Ink, Wink, & Blink Work Out! 2007. (I'm Going to Read Ser.). (J). ***978-1-4287-2855-4(4)*** Sterling Publishing Co., Inc.

Whitter, Jennifer. The Animals of Sycamore Woods, Vol. 1. 2003. 108p. pap. 11.99 (978-1-57921-657-3(9)) Pleasant Word.

Who Hops? Who Hoots? Book Set 800945, 2 vols. 2005. (J). bds. (978-1-59794-099-3(2)) Environments, Inc.

Who's Coming for a Ride? Individual Title, 6 packs. (Literatura 2000 Ser.). (ps-1). 28.00 (978-0-7635-0019-1(4)) Rigby Education.

Whose Egg Is This? Individual Title Six-Packs. (Story Steps Ser.). (gr. k-2). 32.00 (978-0-7635-9607-1(8)) Rigby Education.

Whose Spots. 2005. (J). bds. 5.99 (978-1-933200-05-7(7)) Family Bks. at Home.

Whose Stripes. 2005. (J). bds. 5.99 (978-1-933200-04-0(9)) Family Bks. at Home.

Whybrow, Ian. Dear Little Wolf. Ross, Tony, illus. 2005. (Little Wolf Adventures Ser.). 64p. (gr. 3-6). pap., lib. bdg. 14.95 (978-0-87614-902-7(6)) Lerner Publishing Group.

—Parcel for Stanley. Hobson, Sally, illus. 1998. 32p. (J). (ps-3). 14.95 (978-1-899607-53-2(6)) Sterling Publishing Co., Inc.

—Parcel for Stanley. Hobson, Sally, illus. 1999. (J). (ps-ps). lib. bdg. 15.25 (978-0-613-22155-9(9)) Tandem Library Bks.

—A Parcel for Stanley. Hobson, Sally, illus. 1999. 32p. (J). pap. 6.95 (978-1-86233-082-5(4)) Sterling Publishing Co., Inc.

—Say Hello to the Snowy Animals! Touch & Feel Animals on Every Page. Eaves, Edward, illus. rev. ed. 2007. 20p. 22.95 (***978-0-230-01391-9(0)*** , Macmillan Children's Bks.) Pan Macmillan GBR. *Dist:* Trans-Atlantic Pubns., Inc.

Whybrow, Ian. Where's Bitesize? 2001. (Illus.). (J). (978-0-606-21522-0(0)) Tandem Library Bks.

Wiebe, Trina. Piglets Don't Watch Television. Pavanel, Jane, ed. Sarrazin, Marisol, illus. 2004. (Abby & Tess Pet-Sitters Ser.: Vol. 3). 96p. (J). (gr. 2-4). pap. 5.95 (978-1-894222-16-7(4)) Lobster Pr. CAN. *Dist:* Univ. of Toronto Pr.

Wiersum, Gale. The Animals' Christmas Eve. 2007. (Illus.). 24p. (J). (gr. k-k). 2.99 (***978-0-375-83923-8(2)*** , Golden Inspirational) Random Hse. Children's Bks.

Wild, Margaret. Bobbie Dazzler. Dawson, Janine, illus. 2007. 32p. (J). (ps-1). 15.95 (***978-1-933605-46-3(4)***) Kane/Miller Bk. Pubs., Inc.

—Miss Lily's Fabulous Pink Feather Boa. Argent, Kerry, illus. 2005. 32p. (J). pap. 9.00 (978-0-14-055902-6(7) , Penguin Global) Penguin Group (USA) Inc.

—Nighty Night! Argent, Kerry, illus. 2001. 32p. (J). (ps-1). 15.95 (978-1-56145-246-0(7)); (978-0-7333-0590-0(3)) Peachtree Pubs., Ltd.

Wilder, Laura Ingalls. Animal Adventures. 2004. (Little House Chapter Bks.: No. 3). (Illus.). 48p. (J). (gr. 3-6). (978-0-7666-0608-1(2) , 99170) Modern Publishing.

—Animal Adventures. 2000. (Little House Chapter Bks.). (Illus.). 80p. (J). (gr. 3-6). Teaching Resource Ctr.

—My Little House Book of Animals. Graef, Renee, illus. 1998. (My First Little House Bks.). (J). (ps). lib. bdg. (978-0-06-025993-8(0)) HarperCollins Pubs.

Wildman, Dale. Do You Know the Way to Find an A? A Rhyming ABC Book. Sisung, Peter, illus. 2006. 24p. (J). per. 2.99 (978-1-59958-002-9(0)) Journey Stone Creations, LLC.

Wildsmith, Brian. Jungle Party. Wildsmith, Brian, illus. 2006. (Illus.). 32p. (J). 16.95 (978-1-59572-052-8(9)); pap. 6.95 (978-1-59572-053-5(7)) Star Bright Bks., Inc.

—The Owl & the Woodpecker. Wildsmith, Brian, illus. 2006. (Illus.). 32p. (J). 16.95 (978-1-59572-043-6(X)) Star Bright Bks., Inc.

Wildsmith, Brian, illus. Brian Wildsmith's Animal Colors (Farsi) 2004. (PER.). 16p. (J). bds. 4.95 (978-1-932065-42-8(3)) Star Bright Bks., Inc.

—Brian Wildsmith's Animals to Count (Arabic) 2004. (ARA.). 16p. (J). bds. 4.95 (978-1-932065-45-9(8) , 718-784-9112) Star Bright Bks., Inc.

Wilhelm, Hans. Hello, Sun! Wilhelm, Hans, illus. 2005. (Illus.). 32p. (gr. k-2). 15.25 (978-1-57505-348-6(9)) Lerner Publishing Group.

—With Lots of Love. 2004. (Illus.). 32p. (J). 12.95 (978-0-7641-5767-7(1)) Barron's Educational Series, Inc.

Wilkes, Angela. Animales de la Selva Tropical. 2004. (Ladders Ser.).Tr. of Rain Forest Animals. (SPA., Illus.). 32p. (J). (ps-3). pap. 6.95 (978-1-58728-409-0(X) , Two Can Publishing) T&N Children's Publishing.

William Morrow Publishers Staff. Chicken Little. 1999. (J). (ps-3). pap. (978-0-673-80925-4(0) , Good Year Bks.) Celebration Pr.

Williamgoldenpen. Quacker's Bedtime Stories. 2006. 49p. pap. 12.95 (978-1-4241-2236-3(8)) PublishAmerica, Inc.

Williamgoldenpen. Quacker's Bedtime Stories... Continued. 2007. (ENG.). 68p. per. 12.95 (***978-1-4241-7448-5(1)***) PublishAmerica, Inc.

Williams, Deborah. Artist in the Woods. Dellard, Kristine, illus. 2000. 12p. (J). (gr. k-2). pap. 3.75 (978-1-58323-032-9(7) , Seedling Pubns.) Continental Pr., Inc.

Williams, Sue. I Went Walking. Vivas, Julie, illus. 2002. (J). 14.79 (978-0-7587-2823-4(9)) Book Wholesalers, Inc.

—I Went Walking. Vivas, Julie, illus. 2005. 30p. (ps-ps). bds. 10.95 (978-0-15-205626-1(2) , Red Wagon Bks.) Harcourt Children's Bks.

—I Went Walking. 2003. (Illus.). (J). pap. 18.95 incl. audio compact disk (978-1-59112-719-2(X)) Live Oak Media.

—I Went Walking. Vivas, Julie, illus. 2003. 28.95 incl. audio compact disk (978-1-59112-720-8(3)); 2003. pap. 39.95 incl. audio compact disk (978-1-59112-721-5(1)); 2000. (J). 25.95 incl. audio (978-0-87499-664-7(3)); 2000. (ENG & SPA.). (J). pap. 33.95 incl. audio (978-0-87499-666-1(X)) Live Oak Media.

—I Went Walking/Sali de Paseo: Lap-Sized Board Book. Ada, Alma Flor, tr. from ENG. Vivas, Julie, illus. 2006. (ENG & SPA.). 30p. (J). bds. 10.95 (978-0-15-205895-1(8) , Voyager Bks./Libros Viajeros) Harcourt Children's Bks.

—Sali de Paseo. Ada, Alma Flor, tr. Vivas, Julie, illus. 2005. (SPA.). 30p. (J). (ps-ps). bds. 6.95 (978-0-15-205614-8(9) , Red Wagon Bks.) Harcourt Children's Bks.

Williamson, Stafford. Puppy Goes to Lambergarten. 2005. 11p. 11.18 (978-1-4116-3854-9(9)) Lulu.com.

Willingham, Ellie. Wildwood. Willingham, Ellie, illus. 2007. (Illus.). 136p. (J). pap. 10.00 (***978-0-9792371-0-2(6)*** , Moo Pr.) Keene Publishing.

Willis, Jeanne. Be Gentle, Python! Birchall, Mark, illus. 2005. (Picture Bks.). 28p. (J). (gr. k-2). 7.95 (978-1-57505-508-4(2)) Lerner Publishing Group.

—Be Quiet, Parrot! Birchall, Mark, illus. 2005. (Picture Bks.). 32p. (J). (gr. k-2). 7.25 (978-1-57505-492-6(2)) Lerner Publishing Group.

—No Biting, Puma! Birchall, Mark, illus. 2005. (Picture Bks.). 28p. (J). (gr. k-2). 7.25 (978-1-57505-509-1(0)) Lerner Publishing Group.

—The Wind in the Willows. Ross, Tony, illus. 1998. 32p. (J). (ps-1). 15.99 (978-0-86264-782-7(7)) Andersen GBR. *Dist:* Trafalgar Square Publishing.

Willis, Jeanne & Ross, Tony. Como Era Yo Cuando Era un Bebe? (Buenas Noches Coleccion). (SPA., Illus.). (J). (gr. k-3). 8.95 (978-958-04-6031-2(0)) Norma S.A. COL. *Dist:* Distribuidora Norma, Inc., Lectorum Pubns., Inc.

Willson, Sarah. Class Confusion. Dress, Robert, illus. 2006. (SpongeBob SquarePants Ser.). 24p. (J). pap. 3.99 (978-1-4169-1239-2(8) , Simon Spotlight/Nickelodeon) Simon & Schuster Children's Publishing.

Wilsdon, Christina. A Wild Ride in Texas. Jaekel, Susan, illus. 2006. 26p. (J). 7.99 (978-1-59939-011-6(6) , Reader's Digest Young Families, Inc.) Reader's Digest Children's Publishing, Inc.

Wilson, Budge. The Fear of Angelina Domino. Fernandes, Eugenie, illus. 2000. (J). (ps-3). 32p. pap. 7.95 (978-0-7737-6120-9(9)); 29p. 14.95 (978-0-7737-3217-9(9)) Stoddart Kids CAN. *Dist:* Fitzhenry & Whiteside, Ltd.

—The Fear of Angelina Domino. 2000. (Illus.). (J). (978-0-606-21825-2(4)) Tandem Library Bks.

Wilson, Greg. Three Sensible Adventures. Lytle, William S., illus. 1999. 56p. (J). (gr. k-3). lib. bdg. 18.95 (978-1-55037-599-2(7)) Annick Pr., Ltd. CAN. *Dist:* Firefly Bks., Ltd.

—Three Sensible Adventures. 1999. (gr. k-3). lib. bdg. 16.40 (978-0-613-27242-1(0)) Tandem Library Bks.

Wilson, Henrike & Stohner, Anu. Santa's Littlest Helper. 2004. (Illus.). 32p. (J). 15.95 (978-1-58234-964-0(9) , Bloomsbury Children) Bloomsbury Publishing.

Wilson, Karma. Bear Snores On. Chapman, Jane, illus. 2002. (J). 25.11 (978-0-7587-9751-3(6)) Book Wholesalers, Inc.

—Bear Snores On. Chapman, Jane, illus. (Classic Board Bks.). (J). 2005. 34p. bds. 7.99 (978-1-4169-0272-0(4) , Little Simon); 2002. 40p. 16.95 (978-0-689-83187-4(0) , McElderry, Margaret K.) Simon & Schuster Children's Publishing.

—Bear Snores On. 2005. (J). (ps-2). 29.95 incl. audio compact disk (978-0-439-76664-7(8) , WHCD666); 24.95 incl. audio (978-0-439-76660-9(5) , WHRA666) Weston Woods Studios, Inc.

—Bear Stays up for Christmas. Chapman, Jane, illus. 2004. 40p. (J). (ps-2). 16.95 (978-0-689-85278-7(9) , McElderry, Margaret K.) Simon & Schuster Children's Publishing.

—Bear Wants More. Chapman, Jane, illus. 2008. (Classic Board Bks.). 34p. (J). 7.99 (***978-1-4169-4922-0(4)*** , Little Simon) Simon & Schuster Children's Publishing.

—Bear's New Friend. Chapman, Jane, illus. 2006. 40p. (J). (ps-2). 16.95 (978-0-689-85984-7(8) , McElderry, Margaret K.) Simon & Schuster Children's Publishing.

—Hello, Calico! Erdogan, Buket, illus. 2007. 14p. (J). (ps). bds. 7.99 (***978-1-4169-1356-6(4)*** , Little Simon) Simon & Schuster Children's Publishing.

—Mama Always Comes Home. Dyer, Brooke, illus. 32p. (J). 2007. pap. 6.99 (978-0-06-057507-6(7) , Harper Trophy); 2005. 15.99 (978-0-06-057505-2(0)); 2005. lib. bdg. 16.89 (978-0-06-057506-9(9)) HarperCollins Pubs.

—Sweet Briar Goes to School. Pham, LeUyen, illus. 2005. 32p. (J). pap. 5.99 (978-0-14-240281-8(8) , Puffin) Penguin Group (USA) Inc.

Wilson, Pauline Hutchens & Dengler, Sandy. The Case of the Cold Turkey. 2001. (New Sugar Creek Gang Ser.: Vol. #3). (Illus.). 144p. (J). 5.99 (978-0-8024-8663-9(0)) Moody Pubs.

Wilson, Sarah. Love & Kisses. Sweet, Melissa, illus. (J). (gr. k-ps). 2001. 22p. bds. 6.99 (978-0-7636-1049-4(6)); 2005. 32p. reprint ed. pap. 3.99 (978-0-7636-2011-0(4)) Candlewick Pr.

Wind in the willows CD gift Book. 2006. (J). 9.99 (978-1-934004-02-9(2)) Byeway Bks.

Winder, Michael K. Christmas Animals. 2002. 19.95 (978-1-890718-09-1(2)) Eborn Bks.

Windsor, Jo. Fun Zone: Individual Title Six-Packs. Hawley, Kelvin, illus. (Sails Literacy Ser.). 16p. (gr. 2-3). 27.00 (978-0-7578-0705-3(4)) Rigby Education.

Winnick, Karen B. Barn Sneeze. Winnick, Karen B., illus. 2003. (Illus.). 32p. (J). (gr. k-2). 15.95 (978-1-56397-948-4(9)) Boyds Mills Pr.

Winter, Barbara. Monkey Business. 2002. (Amazing Dictionary Ser.). (Illus.). 64p. pap. 4.95 (***978-0-921156-94-9(4)***) Rubicon Publishing, Inc. CAN. *Dist:* International Publishers Marketing.

Witte, Anna. The Parrot Tico Tango. Witte, Anna, illus. (Illus.). 24p. (J). (gr. k-3). 2005. 15.99 (978-1-84148-243-9(9)); 2004. pap. 6.99 (978-1-905236-11-4(5)) Barefoot Bks., Inc.

Wittek, Lee. Critter Capers: Tales from the Dogcatcher Who Captures Your Heart. 2002. (Illus.). 230p. (J). pap. 15.95 (978-0-9722872-1-0(3)) BBM Pr.

Witzy Plays Hide & Seek. 2001. (Little Suzy's Zoo Ser.). 14p. (J). bds. 5.99 (978-1-58668-155-5(9)) Lyrick Studios.

Witzy's Very First Color & Activity Book. 2001. (Little Suzy's Zoo Ser.). 112p. (J). pap. 2.99 (978-1-58668-084-8(6)) Lyrick Studios.

Wixom, Jason Kay & Wixom, Tedi Tuttle. Cock-a-Doodle-Doo, I Love You. Lancaster, Derek, illus. 2nd ed. 2003. (Ralph Rooster Ser.: Vol. 1). 16p. (J). (ps-2). 6.95 (978-1-885227-05-8(1)) TNT Bks.

Wojack, Craig. Tommy the Skunk. 2004. 24p. pap. 14.95 (978-1-4137-2120-1(6)) PublishAmerica, Inc.

Wojtowycz, David. Come on Dudley! Friends. 2002. (Dudley! Ser.). (Illus.). (J). 3.95 (978-1-58925-668-2(9) , tiger tales) ME Media LLC.

—Get Dressed Dudley! Weather. 2002. (Dudley! Ser.). (Illus.). (J). 3.95 (978-1-58925-670-5(0) , tiger tales) ME Media LLC.

—Roar! 1999. (Illus.). 10p. (J). 7.95 (978-1-86233-089-4(1)) Sterling Publishing Co., Inc.

Wolf, Jackie. Night Night Sleep Tight. Garofoli, Viviana, illus. 2004. 10p. (J). (ps up). bds. 5.99 (978-1-57151-734-0(0)) Playhouse Publishing.

Wolff, Ashley. Miss Bindergarten Plans a Circus with Kindergarten. Slate, Joseph & Wolff, Ashley, illus. 2002. 40p. (J). 16.99 (978-0-525-46884-4(6) , Dutton Juvenile) Penguin Group (USA) Inc.

—Oh, the Colors/De Colores: Sing along in English & Spanish!/Vamos a Cantar Junto en Ingles y Espanol! Wolff, Ashley, illus. 2003. (SPA & ENG., Illus.). 22p. (J). (ps-ps). bds. 5.95 (978-0-316-06563-4(3) , Tingley, Megan Bks.) Little, Brown Bks. for Young Readers.

Wolff, Ashley, illus. Miss Bindergarten Stays Home from Kindergarten. 2002. (Miss Bindergarten Ser.). (J). 25.45 (978-0-7587-3144-9(2)) Book Wholesalers, Inc.

Wood, Audrey. Jubal's Wish. Wood, Don, illus. 2000. 32p. (J). (ps up). pap. 17.99 (978-0-439-16964-6(X)) Scholastic, Inc.

—The Napping House. Wood, Audrey, illus. 2002. (Illus.). (J). 21.70 (978-0-7587-3238-5(4)) Book Wholesalers, Inc.

—The Napping House. Wood, Don, illus. 2000. 16p. (J). (ps-k). bds. 6.95 (978-0-15-202632-5(0) , Red Wagon Bks.) Harcourt Children's Bks.

—Quick As a Cricket: Nrawm Npaum Le Ih Tug Kaab Roj/ Nrawm Npaum Li Ib Tug Kab Npis. Vang, Mao J., tr. Wood, Don, illus. 2000. 32p. (J). (ps-3). pap. 6.95 (978-0-9629298-3-0(2) , MHC-3-2) Minnesota Humanities Commission.

—Silly Sally: Lap-Sized Board Book. 2007. (Illus.). 30p. (J). bds. 10.95 (978-0-15-205902-6(4) , Red Wagon Bks.) Harcourt Children's Bks.

Wood, Doug. When Mama Mirabelle Comes Home. 2007. (Illus.). 32p. (J). (ps-1). 16.95 (***978-1-4263-0194-0(4)***); lib. bdg. 24.90 (***978-1-4263-0195-7(2)***) National Geographic Society. (National Geographic Children's Bks.).

Wood, Jakki. Never Say Boo to a Goose! Beaton, Clare, illus. 2002. 24p. (J). (gr. k-2). 14.99 (978-1-84148-255-2(2)) Barefoot Bks., Inc.

Wood, Janette, tr. from GER. Luvy, the Bull. 1999. (Illus.). 48p. (gr. 1-3). 8.95 (978-1-890841-05-8(6) , S605en) Universal Life - The Inner Religion.

Wood, Kim Marie. Forelocks, Fetlocks & Horse Tales. Graham, Kimberly, illus. 1999. 110p. (J). per. 5.95 (978-0-9671978-2-1(1)) Syncopated Pr

Wood, Nancy C. How the Tiny People Grew Tall: An Original Creation Tale. Walsh, Rebecca, illus. 2005. 32p. (J). (ps-2). 16.99 (978-0-7636-1543-7(9)) Candlewick Pr.

Woodside, Martin & Grahame, Kenneth. The Wind in the Willows. Akib, Jamel, illus. 2007. (Classic Starts Ser.). 152p. (J). (***978-1-4287-4210-9(7)***) Sterling Publishing Co., Inc.

Woolf, Virginia. Nurse Lugton's Curtain. Vivas, Julie, illus. ed. 2004. 32p. (J). 16.00 (978-0-15-205048-1(5) , Gulliver Bks.) Harcourt Children's Bks.

Wormell, Christopher. In the Woods. 2004. (Illus.). 32p. (J). (ps). pap., pap. 9.99 (978-0-09-941767-5(7) , Red Fox) Random Hse. Children's Bks. GBR. *Dist:* Trafalgar Square Publishing.

—The New Alphabet of Animals, Vol. 5. 2002. (Illus.). 64p. (J). (gr. k-3). 18.95 (978-0-7624-1347-8(6) , Running Pr. Kids) Running Pr. Bk. Pubs.

—Through the Animals' Eyes: A Story of the First Christmas. Wormell, Christopher, illus. 2006. (Illus.). 64p. (J). 18.95 (978-0-7624-2669-0(1)) Running Pr. Bk. Pubs.

Wright, Lynn F. Flick on Trial. Waters, Tony, illus. 2000. 97p. (J). (gr. 2-6). 14.95 (978-1-881519-12-6(0)); pap. 7.95 (978-1-881519-13-3(9)) WorryWart Publishing Co.

—Grandma, Tell Me a Story. Pagliughi, Debbie, illus. 1999. (J). 13.95 (978-1-881519-10-2(4)); pap. 6.95 (978-1-881519-11-9(2)) WorryWart Publishing Co.

Wundrow, Deanna. Jungle Drum. Swan, Susan E., illus. 1999. (Our World Ser.). 24p. (gr. k-2). lib. bdg. 22.90 (978-0-7613-1270-3(6) , Millbrook Pr.) Lerner Publishing Group.

Wyatt, Cherokee, as told by. The Adventures of Margaret Mouse: Harvest Carnival. l.t. ed. 2006. (Illus.). 32p. (J). 6.95 (978-0-9761326-5-3(6)) www.margaretmouse.com publishing co.

—The Adventures of Margaret Mouse: The Magic Star. l.t. ed. 2006. (Illus.). 32p. (J). 6.95 (978-0-9761326-6-0(4)) www.margaretmouse.com publishing co.

Wyland Studios Staff, illus. Wyland's Spouty And Friends. 2004. 37p. 20.95 (978-1-884840-59-3(0)) Wyland Galleries.

Yee, Wong Herbert. Detective Small in the Amazing Banana Caper. 2007. (Illus.). 32p. (J). (gr. k-3). 15.00 (978-0-618-47285-7(1)) Houghton Mifflin Co.

—Fireman Small - Fire down Below! 32p. (J). (gr. k-3). 2004. pap. 5.95 (978-0-618-49492-7(8)); 2001. (Illus.). tchr. ed. 15.00 (978-0-618-00707-3(5)) Houghton Mifflin Co. Trade & Reference Div.

—Hamburger Heaven. Yee, Wong Herbert, illus. 1999. (Illus.). 32p. (J). (gr. k-3). tchr. ed. 16.00 (978-0-395-87548-3(X)) Houghton Mifflin Co. Trade & Reference Div.

—Hamburger Heaven. 2005. (Illus.). 32p. (J). (gr. k-3). reprint ed. 5.95 (978-0-618-54885-9(8)) Houghton Mifflin Co. Trade & Reference Div.

—A Small Christmas. 2004. (Illus.). 32p. (J). (gr. k-3). tchr. ed. 12.95 (978-0-618-32612-9(X)) Houghton Mifflin Co. Trade & Reference Div.

—Small Christmas. 2007. (Illus.). 32p. (J). (ps-3). 6.95 (***978-0-618-91534-7(6)***) Houghton Mifflin Co. Trade & Reference Div.

—Tracks in the Snow. 2007. (Illus.). 32p. (J). pap. 6.99 (***978-0-312-37134-0(9)***) Square Fish.

Yenshu In: One Day, One Smile. 2003. 3.99 (978-0-915960-40-8(0)) Ebon Research Systems Publishing, LLC.

Yolen, Jane & Stemple, Heidi E. Y. Sleep, Black Bear, Sleep. Dyer, Brooke, illus. 2007. 32p. (J). (ps-1). 15.99 (978-0-06-081560-8(4) , HarperCollins); lib. bdg. 16.89 (978-0-06-081561-5(2)) HarperCollins Pubs.

Yoon, Salina. Animal Count. Yoon, Salina, illus. 2004. (Illus.). 12p. (J). 6.99 (978-0-689-86185-7(0) , Little Simon) Simon & Schuster Children's Publishing.

—Apples, Apples! 2007. 14p. (J). (ps-k). pap. 7.99 (***978-0-8431-2498-9(9)*** , Price Stern Sloan) Penguin Group (USA) Inc.

—Jungle Colors. Yoon, Salina, illus. 2005. (Sliding Board Books). (Illus.). 12p. (J). 6.99 (978-0-689-86186-4(9) , Little Simon) Simon & Schuster Children's Publishing.

—A Spooktacular Halloween. 2006. (Illus.). 10p. (J). (ps-k). bds. 5.99 (978-0-8431-2018-9(5) , Price Stern Sloan) Penguin Group (USA) Inc.

Yoon, Salina, creator. Country Pals: A Sparkling Little Colors Book. 2005. (Illus.). 12p. (J). 5.95 (978-1-58117-167-9(6) , Intervisual/Piggy Toes) Dalmatian Pr.

—Little Friends: A Sparkling Little Colors Book, 4 vols. 2005. (Illus.). 12p. (J). 5.95 (978-1-58117-168-6(4) , Intervisual/Piggy Toes) Dalmatian Pr.

Yorinks, Arthur. Quack! Written in the International Language of Ducks! Yorinks, Adrienne, illus. 2003. 24p. (J). (ps-1). 12.95 (978-0-8109-3548-8(1)) Abrams, Harry N. , Inc.

Yost-Filgate, Susan. Rip Squeak & His Friends. Filgate, Leonard, illus. 2005. 32p. (J). (ps-3). 14.99 (978-0-9747825-0-8(5)) Rip Squeak, Inc.

—Rip Squeak & His Friends: An Introduction to the Roaring Adventures of Rip Squeak. Filgate, Leonard, illus. 2nd deluxe collector's gif. ed. 1999. (GER.). 64p. 35.00 (978-0-9672422-0-0(7)) Rip Squeak, Inc.

—The Treasure. Filgate, Leonard, illus. 2005. 32p. (J). (ps-3). 14.99 (978-0-9747825-1-5(3)) Rip Squeak, Inc.

Yost-Filgate, Susan & Filgate, Leonard. Rip Squeak Treasures. 2002. (J). 16.95 (978-1-931290-10-4(5) , Smallfellow Pr.) Tallfellow Pr.

Young, James. The Cows Are in the Corn. 2001. (Hello Reader! Ser.). (Illus.). (J). 10.79 (978-0-606-21125-3(X)) Tandem Library Bks.

Yunque, Alvaro. Animalia. 2000. (SPA.). lib. bdg. 15.90 (978-0-613-86732-0(7)) Tandem Library Bks.

Zalben, Jane Breskin. Saturday Night at the Beastro. Date not set. 32p. (J). (gr. 2-4). pap. 5.99 (978-0-06-443736-3(1)) HarperCollins Pubs.

—Saturday Night at the Beastro. Zalben, Jane Breskin, illus. 2004. (Illus.). 40p. (J). (gr. 2-4). lib. bdg. 16.89 (978-0-06-029228-7(8)) HarperCollins Pubs.

Zane, Alex & Zacks, Lewis. The Wheels on the Race Car. Warhola, James, illus. 2005. 32p. (J). pap. 14.95 (978-0-439-59080-8(9) , Orchard Bks.) Scholastic, Inc.

Zarins, Kimberly. Playful Bunny. Pons, Bernadette, illus. 2006. (Cartwheel Books). 32p. (J). pap. 5.99 (978-0-439-72538-5(0) , Cartwheel Bks.) Scholastic, Inc.

Zhaohua, Ji & Xu, Cui. No! That's Wrong! Zhaohua, Ji & Xu, Cui, illus. 2008. (Illus.). 32p. (J). 15.95 (***978-1-933605-66-1(9)***) Kane/Miller Bk. Pubs., Inc.

Ziefert, Harriet. All Dirty! All Clean! Level 2. Jacobson, David & Brown, Richard, illus. 2005. (I'm Going to Read Ser.). 32p. (J). pap. 3.95 (978-1-4027-2715-3(1)) Sterling Publishing Co., Inc.

—Baby Animals. Sami, illus. 2005. 24p. (J). (ps). bds. 8.95 (978-1-59354-104-0(X)) Blue Apple Bks.

—Egad Alligator! McKie, Todd, illus. 2002. 40p. (J). (gr. k-3). 16.00 (978-0-618-14171-5(5) , Walter Lorraine) Houghton Mifflin Co. Trade & Reference Div.

—Noisy Forest! 2004. (Illus.). 7p. bds. 8.95 (978-1-59354-058-6(2)) Blue Apple Bks.

—Swapped My Dog. 2000. (J). 12.75 (978-0-606-19429-7(0)) Tandem Library Bks.

Ziefert, Harriet & Cohen, Santiago. Kitty Says Meow. Cohen, Santiago, illus. 2002. (Illus.). 14p. (J). bds. 5.99 (978-0-448-42608-2(0) , Grosset & Dunlap) Penguin Group (USA) Inc.

Ziegler, Mark. Fur, Feathers, & Fun! A Book of Animal Jokes. Haugen, Ryan, illus. 2005. (Read-It! Readers Ser.). 24p. (J). (ps). lib. bdg. 18.60 (978-1-4048-1161-4(3)) Picture Window Bks.

Zimmer, Elizabeth. The Turtle & the Deep Blue Sky. Zimmer, Eric, illus. 2007. 24p. (J). (ps-2). 12.95 (***978-1-55591-597-1(3)***) Fulcrum Publishing.

Zimmerman, Andrea Griffing & Clemesha, David. Fire! Fire! Hurry! Hurry! Barbour, Karen, illus. 2003. 32p. (J). lib. bdg. 16.89 (978-0-06-029760-2(3)) HarperCollins Pubs.

Zindel, Paul. Confessions of a Teenage Baboon. 1999. mass mkt. (978-0-553-20170-3(0)) Random Hse., Inc.

Zoehfeld, Kathleen Weidner. The Movie Novel. 2006. (Ice Age 2 Ser.). (Illus.). 112p. (J). pap. 4.99 (978-0-06-083974-1(0)) HarperCollins Pubs.

—My Very First Winnie the Pooh: Roo's New Babysitter. 32p. (J). (ps-k). Date not set. pap. 4.99 (978-0-7868-4380-0(2)); No. 12. 1999. (Illus.). 12.99 (978-0-7868-3242-2(8)) Disney Pr.

—My Very First Winnie the Pooh: Tigger's Moving Day. Date not set. 32p. (J). (ps-k). pap. 4.99 (978-0-7868-4379-4(9)) Disney Pr.

—Pooh's Favorite Things about Spring. 2000. (My Very First Winnie the Pooh Ser.). (Illus.). 32p. (J). (ps-k). 12.99 (978-0-7868-3251-4(7)) Disney Pr.

—Tigger's Moving Day. 1999. (My Very First Winnie the Pooh Ser.). (Illus.). 32p. (J). (ps-k). 11.99 (978-0-7868-3225-5(8)) Disney Pr.

Zolotow, Charlotte. The Bunny Who Found Easter. Craig, Helen, illus. 2001. 32p. (J). (gr. k-3). pap. 5.95 (978-0-618-11127-5(1)) Houghton Mifflin Co. Trade & Reference Div.

Zschock, Heather. Whoo's There? A Bedtime Shadow Book. 2005. (Activity Book Ser.). (Illus.). 16p. 12.99 (978-1-59359-904-1(8)) Peter Pauper Pr. Inc.

Zuhdi, Darla L. Finding Your Dream. 2nd l.t. ed. 2001. (Cat Detectives Present Ser.). 88p. (J). (gr. 4-7). per. 6.99 (978-0-9706062-1-1(4)) Aloha Publications.

ANIMALS, FICTITIOUS

see Animals, Mythical

ANIMALS—FOLKLORE

Aardema, Verna. Why Mosquitoes Buzz in People's Ears. 2004. pap. 14.95 incl. audio (978-1-55592-675-5(4)) Weston Woods Studios, Inc.

Amoss, Berthe. Three Little Cajun Pigs. 1999. (Illus.). (J). pap. 13.95 (978-0-922589-67-8(4)) More Than a Card, Inc.

Artell, Mike. Three Little Cajun Pigs. Harris, Jim, illus. 2006. 32p. (J). (ps-3). 16.99 (978-0-8037-2815-8(8), Dial) Penguin Group (USA) Inc.

Buri & the Marrow. 2004. (J). (ENG & HIN.). (978-1-84444-668-1(9)); cd-rom (978-1-84444-454-0(6)) Mantra Publishing, Ltd.

Chocolate, Deborah M. Newton & Boies, Alex. Imani in the Belly. 2002. 32p. (J). (gr. k-3). 15.00 (978-0-9718310-0-1(9)) WaterShed Bks.

Curlee, Lynn. Classical Bestiary. Curlee, Lynn, illus. 2008. 40p. (J). 17.99 (978-1-4169-1453-2(6)) Simon & Schuster Children's Publishing.

Davidson, Susanna. Three Little Pigs. 2007. 48p. (J). 8.99 (978-0-7945-1598-0(3), Usborne) EDC Publishing.

Daykin, Louise, illus. Goldilocks & the Three Bears. 2004. 32p. (J). (ENG & ALB.). (978-1-84444-035-1(4)); (ENG & ARA.). (978-1-84444-036-8(2)); (ENG & BEN.). (978-1-84444-037-5(0)); (ENG & CHI.). (978-1-84444-038-2(9)); (ENG & PER.). (978-1-84444-039-9(7)); (ENG & FRE.). (978-1-84444-040-5(0)); (ENG & GER.). (978-1-84444-041-2(9)); (ENG & GUJ.). (978-1-84444-042-9(7)); (ENG & PAN.). (978-1-84444-043-6(5)); (POR & ENG.). (978-1-84444-044-3(3)); (ENG & SOM.). (978-1-84444-045-0(1)); (ENG & SPA.). (978-1-84444-046-7(X)); (ENG & TUR.). (978-1-84444-047-4(8)); (ENG & URD.). (978-1-84444-048-1(6)); (CZE & ENG.). (978-1-84444-049-8(4)); (ENG & ITA.). (978-1-84444-050-4(8)); (ENG & POL.). (978-1-84444-051-1(6)); (RUS & ENG.). (978-1-84444-052-8(4)); (SBC, ENG & SER.). (978-1-84444-053-5(2)); (TAM & ENG.). (978-1-84444-054-2(0)); (ENG & HIN.). (978-1-84444-059-7(1)) Mantra Publishing, Ltd.

Daykin, Louise, tr. & illus. Goldilocks & the Three Bears. Daykin, Louise, illus. 2004. (J). (ENG & VIE.). 32p. (978-1-84444-055-9(9)); 31p. (978-1-84444-057-3(5)) Mantra Publishing, Ltd.

Dewey, Jennifer Owings. The Shaman & the Water Serpent. Yazzie, Benton, illus. 2007. 40p. (J). 16.95 (978-0-8263-4211-9(6)) Univ. of New Mexico Pr.

Ginsburg, Mirra. Two Greedy Bears: Adapted from a Hungarian Folktale. Aruego, Jose, illus. 1999. pap. 18.95 incl. audio compact disk (978-1-59112-743-7(2)); pap. 35.95 incl. audio compact disk (978-1-59112-864-9(1)) Live Oak Media.

Halls, Kelly Milner & Young, Roxanne K. Tales of the Cryptids: Mysterious Creatures That May or May Not Exist. Spears, Rick, illus. 2006. 72p. (J). (gr. 6 up). 18.95 (978-1-58196-049-5(2)) Darby Creek Publishing.

Hamilton, Virginia. Bruh Rabbit & the Tar Baby Girl. Ransome, James E., illus. 2003. 40p. (J). (gr. k-4). pap. 16.95 (978-0-590-47376-7(X), Blue Sky Pr., The) Scholastic, Inc.

Harris, Joel Chandler. The Complete Tales of Uncle Remus. 2002. (Illus.). 848p. (YA). 35.00 (978-0-618-15429-6(9)) Houghton Mifflin Co. Trade & Reference Div.

—The Story of Brer Rabbit & the Wonderful Tar Baby. Drescher, Henrik, illus. 2005. (Rabbit Ears-A Classic Tale Ser.). 40p. (J). (gr. k-5). 25.65 (978-1-59197-761-2(4)) Spotlight.

Hausman, Gerald & Hausman, Loretta. Horses of Myth. Florczak, Robert, illus. 2005. 116p. (J). (gr. 3-7). 19.99 (978-0-525-46964-3(8), Dutton Juvenile) Penguin Group (USA) Inc.

Jorgensen, David, illus. The Three Little Pigs. 2005. (J). (gr. k-5). 25.65 (978-1-59197-755-1(X)) Spotlight.

Kellogg, Steven. The Three Little Pigs. Kellogg, Steven, illus. 2002. (Illus.). 32p. (J). (ps-3). pap. 6.99 (978-0-06-443779-0(5)) HarperCollins Pubs.

Kessler, Brad & Harris, Joel Chandler. Brer Rabbit & Boss Lion. Mayer, Bill, illus. 2005. (Rabbit Ears-A Classic Tale Ser.). 40p. (J). (gr. k-5). 25.65 (978-1-59197-760-5(6)) Spotlight.

Larson, Bonnie. When Animals Were People: A Huichol Indian Tale. Rivera Lemos, Modesto, illus. 2002. Tr. of Cuando los Animales Fueron Gente. (ENG & SPA.). 32p. (J). (gr. 1-3). pap. 16.95 (978-1-57416-051-2(6)) Clear Light Pubs.

Lester, Julius. Tales of Uncle Remus: The Adventures of Brer Rabbit. Pinkney, Jerry, illus. 2006. (Puffin Modern Classics Ser.). 160p. (J). (gr. 3). pap. 5.99 (978-0-14-240720-2(8), Puffin) Penguin Group (USA) Inc.

MacDonald, Margaret Read. The Squeaky Door. DePalma, Mary Newell, illus. 2006. 40p. (J). (ps-1). 12.99 (978-0-06-028373-5(4)) HarperCollins Pubs.

Mayer, Mercer. Show & Tell. 2002. (Little Critter First Readers Ser.). (Illus.). 24p. (J). (ps-k). pap. 3.95 (978-1-57768-835-8(X)) School Specialty Publishing.

—Show & Tell. 2001. (gr. k-3). lib. bdg. 11.80 (978-0-613-67668-7(8)) Tandem Library Bks.

McGill, Alice. Sure as Sunrise: Stories of Bruh Rabbit & His Walkin' Talkin' Friends. Tate, Don, tr. Tate, Don, illus. 2004. 48p. (J). (gr. k-3). tchr. ed. 17.00 (978-0-618-21196-8(9)) Houghton Mifflin Co. Trade & Reference Div.

McNab, Chris. Mythical Monsters: The Scariest Creatures from Legends, Books, & Movies. 2006. (Illus.). 95p. (J). (***978-0-439-85479-5(2)***) Scholastic, Inc.

Messer, Randy, illus. Tales of Animals: Retold Timeless Classics. 1999. (Cover-to-Cover Timeless Classics Ser.). 54p. (J). pap. (978-0-7891-2858-4(6)); (gr. 1-4). lib. bdg. 13.95 (978-0-7807-7852-8(9)) Perfection Learning Corp.

Mollel, Tololwa M. Rhinos for Lunch & Elephants for Supper! 2000. (ps-2). lib. bdg. 15.25 (978-0-613-30110-7(2)) Tandem Library Bks.

Oseki, Iku, illus. How the Turtle Got Its Shell. 2001. (See-More's Stories Ser.). 32p. (J). pap. 11.95 incl. audio (978-1-882601-35-6(1)); pap. 16.95 incl. audio compact disk (978-1-882601-40-0(8)); pap. 6.95 (978-1-882601-34-9(3)) See-More's Workshop.

Paye, Won-Ldy & Lippert, Margaret H. Mrs. Chicken & the Hungry Crocodile. Paschkis, Julie, illus. rev. ed. 2003. 32p. (J). (ps-2). 16.95 (978-0-8050-7047-7(8), Holt, Henry & Co. Bks. For Young Readers) Holt, Henry & Co.

Peters, Andrew. Monkey's Clever Tale. Montgomery-Higham, Amanda, tr. Montgomery-Higham, Amanda, illus. 2003. 32p. (J). 7.99 (978-0-85953-051-4(5)) Child's Play-International.

The Selkie Girl. 2004. 24.95 incl. audio (978-0-7882-0590-3(0)); pap. 14.95 incl. audio (978-0-7882-0664-1(8)) Weston Woods Studios, Inc.

Vidal, Cesar. Gray Feather & the Big Dog. Torrecilla, Pablo, illus. 2002. (Legends of the Americas Ser.). 32p. (J). (gr. k-7). 18.95 (978-1-57768-973-7(9), Bedrick, Peter Bks.) School Specialty Publishing.

Villaseñor, Victor. Frog & His Friends Save Humanity/la Rana y Sus Amigos Salvan ALA Humanidad. Ochoa, Edna, tr. Ramirez, Jose, illus. (ENG & SPA.). 32p. (J). (ps). 15.95 (978-1-55885-429-1(0), Piñata Books) Arte Publico Pr.

Winch, John, illus. Brother Wolf, Sister Sparrow: Stories about Saints & Animals. 2003. 64p. (J). (gr. 4-6). tchr. ed. 18.95 (978-0-8234-1724-7(7)) Holiday Hse., Inc.

Yolen, Jane. Meow: Cat Stories from Around the World. Date not set. 40p. mass mkt. 6.99 (978-0-06-440931-5(7)) HarperCollins Pubs.

—Meow: Cat Stories from Around the World. Wittwer, Hala, illus. 2005. 40p. (J). 16.99 (978-0-06-029161-7(3)); lib. bdg. 17.89 (978-0-06-029162-4(1)) HarperCollins Pubs.

ANIMALS, FOSSIL

see Fossils

ANIMALS, FRESH-WATER

see Fresh-Water Animals

ANIMALS—GEOGRAPHICAL DISTRIBUTION

see Geographical Distribution of Animals and Plants

ANIMALS—HABITATIONS

Aigner-Clark, Julie. Animal Homes. Zaidi, Nadeem, illus. 2006. 16p. (J). (ps-17). 5.99 (978-1-4231-0021-8(2)) Baby Einstein Co., LLC, The.

Animal Habitats, 6 vols., Set E. (Phonics Readers Ser.). (gr. k-2). 28.95 (978-0-7368-4071-2(0)) Red Brick Learning.

Animal Homes: First Grade Newcomer Books. (On Our Way to English Ser.). (gr. 1 up). 23.50 (978-0-7578-7204-4(2)) Rigby Education.

Animals Building Homes. (Animal Behavior Ser.). 24p. (J). 6.95 (978-0-7368-5161-9(5)) Capstone Pr., Inc.

Animals Go Home: Kindergarten Guided Reading Level C. (On Our Way to English Ser.). (gr. k up). 27.75 (978-0-7578-7021-7(X)) Rigby Education.

Animals Hide: First Grade Guided Reading Level B. (On Our Way to English Ser.). (gr. 1 up). 27.75 (978-0-7578-7032-3(5)) Rigby Education.

Benchmark Education Staff, compiled by. Habitats. 2006. spiral bd. 139.00 (***978-1-4108-7029-2(4)***) Benchmark Education Co.

Bertolucci, Cristiano, et al. Hot & Cold. Cucchiariani, Fer, illus. 2004. (Contrasts Ser.). 32p. (J). (gr. 1-4). 14.95 (978-1-57768-526-5(1), Waterbird Bks.) School Specialty Publishing.

—Night & Day. Cucchiariani, Fer, illus. 2003. (Contrasts Ser.). 32p. (J). (gr. 1-4). 14.95 (978-1-57768-523-4(7), Waterbird Bks.) School Specialty Publishing.

Boothroyd, Jennifer. In a Tree. 2006. (First Step Nonfiction Ser.). (Illus.). 8p. (J). pap. (978-0-8225-5663-3(4), Lerner Pubns.) Lerner Publishing Group.

Breene, Robert G., III. A Widow Spider in Its Web. 2003. (Where Do Animals Live? Ser.). (J). (978-1-58417-186-7(3)); pap. (978-1-58417-187-4(1)) Lake Street Pubs.

Brenner, Barbara. One Small Place in a Tree. Leonard, Tom, illus. 2004. 32p. (J). (gr. k-3). 16.99 (978-0-688-17180-3(X)); lib. bdg. 16.89 (978-0-688-17181-0(8)) HarperCollins Pubs.

Building a Home. 2001. (Animal Marvels Ser.). (Illus.). 32p. (J). (gr. 3 up). lib. bdg. 24.67 (978-0-8368-2814-6(3)) Stevens, Gareth Inc.

Burton, Margie, et al. Animal Homes. Evento, Susan, ed. 1998. (Early Connections Ser.). 16p. (J). (gr. k-2). pap. 4.25 (978-1-892393-58-6(1)) Benchmark Education Co.

Butterfield, Moira. Animals in Cold Places. 1999. (Looking at...Ser.). (Illus.). 32p. (J). (gr. 1-4). lib. bdg. 24.26 (978-0-7398-0111-6(2)) Raintree.

Carle, Eric. My Very First Book of Animal Homes. Carle, Eric, illus. 2007. 20p. (J). (ps-k). bds. 5.99 (978-0-399-24647-0(9), Philomel) Penguin Group (USA) Inc.

Cherrington, Janelle. Where Animals Live. 2003. (Compass Point Phonics Readers Ser.). (Illus.). 16p. (J). (gr. 1 up). 13.26 (978-0-7565-0530-1(5)) Compass Point Bks.

Chinery, Michael. Animal Habitats. (Illus.). 64p. 2004. pap. 8.99 (978-1-84215-990-3(9), Southwater); 2002. (gr. 4-7). 14.95 (978-0-7548-1044-5(5), Lorenz Bks.) Anness Publishing GBR. *Dist:* National Bk. Network.

Clyne, Margaret. Animal Builders. 2000. (gr. k-3). lib. bdg. 11.80 (978-0-613-33325-2(X)) Tandem Library Bks.

—Animal Diggers. 2000. (gr. k-3). lib. bdg. 11.80 (978-0-613-29547-5(1)) Tandem Library Bks.

Cobb, Allan B. Super Science Projects about Animals in Their Habitats. 2005. (Psyched for Science Ser.). (Illus.). 48p. (YA). (gr. 5-8). lib. bdg. 23.95 (978-0-8239-3175-0(7), SCADHO) Rosen Publishing Group, Inc., The.

Dahl, Michael. Do Parrots Have Pillows? A Book about Where Animals Sleep. D'Antonio, Sandra, illus. 2004. (Animals All Around Ser.). 24p. (C). (gr. k-2). 22.60 (978-1-4048-0104-2(9)) Picture Window Bks.

Davies, Nicola. Extreme Animals: The Toughest Creatures on Earth. Layton, Neal, illus. 2006. 64p. (J). (gr. 4-6). 12.99 (978-0-7636-3067-6(5)) Candlewick Pr.

Davis, Lee. Feeding Time. Martin, Linda, ed. 2001. (Readers Ser.). (Illus.). 32p. (J). (ps-3). pap. 3.99 (978-0-7894-7357-8(7)) Dorling Kindersley Publishing, Inc.

Davis, Wendy. City Park. 1998. (Habitats Ser.). (Illus.). 32p. (J). (gr. 2-3). pap. 6.95 (978-0-516-20370-6(3), Children's Pr.) Scholastic Library Publishing.

Donovan, Sandy. A Snake in Its Burrow. 2003. (Where Do Animals Live? Ser.). (J). pap. (978-1-58417-193-5(6)); lib. bdg. (978-1-58417-192-8(8)) Lake Street Pubs.

Drew, David. Find the Way Home. Harradine, Dona, tr. Falla, Dominique, illus. 1999. (Hello! Lote Ser.). (IND.). 17p. (J). pap. 5.99 (978-0-7339-0876-7(4)) Pearson Education Australia AUS. *Dist:* Cheng & Tsui Co.

—Find the Way Home. Batt, Deleece, tr. Falla, Dominique, illus. 1999. (Hello! Lote Ser.). (JPN.). 17p. (J). pap. 5.99 (978-0-7339-0891-0(8)) Pearson Education Australia AUS. *Dist:* Cheng & Tsui Co.

—Habitats. Harradine, Dona, tr. Falla, Dominique, illus. 1999. (Hello! Lote Ser.). (IND.). 17p. (J). pap. 5.99 (978-0-7339-0878-1(0)) Pearson Education Australia AUS. *Dist:* Cheng & Tsui Co.

—Habitats. Batt, Deleece, tr. Falla, Dominique, illus. 1999. (Hello! Lote Ser.). (JPN.). 17p. (J). pap. 5.99 (978-0-7339-0893-4(4)) Pearson Education Australia AUS. *Dist:* Cheng & Tsui Co.

Durney, Ryan. Prairie Town. Durney, Ryan, illus. 2000. (Illus.). 8p. (J). (gr. k-2). pap. 3.75 (978-1-58323-014-5(9), Seedling Pubns.) Continental Pr., Inc.

Fraggalosch, Audrey. Great Grizzy Wilderness: A Story of the Pacific Rain Forest. Eberhart, Donald G., illus. 2000. (Habitat Ser.). (J). (gr. 1-4). 32p. 15.95 (978-1-56899-838-1(4)); 36p. 26.95 (978-1-56899-842-8(2)) Soundprints.

Ganeri, Anita. Animal Homes. 2004. (Nature Files Ser.). (Illus.). 32p. (J). (gr. 4-8). 28.00 (978-0-7910-8217-1(2), Chelsea Hse.) Facts On File, Inc.

—Animal Homes. Donohoe, Bill, illus. 1998. (Launch Pad Library). 32p. (J). (gr. k-4). 11.95 (978-1-58087-002-3(3)) Stampley, C.D. Enterprises, Inc.

—Animal Homes. (Discovery Guides Ser.). 32p. (J). 2003. 11.95 (978-1-58728-226-3(7)); 2002. pap. 6.95 (978-1-58728-232-4(1)) T&N Children's Publishing. (Two Can Publishing).

Gillis, Jennifer B. Can It Live Here? 2006. (Reader's Clubhouse Set A Ser.). (Illus.). 24p. (J). pap. 3.99 (978-0-7641-3291-9(1)) Barron's Educational Series, Inc.

Goldie, Sonia. My Favorite Nature Book: Animals in Their Homes: Includes an Activity Kit with Posters, Stickers & Puzzles. Weiss, Anne & Estellon, Pascale, illus. 2006. 24p. 9.95 (978-1-57990-920-8(5)) Lark Bks.

Gregoire, Elizabeth. Whose House Is This? A Look at Animal Homes - Webs, Nests, & Shells. Alderman, Derrick & Shea, Denise, illus. 2004. (Whose Is It? Ser.). 24p. (C). (gr. k-2). 22.60 (978-1-4048-0608-5(3)) Picture Window Bks.

Habitats, 8 bks., Set. Incl. Coasts. Cumming, David. 1997. lib. bdg. 27.12 (978-0-8172-4520-7(0)); Forests. Ganeri, Anita. 1997. lib. bdg. 27.12 (978-0-8172-4519-1(7)); Grasslands. Waterlow, Julia. 1996. lib. bdg. 18.98 (978-0-8172-4518-4(9)); Islands. Waterlow, Julia. 1995. lib. bdg. 18.98 (978-1-56847-387-1(7), AS387-7); Mountains. Cumming, David. 1999. lib. bdg. 18.98 (978-0-8172-5239-7(8)); Polar Regions. Bonner, Nigel. 1995. lib. bdg. 27.12 (978-1-56847-386-4(9), AS386-9); Seas & Oceans. McLeish, Ewan. 1996. lib. bdg. 27.12 (978-0-8172-4517-7(0)); Wetlands. Raintree Steck-Vaughn Staff. 2000. lib. bdg. 27.12 (978-0-7398-1409-3(5)); (Illus.). 48p. (YA). (gr. 4-9). Set lib. bdg. 151.84 (978-0-7398-4112-9(2)) Raintree.

Habitats, 6 bks., Set. Incl. Home in the Coral Reef. Taylor-Butler, Christine. (Illus.). (gr. 1-3). 19.00 (978-0-516-25344-2(1)); Home in the Rain Forest. Taylor-Butler, Christine. 19.00 (978-0-516-25347-3(6)); Home in the Savannah. LaBella, Susan. (Illus.). 19.00 (978-0-516-25348-0(4)); Home in the Swamp. Lion, David C. (Illus.). 19.00 (978-0-516-25349-7(2)); Home on the Prairie. Lion, David C. (Illus.). (gr. 1-3). 19.00 (978-0-516-25346-6(8)); Home on the Tundra. Marsico, Katie. (Illus.). (gr. 1-3). 19.00 (978-0-516-25345-9(X)); 24p. (J). 2006. (Scholastic News Nonfiction Readers Ser.). (Illus.). 2006. 114.00 (***978-0-516-25221-6(6)***, Children's Pr.) Scholastic Library Publishing.

Halpern, Monica. Underground Towns, Treetops, & Other Animal Hiding Places. 2007. (Science Chapters Ser.). 48p. (J). (gr. 1-4). lib. bdg. 17.90 (***978-1-4263-0183-4(9)***, National Geographic Children's Bks.) National Geographic Society.

Harcourt School Publishers Staff. Animal Homes: On Level. 3rd ed. 2002. (Trophies Reading Program Ser.). (J). pap. 4.10 (978-0-15-322993-0(4)) Harcourt Schl. Pubs.

—Animal Homes: Science Reader. 1999. (SPA., Illus.). (J). pap. 3.70 (978-0-15-316106-3(X)) Harcourt Schl. Pubs.

—Animal Homes 5-Pack, On Level. 3rd ed. 2002. (Trophies Reading Program Ser.). (Illus.). (gr. 1). pap. 20.10 (978-0-15-326843-4(3)) Harcourt Schl. Pubs.

—Every Animal Has a Home. 3rd ed. 2002. (Trophies English Language Learners Ser.). (Illus.). (J). pap. 4.10 (978-0-15-327590-6(1)) Harcourt Schl. Pubs.

—Harcourt Science: Animal Homes Reader. 1999. (Illus.). pap. 3.10 (978-0-15-314852-1(7)) Harcourt Schl. Pubs.

Hardy. Who Lives in the Rain Forest? 1998. (J). pap. 2.95 (978-0-87628-185-7(4)) Ctr. for Applied Research in Education, The.

Hewitt, Sally. All Kinds of Habitats. 1999. (gr. k-3). lib. bdg. 15.25 (978-0-613-37261-9(1)) Tandem Library Bks.

Hickman, Pamela & Valerio, Geraldo. It's Moving Day. 2008. (Illus.). 32p. (***978-1-55453-074-8(1)***) Kids Can Pr., Ltd.

Hiris, Monica. Sharing Homes. 2004. 16p. (J). pap. 4.95 (978-1-57874-045-1(2)) Kaeden Corp.

Holmes, Anita. Who Dug This Hole? 2001. (We Can Read about Nature! Ser.). (Illus.). 32p. (J). (gr. 1-2). lib. bdg. 21.36 (978-0-7614-1112-3(7), Benchmark Bks.) Cavendish, Marshall Corp.

James, Diane. Animal Homes. Lynn, Sara, illus. rev. ed. 2004. (My First Look at Animals Ser.). (SPA.). 24p. (ps-2). (J). pap. 5.95 (978-1-58728-860-9(5)); 9.95 (978-1-58728-859-3(1)) T&N Children's Publishing. (Two Can Publishing).

James, Diane, et al. Casas de Animales. 2004. (Descubre los Animales Ser.).Tr. of Animal Homes. (SPA., Illus.). 20p. (ps-2). 9.95 (978-1-58728-385-7(9), Two Can Publishing) T&N Children's Publishing.

Kalman, Bobbie. ABCs of Habitats. 2007. (Illus.). 32p. (J). (***978-0-7787-3411-6(0)***) Crabtree Publishing Co.

—Homes of Living Things. 2007. (Introducing Living Things Ser.). (Illus.). 24p. (J). (gr. 1-4). pap. (***978-0-7787-3252-5(5)***) Crabtree Publishing Co.

Kightley, Rosalinda. Who Lives Here? A Book of Animal Homes. 1998. (Touch & Cling Bks.). (Illus.). 14p. (J). (ps-1). bds. 11.95 (978-0-590-12820-9(5)) Scholastic, Inc.

Kline, Trish. Prairie Dog's Burrow. Smith, Fred, illus. (Read-and-Discover - Great Plains Ser.). 48p. (J). 2005. (ps-1). pap. 3.95 (978-1-56899-904-3(6), S2013); 2002. (gr. 1-3). 7.95 (978-1-56899-903-6(8), B2013) Soundprints.

—Prairie Dog's Burrow: Including 8" Toy. Smith, Fred, illus. 2005. (Read-and-Discover - Great Plains Ser.). 48p. (J). (ps-1). 12.95 (978-1-56899-905-0(4), PS2063) Soundprints.

Knight, K. R. Where Do You Live? Lift-a-Flap Board Book. Santalucia, Francesco, illus. 2002. (Lift-a-Flap Board Bks.). 10p. (J). bds. 8.99 (978-1-57759-785-8(0)) Dalmatian Pr.

Langeland, Deirdre. Kangaroo Island: A Story of An Australian Mallee Forest. Ordaz, Frank, illus. 1998. (Habitat Ser.). (J). (gr. 1-4). 32p. 19.95 incl. reel tape (978-1-56899-545-8(8), BC7007); 36p. pap. 10.95 incl. audio (978-1-56899-546-5(6)) Soundprints.

Lindeen, Carol K. Living in a Biome. Saunders-Smith, Gail, ed. (Pebble Plus Ser.). (Illus.). (J). (gr. k-1). lib. bdg. 159.44 (978-0-7368-2324-1(7)) Capstone Pr., Inc.

Lithgow, John & Blackaby, Susan. Salty, Sandy, Soggy Homes: Level 2. 2007. (Lithgow Palooza Readers Ser.). (Illus.). 32p. (J). (gr. k-1). pap. 3.95 (978-0-7696-4242-0(X)) School Specialty Publishing.

Lock, David. Animal Homes. 2007. (Dk Readers Ser.). 32p. (J). (gr. k-2). pap. 3.99 (***978-0-7566-3138-3(6)***) Dorling Kindersley Publishing, Inc.

Lovell, Scarlett. Exploring Mountain Habitats. 1999. (gr. 3-6). lib. bdg. 12.95 (978-0-613-17211-0(6)) Tandem Library Bks.

Lynch, Wayne. Whose House Is This? Lynch, Wayne, photos by. 2003. (Name That Animal! Ser.). (Illus.). 32p. (J). (gr. 1 up). lib. bdg. 23.33 (978-0-8368-3641-7(3)) Stevens, Gareth Inc.

—Whose House Is This? 1999. (gr. k-3). lib. bdg. 15.25 (978-0-613-84422-2(X)); (978-0-606-18760-2(X)) Tandem Library Bks.

—Whose House Is This? 1999. (Whose? Animal Ser.). (Illus.). 32p. (J). (ps-2). pap. 6.95 (978-1-55110-861-2(5)) Whitecap Bks., Ltd. CAN. *Dist:* Firefly Bks., Ltd.

Martin, Debbie. Animal Homes. Baker, Alan, illus. 2004. (Luxury Lift-the-Flap Ser.). 16p. (J). (gr. 1 up). 11.95 (978-0-7945-0715-2(8), Usborne) EDC Publishing.

Maze, Stephanie, ed. Peaceful Moments in the Wild: Animals & Their Homes. (Moments in the Wild Ser.). (Illus.). (J). 2006. 36p. pap. 8.00 (978-0-9769542-1-7(4)); 2002. 32p. 15.00 (978-0-9707768-1-5(0)) Moonstone Pr.

McDaniel, Melissa. Busy Builders. 2001. (We Can Read about Nature Ser.). (Illus.). 32p. (J). (gr. 1-2). lib. bdg. 21.36 (978-0-7614-1255-7(7) , Benchmark Bks.) Cavendish, Marshall Corp.

McKay, Sindy. Animals under Our Feet. Hunt, Judith, illus. 2007. 40p. (J). (*978-1-891327-97-1(6)); pap. (*978-1-891327-98-8(4)) Treasure Bay, Inc.

—We Both Read-Animals under Our Feet. Hunt, Judith, illus. 2007. (We Both Read Ser.). 44p. (J). 7.99 (*978-1-60115-003-5(2)); pap. 3.99 (*978-1-60115-004-2(0)) Treasure Bay, Inc.

Meredith, Randy. Guess Where I Live... Dunn, Phoebe, photos by. 2009. (Illus.). 5p. (J). ring bd. 7.99 (978-1-57791-251-4(9)) Brighter Minds Children's Publishing.

Parker, Victoria. Homes. 2006. (Heinemann Read & Learn Ser.). (Illus.). 24p. (J). pap. (978-1-4034-7891-7(0)); lib. bdg. (978-1-4034-7885-6(6)) Steck-Vaughn.

Pascoe, Elaine, ed. Into Wild Borneo. 2003. (Jeff Corwin Experience Ser.). (Illus.). 48p. (J). 24.95 (978-1-56711-859-9(3) , Blackbirch Pr., Inc.) Thomson Gale.

Perkins, Wendy. Animals Building Homes. 2004. (First Facts Ser.). (Illus.). 24p. (J). 15.95 (978-0-7368-2509-2(6)) Capstone Pr., Inc.

Pfeffer, Wendy. A Log's Life. Brickman, Robin, illus. 2007. 32p. (J). 6.99 (978-1-4169-3483-7(9) , Aladdin) Simon & Schuster Children's Publishing.

Phinney, Margaret. Exploring Undergound Habitats. 1999. (gr. 3-6). lib. bdg. 12.95 (978-0-613-27813-3(5)) Tandem Library Bks.

Phinney, Margaret Y. Exploring Underground Habitats. Petruccio, Steven James & Katin, Miriam, illus. 1999. (Exploring Ser.). 24p. (J). (gr. 1-5). pap. 4.95 (978-1-57255-161-9(5)) Mondo Publishing.

Prairie Dogs & Their Burrows. (Animal Homes Ser.). 24p. (J). 6.95 (978-0-7368-5128-2(3)) Capstone Pr., Inc.

Press, Judy. Animal Habitats! Learning about North American Animals & Plants Through Art, Science & Creative Play. Day, Betsy, illus. 2005. (Little Hands! Ser.). 128p. (J). (gr. 3-7). 14.95 (978-0-8249-6778-9(X)); pap. 12.95 (978-0-8249-6756-7(9)) Ideals Pubns. (Williamson Bks.).

Purmell, Ann. Where Wild Babies Sleep. Siomades, Lorianne, illus. 2003. 24p. (J). (ps up). 12.95 (978-1-59078-049-7(3)) Boyds Mills Pr.

Rabbits & Their Burrows. (Animal Homes Ser.). 24p. (J). 6.95 (978-0-7368-5124-4(0)) Capstone Pr., Inc.

Ring, Susan. Quien Construye? 2005. Tr. of Who Builds?. (SPA., Illus.). 16p. (J). (gr. 2 up). lib. bdg. 15.93 (978-0-7368-4170-2(9)) Capstone Pr., Inc.

Robinson, Claire. Penguins. (In the Wild Ser.). (Illus.). 24p. (J). (gr. k-2). 2002. pap. 6.95 (978-1-57572-468-3(5) , 90458); 1998. lib. bdg. 21.36 (978-1-57572-137-8(6)) Heinemann Library.

Rustad, Martha E. H. Foxes & Their Dens. 2004. (Animal Homes Ser.). (Illus.). 24p. (J). lib. bdg. 19.93 (978-0-7368-2583-2(5) , Pebble Bks.) Capstone Pr., Inc.

—Prairie Dogs & Their Burrows. 2004. (Animal Homes Ser.). (Illus.). 24p. (J). lib. bdg. 19.93 (978-0-7368-2584-9(3) , Pebble Bks.) Capstone Pr., Inc.

Salas, Laura Purdie. Do Turtles Sleep in Treetops? A Book about Animal Homes. Yesh, Jeff, illus. 2006. (Animals All Around Ser.). (J). 23.93 (978-1-4048-2232-0(1)) Picture Window Bks.

Saunders-Smith, Gail, ed. Animal Homes. (Pebble Plus Ser.). (Illus.). (J). (gr. k-1). lib. bdg. 199.30 (978-0-7368-2744-7(7)) Capstone Pr., Inc.

Savage. Animals by Habitat, 4 bks., Set. 2000. (Illus.). (J). (978-0-7398-3535-7(1)) Raintree.

Schaefer, Lola M. Honey Bees & Hives. Saunders-Smith, Gail, ed. 1999. (Honey Bees Ser.). (Illus.). 24p. (J). (gr. k-1). lib. bdg. 14.60 (978-0-7368-0230-7(4) , Pebble Bks.) Capstone Pr., Inc.

Scholastic, Inc. Staff. Animal Homes. 2000. (Super Science Readers Ser.). (Illus.). 16p. (J). 10.95 (978-0-439-16762-8(0)) Scholastic, Inc.

Shields, Carol Diggory. Homes. Junakovic, Svjetlan, illus. 2001. (Animagicals Ser.). 32p. (J). (ps-2). 9.95 (978-1-929766-27-7(0)) Handprint Bks.

Silver, D. M. & Wynne, P. J. Instant Habitat Dioramas. 2001. pap. 4.99 (978-0-439-04088-4(4)) Scholastic, Inc.

Spada, Ada. Burrows, Nests & Lairs: Animal Architects. Lark Books Staff, ed. 2007. (Illus.). 48p. (J). (gr. 1). 9.95 (*978-1-60059-149-5(3)) Lark Bks.

Squire, Ann O. Animal Homes. (True Bks.). (J). (gr. 3-5). 2002. pap. 6.95 (978-0-516-25996-3(2)); 2001. (Illus.). 48p. 25.00 (978-0-516-22189-2(2)) Scholastic Library Publishing. (Children's Pr.).

Stetson, Emily. Create a Wildlife Habitat for Urban & Suburban Small Spaces. 2004. (Quick Starts for Kids! Ser.). (Illus.). 128p. (J). pap. 12.95 (978-0-8249-8665-0(2)) Ideals Pubns.

Tagliaferro, Linda. Bears & Their Dens. 2004. (Pebble Plus, Animal Homes Ser.). (Illus.). 24p. (J). 13.95 (978-0-7368-2381-4(6)) Capstone Pr., Inc.

—Rabbits & Their Burrows. 2004. (Pebble Plus, Animal Homes Ser.). (Illus.). 24p. (J). 13.95 (978-0-7368-2384-5(0)) Capstone Pr., Inc.

Taylor, Barbara. Survival. 2002. (ps-2). lib. bdg. 14.15 (978-0-613-57141-8(X)) Tandem Library Bks.

Turner, Matt. Home Makers. 2003. (Amazing Nature Ser.). (Illus.). 32p. (J). lib. bdg. (978-1-4034-4705-0(5)) Heinemann Library.

Tuxworth, Nicola. A First Book about Animal Homes. 1999. (Look & Learn Ser.). (Illus.). 24p. (J). (gr. 1 up). lib. bdg. 22.00 (978-0-8368-2285-4(4)) Stevens, Gareth Inc.

Tuxworth, Nicola & Lorenz Editors. Animal Houses. 2002. (Let's Look at Board Bks.). (Illus.). 20p. (ps-3). 5.95 (978-0-7548-1028-5(3) , Lorenz Bks.) Anness Publishing GBR. *Dist:* National Bk. Network.

Twinem, Neecy. Busy Beasties. 2008. (J). (*978-1-55971-994-0(X) , NorthWord Bks. for Young Readers) T&N Children's Publishing.

VanVoorst, Jennifer. Who Builds? 2003. (Illus.). 17p. (J). 15.93 (978-0-7368-2924-3(5)) Yellow Umbrella Pr.

Welvaert, Scott R. A Bear in Its Den. 2003. (Where Do Animals Live? Ser.). (J). (978-1-58417-184-3(7)); pap. (978-1-58417-185-0(5)) Lake Street Pubs.

A Where Animals Live Set, 6 vols. (Phonics Readers Ser.). (gr. k-2). 17.50 (978-0-7368-3190-1(8)) Red Brick Learning.

Whitehouse, Patricia. What Can Build? 2003. (Illus.). 24p. (J). pap. 5.25 (978-1-4034-4377-9(7)); lib. bdg. 18.50 (978-1-4034-4370-0(X)) Heinemann Library.

—What Can Build? 2003. (ps-2). lib. bdg. 28.65 (978-0-613-87966-8(X)) Tandem Library Bks.

Who Builds? 2006. (Yellow Umbrella Science Ser.). 8,16p. (J). 6.50 (978-0-7368-2883-3(4)) Red Brick Learning.

Wilkes, Angela. Animal Homes. (Science Kids Ser.). (Illus.). 48p. (J). (gr. k-3). 2007. pap. 6.95 (*978-0-7534-6123-5(4)); 2003. tchr. ed. 9.95 (978-0-7534-5616-3(8)) Houghton Mifflin Co. Trade & Reference Div. (Kingfisher).

—Animal Homes. 1999. (Ladders Ser.). (Illus.). 30p. (J). (gr. k-2). (978-0-7166-7717-8(2)) World Bk., Inc.

Wilkes, Angela, contrib. by. Hogares de Animales: Animal Homes. 2004. (Ladders—Spanish Ser.). (SPA., Illus.). 32p. (J). pap. 9.95 (978-1-58728-453-3(7)); 12.95 (978-1-58728-165-5(1)) T&N Children's Publishing. (Two Can Publishing).

Wilkes, Angela, et al. Animal Homes. Dogi, Fiametta, illus. rev. ed. 2004. (Ladders Ser.). (ps-3). 32p. (J). pap. 6.95 (978-1-58728-613-1(0)); 20p. 12.95 (978-1-58728-600-1(9)) T&N Children's Publishing. (Two Can Publishing).

Williams, Brenda & Fowler, Rosamund. Home for a Tiger, Home for a Bear. 2006. (Illus.). 32p. (J). (gr. k-3). 16.99 (*978-1-905236-81-7(6)) Barefoot Bks., Inc.

World Book, Inc Staff, contrib. by. Animal Homes. 2007. (J). (*978-0-7166-7726-0(1)) World Bk., Inc.

Wrobel, Scott, et al. Northern Trek, 8 vols., Set. 2000. (Illus.). (J). (gr. 2-7). lib. bdg. 127.60 (978-1-58340-022-7(2)) Smart Apple Media.

ANIMALS—HABITS AND BEHAVIOR

Here are entered factual books whose aim is to describe and instruct. Fictional or legendary tales about animals are entered under Animals—Stories.

see also Animal Intelligence; Animals—Fiction; Animals—Migration; Nature Study; Tracking and Trailing

also names of animals with the subdivision Habits and Behavior, e.g. Birds—Habits and Behavior; etc.

Agard, John. We Animals Would Like a Word with You. Kitamura, Satoshi, illus. 1998. 64p. (J). (gr. 1 up). pap. 9.99 (978-0-09-968851-8(4)) Random Hse. GBR. *Dist:* Independent Pubs. Group.

Allen, Nancy Kelly. Whose Work Is This? A Look at Things Animals Make - Pearls, Silk, & Honey. Alderman, Derrick & Shea, Denise, illus. 2004. (Whose Is It? Ser.). 24p. (C). (gr. k-2). 22.60 (978-1-4048-0612-2(1)) Picture Window Bks.

Animal Actions: Individual Title Six-Packs. (gr. k-1). 23.00 (978-0-7635-9047-5(9)) Rigby Education.

Animal Behavior. (First Facts Ser.). (Illus.). (J). (gr. 1-2). lib. bdg. 148.82 (978-0-7368-2752-2(8)) Capstone Pr., Inc.

Animal Senses & Defenses. 2002. (Illus.). (J). pap. 5.43 (978-0-7398-5925-4(0)) Steck-Vaughn.

Animals All Around. 2000. (Illus.). 18p. (J). (ps). (978-1-57584-810-5(4)) Reader's Digest Children's Publishing, Inc.

Animals Sleeping. (Animal Behavior Ser.). 24p. (J). 6.95 (978-0-7368-5163-3(1)) Capstone Pr., Inc.

Arnold, Caroline. Did You Hear That? Animals with Super Hearing. Trachok, Cathy, illus. 2001. (J). pap. 6.95 (978-1-57091-405-8(2)); 32p. 16.95 (978-1-57091-404-1(4)) Charlesbridge Publishing, Inc.

—Mother & Baby Zoo Animals. 1999. (Zoo Animals Ser.). (Illus.). 32p. (J). (ps-2). 9.95 (978-1-57505-390-5(X) , Carolrhoda Bks.) Lerner Publishing Group.

—Mother & Baby Zoo Animals. Hewett, Richard, illus. 1999. (Zoo Animals Ser.). 32p. (J). (ps-2). lib. bdg. 21.27 (978-1-57505-285-4(7) , Carolrhoda Bks.) Lerner Publishing Group.

—Playtime for Zoo Animals. 1999. (Zoo Animals Ser.). (Illus.). 32p. (J). (ps-2). pap. 9.95 (978-1-57505-391-2(8) , Carolrhoda Bks.) Lerner Publishing Group.

—Playtime for Zoo Animals. Hewett, Richard, illus. 1999. (Zoo Animals Ser.). 32p. (J). (ps-2). lib. bdg. 21.27 (978-1-57505-287-8(3) , Carolrhoda Bks.) Lerner Publishing Group.

—Playtime for Zoo Animals. 1999. (J). (978-0-606-22862-6(4)) Tandem Library Bks.

—Sleepytime for Zoo Animals. 1999. (Zoo Animals Ser.). (Illus.). 32p. (J). (ps-2). 9.95 (978-1-57505-393-6(4) , Carolrhoda Bks.) Lerner Publishing Group.

—Sleepytime for Zoo Animals. Hewett, Richard, illus. 1999. (Zoo Animals Ser.). 32p. (J). (ps-2). lib. bdg. 21.27 (978-1-57505-290-8(3) , Carolrhoda Bks.) Lerner Publishing Group.

—Splashtime for Zoo Animals. 1999. (Zoo Animals Ser.). (Illus.). 32p. (J). (ps-2). 9.95 (978-1-57505-394-3(2) , Carolrhoda Bks.) Lerner Publishing Group.

—Splashtime for Zoo Animals. Hewett, Richard, illus. 1998. (Zoo Animals Ser.). 32p. (J). (ps-2). lib. bdg. 21.27 (978-1-57505-288-5(1) , Carolrhoda Bks.) Lerner Publishing Group.

Arnold, Katya R. Elephants Can Paint Too! Arnold, Katya R., photos by. 2005. (Illus.). 40p. (J). 16.95 (978-0-689-86985-3(1) , Atheneum) Simon & Schuster Children's Publishing.

Baddiel, Ivor. Fantastic Creatures. 1999. (Mysterious World Ser.). (Illus.). 30p. (J). (gr. 5-9). pap. 6.95 (978-0-7641-1153-2(1)) Barron's Educational Series, Inc.

Baillie, Marilyn. Amazing Things Animals Do. Caron, Romi, illus. 2003. 128p. (J). (gr. k-3). 19.95 (978-1-894379-57-1(8)) Maple Tree Pr. CAN. *Dist:* Firefly Bks., Ltd.

Barbey, Dorine. Animals Around Us. Gibson, Sarah et al, trs. 1998. (Creative Discoveries Ser.). (Illus.). 75p. (J). (gr. 2-8). lib. bdg. 23.95 (978-0-88682-943-8(7) , Creative Education) Creative Co., The.

Barrett, Judi. Los Animales No Se Visten.Tr. of Animals Should Definely Not Wear Clothes. (SPA., Illus.). (J). (gr. k-1). pap. (978-950-515-806-5(8) , FL2766) De La Flor ARG. *Dist:* Lectorum Pubns., Inc.

Barron's Educational Editorial Staff. Animal Behavior. 1999. (Illus.). 128p. (gr. 6-12). pap. 8.95 (978-0-7641-0952-2(9)) Barron's Educational Series, Inc.

Batten, Mary. Hey, Daddy! Animal Fathers & Their Babies. Bond, Higgins, illus. 2002. 32p. (J). (gr. 1-5). 15.95 (978-1-56145-272-9(6) , Q34264) Peachtree Pubs., Ltd.

Benchmark Education Staff, compiled by. Animal Behavior. 2006. spiral bd. 249.00 (*978-1-4108-7028-5(6)) Benchmark Education Co.

Bennett, Paul. Catching a Meal. 1999. (Nature's Secrets Ser.). (Illus.). 32p. (ps-4). 21.40 (978-0-8172-5252-6(5)) Raintree.

Bentley, Dawn. The Icky Sticky Anteater. Castillon, Carly, illus. 2001. 18p. (J). (ps-k). 5.95 (978-1-58117-121-1(8) , Intervisual/Piggy Toes) Dalmatian Pr.

—The Icky Sticky Anteater. Castillion, Carly, illus. 2000. 18p. (J). (ps-k). 9.95 (978-1-58117-079-5(3) , Intervisual/Piggy Toes) Dalmatian Pr.

Berger, Melvin & Berger, Gilda. Dogs Bring Newspapers but Cats Bring Mice: And Other Fascinating Facts about Animal Behavior. 2004. (Illus.). 48p. (J). pap. (978-0-439-66433-2(0)) Scholastic, Inc.

Berger, Melvin, et al. What Do Animals Do in Winter? How Animals Survive the Cold. Harrison, Susan J., illus. 1999. (Discovery Readers Ser.). 48p. (J). (ps-3). lib. bdg. 17.55 (978-0-7910-5070-5(X) , Chelsea Hse.) Facts On File, Inc.

Berkowitz, Henry. Animal Oddities: An Educational Coloring Book. Berkowitz, Henry, illus. 2002. 32p. (J). (gr. k-3). pap. 4.95 (978-0-932855-71-8(7)) Winner Enterprises.

BHB International Staff. All about Animals. 1998. (Images Ser.). (J). (ps-3). pap. (978-2-215-06194-6(4)) Editions Fleurus.

Billings, Henry & Billings, Melissa. Angry Animals. 1998. (Wild Side Ser.). (Illus.). 114p. (YA). (gr. 6-12). 13.00 (978-0-89061-801-1(1) , R0801-1E) Jamestown.

Blackbirch Press Staff, creator. Cheats. 2005. (Planet's Most Extreme Ser.). (Illus.). 48p. (J). (ps-7). lib. bdg. 24.95 (978-1-4103-0381-3(0) , Blackbirch Pr., Inc.) Thomson Gale.

—Dads. 2005. (Planet's Most Extreme Ser.). (Illus.). 48p. (J). (ps-7). lib. bdg. 24.95 (978-1-4103-0391-2(8) , Blackbirch Pr., Inc.) Thomson Gale.

—Eaters. 2005. (Planet's Most Extreme Ser.). (Illus.). 48p. (J). (ps-7). lib. bdg. 24.95 (978-1-4103-0401-8(9) , Blackbirch Pr., Inc.) Thomson Gale.

Brett, Jane & Cooke, Andy. In the Country. 1999. (Animal Noises Ser.). (Illus.). 10p. (J). 2.95 (978-1-57717-098-3(9)) New Line Bks.

Brettle, Jane. My Pets. 1999. (Animal Noises Ser.). (Illus.). 10p. (J). 2.95 (978-1-57717-099-0(7)) New Line Bks.

Brighter Vision Publishing Staff. Animal Families. 1998. (Learning Adventures Preschool Ser.). 32p. (J). (ps-k). pap. 2.25 (978-1-55254-006-0(5) , BV12002) Brighter Vision Pubns.

British Museum of Natural History Staff, contrib. by. What Do Animals Eat Colouring Book. (Illus.). 8p. (J). (ps-6). pap. 2.95 (978-0-565-00808-6(0)) Natural History Museum Pubns. GBR. *Dist:* Parkwest Pubns., Inc.

Brown, Jacqui. Whose Footprint Is That? 2003. (Animal Detectives Ser.). (Illus.). 32p. (J). 5.95 (978-0-7641-5661-8(6)) Barron's Educational Series, Inc.

Bruna, Dick. Animals, 2 vols. 2001. (Illus.). 12p. (J). (ps-k). bds. 5.95 (978-1-56836-310-3(9)) Kodansha America, Inc.

Bryant-Mole, Karen & Ansary, Mir Tamim. Moving. 2002. (Science All Around Me Ser.). (Illus.). 24p. (J). (gr. 1-3). pap. 6.50 (978-1-4034-0054-3(7) , 91498) Heinemann Library.

Bull, Schuyler. Crocodile Crossing. Male, Alan, illus. 2005. (Amazing Animal Adventures Ser.). 36p. (J). (ps-2). 15.95 (978-1-59249-051-6(4) , B7104) Soundprints.

Burgess, Thornton W. The Burgess Animal Book for Children. 2005. 29.95 (978-1-4218-0996-0(6) , 1st World Library - Literary Society) 1st World Publishing, Inc.

—The Burgess Animal Book for Children. 2004. reprint ed. pap. 1.99 (978-1-4192-5555-7(X)) Kessinger Publishing, LLC.

—The Burgess Animal Book for Children. Fuertes, Louis Agassiz, illus. 2004. reprint ed. pap. 37.95 (978-1-4179-2978-8(2)) Kessinger Publishing, LLC.

Burgess, Thornton W. The Burgess Animal Book for Children (Yesterday's Classics) Fuertes, Louis Agassiz, illus. 2006. (J). per. 13.95 (*978-1-59915-171-7(5)) Yesterday's Classics.

Burgess, W. Thornton. The Burgess Animal Book for Children. 2006. pap. 57.99 (*978-1-4280-3431-0(5)) IndyPublish.com.

Burroughs, John. Squirrels & Other Fur-Bearers (Yesterday's Classics) 2006. (Illus.). 144p. (J). per. 8.95 (978-1-59915-070-3(0)) Yesterday's Classics.

Carle, Eric. Eric Carle Animal Family, 2000. 1999. (J). pap. 14.95 (978-0-689-82688-7(5)) Globe Fearon Educational Publishing.

Chinery, Michael. Animal Survival. 2003. (Wild Animal Planet Ser.). (Illus.). 64p. 14.99 (978-0-7548-1164-0(6)) Anness Publishing GBR. *Dist:* National Bk. Network.

—Partners & Parents. 2000. (Secrets of the Rainforest Ser.). (Illus.). 32p. (J). (gr. 3-4). pap. (978-0-7787-0226-9(X)); lib. bdg. (978-0-7787-0216-0(2)) Crabtree Publishing Co.

—Partners & Parents. 2000. (gr. 3-6). lib. bdg. 16.40 (978-0-613-28012-9(1)) Tandem Library Bks.

—Plants & Planteaters. 2000. (Secrets of the Rainforest Ser.). (Illus.). 32p. (J). (gr. 3-4). lib. bdg. (978-0-7787-0218-4(9)) Crabtree Publishing Co.

—Plants & Planteaters. 2000. (gr. 3-6). lib. bdg. 16.40 (978-0-613-28023-5(7)) Tandem Library Bks.

—Predators & Prey. 2000. (Secrets of the Rainforest Ser.). (Illus.). 32p. (J). (gr. 3-4). pap. (978-0-7787-0227-6(8)); lib. bdg. (978-0-7787-0217-7(0)) Crabtree Publishing Co.

Chinery, Michael, et al. Hunters of the Wild. 2003. (Illus.). 512p. 45.00 (978-0-7548-1104-6(2) , Lorenz Bks.) Anness Publishing GBR. *Dist:* National Bk. Network.

Christie, Peter. Well-Schooled Fish & Feathered Bandits: The Wondrous Ways Animals Learn from Animals. 2006. (Illus.). 48p. (J). (gr. 3-6). pap. 8.95 (978-1-55451-045-0(7)); lib. bdg. 19.95 (978-1-55451-046-7(5)) Annick Pr., Ltd. CAN. *Dist:* Firefly Bks., Ltd.

Clarke, Ginjer L. Gross Out! Mueller, Pete, illus. 2006. (All Aboard Science Reader Ser.). 48p. (J). (gr. 1-3). pap. 3.99 (978-0-448-44390-4(2) , Grosset & Dunlap) Penguin Group (USA) Inc.

—Wild Dads! Ogden, Betina, illus. 2002. 24p. (J). (gr. k-ps). pap. 3.25 (978-0-375-81449-5(3) , Random Hse. Bks. for Young Readers) Random Hse. Children's Bks.

Clyne, Margaret. Amazing Journeys. 2001. (gr. k-3). lib. bdg. 11.80 (978-0-613-33324-5(1)) Tandem Library Bks.

Cogan, Karen. When Animals Sleep. Tcherepanova-Smith, Marianna, illus. 1999. 8p. (J). (gr. k-2). pap. (978-1-880612-98-9(4) , Seedling Pubns.) Continental Pr., Inc.

Collard, Sneed B., III. Animal Dads. Jenkins, Steve, illus. 2000. 32p. (J). (gr. k-3). 6.95 (978-0-618-03299-0(1)) Houghton Mifflin Co. Trade & Reference Div.

—Animal Dads. Jenkins, Steve, illus. 2000. (J). (ps-ps). lib. bdg. 14.10 (978-0-613-28403-5(8)) Tandem Library Bks.

—Animal Dads. 2000. (Illus.). (J). 12.75 (978-0-606-18207-2(1)) Tandem Library Bks.

—Animals Asleep. McGrory, Anik, tr. McGrory, Anik, illus. 2004. 32p. (J). (gr. k-3). tchr. ed. 15.00 (978-0-618-27697-4(1)) Houghton Mifflin Co. Trade & Reference Div.

—Leaving Home. Dunning, Joan, illus. 2002. 32p. (J). (gr. k-3). 15.00 (978-0-618-11454-2(8)) Houghton Mifflin Co. Trade & Reference Div.

—Tough Terminators. 2004. (It's Nature! Ser.). (Illus.). 32p. (J). (gr. 3-6). pap. 7.95 (978-1-55971-633-8(9) , Creative Publishing International) Quayside.

Cousins, Lucy. Country Animals. Cousins, Lucy, illus. 2004. (Illus.). 12p. (J). (gr. k-k). bds. 4.99 (978-0-7636-2302-9(4)) Candlewick Pr.

—Garden Animals. Cousins, Lucy, illus. 2004. (Illus.). 12p. (J). (gr. k-k). bds. 4.99 (978-0-7636-2304-3(0)) Candlewick Pr.

—Pet Animals. Cousins, Lucy, illus. 2004. (Illus.). 12p. (J). (gr. k-k). bds. 4.99 (978-0-7636-2305-0(9)) Candlewick Pr.

Creative Publishing international Editors. Amazing Animals. 2004. (It's Nature! Ser.). (Illus.). 160p. (YA). (gr. 3-6). ring bd. 16.95 (978-1-55971-752-6(1) , NorthWord Bks. for Young Readers) T&N Children's Publishing.

Crum, Anna-Maria. Animal Behaviorists. 2004. (Navigators Ser.). (J). pap. 38.00 (978-1-4108-0412-9(7)) Benchmark Education Co.

Cunning Creatures: Individual Title Six-Packs. (gr. k-1). 23.00 (978-0-7635-9032-1(0)) Rigby Education.

Czajkowski, Alexandre C. Amazing Creatures. 2000. (Creative Discoveries Ser.). Orig. Title: The Animal World. (Illus.). 80p. (J). (gr. 4 up). lib. bdg. 25.30 (978-0-88682-945-2(3) , Creative Education) Creative Co., The.

Dahl, Michael. Do Bees Make Butter? A Book about the Things Animals Make. Ouren, Todd, illus. 2004. (Animals All Around Ser.). 24p. (J). (gr. k-2). 22.60 (978-1-4048-0288-9(6)) Picture Window Bks.

—Do Dogs Make Dessert? A Book about How Animals Help Humans. Yesh, Jeff, illus. 2004. (Animals All Around Ser.). 24p. (J). (gr. k-2). 22.60 (978-1-4048-0289-6(4)) Picture Window Bks.

—Do Penguins Have Puppies? A Book about Animal Babies. D'Antonio, Sandra, illus. 2004. (Animals All Around Ser.). 24p. (C). (gr. k-2). 22.60 (978-1-4048-0102-8(2)) Picture Window Bks.

—Do Squirrels Swarm? A Book about Animal Groups. Ayers, Franklin, illus. 2004. (Animals All Around Ser.). 24p. (J). (gr. k-2). 22.60 (978-1-4048-0287-2(8) , 1229503) Picture Window Bks.

Dalgleish, Sharon. Attack & Defense. Cavaluzzo, Laura & McEwen, Rebecca, eds. 1999. (Explorers Ser.). (Illus.). 32p. (J). (978-0-7699-0477-1(7)) Shortland Pubns. (U. S. A.) Inc.

Daly, Catherine. Whiskers. 2000. (Road to Reading Ser.). (J). (978-0-606-18922-4(X)) Tandem Library Bks.

Davies, Nicola. Poop: A Natural History of the Unmentionable. Layton, Neal, illus. 2004. 64p. (J). (gr. 3 up). 12.99 (978-0-7636-2437-8(3)) Candlewick Pr.

Davies, Nicola. Poop Mini: A Natural History of the Unmentionable Mini Edition. Layton, Neal, illus. 2007. 64p. (J). (gr. 3). 5.99 (*978-0-7636-3544-2(8)) Candlewick Pr.

Davis, Jennifer & Mackie, Clare. First Comes Love: All about the Birds & the Bees-and Alligators, Possums, & People, Too. 2001. (Illus.). 48p. (J). (gr. k-6). 10.95 (978-0-7611-2244-9(3) , 12244) Workman Publishing Co., Inc.

de Paola, Tomie & Shapiro, Arnold. Mice Squeak, We Speak. 2002. (Illus.). 32p. (J). (ps-1). pap. 6.99 (978-0-399-23798-0(4) , Putnam Juvenile) Penguin Group (USA) Inc.

Delafosse, Claude. Hidden World: Under the Ground. Moignot, Daniel, illus. 1999. (First Discovery Book Ser.). (J). (978-0-590-43812-4(3)) Scholastic, Inc.

Dendy, Leslie. Tracks, Scats & Signs. Garrow, Linda, illus. 1999. (Young Naturalist Field Guides Ser.). 40p. (J). (gr. 3 up). lib. bdg. 24.67 (978-0-8368-2147-5(5)) Stevens, Gareth Inc.

Dendy, Leslie A. Tracks, Scats & Signs. 2004. (Take-Along Guide Ser.). (Illus.). 48p. (J). (gr. 2-5). pap. 7.95 (978-1-55971-599-7(5) , NorthWord Bks. for Young Readers) T&N Children's Publishing.

Devaney, Sherri. Defenders. 2005. (Planet's Most Extreme Ser.). (Illus.). 48p. (J). (gr. 3-7). 24.95 (978-1-4103-0399-8(3) , Blackbirch Pr., Inc.) Thomson Gale.

—Moms. 2005. (Planet's Most Extreme Ser.). (Illus.). 48p. (J). (gr. 3-7). 24.95 (978-1-4103-0390-5(X) , Blackbirch Pr., Inc.) Thomson Gale.

Discovering Animal Habitats: Interactive Playbook. 1998. (Illus.). 10p. (J). (ps-6). 19.99 (978-1-890647-07-0(1)) RC2 Corp.

Discovery Communications Inc. Staff. Who's for Dinner? Predators & Prey. 1998. (Animal Planet Ser.). (J). (978-0-606-13914-4(1)) Tandem Library Bks.

Doherty, Gillian. 1001 Animales Que Buscar. 2004. (1001 Things to Spot Ser.).Tr. of 1001 Animals to Spot. (SPA., Illus.). (J). pap. 6.95 (978-0-7460-5081-1(X)) EDC Publishing.

Dorling Kindersley Publishing Staff. Baby Animals. Landis, Beth, ed. 2002. (Baby's World Shaped Board Bks.). (Illus.). 36p. (J). bds. 6.99 (978-0-7894-8576-2(1)) Dorling Kindersley Publishing, Inc.

—Do Cows Bark? 2003. (DK See Through Ser.). (Illus.). 21p. (J). 6.99 (978-0-7894-9851-9(0)) Dorling Kindersley Publishing, Inc.

Dorling Kindersley Publishing Staff & Locke, Deborah L. Feathers, Flippers, & Feet, Vol. 2. 2004. (Dk Readers Ser.). (Illus.). 32p. (J). (gr. 5). pap. 3.99 (978-0-7566-0264-2(5)) Dorling Kindersley Publishing, Inc.

Drew, David. What Do They Eat? Harradine, Dona, tr. Falla, Dominique, illus. 1999. (Hello! Lote Ser.). (IND.). 17p. (J). pap. 5.99 (978-0-7339-0879-8(9)) Pearson Education Australia AUS. *Dist:* Cheng & Tsui Co.

—What Do They Eat? Batt, Deleece, tr. Falla, Dominique, illus. 1999. (Hello! Lote Ser.). (JPN.). 17p. (J). pap. 5.99 (978-0-7339-0894-1(2)) Pearson Education Australia AUS. *Dist:* Cheng & Tsui Co.

Du Puy, William Atherton & Nelson, Edward William. Our Animal Friends & Foes. 2004. reprint ed. pap. 28.95 (978-1-4179-4364-7(5)) Kessinger Publishing, LLC.

Dubovoy, Silvia. Orejas. 2002. (SPA.). (gr. k-3). lib. bdg. 15.25 (978-0-613-64569-0(3)) Tandem Library Bks.

Echols, Jean C. Animal Defenses. Bevilacqua, Carol, illus. Hoyt, Richard, photos by. 2003. (Great Explorations in Math & Science Ser.). 40p. (Orig.). (J). reprint ed. pap., tchr. ed. 9.00 (978-0-924886-88-1(9) , GEMS) Univ. of California, Berkeley, Lawrence Hall of Science.

Ehren, Michael. They Sleep Too: An A-Zzz Animal Sleeping Patterns. l.t. ed. 2006. (Illus.). 32p. (J). lib. bdg. 18.95 ***(*978-1-934190-06-7(3))** Ocean Front Bk. Publishing, Inc.

Fabulous Animal Families: Individual Title Six-Packs. (gr. k-1). 23.00 (978-0-7635-9034-5(7)) Rigby Education.

Facklam, Margery. Bugs for Lunch. Long, Sylvia, illus. 1999. 32p. (J). (ps-3). 15.95 (978-0-88106-271-7(5)); pap. 6.95 (978-0-88106-272-4(3)) Charlesbridge Publishing, Inc.

—Bugs for Lunch. 1999. (gr. k-3). lib. bdg. 15.25 (978-0-613-16331-6(1)) Tandem Library Bks.

—Insectos para el Almuerzo (Bugs for Lunch) Valenzuela, Liliana, tr. from SPA. Long, Sylvia, illus. 2004. 32p. (J). (ps-3). pap. 7.95 (978-1-57091-506-2(7)) Charlesbridge Publishing, Inc.

Fancy, Colin, et al. Dydy Crocodeilod Ddim yn Glanhau eu Dannedd. 2005. (WEL., Illus.). 24p. (978-1-85596-660-4(3)) Dref Wen.

Feeney, Kathy. Sharp Shooters. Underwood, Kay Povelite, illus. 2004. (It's Nature! Ser.). 32p. (J). (gr. 3-6). pap. 7.95 (978-1-55971-794-6(7) , NorthWord Bks. for Young Readers) T&N Children's Publishing.

Feldman, Eve B. Animals Don't Wear Pajamas: A Book about Sleeping. 2004. (Illus.). 32p. (J). pap. 16.95 (978-0-9764957-0-3(8)) Saturn International.

Ferrari, Marco. Life Cycles. Stalio, Ivan, illus. 1999. (Everyday Life of Animals Ser.). 64p. (YA). (gr. 4-6). lib. bdg. 19.98 (978-0-8172-4197-1(3)) Raintree.

Fleming, Sally. Ferocious Fangs. Underwood, Kay Povelite, illus. 2004. (It's Nature! Ser.). 32p. (J). (gr. 3-6). pap. 7.95 (978-1-55971-587-4(1) , NorthWord Bks. for Young Readers) T&N Children's Publishing.

Fowler, Allan. Animals on the Move. 2000. (Rookie Read-About Science Ser.). (Illus.). 32p. (J). (gr. 1-2). pap. 4.95 (978-0-516-27055-5(9) , Children's Pr.) Scholastic Library Publishing.

—Animals on the Move. 2000. (gr. k-3). lib. bdg. 12.95 (978-0-613-53922-7(2)) Tandem Library Bks.

—It Could Still Be Endangered. 2000. (Rookie Read-About Science Ser.). (Illus.). 32p. (J). (gr. 1-2). 20.50 (978-0-516-21208-1(7) , Children's Pr.) Scholastic Library Publishing.

—Telling Tails. 1998. (Rookie Read-About Science Ser.). (Illus.). 32p. (J). (gr. 1-2). 19.50 (978-0-516-20803-9(9) , Children's Pr.) Scholastic Library Publishing.

Fraser, Mary Ann. How Animal Babies Stay Safe. Fraser, Mary Ann, illus. 2001. (Let's-Read-and-Find-Out Science Ser.). (Illus.). 40p. (J). (ps-1). 15.95 (978-0-06-028803-7(5)); pap. 5.99 (978-0-06-445211-3(5) , Harper Trophy) HarperCollins Pubs.

—Where Are the Night Animals. 2001. 24.75 (978-0-06-000308-1(1)) HarperCollins Pubs.

Fredericks, Anthony D. Animal Sharpshooters. 1999. (Animals Ser.). (Illus.). 64p. (J). (gr. 5-7). 25.50 (978-0-531-11700-2(6) , Watts, Franklin) Scholastic Library Publishing.

—Clever Camouflagers. 2004. (It's Nature! Ser.). (Illus.). 32p. (J). (gr. 3-6). pap. 7.95 (978-1-55971-751-9(3) , Creative Publishing International) Quayside.

Fredericks, Anthony D. & Collard, Sneed B., III. Amazing Animals: Nature's Most Incredible Creatures! 2000. (Illus.). 160p. (J). pap. (978-1-55971-753-3(X) , NorthWord Bks. for Young Readers) T&N Children's Publishing.

Funston, Sylvia. Animal Feelings. Stephens, Pat, illus. 1998. (Secret Life of Animals Ser.). 48p. (J). (gr. 3-7). 19.95 (978-1-895688-81-8(7)) Maple Tree Pr. CAN. *Dist:* Firefly Bks., Ltd.

Ganeri, Anita. Animal Families. 2004. (Nature Files Ser.). (Illus.). 32p. (J). (gr. 4-8). 28.00 (978-0-7910-8215-7(6) , Chelsea Hse.) Facts On File, Inc.

—I Wonder Why Camels Have Humps: And Other Questions about Animals. 2003. (I Wonder Why Ser.). (Illus.). 32p. (J). (gr. k-3). pap. 6.95 (978-0-7534-5660-6(5) , Kingfisher) Houghton Mifflin Co. Trade & Reference Div.

—I Wonder Why Camels Have Humps: And Other Questions about Animals. 2003. (gr. k-3). lib. bdg. 14.10 (978-0-613-90576-3(8)) Tandem Library Bks.

Gates, Phil. Animal Senses: South African Edition. 1999. (Cambridge Reading Routes Ser.). (Illus.). 24p. pap. 5.50 (978-0-521-77891-6(3)) Cambridge Univ. Pr.

George, Isabel & Jones, Rob Lloyd. Animals at War. 2007. 64p. (J). 8.99 (978-0-7945-1422-8(7) , Usborne) EDC Publishing.

Getting Around. 2001. (Animal Marvels Ser.). (Illus.). 32p. (J). (gr. 3 up). lib. bdg. 24.67 (978-0-8368-2816-0(X)) Stevens, Gareth Inc.

Giles, Bridget. Dwellers & Cleaners. 2003. (Parasites & Partners Ser.). (Illus.). 32p. (J). lib. bdg. 25.70 (978-0-7398-6991-8(4)) Raintree.

—Lodgers & Cleaners. 2003. (Parasites & Partners Ser.). (Illus.). 32p. (J). pap. 7.50 (978-1-4109-0358-7(3)) Raintree.

—Lodgers & Cleaners. 2003. (gr. 5-8). lib. bdg. 15.90 (978-0-613-78251-7(8)) Tandem Library Bks.

Gilpin, Daniel. Animal Families: Penguins, 16 vols. Grolier Educational Staff, ed. 2001. (Illus.). (J). (gr. 3-4). 275.00 (978-0-7172-9585-2(0) , Grolier) Scholastic Library Publishing.

Giogas, Valarie. In My Backyard. Zecca, Katherine, illus. 2007. 32p. (J). (ps-3). 8.95 ***(*978-1-934359-17-4(3))** Sylvan Dell Pubng.

Glaser, Linda. Spectacular Spiders. Holland, Gay W., illus. 1998. (Linda Glaser's Classic Creatures Ser.). 32p. (ps-3). lib. bdg. 22.90 (978-0-7613-0353-4(7) , Millbrook Pr.) Lerner Publishing Group.

Gleason, Katherine. The Social Lives of Animals: A Chapter Book. (True Tales Ser.). (Illus.). 48p. (J). 2006. (gr. 2-4). pap. 4.95 (978-0-516-25458-6(8)); 2005. (ps-ps). 22.50 (978-0-516-25188-2(0)) Scholastic Library Publishing. (Children's Pr.).

Goaman. Animal World. Quinn, David, illus. 1999. (Mysteries & Marvels Ser.). 32p. (YA). (gr. 3-7). lib. bdg. 14.95 (978-0-88110-168-3(0)) EDC Publishing.

Gorbachev, Valeri. When Someone Is Afraid. Gorbachev, Kostya, illus. 2005. 40p. (J). (ps-2). 15.95 (978-1-932065-99-2(7)) Star Bright Bks., Inc.

Graham-Barber, Lynda. Spy Hops & Belly Flops: Curious Behaviors of Woodland Animals. Lies, Brian, tr. Lies, Brian, illus. 2004. 32p. (J). (gr. k-3). tchr. ed. 15.00 (978-0-618-22291-9(X)) Houghton Mifflin Co. Trade & Reference Div.

Grambo, Rebecca L. Families. 2001. (Amazing Animals Ser.). (Illus.). 32p. (J). (gr. 2-5). lib. bdg. 27.07 (978-1-58952-146-9(3)) Rourke Publishing, LLC.

Grolier Educational Staff. Animal Families. 2001. (Illus.). 32p. (J). (978-0-7172-9586-9(9)); (978-0-7172-9587-6(7)); (978-0-7172-9588-3(5)); (978-0-7172-9589-0(3)); (978-0-7172-9590-6(7)); (978-0-7172-9591-3(5)); (978-0-7172-9592-0(3)); (978-0-7172-9593-7(1)); (978-0-7172-9595-1(8)); (978-0-7172-9596-8(6)); (978-0-7172-9597-5(4)); (978-0-7172-9598-2(2)); (978-0-7172-9599-9(0)) Scholastic Library Publishing. (Grolier).

Grolier Educational Staff, contrib. by. Animal Families. 2001. (Illus.). 32p. (J). (978-0-7172-9594-4(X) , Grolier) Scholastic Library Publishing.

Gutman, Anne & Hallensleben, Georg. Los Colores. 2004. (Collection Mira Mira Ser.).Tr. of Colors. (SPA., Illus.). (J). bds. 9.95 (978-84-261-3324-3(X)) Juventud, Editorial ESP. *Dist:* Lectorum Pubns., Inc., Iaconi, Mariuccia Bk. Imports.

Haddon, Jean. It's a Beautiful Day! Enright, Vicky, tr. Enright, Vicky, illus. 2004. (Silly Millies Ser.). 32p. (J). lib. bdg. (978-0-7613-2834-6(3) , Millbrook Pr.) Lerner Publishing Group.

Halfmann, Janet. Life in a Tree. 2000. (Lifeviews Ser.). (Illus.). 32p. (J). lib. bdg. (978-1-58341-077-6(5) , Creative Education) Creative Co., The.

Hall, Kirsten. Tracking Animals: A Chapter Book. (True Tales Ser.). (Illus.). 48p. (J). 2006. (gr. 2-4). pap. 4.95 (978-0-516-25459-3(6)); 2005. (ps-ps). 22.50 (978-0-516-25186-8(4)) Scholastic Library Publishing. (Children's Pr.).

Hansen, Rosanna. Animal Rescuers: A Chapter Book. 2003. (True Tales Ser.). (Illus.). 48p. (J). 22.50 (978-0-516-22915-7(X) , Children's Pr.) Scholastic Library Publishing.

Harcourt School Publishers Staff. Animal Collectors Advanced Level. 3rd ed. 2002. (Trophies Reading Program Ser.). (Illus.). pap. 5.10 (978-0-15-323282-4(X)) Harcourt Schl. Pubs.

—Can We Be Friends: Reader's Choice Book. 2001. (Collections Ser.). (Illus.). (J). 4.70 (978-0-15-314368-7(1)) Harcourt Schl. Pubs.

—How Animals Sleep Big Book. 3rd ed. 2002. (Trophies Ser.). (Illus.). (gr. 1 up). pap. 55.70 (978-0-15-326170-1(6)) Harcourt Schl. Pubs.

—Sweet Dreams Little Book: How Animals Sleep. 3rd ed. 2002. (Trophies Reading Program Ser.). (Illus.). (J). pap. 10.20 (978-0-15-329351-1(9)) Harcourt Schl. Pubs.

Hare, Tony. Animal Fact File: Head-to-Tail Profiles of More Than 90 Mammals. 1999. (gr. 5-8). lib. bdg. 29.20 (978-0-613-76280-9(0)) Tandem Library Bks.

—Animal Habitats: Discovering How Animals Live in the Wild. 2001. (Animal Life Ser.). (Illus.). 188p. (J). (gr. 4-8). 40.00 (978-0-8160-4593-8(3) , Checkmark Bks.) Facts On File, Inc.

Harman, Amanda. Farmers & Slavers. 2003. (Parasites & Partners Ser.). (Illus.). 32p. (J). pap. (978-1-4109-0354-9(0)); lib. bdg. 25.70 (978-0-7398-6987-1(6)) Raintree.

—Farmers & Slavers. 2003. (gr. 5-8). lib. bdg. 15.90 (978-0-613-78246-3(1)) Tandem Library Bks.

Harter, Debbie. Cha-Cha-Cha en la Selva. 2003. (SPA.). (gr. k-3). lib. bdg. 18.80 (978-0-613-67257-3(7)) Tandem Library Bks.

Hatkoff, Craig & Hatkoff, Isabella. Owen & Mzee: A Day Together. 2008. (Fairy House Ser.). 112p. (J). bds. 6.99 ***(*978-0-545-03766-2(2))** Scholastic, Inc.

Hatkoff, Craig, et al. Owen & Mzee: The True Story of a Remarkable Friendship. Greste, Peter, illus. 2006. 40p. (J). (ps-3). pap. 16.99 (978-0-439-82973-1(9) , Scholastic Pr.) Scholastic, Inc.

Hickman, Pamela. Animal Senses: How Animals See, Hear, Taste, Smell & Feel. Stephens, Pat, illus. unabr. ed. 1998. (Animal Behavior Ser.). 40p. (J). (gr. 4-6). (978-1-55074-423-1(2)) Kids Can Pr., Ltd.

Higgins, Maria Mihalik. Cats: From Tigers to Tabbies. 1998. (Animal Planet Ser.). (J). (978-0-606-13259-6(7)) Tandem Library Bks.

Hines, James Gary, II. Friendships in Nature. McGuire, Jan Martin, illus. 32p. 2004. (J). (gr. k-3). pap. 7.95 (978-1-55971-902-5(8)); 2002. (gr. 3-7). 15.95 (978-1-55971-791-5(2)) T&N Children's Publishing. (NorthWord Bks. for Young Readers).

Hirschi Ron. When Morning Comes. 2006. (Illus.). 32p. pap. 9.95 (978-1-59078-416-7(2)) Boyds Mills Pr.

Hoare, Ben. Breeders. 2003. (Parasites & Partners Ser.). (Illus.). 32p. (J). pap. 7.50 (978-1-4109-0353-2(2)); lib. bdg. 25.70 (978-0-7398-6986-4(8)) Raintree.

—Breeders. 2003. (gr. 5-8). lib. bdg. 15.90 (978-0-613-78247-0(X)) Tandem Library Bks.

Hoff, Mary. Fighting Back. 2003. (Illus.). 32p. (J). lib. bdg. (978-1-58341-266-4(2) , Creative Education) Creative Co., The.

Holt, Rinehart and Winston Staff. Animals & Behavior: Chapter Resources: Tennessee Edition. 3rd ed. 2003. (Holt Science & Technology Ser.). pap. 11.40 (978-0-03-069137-9(0)) Holt, Rinehart & Winston.

—Holt Science & Technology Chapter 14: Life Science: Animals & Behavior. 5th ed. 2004. (Illus.). pap. 12.86 (978-0-03-030218-3(8)) Holt, Rinehart & Winston.

Holub, Joan. Why Do Horses Neigh? DiVito, Anna, illus. 2003. (Easy-to-Read Ser.). 48p. (J). (gr. 1-3). pap. 3.99 (978-0-14-230119-7(1) , Puffin) Penguin Group (USA) Inc.

—Why Do Horses Neigh? 2003. (gr. k-3). lib. bdg. 11.80 (978-0-613-61670-6(7)) Tandem Library Bks.

Horenstein, Henry. Arf! Beg! Catch! Dogs from A to Z. Horenstein, Henry, illus. 1999. (Illus.). 40p. (J). (ps-1). pap. 12.95 (978-0-590-03380-0(8) , Cartwheel Bks.) Scholastic, Inc.

Hoy, Ken & Bowring, Isabel. Strange Scavenging Creatures. 1999. (Illus.). 10p. (J). (gr. 3-5). reprint ed. 14.00 (978-0-7881-6552-8(6)) DIANE Publishing Co.

Hull, Mary E. The Rhinoceros. 2001. (Endangered Animals & Habitats Ser.). (Illus.). 96p. (YA). (gr. 4-12). 27.45 (978-1-56006-461-9(7) , Lucent Bks.) Thomson Gale.

Hunter, Tom. Critters for Kids: A North American Wildlife Activity Book. 2004. 80p. (J). pap., act. bk. ed. 7.95 (978-1-895811-69-8(4)) Heritage Hse. Publishing Co., Ltd. CAN. *Dist:* Midpoint Trade Bks., Inc.

Jacquet, Luc. March of the Penguins: The Official Children's Book. Maison, Jérome, photos by. 2005. (Illus.). 32p. (J). (ps). lib. bdg. 22.90 (978-0-7922-6190-2(9) , National Geographic Children's Bks.) National Geographic Society.

Jansen, Curt, et al. Badger & Her Babies. Date not set. (Wildlife Adventure Ser.: Vol. 2). (Orig.). (J). (gr. k-4). pap. (978-0-9614904-2-3(X)) Adventure Productions, Inc.

—Bobcat & Her Babies. Date not set. (Wildlife Adventure Ser.: Vol. 3). (Orig.). (J). (gr. k-4). pap. (978-0-9614904-3-0(8)) Adventure Productions, Inc.

Jarrow, Gail. Animal Baby Sitters. 2001. (gr. 3-6). lib. bdg. 17.60 (978-0-613-51611-2(7)) Tandem Library Bks.

Jarrow, Gail & Sherman, Paul. Animal Baby Sitters. (Watts Library). (Illus.). 64p. (J). (gr. 5-7). 2002. pap. 8.95 (978-0-531-16571-3(X)); 2001. 25.50 (978-0-531-11881-8(9)) Scholastic Library Publishing. (Watts, Franklin).

Jeunesse, Gallimard. Animals on the Move. De Hugo, Pierre, illus. 2002. (Look-It-Up Ser.: No. 6). 14p. (J). bds. 4.95 (978-0-439-29723-3(0) , Cartwheel Bks.) Scholastic, Inc.

Kajikawa, Kimiko. Sweet Dreams: How Animals Sleep. rev. ed. 1999. (Illus.). 32p. (J). (ps-2). 16.95 (978-0-8050-5890-1(7) , Holt, Henry & Co. Bks. For Young Readers) Holt, Henry & Co.

Kalman, Bobbie. Animal Families. 2007. (Introducing Living Things Ser.). (Illus.). 24p. (J). (gr. k-4). lib. bdg. ***(*978-0-7787-3226-6(6))** Crabtree Publishing Co.

—How Do Animals Find Food? 2001. (Science of Living Things Ser.). (Illus.). 32p. (J). (gr. 2-3). (978-0-86505-986-3(1)); pap. (978-0-86505-963-4(2)) Crabtree Publishing Co.

—How Do Animals Find Food? 2001. (gr. 3-6). lib. bdg. 14.10 (978-0-613-52959-4(6)) Tandem Library Bks.

—Life in a Dolphin Pod. 2002. (Dolphin Worlds Ser.). (Illus.). 32p. (J). (gr. 4-5). (978-0-7787-1164-3(1)); pap. (978-0-7787-1184-1(6)) Crabtree Publishing Co.

—Life in a Dolphin Pod. 2003. (gr. 3-6). lib. bdg. 15.25 (978-0-613-52867-2(0)) Tandem Library Bks.

—What Are Camouflage & Mimicry? 2001. (Science of Living Things Ser.). (Illus.). 32p. (J). (gr. 2-3). (978-0-86505-985-6(3)) Crabtree Publishing Co.

—What Are Camouflage & Mimicry? 2001. (gr. 3-6). lib. bdg. 14.10 (978-0-613-43523-9(0)) Tandem Library Bks.

Kalman, Bobbie & Levigne, Heather. What Are Camouflage & Mimicry? 2001. (Science of Living Things Ser.). (Illus.). 32p. (J). (gr. 2-3). pap. (978-0-86505-962-7(4)) Crabtree Publishing Co.

Kaner, Etta. Animal Defenses: How Animals Protect Themselves. Stephens, Pat, illus. unabr. ed. 2004. (Animal Behavior Ser.). 40p. (J). (gr. 4-6). (978-1-55074-421-7(6)); (978-1-55074-419-4(4)) Kids Can Pr., Ltd.

—Animal Defenses: How Animals Protect Themselves. 1999. (gr. 3-6). lib. bdg. 14.10 (978-0-613-16320-0(6)); (Illus.). (J). 12.75 (978-0-606-21745-3(2)) Tandem Library Bks.

—Animal Groups: How Animals Live Together. Stephens, Pat, illus. 2004. (Animal Behavior Ser.). 40p. (J). (gr. 4-6). (978-1-55337-338-4(3)); (978-1-55337-337-7(5)) Kids Can Pr., Ltd.

—Animals at Work: How Animals Build, Dig, Fish & Trap. Stephens, Pat, illus. 2004. (Animal Behavior Ser.). 40p. (J). (gr. 4-6). (978-1-55074-675-4(8)); (978-1-55074-673-0(1)) Kids Can Pr., Ltd.

Knight, Tim. Collage. 2003. (Step-by-Step Ser.). 32p. (J). pap. 7.95 (978-1-4034-0716-0(9)) Heinemann Library.

—Dramatic Displays. 2003. (Amazing Nature Ser.). (Illus.). 32p. (J). pap. 6.95 (978-1-4034-3255-1(4)); (gr. 2-4). lib. bdg. 24.22 (978-1-4034-0721-4(5)) Heinemann Library.

—Ferocious Fighters. 2003. (Amazing Nature Ser.). (Illus.). 32p. (J). pap. 6.95 (978-1-4034-3257-5(0)); (gr. 2-4). lib. bdg. 24.22 (978-1-4034-1145-7(X)) Heinemann Library.

—Ferocious Fighters. 2003. (gr. 3-6). lib. bdg. 15.25 (978-0-613-60966-1(2)) Tandem Library Bks.

Knowlton, Laurie Lazzaro. Hide & Seek. 2005. (J). (978-1-933248-09-7(2)) World Quest Learning.

LaBella, Susan. How Animals Navigate. 2007. (J). pap. ***(*978-0-8368-8421-0(3));** 24p. (gr. 2-4). lib. bdg. 19.93 ***(*978-0-8368-8416-6(7))** Stevens, Gareth Inc. (Weekly Reader Early Learning Library).

Landstrom, Lee Ann & Shragg, Karen. Nature's Yucky! 2: The Desert Southwest. Rogge, Rachel, illus. 48p. (J). pap. 12.00 ***(*978-0-87842-529-7(2))** Mountain Pr. Publishing Co., Inc.

Laskey, Elizabeth. Gross & Gory. 2004. (Heinemann Infosearch Ser.). (Illus.). 32p. (J). pap. 7.50 (978-1-4034-4964-1(3)); lib. bdg. (978-1-4034-4959-7(7)) Heinemann Library.

Lauber, Patricia. Who Eats What? Food Chains & Food Webs. 2001. 24.75 (978-0-06-000332-6(4)) HarperCollins Pubs.

Lewin, Ted. Tooth & Claw: Animal Adventures in the Wild. Lewin, Ted, illus. 2003. (Illus.). 112p. (J). (gr. 3-6). 17.99 (978-0-688-14105-9(6)) HarperCollins Pubs.

Living Together. 2001. (Animal Marvels Ser.). (Illus.). 32p. (J). (gr. 3 up). lib. bdg. 24.67 (978-0-8368-2817-7(8)) Stevens, Gareth Inc.

Lock, Deborah & Dorling Kindersley Publishing Staff. Feathers, Flippers, & Feet. 2004. (Dk Readers Ser.). (Illus.). 32p. (J). 12.99 (978-0-7566-0265-9(3)) Dorling Kindersley Publishing, Inc.

London, Jonathan. Crunch Munch. Rex, Michael, illus. 2002. 22p. (J). bds. 5.95 (978-0-15-216600-7(9) , Red Wagon Bks.) Harcourt Children's Bks.

—Snuggle Wuggle. Rex, Michael, illus. 2002. 22p. (J). bds. 5.95 (978-0-15-216594-9(0) , Red Wagon Bks.) Harcourt Children's Bks.

—Wiggle Waggle. Rex, Michael, illus. 2002. 22p. (J). bds. 5.95 (978-0-15-216588-8(6) , Red Wagon Bks.) Harcourt Children's Bks.

Lorenz Books Staff. Animals. 1999. (Let's Look at... Ser.). (Illus.). 12p. (ps). 4.95 (978-0-7548-0376-8(7)) Anness Publishing, Inc.

Lorenz Books Staff & Savage, Ann. Animals. 2000. (My Big Book of Ser.). (Illus.). 48p. (J). (gr. k-4). pap. 7.95 (978-0-7548-0227-3(2) , Lorenz Bks.) Anness Publishing, Inc.

Lowell House Juvenile Staff. My Big Book of Animals. 2000. (Roxbury Park Board Bks.). (Illus.). 24p. (J). (ps-k). bds. 8.95 (978-0-7373-0410-7(3) , 04103W, Roxbury Park Juvenile) Lowell Hse. Juvenile.

Lynch, Wayne. The Scoop on Poop! Fascinating Science from the Animal World. Lynch, Wayne, photos by. 2001. (Illus.). 32p. (J). (gr. 1-6). pap. 5.95 (978-1-894004-59-6(0)) Fifth Hse. Pubs. CAN. *Dist:* Fitzhenry & Whiteside, Ltd.

—Whose Feet Are These? Lynch, Wayne, photos by. 2003. (Name That Animal! Ser.). (Illus.). 32p. (J). (gr. 1 up). lib. bdg. 23.33 (978-0-8368-3640-0(5)) Stevens, Gareth Inc.

—Whose Feet Are These? 1999. (gr. k-3). lib. bdg. 15.25 (978-0-613-78498-6(7)); (978-0-606-18759-6(6)) Tandem Library Bks.

—Whose Feet Are These? 1999. (Whose? Animal Ser.). (Illus.). 32p. (J). (ps-2). pap. 6.95 (978-1-55110-860-5(7)) Whitecap Bks., Ltd. CAN. *Dist:* Firefly Bks., Ltd.

Lynch, Wayne, photos by. The Scoop on Poop! The Fascinating Science of How Animals Use Poop. 2001. (Illus.). 26p. (978-1-894856-11-9(2)) Fifth Hse. Pubs.

Mackill, Mary. Special Animal Senses. 2006. (Heinemann Read & Learn Ser.). (Illus.). 24p. (J). (978-1-4034-7378-3(1)); pap. (978-1-4034-7385-1(4)) Steck-Vaughn.

Manning, Mick. Supermom. Granstrom, Brita, illus. 2001. 32p. (J). (ps-3). 16.95 (978-0-8075-7666-3(2)) Whitman, Albert & Co.

Martin, James W. R. Killers. 2003. (Parasites & Partners Ser.). (Illus.). 32p. (J). pap. 7.50 (978-1-4109-0357-0(5)); lib. bdg. 25.70 (978-0-7398-6990-1(6)) Raintree.

—Killers. 2003. (gr. 5-8). lib. bdg. 15.90 (978-0-613-78250-0(X)) Tandem Library Bks.

Martín Larrañaga, Ana. Animal Actions. 2000. (Copy Cat Bks.). (Illus.). 8p. (J). bds. 5.95 (978-1-58646-005-1(6)) Polka Dot Pr.

—Animal Noises. 2000. (Copy Cat Bks.). (Illus.). (J). 5.95 (978-1-58646-004-4(8)) Polka Dot Pr.

Mason, Paul. Nature's Tricks. 2007. (J). (***978-1-4109-2970-9(1));*** pap. (***978-1-4109-2991-4(4));*** Steck-Vaughn.

Matthews, Derek. Moo! Noisy Pop-Up Fun, 5 Fun Animal Sounds. 2004. (Snappy Ser.). (Illus.). 10p. (ps-k). 12.95 (978-1-59223-214-7(0)) Advantage Pubs. Group.

Mayo, Margaret. Roar! Ayliffe, Alex, illus. 2007. (Carolrhoda Picture Bks.). 32p. (J). (gr. k-3). 15.95 (***978-0-7613-9473-0(7)*** , Carolrhoda Bks.) Lerner Publishing Group.

Maze, Stephanie. Momentos Divertidos en el Reino Animal: Los Animales y Sus Amigos. (SPA., Illus.). 32p. (J). (gr. k-3). 15.00 (978-0-9707768-5-3(3) , MST31407) Moonstone Pr.

—Momentos Tiernos en el Reino Animal: Los Animales y Sus Bebes. (Coleccion Momentos en el Reino Animal). (SPA., Illus.). (J). (gr. k-3). 15.00 (978-0-9707768-2-2(9) , MST31405) Moonstone Pr.

Maze, Stephanie, ed. Amusing Moments in the Wild: Animals & Their Friends. (Moments in the Wild Ser.). (Illus.). (J). 2006. 36p. pap. 8.00 (978-0-9769542-4-8(9)); 2002. 32p. 15.00 (978-0-9707768-3-9(7)) Moonstone Pr.

—Momentos divertidos en el reino Animal: Los animales y sus Amigos. 2006. (Momentos en el reino Animal Ser.). (SPA., Illus.). 36p. (J). pap. 8.00 (978-0-9769542-6-2(5)) Moonstone Pr.

—Tender Moments in the Wild: Animals & Their Babies. 2001. (Moments in the Wild Series Ser.). (Illus.). 32p. (J). (ps). 15.00 (978-0-9707768-0-8(2)) Moonstone Pr.

McLeod, Beatrice. Courtship. McLeod, Beatrice, illus. 2000. (Nature Undercover Ser.). (Illus.). 40p. (J). (gr. 5-8). 23.70 (978-1-56711-503-1(9) , Blackbirch Pr., Inc.) Thomson Gale.

—Growing Up. 2000. (Nature Undercover Ser.). (Illus.). 40p. (J). (gr. 5-8). 23.70 (978-1-56711-501-7(2) , Blackbirch Pr., Inc.) Thomson Gale.

Miller, Connie Colwell. Disgusting Animals. 2007. (Illus.). 32p. (J). (978-0-7368-6797-9(X)); (***978-0-7368-7875-3(0))*** Capstone Pr., Inc.

Miller, Sara Swan. Horses & Rhinos: What They Have in Common. 1999. (Animals in Order Ser.). (Illus.). 48p. (J). (gr. 4-6). 26.50 (978-0-531-11586-2(0) , Watts, Franklin) Scholastic Library Publishing.

Minshull, Evelyn. Eaglet's World. Gabriel, Andrea, illus. 2002. 32p. (J). (ps-3). 16.95 (978-0-8075-8929-8(2)) Whitman, Albert & Co.

Moor, Jo Ellen. Animals with Backbones. Evans, Marilyn, ed. Davis, Cindy, illus. 1998. (ScienceWorks for Kids Ser.: Vol. 2). 80p. (J). (gr. 1-3). pap., tchr. ed. 9.95 (978-1-55799-683-1(0) , EMC 854) Evan-Moor Educational Pubs.

—Habitats. Evans, Marilyn, ed. Robison, Don, illus. 1998. (ScienceWorks for Kids Ser.: Vol. 7). 80p. (J). (gr. 1-3). pap., tchr. ed. 9.95 (978-1-55799-688-6(1) , EMC 859) Evan-Moor Educational Pubs.

Nichols, Catherine. Animal Masterminds: A Chapter Book. 2003. (True Tales Ser.). (Illus.). 48p. (J). 22.50 (978-0-516-22913-3(3) , Children's Pr.) Scholastic Library Publishing.

—Animal Talk. 2001. (We Can Read about Nature! Ser.). (Illus.). 32p. (J). (gr. 1-2). lib. bdg. 21.36 (978-0-7614-1253-3(0) , Benchmark Bks.) Cavendish, Marshall Corp.

—Going Places. 2001. (We Can Read about Nature! Ser.). (Illus.). 32p. (J). (gr. 1-2). lib. bdg. 21.36 (978-0-7614-1252-6(2) , Benchmark Bks.) Cavendish, Marshall Corp.

Nilsen, Anna. Animal Antics, 4 bks. Axworthy, Anni, illus. Incl. Let's Dig & Burrow. lib. bdg. 22.00 (978-0-8368-2910-5(7)); Let's Hang & Dangle. lib. bdg. 22.00 (978-0-8368-2911-2(5)); Let's Leap & Jump. lib. bdg. 22.00 (978-0-8368-2912-9(3)); Let's Swim & Dive. lib. bdg. 22.00 (978-0-8368-2913-6(1)); 24p. (J). (ps up). (Illus.). 2001. Set lib. bdg. 88.00 (978-0-8368-2909-9(3)) Stevens, Gareth Inc.

—Let's Dig & Burrow. Axworthy, Anni, illus. 2001. (Animal Antics Ser.). 24p. (J). (ps up). lib. bdg. 22.00 (978-0-8368-2910-5(7)) Stevens, Gareth Inc.

—Let's Hang & Dangle. Axworthy, Anni, illus. 2001. (Animal Antics Ser.). 24p. (J). (ps up). lib. bdg. 22.00 (978-0-8368-2911-2(5)) Stevens, Gareth Inc.

—Let's Leap & Jump. Axworthy, Anni, illus. 2001. (Animal Antics Ser.). 24p. (J). (ps up). lib. bdg. 22.00 (978-0-8368-2912-9(3)) Stevens, Gareth Inc.

—Let's Swim & Dive. Axworthy, Anni, illus. 2001. (Animal Antics Ser.). 24p. (J). (ps up). lib. bdg. 22.00 (978-0-8368-2913-6(1)) Stevens, Gareth Inc.

Nol, Sally. Watch Where You Go!Tr. of Attention Ou Tu Vas!. (FRE., Illus.). (J). pap. 5.99 (978-0-590-24231-8(8)) Scholastic, Inc.

Otto, Carolyn B. What Color Is Camouflage. 2001. 24.75 (978-0-06-000304-3(9)) HarperCollins Pubs.

Packard, Mary. Talented Animals: A Chapter Book. 2003. (True Tales Ser.). (Illus.). 48p. (J). 22.50 (978-0-516-22911-9(7) , Children's Pr.) Scholastic Library Publishing.

Pandell, Karen. Animal Action ABC. Sheehan, Nancy, illus. Wolfe, Art & Sheehan, Nancy, photos by. 2003. 32p. (J). (ps-1). 12.95 (978-1-929766-92-5(0)) Handprint Bks.

Parker, Steve. Survival & Change. (Life Processes Ser.). 32p. pap. 7.50 (978-1-4034-4076-1(X)); 2006. (Illus.). (J). (***978-1-4034-8848-0(7));*** 2000. (Illus.). (J). (gr. 4-6). lib. bdg. 21.36 (978-1-57572-340-2(9)) Heinemann Library.

Pascoe, Elaine. Animals Hide. Kuhn, Dwight, photos by. 2002. (Springboards into Science Ser.). (Illus.). 24p. (J). (gr. 1 up). lib. bdg. 20.67 (978-0-8368-3005-7(9)) Stevens, Gareth Inc.

—How & Why Animals Hide. Kupperstein, Joel, ed. Kuhn, Dwight, photos by. 2000. (How & Why Ser.). (Illus.). 16p. (J). (gr. 1-3). pap. 2.99 (978-1-57471-662-7(X) , 2969) Creative Teaching Pr., Inc.

Patterson, Caroline. Who Pooped at the Zoo? San Diego. 2007. (J). pap. 12.95 (***978-1-56037-421-3(7))*** Farcountry Pr.

Pearce, Querida L. Great Predators of the Land. Yakovetic, Joe, illus. rev. ed. 1999. 55p. (J). (gr. 7 up). pap. 12.95 (978-0-312-85981-7(3) , Tor Bks.) Doherty, Tom Assocs., LLC.

Penny, Malcolm, et al. Amazing Nature, 6 bks., Set 2. 2004. (J). (gr. 2-4). lib. bdg. 153.86 (978-1-4034-4709-8(8)) Heinemann Library.

Perkins, Wendy. Animals Finding Food. 2004. (First Facts Ser.). (Illus.). 24p. (J). 15.95 (978-0-7368-2510-8(X) , Bridgestone Bks.) Capstone Pr., Inc.

—Animals Sleeping. 2004. (First Facts Ser.). (Illus.). 24p. (J). 15.95 (978-0-7368-2511-5(8) , Bridgestone Bks.) Capstone Pr., Inc.

Perry, Phyllis Jean. Animals under the Ground. 2001. (Animal Library). (Illus.). 64p. (J). (gr. 5-7). 25.50 (978-0-531-11759-0(6) , Watts, Franklin) Scholastic Library Publishing.

Pocket Chart Science: Animals & Habitats. 2002. (J). pap. 9.95 (978-1-56911-077-5(8)) Learning Resources, Inc.

Powell, Richard. Animal Actions. Martín Larrañaga, Ana, illus. 2001. (Copy Cats Ser.). 10p. (J). 6.95 (978-1-58925-666-8(2) , tiger tales) ME Media LLC.

—Animal Noises. Martín Larrañaga, Ana, illus. 2001. (Copy Cats Ser.). 8p. (J). 6.95 (978-1-58925-665-1(4) , tiger tales) ME Media LLC.

Predator & Prey. 2003. (Science Card Games Ser.). (gr. 3-4). 9.99 (978-0-7682-1979-1(5) , J53007) School Specialty Publishing.

Quadrillion Media Staff. Nature & Animals. 1999. (Start Me Up Ser.). (J). pap. 3.95 (978-1-58185-101-4(4)) Quadrillion Media LLC.

Rake, Jody. Animal Training at SeaWorld, Busch Gardens, & Discovery Cove: Behind the Scenes. 2003. (Seaworld Education Ser.). (Illus.). 68p. per. 7.99 (978-1-893698-09-3(2) , B01, SeaWorld Education Dept.) SeaWorld, Inc.

Renne. Animal Males & Females. Taurel, Alison, tr. from DUT. Renne, illus. 2000. (Animals Up Close Ser.). (Illus.). 38p. (J). (gr. 3 up). lib. bdg. 24.67 (978-0-8368-2712-5(0)) Stevens, Gareth Inc.

—Why Animals Have Tails. Renne, illus. 2000. (Animals Up Close Ser.). (Illus.). 38p. (J). (gr. 3 up). lib. bdg. 24.67 (978-0-8368-2716-3(3)) Stevens, Gareth Inc.

Reproducing. 2001. (Animal Marvels Ser.). (Illus.). 32p. (J). (gr. 3 up). lib. bdg. 24.67 (978-0-8368-2932-7(8)) Stevens, Gareth Inc.

Rice, David. Do Animals Have Feelings Too? 1999. (gr. 3-6). lib. bdg. 16.40 (978-0-613-56748-0(X)) Tandem Library Bks.

Riley, Terry, illus. Night Creatures. 2001. (Trackpack Ser.). 32p. (J). 4.99 (978-0-439-37477-4(4)) Scholastic, Inc.

Roberts, Monty. Man Who Listens to Horses. 1999. (gr. 7-12). lib. bdg. 16.45 (978-0-613-28941-2(2)) Tandem Library Bks.

Robinson, Claire. Crocodiles. 2002. (In the Wild Ser.). (Illus.). 24p. (J). (gr. k-2). pap. 6.95 (978-1-57572-465-2(0) , 90455) Heinemann Library.

—Lions. (In the Wild Ser.). (Illus.). 24p. (J). (gr. k-2). 2002. pap. 6.95 (978-1-57572-467-6(7) , 90457); 1998. lib. bdg. 21.36 (978-1-57572-132-3(5)) Heinemann Library.

—Penguins. (In the Wild Ser.). (Illus.). 24p. (J). (gr. k-2). 2002. pap. 6.95 (978-1-57572-468-3(5) , 90458); 1998. lib. bdg. 21.36 (978-1-57572-137-8(6)) Heinemann Library.

Rustad, Martha E. H. Animals in Fall. 2008. (J). (***978-1-4296-0022-4(5))*** Capstone Pr., Inc.

Salas, Laura Purdie. Do Crocodiles Dance? A Book about Animal Habits. Yesh, Jeff, illus. 2006. (Animals All Around Ser.). (J). 23.93 (978-1-4048-2230-6(5)) Picture Window Bks.

Saunders-Smith, Gail. Animals: Life Cycles, 4 vols., Set. 1998. (J). pap. 53.00 (978-0-516-29776-7(7) , Children's Pr.) Scholastic Library Publishing.

—Animals: Life Cycles, 4 bks. Incl. Butterflies. lib. bdg. 14.60 (978-1-56065-485-8(6)); Chickens. lib. bdg. 14.60 (978-1-56065-483-4(X)); Frogs. lib. bdg. 14.60 (978-1-56065-484-1(8)); Koalas. lib. bdg. 14.60 (978-1-56065-486-5(4)); 24p. (J). (gr. k-1). 1997. (Illus.). Set lib. bdg. 58.40 (978-1-56065-674-6(3) , Pebble Bks.) Capstone Pr., Inc.

—Animals in the Fall. 1998. (J). pap. 13.25 (978-0-516-21248-7(6) , Children's Pr.) Scholastic Library Publishing.

Sayre, April Pulley. Splish! Splash! Animal Baths. 2000. (All about Animals Ser.). (Illus.). 32p. (ps-2). lib. bdg. (978-0-7613-1821-7(6) , Millbrook Pr.) Lerner Publishing Group.

Schaefer, Lola M. Que Esta Despierto?, 8 bks., Set. Cano, Patricia, tr. 2003. (SPA., Illus.). (J). pap. 37.80 (978-1-4034-2674-1(0)) Heinemann Library.

—Tiny-Spiny Animals Series, 6 bks., Set. 2004. (978-1-4034-3324-4(0)) Heinemann Library.

Schubert, Ingrid & Schubert, Dieter. Like People. 2008. (J). (***978-1-59078-576-8(2))*** Lemniscaat B.V., Uitgeverij.

Schuette, Sarah L. Let's Look at Fall. 2007. (Pebble Plus Ser.). (Illus.). 24p. (J). (978-0-7368-6705-4(8) , 1264871) Capstone Pr., Inc.

—Let's Look at Spring. 2007. (Pebble Plus Ser.). (Illus.). 24p. (J). (978-0-7368-6707-8(4) , 1264872) Capstone Pr., Inc.

—Let's Look at Summer. 2007. (Pebble Plus Ser.). (Illus.). 24p. (J). (978-0-7368-6708-5(2) , 1264873) Capstone Pr., Inc.

—Let's Look at Winter. 2007. (Pebble Plus Ser.). (Illus.). 24p. (J). (978-0-7368-6706-1(6) , 1264874) Capstone Pr., Inc.

Settel, Joanne. Exploding Ants: Amazing Facts about How Animals Adapt. 1999. (Illus.). 40p. (J). (gr. 2-7). 17.99 (978-0-689-81739-7(8) , Atheneum) Simon & Schuster Children's Publishing.

Seuling, Barbara. Winter Lullaby. Newbold, Greg, illus. 1998. 32p. (J). (ps-2). 16.00 (978-0-15-201403-2(9)) Harcourt Children's Bks.

Sevaly, Karen. Matching Animals & Babies Lace Up Cards. Chang, Maria, ed. 2007. (It's Happy Bunny Ser.). 16p. 9.99 (***978-0-439-91219-8(9)*** , Teaching Resources) Scholastic, Inc.

—Matching Animals & Habitats Lace up Cards. 2007. 48p. 9.99 (***978-0-439-91221-1(0)*** , Teaching Resources) Scholastic, Inc.

Shattil, Wendy & Rozinski, Bob, photos by. On the Trail of Colorado Critters: Wildlife Watching for Kids. 2000. (Illus.). 96p. (J). (gr. 4-7). 14.95 (978-1-56579-350-7(1) , A195) Westcliffe Pubs.

Simon, Seymour. Animals Nobody Loves. 2002. (Illus.). 48p. (J). pap. 7.95 (978-1-58717-155-0(4) , SeaStar Bks.) Chronicle Bks. LLC.

—Animals Nobody Loves. 2002. (gr. 3-6). lib. bdg. 15.25 (978-0-613-53792-6(0)) Tandem Library Bks.

—Wild Babies. 1998. (Illus.). 32p. (J). (gr. k-3). pap. 7.99 (978-0-06-446206-8(4) , Harper Trophy) HarperCollins Pubs.

—Wild Babies. 1998. (J). (978-0-606-13915-1(X)) Tandem Library Bks.

Soffer, Ruth. Nocturnal Animals Stickers. 1998. 4p. (J). pap. 1.50 (978-0-486-40306-9(8)) Dover Pubns., Inc.

St. Pierre, Stephanie. In the Wild: Facts about Favorite Animals, 16 bks. 2001. (Illus.). (J). (gr. k-2). Set. lib. bdg. 341.76 (978-1-58810-185-3(1)); Set 1. lib. bdg. 213.60 (978-1-57572-866-7(4)) Heinemann Library.

Stalio, Ivan, illus. Life Cycles. 2001. 64p. (978-0-7451-5295-0(3) , Cherrytree Books) Evans Publishing Group.

Staub, Frank. The Signs Animals Leave. 2001. (Animal Library). (Illus.). 64p. (J). (gr. 5-7). 25.50 (978-0-531-11863-4(0) , Watts, Franklin) Scholastic Library Publishing.

—Signs Animals Leave. 2001. (gr. 3-6). lib. bdg. 17.60 (978-0-613-53560-1(X)) Tandem Library Bks.

Stickland, Paul. Animals. Stickland, Paul, illus. 1998. (Working Ser.). (Illus.). 16p. (J). (ps up). lib. bdg. 19.93 (978-0-8368-2156-7(4)) Stevens, Gareth Inc.

Stockdale, Susan, illus. Carry Me! 2005. 32p. (J). 15.95 (978-1-56145-328-3(5)) Peachtree Pubs., Ltd.

Stockland, Patricia M. Strange Dances & Long Flights: A Book about Animal Behavior. Ouren, Todd, illus. 2005. (Animal Wise Ser.). 24p. (C). (gr. k-2). 22.60 (978-1-4048-0936-9(8)) Picture Window Bks.

Stone, Lynn M. Wolves: Family & Pack. 2000. (Wolves Discovery Library). (Illus.). 24p. (J). (gr. 1-4). lib. bdg. 19.27 (978-1-55916-241-8(4)) Rourke Publishing, LLC.

Stonehouse, Bernard. Fighters. Francis, John, illus. 2000. 48p. (J). pap. (978-0-439-20657-0(X)) Scholastic, Inc.

—Growing Up: Protected. Francis, John, illus. 2001. 48p. (J). pap. 6.95 (978-0-439-30531-0(4)) Scholastic, Inc.

—Show-offs. Francis, John, illus. 2000. 48p. (J). pap. (978-0-439-15346-1(8)) Scholastic, Inc.

—Wild Cats. Camm, Martin, illus. (Animal Watch Ser.). 48p. (J). (gr. 4-9). 16.95 (978-0-8160-3925-8(9) , Checkmark Bks.) Facts On File, Inc.

Stonehouse, Bernard & Bertram, Esther. How Animals Live: The Amazing World of Animals in the Wild. Francis, John, tr. Francis, John, illus. 2004. 96p. (J). pap. 16.95 (978-0-439-54834-2(9)) Scholastic, Inc.

Stonehouse, Bernard & Francis, John. Partners. 2000. (Illus.). 48p. (J). pap. (978-0-439-20658-7(8)) Scholastic, Inc.

Swan, Erin Pembrey. Land Predators of North America. 1999. (Animals in Order Ser.). (Illus.). 48p. (J). (gr. 4-6). 26.50 (978-0-531-11451-3(1) , Watts, Franklin) Scholastic Library Publishing.

Swanson, Diane. Animals Can Be So Hard to See. Cowles, Rose, illus. 2002. (Animals Can Be So... Ser.). 24p. (J). 10.95 (978-1-55054-901-0(4) , Greystone Bks.) Douglas & McIntyre, Ltd. CAN. *Dist:* Sterling Publishing Co., Inc.

—Animals Can Be So Hard to See. (Illus.). 22p. (J). (978-1-55041-326-7(0)) Fitzhenry & Whiteside, Ltd.

—Animals Can Be So Hard to See. 2001. (Illus.). 21p. (J). pap. (978-1-55054-905-8(7)) Greystone Bks., Ltd.

—Animals Can Be So Sleepy. Cowles, Rose, illus. 2002. (Animals Can Be So... Ser.). 24p. (J). 5.95 (978-1-55054-855-6(7) , Greystone Bks.) Douglas & McIntyre, Ltd. CAN. *Dist:* Sterling Publishing Co., Inc.

—Animals Can Be So Sleepy. 2001. (Animals Can Be So... Ser.). (Illus.). 24p. (J). 10.95 (978-1-55054-837-2(9) , Greystone Bks.) Douglas & McIntyre, Ltd. CAN. *Dist:* Sterling Publishing Co., Inc.

—Animals Can Be So Sleepy. (Illus.). 22p. (J). (978-1-55041-330-4(9)); pap. (978-1-55041-332-8(5)) Fitzhenry & Whiteside, Ltd.

—Animals Eat the Weirdest Things. Smith, Terry, illus. 1998. 64p. (J). (gr. 3-2). pap. 12.95 (978-1-55110-809-4(7)) Whitecap Bks., Ltd. CAN. *Dist:* Firefly Bks., Ltd.

—Noses That Plow & Poke. 2003. (Up Close Ser.). (Illus.). 32p. (J). 5.95 (978-1-55054-733-7(X)) Sterling Publishing Co., Inc.

—Up Close Headgear That Hides & Plays. 2001. (Up Close Ser.). (Illus.). 32p. (J). (ps-3). 9.95 (978-1-55054-819-8(0)) Sterling Publishing Co., Inc.

Swanson, Diane & Cowles, Rose. Noses That Plow & Poke. 2000. (Up Close Ser.). (Illus.). 32p. (gr. k-2). 9.95 (978-1-55054-715-3(1)) Sterling Publishing Co., Inc.

Swinburne, Stephen R. Black Bear: North America's Bear. 2003. (Illus.). 32p. (YA). (gr. 4-6). 15.95 (978-1-59078-023-7(X)) Boyds Mills Pr.

—Bobcat: North America's Cat. 2003. (Illus.). 32p. (YA). (gr. 4-6). 15.95 (978-1-56397-843-2(1)) Boyds Mills Pr.

—Safe, Warm, & Snug. Aruego, Jose & Dewey, Ariane, illus. 2002. 40p. (J). (ps-ps). pap., pap. 7.00 (978-0-15-216378-5(6) , Voyager Bks./Libros Viajeros) Harcourt Children's Bks.

—Safe, Warm, & Snug. 2002. (ps-2). lib. bdg. 14.15 (978-0-613-83227-4(2)) Tandem Library Bks.

Tagliaferro, Linda. Bears & Their Dens. 2004. (Pebble Plus, Animal Homes Ser.). (Illus.). 24p. (J). 13.95 (978-0-7368-2381-4(6)) Capstone Pr., Inc.

—Rabbits & Their Burrows. 2004. (Pebble Plus, Animal Homes Ser.). (Illus.). 24p. (J). 13.95 (978-0-7368-2384-5(0)) Capstone Pr., Inc.

Tatham, Betty. How Animals Play. 2004. (Watts Library). (Illus.). 64p. (J). (gr. 5-7). pap. 8.95 (978-0-531-16236-1(2)); 25.50 (978-0-531-12173-3(9)) Scholastic Library Publishing. (Watts, Franklin).

Taylor, Barbara. Survival. 2002. (ps-2). lib. bdg. 14.15 (978-0-613-57141-8(X)) Tandem Library Bks.

Theodorou, Rod. Birds. 2007. (Illus.). 32p. (J). (***978-1-4034-9249-4(2)); (978-1-4034-9242-5(5))*** Heinemann Library.

—Fish. 2007. (Illus.). 32p. (J). (***978-1-4034-9250-0(6)); (978-1-4034-9243-2(3))*** Heinemann Library.

Twinem, Neecy. Bathing Beasties. 2008. (J). (***978-1-55971-995-7(8)*** , NorthWord Bks. for Young Readers) T&N Children's Publishing.

—Playful Beasties. 2007. (Little Beasties Ser.). (Illus.). 12p. (J). (ps). bds. 6.95 (978-1-55971-958-2(3) , NorthWord Bks. for Young Readers) T&N Children's Publishing.

—Sleepy Beasties. 2006. (Illus.). 12p. (J). bds. 6.95 (978-1-55971-945-2(1) , 1259987, NorthWord Bks. for Young Readers) T&N Children's Publishing.

Underwood, Deborah. Animal Secrets. 2007. (J). (***978-1-4109-2840-5(3));*** pap. (***978-1-4109-2857-3(8))*** Steck-Vaughn.

Uttridge, Sarah, et al. The Hunt for Food: Wild Animal Planet. 2002. (Wild Animal Planet Ser.). (Illus.). 64p. 14.99 (978-0-7548-1072-8(0) , Lorenz Bks.) Anness Publishing GBR. *Dist:* National Bk. Network.

Valdivia, Manny & Valdivia, Rochelle. Jungle Animals: Let's Draw. Valdivia, Manny & Valdivia, Rochelle, illus. 2000. (Let's Draw Ser.). (Illus.). 32p. (J). (gr. 1-7). mass mkt. 2.99 (978-0-7681-0220-8(0) , 67304, McClanahan Bk.) Learning Horizons, Inc.

Van der Meer, Ron & Van der Meer, Atie. Amazing Animal Senses. Motoyama, Keiko, illus. 2001. 12p. (J). (gr. k-3). 12.95 (978-1-58117-087-0(4) , Intervisual/Piggy Toes) Dalmatian Pr.

Vaughn, Marcia. I Howl, I Growl: Southwest Animal Antics. Powell, Polly, illus. 2003. 26p. (J). (ps-k). bds. 6.95 (978-0-87358-835-5(5) , Rising Moon Bks. for Young Readers) Northland Publishing.

von Kessel, Carola. Understanding Horses with Caddie. Guhe, Irmtraud, illus. 2004. 32p. 22.50 (978-3-86127-948-8(7)) Cadmos Verlag GmbH GBR. *Dist:* Trans-Atlantic Pubns., Inc.

Wallace, Karen & Collins, Ross. It Takes Two. 1998. (Wonderwise Ser.). (Illus.). 32p. (J). (gr. k-3). pap. 6.95 (978-0-531-15325-3(8) , Watts, Franklin) Scholastic Library Publishing.

Walsh, Melanie. Do Monkeys Tweet? Walsh, Melanie, illus. 2002. (Illus.). (J). 24.68 (978-0-7587-2391-8(1)) Book Wholesalers, Inc.

Welch, Ruth. Animal Tails: Individual Title Six-Pack Pouch - Level K. (Lighthouse Ser.). 16p. (gr. 2 up). 28.00 (978-0-7578-0860-9(3)) Rigby Education.

Whitehouse, Patricia. Under My Feet Series, 6 bks., Set. 2004. (978-1-4034-4324-3(6)) Heinemann Library.

—What Can Dig? 2003. (Heinemann Read & Learn Ser.). (Illus.). 24p. (J). pap. 5.25 (978-1-4034-4376-2(9)) Heinemann Library.

—What Can Jump? 2003. (Illus.). 24p. (J). pap. 5.25 (978-1-4034-4373-1(4)) Heinemann Library.

—What's Awake 1 2 3. 2003. (What's Awake? Ser.). (Illus.). 24p. (J). (ps-1). lib. bdg. 17.08 (978-1-58810-885-2(6)) Heinemann Library.

—What's Awake ABC. 2003. (Heinemann Read & Learn Ser.). (Illus.). 24p. (J). (ps-1). lib. bdg. 17.08 (978-1-58810-884-5(8)) Heinemann Library.

—What's Awake ABC. 2002. (ps-2). lib. bdg. 13.30 (978-0-613-89120-2(1)) Tandem Library Bks.

Whittaker, Nicola. Noses. 2002. (Creature Features Ser.). (Illus.). 32p. (J). (ps up). lib. bdg. 23.33 (978-0-8368-3165-8(9)) Stevens, Gareth Inc.

—Tails. 2002. (Creature Features Ser.). (Illus.). 32p. (J). (ps up). lib. bdg. 23.33 (978-0-8368-3166-5(7)) Stevens, Gareth Inc.

Who's Who at the Zoo? 2000. (J). cd-rom 5.00 (978-1-931457-00-2(X)) Stargate Electronic Library, Inc.

Whose Work Is This? 2006. (Whose Is It? Ser.). 24p. (J). 7.95 (978-1-4048-1826-2(X)) Picture Window Bks.

Wildlife Education, Ltd. Staff & Wexo, John Bonnett. Night Animals. Stuart, Walter, illus. 2000. (Zoobooks Ser.). 18p. (Orig.). (YA). (gr. 5 up). pap. 2.95 (978-0-937934-26-5(7)) Wildlife Education, Ltd.

Winer, Yvonne. Frogs Sing Songs. Oliver, Tony, illus. 2003. 32p. (J). pap. 6.95 (978-1-57091-549-9(0)); 16.95 (978-1-57091-548-2(2)) Charlesbridge Publishing, Inc.

Winkelman, Barbara Gaines. Puffer's Surprise. 2005. (Illus.). 32p. (J). (ps-2). 9.95 (978-1-59249-038-7(7) , PB4074) Soundprints.

Woelfle, Gretchen. Animal Families Animal Friends. Hynes, Robert, illus. 2005. 32p. (J). (978-1-55971-901-8(X) , NorthWord Bks. for Young Readers) T&N Children's Publishing.

Wood, Jakki. Animal Hullabaloo. Wood, Jakki, illus. 1999. (Illus.). 32p. (J). (ps). pap. (978-0-7112-0946-6(4)) Lincoln, Frances Ltd. GBR. *Dist:* Transition Vendor.

Wood, Jenny. I Wonder Why Kangaroos Have Pouches: And Other Questions about Baby Animals. 2003. (I Wonder Why Ser.). (Illus.). 32p. (J). (gr. k-3). pap. 6.95 (978-0-7534-5661-3(3) , Kingfisher) Houghton Mifflin Co. Trade & Reference Div.

Woodward, John. Daredevils. 2005. (Planet's Most Extreme Ser.). (Illus.). 48p. (J). (gr. 3-7). 24.95 (978-1-4103-0400-1(0) , Blackbirch Pr., Inc.) Thomson Gale.

—Swarms. 2005. (Planet's Most Extreme Ser.). (J). 23.70 (978-1-4103-0394-3(2)); 9.95 (978-1-4103-0436-0(1)) Thomson Gale. (Blackbirch Pr., Inc.).

Zolotow, Charlotte. Sleepy Book. Date not set. 32p. (J). (ps-3). pap. 5.99 (978-0-06-443737-0(X)) HarperCollins Pubs.

—Sleepy Book. Vitale, Stefano, illus. 2001. 40p. (J). (ps-2). 15.95 (978-0-06-027873-1(0)) HarperCollins Pubs.

ANIMALS—HABITS AND BEHAVIOR—FICTION

Armadillo's Midnight Adventure. 2002. (Backyard Mini Bks.). (Illus.). 32p. (J). (978-1-59069-022-2(2) , H2011) Studio Mouse LLC.

Beaton, Clare. How Loud Is a Lion? 2002. (Illus.). 24p. (J). (gr. k-2). 14.99 (978-1-84148-896-7(8)) Barefoot Bks., Inc.

Beaver's Lodge. 2002. (Wild Heritage Collection Mini Bks.). (Illus.). 32p. (J). (978-1-59069-164-9(4) , H3008) Studio Mouse LLC.

Benchmark Education Staff, compiled by. Habitats. 2006. spiral bd. 215.00 (***978-1-4108-7105-3(3)***) Benchmark Education Co.

Bester, Maryanne. Three Friends & a Taxi. Bester, Shayle, illus. 2007. 24p. (J). pap. 12.00 (***978-1-77009-265-5(X)***) Jacana Media ZAF. *Dist:* Independent Pubs. Group.

Bonnell, Kris. Who Can Wiggle? 2006. (J). 3.95 (***978-1-933727-42-4(X)***) Reading Reading Bks., LLC.

Brown, Jacqui. Who Made Me Jump? 2003. (Animal Detectives Ser.). (Illus.). 32p. (J). 5.95 (978-0-7641-5660-1(8)) Barron's Educational Series, Inc.

Brown, Pamela. Barnyard Buddies I, 22 vols. Hutchins, Annie H., illus. 2002. 84p. (J). (gr. k-4). pap. 16.00 (978-1-928589-15-0(4)) Gival Pr., LLC.

Chaconas, Doris J. One Little Mouse. Pham, Le Uyen, illus. 2002. 32p. (J). 15.99 (978-0-670-88947-1(4) , Viking Juvenile) Penguin Group (USA) Inc.

Dowson, Nick. Tigress. Chapman, Jane, tr. Chapman, Jane, illus. 2004. 32p. (J). (gr. k-3). 15.99 (978-0-7636-2325-8(3)) Candlewick Pr.

George, Lindsay Barrett. In the Garden: Who's Been Here? George, Lindsay Barrett, illus. 2006. (Illus.). 48p. (J). 16.99 (978-0-06-078762-2(7)); lib. bdg. 17.89 (978-0-06-078763-9(5)) HarperCollins Pubs.

Giogas, Valerie. In My Backyard. Zecca, Katherine, illus. 2007. 32p. (J). (ps-3). 15.95 (***978-0-9777423-1-8(8)***) Sylvan Dell Pubng.

Harcourt School Publishers Staff. Looking Back, Unit 5. 3rd ed. 2003. (Horizons Ser.). (Illus.). (gr. 1). pap. 166.70 (978-0-15-340224-1(5)) Harcourt Schl. Pubs.

Hebert, Marie-Francine. John's Day. Hamel, Caroline, illus. 2005. (Read-It! Readers Ser.). 32p. (C). (gr. k-3). 18.60 (978-1-4048-1071-6(4)) Picture Window Bks.

Hosta, Dar. I Love the Night. Hosta, Dar, illus. l.t. ed. 2003. (Illus.). 32p. (J). (gr. k-3). 16.95 (978-0-9721967-0-3(6)) Brown Dog Bks.

Jones, Andrea. The Spitting Twins. Kulka, Joe, illus. 2004. 32p. (J). (978-1-58394-095-2(2) , Frog Ltd.) North Atlantic Bks.

Julietta, Melinda. We Are Wolves. Guamotta, Lucia, illus. 1999. 32p. (ps-3). 12.95 (978-1-55971-713-7(0) , NorthWord Bks. for Young Readers) T&N Children's Publishing.

Lewis, Edwina. Who Eats? Parker, Ant, illus. 2003. (Who. . . Ser.). 16p. (YA). (978-1-85602-470-9(9)) Chrysalis Children's Bks.

London, Jonathan. Eyes of Gray Wolf. Van Zyle, Jon, illus. 2004. 32p. (J). pap. 6.95 (978-0-8118-4141-2(3)) Chronicle Bks. LLC.

Martin, Bill. Brown Bear, Brown Bear, What Do You See? 40th Anniversary Edition. Carle, Eric, illus. 2007. 32p. (J). 19.95 (***978-0-8050-8266-1(2)*** , Holt, Henry & Co. Bks. For Young Readers) Holt, Henry & Co.

Miller, Pat. Substitute Groundhog. Ember, Kathi, illus. 2006. 32p. (J). 15.95 (978-0-8075-7643-4(3)) Whitman, Albert & Co.

Racoon's Night Out. 2002. (Backyard Mini Bks.). (Illus.). 32p. (J). (978-1-59069-019-2(2) , H2008) Studio Mouse LLC.

Rogers, Bettye. Prairie Dog. Howland, Deborah, illus. 2002. (J). (978-1-59069-255-4(1) , HS3001) Studio Mouse LLC.

Spafford, Suzy. Tales from Duckport: Helping Out Day Hooray. Spafford, Suzy, illus. 2003. (Tales from Duckport Ser.). (Illus.). 40p. (J). (gr. k-3). pap. 3.99 (978-0-439-38358-5(7)) Scholastic, Inc.

Tamarin's Treetop. 2002. (Animal's Around the World Mini Bks.). (Illus.). 32p. (J). (978-1-59069-173-1(3) , H4009) Studio Mouse LLC.

Title in Development. 2002. (Wild Heritage Collection Mini Bks.). (Illus.). 32p. (J). (978-1-59069-241-7(1) , H3012); (978-1-59069-175-5(X)) Studio Mouse LLC.

Truman, Dennay H. The Happy Endings. 2007. 65p. per. 8.95 (***978-1-59824-435-9(3)***) E-BookTime LLC.

Walsh, Melanie. My Beak, Your Beak. Walsh, Melanie, illus. 2002. (Illus.). 32p. (J). (gr. k-ps). 15.00 (978-0-618-15079-3(X)) Houghton Mifflin Co. Trade & Reference Div.

ANIMALS—HIBERNATION

Crossingham, John. What Is Hibernation? 2002. (gr. 3-6). lib. bdg. 14.10 (978-0-613-50848-3(3)) Tandem Library Bks.

Crossingham, John & Kalman, Bobbie. Que es la Hibernacion? 2005. (Ciencia de los Seres Vivos Ser.).Tr. of What Is Hibernation?. (SPA., Illus.). 32p. (YA). (gr. 7-12). pap. (978-0-7787-8804-1(0)) Crabtree Publishing Co.

—Qué Es la Hibernacion? 2005. (FRE & SPA., Illus.). 32p. (J). (978-0-7787-8758-7(3)) Crabtree Publishing Co.

Ganeri, Anita. Hibernation. 2005. (Nature's Patterns Ser.). (Illus.). 32p. (J). pap. (978-1-4109-1318-0(X)); lib. bdg. 16.95 (978-1-4034-5895-7(2)) Heinemann Library.

Hall, Margaret. Hibernar. 2008. (ENG & SPA.). (J). (***978-1-4296-0013-2(6)***) Capstone Pr., Inc.

Hall, Margaret. Hibernation. 2007. (Pebble Plus Ser.). (Illus.). 24p. (J). 19.93 (978-0-7368-6339-1(7) , 1258706) Capstone Pr., Inc.

Hickman, Pamela. Animals Hibernating: How Animals Survive Extreme Conditions. Stephens, Pat, illus. 2005. (Animal Behavior Ser.). 40p. (J). (gr. 3-5). (978-1-55337-663-7(3)); (ps-6). (978-1-55337-662-0(5)) Kids Can Pr., Ltd.

Kalman, Bobbie & Crossingham, John. L'hibernation. 2003. (FRE., Illus.). 32p. (J). pap. (978-2-920660-95-3(0)) Crabtree Publishing Co.

—What Is Hibernation? 2001. (Science of Living Things Ser.). (Illus.). 32p. (J). (gr. 2-3). (978-0-86505-987-0(X)); pap. (978-0-86505-964-1(0)) Crabtree Publishing Co.

Larsen, Beverly Jean. Bessy Bear's Winter Dreams. McWaters, Karen, illus. 2000. 34p. (Orig.). (J). (gr. 3-8). pap. 13.95 (978-1-58275-053-8(X)) Black Forest Pr.

Murphy, Patricia J. Why Do Some Animals Hibernate? 2004. (Library of Why?). (Illus.). 24p. (J). lib. bdg. 18.75 (978-0-8239-6232-7(6)) Rosen Publishing Group, Inc., The.

Penny, Malcolm. Hidden Hibernators. 2003. (Amazing Nature Ser.). (Illus.). 32p. (J). pap. (978-1-4034-5400-3(0)); lib. bdg. (978-1-4034-4704-3(7)) Heinemann Library.

Perry, Phyllis Jean. Animals That Hibernate. 2001. (Animal Library). (Illus.). 64p. (J). (gr. 5-7). 25.50 (978-0-531-11864-1(9) , Watts, Franklin) Scholastic Library Publishing.

Salas, Laura Purdie. Do Polar Bears Snooze in Hollow Trees? A Book about Animal Hibernation. Ouren, Todd, illus. 2006. (Animals All Around Ser.). (J). 23.93 (978-1-4048-2231-3(3)) Picture Window Bks.

Scrace, Carolyn. Hibernation. 2002. (gr. k-3). lib. bdg. 15.25 (978-0-613-53041-5(1)) Tandem Library Bks.

Seuling, Barbara. Winter Lullaby. Newbold, Greg, illus. 1998. 32p. (J). (ps-2). 16.00 (978-0-15-201403-2(9)) Harcourt Children's Bks.

Stone, Lynn M. Hibernation. 2007. (Illus.). 24p. (J). (978-1-60044-177-6(7)) Rourke Publishing, LLC.

Turner, Matt. Home Makers. 2003. (Amazing Nature Ser.). (Illus.). 32p. (J). pap. (978-1-4034-5401-0(9)) Heinemann Library.

ANIMALS, IMAGINARY

see Animals, Mythical

ANIMALS—INFANCY

Arnold, Caroline. Mother & Baby Zoo Animals. 1999. (Zoo Animals Ser.). (Illus.). 32p. (J). (ps-2). 9.95 (978-1-57505-390-5(X) , Carolrhoda Bks.) Lerner Publishing Group.

—Mother & Baby Zoo Animals. Hewett, Richard, illus. 1999. (Zoo Animals Ser.). 32p. (J). (ps-2). lib. bdg. 21.27 (978-1-57505-285-4(7) , Carolrhoda Bks.) Lerner Publishing Group.

Ashman, Linda. Babies on the Go. Dyer, Jane, illus. (J). 2007. 30p. bds. 6.95 (978-0-15-205886-9(9) , Red Wagon Bks.); 2003. 32p. 16.00 (978-0-15-201894-8(8)) Harcourt Children's Bks.

Aston, Dianna Hutts. Mama's Wild Child/Papa's Wild Child. Hilb, Nora, illus. 2006. 32p. (J). 14.95 (978-1-57091-590-1(3)) Charlesbridge Publishing, Inc.

Baby Animals. 2005. (Illus.). (J). per. 4.99 (978-1-933581-19-4(0)) Byeway Bks.

Baby Animals. 2002. (Puppy Tales Ser.). (Illus.). 24p. (J). (gr. k-3). 1.49 (978-1-57759-258-7(1)) Dalmatian Pr.

Baby Animals. (Illus.). 24p. (J). 1.99 (978-1-59445-022-8(6)) Dogs in Hats Children's Publishing Co.

Baby Animals. (J). Date not set. (Illus.). 16p. 5.98 (978-0-7525-7696-1(8)); Date not set. (Illus.). 16p. 2.98 (978-0-7525-8137-8(6)); Date not set. (Illus.). 16p. 2.98 (978-0-7525-9760-7(4)); 2003. 32p. 3.98 (978-0-7525-8893-3(1)) Parragon, Inc.

Baby Animals. (Illus.). 2005. 10p. bds. 9.98 (978-0-7853-6671-3(7) , 7167000); 2002. 40p. (J). bds. 7.98 (978-0-7853-6339-2(4) , 7158100) Publications International, Ltd.

Baby Animals. 2006. 16p. (J). pap. 1.99 (978-0-7847-1387-7(1) , 22125) Standard Publishing.

Baby Animals: Individual Title Six-Packs. (Rigby Focus Ser.). 16p. (gr. 1 up). 28.00 (978-0-7578-5304-3(8)); 30.00 (978-0-7578-5536-8(9)) Rigby Education.

Baillie, Marilyn. Small Wonders: Baby Animals in the Wild. Caron, Romi, illus. 2006. 32p. (ps-2). 17.95 (978-1-897066-72-0(4)) Maple Tree Pr. CAN. *Dist:* Perseus Distribution.

Balloon Books Staff, ed. Baby Animals. 2003. (Take-Along Bks.). (Illus.). 12p. (J). bds. 4.95 (978-0-8069-2913-2(8) , Balloon Bks.) Sterling Publishing Co., Inc.

Barbaresi, Nina. Cute Baby Animals Stickers. 2004. (Stickers Ser.). (Illus.). 4p. (J). (ps-5). pap. 1.50 (978-0-486-43304-2(8)) Dover Pubns., Inc.

Barnes, J. Lou. Cats & Kittens. 2002. (PowerPhonics Ser.). (Illus.). 23p. (J). lib. bdg. (978-0-8239-8248-6(3)) Rosen Publishing Group, Inc., The.

—Cats & Kittens: Learning the Hard C & K Sounds. 2002. (PowerPhonics Ser.). (Illus.). 24p. (J). (gr. 1). lib. bdg. 18.50 (978-0-8239-5903-7(1) , PowerKids Pr.) Rosen Publishing Group, Inc., The.

Batten, Mary. Baby Wolf. Stammen, JoEllen McAllister, illus. 1998. (All Aboard Reading Ser.). 48p. (J). (gr. 1-3). pap. 3.99 (978-0-448-41645-8(X) , Grosset & Dunlap) Penguin Group (USA) Inc.

Bauer, Marion Dane. If You Were Born a Kitten. Stammen, JoEllen McAllister, illus. 1999. 32p. (J). (gr. k-3). per. 16.00 (978-0-689-82725-9(3) , Simon & Schuster Children's Publishing) Simon & Schuster Children's Publishing.

—If You Were Born a Kitten. 2001. (Illus.). (J). 13.79 (978-0-606-20719-5(8)) Tandem Library Bks.

Bears Have Cubs. (Animals & Their Young Ser.). 24p. (J). 7.95 (978-0-7565-1235-4(2)) Compass Point Bks.

Berger, Melvin. Bebés de Animales Polares: Polar Animal Babies. 2006. (SPA & ENG., Illus.). (J). (***978-0-439-87986-6(8)***) Scholastic, Inc.

Berger, Melvin & Berger, Gilda. Schol True or False #1 Baby Animals. 2008. 48p. pap. 4.99 (***978-0-545-00391-9(1)*** , Scholastic Reference) Scholastic, Inc.

Bicknell, Joanna. Cuddle Buddy: Baby Animals. 2006. 10p. (ps). 9.95 (978-1-84610-093-2(3)) Make Believe Ideas GBR. *Dist:* Ingram Pub. Services.

Bolam, Emily & Ehrlich, Fred. Does a Duck Have a Daddy? Early Experiences. 2007. (Illus.). 28p. pap. 5.95 (978-1-59354-590-1(8)) Blue Apple Bks.

—Does a Mouse Have a Mommy? Early Experiences. 2007. (Illus.). 28p. pap. 5.95 (978-1-59354-589-5(4)) Blue Apple Bks.

Bonforte, Lisa. Baby Animals Stickers. 2002. (Illus.). 4p. (J). (ps-5). 1.50 (978-0-486-42341-8(7)) Dover Pubns., Inc.

Brown, Carron. Animal Babies in Ponds & Rivers. 2007. (Illus.). 24p. (J). bds. 6.95 (978-0-7534-6059-7(9) , Kingfisher) Houghton Mifflin Co. Trade & Reference Div.

—Animal Babies in Rainforests. 2007. (Animal Babies Ser.). (Illus.). 24p. (J). (ps-k). bds. 6.95 (978-0-7534-6060-3(2) , Kingfisher) Houghton Mifflin Co. Trade & Reference Div.

Burton, Margie, et al. Animals & Their Babies. Evento, Susan, ed. 1998. (Early Connections Ser.). 16p. (J). (gr. k-2). pap. 4.25 (978-1-892393-43-2(3)) Benchmark Education Co.

Butler, John. Whose Baby Am I? 2001. (Illus.). 24p. (J). (ps). 10.99 (978-0-670-89683-7(7) , Viking Juvenile) Penguin Group (USA) Inc.

Camm, Sue, illus. Baby Animals. 2004. 24p. (J). bds. 6.99 (978-1-85854-728-2(8)) Brimax Books Ltd. GBR. *Dist:* Byeway Bks.

Carle, Eric. Does a Kangaroo Have a Mother, Too? El Canguro Tiene Mama? Carle, Eric, illus. 2002. (SPA., Illus.). 32p. (J). (ps-1). 17.99 (978-0-06-001110-9(6) , Rayo) HarperCollins Pubs.

Carlson, Kit. Bringing up Baby: Wild Animal Families. 1998. (Animal Planet Ser.). (978-0-606-13227-5(9)) Tandem Library Bks.

Cartwright, Stephen. Animal Babies. 2004. (Usborne Farmyard Tales Ser.). (Illus.). 10p. (J). (ps-k). 4.95 (978-0-7460-4105-5(5)) EDC Publishing.

Chanko, Pamela. Baby Animals Learn. 1998. (Science Emergent Readers Ser.). (Illus.). 48p. (J). pap. 2.50 (978-0-590-76157-4(9)) Scholastic, Inc.

Clarke, Ginjer. Baby Alligator. Twinem, Neecy, illus. 2000. (All Aboard Reading Ser.). 48p. (J). (gr. 1-3). pap. 3.99 (978-0-448-42095-0(3) , Grosset & Dunlap) Penguin Group (USA) Inc.

—Baby Alligator. 2000. (gr. k-3). lib. bdg. 11.80 (978-0-613-24274-5(2)); (Illus.). (J). (978-0-606-18463-2(5)) Tandem Library Bks.

Collard, Sneed B., III. Leaving Home. Dunning, Joan, illus. 2002. 32p. (J). (gr. k-3). 15.00 (978-0-618-11454-2(8)) Houghton Mifflin Co. Trade & Reference Div.

Cooper, Jason. Calf to Cow. 2003. (Rourke Discovery Library). (Illus.). 24p. (J). 20.64 (978-1-58952-690-7(2)) Rourke Publishing, LLC.

—Canada Goose. 2003. (Life Cycles Ser.). (Illus.). 24p. (gr 1-4). 17.95 (978-1-58952-351-7(2)) Rourke Publishing, LLC.

—Cub to Grizzly. 2003. (Illus.). 24p. (J). 20.64 (978-1-58952-691-4(0)) Rourke Publishing, LLC.

—Cub to Panda. 2003. (Illus.). 24p. (J). 20.64 (978-1-58952-692-1(9)) Rourke Publishing, LLC.

—Fawn to Deer. 2003. (Rourke Discovery Library). (Illus.). 24p. (J). 20.64 (978-1-58952-693-8(7)) Rourke Publishing, LLC.

—Foal to Horse. 2003. (Illus.). 24p. (J). 20.64 (978-1-58952-694-5(5)) Rourke Publishing, LLC.

—Kitten to Tiger. 2003. (Illus.). 24p. (J). 20.64 (978-1-58952-695-2(3)) Rourke Publishing, LLC.

—Pacific Salmon. 2003. (Life Cycles Ser.). (Illus.). 24p. (gr. 1-4). 17.95 (978-1-58952-352-4(0)) Rourke Publishing, LLC.

Craft, Sarah S. Mother Beluga Whales & Their Babies. 1999. (Zoo Life Book Ser.). 24p. (J). (gr. k-4). lib. bdg. 18.75 (978-0-8239-5315-8(7) , PowerKids Pr.) Rosen Publishing Group, Inc., The.

—Mother Giraffes & Their Babies. 1999. (Zoo Life Book Ser.). 24p. (J). (gr. k-4). lib. bdg. 18.75 (978-0-8239-5316-5(5) , PowerKids Pr.) Rosen Publishing Group, Inc., The.

—Mother Gorillas & Their Babies. 1999. (Zoo Life Book Ser.). 24p. (J). (gr. k-4). lib. bdg. 18.75 (978-0-8239-5313-4(0) , PowerKids Pr.) Rosen Publishing Group, Inc., The.

—Mother Indian Rhinos & Their Babies. 1999. (Zoo Life Book Ser.). (Illus.). 24p. (J). (gr. k-4). lib. bdg. 18.75 (978-0-8239-5318-9(1) , PowerKids Pr.) Rosen Publishing Group, Inc., The.

—Mother Snow Leopards & Their Babies. 1999. (Zoo Life Book Ser.). 24p. (J). (gr. k-4). lib. bdg. 18.75 (978-0-8239-5317-2(3) , PowerKids Pr.) Rosen Publishing Group, Inc., The.

—Mother Wallabies & Their Babies. 1999. (Zoo Life Book Ser.). 24p. (J). (gr. k-4). lib. bdg. 18.75 (978-0-8239-5314-1(9) , PowerKids Pr.) Rosen Publishing Group, Inc., The.

Cuidando a los animales/Keeping Baby Animals Safe. 2005. (Take-Home Bks.). (SPA.). (YA). (ps-3). 15.75 (978-0-8215-1206-7(4)) Sadlier, William H. Inc.

Currie, Robin. Baby Bible Animals. 2003. (Baby Bible Ser.). (Illus.). 48p. (J). bds. 12.99 (978-0-7814-3865-0(9) , 0781438659) Cook, David C. Publishing Co.

Dahl, Michael. Do Penguins Have Puppies? A Book about Animal Babies. D'Antonio, Sandra, illus. 2004. (Animals All Around Ser.). 24p. (C). (gr. k-2). 22.60 (978-1-4048-0102-8(2)) Picture Window Bks.

Dalmatian Press Staff, ed. Baby Animals. 2006. 64p. (J). 1.09 (978-1-4037-2541-7(1)) Dalmatian Pr.

Daniels, Lucy & Baglio, Ben M. Chick Challenge. Howard, Paul, illus. 1999. (Animal Ark Pets Ser.: No. 6). 128p. (J). (gr. 3-6). pap. 3.99 (978-0-439-05163-7(0)) Scholastic, Inc.

Darling, Kathy. Desert Babies. Darling, Tara, photos by. 2002. (Illus.). 32p. (J). (gr. k-3). pap. 6.95 (978-0-8027-7533-7(0)) Walker & Co.

—Seashore Babies. 2002. (gr. k-3). lib. bdg. 15.25 (978-0-613-63529-5(9)) Tandem Library Bks.

—Seashore Babies. Darling, Tara, photos by. 2002. (Illus.). 32p. (J). pap. 6.95 (978-0-8027-7534-4(9)) Walker & Co.

Discovery Channel Staff. Animal Planet the Most Extreme Animals. Gerstein, Sherry & Packard, Mary, eds. 2007. (Animal Planet Extreme Animals Ser.). 80p. 15.95 (***978-0-7879-8662-9(3)*** , Jossey-Bass) Wiley, John & Sons, Inc.

DK Publishing. Amazing, Fuzzy, Furry Wild Baby Animals. 2008. (Touchables Ser.). 10p. (J). (ps-ps). bds. 8.99 (***978-0-7566-3792-7(9)***) Dorling Kindersley Publishing, Inc.

—Baby Animals. 2008. (J). (ps-k). 16p. bds. 9.99 (***978-0-7566-3845-0(3));*** 14p. 4.99 (***978-0-7566-3437-7(7)***) Dorling Kindersley Publishing, Inc.

—Fox: See How They Grow. 2008. (See How They Grow Ser.). 1p. (J). (ps-k). pap. 3.99 (***978-0-7566-3763-7(5)***) Dorling Kindersley Publishing, Inc.

—Water Magic Baby Animals 123. 2007. 16p. (J). bds. 7.99 (***978-0-7566-3449-0(0)***) Dorling Kindersley Publishing, Inc.

Dolbear, Emily J. & Primm, E. Russell. Cats Have Kittens. 2001. (Animals & Their Young Ser.). (Illus.). 24p. (J). (gr. 1 up). lib. bdg. 18.60 (978-0-7565-0059-7(1)) Compass Point Bks.

—Dogs Have Puppies. 2001. (Animals & Their Young Ser.). (Illus.). 24p. (J). (gr. 1 up). lib. bdg. 18.60 (978-0-7565-0060-3(5)) Compass Point Bks.

—Kangaroos Have Joeys. 2001. (Animals & Their Young Ser.). (Illus.). 24p. (J). (gr. 1 up). lib. bdg. 18.60 (978-0-7565-0061-0(3)) Compass Point Bks.

—Pandas Have Cubs. 2001. (Animals & Their Young Ser.). (Illus.). 24p. (J). (gr. 1 up). lib. bdg. 18.60 (978-0-7565-0062-7(1)) Compass Point Bks.

Dorling Kindersley Publishing Staff. Baby Animals. (Let's Look Ser.). (Illus.). (J). 2006. 36p. 4.99 (978-0-7566-2592-4(0)); 2003. 16p. pap. 3.99 (978-0-7894-9824-3(3)); 2003. 12p. bds. 6.99 (978-0-7894-4749-4(5)) Dorling Kindersley Publishing, Inc.

—Baby Animals. Landis, Beth, ed. 2002. (Baby's World Shaped Board Bks.). (Illus.). 36p. (J). bds. 6.99 (978-0-7894-8576-2(1)) Dorling Kindersley Publishing, Inc.

—Bear. 2004. (Watch Me Grow Ser.). (Illus.). 24p. (J). 7.99 (978-0-7566-0194-2(0)) Dorling Kindersley Publishing, Inc.

—The Big Book of Baby Animals. 2001. (Illus.). 32p. (J). (ps-3). 12.99 (978-0-7894-3069-4(X)) Dorling Kindersley Publishing, Inc.

—Butterfly. 2004. (Watch Me Grow Ser.). (Illus.). 24p. (J). 7.99 (978-0-7566-0193-5(2)) Dorling Kindersley Publishing, Inc.

—Frog. 2003. (Watch Me Grow Ser.). (Illus.). 24p. (J). pap. 7.99 (978-0-7894-9629-4(1)) Dorling Kindersley Publishing, Inc.

—My First Puppy Touch & Feel. 2003. (My First Touch & Feel Ser.). (Illus.). 12p. (J). bds. 9.99 (978-0-7894-9625-6(9)) Dorling Kindersley Publishing, Inc.

—Playtime Peekaboo! 2005. (Illus.). 12p. (J). (ps-3). bds. 6.99 (978-0-7566-1144-6(X)) Dorling Kindersley Publishing, Inc.

—Show Me: Baby Animals. 2003. (Lift-the-Flap Books Ser.). (Illus.). 16p. (J). bds. 6.99 (978-0-7894-9750-5(6)) Dorling Kindersley Publishing, Inc.

Dorling Kindersley Publishing Staff, contrib. by. Baby Animals. 2004. (Baby Love Ser.). (Illus.). 16p. (J). bds. 4.99 (978-0-7566-0213-0(0)) Dorling Kindersley Publishing, Inc.

—My First Baby Animals Touch & Feel. 2004. (Touch & Feel Ser.). (Illus.). 12p. (J). bds. 9.99 (978-0-7566-0453-0(2)) Dorling Kindersley Publishing, Inc.

Dorling Kindersley Publishing Staff, ed. Baby Animals. 2004. (Ultimate Sticker Bks.). 16p. (J). pap. 6.99 (978-0-7566-0564-3(4)) Dorling Kindersley Publishing, Inc.

—Crias y Cachorros. 2004. (Touch & Feel Ser.).Tr. of Baby Animals. (SPA.). 12p. (J). bds. 6.99 (978-0-7566-0630-5(6)) Dorling Kindersley Publishing, Inc.

Doudna, Kelly. Baby Animals, Set. l.t. ed. Incl. Bunnies. lib. bdg. 19.93 (978-1-57765-184-0(7)); Calves. lib. bdg. 19.93 (978-1-57765-186-4(3)); Foals. lib. bdg. 19.93 (978-1-57765-183-3(9)); Kittens. lib. bdg. 19.93 (978-1-57765-182-6(0)); Piglets. lib. bdg. 19.93 (978-1-57765-185-7(5)); Puppies. lib. bdg. 19.93 (978-1-57765-181-9(2)); 24p. (J). (ps-3). 1999. (Illus.). 1999. Set lib. bdg. 119.58 (978-1-57765-266-3(5) , SandCastle) ABDO Publishing Co.

—Bunnies. l.t. ed. 1999. (Baby Animals Ser.). (Illus.). 24p. (J). (ps-3). lib. bdg. 19.93 (978-1-57765-184-0(7) , SandCastle) ABDO Publishing Co.

—Calves. l.t. ed. 1999. (Baby Animals Ser.). (Illus.). 24p. (J). (ps-3). lib. bdg. 19.93 (978-1-57765-186-4(3) , SandCastle) ABDO Publishing Co.

—Foals. l.t. ed. 1999. (Baby Animals Ser.). (Illus.). 24p. (J). (ps-3). lib. bdg. 19.93 (978-1-57765-183-3(9) , SandCastle) ABDO Publishing Co.

—Kittens. l.t. ed. 1999. (Baby Animals Ser.). (Illus.). 24p. (J). (ps-3). lib. bdg. 19.93 (978-1-57765-182-6(0) , SandCastle) ABDO Publishing Co.

—Piglets. l.t. ed. 1999. (Baby Animals Ser.). (Illus.). 24p. (J). (ps-3). lib. bdg. 19.93 (978-1-57765-185-7(5) , SandCastle) ABDO Publishing Co.

Douglas, Vincent & School Specialty Publishing Staff. My Block Book Schoolhouse of Baby Animals, 4 bks. 2003. (My Block Book Schoolhouse Collection). (Illus.). 88p. (J). (ps up). bds. 12.95 (978-1-58845-503-1(3)) School Specialty Publishing.

Dromgoole, Glenn. What Puppies Teach Us: Life's Lessons Learned from Our Little Friends. 2003. (Illus.). 32p. tchr. ed. 12.95 (978-1-57223-684-4(1) , 6841) Willow Creek Pr., Inc.

Dunn, Phoebe. A Big Treasury of Little Animals. Dunn, Phoebe, illus. 2007. (Illus.). 192p. (J). (gr. k-2). 10.99 ***(978-0-375-84177-4(6)*** , Random Hse. Bks. for Young Readers) Random Hse. Children's Bks.

Feely, Jenny. Looking after Baby Animals. 2004. (Illus.). (J). ***(978-0-7608-7879-8(X))*** Sundance/Newbridge Educational Publishing.

Feeney, Kathy. What Are Baby Koalas Called? A Book about Baby Animals. 2007. (First Facts Ser.). (Illus.). 24p. (J). (978-0-7368-6755-9(4) , 1264906) Capstone Pr., Inc.

Fraser, Mary Ann. How Animal Babies Stay Safe. Fraser, Mary Ann, illus. 2001. (Let's-Read-and-Find-Out Science Ser.). (Illus.). 40p. (J). (ps-1). 15.95 (978-0-06-028803-7(5)); pap. 5.99 (978-0-06-445211-3(5) , Harper Trophy) HarperCollins Pubs.

—How Animal Babies Stay Safe. 2002. (gr. k-3). lib. bdg. 12.95 (978-0-613-56780-0(3)) Tandem Library Bks.

Galbraith, Kathryn Osebold. Traveling Babies. Dippold, Jane, illus. 2006. 32p. 16.95 (978-1-55971-939-1(7) , NorthWord Bks. for Young Readers) T&N Children's Publishing.

Gentle, Victor & Perry, Janet. Baby Sharks. 2001. (Sharks Ser.). (Illus.). 24p. (J). (gr. 2 up). lib. bdg. 22.00 (978-0-8368-2824-5(0)) Stevens, Gareth Inc.

Giogas, Valarie. In My Backyard. Zecca, Katherine, illus. 2007. 32p. (J). (ps-3). 8.95 ***(978-1-934359-17-4(3))*** Sylvan Dell Pubng.

God Made Puppies. 2006. 16p. (J). pap. 1.99 (978-0-7847-1685-4(4) , 02987) Standard Publishing.

Golden Books Staff. Baby Farm Animals. Williams, Garth, illus. 2003. (Little Golden Book Classics). 24p. (J). (gr. k-k). 2.99 (978-0-307-02175-5(0) , Golden Bks.) Random Hse. Children's Bks.

Gunzi, Christiane. Fluffy Babies. 2006. (Feels Real Bks.). (Illus.). 10p. (J). bds. 4.99 (978-0-7641-5948-0(8)) Barron's Educational Series, Inc.

Hall, Margaret. Cows & Their Calves. 2003. (Animal Offspring Ser.). (Illus.). 24p. (J). lib. bdg. 17.26 (978-0-7368-2105-6(8) , Pebble Bks.) Capstone Pr., Inc.

—Ducks & Their Ducklings. 2003. (Animal Offspring Ser.). (Illus.). 24p. (J). lib. bdg. 17.26 (978-0-7368-2106-3(6) , Pebble Bks.) Capstone Pr., Inc.

—Elephants & Their Calves. 2003. (Animal Offspring Ser.). (Illus.). 24p. (J). lib. bdg. 17.26 (978-0-7368-2107-0(4) , Pebble Bks.) Capstone Pr., Inc.

—Gorillas & Their Infants. 2003. (Animal Offspring Ser.). (Illus.). 24p. (J). lib. bdg. 17.26 (978-0-7368-2108-7(2) , Pebble Bks.) Capstone Pr., Inc.

—Penguins & Their Chicks. 2003. (Animal Offspring Ser.). (Illus.). 24p. (J). lib. bdg. 17.26 (978-0-7368-2109-4(0) , Pebble Bks.) Capstone Pr., Inc.

—Tigers & Their Cubs. 2003. (Animal Offspring Ser.). (Illus.). 24p. (J). lib. bdg. 17.26 (978-0-7368-2110-0(4) , Pebble Bks.) Capstone Pr., Inc.

Harcourt School Publishers Staff. Animal Babies That Hatch. 3rd ed. 2002. (Trophies English Language Learners Ser.). (Illus.). pap. 5.10 (978-0-15-327649-1(5)) Harcourt Schl. Pubs.

—A Dog Has Pups: Independent Reader. 3rd ed. 2002. (Trophies Reading Program Ser.). (Illus.). (J). pap. 2.90 (978-0-15-325485-7(8)) Harcourt Schl. Pubs.

—Young Animals: Below Level. 3rd ed. 2002. (Trophies Reading Program Ser.). (Illus.). (J). pap. 4.10 (978-0-15-322967-1(5)) Harcourt Schl. Pubs.

—Young Animals 5-Pack, Below Level. 3rd ed. 2002. (Trophies Reading Program Ser.). (Illus.). (gr. 1). pap. 20.10 (978-0-15-326817-5(4)) Harcourt Schl. Pubs.

Head, Honor. Puppy. Burton, Jane, photos by. 2000. (My Pet Ser.). (Illus.). 32p. (J). (gr. 3-5). lib. bdg. 25.69 (978-0-7398-2885-4(1)) Raintree.

—What's It Like to Be a Baby Chimp? Nichols, Matthew, illus. 1998. (Baby Animals Ser.). 32p. (gr. k-3). lib. bdg. 20.90 (978-0-7613-1253-6(6) , Millbrook Pr.) Lerner Publishing Group.

—What's It Like to Be a Baby Elephant? Nichols, Matthew, illus. 1998. (Baby Animals Ser.). 32p. (gr. k-3). lib. bdg. 20.90 (978-0-7613-1252-9(8) , Millbrook Pr.) Lerner Publishing Group.

—What's It Like to Be a Baby Lion? Nichols, Matthew, illus. 1998. (Baby Animals Ser.). 32p. (gr. k-3). lib. bdg. 20.90 (978-0-7613-1254-3(4) , Millbrook Pr.) Lerner Publishing Group.

—What's It Like to Be a Baby Polar Bear? Nichols, Matthew, illus. 1998. (Baby Animals Ser.). 32p. (gr. k-3). lib. bdg. 20.90 (978-0-7613-1255-0(2) , Millbrook Pr.) Lerner Publishing Group.

Hewett, Joan. A Flamingo Chick Grows Up. Hewett, Richard, photos by. (Baby Animals Ser.). (Illus.). 32p. (gr. k-3). 2005. lib. bdg. 21.27 (978-1-57505-164-2(8)); 2003. (J). pap. 6.95 (978-0-8225-0090-2(6) , Lerner Pubns.) Lerner Publishing Group.

—A Harbor Seal Pup Grows Up. Hewett, Richard, photos by. (Baby Animals Ser.). (Illus.). 32p. (gr. k-3). 2005. lib. bdg. 21.27 (978-1-57505-166-6(4)); 2003. (J). pap. 6.95 (978-0-8225-0092-6(2)) Lerner Publishing Group.

—A Kangaroo Joey Grows Up. Hewett, Richard, photos by. (Baby Animals Ser.). (Illus.). 32p. (gr. k-3). 2005. lib. bdg. 21.27 (978-1-57505-165-9(6)); 2003. (J). pap. 6.95 (978-0-8225-0091-9(4)) Lerner Publishing Group.

—A Tiger Cub Grows Up. Hewett, Richard, photos by. (Baby Animals Ser.). (Illus.). 32p. (gr. k-3). 2005. lib. bdg. 21.27 (978-1-57505-163-5(X)); 2001. (J). pap. 6.95 (978-0-8225-0089-6(2) , Lerner Pubns.) Lerner Publishing Group.

—Tiger Cub Grows Up. 2002. (gr. k-3). lib. bdg. 15.25 (978-0-613-56655-1(6)) Tandem Library Bks.

Hewett, Richard, illus. & photos by. A Giraffe Calf Grows Up. Hewett, Richard, photos by. Hewett, Joan, photos by. 2004. (Baby Animals Ser.). 32p. (J). (gr. k-3). lib. bdg. 21.27 (978-1-57505-197-0(4)) Lerner Publishing Group.

—A Koala Joey Grows Up. Hewett, Richard, photos by. Hewett, Joan, photos by. 2004. (Baby Animals Ser.). 32p. (J). (gr. k-3). lib. bdg. 21.27 (978-1-57505-198-7(2)) Lerner Publishing Group.

—A Monkey Baby Grows Up. Hewett, Richard, photos by. Hewett, Joan, photos by. 2004. (Baby Animals Ser.). 32p. (J). (gr. k-3). lib. bdg. 21.27 (978-1-57505-199-4(0)) Lerner Publishing Group.

—A Penguin Chick Grows Up. Hewett, Richard, photos by. Hewett, Joan, photos by. 2004. (Baby Animals Ser.). 32p. (J). (gr. k-3). lib. bdg. 21.27 (978-1-57505-200-7(8)) Lerner Publishing Group.

Hickman, Pamela. Animals & Their Young: How Animals Produce & Care for Their Young. Stephens, Pat, illus. 2004. (Animal Behavior Ser.). 40p. (J). (gr. 4-6). (978-1-55337-062-8(7)); (978-1-55337-061-1(9)) Kids Can Pr., Ltd.

Higgins, Maria Mihalik. Cats: From Tigers to Tabbies. 1998. (Animal Planet Ser.). (J). (978-0-606-13259-6(7)) Tandem Library Bks.

Holmes, Thom & Holmes, Laurie. Baby Dinosaurs: Eggs, Nests, & Recent Discoveries. Skrepnick, Michael William, illus. 2003. (Dinosaur Library). 104p. (J). (gr. 6-12). lib. bdg. 26.60 (978-0-7660-2074-0(6)) Enslow Pubs., Inc.

Horne, Jane. Baby Animals. 2006. (Touch & Learn (Make Believe Ideas) Ser.). (Illus.). 10p. (ps). per., bds. 6.95 (978-1-84610-278-3(2)) Make Believe Ideas GBR. *Dist:* Ingram Pub. Services.

Hughes, Monica. Orangutan Baby. 2006. (I Love Reading Ser.). (Illus.). 24p. (J). lib. bdg. 19.96 (978-1-59716-153-4(5)) Bearport Publishing Co., Inc.

I Love Baby Animals. 2000. (Show & Tell Ser.). (Illus.). 24p. (J). (978-2-922148-91-6(2)) Presses aventure/Adventure Pr.

Jaffe, Elizabeth Dana. Bears Have Cubs. 2002. (Animals & Their Young Ser.). (Illus.). 24p. (J). (gr. 1 up). lib. bdg. 18.60 (978-0-7565-0168-6(7)) Compass Point Bks.

—Deer Have Fawns. 2002. (Animals & Their Young Ser.). (Illus.). 24p. (J). (gr. 1 up). lib. bdg. 18.60 (978-0-7565-0169-3(5)) Compass Point Bks.

—Ducks Have Ducklings. 2002. (Animals & Their Young Ser.). (Illus.). 24p. (J). (gr. 1 up). lib. bdg. 18.60 (978-0-7565-0170-9(9)) Compass Point Bks.

—Wolves Have Pups. 2002. (Animals & Their Young Ser.). (Illus.). 24p. (J). (gr. 1 up). lib. bdg. 18.60 (978-0-7565-0171-6(7)) Compass Point Bks.

Jansen, Curt, et al. Badger & Her Babies. Date not set. (Wildlife Adventure Ser.: Vol. 2). (Orig.). (J). (gr. k-4). pap. (978-0-9614904-2-3(X)) Adventure Productions, Inc.

—Bobcat & Her Babies. Date not set. (Wildlife Adventure Ser.: Vol. 3). (Orig.). (J). (gr. k-4). pap. (978-0-9614904-3-0(8)) Adventure Productions, Inc.

Johnson, Jinny. Busy Baby Animals, 8 bks. Ch'en-Ling, illus. Incl. Chimp. Murrell, Simon, photos by. lib. bdg. 19.33 (978-0-8368-2921-1(2)); Deer. lib. bdg. 19.33 (978-0-8368-2922-8(0)); Elephant. lib. bdg. 19.33 (978-0-8368-2923-5(9)); Fox. lib. bdg. 19.33 (978-0-8368-2924-2(7)); Koala. lib. bdg. 19.33 (978-0-8368-2925-9(5)); Lemur. Price, Susanna, photos by. lib. bdg. 19.33 (978-0-8368-2926-6(3)); Leopard. Price, Susanna, photos by. lib. bdg. 19.33 (978-0-8368-2927-3(1)); Tiger. Price, Susanna, photos by. lib. bdg. 19.33 (978-0-8368-2928-0(X)); 16p. (J). (ps up). 2001. (Illus.). Set lib. bdg. 154.64 (978-0-8368-2920-4(4)) Stevens, Gareth Inc.

—Chimp. 1999. (Wild Baby Animals Ser.). (Illus.). 16p. (ps-k). 4.99 (978-0-7681-0187-4(5) , McClanahan Bk.) Learning Horizons, Inc.

—Chimp. Ch'en-Ling, illus. Murrell, Simon, photos by. 2001. (Busy Baby Animals Ser.). 16p. (J). (ps up). lib. bdg. 19.33 (978-0-8368-2921-1(2)) Stevens, Gareth Inc.

—Deer. Ch'en-Ling, illus. 2001. (Busy Baby Animals Ser.). 16p. (J). (ps up). lib. bdg. 19.33 (978-0-8368-2922-8(0)) Stevens, Gareth Inc.

—Elephant. Ch'en-Ling, illus. 2001. (Busy Baby Animals Ser.). 16p. (J). (ps up). lib. bdg. 19.33 (978-0-8368-2923-5(9)) Stevens, Gareth Inc.

—Fox. Ch'en-Ling, illus. 2001. (Busy Baby Animals Ser.). 16p. (J). (ps up). lib. bdg. 19.33 (978-0-8368-2924-2(7)) Stevens, Gareth Inc.

—Koala. Ch'en-Ling, illus. 2001. (Busy Baby Animals Ser.). 16p. (J). (ps up). lib. bdg. 19.33 (978-0-8368-2925-9(5)) Stevens, Gareth Inc.

—Lemur. Ch'en-Ling, illus. Price, Susanna, photos by. 2001. (Busy Baby Animals Ser.). 16p. (J). (ps up). lib. bdg. 19.33 (978-0-8368-2926-6(3)) Stevens, Gareth Inc.

—Leopard. Ch'en-Ling, illus. Price, Susanna, photos by. 2001. (Busy Baby Animals Ser.). 16p. (J). (ps up). lib. bdg. 19.33 (978-0-8368-2927-3(1)) Stevens, Gareth Inc.

—Tiger. Ch'en-Ling, illus. Price, Susanna, photos by. 2001. (Busy Baby Animals Ser.). 16p. (J). (ps up). lib. bdg. 19.33 (978-0-8368-2928-0(X)) Stevens, Gareth Inc.

Johnson, Marion. Caillou - At the Zoo. Johnson, Marion et al, illus. rev. ed. 2005. (Playtime Ser.). 24p. (J). (ps-1). pap. 4.95 (978-2-89450-384-3(9)) Chouette Publishing CAN. *Dist:* Independent Pubs. Group.

Kajikawa, Kimiko. Close to You: Baby Animals & Their Parents. 2008. 32p. (J). 16.95 ***(978-0-8050-8123-7(2))*** Holt, Henry & Co.

Keating, Brian. Going Wild: Amazing Animal Adventures Around the World. 2004. (Illus.). 48p. pap. (978-1-894856-12-6(0)) Fifth Hse. Pubs.

Kingfisher Editors, ed. Animal Babies Around the House. 2005. (Animal Babies Ser.). (Illus.). 24p. (J). (ps-k). bds. 6.95 (978-0-7534-5840-2(3) , Kingfisher) Houghton Mifflin Co. Trade & Reference Div.

—Animal Babies in Grasslands. 2006. (Animal Babies Ser.). 24p. (J). (ps-k). bds. 6.95 (978-0-7534-5943-0(4) , Kingfisher) Houghton Mifflin Co. Trade & Reference Div.

—Animal Babies in Polar Lands. 2006. (Animal Babies Ser.). 24p. (J). (ps-k). bds. 6.95 (978-0-7534-5944-7(2) , Kingfisher) Houghton Mifflin Co. Trade & Reference Div.

—Animal Babies in Towns & Cities. 2005. (Animal Babies Ser.). (Illus.). 24p. (J). (ps-k). bds. 6.95 (978-0-7534-5841-9(1) , Kingfisher) Houghton Mifflin Co. Trade & Reference Div.

—Animal Babies on Mountains. 2005. (Animal Babies Ser.). (Illus.). 24p. (J). (ps-k). bds. 6.95 (978-0-7534-5839-6(X) , Kingfisher) Houghton Mifflin Co. Trade & Reference Div.

Know it All Safari Babies with CD. 2007. (J). pap. 5.99 ***(978-1-59545-167-5(6))*** Learning Horizons, Inc.

Knox, Barbara. Baby Animals 1, 2, 3: A Counting Book of Animal Offspring. 2003. (A+ Counting Books). (Illus.). 32p. (J). (gr. k-1). lib. bdg. 22.60 (978-0-7368-1675-5(5) , Aplus Bks.) Capstone Pr., Inc.

Kunhardt, Katharine. Let's Count the Puppies. 2004. (Illus.). 32p. (J). (ps-1). 13.89 (978-0-06-054337-2(X)) HarperCollins Pubs.

Lach, William. Baby Animals. 2008. (J). ***(978-1-58839-182-7(5)*** , Abrams Bks. for Young Readers) Abrams, Harry N. , Inc.

Lach, William & Metropolitan Museum of Art Staff. Baby Animals. 2008. 48p. (J). 14.95 ***(978-0-8109-9457-7(7)*** , Abrams Bks. for Young Readers) Abrams, Harry N. , Inc.

Lambilly-Bresson, Elisabeth de. Baby Animals. 2006. (Illus.). 14p. (J). lib. bdg. ***(978-0-8368-7835-6(3))*** Stevens, Gareth Inc.

Lang, Aubrey. The Adventures of Baby Bear. Lynch, Wayne, photos by. 2001. (Nature Babies Ser.). (Illus.). 36p. (gr. k-3). pap. 5.95 (978-1-894004-71-8(X)) Fifth Hse. Pubs. CAN. *Dist:* Fitzhenry & Whiteside, Ltd.

—The Adventures of Baby Bear. Lynch, Wayne, photos by. 2001. (Nature Babies Ser.). (Illus.). 36p. (J). (gr. k-3). (978-1-55041-670-1(7)) Fitzhenry & Whiteside, Ltd.

—Baby Elephant. Lynch, Wayne, photos by. 2002. (Nature Babies Ser.). (Illus.). 36p. (J). (gr. k-3). (978-1-55041-715-9(0)) Fitzhenry & Whiteside, Ltd.

—Baby Fox. Lynch, Wayne, photos by. 2002. (Nature Babies Ser.). (Illus.). 36p. (J). (gr. k-3). (978-1-55041-688-6(X)) Fitzhenry & Whiteside, Ltd.

—Baby Grizzly. Lynch, Wayne, photos by. 2006. (Nature Babies Ser.). (Illus.). 36p. (J). (gr. k-3). pap. 6.95 (978-1-55041-579-7(4)) Fitzhenry & Whiteside, Ltd. CAN. *Dist:* F & W Pubns., Inc.

—Baby Lion. Lynch, Wayne, photos by. (Nature Babies Ser.). (Illus.). 36p. (J). (gr. k-3). 2003. pap. (978-1-55041-713-5(4)); 2002. (978-1-55041-711-1(8)) Fitzhenry & Whiteside, Ltd.

—Baby Penguin. Lynch, Wayne, photos by. (Nature Babies Ser.). (Illus.). 36p. (J). (gr. k-3). 2002. pap. (978-1-55041-693-0(6)); 2001. (978-1-55041-675-6(8)) Fitzhenry & Whiteside, Ltd.

—Baby Penguin. 2002. (gr. k-3). lib. bdg. 14.10 (978-0-613-62593-7(5)) Tandem Library Bks.

—Baby Seal. Lynch, Wayne, photos by. 2002. (Nature Babies Ser.). (Illus.). 36p. (J). (gr. k-3). (978-1-55041-685-5(5)) Fitzhenry & Whiteside, Ltd.

Lang, Aubrey & Lynch, Wayne. Baby Elephant. 2003. (Nature Babies Ser.). (Illus.). 36p. (J). (gr. k-3). pap. (978-1-55041-717-3(7)) Fitzhenry & Whiteside, Ltd.

Lewellyn, Claire. Crocodile. Mendez, Simon, illus. 2004. (Starting Life Ser.). 24p. (ps-3). 16.95 (978-1-55971-900-1(1) , NorthWord Bks. for Young Readers) T&N Children's Publishing.

Ling, Mary, ed. Chick. 2001. (See How They Grow Ser.). (Illus.). 24p. (J). (ps-3). pap. 5.99 (978-0-7894-7654-8(1)) Dorling Kindersley Publishing, Inc.

—The Kitten. 2001. (See How They Grow Ser.). (Illus.). 24p. (J). (ps-3). pap. 4.99 (978-0-7894-7657-9(6)) Dorling Kindersley Publishing, Inc.

Little & Large Sticker Activity - Baby Animals. 2006. (J). 3.99 (978-1-933581-29-3(8)) Byeway Bks.

Livesey, Claire. Our Polliwogs. Wordsworth, Viki, illus. 1999. (Books for Young Learners). 12p. (J). (gr. k-2). pap. 5.00 (978-1-57274-276-5(3)) Owen, Richard C. Pubs., Inc.

Llewellyn, Claire. Going for a Ride. 2000. (Cambridge Reading Ser.). (Illus.). 10p. pap. 5.00 (978-0-521-77460-4(8)) Cambridge Univ. Pr.

—How Animals Grow. 2006. (Illus.). 24p. (J). (978-1-59771-022-0(9)) Sea-To-Sea Pubns.

Longnecker, Theresa. Who Grows Up in the Desert? A Book about Desert Animals & Their Offspring. Carpenter, Melissa, illus. 2004. (Who Grows Up Here? Ser.). 24p. (C). (gr. k-4). 21.26 (978-1-4048-0024-3(7)) Picture Window Bks.

—Who Grows Up in the Forest? A Book about Forest Animals & Their Offspring. Carpenter, Melissa, illus. 2004. (Who Grows Up Here? Ser.). 24p. (C). (gr. k-4). 21.26 (978-1-4048-0025-0(5)) Picture Window Bks.

—Who Grows Up in the Ocean? A Book about Ocean Animals & Their Offspring. Carpenter, Melissa, illus. 2004. (Who Grows Up Here? Ser.). 24p. (C). (gr. k-4). 21.26 (978-1-4048-0026-7(3)) Picture Window Bks.

—Who Grows Up in the Rain Forest? A Book about Rain Forest Animals & Their Offspring. Carpenter, Melissa, illus. 2004. (Who Grows Up Here? Ser.). 24p. (C). (gr. k-4). 21.26 (978-1-4048-0027-4(1)) Picture Window Bks.

—Who Grows Up on the Farm? A Book about Farm Animals & Their Offspring. Carpenter, Melissa, illus. 2004. (Who Grows Up Here? Ser.). 24p. (C). (gr. k-4). 21.26 (978-1-4048-0029-8(8)) Picture Window Bks.

Lorenz Books Staff & Tuxworth, Nicola. Baby Animals. 2000. (Very First Picture Bks.). (Illus.). 12p. 4.95 (978-0-7548-0061-3(X) , Lorenz Bks.) Anness Publishing, Inc.

Love, Pamela. A Moose's Morning. Sochor, Lesia, illus. 2007. 32p. (gr. k-3). 15.95 (978-0-89272-733-9(0)) Down East Bks.

Lynch, Wayne, illus. Baby Fox. (Nature Babies Ser.). 32p. (J). (gr. k-3). pap. (978-1-55041-724-1(X)) Fitzhenry & Whiteside, Ltd.

Lynch, Wayne, photos by. Baby Seal. (Nature Babies Ser.). (Illus.). 36p. (J). (gr. k-3). pap. (978-1-55041-726-5(6)) Fitzhenry & Whiteside, Ltd.

MacKall, Dandi Daley. Animal Babies. Newton, Jill, illus. 2003. (Imagination Ser.). 12p. 6.99 (978-0-8066-4385-4(4) , Augsburg Bks.) Augsburg Fortress, Pubs.

Markle, Sandra. Creepy, Crawly Baby Bugs. 2003. (Illus.). 32p. (J). pap. 6.95 (978-0-8027-7659-4(0)) Walker & Co.

—Really Wild Animals: Sea Babies. 2002. (Illus.). 30p. (J). (978-0-439-33489-1(6)) Scholastic, Inc.

—Wolves. (Animal Predators Ser.). (J). 2005. 40p. (gr. 4-6). pap. 7.95 (978-1-57505-748-4(4)); 2004. (Illus.). 40p. (gr. 3-6). lib. bdg. 25.26 (978-1-57505-732-3(8)); 2003. lib. bdg. (978-0-8225-5107-2(1) , Lerner Pubns.) Lerner Publishing Group.

—Wolves. 2001. (Growing up Wild Ser.). (Illus.). 32p. (J). (ps-3). 16.00 (978-0-689-81886-8(6) , Atheneum) Simon & Schuster Children's Publishing.

Maze, Stephanie, ed. Tender Moments in the Wild: Animals & Their Babies. (Moments in the Wild Ser.). (Illus.). (J). 2006. 36p. pap. 8.00 (978-0-9769542-0-0(6)); 2001. 32p. 15.00 (978-0-9707768-0-8(2)) Moonstone Pr.

McCurry, Kristen. City Babies. 2007. 22p. (J). ***(978-1-55971-981-0(8)*** , NorthWord Bks. for Young Readers) T&N Children's Publishing.

McCurry, Kristen & Jackson, Aimee. Safari Babies. NorthWord Books for Young Readers Staff, ed. 2004. (Illus.). 22p. (J). (ps up). bds. 5.95 (978-1-55971-899-8(4) , NorthWord Bks. for Young Readers) T&N Children's Publishing.

McDonald, Ronald L. Over in the Meadow: A Counting Rhyme. Voce, Louise, ed. Voce, Louise, illus. 1999. (Reading Together Ser.). 32p. (J). (ps). pap. 3.99 (978-0-7636-0852-1(1)) Candlewick Pr.

McLeod, Beatrice. Growing Up. 2000. (Nature Undercover Ser.). (Illus.). 40p. (J). (gr. 5-8). 23.70 (978-1-56711-501-7(2) , Blackbirch Pr., Inc.) Thomson Gale.

Michels, Dia L. If My Mom Were A Platypus- Hebrew Language Edition. 2006. Orig. Title: #1488;#1501; #1488;#1502;#1497; #1492;#1497;#1514;#1492; #1508;#1500;#1496;#1497;#1508;#1493;#1505;. (HEB.). 64p. (J). 16.95 (978-0-9678020-8-4(3)) Science, Naturally!.

—If My Mom Were A Platypus- Hebrew Language Edition. Barthelmes, Andrew, illus. 2006. Orig. Title: #1488;#1501; #1488;#1502;#1497; #1492;#1497;#1514;#1492; #1508;#1500;#1496;#1497;#1508;#1493;#1505;. 64p. (J). 29.95 (978-0-9678020-9-1(1)) Science, Naturally!.

Millard, Anne. Kitten Games. 2001. (Soft-to-Touch Bk.). (Illus.). 18p. (J). (ps-3). bds. 4.99 (978-0-7894-7400-1(X)) Dorling Kindersley Publishing, Inc.

—Perritos Juguetones/Playful Puppies. 2005. (Soft-to-touch Bks.). 16p. (J). bds. 4.99 (978-0-7566-1201-6(2)) Dorling Kindersley Publishing, Inc.

Mitchell, Melanie S. Ducks. (First Step Nonfiction Ser.). (Illus.). (gr. k-2). 2005. 24p. lib. bdg. 17.27 (978-0-8225-4602-3(7)); 2002. 23p. (J). pap. 3.95 (978-0-8225-4603-0(5) , Lerner Pubns.) Lerner Publishing Group.

—Rabbits. (First Step Nonfiction Ser.). (Illus.). (gr. k-2). 2005. 24p. lib. bdg. 17.27 (978-0-8225-4604-7(3)); 2003. 23p. (J). pap. 5.95 (978-0-8225-4605-4(1) , Lerner Pubns.) Lerner Publishing Group.

—Snakes. (First Step Nonfiction Ser.). (Illus.). (gr. k-2). 2005. 24p. lib. bdg. 17.27 (978-0-8225-4606-1(X)); 2003. 23p. (J). pap. 5.95 (978-0-8225-4607-8(8) , Lerner Pubns.) Lerner Publishing Group.

Moon, Rising. Baby Animals of the Southwest. 2007. (J). bds. 5.95 (*978-0-87358-924-6(6) , Rising Moon Bks. for Young Readers) Northland Publishing.

Moreton, Daniel. Animal Babies: A Counting Book. 1998. (Science Emergent Readers Ser.). 32p. (J). pap. 2.50 (978-0-590-76164-2(1)) Scholastic, Inc.

—Animal Babies: A Counting Book. 1998. lib. bdg. 10.10 (978-0-613-89009-0(4)) Tandem Library Bks.

Murphy, Chuck, intro. Animal Babies A to Z. 2007. 8p. 16.95 (*978-1-58117-652-0(X) , Intervisual/Piggy Toes) Dalmatian Pr.

Nagda, Ann Whitehead & Bickel, Cindy. Chimp Math: Learning about Time from a Baby Chimpanzee. rev. ed. 2002. (Illus.). 32p. (J). (gr. 2-5). 17.95 (978-0-8050-6674-6(8) , Holt, Henry & Co. Bks. For Young Readers) Holt, Henry & Co.

Nagda, Ann Whitehead & Bickel, Cindy. Polar Bear Math: Learning about Fractions from Klondike & Snow. 2007. (Illus.). 32p. (J). pap. 7.99 (*978-0-312-37749-6(5)) Square Fish.

Nault, Jennifer. Project Polar Bear. 2003. (gr. 3-6). lib. bdg. 15.25 (978-0-613-79814-3(7)) Tandem Library Bks.

—Project Polar Bear. Kissock, Heather & Marshall, Diana, eds. 2003. (Zoo Life Ser.). (Illus.). 24p. (J). pap. 6.95 (978-1-59036-060-6(5)) Weigl Pubs., Inc.

—Project Polar Bear. 2002. (Zoo Babies Ser.). (Illus.). 24p. (J). lib. bdg. 15.15 (978-1-59036-014-9(1)) Weigl Pubs., Inc.

Nelson, Robin. From Egg to Chicken. 2003. (J). pap. 4.95 (978-0-8225-4733-4(3) , Lerner Pubns.); (Illus.). 24p. lib. bdg. 18.60 (978-0-8225-4662-7(0)) Lerner Publishing Group.

—From Foal to Horse. 2003. (Start to Finish Ser.). (Illus.). 24p. (J). (gr. k-2). lib. bdg. 18.60 (978-0-8225-0941-7(5)) Lerner Publishing Group.

Neye, Emily. All about Cats & Kittens. 1999. (gr. k-3). lib. bdg. 11.25 (978-0-613-21082-9(4)) Tandem Library Bks.

Nichols, Catherine. Going Places. 2001. (We Can Read about Nature! Ser.). (Illus.). 32p. (J). (gr. 1-2). lib. bdg. 21.36 (978-0-7614-1252-6(2) , Benchmark Bks.) Cavendish, Marshall Corp.

Nicholson, Sue. Animal Babies in Deserts. 2006. (Animal Babies Ser.). (Illus.). 24p. (J). (ps-k). bds. 6.95 (978-0-7534-5942-3(6) , Kingfisher) Houghton Mifflin Co. Trade & Reference Div.

Norma Staff, ed. Animales Bebe. 2005. 14p. (978-958-04-8067-9(2)) Norma S.A.

NorthWord Books for Young Readers Editors, contrib. by. Polar Babies. 2003. (Animal Babies Ser.). (Illus.). 22p. (J). (ps up). bds. 5.95 (978-1-55971-875-2(7) , NorthWord Bks. for Young Readers) T&N Children's Publishing.

—Prairie Babies. 2003. (Animal Babies Ser.). (Illus.). 22p. (J). (ps up). bds. 5.95 (978-1-55971-873-8(0) , NorthWord Bks. for Young Readers) T&N Children's Publishing.

Otto, Carolyn B. Our Puppies Are Growing. Morgan, Mary, illus. 1998. (Let's-Read-and-Find-Out Science Ser.). 32p. (J). (ps-1). 15.89 (978-0-06-027272-2(4)) HarperCollins Pubs.

Otto, Crolyn. Our Puppies Are Growing. Morgan, Mary, illus. 1998. (Let's-Read-and-Find-Out Science Ser.). 32p. (J). (ps-1). pap. 4.95 (978-0-06-445169-7(0)) HarperCollins Pubs.

Pandas Have Cubs. (Animals & Their Young Ser.). 24p. (J). 7.95 (978-0-7565-1244-6(1)) Compass Point Bks.

Parker, Helen. Baby Animals. 2006. (Lift Stick & Learn Ser.). (Illus.). 12p. (J). (ps-k). pap. 4.95 (978-1-84610-280-6(4)) Make Believe Ideas GBR. *Dist:* Ingram Pub. Services.

Petty, Kate. Bears. 2004. (J). lib. bdg. 22.80 (978-1-932799-40-8(0)) Stargazer Bks.

Piggy Toes Press Staff. Fun with Numbers, One to Ten: A Baby Jungle Animals Board Book Set, 10 bks., Set. 2000. (Illus.). (J). (ps-k). bds., act. bk. ed. 16.95 (978-1-58117-080-1(7) , Intervisual/Piggy Toes) Dalmatian Pr.

Pigs Have Piglets. (Animals & Their Young Ser.). 24p. (J). 7.95 (978-0-7565-1245-3(X)) Compass Point Bks.

Pingry, Patricia A. Baby Giraffe. 2003. (San Diego Zoo Animal Library: Vol. 4). (Illus.). 26p. (J). bds. 6.95 (978-0-8249-6529-7(9)) Ideals Pubns.

—Baby Koala. 2003. (San Diego Zoo Animal Library: Vol. 3). (Illus.). 24p. (J). bds. 6.95 (978-0-8249-6528-0(0)) Ideals Pubns.

—Baby Zebra. Sharp, Chris, illus. 2004. (San Diego Zoo Animal Library: Vol. 6). 26p. (J). bds. 6.95 (978-0-8249-6556-3(6)) Ideals Pubns.

Pingry, Patricia A. & Sharp, Chris. Baby Chimpanzee. 2003. (San Diego Zoo Animal Library: Vol. 2). (Illus.). 24p. (J). bds. 6.95 (978-0-8249-6530-3(2)) Ideals Pubns.

—Baby Tiger. 2003. (San Diego Zoo Animal Library). (Illus.). 24p. (J). bds. 6.95 (978-0-8249-6527-3(2)) Ideals Pubns.

Pipe, Jim. Baby Animals. 2006. (Read & Play Ser.). (Illus.). 24p. (J). (ps-k). lib. bdg. 22.80 (978-1-59604-111-0(0)) Stargazer Bks.

Pollack, Pam. Bear Cub. 2001. (gr. k-3). lib. bdg. 11.80 (978-0-613-64395-5(X)) Tandem Library Bks.

Pollack, Pam & Belviso, Meg. Bear Cub. Twinem, Neecy, illus. 2001. (All Aboard Reading Ser.). 48p. (J). pap. 3.99 (978-0-448-42523-8(8) , Grosset & Dunlap) Penguin Group (USA) Inc.

Posada, Mia. Guess What Is Growing Inside This Egg. 2007. 32p. (J). (gr. k-4). spiral bd. 15.95 (978-0-8225-6192-7(1) , Millbrook Pr.) Lerner Publishing Group.

Powell, Jillian. From Calf to Cow. 2001. (How Do They Grow? Ser.). (Illus.). 32p. (J). lib. bdg. 25.69 (978-0-7398-4426-7(1)) Raintree.

—From Kitten to Cat. 2001. (How Do They Grow? Ser.). (Illus.). 32p. (J). lib. bdg. 25.69 (978-0-7398-4424-3(5)) Raintree.

—From Lamb to Sheep. 2001. (How Do They Grow? Ser.). (Illus.). 32p. (J). lib. bdg. 25.69 (978-0-7398-4425-0(3)) Raintree.

—From Piglet to Pig. 2000. (Illus.). 32p. (J). lib. bdg. 25.69 (978-0-7398-4428-1(8)) Raintree.

—From Puppy to Dog. 2001. (How Do They Grow? Ser.). (Illus.). 32p. (J). lib. bdg. 25.69 (978-0-7398-4423-6(7)) Raintree.

Powzyk, Joyce. A Little Lemur Named Mew. 2003. (Illus.). 32p. lib. bdg. 22.90 (978-0-7613-2665-6(0) , Millbrook Pr.) Lerner Publishing Group.

Priddy, Roger. Bright Baby Animals. 2006. 26p. (J). bds. 8.95 (978-0-312-49781-1(4) , Priddy Bks.) St. Martin's Pr.

—Bright Baby Touch & Feel Baby Animals. 2006. 10p. (J). bds. 4.95 (978-0-312-49858-0(6) , Priddy Bks.) St. Martin's Pr.

Priddy, Roger. Happy Baby Animals. (J). 2007. bds. 3.95 (*978-0-312-49956-3(6)); 2001. (Illus.). 24p. bds. 5.95 (978-0-312-49020-1(8)) St. Martin's Pr. (Priddy Bks.).

Rabbits Have Bunnies. (Animals & Their Young Ser.). 24p. (J). 7.95 (978-0-7565-1246-0(8)) Compass Point Bks.

Rappoport, Bernice. Baby Animals. Cassels, Jean, illus. 2004. (Treasure Tree Ser.). 32p. (J). (978-0-7166-1615-3(7)) World Bk., Inc.

Renne. Young Animals & Their Parents. Renne, illus. 2000. (Animals Up Close Ser.). (Illus.). 38p. (J). (gr. 3 up). lib. bdg. 24.67 (978-0-8368-2717-0(1)) Stevens, Gareth Inc.

Rennert, Violette. Little Lions. 2005. (Born to Be Wild Ser.). (Illus.). 24p. (J). (ps). lib. bdg. 22.00 (978-0-8368-4737-6(7)) Stevens, Gareth Inc.

Reproducing. 2001. (Animal Marvels Ser.). (Illus.). 32p. (J). (gr. 3 up). lib. bdg. 24.67 (978-0-8368-2932-7(8)) Stevens, Gareth Inc.

Richardson, Nan. Wild Babies. 2006. (Illus.). 80p. 16.95 (978-1-884167-51-5(9)) Umbrage Editions.

Ring, Susan. Polar Babies. McCue, Lisa, illus. 2000. (Step into Reading Ser.). (J). (978-0-606-19904-9(7)) Tandem Library Bks.

—Project Elephant. 2003. (gr. 3-6). lib. bdg. 15.25 (978-0-613-79813-6(9)) Tandem Library Bks.

—Project Elephant. Kissock, Heather & Marshall, Diana, eds. 2003. (Zoo Life Ser.). 24p. (J). pap. 6.95 (978-1-59036-056-9(7)) Weigl Pubs., Inc.

—Project Elephant. 2002. (Zoo Babies Ser.). (Illus.). 24p. (J). lib. bdg. 15.15 (978-1-59036-016-3(8)) Weigl Pubs., Inc.

—Project Hippopotomus. 2002. (Zoo Babies Ser.). (Illus.). 24p. (J). lib. bdg. 15.15 (978-1-59036-013-2(3)) Weigl Pubs., Inc.

—Project Orangutan. 2003. (gr. 3-6). lib. bdg. 15.25 (978-0-613-79812-9(0)) Tandem Library Bks.

—Project Orangutan. Marshall, Diana & Nault, Jennifer, eds. 2003. (Zoo Life Ser.). (Illus.). 24p. (J). pap. 6.95 (978-1-59036-058-3(3)) Weigl Pubs., Inc.

—Project Orangutan. 2002. (Zoo Babies Ser.). (Illus.). 24p. (J). lib. bdg. 15.15 (978-1-59036-017-0(6)) Weigl Pubs., Inc.

—Project Otter. 2003. (gr. 3-6). lib. bdg. 15.25 (978-0-613-79818-1(X)) Tandem Library Bks.

—Project Otter. Kissock, Heather & Marshall, Diana, eds. 2003. (Zoo Life Ser.). (Illus.). 24p. (J). pap. 6.95 (978-1-59036-059-0(1)) Weigl Pubs., Inc.

—Project Otter. 2002. (Zoo Life Ser.). (Illus.). 24p. (J). lib. bdg. 22.80 (978-1-59036-018-7(4)) Weigl Pubs., Inc.

—Project Tiger. Marshall, Diana & Nault, Jennifer, eds. 2003. (Zoo Life Ser.). (Illus.). 24p. (J). pap. 6.95 (978-1-59036-061-3(3)) Weigl Pubs., Inc.

—Project Tiger. 2002. (Zoo Babies Ser.). (Illus.). 24p. (J). lib. bdg. 15.15 (978-1-59036-015-6(X)) Weigl Pubs., Inc.

Roche, Hannah. Have You Ever Seen a Chicken Hatch? 1998. (Lifecycle Spirals Ser.). (Illus.). 16p. (J). (ps-1). spiral bd. (978-1-84089-004-4(5) , 868221Q, Zero to Ten, Limited) Evans Publishing Group.

Royston. Baby Animals Eye Openers. 1998. (J). 7.95 (978-0-87628-160-4(9)) Ctr. for Applied Research in Education, The.

Royston, Angela. Chick. 2004. (J). lib. bdg. 27.10 (978-1-59389-162-6(8)) Chrysalis Education.

—Chick. 2001. (J). (978-0-606-22322-5(3)) Tandem Library Bks.

—The Kitten. 2001. (978-0-606-22325-6(8)) Tandem Library Bks.

—Kitten. 2004. (J). lib. bdg. 27.10 (978-1-59389-158-9(X)) Chrysalis Education.

—Lamb. 2004. (J). lib. bdg. 27.10 (978-1-59389-161-9(X)) Chrysalis Education.

—Puppy. 2004. (J). lib. bdg. 27.10 (978-1-59389-159-6(8)) Chrysalis Education.

—Rabbit. 2004. (J). lib. bdg. 27.10 (978-1-59389-160-2(1)) Chrysalis Education.

Ruurs, Margriet. Wild Babies. Kiss, Andrew, illus. 2003. 32p. (J). (ps-3). 14.95 (978-0-88776-627-5(7)) Tundra Bks., Inc./Livres Toundra, Inc. CAN. *Dist:* Random Hse., Inc.

Ryan, Pam Muñoz. A Pinky Is a Baby Mouse: And Other Baby Animal Names. 1999. (978-0-606-16665-2(3)) Tandem Library Bks.

Safari Babies Know it All. 2005. (J). pap. 2.79 (*978-1-59545-004-3(1)) Learning Horizons, Inc.

Schindel, John. Busy Doggies. Sparks, Beverly, photos by. 2004. (Illus.). 20p. (J). bds. 6.95 (978-1-58246-090-1(6) , Tricycle Pr.) Ten Speed Pr.

Schmidt, Dennis & Schmidt, Esther. Baby Wild Animals. 2007. (Illus.). 48p. pap. (*978-1-55153-254-7(9)) Altitude Publishing Canada Ltd.

Schofield, Jennifer. Animal Babies in Grasslands. 2004. (Animal Babies Ser.). (Illus.). 32p. (J). (ps-k). 7.95 (978-0-7534-5789-4(X) , Kingfisher) Houghton Mifflin Co. Trade & Reference Div.

—Animal Babies in Polar Lands. 2004. (Animal Babies Ser.). (Illus.). 32p. (J). (ps-k). 7.95 (978-0-7534-5755-9(5) , Kingfisher) Houghton Mifflin Co. Trade & Reference Div.

—Animal Babies in Ponds & Rivers. 2004. (Animal Babies Ser.). (Illus.). 32p. (J). (ps-k). 7.95 (978-0-7534-5790-0(3) , Kingfisher) Houghton Mifflin Co. Trade & Reference Div.

—Animal Babies in Rain Forests. 2004. (Animal Babies Ser.). (Illus.). 32p. (J). (ps-k). 7.95 (978-0-7534-5788-7(1) , Kingfisher) Houghton Mifflin Co. Trade & Reference Div.

Scholastic, Inc. Staff, contrib. by. Animal Babies. (Pictureback Ser.). (J). Random Hse. Children's Bks.

School Specialty Publishing. Baby Animals. 2004. (On-File Ser.). 4p. (J). (gr. k-k). ring bd. 4.99 (978-0-7424-2856-0(7) , Instructional Fair) Schaffer, Frank Pubns.

Schwartz, David M. Horse. Kuhn, Dwight, photos by. 2001. (Springboards into Science Ser.). (Illus.). 24p. (J). (gr. 1 up). lib. bdg. 20.67 (978-0-8368-2974-7(3)) Stevens, Gareth Inc.

Sesame Street Animals Toddler Time. 2007. (J). pap. 2.95 (*978-1-59545-144-6(7)) Learning Horizons, Inc.

Shaw, Marjorie B. & Wexo, John Bonnett. Animal Babies. 2001. (Zoobooks Ser.). (Illus.). 18p. (YA). (gr. 6-12). pap. 2.95 (978-1-888153-05-7(9)) Wildlife Education, Ltd.

Sheather, Allan. Neptune's Nursery. 2000. (J). (978-0-606-19331-3(6)) Tandem Library Bks.

Sheep Have Lambs. (Animals & Their Young Ser.). 24p. (J). 7.95 (978-0-7565-1247-7(6)) Compass Point Bks.

Sidman, Joyce & Swan, Susan. Just Us Two: Poems about Dads. 2003. (Single Titles Ser.: Vol. 3). 32p. pap. 7.95 (978-0-7613-1833-0(X) , Millbrook Pr.) Lerner Publishing Group.

Simon, Seymour. Baby Animals. 2002. (SeeMore Readers Ser.). (Illus.). 32p. (J). pap. 3.95 (978-1-58717-171-0(6) , SeaStar Bks.) Chronicle Bks. LLC.

—Baby Animals. 2002. (ps-2). lib. bdg. 11.80 (978-0-613-89899-7(0)) Tandem Library Bks.

—Wild Babies. 1998. (Illus.). 32p. (J). (gr. k-3). pap. 7.99 (978-0-06-446206-8(4) , Harper Trophy) HarperCollins Pubs.

—Wild Babies. 1998. (J). (978-0-606-13915-1(X)) Tandem Library Bks.

Sjonger, Rebecca & Kalman, Bobbie. Las Cachorros: Puppies. 2006. (Illus.). 32p. pap. (978-0-7787-8477-7(0)) Crabtree Publishing Co.

—Puppies. (Pet Care Ser.). (Illus.). 32p. (J). 2004. pap. (978-0-7787-1783-6(6)); 2003. (978-0-7787-1751-5(8)) Crabtree Publishing Co.

Smith, Alastair. Baby Animals. 2004. (Lift-the-Flap Learners Ser.). (SPA., Illus.). 16p. (J). (gr. 1 up). pap. 8.95 (978-0-7945-0133-4(8) , Usborne) EDC Publishing.

—Baby Animals Lift-the-Flap. Butler, John, illus. 2005. 16p. (J). (gr. 1 up). 11.95 (978-0-7945-0966-8(5) , Usborne) EDC Publishing.

Squire, Ann O. Animal Babies. 2001. (True Animal Bks.). (Illus.). 48p. (J). (gr. 3-5). 25.00 (978-0-516-22188-5(4) , Children's Pr.) Scholastic Library Publishing.

—Animal Babies. 2001. (gr. 3-6). lib. bdg. 15.25 (978-0-613-51610-5(9)) Tandem Library Bks.

Sterling Publishing Company Staff. Baby Animals. 1999. (Balloon Ser.). (Illus.). 6p. (ps-k). 2.95 (978-0-8069-1919-5(1)) Sterling Publishing Co., Inc.

Sterling Publishing Company Staff, ed. My Favorite Baby Animals. 2000. (Illus.). 16p. (J). (ps-k). 5.95 (978-0-8069-2671-1(6)) Sterling Publishing Co., Inc.

Stone, Lynn M. Chickens Have Chicks. 2000. (Animals & Their Young Ser.). (Illus.). 24p. (J). (gr. 1 up). lib. bdg. 18.60 (978-0-7565-0000-9(1)) Compass Point Bks.

—Cows Have Calves. 2000. (Animals & Their Young Ser.). (Illus.). 24p. (J). (gr. 1 up). lib. bdg. 18.60 (978-0-7565-0001-6(X)) Compass Point Bks.

—Horses Have Foals. 2000. (Animals & Their Young Ser.). (Illus.). 24p. (J). (gr. 1 up). lib. bdg. 18.60 (978-0-7565-0002-3(8)) Compass Point Bks.

—Pigs Have Piglets. 2000. (Animals & Their Young Ser.). (Illus.). 24p. (J). (gr. 1 up). lib. bdg. 18.60 (978-0-7565-0003-0(6)) Compass Point Bks.

—Rabbits Have Bunnies. 2000. (Animals & Their Young Ser.). (Illus.). 24p. (J). (gr. 1 up). lib. bdg. 18.60 (978-0-7565-0005-4(2)) Compass Point Bks.

—Sheep Have Lambs. 2000. (Animals & Their Young Ser.). (Illus.). 24p. (J). (gr. 1 up). lib. bdg. 18.60 (978-0-7565-0004-7(4)) Compass Point Bks.

Stonehouse, Bernard. Growing Up: Protected. Francis, John, illus. 2001. 48p. (J). pap. 6.95 (978-0-439-30531-0(4)) Scholastic, Inc.

—Growing Up: Strange Beginnings. Francis, John, illus. 2000. 48p. (J). pap. 6.95 (978-0-439-24959-1(7)) Scholastic, Inc.

Stradling, Jan. Animal Babies: Level H, 6 vols. (First Explorers Ser.). 24p. (gr. 1-2). 29.95 (978-0-7699-1443-5(8)) Shortland Pubns. (U. S. A.) Inc.

Swanson, Diane. Cheetah Cubs & Beetle Grubs: The Wacky Ways We Name Young Animals. Spencer, Mariko Ando, illus. 2007. 24p. (J). (gr. k-2). pap. 7.95 (*978-1-55451-083-2(X)); lib. bdg. 19.95 (*978-1-55451-084-9(8)) Annick Pr., Ltd. CAN. *Dist:* Firefly Bks., Ltd.

Sweeney, Diane & Reddy, Michelle. Dolphin Babies: Making a Splash. Smith, Jeff, photos by. 1998. (Illus.). 64p. (J). (gr. 3-7). pap. 14.95 (978-1-57098-194-4(9)) Rinehart, Roberts Pubs.

Swinburne, Stephen R. Safe, Warm, & Snug. Aruego, Jose & Dewey, Ariane, illus. 2002. 40p. (J). (ps-ps). pap., pap. 7.00 (978-0-15-216378-5(6) , Voyager Bks./Libros Viajeros) Harcourt Children's Bks.

—Safe, Warm, & Snug. 2002. (ps-2). lib. bdg. 14.15 (978-0-613-83227-4(2)) Tandem Library Bks.

Tagliaferro, Linda. Animal Offspring. Saunders-Smith, Gail, ed. (Pebble Plus Ser.). (Illus.). (J). (gr. k-1). lib. bdg. 199.30 (978-0-7368-2539-9(8)) Capstone Pr., Inc.

—Baboons & Their Infants. 2004. (Animal Offspring Ser.). (Illus.). 24p. (J). 13.95 (978-0-7368-2386-9(7) , Pebble Bks.) Capstone Pr., Inc.

—Bears & Their Cubs. 2004. (Animal Offspring Ser.). (Illus.). 24p. (J). 13.95 (978-0-7368-2387-6(5) , Pebble Bks.) Capstone Pr., Inc.

—Dogs & Their Puppies. 2004. (Animal Offspring Ser.). (Illus.). 24p. (J). 13.95 (978-0-7368-2388-3(3) , Pebble Bks.) Capstone Pr., Inc.

—Robins & Their Chicks. 2004. (Animal Offspring Ser.). (Illus.). 29p. (J). 13.95 (978-0-7368-2389-0(1) , Pebble Bks.) Capstone Pr., Inc.

Taylor, Bonnie Highsmith. Callie: A Great Gray Owl. 2000. (Cover-to-Cover Chapter Bks.). (Illus.). (J). 55p. pap. (978-0-7891-5272-5(X)); 56p. (gr. 1-4). lib. bdg. 16.95 (978-0-7807-9652-2(7)) Perfection Learning Corp.

Taylor, Geraldine. Baby Animals. 2003. (Baby Genius Ser.). (Illus.). 16p. (J). bds. 6.99 (978-0-7894-9882-3(0)) Dorling Kindersley Publishing, Inc.

Teora Staff. Baby Animals. 2007. 18p. pap. 5.95 (*978-1-59496-427-5(0)) Teora USA LLC.

Theodorou, Rod. Birds. 2007. (Illus.). 32p. (J). (*978-1-4034-9249-4(2)); (*978-1-4034-9242-5(5)) Heinemann Library.

—Fish. 2007. (Illus.). 32p. (J). (*978-1-4034-9250-0(6)); (*978-1-4034-9243-2(3)) Heinemann Library.

—Insects. 2007. (Illus.). 32p. (J). (*978-1-4034-9251-7(4)); (*978-1-4034-9244-9(1)) Heinemann Library.

—Mammals. 2007. (Illus.). 32p. (J). (*978-1-4034-9252-4(2)); (*978-1-4034-9245-6(X)) Heinemann Library.

—Reptiles. 2007. (Animal Babies Ser.). (Illus.). 32p. (J). (*978-1-4034-9253-1(0)) Heinemann Library.

Theodorou, Rod & Fraser, Alan. Reptiles. 2007. (Animal Babies Ser.). (Illus.). 32p. (J). (*978-1-4034-9246-3(8)) Heinemann Library.

Toft, Kim Michelle. Neptune's Nursery. 2000. (gr. k-3). lib. bdg. 15.25 (978-0-613-35189-8(4)) Tandem Library Bks.

Toft, Kim Michelle & Sheather, Allan. Neptune's Nursery. Toft, Kim Michelle, illus. 2000. (Illus.). 32p. (J). (ps-3). 16.95 (978-1-57091-391-4(9)); pap. 6.95 (978-1-57091-392-1(7)) Charlesbridge Publishing, Inc.

—Neptunes Nursery. Toft, Kim Michelle, illus. 1999. (Illus.). 32p. 19.95 (978-0-7022-3079-0(0)) Univ. of Queensland Pr. AUS. *Dist:* International Specialized Bk. Services.

Toms, Kate. Baby Animals. 2006. (Funny Faces Ser.). (Illus.). (J). (ps-k). per., bds. 9.95 (978-1-84610-118-2(2)) Make Believe Ideas GBR. *Dist:* Ingram Pub. Services.

Torres, Melissa, ed. Baby Animals. 2004. (Hands-On Learning Ser.). (Illus.). 12p. (J). 9.95 (978-0-439-63899-9(2) , Cartwheel Bks.) Scholastic, Inc.

Trumbauer, Lisa. The Life Cycle of a Cat. 2002. (Life Cycles Ser.). (Illus.). 24p. (J). (gr. k-1). lib. bdg. 15.93 (978-0-7368-1182-8(6) , Pebble Bks.) Capstone Pr., Inc.

—The Life Cycle of a Dog. 2002. (Life Cycles Ser.). (Illus.). 24p. (J). (gr. k-1). lib. bdg. 15.93 (978-0-7368-1184-2(2) , Pebble Bks.) Capstone Pr., Inc.

Tuxworth, Nicola. Baby Animals. 2001. (Very First Picture Bks.). (Illus.). 20p. 5.95 (978-0-7548-0938-8(2)) Anness Publishing GBR. *Dist:* National Bk. Network.

—Baby Animals: A Very First Picture Book. 1999. (Pictures & Words Ser.). (Illus.). 24p. (J). (ps up). lib. bdg. 22.00 (978-0-8368-2379-0(6)) Stevens, Gareth Inc.

Tuxworth, Nicole. Baby Animals. 2005. (Illus.). 12p. (ps). bds. 6.99 (978-0-7548-1334-7(7) , Lorenz Bks.) Anness Publishing GBR. *Dist:* National Bk. Network.

Vanasse, Deb. Alaska Animal Babies. Jecan, Gavriel, photos by. 2005. (Illus.). 32p. (J). (ps-7). pap., pap. 10.95 (978-1-57061-433-0(4)) Sasquatch Bks.

Vize, Dania. Lift, Stick & Learn Baby Animals. 2006. (Illus.). 24p. (J). (ps-k). pap. 4.95 (978-1-84610-032-1(1)) Make Believe Ideas GBR. *Dist:* Ingram Pub. Services.

Walker, Niki & Kalman, Bobbie. Kittens. (Pet Care Ser.). (Illus.). 32p. (J). 2004. pap. (978-0-7787-1782-9(8)); 2003. (978-0-7787-1750-8(X)) Crabtree Publishing Co.

Wallace, Karen. Duckling Days. 1999. (Eyewitness Readers). (Illus.). 32p. (J). (ps-4). 12.99 (978-0-7894-3995-6(6)); pap. 3.99 (978-0-7894-3994-9(8)) Dorling Kindersley Publishing, Inc.

—Duckling Days. 1999. (Eyewitness Readers Ser.). (J). 10.75 (978-0-606-16984-4(9)) Tandem Library Bks.

—Wild Baby Animals. 2000. (Eyewitness Readers). (Illus.). 32p. (J). (ps-1). pap. 3.99 (978-0-7894-5419-5(X)) Dorling Kindersley Publishing, Inc.

—Wild Baby Animals. 2000. (gr. k-3). lib. bdg. 11.80 (978-0-613-27577-4(2)) Tandem Library Bks.

Wallace, Karen & Dorling Kindersley Publishing Staff. Wild Baby Animals. 2000. (Eyewitness Readers). (Illus.). 32p. (J). (ps-1). 12.99 (978-0-7894-5420-1(3)) Dorling Kindersley Publishing, Inc.

Watt, Fiona. Animals Baby Jigsaw Book. Wells, Rachel, illus. 2006. 10p. (J). bds. 9.99 (978-0-7945-1227-9(5) , Usborne) EDC Publishing.

Watts, Barrie. Duck. 2002. 32p. (J). lib. bdg. 24.25 (978-1-58340-197-2(0)) Smart Apple Media.

—Mouse. 2004. (Illus.). 32p. (J). (ps-17). lib. bdg. 24.25 (978-1-58340-231-3(4)) Smart Apple Media.

—Snake. 2002. 32p. (J). lib. bdg. 24.25 (978-1-58340-200-9(4)) Smart Apple Media.

Wexo, John Bonnett. Baby Animals. 2001. (Zoobooks Ser.). (Illus.). 24p. (J). (gr. 1-6). 15.95 (978-1-888153-45-3(8)) Wildlife Education, Ltd.

Wildlife Education, Ltd. Staff. Animal Babies 1. 2003. (Zoobooks Ser.). (Illus.). 24p. (J). (gr. k-6). reprint ed. 15.95 (978-1-932396-07-2(1)) Wildlife Education, Ltd.

Wildlife Education, Ltd. Staff, contrib. by. Baby Animals, Set. 2002. (All about Animals Ser.). (Illus.). (J). (gr. k-6). 16.95 incl. VHS (978-1-888153-85-9(7)) Wildlife Education, Ltd.

Wildlife Education, Ltd. Staff & Elwood, Ann. Baby Animals, Vol. 2. Francis, John & Stuart, Walter, illus. (Zoobooks Ser.). (J). 2001. 24p. 15.95 (978-0-937934-75-3(5)); 1999. 18p. pap. 2.95 (978-0-937934-58-6(5)) Wildlife Education, Ltd.

Williams, Garth. Baby Animals. Williams, Garth, illus. 2004. (Little Golden Book Ser.). (Illus.). 24p. (J). (gr. k-k). 2.99 (978-0-375-82933-8(4) , Golden Bks.) Random Hse. Children's Bks.

Wolfe, Art, photos by. Northwest Animal Babies. 2006. (Illus.). 32p. (J). pap. 10.95 (978-1-57061-462-0(8)) Sasquatch Bks.

Wolves Have Pups. (Animals & Their Young Ser.). 24p. (J). 7.95 (978-0-7565-1248-4(4)) Compass Point Bks.

Wood, Jenny. I Wonder Why Kangaroos Have Pouches: And Other Questions about Baby Animals. 2003. (I Wonder Why Ser.). (Illus.). 32p. (J). (gr. k-3). pap. 6.95 (978-0-7534-5661-3(3) , Kingfisher) Houghton Mifflin Co. Trade & Reference Div.

Ziefert, Harriet. Woof-Woof. SAMi, illus. 2006. 12p. (J). bds. 8.95 (978-1-59354-148-4(1)) Blue Apple Bks.

Zoehfeld, Kathleen Weidner. Dinosaur Babies. Washburn, Lucia, illus. 1999. (Let's-Read-and-Find-Out Science Ser.). 40p. (J). (gr. k-4). 15.89 (978-0-06-027142-8(6)); pap. 4.99 (978-0-06-445162-8(3) , Harper Trophy) HarperCollins Pubs.

—Dinosaur Babies. 1999. (Let's-Read-and-Find-Out Science Ser.). (Illus.). 40p. (J). (gr. k-4). 15.95 (978-0-06-027141-1(8)) HarperCollins Pubs.

—Dinosaur Babies. 1999. (Let's-Read-and-Find-Out Ser.). 11.79 (978-0-606-17490-9(7)); lib. bdg. 13.00 (978-0-613-21433-9(1)) Tandem Library Bks.

ANIMALS—INFANCY—FICTION

Abercrombie, Barbara & Gustavson, Adam. Bad Dog, Dodger! 2002. (Illus.). 40p. (J). (gr. 1-5). 14.95 (978-0-689-83782-1(8) , McElderry, Margaret K.) Simon & Schuster Children's Publishing.

Adams, Pam. Elephant. 2005. (Illus.). 8p. (J). (ps). bds. 5.99 (978-1-904550-27-3(4)) Child's Play-International.

—Tiger. 2005. (Illus.). 8p. (J). (ps). bds. 5.99 (978-1-904550-28-0(2)) Child's Play-International.

Alderton, Sylvia. A Real Name for Puppy. McCartney, Michael David, illus. 2006. (J). (978-1-930566-58-3(1) , WestWind Pr.) Scott, D.&F. Publishing, Inc.

Andreae, Giles. Love Is a Handful of Honey. Cabban, Vanessa, illus. 1999. 32p. (J). (ps-2). 14.95 (978-1-888444-58-2(4)) Little Tiger Pr.

—Love Is a Handful of Honey. Cabban, Vanessa, illus. 2004. 32p. (J). (ps-k). 5.95 (978-1-58925-353-7(1)); tchr. ed. 15.95 (978-1-58925-003-1(6)) ME Media LLC. (tiger tales).

—Love Is a Handful of Honey. 2001. (ps-2). lib. bdg. 14.10 (978-0-613-57645-1(4)) Tandem Library Bks.

Animal babies - tummy Time. 2007. 8p. (J). 12.95 (*978-1-59764-293-4(2)) New Line Bks.

Apperley, Dawn. Hello Little Chicks. Apperley, Dawn, illus. 2000. (Hello Bks.). (Illus.). 12p. (J). bds. 3.95 (978-1-86233-181-5(2)) David & Charles Children's Bks. GBR. *Dist:* Sterling Publishing Co., Inc.

—Hello Little Ducklings. Apperley, Dawn, illus. 2000. (Hello Bks.). (Illus.). 12p. (J). bds. 3.95 (978-1-86233-176-1(6)) David & Charles Children's Bks. GBR. *Dist:* Sterling Publishing Co., Inc.

Arnosky, Jim. Babies in the Bayou. Arnosky, Jim, illus. 2007. (Illus.). 32p. (J). (ps-k). 16.99 (978-0-399-22653-3(2) , Putnam Juvenile) Penguin Group (USA) Inc.

—Little Lions. 1998. (Illus.). 1p. (J). (ps-1). 17.99 (978-0-399-22944-2(2) , Putnam Juvenile) Penguin Group (USA) Inc.

Baby Farm Animals Chunky Photo Book. 2006. (J). bds. 3.99 (978-1-934004-00-5(6)) Byeway Bks.

Baby Pets: Chunky photo Book. 2006. (J). bds. 3.99 (978-1-934004-01-2(4)) Byeway Bks.

Bachelet, Gilles. When the Silliest Cat Was Small. Bachelet, Gilles, illus. 2007. (FRE & ENG., Illus.). 32p. (J). (ps-3). 16.95 (*978-0-8109-9415-7(1) , Abrams Bks. for Young Readers) Abrams, Harry N., Inc.

Baddiel, Ivor & Jubb, Sophie. Cock-A-Doodle Quack Quack. Busby, Ailie, illus. 2007. 40p. (J). (ps-3). 15.99 (978-0-385-75104-9(4)); lib. bdg. 18.99 (978-0-385-75105-6(2)) Random Hse. Children's Bks. (Fickling, David Bks.).

Badgley, Catherine. Pippa's First Summer. Miljour, Bonnie, illus. (J). 2006. pap. 8.95 (978-1-58726-313-2(0)); 2005. 112p. 14.95 (978-1-58726-281-4(9)) Ann Arbor Media Group, LLC. (Mitten Pr.).

Barnes, Emma. The Thief of Bracken Farm. 2007. (J). lib. bdg. 16.95 (*978-1-59566-338-2(X)) QEB Publishing Inc.

Bauer, Marion Dane. One Brown Bunny. Bates, Ivan, illus. 2008. (J). (*978-0-439-68010-3(7) , Orchard Bks.) Scholastic, Inc.

Bauer, Marion Dane. Sleep, Little One, Sleep. Stammen, JoEllen McAllister, illus. 2002. 32p. (J). (ps). pap. 6.99 (978-0-689-85269-5(X) , Aladdin) Simon & Schuster Children's Publishing.

—Sleep, Little One, Sleep. 2002. (gr. k-3). lib. bdg. 15.30 (978-0-613-57328-3(5)) Tandem Library Bks.

Baurys, Florence. The Coyote Calf. Holmes, Gerald L., illus. 2000. 32p. (J). (ps-3). 16.95 (978-0-88415-236-1(7)) Lone Star Bks.

Baver, Marion Dane. Sleep, Little One, Sleep. Stammen, JoEllen McAllister, illus. 2005. 29p. (J). (gr. k-3). reprint ed. 16.00 (978-0-7567-9641-9(5)) DIANE Publishing Co.

Becker, John E. Mugambi's Journey. Clapsadle, Mark, illus. 2004. 32p. (J). 14.95 (978-0-7696-3167-7(3) , Gingham Dog Pr.) School Specialty Publishing.

Beckhorn, Susan Williams. Moose Eggs or, Why Moose Has Flat Antlers. Stevens, Helen, illus. 2007. 32p. (gr. k-3). 15.95 (*978-0-89272-689-9(X)) Down East Bks.

Berenstain, Stan & Berenstain, Jan. The Berenstain Bears' New Pup. Berenstain, Stan & Berenstain, Jan, illus. 2005. (Berenstain Bears Ser.). (Illus.). 32p. (J). (ps-3). lib. bdg. 11.19 (978-0-606-33614-7(1)) Tandem Library Bks.

Berenstain, Stan & Berenstain, Jan. Berenstain Bears' New Pup. Berenstain, Stan, illus. 2005. (Illus.). 32p. (J). lib. bdg. 13.85 (*978-1-4242-0816-6(5)) Fitzgerald Bks.

Bergstein, Rita. Your Own Big Bed. Hartung, Susan Kathleen, illus. 2008. 32p. (J). (ps). 15.99 (*978-0-670-06079-5(8) , Viking Juvenile) Penguin Group (USA) Inc.

Blackstone, Stella. Who Are You, Baby Kangaroo? Beaton, Clare, illus. 2004. 32p. (J). 14.99 (978-1-84148-217-0(X)) Barefoot Bks., Inc.

Blomgren, Jennifer. Where Do I Sleep? A Pacific Northwest Lullaby. Gabriel, Andrea, illus. 2002. 32p. (J). (ps-1). 16.95 (978-1-57061-258-9(7)) Sasquatch Bks.

Bonnell, Kris. Mother Animals. 2007. (J). 3.95 (*978-1-933727-49-3(7)) Reading Reading Bks., LLC.

Borgo, Deborah Colvin, illus. Baby Bunny. 1999. (J). (978-0-7853-3353-1(3)) Publications International, Ltd.

Bridwell, Norman. Clifford's First Snow Day. Bridwell, Norman, illus. 1998. (Clifford, the Big Red Dog Ser.). (Illus.). 32p. (J). (gr. k-2). 3.99 (978-0-590-03480-7(4) , Cartwheel Bks.) Scholastic, Inc.

—Clifford's Happy Mother's Day. 2001. (Clifford, the Big Red Dog Ser.). (Illus.). 32p. (J). (gr. k-2). 3.50 (978-0-439-22229-7(X)) Scholastic, Inc.

Brown, Jo. Hoppity Skip Little Chick. 2005. (Illus.). 32p. (J). 15.95 (978-1-58925-045-1(1) , tiger tales) ME Media LLC.

Bunting, Eve. The Baby Shower. Love, Judy, illus. 2007. 28p. (J). (ps-1). 15.95 (978-1-58089-139-4(X)) Charlesbridge Publishing, Inc.

—Little Bear's Little Boat. Carpenter, Nancy, illus. 2003. 32p. (J). (gr. k-ps). tchr. ed. 12.00 (978-0-395-97462-9(3) , Clarion Bks.) Houghton Mifflin Co. Trade & Reference Div.

Butler, John. Hush, Little Ones. Butler, John, illus. 2002. (Illus.). 32p. (J). (ps-k). 15.95 (978-1-56145-269-9(6)) Peachtree Pubs., Ltd.

—Pi-shu the Little Panda. 2001. (Illus.). 32p. (J). (gr. 2). 15.95 (978-1-56145-242-2(4) , Q30580) Peachtree Pubs., Ltd.

—Whose Baby Am I? 2004. 12p. (J). (ps-ps). bds. 4.99 (978-0-670-03696-7(X) , Viking Juvenile) Penguin Group (USA) Inc.

Buzzeo, Toni. Dawdle Duckling. Spengler, Margaret, illus. 2003. 32p. (J). (ps). 15.99 (978-0-8037-2731-1(3) , Dial) Penguin Group (USA) Inc.

—Dawdle Duckling. Spengler, Margaret, illus. 2005. 32p. (J). (ps-k). reprint ed. pap. 5.99 (978-0-14-240277-1(X) , Puffin) Penguin Group (USA) Inc.

Calmenson, Stephanie. Perfect Puppy. Yezerski, Thomas F., illus. 2001. 32p. (J). (gr. k-3). tchr. ed. 15.00 (978-0-618-01139-1(0) , Clarion Bks.) Houghton Mifflin Co. Trade & Reference Div.

Campbell, Rod. Baby's Fluffy Friends. 2003. (Illus.). 10p. (J). bds. 8.99 (978-0-333-74126-9(9)) Macmillan Publishers Ltd. GBR. *Dist:* Trafalgar Square Publishing.

Campoy, F. Isabel, et al. Celebra Kwanzaa con Botitas y Sus Gatitos. Docampo, Valeria, illus. 2006. (J). (978-1-59820-123-9(9)) Santillana USA Publishing Co., Inc.

—Celebrate Kwanzaa with Boots & Her Kittens. Docampo, Valeria, illus. 2006. 31p. (J). (978-1-59820-135-2(2)) Santillana USA Publishing Co., Inc.

Capucilli, Alyssa Satin. Biscuit & the Little Pup. Schories, Pat, illus. 2008. (My First I Can Read Bks.). 32p. (J). pap. 3.99 (*978-0-06-074172-3(4) , Harper Trophy) HarperCollins Pubs.

—Biscuit Wants to Play. Schories, Pat, illus. (My First I Can Read Bks.). 32p. (J). (gr. k). 2002. pap. 3.99 (978-0-06-444315-9(9) , Harper Trophy); 2001. 15.99 (978-0-06-028069-7(7)); 2001. lib. bdg. 15.89 (978-0-06-028070-3(0)) HarperCollins Pubs.

—Biscuit Wants to Play. 2002. (gr. k-3). lib. bdg. 11.80 (978-0-613-44508-5(2)) Tandem Library Bks.

—Biscuit's Valentine's Day. Schories, Pat, illus. 2000. (Biscuit Ser.). 20p. (J). (ps-1). 6.99 (978-0-694-01222-0(X) , Harper Festival) HarperCollins Pubs.

—Happy Easter, Biscuit! Schories, Pat, illus. 2000. (Biscuit Ser.). 20p. (J). (ps-1). pap. 6.99 (978-0-694-01223-7(8) , Harper Festival) HarperCollins Pubs.

—Happy Easter, Biscuit! 2000. (gr. k-3). lib. bdg. 15.25 (978-0-613-70589-9(0)) Tandem Library Bks.

—Happy Halloween, Biscuit! Schories, Pat, illus. 1999. (Biscuit Ser.). 20p. (J). (ps-1). pap. 6.99 (978-0-694-01220-6(3) , Harper Festival) HarperCollins Pubs.

—Happy Thanksgiving, Biscuit! Schories, Pat, illus. 1999. (Biscuit Ser.). 20p. (J). (ps-1). pap. 6.99 (978-0-694-01221-3(1) , Harper Festival) HarperCollins Pubs.

Carrick, Carol. Mothers Are Like That. Carrick, Paul, illus. 32p. (J). (gr. k-ps). 2007. pap. 5.95 (978-0-618-75241-6(2)); 2000. tchr. ed. 15.00 (978-0-395-88351-8(2)) Houghton Mifflin Co. Trade & Reference Div. (Clarion Bks.).

Catalanotto, Peter. Kitten Red, Yellow, Blue. Catalanotto, Peter, illus. 2005. (Illus.). 32p. (J). 15.95 (978-0-689-86562-6(7) , Atheneum/Richard Jackson Bks.) Simon & Schuster Children's Publishing.

Ceelen, Vicky. Baby! Baby! 2008. (Illus.). 24p. (J). (gr. k-ps). bds. 6.99 (*978-0-375-84207-8(1) , Random Hse. Bks. for Young Readers) Random Hse. Children's Bks.

Charlotte Latin School Staff. Ann & the Kitten. Sher, illus. 2001. 32p. (J). per. 4.95 (978-0-9707920-6-8(9)) Charlotte's Storybooks.

—Ann & the Puppy. Sher, illus. 2001. 32p. (J). per. 4.95 (978-0-9707920-2-0(6)) Charlotte's Storybooks.

Christian, Cheryl. Where's the Kitten?/Kote Ti Chat la Ye? Dwight, Laura, photos by. 2005. (CRP., Illus.). 12p. (J). (ps). per. 5.50 (978-1-59572-028-3(6)) Star Bright Bks., Inc.

—Where's the Puppy?/Kote Ti Toutous la Ye? Dwight, Laura, photos by. 2005. (CRP., Illus.). 12p. (J). (ps). per. 5.50 (978-1-59572-029-0(4)) Star Bright Bks., Inc.

The Christmas Star. 2005. (Illus.). 28p. (J). (ps-k). bds. 7.95 (978-0-8249-6620-1(1)) Ideals Pubns.

Clark, Dan. Puppies for Sale. 1999. (Illus.). 28p. (J). (gr. k-5). 6.99 (978-1-57759-262-4(X)) Dalmatian Pr.

Clements, Andrew. Naptime for Slippers. Bynum, Janie, illus. 2005. 32p. (J). (ps). 12.99 (978-0-525-47287-2(8) , Dutton Juvenile) Penguin Group (USA) Inc.

Clements, Andrew & Bynum, Janie. Slippers at Home. 2007. 32p. (J). pap. 5.99 (978-0-14-240781-3(X) , Puffin) Penguin Group (USA) Inc.

Cole, Babette. Lady Lupin's Book of Etiquette. 2002. (Illus.). 32p. (J). (gr. 1-5). 14.95 (978-1-56145-257-6(2)) Peachtree Pubs., Ltd.

Collicott, Sharleen. Mildred & Sam Go to School. Collicott, Sharleen, illus. (I Can Read Bks.). (J). 2008. 64p. 16.99 (978-0-06-058114-5(X) , Geringer, Laura Book); 2008. (Illus.). 64p. lib. bdg. 17.89 (978-0-06-058115-2(8) , Geringer, Laura Book); 2004. (Illus.). 48p. pap. 3.99 (978-0-06-000200-8(X) , Harper Trophy); 2003. (Illus.). 48p. 15.99 (978-0-06-026681-3(3)) HarperCollins Pubs.

—Mildred & Sam Go to School. 2004. (gr. k-3). lib. bdg. 11.80 (978-0-613-82531-3(4)) Tandem Library Bks.

Costello, Emily. Realm of the Panther: A Story of South Florida's Forests. 2005. (Habitat Ser.). (Illus.). 32p. (J). (gr. 1-4). 19.95 incl. audio (978-1-56899-849-7(X)) Soundprints.

—Realm of the Panther: A Story of South Florida's Forests. Siegrist, Wes, illus. (Habitat Ser.). (J). (gr. 1-4). 2005. 32p. 15.95 (978-1-56899-847-3(3)); 2005. 32p. pap. 6.95 (978-1-56899-848-0(1)); 2000. 36p. 26.95 (978-1-56899-851-0(1)) Soundprints.

Cotten, Cynthia. Some Babies Sleep. Tong, Paul, illus. 2007. 32p. (J). 12.99 (978-0-399-24030-0(6) , Philomel) Penguin Group (USA) Inc.

Cowell, Cressida. What Shall We Do with the Boo Hoo Baby? Godon, Ingrid, illus. 2004. 25p. (J). (TAM, CZE, VIE, SPA & GUJ.). (978-1-85269-791-4(1)); (TAM, CZE, VIE, SPA & GUJ.). (978-1-85269-254-4(5)); (TAM, CZE, VIE, SPA & GUJ.). (978-1-85269-255-1(3)); (TAM, CZE, VIE, SPA & GUJ.). (978-1-85269-256-8(1)); (TAM, CZE, VIE, SPA & GUJ.). (978-1-85269-258-2(8)); (TAM, CZE, VIE, SPA & GUJ.). (978-1-85269-270-4(7)); (TAM, CZE, VIE, SPA & GUJ.). (978-1-85269-271-1(5)); (CZE, TAM, VIE, SPA & GUJ.). (978-1-85269-272-8(3)); (TAM, CZE, VIE, SPA & GUJ.). (978-1-85269-273-5(1)); (TAM, CZE, VIE, SPA & GUJ.). (978-1-85269-274-2(X)); (TAM, CZE, SPA, VIE & GUJ.). (978-1-85269-276-6(6)); (TAM, CZE, VIE, SPA & GUJ.). (978-1-85269-679-5(6)); (TAM, CZE, VIE, SPA & GUJ.). (978-1-85269-683-2(4)); (TAM, CZE, VIE, SPA & GUJ.). (978-1-85269-790-7(3)); (TAM, CZE, VIE, SPA & GUJ.). (978-1-85269-792-1(X)); (TAM, CZE, VIE, SPA & GUJ.). (978-1-85269-793-8(8)); (TAM, CZE, VIE, SPA & GUJ.). (978-1-85269-794-5(6)); (TAM, CZE, VIE, SPA & GUJ.). (978-1-85269-795-2(4)); (TAM, CZE, VIE, SPA & GUJ.). (978-1-85269-796-9(2)); (TAM, CZE, VIE, SPA & GUJ.). (978-1-85269-799-0(7)); (TAM, CZE, VIE, SPA & GUJ.). (978-1-85269-862-1(4)) Mantra Publishing, Ltd.

Coxe, Molly. Big Egg. Coxe, Molly, illus. 2002. (Illus.). (J). 11.91 (978-0-7587-6028-9(0)) Book Wholesalers, Inc.

Coxon, Michele. Kitten's Adventure. Coxon, Michele, illus. 1998. (Happy Cat Bks.). (Illus.). 32p. (J). (ps-k). bds. 5.50 (978-1-887734-38-7(4)) Star Bright Bks., Inc.

Coxon, Michèle. Kitten's Adventure / As Aventuras do Gatinho (bilingual) Coxon, Michèle, illus. 2006. (POR, SPA & ENG., Illus.). 32p. (J). pap. 6.00 (978-1-59572-047-4(2)) Star Bright Bks., Inc.

—Kitten's Adventure / Las aventuras del Gatito. Coxon, Michèle, illus. 2006. (SPA., Illus.). 32p. (J). pap. (978-1-59572-048-1(0)) Star Bright Bks., Inc.

Coxon, Michele. Too Big! Coxon, Michele, illus. 2000. (Illus.). 20p. (ps-1). 13.95 (978-1-899248-64-3(1)) Happy Cat Bks. GBR. *Dist:* Star Bright Bks., Inc.

—Too Big! Coxon, Michele, illus. 2000. (Lift-the-Flap Bks.). (Illus.). 20p. (J). (ps-3). pap. 5.95 (978-1-887734-78-3(3)) Star Bright Bks., Inc.

Daddo, Andrew. Goodnight, Me. Quay, Emma, illus. 2007. 32p. (J). (ps). 11.95 (*978-1-59990-153-4(6)) Bloomsbury Publishing.

Dale, Jenny. Bob the Bouncy Kitten. Hellard, Susan, illus. 2000. (Kitten Friends Ser.: Vol. 2). (J). 10.79 (978-0-606-19718-2(4)) Tandem Library Bks.

Dale, Jenny. Snowy the Surprise Puppy. Hellard, Susan, illus. 2005. 60p. (J). (*978-0-439-79124-3(3)) Scholastic, Inc.

Davis, Caroline, illus. My Babies. 2007. 12p. (J). (ps). bds. 6.95 (*978-1-58925-822-8(3) , tiger tales) ME Media LLC.

Day, Nancy Raines. A Kitten's Year. Mortimer, Anne, illus. 2002. (J). 23.98 (978-0-7587-2937-8(5)) Book Wholesalers, Inc.

—A Kitten's Year. Mortimer, Anne, illus. 32p. (J). (ps-4). 2001. pap. 5.95 (978-0-06-443863-6(5) , Harper Trophy); 2000. 16.99 (978-0-06-027230-2(9)) HarperCollins Pubs.

Deprisco Wang, Dorothea. I Love You Little One. Eriksen, Tone, illus. 2007. 10p. (J). (ps). bds. 7.99 (*978-1-84666-173-0(0) , Tide Mill Pr.) Top That! Publishing PLC GBR. *Dist:* Random Hse., Inc.

—My Baby. Gevry, Christine, illus. 2007. 10p. (J). (ps). bds. 7.99 (*978-1-84666-263-8(X) , Tide Mill Pr.) Top That! Publishing PLC GBR. *Dist:* Random Hse., Inc.

Diaz, Katacha. Wild Horse Country. Casale, Paul, illus. 2005. (Wild Reading Adventures! Ser.). (J). (ps-2). 32p. 2.95 (978-1-59249-139-1(1) , S7155); 36p. 9.95 (978-1-59249-140-7(5) , PS7155); 36p. 15.95 (978-1-59249-137-7(5) , B7105); 32p. 8.95 incl. audio (978-1-59249-220-6(7) , SC7105); 36p. pap. 6.95 (978-1-59249-138-4(3) , S7105) Soundprints.

Doepker, David. Animal Babies. Sterling Publishing Company Staff, ed. 2004. (Illus.). 16p. (J). (ps). bds. 4.95 (978-1-4027-1717-8(2)) Sterling Publishing Co., Inc.

—Farm Babies. Sterling Publishing Company Staff, ed. 2004. (Illus.). 16p. (J). (ps). bds. 4.95 (978-1-4027-1714-7(8)) Sterling Publishing Co., Inc.

Doinet, Mymi, et al, illus. The Dolphin. 2000. (My Animal Library). 32p. (J). (ps-1). pap. 6.95 (978-0-7892-0661-9(7) , Abbeville Kids) Abbeville Pr., Inc.

—The Elephant. 2000. (My Animal Library). 32p. (J). (ps-1). pap. 6.95 (978-0-7892-0662-6(5) , Abbeville Kids) Abbeville Pr., Inc.

Dorling Kindersley Publishing Staff, contrib. by. Kitten. 1999. (Touch & Feel Ser.). (Illus.). 12p. (J). (ps-k). bds. 6.99 (978-0-7894-3990-1(5)) Dorling Kindersley Publishing, Inc.

Dorman, Clive & Dorman, Helen. Okomi Wakes up Early, Vol. 6. Hutchings, Tony, illus. 2004. (Sharing Nature with Children Book Ser.). 24p. (J). pap. 4.95 (978-1-58469-056-6(9)) Dawn Pubns.

—Okomi Wanders Too Far, Vol. 8. Hutchings, Tony, illus. 2004. (Sharing Nature with Children Book Ser.). 24p. (J). pap. 4.95 (978-1-58469-058-0(5)) Dawn Pubns.

Dorman, Helen. Okomi & the Tickling Game. 2001. (ps-2). lib. bdg. 12.95 (978-0-613-79614-9(4)) Tandem Library Bks.

—Okomi Climbs a Tree. 2001. (ps-2). lib. bdg. 12.95 (978-0-613-79613-2(6)) Tandem Library Bks.

—Okomi Plays in the Leaves. 2001. (ps-2). lib. bdg. 12.95 (978-0-613-79607-1(1)) Tandem Library Bks.

Dorman, Helen & Dorman, Clive. Okomi & the Tickling Game, Vol. 2. Hutchings, Tony, illus. 2004. (Sharing Nature with Children Book Ser.: 2). 24p. (J). pap. 4.95 (978-1-58469-046-7(1)) Dawn Pubns.

—Okomi Climbs a Tree, Vol. 4. Hutchings, Tony, illus. 2004. (Sharing Nature with Children Book Ser.: 4). 24p. (J). pap. 4.95 (978-1-58469-045-0(3)) Dawn Pubns.

—Okomi Plays in the Leaves, Vol. 3. Hutchings, Tony, illus. 2004. (Sharing Nature with Children Book Ser.: 3). 24p. (J). pap. 4.95 (978-1-58469-047-4(X)) Dawn Pubns.

—Okomi, the New Baby. Hutchings, Tony, illus. 2004. (Sharing Nature with Children Book Ser.: 1). 24p. (J). pap. 4.95 (978-1-58469-044-3(5)) Dawn Pubns.

Dowson, Nick. Tigress. Chapman, Jane, tr. Chapman, Jane, illus. 2004. 32p. (J). (gr. k-3). 15.99 (978-0-7636-2325-8(3)) Candlewick Pr.

—Tigress: Read & Wonder. Chapman, Jane, illus. 2007. (Read & Wonder Ser.). 32p. (J). (gr. k-3). pap. 6.99 (*978-0-7636-3314-1(3)) Candlewick Pr.

—Tracks of a Panda. Rong, Yu, illus. 2007. 32p. (J). (gr. k-3). 16.99 (*978-0-7636-3146-8(9)) Candlewick Pr.

Dussling, Jennifer. Picky Peggy. Adams, Lynn, illus. 2004. 32p. (J). lib. bdg. 20.00 (*978-1-4242-1099-2(2)) Fitzgerald Bks.

—Picky Peggy. Adams, Lynn, tr. Adams, Lynn, illus. 2004. (Science Solves It! Ser.). 32p. (J). 4.99 (978-1-57565-138-5(6)) Kane Pr., The.

Dwire, Joyann. What Kind of Cow Are You? Being Content with How God Made You. Dickson, Bill, illus. 2006. 24p. (J). per. 2.99 (978-1-59958-006-7(3)) Journey Stone Creations, LLC.

Eding, June. Easter Showers. Chauhan, Manhar, illus. 2007. (Puppy Scooby-Doo Ser.). 32p. (J). pap. 3.99 (978-0-448-44485-7(2) , Grosset & Dunlap) Penguin Group (USA) Inc.

Edwards. Wake up Kisses. 2000. pap. 5.95 (978-0-06-443879-7(1)) HarperCollins Pubs.

Equipo Staff. Este No es Mi Conejito. 2004. Tr. of That's Not My Bunny. (SPA., Illus.). 12p. (J). (ps). 7.95 (978-0-7460-4512-1(3)) EDC Publishing.

—Este No Es Mi Gatito. 2004. Tr. of That's Not My Kitten. (SPA., Illus.). 12p. (J). (ps). 7.95 (978-0-7460-4513-8(1)) EDC Publishing.

Farmer Fred's: Baby Animals. 2002. bds. 3.98 (978-0-7525-8174-3(0)) Parragon, Inc.

Fearnley, Jan. Just Like You. Fearnley, Jan, illus. 2003. (Illus.). 32p. (J). (ps-1). pap. 6.99 (978-0-7636-2207-7(9)) Candlewick Pr.

—Just Like You. 2004. (ps-2). lib. bdg. 15.30 (978-0-613-74824-7(7)) Tandem Library Bks.

Fisher, Aileen. Know What I Saw. DeSaix, Deborah Durland, illus. 2005. 32p. (J). 16.95 (978-1-59643-055-6(9)) Roaring Brook Pr.

—You Don't Look Like Your Mother. Jones, Lilith, illus. 2001. 31p. (J). pap. 6.00 (978-1-59034-061-5(2)); 15.95 (978-1-58653-856-9(X)) Mondo Publishing.

Ford, Miela. Mom & Me. Ford, Miela, photos by. 1998. (Illus.). 24p. (J). (ps-3). 15.00 (978-0-688-15889-7(7)) HarperCollins Pubs.

Fraggalosch, Audrey. Let's Explore, Moose! Forest, Crista, illus. 2005. (Soundprints' Read-and-Discover Ser.). 32p. (J). (ps-1). pap. 3.95 (978-1-59249-151-3(0) , S2017) Soundprints.

—Trails above the Tree Line: A Story of a Rocky Mountain Meadow. Bond, Higgins, illus. (Soundprints' Wild Habitats Ser.). (J). 2005. 36p. (gr. 1-4). 15.95 (978-1-56899-941-8(0) , B7021); 2005. 36p. (gr. 1-4). 19.95 incl. reel tape (978-1-56899-943-2(7) , BC7021); 2005. 32p. (gr. 1-4). pap. 6.95 (978-1-56899-942-5(9) , S7021); 2002. 36p. 26.95 (978-1-56899-945-6(3) , Little Soundprints) Soundprints.

Friedman, Mel, et al. Kitten Castle. 2001. (Math Matters Ser.). (Illus.). 32p. (J). (gr. k-2). pap. 4.95 (978-1-57565-103-3(3)) Kane Pr., The.

Giogas, Valerie. In My Backyard. Zecca, Katherine, illus. 2007. 32p. (J). (ps-3). 15.95 (*978-0-9777423-1-8(8)) Sylvan Dell Pubng.

Godwin, Laura. What the Baby Hears. 2002. (Illus.). 32p. (ps-k). 16.49 (978-0-7868-2484-7(0)) Hyperion Bks. for Children.

Gray, Rita. Mama Mine, Mama Mine. Goembel, Ponder, illus. 2008. 32p. (J). (ps). 15.99 (*978-0-525-47206-3(1) , Dutton Juvenile) Penguin Group (USA) Inc.

Greban, Quentin. Nestor. 2001. (Illus.). 27p. (J). pap. 15.95 (978-1-59034-012-7(4)) Mondo Publishing.

—Nestor. Greban, Quentin, illus. 2001. (Illus.). 27p. (J). (ps-4). 15.95 (978-1-58653-855-2(1)) Mondo Publishing.

—Nestor. (Buenas Noches Coleccion). (SPA., Illus.). (J). (gr. k-3). 8.95 (978-958-04-6032-9(9)) Norma S.A. COL. *Dist:* Distribuidora Norma, Inc., Lectorum Pubns., Inc.

Grindley, Sally. Little Elephant Thunderfoot. Butler, John, illus. 1999. 32p. (J). (ps-3). 15.95 (978-1-56145-180-7(0)) Peachtree Pubs., Ltd.

—Polar Star. Butler, John, illus. 1998. 32p. (J). (ps-3). 15.95 (978-1-56145-181-4(9) , Q26655) Peachtree Pubs., Ltd.

Grooms, Molly. We Are Bears. 2002. (Illus.). 32p. (J). (ps-2). pap. 7.95 (978-1-55971-836-3(6) , NorthWord Bks. for Young Readers) T&N Children's Publishing.

—We Are Bears. 2000. (ps-2). lib. bdg. 16.40 (978-0-613-55921-8(5)) Tandem Library Bks.

Guidoux, Valerie, et al, illus. The Lion. 2000. (Abbeville Ser.). 32p. (J). (ps-1). pap. 6.95 (978-0-7892-0663-3(3) , Abbeville Kids) Abbeville Pr., Inc.

Harcourt School Publishers Staff. Off We Go! 3rd ed. 2002. (Illus.). pap. 55.10 (978-0-15-325444-4(0)) Harcourt Schl. Pubs.

—Off We Go! Little Book. 3rd ed. 2002. (Trophies Reading Program Ser.). (Illus.). (J). pap. 10.20 (978-0-15-325449-9(1)) Harcourt Schl. Pubs.

Harvey, Sarah N. Puppies on Board. Cowles, Rose, illus. 2005. 32p. (J). (ps-2). 17.95 (978-1-55143-390-5(7)) Orca Bk. Pubs. USA.

Hedrick, Helen Groves. Baas on the Bus. 2000. (J). 12.00 (978-0-8059-5003-8(6)) Dorrance Publishing Co., Inc.

Henderson, Kathy. Tabby Cat's Secret. 2003. (Illus.). 36p. pap. 9.95 (978-0-7112-1883-3(8)) Lincoln, Frances Ltd. GBR. *Dist:* Transition Vendor.

Henderson, Kathy & Winter, Susan. Tabby Cat's Secret. 2004. (Illus.). 32p. (J). pap. 9.95 (978-1-84507-270-4(7)) Lincoln, Frances Ltd. GBR. *Dist:* Perseus Distribution.

Henkes, Kevin. Kitten's First Full Moon. Henkes, Kevin, illus. 2004. (Illus.). 40p. (J). (ps-k). 16.99 (978-0-06-058828-1(4)); lib. bdg. 16.89 (978-0-06-058829-8(2)) HarperCollins Pubs.

—La Primera Luna Llena de Gatita. Henkes, Kevin, illus. 2006. Orig. Title: Kitten's First Full Moon. (SPA.). 32p. (J). 16.99 (978-0-06-087223-6(3)) HarperCollins Pubs.

Higginson, Hadley. Keeker & Pony Camp Catastrophe, Bk. 5. Parrett, Lisa, illus. 2007. 56p. (J). 15.50 (978-0-8118-5596-9(1)) Chronicle Bks. LLC.

—Keeker & Springtime Surprise. Parrett, Lisa, illus. 2007. (Sneaky Pony Ser.: No. 4). 56p. (J). 15.50 (978-0-8118-5598-3(8)) Chronicle Bks. LLC.

—Keeker & Springtime Surprise. Perrett, Lisa, illus. 2007. (Sneaky Pony Ser.: No. 4). 56p. (J). pap. 3.95 (978-0-8118-5599-0(6)) Chronicle Bks. LLC.

—Keeker & the Pony Camp Catastrophe. Parrett, Lisa, illus. 2007. (Keeker & the Sneaky Pony Ser.: Bk. 5). 56p. (J). (gr. k-3). pap. 3.95 (978-0-8118-5597-6(X)) Chronicle Bks. LLC.

Hill, Eric. Spot Goes to the Farm. 2003. (ps-2). lib. bdg. 15.30 (978-0-613-86708-5(4)) Tandem Library Bks.

Hills, Jodi. Hope-So. Bjornson, Barbara, illus. 2004. 36p. (J). 16.95 (978-0-9726504-2-7(3)) Tristan Publishing, Inc.

Hodgkins, Fran. If You Were My Baby. Bryant, Laura J., illus. 2007. 26p. (J). (ps-ps). bds. 7.95 (*978-1-58469-090-0(9)) Dawn Pubns.

Hodgkins, Fran. If You Were My Baby: A Wildlife Lullaby. Bryant, Laura J., illus. 2005. (Sharing Nature with Children Book Ser.). 32p. (J). (ps-2). pap. 8.95 (978-1-58469-075-7(5)); 16.95 (978-1-58469-074-0(7)) Dawn Pubns.

Howe, James. Pinky & Rex & the Just-Right Pet. 2002. (gr. k-3). lib. bdg. 11.80 (978-0-613-45091-1(4)) Tandem Library Bks.

Hurd, Clement, illus. Johnny Lion's Bad Day. 2002. (Johnny Lion Ser.). (J). 12.34 (978-0-7587-5039-6(0)) Book Wholesalers, Inc.

—Johnny Lion's Book. 2002. (Johnny Lion Ser.). (J). 12.34 (978-0-7587-4936-9(8)) Book Wholesalers, Inc.

—Johnny Lion's Rubber Boots. 2002. (Johnny Lion Ser.). (J). 12.34 (978-0-7587-5040-2(4)) Book Wholesalers, Inc.

Hurd, Edith Thacher. Johnny Lion's Bad Day. Hurd, Clement, illus. 2000. (I Can Read Bks.). 64p. (J). (gr. k-3). 14.95 (978-0-06-029335-2(7)) HarperCollins Pubs.

—Johnny Lion's Book. Hurd, Clement, illus. (I Can Read Bks.). 64p. (J). (gr. k-3). 2001. pap. 3.99 (978-0-06-444297-8(7) , Harper Trophy); 2000. 14.95 (978-0-06-029333-8(0)) HarperCollins Pubs.

—Johnny Lion's Book. 2001. (I Can Read Bks.). (Illus.). (J). 10.79 (978-0-606-20745-4(7)) Tandem Library Bks.

—Johnny Lion's Book. Hurd, Clement, illus. 2001. 63p. (J). (ps-ps). lib. bdg. 11.80 (978-0-613-33707-6(7)) Tandem Library Bks.

—Johnny Lion's Rubber Boots. Hurd, Clement, illus. 2000. (I Can Read Bks.). 64p. (J). (gr. k-3). 14.95 (978-0-06-029337-6(3)) HarperCollins Pubs.

—Johnny Lion's Rubber Boots. Hurd, Clement, illus. 2001. (I Can Read Bks.). (J). (978-0-606-20746-1(5)) Tandem Library Bks.

Jackson, Leona Novy. The Littlest Christmas Kitten. Dupre, Kelly, illus. 2005. 32p. (J). 16.00 (978-0-930643-18-8(6) , 1250560) Images Unlimited.

Johansson, Cecilia, illus. Just Like Daddy. 2006. 16p. (J). bds. 6.99 (978-1-4169-1220-0(7) , Little Simon) Simon & Schuster Children's Publishing.

—Just Like Mommy. 2006. 16p. (J). bds. 6.99 (978-1-4169-1218-7(5) , Little Simon) Simon & Schuster Children's Publishing.

Johnson, Paul Brett. The Goose Who Went off in a Huff. Johnson, Paul Brett, illus. 2001. (Illus.). 40p. (J). (ps-1). pap. 15.95 (978-0-531-30317-7(9) , Orchard Bks.) Scholastic, Inc.

Jones, Christianne C. Busy Bear. 2007. (Illus.). 24p. (J). (*978-1-4048-2426-3(X)) Picture Window Bks.

—Busy Bear. Jensen, Brian, illus. 2006. 24p. (J). lib. bdg. (*978-1-4048-2396-9(4)) Picture Window Bks.

Julietta, Melinda & Groom, Molly. We Are Bears. Guamotta, Lucia, photos by. 2000. (Illus.). 31p. (J). (ps-k). 12.95 (978-1-55971-747-2(5) , NorthWord Bks. for Young Readers) T&N Children's Publishing.

Kahn, Lisa. The Calf Who Fell in Love with a Wolf: And Other Calf Stories from Round Top, Texas. von Schweinitz, Helga, tr. from GER. 1999. (J). (978-1-57168-346-5(1) , Eakin Pr.) Eakin Pr.

Kalz, Jill. Tuckerbean. Mahan, Ben, illus. 2006. (Read-It! Readers Ser.). 24p. (J). (ps-3). 18.60 (978-1-4048-1591-9(0)) Picture Window Bks.

Karon, Jan, et al. Violet Comes to Stay. McCully, Emily Arnold, illus. 2006. (Mitford Ser.). 36p. (J). (gr. k). 15.99 (978-0-670-06073-3(9) , Viking Juvenile) Penguin Group (USA) Inc.

Keiser, Frances. The Adventures of Pelican Pete: A Bird Is Born. Keiser, Hugh, illus. 1999. 32p. (J). (ps-3). 15.00 (978-0-9668845-0-0(7)) Sagaponack Bks.

Kessler, Cristina. Jubela. Stammen, JoEllen McAllister, illus. 2004. 32p. (J). reprint ed. pap. 6.99 (978-0-689-86690-6(9) , Aladdin) Simon & Schuster Children's Publishing.

—Jubela. 2004. (gr. k-3). lib. bdg. 15.30 (978-0-613-88065-7(X)) Tandem Library Bks.

King-Smith, Dick. Funny Frank. Eastwood, John, illus. 2003. 112p. (gr. 2-5). pap. 5.50 (978-0-440-41880-1(1) , Yearling) Random Hse. Children's Bks.

—Funny Frank. Roth, Roger & Eastwood, John, illus. 2002. 112p. (J). (gr. 2-5). 14.95 (978-0-375-81460-0(4) , Knopf Bks. for Young Readers) Random Hse. Children's Bks.

Kopper, Lisa. Daisy Is a Mommy. Kopper, Lisa, illus. 2002. (Illus.). (J). 21.36 (978-0-7587-2336-9(9)) Book Wholesalers, Inc.

Kroll, Virginia L. Motherlove. Washburn, Lucia, illus. 1998. 32p. (J). (ps-3). 16.95 (978-1-883220-81-6(5)); pap. 7.95 (978-1-883220-80-8(7)) Dawn Pubns.

Lacombe, Benjamin. Cherry & Olive. 2007. (J). (*978-0-8027-9708-7(3)) Walker & Co.

—Cherry & Olive. Lacombe, Benjamin, illus. 2007. (Illus.). 32p. (J). (ps-2). 16.95 (*978-0-8027-9707-0(5)) Walker & Co.

Laden, Nina. Grow Up. 2003. (Illus.). 26p. (J). bds. 6.95 (978-0-8118-3761-3(0)) Chronicle Bks. LLC.

Langeland, Deirdre, text. Be Careful, Kangaroo! 2005. (Soundprints' Read-and-Discover Ser.). (Illus.). 32p. (J). (ps-1). pap. 3.95 (978-1-59249-145-2(6) , S2010) Soundprints.

Larson, Verna. Bernie's Forest Adventure: A Case for Secular Humanism. Jones, Sharon, ed. Tagnetti, Nikki, illus. 2nd rev. ed. 1999. (Bearables of Bernie Bear Ser.: No. 1). 24p. (J). (ps-k). 8.95 (978-1-56550-085-3(7)) Vision Bks. International.

Lawrence, John. This Little Chick. Lawrence, John, illus. 2002. (Illus.). 32p. (J). (ps up). 15.99 (978-0-7636-1716-5(4)) Candlewick Pr.

Lee, Jeanie. Baby Snow Friends. 2006. (Flips & Flaps Book Ser.). 10p. (J). 12.95 (978-1-4169-0703-9(3) , Little Simon) Simon & Schuster Children's Publishing.

Lee, Kara, illus. Chelsea & the New Puppy. 2001. (J). (ps-3). 14.00 (978-1-892657-03-9(1)) Town Bk. Pr. The.

Lewis, Kim. Little Baa. 2004. (Illus.). 24p. (J). (gr. k-ps). bds. 6.99 (978-0-7636-2472-9(1)) Candlewick Pr.

—Little Baa. Lewis, Kim, illus. 2001. (Illus.). 32p. (J). (gr. k-k). 15.99 (978-0-7636-1447-8(5)) Candlewick Pr.

Lewison, Wendy Cheyette. The Prince & the Potty. Motoyama, Keiko, illus. 2006. 40p. (J). (ps). 12.95 (978-0-689-87808-4(7) , Simon & Schuster Children's Publishing) Simon & Schuster Children's Publishing.

Linamen, Karen Scalf. Princess Madison & the Paisley Puppy. 2007. (Princess Madison Trilogy Ser.). (Illus.). 32p. (J). 12.99 (978-0-8007-1841-1(0)) Revell.

Lincoln, Hazel. Little Elephant's Trunk. Lincoln, Hazel, illus. 2006. (Illus.). 32p. (J). 15.95 (978-0-8075-4591-1(0)) Whitman, Albert & Co.

Little Airplane Productions Staff & Selig, Josh. Teamwork Saves the Day! Book & Beanie Baby Gift Set. Oxley, Jennifer, illus. 2008. (Wonder Pets! Ser.). 12p. (J). bds. 12.99 (*978-1-4169-4797-4(3) , Simon Spotlight/ Nickelodeon) Simon & Schuster Children's Publishing.

Little Kitten. 2003. (Goodnight Mr. Moon Ser.). (Illus.). (J). bds. 2.98 (978-0-7525-4743-5(7)) Parragon, Inc.

Little Puppy. 2003. (Goodnight Mr. Moon Ser.). (Illus.). (J). bds. 2.98 (978-0-7525-4742-8(9)) Parragon, Inc.

London, Jonathan. Baby Whale's Journey. Van Zyle, Jon, illus. 40p. (J). 2007. pap. 6.95 (978-0-8118-5761-1(1)); 1999. 15.95 (978-0-8118-2496-5(9)) Chronicle Bks. LLC.

—Honey Paw & Lightfoot. Van Zyle, Jon, illus. 1998. 40p. (J). (ps-3). pap. 7.95 (978-0-8118-2037-0(8)) Chronicle Bks. LLC.

—Honey Paw & Lightfoot. Van Zyle, Jon, illus. 1998. (J). (ps-ps). lib. bdg. 15.25 (978-0-613-10133-2(2)) Tandem Library Bks.

Losey, Tori. The Ducks of Congress Park. Liguori, Kathy, illus. 2004. 36p. (J). (978-0-925168-97-9(1)) North Country Bks., Inc.

Lucy Lamb. 2006. (J). per. 3.99 (978-1-934004-16-6(2)) Byeway Bks.

Luther, Jacqueline. Black Bear Cub. Trachock, Cathy, illus. 2006. 32p. (J). pap. 3.95 (978-1-59249-587-0(7)) Soundprints.

Marsh, T. J. & Ward, Jennifer. Way Out in the Desert. Spengler, Kenneth J., illus. 2002. 20p. (J). bds. 6.95 (978-0-87358-802-7(9)); 1999. 32p. 15.95 (978-0-87358-687-0(5)) Northland Publishing. (Rising Moon Bks. for Young Readers).

Marzollo, Jean. Mama Mama. Regan, Laura, illus. 1999. (Growing Tree Ser.). 16p. (J). (ps up). 5.99 (978-0-694-01245-9(9) , Harper Festival) HarperCollins Pubs.

—Papa Papa. Regan, Laura, illus. 2000. (Growing Tree Ser.). 14p. (J). (ps up). 5.99 (978-0-694-01246-6(7) , Harper Festival) HarperCollins Pubs.

Masurel, Claire. Domino. Walker, David, illus. 2007. (Super Sturdy Picture Book Ser.). 24p. (J). (gr. k-ps). 8.99 (978-0-7636-2862-8(X)) Candlewick Pr.

McMullan, Kate. If You Were My Bunny. McPhail, David M., illus. 2002. 15.70 (978-0-7587-2831-9(X)) Book Wholesalers, Inc.

—If You Were My Bunny. McPhail, David M., illus. 1998. (Hello Reader! Ser.). 26p. (J). reprint ed. bds. 6.99 (978-0-590-34126-4(X)) Scholastic, Inc.

Meyers, Susan. Kittens! Kittens! Kittens! Walker, David, illus. 2007. (J). (ps-1). 32p. 15.95 (978-0-8109-1218-2(X)); (*978-1-4287-3986-4(6)) Abrams, Harry N., Inc. (Abrams Bks. for Young Readers).

Millard, Anne. Puppies at Play. 2001. (Soft-to-Touch Bk.). (Illus.). 18p. (J). (ps-3). bds. 4.99 (978-0-7894-7401-8(8)) Dorling Kindersley Publishing, Inc.

Mitchell, Melanie. Mommy & Baby: Pets. 2006. (Illus.). 8p. (J). bds. 6.95 (978-0-8027-8982-2(X)) Walker & Co.

Mitton, Tony. Playful Little Penguins. Parker-Rees, Guy, illus. 2007. 32p. (J). (ps-1). 15.95 (*978-0-8027-9710-0(5)) Walker & Co.

Morgan, Michaela. Bunny Wishes. 2007. 32p. (J). (ps-k). pap. 16.99 (*978-0-439-91812-1(X) , Chicken Hse., The) Scholastic, Inc.

Munsch, Robert. Alligator Baby. 1998. (Illus.). (J). pap. 3.99 (978-0-590-34195-0(2) , Cartwheel Bks.) Scholastic, Inc.

—Alligator Baby. Martchenko, Michael, illus. 1998. 32p. (J). (ps-3). pap. 4.99 (978-0-590-88594-2(4) , Cartwheel Bks.) Scholastic, Inc.

—Alligator Baby. (gr. k-3). 2002. lib. bdg. 11.80 (978-0-613-58282-7(9)); 1998. 10.79 (978-0-606-13117-9(5)) Tandem Library Bks.

Murphy, Stuart J. Pepper's Journal: A Kitten's First Year. Winborn, Marsha, illus. 2000. (Trophy Picture Bk.). 40p. (J). (gr. 1 up). pap. 5.99 (978-0-06-446723-0(6) , Harper Trophy) HarperCollins Pubs.

—Pepper's Journal: A Kitten's First Year. 2000. (Math Start Ser.). (978-0-606-18711-4(1)); lib. bdg. 13.00 (978-0-613-22167-2(2)) Tandem Library Bks.

Murray, Marjorie D. Little Wolf & the Moon. Schuett, Stacey, illus. 2002. 32p. (J). (ps-2). 16.95 (978-0-7614-5100-6(5)) Cavendish, Marshall Corp.

Nakamura, Katherine Riley. Song of Night: It's Time to Go to Bed. Riley, Linnea Asplind, illus. 2002. 40p. (J). (ps-3). pap. 15.95 (978-0-439-26678-9(5) , Blue Sky Pr., The) Scholastic, Inc.

Nolan, Lucy. Jack Quack. Wesson, Andrea, illus. 32p. (J). 2005. pap. 5.95 (978-0-7614-5153-2(6)); 2001. 15.95 (978-0-7614-5091-7(2) , Cavendish Children's Bks.) Cavendish, Marshall Corp.

Nussbaum, Ben. Toko Hippo. Wenzel, Gregory, illus. 2006. 36p. (J). pap. 6.95 (978-1-59249-578-8(8)) Soundprints.

—Toko Hippo Micro Ppb. Wenzel, Gregory, illus. 2006. 32p. (J). pap. 2.95 (978-1-59249-579-5(6)) Soundprints.

—Toko the Hippo. Wenzel, Gregory, illus. 2006. (African Wildlife Foundation Kids Ser.). 27p. (J). pap. 8.95 incl. audio compact disk (978-1-59249-580-1(X)) Soundprints.

Oates, Joyce Carol. Naughty Cherie. Graham, Mark, illus. 2008. (J). 40p. 17.89 (978-0-06-074359-8(X)); 32p. 16.99 (978-0-06-074358-1(1)) HarperCollins Pubs.

O'Hair, Margaret. My Pup. Lyon, Tammie, illus. 2008. (J). (*978-0-7614-5389-5(X)) Cavendish, Marshall Corp.

Oke, Janette. Maury Had a Little Lamb. Munger, Nancy, illus. rev. ed. 2001. (Janette Oke's Animal Friends Ser.). 80p. (Orig.). (J). (gr. 1-5). pap. 6.99 (978-0-7642-2457-7(3)) Bethany Hse. Pubs.

—Maury Had a Little Lamb. 2001. (Orig.). (gr. 3-6). lib. bdg. 14.15 (978-0-613-82431-6(8)) Tandem Library Bks.

—Prairie Dog Town. Munger, Nancy, illus. rev. ed. 2001. (Janette Oke's Animal Friends Ser.). 80p. (J). (gr. 1-5). pap. 6.99 (978-0-7642-2455-3(7)) Bethany Hse. Pubs.

—Spunky's Diary. Munger, Nancy, illus. rev. ed. 2000. (Animal Friends Ser.). 64p. (J). (gr. 1-5). pap. 6.99 (978-0-7642-2405-8(0)) Bethany Hse. Pubs.

—This Little Pig. 2001. (Orig.). (gr. k-3). lib. bdg. 14.15 (978-0-613-85065-0(3)) Tandem Library Bks.

—Trouble in a Fur Coat. 2001. (Orig.). (gr. 3-6). lib. bdg. 14.15 (978-0-613-85067-4(X)) Tandem Library Bks.

—Who's New at the Zoo? Munger, Nancy, illus. rev. ed. 2001. (Animal Friends Ser.). 80p. (J). (gr. 1-5). reprint ed. pap. 6.99 (978-0-7642-2460-7(3)) Bethany Hse. Pubs.

—Who's New at the Zoo? 2001. (gr. k-3). lib. bdg. 14.15 (978-0-613-82432-3(6)) Tandem Library Bks.

Olson, David. The Thunderstruck Stork. Munsinger, Lynn, illus. 2007. (J). (ps-2). 15.95 (*978-0-8075-7910-7(6)) Whitman, Albert & Co.

Parks, Charlsie Austin. The Beautiful Duckling. Moisan, Elizabeth, illus. 2001. 64p. (J). 20.95 (978-1-57736-210-4(1) , Hillsboro Pr.) Providence Hse Pubs.

Partis, Joanne. Stripe. Partis, Joanne, illus. (Carolrhoda Picture Books Ser.). 32p. (J). 2004. pap. 6.95 (978-1-57505-667-8(4)); 2003. (Illus.). 14.95 (978-1-57505-450-6(7)) Lerner Publishing Group.

—Stripe. Partis, Joanne, illus. 2004. (Illus.). 32p. (J). (ps-ps). lib. bdg. 14.15 (978-0-606-30383-5(9)) Tandem Library Bks.

Partis, Joanne. Try Counting Sheep. 2007. (Illus.). (J). (ps-k). bds. 12.95 (*978-0-7696-5342-6(1) , Gingham Dog Pr.) School Specialty Publishing.

Pfeffer, Wendy. Mallard Duck at Meadow View Pond. Oughton, Taylor, illus. 2001. (Smithsonian's Backyard Ser.). 32p. (J). (ps-3). pap. 6.95 (978-1-931465-92-2(4) , S5021) Soundprints.

—Mallard Duck at Mountain View Pond. Oughton, Taylor, illus. 2005. (Smithsonian's Backyard Ser.). 32p. (J). (ps-2). 4.95 (978-1-56899-957-9(7) , B5071); 15.95 (978-1-56899-956-2(9) , B5021) Soundprints.

Pfister, Marcus. Charlie at the Zoo. James, J. Alison, tr. from GER. Pfister, Marcus, illus. 2007. (Illus.). 32p. (J). (ps). 17.95 (*978-0-7358-2144-6(5)) North-South Bks., Inc.

Piquemal, Michel. The Panda. Nomdedeu, Clara & Merlin, C., illus. 2000. (My Animal Library). 32p. (J). (ps-1). pap. 6.95 (978-0-7892-0664-0(1)) Abbeville Pr., Inc.

Pomaska, Anna, illus. Sticker Stories: Baby Animals. 2001. (Sticker Stories Ser.). 16p. (J). (ps-3). mass mkt. 4.99 (978-0-448-42492-7(4) , Grosset & Dunlap) Penguin Group (USA) Inc.

Porter-Gaylord, Laurel. I Love My Daddy Because... Wolff, Ashley, illus. 2004. 24p. (J). (ps). bds. 6.99 (978-0-525-47250-6(9) , Dutton Juvenile) Penguin Group (USA) Inc.

Powell, Richard. Bunny's Tail. Davis, Caroline, illus. 2002. (Animal Tails Ser.). 8p. (J). 3.95 (978-1-58925-676-7(X) , tiger tales) ME Media LLC.

—Kitty's Tail. Davis, Caroline, illus. 2003. (Animal Tails Ser.). 10p. (J). 3.95 (978-1-58925-673-6(5) , tiger tales) ME Media LLC.

Powers, John. The Lion Who Couldn't Roar. Colavecchio, Alan, illus. 2002. 32p. (J). 13.95 (978-1-929039-10-4(7)) Ambassador Bks., Inc.

Prap, Lila. Animal Lullabies. 2006. (Illus.). 40p. (J). 14.95 (978-0-7358-2097-5(X)) North-South Bks., Inc.

Raintree Steck-Vaughn Staff, contrib. by. Stellaluna. 1999. (J). (ps-3). 16.00 (978-0-8172-9782-4(0)); pap. 22.00 (978-0-8172-9784-8(7)) Steck-Vaughn.

Rankin, Laura. Fluffy & Baron. 2006. (Illus.). 32p. (J). (ps). 16.99 (978-0-8037-2953-7(7) , Dial) Penguin Group (USA) Inc.

Raum, Elizabeth. The Christmas Star. Johnson, Meredith, illus. 2007. 32p. (J). pap. 3.99 (*978-0-8249-5567-0(6) , Ideals Children's Bks.) Ideals Pubns.

Raum, Elizabeth. Follow That Star: A Christmas Story. Johnson, Meredith, ed. Johnson, Meredith, illus. 2001. 32p. (J). 12.95 (978-0-8249-4136-9(5) , Candy Cane Pr.) Ideals Pubns.

Reasoner, Charles. Who's Hatching? Reasoner, Charles, illus. 2003. (Sliding Surprise Bks.). (Illus.). 12p. (J). (ps). bds. 7.99 (978-0-8431-0598-8(4) , Price Stern Sloan) Penguin Group (USA) Inc.

—Whose Mommy Is This? Reasoner, Charles, illus. 2002. (Sliding Surprise Bks.). (Illus.). 12p. (J). bds. 7.99 (978-0-8431-4579-3(X) , Price Stern Sloan) Penguin Group (USA) Inc.

Robertson, Susan, illus. Little Kitten. 2002. 8p. (J). (ps). per. 6.99 (978-1-57755-502-5(3)) Allied Publishing.

—Little Puppy. 2005. (Bedtime Babies Ser.). 8p. (J). (ps). per. 6.99 (978-1-57755-501-8(5)) Allied Publishing.

Roddie, Shen. Not Now, Mrs. Wolf. 2000. (J). (978-0-606-19386-3(3)) Tandem Library Bks.

Rohmann, Eric. A Kitten Tale. 2008. (J). (*978-0-517-70915-3(5)); lib. bdg. (*978-0-517-70916-0(3)) Knopf, Alfred A. Inc.

Ross, Michael Elsohn. Mama's Milk. Wolff, Ashley, illus. 2007. 32p. (J). 12.95 (*978-1-58246-181-6(3) , Tricycle Pr.) Ten Speed Pr.

Ross, Tony & Willis, J. What Did I Look Like When I Was a Baby? 2003. (Illus.). 32p. pap. (978-1-84270-210-9(6)) Andersen GBR. *Dist:* Random Hse. of Canada, Ltd.

Rylant, Cynthia. Puppy Mudge Finds a Friend. Stevenson, Sucie, illus. 2005. (Puppy Mudge Ser.). (J). (*978-1-4156-3675-6(3) , Aladdin) Simon & Schuster Children's Publishing.

Rylant, Cynthia. Puppy Mudge Has a Snack. Mones, Isidre, illus. 2003. (Puppy Mudge Ser.). 32p. (J). (ps-k). 14.95 (978-0-689-83981-8(2)) Simon & Schuster Children's Publishing.

Saltzberg, Barney. Baby Animals Kisses. 2001. (Illus.). 14p. (J). (ps). bds. 8.95 (978-0-15-202635-6(5) , Red Wagon Bks.) Harcourt Children's Bks.

Sarrazin, Marisol. Peppy, Patch, & the Postman. 2005. (Read-It! Readers Ser.). (Illus.). 32p. (C). (gr. k-3). 18.60 (978-1-4048-1034-1(X)) Picture Window Bks.

Sarrazin, Marisol, illus. Peppy, Patch, & the Bath. 2005. (Read-It! Readers Ser.). 32p. (C). (gr. k-3). 18.60 (978-1-4048-1032-7(3)) Picture Window Bks.

Schaefer, Lola M. Mittens. Hartung, Susan Kathleen, illus. 2007. (My First I Can Read Bks.). 32p. (J). pap. 3.99 (***978-0-06-054661-8(1)*** , Harper Trophy) HarperCollins Pubs.

—What's That, Mittens? Hartung, Susan Kathleen, illus. 2008. (My First I Can Read Bks.). 32p. (J). 16.99 (***978-0-06-054662-5(X)***); lib. bdg. 17.89 (***978-0-06-054663-2(8)***) HarperCollins Pubs.

Schmauss, Judy Kentor. Ted Saw an Egg. 2006. (Reader's Clubhouse Set A Ser.). (Illus.). 24p. (J). pap. 3.99 (978-0-7641-3283-4(0)) Barron's Educational Series, Inc.

Schneider, Howie. Chewy Louie. Schneider, Howie, illus. 2000. (Illus.). 32p. (ps-3). 15.95 (978-0-87358-765-5(0) , Rising Moon Bks. for Young Readers) Northland Publishing.

Schories, Pat, illus. Biscuit & the Little Pup. 2008. (My First I Can Read Bks.). 32p. (J). 17.89 (***978-0-06-074171-6(6)***); 16.99 (***978-0-06-074170-9(8)***) HarperCollins Pubs.

Schories, Pat, illus. Biscuit Wants to Play. 2002. (Biscuit Ser.). (J). 11.87 (978-0-7587-8903-7(3)) Book Wholesalers, Inc.

Sebring Lowrey, Janette. The Poky Little Puppy. Tenggren, Gustaf, illus. 2007. 26p. (J). (gr. k-ps). bds. 4.99 (978-0-375-83925-2(9) , Golden Bks.) Random Hse. Children's Bks.

Shott, Stephen & Dorling Kindersley Publishing Staff. Puppy. 2000. (Animal Board Bks.). (Illus.). 12p. (J). (ps-2). bds. 6.95 (978-0-7894-5402-7(5)) Dorling Kindersley Publishing, Inc.

Smallman, Steve. The Lamb Who Came for Dinner. Dreidemy, Joelle, illus. 2007. 32p. (J). (ps-2). 15.95 (***978-1-58925-067-3(2)*** , tiger tales) ME Media LLC.

Smith, Stephanie. Gray Wolf Pup's Adventure. Hynes, Robert, illus. 2nd ed. 2005. (Soundprints' Read-And-Discover Ser.). (J). (gr. 1-3). 48p. 7.95 (978-1-931465-14-4(2) , B2027); 32p. pap. 3.95 (978-1-931465-13-7(4) , S2027) Soundprints.

—Gray Wolf Pup's Adventure. 2002. (gr. k-3). lib. bdg. 11.80 (978-0-613-61912-7(9)) Tandem Library Bks.

—Lynx Twins Grow Up. Hynes, Robert, illus. 2nd ed. 2005. (Soundprints' Read-and-Discover Ser.). (J). (gr. 1-3). 48p. 7.95 (978-1-931465-20-5(7) , B2002); 32p. pap. 3.95 (978-1-931465-19-9(3) , S2002) Soundprints.

—Lynx Twins Grow Up. 2002. (gr. k-3). lib. bdg. 11.80 (978-0-613-70879-1(2)) Tandem Library Bks.

—Snowshoe Hare's Family. Hynes, Robert, illus. 2nd ed. 2005. (Soundprints' Read-And-Discover Ser.). (J). (gr. 1-3). 48p. 7.95 (978-1-931465-16-8(9) , B2003); 32p. pap. 3.95 (978-1-931465-15-1(0) , S2003) Soundprints.

—Snowshoe Hare's Family. 2002. (gr. k-3). lib. bdg. 16.40 (978-0-613-70884-5(9)) Tandem Library Bks.

Spafford, Suzy. Witzy & Zoom-Zoom. Spafford, Suzy, illus. 1998. (Illus.). 32p. (J). (ps). 14.95 (978-0-9643588-1-2(6)) Suzy's Zoo.

Spangler, Brie. Peg Leg Peke. 2008. 40p. (J). (ps-1). lib. bdg. 18.99 (***978-0-375-94888-6(0)*** , Knopf Bks. for Young Readers) Random Hse. Children's Bks.

Spinelli, Eileen. Hero Cat. McAllister Stammen, Jo Ellen, illus. 2006. 32p. (J). 16.95 (978-0-7614-5223-2(0)) Cavendish, Marshall Corp.

Springer, Susan Woodward. Seldovia Sam & the Sea Otter Rescue. Meissner, Amy, illus. 2005. (Seldovia Sam Ser.: Vol. 2). 64p. pap. 6.95 (978-0-88240-571-1(3)) Graphic Arts Ctr. Publishing Co.

—Seldovia Sam & the Sea Otter Rescue. 2003. (gr. 3-6). lib. bdg. 15.25 (978-0-613-77295-2(4)) Tandem Library Bks.

Steingold, Rita Whitman. A Kitten Followed Me Home. 2001. (Jellybean Bks.). (Illus.). (J). (ps). (978-0-375-80667-4(9) , Random Hse. Bks. for Young Readers) Random Hse. Children's Bks.

Stewart, Amber. Birthday Countdown. Marlow, Layn, illus. 2007. 20p. (J). (ps-k). bds. 12.95 (***978-0-7696-5352-5(9)*** , Gingham Dog Pr.) School Specialty Publishing.

Stierle, Cynthia. The Mysterious Pup. Nunn, Paul E., illus. 2007. 32p. (J). pap. 3.99 (978-0-448-44484-0(4) , Grosset & Dunlap) Penguin Group (USA) Inc.

Street, Jane. Snow Baby. Yandell, Charlene, illus. 2002. 30p. (J). 11.95 (978-1-887905-56-5(1)) Parkway Pubs., Inc.

Sweeney, Jacqueline. Critter Sitters. 2001. (We Can Read! Ser.). (Illus.). 32p. (J). 21.36 (978-0-7614-1122-2(4) , Benchmark Bks.) Cavendish, Marshall Corp.

Sykes, Julie. Dora's Eggs. Chapman, Jane, illus. 2002. 32p. (J). 5.95 (978-1-58925-365-0(5) , tiger tales) ME Media LLC.

—Dora's Eggs. 2002. (gr. k-3). lib. bdg. 14.10 (978-0-613-56323-9(9)) Tandem Library Bks.

—Rainy Day Adventure. 2001. (gr. k-3). lib. bdg. 11.25 (978-0-613-53545-8(6)) Tandem Library Bks.

Tabby, Abigail. Baby Wants the Moon: Book & Bib Gift Set. Beeke, Tiphanie, illus. gif. ed. 2007. (Little Simon Baby Ser.). 16p. (J). bds. 9.99 (978-1-4169-1902-5(3) , Little Simon) Simon & Schuster Children's Publishing.

Tafuri, Nancy. Five Little Chicks. Tafuri, Nancy, illus. 2006. (Illus.). 32p. (J). (ps-k). 14.95 (978-0-689-87342-3(5)) Simon & Schuster Children's Publishing.

—I Love You, Little One. 2000. (Illus.). 15p. (J). (ps-k). bds. 7.99 (978-0-439-13746-1(2) , Scholastic Reference) Scholastic, Inc.

—You Are Special, Little One. 2005. 15p. (J). bds. 7.99 (978-0-439-68613-6(X)) Scholastic, Inc.

—You Are Special, Little One. Tafuri, Nancy, illus. 2003. (Illus.). 32p. (J). pap. 16.95 (978-0-439-39879-4(7)) Scholastic, Inc.

Thatcher, Fran. Tiger Cub's Jungle Home. 2006. 20p. (J). 7.95 (978-1-59764-191-3(X)) New Line Bks.

Thomas, Rosie. Cowgirl Rosie & Her Five Baby Bison. 2001. (Illus.). 24p. (J). (ps-3). 12.95 (978-0-316-64712-0(8)) Little Brown & Co.

Thompson, Lauren. Little Quack. Anderson, Derek, illus. 2005. (Classic Board Bks.). 32p. (J). bds. 7.99 (978-0-689-87645-5(9) , Little Simon) Simon & Schuster Children's Publishing.

—Little Quack's Bath Book. Anderson, Derek, illus. 2006. 8p. (J). pap. 6.99 (978-1-4169-0803-6(X) , Little Simon) Simon & Schuster Children's Publishing.

Thompson, Lauren. Wee Little Chick. Butler, John, illus. 2008. (Wee Little Ser.). 32p. (J). 14.99 (***978-1-4169-3468-4(5)***) Simon & Schuster Children's Publishing.

Thompson, Lauren & Anderson, Derek. Little Quack. 2003. (Illus.). 32p. (J). (ps-1). 14.95 (978-0-689-84723-3(8)) Simon & Schuster Children's Publishing.

Thomson, Pat. Cat Baby. Shulman, Dee, illus. 2006. (Read-It! Chapter Bks.). 64p. (J). lib. bdg. (***978-1-4048-3123-0(1)*** , 1265800) Picture Window Bks.

Tildes, Phyllis L. Baby Animals Black & White. Tildes, Phyllis L., illus. 1998. (Illus.). 10p. (J). (ps). bds. 5.95 (978-0-88106-313-4(4)) Charlesbridge Publishing, Inc.

—Calico's Curious Kittens. 2003. (Illus.). 32p. (J). 16.95 (978-1-57091-511-6(3)); pap. 6.95 (978-1-57091-512-3(1)) Charlesbridge Publishing, Inc.

Trimble, Marcia. A Name for Kitty. Lapuyade, Gloria, illus. 2000. 32p. (J). (ps-2). 15.95 (978-1-891577-63-5(8)); pap. 7.95 (978-1-891577-64-2(6)) Images Pr.

Tuxworth, Nicola. Puppies: A Very First Picture Book. 1999. (Pictures & Words Ser.). (Illus.). 24p. (J). (ps up). lib. bdg. 22.00 (978-0-8368-2380-6(X)) Stevens, Gareth Inc.

Twinem, Neecy. Baby Coyote Counts. 2004. (New Board Book Ser.).Tr. of Bebe Coyote cuenta. (Illus.). 12p. (J). bds. 5.95 (978-0-87358-852-2(5) , Rising Moon Bks. for Young Readers) Northland Publishing.

—Baby Gecko's Colors. 2004. (New Board Book Ser.).Tr. of Los colores de Bebe Geco. (Illus.). 12p. (J). bds. 5.95 (978-0-87358-851-5(7) , Rising Moon Bks. for Young Readers) Northland Publishing.

—Baby Snake's Shapes. 2004. (New Board Book Ser.).Tr. of Las formas de Bebe Serpiente. (Illus.). 12p. (J). bds. 5.95 (978-0-87358-850-8(9) , Rising Moon Bks. for Young Readers) Northland Publishing.

Tyrrell, Melissa. Busy Little Lamb. Tom-Nellis, Susan, illus. 1998. (Baby Buddy Bks.: Vol. 4). 12p. (YA). (ps up). bds. 4.95 (978-1-888443-71-4(5) , Intervisual/Piggy Toes) Dalmatian Pr.

Ure, Jean. Snow Kittens. 1999. (We Love Animals Bks.). (Illus.). 160p. (J). (gr. 4-7). pap. 3.95 (978-0-7641-0970-6(7)) Barron's Educational Series, Inc.

Venn, Cecilia. Puppy Parade, Level 2. 1998. (Disney's First Readers Ser.). (Illus.). 32p. (J). (gr. 1-3). pap. 2.95 (978-0-7868-4170-7(2)) Disney Pr.

Voce, Louise, ed. & illus. Over in the Meadow: A Counting Rhyme. Voce, Louise, illus. 2000. (Big Books! Ser.). 32p. (J). (gr. k-2). pap. 19.99 (978-0-7636-1285-6(5)) Candlewick Pr.

Waddell, Martin. Tough Ronald. Mould, Chris, illus. 2006. (Read-It! Chapter Books). 64p. (J). lib. bdg. (***978-1-4048-3127-8(4)*** , 1265816) Picture Window Bks.

Wallace, Nancy Elizabeth. El Dia del Bebe. 2003. (SPA & ENG., Illus.). 32p. (J). (gr. k-ps). tchr. ed. 9.95 (978-0-618-38795-3(1)) Houghton Mifflin Co. Trade & Reference Div.

—Recycle Every Day! (Illus.). 32p. (J). 2006. 5.95 (978-0-7614-5290-4(7)); 2003. 16.95 (978-0-7614-5149-5(8)) Cavendish, Marshall Corp.

Wallace, Nancy Elizabeth, illus. Recycle Every Day! 2002. 40p. (J). 15.95 (978-1-58837-018-1(6)) Winslow Pr.

Wang, Margaret. I Love You Every Little Bit. 2006. 10p. 9.95 (978-1-58117-482-3(9) , Intervisual/Piggy Toes) Dalmatian Pr.

Ward, Jennifer. Somewhere in the Ocean. 2000. (J). (978-0-606-19468-6(1)) Tandem Library Bks.

Ward, Jennifer. Way up in the Arctic. Spengler, Kenneth J., illus. 2007. (SPA & ENG.). 32p. 15.95 (***978-0-87358-928-4(9)*** , Rising Moon Bks. for Young Readers) Northland Publishing.

Ward, Jennifer, et al. Somewhere in the Ocean. Spengler, Kenneth J., illus. 2000. 32p. (ps-2). 15.95 (978-0-87358-748-8(0) , Rising Moon Bks. for Young Readers) Northland Publishing.

Warnes, Tim. Mommy Mine. Chapman, Jane, illus. 2005. 32p. (J). (ps-k). 15.99 (978-0-06-058947-9(7)); lib. bdg. 16.89 (978-0-06-058948-6(5)) HarperCollins Pubs.

Weeks, Sarah & Carter, David A. Peek in My Pocket. 2007. (Illus.). 16p. (J). (ps). 10.95 (***978-0-15-205807-4(9)***) Harcourt Trade Pubs.

Wildsmith, Brian. The Little Wood Duck. Wildsmith, Brian, illus. 2006. (Illus.). 32p. (J). 16.95 (978-1-59572-042-9(1)); pap. 6.95 (978-1-59572-049-8(9)) Star Bright Bks., Inc.

Willson, Sarah. Rugrats' Easter Surprise. 2002. (gr. k-3). lib. bdg. 14.15 (978-0-613-51321-0(5)) Tandem Library Bks.

Wilson, Karma. Where Is Home, Little Pip? Chapman, Jane, illus. 2008. 40p. (J). (978-0-689-85983-0(X) , McElderry, Margaret K.) Simon & Schuster Children's Publishing.

Wingfield, David. Little Goose. Apple, Margot, illus. 2007. (J). (***978-1-58246-190-8(2)*** , Tricycle Pr.) Ten Speed Pr.

Wormell, Mary. Why Not? 2003. lib. bdg. 14.10 (978-0-613-59763-0(X)) Tandem Library Bks.

Worth, Bonnie. A Great Day for Pup. Ruiz, Aristides, illus. 2002. (Cat in the Hat's Learning Library). 48p. (J). (gr. k-3). 8.99 (978-0-375-81096-1(X) , Random Hse. Bks. for Young Readers) Random Hse. Children's Bks.

Yolen, Jane. Off We Go! 2002. (Illus.). (J). 18.89 (978-0-7587-3295-8(3)) Book Wholesalers, Inc.

—Off We Go! Molk, Laurel, illus. 2000. 32p. (J). (ps-1). 14.99 (978-0-316-90228-1(4)) Little Brown & Co.

—Off We Go! Molk, Laurel, illus. 2002. 8p. (J). (ps-k). bds. 5.95 (978-0-316-90972-3(6)) Little, Brown Bks. for Young Readers.

Ziefert, Harriet. A Dozen Ducklings Lost & Found: A Counting Story. Dreifuss, Donald, illus. 2003. 32p. (J). (gr. k-3). tchr. ed. 15.00 (978-0-618-14175-3(8) , Walter Lorraine) Houghton Mifflin Co. Trade & Reference Div.

ANIMALS—LANGUAGE

see Animal Communication

ANIMALS—LEGENDS

see Animals—Fiction

ANIMALS, MARINE

see Marine Animals

ANIMALS—MIGRATION

see also names of animals with the subdivision Migration, e.g. Birds—Migration

Allen, Kathy. Why Geese Fly South in Winter? A Book about Migration. 2007. (First Facts Ser.). (J). 21.26 (978-0-7368-6380-3(X)) Capstone Pr., Inc.

Berger, Melvin & Berger, Gilda. Migracion: Migration. 2005. (ENG & SPA., Illus.). (J). (978-0-439-79176-2(6)) Scholastic, Inc.

Bredeson, Carmen. Animals That Migrate. 2001. (Animal Library). (Illus.). 64p. (J). (gr. 5-7). 25.50 (978-0-531-11865-8(7) , Watts, Franklin) Scholastic Library Publishing.

Clyne, Margaret. Amazing Journeys. 2001. (gr. k-3). lib. bdg. 11.80 (978-0-613-33324-5(1)) Tandem Library Bks.

Crossingham, John. What Is Migration? 2002. (gr. 3-6). lib. bdg. 14.10 (978-0-613-50849-0(1)) Tandem Library Bks.

Crossingham, John & Kalman, Bobbie. La Migration. 2002. (FRE., Illus.). 32p. (J). pap. (978-2-920660-90-8(X)) Crabtree Publishing Co.

—What Is Migration? 2001. (Science of Living Things Ser.). (Illus.). 32p. (J). (gr. 2-3). pap. (978-0-86505-965-8(9)) Crabtree Publishing Co.

Hoff, Mary. Migration. 2002. (World of Wonder Ser.). (Illus.). 32p. (J). lib. bdg. (978-1-58341-241-1(7) , Creative Education) Creative Co., The.

Hughes, Monica. Migration. 2004. (Nature's Patterns Ser.). (Illus.). 32p. (J). pap. 7.25 (978-1-4034-5885-8(5)); lib. bdg. 22.79 (978-1-4034-5879-7(0)) Heinemann Library.

Johnson, Rebecca L. Tracking Animal Migrators. 2003. (National Geographic Reading Expeditions Ser.). (Illus.). 32p. (J). pap. (978-0-7922-8449-9(6)) National Geographic Society.

Kalman, Bobbie & Crossingham, John. What Is Migration? 2001. (Science of Living Things Ser.). (Illus.). 32p. (J). (gr. 2-3). (978-0-86505-988-7(8)) Crabtree Publishing Co.

Kaner, Etta. Animals Migrating: How, When, Where & Why Animals Migrate. Stephens, Pat, illus. 2005. 40p. (YA). (gr. 2-6). (978-1-55337-548-7(3)); (978-1-55337-547-0(5)) Kids Can Pr., Ltd.

Knight, Tim. Magnificent Movers. 2003. (Amazing Nature Ser.). 32p. (J). (gr. 2-5). lib. bdg. 24.22 (978-1-4034-0722-1(3)) Heinemann Library.

—Marvelous Migrators. 2003. (Amazing Nature Ser.). (Illus.). 32p. (J). pap. 6.95 (978-1-4034-3260-5(0)); lib. bdg. 24.22 (978-1-4034-1149-5(2)) Heinemann Library.

LaBella, Susan. How Animals Navigate. 2007. (J). pap. (***978-0-8368-8421-0(3)***); 24p. (gr. 2-4). lib. bdg. 19.93 (***978-0-8368-8416-6(7)***) Stevens, Gareth Inc. (Weekly Reader Early Learning Library).

Rylant, Cynthia. The Journey: Stories of Migration. Davis, Lambert, illus. 2006. 48p. (J). (gr. 2-5). pap. 16.99 (978-0-590-30717-8(7) , Blue Sky Pr., The) Scholastic, Inc.

Salas, Laura Purdie. Do Lobsters Leap Waterfalls? A Book about Animal Migration. Ouren, Todd, illus. 2006. (Animals All Around Ser.). (J). 23.93 (978-1-4048-2234-4(8)) Picture Window Bks.

Saunders-Smith, Gail. Animals in the Fall. 1998. (J). pap. 13.25 (978-0-516-21248-7(6) , Children's Pr.) Scholastic Library Publishing.

Sayre, April Pulley. Home at Last: A Song of Migration. Berenzy, Alix, illus. rev. ed. 1998. 32p. (J). (ps-3). 17.95 (978-0-8050-5154-4(6) , Holt, Henry & Co. Bks. For Young Readers) Holt, Henry & Co.

Stone, Lynn M. Migration. 2007. (Illus.). 24p. (J). (978-1-60044-179-0(3)) Rourke Publishing, LLC.

ANIMALS, MYTHICAL

see also names of mythical animals, e.g. Dragons, Unicorn, etc.

Allen, Judy & Hook, Richard. Fantasy Encyclopedia. Howe, John et al, illus. 2005. 144p. (J). (gr. 5-9). 19.95 (978-0-7534-5847-1(0) , Kingfisher) Houghton Mifflin Co. Trade & Reference Div.

Baynes, Pauline. Questionable Creatures: A Bestiary. Baynes, Pauline, illus. 2006. (Illus.). 48p. (YA). (gr. 4 up). 18.00 (978-0-8028-5284-7(X)) Eerdmans, William B. Publishing Co.

Bechtold, Phyliss. Seymour Bluffs & the Legend of the Piasa Bird. 2007. 26p. 9.95 (***978-0-9728532-8-6(6)***) New Horizons Christian Ctr.

Brookes, Diane. Su Lin & the Dragon. Carrareto, Mary-Lynn, illus. 1999. 24p. (J). (ps-3). pap. (978-0-9683640-0-0(4)) Raven Rock Publishing.

Burgess, Thornton W. Old Mother West Wind's Neighbors. (J). (gr. 5-6). 19.95 (978-0-88411-786-5(3)) Amereon LTD.

Clibbon, Meg. Magical Creatures. Clibbon, Lucy, illus. 2006. 32p. (J). (ps-4). 19.95 (978-1-55451-030-6(9)); pap. 8.95 (978-1-55451-029-0(5)) Annick Pr., Ltd. CAN. *Dist:* Firefly Bks., Ltd.

Colbert, David. Magical Worlds of Harry Potter: A Treasury of Myths, Legends, & Fascinating Facts. 2001. (Illus.). 223p. (YA). (gr. 5 up). 14.95 (978-0-9708442-0-0(4)) Lumina Pr. LLC.

Cosson, M. J. Sea Monsters: Myth & Truth. 2000. (Cover-to-Cover Bks.). (Illus.). 56p. (J). pap. 8.95 (978-0-7891-5047-9(6)); (gr. 4-7). lib. bdg. 17.95 (978-0-7807-9013-1(8)) Perfection Learning Corp.

Draw 50 Monsters, Creeps, Superheroes, Demons, Dragons, Nerds, Dirts, Ghouls, Giants, Vampires, Zombies, & Other Curiosal. 2002. (Draw 50 Ser.). (Illus.). (J). 17.60 (978-0-7587-4166-0(9)) Book Wholesalers, Inc.

Edwards, Katie. Myths & Monsters: Secrets Revealed. Mendez, Simon, illus. 2004. 29p. (J). 16.95 (978-1-57091-581-9(4)); pap. 6.95 (978-1-57091-582-6(2)) Charlesbridge Publishing, Inc.

Galeano, Eduardo. Mitos de Memoria del Fuego. (SPA.). 80p. 14.95 (978-84-667-1709-0(9)) Suma de Letras, S.L. ESP. *Dist:* Distribooks, Inc.

Gibbons, Gail. Behold... the Unicorns! Gibbons, Gail, illus. 2001. (Illus.). 32p. (J). 15.89 (978-0-688-17958-8(4)) HarperCollins Pubs.

Hague, Michael. The Book of Dragons. Hague, Michael, illus. 2005. (Illus.). 160p. (J). (ps-7). pap., pap. 9.99 (978-0-06-075968-1(2) , Harper Trophy) HarperCollins Pubs.

Hamilton, John. Unicorns & Other Magical Creatures. 2005. (Fantasy & Folklore Ser.). (Illus.). 32p. (J). (gr. 4-8). lib. bdg. 24.21 (978-1-59197-715-5(0)) ABDO Publishing Co.

Heidbreder, Robert. I Wished for a Unicorn. Denton, Kady MacDonald, illus. 32p. (J). (gr. k-3). 2001. (978-1-55074-557-3(3)); 2000. (978-1-55074-543-6(3)) Kids Can Pr., Ltd.

Johnson, Sandi. Dorp the Scottish Dragon Bk. 5: Witch of the Triangle. Praker, Jon, illus. 2000. 27p. (J). (ps-6). 9.99 (978-1-929063-62-8(8) , 161) Moons & Stars Publishing For Children.

Krensky, Stephen. Creatures from the Deep. 2007. (Monster Chronicles Ser.). 48p. (J). (gr. 4-8). lib. bdg. 26.60 (***978-0-8225-6761-5(X)*** , Lerner Pubns.) Lerner Publishing Group.

Lathrop, Dorothy P. Animals of the Bible. Lathrop, Dorothy P., illus. 1998. (Illus.). 72p. (J). (ps-3). 17.99 (978-0-397-31536-9(8)); lib. bdg. 18.89 (978-0-397-30047-1(6)) HarperCollins Pubs.

Lehner, Ernst & Lehner, Johanna. Big Book of Dragons, Monsters, & Other Mythical Creatures. 2004. (Pictorial Archive Ser.). (Illus.). 192p. pap. 16.95 (978-0-486-43512-1(1)) Dover Pubns., Inc.

Levin, Freddie. 1-2-3 Draw Mythical Creatures: A Step-by-Step Guide. 2003. (One-Two-Three Draw Ser.). (Illus.). 64p. pap. 8.99 (978-0-939217-49-6(X)) Peel Productions, Inc.

Mastin, Colleayn O. Magic of Mythical Creatures. Sovak, Jan, illus. 1999. 32p. (J). (gr. 1). pap. 9.95 (978-1-895910-43-8(9)) Grasshopper Bks. CAN. *Dist:* Orca Bk. Pubs. USA.

McNab, Chris. Mythical Monsters: The Scariest Creatures from Legends, Books, & Movies. 2006. (Illus.). 95p. (J). (***978-0-439-85479-5(2)***) Scholastic, Inc.

Mortensen, Lori. Leprechauns. 2007. (Mysterious Encounters Ser.). (Illus.). 48p. (J). (gr. 4-8). 26.20 (***978-0-7377-3663-2(1)*** , Kidhaven) Thomson Gale.

Nigg, Joe. The Book of Dragons & Other Mythical Beasts. 2002. (Illus.). 128p. 18.99 (978-0-7641-5510-9(5)) Barron's Educational Series, Inc.

Posner, Pat. Fantastic Creatures from Greek Myths. Whelan, Olwyn, illus. 2003. (Greek Myths Ser.). 40p. (J). (gr. 1-4). 18.95 (978-1-57768-507-4(5) , Bedrick, Peter Bks.) School Specialty Publishing.

Reading Friends Staff. Dragon Books. (J). (978-0-8136-3751-8(1)) Modern Curriculum Pr.

Russo, Monica. Mythical Animals Dot-to-Dot. 2003. (Illus.). 64p. (J). (gr. 5-7). pap. 5.95 (978-0-8069-9716-2(8)) Sterling Publishing Co., Inc.

Scamander, Newt, pseud & Rowling, J. K. Fantastic Beasts & Where to Find Them. 2001. (Harry Potter Ser.). (Illus.). 64p. (J). (gr. 3 up). mass mkt. 3.99 (978-0-439-29501-7(7)) Scholastic, Inc.

—Harry Potter Schoolbooks: Quidditch Through the Ages & Fantastic Beasts & Where to Find Them, 2 vols., Set. Incl. Fantastic Beasts & Where to Find Them. (Illus.). 64p. (J). (gr. 3 up). 2001. mass mkt. 3.99 (978-0-439-29501-7(7)); (Harry Potter Ser.). (Illus.). 2001. Set mass mkt. 7.98 (978-0-439-28403-5(1) , Levine, Arthur A. Bks.) Scholastic, Inc.

Thompson, Lauren. Love One Another: The Last Days of Jesus. Uyehara, Elizabeth, illus. 2000. 32p. (J). (gr. 1-5). pap. 5.99 (978-0-590-31837-2(3) , Scholastic Pr.) Scholastic, Inc.

Torpe, Kate. Mythical Beasts. Deener, David R., illus. 2007. 24p. (J). (gr. 2-7). 19.99 (***978-1-58476-618-6(2)*** , IKIDS) Innovative Kids.

Whisp, Kennilworthy, pseud & Scamander, Newt. Harry Potter Schoolbooks: Quidditch Through the Ages & Fantastic Beasts & Where to Find Them, 2 vols., Set. braille ed. 2001. (Harry Potter Ser.). (YA). (gr. 3 up). pap. 8.00 (978-0-939173-47-1(6)) National Braille Pr.

ANIMALS, MYTHICAL—FICTION

Anderson, Al. Pegasus: Adventures with Bingo Borden. Kurzyca, Krystyna Emilia, illus. 2006. 77p. (J). per. 19.50 (***978-1-887250-46-7(8)***) Agora Pubns., Inc.

A B

The check digit for ISBN-10 appears in parentheses after the full ISBN-13

Benz, Derek & Lewis, J. S. The Fall of the Templar. 2008. (Grey Griffins Ser.). 304p. (J). 12.99 (***978-0-439-83776-7(6)*** , Orchard Bks.) Scholastic, Inc.

Breathed, Berkeley. The Last Basselope: One Ferocious Story. Breathed, Berkeley, illus. 2001. (Illus.). 32p. (J). (ps-17). pap. 6.99 (978-0-316-12664-9(0)) Little Brown & Co.

Burgess, Thornton. Happy Jack. 2006. pap. 34.99 (***978-1-4219-7082-0(1))*** IndyPublish.com.

Campbell, Roy. Song of the Jackalope. Bosworth, David, illus. 2nd ed. 2006. 140p. (YA). pap. 12.95 (978-1-933538-04-4(X)) Bridgeway Bks.

Campbell, Roy B. Song of the Jackalope. Bosworth, David, illus. 2002. viii, 108p. (YA). (gr. 4-9). 20.00 (978-0-9718282-0-9(2)) Fireside Bks.

Chancellor, Deborah. Ven a Bordo del Arca de Noe. Miranda, Patricia, tr. Downing, Julie, illus. 2002. (SPA.). (J). (ps). (978-958-42-0301-4(0)) Planeta Colombiana Editorial S.A.

Collins, Ross. Medusa Jones. 2008. (J). (***978-0-439-90101-7(4));*** 144p. pap. 16.99 (***978-0-439-90100-0(6))*** Scholastic, Inc. (Levine, Arthur A. Bks.).

Coville, Bruce. Half Human. 2004. (Illus.). 224p. (J). (gr. 4-7). pap. 5.99 (978-0-590-95588-1(8) , Scholastic Paperbacks) Scholastic, Inc.

DuQuette, Keith. Cock-a-Doodle Moooo! A Mixed-Up Menagerie. DuQuette, Keith, illus. 2004. (Illus.). 32p. (J). (ps-3). 15.99 (978-0-399-23889-5(1) , Putnam Juvenile) Penguin Group (USA) Inc.

Eastwood, J. G. Dragon: Enter the Realm. 2007. (YA). per. (***978-0-9792030-7-7(4))*** Light Sword Publishing LLC.

Egan, Kate & Cameron, Alice. The Movie Storybook. Navarro, Larry, illus. 2007. (Shrek the Third Ser.). 48p. (J). pap. 8.99 (978-0-06-122871-1(0) , Harper Entertainment) HarperCollins Pubs.

Favorite, Deborah. The Tush People. Arinsberg, Norman, illus. (J). 11.95 (978-0-9722514-0-2(5)) Tush People, The.

Figler, Jeanie. Majestic Blue Horses. 1999. (Illus.). (J). 9.95 (978-1-56492-273-1(1)) Laredo Publishing Co., Inc.

Freeman, R. Gregory. A Carpenter¿s Tale: The Mystery of Kidron Valley. 2006. (Illus.). 44p. (J). per. 10.95 (978-1-60002-118-3(2) , 3901, Airleaf Publishing) Airleaf Publishing & Bookselling.

Funke, Cornelia. Dragon Rider. Bell, Anthea, tr. from GER. 2004. Orig. Title: Drachenreiter. (Illus.). 528p. (J). (gr. 3-6). pap. 14.99 (978-0-439-45695-1(9) , Chicken Hse., The) Scholastic, Inc.

Gervais, Ricky. Flanimals. Steen, Rob, illus. 2005. 64p. (J). (ps). 14.99 (978-0-399-24397-4(6) , Putnam Juvenile) Penguin Group (USA) Inc.

Golding, Julia. The Gorgon's Gaze. 2007. (Companions Quartet Ser.). 320p. (YA). (gr. 5 up). 16.99 (***978-0-7614-5377-2(6))*** Cavendish, Marshall Corp.

—Mines of the Minotaur. Wyatt, David, illus. 2008. (J). (***978-0-7614-5302-4(4))*** Cavendish, Marshall Corp.

—Secret of the Sirens. Wyatt, David, illus. 2007. 384p. (YA). (gr. 5 up). 16.99 (***978-0-7614-5371-0(7))*** Cavendish, Marshall Corp.

Goldstein, Gary. The Mythfits. 2005. 280p. (YA). (ps-7). pap. 14.99 (978-1-59092-125-8(9) , Blue Works) Windstorm Creative.

Hartman, Moreta. The Adventures of the Rocky Mountain Tea Twerps. Mantzke, Jurgen, illus. 2003. 56p. (J). lib. bdg. 18.95 (978-0-9743937-0-4(3)) Hallelujah Publishing Co., L.L.C.

Ibbotson, Eva. Island of the Aunts. 2001. 304p. (YA). (gr. 4-7). pap. 5.99 (978-0-14-230049-7(7) , Puffin) Penguin Group (USA) Inc.

—Monster Mission. l.t. ed. 2006. pap. 16.95 (978-1-4056-6057-0(0)) BBC Audio GBR. *Dist:* BBC Audiobooks America.

Jacqueline Jules Staff. The Ziz & the Hanukkah Miracle. 2006. (J). pap. 7.95 (978-1-58013-164-3(6)) Kar-Ben Publishing.

Johnson, Jane. The Secret Country. Stower, Adam, illus. 336p. (J). 2007. (Eidolon Chronicles Ser.). pap. 5.99 (***978-1-4169-3815-6(X)*** , Aladdin); 2006. (Chronicles of Eidolon Ser.: Bk. 1). (gr. 3-7). 14.95 (978-1-4169-0712-1(2)) Simon & Schuster Children's Publishing.

Johnson, Sandi. Dorp the Scottish Dragon Bk. 3: Whacky. Vu, Thien V., illus. 2000. 26p. (J). (ps-6). 9.99 (978-1-929063-59-8(8) , 158) Moons & Stars Publishing For Children.

Jules, Jacqueline. The Hardest Word: A Yom Kippur Story. Kahn, Katherine Janus, illus. 2001. 32p. (J). (ps-2). pap. 7.95 (978-1-58013-028-8(3)) Kar-Ben Publishing.

—The Hardest Word: A Yom Kippur Story. Kahn, Katherine Janus, illus. 2001. 32p. (J). (ps-2). 17.95 (978-1-58013-030-1(5) , Carolrhoda Bks.) Lerner Publishing Group.

—Noah & the Ziz. Kahn, Katherine Janus, illus. 2005. 32p. (J). (ps-2). 17.95 (978-0-929371-01-6(1)); 7.95 (978-1-58013-121-6(2)) Kar-Ben Publishing.

—The Ziz And the Hanukkah Miracle. Kahn, Katherine, illus. 2006. 32p. (J). 17.95 (978-1-58013-160-5(3)) Kar-Ben Publishing.

Katschke, Judy. Shrek the Third: King for a Day, Ogre for Life. 2007. (Shrek the Third Ser.). 64p. (J). pap. 4.99 (978-0-06-122864-3(8) , Harper Entertainment) HarperCollins Pubs.

Kline, Trish. Run, Roadrunner, Run! Smith, Fred, illus. (Read-and-Discover - Great Plains Ser.). 48p. (J). 2005. (ps-1). pap. 3.95 (978-1-56899-907-4(0) , S2004); 2002. (gr. 1-3). 7.95 (978-1-56899-906-7(2) , B2004) Soundprints.

McGough, Roger. Daniel & the Beast of Babylon. Newton, Jill, illus. 2004. 32p. (J). pap. 11.00 (978-0-7459-4753-2(0)) Lion Hudson plc GBR. *Dist:* Independent Pubs. Group.

McKinley, Robin. Dragonhaven. 2007. 342p. (J). (gr. 5 up). 17.99 (***978-0-399-24675-3(4)*** , Putnam Juvenile) Penguin Group (USA) Inc.

McQuerry, Maureen Doyle. Wolfproof. Murphy, John, illus. 2006. (J). 183p. 24.95 (978-1-59597-006-0(1)); 176p. per. 14.95 (978-1-59597-009-1(6)) Idylls Pr.

Meyer, Kai. The Glass Word. Crawford, Elizabeth D., tr. from GER. 2008. (Dark Reflections Trilogy Ser.). 288p. (YA). (gr. 7 up). 16.99 (***978-0-689-87791-9(9)*** , McElderry, Margaret K.) Simon & Schuster Children's Publishing.

Nesbit, E. Phoenix & the Carpet. 2006. pap. (***978-1-4068-3504-5(8))*** Echo Library.

Oldfield, Jenny. Iron Eyes. 2002. (Illus.). 240p. (J). pap. 13.99 (978-0-340-85109-8(0) , Hodder & Stoughton) Hodder General Publishing Division GBR. *Dist:* Trafalgar Square Publishing.

Oppel, Kenneth. Skybreaker. 2007. 560p. (J). (gr. 7 up). pap. 6.99 (978-0-06-053229-1(7)) HarperCollins Pubs.

Owens, Vivian W. How Oswa Came to Own All Music: The Legend of Oswa. Owens, April U., ed. Owens, John D., III, illus. 2000. 84p. (YA). 16.95 (978-0-9623839-9-1(6)) Eschar Pubns.

Riordan, Rick. The Titan's Curse. 3rd rev. ed. 2007. (Percy Jackson & the Olympians Ser.: Bk. 3). 320p. (gr. 5 up). 17.95 (***978-1-4231-0145-1(6))*** Miramax Bks.

Service, Pamela F. Yesterday's Magic. 2008. (J). (gr. 3-7). 224p. 16.99 (***978-0-375-85577-1(7));*** 320p. lib. bdg. 19.99 (***978-0-375-95577-8(1))*** Random Hse. Children's Bks. (Random Hse. Bks. for Young Readers).

Smedman, Lisa. Creature Catchers. Baldwin, Alisa, illus. 2007. 200p. (J). (gr. 4-6). 19.95 (***978-1-55451-058-0(9));*** pap. 9.95 (***978-1-55451-057-3(0))*** Annick Pr., Ltd. CAN. *Dist:* Firefly Bks., Ltd.

Ursu, Anne. The Shadow Thieves. Fortune, Eric, illus. 2006. (Cronus Chronicles Ser.: Bk. 1). 432p. (J). (gr. 3-7). 16.95 (978-1-4169-0587-5(1) , Atheneum) Simon & Schuster Children's Publishing.

—The Siren Song. Fortune, Eric, illus. 2007. (Cronus Chronicles Ser.). 448p. (J). (gr. 3-7). 16.99 (978-1-4169-0589-9(8)) Simon & Schuster Children's Publishing.

West, Tracey. Pikachu in Love. 2003. (gr. k-3). lib. bdg. 11.80 (978-0-613-72182-0(9)) Tandem Library Bks.

—Pokemon Reader No.6: Get Well, Pikachu! 2004. (gr. k-3). lib. bdg. 11.80 (978-0-613-84568-7(4)) Tandem Library Bks.

West, Tracey, adapted by. Pikachu in Love. 2003. (Pokemon Readers Ser.). (Illus.). 32p. (J). (gr. k-2). pap. 3.99 (978-0-439-42990-0(0)) Scholastic, Inc.

Whittle, J. Robert & Sandilands, Joyce. Leprechaun Magic. Galego, Ane M., illus. 2004. 64p. (J). (978-0-9685061-2-7(7)) Whitlands Publishing, Ltd.

Wilson, David J. Lucky & the Pot of Gold. 2001. (J). pap. 6.95 (978-0-533-13633-9(4)) Vantage Pr., Inc.

Ziefert, Harriet. Ode to Humpty Dumpty. Chwast, Seymour, illus. 2001. 32p. (J). (gr. k-3). tchr. ed. 15.00 (978-0-618-05047-5(7) , Walter Lorraine) Houghton Mifflin Co. Trade & Reference Div.

Zoehfeld, Kathleen Weidner. Shrek the Third: The Junior Novel. 2007. (Shrek the Third Ser.). 144p. (J). pap. 4.99 (978-0-06-122870-4(2) , Harper Entertainment) HarperCollins Pubs.

ANIMALS—PHOTOGRAPHY

see Photography of Animals

ANIMALS—PICTORIAL WORKS

Ajmera, Maya & Ivanko, John D. Animal Friends: A Global Celebration of Children & Animals. 2004. (Illus.). 20p. (J). (ps-1). bds. 6.95 (978-1-57091-502-4(4)) Charlesbridge Publishing, Inc.

Aliki. Wild & Woolly Mammoths. rev. ed. 1998. (Trophy Picture Bks.). (J). (978-0-606-13068-4(3)) Tandem Library Bks.

Alvarez, Lourdes M. Animals. Brooks, David, illus. 2005. (My First Book Ser.). 9p. (J). (ps-ps). bds. 3.95 (978-1-933050-09-6(8)) Sweetwater Pr.

Animal Friends. Date not set. 88p. (J). 7.98 (978-0-7525-9845-1(7)) Parragon, Inc.

Animal Marvels, 8 bks. Incl. Building a Home. lib. bdg. 24.67 (978-0-8368-2814-6(3)); Communicating. lib. bdg. 24.67 (978-0-8368-2930-3(1)); Escaping Danger. lib. bdg. 24.67 (978-0-8368-2931-0(X)); Finding Food. lib. bdg. 24.67 (978-0-8368-2815-3(1)); Getting Around. lib. bdg. 24.67 (978-0-8368-2816-0(X)); Living Together. lib. bdg. 24.67 (978-0-8368-2817-7(8)); Reproducing. lib. bdg. 24.67 (978-0-8368-2932-7(8)); Surviving. lib. bdg. 24.67 (978-0-8368-2933-4(6)); 32p. (J). (gr. 3 up). 2001. (Illus.). 2001. Set lib. bdg. 197.36 (978-0-8368-2982-2(4)) Stevens, Gareth Inc.

Animal Wise. 2005. (C). (gr. k-2). 135.60 (978-1-4048-0990-1(2)) Picture Window Bks.

Antionelli, Gina & Antionelli, Gina. Who Is Ollie. 2007. 44p. (J). 10.99 (978-1-883573-07-2(6) , Orchard Academy Pr.) Windstorm Creative.

Barlow, Amanda. Animals. 2004. (Baby Board Bks.). (Illus.). 10p. (J). (ps up). pap. 4.95 (978-0-7460-4102-4(0)) EDC Publishing.

Barlowe, Sy. Learning about Desert Animals. 1998. (Learning about Ser.). 16p. (J). (gr. 3-5). pap. 1.50 (978-0-486-40333-5(5) , 40333-5) Dover Pubns., Inc.

Barney's ABC Animals! 1999. (Barney Ser.). (Illus.). 32p. (J). (ps-k). 6.95 (978-1-57064-624-9(4)) Scholastic, Inc.

Bartholomew, Linda & Bartholomew, Al. Adventures in the Tropics. Bartholomew, Linda & Bartholomew, Al, photos by. 2005. 76p. (J). 15.00 (978-0-9764802-1-2(2)) Solutions for Human Services, LLC.

—The Rain Forest Book for Kids. Bartholomew, Linda & Bartholomew, Al, photos by. 2005. 32p. (J). 9.00 (978-0-9764802-0-4(4)) Solutions for Human Services, LLC.

Beck, Jeanine. Los Animales, Mis Amigos. 2003. (ENG & SPA., Illus.). 64p. 14.99 (978-0-7548-1195-4(6)) Anness Publishing GBR. *Dist:* National Bk. Network.

Branzei, Sylvia. Animal Grossology: The Science of Creatures Gross & Disgusting. Keely, Jack, illus. 2004. 80p. (J). (gr. 3 up). reprint ed. pap. 9.99 (978-0-8431-1011-1(2) , Price Stern Sloan) Penguin Group (USA) Inc.

Brooks, Sue. Fun with African Animal Stencils. 1999. (Illus.). 6p. (J). pap. 1.50 (978-0-486-40758-6(0)) Dover Pubns., Inc.

Burkhard, Balthasar. Click, Said the Camera. 2006. (Illus.). 42p. pap. 30.00 (978-3-907044-56-8(8)) Lars Muller CHE. *Dist:* Chronicle Bks. LLC.

Cerfolli, Fulvio. The Animal Atlas. 1998. (Everyday Life of Animals Ser.). (Illus.). 64p. (YA). (gr. 4-6). lib. bdg. 19.98 (978-0-8172-4198-8(1)) Raintree.

Chancellor, Deborah. The Kingfisher First Animal Picture Atlas. Lewis, Anthony, illus. 2006. (Kingfisher First Ser.). 48p. (J). (gr. k-3). 10.95 (978-0-7534-5988-1(4) , Kingfisher) Houghton Mifflin Co. Trade & Reference Div.

Chang, Lynn. Look at Me! Animals: My Own Photo Book. 2000. (Look at Me! Ser.). (Illus.). 20p. (J). (ps-3). bds. 6.95 (978-0-8118-2255-8(9)) Chronicle Bks. LLC.

Cheney, Martha C. Animal Almanac: A Reference Book. Manwaring, Kerry, illus. 1999. (Gifted & Talented Ser.). 79p. (J). (gr. 1-3). pap. 6.95 (978-0-7373-0052-9(3)) Lowell Hse. Juvenile.

Childrens Press Staff, ed. Wild Animals. 1998. (Rookie Read-About Science Ser.). pap. 33.17 (978-0-516-29982-2(4) , Children's Pr.) Scholastic Library Publishing.

Clements, Andrew. Brave Norman: A True Story. Beier, Ellen, illus. 2001. (Pets to the Rescue Ser.: Bk. 2). 32p. (J). (gr. k-3). 15.00 (978-0-689-82914-7(0)) Simon & Schuster Children's Publishing.

Clements, Andrew & Beier, Ellen. Dolores & the Big Fire: A True Story. Cook, Donald, illus. 2002. (Pets to the Rescue Ser.: Bk. 3). 32p. (J). (gr. k-1). 15.00 (978-0-689-82916-1(7)) Simon & Schuster Children's Publishing.

Dennard, Deborah. Daring Deborah's down under Safari Vol. 3: Animals of Australia. Reinhardt, Megan, illus. Silkstone, Barry, photos by. 1998. (Daring Deborah's Safaris Ser.). (J). (gr. k-5). 59.95 incl. cd-rom (978-1-889081-05-2(1)); cd-rom 49.95 (978-1-889081-03-8(5)) Electronic Bks. for Kids.

Discovery Books Staff & Myers, Philip. Mammals: An Explore Your World Handbook. 2000. (Explore Your World Ser.). (Illus.). 192p. pap. 14.95 (978-1-56331-838-2(5)) Discovery Bks.

Dogi, Fiametta. God Made Animal Families. Dogi, Fiametta, illus. 1999. (God Made Animals Ser.). (Illus.). 10p. (J). (ps). bds. 3.99 (978-0-7847-0883-5(5) , 03760, Bean Sprouts) Standard Publishing.

—God Made Baby Animals. Dogi, Fiametta, illus. 1999. (God Made Animals Ser.). (Illus.). 10p. (J). (ps). bds. 3.99 (978-0-7847-0882-8(7) , 03758, Bean Sprouts) Standard Publishing.

—God Made Jungle Animals. Dogi, Fiametta, illus. 1999. (God Made Animals Ser.). (Illus.). 10p. (J). (ps). bds. 3.99 (978-0-7847-0881-1(9) , 03757, Bean Sprouts) Standard Publishing.

—God Made Sea Animals. Dogi, Fiametta, illus. 1999. (God Made Animals Ser.). (Illus.). 10p. (J). (ps). bds. 3.99 (978-0-7847-0884-2(3) , 03761, Bean Sprouts) Standard Publishing.

Doherty, Berlie. Coconutomes to School. 2003. (Illus.). 32p. (J). pap. 9.99 (978-0-00-710434-5(0)) HarperCollins Pubs. Ltd. GBR. *Dist:* Independent Pubs. Group.

Doyle, Alfreda C. Animals & Their Life Spans: Story Rhyme Coloring Book. 1998. (Illus.). 24p. (J). (gr. 3-8). pap. 8.95 (978-1-56820-325-6(X)) Story Time Stories That Rhyme.

Dunn, Phoebe. A Big Treasury of Little Animals. Dunn, Phoebe, illus. 2007. (Illus.). 192p. (J). (gr. k-2). 10.99 (***978-0-375-84177-4(6)*** , Random Hse. Bks. for Young Readers) Random Hse. Children's Bks.

Ehrich, Joanne. Koalas: Zen in Fur, Hardcover Edition. 2007. (Illus.). 96p. 44.99 (***978-0-9764698-6-5(3))*** Koala Jo Publishing.

Eichenberg, Fritz. Ape in a Cape: An Alphabet of Odd Animals. Eichenberg, Fritz, illus. 2002. (Illus.) (J). 14.04 (978-0-7587-0092-6(X)) Book Wholesalers, Inc.

Farmyard Friends. (Magnets on the Move Ser.). 8p. (J). bds. (978-2-7643-0147-0(2)) Phidal Publishing, Inc./Editions Phidal, Inc.

First Book about Animals, 4 bks. Incl. First Book about Animals in the Water. 2000. lib. bdg. 19.33 (978-0-8368-2653-1(1)); First Book about Animals of the Forests. 1999. lib. bdg. 19.33 (978-0-8368-2650-0(7)); First Book about Animals of the Plains. 1999. lib. bdg. 19.33 (978-0-8368-2651-7(5)); First Book about Animals of the Polar Regions. 1999. lib. bdg. 19.33 (978-0-8368-2652-4(3)); 16p. (J). (ps up). (Illus.). 1999. Set lib. bdg. 77.32 (978-0-8368-2649-4(3)) Stevens, Gareth Inc.

First Book about Animals in the Water. 2000. (First Book about Animals Ser.). (Illus.). 16p. (J). (ps up). lib. bdg. 19.33 (978-0-8368-2653-1(1)) Stevens, Gareth Inc.

First Book about Animals of the Forests. 1999. (First Book about Animals Ser.). (Illus.). 16p. (J). (ps up). lib. bdg. 19.33 (978-0-8368-2650-0(7)) Stevens, Gareth Inc.

First Book about Animals of the Plains. 1999. (First Book about Animals Ser.). (Illus.). 16p. (J). (ps up). lib. bdg. 19.33 (978-0-8368-2651-7(5)) Stevens, Gareth Inc.

First Book about Animals of the Polar Regions. 1999. (First Book about Animals Ser.). (Illus.). 16p. (J). (ps up). lib. bdg. 19.33 (978-0-8368-2652-4(3)) Stevens, Gareth Inc.

Fredericks, Anthony D. Animal Sharpshooters. 2000. (Watts Library). (Illus.). 64p. (gr. 5-7). pap. 8.95 (978-0-531-16417-4(9) , Watts, Franklin) Scholastic Library Publishing.

Freymann, Saxton & Elffers, Joost. Baby Food. 2006. (Illus.). 26p. (J). bds. 6.99 (978-0-439-11021-1(1) , Levine, Arthur A. Bks.) Scholastic, Inc.

—Dog Food. 2006. (Illus.). 26p. (J). bds. 6.99 (978-0-439-11020-4(3) , Levine, Arthur A. Bks.) Scholastic, Inc.

Golden Books Staff. Animal Amigos. 2007. (Color Plus Gatefold Sticker Ser.). (Illus.). 16p. (J). (ps-2). pap. 3.99 (978-0-375-84147-7(4) , Golden Bks.) Random Hse. Children's Bks.

Hale, Rachael. Furry Friends. rev. ed. 2007. (Paw Pals Ser.). 20p. (J). (ps-ps). bds. 6.99 (***978-0-316-11319-9(0))*** Little, Brown Bks. for Young Readers.

—Love Tails. rev. ed. 2007. (Paw Pals Ser.). 20p. (J). (ps-ps). bds. 6.99 (***978-0-316-11321-2(2))*** Little, Brown Bks. for Young Readers.

Hammond Inc. Staff, ed. Hammond Animal Atlas. 2005. (Atlas Ser.). (Illus.). 32p. pap. 10.95 (978-0-8437-0918-6(9) , 709189) Langenscheidt Pubs Inc.

Harcourt School Publishers Staff. A Cat Has Four Paws. 3rd ed. 2002. (Trophies English Language Learners Ser.). (Illus.). (J). pap. 4.10 (978-0-15-327591-3(X)) Harcourt Schl. Pubs.

—A Cat Has Four Paws - 5 Pack - Grade 1. 3rd ed. 2002. (Trophies English Language Learners Ser.). 20.10 (978-0-15-327625-5(8)) Harcourt Schl. Pubs.

Hardy, Caroline, et al. Quiet Places: An Animal Care Book. 2006. (Through the Peephole Ser.). (Illus.). 48p. 9.95 (978-1-84560-016-7(9)) Mercury Bks. Ltd. GBR. *Dist:* International Publishers Marketing.

Harper, Ellen. Fun with Chinese Animals Stencils. 2003. (Dover Little Activity Bks.). (Illus.). 6p. (J). pap. 1.50 (978-0-486-43108-6(8)) Dover Pubns., Inc.

Havard, Christian. Untamed: Animals Around the World. Zicot, Emmanuelle, illus. Bloom, Steve, photos by. 2005. 76p. (J). (gr. 2-7). 18.95 (978-0-8109-5956-9(9) , Abrams Bks. for Young Readers) Abrams, Harry N., Inc.

Hemminger, Marcia. Baby Animals Early Learner Photo Fun Activities. Rogers, Kathy, ed. 2001. (Illus.). 8p. (J). (ps-1). pap. 6.95 (978-1-56472-381-9(X)) Edupress, Inc.

Hicks, R. Animals in Art. 2004. (Children's Art Ser. from the National Gallery of Victoria Ser.). (Illus.). 28p. 9.95 (978-0-7241-0236-5(1)) National Gallery of Victoria AUS. *Dist:* Antique Collectors' Club.

Hills, Tad. My Fuzzy Friends. Hills, Tad, illus. 1999. (Illus.). 14p. (J). (ps-3). 10.95 (978-0-689-82357-2(6) , Little Simon) Simon & Schuster Children's Publishing.

Hirschi Ron. When Morning Comes. 2006. (Illus.). 32p. pap. 9.95 (978-1-59078-416-7(2)) Boyds Mills Pr.

Hogenkamp, Susan. They Crawl! Learning the CR Sound. 2001. (PowerPhonics Ser.). (Illus.). 23p. (J). pap. 26.40 (978-0-8239-8292-9(0) , PowerKids Pr.) Rosen Publishing Group, Inc., The.

Innovative Kids Staff & Schultz, Lucy. Farm Faces: A Book of Masks. Larranaga, Ana, illus. 2006. 12p. (J). (ps-ps). bds. 5.99 (978-1-58476-471-7(6) , IKIDS) Innovative Kids.

Jenkins, Steve. Biggest, Strongest, Fastest. Jenkins, Steve, illus. 2002. (Illus.). (J). 13.77 (978-0-7587-2106-8(4)) Book Wholesalers, Inc.

Jenkins, Steve & Page, Robin. Move! Jenkins, Steve, illus. 2006. (Illus.). 32p. (J). (ps-k). 16.00 (978-0-618-64637-1(X)) Houghton Mifflin Co.

Johnson, Jinny. Skeletons: An Inside Look at Animals. Gray, Elizabeth, illus. 1999. 46p. (J). (gr. 5-7). reprint ed. 25.00 (978-0-7881-6810-9(X)) DIANE Publishing Co.

Knapik, Michael Don. Everything Elephants: A Collector's Pictorial Encyclopedia. 2002. (Schiffer Book for Collectors Ser.). (Illus.). 144p. (gr. 10-13). pap. 29.95 (978-0-7643-1494-0(7)) Schiffer Publishing, Ltd.

Kratter, Paul. The Living Rain Forest: An Animal Alphabet. Kratter, Paul, illus. 2006. (Illus.). 32p. (J). pap. 8.95 (978-1-57091-465-2(6)) Charlesbridge Publishing, Inc.

Krulik, Nancy E. Animal Friends: A Learning-to-Write Book. Baroux, illus. 2004. (My Little Chalkboard Ser.). 16p. (J). pap. 12.95 (978-0-7624-1435-2(9) , Running Pr. Kids) Running Pr. Bk. Pubs.

Kuchler, B. L. That's Life. 2003. (Illus.). 112p. (J). tchr. ed. 14.95 (978-1-57223-709-4(0) , 7090) Willow Creek Pr., Inc.

Kuchler, Bonnie Louise, compiled by. Just Kids: Pictures, Poems & Other Silly Animal Stuff Just for Kids! 2003. (Illus.). 32p. tchr. ed. 12.95 (978-1-57223-598-4(5) , 5985) Willow Creek Pr., Inc.

Ladybird Books Staff. First Picture Book: Animals. (First Picture Bks.: No. 832-3). (Illus.). 52p. (J). (ps). pap. 3.50 (978-0-7214-0751-7(X) , Dutton Juvenile) Penguin Group (USA) Inc.

Lever, E. & Lovett, K. Animals Are Fun!, 4 bks. Parish, Steve, photos by. Incl. Dolphins. Slater, P. lib. bdg. 19.33 (978-0-8368-2612-8(4)); Frogs. Slater, P. lib. bdg. 19.33 (978-0-8368-2613-5(2)); Kangaroos. Slater, P. lib. bdg. 19.33 (978-0-8368-2614-2(0)); Koalas. Slater, S. lib. bdg. 19.33 (978-0-8368-2615-9(9)); 16p. (J). (ps up). (Illus.). 1999. Set lib. bdg. 77.32 (978-0-8368-2611-1(6)) Stevens, Gareth Inc.

Litchfield & Allman. Los Animales (Animals) 2004. (First Words Board Bks.). (SPA., Illus.). 12p. (J). 4.95 (978-0-7460-4519-0(0)) EDC Publishing.

Llewellyn, Claire & Southwater Books Staff. Animals. 2002. (Playschool Ser.). (Illus.). 32p. (ps-2). pap. 5.95 (978-1-84215-606-3(3) , Southwater) Anness Publishing GBR. *Dist:* National Bk. Network.

Lorenz Books Staff & Llewellyn, Claire. Animals. 1999. (Fun to Learn Ser.). (Illus.). 48p. (ps-k). 7.95 (978-0-7548-0033-0(4)) Anness Publishing, Inc.

Lorenz Editors. Animal Friends, 4 vols., Set. 2002. (Mini Board Bks.). (Illus.). 12p. pap. 12.95 (978-0-7548-0878-7(5) , Lorenz Bks.) Anness Publishing, Inc.

Luton, Joanne. Rocky Mountain Wildlife Coloring Book. 2001. (Illus.). 36p. (J). (gr. 1-5). pap. 2.50 (978-0-931895-24-1(3)) Grand Teton Natural History Assn.

Magner Publishing Staff. Meet Your Backyard Friends. Magner Publishing Staff, illus. 1999. (Illus.). 16p. (J). (ps-7). pap. 4.95 (978-1-929416-04-2(0)) Magner Publishing & American Binding & Publishing.

Make Believe Ideas, Ltd. Touch & Learn - God's Animals. 2007. (Illus.). 12p. (J). (ps). bds. 6.97 (978-1-59145-555-4(3)) Nelson, Thomas Inc.

Mason, Cherie & Kellogg Markowsky, Judy. Everybody's Somebody's Lunch: The Role of Predator & Prey in Nature. Giebfried, Rosemary, illus. 1998. 70p. (gr. 3-6). pap., tchr. ed., tchr.'s training gde. ed. 9.95 (978-0-88448-199-7(9)) Tilbury Hse. Pubs.

Mayhew, James. Cluck, Cluck Who's There? Church, Caroline J., illus. 2004. 20p. (J). pap. 9.95 (978-0-439-57737-3(3)) Scholastic, Inc.

Maze, Stephanie, ed. Momentos de paz en el reino Animal: Los animales y sus Hogares. 2006. (Moments in the Wild Ser.). (SPA., Illus.). 36p. (J). pap. 8.00 (978-0-9769542-3-1(0)) Moonstone Pr.

—Momentos tiernos en el reino Animal: Los animales y sus Bebes. 2006. (Moments in the Wild Ser.). (SPA., Illus.). 36p. (J). pap. 8.00 (978-0-9769542-2-4(2)) Moonstone Pr.

Miller, Sara Swan. Horses & Rhinos: What They Have in Common. 2000. (Animals in Order Ser.). (Illus.). 48p. (J). (gr. 4-6). pap. 6.95 (978-0-531-16401-3(2) , Watts, Franklin) Scholastic Library Publishing.

Moday, Jane, illus. God Loves Little Lamb. 1999. (Bend-N-Snuggle Bks.). 18p. (gr. k-ps). 10.99 (978-0-7847-0972-6(6) , 03542, Bean Sprouts) Standard Publishing.

Morgan, Sally. Animals As Friends. 2000. (Animals That Help Us Ser.). (Illus.). 32p. (J). (gr. 1-3). pap. 6.95 (978-0-531-15403-8(3) , Watts, Franklin) Scholastic Library Publishing.

Murray, Kirsty. Man-Eaters & Blood Suckers. 1998. (True Stories Ser.). (Illus.). 100p. (J). (gr. 2-3). 6.95 (978-1-86448-630-8(9)) Allen & Unwin AUS. *Dist:* Independent Pubs. Group.

Oliver, Clare. Animals Helping with Special Needs. 1999. (gr. 3-6). lib. bdg. 15.25 (978-0-613-53917-3(6)) Tandem Library Bks.

—Animals in Dangerous Places. 1999. (gr. 3-6). lib. bdg. 15.25 (978-0-613-53918-0(4)) Tandem Library Bks.

—Animals on the Move. 2000. (Animals That Help Us Ser.). (Illus.). 32p. (J). (gr. 1-3). pap. 6.95 (978-0-531-15405-2(X) , Watts, Franklin) Scholastic Library Publishing.

—Animals on the Move. 1999. (gr. 3-6). lib. bdg. 15.25 (978-0-613-53921-0(4)) Tandem Library Bks.

Pascoe, Elaine, ed. Into Wild California. 2003. (Jeff Corwin Experience Ser.). (Illus.). 48p. (J). 24.95 (978-1-56711-858-2(5) , Blackbirch Pr., Inc.) Thomson Gale.

Paul, Tessa. At the Poles. 1998. (Animal Trackers Ser.). (Illus.). 32p. (J). (gr. 2-3). pap. (978-0-86505-598-8(X)); lib. bdg. (978-0-86505-590-2(4)) Crabtree Publishing Co.

—Down Under. 1998. (Animal Trackers Ser.). (Illus.). 32p. (J). (gr. 2-3). pap. (978-0-86505-596-4(3)); lib. bdg. (978-0-86505-588-9(2)) Crabtree Publishing Co.

—On Safari. 1998. (Animal Trackers Ser.). (Illus.). 32p. (J). (gr. 2-3). lib. bdg. (978-0-86505-589-6(0)) Crabtree Publishing Co.

Porell, John. Amazing Journeys. 2005. (Illus.). 32p. (J). lib. bdg. 18.50 (978-0-7910-8769-5(7)) Facts On File, Inc.

Priddy, Roger & Priddy Books Staff. Sticker Acivity Fun Animals: Play & Learn. rev. ed. 2006. 48p. (J). bds. 3.47 (978-0-312-49795-8(4) , Priddy Bks.) St. Martin's Pr.

Richardson, Nan. Wild Babies. 2006. (Illus.). 80p. 16.95 (978-1-884167-51-5(9)) Umbrage Editions.

Robinson, Gary D. Who Pooped in the Park: Glacier. 2004. 48p. pap. 9.95 (978-1-56037-279-0(6)) Farcountry Pr.

Robson, Gary D. Who Pooped in Park: Grand Teton. 2004. 48p. pap. 9.95 (978-1-56037-280-6(X)) Farcountry Pr.

Ruurs, Margriet. In My Backyard. Broda, Ron, illus. 2007. 32p. (J). (ps-3). 18.95 (978-0-88776-775-3(3)) Tundra Bks., Inc./Livres Toundra, Inc. CAN. *Dist:* Random Hse., Inc.

—Wild Babies. Kiss, Andrew, illus. 2003. 32p. (J). (ps-3). 14.95 (978-0-88776-627-5(7)) Tundra Bks., Inc./Livres Toundra, Inc. CAN. *Dist:* Random Hse., Inc.

Schwartz, David M. Animal Ears. Kuhn, Dwight, photos by. 1999. (Springboards into Science Ser.). (Illus.). 24p. (J). (gr. 1 up). lib. bdg. 20.67 (978-0-8368-2576-3(4)) Stevens, Gareth Inc.

—Animal Eyes. Kuhn, Dwight, photos by. 1999. (Springboards into Science Ser.). (Illus.). 24p. (J). (gr. 1 up). lib. bdg. 20.67 (978-0-8368-2423-0(7)) Stevens, Gareth Inc.

—Animal Feathers & Fur. Kuhn, Dwight, photos by. 1999. (Springboards into Science Ser.). (Illus.). 24p. (J). (gr. 1 up). lib. bdg. 20.67 (978-0-8368-2424-7(5)) Stevens, Gareth Inc.

—Animal Feet. Kuhn, Dwight, photos by. 1999. (Springboards into Science Ser.). (Illus.). 24p. (J). (gr. 1 up). lib. bdg. 20.67 (978-0-8368-2577-0(2)) Stevens, Gareth Inc.

—Animal Mouths. Kuhn, Dwight, photos by. 1999. (Springboards into Science Ser.). (Illus.). 24p. (J). (gr. 1 up). lib. bdg. 20.67 (978-0-8368-2425-4(3)) Stevens, Gareth Inc.

—Animal Noses. Kuhn, Dwight, photos by. 1999. (Springboards into Science Ser.). (Illus.). 24p. (J). (gr. 1 up). lib. bdg. 20.67 (978-0-8368-2578-7(0)) Stevens, Gareth Inc.

—Animal Skin & Scales. Kuhn, Dwight, photos by. 1999. (Springboards into Science Ser.). (Illus.). 24p. (J). (gr. 1 up). lib. bdg. 20.67 (978-0-8368-2579-4(9)) Stevens, Gareth Inc.

—Animal Tails. Kuhn, Dwight, photos by. 1999. (Springboards into Science Ser.). (Illus.). 24p. (J). (gr. 1 up). lib. bdg. 20.67 (978-0-8368-2426-1(1)) Stevens, Gareth Inc.

Seder, Rufus Butler. Gallop! 2007. (Illus.). 12p. 12.95 ***(978-0-7611-4763-3(2))*** Workman Publishing Co., Inc.

Snedden, Robert. Animals Protecting Us. 2000. (Animals That Help Us Ser.). (Illus.). 32p. (J). (gr. 1-3). pap. 6.95 (978-0-531-15406-9(8) , Watts, Franklin) Scholastic Library Publishing.

Sovak, Jan. Learning about Forest Animals. 1998. (Learning about Ser.). (Illus.). 16p. (J). (gr. 3-5). pap. 1.50 (978-0-486-40334-2(3) , 40334-3) Dover Pubns., Inc.

Squire, Ann O. African Animals. 2002. (True Bks.). (J). (gr. 3-5). pap. 6.95 (978-0-516-25994-9(6) , Children's Pr.) Scholastic Library Publishing.

—African Animals. 2001. (gr. 3-6). lib. bdg. 15.25 (978-0-613-51608-2(7)) Tandem Library Bks.

Steck-Vaughn Staff. Animals of the Rain Forest Collection. 2002. (Illus.). (J). pap. (978-0-7398-7818-7(2)) Steck-Vaughn.

Sterling, Mary E. Dinosaurs Photo Fun Activities. Rogers, Kathy, ed. Carrozza, John, illus. 1998. (Science Photo Fun Activities Ser.). 8p. (J). pap. 6.95 (978-1-56472-090-0(X)) Edupress, Inc.

Sterling/Balloon. Animals on the Farm Super Sticker Book. 2003. (Sticker Bks.). (Illus.). 16p. (J). (ps-1). pap. 4.95 (978-0-8069-2667-4(8) , Balloon Bks.) Sterling Publishing Co., Inc.

Stewart, Melissa. Extreme Nature! Q&A. 2006. (Illus.). 48p. (J). 16.99 (978-0-06-089937-0(9)); pap. 6.99 (978-0-06-089936-3(0)) HarperCollins Pubs.

—Eye See You Poster Book. Balmuth, Deborah & Guare, Sarah, eds. Vaughn, Vicky, illus. 2006. 64p. (J). pap. 9.95 (978-1-58017-848-8(0)) Storey Publishing, LLC.

Stimson, Judith A. Animal & Photography Adventures. Stimson, Judith A., photos by. 1999. (Illus.). 115p. (J). (gr. 3-5). wbk. ed. 25.00 (978-0-9669879-0-4(X)) ABConsulting.

Stout, William. William Stout - Animal Sketches from Around the World. 2003. (Illus.). 54p. (YA). per. 15.00 (978-0-9712716-8-5(2)) Stout, William Inc.

—William Stout - Tribute to Ray Harryhausen. 2003. (Illus.). 70p. (YA). per. 20.00 (978-0-9712716-9-2(0)) Stout, William Inc.

Sweeney, Kathie. Science Questions & Answers: Animals. Nolte, Larry, illus. 1999. (Science Questions & Answers Ser.). 63p. (J). (gr. 1-3). pap. 5.95 (978-0-7373-0056-7(6)) Lowell Hse. Juvenile.

Thompson, Richard & Thompson, Ofa. Ko 'eku tohi 'oe fanga Manu. Slutz, Stephani, illus. 2004. (TON.). 16p. (J). (ps up). pap. 5.00 (978-0-9678979-2-9(0)) Friendly Isles Pr.

Thornhill, Jan. The Wildlife ABC & 123: A Nature Alphabet & Counting Book. 2004. (Illus.). 64p. (J). 16.95 (978-1-897066-09-6(0)) Maple Tree Pr. CAN. *Dist:* Perseus Distribution.

Tiere der Nacht. (GER.). (978-3-411-09261-1(0)) Bibliographisches Institut & F. A. Brockhaus AG DEU. *Dist:* i.b.d., Ltd.

Tildes, Phyllis L. Animals Brightly Colored. 1998. (J). (978-0-606-13135-3(3)) Tandem Library Bks.

Toft, Kim Michelle. The World That We Want. 2005. (Illus.). 32p. (J). (ps-ps). pap. 6.95 (978-1-58089-115-8(2)); bds. 16.95 (978-1-58089-114-1(4)) Charlesbridge Publishing, Inc.

Tuxworth, Nicola. Animals. 2005. (Illus.). 12p. (gr. 2-13). bds. 6.99 (978-0-7548-1417-7(3) , Lorenz Bks.) Anness Publishing GBR. *Dist:* National Bk. Network.

—Baby Animals. 2001. (Very First Picture Bks.). (Illus.). 20p. 5.95 (978-0-7548-0938-8(2)) Anness Publishing GBR. *Dist:* National Bk. Network.

—Kittens. (Illus.). (ps). 2005. 12p. bds. 6.99 (978-0-7548-1333-0(9) , Lorenz Bks.); 2001. 20p. 5.95 (978-0-7548-0942-5(0)) Anness Publishing GBR. *Dist:* National Bk. Network.

—Kittens. 1999. (Very First Picture Bks.). (Illus.). 12p. bds. 4.95 (978-0-7548-0067-5(9)) Anness Publishing, Inc.

—Kittens: A Very First Picture Book. 1999. (Pictures & Words Ser.). (Illus.). 24p. (J). (ps up). lib. bdg. 22.00 (978-0-8368-2273-1(0)) Stevens, Gareth Inc.

—Wild Animals, 12 vols. (Illus.). 2006. 12p. bds. 6.99 (978-0-7548-1363-7(0) , Lorenz Bks.); 2001. 20p. 5.95 (978-0-7548-0944-9(7)) Anness Publishing GBR. *Dist:* National Bk. Network.

Tuxworth, Nicole. Baby Animals. 2005. (Illus.). 12p. (ps). bds. 6.99 (978-0-7548-1334-7(7) , Lorenz Bks.) Anness Publishing GBR. *Dist:* National Bk. Network.

Two-Can Publishing Ltd. Staff, contrib. by. Wild Animals. 2004. (Interfact Play & Discover Ser.). (Illus.). 48p. (J). (ps-2). 14.95 incl. cd-rom (978-1-58728-628-5(9) , Two Can Publishing) T&N Children's Publishing.

Vernon, Tannis & Longmore, Rich, illus. Glacier National Park Wildlife. 2004. (Postcard Book Ser.). 40p. 9.95 (978-0-7627-2903-6(1) , Falcon) Globe Pequot Pr., The.

Vess, Deborah, et al. AP World History (REA) - the Best Test Prep for the AP World History. Knight, Theodore, ed. 2006. (Test Preps Ser.). (Illus.). 768p. (gr. 5-12). pap. 17.95 (978-0-7386-0128-1(4)) Research & Education Assn.

Wickings, Ruth. Animals on the Ice. 2006. (First Fun Pop-ups Ser.). (Illus.). 12p. bds. 8.95 (978-1-84560-022-8(3)) Mercury Bks. Ltd. GBR. *Dist:* International Publishers Marketing.

Wild Animals Sticker Activity Book. 2003. (Illus.). 12p. (J). 2.98 (978-1-4054-1183-7(X)) Parragon, Inc.

Wild Cats & Other Dangerous Predators. 2002. (Wild, Wild World Ser.). 32p. (J). 9.95 (978-0-7525-4682-7(1)) Parragon, Inc.

Wilkens, Drew. Gecko's & Other Bead Animals. Wilkens, Kelley, ed. Wilkens, Drew, illus. 1998. (Illus.). 40p. (J). (gr. 1 up). pap. 7.95 (978-0-9663591-0-7(0)) Bead Man Pr.

Wormell, Christopher. New Alphabet of Animals. 2006. (Illus.). 26p. (J). pap. 6.95 (978-0-7624-2729-1(9) , Running Pr. Kids) Running Pr. Bk. Pubs.

—Teeth, Tails & Tentacles. 2006. (Illus.). 22p. (J). pap. 6.95 (978-0-7624-2728-4(0) , Running Pr. Kids) Running Pr. Bk. Pubs.

Yolen, Jane. Animal Train: A Lift-the-Flap Concept Book. Cushman, Doug, illus. 2002. 14p. (J). (ps-1). bds. 8.99 (978-0-689-84838-4(2) , Little Simon) Simon & Schuster Children's Publishing.

ANIMALS—POETRY

Ackerman, Diane. The Senses of Animals. 2000. (J). 14.95 (978-0-375-80400-7(5)); lib. bdg. 16.99 (978-0-375-90400-4(X)) Knopf, Alfred A. Inc.

—The Senses of Animals. 2002. lib. bdg. 17.99 (978-0-517-70918-4(X)) Random Hse., Inc.

Andreae, Giles. Rumble in the Jungle. Wojtowycz, David, illus. 2002. 36p. (J). pap. 7.95 (978-1-58925-367-4(1) , tiger tales) ME Media LLC.

—Rumble in the Jungle. 2002. (ps-2). lib. bdg. 15.25 (978-0-613-46096-5(0)) Tandem Library Bks.

Bagert, Brod. Giant Children. Arnold, Tedd, illus. 2005. 32p. (J). pap. 6.99 (978-0-14-240192-7(7) , Puffin) Penguin Group (USA) Inc.

Banks, Kate. Fox. Hallensleben, Georg, illus. 2007. 40p. (J). (ps-1). 16.00 (978-0-374-39967-2(0) , Farrar, Straus & Giroux (BYR)) Farrar, Straus & Giroux.

Bond, Felicia. Tumble Bumble. Bond, Felicia, illus. 2002. (Illus.). (J). 14.43 (978-0-7587-3873-8(0)) Book Wholesalers, Inc.

—Tumble Bumble. braille ed. 2004. (Illus.). (J). (gr. 1). spiral bd., bds. (978-0-616-03081-3(9)) Canadian National Institute for the Blind/Institut National Canadien pour les Aveugles.

—Tumble Bumble. Bond, Felicia, illus. (Laura Geringer Bks.). (Illus.). (J). (ps-k). 1999. 18p. bds. 7.99 (978-0-694-01344-9(7) , Harper Festival); 2000. 32p. reprint ed. pap. 6.99 (978-0-06-443585-7(7) , Harper Trophy) HarperCollins Pubs.

—Tumble Bumble. 2000. (978-0-606-18724-4(3)); lib. bdg. 14.10 (978-0-613-28682-4(0)) Tandem Library Bks.

Bradman, Tony. Wild & Wonderful: Poems about the Natural World. Wintringham, Susan, illus. 2003. 32p. (978-0-7502-3928-8(X) , Hodder Wayland) Hodder Children's Division.

Carle, Eric. Eric Carle's Animals Animals. 1999. (J). 14.64 (978-0-606-17256-1(4)); (gr. 3-6). lib. bdg. 16.45 (978-0-613-22847-3(2)) Tandem Library Bks.

Charles, Faustin. Once upon an Animal. 1998. (Illus.). 64p. (J). pap. 8.99 (978-0-7475-3865-3(4)) Bloomsbury Publishing Plc GBR. *Dist:* Independent Pubs. Group.

Chorao, Kay. Jumpety-Bumpety-Hop: A Parade of Animal Poems. 2000. (Illus.). (J). (978-0-606-18415-1(5)) Tandem Library Bks.

Cordova, Soledad. Poemas de Perros y Gatos. Graullera, Fabiola, illus. 2003. (SPA.). 21p. (J). (gr. 3-5). pap. 7.95 (978-968-19-0987-1(9)) Santillana USA Publishing Co., Inc.

Cotner, June, ed. Bless the Beasts: Children's Prayers & Poems about Animals. Waldherr, Kris, illus. 2006. 63p. (J). (gr. 4-8). reprint ed. 13.00 (978-0-7567-9952-6(X)) DIANE Publishing Co.

Cricket Magazine Group. Ladybug, Ladybug & Other Favorite Poems. 2007. (Illus.). 40p. (J). 17.95 (978-0-8126-7936-6(9)) Cricket Bks.

Cyrus, Kurt. Hotel Deep: Light Verse from Dark Water. 2005. (Illus.). 40p. (J). 16.00 (978-0-15-216771-4(4)) Harcourt Trade Pubs.

Dahl, Roald. Dirty Beasts. Blake, Quentin, illus. 2002. 14.04 (978-1-4046-1747-6(7)) Book Wholesalers, Inc.

—Dirty Beasts. Blake, Quentin, illus. 2002. 32p. (J). pap. 6.99 (978-0-14-230227-9(9) , Puffin) Penguin Group (USA) Inc.

—Dirty Beasts. 2002. (gr. k-3). lib. bdg. 15.30 (978-0-613-63931-6(6)) Tandem Library Bks.

Dixon, Peter. Peter Dixon's Grand Prix of Poetry. Thomas, David, illus. 2003. 62p. (J). pap. 6.99 (978-0-330-35544-5(9) , Pan) Pan Macmillan GBR. *Dist:* Trafalgar Square Publishing.

Esbensen, Barbara Juster. Words with Wrinkled Knees: Animal Poems. 2003. (Illus.). 48p. (YA). (gr. 2-4). pap. 10.95 (978-1-56397-682-7(X)) Boyds Mills Pr.

—Words with Wrinkled Knees: Animal Poems. 1998. (gr. k-3). lib. bdg. 17.60 (978-0-613-78813-7(3)) Tandem Library Bks.

Ewing, Susan. Lucky Hares & Itchy Bears. Zerbetz, Evon, illus. 2005. 32p. (gr. 1 up). pap. 8.95 (978-0-88240-551-3(9)) Graphic Arts Ctr. Publishing Co.

Fearnley, Jan & Andreae, Giles. Rumble in the Jungle. Wojtowycz, David, illus. 2001. 28p. (J). (ps-k). tchr. ed. 16.95 (978-1-58925-005-5(2) , tiger tales) ME Media LLC.

Florian, Douglas. Beast Feast. Halverson, Deborah, ed. 1998. (Illus.). 48p. (J). (ps-3). pap. 7.00 (978-0-15-201737-8(2) , Harcourt Paperbacks) Harcourt Children's Bks.

—Beast Feast. 1998. (J). 13.80 (978-0-606-13184-1(1)) Tandem Library Bks.

—Omnibeasts: Animal Poems & Paintings. 2004. (Illus.). 96p. (J). 18.00 (978-0-15-205038-2(8)) Harcourt Children's Bks.

—Zoo's Who: Poems & Paintings. 2005. (Illus.). 56p. (J). (gr. k-5). 17.00 (978-0-15-204639-2(9)) Harcourt Children's Bks.

Foster, John. Pet Poems. Paul, Korky, illus. 2nd rev. ed. 2007. 32p. (YA). 9.95 ***(978-0-19-276345-7(8))*** Oxford Univ. Pr., Inc.

Frost, Robert. The Runaway. Lang, Glenna, illus. Date not set. 32p. pap. 9.95 (978-1-56792-243-1(0)) Godine, David R. Pub.

Frost, Robert & Lang, Glenna. The Runaway. 1998. (Illus.). 32p. (YA). (ps-4). 17.95 (978-1-56792-006-2(3)) Godine, David R. Pub.

Galdone, Paul. Over in the Meadow. 1998. (J). pap. 5.95 (978-0-87628-986-0(3)) Ctr. for Applied Research in Education, The.

George, Kristine O'Connell. Fold Me a Poem. Stringer, Lauren, illus. 2005. 56p. (J). 16.00 (978-0-15-202501-4(4)) Harcourt Trade Pubs.

Hague, Michael. Animal Friends: A Collection of Poems for Children. Hague, Michael, illus. rev. ed. 2007. (Illus.). 31p. (J). (ps-3). 16.95 (978-0-8050-3817-0(5)) Holt, Henry & Co.

Harley, Avis. Sea Stars: Saltwater Poems. Butschler, Margaret, photos by. 2006. (Illus.). 32p. (J). 16.95 (978-1-59078-429-7(4)) Boyds Mills Pr.

Hollander, John, ed. Animal Poems. Mulazzani, Simona, illus. 2004. (Poetry for Young People Ser.). 48p. 14.95 (978-1-4027-0926-5(9)) Sterling Publishing Co., Inc.

Hopkins, Lee Bennett. A Pet for Me: Poems. Manning, Jane, illus. (I Can Read Bks.). 48p. (J). (gr. k-3). 2004. pap. 3.99 (978-0-06-443716-5(7) , Harper Trophy); 2003. 15.99 (978-0-06-029111-2(7)) HarperCollins Pubs.

Horton, Joan. Hippopotamus Stew & Other Silly Animal Poems. Adinolfi, JoAnn, illus. rev. ed. 2006. 32p. (J). 16.95 (978-0-8050-7350-8(7) , Holt, Henry & Co. Bks. For Young Readers) Holt, Henry & Co.

Hudson, Beverly J. Bees to Baleens: The Rhyme & the Rhythm of Living Things. Hammons, Marjorie, ed. Hudson, Beverly J., illus. Hudson, Delise L., photos by. 2001. (Illus.). 32p. (J). (ps-3). lib. bdg. 16.95 (978-0-9658040-5-9(4) , 40-5-4) Talents From God.

Hummon, David M. Animal Acrostics. 1999. (gr. 3-6). lib. bdg. 16.40 (978-0-613-27709-9(0)) Tandem Library Bks.

Huseinovic, Andrea Petrlik, illus. Cuddly Critters: Animal Nursery Rhymes. 2006. (Mother Goose Rhymes Ser.). 32p. (J). (ps-2). lib. bdg. 25.26 ***(978-1-4048-2344-0(1)*** , 1265749) Picture Window Bks.

Jones, Tim. Wild Critters (new Edition) Walker, Tom, photos by. 2007. 48p. (J). pap. 9.95 ***(978-0-9790470-2-2(1))*** Epicenter Pr., Inc.

Jubb, Mike. The Ghost of My Pussycat's Bottom. 2006. (ENG.). 96p. per. ***(978-1-904529-23-1(2)*** , Back to Front) Solidus.

Kumin, Maxine. Mites to Mastodons: A Book of Animal Poems. Zagarenski, Pamela, illus. 2006. 32p. (J). (gr. k-3). 16.00 (978-0-618-50753-5(1)) Houghton Mifflin Co.

Kuskin, Karla. Roar & More. ed. 2004. (Illus.). 48p. (J). (ps up). 11.95 (978-1-59078-249-1(6)) Boyds Mills Pr.

Lacome, Julie. Walking Through the Jungle. Lacome, Julie, illus. (Big Books! Ser.). (Illus.). (J). (gr. k-1). 2004. 32p. pap. 19.99 (978-0-7636-2471-2(3)); 1999. 24p. pap. 3.99 (978-0-7636-0876-7(9)) Candlewick Pr.

Landry, Sophamae Dean. A Through Z Animal Poetry. 2000. (Illus.). 64p. (J). 20.00 (978-0-8059-4796-0(5)) Dorrance Publishing Co., Inc.

Larios, Julie Hofstrand. Yellow Elephant: A Bright Bestiary. Paschkis, Julie, illus. 2006. 32p. (J). (gr. k-5). 16.00 (978-0-15-205422-9(7)) Harcourt Trade Pubs.

Larios, Julie Hofstrand & Paschkis, Julie. Imaginary Menagerie: A Book of Curious Creatures. 2008. (Illus.). 32p. (J). 16.00 ***(978-0-15-206325-2(0))*** Harcourt Trade Pubs.

Lear, Edward. Bisky Bats & Pussy Cats: The Animal Nonsense of Edward Lear. Harrison, Matilda, illus. (J). 2001. 32p. pap. 11.00 (978-0-7475-4124-0(8)); 1998. 24p. 19.99 (978-0-7475-3556-0(6)) Bloomsbury Publishing Plc GBR. *Dist:* Trafalgar Square Publishing.

Lear, Edward. The Owl & the Pussycat. Jorisch, Stéphane, illus. 2007. (Visions in Poetry Ser.). 48p. (YA). (gr. 5 up). ***(978-1-55337-828-0(8))***; pap. ***(978-1-55453-232-2(9))*** Kids Can Pr., Ltd.

Lewin, Betsy. Animal Snackers. rev. ed. 2004. (Illus.). 32p. (J). 15.95 (978-0-8050-6748-4(5) , Holt, Henry & Co. Bks. For Young Readers) Holt, Henry & Co.

Lewis, J. Patrick. Swan Song. Wormell, Christopher, illus. 2005. 32p. (J). reprint ed. 17.00 (978-0-7567-8662-5(2)) DIANE Publishing Co.

—Tulip at Bat. Hirao, Amiko, illus. 2007. 32p. (J). (gr. k-3). 16.99 (978-0-316-61280-7(4)) Little Brown & Co.

Lowe, Judith. Animals at the Zoo, on the Loose Too. 2001. (Illus.). (J). (978-1-56492-349-3(5)) Laredo Publishing Co., Inc.

Lujan, Jorge & Monroy, Manuel. Rooster Gallo. Monroy, Manuel & Amado, Elisa, trs. Lujan, Jorge, illus. 2004. (ENG & SPA., Illus.). 24p. (J). 14.95 (978-0-88899-558-2(X)) Groundwood Bks. CAN. *Dist:* Perseus Distribution.

Maioli, Elizabeth, illus. Arrest That Asparagus! Manna, Elizabeth, photos by. 2000. 30p. (J). (gr. 1-5). pap. 9.95 (978-0-9729807-1-5(7)) Murray, David M.

Mann, Kirk. If Dogs Could Talk & Other Animal Poems. Lanz, Lucille, ed. Mann, Kirk, illus. 1998. (Illus.). 128p. (J). (gr. 2-4). pap. 12.95 (978-1-892517-00-5(0)) Flying Snail Pr.

Miranda, Anne. To Market, to Market. Stevens, Janet, illus. 2002. (J). 23.40 (978-0-7587-3820-2(X)) Book Wholesalers, Inc.

—To Market, to Market. Stevens, Janet, illus. 2001. 36p. (J). (ps-ps). pap. 7.00 (978-0-15-216398-3(0) , Voyager Bks./Libros Viajeros) Harcourt Children's Bks.

—To Market, to Market. 2001. (978-0-606-22597-7(8)); lib. bdg. 14.15 (978-0-613-60755-1(4)) Tandem Library Bks.

Montalvo, Margarita. Zoolygico de Poemas / Poetry Zoo. Montalvo, Margarita, illus. 2006. (SPA., Illus.). 48p. (J). (gr. 2-5). pap. 4.99 (978-0-439-70681-0(5) , Scholastic en Espanol) Scholastic, Inc.

Morpurgo, Michael, ed. More Muck & Magic. Blake, Quentin, illus. 2001. 148p. (J). pap. 8.99 (978-0-7497-4094-8(9)) Egmont Bks., Ltd. GBR. *Dist:* Independent Pubs. Group.

Nash, Myrna Lee. Spinman, Katydid & Bump: A Spider Vane Collection. Johnson, Sharon, illus. 2003. 48p. (YA). (gr. 4-10). 11.95 (978-0-9724549-0-2(X)) Chapter & Verse Pr.

Pearson, Susan. Squeal & Squawk: Barnyard Talk. Slonim, David, tr. Slonim, David, illus. 2004. 32p. (J). 16.95 (978-0-7614-5160-0(9)) Cavendish, Marshall Corp.

Pierce, Terry. Cuddly Critters. 2007. (Mother Goose Rhymes Ser.). (Illus.). 32p. (J). ***978-1-4048-2350-1(6)** , 1265749) Picture Window Bks.

Plourde, Lynn. Pigs in the Mud in the Middle of the Rud. Schoenherr, John, illus. ed. 2006. 32p. 15.95 (978-0-89272-719-3(5)) Down East Bks.

Prelutsky, Jack. In Aunt Giraffe's Green Garden. Mathers, Petra, illus. 2007. 64p. (J). (gr. 2-5). 16.99 (978-0-06-623868-5(4)); lib. bdg. 17.89 (978-0-06-623869-2(2)) HarperCollins Pubs.

Ross, Mandy. Animal Exercises: Poems to Keep Fit. Rescek, Sanja, illus. 2006. (Animal Lullabies Ser.). 32p. (J). (ps-2). pap. 7.99 (***978-1-84643-044-2(5)**) Child's Play-International.

—Cuddle Up. Kallai-Nagy, Kristina, illus. 2006. 12p. bds. 4.99 (978-1-904550-56-3(8)) Child's Play-International.

—Night Night. Kallai-Nagy, Kristina, illus. 2006. 12p. bds. 4.99 (978-1-904550-53-2(3)) Child's Play-International.

—Sleepy Time. Kallai-Nagy, Kristina, illus. 2006. 12p. bds. 4.99 (978-1-904550-54-9(1)) Child's Play-International.

—Snuggle Up. Kallai-Nagy, Kristina, illus. 2006. 12p. bds. 4.99 (978-1-904550-55-6(X)) Child's Play-International.

Santore, Charles & Carryl, Charles Edward. The Camel's Lament. 2004. (Illus.). 32p. (J). (ps-1). 16.95 (978-0-375-81426-6(4) , Random Hse. Bks. for Young Readers) Random Hse. Children's Bks.

Shepherd, Donna J. Topsy Turvy Land. Collier, Kevin Scott, illus. 2005. 16p. (J). pap. 6.99 (978-0-9678159-6-1(7)) Hidden Pictures.

Shulman, Mark. Some Ducks. Barton, Joe & Nguyen, Vincent, illus. 2003. (Some Animals Ser.). 20p. (J). 5.95 (978-0-7641-5652-6(7)) Barron's Educational Series, Inc.

Sidman, Joyce. Song of the Water Boatman: And Other Pond Poems. Prange, Beckie, illus. 2005. 32p. (J). (gr. k-3). 16.00 (978-0-618-13547-9(2)) Houghton Mifflin Co. Trade & Reference Div.

Sidman, Joyce & Swan, Susan. Just Us Two: Poems about Dads. 2003. (Single Titles Ser.; Vol. 3). 32p. pap. 7.95 (978-0-7613-1833-0(X) , Millbrook Pr.) Lerner Publishing Group.

Sierra, Judy. Beastly Rhymes to Read after Dark. Biggs, Brian, illus. 2008. (J). (***978-0-375-83747-0(7)**); lib. bdg. (***978-0-375-93747-7(1)**) Knopf, Alfred A. Inc.

Sierra, Judy. There's a Zoo in Room 22. Saltzberg, Barney, illus. 40p. (J). 2004. pap. 6.00 (978-0-15-205020-7(5) , Voyager Bks./Libros Viajeros); 2000. 16.00 (978-0-15-202033-0(0) , Gulliver Bks.) Harcourt Children's Bks.

Silverstein, Shel. Runny Babbit: A Billy Sook. 2005. (Illus.). 96p. (J). 18.99 (978-0-06-025653-1(2)) HarperCollins Pubs.

—Runny Babbit: A Billy Sook. Silverstein, Shel, illus. 2005. (Illus.). 96p. lib. bdg. 18.89 (978-0-06-028404-6(8)) HarperCollins Pubs.

Skene, Pat. What a Hippopota-Mess! Ross, Graham, illus. 2006. 64p. (J). pap. 4.99 (978-1-55143-402-5(4)) Orca Bk. Pubs. USA.

Steinberg, David. Club Pet & Other Funny Poems: All Aboard Poetry Reader Station Stop 2. Sinnott, Adrian C., illus. 2005. (All Aboard Poetry Reader Ser.). 48p. (J). (gr. 1-3). pap. 3.99 (978-0-448-43773-6(2) , Grosset & Dunlap) Penguin Group (USA) Inc.

Stockland, Patricia M., tr. Fur, Fangs, & Footprints: A Collection of Animal Poems. 2004. (Poet's Toolbox Ser.). (Illus.). 32p. (J). (gr. 3 up). 22.60 (978-0-7565-0562-2(3)) Compass Point Bks.

Swados, Elizabeth. The Animal Rescue Store. Wilson, Anne, illus. 2005. 48p. (J). pap. 16.95 (978-0-439-55476-3(4) , Levine, Arthur A. Bks.) Scholastic, Inc.

Van Wassenhove, Sue. The Seldom-Ever-Shady Glades: Poems & Quilts. 2008. (J). (***978-1-59078-352-8(2)** , Wordsong) Boyds Mills Pr.

Wadsworth, Olive A. Over in the Meadow. Thornhill, Jan, illus. 2004. 32p. (J). (gr. k-2). 16.95 (978-1-897066-08-9(2)) Maple Tree Pr. CAN. *Dist:* Perseus Distribution.

Waters, Fiona & Julian-Ottie, Vanessa. Whiskers & Paws. 2003. (Illus.). 24p. (J). (gr. k-3). 12.95 (978-0-7696-3188-2(6) , Gingham Dog Pr.) School Specialty Publishing.

Wilson, Karma. Bear Hugs: Romantically Ridiculous Animal Rhymes. Watts, Suzanne, illus. 32p. (J). 2007. 6.99 (***978-1-4169-4958-9(5)** , Aladdin); 2004. 14.95 (978-0-689-85763-8(2) , McElderry, Margaret K.) Simon & Schuster Children's Publishing.

Worth, Valerie. Animal Poems. Jenkins, Steve, illus. 2007. 48p. (J). (gr. 3-8). 17.00 (978-0-374-38057-1(0)) Farrar, Straus & Giroux.

Yolen, Jane. Count Me a Rhyme: Animal Poems by the Numbers. Stemple, Jason, illus. Stemple, Jason, photos by. 2006. 32p. (J). (gr. 1-5). 17.95 (978-1-59078-345-0(X) , Wordsong) Boyds Mills Pr.

—Wild Wings: Poems for Young People. Stemple, Jason, photos by. 2002. (Illus.). 32p. (YA). (gr. 4-6). 19.95 (978-1-56397-904-0(7)) Boyds Mills Pr.

ANIMALS, PREHISTORIC

see Fossils

ANIMALS—PROTECTION

see Animals—Treatment

ANIMALS, SEA

see Marine Animals

ANIMALS—SONGS AND MUSIC

Cabrera, Jane, illus. If You're Happy & You Know It! 2005. 32p. (J). 16.95 (978-0-8234-1881-7(2)) Holiday Hse., Inc.

Gobo Books Staff. Animal Songs. 2007. (Baby Sing & Play Ser.). 8p. (J). (ps). bds. 12.95 incl. audio compact disk (***978-1-932915-43-3(5)**) Sandvik Innovations, LLC.

Merrill, Bob. How Much Is That Doggie in the Window? Trapani, Iza, illus. 2004. (J). (ps-2). 24p. bds. 6.95 (978-1-58089-031-1(8)); 32p. pap. 6.95 (978-1-58089-030-4(X)) Charlesbridge Publishing, Inc.

—How Much Is That Doggie in the Window? 1999. (Extended Nursery Rhymes Ser.). (Illus.). 32p. (J). (ps up). lib. bdg. 23.33 (978-0-8368-2486-5(5)) Stevens, Gareth Inc.

Penner, Fred. The Cat Came Back. Reichert, Renée, illus. 2005. 32p. (J). (ps-2). 15.95 (978-1-59643-030-3(3)) Roaring Brook Pr.

Schnetzler, Pattie. Earth Day Birthday. Wallace, Chad, illus. 2004. (Sharing Nature with Children Book Ser.). 32p. (J). 16.95 (978-1-58469-053-5(4)); 8.95 (978-1-58469-054-2(2)) Dawn Pubns.

Sweet, Melissa. On Christmas Day in the Morning: A Traditional Carol. 2001. (978-0-606-22503-8(X)) Tandem Library Bks.

Sweet, Melissa & Langstaff, John M. On Christmas Day in the Morning: A Traditional Carol. 1999. (J). (978-0-7636-0634-3(0)) Candlewick Pr.

ANIMALS—TRAINING

see also names of animals with the subdivision Training, e.g., Dogs—Training; Horses—Training; etc.

French, Karen. Dr. Frenchy's Pet Training from a to Z: A Fun, Colorful, Stimulating Alphabet Pattern Book. 2003. (J). per. 9.95 (978-1-888125-07-8(1)) Publication Consultants.

Haas, Jessie. Shaper. 2002. 192p. (J). (gr. 5 up). 16.99 (978-0-06-000170-4(4)) HarperCollins Pubs.

Harcourt School Publishers Staff. Animal Helpers On Level. 3rd ed. 2002. (Trophies Reading Program Ser.). (Illus.). pap. 5.10 (978-0-15-323349-4(4)) Harcourt Schl. Pubs.

Kent, Deborah. Animal Helpers for the Disabled. 2003. (Watts Library). (Illus.). 64p. (J). 25.50 (978-0-531-12017-0(1) , Watts, Franklin) Scholastic Library Publishing.

Rake, Jody. Animal Training at SeaWorld, Busch Gardens, & Discovery Cove: Behind the Scenes. 2003. (Seaworld Education Ser.). (Illus.). 68p. per. 7.99 (978-1-893698-09-3(2) , B01, SeaWorld Education Dept.) SeaWorld, Inc.

ANIMALS—TREATMENT

Adkins, Linda. The Dog Who Couldn't Wag His Tail: A True Story about a Stray Who Made a Difference. Dilworth, Kristopher & Rhodes, Sean C., eds. 2003. (J). 13.95 (978-0-9718632-0-0(2)) Keep Me Company Publishing Co.

Arnold, Caroline. Baby Whale Rescue: The True Story of J. J. 1999. (Illus.). (J). (978-0-606-18663-6(8)) Tandem Library Bks.

Barnes, Simon. Planet Zoo: One Hundred Animals We Can't Afford to Lose. Marks, Alan, illus. 2001. 256p. (J). (gr. 3-7). 29.99 (978-1-85881-488-9(X)) Orion Bks. Ltd. GBR. *Dist:* Trafalgar Square Publishing.

Bass, Sheila M. Because You Cared. 2005. (J). per. (978-0-9766366-0-1(3)) Bass, Sheila.

Brooks, Evelyn, told to. Voice for the Animals, A/la voz de los Animales: English/Spanish Pair, 12 texts, 2 titles, Vol. 2. ed. 2004. (Navigators Ser.). (J). pap., instr.'s gde. ed. 84.00 (978-1-4108-1777-8(6) , 17776) Benchmark Education Co.

Brooks, John L., II. Balloons, Sea Creatures, Me. Spivey, Carlos, illus. l.t. ed. 1999. 20p. (J). (gr. k-3). pap. 7.00 (978-0-9661789-1-3(2)) Canis Lupus Productions.

Browning, Bel. Animal Welfare. 2003. (Face the Facts Ser.). (Illus.). 56p. (YA). lib. bdg. 28.56 (978-0-7398-6430-2(0)) Raintree.

Creative Media Applications Staff. Exploring Animal Rights & Animal Welfare, 4 vols. 2002. (Middle School ESL Ser.). (Illus.). 512p. (J). (gr. 5 up). 135.00 (978-0-313-32245-7(7) , MS2245, Greenwood Pr.) Greenwood Publishing Group, Inc.

—Exploring Animal Rights & Animal Welfare Vol. 1: Using Animals for Food, 4 vols. 2002. (Middle School ESL Ser.). (Illus.). 128p. (J). (978-0-313-32246-4(5)) Greenwood Publishing Group, Inc.

—Exploring Animal Rights & Animal Welfare Vol. 2: Using Animals in the Laboratory & Classroom, 4 vols. 2002. (Middle School ESL Ser.). (Illus.). 128p. (J). (978-0-313-32247-1(3)) Greenwood Publishing Group, Inc.

—Exploring Animal Rights & Animal Welfare Vol. 3: Using Animals for Entertainment, 4 vols. 2002. (Middle School ESL Ser.). (Illus.). 128p. (J). (978-0-313-32248-8(1)) Greenwood Publishing Group, Inc.

—Exploring Animal Rights & Animal Welfare Vol. 4: Using Animals for Clothing, 4 vols. 2002. (Middle School ESL Ser.). (Illus.). 128p. (J). (978-0-313-32249-5(X)) Greenwood Publishing Group, Inc.

Day, Nancy. Animal Experimentation: Cruelty or Science? rev. ed. 2000. (Issues in Focus Ser.). (Illus.). 128p. (YA). (gr. 6-12). lib. bdg. 26.60 (978-0-7660-1244-8(1)) Enslow Pubs., Inc.

Dudley, William. Animal Rights. 2006. 80-244*p. (gr. 7-10). 33.70 (978-0-7377-3457-7(4) , Greenhaven Pr., Inc.) Thomson Gale.

Good Morning Miss Prin. 2002. (J). pap. 7.95 (978-0-9722555-0-9(8)) Sblendido, Barbara.

Hardy, Caroline, et al. Quiet Places: An Animal Care Book. 2006. (Through the Peephole Ser.). (Illus.). 48p. 9.95 (978-1-84560-016-7(9)) Mercury Bks. Ltd. GBR. *Dist:* International Publishers Marketing.

Haugen, David M., ed. Animal Experimentation. 2000. (At Issue Ser.). (Illus.). 94p. (YA). (gr. 9-13). lib. bdg. 26.20 (978-0-7377-0149-4(8) , Greenhaven Pr., Inc.) Thomson Gale.

Hayhurst, Chris. Animal Testing: The Animal Rights Debate. 2000. (Focus on Science & Society Ser.). (Illus.). 64p. (YA). (gr. 4-6). lib. bdg. 26.50 (978-0-8239-3213-9(3) , FSANTE) Rosen Publishing Group, Inc., The.

Jacobs, Shannon K. Healers of the Wild: People Who Care for Injured & Orphaned Wildlife. 1998. (Illus.). ix, 214p. (J). (gr. 4-8). pap. 19.95 (978-0-9661070-0-5(4)) Coyote Moon Pr.

James, Barbara. Animal Rights. 1999. (Talking Points Ser.). (Illus.). 64p. (YA). (gr. 4-7). lib. bdg. 27.12 (978-0-8172-5317-2(3)) Raintree.

Kallgren, Beverly H. A Duck Named Goose. 2004. (Illus.). 48p. (J). per. 10.00 (978-1-930648-90-6(1)) Goose River Pr.

Leduc-Lenmark, MaryAlice. Meet Mister Muttley. Speas, Joann, illus. 2004. 25p. (J). 16.95 (978-0-9760733-0-7(7)) Heartstrings Publishing.

Levine, Herbert M. Animal Rights. 1999. (American Issues Debated Ser.). (Illus.). 128p. (J). (gr. 7-12). lib. bdg. 31.40 (978-0-8172-4350-0(X)) Raintree.

Lishak, Antony. Animal Welfare. 2007. (J). (***978-1-59920-034-7(1)**) Smart Apple Media.

Listen-Read-Think Science: Animals in Danger. 2006. pap. 4.49 (978-1-4206-8148-2(6)) Teacher Created Materials, Inc.

Miller-Schroeder, Patricia. The ASPCA. 2002. (International Organizations Ser.). (Illus.). 32p. (J). lib. bdg. 16.95 (978-1-59036-024-8(9)) Weigl Pubs., Inc.

Newkirk, Ingrid. 50 Awesome Ways Kids Can Help Animals: Fun & Easy Ways to Be a Kind Kid. 2006. (Illus.). 304p. (gr. 8-17). pap. 12.99 (978-0-446-69828-3(8)) Grand Central Publishing.

Patterson, Charles. Animal Rights. 2000. (Illus.). 116p. (gr. 7-12). pap. 11.95 (978-0-595-09494-3(5) , Backinprint-.com) iUniverse, Inc.

Powell, Jillian. Animal Rights. 1999. (Talking about Ser.). (Illus.). 32p. (J). (gr. k-4). lib. bdg. 25.69 (978-0-7398-1374-4(9)) Raintree.

Steele, Philip. Animal Matters. 2001. (Life Files Ser.). (Illus.). 62p. 24.99 (978-0-237-52080-9(X)); pap. 15.99 (978-0-237-52081-6(8)) Evans Publishing Group GBR. (Evans Brothers, Limited). *Dist:* Independent Pubs. Group.

Suen, Anastasia. The American Society for the Prevention of Cruelty to Animals (ASPCA) 2002. (Reading Power Ser.). (Illus.). 24p. (J). (gr. k-3). lib. bdg. 17.25 (978-0-8239-6004-0(8) , PowerKids Pr.) Rosen Publishing Group, Inc., The.

Thomas, Peggy. The Science of Saving Animals, 4 vols. 2004. (Illus.). 64p. (YA). (gr. 5-8). (978-0-7613-3123-0(9) , Twenty-First Century Bks.) Lerner Publishing Group.

Tubbs, Janet. The ABC's of Animals: A Book for Children. 1998. (Illus.). 43p. (J). (gr. 1-5). mass mkt. 6.95 (978-1-881185-06-2(0)) Arcadia Pr.

Vanase, Jessica, ed. Farms As Factories: Issues in Animal Welfare, Environmental Protection & Public Health. 2000. 32p. (YA). 3.00 (978-0-941246-11-8(6)) National Assn. for Humane & Environmental Education.

—Understanding Animal Cruelty. 2001. 24p. (YA). 3.00 (978-0-941246-10-1(8)) National Assn. for Humane & Environmental Education.

Ward, Eva D. Calvin C. Waxwing. York, Deborah Ward, illus. l.t. ed. 2006. 34p. (J). per. 14.00 (***978-0-9776514-5-0(2)**) Beech River Bks.

Wildlife Education, Ltd. Staff, et al. Sharing the World with Animals: Saving Our Animal Friends. 2000. (Zoobooks Ser.). (Illus.). 18p. (J). pap. 2.95 (978-0-937934-68-5(2)) Wildlife Education, Ltd.

Woods, Geraldine. Animal Experimentation & Testing: A Pro/Con Issue. 1999. (Hot Pro/Con Issues Ser.). (Illus.). 64p. (YA). (gr. 6-12). lib. bdg. 27.93 (978-0-7660-1191-5(7)) Enslow Pubs., Inc.

ANIMALS—TREATMENT—FICTION

Anderson, Laurie Halse. Fight for Life, Vol. 1. 2007. (Vet Volunteers Ser.). 144p. (J). (gr. 3). pap. 6.99 (978-0-14-240862-9(X) , Puffin) Penguin Group (USA) Inc.

—Fight for Life. 2003. (Wild at Heart Ser.). (Illus.). 127p. (J). (gr. 4 up). lib. bdg. 23.33 (978-0-8368-3256-3(6)) Stevens, Gareth Inc.

—Fight for Life. 2000. (American Girl Wild at Heart Ser.: Bk. 1). (YA). (978-0-606-18358-1(2)) Tandem Library Bks.

—Trapped. 2003. (Wild at Heart Ser.). (Illus.). 113p. (J). (gr. 4 up). lib. bdg. 23.33 (978-0-8368-3263-1(9)) Stevens, Gareth Inc.

Arensen, Shel. Poachers Beware, Vol. 3. 2003. (Rugendo Rhino Ser.: Vol. 3). 128p. (J). pap. 5.99 (978-0-8254-2039-9(3)) Kregel Pubns.

Banks, Lynne Reid. Tiger, Tiger. 2007. 208p. (YA). (gr. 7-11). mass mkt. 5.99 (978-0-440-42044-6(X) , Laurel Leaf) Random Hse. Children's Bks.

Brooke, Lauren. From This Day On. 2005. 171p. (J). (978-1-4155-9728-6(6)) Scholastic, Inc.

Casanova, Mary. Stealing Thunder. 2000. 144p. (gr. 3-7). pap. 5.99 (978-0-7868-1480-0(2)) Hyperion Bks. for Children.

—Stealing Thunder. 2000. (J). (978-0-606-20192-6(0)); (gr. 3-6). lib. bdg. 14.15 (978-0-613-30762-8(3)) Tandem Library Bks.

Dale, Jenny. Barney's Rescue. Reid, Mick, illus. 2003. 100p. (J). (978-0-439-45356-1(9)) Scholastic, Inc.

Daniels, Lucy. Cub in the Cupboard. 1999. (Animal Ark Ser.: No. 8). (J). (gr. 3-5). 10.64 (978-0-606-19087-9(2)) Tandem Library Bks.

DiCamillo, Kate. The Tiger Rising. Sheban, Chris, illus. 2006. 144p. (J). (gr. 5). pap. 5.99 (978-0-7636-2916-8(2)) Candlewick Pr.

—The Tiger Rising. 2001. (Illus.). 128p. (J). (gr. 5 up). 15.99 (978-0-7636-0911-5(0)) Candlewick Pr.

Dickinson, Peter. Eva. 2005. 220p. (YA). (gr. 7-12). 21.50 (978-0-8446-7274-8(2) , 3589) Smith, Peter Pub., Inc.

Farley, Terri. Challenger. 2003. (gr. 5-8). lib. bdg. 13.00 (978-0-613-66694-7(1)) Tandem Library Bks.

Haas, Jessie. Shaper. 2002. 192p. (J). (gr. 5 up). 16.99 (978-0-06-000170-4(4)); lib. bdg. 17.89 (978-0-06-000171-1(2)) HarperCollins Pubs.

Kehret, Peg. Saving Lilly. 160p. (J). 2002. pap. 4.99 (978-0-671-03423-8(5) , Aladdin); 2001. (gr. 3-6). 16.95 (978-0-671-03422-1(7)) Simon & Schuster Children's Publishing.

—Saving Lilly. 2002. (gr. 3-6). lib. bdg. 13.00 (978-0-613-64783-0(1)) Tandem Library Bks.

Lang, Andrew. The Hut in the Forest: A Tale about Being Kind to Animals. Johnson, Meredith, illus. 2006. (J). (978-1-59939-083-3(3) , Reader's Digest Young Families, Inc.) Reader's Digest Children's Publishing, Inc.

Libster, Bernard. The Bonsai Bear. Cheung, Aries, illus. 2006. 31p. (J). (gr. k-4). reprint ed. 16.00 (***978-1-4223-5857-3(7)**) DIANE Publishing Co.

—The Bonsai Bear. Cheung, Aries, illus. 1999. 32p. (ps-3). 15.95 (978-0-935699-15-9(5)) Illumination Arts Publishing Co., Inc.

Mills, Claudia. Standing up to Mr. O. 2000. (978-0-606-18215-7(2)) Tandem Library Bks.

Nanette. Tootie the Green Kitten. 2004. (Life on Granny's Farm Ser.). (J). 12.95 (978-0-9741269-7-5(7)) St. Bernard Publishing, LLC.

Sewell, Anna. Black Beauty. unabr. ed. 2004. (Chrysalis Children's Classics Ser.). (Illus.). 208p. (YA). pap. (978-1-84365-062-1(2)) Chrysalis Children's Bks.

—Black Beauty. 2001. (Fast Track Classics Ser.). (Illus.). 48p. pap. 9.99 (978-0-237-52284-1(5) , Evans Brothers, Limited) Evans Publishing Group GBR. *Dist:* Independent Pubs. Group.

—Black Beauty. 2001. (gr. 3-6). lib. bdg. 11.80 (978-0-613-63178-5(1)); 2001. (gr. 5-8). lib. bdg. 11.80 (978-0-613-66691-6(7)); 1999. (gr. 3-6). lib. bdg. 10.10 (978-0-613-85409-2(8)) Tandem Library Bks.

Skevington, Andrea. The Little Christmas Tree. Hussey, Lorna, illus. 2002. 32p. (J). (gr. k-2). pap. 8.99 (978-0-7459-4588-0(0) , Lion) Lion Hudson plc GBR. *Dist:* Independent Pubs. Group.

Ure, Jean. Daffy down Donkey. 1999. (We Love Animals Bks.). (Illus.). 144p. (J). (gr. 4-7). pap. 3.95 (978-0-7641-0969-0(3)) Barron's Educational Series, Inc.

Van West, Patricia E. The Crab Man. Lucas, Cedric, illus. 2001. 40p. (J). (ps-3). pap. 8.95 (978-1-890515-25-6(6)) Turtle Bks.

Warner, Sally. Bad Girl Blues. 2001. 224p. (YA). (gr. 5-9). 15.95 (978-0-06-028274-5(6)) HarperCollins Pubs.

Wilson, Pauline Hutchens & Dengler, Sandy. The Case of the Red Hot Possum: The New Sugar Creek Gang. 2001. (New Sugar Creek Gang Ser.). 144p. (J). (gr. 2-8). 5.99 (978-0-8024-8661-5(4)) Moody Pubs.

Wood, Jane Roberts. Mocha the Real Doctor. 2004. (Illus.). 32p. 14.95 (978-1-931721-30-1(0)) Bright Sky Pr.

ANIMALS, USEFUL AND HARMFUL

see Zoology, Economic

ANIMALS, WAR USE OF

Denega, Danielle. The Cold War Pigeon Patrols: And Other Animal Spies. 2007. (24/7: Science Behind the Scenes: Spy Files Ser.). 64p. (YA). (gr. 5 up). pap. 7.95 (***978-0-531-17534-7(0)**); (gr. 8-12). 26.00 (978-0-531-12081-1(3)) Scholastic Library Publishing. (Watts, Franklin).

ANIMALS AND CIVILIZATION

Burt, Jonathan. Rat. 2006. (Animal Ser.). (Illus.). 192p. pap. 19.95 (978-1-86189-224-9(1)) Reaktion Bks., Ltd. GBR. *Dist:* Chicago Distribution Ctr.

Stott, Rebecca. Oyster. 2004. (Animal Ser.). (Illus.). 240p. pap. 19.95 (978-1-86189-221-8(7)) Reaktion Bks., Ltd. GBR. *Dist:* Chicago Distribution Ctr.

Zarin, Cynthia. Saints among the Animals. Gore, Leonid, illus. 2006. 96p. (J). 17.95 (978-0-689-85031-8(X) , Atheneum) Simon & Schuster Children's Publishing.

ANIMALS IN ART

see also Animal Painting and Illustration

Ames, Lee J. Draw 50 Baby Animals: The Step-by-Step Way to Draw Kittens, Lambs, Chicks & Other Adorable Offspring. Zak, Murray, illus. 2003. 64p. pap. 8.95 (978-0-7679-1284-6(5) , Broadway) Broadway Bks.

Barr, Steve. 1-2-3 Draw Cartoon Animals: A Step-by-Step Guide. 2002. (One-Two-Three Draw Ser.). (Illus.). 64p. (J). (gr. 1). pap. 8.99 (978-0-939217-48-9(1)) Peel Productions, Inc.

—1-2-3 Draw Cartoon Animals: A Step-by-Step Guide. 2002. (gr. k-3). lib. bdg. 17.60 (978-0-613-86905-8(2)) Tandem Library Bks.

Baumbusch, Brigitte. Animals in Art. 2005. (Illus.). 32p. (J). lib. bdg. 22.00 (978-0-8368-4442-9(4)) Stevens, Gareth Inc.

Bhatt, Sonal. Beaded Critters. 2006. (Illus.). 80p. (J). pap. 9.95 (978-1-4027-4043-5(3)) Sterling Publishing Co., Inc.

Bingham, Jane. The Living World. 2006. (Illus.). 56p. (J). (978-1-4109-2239-7(1)) Steck-Vaughn.

Blizzard, Gladys S. Come Look with Me: Animals in Art. 2006. (Come Look with Me Ser.). 32p. (YA). (gr. k-12). 15.95 (978-1-56566-013-7(7)) Charlesbridge Publishing, Inc.

Bontinck, Helga, illus. At the Seashore. 2006. (Simple Steps to Drawing Ser.). 24p. (J). 22.00 (978-0-8368-6313-0(5)) Stevens, Gareth Inc.

Bratun, Katy. The Drawing Dogs. 2003. (Illus.). 64p. (J). (gr. 2). pap. 6.99 (978-0-448-43173-4(4) , Grosset & Dunlap) Penguin Group (USA) Inc.

Brocklehurst, Ruth. Animal Stencil Bk. Cleyet-Merle, Laurence, illus. 2006. 14p. (J). bds. 12.99 (978-0-7945-1140-1(6) , Usborne) EDC Publishing.

Carroll, Colleen. How Artists See Animals: Mammal, Fish, Bird, Reptile. 1998. (How Artists See Ser.). (Illus.). 48p. pap. 12.95 (978-0-7892-0475-2(4)) Abbeville Pr., Inc.

Claridge, Marit. Ht Draw Dinosaurs & Prehistoric Life. PRINGLE MIKE ET AL, illus. 2006. 32p. (J). pap. 5.99 (978-0-7945-1372-6(7) , Usborne) EDC Publishing.

Court, Rob. How to Draw Jungle Animals. 2008. (Doodle Bks.). 32p. (J). 21.36 ***(978-1-59296-955-5(0))*** Child's World, Inc.

de Rosamel, Godeleine. Drawing with Nature. de Rosamel, Godeleine, illus. 2003. (Drawing Is Easy Ser.). (Illus.). 24p. (J). (ps up). lib. bdg. 22.00 (978-0-8368-3626-4(X)) Stevens, Gareth Inc.

Douglas, Vincent & School Specialty Publishing Staff. Let's Make Animals. EduSlate, ed. 2006. (Edu-Slates Ser.). (Illus.). 1p. (J). 2.99 (978-0-7696-4889-7(4) , Brighter Child) School Specialty Publishing.

Draw 50 Animals. 2002. (Draw 50 Ser.). (Illus.). (J). 17.60 (978-0-7587-5314-4(4)) Book Wholesalers, Inc.

Foster, Walter & Wyland. Step by Step Painting with Wyland: Favorite Animals of the Sea. 2006. (Wyland Art Ser.). (Illus.). 32p. (J). pap. 5.95 (978-1-56010-970-9(X)) Foster, Walter Publishing, Inc.

Freymann, Saxton, illus. Food for Thought: The Complete Book of Concepts for Growing Minds. 2005. 61p. (J). lib. bdg. (978-1-4155-7707-3(2) , Levine, Arthur A. Bks.) Scholastic, Inc.

Freymann, Saxton & Elffers, Joost. Baby Food. 2006. (Illus.). 26p. (J). bds. 6.99 (978-0-439-11021-1(1) , Levine, Arthur A. Bks.) Scholastic, Inc.

—Dog Food. 2006. (Illus.). 26p. (J). bds. 6.99 (978-0-439-11020-4(3) , Levine, Arthur A. Bks.) Scholastic, Inc.

Fritz, Jean. Leonardo's Horse. Talbott, Hudson, illus. 2001. 48p. (J). (gr. 1-6). 18.99 (978-0-399-23576-4(0) , Putnam Juvenile) Penguin Group (USA) Inc.

Gabriel, Faith K. Nifty Thrifty Animal Crafts. 2007. (Nifty Thrifty Crafts for Kids Ser.). (Illus.). 32p. (J). lib. bdg. 22.60 (978-0-7660-2779-4(1) , Enslow Elementary) Enslow Pubs., Inc.

Ganeri, Anita & Tatchell, Judy. Ht Draw Animals. rev. ed. 2006. 32p. (J). pap. 5.99 (978-0-7945-1373-3(5) , Usborne) EDC Publishing.

Gray, Peter C. How to Draw Manga Animals. 2006. (Kid's Guide to Drawing Ser.). (Illus.). 32p. (J). (978-1-4042-3329-4(6) , PowerKids Pr.) Rosen Publishing Group, Inc., The.

Hankin, Rosie. Cut & Paste Farm Animals. 2006. (Illus.). 32p. (J). lib. bdg. ***(978-0-8368-7719-9(5))*** Stevens, Gareth Inc.

—Cut & Paste Sea Creatures. 2006. (Illus.). 32p. (J). lib. bdg. ***(978-0-8368-7720-5(9))*** Stevens, Gareth Inc.

Harpster, Steve. Animals. 2006. (Pencil, Paper, Draw! Ser.). (Illus.). 64p. (J). pap., pap., spiral bd. 5.95 (978-1-4027-2972-0(3)) Sterling Publishing Co., Inc.

—Dinosaurs. 2006. (Pencil, Paper, Draw! Ser.). (Illus.). 64p. (J). pap., pap., spiral bd. 5.95 (978-1-4027-2974-4(X)) Sterling Publishing Co., Inc.

—Dogs. 2006. (Pencil, Paper, Draw! Ser.). (Illus.). 64p. (J). pap., pap., spiral bd. 5.95 (978-1-4027-2973-7(1)) Sterling Publishing Co., Inc.

Harpster, Steve. Pencil, Paper, Draw!: Baby Animals. 2007. (Pencil, Paper, Draw! Ser.). (Illus.). 64p. (J). pap. 5.95 ***(978-1-4027-4678-9(4))*** Sterling Publishing Co., Inc.

Hart, Christopher. Kids Draw Animals. 2003. (Kids Draw Ser.). (Illus.). 64p. (J). pap. 11.95 (978-0-8230-2631-9(0)) Watson-Guptill Pubns., Inc.

Heller, D. M. Let's Make a Monkey with Everyday Materials. 2006. (Illus.). 24p. (J). (978-1-4042-3061-3(0)) Rosen Publishing Group, Inc., The.

Holub, Joan & Regan, Dana, illus. Magical Creatures. 2003. (Easy-to-Read! Easy-to-Draw! Ser.). 48p. (J). pap. 5.99 (978-0-8431-0436-3(8) , Price Stern Sloan) Penguin Group (USA) Inc.

Hosack, Karen. Animals. 2004. (J). lib. bdg. 24.22 (978-1-4034-4850-7(7)) Heinemann Library.

Hosley, Maria. Cats. 2007. (Illus.). 24p. (J). 21.35 ***(978-1-59679-801-4(7))*** ABDO Publishing Co.

—Dogs. 2007. (Illus.). 24p. (J). 21.35 ***(978-1-59679-803-8(3))*** ABDO Publishing Co.

How to Draw Cartoon Animals Adventure Pack. 2001. (978-1-883772-64-2(8)) Flying Rhinoceros, Inc.

How to Draw Cartoons Adventure Pack. 2001. (978-1-883772-63-5(X)) Flying Rhinoceros, Inc.

Howell, Will C. Zooflakes ABC. 2002. (Illus.). 32p. (J). 16.85 (978-0-8027-8827-6(0)) Walker & Co.

Kidd, Nina. Draw Science: Strange & Weird Animals. 1999. (Illus.). 63p. (YA). (gr. 3 up). pap. 7.95 (978-0-7373-0235-6(6) , 02356W) McGraw-Hill/Contemporary.

Kimble, Warren. The Cat's Meow. 2006. (Illus.). 24p. (J). 17.85 (978-0-8027-8079-9(2)); 16.95 (978-0-8027-8078-2(4)) Walker & Co.

King, Penny & Roundhill, Clare. Amazing Animals. 1998. (Making Pictures Ser.). (J). 21.36 (978-1-57572-192-7(9)) Heinemann Library.

Klutz Press Staff. Draw Thumb Animals. 2002. (Illus.). 44p. (J). spiral bd. 6.95 (978-1-57054-981-6(8)) Klutz.

Klutz Press Staff, creator. How to Make Pompom Animals. 2005. (Illus.). 22p. (J). spiral bd. 9.95 (978-1-59174-095-7(9)) Klutz.

LaFosse, Michael. Making Origami Animals Step by Step. 2002. (Kid's Guide to Origami Ser.). (Illus.). 24p. (J). lib. bdg. 21.25 (978-0-8239-5877-1(9) , PowerKids Pr.) Rosen Publishing Group, Inc., The.

Lee, Justin. How to Draw African Animals. 2002. (Kid's Guide to Drawing Ser.). (Illus.). 24p. (J). lib. bdg. 21.25 (978-0-8239-5790-3(X) , PowerKids Pr.) Rosen Publishing Group, Inc., The.

—How to Draw Animals of the Rain Forest. 2002. (Kid's Guide to Drawing Ser.). (Illus.). 24p. (J). lib. bdg. 21.25 (978-0-8239-5793-4(4) , PowerKids Pr.) Rosen Publishing Group, Inc., The.

Lepp, Royden. How to Draw Big Bad Bible Beasts. 2007. (2:52 Ser.). (Illus.). 48p. (J). pap. 6.99 (978-0-310-71336-4(6)) Zonderkidz.

Levin, Freddie. 1-2-3 Draw Pets & Farm Animals. 2000. (gr. k-3). lib. bdg. 17.60 (978-0-613-87986-6(4)) Tandem Library Bks.

—1-2-3 Draw Pets & Farm Animals: A Step by Step Guide. Levin, Freddie, illus. 2000. (One-Two-Three Draw Ser.). (Illus.). 64p. (J). (gr. 1-5). pap. 8.99 (978-0-939217-40-3(6)) Peel Productions, Inc.

—1-2-3 Draw Wild Animals: A Step-by-Step Guide. 2001. (One-Two-Three Draw Ser.). (Illus.). 64p. (J). (gr. 1-5). pap. 8.95 (978-0-939217-42-7(2)) Peel Productions, Inc.

Levin, Freddie & Gordon, Freddie. 1-2-3 Draw Baby Animals. Levin, Freddie, illus. 2006. (Illus.). 64p. pap. 8.99 (978-0-939217-45-8(7)) Peel Productions, Inc.

Levy, Barbara Soloff. How to Draw Wizards, Dragons & Other Magical Creatures. 2004. lib. bdg. 10.60 (978-0-613-85389-7(X)) Tandem Library Bks.

Makowski, Robin Lee, illus. How to Draw Cats & Dogs. 1999. 128p. (J). (978-1-56156-790-4(6)) Kidsbooks, Inc.

Masiello, Ralph. Ralph Masiello's Ocean Drawing Book. Masiello, Ralph, illus. 2006. (Illus.). (J). 16.95 (978-1-57091-529-1(6) , 1258410); pap. 6.95 (978-1-57091-530-7(X) , 1258410) Charlesbridge Publishing, Inc.

Micklethwait, Lucy. Animals. 2004. (First Art Book Ser.). (Illus.). 24p. (J). 14.95 (978-1-84507-027-4(5)) Lincoln, Frances Ltd. GBR. *Dist:* Perseus Distribution.

Morris, Ting. Animals. 2006. (Illus.). 32p. (J). (978-1-59771-025-1(3)) Sea-To-Sea Pubns.

Mravec, James. Animals. 2005. (Illus.). 96p. spiral bd. (978-0-7853-8378-9(6) , 3439101) Publications International, Ltd.

Patent, Dorothy Hinshaw. Mystery of the Lascaux Cave. 1998. (Frozen in Time Ser.). (Illus.). 64p. (J). (gr. 5-9). lib. bdg. 28.50 (978-0-7614-0784-3(7)) Cavendish, Marshall Corp.

Peffer, J. Neondragon. Dragonart Fantasy Characters. 2007. (Illus.). 128p. pap. 19.99 (978-1-58180-852-0(6) , Impact) F & W Pubns., Inc.

Press, Judy. At the Zoo! Explore the Animal World with Craft Fun. Campbell, Jenny, illus. 2001. (Little Hands Bks.). 128p. (J). (ps-2). pap. 12.95 (978-1-885593-61-0(9) , Williamson Bks.) Ideals Pubns.

Roalf, Peggy. Horses: Looking at Paintings. 2004. (Illus.). 48p. (J). (gr. 4-8). reprint ed. 17.00 (978-0-7567-7531-5(0)) DIANE Publishing Co.

Ross, Kathy. Crafts for Kids Who Are Wild about the Wild. Holm, Sharon Lane, illus. 1998. (Crafts from Kathy Ross Ser.). 176p. (J). (gr. 3-6). spiral bd. 18.95 (978-0-7613-0440-1(1)) Lerner Publishing Group.

Ruemelin, Christian. Paul Klee: Animal Images by Paul Klee: The Twittering Machine. 2002. (Adventures in Art Ser.). (Illus.). 30p. 14.95 (978-3-7913-2759-4(3)) Prestel Publishing.

Sautter, Aaron. How to Draw Ferocious Animals. Stiles, Tim, illus. 2008. (J). ***(978-1-4296-1299-9(1))*** Capstone Pr., Inc.

Silver Dolphin en Español Editors. Libro de actividades con plantillas: Disney Animales: Animals Stencil. 2007. (Illus.). 10p. (J). bds. 12.95 ***(978-970-718-435-0(3)*** , Silver Dolphin en Español) Advanced Marketing, S. de R. L. de C. V. MEX. *Dist:* Perseus Distribution.

Silver Dolphin en Español Editors. Serie Aprendizaje: Let's Draw with Pixar. 2006. (SPA., Illus.). 22p. (J). bds. 16.95 (978-970-718-320-9(9)) Advantage Pubs. Group.

Smith, Lucy. Ht Draw Horses. Chapman, Chris, illus. 2006. 32p. (J). pap. 5.99 (978-0-7945-1368-9(9) , Usborne) EDC Publishing.

Somerville, Louisa & Crowley, Bridget. Animals in Art. 2001. (In Art Ser.). (Illus.). 47p. 19.99 (978-0-7451-5262-2(7) , Cherrytree Books) Evans Publishing Group GBR. *Dist:* Independent Pubs. Group.

Stanley, Robert E., Sr. Northwest Native Arts: Creative Colors, 2 vols. 2003. (Northwest Native Arts Ser.). (Illus.). 32p. (gr. 3 up). pap. 5.95 (978-0-88839-532-0(9)) Hancock Hse. Pubs.

—Northwest Native Arts: Creative Colors 2, 2 vols., Vol. 3. 2003. (North West Native Arts Ser.). (Illus.). 24p. pap. 4.95 (978-0-88839-533-7(7)) Hancock Hse. Pubs.

Sterling/Balloon. Wild Animals. 1998. (Peek-a-Boo Bks.). (Illus.). 20p. (J). bds. 3.95 (978-0-8069-3761-8(0) , Balloon Bks.) Sterling Publishing Co., Inc.

Walsh, Patricia. Wild Animals. Westerfield, David, illus. 2006. 32p. ***(978-1-4034-8925-8(4))*** Heinemann Library.

—Wild Animals. 2002. (Draw It! Ser.). (Illus.). 32p. (J). (gr. 3-6). pap. 7.50 (978-1-58810-295-9(5) , 91045) Heinemann Library.

—Wild Animals. Westerfield, David, illus. 2000. (Draw It! Ser.). 32p. (J). (gr. 3-5). lib. bdg. 22.79 (978-1-57572-351-8(4)) Heinemann Library.

—Wild Animals. 2nd ed. 2006. (Illus.). 32p. pap. ***(978-1-4034-8932-6(7))*** Heinemann Library.

—Woodland Animals. Westerfield, David, illus. 2006. 32p. (J). ***(978-1-4034-8926-5(2))*** Heinemann Library.

—Woodland Animals. (Illus.). 32p. (J). 2002. (gr. 3-6). pap. 7.50 (978-1-58810-296-6(3) , 91046); 2nd ed. 2006. pap. ***(978-1-4034-8933-3(5))*** Heinemann Library.

Walsh, Patricia & Westerfield, David. Woodlands Animals. 2000. (Draw It! Ser.). (Illus.). 32p. (J). (gr. 3-5). lib. bdg. 22.79 (978-1-57572-352-5(2)) Heinemann Library.

Wild Animals. 1998. (Illus.). 8p. (J). pap. 2.00 (978-0-9703548-2-2(7)) Belle River Readers, Inc.

Wild Animals. (J). Date not set. (Illus.). 16p. 5.98 (978-0-7525-7699-2(2)); Date not set. (Illus.). 16p. 2.98 (978-0-7525-9763-8(9)); 2002. bds. 7.98 (978-0-7525-8732-5(3)); 2001. 12p. bds. 11.95 (978-0-7525-5261-3(9)) Parragon, Inc.

Wild Animals. 2001. (Early Learning Ser.). (J). (gr. k-12). vinyl bd. 4.95 (978-1-58845-043-2(0)) School Specialty Publishing.

Winter, Jeanette. Beatrix: Various Episodes from the Life of Beatrix Potter. Winter, Jeanette, illus. 2003. (Illus.). 64p. (J). (gr. k-3). 15.00 (978-0-374-30655-7(9) , Farrar, Straus & Giroux (BYR)) Farrar, Straus & Giroux.

Yuan, Margaret Speaker. Beatrix Potter. 2005. (Who Wrote That? Ser.). (Illus.). 114p. (J). (gr. 6-12). lib. bdg. 30.00 (978-0-7910-8655-1(0) , Chelsea Hse.) Facts On File, Inc.

Zuffi, Stefano. The Cat in Art. 2007. 360p. 35.00 ***(978-0-8109-9328-0(7))*** Abrams, Harry N. , Inc.

ANIMATED CARTOONS

see Animated Films

ANIMATED FILMS

Bellen-Berthel[81]zel(UNKNOWN CHARACTER)ne, Cyndie. Flipping Out! How to Draw Flip Animation. Steck, Jim, illus. 2005. 48p. (J). ***(978-0-439-81335-8(2))*** Scholastic, Inc.

Bulloch, Ivan. Cartoons & Animation. 1999. (Arts & Crafts Skills Ser.). (Illus.). 32p. (J). (gr. 3-6). pap. 6.95 (978-0-516-26342-7(0) , Children's Pr.) Scholastic Library Publishing.

Bulloch, Ivan, et al. Cartoons & Animation. 2005. (Illus.). 32p. (J). (gr. 3-7). lib. bdg. 27.10 (978-1-932889-81-9(7) , 1247651) Sea-To-Sea Pubns.

Cartwright, Nancy. My Life As a Ten Year-Old Boy. 2001. 304p. pap. 17.95 (978-0-7868-8600-5(5)) Hyperion Pr.

—My Life as a Ten Year-Old Boy: Bart, the Simpsons & Me. 2000. (Illus.). 288p. 27.95 (978-0-7868-6696-0(9)) Hyperion Pr.

Cervone, Tony. Animating the Looney Tunes Way. Foster, Walter T., ed. 2000. (Looney Tunes Collection). (Illus.). 96p. (J). (gr. 3). pap. 14.95 (978-1-56010-303-5(5)) Foster, Walter Publishing, Inc.

Disney Staff. Toy Story Sketchbook. 2000. (Illus.). 112p. 125.00 (978-1-55709-340-0(7)) Applewood Bks.

Ford, Carin T. Walt Disney: Meet the Cartoonist. 2003. (Meeting Famous People Ser.). (Illus.). 32p. (J). (gr. 1-4). lib. bdg. 22.60 (978-0-7660-1857-0(1)) Enslow Pubs., Inc.

Freleng, Hope & Freleng, Sybil. Meet the Pink Panther. 2005. (Illus.). 64p. 17.95 (978-0-7893-1308-9(1)) Universe Publishing.

Hahn, Don. Animation Magic: A Behind-the-Scenes Look at How an Animated Film Is Made. Disney Art Archives Staff, illus. rev. ed. 2000. 96p. (ps-17). 16.99 (978-0-7868-3261-3(4)) Hyperion Pr.

Horn, Geoffrey M. Movie Animation. 2006. (Making Movies Ser.). 32p. (J). (gr. 4-6). lib. bdg. 23.93 (978-0-8368-6837-1(4)) Stevens, Gareth Inc.

Marcovitz, Hal. Anime. 2007. (Eye on Art Ser.). (Illus.). 128p. (J). (gr. 7-10). 31.20 ***(978-1-59018-995-5(7)*** , Lucent Bks.) Thomson Gale.

Peterson, Monique, text. The Little Big Book of Disney Family Classics. (Illus.). 352p. 24.95 (978-1-932183-16-0(7) , Welcome Bks.) Welcome Enterprises, Inc.

Rauf, Don & Vescia, Monique. Virtual Apprentice. 2008. (Virtual Apprentice Ser.). 64p. (J). (gr. 6-12). 29.95 ***(978-0-8160-6760-2(0)*** , Ferguson Publishing Co.) Facts On File, Inc.

Shudo, Takeshi. Art of Pokemon: The Movie. 2000. (gr. 3-6). lib. bdg. 18.75 (978-0-613-79038-3(3)) Tandem Library Bks.

Spilsbury, Richard. Cartoons & Animation. 2006. (Art off the Wall Ser.). (Illus.). 56p. (J). (978-1-4034-8287-7(X)) Heinemann Library.

Tezuka Productions. Tezuka School of Animation 1: Learning the Basics. 2003. (Illus.). 108p. pap. 13.95 (978-1-56970-995-5(5)) Macmillan.

ANIMORPHS (FICTITIOUS CHARACTERS)—FICTION

Applegate, Katherine. L' Alerte. 2nd ed. 1999. (Animorphs Ser.: No. 16). Tr. of Animorphs. (FRE.). (J). (gr. 3-7). pap. 12.95 (978-2-07-052191-3(5)) Distribooks, Inc.

—Animorphs Boxed Set: The Change; The Unknown; The Escape; The Warning, No. 4. 2001. (Animorphs Ser.). (J). (gr. 3-7). 19.96 (978-0-590-28434-9(7) , Scholastic Paperbacks) Scholastic, Inc.

—Animorphs Boxed Set: The Invasion; The Visitor; The Encounter; The Message, No. 1. 2001. (Animorphs Ser.). (J). (gr. 3-7). 19.96 (978-0-590-38187-1(3)) Scholastic, Inc.

—Animorphs Boxed Set: The Predator; The Capture; The Stranger; The Alien, No. 2. 2001. (Animorphs Ser.). (J). (gr. 3-7). 19.96 (978-0-590-90725-5(5)) Scholastic, Inc.

—Animorphs Boxed Set: The Separation; The Illusion; The Prophecy; The Proposal; The Mutation; The Weakness; The Arrival; The Hidden; The Other; The Familiar; The Journey, 12 bks. l.t. ed. Incl. Arrival. 148p. 2001. lib. bdg. 23.33 (978-0-8368-2771-2(6)); Conspiracy. 138p. 2000. lib. bdg. 23.33 (978-0-8368-2754-5(6)); Familiar. 143p. 2001. lib. bdg. 23.33 (978-0-8368-2774-3(0)); Hidden. 121p. 2001. lib. bdg. 23.33 (978-0-8368-2772-9(4)); Illusion. 156p. 2000. lib. bdg. 23.33 (978-0-8368-2755-2(4)); Journey. 139p. 2001. lib. bdg. 23.33 (978-0-8368-2775-0(9)); Mutation. 142p. 2000. lib. bdg. 23.33 (978-0-8368-2756-9(2)); Other. 130p. 2001. lib. bdg. 23.33 (978-0-8368-2773-6(2)); Prophecy. 141p. 2000. lib. bdg. 23.33 (978-0-8368-2757-6(0)); Proposal. 147p. 2000. lib. bdg. 23.33 (978-0-8368-2758-3(9)); Separation. 158p. 2000. lib. bdg. 23.33 (978-0-8368-2759-0(7)); Weakness. (Illus.). 129p. 2001. lib. bdg. 23.33 (978-0-8368-2770-5(8)); (J). (gr. 4 up). (Animorphs Ser.: Nos. 32-42). 2001. Set lib. bdg. 279.96 (978-0-8368-2862-7(3)) Stevens, Gareth Inc.

—Animorphs Boxed Set: The Sickness; The Reunion, The Conspiracy; The Separation, No. 8. 2001. (Animorphs Ser.: 29-32). (J). 19.96 (978-0-439-10684-9(2)) Scholastic, Inc.

—Animorphs Boxed Set: The Threat; The Solution; The Pretender; The Suspicion, 4 vols., No. 6. 2001. (Animorphs Ser.: Nos. 21-24). (J). (gr. 3-7). 19.96 (978-0-590-28543-8(2)) Scholastic, Inc.

—Animorphs Boxed Set: The Undergound; The Decision; The Departure; The Discovery, No. 5. 2001. (Animorphs Ser.). (J). (gr. 3-7). 19.96 (978-0-590-28497-4(5) , Scholastic Paperbacks) Scholastic, Inc.

—Animorphs Boxed Set: The Weakness; the Arrival; the Hidden; the Other, No. 10. 2000. (Animorphs Ser.: Nos. 37-40). (Illus.). (J). (gr. 3-7). 19.96 (978-0-439-10688-7(5) , Scholastic Paperbacks) Scholastic, Inc.

—Animorphs Series Boxed Set. 1998. (Animorphs Ser.). (J). (gr. 3-7). pap. 143.64 (978-0-590-51066-0(5)) Scholastic, Inc.

—The Arrival. 2000. (Animorphs Ser.: No. 38). (Illus.). (J). (gr. 3-7). 11.64 (978-0-606-18509-7(7)) Tandem Library Bks.

—The Attack. 1999. (Animorphs Ser.: No. 26). (gr. 3-6). lib. bdg. 13.00 (978-0-613-11262-8(8)); (J). (978-0-606-15834-3(0)) Tandem Library Bks.

—Back to Before. 2000. (Animorphs Ser.: No. 4). (Illus.). 192p. (J). (gr. 3-7). pap. 5.99 (978-0-439-17307-0(8) , Scholastic Paperbacks) Scholastic, Inc.

—Back to Before. 2000. (Animorphs Ser.: No. 4). (Illus.). (J). (gr. 3-7). (978-0-606-18513-4(5)) Tandem Library Bks.

—The Conspiracy. l.t. ed. 2000. (Animorphs Ser.: No. 31). 138p. (J). (gr. 4 up). lib. bdg. 23.33 (978-0-8368-2754-5(6)) Stevens, Gareth Inc.

—The Conspiracy. 1999. (Animorphs Ser.: No. 31). (Illus.). (J). (gr. 3-7). 11.64 (978-0-606-16928-8(8)) Tandem Library Bks.

—The Decision. 1998. (Animorphs Ser.: No. 18). (J). (gr. 3-7). 11.64 (978-0-606-13138-4(8)) Tandem Library Bks.

—The Departure. 1998. (Animorphs Ser.: No. 19). 176p. (J). (gr. 3-7). pap. 4.99 (978-0-590-49451-9(1) , Scholastic Paperbacks) Scholastic, Inc.

—The Departure. 1998. (Animorphs Ser.: No. 19). (J). (gr. 3-7). 11.64 (978-0-606-13139-1(6)) Tandem Library Bks.

—The Discovery. 1998. (Animorphs Ser.: No. 20). 153p. (J). (gr. 3-7). pap. 4.99 (978-0-590-49637-7(9) , Scholastic Paperbacks) Scholastic, Inc.

—The Discovery. 1998. (Animorphs Ser.: No. 20). (J). (gr. 3-7). (978-0-606-13140-7(X)) Tandem Library Bks.

—Elfangor's Secret. 1999. (Animorphs Ser.: No. 3). (J). (gr. 3-7). 12.64 (978-0-606-16619-5(X)) Tandem Library Bks.

—The Ellimist Chronicles. 2000. (Animorphs Ser.). (Illus.). 288p. (J). (gr. 3-7). pap. 5.99 (978-0-439-21798-9(9)) Scholastic, Inc.

—The Ellimist Chronicles. 2000. (Animorphs Ser.). (J). (gr. 3-7). (978-0-606-19533-1(5)) Tandem Library Bks.

—El Encuentro. 1999. (Animorphs Ser.: Vol. 3). (SPA., Illus.). (J). (gr. 4-7). pap. 4.99 (978-0-439-08627-1(2) , SO1649) Scholastic, Inc.

—El Encuentro. 1999. (Animorphs Ser.: No. 3). (J). (gr. 3-7). (978-0-606-17286-8(6)) Tandem Library Bks.

—The Escape. 1998. (Animorphs Ser.: No. 15). 170p. (J). (gr. 3-7). pap. 4.99 (978-0-590-49424-3(4)) Scholastic, Inc.

—The Escape. 1998. (Animorphs Ser.: No. 15). (J). (gr. 3-7). (978-0-606-12876-6(X)) Tandem Library Bks.

—The Experiment. 1999. (Animorphs Ser.: No. 28). 160p. (J). (gr. 3-7). pap. 4.99 (978-0-590-76261-8(3)) Scholastic, Inc.

—The Experiment. 1999. (Animorphs Ser.: No. 28). (gr. 3-6). lib. bdg. 13.00 (978-0-613-16892-2(5)); (J). (978-0-606-16608-9(4)) Tandem Library Bks.

—The Exposed. 1999. (Animorphs Ser.: No. 27). (J). (gr. 3-7). (978-0-606-16589-1(4)) Tandem Library Bks.

—The Extreme. 1999. (Animorphs Ser.: No. 25). (J). (gr. 3-7). 146p. pap. 4.99 (978-0-590-76258-8(3)); pap. 179.64 (978-0-439-04365-6(4)) Scholastic, Inc.

—The Extreme. 1999. (Animorphs Ser.: No. 25). (J). (gr. 3-7). 11.64 (978-0-606-15437-6(X)) Tandem Library Bks.

—The Familiar. 2000. (Animorphs Ser.: No. 41). (Illus.). (J). (gr. 3-7). 11.64 (978-0-606-18512-7(7)) Tandem Library Bks.

—The First Journey. 1999. (Animorphs Ser.: No. 1). (J). (gr. 3-7). (978-0-606-16606-5(8)) Tandem Library Bks.

—The Hork-Bajir Chronicles. 1998. (Animorphs Ser.). (J). (gr. 3-7). (Illus.). 206p. pap. 13.95 (978-0-439-04291-8(7)); 12.95 (978-0-590-38198-7(9)) Scholastic, Inc.

—The Hork-Bajir Chronicles. 1999. (Animorphs Ser.). (J). (gr. 3-7). (978-0-606-17284-4(X)) Tandem Library Bks.

—The Illusion. l.t. ed. 2000. (Animorphs Ser.: No. 33). 156p. (J). (gr. 4 up). lib. bdg. 23.33 (978-0-8368-2755-2(4)) Stevens, Gareth Inc.

—The Illusion. 1999. (Animorphs Ser.: No. 33). (J). (gr. 3-7). 11.64 (978-0-606-17287-5(4)) Tandem Library Bks.

—In the Time of Dinosaurs. 1998. (Animorphs Ser.: No. 2). 229p. (J). (gr. 3-7). pap. 4.99 (978-0-590-95615-4(9) , Scholastic Paperbacks) Scholastic, Inc.

A B

—In the Time of Dinosaurs. 1998. (Animorphs Ser.: No. 2). (J). (gr. 3-7). (978-0-606-13142-1(6)) Tandem Library Bks.

—L' Invasion. 1999. (Animorphs Ser.: No. 1). Tr. of Invasion. (FRE & SPA.). 128p. (J). (gr. 3-7). pap. 4.99 (978-0-439-05602-1(0)) Scholastic, Inc.

—The Journey. 2000. (Animorphs Ser.: No. 42). (Illus.). (J). (gr. 3-7). 11.64 (978-0-606-18860-9(6)) Tandem Library Bks.

—El Mensaje. 1999. (Animorphs Ser.: No. 4). (SPA., Illus.). 164p. (J). (gr. 3-7). pap. 4.99 (978-0-439-08783-4(X), SO5398) Scholastic, Inc.

—El Mensaje. 1999. No. 4. (J). (978-0-606-17290-5(4)) Tandem Library Bks.

—The Message. 2000. (Animorphs Ser.: No. 4). (Illus.). (J). (gr. 3-7). 11.64 (978-0-606-18510-3(0)) Tandem Library Bks.

—The Mutation. l.t. ed. 2000. (Animorphs Ser.: No. 36). 142p. (J). (gr. 4 up). lib. bdg. 23.33 (978-0-8368-2756-9(2)) Stevens, Gareth Inc.

—The Mutation. 1999. (Animorphs Ser.: No. 36). (Illus.). (J). (gr. 3-7). (978-0-606-18507-3(0)) Tandem Library Bks.

—The Next Passage. 2000. (Animorphs Ser.: No. 2). (Illus.). 128p. (J). (gr. 3-7). pap. 4.99 (978-0-439-14263-2(6)) Scholastic, Inc.

—The Next Passage. 2000. (Animorphs Ser.: No. 2). (Illus.). (J). (gr. 3-7). (978-0-606-18506-6(2)) Tandem Library Bks.

—The Other. 2000. (Animorphs Ser.: No. 40). (Illus.). 144p. (J). (gr. 3-7). pap. 4.99 (978-0-439-10679-5(6)) Scholastic, Inc.

—The Other. 2000. (Animorphs Ser.: No. 40). (Illus.). (J). (gr. 3-7). (978-0-606-18511-0(9)) Tandem Library Bks.

—The Prophecy. l.t. ed. 2000. (Animorphs Ser.: No. 34). 141p. (J). (gr. 4 up). lib. bdg. 23.33 (978-0-8368-2757-6(0)) Stevens, Gareth Inc.

—The Prophecy. 1999. (Animorphs Ser.: No. 34). (J). (gr. 3-7). (978-0-606-17283-7(1)) Tandem Library Bks.

—The Proposal. l.t. ed. 2000. (Animorphs Ser.: No. 35). 147p. (J). (gr. 4 up). lib. bdg. 23.33 (978-0-8368-2758-3(9)) Stevens, Gareth Inc.

—The Proposal. 1999. (Animorphs Ser.: No. 35). (gr. 3-6). lib. bdg. 13.00 (978-0-613-21114-7(6)); (J). (978-0-606-17289-9(0)) Tandem Library Bks.

—The Resistance. 2000. (Animorphs Ser.: No. 47). (J). (gr. 3-7). (978-0-606-19530-0(0)) Tandem Library Bks.

—The Reunion. 1999. (Animorphs Ser.: No. 30). (J). (978-0-606-16657-7(2)) Tandem Library Bks.

—The Revelation. 2000. (Animorphs Ser.: No. 45). (Illus.). 144p. (J). (gr. 3-7). pap. 4.99 (978-0-439-11519-3(1)) Scholastic, Inc.

—The Revelation. 2000. (Animorphs Ser.: No. 45). (Illus.). (J). (gr. 3-7). (978-0-606-18863-0(0)) Tandem Library Bks.

—The Separation. 1999. (Animorphs Ser.: No. 32). 176p. (J). (gr. 3-7). pap. 4.99 (978-0-439-07032-4(5)) Scholastic, Inc.

—The Separation. l.t. ed. 2000. (Animorphs Ser.: No. 32). 158p. (J). (gr. 4 up). lib. bdg. 23.33 (978-0-8368-2759-0(7)) Stevens, Gareth Inc.

—The Separation. 1999. (Animorphs Ser.: No. 32). (gr. 3-6). lib. bdg. 13.00 (978-0-613-16895-3(X)); (J). (978-0-606-17060-4(X)) Tandem Library Bks.

—The Sickness. 1999. (Animorphs Ser.: No. 29). 176p. (J). (gr. 3-7). pap. 4.99 (978-0-590-76262-5(1)) Scholastic, Inc.

—The Sickness. 1999. (Animorphs Ser.: No. 29). (J). (978-0-606-16618-8(1)); (gr. 3-6). lib. bdg. 13.00 (978-0-613-16896-0(8)) Tandem Library Bks.

—The Solution. 1998. (Animorphs Ser.: No. 22). 152p. (J). (gr. 3-7). pap. 4.99 (978-0-590-76255-7(9)) Scholastic, Inc.

—The Suspicion. 1998. (Animorphs Ser.: No. 24). (J). (gr. 3-7). pap. 179.64 (978-0-590-63052-8(0)); 176p. pap. 4.99 (978-0-590-76257-1(5)) Scholastic, Inc.

—The Test. 2000. (Animorphs Ser.: No. 43). (Illus.). (J). (gr. 3-7). (978-0-606-18861-6(4)) Tandem Library Bks.

—The Threat. 1998. (Animorphs Ser.: No. 21). 158p. (J). (gr. 3-7). pap. 4.99 (978-0-590-76254-0(0), Scholastic Paperbacks) Scholastic, Inc.

—The Threat. 1998. (Animorphs Ser.: No. 21). (J). (gr. 3-7). (978-0-606-13141-4(8)) Tandem Library Bks.

—The Underground. 1998. (Animorphs Ser.: No. 17). (J). (gr. 3-7). (978-0-606-13137-7(X)) Tandem Library Bks.

—The Unexpected. 2000. (Animorphs Ser.: No. 44). (Illus.). (J). (gr. 3-7). (978-0-606-18862-3(2)) Tandem Library Bks.

—El Visitante. 1999. (Animorphs Ser.: No. 2). (SPA., Illus.). 192p. (J). (gr. 3-7). pap. 4.99 (978-0-439-07163-5(1), SO5396) Scholastic, Inc.

—El Visitante. 1999. (Animorphs Ser.: No. 2). (J). (gr. 3-7). (978-0-606-16929-5(6)) Tandem Library Bks.

—The Warning. 1998. (Animorphs Ser.: No. 16). (J). (gr. 3-7). (978-0-606-13136-0(1)) Tandem Library Bks.

—The Weakness. 2000. (Animorphs Ser.: No. 37). (Illus.). (J). (gr. 3-7). (978-0-606-18508-0(9)) Tandem Library Bks.

Reisfeld, Randi. Meet the Stars of Animorphs. 1999. (Animorphs Ser.). (J). (gr. 3-7). 144p. pap. 4.99 (978-0-439-06165-0(2)); pap. 59.88 (978-0-439-07272-4(7)) Scholastic, Inc.

ANNAPOLIS NAVAL ACADEMY

see United States Naval Academy, Annapolis

ANNE BOLEYN, QUEEN, CONSORT OF HENRY VIII, KING OF ENGLAND, 1507-1536

Ross, Stewart. Beware the King. 2007. (Flashbacks Ser.). (Illus.). 64p. (J). (gr. 4-7). pap. 8.95 (***978-0-237-53151-5(8)***, Evans Brothers, Limited) Evans Publishing Group GBR. *Dist:* Independent Pubs. Group.

ANNE OF GREEN GABLES (FICTITIOUS CHARACTER)—FICTION

see Shirley, Anne (Fictitious Character)—Fiction

ANNING, MARY, 1799-1847

Brown, Don. Rare Treasure: Mary Anning & Her Remarkable Discoveries. 2003. (Illus.). 32p. (J). (gr. k-3). pap. 5.95 (978-0-618-31081-4(9)) Houghton Mifflin Co. Trade & Reference Div.

—Rare Treasure: Mary Anning & Her Remarkable Discoveries. 1999. (gr. k-3). lib. bdg. 14.10 (978-0-613-60833-6(X)) Tandem Library Bks.

Goodhue, Thomas W. Curious Bones: Mary Anning & the Birth of Paleontology. 2004. (Profiles in Science Ser.). (Illus.). 112p. (YA). (gr. 6-12). lib. bdg. 23.95 (978-1-883846-93-0(5), First Biographies) Reynolds, Morgan Inc.

Mary Anning: Fossil Hunter. 2007. (J). pap. 5.95 (***978-1-57505-457-5(4)***, First Avenue Editions) Lerner Publishing Group.

Walker, Sally M. Mary Anning: Fossil Hunter. Saroff, Phyllis V., illus. 2000. (On My Own Biographies Ser.). 64p. (J). (gr. 1-3). lib. bdg. 23.93 (978-1-57505-425-4(6), Carolrhoda Bks.) Lerner Publishing Group.

ANNIVERSARIES

see Holidays

ANNULMENT OF MARRIAGE

see Divorce

ANOREXIA NERVOSA

see Eating Disorders

ANSWERS TO QUESTIONS

see Questions and Answers

ANT

see Ants

ANTARCTIC REGIONS

see Antarctica

ANTARCTICA

see also Scientific Expeditions; South Pole

Alderfer, Zoe, et al. Ann & Liv Cross Antarctica: A Dream Come True! 2003. (Illus.). 32p. (J). 15.95 (978-0-7382-0934-0(1)) Da Capo Pr., Inc.

Aloian, Molly. El Habitat de la Antartida. 2007. (SPA & ENG.). 32p. (J). (gr. 1-2). (***978-0-7787-8332-9(4)***) Crabtree Publishing Co.

Aloian, Molly & Kalman, Bobbie. An Antarctic Habitat. 2006. (Introducing Habitats Ser.). (Illus.). 32p. (J). (gr. 2-4). pap. (978-0-7787-2984-6(2)) Crabtree Publishing Co.

—The Antarctic Habitat. 2006. (Introducing Habitats Ser.). (Illus.). 32p. (J). (gr. 2-4). lib. bdg. (978-0-7787-2956-3(7)) Crabtree Publishing Co.

Aloian, Molly & Kalman, Bobbie. El Habitat de la Antartida. rev. ed. 2007. (SPA & ENG.). 32p. (J). (gr. 1-2). pap. (***978-0-7787-8356-5(1)***) Crabtree Publishing Co.

Antarctica: Individual Title, 6 Packs. (On Deck Ser.). 24p. (gr. 4-5). 35.00 (978-0-7578-1079-4(9)) Rigby Education.

Antarctica (30), Vol. 30. (Early Intervention Levels Ser.). 5.31 (978-0-7362-0652-5(3)) Hampton-Brown Bks.

Antarctica. (Continents Ser.). 24p. (J). 6.95 (978-0-7368-3357-8(9)) Capstone Pr., Inc.

Armstrong, Jennifer. Shipwreck at the Bottom of the World: The Extraordinary True Story of Shackleton & the Endurance. Boughton, Simon, ed. 2000. 144p. (J). (gr. 5-7). 12.95 (978-0-375-81049-7(8), Crown Books For Young Readers) Random Hse. Children's Bks.

Aspen-Baxter, Linda. Antarctica. 2005. (Illus.). 32p. (J). (ps-6). lib. bdg. 26.00 (978-1-59036-317-1(5)); pap. 7.95 (978-1-59036-324-9(8)) Weigl Pubs., Inc.

Bagley, Katie. Antarctica. 2002. (Continents Ser.). (Illus.). 79p. (J). (gr. 1-2). 18.60 (978-0-7368-1415-7(9), Bridgestone Bks.) Capstone Pr., Inc.

Binns, Tristan Boyer. Antarctica. 2006. (Exploring Continents Ser.). (Illus.). 32p. (J). (978-1-4034-8242-6(X)); pap. (978-1-4034-8250-1(0)) Heinemann Library.

Bledsoe, Lucy Jane. How to Survive in Antarctica. 2005. (Illus.). 96p. (J). (gr. 5-9). 16.95 (978-0-8234-1890-9(1)) Holiday Hse., Inc.

Bowman, Lucy. Antarctica (Level 1) - Internet Referenced. 2007. (Beginners Nature Ser.). 32p. (J). 4.99 (***978-0-7945-1691-8(2)***, Usborne) EDC Publishing.

Bredeson, Carmen. After the Last Dog Died: The True-Life, Hair-Raising Adventure of Douglas Mawson's 1912 Antarctic Expedition. 2003. (Illus.). 64p. (J). (gr. 5). 18.95 (978-0-7922-6140-7(2), National Geographic Children's Bks.) National Geographic Society.

Burleigh, Robert. Black Whiteness: Admiral Byrd Alone in the Antarctic. Krudop, Walter Lyon, illus. 1998. 40p. (J). (gr. 2-7). 17.95 (978-0-689-81299-6(X), Atheneum) Simon & Schuster Children's Publishing.

Calvert, Patricia. Sir Ernest Shackleton: By Endurance We Conquer. 2002. (Great Explorations Ser.). (Illus.). 80p. (J). 29.93 (978-0-7614-1485-8(1), Benchmark Bks.) Cavendish, Marshall Corp.

Coady, Christopher & Hooper, Meredith. The Island That Moved. 2004. (Illus.). 32p. (J). (gr. k). 16.99 (978-0-670-05882-2(3), Viking Juvenile) Penguin Group (USA) Inc.

Cowcher, Helen. Antarctica. 2001. (Illus.). 40p. (VIE, ENG, URD, TUR & CHI.). 16.95 (978-1-84059-006-7(8)); (GRE, ENG, URD, TUR & VIE., (YA). 16.95 (978-1-84059-002-9(5)); (GUJ, ENG, URD, TUR & VIE., (YA). 16.95 (978-1-84059-003-6(3)); (URD, ENG, TUR, VIE & CHI., (YA). 16.95 (978-1-84059-005-0(X)); (BEN, ENG, URD, TUR & VIE., (YA). 16.95 (978-1-84059-000-5(9)); (TUR., (YA). 16.95 (978-1-84059-007-4(6)) Milet Publishing.

Currie, Stephen. Antarctica. 2004. (Illus.). 112p. (J). (gr. 7-10). 29.95 (978-1-59018-495-0(5), Lucent Bks.) Thomson Gale.

Darian-Smith, Kate. Australia, Antarctica, & the Pacific. (Continents of the World Ser.). 2006. (Illus.). 64p. (YA). (gr. 7-10). lib. bdg. 32.67 (978-0-8368-5912-6(X)); 2005. (J). (978-0-8368-5919-5(7)) Stevens, Gareth Inc. (World Almanac Library).

Dewey, John. The Antarctic Journal. 1999. 48p. (J). (gr. 1 up). pap. 6.95 (978-0-06-446225-9(0)) HarperCollins Pubs.

Discovering Antarctica. 2005. (Illus.). 32p. (J). pap. 112.00 (978-0-7910-7057-4(3)) Facts On File, Inc.

Donaldson, Madeline. Antarctica. 2005. (Pull Ahead Bks.). (Illus.). 32p. (J). (gr. k-3). lib. bdg. 22.60 (978-0-8225-4724-2(4)) Lerner Publishing Group.

—Antarctica. 2005. (Illus.). 32p. (YA). (978-0-8225-2490-8(2), Lerner Pubns.) Lerner Publishing Group.

Fine, Jil. The Shackleton Expedition. 2002. (Survivors Ser.). (Illus.). 48p. (J). (gr. 7-12). 24.00 (978-0-516-23904-0(X), Children's Pr.) Scholastic Library Publishing.

—Shackleton Expedition. 2002. (gr. 7-12). lib. bdg. 15.25 (978-0-613-58800-3(2)) Tandem Library Bks.

Foster, Leila Merrell. Antarctica. 2001. (Continents Ser.). (Illus.). 32p. (J). (gr. k-2). lib. bdg. 21.36 (978-1-57572-447-8(2)) Heinemann Library.

Foster, Leila Merrell & Fox, Mary Virginia. Antarctica. 2002. (Continents Ser.). (Illus.). 32p. (J). (gr. k-2). pap. 6.95 (978-1-58810-946-0(1), 91436) Heinemann Library.

Fowler, Allan. Antarctica. 2001. (Rookie Read-About Geography Ser.). (Illus.). 32p. (J). (gr. 1-2). pap. 5.95 (978-0-516-27297-9(7)); 20.50 (978-0-516-21669-0(4)) Scholastic Library Publishing. (Children's Pr.).

—Antarctica. 2001. (gr. k-3). lib. bdg. 14.10 (978-0-613-53924-1(9)) Tandem Library Bks.

George, Michael. Antarctica: Land of Endless Water. 2002. (J). pap. 12.80 (978-0-89812-327-2(5), Creative Paperbacks) Creative Co., The.

Gogerly, Liz. Amundsen & Scott's Race to the South Pole. 2007. (J). (***978-1-4034-9761-1(3)***) Heinemann Library.

Graham, Amy. Discovering Antarctica's Land, People, & Wildlife: A MyReportLinks. com Book. 2004. (Continents of the World Ser.). (Illus.). 48p. (J). lib. bdg. 25.26 (978-0-7660-5205-5(2), MyReportLinks.com Bks.) Enslow Pubs., Inc.

Green, Jen. You Wouldn't Want to Be a Polar Explorer. 2001. (gr. 3-6). lib. bdg. 18.75 (978-0-613-44276-3(8)) Tandem Library Bks.

—You Wouldn't Want to Be a Polar Explorer! An Expedition You'd Rather Not Go On. Antram, David, illus. 2001. (You Wouldn't Want to Ser.). 32p. (J). (gr. 2-5). 28.50 (978-0-531-14601-9(4)); pap. 9.95 (978-0-531-16207-1(9)) Scholastic Library Publishing. (Watts, Franklin).

Harcourt School Publishers Staff. Animals of the Frozen South On Level. 3rd ed. 2002. (Trophies Reading Program Ser.). (Illus.). pap. 5.10 (978-0-15-323439-2(3)) Harcourt Schl. Pubs.

—Living in Antarctica. 3rd ed. 2002. (Horizons Ser.). (Illus.). (J). pap. 5.50 (978-0-15-333296-8(4)) Harcourt Schl. Pubs.

Hoena, B. A. Shackleton & the Lost Antarctic Expedition. Hoover, Dave & Barnett, Charles, illus. 2006. (Graphic Library). 32p. (J). (978-0-7368-5482-5(7)) Capstone Pr., Inc.

Hook, Cheryl. The Antarctic. 2001. (Water Worlds Ser.). (Illus.). 32p. (J). (gr. 4 up). 28.00 (978-0-7910-6566-2(9), 010351, Chelsea Hse.) Facts On File, Inc.

Hooper, Meredith. Antarctic Adventure: Exploring the frozen Continent. Martin, Linda, ed. 2000. (Eyewitness Bks.). (Illus.). 48p. (J). (gr. 2-4). pap. 3.99 (978-0-7894-6684-6(8)) Dorling Kindersley Publishing, Inc.

—Antarctic Adventure: Exploring the Frozen South. 2000. (Illus.). (J). (ps-ps). 48p. lib. bdg. 11.80 (978-0-613-32278-2(9)); 10.75 (978-0-606-20550-4(0)) Tandem Library Bks.

—Antarctic Journal: Hidden Worlds of Antarctica's Animals. DeLeiris, Lucia, illus. 2001. 40p. (J). (gr. 2-5). 16.95 (978-0-7922-7188-8(2), National Geographic Children's Bks.) National Geographic Society.

—Tom's Rabbit: A Surprise on the Way to Antarctica. Kitchen, Bert, illus. 2002. 27p. reprint ed. 16.00 (978-0-7567-5620-8(0)) DIANE Publishing Co.

Hooper, Meredith & Robertson, M. P. The Endurance: Shackleton's Perilous Expedition in Antarctica. 2001. (Illus.). 32p. 16.95 (978-0-7892-0704-3(4)) Abbeville Pr., Inc.

Hovanec, Erin M. An Online Visit to Antarctica. (Internet Field Trips Ser.). 24p. (J). 2002. lib. bdg. 18.75 (978-0-8239-6423-9(X)); 2001. (Illus.). (gr. 3). lib. bdg. 18.75 (978-0-8239-5656-2(3)) Rosen Publishing Group, Inc., The. (PowerKids Pr.).

Journey to Antarctica: Individual Title, 6 Packs. 32p. (gr. 5 up). 44.00 (978-0-7578-0992-7(8)) Rigby Education.

Kalman, Bobbie. Polar Oceans. 2003. (gr. 3-6). lib. bdg. 15.25 (978-0-613-59135-5(6)) Tandem Library Bks.

Kalman, Bobbie & Aloian, Molly. Polar Oceans. 2003. (Living Ocean Ser.). (Illus.). 32p. (J). (gr. 2-9). (978-0-7787-1297-8(4)); pap. (978-0-7787-1319-7(9)) Crabtree Publishing Co.

Kalman, Bobbie & Sjonger, Rebecca. Explora la Antartida. 2007. (SPA.). 32p. (gr. 6-10). pap. (***978-0-7787-8296-4(4)***) Crabtree Publishing Co.

—Explore Antarctica. 2007. (Explore the Continents Ser.). (Illus.). 32p. (J). (gr. 1-7). (***978-0-7787-3071-2(9)***); pap. (***978-0-7787-3085-9(9)***) Crabtree Publishing Co.

Karner, Julie. Roald Amundsen: The Conquest of the South Pole. 2006. (In the Footsteps of Explorers Ser.). (Illus.). 32p. (J). (gr. 3-9). lib. bdg. (978-0-7787-2432-2(8)) Crabtree Publishing Co.

Kimmel, Elizabeth Cody. Ice Story: Shackleton's Lost Expedition. 1999. (Illus.). 128p. (J). (gr. 4-6). tchr. ed. 19.00 (978-0-395-91524-0(4), Clarion Bks.) Houghton Mifflin Co. Trade & Reference Div.

l@Heureux, J. J. Good Day Book. 2006. spiral bd. (***978-0-9785892-0-2(3)***) Jian Media Ltd.

Loewen, Nancy & Bancroft, Ann. Four to the Pole: The American Women's Expedition to Antarctica, 1992-93. 2001. (Illus.). xi, 84p. (J). (gr. 7 up). 25.00 (978-0-208-02518-0(9), Linnet Bks.) Shoe String Pr., Inc.

Loves, June. Discovering Antarctica: Plants & Animals. 2002. (Discovering Antarctica Ser.). (Illus.). 32p. (gr. 4-8). 28.00 (978-0-7910-7022-2(0), Chelsea Hse.) Facts On File, Inc.

—Discovering Antarctica: The Future. 2002. (Discovering Antarctica Ser.). (Illus.). 32p. (gr. 4-8). 28.00 (978-0-7910-7025-3(5), Chelsea Hse.) Facts On File, Inc.

—Discovering Antarctica: The Land. 2002. (Discovering Antarctica Ser.). (Illus.). 32p. (gr. 4-8). 28.00 (978-0-7910-7023-9(9), Chelsea Hse.) Facts On File, Inc.

—Discovering Antarctica: The People. 2002. (Discovering Antarctica Ser.). (Illus.). 32p. (gr. 4-8). 28.00 (978-0-7910-7024-6(7), Chelsea Hse.) Facts On File, Inc.

Matsen, Bradford. An Extreme Dive under the Antarctic Ice. 2003. (Incredible Deep-Sea Adventures Ser.). (Illus.). 48p. (J). lib. bdg. 23.93 (978-0-7660-2190-7(4)) Enslow Pubs., Inc.

Mattern, Joanne. Antarctica: World's Biggest Glacier. 2002. (Reading Power Ser.). (Illus.). 24p. (J). lib. bdg. 17.25 (978-0-8239-6017-0(X), PowerKids Pr.) Rosen Publishing Group, Inc., The.

McCurdy, Michael. Trapped by the Ice! Shackleton's Amazing Antarctic Adventure. McCurdy, Michael, illus. 2002. (Illus.). 40p. (J). pap. 8.95 (978-0-8027-7633-4(7)) Walker & Co.

McNeil, Niki, et al. HOCPP 1057 Antarctica. 2006. spiral bd. 21.00 (***978-1-60308-057-6(0)***) In the Hands of a Child.

Moore, Jo Ellen. Antarctica. Evans, Marilyn, ed. Davis, Cindy & Winters, Keli, illus. 1999. (Geography Units Ser.). 80p. (J). (gr. 3-6). pap., tchr. ed. 12.95 (978-1-55799-715-9(2), EMC 768) Evan-Moor Educational Pubs.

Pelusey, Michael & Pelusey, Jane. Antarctica. 2004. (Continents Ser.). (Illus.). 32p. (J). (gr. 2-4). 23.00 (978-0-7910-8282-9(2), Chelsea Hse.) Facts On File, Inc.

Penner, Lucille Recht. Ice Wreck. LaFleur, David, illus. 2004. (Stepping Stones Ser.). 48p. (J). (gr. k-3). pap. 3.99 (978-0-307-26408-4(4), Random Hse. Bks. for Young Readers) Random Hse. Children's Bks.

Pipe, Jim. The Race to the South Pole. 2006. (Stories from History Ser.). 48p. (J). pap. 6.95 (***978-0-7696-4702-9(2)***) School Specialty Publishing.

Rau, Dana Meachen. Antarctica. 2003. (Continents Ser.). (Illus.). 32p. (J). (gr. 2-6). 27.07 (978-1-59296-064-4(2)) Child's World, Inc.

Reid, Greg. Exploration. 2005. (Illus.). 32p. (J). (gr. 4-7). lib. bdg. 27.10 (978-1-58340-762-2(6)) Smart Apple Media.

—The Frozen Continent. 2005. (Illus.). 32p. (J). (gr. 4-7). lib. bdg. 27.10 (978-1-58340-761-5(8)) Smart Apple Media.

Rink, Paul. Admiral Richard Byrd: Alone in the Antarctic. 2006. (Sterling Point Bks.). (Illus.). 192p. (J). 12.95 (978-1-4027-3189-1(2)) Sterling Publishing Co., Inc.

Roop, Connie, et al. Escape from the Ice: Shackleton & the Endurance. 2001. (Hello Reader! Ser.). (Illus.). 48p. (J). (gr. 2-4). pap. 3.99 (978-0-439-20640-2(5), Cartwheel Bks.) Scholastic, Inc.

Ryan, Zoe Alderfer. Ann & Liv Cross Antarctica: A Dream Come True! 2001. (J). (gr. 1-6). pap. 10.95 (978-0-9711527-0-0(5)) yourexpedition.

Sanford, Candace. Captain Nathaniel Brown Palmer. Scala, Susan, illus. 2007. 96p. (YA). pap. 14.95 (***978-0-9773725-9-1(6)***) Flat Hammock Pr.

Sayre, April Pulley. Antarctica. 1998. (Seven Continents Ser.: 8). (Illus.). 64p. (gr. 5-8). lib. bdg. 25.90 (978-0-7613-3227-5(8), Millbrook Pr.) Lerner Publishing Group.

—Hooray for Antarctica! 2003. 32p. (J). (gr. 2-5). pap. 7.95 (978-0-7613-1992-4(1)); (Our Amazing Continents Ser.: 4). (Illus.). lib. bdg. 21.90 (978-0-7613-2152-1(7)) Lerner Publishing Group. (Millbrook Pr.).

Schaefer, A. R. Antarctica. 2006. (Illus.). 24p. (J). (978-0-7368-5426-9(6)) Capstone Pr., Inc.

Striveildi, Cheryl. Antarctica. 2003. (Continents Ser.). (Illus.). 32p. (J). (gr. k-4). lib. bdg. 22.78 (978-1-57765-959-4(7)) ABDO Publishing Co.

Tulloch, Coral. Antarctica: The Heart of the World. 2006. 48p. (J). 17.95 (978-1-59270-054-7(3)) Enchanted Lion Bks., LLC.

Vierow, Wendy. Antarctica. 2004. (Atlas of the Seven Continents Ser.). (Illus.). 24p. (J). lib. bdg. 21.25 (978-0-8239-6688-2(7), PowerKids Pr.) Rosen Publishing Group, Inc., The.

Webb, Sophie. My Season with Penguins: An Antarctic Journal. (Illus.). 48p. (J). (gr. 4-6). 2000. tchr. ed. 15.00 (978-0-395-92291-0(7)); 2004. reprint ed. pap. 5.95 (978-0-618-43234-9(5)) Houghton Mifflin Co. Trade & Reference Div.

—My Season with Penguins: An Antarctic Journal. 2004. (Illus.). 48p. (J). (gr. 3-7). lib. bdg. 13.15 (978-0-606-30319-4(7)) Tandem Library Bks.

Werther, Scott P. Dr. Jerri Nielsen: Cheating Death in Antarctica. 2003. (Illus.). 48p. (J). (gr. 4-7). lib. bdg. 15.25 (978-0-613-67881-0(8)) Tandem Library Bks.

White, Matt. Endurance: Shipwreck & Survival on a Sea of Ice. 2001. (Illus.). 64p. (J). pap. (978-0-7368-9500-2(0)); (gr. 4-5). lib. bdg. 22.60 (978-0-7368-4000-2(1), Capstone High-Interest Bks.) Capstone Pr., Inc.

Ylvisaker, Anne. The Antarctic Ocean. 2002. (Oceans Ser.). (Illus.). 24p. (J). (gr. 1-2). lib. bdg. 18.60 (978-0-7368-1420-1(5), Bridgestone Bks.) Capstone Pr., Inc.

ANTARCTICA—FICTION

Antarctica: The Last Frontier. 2005. (J). audio, cd-rom 24.95 (978-0-9771381-9-7(4)) Williams, Geoffrey T.

Goldfrap, John Henry. The Boy Aviators' Polar Dash: Or Facing Death in the Antarctic. 2006. 180p. pap. 11.99 ***(978-1-4264-5072-3(9));*** 200p. pap. 15.99 ***(978-1-4264-5373-1(6))*** BiblioBazaar.

Hooper. Pole-Seekers. 2000. (Illus.). 165p. pap. 8.99 (978-0-340-75734-5(5) , Hodder & Stoughton) Hodder General Publishing Division GBR. *Dist:* Trafalgar Square Publishing.

Hooper, Meredith. Tom Crean's Rabbit: A True Story from Scott's Last Voyage. Kitchen, Bert, illus. 2005. 32p. (J). (ps-7). pap., pap. 7.95 (978-1-84507-393-0(2)) Lincoln, Frances Ltd. GBR. *Dist:* Perseus Distribution.

Lerangis, Peter. Journey to the North Pole. 2000. (Illus.). (J). (978-0-606-18864-7(9)) Tandem Library Bks.

Lumry, Amanda & Hurwitz, Laura. South Pole Penguins. 2007. 36p. 18.95 (978-0-9748411-8-2(8)); 15.95 (978-0-9748411-5-1(3)) Eaglemont Pr.

McCaughrean, Geraldine. The White Darkness. 2007. 384p. (J). (gr. 7 up). 16.99 (978-0-06-089035-3(5)); lib. bdg. 17.89 (978-0-06-089036-0(3)) HarperCollins Pubs. (HarperTeen).

Reilly, Matthew. Ice Station. 2000. (gr. 7-12). lib. bdg. 15.30 (978-0-613-36423-2(6)) Tandem Library Bks.

Smith, Noah. Antarctica: A Storybook Record. Smith, Noah, illus. 2006. (Illus.). (YA). per. 20.00 (978-1-59715-019-4(3)) Chapel Hill Pr.

Stamper, Judith Bauer. Penguin Puzzle. 2001. (gr. 3-6). lib. bdg. 11.80 (978-0-613-50722-6(3)) Tandem Library Bks.

Warner, Ross. Happy Feet Jr Cine-Manga. 2006. 32p. pap. 3.99 ***(978-1-59816-997-3(1)*** , Tokyopop Kids) TOKYOPOP, Inc.

Wilson, Karma. Where Is Home, Little Pip? Chapman, Jane, illus. 2008. 40p. (J). (978-0-689-85983-0(X) , McElderry, Margaret K.) Simon & Schuster Children's Publishing.

Young, Louise O. Penguin Comes Home. Elmore, Larry, illus. 2005. (Amazing Animal Adventures Ser.). (J). (ps-2). 36p. 15.95 (978-1-59249-324-1(6) , B7108); 32p. 2.95 incl. cd-rom (978-1-59249-325-8(4) , S7158); 36p. 6.95 (978-1-59249-326-5(2) , S7108) Soundprints.

ANTEATERS

Dollar, Sam. Anteaters. Sloan, Frank, ed. 2001. (Animals of the Rain Forest Ser.). (Illus.). 32p. (J). (gr. 4-7). lib. bdg. 22.83 (978-0-7398-3552-4(1)) Raintree.

Rebman, Renee C. Anteaters. 2006. (Animals Animals Ser.). (Illus.). 48p. (J). lib. bdg. 28.50 (978-0-7614-2234-1(X) , Benchmark Bks.) Cavendish, Marshall Corp.

Schaefer, Lola M. Spiny Echidna. 2003. (Heinemann Read & Learn Ser.). (Illus.). 24p. (J). lib. bdg. 18.50 (978-1-4034-3242-1(2)) Heinemann Library.

Seiple, Samantha & Seiple, Todd. Giant Anteaters. 2008. (Early Bird Nature Books Ser.). (J). lib. bdg. 26.60 ***(978-0-8225-7887-1(5)*** , Lerner Pubns.) Lerner Publishing Group.

ANTEATERS—FICTION

Anfousse, Ginette. Mon Ami Pichou. ed. 2004. (FRE.). (J). (ps-1). spiral bd. (978-0-616-01824-8(X)) Canadian National Institute for the Blind/Institut National Canadien pour les Aveugles.

Curry, Peter. Nosy Rosy. 2000. (Illus.). 28p. (J). 19.99 (978-0-00-198356-4(3)) HarperCollins Pubs. Ltd. GBR. *Dist:* Independent Pubs. Group.

—Nosy Rosy. 2002. (Illus.). 28p. (J). pap. 9.99 (978-0-00-664724-9(3)) Zondervan.

Cushman, Doug. Aunt Eater Loves a Mystery. Cushman, Doug, illus. 2002. (Aunt Eater Mysteries Ser.). (Illus.). (J). 12.30 (978-0-7587-5990-0(8)) Book Wholesalers, Inc.

—Aunt Eater's Mystery Christmas. Cushman, Doug, illus. 2002. (Aunt Eater Mysteries Ser.). (Illus.). (J). 12.30 (978-0-7587-5991-7(6)) Book Wholesalers, Inc.

—Aunt Eater's Mystery Halloween. Cushman, Doug, illus. 2002. (Aunt Eater Mysteries Ser.). (Illus.). (J). 11.91 (978-0-7587-5992-4(4)) Book Wholesalers, Inc.

—Aunt Eater's Mystery Halloween. Cushman, Doug, illus. 1999. (I Can Read Bks.). (Illus.). 64p. (J). (gr. k-3). pap. 3.99 (978-0-06-444266-4(7) , Harper Trophy) HarperCollins Pubs.

—Aunt Eater's Mystery Halloween. 1998. (I Can Read Bks.). (Illus.). (J). (gr. k-3). 64p. 14.95 (978-0-06-027803-8(X)); 40p. 14.89 (978-0-06-027804-5(8)) HarperCollins Pubs.

—Aunt Eater's Mystery Halloween. Cushman, Doug, illus. 1999. (I Can Read Bks.). (Illus.). 64p. lib. bdg. 10.79 (978-0-606-17301-8(3)) Tandem Library Bks.

—Aunt Eater's Mystery Halloween. 1999. (gr. k-3). lib. bdg. 11.80 (978-0-613-22814-5(6)) Tandem Library Bks.

—Aunt Eater's Mystery Vacation. Cushman, Doug, illus. 2002. (Aunt Eater Mysteries Ser.). (Illus.). (J). 12.30 (978-0-7587-5993-1(2)) Book Wholesalers, Inc.

DeSmet, Sara. Scared Silly. DeSmet, Sara, illus. 2006. (Illus.). 32p. (J). 15.95 (978-1-60108-009-7(3)) Red Cygnet Pr.

Emerson, Carl. Nosy Arnie the Anteater. Trover, Zachary, illus. 2007. (Animal Underdogs Ser.). 32p. (J). (ps-4). lib. bdg. 27.07 ***(978-1-60270-016-1(8)*** , Looking Glass Library) Magic Wagon.

Reed, Lynn R. Julius Anteater, Misunderstood. rev. ed. 2005. (Illus.). 32p. (J). 15.95 (978-1-59643-042-6(7)) Roaring Brook Pr.

Wallace, Karen. Alice Goes to Hollywood. Dewar, Bob, illus. 2006. (Read-It! Chapter Books). 48p. (J). (gr. 2-4). 19.95 (978-1-4048-1678-7(X)) Picture Window Bks.

ANTELOPES

Frisch, Aaron. Pronghorn Antelope. 2001. (Northern Trek Ser.). (Illus.). 24p. (J). lib. bdg. 22.80 (978-1-58340-054-8(0)) Smart Apple Media.

Schemenauer, Elma & Switzer, Merebeth. Pronghorns. 1999. (Getting to Know ... Nature's Children Ser.). (Illus.). 47p. (J). (978-0-7172-8842-7(0) , Grolier) Scholastic Library Publishing.

Stewart, Melissa. Antelope. 2002. (True Book Ser.). (Illus.). 48p. (J). (gr. 3-5). 25.00 (978-0-516-22198-4(1) , Children's Pr.) Scholastic Library Publishing.

—Antelope. 2002. (gr. 3-6). lib. bdg. 15.25 (978-0-613-53925-8(7)) Tandem Library Bks.

ANTHONY, SUSAN B. (SUSAN BROWNELL), 1820-1906

Auch, Allison. Mujeres que se atrevieron & Women Who Dared. 2005. spiral bd. 84.00 ***(978-1-4108-5692-0(5))*** Benchmark Education Co.

Bohannon, Lisa Frederiksen. Failure Is Impossible: The Story of Susan B. Anthony. 2004. (Feminist Voices Ser.). (Illus.). 112p. (YA). (gr. 6-12). 23.95 (978-1-883846-77-0(3) , First Biographies) Reynolds, Morgan Inc.

Boothroyd, Jennifer. Susan B. Anthony: A Life of Fairness. 2006. (Pull Ahead Books). (J). lib. bdg. (978-978-082-253-8(4)); (Illus.). 32p. 22.60 (978-0-8225-3479-2(7)) Lerner Publishing Group. (Lerner Pubns.).

—Susan B. Anthony: Una vida de igualdad. 2006. (Libros para Avanzar Ser.). (ENG & SPA., Illus.). 32p. (J). lib. bdg. 22.60 (978-0-8225-6234-4(0)) Lerner Publishing Group.

Collier, James Lincoln. The Susan B. Anthony You Never Knew. 2004. (You Never Knew Ser.). (J). 25.50 (978-0-516-24428-0(0) , Children's Pr.) Scholastic Library Publishing.

Connell, Kate. They Shall Be Heard: Susan B. Anthony & Elizabeth Cady Stanton. 2001. (Nonfiction Bookbag Ser.). (YA). (gr. 7-8). per. 8.45 (978-1-58830-207-6(5)) Metropolitan Teaching & Learning Co.

Davis, Lucile. Susan B. Anthony. 1998. (Read-and-Discover Biographies Ser.). (J). pap. 14.00 (978-0-516-21273-9(7) , Children's Pr.) Scholastic Library Publishing.

Fry, Erin. The Power of Friendship. 2005. (Illus.). 16p. (J). pap. (978-0-7367-2920-8(8)) Zaner-Bloser, Inc.

Gehret, Jeanne. Susan B. Anthony: And Justice for All. 2003. (Illus.). 120p. (J). (gr. 4 up). 14.95 (978-0-9625136-9-5(5)); pap. 6.95 (978-0-9625136-8-8(7)) Verbal Images Pr.

Ghiglieri, Carol. Easy Reader Biographies: Susan B. Anthony: Fighter for Women's Rights. 2007. 16p. pap. 2.99 ***(978-0-439-77413-0(6)*** , Teaching Resources) Scholastic, Inc.

Harcourt School Publishers Staff. Susan B. Anthony: Take-Home Book. 2001. (Collections Ser.). (Illus.). (J). pap. 1.90 (978-0-15-319542-6(8)) Harcourt Schl. Pubs.

—Susan B Anthony Below Level. 3rd ed. 2002. (Trophies Reading Program Ser.). (Illus.). pap. 5.10 (978-0-15-323337-1(0)) Harcourt Schl. Pubs.

Hopkinson, Deborah. Susan B. Anthony: Fighter for Women's Rights. Bates, Amy, illus. 2005. 32p. (J). lib. bdg. 15.00 ***(978-1-4242-1563-8(3))*** Fitzgerald Bks.

—Susan B. Anthony: Fighter for Women's Rights. Bates, Amy June, illus. 2005. (Ready-To-Read Stories of Famous Americans Ser.). 32p. (J). (gr. 1-3). pap. 3.99 (978-0-689-86909-9(6)); lib. bdg. 11.89 (978-0-689-86910-5(X)) Simon & Schuster Children's Publishing. (Aladdin).

Isaacs, Sally Senzell. America in the Time of Susan B. Anthony: 1845 to 1928. 2002. (America in the Time of... Ser.). (Illus.). 48p. (J). (gr. 4-7). pap. 8.50 (978-1-57572-941-1(5)) Heinemann Library.

Kendall, Martha E. Failure Is Impossible! The History of American Women's Rights. 3rd ed. 2005. (People's History Ser.). (Illus.). 96p. (gr. 6-12). lib. bdg. 26.60 (978-0-8225-1744-3(2)) Lerner Publishing Group.

Marsh, Carole. Susan B. Anthony. 2002. (One Thousand Readers Ser.). (Illus.). 12p. (J). (gr. k-4). 2.95 (978-0-635-01473-3(4) , 14734) Gallopade International.

—The Virginia Reader: Susan B. Anthony. 2001. (Virginia Experience! Ser.). (Illus.). 12p. (J). (gr. k-5). pap. 2.95 (978-0-635-00356-0(2)) Gallopade International.

Mattern, Joanne. Elizabeth Cady Stanton & Susan B. Anthony: Fighting Together for Women's Rights. 2003. (Reading Power Ser.). (Illus.). 24p. (J). lib. bdg. 17.25 (978-0-8239-6503-8(1) , PowerKids Pr.) Rosen Publishing Group, Inc., The.

McLeese, Don. Susan B. Anthony. 2002. (Illus.). 24p. (J). lib. bdg. 20.64 (978-1-58952-284-8(2)) Rourke Publishing, LLC.

McPherson, Stephanie Sammartino. Susan B. Anthony. 2006. (History Maker Bios Ser.). (Illus.). 48p. (J). 26.60 (978-0-8225-5938-2(2) , Lerner Pubns.) Lerner Publishing Group.

Monroe, Judy. The Susan B. Anthony Women's Voting Rights Trial: A Headline Court Case. 2002. (Headline Court Cases Ser.). (Illus.). 112p. (YA). (gr. 6-12). lib. bdg. 26.60 (978-0-7660-1759-7(1)) Enslow Pubs., Inc.

Noyed, Robert B. Susan B. Anthony: Reformer. 2002. (Spirit of America: Our People Ser.). (Illus.). 32p. (J). (gr. 2-6). 27.07 (978-1-56766-171-2(8)) Child's World, Inc.

Orr, Tamra B. Susan B. Anthony. 2006. (Profiles in American History Ser.). (Illus.). 48p. (J). (gr. 4-8). lib. bdg. 29.95 ***(978-1-58415-445-7(4))*** Mitchell Lane Pubs., Inc.

Parker, Barbara Keevil. Susan B. Anthony: Daring to Vote. 2000. (Gateway Biography Ser.: 4). (Illus.). 48p. (J). (gr. 2-4). pap. (978-0-7613-1378-6(8) , Millbrook Pr.) Lerner Publishing Group.

Raatma, Lucia. Susan B. Anthony. 2001. (Compass Point Early Biographies Ser.). (Illus.). 32p. (J). (gr. 2 up). lib. bdg. 21.26 (978-0-7565-0069-6(9)) Compass Point Bks.

Rustad, Martha E. H. Susan B. Anthony. Saunders-Smith, Gail, ed. 2001. (First Biographies Ser.). (Illus.). 24p. (J). (gr. k-1). lib. bdg. 15.93 (978-0-7368-0998-6(8) , Pebble Bks.) Capstone Pr., Inc.

—Susan B Anthony. 2005. (First Biographies Ser.). 24p. (YA). (gr. k-3). pap. (978-0-7368-9448-7(9) , Pebble Bks.) Capstone Pr., Inc.

Slade, Suzanne. Susan B. Anthony: Fighter for Freedom & Equality. Orback, Craig, illus. 2006. (Biographies Ser.). 24p. (J). (gr. k-3). lib. bdg. 23.93 ***(978-1-4048-3104-9(5))*** Picture Window Bks.

Susan B Anthony. (Photo Illustrated Biographies Ser.). 24p. (J). 6.95 (978-0-7368-8422-8(X)) Capstone Pr., Inc.

Susan B Anthony. (Compass Point Early Biographies Ser.). 32p. (J). 7.95 (978-0-7565-1181-4(X)) Compass Point Bks.

Susan B. Anthony: A Life of Fairness. 2006. (J). pap. 5.95 (978-0-8225-5699-2(5)) Lerner Publishing Group.

Susan B. Anthony: Una vida de igualdad (A Life of Fairness) 2007. (J). pap. 5.95 (978-0-8225-6558-1(7) , Ediciones Lerner) Lerner Publishing Group.

Wheeler, Jill C. Susan B. Anthony. 2003. (Breaking Barriers Ser.). (Illus.). 64p. (J). (gr. 3-8). lib. bdg. 25.65 (978-1-57765-903-7(1)) ABDO Publishing Co.

ANTHROPOGEOGRAPHY

see Human Geography

ANTHROPOLOGY

see also Anthropometry; Archaeology; Civilization; Ethnology; Human Beings; Human Geography; Human Skin Color; Language and Languages; Social Change

also names of races and tribes

Adams, Bradley J. Forensic Anthropology. 2006. (Inside Forensic Science Ser.). (Illus.). 112p. (J). (gr. 9 up). 30.00 (978-0-7910-9198-2(8) , Chelsea Hse.) Facts On File, Inc.

Barnett, Annette. Myth, Magic, & Mystery: An Introduction to Anthropology for Kids in the 21st Century. 2004. 41p. per. 17.30 (978-1-4116-0598-5(5)) Lulu.com.

Batten, Mary. Anthropologist: Scientist of the People. Hurtado, Magdalena & Hill, Kim, photos by. 2001. (Scientists in the Field Ser.). (Illus.). 64p. (J). (gr. 4-6). tchr. ed. 16.00 (978-0-618-08368-8(5)) Houghton Mifflin Co. Trade & Reference Div.

Boyd, R. How Humans Evolved. 3rd ed. 2002. ix, 372p. (YA). pap., tchr. ed. (978-0-393-97964-0(4)) Norton, W. W. & Co., Inc.

Delasfosse, Claude & Jeunesse, Gallimard. Houses. Grant, Donald, illus. 1998. (First Discovery Book Ser.). 24p. (J). (ps-2). 12.95 (978-0-590-38152-9(0)) Scholastic, Inc.

Discovering Cultures - Group 2, 6 vols. 2003. 288p. (YA). (gr. 2 up). lib. bdg. 158.86 (978-0-7614-1514-5(9)) Cavendish, Marshall Corp.

Doherty, Gillian. Usborne Book of Peoples of the World: Internet-Linked. 2001. (978-0-606-22545-8(5)) Tandem Library Bks.

Doudna, Kelly. Boys & Girls Around the World. 2004. (Illus.). (J). (ps-3). lib. bdg. 119.58 (978-1-59197-563-2(8) , SandCastle) ABDO Publishing Co.

Facchini, Fiorenzo. A Day with Homo Erectus: Life 400,000 Years Ago. Baldanzi, Alessandro, illus. 2003. (Early Humans Ser.). 48p. (gr. 6 up). lib. bdg. 23.90 (978-0-7613-2766-0(5) , Twenty-First Century Bks.) Lerner Publishing Group.

Haywood, John. The War for Power & Knowledge. 2003. (Illus.). 264p. pap. 19.99 (978-0-7548-1201-2(4)) Anness Publishing GBR. *Dist:* National Bk. Network.

Hopping, Lorraine Jean. Bone Detective: The Story of Forensic Anthropologist Diane France. 2006. (Women's Adventures in Science Ser.). 128p. pap. 9.95 (978-0-309-09550-1(6) , Joseph Henry Pr.) National Academies Pr.

Hossell, Karen Price. Sonar. 2003. (gr. 3-6). lib. bdg. 16.40 (978-0-613-45837-5(0)) Tandem Library Bks.

Lambert, David & Diagram Group. The Field Guide to Early Man. 1999. (Illus.). 256p. (YA). (gr. 8-12). pap. 32.95 (978-0-7351-0215-6(5)) Replica Bks.

Libal, Angela. Forensic Anthropology. 2006. (Forensics, the Science of Crime-Solving Ser.). (Illus.). 112p. (J). (gr. 7 up). 22.95 (978-1-4222-0030-8(2) , 1248052) Mason Crest Pubs.

MacDonald, Fiona. Tribes, Empires & Civilizations. 2001. (Through the Ages Ser.). (Illus.). 64p. (gr. 3-7). 12.95 (978-0-7548-0851-0(3)) Anness Publishing GBR. *Dist:* National Bk. Network.

Museo de Antropologia (Para Colorear) 2003. (SPA.). 4.48 (978-968-855-273-5(9)) Suromex, Ediciones, S.A. MEX. *Dist:* Giron Bks.

One World, Many People: Anthropology made fun for kids:an illustrated textbook & activity Guide. 2006. (J). per. 19.95 net. ***(978-0-9787138-0-5(X))*** Young Scholars Pr.

Sager. People, Places & Change: Intro to World Studies - Eastern. 3rd ed. 2003. (Illus.). (gr. 6-8). 58.00 (978-0-03-053637-3(5)) Holt, Rinehart & Winston.

Walker, Sally M. Written in Bone. 2008. (J). lib. bdg. ***(978-0-8225-7135-3(8)*** , Carolrhoda Bks.) Lerner Publishing Group.

Waters, Jennifer. All Kinds of People: What Makes Us Different. 2002. (Spyglass Books). (Illus.). 24p. (J). (gr. 1 up). lib. bdg. 18.60 (978-0-7565-0377-2(9)) Compass Point Bks.

Woolf, Alex. History Mysteries. 2004. (Forensic Files Ser.). (Illus.). 48p. (J). lib. bdg. (978-1-4034-4830-9(2)) Heinemann Library.

—Investigating History Mysteries. 2004. (Forensic Files Ser.). (Illus.). 48p. (J). pap. 8.50 (978-1-4034-5470-6(1)) Heinemann Library.

ANTHROPOLOGY—BIOGRAPHY

Horn, Geoffrey M. Margaret Mead. 2004. (Trailblazers of the Modern World Ser.). (Illus.). 48p. (J). (gr. 5 up). pap. 11.95 (978-0-8368-5259-2(1) , World Almanac Library) Stevens, Gareth Inc.

Poynter, Margaret. The Leakeys: Uncovering the Origins of Humankind. 2001. (Great Minds of Science Ser.). (Illus.). 128p. (YA). (gr. 4-10). pap. 10.95 (978-0-7660-1873-0(3)) Enslow Pubs., Inc.

ANTHROPOLOGY—DICTIONARIES

Cultures of the World, 6 vols., Set. 2003. 864p. (gr. 5 up). 222.43 (978-0-7614-1496-4(7)); 2nd ed. 222.43 (978-0-7614-1472-8(X)) Cavendish, Marshall Corp. (Cavendish, Marshall Reference Bks.).

Cultures of the World, 6 bks., Group 9. Incl. Cuba. Sheehan, Sean & Jermyn, Leslie. lib. bdg. (978-0-7614-1965-5(9)); Dominican Republic. Foley, Erin & Jermyn, Leslie. lib. bdg. (978-0-7614-1966-2(7)); Haiti. Ngcheong-Lum, Roseline & Jermyn, Leslie. lib. bdg. (978-0-7614-1968-6(3)); Nicaragua. Kott, Jennifer & Streiffert, Kristi. lib. bdg. (978-0-7614-1969-3(1)); Puerto Rico. Levy, Patricia & Bahrawi, Nazry. lib. bdg. (978-0-7614-1970-9(5)); Salvador. Foley, Erin & Hapipi, Rafiz. lib. bdg. (978-0-7614-1967-9(5)); 2nd ed. (Illus.). 144p. (J). (gr. 6-10). 2005. (978-0-7614-1964-8(0) , Benchmark Bks.) Cavendish, Marshall Corp.

ANTHROPOMETRY

Lockie, Mark. Biometric Technology. (Science at the Edge Ser.). 64p. pap. 8.95 (978-1-4034-4119-5(7)); 2002. (Illus.). (J). (gr. 6-8). lib. bdg. 27.86 (978-1-58810-701-5(9)) Heinemann Library.

ANTIBIOTICS

see also names of specific antibiotics, e.g. Penicillin; etc.

Ballard, Carol. From Cowpox to Antibiotics: Discovering Vaccines & Medicines. 2006. (Chain Reactions Ser.). (Illus.). 62p. (YA). (gr. 6-9). lib. bdg. 34.29 (978-1-4034-8839-8(8)) Heinemann Library.

Day, Nancy. Killer Superbugs: The Story of Drug-Resistant Diseases. 2001. (Issues in Focus Ser.). (Illus.). 128p. (YA). (gr. 6-12). lib. bdg. 26.60 (978-0-7660-1588-3(2)) Enslow Pubs., Inc.

Goldsmith, Connie. Superbugs Strike Back: When Antibiotics Fail. 2007. (Discovery! Ser.). (Illus.). 112p. (J). (gr. 6-12). 29.27 (978-0-8225-6607-6(9) , Twenty-First Century Bks.) Lerner Publishing Group.

ANTI-COMMUNIST MOVEMENTS

Brooks, Philip. The McCarthy Hearings. 2003. (20th-Century Perspectives Ser.). (Illus.). 48p. (J). pap. (978-1-4034-4178-2(2)); lib. bdg. 27.07 (978-1-4034-3808-9(0)) Heinemann Library.

Fitzgerald, Brian. McCarthyism: The Red Scare. 2006. 96p. (YA). (gr. 7 up). lib. bdg. (978-0-7565-2007-6(X)) Compass Point Bks.

Zeinert, Karen. McCarthy & the Fear of Communism in American History. 1998. (In American History Ser.). (Illus.). 128p. (YA). (gr. 5-12). lib. bdg. 26.60 (978-0-89490-987-0(8)) Enslow Pubs., Inc.

ANTIPATHIES

see Prejudices

ANTIQUES

see also Art Objects; Collectors and Collecting

Cunningham, Jo & Nossaman, Darlene. Homer Laughlin China: Guide to Shapes & Patterns. 2002. (Schiffer Book for Collectors Ser.). (Illus.). 240p. (gr. 10-13). pap. 29.95 (978-0-7643-1483-4(1)) Schiffer Publishing, Ltd.

Deel, Kathleen. Enesco Then & Now: An Unauthorized Collector's Guide. 2001. (Schiffer Book for Collectors Ser.). (Illus.). 184p. (gr. 10-13). pap. 29.95 (978-0-7643-1453-7(X)) Schiffer Publishing, Ltd.

Hobby House Press Staff. My Antiques Organizer. 2000. 24p. (YA). 19.95 (978-0-87588-579-7(9)) Hobby Hse. Pr., Inc.

Miller, Judith. Antiques Price Guide 2005. 2004. 752p. 35.00 (978-0-7566-0432-5(X)) Dorling Kindersley Publishing, Inc.

Schiffer, Nancy N. Rhinestones! A Collector's Handbook & Price Guide. 4th rev. ed. 2003. (Illus.). 160p. (gr. 10-13). pap. 16.95 (978-0-7643-1751-4(2)) Schiffer Publishing, Ltd.

Shalhoub, Michael. The Pinball Compendium, 1930s-1960s. 2002. (Illus.). 256p. (gr. 10-13). 49.95 (978-0-7643-1527-5(7)) Schiffer Publishing, Ltd.

ANTIQUITIES

see Archaeology; Bible—Antiquities; Classical Antiquities; Human Beings—Origin; Indians of North America—Antiquities; Prehistoric Peoples

see names of countries, cities, etc. with the subdivision Antiquities, e.g. United States—Antiquities; etc

ANTIQUITIES, BIBLICAL

see Bible—Antiquities

ANTIQUITIES, CLASSICAL

see Classical Antiquities

ANTIQUITY OF MAN

see Human Beings—Origin

ANTI-REFORMATION

see Reformation

ANTISEMITISM

see also Jews—Persecutions

Cohn, Janice. The Christmas Menorahs: How a Town Fought Hate. 2000. (J). 13.75 (978-0-606-19688-8(9)) Tandem Library Bks.

Finkelstein, Norman H. Captain of Innocence: France & the Dreyfus Affair. 2000. (gr. 7-12). lib. bdg. 23.40 (978-0-613-81391-4(X)) Tandem Library Bks.

A B

—Captain of Innocence: France & the Dreyfus Affair. 2001. (Illus.). 160p. (YA). (gr. 7-12). pap. 13.95 (978-0-595-15651-1(7) , Backinprint.com) iUniverse, Inc.

Gottfried, Ted. Nazi Germany: The Face of Tyranny. Alcorn, Stephen, illus. (Holocaust History Ser.). 112p. (YA). (gr. 7-12). 22.95 (978-1-58013-203-9(0)) Kar-Ben Publishing.

—Nazi Germany: The Face of Tyranny. 2000. (Holocaust Ser.: up). (Illus.). 128p. (gr. 7 up). lib. bdg. (978-0-7613-1714-2(7) , Twenty-First Century Bks.) Lerner Publishing Group.

Hasday, Judy L. The Holocaust. 2001. (Great Disasters, Reforms & Ramifications Ser.). (Illus.). 112p. (J). 30.00 (978-0-7910-5790-2(9) , Chelsea Hse.) Facts On File, Inc.

Ramen, Fred. Hermann Goering: Hitler's Second in Command. 2005. (Holocaust Biographies Ser.). (Illus.). 112p. (YA). (gr. 7-12). lib. bdg. 26.50 (978-0-8239-3307-5(5) , HBGORI) Rosen Publishing Group, Inc., The.

Roberts, Jeremy. Joseph Goebbels: Nazi Propaganda Minister. 2005. (Holocaust Biographies Ser.). (Illus.). 112p. (J). (gr. 7-12). lib. bdg. 26.50 (978-0-8239-3309-9(1) , HBGOEB) Rosen Publishing Group, Inc., The.

ANTISEMITISM—FICTION

Bell, Mary Reeves. Secret of Mezuzah. 1999. (J). (978-0-606-18974-3(2)) Tandem Library Bks.

Griffis, Molly Levite. Simon Says. 2004. vi, 263p. (J). 22.95 (978-1-57168-836-1(6)); pap. (978-1-57168-847-7(1)) Eakin Pr. (Eakin Pr.).

Levitin, Sonia. The Cure. 1999. 192p. (YA). (gr. 5 up). 16.00 (978-0-15-201827-6(1) , Silver Whistle) Harcourt Trade Pubs.

—The Cure. 2000. 272p. (J). (gr. 7 up). pap. 6.99 (978-0-380-73298-2(X) , Harper Trophy) HarperCollins Pubs.

—The Cure. 2000. (J). 12.64 (978-0-606-19967-4(5)) Tandem Library Bks.

—Cure. 2000. (gr. 5-8). lib. bdg. 14.15 (978-0-613-29918-3(3)) Tandem Library Bks.

Rappaport, Doreen. The Year of the Paper Menorahs. Alcorn, Stephen, illus. 2000. 32p. (J). 15.99 (978-0-7868-0400-9(9)) Hyperion Bks. for Children.

Shapiro, David L. Sara's Journey. 2005. 293p. (YA). (gr. 7-12). pap. 12.95 (978-0-8276-0776-7(8)) Jewish Pubn. Society.

Tunis, John R. Keystone Kids. 2006. (Illus.). 252p. (J). pap. 5.95 (978-0-15-205634-6(3) , Odyssey Classics) Harcourt Children's Bks.

ANTISLAVERY

see Slavery

ANTS

Alexander Ant Cools Off. 2005. (Early Library). (YA). (ps-3). 23.94 (978-0-8215-8950-2(4)) Sadlier, William H. Inc.

All about Ants. (Rosen Real Readers Big Bookstm Ser.). 12p. (J). (gr. 1-2). 31.95 (978-1-4042-6213-3(X)) Rosen Publishing Group, Inc., The.

All about Ants, 6 vols. (Book2WebTM Ser.). (gr. 4-8). 36.50 (978-0-322-02977-4(5)) Wright Group, The.

Allen, Judy. Are You an Ant? Humphries, Tudor, illus. 2002. (Backyard Bks.). 32p. (J). (gr. k-3). tchr. ed. 9.95 (978-0-7534-5365-0(7) , Kingfisher) Houghton Mifflin Co. Trade & Reference Div.

—Are you an Ant? Humphries, Tudor, illus. 2004. (Backyard Bks.). 32p. (J). (ps up). pap. 5.95 (978-0-7534-5803-7(9) , Kingfisher) Houghton Mifflin Co. Trade & Reference Div.

Anderson, Catherine & Harris, Monica. Bug Books, 6 bks., Set 5. 2003. (Illus.). (J). (gr. k-2). lib. bdg. 136.74 (978-1-58810-867-8(8)) Heinemann Library.

Anderson, Catherine, et al. Bug Books, 1 bks., Set. 2003. (Illus.). (J). lib. bdg. 592.54 (978-1-4034-0768-9(1)) Heinemann Library.

Ants. (Bugs, Bugs, Bugs! Ser.). 24p. (J). 6.95 (978-0-7368-5094-0(5)) Capstone Pr., Inc.

Ants. (Nature's Friends Ser.). 32p. (J). 7.95 (978-0-7565-1223-1(9)) Compass Point Bks.

Ants, 6 vols. (gr. k-2). 28.95 (978-0-7368-8245-3(6)) Red Brick Learning.

Ants, 6 vols. (Sunshinetm Science Ser.). 24p. (gr. 1-2). 31.50 (978-0-7802-0287-0(2)); 36.95 (978-0-7802-0538-3(3)) Wright Group, The.

Ants: Level K, 6 vols. (Wonder Worldtm Ser.). 16p. 34.95 (978-0-7802-1193-3(6)) Wright Group, The.

Ants & Their Nests. (Animal Homes Ser.). 24p. (J). 6.95 (978-0-7368-5120-6(8)) Capstone Pr., Inc.

Ants, Ants, Ants, 6 vols. (Sunshinetm Science Ser.). 24p. (gr. 1-2). 31.50 (978-0-7802-0286-3(4)); 36.95 (978-0-7802-0537-6(5)) Wright Group, The.

Ants Aren't Antisocial: Individual Title Six-Packs. (Action Packs Ser.). 104p. (gr. 3-5). 44.00 (978-0-7635-2986-4(9)) Rigby Education.

Ants Sets: 1 Each of 3 Student Books. (Sunshinetm Science Ser.). (gr. 1-2). 17.95 (978-0-7802-0267-2(8)) Wright Group, The.

Ants World of Insects. 2006. (Illus.). 24p. (J). (gr. k-2). 18.50 (*978-0-531-17858-4(7)) Scholastic Library Publishing.

Armies of Ants. 1998. (J). pap. 3.95 (978-0-439-04452-3(9)) Scholastic, Inc.

Ashley, Susan. Ants. 2004. (Weekly Reader Early Learning Library). (Illus.). 24p. (gr. 1 up). (J). pap. 5.95 (978-0-8368-4057-5(7)); (YA). lib. bdg. 19.33 (978-0-8368-4050-6(X)) Stevens, Gareth Inc. (Weekly Reader Early Learning Library).

Barraclough, Sue. Ants. 2005. (Creepy Creatures Ser.). (Illus.). 24p. (J). (978-1-4109-1505-4(0)); pap. (978-1-4109-1510-8(7)) Steck-Vaughn.

Berger, Melvin & Berger, Gilda. Ants. 2002. (Scholastic Readers Ser.). (Illus.). (J). (978-0-439-44537-5(X)) Scholastic, Inc.

Birch. Ants up Close 6 Pack. 2004. pap. 40.50 (978-1-4109-1151-3(9)) Harcourt Schl. Pubs.

Birch, Robin. Ants up Close. 2004. (J). pap. 7.50 (978-1-4109-1144-5(6)); (Illus.). 32p. (gr. 3-5). 25.70 (978-1-4109-1137-7(3)) Harcourt Schl. Pubs.

Brimner, Larry Dane. How Many Ants? 1998. (Rookie Reader Skill Set Ser.). (Illus.). 32p. (J). (gr. k-2). pap. 4.95 (978-0-516-26251-2(3) , Children's Pr.) Scholastic Library Publishing.

Chapman, Joan. An Ant: Learning the Short A Sound. (PowerPhonics Ser.). (Illus.). (J). 2002. 24p. (gr. 1). lib. bdg. 18.50 (978-0-8239-5916-7(3)); 2001. 23p. pap. 26.40 (978-0-8239-8261-5(0)) Rosen Publishing Group, Inc., The. (PowerKids Pr.).

Christian, Eleanor & Roth-Singer, Lyzz. Looking at Ants. 2000. (Yellow Umbrella Books). (Illus.). 16p. (J). (gr. 1). lib. bdg. 14.60 (978-0-7368-0725-8(X) , Pebble Bks.) Capstone Pr., Inc.

Claybourne, Anna. Ants & Termites. (Illus.). 32p. (YA). (gr. 3 up). lib. bdg. 27.10 (978-1-932799-57-6(5)) Stargazer Bks.

Cooper, Jason. Ants. (Insects Ser.). 24p. (gr. k-2). 2006. (Illus.). 14.95 (978-1-59515-424-8(8)); 2005. pap. 5.45 (978-1-59515-738-6(7)) Rourke Publishing, LLC.

—Hormigas. 2005. (Biblioteca del Descubrimiento de los Insectos Ser.). (SPA.). 24p. pap. 5.45 (978-1-59515-694-5(1)) Rourke Publishing, LLC.

Coughlan, Cheryl. Ants. 2005. (Bugs, Bugs, Bugs Ser.). 24p. (YA). (gr. k-3). pap. (978-0-7368-8205-7(7) , Pebble Bks.) Capstone Pr., Inc.

—Ants. Saunders-Smith, Gail, ed. 1999. (Insects Ser.). (Illus.). 24p. (J). (gr. k-1). lib. bdg. 15.93 (978-0-7368-0234-5(7) , Pebble Bks.) Capstone Pr., Inc.

Dahl, Michael. Ants at the Picnic: Counting by 10s. Trover, Zachary, illus. 2006. 24p. (J). (ps-2). 22.60 (978-1-4048-1318-2(7)) Picture Window Bks.

Dorros, Arthur. Ciudades de Hormigas. Dorros, Arthur, illus. 2006. (Let's-Read-and-Find-Out Science Ser.). (SPA.). 32p. (J). pap. 6.99 (978-0-06-088715-5(X)) HarperCollins Pubs.

Dyer, Hadley & Kalman, Bobbie. Les Fourmis. rev. ed. 2007. (FRE., Illus.). 32p. (J). (gr. 2-3). pap. (*978-2-89579-125-6(2)) Editions Banjo.

Dyer, Hadley & Kalman, Bobbie. The Life Cycle of an Ant. 2005. (Life Cycle Ser.). (Illus.). 32p. (J). (gr. k-6). (978-0-7787-0670-0(2)); pap. (978-0-7787-0700-4(8)) Crabtree Publishing Co.

Fleisher, Paul. Ants. 2001. (Animalways Ser.). (Illus.). 112p. (J). (gr. 5 up). lib. bdg. 31.36 (978-0-7614-1269-4(7) , Benchmark Bks.) Cavendish, Marshall Corp.

Fowler, Allan. Inside an Ant Colony. Rau, Dana, ed. 1998. (Rookie Read-About Science Ser.). (Illus.). 32p. (J). (gr. 1-2). pap. 4.95 (978-0-516-26365-6(X) , Children's Pr.) Scholastic Library Publishing.

—Inside an Ant Colony. 1998. (Rookie Read-About Science Ser.). (Illus.). 32p. (J). (gr. 1-2). 20.50 (978-0-516-20804-6(7) , Children's Pr.) Scholastic Library Publishing.

—Inside an Ant Colony. 1998. (Illus.). 31p. (J). (gr. 1-2). lib. bdg. 12.95 (978-0-613-37400-2(2)) Tandem Library Bks.

Frost, Helen. Leaf-Cutting Ants. Saunders-Smith, Gail, ed. 2002. (Rain Forest Animals Ser.). (Illus.). 24p. (J). (gr. k-1). lib. bdg. 15.93 (978-0-7368-1457-7(4) , Pebble Bks.) Capstone Pr., Inc.

Furgang, Kathy. Let's Take a Field Trip to an Ant Colony. 2000. (Neighborhoods in Nature Ser.). (Illus.). 24p. (J). (gr. k-4). lib. bdg. 18.75 (978-0-8239-5444-5(7) , PowerKids Pr.) Rosen Publishing Group, Inc., The.

Gillis, Jennifer B. Dan the Ant. 2006. (Reader's Clubhouse Set A Ser.). (Illus.). 24p. (J). pap. 3.99 (978-0-7641-3282-7(2)) Barron's Educational Series, Inc.

Gomel, Luc. Face-to-Face with the Ant: Energetic Worker. Amann, Remy & Stoffel, Dominique, photos by. 2004. (Face to Face Ser.). (Illus.). 28p. (J). (ps-2). 9.95 (978-1-57091-451-5(6)) Charlesbridge Publishing, Inc.

Green, Emily K. Ants. 2006. (Blastoff! Readers Ser.). (Illus.). 24p. (J). lib. bdg. 16.95 (978-1-60014-008-2(4)) Bellwether Media.

Green, Jen. Ants, Bees, Wasps & Termites. 2004. (Illus.). 64p. pap. 8.99 (978-1-84215-977-4(1) , Southwater) Anness Publishing GBR. *Dist:* National Bk. Network.

Greenaway, Theresa. Ants. 2001. (Secret World Of... Ser.). (Illus.). 48p. (J). (gr. 4-7). lib. bdg. 27.12 (978-0-7398-3511-1(4)) Raintree.

—Ants. Fairclough, Chris, illus. 1999. (Minipets Ser.). 32p. (J). (gr. 1-5). lib. bdg. 25.69 (978-0-7398-1830-5(9)) Raintree.

—Ants. 2000. (Minipets Ser.). (Illus.). 32p. (J). (gr. 1-5). pap. 7.95 (978-0-7398-2193-0(8)) Steck-Vaughn.

Gunson, Dave, illus. The Ants: First Wave Satellite Individual Title Six-Packs. (Sails Literacy Ser.). 16p. (gr. k up). 27.00 (978-0-7578-6869-6(X)) Rigby Education.

Halfmann, Janet. Ants. 1998. (Bugs Ser.). (Illus.). 32p. (J). (gr. 4-7). lib. bdg. 16.95 (978-1-887068-29-1(5)) Smart Apple Media.

Hall, Margaret. Ants. 2004. (Bugs, Bugs, Bugs! Ser.). (Illus.). 24p. (J). lib. bdg. 19.93 (978-0-7368-2586-3(X) , Pebble Bks.) Capstone Pr., Inc.

Harcourt School Publishers Staff. Amazing Ants: Independent Reader. 3rd ed. 2002. (Trophies Reading Program Ser.). (Illus.). (J). pap. 2.90 (978-0-15-325488-8(2)) Harcourt Schl. Pubs.

—Ants Are Busy: On Level. 3rd ed. 2002. (Trophies Reading Program Ser.). (Illus.). pap. 5.10 (978-0-15-322998-5(5)) Harcourt Schl. Pubs.

Hartley, Karen. Ant. 2002. (Bug Bks.). (Illus.). 32p. (J). (gr. k-2). pap. 6.95 (978-1-57572-456-0(1) , 90446) Heinemann Library.

—Ant. 1999. (Bug Bks.). (Illus.). (J). 13.75 (978-0-606-21976-1(5)) Tandem Library Bks.

Hartley, Karen & Macro, Chris. Ant. 2006. (Illus.). 32p. (J). (*978-1-4034-8292-1(6)) Heinemann Library.

Hartley, Karen & Marco, Chris. Ant. 1998. (Bug Books Ser.). (Illus.). 32p. (J). (gr. k-2). lib. bdg. 21.36 (978-1-57572-660-1(2)) Heinemann Library.

HEINEMANN LIBRARY. Ant. 2nd ed. 2006. (Illus.). 32p. (J). pap. (*978-1-4034-8305-8(1)) Heinemann Library.

Heinrichs, Ann. Ants. 2002. (Nature's Friends Ser.). (Illus.). 32p. (J). (gr. 2 up). lib. bdg. 21.26 (978-0-7565-0164-8(4)) Compass Point Bks.

Hipp, Andrew. Gardening Ants. 2003. (Really Wild Life Of... Ser.). (Illus.). 24p. (J). lib. bdg. 18.75 (978-0-8239-6243-3(1) , PowerKids Pr.) Rosen Publishing Group, Inc., The.

Hodge, Deborah. Ants. Mulock, Julian, tr. Mulock, Julian, illus. 2004. (Denver Museum of Nature & Science Bks.). 32p. (J). (gr. k-3). (978-1-55337-655-2(2)); (978-1-55337-066-6(X)) Kids Can Pr., Ltd.

Hovanec, Erin M. I Wonder What It's Like to Be an Ant. 2000. (Life Science Wonder Bks.). (Illus.). 24p. (J). (gr. k-4). lib. bdg. 18.75 (978-0-8239-5449-0(8) , PowerKids Pr.) Rosen Publishing Group, Inc., The.

How Ants Live, 6 vols. (Sunshinetm Science Ser.). 24p. (gr. 1-2). 31.50 (978-0-7802-0288-7(0)); 36.95 (978-0-7802-0539-0(1)) Wright Group, The.

Iasevoli, Brenda. Ants! 2005. 32p. (J). lib. bdg. 15.00 (*978-1-4242-0855-5(6)) Fitzgerald Bks.

Jacobs, Liza. Ants. 2003. (Wild Wild World Ser.). (Illus.). 24p. (J). 22.45 (978-1-4103-0054-6(4) , Blackbirch Pr., Inc.) Thomson Gale.

Krudwig, Vickie Leigh. Cucumber Soup. Madrigal, Antonio Hernandez, tr. Brown, Craig McFarland, illus. 1998. 32p. (gr. 2-3). reprint ed. 16.95 (978-1-55591-380-9(6) , FU9806) Fulcrum Publishing.

Lockwood, Sophie. Ants. 2007. (World of Insects Ser.). 40p. (J). (gr. 2-6). 29.93 (*978-1-59296-817-6(1)) Child's World, Inc.

Loewen, Nancy. Tiny Workers: Ants in Your Backyard. Reibeling, Brandon, illus. 2004. (Backyard Bugs Ser.). 24p. (C). (gr. k-3). 22.60 (978-1-4048-0141-7(3)) Picture Window Bks.

The Magic School Bus Gets Ants in Its Pants: A Book about Ants. 2002. (Magic School Bus Ser.). (Illus.). (J). 11.45 (978-0-7587-6509-3(6)) Book Wholesalers, Inc.

Markle, Sandra. Army Ants. (Illus.). (J). 2006. 39p. pap. 7.95 (978-0-8225-3472-3(X) , First Avenue Editions); 2005. 40p. 25.26 (978-0-8225-3196-8(8) , Lerner Pubns.) Lerner Publishing Group.

Markle, Sandra. Las Hormigas Legionarias (Army Ants) 2007. (Animales carroñeros (Animal Scavengers) Ser.). 40p. (J). (gr. 3-6). pap. 7.95 (*978-0-8225-7734-8(8)); (SPA.). lib. bdg. 25.26 (*978-0-8225-7730-0(5)) Lerner Publishing Group. (Ediciones Lerner).

Micucci, Charles. The Life & Times of the Ant. 2006. (Illus.). 32p. (J). (gr. k-3). reprint ed. pap. 6.95 (978-0-618-68949-1(4)) Houghton Mifflin Co.

—The Life & Times of the Ant. 2003. (Illus.). 32p. (J). (gr. k-3). tchr. ed. 16.00 (978-0-618-00559-8(5)) Houghton Mifflin Co. Trade & Reference Div.

Morgan, Sally. Ants, Bees, & Wasps. 2001. (Illus.). 32p. (J). lib. bdg. 24.25 (978-1-930643-10-9(1)) Chrysalis Education.

Morris, Neil & Morris, Ting. Ant. 2003. (Illus.). 32p. (J). lib. bdg. 27.10 (978-1-58340-376-1(0)) Smart Apple Media.

Nelson, Kristin L. Busy Ants. 2004. (Pull Ahead Bks.). 32p. (J). (gr. k-2). pap. 5.95 (978-0-8225-9885-5(X)); (Illus.). lib. bdg. 22.60 (978-0-8225-3775-5(3)) Lerner Publishing Group.

Orr, Tamra. Fire Ants. 2003. (Animal Attacks Ser.). (Illus.). 48p. (J). 26.20 (978-0-7377-1526-2(X) , Greenhaven Pr., Inc.) Thomson Gale.

Pascoe, Elaine. Ants. Kuhn, Dwight, photos by. 1998. (Nature Close-Up Ser.). (Illus.). 48p. (J). (gr. 4-8). 23.70 (978-1-56711-183-5(1) , Blackbirch Pr., Inc.) Thomson Gale.

Prischmann, Deirdre A. Ants. 2005. (Illus.). 24p. (J). 21.26 (978-0-7368-3705-7(1)) Capstone Pr., Inc.

Retan, Walter. Armies of Ants: Level. 4. Cassels, Jean, illus. 2002. (Coleccion "Hola, Lector" Ser.). (SPA.). 48p. (J). (gr. 2-4). pap. 3.99 (978-0-439-08742-1(2) , SO0769, Scholastic en Espanol) Scholastic, Inc.

—Ejercitos de Hormigas. 1999. (SPA.). (gr. k-3). lib. bdg. 11.80 (978-0-613-28290-1(6)) Tandem Library Bks.

Robinson, W. Wright. How Insects Build Their Amazing Homes. Iverson, Carlyn, illus. 1999. (Animal Architects Ser.). 64p. (J). (gr. 5-9). 24.95 (978-1-56711-375-4(3) , Blackbirch Pr., Inc.) Thomson Gale.

Ross, Edward S. Ants. 2003. (Naturebooks: Creepy Crawlers Ser.). (Illus.). 32p. (J). (gr. 1-5). 25.64 (978-1-56766-398-3(2)) Child's World, Inc.

Sayre, April Pulley. Army Ant Parade. Chrustowski, Rick, illus. rev. ed. 2002. 32p. (J). (ps-2). 17.95 (978-0-8050-6353-0(6) , Holt, Henry & Co. Bks. For Young Readers) Holt, Henry & Co.

Spilsbury, Louise & Spilsbury, Richard. A Colony of Ants. 2003. (Animal Groups Ser.). (Illus.). 32p. pap. 6.95 (978-1-4034-3283-4(X)); (J). lib. bdg. 24.22 (978-1-4034-0741-2(X)) Heinemann Library.

Squire, Ann O. Ants. (True Bks.). (J). 2004. (gr. 3-5). pap. 6.95 (978-0-516-29359-2(1)); 2003. (Illus.). 48p. 25.00 (978-0-516-22659-0(2)) Scholastic Library Publishing. (Children's Pr.).

Steele. Ants. 2001. (Animals of the Rain Forest Ser.). (SPA., Illus.). pap. (978-0-7398-3358-2(8)) Steck-Vaughn.

Steele, Christy. Ants. 2000. (Animals of the Rain Forest Ser.). (Illus.). 32p. (J). (gr. 4-7). lib. bdg. 22.83 (978-0-7398-3098-7(8)) Raintree.

Tabletop Zoo: Ants. 2003. 43.95 (978-0-673-57978-2(6)) Celebration Pr.

Tagliaferro, Linda. Ants & Their Nests. 2004. (Pebble Plus, Animal Homes Ser.). (Illus.). 29p. (J). 13.95 (978-0-7368-2380-7(8)) Capstone Pr., Inc.

Tenorio-Coscarelli, Jane. The Ants. Coscarelli, Nicole, tr. l.t. ed. 1998. Tr. of Hormigas. (SPA & ENG.). 32p. (J). (gr. k-4). pap. 11.95 (978-0-9653422-2-3(0)) Quarter-Inch Publishing.

Time for Kids Editors. Ants. 2005. (Time for Kids Ser.). (Illus.). 32p. (J). pap. 3.99 (978-0-06-057640-0(5) , Harper Trophy) HarperCollins Pubs.

—Ants! 2005. (Time for Kids Ser.). (Illus.). 32p. (J). 14.99 (978-0-06-057641-7(3)) HarperCollins Pubs.

Tiny Workers. (Backyard Bugs Ser.). 24p. (J). 7.95 (978-1-4048-0443-2(9)) Picture Window Bks.

Twist, Clint. Army Ants, 6 Vols. 2006. (Illus.). 32p. (J). 23.33 (978-0-8368-6372-7(0)) Stevens, Gareth Inc.

Venn, Cecilia. Ants & Other Social Insects, Vol. 1. World Book, Inc. Staff, ed. 2002. (World Book's Animals of the World Ser.: Set 1). 64p. (J). (978-0-7166-1238-4(0)) World Bk., Inc.

Weingartz, Jill. Ant Colonies. 2001. (Created Environments Ser.). (Illus.). 24p. (J). 21.35 (978-1-58340-103-3(2)) Smart Apple Media.

Whitecap Books Staff. Ants. 2000. (Investigate Ser.). (Illus.). 64p. (J). (gr. 1-7). pap. 3.95 (978-1-55285-129-6(X)) Whitecap Bks., Ltd. CAN. *Dist:* Firefly Bks., Ltd.

Whitehouse, Patricia. Ants. 2003. (Heinemann Read & Learn Ser.). (Illus.). 24p. (J). pap. 5.25 (978-1-4034-4325-0(4)); lib. bdg. 18.50 (978-1-4034-4316-8(5)) Heinemann Library.

Whiting, Sue. All about Ants. 2006. (National Geographic Science Chapters Ser.). (Illus.). 40p. (gr. 1-4). 17.90 (978-0-7922-5948-0(3) , National Geographic Children's Bks.) National Geographic Society.

Wimmer, Theresa. Ants. 2006. (My First Look at: Insects Ser.). 24p. 15.95 (978-1-58341-453-8(3) , Creative Education) Creative Co., The.

The Word of Our Little Friend, the Ants. l.t. ed. 2001. 32p. (J). pap. 1.74 (978-81-7898-010-2(X)) Goodword Bks. Pvt. Ltd. IND. *Dist:* Lodhia Ctr., The.

ANTS—FICTION

Ada, Alma Flor. One More Friend. Fatus, Sophie, illus. 2007. 24p. (J). (*978-0-15-206278-1(5)); pap. (*978-0-15-206284-2(X)) Harcourt Trade Pubs.

Adair, Virginia Hamilton. Ants on the Melon: A Collection of Poems. 1999. (Modern Library Ser.). 176p. (J). pap. 15.00 (978-0-375-75229-2(3) , Modern Library) Random House Publishing Group.

Aesop. The Grasshopper & the Ant: A Tale about Planning. Hockerman, Dennis, illus. 2006. (J). (978-1-59939-082-6(5) , Reader's Digest Young Families, Inc.) Reader's Digest Children's Publishing, Inc.

Alatorcida. 2001. (SPA.). (J). (gr. 1-3). 16.95 (978-84-261-3159-1(X)) Juventud, Editorial ESP. *Dist:* Lectorum Pubns., Inc.

Ammerman, Michelle. Amos's Beautiful Day. 2005. 12p. 6.99 (978-1-4116-3819-8(0)) Lulu.com.

Anderson, Jane. Inspector Insector. 2005. 22.00 (*978-1-4108-4196-4(0)) Benchmark Education Co.

The Ant & the Grasshopper: Individual Title Six-Packs. (Story Steps Ser.). (gr. k-2). 32.00 (978-0-7635-9846-4(1)) Rigby Education.

The Ant & the Grasshopper: Small Book. (Pebble Soup Explorations Ser.). 16p. (ps up). 5.00 (978-0-7635-7049-1(4)) Rigby Education.

Anthony, Ross. Please Don't Step on the Ants. Anthony, Ross, illus. 2006. (ENG, CHI, SPA & JPN.). (J). per. (*978-0-9727894-4-8(8)) Arizona Blueberry Studios.

Avi. A Beginning, a Muddle, & an End: The Return of the End of the Beginning. Tusa, Tricia, illus. 2008. 176p. (J). 14.95 (*978-0-15-205555-4(X)) Harcourt Trade Pubs.

—The End of the Beginning: Being the Adventures of a Small Snail (and an Even Smaller Ant) Tusa, Tricia, illus. 144p. (J). 2008. pap. 6.95 (*978-0-15-205532-5(0) , Harcourt Paperbacks); 2004. 14.95 (978-0-15-204968-3(1)) Harcourt Children's Bks.

Azordegan, Kambiz. The Ant & the Honey: Andy the Ant. Sajem, Johnny, illus. abr. l.t. ed. 1998. (Tootee's Magical Stories Ser.: Vol. 2). 40p. (J). 9.95 (978-1-890571-26-9(1)) Positive Children's Programming Corp.

Bahz, Kahanni. Ants? in My Pants? An Antimated Tale. Fraser, Kevin, illus. 2005. 72p. (J). (gr. k-4). reprint ed. 22.00 (978-0-7567-8705-9(X)) DIANE Publishing Co.

Beall, Pamela Conn & Nipp, Susan Hagen. Ants Go Marching. Wittwer, Hala, illus. 2002. (Wee Sing Ser.). 24p. (J). bds. 4.99 (978-0-8431-7709-1(8) , Price Stern Sloan) Penguin Group (USA) Inc.

Beatty, Susi. Angie the Ant & the Bumblebee Tree. 2006. (J). 19.95 (978-0-9773653-0-2(1)) Susi B. Marketing, Inc.

Benson, Laura. The Tiny Ant. Heard, Nancy, illus. 2002. (Two Can Read Ser.). 16p. (J). 2.99 (978-1-56472-665-0(7)) Edupress, Inc.

Berenstain, Stan & Berenstain, Jan. The Berenstain Bears & the Great Ant Attack. 2000. (Berenstain Bears Big Chapter Bks.). (Illus.). (J). (gr. 2-6). (978-0-606-18487-8(2)) Tandem Library Bks.

Brennan, Herbie. Fairy Nuff: A Tale of Bluebell Ball. Collins, Ross, illus. 2002. 128p. (J). (gr. 2-4). 13.95 (978-1-58234-770-7(0) , Bloomsbury Children) Bloomsbury Publishing.

—Nuff Said: Another Tale of Bluebell Wood. Collins, Ross, illus. 2002. 128p. (J). (gr. 2-5). 13.95 (978-1-58234-771-4(9) , Bloomsbury Children) Bloomsbury Publishing.

Brouwer, Sigmund. Bug's Eye View: Annie Ant, Don't Cry! 2004. (Bug's-Eye View Bks.). (Illus.). 18p. (J). bds. 4.99 (978-0-8499-7757-2(6)) Nelson, Thomas Inc.

—Bug's Eye View: Baby Ant Has Stinky Pants. 2001. (Bug's-Eye View Bks.). (Illus.). (J). bds. 4.99 (978-0-8499-7754-1(1)) Nelson, Thomas Inc.

—Daddy Ant, You Never Listen. 2004. (Bug's-Eye View Bks.). (Illus.). 18p. (J). bds. 4.99 (978-0-8499-7755-8(X)) Nelson, Thomas Inc.

—Mommy Ant, Eat Your Vegetables. 2004. (Bug's-Eye View Bks.). (Illus.). 18p. (J). bds. 4.99 (978-0-8499-7756-5(8)) Nelson, Thomas Inc.

Byars, Betsy. Ant Series, 2 bks., Set. Simont, Marc, illus. (gr. k-3). 2000. (J). pap. 29.95 incl. audio ; 1999. pap. 30.95 incl. audio (978-0-87499-704-0(6)); 1999. pap. 34.95 incl. audio compact disk (978-1-59112-857-1(9)) Live Oak Media.

—My Brother, Ant. Simont, Marc, illus. 2000. (J). pap. 19.97 incl. audio (978-0-7366-9214-4(2)) Books on Tape, Inc.

—My Brother, Ant. Simont, Marc, illus. unabr. ed. 1999. (Ant Ser.). (J). (gr. k-3). 25.95 incl. audio (978-0-87499-517-6(5)); pap. 16.95 incl. audio (978-0-87499-516-9(7)); pap., tchr. ed. 29.95 incl. audio (978-0-87499-518-3(3)) Live Oak Media.

Carney, Mary Lou. Tyler Timothy Bradford & the Birthday Surprise. Warren, Shari, illus. 2004. 32p. (J). 14.95 (978-0-7696-3168-4(1)) School Specialty Publishing.

Clairmont, Patsy. Stinky. Oeltjenbruns, Joni, illus. 2006. (Tails from the Pantry Ser.). 32p. (J). 9.99 (978-1-4003-0803-3(8)) Nelson, Thomas Inc.

Climo, Shirley. The Little Red Ant & the Great Big Crumb. Mora, Francisco X., illus. 1999. 40p. (J). (gr. k-3). pap. 5.95 (978-0-395-72097-4(4) , Clarion Bks.) Houghton Mifflin Co. Trade & Reference Div.

Cooper, Ann Goode. Zebordee Goes to the Races. Jessee, Diana, illus. 2005. 30p. (J). (978-1-933251-01-1(8)) Parkway Pubs., Inc.

Dargon, J. Beetle & Lady Bug. 2005. 48p. pap. 12.95 (978-1-4137-6701-8(X)) PublishAmerica, Inc.

Edwards, Pamela Duncan. The Wacky Wedding: A Book of Alphabet Antics. 2005. 32p. (J). pap. (978-0-7868-1172-4(2)) Hyperion Bks. for Children.

—The Wacky Wedding: A Book of Alphabet Antics. Cole, Henry, illus. 1999. 32p. (ps-2). 14.99 (978-0-7868-0308-8(8)) Hyperion Bks. for Children.

Frontiera, Deborah K. New South Dairy Colony 50. 2nd ed. 2004. (Chronicles of Henry Roach-Dairier: Bk. 2). 247p. (YA). (gr. 5 up). per. 15.95 (978-0-9753410-2-5(2)) Jade Enterprises.

—To Build a Tunnel. 2nd ed. 2004. (Chronicles of Henry Roach-Dairier: Bk. 1). 218p. (YA). (gr. 5 up). per. 15.95 (978-0-9753410-1-8(4)) Jade Enterprises.

Garcia, Lionel. El Elefante y la Hormiga. 2000. 28p. 16.99 (978-0-9678364-1-6(7)) Wisdom Pr.

—The Elephant & the Ant. 2000. 28p. 16.99 (978-0-9678364-0-9(9)) Wisdom Pr.

George, Lindsay Barrett. Alfred Digs. 2008. 40p. (J). 16.99 (***978-0-06-078760-8(0)***); lib. bdg. 17.89 (***978-0-06-078761-5(9)***) HarperCollins Pubs. (Greenwillow Bks.).

Gill, Janie S. The Ant's Journey. 2001. (Predictable Readers Ser.). (Illus.). (J). (gr. k-2). lib. bdg. 11.95 (978-0-89868-531-2(1)) ARO Publishing Co.

Giovanni, Nikki. Jimmy Grasshopper Versus the Ants. Raschka, Christopher, illus. 2007. (J). (***978-0-7636-3021-8(7)***) Candlewick Pr.

Greenburg, Dan. Evil Queen Tut & the Great Ant Pyramids. Davis, Jack E., illus. 1999. (Zack Files Ser.: No. 16). 64p. (J). (gr. 2-5). pap. 4.99 (978-0-448-41876-6(2) , Grosset & Dunlap) Penguin Group (USA) Inc.

—Evil Queen Tut & the Great Ant Pyramids. 1999. (gr. 3-6). lib. bdg. 13.00 (978-0-613-14708-8(1)); (Zack Files Ser.: No. 16). (J). (gr. 2-5). 11.79 (978-0-606-17782-5(5)) Tandem Library Bks.

—Fall of the House of Mandible. Fischer, Scott M., illus. 2006. (Outrageously Funny Ser.: Bk. 4). 160p. (J). 9.95 (978-0-15-205475-5(8)) Harcourt Children's Bks.

—The Onts. Fischer, Scott M., illus. 2006. (Secrets of Dripping Fang Ser.: Bk. 1). 144p. (J). 2.99 (978-0-15-205995-8(4) , Harcourt Paperbacks) Harcourt Children's Bks.

—Please Don't Eat the Children. Fischer, Scott M., illus. 2007. (Secrets of Dripping Fang Ser.: Bk. 7). 160p. (J). 9.95 (978-0-15-206047-3(2)) Harcourt Children's Bks.

—Treachery & Betrayal at Jolly Days. Fischer, Scott M., illus. 2006. (Secrets of Dripping Fang Ser.: Bk. 2). 144p. (J). 9.95 (978-0-15-205463-2(4)) Harcourt Children's Bks.

Greenburg, Dan & Diterlizzi, Angela. The Vampire's Curse. Fischer, Scott M., illus. 2006. (Secrets of Dripping Fang Ser.: Bk. 3). 144p. (J). 9.95 (978-0-15-205469-4(3)) Harcourt Children's Bks.

Groves. Ant Eggs, Bk. 2. Date not set. (Illus.). 16p. (J). pap. 129.15 (978-0-582-18793-1(0)) Addison-Wesley Longman, Ltd. GBR. *Dist:* Trans-Atlantic Pubns., Inc.

Hanson, Anders. Ant King. Haberstroh, Anne, illus. (Fact & Fiction Ser.). 24p. (J). 2007. 21.35 (978-1-59928-430-9(8)); 2006. (978-1-59928-431-6(6)) ABDO Publishing Co.

Harcourt School Publishers Staff. The Ants Picnic: Take-Home Book. 1999. (Illus.). (J). pap. 1.90 (978-0-15-317191-8(X)) Harcourt Schl. Pubs.

—The Edge of the Puddle: On Level. 3rd ed. 2002. (Trophies Reading Program Ser.). (Illus.). pap. 5.10 (978-0-15-323003-5(7)) Harcourt Schl. Pubs.

—Step by Step: Library Book. 1999. (Collections Ser.). (Illus.). pap. 14.90 (978-0-15-313416-6(X)) Harcourt Schl. Pubs.

—Trofeos Advanced Level: Cuca y Biba. 3rd ed. 2002. (SPA., Illus.). pap. 5.50 (978-0-15-323920-5(4)) Harcourt Schl. Pubs.

—Trofeos Below Level: Que Es Eso? 3rd ed. 2002. (SPA., Illus.). (J). pap. 3.50 (978-0-15-323852-9(6)) Harcourt Schl. Pubs.

—Two Little Ants, 5 Packs., Advanced Level. 3rd ed. 2002. (Trophies Reading Program Ser.). (Illus.). (gr. 1). pap. 20.10 (978-0-15-326859-5(X)) Harcourt Schl. Pubs.

—Two Little Ants Advanced Level. 3rd ed. 2002. (Trophies Reading Program Ser.). (Illus.). (J). pap. 3.70 (978-0-15-323009-7(6)) Harcourt Schl. Pubs.

—What Do They Make? Below Level. 3rd ed. 2002. (Trophies Reading Program Ser.). (Illus.). (J). pap. 3.20 (978-0-15-322941-1(1)) Harcourt Schl. Pubs.

Harley Bill. Sarahs Story. Aldridge Eve, illus. 2006. 32p. (J). 6.95 (978-1-58246-178-6(3) , Tricycle Pr.) Ten Speed Pr.

Harper, Ben. Revenge of the Ants. Harris, Annmarie, ed. 2006. (Ant Bully Ser.). (Illus.). 24p. (J). pap. 3.50 (978-0-439-85679-9(5) , Scholastic) Scholastic, Inc.

Harris, Nelson. Andrew of the Antimites. 2006. 83p. pap. 14.95 (978-1-4241-3429-8(3)) PublishAmerica, Inc.

Heiner, Garth Farr. Arty Puts the Bite on Hopper. Melander, Eric, illus. unabr. ed. 2001. (Fun-with-the-Law Ser.: No. 1). 32p. (J). (gr. k-7). pap. 5.95 (978-1-929905-01-0(7)) Fun With the Law, Inc.

—Finders Keepers. Melander, Eric, illus. l.t. unabr. ed. 2001. (Fun-with-the-Law Ser.: No. 4). 32p. (J). (gr. k-7). pap. 5.95 (978-1-929905-04-1(1)) Fun With the Law, Inc.

—Unwanted Muddy. Melander, Eric, illus. l.t. unabr. ed. 2001. (Fun-with-the-Law Ser.: No. 5). 32p. (J). (gr. k-7). pap. 5.95 (978-1-929905-05-8(X)) Fun With the Law, Inc.

Hillary, Robert. Ernie the Ant. 2005. 24p. per. 9.95 (978-1-59453-668-7(6) , 2813) Airleaf Publishing & Bookselling.

Hofmeister, Alan, et al. Ben the Ant. (Reading for All Learners Ser.). (Illus.). (J). pap. (978-1-56861-123-5(4)) Swift Learning Resources.

Holub, Joan. Big Heart! A Valentine's Day Tale. Terry, Will, illus. 2007. (Ant Hill Ser.). 24p. (J). lib. bdg. 13.89 (***978-1-4169-2562-0(7)***); pap. 3.99 (***978-1-4169-0957-6(5)***) Simon & Schuster Children's Publishing. (Aladdin).

—Good Luck! A St. Patrick's Day Story. Terry, Will, illus. 2007. (Ant Hill Ser.). 24p. (J). pap. 3.99 (978-1-4169-0955-2(9) , Aladdin); lib. bdg. 11.89 (978-1-4169-2560-6(0) , Aladdin Library) Simon & Schuster Children's Publishing.

—Scaredy-Pants: A Halloween Story. Terry, Will, illus. 2007. (Ant Hill Ser.). 24p. (J). lib. bdg. 13.89 (***978-1-4169-2561-3(9)*** , Aladdin) Simon & Schuster Children's Publishing.

—Scaredy-Pants! A Halloween Story. Terry, Will, illus. 2007. (Ant Hill Ser.). 24p. (J). pap. 3.99 (***978-1-4169-0956-9(7)*** , Aladdin) Simon & Schuster Children's Publishing.

—Spring Time! A Story about Seeds. Terry, Will, illus. 2008. (Ant Hill Ser.). 24p. (J). 13.89 (***978-1-4169-5132-2(6)***); pap. 3.99 (***978-1-4169-5131-5(8)***) Simon & Schuster Children's Publishing. (Aladdin).

Hoose, Philip M. & Hoose, Hannah. Hey, Little Ant. Tilley, Debbie, illus. 2004. 30p. (J). (ps-3). tchr. ed. 14.95 (978-1-883672-54-6(6) , Tricycle Pr.) Ten Speed Pr.

Hoose, Phillip & Hoose, Hannah. Oye, Hormiguita. 2004. (SPA., Illus.). 30p. (J). 6.95 (978-1-58246-089-5(2) , Tricycle Pr.) Ten Speed Pr.

—Oye, Hormiguita. Tilley, Debbie, illus. 2003. (SPA.). 30p. (J). 14.95 (978-1-58246-088-8(4) , Tricycle Pr.) Ten Speed Pr.

La Hormiga y el Saltamontes: Lap Book. (Pebble Soup Exploraciones Ser.). (SPA.). 16p. (ps up). 21.00 (978-0-7578-1682-6(7)) Rigby Education.

La hormiga y el Saltamontes: Small Book. (Pebble Soup Exploraciones Ser.). (SPA.). 16p. (ps up). 5.00 (978-0-7578-1722-9(X)) Rigby Education.

Ibbotson, Eva. Island of the Aunts. 2000. (J). (978-0-525-46516-4(2) , Dutton Juvenile) Penguin Group (USA) Inc.

Ives, Bob. The Three Ants & Mother Bird. Deskov, Vladimir, ed. Fairy, Meg, illus. 2004. 40p. (J). (978-1-920832-06-3(8)) Four Heads Publishing Group Pty, Ltd.

James, Anne. Ant Attack! Lewis, Anthony, illus. 2002. (Science Solves It! Ser.). 32p. (J). 4.95 (978-1-57565-117-0(3)) Kane Pr., The.

—Ant Attack! 2002. (gr. k-3). lib. bdg. 13.00 (978-0-613-53699-8(1)) Tandem Library Bks.

Johnson, Steve & Fancher, Lou. The Quest for the One Big Thing: A Counting Book. 1998. (Illus.). 32p. (J). (gr. k-4). 10.95 (978-0-7868-3198-2(7)) Disney Pr.

Kalar, Bonnie. The Cat & the Ant. Spreen, Kathe, illus. 1998. 8p. (J). (ps-2). pap. (978-1-891619-02-1(0)) Corona Pr.

Katschke, Judy. The Movie Novel. Harris, Annmarie, ed. 2006. (Ant Bully Ser.). (Illus.). 96p. (J). pap. 4.99 (978-0-439-85683-6(3)) Scholastic, Inc.

Krishnaswami, Uma. The Ants Have a Picnic. 2006. (Early Explorers Ser.). (J). 34.00 (***978-1-4108-6115-3(5)***) Benchmark Education Co.

Krudwig, Vickie Leigh. Sopa de Pepino. Madrigal, Antonio Hernandez, tr. Brown, Craig McFarland, illus. 1998. (SPA.). 32p. (gr. 3-4). reprint ed. 16.95 (978-1-55591-982-5(0) , FU9820) Fulcrum Publishing.

Kurtzman, Harvey. The Grasshopper & the Ant. 2002. (Illus.). (YA). (gr. 10 up). 25.00 (978-0-9710080-0-7(0)) Kitchen, Denis Publishing Co.

Learning Wrap-Ups: The Grasshopper & the Ants, The Turtle & the Rabbit. 2006. 66p. (J). 12.99 (978-1-59204-203-6(1)) Learning Wrap-Ups.

Lee, Quinlan B. The Great Ant Adventure. Harris, Annmarie, ed. 2006. (Ant Bully Ser.). (Illus.). 32p. (J). pap. 3.99 (978-0-439-85680-5(9) , Scholastic) Scholastic, Inc.

The Little Ant. (Lexile Levels Ser.). 7.98 (978-1-56334-689-7(3)); 47.88 (978-0-7362-1103-1(9)) Hampton-Brown Bks.

Martin, David. All for Pie, Pie for All. Gorbachev, Valeri, illus. 2006. 32p. (J). (ps-k). 15.99 (978-0-7636-2393-7(8)) Candlewick Pr.

McDonald, Megan & Payne, Tom. Ant & Honey Bee: What a Pair! Karas, G. Brian, illus. 2005. 32p. (J). (gr. k-3). 13.99 (978-0-7636-1265-8(0)) Candlewick Pr.

McElligott, Matthew. Absolutely Not. 2006. (Illus.). 32p. (J). pap. 6.95 (978-0-8027-8934-1(X)) Walker & Co.

McGough, Wallace D. The Adventures of Walter Ant Bk. I: The Unknown. 56p. (J). pap. 9.95 (978-0-9645180-0-1(7)) Family Value Publishing.

McLaughlin, Diane & Tully, Lisa. The WhizAnt Who Isn't Coloring & Activity Book. 2003. (Illus.). 32p. (J). cd-rom 15.95 (978-0-9722249-1-8(2)) Bugeye Bks.

Miller, Roger Carlton. The Ant & the Grasshopper, l.t. ed. 2003. Orig. Title: Same. (Illus.). 14p. (978-0-9712104-2-4(X)) Texas Woman's Univ. Pr.

Moeller mé illuminé, Jo, illus. La Hormiguita ¿ A Folktale about the Perseverant Little Ant. 2005. (SPA.). (J). (978-0-9644678-4-2(4)) Bilingual Pubns.

Mora, Pat. Una Cesta de Cumpleanos para Tia Abuela. Lang, Cecily, illus. (SPA.). (J). (gr. k-2). pap. 3.16 net. (978-0-395-78817-2(X) , HMS088) Houghton Mifflin Co.

Moran, Alex. What Day Is It?/Que dia es Hoy? Moreton, Daniel, illus. 2008. (Green Light Readers Level 1 Ser.). 28p. (J). pap. 3.95 (***978-0-15-206281-1(5)*** , Green Light Readers) Harcourt Children's Bks.

—What Day Is It?/Que dia es Hoy? Campoy, F. Isabel & Ada, Alma Flor, trs. Moreton, Daniel, illus. 2008. (Green Light Readers Level 1 Ser.). 28p. (J). 12.95 (***978-0-15-206275-0(0)*** , Green Light Readers) Harcourt Children's Bks.

Nickle, John. The Ant Bully. 2006. (Illus.). 32p. (J). pap. 5.99 (978-0-439-85116-9(5) , Scholastic); pap. 16.99 (978-0-590-39591-5(2)) Scholastic, Inc.

Owens, Jeffrey A. The Ant That Tunrned His Burden into a Bridge. 1999. 44p. (J). pap. 5.00 (978-0-9649393-2-5(0)) Owens Pubns.

Paloma y la Hormiga. (SPA.). pap. 7.95 (978-88-8148-801-8(9)) European Language Institute ITA. *Dist:* Distribooks, Inc.

Paropillo, Guisopete de. La Hormiga Gertrudis (Gertrude the Ant) Radosh, Ricardo, illus. 2001. (SPA.). 28p. (J). 18.95 (978-968-494-102-1(1)) Centro de Informacion y Desarrollo de la Comunicacion y la Literatura MEX. *Dist:* AIMS International Bks., Inc.

Paterson, Brian. Zigby & the Ants. 2004. (J). (978-0-06-053796-8(5)) HarperCollins Pubs.

Phillippe, Esther. The Ants Will Carry the Elephant. 2000. (Illus.). 24p. (J). (gr. 1-3). pap. 3.99 (978-0-89827-211-6(4)) Wesleyan Publishing Hse.

Phillips, Gina & Martin, Stuart. Ants & Caterpillars. 2003. (Busy Bugs Ser.). 12p. (J). bds. 14.95 (978-1-74047-240-1(3)) Book Co. Publishing Pty, Ltd., The AUS. *Dist:* Penton Overseas, Inc.

Philpot, Lorna & Philpot, Graham. Find Anthony Ant. 2006. (Illus.). 24p. (J). 12.95 (978-1-905417-10-0(1)) Boxer Bks., Ltd. GBR. *Dist:* Sterling Publishing Co., Inc.

Poe. Breve Ant de Ctos Policiales. (SPA.). pap. 11.95 (978-950-07-1006-0(4)) Editorial Sudamericana S.A. ARG. *Dist:* Distribooks, Inc.

Porte, Barbara Ann. Ma Jiang & the Orange Ants. Cannon, Annie, illus. 2000. 32p. (J). 17.99 (978-0-531-33241-2(1) , Orchard Bks.) Scholastic, Inc.

Powell, Glenda. Cassie & Mr. Ant. Mitchell, Hazel, illus. 2008. (J). 7.95 (978-0-9779445-6-9(5)) Zoe Life Publishing.

Prince, Joshua. I Saw an Ant in a Parking Lot. Pamintuan, Macky, illus. 2007. 24p. (J). (ps-k). 14.95 (978-1-4027-3823-4(4)) Sterling Publishing Co., Inc.

—I Saw an Ant on the Railroad Track. Pamintuan, Macky, illus. 2006. 24p. (J). 14.95 (978-1-4027-2183-0(8) , 1252268) Sterling Publishing Co., Inc.

Quackenbush, Robert. Henry's Awful Mistake. Quackenbush, Robert, illus. rev. deluxe ed. 2005. (Illus.). 40p. (J). (gr. k-2). reprint ed. 12.95 (978-0-9712757-0-6(X)) Quackenbush, Robert Studios.

Quinlan, Janet, adapted by. Hard Work: The Ant & the Grasshopper. 2005. (Illus.). (***978-1-4127-3761-6(3)***) Publications International, Ltd.

Raudenbush, Brenda. Brilly & the Boot. Meyers, Holly B., illus. 1998. 97p. (J). (gr. 4-6). pap. 9.95 (978-0-9661531-0-1(3)) Panola Publishing Co.

Rogers, Scott. Once More. 2001. (Illus.). 92p. (J). (gr. k-3). pap. 15.95 (978-0-9705237-1-6(8)) 1stCoBooks.

Rosenblatt, Joe. Tommy Fry & the Ant Colony. 2003. (Illus.). 30p. pap. 4.95 (978-0-88753-054-8(0)) Black Moss Pr. CAN. *Dist:* LitDistCo.

Ross, Andrea. Chester Earth And & Friends. Ross, Andrea, illus. 2001. (Illus.). 25p. (J). (gr. 1-3). pap. 7.95 (978-1-887683-44-9(5)) Storybook Pr. & Productions.

—Chester Earth Ant in School. Ross, Andrea, illus. 1999. (Chester Earth Ant Ser.). (Illus.). 26p. (J). (gr. k-3). pap. 1.95 (978-1-887683-20-3(8)) Storybook Pr. & Productions.

—Chester Earth Ant Meets Rachel Reindeer. Ross, Andrea, illus. 2000. (Chester Earth Ant Ser.). (Illus.). 26p. (J). (gr. k-3). 7.95 (978-1-887683-31-9(3)) Storybook Pr. & Productions.

—Chester Earth Ant Pack Facts. Ross, Andrea, illus. 2nd ed. 2002. (Illus.). 19p. (J). (gr. 1-4). pap. 7.95 (978-1-887683-47-0(X)) Storybook Pr. & Productions.

—Chester Earth Ant (Possessed) Ross, Andrea, illus. 2002. (Illus.). 30p. (J). (gr. 1-3). pap. 7.95 (978-1-887683-48-7(8)) Storybook Pr. & Productions.

—Chester Goes to the Moon. 1999. (Chester Earth Ant Ser.). (Illus.). 25p. (J). (gr. k-3). pap. 7.95 (978-1-887683-08-1(9)) Storybook Pr. & Productions.

Ross, Andrea, illus. Chester Goes to the City. 1999. (Chester Earth Ant Ser.). 25p. (J). (gr. k-3). pap. 7.97 (978-1-887683-04-3(6)) Storybook Pr. & Productions.

—Storybook Castle with Chester. 1999. (Chester Earth Ant Ser.). 25p. (J). (gr. k-3). pap. 6.95 (978-1-887683-05-0(4)) Storybook Pr. & Productions.

Rucker, Rudolf V. B. Hacker & the Ants. 2000. (J). 20.00 (978-0-380-97236-4(0)) HarperCollins Pubs.

Santillo, LuAnn. The Seeds. Santillo, LuAnn, ed. 2003. (Half-Pint Kids Readers Ser.). (Illus.). 7p. (J). (ps-1). pap. (978-1-59256-109-4(8)) Half-Pint Kids, Inc.

Scholastic, Inc. Staff. The Ant Bully: Play-Along Sticker Storybook. Harris, Annmarie, ed. 2006. (Ant Bully Ser.). 16p. (J). pap. 4.99 (978-0-439-85682-9(5) , Scholastic) Scholastic, Inc.

The Secret Song & Other Stories: Individual Title Six-Pack. (Story Steps Ser.). (gr. k-2). 48.00 (978-0-7635-9808-2(9)) Rigby Education.

Smith, Timotyh R. The Ants Dig to China. 2007. (Buck Wilder's Adventure Ser.: 3). (Illus.). 98p. (J). pap. (978-1-934133-07-1(8)) Mackinac Island Pr., Inc.

Sneed, Brad. Deputy Harvey & the Ant Cow Caper. 2005. (Illus.). 32p. (J). (ps). 16.99 (978-0-8037-3023-6(3) , Dial) Penguin Group (USA) Inc.

Sommer, Carl. No Longer a Dilly Dally, 1 bk. 2003. (Another Sommer-Time Story Ser.). (Illus.). 48p. (J). 16.95 incl. audio (978-1-57537-550-2(8)); (gr. 1-4). 16.95 incl. audio compact disk (978-1-57537-501-4(X)) Advance Publishing, Inc.

Steggall, Vicki. Lunchtime Rules. Oswald, Ash, illus. 2007. (Go Girl! Ser.: Bk. 4). 96p. (Orig.). (J). (gr. 2 up). pap. 3.99 (***978-0-312-34644-7(1)***) Feiwel & Friends.

Stone, Forrest. The Ant & Grasshopper Show. 2006. 42.00 (***978-1-4108-6183-2(X)***) Benchmark Education Co.

Tozer, Al. Mr. Ant & His Friends: A Fun Insect Story. 2002. (J). 19.95 (978-0-9720493-0-6(4)) Junebug Pr.

Trimble, Patti. Lost! 2000. (ps-2). lib. bdg. 11.80 (978-0-613-64539-3(1)) Tandem Library Bks.

—What Day Is It? (gr. k-3). 2003. lib. bdg. 11.80 (978-0-613-66388-5(8)); 2000. (978-0-606-18195-2(4)) Tandem Library Bks.

Trimble, Patti & Moran, Alex. Lost! Moreton, Daniel, illus. 2003. (Green Light Readers Level 1 Ser.). 24p. (J). 11.95 (978-0-15-204824-2(3)); pap. 3.95 (978-0-15-204864-8(2)) Harcourt Children's Bks. (Green Light Readers).

—What Day Is It? Moreton, Daniel, illus. 2003. (Green Light Readers Level 1 Ser.). 24p. (J). 11.95 (978-0-15-204806-8(5)); pap. 3.95 (978-0-15-204846-4(4)) Harcourt Children's Bks. (Green Light Readers).

Van Allsburg, Chris. Two Bad Ants. Van Allsburg, Chris, illus. 2002. (Illus.). (J). 25.28 (978-0-7587-3885-1(4)) Book Wholesalers, Inc.

Van Laan, Nancy. Nit-Pickin' 2001. (Illus.). 32p. (J). 16.00 (978-0-689-83898-9(0) , Atheneum/Anne Schwartz Bks.) Simon & Schuster Children's Publishing.

Vantrease, Norma. Ants in My Pants. Cox, Steve, illus. 2004. (Rookie Reader Skill Set Ser.). 32p. (J). (gr. k-2). pap. 4.95 (978-0-516-25839-3(7) , Children's Pr.) Scholastic Library Publishing.

—Ants in My Pants. Vantrease, Norma & Cox, Steve, trs. Cox, Steve, illus. 2004. (Rookie Reader Ser.). 31p. (J). 19.50 (978-0-516-23443-4(9) , Children's Pr.) Scholastic Library Publishing.

Vaughan, Laura. Andy Ant: And What Could Be on the Other Side to See? Vaughan, Laura, illus. 2001. (Illus.). 32p. (J). (ps-2). 14.95 (978-0-9702979-0-7(4)) Terrapin Publishing.

Walker, Wayne. The Proud Little Ant. Powers, Daniel, illus. 1999. (J). (gr. 1-6). (978-0-944576-19-9(2)) Rocky River Pubs., LLC.

Watier, Matt. Ants. 32p. 12.95 (978-1-58330-736-6(2)) Feldheim Pubs.

Watson, Regal. The Ant That Can't, 1. l.t. ed. 2005. (Illus.). 50p. (J). per. 10.95 (978-0-9763686-0-1(9)) Rapha Publishing.

White, Mark. La Cigarra y la Hormiga: Version de la Fabula de Esopo. Rojo, Sara, illus. 2006. (Read-It! Readers en Espanol Ser.).Tr. of Ant & the Grasshopper: A Retelling of Aesop's Fable. (SPA.). 32p. (J). (ps-3). 19.95 (978-1-4048-1614-5(3)) Picture Window Bks.

Willson, Sarah. Can't Have Ants. 2000. (gr. k-3). lib. bdg. 11.25 (978-0-613-24470-1(2)) Tandem Library Bks.

ANXIETY

see also Fear

Apel, Melanie Ann. Let's Talk about Feeling Worried. 2001. (Let's Talk Library). (Illus.). 24p. (J). (gr. 3). lib. bdg. 18.75 (978-0-8239-5622-7(9) , PowerKids Pr.) Rosen Publishing Group, Inc., The.

Brinkerhoff, Shirley. Drug Therapy & Anxiety Disorders. 2003. (Encyclopedia of Psychiatric Drugs & Their Disorders Ser.). (Illus.). 128p. (J). lib. bdg. (978-1-59084-561-5(7)) Mason Crest Pubs.

Campbell, Nancy M. Panic Disorder. 2000. (Perspectives on Mental Health Ser.). (Illus.). 64p. (J). (gr. 4-6). lib. bdg. 23.93 (978-0-7368-1030-2(7) , LifeMatters Bks.) Capstone Pr., Inc.

Freedom from Fear, Worry & Anxiety. 2002. 5.00 (978-0-9718012-3-3(1)) Fresh Word.

Giacobello, John. Everything You Need to Know about Anxiety & Panic Attacks. 2005. (Need to Know Library). (Illus.). 64p. (YA). (gr. 7-12). lib. bdg. 25.25 (978-0-8239-3219-1(2) , NTANPA) Rosen Publishing Group, Inc., The.

Gray, Shirley W. Good Mental Health. 2003. (Living Well). (Illus.). 32p. (J). (gr. 2-6). 27.07 (978-1-59296-082-8(0)) Child's World, Inc.

Hovanec, Erin M. Everything You Need to Know about Phobias. 2005. (Need to Know Library). (Illus.). 64p. (YA). (gr. 7-12). lib. bdg. 25.25 (978-0-8239-3226-9(5) , NTPHOB) Rosen Publishing Group, Inc., The.

Huebner, Dawn. What to do When You Worry Too Much: A Kid's Guide to Overcoming Anxiety. Matthews, Bonnie, illus. 2005. ("What to Do" Workbooks for Kids). 80p. (J). pap. 14.95 (978-1-59147-314-5(4) , Magination Pr.) American Psychological Assn.

Lee, Jordan. Coping with Anxiety & Panic Attacks. rev. ed. 2000. (Coping Ser.). (Illus.). 128p. (YA). (gr. 7-12). lib. bdg. 26.50 (978-0-8239-3202-3(8) , COANPA) Rosen Publishing Group, Inc., The.

Medina, Sarah. Worried. Brooker, Jo, illus. 2007. (J). ***978-1-4034-9796-3(6));** pap. (***978-1-4034-9803-8(2))** Heinemann Library.

Moehn, Heather. Coping with Social Anxiety. 2005. (Coping Ser.). (Illus.). 192p. (YA). (gr. 7-12). lib. bdg. 26.50 (978-0-8239-3363-1(6)) Rosen Publishing Group, Inc., The.

O'Connor, Frances. Frequently Asked Questions about Academic Anxiety. 2007. (J). (***978-1-4042-1937-3(4))** Rosen Publishing Group, Inc., The.

Powell, Mark. Stress Relief: The Ultimate Teen Guide. Adams, Kelly, illus. 2002. (It Happened to Me Ser.: No. 3). 112p. 37.50 (978-0-8108-4433-9(8)) Scarecrow Pr., Inc.

Rosen, Marvin. The Effects of Stress & Anxiety on the Family. 2002. (Focus on Family Matters Ser.). (Illus.). 64p. (YA). (gr. 6-12). 25.00 (978-0-7910-6950-9(8)) Facts On File, Inc.

Ross, Allison J. Everything You Need to Know about Social Anxiety. 2005. (Need to Know Library). (Illus.). 64p. (YA). (gr. 7-12). 25.25 (978-0-8239-3324-2(5)) Rosen Publishing Group, Inc., The.

Shuman, Carol. Jenny Is Scared! When Sad Things Happen in the World. Pillo, Cary, tr. Pillo, Cary, illus. 2003. 32p. (J). (gr. k-3). 14.95 (978-1-59147-002-1(1)); pap. 8.95 (978-1-59147-003-8(X)) American Psychological Assn. (Magination Pr.).

Sunderland, Margot & Hancock, Nicky. Helping Children with Fear: A Guidebook, 2 vols. Armstrong, Nicky, tr. (Illus.). 140p. spiral bd. (978-0-86388-464-1(4) , 002-5151) Speechmark Publishing Ltd.

—Willy & the Wobbly House: Storybook: Guidebook:Helping Children Who Are Anxious & Obsessional, 2 vols. Armstrong, Nicky, tr. Armstrong, Nicky, illus. 100p. (978-0-86388-499-3(7) , 002-4774) Speechmark Publishing Ltd.

Van Duyne, Sara. Stress & Anxiety-Related Disorders. 2003. (Diseases & People Ser.). (Illus.). 112p. (J). lib. bdg. 26.60 (978-0-7660-1900-3(4)) Enslow Pubs., Inc.

APARTHEID

Here are entered works on the political, economic and social policies of the government of South Africa designed to keep racial groups in South Africa and Namibia separated.

Connolly. Apartheid in South Africa. 2002. (Troubled World Ser.). (Illus.). 64p. (J). (gr. 6 up). lib. bdg. 28.54 (978-0-7398-6339-8(8)) Raintree.

Downing, David. Apartheid in South Africa. 2004. (Illus.). 56p. (J). 27.07 (978-1-4034-4870-5(1)); pap. (978-1-4034-6258-9(5)) Heinemann Library.

Gaines, Ann Graham. Nelson Mandela & Apartheid in World History. 2001. (In World History Ser.). (Illus.). 128p. (J). (gr. 5-12). lib. bdg. 26.60 (978-0-7660-1463-3(0)) Enslow Pubs., Inc.

Martin, Michael. Apartheid in South Africa. 2006. (World History Ser.). 112p. (J). (gr. 7-10). 32.45 (978-1-59018-696-1(6) , Lucent Bks.) Thomson Gale.

Tames, Richard. End of Apartheid: A New South Africa. 2000. (Point of Impact Ser.). (Illus.). 32p. (J). (gr. 5-7). lib. bdg. 24.22 (978-1-57572-412-6(X)) Heinemann Library.

APARTMENT HOUSES

see also Housing

Schaefer, Lola M. Apartment. 2003. 24p. (Illus.). pap. 5.25 (978-1-4034-0481-7(X)); Set. (J). lib. bdg. 18.50 (978-1-4034-0258-5(2)) Heinemann Library.

Schwartz, Stuart B. Finding an Apartment. 1998. (Life Skills Ser.). (J). lib. bdg. (978-0-516-21462-7(4) , Children's Pr.) Scholastic Library Publishing.

Schwartz, Stuart B. & Conley, Craig. Finding an Apartment. (Life Skills-Career Bks.). 48p. pap. 6.95 (978-0-7368-8508-9(0)); 1998. (Illus.). 32p. (J). (gr. 3-4). lib. bdg. 21.26 (978-0-7368-0046-4(8)) Capstone Pr., Inc. (Life-Matters Bks.).

APARTMENT HOUSES—FICTION

Ahrens, Robin Isabel. My Building. Bereznickas, Ilja, illus. 1998. 40p. (J). (ps-1). 15.95 (978-1-890817-06-0(6)) Winslow Pr.

Avi. The Christmas Rat. 2002. (gr. 3-6). lib. bdg. 13.00 (978-0-613-88162-3(1)) Tandem Library Bks.

Briant, Ed. Seven Stories. 2005. (Illus.). 32p. (J). (ps-3). 16.95 (978-1-59643-056-3(7)) Roaring Brook Pr.

Darryl the Doorman: Individual Title, 6 Packs. (ps-2). 27.00 (978-0-7635-9444-2(X)) Rigby Education.

DiCerto, Joseph. The Wall People. 2006. 19.95 (978-1-58752-112-6(1)) Timberwolf Pr., Inc.

Frank, Lucy. Just Ask Iris. 2003. (Illus.). 224p. (J). pap. 4.99 (978-0-689-84454-6(9) , Aladdin) Simon & Schuster Children's Publishing.

—Just Ask Iris. 2003. (gr. 5-8). lib. bdg. 13.00 (978-0-613-66417-2(5)) Tandem Library Bks.

Fries, Claudia. A Pig Is Moving In! Fries, Claudia, illus. 2000. (Illus.). 32p. (J). (ps-2). 16.99 (978-0-531-33307-5(8)); pap. 15.95 (978-0-531-30307-8(1)) Scholastic, Inc. (Orchard Bks.).

Fudge, Keith. The Rainy Day Discovery. 2006. (J). per. 11.95 (978-1-889743-37-0(2)) Robbie Dean Pr.

Good Night, City Lights: Individual Title Six-Packs. (ps-2). 27.00 (978-0-7635-9451-0(2)) Rigby Education.

Goode, Diane. Tiger Trouble! Goode, Diane, illus. 2001. (Illus.). 40p. (J). (ps up). pap. 15.95 (978-0-439-20866-6(1) , Blue Sky Pr., The) Scholastic, Inc.

Grimm, Edward. The Doorman. Lewin, Ted, illus. 2000. 32p. (J). (gr. k-4). 17.99 (978-0-531-33280-1(2) , Orchard Bks.) Scholastic, Inc.

Harper, Charise Mericle. The Trouble with Normal. 2003. (Illus.). 32p. (J). (gr. k-3). tchr. ed. 15.00 (978-0-618-15626-9(7)) Houghton Mifflin Co. Trade & Reference Div.

Harrison, Dorothy. A Better Tomorrow? 2003. 128p. pap. 13.95 (978-0-595-28429-0(9) , Backinprint.com) iUniverse, Inc.

Hearne, Betsy. Who's in the Hall? A Mystery in Four Chapters. 2000. (Illus.). 32p. (J). (gr. 2 up). 16.89 (978-0-688-16262-7(2)) HarperCollins Pubs.

Hirsch, Odo. Have Courage, Hazel Green! (J). 2007. (Illus.). 256p. pap. 6.95 (978-1-59990-003-2(3)); 2006. 262p. 15.95 (978-1-58234-659-5(3)) Bloomsbury Publishing. (Bloomsbury Children).

Howard, Arthur. The Hubbub Above. 2005. (Illus.). 32p. (J). 16.00 (978-0-15-204592-0(9)) Harcourt Trade Pubs.

Hurwitz, Johanna. Nora & Mrs. Mind-Your-Own-Business. 2001. (gr. 3-6). lib. bdg. 12.10 (978-0-613-35646-6(2)) Tandem Library Bks.

—Rip-Roaring Russell. Tilley, Debbie, illus. 2001. (Riverside Kids Ser.). 112p. (J). (gr. 1-4). pap. 4.99 (978-0-06-442155-3(4) , Harper Trophy) HarperCollins Pubs.

—Rip-Roaring Russell. 1999. (Beech Tree Chapter Bks.). (Illus.). 96p. (gr. k-4). mass mkt. 4.95 (978-0-688-16664-9(4)) HarperCollins Pubs.

—Rip-Roaring Russell. Tilley, Debbie, illus. 2001. 110p. (J). (ps-ps). per. 12.10 (978-0-613-34915-4(6)) Tandem Library Bks.

Johnson, D. B. Eddie's Kingdom. 2005. (Illus.). 32p. (J). (gr. k-3). 16.00 (978-0-618-56299-2(0)) Houghton Mifflin Co. Trade & Reference Div.

Keats, Ezra Jack. Apt. 3. Keats, Ezra Jack, illus. 2002. (Illus.). (J). 22.72 (978-0-7587-1965-2(5)) Book Wholesalers, Inc.

—Apt. 3. Keats, Ezra Jack, illus. 1999. (Illus.). 32p. (J). (ps-3). 15.99 (978-0-670-88342-4(5) , Viking Juvenile); pap. 6.99 (978-0-14-056507-2(8) , Puffin) Penguin Group (USA) Inc.

—Apt. 3. 1999. (J). 13.79 (978-0-606-16772-7(2)) Tandem Library Bks.

Lakin, Patricia. Fat Chance Thanksgiving. Schuett, Stacey, illus. 2001. 32p. (J). (gr. 2-5). 15.95 (978-0-8075-2288-2(0)) Whitman, Albert & Co.

The Lil Dudes. 2006. (YA). per. (978-1-59872-308-3(1)) Instantpublisher.com.

MacPhail, Catherine. Fighting Back. (Illus.). 128p. (J). 7.95 (978-0-14-038270-9(4)) Penguin Bks., Ltd. GBR. *Dist:* Trafalgar Square Publishing.

Naylor, Phyllis Reynolds. Cuckoo Feathers. Ramsey, Marcy Dunn, illus. 2006. 96p. (J). 14.95 (978-0-7614-5285-0(0)) Cavendish, Marshall Corp.

Pennypacker, Sara. Clementine. Frazee, Marla, illus. 2006. 144p. (gr. 1-5). 14.99 (978-0-7868-3882-0(5)) Hyperion Pr.

Potter, Ellen. Olivia Kidney. Reynolds, Peter, illus. 2003. 160p. (J). (gr. 3-6). 15.99 (978-0-399-23850-5(6) , Philomel) Penguin Group (USA) Inc.

—Olivia Kidney. Aguilar, Carmen, tr. Reynolds, Peter H., illus. 2006. (SPA.). 159p. (J). pap. 16.99 (***978-84-7871-408-7(1))** RBA Libros, S.A. ESP. *Dist:* Lectorum Pubns., Inc.

Potter, Ellen. Olivia Kidney. Reynolds, Peter, illus. 2004. 176p. (J). (gr. 3). reprint ed. pap. 5.99 (978-0-14-240234-4(6) , Puffin) Penguin Group (USA) Inc.

Raskin, Ellen. Westing Game. 2003. 182p. (J). lib. bdg. 15.00 (***978-1-4242-2271-1(0))** Fitzgerald Bks.

Rylant, Cynthia. The Case of the Climbing Cat. Karas, G. Brian, illus. 2000. (High-Rise Private Eyes Ser.: No. 2). 48p. (J). (gr. 1 up). 14.89 (978-0-688-16309-9(2)) HarperCollins Pubs.

—The Case of the Sleepy Sloth. Karas, G. Brian, illus. 2004. (High-Rise Private Eyes Ser.: No. 5). 48p. (J). (gr. k-3). pap. 3.99 (978-0-06-009100-2(2) , Harper Trophy) HarperCollins Pubs.

—The Case of the Sleepy Sloth. Karas, G. Brian, illus. unabr. ed. 2005. (High-Rise Private Eyes Ser.: No. 5). (J). (gr. k-4). 29.95 incl. audio (978-1-59519-413-8(4)); 28.95 incl. audio compact disk (978-1-59519-417-6(7)); pap. 18.95 incl. audio compact disk (978-1-59519-416-9(9)); pap. 16.95 incl. audio (978-1-59519-412-1(6)); Set. pap. 29.95 incl. audio (978-1-59519-414-5(2)); Set. pap. 31.95 incl. audio compact disk (978-1-59519-418-3(5)) Live Oak Media.

Sachs, Marilyn. The Four Ugly Cats in Apartment 3D. Litzinger, Rosanne, illus. 2003. (Ready-for-Chapters Ser.). 80p. (J). pap. 3.99 (978-0-689-86353-0(5) , Aladdin) Simon & Schuster Children's Publishing.

Schotter, Roni. The House of Joyful Living. Widener, Terry, illus. 2008. (J). (***978-0-374-33429-1(3))** Farrar, Straus & Giroux.

Schraff, Anne. The White Room: Set 2. 2002. 32p. (YA). 2.95 (978-1-56254-424-9(1) , SP 4241) Saddleback Educational Publishing.

Schwartz, Amy. A Glorious Day. Schwartz, Amy, illus. 2004. (Illus.). 32p. (J). 16.95 (978-0-689-84802-5(1) , Atheneum/Richard Jackson Bks.) Simon & Schuster Children's Publishing.

Stadler, John. The Cats of Mrs. Calamari. Stadler, John, illus. 1999. (Illus.). 32p. (J). (ps-1). pap. 5.95 (978-0-531-07140-3(5) , Orchard Bks.) Scholastic, Inc.

—The Cats of Mrs. Calamari. 1999. (Illus.). (J). (978-0-606-18332-1(9)) Tandem Library Bks.

Thompson, Kay. Eloise the Ultimate Edition. Knight, Hilary, illus. 2000. 304p. (J). (ps-3). 39.99 (978-0-689-83990-0(1)) Simon & Schuster Children's Publishing.

Tiddle, Deanna Hessedal. Apartment Horse & Friends. 2003. 62p. (J). pap. 9.95 (978-0-7414-1724-4(3)) Infinity Publishing.

Yin & Soentpiet, Chris K. Dear Santa, Please Come to the 19th Floor. Soentpiet, Chris K., illus. 2002. (Illus.). 32p. (J). (gr. k-3). 17.99 (978-0-399-23636-5(8) , Philomel) Penguin Group (USA) Inc.

APES

see also Chimpanzees; Gorilla; Orangutan

Armentrout, David & Armentrout, Patricia. Gibbons. 2008. (J). (***978-1-60044-566-8(7))** Rourke Publishing, LLC.

Chambers, Catherine E. Ape Adventures. 2008. (Dk Readers Ser.). 48p. (J). (gr. 2-4). 14.99 (***978-0-7566-3750-7(3));** pap. 3.99 (***978-0-7566-3751-4(1))** Dorling Kindersley Publishing, Inc.

Dennard, Deborah. Apes & Monkeys. McGee, John F., illus. 2004. (Our Wild World Ser.). 192p. (J). (gr. 2-5). ring bd. 16.95 (978-1-55971-863-9(3) , NorthWord Bks. for Young Readers) T&N Children's Publishing.

Dorling Kindersley Publishing Staff. Ape. 2006. (Watch Me Grow Ser.). (Illus.). 24p. (J). 7.99 (978-0-7566-1976-3(9)) Dorling Kindersley Publishing, Inc.

Gikow, Louise. Ripley's Apes & Monkeys. 2004. (Illus.). 60p. (J). (978-0-439-63364-2(8)) Scholastic, Inc.

Gilders, Michelle A. The Nature of Great Apes: Our Next of Kin. 2003. (Selection from the Nature Ser.). (Illus.). 112p. (gr. 4-7). 24.95 (978-1-55054-762-7(3) , Greystone Bks.) Douglas & McIntyre, Ltd. CAN. *Dist:* Transition Vendor.

Goecke, Michael P. Giant Ape. 2003. (Prehistoric Animals Ser.). (Illus.). 24p. (J). (gr. k-4). lib. bdg. 21.35 (978-1-57765-967-9(8)) ABDO Publishing Co.

Great Apes. 2006. (Zootles Ser.). (J). 4.95 (978-1-932396-19-5(5)) Wildlife Education, Ltd.

Harrison, Carol. Apes! Harris, Greg, photos by. 1999. (Know-It-Alls Ser.). (Illus.). 24p. (J). (ps-3). 2.79 (978-0-7681-0180-5(8) , 57006, McClanahan Bk.) Learning Horizons, Inc.

Hoare, Ben. Gibbons. 2004. (Nature's Children Ser.). (J). (978-0-7172-5965-6(X) , Grolier) Scholastic Library Publishing.

Jenkins, Martin. Ape. White, Vicky, illus. 2007. 48p. (J). (ps-2). 16.99 (***978-0-7636-3471-1(9))** Candlewick Pr.

Jeunesse, Gallimard. Monkeys & Apes. Prunier, James, illus. 1999. (First Discovery Book Ser.). 24p. (J). (ps-2). 12.95 (978-0-590-87610-0(4)) Scholastic, Inc.

Redmond, Ian. Gorilas. Anderson, Peter & Brightling, Geoff, illus. 2003. (SPA.). 64p. 14.95 (978-84-372-2323-0(7)) Altea, Ediciones, S.A. - Grupo Santillana ESP. *Dist:* Santillana USA Publishing Co., Inc.

—Gorilla. 2000. (Eyewitness Bks.). (Illus.). 64p. (J). (gr. 4-7). 15.99 (978-0-7894-6036-3(X)) Dorling Kindersley Publishing, Inc.

Redmond, Ian & Dorling Kindersley Publishing Staff. Gorilla. 2000. (Eyewitness Bks.). (Illus.). 64p. (J). (gr. 4-7). lib. bdg. 19.99 (978-0-7894-6613-6(9)) Dorling Kindersley Publishing, Inc.

Saign, Geoffrey C. The Great Apes. 1998. (First Bks.). (Illus.). 64p. (J). (gr. 4 up). 23.00 (978-0-531-20361-3(1) , Watts, Franklin) Scholastic Library Publishing.

—The Great Apes. 1998. (Illus.). 63p. (J). (ps-6). lib. bdg. 15.25 (978-0-613-18707-7(5)) Tandem Library Bks.

Stonehouse, Bernard. Monkeys & Apes: A Visual Introduction to Monkeys & Apes. Camm, Martin & Orr, Richard, illus. (Animal Watch Ser.). 48p. (J). (gr. 4-9). 16.95 (978-0-8160-3927-2(5) , Checkmark Bks.) Facts On File, Inc.

Taylor, Barbara. Apes & Monkeys. (Science Kids Ser.). (Illus.). 48p. (J). 2007. pap. 6.95 (***978-0-7534-6163-1(3));** 2004. 9.95 (978-0-7534-5760-3(1)) Houghton Mifflin Co. Trade & Reference Div. (Kingfisher).

Taylor, Barbara. Great Apes. (Nature Fact File... Ser.). (Illus.). 64p. 2003. pap. 7.99 (978-1-84215-714-5(0) , Southwater); 2001. (gr. 3-7). 14.95 (978-0-7548-0655-4(3)) Anness Publishing GBR. *Dist:* National Bk. Network.

Taylor, Barbara & Jackson, Tom. Apes & Monkeys. 2004. (Illus.). 128p. pap. 17.99 (978-1-84215-955-2(0) , Southwater) Anness Publishing GBR. *Dist:* National Bk. Network.

Wildlife Education, compiled by. Great Apes. 2005. (Zootles Ser.). (Illus.). 23p. (J). lib. bdg. 10.95 (978-1-932396-08-9(X)) Wildlife Education, Ltd.

Wildlife Education, Ltd. Staff & Wexo, John Bonnett. Apes. Hynes, Robert et al, illus. 2001. (Zoobooks Ser.). 18p. (Orig.). (YA). (gr. 5 up). pap. 2.95 (978-0-937934-03-6(8)) Wildlife Education, Ltd.

World Book, Inc. Staff, contrib. by. Gorillas & Other Apes. 2005. (World Book's Animals of the World Ser.). (Illus.). 64p. (J). (978-0-7166-1263-6(1)) World Bk., Inc.

APES—FICTION

Buehner, Caralyn. Escape of Marvin the Ape. Buehner, Mark, illus. 1999. 32p. (J). (ps-3). pap. 5.99 (978-0-14-056503-4(5) , Puffin) Penguin Group (USA) Inc.

—Escape of Marvin the Ape. 1999. (gr. k-3). lib. bdg. 14.15 (978-0-613-17791-7(6)) Tandem Library Bks.

Buehner, Caralyn. Escape of Marvin the Ape Board Book. Buehner, Mark, illus. 2007. 24p. (J). (ps). bds. 7.99 (***978-0-8037-3244-5(9)** , Dial) Penguin Group (USA) Inc.

Bynum, Janie. Altoona Baboona. 2002. (Illus.). 36p. (J). (ps-2). pap. 7.00 (978-0-15-216404-1(9) , Voyager Bks./Libros Viajeros) Harcourt Children's Bks.

Carlson, Dale Bick, et al, illus. The Human Apes. 2nd ed. 2005. 155p. (gr. 8-12). reprint ed. pap. 14.95 (978-1-884158-31-5(5)) Bick Publishing Hse.

Greco, Francesca. Cyril the Mandrill. 2004. (Illus.). 40p. (J). (ps-ps). 16.95 (978-1-932065-92-3(X)) Star Bright Bks., Inc.

McMullan, Kate. A Wedding for Wiglaf? 2007. (Dragon Slayers' Academy Ser.: No. 4). 112p. (J). (gr. 1-6). 24.21 (***978-1-59961-380-2(8))** Spotlight.

Morris, Gilbert. Dixie & Dolly. 1998. (Dixie Morris Animal Adventure Ser.: No. 3). 160p. (J). (gr. 4-7). pap. 5.99 (978-0-8024-3365-7(0)) Moody Pubs.

Pinkwater, Daniel M. Second-Grade Ape. 1998. (978-0-606-13768-3(8)) Tandem Library Bks.

Rey, H. A. & Rey, Margret. A Treasury of Curious George. 2004. (Illus.). 208p. (J). (gr. k-3). 10.99 (978-0-618-53822-5(4)) Houghton Mifflin Co. Trade & Reference Div.

Souci, Robert D. San & Burroughs, Edgar Rice. Tarzan. McCurdy, Michael, illus. 2004. 31p. (J). (gr. k-4). reprint ed. 16.00 (978-0-7567-7576-6(0)) DIANE Publishing Co.

APICULTURE

see Bees

APOLLO PROJECT

see Project Apollo

APOSTLES

Aquilina, Michael, III. St. Jude: A Friend in Hard Times. Neely, Keith, illus. 2004. 76p. (J). 14.95 (978-0-8198-7075-9(7) , 332-371) Pauline Bks. & Media.

Lovasik, Lawrence G. & Winkler, J. The Twelve Apostles. (Illus.). (J). 1.25 (978-0-89942-520-7(8)) Catholic Bk. Publishing Corp.

Walters, Steve B. A Shepherd's Journey: The Life Story of Apostle Lymus Johnson. 2002. 216p. 20.00 (978-0-9719767-0-2(8) , 770-409-1633) Walters, Steve Ministries.

APPALACHIAN MOUNTAINS

Bollich, James J. Innocents at War. Turner, Bruce et al, eds. 2001. 270p. (YA). pap. 20.00 (978-0-9643275-5-9(4)) Bollich, James J.

Mader, Jan. Appalachian Mountains. 2004. (Rookie Read-About Geography Ser.). (J). 32p. (gr. 1-2). pap. 5.95 (978-0-516-26834-7(1)); 31p. 20.50 (978-0-516-22757-3(2)) Scholastic Library Publishing. (Children's Pr.).

Maynard, Charles W. The Appalachians. 2004. (Great Mountain Ranges of the World Ser.). (Illus.). 24p. (J). lib. bdg. 21.25 (978-0-8239-6695-0(X) , PowerKids Pr.) Rosen Publishing Group, Inc., The.

APPALACHIAN MOUNTAINS—FICTION

Bradfield, Carl. Tecumseh's Trail: The Appalachian Trail, Then & Now. (Illus.). 137p. (Orig.). (YA). (gr. 8-12). pap. (978-0-9632319-3-2(6)) ASDA Publishing, Inc.

Bradley, Kimberly Brubaker. Halfway to the Sky. 2003. 176p. (J). (gr. 3-7). pap. 5.99 (978-0-440-41830-6(5) , Yearling) Random Hse. Children's Bks.

—Halfway to the Sky. 2003. (gr. 5-8). lib. bdg. 13.00 (978-0-613-62771-9(7)) Tandem Library Bks.

Davis, Donald. The Pig Who Went Home on Sunday: An Appalachian Folktale. 2007. 40p. pap. 7.95 (***978-0-87483-851-0(7))** August Hse. Pubs., Inc.

Dreibrodt, Stacie Champlin. Where the Lilies Bloom. 2000. (YA). 9.95 (978-1-58130-634-7(2)); 11.95 (978-1-58130-635-4(0)) Novel Units, Inc.

Ernst, Kathleen. Midnight in Lonesome Hollow: A Kit Mystery. Tibbles, Jean-Paul, illus. 2007. 192p. (J). 10.95 (***978-1-59369-161-5(0));** pap. 6.95 (***978-1-59369-160-8(2))** American Girl Publishing, Inc. (American Girl).

Francis, M. Stella. Campfire Girls in the Allegheny Mountain. 2006. 32.99 (***978-1-4280-3392-4(0));** pap. 25.99 (***978-1-4280-3395-5(5))** IndyPublish.com.

Gibbons, Faye. Emma Jo's Song. Meidell, Sherry, illus. 2003. 32p. (J). (gr. k-2). 15.95 (978-1-56397-935-4(7)) Boyds Mills Pr.

Harcourt School Publishers Staff. Mountain Home Advanced Level. 3rd ed. 2002. (Trophies Reading Program Ser.). (Illus.). pap. 5.10 (978-0-15-323210-7(2)) Harcourt Schl. Pubs.

—Trofeos Advanced Level: La Casa en Montana. 3rd ed. 2002. (SPA., Illus.). pap. 6.80 (978-0-15-324121-5(7)) Harcourt Schl. Pubs.

Henson, Heather. That Bookwoman. Small, David, illus. 2008. (J). (***978-1-4169-0812-8(9))** Simon & Schuster Children's Publishing.

Kingsolver, Barbara. Prodigal Summer. 2001. (gr. 7-12). lib. bdg. 23.45 (978-0-613-64446-4(8)) Tandem Library Bks.

Lunn, Janet. Hollow Tree. 1998. 272p. (J). mass mkt. (978-0-676-97143-9(1) , Knopf Canada) Knopf Canada CAN. *Dist:* Random Hse., Inc.

Martin, Ann M. Belle Teale. 224p. (J). 2004. pap. 5.99 (978-0-439-09824-3(6) , Scholastic Paperbacks); 2001. (gr. 5-9). pap. 16.95 (978-0-439-09823-6(8)) Scholastic, Inc.

Morgan, Robert. Gap Creek: The Story of A Marriage. 2001. (gr. 5-8). lib. bdg. 16.45 (978-0-613-58965-9(3)) Tandem Library Bks.

Naylor, Phyllis Reynolds. Sang Spell. 224p. (YA). (gr. 5 up). pap. 4.99 (978-0-8072-8294-6(4)); 2000. pap. 35.00 incl. audio (978-0-8072-8293-9(6) , YYA153SP) Random Hse. Audio Publishing Group. (Listening Library).

—Sang Spell. 2000. (978-0-606-17828-0(7)); (gr. 5-8). lib. bdg. 13.00 (978-0-613-28632-9(4)) Tandem Library Bks.

Naylor, Phyllis Reynolds & Duda, Jana. Sang Spell. 2000. (Illus.). 224p. (YA). (gr. 6-12). pap. 5.99 (978-0-689-82006-9(2) , Simon Pulse) Simon & Schuster Children's Publishing.

Nolan, Han. When We Were Saints. (YA). 2005. 312p. pap. 6.95 (978-0-15-205322-2(0) , Harcourt Paperbacks); 2003. (Illus.). 304p. 17.00 (978-0-15-216371-6(9) , 53586153) Harcourt Children's Bks.

Pace, Dianne. Odel's Diner. 2007. (J). per. 12.95 (***978-0-89315-419-6(9))** Lambert Bk. Hse., Inc.

Rinaldi, Ann. The Coffin Quilt: The Feud Between the Hatfields & the McCoys. 2001. (gr. 5-8). lib. bdg. 14.15 (978-0-613-35451-6(6)) Tandem Library Bks.

Showell, Ellen Harvey. The Ghost of Tillie Jean Cassaway. 2000. (Illus.). 128p. (YA). (gr. 4-7). pap. 9.95 (978-0-595-14292-7(3) , Backinprint.com) iUniverse, Inc.

Smith, Doris Buchanan. Return to Bitter Creek. 2002. (J). (gr. 3-7). 19.75 (978-0-8446-7212-0(2)) Smith, Peter Pub., Inc.

Vaughn, Margaret Britton, et al. The Birthday Dolly. 2000. (Illus.). 47p. (J). pap. (978-1-882845-09-5(9)) Bell Buckle Pr.

Wood, D. K. Nightmare at Indian Cave. 2006. pap. 10.00 (***978-1-4257-1640-0(7)***) Xlibris Corp.

APPALACHIAN MOUNTAINS—SOCIAL LIFE AND CUSTOMS

Rylant, Cynthia. Appalachia: The Voices of Sleeping Birds. Moser, Barry, illus. 1998. 32p. (J). pap. 7.00 (978-0-15-201893-1(X) , Harcourt Paperbacks) Harcourt Children's Bks.

APPARATUS, SCIENTIFIC

see Scientific Apparatus and Instruments

APPARITIONS

see also Ghosts

Montague, Darlana. Messages from Your Angels, 3 vols. Brooks, Deborah J., illus. 1998. (Orig.). (J). (gr. 1-5). Set. pap. 22.95 (978-1-889529-09-7(5)); Vol. II. 18p. pap. 7.95 (978-1-889529-07-3(9)); Vol. III. 20p. pap. 7.95 (978-1-889529-08-0(7)) Two Feathers Publishing.

Serrano, Francisco. La Virgen de Guadalupe. Davalos, Felipe, illus. Tr. of Virgin of Guadalupe. (SPA.). (J). (gr. 2-4). 18.00 (978-968-494-070-3(X)) Centro de Informacion y Desarrollo de la Comunicacion y la Literatura MEX. *Dist:* Lectorum Pubns., Inc.

Serrano, Francisco & Guzman, Eugenia. La Virgen de Guadalupe. Davalos, Felipe, illus. 1998. Tr. of Virgin of Guadalupe. (SPA.). 12p. (J). 16.95 (978-0-88899-340-3(4)) Groundwood Bks. CAN. *Dist:* Perseus Distribution.

APPLE

Anderson, Catherine. Apple Orchard. 2004. (Field Trip! Ser.). (Illus.). 24p. (J). pap. 5.50 (978-1-4034-6166-7(X)); lib. bdg. 20.64 (978-1-4034-6159-9(7)) Heinemann Library.

Apples in a Box, Vol. 4. (Early Intervention Levels Ser.). 3.55 (978-0-7362-0166-7(1)) Hampton-Brown Bks.

Apples Set. (gr. k-2). 114.95 (978-0-7368-9050-2(5)) Red Brick Learning.

Bauer, David. My Apple Tree. 2006. (Yellow Umbrella Books for Early Readers). (Illus.). (J). 16p. (978-0-7368-5974-5(8)); (ENG & SPA., 18p. (978-0-7368-6010-9(X)) Yellow Umbrella Pr.

Bulla, Clyde Robert. Tree Is a Plant. 2001. (gr. k-3). lib. bdg. 12.95 (978-0-613-45558-9(4)) Tandem Library Bks.

—A Tree Is a Plant. Schuett, Stacey, illus. 2001. (J). (ps-ps). lib. bdg. 12.19 (978-0-606-22286-0(3)) Tandem Library Bks.

Driscoll, Laura. Apples & How They Grow. 2003. (gr. k-3). lib. bdg. 11.80 (978-0-613-70544-8(0)) Tandem Library Bks.

Flanagan, Alice K. The Zieglers & Their Apple Orchard. Flanagan, Romie, illus. 1999. (Our Neighborhood Ser.). 32p. (J). (gr. 1-2). 20.00 (978-0-516-21134-3(X) , Children's Pr.) Scholastic Library Publishing.

Franck, Irene M. & Brownstone, David M. Apples. 2003. (Illus.). 32p. (J). (978-0-7172-5713-3(4) , Grolier) Scholastic Library Publishing.

—Riches of the Earth, 16 vols. 2003. (Illus.). 32p. (J). 269.00 (978-0-7172-5730-0(4) , Grolier) Scholastic Library Publishing.

Gibbons, Gail. Apples. Gibbons, Gail, illus. 2005. (Illus.). 32p. (J). (gr. k-3). 6.95 (978-0-8234-1669-1(0)) Holiday Hse., Inc.

Harcourt School Publishers Staff. Apple Picking Time Below Level. 3rd ed. 2002. (Trophies Reading Program Ser.). (Illus.). pap. 5.10 (978-0-15-323055-4(X)) Harcourt Schl. Pubs.

—Apples: Below Level. 3rd ed. 2002. (Trophies Reading Program Ser.). (Illus.). (J). pap. 3.20 (978-0-15-322945-9(4)) Harcourt Schl. Pubs.

Hazelwood, Drema. The Apple Orchard Gang: Featuring Red Delicious. l.t. ed. 1999. (Illus.). 20p. (J). (ps-3). pap. 5.95 (978-1-891029-45-5(2)) Henderson Publishing.

Hibbert, Clare. The Life of an Apple. 2004. (Illus.). pap. 7.50 (978-1-4109-0922-0(0)) Raintree.

—The Life of an Apple 6-Pack. 2004. (Illus.). pap. 40.50 (978-1-4109-0929-9(8)) Raintree.

Hubbell, William, illus. Apples Here! 2002. 32p. (J). (ps-3). 16.95 (978-0-8075-0397-3(5)) Whitman, Albert & Co.

Hutchings, Amy & Hutchings, Richard. Growing Apples & Pumpkins. 2001. (Illus.). (J). (978-0-439-22352-2(0)) Scholastic, Inc.

Keller, Kristin Thoennes. Apples to Applesauce. 2004. (First Facts Ser.). 24p. (J). lib. bdg. 21.26 (978-0-7368-2633-4(5)) Capstone Pr., Inc.

Landau, Elaine. Apples. 1999. (True Bks.). (Illus.). 48p. (J). (gr. 3-5). 25.00 (978-0-516-21024-7(6) , Children's Pr.) Scholastic Library Publishing.

Llewellyn, Claire. Apples. 2005. (Illus.). 24p. (YA). (gr. 1 up). lib. bdg. 22.80 (978-1-932889-39-0(6)) Sea-To-Sea Pubns.

—Tree. Mendez, Simon, tr. Mendez, Simon, illus. 2004. (Starting Life Ser.). 24p. (J). (ps-3). ring bd. 16.95 (978-1-55971-879-0(X) , NorthWord Bks. for Young Readers) T&N Children's Publishing.

Mattern, Joanne. How Apple Trees Grow: Como Crecen Los Manzanos. 2006. (ENG & SPA., Illus.). 24p. (J). pap. (978-0-8368-6467-0(0) , Weekly Reader Early Learning Library) Stevens, Gareth Inc.

—How Apple Trees Grow/ Como crecen los manzanos. 2006. (ENG & SPA., Illus.). 24p. (J). 19.33 (978-0-8368-6460-1(3)) Stevens, Gareth Inc.

Mayo, Gretchen Will. Applesauce. 2004. (Weekly Reader Early Learning Library). (Illus.). 24p. (gr. 2 up). (J). pap. 5.95 (978-0-8368-4071-1(2)); (YA). lib. bdg. 19.33 (978-0-8368-4064-3(X)) Stevens, Gareth Inc. (Weekly Reader Early Learning Library).

Murphy, Patricia J. The Apple Orchard. 2004. (Visit To Ser.). (Illus.). 24p. (J). lib. bdg. 19.93 (978-0-7368-2579-5(7) , Pebble Bks.) Capstone Pr., Inc.

Murray, Julie. Apples. 2007. (Life Cycles Ser.). 24p. (J). (gr. k-4). lib. bdg. 21.35 (***978-1-59928-701-0(3)*** , Buddy Bks.) ABDO Publishing Co.

My Apple Tree. 2006. (Yellow Umbrella Science Ser.). 8,16p. (J). 6.50 (978-0-7368-1707-3(7)) Red Brick Learning.

Naslund, Gorel Kristina. Our Apple Tree. Digman, Kristina, illus. 2006. 32p. (J). pap. 6.95 (978-1-59643-191-1(1)) Roaring Brook Pr.

Naslund, Gorel Kristina & Wormell, Christopher. Our Apple Tree. Digman, Kristina, illus. rev. ed. 2005. 32p. (J). 15.95 (978-1-59643-052-5(4)) Roaring Brook Pr.

Out & about at the Apple Orchard. (Field Trips Ser.). 24p. (J). 8.95 (978-1-4048-0164-6(2)) Picture Window Bks.

Pascoe, Elaine. The Ecosystem of an Apple Tree. 2003. (Library of Small Ecosystems Ser.). (Illus.). 24p. (J). lib. bdg. 21.25 (978-0-8239-6304-1(7) , PowerKids Pr.) Rosen Publishing Group, Inc., The.

Raintree Steck-Vaughn Staff. Manzanas y Mas Manzanas. 1999. (SPA.). (J). pap., stu. ed. 31.05 (978-0-7398-0760-6(9)) Steck-Vaughn.

Rau, Dana Meachen. Applesauce. 2008. (J). (***978-0-7614-2894-7(1)***) Cavendish, Marshall Bks., Ltd.

Royston, Angela. Apple. 2002. (Life Cycle of a... Ser.). (Illus.). 32p. (J). (gr. k-2). pap. 6.95 (978-1-57572-472-0(3) , 90461) Heinemann Library.

Saunders-Smith, Gail. Apple Trees. 1998. (Plants Ser.). pap. 13.25 (978-0-516-21237-1(0) , Children's Pr.) Scholastic Library Publishing.

—Apples, 3 vols, Set. 1998. (J). pap. (978-0-516-29777-4(5) , Children's Pr.) Scholastic Library Publishing.

—Eating Apples. 1998. (J). pap. 13.25 (978-0-516-21242-5(7) , Children's Pr.) Scholastic Library Publishing.

—From Bud to Blossom. 1998. (J). pap. 13.25 (978-0-516-21243-2(5) , Children's Pr.) Scholastic Library Publishing.

—Picking Apples. 1998. (J). pap. 13.25 (978-0-516-21245-6(1) , Children's Pr.) Scholastic Library Publishing.

Snyder, Inez. Apples. 2004. (Harvesttime Ser.). (J). 18.00 (978-0-516-27595-6(X)); pap. 4.95 (978-0-516-25910-9(5)) Scholastic Library Publishing. (Children's Pr.).

Tagliaferro, Linda. The Life Cycle of an Apple Tree. 2007. (Pebble Plus Ser.). (Illus.). 24p. (J). (978-0-7368-6709-2(0) , 1264875, Pebble Bks.) Capstone Pr., Inc.

Taus-Bolstad, Stacy. From Seed to Apple. 2003. (From Start to Finish Ser.). (Illus.). 24p. (J). 18.60 (978-0-8225-0719-2(6) , Lerner Pubns.) Lerner Publishing Group.

—From Shoot to Apple. 2002. (From Start to Finish Ser.). (J). pap. 4.95 (978-0-8225-0670-6(X)) Lerner Publishing Group.

Ward, Kristin. Apples. 2000. (PowerKids Readers Ser.). (Illus.). 24p. (J). (gr. 1). lib. bdg. 16.00 (978-0-8239-5528-2(1) , PKNAAP, PowerKids Pr.) Rosen Publishing Group, Inc., The.

APPLE COMPUTERS

see also Macintosh (Computer)

Brackett, Virginia. Steve Jobs: Computer Genius of Apple. 2003. (Internet Biographies Ser.). (Illus.). 48p. (J). (gr. 4-10). lib. bdg. 23.93 (978-0-7660-1970-6(5)) Enslow Pubs., Inc.

Brashares, Ann. Steve Jobs: Thinks Different. 2001. (978-0-606-22376 8(2)) Tandem Library Bks.

Kendall, Martha E. Steve Wozniak: Inventor of the Apple Computer. 2000. (Illus.). 112p. (YA). (gr. 4 up). pap. 10.95 (978-0-945783-08-4(6)) Highland Publishing Group.

Lemke, Donald B. Steve Jobs & Steve Wozniak & the Personal Computer. 2007. (Graphic Library). (Illus.). 32p. (J). 25.26 (978-0-7368-6488-6(1)) Capstone Pr., Inc.

Lemke, Donald B. Steve Jobs, Steve Wozniak & the Personal Computer. 2007. (Illus.). 32p. (J). (***978-0-7368-9650-4(3)***) Capstone Pr., Inc.

Riddle, John & Whiting, Jim. Stephen Wozniak & the Story of Apple Computer. l.t. ed. 2002. (Unlocking the Secrets of Science Ser.). (Illus.). 56p. (gr. 4-10). lib. bdg. 17.95 (978-1-58415-109-8(9)) Mitchell Lane Pubs., Inc.

Wilson, Suzan. Steve Jobs: Wizard of Apple Computer. 2001. (People to Know Ser.). (Illus.). 128p. (YA). (gr. 6-12). lib. bdg. 26.60 (978-0-7660-1536-4(X)) Enslow Pubs., Inc.

APPLESEED, JOHNNY, 1774-1845

Adil, Janeen. Johnny Appleseed. 2003. (Folk Heroes Ser.). (Illus.). 24p. (J). lib. bdg. 15.95 (978-1-59036-075-0(3)) Weigl Pubs., Inc.

Balcziak, Bill. Johnny Appleseed. 2003. (Tall Tales Ser.). (Illus.). 32p. (C). (gr. 3-5). 22.60 (978-0-7565-0458-8(9)) Compass Point Bks.

Blair, Eric. Johnny Appleseed. Muehlenhardt, Amy Bailey, illus. 2006. (Read-It! Readers en Espanol Ser.).Tr. of Johnny Appleseed. (SPA.). 32p. (J). (ps-3). 19.95 (978-1-4048-1655-8(0)) Picture Window Bks.

—Johnny Appleseed's Fruitful Adventure: A Retelling of the Classic Traditional Tale. Muehlenhardt, Amy Bailey, illus. 2005. (Read-It! Readers Ser.). 32p. (C). (gr. k-3). 18.60 (978-1-4048-0971-0(6)) Picture Window Bks.

Boskey, Madeline. Johnny Appleseed. Petruccio, Steven James, illus. 2001. (Hello Reader! Ser.). (J). (978-0-439-31705-4(3)) Scholastic, Inc.

Ditchfield, Christin. Johnny Appleseed. 2003. (Rookie Biographies Ser.). (gr. 1-2). pap. 4.95 (978-0-516-27816-2(9)); (Illus.). 32p. (J). 20.50 (978-0-516-22853-2(6)) Scholastic Library Publishing. (Children's Pr.).

—Johnny Appleseed. 2003. (gr. k-3). lib. bdg. 12.95 (978-0-613-67637-3(8)) Tandem Library Bks.

Feinstein, Stephen. Read about Johnny Appleseed. 2006. (I Like Biographies! Ser.). (Illus.). 24p. (J). lib. bdg. 21.26 (978-0-7660-2599-8(3) , Enslow Elementary) Enslow Pubs., Inc.

Fischer, Jeff, illus. Johnny Appleseed. 2006. (Famous Fables Ser.). (J). 6.99 (978-1-59939-028-4(0)) Reader's Digest Young Families, Inc.

Harrison, David L. Johnny Appleseed: My Story. 2001. (gr. k-3). lib. bdg. 11.80 (978-0-613-36831-5(2)) Tandem Library Bks.

Harrison, David Lee. Johnny Appleseed: My Story. Wohnoutka, Mike, illus. 2001. (Step into Reading Step 2 Bks.). 48p. (J). (gr. k-2). pap. 3.99 (978-0-375-81247-7(4) , Random Hse. Bks. for Young Readers) Random Hse. Children's Bks.

Johnston, Marianne. Johnny Appleseed. 2001. (American Legends Ser.). (Illus.). 24p. (J). (gr. 3). lib. bdg. 18.75 (978-0-8239-5577-0(X) , PowerKids Pr.) Rosen Publishing Group, Inc., The.

Kunstler, James Howard. Johnny Appleseed. Olson, Stan, illus. 2005. (Rabbit Ears-A Classic Tale Ser.). 40p. (J). (gr. k-5). 25.65 (978-1-59197-765-0(7)) Spotlight.

Kurtz, Jane & Haverfield, Mary. Johnny Appleseed. 2004. (Ready-to-Read Ser.). (Illus.). 32p. (J). pap. 3.99 (978-0-689-85958-8(9) , Aladdin) Simon & Schuster Children's Publishing.

Marsh, Carole. Johnny Appleseed. 2002. (One Thousand Readers Ser.). (Illus.). 12p. (J). (gr. k-4). 2.95 (978-0-635-01471-9(8) , 14718) Gallopade International.

—Johnny Appleseed: An Ohio Experience Reader. 2001. (J). (gr. k-5). pap. 1.95 (978-0-635-00424-6(0)) Gallopade International.

—The Virginia Reader: Johnny Appleseed. 2001. (Virginia Experience! Ser.). 12p. (J). (gr. k-5). pap. 2.95 (978-0-635-00350-8(3)) Gallopade International.

Moore, Eva. Johnny Appleseed. 2000. (J). (ps-3). pap. 4.99 (978-0-590-40297-2(8)) Scholastic, Inc.

Moses, Will. Johnny Appleseed: The Story of a Legend. Moses, Will, illus. 2004. (Illus.). 48p. (J). pap. 6.99 (978-0-14-240138-5(2) , Puffin) Penguin Group (USA) Inc.

Schaefer, Lola M. Johnny Appleseed. Saunders-Smith, Gail, ed. 2003. (First Biographies Ser.). (Illus.). 24p. (J). (gr. k-1). lib. bdg. 15.93 (978-0-7368-1645-8(3) , Pebble Bks.) Capstone Pr., Inc.

—Johnny Appleseed. 2005. (First Biographies Ser.). 24p. (YA). (gr. k-3). pap. (978-0-7368-3380-6(3) , Pebble Bks.) Capstone Pr., Inc.

Snyder, Geraldine Ann. Johnny Appleseed: Musical. 2003. (Illus.). 41p. (YA). pap. 6.95 (978-1-58342-127-7(0) , J04) Dramatic Publishing Co.

Swain, Gwenyth. Johnny Appleseed. Porter, Janice Lee, illus. (On My Own Biographies Ser.). 48p. (J). (gr. 1-3). 2003. pap. 5.95 (978-1-57505-534-3(1)); 2001. lib. bdg. 23.93 (978-1-57505-519-0(8) , Carolrhoda Bks.) Lerner Publishing Group.

—Johnny Appleseed. 2001. (gr. 3-6). lib. bdg. 14.10 (978-0-613-79236-3(X)) Tandem Library Bks.

Sweeney, Alyse. Easy Reader Biographies: Johnny Appleseed: An American Who Made a Difference. 2007. 16p. pap. 2.99 (***978-0-439-77414-7(4)*** , Teaching Resources) Scholastic, Inc.

Warrick, Karen Clemens. John Chapman: The Legendary Johnny Appleseed. 2001. (Historical American Biographies Ser.). (Illus.). 128p. (J). (gr. 6-12). lib. bdg. 26.60 (978-0-7660-1443-5(6)) Enslow Pubs., Inc.

Winters, Kay. John Appleseed: A Trail of Trees. Pullen, Zachary, illus. 2007. (J). (978-1-4263-0101 8(4)) National Geographic Society.

Zarzycki, Daryl. Johnny Appleseed. 2006. (What's So Great About... ? Ser.). (Illus.). 32p. (J). (gr. 1-4). lib. bdg. (978-1-58415-483-9(7)) Mitchell Lane Pubs., Inc.

APPLESEED, JOHNNY, 1774-1845—FICTION

Brown, Gregory. Johnny Appleseed: An AMER Tall Tale. 2006. spiral bd. 42.00 (***978-1-4108-7157-2(6)***) Benchmark Education Co.

Christopher, Matt. Johnny Long Legs. ed. 2005. (Sports Classics II Ser.). 117p. (J). lib. bdg. 15.00 (978-1-59054-760-1(8)) Fitzgerald Bks.

Durrant, Lynda. The Sun, the Rain, & the Apple Seed: A Novel of Johnny Appleseed's Life. 2003. 208p. (J). (gr. 5-9). tchr. ed. 15.00 (978-0-618-23487-5(X) , Clarion Bks.) Houghton Mifflin Co. Trade & Reference Div.

Glass, Andrew. Folks Call Me Appleseed John. unabr. ed. 1998. (J). Class Set. 102.70 incl. audio (978-0-7887-2552-4(1) , 46722); Homework. 27.24 incl. audio (978-0-7887-2247-9(6) , 40731) Recorded Bks., LLC.

—Folks Call Me Appleseed John. 1998. (978-0-606-13393-7(3)) Tandem Library Bks.

Kurtz, Jane. Johnny Appleseed. Haverfield, Mary, illus. ed. 2005. 32p. (J). lib. bdg. 15.00 (978-1-59054-928-5(7)) Fitzgerald Bks.

APPLIANCES, ELECTRIC

see Household Appliances, Electric

APPLIED SCIENCE

see Technology

APPRAISAL OF BOOKS

see Books and Reading; Criticism; Literature—History and Criticism

APPRECIATION OF ART

see Art Appreciation

APPRECIATION OF MUSIC

see Music—Analysis, Appreciation

APPRENTICES—FICTION

Blackwood, Gary L. Shakespeare's Spy. 2005. 288p. (J). (gr. 5-9). pap. 6.99 (978-0-14-240311-2(3) , Puffin) Penguin Group (USA) Inc.

Cadnum, Michael. Ship of Fire. 2003. 208p. (J). (gr. 7). 16.99 (978-0-670-89907-4(0) , Viking Juvenile) Penguin Group (USA) Inc.

Czernecki, Stefan. Paper Lanterns. 2004. (Illus.). 32p. (J). (ps-13). pap. 6.95 (978-1-57091-411-9(7)) Charlesbridge Publishing, Inc.

—Paper Lanterns. Czernecki, Stefan, illus. 2001. (Illus.). 32p. (J). (ps-3). 15.95 (978-1-57091-410-2(9)) Charlesbridge Publishing, Inc.

DeFelice, Cynthia. The Apprenticeship of Lucas Whitaker. 2007. 160p. (J). pap. 6.95 (978-0-374-40014-9(8) , Farrar, Straus & Giroux (BYR)) Farrar, Straus & Giroux.

DeFelice, Cynthia C. The Apprenticeship of Lucas Whitaker. 1998. (J). 12.64 (978-0-606-13078-3(0)) Tandem Library Bks.

Delaney, Joseph. Curse of the Bane. Arrasmith, Patrick, illus. 2006. (Last Apprentice Ser.). 480p. (J). 16.99 (978-0-06-076621-4(2) , Greenwillow Bks.); lib. bdg. 17.89 (978-0-06-076622-1(0)) HarperCollins Pubs.

—Last Apprentice Curse of Bane. 2007. (Last Apprentice Ser.). 480p. (J). pap. 7.99 (***978-0-06-076623-8(9)*** , Harper Trophy) HarperCollins Pubs.

—Night of the Soul Stealer, No. 3. 2007. (Last Apprentice Ser.). 512p. (J). (gr. 5 up). lib. bdg. 17.89 (***978-0-06-076625-2(5)*** , Greenwillow Bks.) HarperCollins Pubs.

—Night of the Soul Stealer, No. 3. Arrasmith, Patrick, illus. 2007. (Last Apprentice Ser.). 512p. (J). (gr. 5 up). 16.99 (***978-0-06-076624-5(7)*** , Greenwillow Bks.) HarperCollins Pubs.

Delaney, Joseph. Revenge of the Witch. Arrasmith, Patrick, illus. (Last Apprentice Ser.). (J). 2005. 368p. 16.99 (978-0-06-076618-4(2)); 2005. 368p. lib. bdg. 17.89 (978-0-06-076619-1(0)); 2006. 384p. reprint ed. pap. 7.99 (978-0-06-076620-7(4) , Harper Trophy) HarperCollins Pubs.

Jarvis, Robin. The Alchemist's Cat. 2006. 304p. (YA). pap. 6.95 (978-0-8118-5450-4(7)) Chronicle Bks. LLC.

Joseph Delaney. Revenge of the Witch. l.t. ed. 2006. 375p. 21.95 (978-0-7862-8641-6(5)) Thorndike Pr.

Koller, Jackie French. The Wizard's Apprentice. Guay, Rebecca, illus. 2003. 192p. (J). pap. 4.99 (978-0-689-85592-4(3) , Aladdin) Simon & Schuster Children's Publishing.

L'Engle, Madeleine. The Joys of Love. 2008. 272p. (YA). 16.95 (***978-0-374-33870-1(1)***) Farrar, Straus & Giroux.

Llorente, Pilar Molina. El Aprendiz. (SPA.). 140p. (YA). (gr. 5-8). (978-84-321-2532-4(6) , RP4335) Rialp, Ediciones, S.A. ESP. *Dist:* Lectorum Pubns., Inc.

Meyer, Kai. The Water Mirror. Crawford, Elizabeth D., tr. 2006. (Dark Reflections Trilogy Ser.). 272p. (YA). pap. 7.99 (978-0-689-87788-9(9) , Simon Pulse) Simon & Schuster Children's Publishing.

—The Water Mirror. l.t. ed. 2006. 260p. (YA). 22.95 (978-0-7862-8288-3(6)) Thorndike Pr.

Meyer, Kai & Crawford, Elizabeth D. The Water Mirror. 2005. (J). (978-978-068-987-2(7) , McElderry, Margaret K.) Simon & Schuster Children's Publishing.

Nikola-Lisa, W. Magic in the Margins: A Medieval Tale of Bookmaking. Christensen, Bonnie, illus. 2007. 32p. (J). (gr. 3-5). 17.00 (978-0-618-49642-6(4)) Houghton Mifflin Co. Trade & Reference Div.

Olasky, Susan. Will Northaway & the Price of Loyalty. 2005. (Young American Patriots Ser.: #3). 93p. (J). (ps-7). pap. 5.99 (978-1-58134-477-6(5) , Crossway Bibles) Crossway Bks.

Prineas, Sarah. Stolen. 2008. (Magic Thief Ser.). 416p. (J). 16.99 (***978-0-06-137587-3(X)***) HarperCollins Pubs.

Regan, Dian Curtis. Cam's Quest: The Continuing Story of Princess Nevermore & the Wizard's Apprentice. 2007. 256p. (J). (gr. 4-8). 17.95 (***978-1-58196-056-3(5)***) Darby Creek Publishing.

Ross, Andrea. To Touch the Sun. Davenport, May, ed. l.t. ed. 2000. 195p. (YA). (gr. 9-12). pap. 15.95 (978-0-943864-99-0(2)) Davenport, May Pubs.

Sage, Angie. Physik. Zug, Mark, illus. 2008. (Septimus Heap Ser.: Bk. 3). 560p. (J). (gr. 4-6). pap. 7.99 (***978-0-06-057739-1(8)*** , Harper Trophy) HarperCollins Pubs.

Stroud, Jonathan. The Amulet of Samarkand. 2003. (Bartimaeus Trilogy Ser.: Bk. 1). (Illus.). 464p. (gr. 5-17). 17.95 (978-0-7868-1859-4(X)) Hyperion Bks. for Children.

—The Golem's Eye. 2nd rev. ed. 2006. (Bartimaeus Trilogy Ser.: Bk. 2). 576p. (gr. 5-17). reprint ed. pap. 7.99 (978-0-7868-3654-3(7)) Miramax Bks.

Walsh, Ann. The Doctors Apprentice. 2007. 160p. (J). pap. 9.99 (***978-1-55002-633-7(X)*** , Sandcastle Bks.) Dundurn Group, The CAN. *Dist:* Univ. of Toronto Pr.

Watts, Leander. Stonecutter. 2006. 182p. (J). (gr. 5-9). reprint ed. pap. 7.99 (978-0-618-60577-4(0) , Graphia) Houghton Mifflin Co. Trade & Reference Div.

APRIL FOOLS' DAY

Kroll, Steven & Bassett, Jeni C. Poisson d'Avril. (FRE.). (J). pap. 6.99 (978-0-590-73953-5(0)) Scholastic, Inc.

Schiller, Melissa. April Fool's Day. 2003. (Rookie Read-About Holidays Ser.). (Illus.). 31p. (J). (gr. 1-2). pap. 5.95 (978-0-516-27942-8(4) , Children's Pr.) Scholastic Library Publishing.

—April Fool's Day. 2003. (gr. k-3). lib. bdg. 14.10 (978-0-613-63578-3(7)) Tandem Library Bks.

Williams, Colleen Madonna Flood. My Adventure on April Fool's Day. 2007. 44p. (J). 8.99 (978-1-59092-544-7(0) , Orchard Academy Pr.) Windstorm Creative.

APRIL FOOLS' DAY—FICTION

Bateman, Teresa. April Foolishness. Westcott, Nadine Bernard, illus. 32p. (J). 2007. pap. 6.95 (***978-0-8075-0405-5(X)***); 2004. 16.95 (978-0-8075-0404-8(1)) Whitman, Albert & Co.

Katschke, Judy. April Fools' Rules. 2002. (gr. 3-6). lib. bdg. 13.00 (978-0-613-50406-5(2)) Tandem Library Bks.

King, Susan. Amy & the Real April Fool; Amy & the Easter Basket. King, Susan, illus. 2002. (Illus.). 81p. (J). (ps-6). 7.00 (978-0-9714446-3-8(3)) King RIT - ACKS Pubs.

Maguire, Gregory. A Couple of April Fools. Clayton, Elaine, illus. 2004. (Hamlet Chronicles Ser.). 192p. (J). (gr. 3-5). tchr. ed. 16.00 (978-0-618-27474-1(X) , Clarion Bks.) Houghton Mifflin Co. Trade & Reference Div.

Pascal, Francine. Bromas de Primavera. Orig. Title: April Fool. (SPA.). 120p. (J). 6.95 (978-84-272-3798-8(7)) Molino, Editorial ESP. *Dist:* AIMS International Bks., Inc.

Stevenson, James. Mud Flat April Fool. 1998. (Illus.). 48p. (J). (gr. k-3). 15.89 (978-0-688-15164-5(7)) HarperCollins Pubs.

Stone, Tom B. Dia de los Inocentes. 2002. (SPA.). (J). 5.95 (978-950-24-0789-0(X) , AL30664) Albatros ARG. *Dist:* Lectorum Pubns., Inc.

Welling, Peter J. Michael le Souffle & the April Fool. Welling, Peter J., illus. 2003. (Illus.). 32p. (J). 15.95 (978-1-58980-105-9(9)) Pelican Publishing Co., Inc.

Ziefert, Harriet. April Fool! 2000. (ps-2). lib. bdg. 11.80 (978-0-613-24229-5(7)) Tandem Library Bks.

AQUARIUMS

see also Fish-Culture; Goldfish

Alexander, Zhauna. Amelia's Aquarium. 1999. (Illus.). iii, 65p. (J). (978-1-895836-66-0(2)) Tesseract Bks.

The Aquarium, 6 vols., Pack. (Kinderstarters Ser.). 8p. (ps-1). 21.00 (978-0-7635-8706-2(0)) Rigby Education.

Beylon, Cathy. At the Aquarium. 2003. (Dover Coloring Bks.). (Illus.). 32p. (J). pap. 2.95 (978-0-486-42371-5(9)) Dover Pubns., Inc.

Binns, Tristan Boyer. Freshwater Fish. 2006. (Keeping Pets Ser.). (Illus.). 48p. (J). (978-1-4034-7700-2(0)) Heinemann Library.

Canizares, Susan, et al. Aquarium. 2000. (Scholastic Placebook Ser.). (Illus.). (J). pap. (978-0-439-15372-0(7)) Scholastic, Inc.

Chelsea House Publishing Staff. Marine Aquarium. 1999. (Fish). (Illus.). 64p. (YA). (gr. 4-7). lib. bdg. 19.75 (978-0-7910-5092-7(0) , Chelsea Hse.) Facts On File, Inc.

Dalmatian Press Staff. Setting up & Caring for Your Aquarium. 2005. (Illus.). 64p. (J). pap. 5.99 (978-1-4037-1202-8(6)) Dalmatian Pr.

Elson, Gary & Lucanus, Oliver. Catfish: Everything about Natural History, Purchase, Health, Care, Breeding, & Species Identification. 2003. (Complete Pet Owner's Manual Ser.). (Illus.). 96p. pap. 7.99 (978-0-7641-2397-9(1)) Barron's Educational Series, Inc.

Fabiny, Sarah. Under the Sea. Smith, Jan, illus. 2004. (Pinwheel Ser.). 12p. (J). 9.95 (978-1-4027-1213-5(8)) Sterling Publishing Co., Inc.

Foley, Cate. Let's Go to the Aquarium. 2001. (Weekend Fun Ser.). (Illus.). 24p. (J). (ps-2). 17.00 (978-0-516-23192-1(8)) ; pap. 4.95 (978-0-516-29582-4(9)) Scholastic Library Publishing. (Children's Pr.).

Frost, Helen. Fish. 2000. (All about Pets Ser.). (Illus.). 24p. (J). (gr. k-1). lib. bdg. 15.93 (978-0-7368-0657-2(1) , Pebble Bks.) Capstone Pr., Inc.

Geis, Richard. Catfish. 1999. (Fish). (Illus.). 64p. (J). (gr. 4-7). lib. bdg. 19.75 (978-0-7910-5089-7(0) , Chelsea Hse.) Facts On File, Inc.

Gillis, Jennifer Blizin. Aquariums. 2008. (J). (***978-1-60044-558-3(6)***) Rourke Publishing, LLC.

Glass, Spencer. Goldfish. 1999. (Fish). (Illus.). 64p. (YA). (gr. 4-7). 32.00 (978-0-7910-5090-3(4) , Chelsea Hse.) Facts On File, Inc.

Gorman, Jacqueline Laks. The Aquarium. 2005. (I Like to Visit Ser.). (Illus.). 24p. (J). pap. (978-0-8368-4458-0(0)) ; (YA). lib. bdg. 19.93 (978-0-8368-4451-1(3)) Stevens, Gareth Inc.

—The Aquarium: El Acuario. 2005. (ENG & SPA., Illus.). 24p. (J). pap. (978-0-8368-4602-7(8)) Stevens, Gareth Inc.

—The Aquarium/El Acuario. Acosta, Tatiana & Gutiérrez, Guillermo, trs. 2005. (I Like to Visit/Me Gusta Visitar Ser.). (ENG & SPA., Illus.). 24p. (J). lib. bdg. 19.33 (978-0-8368-4595-2(1)) Stevens, Gareth Inc.

Hamilton, Lynn. Caring for Your Fish. 2002. (Caring for Your Pet Ser.). (Illus.). 32p. (J). lib. bdg. 16.95 (978-1-59036-035-4(4)) Weigl Pubs., Inc.

Hibbert, Clare. Fish. 2004. (Illus.). 32p. (J). lib. bdg. (978-1-58340-435-5(X)) Smart Apple Media.

Jeffrey, Laura S. Fish: How to Choose & Care for a Fish. 2004. (American Humane Pet Care Library). (Illus.). 48p. (J). lib. bdg. 23.93 (978-0-7660-2517-2(9)) Enslow Pubs., Inc.

Jerome, Kate Boehm. Science at the Aquarium. 2004. (National Geographic Reading Expeditions Ser.). (Illus.). 24p. (J). pap. (978-0-7922-8625-7(1)) National Geographic Society.

Kloes, Carol. A Trip to the Aquarium. 2005. 8p. (J). pap. 4.25 (978-1-57874-083-3(5)) Kaeden Corp.

Mary, Ginder, ed. Setting up Aquarium. 2004. 64p. pap. 5.99 (978-1-4037-0883-0(5)) Dalmatian Pr.

McReynolds, Stacy. San Antonio Zoo. 2003. (Great Zoos of the United States Ser.). (Illus.). 24p. (J). lib. bdg. 18.75 (978-0-8239-6319-5(5) , PowerKids Pr.) Rosen Publishing Group, Inc., The.

Mills, Dick. Aquarium Fish. 2004. (101 Essential Tips Ser.). (Illus.). 72p. pap. 5.00 (978-0-7566-0611-4(X)) Dorling Kindersley Publishing, Inc.

Mozart, Homer. Guppies. 1999. (Fish). (Illus.). 64p. (YA). (gr. 4-7). lib. bdg. 19.75 (978-0-7910-5091-0(2) , Chelsea Hse.) Facts On File, Inc.

Out & about at the Aquarium. (Field Trips Ser.). 24p. (J). 8.95 (978-1-4048-0203-2(7)) Picture Window Bks.

Pinkguni, Manolito. Piranhas. 1999. (Fish). (Illus.). 64p. (YA). (gr. 4-7). lib. bdg. 19.75 (978-0-7910-5093-4(9) , Chelsea Hse.) Facts On File, Inc.

Pronek, Neal. Tropical Fish. 1999. (Fish). (Illus.). 64p. (YA). (gr. 4-7). 32.00 (978-0-7910-5094-1(7) , Chelsea Hse.) Facts On File, Inc.

Rechner, Amy. Out & About at the Aquarium. Shipe, Becky, illus. 2004. (Field Trips Ser.). 24p. (C). (gr. k-3). 23.93 (978-1-4048-0298-8(3)) Picture Window Bks.

Richardson, Adele. Caring for Your Fish. 2007. (First Facts Ser.). (Illus.). 24p. (J). (gr. k-3). lib. bdg. 21.26 (978-0-7368-6386-5(9)) Capstone Pr., Inc.

Salzmann, Mary Elizabeth. Flashy Fish. Nobens, C. A., illus. 2007. (Perfect Pets Ser.). 24p. (J). (gr. k-3). lib. bdg. 19.93 (***978-1-59928-747-8(1)*** , SandCastle) ABDO Publishing Co.

Silverstein, Alvin, et al. Fabulous Fish. 2003. (What a Pet! Ser.). (Illus.). 48p. (gr. 5-8). lib. bdg. 23.90 (978-0-7613-2514-7(X) , Millbrook Pr.) Lerner Publishing Group.

Weingartz, Jill. Aquariums. 2001. (Created Environments Ser.). (Illus.). 24p. (J). 21.35 (978-1-58340-104-0(0)) Smart Apple Media.

Williams, Colleen Madonna Flood. My Adventure at the Sea Life Park. 2007. 44p. (J). 8.99 (978-1-59092-578-2(5) , Orchard Academy Pr.) Windstorm Creative.

Williams, Sarah, et al. 101 Facts about Tropical Fish. 2001. (One Hundred One Facts about Pets Ser.). (Illus.). 32p. (J). (gr. 3 up). lib. bdg. 23.33 (978-0-8368-2892-4(5)) Stevens, Gareth Inc.

Wolfsheimer, Gene. Siamese Fighting Fish. 1999. (Fish). (Illus.). 64p. (YA). (gr. 4-7). lib. bdg. 19.75 (978-0-7910-5088-0(2) , Chelsea Hse.) Facts On File, Inc.

Wood, Selina. Fish. 2006. (Owning a Pet Ser.). (J). (978-1-59771-057-2(1)) Sea-To-Sea Pubns.

AQUATIC ANIMALS

see also Fresh-Water Animals; Marine Animals

Aquatic Animals, 8 vols., set. 2002. (Zoobooks). (Illus.). (J). (gr. k-7). pap. 19.80 (978-1-888153-68-2(7)) Wildlife Education, Ltd.

Arnosky, Jim. Hook, Line & Seeker: A Beginner's Guide to Fishing, Boating & Watching Water Wildlife. Arnosky, Jim, illus. 2005. (Hook, Line & Seeker Ser.). (Illus.). 192p. (J). pap. 12.95 (978-0-439-45584-8(7) , Scholastic Reference) Scholastic, Inc.

Baker, Charles F., ed. Water Animals. 2005. (Illus.). 32p. (J). 17.95 (978-0-8126-7927-4(X)) Cobblestone Publishing Co.

Basic Exploring Ocean Ecosystems Set. 2002. (Zoobooks). (Illus.). (J). (gr. k-7). mass mkt. 34.95 (978-1-888153-70-5(9)) Wildlife Education, Ltd.

Bertolucci, Cristiano, et al. Animals above & below Water. Bartolozzi, Alle, illus. 2004. (Contrasts Ser.). 32p. (J). (gr. 1-4). 14.95 (978-1-57768-524-1(5) , Waterbird Bks.) School Specialty Publishing.

Bingham, Caroline & Dorling Kindersley Publishing Staff. Whales & Dolphins. 2003. (Eye Wonder Ser.). (Illus.). 48p. (J). lib. bdg. 17.99 (978-0-7894-9613-3(5)) Dorling Kindersley Publishing, Inc.

Blaxland, Beth. Crustaceans: Crabs, Crayfishes, & Their Relatives. 2002. (Invertebrates Ser.). (Illus.). 32p. (gr. 4-8). 28.00 (978-0-7910-6994-3(X) , Chelsea Hse.) Facts On File, Inc.

Boothroyd, Jennifer. In the Water. 2006. (First Step Nonfiction Ser.). (Illus.). 8p. (J). pap. (978-0-8225-5664-0(2) , Lerner Pubns.) Lerner Publishing Group.

Bullard, Lisa. Wet & Dry: An Animal Opposites Book. Saunders-Smith, Gail, ed. 2005. (Illus.). 32p. (J). (ps-7). 22.60 (978-0-7368-4278-5(0)) Capstone Pr., Inc.

Dorling Kindersley Publishing Staff. Rivers & Lakes. (Eye Wonder Ser.). (Illus.). 48p. (J). (gr. k-3). 2003. 9.99 (978-0-7894-9046-9(3)); 2002. lib. bdg. 17.99 (978-0-7894-9047-6(1)) Dorling Kindersley Publishing, Inc.

Dorling Kindersley Publishing Staff, contrib. by. Diving Dolphin. 2001. (Readers Ser.). (Illus.). 32p. (J). (ps-k). 14.99 (978-0-7894-7356-1(9)) Dorling Kindersley Publishing, Inc.

Feeney, Kathy. Manatees. 2004. (Our Wild World Ser.). (Illus.). 48p. (J). (gr. 2-5). pap. 7.95 (978-1-55971-778-6(5) , NorthWord Bks. for Young Readers) T&N Children's Publishing.

—Manatees. 2001. (gr. 3-6). lib. bdg. 16.40 (978-0-613-55869-3(3)) Tandem Library Bks.

Gambrell, Linda B. DK Readers Level 1: Pre - Level 1. 2003. (ps-2). lib. bdg. 11.80 (978-0-613-75170-4(1)) Tandem Library Bks.

Harcourt School Publishers Staff. Who Is in the Pond Advanced Level. 3rd ed. 2002. (Trophies Reading Program Ser.). (Illus.). pap. 5.10 (978-0-15-323040-0(1)) Harcourt Schl. Pubs.

James, Diane, et al. Bajo el Agua. 2004. (Descubre los Animales Ser.).Tr. of Underwater. (SPA., Illus.). 24p. (ps-2). 9.95 (978-1-58728-384-0(0) , Two Can Publishing) T&N Children's Publishing.

Klingel, Cynthia Fitterer & Noyed, Robert B. Manatees. 2001. (Wonder Books Ser.: Level 1). (Illus.). 24p. (J). (ps-3). 22.79 (978-1-56766-944-2(1)) Child's World, Inc.

Lithgow, John & Blackaby, Susan. Salty, Sandy, Soggy Homes: Level 2. 2007. (Lithgow Palooza Readers Ser.). (Illus.). 32p. (J). (gr. k-1). pap. 3.95 (978-0-7696-4242-0(X)) School Specialty Publishing.

May, Suellen. Invasive Aquatic & Wetland Animals. 2006. (Invasive Species Ser.). (Illus.). 104p. (J). (gr. 6-12). 30.00 (978-0-7910-9129-6(5) , Chelsea Hse.) Facts On File, Inc.

Nuzzolo, Deborah. Seaworld Preschool Funbook: Activities & Songs. 2002. (Illus.). 24p. (J). 3.99 (978-1-893698-21-5(1) , E02) SeaWorld, Inc.

Radley, Gail. Waterways. Sherlock, Jean, illus. 2003. (Vanishing from Ser.). 32p. (J). (gr. 3-5). 6.95 (978-1-57505-569-5(4)) Lerner Publishing Group.

—Waterways. 2001. (gr. 3-6). lib. bdg. 15.25 (978-0-613-64614-7(2)) Tandem Library Bks.

Rake, Jody. Ocean Animals A to Z: Aquatic AnimalZ. 2001. (Illus.). 28p. (J). per. 7.99 (978-1-893698-20-8(3) , E01, SeaWorld Bks. for Young Learners) SeaWorld, Inc.

Rechner, Amy. Out & About at the Aquarium. Shipe, Becky, illus. 2004. (Field Trips Ser.). 24p. (C). (gr. k-3). 23.93 (978-1-4048-0298-8(3)) Picture Window Bks.

Renne. Animals That Live in Water. Renne, illus. 2000. (Animals Up Close Ser.). (Illus.). 38p. (J). (gr. 3 up). lib. bdg. 24.67 (978-0-8368-2715-6(5)) Stevens, Gareth Inc.

Ring, Elizabeth. Inland Waters. 2005. (Communities in Nature Ser.). 48p. (J). (gr. 2-5). 24.95 (978-1-4103-0317-2(9) , Blackbirch Pr., Inc.) Thomson Gale.

Rosenberg, Pam. Yikes! Icky, Sticky, Gross Stuff Underwater. 2007. (Icky, Sticky, Gross-Out Bks.). 24p. (J). (gr. 2-6). 22.79 (***978-1-59296-901-2(1)***) Child's World, Inc.

Rustad, Martha E. H. Manatees. 2003. (Ocean Life Ser.). (Illus.). 24p. (J). (gr. k-1). lib. bdg. 15.93 (978-0-7368-1657-1(7) , Pebble Bks.) Capstone Pr., Inc.

Sackett, Hannah Kate & Camm, Martin. Animal Faces in the Water. 2002. (Animal Faces Ser.). (Illus.). 32p. (J). (gr. k-3). 16.95 (978-1-57768-417-6(6) , Waterbird Bks.) School Specialty Publishing.

Wallace, Karen. Diving Dolphin. 2001. (Readers Ser.). (Illus.). 32p. (J). (ps-k). pap. 3.99 (978-0-7894-7355-4(0)) Dorling Kindersley Publishing, Inc.

Windsor, Jo. Animals in the Water: Early Level Satellite Individual Title Six-Packs. (Sails Literacy Ser.). 16p. (gr. 1-2). 27.00 (978-0-7578-2917-8(1)) Rigby Education.

AQUATIC PLANTS

see also Fresh-Water Plants; Marine Plants

Rushworth, Gary. The Life Cycle of Water Plants. 2006. (Navigators Ser.). (J). pap. 38.00 (***978-1-4108-6225-9(9)***) Benchmark Education Co.

AQUATIC SPORTS

see also Boats and Boating; Canoes and Canoeing; Diving; Fishing; Sailing; Skin Diving; Swimming

Barraclough, Sue. Water Safety. 2007. (J). (***978-1-4034-9855-7(5)***); pap. (***978-1-4034-9862-5(8)***) Heinemann Library.

Budd, E. S. Jet Watercraft. 2004. (Machines at Work Ser.). 24p. (J). (ps-3). 21.36 (978-1-59296-163-4(0)) Child's World, Inc.

Carey, Craig Robert. Wave Craze. 2000. (Extreme Sports Ser.). (Illus.). (J). (978-0-606-21697-5(9)) Tandem Library Bks.

Covert, Kim. Skeleton: High-Speed Ice Sliding. 2005. (X-Sports Ser.). (Illus.). 32p. (J). 22.60 (978-0-7368-3784-2(1)) Capstone Pr., Inc.

Dallas Friday. 2007. (J). pap. 5.95 (***978-0-8225-6599-4(4)*** , First Avenue Editions) Lerner Publishing Group.

Endres, Hollie. Wakeboarding. 2007. (Illus.). 24p. (J). lib. bdg. 19.95 (978-1-60014-129-4(3)) Bellwether Media.

—Wakeboarding. 2007. (Torque: Action Sports Ser.). (Illus.). 24p. (J). (gr. 3-7). lib. bdg. 20.00 (***978-0-531-18496-7(X)*** , Children's Pr.) Scholastic Library Publishing.

Fraioli, James O. Water Sports. 2005. (Kids' Guides Ser.). (Illus.). 32p. (J). (gr. 1-5). 25.64 (978-1-59296-212-9(2)) Child's World, Inc.

Hayhurst, Chris. Wakeboarding! Throw a Tantrum. 2000. (Illus.). 64p. (YA). per. 9.95 (978-1-56254-307-5(5) , SP 3075) Saddleback Educational Publishing.

Hedlund, Stephanie F. Windsurfing. 2003. (X-Treme Sports Ser.). (Illus.). 32p. (J). (gr. k-6). lib. bdg. 22.78 (978-1-57765-931-0(7)) ABDO Publishing Co.

Pendziwol, Jean. Treasure at Sea for Dragon & Me: Water Safety for Kids (and Dragons) Gourbault, Martine, illus. 2005. 32p. (J). (ps-2). (978-1-55337-721-4(4)) Kids Can Pr., Ltd.

Perry, Phyllis Jean. Boardsailing. 2000. (Extreme Sports Ser.). (Illus.). 48p. (J). (gr. 3-4). lib. bdg. 21.26 (978-0-7368-0481-3(1) , Capstone High-Interest Bks.) Capstone Pr., Inc.

Peterson, Christine. Wakeboarding. 2005. (Blazers—To the Extreme Ser.). (Illus.). 149p. (J). 19.33 (978-0-7368-3788-0(4)) Capstone Pr., Inc.

Savage, Jeff. Dallas Friday. 2007. (Amazing Athletes Ser.). (J). 23.93 (978-0-8225-6595-6(1) , Lerner Pubns.) Lerner Publishing Group.

Thompson, Luke. Jet Ski. 2001. (High Interest Bks.). (Illus.). 48p. (YA). (gr. 7-12). pap. 6.95 (978-0-516-23264-5(9) , Children's Pr.) Scholastic Library Publishing.

—Jet Ski. 2001. (gr. 7-12). lib. bdg. 15.25 (978-0-613-52103-1(X)) Tandem Library Bks.

Turner, Brock. Dash! Crash! Splash! Dickson, David, illus. 2006. 64p. (J). (gr. 2-4). 19.95 (978-1-4048-1662-6(3)) Picture Window Bks.

Water Safety. 2000. (Adventures in the Roo World - Young Roo Ser.: Vol. 5). 24p. (J). pap. (978-0-9652579-5-4(9)) Roo Pubns.

Woods, Bob. Water Sports. 2003. (Extreme Sports Ser.). (Illus.). 24p. (J). (gr. 2 up). lib. bdg. 22.00 (978-0-8368-3727-8(4)) Stevens, Gareth Inc.

AQUATIC SPORTS—FICTION

Hobbs, Will. River Thunder. 1999. (Learn-Along Board Bks. Ser.). 224p. (YA). (gr. 7-12). pap. 5.99 (978-0-440-22681-9(3) , Laurel Leaf) Random Hse. Children's Bks.

Jones, Penri. Dan Leuad Llyn. 2005. (WEL.). 196p. pap. (978-0-86243-028-3(3)) Y Lolfa.

McEwan, Jamie. Whitewater Scrubs. Margeson, John, illus. 2005. 64p. (J). (gr. 4-7). per. 14.99 (978-1-58196-038-9(7)) Darby Creek Publishing.

Strasser, Todd. Take Off. 2004. 320p. (YA). pap. 5.99 (978-0-689-87029-3(9) , Simon Pulse) Simon & Schuster Children's Publishing.

AQUATIC SPORTS—SAFETY MEASURES

Hill, Mary. Signs at the Pool. 2003. (Welcome Bks.). (Illus.). 24p. (J). (ps-2). pap. 4.95 (978-0-516-24367-2(5) , Children's Pr.) Scholastic Library Publishing.

Pendziwol, Jean E., et al. A Treasure at Sea for Dragon & Me: Water Safety for Kids (and Dragons) 2006. (Illus.). 32p. 6.95 (978-1-55337-880-8(6)) Kids Can Pr., Ltd. CAN. *Dist:* Wybel Marketing Group.

Raatma, Lucia. Water Safety. 2003. (Living Well). (Illus.). 32p. (J). (gr. 2-6). 27.07 (978-1-59296-090-3(1)) Child's World, Inc.

ARAB COUNTRIES

Anderson, Marilyn D. Arab Americans. 2006. (World Almanac Library of American Immigration). (Illus.). 48p. (J). pap. (978-0-8368-7320-7(3)); lib. bdg. (978-0-8368-7307-8(6)) Stevens, Gareth Inc. (World Almanac Library).

Beardwood, Mary. Children's Encyclopedia of Arabia. 2002. (Illus.). 16p. (J). (gr. 4-7). 29.95 (978-1-900988-33-9(X)) Interlink Publishing Group, Inc.

Cromwell, Sharon. Arab Americans. 2008. (J). (***978-1-60044-610-8(8)***) Rourke Publishing, LLC.

Losleben, Elizabeth. The Bedouin of the Middle East. 2005. (First Peoples Ser.). (Illus.). 48p. (gr. 4-8). lib. bdg. 23.95 (978-0-8225-0663-8(7)) Lerner Publishing Group.

Marín-Guzman, Roberto & Zéraoui, Zidane. Arab Immigration in Mexico in the Nineteenth & Twentieth Centuries: Assimilation & Arab Heritage. 2003. (Illus.). 208p. per. 18.95 (978-0-9636882-2-4(7)) Augustine Pr.

McCoy, Lisa. Bahrain. 2003. (Modern Middle East Nations & Their Strategic Place in the World Ser.). (Illus.). 112,128p. (YA). (gr. 7 up). lib. bdg. (978-1-59084-522-6(6)) Mason Crest Pubs.

Orr, Tamra. Qatar. 2008. (Cultures of the World Ser.). (J). lib. bdg. (***978-0-7614-2566-3(7)*** , Benchmark Bks.) Cavendish, Marshall Corp.

Schur, Joan Brodsky. The Arab Americans. 2004. (Immigrants in America Ser.). (Illus.). 112p. (J). 29.95 (978-1-59018-075-4(5) , Lucent Bks.) Thomson Gale.

Sonneborn, Liz. United Arab Emirates. 2007. (Enchantment of the World, Second Ser.). 144p. (J). spiral bd. 37.00 (***978-0-531-18487-5(0)*** , Children's Pr.) Scholastic Library Publishing.

Spilsbury, Louise & Spilsbury, Richard. The Islamic Empires. 2007. (J). (***978-1-4109-2911-2(6)***); pap. (***978-1-4109-2917-4(5)***) Steck-Vaughn.

ARAB-ISRAEL WAR, 1967

see Israel-Arab War, 1967

ARAB-JEWISH RELATIONS

see Jewish-Arab Relations

ARABIA

see Arabian Peninsula

ARABIAN PENINSULA

Beardwood, Mary. Childrens Encyclopaedia of Arabia. 2006. (Illus.). 152p. 39.95 (***978-1-905299-21-8(4)***) Stacey International Pubs. GBR. *Dist:* Brown, David Bk. Co., The.

Cooper, Robert. Bahrain. 2000. (Cultures of the World Ser.). (Illus.). 128p. (gr. 5-12). lib. bdg. 37.07 (978-0-7614-1161-1(5) , Benchmark Bks.) Cavendish, Marshall Corp.

Johnson, Julia. A Is for Arabia. Styles, Emily, illus. 2004. 32p. 12.95 (978-1-900988-55-1(0)) Stacey International Pubs. GBR. *Dist:* Interlink Publishing Group, Inc.

Marcovitz, Hal. Yemen. 2003. (Modern Middle East Nations & Their Strategic Place in the World Ser.). (Illus.). 112,128p. (YA). (gr. 7 up). lib. bdg. (978-1-59084-521-9(8)) Mason Crest Pubs.

McCoy, Lisa. Qatar. 2003. (Modern Middle East Nations & Their Strategic Place in the World Ser.). (Illus.). 112,128p. (YA). (gr. 7 up). lib. bdg. (978-1-59084-523-3(4)) Mason Crest Pubs.

Sonneborn, Liz. Yemen. 2007. 144p. (J). 37.00 (***978-0-516-25296-4(8)*** , Children's Pr.) Scholastic Library Publishing.

ARABIAN PENINSULA—FICTION

Clynes, Kate. Ali Baba. Anstey, David, illus. 2005. (ENG & SWA.). 32p. (J). pap. 12.95 (978-1-84444-429-8(5)) Mantra Lingua GBR. *Dist:* Mantra Publishing, Ltd.

Croall, Marie P. & Hilinski, Clint. Ali Baba Fooling the Forty Thieves: An Arabian Tale: Story. 2008. (Graphic Myths & Legends Ser.). (J). lib. bdg. 26.60 (***978-0-8225-7525-2(6)*** , Graphic Universe) Lerner Publishing Group.

Fine, Anne. Goldnebel. Koesters-Roth, Ursula, tr. from ENG. Kernke, Gabriele, photos by. 1999. Orig. Title: A Sudden Glow of Gold. (GER., Illus.). 64p. (J). pap. (978-3-257-00853-1(8)) Diogenes Verlag AG CHE. *Dist:* International Bk. Import Service, Inc.

Gallego Garcia, Laura. The Legend of the Wandering King. 2005. (Illus.). 224p. (J). (gr. 7-17). pap. 16.95 (978-0-439-58556-9(2) , Levine, Arthur A. Bks.) Scholastic, Inc.

Gallego Garcia, Laura & Bellm, Dan. The Legend of the Wandering King. 2005. (J). (978-0-439-58557-6(0) , Levine, Arthur A. Bks.) Scholastic, Inc.

Wein, Elizabeth. The Empty Kingdom. 2008. (YA). (gr. 5). 16.99 (***978-0-670-06273-7(1)*** , Viking Juvenile) Penguin Group (USA) Inc.

Zwemer, M. Samuel. Topsy-Turvy Land (Arabia Pictured for Ch. 2006. 77.99 (***978-1-4280-4803-4(0)***); pap. 70.99 (***978-1-4280-4810-2(3)***) IndyPublish.com.

ARABIC ART

see Art, Islamic

ARABIC LANGUAGE

Adly, Muhammad S. Let's Count in Arabic, Bk. 1. 24p. (978-1-894264-46-4(0)) Al-Attique Pubs., Inc.

Al-Mouhawaka, Kira. Learn to Read Arabic. (ARA & ENG., Illus.). 68p. (J). (ps-5). pap., wbk. ed. 6.95 (978-0-86685-769-7(9)) International Bk. Ctr., Inc.

—Learn to Read Arabic: Drills. (ARA & ENG., Illus.). 68p. (J). (ps-5). pap. 6.95 (978-0-86685-770-3(2)) International Bk. Ctr., Inc.

—Learn to Read Arabic: Exercise Book. (ARA & ENG., Illus.). 68p. (J). (ps-5). pap. 7.95 (978-0-86685-407-8(X)) International Bk. Ctr., Inc.

Amery, Heather. First Thousand Words in Arabic. Cartwright, Stephen, illus. 2004. (First Thousand Words Ser.). 64p. (J). 12.99 (978-0-7945-0030-6(7) , Usborne) EDC Publishing.

Corbeil, Jean-Claude, et al. Milet Bilingual Visual Dictionary: Arabic-English. 2005. (ENG & ARA., Illus.). 232p. (gr. 1-3). pap. 29.95 (978-1-84059-256-6(7)) Milet Publishing.

Dumont, Deborah, intro. Hippocrene Children's Illustrated Arabic Dictionary: English-Arabic/Arabic-English. 2002. (Children's Illustrated Foreign Language Dictionaries Ser.). (ARA & ENG., Illus.). 122p. (gr. k-5). pap. 11.95 (978-0-7818-0891-0(X)) Hippocrene Bks., Inc.

El-Halees, Yousef & Wiig, Elisabeth H. Arabic Language Screening Tests: Pre-School & School Age. unabr. ed. 2000. (ARA., Illus.). 250p. (J). (ps-8). pap. 150.00 (978-0-9638925-5-3(X)) Schema Pr., Ltd.

—Arabic Receptive-Expressive Vocabulary Test. unabr. ed. 2000. (ARA., Illus.). 200p. (J). (ps-8). pap. 150.00 (978-0-9638925-6-0(8)) Schema Pr., Ltd.

Elias, Joseph. Dictionary for Children: Arabic-Arabic. (ARA., Illus.). 378p. (J). 18.95 (978-0-86685-754-3(0)) International Bk. Ctr., Inc.

The Phoenicians. (Butterfly Bks.). (J). (gr. 4-8). 9.95 (978-0-86685-705-5(2) , LDL60E) International Bk. Ctr., Inc.

Speak Arabic: Arabic Script Version. 144p. (YA). pap. 180.00 incl. audio, VHS (978-0-88432-519-2(9) , SAR202) Norton, Jeffrey Pubs., Inc.

Speak Arabic: Transliterated Version. 160p. (YA). pap. 180.00 incl. audio, VHS (978-0-88432-518-5(0) , SAR201) Norton, Jeffrey Pubs., Inc.

ARABS

see also Bedouins

Carew-Miller, Anna. The Palestinians. 2003. (Modern Middle East Nations & Their Strategic Place in the World Ser.). (Illus.). 112,128p. (YA). (gr. 7 up). lib. bdg. (978-1-59084-513-4(7)) Mason Crest Pubs.

McCoy, Lisa. United Arab Emirates. 2003. (Modern Middle East Nations & Their Strategic Place in the World Ser.). (Illus.). 112,128p. (YA). (gr. 7 up). lib. bdg. (978-1-59084-514-1(5)) Mason Crest Pubs.

Rosaler, Maxine. Hamas: (Rev) Palestinian Terrorists. 2005. (Illus.). 64p. (J). (ps-7). lib. bdg. 26.50 (978-1-4042-0634-2(5)) Rosen Publishing Group, Inc., The.

Sharp, Anne Wallace. The Palestinians. 2004. (Lucent Library of Conflict in the Middle East). (Illus.). 112p. (J). (gr. 7-10). 29.95 (978-1-59018-493-6(9) , Lucent Bks.) Thomson Gale.

Stotsky, Sandra, ed. The Arab Americans. 1999. (Immigrant Experience Ser.). (Illus.). 110p. (YA). (gr. 4-7). 21.95 (978-0-7910-5051-4(3)) ; pap. 13.25 (978-0-7910-5053-8(X)) Facts On File, Inc. (Chelsea Hse.).

Temple, Bob. The Arab Americans. 2002. (Welcome to America Ser.). (Illus.). 64p. (J). (gr. 5 up). lib. bdg. (978-1-59084-102-0(6)) Mason Crest Pubs.

ARABS—FICTION

Croall, Marie. Sinbad. Hilinski, Clint, illus. 2007. (Graphic Myths & Legends Ser.). 48p. (J). (gr. 4-8). 26.60 (978-0-8225-6375-4(4)) Lerner Publishing Group.

Fairy Tale- Aladdin. 2005. (J). bds. (978-1-4194-0037-7(1)) Paradise Pr., Inc.

Samira's Eid. 2004. (ENG & KUR.). (J). (978-1-84444-667-4(0)) Mantra Publishing, Ltd.

Sasson, Jean. Ester's Child. 2003. (gr. 7-12). lib. bdg. 22.20 (978-0-613-70913-2(6)) Tandem Library Bks.

Siks, Geraldine B. Ali Baba & the Forty Thieves. (Illus.). (YA). (gr. 6-12). 6.00 (978-0-87602-103-3(8)) Anchorage Pr.

Yamani, Muhammad Abdo. A Boy from Makkah, Vol. 1. Mohiuddin, Khadija & De Backer, Talha, eds. Lipton, Abdallah, illus. novel ed. 2002. 149p. (J). 10.00 (978-1-56316-057-8(9)) IQRA International Educational Foundation.

ARABS—HISTORY

Marschner, Janice. California's Arab Americans. 2003. (Illus.). 160p. lib. bdg. 18.95 (978-0-9677069-7-9(1)) Coleman Ranch Pr.

Schur, Joan Brodsky. The Arabs. 2004. (gr. 10-12). 22.45 (978-0-7377-2149-2(9) , Greenhaven Pr., Inc.) Thomson Gale.

Schur, Joan Brodsky, ed. The Arabs. 2004. (Illus.). 218p. (YA). (gr. 10-13). lib. bdg. 34.95 (978-0-7377-2148-5(0) , Greenhaven Pr., Inc.) Thomson Gale.

ARBOR DAY

Ansary, Mir Tamim. Arbor Day. (Holiday Histories Ser.). (Illus.). 32p. (J). 2006. (***978-1-4034-8882-4(7)***); 2001. lib. bdg. 21.36 (978-1-58810-219-5(X)) Heinemann Library.

—Arbor Day. 2001. (Holiday Histories Ser.). 13.75 (978-0-606-22383-6(5)) Tandem Library Bks.

Ansary, Tamim. Arbor Day. 2002. (Holiday Histories Ser.). (Illus.). 32p. (J). (gr. k-2). pap. 6.95 (978-1-58810-569-1(5) , 91684) Heinemann Library.

Beaty, Sandy & Wilkerson, J. L. Champion of Arbor Day: J. Sterling Morton. Parkison, Jami, ed. 1999. (Great Heartlanders Ser.). (Illus.). 130p. (YA). (gr. 4-12). pap. 8.95 (978-0-9664470-1-9(8)) Acorn Bks.

Bennett, Kelly. Arbor Day. 2003. (Rookie Read-About Holidays Ser.). (Illus.). 32p. (J). (gr. 1-2). 20.50 (978-0-516-22861-7(7)); pap. 5.95 (978-0-516-27754-7(5)) Scholastic Library Publishing. (Children's Pr.).

—Arbor Day. 2003. (gr. k-3). lib. bdg. 14.10 (978-0-613-59571-1(8)) Tandem Library Bks.

Cooper, Jason. Arbor Day. 2002. (Illus.). 24p. (J). lib. bdg. 20.64 (978-1-58952-217-6(6)) Rourke Publishing, LLC.

ARCHAEOLOGISTS

Fagan, Brian. Archaeologists: Explorers of the Human Past. 2003. (Oxford Profiles Ser.). (Illus.). 192p. (YA). (ps-3). 50.00 (978-0-19-511946-6(0)) Oxford Univ. Pr., Inc.

Inserra, Rose. Archaeologists. 2004. (J). lib. bdg. 27.10 (978-1-58340-544-4(5)) Smart Apple Media.

Pickering, Robert. In the Footsteps of the Mummy: The Journal of an Archaeologist. Gemmell, Alice, illus. 2002. 64p. (gr. 3-7). pap. 14.95 (978-1-57098-383-2(6)) Rinehart, Roberts Pubs.

Schlitz, Laura Amy. The Hero Schliemann: The Dreamer Who Dug up Troy. Byrd, Robert, illus. 2006. 80p. (J). (gr. 4-8). 17.99 (978-0-7636-2283-1(4)) Candlewick Pr.

Spilsbury, Louise & Spilsbury, Richard. Scientists at Work: History Detectives: Archaeologists Hardback. 2007. (Illus.). 32p. (J). (***978-0-431-14924-0(0)***) Heinemann Library.

—Scientists at Work: History Detectives: Archaeologists Paperback. 2007. (Illus.). 32p. (J). (***978-0-431-14931-8(3)***) Heinemann Library.

ARCHAEOLOGY

see also Arms and Armor; Art, Primitive; Bible—Antiquities; Bronzes; Christian Art and Symbolism; Cities and Towns, Ruined, Extinct, Etc.; Classical Antiquities; Cliff Dwellers and Cliff Dwellings; Ethnology; Excavations (Archaeology); Funeral Rites and Ceremonies; Gems; Heraldry; Indians of North America—Antiquities; Mounds and Mound Builders; Mummies; Numismatics; Pottery; Prehistoric Peoples; Pyramids; Stone Age; Temples

also subdivision Antiquities under names of countries, cities, etc.

Anderson, Dale. How Do We Know the Nature of Humankind. 2005. (Great Scientific Questions & the Scientists Who Answered Them Ser.). (Illus.). 112p. (J). (gr. 7-12). lib. bdg. 26.50 (978-1-4042-0077-7(0)) Rosen Publishing Group, Inc., The.

Armentrout, David & Armentrout, Patricia. Treasures from China. 2000. (Treasures from the Past Ser.). (Illus.). 48p. (J). (gr. 4-8). lib. bdg. 29.93 (978-1-55916-288-3(0)) Rourke Publishing, LLC.

—Treasures from Egypt. 2000. (Treasures from the Past Ser.). (Illus.). 48p. (J). (gr. 4-8). lib. bdg. 29.93 (978-1-55916-289-0(9)) Rourke Publishing, LLC.

—Treasures from Greece. 2000. (Treasures from the Past Ser.). (Illus.). 48p. (J). (gr. 4-8). lib. bdg. 29.93 (978-1-55916-291-3(0)) Rourke Publishing, LLC.

—Treasures from Italy. 2000. (Treasures from the Past Ser.). (Illus.). 48p. (J). (gr. 4-8). lib. bdg. 29.93 (978-1-55916-292-0(9)) Rourke Publishing, LLC.

—Treasures from Mexico. 2000. (Treasures from the Past Ser.). (Illus.). 48p. (J). (gr. 4-8). lib. bdg. 29.93 (978-1-55916-290-6(2)) Rourke Publishing, LLC.

—Treasures from Spain. 2000. (Treasures from the Past Ser.). (Illus.). 48p. (J). (gr. 4-8). lib. bdg. 29.93 (978-1-55916-293-7(7)) Rourke Publishing, LLC.

Bailey, Linda. Adventures in the Ice Age. Slavin, Bill, illus. 2005. (Good Times Travel Agency Ser.). 48p. (YA). (gr. 3-7). (978-1-55337-504-3(1)) Kids Can Pr., Ltd.

Barnes, Trevor. Archaeology. (Kingfisher Knowledge Ser.). (Illus.). 64p. (J). 2007. pap. 8.95 (***978-0-7534-6158-7(7)***); 2004. (gr. 4-8). 12.95 (978-0-7534-5768-9(7)) Houghton Mifflin Co. Trade & Reference Div. (Kingfisher).

Barrett, Katherine, et al. Investigating Artifacts: Making Masks, Creating Myths, Exploring Middens. Bergman, Lincoln et al, eds. Klofkorn, Lisa, illus. Hoyt, Richard, photos by. 2000. (Great Explorations in Math & Science Ser.). 120p. (J). reprint ed. pap., tchr. ed. 13.50 (978-0-924886-49-2(8) , GEMS) Univ. of California, Berkeley, Lawrence Hall of Science.

Behr, Alexandra. Lost in Time. 2005. (Real Deal Ser.). (Illus.). 32p. (J). 18.50 (978-0-7910-8771-8(9) , Chelsea Hse.) Facts On File, Inc.

Bodies from the Past. 2000. (Digging Up the Past Ser.). 48p. (J). (gr. 4-7). lib. bdg. (978-0-8172-4641-9(X)) Raintree.

Bowkett, L. C. Classical Archaeology in the Field: Approaches. (Illus.). ix, 138p. pap. 18.00 (978-1-85399-617-7(3)) Bristol Classical Pr. GBR. *Dist:* International Publishers Marketing.

Cassells, E. Steve. Tracing the Past: Archaeology along the Rocky Mountain Expansion Loop Pipeline, 1. 2003. (Illus.). 40p. 6.95 (978-0-9743137-0-2(X)) Alpine Archaeological Consultants, Inc.

Cutchins, Judy. Ice Age Giants of the South. 2000. (Southern Fossil Discoveries Ser.: Vol. 1). (Illus.). 48p. (J). (gr. 3-7). 14.95 (978-1-56164-195-6(2)) Pineapple Pr., Inc.

Davidson, Avelyn & Morrison, Yvonne. Carved in Stone: Clues about Cultures. 2007. (Shockwave: Arts & Culture Ser.). (Illus.). 36p. (J). (gr. 4-6). lib. bdg. 25.00 (***978-0-531-17785-3(8)*** , Children's Pr.) Scholastic Library Publishing.

De Magalhaes, Roberto Carvalho. Prehistory. 2000. (Art & Civilization Ser.). (Illus.). 40p. (J). (gr. 3 up). 16.95 (978-0-87226-615-5(X) , 6615XB, Bedrick, Peter Bks.) School Specialty Publishing.

Devereux, Paul. Archaeology: The Study of Our Past. 2002. (Investigating Science Ser.). (Illus.). 36p. (J). (gr. 4 up). lib. bdg. 24.67 (978-0-8368-3228-0(0)) Stevens, Gareth Inc.

Dig This! How Archaeologists Uncover Our Past. 2003. (Illus.). 96p. (J). 17.95 (978-1-58013-078-3(X)) Kar-Ben Publishing.

Dixon, Dougal. Dinosaur Dig. 2003. (History Hunters Ser.). (Illus.). 32p. (J). (gr. 3 up). lib. bdg. 24.67 (978-0-8368-3739-1(8)) Stevens, Gareth Inc.

Fisher, Enid Broderick. The Great Dinosaur Record Book. Grant, Richard, illus. 1998. 32p. (J). (gr. 4 up). lib. bdg. 22.60 (978-0-8368-2176-5(9)) Stevens, Gareth Inc.

Green, Tamara. Cretaceous Dinosaur World. Grant, Richard, illus. 1998. 32p. (J). (gr. 4 up). lib. bdg. 22.60 (978-0-8368-2173-4(4)) Stevens, Gareth Inc.

—Jurassic Dinosaur World. Grant, Richard, illus. 1998. 32p. (J). (gr. 4 up). lib. bdg. 22.60 (978-0-8368-2174-1(2)) Stevens, Gareth Inc.

Greenberg, Lorna & Horwitz, Margot F. Digging into the Past: Pioneers of Archeology. 2001. (Lives in Science Ser.). (Illus.). 128p. (YA). (gr. 8-12). 21.50 (978-0-531-11857-3(6) , Watts, Franklin) Scholastic Library Publishing.

Greene, Meg. Buttons, Bones & the Organ Grinder's Monkey: Tales of Historical Archaeology. 2001. (Illus.). 128p. (J). (gr. 7 up). 25.00 (978-0-208-02498-5(0) , Linnet Bks.) Shoe String Pr., Inc.

Grolier Educational Staff, contrib. by. Ancient Civilizations. 2000. (J). (978-0-7172-9473-2(0) , Grolier) Scholastic Library Publishing.

Halls, Kelly Milner. Mysteries of the Mummy Kids. 2007. (Illus.). 72p. (J). (gr. 4-8). 18.95 (***978-1-58196-059-4(X)***) Darby Creek Publishing.

Holdcroft, Tina. Hidden Treasures: Amazing Stories of Discovery. Holdcroft, Tina, illus. 2003. (Hidden! Ser.). (Illus.). 32p. (J). (gr. 2-5). pap. 6.95 (978-1-55037-802-3(3)); lib. bdg. 19.95 (978-1-55037-803-0(1)) Annick Pr., Ltd. CAN. *Dist:* Firefly Bks., Ltd.

—Hidden Treasures: Amazing Stories of Discovery. 2003. (gr. 3-6). lib. bdg. 15.25 (978-0-613-78464-1(2)) Tandem Library Bks.

Inserra, Rose. Archaeologists. 2004. (J). lib. bdg. 27.10 (978-1-58340-544-4(5)) Smart Apple Media.

Kirkpatrick, Naida. The Maya. 2003. (Understanding People in the Past Ser.). (Illus.). 64p. (J). pap. 28.50 (978-1-4034-0386-5(4)) Heinemann Library.

Lauber, Patricia. Who Came First? New Clues to Prehistoric Americans. 2003. (Illus.). 64p. (J). (gr. 5). 18.95 (978-0-7922-8228-0(0)' , National Geographic Children's Bks.) National Geographic Society.

Malam, John. Gladiator's Secret. 2003. (History Hunters Ser.). (Illus.). 32p. (J). (gr. 3 up). lib. bdg. 24.67 (978-0-8368-3741-4(X)) Stevens, Gareth Inc.

McIntosh, Jane. Archeology. 2000. (Eyewitness Bks.). (Illus.). 64p. (J). (gr. 4-7). 15.99 (978-0-7894-5864-3(0)) Dorling Kindersley Publishing, Inc.

McIntosh, Jane & Dorling Kindersley Publishing Staff. Archeology. 2000. (Eyewitness Bks.). (Illus.). 64p. (J). (gr. 4-7). lib. bdg. 19.99 (978-0-7894-6605-1(8)) Dorling Kindersley Publishing, Inc.

Mitchell, Mark. Raising la Belle. Mitchell, Mark, illus. (Professor Wigglestix & the Weather Ser.). (Illus.). 112p. 10.95 (978-1-57168-703-6(3)) Eakin Pr.

Nathan, Emma. Lugares Conocidos. 2002. (Abre los Ojos y Aprende Serie).Tr. of Eyeopeners: Landmarks. (SPA.). 24p. (J). (-3). 24.94 (978-1-4103-0026-3(9) , Blackbirch Pr., Inc.) Thomson Gale.

Newton, Afton Lisette. The Mystery of the Sabotaged Dig. 2004. 100p. (J). per. 4.99 (978-0-9762326-0-5(X)) ACT-New Bks.

Nicholson, Robert & Watts, Claire. Los Egipcios. 2004. (Interfact Ser.). (SPA., Illus.). 48p. (J). (gr. 3-6). 14.95 incl. cd-rom (978-1-58728-975-0(X) , Two Can Publishing) T&N Children's Publishing.

—Los Egipcios: El Libro Y El Que Interactuan. 2004. (Interfact Ser.). (SPA., Illus.). 32p. (J). (gr. 2-7). pap. 9.95 (978-1-58728-474-8(X) , Two Can Publishing) T&N Children's Publishing.

O'Connor, Jane. The Emperor's Silent Army: Terracotta Warriors of Ancient China. 2002. (Illus.). 48p. (J). (gr. 4-6). 17.99 (978-0-670-03512-0(2) , Viking Juvenile) Penguin Group (USA) Inc.

Orna-Ornstein, John. Archaeology: Discovering the Past. 2002. (Illus.). 48p. (YA). 21.95 (978-0-19-521909-8(0)) Oxford Univ. Pr., Inc.

Osborne, Will & Osborne, Mary Pope. Mummies & Pyramids: A Nonfiction Companion to Mummies in the Morning. 2001. (Magic Tree House Research Guide Ser.: No. 3). (Illus.). (J). (gr. k-3). (978-0-606-20781-2(3)) Tandem Library Bks.

Panchyk, Richard. Archaeology for Kids: Uncovering the Mysteries of Our Past. 2001. (For Kids Ser.). (Illus.). 160p. (J). pap. 14.95 (978-1-55652-395-3(5)) Chicago Review Pr., Inc.

Patent, Dorothy Hinshaw. The Incredible Story of China's Buried Warriors. 2000. (Frozen in Time Ser.). (Illus.). (J). (gr. 5-9). lib. bdg. 27.07 (978-0-7614-0783-6(9) , Benchmark Bks.) Cavendish, Marshall Corp.

—Treasures of the Spanish Main. 2000. (Frozen in Time Ser.). (Illus.). (J). (gr. 5-9). lib. bdg. 28.50 (978-0-7614-0786-7(3) , Benchmark Bks.) Cavendish, Marshall Corp.

Phillips, Dee. Sunken Treasure. 2003. (History Hunters Ser.). (Illus.). 32p. (J). (gr. 3 up). lib. bdg. 24.67 (978-0-8368-3743-8(6)) Stevens, Gareth Inc.

Pickering, Robert. In the Footsteps of the Mummy: The Journal of an Archaeologist. Gemmell, Alice, illus. 2002. 64p. (gr. 3-7). pap. 14.95 (978-1-57098-383-2(6)) Rinehart, Roberts Pubs.

Pirotta, Saviour. Buried Treasure. 2003. (Mysteries of the Past Ser.). (Illus.). 32p. pap. 7.95 (978-1-4109-0061-6(4)) Raintree.

Rinaldo, Denise. Cities of the Dead: Finding Lost Civilizations. 2008. (24/7: Science Behind the Scenes: Mystery Files Ser.). 64p. (J). pap. 7.95 (***978-0-531-18739-5(X)*** , Watts, Franklin) Scholastic Library Publishing.

Scarre, Chris & Stefoff, Rebecca. The Palace of Minos at Knossos. 2003. (Digging for the Past Ser.). (Illus.). 48p. (YA). 22.95 (978-0-19-514272-3(1)) Oxford Univ. Pr., Inc.

Shone, Rob. Ancient Treasures. Spender, Nick, illus. 2007. (Graphic Discoveries Ser.). (J). 48p. (gr. 3-7). lib. bdg. (***978-1-4042-1089-9(X)***); (***978-1-4042-9594-0(1)***); pap. (***978-1-4042-9593-3(3)***) Rosen Publishing Group, Inc., The.

Smith, Stuart Tyson & Bernard, Nancy S. The Valley of the Kings. 2002. (Digging for the Past Ser.). (Illus.). 48p. (YA). 22.95 (978-0-19-514770-4(7)) Oxford Univ. Pr., Inc.

Spilsbury, Louise & Spilsbury, Richard. Scientists at Work: History Detectives: Archaeologists Hardback. 2007. (Illus.). 32p. (J). (***978-0-431-14924-0(0)***) Heinemann Library.

—Scientists at Work: History Detectives: Archaeologists Paperback. 2007. (Illus.). 32p. (J). (***978-0-431-14931-8(3)***) Heinemann Library.

Taylor, Barbara & MacDonald, Fiona. Mummies & Tombs. 2000. (Discovery Ser.). (Illus.). 64p. (gr. 3-7). 14.95 (978-0-7548-0505-2(0) , Lorenz Bks.) Anness Publishing GBR. *Dist:* National Bk. Network.

Thompson, Gare. Monitor: The Iron Warship That Changed the World. Day, Larry, illus. 2003. (All Aboard Reading Ser.). 48p. (J). (gr. 4-4). pap. 3.99 (978-0-448-43245-8(5) , Grosset & Dunlap) Penguin Group (USA) Inc.

—Monitor: The Iron Warship That Changed the World. 2003. (gr. k-3). lib. bdg. 11.80 (978-0-613-72533-0(6)) Tandem Library Bks.

Wheatley, Abigail & Reid, Struan. Archaeology Internet Linked. 2005. 128p. (J). 19.95 (978-0-7945-0806-7(5) , Usborne) EDC Publishing.

Wilcox, Charlotte. Animal Mummies: Preserved Through the Ages. 2002. (Mummies Ser.). (Illus.). 32p. (J). (gr. 3-4). lib. bdg. 21.26 (978-0-7368-1305-1(5) , Capstone High-Interest Bks.) Capstone Pr., Inc.

—Mummies, Bones & Body Parts. (Photo Bks.). (Illus.). 64p. (J). 2003. (gr. 3-6). 7.95 (978-1-57505-486-5(8)); 2000. (gr. 4-7). 25.26 (978-1-57505-428-5(0) , Carolrhoda Bks.) Lerner Publishing Group.

Woolf, Alex. History Mysteries. 2004. (Forensic Files Ser.). (Illus.). 48p. (J). lib. bdg. (978-1-4034-4830-9(2)) Heinemann Library.

—Investigating History Mysteries. 2004. (Forensic Files Ser.). (Illus.). 48p. (J). pap. 8.50 (978-1-4034-5470-6(1)) Heinemann Library.

ARCHAEOLOGY, BIBLICAL

see Bible—Antiquities

ARCHAEOLOGY, CLASSICAL

see Classical Antiquities

ARCHAEOLOGY—FICTION

Barrett, Tracy. On Etruscan Time. rev. ed. 2005. 176p. (J). 17.95 (978-0-8050-7569-4(0) , Holt, Henry & Co. Bks. For Young Readers) Holt, Henry & Co.

Bernard, Virginia. Eliza & the Sacred Mountain. 2000. (Going to Ser.). (Illus.). 121p. (J). (gr. 4-8). pap. 6.95 (978-1-893577-05-3(8)) Four Corners Publishing Co., Inc.

Carson, Drew. Summer Discovery. Thatch, Nancy R., ed. Carson, Drew, illus. 1998. (Books for Students by Students). (Illus.). 29p. (J). (gr. 2-4). lib. bdg. 15.95 (978-0-933849-68-6(0)) Landmark Editions, Inc.

Erickson, John R. The Case of the Most Ancient Bone. Holmes, Gerald L., illus. 2007. (Hank the Cowdog Ser.). 192p. (J). (gr. 3). 16.99 (978-0-670-06224-9(3) , Viking Juvenile) Penguin Group (USA) Inc.

—The Case of the Most Ancient Bone, No. 50. Holmes, Gerald L., illus. 2007. (Hank the Cowdog Ser.: No. 50). 256p. (J). (gr. 3). pap. 5.99 (978-0-14-240800-1(X) , Puffin) Penguin Group (USA) Inc.

Fisher, Catherine. Darkhenge. 2007. 432p. (J). pap. 7.99 (978-0-06-078584-0(5)) HarperCollins Pubs.

Gordon, Roderick. Tunnels. 2008. 480p. (J). pap. 17.99 (***978-0-439-87177-8(8)*** , Chicken Hse., The) Scholastic, Inc.

Hapka, Cathy, et al. Curious George's Dinosaur Discovery. Hines, Anna Grossnickle, illus. 2006. 24p. (J). (ps-k). 12.95 (978-0-618-66376-7(2)); pap. 3.95 (978-0-618-66377-4(0)) Houghton Mifflin Co.

Harcourt School Publishers Staff. An Interview with Otzi Advanced Level. 3rd ed. 2002. (Trophies Reading Program Ser.). (Illus.). pap. 5.10 (978-0-15-323471-2(7)) Harcourt Schl. Pubs.

—Journey to Kush: Take-Home Book. 2001. (Collections Ser.). (Illus.). (J). pap. 1.90 (978-0-15-319555-6(X)) Harcourt Schl. Pubs.

—Journey to the Pyramids Below Level. 3rd ed. 2002. (Trophies Reading Program Ser.). (Illus.). pap. 5.10 (978-0-15-323413-2(X)) Harcourt Schl. Pubs.

Herr, Melody. Summer of Discovery. 2006. 111p. (J). pap. 10.95 (978-0-8032-2437-7(0)); 112p. pap. 10.95 (978-0-8032-7362-7(2) , A Bison Original) Univ. of Nebraska Pr.

Hill, Pamela Smith. The Last Grail Keeper. 2001. 240p. (J). (gr. 7 up). tchr. ed. 17.95 (978-0-8234-1574-8(0)) Holiday Hse., Inc.

Hobbs, William. Wild Man Island. 192p. (J). (gr. 5 up). 2003. pap. 5.99 (978-0-380-73310-1(2) , Harper Trophy); 2002. (Illus.). 19.99 (978-0-688-17473-6(6)); 2002. (Illus.). lib. bdg. 16.89 (978-0-06-029810-4(3)) HarperCollins Pubs.

—Wild Man Island. 2003. (gr. 5-8). lib. bdg. 14.15 (978-0-613-61741-3(X)) Tandem Library Bks.

Hoeye, Michael. The Sands of Time. (J). 2007. 304p. (gr. 1). pap. 7.99 (***978-0-14-240983-1(9)*** , Puffin); 2002. (Hermux Tantamoq Adventure Ser.: Bk. 2). (Illus.). 288p. (gr. 5-8). 14.99 (978-0-399-23879-6(4) , Putnam Juvenile) Penguin Group (USA) Inc.

—The Sands of Time. 2001. (Hermux Tantamoq Adventure Ser.: Bk. 2). (Illus.). (YA). (gr. 5-8). pap. 12.95 (978-0-9675111-2-2(7)) Terfle Bks.

—The Sands of Time: A Hermux Tantamoq AdventureTM. 2004. 288p. (J). (gr. 5-9). pap. 40.00 incl. audio (978-1-4000-9016-7(4) , Listening Library) Random Hse. Audio Publishing Group.

—The Sands of Time: A New Hermux Tantamoq Adventure. 2003. 288p. pap. 6.99 (978-0-14-250176-4(X) , Puffin) Penguin Group (USA) Inc.

Jones, Allan Frewin. Ghostlight, Vol. 8. 2003. 176p. (J). mass mkt. 6.99 (978-0-330-39239-6(5) , Pan) Pan Macmillan GBR. *Dist:* Trafalgar Square Publishing.

Jones, Allan Frewin. Legend of the Anaconda King. 2006. 186p. (J). pap. (*978-0-439-85670-6(1)) Scholastic, Inc.

Koops, Sheena. Voice of the Valley. 2006. 208p. (J). pap. 8.95 (978-1-55143-514-5(4)) Orca Bk. Pubs. USA.

Logan, Claudia. The 5,000-Year-Old Puzzle: Solving a Mystery at Giza. Sweet, Melissa, illus. 2001. (J). (978-0-7894-2635-2(8)) Dorling Kindersley Publishing, Inc.

—The 5,000-Year-Old Puzzle: Solving a Mystery of Ancient Egypt. Sweet, Melissa, illus. 2002. 48p. (J). 17.00 (978-0-374-32335-6(6) , Farrar, Straus & Giroux (BYR)) Farrar, Straus & Giroux.

McMurchy-Barber, Gina. Reading the Bones. 2008. 152p. (YA). pap. 9.99 (*978-1-55002-732-7(8) , Sandcastle Bks.) Dundurn Group, The CAN. *Dist:* Univ. of Toronto Pr.

Moreno, Elena. El Misterio de la Llave. 1998. (SPA.). (gr. 7-12). lib. bdg. 14.10 (978-0-613-80728-9(6)) Tandem Library Bks.

Peel, John. The Invaders. 1998. (Outer Limits Ser.: No. 5). (J). (gr. 4-7). (978-0-606-13689-1(4)) Tandem Library Bks.

Peters, Elizabeth, pseud. The Falcon at the Portal. 2000. 450p. (gr. 7-12). per. 15.90 (978-0-613-25117-4(2)) Tandem Library Bks.

Poulsen, David A. No Time Like the Past. 3rd rev. ed. 2007. (Salt & Pepper Chronicles). 160p. (gr. 3-7). pap. 6.95 (*978-1-55263-807-1(3)) Key Porter Bks. CAN. *Dist:* Perseus Distribution.

Robinson, Fay. Un Dinosaurio Llamado Sue: El Hallzgo del Siglo. 2002. (SPA., Illus.). 32p. (J). (gr. k-2). pap. 3.99 (978-0-439-42110-2(1) , Scholastic en Espanol) Scholastic, Inc.

Russell, Elaine. Martin Mcmillan & the Lost Inca City. Cornell du Houx, Emily M. D., illus. 2005. 128p. (gr. 5 up). pap. 10.00 (978-1-882190-86-7(6)) Polar Bear & Co.

Stanley, Diane. A Time Apart. 1999. (Illus.). 256p. (J). (gr. 5 up). 15.95 (978-0-688-16997-8(X)) HarperCollins Pubs.

Stine, Megan. Power of the Rat. 2002. (gr. 3-6). lib. bdg. 13.00 (978-0-613-72454-8(2)) Tandem Library Bks.

Thomas, Jerry D. The Red Hat Mystery. Odell, Lad, illus. 2003. (Detective Zack Ser.). 132p. (J). pap., pap. 6.99 (978-0-7814-3802-5(0) , 0781438020) Cook, David C. Publishing Co.

—The Secrets in the Sand. Odell, Lad, illus. 2003. (Detective Zack Ser.). 132p. (J). pap., pap. 6.99 (978-0-7814-3803-2(9) , 0781438039) Cook, David C. Publishing Co.

West, Tracey. Mr. Peale's Bones. 2000. (gr. 3-6). lib. bdg. 14.10 (978-0-613-80357-1(4)) Tandem Library Bks.

ARCHAEOLOGY—HISTORY

Allison, Amy. Machu Picchu. 2003. (Building History Ser.). (Illus.). 112p. (YA). 32.45 (978-1-59018-020-4(8) , Lucent Bks.) Thomson Gale.

Conley, Kate A. Digging up Greece. 2005. (Life in Ancient Days: Greece Ser.). (J). (978-1-59197-864-0(5)) ABDO Publishing Co.

Patent, Dorothy Hinshaw. Frozen in Time - Group 1, 3 bks., Set. Incl. In Search of the Maiasaurs. 1998. lib. bdg. 28.50 (978-0-7614-0787-4(1) , Benchmark Bks.); Mystery of the Lascaux Cave. 64p. 1998. lib. bdg. 28.50 (978-0-7614-0784-3(7)); Secrets of the Ice Man. 72p. 1999. lib. bdg. 28.50 (978-0-7614-0782-9(0) , Benchmark Bks.); (J). (gr. 5-9). (Illus.). 1999. Set lib. bdg. 81.21 (978-0-7614-0781-2(2) , Benchmark Bks.) Cavendish, Marshall Corp.

ARCHAEOLOGY—VOCATIONAL GUIDANCE

Bryan, Betsy M. & Cohen, Judith Love. You Can Be a Woman Egyptologist. Martin, Janice, ed. Katz, David Arthur, illus. rev. ed. 1999. 40p. (J). (gr. 3-6). reprint ed. 13.95 (978-1-880599-45-7(7)) Cascade Pass, Inc.

Inserra, Rose. Archaeologists. 2004. (J). lib. bdg. 27.10 (978-1-58340-544-4(5)) Smart Apple Media.

ARCHEOLOGY

see Archaeology

ARCHER, JENNY (FICTITIOUS CHARACTER)—FICTION

Conford, Ellen. Get the Picture, Jenny Archer? 2000. (J). 11.79 (978-0-606-19838-7(5)) Tandem Library Bks.

—Nibble, Nibble, Jenny Archer. 1999. (978-0-606-17505-0(9)); (gr. 3-6). lib. bdg. 13.00 (978-0-613-22906-7(1)) Tandem Library Bks.

—Nibble, Nibble Jenny Archer. Palmisciano, Diane, illus. 1999. 64p. (J). (gr. 2-4). pap. 4.99 (978-0-316-15206-8(4) , Tingley, Megan Bks.) Little, Brown Bks. for Young Readers.

ARCHERY

Ascham, Roger & Ford, Horace. Toxophilus: Archery - Theory & Practice, 2 vols. in 1. Manley, Dean V., ed. 1998. (Legends of the Longbow Ser.: Vol. 6). (Illus.). 104p. reprint ed. lthr. 45.00 (978-1-56416-092-8(0)) Derrydale Pr., The.

Rowe, Ruth & Anderson, Alan. Simple Maintenance for Archery: Easy Things You Can Do to Maintain Your Equipment, 1. 2003. (Illus.). 96p. spiral bd. 11.99 (978-0-9715298-1-6(7)) Quintessential Corp.

ARCHIMEDES

Gow, Mary. Archimedes: Mathematical Genius of the Ancient World. 2005. (Great Minds of Science Ser.). (Illus.). 128p. (J). (gr. 5-8). lib. bdg. 26.60 (978-0-7660-2502-8(0)) Enslow Pubs., Inc.

Hasan, Heather. Archimedes: The Father of Mathematics. 2005. (Library of Greek Philosophers). (Illus.). 112p. (J). 33.25 (978-1-4042-0774-5(0)) Rosen Publishing Group, Inc., The.

Keating, Susan K. Archimedes: Ancient Greek Mathematician. 2002. (Great Names Ser.). (Illus.). 32p. (J). (gr. 3 up). lib. bdg. (978-1-59084-152-5(2)) Mason Crest Pubs.

Zannos, Susan. The Life & Times of Archimedes. 2004. (Biography from Ancient Civilizations Ser.). (Illus.). 48p. (J). (gr. 4-8). lib. bdg. 29.95 (978-1-58415-242-2(7)) Mitchell Lane Pubs., Inc.

ARCHITECTS

African-American Architects. 2000. (My Ancestors—My Heroes Ser.: Vol. 40). (J). (gr. 3-4). (978-1-893091-39-9(2)) Parker Publishing Co.

Architects: Artists Who Build, 4 bks. Incl. César Pelli. Anger, David. 48p. lib. bdg. 22.60 (978-1-56065-313-4(2)); Gyo Obata. Kudalis, Eric. 48p. lib. bdg. 22.60 (978-1-56065-311-0(6)); Michael Graves. Kudalis, Eric. 48p. lib. bdg. 22.60 (978-1-56065-310-3(8)); Robert A. M. Stern. Anger, David. 24p. lib. bdg. 22.60 (978-1-56065-312-7(4)); (J). (gr. 3-4). 1996. (Illus.). Set lib. bdg. 90.40 (978-1-56065-627-2(1) , Bridgestone Bks.) Capstone Pr., Inc.

Bodden, Valerie & Gehry, Frank O. Frank Gehry. 2008. (J). (*978-1-58341-662-4(5) , Creative Education) Creative Co., The.

Boekhoff, P. M. What Does a Construction Worker Do? 2006. (What Does a Community Helper Do? Ser.). (Illus.). 24p. (J). lib. bdg. 21.26 (978-0-7660-2326-0(5) , Enslow Elementary) Enslow Pubs., Inc.

Chandler, Alton. A Salute to African American Architects: Learning Activities. Chapman, Loring F., ed. Still, Wayne A., illus. 24p. (Orig.). (J). (gr. 3-8). pap. 1.75 (978-1-877804-16-8(9)) Chandler/White Publishing Co.

Englart, Mindi. Architect. 2002. (How Do I Become a... Ser.). (Illus.). 32p. (J). 23.70 (978-1-56711-686-1(8) , Blackbirch Pr., Inc.) Thomson Gale.

Fandel, Jennifer. Frank Lloyd Wright. 2005. (Extraordinary Artists Ser.). (Illus.). 48p. (gr. 7 up). 21.95 (978-1-58341-378-4(2) , Creative Education) Creative Co., The.

Gwilliam, Heather. Livewire Real Lives Sir John Monash. 1999. (Livewires Real Lives Ser.). 32p. (gr. 6-9). pap. 6.00 (978-0-521-77629-5(5)) Cambridge Univ. Pr.

Ingram, Scott. Frank Lloyd Wright. 2003. (Raintree Biographies Ser.). (J). lib. bdg. 25.70 (978-0-7398-6866-9(7)) Raintree.

—Frank Lloyd Wright. 2003. (gr. 3-6). lib. bdg. 15.90 (978-0-613-78232-6(1)) Tandem Library Bks.

Lashnits, Tom. Maya Lin. 2007. (Asian Americans of Achievement Ser.). 128p. (YA). (gr. 6-10). lib. bdg. 30.00 (978-0-7910-9268-2(2) , Chelsea Hse.) Facts On File, Inc.

Lazo, Caroline Evensen. Frank Gehry. 2005. (Biography(R) Ser.). (Illus.). 112p. (J). (ps-7). pap. 7.95 (978-0-8225-3388-7(X)) Lerner Publishing Group.

Manatt, Kathleen. Architect. 2008. (J). pap. 7.95 (*978-1-60279-078-0(7)) Cherry Lake Publishing.

Manatt, Kathleen G. Architect. 2008. (J). lib. bdg. 25.26 (*978-1-60279-052-0(3)) Cherry Lake Publishing.

Mannis, Celeste Davidson. Julia Morgan Built a Castle. Hyman, Miles, illus. 2006. 40p. (J). (ps). 17.99 (978-0-670-05964-5(1) , Viking Adult) Penguin Group (USA) Inc.

Marsh, Carole. Frank Lloyd Wright. 2002. (One Thousand Readers Ser.). (Illus.). 12p. (J). (gr. k-4). 2.95 (978-0-635-01503-7(X) , 1503X) Gallopade International.

Matuz, Roger. Albert Kahn: Architect of Detroit. 2002. (Detroit Biography Series for Young Readers). (Illus.). 104p. (YA). (gr. 5 up). pap. 14.95 (978-0-8143-2957-3(8)) Wayne State Univ. Pr.

—Albert Kahn: Builder of Detroit. 2002. (Detroit Biography Series for Young Readers). (Illus.). 104p. (J). 27.95 (978-0-8143-2956-6(X) , Great Lakes Bks.) Wayne State Univ. Pr.

Mayo, Gretchen Will. Frank Lloyd Wright. 2004. (Trailblazers of the Modern World Ser.). (Illus.). 48p. (J). (gr. 5 up). pap. 11.95 (978-0-8368-5261-5(3)); lib. bdg. 30.00 (978-0-8368-5101-4(3)) Stevens, Gareth Inc. (World Almanac Library).

Middleton, Haydn. Frank Lloyd Wright. 2001. (Creative Lives Ser.). (Illus.). 64p. (YA). (gr. 6-8). lib. bdg. 27.07 (978-1-58810-203-4(3)) Heinemann Library.

Olmstead. I. M. Pei: A Biography. 2004. (Asian-American Biographies Ser.). (Illus.). 64p. (J). pap. 9.50 (978-1-4109-1129-2(2)) Raintree.

Poulakidas, Georgene. The Guggenheim Museum Bilbao: Transforming a City. 2004. (High Interest Bks.). (Illus.). 48p. (J). (gr. 7-12). pap. 6.95 (978-0-516-25907-9(5) , Children's Pr.) Scholastic Library Publishing.

Stinson, Kathy. Cornelia Oberlander: The Art of the Possible. 2008. 96p. 22.95 (*978-0-88776-804-0(0)) Tundra Bks., Inc./Livres Toundra, Inc. CAN. *Dist:* Random Hse. of Canada, Ltd.

Stone, Amy. Maya Lin. 2003. (Raintree Biographies Ser.). (Illus.). 32p. (J). lib. bdg. 25.70 (978-0-7398-6863-8(2)) Raintree.

—Maya Lin. 2003. (gr. 3-6). lib. bdg. 15.90 (978-0-613-78165-7(1)) Tandem Library Bks.

Winegarten, Debra L. Katherine Stinson: The Flying Schoolgirl. 2004. (Illus.). 133p. (gr. 4-7). 26.95 (978-1-57168-459-2(X)) Eakin Pr.

Wright, David K. Frank Lloyd Wright: Visionary Architect. 1999. (People to Know Ser.). (Illus.). 128p. (YA). (gr. 6-12). lib. bdg. 26.60 (978-0-7660-1032-1(5)) Enslow Pubs., Inc.

Zaunders, Bo. Gargoyles, Girders, & Glass Houses: Magnificent Master Builders. Munro, Roxie, illus. 2004. 48p. (J). (gr. 3-7). 17.99 (978-0-525-47284-1(3) , Dutton Juvenile) Penguin Group (USA) Inc.

—The Great Bridge-Building Contest. Munro, Roxie, illus. 2004. 32p. (J). (gr. k-4). 16.95 (978-0-8109-4929-4(6)) Abrams, Harry N., Inc.

—The Great Bridge-Building Contest. Munro, Roxie, illus. 2006. 30p. (J). (gr. 4-8). reprint ed. 17.00 (978-1-4223-5239-7(0)) DIANE Publishing Co.

ARCHITECTS—FICTION

Wells, Rosemary & Wells, Tom. The House in the Mail. 2004. (Illus.). 48p. (J). pap. 6.99 (978-0-14-240061-6(0) , Puffin) Penguin Group (USA) Inc.

—The House in the Mail. Andreasen, Dan, illus. 2002. 32p. (J). (gr. 1-5). 16.99 (978-0-670-03545-8(9) , Viking Juvenile) Penguin Group (USA) Inc.

ARCHITECTURAL ENGINEERING

see Building

ARCHITECTURAL PERSPECTIVE

see Perspective

ARCHITECTURE

see also Building; Castles; Cathedrals; Church Architecture; Monuments; Naval Architecture; Palaces; Skyscrapers; Synagogues; Temples; Theaters

also headings beginning with the word Architectural

Allison, Carol. Made by Humans: Astonishing Achievements. 2007. (Shockwave: Arts & Culture Ser.). (Illus.). 36p. (J). (gr. 4-6). lib. bdg. 25.00 (*978-0-531-17789-1(0) , Children's Pr.) Scholastic Library Publishing.

Arbogast, Joan Marie. Buildings in Disguise: Architecture That Looks Like Animals, Food, & Other Things, 2004. (Illus.). 48p. (J). (gr. 3-7). 16.95 (978-1-59078-099-2(X)) Boyds Mills Pr.

Beasant, Pam. Ht Draw Buildings. Ashman, Iain, illus. 2006. 32p. (J). pap. 5.99 (978-0-7945-1371-9(9) , Usborne) EDC Publishing.

Bigger, Better, Bolder! Individual Title Six-Packs. (Bookweb Ser.). 32p. (gr. 6 up). 34.00 (978-0-7578-0910-1(3)) Rigby Education.

Bode, Adrian, et al. Where We Live. 2000. (Adventures in Architecture Ser.). (ENG & GER., Illus.). 27p. (J). (gr. 3-10). 14.95 (978-3-7913-2104-2(8)) Prestel Publishing.

Brooks, Philip. Superstructures. 2002. (Inside Look Ser.). (Illus.). 48p. (J). (gr. 4 up). lib. bdg. 26.00 (978-0-8368-3177-1(2)) Stevens, Gareth Inc.

Building with Shapes. 24p. (J). 7.95 (978-0-7565-1055-8(4)) Compass Point Bks.

Buildings, 6, Pack. (Sails Literacy Ser.). (gr. 1-2). 36.00 (978-0-7578-4022-7(1)) Rigby Education.

Campadonica, Carol. How to Build a California Mission: San Juan Capistiano, 20 vols. Mueller, Bondell et al, eds. Anderson, Bill, illus. Sousa, Jay, photos by. 1998. (How to Build a California Mission Ser.). (J). (gr. 4-5). pap. (978-0-9648488-8-7(0)) Buzzard Pr. International.

Campbell, Ellen Langas. Raising the Roof. 2005. (Girls Know How Ser.: No. 2 - Construction). (Illus.). 128p. (J). pap. 4.95 (978-0-9743604-1-6(4) , GIRLS KNOW HOW) NouSoma Communications, Inc.

Campodonica, Carol A. How to Build a California Mission: Santa Barbara, 20 vols. Wardup, Shirley et al, eds. Sousa, Jay, photos by. Date not set. (How to Build a California Mission Ser.). (Illus.). (J). (gr. 4-5). pap. (978-0-9648488-3-2(X)) Buzzard Pr. International.

—How to Build a California Mission: Santa Cruz, 20 vols. Weber, Francis J. et al, eds. Anderson, Bill, illus. Anderson, Jay, photos by. Date not set. (How to Build a California Mission Ser.). (J). (gr. 4-5). pap. (978-0-9648488-5-6(6)) Buzzard Pr. International.

—How to Build the White House, Vol. 3. Scouten, Rex et al, eds. Anderson, Bill, illus. White House Historical Society Staff, photos by. 1998. 40p. (J). (gr. 4-5). pap. 19.95 (978-0-9648488-6-3(4)) Buzzard Pr. International.

Clements, Gillian. A Picture History of Great Buildings. 2008. (Illus.). 64p. (J). 19.95 (*978-1-84507-488-3(2)) Lincoln, Frances Ltd. GBR. *Dist:* Perseus Distribution.

Construction TCG. 3rd rev. ed. 2004. 56p. pap. (978-0-86657-512-6(X)) Lab-Volt Systems, Inc.

Cormand, Bernat. Barcelona, Tell Us about Gaudi. Kliczkowski, H., ed. Rifa, Fina, illus. 80p. (978-84-89439-29-0(X)) Asppan, A., S.L. Distribuidora Internacional de Libros y Revistas.

Craats, Rennay. The Science of Construction: Style, Structures, & Building. 2003. (J). lib. bdg. 27.14 (978-0-7398-6993-2(0)) Raintree.

Cruikshank, Dan. The Story of Britain's Best Buildings. Parker, John, photos by. 2003. (Illus.). 240p. (gr. 7-12). pap. 24.95 (978-1-55297-748-4(X)) Firefly Bks., Ltd.

Crum, Anna-Maria. Matematicas para construir & Math to Build On. 2005. spiral bd. 84.00 (*978-1-4108-5696-8(8)) Benchmark Education Co.

Dargie, Richard. A Roman Villa. Hook, Adam, illus. 2000. (Look Inside Ser.). 32p. (J). (gr. 4-7). lib. bdg. 25.69 (978-0-7398-2380-4(9)) Raintree.

Del cemento al puente (from Cement to Bridge) 2007. (J). pap. 4.95 (978-0-8225-6630-4(3) , Ediciones Lerner) Lerner Publishing Group.

DK Publishing. Inside-Out Buildings. 2008. 80p. (J). (gr. 8). 19.99 (*978-0-7566-3436-0(9)) Dorling Kindersley Publishing, Inc.

DuTemple, Lesley A. The Taj Mahal. 2003. (Great Building Feats Ser.). (Illus.). 96p. (J). (gr. 5-9). 27.93 (978-0-8225-4694-8(9)) Lerner Publishing Group.

Fisher, Leonard Everett. The Architects. 1999. (Colonial Craftsmen Ser.). (Illus.). 48p. (J). (gr. 4-8). lib. bdg. 21.36 (978-0-7614-0931-1(9) , Benchmark Bks.) Cavendish, Marshall Corp.

Foran, Jill. Buildings. 2004. (American Symbols Ser.). (J). pap. 6.95 (978-1-59036-175-7(X)); (Illus.). 24p. lib. bdg. 15.95 (978-1-59036-132-0(6)) Weigl Pubs., Inc.

Ganeri, Anita. Religious Buildings. 2000. (What's Sacred to Me Ser.). (Illus.). 32p. (J). (ps-3). pap. 10.34 (978-0-7398-3123-6(2)) Steck-Vaughn.

Gonzales, Doreen. Seven Wonders of the Modern World: A MyReportLinks. com Book. 2005. (Seven Wonders of the World Ser.). (Illus.). 48p. (J). lib. bdg. 25.26 (978-0-7660-5292-5(3) , MyReportLinks.com Bks.) Enslow Pubs., Inc.

Greene, Meg. The Russian Kremlin. 2001. (Building History Ser.). (Illus.). 96p. (YA). (gr. 6-9). 32.45 (978-1-56006-840-2(X) , Lucent Bks.) Thomson Gale.

Grimshaw, Caroline. Buildings. 2000. (Connections Ser.). (Illus.). 32p. (J). (gr. 3-6). 9.95 (978-1-58728-314-7(X)); pap. 5.95 (978-1-58728-320-8(4)) T&N Children's Publishing. (Two Can Publishing).

Grinberg, Delphine. Construction. Sapin, Mathieu, illus. 2006. (Explore Your World Ser.). (ENG & FRE.). 28p. (J). (ps-1). 15.95 (978-1-55407-004-6(X)) Firefly Bks., Ltd.

Gunderson, Jessica. Gothic Art. 2008. (J). (*978-1-58341-610-5(2) , Creative Education) Creative Co., The.

Harcourt School Publishers Staff. Building the Past On Level. 3rd ed. 2002. (Trophies Reading Program Ser.). (Illus.). pap. 5.10 (978-0-15-323444-6(X)) Harcourt Schl. Pubs.

Harris, Phyllis, illus. St. Louis Architecture for Kids. Obata, Gen, photos by. 2005. 32p. 15.95 (978-1-883982-42-3(1)) Missouri Historical Society Pr.

Ichord, Loretta Frances. Raising the Roof. 2004. 96p. lib. bdg. (978-0-7613-2369-3(4) , Millbrook Pr.) Lerner Publishing Group.

Isaacson, Philip M. Round Buildings, Square Buildings, Buildings That Wiggle Like a Fish. Isaacson, Philip M., photos by. 2005. (Illus.). 121p. (J). (gr. 4-8). reprint ed. 20.00 (978-0-7567-8940-4(0)) DIANE Publishing Co.

Jefferis, David. Extreme Structures: Mega-Construction of the 21st Century. 2006. (Science Frontiers Ser.). (Illus.). 32p. (J). (gr. 3-9). (978-0-7787-2858-0(7)) Crabtree Publishing Co.

Jomann, Carol. Skyscrapers! Super Structures to Design & Build. 2001. (gr. 3-6). lib. bdg. 19.90 (978-0-613-55900-3(2)) Tandem Library Bks.

Kalman, Bobbie. Everyday Structures from A to Z. 1999. (AlphaBasiCs Ser.). (Illus.). 32p. (J). (gr. 2-3). pap. (978-0-86505-417-2(7)); lib. bdg. (978-0-86505-387-8(1)) Crabtree Publishing Co.

Kent, Peter. Great Building Stories of the Past. Kent, Peter, illus. 2001. (Illus.). 48p. (YA). (gr. 4-6). 19.95 (978-0-19-521846-6(9)) Oxford Univ. Pr., Inc.

Keoke, Emory Dean & Porterfield, Kay Marie. American Indian Contributions to the World: Buildings, Clothing, & Art. 2005. (American Indian Contributions to the World Ser.). (Illus.). 160p. (J). (gr. 4-9). 35.00 (978-0-8160-5394-0(4)) Facts On File, Inc.

Klobuchar, Lisa. How Did They Do That? 2005. (Real Deal - Green Plus Ser.). (Illus.). 32p. (gr. 4-8). 19.00 (978-0-7910-8901-9(0)) Facts On File, Inc.

Die Kunst des Bauens.Tr. of Art of Building. (GER., Illus.). (YA). 31.95 (978-3-411-09101-0(0) , MY9101E) Bibliographisches Institut & F. A. Brockhaus AG DEU. *Dist:* Continental Bk. Co., Inc.

Kuntz, Lynn. The Roman Colosseum. 2004. (Great Structures in History Ser.). (Illus.). 48p. (J). (gr. 4-7). 26.20 (978-0-7377-1561-3(8) , Greenhaven Pr., Inc.) Thomson Gale.

Levy, Janey. The Architecture of Frank Lloyd Wright: Understanding the Concepts of Parallel & Perpendicular. 2005. (PowerMath Ser.). (Illus.). 32p. (J). 22.50 (978-1-4042-2940-2(X)); (978-1-4042-5145-8(6)); pap. 22.50 (978-1-4042-5144-1(8)) Rosen Publishing Group, Inc., The. (PowerKids Pr.).

Lusted, Marcia Amidon. The Holy City of Jerusalem. 2002. (Building History Ser.). (Illus.). 112p. (J). (gr. 6-9). 32.45 (978-1-59018-028-0(3) , Lucent Bks.) Thomson Gale.

Lynette, Rachel. The Taj Mahal. 2005. (Great Structures in History Ser.). (Illus.). 48p. (J). (ps-8). lib. bdg. 26.20 (978-0-7377-3154-5(0) , Greenhaven Pr., Inc.) Thomson Gale.

Macaulay, David. Building Big. Macaulay, David, illus. 2006. (Illus.). 192p. reprint ed. 30.00 (978-1-4223-5328-8(1)) DIANE Publishing Co.

Malam, John. Super Structures. 2000. (Fast Forward Ser.). (Illus.). 32p. (J). (gr. 4-8). 29.00 (978-0-531-11875-7(4) , Watts, Franklin) Scholastic Library Publishing.

—Super Structures. 2000. (J). (978-0-606-19796-0(6)) Tandem Library Bks.

Mann, Elizabeth. Empire State Building: When New York Reached for the Skies. Witschonke, Alan, illus. Hine, Lewis, photos by. (Wonders of the World Book Ser.). 48p. (J). (gr. 4-8). 2006. pap. 9.95 (978-1-931414-08-1(4)); 2003. 19.95 (978-1-931414-06-7(8)) Mikaya Pr.

Mason, Adrienne. Build it Structures Systems. Davila, Claudia, illus. 2006. 32p. (978-1-55337-836-5(9)); (978-1-55337-835-8(0)) Kids Can Pr., Ltd.

Michelle Keller. The Akashi-Kaiko Bridge. 2004. (Building World Landmarks Ser.). (Illus.). 48p. (J). (gr. 4-7). 24.95 (978-1-4103-0140-6(0) , Blackbirch Pr., Inc.) Thomson Gale.

Moskal, Greg. Modern Buildings: Identifying Bilateral & Rotational Symmetry. 2004. (PowerMath Ser.). (Illus.). 32p. (J). lib. bdg. (978-0-8239-8902-7(X)); lib. bdg. 22.50 (978-0-8239-8989-8(5)) Rosen Publishing Group, Inc., The. (PowerKids Pr.).

Naranjo, Tito S. A Pueblo. Bacchin, Giorgio, illus. 1999. (Day with Ser.). 48p. (J). (gr. 5-7). lib. bdg. (978-0-8225-1919-5(4)) Lerner Publishing Group.

Nardo, Don. Architecture. 2007. (Eye on Art Ser.). (Illus.). 128p. (J). (gr. 7-10). 31.20 (*978-1-4205-0003-5(1)*, Lucent Bks.) Thomson Gale.

Nardo, Don. The Parthenon of Ancient Greece. 1998. (Building History Ser.). (Illus.). 96p. (YA). (gr. 6-9). 27.45 (978-1-56006-431-2(5), Lucent Bks.) Thomson Gale.

Neumann, Dietrich. Joe & the Skyscraper. Heritage, Anne, tr. from GER. 2000. (Adventures in Architecture Ser.). (Illus.). 30p. (gr. 3-10). 14.95 (978-3-7913-2103-5(X)) Prestel Publishing.

Oxlade, Chris. Stadiums. 2nd ed. 2005. (Illus.). 32p. (J). (978-1-4034-7905-1(4)) Heinemann Library.

Pascoe, Elaine, ed. Skyscrapers. 2003. (Super Structures of the World Ser.). (J). 11.20 (978-1-4103-0192-5(3), Blackbirch Pr., Inc.) Thomson Gale.

Potter, Tony, prod. Plantation Home Model. 2005. 3p. (J). pap. 19.95 (978-1-58980-274-2(8)) Pelican Publishing Co., Inc.

Poulakidas, Georgene. The Guggenheim Museum Bilbao: Transforming a City. 2004. (High Interest Bks.). (Illus.). 48p. (J). (gr. 7-12). pap. 6.95 (978-0-516-25907-9(5), Children's Pr.) Scholastic Library Publishing.

Radevsky, Anton. Architecture Pop-Up Book. Radevsky, Anton, illus. 2004. (Illus.). 6p. 39.95 (978-0-7893-1188-7(7)) Universe Publishing.

Renaissance Art/Architecture DBA. 2002. spiral bd. 16.95 (978-1-56004-139-9(0)) Social Studies Schl. Service.

Ruffin, Frances E. The Gateway Arch. 2006. (Illus.). 24p. (J). pap. (978-0-8368-6416-8(6), Weekly Reader Early Learning Library) Stevens, Gareth Inc.

Rufin, Farncis & Ashley, Susan A. The Gateway Arch. 2006. (Illus.). 24p. (J). 19.33 (978-0-8368-6409-0(3)) Stevens, Gareth Inc.

Sample, Ann. Houses & Homes in Colonial America. 2003. (Everyday Life Long Ago Ser.). (J). (978-0-7368-2163-6(5), Blue Earth Bks.) Capstone Pr., Inc.

Sheehan, Pat. Make Your Own Roman Villa. 1999. 24p. pap. 9.95 (978-0-688-17020-2(X)) HarperCollins Pubs.

Shemie, Bonnie. Building Canada. 2001. (Illus.). 40p. (J). (gr. 4). 18.95 (978-0-88776-504-9(1)) Tundra Bks., Inc./Livres Toundra, Inc. CAN. *Dist:* Random Hse., Inc.

Simon, Seymour. Seemore Skyscrapers. 2005. (Illus.). 32p. (J). 14.50 (978-1-58717-266-3(6), SeaStar Bks.) Chronicle Bks. LLC.

Sims, Lesley. El Gran Libro de Los Castillos - Internet Linked. Groebner, Dominic, illus. 2004. (Titles in Spanish Ser.). (SPA.). 104p. (J). pap. 14.95 (978-0-7460-5089-7(5), Usborne) EDC Publishing.

Steele, Philip. Wonders of the World. 2007. (Kingfisher Knowledge Ser.). (Illus.). 64p. (J). (gr. 3-5). 12.95 (978-0-7534-5979-9(5), Kingfisher) Houghton Mifflin Co. Trade & Reference Div.

Sterling Publishing Company Staff. Make a Small House. 1999. (Illus.). 8p. (J). (gr. k-2). pap. 2.95 (978-0-8069-1947-8(7)) Sterling Publishing Co., Inc.

Tagliapietra, Ron. The Seven Wonders of the World. 1999. (Illus.). 238p. (J). pap. 6.95 (978-1-57924-234-3(0)) Jones, Bob Univ. Pr.

Thomas, Mark. Discoverer Enterprise: La Plataforma de Perforacion Mas Grande Del Mundo. 2004. (Estructuras Extraordinarias Ser.). (SPA & ENG., Illus.). 24p. (J). (gr. 3-6). lib. bdg. 17.25 (978-0-8239-6864-0(2), Buenas Letra) Rosen Publishing Group, Inc., The.

—Maracana: El Estadio de Futbol Mas Grande del Mundo. 2004. (Estructuras Extraordinarias Ser.). (SPA & ENG., Illus.). 24p. (J). (gr. 3-6). lib. bdg. 17.25 (978-0-8239-6863-3(4), Buenas Letra) Rosen Publishing Group, Inc., The.

—La Represa de Itaipu: La Represa Mas Grande Del Mundo. 2004. (Estructuras Extraordinarias Ser.). (SPA & ENG., Illus.). 24p. (J). (gr. 3-6). lib. bdg. 17.25 (978-0-8239-6865-7(0), Buenas Letra) Rosen Publishing Group, Inc., The.

Thorne-Thomsen, Kathleen. Greene & Greene for Kids. 2004. (Illus.). 128p. 17.95 (978-1-58685-440-9(2)) Gibbs Smith, Publisher.

Los Tuneles Son Redondos. (Enciclopedia Me Pregunto Por Que). (SPA., Illus.). 32p. (J). (gr. 3-5). (978-84-241-1967-6(3), EV2040) Everest de Ediciones y Distribucion, S.L. ESP. *Dist:* Lectorum Pubns., Inc.

Viereckskonstruktionen. (Duden-Schuelerhilfen Ser.). (GER.). 112p. (YA). (gr. 7-8). (978-3-411-06181-5(2)) Bibliographisches Institut & F. A. Brockhaus AG DEU. *Dist:* International Bk. Import Service, Inc.

Wallach, Paul Ross. Chief Architect 9. 5 tutorials Workbook. 2004. 77p. spiral bd. 24.95 (978-0-9740796-4-6(2)) Technology Education Concepts Inc.

Weber, Rebecca. Building with Shapes. 2004. (Spyglass Books). 24p. (J). (gr. 1 up). lib. bdg. 19.93 (978-0-7565-0655-1(7)) Compass Point Bks.

Webster, Christine. Taj Mahal. 2007. (J). (*978-1-59036-729-2(4)*); (*978-1-59036-730-8(8)*) Weigl Pubs., Inc.

Zaunders, Bo. Gargoyles, Girders, & Glass Houses: Magnificent Master Builders. Munro, Roxie, illus. 2004. 48p. (J). (gr. 3-7). 17.99 (978-0-525-47284-1(3), Dutton Juvenile) Penguin Group (USA) Inc.

ARCHITECTURE, DOMESTIC

see also Apartment Houses; Houses

Anon. History Detective Investigates. (Illus.). 32p. pap. (978-0-7502-3750-5(3), Hodder Wayland) Hodder Children's Division.

Barber, Nicola. City Home. 2007. (Homes Around the World Ser.). 32p. (J). (gr. 2-5). pap. (*978-0-7787-3554-0(0)*) Crabtree Publishing Co.

Bass, Hester Thompson & Arzoumanian, Alik. So Many Houses. 2006. (Illus.). 32p. (YA). pap. 4.95 (978-0-516-24999-5(1), Children's Pr.) Scholastic Library Publishing.

Bingham, Jane. Look Around a Roman Villa. 2007. (J). (*978-1-84193-723-6(1)*) Smart Apple Media.

Bode, Achim, et al. Where We Live. 2005. (GER., Illus.). 27p. (J). (gr. 4-8). reprint ed. pap. 17.00 (978-0-7567-9381-4(5)) DIANE Publishing Co.

Burton, Margie, et al. Where People Live. Adams, Alison, ed. 1999. (Early Connections Ser.). 16p. (J). (gr. k-2). pap. 4.50 (978-1-58344-087-2(9)) Benchmark Education Co.

Canizares, Susan. Shelter. (J). 2000. pap. (978-0-439-04552-0(5)); 1999. 2.50 (978-0-439-04550-6(9)) Scholastic, Inc.

Doering, Amanda. World Homes ABC: An Alphabet Book. 2005. (A+ Alphabet Books). (Illus.). 32p. (J). 22.60 (978-0-7368-3665-4(9)) Capstone Pr., Inc.

Flanagan, Alice K. The Pueblos. 1998. (True Bks.). (Illus.). 47p. (J). (gr. 3-5). pap. 6.95 (978-0-516-26383-0(8), Children's Pr.) Scholastic Library Publishing.

Gallagher, Debbie. City & Country Homes. 2007. (J). (*978-1-59920-153-5(4)*) Smart Apple Media.

Guin, Valerie. Where We Live. 2005. (Illus.). 30p. (J). (gr. 3-7). lib. bdg. 27.10 (978-1-58340-698-4(0)) Smart Apple Media.

Halstead, Rachel & Reid, Struan, eds. Homes: Bring the Past Alive with 30 Great Projects. 2003. (Hands-On History Ser.). (Illus.). 64p. (gr. 3-7). pap. 10.99 (978-1-84215-759-6(0), Southwater) Anness Publishing GBR. *Dist:* National Bk. Network.

Hayden, Kate. Amazing Buildings, Vol. 2. 2003. (Readers Ser.). (Illus.). 32p. (J). pap. 3.99 (978-0-7894-9220-3(2)) Dorling Kindersley Publishing, Inc.

—Amazing Buildings. 2003. (gr. k-3). lib. bdg. 11.80 (978-0-613-62431-2(9)) Tandem Library Bks.

Hayden, Kate & Dorling Kindersley Publishing Staff. Amazing Buildings. 2003. (Readers Ser.). (Illus.). 32p. (J). 14.99 (978-0-7894-9308-8(X)) Dorling Kindersley Publishing, Inc.

Hill, Lee Sullivan. Homes Keep Us Warm. 2000. (Building Block Bks.). (Illus.). 32p. (J). (gr. k-3). lib. bdg. (978-1-57505-430-8(2), Carolrhoda Bks.) Lerner Publishing Group.

Jackson, Abby. Homes. 2003. (Yellow Umbrella Books for Early Readers). (Illus.). 17p. (J). 15.93 (978-0-7368-2927-4(X)); pap. (978-0-7368-2886-4(9)) Yellow Umbrella Pr.

Kalman, Bobbie & Crossingham, John. Colonial Home. 2000. (Historic Communities Ser.). (Illus.). 32p. (J). (gr. 3). pap. (978-0-86505-469-1(X)) Crabtree Publishing Co.

Komatsu, Yoshio. Wonderful Houses Around the World. Nishiyama, Akira & Komatsu, Eiko, illus. 2004. 48p. 14.95 (978-0-936070-35-3(8)) Shelter Pubns., Inc.

Konemann Staff. The Victorian House. 1999. (Illus.). 4p. (J). (gr. 4-7). 19.95 (978-3-8290-2529-4(7)) Konemann.

McLeish, Ewan. Sustainable Homes. 2006. (Sustainable Futures Ser.). (Illus.). 48p. (J). (978-1-58340-982-4(3), 1262624) Smart Apple Media.

Nelson, Robin. Homes. 2003. (First Step Nonfiction Ser.). (Illus.). 8p. (J). pap. 3.95 (978-0-8225-3930-8(6), Lerner Pubns.) Lerner Publishing Group.

Nishiyama, Akira & Komatsu, Eiko, illus. Wonderful Houses Around the World. Komatsu, Yoshio, photos by. 2004. 48p. (J). pap. 8.95 (978-0-936070-34-6(X)) Shelter Pubns., Inc.

Ring, Susan. Places We Live. 2005. (J). (978-0-7368-5316-3(2)); (Illus.). 16p. (978-0-7368-5280-7(8)) Capstone Pr., Inc.

Schaefer, Lola M. Homes 123. 2003. (Home for Me Ser.). (Illus.). 24p. (J). (ps-1). lib. bdg. 18.50 (978-1-4034-0259-2(0)) Heinemann Library.

Schmauss, Judy Kentor. Just the Right Home. 2006. (Reader's Clubhouse Set B Ser.). (Illus.). 24p. (J). pap. 3.99 (978-0-7641-3299-5(7)) Barron's Educational Series, Inc.

Shoulders, Michael. The ABC Book of American Homes. Brannen, Sarah, illus. 2008. (J). (*978-1-57091-565-9(2)*) Charlesbridge Publishing, Inc.

Shuter, Jane. Life in a Roman Villa. 2004. (Picture the Past Ser.). (Illus.). 32p. (J). 24.22 (978-1-4034-5830-8(8)) Heinemann Library.

Skinner, Tina. Log & Timber Frame Homes. 2003. (Schiffer Design Book Ser.). (Illus.). 224p. (gr. 10-13). 44.95 (978-0-7643-1754-5(7)) Schiffer Publishing, Ltd.

Skinner, Tina, ed. Radford's Artistic Homes. 2001. (Illus.). 264p. (gr. 10-13). pap. 19.95 (978-0-7643-1455-1(6)) Schiffer Publishing, Ltd.

Smith, A. G. Victorian Houses. 2001. (Illus.). 32p. (J). (gr. k up). pap. 3.95 (978-0-486-41551-2(1)) Dover Pubns., Inc.

Smith, Alastair, ed. Homes & Houses Then & Now. 2004. (Then & Now Flip Flaps Ser.). (SPA., Illus.). 16p. (J). (gr. 2 up). pap. 7.95 (978-0-7460-3100-1(9)) EDC Publishing.

Stone, Lynn M. Houses. 2001. (How are They Built? Ser.). (Illus.). 48p. (J). (gr. 4-8). lib. bdg. 29.93 (978-1-58952-137-7(4)) Rourke Publishing, LLC.

Thomas, Mark. Homes in Colonial America. 2002. (Welcome Colonial America Ser.). (Illus.). 24p. (J). (ps-2). 18.00 (978-0-516-23933-0(3), Children's Pr.) Scholastic Library Publishing.

—Homes in Colonial America. 2002. (gr. k-3). lib. bdg. 12.95 (978-0-613-58778-5(2)) Tandem Library Bks.

Townsend, John. Dreary Dwellings & Frightful Families. 2006. (Illus.). 48p. (J). (978-1-4109-1873-4(4)) Steck-Vaughn.

Williams, Brian. Ancient Roman Homes. (People in the Past Ser.). (Illus.). 48p. (J). 2003. (gr. 4-6). lib. bdg. 25.64 (978-1-58810-631-5(4)); 2002. pap. 8.50 (978-1-4034-0519-7(0)) Heinemann Library.

ARCHITECTURE, ECCLESIASTICAL

see Church Architecture

ARCHITECTURE, EGYPTIAN

Rau, Dana Meachen. Pyramid. 2006. (Bookworms Ser.). (Illus.). 32p. (J). (gr. k-2). lib. bdg. 22.79 (*978-0-7614-2275-4(7)*, Benchmark Bks.) Cavendish, Marshall Corp.

School Zone Publishing Company Staff. Addition & Subraction 1-2: I Know It! deluxe ed. 2005. 64p. (J). (gr. 1-2). pap., wbk. ed. 3.79 (978-1-58947-323-2(X)) School Zone Publishing Co.

ARCHITECTURE—FICTION

Konigsburg, E. L. The Second Mrs. Gioconda. 2005. 160p. (YA). pap. 7.99 (978-1-4169-0342-0(9), Simon Pulse) Simon & Schuster Children's Publishing.

Macaulay, David. Angelo. 2002. (Illus.). 48p. (J). (gr. 1-4). 16.00 (978-0-618-16826-2(5), Walter Lorraine) Houghton Mifflin Co. Trade & Reference Div.

MacKall, Dandi Daley. Made for a Purpose. Dibley, Glin, illus. 2004. 40p. (J). 15.99 (978-0-310-70953-4(9)) Zonderkidz.

Valentine, Sally. The Ghost of the Charlotte Lighthouse. 2006. (J). (*978-1-59531-013-2(4)*) North Country Bks., Inc.

Warren, Rick. Made for a Purpose AMS. 2004. (J). 287.82 (978-0-310-60329-0(3)) Zonderkidz.

ARCHITECTURE—HISTORY

Adams, Cynthia. Circling the World: World Famous Landmarks. 2003. (Circling the World Ser.). (Illus.). 176p. (gr. 4-6). 15.99 (978-1-56822-674-3(8), IF20538) School Specialty Publishing.

Arnold, Caroline & Comora, Madeleine. Taj Mahal. Bhushan, Rahul, illus. 2007. 32p. (J). (gr. k up). spiral bd. 17.95 (978-0-7613-2609-0(X), Millbrook Pr.) Lerner Publishing Group.

Barter, James E. The Palace of Versailles. 1998. (Building History Ser.). (Illus.). 112p. (YA). (gr. 6-9). 27.45 (978-1-56006-433-6(1), Lucent Bks.) Thomson Gale.

Bussagli, Marco. Understanding Architecture, 2 vols. Bettinelli, Sara & Galleschi, M. Lucrezia, eds. Frost, Catherine, tr. from ITA. 2004. (Illus.). 384p. lib. bdg. 199.00 (978-0-7656-8071-6(8), Sharpe Reference) Sharpe, M.E. Inc.

DuTemple, Lesley A. The Colosseum. 2003. (Great Building Feats Ser.). (Illus.). 96p. (J). (gr. 5-9). 27.93 (978-0-8225-4693-1(0)) Lerner Publishing Group.

Halfmann, Janet. Greek Temples. 1999. (Designing the Future Ser.). (Illus.). 32p. (J). (gr. 4-7). lib. bdg. 21.30 (978-0-88682-654-3(3), Creative Education) Creative Co., The.

Lace, William W. The Medieval Cathedral. 2000. (Building History Ser.). (Illus.). 96p. (J). (gr. 6-9). 32.45 (978-1-56006-720-7(9), Lucent Bks.) Thomson Gale.

Lectorum Publications Staff & Milo, Francesco. La Historia de la Arquitectura. 2000. (Maestros del Arte Ser.). (SPA., Illus.). 72p. (J). (gr. 4-7). 22.95 (978-84-88061-98-0(6)) Serres, Ediciones, S. L. ESP. *Dist:* Lectorum Pubns., Inc.

Levick, Melba, photos by. Antonio Gaudi: Master Architect. 2000. (Tiny Folio Ser.). (Illus.). 144p. 35.00 (978-0-7892-0220-8(4)) Abbeville Pr., Inc.

Macaulay, David. Mosque. Macaulay, David, illus. 2003. (Illus.). 96p. (YA). (gr. 5 up). 18.00 (978-0-618-24034-0(9), Walter Lorraine) Houghton Mifflin Co. Trade & Reference Div.

Mann, Elizabeth. The Roman Colosseum: The Story of the World's Most Famous Stadium & Its Deadly Games. Racz, Michael, illus. 1998. (Wonders of the World Ser.). 48p. (J). (gr. 4-7). 19.95 (978-0-9650493-3-7(7)) Mikaya Pr.

Meg Greene. The CN Tower. 2004. (Building World Landmarks Ser.). (Illus.). 48p. (J). 24.95 (978-1-4103-0141-3(9), Blackbirch Pr., Inc.) Thomson Gale.

Nardo, Don. Roman Amphitheaters. 2002. (Watts Library). (Illus.). 64p. (J). (gr. 5-7). pap. 8.95 (978-0-531-16224-8(9)); 25.50 (978-0-531-12036-1(8)) Scholastic Library Publishing. (Watts, Franklin).

—Roman Amphitheaters. 2002. (gr. 3-6). lib. bdg. 17.60 (978-0-613-53859-6(5)) Tandem Library Bks.

Severance, John B. Skyscrapers: How America Grew Up. 2000. (Illus.). 112p. (J). (gr. 7 up). tchr. ed. 18.95 (978-0-8234-1492-5(2)) Holiday Hse., Inc.

Shemie, Bonnie. Ainsi S'est Construit le Canada. Levesque, Suzanne, tr. from ENG. 2002. (FRE & SPA., Illus.). 40p. (J). (gr. 4). 18.95 (978-0-88776-555-1(6), Livres Toundra) Tundra Bks., Inc./Livres Toundra, Inc. CAN. *Dist:* Random Hse., Inc.

Simply Wright: A Journey into the Ideas of Frank Lloyd Wright's Architecture. 2004. (J). spiral bd. 17.95 (978-0-9677348-3-5(5)) Castleconal Pr.

Smith, A. G. Victorian Houses. 2001. (Illus.). 32p. (J). (gr. k up). pap. 3.95 (978-0-486-41551-2(1)) Dover Pubns., Inc.

Yuan, Margaret. The Arc D'Triomphe. 2004. (Building World Landmarks Ser.). (Illus.). 48p. (J). (gr. 4-7). 24.95 (978-1-4103-0138-3(9), Blackbirch Pr., Inc.) Thomson Gale.

ARCHITECTURE, NAVAL

see Naval Architecture; Shipbuilding

ARCHITECTURE, RURAL

see Architecture, Domestic

ARCHITECTURE—VOCATIONAL GUIDANCE

Architecture & Construction Careers (AVA) 2001. (YA). pap. 6.00 (978-1-57078-016-5(1), CEV00016) C E V Multimedia, Ltd.

Cohen, Judith Love & Siegel, Margot. You Can Be a Woman Architect. Katz, David Arthur, illus. rev. ed. 1999. 40p. (J). pap. 7.00 (978-1-880599-04-4(X)) Cascade Pass, Inc.

Englart, Mindi. Architect. 2002. (How Do I Become a... Ser.). (Illus.). 32p. (J). 23.70 (978-1-56711-686-1(8), Blackbirch Pr., Inc.) Thomson Gale.

Ferguson. Careers in Focus: Architecture & Building. 2007. (Careers in Focus Ser.). 192p. (gr. 6-12). 29.95 (*978-0-8160-6569-1(1)*, Ferguson Publishing Co.) Facts On File, Inc.

Manatt, Kathleen. Architect. 2008. (J). pap. 7.95 (*978-1-60279-078-0(7)*) Cherry Lake Publishing.

Manatt, Kathleen G. Architect. 2008. (J). lib. bdg. 25.26 (*978-1-60279-052-0(3)*) Cherry Lake Publishing.

Reeves, Diane Lindsey, et al. Career Ideas for Teens in Construction & Architecture. 2005. (Career Ideas for Teens Ser.). (Illus.). 176p. (J). (gr. 6-12). 40.00 (978-0-8160-5289-9(1), Ferguson Publishing Co.) Facts On File, Inc.

ARCTIC EXPEDITIONS

see Arctic Regions

ARCTIC REGIONS

see also North Pole; Northwest Passage; Scientific Expeditions

Albanov, Valerian. In the Land of White Death: An Epic Story of Survival in the Siberian Arctic. 2000. (gr. 7-12). lib. bdg. 22.20 (978-0-613-70851-7(2)) Tandem Library Bks.

Alexander, Bryan & Alexander, Cherry. Journey into the Arctic. 2003. (Illus.). 48p. (YA). 22.00 (978-0-19-522004-9(8)); 19.95 (978-0-19-522005-6(6)) Oxford Univ. Pr., Inc.

Aloian, Molly. El Habitat del Artico. 2007. (SPA & ENG.). 32p. (J). (gr. 1-2). (*978-0-7787-8330-5(8)*) Crabtree Publishing Co.

Aloian, Molly & Kalman, Bobbie. The Arctic Habitat. 2006. (Introducing Habitats Ser.). (Illus.). 32p. (J). (gr. 2-4). pap. (978-0-7787-2981-5(8)); lib. bdg. (978-0-7787-2953-2(2)) Crabtree Publishing Co.

Aloian, Molly & Kalman, Bobbie. El Habitat del Artico. rev. ed. 2007. (SPA & ENG.). 32p. (J). (gr. 1-2). pap. (*978-0-7787-8354-1(5)*) Crabtree Publishing Co.

Anema, Durlynn. Louise Arner Boyd: Arctic Explorer. 2004. (Women Adventurers Ser.). (Illus.). 112p. (gr. 5 up). 21.95 (978-1-883846-42-8(0)) Reynolds, Morgan Inc.

Blue, Rose. Exploring the Arctic. 2004. (Illus.). (J). pap. 9.50 (978-1-4109-0675-5(2)) Raintree.

Blue, Rose & Naden, Corinne J. Exploring the Arctic. 2004. (J). lib. bdg. 32.79 (978-1-4109-0673-1(6)) Raintree.

Borucki, Kenneth. Penn Guinn & the Arctic Adventurers: Voyage North. 2001. (Illus.). 128p. (J). (ps-6). 19.95 (978-0-9708337-0-9(9)) Brimstone Ventures.

Brelsfoard, Sam. Life Inside the Arctic Circle. 2005. (Illus.). 24p. (J). (*978-0-328-13638-4(7)*, Scott Foresman) Addison-Wesley Educational Pubs., Inc.

Brennan, Kristine. Sir Edmund Hillary: Modern Day Explorer. 2001. (Explorers of the New World Ser.). (Illus.). 63p. (J). (gr. 4-7). pap. 25.00 (978-0-7910-6163-3(9), Chelsea Hse.) Facts On File, Inc.

—Sir Edmund Hillary: Modern Day Explorer. 2001. (gr. 3-6). lib. bdg. 17.60 (978-0-613-33056-5(0)) Tandem Library Bks.

Butterfield, Moira. Arctic. 1999. (Where Am I? Ser.). (Illus.). 32p. (J). (gr. 2-6). lib. bdg. 16.95 (978-1-929298-34-1(X)) Chrysalis Education.

Calvert, Patricia, et al. Robert E. Peary: To the Top of the World. 2001. (Great Explorations Ser.). (Illus.). 80p. (J). (gr. 4 up). lib. bdg. 29.93 (978-0-7614-1242-7(5), Benchmark Bks.) Cavendish, Marshall Corp.

Chapman, Simon. At the North Pole. 2005. (Illus.). 115p. (J). lib. bdg. 20.00 (*978-1-4242-0629-2(4)*) Fitzgerald Bks.

Clarke, Penny. Life in the Tundra. 2005. (What on Earth? Ser.). (Illus.). 32p. (J). 25.50 (978-0-516-25316-9(6), Children's Pr.) Scholastic Library Publishing.

Clarke, Penny. Scary Creatures of the Arctic! (Scary Creatures Ser.). 32p. (J). 2008. pap. 8.95 (*978-0-531-21008-6(1)*, Watts, Franklin); 2007. spiral bd. 26.00 (*978-0-531-20449-8(9)*, Children's Pr.) Scholastic Library Publishing.

Cookman, Scott. Ice Blink: The Tragic Fate of Sir John Franklin's Lost Polar Expedition. 2000. (gr. 7-12). lib. bdg. 25.70 (978-0-613-35414-1(1)) Tandem Library Bks.

Curlee, Lynn. Into the Ice: The Story of Arctic Exploration. 1998. (Illus.). 40p. (J). (gr. 4-6). tchr. ed. 16.00 (978-0-395-83013-0(3)) Houghton Mifflin Co. Trade & Reference Div.

Dorling Kindersley Publishing Staff. Arctic. 2006. (Dk 24 Hours Ser.). (Illus.). 48p. (J). 12.99 (978-0-7566-2214-5(X)) Dorling Kindersley Publishing, Inc.

Dwyer, Mindy. The Northern Lights A to Z. 2007. (Illus.). 32p. (J). (gr. k-3). pap. 10.95 (978-1-57061-515-3(2)) Sasquatch Bks.

Flowers, Pam. Big-Enough Anna: The Little Sled Dog Who Braved the Arctic. 2003. (gr. k-3). lib. bdg. 17.60 (978-0-613-77220-4(2)) Tandem Library Bks.

Flowers, Pam & Dixon, Ann. Alone Across the Arctic: One Woman's Epic Journey by Dog Team. 2005. (Illus.). 120p. (gr. 5-10). pap. 15.95 (978-0-88240-539-1(X)) Graphic Arts Ctr. Publishing Co.

—Big-Enough Anna: The Little Sled Dog Who Braved the Arctic. Farnsworth, Bill, illus. 2005. (Seldovia Sam Ser.). 32p. (ps up). 15.95 (978-0-88240-577-3(2)) Graphic Arts Ctr. Publishing Co.

—Big-Enough Anna: The Little Sled Dog Who Braved the Arctic. Farnsworth, Bill, tr. Farnsworth, Bill, illus. 2005. 32p. pap. 8.95 (978-0-88240-580-3(2)) Graphic Arts Ctr. Publishing Co.

Foran, Jill. Search for the Northwest Passage. 2004. (Great Journeys Ser.). (Illus.). 32p. (J). lib. bdg. 26.00 (978-1-59036-205-1(5)) Weigl Pubs., Inc.

A B

—The Search for the Northwest Passage. 2005. (Great Journeys Ser.). 32p. pap. 7.95 (978-1-59036-259-4(4)) Weigl Pubs., Inc.

Fowler, Allan. Living in the Arctic. 2001. (Rookie Read-About Geography Ser.). (Illus.). 32p. (J). (gr. 1-2). pap. 5.95 (978-0-516-27084-5(2) , Children's Pr.) Scholastic Library Publishing.

—Living in the Arctic. 2000. (gr. k-3). lib. bdg. 14.10 (978-0-613-54733-8(0)) Tandem Library Bks.

George, Michael. Tundra: The Barren Wilderness. 2001. (Life on Earth Ser.). (Illus.). 32p. (J). lib. bdg. (978-1-58341-023-3(6) , Creative Education) Creative Co., The.

Green, Jen. Arctic World: Step Into. 2000. (Step into Ser.). (Illus.). 64p. (gr. 3-7). 12.95 (978-0-7548-0474-1(7) , Lorenz Bks.) Anness Publishing GBR. *Dist:* National Bk. Network.

—On the Tundra. 2002. (Small Worlds Ser.). (Illus.). 32p. (J). (gr. 3-4). pap. (978-0-7787-0153-8(0)); lib. bdg. (978-0-7787-0139-2(5)) Crabtree Publishing Co.

—On the Tundra. 2002. (gr. 3-6). lib. bdg. 17.60 (978-0-613-52986-0(3)) Tandem Library Bks.

—People of the Polar Regions. 1998. (Wide World Ser.). (Illus.). 48p. (J). (gr. 3-7). 18.98 (978-0-8172-5065-2(4)) Raintree.

Harper, Kenn. Give Me My Fathers Body: The Life of Minik the New York Eskimo. 2001. (gr. 7-12). lib. bdg. 23.40 (978-0-613-45765-1(X)) Tandem Library Bks.

Harrington, Fred H. The Arctic Wolf. 2002. (Library of Wolves & Wild Dogs). (Illus.). 24p. (J). lib. bdg. 18.75 (978-0-8239-5766-8(7)) Rosen Publishing Group, Inc., The.

Haslam, Andrew. Arctic Peoples. 2004. (Make It Work! History Ser.). (Illus.). 64p. (J). (gr. 3-6). pap. 7.95 (978-1-58728-304-8(2) , Two Can Publishing) T&N Children's Publishing.

Hess, Paul, illus. Polar Animals. 1998. (Animal Worlds Ser.). (YA). (ps up). (978-1-84089-009-9(6) , 868229, Zero to Ten, Limited) Evans Publishing Group.

Kalman, Bobbie. Life in the Far North. 2003. (gr. 3-6). lib. bdg. 17.60 (978-0-613-85053-7(X)) Tandem Library Bks.

—Polar Oceans. 2003. (gr. 3-6). lib. bdg. 15.25 (978-0-613-59135-5(6)) Tandem Library Bks.

Kalman, Bobbie & Aloian, Molly. Polar Oceans. 2003. (Living Ocean Ser.). (Illus.). 32p. (J). (gr. 2-9). (978-0-7787-1297-8(4)); pap. (978-0-7787-1319-7(9)) Crabtree Publishing Co.

Kalman, Bobbie & Sjonger, Rebecca. Life in the Far North. 2003. (Native Nations of North America Ser.). (Illus.). 32p. (J). (gr. 5). (978-0-7787-0377-8(0)); pap. (978-0-7787-0469-0(6)) Crabtree Publishing Co.

Kirkpatrick, Katherine. The Snow Baby: The Arctic Childhood of Robert E. Peary's Daring Daughter. 2006. (Illus.). 48p. (J). 16.95 (978-0-8234-1973-9(8)) Holiday Hse., Inc.

Knudsen, Anders. Sir John Franklin: The Search for the Northwest Passage. 2007. (Illus.). 32p. (J). (gr. 3-9). ***(978-0-7787-2420-9(4))***; pap. ***(978-0-7787-2456-8(5))*** Crabtree Publishing Co.

Latreille, Francis & Guigon, Catherine. The Great North. Malenfer, Frédéric, illus. 2007. 72p. (J). (gr. 4-6). 18.95 (978-0-8109-1428-5(X) , Abrams Bks. for Young Readers) Abrams, Harry N., Inc.

Leeson, Cole. Arctic. 2003. (Wild America Habitats Ser.). (Illus.). 24p. (J). 21.20 (978-1-56711-798-1(8) , Blackbirch Pr., Inc.) Thomson Gale.

Levy, Janey. Discovering the Arctic Tundra. 2008. (J). lib. bdg. ***(978-1-4042-3787-2(9)*** , PowerKids Pr.) Rosen Publishing Group, Inc., The.

Litwin, Laura Baskes. Matthew Henson: Co-Discoverer of the North Pole. 2001. (African-American Biographies Ser.). (Illus.). 128p. (J). (gr. 6-12). lib. bdg. 26.60 (978-0-7660-1546-3(7)) Enslow Pubs., Inc.

Loughran, Donna. Living in the Tundra. 2004. (Rookie Read-About Geography Ser.). (Illus.). 31p. (J). (gr. 1-2). pap. 5.95 (978-0-516-27331-0(0) , Children's Pr.) Scholastic Library Publishing.

Love, Ann, et al. The Kids Book of the Far North. Bouchard, Jocelyne, illus. 2000. 48p. (J). (gr. 4-6). (978-1-55074-563-4(8)) Kids Can Pr., Ltd.

Lynch, Wayne. Arctic. Lynch, Wayne, photos by. 2007. (Our Wild World Ecosystems Ser.). (Illus.). 64p. (J). (gr. 3-7). 16.95 (978-1-55971-960-5(5)); pap. 8.95 (978-1-55971-961-2(3)) T&N Children's Publishing. (NorthWord Bks. for Young Readers).

—Arctic Alphabet: Exploring the North from A to Z. 1999. (Illus.). 32p. (J). (gr. k-5). lib. bdg. 19.95 (978-1-55209-336-8(0)) Firefly Bks., Ltd.

Martin, Jacqueline Briggs. The Lamp, the Ice, & the Boat Called Fish. Krommes, Beth, illus. 2001. 48p. (J). (gr. k-3). tchr. ed. 15.00 (978-0-618-00341-9(X)) Houghton Mifflin Co. Trade & Reference Div.

—The Lamp, the Ice, & the Boat Called Fish: Based on a True Story. Krommes, Beth, illus. 2005. 48p. (J). (gr. k-3). 6.95 (978-0-618-54895-8(5)) Houghton Mifflin Co. Trade & Reference Div.

Mazur, Ivan & Mazur, Elena. Treasures of the North. Freedman, Stella, ed. Piatikop, Alexander, illus. 1998. (Ecology for Children Ser.: Vol. 2). 48p. (J). (gr. 2-6). 11.95 (978-1-892316-04-2(8)) Rama Pr., Inc.

Miller, Chuck. Tundra Scientists. 2001. (Scientists of the Biomes Ser.). (Illus.). 48p. (J). (gr. 4-7). lib. bdg. 24.26 (978-0-7398-4752-7(X)) Raintree.

Miller, Debbie. Arctic Lights, Arctic Nights. Van Zyle, Jon, illus. 2007. 32p. (J). pap. 7.95 (978-0-8027-9636-3(2)) Walker & Co.

Miller, Debbie S. Arctic Lights, Arctic Nights. Van Zyle, Jon, illus. 2003. 32p. (J). (gr. 1-4). 16.95 (978-0-8027-8856-6(4)) Walker & Co.

Montgomery, Richard. Pechuck. 2005. reprint ed. pap. 31.95 (978-1-4179-9755-8(9)) Kessinger Publishing, LLC.

Morris, Neil. Living in the Arctic. 2007. (J). pap. ***(978-1-4109-2824-5(1))***; lib. bdg. ***(978-1-4109-2815-3(2))*** Steck-Vaughn.

Nelson, Julie. Tundra. Sloan, Frank, ed. 2001. (Biomes Ser.). (Illus.). 32p. (J). (gr. 4-7). lib. bdg. 22.83 (978-0-7398-3565-4(3)) Raintree.

Nichols, Catherine. An Arctic Year. 2002. (We Can Read about Nature Ser.). (Illus.). 32p. (J). 21.36 (978-0-7614-1430-8(4) , Benchmark Bks.) Cavendish, Marshall Corp.

Osborne, Mary Pope & Boyce, Natalie Pope. Polar Bears & the Arctic. Murdocca, Sal, illus. 2007. 128p. (J). (gr. 2-5). pap. 4.99 (978-0-375-83222-2(X) , Random Hse. Bks. for Young Readers) Random Hse. Children's Bks.

—Polar Bears & the Arctic: A Nonfiction Companion to Polar Bears Past Bedtime. Murdocca, Salvatore, illus. 2007. (Magic Tree House Research Guides (Library) Ser.). 119p. (J). (gr. 2-5). lib. bdg. 11.99 (978-0-375-93222-9(4) , Random Hse. Bks. for Young Readers) Random Hse. Children's Bks.

Petersen, David. Antarctica. 1999. (True Bks.). (Illus.). 48p. (J). (gr. 3-5). pap. 6.95 (978-0-516-26426-4(5) , Children's Pr.) Scholastic Library Publishing.

Prevost, John F. Arctic Ocean. 2003. (Oceans & Seas Ser.). (Illus.). 24p. (J). (gr. k-6). lib. bdg. 21.35 (978-1-57765-095-9(6)) ABDO Publishing Co.

Revkin, Andrew. New York Times the North Pole Was Here: Puzzles & Perils at the Top of the World. 2006. (New York Times Ser.). (Illus.). 128p. (J). (gr. 5). 15.95 (978-0-7534-5993-5(0) , Kingfisher) Houghton Mifflin Co. Trade & Reference Div.

Revkin, Andrew. North Pole Was Here. 2007. 128p. (J). pap. 10.95 ***(978-0-7534-6138-9(2)*** , Kingfisher) Houghton Mifflin Co. Trade & Reference Div.

Robinson, Barbara. The Arctic Life. 1999. (Illus.). (J). pap. 5.18 (978-0-7398-2409-2(0)) Steck-Vaughn.

Sis, Peter. A Small, Tall Tale from the Far Far North. 2001. (J). (978-0-606-21435-3(6)) Tandem Library Bks.

Somervill, Barbara A. Animal Survivors of the Arctic. 2004. (Watts Library). (Illus.). 64p. (J). 25.50 (978-0-531-12204-4(2) , Watts, Franklin) Scholastic Library Publishing.

Tarbox, A. D. The Arctic Tundra. 2008. (J). ***(978-1-58341-596-2(3)*** , Creative Education) Creative Co., The.

Taylor, Barbara. Arctic & Antarctic. Brightling, Geoff, photos by. 2000. (Eyewitness Bks.). (Illus.). 64p. (J). (gr. 4-7). 15.99 (978-0-7894-5850-6(0)) Dorling Kindersley Publishing, Inc.

Taylor, Barbara & Dorling Kindersley Publishing Staff. Arctic & Antarctic. 2000. (Eyewitness Bks.). (Illus.). 64p. (J). (gr. 4-7). lib. bdg. 19.99 (978-0-7894-6606-8(6)) Dorling Kindersley Publishing, Inc.

Tocci, Salvatore. Alpine Tundra. 2005. (Biomes & Habitats Ser.). (Illus.). 64p. (J). (gr. 5-7). 24.50 (978-0-531-12365-2(0) , Watts, Franklin) Scholastic Library Publishing.

—Arctic Tundra. 2005. (Biomes & Habitats Ser.). (Illus.). 64p. (J). (gr. 5-7). 24.50 (978-0-531-12366-9(9) , Watts, Franklin) Scholastic Library Publishing.

Two-Can Publishing Ltd. Staff. Arctic Peoples. 2004. (Make It Work! History Ser.). (Illus.). 64p. (gr. 3-6). 14.95 (978-1-58728-310-9(7) , Two Can Publishing) T&N Children's Publishing.

Wadsworth, Ginger. Tundra Discoveries. Carrozza, John, illus. 1999. (Discoveries Ser.). 32p. (J). (ps-3). 15.95 (978-0-88106-875-7(6)); pap. 6.95 (978-0-88106-876-4(4)) Charlesbridge Publishing, Inc.

—Tundra Discoveries. Carrozza, John, illus. 1999. (J). (ps-ps). lib. bdg. 16.40 (978-0-613-23995-0(4)) Tandem Library Bks.

—Tundra Discoveries. 1999. (978-0-606-17337-7(4)) Tandem Library Bks.

Warrick, Karen Clemens. The Perilous Search for the Fabled Northwest Passage in American History. 2004. (In American History Ser.). (Illus.). 128p. (J). lib. bdg. 26.60 (978-0-7660-2148-8(3)) Enslow Pubs., Inc.

Whitehouse, Patricia. Living in the Arctic. 2007. (Illus.). 24p. (J). (978-1-60044-188-2(2)) Rourke Publishing, LLC.

Wilson, John. Discovering the Arctic: The Story of John Rae. 2004. (Illus.). 73p. (J). 14.95 (978-0-929141-88-6(1)) Napoleon Publishing/Rendezvous Pr. CAN. *Dist:* AtlasBooks Distribution.

Woodford. Arctic Tundra & Polar Deserts. 2003. (Biomes Atlas Ser.). (Illus.). 64p. pap. 9.50 (978-1-4109-0020-3(7)) Raintree.

Wulffson, Don L. The Upside-Down Voyage. Lyall, Dennis, illus. 2005. (J). (978-1-59336-334-5(6)); pap. (978-1-59336-335-2(4)) Mondo Publishing.

Yolen, Jane. Welcome to the Icehouse. Regan, Laura, illus. 1998. 1p. (J). (ps-3). 16.99 (978-0-399-23011-0(4) , Putnam Juvenile) Penguin Group (USA) Inc.

Young. Arctic Investigations. 1999. (Illus.). (J). pap. (978-0-7398-0009-6(4)) Steck-Vaughn.

Young, Karen Romano. Arctic Investigations: Exploring the Frozen Ocean. 1999. (Turnstone Ocean Pilot Bks.). (Illus.). 48p. (J). (gr. 3-7). pap. 7.95 (978-0-7398-1233-4(5)) Steck-Vaughn.

—Arctic Investigations: Exploring the Frozen Ocean. 1999. (Illus.). (J). (978-0-606-18477-9(5)) Tandem Library Bks.

ARCTIC REGIONS—FICTION

Arctic. 2003. (J). per. (978-1-57657-885-8(2)) Paradise Pr., Inc.

Ballantyne, R. M. The Walrus Hunters. 2004. reprint ed. pap. 26.95 (978-1-4191-8706-3(6)); pap. 1.99 (978-1-4192-8706-0(0)) Kessinger Publishing, LLC.

Bania, Michael. Kumak's Fish: A Tall Tale from the Far North. 2005. (Illus.). 32p. 15.95 (978-0-88240-583-4(7)); pap. 8.95 (978-0-88240-584-1(5)) Graphic Arts Ctr. Publishing Co.

Barg, Lois. Muktuk Makes It. 2003. 33 p. pap. 17.95 (978-1-4137-0930-8(3)) PublishAmerica, Inc.

Bilgrami, Shaheen. Icy Antics. Chambers, Sally & Ratie, Patricia, illus. 2003. (Curious Creatures Bks.). 12p. (J). bds. 12.95 (978-1-4027-0820-6(3) , Sterling/Pinwheel) Sterling Publishing Co., Inc.

Blaikie, Lynn. Beyond the Northern Lights. 2006. (Illus.). 24p. (J). (ps-k). ***(978-1-55005-123-0(7))*** Fitzhenry & Whiteside, Ltd.

Colfer, Eoin. The Arctic Incident. 2004. (Artemis Fowl Ser.: Bk. 2). 416p. (J). (gr. 8-17). reprint ed. pap. 5.99 (978-0-7868-5147-8(3)) Hyperion Bks. for Children.

Crawford, Laura. In Arctic Waters. Hodson, Ben, illus. 2007. 32p. (J). pap. 8.95 ***(978-1-934359-34-1(3))*** Sylvan Dell Pubng.

D'Lacey, Chris. Fire Star. 560p. (J). 2008. pap. 7.99 (978-0-439-90185-7(5)); 2007. (gr. 4-7). pap. 15.99 (978-0-439-84582-3(3)) Scholastic, Inc. (Orchard Bks.).

—Icefire. 432p. (J). 2007. pap. 7.99 (978-0-439-67246-7(5)); 2006. pap. 14.99 (978-0-439-67245-0(7)) Scholastic, Inc. (Orchard Bks.).

Dunphy, Madeleine. Here Is the Arctic Winter. Robinson, Alan James, illus. 2007. (Web of Life Ser.). 32p. (J). 16.95 (978-0-9777539-1-8(3)); pap. 9.95 (978-0-9777539-0-1(5)) Web of Life Children's Bks.

Dwyer, Mindy. Aurora: A Tale of the Northern Lights. Dwyer, Mindy, illus. 2005. (Illus.). 32p. (ps up). pap. 8.95 (978-0-88240-549-0(7)) Graphic Arts Ctr. Publishing Co.

—Aurora: A Tale of the Northern Lights. 2001. (gr. k-3). lib. bdg. 17.60 (978-0-613-77291-4(1)) Tandem Library Bks.

—Sweet Dreams, Polar Bear. 2005. (Illus.). 32p. (J). 15.95 (978-0-88240-554-4(3)); pap. 8.95 (978-0-88240-555-1(1)) Graphic Arts Ctr. Publishing Co.

Fardell, John. The Seven Professors of the Far North. 2005. (Illus.). 192p. (YA). (gr. 3-7). 14.99 (978-0-399-24381-3(X) , Putnam Juvenile) Penguin Group (USA) Inc.

George, Jean Craighead. Arctic Son. 1999. (J). (978-0-606-17381-0(1)) Tandem Library Bks.

—Nutik & Amaroq Play Ball. 2000. 32p. (J). (gr. k-3). pap. 5.95 (978-0-06-443523-9(7)) HarperCollins Pubs.

—Nutik, the Wolf Pup. Rand, Ted, illus. 2001. 40p. (J). (gr. k-3). 15.99 (978-0-06-028164-9(2)); lib. bdg. 17.89 (978-0-06-028165-6(0)) HarperCollins Pubs.

—Nutik, the Wolf Pup. 2000. 32p. (J). (gr. k-3). pap. 5.95 (978-0-06-443522-2(9)) HarperCollins Pubs.

—Snow Bear. 2003. (gr. k-3). lib. bdg. 14.15 (978-0-613-75033-2(0)) Tandem Library Bks.

Gerber, Carole. Arctic Dreams. Husted, Marty, illus. 1999. (J). (ps-2). 15.95 (978-1-58089-021-2(0)) Charlesbridge Publishing, Inc.

Grigg, Carol. The Singing Snowbear. Grigg, Carol, illus. 1999. (Illus.). 32p. (J). (gr. k-3). tchr. ed. 15.00 (978-0-395-94223-9(3)) Houghton Mifflin Co. Trade & Reference Div.

Halfman, Janet. Polar Bear Horizon. Chesterman, Adrian, illus. 2006. (Smithsonian Oceanic Collection). 32p. (J). 19.95 incl. audio (978-1-59249-568-9(0)); 9.95 (978-1-59249-570-2(2)) Soundprints.

Halfmann, Janet. Polar Bear Horizon. Chesterman, Adrian, illus. 2006. 32p. pap. 8.95 incl. reel tape (978-1-59249-569-6(9)); (J). 15.95 (978-1-59249-565-8(6)); (J). pap. 4.95 (978-1-59249-567-2(2)); (J). mass mkt. 6.95 (978-1-59249-566-5(4)) Soundprints.

Harris, Sue. The Little Seal. Boey, Stephanie, illus. 2007. 28p. (J). (ps). pap. 15.99 ***(978-0-525-47839-3(6)*** , Dutton Juvenile) Penguin Group (USA) Inc.

Heinz, Brian J. Kayuktuk: An Arctic Quest. Van Zyle, Jon, illus. 2004. (J). pap. 6.95 (978-0-936335-09-4(2)); 14.95 (978-0-936335-08-7(4)) Ballyhoo BookWorks, Inc.

Himmelman, John. Pipaluk & the Whales. 2002. (Illus.). 32p. (J). (gr. 3-7). 16.95 (978-0-7922-8217-4(5) , National Geographic Children's Bks.) National Geographic Society.

Jalonen, Riitta. Tundra Mouse Mountain. Ledgard, J. M., tr. Louhi, Kristiina, illus. 2006. (Picture books from around the World Seri Ser.). 56p. (J). 19.95 (978-1-905341-05-4(9)) WingedChariot Pr. GBR. *Dist:* Independent Pubs. Group.

Joosse, Barbara M. Mama Do You Love Me? Lavallee, Barbara, illus. 1998. 24p. (J). (ps). bds. 6.95 (978-0-8118-2131-5(5)) Chronicle Bks. LLC.

Kusugak, Michael Arvaarluk. Arctic Stories. Krykorka, Vladyana Langer, illus. 1998. 40p. (J). (gr. k-4). pap. 7.95 (978-1-55037-452-0(4)); lib. bdg. 19.95 (978-1-55037-453-7(2)) Annick Pr., Ltd. CAN. *Dist:* Firefly Bks., Ltd.

—Arctic Stories. 1999. (J). (978-0-606-16482-5(0)) Tandem Library Bks.

Lincoln, Hazel. Little Snow Bear. Lincoln, Hazel, illus. 2004. (Illus.). 32p. (J). pap. 17.95 (978-0-86315-454-6(9)) Floris Bks. GBR. *Dist:* SteinerBooks, Inc.

Luenn, Nancy. Nessa's Fish. Waldman, Neil, illus. unabr. ed. 2001. (J). (gr. k-3). pap. 16.95 incl. audio (978-0-8045-6844-9(8) , 6844) Spoken Arts, Inc.

Oberman, Sheldon. The Shaman's Nephew: A Life in the Far North. Tookoome, Simon, illus. 2001. 55p. (gr. 4 up). pap. 13.95 (978-0-7737-6189-6(6)) Stoddart Kids CAN. *Dist:* Fitzhenry & Whiteside, Ltd.

Prater, John. The Big Dark. 2008. (Illus.). 32p. (J). pap. ***(978-0-09-948752-4(7)*** , Red Fox) Random Hse. Children's Bks. GBR. *Dist:* Random Hse., Inc.

Rockwood, Roy. Through the Air to the North Pole or the. 2006. 33.99 ***(978-1-4280-2972-9(9))*** IndyPublish.com.

Sabuda, Robert. The Blizzard's Robe. 1999. (J). (gr. k-3). 16.00 (978-0-689-81161-6(6) , Atheneum) Simon & Schuster Children's Publishing.

—The Blizzard's Robe. Sabuda, Robert, illus. 1999. (Illus.). 32p. (J). (gr. k-3). 16.95 (978-0-689-31988-4(6) , Atheneum) Simon & Schuster Children's Publishing.

Sis, Peter. A Small, Tall Tale from the Far Far North. (Illus.). (J). pap. 7.95 (978-0-88899-431-8(1)) Groundwood Bks. CAN. *Dist:* Transition Vendor.

—Small Tall Tale from the Far Far North. 2001. (gr. k-3). lib. bdg. 15.25 (978-0-613-82503-0(9)) Tandem Library Bks.

—A Small Tall Tale from the Far Far North. Sis, Peter, illus. 2001. (Illus.). 40p. (J). (gr. 1-4). 17.00 (978-0-374-37075-6(3) , Farrar, Straus & Giroux (BYR)); pap. 6.95 (978-0-374-46725-8(0) , Sunburst) Farrar, Straus & Giroux.

Snell, J. Roy. Lost in the Air. 2006. 95.99 ***(978-1-4280-0442-9(4))***; pap. 88.99 ***(978-1-4280-0450-4(5))*** IndyPublish.com.

Snell, Roy J. Lost in the Air. 2006. 132p. pap. 10.99 ***(978-1-4264-4244-5(0))***; 148p. pap. 13.99 ***(978-1-4264-4308-4(0))*** BiblioBazaar.

—Lost in the Air. 2004. reprint ed. pap. 20.95 (978-1-4191-3128-8(1)); pap. 1.99 (978-1-4192-3128-5(6)) Kessinger Publishing, LLC.

Sollinger, Emily. Diego's Arctic Adventure: A Book of Facts about Arctic Animals. Mawhinney, Art, illus. 2007. (Go, Diego, Go! Ser.). 16p. (J). pap. 6.99 ***(978-1-4169-3822-4(2)*** , Simon Spotlight/Nickelodeon) Simon & Schuster Children's Publishing.

Taulbert, Clifton L. Little Cliff & the Cold Place. Lewis, Earl, illus. 2002. 32p. (J). (gr. k-3). 16.99 (978-0-8037-2558-4(2) , Dial) Penguin Group (USA) Inc.

Taylor, Theodore. Hello, Arctic! Chodos-Irvine, Margaret, illus. 2002. 40p. (J). (gr. k-2). 17.00 (978-0-15-201577-0(9)) Harcourt Children's Bks.

—Ice Drift. 2006. (Illus.). 240p. (J). pap. 5.95 (978-0-15-205550-9(9) , Harcourt Paperbacks) Harcourt Children's Bks.

Thompson, Kate. Switchers. 220p. (J). (gr. 4-7). pap. 5.99 (978-0-8072-1553-1(8)); 2004. (Switchers Ser.: Vol. 1). (gr. 5-9). pap. 38.00 incl. audio (978-0-8072-8138-3(7) , YA115SP) Random Hse. Audio Publishing Group. (Listening Library).

—Switchers. 1999. (978-0-606-17387-2(0)); (gr. 5-8). lib. bdg. 14.15 (978-0-613-20224-4(4)) Tandem Library Bks.

Turner, Bonnie. Haunted Igloo. 2002. (gr. 7-12). lib. bdg. 24.00 (978-0-613-74646-5(5)) Tandem Library Bks.

Verne, Jules. The Field of Ice: Part II of the Adventures of Captain Hatteras. 2006. 154p. pap. 11.99 ***(978-1-4264-3591-1(6))***; 168p. pap. 12.99 ***(978-1-4264-3642-0(4))*** BiblioBazaar.

Ward, Jennifer. Way up in the Arctic. Spengler, Kenneth J., illus. 2007. (SPA & ENG.). 32p. 15.95 ***(978-0-87358-928-4(9)*** , Rising Moon Bks. for Young Readers) Northland Publishing.

White, Kathryn. Snowshoe the Hare. Rivers, Ruth, illus. 2005. (Red Go Bananas Ser.). 43p. (J). lib. bdg. (978-0-7787-2677-7(0) , 1253648) Crabtree Publishing Co.

Whyman, Matt. Icecore: A Carl Hobbes Thriller. 2007. 320p. (YA). (gr. 7 up). 16.99 ***(978-1-4169-4907-7(0))*** Simon & Schuster Children's Publishing.

Wiebe, Rudy. The Mad Trapper. rev. ed. 2004. (Illus.). 184p. (YA). (gr. 9 up). pap. 9.95 (978-0-88995-268-3(X)) Red Deer Pr. CAN. *Dist:* Fitzhenry & Whiteside, Ltd.

ARDENNES, BATTLE OF THE, 1944-1945

Abnett, Dan & Verma, Dheeraj. Hitler's Last Gamble: Battle of the Bulge. Wagner, Ron & Cain, Bill, illus. 2007. (Graphic History Ser.). 48p. (J). pap. 9.95 ***(978-1-84603-057-4(9))*** Osprey Publishing, Ltd. GBR. *Dist:* Random Hse., Inc.

Anderson, Christopher A. The Fall of Fortress Europe. 2001. (G. I. Ser.). (Illus.). 80p. (J). 27.50 (978-0-7910-6669-0(X) , Chelsea Hse.) Facts On File, Inc.

McNeese, Tim. Battle of the Bulge. (Great Battles Through the Ages Ser.). (Illus.). 112p. (gr. 6-12). 2004. pap. 13.25 (978-0-7910-7794-8(2)); 2003. 30.00 (978-0-7910-7435-0(8)) Facts On File, Inc. (Chelsea Hse.).

Sears, Stephen W. The Battle of the Bulge. 2005. 160p. pap. 9.95 (978-0-7434-9333-8(8)) ibooks, Inc.

ARGENTINA

Argentina, a Primary Source. 2005. (Countries of the World Ser.). 19.95 (978-1-4042-2749-1(0) , PowerKids Pr.) Rosen Publishing Group, Inc., The.

Blashfield, Jean F. Argentina. 2007. (Enchantment of the World, Second Ser.). 144p. (YA). (gr. 5-9). 36.00 (978-0-516-24872-1(3) , Children's Pr.) Scholastic Library Publishing.

Burgan, Michael. Argentina. 1999. (True Bks.). (Illus.). 48p. (J). (gr. 3-5). 25.00 (978-0-516-21188-6(9) , Children's Pr.) Scholastic Library Publishing.

—Argentina. 1999. (Illus.). 47p. (J). (gr. 4-7). lib. bdg. 15.25 (978-0-613-54823-6(X)) Tandem Library Bks.

Conley, Kate A. Argentina. 2004. (Countries Ser.). (Illus.). 40p. (J). (gr. k-6). lib. bdg. 22.78 (978-1-59197-290-7(6)) ABDO Publishing Co.

Crooker, Richard A. Argentina. 2003. (Modern World Nations Ser.). (Illus.). 150p. (gr. 6-12). 30.00 (978-0-7910-7480-0(3) , Chelsea Hse.) Facts On File, Inc.

Dell'Oro, Suzanne Paul. Argentina. 1998. (Ticket to Ser.). (Illus.). 48p. (gr. 2-4). lib. bdg. 22.60 (978-1-57505-139-0(7)); (J). (gr. 3-5). lib. bdg. 22.60 (978-1-57505-114-7(1) , Carolrhoda Bks.) Lerner Publishing Group.

Dougherty, Terri. Argentina. 2003. (Modern Nations of the World Ser.). (Illus.). 112p. (J). 29.95 (978-1-59018-108-9(5) , Lucent Bks.) Thomson Gale.

Dubois, Muriel L. Argentina. 2001. (Countries of the World Ser.). (Illus.). 126p. (J). (gr. 2-3). 18.60 (978-0-7368-0811-8(6) , Bridgestone Bks.) Capstone Pr., Inc.

Englar, Mary. Argentina: A Question & Answer Book. 2006. (Fact Finders Ser.). (Illus.). 32p. (J). (978-0-7368-4350-8(7)) Capstone Pr., Inc.

Fearns, Daisy & Fearns, Les. Argentina. 2003. (Changing Face Of... Ser.). (Illus.). 48p. (J). 28.56 (978-0-7398-6040-3(2)); 28.56 (978-0-7398-5486-0(0)) Raintree.

Fearns, Les & Fearns, Daisy. Argentina. 2005. (Countries of the World Ser.). 64p. (J). (gr. 6-12). 30.00 (978-0-8160-6008-5(8)); Set 3. (Illus.). (gr. 9-12). 180.00 (978-0-8160-6320-8(6)) Facts On File, Inc.

Fontanarrosa, Roberto. Argentina Para Principiantes. 2002. (SPA.). 160p. (978-84-7901-891-7(7) , 8100) Oasis, Producciones Generales de Comunicacion, S.L.

Frank, Nicole. Argentina, , 1999. (Countries of the World Ser.). (Illus.). 96p. (J). (gr. 6 up). lib. bdg. 30.00 (978-0-8368-2315-8(X)) Stevens, Gareth Inc.

Furstinger, Nancy. Buenos Aires. 2005. (Cities Ser.). (Illus.). 32p. (J). (gr. k-6). lib. bdg. 22.78 (978-1-59197-855-8(6)) ABDO Publishing Co.

Gofen, E. & Jermyn, L. Argentina. 2nd ed. 2001. (Cultures of the World Ser.). (Illus.). 144p. (gr. 5 up). lib. bdg. 37.07 (978-0-7614-1358-5(8) , Benchmark Bks.) Cavendish, Marshall Corp.

Grolier Educational Staff, contrib. by. Argentina. 2003. (Illus.). 32p. (J). (978-0-7172-5789-8(4) , Grolier) Scholastic Library Publishing.

Harcourt School Publishers Staff. Social Studies: Argentina, Chile, Paraguay & Uruguay. 2000. (Harcourt Brace Social Studies). (Illus.). (gr. k-7). pap. 33.90 (978-0-15-317433-9(1)) Harcourt Schl. Pubs.

Hintz, Martin. Argentina. 2nd ed. 1998. (Enchantment of the World, Second Ser.). (Illus.). 144p. (J). (gr. 5-9). 36.00 (978-0-516-20647-9(8) , Children's Pr.) Scholastic Library Publishing.

Kent, Deborah. Buenos Aires. Downing, Joan, ed. 1998. (Cities of the World Ser.). (Illus.). 64p. (J). (gr. 4-9). pap. 9.95 (978-0-516-26326-7(9) , Children's Pr.) Scholastic Library Publishing.

Liebowitz, Sol. Argentina. 1999. (Major World Nations Ser.). (Illus.). 144p. (YA). (gr. 4-7). 29.95 (978-0-7910-4730-9(X) , Chelsea Hse.) Facts On File, Inc.

Link, Theodore & McCarthy, Rose. Argentina: A Primary Source Cultural Guide. 2004. (Primary Sources of World Cultures Ser.). (Illus.). 128p. (YA). lib. bdg. 34.60 (978-0-8239-3997-8(9)) Rosen Publishing Group, Inc., The.

Mesenas, Geraldine & Frank, Nicole. Welcome to Argentina. 2001. (Welcome to My Country Ser.). (Illus.). 48p. (J). (gr. 2 up). lib. bdg. 26.00 (978-0-8368-2515-2(2)) Stevens, Gareth Inc.

Morrison, Marion. Buenos Aires. 2005. (Great Cities of the World Ser.). (Illus.). 48p. (J). pap. (978-0-8368-5204-2(4)); (YA). lib. bdg. 30.00 (978-0-8368-5044-4(0)) Stevens, Gareth Inc. (World Almanac Library).

—Guide to Argentina. 1998. (World Guides Ser.). (Illus.). 32p. (J). (gr. 2-6). lib. bdg. 21.27 (978-1-884756-57-3(3)) Davidson Titles, Inc.

Nickles, Greg. Argentina: The Culture. 2001. (gr. 3-6). lib. bdg. 16.40 (978-0-613-32285-0(1)) Tandem Library Bks.

—Argentina: The Land. 2001. (gr. 3-6). lib. bdg. 16.40 (978-0-613-32286-7(X)) Tandem Library Bks.

—Argentina: The People. 2001. (gr. 3-6). lib. bdg. 16.40 (978-0-613-32287-4(8)) Tandem Library Bks.

—Argentina - The Culture. 2000. (Lands, Peoples & Cultures Ser.). (Illus.). 32p. (J). (gr. 4-5). (978-0-86505-246-8(8)); pap. (978-0-86505-326-7(X)) Crabtree Publishing Co.

—Argentina - The Land. 2000. (Lands, Peoples & Cultures Ser.). (Illus.). 32p. (J). (gr. 4-5). (978-0-86505-244-4(1)); pap. (978-0-86505-324-3(3)) Crabtree Publishing Co.

—Argentina - The People. 2000. (Lands, Peoples & Cultures Ser.). (Illus.). 32p. (J). (gr. 4-5). (978-0-86505-245-1(X)); pap. (978-0-86505-325-0(1)) Crabtree Publishing Co.

Park. Taking Your Camera To..., 6 vols., Set 3. 2000. pap. (978-0-7398-4136-5(X)) Steck-Vaughn.

Park, Ted. Taking Your Camera To..., Set 3. 2000. pap., tchr. ed. (978-0-7398-4135-8(1)) Steck-Vaughn.

—Taking Your Camera to Argentina. Sloan, Frank, ed. 2001. (Taking Your Camera to Ser.). (Illus.). 32p. (J). (gr. 4-7). lib. bdg. 22.83 (978-0-7398-3567-8(X)) Raintree.

—Taking Your Camera to Argentina. 2000. (Illus.). pap. (978-0-7398-4129-7(7)) Steck-Vaughn.

Selby, Anna. Argentina, Chile, Paraguay, Uruguay. 1999. (Country Fact Files Ser.). (Illus.). 48p. (J). (gr. 4-8). lib. bdg. 27.12 (978-0-8172-5408-7(0)) Raintree.

Shields, Charles J. Argentina. 2003. (Discovering Latin America Ser.). (Illus.). 64p. (J). (gr. 5 up). lib. bdg. (978-1-59084-285-0(5)) Mason Crest Pubs.

Spengler, Kremena. Eva Peron: First Lady of the People. 2006. (Fact Finders Ser.). 32p. (J). (gr. 1-3). 22.60 (978-0-7368-6415-2(6)) Capstone Pr., Inc.

Stille, Darlene R. Eva Peron, First Lady of Argentina. 2006. (Signature Lives Ser.). (Illus.). 112p. (J). (gr. 5-7). 30.60 (978-0-7565-1585-0(8)) Compass Point Bks.

Streissguth, Thomas & Streissguth, Tom. Argentina in Pictures. 2nd ed. 2003. (Visual Geography Ser.). (Illus.). 80p. (J). (gr. 5-12). 27.93 (978-0-8225-0372-9(7)) Lerner Publishing Group.

Taking Your Camera To... Includes: Argentina, China, Germany, India, South Africa, Vietnam, 6 bks., Set. 2001. (Taking Your Camera to Ser.). (Illus.). (J). (gr. 4-7). 136.98 (978-0-7398-3573-9(4)) Raintree.

ARGENTINA—FICTION

Ahrens, Mario. Tapiz Argentino. 2004. Orig. Title: Argentine Tapestry. (SPA.). 167p. per. 20.00 (978-0-9744675-1-1(0)) Pampa Publishing.

Alcantara, Ricardo. La Ronda de Cada Día. 2003. (SPA., Illus.). 176p. (978-84-236-3872-7(3) , ED1602) Edebé ESP. *Dist:* Lectorum Pubns., Inc.

Otero, Rodolfo. La Travesia. (SPA.). 112p. (YA). (gr. 5-8). (978-84-279-3152-7(2) , NG3670) Noguer y Caralt Editores, S. A. ESP. *Dist:* Lectorum Pubns., Inc.

Palermo, Miguel Angel. Lo Que Cuentan los Mapuches. Rojas, María P, illus. 2000. (Cuentamerica Ser.). (SPA.). 62p. (YA). (gr. 4). 7.95 (978-950-07-1738-0(7) , SA30065) Editorial Sudamericana S.A. ARG. *Dist:* Lectorum Pubns,, Inc.

Pechero-Loewen, Mariella. I Want to Know How You Found Me. 2004. 39p. pap. 17.95 (978-1-4137-2955-9(X)) PublishAmerica, Inc.

Roldan, Gustavo. Cuentos de Pedro Urdemales. Roldan, Gustavo, Jr., illus. 2000. (Cuentamerica Ser.). (SPA.). 62p. (YA). (gr. 4 up). pap. 7.95 (978-950-07-1760-1(3) , SA30060) Editorial Sudamericana S.A. ARG. *Dist:* Lectorum Pubns., Inc.

Smith, Roland. Jack's Run. 256p. (gr. 5-17). 2007. pap. 5.99 (*978-1-4231-0407-0(2)); 2005. 15.99 (978-0-7868-5592-6(4)) Hyperion Pr.

ARGENTINE REPUBLIC

see Argentina

ARGONAUTS

Colum, Padraic. The Golden Fleece & the Heroes Who Lived Before Achilles. Pogany, Willy, illus. 2004. 316p. (J). (gr. 4-8). reprint ed. pap. 10.00 (978-0-7567-7961-0(8)) DIANE Publishing Co.

Malam, John. Jason & the Argonauts. Antram, David, illus. 2004. (Ancient Myths Ser.). (J). (978-0-7565-0667-4(0)) Compass Point Bks.

—Jason & the Argonauts. Antram, David, illus. 2004. (Ancient Myths Ser.). 32p. (gr. 3-5). 23.93 (978-1-4048-0902-4(3)) Picture Window Bks.

ARGUMENTATION

see Debates and Debating; Logic

ARISTOTLE

Anderson, Margaret J. & Stephenson, Karen F. Aristotle: Philosopher & Scientist. 2004. (Great Minds of Science Ser.). (Illus.). 112p. (J). lib. bdg. 26.60 (978-0-7660-2096-2(7)) Enslow Pubs., Inc.

Whiting, Jim. Aristotle. 2006. (Biography from Ancient Civilizations Ser.). (Illus.). 48p. (J). lib. bdg. 20.95 (978-1-58415-508-9(6)) Mitchell Lane Pubs., Inc.

Williams, Brian. Aristotle. (Historical Biographies Ser.). 32p. 2003. pap. 7.50 (978-1-58810-997-2(6)); 2002. (Illus.). (J). (gr. 2-4). lib. bdg. 22.79 (978-1-58810-563-9(6)) Heinemann Library.

ARITHMETIC

Aboff, Marcie. The Lemonade Standoff. Olin, Troy, illus. 2007. (J). lib. bdg. (*978-1-4048-3668-6(3)) Picture Window Bks.

—Mike's Mystery. Muehlenhardt, Amy Bailey, illus. 2007. (J). lib. bdg. (*978-1-4048-3667-9(5)) Picture Window Bks.

—The Pizza Palace. Doerrfeld, Cori, illus. 2007. (J). lib. bdg. (*978-1-4048-3665-5(9)) Picture Window Bks.

Adams, Colleen. Magic Squares. 2006. (Rosen Publishing Group's Reading Room Collection). (Illus.). 16p. (J). lib. bdg. (978-1-4042-3335-5(0) , PowerKids Pr) Rosen Publishing Group, Inc., The.

Adding & Subtracting. 2003. (Gold Star Workbooks Ser.). (Illus.). 32p. (J). 2.98 (978-1-4054-1188-2(0)); 2.98 (978-1-4054-1189-9(9)) Parragon, Inc.

Addition. 2004. (Help with Homework Ser.). 32p. (J). (gr. k-2). wbk. ed. 3.99 (978-1-904586-23-4(6)) Byeway Bks.

Addition. 2000. (Math Windows Ser.). (J). pap. 0.99 (978-0-88724-849-8(7) , CD-3061) Carson-Dellosa Publishing Co., Inc.

Addition. (Classroom Helpers Ser.). 24p. (gr. k up). 3.99 (978-0-7682-0806-1(8) , FS194105) Schaffer, Frank Pubns.

Addition. 1998. (Play & Learn Ser.). (Illus.). 16p. (J). (gr. k-2). pap., wbk. ed. 3.95 (978-0-8069-3791-5(2) , Balloon Bks.) Sterling Publishing Co., Inc.

Addition: With Re-Usable Stickers. 1999. (Fun to Learn Ser.). (Illus.). 32p. (ps-3). 1.99 (978-1-58279-013-8(2) , 97) Trident Pr. International.

Addition Basic Facts Pack. 2000. (Math Windows Ser.). (J). pap. 4.50 (978-0-88724-855-9(1) , CD-3068) Carson-Dellosa Publishing Co., Inc.

Addition Basic Facts with Answers. 2000. (Math Windows Ser.). (J). pap. 0.99 (978-0-88724-861-0(6) , CD-3074) Carson-Dellosa Publishing Co., Inc.

Addition Sums 0-12. 2003. (Illus.). (gr. k up). 9.99 (978-0-7682-1896-1(9) , J41006) School Specialty Publishing.

Alpha Omega Publishing Staff. Horizons Math Kindergarten, Bk. 2. 2000. (Illus.). (J). pap., stu. ed. 12.50 (978-0-7403-0310-4(4) , JKS022) Alpha Omega Pubns., Inc.

—Mathematics, 2 bks., Set. 2004. (Illus.). pap. 59.95 (978-0-7403-0313-5(9) , JKC120, Horizons) Alpha Omega Pubns., Inc.

American Education Publishing Staff. Addition. 2003. (Brighter Child Learning Flash Cards Ser.). (Illus.). 36p. (J). 2.99 (978-1-56189-462-8(1) , 31045, American Education Publishing) School Specialty Publishing.

—Division. 2003. (Brighter Child Learning Flash Cards Ser.). (Illus.). 36p. (J). 2.99 (978-1-56189-465-9(6) , 31048, American Education Publishing) School Specialty Publishing.

—Subtraction. 2003. (Brighter Child Learning Flash Cards Ser.). (Illus.). 36p. (J). 2.99 (978-1-56189-463-5(X) , 31046, American Education Publishing) School Specialty Publishing.

Atkinson, Sue, et al. Seven Dizzy Dragons & Other Maths Rhymes Big Book. 1998. (New Cambridge Mathematics Ser.). (Illus.). 32p. (ps-1). pap. 50.00 (978-0-521-63421-2(0)) Cambridge Univ. Pr.

Ayers, Amy. Using Math at the Class Party. 2007. (J). pap. (*978-0-8368-8484-5(1)); 24p. (gr. 1-3). lib. bdg. 19.93 (*978-0-8368-8475-3(2)) Stevens, Gareth Inc. (Weekly Reader Early Learning Library).

Back to Basics: Multiplication. (Math Ser.). (J). incl. audio NewSound, LLC.

Back to Basics: Subtraction. (Math Ser.). (J). incl. audio NewSound, LLC.

Basic Skills Math Books: Addition & Subtraction. (Basic Skills Ser.). 48p. (gr. 4 up). 5.99 (978-1-56822-086-4(3) , IF5106) School Specialty Publishing.

Basic Skills Math Books: Addition, Subtraction, Multiplication, & Division. (Basic Skills Ser.). 48p. (gr. 5 up). 5.99 (978-1-56822-089-5(8) , IF5109) School Specialty Publishing.

Bauer, David. Sumando Animales del Artico. 2005. Tr. of Adding Arctic Animals. (SPA., Illus.). 16p. (J). (gr. k-1). lib. bdg. 15.93 (978-0-7368-4147-4(4)) Capstone Pr., Inc.

Beginning Multiplication & Division with Mr Wiggle. 32p. (gr. k up). 4.99 (978-1-56451-980-1(5) , ID99003); (gr. 1 up). 4.99 (978-1-56451-981-8(3) , ID99004); (gr. 2 up). 4.99 (978-1-56451-982-5(1) , ID99005) School Specialty Publishing.

Benchmark Education Staff, compiled by. Adding & Subtracting. 2006. spiral bd. 315.00 (*978-1-4108-7073-5(1)) Benchmark Education Co.

—Addition & Subtraction. 2006. spiral bd. 125.00 (*978-1-4108-7052-0(9)) Benchmark Education Co.

—Comparing Numbers. 2006. spiral bd. 99.00 (*978-1-4108-7093-3(6)) Benchmark Education Co.

Blood, Danielle. Multiplication. 2004. (Fun-flap Facts Ser.). 32p. pap. 8.99 (978-0-439-36544-4(9) , Teaching Resources) Scholastic, Inc.

Boothroyd, Jennifer. Skip Counting. 2007. (First Step Nonfiction Ser.). (J). pap. (978-0-8225-6828-5(4)) Lerner Publishing Group.

Brooks, Felicity. First Numbers. 2004. 48p. (J). pap. 8.99 (978-0-7945-0746-6(8) , Usborne) EDC Publishing.

Brown, Sam E. One, Two, Buckle My Shoe: Math Activities for Young Children. Libonn, Jula, illus. 2004. 112p. (Orig.). (ps). pap. 8.95 (978-0-87659-103-1(9) , 10300) Gryphon Hse., Inc.

Burstein, John. Making Tens: Groups of Gollywomples. Destiny Images Staff, illus. 2003. (Math Monsters Ser.). 24p. (YA). (gr. 1 up). lib. bdg. 19.33 (978-0-8368-3812-1(2) , Weekly Reader Early Learning Library) Stevens, Gareth Inc.

Cameron, Antonia, et al. Addition & Subtraction Minilessons, Grades PreK-3. 2004. (Young Mathematicians at Work Ser.). 64p. 49.50 (978-0-325-00675-8(X) , E00675) Heinemann.

Campbell, Mel. Grupos Desfilando. 2007. (J). (*978-1-60044-286-5(2)) Rourke Publishing, LLC.

Campbell, Mel. Parades of Arrays. 2007. (Illus.). 24p. (J). (978-1-59515-980-9(0)) Rourke Publishing, LLC.

Carder, Ken, et al. Songs That Teach Multiplication. 2006. (Songs That Teach Ser.). 72p. (J). pap. 14.95 (978-0-7696-7693-7(6) , American Education Publishing) School Specialty Publishing.

Caroll, Danielle. The Great Divide. 2006. 16p. (J). (gr. k-2). 15.93 (978-0-7368-5861-8(X) , Yellow Umbrella Bks.) Capstone Pr., Inc.

Caron, Lucille & St. Jacques, Philip M. Addition & Subtraction. 2001. (Math Success Ser.). (Illus.). 64p. (YA). (gr. 4-10). lib. bdg. 22.60 (978-0-7660-1432-9(0)) Enslow Pubs., Inc.

—Multiplication & Division. 2001. (Math Success Ser.). (Illus.). 64p. (YA). (gr. 4-10). lib. bdg. 22.60 (978-0-7660-1431-2(2)) Enslow Pubs., Inc.

—Percents & Ratios. 2000. (Math Success Ser.). (Illus.). 64p. (YA). (gr. 4-10). lib. bdg. 22.60 (978-0-7660-1435-0(5)) Enslow Pubs., Inc.

Carroll, Danielle. The Great Divide. 2005. (Yellow Umbrella Books for Early Readers). (Illus.). 16p. (J). (978-0-7368-5291-3(3)); (978-0-7368-5327-9(8)) Capstone Pr., Inc.

—Is It Odd or Even? 2005. (Yellow Umbrella Books for Early Readers). (Illus.). 17p. (J). (978-0-7368-5285-2(9)); (978-0-7368-5321-7(9)) Capstone Pr., Inc.

Catala, Ellen. Restar. 2005. Tr. of Take Away. (SPA., Illus.). 16p. (J). (gr. k-1). lib. bdg. 15.93 (978-0-7368-4132-0(6)) Capstone Pr., Inc.

Cato, Sheila. Addition. Sweeten, Sami, illus. 1998. (Question of Math Ser.). 32p. (J). (gr. k-3). lib. bdg. 25.26 (978-1-57505-320-2(9) , Carolrhoda Bks.) Lerner Publishing Group.

—Division. Sweeten, Sami, illus. 1999. (Question of Math Ser.). 32p. (J). (gr. k-3). lib. bdg. 25.26 (978-1-57505-319-6(5) , Carolrhoda Bks.) Lerner Publishing Group.

—Multiplication. Sweeten, Sami, illus. 1999. (Question of Math Ser.). 32p. (J). (gr. k-3). lib. bdg. 25.26 (978-1-57505-321-9(7) , Carolrhoda Bks.) Lerner Publishing Group.

—Subtraction. Sweeten, Sami, illus. 1999. (Question of Math Ser.). 32p. (J). (gr. k-3). lib. bdg. 25.26 (978-1-57505-318-9(7) , Carolrhoda Bks.) Lerner Publishing Group.

Chrismer, Melanie. Multiply This! 2005. (Rookie Read-About Math Ser.). (Illus.). 31p. (J). (ps-ps). 20.50 (978-0-516-25264-3(X) , Children's Pr.) Scholastic Library Publishing.

Cipriano, Jeri. Arithmetricks. 2nd ed. 2006. 160p. pap. (978-1-59647-112-2(3)) Good Year Bks.

Cipriano, Jeri S. Arithmetricks. 2004. (Illus.). 160p. pap. (978-0-673-58896-8(3)) Good Year Bks.

Cleary, Brian P. The Action of Subtraction. Gable, Brian, illus. 2006. (Math Is CATegorical Ser.). 32p. (J). 15.95 (978-0-7613-9461-7(3) , Millbrook Pr.) Lerner Publishing Group.

—The Mission of Addition. Gable, Brian, illus. 2005. (Math Is CATegorical Ser.). 32p. (J). (gr. k-2). lib. bdg. 15.95 (978-1-57505-859-7(6)) Lerner Publishing Group.

Clemson, Wendy. Adding & Subtracting. 2002. (gr. k-3). lib. bdg. 14.10 (978-0-613-45337-0(9)) Tandem Library Bks.

Clemson, Wendy & Clemson, David. Adding & Subtracting. 2004. (Math Magic Ser.). (Illus.). 32p. (gr. k-3). (J). pap. 5.95 (978-1-58728-272-0(0)); 9.95 (978-1-58728-268-3(2)) T&N Children's Publishing. (Two Can Publishing).

Clemson, Wendy & Clemson, David. Zookeeper for a Day. 2006. (Illus.). 32p. (J). pap. (*978-0-8368-8142-4(7)); (gr. 2-4). lib. bdg. 25.27 (*978-0-8368-7843-1(4)) Stevens, Gareth Inc.

Cole, Kate. Addition & Subtraction, No. 2. 1999. (Step Ahead Workbooks Ser.). (Illus.). 64p. (J). (gr. 1-2). pap., wbk. ed. 3.99 (978-0-307-03652-0(9) , 03652, Golden Bks.) Random Hse. Children's Bks.

Collins, Kathleen. Our New Fish Tank. 2006. (Illus.). 16p. (J). lib. bdg. 25.25 (978-1-4042-3338-6(5) , PowerKids Pr.) Rosen Publishing Group, Inc., The.

Dahl, Michael. Eggs & Legs: Counting by Twos. Ouren, Todd, illus. 2004. (Know Your Numbers Ser.). 24p. (C). (gr. k-3). 22.60 (978-1-4048-0945-1(7)) Picture Window Bks.

—Plenty of Petals: Counting by 10s. Trover, Zachary, illus. 2006. 24p. (J). (ps-2). 22.60 (978-1-4048-1317-5(9)) Picture Window Bks.

—Speed, Speed Centipede! Counting by 10s. Trover, Zachary, illus. 2006. 24p. (J). (ps-2). 22.60 (978-1-4048-1316-8(0)) Picture Window Bks.

—Tail Feather Fun: Counting by 10s. Trover, Zachary, illus. 2006. 24p. (J). (ps-2). 22.60 (978-1-4048-1319-9(5)) Picture Window Bks.

—Toasty Toes: Counting by 10s. Trover, Zachary, illus. 2006. 24p. (J). (ps-2). 22.60 (978-1-4048-1320-5(9)) Picture Window Bks.

Dalton, Julie. Farmers Market Rounding. 2006. (Rookie Read-About Math Ser.). (Illus.). 31p. (J). (978-0-516-25424-1(3)) Children's Pr., Ltd.

Davis, Rebecca Fjelland. More or Less: A Rain Forest Counting Book. 2007. (Illus.). 32p. (J). 23.93 (978-0-7368-6376-6(1)) Capstone Pr., Inc.

DeGroat, Harry De W. & Firman, Sidney G. The Iroquois Arithmetics for School & Life Book: Grades Five & Six. 2005. reprint ed. pap. 31.95 (978-1-4179-3343-3(7)) Kessinger Publishing, LLC.

—The Iroquois Arithmetics for School & Life Book: Grades Seven & Eight. 2005. reprint ed. pap. 33.95 (978-1-4191-7680-7(3)) Kessinger Publishing, LLC.

Dillon, Susan. Addition & Subtraction: Dozens of Leveled Practice Pages to Improve Students' Speed & Accuracy with Math Facts. 2006. 48p. pap. 10.99 (978-0-439-54885-4(3) , Teaching Resources) Scholastic, Inc.

—Addition Subtraction Flashcard Games: 25 Fun Games to Improve Speed & Accuracy in Computation. 2004. 48p. pap. 14.99 (978-0-439-64015-2(6) , Teaching Resources) Scholastic, Inc.

—Multiplication & Division: Dozens of Leveled Practice Pages to Improve Students' Speed & Accuracy with Math Facts. 2006. 48p. pap. 10.99 (978-0-439-54886-1(1) , Teaching Resources) Scholastic, Inc.

—Multiplication & Division Flashcard Games: 25 Fun Games to Improve Speed & Accuracy in Computation. 2004. 48p. pap. 14.99 (978-0-439-64225-5(6) , Teaching Resources) Scholastic, Inc.

Disney Magic Math Machine: Addition & Subtraction. 2005. (Illus.). 16p. (ps-1). 14.99 (978-0-7868-3644-4(X)) Disney Pr.

Division. 2000. (Math Windows Ser.). (J). pap. 0.99 (978-0-88724-852-8(7) , CD-3065) Carson-Dellosa Publishing Co., Inc.

Division. 2003. (Sabio y Prudente Ser.). (SPA., Illus.). 64p. (J). 4.99 (978-0-8254-0912-7(8)) Kregel Pubns.

Division. 2001. (Early Math Ser.). (J). (gr. k-12). vinyl bd. 4.95 (978-1-58845-065-4(1)) School Specialty Publishing.

Diyan Leake. Adding & Counting On. 2006. (Illus.). 24p. (J). pap. (*978-1-4034-8160-3(1)) Heinemann Library.

Dorling Kindersley Publishing Staff, ed. Animal Counting. 2004. (Baby Genius Ser.). (Illus.). 12p. (J). bds. 6.99 (978-0-7566-0570-4(9)) Dorling Kindersley Publishing, Inc.

Douglas, Vincent. Math, Time, & Money. 2004. (Flash Card Collection). 324p. (C). 16.95 (978-1-58845-663-2(3)) School Specialty Publishing.

Douglas, Vincent & School Specialty Publishing Staff. Addition. 2003. (Brighter Child Flash Cards Ser.). (Illus.). 54p. (J). (ps up). 2.99 (978-0-7696-2365-8(4) , Brighter Child) School Specialty Publishing.

—Division. (Brighter Child Flash Cards Ser.). (Illus.). (J). (ps up). 2003. 54p. 2.99 (978-0-7696-2368-9(9) , Brighter Child); 2000. 50p. 2.99 (978-1-57768-158-8(4) , Spectrum) School Specialty Publishing.

—Subtraction. (Brighter Child Flash Cards Ser.). (Illus.). (J). (ps up). 2003. 54p. 2.99 (978-0-7696-2397-9(2) , Brighter Child); 2000. 50p. 2.99 (978-1-57768-168-7(1) , Spectrum) School Specialty Publishing.

Douglas, Vincent F. & School Specialty Publishing Staff. Multiplication. 2003. (Brighter Child Flash Cards Ser.). (Illus.). 54p. (J). (ps up). 2.99 (978-0-7696-2379-5(4) , Brighter Child) School Specialty Publishing.

Ehrlich, Fred. You Can't Buy a Dinosaur with Dime. 2007. (Illus.). 32p. pap. 6.95 (*978-1-59354-591-8(6)) Blue Apple Bks.

Endres, Hollie J. Fair Share. (J). (gr. k-2). 2006. 16p. 15.93 (978-0-7368-5852-6(0) , Yellow Umbrella Bks.); 2005. (Illus.). 17p. (978-0-7368-5318-7(9)); 2005. (Illus.). 17p. (978-0-7368-5282-1(4)) Capstone Pr., Inc.

—How Much Money? (J). (gr. k-2). 2006. (Illus.). 16p. 15.93 (978-0-7368-5859-5(8) , Yellow Umbrella Bks.); 2005. (978-0-7368-5325-5(1)); 2005. (Illus.). 16p. (978-0-7368-5289-0(1)) Capstone Pr., Inc.

Evans, Renee Call & Perucca, Nancy Call. Multiplication Camp. Perucca, Nancy Call, illus. 2004. (J). pap. 29.95 (978-0-9748074-0-9(0)) Nancy's Artworks.

Faulkner, Keith. Flip-Flap Math: Flip the Flpas to Check Your Answers! Irish, Martin, illus. 2005. 12 p.p. (J). (***978-0-439-78578-5(2)***) Scholastic, Inc.

—Maths Machine: A Fun New Way to Do Maths! Tyger, Rory, illus. 2004. (J). (***978-0-439-72174-5(1)***) Scholastic, Inc.

Faulkner, Keith & Holmes, Stephen. Animal ? Math. Faulkner, Keith & Holmes, Stephen, illus. 2003. (Illus.). (J). (978-0-439-62755-9(9)) Scholastic, Inc.

Fayen, Rosemary. Seven Times Down Eight Times Up. 2001. 45p. (J). (gr. 5-7). pap. (978-0-9706494-0-9(1)) Fajen, Rosemary Faces In Education.

Ferris, Julie. Galaxy Getaway: A Math Puzzle Adventure. Tassie, Jane, illus. 2000. (Math for Martians Ser.). 32p. (J). (gr. 1-3). pap. (978-0-7534-5276-9(6)) Kingfisher Publications, plc.

Finifrock, Jacob E. & Pierson, Melinda. Multiplicity: Lesson Planning Guide. 2004. 85p. spiral bd. 21.95 (978-1-930731-18-9(3)) DAC Educational Pubns.

Fisher, Valorie. How High Can a Dinosaur Count? ...and Other Math Mysteries. Fisher, Valorie, illus. 2006. (Illus.). 40p. (J). (gr. k-4). 16.95 (978-0-375-83608-4(X) , Schwartz & Wade Bks.) Random Hse. Children's Bks.

Fontes, Justine. Cheerios Count to 100. Croll, Carolyn, illus. 2005. (***978-0-439-70341-3(7)***) Scholastic, Inc.

Fosnot, Catherine Twomey & Dolk, Maarten. Multiplication & Division Minilessons, Grades 3-5. 2005. (Young Mathematicians at Work Ser.). (J). (gr. 3-5). cd-rom 25.00 (978-0-325-00775-5(6) , E00775) Heinemann.

Fractions, Decimals & Percents: The Three Mathketeers. 2002. (J). pap., stu. ed. 10.95 (978-1-58123-326-1(4)) Larson Learning, Inc.

Francis, Eugenia. Ensene a Su Hijo: Las Tablas de Multiplicas (Written in Spanish) 2007. 169p. pap. 14.95 (***978-0-7414-3998-7(0)***) Infinity Publishing.

Franco, Betsy. Subtraction Fun. 2002. (Yellow Umbrella Books). (Illus.). 16p. (J). (gr. 1). lib. bdg. 14.60 (978-0-7368-1287-0(3) , Pebble Bks.) Capstone Pr., Inc.

Freeman, Marcia S. More Ice Cream: Words for Math Comparisons. 2008. (J). (***978-1-60044-641-2(8)***) Rourke Publishing, LLC.

—Multiply by Hand: The Nines Facts. 2008. (J). (***978-1-60044-643-6(4)***) Rourke Publishing, LLC.

Gant, Robert, illus. My Big Box of Addition & Subtraction. gif. ed. 2005. 64p. (J). cd-rom 24.95 (978-1-57791-196-8(2)) Brighter Minds Children's Publishing.

Geisert, Arthur. Roman Numerals I to MM: Liber de Difficillimo Computando Numerum. Geisert, Arthur, illus. 2001. Tr. of Numerabilia Romana Uno ad Duo Mila. (Illus.). 32p. (J). (gr. k-3). pap. 6.95 (978-0-618-15321-3(7) , Walter Lorraine) Houghton Mifflin Co. Trade & Reference Div.

Glenn, Suki & Carpenter, Susan. Patterns in Arithmetic: Book 1. Minns, Karen M. C., illus. 2004. 305p. (YA). spiral bd. 45.00 (978-0-9729248-2-5(5)) Pattern Pr.

—Patterns in Arithmetic: Student Workbook: Book 1, 2 vols. 2004. (Illus.). 150p. (YA). ring bd., wbk. ed. 15.00 (978-0-9729248-1-8(7)) Pattern Pr.

—Patterns in Arithmetic 2: Parent/Teacher Guide & Student Workbook: Book 2. Minns, Karen Marie Christa, illus. 2005. (ENG.). 536p. (gr. 2 up). spiral bd. 62.50 (978-0-9729248-5-6(X)) Pattern Pr.

—Patterns in Arithmetic Bk. 2: Student Workbook. 2005. (Illus.). 278p. (J). (gr. 2 up). ring bd., wbk. ed. 22.00 (978-0-9729248-4-9(1)) Pattern Pr.

Great Leaps Oral Calculations - Easel. 2006. 10.00 (978-1-59347-632-8(9)) Diarmuid Inc.

Great Leaps Oral Calculations Addition. 2006. spiral bd. 20.00 (978-1-59347-628-1(0)) Diarmuid Inc.

Great Leaps Oral Calculations addition & Subtraction. 2006. (J). (gr. 1-4). spiral bd. 49.50 net. (978-1-59347-626-7(4)) Diarmuid Inc.

Great Leaps Oral Calculations Division. 2006. spiral bd. 20.00 (978-1-59347-631-1(0)) Diarmuid Inc.

Great Leaps Oral Calculations Multiplication. 2006. spiral bd. 20.00 (978-1-59347-630-4(2)) Diarmuid Inc.

Great Leaps Oral Calculations Multiplication & Division. 2006. (J). (gr. 3-7). spiral bd. 49.50 net. (978-1-59347-627-4(2)) Diarmuid Inc.

Great Leaps Oral Calculations Package: Addition, Subtraction, Mutiplication & Division. 2006. (J). (gr. 1). spiral bd. 72.60 net. (978-1-59347-625-0(6)) Diarmuid Inc.

Great Leaps Oral Calculations Subtraction. 2006. spiral bd. 20.00 (978-1-59347-629-8(9)) Diarmuid Inc.

Grundrechenarten 1. (Duden-Schuelerhilfen Ser.). (GER.). 96p. (J). (978-3-411-02636-4(7)) Bibliographisches Institut & F. A. Brockhaus AG DEU. *Dist:* International Bk. Import Service, Inc.

Grundrechenarten 2. (Duden-Schuelerhilfen Ser.). (GER.). 96p. (J). (gr. 3-4). (978-3-411-04561-7(2)) Bibliographisches Institut & F. A. Brockhaus AG DEU. *Dist:* International Bk. Import Service, Inc.

Handley, Bill. Speed Math for Kids: The Fast, Fun Way to Do Basic Calculations. 2007. 256p. pap. 12.95 (978-0-7879-8863-0(4) , Jossey-Bass) Wiley, John & Sons, Inc.

Harcourt, Lalie & Wortzman, Rickie. Red Riding Hood's Math Adventure. Mazille, Capucine, illus. 2006. 19p. (J). (gr. k-4). reprint ed. 15.00 (978-0-7567-9957-1(0)) DIANE Publishing Co.

Harris, Trudy. 100 Days of School. 2000. (J). (978-0-606-20193-3(9)) Tandem Library Bks.

Hein, Marilyn B. Math Phonics, Multiplication & Division Bonus Book. Mitchell, Judy, ed. Wheeler, Ron, illus. 2002. 96p. (J). (gr. 3-6). pap. 9.95 (978-1-57310-346-6(2)) Teaching & Learning Co.

Hirschmann, Kris. Necco Sweethearts: Math Magic. 2001. (978-0-606-22249-5(9)) Tandem Library Bks.

Hoffman, Mary Ann. Numbers Operations. 2004. 48p. pap. 6.95 (978-1-4042-8542-2(3)) Rosen Publishing Group, Inc., The.

Hofmeyr, Dianne. Mama Mabena's Magic: Ndebele Version. Dube, Grace, tr. 1999. (Cambridge African Language Library Ser.). (NBL & NDE., Illus.). 16p. pap. 3.70 (978-0-521-65828-7(4)) Cambridge Univ. Pr.

Hop, L. L. C. Hooked on First Grade: Simple Addition & Subtraction. 2006. 64p. 3.79 (978-1-931020-69-5(8)) HOP, LLC.

—Hooked on First-Grade Super Workbook. 2006. 320p. 12.99 (978-1-931020-74-9(4)) HOP, LLC.

—Hooked on Kindergarten Super Workbook. 2006. 320p. 12.99 (978-1-931020-73-2(6)) HOP, LLC.

HOP LLC Staff. Hooked on Math - Division. 2005. (J). (gr. 3-5). 64.99 (978-1-931020-52-7(3)) HOP, LLC.

—Hooked on Math - Multiplication. 2005. (J). (gr. 2-4). 64.99 (978-1-931020-51-0(5)) HOP, LLC.

Howett, Jerry. Contemporary's Number Power: Addition, Subtraction, Multiplication, & Division, Vol. 1. 2nd ed. 2000. (Number Power Ser.: Vol. 1). (Illus.). 192p. pap. 15.55 (978-0-8092-2380-0(5) , Contemporary Bks.) McGraw-Hill Trade.

HSP. Addition, Bk. B. 2nd ed. 2002. (First-Place Math Ser.). (gr. 2 up). pap. 12.60 (978-0-15-334616-3(7)) Harcourt Schl. Pubs.

—Addition & Subtraction. 2nd ed. 2002. (First-Place Math Ser.). Bk. D. (gr. 2 up). pap. 12.60 (978-0-15-334618-7(3)); Bk. A. (gr. 3 up). pap. 12.60 (978-0-15-334621-7(3)); Bk. A. (gr. 4 up). pap. 12.60 (978-0-15-334627-9(2)) Harcourt Schl. Pubs.

—Addition & Subtraction Facts to 10, Bk. B. 2nd ed. 2002. (First-Place Math Ser.). (gr. 1 up). pap. 12.60 (978-0-15-334610-1(8)) Harcourt Schl. Pubs.

—Addition Facts to 18, Bk. C. 2nd ed. 2002. (First-Place Math Ser.). (gr. 1 up). pap. 12.60 (978-0-15-334611-8(6)) Harcourt Schl. Pubs.

—Book F: Addition & Subtraction. 2nd ed. 2002. (First-Place Math Ser.). (gr. k up). pap. 9.60 (978-0-15-334608-8(6)) Harcourt Schl. Pubs.

—Numbers to 100, Bk. A. 2nd ed. 2002. (First-Place Math Ser.). (gr. 1 up). pap. 12.60 (978-0-15-334609-5(4)) Harcourt Schl. Pubs.

—Subtraction, Bk. C. 2nd ed. 2002. (First-Place Math Ser.). (gr. 2 up). pap. 12.60 (978-0-15-334617-0(5)) Harcourt Schl. Pubs.

—Subtraction Facts to 18, Bk. D. 2nd ed. 2002. (First-Place Math Ser.). (gr. 1 up). pap. 12.60 (978-0-15-334612-5(4)) Harcourt Schl. Pubs.

Hudson, Dave. Multiplication I: Facts 0-81. Rogers, Kathy, ed. 1999. (Best Value Drillbooks Ser.). (Illus.). 32p. (J). pap., wbk. ed. 3.99 (978-1-56472-137-2(X) , EP137) Edupress, Inc.

—Multiplication II: Multi-Digit. Rogers, Kathy, ed. 1999. (Best Value Drillbooks Ser.). 32p. (J). pap. 3.99 (978-1-56472-138-9(8) , EP138) Edupress, Inc.

Hunt, Roger & Hunt, Mary. Fun with Subtraction. (Basic Math Ser.: No. 678-2). (Illus.). 52p. (J). (gr. 1-3). 3.50 (978-0-7214-0705-0(6) , Dutton Juvenile) Penguin Group (USA) Inc.

Ideal. Addition, 100 Cards. 1999. (Vertical Flash Cards Ser.). (J). (gr. k-9). 7.99 (978-1-56451-551-3(6) , ID7236) School Specialty Publishing.

—Division, 90 Cards. 1999. (Vertical Flash Cards Ser.). (J). (gr. 4-9). 7.99 (978-1-56451-554-4(0) , ID7239) School Specialty Publishing.

—Multiplication, 100 Cards. 1999. (Vertical Flash Cards Ser.). (J). (gr. 3-9). 7.99 (978-1-56451-553-7(2) , ID7238) School Specialty Publishing.

—Subtraction, 100 Cards. 1999. (Vertical Flash Cards Ser.). (J). (gr. 1-9). 7.99 (978-1-56451-552-0(4) , ID7237) School Specialty Publishing.

I'm Learning to Add. 2004. (Flash Card + Music CD Learning Kits Ser.). (Illus.). 20p. 18.99 (978-1-894677-62-2(5)) Kidzup Productions.

Instructional Fair. Timed Math Tests: Addition & Subtraction. 2002. (100+ Seriestm Ser.). 128p. (J). (gr. 2-5). pap. 12.99 (978-0-7424-0226-3(6) , IF87115) School Specialty Publishing.

—Timed Math Tests: Multiplication & Division. 2002. (100+ Seriestm Ser.). 128p. (J). (gr. 2-5). pap. 12.99 (978-0-7424-0227-0(4) , IF87116) School Specialty Publishing.

Jaffe, Elizabeth Dana. Can You Eat a Fraction? 2002. (Yellow Umbrella Books). (Illus.). 16p. (J). (gr. 1). lib. bdg. 14.60 (978-0-7368-1279-5(2) , Pebble Bks.) Capstone Pr., Inc.

John, Nelson A. Multiplication Tables Plus. 1999. 64p. (YA). (gr. 3 up). 9.95 (978-1-877633-48-5(8)) Luthers.

Kidzup Productions Staff. I'm Learning to Multiply. 2004. 54p. (J). (gr. 1-3). audio compact disk 18.99 (978-1-894677-65-3(X)) Kidzup Productions.

Kiernan, Denise. Math Games to Master Basic Skills: Multiplication & Division: Familiar & Flexible Games with Dozens of Variations That Help Struggling Learners Practice & Really Master Multiplication & Division Facts. 2007. 48p. pap. 10.99 (978-0-439-51773-7(7) , Teaching Resources) Scholastic, Inc.

Kirkby, David. Numbers. 1998. (Mini Math Ser.). (J). (978-1-57572-001-2(9)) Heinemann Library.

Klein, Adria. El Numero Impar Trece: Metro Math Readers Yellow Level. 2000. (Metro Math Readers Yellow Level Ser.). (J). (gr. 1-2). 3.75 (978-1-58120-481-0(7)) Metropolitan Teaching & Learning Co.

—Which One is More? Metro Math Readers Yellow Level. 2000. (Metro Math Readers Yellow Level Ser.). (J). (gr. 1-2). 3.75 (978-1-58120-420-9(5)) Metropolitan Teaching & Learning Co.

Kompelien, Tracy. I Can Add, It's Not So Bad! (Math Made Fun Ser.). (Illus.). 24p. (J). 2007. 19.93 (978-1-59928-513-9(4)); 2006. pap. (978-1-59928-514-6(2)) ABDO Publishing Co.

—I Can Divide, I Need No Guide! (Math Made Fun Ser.). (Illus.). 24p. (J). 2007. 19.93 (978-1-59928-515-3(0)); 2006. pap. (978-1-59928-516-0(9)) ABDO Publishing Co.

—I Can Multiply, It's Not a Lie! (Math Made Fun Ser.). (Illus.). 24p. (J). 2007. 19.93 (978-1-59928-521-4(5) , SandCastle); 2006. pap. (978-1-59928-522-1(3)) ABDO Publishing Co.

—I Can Subtract, It's Not an ACT! (Math Made Fun Ser.). (Illus.). 24p. (J). 2007. 19.93 (978-1-59928-523-8(1)); 2006. pap. (978-1-59928-524-5(X)) ABDO Publishing Co.

—I Know about Money, It Is so Funny! 2007. (Math Made Fun Ser.). (Illus.). 24p. (J). 19.93 (978-1-59928-527-6(4) , SandCastle) ABDO Publishing Co.

—Skip Count by 10, Let's Do It Again. 2007. (Math Made Fun Ser.). (Illus.). 24p. (J). 19.93 (978-1-59928-541-2(X) , SandCastle) ABDO Publishing Co.

—Skip Count by 10, Let's Do It Again! 2006. (Math Made Fun Ser.). (Illus.). 24p. (J). pap. (978-1-59928-542-9(8)) ABDO Publishing Co.

—Skip Count by 2, Now Can You? (Math Made Fun Ser.). (Illus.). 24p. (J). 2007. 19.93 (978-1-59928-545-0(2) , SandCastle); 2006. pap. (978-1-59928-546-7(0)) ABDO Publishing Co.

—Skip Count by 5, It's No Jive. 2007. (Math Made Fun Ser.). (Illus.). 24p. (J). 19.93 (978-1-59928-543-6(6) , SandCastle) ABDO Publishing Co.

—Skip Count by 5, It's No Jive! 2006. (Math Made Fun Ser.). (Illus.). 24p. (J). pap. (978-1-59928-544-3(4)) ABDO Publishing Co.

Kumon Publishing, creator. My Book of Simple Addition. 2005. (Illus.). 80p. per. 6.95 (978-1-933241-00-5(4)) Kumon Publishing North America, Inc.

—My Book of Simple Subtraction, 20 vols. 2005. (Illus.). 80p. (J). (ps-3). per. 6.95 (978-1-933241-06-7(3)) Kumon Publishing North America, Inc.

—My Book of Subtraction, 20 vols. 2005. (Illus.). 80p. (J). (gr. 4-7). per. 6.95 (978-1-933241-07-4(1)) Kumon Publishing North America, Inc.

Lalley, Kristine. How Many Legs? 2006. (Rosen Publishing Group's Reading Room Collection). (Illus.). 16p. (J). lib. bdg. (978-1-4042-3336-2(9) , PowerKids Pr.) Rosen Publishing Group, Inc., The.

Leap Frog Awesome Addition Wipe off Mat. 2006. (J). 3.95 (***978-1-59545-089-0(0)***) Learning Horizons, Inc.

Learning Horizons, creator. Addition: Decoder Workbook. 2005. (Illus.). 24p. (J). (gr. k-1). pap. 3.95 (978-1-58610-883-0(2) , 72006) Learning Horizons, Inc.

Learning Wrap-Ups Addition. 2004. 7.99 (978-0-943343-26-6(7)) Learning Wrap-Ups.

Learning Wrap-Ups Division. 2004. 7.99 (978-0-943343-29-7(1)); 18.99 (978-0-943343-98-3(4)) Learning Wrap-Ups.

Learning Wrap-Ups Multiplication. 2004. 18.99 (978-0-943343-00-6(3)); 7.99 (978-0-943343-28-0(3)) Learning Wrap-Ups.

Learning Wrap-Ups Subtraction. 2004. 7.99 (978-0-943343-27-3(5)); 18.99 (978-0-943343-99-0(2)) Learning Wrap-Ups.

Leedy, Loreen. Subtraction Action. Leedy, Loreen, illus. 2005. (Illus.). 32p. (J). (gr. k-3). 6.95 (978-0-8234-1764-3(6)) Holiday Hse., Inc.

Leffingwell, Richard. Adding & Counting On. 2006. (J). pap. (978-1-4034-8165-8(2)); (Illus.). 24p. 21.36 (978-1-4034-8155-9(5)) Steck-Vaughn.

—Compartir y Dividir. 2006. (ENG & SPA.). (J). (***978-1-4034-9189-3(5)); pap. (978-1-4034-9194-7(1))*** Heinemann Library.

—Duplicar y Multiplicar. 2006. (ENG & SPA.). (J). (***978-1-4034-9188-6(7)); pap. (978-1-4034-9193-0(3))*** Heinemann Library.

—Restar y Quitar. 2006. (ENG & SPA.). (J). (***978-1-4034-9187-9(9)); pap. (978-1-4034-9192-3(5))*** Heinemann Library.

—Sharing & Dividing. 2006. (Illus.). 24p. (J). 21.36 (978-1-4034-8158-0(X)); pap. (978-1-4034-8163-4(6)) Steck-Vaughn.

—Subtracting & Taking Away. 2006. (Illus.). 24p. (J). 21.36 (978-1-4034-8156-6(3)); pap. (978-1-4034-8161-0(X)) Steck-Vaughn.

Leffingwell, Richard. Sumar y Contar Hacia Adelante. 2006. (ENG & SPA.). (J). (***978-1-4034-9186-2(0)); pap. (978-1-4034-9191-6(7))*** Heinemann Library.

Leffingwell, Richard & Leake, Diyan. Doubling & Multiplying: Creating an Image. 2006. (Illus.). 24p. (J). 21.36 (978-1-4034-8157-3(1)); pap. (978-1-4034-8162-7(8)) Steck-Vaughn.

Levy, Janey. At Sea on a Viking Ship. 2004. (PowerMath Ser.). (Illus.). 24p. (J). lib. bdg. 21.25 (978-0-8239-8977-5(1) , PowerKids Pr.) Rosen Publishing Group, Inc., The.

—At Sea on a Viking Ship: Solving Problems of Length & Weight Using the Four Math Operations. 2004. (PowerMath Ser.). (Illus.). 24p. (J). pap. (978-0-8239-8922-5(4) , PowerKids Pr.) Rosen Publishing Group, Inc., The.

—Numbers Operations. 2005. 48p. pap. 6.95 (978-1-4042-8572-9(5)) Rosen Publishing Group, Inc., The.

—Recipes for a Medieval Feast: Working Flexibly with Fractions. 2006. (Math for the Real World Ser.). (Illus.). 32p. (J). pap. (978-1-4042-6061-0(7)); lib. bdg. (978-1-4042-3354-6(7)) Rosen Publishing Group, Inc., The.

Lewis, J. Patrick. Arithme-Tickle: An Even Number of Odd Riddle-Rhymes. Remkiewicz, Frank, illus. 2007. 32p. (J). (gr. 1-4). pap. 6.00 (978-0-15-205848-7(6) , Voyager Bks./Libros Viajeros) Harcourt Children's Bks.

—Arithme-Tickle: An Even Number of Odd Riddle-Rhymes. Remkiewicz, Frank, illus. 2002. 32p. (J). (gr. 1-4). 16.00 (978-0-15-216418-8(9) , Silver Whistle) Harcourt Trade Pubs.

Liautaud, Judy. Times Tables the Fun Way Activity Book: Color your own posters & make your own flash Cards black & white version of Times Tables the Fun Way Book for Kids. Bagley, Val Chadwick, illus. 1998. 98p. (J). (gr. 2-8). pap. 11.95 (978-1-883841-48-5(8)) City Creek Pr., Inc.

Lin, Jonathon. Discovering Multiplication & Division. Abouzhar, H. & Nowakowski, P., illus. 2002. 40p. cd-rom 19.95 (978-1-59022-015-3(3)) Glory Educational Resource, Inc.

Linde, Barbara M. The Price of a Pioneer Journey. 2006. (Rosen Publishing Group's Reading Room Collection). (Illus.). 16p. (J). lib. bdg. (978-1-4042-3337-9(7) , PowerKids Pr.) Rosen Publishing Group, Inc., The.

—Working at the Farmers' Market: Solving Money Problems Involving the Four Math Operations. 2004. (PowerMath Ser.). (Illus.). 24p. (J). lib. bdg. (978-0-8239-8920-1(8)); lib. bdg. 21.25 (978-0-8239-8975-1(5)) Rosen Publishing Group, Inc., The. (PowerKids Pr.).

Linderman, Bill. Basic Skills Math Books: Addition & Subtraction. 1999. (Basic Skills Ser.). 43p. (J). (gr. 2-3). pap. 6.99 (978-1-56822-084-0(7) , IF5104) School Specialty Publishing.

—Basic Skills Math Books: Multiplication & Division. 1999. (Basic Skills Ser.). (J). 43p. (gr. 2-3). pap. 6.99 (978-1-56822-085-7(5) , IF5105); 48p. (gr. 4 up). pap. 5.99 (978-1-56822-087-1(1) , IF5107) School Specialty Publishing.

—Fractions. 1999. (Basic Skills Ser.). 48p. (J). (gr. 4-4). pap. 6.99 (978-1-56822-088-8(X) , IF5108, Instructional Fair) Schaffer, Frank Pubns.

Llewellyn, Claire. Sums. Anness Publishing Staff, ed. 1999. (Fun to Learn Ser.). (Illus.). 48p. (ps-1). 7.95 (978-0-7548-0210-5(8) , Lorenz Bks.) Anness Publishing GBR. *Dist:* National Bk. Network.

—Sums. 2003. (Playschool Ser.). (Illus.). 32p. pap. 5.99 (978-1-84215-855-5(4) , Southwater) Anness Publishing GBR. *Dist:* National Bk. Network.

Long, Lynette. Dealing with Addition. 1998. (978-0-606-13322-7(4)) Tandem Library Bks.

Lucas, Jerry. The Times Tables: A Fun & Easy Way to Learn Through Pictures! 2000. (Ready - Set - Remember Ser.). (Illus.). 112p. (J). pap. 23.95 (978-1-930853-05-8(X) , 967-006) Lucas Educational Systems.

Mahlangu, Lindi. Scary Footsteps. Tadjo, Veronique, tr. from ENG. 1998. (Cambridge African Language Library). (FRE., Illus.). 16p. pap. 3.75 (978-0-521-64791-5(6)) Cambridge Univ. Pr.

Martin, Susan. The Combiners: Understanding Addition & Multiplication Word Problems. Martin, Susan, illus. l.t. ed. 1999. (Illus.). 80p. (J). (gr. 3-6). pap. 14.95 (978-0-941530-39-2(6)) Move It Math.

Martyr, Paula. Dial-a-Times Table. 2000. (Illus.). 12p. (J). (ps-3). 7.99 (978-0-7858-1234-0(2)) Book Sales, Inc.

Math Art Gr. 1-2 Spanish Version. 2007. (J). per. (***978-1-58232-164-6(7)***) Bryan Hse. Pubs., Inc.

Math Art Gr. 2-3 Spanish Version. 2007. (J). per. (***978-1-58232-165-3(5)***) Bryan Hse. Pubs., Inc.

Math Core Assignments: From Addition to Subtraction Student Materials. 1999. 75p. (J). pap., stu. ed. 5.00 (978-1-889630-01-4(2)) National Ctr. on Education & The Economy.

Matross, Vuyokazi. Vusirala the Giant. Tadjo, Veronique, tr. from ENG. 1998. (Cambridge African Language Library). (FRE., Illus.). 16p. pap. 3.75 (978-0-521-64790-8(8)) Cambridge Univ. Pr.

Mattern, Joanne. At the Football Game. 2006. (Rosen Publishing Group's Reading Room Collection). (Illus.). 16p. (J). lib. bdg. (978-1-4042-3339-3(3) , PowerKids Pr.) Rosen Publishing Group, Inc., The.

—I Use Math at the Doctor's: Uso Las Matematicas en el Médico. 2005. (Illus.). 24p. (SPA.). pap. (978-0-8368-6006-1(3)); (ENG & SPA., lib. bdg. 19.33 (978-0-8368-5999-7(5)) Stevens, Gareth Inc.

—I Use Math at the Game. 2005. (Illus.). 24p. (J). pap. (978-0-8368-4862-5(4)); lib. bdg. 19.33 (978-0-8368-4855-7(1)) Stevens, Gareth Inc.

—I Use Math at the Game: Uso Las Matematicas el Juego de Pelota. 2005. (SPA., Illus.). 24p. (J). pap. (978-0-8368-6007-8(1)); lib. bdg. 19.33 (978-0-8368-6000-9(4)) Stevens, Gareth Inc.

—I Use Math at the Store. 2005. (Illus.). 24p. (J). pap. (978-0-8368-4863-2(2)); lib. bdg. 19.33 (978-0-8368-4856-4(X)) Stevens, Gareth Inc.

—I Use Math at the Store: Uso Las Matematicas en la Tienda. 2005. (Illus.). 24p. (J). (SPA.). pap. (978-0-8368-6008-5(X)); (ENG & SPA., lib. bdg. 19.33 (978-0-8368-6001-6(2)) Stevens, Gareth Inc.

—I Use Math in the Kitchen. 2005. (Illus.). 24p. (J). pap. (978-0-8368-4864-9(0)); lib. bdg. 19.33 (978-0-8368-4857-1(8)) Stevens, Gareth Inc.

—I Use Math in the Kitchen: Uso Las Matematicas en la Cocina. 2005. (Illus.). 24p. (SPA.). (978-0-8368-6009-2(8)); (ENG & SPA., lib. bdg. 19.33 (978-0-8368-6002-3(0)) Stevens, Gareth Inc.

—I Use Math in the Workshop. 2005. (Illus.). 24p. (J). pap. (978-0-8368-4865-6(9)); lib. bdg. 19.33 (978-0-8368-4858-8(6)) Stevens, Gareth Inc.

—I Use Math in the Workshop: Uso Las Matematicas en el Taller. 2005. (SPA., Illus.). 24p. (978-0-8368-6010-8(1)); lib. bdg. 19.33 (978-0-8368-6003-0(9)) Stevens, Gareth Inc.

—I Use Math on a Trip. 2005. (Illus.). 24p. (J). pap. (978-0-8368-4866-3(7)); lib. bdg. 19.33 (978-0-8368-4859-5(4)) Stevens, Gareth Inc.

—I Use Math on a Trip: Uno Las Matematicas en un Viaje. 2005. (Illus.). 24p. (J). pap. (978-0-8368-6011-5(X)); (ENG & SPA., lib. bdg. 19.33 (978-0-8368-6004-7(7)) Stevens, Gareth Inc.

McGrath, Barbara Barbieri. The Cheerios Counting Book. Bolster, Rob & Mazzola, Frank, Jr., illus. 1998. 32p. (J). (gr. k-1). pap. 10.95 (978-0-590-00321-6(6) , Cartwheel Bks.) Scholastic, Inc.

—The M & M's' Brand Addition Book. 2004. (Illus.). 24p. (J). 16.95 (978-0-88106-348-6(7)); pap. 6.95 (978-0-88106-349-3(5)) Charlesbridge Publishing, Inc.

—The M&M's' Brand Subtraction Book. 2005. (Illus.). 32p. (J). 16.95 (978-1-57091-358-7(7)); pap. 6.95 (978-1-57091-359-4(5)) Charlesbridge Publishing, Inc.

McGraw-Hill Staff & School Specialty Publishing Staff. Addition. 2001. (Homework Helpers Activity Bks.). (Illus.). 56p. (J). (gr. 1-1). pap., act. bk. ed. 2.99 (978-0-7682-0706-4(1) , FS109035, Schaffer, Frank) Schaffer, Frank Pubns.

Miles Moran, Andrea. Decimals & Percents. 1999. (Basic Skills Ser.). 48p. (J). (gr. 6-6). pap. 6.99 (978-1-56822-093-2(6) , IF5113, Instructional Fair) Schaffer, Frank Pubns.

Minden, Cecilia. Gardening by the Numbers. 2008. (J). lib. bdg. 25.26 (***978-1-60279-008-7(6)***) Cherry Lake Publishing.

—Lunch by the Numbers. 2008. (J). lib. bdg. 25.26 (***978-1-60279-012-4(4)***) Cherry Lake Publishing.

—Restaurants by the Numbers. 2008. (J). lib. bdg. 25.26 (***978-1-60279-009-4(4)***) Cherry Lake Publishing.

Mitzo Thompson, Kim & Mitzo Hilderbrand, Karen. Addition: Songs That Teach Addition. 2005. (Sing along Activity Books with CDs Ser.). (Illus.). 32p. (J). pap. 4.99 (978-0-7696-4451-6(1)) School Specialty Publishing.

Mitzo Thompson, Kim, et al. Songs That Teach Addition. 2006. (Songs That Teach Ser.). 72p. (J). pap. 14.95 (978-0-7696-7691-3(X) , American Education Publishing) School Specialty Publishing.

—Songs That Teach Division. 2006. (Songs That Teach Ser.). 72p. (J). pap. 14.95 (978-0-7696-7703-3(7) , American Education Publishing) School Specialty Publishing.

—Songs That Teach Subtraction. 2006. (Songs That Teach Ser.). 72p. (J). pap. 14.95 (978-0-7696-7701-9(0) , American Education Publishing) School Specialty Publishing.

Montague-Smith, Ann. Adding, 8 vols. 2005. (QEB Math Club Ser.). (Illus.). 24p. (J). (gr. k-1). lib. bdg. 15.95 (978-1-59566-096-1(8)) QEB Publishing Inc.

—Adding & Subtracting Book One, 8 vols. 2005. (QEB Math Club Ser.). (Illus.). 24p. (J). (gr. k-1). lib. bdg. 15.95 (978-1-59566-098-5(4)) QEB Publishing Inc.

—Adding & Subtracting Book Two, 8 vols. 2005. (QEB Math Club Ser.). (Illus.). 24p. (J). (gr. k-1). lib. bdg. 15.95 (978-1-59566-116-6(6)) QEB Publishing Inc.

—Multiplying, 8 vols. 2005. (QEB Start Math Ser.). (Illus.). 24p. (J). (gr. k-1). lib. bdg. 15.95 (978-1-59566-114-2(X)) QEB Publishing Inc.

Montessori ADvantage, des. Addition Wokbook. 2005. (J). pap. (978-0-9766453-0-6(0)) Montessori Advantage.

Mr. R.'s Math Poems. 2003. spiral bd. 20.00 (978-0-9702641-1-4(9)) MATHSTORY.COM.

Multiplication. 2000. (Math Windows Ser.). (J). pap. 0.99 (978-0-88724-851-1(9) , CD-3064) Carson-Dellosa Publishing Co., Inc.

Multiplication. (Illus.). (J). pap. 2.79 (978-0-88743-715-1(X)) School Zone Publishing Co.

Multiplication. 2001. (Early Math Ser.). (J). (gr. k-12). vinyl bd. 4.95 (978-1-58845-064-7(3)) School Specialty Publishing.

Multiplication 0-12. 2003. (Math Card Games Ser.). (Illus.). (gr. 3 up). 9.99 (978-0-7682-1987-6(6) , J53015) School Specialty Publishing.

Multiplication & Division 3-4. 2004. (Basic Skills Ser.). 48p. (J). pap. 6.99 (978-0-88724-182-6(4) , CD-4729) Carson-Dellosa Publishing Co., Inc.

Multiplication & Division 4-5. 2004. (Basic Skills Ser.). 48p. (J). pap. 6.99 (978-0-88724-183-3(2) , CD-4730) Carson-Dellosa Publishing Co., Inc.

Multiplication Basic Facts Pack. 2000. (Math Windows Ser.). (J). pap. 4.50 (978-0-88724-857-3(8) , CD-3070) Carson-Dellosa Publishing Co., Inc.

Multiplication Basic Facts with Answers. 2000. (Math Windows Ser.). (J). pap. 0.99 (978-0-88724-863-4(2) , CD-3076) Carson-Dellosa Publishing Co., Inc.

Multiplication Dot-to-Dot (Gr. 3-4) 2003. (J). (978-1-58232-107-3(8)) Bryan Hse. Pubs., Inc.

Multiplication Facts (Gr. 3-4) 2003. (J). (978-1-58232-086-1(1)) Bryan Hse. Pubs., Inc.

Multiplication Rap & Hip Hop. 2004. pap. 12.99 (978-1-57583-269-2(0)) Twin Sisters Productions, LLC.

Multiplication Skills (Gr. 3-5) 2003. (J). (978-1-58232-087-8(X)) Bryan Hse. Pubs., Inc.

Multiplication Tables: With Re-Usable Stickers. 1999. (Fun to Learn Ser.). (Illus.). 32p. (ps-5). 1.99 (978-1-58279-012-1(4) , 99) Trident Pr. International.

Mumford, Jeanette. Cambridge Mathematics Direct 1 Maths Review, 10 vols., Pack. 2002. (Cambridge Mathematics Direct Ser.). (Illus.). 160p. pap., wbk. ed. 14.30 (978-0-521-01135-8(3)) Cambridge Univ. Pr.

Mumford, Jeanette, et al. Cambridge Mathematics Direct 1 Interactive Pictures User Guide. 2002. (Cambridge Mathematics Direct Ser.). (Illus.). 40p. pap. 16.00 (978-0-521-01144-0(2)) Cambridge Univ. Pr.

Murphy, Patricia J. Adding Puppies & Kittens. 2007. (Puppy & Kitten Math Ser.). (Illus.). 32p. (J). lib. bdg. 22.60 (978-0-7660-2726-8(0) , Enslow Elementary) Enslow Pubs., Inc.

—Counting Puppies & Kittens. 2007. (Puppy & Kitten Math Ser.). (Illus.). 32p. (J). lib. bdg. 22.60 (978-0-7660-2724-4(4) , Enslow Elementary) Enslow Pubs., Inc.

—Subtracting Puppies & Kittens. 2007. (Puppy & Kitten Math Ser.). (Illus.). 32p. (J). lib. bdg. 22.60 (978-0-7660-2725-1(2) , Enslow Elementary) Enslow Pubs., Inc.

Murphy, Stuart J. Leaping Lizards. Adinolfi, JoAnn, illus. 2005. (MathStart Ser.). 40p. (J). 15.99 (978-0-06-000130-8(5)); pap. 5.99 (978-0-06-000132-2(1)) HarperCollins Pubs.

—Less Than Zero. Remkiewicz, Frank, illus. 2003. (MathStart Ser.: Vol. 49). 40p. (J). (gr. 2 up). 16.99 (978-0-06-000124-7(0)); pap. 5.99 (978-0-06-000126-1(7)) HarperCollins Pubs.

—Less Than Zero. 2003. (gr. k-3). lib. bdg. 13.00 (978-0-613-68443-9(5)) Tandem Library Bks.

—Monster Musical Chairs: Subtracting One. Nash, Scott, illus. 2000. (Mathstart Ser.). (J). (978-0-606-19986-5(1)) Tandem Library Bks.

—More or Less. Wenzel, David, illus. 2005. (MathStart Ser.). 40p. (J). (gr. 1 up). 15.99 (978-0-06-053165-2(7)) HarperCollins Pubs.

—More or Less. Wenzel, David T., illus. 2005. (MathStart Ser.). 40p. (J). (gr. 1 up). pap. 5.99 (978-0-06-053167-6(3)) HarperCollins Pubs.

—The Shark Swimathon. Cravath, Lynne W., illus. 2000. (MathStart Ser.). 40p. (J). (gr. 2 up). 15.95 (978-0-06-028030-7(1)) HarperCollins Pubs.

—Shark Swimathon Level 3. Cravath, Lynne W., illus. 2001. (MathStart Ser.). 40p. (J). (gr. 2 up). pap. 5.99 (978-0-06-446735-3(X) , Harper Trophy) HarperCollins Pubs.

—The Shark Swimathon Level 3: Subtracting Two Digit Numbers. Cravath, Lynne W., illus. 2000. (MathStart Ser.). 40p. (J). (gr. 2 up). 15.89 (978-0-06-028031-4(X)) HarperCollins Pubs.

—Sluggers' Car Wash. Saltzberg, Barney, illus. 2002. (MathStart Ser.). 40p. (J). (gr. 2 up). pap. 5.99 (978-0-06-446248-8(X)) HarperCollins Pubs.

Murray, James K. How to Add Without Using Fingers. 2002. 48p. (YA). (gr. 1 up). tchr. ed. (978-0-9718812-0-4(0)); stu. ed. (978-0-9718812-1-1(9)) Murray's Pubns.

—How to Add Without Using Fingers: Home Edition. 2002. 62p. (YA). (gr. 1 up). per. 8.99 (978-0-9718812-2-8(7)) Murray's Pubns.

My Book of Addition. 2005. (Illus.). 80p. (J). per. 6.95 (978-1-933241-01-2(2)) Kumon Publishing North America, Inc.

Nagda, Ann Whitehead. Cheetah Math: Learning about Division from Baby Cheetahs. rev. ed. 2007. (Illus.). 32p. (J). (gr. 2-5). 16.95 (***978-0-8050-7645-5(X)***) Holt, Henry & Co.

Naruse, Kaori & Satou, Junichi. Pretear Vol. 3: The New Legend of Snow White. Forsyth, Amy, tr. from JPN. 2004. (Illus.). 172p. (YA). pap. (978-1-4139-0146-7(8)) ADV Manga.

O'Donnell, Kerri. The California Gold Rush: Multiplying & Dividing Using Three- & Four-Digit Numbers. 2005. (PowerMath Ser.). (Illus.). 32p. (J). 22.50 (978-1-4042-2934-1(5)); pap. 22.50 (978-1-4042-5131-1(6)) Rosen Publishing Group, Inc., The. (PowerKids Pr.).

—Explorers in North America: Solving Addition & Subtraction Problems Using Timelines. 2004. (PowerMath Ser.). (Illus.). 32p. (J). lib. bdg. (978-0-8239-8898-3(8)); lib. bdg. 22.50 (978-0-8239-8987-4(9)) Rosen Publishing Group, Inc., The. (PowerKids Pr.).

Osborne, Amy, ed. Multables, Inc. McGee, Thomas, illus. 3p. (J). (gr. 2-5). 13.99 (978-0-9645004-0-2(X)) Multables, Inc.

Pallotta, Jerry. Hershey's Kisses Addition Book. Bolster, Rob, illus. 2001. 32p. (J). (gr. k-3). pap. 10.95 (978-0-439-26728-1(5)); pap. 5.99 (978-0-439-24173-1(1)) Scholastic, Inc.

—The Hershey's Kisses Subtraction Book. Bolster, Rob, illus. 2002. (Hershey's Ser.). 32p. (J). pap. 5.99 (978-0-439-33779-3(8) , Cartwheel Bks.) Scholastic, Inc.

—Hershey's Kisses Subtraction Book. 2002. (gr. k-3). lib. bdg. 14.15 (978-0-613-52853-5(0)) Tandem Library Bks.

—Hershey's Milk Chocolate Multiplication Book. 2002. 12.75 (978-0-606-22266-2(9)) Tandem Library Bks.

Pallotta, Jerry. The Subtraction Book. Bolster, Rob, illus. 2007. 32p. (J). (***978-0-439-89638-2(X)***) Scholastic, Inc.

Park, Margaret. Now for My Next Number! Songs for Multiplying Fun. Esterman, Sophia, illus. 2007. 48p. (J). (gr. 3-6). 16.95 (***978-0-915556-38-0(3)***) Great River Bks.

Patilla, Peter. Starting off with Adding & Subtracting. 2001. (Starting Off Ser.). (Illus.). (J). (978-0-606-21460-5(7)) Tandem Library Bks.

Pegoraro, Laura. We'll Practice Addition 1. Petertil Design Partners Staff, illus. 1998. (Powertools for Kids Ser.). 4p. (J). (ps-2). pap., wbk. ed. 4.95 (978-1-58220-000-2(9) , 32101, PowerTools for Kids) Navigator Systems, Inc.

—We'll Practice Addition 2. Petertil Design Partners Staff, illus. 1998. (Powertools for Kids Ser.: No. 5). 4p. (J). (gr. 1-4). pap., wbk. ed. 4.95 (978-1-58220-004-0(1) , 32105, PowerTools for Kids) Navigator Systems, Inc.

—We'll Practice Division. Petertil Design Partners Staff, illus. 1998. (Powertools for Kids Ser.: No. 4). 4p. (J). (gr. k-4). pap., wbk. ed. 4.95 (978-1-58220-003-3(3) , 32104, PowerTools for Kids) Navigator Systems, Inc.

—We'll Practice Multiplication 2. Petertil Design Partners Staff, illus. 1998. (Powertools for Kids Ser.: No. 7). 4p. (J). (gr. 1-4). pap., wbk. ed. 4.95 (978-1-58220-006-4(8) , 32107, PowerTools for Kids) Navigator Systems, Inc.

—We'll Practice Subtraction 1. Petertil Design Partners Staff, illus. 1998. (Powertools for Kids Ser.: No. 2). 4p. (J). (ps-3). pap., wbk. ed. 4.95 (978-1-58220-001-9(7) , 32102, PowerTools for Kids) Navigator Systems, Inc.

—We'll Practice Subtraction 2. Petertil Design Partners Staff, illus. 1998. (Powertools for Kids Ser.: No. 6). 4p. (J). (gr. 1-4). pap., wbk. ed. 4.95 (978-1-58220-005-7(X) , 32106, PowerTools for Kids) Navigator Systems, Inc.

Pegoraro, Laura, ed. We'll Practice Multiplication 1. Petertil Design Partners Staff, illus. 1998. (Powertools for Kids Ser.: No. 3). 4p. (J). (gr. 1-3). pap., wbk. ed. 4.95 (978-1-58220-002-6(5) , 32103, PowerTools for Kids) Navigator Systems, Inc.

Pluckrose, Henry. Numbers & Counting. 2001. (Let's Explore Ser.). (Illus.). 32p. (J). (gr. 1 up). lib. bdg. 23.33 (978-0-8368-2964-8(6)) Stevens, Gareth Inc.

Pluckrose, Henry Arthur. How Many Are There? 2007. (Illus.). 32p. (J). (***978-1-59771-037-4(7)***) Sea-To-Sea Pubns.

Practice Pals Bilingual Practice Book: Addition & Subtraction. 2006. (ENG & FRE., Illus.). 16p. (J). (gr. k-2). spiral bd. (978-1-930355-52-1(1)) Greenbrier/Scentex.

Practice Power Bilingual Practice Book: Addition. 2003. (Illus.). 16p. (J). (gr. k-2). spiral bd. (978-1-930355-47-7(5)) Greenbrier/Scentex.

Practice Power Bilingual Practice Book: Subtraction. 2003. (Illus.). 16p. (J). (gr. k-2). spiral bd. (978-1-930355-48-4(3)) Greenbrier/Scentex.

Practice Power Flip & Learn Multiplication. 2000. (Illus.). 16p. (J). (gr. 2-5). spiral bd. (978-1-930355-21-7(1)) Greenbrier/Scentex.

Practice Power Practice Book - Fractions & Measures. 2000. (Illus.). 16p. (J). (gr. 3-5). spiral bd. (978-1-930355-19-4(X)) Greenbrier/Scentex.

Practice Power Practice Book Fractions & Measures. 2001. (Illus.). 18p. (J). (gr. 3-5). spiral bd., wbk. ed. (978-1-930355-33-0(5)) Greenbrier/Scentex.

Practice Power Practice Book Multiplication. 2001. (Illus.). 18p. (J). (gr. 2-5). spiral bd., wbk. ed. (978-1-930355-27-9(0)) Greenbrier/Scentex.

Prior, Jennifer. Math Games to Master Basic Skills: Addition & Subtraction: 14 Reproducible Games That Help Struggling Learners Practice & Really Master Basic Addition & Subtraction Skills. 2007. 48p. pap. 10.99 (978-0-439-55415-2(2) , Teaching Resources) Scholastic, Inc.

Pulse- Fun with Multiplication & Division. 2006. cd-rom 4.99 (***978-1-60245-038-7(2)***) GDL Multimedia, LLC.

QEB Maths Club National Book Stores Edition: Adding. 2006. (J). per. (978-1-59566-287-3(1)) QEB Publishing Inc.

QEB Maths Club National Book Stores Edition: Adding & Subtracting. 2006. (J). per. (978-1-59566-285-9(5)) QEB Publishing Inc.

QEB Maths Club National Book Stores Edition: Adding & Subtracting Book 2. 2006. (J). per. (978-1-59566-289-7(8)) QEB Publishing Inc.

QEB Maths Club National Book Stores Edition: Dividing. 2006. (J). per. (978-1-59566-292-7(8)) QEB Publishing Inc.

QEB Maths Club National Book Stores Edition: Multiplying. 2006. (J). per. (978-1-59566-291-0(X)) QEB Publishing Inc.

QEB Maths Club National Book Stores Edition: Subtracting. 2006. (J). per. (978-1-59566-288-0(X)) QEB Publishing Inc.

QEB Start Math Book National Book Stores Edition: Numbers - Book 1. 2006. (J). per. (978-1-59566-272-9(3)) QEB Publishing Inc.

Rauen, Amy. Adding & Subtracting at the Lake. 2008. (J). pap. (***978-0-8368-8988-8(6)***); lib. bdg. (***978-0-8368-8983-3(5)***) Stevens, Gareth Inc. (Weekly Reader Early Learning Library).

—Adding & Subtracting in the City. 2007. (J). pap. (***978-0-8368-8479-1(5)***); 24p. (gr. 1-3). lib. bdg. 19.93 (***978-0-8368-8470-8(1)***) Stevens, Gareth Inc. (Weekly Reader Early Learning Library).

—Usamos Matematicas en la Fiesta Del Salon. 2007. (SPA & ENG.). (J). pap. (***978-0-8368-8502-6(3)*** , Weekly Reader Early Learning Library) Stevens, Gareth Inc.

—Usamos Matematicas en la Fiesta del Salon (Using Math at the Class Party) 2007. (Matimaticas en Nuestro Mundo (Math in Our World) Ser.). (SPA.). 24p. (J). (gr. 1-3). lib. bdg. 19.93 (***978-0-8368-8493-7(0)*** , Weekly Reader Early Learning Library) Stevens, Gareth Inc.

Read-Think-Do Math: Adding. 2006. pap. 4.49 (978-1-4206-8174-1(5)) Teacher Created Materials, Inc.

Read-Think-Do Math: Adding & Subtracting Book 1. 2006. pap. 4.49 (978-1-4206-8176-5(1)) Teacher Created Materials, Inc.

Read-Think-Do Math: Adding & Subtracting Book 2. 2006. pap. 4.49 (978-1-4206-8177-2(X)) Teacher Created Materials, Inc.

Read-Think-Do Math: Dividing. 2006. pap. 4.49 (978-1-4206-8179-6(6)) Teacher Created Materials, Inc.

Read-Think-Do Math: Multiplying. 2006. pap. 4.49 (978-1-4206-8178-9(8)) Teacher Created Materials, Inc.

Read-Think-Do Math: Subtracting. 2006. pap. 4.49 (978-1-4206-8175-8(3)) Teacher Created Materials, Inc.

Realtime Associates and Mazer Corporation Staff & LeapFrog Staff, compiled by. Add & Subtract Decimals. 2002. (J). (gr. 4). 66.75 (978-1-58605-466-3(X) , LeapFrog Schl. Hse.) LeapFrog Enterprises, Inc.

—Add Decimals. 2002. (J). (gr. 3). 66.75 (978-1-58605-394-9(9) , LeapFrog Schl. Hse.) LeapFrog Enterprises, Inc.

—Add Fractions with Like Denominators. 2002. (J). (gr. 4). 66.75 (978-1-58605-455-7(4) , LeapFrog Schl. Hse.) LeapFrog Enterprises, Inc.

—Add Fractions with Unlike Denominators. 2002. (J). (gr. 5). 66.75 (978-1-58605-512-7(7) , LeapFrog Schl. Hse.) LeapFrog Enterprises, Inc.

—Add Three Numbers up to Three Digits Each. 2002. (J). (gr. 3). 66.75 (978-1-58605-406-9(6) , LeapFrog Schl. Hse.) LeapFrog Enterprises, Inc.

—Add Three One-Digit Numbers. 2002. (J). (gr. 2). 66.75 (978-1-58605-333-8(7) , LeapFrog Schl. Hse.) LeapFrog Enterprises, Inc.

—Adding One-Digit & Two-Digit Numbers. 2002. (J). (gr. 2). 66.75 (978-1-58605-334-5(5) , LeapFrog Schl. Hse.) LeapFrog Enterprises, Inc.

Reynolds, Patricia A. I Can Add (Grades K - 1) 1999. (Step Ahead Workbooks Ser.). (Illus.). 32p. (J). (ps-3). pap. 2.99 (978-0-307-03590-5(5) , 03590, Golden Bks.) Random Hse. Children's Bks.

Ribke, Simone T. Pet Store Subtraction. 2006. (Rookie Read-About Math Ser.). (Illus.). 32p. (J). (gr. k-2). 20.50 (978-0-516-29673-9(6) , Children's Pr.) Scholastic Library Publishing.

Robinson, C. L. MATH1on1 Add & Subtract Fractions. 2006. (YA). per. 9.99 (978-0-9786767-2-8(6)) Robinson, Consuelo.

—MATH1on1 Multiply & Divide Fractions. 2006. (YA). per. 9.99 (978-0-9786767-3-5(4)) Robinson, Consuelo.

Rosenberg, Pam. Is It Still a Number? 2006. (Rookie Read-About Math Ser.). (Illus.). 31p. (J). (978-0-516-25443-2(X)) Children's Pr., Ltd.

Rosenberg, Pam. Is It Still a Number. 2007. (Rookie Read-About Math Ser.). (Illus.). 31p. (J). pap. (***978-0-516-25594-1(0)***) Children's Pr., Ltd.

Roy, Jennifer Rozines & Roy, Gregory. Addition in the Forest. 2005. (Math All Around Ser.). (Illus.). 31p. (J). (978-0-7614-2000-2(2) , Benchmark Bks.) Cavendish, Marshall Corp.

—Division with Toys. 2006. (Math All Around Ser.). (Illus.). 32p. (J). lib. bdg. 28.50 (978-0-7614-2269-3(2) , Benchmark Bks.) Cavendish, Marshall Corp.

—Multiplication on the Farm. 2006. (Math All Around Ser.). (Illus.). 32p. (J). lib. bdg. 28.50 (978-0-7614-2268-6(4) , Benchmark Bks.) Cavendish, Marshall Corp.

—Numbers on the Street. 2005. (Math All Around Ser.). (Illus.). 31p. (J). (978-0-7614-2002-6(9) , Benchmark Bks.) Cavendish, Marshall Corp.

—Subtraction at School. 2005. (Math All Around Ser.). (Illus.). 31p. (J). 25.64 (978-0-7614-2003-3(7) , Benchmark Bks.) Cavendish, Marshall Corp.

Safro, Jill. Multiplication & Division. 2003. (5-Minute Daily Practice Ser.). (Illus.). 64p. pap., tchr. ed. 11.95 (978-0-439-40916-2(0) , Teaching Resources) Scholastic, Inc.

Sargent, Brian. Pen Pals Compare. (J). 2006. 32p. (gr. 1-2). pap. 5.95 (978-0-516-25363-3(8)); 2005. (Illus.). 31p. (ps-ps). 20.50 (978-0-516-25262-9(3)) Scholastic Library Publishing. (Children's Pr.).

—Slumber Party Problem Solving. 2006. 32p. (gr. 1-2). (YA). pap. 5.95 (978-0-516-29829-0(1)); (Illus.). (J). 20.50 (978-0-516-24962-9(2)) Scholastic Library Publishing. (Children's Pr.).

Saviola, Joseph A. The Tour de France: Solving Addition Problems Involving Renaming. 2004. (PowerMath Ser.). (Illus.). 24p. (J). lib. bdg. (978-0-8239-8851-8(1) , PowerKids Pr.) Rosen Publishing Group, Inc., The.

—The Tour de France: Solving Addition Problems Using Regrouping. 2004. (PowerMath Ser.). (Illus.). 24p. (J). lib. bdg. 21.25 (978-0-8239-8963-8(1) , PowerKids Pr.) Rosen Publishing Group, Inc., The.

Scarpone, Janet. Addition: Learn Math Quickly Video A, 1998. (Learn Math Quickly Ser.). pap., wbk. ed. 49.99 incl. VHS (978-1-889434-22-3(1)) Learn Quickly.

—Division: Learn Math Quickly Video E, 1998. (Learn Math Quickly Ser.). pap., wbk. ed. 49.99 incl. VHS (978-1-889434-25-4(6)) Learn Quickly.

—Learn Math Quickly Basic Math Workbook: Math Workbook for Videos A-E. 1998. (Learn Math Quickly Ser.). (J). pap., wbk. ed. 12.99 (978-1-889434-26-1(4)) Learn Quickly.

—Multiplication: Learn Math Quickly Video D, Video D. 1998. (Learn Math Quickly Ser.:). pap., wbk. ed. 49.99 incl. VHS (978-1-889434-24-7(8)) Learn Quickly.

—Subtraction: Learn Math Quickly Video B, Video B. 1998. (Learn Math Quickly Ser.). pap., wbk. ed. 49.99 incl. VHS (978-1-889434-23-0(X)) Learn Quickly.

School Specialty Publishing. Addition. 2001. (Teddy Bear Math Ser.). 20p. (J). (gr. k-1). pap. 5.99 (978-0-7682-0518-3(2) , FS8403) Schaffer, Frank Pubns.

—Addition. 2004. (On-File Ser.). 4p. (J). (gr. 1-3). ring bd. 4.99 (978-0-7424-2907-9(5) , Instructional Fair) Schaffer, Frank Pubns.

—Addition 0 to 20. 2006. (Brighter Child Flash Cards Ser.). 54p. (J). 2.99 (978-0-7696-7711-8(8) , Brighter Child) School Specialty Publishing.

—Addition & Subtraction - Missing Facts. 2002. (Flip-Flashtm Ser.). 160p. (J). (gr. 1 up). pap. 7.99 (978-1-56451-389-2(0) , ID7878) School Specialty Publishing.

—Addition & Subtraction 1-10, Grades 1-2. 2006. 48p. (J). (gr. 1-2). pap. 6.99 (978-0-7682-3511-1(1) , Schaffer, Frank) Schaffer, Frank Pubns.

—Addition & Subtraction 11-20, Grades 1-2. 2006. 48p. (C). pap. 6.99 (***978-0-7682-3521-0(9)*** , Schaffer, Frank) Schaffer, Frank Pubns.

—Addition & Subtraction Facts: Vertical. 1999. (Flip-Flashtm Ser.). 160p. (J). (gr. 1 up). pap. 7.99 (978-1-56451-351-9(3) , ID7875) School Specialty Publishing.

—Addition Through 12+12. 2002. 170p. (C). 12.99 (***978-0-7682-0839-9(4)*** , Schaffer, Frank) Schaffer, Frank Pubns.

—Basic Skills Math Books: Addition & Subtraction. 1999. (Basic Skills Ser.). 48p. (J). (gr. 1 up). pap. 5.99 (978-1-56822-082-6(0) , IF5102) School Specialty Publishing.

—Division. 2004. (On-File Ser.). 4p. (J). (gr. 3-5). ring bd. 4.99 (978-0-7424-2909-3(1) , Instructional Fair) Schaffer, Frank Pubns.

—Division 0 to 12. 2006. (Brighter Child Flash Cards Ser.). 54p. (J). 2.99 (978-0-7696-7723-1(1) , Brighter Child) School Specialty Publishing.

—Division Through 144/12. 2002. 170p. (C). 12.99 (***978-0-7682-0842-9(4)*** , Schaffer, Frank) Schaffer, Frank Pubns.

—Easy Addition War. 2006. (Brighter Child Flash Cards Ser.). 54p. (J). 2.99 (978-0-7696-4709-8(X) , Brighter Child) School Specialty Publishing.

—Fractions & Decimals. 1999. (Basic Skills Ser.). 48p. (J). (gr. 5-5). pap. 6.99 (978-1-56822-090-1(1) , IF5110, Instructional Fair) Schaffer, Frank Pubns.

—Funtastic Frogs Math Vol. 2: Addition & Subtraction; Fast Facts; Beginning Multiplication & Division; Making Graphs; Beginning Problem Solving. 2004. 160p. (J). (gr. k-2). pap. 16.99 (978-0-7424-2771-6(4) , ID99077) School Specialty Publishing.

—Mathematics: A Step-by-Step Approach. 1999. (Practice Drills Ser.). 86p. (J). (gr. 1-1). pap. 2.99 (978-0-88012-452-2(0) , IF0110); (gr. 6-6). pap. 2.99 (978-0-88012-481-2(4) , IF0160) Schaffer, Frank Pubns. (Instructional Fair).

—Multiplication. 2004. (On-File Ser.). 4p. (J). (gr. 3-5). ring bd. 4.99 (978-0-7424-2914-7(8) , Instructional Fair) Schaffer, Frank Pubns.

—Multiplication 0 to 12. 2006. (Brighter Child Flash Cards Ser.). 54p. (J). 2.99 (978-0-7696-7743-9(6) , Brighter Child) School Specialty Publishing.

—Multiplication & Division - Missing Facts. 2002. 160p. (J). (gr. 3 up). pap. 7.99 (978-1-56451-390-8(4) , ID7879) School Specialty Publishing.

—Multiplication & Division Facts: Vertical. 1999. (Flip-Flashtm Ser.). 160p. (J). (gr. 3 up). pap. 7.99 (978-1-56451-352-6(1) , ID7876) School Specialty Publishing.

—Multiplication, Grades 3-4. 2006. 48p. (C). pap. 6.99 (***978-0-7682-3443-5(3)** , Schaffer, Frank) Schaffer, Frank Pubns.

—Multiplying & Dividing I Gr 3. 2005. (Math 2 Master Ser.). 32p. (J). pap. 3.99 (978-0-7696-3913-0(5) , Brighter Child) School Specialty Publishing.

—Multiplying & Dividing II Gr 4. 2005. (Math 2 Master Ser.). 32p. (J). pap. 3.99 (978-0-7696-3914-7(3) , Brighter Child) School Specialty Publishing.

—Place Values. 2004. (On-File Ser.). 4p. (J). (gr. 3-5). ring bd. 4.99 (978-0-7424-2915-4(6) , Instructional Fair) Schaffer, Frank Pubns.

—Subtraction. 2001. (Teddy Bear Math Ser.). 20p. (J). (gr. k-1). pap. 5.99 (978-0-7682-0519-0(0) , FS8404) Schaffer, Frank Pubns.

—Subtraction. 2004. (On-File Ser.). 4p. (J). (gr. 5-7). ring bd. 4.99 (978-0-7424-2918-5(0) , Instructional Fair) Schaffer, Frank Pubns.

—Subtraction 0 to 12. 2006. (Brighter Child Flash Cards Ser.). 54p. (J). 2.99 (978-0-7696-7721-7(5) , Brighter Child) School Specialty Publishing.

—Subtraction Through 24-12. 2002. 170p. (C). 12.99 (***978-0-7682-0840-5(8)** , Schaffer, Frank) Schaffer, Frank Pubns.

School Specialty Publishing. Times Table. 2004. (On-File Ser.). 4p. (J). (gr. 3-5). ring bd. 4.99 (978-0-7424-2919-2(9) , Instructional Fair) Schaffer, Frank Pubns.

School Zone Publishing Company Staff. Addition 0-12. rev. ed. 1999. (Flash Cards Ser.). 52p. (J). (ps-3). 2.79 (978-0-938256-91-5(2) , 04006) School Zone Publishing Co.

—Addition & Subtraction 2. (Illus.). (J). 19.99 incl. audio compact disk (978-0-88743-950-6(0)) School Zone Publishing Co.

—Addition & Subtraction Grade 1-2 A Wipe-off Book: Hours of Reusable Fun. rev. ed. 2005. 26p. (J). (gr. k-1). pap. 3.79 (978-1-58947-784-1(7)) School Zone Publishing Co.

—Multiplication & Division 3-4 Bilingual: I Know It! 2004. 64p. (J). (gr. 3-4). pap. 3.79 (978-1-58947-963-0(7)) School Zone Publishing Co.

—Multiplication Facts Made Easy: I Know It! 2004. 64p. (J). (gr. 3-4). pap. 3.79 (978-1-58947-965-4(3)) School Zone Publishing Co.

—Multiplication Made Easy Grade 3-4 a Wipe-Off Book: Hours of Reusable Fun! rev. ed. 2005. 26p. (J). (gr. 3-4). pap. 3.79 (978-1-58947-785-8(5)) School Zone Publishing Co.

—Numbers 1-12. (Illus.). (J). 19.99 incl. audio compact disk (978-0-88743-949-0(7)) School Zone Publishing Co.

School Zone Staff. Addition. rev. ed. 2004. 55p. (J). 2.79 (978-1-58947-984-5(X)) School Zone Publishing Co.

—Division. rev. ed. 2004. 56p. (J). 2.79 (978-1-58947-987-6(4)) School Zone Publishing Co.

—Math War Addition & Subtraction. 2004. (J). 2.79 (978-1-58947-993-7(9)) School Zone Publishing Co.

—Math War Multiplication. 2004. (J). 2.79 (978-1-58947-994-4(7)) School Zone Publishing Co.

—Multiplication. rev. ed. 2004. 56p. (J). 2.79 (978-1-58947-986-9(6)) School Zone Publishing Co.

—Subtraction. rev. ed. 2004. (J). 2.79 (978-1-58947-985-2(8)) School Zone Publishing Co.

School Zone Staff, ed. Multiplication & Division 3-4. deluxe ed. 2004. (Activity Zone Workbook Ser.). 64p. (J). (gr. 3-4). pap. 3.79 (978-1-58947-329-4(9) , 02215) School Zone Publishing Co.

Schwartz, David M. How Much Is a Million? Kellogg, Steven, illus. 2000. (J). (gr. 1-4). pap. 12.95 incl. audio Weston Woods Studios, Inc.

—If Dogs Were Dinosaurs. Warhola, James, illus. 2005. 32p. (J). (gr. 2-5). pap. 16.99 (978-0-439-67612-0(6) , Scholastic Pr.) Scholastic, Inc.

Shea. Decimals & Percents Core Skills. 2001. pap. (978-0-7398-4898-2(4)) Steck-Vaughn.

Silate, Jennifer. Number Operations. 2005. 48p. pap. 6.95 (978-1-4042-8574-3(1)) Rosen Publishing Group, Inc., The.

—Numbers Operations. 2005. 48p. pap. 6.95 (978-1-4042-8571-2(7)); pap. 6.95 (978-1-4042-8576-7(8)) Rosen Publishing Group, Inc., The.

Simpson, Jeff. Addition, Subtraction & Place Value Student Edition: Count, Notice & Remember Math Intervention Volume I, AS. Simpson, Marilyn, ed. 2007. (Count, Notice & Remember Ser. : Volume I, AS). ring bd. 50.00 (***978-1-888976-41-0(1))** Mastery Learning Systems.

—The Best Stuff for Adding & Subtracting. 1998. (Count, Notice, & Remember Ser.: Vol. 512). (Illus.). 350p. (J). (gr. k-8). ring bd. 50.00 (978-1-888976-33-5(0) , 512) Mastery Learning Systems.

Simpson, Jeff. The Best Stuff for Multiplying & Dividing, Student Edition: Count, Notice & Remember Math Intervention MD-1. Simpson, Marilyn, ed. 2nd ed. 2006. (Count, Notice, & Remember Ser.: 14). stu. ed., ring bd. (***978-1-888976-38-0(1)** , 530S) Mastery Learning Systems.

Simpson, Jeffrey L. Core Processes of Mathematics, Student Edition: Count, Notice & Remember Math Intervention, Volume 4. Simpson, Marilyn Bohlen, ed. 2007. ring bd. 59.95 (***978-1-888976-53-3(5))** Mastery Learning Systems.

—Fractions & Decimals, Student Edition: Count, Notice & Remember Math Intervention, Volume 2. Simpson, Marilyn Bohlen, ed. 2007. stu. ed., ring bd. 69.95 (***978-1-888976-47-2(0))** Mastery Learning Systems.

—Functions & Equations, Student Edition: Count, Notice & Remember Math Intervention, Volume 5. Simpson, Marilyn Bohlen, ed. 2007. ring bd. 59.95 (***978-1-888976-56-4(X))** Mastery Learning Systems.

Southwater Books Staff. Let's Stick & Learn. 2000. (Illus.). 64p. pap. 7.95 (978-1-84215-124-2(X) , Southwater) Anness Publishing GBR. *Dist:* National Bk. Network.

Spann, Mary Beth. Times Table Mini-Books & Lift-N-Look Flash Cards: Reproducible Learning Tools That Make Mastering the Multiplication Facts Fun, Fun, Fun! 2000. (Illus.). 48p. (J). pap. 9.95 (978-0-439-10438-8(6)) Scholastic, Inc.

Steck-Vaughn Staff. Early Math: 2 Digit Addition & Subtraction, 10 Pack. 2005. pap. 29.95 (978-1-4190-0356-1(9)) Steck-Vaughn.

—Early Math: 2 Digit Addition with Regrouping, 10 Pack. 2005. pap. 29.95 (978-1-4190-0357-8(7)) Steck-Vaughn.

—Early Math: 2 Digit Subtraction with Regrouping. 2005. pap. 2.99 (978-1-4190-0335-6(6)); pap. 29.95 (978-1-4190-0359-2(3)) Steck-Vaughn.

—Early Math: 3 Digit Addition & Subtraction with Regrouping. 2005. pap. 2.99 (978-1-4190-0336-3(4)); pap. 29.95 (978-1-4190-0360-8(7)) Steck-Vaughn.

—Early Math: Addition. 2005. (gr. k-5). pap. 2.99 (978-1-4190-0323-3(2)); (gr. 6-10). pap. 2.99 (978-1-4190-0324-0(0)); (gr. 6-10). pap. 29.95 (978-1-4190-0348-6(8)) Steck-Vaughn.

—Early Math: Fractions I. 2005. pap. 2.99 (978-1-4190-0330-1(5)) Steck-Vaughn.

—Early Math: Fractions II. 2005. pap. 2.99 (978-1-4190-0340-0(2)) Steck-Vaughn.

—Early Math: Place Value. 2005. (J). (gr. 1). pap. 2.99 (978-1-4190-0322-6(4)) Steck-Vaughn.

—Early Math: Place Value 1, 10 Pack. 2005. (gr. 1). pap. 29.95 (978-1-4190-0346-2(1)) Steck-Vaughn.

—Early Math: Place Value II. 2005. pap. 2.99 (978-1-4190-0334-9(8)) Steck-Vaughn.

—Early Math: Subtraction. 2005. (gr. 1-10). pap. 2.99 (978-1-4190-0325-7(9)) Steck-Vaughn.

—Early Math 10-pack: Place Value II. 2005. pap. 29.95 (978-1-4190-0358-5(5)) Steck-Vaughn.

—Early Math 10-pack: Subtraction. 2005. (gr. 1-10). pap. 29.95 (978-1-4190-0349-3(6)) Steck-Vaughn.

—Focus on Math Level C: Addition & Subtraction. 2005. pap. 2.99 (978-1-4190-0265-6(1)) Harcourt Schl. Pubs.

—Focus on Math Level C: Multiplication & Division. 2005. pap. 2.99 (978-1-4190-0266-3(X)) Harcourt Schl. Pubs.

—Focus on Math Level C 10-pack: Addition & Subtractions. 2005. pap. 29.95 (978-1-4190-0289-2(9)) Harcourt Schl. Pubs.

—Focus on Math Level C 10-pack: Multiplication & Division. 2005. pap. 29.95 (978-1-4190-0290-8(2)) Harcourt Schl. Pubs.

—Focus on Math Level E 10-pack: Ratio Percent. 2005. pap. 29.95 (978-1-4190-0306-6(2)) Harcourt Schl. Pubs.

—Focus on Math Level F: Ration Percent. 2005. pap. 2.99 (978-1-4190-0287-8(2)) Harcourt Schl. Pubs.

—Focus on Math Level F 10-pack: Ratio Percent. 2005. pap. 29.95 (978-1-4190-0311-0(9)) Harcourt Schl. Pubs.

—Multiplication & Division. 1999. (Illus.). (J). (gr. 3). pap. 6.95 (978-0-7398-2712-3(X)) Harcourt Trade Pubs.

—Multiplication & Division. 1999. (Illus.). (J). (gr. 4). pap. (978-0-7398-2713-0(8)); (gr. 5). pap. (978-0-7398-2714-7(6)); (gr. 6). pap. (978-0-7398-2715-4(4)) Steck-Vaughn.

Steck-Vaughn Staff, ed. Early Math: Addition. 2005. (gr. k-5). pap. 29.95 (978-1-4190-0347-9(X)) Steck-Vaughn.

Strazzabosco, John. Aircraft Carriers, Supplies for a City at Sea: Multiplying Multidigit Numbers with Regrouping. 2004. (PowerMath Ser.). (Illus.). 32p. (J). lib. bdg. 22.50 (978-0-8239-8995-9(X) , PowerKids Pr.) Rosen Publishing Group, Inc., The.

—Aircraft Carriers, Supplies for a City at Sea: Multiplying Multidigit Numbers with Renaming. 2004. (PowerMath Ser.). (Illus.). 32p. (J). lib. bdg. (978-0-8239-8919-5(4) , PowerKids Pr.) Rosen Publishing Group, Inc., The.

Strombosky, Jerome D. Adding & Subtracting Numbers with EUCLID & the Number Line: An Institute Math Book for Children. Strombosky, Jerome D., illus. 1998. (Illus.). 30p. (J). (ps-1). pap. 6.95 (978-0-9665579-0-9(5)) Strombosky, Jerome D.

Stuart, Marion W. Subtraction Wrap-Ups: Individual Sets. (J). (gr. 1-3). (978-0-943343-02-0(X)) Learning Wrap-Ups.

Subtraction. 2004. (Help with Homework Ser.). 32p. (J). (gr. k-2). wbk. ed. 3.99 (978-1-904586-25-8(2)) Byeway Bks.

Subtraction. 2000. (Math Windows Ser.). (J). pap. 0.99 (978-0-88724-850-4(0) , CD-3063) Carson-Dellosa Publishing Co., Inc.

Subtraction. (Substitute Teaching Ser.). (J). 2.50 (978-0-931993-14-5(8) , GP-014) Garlic Pr.

Subtraction. 2001. (Early Math Ser.). (J). (gr. k-12). vinyl bd. 4.95 (978-1-58845-063-0(5)) School Specialty Publishing.

Subtraction. 1998. (Play & Learn Ser.). (Illus.). 16p. (J). (gr. k-2). pap., wbk. ed. 3.95 (978-0-8069-3793-9(9) , Balloon Bks.) Sterling Publishing Co., Inc.

Subtraction: With Re-Usable Stickers. 1999. (Fun to Learn Ser.). (Illus.). 32p. (ps-4). 1.99 (978-1-58279-014-5(0) , 98) Trident Pr. International.

Subtraction 0-12: Flash Cards. rev. ed. 1999. (Flash Cards Ser.). 56p. (J). (ps-3). 2.79 (978-0-938256-92-2(0) , 04007) School Zone Publishing Co.

Subtraction Basic Facts Pack. 2000. (Math Windows Ser.). (J). pap. 4.50 (978-0-88724-856-6(X) , CD3069) Carson-Dellosa Publishing Co., Inc.

Subtraction Basic Facts with Answers. 2000. (Math Windows Ser.). (J). pap. 0.99 (978-0-88724-862-7(4) , CD-3075) Carson-Dellosa Publishing Co., Inc.

Tang, Greg. Math for All Seasons: Mind-Stretching Math Riddles. Briggs, Harry, illus. 2002. 40p. (J). pap. 16.95 (978-0-439-21042-3(9) , Scholastic Pr.) Scholastic, Inc.

—Mind-Stretching Brain Food. Briggs, Harry, illus. 2005. (Math Potatoes Ser.). 40p. (J). (ps-k). pap. 16.95 (978-0-439-44390-6(3) , Scholastic Pr.) Scholastic, Inc.

Thompson, Karen & Mitzo Thompson, Kim. Subtraction: Songs That Teach Subtraction. 2006. (Sing along Activity Books with CDs Ser.). (Illus.). 32p. (J). pap. 4.99 (978-0-7696-4575-9(5)) School Specialty Publishing.

Thompson, Kim Mitzo & Hilderbrand, Karen Mitzo. Addition. 2000. (J). pap. 13.99 incl. audio compact disk (978-1-57583-332-3(8) , Twin 443CD) Twin Sisters Productions, LLC.

—Division. 2000. (J). pap. 13.99 incl. audio compact disk (978-1-57583-334-7(4) , TWIN 445CD) Twin Sisters Productions, LLC.

—Multiplication. 2000. (J). pap. 13.99 incl. audio compact disk (978-1-57583-331-6(X) , Twin 442CD) Twin Sisters Productions, LLC.

—Multiplication Rap Hip Hop. 2001. (J). pap. 13.99 incl. audio compact disk (978-1-57583-335-4(2) , Twin 446CD) Twin Sisters Productions, LLC.

Times Tables. 2004. (Help with Homework Ser.). 32p. (J). (gr. 1-4). wbk. ed. 3.99 (978-1-904586-28-9(7)) Byeway Bks.

Times Tables. 2001. (Early Math Ser.). (J). (gr. k-12). vinyl bd. 4.95 (978-1-58845-066-1(X)) School Specialty Publishing.

Trumbauer, Lisa. Double the Animals. (J). (gr. k-2). 2006. 16p. 15.93 (978-0-7368-5854-0(7) , Yellow Umbrella Bks.); 2005. (Illus.). 17p. (978-0-7368-5320-0(0)); 2005. (Illus.). 17p. (978-0-7368-5284-5(0)) Capstone Pr., Inc.

—Take Away. 2003. (Yellow Umbrella Books). (Illus.). 16p. (J). (gr. 1). lib. bdg. 14.60 (978-0-7368-2015-8(9) , Pebble Bks.) Capstone Pr., Inc.

—Take Away. 2003. (Math Ser.). (J). (978-0-7368-1702-8(6)) Yellow Umbrella Pr.

—What Makes Ten? 2006. (Illus.). 18p. (J). (978-0-7368-5980-6(2)) Yellow Umbrella Pr.

—What Makes Ten. 2006. (Yellow Umbrella Books for Early Readers). (SPA & ENG., Illus.). 18p. (J). (978-0-7368-6016-1(9)) Yellow Umbrella Pr.

Tucker, Shirley & Rambo, Jane. Odd & Even Numbers. 2002. (Yellow Umbrella Books). (Illus.). 16p. (J). (gr. 1). lib. bdg. 14.60 (978-0-7368-1286-3(5) , Pebble Bks.) Capstone Pr., Inc.

Tulip, Jenny. My First Book of Numbers. 2004. (Early Learning Ser.). (Illus.). 18p. (J). bds. 5.99 (978-1-85854-216-4(2)) Brimax Books Ltd. GBR. *Dist:* Byeway Bks.

Two-Minute Math Drills: Addition & Subtraction, Grades 1 & Up. 2003. 64p. (J). (gr. 1-5). pap. 8.99 (978-0-7424-1741-0(7) , IFG99047) School Specialty Publishing.

Two-Minute Math Drills: Fractions & Decimals, Grades 5 & Up. 2003. 64p. (J). (gr. 5-12). pap. 8.99 (978-0-7424-1745-8(X) , IFG99049) School Specialty Publishing.

Two-Minute Math Drills: Multiplication & Division, Grades 3 & Up. 2003. 64p. (J). (gr. 3-8). pap. 8.99 (978-0-7424-1743-4(3) , IFG99048) School Specialty Publishing.

Unknown. Flip Flash Addition. 2004. (Flip Flash Pads Ser.). 64p. (J). act. bk. ed. 6.99 (978-1-85997-585-5(2)) Byeway Bks.

—Flip Flash Subtraction. 2004. (Flip Flash Pads Ser.). 64p. (J). act. bk. ed. 6.99 (978-1-85997-586-2(0)) Byeway Bks.

Uriah, Parke. Lectures on the Philosophy of Arithmetic & the Adaptation of That Science to the Business Purposes of Life with Numerous Problems, Curious & Useful, Solved by Various Modes; with Explanations Designed to Make the Study & Application of Arithmetic Pleasant & Profitable to Such As Have Not the Aid of a Teacher; As Well As to Exercise Advanced Classes in Schools, 5 vols. 2006. (Illus.). cd-rom (978-1-892824-24-0(8)) AFCHRON.

Using Cuisenaire Rods: Addition & Subtraction. 2001. (J). pap. 7.95 (978-1-56911-736-1(5)) Learning Resources, Inc.

Using Cuisenaire Rods: Multiplication & Division. 2001. (J). pap. 7.95 (978-1-56911-737-8(3)) Learning Resources, Inc.

Walsh, Kieran. Animal Math. 2005. (Math & My World Ser.). (Illus.). 48p. (gr. 4-6). 20.95 (978-1-59515-491-0(4)) Rourke Publishing, LLC.

—Construction Math. 2005. (Math & My World Ser.). (Illus.). 48p. (gr. 4-6). 20.95 (978-1-59515-492-7(2)) Rourke Publishing, LLC.

—Music Math. 2005. (Math & My World Ser.). (Illus.). 48p. (gr. 4-6). 20.95 (978-1-59515-493-4(0)) Rourke Publishing, LLC.

—Space Math. 2005. (Math & My World Ser.). (Illus.). 48p. (gr. 4-6). 20.95 (978-1-59515-494-1(9)) Rourke Publishing, LLC.

—Sports Math. 2005. (Math & My World Ser.). (Illus.). 48p. (gr. 4-6). 20.95 (978-1-59515-495-8(7)) Rourke Publishing, LLC.

—Time Math. 2005. (Math & My World Ser.). (Illus.). 48p. (gr. 4-6). 20.95 (978-1-59515-496-5(5)) Rourke Publishing, LLC.

Wasson Warfel, Laura. Basic Skills Math Books: Addition & Subtraction. 1999. (Basic Skills Ser.). 48p. (J). (gr. 2-3). pap. 6.99 (978-1-56822-083-3(9) , IF5103) School Specialty Publishing.

Watt, F. & Wells, R. Sticker Math Fun for 6 - 7 Years Olds. 2004. (Sticker Math Ser.). (Illus.). 102p. (J). pap., act. bk. ed. 14.95 (978-0-7945-0566-0(X)) EDC Publishing.

Watt, Fiona & Wells, Rachel. Starting Times Tables. 2004. (Usborne Sticker Math Ser.). (Illus.). 28p. (J). (gr. k-1). pap., act. bk. ed. 6.95 (978-0-7460-3735-5(X)) EDC Publishing.

Weatherall, Donald M. & Quinn. Addition & Subtraction Learning Module. pap. (978-0-89290-131-9(4)) S V E & Churchill Media.

Weekly Reader Early Learning Library (Firm) Staff, contrib. by. I Know Same & Different. 2006. (I'm Ready for Math Ser.). (Illus.). 16p. (J). pap. (978-0-8368-6481-6(6)); lib. bdg. 16.67 (978-0-8368-6476-2(X)) Stevens, Gareth Inc.

—I Know Same & Different: Igual y Diferente. 2006. (ENG & SPA., Illus.). 16p. (J). pap. 4.50 (978-0-8368-6491-5(3)); lib. bdg. 16.67 (978-0-8368-6486-1(7)) Stevens, Gareth Inc.

Wells, Robert E. Can You Count to a Googol? 2000. (Illus.). (J). 13.75 (978-0-606-18773-2(1)) Tandem Library Bks.

—Can You Count to a Googol? Wells, Robert E., illus. 2000. (Illus.). 32p. (J). (gr. 1-5). 15.95 (978-0-8075-1060-5(2)) Whitman, Albert & Co.

—Can You Count to a Googol? 2000. (Illus.). 32p. (J). (gr. 1-5). pap. 6.95 (978-0-8075-1061-2(0)) Whitman, Albert & Co.

Wen, Dref. Fy Llyfr Rhifau Cyntaf. 2005. Tr. of My First Numbers. (WEL., Illus.). 32p. bds. (978-1-85596-672-7(7)) Dref Wen.

What Makes Ten? 2006. (Yellow Umbrella Math Ser.). 8,16p. (J). 6.50 (978-0-7368-1697-7(6)) Red Brick Learning.

Wickett, Maryann. Lessons for Extending Place Value: Grade 3. 2005. (Teaching Arithmetic Ser.). (Illus.). 256p. pap. 26.95 (978-0-941355-57-5(8)) Math Solutions Pubns.

Wingard-Nelson, Rebecca. Division Made Easy. LaBaff, Tom, illus. 2005. (Making Math Easy Ser.). 48p. (J). (ps-ps). lib. bdg. 23.93 (978-0-7660-2511-0(X) , Enslow Elementary) Enslow Pubs., Inc.

—Multiplication Made Easy. LaBaff, Tom, illus. 2005. (Making Math Easy Ser.). 48p. (J). (ps-ps). lib. bdg. 23.93 (978-0-7660-2510-3(1) , Enslow Elementary) Enslow Pubs., Inc.

—Subtraction & Addition. 2008. (Math Busters Ser.). (Illus.). 64p. (J). (gr. 5 up). lib. bdg. 27.93 (***978-0-7660-2875-3(5))** Enslow Pubs., Inc.

Wingard-Nelson, Rebecca. Subtraction Made Easy. LaBaff, Tom, illus. 2005. (Making Math Easy Ser.). 48p. (J). (gr. 1-4). lib. bdg. 23.93 (978-0-7660-2509-7(8) , Enslow Elementary) Enslow Pubs., Inc.

Wipe-Away Books: Addition. 2003. (Illus.). 16p. (J). (ps up). pap. 3.99 (978-0-7682-0072-0(5)) School Specialty Publishing.

Wipe-Away Books: Subtraction. 2003. (Illus.). 16p. (YA). (ps up). pap. 3.99 (978-0-7682-0073-7(3)) School Specialty Publishing.

Wojtowycz, David. Animal Antics from 1 to 10. Wojtowycz, David, illus. 2000. (Illus.). 32p. (J). (gr. k-3). 16.95 (978-0-8234-1552-6(X)) Holiday Hse., Inc.

Worth, Bonnie. One Cent, Two Cent, Old Cent, New Cent: All about Money. Ruiz, Aristides & Mathieu, Joseph, illus. 2008. (J). (***978-0-375-82881-2(8)**); lib. bdg. (***978-0-375-92881-9(2))** Random Hse., Inc.

Wortzman, Ricki, et al. Red Riding Hood's Math Adventure. Mazille, Capucine, illus. 2001. 24p. (J). (ps-5). 14.95 (978-1-57091-477-5(X)) Charlesbridge Publishing, Inc.

Ziefert, Harriet. Rockheads. McKie, Todd, tr. McKie, Todd, illus. 2004. 32p. (J). (gr. k-3). 16.00 (978-0-618-34574-8(4) , Walter Lorraine) Houghton Mifflin Co. Trade & Reference Div.

Zuravicky, Orli. Amazing Animals: Multiplying Multidigit Numbers by a One-Digit Number with Renaming. 2004. (PowerMath Ser.). (Illus.). 24p. (J). lib. bdg. (978-0-8239-8861-7(9)); lib. bdg. 21.25 (978-0-8239-8964-5(X)) Rosen Publishing Group, Inc., The. (PowerKids Pr.).

1st Subtraction Booster. 2005. 64p. (J). per. 1.49 (978-1-59441-338-4(X) , C04014) Carson-Dellosa Publishing Co., Inc.

2-Sided Math Puzzles: Addition. 2002. (J). 15.95 (978-1-930820-13-5(5)) Garlic Pr.

2-Sided Math Puzzles: Division. 2002. (J). 15.95 (978-1-930820-16-6(X)) Garlic Pr.

2-Sided Math Puzzles: Multiplication. 2002. (J). 15.95 (978-1-930820-15-9(1)) Garlic Pr.

2-Sided Math Puzzles: Multiplication/Division. 2002. (J). 15.95 (978-1-930820-22-7(4)) Garlic Pr.

2-Sided Math Puzzles: Subtraction. 2002. (J). 15.95 (978-1-930820-14-2(3)) Garlic Pr.

2nd Subtraction Booster. 2005. 64p. (J). per. 1.49 (978-1-59441-342-1(8) , C04018) Carson-Dellosa Publishing Co., Inc.

3rd Multiplication Booster. 2005. 64p. (J). per. 1.49 (978-1-59441-346-9(0) , C04022) Carson-Dellosa Publishing Co., Inc.

ARITHMETIC—FICTION

Axelrod, Amy. Pigs Go to Market: Fun with Math & Shopping. McGinley-Nally, Sharon, illus. 1999. 40p. (J). (ps-3). 6.99 (978-0-689-82553-8(6) , 076714005990, Aladdin) Simon & Schuster Children's Publishing.

—Pigs Go to Market: Halloween Fun with Math & Shopping. 1999. (978-0-606-16330-9(1)); lib. bdg. 14.15 (978-0-613-19419-8(5)) Tandem Library Bks.

Bauer, Joan. Sticks. 2002. 192p. (YA). 18.99 (978-0-399-23752-2(6) , Putnam Juvenile) Penguin Group (USA) Inc.

Calvert, Pam. Multiplying Menace: The Revenge of Rumpelstiltskin: A Math Adventure. Geehan, Wayne, illus. (Math Adventures Ser.). 32p. (J). 2006. pap. 6.95 (978-1-57091-890-2(2)); 2005. 16.95 (978-1-57091-889-6(9)) Charlesbridge Publishing, Inc.

Davies, Jacqueline. The Lemonade War. 2007. 192p. (J). (gr. 3-5). 16.00 (***978-0-618-75043-6(6)***) Houghton Mifflin Co.

deRubertis, Barbara. A Collection for Kate: Math Concept: Addition. Fiammenghi, Gioia, illus. 1999. (Math Matters Ser.). 32p. (J). (gr. k-2). pap. 4.95 (978-1-57565-089-0(4)) Kane Pr., The.

—A Collection for Kate: Math Concept: Addition. 1999. (Math Matters Ser.). (Illus.). (J). 11.75 (978-0-606-18216-4(0)) Tandem Library Bks.

Fisher, Doris & Sneed, Dani. My Even Day. Lee, Karen, illus. 2007. 32p. (J). (ps-3). 8.95 (***978-1-934359-22-8(X)***) Sylvan Dell Pubng.

—One Odd Day, 2 Books, Book 1. Lee, Karen, illus. 2007. 32p. (J). pap. 8.95 (***978-1-934359-33-4(5)***) Sylvan Dell Pubng.

Fromental, Jean-Luc. 365 Penguins. Jolivet, Joelle, illus. 2006. 48p. (J). (ps-3). 17.95 (978-0-8109-4460-2(X)) Abrams, Harry N., Inc.

Gerth, Melanie. Ten Little Ladybugs. Huliska-Beith, Laura, illus. 22p. (ps-k). 2005. (J). 10.95 (978-1-58117-091-7(2)); 2000. (YA). lp 12.95 (978-1-58117-122-8(6)) Dalmatian Pr. (Intervisual/Piggy Toes).

Giganti, Paul. How Many Blue Birds Flew Away? A Counting Book with a Difference. Crews, Donald, illus. 2005. 32p. (J). lib. bdg. 16.89 (978-0-06-000763-8(X)) HarperCollins Pubs.

Keenan, Sheila & Burns, Marilyn. Lizzy's Dizzy Day. Snider, Jackie, illus. 2001. (Hello Reader! Math Ser.). (J). (gr. k-2). pap. 3.99 (978-0-439-05963-3(1) , Cartwheel Bks.) Scholastic, Inc.

—Myrtle's Turtles. Coyle, Laura, illus. 2001. (Hello Reader! Math Ser.). (J). (978-0-439-30472-6(5)) Scholastic, Inc.

Kids Can Press Staff, Press Can. Math Stories: Addition. 2004. (Kids Can Learn with Franklin Ser.). (Illus.). 32p. (J). (gr. k-3). (978-1-55337-593-7(9)) Kids Can Pr., Ltd.

Manos, John. The Mail Comes to Main Street. 2006. (Early Explorers Ser.). (J). 34.00 (***978-1-4108-6118-4(X)***) Benchmark Education Co.

McNamara, Margaret. Eloise Has a Lesson. Mitter, Kathryn, illus. 2004. (Eloise Ser.). 32p. (J). pap. 3.99 (978-0-689-87367-6(0) , Aladdin) Simon & Schuster Children's Publishing.

—Eloise Has a Lesson. Mitter, Kathryn, illus. 2005. (Eloise Ser.). 32p. (J). (ps-1). lib. bdg. 11.19 (978-0-606-33476-1(9)) Tandem Library Bks.

Mills, Claudia. 7 x 9 = Trouble! Karas, G. Brian, illus. 2002. 112p. (J). (gr. 2-3). 16.00 (978-0-374-36746-6(9) , Farrar, Straus & Giroux (BYR)) Farrar, Straus & Giroux.

Neuschwander, Cindy, et al. Amanda Bean's Amazing Dream: A Mathematical Story. Litzinger, Rosanne, illus. 1998. 40p. (J). (gr. 1-4). pap. 16.95 (978-0-590-30012-4(1)) Scholastic, Inc.

Rand, Ann & Rand, Paul. Little 1. 2006. (Illus.). 40p. (J). 15.95 (978-0-8118-5004-9(8)) Chronicle Bks. LLC.

Rocklin, Joanne. Just Add Fun! Lemelman, Martin, illus. 2000. (Hello Reader! Math Ser.). 48p. (J). (ps-3). pap. 3.99 (978-0-590-64399-3(1)) Scholastic, Inc.

—Just Add Fun! 2000. (Hello Reader! Ser.). (Illus.). (J). (978-0-606-18572-1(0)) Tandem Library Bks.

Schwartz, Betty Ann. One to Ten... And back Again: An Amazing Pull-the-Ribbon Book. Shakir, Susie, illus. 2007. 24p. (J). (ps). 12.95 (***978-1-932403-27-5(2)***) Handprint Bks.

Scieszka, Jon. Math Curse. ed. 2004. (Illus.). (J). (gr. k-4). spiral bd. (978-0-616-01778-4(2)) Canadian National Institute for the Blind/Institut National Canadien pour les Aveugles.

Slater, David Michael. Seven Ate Nine! Trover, Zachary, illus. 2007. (Missy Swiss & More Ser.). 32p. (J). (ps-4). lib. bdg. 27.07 (***978-1-60270-012-3(5)*** , Looking Glass Library) Magic Wagon.

Stamper, Judith Bauer. Bowwow Bake Sale. 2002. (gr. k-3). lib. bdg. 11.80 (978-0-613-64026-8(8)) Tandem Library Bks.

Top That!, ed. In My Little Blue Bed. Henley, Claire, illus. 2007. 11p. (J). (ps). bds. 9.99 (***978-1-84666-280-5(X)*** , Tide Mill Pr.) Top That! Publishing PLC GBR. *Dist:* Random Hse., Inc.

—In My Little Pink Bed. Henley, Claire, illus. 2007. 11p. (J). (ps). bds. 9.99 (***978-1-84666-285-0(0)*** , Tide Mill Pr.) Top That! Publishing PLC GBR. *Dist:* Random Hse., Inc.

ARITHMETIC—STUDY AND TEACHING

see also Counting Books

Douglas, Kathy. Calculation Station. Bittinger, Gayle, ed. Barr, Marilynn G. & Mohrman, Gary, illus. 1998. (Kinderstation Ser.). 160p. (J). (ps). pap. 15.95 (978-1-57029-158-6(6) , WPH 4501, Totline Pubns.) Schaffer, Frank Pubns.

Engelbrite, Eve. Arithmability: Addition & Subtraction of Whole Numbers: Dyscalculia Workbook. 2003. 68p. spiral bd. 19.95 (978-1-931203-07-4(5)) Inspired Idea.

Musson, Gloria J. & Musson, Cyril D. RAPmetic, the Arithmetic Rap. Miller, Benjamin S., illus. 1998. 48p. (J). (gr. 3 up). pap. 3.50 (978-0-9619321-0-7(4)) Square 1 Pubns.

Saunders, Nicholas & Faber, Laurie. The Times Table Rap. 2004. (J). audio compact disk 15.00 (978-0-9761132-0-1(1)) Blue Lion Productions, Ltd.

School Zone Publishing Company Staff. First Grade Scholar. rev. ed. 2001. (Super-Deluxe Wkbks.). (Illus.). 128p. (J). (gr. k-1). pap. 7.99 (978-1-58947-009-5(5) , 02460) School Zone Publishing Co.

—Multiplication Made Easy. rev. ed. 2002. (I Know It! Workbooks Ser.). (Illus.). 32p. (J). (gr. 3-4). pap. 2.49 (978-0-88743-796-0(6) , 02108) School Zone Publishing Co.

ARIZONA

Adamson, Thomas K. Arizona. 2003. (Land of Liberty Ser.). (Illus.). 64p. (J). (gr. 3-4). lib. bdg. 23.93 (978-0-7368-1571-0(6) , Bridgestone Bks.) Capstone Pr., Inc.

Andres, Dennis Michael. The Insider's Guide to Sedona. Lindahl, Larry, photos by. 2003. (Illus.). 222p. per. 16.95 (978-0-9721202-1-0(1) , 825-694) Meta AdventuresPublishing & DIA Publishing.

Becker, Michelle Aki. Arizona. Risco, Eida del, tr. Ancona, George, photos by. 2004. (Rookie Readers - Spanish Ser.). (SPA., Illus.). 32p. (J). 19.50 (978-0-516-25106-6(6) , Watts, Franklin) Scholastic Library Publishing.

—Arizona. 2004. (Rookie Read-About Geography Ser.). (Illus.). 31p. (J). 20.50 (978-0-516-22734-4(3) , Children's Pr.) Scholastic Library Publishing.

Bereit, Rebekah, ed. A-Maze-Ing Arizona. 2002. (Illus.). 56p. (J). act. bk. ed. 7.95 (978-0-87358-809-6(6) , Rising Moon Bks. for Young Readers) Northland Publishing.

Brew, Virginia & McCabe, Michael. Arizona: Studies. rev. ed. 2000. (Illus.). 160p. (YA). (gr. 4-6). 21.50 (978-0-911981-58-2(6)) Cloud Publishing.

Brown, Jonatha A. Arizona. 2006. (Portraits of the States Ser.). (Illus.). 32p. (J). pap. 8.95 (978-0-8368-4679-9(6)); lib. bdg. 23.33 (978-0-8368-4660-7(5)) Stevens, Gareth Inc.

Brown, Vanessa. Arizona. (Bilingual Library of the United States of America). (ENG & SPA.). (J). 2007. lib. bdg. (978-1-4042-3139-9(0)); 2005. (Illus.). 32p. lib. bdg. 22.50 (978-1-4042-3067-5(X) , Buenas Letra) Rosen Publishing Group, Inc., The.

Capstone Press Staff, contrib. by. Arizona. rev. ed. 2002. (One Nation Ser.). (Illus.). 48p. (J). (gr. 3-4). lib. bdg. 22.60 (978-0-7368-1227-6(X) , Bridgestone Bks.) Capstone Pr., Inc.

Cloud Publishing Editorial Staff, contrib. by. Arizona: Resource Binder. 2000. (J). (gr. 4-7). ring bd. 124.95 (978-0-911981-62-9(4)) Cloud Publishing.

Corrick, James A. Uniquely Arizona. 2003. (Heinemann State Studies). (Illus.). 48p. (J). 27.07 (978-1-4034-4486-8(2)); pap. 8.50 (978-1-4034-4501-8(X)) Heinemann Library.

Corwin, Jeff. Into Wild Arizona. Pascoe, Elaine, ed. 2003. (Jeff Corwin Experience Ser.). (Illus.). 48p. (J). 24.95 (978-1-4103-0058-4(7)); 11.20 (978-1-4103-0179-6(6)) Thomson Gale. (Blackbirch Pr., Inc.).

Craats, Rennay. A Guide to Arizona. 2001. (American States Ser.). (Illus.). 32p. (J). lib. bdg. 16.95 (978-1-930954-77-9(8)); per. 7.95 (978-1-930954-68-7(9)) Weigl Pubs., Inc.

Feinstein, Stephen. Arizona: A MyReportLinks.com Book. 2002. (States Ser.). (Illus.). 48p. (J). (gr. 4-10). lib. bdg. 25.26 (978-0-7660-5023-5(8) , MyReportLinks.com Bks.) Enslow Pubs., Inc.

Filbin, Dan. Arizona. 2nd exp. rev. ed. (Hello U. S. A. Ser.). (Illus.). 84p. (J). (gr. 3-6). 2003. pap. 6.95 (978-0-8225-4133-2(5)); 2002. lib. bdg. 25.26 (978-0-8225-4063-2(0)) Lerner Publishing Group.

—Arizona. 2001. (gr. 3-6). lib. bdg. 15.25 (978-0-613-89180-6(5)) Tandem Library Bks.

Gordon, David. Kid's Guide to Chiricahua. 2002. 16p. (J). pap. 3.95 (978-1-58369-027-7(1)) Western National Parks Assn.

Gowan, Barb. G Is for Grand Canyon: An Arizona Alphabet. Larson, Katherine, illus. 2002. 40p. (J). 17.95 (978-1-58536-068-0(6)) Sleeping Bear Pr.

Gowan, Barbara. Desert Digits: An Arizona Number Book. Toddy, Irving, illus. 2006. 40p. (J). 17.95 (978-1-58536-162-5(3)) Sleeping Bear Pr.

Harcourt School Publishers Staff. Life in a Canyon. 3rd ed. 2002. (Horizons Ser.). (Illus.). (J). pap. 5.50 (978-0-15-333386-6(3)) Harcourt Schl. Pubs.

Heidinger, Lisa Schnebly. The Three Sedonas. Swanson, Trevor V., illus. 2nd ed. 2000. 32p. (J). (ps-5). 15.95 (978-0-916179-97-7(4)) Arizona Highways.

Heinrichs, Ann. Arizona. 2005. (Welcome to the USA Ser.). 40p. (J). (gr. 1-5). 27.07 (978-1-59296-468-0(0)) Child's World, Inc.

—Arizona. 2003. (This Land Is Your Land Ser.). (Illus.). 48p. (J). (gr. 3 up). lib. bdg. 22.60 (978-0-7565-0333-8(7)) Compass Point Bks.

Kid's Guide to Canyon de Chelly National Monument. l.t. ed. 2001. 16p. per. 1.00 (978-1-58369-012-3(3)) Western National Parks Assn.

Labairon, Cassandra Sharri. Arizona. 2008. (J). (***978-1-58341-628-0(5)*** , Creative Education) Creative Co., The.

Marsh, Carole. Arizona Classic Christmas Trivia. 2002. (Carole Marsh Arizona Bks.). (Illus.). 32p. pap. 6.95 (978-0-635-01373-6(8) , 13738, Marsh, Carole Bks.); lib. bdg. 21.95 (978-0-635-01374-3(6) , 13746) Gallopade International.

—Arizona Current Events Projects: 30 Cool, Activities, Crafts, Experiments & More for Kids to Do to Learn about Your State! 2003. (Arizona Experience Ser.). 32p. (gr. k-5). pap. 5.95 (978-0-635-02022-2(X) , Marsh, Carole Bks.) Gallopade International.

—The Arizona Experience Pocket Guide. 2001. (Illus.). 96p. (J). (gr. 3-8). pap. 6.95 (978-0-7933-9907-9(6)) Gallopade International.

—Arizona Geography Projects: 30 Cool, Activities, Crafts, Experiments & More for Kids to Do to Learn about Your State! 2003. (Arizona Experience Ser.). 32p. (gr. k-5). pap. 5.95 (978-0-635-01822-9(5) , Marsh, Carole Bks.) Gallopade International.

—Arizona Government Projects: 30 Cool, Activities, Crafts, Experiments & More for Kids to Do to Learn about Your State! 2003. (Arizona Experience Ser.). 32p. (gr. k-5). pap. 5.95 (978-0-635-01922-6(1) , Marsh, Carole Bks.) Gallopade International.

—Arizona Jeopardy! Answers & Questions about Our State! 2001. (Carole Marsh Arizona Bks.). (Illus.). 32p. (J). (gr. 3-8). pap. 7.95 (978-0-7933-9791-4(X)) Gallopade International.

—Arizona "Jography" A Fun Run Thru Our State! 2001. (Carole Marsh Arizona Bks.). 32p. (J). (gr. 3-8). pap. 7.95 (978-0-7933-9820-1(7)) Gallopade International.

—Arizona Millionaire: Game Book. 2001. (Carole Marsh Arizona Bks.). (Illus.). 32p. (J). (gr. 3-8). pap., act. bk. ed. 9.95 (978-0-635-00022-4(9)) Gallopade International.

—Arizona People Projects: 30 Cool, Activities, Crafts, Experiments & More for Kids to Do to Learn about Your State! 2003. (Arizona Experience Ser.). 32p. (gr. k-5). pap. 5.95 (978-0-635-01972-1(8) , Marsh, Carole Bks.) Gallopade International.

—Arizona Survivor: Game Book. 2001. (Carole Marsh Arizona Bks.). (Illus.). 32p. (J). (gr. 3-8). pap., act. bk. ed. 9.95 (978-0-635-00524-3(7)) Gallopade International.

—Arizona Symbols & Facts Projects: 30 Cool, Activities, Crafts, Experiments & More for Kids to Do to Learn about Your State! 2003. (Arizona Experience Ser.). 32p. (gr. k-5). pap. 5.95 (978-0-635-01871-7(3) , Marsh, Carole Bks.) Gallopade International.

—The Big Arizona Reproducible Activity Book. 2001. (Carole Marsh Arizona Bks.). (Illus.). 96p. (J). (gr. 2-6). pap. 9.95 (978-0-7933-9936-9(X)) Gallopade International.

—My First Book about Arizona. 2001. (Carole Marsh Arizona Bks.). (Illus.). 32p. (J). (gr. k-4). pap. 7.95 (978-0-7933-9878-2(9)) Gallopade International.

—My First Pocket Guide Arizona. 2000. (Arizona Experience! Ser.). (Illus.). 96p. (J). (gr. 3-8). 12.95 (978-0-635-01293-7(6) , 12936) Gallopade International.

—The Survivor: A Class Challenge. 2001. (Carole Marsh Arizona Bks.). lib. bdg. 29.95 (978-0-635-00649-3(9)) Gallopade International.

Martin, Michael A. Arizona: The Grand Canyon State. 2002. (World Almanac Library of the States). (Illus.). 48p. (J). (gr. 5 up). lib. bdg. 30.00 (978-0-8368-5128-1(5)); pap. 14.95 (978-0-8368-5298-1(2)) Stevens, Gareth Inc. (World Almanac Library).

Maruca, Mary. A Kid's Guide to Exploring Montezuma Castle National Monument. 2000. (Illus.). 12p. (J). pap. (978-1-58369-010-9(7)) Western National Parks Assn.

—A Kid's Guide to Exploring Walnut Canyon National Monument. 2002. (Illus.). 12p. (J). pap. 1.00 (978-1-58369-017-8(4)) Western National Parks Assn.

McAuliffe, Emily. Arizona Facts & Symbols. (States & Their Symbols Ser.). 24p. (J). 1998. (Illus.). (gr. 2-3). lib. bdg. 18.60 (978-0-7368-0080-8(8) , Bridgestone Bks.); 2003. lib. bdg. 19.93 (978-0-7368-2233-6(X)) Capstone Pr., Inc.

McCabe, Michael. Arizona: Studies. 2000. (Illus.). 48p. (J). (gr. 4-6). pap., act. bk. ed. 6.65 (978-0-911981-59-9(4)) Cloud Publishing.

McDaniel, Melissa. Arizona. 2000. (Celebrate the States Ser.). (Illus.). 144p. (J). (gr. 4-8). lib. bdg. 37.07 (978-0-7614-0647-1(6) , Benchmark Bks.) Cavendish, Marshall Corp.

McHugh, Erin. State Shapes: Arizona. Schrier, Alfred, illus. 2007. 48p. (J). 9.95 (978-1-57912-701-5(0)) Black Dog & Leventhal Pubs., Inc.

Murray, Julie. Arizona. 2005. (Buddy Book Ser.). (Illus.). 32p. (J). (gr. k-4). lib. bdg. 22.78 (978-1-59197-662-2(6) , Buddy Bks.) ABDO Publishing Co.

Peterson, David. Saguaro National Park. (True Bks.). (Illus.). 48p. (J). (gr. 3-5). 2000. pap. 6.95 (978-0-516-26771-5(X)); 1999. 25.00 (978-0-516-20944-9(2)) Scholastic Library Publishing. (Children's Pr.).

Phoenix Sold C 2005. 2004. 372p. (YA). pap. 15.00 (978-1-58553-961-1(9) , 05GC0020) Entertainment Publications, Inc.

Pratt-Serafini, Kristin Joy. Saguaro Moon: A Desert Journal. 2002. (gr. 3-6). lib. bdg. 16.40 (978-0-613-52786-6(0)) Tandem Library Bks.

Sosaz. Arizona. 2000. (Switched on Schoolhouse Ser.). (Illus.). (YA). (gr. 7-12). pap. 24.95 incl. cd-rom (978-0-7403-0255-8(8) , SOSAZ) Alpha Omega Pubns., Inc.

Stacy, Darryl. Arizona: Government & Citizenship. rev. ed. 1999. (Illus.). (J). (gr. 7-9). 160p. 21.50 (978-0-911981-56-8(X)); 48p. pap., stu. ed. 6.45 (978-0-911981-57-5(8)) Cloud Publishing.

Stacy, Darryl & McCabe, Michael. Arizona: Studies: Map Skills Program Binder. 2000. (Illus.). 59p. (J). (gr. 4-6). ring bd. 59.95 (978-0-911981-53-7(5)) Cloud Publishing.

Standard, Carole K. Arizona. 2002. (From Sea to Shining Sea Ser.: 2). (Illus.). 80p. (J). (gr. 3-5). 30.50 (978-0-516-22315-5(1) , Children's Pr.) Scholastic Library Publishing.

Storad, Conrad J. Head over Heels about Arizona: A Color & Learning Book. Rumphorst, John, illus. 1999. 32p. (J). (gr. 1-4). pap. 2.95 (978-1-891795-10-7(4)) RGU Group, The.

ARIZONA—FICTION

Adler, C. S. The No Place Cat. 2002. 160p. (YA). (gr. 5-9). 15.00 (978-0-618-09644-2(2) , Clarion Bks.) Houghton Mifflin Co. Trade & Reference Div.

Allen, J. Kent. Embritt Waters & the Mark of the Rattlesnake. 2006. 229p. (J). pap. 14.95 (978-0-7414-2769-4(9)) Infinity Publishing.

Allred, Sylvester. Rascal, the Tassel-Eared Squirrel. Iverson, Diane, illus. 2007. (J). (***978-0-938216-88-9(0)***) Grand Canyon Assn.

Avalos, Cecilia O. El Sombrero de Luis Lucero. 2003. (SPA.). pap. 15.96 net. (978-0-7608-2262-3(X) , SW3166) Sundance/Newbridge Educational Publishing.

Avrech, Robert J. The Hebrew Kid & the Apache Maiden. 2006. 228p. (J). pap. 11.95 (978-0-9754382-2-0(0)) Seraphic Pr.

Baxter, Linda. The Winter of the Stone Woman. Marks, Dea, illus. 1999. (Cover-to-Cover Novels Ser.). 75p. (J). (gr. 2-5). lib. bdg. 13.95 (978-0-7807-8965-4(2) , Covercraft); (gr. 4-8). pap. 5.60 (978-0-7891-2926-0(4)) Perfection Learning Corp.

Bly, Stephen A. Daring Rescue at Sonora Pass. 2005. (Adventures of the American Frontier Ser.). 144p. pap. 6.99 (978-1-58134-471-4(6) , Crossway Bibles) Crossway Bks.

Bury, Laurie D. The Adventures of Dalbert Juan: Dalbert Goes to Arizona. Gallo, Karen A., illus. 2000. (J). (ps-2). 12.95 (978-0-9702319-2-5(X)) Rhette Enterprises, Inc.

Campbell, Julie. Mystery in Arizona, Vol. 6. Stevens, Mary, illus. 2004. (Trixie Belden Ser.: No. 6). 272p. (J). (gr. 3-7). 6.99 (978-0-375-82741-9(2) , Random Hse. Bks. for Young Readers) Random Hse. Children's Bks.

Carabine, Sue. The Night Before Christmas in Arizona. Kawasaki, Shauna Mooney, illus. 2002. 60p. 5.95 (978-1-58685-169-9(1)) Gibbs Smith, Publisher.

Charlie Moves to Arizona Vol. 2: Charlie's Great Adventure. 2001. 88p. (J). per. 5.95 (978-0-9702546-9-6(5)) GoodyGoody Bks.

Gamble, Adam. Good Night Arizona. Hansen, Red, illus. 2008. (Good Night Our World Ser.). 20p. (J). bds. 9.95 (***978-1-60219-000-9(3)***) Our World of Books.

Giacomucci, Carol. A New Home. 2006. 23p. pap. 10.95 (978-0-7414-3498-2(9)) Infinity Publishing.

Golio, Janet & Golio, Mike. Present from the Past. 2nd ed. 2007. 120p. (YA). pap. 14.99 (***978-1-59092-145-6(3)*** , Blue Works) Windstorm Creative.

—Puzzle from the Past. 2nd ed. 2007. 120p. (YA). pap. 14.99 (***978-1-59092-146-3(1)*** , Blue Works) Windstorm Creative.

Golio, Janet, et al. A Present from the Past: Multimedia Edition. 2000. (Illus.). III, 157p. (J). (gr. 4-7). cd-rom 14.95 (978-0-9704202-0-6(X)) GAGA.

Goodridge, Jim. A Sterling Plan: The Yankees, the Durang. 2005. 156p. pap. 19.95 (978-1-4137-4088-2(X)) PublishAmerica, Inc.

Gutman, Dan. The Homework Machine. 2006. (Illus.). 160p. (J). (gr. 3-7). 15.95 (978-0-689-87678-3(5)) Simon & Schuster Children's Publishing.

—The Homework Machine. 2006. (YA). 21.95 (978-0-7862-8883-0(3)) Thorndike Pr.

Hamilton, Elizabeth L. Lost on Superstition Mountain. 2004. (Character Mystery Ser.: No. 3). (Illus.). 144p. (J). per. 9.95 (978-0-9754629-5-9(4) , Character-in-Action) Quiet Impact, Inc.

Hancock, H. Irving. The Young Engineers in Arizona. rev. ed. 2006. 216p. 27.95 (978-1-4218-1751-4(9)); pap. 12.95 (978-1-4218-1851-1(5)) 1st World Publishing, Inc. (1st World Library - Literary Society).

—The Young Engineers in Arizona or Laying. 2004. reprint ed. pap. 21.95 (978-1-4191-8913-5(1)) Kessinger Publishing, LLC.

—The Young Engineers in Arizona or Laying Tracks on the Man Killer Quicksand. 2004. reprint ed. pap. 1.99 (978-1-4192-8913-2(6)) Kessinger Publishing, LLC.

Harris, Marian. Tuesday in Arizona. Harris, Jim, illus. 1998. 32p. (J). (ps-3). 15.95 (978-1-56554-233-4(9)) Pelican Publishing Co., Inc.

Hart, J. J. Zombie Monkey Monster Jamboree. Meugniot, Will, illus. 2006. 141p. (J). 12.95 (978-1-933925-07-3(8) , Actionopolis) Komikwerks, LLC.

Hayes, Joe. Ghost Fever.Tr. of Mal de Fantasma. (J). 2006. (SPA.). 90p. pap. 8.95 (978-1-933693-03-3(7)); 2004. (ENG & SPA., Illus.). 80p. (gr. 3-6). 14.95 (978-0-938317-83-8(0)) Cinco Puntos Pr.

Henry, Marguerite. Brighty: Of the Grand Canyon. 2002. (Illus.). (YA). 13.40 (978-1-4046-1351-5(X)) Book Wholesalers, Inc.

—Brighty: Of the Grand Canyon. 2001. (J). (gr. 3-6). 21.50 (978-0-8446-7176-5(2)) Smith, Peter Pub., Inc.

Hobbs, Will. River Thunder. 1999. (gr. 7-12). lib. bdg. 13.55 (978-0-613-12037-1(X)) Tandem Library Bks.

Hobbs, William. River Thunder. 1999. (978-0-606-15817-6(0)) Tandem Library Bks.

Hopkins, Suzette. Little Wolf's Christmas. Taylor, Jill, illus. 2004. 19p. (J). 12.95 (978-1-932133-72-1(0)) Writers' Collective, The.

Howey, Paul M. Freckles: The Mystery of the Little White Dog in the Desert. Zabriskie, Judy Mehn, illus. 2003. 72p. (gr. 2-5). lib. bdg. 14.95 (978-0-9677292-1-3(1)) AZTexts Publishing, Inc.

Jenkins, Jerry B. & Fabry, Chris. Canyon Echoes. 2005. (Tyndale Kids Ser.). 240p. (J). pap. 5.99 (978-1-4143-0147-1(2)) Tyndale Hse. Pubs.

Johnson, Tim. Lost Dutchman in Cochise County? Incidents & Coincidences. 2003. (Illus.). 52p. 19.95 (978-0-9742351-0-3(5)) MCM Prime, Inc.

Kadohata, Cynthia. Weedflower. 2006. (J). (978-0-689-04937-8(4)); (Illus.). 272p. (gr. 5 up). 16.95 (978-0-689-86574-9(0)) Simon & Schuster Children's Publishing. (Atheneum).

Koertge, Ronald. The Arizona Kid. 2005. 304p. (YA). (gr. 9-12). 16.99 (978-0-7636-2542-9(6)) Candlewick Pr.

—Arizona Kid. 2005. 304p. (YA). (gr. 9 up). pap. 6.99 (978-0-7636-2695-2(3)) Candlewick Pr.

Lewis, Floyd. The Foundered Mule. 2006. (YA). ***978-0-9788283-2-5(1)*** Acacia Publishing, Inc.

The Little Saguaro. 2007. (YA). pap. 15.95 ***(*978-1-886679-37-5(1))*** Arizona Sonora Desert Museum Pr.

Marsden, Carolyn. Bird Springs. 2007. 128p. (J). (gr. 3 up). 14.99 (978-0-670-06193-8(X) , Viking Juvenile) Penguin Group (USA) Inc.

Martin, Gayle. Gunfight at the O. K. Corral: Luke & Jenny Visit Tombstone. 2006. (J). per. 14.95 net. (978-1-58985-050-7(5)) Five Star Pubns., Inc.

Matthews. Death in the Desert. (Thumbprint Mysteries Ser.). 32.86 (978-0-8092-0416-8(9)) McGraw-Hill/ Contemporary.

Mayaprua, Alejandro Taish. Nantu & Auju: How the Moon & the Potoo Bird Came to Be. Youth of the Achuar Tribe of Ecuador, illus. 2005. (J). 15.95 (978-0-9745477-0-1(0)) Arutam Pr.

Mesta, Robert I. Condor: Spirit of the Canyon. Ormsby, Lawrence, illus. 2007. (J). ***(*978-0-938216-85-8(6))*** Grand Canyon Assn.

Mosier, Elizabeth. My Life As a Girl. 2000. 204p. (gr. 7). pap. 12.00 (978-0-375-89522-7(1) , Random Hse. Bks. for Young Readers) Random Hse. Children's Bks.

—My Life As a Girl. 2000. (J). (978-0-606-19082-4(1)) Tandem Library Bks.

Oneill, Elizabeth. Alfred Visits Arizona. 2006. 24p. pap. 12.00 ***(*978-0-9790240-0-9(5))*** Funny Bone Bks.

Organick, Avrum B. Canyon Boy. Toddy, Irving, illus. 2002. 40p. (YA). (gr. 4-8). 11.95 (978-0-9671068-4-7(2)) Red Lake Pr.

Peschke, M. Dead Man's Map. Smith, Tod, illus. 2008. (J). pap. ***(*978-1-59889-921-4(X));*** (YA). (gr. 5-9). lib. bdg. 17.95 ***(*978-1-59889-855-2(8))*** Stone Arch Bks.

Pintozzi, Nick. Bentley & the Great Fire. Pintozzi, Nick et al, illus. 2004. 16.95 (978-0-9749465-2-8(4)) Bent-DaiSha, LLC.

Samantha's Arizona Adventure. 1998. (Illus.). 2p. (J). (ps-1). 15.00 (978-1-888074-84-0(1)) Pockets of Learning.

Sandin, Joan. Coyote School News. Sandin, Joan, illus. rev. ed. 2003. (Illus.). 48p. (J). 17.95 (978-0-8050-6558-9(X) , Holt, Henry & Co. Bks. For Young Readers) Holt, Henry & Co.

Sargent, Dave & Sargent, Pat. Buttons: (Muddy Dun) Have Courage, 9. Lenoir, Jane, illus. 2003. (Saddle Up Ser.: Vol. 9). 42p. (J). pap. 6.95 (978-1-56763-688-8(8)); lib. bdg. 22.60 (978-1-56763-687-1(X)) Ozark Publishing.

Schurch, Maylan. The Desert Temple Mystery. 2001. (Justin Case Adventures Ser.: 2). 128p. (YA). pap. (978-0-8280-1612-4(7) , 042-430) Review & Herald Publishing Assn.

Skurzynski, Gloria. Over the Edge. 2002. (gr. 3-6). lib. bdg. 14.10 (978-0-613-62819-8(5)) Tandem Library Bks.

Skurzynski, Gloria & Ferguson, Alane. Over the Edge. 2002. (Mysteries in Our National Parks Ser.: Vol. 7). 160p. (J). (gr. 3-7). pap. 5.95 (978-0-7922-6686-0(2)); Vol. 7. 15.95 (978-0-7922-6677-8(3)) National Geographic Society. (National Geographic Children's Bks.).

Smith, Roland. The Last Lobo. 2001. (gr. 3-6). lib. bdg. 14.15 (978-0-613-74960-2(X)) Tandem Library Bks.

Spinelli, Jerry. Star Girl. 2000. 192p. (J). (gr. 5-8). 15.95 (978-0-679-88637-2(0) , Knopf Bks. for Young Readers) Random Hse. Children's Bks.

—Stargirl. 2002. (EMC Masterpiece Series Access Editions). xiv, 199p. (YA). 10.95 (978-0-8219-2504-1(0) , 35378) EMC/Paradigm Publishing.

—Stargirl. unabr. ed. 2004. 192p. (J). (gr. 7 up). pap. 40.00 incl. audio (978-0-8072-0855-7(8) , LYA 323 SP, Listening Library) Random Hse. Audio Publishing Group.

—Stargirl. (YA). 2004. 208p. (gr. 5). mass mkt. 6.99 (978-0-440-41677-7(9) , Laurel Leaf); 2000. 192p. (gr. 5-8). lib. bdg. 17.99 (978-0-679-98637-9(5) , Knopf Bks. for Young Readers); 2002. 208p. (gr. 7 up). reprint ed. pap. 8.95 (978-0-375-82233-9(X) , Knopf Bks. for Young Readers) Random Hse. Children's Bks.

—Stargirl. Tino, illus. (SPA.). 224p. (J). (gr. 5-8). pap. 9.95 (978-1-59437-815-7(0)) Santillana USA Publishing Co., Inc.

—Stargirl. 2002. (gr. 7-12). lib. bdg. 17.60 (978-0-613-49417-5(2)) Tandem Library Bks.

—Stargirl. l.t. ed. 2001. 240p. (J). (gr. 8-12). 24.95 (978-0-7862-3218-5(8)) Thorndike Pr.

Stewart, Jennifer. If That Breathes Fire, We're Toast! 1999. 128p. (J). (gr. 4-6). tchr. ed. 15.95 (978-0-8234-1430-7(2)) Holiday Hse., Inc.

—If That Breathes Fire, We're Toast! 2001. (978-0-606-22151-1(4)); 2000. (gr. 3-6). lib. bdg. 12.40 (978-0-613-35730-2(2)) Tandem Library Bks.

Stewart, Jennifer J. The Bean King's Daughter. 2002. 144p. (J). (gr. 4-6). tchr. ed. 15.95 (978-0-8234-1644-8(5)) Holiday Hse., Inc.

Stoneskipper. 2005. (J). per. 19.95 (978-0-9743789-0-9(9)) Freeverse Enterprises Inc.

Taylor, Theodore. Billy the Kid: A Novel. 2005. (Illus.). 224p. (YA). (gr. 7-12). 17.00 (978-0-15-204930-0(4)) Harcourt Children's Bks.

Turner, Nancy E. These Is My Words: The Diary of Sarah Agnes Prine, 1881-1902 Arizona Territories. 1999. (978-0-606-17597-5(0)) Tandem Library Bks.

Ware, Jim. Canyon Quest. 2004. (Last Chance Detectives Ser.). 272p. (YA). per. 7.99 (978-1-58997-239-1(2)) Focus on the Family Publishing.

Wilson, Pauline Hutchens & Dengler, Sandy. The Case of the Dinosaur in the Desert, Vol. 4. 2001. (New Sugar Creek Gang Ser.: Vol. #4). (Illus.). 144p. (J). 5.99 (978-0-8024-8664-6(9)) Moody Pubs.

Wood, Elizabeth Lamb. There Go the Apaches. 2005. pap. 26.95 (978-1-4191-5979-4(8)) Kessinger Publishing, LLC.

Worley, Rob. Heir to Fire: Gila Flats. Dubisch, Mike, illus. 2006. 129p. (J). (gr. 5-8). 12.95 (978-0-9742803-7-0(2) , Actionopolis) Komikwerks, LLC.

Zambarano, Richard, illus. Wilbur & Wilma's Colorful Campus Tour - University of Arizona A-Z. 2004. (J). 9.99 (978-1-933069-02-9(3)) Odd Duck Ink, Inc.

ARIZONA—HISTORY

Aki, Becker Michelle. Arizona. 2004. (Rookie Read-About Geography Ser.). 32p. (J). (gr. 1-2). pap. 5.95 (978-0-516-24434-1(5) , Children's Pr.) Scholastic Library Publishing.

Alagna, Magdalena. Wyatt Earp: Lawman of the American West. (Famous People in American History Ser.). (Illus.). 32p. (J). (ps-7). 2004. 21.25 (978-0-8239-4123-0(X) , Rosen Central); 2003. pap. (978-0-8239-4195-7(7)) Rosen Publishing Group, Inc., The.

The Arizona Constitution. 4th ed. 2003. (YA). pap., wbk. ed. 7.00 (978-0-9740200-0-6(1)) Academic Solutions, Inc.

Becker, Michelle Aki. Arizona. 2005. (Rookie Espanol: Geografia Ser.). (SPA., Illus.). 32p. (J). (gr. k-2). pap. 5.95 (978-0-516-25512-5(6) , Children's Pr.) Scholastic Library Publishing.

Buscher, Dick, et al. Ali-shonak: The Story of Arizona - Roaring into the Millennium: Roaring into the Millennium, 10 vols., Vol. 10. 2000. (Al-shonak: The Story of Arizona: Vol. 10). 62p. (J). pap. 14.95 (978-1-887273-12-1(3)) Amigos de Arizonac, Inc.

Durrett, Deanne. Arizona. 2003. (Seeds of a Nation Ser.). (Illus.). 48p. (J). (gr. 3-5). 23.70 (978-0-7377-1537-8(5) , Kidhaven) Thomson Gale.

Goodman, Michael E. Wyatt Earp. 2005. (Legends of the West Ser.). (Illus.). 48p. (J). (gr. 5-9). 21.95 (978-1-58341-339-5(1) , Creative Education) Creative Co., The.

Hall, Carol S. & Hansen, T. J. This Is Arizona. (Illus.). 298p. (J). (gr. 1-6). pap. 49.95 (978-1-56861-061-0(0)) Swift Learning Resources.

Jastrzembski, Joseph C. The Apache Wars: The Final Resistance. 2007. (Landmark Events in Native American History Ser.). 136p. (gr. 9). 35.00 ***(*978-0-7910-9343-6(3)*** , Chelsea Hse.) Facts On File, Inc.

Marsh, Carole. Arizona History Projects: 30 Cool, Activities, Crafts, Experiments & More for Kids to Do to Learn about Your State! 2003. (Arizona Experience Ser.). 32p. (gr. k-5). pap. 5.95 (978-0-635-01772-7(5) , Marsh, Carole Bks.) Gallopade International.

Ruffner, Melissa. Whatever Happened to Baby Harry: The True Story of the First Child Born to an Officer's Family at Camp Apache, Arizona Territory. Summerhayes, Roger, photos by. 2003. (Illus.). (YA). pap. 12.95 (978-0-9673171-1-3(8)) Primrose Pr.

Tucker, Regina E. The Legend of the Lost Dutchman's Gold Mine. 2004. (J). (gr. 3-7). 250.00 (978-0-9754261-2-8(5)); 96p. (gr. 3-7). spiral bd. 15.00 (978-0-9754261-1-1(7)); 2nd l.t. ed. (Tales of the Old West Ser.: 1). (Illus.). 88p. per. 15.00 (978-0-9754261-0-4(9)) Sol de Oro Pubns.

Urban, William. Wyatt Earp: The OK Corral & the Law of the American West. 2005. (Library of American Lives & Times). (Illus.). 112p. (YA). (gr. 4-8). lib. bdg. 31.95 (978-0-8239-5740-8(3)) Rosen Publishing Group, Inc., The.

Watson, Marilyn Myrick. Rose Mofford. 2007. (J). per. 6.95 ***(*978-0-9790826-1-0(7))*** Acacia Publishing, Inc.

ARKANSAS

Bailer, Darice. Arkansas: The Natural State. 2002. (World Almanac Library of the States). (Illus.). 48p. (J). (gr. 5 up). lib. bdg. 30.00 (978-0-8368-5129-8(3)); pap. 14.95 (978-0-8368-5299-8(0)) Stevens, Gareth Inc. (World Almanac Library).

Brown, Vanessa. Arkansas. 2006. (Bilingual Library of the United States of America). (SPA.). (J). lib. bdg. (978-1-4042-3144-3(7) , PowerKids Pr.) Rosen Publishing Group, Inc., The.

—Arkansas. Brusca, Maria Cristina, tr. 2005. (Bilingual Library of the United States of America: Set 1). (ENG & SPA., Illus.). 32p. (J). (gr. 2-5). lib. bdg. 22.50 (978-1-4042-3068-2(8) , Buenas Letra) Rosen Publishing Group, Inc., The.

Di Piazza, Domenica. Arkansas. 2nd exp. rev. ed. (Hello U. S. A. Ser.). (Illus.). 84p. (J). (gr. 3-6). 2002. lib. bdg. 25.26 (978-0-8225-4073-1(8)); 2003. pap. 6.95 (978-0-8225-4136-3(X)) Lerner Publishing Group.

—Arkansas. 2001. (gr. 3-6). lib. bdg. 15.25 (978-0-613-89181-3(3)) Tandem Library Bks.

Dougan, Michael B. Uniquely Arkansas. 2004. (Heinemann State Studies). (Illus.). 48p. (J). 27.07 (978-1-4034-4643-5(1)); pap. 8.50 (978-1-4034-4712-8(8)) Heinemann Library.

Heinrichs, Ann. Arkansas. 2005. (Welcome to the USA Ser.). 40p. (J). (gr. 1-5). 27.07 (978-1-59296-469-7(9)) Child's World, Inc.

—Arkansas. 2003. (This Land Is Your Land Ser.). (Illus.). 48p. (J). (gr. 3 up). lib. bdg. 22.60 (978-0-7565-0339-0(6)) Compass Point Bks.

King, David C. Arkansas. 2007. (J). ***(*978-0-7614-2215-0(3))*** Cavendish, Marshall Bks., Ltd.

Kjelle, Marylou Morano. Arkansas: A MyReportLinks. Com Book. 2003. (States Ser.). (Illus.). 48p. (J). lib. bdg. 25.26 (978-0-7660-5152-2(8) , MyReportLinks.com Bks.) Enslow Pubs., Inc.

Kule, Elaine A. Arkansas Facts & Symbols. (States & Their Symbols Ser.). 24p. (J). 2000. (Illus.). (gr. 2-3). lib. bdg. 18.60 (978-0-7368-0634-3(2) , Bridgestone Bks.); 2003. lib. bdg. 19.93 (978-0-7368-2234-3(8)) Capstone Pr., Inc.

Kummer, Patricia K. Arkansas. rev. ed. 2002. (One Nation Ser.). (Illus.). 48p. (J). (gr. 3-4). lib. bdg. 22.60 (978-0-7368-1228-3(8) , Bridgestone Bks.) Capstone Pr., Inc.

Lantier, Patricia. Arkansas. 2006. (Portraits of the States Ser.). (Illus.). 32p. (J). 8.95 (978-0-8368-4680-5(X)); lib. bdg. 23.33 (978-0-8368-4661-4(3)) Stevens, Gareth Inc.

Leber, Nancy. Arkansas. 2004. (Rookie Read-About Geography Ser.). (Illus.). 31p. (J). 20.50 (978-0-516-22746-7(7) , Children's Pr.) Scholastic Library Publishing.

Macaulay, Ellen. Arkansas. 2002. (From Sea to Shining Sea Ser.: 2). (Illus.). 80p. (J). (gr. 3-5). pap. 30.50 (978-0-516-22296-7(1) , Children's Pr.) Scholastic Library Publishing.

Marsh, Carole. Arkansas Classic Christmas Trivia. 2002. (Carole Marsh Arkansas Bks.). (Illus.). 32p. pap. 6.95 (978-0-635-01375-0(4) , 13754); lib. bdg. 21.95 (978-0-635-01376-7(2) , 13762) Gallopade International. (Marsh, Carole Bks.).

—Arkansas Current Events Projects: 30 Cool, Activities, Crafts, Experiments & More for Kids to Do to Learn about Your State! 2003. (Arkansas Experience Ser.). 32p. (gr. k-8). pap. 5.95 (978-0-635-02023-9(8) , Marsh, Carole Bks.) Gallopade International.

—The Arkansas Experience Pocket Guide. 2001. (Carole Marsh Arkansas Bks.). (Illus.). 96p. (J). (gr. 3-8). pap. 6.95 (978-0-7933-9908-6(4)) Gallopade International.

—Arkansas Geography Projects: 30 Cool, Activities, Crafts, Experiments & More for Kids to Do to Learn about Your State! 2003. (Arkansas Experience Ser.). 32p. (gr. k-5). pap. 5.95 (978-0-635-01823-6(3) , Marsh, Carole Bks.) Gallopade International.

—Arkansas Government Projects: 30 Cool, Activities, Crafts, Experiments & More for Kids to Do to Learn about Your State! 2003. (Arkansas Experience Ser.). 32p. (gr. k-5). pap. 5.95 (978-0-635-01923-3(X) , Marsh, Carole Bks.) Gallopade International.

—Arkansas Jeopardy! Answers & Questions about Our State! 2004. (Illus.). 32p. (J). (gr. 3-8). pap. 7.95 (978-0-7933-9792-1(8)) Gallopade International.

—Arkansas "Jography" A Fun Run Thru Our State! 2004. (Carole Marsh Arkansas Bks.). (Illus.). 32p. (J). (gr. 3-8). pap. 7.95 (978-0-7933-9821-8(5)) Gallopade International.

—Arkansas Millionaire: Game Book. 2001. (Carole Marsh Arkansas Bks.). (Illus.). 32p. (J). (gr. 3-8). pap., act. bk. ed. 9.95 (978-0-635-00024-8(5)) Gallopade International.

—Arkansas People Projects: 30 Cool, Activities, Crafts, Experiments & More for Kids to Do to Learn about Your State! 2003. (Arkansas Experience Ser.). 32p. (gr. k-5). pap. 5.95 (978-0-635-01973-8(6) , Marsh, Carole Bks.) Gallopade International.

—Arkansas Survivor: Game Book. 2001. (Carole Marsh Arkansas Bks.). (Illus.). 32p. (J). (gr. 3-8). pap., act. bk. ed. 9.95 (978-0-635-00525-0(5)) Gallopade International.

—Arkansas Symbols & Facts Projects: 30 Cool, Activities, Crafts, Experiments & More for Kids to Do to Learn about Your State! 2003. (Arkansas Experience Ser.). 32p. (gr. k-5). pap. 5.95 (978-0-635-01872-4(1) , Marsh, Carole Bks.) Gallopade International.

—The Big Arkansas Reproducible Activity Book. 2001. (Carole Marsh Arkansas Bks.). 96p. (J). (gr. 2-6). pap. 9.95 (978-0-7933-9937-6(8)) Gallopade International.

—My First Book about Arkansas. 2001. (Illus.). 32p. (J). (gr. k-4). pap. 7.95 (978-0-7933-9879-9(7)) Gallopade International.

—My First Pocket Guide Arkansas. 2000. (Arkansas Experience! Ser.). (Illus.). 96p. (J). (gr. 3-8). 12.95 (978-0-635-01294-4(4) , 12944) Gallopade International.

—The Survivor: A Class Challenge. 2001. (Carole Marsh Arkansas Bks.). lib. bdg. 29.95 (978-0-635-00650-9(2)) Gallopade International.

—Who Wants to Be an Arkansas Millionaire? 2001. (Carole Marsh Arkansas Bks.). lib. bdg. 29.95 (978-0-635-00025-5(3)) Gallopade International.

Murray, Julie. Arkansas. 2005. (Buddy Book Ser.). (Illus.). 32p. (J). (gr. k-4). lib. bdg. 22.78 (978-1-59197-663-9(4) , Buddy Bks.) ABDO Publishing Co.

Olien, Rebecca. Arkansas. 2003. (Land of Liberty Ser.). (Illus.). 64p. (J). (gr. 3-4). lib. bdg. 23.93 (978-0-7368-1572-7(4) , Bridgestone Bks.) Capstone Pr., Inc.

Pezzi, Bryan. A Guide to Arkansas. 2001. (American States Ser.). (Illus.). 32p. (J). lib. bdg. 16.95 (978-1-930954-82-3(4)); per. 7.95 (978-1-930954-73-1(5)) Weigl Pubs., Inc.

Shofner, Shawndra. Arkansas. 2008. (J). ***(*978-1-58341-629-7(3)*** , Creative Education) Creative Co., The.

Shoulders, Michael. N Is for Natural State: An Arkansas Alphabet. Anderson, Rick, illus. 2003. 40p. (J). 17.95 (978-1-58536-067-3(8)) Sleeping Bear Pr.

Sosare, M. Arkansas. 2000. (Switched on Schoolhouse Ser.). (Illus.). (YA). (gr. 7-12). pap. 24.95 incl. cd-rom (978-0-7403-0256-5(6) , SOSAR) Alpha Omega Pubns., Inc.

Ward, Margaret & Halpom, Roberta. At Home in Green-Wood: The Lives of Some Famous Inhabitants. 1998. (Illus.). 50p. (YA). pap. 6.95 (978-0-930194-57-4(8)) Ctr. for Thanatology Research & Education, Inc.

ARKANSAS—FICTION

Bennett, W. J., Jr. Sydney & Garrett's Great Arkansas Adventury. 2005. (J). pap. ***(*978-0-9794044-6-7(0))*** Archeological Assessments, Inc.

—Vivianna Becomes an Arkansan. 2005. (J). pap. ***(*978-0-9794044-7-4(9))*** Archeological Assessments, Inc.

Bowman, Eddie. Gravy on a Bucket Lid. Prater, Howard, illus. 1998. (Silly Songs Ser.). (J). pap. 6.95 (978-1-56763-430-3(3)); lib. bdg. 19.95 (978-1-56763-429-7(X)) Ozark Publishing.

Chesne, Sabrina. Lillie's Treasures/Los tesoros de Lili. Capasso, Diana, tr. Patagonia School, illus. 2004. (ENG & SPA.). 32p. per. 15.00 ***(*978-0-9630310-9-9(0))*** Will Hall Bks.

Darrow, Sharon. Painters of Lexieville. 2003. (Illus.). 192p. (YA). (gr. 9). 16.99 (978-0-7636-1437-9(8)) Candlewick Pr.

Draper, Sharon. Fire from the Rock. 2007. 240p. (YA). (gr. 7). 16.99 ***(*978-0-525-47720-4(9)*** , Dutton Juvenile) Penguin Group (USA) Inc.

Fickey, Brenda. Whispering Darkness. 2007. (ENG.). 136p. pr. 19.95 ***(*978-1-4241-6932-0(1))*** PublishAmerica, Inc.

Greene, Bette. I've Already Forgotten Your Name, Philip Hall! Jenkins, Leonard, illus. 2004. 176p. (J). (gr. 5 up). 15.99 (978-0-06-051835-6(9)) HarperCollins Pubs.

—Summer of My German Soldier. 1999. (Illus.). 208p. (J). (gr. 5-9). pap. 6.99 (978-0-14-130636-0(X) , Puffin) Penguin Group (USA) Inc.

—Summer of My German Soldier. 2000. (J). (gr. 6 up). 20.50 (978-0-8446-7144-4(4)) Smith, Peter Pub., Inc.

—Summer of My German Soldier. 1999. (978-0-606-17432-9(X)) Tandem Library Bks.

—Summer of My German Soldier. 2006. (Puffin Modern Classics Ser.). 240p. (J). (gr. 5). pap. 6.99 (978-0-14-240651-9(1) , Puffin) Penguin Group (USA) Inc.

—Summer of My German Soldier. l.t. ed. 2000. (LRS Large Print Cornerstone Ser.). 305p. (YA). (gr. 6-12). lib. bdg. 29.95 (978-1-58118-059-6(4) , 23473) LRS.

—Summer of My German Soldier. l.t. ed. 2005. 330p. pap. 10.95 (978-0-7862-7361-4(5) , Large Print Pr.) Thorndike Pr.

Greene, Bette & Hunt, Robert, illus. Summer of My German Soldier. 2003. 256p. (J). (gr. 5). 18.99 (978-0-8037-2869-1(7) , Dial) Penguin Group (USA) Inc.

Hess, Joan. Murder@Maggody.com. 2001. (Arly Hanks Mystery Ser.). (gr. 7-12). lib. bdg. 15.30 (978-0-613-36535-2(6)) Tandem Library Bks.

Mason, Richard. The Red Scarf: A Country Boy's Christmas Story. 2007. 160p. 14.95 ***(*978-0-87483-850-3(9))*** August Hse. Pubs., Inc.

Milligan, Bryce. Battle of the Alamo: You Are There. (Illus.). 176p. 9.95 (978-1-57168-286-4(4)) Eakin Pr.

Parkhurst, Liz S. Under One Flag: A Year at Rohwer. Clifton, Tom, illus. 2005. 32p. (J). 16.95 (978-0-87483-759-9(6) , 1241971) August Hse. Pubs., Inc.

Sandage, Charley. ALL AROUND ARKANSAS Big Book. 2005. (J). pap. ***(*978-0-9794044-2-9(8))*** Archeological Assessments, Inc.

—ALL AROUND ARKANSAS student Edition. 2005. (J). pap. ***(*978-0-9638956-5-3(6))*** Archeological Assessments, Inc.

—Big Bear's Arkansas ABCs. Przybylek, Leslie, illus. 2004. 56p. (J). (gr. k-2). pap. 14.95 (978-0-9638956-9-1(9)) Archeological Assessments, Inc.

—Big Bear's Arkansas ABCs Big Book. 2005. (J). pap. ***(*978-0-9794044-1-2(X))*** Archeological Assessments, Inc.

—"I Can Tell You Stories, If You Gather Near"... The Big Bear of Arkansas. Daniel, R. F., illus. 2004. 46p. (J). (gr. k-2). pap. 14.95 (978-0-9638956-7-7(2)) Archeological Assessments, Inc.

—I can tell you stories, if you gather round Big Book. 2005. (J). pap. ***(*978-0-9794044-3-6(6))*** Archeological Assessments, Inc.

—Where did we come from, Grandpa? Big Book. 2005. (J). pap. ***(*978-0-9794044-5-0(2))*** Archeological Assessments, Inc.

—Where did we come from, Grandpa? student Edition. 2005. (J). pap. ***(*978-0-9794044-4-3(4))*** Archeological Assessments, Inc.

Sargent, Daina. Arkansas: Dream Big. Lenoir, Jane, illus. l.t. ed. 2004. (Double Trouble Ser.). 48p. (J). pap. 6.95 (978-1-59381-123-5(3)); lib. bdg. (978-1-59381-122-8(5)) Ozark Publishing.

Sargent, Dave & Sargent, Pat. Kenny Kangaroo: Fighting, 56 vols., 49. Lenoir, Jane, illus. 2001. (Animal Pride Ser.: Vol. 49). 36p. (J). lib. bdg. 19.95 (978-1-56763-539-3(3)) Ozark Publishing.

Sargent, Dave, et al. Kenny Kangaroo: Fighting, 17, 49. 2000. (Animal Pride Ser.: 48). (Illus.). 42p. (J). pap. 6.95 (978-1-56763-540-9(7)) Ozark Publishing.

Summer of My German Soldier. 1999. (YA). 9.95 (978-1-56137-113-6(0)) Novel Units, Inc.

Summer of the Secret Squadron. 2005. Orig. Title: Return of the Secret Squadron. (YA). kivar 14.95 (978-0-9765750-0-9(0)) Ball, Michael.

Woody, Velma B. Branscum. Bandits, Bears & Backaches: A Collection of Short Stories Based on Arkansas History. 2004. (J). per. 12.50 (978-0-9708574-2-2(X)) Butler Ctr. for Arkansas Studies.

ARKANSAS—HISTORY

Fitzgerald, Stephanie. Little Rock Nine: Struggle for Integration. 2006. (J). (978-0-7565-2011-3(8)) Compass Point Bks.

Fradin, Judith Bloom & Fradin, Dennis Brindell. The Power of One: Daisy Bates & the Little Rock Nine. 2004. (Illus.). 192p. (YA). (gr. 5-9). tchr. ed. 19.00 (978-0-618-31556-7(X) , Clarion Bks.) Houghton Mifflin Co. Trade & Reference Div.

Harcourt School Publishers Staff. A Certain Courage. 3rd ed. 2002. (Horizons Ser.). (Illus.). (J). pap. 7.30 (978-0-15-333589-1(0)) Harcourt Schl. Pubs.

Harmon, Daniel E. Fort Smith. 2004. (American Forts & Their Strategic Importance Ser.). (J). (978-1-59084-717-6(2)) Mason Crest Pubs.

Hopper, et al. Arkansas Hist Young. 4th ed. 2007. (***978-1-55728-845-5(3)***) Univ. of Arkansas Pr.

Leber, Nancy. Arkansas. 2004. (Rookie Read-About Geography Ser.). 32p. (J). (gr. 1-2). pap. 5.95 (978-0-516-27946-6(7) , Children's Pr.) Scholastic Library Publishing.

Lucas, Eileen. Cracking the Wall: The Story of the Little Rock Nine. Anthony, Mark, illus. 2007. pap. 16.95 incl. audio (***978-1-59519-937-9(3)***); pap. 18.95 incl. audio compact disk (***978-1-59519-941-6(1)***) Live Oak Media.

—Cracking the Wall (4 PB/1 Cass) Anthony, Mark, illus. 2007. pap. 37.95 incl. audio (***978-1-59519-939-3(X)***) Live Oak Media.

—Cracking the Wall (4 PB/1 CD) Anthony, Mark, illus. 2007. pap. 39.95 incl. audio compact disk (***978-1-59519-943-0(8)***) Live Oak Media.

Marsh, Carole. Arkansas History Projects: 30 Cool, Activities, Crafts, Experiments & More for Kids to Do to Learn about Your State! 2003. (Arkansas Experience Ser.). 32p. (gr. k-5). pap. 5.95 (978-0-635-01773-4(3) , Marsh, Carole Bks.) Gallopade International.

Polakow, Amy. Daisy Bates: Civil Rights Crusader. 2002. (Illus.). 128p. (J). 25.00 (978-0-208-02513-5(8) , Linnet Bks.) Shoe String Pr., Inc.

ARMADA, 1588

Hynson, Colin. Elizabeth I & the Spanish Armada. 2006. (Stories from History Ser.). 48p. (J). 14.95 (978-0-7696-4703-6(0)); pap. 6.95 (978-0-7696-4629-9(8)) School Specialty Publishing.

Malam, John. You wouldn't/sail in spanish Armada. 2006. (Illus.). 32p. (J). (gr. 2-5). 28.50 (***978-0-531-14974-4(9)***) Scholastic Library Publishing.

Malam, John & Antram, David. You Wouldn't Want to Sail in the Spanish Armada! 2006. (Illus.). 32p. (YA). (gr. 2-5). pap. 9.95 (978-0-531-16999-5(5) , Watts, Franklin) Scholastic Library Publishing.

Ross, Stewart. Sink the Armada! Sir Francis Drake & the Spanish Armada of 1588. Shields, Susan, illus. 62p. (J). pap. (978-0-237-51959-9(3) , Evans Brothers, Limited) Evans Publishing Group.

ARMADILLOS

The Armadillo. (Wildlife of North America Ser.). 48p. (YA). 7.95 (978-0-7368-8482-2(3)) Capstone Pr., Inc.

The Armadillo, 6 vols. (gr. 4 up). 39.95 (978-0-7368-8494-5(7)) Red Brick Learning.

Cherry, Lynne. The Armadillo from Amarillo. 1999. (Illus.). 40p. (J). pap. 7.00 (978-0-15-201955-6(3) , Harcourt Paperbacks) Harcourt Children's Bks.

—The Armadillo from Amarillo. 1999. (J). 12.80 (978-0-606-16507-5(X)) Tandem Library Bks.

Cohen, Judith. Digging Armadillos. 1999. (gr. k-3). lib. bdg. 14.10 (978-0-613-43816-2(7)) Tandem Library Bks.

Goecke, Michael P. Giant Armadillo. 2004. (Prehistoric Animals Set II Ser.). (Illus.). 24p. (J). (gr. k-4). lib. bdg. 21.35 (978-1-57765-974-7(0)) ABDO Publishing Co.

Harcourt School Publishers Staff. The Amazing Armadillo On Level. 3rd ed. 2002. (Trophies Reading Program Ser.). (Illus.). pap. 5.10 (978-0-15-323189-6(0)) Harcourt Schl. Pubs.

Harman, Amanda. Armadillos. 2004. (Nature's Children Ser.). (J). (978-0-7172-5958-8(7) , Grolier) Scholastic Library Publishing.

Robb, Jackie & Stringle, Berny. The Story of Armadillo. Duncan, Karen & Stringle, Sam, illus. 2003. (Bang on the Door Ser.). 32p. (YA). pap. (978-1-85602-337-5(0)) Chrysalis Children's Bks.

Schaefer, Lola M. Armadillos. 2004. (J). pap. 5.25 (978-1-4034-5732-5(8)); (Illus.). 24p. (gr. 1-3). lib. bdg. (978-1-4034-5044-9(7)) Heinemann Library.

Soundprints Staff, ed. Backyard Collection: Daddy Longlegs, Owl, Armadillo & Ladybug Books, 4 microbks., No. III. (Smithsonian's Backyard Ser.). (Illus.). 128p. (J). (ps-2). 18.95 (978-1-56899-634-9(9)) Soundprints.

Townsend, Emily Rose. Armadillos. Saunders-Smith, Gail, ed. 2003. (Desert Animals Ser.). (Illus.). 24p. (J). (gr. k-1). lib. bdg. 15.93 (978-0-7368-2075-2(2) , Pebble Bks.) Capstone Pr., Inc.

ARMED FORCES

see Armies; Soldiers

see names of countries and international organizations with the subdivision Armed Forces, e.g. U. S.—Armed Forces; etc.

ARMENIA (REPUBLIC)

Giragosian, Richard & Streissguth, Thomas. The Transcaucasus. 2002. (Former Soviet Republics Ser.). (Illus.). 112p. (J). (gr. 6-9). 29.95 (978-1-56006-736-8(5) , Lucent Bks.) Thomson Gale.

Hintz, Martin. Armenia. 2004. (Enchantment of the World, Second Ser.). (Illus.). 144p. (YA). (gr. 5-9). 36.00 (978-0-516-24257-6(1) , Children's Pr.) Scholastic Library Publishing.

ARMIES

see also Disarmament; Military Art and Science; Military Service, Compulsory; Soldiers; War

also names of countries with the subhead Army (e.g. United States—Army; etc.); and headings beginning with the word Military

Ashabranner, Brent. A Date with Destiny: The Women in Military Service for America Memorial. Ashabranner, Jennifer, photos by. 2000. (Great American Memorials Ser.). (Illus.). 64p. (gr. 4-8). lib. bdg. (978-0-7613-1472-1(5) , Twenty-First Century Bks.) Lerner Publishing Group.

Sofer, Barbara. Keeping Israel Safe: The Israel Defense Forces. 2008. (Israel Ser.). (J). lib. bdg. 16.95 (***978-0-8225-7221-3(4)***) Kar-Ben Publishing.

ARMORED CARS (TANKS)

see Tanks (Military Science)

ARMS, COATS OF

see Heraldry

ARMS AND ARMOR

see also Firearms; Ordnance; Rifles

Beyer, Mark. Nuclear Weapons & the Cold War. 2005. (Library of Weapons of Mass Destruction). (Illus.). 64p. (J). lib. bdg. 26.50 (978-1-4042-0290-0(0)) Rosen Publishing Group, Inc., The.

Bingley. The Arms Trade. 2003. (Face the Facts Ser.). 56p. pap. 8.95 (978-1-4109-0046-3(0)) Raintree.

Bingley, Richard. The Arms Trade. 2003. (Face the Facts Ser.). (Illus.). 56p. (J). lib. bdg. 28.56 (978-0-7398-6431-9(9)) Raintree.

Brewer, Paul. Warfare in the Ancient World. 1999. (History of Warfare Ser.). (Illus.). 80p. (YA). (gr. 7-12). lib. bdg. 29.97 (978-0-8172-5442-1(0)) Raintree.

—Warfare in the Renaissance World. 1999. (History of Warfare Ser.). (Illus.). 80p. (YA). (gr. 7-12). lib. bdg. 29.97 (978-0-8172-5444-5(7)) Raintree.

Brezina, Corona. Weapons of Mass Destruction: Proliferation & Control. 2004. (Library of Weapons of Mass Destruction). (Illus.). 64p. (J). lib. bdg. 26.50 (978-1-4042-0298-6(6)) Rosen Publishing Group, Inc., The.

Byam, Michele. Arms & Armor. (Dk Eyewitness Books Ser.). (J). pap. 8.95 (978-0-7894-5837-7(3)); 2004. (Illus.). 72p. 15.99 (978-0-7566-0654-1(3)) Dorling Kindersley Publishing, Inc.

Byam, Michele & Dorling Kindersley Publishing Staff. Arms & Armor. King, Dave, illus. 2004. (Eyewitness Books). 72p. (J). lib. bdg. 19.99 (978-0-7566-0653-4(5)) Dorling Kindersley Publishing, Inc.

Chapman, Caroline. Battles & Weapons: Exploring History Through Art. 2007. (Picture That! Ser.). 64p. (gr. 3-7). 19.95 (***978-1-58728-588-2(6)*** , Two Can Publishing) T&N Children's Publishing.

Clarke, Catriona. Armor - Internet Referenced (Level 2) 2007. 32p. (J). 4.99 (978-0-7945-1578-2(9) , Usborne) EDC Publishing.

Egan, Tracie. Weapons of Mass Destruction & North Korea. 2004. (Library of Weapons of Mass Destruction). (Illus.). 64p. (J). lib. bdg. 26.50 (978-1-4042-0296-2(X)) Rosen Publishing Group, Inc., The.

Firth, Rachel. Knights & Armor - Internet Linked. 2006. (Illus.). 96p. (J). 17.99 (978-0-7945-1279-8(8) , Usborne) EDC Publishing.

Fowler, William. Modern Weapons: Discover the Technology of War from 1700 to the Present Day. 2003. (History Detectives Ser.). (Illus.). 64p. (gr. 3-7). pap. 7.99 (978-1-84215-782-4(5) , Southwater) Anness Publishing GBR. *Dist:* National Bk. Network.

Gifford, Clive. The Arms Trade. 2004. (World Issues Ser.). (J). lib. bdg. 28.50 (978-1-59389-154-1(7)) Chrysalis Education.

Gilbert, Adrian. Going to War in Ancient Greece. 2001. (gr. 3-6). lib. bdg. 15.25 (978-0-613-54518-1(4)) Tandem Library Bks.

Green, Michael. Self-Propelled Howitzers: the M109a6 Paladins. 2004. (War Machines Ser.). (Illus.). 32p. (J). lib. bdg. 22.60 (978-0-7368-2723-2(4) , Edge Bks.) Capstone Pr., Inc.

Hamilton, John. Pirate Ships & Weapons. 2007. (ENG., Illus.). 32p. (J). lib. bdg. 24.21 (***978-1-59928-763-8(3)*** , ABDO & Daughters) ABDO Publishing Co.

—Weapons of Science Fiction. 2007. (Illus.). 32p. (J). 24.21 (978-1-59679-997-4(8) , ABDO & Daughters) ABDO Publishing Co.

—Weapons of War. 2002. (War on Terrorism Ser.). (Illus.). 64p. (J). (gr. 4-8). lib. bdg. 25.65 (978-1-57765-673-9(3) , ABDO & Daughters) ABDO Publishing Co.

Holder, Bill & Vadnais, Scott. Air Launch! A Pictorial History of Airborne Weapons. 2001. (Schiffer Military History Book Ser.). (Illus.). 96p. (gr. 10-13). pap. 19.95 (978-0-7643-1392-9(4)) Schiffer Publishing, Ltd.

Kenney, Karen Latchana. The Spoils of War. 2008. (Shockwave: History & Politics Ser.). 32p. (J). pap. 6.95 (***978-0-531-18837-8(X)*** , Children's Pr.) Scholastic Library Publishing.

The Library of Weapons of Mass Destruction. 2005. Set. (YA). (gr. 7-12). lib. bdg. 239.40 (978-1-4042-0384-6(2)); Set 1. (J). 159.00 (978-1-4042-0382-2(6)); Set 2. (YA). 159.00 (978-1-4042-0383-9(4)) Rosen Publishing Group, Inc., The.

Malam, John. War & Weapons. 2002. (People in the Past Ser.). (Illus.). 48p. (J). pap. (978-1-4034-0516-6(6)) Heinemann Library.

Marshall, Chris. Warfare in the Medieval World. 1999. (History of Warfare Ser.). (Illus.). 80p. (YA). (gr. 7-12). lib. bdg. 29.97 (978-0-8172-5443-8(9)) Raintree.

McGoldrick, Megan. All about Armor. 2005. (Real Deal-Red Plus Ser.). (Illus.). 32p. (gr. 4-8). 19.00 (978-0-7910-8893-7(6)) Facts On File, Inc.

McManners, Hugh. Ultimate Special Forces. 2003. (Illus.). 192p. 30.00 (978-0-7894-9973-8(8)) Dorling Kindersley Publishing, Inc.

Middleton, Haydn. Ancient Greek War & Weapons. 2002. (People in the Past Ser.). (Illus.). 48p. (J). (gr. 4-6). lib. bdg. 27.07 (978-1-58810-635-3(7)) Heinemann Library.

—Ancient Greek War & Weapons. 2002. (gr. 3-6). lib. bdg. 17.05 (978-0-613-87483-0(8)) Tandem Library Bks.

Middleton, Haydn & Tames, Richard. Ancient Greek War & Weapons. 2002. (People in the Past Ser.). 64p. (J). (gr. 4-7). pap. 8.50 (978-1-4034-0134-2(9) , 91639) Heinemann Library.

Moe, Barbara A. The Search for Weapons of Mass Destruction in Iraq. 2004. (Library of Weapons of Mass Destruction). (Illus.). 64p. (J). lib. bdg. 26.50 (978-1-4042-0295-5(1)) Rosen Publishing Group, Inc., The.

Morgan, Sally & Morgan, Adrian. Warfare in a Hi-Tech Age. 2005. (Science at the Edge Ser.). (Illus.). 64p. (J). (978-1-4034-7765-1(5)) Heinemann Library.

Morris, Mark. Weapons: Bigger, Stronger, & Smarter. 2006. (Cutting Edge Ser.). 56p. (J). (Illus.). lib. bdg. 32.86 (978-1-4034-7430-8(3)); pap. 8.90 (***978-1-4034-7436-0(2)***) Heinemann Library.

Murray, Stuart. Encyclopedia of War & Weaponry. 2003. (gr. 3-6). lib. bdg. 30.35 (978-0-613-72674-0(X)) Tandem Library Bks.

Nardo, Don. The Civil War. 2002. (History of Weapons & Warfare Ser.). (Illus.). 112p. (J). 29.95 (978-1-59018-068-6(2) , Lucent Bks.) Thomson Gale.

Oakeshott, R. Ewart. A Knight & His Horse. 2nd rev. ed. 1999. (Illus.). 128p. (gr. 5-12). pap. 13.95 (978-0-8023-1297-6(7)) Dufour Editions, Inc.

O'Connor, Rebecca. Weapons of Mass Destruction. 2007. (Introducing Issues with Opposing Viewpoints Ser.). 144p. (gr. 7-10). 32.45 (***978-0-7377-3617-5(8)*** , Greenhaven Pr., Inc.) Thomson Gale.

O'Donnell, Liam. Pirate Gear: Cannons, Swords, & the Jolly Roger. 2007. (Edge Books, the Real World of Pirates). (Illus.). 32p. (J). 23.93 (978-0-7368-6425-1(3)) Capstone Pr., Inc.

Orr, Tamra. The Hydrogen Bomb: Unleashing the Nuclear & Arms Race. 2004. (Library of Weapons of Mass Destruction). (Illus.). 64p. (J). lib. bdg. 26.50 (978-1-4042-0293-1(5)) Rosen Publishing Group, Inc., The.

Quinlan. The History of Weapons of War. 2004. (World History Ser.). (Illus.). 112p. (J). 32.45 (978-1-59018-183-6(2) , Lucent Bks.) Thomson Gale.

Ripley, Tim. Weapon Technology. 2004. (History of Invention Ser.). (Illus.). 96p. (YA). (gr. 6-12). 35.00 (978-0-8160-5438-1(X)) Facts On File, Inc.

Rivera, Sheila. Weapons of Mass Destruction. 2004. (World in Conflict-the Middle East Ser.). (Illus.). 48p. (J). (gr. 4-8). lib. bdg. 25.65 (978-1-59197-421-5(6)) ABDO Publishing Co.

Schaefer, Lola M. Brazos, Codos, Manos y Dedos. (Es Mi Cuerpo (It's My Body) Ser.).Tr. of Arms, Elbows, Hands & Fingers. 24p. pap. 5.25 (978-1-4034-3380-0(1)) Heinemann Library.

Schmidt, Roderic D. Infantry of the Future. 2005. (Library of Future Weaponry). (Illus.). 64p. (J). (978-1-4042-0525-3(X)) Rosen Publishing Group, Inc., The.

Southwater Books Staff. Ancient Weapons. 2002. (History Detectives Ser.). (Illus.). 64p. (gr. 3-7). pap. 7.95 (978-1-84215-628-5(4) , Southwater) Anness Publishing GBR. *Dist:* National Bk. Network.

Speakman, Jay. Weapons of War. 2000. (American War Library). (Illus.). 112p. (YA). (gr. 4-12). lib. bdg. 29.95 (978-1-56006-649-1(0) , LML00902-178003, Lucent Bks.) Thomson Gale.

Star, Fleur & Dorling Kindersley Publishing Staff. Castle & Knight. 2005. (Eye Wonder Ser.). (Illus.). 48p. (J). 9.99 (978-0-7566-1417-1(1)); lib. bdg. 17.99 (978-0-7566-1418-8(X)) Dorling Kindersley Publishing, Inc.

Stewart, Gail B. World War I: Weapons of War. 2001. (American War Library). (Illus.). 112p. (YA). (gr. 4-12). lib. bdg. 27.45 (978-1-56006-837-2(X) , LML00902-178169, Lucent Bks.) Thomson Gale.

TBC Staff. Cutting Edge Weapons: Bigger, Stronger & Smarter. 2006. (Illus.). 56p. (J). (978-0-431-13271-6(2)) Heinemann.

Torr, James D. Responding to Attack: Firefighters & Police. 2003. (Lucent Library of Homeland Security). (Illus.). 112p. (J). 29.95 (978-1-59018-375-5(4) , Lucent Bks.) Thomson Gale.

Weapons & Warfare. 2003. (Illus.). 32p. (YA). pap. (978-1-904516-31-6(9)) Chrysalis Children's Bks.

Woods, Mary B. & Woods, Michael. Ancient Warfare: From Clubs to Catapults. 2005. (Ancient Technology Ser.). (Illus.). 96p. (gr. 6-12). 25.26 (978-0-8225-2999-6(8)) Lerner Publishing Group.

Wright, Susan. Weapons of Mass Destruction: Illicit Trade & Trafficking. 2004. (Library of Weapons of Mass Destruction). (Illus.). 64p. (J). lib. bdg. 26.50 (978-1-4042-0297-9(8)) Rosen Publishing Group, Inc., The.

ARMS CONTROL

see Disarmament

ARMSTRONG, ANNIE, 1850-1938

The Lottie & Annie Upside-down Book. 2003. 8.99 (978-1-56309-627-3(7)) Woman's Missionary Union.

ARMSTRONG, LANCE, 1971-

Armentrout, David & Armentrout, Patricia, trs. Lance Armstrong. 2003. (Discover the Life of a Sports Star Ser.). (Illus.). 24p. (J). 20.64 (978-1-58952-651-8(1)) Rourke Publishing, LLC.

Armstrong, Kristin. Lance Armstrong: The Race of His Life. Call, Ken, illus. 2000. (All Aboard Reading Ser.). 48p. (J). (gr. 2-3). 13.89 (978-0-448-42415-6(0)); (gr. 4-7). pap. 3.99 (978-0-448-42407-1(X)) Penguin Group (USA) Inc. (Grosset & Dunlap).

—Lance Armstrong: The Race of His Life. 2000. (All Aboard Reading Ser.). (J). (978-0-606-20267-1(6)); lib. bdg. 11.80 (978-0-613-31402-2(6)); (Illus.). (J). (978-0-606-20403-3(2)) Tandem Library Bks.

Bankston, John. Lance Armstrong. 2004. (Blue Banner Biography Ser.). (Illus.). 32p. (J). lib. bdg. (978-1-58415-334-4(2)) Mitchell Lane Pubs., Inc.

Benson, Michael. Lance Armstrong, Cyclist. 2003. (Ferguson Career Biographies Ser.). (Illus.). 144p. (J). (gr. 6-12). 25.00 (978-0-8160-5479-4(7) , Ferguson Publishing Co.) Facts On File, Inc.

Brocker, Susan. Leyendas del deporte & Sports Legends. 2005. spiral bd. 77.00 (***978-1-4108-5678-4(X)***) Benchmark Education Co.

Christopher, Matt. On the Bike with... Lance Armstrong. 2003. (Illus.). 112p. (J). (gr. 5-8). pap. 4.99 (978-0-316-07549-7(3)) Little, Brown Bks. for Young Readers.

—On the Bike with... Lance Armstrong. 2003. (gr. 3-6). lib. bdg. 13.00 (978-0-613-71601-7(9)) Tandem Library Bks.

Doeden, Matt. Lance Armstrong. 2006. (Sports Heroes & Legends Ser.). (J). 27.93 (978-0-8225-5959-7(5) , Lerner Pubns.) Lerner Publishing Group.

Donovan, Sandra. Lance Armstrong. 2nd rev. ed. 2005. (Amazing Athletes Ser.). (Illus.). 32p. (J). lib. bdg. 22.60 (978-0-8225-6052-4(6) , Lerner Pubns.) Lerner Publishing Group.

Donovan, Sandy. Lance Armstrong. 2005. (Amazing Athletes Ser.). (Illus.). 32p. (J). (gr. 3-4). lib. bdg. 23.93 (978-0-8225-3691-8(9)) Lerner Publishing Group.

Donovan Sandy. Lance Armstrong (Revised Edition) 2007. (Amazing Athletes Ser.). (J). pap. 6.95 (***978-0-8225-8748-4(3)*** , First Avenue Editions) Lerner Publishing Group.

Ellwood, Nancy. Lance Armstrong: With a Discussion of Determination. 2004. (Values in Action Ser.). (J). (978-1-59203-073-6(4)) Learning Challenge, Inc.

Garcia, Kimberly. Lance Armstrong. 2002. (Real-Life Reader Biographies Ser.). (Illus.). 32p. (gr. 3-8). lib. bdg. 15.95 (978-1-58415-125-8(0)) Mitchell Lane Pubs., Inc.

Grabowski, John F. Lance Armstrong. 2005. (People in the News Ser.). (Illus.). 112p. (J). (ps-7). lib. bdg. 32.45 (978-1-59018-711-1(3) , Lucent Bks.) Thomson Gale.

Gutman, Bill. Lance Armstrong: A Biography. 2005. 192p. (YA). mass mkt. 6.99 (978-1-4169-1797-7(7) , Simon Pulse) Simon & Schuster Children's Publishing.

Hill, Christine M. Lance Armstrong: Cycling, Surviving, Inspiring Hope. 2007. (People to Know Today Ser.). (Illus.). 128p. (J). (gr. 6). lib. bdg. 31.93 (***978-0-7660-2694-0(9)***) Enslow Pubs., Inc.

Jones, Brenn. Learning about Resilience from the Life of Lance Armstrong. 2002. (Character Building Book Ser.). (Illus.). 24p. (J). (gr. 3). lib. bdg. 18.75 (978-0-8239-5779-8(9) , PowerKids Pr.) Rosen Publishing Group, Inc., The.

Kramer, Barbara. Lance Armstrong: Determined to Beat the Odds. 2005. (Awesome Values in Famous Lives Ser.). (Illus.). 48p. (J). (ps-7). lib. bdg. 23.93 (978-0-7660-2377-2(X) , Enslow Elementary) Enslow Pubs., Inc.

Lance Armstrong. 2004. (J). 27.07 (978-0-7614-1761-3(3)) Cavendish, Marshall Corp.

MacEachern, Ashley. Lance in France. Barbera, Michelle, illus. 2008. 32p. (J). 16.99 (***978-0-06-113192-9(X)***); lib. bdg. 17.89 (***978-0-06-113193-6(8)***) HarperCollins Pubs. (Collins).

Sandler, Michael. Cycling: Lance Armstrong's Impossible Ride. 2006. (Upsets & Comebacks Ser.). (Illus.). 32p. (J). lib. bdg. 25.27 (978-1-59716-167-1(5)) Bearport Publishing Co., Inc.

Stewart, Mark. Sweet Victory: Lance Armstrong's Incredible Journey. 2000. 64p. (gr. 4-7). (Single Titles Ser.: up). pap. (978-0-7613-1387-8(7) , Millbrook Pr.); (Inspiring People Ser.). (Illus.). lib. bdg. 24.90 (978-0-7613-1861-3(5) , Twenty-First Century Bks.) Lerner Publishing Group.

—Sweet Victory: Lance Armstrong's Incredible Journey. 2000. (J). (978-0-606-19176-0(3)); (gr. 3-6). lib. bdg. 16.40 (978-0-613-27144-8(0)) Tandem Library Bks.

Thompson, John. Lance Armstrong. 2001. (Overcoming Adversity Ser.). (Illus.). (J). 100p. pap. 9.95 (978-0-7910-5880-0(8)); 112p. (gr. 5 up). 30.00 (978-0-7910-5879-4(4)) Facts On File, Inc. (Chelsea Hse.).

Young, Ian. Lance Armstrong: Champion for Life!, 6 vols. (gr. 4 up). 49.95 (978-0-7368-3868-9(6) , High Five) Red Brick Learning.

Young, Ian & Rasinski, Timothy V. Lance Armstrong: Champion for Life! 2004. (High Five Reading Ser.). (J). (978-0-7368-3850-4(3)); 23.93 (978-0-7368-3878-8(3)) Capstone Pr., Inc.

ARMSTRONG, LOUIS, 1900-1971

Elish, Dan. Louis Armstrong & the Jazz Age. 2005. (Cornerstones of Freedom Ser.). (Illus.). 48p. (J). (gr. 4-6). 26.00 (978-0-516-23629-2(6) , Children's Pr.) Scholastic Library Publishing.

Holland, Gini. Louis Armstrong. 2003. (Trailblazers of the Modern World Ser.). (Illus.). 48p. (J). (gr. 5 up). lib. bdg. 30.00 (978-0-8368-5089-5(0) , World Almanac Library) Stevens, Gareth Inc.

January, Brendan. Louis Armstrong. 2002. (Great Names Ser.). (Illus.). 32p. (J). (gr. 3 up). lib. bdg. (978-1-59084-135-8(2)) Mason Crest Pubs.

Josephson, Judith Pinkerton. Louis Armstrong. 2008. (History Maker Biographies Ser.). (J). lib. bdg. 26.60 (***978-0-8225-7169-8(2)*** , Lerner Pubns.) Lerner Publishing Group.

Kimmel, Eric A. A Horn for Louis. 96p. (J). (gr. 1-4). 2006. pap. 3.99 (978-0-375-84005-0(2)); 2005. (Illus.). 11.95 (978-0-375-83252-9(1)); 2005. (Illus.). lib. bdg. 13.99 (978-0-375-93252-6(6)) Random Hse. Children's Bks. (Random Hse. Bks. for Young Readers).

Marsh, Carole. Louis Armstrong. 2002. (One Thousand Readers Ser.). (Illus.). 12p. (J). (gr. k-4). 2.95 (978-0-635-01516-7(1) , 15161) Gallopade International.

McDonough, Yona Zeldis. Who Was Louis Armstrong? O'Brien, John & Harrison, Nancy, illus. 2004. (Who Was...? Ser.). 112p. (J). 13.89 (978-0-448-43560-2(8)); (gr. 3-7). pap. 4.99 (978-0-448-43368-4(0)) Penguin Group (USA) Inc. (Grosset & Dunlap).

McKissack, Patricia C. & McKissack, Fredrick L. Louis Armstrong: Jazz Musician. rev. ed. 2001. (Great African Americans Ser.). (Illus.). 32p. (J). (gr. 1-4). lib. bdg. 18.60 (978-0-7660-1675-0(7)) Enslow Pubs., Inc.

A B

Old, Wendie C. Louis Armstrong: King of Jazz. 1998. (African-American Biographies Ser.). (Illus.). 128p. (YA). (gr. 6-12). lib. bdg. 26.60 (978-0-89490-997-9(5)) Enslow Pubs., Inc.

Schuman, Michael. Louis Armstrong: Jazz Is Played from the Heart. 2007. (African-American Biography Library). (Illus.). 128p. (J). (gr. 6 up). lib. bdg. 31.93 (978-0-7660-2700-8(7)) Enslow Pubs., Inc.

Trailblazers of the Modern World: Louis Armstrong; Anne Frank; Martin Luther King, Jr.; Theodore Roosevelt; Gloria Steinem; The Wright Brothers, 6 bks. 2003. (Illus.). (J). (gr. 5 up). lib. bdg. 175.60 (978-0-8368-5088-8(2) , World Almanac Library) Stevens, Gareth Inc.

Weinstein. How Louis Armstrong Taught Me. 2008. (J). 15.95 (978-0-8118-5131-2(1)) Chronicle Bks. LLC.

ARMY

see Armies; Military Art and Science

ARMY SCHOOLS

see Military Education

ARMY VEHICLES

see Vehicles, Military

ARNOLD, BENEDICT, 1741-1801

Benedict Arnold, 6 vols. (gr. 2-5). 39.95 (978-0-7368-4586-1(0)) Red Brick Learning.

Burgan, Michael. Benedict Arnold: American Hero & Traitor. Beatty, Terry, illus. 2007. (Graphic Library). 32p. (J). (gr. 3-5). lib. bdg. 25.26 (*978-0-7368-6854-9(2)) Capstone Pr., Inc.

—Benedict Arnold: American Hero & Traitor. 2007. (Graphic Library). (Illus.). 32p. (J). (gr. 3-5). pap. 7.95 (*978-0-7368-7906-4(4)) Capstone Pr., Inc.

Capstone Press, contrib. by. Benedict Arnold. (American Revolution Biographies Ser.). 48p. (YA). pap. 7.95 (978-0-7368-4500-7(3)) Capstone Pr., Inc.

Dell, Pamela. Benedict Arnold: From Patriot to Traitor. 2004. (Signature Lives Ser.). (Illus.). 112p. (J). 30.60 (978-0-7565-0825-8(8) , 1240127) Compass Point Bks.

Draper, Allison Stark. America's First Traitor: Benedict Arnold Betrays the Colonies. 2001. (Headlines from History Ser.). (Illus.). 24p. (J). (gr. 3). lib. bdg. 19.95 (978-0-8239-5673-9(3) , PKTRAI, PowerKids Pr.) Rosen Publishing Group, Inc., The.

Gaines, Ann Graham. Benedict Arnold: Patriot or Traitor? 2001. (Historical American Biographies Ser.). (Illus.). 128p. (J). (gr. 6-12). lib. bdg. 26.60 (978-0-7660-1393-3(6)) Enslow Pubs., Inc.

Gregson, Susan R. Benedict Arnold. 2001. (Let Freedom Ring Ser.). (Illus.). 48p. (J). (gr. 3-4). lib. bdg. 22.60 (978-0-7368-1032-6(3) , Bridgestone Bks.) Capstone Pr., Inc.

King, David C. Benedict Arnold & the American Revolution. 1998. (Notorious Americans & Their Times Ser.). (Illus.). 80p. (YA). (gr. 5 up). 28.70 (978-1-56711-221-4(8) , Blackbirch Pr., Inc.) Thomson Gale.

Lutz, Norma Jean. Benedict Arnold: Traitor to the Cause. 1999. (Revolutionary Leaders Ser.). (Illus.). 80p. (J). (gr. 3 up). 20.85 (978-0-7910-5358-4(X)); pap. 8.95 (978-0-7910-5701-8(1)) Facts On File, Inc. (Chelsea Hse.).

—Benedict Arnold: Traitor to the Cause. 2000. (gr. 5-8). lib. bdg. 17.60 (978-0-613-43301-3(7)) Tandem Library Bks.

Murphy, Jim. The Real Benedict Arnold. 2007. (Illus.). 272p. (YA). (gr. 5 up). 20.00 (*978-0-395-77609-4(0) , Clarion Bks.) Houghton Mifflin Co. Trade & Reference Div.

Powell, Walter Louis. Benedict Arnold: Revolutionary War Hero & Traitor. 2005. (Library of American Lives & Times). (Illus.). 112p. (YA). (gr. 4-8). lib. bdg. 31.95 (978-0-8239-6627-1(5)) Rosen Publishing Group, Inc., The.

Price Hossell, Karen. Benedict Arnold. 2004. (American War Biographies Ser.). (J). pap. 8.50 (978-1-4034-5085-2(4)); lib. bdg. 29.93 (978-1-4034-5076-4(1)) Heinemann Library.

Sonneborn, Liz. Benedict Arnold: Hero & Traitor. 2005. (Leaders of the American Revolution Ser.). (Illus.). 130p. (J). (ps-8). lib. bdg. 30.00 (978-0-7910-8617-9(8) , Chelsea Hse.) Facts On File, Inc.

ARNOLD, BENEDICT, 1741-1801—FICTION

Rinaldi, Ann. Finishing Becca: A Story about Peggy Shippen & Benedict Arnold. 2004. (Great Episodes Ser.). 384p. (YA). pap. 6.95 (978-0-15-205079-5(5) , Gulliver Bks.) Harcourt Children's Bks.

ART

see also African Americans in Art; Anatomy, Artistic; Animals in Art; Archaeology; Architecture; Art Objects; Bronzes; Christian Art and Symbolism; Collage; Collectors and Collecting; Design, Decorative; Drawing; Folk Art; Forgery of Works of Art; Gems; Graphic Arts; Illustration of Books; Painting; Photography, Artistic; Pictures; Portraits; Sculpture; Symbolism

Aigner-Clark, Julie. The ABC's of Art. Zaidi, Nadeem, illus. 2002. (Baby Einstein Ser.). 64p. (ps-ps). 15.99 (978-0-7868-0882-3(9)) Disney Pr.

Ajmera, Maya & Ivanko, John D. To Be an Artist. 2004. (Illus.). 32p. (J). 15.95 (978-1-57091-503-1(2)) Charlesbridge Publishing, Inc.

Albright, Tawnya, et al, illus. Puppetry Clip Art Book & CD. rev. ed. 2003. 44p. (YA). 25.00 (978-1-58302-229-0(5)) One Way St., Inc.

Allison, Amy. Gargoyles on Guard. Brammer, Erin McGonigle, illus. 2002. (Books for Young Learners). 16p. (J). pap. 5.00 (978-1-57274-260-4(7)) Owen, Richard C. Pubs., Inc.

American Girl Editorial Staff, creator. Art Studio Felicity. 2005. (American Girls Collection). (Illus.). 64p. (J). (gr. 3). 14.95 (978-1-59369-055-7(X) , American Girl) American Girl Publishing, Inc.

Andelin, Darline. Easy String Art for All Seasons. 70p. (J). (gr. 1-6). pap. 7.95 (978-1-56861-047-4(5)) Swift Learning Resources.

Anderson, Dale. Ancient China. 2005. (History in Art Ser.). (Illus.). 48p. (J). lib. bdg. 29.93 (978-1-4109-0519-2(5)) Steck-Vaughn.

Andrich, Tom. Decorate Yourself: Cool Designs for Temporary Tattoos, Face Painting, Henna & More. 2004. (Illus.). 96p. pap. 9.95 (978-1-4027-1759-8(8)) Tamos Bks., Inc. CAN. *Dist:* Sterling Publishing Co., Inc.

Angelou, Maya. My Painted House, My Friendly Chicken & Me. Courtney-Clarke, Margaret, illus. 2003. 48p. (J). (gr. 1-4). pap. 7.99 (978-0-375-82567-5(3)); lib. bdg. 17.99 (978-0-375-92567-2(8)) Random Hse. Children's Bks. (Crown Books For Young Readers).

Die Arbeit des Bildhausers.Tr. of Sculptor's Work. (GER., Illus.). (YA). 31.95 (978-3-411-09081-5(2) , MY9081E) Bibliographisches Institut & F. A. Brockhaus AG DEU. *Dist:* Continental Bk. Co., Inc.

Art Across the Curriculum. 116p. (gr. 5-9). 21.99 (978-0-7682-0473-5(9) , GA131698) School Specialty Publishing.

Art and Poetry Datebook from the InsideOut Writing Project Staff. Feels Like Jazz 2002: Arts & Poetry Datebook. Blackhawk, Terry, ed. 2001. 116p. spiral bd. 15.00 (978-0-9713562-0-7(3)) Inside Out, Inc.

Art for Children. 2005. pap. 225.00 (978-0-7910-9192-0(9) , Chelsea Hse.) Facts On File, Inc.

Art for You. 2002. (Illus.). (J). pap. 3.74 (978-0-7398-5850-9(5)) Steck-Vaughn.

Arte. (SPA.). (J). 29.00 (978-958-04-5746-6(8)) Norma S.A. COL. *Dist:* Distribuidora Norma, Inc.

Artist's Easel. 2003. (Gateways to the Sun Ser.). 32p. (J). (gr. 2-3). pap. 11.95 (978-1-58105-576-4(5)) Santillana USA Publishing Co., Inc.

The Artist's Handbook. 2003. 384p. (YA). pap. 30.00 (978-0-7566-0184-3(3)) Dorling Kindersley Publishing, Inc.

Aveline, Erick & Chargueraud, Joyce. Temporary Tattoos. 2001. (Illus.). 64p. (J). (gr. 4-8). lib. bdg. 18.75 (978-0-613-78563-1(0)) Tandem Library Bks.

Avi Video. 2000. (J). pap. (978-0-380-29937-9(2) , Harper Trophy) HarperCollins Pubs.

Backus, Karen. 25 Terrific & Easy Art Projects Based on Favorite Picture Books. 2002. 80p. (J). 13.95 (978-0-439-22263-1(X)) Scholastic, Inc.

Bacon, Dolores. Pictures Every Child Should Know (a Sele. 2006. 27.99 (*978-1-4219-7621-1(8)); pap. 21.99 (*978-1-4219-7620-4(X)) IndyPublish.com.

Ballweg, Judy K. Kid Pix ABC: Art, Books & Computers. 2000. (Illus.). 150p. (J). (gr. k-2). spiral bd. 25.95 (978-1-56484-155-1(3)) International Society for Technology in Education.

Bank Street College of Education Staff. Children's Guide to the Prado. 2006. (Illus.). 8p. pap. 9.95 (978-1-85759-369-3(3)) Scala Pubs., Ltd. GBR. *Dist:* Antique Collectors' Club.

Bartfeld, Martha. Mandala Designs. 2000. 48p. (J). pap. 3.95 (978-0-486-41034-0(X)) Dover Pubns., Inc.

Baumbusch, Brigitte. Clothing in Art. 2005. (Illus.). 32p. (J). lib. bdg. 22.00 (978-0-8368-4780-2(6)) Stevens, Gareth Inc.

—Faces in Art. 2004. (What Makes a Masterpiece? Ser.). (J). lib. bdg. 22.00 (978-0-8368-4378-1(9)) Stevens, Gareth Inc.

—Figures in Art. 2004. (What Makes a Masterpiece? Ser.). (J). lib. bdg. 22.00 (978-0-8368-4379-8(7)) Stevens, Gareth Inc.

—Food in Art. 2004. (What Makes a Masterpiece? Ser.). (J). lib. bdg. 22.00 (978-0-8368-4380-4(0)) Stevens, Gareth Inc.

—Houses in Art. 2004. (What Makes a Masterpiece? Ser.). (J). lib. bdg. 22.00 (978-0-8368-4381-1(9)) Stevens, Gareth Inc.

—The Sky in Art. 2005. (Illus.). 32p. (J). (ps-7). lib. bdg. 22.00 (978-0-8368-4783-3(0)) Stevens, Gareth Inc.

Bayles, Jennifer L. An Adventure in Looking & Listening: Exploring Masterworks at the Albright-Knox Art Gallery. Barnett, Janet, illus. 2003. (J). (978-1-887457-01-9(1)) Buffalo Fine Arts/Albright-Knox Art Gallery.

Be a Plant Scientist: Level L, 6 vols. (Take-Twostm Ser.). 16p. 36.95 (978-0-322-03403-7(5)) Wright Group, The.

Beery, Barbara. Fairies Cookbook. 2007. (Illus.). 64p. (J). (gr. 1 up). 14.95 (*978-1-4236-0290-3(0)) Gibbs Smith, Publisher.

Beyond the Wall: Ten Artists from Berlin. 2001. (Illus.). 28p. pap. 10.00 (978-1-889136-10-3(7)) Ursinus College.

Bingham, Jane. African Art & Culture. 2003. (World Art & Culture Ser.). (Illus.). 56p. (J). lib. bdg. 29.99 (978-0-7398-6606-1(0)) Raintree.

—Indian Art & Culture. 2003. (World Art & Culture Ser.). (Illus.). 56p. (J). lib. bdg. 29.99 (978-0-7398-6607-8(9)) Raintree.

—Landscape & the Environment. 2006. (Through Artists' Eyes Ser.). (Illus.). 56p. (J). (gr. 4-7). 32.86 (978-1-4109-2240-3(5)) Raintree.

—Relationships & Emotions. 2006. (Through Artists' Eyes Ser.). (Illus.). 56p. (J). (gr. 4-7). 32.86 (978-1-4109-2238-0(3)) Raintree.

—Science & Technology. 2006. (Through Artists' Eyes Ser.). (Illus.). 56p. (J). (gr. 4-7). 32.86 (978-1-4109-2241-0(3)) Raintree.

—Society & Class. 2006. (Through Artists' Eyes Ser.). (Illus.). 56p. (J). (gr. 4-7). 32.86 (978-1-4109-2237-3(5)) Raintree.

—War & Conflict. 2006. (Illus.). 56p. (J). (978-1-4109-2236-6(7)) Steck-Vaughn.

Blauer, Ettagale. African Art. Laurbe, Jason, illus. 2001. (Art in History Ser.). (J). 23.58 (978-1-58810-089-4(8)) Heinemann Library.

Blizzard, Gladys S. Come Look with Me: Enjoying Art with Children. 2006. (Come Look with Me Ser.). (Illus.). 32p. (YA). (ps-2). 15.95 (978-0-934738-76-7(9)) Charlesbridge Publishing, Inc.

—Come Look with Me: Exploring Landscape Art with Children. 2006. (Come Look with Me Ser.). (Illus.). 32p. (YA). (gr. 1-8). 15.95 (978-0-934738-95-8(5)) Charlesbridge Publishing, Inc.

Blue & Green. 2003. (Gateways to the Sun Ser.). 32p. (J). (gr. k-1). pap. 11.95 (978-1-58105-574-0(9)) Santillana USA Publishing Co., Inc.

Bratton, Catherine. Art Vol. 1: Impressionism. 2002. (Illus.). 2p. (J). pap. 2.00 (978-0-9719268-1-3(6)) davishooligans.

—Art Vol. 2: Post-Impressionism. 2002. (Illus.). 2p. (J). pap. 2.00 (978-0-9719268-2-0(4)) davishooligans.

Brooke, Charles A. Ten years in Sarbwak, Vol. 2. fac. ed. 2001. 364p. pap. 18.95 (978-1-4021-9329-3(7) , Elibron Classics) Adamant Media.

Brothers, Blues. Flute: the Blues Brothers. 2000. 13.95 incl. audio compact disk (978-1-85909-725-0(1) , Warner Bros. Pubns.) Alfred Publishing Co., Inc.

Brown Reference Group PLC. Encyclopedia of Art for Young People, 8 Vols., Set. 2007. (Encyclopedia of Art for Young People Ser.). 768p. (gr. 6-12). 280.00 (*978-0-7910-9477-8(4) , Chelsea Hse.) Facts On File, Inc.

Brush & Paint. 2003. (Gateways to the Sun Ser.). 32p. (J). (gr. 1-2). pap. 11.95 (978-1-58105-575-7(7)) Santillana USA Publishing Co., Inc.

Burton, Margie, et al. Art Around the World. Adams, Alison, ed. 1999. (Early Connections Ser.). 16p. (J). (gr. k-2). pap. 4.50 (978-1-58344-054-4(2)) Benchmark Education Co.

Canvas & Paper. 2003. (Gateways to the Sun Ser.). 32p. (J). (gr. 3-4). pap. 11.95 (978-1-58105-577-1(3)) Santillana USA Publishing Co., Inc.

Carter, David A. & Diaz, James. Let's Make It Pop-Up. Carter, David A. & Diaz, James, illus. 2004. (Illus.). 10p. (J). 12.95 (978-0-689-86508-4(2) , Little Simon) Simon & Schuster Children's Publishing.

Carter, David A. & Diaz, James R. The Elements of Pop-Up: A Pop-up Book for Aspiring Paper Engineers. Carter, David A. & Diaz, James R., illus. 1999. (Illus.). 18p. (YA). (gr. 3-7). pap. 35.99 (978-0-689-82224-7(3) , Little Simon) Simon & Schuster Children's Publishing.

Carver Middle School, compiled by. Voices from the Middle: Stepping into the Real World. Carver Middle School, . 2004. 224p. (YA). per. 9.99 (978-0-9749811-3-0(3) , Sonship Pr.) 21st Century Pr.

Chandler, Virginia. Telling Tales: Stories in Art. 2005. (Artventure Ser.). (Illus.). 32p. (J). (gr. 4-7). lib. bdg. 27.10 (978-1-58340-623-6(9)) Smart Apple Media.

Chapman. Artist Cards 1. 2003. (Adventures in Art Ser.). (Illus.). (gr. 1 up). pap. 22.95 (978-0-87192-369-1(6)) Davis Pubns., Inc.

—Artist Cards 2. 2003. (Adventures in Art Ser.). (Illus.). (gr. 2 up). pap. 22.95 (978-0-87192-370-7(X)) Davis Pubns., Inc.

—Artist Cards 5. 2003. (Adventures in Art Ser.). (Illus.). (gr. 5 up). pap. 22.95 (978-0-87192-373-8(4)) Davis Pubns., Inc.

Chapman, Laura H. Big Book Bk. 1: Level One, Vol. 1. (Illus.). 70p. (gr. 1 up). 334.95 (978-0-87192-263-2(0)) Davis Pubns., Inc.

Cikanova, Karla. Let's Talk with the World: A Child's Guide to Art & the Natural World. 1998. (Illus.). 128p. 22.50 (978-90-5703-311-7(9) , Harwood Academic Pubs.) Gordon & Breach Publishing Group.

Civardi, Anne. Action! Movement in Art. 2005. (Artventures Ser.). (Illus.). 32p. (J). (gr. 4-7). lib. bdg. 27.10 (978-1-58340-625-0(5) , 1247312) Smart Apple Media.

Como Usted Vea: Fernando Botero. 2005. (Coleccion Los Grandes Para Los Mas Pequenos Ser.). (SPA.). (J). pap. 8.95 (978-968-7381-37-4(X)) Tecolote, Ediciones, S.A. de C.V. MEX. *Dist:* Iaconi, Mariuccia Bk. Imports.

Conroy, Don. Cartoon Animals. 2000. (Draw with Don Ser.: No. 3). 31p. (J). (gr. 1-4). pap. (978-1-84210-030-1(0)) Mentor Bks.

Conway, Ethel Agnes. The Book of Art for Young People. 2006. 94.99 (*978-1-4280-0411-5(4)); pap. 88.99 (*978-1-4280-0410-8(6)) IndyPublish.com.

Crey, Joanna. The World of Eric Carle: A Visit to Eric Carle's Studio. 2002. per. 12.00 (978-1-59288-000-3(2)) Carle, Eric Museum of Picture Bk. Art, The.

Crismon, Joy. Start with Art. 339p. (J). (gr. 1-7). pap. 59.95 (978-1-56861-046-7(7)) Swift Learning Resources.

Dalmatian Press Staff. Precious Moments Activity Art Tablet. 1998. (Precious Moments Ser.). (Illus.). (J). (ps-3). pap. 2.29 (978-1-57759-057-6(0)) Dalmatian Pr.

—Precious Moments Activity Fun Tablet. 1998. (Precious Moments Ser.). (Illus.). (J). (ps-3). pap. 2.29 (978-1-57759-058-3(9)) Dalmatian Pr.

—Ultimate Holiday Fun Book: The Greatest Collection of Fun & Learning Ever Assembled. 1998. (Ultimate Fun Bks.). (J). pap. 5.99 (978-1-888567-74-8(0)) Dalmatian Pr.

Davis Publications Inc. Art a Personal Journey. 2002. pap. 149.95 (978-0-87192-561-9(3)) Davis Pubns., Inc.

DeLong, Ron, ed. Dream-Makers: Visual Art & Literacy. 2003. (Illus.). 48p. 6.00 (978-0-86696-315-2(4)) Binney & Smith, Inc.

Destefano, Tanya. Art. 2000. (gr. k-3). lib. bdg. 11.80 (978-0-613-29551-2(X)) Tandem Library Bks.

Di Pasquale, Giovanni & Bardi, Matilde. Medieval Times. 2002. (Art & Civilization Ser.). (Illus.). 40p. (J). (gr. 3 up). 16.95 (978-0-87226-686-5(9) , Bedrick, Peter Bks.) School Specialty Publishing.

Dickens, Rosie. Introduction to Modern Art - Internet Linked. 2005. (Introduction to Art Ser.). 96p. (J). 19.95 (978-0-7945-0923-1(1) , Usborne) EDC Publishing.

Dickins, Rosie. Book of Art - Internet Linked. Cartwright, Mary, illus. 2006. 196p. (J). 22.95 (978-0-7945-1222-4(4) , Usborne) EDC Publishing.

—Children's Book of Art - Internet Linked. Butler, Nickey, illus. 2006. 64p. (J). 14.99 (978-0-7945-1223-1(2) , Usborne) EDC Publishing.

Domeniconi, David. M Is for Masterpiece: An Art Alphabet. Bullas, Will, illus. rev. ed. 2006. 48p. (J). 17.95 (978-1-58536-276-9(X)) Sleeping Bear Pr.

Dragon World. 2005. (Illus.). 76p. 19.95 (978-0-7631-8183-3(8)) BrownTrout Pubs., Inc.

Drucker, Janet & Drucker, William, prefs. Georg Jensen: 20th Century Designs. 2002. (Schiffer Book for Collectors Ser.). (Illus.). 256p. (gr. 10-13). 69.95 (978-0-7643-1568-8(4)) Schiffer Publishing, Ltd.

Dunn, Mary. My Adventure at an Artist's Studio. 2006. 44p. (J). 8.99 (978-1-59092-290-3(5) , Orchard Academy Pr.) Windstorm Creative.

Equipo Staff. El Circo: Un Acercamiento al Arte a Traves del Juego. (Arte en Puzzle Ser.). (SPA., Illus.). 12p. (J). 12.95 (978-84-8488-026-4(5)) Serres, Ediciones, S. L. ESP. *Dist:* Lectorum Pubns., Inc.

Evans, Alwyn, ed. Destination Unknown. 2001. (Illus.). 112p. (J). pap. 13.95 (978-1-86368-341-8(0)) Fremantle Pr. AUS. *Dist:* International Specialized Bk. Services.

Express Yourself! Scholastic Edition. 2005. 7.95 (978-0-8230-2492-6(X)) Watson-Guptill Pubns., Inc.

Fallen, Anne-Catherine. Exploring Art: A Student Guide to Viewing Museum Exhibitions in the Arts. McNamee, Harriet, ed. 1999. (Illus.). 24p. (YA). (gr. 7-10). pap., stu. ed. 9.95 (978-0-940979-39-0(X)) National Museum of Women in the Arts.

Fine, Jil. Art. 2004. (High Interest Bks.). (Illus.). 48p. (J). (gr. 7-12). pap. 6.95 (978-0-516-25942-0(3) , Children's Pr.) Scholastic Library Publishing.

Finger, Shari & Tumblety, Susan. Fabulous Nails. 2000. (Funtastic Kits Ser.). (Illus.). 48p. (J). 12.98 (978-0-7853-3869-7(1)) Publications International, Ltd.

A First Look At. 2005. 32p. pap. 184.00 (978-0-7910-8461-8(2) , Chelsea Hse.) Facts On File, Inc.

Fisher, Leonard Everett. Colonial Craftsmen - Group 3, 5 bks., Set. Incl. Architects. lib. bdg. 21.36 (978-0-7614-0931-1(9)); Blacksmiths. lib. bdg. 24.21 (978-0-7614-0930-4(0)); Limners : America's Earliest Portrait Painters. lib. bdg. 24.21 (978-0-7614-0932-8(7)); Printers. lib. bdg. 24.21 (978-0-7614-0929-8(7)); Wigmakers. lib. bdg. 24.21 (978-0-7614-0933-5(5)); 48p. (J). (gr. 4-8). 1999. (Illus.). 1999. Set lib. bdg. 106.79 (978-0-7614-0928-1(9) , Benchmark Bks.) Cavendish, Marshall Corp.

Fitzpatrick, Anne. The Baroque Period. 2005. (Movements in Art Ser.). (Illus.). 48p. (gr. 5-9). 21.95 (978-1-58341-346-3(4) , Creative Education) Creative Co., The.

Fleming, Christine. Art As Science. 2007. (Shockwave: Arts & Culture Ser.). (Illus.). 36p. (J). (gr. 4-6). lib. bdg. 25.00 (*978-0-531-17784-6(X) , Children's Pr.) Scholastic Library Publishing.

Flux, Paul. How Artists Use... Techniques for Young Artists, 5 bks., Set. 2001. (Illus.). 32p. (J). (gr. 1-3). lib. bdg. 113.95 (978-1-58810-014-6(6)) Heinemann Library.

—Perspective. 2002. (How Artists Use Ser.). (Illus.). 32p. (J). (gr. 1-4). pap. 6.95 (978-1-58810-439-7(7) , 91167) Heinemann Library.

Fraser, Fil. Alberta's Camelot Vol. 1: Culture & the Arts in the Lougheed Years. rev. ed. 2003. (Illus.). 240p. (J). (gr. 4). pap. 18.95 (978-1-55105-393-6(4)) Lone Pine Publishing USA.

Garbo, Beth. Renoir to Matisse: A Calendar Book - 1999. 1998. (Illus.). 106p. spiral bd. 12.95 (978-1-892373-38-0(6) , 38-6) Especially Bks.

God & the History of Art. 2nd ed. 2000. 456p. (YA). spiral bd. 49.95 (978-0-9700405-6-5(3)) How Great Thou Art Pubns.

Gooding, Mel, et al. Artists, Land, Nature. 2002. (Illus.). 168p. 49.95 (978-0-8109-4189-2(9)) Abrams, Harry N. , Inc.

Gottesman, Eric. I Love America Tattoos. 2004. (Tattoos Ser.). (Illus.). 2p. (J). (gr. k-5). pap. 1.50 (978-0-486-43490-2(7)) Dover Pubns., Inc.

Gowing, Lawrence, ed. Facts on File Encyclopedia of Art & Artists Set. 2005. 1840p. (gr. 9). 585.00 (978-0-8160-6378-9(8)) Facts On File, Inc.

Greenway, Shirley. Art: An A-Z Guide. 2001. (Watts Reference Ser.). (Illus.). 128p. (YA). (gr. 6-8). pap. 19.95 (978-0-531-16553-9(1) , Watts, Franklin) Scholastic Library Publishing.

—Art: An A-Z Guide. 2001. (Illus.). 128p. (J). (gr. 6-8). lib. bdg. 30.35 (978-0-613-72729-7(0)) Tandem Library Bks.

Gunderson, Jessica. Gothic Art. 2008. (J). (*978-1-58341-610-5(2) , Creative Education) Creative Co., The.

—Realism. 2008. (J). (*978-1-58341-612-9(9) , Creative Education) Creative Co., The.

—Romanticism. 2008. (J). (*978-1-58341-613-6(7) , Creative Education) Creative Co., The.

Harcourt School Publishers Staff. Art 2006. 2nd ed. 2002. (J). (gr. 1). stu. ed. 45.40 (978-0-15-336446-4(7)); (gr. 1). tchr. ed. 102.70 (978-0-15-336452-5(1)); (J). (gr. 2). stu. ed. 45.40 (978-0-15-336447-1(5)); (gr. 2). tchr. ed. 102.70 (978-0-15-336453-2(X)); (J). (gr. 3). stu. ed. 45.40 (978-0-15-336448-8(3)); (gr. 3). tchr. ed. 102.70 (978-0-15-336454-9(8)); (J). (gr. 4). stu. ed. 45.40 (978-0-15-336449-5(1)); (gr. 4). tchr. ed. 102.70 (978-0-15-336457-0(2)); (J). (gr. 5). stu. ed. 45.40 (978-0-15-336451-8(3)); (gr. 5). tchr. ed. 102.70 (978-0-15-336456-3(4)) Harcourt Schl. Pubs.

—Art Around the World. 3rd ed. 2002. (Horizons Ser.). (Illus.). (J). pap. 3.70 (978-0-15-333170-1(4)) Harcourt Schl. Pubs.

—Art Big Book. 4th ed. 2004. (Illus.). (gr. 3). 207.80 (978-0-15-343688-8(3)); (gr. 4). 207.80 (978-0-15-343689-5(1)); (gr. 5). 207.80 (978-0-15-343690-1(5)) Harcourt Schl. Pubs.

—Art, Grade 1. 4th ed. 2004. pap., tchr. ed. 97.10 (978-0-15-342012-2(X)) Harcourt Schl. Pubs.

—Art, Grade 1: Teacher Resource Book. 3rd ed. 2003. (Illus.). pap., tchr. ed. 39.00 (978-0-15-339496-6(X)) Harcourt Schl. Pubs.

—Art, Grade 2. 4th ed. 2004. pap., tchr. ed. 97.10 (978-0-15-342013-9(8)) Harcourt Schl. Pubs.

—Art, Grade 2: Teacher Resource Book. 3rd ed. 2003. (Illus.). pap., tchr. ed. 39.00 (978-0-15-339497-3(8)) Harcourt Schl. Pubs.

—Art, Grade 3. 4th ed. 2004. pap., tchr. ed. 97.10 (978-0-15-342014-6(6)) Harcourt Schl. Pubs.

—Art, Grade 3: Teacher Resource Book. 3rd ed. 2003. pap., tchr. ed. 39.00 (978-0-15-339498-0(6)) Harcourt Schl. Pubs.

—Art, Grade 4. 4th ed. 2004. pap., tchr. ed. 97.10 (978-0-15-342015-3(4)) Harcourt Schl. Pubs.

—Art, Grade 4: Teacher Resource Book. 3rd ed. 2003. (Illus.). pap., tchr. ed. 39.00 (978-0-15-339499-7(4)) Harcourt Schl. Pubs.

—Art, Grade 5. 4th ed. 2004. pap., tchr. ed. 97.10 (978-0-15-342016-0(2)) Harcourt Schl. Pubs.

—Art, Grade 5: Teacher Resource Book. 3rd ed. 2003. pap., tchr. ed. 39.00 (978-0-15-339501-7(X)) Harcourt Schl. Pubs.

—Artist Workshop. 3rd ed. 2003. (SPA & ENG., Illus.). pap. 15.60 (978-0-15-339899-5(X)); pap. 15.60 (978-0-15-339900-8(7)); pap. 15.60 (978-0-15-339901-5(5)); pap. 15.60 (978-0-15-339902-2(3)); pap. 15.60 (978-0-15-339903-9(1)) Harcourt Schl. Pubs.

—Big Book Art 2006 - Grade 1. 3rd ed. 2003. (Illus.). pap. 207.80 (978-0-15-339507-9(9)) Harcourt Schl. Pubs.

—Big Book Art 2006 - Grade 2. 3rd ed. 2003. (Illus.). pap. 207.80 (978-0-15-339508-6(7)) Harcourt Schl. Pubs.

Haring, Keith. Big. 1998. (Illus.). 14p. (J). pap. 6.95 (978-0-7868-0390-3(8)) Hyperion Bks. for Children.

—Ten. 1998. (Illus.). 14p. (J). 6.95 (978-0-7868-0391-0(6)) Hyperion Bks. for Children.

Haruch, Tony. Kurtal Explores Aboriginal Art. 2007. (J). (***978-1-56290-533-0(3)***) Crystal Productions.

Heard, Georgia. Songs of Myself: An Anthology of Poems & Art. 2000. (Illus.). 32p. (J). (gr. 2-5). 15.95 (978-1-57255-723-9(0)) Mondo Publishing.

Heard, Georgia, compiled by. Songs of Myself: An Anthology of Poems & Art. 2000. (Illus.). 32p. (J). 17.00 (978-1-57255-854-0(7)); pap. 4.95 (978-1-57255-722-2(2)) Mondo Publishing.

Hilyear, D. The ABC of Art. 2004. (Children's Art Ser. from the National Gallery of Victoria Ser.). (Illus.). 56p. 9.95 (978-0-7241-0235-8(3)) National Gallery of Victoria AUS. *Dist:* Antique Collectors' Club.

Hodge, Susie. Prehistoric Art. 2006. (Illus.). 32p. (J). (***978-1-4034-8770-4(7)***) Heinemann Library.

Holiday - Art Projects, Stationary, Invitations, Greet Cards, & More! 2005. 73p. (J). spiral bd. 14.99 (978-1-59441-473-2(4) , K04024) Carson-Dellosa Publishing Co., Inc.

Holland, William R., et al. Icart: The Complete Etchings. 4th rev. exp. ed. 2002. (Schiffer Book for Collectors Ser.). (Illus.). 248p. (gr. 10-13). 79.95 (978-0-7643-1584-8(6)) Schiffer Publishing, Ltd.

Hook, Dianne. Funtastic Fall. 2005. 128p. (J). per. 19.99 (978-1-59441-310-0(X) , DJ-604012) Carson-Dellosa Publishing Co., Inc.

—School Stuff Clip Art Smiles. 2005. 128p. (J). per. 19.99 (978-1-59441-312-4(6) , DJ-604014) Carson-Dellosa Publishing Co., Inc.

—Winter Whimsey. 2005. 128p. (J). per. 19.99 (978-1-59441-309-4(6) , DJ-604011) Carson-Dellosa Publishing Co., Inc.

Hook, Dianne J., creator. School Stuff Clip Art Smiles. 2004. 128p. (978-1-59441-005-5(4) , DJ-604001) Carson-Dellosa Publishing Co., Inc.

Hook, Dianne J., creator & des. Winter Whimsy. Hook, Dianne J., des. 2004. (Illus.). 64p. per. 11.99 (978-1-59441-178-6(6) , DJ-604003) Carson-Dellosa Publishing Co., Inc.

Hosack, Karen. Families. 2004. (J). lib. bdg. 24.22 (978-1-4034-4851-4(5)) Heinemann Library.

—Food. 2004. (J). lib. bdg. 24.22 (978-1-4034-4852-1(3)) Heinemann Library.

—Homes. 2004. (J). lib. bdg. 24.22 (978-1-4034-4853-8(1)) Heinemann Library.

—Nature. 2004. (J). lib. bdg. 24.22 (978-1-4034-4854-5(X)) Heinemann Library.

Hughes, Fenella, et al. Art for Children. 1999. (Art for Children Ser.: Vol. 4). (Illus.). 264p. (ps-3). 19.99 (978-0-7858-1046-9(3)) Book Sales, Inc.

It's All About Baby. 2004. (J). mass mkt. (978-0-9728472-3-0(5)) Signator Publishing Group Inc.

Jane Shuter. Ancient Chinese Art. 2nd ed. 2006. (Illus.). 32p. (J). pap. (***978-1-4034-8772-8(3)***) Heinemann Library.

Jenkins, Martin. The Art of Science: A Pop-Up Adventure in Art. Young, Jay, illus. 1999. 41p. (YA). (gr. 7-9). reprint ed. 28.00 (978-0-7567-5831-8(9)) DIANE Publishing Co.

Katter, Eldon & Stewart. Art a Global Experience: Student Art Gallery. 2001. (Illus.). stu. ed. incl. cd-rom (978-0-87192-502-2(8)) Davis Pubns., Inc.

Katz, Elizabeth, et al. Themes & Foundations of Art. 1999. (C). stu. ed. 83.32 (978-0-538-42973-3(9) , 9780538429733) Glencoe/McGraw-Hill.

Keoke, Emory Dean & Porterfield, Kay Marie. American Indian Contributions to the World: Buildings, Clothing, & Art. 2005. (American Indian Contributions to the World Ser.). (Illus.). 160p. (J). (gr. 4-9). 35.00 (978-0-8160-5394-0(4)) Facts On File, Inc.

Kim, H. Y. Michelle. Art Play-Ground A-1: A Complete & Self-Contained Curriculum for Art Education. 2005. 42p. spiral bd., wbk. ed. 12.95 (978-89-91302-05-1(X)) Michelle's A & E KOR. *Dist:* APG Sales and Fulfillment.

—Art Play-Ground A-2: A Complete & Self-Contained Curriculum for Art Education. 2005. 42p. spiral bd., wbk. ed. 12.95 (978-89-91302-06-8(8)) Michelle's A & E KOR. *Dist:* APG Sales and Fulfillment.

—Art Play-Ground A-3: A Complete & Self-Contained Curriculum for Art Education. 2005. 42p. spiral bd., wbk. ed. 12.95 (978-89-91302-07-5(6)) Michelle's A & E KOR. *Dist:* APG Sales and Fulfillment.

—Art Play-Ground B-1: A Complete & Self-Contained Curriculum for Art Education. 2005. 42p. spiral bd., wbk. ed. 12.95 (978-89-91302-02-0(5)) Michelle's A & E KOR. *Dist:* APG Sales and Fulfillment.

—Art Play-Ground C-1: A Complete & Self-Contained Curriculum for Art Education. 2005. 42p. spiral bd. 12.95 (978-89-91302-08-2(4)) Michelle's A & E KOR. *Dist:* APG Sales and Fulfillment.

—Art Play-Ground C-2: A Complete & Self-Contained Curriculum for Art Education. 2005. 42p. spiral bd., wbk. ed. 12.95 (978-89-91302-09-9(2)) Michelle's A & E KOR. *Dist:* APG Sales and Fulfillment.

—Art Play-Ground C-3: A Complete & Self-Contained Curriculum for Art Education. 2005. 42p. spiral bd. 12.95 (978-89-91302-10-5(6)) Michelle's A & E KOR. *Dist:* APG Sales and Fulfillment.

—Art Play-Ground E-1: A Complete & Self-Contained Curriculum for Art Education. 2005. 42p. spiral bd. 12.95 (978-89-91302-11-2(4)) Michelle's A & E KOR. *Dist:* APG Sales and Fulfillment.

—Art Play-Ground E-2: A Complete & Self-Contained Curriculum for Art Education. 2005. 42p. spiral bd. 12.95 (978-89-91302-12-9(2)) Michelle's A & E KOR. *Dist:* APG Sales and Fulfillment.

—Art Play-Ground E-3: A Complete & Self-Contained Curriculum for Art Education. 2005. 42p. spiral bd., wbk. ed. 12.95 (978-89-91302-13-6(0)) Michelle's A & E KOR. *Dist:* APG Sales and Fulfillment.

—Art Play-Ground F-1: A Complete & Self-Contained Curriculum for Art Education. 2005. 42p. spiral bd. 12.95 (978-89-954869-1-7(0)) Michelle's A & E KOR. *Dist:* APG Sales and Fulfillment.

—Art Play-Ground F-2: A Complete & Self-Contained Curriculum for Art Education. 2005. 42p. spiral bd., wbk. ed. 12.95 (978-89-954869-2-4(9)) Michelle's A & E KOR. *Dist:* APG Sales and Fulfillment.

—Art Play-Ground F-3: A Complete & Self-Contained Curriculum for Art Education. 2005. 42p. spiral bd. 12.95 (978-89-954869-3-1(7)) Michelle's A & E KOR. *Dist:* APG Sales and Fulfillment.

Kim, Michelle. Art Play-Ground B-2. 2005. 42p. pap., wbk. ed. 12.95 (978-89-91302-03-7(3)) Michelle's A & E KOR. *Dist:* APG Sales and Fulfillment.

—Art Play-Ground B-3. 2005. 42p. pap. 12.95 (978-89-91302-04-4(1)) Michelle's A & E KOR. *Dist:* APG Sales and Fulfillment.

—Art Play-Ground D-1. 2005. 42p. pap., wbk. ed. 12.95 (978-89-954869-4-8(5)) Michelle's A & E KOR. *Dist:* APG Sales and Fulfillment.

—Art Play-Ground D-2. 2005. 42p. pap. 12.95 (978-89-91302-00-6(9)) Michelle's A & E KOR. *Dist:* APG Sales and Fulfillment.

—Art Play-Ground D-3. 2005. 42p. pap. 12.95 (978-89-91302-01-3(7)) Michelle's A & E KOR. *Dist:* APG Sales and Fulfillment.

King, Ginger. Stay Connected. 2000. 114p. 9.99 (978-0-9709081-0-0(5)) Stay Connected.

Kinghorn, Harriet R. Let's Meet Famous Artists: A Creative Art Activity Book. 1999. (Illus.). 104p. (J). (gr. 1-6). pap., act. bk. ed. 10.99 (978-0-513-02050-4(0) , TSD20500, Instructional Fair) Schaffer, Frank Pubns.

Knight, Ernie C. Bean Heads, Another Batch. 2003. (Illus.). 58p. per. 16.99 (978-1-932338-06-5(3)) Lifevest Publishing, Inc.

Kohl, MaryAnn F. & Potter, Jean. Storybook Art: Hands-on Art for Children in the Styles of 100 Great Picture Book Illustrators. Davis, Katheryn & Van Slyke, Rebecca, illus. 2003. (Bright Ideas for Learning Ser.). 144p. (J). pap. 18.95 (978-0-935607-03-1(X)) Bright Ring Publishing, Inc.

Kramer, Ann. Egyptian Myth: A Treasury of Legends, Art, & History. 2007. (World of Mythology Ser.). (Illus.). 96p. (YA). (gr. 6 up). 35.95 (***978-0-7656-8105-8(6)***) Sharpe, M.E. Inc.

Kunst. (Duden-Schuelerduden Ser.). (YA). (978-3-411-05942-3(7)) Bibliographisches Institut & F. A. Brockhaus AG DEU. *Dist:* International Bk. Import Service, Inc.

Kunst und Kultur, 6 Bands, Set. (Bibliothek Ser.). (GER., Illus.). (978-3-7653-6700-7(1)) Brockhaus, F. A., GmbH DEU. *Dist:* International Bk. Import Service, Inc.

Langley, Andrew. Ancient Egypt. 2002. (History in Stone Ser.). 64p. (J). (gr. 3-7). 16.95 (978-1-57145-552-9(3) , Silver Dolphin Bks.) Advantage Pubs. Group.

—Ancient Egypt. 2005. (History in Art Ser.). (Illus.). 48p. (J). lib. bdg. 29.93 (978-1-4109-0518-5(7)) Steck-Vaughn.

—Ancient Greece. 2005. (History in Art Ser.). (Illus.). 48p. (J). lib. bdg. 29.93 (978-1-4109-0517-8(9)) Steck-Vaughn.

Langley, Andrew & Wolfe, Gillian. Oxford First Book of Art. 2nd rev. ed. 2005. (Illus.). 48p. (YA). 12.95 (978-0-19-910981-4(8)) Oxford Univ. Pr., Inc.

Levithan, David. You Are Here This Is Now: Poems, Stories Essays, & Art from the Best Young Writers & Artists in America. 2002. (gr. 7-12). lib. bdg. 15.30 (978-0-613-72042-7(3)) Tandem Library Bks.

Lewis, Elizabeth. Mexican Art & Culture. 2003. (World Art & Culture Ser.). (Illus.). 56p. (J). lib. bdg. 29.99 (978-0-7398-6610-8(9)) Raintree.

Louchard, Antonin & Couprie, Katy. A Whole World. 2002. (Illus.). 256p. (J). 15.95 (978-1-84059-342-6(3)) Milet Publishing.

Luo, Keyi, illus. Colorful Childhood. 2004. (CHI.). (J). pap. 27.50 (978-1-932002-47-8(2) , Cozy Hse. Publisher) Cozy Graphics Corp.

MacDonald, Fiona. Design. 2002. (Culture Encyclopedia Ser.). (Illus.). 40p. (J). (gr. 5 up). lib. bdg. (978-1-59084-476-2(9)) Mason Crest Pubs.

MacDonald, Fiona, intro. Art, Culture & Entertainment. 2001. (Through the Ages Ser.). (Illus.). 64p. (gr. 3-7). 12.95 (978-0-7548-0785-8(1)) Anness Publishing GBR. *Dist:* National Bk. Network.

Marcovitz, Hal. Art Conservation. 2006. (Eye on Art Ser.). 112p. (J). (gr. 7-10). 32.45 (978-1-59018-964-1(7) , Lucent Bks.) Thomson Gale.

Marcovitz, Hal. Surrealism. 2007. (Eye on Art Ser.). (Illus.). 128p. (J). (gr. 7-10). 31.20 (***978-1-4205-0005-9(8)*** , Lucent Bks.) Thomson Gale.

Marotske, Michelle R. & Yoakum, Kimberly H. Color Creations Coloring Book: Impressionism, Cubism, Modernism. Marotske, Michelle R. & Yoakum, Kimberly H., illus. 1998. (Illus.). 60p. (J). (gr. 1-6). (978-1-893397-00-2(9)) Painted in the Corner Productions, L.L.C.

—Cubism. Marotske, Michelle R. & Yoakum, Kimberly H., illus. 1998. (Illus.). 20p. (J). (gr. 1-6). pap. (978-1-893397-02-6(5)) Painted in the Corner Productions, L.L.C.

Martha Day Zschock. Super Sand Art. 2006. (Activity Book Ser.). 56p. (J). 12.99 (978-1-59359-934-8(X)) Peter Pauper Pr. Inc.

Mason, Antony. Art. 2002. (Culture Encyclopedia Ser.). (Illus.). 40p. (J). (gr. 5 up). lib. bdg. (978-1-59084-475-5(0)) Mason Crest Pubs.

—El arte Impresionista: En los tiempos de Renoir. Llaca, Martha, tr. 2005. (Arte Alrededor del Mundo Ser.). 48p. (J). pap. 9.95 (978-85-7416-229-4(9)) Callis Editora Ltda BRA. *Dist:* Independent Pubs. Group.

—El arte Moderna: En los tiempos de Picasso. 2005. (Arte Alrededor del Mundo Ser.). 48p. (J). pap. 9.95 (978-85-7416-217-1(5)) Callis Editora Ltda BRA. *Dist:* Independent Pubs. Group.

—El Arte Moderno: En los Tiempos de Picasso. 2005. (Arte Alrededor del Mundo Ser.). 48p. (J). pap. 9.95 (978-85-7416-240-9(X)) Callis Editora Ltda BRA. *Dist:* Independent Pubs. Group.

—El arte Renacentista: En los tiempos de Miguel Angel. 2005. (Arte Alrededor del Mundo Ser.). 48p. (J). pap. 9.95 (978-85-7416-228-7(0)) Callis Editora Ltda BRA. *Dist:* Independent Pubs. Group.

Micklethwait, Lucy. I Spy Shapes in Art. 2004. (Illus.). 40p. (J). 19.99 (978-0-06-073193-9(1)) HarperCollins Pubs.

Minond, Edgardo. Drac, Tell Us about Modernism. (SPA.). 80p. (978-84-96137-13-4(9)) Asppan, A., S.L. Distribuidora Internacional de Libros y Revistas.

Mis, Melody S. How to Draw Mexico's Sights & Symbols. 2004. (Kid's Guide to Drawing the Countries of the World Ser.). (Illus.). 48p. (J). lib. bdg. 26.50 (978-0-8239-6668-4(2) , PowerKids Pr.) Rosen Publishing Group, Inc., The.

Mittler & McGraw-Hill Staff. Introducing Art. 1999. (Illus.). stu. ed. 73.96 (978-0-02-662363-6(3) , 9780026623636) Glencoe/McGraw-Hill.

Mittler, et al. Exploring Art. 3rd ed. 2004. stu. ed. 75.96 (978-0-07-846514-7(1) , 9780078465147) Glencoe/McGraw-Hill.

—Introducing Art. 2nd ed. 2004. stu. ed. 75.96 (978-0-07-846499-7(4) , 9780078464997) Glencoe/McGraw-Hill.

—Understanding Art. 3rd ed. 2004. (C). stu. ed. 75.96 (978-0-07-846529-1(X) , 9780078465291) Glencoe/McGraw-Hill.

Moyer, Bernadette A. Bee an Artist & Bee Creative: Sketch Book. 1999. (Illus.). 50p. (J). (gr. k-12). spiral bd. 12.95 (978-0-9666183-6-5(X)) Two Bee-A-TwinBee Publishing, LLC.

Murray, Carol. ABC Art Riddles. Levin, Freddie, illus. 2005. (J). (978-0-939217-58-8(9)) Peel Productions, Inc.

National Gallery of Australia Staff. Parole Grande per Persone Piccole: Big Words for Little People. 2003. (Illus.). 56p. pap. 12.95 (978-0-642-54207-6(4)) National Gallery of Australia AUS. *Dist:* Univ. of Washington Pr.

Nelson, Andy. The Impressionists Coloring Book. Nelson, Andy, illus. 2nd ed. 2004. (Illus.). 96p. (Orig.). (J). (gr. 1-6). pap. 8.95 (978-0-929636-26-9(0)) Syren Bk. Co.

Nelson, Libby & Cornell, Kari. Projects & Layouts. 1999. (California Missions Ser.). (Illus.). 80p. (gr. 4-7). pap. 8.95 (978-0-8225-9831-2(0)) Lerner Publishing Group.

Nestler, David, illus. The Art of Dave Nestler. 2003. 48p. (YA). (gr. 12 up). pap. (978-0-86562-065-0(2)) Anabas Marketing Limited.

Newbury, Elizabeth. Art to Make You Smile! 2008. (Illus.). 24p. (J). 15.95 (***978-1-84507-583-5(8)***) Lincoln, Frances Ltd. GBR. *Dist:* Perseus Distribution.

Nicholson, Sue. Collage, 6 vols. 2005. (QEB Let's Start! Art Ser.). (Illus.). 24p. (J). (gr. 2-5). lib. bdg. 16.95 (978-1-59566-082-4(8)) QEB Publishing Inc.

—World Art, 6 vols. (QEB Let's Start! Art Ser.). (Illus.). (J). 2005. 24p. (gr. 2-5). lib. bdg. 16.95 (978-1-59566-081-7(X)); 2005. 32p. per. 8.95 (978-1-59566-124-1(7)); 2004. 32p. lib. bdg. 18.95 (978-1-59566-049-7(6)) QEB Publishing Inc.

Nicholson Sue. World Art. 2006. (Art Smart Ser.). (Illus.). 32p. (J). 9.95 (978-1-58728-536-3(3) , 1253683, Two Can Publishing) T&N Children's Publishing.

Nye, Naomi Shihab. The Space Between Our Footsteps: Poems & Paintings from the Middle East. 1998. (Illus.). 144p. (J). (gr. 7-12). 22.95 (978-0-689-81233-0(7)) Simon & Schuster Children's Publishing.

O'Brien, Gregory. Welcome to the South Seas: Contemporary New Zealand Art for Young People. 2005. (Illus.). 96p. 24.95 (978-1-86940-328-7(2)) Auckland Univ. Pr. NZL. *Dist:* Independent Pubs. Group.

Obrist, Hans-Ulrich, contrib. by. Hans Ulrich Obrist: Interviews. 2004. (Illus.). 1000p. (YA). (gr. 13 up). 59.95 (978-88-8158-431-4(X)) Charta ITA. *Dist:* D.A.P./Distributed Art Pubs.

Olson, Michael Keith. How I Feel: A Book about Diabetes. 2002. (Illus.). 48p. 15.00 (978-1-59056-037-2(X)) Lantern Bks.

O'Reilly, Wenda. Art Ditto. 2007. 24.95 (978-1-889613-56-7(8)) Birdcage Pr.

Parsonage, Betty. Butterfly Wings. 2003. (Illus.). 50p. 12.95 (978-1-59094-013-6(X) , 159094013X) Jawbone Publishing Corp.

Patten, Dennis. The Matchstick Fun Book. 1999. (Illus.). 48p. (J). (gr. 6-12). pap. 9.95 (978-0-7641-1215-7(5)) Barron's Educational Series, Inc.

Pfleger, Susanne. Henri Rousseau: A Jungle Expedition. 1998. (Adventures in Art Ser.). (Illus.). 30p. (J). (ps-7). 14.95 (978-3-7913-1987-2(6)) Prestel Publishing.

Phaidon Press Editors. El ABC del Arte. 2004. (SPA., Illus.). pap. 9.95 (978-0-7148-9806-3(6)) Phaidon Pr. GBR. *Dist:* Hachette Bk. Group.

—El ABC Del la Fotografia. rev. ed. 2004. (SPA., Illus.). pap. 9.95 (978-0-7148-9797-4(3)) Phaidon Pr. GBR. *Dist:* Hachette Bk. Group.

Phaidon Press Editors. The Art Book for Children. 2006. 19.95 (***978-0-7148-9863-6(5)***) Phaidon Pr., Inc.

Phaidon Press Editors & Renshaw, Amanda. Art Book for Children, Bk. 2. rev. ed. 2007. (Illus.). 80p. (gr. 8-17). 19.95 (978-0-7148-4706-1(2)) Phaidon Pr., Inc.

Picthall, Chez, illus. Hearts & Stars. 2007. 10p. (J). (ps). bds. 5.95 (***978-1-58728-595-0(9)*** , Two Can Publishing) T&N Children's Publishing.

—Spots & Dots. 2007. 10p. (J). bds. 5.95 (***978-1-58728-594-3(0)***) T&N Children's Publishing.

Pina, Leslie & Vigier, Lorenzo. Scandinavian Glass, 1930-2000: Smoke & Ice. 2002. (Illus.). 224p. (gr. 10-13). 59.95 (978-0-7643-1653-1(2)) Schiffer Publishing, Ltd.

Piven, Hanoch. Untitled. 2006. (J). (978-0-316-76613-5(5)) Little Brown & Co.

QEB Learn Art National Book Stores Edition: Special Effects. 2006. (J). per. (978-1-59566-282-8(0)) QEB Publishing Inc.

QEB Learn Art National Book Stores Edition: World Art. 2006. (J). per. (978-1-59566-284-2(7)) QEB Publishing Inc.

Raimondo, Joyce. Make it Pop! Activities & Adventures in Pop Art. 2006. (Art Explorers Ser.). (Illus.). 48p. (J). 12.95 (978-0-8230-2507-7(1)) Watson-Guptill Pubns., Inc.

Reynolds, Virginia. Fine Art Scratch & Sketch: A Cool Art Activity Book for Budding Fine Artists of All Ages. 2005. (Activity Journal Ser.). (Illus.). (J). 12.99 (978-0-88088-596-6(3)) Peter Pauper Pr. Inc.

Robins, Deri. Special Effects. 2004. (QEB Learn Art Ser.). (Illus.). 32p. (J). lib. bdg. 27.10 (978-1-59566-047-3(X)) QEB Publishing Inc.

—Stencils & Prints. 2006. (Illus.). 32p. (J). 9.95 (978-1-58728-544-8(4) , Two Can Publishing) T&N Children's Publishing.

Robinson, Shannon. Cubism: Movements in Art. 2005. (Movements in Art Ser.). (Illus.). 48p. (gr. 5-9). 21.95 (978-1-58341-347-0(2) , Creative Education) Creative Co., The.

Roca, Nuria. What Is Art? Painting & Sculpture. 2004. (gr. k-3). lib. bdg. 15.25 (978-0-613-84061-3(5)) Tandem Library Bks.

Roche, Denis. Oodles to Do with Loo-Loo & Boo: The Collected Art Adventures. Roche, Denis, illus. 2001. (Illus.). 64p. (J). (gr. k-3). pap. 9.95 (978-0-618-15423-4(X)) Houghton Mifflin Co. Trade & Reference Div.

Rubin, Susan Goldman. Art Against the Odds: From Slave Quilts to Prison Paintings. 2004. (Illus.). 64p. (J). (gr. 5-9). 19.95 (978-0-375-82406-7(5) , Crown Books For Young Readers) Random Hse. Children's Bks.

Running Press Staff & Langley, Andrew. Leonardo da Vinci & the Renaissance. 2001. (Illus.). 32p. (J). pap. 19.95 (978-0-7624-0746-0(8) , Running Pr. Kids) Running Pr. Bk. Pubs.

Ruth, Annie. I Can Read. Ruth, Annie, illus. l.t. ed. 2005. (Illus.). 32p. (J). 9.95 (978-0-9656306-7-2(6)) Ruth, A. Creations.

Salmansohn, Karen. Art. Stauffer, Brian, illus. 2004. (Petit Connoisseur Ser.). 16p. bds. 6.95 (978-1-58246-103-8(1) , Tricycle Pr.) Ten Speed Pr.

Schaefer, Lola M. Un Hogar para Mi, 5 vols., Set. 2003. (SPA.). (J). (ps-1). lib. bdg. 92.50 (978-1-4034-0271-4(X)) Heinemann Library.

Schlageck, Kathrine Walker. Beyond Oz: Children's Book Illustrations from the Region. 2002. (Illus.). 100p. per. 10.00 (978-1-890751-10-4(3)) Kansas State Univ., Marianna Kistler Beach Museum of Art, The.

Schooltime Borders. 2005. 128p. (J). per. 19.99 (978-1-59441-187-8(5) , DJ-604006) Carson-Dellosa Publishing Co., Inc.

Schooltime Toppers. 2005. 128p. (J). per. 19.99 (978-1-59441-188-5(3) , DJ-604007) Carson-Dellosa Publishing Co., Inc.

Schwartz, Linda. Jewish Superdoubles: Step by Step Drawing Fun for Kids 6-12. Clark Editorial and Design Staff, ed. Armstrong, Beverly, illus. 1999. 32p. (J). (gr. 1-7). pap. 4.95 (978-0-88160-322-4(8) , LW385) Creative Teaching Pr., Inc.

Seidel, Ruthanna. What Is an Icon? Larsen, Anya, illus. 1999. 32p. (J). (GRE.). pap. (978-1-930224-02-5(8)); (RUS.). pap. (978-1-930224-01-8(X)); pap. (978-1-930224-00-1(1)) Talanton Pr.

A B

Seif, Adam. Adam & Jeremy's Artistic Adventure: The World Isn't Flat... Learn to Draw Pictures That Jump Out at You. Cutcliff, Linda & Havenga, Marilyn, eds. Seif, Adam, illus. 2001. (Illus.). (J). (gr. 1-8). pap. 19.95 (978-0-9678810-8-9(0)) DreamCatcherPress, Inc.

Servello, Joe. You Are an Artist: Ideas & Encouragement for Children. Servello, Joe, illus. 2001. 24p. (J). spiral bd. 12.95 (978-0-939195-30-5(5) , 500) Parent Child Pr., Inc.

Settembrini, Luigi, ed. The Ideal City. 2003. (Illus.). 516p. (YA). (gr. 13 up). pap. 42.95 (978-88-8158-437-6(9)) Charta ITA. *Dist:* D.A.P./Distributed Art Pubs.

Sevaly, Karen. Nothing But... Borders! Reproducible Borders for All Occasions. Sevaly, Karen, illus. 1999. (Illus.). 80p. (J). pap. 9.95 (978-1-57882-020-7(0) , TF-1652) Teacher's Friend Pubns., Inc.

Shepherd, Nellie. Puppets. 2003. (My Art Class Ser.). (Illus.). 48p. (J). 12.99 (978-0-7894-9856-4(1)) Dorling Kindersley Publishing, Inc.

Shuter, Jane. Ancient Chinese Art. 2006. (Illus.). 32p. (J). ***978-1-4034-8764-3(2))** Heinemann Library.

Shyam, Bhajju. The London Jungle Book. 2005. (Illus.). 48p. 19.95 (978-81-86211-87-8(X)) Tara Publishing IND. *Dist:* Consortium Bk. Sales & Distribution.

So You Want to Be an Artist. 2001. 52p. pap. 7.95 (978-0-9707469-0-0(3) , DLS Bks.) Denney Literary Services.

Solotareff, Gregoire. Nieve. 2003. (SPA.). 86p. 21.99 (978-84-8470-039-5(9)) Corimbo, Editorial S.L. ESP. *Dist:* Lectorum Pubns., Inc.

Sommers, Joan. A Sunday on la Grande Jatte Tunnel Book. 2004. (Take a Peek Ser.). (Illus.). 5p. 9.95 (978-0-9754150-0-9(X)) Tunnel Vision.

Sovak, Jan. Spiders Tattoos. 2000. 2p. (J). pap. 1.50 (978-0-486-41013-5(7)) Dover Pubns., Inc.

Spates, Tracy V. Picture the World: Children's Art Around the Globe. 2001. (Illus.). 68p. (J). (gr. 1-3). 24.95 (978-1-84059-296-2(6)) Milet Publishing.

Spring & Summer Clip Art Smiles. 2005. 128p. (J). per. 19.99 (978-1-59441-186-1(7) , DJ-604005) Carson-Dellosa Publishing Co., Inc.

Steck-Vaughn Staff. See What I Can Do. 2000. (Illus.). (J). bds. (978-0-7398-4445-8(8)) Steck-Vaughn.

Step-by-Step, 12 vols. (Illus.). (gr. 3-5). Set. 2003. lib. bdg. 307.68 (978-1-4034-0701-6(0)); Set 3. 2002. lib. bdg. 102.56 (978-1-4034-0700-9(2)) Heinemann Library.

Stephens, Pamela Geiger. Dropping in on Picasso. McNeill, Jim, illus. 2004. (J). (978-1-56290-325-1(X)) Crystal Productions.

Stephens, Pamela Geiger & Walkup, Nancy Elizabeth. Bridging the Curriculum Through Art - Interdisciplinary Connections. 2001. 142p. (YA). spiral bd. 29.95 net. (978-1-56290-270-4(9)) Crystal Productions.

Susie Hodge. Prehistoric Art. 2nd ed. 2006. (Illus.). 32p. (J). pap. ***978-1-4034-8778-0(2))** Heinemann Library.

Tarbox, Charlene. Floral Fingernail Tattoos. 2000. 2p. (J). (gr. k-5). pap. 1.50 (978-0-486-41017-3(X)) Dover Pubns., Inc.

—Jewel Ankle Bracelet's Tattoos. 2000. 2p. (J). pap. 1.50 (978-0-486-41015-9(3)) Dover Pubns., Inc.

Thomsen, Ruth. Ghastly & Gruesome. 2004. (Illus.). (J). lib. bdg. 16.95 (978-1-931983-70-9(4)) Chrysalis Education.

—Myths & Legends. 2004. (Illus.). lib. bdg. 16.95 (978-1-931983-68-6(2)) Chrysalis Education.

Thomson, Ruth. Celebrations. 2005. (First Look at Art Ser.). (Illus.). 32p. (J). (gr. 3-5). 23.00 (978-0-7910-8315-4(2) , Chelsea Hse.) Facts On File, Inc.

—Creatures. 2003. (First Look at Art Ser.). (Illus.). 32p. (gr. 3-5). 23.00 (978-0-7910-7945-4(7) , Chelsea Hse.) Facts On File, Inc.

—Families: Relationships in Art. 2005. (Artventures Ser.). (Illus.). 32p. (J). (gr. 4-7). lib. bdg. 27.10 (978-1-58340-627-4(1)) Smart Apple Media.

—Journeys. 2005. (First Look at Art Ser.). (Illus.). 32p. (J). (gr. 3-5). 23.00 (978-0-7910-8317-8(9) , Chelsea Hse.) Facts On File, Inc.

—Weather. 2005. (First Look at Art Ser.). (Illus.). 32p. (J). (gr. 3-5). 23.00 (978-0-7910-8318-5(7) , Chelsea Hse.) Facts On File, Inc.

Timeless Voices, Timeless Themes: Gold, Fine Art. 2000. (YA). (gr. 9). trans. 31.97 (978-0-13-051234-5(6)) Prentice Hall PTR.

Timeless Voices, Timeless Themes: Gold, Spanish Support Planning Guide. 2000. (YA). (gr. 9). pap. 4.97 (978-0-13-050916-1(7)) Prentice Hall PTR.

Timeless Voices, Timeless Themes: Platinum, Fine Art. 2000. (YA). (gr. 10). pap. 4.97 (978-0-13-050917-8(5)) Prentice Hall PTR.

Top That Publishing Staff, ed. Celtic Double Cross. 2004. (Wicked Tattoos Ser.). (Illus.). 16p. (J). pap. (978-1-84510-113-8(8)) Top That! Publishing PLC.

Vaughan, Carolyn. The Painters. 2001. (Illus.). 50p. (J). (gr. 4-7). 9.95 (978-0-7611-2359-0(8) , 12359) Workman Publishing Co., Inc.

Watt, Fiona. Art Projects. 2004. (Art Ideas Ser.). 96p. (J). lib. bdg. 26.95 (978-1-58086-638-5(7)); (Illus.). 18.95 (978-0-7945-0657-5(7)) EDC Publishing. (Usborne).

—Mini Art Ideas. Barlow, Amanda, illus. 2004. 96p. (J). 7.95 (978-0-7945-0842-5(1) , Usborne) EDC Publishing.

—Mini art Projects. 2005. 96p. (J). 7.99 (978-0-7945-1111-1(2) , Usborne) EDC Publishing.

White, Lee, ed. Poetry 4 Ya Mind: A Collection of Poetry & Artwork from Getting Ready. 1999. (Illus.). 128p. (J). (gr. 7-12). pap. 9.95 (978-1-892194-22-0(8)) Northwest Media, Inc.

Whitely, H. Ellen. Line. 2004. (Children's Art Ser. from the National Gallery of Victoria Ser.). (Illus.). 28p. 9.95 (978-0-7241-0238-9(8)) National Gallery of Victoria AUS. *Dist:* Antique Collectors' Club.

Wickham, Geoffrey. Rapid Perspective. (YA). (gr. 10 up). 9.95 (978-0-85458-050-7(6)); pap. 7.95 (978-0-85458-051-4(4)) Transatlantic Arts, Inc.

Wilkinson, Philip. Chinese Myth: A Treasury of Legends, Art, & History. 2007. (World of Mythology Ser.). (Illus.). 96p. (YA). (gr. 6 up). 35.95 ***978-0-7656-8103-4(X))** Sharpe, M.E. Inc.

Wistow, David. Meet the Group of Seven. McKinley, Kelly, illus. 1999. (Snapshots: Images of People & Places in History Ser.). 48p. (J). (gr. 3-7). (978-1-55074-494-1(1)) Kids Can Pr., Ltd.

Wistow, David & McKinley, Kelly. Meet the Group of Seven. 2005. (Snapshots: Images of People & Places in History Ser.). (Illus.). (J). (gr. 3-7). (978-1-55074-694-5(4)) Kids Can Pr., Ltd.

Wolfe, Gillian. Look! Body Language in Art. 2004. (Look! Ser.). (Illus.). 40p. (J). 16.95 (978-1-84507-034-2(8)) Lincoln, Frances Ltd. GBR. *Dist:* Perseus Distribution.

World Art, 6 bks. 2005. (QEB Learn Art Ser.). (Illus.). 32p. (J). per. 8.95 (978-1-59566-128-9(X)) QEB Publishing Inc.

World Art & Culture, 4 vols., Set 1. 2003. (Illus.). 119.96 (978-0-7398-6611-5(7)) Raintree.

Wybomy, Sheila. Gargoyles. 2006. (Illus.). 48p. (J). (gr. 4-8). 26.20 (978-0-7377-3627-4(5) , Kidhaven) Thomson Gale.

Yenawine, Philip. Places. 2006. (Illus.). 22p. (J). (gr. 4-8). reprint ed. 15.00 (978-1-4223-5407-0(5)) DIANE Publishing Co.

Zagon, Laurie. Art for Healing: A Beginner's Workshop, 1. 2003. 34p. (J). spiral bd. 20.00 (978-0-9748462-0-0(1)) Art & Creativity For Healing, Inc.

Zemke, Deborah. D Is for Doodle: Doodles from A. 2004. (Illus.). 64p. pap. 12.95 (978-1-59354-029-6(9)) Blue Apple Bks.

ART, ABSTRACT

Barnes, Rachel. Abstract Expressionists. 2002. (Artists in Profile Ser.). (Illus.). 64p. (J). lib. bdg. 28.50 (978-1-58810-644-5(6)) Heinemann Library.

Bocchino, Serena. What Am I? the Story of an Abstract Painting. Bocchino, Serena, illus. l.t. ed. 2005. (Illus.). 32p. (J). per. 19.95 (978-0-9767674-0-4(6)) Serena Bocchino/In His Perfect Time Collection.

Gaff, Jackie & Oliver, Clare. 1920-1940: Realism & Surrealism. 2001. (Twentieth Century Art Ser.). (Illus.). 32p. (J). (gr. 5 up). lib. bdg. 26.00 (978-0-8368-2850-4(X)) Stevens, Gareth Inc.

ART, AFRICAN AMERICAN

see African American Art

ART, AMERICAN

Baverstock, Alison. Joseph Cornell: Secrets in a Box. 2003. (Adventures in Art Ser.). (Illus.). 30p. 14.95 (978-3-7913-2928-4(6)) Prestel Publishing.

Blevins, Wiley. Found Underground: Art, Music, & Poetry of the New York City Subways. 2002. (Illus.). 16p. (J). pap. (978-0-439-35143-0(X)) Scholastic, Inc.

Danneberg, Julie. Women Artists of the West: Five Portraits in Creativity & Courage. 2004. (Illus.). 96p. pap. 12.95 (978-1-55591-861-3(1)) Fulcrum Publishing.

Fitzpatrick, Anne. Late Modernism. 2005. (Movements in Art Ser.). (Illus.). 48p. (gr. 5-9). 21.95 (978-1-58341-348-7(0) , Creative Education) Creative Co., The.

Haskins, James. Harlem Renaissance. 2004. (J). pap. 10.95 (978-0-940975-95-8(5) , Sankofa Bks.) Just Us Bks., Inc.

Kallen, Stuart A. Arts & Entertainment. 2004. (Lucent Library of Historical Eras). (Illus.). 112p. (J). 32.45 (978-1-59018-388-5(6) , Lucent Bks.) Thomson Gale.

Mason, Antony. El arte Contemporanea: En los tiempos de Warhol. 2005. (Arte Alrededor del Mundo Ser.). 48p. (J). pap. 9.95 (978-85-7416-218-8(3)) Callis Editora Ltda BRA. *Dist:* Independent Pubs. Group.

—El Arte Contemporanea: En los Tiempos de Warhol. 2005. (Arte Alrededor del Mundo Ser.). 48p. (J). pap. 9.95 (978-85-7416-241-6(8)) Callis Editora Ltda BRA. *Dist:* Independent Pubs. Group.

Merrill, Yvonne Y. Hands-on America Vol. 2: Art Activities about Colonial America, African-Americans, & Southeast Indians. 2006. (Hands-on Ser.). 71p. (J). pap. 20.00 (978-0-9778797-0-0(4)) KITS Publishing.

Nichols, Catherine. Early American Culture. 2006. (Discovering the Arts Ser.). (Illus.). 48p. (gr. 4-8). 20.95 (978-1-59515-518-4(X)) Rourke Publishing, LLC.

Osofsky, Randy. Come Look with Me: Art in Early America. 2006. (Come Look with Me Ser.). (J). 15.95 ***978-1-890674-12-0(5))** Charlesbridge Publishing, Inc.

Pearlman, Debra. Where Is Jasper Johns. 2006. (Illus.). 30p. (J). 14.95 (978-3-7913-3711-1(4)) Prestel Publishing.

Press, Petra. Native American Art. (Art in History Ser.). 32p. 2003. pap. 6.95 (978-1-4034-4020-4(4)); 2001. (Illus.). (J). (gr. 4-6). lib. bdg. 24.22 (978-1-58810-092-4(8)) Heinemann Library.

Raczka, Bob. The Art of Freedom: How Artists See America. 2008. (J). lib. bdg. ***978-0-8225-7508-5(6)** , Millbrook Pr.) Lerner Publishing Group.

Raintree Steck-Vaughn Staff. Artists & Their Art. 1999. (Illus.). (J). pap. 35.60 (978-0-7398-0898-6(2)) Steck-Vaughn.

Roche, Judith, ed. The Bottom of Heaven: Artwork & Poetry of the Remann Hall Women's Project. 2003. (J). per. 19.95 (978-0-9726649-0-5(4)) Museum of Glass.

Salomon, Stephanie. Come Look with Me: American Indian Art. 2006. (Come Look with Me Ser.). (J). 15.95 ***978-1-890674-11-3(7))** Charlesbridge Publishing, Inc.

Smithsonian American Art Museum Staff, compiled by. Scenes of American Life: Treasures from the Smithsonian American Art Museum. 2000. (YA). pap. 75.00 net. incl. 3/4" U-Matic, sl. (978-1-56290-229-2(6)) Crystal Productions.

Sommers, Joan. The Dancing Skeletons Tunnel Book / el Gran Baile de Calaveras Libro del Tunel. 2006. (Take a Peek Ser.). (Illus.). 16p. (J). 14.95 (978-0-9754150-3-0(4)) Tunnel Vision.

Thomas, Dina M. & Thomas, Andy, eds. The Artful Journey: The Artwork of Andy Thomas. Thomas, Tria M., photos by. l.t. ed. 2003. (Illus.). 122p. 50.00 (978-0-9742285-0-1(8)) Maze Creek Studio.

ART—ANALYSIS, INTERPRETATION, APPRECIATION

see Art—Study and Teaching; Art Appreciation

ART, ANCIENT

see also Art, Primitive; Classical Antiquities

Campbell-Hinshaw, Kelly. Ancient Egypt. 2007. (Art Across the Ages Ser.). (Illus.). 32p. (J). (gr. k-2). 14.95 (978-0-8118-5668-3(2)); pap. 4.95 (978-0-8118-5669-0(0)) Chronicle Bks. LLC.

—Ancient Mexico. 2007. (Art Across the Ages Ser.). (Illus.). 32p. (J). (gr. k-2). 14.95 (978-0-8118-5670-6(4)); pap. 4.95 (978-0-8118-5671-3(2)) Chronicle Bks. LLC.

Conley, Kate A. Greek Arts & Sciences. 2005. (Life in Ancient Days: Greece Ser.). (J). (978-1-59197-866-4(1)) ABDO Publishing Co.

Hodge, Susie. Ancient Egyptian Art. 32p. 2006. (Illus.). (J). ***978-1-4034-8765-0(0));** 2003. 6.95 (978-1-4034-4016-7(6)) Heinemann Library.

—Ancient Egyptian Art. 2003. (gr. 5-8). lib. bdg. 15.25 (978-0-613-87161-7(8)) Tandem Library Bks.

—Ancient Greek Art. 32p. 2006. (Illus.). (J). ***978-1-4034-8766-7(9));** 2003. pap. 6.95 (978-1-4034-4017-4(4)) Heinemann Library.

—Ancient Roman Art. 32p. 2006. (Illus.). (J). ***978-1-4034-8767-4(7));** 2003. pap. 6.95 (978-1-4034-4018-1(2)) Heinemann Library.

Hodge, Susie. Prehistoric Art. 2003. (Art in History Ser.). (Illus.). 32p. (J). (gr. 5-7). pap. 6.95 (978-1-4034-4021-1(2)) Heinemann Library.

Kaplan, Leslie C. Art & Religion in Ancient Egypt. 2004. (Primary Sources of Ancient Civilizations Ser.). (J). lib. bdg. (978-0-8239-8932-4(1)); (Illus.). 24p. lib. bdg. 19.95 (978-0-8239-6782-7(4)) Rosen Publishing Group, Inc., The. (PowerKids Pr.).

Knapp, Ruthie & Lehmberg, Janice. Egyptian Art. 1998. (Off the Wall Museum Guides for Kids). (Illus.). 64p. (J). (gr. 2-7). pap. 10.95 (978-0-87192-384-4(X)) Davis Pubns., Inc.

Samuel, Anna, ed. Egyptian Art: 16 Art Stickers. 2001. (Illus.). 4p. pap. 1.50 (978-0-486-41354-9(3)) Dover Pubns., Inc.

Susie Hodge. Ancient Egyptian Art. 2nd ed. 2006. (Illus.). 32p. (J). pap. ***978-1-4034-8773-5(1))** Heinemann Library.

—Ancient Greek Art. 2nd ed. 2006. (Illus.). 32p. (J). pap. ***978-1-4034-8774-2(X))** Heinemann Library.

—Ancient Roman Art. 2nd ed. 2006. (Illus.). 32p. (J). pap. ***978-1-4034-8775-9(8))** Heinemann Library.

ART, APPLIED

see Art Industries and Trade

ART, ARABIC

see Art, Islamic

ART, ASIAN

Major, John & Belanus, Betty J. Caravan to America: Living Arts of the Silk Road. 2002. (Illus.). 144p. (J). (gr. 3-6). pap. 15.95 (978-0-8126-2677-3(X)); (gr. 4-6). 24.95 (978-0-8126-2666-7(4)) Cricket Bks.

Mis, Melody S. How to Draw China's Sights & Symbols. 2004. (Kid's Guide to Drawing the Countries of the World Ser.). (Illus.). 48p. (J). lib. bdg. 26.50 (978-0-8239-6664-6(X) , PowerKids Pr.) Rosen Publishing Group, Inc., The.

ART, CHRISTIAN

see Christian Art and Symbolism

ART, CLASSICAL

see Art, Greek; Art, Roman

ART—CRITICISM

see Art Criticism

ART, DECORATIVE

Here are entered general works on the decoration and use of artistic objects. Works limited to the external ornamentation of objects are entered under Design, Decorative.

see also Bronzes; Calligraphy; Decoration and Ornament; Design, Decorative; Furniture; Illustration of Books; Mosaics; Needlework; Pottery

Balchin, Judy. Decorative Painting. 2001. (Step-by-Step Children's Crafts Ser.). (Illus.). 32p. pap. 7.95 (978-0-85532-910-5(6) , 9106) Search Pr., Ltd. GBR. *Dist:* Independent Pubs. Group.

Chapman. Artist Cards 3. 2003. (Adventures in Art Ser.). (Illus.). (gr. 3 up). pap. 22.95 (978-0-87192-371-4(8)) Davis Pubns., Inc.

—Artist Cards 4. 2003. (Adventures in Art Ser.). (Illus.). (gr. 4 up). pap. 22.95 (978-0-87192-372-1(6)) Davis Pubns., Inc.

Haab, Rachel. Fairies: Petal People You Make Yourself. 2001. (Illus.). 40p. (J). spiral bd. 16.95 (978-1-57054-649-5(5)) Klutz.

Paris Moderne: Art Deco Works from the Musee d'Art Moderne de la Ville de Paris. 2004. per. (978-0-9662859-4-9(8)) International Arts & Artists.

Pfouts, Chris. The Art of the Decal: Just Add Water. 2002. (Illus.). 112p. (gr. 10-13). pap. 19.95 (978-0-7643-1541-1(2)) Schiffer Publishing, Ltd.

Rhodes, Vicki. Pumpkin Decorating. 2002. (gr. 3-6). lib. bdg. 15.25 (978-0-613-75551-1(0)) Tandem Library Bks.

Sunderlage, Barb, ed. The Best of Holiday Wearables. 2002. 32p. pap. 11.99 (978-0-9652041-5-6(4) , Pack-O-Fun, Inc.) Clapper Publishing Co.

ART—DICTIONARIES

Greenway, Shirley. Art: An A-Z Guide. 2000. (Pictures & Words Ser.). (Illus.). 128p. (YA). (gr. 6-8). 34.00 (978-0-531-11729-3(4) , Watts, Franklin) Scholastic Library Publishing.

—Art: An A-Z of the Visual Arts—Styles, Methods & History. 2000. (Pictures & Words Ser.). (Illus.). 128p. (J). (gr. 2-6). lib. bdg. 32.50 (978-0-531-11771-2(5) , Watts, Franklin) Scholastic Library Publishing.

ART, ECCLESIASTICAL

see Christian Art and Symbolism

ART—EDUCATION

see Art—Study and Teaching

ART—FICTION

Aigner-Clark, Julie. Master Pieces. Zaidi, Nadeem, illus. 2003. (Baby Einstein Ser.). 10p. (ps-17). 9.99 (978-0-7868-1905-8(7)) Hyperion Bks. for Children.

Anholt, Laurence. Camille y los Girasoles: Un Cuento Sobre Vincent van Gogh. 2000. (Illus.). (J). (ps-3). (CAT.). 32p. 14.95 (978-84-95040-34-3(4)); (SPA., 28p. 14.95 (978-84-88061-35-5(8)) Serres, Ediciones, S. L. ESP. *Dist:* Lectorum Pubns., Inc.

—The Child's Gift of Art. 2002. (Illus.). 128p. (J). (gr. k-3). 16.95 (978-0-7641-7524-4(6)) Barron's Educational Series, Inc.

—Degas y la Pequena Bailarina: Un Cuento Sobre Edgar Degas. 2000. Tr. of Degas & the Little Dancer. (Illus.). (J). (ps-3). (CAT.). 32p. 14.95 (978-84-95040-86-2(7)); (SPA., 29p. 16.99 (978-84-88061-36-2(6)) Serres, Ediciones, S. L. ESP. *Dist:* Lectorum Pubns., Inc.

Avignone, June. A Peek into the Secret Little Ones of Turtle Back Island. My Wolf Dog, illus. 2004. 40p. (J). pap. (978-0-9654628-2-2(X)) Mill Street Forward, The.

Balliett, Blue. Chasing Vermeer. Helquist, Brett, illus. 2004. 272p. (J). (gr. 3-6). pap. 16.95 (978-0-439-37294-7(1)) Scholastic, Inc.

Bersson, Robert & Shoup, Dolores. Stripes & Stars. Bersson, Robert & Trobaugh, Scott, illus. l.t. ed. 2003. 40p. (J). (gr. 1-4). per. 16.95 (978-0-9740585-0-4(5)) Legacy Group Productions, LLC.

Boyce, Frank Cottrell, ed. Framed. 2006. 320p. (J). 16.99 (978-0-06-073402-2(7)); lib. bdg. 17.89 (978-0-06-073403-9(5)) HarperCollins Pubs.

Brezina, Thomas. Who Can Save Vincent's Hidden Treasure? Museum of Adventures. Sartin, Laurence, illus. 2005. 96p. (J). (gr. 4-7). pap. 16.95 (978-3-7913-3432-5(8)) Prestel Publishing.

Brownrigg. I'm an Artist. 2003. (J). 16.00 (978-0-689-80250-8(1) , Simon & Schuster Children's Publishing) Simon & Schuster Children's Publishing.

Burkett, Larry. Sarah & the Art Contest. 2000. (Great Smoky Mountain Storybook Ser.). (Illus.). 32p. (J). (ps-3). 7.99 (978-0-8024-0984-3(9)) Moody Pubs.

Camossa, Silvia. Elecciones Que Brillan. Mesquita, Camila, illus. 2004. 64p. pap. 8.95 (978-85-7416-193-8(4)) Callis Editora Ltda BRA. *Dist:* Independent Pubs. Group.

Culbertson, Jan E. The Legend of the Lost Tiki. 2006. 95p. (YA). pap. 13.95 (978-1-58909-315-7(1)) Bookstand Publishing.

de Paola, Tomie. The Art Lesson. de Paola, Tomie, illus. 2002. (Illus.). (J). 13.19 (978-0-7587-1969-0(8)) Book Wholesalers, Inc.

De Rolf, Shane. Crayon-Maker. 1998. (978-0-679-88453-8(X) , Random Hse. Bks. for Young Readers) Random Hse. Children's Bks.

DePaola, Tomie. Mr. Satie & the Great Art Contest. 2007. 32p. (J). (ps). pap. 5.99 (978-0-14-240771-4(2) , Puffin) Penguin Group (USA) Inc.

Disney Publishing Staff. An Arts & Crafts Day, 15 vols. 2003. (It's Fun to Learn Ser.). (Illus.). 32p. (J). (ps-3). 3.99 (978-1-57973-130-4(9)) Advance Pubs. LLC.

Doran-Smith, Eileen J. How the Youngest Angel Learned to Fly, No. 1. Smith, Douglas M., ed. 2000. (Illus.). 32p. (J). (ps-3). 14.99 (978-1-929489-50-3(1)) Platinum Medallion Children's Bks.

Doyle, Bill. Trapped! The 2031 Journal of Otis Fitzmorgan. Pamituan, Macky, illus. 2006. 141p. (J). lib. bdg. 18.46 ***978-1-4242-1738-0(5))** Fitzgerald Bks.

Dream Catchers - Evaluation Guide: Evaluation Guide. 2006. (J). (978-1-55942-403-5(6)) Marsh Media.

Dream Catchers - Teaching Guide. 2001. (J). 17.95 (978-1-55942-183-6(5)) Marsh Media.

Drew, James. Rackstraw: The Magical Thoughts & Adventures of A Brilliant Young Art Mouse. George, Mary G., ed. Drew, James, illus. 2000. (Illus.). 168p. (J). (gr. 2-9). 18.95 (978-0-9625023-9-2(1)) Artistry Pr. International.

Edwards, Pamela Duncan. The Neat Line: Scribbling Through Mother Goose. Bluthenthal, Diana Cain, illus. 2005. 32p. (J). lib. bdg. 17.89 (978-0-06-623971-2(0)); 15.99 (978-0-06-623970-5(2)) HarperCollins Pubs.

Ehlert, Lois. Hands: Growing up to be an Artist. 2004. (Illus.). 48p. (J). 14.95 (978-0-15-205107-5(4) , Harcourt Children's Bks) Harcourt Children's Bks.

Fox, Mem. The Straight Line Wonder. (978-1-57255-567-9(5)) Mondo Publishing.

Gallagher, Liz. The Opposite of Invisible. 2008. (YA). ***978-0-375-84152-1(0)); *978-0-375-94329-4(3))** Dell Publishing. (Delacorte Pr.).

Garmon, Larry Mike. The Calamari Code: an Agatha Pixie Mystery. 2007. 244p. pap. 15.49 ***978-0-615-15267-7(8))** Zu Bks.

Gatou, Shouji. Full Metal Panic! Film Book. 2003. (JPN & ENG., Illus.). 100p. pap. 19.98 (978-1-4139-0027-9(5)) A. D. Vision, Inc.

Gordon, Amy. Return to Gill Park. 2006. (Illus.). 240p. (J). (gr. 3-7). 16.95 (978-0-8234-1998-2(3)) Holiday Hse., Inc.

Griek, Susan Vande. The Art Room. Milelli, Pascal, illus. 2002. 24p. (J). (ps-2). 15.95 (978-0-88899-449-3(4)) Groundwood Bks. CAN. *Dist:* Perseus Distribution.

Gutierrez, Elisa. Picturescape. 2005. (Illus.). 32p. (J). (gr. k). 16.95 (978-1-894965-24-8(8)) Simply Read Bks. CAN. *Dist:* Perseus Distribution.

Harcourt School Publishers Staff. Collections: The Art Lesson: Grade Level Library. 1999. (Illus.). (J). pap. 4.70 (978-0-15-315205-4(2)) Harcourt Schl. Pubs.

—The Four Treasures Advanced Level. 3rd ed. 2002. (Trophies Reading Program Ser.). (Illus.). pap. 5.10 (978-0-15-323472-9(5)) Harcourt Schl. Pubs.

Hergé. Tintín: Descubro Los Numeros. 2004. (SPA., Illus.). 48p. 19.95 (978-1-59497-067-2(X)) Public Square Bks.

Hill, Sandi. Just Graph It!, Vol. 4468. Kupperstein, Joel, ed. Jarrett, Michael, photos by. 1998. (Learn to Read Math Ser.). (Illus.). 16p. (J). pap. 2.75 (978-1-57471-375-6(2) , 4468) Creative Teaching Pr., Inc.

Holwitz, Peter. Scribbleville. Holwitz, Peter, illus. 2005. (Illus.). 40p. (J). (ps-3). 15.99 (978-0-399-24303-5(8) , Philomel) Penguin Group (USA) Inc.

Hooper, Meredith & Curless, Allan. Dogs' Night. Burgess, Mark, illus. 2006. 36p. pap. 7.95 (978-1-84507-688-7(5)) Lincoln, Frances Ltd. GBR. *Dist:* Perseus Distribution.

Hutchins, Hazel J. Robyn's Art Attack. Cathcart, Yvonne, illus. 2002. 64p. (gr. 1-5). (First Novel Ser.). (J). ***(978-0-88780-565-3(5));*** (First Novels Ser.: Vol. 23). 4.95 (978-0-88780-564-6(7)) Formac Publishing Co., Ltd. CAN. *Dist:* Casemate Pubs. & Bk. Distributors, LLC.

Jacobson, Rick. The Mona Lisa Caper. Jacobson, Rick & Fernandez, Laura, illus. 2005. 24p. (J). (gr. k-2). 15.95 (978-0-88776-726-5(5)) Tundra Bks., Inc./Livres Toundra, Inc. CAN. *Dist:* Random Hse., Inc.

Karr, Kathleen. The Seventh Knot. 2003. (Illus.). 192p. (J). 15.95 (978-0-7614-5135-8(8)) Cavendish, Marshall Corp.

Kerr, Kathleen. 7th Knot. 2007. 192p. (J). pap. 5.99 ***(978-0-7614-5368-0(7))*** Cavendish, Marshall Corp.

Kidd, Richard. Almost Famous Daisy: Around the World in Famous Paintings. Kidd, Richard, illus. 2000. (Illus.). 32p. (J). (gr. k-4). pap. 9.99 (978-0-7112-1070-7(5)) Lincoln, Frances Ltd. GBR. *Dist:* Transition Vendor.

—Daisy Quiere Ser Famosa. 2002. Tr. of Almost Famous Daisy!. (Illus.). (J). (gr. k-3). (SPA.). 200p. 14.95 (978-84-8488-008-0(7)); (CAT., 32p. 14.95 (978-84-8488-012-7(5)) Serres, Ediciones, S. L. ESP. *Dist:* Lectorum Pubns., Inc.

Klutz Editors. Button Rings. 2007. 30p. (J). pap. 5.95 ***(978-1-59174-477-1(6))*** Klutz.

Knight, Jean MacPhail. Charlotte en Giverny. Sweet, Melissa, illus. 2002. Tr. of Charlotte in Giverny. 64p. (J). (SPA.). 14.95 (978-84-8488-006-6(0)); (CAT.). 14.95 (978-84-8488-015-8(X)) Serres, Ediciones, S. L. ESP. *Dist:* Lectorum Pubns., Inc.

Leavitt, Martine. Heck, Superhero! 2004. 144p. (YA). 16.95 (978-1-886910-94-2(4) , Lemniscaat) Boyds Mills Pr.

Light, John. Dotty. 2005. (Illus.). 28p. (978-1-897968-26-0(4)) Photon Pr.

Lincoln, Kelly J. Making a Grass Basket. Nevak, Caroline, illus. l.t. ed. 1999. 16p. (J). (gr. k-3). pap. 21.00 (978-1-58084-062-0(0)) Lower Kuskokwim Schl. District.

—Mingqiller Tapernarneg. Nevak, Caroline, illus. l.t. ed. 1999. Tr. of Making a Grass Basket. (ESK.). 16p. (J). (gr. k-3). pap. 21.00 (978-1-58084-063-7(9)); pap. 21.00 (978-1-58084-110-8(4)) Lower Kuskokwim Schl. District.

Lowenstein, Sallie Claire. Waiting for Eugene. 2006. (Illus.). 201p. (J). ***(978-1-4156-6166-6(9))*** Book Wholesalers, Inc.

Mayer, Mercer. Little Christmas Tree. 2003. (gr. k-3). lib. bdg. 11.80 (978-0-613-84261-7(8)) Tandem Library Bks.

Mayhew, James. Carlota Descubre a los Impresionistas. 38p. (J). 2002. (CAT.). (ps-3). 14.95 (978-84-95040-27-5(1)); 3rd ed. 2000. (SPA., Illus.). (gr. 2-4). 14.95 (978-84-88061-80-5(3) , RR7203) Serres, Ediciones, S. L. ESP. *Dist:* Lectorum Pubns., Inc.

—Carlota y Monna Lisa. 2000. 38p. (J). (ps-3). (CAT.). 14.95 (978-84-95040-99-2(9)); (SPA., Illus.). 14.95 (978-84-95040-00-8(X) , RR5709) Serres, Ediciones, S. L. ESP. *Dist:* Lectorum Pubns., Inc.

—El Museo de Carlota. 38p. (J). (ps-3). 2001. (CAT.). pap. 14.95 (978-84-95040-59-6(X)); 2000. (SPA., Illus.). 14.95 (978-84-88061-57-7(9)) Serres, Ediciones, S. L. ESP. *Dist:* Lectorum Pubns., Inc.

McOmber, Rachel B., ed. String Art Vol. 1: For All Seasons. rev. ed. (Illus.). (J). (978-0-944991-95-4(5)) Swift Learning Resources.

—String Art Vol. 2: For All Seasons. rev. ed. (Illus.). (J). (978-0-944991-96-1(3)) Swift Learning Resources.

Mitchell, Rhonda. The Talking Cloth. 2001. (Illus.). 32p. (J). (ps-2). pap. 6.95 (978-0-531-07182-3(0) , Orchard Bks.) Scholastic, Inc.

Mona, Larkins. Pablo's Art Adventures: Exploring the Studio. Mona, Larkins, illus. 2004. (Illus.). 27p. (J). 14.99 (978-0-9740841-3-8(1)) K&B Products.

Neff, Henry H. The Hound of Rowan. 2007. (Tapestry Ser.: Bk. 1). (Illus.). 414p. (J). (gr. 3-7). 17.99 (978-0-375-83894-1(5) , Random Hse. Bks. for Young Readers) Random Hse. Children's Bks.

—The Hound of Rowan. Neff, Henry H., illus. 2007. (Tapestry Ser.: Bk. 1). (Illus.). 414p. (J). (gr. 3-7). lib. bdg. 20.99 (978-0-375-93894-8(X) , Random Hse. Bks. for Young Readers) Random Hse. Children's Bks.

—The Hound of Rowan. 2007. (J). pap. (978-0-375-83895-8(3)) Random Hse., Inc.

Nesbit, E. The Incomplete Amorist. 2006. 65.99 ***(978-1-4280-2983-5(4))*** IndyPublish.com.

O'Connor, Jane. Fancy Nancy at the Museum. Glasser, Robin Preiss & Enik, Ted, illus. 2008. (I Can Read Bks.). 32p. (J). 16.99 ***(978-0-06-123608-2(X))*** HarperCollins Pubs.

—Fancy Nancy at the Museum. Glasser, Robin Preiss, illus. 2008. (I Can Read Bks.). 32p. (J). pap. 3.99 ***(978-0-06-123607-5(1)*** , Harper Trophy) HarperCollins Pubs.

Parish, Herman. Amelia Bedelia's Masterpiece. Sweat, Lynn, illus. 2007. 64p. (J). 15.99 (978-0-06-084355-7(1)); lib. bdg. 16.89 (978-0-06-084356-4(X)) HarperCollins Pubs.

Paterson, Brian. Zigby & the Ant Invaders. (Illus.). 32p. (J). (ps). 2004. 17.99 (978-0-00-713166-2(6)); 2003. pap. 8.99 (978-0-00-713182-2(8)) HarperCollins Pubs. Ltd. GBR. (HarperCollins Children's Bks.). *Dist:* Independent Pubs. Group.

Paulsen, Gary. The Glass Cafe: Or the Stripper & the State; How My Mother Started a War with the System That Made Us Kind of Rich & a Little Bit Famous. 2004. 112p. (J). (gr. 5). pap. 5.99 (978-0-440-23843-0(9) , Laurel Leaf) Random Hse. Children's Bks.

Pedrow, Debra A. Aunt Debra & My Favorite Things Poster. Karper, Deborah, ed. Reynolds, Sarah, illus. 2003. 40p. (J). 15.95 (978-1-928681-09-0(3)) Gladstone Publishing.

Pozzi, Gianni. Chagall: Un Siglo de Pintura. 2000. (Maestros del Arte Ser.). (SPA., Illus.). 72p. (J). (gr. 4-7). 22.95 (978-84-88061-75-1(7)) Serres, Ediciones, S. L. ESP. *Dist:* Lectorum Pubns., Inc.

Rabley, Stephen. Marcel & the Mona Lisa. 2002. (Illus.). 16p. pap. (978-0-582-40173-0(9) , Putnam Juvenile) Penguin Group (USA) Inc.

Reynolds, Peter H. The Dot. 2003. (Illus.). 32p. (J). (gr. k). 14.00 (978-0-7636-1961-9(2) , 53509533) Candlewick Pr.

—El Punto. 2004. (SPA., Illus.). 48p. (J). 16.99 (978-84-8488-110-0(5)) Serres, Ediciones, S. L. ESP. *Dist:* Lectorum Pubns., Inc.

Robishaw, Sue. Rosita & Sian Search for a Great Work of Art. Schmeck, Steve, illus. 1999. 160p. (gr. 3-12). 16.98 (978-0-9652036-3-0(8)) ManyTracks Publishing.

Roy, Ron. The Orange Outlaw. Gurney, John Steven, illus. 2001. (A to Z Mysteries Ser.: No. 15). 96p. (J). (gr. 2-5). lib. bdg. 11.99 (978-0-375-90270-3(8) , Random Hse. Bks. for Young Readers) Random Hse. Children's Bks.

Roy, Ron & Gurney, John Steven. The Orange Outlaw. 2001. (A to Z Mysteries Ser.: No.15). (Illus.). 96p. (J). (gr. 2-5). mass mkt. 3.99 (978-0-375-80270-6(3) , Random Hse. Bks. for Young Readers) Random Hse. Children's Bks.

Rylant, Cynthia. The Van Gogh Cafe. 1998. (Apple Signature Edition Ser.). 64p. (J). (gr. 3-7). mass mkt. 4.99 (978-0-590-90717-0(4)) Scholastic, Inc.

Say, Allen. Emma's Rug. Say, Allen, illus. 2002. (Illus.). (J). 24.30 (978-0-7587-2457-1(8)) Book Wholesalers, Inc.

—Emma's Rug. 2003. (Illus.). 32p. (J). pap. 6.95 (978-0-618-33523-7(4) , Walter Lorraine) Houghton Mifflin Co. Trade & Reference Div.

Scieszka, Jon. Seen Art? Smith, Lane, illus. 2005. 48p. (J). (gr. 1). 16.99 (978-0-670-05986-7(2) , Viking Juvenile) Penguin Group (USA) Inc.

Seltzer, Eric. Doodle Dog. Seltzer, Eric, illus. 2005. (Ready-to-Reads Ser.). (Illus.). 32p. (J). pap. 3.99 (978-0-689-85910-6(4) , Aladdin) Simon & Schuster Children's Publishing.

—Doodle Dog. 2005. (Ready-to-Reads Ser.). (Illus.). 32p. (J). lib. bdg. 11.89 (978-0-689-85913-7(9) , Aladdin Library) Simon & Schuster Children's Publishing.

—Doodle Dog in Space. Seltzer, Eric, illus. 2005. (Ready-to-Reads Ser.). (Illus.). 32p. (J). (ps-3). pap. 3.99 (978-0-689-85912-0(0) , Aladdin) Simon & Schuster Children's Publishing.

Solotareff, Gregoire. Pequeno Museo. 2003. (SPA.). 275p. (978-84-95150-78-3(6)) Corimbo, Editorial S.L.

Spinelli, Eileen. La Obra de Sofia. Dyer, Jane, illus. 32p. (J). 2004. (SPA.). 16.99 (978-84-8488-052-3(4)); 2002. (CAT.). 14.95 (978-84-8488-053-0(2)) Serres, Ediciones, S. L. ESP. *Dist:* Lectorum Pubns., Inc.

Stallings, Jimmy. How to Draw Fala. Pinto, Israel, illus. 1998. 12p. (J). pap. 5.95 (978-1-879295-26-1(1)) Prince, L.B. Co., Inc.

Stilton, Geronimo. The Mona Mousa Code. Wolf, Matt, illus. 2005. (Geronimo Stilton Ser.: No. 15). 113p. (J). lib. bdg. 10.00 ***(978-1-4242-0284-3(1))*** Fitzgerald Bks.

—The Mona Mousa Code. Wolf, Matt, illus. 2005. (Geronimo Stilton Ser.: No. 15). 113p. (J). (ps-k). lib. bdg. 13.54 (978-0-606-33278-1(2)) Tandem Library Bks.

Stone, Sadie. Jamal Martin & All That Jazz. Southivorarat, Sombat, illus. 2005. 71p. pap. 14.95 (978-1-4137-4768-3(X)) PublishAmerica, Inc.

Strom, Maria Diaz. Rainbow Joe & Me. ed. 2004. (J). (gr. k-3). spiral bd. (978-0-616-03097-4(5)) Canadian National Institute for the Blind/Institut National Canadien pour les Aveugles.

—Rainbow Joe & Me. Strom, Maria Diaz, illus. (Illus.). 32p. (J). 2002. 6.95 (978-1-58430-050-2(7)); 1999. 15.95 (978-1-880000-93-9(8)) Lee & Low Bks., Inc.

Sturgis, Alexander. Dan's Angel: A Detective's Guide to the Language of Painting. Child, Lauren, illus. 2004. 40p. (J). 16.95 (978-1-929132-47-8(6)) Kane/Miller Bk. Pubs., Inc.

Suen, Anastasia. Scissors, Paper, & Sharing. Ebbeler, Jeffrey, illus. 2007. (Main Street School - Kids with Character Ser.). 32p. (J). (ps-4). lib. bdg. 27.07 ***(978-1-60270-032-1(X)*** , Looking Glass Library) Magic Wagon.

Thompson, Lisa. Artrageous! Thompson, Lisa & Stapleton, Matthew, illus. 2005. (Read-It! Chapter Bks.). 48p. (J). (ps-k). lib. bdg. 19.95 (978-1-4048-1348-9(9)) Picture Window Bks.

Tusa, Tricia. Bunnies in My Head, 1. Tusa, Tricia et al, illus. 1998. (Illus.). (J). (gr. k-5). 20.00 (978-0-9664551-8-2(5)) Univ. of Texas, M.D. Anderson Cancer Ctr.

Van Draanen, Wendelin. Sammy Keyes & the Art of Deception. 2003. (Sammy Keyes Ser.: Bk. 8). 288p. (gr. 5). 15.95 (978-0-375-81176-0(1)); lib. bdg. 17.99 (978-0-375-91176-7(6)) Random Hse. Children's Bks. (Knopf Bks. for Young Readers).

Wallace, Nancy Elizabeth & Friedlaender, Linda. Look! Look! Look! Wallace, Nancy Elizabeth & Friedlaender, Linda, illus. 2006. (Illus.). 40p. (J). 16.95 (978-0-7614-5282-9(6)) Cavendish, Marshall Corp.

Watt, Mélanie. Augustine. 2006. (Illus.). 32p. (J). (978-1-55337-885-3(7)) Kids Can Pr., Ltd.

Webb, Mack Henry, Jr. Little Bianca. Tuck, Beverly, illus. 2006. 52p. (J). per. 15.95 (978-0-9779576-0-6(8)) Pilinut Pr., Inc.

Weitzman, Jacqueline Preiss. Mi Globo Paseando por Nueva York: Yo en el Metropolitan Museum. Glasser, Robin Preiss, illus. 2000. (SPA.). 32p. (J). (gr. k-2). 17.95 (978-84-95040-49-7(2) , RR1515) Serres, Ediciones, S. L. ESP. *Dist:* Lectorum Pubns., Inc.

ART—FORGERIES

see Forgery of Works of Art

ART—GALLERIES AND MUSEUMS

see Art Galleries, Commercial; Art Museums

ART, GRAPHIC

see Graphic Arts

ART, GREEK

Apel, Melanie Ann. Art & Religion in Ancient Greece. 2004. (Primary Sources of Ancient Civilizations Ser.). (Illus.). 24p. (J). lib. bdg. 19.95 (978-0-8239-6770-4(0) , PowerKids Pr.) Rosen Publishing Group, Inc., The.

Bingham, Jane. Classical Myth: A Treasury of Greek & Roman Legends, Art, & History. 2007. (World of Mythology Ser.). (Illus.). 96p. (YA). (gr. 6 up). 35.95 ***(978-0-7656-8104-1(8))*** Sharpe, M.E. Inc.

Blanco Freijeiro, Antonio. Arte Griego. (SPA.). 96p. (J). (978-84-207-3730-0(5)) Grupo Anaya, S.A.

Conley, Kate A. Greek Arts & Sciences. 2005. (Life in Ancient Days: Greece Ser.). (J). (978-1-59197-866-4(1)) ABDO Publishing Co.

Harcourt School Publishers Staff. The Elgin Marbles. 3rd ed. 2002. (Horizons Ser.). (Illus.). (J). pap. 7.30 (978-0-15-333622-5(6)) Harcourt Schl. Pubs.

Hodge, Susie. Ancient Greek Art. 32p. 2006. (Illus.). (J). ***(978-1-4034-8766-7(9));*** 2003. pap. 6.95 (978-1-4034-4017-4(4)) Heinemann Library.

Knapp, Ruthie & Lehmberg, Janice. Greek & Roman Art: Off the Wall Museum Guides for Kids. 2001. (Off the Wall Museum Guides for Kids). (ENG., Illus.). 72p. (J). (gr. 2-5). pap. 8.95 (978-0-87192-549-7(4)) Davis Pubns., Inc.

Morison, Bill & Morison, Melissa. The Odyssey. Conkle, Nancy, illus. 1998. 48p. (YA). (gr. 3 up). pap. 4.95 (978-0-88388-207-8(8)) Bellerophon Bks.

Nardo, Don. Leisure Life of the Ancient Greeks. 2004. (Lucent Library of Historical Eras). (Illus.). 112p. (J). (gr. 7-10). 32.45 (978-1-59018-528-5(5) , Lucent Bks.) Thomson Gale.

—The Parthenon of Ancient Greece. 1998. (Building History Ser.). (Illus.). 96p. (YA). (gr. 6-9). 27.45 (978-1-56006-431-2(5) , Lucent Bks.) Thomson Gale.

Susie Hodge. Ancient Greek Art. 2nd ed. 2006. (Illus.). 32p. (J). pap. ***(978-1-4034-8774-2(X))*** Heinemann Library.

ART—HISTORY

Avp, prod. Impressionism to the Twentieth Century. (YA). cd-rom 149.95 (978-0-7365-0614-4(4)) Films Media Group.

Barbe-Gall, Francoise. How to Talk to Children about Art. 2005. (Illus.). 208p. (J). pap. 16.95 (978-1-55652-580-3(X)) Chicago Review Pr., Inc.

Blauer, Ettagale, et al. Art in History: The Origins of Art, 3 bks., Set 2. 2001. (Illus.). 32p. (J). (gr. 5-7). lib. bdg. 72.66 (978-1-58810-020-7(0)) Heinemann Library.

Bolton, Linda. Surrealists. 2002. (Artists in Profile Ser.). (Illus.). 64p. (J). lib. bdg. 28.50 (978-1-58810-648-3(9)) Heinemann Library.

Burton, Margie, et al. Art Around the World. Adams, Alison, ed. 1999. (Early Connections Ser.). 16p. (J). (gr. k-2). pap. 4.50 (978-1-58344-054-4(2)) Benchmark Education Co.

Carnibucci, Patricia. The Arts & Art History: Over 15 Complete Printable Unit Studies with Interactive Links. 2002. 160p. (gr. k-12). cd-rom 15.95 (978-1-891400-82-7(7)) Champion Pr., Ltd.

Carroll, Colleen. How Artists See Heroes: Myth History War Everyday. 2003. (How Artists See Ser.). (Illus.). 48p. (gr. 3-6). 12.95 (978-0-7892-0773-9(7)) Abbeville Pr., Inc.

Carter, David A. One Red Dot: A Pop-up Book for Children of All Ages. Carter, David A., illus. ltd. ed. 2006. 18p. (J). 250.00 (978-1-4169-0979-8(6) , Little Simon) Simon & Schuster Children's Publishing.

Chapman. Vocabulary Cards. 2003. No. 1. (gr. 1 up). 22.95 (978-0-87192-349-3(1)); No. 2. (gr. 2 up). 22.95 (978-0-87192-350-9(5)); No. 3. (gr. 3 up). 22.95 (978-0-87192-351-6(3)); No. 4. (gr. 4 up). 22.95 (978-0-87192-352-3(1)); No. 5. (gr. 5 up). 22.95 (978-0-87192-353-0(X)); No. 6. (gr. 6 up). 22.95 (978-0-87192-354-7(8)) Davis Pubns., Inc.

Copmbined, Slide. Discovering Art History. (978-0-87192-311-0(4)) Davis Pubns., Inc.

Corrain, Lucia. La Europa del Renacimiento: Un Itinerio Artistico. 2000. (Maestros del Arte Ser.). (SPA., Illus.). 72p. (J). (gr. 4-7). 22.95 (978-84-88061-74-4(9)) Serres, Ediciones, S. L. ESP. *Dist:* Lectorum Pubns., Inc.

—Giotto y el Arte de la Edad Media: Los Talleres, las Tecnicas, los Lugares y las Historias. 2000. (Maestros del Arte Ser.). (SPA., Illus.). 72p. (J). (gr. 4-7). 22.95 (978-84-88061-53-9(6)) Serres, Ediciones, S. L. ESP. *Dist:* Lectorum Pubns., Inc.

Court, Rob. Art of Native America. 2003. (Scribbles Institute). 32p. (J). (gr. 1-5). 21.36 (978-1-56766-589-5(6)) Child's World, Inc.

—Art of the Incas. 2003. (Scribbles Institute). 32p. (J). (gr. 1-5). 21.36 (978-1-56766-557-4(8)) Child's World, Inc.

—Art of the Maya. 2003. (Scribbles Institute). 32p. (J). (gr. 1-5). 21.36 (978-1-56766-566-6(7)) Child's World, Inc.

Dickins, Rosie. Art Treasury. 2007. 96p. (J). 19.99 (978-0-7945-1452-5(9) , Usborne) EDC Publishing.

—Introduction to Art - Internet Linked. Chisholm, Jane, ed. 2004. (Introduction to Art Ser.). 144p. (J). 19.95 (978-0-7945-0661-2(5) , Usborne) EDC Publishing.

Dickins, Rosie, et al. The Usborne Introduction to Art: In Association with the National Gallery, London. 2005. (Illus.). 144p. (J). (978-0-439-79202-8(9)) Scholastic, Inc.

Flux, Paul. Wassily Kandinsky. 2002. (Life & Work of. . . Ser.). (Illus.). 32p. (J). (gr. k-2). lib. bdg. 22.79 (978-1-58810-607-0(1)) Heinemann Library.

Gaff, Jackie & Oliver, Clare. 1900-1910: New Ways of Seeing. 2001. (Twentieth Century Art Ser.). (Illus.). 32p. (J). (gr. 5 up). lib. bdg. 26.00 (978-0-8368-2848-1(8)) Stevens, Gareth Inc.

—1910-1920: Birth of Abstract Art. 2001. (Twentieth Century Art Ser.). (Illus.). 32p. (J). (gr. 5 up). lib. bdg. 26.00 (978-0-8368-2849-8(6)) Stevens, Gareth Inc.

—1920-1940: Realism & Surrealism. 2001. (Twentieth Century Art Ser.). (Illus.). 32p. (J). (gr. 5 up). lib. bdg. 26.00 (978-0-8368-2850-4(X)) Stevens, Gareth Inc.

—1940-1960: Emotion & Expression. 2001. (Twentieth Century Art Ser.). (Illus.). 32p. (J). (gr. 5 up). lib. bdg. 26.00 (978-0-8368-2851-1(8)) Stevens, Gareth Inc.

—1960-1980: Experiments & New Directions. 2001. (Twentieth Century Art Ser.). (Illus.). 32p. (J). (gr. 5 up). lib. bdg. 26.00 (978-0-8368-2852-8(6)) Stevens, Gareth Inc.

—1980-2000: New Media, New Messages. 2001. (Twentieth Century Art Ser.). (Illus.). 32p. (J). (gr. 5 up). lib. bdg. 26.00 (978-0-8368-2853-5(4)) Stevens, Gareth Inc.

Greenway, Shirley. Art: An A-Z Guide. 2001. (Watts Reference Ser.). (Illus.). 128p. (YA). (gr. 6-8). pap. 19.95 (978-0-531-16553-9(1) , Watts, Franklin) Scholastic Library Publishing.

—Art: An A-Z Guide. 2001. (Illus.). 128p. (J). (gr. 6-8). lib. bdg. 30.35 (978-0-613-72729-7(0)) Tandem Library Bks.

Harcourt School Publishers Staff. The First Artists: Take-Home Book. 2001. (Collections Ser.). (Illus.). (J). pap. 1.90 (978-0-15-319553-2(3)) Harcourt Schl. Pubs.

Hollingsworth, Patricia L., ed. & illus. SAILS Interdisciplinary Curriculum Kit. Hollingsworth, Patricia L., illus. 2000. (Students' Active Interdisciplinary Learning Ser.). (YA). (gr. 1-12). pap. 20.00 (978-1-893413-10-8(1)) Univ. Schl. at the Univ. of Tulsa.

Hollingsworth, Patricia L., et al. Baroque & Rococo. 1998. (Sails - Students' Active Interdisciplinary Learning Ser.: Vol. 4). (Illus.). (YA). (gr. 3-12). pap. 20.00 (978-1-893413-03-0(9)) Univ. Schl. at the Univ. of Tulsa.

—Neoclassicism. 1998. (Sails - Students' Active Interdisciplinary Learning Ser.: Vol. 5). (Illus.). (YA). (gr. 3-12). pap. 20.00 (978-1-893413-04-7(7)) Univ. Schl. at the Univ. of Tulsa.

—The Renaissance. 1998. (Sails - Students' Active Interdisciplinary Learning Ser.: Vol. 3). (Illus.). (YA). (gr. 3-12). pap. 20.00 (978-1-893413-02-3(0)) Univ. Schl. at the Univ. of Tulsa.

—Romanticism. 1998. (Sails - Students' Active Interdisciplinary Learning Ser.: Vol. 6). (Illus.). (YA). (gr. 3-12). pap. 20.00 (978-1-893413-05-4(5)) Univ. Schl. at the Univ. of Tulsa.

Holme, Marilyn & McKinzie, Bridget. Expressionists. 2002. (Artists in Profile Ser.). (Illus.). 64p. (J). lib. bdg. 28.50 (978-1-58810-647-6(0)) Heinemann Library.

Klimt, Gustav. Klimt Art Tattoos. 2003. (Illus.). 2p. pap. 1.50 (978-0-486-42659-4(9)) Dover Pubns., Inc.

Knapp, Ruthie & Lehmberg, Janice. Greek & Roman Art: Off the Wall Museum Guides for Kids. 2001. (Off the Wall Museum Guides for Kids). (ENG., Illus.). 72p. (J). (gr. 2-5). pap. 8.95 (978-0-87192-549-7(4)) Davis Pubns., Inc.

Kunstgeschichte I: Von den Anfaengen bis zum 18. Jahrhundert. 2nd ed. (Duden Abiturhilfen Ser.). (GER.). 112p. (YA). (gr. 12-13). (978-3-411-04142-8(0)) Bibliographisches Institut & F. A. Brockhaus AG DEU. *Dist:* International Bk. Import Service, Inc.

Kunstgeschichte II: 19. und 20. Jahrhundert. 2nd ed. (Duden Abiturhilfen Ser.). (GER.). 112p. (YA). (gr. 12-13). (978-3-411-04192-3(7)) Bibliographisches Institut & F. A. Brockhaus AG DEU. *Dist:* International Bk. Import Service, Inc.

Loria, Stefano. Picasso: El Genio de la Pintura del Siglo XX. 2000. (Maestros del Arte Ser.). (SPA., Illus.). 64p. (J). (gr. 4-7). 22.95 (978-84-88061-91-1(9)) Serres, Ediciones, S. L. ESP. *Dist:* Lectorum Pubns., Inc.

Mines, Cynthia J. Cubism. 2006. (Eye on Art Ser.). 112p. (J). (gr. 7-10). 32.45 (978-1-59018-961-0(2) , Lucent Bks.) Thomson Gale.

Nilsen, Anna. Art Fraud Detective: Spot the Difference, Solve the Crime! Parker, Andy, illus. 2000. 48p. (J). (gr. 3-5). tchr. ed. 17.95 (978-0-7534-5308-7(8) , Kingfisher) Houghton Mifflin Co. Trade & Reference Div.

Olmstead, Jennifer. Art of the Middle Ages. 2001. (Art in History Ser.). (Illus.). 32p. (J). (gr. 5-7). pap. 6.95 (978-1-4034-4019-8(0)) Heinemann Library.

Palermo, Blinky. Blinky Palermo: To the People of New York City. Cooke, Lynne & Kelly, Karen, eds. 2005. (Illus.). 112p. (YA). (gr. 13 up). 45.00 (978-0-944521-48-9(7)) Dia Ctr. for the Arts.

Papunya School Staff & Wheatley, Nadia. Papunya School Book of Country & History. Searle, Ken, illus. 2001. 48p. pap. 7.95 (978-1-86508-525-8(1)) Allen & Unwin AUS. *Dist:* Independent Pubs. Group.

Parker, G. Art of Counting. 2004. (Children's Art Ser. from the National Gallery of Victoria Ser.). (Illus.). 24p. 9.95 (978-0-7241-0234-1(5)) National Gallery of Victoria AUS. *Dist:* Antique Collectors' Club.

Parry, Charles H. H. The Evolution of the Art & Music. 2001. 342p. (YA). reprint ed. 98.00 (978-0-7222-5043-3(6)) Library Reprints, Inc.

Pescio, Claudio. Rembrandt y la Pintura Holandesa del Siglo XVII. 2000. (Maestros del Arte Ser.). (SPA., Illus.). 72p. (J). 22.95 (978-84-88061-54-6(4)) Serres, Ediciones, S. L. ESP. *Dist:* Lectorum Pubns., Inc.

Phaidon Press Editors. The Art Book for Children. 2006. 19.95 (*978-0-7148-9863-6(5)) Phaidon Pr., Inc.

Press, Petra. Native American Art. (Art in History Ser.). 32p. 2003. pap. 6.95 (978-1-4034-4020-4(4)); 2001. (Illus.). (J). (gr. 4-6). lib. bdg. 24.22 (978-1-58810-092-4(8)) Heinemann Library.

Ramirez, Juan Antonio. Arte Prehistorico y Primitivo. (SPA.). 96p. (YA). (978-84-207-3190-2(0)) Grupo Anaya, S.A.

Romei, Francesca. La Escultura Desde la Antiguedad Hasta Hoy: Las Epocas, las Tecnicas, los Artistas. 2000. (Maestros del Arte Ser.). (SPA., Illus.). 64p. (J). (gr. 4-7). 22.95 (978-84-88061-92-8(7)) Serres, Ediciones, S. L. ESP. *Dist:* Lectorum Pubns., Inc.

Ruggi, Gilda Williams. The Art Book for Children. rev. ed. 2005. (Illus.). 80p. (gr. 4-7). 19.95 (978-0-7148-4530-2(2)) Phaidon Pr. GBR. *Dist:* Hachette Bk. Group.

Sabbeth, Carol. Monet & the Impressionists for Kids: Their Lives & Ideas, 21 Activities. 2002. (For Kids Ser.). (Illus.). 152p. (J). (gr. 4 up). pap. 17.95 (978-1-55652-397-7(1)) Chicago Review Pr., Inc.

—Monet & the Impressionists for Kids: Their Lives & Ideas, 21 Activities. 2002. (gr. 3-6). lib. bdg. 28.00 (978-0-613-64194-4(9)) Tandem Library Bks.

Salvi, Francesco. Los Impresionistas: En los Origenes de la Pintura Contemporaneo. 2000. (Maestros del Arte Ser.).Tr. of Impressionists. (SPA., Illus.). 72p. (J). (gr. 4-7). 22.95 (978-84-88061-56-0(0)) Serres, Ediciones, S. L. ESP. *Dist:* Lectorum Pubns., Inc.

The Sharpe Library of the Arts: Understanding Art; Music in the Twentieth Century; Lives & Works in the Arts, 14 vols., Set. 1999. 2302p. (YA). 775.00 (978-0-7656-8037-2(8)) Sharpe, M.E. Inc.

Shuter, Jane. Ancient Chinese Art. (Art in History Ser.). 32p. 2003. pap. 6.95 (978-1-4034-4015-0(8)); 2001. (Illus.). (J). (gr. 4-6). lib. bdg. 24.22 (978-1-58810-090-0(1)) Heinemann Library.

Slides. African Arts & Cultures. 4th ed. 2007. (Illus.). xix, 638p. (J). (*978-0-87192-719-4(5)) Davis Pubns., Inc.

Uecker, Jeffry. History Through Art Timeline. 2001. 196p. 69.95 (978-0-87192-480-3(3)) Davis Pubns., Inc.

Vadeboncoeur, Jim, Jr., prod. Black & White Images: 2004. 2004. (Illus.). 112p. per. 20.00 (978-0-9724697-1-5(0)) Vadeboncoeur, Jim.

Wallis, Jeremy. Cubists. 2002. (Artists in Profile Ser.). (Illus.). 64p. (J). (gr. 6-8). lib. bdg. 28.50 (978-1-58810-645-2(4)) Heinemann Library.

Wenzel, Angela. The Mad, Mad, Mad World of Salvador Dali. 2003. (Adventures in Art Ser.). (Illus.). 30p. 14.95 (978-3-7913-2944-4(8)) Prestel Publishing.

Zohorsky, Janet R. Colonial Craftsman. 2004. (Working Life Ser.). (Illus.). 112p. (J). (gr. 7-10). 29.95 (978-1-59018-176-8(X) , Lucent Bks.) Thomson Gale.

ART, INDIAN

see Indians of North America—Art

ART, ISLAMIC

Barber, Nicola. Islamic Empires. 2005. (History in Art Ser.). (Illus.). 48p. (J). (ps-7). per. 29.93 (978-1-4109-0522-2(5)) Steck-Vaughn.

Barkow, Henriette. Journey Through Islamic Art. Lamont, Priscilla, illus. 2004. (J). (ALB, ENG & ITA.). 31p. (978-1-84444-571-4(2)); (ARA, ENG & JPN.). (978-1-84444-572-1(0)); (BEN, ENG & MAL.). (978-1-84444-573-8(9)); (CHI, ENG & KUR.). (978-1-84444-574-5(7)); (CHI, ENG & PAN.). (978-1-84444-575-2(5)); (CRO, ENG & POL.). 31p. (978-1-84444-576-9(3)); (ENG, PER & POR.). 31p. (978-1-84444-577-6(1)); (ENG, GUJ & RUS.). (978-1-84444-579-0(8)); (ENG, HIN & TAG.). 31p. (978-1-84444-580-6(1)); (ENG, KUR & TUR.). 31p. (978-1-84444-582-0(8)); (ENG, POL & VIE.). (978-1-84444-584-4(4)) Mantra Publishing, Ltd.

Barkow, Henriette & Lamont, Priscilla. Journey Through Islamic Art. 2004. (ENG, POR & SOM., Illus.). 31p. (J). (978-1-84444-585-1(2)); (978-1-84444-586-8(0)) Mantra Publishing, Ltd.

Davis, Lucile. The Ottoman Empire. 2004. (Life During the Great Civilizations Ser.). (Illus.). 48p. (J). (gr. 3-5). 24.95 (978-1-56711-739-4(2) , Blackbirch Pr., Inc.) Thomson Gale.

Journey Through Islamic Art. 2004. (ENG & PER.). (J). (978-1-84444-669-8(7)); (978-1-84444-578-3(X)); (978-1-84444-581-3(X)); (978-1-84444-583-7(6)); (978-1-84444-587-5(9)); (978-1-84444-588-2(7)); (978-1-84444-589-9(5)); (978-1-84444-590-5(9)); (978-1-84444-591-2(7)); (978-1-84444-592-9(5)); (978-1-84444-593-6(3)) Mantra Publishing, Ltd.

Levy, Janey. Islamic Art: Recognizing Geometric Ideas in Art. 2006. (Math for the Real World Ser.). (Illus.). 32p. (J). pap. (978-1-4042-6081-8(1)); lib. bdg. (978-1-4042-3364-5(4)) Rosen Publishing Group, Inc., The.

Smith, A. G. Arabic Patterns Stained Glass Coloring Book. 2006. 16p. (J). pap. 5.95 (978-0-486-44839-8(8)) Dover Pubns., Inc.

Toor, Atif. Islamic Culture. 2006. (Discovering the Arts Ser.). (Illus.). 48p. (gr. 4-8). 20.95 (978-1-59515-521-4(X)) Rourke Publishing, LLC.

ART, JAPANESE

Finley, Carol. Art of Japan: Wood-Block Color Prints. 1998. (Art Around the World Ser.). (Illus.). 56-64p. (gr. 4-8). 23.93 (978-0-8225-2077-1(X)) Lerner Publishing Group.

Khanduri, Kamini. Japanese Art & Culture. 2003. (World Art & Culture Ser.). (Illus.). 56p. (J). lib. bdg. 29.99 (978-0-7398-6609-2(5)) Raintree.

ART, MEDIEVAL

Cels, Marc. Arts & Literature in the Middle Ages. 2004. (Medieval World Ser.). (Illus.). 32p. (J). (978-0-7787-1355-5(5)); pap. (978-0-7787-1387-6(3)) Crabtree Publishing Co.

Living Art Seminars Staff, et al. Teaching the Middle Ages with Magnificent Art Masterpieces: Explore the Middle Ages with 4 Posters & Background Information to Use As Springboards for Engaging Writing Activities, Art Projects, & More. 2000. (Illus.). 64p. (gr. 4-8). pap. 14.95 (978-0-590-64435-8(1)) Scholastic, Inc.

MacDonald, Fiona. The Middle Ages. 2005. (History in Art Ser.). (Illus.). 48p. (J). lib. bdg. 29.93 (978-1-4109-0521-5(7)) Steck-Vaughn.

Medieval Times. 2002. (First Book of History Questions & Answers Ser.). 32p. (J). 9.95 (978-0-7525-7580-3(5)) Parragon, Inc.

Olmsted, Jennifer. Art of the Middle Ages. (Illus.). 32p. (J). 2006. (*978-1-4034-8768-1(5)); 2001. (gr. 4-7). lib. bdg. 24.22 (978-1-58810-091-7(X)); 2nd ed. 2006. pap. (*978-1-4034-8776-6(6)) Heinemann Library.

ART, MOHAMMEDAN

see Art, Islamic

ART, MOORISH

see Art, Islamic

ART—MUSEUMS

see Art Museums

ART, NONOBJECTIVE

see Art, Abstract

ART, ORIENTAL

see Art, Asian

ART, PRIMITIVE

see also Cave Drawings; Folk Art; Indians of North America—Art

also names of countries, cities, etc. with the subdivision Antiquities, e.g. United States—Antiquities; etc.

Hodge, Susie. Prehistoric Art. 2003. (Art in History Ser.). (Illus.). 32p. (J). (gr. 5-7). pap. 6.95 (978-1-4034-4021-1(2)) Heinemann Library.

Lewis, Richard. Cave: An Evocation of the Beginnings of Art. Crawford, Elizabeth, illus. Hirose, George, photos by. 2003. 56p. pap. 14.00 (978-1-929299-03-4(6)) Touchstone Ctr. Pubns.

Patent, Dorothy Hinshaw. Mystery of the Lascaux Cave. 1998. (Frozen in Time Ser.). (Illus.). 64p. (J). (gr. 5-9). lib. bdg. 28.50 (978-0-7614-0784-3(7)) Cavendish, Marshall Corp.

Stephens, Pam. Dropping in on Rousseau. 2003. (Illus.). (J). (978-1-56290-303-9(9)) Crystal Productions.

ART—PSYCHOLOGY

Carroll, Colleen. How Artists See Feelings: Joy, Sadness, Fear, Love. 2001. (How Artists See Ser.). (Illus.). 48p. (ps-3). 12.95 (978-0-7892-0616-9(1)) Abbeville Pr., Inc.

ART, RENAISSANCE

Barter, James E. Artists of the Renaissance. 1998. (History Makers Ser.). (Illus.). 112p. (YA). (gr. 4-12). 28.70 (978-1-56006-439-8(0) , Lucent Bks.) Thomson Gale.

Corrain, Lucia. The Art of the Renaissance. 2008. (YA). lib. bdg. 24.95 net. (*978-1-934545-04-1(X)) Oliver Pr., Inc.

Fitzpatrick, Anne. The Renaissance. 2005. (Movements in Art Ser.). (Illus.). 48p. (gr. 5-9). 21.95 (978-1-58341-349-4(9) , Creative Education) Creative Co., The.

Langley, Andrew. Da Vinci & His Times. 2006. (DK Eyewitness Bks.). (Illus.). 72p. (J). 15.99 (978-0-7566-1768-4(5)); lib. bdg. 19.99 (978-0-7566-1767-7(7)) Dorling Kindersley Publishing, Inc.

Meyer, Eric Christopher. Art in the Renaissance. 2006. (Navigators Ser.). (J). pap. 44.00 (*978-1-4108-6265-5(8)) Benchmark Education Co.

O'Reilly, Wenda B. The Renaissance Art Book: Discover Thirty Glorious Masterpieces by Leonardo da Vinci, Michelangelo, Raphael, Fra Angelico, Botticelli. 2000. (Illus.). 76p. (J). pap. 14.95 (978-1-889613-03-1(7)) Birdcage Pr.

Renaissance Art/Architecture DBA. 2002. spiral bd. 16.95 (978-1-56004-139-9(0)) Social Studies Schl. Service.

ART, ROMAN

Bingham, Jane. Classical Myth: A Treasury of Greek & Roman Legends, Art, & History. 2007. (World of Mythology Ser.). (Illus.). 96p. (YA). (gr. 6 up). 35.95 (*978-0-7656-8104-1(8)) Sharpe, M.E. Inc.

Court, Rob. Art of Early Rome. 2003. (Scribbles Institute). 32p. (J). (gr. 1-5). 21.36 (978-1-56766-590-1(X)) Child's World, Inc.

Gedacht, Daniel C. Art & Religion in Ancient Rome. 2004. (Primary Sources of Ancient Civilizations Ser.). (Illus.). 24p. (J). lib. bdg. (978-0-8239-8944-7(5)); lib. bdg. 19.95 (978-0-8239-6776-6(X)) Rosen Publishing Group, Inc., The. (PowerKids Pr.).

Hodge, Susie. Ancient Roman Art. 32p. 2006. (Illus.). (J). (*978-1-4034-8767-4(7)); 2003. pap. 6.95 (978-1-4034-4018-1(2)) Heinemann Library.

Knapp, Ruthie & Lehmberg, Janice. Greek & Roman Art: Off the Wall Museum Guides for Kids. 2001. (Off the Wall Museum Guides for Kids). (ENG., Illus.). 72p. (J). (gr. 2-5). pap. 8.95 (978-0-87192-549-7(4)) Davis Pubns., Inc.

Susie Hodge. Ancient Roman Art. 2nd ed. 2006. (Illus.). 32p. (J). pap. (*978-1-4034-8775-9(8)) Heinemann Library.

ART—STUDY AND TEACHING

Ada, Alma Flor. Azul y Verde. 1999. (Puertas al Sol Ser.). (SPA., Illus.). 32p. (J). (gr. k-6). pap. 11.95 (978-1-58105-417-0(3)) Santillana USA Publishing Co., Inc.

—Brocha y Pincel. 2004. (Puertas al Sol Ser.). (SPA., Illus.). 32p. (YA). (gr. 1-2). 11.95 (978-1-58105-419-4(X)) Santillana USA Publishing Co., Inc.

—Caballete. 2004. (Puertas al Sol Ser.). (SPA., Illus.). 32p. (YA). (gr. 2-3). 11.95 (978-1-58105-421-7(1)) Santillana USA Publishing Co., Inc.

—Lienzo y Papel. 2004. (Puertas al Sol Ser.). (SPA., Illus.). 32p. (YA). (gr. 3-4). 11.95 (978-1-58105-423-1(8)) Santillana USA Publishing Co., Inc.

Bittinger, Gayle & Warren, Jean. Creation Station. Barr, Marilynn G., illus. 1998. (Kinderstation Ser.). 160p. (J). (ps). pap. 15.95 (978-1-57029-161-6(6) , WPH 4503, Totline Pubns.) Schaffer, Frank Pubns.

Daniel, Vesta A. H., et al. Teacher's Editions. 98th ed. 1999. (Art Express(R) Ser.). (gr. 3 up). tchr. ed. 100.00 (978-0-15-309076-9(6)) Harcourt Schl. Pubs.

Finley, Carol. Aboriginal Art of Australia: Exploring Cultural Traditions. 1998. (Art Around the World Ser.). (Illus.). 56-64p. (gr. 4-8). 23.93 (978-0-8225-2076-4(1)) Lerner Publishing Group.

Gross, Ila Lane. Cinderella Around the World. 2001. (Global Understanding - Cultural Literacy Ser.). (Illus.). 104p. (J). (gr. 3-5). pap. 4.95 (978-0-9713649-1-2(5)) L.E.A.P. (Learning through an Expanded Arts Program, Inc).

Harcourt School Publishers Staff. Art Express: Big Book: California/National Edition. 98th ed. 1999. (Art Express(R) Ser.). (Illus.). (gr. 2 up). pap. 151.50 (978-0-15-312658-1(2)) Harcourt Schl. Pubs.

Hendler, Muncie. Color Your Own Abstract Art Masterpieces. 1999. (Dover Super Value Editions Ser.). (Illus.). 32p. (J). pap. 3.95 (978-0-486-40800-2(0)) Dover Pubns., Inc.

Herman, Gail Neary & Hollingsworth, Patricia L. Kinetic Kaleidoscope: Exploring Movement & Energy in the Visual Arts. Hollingsworth, Patricia L., illus. 2001. (Illus.). 96p. (YA). (gr. 1-12). pap. 20.00 (978-1-893413-11-5(X)) Univ. Schl. at the Univ. of Tulsa.

Hodges, Susan. Toddler Art. Toutillotte, Barb, illus. 2001. (Art Ser.). 80p. (J). (ps). pap. 10.99 (978-1-57029-205-7(1) , WPH4801, Totline Pubns.) Schaffer, Frank Pubns.

Hollenbeck, Kathleen M. Teaching with Favorite Leo Lionni Books: Creative Activities for Exploring Friendship, Self-Esteem, Cooperation & Other Themes in These Beloved Books. 1999. (Illus.). 64p. pap. 10.95 (978-0-439-04388-5(3)) Scholastic, Inc.

Literature: Timeless Voices, Timeless Themes, Copper Level 2001. (J). (gr. 6). trans. 33.47 (978-0-13-052376-1(3)) Prentice Hall PTR.

Living Art Seminars Staff, et al. Teaching the Middle Ages with Magnificent Art Masterpieces: Explore the Middle Ages with 4 Posters & Background Information to Use As Springboards for Engaging Writing Activities, Art Projects, & More. 2000. (Illus.). 64p. (gr. 4-8). pap. 14.95 (978-0-590-64435-8(1)) Scholastic, Inc.

Macken, JoAnn Early. Art Classes. 2005. (Illus.). 24p. (J). pap. (978-0-8368-4518-1(8)); (YA). lib. bdg. 19.33 (978-0-8368-4511-2(0) , Weekly Reader Early Learning Library) Stevens, Gareth Inc.

Micklethwait, Lucy. I Spy Two Eyes: Numbers in Art. 1999. (Illus.). (J). 17.79 (978-0-606-15581-6(3)) Tandem Library Bks.

Press, Judy. ArtStarts for Little Hands! Fun & Discoveries for 3- to 7-Year-Olds. 2000. (Little Hands Bks.). (Illus.). 144p. (J). (ps-3). pap. 12.95 (978-1-885593-37-5(6) , Williamson Bks.) Ideals Pubns.

Raimondo, Joyce. Express Yourself! Activities & Adventures in Expressionism. 2005. (Art Explorers Ser.). (Illus.). 48p. (J). (gr. 4-6). 12.95 (978-0-8230-2506-0(3)) Watson-Guptill Pubns., Inc.

Richardson, Joy. How to Look at Art, 6 bks. Incl. Looking at Faces in Art. lib. bdg. 23.33 (978-0-8368-2624-1(8)); Showing Distance in Art. lib. bdg. 23.33 (978-0-8368-2627-2(2)); Showing Motion in Art. lib. bdg. 22.60 (978-0-8368-2626-5(4)); Telling Stories in Art. lib. bdg. 22.60 (978-0-8368-2628-9(0)); Using Color in Art. lib. bdg. 23.33 (978-0-8368-2629-6(9)); Using Shadows in Art. lib. bdg. 23.33 (978-0-8368-2625-8(6)); 32p. (J). (gr. 1 up). (Illus.). 1999. Set lib. bdg. 69.99 (978-0-8368-2623-4(X)) Stevens, Gareth Inc.

—Looking at Faces in Art. 1999. (How to Look at Art Ser.). (Illus.). 32p. (J). (gr. 1 up). lib. bdg. 23.33 (978-0-8368-2624-1(8)) Stevens, Gareth Inc.

—Showing Distance in Art. 1999. (How to Look at Art Ser.). (Illus.). 32p. (J). (gr. 1 up). lib. bdg. 23.33 (978-0-8368-2627-2(2)) Stevens, Gareth Inc.

—Showing Motion in Art. 1999. (How to Look at Art Ser.). (Illus.). 32p. (J). (gr. 1 up). lib. bdg. 22.60 (978-0-8368-2626-5(4)) Stevens, Gareth Inc.

—Telling Stories in Art. 1999. (How to Look at Art Ser.). (Illus.). 32p. (J). (gr. 1 up). lib. bdg. 22.60 (978-0-8368-2628-9(0)) Stevens, Gareth Inc.

—Using Shadows in Art. 1999. (How to Look at Art Ser.). (Illus.). 32p. (J). (gr. 1 up). lib. bdg. 23.33 (978-0-8368-2625-8(6)) Stevens, Gareth Inc.

Rodda, Emily. How to Draw Deltora Monsters. McBride, Marc, illus. 2005. 48p. (J). pap. 5.99 (978-0-439-73647-3(1) , Scholastic Paperbacks) Scholastic, Inc.

Somerville, Louisa & Crowley, Bridget. Animals in Art. 2001. (In Art Ser.). (Illus.). 47p. 19.99 (978-0-7451-5262-2(7) , Cherrytree Books) Evans Publishing Group GBR. *Dist:* Independent Pubs. Group.

Taylor, Barbara. Structures, Materials, & Art Activities. (Arty Facts Ser.). (Illus.). 48p. (J). (gr. 3-4). 2011. pap. (978-0-7787-1141-4(2)); 2002. lib. bdg. (978-0-7787-1113-1(7)) Crabtree Publishing Co.

Timeless Voices, Timeless Themes: Bronze, Fine Art. 2001. (YA). (gr. 7). trans. 31.97 (978-0-13-052377-8(1)) Prentice Hall PTR.

Timeless Voices, Timeless Themes: Silver, Fine Art. 2001. (YA). (gr. 8). trans. 31.97 (978-0-13-052378-5(X)) Prentice Hall PTR.

Wright, Suzanne. The Choice Is Yours: An Art Activity Handbook for Young Artists Highlighting the Art & Life of Jacob Lawrence. 2002. (Illus.). 64p. (J). pap. (978-0-943044-30-9(8)) Phillips Collection, The.

Yenawine, Philip. Places. 3rd ed. 2006. (Illus.). 24p. (gr. 13 up). 14.95 (978-0-87070-173-3(8)) D.A.P./Distributed Art Pubs.

ART—TECHNIQUE

AGC Editors. The American Girls Art Studio. 2003. (American Girls Collection Ser.). (Illus.). 64p. 14.95 (978-1-58485-725-9(0)) American Girl Publishing, Inc.

—American Girls Art Studio: Kaya. 2003. (American Girls Collection Ser.). 64p. (J). 14.95 (978-1-58485-724-2(2)) American Girl Publishing, Inc.

—American Girls Art Studio: Molly. 2003. (American Girls Collection Ser.). 64p. (J). 14.95 (978-1-58485-727-3(7)) American Girl Publishing, Inc.

—American Girls Art Studio: Samantha. 2003. (American Girls Collection Ser.). 64p. (J). 14.95 (978-1-58485-726-6(9)) American Girl Publishing, Inc.

Alex Toys Staff. My First Art Book & Easel: Color, Draw, Paint, Create! Silver-Thompson, Pattie, illus. 2006. (Everything... Art! Ser.). 42p. (J). (ps-1). 14.99 (978-0-316-15381-2(8)) Little Brown & Co.

Appel, Julie & Guglielmo, Amy. Touch the Art: Make Van Gogh's Bed. 2006. (Touch the Art Ser.). (Illus.). 20p. (J). bds. 9.95 (978-1-4027-3567-7(7)) Sterling Publishing Co., Inc.

—Touch the Art: Pop Warhol's Top. 2006. (Touch the Art Ser.). (Illus.). 24p. (J). bds. 9.95 (978-1-4027-3569-1(3)) Sterling Publishing Co., Inc.

Barr, Steve. 1-2-3 Draw Cartoon Cars: A Step-By-Step Guide. 2005. (Illus.). 64p. (J). pap. 8.99 (978-0-939217-75-5(9)) Peel Productions, Inc.

Bingham, Jane. Illusion Art. 2006. (Art off the Wall Ser.). (Illus.). 56p. (J). (978-1-4034-8290-7(X)) Heinemann Library.

Booth, Scott, illus. How to Draw Superheroes & Super Villains. 2003. 64p. (J). (978-0-439-55133-5(1)) Scholastic, Inc.

Creative Kids: Arts, Crafts, & More. 2004. pap. 15.99 (978-0-7439-3200-4(5)) Teacher Created Materials, Inc.

Day, Eileen. I'm Good at Making Art. 2003. (Heinemann Read & Learn Ser.). (Illus.). 24p. (J). pap. 5.25 (978-1-4034-3446-3(8)); lib. bdg. 18.50 (978-1-4034-0898-3(X)) Heinemann Library.

—I'm Good at Making Art. 2003. (gr. k-3). lib. bdg. 13.30 (978-0-613-70657-5(9)) Tandem Library Bks.

de Rosamel, Godeleine. Drawing with Circles. de Rosamel, Godeleine, illus. 2003. (Drawing Is Easy Ser.). (Illus.). 24p. (J). (ps up). lib. bdg. 22.00 (978-0-8368-3625-7(1)) Stevens, Gareth Inc.

—Drawing with Nature. de Rosamel, Godeleine, illus. 2003. (Drawing Is Easy Ser.). (Illus.). 24p. (J). (ps up). lib. bdg. 22.00 (978-0-8368-3626-4(X)) Stevens, Gareth Inc.

—Drawing with Objects. de Rosamel, Godeleine, illus. 2003. (Drawing Is Easy Ser.). (Illus.). 24p. (J). (ps up). lib. bdg. 22.00 (978-0-8368-3627-1(8)) Stevens, Gareth Inc.

—Drawing with Your Fingerprints. de Rosamel, Godeleine, illus. 2003. (Drawing Is Easy Ser.). (Illus.). 24p. (J). (ps up). lib. bdg. 22.00 (978-0-8368-3628-8(6)) Stevens, Gareth Inc.

—Drawing with Your Hands. de Rosamel, Godeleine, illus. 2003. (Drawing Is Easy Ser.). (Illus.). 24p. (J). (ps up). lib. bdg. 22.00 (978-0-8368-3629-5(4)) Stevens, Gareth Inc.

Distance-It with Space/Build-It with Form. 2005. (J). spiral bd. 45.00 (978-0-9755413-9-5(0)) ArtAnswer.

Emert, Phyllis. Art in Glass. 2007. (Eye on Art Ser.). 128p. (gr. 7-10). 31.20 (*978-1-59018-983-2(3) , Lucent Bks.) Thomson Gale.

Ewing, Patrick & Lewis, Linda. In the Paint. 1999. (Illus.). 64p. (gr. 2-5). 15.95 (978-0-7892-0542-1(4)) Abbeville Pr., Inc.

Fish, Jeremy & Rock, Aesop. The Next Best Thing. 2006. 24p. 25.00 (978-0-9778854-7-3(X)) Upper Playground Pubng.

Flux, Paul. Color. (How Artists Use Ser.). (Illus.). 32p. (J). (gr. 1-4). 2002. pap. 6.95 (978-1-58810-436-6(2) , 91164); 2001. lib. bdg. 22.79 (978-1-58810-078-8(2)) Heinemann Library.

—Pattern & Texture. (Illus.). 32p. (J). 2007. (*978-1-4034-9631-7(5)); 2002. (gr. 1-4). pap. 6.95 (978-1-58810-438-0(9) , 91166); 2001. lib. bdg. 21.36 (978-1-58810-082-5(0)) Heinemann Library.

—Pattern & Texture (2nd Edition) 2007. (Illus.). 32p. (J). (*978-1-4034-9637-9(4)) Heinemann Library.

—Shape. (Illus.). 32p. (J). 2007. (*978-1-4034-9633-1(1)); 2002. (gr. 1-4). pap. 6.95 (978-1-58810-440-3(0) , 91168); 2001. (gr. 1-3). lib. bdg. 22.79 (978-1-58810-081-8(2)) Heinemann Library.

—Shape (2nd Edition) 2007. (Illus.). 32p. (J). (*978-1-4034-9639-3(0)) Heinemann Library.

Golightly, Holly. Witches n Whatnot. Golightly, Holly, . 2004. (Illus.). 48p. (YA). per. 9.99 (978-0-9745367-6-7(8)) BroadSword Comics/ Jim Balent Studios.

Hart, Christopher. Kids Draw Animals. 2003. (Kids Draw Ser.). (Illus.). 64p. (J). pap. 11.95 (978-0-8230-2631-9(0)) Watson-Guptill Pubns., Inc.

Henry, Sandi. Kids' Art Works! Creating with Color, Design, Texture & More. 1999. (Kids Can Bks.). (Illus.). 138p. (J). (gr. 1-7). pap. 12.95 (978-1-885593-35-1(X) , Williamson Bks.) Ideals Pubns.

—Kids' Art Works! Creating with Color, Design, Texture & More. 1999. lib. bdg. 22.20 (978-0-613-57606-2(3)) Tandem Library Bks.

—Using Color in Your Art! 2006. 128p. (J). 14.95 (978-0-8249-6772-7(0) , Williamson Bks.) Ideals Pubns.

Hodge, Anthony. Collage. 2006. 32p. pap. (978-958-30-1835-0(X)) Panamericana Editorial.

El Impresionismo. 2003. (Coleccion Mundo Maravilloso). (SPA., Illus.). (J). (gr. 3-5). 13.56 (978-84-348-6570-9(X)) SM Ediciones ESP. *Dist:* Lectorum Pubns., Inc.

Jones, William. Arte de la Manipulacion.Tr. of Art of Manipulation. (SPA.). 9.98 (978-968-403-964-3(6)) Selector, S.A. de C.V. MEX. *Dist:* AIMS International Bks., Inc.

Kallen, Stuart A. The Artist's Tools. 2006. (Illus.). 112p. (gr. 7-10). 32.45 (978-1-59018-957-3(4) , Lucent Bks.) Thomson Gale.

Lacey, Sue. Sports & Leisure. 2000. (gr. 3-6). lib. bdg. 15.25 (978-0-613-27041-0(X)) Tandem Library Bks.

Lapointe, Claude. The Aspiring Artist's Journal. Guindolet, Sylvette, illus. 2007. 372p. (J). (gr. 3-7). pap. 16.95 (***978-0-8109-9420-1(8)***) Abrams, Harry N. , Inc.

Luxbacher, Irene. The Jumbo Book of Art. 2003. (gr. 3-6). lib. bdg. 24.55 (978-0-613-81039-5(2)) Tandem Library Bks.

Luxbacher, Irene, illus. The Jumbo Book of Art. 2004. (Jumbo Bks.). 208p. (J). (gr. 4-6). (978-1-55074-762-1(2)) Kids Can Pr., Ltd.

—The Jumbo Book of Outdoor Art. Boudreau, Ray & Hall, Doug, photos by. 2006. 144p. (J). (gr. 3-6). (978-1-55337-680-4(3)) Kids Can Pr., Ltd.

Making Amazing Art: 40 Activities Using the 7 Elements of Art Design. 2007. (Illus.). 128p. (J). (gr. 2-8). 16.99 (***978-0-8249-6794-9(1)***); pap. 12.99 (***978-0-8249-6795-6(X)***) Ideals Pubns. (Williamson Bks.).

Mis, Melody S. How to Draw Brazil's Sights & Symbols. 2004. (Kid's Guide to Drawing the Countries of the World Ser.). (Illus.). 48p. (J). lib. bdg. 26.50 (978-0-8239-6667-7(4) , PowerKids Pr.) Rosen Publishing Group, Inc., The.

—How to Draw Poland's Sights & Symbols. 2004. (Kid's Guide to Drawing the Countries of the World Ser.). (Illus.). 48p. (J). lib. bdg. 26.50 (978-0-8239-6669-1(0) , PowerKids Pr.) Rosen Publishing Group, Inc., The.

—How to Draw Russia's Sights & Symbols. 2004. (Kid's Guide to Drawing the Countries of the World Ser.). (Illus.). 48p. (J). lib. bdg. 26.50 (978-0-8239-6666-0(6) , PowerKids Pr.) Rosen Publishing Group, Inc., The.

—How to Draw South Africa's Sights & Symbols. 2004. (Kid's Guide to Drawing the Countries of the World Ser.). (Illus.). 48p. (J). lib. bdg. 26.50 (978-0-8239-6665-3(8) , PowerKids Pr.) Rosen Publishing Group, Inc., The.

Murphy, Patricia J. Creative Minds. 2005. (Real Deal - Green Plus Ser.). (Illus.). 32p. (gr. 4-8). 19.00 (978-0-7910-8899-9(5)) Facts On File, Inc.

Newbery, Elizabeth. How Is Art Made? 2001. (Art for All Ser.). (Illus.). 32p. (J). lib. bdg. 24.25 (978-1-930643-31-4(4)) Chrysalis Education.

—The Secrets of Art. 2001. (Art for All Ser.). (Illus.). 32p. (J). lib. bdg. 24.25 (978-1-930643-32-1(2)) Chrysalis Education.

Newbury, Elizabeth. Art to Make You Scared! 2008. (Illus.). 24p. (J). 15.95 (***978-1-84507-584-2(6)***) Lincoln, Frances Ltd. GBR. *Dist:* Perseus Distribution.

Nicholson, Sue. World Art. 2005. (Learn Art Ser.). (Illus.). 32p. (J). (***978-1-84538-161-5(0)***); pap. (***978-1-84538-130-1(0)***) QED Publishing.

Peffer, J. Neondragon. Dragonart Mythical Monsters. 2007. 32p. 9.99 (***978-1-60061-074-5(9)*** , Impact) F & W Pubns., Inc.

Pocket Artist. 2004. (Young Artist Ser.). (Illus.). 288p. (J). (gr. 2 up). 8.95 (978-0-7945-0100-6(1) , Usborne) EDC Publishing.

Press, Judy. ArtStarts for Little Hands! 2000. (gr. k-3). lib. bdg. 22.20 (978-0-613-27715-0(5)) Tandem Library Bks.

Randolph, Joanne. Drawing Birds. 2005. (Let's Draw with Shapes Ser.). (Illus.). 24p. (J). 17.25 (978-1-4042-2792-7(X) , PowerKids Pr.) Rosen Publishing Group, Inc., The.

Reinagle, Damon J. Draw: A Step-by-Step Guide. 2005. (Illus.). 64p. pap. 8.99 (978-0-939217-34-2(1)) Peel Productions, Inc.

Robins, Deri. Special Effects. 2005. (Learn Art Ser.). (Illus.). 32p. (J). pap. (***978-1-84538-280-3(3)***); pap. (***978-1-84538-128-8(9)***) QED Publishing.

Robins, Deri. Stencils & Prints. 2004. (QEB Learn Art Ser.). (Illus.). 32p. (J). lib. bdg. 18.95 (978-1-59566-048-0(8) , 1236548) QEB Publishing Inc.

Roca, Nuria. What Is Art? Painting & Sculpture. 2004. (gr. k-3). lib. bdg. 15.25 (978-0-613-84061-3(5)) Tandem Library Bks.

Ros, Jordina & Estadella, Pere. Fun Crafts with 2D & 3D Figures. 2006. (Arts & Crafts Fun Ser.). (Illus.). 48p. (J). (gr. 3-7). lib. bdg. 23.93 (978-0-7660-2652-0(3) , Enslow Elementary) Enslow Pubs., Inc.

—Fun Crafts with Colors. 2006. (Arts & Crafts Fun Ser.). (Illus.). 48p. (J). (gr. 3-7). lib. bdg. 23.93 (978-0-7660-2655-1(8) , Enslow Elementary) Enslow Pubs., Inc.

—Fun Crafts with Dots & Lines. 2006. (Arts & Crafts Fun Ser.). (Illus.). 48p. (J). (gr. 3-7). lib. bdg. 23.93 (978-0-7660-2656-8(6) , Enslow Elementary) Enslow Pubs., Inc.

—Fun Crafts with Shapes. 2006. (Arts & Crafts Fun Ser.). (Illus.). 48p. (J). (gr. 3-7). lib. bdg. 23.93 (978-0-7660-2657-5(4) , Enslow Elementary) Enslow Pubs., Inc.

—Fun Crafts with Sizes & Spaces. 2006. (Arts & Crafts Fun Ser.). (Illus.). 48p. (J). (gr. 3-7). lib. bdg. 23.93 (978-0-7660-2653-7(1) , Enslow Elementary) Enslow Pubs., Inc.

—Fun Crafts with Textures. 2006. (Arts & Crafts Fun Ser.). (Illus.). 48p. (J). (gr. 3-7). lib. bdg. 23.93 (978-0-7660-2654-4(X) , Enslow Elementary) Enslow Pubs., Inc.

Sherwyn, Art. Creative Coloring Vol. 1: Design Elements. 2001. (Illus.). 48p. pap. 9.95 (978-0-87192-584-8(2)) Davis Pubns., Inc.

Sterling Publishing Co., Inc. Visual Magic. 2007. (Illus.). 64p. pap. 8.95 (978-1-4027-4361-0(0)) Sterling Publishing Co., Inc.

Tecco, Betsy Dru. How to Draw Egypt's Sights & Symbols. 2004. (Kid's Guide to Drawing the Countries of the World Ser.). (Illus.). 48p. (J). lib. bdg. 26.50 (978-0-8239-6682-0(8) , PowerKids Pr.) Rosen Publishing Group, Inc., The.

—How to Draw France's Sights & Symbols. 2004. (Kid's Guide to Drawing the Countries of the World Ser.). (Illus.). 48p. (J). lib. bdg. 26.50 (978-0-8239-6683-7(6) , PowerKids Pr.) Rosen Publishing Group, Inc., The.

—How to Draw Germany's Sights & Symbols. 2004. (Kid's Guide to Drawing the Countries of the World Ser.). (Illus.). 48p. (J). lib. bdg. 26.50 (978-0-8239-6685-1(2) , PowerKids Pr.) Rosen Publishing Group, Inc., The.

—How to Draw Italy's Sights & Symbols. 2004. (Kid's Guide to Drawing the Countries of the World Ser.). (Illus.). 48p. (J). lib. bdg. 26.50 (978-0-8239-6686-8(0) , PowerKids Pr.) Rosen Publishing Group, Inc., The.

—How to Draw Japan's Sights & Symbols. 2004. (Kid's Guide to Drawing the Countries of the World Ser.). 48p. (J). lib. bdg. 26.50 (978-0-8239-6681-3(X) , PowerKids Pr.) Rosen Publishing Group, Inc., The.

—How to Draw the United Kingdom's Sights & Symbols. 2004. (Kid's Guide to Drawing the Countries of the World Ser.). (Illus.). 48p. (J). lib. bdg. 26.50 (978-0-8239-6684-4(4) , PowerKids Pr.) Rosen Publishing Group, Inc., The.

Thompson, Ruth. What Is a Still Life? 2005. (Illus.). 30p. (J). (gr. 3-7). lib. bdg. 27.10 (978-1-932889-88-8(4)) Sea-To-Sea Pubns.

Top That Publishing Staff, ed. Cartoon Sculpture. 2005. (Illus.). 48p. (978-1-84510-305-7(X)) Top That! Publishing PLC.

Visca, Curt & Visca, Kelley. How to Draw Cartoon Holiday Symbols. 2004. (Kid's Guide to Drawing Ser.). (Illus.). 24p. (J). lib. bdg. 21.25 (978-0-8239-6726-1(3) , PowerKids Pr.) Rosen Publishing Group, Inc., The.

Watt, F. Art Ideas Pack. 2004. (Activity Kits Ser.). (Illus.). 32p. (J). act. bk. ed. 16.95 (978-0-7945-0119-8(2) , Usborne) EDC Publishing.

—Art Skills. 2004. (Art Ideas Ser.). (Illus.). 96p. (J). 18.95 (978-0-7945-0351-2(9)); lib. bdg. 26.95 (978-1-58086-497-8(X)) EDC Publishing.

Watt, Fiona. Art Ideas. rev. ed. 2006. (Illus.). 96p. (J). 14.99 (978-0-7945-0893-7(6) , Usborne) EDC Publishing.

—Art Ideas Drawing Pack: Internet-Linked. 2004. (Activity Kits Ser.). 32p. (J). act. bk. ed. 16.95 (978-0-7945-0539-4(2)) EDC Publishing.

—Compl Bk of Art Ideas (Reduced Format) Miller, Antonia Et Al, illus. 2005. 288p. (J). pap. 19.99 (978-0-7945-1439-6(1) , Usborne) EDC Publishing.

—The Usborne Book of Art Skills. 2005. (Illus.). 96p. (J). 7.95 (978-0-7945-1110-4(4) , Usborne) EDC Publishing.

Wheeler, Annie. Painting on A Canvas. Dixon, Debra, illus. 2006. 64p. (J). pap. 9.95 (978-1-58685-839-1(4)) Gibbs Smith, Publisher.

Witty One Restickable Art Frames. 2003. per. (978-1-932435-02-3(6)) Cardinal Brands, Inc.

Wright, Suzanne. The Choice Is Yours: An Art Activity Handbook for Young Artists Highlighting the Art & Life of Jacob Lawrence. 2002. (Illus.). 64p. (J). pap. (978-0-943044-30-9(8)) Phillips Collection, The.

Yenawine, Philip. Colors. 3rd ed. 2006. (Illus.). 32p. (gr. 13 up). 9.95 (978-0-87070-176-4(2)) D.A.P./Distributed Art Pubs.

ART—VOCATIONAL GUIDANCE

Burton, Marilee Robin. Artists at Work. 2003. (On the Job Ser.). (Illus.). 32p. (gr. 3-5). 23.00 (978-0-7910-7410-7(2) , Chelsea Hse.) Facts On File, Inc.

Clark, Richard & Fehl, Pamela. Career Opportunities in the Visual Arts. (Career Opportunities Ser.). (YA). (gr. 9). 288p. pap. 18.95 (978-0-8160-5928-7(4) , Checkmark Bks.); 2006. 240p. 49.50 (978-0-8160-5927-0(6) , Ferguson Publishing Co.) Facts On File, Inc.

Facts on File, Inc. Staff, contrib. by. Top Careers for Art Graduates. 2004. (Top Careers Ser.). (Illus.). 368p. (gr. 9). pap. 14.95 (978-0-8160-5565-4(3) , Checkmark Bks.) Facts On File, Inc.

Ferguson. What Can I Do Now? 2007. (What Can I Do Now Ser.). 176p. (YA). (gr. 6-12). 29.95 (***978-0-8160-6025-2(8)*** , Ferguson Publishing Co.) Facts On File, Inc.

Kohl, MaryAnn F. & Solga, Kim. Discovering Great Artists: Hands-on Art for Children in the Styles of the Great Masters. Van Slyke, Rebecca, illus. 2003. (Bright Ideas for Learning Ser.: Vol. 6). 144p. (Orig.). (J). (ps-12). pap. 18.95 (978-0-935607-09-3(9)) Bright Ring Publishing, Inc.

Lehn, Barbara. What Is an Artist? Krauss, Carol, photos by. 2002. (What Is...? Ser.). (Illus.). 32p. (gr. k-3). lib. bdg. 21.90 (978-0-7613-2259-7(0) , Millbrook Pr.) Lerner Publishing Group.

Miller, Heather. Artista. 2003. Tr. of Artist. (SPA.). 24p. (J). pap. 5.25 (978-1-4034-3393-0(3)) Heinemann Library.

Reeves, Diane Lindsey, et al. Career Ideas for Teens in the Arts & Communications. (Career Ideas for Teens Ser.). (gr. 6-12). 176p. pap. 16.95 (978-0-8160-6918-7(2) , Checkmark Bks.); 2005. (Illus.). 170p. (YA). per. 40.00 (978-0-8160-5288-2(3) , Ferguson Publishing Co.) Facts On File, Inc.

Yehling, Carol B., ed. Discovering Careers for Your Future/ Art. 2001. (Discovering Careers for Your Future Ser.). (Illus.). 96p. (J). (gr. 4-9). 21.95 (978-0-89434-388-9(2) , Ferguson Publishing Co.) Facts On File, Inc.

ART ANATOMY

see Anatomy, Artistic

ART AND MYTHOLOGY

Holub, Joan & Regan, Dana, illus. Magical Creatures. 2003. (Easy-to-Read! Easy-to-Draw! Ser.). 48p. (J). pap. 5.99 (978-0-8431-0436-3(8) , Price Stern Sloan) Penguin Group (USA) Inc.

Levin, Freddie. 1-2-3 Draw Mythical Creatures: A Step-by-Step Guide. 2003. (One-Two-Three Draw Ser.). (Illus.). 64p. pap. 8.99 (978-0-939217-49-6(X)) Peel Productions, Inc.

ART APPRECIATION

see also Art—Study and Teaching; Art Criticism; Painting; Pictures

Aigner-Clark, Julie. Van Gogh's World of Color. Zaidi, Nadeem, illus. 2001. (Baby Einstein Ser.). 12p. (J). (ps-ps). 7.99 (978-0-7868-0805-2(5)) Hyperion Bks. for Children.

Anderson, Robert. Salvador Dali. 2002. (Artists in Their Time Ser.). (Illus.). 48p. (J). (gr. 5-7). pap. 23.50 (978-0-531-12231-0(X) , Watts, Franklin) Scholastic Library Publishing.

Barbe-Gall, Francoise. How to Talk to Children about Art. 2005. (Illus.). 208p. (J). pap. 16.95 (978-1-55652-580-3(X)) Chicago Review Pr., Inc.

Bayles, Jennifer L. An Adventure in Looking & Listening: Exploring Masterworks at the Albright-Knox Art Gallery. Barnett, Janet, illus. 2003. (J). (978-1-887457-01-9(1)) Buffalo Fine Arts/Albright-Knox Art Gallery.

Bieringer, Kelley. Is Modern Art Really Art? 2007. (J). (***978-1-4329-0356-5(X)***) Heinemann Library.

Blake, Quentin. Tell Me a Picture. Blake, Quentin, illus. 2003. (Single Titles Ser.). (Illus.). 128p. lib. bdg. 29.90 (978-0-7613-2748-6(7) , Millbrook Pr.) Lerner Publishing Group.

—Tell Me a Picture. 2003. (Illus.). 128p. (gr. 3 up). pap. (978-0-7613-1893-4(3) , Millbrook Pr.) Lerner Publishing Group.

—Tell Me a Picture. 2006. (Illus.). 128p. pap. 17.95 (978-1-84507-687-0(7)) Lincoln, Frances Ltd. GBR. *Dist:* Perseus Distribution.

Blizzard, Gladys S. Come Look with Me: World of Play. 2006. (Come Look with Me Ser.). (Illus.). 32p. (YA). (gr. k-12). 15.95 (978-1-56566-031-1(5)) Charlesbridge Publishing, Inc.

Browne, Anthony. The Shape Game. Browne, Anthony, illus. 2003. (Illus.). 32p. (J). (gr. k up). 16.00 (978-0-374-36764-0(7) , Farrar, Straus & Giroux (BYR)) Farrar, Straus & Giroux.

Burleigh, Robert. Seurat & la Grande Jatte: Connecting the Dots. 2004. (Illus.). 32p. (J). (gr. k-4). 17.95 (978-0-8109-4811-2(7)) Abrams, Harry N. , Inc.

Carew-Miller, Anna. Mexican Art & Architecture. 2002. (Encyclopedia of Mexico Ser.). (Illus.). 64,80p. (YA). (gr. 5 up). lib. bdg. (978-1-59084-081-8(X)) Mason Crest Pubs.

Carroll, Colleen. Elements: Earth, Air, Fire & Water. 1998. (How Artists See Ser.). (Illus.). 48p. (gr. 3 up). 12.95 (978-0-7892-0476-9(2)) Abbeville Pr., Inc.

—How Artists See America: East, West, South, Midwest. 2002. (How Artists See Ser.). (Illus.). 48p. (gr. 2-5). 12.95 (978-0-7892-0772-2(9)) Abbeville Pr., Inc.

—How Artists See Animals: Mammal, Fish, Bird, Reptile. 1998. (How Artists See Ser.). (Illus.). 48p. pap. 12.95 (978-0-7892-0475-2(4)) Abbeville Pr., Inc.

—How Artists See Artists: Actor, Painter, Dancer, Musician. 2001. (How Artists See Ser.). (Illus.). 48p. (ps-3). 12.95 (978-0-7892-0618-3(8)) Abbeville Pr., Inc.

—How Artists See Cities. 1999. (How Artists See Ser.). (Illus.). 48p. (gr. 3-6). 12.95 (978-0-7892-0187-4(9)) Abbeville Pr., Inc.

—How Artists See Feelings: Joy, Sadness, Fear, Love. 2001. (How Artists See Ser.). (Illus.). 48p. (ps-3). 12.95 (978-0-7892-0616-9(1)) Abbeville Pr., Inc.

—How Artists See Play. 1999. (How Artists See Ser.). (Illus.). 48p. (gr. 3-6). 12.95 (978-0-7892-0393-9(6)) Abbeville Pr., Inc.

—How Artists See Work: Farm, Factory, Home, Office. 2000. (How Artists See Ser.). (Illus.). 48p. 10.95 (978-0-7892-0672-5(2)) Abbeville Pr., Inc.

—The Weather: Sun, Rain, Wind, Snow. 1998. (How Artists See Ser.). (Illus.). 48p. (gr. 4-7). 12.95 (978-0-7892-0478-3(9)) Abbeville Pr., Inc.

Cole, Alison. Perspective. 2000. (Eyewitness Bks.). (Illus.). 64p. (J). (gr. 4-7). 15.99 (978-0-7894-5585-7(4)) Dorling Kindersley Publishing, Inc.

Cole, Alison & Dorling Kindersley Publishing Staff. Perspective. 2000. (Eyewitness Bks.). (Illus.). 64p. (J). (gr. 4-7). lib. bdg. 19.99 (978-0-7894-6818-5(2)) Dorling Kindersley Publishing, Inc.

Colleen, Carroll & Carroll, Colleen. How Artists See Families: Mother, Father, Sister, Brother. 2000. (How Artists See Ser.). (Illus.). 48p. 12.95 (978-0-7892-0671-8(4)) Abbeville Pr., Inc.

Connolly, Sean. Leonardo Da Vinci. 2006. (Heinemann First Library). (Illus.). 32p. (J). lib. bdg. (***978-1-4034-8492-5(9)***) Heinemann Library.

—Vincent Van Gogh. 2006. (Heinemann First Library). (Illus.). 32p. (J). lib. bdg. (***978-1-4034-8497-0(X)***) Heinemann Library.

Copmbined, Slide. Discovering Art History. (978-0-87192-311-0(4)) Davis Pubns., Inc.

Cormack, Malcolm. Tigers & Sails & ABC Tales. 2003. (Illus.). 64p. 14.95 (978-0-917046-65-0(X)) Virginia Museum of Fine Arts.

Cressy, Judith. Can You Find It? Search & Discover More Than 150 Details in 19 Works of Art. 2002. (Illus.). 48p. (J). (gr. k-4). 15.95 (978-0-8109-3279-1(2)) Abrams, Harry N. , Inc.

—Can You Find It, Too? Search & Discover More Than 150 Details in 20 Works of Art. 2004. (Illus.). 40p. (J). (gr. k-4). 15.95 (978-0-8109-5046-7(4)) Abrams, Harry N. , Inc.

—Can You Find It, Too? Search & Discover More Than 150 Details in 20 Works of Art. 2004. (Illus.). 40p. (J). (978-1-58839-053-0(5)) Metropolitan Museum of Art, The.

Danzis, Steve. Behind the Lions: A Family Guide to the Art Institute of Chicago. Csicsko, David L., illus. 1998. 112p. (J). (gr. 2-8). pap. 15.95 (978-0-86559-156-1(3)) Art Institute of Chicago.

D'Harcourt, Claire. Art up Close. 6th ed. 2006. 64p. (J). 22.95 (978-0-8118-5464-1(7)) Chronicle Bks. LLC.

—Louvre in Close Up. 2007. (Illus.). 64p. (J). 22.95 (978-0-8118-5510-5(4)) Chronicle Bks. LLC.

d'Harcourt, Claire. Masterpieces up Close: Western Painting from the 14th to 20th Centuries. Kirk, Shoshanna, tr. from FRE. 2006. (Illus.). 64p. (J). (gr. 6-8). 22.95 (978-0-8118-5403-0(5)) Chronicle Bks. LLC.

Dickens, Rosie. The Children's Book of Art: Internet Linked. 2005. (Illus.). 64p. (J). (***978-0-439-88981-0(2)***) Scholastic, Inc.

Dickins, Rosie, et al. The Usborne Introduction to Art: In Association with the National Gallery, London. 2005. (Illus.). 144p. (J). (978-0-439-79202-8(9)) Scholastic, Inc.

Dickins, Rosie, et al. The Usborne Introduction to Modern Art. 2006. (Illus.). 96p. (J). (***978-0-439-89532-3(4)***) Scholastic, Inc.

Duggleby, John. Story Painter: The Life of Jacob Lawrence. 1998. (Illus.). 64p. (J). (gr. 1-7). 16.95 (978-0-8118-2082-0(3)) Chronicle Bks. LLC.

Gaff, Jackie. Alberto Giacometti. 2002. (Artists in Their Time Ser.). (Illus.). (J). (gr. 5-7). 46p. pap. 6.95 (978-0-531-16617-8(1)); 48p. pap. 23.50 (978-0-531-12224-2(7)) Scholastic Library Publishing. (Watts, Franklin).

—Alberto Giacometti. 2002. (Illus.). 46p. (J). (gr. 3-7). lib. bdg. 15.25 (978-0-613-53900-5(1)) Tandem Library Bks.

Gherman, Beverly & Rockwell, Family Trust. Norman Rockwell: Storyteller with a Brush. 2000. (Illus.). 64p. (J). (gr. 3-7). 20.99 (978-0-689-82001-4(1) , Atheneum) Simon & Schuster Children's Publishing.

Giesecke, Ernestine. Frederic Remington. (Illus.). 32p. 2003. pap. 6.50 (978-1-58810-281-2(5)); 1999. (J). lib. bdg. 21.36 (978-1-57572-951-0(2)) Heinemann Library.

—Frederic Remington. 2001. (gr. k-3). lib. bdg. 14.75 (978-0-613-89893-5(1)) Tandem Library Bks.

Giesecke, Ernestine. Mary Cassatt. 2006. (Heinemann First Library). (Illus.). 32p. (J). lib. bdg. (***978-1-4034-8493-2(7)***) Heinemann Library.

Granat, Diana. Exploring Cultures Through Art: China & Japan. 2002. (Exploring Cultures Through Art Ser.). (Illus.). 64p. (gr. 4-8). pap. 11.95 (978-0-439-11106-5(4)) Scholastic, Inc.

Hodge, Susie. Claude Monet. 2002. (Artists in Their Time Ser.). (J). (gr. 5-7). pap. 6.95 (978-0-531-16619-2(8)); (Illus.). 48p. pap. 23.50 (978-0-531-12226-6(3)) Scholastic Library Publishing. (Watts, Franklin).

—Claude Monet. 2002. (gr. 5-8). lib. bdg. 15.25 (978-0-613-54133-6(2)) Tandem Library Bks.

Hopps, Walter, ed. & contrib. by. Andy Warhol. Hopps, Walter, contrib. by. 2002. (Art Ed Books & Kits Ser.). (Illus.). 24p. (J). 19.95 (978-0-8109-6793-9(6)) Abrams, Harry N. , Inc.

—Georgia O'Keeffe. Hopps, Walter, contrib. by. 2002. (Art Ed Books & Kits Ser.). (Illus.). 32p. (J). 19.95 (978-0-8109-6792-2(8)) Abrams, Harry N. , Inc.

—Henri Matisse. Hopps, Walter, contrib. by. 2002. (Art Ed Books & Kits Ser.). (Illus.). 24p. (J). 19.95 (978-0-8109-6794-6(4)) Abrams, Harry N. , Inc.

Hosack, Karen. Animals. 2004. (J). lib. bdg. 24.22 (978-1-4034-4850-7(7)) Heinemann Library.

—Families. 2004. (J). lib. bdg. 24.22 (978-1-4034-4851-4(5)) Heinemann Library.

—Food. 2004. (J). lib. bdg. 24.22 (978-1-4034-4852-1(3)) Heinemann Library.

—Homes. 2004. (J). lib. bdg. 24.22 (978-1-4034-4853-8(1)) Heinemann Library.

—Nature. 2004. (J). lib. bdg. 24.22 (978-1-4034-4854-5(X)) Heinemann Library.

—Weather. 2005. (Illus.). 32p. (J). (gr. 1-3). lib. bdg. 24.22 (978-1-4034-4855-2(8)) Heinemann Library.

Kelley, True. Pablo Picasso: Breaking All the Rules. Kelley, True, illus. 2002. (Smart about Art Ser.). (Illus.). 32p. (J). pap. 5.99 (978-0-448-42862-8(8) , Grosset & Dunlap) Penguin Group (USA) Inc.

—Pablo Picasso: Breaking All the Rules. 2002. (gr. 3-6). lib. bdg. 14.15 (978-0-613-62151-9(4)) Tandem Library Bks.

Knapp, Ruthie & Lehmberg, Janice. American Art: Museum Guide for Kids. 1998. (Off the Wall Museum Guides for Kids). (ENG., Illus.). 72p. (J). pap. 10.95 (978-0-87192-386-8(6)) Davis Pubns., Inc.

—Egyptian Art. 1998. (Off the Wall Museum Guides for Kids). (Illus.). 64p. (J). (gr. 2-7). pap. 10.95 (978-0-87192-384-4(X)) Davis Pubns., Inc.

—Impressionist Art. 1998. (Off the Wall Museum Guides for Kids). (Illus.). 72p. (J). pap. 10.95 (978-0-87192-385-1(8)) Davis Pubns., Inc.

Lacey, Sue. Sports & Leisure. 2000. (gr. 3-6). lib. bdg. 15.25 (978-0-613-27041-0(X)) Tandem Library Bks.

Le Tord, Bijou. A Bird or Two: A Story about Henri Matisse. Le Tord, Bijou, illus. 2004. (Illus.). 32p. (gr. 2-7). 17.00 (978-0-8028-5184-0(3)) Eerdmans, William B. Publishing Co.

A B

Living Art Seminars Staff, et al. Teaching the Middle Ages with Magnificent Art Masterpieces: Explore the Middle Ages with 4 Posters & Background Information to Use As Springboards for Engaging Writing Activities, Art Projects, & More. 2000. (Illus.). 64p. (gr. 4-8). pap. 14.95 (978-0-590-64435-8(1)) Scholastic, Inc.

MacDonald, Patricia & Picasso, Pablo. Pablo Picasso: Great-est Artist of the 20th Century. 2001. (Giants of Art & Culture Ser.). (Illus.). 128p. (J). (gr. 5-8). 29.94 (978-1-56711-504-8(7) , Blackbirch Pr., Inc.) Thomson Gale.

Mason, Antony. El arte Contemporanea: En los tiempos de Warhol. 2005. (Arte Alrededor del Mundo Ser.). 48p. (J). pap. 9.95 (978-85-7416-218-8(3)) Callis Editora Ltda BRA. *Dist:* Independent Pubs. Group.

—El Arte Contemporanea: En los Tiempos de Warhol. 2005. (Arte Alrededor del Mundo Ser.). 48p. (J). pap. 9.95 (978-85-7416-241-6(8)) Callis Editora Ltda BRA. *Dist:* Independent Pubs. Group.

—El arte Moderna: En los tiempos de Picasso. 2005. (Arte Alrededor del Mundo Ser.). 48p. (J). pap. 9.95 (978-85-7416-217-1(5)) Callis Editora Ltda BRA. *Dist:* Independent Pubs. Group.

—El Arte Moderno: En los Tiempos de Picasso. 2005. (Arte Alrededor del Mundo Ser.). 48p. (J). pap. 9.95 (978-85-7416-240-9(X)) Callis Editora Ltda BRA. *Dist:* Independent Pubs. Group.

—In the Time of Picasso. 2002. (gr. 3-6). lib. bdg. 17.60 (978-0-613-85063-6(7)) Tandem Library Bks.

Merberg, Julie & Bober, Suzanne. Dancing with Degas. 2003. (Illus.). 22p. (J). bds. 6.95 (978-0-8118-4047-7(6)) Chronicle Bks. LLC.

—A Picnic with Monet. 2003. (Illus.). 22p. (J). bds. 6.95 (978-0-8118-4046-0(8)) Chronicle Bks. LLC.

Merlo, Claudio & Ganeri, Anita. The History of Art. 2001. (Masters of Art Ser.). (Illus.). 128p. (J). (gr. 3 up). 29.95 (978-0-87226-531-8(5) , 65315B, Bedrick, Peter Bks.) School Specialty Publishing.

Metropolitan Museum of Art Staff, contrib. by. Museum Shapes. 2005. (Illus.). 48p. (J). (ps-1). 16.99 (978-0-316-05698-4(7)) Little Brown & Co.

Micklethwait, Lucy. I Spy Shapes in Art. 2004. (Illus.). 40p. (J). 19.99 (978-0-06-073193-9(1)) HarperCollins Pubs.

—I Spy Two Eyes: Numbers in Art. 1999. (Illus.). (J). 17.79 (978-0-606-15581-6(3)) Tandem Library Bks.

Minnerly, Denise Bennett, illus. Molly Meets Mona & Friends: A Magical Day in the Museum. 2004. 40p. (J). (978-1-56290-324-4(1)) Crystal Productions.

Morris, Neil & Foglia, Enrico. The Life of Moses. 2003. (Art Revelations Ser.). (Illus.). 32p. (J). (gr. 6-9). 18.95 (978-1-59270-001-1(2)) Enchanted Lion Bks., LLC.

Muhlberger, Richard. What Makes a Degas a Degas? 2002. (Illus.). 48p. (YA). 16.99 (978-0-670-03571-7(8) , Viking Juvenile) Penguin Group (USA) Inc.

—What Makes a Monet a Monet? 2002. (Illus.). 48p. (YA). 16.99 (978-0-670-03570-0(X) , Viking Juvenile) Penguin Group (USA) Inc.

—What Makes a Rembrandt a Rembrandt? 2002. (Illus.). 48p. (J). 16.99 (978-0-670-03572-4(6) , Viking Juvenile) Penguin Group (USA) Inc.

—What Makes a Van Gogh a Van Gogh? 2002. (Illus.). 48p. (YA). 16.99 (978-0-670-03573-1(4) , Viking Juvenile) Penguin Group (USA) Inc.

Murphy, Patricia J. Creative Minds. 2005. (Real Deal Ser.). (Illus.). 32p. (J). (978-0-7608-9637-2(2)) Sundance/Newbridge Educational Publishing.

Newbery, Elizabeth. Color in Art. 2001. (Art for All Ser.). (Illus.). 32p. (J). lib. bdg. 24.25 (978-1-930643-30-7(6)) Chrysalis Education.

—How Is Art Made? 2001. (Art for All Ser.). (Illus.). 32p. (J). lib. bdg. 24.25 (978-1-930643-31-4(4)) Chrysalis Education.

—Why Make Art? 2001. (Art for All Ser.). (Illus.). 32p. (J). lib. bdg. 24.25 (978-1-930643-33-8(0)) Chrysalis Education.

O'Reilly, Wenda B. The Renaissance Art Book: Discover Thirty Glorious Masterpieces by Leonardo da Vinci, Michelangelo, Raphael, Fra Angelico, Botticelli. 2000. (Illus.). 76p. (J). pap. 14.95 (978-1-889613-03-1(7)) Birdcage Pr.

Osofsky, Randy. Come Look with Me: Art in Early America. 2006. (Come Look with Me Ser.). (J). 15.95 (***978-1-890674-12-0(5)***) Charlesbridge Publishing, Inc.

Phaidon Press Editors. The Art Book for Children. 2006. 19.95 (***978-0-7148-9863-6(5)***) Phaidon Pr., Inc.

Raczka, Bob. Art Is... 2003. (Illus.). 32p. (J). (gr. k-3). pap. 9.95 (978-0-7613-1832-3(1) , First Avenue Editions) Lerner Publishing Group.

—Art Is... 2003. (Illus.). 32p. (J). (ps-ps). lib. bdg. 18.75 (978-0-613-58956-7(4)) Tandem Library Bks.

—More Than Meets the Eye: Seeing Art with All Five Senses. 2003. (Illus.). 32p. (J). pap. 9.95 (978-0-7613-1994-8(8) , First Avenue Editions) Lerner Publishing Group.

—More Than Meets the Eye: Seeing Art with All Five Senses. 2003. (gr. k-3). lib. bdg. 18.75 (978-0-613-90443-8(5)) Tandem Library Bks.

—No One Saw. 2001. (gr. k-3). lib. bdg. 18.75 (978-0-613-90694-4(2)) Tandem Library Bks.

—No One Saw... Ordinary Things Through the Eyes of an Artist. 2001. (Illus.). 32p. (J). (gr. k-2). pap. 9.95 (978-0-7613-1648-0(5) , First Avenue Editions) Lerner Publishing Group.

—Unlikely Pairs: Fun with Famous Works of Art. (Bob Raczka's Art Adventures Ser.). (Illus.). (J). (gr. 4 up). 2006. 32p. lib. bdg. 23.93 (978-0-7613-2936-7(6)); 2005. 31p. pap. 9.95 (978-0-7613-2378-5(3) , First Avenue Editions) Lerner Publishing Group.

—Where in the World? Around the Globe in Thirteen Works of Art. 2007. (Illus.). 32p. (J). (gr. 3-8). spiral bd. 23.93 (978-0-8225-6371-6(1) , Millbrook Pr.) Lerner Publishing Group.

Raimondo, Joyce. Imagine That! Activities & Adventures in Surrealism. 2004. (New Children's Ser.). (Illus.). 48p. (J). 12.95 (978-0-8230-2502-2(0)) Watson-Guptill Pubns., Inc.

—Picture This! Activities & Adventures in Impressionism. 2004. (Art Explorers Ser.). (Illus.). 48p. (J). (gr. 1-5). 12.95 (978-0-8230-2503-9(9)) Watson-Guptill Pubns., Inc.

Renshaw, Amanda. Art Book for Children, Bk. 2. 2007. (Illus.). 80p. (YA). (gr. 3 up). 19.95 (***978-0-7148-4705-4(4)***) Phaidon Pr., Inc.

Richardson, Joy. Using Color in Art. 1999. (How to Look at Art Ser.). (Illus.). 32p. (J). (gr. 1 up). lib. bdg. 23.33 (978-0-8368-2629-6(9)) Stevens, Gareth Inc.

Richardson, R. Sarah. Come Look with Me: The Artist at Work. 2006. (Come Look with Me Ser.). (J). 15.95 (***978-1-890674-09-0(5)***) Charlesbridge Publishing, Inc.

Richardson, Sarah. Art in a Box. 2005. (Illus.). 20p. (J). (gr. 1-7). 19.95 (978-1-85437-536-0(9)) Tate Gallery Publishing, Ltd. GBR. *Dist:* Hachette Bk. Group.

Roy, Jennifer Rozines & Roy, Gregory. Jacob Lawrence: Painter of African-American Life. 2003. (J). 18.95 (978-0-7660-1878-5(4)) Enslow Pubs., Inc.

Ruggi, Gilda Williams. The Art Book for Children. rev. ed. 2005. (Illus.). 80p. (gr. 4-7). 19.95 (978-0-7148-4530-2(2)) Phaidon Pr. GBR. *Dist:* Hachette Bk. Group.

Sabbeth, Carol. Frida Kahlo & Diego Rivera: Their Lives & Ideas, 24 Activities. 2005. (For Kids Ser.). (Illus.). 160p. (J). pap. 17.95 (978-1-55652-569-8(9) , 1241061) Chicago Review Pr., Inc.

Sateren, Shelley Swanson. Michaelangelo. 2002. (Masterpieces). (Illus.). 24p. (J). (gr. 2-3). lib. bdg. 18.60 (978-0-7368-1125-5(7) , Bridgestone Bks.) Capstone Pr., Inc.

Sayre, Henry M. Cave Paintings to Picasso: The Inside Scoop on 50 Famous Masterpieces. 2004. (Illus.). 96p. (J). 22.95 (978-0-8118-3767-5(X)) Chronicle Bks. LLC.

Scarborough, Kate. Pablo Picasso. 2002. (Artists in Their Time Ser.). (Illus.). (J). (gr. 5-7). 46p. pap. 6.95 (978-0-531-16622-2(8)); 48p. pap. 23.50 (978-0-531-12229-7(8)) Scholastic Library Publishing. (Watts, Franklin).

—Pablo Picasso. 2002. (Illus.). 46p. (J). (gr. 3-7). lib. bdg. 15.25 (978-0-613-54067-4(0)) Tandem Library Bks.

Schaefer, A. R. Alexander Calder. (Life & Work of. . . Ser.). (Illus.). 32p. (J). (gr. k-2). 2003. lib. bdg. 22.79 (978-1-4034-0287-5(6)); 2002. pap. 6.50 (978-1-4034-0493-0(3)) Heinemann Library.

—Diego Rivera. (Life & Work of. . . Ser.). (Illus.). 32p. (J). (gr. k-2). 2003. lib. bdg. 22.79 (978-1-4034-0288-2(4)); 2002. pap. 6.50 (978-1-4034-0494-7(1)) Heinemann Library.

—Grandma Moses. (Life & Work of. . . Ser.). (Illus.). 32p. (J). (gr. k-2). 2003. lib. bdg. 22.79 (978-1-4034-0289-9(2)); 2002. pap. 6.50 (978-1-4034-0495-4(X)) Heinemann Library.

—Jacob Lawrence. 2002. (Life & Work of. . . Ser.). (J). pap. 6.50 (978-1-4034-0496-1(8)); 32p. lib. bdg. 21.36 (978-1-4034-0290-5(6)) Heinemann Library.

Schulte, Jessica. Can You Find It Inside? Search & Discover for Young Art Lovers. 2005. (Illus.). 32p. (J). (gr. k-4). 10.95 (978-0-8109-5794-7(9) , Abrams Bks. for Young Readers) Abrams, Harry N. , Inc.

Slides. African Arts & Cultures. 4th ed. 2007. (Illus.). xix, 638p. (J). (***978-0-87192-719-4(5)***) Davis Pubns., Inc.

Somerville, Louisa & Crowley, Bridget. Animals in Art. 2001. (In Art Ser.). (Illus.). 47p. 19.99 (978-0-7451-5262-2(7) , Cherrytree Books) Evans Publishing Group GBR. *Dist:* Independent Pubs. Group.

Stephens, Pamela Geiger. Dropping in on Matisse. McNeill, Jim, illus. 2004. 32p. (J). (978-1-56290-322-0(5)) Crystal Productions.

Sturgis, Alexander. Optical Illusions in Art: Or - Discover How Paintings Aren't Always What They Seem to Be. 2003. (Illus.). 32p. (J). pap. 5.95 (978-1-4027-0650-9(2)) Sterling Publishing Co., Inc.

Tames, Richard. Auguste Rodin. (Heinemann First Library). 32p. (J). (gr. k-2). 2000. lib. bdg. 21.36 (978-1-57572-342-6(5)); Set 1. 2002. (Illus.). pap. 6.50 (978-1-58810-288-1(2) , 91051) Heinemann Library.

Taylor, Rod. Understanding & Investigating Art. 1998. (Illus.). 192p. (YA). pap. 35.00 (978-0-340-67989-0(1)) Hodder Education GBR. *Dist:* Trafalgar Square Publishing.

Thomson, Ruth. Families. 2003. (First Look at Art Ser.). (Illus.). 32p. (J). (gr. 3-5). 23.00 (978-0-7910-7946-1(5) , Chelsea Hse.) Facts On File, Inc.

—Places. 2003. (First Look at Art Ser.). (Illus.). 32p. (gr. 3-5). 23.00 (978-0-7910-7947-8(3) , Chelsea Hse.) Facts On File, Inc.

Venezia, Mike. Diego Velazquez. Venezia, Mike, illus. 2004. (Getting to Know the World's Greatest Artists Ser.). (Illus.). 32p. (J). (gr. 3-4). pap. 6.95 (978-0-516-26980-1(1) , Children's Pr.) Scholastic Library Publishing.

—Edgar Degas. Venezia, Mike, illus. 2001. (Getting to Know the World's Greatest Artists Ser.). (Illus.). 32p. (J). (gr. 3-4). pap. 6.95 (978-0-516-27172-9(5) , Children's Pr.) Scholastic Library Publishing.

—Edgar Degas. 2000. (Getting to Know the World's Greatest Artists Ser.). (Illus.). 32p. (J). (gr. 3-4). 27.00 (978-0-516-21593-8(0) , Children's Pr.) Scholastic Library Publishing.

—Edgar Degas. Venezia, Mike, illus. 2001. (Illus.). 31p. (J). (ps-ps). lib. bdg. 15.25 (978-0-613-50683-0(9)) Tandem Library Bks.

—Eugene Delacroix. 2003. (Getting to Know World Artists Ser.). (Illus.). 32p. (J). 27.00 (978-0-516-22576-0(6) , Children's Pr.) Scholastic Library Publishing.

—Jacob Lawrence. 1999. (Getting to Know the World's Greatest Artists Ser.). (Illus.). 32p. (J). (gr. 3-4). 27.00 (978-0-516-21012-4(2) , Children's Pr.) Scholastic Library Publishing.

—Norman Rockwell. Venezia, Mike, illus. 2001. (Getting to Know the World's Greatest Artists Ser.). (Illus.). 32p. (J). (gr. 3-4). pap. 6.95 (978-0-516-27173-6(3) , Children's Pr.) Scholastic Library Publishing.

—Norman Rockwell. 2000. (Getting to Know the World's Greatest Artists Ser.). (Illus.). 32p. (J). (gr. 3-4). 27.00 (978-0-516-21594-5(9) , Children's Pr.) Scholastic Library Publishing.

—Norman Rockwell. 2000. (gr. 3-6). lib. bdg. 15.25 (978-0-613-50720-2(7)) Tandem Library Bks.

—Roy Lichtenstein. Venezia, Mike, illus. 2002. (Getting to Know the World's Greatest Artists Ser.). (Illus.). 32p. (J). (gr. 3-4). pap. 6.95 (978-0-516-25963-5(6) , Children's Pr.) Scholastic Library Publishing.

—Roy Lichtenstein. Lichtenstein, Roy, illus. 2001. (Getting to Know the World's Greatest Artists Ser.). 32p. (J). (gr. 3-4). 27.00 (978-0-516-22030-7(6) , Children's Pr.) Scholastic Library Publishing.

—Roy Lichtenstein. 2001. (gr. 3-6). lib. bdg. 15.25 (978-0-613-50362-4(7)) Tandem Library Bks.

Woodhouse, Jayne. Joseph Turner. 2000. (Life & Work of. . . Ser.). (Illus.). 32p. (J). (gr. k-2). lib. bdg. 21.36 (978-1-57572-345-7(X)) Heinemann Library.

—Peter Bruegel. 2000. (Heinemann First Library). (Illus.). 32p. (J). (gr. k-2). lib. bdg. 21.36 (978-1-57572-344-0(1)) Heinemann Library.

—Pieter Bruegel. 2001. (gr. k-3). lib. bdg. 14.75 (978-0-613-45811-5(7)) Tandem Library Bks.

Wright, Jessica Noelani. Come Look with Me: Exploring Modern Art. 2006. (J). 15.95 (***978-1-890674-10-6(9)***) Charlesbridge Publishing, Inc.

Yenawine, Philip. People. 3rd ed. 2006. (Illus.). 24p. (gr. 13 up). 14.95 (978-0-87070-174-0(6)) D.A.P./Distributed Art Pubs.

—Places. 2006. (Illus.). 22p. (J). (gr. 4-8). reprint ed. 15.00 (978-1-4223-5407-0(5)) DIANE Publishing Co.

—Stories. 2006. (Illus.). 32p. (gr. 13 up). 9.95 (978-0-87070-178-8(9)) D.A.P./Distributed Art Pubs.

ART APPRECIATION—FICTION

Baker, Sharon. A Nickel, a Trolley, a Treasure House. Peck, Beth, illus. 2007. 32p. (J). (gr. k-5). 16.99 (978-0-670-05982-9(X) , Viking Juvenile) Penguin Group (USA) Inc.

Boehm, Arlene P. Jack in Search of Art. Boehm, Arlene P., illus. (Illus.). 32p. (ps-3). 2001. pap. 7.95 (978-1-57098-234-7(1)); 1998. 16.95 (978-1-57098-244-6(9)) Rinehart, Roberts Pubs.

Gutman, Dan. Ms. Hannah Is Bananas! Paillot, Jim, illus. 2005. 84p. (J). (gr. 2-5). lib. bdg. 11.19 (978-0-606-33041-1(0)) Tandem Library Bks.

Mayhew, James. Katie Meets the Impressionists. 2007. 32p. (J). pap. 5.99 (***978-0-439-93508-1(3)***) Scholastic, Inc.

—Katie Meets the Impressionists. Mayhew, James, illus. 1999. (Illus.). 32p. (J). (ps-2). pap. 16.95 (978-0-531-30151-7(6) , Orchard Bks.) Scholastic, Inc.

—Katie's Sunday Afternoon. 2005. (Illus.). 32p. (J). pap. 16.95 (978-0-439-60678-3(0) , Orchard Bks.) Scholastic, Inc.

Montanari, Eva. The Crocodile's True Colors. 2002. (Illus.). 32p. (J). (gr. k-3). 14.95 (978-0-8230-2435-3(0)) Watson-Guptill Pubns., Inc.

Raintree Steck-Vaughn Staff. The Art Riddle Contest. 1999. (Illus.). (J). pap. 35.60 (978-0-7398-0897-9(4)) Steck-Vaughn.

Scieszka, Jon & Smith, Lane. Seen Art? 2005. (Illus.). (J). (978-1-4155-7784-4(6)) Museum of Modern Art.

Sortland, Bjorn. Anna's Art Adventure. Elling, Lars, illus. 2005. (Picture Bks.). 32p. (gr. k-2). 15.25 (978-1-57505-376-9(4)) Lerner Publishing Group.

ART CRITICISM

see also Art Appreciation

Aronson, Marc. Art Attack: A Brief Cultural History of the Avant-Garde. 1998. (Illus.). 192p. (YA). (gr. 7-12). tchr. ed. 24.00 (978-0-395-79729-7(2) , Clarion Bks.) Houghton Mifflin Co. Trade & Reference Div.

Blizzard, Gladys S. Come Look with Me: Animals in Art. 2006. (Come Look with Me Ser.). 32p. (YA). (gr. k-12). 15.95 (978-1-56566-013-7(7)) Charlesbridge Publishing, Inc.

—Come Look with Me: Exploring Landscape Art with Children. 2006. (Come Look with Me Ser.). (Illus.). 32p. (YA). (gr. 1-8). 15.95 (978-0-934738-95-8(5)) Charlesbridge Publishing, Inc.

Holzhey, Magdalena. Frida Kahlo: The Artist in the Blue House. 2003. (Adventures in Art Ser.). (Illus.). 30p. (J). (gr. 5 up). 14.95 (978-3-7913-2863-8(8)) Prestel Publishing.

Khu, Jannell. Drawing Fire Trucks. 2005. (Let's Draw with Shapes Ser.). (Illus.). 24p. (J). 17.25 (978-1-4042-2794-1(6) , PowerKids Pr.) Rosen Publishing Group, Inc., The.

Langmuir, Erika & Thomson, Ruth. Looking at Paintings: An Introduction to Fine Art for Young People. 2003. (Disney Manuels Ser.). (Illus.). 160p. 14.95 (978-1-59373-008-6(X)) Bunker Hill Publishing, Inc.

Randolph, Joanne. Drawing Dinosaurs. 2005. (Let's Draw with Shapes Ser.). (J). 17.25 (978-1-4042-2793-4(8) , PowerKids Pr.) Rosen Publishing Group, Inc., The.

—Drawing Trucks. 2005. (Let's Draw with Shapes Ser.). (J). 17.25 (978-1-4042-2796-5(2) , PowerKids Pr.) Rosen Publishing Group, Inc., The.

Wenzel, Angela. The Mad, Mad, Mad World of Salvador Dali. 2003. (Adventures in Art Ser.). (Illus.). 30p. 14.95 (978-3-7913-2944-4(8)) Prestel Publishing.

Wright, Suzanne. The Choice Is Yours: An Art Activity Handbook for Young Artists Highlighting the Art & Life of Jacob Lawrence. 2002. (Illus.). 64p. (J). pap. (978-0-943044-30-9(8)) Phillips Collection, The.

ART EDUCATION

see Art—Study and Teaching

ART FORGERIES

see Forgery of Works of Art

ART GALLERIES, COMMERCIAL

Katter, Eldon & Stewart. Art a Global Pursuit: Davis E-Gallery. 2001. (Illus.). cd-rom (978-0-87192-501-5(X)) Davis Pubns., Inc.

3D Gallery: Stereo Images by Members of Cascade Stereoscopic Club. 2001. 73p. (J). spiral bd. 20.00 (978-0-9669801-1-0(5)) Chameleon Enterprises, Inc.

ART INDUSTRIES AND TRADE

see also Folk Art

also special industries, trades, etc., e.g. Glass painting and staining; Leather Work

MacConnel, Kim. A Collection of Applied Design. 2004. (Illus.). (YA). 5.00 (978-0-9744804-6-6(0) , Athenaeum Music & Arts Library) Library Assn. of La Jolla.

ART MUSEUMS

see also Art Galleries, Commercial

Blake, Quentin. Tell Me a Picture. Blake, Quentin, illus. 2003. (Single Titles Ser.). (Illus.). 128p. lib. bdg. 29.90 (978-0-7613-2748-6(7) , Millbrook Pr.) Lerner Publishing Group.

—Tell Me a Picture. 2003. (Illus.). 128p. (gr. 3 up). pap. (978-0-7613-1893-4(3) , Millbrook Pr.) Lerner Publishing Group.

—Tell Me a Picture. 2006. (Illus.). 128p. pap. 17.95 (978-1-84507-607-0(7)) Lincoln, Frances Ltd. GBR. *Dist:* Perseus Distribution.

Browne, Anthony. The Shape Game. Browne, Anthony, illus. 2003. (Illus.). 32p. (J). (gr. k up). 16.00 (978-0-374-36764-0(7) , Farrar, Straus & Giroux (BYR)) Farrar, Straus & Giroux.

Danzis, Steve. Behind the Lions: A Family Guide to the Art Institute of Chicago. Csicsko, David L., illus. 1998. 112p. (J). (gr. 2-8). pap. 15.95 (978-0-86559-156-1(3)) Art Institute of Chicago.

Knapp, Ruthie & Lehmberg, Janice. American Art: Museum Guide for Kids. 1998. (Off the Wall Museum Guides for Kids). (ENG., Illus.). 72p. (J). pap. 10.95 (978-0-87192-386-8(6)) Davis Pubns., Inc.

—Egyptian Art. 1998. (Off the Wall Museum Guides for Kids). (Illus.). 64p. (J). (gr. 2-7). pap. 10.95 (978-0-87192-384-4(X)) Davis Pubns., Inc.

—Impressionist Art. 1998. (Off the Wall Museum Guides for Kids). (Illus.). 72p. (J). pap. 10.95 (978-0-87192-385-1(8)) Davis Pubns., Inc.

Koelsch, Patrice. Museums. 2001. (Designing the Future Ser.). (Illus.). 32p. (J). (978-1-58341-132-2(1) , Creative Education) Creative Co., The.

Minnerly, Denise Bennett, illus. Molly Meets Mona & Friends: A Magical Day in the Museum. 2004. 40p. (J). (978-1-56290-324-4(1)) Crystal Productions.

Monk, Jonathan. Jonathan Monk: P. 2000. (Revolver Children's Book Ser.). (Illus.). 72p. 30.95 (978-3-934823-80-8(7)) Keller, Christoph Revolver Verlag DEU. *Dist:* RAM Pubns. & Distribution.

Thomson, Ruth. Museum of Art: Masterpieces. 2001. (Museum Kits Ser.). (Illus.). 64p. (J). (gr. 3 up). pap. 19.95 (978-0-7624-1067-5(1) , Running Pr. Kids) Running Pr. Bk. Pubs.

Wright, Wayne. Thornton Burgess-A Descriptive Book Bibliography. 2000. (YA). 23.95 (978-0-8488-2869-1(0)) Amereon LTD.

ART OBJECTS

see also classes of art objects, e.g. Furniture; pottery; etc.

Trash Art. 2002. (Illus.). (J). pap. 3.74 (978-0-7398-5841-7(6)) Steck-Vaughn.

ART OBJECTS, FORGERY OF

see Forgery of Works of Art

ART SCHOOLS

see Art—Study and Teaching

ARTESIAN WELLS

see Wells

ARTHRITIS

Fall, Guy. Everything You Need to Know about Juvenile Arthritis. 2005. (Need to Know Library). (Illus.). 64p. (YA). (gr. 4-6). lib. bdg. 25.25 (978-0-8239-3614-4(7)) Rosen Publishing Group, Inc., The.

Gold, Susan Dudley. Arthritis. rev. ed. 2001. (Health Watch Ser.). (Illus.). 48p. (YA). (gr. 4-10). lib. bdg. 23.93 (978-0-7660-1659-0(5)) Enslow Pubs., Inc.

Gray, Susan Heinrichs. Living with Juvenile Rheumatoid Arthritis. 2002. (Living Well: Chronic Conditions Ser.). (Illus.). 32p. (J). (gr. 2-6). 27.07 (978-1-56766-104-0(1)) Child's World, Inc.

Llewellyn, Claire. Arthritis. 2001. (Illus.). 32p. (J). lib. bdg. 24.25 (978-1-929298-99-0(4)) Chrysalis Education.

Sheen, Barbara. Arthritis. 2002. (Diseases & Disorders Ser.). (Illus.). 120p. (YA). (gr. 6-9). 32.45 (978-1-56006-904-1(X) , Lucent Bks.) Thomson Gale.

ARTHRITIS—FICTION

Hartmann, April. Keeping a Secret: A Story about Juvenile Rheumatoid Arthritis. Hartmann, April, illus. 2002. 32p. (J). 14.95 (978-0-929173-34-4(1)) Health Pr. NA, Inc.

Mercer, Adrienne. Rebound. 2002. (gr. 3-6). lib. bdg. 13.55 (978-0-613-78322-4(0)) Tandem Library Bks.

Miller, DeeDee L. Taking Arthritis to School. Dineen, Tom, illus. 2002. (Special Kids in School Ser.: 13). 32p. (J). pr. 11.95 (978-1-891383-21-2(3) , 70013) JayJo Bks., LLC.

ARTHROPODA

see also Centipedes; Crabs; Insects; Lobsters; Millipedes; Scorpions; Spiders

Bonotaux, Giles. Dirty Rotten Bugs? Bonotaux, Giles, illus. 2007. (Illus.). 48p. (gr. 3-6). 14.95 (***978-1-58728-593-6(2)*** , Two Can Publishing) T&N Children's Publishing.

Dixon, Dougal. Early Life. 2006. (Prehistoric World Bks.). 32p. (J). pap. 4.99 (978-0-7641-3482-1(5)) Barron's Educational Series, Inc.

Domnauer, Teresa. Arachnid Attack!, Level 2. 2007. (Extreme Readers Ser.). 32p. (J). (gr. k-1). pap. 3.95 (*978-0-7696-6550-4(0)) School Specialty Publishing.

Gingold, Janet. My Adventure with Arthropods: Advanced My Adventure. 2007. 44p. (J). pap. 8.99 (978-1-59092-447-1(9) , Orchard Academy Pr.) Windstorm Creative.

Harrison, Paul. Micro Bugs. 2007. (Up Close Ser.). (Illus.). 24p. (J). (gr. 3-5). lib. bdg. 23.95 (*978-1-4042-3760-5(7) , PowerKids Pr.) Rosen Publishing Group, Inc., The.

Harvey, Bev. Arthropods. 2002. (Chelsea Clubhouse Science Exploration Ser.). (Illus.). 32p. (gr. k-2). 23.00 (978-0-7910-6986-8(9) , Chelsea Hse.) Facts On File, Inc.

Healy, Nick. The World's Most Dangerous Bugs. 2006. (Edge Books, the World's Top Tens). (Illus.). 32p. (978-0-7368-5456-6(8)) Capstone Pr., Inc.

Himmelman, John. A Pill Bug's Life. 1999. (gr. k-3). lib. bdg. 15.25 (978-0-613-37504-7(1)) Tandem Library Bks.

Huggins-Cooper, Lynn. Beastly Bugs. 2007. (Killer Nature! Ser.). (Illus.). 32p. (J). (gr. 3-5). lib. bdg. 28.50 (*978-1-58340-936-7(X)) Smart Apple Media.

Kalman, Bobbie. What Is an Arthropod? 2002. (Science of Living Things Ser.). (Illus.). 32p. (J). (gr. 2-3). (978-0-86505-991-7(8)); pap. (978-0-86505-968-9(3)) Crabtree Publishing Co.

Minnis, Ivan. I Like Bugs. 2007. 24p. (J). (978-1-4034-9280-7(8)); (978-1-4034-9271-5(9)) Heinemann Library.

Morgan, Sally. Arthropods. 2004. (Illus.). 64p. (J). 25.70 (978-1-4109-1049-3(0)); pap. 9.50 (978-1-4109-1343-2(0)) Harcourt Schl. Pubs.

Pyers. Pill Bugs 6-Pack. 2004. (Minibeasts up Close Ser.). pap. 40.50 (978-1-4109-1545-0(X)) Harcourt Schl. Pubs.

Smithyman, Kathryn & Kalman, Bobbie. Les Arthropodes. 2005. (FRE., Illus.). 32p. (J). pap. (978-2-89579-026-6(4)) Crabtree Publishing Co.

Townsend. Incredible Crustaceans. 2004. (Illus.). (J). 31.36 (978-1-4109-0528-4(4)); Pack. pap. 51.30 (978-1-4109-0861-2(5)) Harcourt Schl. Pubs.

—Incredible Mollusks. 2004. (Illus.). (J). pap. 9.50 (978-1-4109-0852-0(6)) Harcourt Schl. Pubs.

ARTHROPODA—FICTION

Nickel, Scott. Curse of the Red Scorpion. Harpster, Steve, illus. 2006. (Graphic Sparks Ser.). 33p. (J). 19.93 (978-1-59889-034-1(4)) Stone Arch Bks.

ARTHUR (FICTITIOUS CHARACTER : BROWN)—FICTION

Arthur. 2001. (Illus.). (J). 7.98 (978-0-7853-4852-8(2)) Publications International, Ltd.

Brown, Marc. Arthur, Bk. 4 to 6. 2002. (Illus.). 196p. (J). (gr. 2-4). 9.95 (978-0-316-07595-4(7)) Little, Brown Bks. for Young Readers.

—Arthur & the 1,001 Dads. ed. 2005. (Arthur Chapter Bks.: No. 28). (Illus.). 57p. (J). lib. bdg. 15.00 (978-1-59054-716-8(0)) Fitzgerald Bks.

—Arthur & the Babysitter. 2004. 32p. (J). 15.95 (978-0-316-12128-6(2)) Little Brown & Co.

—Arthur & the Bad-Luck Brain. ed. 2005. (Arthur Chapter Bks.: Bk. 30). (Illus.). 55p. (J). lib. bdg. 15.00 (978-1-59054-717-5(9)) Fitzgerald Bks.

—Arthur & the Bad-Luck Brain. 30th ed. 2003. (Arthur Chapter Bks.: Bk. 30). (Illus.). 64p. (J). (gr. 2-4). pap. 4.25 (978-0-316-12377-8(3)) Little Brown & Co.

—Arthur & the Bad-Luck Brain. 30th ed. 2003. (Arthur Chapter Bks. : Bk. 30). (Illus.). 64p. (J). (gr. 2-4). 14.95 (978-0-316-12650-2(0)) Little, Brown Bks. for Young Readers.

—Arthur & the Best Coach Ever. Brown, Marc, illus. 4th ed. 2001. (Arthur Good Sports Ser.: Bk. 4). (Illus.). 64p. (J). (gr. 2-4). 13.95 (978-0-316-11965-8(2)); pap. 4.25 (978-0-316-12117-0(7)) Little, Brown Bks. for Young Readers.

—Arthur & the Best Coach Ever. 2001. (Arthur Good Sports Ser.: Bk. 4). (gr. 3-6). lib. bdg. 11.80 (978-0-613-35627-5(6)); (Illus.). (J). 10.75 (978-0-606-21910-5(2)) Tandem Library Bks.

—Arthur & the Big Blow-Up. 2002. (Arthur Chapter Bks.: Bk. 20). (Illus.). (J). 11.45 (978-0-7587-0000-1(8)) Book Wholesalers, Inc.

—Arthur & the Big Blow-Up. 1999. (Arthur Chapter Bks. : Bk. 20). (J). (gr. 3-6). pap. 3.95 (978-0-316-12326-6(9)) Little, Brown Bks. for Young Readers.

—Arthur & the Big Blow-Up. 2000. (Arthur Chapter Bks.: Bk. 20). (gr. k-3). lib. bdg. 11.80 (978-0-613-24244-8(0)); (Illus.). (J). (gr. 3-6). 10.75 (978-0-606-18251-5(9)) Tandem Library Bks.

—Arthur & the Big Blow-up. ed. 2005. (Arthur Chapter Bks.: No. 20). (Illus.). 54p. (J). lib. bdg. 15.00 (978-1-59054-718-2(7)) Fitzgerald Bks.

—Arthur & the Big Blow-Up. Brown, Marc, illus. 20th ed. 2000. (Arthur Chapter Bks. : Bk. 20). (Illus.). 64p. (J). (gr. 2-4). pap. 4.25 (978-0-316-12203-0(3)) Little, Brown Bks. for Young Readers.

—Arthur & the Big Snow. Brown, Marc, illus. 2005. (Illus.). 24p. (J). (ps-1). pap. 3.99 (978-0-316-05770-7(3)) Little Brown & Co.

—Arthur & the Comet Crisis. 2002. (Arthur Chapter Bks.: Bk. 27). (Illus.). (J). 11.70 (978-1-4046-1061-3(8)) Book Wholesalers, Inc.

—Arthur & the Comet Crisis. ed. 2005. (Arthur Chapter Bks.: No. 27). (Illus.). 54p. (J). lib. bdg. 15.00 (978-1-59054-719-9(5)) Fitzgerald Bks.

—Arthur & the Comet Crisis. Brown, Marc, illus. 2002. (Arthur Chapter Bks. : Bk. 27). (Illus.). 64p. (J). (gr. 2-4). 14.95 (978-0-316-12462-1(1)); 27th ed. pap. 4.25 (978-0-316-12199-6(1)) Little, Brown Bks. for Young Readers.

—Arthur & the Comet Crisis. 2002. (Arthur Chapter Bks.: Bk. 27). (gr. k-3). lib. bdg. 12.10 (978-0-613-50585-7(9)) Tandem Library Bks.

—Arthur & the Cootie-Catcher. ed. 2005. (Arthur Chapter Bks.: Bk. 15). (Illus.). 60p. (J). lib. bdg. 15.00 (978-1-59054-720-5(9)) Fitzgerald Bks.

—Arthur & the Cootie-Catcher. 1999. (Arthur Chapter Bks. : Bk. 15). (J). (gr. 3-6). pap. 3.95 (978-0-316-12085-2(5)) Little, Brown Bks. for Young Readers.

—Arthur & the Cootie-Catcher. Brown, Marc, illus. 15th ed. 1999. (Arthur Chapter Bks. : Bk. 15). (Illus.). 64p. (J). (gr. 2-4). pap. 4.25 (978-0-316-12266-5(1)) Little, Brown Bks. for Young Readers.

—Arthur & the Double Dare. 2002. (Arthur Chapter Bks.: Bk. 25). (Illus.). (J). 11.70 (978-0-7587-9423-9(1)) Book Wholesalers, Inc.

—Arthur & the Double Dare. ed. 2005. (Arthur Chapter Bks.: Bk. 25). (Illus.). 56p. (J). lib. bdg. 15.00 (978-1-59054-722-9(5)) Fitzgerald Bks.

—Arthur & the Double Dare. Brown, Marc, illus. 2002. (Arthur Chapter Bks. : Bk. 25). (Illus.). 64p. (J). (gr. 2-4). 13.95 (978-0-316-12264-1(5)); pap. 4.25 (978-0-316-12087-6(1)) Little, Brown Bks. for Young Readers.

—Arthur & the Double Dare. 2002. (Arthur Chapter Bks.: Bk. 25). (gr. k-3). lib. bdg. 12.10 (978-0-613-50586-4(7)) Tandem Library Bks.

—Arthur & the Goalie Ghost. 2001. (Arthur Good Sports Ser.). (gr. k-3). lib. bdg. 11.80 (978-0-613-44164-3(8)); (Illus.). (J). 10.75 (978-0-606-22027-9(5)) Tandem Library Bks.

—Arthur & the Lost Diary. ed. 2005. (Arthur Chapter Bks.: Bk. 9). (Illus.). 55p. (J). lib. bdg. 15.00 (978-1-59054-723-6(3)) Fitzgerald Bks.

—Arthur & the Lost Diary. 2002. (Arthur Chapter Bks. : Bk. 9). (Illus.). (J). (gr. k-3). 14.95 (978-1-58605-916-3(5) , LeapFrog Schl. Hse.) LeapFrog Enterprises, Inc.

—Arthur & the Lost Diary. 1998. (Arthur Chapter Bks. : Bk. 9). (J). (gr. 3-6). pap. 3.95 (978-0-316-61004-9(6)); 9th ed. (Illus.). 64p. (gr. 2-4). pap. 4.25 (978-0-316-11537-7(1)) Little, Brown Bks. for Young Readers.

—Arthur & the Lost Diary. (Arthur Chapter Bks.: Bk. 9). 55p. (J). (gr. 3-6). pap. 3.95 (978-0-8072-1305-6(5)); 1999. (gr. 2-4). pap. 17.00 incl. audio (978-0-8072-0404-7(8) , EFTR200SP) Random Hse. Audio Publishing Group. (Listening Library).

—Arthur & the Nerves of Steal. ed. 2005. (Arthur Chapter Bks.: Bk. 32). (Illus.). 53p. (J). lib. bdg. 15.00 (978-1-59054-724-3(1)) Fitzgerald Bks.

—Arthur & the Nerves of Steal. 2004. (Arthur Chapter Bks. : Bk. 32). (Illus.). 64p. (J). (gr. 2-4). 14.99 (978-0-316-12895-7(3)); pap. 4.25 (978-0-316-12618-2(7)) Little, Brown Bks. for Young Readers. (Tingley, Megan Bks.).

—Arthur & the New Kid. 2004. (Arthur Ser.). (Illus.). 24p. (J). (gr. k-3). pap. 3.99 (978-0-375-81381-8(0)); lib. bdg. 11.99 (978-0-375-91381-5(5)) Random Hse. Children's Bks. (Random Hse. Bks. for Young Readers).

—Arthur & the No-Brainer. ed. 2005. (Arthur Chapter Bks.: Bk. 26). (Illus.). 55p. (J). lib. bdg. 15.00 (978-1-59054-725-0(X)) Fitzgerald Bks.

—Arthur & the No-Brainer. Brown, Marc, illus. 26th ed. 2002. (Arthur Chapter Bks. : Bk. 26). (Illus.). 64p. (J). (gr. 2-4). 14.95 (978-0-316-12332-7(3)); pap. 4.25 (978-0-316-12132-3(0)) Little, Brown Bks. for Young Readers.

—Arthur & the No-Brainer. 2002. (Arthur Chapter Bks.: Bk. 26). (gr. k-3). lib. bdg. 12.10 (978-0-613-50587-1(5)) Tandem Library Bks.

—Arthur & the Pen-Pal Playoff. 2002. (Arthur Good Sports Ser.: Bk. 6). (Illus.). (J). 11.70 (978-0-7587-6863-6(X)) Book Wholesalers, Inc.

—Arthur & the Pen-Pal Playoff. Brown, Marc, illus. 6th ed. 2001. (Arthur Good Sports Ser.: Bk. 6). (Illus.). 64p. (J). (gr. 2-4). 14.95 (978-0-316-12054-8(5)); pap. 4.25 (978-0-316-12170-5(3)) Little, Brown Bks. for Young Readers.

—Arthur & the Pen-Pal Playoff. 2001. (Arthur Good Sports Ser.: Bk. 6). (ps-3). (Illus.). 55p. (J). lib. bdg. 12.10 (978-0-613-44165-0(6)); 11.05 (978-0-606-22556-4(0)) Tandem Library Bks.

—Arthur & the Perfect Brother. Brown, Marc, illus. 21st ed. 2000. (Arthur Chapter Bks. : Bk. 21). (Illus.). 64p. (J). (gr. 2-4). pap. 4.25 (978-0-316-12226-9(2)) Little, Brown Bks. for Young Readers.

—Arthur & the Perfect Brother. 2000. (Illus.). (J). 54p. (ps-ps). lib. bdg. 11.80 (978-0-613-24245-5(9)); (Arthur Chapter Bks.: Bk. 21). (gr. 3-6). 10.75 (978-0-606-18252-2(7)) Tandem Library Bks.

—Arthur & the Poetry Contest. ed. 2005. (Arthur Chapter Bks.: No. 18). (Illus.). 60p. (J). lib. bdg. 15.00 (978-1-59054-727-4(6)) Fitzgerald Bks.

—Arthur & the Poetry Contest. 1999. (Arthur Chapter Bks. : Bk. 18). (J). (gr. 3-6). pap. 3.95 (978-0-316-12153-8(3)) Little, Brown Bks. for Young Readers.

—Arthur & the Poetry Contest. Brown, Marc, illus. 18th ed. 1999. (Arthur Chapter Bks. : Bk. 18). (Illus.). 64p. (J). (gr. 2-4). pap. 4.25 (978-0-316-12295-5(5)) Little, Brown Bks. for Young Readers.

—Arthur & the Poetry Contest. 1999. (Arthur Chapter Bks.: Bk. 18). (gr. k-3). lib. bdg. 11.80 (978-0-613-21137-6(5)); (J). (gr. 3-6). 10.75 (978-0-606-17238-7(6)) Tandem Library Bks.

—Arthur & the Popularity Test. ed. 2005. (Arthur Chapter Bks.: Bk. 12). (Illus.). 58p. (J). lib. bdg. 15.00 (978-1-59054-728-1(4)) Fitzgerald Bks.

—Arthur & the Popularity Test. (Arthur Chapter Bks. : Bk. 12). (J). 1999. (gr. 3-6). pap. 3.95 (978-0-316-11999-3(7)); 12th ed. 1998. (Illus.). 64p. (gr. 2-4). pap. 4.25 (978-0-316-11545-2(2)) Little, Brown Bks. for Young Readers.

—Arthur & the Popularity Test. (Arthur Chapter Bks.: Bk. 12). 58p. (J). (gr. 3-6). pap. 3.95 (978-0-8072-1308-7(X)); 2004. (gr. 2-4). pap. 17.00 incl. audio (978-0-8072-0413-9(7) , FTR204SP) Random Hse. Audio Publishing Group. (Listening Library).

—Arthur & the Race to Read. 2001. (Arthur Good Sports Ser.: Bk. 1). (Illus.). (J). (ps). 58p. lib. bdg. 12.10 (978-0-613-35628-2(4)); 11.05 (978-0-606-21041-6(5)) Tandem Library Bks.

—Arthur & the Recess Rookie. 2001. (Arthur Good Sports Ser.: Bk. 3). (Illus.). 64p. (J). (gr. 2-4). 13.95 (978-0-316-11916-0(4)); 3rd ed. pap. 4.25 (978-0-316-12105-7(3)) Little, Brown Bks. for Young Readers.

—Arthur & the Recess Rookie. 2001. (Arthur Good Sports Ser.: Bk. 3). (gr. 3-6). lib. bdg. 11.80 (978-0-613-35629-9(2)); (Illus.). (J). 10.75 (978-0-606-21909-9(9)) Tandem Library Bks.

—Arthur & the School Pet. 2003. (Arthur Ser.). (Illus.). 24p. (J). (gr. k-2). pap. 3.99 (978-0-375-81001-5(3) , Random Hse. Bks. for Young Readers) Random Hse. Children's Bks.

—Arthur & the School Pet. 2003. (Arthur Ser.). (ps-2). lib. bdg. 11.80 (978-0-613-57492-1(3)) Tandem Library Bks.

—Arthur & the Seventh-Inning Stretcher. Brown, Marc, illus. 2nd ed. 2001. (Arthur Good Sports Ser.: Bk. 2). (Illus.). 64p. (J). (gr. 2-4). 13.95 (978-0-316-11861-3(3)) Little, Brown Bks. for Young Readers.

—Arthur & the True Francine. 1998. (Arthur Adventure Ser.). (Illus.). 32p. (J). (ps-3). 9.95 (978-0-316-11946-7(6)) Little, Brown Bks. for Young Readers.

—Arthur & the True Francine. (Arthur Adventure Ser.). (J). (gr. k-3). 7.98 incl. audio NewSound, LLC.

—Arthur & the World Record. 33rd ed. 2005. (Arthur Chapter Bks. : Bk. 33). (Illus.). 64p. (J). (gr. 2-4). 14.99 (978-0-316-12949-7(6) , Tingley, Megan Bks.); pap. 4.25 (978-0-316-12681-6(0)) Little, Brown Bks. for Young Readers.

—Arthur Babysits. Brown, Marc, illus. 2002. (Arthur Adventure Ser.). (Illus.). (J). 13.15 (978-0-7587-1971-3(X)) Book Wholesalers, Inc.

—Arthur Babysits. 1999. (Arthur Adventure Ser.). (Illus.). (J). (gr. k-3). lib. bdg. 14.10 (978-0-7857-5838-9(0)) Tandem Library Bks.

—Arthur, Clean Your Room! (Arthur Ser.). (Illus.). 24p. (gr. k-3). 2003. lib. bdg. 11.99 (978-0-679-98467-2(4)); 1999. (J). pap. 3.99 (978-0-679-88467-5(X)) Random Hse. Children's Bks. (Random Hse. Bks. for Young Readers).

—Arthur, Clean Your Room! 1999. (Arthur Ser.). (gr. k-3). lib. bdg. 11.80 (978-0-613-23105-3(8)) Tandem Library Bks.

—Arthur Flips!, 18 vols., Vol. 14. 2001. (Illus.). 28p. (J). 3.79 (978-1-57973-120-5(1)) Advance Pubs. LLC.

—Arthur Goes to Camp. Brown, Marc, illus. 2002. (Arthur Adventure Ser.). (Illus.). (J). 13.15 (978-0-7587-1972-0(8)) Book Wholesalers, Inc.

—Arthur Goes to Camp. Brown, Marc, illus. 1998. (Arthur Adventure Ser.). (Illus.). 32p. (J). (gr. k-3). pap. 5.95 (978-0-316-11529-2(0)) Little, Brown Bks. for Young Readers.

—Arthur Helps Out. 2005. (Illus.). 24p. (J). (ps-1). pap. 3.99 (978-0-316-05772-1(X)) Little Brown & Co.

—Arthur in a Pickle. 1999. (Arthur Ser.). lib. bdg. 11.80 (978-0-613-65119-6(7)) Tandem Library Bks.

—Arthur, It's Only Rock 'n' Roll. Brown, Marc, illus. 2002. (Illus.). 32p. (J). (ps-3). 15.95 (978-0-316-11854-5(0)) Little, Brown Bks. for Young Readers.

—Arthur Loses His Marbles. ed. 2005. (Arthur Chapter Bks.: Bk. 31). (Illus.). 56p. (J). lib. bdg. 15.00 (978-1-59054-730-4(6)) Fitzgerald Bks.

—Arthur Loses His Marbles. 2004. (Arthur Chapter Bks.: Bk. 31). (Illus.). 64p. (J). (gr. 2-4). 14.95 (978-0-316-12711-0(6)); pap. 4.25 (978-0-316-12557-4(1)) Little Brown & Co.

—Arthur Loses His Patience, 18 vols. 2001. (Arthur's Family Values: Vol. 11). (Illus.). 28p. 3.79 (978-1-57973-117-5(1)) Advance Pubs. LLC.

—Arthur Lost & Found. ed. 2004. (Arthur Adventure Ser.). (J). (gr. k-3). spiral bd. (978-0-616-11102-4(9)) Canadian National Institute for the Blind/Institut National Canadien pour les Aveugles.

—Arthur Lost & Found. Brown, Marc, illus. (Arthur Adventure Ser.). (Illus.). 32p. (J). (ps-3). 2000. pap. 6.99 (978-0-316-10824-9(3)); 1998. 15.95 (978-0-316-10912-3(6)) Little, Brown Bks. for Young Readers.

—Arthur Lost & Found. 2000. (Arthur Adventure Ser.). (J). (gr. k-3). 12.75 (978-0-606-19835-6(0)) Tandem Library Bks.

—Arthur Plays the Blues. ed. 2005. (Arthur Chapter Bks.: Bk. 29). (Illus.). 53p. (J). lib. bdg. 15.00 (978-1-59054-732-8(2)) Fitzgerald Bks.

—Arthur Plays the Blues. 29th ed. 2003. (Arthur Chapter Bks.: Bk. 29). (Illus.). 64p. (J). (gr. 2-4). pap. 4.25 (978-0-316-12314-3(5)) Little Brown & Co.

—Arthur Plays the Blues. 29th ed. 2003. (Arthur Chapter Bks. : Bk. 29). (Illus.). 64p. (J). (gr. 2-4). 14.95 (978-0-316-12586-4(5)) Little, Brown Bks. for Young Readers.

—Arthur Rocks with Binky. Brown, Marc, illus. 2002. (Arthur Chapter Bks.: Bk. 11). (Illus.). (J). 11.70 (978-0-7587-0439-9(9)) Book Wholesalers, Inc.

—Arthur Rocks with Binky. ed. 2005. (Arthur Chapter Bks.: No. 11). (Illus.). 61p. (J). lib. bdg. (978-1-59054-733-5(0)) Fitzgerald Bks.

—Arthur Rocks with Binky. (Arthur Chapter Bks. : Bk. 11). (Illus.). (J). ed. 1999. (gr. 3-6). pap. 3.95 (978-0-316-10422-7(1)); 11th ed. 1998. 64p. (gr. 2-4). pap. 4.25 (978-0-316-11543-8(6)) Little, Brown Bks. for Young Readers.

—Arthur Rocks with Binky. (Arthur Chapter Bks.: Bk. 11). 61p. (J). (gr. 3-6). pap. 3.95 (978-0-8072-1307-0(1)); Vol. 11. 2004. (gr. 2-4). pap. 17.00 incl. audio (978-0-8072-0410-8(2) , FTR203SP) Random Hse. Audio Publishing Group. (Listening Library).

—Arthur the Brave, 18 vols., Vol. 10. 2001. (Arthur's Family Values: Vol. 10). (Illus.). 28p. (J). 3.79 (978-1-57973-116-8(3)) Advance Pubs. LLC.

—Arthur Tricks the Tooth Fairy. 1998. (Arthur Ser.). (Illus.). 24p. (J). (gr. k-3). pap. 3.99 (978-0-679-88464-4(5)); lib. bdg. 11.99 (978-0-679-98464-1(X)) Random Hse. Children's Bks. (Random Hse. Bks. for Young Readers).

—Arthur Writes a Story. Brown, Marc, illus. 2002. (Arthur Adventure Ser.). (Illus.). (J). 13.15 (978-0-7587-1974-4(4)) Book Wholesalers, Inc.

—Arthur Writes a Story. ed. 2004. (Arthur Adventure Ser.). (J). (gr. k-3). spiral bd. (978-0-616-01604-6(2)); spiral bd. (978-0-616-01605-3(0)) Canadian National Institute for the Blind/Institut National Canadien pour les Aveugles.

—Arthur Writes a Story. 2003. (Arthur Adventure Ser.). (Illus.). 14.95 (978-1-59319-021-7(2)) LeapFrog Enterprises, Inc.

—Arthur Writes a Story. Brown, Marc, illus. (Arthur Adventure Ser.). (Illus.). 32p. (J). (ps-3). 1999. 9.95 (978-0-316-11976-4(8)); 1998. pap. 6.99 (978-0-316-11164-5(3)); 2007. pap. 10.99 incl. audio compact disk (*978-0-316-11865-1(6)) Little, Brown Bks. for Young Readers.

—Arthur Writes a Story. 1998. (Arthur Adventure Ser.). (J). (gr. k-3). 12.75 (978-0-606-13153-7(1)) Tandem Library Bks.

—Arthur's Baby. 1998. (Arthur Adventure Ser.). (Illus.). 30p. (J). (ps-k). bds. 5.95 (978-0-316-11858-3(3)) Little, Brown Bks. for Young Readers.

—Arthur's Back-to-School Surprise. 2002. (Arthur Ser.). (Illus.). 24p. (J). (gr. k-3). pap. 3.99 (978-0-375-81000-8(5)); lib. bdg. 11.99 (978-0-375-91000-5(X)) Random Hse. Children's Bks. (Random Hse. Bks. for Young Readers).

—Arthur's Birthday. 1998. (Arthur Adventure Ser.). (Illus.). 30p. (J). (ps-3). bds. 5.95 (978-0-316-11857-6(5)) Little, Brown Bks. for Young Readers.

—Arthur's Birthday Activity Book. Brown, Marc, illus. 2001. (Arthur Ser.). (Illus.). 18p. (J). (ps-3). pap., act. bk. ed. 7.95 (978-0-316-11851-4(6)) Little Brown & Co.

—Arthur's Birthday Surprise. 2004. (Arthur's 8 x 8 Bks.). (Illus.). 24p. (J). (ps-1). pap. 3.99 (978-0-316-73379-3(2)) Little, Brown Bks. for Young Readers.

—Arthur's Chicken Pox. Brown, Marc, illus. 2002. (Arthur Adventure Ser.). (Illus.). (J). 13.15 (978-0-7587-1978-2(7)) Book Wholesalers, Inc.

—Arthur's Chicken Pox. Brown, Marc, illus. 1999. (Arthur Adventure Ser.). (Illus.). 30p. (J). (ps-k). bds. 5.95 (978-0-316-11953-5(9)) Little, Brown Bks. for Young Readers.

—Arthur's Chicken Pox. 1998. (Arthur Adventure Ser.). 32p. (J). (ps-3). 9.95 (978-0-316-11947-4(4)) Little, Brown Bks. for Young Readers.

—Arthur's Christmas. Brown, Marc, illus. 2002. (Arthur Adventure Ser.). (Illus.). (J). 13.15 (978-0-7587-1979-9(5)) Book Wholesalers, Inc.

—Arthur's Christmas. Brown, Marc, illus. 1999. (Arthur Adventure Ser.). 32p. (J). (ps-3). 9.95 (978-0-316-11964-1(4)) Little, Brown Bks. for Young Readers.

—Arthur's Computer Disaster. 1999. (Arthur Adventure Ser.). (J). (gr. k-3). pap. 5.95 (978-0-316-12373-0(0)) Little, Brown Bks. for Young Readers.

—Arthur's Computer Disaster. Brown, Marc, illus. 1999. (Arthur Adventure Ser.). (Illus.). 32p. (J). (ps-3). pap. 6.99 (978-0-316-10534-7(1)) Little, Brown Bks. for Young Readers.

—Arthur's Family Feud. 2003. 32p. (J). 15.95 (978-0-316-12093-7(6)) Little Brown & Co.

—Arthur's Family Treasury: Three Arthur Adventures in One Volume. Brown, Marc, illus. 2000. (Illus.). 112p. (J). (ps-3). 18.95 (978-0-316-12147-7(9)) Little Brown & Co.

—Arthur's Family Vacation. Brown, Marc, illus. 2002. (Arthur Adventure Ser.). (Illus.). (J). 13.15 (978-0-7587-1981-2(7)) Book Wholesalers, Inc.

—Arthur's Family Vacation. ed. 2004. (Arthur Adventure Ser.). (J). (gr. k-3). spiral bd. (978-0-616-01601-5(8)); spiral bd. (978-0-616-01602-2(6)) Canadian National Institute for the Blind/Institut National Canadien pour les Aveugles.

—Arthur's Family Vacation. Brown, Marc, illus. 1998. (Arthur Adventure Ser.). (Illus.). (J). (gr. k-3). pap. 5.95 (978-0-316-11528-5(2)) Little, Brown Bks. for Young Readers.

—Arthur's First Kiss. Brown, Marc, illus. 2001. (Arthur Ser.). (Illus.). 24p. (J). (gr. k-3). pap. 3.99 (978-0-375-80602-5(4)); lib. bdg. 11.99 (978-0-375-90602-2(9)) Random Hse. Children's Bks. (Random Hse. Bks. for Young Readers).

—Arthur's First Kiss with Sticker. 2001. (Arthur Ser.). (gr. k-3). lib. bdg. 11.80 (978-0-613-84580-9(3)) Tandem Library Bks.

—Arthur's First Sleepover. Brown, Marc, illus. 2002. (Arthur Adventure Ser.). (Illus.). (J). 13.15 (978-0-7587-1982-9(5)) Book Wholesalers, Inc.

—Arthur's First Sleepover. Brown, Marc, illus. 1999. (Arthur Adventure Ser.). (Illus.). 30p. (J). (ps-k). bds. 5.95 (978-0-316-10560-6(0)) Little, Brown Bks. for Young Readers.

A B

—Arthur's First Sleepover. 1998. (Arthur Adventure Ser.). (J). (gr. k-3). pap. 5.95 (978-0-316-11974-0(1)); 32p. 9.95 (978-0-316-11948-1(2)) Little, Brown Bks. for Young Readers.

—Arthur's Halloween. Brown, Marc, illus. 2002. (Arthur Adventure Ser.). (Illus.). (J). 13.15 (978-0-7587-1983-6(3)) Book Wholesalers, Inc.

—Arthur's Halloween. movie tie-in ed. Date not set. (Arthur Adventure Ser.). (J). 16.95 (978-0-316-11855-2(9)) Little Brown & Co.

—Arthur's Heart Mix-Up. 2004. (Arthur's 8 x 8 Bks.). (Illus.). 24p. (J). (ps-1). pap. 3.99 (978-0-316-73381-6(4)) Little Brown & Co.

—Arthur's Heart Mix-Up. 2004. (Arthur's 8 x 8 Bks.). (ps-2). lib. bdg. 11.80 (978-0-613-71772-4(4)) Tandem Library Bks.

—Arthur's Hiccups. 2001. (Arthur Ser.). (Illus.). (J). (ps-3). lib. bdg. (978-0-375-90699-2(1) , Random Hse. Bks. for Young Readers) Random Hse. Children's Bks.

—Arthur's Hiccups. 2001. (Arthur Ser.). (gr. k-3). lib. bdg. 11.80 (978-0-613-85128-2(5)); 10.79 (978-0-606-22767-4(9)) Tandem Library Bks.

—Arthur's in Charge, 18 vols., Vol. 13. 2001. (Illus.). 28p. (J). 3.79 (978-1-57973-119-9(8)) Advance Pubs. LLC.

—Arthur's Jelly Beans. 2004. (Arthur's 8 x 8 Bks.). (Illus.). 24p. (J). (ps-1). pap. 3.99 (978-0-316-73382-3(2)) Little Brown & Co.

—Arthur's Jelly Beans. 2004. (Arthur's 8 x 8 Bks.). (ps-2). lib. bdg. 11.80 (978-0-613-71774-8(0)) Tandem Library Bks.

—Arthur's Lost Ducklin, 18 vols., Vol. 18. 2001. (Illus.). 28p. (J). 3.79 (978-1-57973-124-3(4)) Advance Pubs. LLC.

—Arthur's Lost Puppy. Brown, Marc, illus. 2000. (Arthur Ser.). (Illus.). 24p. (J). (gr. k-3). pap. 3.99 (978-0-679-88466-8(1) , Random Hse. Bks. for Young Readers) Random Hse. Children's Bks.

—Arthur's Mystery Babysitter. Brown, Marc, illus. 2004. (Arthur's 8 x 8 Bks.). (Illus.). 24p. (J). (ps-3). pap. 3.99 (978-0-316-73394-6(6) , Tingley, Megan Bks.) Little, Brown Bks. for Young Readers.

—Arthur's New Puppy. Brown, Marc, illus. 2002. (Arthur Adventure Ser.). (Illus.). (J). 13.15 (978-0-7587-1984-3(1)) Book Wholesalers, Inc.

—Arthur's New Puppy. 1998. (Arthur Adventure Ser.). (Illus.). 32p. (J). (ps-3). 9.95 (978-0-316-11949-8(0)) Little, Brown Bks. for Young Readers.

—Arthur's New Puppy. (Arthur Adventure Ser.). (J). (gr. k-3). 7.98 incl. audio NewSound, LLC.

—Arthur's off to School. 2004. (Arthur's 8 x 8 Bks.). (Illus.). 24p. (J). (ps-1). pap. 3.99 (978-0-316-73378-6(4)) Little, Brown Bks. for Young Readers.

—Arthur's off to School. 2004. (Arthur's 8 x 8 Bks.). (ps-2). lib. bdg. 11.80 (978-0-613-71773-1(2)) Tandem Library Bks.

—Arthur's Perfect Christmas. 2004. (Arthur Adventure Ser.). (Illus.). 40p. (J). (ps-1). pap. 6.99 (978-0-316-00130-4(9) , Tingley, Megan Bks.) Little, Brown Bks. for Young Readers.

—Arthur's Perfect Christmas. Brown, Marc, illus. 2000. (Arthur Adventure Ser.). (Illus.). 48p. (J). (ps-3). 15.95 (978-0-316-11968-9(7)) Little, Brown Bks. for Young Readers.

—Arthur's Pet Business. Brown, Marc, illus. rev. ed. 2007. (Arthur Adventure Ser.). (Illus.). 32p. (J). (ps-1). pap. 10.99 incl. audio compact disk ***978-0-316-11863-7(X))** Little, Brown Bks. for Young Readers.

—Arthur's Science Fair Trouble. Brown, Marc, illus. 2003. (Arthur Ser.). (Illus.). 24p. (J). (gr. k-3). pap. 3.99 (978-0-375-81003-9(X)); lib. bdg. 11.99 (978-0-375-91003-6(4)) Random Hse. Children's Bks. (Random Hse. Bks. for Young Readers).

—Arthur's Science Fair Trouble. 2003. (Arthur Ser.). (gr. k-3). lib. bdg. 11.80 (978-0-613-70564-6(5)) Tandem Library Bks.

—Arthur's Science Project, 18 vols., Vol. 9. 2001. (Arthur's Family Values: Vol. 9). (Illus.). 28p. (J). 3.79 (978-1-57973-115-1(5)) Advance Pubs. LLC.

—Arthur's Teacher Moves In. Brown, Marc, illus. 2000. (Arthur Adventure Ser.). (Illus.). 32p. (J). (ps-3). 15.95 (978-0-316-11979-5(2)) Little, Brown Bks. for Young Readers.

—Arthur's Teacher Moves In. 2000. (Arthur Adventure Ser.). (J). (gr. k-3). 15.95 (978-0-316-11856-9(7)) Little, Brown Bks. for Young Readers.

—Arthur's Teacher Trouble. ed. 2004. (Arthur Adventure Ser.). (J). (gr. k-3). spiral bd. (978-0-616-00406-7(0)); spiral bd. (978-0-616-01603-9(4)) Canadian National Institute for the Blind/Institut National Canadien pour les Aveugles.

—Arthur's Tooth. Brown, Marc, illus. 2002. (Arthur Adventure Ser.). (Illus.). (J). 13.15 (978-0-7587-1989-8(2)) Book Wholesalers, Inc.

—Arthur's Tree House. 2007. (Arthur's 8 x 8 Bks.). (Illus.). (J). ***978-1-4287-1970-5(9))** Little Brown & Co.

—Arthur's Tree House. 2007. (Arthur's 8 x 8 Bks.). (Illus.). 24p. (J). (ps-1). mass mkt. 3.99 (978-0-316-05776-9(2)) Little, Brown Bks. for Young Readers.

—Arthur's TV Trouble. Brown, Marc, illus. 2002. (Arthur Adventure Ser.). (Illus.). (J). 13.15 (978-0-7587-1990-4(6)) Book Wholesalers, Inc.

—Arthur's TV Trouble. Brown, Marc, illus. 1999. (Arthur Adventure Ser.). (Illus.). 32p. (J). (ps-3). 9.95 (978-0-316-11594-0(0)) Little, Brown Bks. for Young Readers.

—Arthur's Underwear. ed. 2004. (Arthur Adventure Ser.). (Illus.). (J). (gr. k-3). spiral bd. (978-0-616-14563-0(2)); spiral bd. (978-0-616-14564-7(0)) Canadian National Institute for the Blind/Institut National Canadien pour les Aveugles.

—Arthur's Underwear. Brown, Marc, illus. 2001. (Arthur Adventure Ser.). (Illus.). 32p. (J). (ps-3). pap. 6.99 (978-0-316-10619-1(4)) Little, Brown Bks. for Young Readers.

—Arthur's Underwear. 2001. (Arthur Adventure Ser.). 12.75 (978-0-606-22553-3(6)); lib. bdg. 14.10 (978-0-613-43675-5(X)) Tandem Library Bks.

—Arthur's Underwear: An Arthur Adventure. Brown, Marc, illus. 1999. (Arthur Adventure Ser.). (Illus.). 32p. (J). (ps-3). 15.95 (978-0-316-11012-9(4)) Little, Brown Bks. for Young Readers.

—Arthur's Valentine. Brown, Marc, illus. 2002. (Arthur Adventure Ser.). (Illus.). (J). 13.15 (978-0-7587-1991-1(4)) Book Wholesalers, Inc.

—Arthur's Valentine. Brown, Marc, illus. 2000. (Arthur Adventure Ser.). 32p. (J). (ps-3). 9.95 (978-0-316-11866-8(4)) Little, Brown Bks. for Young Readers.

—Arturo Tiene Varicela. Sarfatti, Esther, tr. from ENG. 2001. (SPA., Illus.). (J). (gr. k-2). pap. 6.95 (978-1-930332-00-3(9) , LC30182) Lectorum Pubns., Inc.

—Arturo Tiene Varicela. 2001. (SPA.). (gr. k-3). lib. bdg. 15.25 (978-0-613-64340-5(2)) Tandem Library Bks.

—Arturo y el Desastre de la Computadora. Sarfatti, Esther, tr. (SPA.). (J). (gr. k-2). pap. 6.95 (978-1-930332-01-0(7) , LC30180) Lectorum Pubns., Inc.

—Arturo y el Desastre de la Computadora. 2001. (SPA.). (gr. k-3). lib. bdg. 15.25 (978-0-613-35900-9(3)); (Illus.). (J). 13.75 (978-0-606-21044-7(X)) Tandem Library Bks.

—Arturo y el Negocio de Mascotas. Sarfatti, Esther, tr. (SPA.). (J). (gr. k-2). pap. 6.95 (978-1-880507-94-0(3) , LC8511) Lectorum Pubns., Inc.

—Arturo y el Negocio de Mascotas. 2001. (SPA.). (gr. k-3). lib. bdg. 15.25 (978-0-613-35901-6(1)); (Illus.). (J). 13.75 (978-0-606-21045-4(8)) Tandem Library Bks.

—Arturo y los Terribles Gemelos. Sarfatti, Esther, tr. from ENG. 2000. (Arthur Adventure Ser.). (SPA., Illus.). (J). (gr. k-3). pap. 6.95 (978-1-880507-65-0(X) , LC2344) Lectorum Pubns., Inc.

—Arturo y los Terribles Gemelos. 2000. (Arthur Adventure Ser.). (J). (gr. k-3). 13.75 (978-0-606-17569-2(5)) Tandem Library Bks.

—Binky Rules. ed. 2005. (Arthur Chapter Bks.: Bk. 24). (Illus.). 57p. (J). lib. bdg. 15.00 (978-1-59054-735-9(7)) Fitzgerald Bks.

—Binky Rules. Brown, Marc, illus. 24th ed. 2000. (Arthur Chapter Bks.: Bk. 24). (Illus.). 64p. (J). (gr. 2-4). pap. 3.95 (978-0-316-12333-4(1)) Little Brown & Co.

—Binky Rules. Brown, Marc, illus. 24th ed. 2000. (Arthur Chapter Bks. : Bk. 24). (Illus.). 64p. (J). (gr. 2-4). 13.95 (978-0-316-12193-4(2)) Little, Brown Bks. for Young Readers.

—Binky Rules. 2000. (Arthur Chapter Bks.: Bk. 24). (gr. k-3). lib. bdg. 11.80 (978-0-613-30275-3(3)); (J). (gr. 3-6). 10.75 (978-0-606-19447-1(9)) Tandem Library Bks.

—Buried Treasure, 18 vols., Vol. 8. 2001. (Illus.). 28p. (J). 3.79 (978-1-57973-114-4(7)) Advance Pubs. LLC.

—Buster Makes the Grade. 1999. (Arthur Chapter Bks. : Bk. 16). (J). (gr. 3-6). pap. 3.95 (978-0-316-12262-7(9)) Little, Brown Bks. for Young Readers.

—Buster Makes the Grade. Brown, Marc, illus. 16th ed. 1999. (Arthur Chapter Bks. : Bk. 16). (Illus.). 64p. (J). (gr. 2-4). pap. 4.25 (978-0-316-12277-1(7)) Little, Brown Bks. for Young Readers.

—Buster Makes the Grade. 1999. (Arthur Chapter Bks.: Bk. 16). (J). (gr. 3-6). 10.75 (978-0-606-17235-6(1)) Tandem Library Bks.

—Buster's Dino Dilemma. 7th ed. 1998. (Arthur Chapter Bks. : Bk. 7). (Illus.). 64p. (J). (gr. 2-4). pap. 4.25 (978-0-316-11560-5(6)); 13.95 (978-0-316-11559-9(2)) Little, Brown Bks. for Young Readers.

—Buster's Dino Dilemma. (Arthur Chapter Bks.: Bk. 7). 58p. (J). (gr. 3-6). pap. 3.95 (978-0-8072-1303-2(9)); 1999. (gr. 2-4). pap. 17.00 incl. audio (978-0-8072-0397-2(1) , EFTR198SP) Random Hse. Audio Publishing Group. (Listening Library).

—Buster's New Friend. Brown, Marc, illus. 23rd ed. 2000. (Arthur Chapter Bks.: Bk. 23). (Illus.). 64p. (J). (gr. 2-4). pap. 4.25 (978-0-316-12307-5(2)) Little Brown & Co.

—Buster's New Friend. Brown, Marc, illus. 23rd ed. 2000. (Arthur Chapter Bks. : Bk. 23). (Illus.). 64p. (J). (gr. 2-4). 13.95 (978-0-316-12212-2(2)) Little, Brown Bks. for Young Readers.

—Buster's New Friend. 2000. (Arthur Chapter Bks.: Bk. 23). (gr. k-3). lib. bdg. 12.10 (978-0-613-30292-0(3)); (J). (gr. 3-6). 10.75 (978-0-606-19446-4(0)) Tandem Library Bks.

—D. W., Go to Your Room! Brown, Marc, illus. 1999. (D. W. Ser.). (Illus.). 32p. (J). (ps-1). 13.95 (978-0-316-10905-5(3)) Little, Brown Bks. for Young Readers.

—D. W. Saves the Day. 2001. (D. W. Ser.). (Illus.). 28p. (J). 3.79 (978-1-57973-121-2(X)) Advance Pubs. LLC.

—D. W.'s Lost Blankie. Brown, Marc, illus. 2002. (D. W. Ser.). (Illus.). (J). 13.15 (978-0-7587-2330-7(X)) Book Wholesalers, Inc.

—La Fiesta de Arturo. 1999. (Arthur Adventure Ser.). (SPA., Illus.). (J). (gr. k-3). pap. 6.95 (978-1-880507-64-3(1) , LC2343) Lectorum Pubns., Inc.

—Fiesta de Arturo. 2000. (SPA.). (gr. k-3). lib. bdg. 15.25 (978-0-613-18106-8(9)) Tandem Library Bks.

—Francine, Believe It or Not. ed. 2005. (Arthur Chapter Bks.: Bk. 14). (Illus.). 58p. (J). lib. bdg. 15.00 (978-1-59054-741-0(1)) Fitzgerald Bks.

—Francine, Believe It or Not! ed. 1999. (Arthur Chapter Bks. : Bk. 14). (J). (gr. 3-6). pap. 3.95 (978-0-316-10463-0(9)) Little, Brown Bks. for Young Readers.

—Francine, Believe It or Not! Brown, Marc, illus. 14th ed. 1999. (Arthur Chapter Bks. : Bk. 14). (Illus.). 64p. (J). (gr. 2-4). pap. 4.25 (978-0-316-12258-0(0)) Little, Brown Bks. for Young Readers.

—The Good Sport, 18 vols., Vol. 16. 2001. (Illus.). 28p. (J). (ps-3). 3.79 (978-1-57973-122-9(8)) Advance Pubs. LLC.

—King Arthur. Brown, Marc, illus. 2002. (Arthur Chapter Bks.: Bk. 13). (Illus.). (J). 11.45 (978-0-7587-0631-7(6)) Book Wholesalers, Inc.

—King Arthur. ed. 2005. (Arthur Chapter Bks.: Bk. 13). (Illus.). 58p. (J). lib. bdg. 15.00 (978-1-59054-742-7(X)) Fitzgerald Bks.

—King Arthur. 1999. (Arthur Chapter Bks. : Bk. 13). (J). (gr. 3-6). pap. 3.95 (978-0-316-10667-2(4)) Little, Brown Bks. for Young Readers.

—King Arthur. Brown, Marc, illus. 13th ed. 1999. (Arthur Chapter Bks. : Bk. 13). (Illus.). 64p. (J). (gr. 2-4). pap. 4.25 (978-0-316-12241-2(6)) Little, Brown Bks. for Young Readers.

—King Arthur. unabr. ed. 2004. (Arthur Chapter Bks.: Bk. 13). 58p. (J). (gr. 2-4). pap. 17.00 incl. audio (978-0-8072-0344-6(0) , Listening Library) Random Hse. Audio Publishing Group.

—King Arthur. 1999. (Arthur Chapter Bks.: Bk. 13). (gr. k-3). lib. bdg. 12.10 (978-0-613-14900-6(9)); (J). (gr. 3-6). (978-0-606-16804-5(4)) Tandem Library Bks.

—Manners Matter. Brown, Marc, ed. 2001. (Arthur's Family Values: Vol. 1). (Illus.). 28p. (J). 3.49 (978-1-57973-108-3(2)) Advance Pubs. LLC.

—Marc Brown Arthur: King Arthur; Francine, Believe it or Not; Arthur & the Cootie-Catcher; (Arthur Chapter Bks.: No. 5). 58p. (J). (gr. 3-6). pap. 3.95 (978-0-8072-1299-8(7)); Vol. 5. 1998. (gr. 2-4). pap. 17.00 incl. audio (978-0-8072-0385-9(8) , FTR191SP) Random Hse. Audio Publishing Group. (Listening Library).

—Marc Brown's Arthur: Arthur & the Crunch Cereal Contest; Arthur Accused!; Locked in the Library. (Arthur Chapter Bks.: No. 2). 58p. (J). (gr. 3-6). pap. 3.95 (978-0-8072-1296-7(2) , Listening Library) Random Hse. Audio Publishing Group.

—Marc Brown's Arthur: Arthur & the Scare-Your-Pants-off Club; Arthur Makes the Team. (Arthur Chapter Bks.: No. 1). (J). (gr. 3-6). 12.78 incl. audio NewSound, LLC.

—Marc Brown's Arthur: Arthur & the Scare-Your-Pants-off Club; Arthur Makes the Team. (Arthur Chapter Bks.: No. 1). 58p. (J). (gr. 3-6). pap. 3.95 (978-0-8072-1295-0(4) , Listening Library) Random Hse. Audio Publishing Group.

—Marc Brown's Arthur: Buster's Dino Dilemma; The Mystery of the Stolen Bike; Arthur & the Lost Diary. (Arthur Chapter Bks.: No. 3). 61p. (J). (gr. 3-6). pap. 3.95 (978-0-8072-1297-4(0)); pap. 3.95 (978-0-8072-1298-1(9)) Random Hse. Audio Publishing Group. (Listening Library).

—Muffy's Secret Admirer. ed. 2005. (Arthur Chapter Bks.: Bk. 17). (Illus.). 58p. (J). lib. bdg. 15.00 (978-1-59054-744-1(6)) Fitzgerald Bks.

—Muffy's Secret Admirer. 1999. (Arthur Chapter Bks. : Bk. 17). (J). (gr. 3-6). pap. 3.95 (978-0-316-12047-0(2)) Little, Brown Bks. for Young Readers.

—Muffy's Secret Admirer. Brown, Marc, illus. 17th ed. 1999. (Arthur Chapter Bks. : Bk. 17). (Illus.). 64p. (J). (gr. 2-4). 13.95 (978-0-316-12017-3(0)); pap. 3.95 (978-0-316-12230-6(0)) Little, Brown Bks. for Young Readers.

—Muffy's Secret Admirer. 1999. (Arthur Chapter Bks.: Bk. 17). (gr. k-3). lib. bdg. 11.80 (978-0-613-22040-8(4)); (J). (gr. 3-6). (978-0-606-17237-0(8)) Tandem Library Bks.

—The Mystery of the Stolen Bike. ed. 2005. (Arthur Chapter Bks.: Bk. 8). (Illus.). 59p. (J). lib. bdg. 15.00 (978-1-59054-745-8(4)) Fitzgerald Bks.

—The Mystery of the Stolen Bike. 8th ed. 1998. (Arthur Chapter Bks. : Bk. 8). (Illus.). 64p. (J). (gr. 2-4). pap. 4.25 (978-0-316-11571-1(1)) Little, Brown Bks. for Young Readers.

—The Mystery of the Stolen Bike. (Arthur Chapter Bks.: Bk. 8). 59p. (J). (gr. 3-6). pap. 3.95 (978-0-8072-1304-9(7)); 1999. (gr. 2-4). pap. 17.00 incl. audio (978-0-8072-0401-6(3) , EFTR199SP) Random Hse. Audio Publishing Group. (Listening Library).

—Queen for a Day, 18 vols., Vol. 3. 2001. (Arthur's Family Values: Vol. 3). (Illus.). 28p. (J). 3.79 (978-1-57973-109-0(0)) Advance Pubs. LLC.

—Say Cheese, 18 vols., Vol. 17. 2001. (Arthur's Family Values: Vol. 17). (Illus.). 28p. (J). 3.79 (978-1-57973-123-6(6)) Advance Pubs. LLC.

—Sir Arthur to the Rescue, 18 vols., Vol. 6. 2001. (Illus.). 28p. (J). 3.79 (978-1-57973-112-0(0)) Advance Pubs. LLC.

—The Truth Pops Out, 18 vols., Vol. 5. 2001. (Arthur's Family Values: Vol. 5). (Illus.). 28p. (J). 3.79 (978-1-57973-111-3(2)) Advance Pubs. LLC.

—Try It, You'll Like It!, 18 vols., Vol. 4. 2001. (Arthur's Family Values: Vol. 4). (Illus.). 28p. (J). 3.79 (978-1-57973-110-6(4)) Advance Pubs. LLC.

—La Visita del Señor Rataquemada. Sarfatti, Esther, tr. from ENG. 2003. (SPA.). (J). (gr. k-2). pap. 6.95 (978-1-930332-41-6(6)) Lectorum Pubns., Inc.

—Volunteer of the Year, 18 vols., Vol. 7. 2001. (Illus.). 28p. (J). 3.79 (978-1-57973-113-7(9)) Advance Pubs. LLC.

—What a Mess!, 18 vols., Vol. 12. 2001. (Arthur's Family Values: Vol. 12). (Illus.). 28p. (J). 3.79 (978-1-57973-118-2(X)) Advance Pubs. LLC.

—Who's in Love with Arthur? ed. 2005. (Arthur Chapter Bks.: Bk. 10). (Illus.). 57p. (J). lib. bdg. 15.00 (978-1-59054-746-5(2)) Fitzgerald Bks.

—Who's in Love with Arthur? (Arthur Chapter Bks. : Bk. 10). (J). 1999. (gr. 3-6). pap. 3.95 (978-0-316-10671-9(2)); 10th ed. 1998. (Illus.). 64p. (gr. 2-4). pap. 4.25 (978-0-316-11540-7(1)) Little, Brown Bks. for Young Readers.

—Who's in Love with Arthur? (Arthur Chapter Bks.: Bk. 10). 57p. (J). (gr. 3-6). pap. 3.95 (978-0-8072-1306-3(3) , Listening Library) Random Hse. Audio Publishing Group.

Brown, Marc, illus. Arthur & the Goalie Ghost. 2002. (Arthur Good Sports Ser.: Bk. 5). (J). 11.45 (978-0-7587-6862-9(1)) Book Wholesalers, Inc.

Brown, Marc & Sarfatti, Esther. Arturo y la Navidad. 2004. (SPA.). (J). pap. 6.95 (978-1-930332-48-5(3)) Lectorum Pubns., Inc.

Brown, Marc & Schulman, Janet. Arthur's Hiccups. Brown, Marc, illus. 2001. (Arthur Ser.). (Illus.). 24p. (J). (gr. k-3). lib. bdg. 11.99 (978-0-375-90698-5(3) , Random Hse. Bks. for Young Readers) Random Hse. Children's Bks.

Brown, Marc & Schulman, Lester. Arthur Breaks the Bank. 2004. (Arthur Ser.). (Illus.). 24p. (J). (gr. k-3). pap. 3.99 (978-0-375-81002-2(1)); lib. bdg. 11.99 (978-0-375-91002-9(6)) Random Hse. Children's Bks. (Random Hse. Bks. for Young Readers).

Brown, Marc, et al. Arthur & the Lost Diary. 9th ed. 1998. (Arthur Chapter Bks.: Bk. 9). (Illus.). 64p. (J). (gr. 2-4). 14.95 (978-0-316-11573-5(8)) Little, Brown Bks. for Young Readers.

—Buster Makes the Grade. Brown, Marc, illus. 16th ed. 1999. (Arthur Chapter Bks. : Bk. 16). (Illus.). 64p. (J). (gr. 2-4). 13.95 (978-0-316-11960-3(1)) Little, Brown Bks. for Young Readers.

Krensky, Stephen. Arthur Accused! 1998. (Arthur Chapter Bks. : Bk. 5). (J). (gr. 3-6). pap. 3.95 (978-0-316-12150-7(9)); 5th ed. (Illus.). 64p. (gr. 2-4). pap. 4.25 (978-0-316-11556-8(8)) Little, Brown Bks. for Young Readers.

—Arthur & the Crunch Cereal Contest. 1998. (Arthur Chapter Bks. : Bk. 4). (J). (gr. 3-6). pap. 3.95 (978-0-316-10546-0(5)); Bk. 4. (Illus.). 64p. (gr. 2-4). pap. 4.25 (978-0-316-11553-7(3)) Little, Brown Bks. for Young Readers.

—Arthur & the Crunch Cereal Contest. unabr. ed. 1998. (Arthur Chapter Bks.: Bk. 4). 61p. (J). (gr. 2-4). pap. 17.00 incl. audio (978-0-8072-0382-8(3) , FTR190SP, Listening Library) Random Hse. Audio Publishing Group.

—Arthur & the Crunch Cereal Contest. 1998. (Arthur Chapter Bks.: Bk. 4). (J). (gr. 3-6). 11.05 (978-0-606-13150-6(7)); (Illus.). 61p. (ps). lib. bdg. 12.10 (978-0-613-06882-6(3)) Tandem Library Bks.

—Arthur & the Scare-Your-Pants-off Club. 1998. (Arthur Chapter Bks. : Bk. 2). (J). (gr. 3-6). pap. 3.95 (978-0-316-10496-8(5)); (Illus.). 64p. (gr. 2-4). pap. 4.25 (978-0-316-11549-0(5)) Little, Brown Bks. for Young Readers.

—Arthur & the Scare-Your-Pants-off Club. unabr. ed. 1998. (Arthur Chapter Bks.: Bk. 2). 58p. (J). (gr. 2-4). pap. 17.00 incl. audio (978-0-8072-0376-7(9) , FTR188SP, Listening Library) Random Hse. Audio Publishing Group.

—Arthur & the Scare-Your-Pants-off Club. 1998. (Arthur Chapter Bks.: Bk. 2). (J). (gr. 3-6). 11.05 (978-0-606-13151-3(5)) Tandem Library Bks.

—Arthur Makes the Team. 2002. (Arthur Chapter Bks. : Bk. 3). (J). (gr. k-3). 14.95 (978-1-58605-914-9(9) , LeapFrog Schl. Hse.) LeapFrog Enterprises, Inc.

—Arthur Makes the Team. 1998. (Arthur Chapter Bks. : Bk. 3). (J). (gr. 3-6). pap. 3.95 (978-0-316-10536-1(8)); (Illus.). 64p. (gr. 2-4). pap. 4.25 (978-0-316-11551-3(7)) Little, Brown Bks. for Young Readers.

—Arthur Makes the Team. unabr. ed. 1998. (Arthur Chapter Bks.: Bk. 3). 61p. (J). (gr. 2-4). pap. 17.00 incl. audio (978-0-8072-0379-8(3) , FTR189SP, Listening Library) Random Hse. Audio Publishing Group.

—Arthur Makes the Team. 1998. (Arthur Chapter Bks.: Bk. 3). (J). (gr. 3-6). 11.05 (978-0-606-13152-0(3)); (Illus.). 61p. (ps). lib. bdg. 12.10 (978-0-613-06884-0(X)) Tandem Library Bks.

—Arthur's Mystery Envelope. 1998. (Arthur Chapter Bks. : Bk. 1). (J). (gr. 3-6). pap. 3.95 (978-0-316-10464-7(7)); (Illus.). 64p. (gr. 2-4). pap. 4.25 (978-0-316-11547-6(9)) Little, Brown Bks. for Young Readers.

—Arthur's Mystery Envelope. unabr. ed. 1998. (Arthur Chapter Bks.: Bk. 1). 58p. (J). (gr. 2-4). pap. 17.00 incl. audio (978-0-8072-0372-9(6) , FTR187SP, Listening Library) Random Hse. Audio Publishing Group.

—Arthur's Mystery Envelope. 1998. (Arthur Chapter Bks.: Bk. 1). (J). (gr. 3-6). 11.05 (978-0-606-13154-4(X)) Tandem Library Bks.

—Locked in the Library! Krensky, Stephen, illus. 1998. (Arthur Chapter Bks. : Bk. 6). (Illus.). 64p. (J). (gr. 2-4). pap. 4.25 (978-0-316-11558-2(4)) Little, Brown Bks. for Young Readers.

—Locked in the Library! (Arthur Chapter Bks.: Bk. 6). 58p. (J). (gr. 3-6). pap. 3.95 (978-0-8072-1300-1(4)); 1998. (gr. 2-4). pap. 17.00 incl. audio (978-0-8072-0388-0(2) , FTR192SP) Random Hse. Audio Publishing Group. (Listening Library).

Krensky, Stephen, text. Arthur Accused! ed. 2005. (Arthur Chapter Bks.: Bk. 5). (Illus.). (J). lib. bdg. 15.00 (978-1-59054-715-1(2)) Fitzgerald Bks.

—Arthur & the Crunch Cereal Contest. ed. 2005. (Arthur Chapter Bks.: Bk. 4). (Illus.). 61p. (J). lib. bdg. 15.00 (978-1-59054-721-2(7)) Fitzgerald Bks.

—Arthur & the Scare-Your-Pants-off Club. ed. 2005. (Arthur Chapter Bks.: Bk. 2). (Illus.). (J). lib. bdg. 15.00 (978-1-59054-729-8(2)) Fitzgerald Bks.

—Arthur Makes the Team. ed. 2005. (Arthur Chapter Bks.: Bk. 3). (Illus.). (J). lib. bdg. 15.00 (978-1-59054-731-1(4)) Fitzgerald Bks.

—Arthur's Mystery Envelope. ed. 2005. (Arthur Chapter Bks.: Bk. 1). (Illus.). 58p. (J). lib. bdg. 15.00 (978-1-59054-734-2(9)) Fitzgerald Bks.

—Buster's New Friend. ed. 2005. (Arthur Chapter Bks.: Bk. 23). (Illus.). 54p. (J). lib. bdg. 15.00 (978-1-59054-739-7(X)) Fitzgerald Bks.

—Locked in the Library! ed. 2005. (Arthur Chapter Bks.: Bk. 6). (Illus.). 58p. (J). lib. bdg. 15.00 (978-1-59054-743-4(8)) Fitzgerald Bks.

ARTHUR (FICTITIOUS CHARACTER : HOBAN)—FICTION

Hoban, Lillian. Arthur's Back to School Day. Hoban, Lillian, illus. 64th ed. 1998. (I Can Read Bks.). (Illus.). 48p. (J). (ps-3). pap. 3.99 (978-0-06-444245-9(4) , Harper Trophy) HarperCollins Pubs.

—Arthur's Back to School Day. Hoban, Lillian, illus. 1998. (Illus.). (J). (ps-ps). lib. bdg. 11.80 (978-0-613-11282-6(2)) Tandem Library Bks.

—Arthur's Birthday Party. Hoban, Lillian, illus. 1999. (I Can Read Bks.). (Illus.). 64p. (J). (gr. k-4). 14.89 (978-0-06-027799-4(8)); 14.95 (978-0-06-027798-7(X)) HarperCollins Pubs.

—Arthur's Funny Money. Hoban, Lillian, illus. 2002. (Arthur the Chimpanzee Ser.). (Illus.). (J). 12.34 (978-0-7587-5985-6(1)) Book Wholesalers, Inc.

—Arthur's Halloween Costume. Hoban, Lillian, illus. 2002. (Arthur the Chimpanzee Ser.). (Illus.). (J). 12.30 (978-0-7587-5553-7(8)) Book Wholesalers, Inc.

—Arthur's Honey Bear. Hoban, Lillian, illus. 2002. (Arthur the Chimpanzee Ser.). (Illus.). (J). 11.91 (978-0-7587-5986-3(X)) Book Wholesalers, Inc.

—Arthur's Loose Tooth. Hoban, Lillian, illus. 2002. (Arthur the Chimpanzee Ser.). (Illus.). (J). 11.37 (978-0-7587-5987-0(8)) Book Wholesalers, Inc.

—Arthur's Pen Pal. Hoban, Lillian, illus. 2002. (Arthur the Chimpanzee Ser.). (Illus.). (J). 12.34 (978-0-7587-5989-4(4)) Book Wholesalers, Inc.

—Arthur's Prize Reader. Hoban, Lillian, illus. 2002. (Arthur the Chimpanzee Ser.). (Illus.). (J). 12.30 (978-0-7587-5554-4(6)) Book Wholesalers, Inc.

ARTHUR, KING

see also Grail

Baker, Alan, illus. The Story of King Arthur. 2005. (Kingfisher Epics Ser.). 176p. (J). (gr. 4-6). pap. 7.95 (978-0-7534-5724-5(5) , Kingfisher) Houghton Mifflin Co. Trade & Reference Div.

Colum, Padraic. The Story of King Arthur & Other Celtic Heroes. Jones, Wilfred, illus. 2005. 208p. pap. 9.95 (978-0-486-44061-3(3)) Dover Pubns., Inc.

Flynn, Benedict. King Arthur & the Knights of the Round Table. 2008. (Hear It Read It Ser.). 160p. (J). (gr. 2 up). 9.95 (***978-1-4022-1243-7(7)*** , Sourcebooks Jabberwocky) Sourcebooks, Inc.

Gilbert, Henry. King Arthur's Knights: The Tales Retold for Boys & Girls. 2004. reprint ed. pap. 27.95 (978-1-4191-2865-3(5)); pap. 1.99 (978-1-4192-2865-0(X)) Kessinger Publishing, LLC.

Green, John. King Arthur Stained Glass Coloring Book. 1999. 8p. (J). (gr. k-5). pap. 1.50 (978-0-486-40496-7(X)) Dover Pubns., Inc.

Harkins, Susan. The Life & Times of King Arthur: The Evolution of a Legend. 2006. (Biography from Ancient Civilizations Ser.). (Illus.). 48p. (J). (gr. 6 up). lib. bdg. 29.95 (978-1-58415-513-3(2)) Mitchell Lane Pubs., Inc.

Korn, David M. Young King Arthur in Brooklyn. 2003. 210p. (YA). (gr. 6-10). pap. 9.95 (978-0-9723382-0-2(9)) Jester Bks.

Lang, Andrew. The Book of Romance. 2004. reprint ed. pap. 34.95 (978-0-7661-8836-5(1)) Kessinger Publishing, LLC.

Lang, Andrew, ed. The Book of Romance. Ford, H. J., illus. 2004. reprint ed. pap. 34.95 (978-1-4179-1718-1(0)) Kessinger Publishing, LLC.

Morpurgo, Michael. Sir Gawain & the Green Knight. Foreman, Michael, illus. 2004. 112p. (J). (gr. 3-7). 18.99 (978-0-7636-2519-1(1)) Candlewick Pr.

Nardo, Don. King Arthur. 2002. (Heroes & Villains Ser.). (Illus.). 112p. (J). (gr. 6). 27.45 (978-1-56006-948-5(1) , Lucent Bks.) Thomson Gale.

Pryor, Francis. Britain Ad: A Quest for Authur, England & the Anglo-Saxon. movie tie-in ed. 2006. (Illus.). 268p. 35.00 (***978-0-00-718186-5(8))*** HarperCollins Pubs. Ltd. GBR. *Dist:* Independent Pubs. Group.

Pyle, Howard. The Story of the Champions of the Round Table. 2004. reprint ed. pap. 28.95 (978-1-4191-8405-5(9)); pap. 1.99 (978-1-4192-8405-2(3)) Kessinger Publishing, LLC.

Roberts, Jeremy. King Arthur. 2005. (How History Is Invented Ser.). (Illus.). 112p. (J). (gr. 6-12). lib. bdg. 23.93 (978-0-8225-4891-1(7)) Lerner Publishing Group.

Ryan, Pamela. A Dictionary of King Arthur's Knights. 2001. (Illus.). 112p. (YA). (gr. 7 up). 26.95 (978-1-877853-61-6(5)) Nautical & Aviation Publishing Co. of America, Inc., The.

San Souci, Robert D. Young Arthur. 1999. (978-0-606-15904-3(5)) Tandem Library Bks.

—Young Lancelot. 1998. (J). (978-0-606-13937-3(0)) Tandem Library Bks.

Spinner, Stephanie. King Arthur's Courage. Sokolova, Valerie, illus. 2006. (Stepping Stones Ser.). 48p. (J). (gr. 1-4). pap. 3.99 (978-0-307-26410-7(6) , Random Hse. Bks. for Young Readers) Random Hse. Children's Bks.

Thompson, Frank. King Arthur. 2004. 368p. mass mkt. 6.50 (978-0-7868-9083-5(5)) Hyperion Pr.

Wilkes, Angela. King Arthur. 2003. (gr. 3-6). lib. bdg. 14.10 (978-0-613-90430-8(3)) Tandem Library Bks.

Wolfson, Evelyn. King Arthur & His Knights in Mythology. Bock, William Sauts, illus. 2002. (Mythology Ser.). 128p. (YA). (gr. 6-12). lib. bdg. 26.60 (978-0-7660-1914-0(4)) Enslow Pubs., Inc.

Wyly, Michael J. King Arthur. 2001. (Mystery Library). (Illus.). 112p. (YA). (gr. 4-12). 27.45 (978-1-56006-771-9(3) , Lucent Bks.) Thomson Gale.

ARTHUR, KING—FICTION

Barkan, Joanne. A Pup in King Arthur's Court. l.t. ed. 1999. (Adventures of Wishbone Ser.: No. 15). (Illus.). 164p. (J). (gr. 2-5). lib. bdg. 22.60 (978-0-8368-2593-0(4)) Stevens, Gareth Inc.

Brassey, Richard. Brilliant BritsGuy Fawkes. Brassey, Richard, illus. 2005. (Brilliant Brits Ser.). (Illus.). 24p. (J). pap. 8.99 (978-1-84255-231-5(7)) Orion Children's Bks. GBR. *Dist:* Independent Pubs. Group.

Brooks, Felicity. King Arthur. rev. ed. 2007. 144p. (J). pap. 4.99 (***978-0-7945-1483-9(9)*** , Usborne) EDC Publishing.

Brooks, Felicity. Tales of King Arthur. 2004. (Paperback Classics Ser.). 144p. (J). lib. bdg. 12.95 (978-1-58086-433-6(3)) EDC Publishing.

—Tales of King Arthur. 2002. (gr. 3-6). lib. bdg. 12.95 (978-0-613-75320-3(8)) Tandem Library Bks.

Brown, Marc. La Visita del Senor Rataquemada. 2003. (SPA.). (gr. k-3). lib. bdg. 15.25 (978-0-613-64613-0(4)) Tandem Library Bks.

Browne, N. M. Warriors of Camlann. 2003. (Illus.). 275p. (J). 16.95 (978-1-58234-817-9(0) , Bloomsbury Children) Bloomsbury Publishing.

Bulla, Clyde Robert. The Sword in the Tree. 2000. (gr. 3-6). lib. bdg. 12.10 (978-0-613-27147-9(5)) Tandem Library Bks.

Los Caballeros del Rey Arturo. (SPA., Illus.). (YA). 14.95 (978-84-7281-107-2(7) , AF1107) Auriga, Ediciones S.A. ESP. *Dist:* Continental Bk. Co., Inc.

Cabot, Meg. Avalon High. (J). 2007. 320p. pap. 8.99 (***978-0-06-075588-1(1)*** , HarperTeen); 2006. 304p. 16.99 (978-0-06-075586-7(5)); 2006. 304p. lib. bdg. 17.89 (978-0-06-075587-4(3)) HarperCollins Pubs.

—Avalon High. l.t. ed. 2006. 335p. (YA). 23.95 (978-0-7862-9032-1(3)) Thorndike Pr.

Cabot, Meg. The Merlin Prophecy. Coronado, Jinky, illus. 2007. (Avalon High Coronation Ser.: No. 1). 208p. (J). (gr. 7 up). pap. 7.99 (***978-0-06-117707-1(5))*** TOKYOPOP, Inc.

Clay, Beatrice. Stories from le Morte d'Arthur & the M. 2006. 78.99 (***978-1-4280-4717-4(4));*** pap. 71.99 (***978-1-4280-4712-9(3))*** IndyPublish.com.

Clement-Davies, David. The Telling Pool. (gr. 7-17). 2007. 382p. (YA). pap. 7.95 (***978-0-8109-9257-3(4));*** 2005. (Illus.). 376p. (J). 19.95 (978-0-8109-5758-9(2) , Abrams Bks. for Young Readers) Abrams, Harry N., Inc.

Crossley-Holland, Kevin. At the Crossing Places. 2002. (Arthur Trilogy: Bk. 2). 416p. (J). (gr. 9 up). 17.95 (978-0-439-26598-0(3) , Levine, Arthur A. Bks.) Scholastic, Inc.

—At the Crossing-Places. 2004. (Illus.). 394p. (YA). (gr. 7-12). lib. bdg. 13.64 (978-0-606-32761-9(4)) Tandem Library Bks.

—At the Crossing Places. 2004. (Arthur Trilogy: Bk. 2). 416p. (J). (gr. 4-7). reprint ed. pap. 7.99 (978-0-439-26599-7(1) , Levine, Arthur A. Bks.) Scholastic, Inc.

—King of the Middle March. 432p. (J). 2006. pap. 7.99 (978-0-439-26601-7(7)); Book 3. 2004. (gr. 7 up). 17.95 (978-0-439-26600-0(9) , Levine, Arthur A. Bks.) Scholastic, Inc.

—The Seeing Stone. 2002. (Arthur Trilogy: Vol. 1). 368p. (J). (gr. 5 up). mass mkt. 6.99 (978-0-439-43524-6(2) , Levine, Arthur A. Bks.) Scholastic, Inc.

—Seeing Stone. 2002. (gr. 7-12). lib. bdg. 15.30 (978-0-613-50642-7(1)) Tandem Library Bks.

—The Seeing Stone, Book 1. 2002. (Arthur Trilogy: Bk. 1). 368p. (J). (gr. 4-7). mass mkt. 7.99 (978-0-439-26327-6(1) , Levine, Arthur A. Bks.) Scholastic, Inc.

—The World of King Arthur & His Court: People, Places, Legend, & Lore. Maloney, Peter, illus. 2004. 128p. (J). (gr. 5). pap. 14.99 (978-0-525-47321-3(1) , Dutton Juvenile) Penguin Group (USA) Inc.

Darden, Amy Yesterday Once Again: Guenevere's Quest. 2003. (J). pap. 11.00 (978-0-8059-9238-0(3) , RoseDog Bks.) Dorrance Publishing Co., Inc.

Dixon, Andy. Los Caballeros del Rey Arturo. 2001. (SPA., Illus.). 32p. (YA). (gr. 3 up). lib. bdg. 16.95 (978-1-58086-318-6(3)) EDC Publishing.

Duey, Kathleen. Arthur. Epstein, Eugene, illus. Gould, Robert, photos by. 2004. (Time Soldiers Ser.: Bk. 4). 48p. (J). 15.95 (978-1-929945-05-4(1)) Big Guy Bks., Inc.

—Arthur. 2007. (Illus.). 96p. (J). 24.21 (978-1-59961-224-9(0)) Spotlight.

Engler, L. E. The Forgotten Isle. 2004. 108p. pap. 16.95 (978-1-4137-1941-3(4)) PublishAmerica, Inc.

Gelders-Sterne, Emma & Lindsay, Barbara. King Arthur & the Knights of the Round Table. Tenggren, Gustaf, illus. 2002. 160p. (J). (gr. 1). 21.99 (978-0-307-90432-4(6) , Golden Bks.) Random Hse. Children's Bks.

Gilman, Laura Anne. The Camelot Spell. 2006. (Grail Quest Trilogy Ser.: No. 1). 304p. (J). 10.99 (978-0-06-077279-6(4)); lib. bdg. 14.89 (978-0-06-077280-2(8)) HarperCollins Pubs.

—Morgain's Revenge. 2006. (Grail Quest Trilogy Ser.: No. 2). 288p. (J). lib. bdg. 14.89 (978-0-06-077283-3(2)) HarperCollins Pubs.

Hill, Pamela Smith. The Last Grail Keeper. 2001. 240p. (J). (gr. 7 up). tchr. ed. 17.95 (978-0-8234-1574-8(0)) Holiday Hse., Inc.

Hodges, Margaret & Malory, Thomas. Merlin & the Making of the King. Hyman, Trina Schart, tr. Hyman, Trina Schart, illus. 2004. 40p. (J). (gr. 4-6). tchr. ed. 16.95 (978-0-8234-1647-9(X)) Holiday Hse., Inc.

Hoffman, Mary. Women of Camelot: Queens & Enchantresses at the Court of King Arthur. 2000. (Illus.). 72p. (J). 19.95 (978-0-7892-0646-6(3)) Abbeville Pr., Inc.

—Women of Camelot: Queens & Enchantresses at the Court of King Arthur. Balit, Christina, illus. 2006. 69p. (YA). (gr. 5-9). 20.00 (978-1-4223-5260-1(9)) DIANE Publishing Co.

Ioan, Elwyn & Gruffudd, Garmon. Arthur A'r Cleddyf: Llyfr Lliwio. 2005. (WEL., Illus.). 16p. pap. (978-0-86243-378-9(9)) Y Lolfa.

Limke, Jeff. King Arthur: Excalibur Unsheathed. Yeates, Thomas, illus. 2007. (Graphic Myths & Legends Ser.). 48p. (YA). (gr. 4-9). pap. 8.95 (***978-0-8225-6483-6(1))*** Lerner Publishing Group.

Limke Jeff. El rey Arturo (King Arthur) La espada Excalibur desenvainada (Excalibur Unsheathed) Yeates, Thomas, illus. 2007. (Mitos y leyendas en viñetas (Graphic Myths & Legends) Ser.). (J). pap. 8.95 (***978-0-8225-7968-7(5)*** , Ediciones Lerner) Lerner Publishing Group.

Malone, Patricia. Lady Ilena: Way of the Warrior. 2007. 176p. (YA). (gr. 7-11). mass mkt. 5.99 (***978-0-440-23901-7(X)*** , Laurel Leaf) Random Hse. Children's Bks.

Malory, Thomas & Lanier, Sidney. The Boy's King Arthur. Wyeth, N. C., illus. 2006. 352p. pap. 14.95 (978-0-486-44800-8(2)) Dover Pubns., Inc.

Matthews, John. Arthur of Albion: Marvellous Tales of the Round Table. Tatarnikau, Pavel, illus. 2007. (J). (***978-1-84686-049-2(0))*** Barefoot Bks., Inc.

McCaughrean, Geraldine & Marks, Alan. King Arthur. 2007. (Illus.). (J). pap. (***978-0-340-89437-8(7)*** , Hodder Children's Books) Hodder Children's Division.

McKenzie, Nancy. Guinevere's Gift. 2008. 336p. (J). (gr. 5-9). 15.99 (***978-0-375-84345-7(0)*** , Knopf Bks. for Young Readers) Random Hse. Children's Bks.

Milbourne, Anna. Stories of Knights & Castles. 2007. 96p. (J). 16.99 (978-0-7945-1466-2(9) , Usborne) EDC Publishing.

Morris, Gerald. Parsifal's Page. (Squire's Tales Ser.). 240p. (J). (gr. 5-9). 2004. pap. 5.95 (978-0-618-43237-0(X)); 2001. (Illus.). tchr. ed. 16.00 (978-0-618-05509-8(6)) Houghton Mifflin Co. Trade & Reference Div.

Pyle, Howard. The Story of King Arthur & His Knights. McKowen, Scott, illus. 2005. (Unabridged Classics Ser.). 320p. (gr. 5-9). 9.95 (978-1-4027-2503-6(5) , 1252056) Sterling Publishing Co., Inc.

—The Story of Sir Lancelot & His Companions. 2004. reprint ed. pap. 27.95 (978-1-4179-5609-8(7)) Kessinger Publishing, LLC.

Richards, Christopher, illus. King Arthur & the Knights of the Round Table. 2007. (Graphic Revolve Ser.). 63p. (J). (gr. 4-6). lib. bdg. 22.60 (978-1-59889-048-8(4)) Stone Arch Bks.

Sandell, Lisa Ann. Song of the Sparrow. 2007. 416p. (YA). (gr. 7 up). pap. 16.99 (***978-0-439-91848-0(0)*** , Scholastic Pr.) Scholastic, Inc.

Sanderson, Jeannette. The Sword in Stone: A King Arthur Legend. 2006. 42.00 (***978-1-4108-6179-5(1))*** Benchmark Education Co.

Service, Pamela F. Tomorrow's Magic. 2007. 448p. (J). (gr. 3-7). 15.99 (978-0-375-84087-6(7)); (gr. 4-9). lib. bdg. 18.99 (978-0-375-94087-3(1)) Random Hse. Children's Bks. (Random Hse. Bks. for Young Readers).

—Tomorrow's Magic. 2007. (J). pap. (978-0-375-84088-3(5)) Random Hse., Inc.

Service, Pamela F. Yesterday's Magic. 2008. (J). (gr. 3-7). 224p. 16.99 (***978-0-375-85577-1(7));*** 320p. lib. bdg. 19.99 (***978-0-375-95577-8(1))*** Random Hse. Children's Bks. (Random Hse. Bks. for Young Readers).

Spence, Stephen Mark. Merlin's Curse. 2000. (Round Table Cycle: 3). 226p. (YA). (gr. 4-12). pap. 11.99 (978-0-9705324-2-8(3)) Spence, Stephen Mark.

—The Round Table Cycle, 3 vols. 2000. (Round Table Cycle). 658p. (YA). (gr. 4-12). pap. 33.00 (978-0-9705324-3-5(1)) Spence, Stephen Mark.

Springer, Nancy. I Am Mordred: A Tale from Camelot. 2002. (Firebird Ser.). 192p. (J). (gr. 7 up). pap. 6.99 (978-0-698-11841-6(3) , Puffin) Penguin Group (USA) Inc.

—I Am Mordred: A Tale from Camelot. unabr. ed. 2000. (YA). pap. 68.99 incl. audio (978-0-7887-3006-1(1) , 40888X4) Recorded Bks., LLC.

—I Am Mordred: A Tale from Camelot. 2002. (gr. 5-8). lib. bdg. 14.15 (978-0-613-44457-6(4)) Tandem Library Bks.

—I Am Morgan le Fay: A Tale from Camelot. 2002. (Firebird Ser.). 240p. (YA). pap. 6.99 (978-0-698-11974-1(6) , Puffin) Penguin Group (USA) Inc.

—I Am Morgan le Fay: A Tale from Camelot. 2002. (gr. 7-12). lib. bdg. 14.15 (978-0-613-55214-1(8)) Tandem Library Bks.

Stewart, Mary. The Last Enchantment. 2003. (gr. 7-12). lib. bdg. 24.55 (978-0-613-66978-8(9)) Tandem Library Bks.

—The Wicked Day. 2003. (gr. 7-12). lib. bdg. 24.55 (978-0-613-67236-8(4)) Tandem Library Bks.

Thomson, Sarah L. The Dragon's Son. 2001. (Illus.). 148p. (J). (gr. 7 up). 17.95 (978-0-531-30333-7(0) , Orchard Bks.) Scholastic, Inc.

Twain, Mark. A Connecticut Yankee in King Arthur's Court. 1999. reprint ed. pap. 28.00 (978-1-4047-1121-1(X)) Classic Textbooks.

Uletilovuic, Patricia. Merlin's Return. 2004. (YA). lib. bdg. 5.50 (978-1-59431-135-2(8)) ebooksonthe.net.

Vande Velde, Vivian. The Book of Mordred. 2005. (Illus.). 352p. (YA). (gr. 7-7). 18.00 (978-0-618-50754-2(X)) Houghton Mifflin Co. Trade & Reference Div.

Velde, Vivian Vande. The Book of Mordred. 2007. 352p. (YA). (gr. 7). pap. 8.99 (***978-0-618-80916-5(3)*** , Graphia) Houghton Mifflin Co. Trade & Reference Div.

Wilkes, Angela & Rawson, Christopher. The Adventures of King Arthur. 2004. (Young Reading Ser.). (Illus.). 64p. (J). (gr. 2 up). pap. 5.99 (978-0-7945-0447-2(7) , Usborne) EDC Publishing.

Yancey, Rick. The Extraordinary Adventures of Alfred Kropp. 2006. (Illus.). 352p. (YA). reprint ed. pap. 7.95 (978-1-59990-044-5(0) , Bloomsbury Children) Bloomsbury Publishing.

Yeates, Thomas, illus. Arthur & Lancelot: The Fight for Camelot. 2007. (Graphic Myths & Legends Ser.). 48p. (J). (gr. 4-8). lib. bdg. 26.60 (***978-0-8225-6296-2(0)*** , Graphic Universe) Lerner Publishing Group.

Yolen, Jane. The Dragon's Boy: A Tale of Young King Arthur. 2001. (Illus.). (J). 11.64 (978-0-606-21161-1(6)) Tandem Library Bks.

—Sword of the Rightful King: A Novel of King Arthur. 2004. (Illus.). 376p. (YA). reprint ed. pap. 6.95 (978-0-15-202533-5(2)) Harcourt Children's Bks.

ARTHURIAN ROMANCES

see Arthur, King

ARTIFICIAL FLOWERS

Chicken Socks Editors. Make Your Own Paper Flowers. 2007. 18p. (J). (ps up). spiral bd. 12.95 (***978-1-59174-443-6(1))*** Klutz.

ARTIFICIAL INTELLIGENCE

Fritz, Sandy. Robotics & Artificial Intelligence. 2003. (Hot Science Ser.). (J). lib. bdg. 28.50 (978-1-58340-364-8(7)) Smart Apple Media.

Graham, Ian. Artificial Intelligence. 2003. (Science at the Edge Ser.). (Illus.). 64p. (J). (gr. 6-8). lib. bdg. 27.86 (978-1-4034-0323-0(6)) Heinemann Library.

Jefferis, David. Artificial Intelligence: Robotics & Machine Evolution. 1999. (Megatech Ser.). (Illus.). 32p. (J). (gr. 4-5). pap. (978-0-7787-0056-2(9)); lib. bdg. (978-0-7787-0046-3(1)) Crabtree Publishing Co.

Margulies, Phillip. Artificial Intelligence. 2003. (Science on the Edge Ser.). 48p. (J). 24.95 (978-1-56711-783-7(X) , Blackbirch Pr., Inc.) Thomson Gale.

Perry, Robert. Artificial Intelligence. 2000. (gr. 5-8). lib. bdg. 17.60 (978-0-613-37275-6(1)) Tandem Library Bks.

Thomas, Peggy. Artificial Intelligence. 2005. (Lucent Library of Science & Technology). (Illus.). 112p. (J). (gr. 3-7). lib. bdg. 29.95 (978-1-59018-437-0(8) , Lucent Bks.) Thomson Gale.

Woolf, Alex. Artificial Intelligence: The Impact on Our Lives. 2003. (21st Century Debates Ser.). (Illus.). 64p. (J). lib. bdg. 27.12 (978-0-7398-5504-1(2)) Raintree.

ARTIFICIAL SATELLITES

see also Meteorological Satellites; Space Stations; Space Vehicles

Asimov, Isaac & Hantula, Richard. Exploring Outer Space. 2005. (Isaac Asimov's 21st Century Library of the Universe). (Illus.). 32p. (J). (gr. 3-7). lib. bdg. 24.67 (978-0-8368-3981-4(1)) Stevens, Gareth Inc.

Bailey, Gerry. Journey into Space. Boulter, Steve & Smith, Jan, illus. 2005. (Crafty Inventions Ser.). 48p. (C). (gr. 4-6). 26.60 (978-1-4048-1042-6(0)) Picture Window Bks.

Deady, Kathleen W. Satellites. 2002. (Explore Space! Ser.). (Illus.). 24p. (J). (gr. 1-2). lib. bdg. 18.60 (978-0-7368-1400-3(0) , Bridgestone Bks.) Capstone Pr., Inc.

Elish, Dan. Satellites. 2006. (Kaleidoscope Space Ser.). (Illus.). 48p. (J). lib. bdg. 28.50 (978-0-7614-2098-9(3) , Benchmark Bks.) Cavendish, Marshall Corp.

Feldman, Heather. Sputnik: The First Satellite. 2003. (Space Firsts Ser.). (Illus.). 24p. (J). lib. bdg. 19.95 (978-0-8239-6244-0(X) , PowerKids Pr.) Rosen Publishing Group, Inc., The.

Goldberg, Jan. Earth Imaging Satellites. 2003. (Library of Satellites). (Illus.). 64p. (YA). (gr. 5-8). lib. bdg. 26.50 (978-0-8239-3853-7(0) , Rosen Central) Rosen Publishing Group, Inc., The.

Graham, Ian. The Best Book of Spaceships. 1998. (Best Book of... Ser.). (Illus.). 32p. (J). (gr. k-3). tchr. ed. 12.95 (978-0-7534-5133-5(6) , Kingfisher) Houghton Mifflin Co. Trade & Reference Div.

—Satellites & Communications. 2001. (Technoworld Ser.). (Illus.). 32p. (J). lib. bdg. 25.69 (978-0-7398-3255-4(7)) Raintree.

Johnson, Rebecca L. Satellites. 2006. (Cool Science Ser.). (Illus.). 48p. (J). (gr. 4-8). lib. bdg. 26.60 (978-0-8225-2908-8(4) , Lerner Pubns.) Lerner Publishing Group.

The Library of Satellites, 6 bks. Incl. Communication Satellites. Byers, Ann. lib. bdg. 26.50 (978-0-8239-3851-3(4)); Deep Space Observation Satellites. Sherman, Josepha. lib. bdg. 26.50 (978-0-8239-3852-0(2)); Earth Imaging Satellites. Goldberg, Jan. lib. bdg. 26.50 (978-0-8239-3853-7(0)); Spy Satellites. Kupperberg, Paul. lib. bdg. 26.50 (978-0-8239-3854-4(9)); Weapons Satellites. Wolny, Philip. lib. bdg. 26.50 (978-0-8239-3855-1(7)); Weather Observation Satellites. Cobb, Allan B. lib. bdg. 26.50 (978-0-8239-3856-8(5)); 64p. (YA). (gr. 5-8). 2003. (Illus.). 2002. Set lib. bdg. 159.00 (978-0-8239-4055-4(1) , Rosen Central) Rosen Publishing Group, Inc., The.

Miller, Ron. Satellites. 2007. (Space Innovations Ser.). 112p. (YA). (gr. 6-8). lib. bdg. 31.93 (***978-0-8225-7154-4(4)*** , Twenty-First Century Bks.) Lerner Publishing Group.

Parker, Steve. Satellites. 2002. (Tomorrow's Technology Ser.). (Illus.). 32p. (J). lib. bdg. 24.25 (978-1-931983-25-9(9)) Chrysalis Education.

Rosinsky, Natalie M. Satellites & the GPS. 2004. (Illus.). 32p. (J). (gr. 3 up). 21.26 (978-0-7565-0597-4(6)) Compass Point Bks.

Rudy, Lisa Jo. Eyes in the Sky: Satellite Spies Are Watching You! 2007. (24/7: Science Behind the Scenes: Spy Files Ser.). 64p. (J). pap. 7.95 (***978-0-531-18732-6(2)*** , Watts, Franklin) Scholastic Library Publishing.

Sherman, Josepha. Deep Space Observation Satellites. 2003. (Library of Satellites). (Illus.). 64p. (YA). (gr. 5-8). lib. bdg. 26.50 (978-0-8239-3852-0(2) , Rosen Central) Rosen Publishing Group, Inc., The.

Simon, Seymour. Tornadoes. 1999. (Illus.). 32p. (J). (gr. k-3). 16.89 (978-0-688-14647-4(3)) HarperCollins Pubs.

A
B

Spangenburg, Ray. Artificial Satellites. 2001. (gr. 5-8). lib. bdg. 24.55 (978-0-613-53933-3(8)) Tandem Library Bks.

Stille, Darlene R. Satellite. 2001. (Communications Ser.). (Illus.). 24p. (J). (gr. 1 up). lib. bdg. 18.60 (978-0-7565-0137-2(7)) Compass Point Bks.

Vogt, Gregory L. Moons. 2002. (Galaxy Ser.). (Illus.). 24p. (J). (gr. 2-3). lib. bdg. 18.60 (978-0-7368-1383-9(7), Bridgestone Bks.) Capstone Pr., Inc.

—Moons. 2000. (Our Universe Ser.). (Illus.). 48p. (YA). (gr. 5-12). lib. bdg. 22.83 (978-0-7398-3106-9(2)) Raintree.

—Moons. 2000. (Our Universe Ser.). (Illus.). (J). pap. (978-0-7398-3345-2(6)) Steck-Vaughn.

Wolny, Philip. Weapons Satellites. 2003. (Library of Satellites). (Illus.). 64p. (YA). (gr. 5-8). lib. bdg. 26.50 (978-0-8239-3855-1(7), Rosen Central) Rosen Publishing Group, Inc., The.

ARTIFICIAL SATELLITES IN TELECOMMUNICATION

Byers, Ann. Communication Satellites. 2003. (Library of Satellites). (Illus.). 64p. (YA). (gr. 5-8). lib. bdg. 26.50 (978-0-8239-3851-3(4), Rosen Central) Rosen Publishing Group, Inc., The.

Gaines, Ann Graham. Satellite Communications. 1999. (Making Contact Ser.). (Illus.). 32p. (YA). (gr. 4 up). lib. bdg. 16.95 (978-1-887068-63-5(5)) Smart Apple Media.

Whiting, Jim. John R. Pierce: Pioneer in Satellite Communication. 2003. (Unlocking the Secrets of Science Ser.). (Illus.). 56p. (gr. 4-10). lib. bdg. 25.70 (978-1-58415-205-7(2)) Mitchell Lane Pubs., Inc.

ARTILLERY

see also Ordnance

Baker, David. M109 Paladin. 2007. (Fighting Forces on Land Ser.). (Illus.). 32p. (J). (978-1-60044-245-2(5)) Rourke Publishing, LLC.

Katcher, Philip R. N. Confederate Artillerymen of the Civil War. 2003. (Soldier's Life Ser.). (Illus.). 64p. (J). 31.42 (978-1-4109-0113-2(0)) Raintree.

ARTISTIC ANATOMY

see Anatomy, Artistic

ARTISTIC PHOTOGRAPHY

see Photography, Artistic

ARTISTS

see also Architects; Art—Vocational Guidance; Painters; Sculptors; Women Artists

Ada, Alma Flor & Campoy, F. Isabel. Brocha y Pincel. (Literature Collection of Puertas Al Sol Ser.). (SPA.). 32p. (J). (gr. k-6). pap. 13.95 (978-1-59437-705-1(7)) Santillana USA Publishing Co., Inc.

—Caballete. (Literature Collection of Puertas Al Sol Ser.). (SPA.). 32p. (J). (gr. k-6). pap. 13.95 (978-1-59437-708-2(1)) Santillana USA Publishing Co., Inc.

—Lienzo y Papel. (Literature Collection of Puertas Al Sol Ser.). (SPA.). 32p. (J). (gr. k-6). pap. 13.95 (978-1-59437-711-2(1)) Santillana USA Publishing Co., Inc.

Ada, Alma Flor & Campoy, F. Isabel, contrib. by. Artist's Easel. (Literature Collection of Gateways to the Sun Ser.). 32p. (J). (gr. k-6). pap. 13.95 (978-1-59437-720-4(0)) Santillana USA Publishing Co., Inc.

—Azul y Verde. (Literature Collection of Puertas Al Sol Ser.). (SPA.). 32p. (J). (gr. k-6). pap. 13.95 (978-1-59437-702-0(2)) Santillana USA Publishing Co., Inc.

Agnes & Aubrey. Art Songs: Ten Songs about Artists. 2006. (Illus.). 24p. (gr. k-4). 14.95 (978-1-85437-683-1(7)) Tate Gallery Publishing, Ltd. GBR. *Dist:* Hachette Bk. Group.

Ajmera, Maya & Ivanko, John D. To Be an Artist. 2005. (Illus.). 32p. (J). (ps-ps). pap. 6.95 (978-1-57091-576-5(8)) Charlesbridge Publishing, Inc.

Armstrong, Jennifer. Audubon: Painter of Birds in the Wild Frontier. Smith, Joseph A., illus. 2003. 40p. (J). (gr. k-4). 17.95 (978-0-8109-4238-7(0)) Abrams, Harry N., Inc.

Artists in Profile, 8 bks., Set. 2002. (YA). (gr. 6-8). lib. bdg. 228.00 (978-1-58810-467-0(2)) Heinemann Library.

Authors & Artists for Young Adults. 1998. (Authors & Artists for Young Adults Ser.: Vol. 24). 250p. (gr. 8-12). 130.00 (978-0-7876-1971-8(X), 00157487); 51. 2003. (Illus.). 250p. (YA). 130.00 (978-0-7876-5180-0(X), UXL); Vol. 27. 1998. (Authors & Artists for Young Adults Ser.: Vol. 27). (Illus.). 250p. (gr. 8-12). 130.00 (978-0-7876-2070-7(X), GML14099-111588); Vol. 28. 1999. (Authors & Artists for Young Adults Ser.: Vol. 28). (Illus.). 250p. (gr. 8-12). 130.00 (978-0-7876-2071-4(8), GML14099-111589); Vol. 45. 2002. (Authors & Artists Ser.). 250p. 130.00 (978-0-7876-5174-9(5), GML00502-173184); Vol. 49. 2003. (Illus.). 250p. (YA). 105.00 (978-0-7876-5178-7(8), UXL); Vol. 50. 2003. (Illus.). 250p. (YA). 130.00 (978-0-7876-5179-4(6), UXL); Vol. 52. 2003. (YA). 130.00 (978-0-7876-5181-7(8)); Vol. 55. 2004. (Authors & Artists for Young Adults Ser.). 130.00 (978-0-7876-6643-9(2)); Vol. 56. 2004. (Authors & Artists for Young Adults Ser.). 130.00 (978-0-7876-6644-6(0)); Vol. 57. 2004. (Authors & Artists for Young Adults Ser.). 130.00 (978-0-7876-6645-3(9)); Vol. 58. 2004. (Authors & Artists for Young Adults Ser.). 130.00 (978-0-7876-6646-0(7)) Thomson Gale.

Bankston, John. Diego Rivera. 2003. (Latinos in American History Ser.). (Illus.). 56p. (gr. 4-8). lib. bdg. 29.95 (978-1-58415-208-8(7)) Mitchell Lane Pubs., Inc.

Barnett, Michelle Noble, et al. Theme Pockets - June: Amazon Rainforest; Artists; Farmers Feed Us. Evans, Marilyn, ed. Larsen, Jo, illus. 1999. (Making Books with Pockets). 96p. (J). pap., tchr. ed. 12.99 (978-1-55799-703-6(9), EMC 589) Evan-Moor Educational Pubs.

Barter, James E. Artists of the Renaissance. 1998. (History Makers Ser.). (Illus.). 112p. (YA). (gr. 4-12). 28.70 (978-1-56006-439-8(0), Lucent Bks.) Thomson Gale.

—A Renaissance Painter's Studio. 2002. (Working Life Ser.). (Illus.). 112p. (J). 29.95 (978-1-59018-178-2(6)) Thomson Gale.

Bennett, Leonie. Life & Work of Pablo Picasso. 2004. (Life & Work Of- Ser.). (Illus.). 32p. (J). pap. 7.25 (978-1-4034-5563-5(5)) Heinemann Library.

Bolton, Linda. Andy Warhol. 2002. (Artists in Their Time Ser.). (Illus.). 48p. (J). (gr. 5-7). pap. 23.50 (978-0-531-12225-9(5), Watts, Franklin) Scholastic Library Publishing.

—Andy Warhol. 2002. (gr. 5-8). lib. bdg. 15.25 (978-0-613-53914-2(1)) Tandem Library Bks.

—Surrealists. 2002. (Artists in Profile Ser.). (Illus.). 64p. (J). lib. bdg. 28.50 (978-1-58810-648-3(9)) Heinemann Library.

Braun, Eric. Tomie DePaola. 2005. (First Biographies Ser.). (Illus.). 24p. (J). 15.93 (978-0-7368-3641-8(1), Pebble Bks.) Capstone Pr., Inc.

Brenner, Barbara. The Boy Who Loved to Draw: Benjamin West. Dunrea, Olivier, illus. 48p. (J). (gr. k-3). 2003. pap. 5.95 (978-0-618-31089-0(4)); 1999. tchr. ed. 15.00 (978-0-395-85080-0(0)) Houghton Mifflin Co. Trade & Reference Div.

Burleigh, Robert. Toulouse-Lautrec: The Moulin Rouge & the City of Light. 2005. (Illus.). 32p. (J). (gr. k-4). 17.95 (978-0-8109-5867-8(8)) Abrams, Harry N., Inc.

—Toulouse-Lautrec: The Moulin Rouge & the City of Light. 2006. (Illus.). 32p. (J). (gr. 4-8). 18.00 (978-1-4223-5493-3(8)) DIANE Publishing Co.

Burnett, Craig. Jeff Wall. 2006. (Modern Artists Ser.). (Illus.). 128p. pap. 24.95 (978-1-85437-611-4(X)) Tate Gallery Publishing, Ltd. GBR. *Dist:* Hachette Bk. Group.

Burton, Marilee Robin. Artists at Work. 2003. (On the Job Ser.). (Illus.). 32p. (gr. 3-5). 23.00 (978-0-7910-7410-7(2), Chelsea Hse.) Facts On File, Inc.

Button, Beth. Early Modern Artists. Rogers, Kathy, ed. Adams, Elizabeth, illus. 2000. (Famous Faces Ser.). 8p. (J). pap., wbk. ed. 6.95 (978-1-56472-282-9(1)) Edupress, Inc.

Caravan to America: Living Arts of the Silk Road. 2002. (gr. 3-6). lib. bdg. 25.70 (978-0-613-76180-2(4)) Tandem Library Bks.

Civardi, A. First Experiences. 2004. 144p. (J). 19.95 (978-0-7460-2254-2(9), Usborne) EDC Publishing.

Connolly, Sean. Leonardo Da Vinci. 2006. (Heinemann First Library). (Illus.). 32p. (J). lib. bdg. ***978-1-4034-8492-5(9)*** Heinemann Library.

Cook, Diane. Paul Gaugin: 18th Century French Painter. 2002. (Great Names Ser.). (Illus.). 32p. (J). (gr. 3 up). lib. bdg. (978-1-59084-153-2(0)) Mason Crest Pubs.

Covington, Karen. The Creators: Artists, Designers, Craftswomen. 2000. (Remarkable Women). (Illus.). 80p. (YA). (gr. 6-9). lib. bdg. 32.85 (978-0-8172-5725-5(X)) Raintree.

Cummings, Pat. Talking with Artists. 1999. (Talking with Artists Ser.: Vol. 3). (Illus.). 96p. (J). (gr. 5-9). tchr. ed. 22.00 (978-0-395-89132-2(9), Clarion Bks.) Houghton Mifflin Co. Trade & Reference Div.

Danneberg, Julie. Women Artists of the West: Five Portraits in Creativity & Courage. 2004. (Illus.). 96p. pap. 12.95 (978-1-55591-861-3(1)) Fulcrum Publishing.

Davies, Carolyn. Josef Herman in Wales. 2004. (Illus.). 31p. pap. 15.95 (978-1-85902-999-2(X)) Beekman Bks., Inc.

Delgado, M. E. First Sandcastle. 2002. (ENG.). 360p. 28.95 (***978-0-595-65106-1(2)***, Writers Club Pr.) iUniverse, Inc.

Dickens, Rosie. The Children's Book of Art: Internet Linked. 2005. (Illus.). 64p. (J). (***978-0-439-88981-0(2)***) Scholastic, Inc.

Dorling Kindersley Publishing Staff & Fedele, Frank. The Artist's Palate: Cooking with the World's Great Artists. 2003. (Illus.). 192p. 30.00 (978-0-7894-7768-2(8)) Dorling Kindersley Publishing, Inc.

Duggleby, John. Artist in Overalls: The Life of Grant Wood. 2005. (Illus.). 64p. (J). (ps-7). pap. 7.95 (978-0-8118-4908-1(2)) Chronicle Bks. LLC.

Durham, Jimmie. Jimmie Durham: From the West Pacific to the East Atlantic. Arkesteijn, Roel, ed. 2004. (Illus.). 256p. 50.00 (978-90-75380-74-3(7)) Artimo Foundation NLD. *Dist:* D.A.P./Distributed Art Pubs.

Falconer, Shelley & White, Shawna. Stones, Bones & Stitches: Storytelling Through Inuit Art. 2007. 40p. (YA). (gr. 3 up). 22.95 (***978-0-88776-854-5(7)***) Tundra Bks. of Northern New York.

Ferrara, Cos. Mary Cassatt: The Life & Art of a Genteel Rebel. 2004. (Girls Explore, Reach for the Stars Ser.). (Illus.). 101p. (J). 20.00 (978-0-9749456-3-7(3), Girls Explore) Girls Explore LLC.

Fleischman, Sid. Escape! The Story of the Great Houdini. 2006. (Illus.). 224p. (J). (gr. 4-8). 18.99 (978-0-06-085094-4(9)); lib. bdg. 19.89 (978-0-06-085095-1(7)) HarperCollins Pubs.

Flux, Paul. The Life & Work of Wassily Kandinsky, Set 2. 2002. (Illus.). 32p. (J). (gr. k-2). pap. 6.50 (978-1-4034-0006-2(7), 91624) Heinemann Library.

Framis, Alicia. Alicia Framis. Breddels, Lilet, ed. 2004. (Illus.). 128p. (YA). (gr. 13 up). 35.00 (978-90-75380-77-4(1)) Artimo Foundation NLD. *Dist:* D.A.P./Distributed Art Pubs.

Frey, Lisa A. The Story of Monet & Renoir. Frey, Lisa A. & Darroch, Jane, eds. Darroch, Jane & Riley, Scott, illus. 2004. (Color & Learn Book Ser.). 32p. (gr. k-4). pap. 12.99 (978-0-9707110-1-4(8)) Starshell Pr., Ltd.

Frith, Margaret. The Artist Who Painted Herself. de Paola, Tomie, illus. 2003. (Smart about the Arts Ser.). 32p. (J). (gr. k-5). pap. 5.99 (978-0-448-42677-8(3), Grosset & Dunlap) Penguin Group (USA) Inc.

Gaff, Jackie. Alberto Giacometti. 2002. (Artists in Their Time Ser.). (Illus.). (J). (gr. 5-7). 46p. pap. 6.95 (978-0-531-16617-8(1)); 48p. pap. 23.50 (978-0-531-12224-2(7)) Scholastic Library Publishing. (Watts, Franklin).

—Alberto Giacometti. 2002. (Illus.). 46p. (J). (gr. 3-7). lib. bdg. 15.25 (978-0-613-53900-5(1)) Tandem Library Bks.

Gauch, Patricia Lee, et al, eds. Artist to Artist: 23 Major Illustrators Talk to Children about Their Art. 2007. (Illus.). 105p. (J). (ps). 30.00 (***978-0-399-24600-5(2)***, Philomel) Penguin Group (USA) Inc.

Getting to Know the World's Greatest Creative Minds. 2004. 624.00 (978-0-516-24708-3(5)) Scholastic Library Publishing.

Giesecke, Ernestine. Mary Cassatt. 2006. (Heinemann First Library). (Illus.). 32p. (J). lib. bdg. (***978-1-4034-8493-2(7)***) Heinemann Library.

Goldberg, Dana. On My Block: Stories & Paintings by Fifteen Artists. 2007. (Illus.). 32p. (J). (gr. 1 up). 16.95 (***978-0-89239-220-9(7)***) Children's Bk. Pr.

Goldman-Rubin, Susan. Delicious: The Art & Life of Wayne Thiebaud. 2007. (Illus.). 104p. (J). (gr. 4-9). 15.95 (978-0-8118-5168-8(0)) Chronicle Bks. LLC.

Gowing, Lawrence, ed. Facts on File Encyclopedia of Art & Artists Set. 2005. 1840p. (gr. 9). 585.00 (978-0-8160-6378-9(8)) Facts On File, Inc.

Granada Learning Ltd., prod. Great Artists. (YA). cd-rom 99.95 (978-0-7365-0363-1(3)) Films Media Group.

Great Artists. 2005. (J). (gr. k-6). lib. bdg. 22.78 (978-1-59197-838-1(6)) ABDO Publishing Co.

Great Artists Set 2. 2007. 273.36 (978-1-59679-726-0(6), Checkerboard Library) ABDO Publishing Co.

Greenberg, Jan & Jordan, Sandra. Action Jackson. Parker, Robert Andrew, illus. rev. ed. 2002. 32p. (J). (gr. 1-5). 23.90 (978-0-7613-2770-7(3)); 16.95 (978-0-7613-1682-4(5)) Roaring Brook Pr.

—Runaway Girl: The Artist Louise Bourgeois. 2003. (Illus.). 80p. (J). (gr. 7-17). 19.95 (978-0-8109-4237-0(2)) Abrams, Harry N., Inc.

Guerrero, Ernesto, tr. Family Stories (Cuentos Familiares) Castro, Maria Elena et al, illus. 2006. (ENG & SPA.). 27p. 15.95 (***978-0-9716580-7-3(2)***) Lectura Bks.

Hall, Margaret. Leonardo Da Vinci. 2007. (Essential Lives Ser.). (ENG., Illus.). 112p. (J). (gr. 6-8). lib. bdg. 32.79 (***978-1-59928-844-4(3)***, Essential Library) ABDO Publishing Co.

Hall, Margaret. Samuel Morse. 2004. (J). pap. 6.50 (978-1-4034-5337-2(3)); lib. bdg. 22.79 (978-1-4034-5329-7(2)) Heinemann Library.

Halliwell, Sarah. The Romantics: Artists, Writers & Composers. 1998. (Who & When Ser.: Vol. 4). (Illus.). 96p. (J). (gr. 7-12). lib. bdg. 29.97 (978-0-8172-4729-4(7)) Raintree.

—The 19th Century: Artists, Writers & Composers. 1998. (Who & When Ser.). (Illus.). 96p. (J). (gr. 7-12). lib. bdg. 29.97 (978-0-8172-4728-7(9)) Raintree.

—The 20th Century: Post-1945 - Artists, Writers & Composers. 1998. (Who & When Ser.). (Illus.). 96p. (J). (gr. 7-12). lib. bdg. 29.97 (978-0-8172-4732-4(7)) Raintree.

Harcourt School Publishers Staff. The Young Artist: Reader's Choice Book. 2001. (Collections Ser.). (Illus.). (J). 4.70 (978-0-15-314395-3(9)) Harcourt Schl. Pubs.

Harris, Lois V. Mary Cassatt: Impressionist Painter. 2007. 32p. (J). (gr. k-3). 15.95 (***978-1-58980-452-4(X)***) Pelican Publishing Co., Inc.

Hartland, Jessie, illus. Henri Matisse: Drawing with Scissors. 2002. (J). (ps-ps). lib. bdg. 14.15 (978-0-613-45270-0(4)) Tandem Library Bks.

Hawes, Louise. Willem de Kooning: The Life of an Artist. 2002. (Artist Biographies Ser.). (Illus.). 48p. (J). (gr. 1-4). lib. bdg. 23.93 (978-0-7660-1884-6(9)) Enslow Pubs., Inc.

Heinrichs, Ann. Gerardus Mercator: Father of Modern Mapmaking. 2007. (Signature Lives Ser.). (J). lib. bdg. 31.93 (***978-0-7565-3312-0(0)***) Compass Point Bks.

Holme, Marilyn & McKinzie, Bridget. Expressionists. 2002. (Artists in Profile Ser.). (Illus.). 64p. (J). lib. bdg. 28.50 (978-1-58810-647-6(0)) Heinemann Library.

Holmes, Burnham. Edward Hopper. 2003. (Raintree Biographies Ser.). (J). lib. bdg. 25.70 (978-0-7398-6861-4(6)) Raintree.

—Edward Hopper. 2003. (gr. 3-6). lib. bdg. 15.90 (978-0-613-78231-9(3)) Tandem Library Bks.

Hopps, Walter, ed. & contrib. by. Andy Warhol. Hopps, Walter, contrib. by. 2002. (Art Ed Books & Kits Ser.). (Illus.). 24p. (J). 19.95 (978-0-8109-6793-9(6)) Abrams, Harry N., Inc.

—Georgia O'Keeffe. Hopps, Walter, contrib. by. 2002. (Art Ed Books & Kits Ser.). (Illus.). 32p. (J). 19.95 (978-0-8109-6792-2(8)) Abrams, Harry N., Inc.

Hunter, Shaun. Visual & Performing Artists. 1999. (Illus.). 48p. (J). (ps-11). lib. bdg. 17.60 (978-0-613-12237-5(2)) Tandem Library Bks.

Hutchinson, illus. Atlas/Explorador Advent. 2002. Tr. of Atlas for the Young Explorer. (SPA.). 32p. (J). 29.95 (978-84-272-2231-1(9)) Molino, Editorial ESP. *Dist:* AIMS International Bks., Inc.

Hyde, Margaret E., ed. Impressionists for Kids. 2004. (Great Art for Kids Ser.). (Illus.). 14p. ring bd. 8.95 (978-1-58980-265-0(9)); 12p. (J). pap. 8.95 (978-1-58980-203-2(9)) Pelican Publishing Co., Inc.

Hyman, Trina Schart. A Self Portrait: Trina. 12.95 (978-0-201-09308-7(1)) HarperCollins Pubs.

January, Brendan. Leonardo Da Vinci. 2002. (Great Names Ser.). (Illus.). 32p. (J). (gr. 3 up). lib. bdg. (978-1-59084-134-1(4)) Mason Crest Pubs.

Julio, Paredes. Eugène Delacroix. 2005. 132p. pap. (978-958-30-1358-4(7)) Panamericana Editorial.

Klein, Adam G. & Dalí, Salvador. Salvador Dalí. 2007. (Great Artists Ser.). (Illus.). 32p. (J). (gr. 2-5). lib. bdg. 22.78 (978-1-59679-728-4(2)) ABDO Publishing Co.

Klein, Adam G. & Picasso, Pablo. Pablo Picasso. 2007. (Great Artists Ser.). (Illus.). 32p. (J). (gr. 2-5). lib. bdg. 22.78 (978-1-59679-733-8(9)) ABDO Publishing Co.

Klein, Adam G. & Rembrandt Harmenszoon van Rijn. Rembrandt. 2007. (Illus.). 32p. (J). 22.78 (978-1-59679-735-2(5)) ABDO Publishing Co.

Klingel, Cynthia Fitterer & Court, Rob. Art of Early Africa. 2003. (Scribbles Institute : Art in Ancient Civilizations Ser.). (Illus.). 32p. (J). (gr. 1-5). 21.36 (978-1-56766-551-2(9), 65519) Child's World, Inc.

Koestler-Grack, Rachel A. Leonardo Da Vinci: Artist, Inventor, & Renaissance Man. 2005. (Makers of the Middle Ages & Renaissance Ser.). (Illus.). 146p. (J). (gr. 4-8). lib. bdg. 30.00 (978-0-7910-8626-1(7), Chelsea Hse.) Facts On File, Inc.

Krystal, Barbara. 100 Artists Who Changed the World. 2003. (People Who Changed the World Ser.). (Illus.). 112p. (J). (gr. 5 up). lib. bdg. 30.00 (978-0-8368-5469-5(1), World Almanac Library) Stevens, Gareth Inc.

Kudlinski, Kathleen. Dr. Seuss: Young Author & Artist. Henderson, Meryl, illus. 2005. 184p. (J). lib. bdg. 18.46 (***978-1-4242-2201-8(X)***) Fitzgerald Bks.

Lacey, Sue. In the Time of Renoir. 2001. (gr. 3-6). lib. bdg. 17.60 (978-0-613-45192-5(9)) Tandem Library Bks.

Laidlaw, Jill A. Paul Klee. 2002. (Artists in Their Time Ser.). (Illus.). 48p. (J). (gr. 5-7). pap. 23.50 (978-0-531-12230-3(1), Watts, Franklin) Scholastic Library Publishing.

Landmann, Bimba, illus. I Am Marc Chagall. 2006. (Eerdmans Books for Young Readers). 40p. (J). 18.00 (978-0-8028-5305-9(6), Eerdmans Bks For Young Readers) Eerdmans, William B. Publishing Co.

Langley, Andrew. Da Vinci & His Times. 2006. (DK Eyewitness Bks.). (Illus.). 72p. (J). 15.99 (978-0-7566-1768-4(5)); lib. bdg. 19.99 (978-0-7566-1767-7(7)) Dorling Kindersley Publishing, Inc.

—Pablo Picasso. 2003. pap. 37.50 (978-1-4109-0290-0(0)) Raintree.

The Life & Contributions of Leonardo Da Vinci. 2006. 58p. (J). pap. (978-0-935047-60-8(3)) Americas Group, The.

Lives of the Artists, 4 bks. Incl. Leonardo da Vinci. Mason, Antony & da Vinci, Leonardo. pap. 29.26 (978-0-8368-5604-0(X)); Michelangelo. Connolly, Sean & Michelangelo Buonarroti. pap. 29.26 (978-0-8368-5605-7(8)); Pablo Picasso. Hodge, Susie & Picasso, Pablo. pap. 29.26 (978-0-8368-5606-4(6)); Vincent Van Gogh. Bassil, Andrea & Van Gogh, Vincent. pap. 29.26 (978-0-8368-5607-1(4)); 48p. (J). (gr. 5 up). (Illus.). 2004. Set pap. 47.80 (978-0-8368-5603-3(1)); Set lib. bdg. 117.06 (978-0-8368-5598-2(1)) Stevens, Gareth Inc. (World Almanac Library).

Lynch, Wendy, contrib. by. Janet & Allan Ahlberg. 2000. (Lives & Times Ser.). (Illus.). 24p. (J). lib. bdg. 19.92 (978-1-57572-218-4(6)) Heinemann Library.

MacDonald, Patricia & Picasso, Pablo. Pablo Picasso: Greatest Artist of the 20th Century. 2001. (Giants of Art & Culture Ser.). (Illus.). 128p. (J). (gr. 5-8). 29.94 (978-1-56711-504-8(7), Blackbirch Pr., Inc.) Thomson Gale.

Major, John & Belanus, Betty J. Caravan to America: Living Arts of the Silk Road. 2002. (Illus.). 144p. (J). (gr. 3-6). pap. 15.95 (978-0-8126-2677-3(X)); (gr. 4-6). 24.95 (978-0-8126-2666-7(4)) Cricket Bks.

Malone, Richard & Shettleworth, Earle. Rediscovering S. P. Rolt Triscott: Monhegan Island Artist & Photographer. 2002. (Illus.). xi, 196p. pap. 30.00 (978-0-88448-240-6(5)) Tilbury Hse. Pubs.

Marcovitz, Hal. Maurice Sendak. 2006. (Who Wrote That? Ser.). (Illus.). 136-144p. (J). 30.00 (978-0-7910-8796-1(4), Chelsea Hse.) Facts On File, Inc.

Marsh, Carole. Georgia O'Keeffe. 2002. (One Thousand Readers Ser.). (Illus.). 12p. (J). (gr. k-4). 2.95 (978-0-635-01507-5(2), 15072) Gallopade International.

Mason, Antony. El arte Impresionista: En los tiempos de Renoir. Llaca, Martha, tr. 2005. (Arte Alrededor del Mundo Ser.). 48p. (J). pap. 9.95 (978-85-7416-229-4(9)) Callis Editora Ltda BRA. *Dist:* Independent Pubs. Group.

Mason, Paul. Pop Artists. 2002. (Artists in Profile Ser.). (Illus.). 64p. (J). lib. bdg. 28.50 (978-1-58810-646-9(2)) Heinemann Library.

Masterpieces: Artists & Their Works. (Illus.). (J). (gr. 2-3). lib. bdg. 170.08 (978-0-7368-2347-0(6)) Capstone Pr., Inc.

Mattern, Joanne. Andy Warhol. 2005. (Great Artists Ser.). (Illus.). 32p. (J). (gr. k-6). lib. bdg. 22.78 (978-1-59197-850-3(5)) ABDO Publishing Co.

—Leonardo Da Vinci. 2005. (Checkerboard Biography Library). (Illus.). 32p. (J). (gr. k-6). lib. bdg. 22.78 (978-1-59197-842-8(4)) ABDO Publishing Co.

—Marc Chagall. 2005. (Checkerboard Biography Library). (Illus.). 32p. (J). (gr. k-6). lib. bdg. 22.78 (978-1-59197-841-1(6)) ABDO Publishing Co.

—Mary Cassatt. 2005. (Checkerboard Biography Library). (Illus.). 32p. (J). (gr. k-6). lib. bdg. 22.78 (978-1-59197-840-4(8)) ABDO Publishing Co.

—Michelangelo. 2005. (Checkerboard Biography Library). (Illus.). 32p. (J). (gr. k-6). lib. bdg. 22.78 (978-1-59197-845-9(9)) ABDO Publishing Co.

McNeese, Tim. Michelangelo: Painter, Sculptor & Architect. 2005. (Makers of the Middle Ages & Renaissance Ser.). (Illus.). 148p. (J). (gr. 4-8). lib. bdg. 30.00 (978-0-7910-8627-8(5), Chelsea Hse.) Facts On File, Inc.

—Pablo Picasso. 2006. (Great Hispanic Heritage Ser.). (Illus.). 128p. (J). 30.00 (978-0-7910-8843-2(X), Chelsea Hse.) Facts On File, Inc.

—Salvador Dali. 2006. (Great Hispanic Heritage Ser.). (Illus.). 128p. (J). 30.00 (978-0-7910-8837-1(5), Chelsea Hse.) Facts On File, Inc.

Medearis, Michael. Artists & Their Art. 2000. (Pair-It Books). (Illus.). 32p. (J). pap. (978-0-7398-0867-2(2)) Steck-Vaughn.

Miller, Heather. Artist. 2003. (This Is What I Want to Be Ser.). (Illus.). 24p. (J). lib. bdg. 18.50 (978-1-4034-0913-3(7)); pap. 5.25 (978-1-4034-3606-1(1)) Heinemann Library.

—Artist. 2003. (ps-2). lib. bdg. 13.30 (978-0-613-60953-1(0)) Tandem Library Bks.

—Artista. 2003. Tr. of Artist. (SPA.). 24p. (J). pap. 5.25 (978-1-4034-3393-0(3)); (Illus.). lib. bdg. 18.50 (978-1-4034-0948-5(X)) Heinemann Library.

Mitchell Lane Publishers. Art Profiles for Kids. 2007. (Art Profiles for Kids Ser.). (YA). lib. bdg. 179.70 (***978-1-58415-567-6(1)***) Mitchell Lane Pubs., Inc.

Morrissey, Simon. Richard Wilson. 2006. (Tate Modern Artists Ser.). (Illus.). 128p. pap. 27.50 (978-1-85437-570-4(9)) Tate Gallery Publishing, Ltd. GBR. *Dist:* Hachette Bk. Group.

Nichols, Catherine. Leonardo Da Vinci. 2006. (Primary Source Library of Famous Artists). (Illus.). 32p. (J). 21.95 (978-1-4042-2762-0(8) , PowerKids Pr.) Rosen Publishing Group, Inc., The.

—Michelangelo Buonarroti. 2006. (Primary Source Library of Famous Artists). (Illus.). 32p. (J). 21.95 (978-1-4042-2763-7(6) , PowerKids Pr.) Rosen Publishing Group, Inc., The.

—Pablo Picasso. 2006. (Primary Source Library of Famous Artists). (Illus.). 32p. (J). 21.95 (978-1-4042-2764-4(4) , PowerKids Pr.) Rosen Publishing Group, Inc., The.

—Vincent Van Gogh. 2006. (Primary Source Library of Famous Artists). (Illus.). 32p. (J). 21.95 (978-1-4042-2766-8(0) , PowerKids Pr.) Rosen Publishing Group, Inc., The.

Northeast, Brenda V. Vincent con Amor. 2000. (CAT., Illus.). 32p. (J). (gr. k-2). (978-84-95040-53-4(0)) Serres, Ediciones, S. L.

—Vincent con Amor. 2000. (SPA., Illus.). 36p. (J). (gr. k-2). 14.95 (978-84-95040-48-0(4)) Serres, Ediciones, S. L. ESP. *Dist:* Lectorum Pubns., Inc.

Oberman, Sheldon. Shaman's Nephew: A Life in the Far North. 2000. (gr. 3-6). lib. bdg. 23.40 (978-0-613-65096-0(4)) Tandem Library Bks.

O'Connor, Barbara. Leonardo Da Vinci: Renaissance Genuis. 2005. (Trailblazer Biographies Ser.). (Illus.). 112p. (gr. 5-9). 27.93 (978-0-87614-467-1(9)) Lerner Publishing Group.

Olmstead. Yo Yo Ma: A Biography. 2004. (Asian-American Biographies Ser.). (Illus.). 64p. pap. 9.50 (978-1-4109-1127-8(6)) Raintree.

Olmstead, Mary. Judy Baca. 2004. (Hispanic-American Biographies Ser.). (Illus.). 64p. (J). pap. 9.50 (978-1-4109-0915-2(8)) Harcourt Schl. Pubs.

—Judy Baca. 2004. (Hispanic-American Biographies Ser.). (Illus.). 64p. (J). (gr. 4-6). 32.86 (978-1-4109-0709-7(0)) Raintree.

Pieter Brueger. 2002. 32p. (J). (gr. k-2). pap. 6.50 (978-1-4034-0500-5(X) , 91809) Heinemann Library.

Plain, Nancy. Frederic Remington: Artist of the American West. 2003. (Historical American Biographies Ser.). (Illus.). 160p. (J). (gr. 6-12). lib. bdg. 26.60 (978-0-7660-1975-1(6)) Enslow Pubs., Inc.

—Leonardo Da Vinci. 1999. (J). (978-0-7614-0790-4(1) , Benchmark Bks.) Cavendish, Marshall Corp.

Podoshen, Lois. The Artist. Finch, Linda, illus. 1999. (Books for Young Learners). 12p. (J). (gr. k-2). pap. 5.00 (978-1-57274-137-9(6)) Owen, Richard C. Pubs., Inc.

Prestel. Coloring Book Kandinsky. 2006. (Illus.). 32p. 8.95 (978-3-7913-3712-8(2)) Prestel Publishing.

The Primary Source Library of Famous Artists. (Illus.). (J). (gr. 3-5). 127.50 (978-1-4042-3302-7(4)) Rosen Publishing Group, Inc., The.

Raczka, Bob. Here's Looking at Me: How Artists See Themselves. 32p. (J). 2007. pap. 9.95 (***978-0-8225-7305-0(9)*** , First Avenue Editions); 2006. (Illus.). 23.93 (978-0-7613-3404-0(1) , Millbrook Pr.) Lerner Publishing Group.

Raintree Steck-Vaughn Staff. Artists & Their Art. 1999. (Illus.). (J). pap. 35.60 (978-0-7398-0898-6(2)) Steck-Vaughn.

Reed, Jennifer. Leonardo da Vinci: Genius of Art & Science. 2005. (Great Minds of Science Ser.). (Illus.). 128p. (J). lib. bdg. 26.60 (978-0-7660-2500-4(4)) Enslow Pubs., Inc.

Remington, Frederic. Remington: 16 Art Stickers. 2001. (Illus.). 4p. pap. 1.50 (978-0-486-41353-2(5)) Dover Pubns., Inc.

Richardson, Adele. Michelangelo. 2005. (Extraordinary Artists Ser.). (Illus.). 48p. (gr. 5-9). 21.95 (978-1-58341-379-1(0) , Creative Education) Creative Co., The.

Richardson, R. Sarah. Come Look with Me: The Artist at Work. 2006. (Come Look with Me Ser.). (J). 15.95 (***978-1-890674-09-0(5)***) Charlesbridge Publishing, Inc.

Rinaldo, Denise. Leonardo Da Vinci: With a Discussion of Imagination. 2003. (Values in Action Ser.). (J). (978-1-59203-066-8(1)) Learning Challenge, Inc.

Rohmer, Harriet, ed. Honoring Our Ancestors. 1999. (Illus.). 32p. pap. 21.27 (978-0-516-21697-3(X) , Children's Pr.) Scholastic Library Publishing.

Romei, Francesca. Leonardo Da Vinci. 2000. (Maestros del Arte Ser.). (SPA., Illus.). 72p. (J). (gr. 4-7). 22.95 (978-84-88061-55-3(2)) Serres, Ediciones, S. L. ESP. *Dist:* Lectorum Pubns., Inc.

Rubin, Susan Goldman. Fireflies in the Dark: The Story of Freidl Dicker-Brandeis & the Children of Terezin. (Illus.). 48p. (J). (gr. 4-6). 2005. pap. 8.95 (978-0-8234-1681-3(X)); 2000. tchr. ed. 18.95 (978-0-8234-1461-1(2)) Holiday Hse., Inc.

—The Yellow House: Vincent Van Gogh & Paul Gauguin Side by Side. Smith, Joseph A., illus. 2001. 40p. (J). (gr. k-4). 17.95 (978-0-8109-4588-3(6)) Abrams, Harry N. , Inc.

Rulers, Scholars, & Artists of the Renaissance, 6 bk. set. 2005. (YA). (gr. 5-8). lib. bdg. 191.70 (978-1-4042-0370-9(2)) Rosen Publishing Group, Inc., The.

Sateren, Shelley Swanson. Masterpieces: Artists & Their Works, 4 bks. Incl. Michaelangelo. 2002. lib. bdg. 18.60 (978-0-7368-1125-5(7)); Monet. 2001. lib. bdg. 18.60 (978-0-7368-1123-1(0)); Picasso. Picasso, Pablo. 2002. lib. bdg. 18.60 (978-0-7368-1122-4(2)); Van Gogh. 2002. lib. bdg. 18.60 (978-0-7368-1124-8(9)); 24p. (J). (gr. 2-3). (Illus.). Set lib. bdg. 74.40 (978-0-7368-1160-6(5) , Bridgestone Bks.) Capstone Pr., Inc.

Schaefer, A. R. Alexander Calder. (Life & Work of. . . Ser.). (Illus.). 32p. (J). (gr. k-2). 2003. lib. bdg. 22.79 (978-1-4034-0287-5(6)); 2002. pap. 6.50 (978-1-4034-0493-0(3)) Heinemann Library.

—Diego Rivera. (Life & Work of. . . Ser.). (Illus.). 32p. (J). (gr. k-2). 2003. lib. bdg. 22.79 (978-1-4034-0288-2(4)); 2002. pap. 6.50 (978-1-4034-0494-7(1)) Heinemann Library.

—Grandma Moses. (Life & Work of. . . Ser.). (Illus.). 32p. (J). (gr. k-2). 2003. lib. bdg. 22.79 (978-1-4034-0289-9(2)); 2002. pap. 6.50 (978-1-4034-0495-4(X)) Heinemann Library.

Schaefer, Adam. The Life & Work of... Series, 3 bks., Set 4. 2003. (Illus.). (J). 68.37 (978-1-4034-0292-9(2)) Heinemann Library.

Smiles: Pablo Picasso, Gabriela Mistral, Benito Juarez. 2001. (Gateways to the Sun Ser.). (Illus.). (J). (gr. k-1). pap. 10.95 (978-1-58105-570-2(6)) Santillana USA Publishing Co., Inc.

Somervill, Barbara A. Michelangelo: Sculptor & Painter. 2004. (Signature Lives Ser.). (Illus.). 112p. (J). 30.60 (978-0-7565-0814-2(2)) Compass Point Bks.

Stanley, Diane. Michelangelo. Stanley, Diane, illus. (Illus.). 48p. (J). 2003. (gr. 2 up). pap. 6.99 (978-0-06-052113-4(9)); 2000. (gr. 3 up). 17.99 (978-0-688-15085-3(3)) HarperCollins Pubs.

Stephens, Pamela Geiger. Dropping in on Andy Warhol. McNeill, Jim, illus. 2006. (J). 15.95 (978-1-56290-433-3(7)) Crystal Productions.

Steps: Rita Moreno, Fernando Botero, Evelyn Cisneros. 2001. (Gateways to the Sun Ser.). (Illus.). (J). (gr. 1-2). pap. 11.95 (978-1-58105-571-9(4)) Santillana USA Publishing Co., Inc.

Sturm, Ellen. Matisse. 2003. (Masterpieces, Artists & Their Works). (Illus.). 24p. (J). lib. bdg. 19.93 (978-0-7368-2227-5(5) , Bridgestone Bks.) Capstone Pr., Inc.

Stux, Erica. Eight Who Made a Difference: Pioneer Women in the Arts 1999. (Avisson Young Adult Ser.). (YA). lib. bdg. 19.95 (978-1-888105-37-7(2)) Avisson Pr., Inc.

Tames, Richard. Michelangelo Buonarotti. 2000. (Life & Work of. . . Ser.). (Illus.). 32p. (J). (gr. k-2). pap. 21.36 (978-1-57572-343-3(3)) Heinemann Library.

Thomas, Dina M. & Thomas, Andy, eds. The Artful Journey: The Artwork of Andy Thomas. Thomas, Tria M., photos by. l.t. ed. 2003. (Illus.). 122p. 50.00 (978-0-9742285-0-1(8)) Maze Creek Studio.

Triumph Books Staff. Hilary Rocks: On Stage & Screen, & in Between, Hilary Duff Living a Fairy Tale Life. 2004. (Illus.). 80p. pap. 9.95 (978-1-57243-727-2(8)) Triumph Bks.

Venezia, Mike. Diego Velazquez. Venezia, Mike, illus. 2004. (Getting to Know the World's Greatest Artists Ser.). (Illus.). 32p. (J). (gr. 3-4). pap. 6.95 (978-0-516-26980-1(1) , Children's Pr.) Scholastic Library Publishing.

—Georges Seurat. Venezia, Mike, illus. 2002. (Getting to Know the World's Greatest Artists Ser.). (Illus.). 32p. (J). (gr. 3-4). pap. 27.00 (978-0-516-22496-1(4) , Children's Pr.) Scholastic Library Publishing.

—Getting to Know the World's Greatest Artists, 2 bks. 2004. 48.00 (978-0-516-23723-7(3) , Children's Pr.) Scholastic Library Publishing.

—El Greco. 1998. (Getting to Know the World's Greatest Artists Ser.). (Illus.). 32p. (J). (gr. 3-4). pap. 6.95 (978-0-516-26243-7(2) , Children's Pr.) Scholastic Library Publishing.

—Marc Chagall. 2000. (Getting to Know the World's Greatest Artists Ser.). (Illus.). 32p. (J). (gr. 3-4). pap. 6.95 (978-0-516-27041-8(9)); 27.00 (978-0-516-21055-1(6)) Scholastic Library Publishing. (Children's Pr.).

—Marc Chagall. 2000. (gr. 3-6). lib. bdg. 15.25 (978-0-613-37447-7(9)) Tandem Library Bks.

—Rene Magritte. Venezia, Mike, illus. 2002. (Getting to Know World Artists Ser.). (Illus.). 32p. (J). (gr. 3-4). pap. 27.00 (978-0-516-22029-1(2) , Children's Pr.) Scholastic Library Publishing.

—Rene Magritte. 2002. (gr. 3-6). lib. bdg. 15.25 (978-0-613-59544-5(0)) Tandem Library Bks.

—Winslow Homer. Venezia, Mike, illus. 2004. (Getting. . Know Artists Pb Ser.). (Illus.). 32p. (J). (gr. 3-4). pap. 6.95 (978-0-516-26979-5(8) , Children's Pr.) Scholastic Library Publishing.

Venezia, Mike & Magritte, Rene. Rene Magritte. 2003. (Getting to Know the World's Greatest Artists Ser.). (Illus.). 32p. (J). (gr. 3-4). pap. 6.95 (978-0-516-27814-8(2) , Children's Pr.) Scholastic Library Publishing.

Voices: Luis Valdez, Judith Francisca Baca, Carlos Juan Finlay. 2001. (Gateways to the Sun Ser.). (J). (gr. 2-3). pap. 11.95 (978-1-58105-572-6(2)) Santillana USA Publishing Co., Inc.

Wagstaff, Sheena. Jeff Wall: Photographs 1978-2004. 2005. (Illus.). 80p. 22.50 (978-1-85437-613-8(6)) Tate Gallery Publishing, Ltd. GBR. *Dist:* Hachette Bk. Group.

Waldman, Neil. Out of the Shadows. 2006. (Illus.). 144p. (J). 21.95 (978-1-59078-411-2(1)) Boyds Mills Pr.

Wallis, Jeremy. Cubists. 2002. (Artists in Profile Ser.). (Illus.). 64p. (J). (gr. 6-8). lib. bdg. 28.50 (978-1-58810-645-2(4)) Heinemann Library.

—Impressionists. 2002. (Artists in Profile Ser.). (Illus.). 64p. (J). lib. bdg. 28.50 (978-1-58810-642-1(X)) Heinemann Library.

Warhola, James. Uncle Andy's. Warhola, James, illus. 2005. (Illus.). 32p. (J). reprint ed. pap. 5.99 (978-0-14-240347-1(4) , Puffin) Penguin Group (USA) Inc.

—Uncle Andy's: A Faabbulous Visit with Andy Warhol. Warhola, James, illus. 2003. (Illus.). 32p. (J). (ps-3). 16.99 (978-0-399-23869-7(7) , Putnam Juvenile) Penguin Group (USA) Inc.

Welton, Jude. Henri Matisse. 2002. (Artists in Their Time Ser.). (Illus.). 48p. (J). (gr. 5-7). pap. 23.50 (978-0-531-12228-0(X) , Watts, Franklin) Scholastic Library Publishing.

—Henri Matisse. 2002. (gr. 5-8). lib. bdg. 15.25 (978-0-613-54241-8(X)) Tandem Library Bks.

—Marc Chagall. 2003. (Artists in Their Time Ser.). (Illus.). 48p. (J). 23.50 (978-0-531-12235-8(2)); (gr. 5-7). pap. 6.95 (978-0-531-16645-1(7)) Scholastic Library Publishing. (Watts, Franklin).

—Marc Chagall. 2003. (gr. 5-8). lib. bdg. 15.25 (978-0-613-59517-9(3)) Tandem Library Bks.

Wheeler, Jill C. Chris Van Allsburg. 2005. (Children's Illustrators Set I Ser.). (J). (gr. k-6). lib. bdg. 21.35 (978-1-59197-721-6(5)) ABDO Publishing Co.

—Garth Williams. 2005. (Children's Illustrators Set I Ser.). (Illus.). 24p. (J). (gr. k-6). lib. bdg. 21.35 (978-1-59197-723-0(1)) ABDO Publishing Co.

—Robert McCloskey. 2005. (Children's Illustrators Set I Ser.). (Illus.). 24p. (J). (gr. k-6). lib. bdg. 21.35 (978-1-59197-719-3(3)) ABDO Publishing Co.

—William Steig. 2005. (Children's Illustrators Set I Ser.). (Illus.). 24p. (J). (gr. k-6). lib. bdg. 21.35 (978-1-59197-720-9(7)) ABDO Publishing Co.

Whitehead, Kathy. Art from Her Heart: Folk Artist Clementine Hunter. Evans, Shane, illus. 2008. (J). (***978-0-399-24219-9(8)*** , Putnam Juvenile) Penguin Group (USA) Inc.

Winter, Jeanette. Beatrix: Various Episodes from the Life of Beatrix Potter. Winter, Jeanette, illus. 2003. (Illus.). 64p. (J). (gr. k-3). 15.00 (978-0-374-30655-7(9) , Farrar, Straus & Giroux (BYR)) Farrar, Straus & Giroux.

—My Name Is Georgia. 2003. (gr. k-3). lib. bdg. 14.15 (978-0-613-59912-2(8)) Tandem Library Bks.

Woodhouse, Jayne. Edgar Degas. 2002. (Life & Work of. . . Ser.). (Illus.). 32p. (J). (gr. k-2). lib. bdg. 22.79 (978-1-58810-602-5(0)) Heinemann Library.

—Joseph Turner. 2000. (Life & Work of. . . Ser.). (Illus.). 32p. (J). (gr. k-2). lib. bdg. 21.36 (978-1-57572-345-7(X)) Heinemann Library.

—The Life & Work of Rembrandt Van Rijn, Set 2. 2002. (Illus.). 32p. (J). (gr. k-2). pap. 6.50 (978-1-4034-0005-5(9) , 91623) Heinemann Library.

—Peter Bruegel. 2000. (Heinemann First Library). (Illus.). 32p. (J). (gr. k-2). lib. bdg. 21.36 (978-1-57572-344-0(1)) Heinemann Library.

Wright, Patricia. Goya. 1999. (Dk Eyewitness Books Ser.). (Illus.). 64p. (J). (gr. 3-12). 15.99 (978-0-7894-4877-4(7)) Dorling Kindersley Publishing, Inc.

Yuan, Margaret Speaker. Beatrix Potter. 2005. (Who Wrote That? Ser.). (Illus.). 114p. (J). (gr. 6-12). lib. bdg. 30.00 (978-0-7910-8655-1(0) , Chelsea Hse.) Facts On File, Inc.

Zannos, Susan. Samuel Morse & the Telegraph. 2004. (Uncharted, Unexplored, & Unexplained Ser.). (Illus.). 48p. (J). (gr. 4-8). lib. bdg. 29.95 (978-1-58415-269-9(9)) Mitchell Lane Pubs., Inc.

ARTISTS, AFRICAN AMERICAN

see African American Artists

ARTISTS, AMERICAN

Blitz, Bruce. Bruce Blitz. 2007. 56p. 12.95 (***978-0-7624-2865-6(1)***) Running Pr. Bk. Pubs.

Bolton, Linda. Andy Warhol. 2002. (Artists in Their Time Ser.). (J). (gr. 5-7). pap. 6.95 (978-0-531-16618-5(X) , Watts, Franklin) Scholastic Library Publishing.

Chelsea House Publishing Staff. Georgia O'Keeffe. 1999. (J). 16.75 (978-0-606-16414-6(6)) Tandem Library Bks.

Flanagan, Alice K. Mrs. Scott's Beautiful Art. Flanagan, Romie, illus. 1999. (Our Neighborhood Ser.). 32p. (J). (gr. 1-2). 20.00 (978-0-516-21135-0(8) , Children's Pr.) Scholastic Library Publishing.

Foa, Emma. Edward Hopper. 2003. (Artists in Their Time Ser.). (Illus.). 48p. (J). 23.50 (978-0-531-12240-2(9)); (gr. 5-7). pap. 6.95 (978-0-531-16641-3(4)) Scholastic Library Publishing. (Watts, Franklin).

—Edward Hopper. 2003. (Illus.). 46p. (J). (gr. 4-7). lib. bdg. 15.25 (978-0-613-59466-0(5)) Tandem Library Bks.

Ford, Carin T. Andy Warhol: Pioneer of Pop Art. Warhol, Andy, illus. 2001. (People to Know Ser.). 112p. (YA). (gr. 6-12). lib. bdg. 26.60 (978-0-7660-1531-9(9)) Enslow Pubs., Inc.

—Andy Warhol: The Life of an Artist. 2002. (Artist Biographies Ser.). (Illus.). 48p. (J). (gr. 1-4). lib. bdg. 23.93 (978-0-7660-1880-8(6)) Enslow Pubs., Inc.

Ford, Jeffrey. Portrait of Mrs. Charbuque. 2003. lib. bdg. 22.20 (978-0-613-68375-3(7)) Tandem Library Bks.

Foxley Leach, Deba. Grant Wood: The Artist in the Hayloft. 2005. (Adventures in Art Ser.). (Illus.). 29p. 14.95 (978-3-7913-3401-1(8)) Prestel Publishing.

Giesecke, Ernestine. Frederic Remington. (Illus.). 32p. 2003. pap. 6.50 (978-1-58810-281-2(5)); 1999. (J). lib. bdg. 21.36 (978-1-57572-951-0(2)) Heinemann Library.

—Frederic Remington. 2001. (gr. k-3). lib. bdg. 14.75 (978-0-613-89893-5(1)) Tandem Library Bks.

Greenberg, Jan & Jordan, Sandra. Andy Warhol, Prince of Pop. (YA). (gr. 7). 2007. 224p. mass mkt. 6.99 (***978-0-385-73275-8(9)*** , Laurel Leaf); 2004. (Illus.). 208p. 16.95 (978-0-385-73056-3(X) , Delacorte Bks. for Young Readers); 2004. (Illus.). 208p. lib. bdg. 18.99 (978-0-385-90079-9(1) , Delacorte Bks. for Young Readers) Random Hse. Children's Bks.

Greenberg, Jan & Jordan, Sandra. Chuck Close, up Close. 2000. (978-0-606-17800-6(7)) Tandem Library Bks.

Hamilton, Sue L. Stan Lee. 2007. (Comic Book Creators Ser.). (Illus.). 32p. (J). (gr. 3-5). lib. bdg. 24.21 (978-1-59928-301-2(8)) ABDO Publishing Co.

Hillstrom, Laurie. Kelly Clarkson. 2007. (People in the News Ser.). (Illus.). 128p. (gr. 7-10). 31.20 (***978-1-4205-0013-4(9)*** , Lucent Bks.) Thomson Gale.

Hoena, Blake A. Mary Cassatt. 2003. (Masterpieces, Artists & Their Works). (Illus.). 24p. (J). lib. bdg. 19.93 (978-0-7368-2229-9(1) , Bridgestone Bks.) Capstone Pr., Inc.

Koerner, Henry. The Early Works of Henry Koerner 1945-1957. 2004. (Illus.). 96p. (YA). (gr. 13 up). pap. 35.00 (978-0-9703425-5-3(1)) Frick Art & Historical Ctr.,The.

Krull, Kathleen. Houdini: World's Greatest Mystery Man & Escape King. Velasquez, Eric, illus. 2007. 32p. (J). pap. 6.95 (***978-0-8027-9646-2(X)***) Walker & Co.

Lyons, Deborah. Edward Hopper: Summer at the Seaside. 2003. (Adventures in Art Ser.). (Illus.). 30p. (gr. 5 up). 14.95 (978-3-7913-2737-2(2)) Prestel Publishing.

Mason, Antony. El arte Contemporanea: En los tiempos de Warhol. 2005. (Arte Alrededor del Mundo Ser.). 48p. (J). pap. 9.95 (978-85-7416-218-8(3)) Callis Editora Ltda BRA. *Dist:* Independent Pubs. Group.

—El Arte Contemporanea: En los Tiempos de Warhol. 2005. (Arte Alrededor del Mundo Ser.). 48p. (J). pap. 9.95 (978-85-7416-241-6(8)) Callis Editora Ltda BRA. *Dist:* Independent Pubs. Group.

Miller, Raymond H. Stan Lee: Creator of Spider-Man. 2006. (Inventors & Creators Ser.). (Illus.). 48p. (gr. 4-8). 26.20 (978-0-7377-3447-8(7) , Greenhaven Pr., Inc.) Thomson Gale.

Neysters, Silvia & Soll-Tauchert, Sabine. Andy Warhol: Paintings for Children. 2004. (Adventures in Art Ser.). (Illus.). 30p. (J). 14.95 (978-3-7913-3063-1(2)) Prestel Publishing.

Roy, Jennifer Rozines & Roy, Gregory. Norman Rockwell: The Life of an Artist. 2002. (Artist Biographies Ser.). (Illus.). 48p. (J). (gr. 1-4). lib. bdg. 23.93 (978-0-7660-1883-9(0)) Enslow Pubs., Inc.

Slaymaker, Melissa Eskridge. Bottle Houses: The Creative World of Grandma Prisbrey. Paschkis, Julie, tr. Paschkis, Julie, illus. rev. ed. 2004. 32p. (J). 17.95 (978-0-8050-7131-3(8) , Holt, Henry & Co. Bks. For Young Readers) Holt, Henry & Co.

Spangenburg, Ray & Moser, Kit. Edward Hopper: The Life of an Artist. 2002. (Artist Biographies Ser.). (Illus.). 48p. (J). (gr. 1-4). lib. bdg. 23.93 (978-0-7660-1881-5(4)) Enslow Pubs., Inc.

—Georgia O'Keeffe: The Life of an Artist. 2002. (Artist Biographies Ser.). (Illus.). 48p. (J). (gr. 1-4). lib. bdg. 23.93 (978-0-7660-1882-2(2)) Enslow Pubs., Inc.

Stalcup, Ann & Politi, Leo. Leo Politi: Artist of the Angels. 2004. (J). 24.95 (978-1-893110-38-0(9)) Silver Moon Pr.

Venezia, Mike. Alexander Calder. Venezia, Mike, illus. 1998. (Getting to Know the World's Greatest Artists Ser.). (Illus.). 32p. (J). (gr. 3-4). 23.00 (978-0-516-20966-1(3) , Children's Pr.) Scholastic Library Publishing.

—Faith Ringgold. 2008. (Getting to Know the World's Greatest Artists Ser.). 32p. (J). pap. 6.95 (***978-0-531-14757-3(6)*** , Children's Pr.) Scholastic Library Publishing.

—Faith Ringgold. Venezia, Mike, illus. 2007. (Getting to Know the World's Greatest Artists Ser.). 32p. (J). 28.00 (***978-0-531-18526-1(5)*** , Children's Pr.) Scholastic Library Publishing.

—Frederic Remington. Venezia, Mike, illus. (Getting to Know the World's Greatest Artists Ser.). (Illus.). 32p. (J). (gr. 3-4). 2003. pap. 6.95 (978-0-516-27812-4(6)); 2002. 27.00 (978-0-516-22497-8(2)) Scholastic Library Publishing. (Children's Pr.).

—Frederic Remington. 2002. (gr. 3-6). lib. bdg. 15.25 (978-0-613-59482-0(7)) Tandem Library Bks.

—James McNeill Whistler. 2003. (Getting to Know World Artists Ser.). (Illus.). 32p. (J). 27.00 (978-0-516-22578-4(2) , Children's Pr.) Scholastic Library Publishing.

—Norman Rockwell. Venezia, Mike, illus. 2001. (Getting to Know the World's Greatest Artists Ser.). (Illus.). 32p. (J). (gr. 3-4). pap. 6.95 (978-0-516-27173-6(3) , Children's Pr.) Scholastic Library Publishing.

—Norman Rockwell. 2000. (Getting to Know the World's Greatest Artists Ser.). (Illus.). 32p. (J). (gr. 3-4). 27.00 (978-0-516-21594-5(9) , Children's Pr.) Scholastic Library Publishing.

—Norman Rockwell. 2000. (gr. 3-6). lib. bdg. 15.25 (978-0-613-50720-2(7)) Tandem Library Bks.

—Roy Lichtenstein. Venezia, Mike, illus. 2002. (Getting to Know the World's Greatest Artists Ser.). (Illus.). 32p. (J). (gr. 3-4). pap. 6.95 (978-0-516-25963-5(6) , Children's Pr.) Scholastic Library Publishing.

—Roy Lichtenstein. Lichtenstein, Roy, illus. 2001. (Getting to Know the World's Greatest Artists Ser.). 32p. (J). (gr. 3-4). 27.00 (978-0-516-22030-7(6) , Children's Pr.) Scholastic Library Publishing.

—Roy Lichtenstein. 2001. (gr. 3-6). lib. bdg. 15.25 (978-0-613-50362-4(7)) Tandem Library Bks.

Wheeler, Jill C. David Wiesner. 2005. (Children's Illustrators Set I Ser.). (J). (gr. k-6). lib. bdg. 21.35 (978-1-59197-722-3(3)) ABDO Publishing Co.

Wilkerson, J. L. American Illustrator: Rose O'Neill. 2001. (Great Heartlanders Ser.). (Illus.). iii, 114p. (J). (gr. 4-6). pap. 9.95 (978-0-9664470-6-4(9)) Acorn Bks.

Winter, Jeanette. My Name Is Georgia. 2003. (gr. k-3). lib. bdg. 14.15 (978-0-613-59912-2(8)) Tandem Library Bks.

—My Name Is Georgia: A Portrait by Jeanette Winter. 2003. (Illus.). 48p. (J). pap. 7.00 (978-0-15-204597-5(X) , Voyager Bks./Libros Viajeros) Harcourt Children's Bks.

—My Name Is Georgia: A Portrait by Jeanette Winter. 1998. (Illus.). 48p. (J). (gr. 1-5). 16.00 (978-0-15-201649-4(X) , Silver Whistle) Harcourt Trade Pubs.

ARTISTS, BRITISH

Browne, Anthony. The Shape Game. Browne, Anthony, illus. 2003. (Illus.). 32p. (J). (gr. k up). 16.00 (978-0-374-36764-0(7) , Farrar, Straus & Giroux (BYR)) Farrar, Straus & Giroux.

Dickens, Archie, illus. The Pin up Art of Archi Dickens. 2003. 48p. (YA). (gr. 11 up). pap. 14.95 (978-0-86562-070-4(9)) S.Q. Productions, Inc.

Hegel, Claudette. Randolph Caldecott: An Illustrated Life. 2004. (Avisson Young Adult Ser.). (Illus.). 176p. (J). lib. bdg. 27.50 (978-1-888105-60-5(7)) Avisson Pr., Inc.

Wallis, Jeremy. Henry Moore. 2001. (Creative Lives Ser.). (J). 26.50 (978-1-58810-204-1(1)) Heinemann Library.

ARTISTS, DUTCH

Bassil, Andrea & Van Gogh, Vincent. Vincent Van Gogh. 2004. (Lives of the Artists Ser.). (Illus.). 48p. (J). (gr. 5 up). pap. 29.26 (978-0-8368-5607-1(4)); lib. bdg. 30.00 (978-0-8368-5602-6(3)) Stevens, Gareth Inc. (World Almanac Library).

Crispino, Enrica. Van Gogh. 2008. (YA). lib. bdg. 24.95 net. (***978-1-934545-05-8(8)***) Oliver Pr., Inc.

Crispino, Enrica. Van Gogh: La Experiencia Extraordinaria del Color. 2000. (Maestros del Arte Ser.). (SPA., Illus.). 64p. (J). (gr. 4-7). 22.95 (978-84-88061-78-2(1)) Serres, Ediciones, S. L. ESP. *Dist:* Lectorum Pubns., Inc.

Mis, Melody S. Rembrandt. 2008. (J). lib. bdg. (***978-1-4042-3840-4(9)*** , PowerKids Pr.) Rosen Publishing Group, Inc., The.

Niz, Xavier. Rembrandt. 2003. (Masterpieces, Artists & Their Works). (Illus.). 24p. (J). lib. bdg. 19.93 (978-0-7368-2230-5(5) , Bridgestone Bks.) Capstone Pr., Inc.

Pescio, Claudio. Rembrandt. 2008. (YA). lib. bdg. 24.95 net. (***978-1-934545-02-7(3)***) Oliver Pr., Inc.

Pescio, Claudio. Rembrandt y la Pintura Holandesa del Siglo XVII. 2000. (Maestros del Arte Ser.). (SPA., Illus.). 72p. (J). 22.95 (978-84-88061-54-6(4)) Serres, Ediciones, S. L. ESP. *Dist:* Lectorum Pubns., Inc.

ARTISTS—FICTION

Alfaro Sifontes, Manuel Guillermo. Alboroto en un Lugar Remoto. 2005. (Illus.). 32p. (J). (978-1-58018-052-8(3)) Versal Editorial Group.

Alphin, Elaine Marie. Simon Says. (YA). (gr. 9-12). 2005. 264p. pap. 6.95 (978-0-15-204678-1(X) , Harcourt Paperbacks); 2002. (Illus.). 272p. 17.00 (978-0-15-216355-6(7)) Harcourt Children's Bks.

Anholt, Laurence. The Child's Gift of Art. 2002. (Illus.). 128p. (J). (gr. k-3). 16.95 (978-0-7641-7524-4(6)) Barron's Educational Series, Inc.

—Leonardo y el Aprendiz Volador: Un Cuento Sobre Leonardo Da Vinci. 2000. Tr. of Leonardo & the Flying Boy. (CAT., Illus.). 30p. (J). (gr. 3-5). 14.95 (978-84-95040-79-4(4)) Serres, Ediciones, S. L. ESP. *Dist:* Lectorum Pubns., Inc.

—The Magical Garden of Claude Monet. 2003. (Illus.). 32p. (J). 14.95 (978-0-7641-5574-1(1)) Barron's Educational Series, Inc.

—Matisse: The King of Color. 2007. (Anholt's Artists Books for Children Ser.). 32p. (J). (ps-3). 14.99 (***978-0-7641-6047-9(8)***) Barron's Educational Series, Inc.

—Picasso & the Girl with a Ponytail. 2007. (Anholt's Artists Books for Children Ser.). 32p. (J). (ps-3). pap. 7.99 (***978-0-7641-3853-9(7)***) Barron's Educational Series, Inc.

—Picasso y Sylvette: Un Cuento Sobre Pablo Picasso. 2000. (Illus.). (J). (gr. 3-5). (CAT.). 32p. 14.95 (978-84-8488-003-5(6)); (SPA., 200p. 14.95 (978-84-95040-01-5(8)) Serres, Ediciones, S. L. ESP. *Dist:* Lectorum Pubns., Inc.

Anholt, Laurence. Van Gogh & the Sunflowers. 2007. (Anholt's Artists Books for Children Ser.). 32p. (J). (ps-3). pap. 7.99 (***978-0-7641-3854-6(5)***) Barron's Educational Series, Inc.

Bauer, Cat. Harley's Ninth. 2007. 208p. (YA). (gr. 9). 15.99 (978-0-375-83736-4(1)); lib. bdg. 18.99 (978-0-375-93736-1(6)) Random Hse. Children's Bks. (Knopf Bks. for Young Readers).

Becker, Bonny. Holbrook, a Lizard's Tale. Carter, Abby, illus. 2006. 128p. (J). (gr. 3-5). 15.00 (978-0-618-71458-2(8) , Clarion Bks.) Houghton Mifflin Co. Trade & Reference Div.

Bergen, Lara. A Masterpiece for Bess. Clarke, Judith H., illus. 2006. (Stepping Stone Bks.). 128p. (J). (gr. 1-5). 5.99 (978-0-7364-2418-9(0) , RH/Disney) Random Hse. Children's Bks.

Bingham, Kelly. Shark Girl. 2007. (Illus.). 288p. (YA). (gr. 7 up). 16.99 (***978-0-7636-3207-6(4)***) Candlewick Pr.

Bingham, Kelly L. Shark Girl. 2007. 276p. (YA). (***978-1-4287-4705-0(2)***) Candlewick Pr.

Blackaby, Susan. Mary's Art. Haugen, Ryan, illus. 2005. (Read-It! Readers Ser.). 32p. (J). (gr. k-3). 18.60 (978-1-4048-1056-3(0)) Picture Window Bks.

Bowler, Tim. River Boy. 2002. (Illus.). 160p. (YA). mass mkt. 4.99 (978-0-689-84804-9(8) , Simon Pulse) Simon & Schuster Children's Publishing.

—River Boy. l.t. ed. 2001. 190p. (J). 22.95 (978-0-7862-3507-0(1)) Thorndike Pr.

Bradford, Emma. Kat & the Missing Notebooks. Sano, Kazuhiko, illus. 1999. (Stardust Classics: No. 4). 119p. (J). (gr. 2-5). 12.95 (978-1-889514-27-7(6)); pap. 5.95 (978-1-889514-28-4(4)) Dolls Corp.

Brokaw, Nancy Steele. Leaving Emma. 1999. 144p. (J). (gr. 4-6). tchr. ed. 15.00 (978-0-395-90699-6(7) , Clarion Bks.) Houghton Mifflin Co. Trade & Reference Div.

Bryant, Jen. Georgia's Bones. Andersen, Bethanne, illus. 2005. 32p. (J). 16.00 (978-0-8028-5217-5(3)) Eerdmans, William B. Publishing Co.

Bryant, Jennifer. Pieces of Georgia. 176p. (J). 2007. (gr. 5-9). 5.99 (***978-0-440-42055-2(5)*** , Yearling); 2006. (gr. 6-9). 15.95 (978-0-375-83259-8(9) , Knopf Bks. for Young Readers); 2006. (gr. 6-9). lib. bdg. 17.99 (978-0-375-93259-5(3) , Knopf Bks. for Young Readers) Random Hse. Children's Bks.

Bulla, Clyde Robert. The Paint Brush Kid. 1998. (Stepping Stone Bks.). (Illus.). 80p. (J). (gr. k-3). pap. 3.99 (978-0-679-89282-3(6) , Random Hse. Bks. for Young Readers) Random Hse. Children's Bks.

—The Paint Brush Kid. 1999. (Stepping Stone Bks.). (978-0-606-15668-4(2)) Tandem Library Bks.

Burns, Suzanne. The Moon Painters. 2003. 192p. 14.00 (978-1-894942-36-2(1)) Zumaya Pubns. LLC.

Capatti, Bérénice. Klimt & His Cat. Monaco, Octavia, illus. 2005. 40p. (J). 18.00 (978-0-8028-5282-3(3)) Eerdmans, William B. Publishing Co.

Carle, Eric. Draw Me a Star. Carle, Eric, illus. 2002. (Illus.). (J). 14.04 (978-0-7587-2416-8(0)) Book Wholesalers, Inc.

Cassels, Jean. Br'er Rabbit Captured! A Dr. David Harleyson Adventure. Cassels, Jean, illus. 2007. (Illus.). 32p. (J). 18.85 (***978-0-8027-9557-1(9)***); 17.95 (***978-0-8027-9556-4(0)***) Walker & Co.

Cassels, Jean. The Mysterious Collection of Dr. David Harleyson. Cassels, Jean, illus. 2004. (Illus.). 32p. (J). 17.95 (978-0-8027-8916-7(1)) Walker & Co.

Catalanotto, Peter. Emily's Art. Catalanotto, Peter, illus. (Illus.). 32p. (J). 2006. pap. 6.99 (978-1-4169-2688-7(7) , Aladdin); 2001. 17.99 (978-0-689-83831-6(X) , Atheneum/Richard Jackson Bks.) Simon & Schuster Children's Publishing.

—The Painter. Catalanotto, Peter, illus. 1999. (Illus.). 32p. (J). (ps-2). pap. 5.95 (978-0-531-07116-8(2) , Orchard Bks.) Scholastic, Inc.

Clinton, Cathryn. The Eyes of Van Gogh. 2007. (Illus.). 224p. (YA). (gr. 9 up). 16.99 (***978-0-7636-2245-9(1)***) Candlewick Pr.

Comora, Madeleine. Rembrandt & Titus: Father & Son. Locker, Thomas, illus. 2005. 32p. (J). (gr. 2-5). 17.95 (978-1-55591-490-5(X)) Fulcrum Publishing.

Cornwell, Autumn. Carpe Diem. 2007. 368p. (YA). (gr. 7 up). 16.95 (***978-0-312-36792-3(9)***) Feiwel & Friends.

Danziger, Paula. United Tates of America. 2006. 144p. (J). pap. 5.99 (978-0-439-83883-2(5) , Scholastic Paperbacks) Scholastic, Inc.

—United Tates of America. Danziger, Paula, illus. 2002. (Illus.). 144p. (J). (gr. 3-7). pap. 17.95 (978-0-590-69221-2(6) , Scholastic Pr.) Scholastic, Inc.

—United Tates of America: The Story & the Scrapbook. 2002. (gr. 3-6). lib. bdg. 14.15 (978-0-613-67042-5(6)) Tandem Library Bks.

de Paola, Tomie. The Art Lesson. de Paola, Tomie, illus. 2002. (Illus.). (J). 13.19 (978-0-7587-1969-0(8)) Book Wholesalers, Inc.

Demi. The Boy Who Painted Dragons. Demi, illus. 2007. 52p. (J). (gr. 2-5). 21.99 (978-1-4169-2469-2(8) , McElderry, Margaret K.) Simon & Schuster Children's Publishing.

DeSantis, Anthony John & Namorato, Carmine, Jr. Vincent Van Mouse. 2001. 32p. (J). per. 16.50 (978-0-9712994-0-5(4)) Black Cat Pubns., Inc.

DiMare, Loren Spiotta. Rockwell: A Boy & His Dog. Miller, Cliff, illus. 2005. 32p. (J). 14.95 (978-0-7641-5790-5(6)) Barron's Educational Series, Inc.

Dines, Carol. The Queen's Soprano. 2007. (Illus.). 336p. (YA). pap. 6.95 (***978-0-15-206102-9(9)*** , Harcourt Paperbacks) Harcourt Children's Bks.

Ehlert, Lois. Hands: Growing up to be an Artist. 2004. (Illus.). 48p. (J). 14.95 (978-0-15-205107-5(4) , Harcourt Children's Bks) Harcourt Children's Bks.

Ellis, Deborah. Jackal in the Garden: An Encounter with Bihzad. 2006. (Art Encounters Ser.). (Illus.). 176p. (YA). (gr. 7 up). 16.95 (978-0-8230-0415-7(5)) Watson-Guptill Pubns., Inc.

Everson, Chance. Discoveries: Tales of the Mandrasaurs, Volume the Third. Geary, Steve, illus. 2004. cd-rom 9.95 (978-0-9760303-2-4(2)) R.A.R.E. TALES.

Fiorello, Frank. Frankie Big Head Becomes an Artist. Fiorello, Frank, illus. 2002. 40p. (J). lib. bdg. 12.95 (978-0-9708400-3-5(9)); per. 8.95 (978-0-9708400-2-8(0)) Pumpkin Patch Publishing.

Fitzgerald, John D. Great Brain. 2004. (gr. 3-6). lib. bdg. 14.15 (978-0-613-86709-2(2)) Tandem Library Bks.

Francis, Dorothy Brenner. The Jayhawk Horse Mystery. Ersland, William, illus. 2001. (Cover-to-Cover Novel Ser.). 80p. (J). pap. (978-0-7891-5349-4(1)); (gr. 2-5). lib. bdg. 13.95 (978-0-7807-9728-4(0)) Perfection Learning Corp.

Gallup, Tracy. Stone Crazy. Gallup, Tracy, illus. 2007. (Crazy Little Ser.). (Illus.). 40p. (J). (***978-1-934133-13-2(2)***) Mackinac Island Pr., Inc.

Gammell, Stephen. The Art Contest. 2001. (J). (978-0-15-202048-4(9)) Harcourt Trade Pubs.

Geeslin, Campbell. Clara & Senor Frog. Sanchez, Ryan, illus. 2007. 40p. (J). (ps-3). 16.99 (978-0-375-83613-8(6)); lib. bdg. 19.99 (978-0-375-93613-5(0)) Random Hse. Children's Bks. (Schwartz & Wade Bks.).

Geisert, Arthur. The Etcher's Studio. 2005. (Illus.). 32p. (J). (gr. k-3). reprint ed. 5.95 (978-0-618-55614-4(1) , Walter Lorraine) Houghton Mifflin Co. Trade & Reference Div.

Gelman, Rita Golden. Doodler Doodling. Zelinsky, Paul O., illus. 2004. 24p. (J). 15.99 (978-0-688-16645-8(8)) HarperCollins Pubs.

Giff, Patricia Reilly. Pictures of Hollis Woods. 176p. (gr. 3-8). 2004. (J). pap. 6.50 (978-0-440-41578-7(0) , Yearling); 2002. lib. bdg. 17.99 (978-0-385-90070-6(8) , Lamb, Wendy) Random Hse. Children's Bks.

—Pictures of Hollis Woods. Giff, Patricia Reilly, illus. 2002. (Illus.). 176p. (gr. 3-8). 15.95 (978-0-385-32655-1(6) , Lamb, Wendy) Random Hse. Children's Bks.

—Pictures of Hollis Woods. l.t. ed. 2003. 158p. (J). 23.95 (978-0-7862-5094-3(1)) Thorndike Pr.

Gilson, Jamie. Stink Alley. 2002. 192p. (J). (gr. 3 up). 15.95 (978-0-688-17864-2(2)); lib. bdg. 15.89 (978-0-06-029217-1(2)) HarperCollins Pubs.

Grey, Christopher Peter. Leonardo's Shadow: Or, My Astonishing Life as Leonardo da Vinci's Servant. 2006. 400p. (YA). 16.95 (978-1-4169-0543-1(X) , Atheneum) Simon & Schuster Children's Publishing.

Grove, Vicki. Destiny. 2001. 12.64 (978-0-606-22525-0(0)) Tandem Library Bks.

Harcourt School Publishers Staff. How the Leaves Got Their Color On Level. 3rd ed. 2002. (Trophies Reading Program Ser.). (Illus.). pap. 5.10 (978-0-15-323073-8(8)) Harcourt Schl. Pubs.

Harris, Ruth Elwin. Gwen's Story. 2002. (gr. 7-12). lib. bdg. 14.15 (978-0-613-74775-2(5)) Tandem Library Bks.

—Gwen's Story: Sisters of the Quantock Hills. 2002. (Quantock's Quartet Ser.). (Illus.). 288p. (YA). (gr. 7 up). pap. 5.99 (978-0-7636-1705-9(9)) Candlewick Pr.

—Julia's Story. 2002. (gr. 7-12). lib. bdg. 14.15 (978-0-613-74777-6(1)) Tandem Library Bks.

Hartfield, Claire. Me & Uncle Romie: A Story Inspired by the Life & Art of Romare Beardon. Lagarrigue, Jerome, illus. 2002. 40p. (J). 16.99 (978-0-8037-2520-1(5) , Dial) Penguin Group (USA) Inc.

Hasley, Dennis. Painting A Horse. 2008. (Illus.). 32p. (J). 16.95 (***978-1-59643-238-3(1)***) Roaring Brook Pr.

Hayes, Daniel. Eye of the Beholder. 1998. 192p. (YA). (gr. 7-12). pap. 6.99 (978-0-449-00235-3(7) , Fawcett) Random House Publishing Group.

Henkes, Kevin. The Birthday Room. 2001. (gr. 5-8). lib. bdg. 14.15 (978-0-613-44190-2(7)) Tandem Library Bks.

Hershenhorn, Esther. Fancy That. Lloyd, Megan, illus. 2003. 32p. (J). (gr. k-3). tchr. ed. 16.95 (978-0-8234-1605-9(4)) Holiday Hse., Inc.

Hill, Laban Carrick. Casa Azul: An Encounter with Frida Kahlo. 2005. (Art Encounters Ser.). (Illus.). 160p. (YA). 15.95 (978-0-8230-0411-9(2)) Watson-Guptill Pubns., Inc.

Holmes, Barbara W. Following Fake Man. 2002. (gr. 3-6). lib. bdg. 13.00 (978-0-613-61839-7(4)) Tandem Library Bks.

Hurd, Thacher. Art Dog. 2004. (Live Oak Readalong Ser.). (Illus.). (J). pap. 18.95 incl. audio compact disk (978-1-59112-308-5(7)) Live Oak Media.

—Art Dog. Hurd, Thacher, illus. 1999. (Illus.). pap. 43.95 incl. audio compact disk (978-1-59112-526-6(X)) Live Oak Media.

—Art Dog. 1999. (Illus.). (J). (gr. k-3). 24.95 incl. audio (978-0-87499-509-1(4)); pap., tchr. ed. 41.95 incl. audio (978-0-87499-510-7(8)) Live Oak Media.

Inui, Sekihiko, illus. & creator. Comic Party, Vol. 5. Inui, Sekihiko, creator. 5th rev. ed. 2006. 248p. pap. 9.99 (978-1-59816-272-1(1) , Tokyopop Adult) TOKYOPOP, Inc.

Isom, Joan Shaddox. The First Starry Night. 2001. (gr. k-3). lib. bdg. 15.25 (978-0-613-35118-8(5)) Tandem Library Bks.

Jackson, Shelley. Sophia, the Alchemist's Dog. 2000. (Illus.). (J). (978-0-7894-2639-0(0)) Dorling Kindersley Publishing, Inc.

Jahn-Clough, Lisa. Little Dog. 2006. (Illus.). 32p. (J). (gr. k-3). 16.00 (978-0-618-57405-6(0) , Walter Lorraine) Houghton Mifflin Co. Trade & Reference Div.

Jefferies, Cindy. Reach for the Stars. 2007. (Fame School Ser.: No. 1). 128p. (J). 4.99 (978-0-14-240715-8(1) , Puffin) Penguin Group (USA) Inc.

Jeffers, Susan. My Pony. (Illus.). (J). (ps-17). 2003. 28p. 15.99 (978-0-7868-1995-9(2)); 2002. lib. bdg. (978-0-7868-2673-5(8)) Hyperion Bks. for Children.

Karas, G. Brian. The Class Artist. 2001. (Illus.). 32p. (J). 15.89 (978-0-688-17815-4(4)) HarperCollins Pubs.

Kimmel, Eric A. A Picture for Marc. Trueman, Matthew, illus. 2007. (Stepping Stone Bks.). 101p. (J). (gr. 1-4). 11.99 (***978-0-375-83253-6(X)***); lib. bdg. 13.99 (***978-0-375-93253-3(4)***) Random Hse. Children's Bks. (Random Hse. Bks. for Young Readers).

Kinkade, Thomas. Katherine's Story. 2004. (Girls of Lighthouse Lane Ser.). 176p. (J). (gr. 5 up). 13.89 (978-0-06-054342-6(6)) HarperCollins Pubs.

Kinkade, Thomas & Tamar, Erika. Rose's Story. 2004. (Girls of Lighthouse Lane Ser.: No. 2). (Illus.). 192p. (J). (gr. 5 up). 12.99 (978-0-06-054344-0(2)) HarperCollins Pubs.

Kinsey-Warnock, Natalie. Canada Geese Quilt. 2000. 11.79 (978-0-606-20354-8(0)) Tandem Library Bks.

Kitamura, Satoshi. Pablo the Artist. 2006. (Illus.). 32p. (J). 16.00 (978-0-374-35687-3(4)) Macmillan.

Knight, Joan. Charlotte in New York. Sweet, Melissa, illus. 2006. 52p. (J). 16.95 (978-0-8118-5005-6(6)) Chronicle Bks. LLC.

—Charlotte in Paris. Sweet, Melissa, illus. 2003. 52p. (J). 16.95 (978-0-8118-3766-8(1)) Chronicle Bks. LLC.

Knight, Joan MacPhail. Charlotte in Giverny. Rock, Victoria, ed. Sweet, Melissa, illus. 2000. 64p. (J). (gr. 4-7). 16.95 (978-0-8118-2383-8(0)) Chronicle Bks. LLC.

Koja, Kathe. The Blue Mirror. 2004. 128p. (YA). 16.00 (978-0-374-30849-0(7) , Farrar, Straus & Giroux (BYR)) Farrar, Straus & Giroux.

—The Blue Mirror. 2006. 128p. (YA). (gr. 8). pap. 6.99 (978-0-14-240693-9(7) , Puffin) Penguin Group (USA) Inc.

—The Blue Mirror. l.t. ed. 2004. 134p. 21.95 (978-0-7862-6960-0(X) , Large Print Pr.) Thorndike Pr.

—Buddha Boy. 2003. 128p. (YA). (gr. 7 up). 16.00 (978-0-374-30998-5(1) , Farrar, Straus & Giroux (BYR)) Farrar, Straus & Giroux.

—Buddha Boy. 2004. 128p. (YA). (gr. 6-11). reprint ed. pap. 5.99 (978-0-14-240209-2(5) , Puffin) Penguin Group (USA) Inc.

—Buddha Boy. l.t. ed. 2003. 113p. (J). 24.95 (978-0-7862-6012-6(2)) Thomson Gale.

Kudlinski, Kathleen V. The Spirit Catchers: An Encounter with Georgia O'Keeffe. 2005. (Art Encounters Ser.). (Illus.). 176p. (YA). 15.95 (978-0-8230-0408-9(2)) Watson-Guptill Pubns., Inc.

Laden, Nina. When Pigasso Met Mootisse. 1998. (Illus.). 40p. (J). (ps-5). 16.95 (978-0-8118-1121-7(2)) Chronicle Bks. LLC.

Laird, Elizabeth. Karen & the Artist. 1999. (Illus.). 144p. (J). pap. 7.00 (978-0-582-37174-3(0)) Addison-Wesley Longman, Inc.

Lakin, Patricia. Subway Sonata. Maione, Heather Harms, illus. 2001. 32p. (J). (gr. k-4). lib. bdg. (978-0-7613-1464-6(4) , Millbrook Pr.) Lerner Publishing Group.

Lamm, Drew. Bittersweet. 2003. 224p. (YA). (gr. 7 up). tchr. ed. 15.00 (978-0-618-16443-1(X) , Clarion Bks.) Houghton Mifflin Co. Trade & Reference Div.

Lantz, Frances L. Fade Far Away. 1999. 176p. (YA). (gr. 7-12). pap. 6.99 (978-0-380-79372-3(5)) HarperCollins Pubs.

—Fade Far Away. 1999. (J). (978-0-606-16361-3(1)) Tandem Library Bks.

Law, Felicia. Rumble Meets Sylvia & Sally Swan. 2005. (Read-It! Readers Ser.). (Illus.). 32p. (J). (ps-k). lib. bdg. 18.60 (978-1-4048-1541-4(4)) Picture Window Bks.

Lester, Julius. When Dad Killed Mom. 2003. (YA). 216p. pap. 6.95 (978-0-15-204698-9(4)); (gr. 7-12). mass mkt. 6.95 (978-0-15-524698-0(4)) Harcourt Trade Pubs. (Silver Whistle).

—When Dad Killed Mom. 2003. (gr. 7-12). lib. bdg. 15.25 (978-0-613-59932-0(2)) Tandem Library Bks.

Lisle, Janet Taylor. The Art of Keeping Cool. 2002. 256p. (J). (gr. 5-9). pap. 5.99 (978-0-689-83788-3(7) , Aladdin) Simon & Schuster Children's Publishing.

—The Art of Keeping Cool. Goldstrom, Robert, illus. 2000. 216p. (J). (gr. 5-7). 17.00 (978-0-689-83787-6(9) , Atheneum/Richard Jackson Bks.) Simon & Schuster Children's Publishing.

—The Art of Keeping Cool. 2002. (gr. 5-8). lib. bdg. 13.00 (978-0-613-54109-1(X)) Tandem Library Bks.

Lithgow, John. Micawber. Payne, C. F., illus. 2002. 44p. (J). (gr. k-3). 17.95 incl. audio compact disk (978-0-689-83341-0(5)) Simon & Schuster Children's Publishing.

—Micawber. Payne, C. F., illus. 2005. 40p. (J). reprint ed. pap. 6.99 (978-0-689-83542-1(6) , Aladdin) Simon & Schuster Children's Publishing.

Locker, Thomas. In Blue Mountains: An Artist's Return to America's First Wilderness. Locker, Thomas, illus. rev. ed. 2000. (Illus.). 36p. (J). (ps-3). 18.00 (978-0-88010-471-5(6)) SteinerBooks, Inc.

Lockhart, E. Fly on the Wall. 2007. 192p. (YA). (gr. 7). pap. 8.99 (***978-0-385-73282-6(1)*** , Delacorte Bks. for Young Readers) Random Hse. Children's Bks.

Lockhart, E. Fly on the Wall: How One Girl Saw Everything. 2006. 192p. (YA). (gr. 7). 15.95 (978-0-385-73281-9(3)); lib. bdg. 17.99 (978-0-385-90299-1(9)) Random Hse. Children's Bks. (Delacorte Bks. for Young Readers).

Lowry, Lois. Gathering Blue. 2000. (Illus.). 224p. (YA). (gr. 7 up). 16.00 (978-0-618-05581-4(9) , Mariner Bks.) Houghton Mifflin Co. Trade & Reference Div.

—Gathering Blue. unabr. ed. 2004. (Middle Grade Cassette Librariestm Ser.). 224p. (J). (gr. 5-9). pap. 38.00 incl. audio (978-0-8072-0989-9(9) , S YA 250 SP, Listening Library) Random Hse. Audio Publishing Group.

—Gathering Blue. (YA). (gr. 7). 2006. 240p. pap. 8.95 (978-0-385-73256-7(2) , Delacorte Bks. for Young Readers); 2005. 224p. mass mkt. 6.99 (978-0-553-49478-5(3) , Bantam Bks. for Young Readers); 2002. 224p. mass mkt. 6.50 (978-0-440-22949-0(9) , Laurel Leaf) Random Hse. Children's Bks.

—Gathering Blue. 2002. (gr. 5-8). lib. bdg. 14.75 (978-0-613-57593-5(8)) Tandem Library Bks.

—Gathering Blue. l.t. ed. 2000. 256p. (J). (gr. 8-12). 22.95 (978-0-7862-3048-8(7)) Thorndike Pr.

Luna, Rachel Nickerson. Darinka, the Little Artist Deer. Luna, Rachel Nickerson, illus. 1999. (Illus.). 36p. (J). (gr. 3-4). 12.95 (978-1-886551-06-0(5)) Howard, Emma Bks.

Mack, Tracy. Drawing Lessons. (Illus.). 176p. (J). 2002. (gr. 5-9). pap. 4.99 (978-0-439-11203-1(6) , Scholastic Paperbacks); 2000. (gr. 7-12). pap. 15.95 (978-0-439-11202-4(8) , Scholastic Reference) Scholastic, Inc.

—Drawing Lessons. 2002. (gr. 5-8). lib. bdg. 13.00 (978-0-613-72015-1(6)) Tandem Library Bks.

Mackall, Dandi Daley. Just Jazz Bk. 3: Blog On! 2006. (Faithgirlz Ser.). (Illus.). 128p. (J). pap. 6.99 (978-0-310-71095-0(2)) Zonderkidz.

MacLachlan, Patricia & MacLachlan, Emily. Painting the Wind. Schneider, Katy, illus. 40p. (J). (ps-3). 2003. 15.99 (978-0-06-029798-5(0) , Cotler, Joanna Books); 2003. lib. bdg. 16.89 (978-0-06-029799-2(9) , Cotler, Joanna Books); 2006. reprint ed. pap. 6.99 (978-0-06-443825-4(2) , Harper Trophy) HarperCollins Pubs.

Magoon, Scott. Hugo & Miles in: I've Painted Everything! 2007. (Illus.). (J). (***978-1-4287-3565-1(8)***) Houghton Mifflin Co.

Magoon, Scott. Hugo & Miles in I've Painted Everything! 2007. (Illus.). 40p. (J). (gr. 3-5). 16.00 (978-0-618-64638-8(8)) Houghton Mifflin Co.

Maltbie, P. I. Picasso & Minou. Estrada, Pau, illus. 2005. 32p. (J). 15.95 (978-1-57091-620-5(9)) Charlesbridge Publishing, Inc.

Maltby Jr., Richard. Miss Potter. 2006. 196p. (J). pap. 7.99 (978-0-7232-5899-5(6) , Warne) Penguin Group (USA) Inc.

Mariconda, Barbara. Turn the Cup Around. 1998. (978-0-606-13878-9(1)) Tandem Library Bks.

Maynard, Bill. Incredible Ned: If You Could See What He Said. 1999. (J). (978-0-606-17417-6(6)) Tandem Library Bks.

McClintock, Barbara. The Fantastic Drawings of Danielle. 2004. (Illus.). 32p. (J). (gr. k-3). pap. 5.95 (978-0-618-43230-1(2)) Houghton Mifflin Co. Trade & Reference Div.

McKay, Hilary. Saffy's Angel. 2002. 160p. (J). (gr. 3-7). 16.99 (978-0-689-84933-6(8) , McElderry, Margaret K.) Simon & Schuster Children's Publishing.

McNamara, Margaret. Dad Goes to School. Gordon, Mike, illus. 2007. (Robin Hill School Ser.). 32p. (J). lib. bdg. 13.89 (978-1-4169-1542-3(7) , Aladdin Library) Simon & Schuster Children's Publishing.

McNamara, Margaret & Gordon, Mike. Dad Goes to School. 2007. (Robin Hill School Ser.). 32p. (J). pap. 3.99 (978-1-4169-1541-6(9) , Aladdin) Simon & Schuster Children's Publishing.

McPhail, David M. Drawing Lessons from a Bear. McPhail, David M., illus. 2000. (Illus.). 32p. (J). (ps-3). 15.99 (978-0-316-56345-1(5)) Little Brown & Co.

Merberg, Julie & Bober, Suzanne. In the Garden with Van Gogh. 2002. (Illus.). 22p. (J). (ps). bds. 6.95 (978-0-8118-3415-5(8)) Chronicle Bks. LLC.

—A Magical Day with Matisse. 2002. (Illus.). 22p. (J). (ps). bds. 6.95 (978-0-8118-3414-8(X)) Chronicle Bks. LLC.

—Sharing with Renoir. 2005. (Illus.). 22p. (J). (ps-ps). bds. 6.95 (978-0-8118-4757-5(8)) Chronicle Bks. LLC.

—Sunday with Seurat. 2005. (Illus.). 16p. (J). (ps-ps). bds. 6.95 (978-0-8118-4758-2(6)) Chronicle Bks. LLC.

Moss, Marissa. Amelia Works It Out. 2000. (Amelia - American Girl Ser.). (J). 12.75 (978-0-606-20544-3(6)) Tandem Library Bks.

Nelson, Sherrie. The Boy of Color. Cantrell, Jaquese, illus. 2006. 32p. (J). 12.99 (978-1-4003-0910-8(7)) Nelson, Thomas Inc.

Nikola-Lisa, W. Magic in the Margins: A Medieval Tale of Bookmaking. Christensen, Bonnie, illus. 2007. 32p. (J). (gr. 3-5). 17.00 (978-0-618-49642-6(4)) Houghton Mifflin Co. Trade & Reference Div.

—Setting the Turkeys Free. Wilson-Max, Ken, illus. 2004. 32p. (ps-1). 15.99 (978-0-7868-1952-2(9) , Jump at the Sun) Hyperion Bks. for Children.

Nixon, Joan Lowery. Who Are You? 2001. (YA). (978-0-606-21525-1(5)); (gr. 5-8). lib. bdg. 13.00 (978-0-613-35478-3(8)) Tandem Library Bks.

Noble, Trinka Hakes. The Orange Shoes. Ettlinger, Doris, illus. rev. ed. 2007. (General Ser.). 40p. (J). (gr. 1-7). 16.95 (***978-1-58536-277-6(8)***) Sleeping Bear Pr.

Nolan, Han. Send Me down a Miracle. 2003. 276p. (YA). pap. 6.95 (978-0-15-204680-4(1)) Harcourt Children's Bks.

—Send Me down a Miracle. 2003. (gr. 7-12). lib. bdg. 15.25 (978-0-613-59926-9(8)) Tandem Library Bks.

Pedersen, Janet. Millie in the Meadow. Pedersen, Janet, illus. 2003. (Illus.). 32p. (J). (ps-1). 14.99 (978-0-7636-1725-7(3)) Candlewick Pr.

Pfister, Marcus. Henri Egg Artiste. Pfister, Marcus, illus. 2008. 32p. (J). (ps). 15.95 (***978-0-7358-2130-9(5)***) North-South Bks., Inc.

Pilegard, Virginia Walton. The Warlord's Fish. Debon, Nicolas, illus. 2002. 32p. (J). 15.95 (978-1-56554-964-7(3)) Pelican Publishing Co., Inc.

Pinkwater, Daniel M. The Artsy Smartsy Club. Pinkwater, Jill, illus. 2005. 176p. (J). 16.89 (978-0-06-053558-2(X)); 15.99 (978-0-06-053557-5(1)) HarperCollins Pubs.

Place, Francois. The Old Man Mad about Drawing: A Tale of Hokusai. Rodarmor, William, tr. from FRE. 2004. (Illus.). 108p. (J). 19.95 (978-1-56792-260-8(0)) Godine, David R. Pub.

Ploss, Skip. If Picasso Were a Fish. Ploss, Skip, illus. 2006. 40p. (gr. k-2). 15.99 (978-1-4116-9220-6(9)) Lulu.com.

Pullman, Philip. The Broken Bridge. 2002. 20.50 (978-0-8446-7229-8(7)) Smith, Peter Pub., Inc.

Rayban, Chloe. Hollywood Bliss: My Life Starring Mum. 2007. 304p. (J). pap. 7.95 (***978-1-59990-097-1(1)*** , Bloomsbury Children) Bloomsbury Publishing.

Rees, Douglas. The Janus Gate: An Encounter with John Singer Sargent. 2006. (Art Encounters Ser.). (Illus.). 176p. (YA). 15.95 (978-0-8230-0406-5(6)) Watson-Guptill Pubns., Inc.

—Smoking Mirror. 2005. (Art Encounters Ser.). (Illus.). 176p. (YA). 15.95 (978-0-8230-4863-2(2)) Watson-Guptill Pubns., Inc.

Rees, Elizabeth M. The Wedding: An Encounter with Jan Van Eyck. 2005. (Art Encounters Ser.). (Illus.). 176p. (ps-7). 15.95 (978-0-8230-0407-2(4)) Watson-Guptill Pubns., Inc.

Reiss, Kathryn. Blackthorn Winter: A Murder Mystery. (YA). 2007. (Illus.). 348p. pap. 6.95 (***978-0-15-206109-8(6)*** , Harcourt Paperbacks); 2006. 352p. 17.00 (978-0-15-205479-3(0)) Harcourt Children's Bks.

Resnick, Mike. Lady with an Alien: An Encounter with Leonardo da Vinci. 2005. (Art Encounterstm Series- Ser.). 244p. pap. 6.99 (978-0-8230-0419-5(8)) Watson-Guptill Pubns., Inc.

—Lady with an Alien: An Encounter with Leonardo Da Vinci. 2005. (Art Encounters Ser.). (Illus.). 176p. (YA). (gr. 3-7). 15.95 (978-0-8230-0323-5(X)) Watson-Guptill Pubns., Inc.

Rodowsky, Colby F. That Fernhill Summer. 2006. 176p. (J). 16.00 (978-0-374-37442-6(2)) Farrar, Straus & Giroux.

Russo, Marisabina. A Portrait of Pia. 2007. (Illus.). 240p. (YA). (gr. 6-8). 17.00 (978-0-15-205577-6(0)) Harcourt Trade Pubs.

Sally, Dick & Jane Sketchbooks Vol. 1: Fun Wherever We Are. 2004. (J). per. 14.95 (978-1-933002-00-2(X)) PublishingWorks.

Say, Allen. The Ink-Keeper's Apprentice. 2006. 160p. (YA). (gr. 7). reprint ed. pap. 6.95 (978-0-618-21613-0(8) , Walter Lorraine) Houghton Mifflin Co. Trade & Reference Div.

—The Sign Painter. Say, Allen, illus. 2000. (Illus.). 32p. (J). (gr. k-3). tchr. ed. 17.00 (978-0-395-97974-7(9) , Walter Lorraine) Houghton Mifflin Co. Trade & Reference Div.

Scott, Elaine. The Spanish Web: An Encounter with Picasso. 2004. (Art Encounters Ser.). (J). 15.95 (978-0-8230-0410-2(4)); pap. 6.99 (978-0-8230-0413-3(9)) Watson-Guptill Pubns., Inc.

Seidler, Tor. Brothers below Zero. McCarty, Peter, illus. 2003. 144p. (J). (gr. 5 up). pap. 5.99 (978-0-06-440936-0(8) , Harper Trophy) HarperCollins Pubs.

—Brothers below Zero. 2002. (Illus.). 144p. (J). (gr. 3 up). 14.95 (978-0-06-029179-2(6) , Geringer, Laura Book) HarperCollins Pubs.

—Brothers below Zero. McCarty, Peter, illus. 2002. 144p. (J). (gr. 5 up). lib. bdg. 15.89 (978-0-06-029180-8(X) , Geringer, Laura Book) HarperCollins Pubs.

—Brothers below Zero. 2003. (gr. 3-6). lib. bdg. 14.15 (978-0-613-57705-2(1)) Tandem Library Bks.

—A Rat's Tale. Marcellino, Fred, illus. 1999. 192p. (J). (gr. 5 up). pap. 5.99 (978-0-06-440779-3(9) , Harper Trophy) HarperCollins Pubs.

—Rat's Tale. 1999. (978-0-606-16698-0(X)); (gr. 3-6). lib. bdg. 15.25 (978-0-613-12367-9(0)) Tandem Library Bks.

Slate, Joseph. Crossing the Trestle. 1999. (Accelerated Reader Bks.). 144p. (J). (gr. 3-7). 14.95 (978-0-7614-5053-5(X) , Cavendish Children's Bks.) Cavendish, Marshall Corp.

Sones, Sonya. What My Girlfriend Doesn't Know. 2007. 304p. (YA). (gr. 7 up). 16.99 (978-0-689-87602-8(5)) Simon & Schuster Children's Publishing.

Stadler, John. What's So Scary? (Illus.). (J). (gr. k-4). 2001. 32p. pap. 16.95 (978-0-531-30301-6(2)); 2000. lib. bdg. 16.95 (978-0-531-33301-3(9)) Scholastic, Inc. (Orchard Bks.).

Stock, Catherine. Gugu's House. 2001. (Illus.). 32p. (J). (gr. k-3). tchr. ed. 16.00 (978-0-618-00389-1(4) , Clarion Bks.) Houghton Mifflin Co. Trade & Reference Div.

Stuchner, Joan Betty. Josephine's Dream. Walther, Chantelle, illus. 2008. 32p. 16.95 (***978-1-934393-04-8(5)***) Silverleaf Pr.

Sweeney, Joan. Suzette & the Puppy: A Story about Mary Cassatt. Wharton, Jennifer Heyd, illus. 2000. 28p. (J). (ps-3). 14.99 (978-0-7641-5294-8(7)) Barron's Educational Series, Inc.

Tada, Joni Eareckson. I'll Be with You Always. Nelson, Craig, illus. 2004. 32p. (gr. 8-12). 14.99 (978-1-58134-000-6(1)) Crossway Bks.

Trottier, Maxine. A Circle of Silver. 2000. (Circle of Silver Chronicles Ser.). 216p. (J). (gr. 7-12). pap. 7.95 (978-0-7737-6055-4(5)) Stoddart Kids CAN. *Dist:* Fitzhenry & Whiteside, Ltd.

—Circle of Silver. 2000. (gr. 7-12). lib. bdg. 16.40 (978-0-613-81347-1(2)) Tandem Library Bks.

—The Paint Box. East, Stella, illus. 32p. (J). (978-1-55041-804-0(1)) Fitzhenry & Whiteside, Ltd.

Trottier, Maxine & East, Stella. The Paint Box. 2004. (Illus.). 32p. pap. (978-1-55041-808-8(4)) Fitzhenry & Whiteside, Ltd.

Tullson, Diane. Zero. 2006. 176p. (YA). (gr. 7 up). pap. (***978-1-55041-950-4(1)***) Fitzhenry & Whiteside, Ltd.

Tunnell, Michael. Joke's on George. 2001. (gr. 3-6). lib. bdg. 18.75 (978-0-613-49572-1(1)) Tandem Library Bks.

Tunnell, Michael O. The Joke's on George. Osborn, Kathy, illus. 2003. 32p. (J). (gr. k-2). 9.95 (978-1-56397-970-5(5)) Boyds Mills Pr.

Van Draanen, Wendelin. Sammy Keyes & the Art of Deception. 2003. (Sammy Keyes Ser.: Bk. 8). 288p. (gr. 5). 15.95 (978-0-375-81176-0(1)); lib. bdg. 17.99 (978-0-375-91176 7(6)) Random Hse. Children's Bks. (Knopf Bks. for Young Readers).

Velthuijs, Max. Crocodile's Masterpiece. 2001. (Illus.). 32p. pap. 9.95 (978-1-84270-002-0(2)) Andersen GBR. *Dist:* Trafalgar Square Publishing.

Wade, Rebecca. The Theft & the Miracle. 2007. 368p. (J). (gr. 5-9). 16.99 (978-0-06-077493-6(2)); lib. bdg. 17.89 (978-0-06-077495-0(9)) HarperCollins Pubs.

Waldman, Neil. The Starry Night. 2003. (Illus.). 32p. (J). (gr. 2-4). 16.95 (978-1-56397-736-7(2)) Boyds Mills Pr.

Walter, Mildred Pitts. Suitcase. Flavin, Teresa, illus. 1999. 112p. (J). (gr. 3 up). 16.99 (978-0-688-16547-5(8)) HarperCollins Pubs.

Warner, Gertrude Chandler. Midnight Mystery. 2003. (gr. 3-6). lib. bdg. 11.80 (978-0-613-75712-6(2)) Tandem Library Bks.

—Tattletale Mystery. 2003. (gr. 3-6). lib. bdg. 11.80 (978-0-613-65061-8(1)) Tandem Library Bks.

Webb, Mack Henry, Jr. Little Bianca. Tuck, Beverly, illus. 2006. 52p. (J). per. 15.95 (978-0-9779576-0-6(8)) Pilinut Pr., Inc.

Wegman, Marcia. Lula Belle. 2007. (ENG.). 32p. per. 16.95 (***978-1-4327-0146-8(0)***) Outskirts Press, Inc.

Wheatley, Nadia & Ottley, Matt. Luke's Way of Looking. 2001. (Illus.). 36p. (J). (gr. k up). 15.95 (978-1-929132-18-8(2)) Kane/Miller Bk. Pubs., Inc.

Williams, Deborah. Artist in the Woods. Dellard, Kristine, illus. 2000. 12p. (J). (gr. k-2). pap. 3.75 (978-1-58323-032-9(7) , Seedling Pubns.) Continental Pr., Inc.

Wilson, Jacqueline. Girls in Tears. 176p. (YA). (gr. 7). 2004. (Girls Quartet: Bk. 4). mass mkt. 4.99 (978-0-440-23807-2(2) , Laurel Leaf); 2003. lib. bdg. 11.99 (978-0-385-90104-8(6) , Delacorte Bks. for Young Readers) Random Hse. Children's Bks.

—Girls in Tears. 2004. (gr. 7-12). lib. bdg. 13.00 (978-0-613-72253-7(1)) Tandem Library Bks.

—Girls Out Late. 2003. 224p. (YA). (gr. 7). mass mkt. 5.50 (978-0-440-22959-9(6) , Laurel Leaf) Random Hse. Children's Bks.

—Girls Out Late. Sharratt, Nick, illus. 2003. 192p. (YA). mass mkt. (978-0-552-54523-5(6) , Corgi) Transworld Publishers Ltd. GBR. *Dist:* Random Hse. of Canada, Ltd.

Wojciechowski, Susan. The Christmas Miracle of Jonathan Toomey. Lynch, P. J., illus. 1998. 40p. (J). (ps-3). 18.99 incl. cd-rom (978-0-8499-5905-9(5)) Nelson, Thomas Inc.

Wong, Joyce Lee. Seeing Emily. 2005. (Illus.). 288p. (J). (gr. 7-11). 16.95 (978-0-8109-5757-2(4) , Abrams Bks. for Young Readers) Abrams, Harry N., Inc.

Wyeth, Sharon Dennis. Orphea Proud. 2006. 208p. (YA). (gr. 9). pap. 5.99 (978-0-440-22706-9(2) , Laurel Leaf) Random Hse. Children's Bks.

ARTISTS, FLEMISH

Malam, John. Pieter Bruegel. 1999. (Tell Me about Ser.). (Illus.). 24p. (gr. 2-5). lib. bdg. 19.93 (978-1-57505-366-0(7)) Lerner Publishing Group.

ARTISTS, ITALIAN

Connolly, Sean & Michelangelo Buonarroti. Michelangelo. 2004. (Lives of the Artists Ser.). (Illus.). 48p. (J). (gr. 5 up). pap. 29.26 (978-0-8368-5605-7(8)); lib. bdg. 30.00 (978-0-8368-5600-2(7)) Stevens, Gareth Inc. (World Almanac Library).

Di Cagno, Gabriella. Michelangelo. 2008. (YA). lib. bdg. 24.95 net. (***978-1-934545-01-0(5)***) Oliver Pr., Inc.

Kalz, Jill. The Mona Lisa. 2004. (What in the World? Ser.). (Illus.). 48p. 19.95 (978-1-58341-272-5(7) , Creative Education) Creative Co., The.

Mason, Antony & da Vinci, Leonardo. Leonardo da Vinci. 2004. (Lives of the Artists Ser.). (Illus.). 48p. (J). (gr. 5 up). pap. 29.26 (978-0-8368-5604-0(X)); lib. bdg. 30.00 (978-0-8368-5599-9(X)) Stevens, Gareth Inc. (World Almanac Library).

Pignatelli, Luca. Italia. 2004. (Illus.). 144p. (YA). (gr. 13 up). pap. 39.95 (978-88-8158-424-6(7)) Charta ITA. *Dist:* D.A.P./Distributed Art Pubs.

Quill, Charles G. Michelangelo: His Life & Art. 2002. (Reading Room Collection). (Illus.). 24p. (J). lib. bdg. 18.75 (978-0-8239-3749-3(6)) Rosen Publishing Group, Inc., The.

Rice, Earle, Jr. Canaletto. 2007. (Art Profiles for Kids Ser.). (Illus.). 48p. (J). lib. bdg. 29.95 (***978-1-58415-561-4(2)***) Mitchell Lane Pubs., Inc.

Romeo, Francesca. Leonardo Da Vinci. 2008. (YA). lib. bdg. 24.95 net. (***978-1-934545-00-3(7)***) Oliver Pr., Inc.

Ross, Stewart. Leonardo Da Vinci. 2002. (Scientists Who Made History Ser.). (Illus.). 48p. (J). lib. bdg. 27.12 (978-0-7398-5223-1(X)) Raintree.

Ruggeri, Ileana. Isolari. 2004. (Illus.). 56p. (YA). (gr. 13 up). pap. 16.95 (978-88-8158-421-5(2)) Charta ITA. *Dist:* D.A.P./Distributed Art Pubs.

Sateren, Shelley Swanson. Michaelangelo. 2002. (Masterpieces). (Illus.). 24p. (J). (gr. 2-3). lib. bdg. 18.60 (978-0-7368-1125-5(7) , Bridgestone Bks.) Capstone Pr., Inc.

Stanley, George Edward. Leonardo Da Vinci: Young Artist, Writer, & Inventor. 2005. (Childhood of World Figures Ser.). 166p. (J). (978-1-4156-3039-6(9) , Aladdin) Simon & Schuster Children's Publishing.

Strom, Laura Layton. Leonardo da Vinci: Artist & Scientist. 2007. (Shockwave: Life Stories Ser.). 36p. (J). (gr. 3-5). pap. 6.95 (***978-0-531-18798-2(5)*** , Children's Pr.) Scholastic Library Publishing.

Strom, Laura Layton & Leonardo. Leonardo Da Vinci: Artist & Scientist. 2007. (Shockwave: Life Stories Ser.). (Illus.). 36p. (J). (gr. 4-6). lib. bdg. 25.00 (***978-0-531-17771-6(8)*** , Children's Pr.) Scholastic Library Publishing.

Tames, Richard. Michelangelo Buonarotti. 2000. (Life & Work of. . . Ser.). (Illus.). 32p. (J). (gr. k-2). pap. 21.36 (978-1-57572-343-3(3)) Heinemann Library.

Whiting, Jim. Michelangelo. 2007. (Art Profiles for Kids Ser.). (Illus.). 48p. (J). lib. bdg. 29.95 (***978-1-58415-562-1(0)***) Mitchell Lane Pubs., Inc.

Witteman, Barbara. Leonardo Da Vinci. 2003. (Masterpieces, Artists & Their Works). (Illus.). 24p. (J). lib. bdg. 19.93 (978-0-7368-2228-2(3) , Bridgestone Bks.) Capstone Pr., Inc.

ARTISTS, MEXICAN

Cruz, Barbara C. Jose Clemente Orozco: Mexican Artist. 1998. (Hispanic Biographies Ser.). (Illus.). 128p. (YA). (gr. 6-12). lib. bdg. 26.60 (978-0-7660-1041-3(4)) Enslow Pubs., Inc.

Frith, Margaret. Frida Kahlo: The Artist Who Painted Herself. 2003. (gr. k-3). lib. bdg. 14.15 (978-0-613-68237-4(8)) Tandem Library Bks.

Holzhey, Magdalena. Frida Kahlo: The Artist in the Blue House. 2003. (Adventures in Art Ser.). (Illus.). 30p. (J). (gr. 5 up). 14.95 (978-3-7913-2863-8(8)) Prestel Publishing.

Kent, Deborah. Frida Kahlo: An Artist Celebrates Life. 2004. (Proud Heritage: the Hispanic Library Ser.). 40p. (J). (gr. 3-7). 28.50 (978-1-59296-167-2(3)) Child's World, Inc.

Laidlaw, Jill A. Frida Kahlo. 2003. (Artists in Their Time Ser.). (Illus.). 48p. (J). 23.50 (978-0-531-12236-5(0)); (gr. 5-7). pap. 6.95 (978-0-531-16642-0(2)) Scholastic Library Publishing. (Watts, Franklin).

—Frida Kahlo. 2003. (gr. 5-8). lib. bdg. 15.25 (978-0-613-59483-7(5)) Tandem Library Bks.

Morrison, John F. Frida Kahlo. 2003. (Great Hispanic Heritage Ser.). (Illus.). 112p. (J). (gr. 6-12). 30.00 (978-0-7910-7254-7(1)); pap. 30.00 (978-0-7910-7517-3(6)) Facts On File, Inc. (Chelsea Hse.).

Muro, Claudia Burr. Yo Miro, Miro Todo el Tiempo: Basada en Pinturas y Textos de Rufino Tamayo. 2005. (Coleccion Los Grandes Para Los Mas Pequenos Ser.). (SPA., Illus.). 35p. (J). (gr. 3-5). pap. 8.95 (978-968-7381-28-2(0)) Tecolote, Ediciones, S.A. de C.V. MEX. *Dist:* Iaconi, Mariuccia Bk. Imports.

Sabbeth, Carol. Frida Kahlo & Diego Rivera: Their Lives & Ideas, 24 Activities. 2005. (For Kids Ser.). (Illus.). 160p. (J). pap. 17.95 (978-1-55652-569-8(9) , 1241061) Chicago Review Pr., Inc.

Venezia, Mike. Frida Kahlo. 1999. (Getting to Know the World's Greatest Artists Ser.). (Illus.). 32p. (gr. 3-4). pap. 6.95 (978-0-516-26466-0(4)); (J). 27.00 (978-0-516-20975-3(2)) Scholastic Library Publishing. (Children's Pr.).

—Frida Kahlo. 1999. (gr. 3-6). lib. bdg. 15.25 (978-0-613-37352-4(9)) Tandem Library Bks.

Woronoff, Kristen. Frida Kahlo: Mexican Painter. 2002. (Famous Women Juniors Ser.). (Illus.). 32p. (J). (gr. 3-5). 23.70 (978-1-56711-594-9(2) , Blackbirch Pr., Inc.) Thomson Gale.

ARTISTS, NEGRO

see African American Artists

ARTISTS, SPANISH

Anderson, Robert. Salvador Dali. 2002. (Artists in Their Time Ser.). (J). (gr. 5-7). pap. 6.95 (978-0-531-16624-6(4) , Watts, Franklin) Scholastic Library Publishing.

—Salvador Dali. 2002. (gr. 5-8). lib. bdg. 15.25 (978-0-613-54336-1(X)) Tandem Library Bks.

Bennett, Leonie. Salvador Dali. 2004. (Life & Work Of-Ser.). (Illus.). 32p. (J). pap. 7.25 (978-1-4034-5561-1(9)); lib. bdg. 22.79 (978-1-4034-5071-5(4)) Heinemann Library.

Giraudy, Daniele & De Maupeou, Patrick. Picasso & His Times. 1999. (W5 Who, What, Where, When & Why Ser.). 96p. (YA). (gr. 6 up). 19.95 (978-0-8050-5061-5(2)) Holt, Henry & Co.

Lowery, Linda. Pablo Picasso. Porter, Janice Lee, illus. 1999. (On My Own Biographies Ser.). 48p. (J). (gr. 1-3). lib. bdg. 23.93 (978-1-57505-331-8(4) , Carolrhoda Bks.) Lerner Publishing Group.

Picasso, Pablo. Introducing Pablo Picasso: His Life & Art with 16 Stickers. Negri, Paul, ed. 2001. (Illus.). 16p. (YA). 5.95 (978-0-486-41559-8(7)) Dover Pubns., Inc.

Ross, Michael Elsohn. Salvador Dali & the Surrealists: Their Lives & Ideas, 21 Activities. 2003. (For Kids Ser.). (Illus.). 144p. (J). (gr. 6 up). pap. 17.95 (978-1-55652-479-0(X)) Chicago Review Pr., Inc.

ARTISTS' MATERIALS

Canizares, Susan & Berger, Samantha. What Do Artists Use? 1999. (Learning Center Emergent Readers Ser.). (J). 2.50 (978-0-439-04591-9(6)) Scholastic, Inc.

Cunningham, Kevin. Pencils. 2008. (J). lib. bdg. 25.26 (***978-1-60279-122-0(8)***) Cherry Lake Publishing.

Hannah, Sue. Crafty Concoctions: 101 Craft Supply Recipes. 2003. (Illus.). xi, 140p. (J). 7.95 (978-0-88166-462-1(6)) Meadowbrook Pr.

Munton, Gill. How Crayons Are Made. 2000. (Cambridge Reading Ser.). (Illus.). 14p. pap. 5.00 (978-0-521-77452-9(7)) Cambridge Univ. Pr.

Murray, Julie. Wax to Crayon. 2007. (Illus.). 24p. (J). 21.35 (978-1-59679-915-8(3) , Buddy Bks.) ABDO Publishing Co.

Newbery, Elizabeth. How Is Art Made? 2001. (Art for All Ser.). (Illus.). 32p. (J). lib. bdg. 24.25 (978-1-930643-31-4(4)) Chrysalis Education.

Rau, Dana Meachen. Los Artistas. 2007. (Instrumentos de Trabajo Ser.). (SPA.). 32p. (J). lib. bdg. 22.79 (***978-0-7614-2796-4(1)*** , Benchmark Bks.) Cavendish, Marshall Corp.

—Artists. 2007. (Tools We Use Ser.). 32p. (J). lib. bdg. 22.79 (***978-0-7614-2655-4(8)*** , Benchmark Bks.) Cavendish, Marshall Corp.

—Artists/Los Artistas. 2007. (Tools We Use/Instrumentos de Trabajo Ser.). (SPA & ENG., Illus.). 32p. (J). lib. bdg. 22.79 (***978-0-7614-2820-6(8)*** , Benchmark Bks.) Cavendish, Marshall Corp.

—Tools We Use, 6 vols., Set. Incl. Artists. lib. bdg. 22.79 (***978-0-7614-2655-4(8)***); Builders. lib. bdg. 22.79 (***978-0-7614-2656-1(6)***); Chefs. lib. bdg. 22.79 (***978-0-7614-2657-8(4)***); Doctors. lib. bdg. 22.79 (***978-0-7614-2659-2(0)***); Emergency Medical Technicians (EMT) lib. bdg. 22.79 (***978-0-7614-2660-8(4)***); Librarians. lib. bdg. 22.79 (***978-0-7614-2662-2(0)***); 32p. (J). 2007. 136.71 (***978-0-7614-2654-7(X)*** , Benchmark Bks.) Cavendish, Marshall Corp.

ARTS, GRAPHIC

see Graphic Arts

ARTS, USEFUL

see Technology

ARTS AND CRAFTS

see Handicraft

ASHE, ARTHUR, 1943-1993

Cunningham, Kevin. Arthur Ashe: Athlete & Activist. 2005. (Journey to Freedom). (Illus.). 40p. (J). (gr. 3-7). 28.50 (978-1-59296-228-0(9)) Child's World, Inc.

Fry, Erin. Arthur Ashe Against the Odds. 2005. (Voices Reading Ser.). (Illus.). 16p. (J). (978-0-7367-2915-4(1)) Zaner-Bloser, Inc.

Lazo, Caroline Evensen. Arthur Ashe. 1998. (Biography Ser.). (Illus.). 128p. (YA). (gr. 6-12). lib. bdg. 25.26 (978-0-8225-4932-1(8) , Lerner Pubns.) Lerner Publishing Group.

Mantell, Paul. Arthur Ashe: Young Tennis Champion. Henderson, Meryl, illus. 2006. 213p. (J). lib. bdg. 18.46 (***978-1-4242-2203-2(6)***) Fitzgerald Bks.

—Arthur Ashe: Young Tennis Champion. Henderson, Meryl, illus. 2006. (Childhood of Famous Americans Ser.). 224p. (J). pap. 5.99 (978-0-689-87346-1(8) , Aladdin) Simon & Schuster Children's Publishing.

Marsh, Carole. Arthur Ashe. 2002. (One Thousand Readers Ser.). (Illus.). 12p. (J). (gr. k-4). 2.95 (978-0-635-01536-5(6) , 15366) Gallopade International.

—The Virginia Reader: Arthur Ashe. 2001. (Virginia Experience! Ser.). (Illus.). 12p. (J). (gr. k-5). pap. 2.95 (978-0-635-00376-8(7)) Gallopade International.

Martin, Marvin. Arthur Ashe: Of Tennis & the Human Spirit. 1999. (Impact Biographies Ser.). (Illus.). 176p. (J). (gr. 8-12). 18.95 (978-0-531-11432-2(5) , Watts, Franklin) Scholastic Library Publishing.

ASIA

see also Southeast Asia

Aretha, David. Discovering Asia's Land, People, & Wildlife: A MyReportLinks. com Book. 2004. (Continents of the World Ser.). (Illus.). 48p. (J). lib. bdg. 25.26 (978-0-7660-5183-6(8) , MyReportLinks.com Bks.) Enslow Pubs., Inc.

Asia: Individual Title Six-Packs. (On Deck Ser.). 24p. (gr. 4-5). 35.00 (978-0-7578-1077-0(2)); (SPA.). 35.00 (978-0-7578-6448-3(1)) Rigby Education.

Bandon, Alex & O'Brien, Patrick. The Travels of Marco Polo. 1999. (Explorers & Exploration Ser.). (Illus.). 48p. (J). (gr. 4-7). lib. bdg. 22.83 (978-0-7398-1485-7(0)) Raintree.

Benhart, John & Pomeroy, George. South Asia. Gritzner, Charles F., ed. 2005. (Modern World Cultures Ser.). (Illus.). 120p. (J). (ps-7). lib. bdg. 30.00 (978-0-7910-8147-1(8) , Chelsea Hse.) Facts On File, Inc.

Bramwell, Martyn. Northern & Western Asia. 2000. (World in Maps Ser.). (Illus.). 40p. (J). (gr. 5-12). lib. bdg. 23.93 (978-0-8225-2915-6(7) , Lerner Pubns.) Lerner Publishing Group.

—Southern & Eastern Asia. 2000. (World in Maps Ser.). (Illus.). 48p. (YA). (gr. 5-12). lib. bdg. 23.93 (978-0-8225-2916-3(5) , Lerner Pubns.) Lerner Publishing Group.

Conyers, Karen Elizabeth & Compass Point Books Staff. Teens in China. 2006. (Global Connections Ser.). (Illus.). 96p. (J). (gr. 5-7). 31.93 (978-0-7565-2060-1(6) , 1265891) Compass Point Bks.

Cooper, Robert. Bhutan. 2001. (Cultures of the World Ser.). (Illus.). 128p. (gr. 5-12). lib. bdg. 37.07 (978-0-7614-1191-8(7) , Benchmark Bks.) Cavendish, Marshall Corp.

CultureGrams 2005 World Edition - Asia & Oceania. 2004. (YA). per. 39.99 (978-1-931694-92-6(3)) ProQuest CSA.

Dalby, Elizabeth, et al. Introduction to Asia. 2006. (Illus.). 96p. (J). (***978-0-439-88982-7(0)***) Scholastic, Inc.

Encyclopaedia Britannica Publishers, Inc. Staff. Views of Asia & Australia. 2004. (Britannica Learning Library). (Illus.). (J). lib. bdg. 14.95 (978-1-59339-010-5(6)) Encyclopaedia Britannica, Inc.

Foster, Leila Merrell. Asia. 2001. (Continents Ser.). (Illus.). 32p. (J). (gr. k-2). lib. bdg. 21.36 (978-1-57572-448-5(0)) Heinemann Library.

—Asia. 2001. (gr. k-3). lib. bdg. 14.75 (978-0-613-45709-5(9)) Tandem Library Bks.

Foster, Leila Merrell & Fox, Mary Virginia. Asia. 2002. (Continents Ser.). (Illus.). 32p. (J). (gr. k-2). pap. 6.95 (978-1-58810-947-7(X) , 91437) Heinemann Library.

Fowler, Allan. Asia. (Rookie Read-About Geography Ser.). (Illus.). 32p. (J). (gr. 1-2). 2002. pap. 5.95 (978-0-516-25980-2(6)); 2001. 20.50 (978-0-516-22234-9(1)) Scholastic Library Publishing. (Children's Pr.).

—Asia. 2001. (gr. k-3). lib. bdg. 14.10 (978-0-613-53934-0(6)) Tandem Library Bks.

Fpri. Tajikistan. 2005. (Growth & Influence of Islam in the Nations of Asia & Central Asia Ser.). (Illus.). 120p. (J). (ps-7). lib. bdg. 25.95 (978-1-59084-885-2(3)) Mason Crest Pubs.

Ganeri, Anita. Asia. 2006. (Exploring Continents Ser.). (Illus.). 32p. (J). (978-1-4034-8243-3(8)); pap. (978-1-4034-8251-8(9)) Heinemann Library.

Graf, Mike. Asia. 2002. (Continents Ser.). (Illus.). 79p. (J). (gr. 1-2). 18.60 (978-0-7368-1416-4(7) , Bridgestone Bks.) Capstone Pr., Inc.

Grahame, Deborah. Asia. 2003. (Continents Ser.). (Illus.). 32p. (J). (gr. 2-6). 27.07 (978-1-59296-058-3(8)) Child's World, Inc.

Hovanec, Erin M. An Online Visit to Asia. (Internet Field Trips Ser.). 24p. (J). 2002. lib. bdg. 18.75 (978-0-8239-6422-2(1)); 2001. (Illus.). (gr. 3). lib. bdg. 18.75 (978-0-8239-5652-4(0)) Rosen Publishing Group, Inc., The. (PowerKids Pr.).

Kalman, Bobbie & Sjonger, Rebecca. Explore Asia. 2007. (Explore the Continents Ser.). (Illus.). 32p. (J). (gr. 1-7). (***978-0-7787-3072-9(7));*** pap. (***978-0-7787-3086-6(7))*** Crabtree Publishing Co.

Karecki, Jason, illus. The Adventures of Drake Montana Vol. 2: Asian Mountains. 1998. 24p. (J). (gr. k-5). (978-1-890716-08-0(1)) K&M International.

Knowlton, MaryLee. Turkmenistan. 2006. (Cultures of the World Ser.). (Illus.). 144p. (J). (978-0-7614-2014-9(2) , Benchmark Bks.) Cavendish, Marshall Corp.

Mattern, Joanne. Asia. 2004. (Natures Greatest Hits Ser.). (SPA.). 24p. (J). (gr. 3-6). lib. bdg. 17.25 (978-0-8239-6875-6(8) , Buenas Letra) Rosen Publishing Group, Inc., The.

—Asia: World's Largest Continent. 2002. (Reading Power Ser.). (Illus.). 24p. (J). (gr. 2). lib. bdg. 17.25 (978-0-8239-6015-6(3) , PowerKids Pr.) Rosen Publishing Group, Inc., The.

McGraw-Hill Staff. Exploring Our World, Eastern Hemisphere, Interactive Tutor Self Assessment CD-ROM. 2007. (C). cd-rom 93.32 (***978-0-07-879098-0(0)*** , 9780078790980) Glencoe/McGraw-Hill.

—Exploring Our World, Eastern Hemisphere, Reading Essentials & Note-Taking Guide Workbook. 2007. (C). pap. 18.00 (***978-0-07-878166-7(3)*** , 9780078781667) Glencoe/McGraw-Hill.

—Exploring Our World, Eastern Hemisphere, Standardized Test Practice Workbook. 2007. (C). pap. 10.00 (***978-0-07-877743-1(7)*** , 9780078777431) Glencoe/McGraw-Hill.

—Exploring Our World, Eastern Hemisphere, Student Edition. 2nd ed. 2007. 69.32 (***978-0-07-874578-2(0)*** , 9780078745782) Glencoe/McGraw-Hill.

McNeil, Niki, et al. HOCPP 1065 Asia. 2006. spiral bd. 22.00 (***978-1-60308-065-1(1))*** In the Hands of a Child.

Merrill, Yvonne Y. Asia: Art Activities for All Ages. Simpson, Mary, illus. 1999. (Hands-on Ser.). 90p. (J). (gr. 5 up). pap. 20.00 (978-0-9643177-5-8(3)) KITS Publishing.

Moore, Jo Ellen. Asia. Evans, Marilyn, ed. Davis, Cindy & Winters, Keli, illus. 1999. (Geography Units Ser.). 80p. (gr. 3-6). pap., tchr. ed. 12.95 (978-1-55799-713-5(6) , EMC 766) Evan-Moor Educational Pubs.

Pascoe, Elaine. The Pacific Rim: East Asia at the Dawn of a New Century. 1999. (Single Titles Ser.). 128p. (gr. 7 up). lib. bdg. 25.90 (978-0-7613-3015-8(1) , Twenty-First Century Bks.) Lerner Publishing Group.

Pelusey, Michael & Pelusey, Jane. Asia. 2004. (Continents Ser.). (Illus.). 32p. (J). (gr. 2-4). 23.00 (978-0-7910-8280-5(6) , Chelsea Hse.) Facts On File, Inc.

Petersen, David. Asia. Taft, James, ed. 1998. (True Bks.). (Illus.). 48p. (J). (gr. 3-5). pap. 6.95 (978-0-516-26371-7(4) , Children's Pr.) Scholastic Library Publishing.

—Asia. 1998. (Illus.). 47p. (J). (ps-3). lib. bdg. 15.25 (978-0-613-37276-3(X)) Tandem Library Bks.

Rogers, Kirsteen. Introduction to Asia - Internet Linked. 2005. (Introduction to Asia Ser.). 96p. (J). 17.95 (978-0-7945-0941-5(X) , Usborne) EDC Publishing.

Sammis, Fran. Asia. 1998. (Mapping Our World Ser.). (Illus.). 64p. (J). (gr. 4-8). lib. bdg. 27.07 (978-0-7614-0371-5(X) , Benchmark Bks.) Cavendish, Marshall Corp.

Sayre, April Pulley. Asia. 1999. (Seven Continents Ser.: 8). (Illus.). 64p. (gr. 5-8). lib. bdg. 25.90 (978-0-7613-1368-7(0) , Millbrook Pr.) Lerner Publishing Group.

—Greeting, Asia! The Ultimate Guide to America's 4 Regional Styles of 'Cue. 2003. (Illus.). 32p. lib. bdg. 21.90 (978-0-7613-2124-8(1) , Millbrook Pr.) Lerner Publishing Group.

—Greetings, Asia! 2003. 32p. (J). (gr. 2-5). pap. 7.95 (978-0-7613-1991-7(3) , Millbrook Pr.) Lerner Publishing Group.

Schaefer, A. R. Asia. 2006. (Illus.). 24p. (J). (978-0-7368-5427-6(4)) Capstone Pr., Inc.

Senker, Cath. Marco Polo's Travels on Asia's Silk Road. 2007. (J). (***978-1-4034-9751-2(6))*** Heinemann Library.

Simpson, Judith. Ask about Asia, 10 vols., Set. 2002. (Ask about Asia Ser.). (Illus.). 48p. (J). (gr. 4 up). lib. bdg. (978-1-59084-198-3(0)) Mason Crest Pubs.

Stewart, Mark. South Asia. 2007. (J). (***978-1-4034-9899-1(7));*** pap. (***978-1-4034-9908-0(X))*** Heinemann Library.

Striveildi, Cheryl. Asia. 2003. (Continents Ser.). (Illus.). 32p. (J). (gr. k-4). lib. bdg. 22.78 (978-1-57765-960-0(0)) ABDO Publishing Co.

Waters, Bella. Uzbekistan in Pictures. 2007. (Visual Geography Ser.). (Illus.). 80p. (J). 27.93 (978-0-8225-2673-5(5) , Twenty-First Century Bks.) Lerner Publishing Group.

ASIA, CENTRAL

Bausum, Ann. Dragon Bones & Dinosaur Eggs: A Photo-Biography of Explorer Roy Chapman Andrews. 2000. (Illus.). 64p. (J). (gr. 3-7). 17.95 (978-0-7922-7123-9(8) , National Geographic Children's Bks.) National Geographic Society.

Cartlidge, Cherese & Clark, Charles. The Central Asian States. 2001. (Former Soviet Republics Ser.). (Illus.). 128p. (J). (gr. 6-9). 29.95 (978-1-56006-735-1(7) , Lucent Bks.) Thomson Gale.

Harmon, Daniel E. Kyrgyzstan. 2005. (Growth & Influence of Islam in the Nations of Asia & Central Asia Ser.). (Illus.). 120p. (J). (ps-7). lib. bdg. (978-1-59084-883-8(7)) Mason Crest Pubs.

King, David C. Kyrgyzstan. 2005. (Cultures of the World Ser.). (Illus.). 144p. (J). (978-0-7614-2013-2(4)) Cavendish, Marshall Corp.

Libal, Joyce. Uzbekistan. 2005. (Growth & Influence of Islam in the Nations of Asia & Central Asia Ser.). (Illus.). 128p. (J). lib. bdg. (978-1-59084-887-6(X)) Mason Crest Pubs.

Morris, Neil. North & East Asia. 2007. (J). (***978-1-4034-9898-4(9));*** pap. (***978-1-4034-9907-3(1))*** Heinemann Library.

Pavlovic, Zoran. Kazakhstan. 2003. (Modern World Nations Ser.). (Illus.). 150p. (gr. 6-12). 30.00 (978-0-7910-7231-8(2) , Chelsea Hse.) Facts On File, Inc.

ASIA—DESCRIPTION AND TRAVEL

Bateman, Helen & Denshire, Jayne. Asia. 2006. (Illus.). 32p. (J). (978-1-58340-800-1(2) , 1262715) Smart Apple Media.

Bowden, Rob. Asia. 2005. (Illus.). 64p. (J). (978-0-8368-5918-8(9)); lib. bdg. 32.67 (978-0-8368-5911-9(1)) Stevens, Gareth Inc. (World Almanac Library).

Di Piazza, Francesca Davis. Yemen in Pictures. 2007. lib. bdg. (***978-0-8225-7149-0(8))*** Twenty First Century Bks.

DiPiazza, Francesca. Kuwait in Pictures. 2nd ed. 2007. (Visual Geography Ser.). (Illus.). 80p. (J). (gr. 5-12). 27.93 (978-0-8225-6589-5(7) , Twenty-First Century Bks.) Lerner Publishing Group.

Doeden, Matt. Laos in Pictures. 2007. (Visual Geography Ser.). (Illus.). 80p. (J). (gr. 5-12). 27.93 (978-0-8225-6590-1(0) , Twenty-First Century Bks.) Lerner Publishing Group.

Donaldson, Madeline. Asia. 2005. (Illus.). 32p. (YA). (978-0-8225-2491-5(0) , Lerner Pubns.); (J). lib. bdg. 22.60 (978-0-8225-4721-1(X)) Lerner Publishing Group.

Feeney, Kathy. Marco Polo: Explorer of China. 2004. (Explorers! Ser.). (Illus.). 48p. (J). lib. bdg. 23.93 (978-0-7660-2145-7(9)) Enslow Pubs., Inc.

Gefen, Keren. Marco Polo. (Great Explorers Ser.). (Illus.). 48p. (J). (gr. 5 up). 2002. pap. 14.60 (978-0-8368-5177-9(3)); 2001. lib. bdg. 30.00 (978-0-8368-5017-8(3)) Stevens, Gareth Inc. (World Almanac Library).

Hare, Eric B. Jungle Heroes & Other Stories. 2005. (Illus.). 106p. (J). (978-0-8163-2063-9(2)) Pacific Pr. Publishing Assn.

Herbert, Janis. Marco Polo for Kids: His Marvelous Journey to China, 21 Activities. 2001. (For Kids Ser.). (Illus.). 144p. (J). (gr. 4-7). pap. 16.95 (978-1-55652-377-9(7)) Chicago Review Pr., Inc.

Holub, Joan. Who Was Marco Polo? O'Brien, John & Harrison, Nancy, illus. 2007. (Who Was... ? Ser.). 112p. (J). (gr. 2-6). pap. 4.99 (978-0-448-44540-3(9) , Grosset & Dunlap) Penguin Group (USA) Inc.

Lyle, Garry. Turkey. 1999. (Major World Nations Ser.). (Illus.). 103p. (J). (gr. 4-7). 19.95 (978-0-7910-5401-7(2) , Chelsea Hse.) Facts On File, Inc.

Marcovitz, Hal. Marco Polo & the Wonders of the East. 1999. (Explorers of the New World Ser.). (Illus.). 63p. (J). (gr. 4 up). 31.00 (978-0-7910-5511-3(6) , Chelsea Hse.) Facts On File, Inc.

McFarren, Kathleen. Marco Polo. 2004. (Fact Finders Ser.). (Illus.). 32p. (J). 16.95 (978-0-7368-2490-3(1)) Capstone Pr., Inc.

McNeese, Tim. Marco Polo: And the Realm of Kublai Khan. Goetzmann, William H., ed. 2005. (Explorers of New Lands Ser.). (Illus.). 158p. (J). (gr. 4-8). lib. bdg. 30.00 (978-0-7910-8612-4(7) , Chelsea Hse.) Facts On File, Inc.

Smalley, Roger. The Adventures of Marco Polo. Carter, Greg, illus. 2005. (Graphic Library). 32p. (J). 22.60 (978-0-7368-3830-6(9)) Capstone Pr., Inc.

Vierow, Wendy. Asia. 2004. (Atlas of the Seven Continents Ser.). (Illus.). 24p. (J). lib. bdg. 21.25 (978-0-8239-6689-9(5) , PowerKids Pr.) Rosen Publishing Group, Inc., The.

Waters, Bella. Kazakhstan in Pictures. 2007. (Visual Geography Ser.). (Illus.). 80p. (J). (gr. 5-12). 27.93 (978-0-8225-6588-8(9) , Twenty-First Century Bks.) Lerner Publishing Group.

Worth, Richard. The Great Empire of China & Marco Polo in World History. 2003. (In World History Ser.). (Illus.). 112p. (J). lib. bdg. 26.60 (978-0-7660-1939-3(X)) Enslow Pubs., Inc.

ASIA—FICTION

Baker, Barrie. The Village of a Hundred Smiles. Jorisch, Stephane, illus. 1998. 48p. (J). (gr. k-3). pap. 7.95 (978-1-55037-535-0(0)) Annick Pr., Ltd. CAN. *Dist:* Firefly Bks., Ltd.

—The Village of a Hundred Smiles. Jorisch, Stephane, illus. 1998. 48p. (J). (gr. k-3). lib. bdg. 18.95 (978-1-55037-522-0(9)) Firefly Bks., Ltd.

Bird, Helen. Fighting Back. 2005. (Shades Ser.). 64p. (J). pap. 7.99 (978-0-237-52845-4(2) , Evans Brothers, Limited) Evans Publishing Group GBR. *Dist:* Independent Pubs. Group.

Chen, Chih-Yuan. On My Way to Buy Eggs. Chen, Chih-Yuan, illus. 2003. (Illus.). 36p. (J). (ps up). 15.95 (978-1-929132-49-2(2)) Kane/Miller Bk. Pubs., Inc.

Conger, David, et al. Asian Children's Favorite Stories: A Treasury of Folktales from China, Japan, Korea, India, the Philippines, Thailand, Indonesia & Malaysia. Yee, Patrick, illus. 2006. 112p. (J). (gr. k-4). 24.95 (978-0-8048-3669-2(8)) Tuttle Publishing.

Harcourt School Publishers Staff. People of Our Nation. 3rd ed. 2002. (Trophies English Language Learners Ser.). (Illus.). pap. 5.10 (978-0-15-327880-8(3)) Harcourt Schl. Pubs.

—The Serai: Take-Home Book. 2001. (Collections Ser.). (Illus.). (J). pap. 1.90 (978-0-15-319554-9(1)) Harcourt Schl. Pubs.

Hightman, Jason. Samurai. 2007. 416p. (J). pap. 6.99 (***978-0-06-054016-6(8)*** , Eos) HarperCollins Pubs.

Kilborne, Sarah S. Leaving Vietnam: The Journey of Tuan Ngo, a Boat Boy. 1999. (Ready-to-Read Ser.). (J). (978-0-606-15940-1(1)) Tandem Library Bks.

Masson, J. Moussaieff. The Cat Who Came in from the Cold: A Fable. 2004. 107p. (978-0-345-47867-2(3) , Ballantine Bks.) Random House Publishing Group.

Perkins, Mitali. Rickshaw Girl. Hogan, Jamie, illus. 2007. 91p. (J). (gr. 2-5). 13.95 (978-1-58089-308-4(2)) Charlesbridge Publishing, Inc.

Place, Francois. The Last Giants. 2001. (Illus.). 74p. (J). pap. 11.00 (978-1-86205-289-5(1) , Pavilion Bks., Ltd.) Anova Bks. GBR. *Dist:* Trafalgar Square Publishing.

Pullman, Philip. The Firework-Maker's Daughter. 1999. 120p. (J). 16.95 (978-0-7540-6055-0(1) , Galaxy Children's Large Print) BBC Audiobooks America.

Trottier, Maxine. Mr Hiroshis Garden. Morin, Paul, illus. 2006. 32p. (J). pap. 7.95 (978-1-55005-152-0(0)) Fitzhenry & Whiteside, Ltd. CAN. *Dist:* F & W Pubns., Inc.

Zhang, Song Nan. Balada de Mulan (Ballad of Mulan) Zhang, Song Nan, illus. 1998. (SPA., Illus.). 32p. (J). (gr. 2-4). 16.95 (978-1-57227-056-5(X)) Pan Asia Pubns. (USA), Inc.

—The Ballad of Mulan. Zhang, Song Nan, illus. 1998. (Illus.). 32p. (J). (gr. 2-4). (ENG & VIE.). 16.95 (978-1-57227-057-2(8)); (CHI & ENG., 16.95 (978-1-57227-054-1(3)) Pan Asia Pubns. (USA), Inc.

—The Ballad of Mulan: English/Hmong. Moua, Xe S., tr. from SIT. Zhang, Song Nan, illus. 1998. (Illus.). 32p. (J). (gr. 2-4). 16.95 (978-1-57227-058-9(6)) Pan Asia Pubns. (USA), Inc.

—The Legend of Hua Mu Lan. Kobylinski, Paulina & Ngan, Nguyen N., trs. Zhang, Song Nan, illus. 1998. (ENG & SPA., Illus.). 32p. (J). (gr. 2-4). 16.95 (978-1-57227-055-8(1)) Pan Asia Pubns. (USA), Inc.

ASIA—HISTORY

Abazov, Rafis. Tajikistan. 2006. (Cultures of the World Ser.). (Illus.). 144p. (J). (978-0-7614-2012-5(6)) Cavendish, Marshall Corp.

Adams, Simon. Russian Republics. 2005. (Illus.). 44p. (J). (gr. 6-9). lib. bdg. 29.95 (978-1-58340-606-9(9)) Smart Apple Media.

Aspen-Baxter, Linda. Asia. 2005. (Illus.). 32p. (J). (978-1-59036-325-6(6)); lib. bdg. 26.00 (978-1-59036-318-8(3)) Weigl Pubs., Inc.

Barber, Nicola. Everyday Life in the Ancient Arab & Islamic World. 2005. (Uncovering History Ser.). (Illus.). 46p. (J). (gr. 6-9). lib. bdg. 29.95 (978-1-58340-707-3(3)) Smart Apple Media.

Corrigan, Jim. Kazakhstan. 2005. (Growth & Influence of Islam in the Nations of Asia & Central Asia Ser.). (Illus.). 128p. (J). (ps-7). lib. bdg. 25.95 (978-1-59084-882-1(9)) Mason Crest Pubs.

Dillon, Doug. A Brief Political & Geographic History of Asia: Where Are Saigon, Kampuchea, & Burma? 2007. (Places in Time Ser.). (Illus.). 112p. (YA). (gr. 5-10). lib. bdg. 37.10 (***978-1-58415-623-9(6))*** Mitchell Lane Pubs., Inc.

Downing, David. Afghanistan. 2004. (Illus.). 56p. (J). pap. 8.95 (978-1-4034-5523-9(6)); lib. bdg. (978-1-4034-4864-4(7)) Heinemann Library.

Ellis, Deborah. Three Wishes: Palestinian & Israeli Children Speak. 2004. (Illus.). 144p. (J). 16.95 (978-0-88899-554-4(7)) Groundwood Bks. CAN. *Dist:* Perseus Distribution.

Events That Changed the World - 1940-1960. 2003. (Illus.). lib. bdg. 36.20 (978-0-7377-1756-3(4)) Thomson Gale.

Everything You Need to Teach Asia. 2005. (YA). ring bd. 149.95 (978-1-933558-01-1(6)) InspirEd Educators.

Foreign Policy Research Institute Staff, ed. The Growth & Influence of Islam in the Nations of Asia & Central Asia, 17 vols., Set. 2006. (Illus.). 112,128p. (YA). lib. bdg. 441.15 (978-1-59084-832-6(2)) Mason Crest Pubs.

Group/McGraw-Hill, Wright. Amazing Asia, 6 vols. (Book2WebTM Ser.). (gr. 4-8). 36.50 (978-0-322-04437-1(5)) Wright Group, The.

Habeeb, William Mark. Turkmenistan. 2005. (Growth & Influence of Islam in the Nations of Asia & Central Asia Ser.). (Illus.). 128p. (J). lib. bdg. (978-1-59084-886-9(1)) Mason Crest Pubs.

Hart, Joyce. Kim Jong Il: Leader of North Korea. 2007. (J). (***978-1-4042-1901-4(3))*** Rosen Publishing Group, Inc., The.

Ingram, Scott. Kim il Sung. 2003. (History's Villains Ser.). (Illus.). 112p. (J). 28.70 (978-1-4103-0259-5(8) , Blackbirch Pr., Inc.) Thomson Gale.

Kaeter, Margaret. The Caucasian Republics. 2004. (Nations in Transition Ser.). (Illus.). 176p. (YA). (gr. 6-12). 40.00 (978-0-8160-5268-4(9)) Facts On File, Inc.

Kalman, Bobbie & Sjonger, Rebecca. Explora Asia. 2007. (SPA.). 32p. (gr. 6-10). pap. (***978-0-7787-8297-1(2))*** Crabtree Publishing Co.

Kenoyer, Jonathan M. & Heuston, Kimberley Burton. The Ancient South Asian World. 2006. (World in Ancient Times Ser.). 32.95 (978-0-19-522243-2(1)) Oxford Univ. Pr., Inc.

Kenoyer, Jonathan Mark & Heuston, Kimberly. Student Study Guide to the South Asian World. 2005. (World in Ancient Times Ser.). 58p. (YA). 9.95 (978-0-19-522166-4(4)) Oxford Univ. Pr., Inc.

King, David C. Azerbaijan. 2006. (Cultures of the World Ser.). (Illus.). 144p. (J). (978-0-7614-2011-8(8)) Cavendish, Marshall Corp.

Knowlton, MaryLee. Uzbekistan. 2005. (Cultures of the World Ser.). (Illus.). 144p. (J). (978-0-7614-2016-3(9)) Cavendish, Marshall Corp.

Matray, James Irving. Korea Divided: The Thirty-Eighth Parallel & the Demilitarized Zone. 2004. (Arbitrary Borders Ser.). (Illus.). 112p. (gr. 9-13). 35.00 (978-0-7910-7829-7(9) , Chelsea Hse.) Facts On File, Inc.

Miller, Debra A. North Korea. 2004. (Modern Nations of the World Ser.). (Illus.). 112p. (J). 29.95 (978-1-59018-118-8(2) , Lucent Bks.) Thomson Gale.

—United Arab Emirates. 2004. (Modern Nations of the World Ser.). (Illus.). 112p. (YA). (gr. 7-12). lib. bdg. 29.95 (978-1-59018-627-5(3) , Lucent Bks.) Thomson Gale.

NgCheong-Lum, Roseline. Maldives. 2000. (Cultures of the World Ser.). (Illus.). 128p. (gr. 5-12). lib. bdg. 37.07 (978-0-7614-1157-4(7) , Benchmark Bks.) Cavendish, Marshall Corp.

Piddock, Charles. Kazakhstan. 2006. 48p. (J). pap. (978-0-8368-6715-2(7)); lib. bdg. (978-0-8368-6708-4(4)) Stevens, Gareth Inc. (World Almanac Library).

Rutsala, David. The Sea Route to Asia. 2002. (Exploration & Discovery Ser.). (Illus.). 64p. (YA). (gr. 5 up). lib. bdg. (978-1-59084-046-7(1)) Mason Crest Pubs.

Shuter, Jane. The Indus Valley. 2003. (History Opens Windows Ser.). (Illus.). 32p. (J). (gr. 2-4). lib. bdg. 22.79 (978-1-4034-0253-0(1)); pap. 7.50 (978-1-4034-0081-9(4)) Heinemann Library.

Sonnier, Suzanne. Shinto, Spirits, & Shrines: Religion in Japan. 2007. (Lucent Library of Historical Eras:Twentieth-Century Japan Ser.). (Illus.). 128p. (gr. 7-10). 31.20 (***978-1-4205-0029-5(5)*** , Lucent Bks.) Thomson Gale.

Tay, Alan. Welcome to Kazakhstan. 2005. (Welcome to My Country Ser.). (Illus.). 48p. (J). lib. bdg. 26.00 (978-0-8368-3134-4(9)) Stevens, Gareth Inc.

The War at Home: Japan during World War II. 2007. (Lucent Library of Historical Eras:Twentieth-Century Japan Ser.). (Illus.). 128p. (gr. 7-10). 31.20 (***978-1-4205-0027-1(9)*** , Lucent Bks.) Thomson Gale.

Weber, Sandra. Yemen. 2002. (Creation of the Modern Middle East Ser.). (Illus.). 125p. (gr. 6-12). 35.00 (978-0-7910-6513-6(8) , Chelsea Hse.) Facts On File, Inc.

Wells, Donald. The Silk Road. 2004. (Great Journeys Ser.). (Illus.). 32p. (J). lib. bdg. 26.00 (978-1-59036-207-5(1)) Weigl Pubs., Inc.

ASIA, SOUTHEASTERN

see Southeast Asia

ASIAN AMERICANS

Barr, Linda. Long Road to Freedom: Journey of the Hmong. (High Five Reading Ser.). (J). (ps-k). 2005. (Illus.). 64p. lib. bdg. 23.93 (978-0-7368-3880-1(5)); 2004. pap. (978-0-7368-3852-8(X)) Capstone Pr., Inc.

Cha, Dia. Dia's Story Cloth: Diav Daim Paj Ntaub Dab Neeg/Dlav Dlaim Paaj Ntaub Lug Nruag. 2002. (ENG., Illus.). (J). pap. 6.95 (978-1-931016-11-7(9) , MHC-11-9) Minnesota Humanities Commission.

Corrigan, Jim. Filipino Immigration. 2003. (Changing Face of North America Ser.). (Illus.). 112p. (YA). lib. bdg. (978-1-59084-684-1(2)) Mason Crest Pubs.

Darraj, Susan Muaddi. Amy Tan. 2007. (Asian Americans of Achievement Ser.). 112p. (gr. 6-12). 30.00 (978-0-7910-9269-9(0) , Chelsea Hse.) Facts On File, Inc.

Glencoe McGraw-Hill Staff. Glencoe Asian American Literature. 2001. 397p. 31.96 (978-0-07-822929-9(4) , 9780078229299) Glencoe/McGraw-Hill.

Hansen-Krening, Nancy, et al, eds. Kaleidoscope: A Multicultural Booklist for Grades K-8. 4th ed. 2003. (NCTE Bibliography Ser.). (Illus.). 118p. (J). pap. 30.95 (978-0-8141-2539-7(5) , 25395) National Council of Teachers of English.

Ishizuka, Kathy. Asian-American Authors. 2000. (Collective Biographies Ser.). (Illus.). 128p. (YA). (gr. 6-12). lib. bdg. 26.60 (978-0-7660-1376-6(6)) Enslow Pubs., Inc.

Kule, Elaine A. Kristi Yamaguchi. 2005. (Asian-American Biographies Ser.). (Illus.). 64p. (J). (gr. 6-9). pap. 9.50 (978-1-4109-1130-8(6)) Raintree.

Louie, Ai-Ling. Vera Wang Queen of Fashion; Amazing Chinese American: Biographies of Amazing Asian Americans. 2007. (Illus.). 48p. (J). pap. 12.99 (***978-0-9787465-3-7(8)***) Dragoneagle Pr.

Marvis, Barbara J. Famous People of Asian Ancestry, 5 vols. Incl. Vol. I. 1993. pap. 10.95 (978-1-883845-06-3(8)); Vol. II. 1993. pap. 10.95 (978-1-883845-07-0(6)); Vol. III. (Illus.). 1993. pap. 10.95 (978-1-883845-08-7(4)); Vol. IV. (Illus.). 1994. pap. 10.95 (978-1-883845-09-4(2)); Vol. V. (Illus.). 1994. pap. 10.95 (978-1-883845-11-7(4)); 96p. (YA). (gr. 5 up). (Contemporary American Success Stories Ser.). (Illus.). Set pap. 54.75 (978-1-883845-13-1(0)) Mitchell Lane Pubs., Inc.

Media Projects, Inc., Staff. Almanac of Asian American History, 2 vols. 2004. (Illus.). 144p. (J). (gr. 6-8). stu. ed. 83.95 (978-0-313-32602-8(9) , MS2602, Greenwood Pr.) Greenwood Publishing Group, Inc.

Media Projects, Inc., Staff, contrib. by. Students Almanac of Asian American History, 2 vols. 2003. (Illus.). (J). (978-0-313-32603-5(7)); (978-0-313-32604-2(5)) Greenwood Publishing Group, Inc. (Greenwood Pr.).

Moore, Dave, compiled by. A Free People: Tracing Our Hmong Roots. 2nd ed. 2003. (ENG., Illus.). 144p. (J). per. 14.95 (978-1-888194-42-5(1)) Master Communications, Inc.

Nam, Vickie. A Yell-Oh Girls! Emerging Voices Explore Culture, Identity & Growing up Asian. 2001. (gr. 7-12). lib. bdg. 22.25 (978-0-613-49389-5(3)) Tandem Library Bks.

Petrillo, Valerie. A Kid's Guide to Asian American History: More Than 70 Activities. 2007. (Kid's Guide Ser.). 256p. (J). pap. 14.95 (***978-1-55652-634-3(2)***) Chicago Review Pr., Inc.

Price Hossell, Karen. Thai Americans. 2004. (We Are America Ser.). (Illus.). 32p. (J). lib. bdg. 24.22 (978-1-4034-5025-8(0)) Heinemann Library.

Smith, Carter & Lindroth, David, eds. Asian-American Experience on File. 1999. (Ethnic Minorities in America Ser.: Vol. 2). (Illus.). 150p. (YA). (gr. 6-12). ring bd. 140.00 (978-0-8160-3696-7(9)) Facts On File, Inc.

Stauffer, Stacey & Koslow, Philip. Histories. 1998. (Asian American Experience Ser.). (YA). (gr. 5 up). (978-0-7910-4457-5(2) , Chelsea Hse.) Facts On File, Inc.

Sterngass, Jon. Filipino Americans. 2007. (New Immigrants Ser.). (Illus.). 144p. (J). (gr. 6-12). 27.95 (978-0-7910-8791-6(3) , Chelsea Hse.) Facts On File, Inc.

Yoder, Carolyn. Filipino Americans. 2003. (We Are America Ser.). (Illus.). 32p. (J). (gr. 2-4). pap. 6.95 (978-1-4034-0419-0(4)); lib. bdg. (978-1-4034-0164-9(0)) Heinemann Library.

—Filipino Americans. 2003. (gr. k-3). lib. bdg. 15.25 (978-0-613-60869-5(0)) Tandem Library Bks.

Yount, Lisa. Asian-American Scientists. 1998. (American Profiles Ser.). (Illus.). 144p. (J). (gr. 5-12). 25.00 (978-0-8160-3756-8(6)) Facts On File, Inc.

ASIAN AMERICANS—FICTION

Asai, Carrie. The Book of the Pearl. Verhoye, Annabelle & Alarcao, Renato, illus. 2003. (Samurai Girl Ser.: Bk. 3). 240p. (YA). pap. 6.99 (978-0-689-86432-2(9) , Simon Pulse) Simon & Schuster Children's Publishing.

—The Book of the Sword. Verhoye, Annabelle, illus. 2003. (Samurai Girl Ser.). 224p. (YA). pap. 6.99 (978-0-689-85948-9(1) , Simon Pulse) Simon & Schuster Children's Publishing.

Asai, Carrie & Gray, Mitchel. The Book of the Wind. Verhoye, Annabelle & Alarcao, Renato, illus. 2003. (Samurai Girl Ser.). 224p. (YA). pap. 6.99 (978-0-689-86433-9(7) , Simon Pulse) Simon & Schuster Children's Publishing.

Blackaby, Susan. Jake Skates. Olin, Troy, illus. 2007. (Read-It! Readers Ser.). (J). 19.93 (978-1-4048-2412-6(X)) Picture Window Bks.

—Tricky Twins. Epstein, Len, illus. 2006. (Read-It! Readers Ser.). (J). 19.93 (978-1-4048-2419-5(7)) Picture Window Bks.

Brown, Jackie. Little Cricket. 2004. (Illus.). 224p. (gr. 4-7). 15.99 (978-0-7868-1852-5(2)) Hyperion Bks. for Children.

Chiu, Esther. The Lobster & the Sea. Takahashi, Mika, illus. 1998. 32p. (J). (gr. 2-5). pap. 14.95 (978-1-879965-14-0(3)) Polychrome Publishing Corp.

Dougherty, Terri. The Flying Fish. Visser, Kristy, illus. 2006. (Read-It! Readers Ser.). (J). 19.93 (978-1-4048-2410-2(3)) Picture Window Bks.

Lewis, Rose A. Every Year on Your Birthday. Dyer, Jane, illus. 2007. 32p. (J). (ps-3). 16.99 (978-0-316-52552-7(9)) Little Brown & Co.

Namioka, Lensey. Yang the Second & Her Secret Admirers. 2000. (978-0-606-18794-7(4)) Tandem Library Bks.

Shaskan, Trisha Speed. Another Pet. Vincent, Kenneth, illus. 2006. (Read-It! Readers Ser.). (J). 19.93 (978-1-4048-2404-1(9)) Picture Window Bks.

Sheth, Kashmira. Blue Jasmine. 2004. 192p. (gr. 4-7). 15.99 (978-0-7868-1855-6(7)) Hyperion Bks. for Children.

Sonnenblick, Jordan. Zen & the Art of Faking It. 2007. 272p. (J). pap. 16.99 (***978-0-439-83707-1(3)*** , Scholastic Pr.) Scholastic, Inc.

Suen, Anastasia. Toddler Two. Cheon, Winnie, illus. (J). 2002. 20p. bds. 6.95 (978-1-58430-052-6(3)); 2000. 22p. 6.95 (978-1-58430-015-1(9)) Lee & Low Bks., Inc.

—Toddler Two: Dos Anos. Cheon, Winnie, illus. 2002. (ENG & SPA.). (J). bds. 5.95 (978-1-58430-054-0(X)) Lee & Low Bks., Inc.

Yamanaka, Lois-Ann. Name Me Nobody. 2000. 240p. (gr. 8-17). pap. 5.99 (978-0-7868-1466-4(7)) Disney Pr.

—Name Me Nobody. 2000. (gr. 7-12). lib. bdg. 14.15 (978-0-613-31521-0(9)) Tandem Library Bks.

ASIMOV, ISAAC, 1920-1992

Boerst, William J. Isaac Asimov: Writer of the Future. 2004. (World Writers Ser.). (Illus.). 112p. (YA). (gr. 6-12). 23.95 (978-1-883846-32-9(3) , First Biographies) Reynolds, Morgan Inc.

Judson, Karen. Isaac Asimov: Master of Science Fiction. 1998. (People to Know Ser.). (Illus.). 112p. (YA). (gr. 6-12). lib. bdg. 26.60 (978-0-7660-1031-4(7)) Enslow Pubs., Inc.

ASSASSINATION

see also names of persons and groups of persons with the subdivision Assassination, e.g. Presidents—United States—Assassination

Kingsbury, Robert. The Assassination of James A. Garfield. 2003. (Library of Political Assassinations). (Illus.). 64p. (YA). (gr. 7-12). lib. bdg. 26.50 (978-0-8239-3540-6(X)) Rosen Publishing Group, Inc., The.

Townsend, John. Kidnappers & Assassins. 48p. (J). 2006. pap. 8.90 (978-1-4109-1432-3(1)); 2005. lib. bdg. 31.43 (978-1-4109-1426-2(7)) Raintree.

ASSEMBLY, RIGHT OF

see also Freedom of Speech

Smith, Rich. First Amendment: The Right of Expression. 2007. (Bill of Rights Ser.). (ENG., Illus.). 32p. (J). (gr. 4-8). lib. bdg. 25.65 (***978-1-59928-914-4(8)*** , ABDO & Daughters) ABDO Publishing Co.

ASSERTIVENESS (PSYCHOLOGY)

Cordes, Helen. Girl Power in the Mirror: Your Body, Your Self. 1999. (Girl Power Ser.). (Illus.). 64p. (YA). (gr. 6-9). lib. bdg. (978-0-8225-2691-9(3) , Lerner Pubns.) Lerner Publishing Group.

Havelin, Kate. Assertiveness: "How Can I Say What I Mean?" 1999. (Perspectives on Relationships Ser.). (Illus.). 64p. (J). (gr. 4-6). lib. bdg. 23.93 (978-0-7368-0290-1(8) , LifeMatters Bks.) Capstone Pr., Inc.

Kaufman, Gershen, et al. Stick up for Yourself! Every Kid's Guide to Personal Power & Positive Self-Esteem. 2nd rev. ed. 2004. (Illus.). 128p. (YA). (gr. 3-7). pap. 11.95 (978-1-57542-068-4(6)) Free Spirit Publishing, Inc.

Ward, Kristin. Learning about Assertiveness from the Life of Oprah Winfrey. 1999. (Character Building Book Ser.). (Illus.). 24p. (J). (gr. 3). lib. bdg. 18.75 (978-0-8239-5348-6(3) , PowerKids Pr.) Rosen Publishing Group, Inc., The.

ASSERTIVENESS (PSYCHOLOGY)—FICTION

Asher, Sandy. Too Many Frogs! Graves, Keith, illus. 2005. 32p. (J). (ps-1). 15.99 (978-0-399-23978-6(2) , Philomel) Penguin Group (USA) Inc.

Berenstain, Stan & Berenstain, Jan. The Berenstain Bears & the Bully. Berenstain, Stan & Berenstain, Jan, illus. 2002. (Berenstain Bears First Time Bks.). (Illus.). (J). 11.19 (978-0-7587-0947-9(1)) Book Wholesalers, Inc.

Brumbeau, Jeff. Miss Hunnicutt's Hat. de Marcken, Gail, illus. 2003. 48p. (J). (gr. k-3). pap. 16.95 (978-0-439-31895-2(5) , Orchard Bks.) Scholastic, Inc.

Gormley, Beatrice. More Fifth Grade Magic. McCully, Emily Arnold, illus. 2001. 116p. (YA). (gr. 4-7). pap. 9.95 (978-0-595-15203-2(1) , Backinprint.com) iUniverse, Inc.

Mackler, Carolyn. The Earth, My Butt & Other Big Round Things. 2003. (Illus.). 256p. (YA). (gr. 9). 15.99 (978-0-7636-1958-9(2)) Candlewick Pr.

—The Earth, My Butt, & Other Big Round Things. 2005. 256p. (YA). (gr. 9 up). reprint ed. pap. 8.99 (978-0-7636-2091-2(2)) Candlewick Pr.

MacRae, Tom. The Opposite. Odriozola, Elena, illus. 2006. 32p. (J). 15.95 (978-1-56145-371-9(4) , Peachtree Junior) Peachtree Pubs., Ltd.

Moss, Peggy. Say Something. Lyon, Lea, illus. 2005. 32p. (J). (gr. 2-6). 16.95 (978-0-88448-261-1(8)) Tilbury Hse. Pubs.

ASSIMILATION (SOCIOLOGY)—FICTION

Krishnaswami, Uma. Chachaji's Cup. Sitaraman, Soumya, illus. 2003. 32p. (J). (gr. 1 up). 16.95 (978-0-89239-178-3(2)) Children's Bk. Pr.

Scott, Mary Ann. New Girl. 2003. 208p. (YA). (978-1-55041-725-8(8)) Fitzhenry & Whiteside, Ltd.

ASSISI (ITALY)

Alves, Mary E. & Kelley, Patrick, illus. Saint Francis of Assisi: Gentle Revolutionary. rev. ed. 1999. (Encounter the Saints Ser.: No. 4). 120p. (J). (gr. 5-9). pap. 5.95 (978-0-8198-7030-8(7) , 332-342) Pauline Bks. & Media.

Gray, Tricia. The Wondrous Adventures of St. Francis of Assisi. rev. ed. 2003. (Illus.). 164p. (J). pap. 14.95 (978-0-86716-480-0(8)) St. Anthony Messenger Pr. & Franciscan Communications.

Kennedy, Robert F., Jr. Saint Francis of Assisi: A Life of Joy. Nolan, Dennis, illus. 2005. 32p. (J). (gr. k-17). 18.99 (978-0-7868-1875-4(1)) Hyperion Bks. for Children.

ASSISTANCE TO UNDERDEVELOPED AREAS

see Economic Assistance

ASSISTED SUICIDE

see also Euthanasia

Engdahl, Sylvia Louise. Euthanasia. 2006. 192p. (J). (gr. 10-12). 36.20 (978-0-7377-3251-1(2)); pap. 24.95 (978-0-7377-3252-8(0)) Thomson Gale. (Greenhaven Pr., Inc.).

Fireside, Bryna J. & Ferguson, John E. The Right to Die. 2007. (Point/Counterpoint Ser.). 112p. (J). (gr. 9). 32.95 (***978-0-7910-9287-3(9)*** , Chelsea Hse.) Facts On File, Inc.

Lauri S. Friedman. Assisted Suicide. 2006. (Writing the Critical Essay Ser.). (Illus.). 244p. (J). 29.95 (978-0-7377-3640-3(2) , Greenhaven Pr., Inc.) Thomson Gale.

Marzilli, Alan. Physician-Assisted Suicide. 2003. (Point/Counterpoint Ser.). (Illus.). 112p. (gr. 9-13). 32.95 (978-0-7910-7485-5(4) , Chelsea Hse.) Facts On File, Inc.

Ondrey, James H. Physician-Assisted Suicide. 2006. (Illus.). 128p. (J). (gr. 10-12). 21.20 (978-0-7377-3246-7(6)); pap. 29.95 (978-0-7377-3245-0(8)) Thomson Gale. (Greenhaven Pr., Inc.).

Walker, Richard. The Right to Die? 2005. (Illus.). 32p. (J). (gr. 5-9). lib. bdg. 27.10 (978-1-932889-56-7(6)) Sea-To-Sea Pubns.

ASSYRIA

Matthews, Rupert. You Wouldn't Want to Be an Assyrian Soldier! An Ancient Army You'd Rather Not Join. Antram, David, illus. 2007. (You Wouldn't Want to Ser.). 32p. (J). (gr. 2-5). 28.50 (***978-0-531-18727-2(6)*** , Watts, Franklin) Scholastic Library Publishing.

ASSYRIA—ANTIQUITIES

Oakes, Lorna. Assyria & Mesopotamia. 2001. (Step into Ser.). (Illus.). 64p. (gr. 3-7). 14.95 (978-0-7548-0656-1(1) , Lorenz Bks.) Anness Publishing, Inc.

ASSYRIA—FICTION

Bower, Tamara. How the Amazon Queen Fought the Prince of Egypt. Bower, Tamara, illus. 2005. (Illus.). 40p. (J). (gr. 2-6). 17.99 (978-0-689-84434-8(4) , Atheneum) Simon & Schuster Children's Publishing.

ASTERIX (FICTITIOUS CHARACTER)—FICTION

Distribooks Inc. Staff. Asterix Bind-Ups: Asterix & Friends. 1998. (Asterix Ser.). (Illus.). 240p. (J). (978-0-340-72755-3(1) , Hodder & Stoughton) Hodder General Publishing Division.

Goscinny, René. Absolutely Asterix. 1998. (Illus.). 204p. (J). 24.95 (978-0-340-72756-0(X) , Hodder & Stoughton) Hodder General Publishing Division GBR. *Dist:* Trafalgar Square Publishing.

—Asterix & Caesar's Gift. Uderzo, Albert, illus. 2005. 48p. 12.95 (978-0-7528-6645-1(1)) Orion Bks. Ltd. GBR. *Dist:* Sterling Publishing Co., Inc.

—Asterix & Cleopatra. Uderzo, Albert, illus. 2004. 48p. 12.95 (978-0-7528-6606-2(0)) Orion Bks. Ltd. GBR. *Dist:* Sterling Publishing Co., Inc.

—Asterix & Obelix All at Sea. Uderzo, Albert, illus. 2002. 48p. (978-0-7528-4717-7(1)) Orion Media.

—Asterix & the Banquet. Uderzo, Albert, illus. 2004. 48p. 12.95 (978-0-7528-6608-6(7)) Orion Bks. Ltd. GBR. *Dist:* Sterling Publishing Co., Inc.

—Asterix & the Big Fight. Uderzo, Albert, illus. 2004. 48p. 12.95 (978-0-7528-6616-1(8)) Orion Bks. Ltd. GBR. *Dist:* Sterling Publishing Co., Inc.

—Asterix & the Cauldron. Uderzo, Albert, illus. 2004. 48p. 12.95 (978-0-7528-6628-4(1)) Orion Bks. Ltd. GBR. *Dist:* Sterling Publishing Co., Inc.

—Asterix & the Cheiftan's Sheild. Uderzo, Albert, illus. 2004. 48p. 12.95 (978-0-7528-6624-6(9)) Orion Bks. Ltd. GBR. *Dist:* Sterling Publishing Co., Inc.

—Asterix & the Goths. Uderzo, Albert, illus. 2004. 48p. 12.95 (978-0-7528-6614-7(1)) Orion Bks. Ltd. GBR. *Dist:* Sterling Publishing Co., Inc.

—Asterix & the Great Crossing. Uderzo, Albert, illus. 2005. 48p. 12.95 (978-0-7528-6647-5(8)); pap. 9.95 (978-0-7528-6648-2(6)) Orion Bks. Ltd. GBR. *Dist:* Sterling Publishing Co., Inc.

—Asterix & the Great Divide. Uderzo, Albert, illus. 2007. 48p. (***978-0-7528-4712-2(0)***) Orion Media.

—Asterix & the Normans. (Illus.). (J). pap. 9.95 (978-0-02-497290-3(8)) International Language Centre.

—Asterix & the Normans. Uderzo, Albert, illus. 2004. 48p. 12.95 (978-0-7528-6622-2(2)) Orion Bks. Ltd. GBR. *Dist:* Sterling Publishing Co., Inc.

—Asterix & the Roman Agent. Uderzo, Albert, illus. 2004. 48p. 12.95 (978-0-7528-6632-1(X)) Orion Bks. Ltd. GBR. *Dist:* Sterling Publishing Co., Inc.

—Asterix at the Olympic Games. Uderzo, Albert, illus. 2004. 48p. 12.95 (978-0-7528-6626-0(5)) Orion Bks. Ltd. GBR. *Dist:* Sterling Publishing Co., Inc.

—Asterix aux Jeux Olympiques. (FRE.). (J). pap. 21.95 (***978-2-01-210144-9(5)***) Hachette Groupe Livre FRA. *Dist:* Distribooks, Inc.

—Asterix en Hispanie. (FRE.). (J). pap. 21.95 (***978-2-01-210146-3(1)***) Hachette Groupe Livre FRA. *Dist:* Distribooks, Inc.

—Asterix et Cleopatre. (FRE.). (J). pap. 21.95 (***978-2-01-210138-8(0)***); (Illus.). 21.95 (978-2-01-210111-1(9)) Hachette Groupe Livre FRA. *Dist:* Distribooks, Inc.

—Asterix et les Normaands. (FRE.). (J). pap. 21.95 (***978-2-01-210141-8(0)***) Hachette Groupe Livre FRA. *Dist:* Distribooks, Inc.

—Asterix in Belgium. Uderzo, Albert, illus. 2005. 48p. 12.95 (978-0-7528-6649-9(4)); pap. 9.95 (978-0-7528-6650-5(8)) Orion Bks. Ltd. GBR. *Dist:* Sterling Publishing Co., Inc.

—Asterix in Britain. Uderzo, Albert, illus. 2004. 48p. 12.95 (978-0-7528-6618-5(4)) Orion Bks. Ltd. GBR. *Dist:* Sterling Publishing Co., Inc.

—Asterix in Corsica. Uderzo, Albert, illus. 2005. 48p. 12.95 (978-0-7528-6643-7(5)) Orion Bks. Ltd. GBR. *Dist:* Sterling Publishing Co., Inc.

—Asterix in Spain. Uderzo, Albert, illus. 2004. 48p. 12.95 (978-0-7528-6630-7(3)) Orion Bks. Ltd. GBR. *Dist:* Sterling Publishing Co., Inc.

—Asterix in Switzerland. Uderzo, Albert, illus. 2004. 48p. 12.95 (978-0-7528-6634-5(6)) Orion Bks. Ltd. GBR. *Dist:* Sterling Publishing Co., Inc.

—Asterix le Gaulois. 2005. audio compact disk 45.00 (978-0-320-06624-5(X)) French & European Pubns., Inc.

—Asterix le Gaulois. (FRE.). (J). pap. 21.95 (***978-2-01-210133-3(X)***) Hachette Groupe Livre FRA. *Dist:* Distribooks, Inc.

—Asterix the Gaul. Uderzo, Albert, illus. 2004. 48p. 12.95 (978-0-7528-6604-8(4)) Orion Bks. Ltd. GBR. *Dist:* Sterling Publishing Co., Inc.

—Asterix the Gladiator. Uderzo, Albert, illus. 2004. 48p. 12.95 (978-0-7528-6610-9(9)) Orion Bks. Ltd. GBR. *Dist:* Sterling Publishing Co., Inc.

—Asterix the Legionary. Uderzo, Albert, illus. 2004. 48p. 12.95 (978-0-7528-6620-8(6)) Orion Bks. Ltd. GBR. *Dist:* Sterling Publishing Co., Inc.

—Asterix the Mansions of the Gods. Uderzo, Albert, illus. 2005. 48p. 12.95 (978-0-7528-6638-3(9)) Orion Bks. Ltd. GBR. *Dist:* Sterling Publishing Co., Inc.

—Obelix & Co. Uderzo, Albert, illus. 2005. 48p. (J). 12.95 (978-0-7528-6651-2(6)) Orion Bks. Ltd. GBR. *Dist:* Sterling Publishing Co., Inc.

Goscinny, René & Uderzo. Asterix French. 21.95 (978-2-01-210022-0(8)) Hachette Groupe Livre FRA. *Dist:* Distribooks, Inc.

Goscinny, René & Uderzo, Albert. Asterix & Caesar's Gift. 2005. (Illus.). 48p. pap. 9.95 (978-0-7528-6646-8(X)) Orion Bks. Ltd. GBR. *Dist:* Sterling Publishing Co., Inc.

—Asterix & Cleopatra. Uderzo, Albert, illus. 2004. (Illus.). 48p. pap. 9.95 (978-0-7528-6607-9(9)) Orion Bks. Ltd. GBR. *Dist:* Sterling Publishing Co., Inc.

—Asterix & the Banquet. Uderzo, Albert, illus. 2004. (Illus.). 48p. pap. 9.95 (978-0-7528-6609-3(5)) Orion Bks. Ltd. GBR. *Dist:* Sterling Publishing Co., Inc.

—Asterix & the Big Fight. Uderzo, Albert, illus. 2004. (Illus.). 48p. pap. 9.95 (978-0-7528-6617-8(6)) Orion Bks. Ltd. GBR. *Dist:* Sterling Publishing Co., Inc.

—Asterix & the Cauldron. Uderzo, Albert, illus. 2004. (Illus.). 48p. pap. 9.95 (978-0-7528-6629-1(X)) Orion Bks. Ltd. GBR. *Dist:* Sterling Publishing Co., Inc.

—Asterix & the Chieftain's Shield. Uderzo, Albert, illus. 2004. (Illus.). 48p. pap. 9.95 (978-0-7528-6625-3(7)) Orion Bks. Ltd. GBR. *Dist:* Sterling Publishing Co., Inc.

—Asterix & the Falling Sky. (Illus.). 48p. 2006. pap. 9.95 (978-0-7528-7548-4(5)); 2005. 12.95 (978-0-7528-7301-5(6)) Orion Bks. Ltd. GBR. *Dist:* Sterling Publishing Co., Inc.

—Asterix & the Golden Sickle. 2004. (Illus.). 48p. 12.95 (978-0-7528-6612-3(5)) Orion Bks. Ltd. GBR. *Dist:* Sterling Publishing Co., Inc.

—Asterix & the Golden Sickle. Uderzo, Albert, illus. 2004. (Illus.). 48p. pap. 9.95 (978-0-7528-6613-0(3)) Orion Bks. Ltd. GBR. *Dist:* Sterling Publishing Co., Inc.

—Asterix & the Goths. Uderzo, Albert, illus. 2004. (Illus.). 48p. pap. 9.95 (978-0-7528-6615-4(X)) Orion Bks. Ltd. GBR. *Dist:* Sterling Publishing Co., Inc.

—Asterix & the Laurel Wreath. Uderzo, Albert, illus. 2005. (Illus.). 48p. 12.95 (978-0-7528-6636-9(2)); pap. 9.95 (978-0-7528-6637-6(0)) Orion Bks. Ltd. GBR. *Dist:* Sterling Publishing Co., Inc.

—Asterix & the Normans. Uderzo, Albert, illus. 2004. (Illus.). 48p. pap. 9.95 (978-0-7528-6623-9(0)) Orion Bks. Ltd. GBR. *Dist:* Sterling Publishing Co., Inc.

—Asterix & the Roman Agent. Uderzo, Albert, illus. 2004. (Illus.). 48p. pap. 9.95 (978-0-7528-6633-8(8)) Orion Bks. Ltd. GBR. *Dist:* Sterling Publishing Co., Inc.

—Asterix & the Soothsayer. Uderzo, Albert, illus. 2005. (Illus.). 48p. 12.95 (978-0-7528-6641-3(9)); pap. 9.95 (978-0-7528-6642-0(7)) Orion Bks. Ltd. GBR. *Dist:* Sterling Publishing Co., Inc.

—Asterix & the Vikings. 2007. (Illus.). 72p. per. 9.95 (***978-0-7528-8876-7(5)***) Orion Bks. Ltd. GBR. *Dist:* Sterling Publishing Co., Inc.

—Asterix at the Olympic Games. Uderzo, Albert, illus. 2004. (Illus.). 48p. pap. 9.95 (978-0-7528-6627-7(3)) Orion Bks. Ltd. GBR. *Dist:* Sterling Publishing Co., Inc.

—Asterix Chez les Helvetes. (FRE.). (J). pap. 21.95 (978-2-01-210016-9(3)) Hachette Groupe Livre FRA. *Dist:* Distribooks, Inc.

—Asterix en Corse. (FRE.). 21.95 (978-2-01-210020-6(1)) Hachette Groupe Livre FRA. *Dist:* Distribooks, Inc.

—Asterix en Hispanie. (FRE.). 21.95 (978-2-01-210014-5(7)) Hachette Groupe Livre FRA. *Dist:* Distribooks, Inc.

—Asterix et le Bombe. (FRE.). 21.95 (978-2-01-210008-4(2)) Hachette Groupe Livre FRA. *Dist:* Distribooks, Inc.

—Asterix French. 21.95 (978-2-01-210009-1(0)) Hachette Groupe Livre FRA. *Dist:* Distribooks, Inc.

—Asterix in Britain. Uderzo, Albert, illus. 2004. (Illus.). 48p. pap. 9.95 (978-0-7528-6619-2(2)) Orion Bks. Ltd. GBR. *Dist:* Sterling Publishing Co., Inc.

—Asterix in Spain. Uderzo, Albert, illus. 2004. (Illus.). 48p. pap. 9.95 (978-0-7528-6631-4(1)) Orion Bks. Ltd. GBR. *Dist:* Sterling Publishing Co., Inc.

—Asterix in Switzerland. Uderzo, Albert, illus. 2004. (Illus.). 48p. pap. 9.95 (978-0-7528-6635-2(4)) Orion Bks. Ltd. GBR. *Dist:* Sterling Publishing Co., Inc.

—Asterix Omnibus 1. 2008. (Illus.). 144p. pap. 19.95 (***978-0-7528-9155-2(3)***) Orion Bks. Ltd. GBR. *Dist:* Sterling Publishing Co., Inc.

—Asterix Omnibus 2: Three Great Asterix Stories in One Volume. 2008. (Illus.). 144p. per. 19.95 (***978-0-7528-9158-3(8)***) Orion Bks. Ltd. GBR. *Dist:* Sterling Publishing Co., Inc.

—Asterix the Gaul. Uderzo, Albert, illus. 2004. (Illus.). 48p. pap. 9.95 (978-0-7528-6605-5(2)) Orion Bks. Ltd. GBR. *Dist:* Sterling Publishing Co., Inc.

—Asterix the Gladiator. Uderzo, Albert, illus. 2004. (Illus.). 48p. pap. 9.95 (978-0-7528-6611-6(7)) Orion Bks. Ltd. GBR. *Dist:* Sterling Publishing Co., Inc.

—Asterix the Legionary. Uderzo, Albert, illus. 2004. (Illus.). 48p. pap. 9.95 (978-0-7528-6621-5(4)) Orion Bks. Ltd. GBR. *Dist:* Sterling Publishing Co., Inc.

Goscinny, René & Uderzo, M. Asterix el Galo. (SPA., Illus.). (J). (gr. 7-10). 24.95 (978-0-8288-4933-3(1)) French & European Pubns., Inc.

—Streit um Asterix. (GER., Illus.). (J). 24.95 (978-0-8288-4906-7(4)) French & European Pubns., Inc.

Uderzo, Albert. Asterix & Son. Bell, Anthea & Hockbridge, Derek, trs. from FRE. 2002. (Asterix Ser.). (Illus.). 48p. pap. 9.95 (978-0-7528-4775-7(9)) Orion Bks. Ltd. GBR. *Dist:* Sterling Publishing Co., Inc.

Uderzo, Albert & Goscinny, René. Asterix & Obelix All at Sea. 2002. (Asterix Ser.). (Illus.). 48p. pap. 9.95 (978-0-7528-4778-8(3)) Orion Bks. Ltd. GBR. *Dist:* Sterling Publishing Co., Inc.

—Asterix & Son. 2007. (Illus.). 48p. (***978-0-7528-4714-6(7)***) Orion Media.

—Asterix & the Actress. 2002. (Asterix Ser.). (Illus.). 48p. pap. 9.95 (978-0-7528-4658-3(2)) Orion Bks. Ltd. GBR. *Dist:* Sterling Publishing Co., Inc.

—Asterix & the Actress. Bell, Anthea & Hockridge, Derek, trs. from FRE. 2001. (Illus.). 48p. (J). (gr. 5). (978-0-7528-4657-6(4)) Orion Media.

—Asterix & the Magic Carpet. 2002. (Asterix Ser.). (Illus.). 48p. pap. 9.95 (978-0-7528-4776-4(7)) Orion Bks. Ltd. GBR. *Dist:* Sterling Publishing Co., Inc.

—Asterix & the Magic Carpet. 2002. (Illus.). 48p. (978-0-7528-4715-3(5)) Orion Media.

—Asterix & the Secret Weapon. 2002. (Asterix Ser.). (Illus.). 48p. pap. 9.95 (978-0-7528-4777-1(5)) Orion Bks. Ltd. GBR. *Dist:* Sterling Publishing Co., Inc.

—Asterix & the Secret Weapon. 2002. (Illus.). 48p. (978-0-7528-4716-0(3)) Orion Media.

ASTHMA

Asthma in Action. 2005. (Book Treks Ser.). (J). (gr. 3 up). stu. ed. 34.95 (978-0-673-62843-5(4)) Celebration Pr.

Baldwin, Carol. Asthma. 2003. (Health Matters Ser.). (Illus.). 32p. (J). (gr. 3-5). lib. bdg. 24.22 (978-1-4034-0248-6(5)) Heinemann Library.

Bee, Peta. Living with Asthma. (J). 2000. 32 p. lib. bdg. 27.12 (978-0-8172-5568-8(0)); 1999. (Illus.). 32p. (gr. 1-5). lib. bdg. 25.69 (978-0-8172-5576-3(1)) Raintree.

Berger, William E. Teen's Guide to Living with Asthma. 2007. (Teen's Guides). 192p. (J). (gr. 6-12). 34.95 (***978-0-8160-6483-0(0)***) Facts On File, Inc.

Bjorklund, Ruth. Asthma. 2004. (Illus.). 64p. (J). 28.50 (978-0-7614-1803-0(2) , Benchmark Bks.) Cavendish, Marshall Corp.

Boldt, Mark. U-Do Book Project "Science Fair" Vol. 7: An Asthma Action Plan U-Do Book. 2001. (Illus.). 24p. (J). (gr. k-8). pap. (978-0-9662556-6-9(6)) Boldt.Entertainment.

Bryan, Jenny. Asthma. 2003. (Just the Facts Ser.). (Illus.). 56p. (J). lib. bdg. (978-1-4034-4599-5(0)) Heinemann Library.

Ford, Jean. Breathe Easy! A Teen's Guide to Allergies & Asthma. 2004. (Science of Health Ser.). (Illus.). 128p. (J). (978-1-59084-842-5(X)) Mason Crest Pubs.

Glaser, Jason. Asthma. 2005. (First Facts Ser.). (Illus.). 24p. (J). (978-0-7368-4287-7(X) , 1243922) Capstone Pr., Inc.

Gold, Susan Dudley. Asthma. 2000. (Health Watch Ser.). (Illus.). 48p. (J). (gr. 4-10). lib. bdg. 23.93 (978-0-7660-1656-9(0)) Enslow Pubs., Inc.

Gordon, Sharon. Asthma. 2003. (Rookie Read-About Health Ser.). (Illus.). (J). (gr. k-2). 31p. pap. 5.95 (978-0-516-27395-2(7)); 32p. 20.50 (978-0-516-22582-1(0)) Scholastic Library Publishing. (Children's Pr.).

—Asthma. 2003. (gr. k-3). lib. bdg. 14.10 (978-0-613-67870-4(2)) Tandem Library Bks.

Gosselin, Kim. Taking Asthma to School. Mitchell, Barbara, ed. Freedman, Moss, illus. 2nd rev. ed. 1998. (Special Kids in School Ser.: Vol. 2). 24p. (J). (gr. k-5). pap. 11.95 (978-1-891383-01-4(9)) JayJo Bks., LLC.

Greenberg, Alissa. Asthma. 2000. (Single Titles Ser.). (Illus.). 128p. (J). (gr. 9-12). 21.00 (978-0-531-11331-8(0) , Watts, Franklin) Scholastic Library Publishing.

Hyde, Margaret. Living with Asthma: A Guide for Parents & Children. 2000. (gr. 3-6). lib. bdg. 17.60 (978-0-613-26043-5(0)) Tandem Library Bks.

Hyde, Margaret O. & Forsyth, Elizabeth. Living with Asthma: A Guide for Parents & Children. 2000. (Illus.). 112p. (J). (gr. 3-7). pap. 8.95 (978-0-8027-7585-6(3)) Walker & Co.

Lennard-Brown, Sarah. Asthma. 2002. (Health Issues Ser.). (Illus.). 64p. (J). (gr. 6-8). lib. bdg. 28.54 (978-0-7398-5218-7(3)) Raintree.

Levene, Anna. My Friend Has Asthma. 2003. (Illus.). (J). (gr. 3-5). lib. bdg. 16.95 (978-1-932333-25-1(8)) Chrysalis Education.

Llewellyn, Claire. Asthma. 2001. (Illus.). 32p. (J). lib. bdg. 24.25 (978-1-929298-95-2(1)) Chrysalis Education.

Moore-Malinos, Jennifer. Tengo Asma: I Have Asthma (Spanish Edition) Fabrega, Marta, illus. 2007. (Let's Talk about It Bks.). (SPA.). 36p. (J). (ps-2). pap. 6.99 (***978-0-7641-3786-0(7)***) Barron's Educational Series, Inc.

Murphy, Wendy B. Asthma. 1998. (Medical Library: up). (Illus.). 112p. (gr. 7 up). lib. bdg. (978-0-7613-0364-0(2) , Twenty-First Century Bks.) Lerner Publishing Group.

O'Neill, Linda. Imagine Having Asthma. 2000. (Imagine Ser.). (Illus.). 32p. (J). (gr. 1-4). lib. bdg. 26.60 (978-1-57103-379-6(3)) Rourke Publishing, LLC.

Paquette, Penny. Asthma: The Ultimate Teen Guide. 2006. (Illus.). 184p. pap. 14.95 (978-0-8108-5759-9(6)) Scarecrow Pr., Inc.

Paquette, Penny Hutchins. Asthma: The Ultimate Teen Guide. 2003. (It Happened to Me Ser.: No. 5). (Illus.). 184p. 37.50 (978-0-8108-4633-3(0)) Scarecrow Pr., Inc.

Powell, Jillian. Asthma. 2007. (***978-1-84234-472-9(2)***) Cherrytree Pubns., Inc.

Powell, Jillian. Zack has Asthma. 2004. (Like Me Like You Ser.). (Illus.). 32p. (gr. 2-4). 23.00 (978-0-7910-8181-5(8) , Chelsea Hse.) Facts On File, Inc.

Royston, Angela. Asthma. 2004. (Illus.). 32p. (J). lib. bdg. 15.95 (978-1-4034-4821-7(3)) Heinemann Library.

Sheen, Barbara. Asthma. 2002. (Diseases & Disorders Ser.). (Illus.). 120p. (J). (gr. 6-9). 32.45 (978-1-59018-235-2(9) , Lucent Bks.) Thomson Gale.

Silverstein, Alvin. Asthma. 2002. (gr. 3-6). lib. bdg. 15.25 (978-0-613-59446-2(0)) Tandem Library Bks.

Silverstein, Alvin, et al. Asthma. 2002. (My Health Ser.). (Illus.). 48p. (J). (gr. 3-5). pap. 25.50 (978-0-531-12048-4(1) , Watts, Franklin) Scholastic Library Publishing.

—The Asthma Update. 2006. (Disease Update Ser.). (Illus.). 104p. (J). (gr. 5 up). lib. bdg. 31.93 (978-0-7660-2482-3(2)) Enslow Pubs., Inc.

Simpson, Carolyn. Coping with Asthma. rev. ed. 1999. (Coping Ser.). (Illus.). 140p. (YA). (gr. 7-12). lib. bdg. 26.50 (978-0-8239-2969-6(8) , COASTH) Rosen Publishing Group, Inc., The.

Weiss, Jonathan H. Breathe Easy: Young People's Guide to Asthma. Chesworth, Michael, illus. 2nd ed. 2003. 80p. (YA). 14.95 (978-1-55798-956-7(7)); pap. 9.95 (978-1-55798-957-4(5)) American Psychological Assn. (Magination Pr.).

ASTHMA—FICTION

Bradley, Kimberly Brubaker. Weaver's Daughter. l.t. ed. 2002. 173p. (J). 21.95 (978-0-7862-3763-0(5)) Thomson Gale.

Deem, Saitofi Anne. Myrtle Learns about Asthma. 1998. (Teachable Moments Ser.). (Illus.). 8p. (J). (ps-3). pap. 7.95 (978-1-930694-00-2(8)) Myrtle Learns.

Gosselin, Kim. Sportsercise: A School Story about Exercise-Induced Asthma. Ravanelli, Terry, illus. 2nd ed. 2004. (Children's Asthma Ser.). (J). per. 9.95 (978-1-891383-25-0(6)) JayJo Bks., LLC.

Hurwitz, Johanna. Mostly Monty. McGrory, Anik, illus. 2007. 96p. (J). (gr. 1-4). 15.99 (978-0-7636-2831-4(X)) Candlewick Pr.

Kaufman, Dan. Red Flags & Pixies. 2004. 81p. pap. 14.95 (978-1-4137-0244-6(9)) PublishAmerica, Inc.

Kroll, Virginia. Brianna Breathes Easy: A Story about Asthma. Cho, Jayoung, illus. 2005. 32p. (J). (gr. k-3). 15.95 (978-0-8075-0880-0(2)) Whitman, Albert & Co.

McCormick, Shawn R. Zoey & the Zones: A Story for Children with Asthma. 2003. per. 8.95 (978-0-9718120-8-6(X)); 2002. (Illus.). (J). per. 8.95 (978-0-9740697-3-9(6)) HealthSprings, LLC.

McCormick, Shawn R. & Trevino, Ginny. Zoey & the Zones: A Story for Children with Asthma. 2002. (J). per. 8.95 (978-0-9718120-0-0(4) , ZC-2004) HealthSprings, LLC.

McNish, Cliff. Breathe: A Ghost Story. 2006. 264p. (J). 15.95 (978-0-8225-6443-0(2) , Carolrhoda Bks.) Lerner Publishing Group.

Moore-Malinos, Jennifer. I Have Asthma. Fabrega, Marta, illus. 2007. (Let's Talk about It Bks.). 36p. (J). (ps-2). pap. 6.99 (***978-0-7641-3785-3(9)***) Barron's Educational Series, Inc.

Robert, G. Sillwee Wobbert & Wheezing Will in the Big Game. 2002. (Illus.). 32p. (J). per. 9.95 (978-0-9704861-2-7(X)) Dream Publishing Co.

Sander, Nancy. Go Blow Your Nose, Robert! Brown, Jim, illus. 1999. 28p. (J). (gr. k-6). pap. 6.95 (978-1-885543-02-8(6)) Allergy & Asthma Network-Mothers of Asthmatic, Inc.

Wheelus, Doris. Wind Chasers. 2005. 109p. pap. 16.95 (978-1-4137-5734-7(0)) PublishAmerica, Inc.

Zevy, Aaron. Once upon a Breath: The Story of a Wolf, 3 Pigs & Asthma. 1998. (J). pap. 6.99 (978-0-9680678-1-9(6)) Tumbleweed Pr.

ASTOR, JOHN JACOB, 1763-1848

Parker, Lewis K. John Jacob Astor & the Fur Trade. 2003. (Reading Power Ser.). (Illus.). 24p. (J). lib. bdg. 17.25 (978-0-8239-6447-5(7) , PowerKids Pr.) Rosen Publishing Group, Inc., The.

—John Jacob Astor & the Fur Trade: Individual Title Six-Packs. (On Deck Ser.: Vol. 2). 24p. (gr. 4-5). 35.00 (978-0-7578-5852-9(X)) Rigby Education.

ASTROLOGY

see also Occultism

Abadie, M. J. Tarot for Teens. 2002. (Illus.). 256p. 14.95 (978-0-89281-917-1(0) , Bindu Bks.) Inner Traditions International, Ltd.

Adams, Jessica. Astrology: What Do the Stars Say about You? 2004. (Amazing You Ser.). (Illus.). (J). pap. 7.99 (978-0-340-88204-7(2) , Hodder & Stoughton) Hodder General Publishing Division GBR. *Dist:* Trafalgar Square Publishing.

Aslan, Madalyn. What's Your Sign? A Cosmic Guide for Young Astrologers. Kalis, Jennifer, illus. 2002. 128p. (J). 12.99 (978-0-448-42693-8(5) , Grosset & Dunlap) Penguin Group (USA) Inc.

Benton, Jim. What's Your Sign? 2005. (It's Happy Bunny Ser.: No. 3). (Illus.). 80p. (J). (gr. 10). pap. 7.99 (978-0-439-70592-9(4) , Scholastic Paperbacks) Scholastic, Inc.

Beyerl, Paul V. The Symbols & Magick of Tarot. 2005. (Illus.). xvi, 212p. pap. (978-0-9655687-4-6(1)) Hermit's Grove, The.

Brandis, Marianne. The Sign of the Scales. 2003. (Illus.). 264p. (J). (gr. 6-9). pap. 9.95 (978-0-88776-625-1(0)) Tundra Bks., Inc./Livres Toundra, Inc. CAN. *Dist:* Random Hse., Inc.

Cheung, Theresa. Face & Hand Reading: Discover Their Secret Meanings! 2004. (Illus.). (J). pap. 7.99 (978-0-340-88250-4(6) , Hodder & Stoughton) Hodder General Publishing Division GBR. *Dist:* Trafalgar Square Publishing.

Faulkner, Danny. Universe by Design. 2004. (Illus.). 160p. (YA). pap. 13.99 (978-0-89051-415-3(1) , 303-029) New Leaf Pr., Inc.

Gravelle, Karen. Five Ways to Know about You. Blasutta, Mary Lynn, illus. 2002. 166p. (J). (gr. 4-9). pap. 10.95 (978-0-8027-7586-3(1)) Walker & Co.

Hamanaka, Sheila. Space. 2005. (J). (978-0-7868-0144-2(1)); (978-0-7868-2117-4(5)) Hyperion Pr.

Hopping, Lorraine Jean. Space Rocks: The Story of Planetary Geologist Adriana Ocampo. 2005. (Women's Adventures in Science Ser.). (Illus.). 118p. (YA). (gr. 7-9). 31.00 (978-0-531-16783-0(6) , Watts, Franklin) Scholastic Library Publishing.

Kallen, Stuart A. Fortune Telling. 2003. (Illus.). 112p. (J). 29.95 (978-1-59018-289-5(8) , Lucent Bks.) Thomson Gale.

Martin, Ann M. A Corner of the Universe. 2005. 224p. (J). (gr. 8-12). pap. 2.99 (978-0-439-77124-5(2)) Scholastic, Inc.

Morningstar, Sally. La Sabiduria de la Luna. (SPA.). 64p. (J). 12.00 (978-84-342-3018-7(6)) Parramon Ediciones S.A. ESP. *Dist:* Distribuidora Norma, Inc.

Noble, Marty. Sun Signs Stained Glass Coloring Book. 2007. 16p. pap. 5.95 (***978-0-486-46230-1(7)***) Dover Pubns., Inc.

Page, Jason. The Secret Side of You: A Fun Guide to Your Star Signs, Dreams, Lucky Numbers & More! 1999. (Illus.). 128p. (YA). (gr. 4-7). pap. 5.95 (978-1-902618-21-0(1)) Element Children's Bks.

Parker, Julia. Kiss Guide to Astrology. 2000. (gr. 7-12). lib. bdg. 30.40 (978-0-613-32745-9(4)) Tandem Library Bks.

Paterson, Helena. The Celtic Moon Sign Kit: Everything You Need to Cast a Lunar Horoscope. 1999. (Illus.). 176p. pap. 24.95 (978-0-684-86218-7(2) , Fireside) Simon & Schuster.

Pluto Project Staff & Semkiw, Walter. Astrology for Regular People. Milner, Fran & Brewer, Trish, illus. 1998. (For Regular People Ser.). 198p. pap. 24.95 (978-0-9662982-7-7(6)) Pluto Project.

Realtime Associates and Mazer Corporation Staff & LeapFrog Staff, compiled by. Predict Events or Outcomes. 2002. (J). (gr. 2). 66.75 (978-1-58605-298-0(5) , LeapFrog Schl. Hse.); (gr. 3). 66.75 (978-1-58605-360-4(4) , LeapFrog Schl. Hse.); (gr. 4). 66.75 (978-1-58605-416-8(3)); (gr. 5). 66.75 (978-1-58605-475-5(9) , LeapFrog Schl. Hse.) LeapFrog Enterprises, Inc.

Roberts, Russell. The Life & Times of Nostradamus. 2007. (Biography from Ancient Civilizations Ser.). 48p. (J). lib. bdg. 29.95 (***978-1-58415-544-7(2)***) Mitchell Lane Pubs., Inc.

Shaw, Maria. Maria Shaw's Star Gazer. Willis, Joanna, ed. 2003. (Illus.). 336p. pap. 17.95 (978-0-7387-0422-7(9)) Llewellyn Pubns.

Stacy, Lori. Get a Cosmic Clue: Astrology, Numerology, Fengshui, & Other Help from the Heavens. 2001. (Among Teens Ser.). (Illus.). 106p. (J). (978-0-439-27221-6(1)) Scholastic, Inc.

Starr, Amanda. My Sign Is Aries. 2000. (gr. 7-12). lib. bdg. 12.95 (978-0-613-86274-5(0)) Tandem Library Bks.

—My Sign Is Capricorn. 2000. (gr. 7-12). lib. bdg. 12.95 (978-0-613-85750-5(X)) Tandem Library Bks.

—My Sign Is Gemini. 2000. (gr. 7-12). lib. bdg. 12.95 (978-0-613-86276-9(7)) Tandem Library Bks.

—My Sign Is Leo. 2000. (gr. 7-12). lib. bdg. 12.95 (978-0-613-83573-2(5)) Tandem Library Bks.

—My Sign Is Libra. 2000. (gr. 7-12). lib. bdg. 12.95 (978-0-613-86278-3(3)) Tandem Library Bks.

—My Sign Is Pisces. 2000. (gr. 7-12). lib. bdg. 12.95 (978-0-613-85751-2(8)) Tandem Library Bks.

—My Sign Is Sagittarius. 2000. (gr. 7-12). lib. bdg. 12.95 (978-0-613-86280-6(5)) Tandem Library Bks.

—My Sign Is Scorpio. 2000. (gr. 7-12). lib. bdg. 12.95 (978-0-613-86279-0(1)) Tandem Library Bks.

—My Sign Is Taurus. 2000. (gr. 7-12). lib. bdg. 12.95 (978-0-613-86275-2(9)) Tandem Library Bks.

—My Sign Is Virgo. 2000. (gr. 7-12). lib. bdg. 12.95 (978-0-613-86277-6(5)) Tandem Library Bks.

Wand, Kelly. Astrology. 2006. (Illus.). 168p. (gr. 10-12). 32.45 (978-0-7377-3506-2(6) , Greenhaven Pr., Inc.) Thomson Gale.

Whitfield, Susan. Animals of the Chinese Zodiac. 1999. (J). (978-0-606-17229-5(7)) Tandem Library Bks.

Xuan, Yong-Sheng, illus. The Rooster's Antlers: A Story of the Chinese Zodiac. 1999. 32p. (J). (gr. k-3). tchr. ed. 16.95 (978-0-8234-1385-0(3)) Holiday Hse., Inc.

Zenkel, Suzanne Siegel. Fashion Astrology. Bigda, Diane, illus. 2005. (Charming Petites Ser.). 80p. 4.95 (978-0-88088-842-4(3)) Peter Pauper Pr. Inc.

ASTRONAUTICS

Here are entered general works on the scientific, technological, and engineering disciplines needed for the exploration of outer space. Works on the physics and technical details of locomotion beyond earth's atmosphere are entered under Space Flight.

see also Artificial Satellites; Interplanetary Voyages; Manned Space Flight; Outer Space; Rocketry; Space Flight; Space Flight to the Moon; Space Sciences; Space Stations; Space Vehicles

Ackroyd, Peter. Escape from Earth. 2005. (Voyages Through Time Ser.). 144p. (J). pap. 9.99 (978-0-7566-0831-6(7)) Dorling Kindersley Publishing, Inc.

Adair, Amy. Space Adventure: Ligt-A-Flap Fun. Birmingham, Lloyd, tr. Birmingham, Lloyd, illus. 2002. (Leap Frog Ser.). 12p. (J). bds. 7.98 (978-0-7853-6347-7(5) , 7159300) Publications International, Ltd.

Adamson, Thomas K. Astronauts. 2007. (J). (978-0-7368-6758-0(9)) Capstone Pr., Inc.

Allman, Toney. Space Travel. 2005. (Science on the Edge Ser.). (Illus.). 48p. (J). (gr. 4-7). 24.95 (978-1-4103-0532-9(5) , Blackbirch Pr., Inc.) Thomson Gale.

Angelo, Joseph A., Jr. Human Spaceflight. 2007. (Frontiers in Space Ser.). 384p. (J). (gr. 9). 39.50 (978-0-8160-5775-7(3)) Facts On File, Inc.

Angelo, Joseph A. Robot Spacecraft. 2006. (Frontiers in Space Ser.). (Illus.). 320p. (J). (gr. 9). 39.50 (978-0-8160-5773-3(7)) Facts On File, Inc.

Asimov, Isaac & Hantula, Richard. Global Space Programs. 2005. (Isaac Asimov's 21st Century Library of the Universe). (Illus.). 32p. (J). lib. bdg. 24.67 (978-0-8368-3982-1(X)) Stevens, Gareth Inc.

Aylmore, Angela. We Work in Space. 2006. (Where We Work Ser.). (Illus.). 24p. (J). (978-1-4109-2249-6(9)); 21.36 (978-1-4109-2244-1(8)) Steck-Vaughn.

Bailey, Gerry. Journey into Space. Boulter, Steve & Smith, Jan, illus. 2005. (Crafty Inventions Ser.). 48p. (C). (gr. 4-6). 26.60 (978-1-4048-1042-6(0)) Picture Window Bks.

Becklake, Sue. Space. 2004. (Picture Reference Ser.). (SPA., Illus.). 48p. (gr. 3-6). (J). pap. 7.95 (978-1-58728-660-5(2)); 13.95 (978-1-58728-653-7(X)) T&N Children's Publishing. (Two Can Publishing).

—Space: The Book & Disk That Work Together. 2000. (Interfact Reference Ser.). (Illus.). 48p. (J). (gr. 3-6). 19.95 incl. cd-rom (978-1-58728-473-1(1) , Two Can Publishing) T&N Children's Publishing.

Berger, Gilda & Berger, Melvin. Se Puede Escuchar un Grito en el Espacio. 2007. Tr. of Can You Hear a Shout in Space?. (SPA., Illus.). 48p. (J). (gr. 3-5). pap. 5.99 (978-0-439-76538-1(2) , SO33881, Scholastic en Espanol) Scholastic, Inc.

Berger, Melvin. Can You Hear a Shout in Space? 2000. (gr. 3-6). lib. bdg. 14.10 (978-0-613-32367-3(X)) Tandem Library Bks.

Berger, Melvin & Berger, Gilda. Can You Hear a Shout in Space? Questions & Answers about Space Exploration. Di Fate, Vincent, illus. 2001. (Question & Answer Ser.). 48p. (J). (gr. 2-4). pap. 14.95 (978-0-439-09582-2(4)) Scholastic, Inc.

Beyer, Mark. Crisis in Space: Apollo 13. 2002. (Survivors Ser.). (Illus.). 48p. (YA). (gr. 7-12). 24.00 (978-0-516-23903-3(1)); pap. 6.95 (978-0-516-23485-4(4)) Scholastic Library Publishing. (Children's Pr.).

—Space Exploration. 2002. (Life in the Future Ser.). (Illus.). 48p. (YA). (gr. 7-12). pap. 23.00 (978-0-516-23917-0(1)); pap. 6.95 (978-0-516-24008-4(0)) Scholastic Library Publishing. (Children's Pr.).

—Space Exploration. 2002. (gr. 7-12). lib. bdg. 15.25 (978-0-613-58734-1(0)) Tandem Library Bks.

Birch, Robin. Exploring Space. 2002. (Space Ser.). (Illus.). 32p. (gr. k-2). 23.00 (978-0-7910-6974-5(5) , Chelsea Hse.) Facts On File, Inc.

Braulick, Carrie A. The U.S. Air Force Space Command. 2008. (J). (***978-1-4296-0829-9(3)***) Capstone Pr., Inc.

Bredeson, Carmen. Astronauts. 2003. (Rookie Read-About Science Ser.). (Illus.). 32p. (J). (gr. 1-2). 20.50 (978-0-516-22529-6(4) , Children's Pr.) Scholastic Library Publishing.

—Our Space Program. 1999. (I Know America Ser.: 4). (Illus.). 48p. (gr. 2-4). lib. bdg. 24.90 (978-0-7613-0952-9(7) , Millbrook Pr.) Lerner Publishing Group.

Bredeson, Carmen. What Do Astronauts Do? 2008. (I Like Space! Ser.). (Illus.). 32p. (J). (gr. 1-3). lib. bdg. 22.60 (***978-0-7660-2942-2(5)*** , Enslow Elementary) Enslow Pubs., Inc.

Canizares, Susan & Berger, Samantha. The Voyage of Mae Jemison. 1999. (J). 2.50 (978-0-439-04579-7(7)) Scholastic, Inc.

—Voyage of Mae Jemison. 1999. (ps-2). lib. bdg. 10.10 (978-0-613-22577-9(5)) Tandem Library Bks.

Carlisle, Rodney P. Exploring Space. 2004. (Discovery & Exploration Ser.). (Illus.). 160p. (J). (gr. 6-12). 40.00 (978-0-8160-5265-3(4)) Facts On File, Inc.

Casanellas, Antonio. Great Discoveries & Inventions That Helped Explore Earth & Space. Garousi, Ali, illus. 2000. (Great Discoveries & Inventions Ser.). 32p. (J). (gr. 4 up). lib. bdg. 24.67 (978-0-8368-2584-8(5)) Stevens, Gareth Inc.

Cole, Michael D. The Columbia Space Shuttle Disaster: From First Liftoff to Tragic Final Flight. 2003. (Countdown to Space Ser.). (Illus.). 48p. (J). lib. bdg. 23.93 (978-0-7660-2295-9(1)) Enslow Pubs., Inc.

—Hubble Space Telescope: Exploring the Universe. 1999. (Countdown to Space Ser.). (Illus.). 48p. (YA). (gr. 4-10). lib. bdg. 23.93 (978-0-7660-1120-5(8)) Enslow Pubs., Inc.

—International Space Station: A Space Mission. 1999. (Countdown to Space Ser.). (Illus.). 48p. (YA). (gr. 4-10). lib. bdg. 23.93 (978-0-7660-1117-5(8)) Enslow Pubs., Inc.

—Space Emergency: Astronauts in Danger. 2000. (Countdown to Space Ser.). (Illus.). 48p. (YA). (gr. 4-10). lib. bdg. 23.93 (978-0-7660-1307-0(3)) Enslow Pubs., Inc.

—Space Launch Disaster: When Liftoff Goes Wrong. 2000. (Countdown to Space Ser.). (Illus.). 48p. (YA). (gr. 4-10). lib. bdg. 23.93 (978-0-7660-1309-4(X)) Enslow Pubs., Inc.

Collison, Cathy. An Out of This World Alphabet. rev. ed. 2007. 40p. pap. 7.95 (***978-1-58536-335-3(9)***) Sleeping Bear Pr.

Countdown to Space, 40 bks. , Set. (Illus.). (YA). (gr. 4-10). lib. bdg. 758.00 (978-0-89490-562-9(7)) Enslow Pubs., Inc.

Crompton, Samuel Willard. Sputnik/Explorer I: The Race to Conquer Space. 2007. (Milestones in American History Ser.). 112p. (gr. 6-12). 35.00 (***978-0-7910-9357-3(3)*** , Chelsea Hse.) Facts On File, Inc.

Dahl, Michael. On the Launch Pad: A Counting Book about Rockets. Aldermand, Derrick & Shea, Denise, illus. 2004. (Know Your Numbers Ser.). 24p. (J). (gr. k-3). 22.60 (978-1-4048-0581-1(8)) Picture Window Bks.

Davis, Lucile. The Mars Rovers. 2004. (KidHaven Science Library). (Illus.). 48p. (J). (gr. 4-7). 26.20 (978-0-7377-3074-6(9) , Greenhaven Pr., Inc.) Thomson Gale.

Daynes, Katie. Living in Space. 2003. (gr. 3-6). lib. bdg. 12.95 (978-0-613-88628-4(3)) Tandem Library Bks.

De Goursac, Olivier. Space: Exploring the Moon, the Planets, & Beyond. Laye, Pascal, illus. 2006. 76p. (J). (gr. 3-7). 18.95 (978-0-8109-5719-0(1)) Abrams, Harry N. , Inc.

Dorling Kindersley Publishing Staff. Astronaut for A Day. 2005. (Illus.). 12p. (J). bds. 12.99 (978-0-7566-1117-0(2)) Dorling Kindersley Publishing, Inc.

Dunn, Joeming W. Moon Landing. Wight, Joseph et al, illus. 2007. (Graphic History Ser.). 32p. (J). (gr. 3-6). lib. bdg. 27.07 (***978-1-60270-078-9(8)*** , Graphic Planet) Magic Wagon.

Dyson, Marianne J. & Klug, Dave. Space Station Science: Life in Free Fall. 1999. (Illus.). 128p. (J). (gr. 4-9). pap. 16.95 (978-0-590-05889-6(4) , Scholastic Reference) Scholastic, Inc.

Elish, Dan. Nasa. 2006. (Kaleidoscope Space Ser.). (Illus.). 48p. (J). lib. bdg. 28.50 (***978-0-7614-2046-0(0)*** , Benchmark Bks.) Cavendish, Marshall Corp.

Eugene, Toni. Exploring Space. 1999. (978-0-7922-9433-7(5)) National Geographic Society.

Franklin, Kent. Exploring Earth & Space Systems. 2006. 96p. pap. 9.95 (978-1-4116-3469-5(1)) Lulu.com.

Gifford, Clive. Space Exploration. 2005. (Technology All Around Us Ser.). (Illus.). 32p. (J). (gr. 4-7). lib. bdg. 27.10 (978-1-58340-753-0(7)) Smart Apple Media.

Grace, N. B. Women in Space. 2006. (Girls Rock! Ser.). (Illus.). 32p. (J). (gr. 1-5). 24.21 (978-1-59296-751-3(5)) Child's World, Inc.

Hansen, Ole Steen. Space Flight. 2003. (Story of Flight Ser.). (Illus.). 32p. (J). (gr. 2-9). lib. bdg. (978-0-7787-1207-7(9)); (gr. 4). pap. (978-0-7787-1223-7(0)) Crabtree Publishing Co.

Hansen, Rosanna. Space: A Chapter Book. 2003. (True Tales Ser.). (Illus.). 48p. (J). 22.50 (978-0-516-22919-5(2) , Children's Pr.) Scholastic Library Publishing.

Harcourt School Publishers Staff. Apollo Below Level: To the Moon. 3rd ed. 2002. (Trophies Reading Program Ser.). (Illus.). pap. 5.10 (978-0-15-323325-8(7)) Harcourt Schl. Pubs.

—J. Glenn in Space: Take-Home Book. 1999. (Collections Ser.). (Illus.). (J). pap. 1.90 (978-0-15-317214-4(2)) Harcourt Schl. Pubs.

Hayhurst, Chris. Astronauts: Life Exploring Outer Space. 2005. (Extreme Careers Ser.). (Illus.). 64p. (YA). (gr. 5-8). 26.50 (978-0-8239-3364-8(4)) Rosen Publishing Group, Inc., The.

Hermsen, Sarah. Space Exploration Library Cumulative Index. 2004. 42p. (J). lib. bdg. 5.00 (978-0-7876-9214-8(X) , UXL) Thomson Gale.

Herrod, Robin. Dawn of the Space Age. 2004. (History of Space Exploration Ser.). (Illus.). 48p. (J). pap. 11.95 (978-0-8368-5712-2(7)); lib. bdg. 30.00 (978-0-8368-5705-4(4)) Stevens, Gareth Inc. (World Almanac Library).

Hilliard, Richard. Neil, Buzz, & Mike Go to the Moon. 2005. (Illus.). 32p. (J). (ps-7). 16.95 (978-1-59078-293-4(3)) Boyds Mills Pr.

Jedicke, Peter. Scientific American. 2007. (Scientific American Ser.). 72p. (J). (gr. 5-8). 30.00 (978-0-7910-9046-6(9) , Chelsea Hse.) Facts On File, Inc.

Jefferis, David. Flight into Orbit. 2007. (Illus.). 32p. (J). (gr. 3-7). (***978-0-7787-3101-6(4)***); pap. (***978-0-7787-3115-3(4))*** Crabtree Publishing Co.

—Future Space: Beyond Earth. Quigley, Sebastian, illus. 2001. 48p. (J). 6.95 (978-0-439-31460-2(7)) Scholastic, Inc.

—Into Infinity: From Earth to the Stars. 2001. (Megatech Ser.). (Illus.). 32p. (J). (gr. 4-5). pap. (978-0-7787-0060-9(7)); lib. bdg. (978-0-7787-0050-0(X)) Crabtree Publishing Co.

—Into Infinity: From Earth to the Stars. 2002. (gr. 3-6). lib. bdg. 17.60 (978-0-613-52963-1(4)) Tandem Library Bks.

Jefferis, David. Race into Space. 2007. (Illus.). 32p. (J). (gr. 3-7). (***978-0-7787-3102-3(2)***); pap. (***978-0-7787-3116-0(2))*** Crabtree Publishing Co.

Jeffrey, Gary. Incredible Space Missions. Lacey, Mike, illus. 2007. (Graphic Discoveries Ser.). 48p. (J). (gr. 3-7). lib. bdg. (***978-1-4042-1090-5(3))*** Rosen Publishing Group, Inc., The.

—Incredible Space Missions: By Gary Jeffrey: Illustrated by Mike Lacey. Lacey, Mike, illus. 2007. (J). (***978-1-4042-9595-7(X)***); pap. (***978-1-4042-9596-4(8))*** Rosen Publishing Group, Inc., The.

Johnstone, Michael. History News in Space. 1999. (History News Ser.). (Illus.). 32p. (J). (gr. 5-9). 16.99 (978-0-7636-0490-5(9)) Candlewick Pr.

—In Space. 2001. (History News Ser.). (Illus.). 32p. (J). (gr. 3 up). lib. bdg. 24.67 (978-0-8368-2876-4(3)) Stevens, Gareth Inc.

Karner, Julie. Space Disaster & Meteorite Alert! 2005. (Disaster Alert! Ser.). (Illus.). 32p. (J). (978-0-7787-1583-2(3)) Crabtree Publishing Co.

Khan, Hena & Dyson, Marianne J. The Space Explorer's Guide to Out-Of-This-World Science. 2004. (Space University Ser.). (Illus.). 48p. (J). (***978-0-439-55747-4(X))*** Scholastic, Inc.

King, Penny & Roundhill, Clare. Out of This World. 1998. (Making Pictures Ser.). (J). (978-1-57572-193-4(7)) Rigby Education.

Kuhn, Betsy. The Race for Space. 2007. (People's History Ser.). 112p. (J). (gr. 5-8). 29.27 (978-0-8225-5984-9(6) , Twenty-First Century Bks.) Lerner Publishing Group.

Lassieur, Allison. Astronauts. 2001. (True Bks.). (Illus.). 48p. (J). (gr. 3-5). pap. 6.95 (978-0-516-27185-9(7) , Children's Pr.) Scholastic Library Publishing.

Mason. Space Race - Space Busters. 2004. pap. 48.30 (978-1-4109-0294-8(3)) Harcourt Schl. Pubs.

Mason, Paul. Space Race. 2002. (Young Library - Space Busters Ser.). (Illus.). 32p. (J). (gr. 3-5). lib. bdg. 25.69 (978-0-7398-4851-7(8)) Raintree.

Mattern, Joanne. Astronautas. 2004. (Trabajo en Grupo Ser.). (SPA & ENG., Illus.). 24p. (J). (gr. 3-6). lib. bdg. 17.25 (978-0-8239-6842-8(1) , Buenas Letra) Rosen Publishing Group, Inc., The.

McCarthy, Meghan. Astronaut Handbook. 2008. 40p. (J). (gr. k-3). 16.99 (***978-0-375-84459-1(7)***); lib. bdg. 19.99 (***978-0-375-94459-8(1))*** Random Hse. Children's Bks. (Knopf Bks. for Young Readers).

McConnell, Bill. Living Through the Space Race. 2006. 192p. (gr. 10-12). 33.70 (978-0-7377-2134-8(0) , Greenhaven Pr., Inc.) Thomson Gale.

McNeese, Tim. The Space Race. 2003. (Cornerstones of Freedom). (Illus.). 48p. (J). (gr. 4-6). 26.00 (978-0-516-24201-9(6) , Children's Pr.) Scholastic Library Publishing.

Miller, Ron. Space Exploration. 2007. (Space Innovations Ser.). 112p. (YA). (gr. 6-8). lib. bdg. 31.93 (***978-0-8225-7155-1(2)*** , Twenty-First Century Bks.) Lerner Publishing Group.

Mission Control. (Explore Space! Ser.). 24p. (J). 6.95 (978-0-7368-4532-8(1)) Capstone Pr., Inc.

Mitchell, Don. Liftoff: A Photobiography of John Glenn. 2006. (Illus.). 64p. (J). (gr. 4-8). lib. bdg. 27.90 (978-0-7922-5900-8(9)); (gr. 5-9). pap. 17.95 (978-0-7922-5899-5(1)) National Geographic Society. (National Geographic Children's Bks.).

Moskal, Greg. The History of Space Exploration: Sequencing Events Chronologically on a Timeline. 2004. (PowerMath Ser.). (Illus.). 24p. (J). lib. bdg. (978-0-8239-8850-1(3)); lib. bdg. 21.25 (978-0-8239-8962-1(3)) Rosen Publishing Group, Inc., The. (PowerKids Pr.).

Murphy, Patricia J., tr. Exploring Space with an Astronaut. 2004. (I Like Science! Ser.). (Illus.). 24p. (J). lib. bdg. 21.26 (978-0-7660-2268-3(4)) Enslow Pubs., Inc.

Nicolson, Cynthia. Discover Space. Slavin, Bill, illus. 2005. 32p. (J). lib. bdg. 15.38 (***978-1-4242-1193-7(X))*** Fitzgerald Bks.

Outer Space. Date not set. (Illus.). 12p. (J). 3.98 (978-1-4054-0498-3(1)) Parragon, Inc.

Outer Space, 12 vols., Set. 1998. (Illus.). (YA). lib. bdg. 285.00 (978-0-7172-9179-3(0) , Grolier) Scholastic Library Publishing.

Priddy, Roger. Space IQ. rev. ed. 2006. (Smart Kids Ser.). 18p. (J). bds. 14.95 (978-0-312-49699-9(0) , Priddy Bks.) St. Martin's Pr.

Red Bird Press Staff. Amazing Spaceships. 2004. (Build Your Own Ser.). 20p. (J). pap. 5.95 (978-1-902626-70-3(2)) Red Bird Publishing GBR. *Dist:* Weatherhill, Inc.

Saari, Peggy. Primary Sources, Space Explorer. 2004. (Space Exploration Reference Library). (Illus.). 203p. (J). lib. bdg. 67.00 (978-0-7876-9213-1(1) , UXL) Thomson Gale.

Shearer, Deborah A. Astronauts at Work. 2002. (Explore Space! Ser.). (Illus.). 24p. (J). (gr. 1-2). lib. bdg. 18.60 (978-0-7368-1142-2(7) , Bridgestone Bks.) Capstone Pr., Inc.

—Mission Control. 2002. (Explore Space! Ser.). (Illus.). 24p. (J). (gr. 1-2). lib. bdg. 18.60 (978-0-7368-1143-9(5) , Bridgestone Bks.) Capstone Pr., Inc.

—Space Missions. 2002. (Explore Space! Ser.). (Illus.). 24p. (J). (gr. 1-2). lib. bdg. 18.60 (978-0-7368-1401-0(9) , Bridgestone Bks.) Capstone Pr., Inc.

Simon, Seymour. Space Travelers. 2004. (See More Readers). (Illus.). 48p. (J). 14.50 (978-1-58717-250-2(X)); Vol. 3. pap. 3.95 (978-1-58717-251-9(8)) Chronicle Bks. LLC. (SeaStar Bks.).

Solway, Andrew. Can We Travel to the Stars? Space Flight & Space Exploration. 2006. (Stargazers Guides Ser.). (Illus.). 48p. (J). (978-1-4034-7711-8(6)); pap. (978-1-4034-7718-7(3)) Heinemann Library.

Space Missions. (Explore Space! Ser.). 24p. (J). 6.95 (978-0-7368-4533-5(X)) Capstone Pr., Inc.

Spangenburg, Ray. The History of NASA. 2000. (978-0-606-20706-5(6)) Tandem Library Bks.

Spangenburg, Ray & Moser, Kit. The History of NASA. 2001. (Out of This World Ser.). (Illus.). 128p. (YA). (gr. 7-9). pap. 14.95 (978-0-531-16511-9(6) , Watts, Franklin) Scholastic Library Publishing.

Spilsbury, Louise & Spilsbury, Richard. Scientists at Work: Space Pioneers: Astronauts Hardback. 2007. (Illus.). 32p. (J). (***978-0-431-14927-1(5))*** Heinemann Library.

—Scientists at Work: Space Pioneers: Astronauts Paperback. 2007. (Illus.). 32p. (J). (***978-0-431-14934-9(8))*** Heinemann Library.

Spilsbury, Richard & Spilsbury, Louise. Space Pioneers: Astronauts. 2007. (J). (***978-1-4034-9951-6(9)***); pap. (***978-1-4034-9958-5(6))*** Heinemann Library.

Taylor, Robert. Space Stations. 2004. (Lucent Library of Science). (Illus.). 112p. (J). 29.95 (978-1-59018-106-5(9)) Thomson Gale.

Tocci, Salvatore. Space Experiments. 2002. (True Book Ser.). (Illus.). 48p. (J). (gr. 3-5). 25.00 (978-0-516-22509-8(X) , Children's Pr.) Scholastic Library Publishing.

—Space Experiments. 2002. (gr. 3-6). lib. bdg. 15.25 (978-0-613-54358-3(0)) Tandem Library Bks.

Vogt, Greg. John Glenn's Return to Space. 2000. (Illus.). 72p. (gr. 5-8). lib. bdg. 24.90 (978-0-7613-1614-5(0) , Millbrook Pr.) Lerner Publishing Group.

Vogt, Gregory L. Exploring Space. 2000. (Our Universe Ser.). (Illus.). 48p. (J). (gr. 5-12). lib. bdg. 22.83 (978-0-7398-3113-7(5)) Raintree.

—Exploring Space. 2000. (Our Universe Ser.). (Illus.). (J). pap. (978-0-7398-3352-0(9)) Steck-Vaughn.

—The Milky Way & Other Galaxies. 2000. (Our Universe Ser.). (Illus.). 48p. (YA). (gr. 5-12). lib. bdg. 22.83 (978-0-7398-3107-6(0)) Raintree.

—The Milky Way & Other Galaxies. 2000. (Our Universe Ser.). (Illus.). (J). pap. (978-0-7398-3346-9(4)) Steck-Vaughn.

—Space Mission Patches. 2001. (Enthusiastic Astronomy Ser.). (Illus.). 80p. (gr. 5-8). lib. bdg. (978-0-7613-1613-8(2) , Millbrook Pr.) Lerner Publishing Group.

—Space Stations. 1999. (Explore Space! Ser.). (Illus.). 24p. (J). (gr. 1-2). lib. bdg. 18.60 (978-0-7368-0201-7(0) , Bridgestone Bks.) Capstone Pr., Inc.

Walker, Niki. The Life of an Astronaut. 2000. (Eye on the Universe Ser.). (Illus.). 32p. (J). (gr. 3-4). (978-0-86505-683-1(8)); pap. (978-0-86505-693-0(5)) Crabtree Publishing Co.

—Life of an Astronaut. 2001. (gr. 3-6). lib. bdg. 14.10 (978-0-613-32783-1(7)) Tandem Library Bks.

Whitehouse, Patricia. Space Equipment. 2004. (J). 24.21 (978-1-4034-5154-5(0)); pap. 7.25 (978-1-4034-5658-8(5)) Heinemann Library.

—Space Travel. 2004. (Heinemann First Library). (Illus.). 32p. (J). 24.21 (978-1-4034-5155-2(9)); pap. 7.25 (978-1-4034-5659-5(3)) Heinemann Library.

Wilkinson, Philip. Al Espacio: La Carrera a la Luna. 2006. (Dk Readers Ser.). 48p. (J). 14.99 (978-0-7566-2128-5(3)); (gr. 5). pap. 3.99 (978-0-7566-2127-8(5)) Dorling Kindersley Publishing, Inc.

Williams, Brian. Space. 2001. (Great Inventions Ser.). (Illus.). 48p. (YA). (gr. 6-8). lib. bdg. 25.64 (978-1-58810-215-7(7)) Heinemann Library.

Woodford. Space Dramas. 2003. (Space Busters Ser.). (Illus.). 32p. (J). pap. 7.95 (978-1-4109-0073-9(8)) Raintree.

Woodford, Chris. Air & Space Travel. 2004. (History of Invention Ser.). (Illus.). 96p. (YA). (gr. 6-12). 35.00 (978-0-8160-5436-7(3)) Facts On File, Inc.

Yoon, Salina. What's in Space? 2006. (Illus.). 10p. (J). (ps-k). bds. 5.99 (978-0-8431-2017-2(7) , Price Stern Sloan) Penguin Group (USA) Inc.

York, Pat. Exploring Space. 2002. (Science Matters Ser.). (Illus.). 24p. (J). lib. bdg. 15.95 (978-1-59036-085-9(0)) Weigl Pubs., Inc.

Zelon, Helen. The Apollo 13 Mission: Surviving an Explosion in Space. 2002. (Space Missions Ser.). (Illus.). 24p. (J). (gr. 2-4). lib. bdg. 19.95 (978-0-8239-5773-6(X) , PowerKids Pr.) Rosen Publishing Group, Inc., The.

ASTRONAUTICS—BIOGRAPHY

Aldrin, Buzz, Jr. Reaching for the Moon. Minor, Wendell, illus. 2005. 40p. (J). 16.99 (978-0-06-055445-3(2)); lib. bdg. 17.89 (978-0-06-055446-0(0)) HarperCollins Pubs.

—Reaching for the Moon. Minor, Wendell, illus. unabr. ed. 2006. (Picture Book Readalong Ser.). (J). (gr. k-4). 25.95 incl. audio (978-1-59519-581-4(5)); 28.95 incl. audio compact disk (978-1-59519-582-1(3)) Live Oak Media.

Benge, Janet & Benge, Geoff. Alan Shepard: Higher & Faster. 2007. (J). (***978-1-932096-41-5(8))*** YWAM Publishing.

Bredeson, Carmen. Shannon Lucid: Space Ambassador. 2000. (Gateway Biography Ser.: 4). (Illus.). 48p. (J). (gr. 4-8). pap. 8.95 (978-0-7613-1375-5(3) , Millbrook Pr.) Lerner Publishing Group.

Gueldenpfennig, Sonia. Spectacular Women in Space. 2005. (Illus.). 112p. (YA). pap. 7.95 (978-1-896764-88-7(6)) Second Story Pr. CAN. *Dist:* Orca Bk. Pubs. USA, Univ. of Toronto Pr.

Holden, Henry M. Pioneering Astronaut Sally Ride: A MyReportLinks. com Book. 2004. (Space Flight Adventures & Disasters Ser.). (Illus.). 48p. (J). lib. bdg. 25.26 (978-0-7660-5169-0(2) , MyReportLinks.com Bks.) Enslow Pubs., Inc.

Jeffrey, Laura S. Christa McAuliffe: A Space Biography. 1998. (Countdown to Space Ser.). (Illus.). 48p. (YA). (gr. 4-10). lib. bdg. 23.93 (978-0-89490-976-4(2)) Enslow Pubs., Inc.

Latham, Donna. Ellen Ochoa: Reach for the Stars! 2005. (Defining Moments Ser.). (Illus.). 32p. (J). (gr. 3-7). lib. bdg. 25.27 (978-1-59716-076-6(8)) Bearport Publishing Co., Inc.

Padmanabhan, Anil. Kalpana Chawla: A Life. 2003. (Illus.). xi, 94p. pap. (978-0-14-333586-3(3) , Puffin) Penguin Group (USA) Inc.

Stone, Tanya Lee. Ilan Ramon: Israel's First Astronaut. 2003. 48p. pap. 7.95 (978-0-7613-2376-1(7)); lib. bdg. 23.90 (978-0-7613-2888-9(2)) Lerner Publishing Group. (Twenty-First Century Bks.).

Thomson, Sarah L. Astronauts & Other Space Heroes FYI. 2007. 80p. (J). 16.99 (***978-0-06-089945-5(X)***); pap. 7.99 (***978-0-06-089944-8(1))*** Smithsonian Institution Pr.

Wukovitz, John F. Ellen Ochoa, First Female Hispanic Astronaut. 2006. (Twentieth Century's Most Influential Hispanics Ser.). (Illus.). 112p. (J). (gr. 7-10). lib. bdg. 32.45 (978-1-59018-976-4(0) , 1256844, Lucent Bks.) Thomson Gale.

Yannuzzi, Della A. Mae Jemison: A Space Biography. 1998. (Countdown to Space Ser.). (Illus.). 48p. (YA). (gr. 4-10). lib. bdg. 23.93 (978-0-89490-813-2(8)) Enslow Pubs., Inc.

ASTRONAUTICS—DICTIONARIES

Dowswell, Paul. First Encyclopedia of Space. 2004. (First Encyclopedia Ser.). (SPA., Illus.). 64p. (J). (gr. 3 up). pap. 9.99 (978-0-7945-0035-1(8) , Usborne); lib. bdg. 17.95 (978-1-58086-357-5(4)) EDC Publishing.

Nagel, Rob. Space Exploration - Almanac, 2 vols. 2004. (Space Exploration Reference Library). (Illus.). lib. bdg. 120.00 (978-0-7876-9209-4(3) , UXL) Thomson Gale.

ASTRONAUTICS—VOCATIONAL GUIDANCE

Ferguson. Careers in Focus: Space Exploration. 2007. (Careers in Focus Ser.). 192p. (gr. 6-12). 29.95 (***978-0-8160-6570-7(5)*** , Ferguson Publishing Co.) Facts On File, Inc.

Hutson, Matt. Totally Amazing Careers in Aerospace. 2006. (J). 7.80 (978-1-933798-03-5(3)) Sally Ride Science.

Hyland, Tony. Astronauts. 2006. (Extreme Jobs Ser.). (Illus.). 32p. (J). (gr. 4-6). lib. bdg. 27.10 (978-1-58340-743-1(X)) Smart Apple Media.

Mattern, Joanne. Astronauts. 2002. (Reading Power Ser.). (Illus.). 24p. (J). (gr. 1). lib. bdg. 17.25 (978-0-8239-5977-8(5) , PowerKids Pr.) Rosen Publishing Group, Inc., The.

Miller, Heather. Astronaut. 2003. (This is What I Want To Be Ser.). (Illus.). 24p. (ps-1). (J). lib. bdg. 18.50 (978-1-4034-0364-3(3)); pap. 5.25 (978-1-4034-0586-9(7)) Heinemann Library.

—Astronaut. 2003. (ps-2). lib. bdg. 13.30 (978-0-613-88522-5(8)) Tandem Library Bks.

Parks, Peggy J. Astronaut. 2005. (Exploring Careers Ser.). (Illus.). 48p. (J). (gr. 4-8). 26.20 (978-0-7377-3016-6(1) , Kidhaven) Thomson Gale.

Sparrow, Giles. Astronauts. 2006. (Illus.). 48p. (J). pap. (978-0-8368-7282-8(7)); lib. bdg. (978-0-8368-7275-0(4)) Stevens, Gareth Inc. (World Almanac Library).

Whitehouse, Patricia. Working in Space. 2004. (J). 24.21 (978-1-4034-5158-3(3)); pap. 6.95 (978-1-4034-5662-5(3)) Heinemann Library.

Willett, Edward. Careers in Outer Space: New Business Opportunities. 2005. (Career Resource Library). (Illus.). 192p. (YA). (gr. 7-12). lib. bdg. 26.50 (978-0-8239-3358-7(X)) Rosen Publishing Group, Inc., The.

ASTRONAUTS

Adamson, Heather. The Challenger Explosion. Bascle, Brian, illus. 2006. (Graphic Library). 32p. (J). (978-0-7368-5478-8(9) , 1252837) Capstone Pr., Inc.

African American Astronauts. 2000. (My Ancestors—My Heroes Ser.: Vol. 19). (J). (gr. 3-4). (978-1-893091-18-4(X)) Parker Publishing Co.

Agle, D. C. Heroes of Space: A Three-Dimensional Tribute to 40 Years of Space Exploration. 1999. (Illus.). 8p. 19.95 (978-1-58117-054-2(8) , Intervisual/Piggy Toes) Dalmatian Pr.

Aldrin, Buzz, Jr. Reaching for the Moon. Minor, Wendell, illus. 2005. 40p. (J). 16.99 (978-0-06-055445-3(2)); lib. bdg. 17.89 (978-0-06-055446-0(0)) HarperCollins Pubs.

—Reaching for the Moon. Minor, Wendell, illus. unabr. ed. 2006. (Picture Book Readalong Ser.). (J). (gr. k-4). 25.95 incl. audio (978-1-59519-581-4(5)); 28.95 incl. audio compact disk (978-1-59519-582-1(3)) Live Oak Media.

Astronauts. (Community Helpers Ser.). 24p. (J). 6.95 (978-0-7368-8029-9(1)) Capstone Pr., Inc.

Astronauts. (Awesome Adventures Ser.). 16p. (J). (978-2-7643-0119-7(7)) Phidal Publishing, Inc./Editions Phidal, Inc.

Astronauts, 6 vols. (gr. 2-5). 36.95 (978-0-7368-8047-3(X)) Red Brick Learning.

Astronauts: Individual Title Six-Packs. (On Deck Ser.). 24p. (gr. 4-5). 35.00 (978-0-7578-1030-5(6)) Rigby Education.

Astronauts: Level K, 6 vols. (Wonder Worldtm Ser.). 16p. 34.95 (978-0-7802-4595-2(4)) Wright Group, The.

Astronauts at Work, 6 vols. (gr. 2-5). 36.95 (978-0-7368-4608-0(5)) Red Brick Learning.

Astronauts Set B, 6 vols. (Phonics Readers Ser.). (gr. k-2). 17.50 (978-0-7368-3197-0(5)) Red Brick Learning.

Atkins, Jeannine. Wings & Rockets: The Story of Women in Air & Space. Petricic, Dusan, illus. 2003. 208p. (J). 17.00 (978-0-374-38450-0(9) , Farrar, Straus & Giroux (BYR)) Farrar, Straus & Giroux.

Black, Sonia W. Mae Jemison. 2000. (Illus.). 64p. (J). (gr. 3-7). pap. 3.95 (978-1-57255-801-4(6)) Mondo Publishing.

—Mae Jemison. 2000. (978-0-606-22649-3(4)); (gr. 3-6). lib. bdg. 11.80 (978-0-613-35854-5(6)) Tandem Library Bks.

A B

Branley, Franklyn M. Floating in Space. Kelley, True, illus. 1998. (Let's-Read-and-Find-Out Science Ser.). 32p. (J). (gr. k-4). 15.89 (978-0-06-025433-9(5)); pap. 5.99 (978-0-06-445142-0(9)) HarperCollins Pubs.

Bredeson, Carmen. Astronautas. 2005. (Rookie Espanol: Ciencias Ser.). (SPA., Illus.). 32p. (J). (gr. k-2). pap. 5.95 (978-0-516-24699-4(2) , Children's Pr.) Scholastic Library Publishing.

—Astronauts. (Rookie Readers - Spanish Ser.). (J). 2004. 19.50 (978-0-516-24441-9(8) , Watts, Franklin); 2003. (Illus.). 32p. (gr. 1-2). 20.50 (978-0-516-22529-6(4) , Children's Pr.) Scholastic Library Publishing.

—Astronauts. 2003. (gr. k-3). lib. bdg. 12.95 (978-0-613-67871-1(0)) Tandem Library Bks.

—Neil Armstrong: A Space Biography. 1998. (Countdown to Space Ser.). (Illus.). 48p. (YA). (gr. 4-10). lib. bdg. 23.93 (978-0-89490-973-3(8)) Enslow Pubs., Inc.

—Our Space Program. 2000. (I Know America Ser.: 4). (Illus.). 48p. (gr. 2-4). pap. (978-0-7613-1349-6(4) , Millbrook Pr.) Lerner Publishing Group.

—Our Space Program. 2000. (I Know America Ser.). (Illus.). (J). (978-0-606-18292-8(6)) Tandem Library Bks.

Bredeson, Carmen. What Do Astronauts Do? 2008. (I Like Space! Ser.). (Illus.). 32p. (J). (gr. 1-3). lib. bdg. 22.60 (*978-0-7660-2942-2(5) , Enslow Elementary) Enslow Pubs., Inc.

Bricker, Sandra D. Challenger. 2000. (gr. 5-8). lib. bdg. 11.80 (978-0-613-51203-9(0)) Tandem Library Bks.

Briggs, Carole S. Women in Space. rev. ed. 1998. (Biography Ser.). (Illus.). 128p. (YA). (gr. 6-12). lib. bdg. 27.93 (978-0-8225-4937-6(9) , Lerner Pubns.) Lerner Publishing Group.

Brown, Don. One Giant Leap: The Story of Neil Armstrong. Brown, Don, illus. 2001. (Illus.). 32p. (J). (gr. k-3). pap. 6.95 (978-0-618-15239-1(3)) Houghton Mifflin Co. Trade & Reference Div.

—One Giant Leap: The Story of Neil Armstrong. 1998. 32p. (J). (gr. k-3). tchr. ed. 16.00 (978-0-395-88401-0(2)) Houghton Mifflin Co. Trade & Reference Div.

—One Giant Leap: The Story of Neil Armstrong. 2001. (978-0-606-22589-2(7)) Tandem Library Bks.

Brown, Jonatha A. Neil Armstrong. (People We Should Know Ser.). 24p. (J). 2006. pap. 5.95 (978-0-8368-4765-9(2)); 2006. lib. bdg. 19.33 (978-0-8368-4758-1(X)); 2005. (Illus.). pap. (978-0-8368-4751-2(2)); 2005. (Illus.). lib. bdg. 19.33 (978-0-8368-4744-4(X)) Stevens, Gareth Inc.

Buckley, Annie. Ellen Ochoa. 2008. (J). lib. bdg. 26.00 (*978-1-60279-075-9(2)) Cherry Lake Publishing.

Buckley, James & Dorling Kindersley Publishing Staff. Space Heroes: Amazing Astronauts. 2003. (Readers Ser.). (Illus.). 48p. (J). 12.99 (978-0-7894-9895-3(2)) Dorling Kindersley Publishing, Inc.

Buckley, James, Jr. & Dorling Kindersley Publishing Staff. Space Heroes Vol. 3: Amazing Astronauts. 2003. (DK Readers Ser.: Level. 2). (Illus.). 48p. (J). (gr. 5). pap. 3.99 (978-0-7894-9896-0(0)) Dorling Kindersley Publishing, Inc.

Capstone Press, contrib. by. Astronauts at Work. (Explore Space! Ser.). 24p. (J). pap. 6.95 (978-0-7368-4531-1(3)) Capstone Pr., Inc.

Clemson, Wendy & Clemson, David. Rocket to the Moon. 2006. (Illus.). 32p. (J). pap. (*978-0-8368-8140-0(0)); lib. bdg. (*978-0-8368-7841-7(8)) Stevens, Gareth Inc.

Cohen, Judith Love & Ghez, Andrea M. You Can Be a Woman Astronomer. Katz, David Arthur, illus. 1998. 40p. (J). (gr. 1-6). 19.95 incl. cd-rom (978-1-880599-27-3(9)) Cascade Pass, Inc.

Cole, Michael D. Astronauts: Training for Space. 1999. (Countdown to Space Ser.). (Illus.). 48p. (YA). (gr. 4-10). lib. bdg. 23.93 (978-0-7660-1116-8(X)) Enslow Pubs., Inc.

Cooper, Sharon Katz. Whose Vehicle Is This? A Look at Vehicles Workers Drive—Fast, Loud, & Bright. Muehlenhardt, Amy Bailey, illus. 2006. (Whose Is It? Ser.). 24p. (J). (ps-2). 22.60 (978-1-4048-1603-9(8) , 1253206) Picture Window Bks.

Cullen, David. The First Man in Space. 2004. (Days That Changed the World Ser.). (Illus.). 48p. (J). (gr. 5 up). pap. 11.95 (978-0-8368-5577-7(9)); lib. bdg. 30.00 (978-0-8368-5570-8(1)) Stevens, Gareth Inc. (World Almanac Library).

Dorling Kindersley Publishing Staff. DK Readers: Space Heroes - Amazing Astronauts. 2004. (gr. k-3). lib. bdg. 11.80 (978-0-613-75239-8(2)) Tandem Library Bks.

Dunn, Herb. John Glenn: Young Astronaut. Brown, Robert S., illus. 2000. (Childhood of Famous Americans Ser.). (J). 11.64 (978-0-606-19714-4(1)) Tandem Library Bks.

Ellen Ochoa: Reaching for the Stars. 2005. (Book Treks Ser.). (J). (gr. 3 up). stu. ed. 34.95 (978-0-673-62081-1(6)) Celebration Pr.

Feinstein, Stephen. Read about Neil Armstrong. 2005. (I Like Biographies! Ser.). (Illus.). 24p. (J). lib. bdg. 21.26 (978-0-7660-2593-6(4) , Enslow Elementary) Enslow Pubs., Inc.

Feldman, Heather. Valentina Tereshkova: The First Woman in Space. 2003. (Space Firsts Ser.). (Illus.). 24p. (J). lib. bdg. 19.95 (978-0-8239-6246-4(6) , PowerKids Pr.) Rosen Publishing Group, Inc., The.

—Yuri Gagarin: The First Man in Space. 2003. (Space Firsts Ser.). (Illus.). 24p. (J). lib. bdg. 19.95 (978-0-8239-6245-7(8) , PowerKids Pr.) Rosen Publishing Group, Inc., The.

Ganeri, Anita. Neil Armstrong. 1999. (What Would You Ask...? Ser.). (Illus.). 32p. (J). (gr. 2-6). lib. bdg. 16.95 (978-1-929298-03-7(X)) Chrysalis Education.

Gelletly, LeeAnne. Mae Jemison. 2002. (Black Americans of Achievement Ser.). (Illus.). 112p. (J). 30.00 (978-0-7910-6293-7(7) , Chelsea Hse.) Facts On File, Inc.

Gomez, Rebecca. Sally Ride. 2003. (First Biographies Ser.). (Illus.). 32p. (J). (gr. k-4). lib. bdg. 22.78 (978-1-57765-948-8(1)) ABDO Publishing Co.

Goodman, Susan E. Blasting off to Space Academy. 2002. (gr. 3-6). lib. bdg. 15.30 (978-0-613-45013-3(2)) Tandem Library Bks.

Goss, Tim. Neil Armstrong. 2002. (Trailblazers of the Modern World Ser.). (Illus.). 48p. (J). (gr. 5 up). pap. 14.95 (978-0-8368-5235-6(4)); lib. bdg. 30.00 (978-0-8368-5075-8(0)) Stevens, Gareth Inc. (World Almanac Library).

Grace, N. B. Women in Space. 2006. (Girls Rock! Ser.). (Illus.). 32p. (J). (gr. 1-5). 24.21 (978-1-59296-751-3(5)) Child's World, Inc.

Graham, Ian. The Best Book of Spaceships. 1998. (Best Book of... Ser.). (Illus.). 32p. (J). (gr. k-3). tchr. ed. 12.95 (978-0-7534-5133-5(6) , Kingfisher) Houghton Mifflin Co. Trade & Reference Div.

—Wright Brothers: Pioneers of Flight. Antram, David, illus. 2003. (Explosion Zone Ser.). 32p. (J). pap. 6.95 (978-0-7641-2591-1(5)) Barron's Educational Series, Inc.

Green, Robert. John Glenn: Astronaut & U. S. Senator. 2000. (Career Biographies Ser.). (Illus.). 128p. (YA). (gr. 6-12). 25.00 (978-0-89434-341-4(6) , F403, Ferguson Publishing Co.) Facts On File, Inc.

Guzman, Lila & Guzman, Rick. Ellen Ochoa: First Latina Astronaut. 2006. (Famous Latinos Ser.). (Illus.). 32p. (J). lib. bdg. 22.60 (978-0-7660-2642-1(6) , Enslow Elementary) Enslow Pubs., Inc.

Guzman, Lila & Guzman, Rick. Ellen Ochoa: La primera astronauta Latina. 2007. (Latinos Famosos Ser.). (SPA., Illus.). 32p. (J). (gr. 3-4). lib. bdg. 22.60 (*978-0-7660-2677-3(9) , Enslow Elementary) Enslow Pubs., Inc.

Harcourt School Publishers Staff. Guion Bluford: A Space Biography. 2001. (Reader's Choice Bks.). (Illus.). (J). pap. 7.20 (978-0-15-314430-1(0)) Harcourt Schl. Pubs.

Hayden, Kate. Astronaut: Living in Space. 2000. (Readers Ser.). (Illus.). 32p. (J). (gr. 1-3). pap. 3.99 (978-0-7894-5421-8(1)) Dorling Kindersley Publishing, Inc.

—Astronaut: Living in Space. 2000. (Eyewitness Readers Ser.). (J). 10.79 (978-0-606-19376-4(6)) Tandem Library Bks.

—Astronaut Living in Space. 2000. (gr. k-3). lib. bdg. 11.80 (978-0-613-24252-3(1)) Tandem Library Bks.

Hayden, Kate & Dorling Kindersley Publishing Staff. Astronaut: Living in Space. 2000. (Eyewitness Readers). (Illus.). 32p. (J). (gr. 1-3). 14.99 (978-0-7894-5422-5(X)) Dorling Kindersley Publishing, Inc.

Hayhurst, Chris. Astronauts: Life Exploring Outer Space. 2005. (Extreme Careers Ser.). (Illus.). 64p. (YA). (gr. 5-8). 26.50 (978-0-8239-3364-8(4)) Rosen Publishing Group, Inc., The.

Hilliard, Richard. Godspeed, John Glenn. 2006. (Illus.). (J). 16.95 (978-1-59078-384-9(0)) Boyds Mills Pr.

Hoenecke, Karen. Astronaut. 2004. 8p. (J). pap. 4.50 (978-1-57874-047-5(9)) Kaeden Corp.

Holden, Henry M. Pioneering Astronaut Sally Ride: A MyReportLinks. com Book. 2004. (Space Flight Adventures & Disasters Ser.). (Illus.). 48p. (J). lib. bdg. 25.26 (978-0-7660-5169-0(2) , MyReportLinks.com Bks.) Enslow Pubs., Inc.

—Trailblazing Astronaut John Glenn: A MyReportLinks. com Book. 2004. (Space Flight Adventures & Disasters Ser.). (Illus.). 48p. (J). lib. bdg. 25.26 (978-0-7660-5166-9(8) , MyReportLinks.com Bks.) Enslow Pubs., Inc.

Hyland, Tony. Astronauts. 2006. (Extreme Jobs Ser.). (Illus.). 32p. (J). (gr. 4-6). lib. bdg. 27.10 (978-1-58340-743-1(X)) Smart Apple Media.

Iverson, Teresa. Ellen Ochoa. (Hispanic-American Biographies Ser.). (Illus.). 64p. (J). 2005. pap. 9.50 (978-1-4109-1307-4(4)); 2004. (gr. 4-6). 32.86 (978-1-4109-1299-2(X)) Raintree.

—Ellen Ochoa. 2006. (Biografías de Hispanoamericanos Ser.). (ENG & SPA.). (J). 32.86 (978-1-4109-2128-4(X)); pap. 9.90 (978-1-4109-2135-2(2)) Steck-Vaughn.

Jaffe, Elizabeth Dana. Ellen Ochoa. (Rookie Biographies(R) Ser.). (Illus.). 2005. 32p. (J). (gr. 1-2). pap. 4.95 (978-0-516-25827-0(3)); 2004. 31p. 20.50 (978-0-516-21721-5(6)) Scholastic Library Publishing. (Children's Pr.).

Jeffrey, Laura S. Christa McAuliffe: A Space Biography. 1998. (Countdown to Space Ser.). (Illus.). 48p. (YA). (gr. 4-10). lib. bdg. 23.93 (978-0-89490-976-4(2)) Enslow Pubs., Inc.

—Guion Bluford: A Space Biography. 1998. (Countdown to Space Ser.). (Illus.). 48p. (YA). (gr. 4-10). lib. bdg. 23.93 (978-0-89490-977-1(0)) Enslow Pubs., Inc.

Jemison, Mae. Find Where the Wind Goes: Moments from My Life. (Find Where the Wind Goes Ser.). (Illus.). 208p. (J). 2003. pap. 4.99 (978-0-439-13196-4(0) , Scholastic Paperbacks); 2001. (gr. 5-9). pap. 16.95 (978-0-439-13195-7(2)) Scholastic, Inc.

—Find Where the Wind Goes: Moments from My Life. 2003. (gr. 5-8). lib. bdg. 13.00 (978-0-613-72017-5(2)) Tandem Library Bks.

Johnston, Lissa Jones. Ellen Ochoa: Pioneering Astronaut. 2006. (Fact Finders Ser.). (Illus.). 32p. (J). (978-0-7368-5438-2(X)) Capstone Pr., Inc.

Karner, Julie. Space Disaster & Meteorite Alert! 2005. (Disaster Alert Ser.). (Illus.). 32p. (J). pap. (978-0-7787-1615-0(5)) Crabtree Publishing Co.

Kortenkamp, Steve. Working in Space. 2008. (*978-1-4296-1261-6(4)) Capstone Pr., Inc.

Kramer, Barbara. John Glenn: A Space Biography. 1998. (Countdown to Space Ser.). (Illus.). 48p. (YA). (gr. 4-10). lib. bdg. 23.93 (978-0-89490-964-1(9)) Enslow Pubs., Inc.

—Neil Armstrong: Meet the Famous Astronaut. 2003. (Meeting Famous People Ser.). (Illus.). 32p. (J). lib. bdg. 22.60 (978-0-7660-2007-8(X)) Enslow Pubs., Inc.

Kraske, Robert. Mae Jemison: Space Pioneer. 2006. (Illus.). 32p. (J). (gr. 1-3). 22.60 (978-0-7368-6420-6(2)) Capstone Pr., Inc.

Levin, Amy. Astronauts. 2003. (Compass Point Phonics Readers Ser.). (Illus.). 16p. (J). (gr. 1 up). 13.26 (978-0-7565-0503-5(8)) Compass Point Bks.

Lock, Deborah. Astronaut: La Vida in Espacio. 2006. (Dk Readers Ser.). 32p. (J). pap. 3.99 (978-0-7566-2345-6(6)) Dorling Kindersley Publishing, Inc.

—Astronaut: Living in Space. 2006. (Dk Readers Ser.). 32p. (J). 14.99 (978-0-7566-2346-3(4)) Dorling Kindersley Publishing, Inc.

Marcovitz, Hal. Reaching for the Moon: The Apollo Astronauts. 2000. (Explorers of the New World Ser.). (Illus.). (J). 63p. (gr. 4-7). pap. 25.00 (978-0-7910-6167-1(1)); 64p. (gr. 8-12). 25.00 (978-0-7910-5957-9(X)) Facts On File, Inc. (Chelsea Hse.).

—Reaching for the Moon: The Apollo Astronauts. 2001. (gr. 3-6). lib. bdg. 17.60 (978-0-613-32989-7(9)) Tandem Library Bks.

Marsh, Carole. Neil Armstrong. 2002. (One Thousand Readers Ser.). (Illus.). 12p. (J). (gr. k-4). 2.95 (978-0-635-01565-5(X) , 1565X) Gallopade International.

—Neil Armstrong: An Ohio Experience Reader. 2001. (J). (gr. k-5). pap. 1.95 (978-0-635-00438-3(0)) Gallopade International.

Mattern, Jeanne. Astronautas: Individual Title Six-Packs. (On Deck en Espanol Ser.).Tr. of Astronauts. (SPA.). 24p. (gr. 4-5). 35.00 (978-0-7578-6409-4(0)) Rigby Education.

Mattern, Joanne. Astronautas. 2004. (Trabajo en Grupo Ser.). (SPA & ENG., Illus.). 24p. (J). (gr. 3-6). lib. bdg. 17.25 (978-0-8239-6842-8(1) , Buenas Letra) Rosen Publishing Group, Inc., The.

—Astronauts. 2002. (Reading Power Ser.). (Illus.). 24p. (J). (gr. 1). lib. bdg. 17.25 (978-0-8239-5977-8(5) , PowerKids Pr.) Rosen Publishing Group, Inc., The.

—Sally Ride: Astronaut & Physicist. 2005. (Ferguson Career Biographies Ser.). (Illus.). 128p. (J). (gr. 6-12). 25.00 (978-0-8160-5892-1(X) , Ferguson Publishing Co.) Facts On File, Inc.

Maze, Stephanie. I Want to Be an Astronaut. 1999. (I Want to Be Ser.). (Illus.). 48p. (J). (gr. 3-9). pap. 10.00 (978-0-15-201966-2(9) , Harcourt Paperbacks) Harcourt Children's Bks.

—I Want to Be an Astronaut. 1999. (I Want to Be Ser.). (Illus.). 48p. (YA). (gr. 4-9). lib. bdg. 18.98 (978-0-8172-4159-9(0)) Raintree.

Miller, Heather. Astronaut. 2003. (This is What I Want To Be Ser.). (Illus.). 24p. (ps-1). (J). lib. bdg. 18.50 (978-1-4034-0364-3(3)); pap. 5.25 (978-1-4034-0586-9(7)) Heinemann Library.

—Astronaut. 2003. (ps-2). lib. bdg. 13.30 (978-0-613-88522-5(8)) Tandem Library Bks.

—Astronauta. Prieto, Carlos, tr. 2003. (Esto es lo Que Quiero Ser (This Is What I Want to Be) Ser.).Tr. of Astronaut. (SPA.). 24p. (J). (ps-1). lib. bdg. 18.50 (978-1-4034-0374-2(0)); pap. 5.25 (978-1-4034-0596-8(4)) Heinemann Library.

Mitchell, Don. Liftoff: A Photobiography of John Glenn. 2006. (Illus.). 64p. (J). (gr. 4-8). lib. bdg. 27.90 (978-0-7922-5900-8(9)); (gr. 5-9). pap. 17.95 (978-0-7922-5899-5(1)) National Geographic Society. (National Geographic Children's Bks.).

Naden, Corinne J. & Blue, Rose. Mae Jeminson: Out of This World. 2003. (Gateway Biography Ser.: 4). (Illus.). 48p. lib. bdg. 23.90 (978-0-7613-2570-3(0) , Millbrook Pr.) Lerner Publishing Group.

Nettleton, Pamela Hill. Sally Ride. Yesh, Jeff, illus. 2004. (Biographies Ser.). 24p. (C). (gr. k-3). 22.60 (978-1-4048-0189-9(8)) Picture Window Bks.

Nichols, Catherine. Sally Ride. 2005. (Scholastic News Nonfiction Readers Ser.). (Illus.). 24p. (J). (gr. 1-2). 19.00 (978-0-516-24942-1(8) , Children's Pr.) Scholastic Library Publishing.

O'Brien, Eileen & Denne, Ben. Space. 2004. (Discovery Program Ser.). (SPA., Illus.). 48p. (J). pap. 8.95 (978-0-7945-0126-6(5) , Usborne); lib. bdg. 16.95 (978-1-58086-388-9(4)) EDC Publishing.

Parks, Peggy J. Astronaut. 2005. (Exploring Careers Ser.). (Illus.). 48p. (J). (gr. 4-8). 26.20 (978-0-7377-3016-6(1) , Kidhaven) Thomson Gale.

Peck, George K. The Birdbook, 8 vols. in 1. Peck, George K., photos by. 1999. (Illus.). 216p. (J). (gr. 2-7). lib. bdg. 25.95 (978-1-887068-98-7(8)) Smart Apple Media.

Putnam, Jeff. Explorers of the Sky. 2004. (Illus.). 74p. (978-0-7367-1796-0(X)) Zaner-Bloser, Inc.

Raintree Steck-Vaughn Staff. Overcoming Challenges: The Life of Charles F. Bolden, Jr. 1999. (Illus.). (J). pap. 35.60 (978-0-7398-0910-5(5)) Steck-Vaughn.

Rau, Dana Meachen. Neil Armstrong. 2003. (Rookie Biographies Ser.). (gr. 1-2). pap. 4.95 (978-0-516-26963-4(1)); (Illus.). 32p. (J). 20.50 (978-0-516-22592-0(8)) Scholastic Library Publishing. (Children's Pr.).

—Neil Armstrong. 2003. (gr. k-3). lib. bdg. 12.95 (978-0-613-67650-2(5)) Tandem Library Bks.

Raum, Elizabeth. Edwin "Buzz" Aldrin. 2005. (American Lives Ser.). (Illus.). 32p. (978-1-4034-6939-7(3)); pap. (978-1-4034-6946-5(6)) Heinemann Library.

—Eileen Collins. 2005. (American Lives Ser.). (Illus.). 32p. (J). (978-1-4034-6943-4(1)); pap. (978-1-4034-6950-2(4)) Heinemann Library.

—John Glenn. 2005. (American Lives Ser.). (Illus.). 32p. (J). (978-1-4034-6940-3(7)); pap. (978-1-4034-6947-2(4)) Heinemann Library.

—Mae Jemison. 2005. (American Lives Ser.). (Illus.). 32p. (J). (978-1-4034-6942-7(3)); pap. (978-1-4034-6949-6(0)) Heinemann Library.

—Neil Armstrong. 2005. (American Lives Ser.). (Illus.). 32p. (J). (978-1-4034-6938-0(5)); pap. (978-1-4034-6945-8(8)) Heinemann Library.

—Sally Ride. 2005. (American Lives Ser.). (Illus.). 32p. (J). (978-1-4034-6941-0(5)); pap. (978-1-4034-6948-9(2)) Heinemann Library.

Richardson, Adele D. Astronauts. 1999. (Above & Beyond Ser.). (Illus.). 32p. (J). (gr. 4-7). lib. bdg. 16.95 (978-1-58340-046-3(X)) Smart Apple Media.

Richie, Jason. Spectacular Space Travelers. Sterling, Denise, ed. 2001. (Profiles Ser.: Vol. No. 31). (Illus.). 160p. (gr. 5 up). lib. bdg. 19.95 (978-1-881508-71-7(4)) Oliver Pr., Inc.

Saari, Peggy. Biography, Space Exploration. 2004. (Space Exploration Reference Library). (J). lib. bdg. 67.00 (978-0-7876-9212-4(3) , UXL) Thomson Gale.

Sally Ride. (Biographies Ser.). 24p. (J). 7.95 (978-1-4048-0462-3(5)) Picture Window Bks.

Schyffert, Bea Uusma. Man Who Went to the Far Side of the Moon: The Story of Apollo 11 Astronaut Michael Collins. 2003. (Illus.). 80p. (J). (gr. 5 up). 14.95 (978-0-8118-4007-1(7)) Chronicle Bks. LLC.

Sipiera, Diane M. & Sipiera, Paul P. Project Mercury. 1998. (True Bks.). (Illus.). 48p. (J). (gr. 3-5). pap. 6.95 (978-0-516-26275-8(0) , Children's Pr.) Scholastic Library Publishing.

Sofer, Barbara. Ilan Ramon: Israel's Space Hero. 2003. (Illus.). 64p. (J). (gr. 3-6). 16.95 (978-1-58013-115-5(8)); pap. (978-1-58013-116-2(6)) Kar-Ben Publishing.

Sparrow, Giles. Astronauts. 2006. (Illus.). 48p. (J). pap. (978-0-8368-7282-8(7)); lib. bdg. (978-0-8368-7275-0(4)) Stevens, Gareth Inc. (World Almanac Library).

Speregen, Devra Newberger. Ilan Ramon: Jewish Star. 2004. (Illus.). 120p. pap. 9.95 (978-0-8276-0769-9(5)) Jewish Pubn. Society.

Spilsbury, Louise & Spilsbury, Richard. Scientists at Work: Space Pioneers: Astronauts Hardback. 2007. (Illus.). 32p. (J). (*978-0-431-14927-1(5)) Heinemann Library.

—Scientists at Work: Space Pioneers: Astronauts Paperback. 2007. (Illus.). 32p. (J). (*978-0-431-14934-9(8)) Heinemann Library.

Spilsbury, Richard & Spilsbury, Louise. Space Pioneers: Astronauts. 2007. (J). (*978-1-4034-9951-6(9)); pap. (*978-1-4034-9958-5(6)) Heinemann Library.

Steck-Vaughn Staff. The Moon & Beyond. 2002. (Illus.). pap. 41.60 incl. audio compact disk (978-0-7398-6978-9(7)) Steck-Vaughn.

Stone, Tanya Lee. Ilan Ramon: Israel's First Astronaut. 48p. (J). (gr. 4-7). 17.95 (978-1-58013-204-6(9)) Kar-Ben Publishing.

—Ilan Ramon: Israel's First Astronaut. 2003. (gr. 3-6). lib. bdg. 16.40 (978-0-613-88042-8(0)) Tandem Library Bks.

Streissguth, Thomas. Christa McAuliffe. 2003. (Explore Space! Ser.). (Illus.). 24p. (J). (gr. 1-2). lib. bdg. 18.60 (978-0-7368-1624-3(0) , Bridgestone Bks.) Capstone Pr., Inc.

—Mae Jemison. 2003. (Explore Space! Ser.). (Illus.). 24p. (J). (gr. 1-2). lib. bdg. 18.60 (978-0-7368-1626-7(7) , Bridgestone Bks.) Capstone Pr., Inc.

—Neil Armstrong. 2003. (Explore Space! Ser.). (Illus.). 24p. (J). (gr. 1-2). lib. bdg. 18.60 (978-0-7368-1627-4(5) , Bridgestone Bks.) Capstone Pr., Inc.

Streissguth, Tom. John Glenn. 2005. (Bios for Challenged Readers Ser.). (Illus.). 112p. (J). (gr. 6-12). lib. bdg. 27.93 (978-0-8225-2274-4(8)) Lerner Publishing Group.

—John Glenn. 1999. (gr. 7-12). lib. bdg. 16.40 (978-0-613-81316-7(2)) Tandem Library Bks.

Taylor, Robert. Life Aboard the Space Shuttle. 2002. (Way People Live Ser.). (Illus.). 112p. (J). (gr. 7-10). 29.95 (978-1-59018-154-6(9) , LML00902-181109, Lucent Bks.) Thomson Gale.

Trailblazers of the Modern World: Neil Armstrong; Bob Dylan; Bill Gates; Nelson Mandela; Eleanor Roosevelt; Steven Spielberg, 6 bks. 2002. (Illus.). (J). (gr. 5 up). pap. 87.60 (978-0-8368-5234-9(6) , World Almanac Library) Stevens, Gareth Inc.

Visca, Curt & Visca, Kelley. How to Draw Cartoon Spacecraft & Astronauts in Action. 2004. (Kid's Guide to Drawing Ser.). (Illus.). 24p. (J). lib. bdg. 21.25 (978-0-8239-6729-2(8) , PowerKids Pr.) Rosen Publishing Group, Inc., The.

Vogt, Greg. John Glenn's Return to Space. 2000. (Illus.). 72p. (gr. 5-8). lib. bdg. 24.90 (978-0-7613-1614-5(0) , Millbrook Pr.) Lerner Publishing Group.

Wade, Linda R. Sally Ride: First American Female in Space. l.t. ed. 2002. (Unlocking the Secrets of Science Ser.). (Illus.). 56p. (gr. 4-10). lib. bdg. 25.70 (978-1-58415-139-5(0)) Mitchell Lane Pubs., Inc.

Walker, Niki. The Life of an Astronaut. 2000. (Eye on the Universe Ser.). (Illus.). 32p. (J). (gr. 3-4). (978-0-86505-683-1(8)); pap. (978-0-86505-693-0(5)) Crabtree Publishing Co.

—Life of an Astronaut. 2001. (gr. 3-6). lib. bdg. 14.10 (978-0-613-32783-1(7)) Tandem Library Bks.

Walker, Pamela. Ellen Ochoa. 2001. (Real People Ser.). (Illus.). 24p. (J). (ps-2). 17.00 (978-0-516-23433-5(1)); pap. 4.95 (978-0-516-23587-5(7)) Scholastic Library Publishing. (Children's Pr.).

—Ellen Ochoa. 2001. (gr. k-3). lib. bdg. 12.95 (978-0-613-58832-4(0)) Tandem Library Bks.

Walton, Darwin McBeth. Overcoming Challenges: The Life of Charles F. Bolden, Jr. 2000. (Pair-It Books). (Illus.). 40p. (J). (978-0-7398-0879-5(6)) Steck-Vaughn.

Weil, Ann. The Moon & Beyond. 2003. (Illus.). 60p. (J). (978-0-7398-5173-9(X)) Steck-Vaughn.

Whitehouse, Patricia. Living in Space. 2004. (J). 24.21 (978-1-4034-5151-4(6)); pap. 6.95 (978-1-4034-5655-7(0)) Heinemann Library.

—Working in Space. 2004. (J). 24.21 (978-1-4034-5158-3(3)); pap. 6.95 (978-1-4034-5662-5(3)) Heinemann Library.

Yannuzzi, Della A. Mae Jemison: A Space Biography. 1998. (Countdown to Space Ser.). (Illus.). 48p. (YA). (gr. 4-10). lib. bdg. 23.93 (978-0-89490-813-2(8)) Enslow Pubs., Inc.

Zelon, Helen. The Mercury 6 Mission: The First American Astronaut to Orbit Earth. 2002. (Space Missions Ser.). (Illus.). 24p. (J). (gr. 2-4). lib. bdg. 19.95 (978-0-8239-5770-5(5) , PowerKids Pr.) Rosen Publishing Group, Inc., The.

Zemlicka, Shannon. Neil Armstrong. (History Maker Bios Ser.). (Illus.). 48p. (J). 2003. (gr. 2-4). 26.60 (978-0-8225-0395-8(6)); 2002. pap. 6.95 (978-0-8225-1563-0(6)) Lerner Publishing Group. (Lerner Pubns.).

ASTRONAUTS—CLOTHING

Shearer, Deborah A. Space Suits. 2002. (Explore Space! Ser.). (Illus.). 24p. (J). (gr. 1-2). lib. bdg. 18.60 (978-0-7368-1144-6(3) , Bridgestone Bks.) Capstone Pr., Inc.

ASTRONAUTS—FICTION

Brett, Jan. Hedgie Blasts Off! Brett, Jan, illus. 2006. (Illus.). 32p. (J). (ps-3). 16.99 (978-0-399-24621-0(5) , Putnam Juvenile) Penguin Group (USA) Inc.

Carbin, Eddie. Arty the Part-Time Astronaut. Savoia, Greg & Peters, Ron, illus. 2000. 36p. (J). (gr. 1-7). pap. 19.95 (978-0-9675299-0-5(5)) 3 Pounds Pr.

Casey, Joe & Gerard, Caleb. Full Moon Fever. 2005. (Illus.). 88p. (YA). pap. 12.95 (978-1-932051-35-3(X)) A i T/Planet Lar.

Cole, Steve. The Hatching Horror. Fowkes, Charlie, illus. 2006. (Astrosaurs Ser.). 144p. (J). pap. 4.99 (978-0-689-87842-8(7) , Aladdin) Simon & Schuster Children's Publishing.

—The Mind-Swap Menace. Fox, Woody, illus. 2007. (Astrosaurs Ser.). 128p. (Orig.). (J). pap. 4.99 (978-0-689-87844-2(3) , Aladdin) Simon & Schuster Children's Publishing.

—Riddle of the Raptors. Fowkes, Charlie, illus. 2006. (Astrosaurs Ser.). 144p. (J). (gr. 3-7). pap. 4.99 (978-0-689-87841-1(9) , Aladdin) Simon & Schuster Children's Publishing.

Cress, Michelle H. Annie the Astronaut Meets Gussie the Green Man. l.t. ed. 1999. (LB Ser.). (Illus.). 8p. (J). (ps-1). pap. 10.95 (978-1-57332-153-2(2)) HighReach Learning, Inc.

—Annie the Astronaut Meets Gussie the Green Man. Cress, Michelle H., illus. l.t. ed. 1999. (BB Ser.). (Illus.). 8p. (J). (ps-1). pap. 10.95 (978-1-57332-152-5(4)) HighReach Learning, Inc.

Draper, Sharon M. The Space Mission Adventure. Watson, Jesse Joshua, illus. 2006. (Ziggy & the Black Dinosaurs Ser.: No. 4). 128p. (J). pap. 4.99 (978-0-689-87914-2(8) , Aladdin) Simon & Schuster Children's Publishing.

Fox, Christyan & Fox, Diane. Astronaut PiggyWiggy. 2002. (Illus.). 24p. (J). (ps-k). 9.95 (978-1-929766-41-3(6)) Handprint Bks.

Gerritsen, Tess. Gravity: A Novel of Medical Suspense. 2000. (gr. 7-12). lib. bdg. 16.45 (978-0-613-36378-5(7)) Tandem Library Bks.

Graves, Robin. Space Diaries: The Saga of Robby, Boy Astronaut. 2005. pap. 6.95 (978-1-57646-915-6(8)) Quiet Vision Publishing.

Hart, Anne. Four Astronauts & a Kitten. 2001. 144p. (J). pap. 11.95 (978-0-595-19202-1(5) , Authors Choice Pr.) iUniverse, Inc.

Kirk, Daniel. Moondogs. 1999. (Illus.). 1p. (J). (ps-3). 16.99 (978-0-399-23128-5(5) , Putnam Juvenile) Penguin Group (USA) Inc.

Latta, Sara L. Stella Brite & the Dark Matter Mystery. Johnson, Meredith, illus. 2006. 32p. (J). 16.95 (978-1-57091-883-4(X)); pap. 6.95 (978-1-57091-884-1(8)) Charlesbridge Publishing, Inc.

Mackinnon, Debbie & Sieveking, Anthea. What Am I? 2004. (Illus.). 24p. (J). pap. 7.95 (978-1-84507-243-8(X)) Lincoln, Frances Ltd. GBR. *Dist:* Perseus Distribution.

Mullican, Judy. An Atronaut at Last. 2006. (J). pap. (978-1-57332-424-3(8)) HighReach Learning, Inc.

—An Atronaut at Last children's Booklet. 2006. (J). (978-1-57332-425-0(6)) HighReach Learning, Inc.

Reiser, Lynn W. Earthdance. Reiser, Lynn W., illus. 1999. (Illus.). 40p. (J). (gr. k-3). 15.89 (978-0-688-16327-3(0)) HarperCollins Pubs.

Rouss, Sylvia A. Reach for the Stars. 2005. (Illus.). 40p. (J). (gr. 3-7). 16.95 (978-1-930143-82-1(6)); pap. 9.95 (978-1-930143-83-8(4)) Pitspopany Pr. (Devora Publishing).

Sleep Tight Spaceboy. 2003. (J). (978-1-932570-02-1(0)) Literacy Footprints Inc.

Smith, A. G. Glenn the Astronaut: With 4 Sticker Uniforms. 1998. (Dover Little Activity Bks.). 4p. (J). (gr. k-5). pap. 1.50 (978-0-486-40517-9(6)) Dover Pubns., Inc.

Spaceboy Finds a Friend. 2003. (J). (978-1-932570-01-4(2)) Literacy Footprints Inc.

Spaceboy Plays Hide & Seek. 2003. (J). (978-1-932570-05-2(5)) Literacy Footprints Inc.

Spaceboy Set 1. 2003. (J). (978-1-932570-00-7(4)) Literacy Footprints Inc.

Spence, Kenlyn Foster. Astronaut Noodle on Planet Velocity. 2005. (Illus.). 31p. (J). 14.95 (978-0-9768760-1-4(9)) BelleBks.

Tremblay, Carole. Matt Goes to Mars. Crovatto, Lucie, illus. 2005. (Read-It! Readers Ser.). (J). (978-1-4048-1178-2(8)); 32p. 18.60 (978-1-4048-1269-7(5)) Picture Window Bks.

Westover, Alli. My Daddy Works at NASA. 2005. (J). 15.95 (978-1-888237-59-7(7)) Baxter Pr.

Woodward, Kay. La Cuenta Regresiva Level P. AMIT, Ofra, illus. 2006. (Lightning Readers Ser.). 32p. (J). pap. 3.95 (978-0-7696-4205-5(5) , Gingham Dog Pr.) School Specialty Publishing.

ASTRONOMERS

Anderson, Dale. Maria Mitchell. 2003. (Women in Science Ser.). (Illus.). 112p. (gr. 6-12). 30.00 (978-0-7910-7249-3(5) , Chelsea Hse.) Facts On File, Inc.

Andronik, Catherine M. Copernicus: Founder of Modern Astronomy. 2002. (Great Minds of Science Ser.). (Illus.). 112p. (J). (gr. 4-10). lib. bdg. 26.60 (978-0-7660-1755-9(5)) Enslow Pubs., Inc.

Blashfield, Jean F. Carl Sagan: Astronomer. 2001. (Career Biographies Ser.). (Illus.). 128p. (YA). (gr. 6-12). 25.00 (978-0-89434-374-2(2) , F417, Ferguson Publishing Co.) Facts On File, Inc.

Boekhoff, P. M. Galileo. 2003. (Inventors & Creators Ser.). (Illus.). 48p. (J). 23.70 (978-0-7377-1891-1(9) , Greenhaven Pr., Inc.) Thomson Gale.

Boerst, William J. Johannes Kepler: Discovering the Laws of Celestial Motion. 2004. (Profiles in Science Ser.). (Illus.). 144p. (YA). (gr. 6-12). lib. bdg. 26.95 (978-1-883846-98-5(6) , First Biographies) Reynolds, Morgan Inc.

—Nicholas Copernicus & the Founding of Modern Astronomy. 2004. (Profiles in Science Ser.). (Illus.). 144p. (YA). (gr. 6-12). lib. bdg. 26.95 (978-1-883846-99-2(4) , First Biographies) Reynolds, Morgan Inc.

—Tycho Brahe: Mapping the Heavens. 2004. (Profiles in Science Ser.). (Illus.). 144p. (YA). (gr. 6-12). 26.95 (978-1-883846-97-8(8) , First Biographies) Reynolds, Morgan Inc.

Boothroyd, Jennifer. Galileo Galilei: A Life of Curiosity. 2007. (Pull Ahead Books-Biographies Ser.). (J). 22.60 (978-0-8225-6460-7(2) , Lerner Pubns.) Lerner Publishing Group.

Bortz, Fred. Beyond Jupiter: The Story of Planetary Astronomer Heidi Hammel. 2005. (Women's Adventures in Science Ser.). (Illus.). 110p. (YA). (gr. 7-9). 31.00 (978-0-531-16775-5(5) , Watts, Franklin) Scholastic Library Publishing.

Burke, Rick. Benjamin Banneker. 2003. (American Lives Ser.). (Illus.). 32p. (J). lib. bdg. 24.22 (978-1-4034-0725-2(8)); pap. 6.50 (978-1-4034-3100-4(0)) Heinemann Library.

Butts, Ellen R. & Schwartz, Joyce R. Carl Sagan. 2005. (Biography Ser.). (Illus.). 112p. (gr. 6-12). lib. bdg. 27.93 (978-0-8225-4986-4(7)) Lerner Publishing Group.

Datnow, Claire L. Edwin Hubble: Discoverer of Galaxies. (Great Minds of Science Ser.). (Illus.). 128p. 2001. (YA). (gr. 4-10). pap. 13.26 (978-0-7660-1869-3(5)); 2007. (J). lib. bdg. 31.93 (978-0-7660-2791-6(0)) Enslow Pubs., Inc.

Doak, Robin S. Galileo: Astronomer & Physicist. 2004. (Signature Lives Ser.). (Illus.). 112p. (J). 30.60 (978-0-7565-0813-5(4)) Compass Point Bks.

Don Nardo. The Trial of Galileo. 2004. (Famous Trials Ser.). (Illus.). 112p. (J). 29.95 (978-1-59018-423-3(8)) Thomson Gale.

Fradin, Dennis Brindell. Nicolaus Copernicus: The Earth Is a Planet. Buhler, Cynthia von, tr. Buhler, Cynthia von, illus. 2003. 32p. (J). (gr. 2-6). 15.95 (978-1-59336-006-1(1)); pap. (978-1-59336-007-8(X)) Mondo Publishing.

Germadnik, Mary Lynn. How Do We Know the Age of the Universe? 2001. (Great Scientific Questions & the Scientists Who Answered Them Ser.). (Illus.). 112p. (YA). (gr. 4-6). lib. bdg. 26.50 (978-0-8239-3382-2(2)) Rosen Publishing Group, Inc., The.

Ghez, Andrea Mia & Cohen, Judith Love. You Can Be A Woman Astronomer. Katz, David Arthur, illus. l.t. ed. 40p. (J). 2006. pap. 12.95 incl. DVD (978-1-880599-77-8(5)); 2005. 17.95 incl. DVD (978-1-880599-78-5(3)) Cascade Pass, Inc.

Gingerich, Owen & MacLachlan, James H. Nicolaus Copernicus: Making the Earth a Planet. 2005. (Oxford Portraits in Science Ser.). (Illus.). 128p. (YA). 30.00 (978-0-19-516173-1(4)) Oxford Univ. Pr., Inc.

Gormley, Beatrice. Maria Mitchell: The Soul of an Astronomer. 2004. (Illus.). 166p. (J). pap. 12.00 (978-0-8028-5264-9(5)) Eerdmans, William B. Publishing Co.

Gow, Mary. Johannes Kepler: Discovering the Laws of Planetary Motion. 2003. (Great Minds of Science Ser.). (Illus.). 128p. (J). lib. bdg. 26.60 (978-0-7660-2098-6(3)) Enslow Pubs., Inc.

—Tycho Brahe: Astronomer. 2002. (Great Minds of Science Ser.). (Illus.). 128p. (J). (gr. 4-10). lib. bdg. 26.60 (978-0-7660-1757-3(5)) Enslow Pubs., Inc.

Hasan, Heather. Kepler & the Laws of Planetary Motion. 2004. (Primary Sources of Revolutionary Scientific Discoveries & Theories Ser.). (Illus.). 64p. (J). lib. bdg. 29.25 (978-1-4042-0308-2(7)) Rosen Publishing Group, Inc., The.

Haydon, Julie. Astronomers. 2004. (J). lib. bdg. 27.10 (978-1-58340-541-3(0)) Smart Apple Media.

Hightower, Paul. Galileo: Astronomer & Physicist. 2008. (J). ***(978-0-7660-3008-4(3))*** Enslow Pubs., Inc.

Hilliam, Rachel. Galileo Galilei: Father of Modern Science. 2004. (Rulers, Scholars, & Artists of Renaissance Europe Ser.). (Illus.). 112p. (J). lib. bdg. 31.95 (978-1-4042-0314-3(1)) Rosen Publishing Group, Inc., The.

Hinman, Bonnie. Benjamin Banneker. 1999. (Colonial Leaders Ser.). (Illus.). 79p. (J). (gr. 3 up). pap. 8.95 (978-0-7910-5691-2(0) , Chelsea Hse.) Facts On File, Inc.

—Benjamin Banneker: American Mathematician & Astronomer. 2000. (Colonial Leaders Ser.). (Illus.). 80p. (J). (gr. 3 up). 27.50 (978-0-7910-5348-5(2) , Chelsea Hse.) Facts On File, Inc.

Ingram, Scott. Nicolaus Copernicus: Father of Modern Astronomy. 2004. (Illus.). 64p. (J). 26.20 (978-1-56711-489-8(X) , Blackbirch Pr., Inc.) Thomson Gale.

Kupperberg, Paul. Hubble & the Big Bang. 2004. (Primary Sources of Revolutionary Scientific Discoveries & Theories Ser.). (Illus.). 64p. (J). lib. bdg. 29.25 (978-1-4042-0307-5(9)) Rosen Publishing Group, Inc., The.

Lassieur, Allison. Benjamin Banneker: Astronomer & Mathematician. 2006. (Fact Finders Ser.). (Illus.). 32p. (J). (978-0-7368-5432-0(0)) Capstone Pr., Inc.

Litwin, Laura Baskes. Benjamin Banneker: Astronomer & Mathematician. 1999. (African-American Biographies Ser.). (Illus.). 112p. (YA). (gr. 6-12). lib. bdg. 26.60 (978-0-7660-1208-0(5)) Enslow Pubs., Inc.

MacDonald, Fiona. Edwin Hubble. 48p. pap. 8.50 (978-1-4034-4062-4(X)); 2001. (Groundbreakers Ser.: Vol. 2). (Illus.). (J). (gr. 5-7). lib. bdg. 25.64 (978-1-58810-054-2(5)) Heinemann Library.

—Edwin Hubble. 2003. (gr. 5-8). lib. bdg. 17.05 (978-0-613-84427-7(0)) Tandem Library Bks.

Marsh, Carole. Dr. Mae Jemison. 2002. (One Thousand Readers Ser.). (Illus.). 12p. (J). (gr. k-4). 2.95 (978-0-635-01512-9(9) , 15129) Gallopade International.

Mason, Paul. Galileo. (Groundbreakers Ser.). (Illus.). 48p. (J). (gr. 5-7). 2002. pap. 8.50 (978-1-58810-991-0(7) , 91466); 2001. lib. bdg. 25.64 (978-1-58810-052-8(9)) Heinemann Library.

McCutcheon, Scott & McCutcheon, Bobbi. Space & Astronomy. 2005. (Pioneers in Science Ser.). (Illus.). 208p. (J). (gr. 6-12). 29.95 (978-0-8160-5467-1(3)) Facts On File, Inc.

Morris, Neil. Astronomers. (Illus.). 48p. (YA). (gr. 5 up). lib. bdg. 29.95 (978-1-932333-78-7(9)) Chrysalis Education.

Nardo, Don. Tycho Brahe: Pioneer of Astronomy. 2007. (J). lib. bdg. ***(978-0-7565-3309-0(0))*** Compass Point Bks.

Panchyk, Richard. Galileo for Kids: His Life & Ideas, 25 Activities. 2005. (For Kids Ser.). (Illus.). 184p. (J). pap. 16.95 (978-1-55652-566-7(4)) Chicago Review Pr., Inc.

Pinkney, Andrea Davis. Dear Benjamin Banneker. Pinkney, Brian, illus. 1998. 32p. (J). (gr. 1-5). pap. 7.00 (978-0-15-201892-4(1) , Harcourt Paperbacks) Harcourt Children's Bks.

—Dear Benjamin Banneker. 1998. 12.80 (978-0-606-13324-1(0)) Tandem Library Bks.

Robinson, Ella M. Stars in her Heart. 2005. 127p. per. 10.95 (978-1-57258-318-4(5)) TEACH Services, Inc.

Rodríguez, Ruiz & Jaime, Alejandro. Johannes Kepler -Del otro lado esta Dios. 2005. 124p. pap. (978-958-30-1647-9(0)) Panamericana Editorial.

Romero, Libby. Comets. 2006. pap. 39.00 ***(978-1-4108-6505-2(3))*** Benchmark Education Co.

Rusch, Elizabeth. The Planet Hunter. Francis, Guy, illus. 2007. 32p. 15.95 ***(978-0-87358-926-0(2)*** , Rising Moon Bks. for Young Readers) Northland Publishing.

Sakolsky, Josh. Copernicus & Modern Astronomy. 2004. (Primary Sources of Revolutionary Scientific Discoveries & Theories Ser.). (Illus.). 64p. (J). lib. bdg. 29.25 (978-1-4042-0305-1(2)) Rosen Publishing Group, Inc., The.

Silman, Roberta. Astronomers/Los Astronomos: English/Spanish Pair, 12 texts, 2 titles, Vol. 2. ed. 2004. (Navigators Ser.). (J). pap., instr.'s gde. ed. 84.00 (978-1-4108-1778-5(4) , 17784) Benchmark Education Co.

—Los Astronomos. ed. 2004. (Navigators Ser.). (SPA.). (J). pap. 42.00 (978-1-4108-1763-1(6)) Benchmark Education Co.

Sis, Peter. Starry Messenger. 2000. (gr. 3-6). lib. bdg. 15.25 (978-0-8085-0262-3(X)) Tandem Library Bks.

—Starry Messenger: Galileo Galilei. Sis, Peter, illus. 2000. (Illus.). 40p. (J). (ps-3). pap. 6.95 (978-0-374-47027-2(8) , Sunburst) Farrar, Straus & Giroux.

Somervill, Barbara A. Nicolaus Copernicus: Father of Modern Astronomy. 2004. (Signature Lives Ser.). (Illus.). 112p. (J). 30.60 (978-0-7565-0812-8(6)) Compass Point Bks.

Steele, Philip. Galileo: The Genius Who Faced the Inquisition. 2005. (World History Biographies Ser.). (Illus.). 64p. (J). (gr. 3-7). 17.95 (978-0-7922-3656-6(4)); 27.90 (978-0-7922-3657-3(2)) National Geographic Society. (National Geographic Children's Bks.).

Wadsworth, Ginger. Benjamin Banneker: Pioneering Scientist. Orback, Craig, illus. 2003. (On My Own Biographies Ser.). 48p. (J). (gr. 2-5). 25.26 (978-0-87614-916-4(0)) Lerner Publishing Group.

Weatherly, Myra. Benjamin Banneker: American Scientific Pioneer. 2006. (Signature Lives Ser.). (Illus.). 112p. (J). (gr. 5-7). 30.60 (978-0-7565-1579-9(3)) Compass Point Bks.

Welch, Catherine A. Benjamin Banneker. 2008. (History Maker Biographies Ser.). (J). lib. bdg. 26.60 ***(978-0-8225-7167-4(6)*** , Lerner Pubns.) Lerner Publishing Group.

Wills, Susan & Wills, Steven R. Astronomy: Looking at the Stars. Anderson, Jenna, ed. 2001. (Innovators Ser.: Vol. No. 8). (Illus.). 144p. (gr. 5 up). lib. bdg. 21.95 (978-1-881508-76-2(5)) Oliver Pr., Inc.

ASTRONOMICAL INSTRUMENTS

see also Telescopes

Angelo, Joseph A. Spacecraft for Astronomy. 2006. (Frontiers in Space Ser.). 304p. (YA). (gr. 9). 39.50 (978-0-8160-5774-0(5)) Facts On File, Inc.

ASTRONOMICAL OBSERVATORIES

see also Telescopes

Angelo, Joseph A. Spacecraft for Astronomy. 2006. (Frontiers in Space Ser.). 304p. (YA). (gr. 9). 39.50 (978-0-8160-5774-0(5)) Facts On File, Inc.

Julivert, Maria Angeles & Banqueri, Eduardo. Night Sky. 2007. (Field Guides Ser.). (Illus.). 32p. (J). (gr. 4-6). 16.95 (978-1-59270-066-0(7)) Enchanted Lion Bks., LLC.

ASTRONOMICAL PHYSICS

see Astrophysics

ASTRONOMICAL SPECTROSCOPY

see Astrophysics

ASTRONOMY

see also Almanacs; Astrology; Astrophysics; Life on Other Planets; Meteorites; Meteors; Moon; Outer Space; Planets; Radio Astronomy; Seasons; Solar System; Space Sciences; Stars; Sun; Tides

Adamson, Thomas K. Exploring the Galaxy. Saunders-Smith, Gail, ed. (Pebble Plus Ser.). (Illus.). (J). (gr. k-1). lib. bdg. 179.37 (978-0-7368-2326-5(3)) Capstone Pr., Inc.

Alberti, Theresa Jarosz. Out & About at the Planetarium. Shipe, Becky, illus. 2004. (Field Trips Ser.). 24p. (C). (gr. k-3). 23.93 (978-1-4048-0299-5(1)) Picture Window Bks.

Alex, Joanne DeFilipp. I Wonder What's Out There: A Vision of the Universe for Primary Classes. 2003. (Illus.). 64p. (J). spiral bd. (978-0-939195-32-9(1)) Parent Child Pr., Inc.

Allen, Tracey J. & Harmon, Jacque L. APOK Space Explorers. Allen, Tracey J. & Harmon, Jacque L., eds. Krudwig, Vickie Leigh & Stroud, Ricki, illus. 1999. 64p. (J). (gr. 1-6). pap. 14.95 (978-0-9664107-0-9(X)) APOK Kreations.

Amazing Science: Exploring the Sky. (C). 135.60 (978-1-4048-1523-0(6)) Picture Window Bks.

American Education Publishing Staff & School Specialty Publishing Staff. Astronomy. 2001. (Brighter Child Fact Card Ser.). (Illus.). 54p. (J). (gr. 3-5). 2.99 (978-1-56189-690-5(X) , 31386, American Education Publishing) School Specialty Publishing.

Artell, Mike. Starry Skies. 2007. 96p. pap. ***(978-1-59647-022-4(4))*** Good Year Bks.

Asimov, Isaac & Hantula, Richard. Asteroids. rev. ed. 2003. (Isaac Asimov's 21st Century Library of the Universe). (Illus.). 32p. (YA). (gr. 3 up). lib. bdg. 24.67 (978-0-8368-3233-4(7)) Stevens, Gareth Inc.

—Astronomy Projects. 2005. (Isaac Asimov's 21st Century Library of the Universe). (Illus.). 32p. (J). (gr. 3). lib. bdg. 24.67 (978-0-8368-3979-1(X)) Stevens, Gareth Inc.

—Astronomy Today. 2005. (Isaac Asimov's 21st Century Library of the Universe). (Illus.). 32p. (J). lib. bdg. 24.67 (978-0-8368-3980-7(3)) Stevens, Gareth Inc.

—Black Holes, Pulsars, & Quasars. 2005. (Isaac Asimov's 21st Century Library of the Universe). (Illus.). 32p. (J). lib. bdg. 24.67 (978-0-8368-3965-4(X)) Stevens, Gareth Inc.

—Isaac Asimov's 21st Century Library of the Universe: Set 2 : Fact & Fantasy, 6 Vols. 148.02 (978-0-8368-3949-4(8)) Stevens, Gareth Inc.

—Isaac Asimov's 21st Century Library of the Universe: Set 3 : Near & Far, 6 Vols. 148.02 (978-0-8368-3963-0(3)) Stevens, Gareth Inc.

—Legends, Folklore, & Outer Space. 2004. (Isaac Asimov's 21st Century Library of the Universe). (Illus.). 32p. (J). 24.67 (978-0-8368-3951-7(X)) Stevens, Gareth Inc.

—The Milky Way & Other Galaxies. 2005. (Isaac Asimov's 21st Century Library of the Universe). (Illus.). 32p. (J). lib. bdg. 24.67 (978-0-8368-3968-5(4)) Stevens, Gareth Inc.

—A Stargazer's Guide. 2004. (Isaac Asimov's 21st Century Library of the Universe). (Illus.). 32p. (J). lib. bdg. 24.67 (978-0-8368-3953-1(6)) Stevens, Gareth Inc.

Astronaut. 2002. (Risky Business Ser.). 24.94 (978-1-56711-672-4(8) , Blackbirch Pr., Inc.) Thomson Gale.

Astronaut Adventure, Vol. 2. (Early Intervention Levels Ser.). 3.55 (978-0-7362-0099-8(1)) Hampton-Brown Bks.

Astronomy Assessment Book: Unit 4: Astronomy. 2000. (McGraw-Hill Science Ser.). (gr. 6 up). (978-0-02-277774-6(1)) Macmillan/McGraw-Hill Schl. Div.

Astronomy Pupil Edition: Unit 4: Astronomy. 2000. (McGraw-Hill Science Ser.). (gr. 6 up). (978-0-02-278234-4(6)) Macmillan/McGraw-Hill Schl. Div.

Aylmore, Angela. I Like Outer Space. 2007. (Illus.). 24p. (J). (978-1-4034-9274-6(3)); lib. bdg. 21.36 (978-1-4034-9265-4(4)) Heinemann Library.

Bailey, Jacqui. The Birth of the Earth: A Cartoon History of the Earth, 4 vols. Lilly, Matthew, illus. 2001. (Cartoon History of the Earth Ser.). 32p. (J). (gr. 4-6). No. 1. (978-1-55337-080-2(5)); Vol. 1. (978-1-55337-071-0(6)) Kids Can Pr., Ltd.

Barnes, Mary. CX Ultimate Asteroid Book: The Inside Story on the Threat from the Skies. 1998. (gr. 3-6). lib. bdg. 11.80 (978-0-613-90609-8(8)) Tandem Library Bks.

Barnes-Svarney, Patricia L. A Traveler's Guide to the Solar System. 2008. (Illus.). 96p. (J). pap. 6.95 ***(978-1-4027-2628-6(7))*** Sterling Publishing Co., Inc.

Barnett, Alex. Black Holes. 2002. (ps-2). lib. bdg. 14.15 (978-0-613-57014-5(6)) Tandem Library Bks.

Basso, Bill, illus. Starry Skies. 2000. (Glow Sticker Stories Ser.). 20p. (J). (ps-3). mass mkt. 4.99 (978-0-448-42173-5(9) , Grosset & Dunlap) Penguin Group (USA) Inc.

BBC Staff, contrib. by. The Blue Planet Sticker Book. 2002. (Blue Planet Ser.). (Illus.). 16p. (J). (gr. 1-4). pap. 4.95 (978-0-439-33414-3(4)) Scholastic, Inc.

Becklake, Sue. Space. 2004. (Picture Reference Ser.). (SPA., Illus.). 48p. (gr. 3-6). (J). pap. 7.95 (978-1-58728-660-5(2)); 13.95 (978-1-58728-653-7(X)) T&N Children's Publishing. (Two Can Publishing).

—Space: The Book & Disk That Work Together. 2000. (Interfact Reference Ser.). (Illus.). 48p. (J). (gr. 3-6). 19.95 incl. cd-rom (978-1-58728-473-1(1) , Two Can Publishing) T&N Children's Publishing.

Bell, Trudy E. Comets, Meteors, Asteroids, & the Outer Reaches. 2003. (New Solar System Ser.). (J). lib. bdg. 28.50 (978-1-58340-289-4(6)) Smart Apple Media.

Bell, Trudy E. Earth's Journey Through Space. 2007. (Scientific American Ser.). 72p. (gr. 5-8). 30.00 ***(978-0-7910-9050-3(7)*** , Chelsea Hse.) Facts On File, Inc.

Benchmark Education Staff, compiled by. Earth & Space. 2006. spiral bd. 215.00 ***(978-1-4108-7106-0(1));*** 2006. spiral bd. 239.00 ***(978-1-4108-7120-6(7));*** 2005. spiral bd. 110.00 ***(978-1-4108-3873-5(0))*** Benchmark Education Co.

A
B

Bennett, Lorna & Galat, Joan Marie. Dot-to-Dot in the Sky: Stories in the Stars. Bennett, Lorna et al, illus. 2001. (Dot to Dot in the Sky Ser.). 64p. (J). (gr. 2-6). pap. 12.95 (978-1-55285-182-1(6)) Whitecap Bks., Ltd. CAN. *Dist:* Firefly Bks., Ltd.

Berger, Melvin. Do Stars Have Points? 1999. (Question & Answer Ser.). (J). 12.75 (978-0-606-20054-7(1)) Tandem Library Bks.

Berger, Melvin & Berger, Gilda. Do Stars Have Points? Questions & Answers about Stars & Planets. Di Fate, Vincent, illus. 1999. (Scholastic Question & Answer Ser.). 48p. (J). (gr. 2-4). pap. 12.95 (978-0-590-13080-6(3)); pap. 6.99 (978-0-439-08570-0(5)) Scholastic, Inc. (Scholastic Reference).

Between the Lions - Early Literacy Kit - Shooting Stars, 1 cass., 1 bk. 2005. (Between the Lions Ser.). 36p. (J). VHS 29.95 (978-1-59375-285-9(7) , WG38633) WGBH Boston Video.

Bhathal, Ragbir & Jenny, Bhathal. Australian Backyard Astronomy. 2006. (Illus.). 132p. (J). pap. (***978-0-642-27632-2(3)***) National Library of Australia.

Birch, Robin. Space Series, 6 vols., Set. 2005. (Illus.). 32p. (gr. 2-4). pap. 138.00 (978-0-7910-7053-6(0) , Chelsea Hse.) Facts On File, Inc.

—Stars. (Solar System Ser.). (Illus.). 32p. 2004. (gr. 3-5). 23.00 (978-0-7910-7933-1(3)); 2002. (gr. k-2). 23.00 (978-0-7910-6971-4(0)) Facts On File, Inc. (Chelsea Hse.).

Blast Off!, 6 Pack. (gr. k-1). 23.00 (978-0-7635-9078-9(9)) Rigby Education.

Boerst, William J. Johannes Kepler: Discovering the Laws of Celestial Motion. 2004. (Profiles in Science Ser.). (Illus.). 144p. (YA). (gr. 6-12). lib. bdg. 26.95 (978-1-883846-98-5(6) , First Biographies) Reynolds, Morgan Inc.

Bonar, Samantha. Asteroids. 1999. (gr. 5-8). lib. bdg. 17.60 (978-0-613-29399-0(1)) Tandem Library Bks.

Bond, Peter. Guide to Space: A Photographic Journey Through the Universe. 1999. (DK Guides Ser.). (Illus.). 64p. (J). (gr. 4-7). 19.99 (978-0-7894-3946-8(8)) Dorling Kindersley Publishing, Inc.

—Space. 2006. 64p. (J). (gr. 8). pap. 7.99 (978-0-7566-2230-5(1)) Dorling Kindersley Publishing, Inc.

Bortolotti, Dan. Exploring Saturn: From Galileo to Cassini. 2003. (Illus.). 64p. (J). (gr. 4-8). 19.95 (978-1-55297-766-8(8)); pap. 9.95 (978-1-55297-765-1(X)) Firefly Bks., Ltd.

Bourgeois, Paulette & Slavin, Bill. Starting with Space: The Moon.Tr. of Destination Univers: La Lune. (FRE., Illus.). 40p. (J). pap. 8.99 (978-0-590-16020-9(6)) Scholastic, Inc.

—Starting with Space: The Sun.Tr. of Destination Univers: Le Soleil. (FRE., Illus.). 40p. (J). pap. 8.99 (978-0-590-16019-3(2)) Scholastic, Inc.

Bramwell, Martyn. Mapping the Planets & Space. 1998. (Maps & Mapmakers Ser.). (Illus.). 48p. (J). (gr. 5-7). lib. bdg. 22.60 (978-0-8225-2922-4(X) , Lerner Pubns.) Lerner Publishing Group.

Braun, Eric. Mae Jemison. 2006. (Illus.). 24p. (J). 15.93 (978-0-7368-4231-0(4) , 1243882, Pebble Bks.) Capstone Pr., Inc.

Bulletpoints Astronomy. 2005. (Illus.). (J). per. 4.99 (978-1-933581-00-2(X) , Byeway) Byeway Bks.

Bullock, Linda. Looking Through a Telescope. (Rookie Read-About Science Ser.). (Illus.). (J). 2004. 31p. (gr. 1-2). pap. 4.95 (978-0-516-27906-0(8)); 2003. 32p. 20.50 (978-0-516-22873-0(0)) Scholastic Library Publishing. (Children's Pr.).

Campbell, Ann-Jeanette. Espacio Asombroso. 2001. Tr. of Amazing Space. 19.60 (978-0-606-22716-2(4)) Tandem Library Bks.

Capogna, Vera Vullo. Did You Ever Wonder about Things You See in the Sky? 1999. (Did You Ever Wonder? Ser.). (Illus.). 32p. (J). (gr. k-3). lib. bdg. 22.79 (978-0-7614-0853-6(3) , Benchmark Bks.) Cavendish, Marshall Corp.

Carson, Jana. We Both Read-about Space. 2001. (We Both Read Ser.). (Illus.). 44p. (J). (gr. 1-2). 7.99 (978-1-891327-39-1(9)); pap. 3.99 (978-1-891327-40-7(2)) Treasure Bay, Inc.

Carson, Mary Kay. Exploring the Solar System: A History with 22 Activities. rev. ed. 2008. 176p. (J). (gr. 4 up). pap. 17.95 (***978-1-55652-715-9(2)***) Chicago Review Pr., Inc.

Caviezel, Giovanni. Our Planet Earth. Pagnoni, Roberta, illus. 2004. 40p. (J). bds. 8.95 (978-0-7641-5750-9(7)) Barron's Educational Series, Inc.

Cefrey, Holly. What If an Asteroid Hit Earth? 2002. (What If Ser.). (Illus.). 48p. (YA). (gr. 7-12). 24.00 (978-0-516-23911-8(2) , Children's Pr.) Scholastic Library Publishing.

Chaisson, Eric & McMillan, Steve. Astronomy Today. 2002. 688p. (YA). (gr. 9-12). stu. ed. (978-0-13-094334-7(7)) Prentice Hall Pr.

Chapman, Cindy. What Is in the Sky? 2003. (Compass Point Phonics Readers Ser.). (Illus.). 16p. (J). (gr. 1 up). 13.26 (978-0-7565-0513-4(5)) Compass Point Bks.

Chrisp, Peter. Space Exploration. 2004. (Discovery Guides Ser.). (SPA., Illus.). 32p. (gr. 2-5). 11.95 (978-1-58728-231-7(3) , Two Can Publishing) T&N Children's Publishing.

Clark, Stuart. Discovering the Universe. 2000. (Inside Look Ser.). (Illus.). 48p. (J). (gr. 4 up). lib. bdg. 26.00 (978-0-8368-2724-8(4)) Stevens, Gareth Inc.

Cole, Michael D. Hubble Space Telescope: Exploring the Universe. 1999. (Countdown to Space Ser.). (Illus.). 48p. (YA). (gr. 4-10). lib. bdg. 23.93 (978-0-7660-1120-5(8)) Enslow Pubs., Inc.

Collins, Heather, illus. Twinkle, Twinkle Little Star. 2004. (Traditional Nursery Rhyme Board Bks.). 12p. (J). (ps-k). (978-1-55074-566-5(2)) Kids Can Pr., Ltd.

Collison, Cathy. An Out of This World Alphabet. rev. ed. 2007. 40p. pap. 7.95 (***978-1-58536-335-3(9)***) Sleeping Bear Pr.

Collison, Cathy & Campbell, Janis. G Is for Galaxy: An Out of This World Alphabet. Stacy, Alan, illus. 2005. (World/Country Alphabet Ser.). 40p. (J). (gr. k-5). 16.95 (978-1-58536-255-4(7)) Sleeping Bear Pr.

Conrad, David. Out in Space. 2002. (Spyglass Books). (Illus.). 24p. (J). (gr. 1 up). 18.60 (978-0-7565-0242-3(X)) Compass Point Bks.

Contemporary Discourse in the Field of Astronomy, 6 bks., Set. 2006. (YA). lib. bdg. 183.60 (978-1-4042-0628-1(0)) Rosen Publishing Group, Inc., The.

Croswell, Ken. See the Stars: Your First Guide to the Night Sky. 2003. (Illus.). 32p. (YA). (gr. 2-4). 16.95 (978-1-56397-757-2(5)) Boyds Mills Pr.

Davies, Francis. The Universe. Davico, Francesco & Cecchi, Lorenzo, illus. 2000. (Nature's Record-Breakers Ser.). 32p. (J). (gr. 3 up). lib. bdg. 23.33 (978-0-8368-2476-6(8)) Stevens, Gareth Inc.

Davis, Kenneth C. Don't Know Much about Space. Ruzzier, Sergio, illus. 2001. (Don't Know Much About Ser.). 144p. (J). (gr. 2 up). pap. 6.99 (978-0-06-440835-6(3) , Harper Trophy); 19.89 (978-0-06-028602-6(4)) HarperCollins Pubs.

—Don't Know Much about Space. unabr. ed. 2004. (Don't Know Much about(R) Ser.). 144p. (J). (gr. 4-7). pap. 29.00 incl. audio (978-0-8072-0661-4(X) , Listening Library) Random Hse. Audio Publishing Group.

—Don't Know Much about Space. 2001. 13.64 (978-0-606-22305-8(3)) Tandem Library Bks.

Davis, Phyllis Rowe. On a Clear Night: Poetic Description of Constellations. Wolff, Glenn, illus. 2001. 60p. (Orig.). (YA). (gr. 10 up). pap. 11.95 (978-0-9714964-0-8(4)) Fidjus.

Deboo, Ana. Mapping the Seas & Skies. 2006. (Illus.). 32p. (J). (978-1-4034-6793-5(5)); pap. (978-1-4034-6800-0(1)) Heinemann Library.

Delafosse, Claude. Space. Grant, Donald, illus. 2000. (Hidden World Ser.). 30p. (J). (ps-2). 12.95 (978-0-439-14826-9(X)) Scholastic, Inc.

Delano, Marfe Ferguson. Sky. 1998. (National Geographic Nature Library). (J). (978-0-7922-7047-8(9)) National Geographic Society.

Di Gesu, V., et al, eds. Data Analysis in Astronomy: Proceedings of the 5th Workshop Ettore Majorana Center for Scientific Culture, Erice, Italy, 27 October-3 November 1996. 1998. (Science & Culture Ser.). 440p. 86.00 (978-981-02-3171-2(7)) World Scientific Publishing Co., Inc.

Diagram Group. Space & Astronomy. 2006. (Science Visual Resources Ser.). 208p. (gr. 6-12). 49.50 (978-0-8160-6168-6(8)) Facts On File, Inc.

Dickinson, Terence. The Universe & Beyond. 4th rev. ed. 2004. (Illus.). 180p. (gr. 7). 40.00 (978-1-55297-937-2(7)); pap. 29.95 (978-1-55297-901-3(6)) Firefly Bks., Ltd.

DiSpezio, Michael Anthony. Space Mania: Discovering Distant Worlds Without Leaving Your Own. 2004. (Illus.). 80p. (J). pap. 6.95 (978-1-4027-1772-7(5)) Sterling Publishing Co., Inc.

DK Publishing Staff. Night Sky Atlas. 2007. 48p. (J). (gr. 3-8). 19.99 (978-0-7566-2839-0(3)) Dorling Kindersley Publishing, Inc.

—Secrets of the Night Sky: Cub Scout Activity Series. 2006. 24p. (J). pap. 2.49 (978-0-7566-2796-6(0)) Dorling Kindersley Publishing, Inc.

Dorling Kindersley Publishing Staff. Smithsonian Stargazer. 2005. (Nature Activities Ser.). (Illus.). 72p. (J). (gr. 8). pap. 9.99 (978-0-7566-1031-9(1)) Dorling Kindersley Publishing, Inc.

—Starry Sky. 2006. (Dk Readers Ser.). (Illus.). 32p. (J). 14.99 (978-0-7566-1960-2(2)); (gr. 5). pap. 3.99 (978-0-7566-1959-6(9)) Dorling Kindersley Publishing, Inc.

—Universe. 2003. (Eyewitness Bks.). (Illus.). 64p. (J). (gr. 3). lib. bdg. 19.99 (978-0-7894-9549-5(X)) Dorling Kindersley Publishing, Inc.

—1001 Facts about Space. 2002. (gr. 3-6). lib. bdg. 17.60 (978-0-613-75144-5(2)) Tandem Library Bks.

Dorling Kindersley Publishing Staff & Kerrod, Robin. Universe. 2003. (Eyewitness Bks.). (Illus.). 64p. (J). pap. 15.99 (978-0-7894-9238-8(5)) Dorling Kindersley Publishing, Inc.

Dowswell, Paul. Mi Primera Enciclopedia del Espacio. rev. ed. 2004. (Bible Tales Readers Ser.).Tr. of First Encyclopedia of Space. (SPA.). 16p. (J). lib. bdg. 17.95 (978-1-58086-495-4(3)) EDC Publishing.

Doyle, Bill. The Space Explorer's Guide to the Universe. Labat, Yancey C., illus. 2003. (Space University Ser.). 48p. (J). (978-0-439-55739-9(9)) Scholastic, Inc.

Driscoll, Michael & Hamilton, Meredith. Child's Introduction to the Night Sky: The Story of the Stars, Planets & Constellations—And How You Can Find Them in the Sky. 2004. (Illus.). 96p. tchr. ed. 19.95 (978-1-57912-366-6(X) , 81366) Black Dog & Leventhal Pubs., Inc.

Dyer, Alan. Space. 2007. (Insiders Ser.). 64p. (J). 16.99 (***978-1-4169-3860-6(5)***) Simon & Schuster Children's Publishing.

Elish, Dan. The Galaxies. 2006. (Kaleidoscope Space Ser.). (Illus.). 48p. (J). lib. bdg. 28.50 (978-0-7614-2047-7(9) , Benchmark Bks.) Cavendish, Marshall Corp.

Elkins-Tanton, Linda T. Asteroids, Meteorites, & Comets. 2006. (Solar System Ser.). (Illus.). 232p. (YA). (gr. 6-12). lib. bdg. 37.50 (978-0-8160-5195-3(X)) Facts On File, Inc.

Eugene, Toni. Discover Stars & Planets. 2005. (Discover Ser.). (Illus.). 48p. (J). (978-0-7853-6113-8(8) , 3013606) Publications International, Ltd.

—Exploring Space. 1999. (978-0-7922-9433-7(5)); (978-0-7922-9426-9(2)) National Geographic Society.

Explore Space!, 12 bks. (Illus.). (J). (gr. 1-2). lib. bdg. 223.20 (978-0-7368-1403-4(5) , Bridgestone Bks.) Capstone Pr., Inc.

Explore Space!, 8 bks. Incl. Astronauts at Work. Shearer, Deborah A. 2002. lib. bdg. 18.60 (978-0-7368-1142-2(7)); Christa McAuliffe. Streissguth, Thomas. 2003. lib. bdg. 18.60 (978-0-7368-1624-3(0)); Exploring Mars. Shearer, Deborah A. 2002. lib. bdg. 18.60 (978-0-7368-1399-0(3)); John Glenn. Streissguth, Thomas. 2003. lib. bdg. 18.60 (978-0-7368-1625-0(9)); Mae Jemison. Streissguth, Thomas. 2003. lib. bdg. 18.60 (978-0-7368-1626-7(7)); Mission Control. Shearer, Deborah A. 2002. lib. bdg. 18.60 (978-0-7368-1143-9(5)); Neil Armstrong. Streissguth, Thomas. 2003. lib. bdg. 18.60 (978-0-7368-1627-4(5)); Rockets. Vogt, Gregory L. 1999. lib. bdg. 18.60 (978-0-7368-0198-0(7)); Satellites. Deady, Kathleen W. 2002. lib. bdg. 18.60 (978-0-7368-1400-3(0)); Space Missions. Shearer, Deborah A. 2002. lib. bdg. 18.60 (978-0-7368-1401-0(9)); Space Robots. Vogt, Gregory L. 1999. lib. bdg. 18.60 (978-0-7368-0199-7(5)); Space Shuttles. Vogt, Gregory L. 1999. lib. bdg. 18.60 (978-0-7368-0200-0(2)); Space Stations. Vogt, Gregory L. & Vogt, Gregory L. 1999. lib. bdg. 18.60 (978-0-7368-0201-7(0)); Space Suits. Shearer, Deborah A. 2002. lib. bdg. 18.60 (978-0-7368-1144-6(3)); Space Walks. Deady, Kathleen W. 2002. lib. bdg. 18.60 (978-0-7368-1402-7(7)); Walking on the Moon. Shearer, Deborah A. 2002. lib. bdg. 18.60 (978-0-7368-1145-3(1)); 24p. (J). (gr. 1-2). (Illus.). Set lib. bdg. 297.60 (978-0-7368-1638-0(0) , Bridgestone Bks.) Capstone Pr., Inc.

Farndon, John. From Ptolemy's Spheres to Dark Energy: Discovering the Universe. 2007. (Illus.). 64p. (J). (***978-1-4034-9553-2(X)***) Heinemann Library.

Feely, Jenny. In the Sky. 2001. (gr. k-3). lib. bdg. 11.95 (978-0-613-33381-8(0)) Tandem Library Bks.

Firestone, Mary. Astrobiologist. 2005. (Weird Careers in Science Ser.). (Illus.). 65p. (J). (gr. 4-8). lib. bdg. 25.00 (978-0-7910-8971-2(1) , Chelsea Hse.) Facts On File, Inc.

Firth, Rachel. Astronomy. 48p. (J). lib. bdg. 16.95 (978-1-58086-689-7(1) , Usborne) EDC Publishing.

—Astronomy - Internet Linked. Woodcock, John, illus. 2004. (Discovery Program Ser.). 48p. (J). pap. 8.95 (978-0-7945-0484-7(1) , Usborne) EDC Publishing.

Flight Science. 2004. (Formula Fun Ser.). (Illus.). 48p. (J). (978-1-84229-589-2(6)) Top That! Publishing PLC.

Fontany, Elena. Other Worlds Than This. 2005. reprint ed. pap. 19.95 (978-1-4179-9707-7(9)) Kessinger Publishing, LLC.

Fredette, Nathalie & Lafleur, Claude. Exploring the Universe. 2001. (Twenty-First Century Science Ser.). (Illus.). 64p. (J). (gr. 5 up). lib. bdg. 32.67 (978-0-8368-5001-7(7) , World Almanac Library) Stevens, Gareth Inc.

Fried, Ellen. Stars & Galaxies. 2004. (National Geographic Reading Expeditions Ser.). (Illus.). 32p. (J). pap. (978-0-7922-4574-2(1)) National Geographic Society.

Furniss, Tim. Moon. 2000. (gr. k-3). lib. bdg. 17.60 (978-0-613-74045-6(9)) Tandem Library Bks.

Gaff, Jackie. Superman's Guide to the Universe. 2003. (Dk Readers Ser.). (Illus.). 48p. (J). pap. 3.99 (978-0-7894-9754-3(9)) Dorling Kindersley Publishing, Inc.

Gaff, Jackie & Dorling Kindersley Publishing Staff. Superman's Guide to the Universe. 2003. (Readers Ser.). (Illus.). 48p. (J). 12.99 (978-0-7894-9746-8(8)) Dorling Kindersley Publishing, Inc.

Galat, Joan Marie. Dot to Dot in the Sky: Stories in the Planets. 2003. (gr. 3-6). lib. bdg. 22.20 (978-0-613-78525-9(8)) Tandem Library Bks.

—Stories in the Planets. Bennett, Lorna & Yu, Chao, illus. 2003. (Dot to Dot in the Sky Ser.). 64p. (J). (gr. 2-6). pap. 12.95 (978-1-55285-392-4(6)) Whitecap Bks., Ltd. CAN. *Dist:* Firefly Bks., Ltd.

—Stories of the Zodiac. Bennett, Lorna, illus. 2007. (Dot to Dot in the Sky Ser.). 64p. (J). (gr. 2-6). pap. 14.95 (978-1-55285-805-9(7) , Walrus Bks.) Whitecap Bks., Ltd. CAN. *Dist:* Firefly Bks., Ltd.

Galaxies & the Universe. 2006. (World Book's Solar System & Space Exploration Library). 63p. (J). (978-0-7166-9508-0(1)) World Bk., Inc.

The Galaxy, 14 bks. Incl. Asteroids. Vogt, Gregory L. 2002. lib. bdg. 18.60 (978-0-7368-1118-7(4)); Comets. Vogt, Gregory L. 2002. lib. bdg. 18.60 (978-0-7368-1119-4(2)); Constellations. Vogt, Gregory L. 2002. lib. bdg. 18.60 (978-0-7368-1382-2(9)); Earth. Kipp, Steven L. 2000. lib. bdg. 18.60 (978-0-7368-0521-6(4)); Jupiter. Vogt, Gregory L. 2000. lib. bdg. 18.60 (978-0-7368-0512-4(5)); Mars. Kipp, Steven L. 2000. lib. bdg. 18.60 (978-0-7368-0520-9(6)); Mercury. Kipp, Steven L. 2000. lib. bdg. 18.60 (978-0-7368-0518-6(4)); Meteors & Meteorites. Vogt, Gregory L. 2002. lib. bdg. 18.60 (978-0-7368-1120-0(6)); Milky Way. Vogt, Gregory L. 2002. lib. bdg. 18.60 (978-0-7368-1384-6(5)); Moons. Vogt, Gregory L. 2002. lib. bdg. 18.60 (978-0-7368-1383-9(7)); Neptune. Vogt, Gregory L. 2000. lib. bdg. 18.60 (978-0-7368-0513-1(3)); Pluto. Vogt, Gregory L. 2000. lib. bdg. 18.60 (978-0-7368-0514-8(1)); Saturn. Vogt, Gregory L. 2000. lib. bdg. 18.60 (978-0-7368-0515-5(X)); Solar System. Vogt, Gregory L. 2002. lib. bdg. 18.60 (978-0-7368-1385-3(3)); Stars. Vogt, Gregory L. 2002. lib. bdg. 18.60 (978-0-7368-1121-7(4)); Sun. Vogt, Gregory L. 2000. lib. bdg. 18.60 (978-0-7368-0516-2(8)); Uranus. Vogt, Gregory L. 2000. lib. bdg. 18.60 (978-0-7368-0517-9(6)); Venus. Kipp, Steven L. 2000. lib. bdg. 18.60 (978-0-7368-0519-3(2)); 24p. (J). (gr. 2-3). (Illus.). Set lib. bdg. 334.80 (978-0-7368-1386-0(1) , Bridgestone Bks.) Capstone Pr., Inc.

The Galaxy Classroom Library. (gr. 2-5). lib. bdg. 57.95 (978-0-7368-8977-3(9)) Red Brick Learning.

The Galaxy Complete Unit. (gr. 2-5). 331.95 (978-0-7368-8978-0(7)) Red Brick Learning.

Gallant, Roy A. Comets, Asteroids & Meteorites. 2001. (Kaleidoscope Ser.). (Illus.). 48p. (J). (gr. 3 up). lib. bdg. 25.64 (978-0-7614-1034-8(1) , Benchmark Bks.) Cavendish, Marshall Corp.

—Eyes on the Universe. 2000. (Story of Science Ser.). (Illus.). 80p. (J). (gr. 5 up). lib. bdg. 29.93 (978-0-7614-1154-3(2) , Benchmark Bks.) Cavendish, Marshall Corp.

Gardner, Robert. Astronomy Projects with an Observatory You Can Build. 2007. (Build-a-Lab! Science Experiments Ser.). (Illus.). 128p. (J). (gr. 5). lib. bdg. 31.93 (***978-0-7660-2808-1(9)***) Enslow Pubs., Inc.

Gareth Stevens Publishing Staff, contrib. by. The Universe. 2003. (Discovery Channel School Science Ser.). (Illus.). 32p. (J). (gr. 5 up). lib. bdg. 24.67 (978-0-8368-3374-4(0)) Stevens, Gareth Inc.

Gentle, Victor & Perry, Janet. Asteroid Strikes. 2001. (Natural Disasters Ser.). (Illus.). 24p. (J). (gr. 2 up). lib. bdg. 22.00 (978-0-8368-2831-3(3)) Stevens, Gareth Inc.

George, Michael. Stars: Beacons in the Sky. 2003. (LifeViews Ser.). (Illus.). 32p. (J). lib. bdg. (978-1-58341-250-3(6) , Creative Education) Creative Co., The.

Gibbons, Gail. Galaxies, Galaxies! Gibbons, Gail, illus. 2006. (Illus.). 32p. (J). 16.95 (978-0-8234-2002-5(7)) Holiday Hse., Inc.

Gifford, Clive. The Kingfisher Facts & Records Book of Space: The Ultimate Information Database. 2001. (Facts & Records Ser.). (Illus.). 64p. (J). (gr. 4-6). tchr. ed. 14.95 (978-0-7534-5363-6(0) , Kingfisher) Houghton Mifflin Co. Trade & Reference Div.

—The Kingfisher Geography Encyclopedia. 2003. (Kingfisher Encyclopedias Ser.). (Illus.). 498p. (J). (gr. 4-8). tchr. ed. 39.95 (978-0-7534-5591-3(9) , Kingfisher) Houghton Mifflin Co. Trade & Reference Div.

Gillis, Jennifer Blizin. Planetariums. 2008. (J). (***978-1-60044-562-0(4)***) Rourke Publishing, LLC.

Glover, David. Space: The Hands-on Approach to Science. 2000. (gr. 3-6). lib. bdg. 15.25 (978-0-613-43381-5(5)) Tandem Library Bks.

Goldsmith, Mike. Space Mysteries. 2001. (Spinning Through Space Ser.). (Illus.). 32p. (J). (gr. 2-4). lib. bdg. 25.69 (978-0-7398-2745-1(6)) Raintree.

Goodman, Polly. Space & Art Activities. 2002. (Arty Facts Ser.). (Illus.). 48p. (J). (gr. 3-4). pap. (978-0-7787-1140-7(4)); lib. bdg. (978-0-7787-1112-4(9)) Crabtree Publishing Co.

—Space & Art Activities. 2002. (ps-2). lib. bdg. 17.60 (978-0-613-57136-4(3)) Tandem Library Bks.

Gore, Bryson. Astronomy: Every Galaxy Has a Black Hole. 2005. (Wow Science Ser.). (Illus.). 32p. (J). (gr. 4). lib. bdg. 27.10 (978-1-59604-068-7(8)) Stargazer Bks.

Goss, Tim & Gyuk, Geza. The Universe: The Outer Planets. 2007. (J). (***978-1-4329-0168-4(0)***); pap. (***978-1-4329-0180-6(X)***) Heinemann Library.

Gottlieb. Earth & Beyond. 2004. pap., tchr. ed. 17.60 incl. cd-rom (978-0-7398-9187-2(1)) Steck-Vaughn.

Graun, Ken. Our Constellations & Their Stars. 2004. (Twenty-First Century Astronomy Ser.: 3). (Illus.). 36p. (J). 15.95 (978-1-928771-09-8(2)) Ken Pr.

Graun, Ken & Maly, Suzanne. Our Galaxy & the Universe. 2002. (Twenty-First Century Astronomy Ser.: 2). (Illus.). 36p. (J). 15.95 (978-1-928771-08-1(4)) Ken Pr.

Grice, Noreen. The Little Moon Phase Book. Gendler, Robert, photos by. 2005. (Illus.). 12p. (J). spiral bd. 23.95 (978-0-9773285-0-5(3)) Ozone Publishing, Corp.

Guidici, Cynthia. Adriana Ocampo. 2006. (Biografías Hispanoamericanas Ser.). (J). (978-1-4109-2127-7(1)); pap. (978-1-4109-2134-5(4)) Steck-Vaughn.

Halls, Kelly Milner. Astronomy & Space. 2006. (Science Fair Projects Ser.). (Illus.). 48p. (J). (gr. 6-9). lib. bdg. 30.00 (978-1-4034-7908-2(9)) Heinemann Library.

Handwerker, Mark J. Ready-to-Use Earth & Astronomical Activities for Grades 5-12. 2000. (Secondary Science Curriculum Activities Library: Vol. 4). (Illus.). 256p. (J). pap. 27.50 (978-0-13-029100-4(5) , Addison Wesley) Benjamin-Cummings Publishing Co.

Hans, E. M. Constellations. Sloan, Frank, ed. 2001. (Spinning Through Space Ser.). (Illus.). 32p. (J). (gr. 3-4). lib. bdg. 25.69 (978-0-7398-2743-7(X)) Raintree.

Hansen, Rosanna. Mysteries in Space: A Chapter Book. 48p. (J). 2006. (gr. 2-4). pap. 4.95 (978-0-516-25450-0(2)); 2005. (Illus.). (ps-ps). 22.50 (978-0-516-25185-1(6)) Scholastic Library Publishing. (Children's Pr.).

—Seeing Stars: The Milky Way & Its Constellations. Harris, Greg, illus. 2002. (J). 3.99 (978-0-439-32100-6(X)) Scholastic, Inc.

Harcourt School Publishers Staff. Hale y Bopp Below Level. 3rd ed. 2002. (Trofeos Ser.). (SPA., Illus.). pap. 6.80 (978-0-15-324071-3(7)) Harcourt Schl. Pubs.

—How the Sky Got Its Starr. 3rd ed. 2004. (Trophies Reading Program Ser.). (Illus.). (J). (gr. k). pap. 11.50 (978-0-15-340895-3(2)) Harcourt Schl. Pubs.

—Sky Life On Level: Living in Space. 3rd ed. 2002. (Trophies Reading Program Ser.). (Illus.). pap. 5.10 (978-0-15-323458-3(X)) Harcourt Schl. Pubs.

Harrington, Philip S. & Pascuzzi, Edward. Astronomy for All Ages: Discovering the Universe Through Activities for Children & Adults. 2nd ed. 2000. (Illus.). 224p. pap. 19.95 (978-0-7627-0809-3(3)) Globe Pequot Pr., The.

Henry, Jonathan. The Astronomy Book. 2005. pap., stu. ed. 3.99 (978-1-893345-61-4(0)) Answers in Genesis Ministries.

Heudier, Jean-Louis. The Night Sky Month by Month: January to December 2005. 2004. (Night Sky Month by Month Ser.). (Illus.). 240p. pap. 24.95 (978-1-55297-972-3(5)) Firefly Bks., Ltd.

Holland, Simon & Dorling Kindersley Publishing Staff. Space. 2001. (Eye Wonder Ser.). (Illus.). 48p. (J). (gr. k-3). lib. bdg. 17.95 (978-0-7894-8182-5(0)) Dorling Kindersley Publishing, Inc.

Holland, Simon & Stott, Carole. Space. Holland, Simon & Ling, Mary, eds. 2001. (Eye Wonder Ser.). (Illus.). 48p. (J). (gr. k-3). 9.99 (978-0-7894-7854-2(4)) Dorling Kindersley Publishing, Inc.

Holt, Laurence. Stikky Night Skies. 2003. (Illus.). 240p. (YA). 12.00 (978-1-56858-253-5(6)) Avalon Publishing Group.

Holt, Rinehart and Winston Staff. Astronomy, Vol. J. 3rd ed. 2003. (Holt Science & Technology Ser.). (SPA.). 18.60 (978-0-03-069319-9(5)) Holt, Rinehart & Winston.

—Astronomy: Item Listing, Group J. 2nd ed. 2001. (Holt Science & Technology Ser.). pap. 11.26 (978-0-03-065519-7(6)) Holt, Rinehart & Winston.

—Astronomy 2002, Pt. J. 2nd ed. 2002. (Holt Science & Technology Ser.). (Illus.). 18.60 (978-0-03-064794-9(0)); tchr. ed. 46.66 (978-0-03-064796-3(7)) Holt, Rinehart & Winston.

—Astronomy Science Kit: Consumable Edition, Module J. 2nd ed. 2002. (Holt Science & Technology Ser.). 141.86 (978-0-03-067642-0(8)) Holt, Rinehart & Winston.

—Astronomy Science Kit: Non-Consumable Edition, Module J. 2nd ed. 2002. (Holt Science & Technology Ser.). 349.86 (978-0-03-067623-9(1)) Holt, Rinehart & Winston.

Hunter, Rebecca M. Space. 2001. (Discovering Science Ser.). (Illus.). 32p. (J). (gr. 4-7). lib. bdg. 25.69 (978-0-7398-3248-6(4)) Raintree.

Irion, Robert. Galaxies: Island Universes. 2001. (Out There Ser.). (Illus.). 66p. (J). 6.98 (978-0-7621-0312-6(4)) Reader's Digest Assn., Inc., The.

Isaac Asimov's 21st Century Library of the Universe: Set 4 : Past & Present, 6 Vols. 148.02 (978-0-8368-3977-7(3)) Stevens, Gareth Inc.

Jerome, Kate Boehm. Exploring Space. 2002. (Earth Science Ser.). (Illus.). 32p. (J). (978-0-7922-8870-1(X)) National Geographic Society.

Jobb, Jamie. Brown Paper School Book: The Night Sky Book. 2006. 128p. (J). pap. 12.99 (978-0-316-05983-1(8)) Little Brown & Co.

—The Night Sky Book: An Everyday Guide to Every Night. Bennett, Linda, illus. 1999. 127p. (YA). (gr. 7-10). reprint ed. pap. 10.00 (978-0-7881-6695-2(6)) DIANE Publishing Co.

Johnstone, Michael. Space News. 2001. (978-0-606-22540-3(4)) Tandem Library Bks.

Kenah, Katharine. Space Mysteries. 2004. (Extreme Readers Ser.). (Illus.). 32p. (J). (gr. 1-2). pap. 3.95 (978-0-7696-3187-5(8)) School Specialty Publishing.

Kerrod, Robin. Astronomy. 2000. (Fantastic Facts Ser.). (Illus.). 64p. (gr. 3-7). pap. 6.95 (978-1-84215-201-0(7) , Southwater) Anness Publishing GBR. *Dist:* National Bk. Network.

—Night Sky. 2001. (Illus.). 32p. (J). lib. bdg. 24.25 (978-1-930643-25-3(X)) Chrysalis Education.

—The Night Sky. 2001. (Exploring the Universe Ser.). (Illus.). 48p. (J). lib. bdg. 27.12 (978-0-7398-2815-1(0)) Raintree.

—The Sun's Family. 1999. (J). (978-1-57505-363-9(2) , Carolrhoda Bks.) Lerner Publishing Group.

Kerrod, Robin & Sparrow, Giles. The Way the Universe Works: Discover the Secrets of Space. Parsons, Jayne, ed. 2002. (Illus.). 160p. (J). (gr. 3-12). 24.99 (978-0-7894-8890-9(6)) Dorling Kindersley Publishing, Inc.

Khan, Hena. The Space Explorer's Guide to Earth's Neighborhood. 2003. (Space University Ser.). (Illus.). 48p. (J). (978-0-439-55741-2(0)) Scholastic, Inc.

Khan, Sarah. Night Sky Sticker Bk. 2007. 24p. (J). pap. 8.99 (978-0-7945-1563-8(0) , Usborne) EDC Publishing.

King, Penny & Roundhill, Clare. Out of This World. 1998. (Making Pictures Ser.). (J). (978-1-57572-193-4(7)) Rigby Education.

Klutz Press Staff. Backyard Stars. 1998. (Klutz Guides). (Illus.). (YA). (gr. 4-7). 4.95 (978-1-57054-172-8(8)) Klutz.

Knocke, Melanie Melton. Astronomy. Garbot, Dave, illus. 2008. (Little Giant Bks.). 352p. (J). pap. 6.95 (*978-1-4027-3234-8(1)) Sterling Publishing Co., Inc.

Koltenkamp, Steve. The Milky Way. 2008. (J). (*978-1-4296-0061-3(6)) Capstone Pr., Inc.

Kranz, Rachel. Our Solar System/el sistema Solar: English/Spanish Pair, 12 texts, 2 titles, Vol. 2. ed. 2004. (Navigators Ser.). (J). pap., instr.'s gde. ed. 84.00 (978-1-4108-1766-2(0) , 17660) Benchmark Education Co.

LaFontaine, Bruce. Constellations of the Night Sky. 2003. (Dover Coloring Bks.). (Illus.). 48p. (J). pap. 3.95 (978-0-486-42648-8(3)) Dover Pubns., Inc.

Larousse Kingfisher Chambers Staff & Kerrod, Robin. Stars & Planets. 2000. (Questions & Answers about... Ser.). (Illus.). 40p. (J). (gr. 4-6). pap. 7.95 (978-0-7534-5312-4(6) , Kingfisher) Houghton Mifflin Co. Trade & Reference Div.

Las Galaxias. (SPA.). (J). 10.00 (978-84-342-1815-4(1)) Parramon Ediciones S.A. ESP. *Dist:* Distribuidora Norma, Inc.

Latham, Donna. Space: Surviving in Zero-G. 2005. (X-treme Places Ser.). (Illus.). 32p. (J). (gr. 3-7). lib. bdg. 25.27 (978-1-59716-090-2(3)) Bearport Publishing Co., Inc.

Lawrence, Debbie & Lawrence, Richard. Our Universe. 2004. (Illus.). vi, 134p. (gr. 1-6). pap. 18.00 (978-0-9725365-4-7(X)) R & D Educational Ctr.

The Library of the Nine Planets, 9 Bks, Set. 2004. (J). 238.50 (978-1-4042-0346-4(X)) Rosen Publishing Group, Inc., The.

Lippincott, Kristen. Astronomy. 2008. (DK Eyewitness Bks.). 72p. (J). (gr. 3-8). 15.99 (*978-0-7566-3767-5(8)) Dorling Kindersley Publishing, Inc.

Lippincott, Kristen & Dorling Kindersley Publishing Staff. Astronomy. 2004. (Eyewitness Books). (Illus.). 72p. (J). lib. bdg. 19.99 (978-0-7566-0655-8(1)) Dorling Kindersley Publishing, Inc.

Love, Ann & Drake, Jane. The Kids Book of the Night Sky. Collins, Heather, tr. Collins, Heather, illus. 2004. (Fun for All Seasons Ser.). 144p. (J). (gr. 4-6). (978-1-55337-128-1(3)); (978-1-55337-357-5(X)) Kids Can Pr., Ltd.

Lucas, Debra. Our Moon. 2005. (Yellow Umbrella Books for Early Readers). (Illus.). 17p. (J). (978-0-7368-5260-9(3)); (978-0-7368-5296-8(4)) Capstone Pr., Inc.

Lunis, Natalie. Watching the Night Sky. Date not set. (Thinking Like a Scientist Ser.). (Illus.). 20p. (J). pap. 16.95 (978-1-58273-079-0(2)) Sundance/Newbridge Educational Publishing.

MacDonald, Fiona. Space. 2000. (Topic Bks.). (Illus.). 32p. (J). (gr. 2-5). 23.50 (978-0-531-14542-5(5)); pap. 6.95 (978-0-531-15426-7(2)) Scholastic Library Publishing. (Watts, Franklin).

—Space. 2000. (J). (978-0-606-19794-6(X)); (gr. 3-6). lib. bdg. 15.25 (978-0-613-54680-5(6)) Tandem Library Bks.

Mahoney, Terry. Astronomy: The Study of the Universe. 2002. (Investigating Science Ser.). (Illus.). 36p. (J). (gr. 4 up). lib. bdg. 24.67 (978-0-8368-3229-7(9)) Stevens, Gareth Inc.

Matloff, Gregory L. More Telescope Power: All New Activities & Projects for Young Astronomers. 2002. (Illus.). 128p. pap. 12.95 (978-0-471-40985-4(5) , Wiley) Wiley, John & Sons, Inc.

McCutcheon, Scott & McCutcheon, Bobbi. Space & Astronomy. 2006. (Science News for Kids Ser.). (Illus.). 64p. 30.00 (978-0-7910-9125-8(2) , Chelsea Clubhouse) Facts On File, Inc.

McGinley, Kathryn M., ed. Create Your Own Night Sky Calendar 2005: Rose Center for Earth & Space/American Museum of Natural History. 2004. 24p. (YA). (978-1-57641-122-3(2)) Hudson Park Pr.

McGraw-Hill Staff. Astronomy. 2nd ed. 2004. (Glencoe Science Ser.). stu. ed. 20.64 (978-0-07-861761-4(8) , 9780078617614) Glencoe/McGraw-Hill.

McNeil, Niki, et al. HOCPP 1081 Galaxies. 2006. spiral bd. 16.50 (*978-1-60308-081-1(3)) In the Hands of a Child.

—HOCPP 1088 Advanced Astronomy. 2006. spiral bd. 26.50 (*978-1-60308-088-0(0)) In the Hands of a Child.

Mechler, Gary. National Audubon Society First Field Guide: Night Sky. 1999. (978-0-606-18583-7(6)) Tandem Library Bks.

Menges, Jeff A. Glow-in-the-Dark Night Sky Stickers. 2006. 2p. (J). 1.50 (978-0-486-44915-9(7)) Dover Pubns., Inc.

Miles, Lisa. Usborne Internet-Linked Book of Astronomy & Space. 2002. (gr. 3-6). lib. bdg. 24.55 (978-0-613-58392-3(2)) Tandem Library Bks.

Miles, Lisa & Smith, Alastair. Astronomy & Space. 1998. (Complete Bks.). (Illus.). 96p. (YA). (gr. 3 up). lib. bdg. 22.95 (978-1-58086-130-4(X)) EDC Publishing.

Miller, Ron. Worlds Beyond, 10 vols. 2004. (Illus.). (YA). (gr. 7 up). (978-0-7613-3174-2(3) , Twenty-First Century Bks.) Lerner Publishing Group.

Mission Control, 6 vols. (gr. 2-5). 36.95 (978-0-7368-4609-7(3)) Red Brick Learning.

Mitton, Jacqueline. Zodiac: Celestial Circle of the Sun. 2005. (Illus.). 40p. (J). 16.95 (978-1-84507-074-8(7)) Lincoln, Frances Ltd. GBR. *Dist:* Perseus Distribution.

—Zoo in the Sky: A Book of Animal Constellations. Balit, Christina, illus. 2006. 32p. (J). (gr. 1-4). pap. 7.95 (978-0-7922-5935-0(1) , National Geographic Children's Bks.) National Geographic Society.

Mitton, Jacqueline & Balit, Christina. Once upon a Starry Night: A Book of Constellations. 2004. (Illus.). 32p. (J). (gr. 1-4). 16.95 (978-0-7922-6332-6(4) , National Geographic Children's Bks.) National Geographic Society.

Mobberley, Martin. Space. 2007. (Illus.). 48p. (J). (*978-1-60044-262-9(5)) Rourke Publishing, LLC.

Moeschl, Richard. Exploring the Sky: Projects for Beginning Astronomers. rev. ed. 2003. (Ziggurat Bks.). (Illus.). 432p. (J). (gr. 6 up). pap. 16.95 (978-1-55652-160-7(X)) Chicago Review Pr., Inc.

Moore, Eva. Space Explorers. 2000. (gr. 3-6). lib. bdg. 11.80 (978-0-613-33078-7(1)) Tandem Library Bks.

Moore, Patrick. Philip's Guide to the Night Sky: A Guided Tour of the Stars & Constellations. 2001. (Illus.). 48p. (J). (gr. 4-7). pap. (978-0-540-06315-4(0) , Philip's) Octopus Publishing Group.

—The Young Astronomer & his Telescope. 2004. (Illus.). 80p. pap. 8.00 (978-0-904094-09-1(X)) Reid, Keith Ltd. GBR. *Dist:* Parkwest Pubns., Inc.

Morris, Rick. Stars & Planets. 2005. (Time for Learning Ser.). (Illus.). 96p. (J). (978-1-4127-1135-7(5) , 7255300) Publications International, Ltd.

Moser, Richard. The Examined Universe. 2004. per. 24.00 (978-0-9746865-0-9(6)) MEC Publishing.

Naaeye, Robert. Signals from Outer Space: The Chandra X-Ray Observatory. 2000. (Space Explorer Ser.). (Illus.). 64p. (J). (gr. 6-8). lib. bdg. 28.54 (978-0-7398-2215-9(2)) Raintree.

Naeye. Signals from Space: Chandra X. 1999. (Illus.). (J). pap. (978-0-7398-2506-8(2)) Steck-Vaughn.

Nardo, Don. Black Holes. 2003. (Lucent Science & Technology Library). (Illus.). 112p. (J). 29.95 (978-1-59018-101-0(8) , Lucent Bks.) Thomson Gale.

Nicolson, Cynthia Pratt. Comets, Asteroids & Meteorites. 1999. (gr. 3-6). lib. bdg. 15.25 (978-0-613-21370-7(X)) Tandem Library Bks.

—Discover Space. Slavin, Bill, illus. 2005. (Kids Can Read Alone Ser.). 32p. (J). (ps-ps). (978-1-55337-823-5(7)) Kids Can Pr., Ltd.

Night Sky Spotter's Guide - Internet Linked. rev. ed. 2006. 64p. (J). pap. 5.99 (978-0-7945-1301-6(8) , Usborne) EDC Publishing.

Oceanor Staff. Astronomia - Atlas Visual. 1999. (SPA.). (gr. 3-6). lib. bdg. 20.00 (978-0-613-80883-5(5)) Tandem Library Bks.

Oleksy, Walter G. Mapping the Skies. 2003. (Illus.). 63p. (J). (gr. 4-7). lib. bdg. 17.60 (978-0-613-59514-8(9)) Tandem Library Bks.

Osborne, Mary Pope & Osborne, Will. Space: A Nonfiction Companion to Midnight on the Moon. Murdocca, Sal, illus. 2002. (Magic Tree House Research Guide Ser.: No. 6). 144p. (J). (gr. k-3). pap. 4.99 (978-0-375-81356-6(X)); lib. bdg. 11.99 (978-0-375-91356-3(4)) Random Hse. Children's Bks. (Random Hse. Bks. for Young Readers).

—Space: A Nonfiction Companion to Midnight on the Moon. 2002. (Magic Tree House Research Guide Ser.: No. 6). (J). (gr. k-3). lib. bdg. 13.00 (978-0-613-62996-6(5)) Tandem Library Bks.

Out & about at the Planetarium. (Field Trips Ser.). 24p. (J). 8.95 (978-1-4048-0204-9(5)) Picture Window Bks.

Outer Space. Date not set. (Illus.). 12p. (J). 3.98 (978-1-4054-0498-3(1)) Parragon, Inc.

Outer Space, 12 vols., Set. 1998. (Illus.). (YA). lib. bdg. 285.00 (978-0-7172-9179-3(0) , Grolier) Scholastic Library Publishing.

Oxlade, Chris. The Mystery of Black Holes. (Can Science Solve? Ser.). (Illus.). 32p. (J). (gr. 4-6). 1999. lib. bdg. 22.79 (978-1-57572-808-7(7)); Set 1. 2002. pap. 7.50 (978-1-58810-311-6(0) , 91035) Heinemann Library.

Papa Cardinal Finds Breakfast. 2001. cd-rom 5.00 (978-1-931457-06-4(9)) Stargate Electronic Library, Inc.

Parker. Space Mysteries - Space Busters. 2004. (YA). pap. 48.30 (978-1-4109-0293-1(5)) Harcourt Schl. Pubs.

Parker, Steve. Space Mysteries. 2002. (Young Library - Space Busters Ser.). (Illus.). 32p. (J). (gr. 3-5). lib. bdg. 25.69 (978-0-7398-4853-1(4)) Raintree.

Pasachoff, Jay M. Field Guide to the Stars & Planets. 4th ed. 2000. (Illus.). x, 578p. (gr. 7-12). lib. bdg. 29.25 (978-0-613-35406-6(0)) Tandem Library Bks.

Perez, Miguel. Stars & Galaxies. Rius, María, illus. 1998. (Universe Ser.). 36p. (J). (ps-1). pap. 6.95 (978-0-7641-0686-6(4)) Barron's Educational Series, Inc.

—The Universe: The Solar System; Stars & Galaxies; The Earth & the Universe, 3 bks., Set. Rius, María, illus. 1998. 36p. (J). (ps-2). pap. 17.95 (978-0-7641-7203-8(4)) Barron's Educational Series, Inc.

Peritz, Judith, et al. ARIES Exploring the Moon & Stars: Cycles, Phases & Patterns: Science Journal. 2000. (Aries Ser.). (Illus.). (J). (gr. 3-8). pap. 3.80 (978-1-57091-256-6(4)) Charlesbridge Publishing, Inc.

Pfeffer, Wendy. A New Beginning. Bleck, Linda, illus. 2008. 40p. (J). (gr. 1). 17.99 (*978-0-525-47874-4(4) , Dutton Juvenile) Penguin Group (USA) Inc.

Phelan, Glen. Earth, Sun, Moon. 2004. (National Geographic Reading Expeditions Ser.). (Illus.). 32p. (J). pap. (978-0-7922-4573-5(3)) National Geographic Society.

Proctor, Mary. Stories of Starland. 2006. pap. 22.95 (*978-1-4286-0644-9(0)) Kessinger Publishing, LLC.

Purslow, Frances. Constellations. 2006. (Science Matters Ser.). (J). (978-1-59036-410-9(4)); pap. (978-1-59036-416-1(3)) Weigl Pubs., Inc.

Que Vemos en el Cielo, 6 vols. (Explorers. Exploradores Nonfiction Sets Ser.). (SPA.). 32p. (gr. 3-6). 44.95 (978-0-7699-0631-7(1)) Shortland Pubns. (U. S. A.) Inc.

Rau, Dana Meachen. Black Holes. 2004. (Our Solar System Ser.). (Illus.). 32p. (J). 22.60 (978-0-7565-0849-4(5)) Compass Point Bks.

—The Milky Way & Other Galaxies. 2004. (Our Solar System Ser.). (Illus.). 32p. (J). 22.60 (978-0-7565-0853-1(3)) Compass Point Bks.

Redfern, Martin. The Kingfisher Young Peoples Book of Space. 1998. (Kingfisher Book of Ser.). (Illus.). 96p. (J). (gr. 4-8). 22.95 (978-0-7534-5136-6(0) , Kingfisher) Houghton Mifflin Co. Trade & Reference Div.

Rhatigan, Joe, et al. Out-of-This-World Astronomy. 2005. (Illus.). 128p. (J). pap. 12.95 (978-1-57990-675-7(3)) Lark Bks.

Ridpath, Ian. Facts on File Stars & Planets Atlas: New Edition. 3rd ed. (Facts on File Atlas Ser.). 80p. (gr. 4-9). 18.95 (978-0-8160-6294-2(3) , Checkmark Bks.) Facts On File, Inc.

—Stars & Planets Atlas. 2nd rev. ed. 2001. (Illus.). 80p. (YA). (gr. 4-9). 18.95 (978-0-8160-4800-7(2)) Facts On File, Inc.

Riley, Peter D. The Earth & Space. 2005. (Illus.). 32p. (J). (gr. 4-7). lib. bdg. 27.10 (978-1-58340-713-4(8)) Smart Apple Media.

—Earth in Space. 1999. (gr. 3-6). lib. bdg. 15.25 (978-0-613-31148-9(5)) Tandem Library Bks.

Robinson, Ella M. Stars in her Heart. 2005. 127p. per. 10.95 (978-1-57258-318-4(5)) TEACH Services, Inc.

Rockwell, Anne F. Our Stars. 2002. (Illus.). 24p. (J). (gr. k-2). pap. 6.00 (978-0-15-216360-0(3) , Voyager Bks./Libros Viajeros) Harcourt Children's Bks.

—Our Stars. 2002. (gr. k-3). lib. bdg. 14.15 (978-0-613-53848-0(X)) Tandem Library Bks.

Rooney, Anne. Outer Space. 2007. (J). (*978-1-4329-0112-7(5)); pap. (*978-1-4329-0118-9(4)) Heinemann Library.

Saffer, Barbara. Science Questions & Answers: Space. 2000. (Questions & Answers Ser.). (Illus.). 64p. (J). (gr. 1-3). pap. 5.95 (978-0-7373-0531-9(2)) Lowell Hse. Juvenile.

Sasaki, Chris. Constellations: A Glow-in-the-Dark Guide to the Night Sky. Flinn, Alan, illus. 2006. 48p. (J). (gr. 1-4). 12.95 (978-1-4027-0385-0(6)) Sterling Publishing Co., Inc.

Scagell, Robin. Night Sky Atlas: The Moon, Planets, Stars & Deep Sky Objects. Tirion, Wil, illus. 2005. 128p. pap. 29.95 (978-1-55407-026-8(0)) Firefly Bks., Ltd.

Scholastic, Inc. Staff. Night Sky: Teaching Kit. Cooper, Terry, ed. 2000. (Super Science Readers Ser.). (Illus.). 16p. pap. 10.95 (978-0-439-18618-6(8)) Scholastic, Inc.

Scholastic, Inc. Staff. The Universe. 2007. (Scholastic First Discovery Ser.). 24p. (J). (ps-k). pap. 5.99 (*978-0-545-00146-5(3) , Scholastic Reference) Scholastic, Inc.

Segal, Justin. The Amazing Space Almanac. 1999. (Illus.). 128p. (J). (gr. 3-7). 9.95 (978-1-56565-691-8(1) , 06911W); (gr. 4-7). 15.95 (978-1-56565-690-1(3) , 06903W) Lowell Hse. Juvenile. (Roxbury Park Juvenile).

Seuling, Barbara. Earth Is Like a Giant Magnet & Other Freaky Facts about Planets, Oceans, & Volcanoes. Skeens, Matthew, illus. 2007. (J). lib. bdg. (*978-1-4048-3752-2(3)) Picture Window Bks.

Shapiro, Irwin I., et al. ARIES Exploring the Earth in Motion: Daylight, Sun, & Shadow Patterns: Science Journal. 2000. (Aries Ser.). Orig. Title: Project Aries: Astronomy I. (Illus.). (J). (gr. 3-8). pap. 3.80 (978-1-57091-253-5(X)) Charlesbridge Publishing, Inc.

Silver, Donald M. The Night Sky. Wynne, Patricia J., illus. 1998. (One Small Square). 48p. (gr. 1-4). pap. 7.95 (978-0-07-058045-9(6) , 9780070580459) McGraw-Hill Cos., The.

—One Small Square, the Night Sky. 1998. (gr. k-3). lib. bdg. 16.40 (978-0-613-71490-7(3)) Tandem Library Bks.

Silverstein, Alvin, et al. The Universe. 2003. (Science Concepts Ser.). (Illus.). 64p. (gr. 5-8). lib. bdg. 26.90 (978-0-7613-2255-9(8) , Twenty-First Century Bks.) Lerner Publishing Group.

Simon, Seymour. Comets, Meteors & Asteroids. 1998. (J). 13.79 (978-0-606-13288-6(0)) Tandem Library Bks.

—Destination: Jupiter. (Illus.). 32p. (J). 2000. (gr. k up). pap. 6.99 (978-0-06-443759-2(0) , Harper Trophy); 1998. (gr. 5 up). 15.95 (978-0-688-15620-6(7)) HarperCollins Pubs.

—Destination: Jupiter. 2000. (gr. 3-6). lib. bdg. 15.30 (978-0-613-33691-8(7)) Tandem Library Bks.

—Destination: Mars. 2000. (Illus.). 32p. (J). (ps-3). 15.95 (978-0-688-15770-8(X)) HarperCollins Pubs.

—Destination: Space. 32p. (J). 2006. 16.99 (978-0-06-087722-4(7)); 2006. (Illus.). pap. 6.99 (978-0-06-087723-1(5)); 2004. pap. 6.99 (978-0-06-059681-1(3) , Harper Trophy); 2002. (Illus.). (gr. 4-7). 15.99 (978-0-688-16289-4(4)) HarperCollins Pubs.

—Galaxies. 2000. (Illus.). 28p. (YA). (gr. 6-7). reprint ed. 18.00 (978-0-7881-9202-9(7)) DIANE Publishing Co.

—The Universe. 1998. (Illus.). 32p. (J). (gr. k-3). lab manual ed. 17.89 (978-0-688-15302-1(X)) HarperCollins Pubs.

Smith, A. Book of Astronomy & Space. 2004. (Complete Bks.). (SPA., Illus.). 96p. (J). lib. bdg. 22.95 (978-1-58086-385-8(X)) EDC Publishing.

Smith, Alastair & Miles, Lisa. Book of Astronomy & Space. 2004. (Complete Bks.). (SPA., Illus.). 96p. (J). pap. 14.95 (978-0-7945-0116-7(8) , Usborne) EDC Publishing.

Smith, Ian. What's in the Sky? 2004. (QEB Start Writing Ser.). (Illus.). 24p. (J). lib. bdg. 15.95 (978-1-59566-019-0(4)) QEB Publishing Inc.

Solway, Andrew. What's Inside a Black Hole? Deep Space Objects & Mysteries. 2006. (Stargazers Guides Ser.). (Illus.). 48p. (J). (978-1-4034-7710-1(8)); pap. (978-1-4034-7717-0(5)) Heinemann Library.

Somervill, Barbara A. Nicolaus Copernicus: Father of Modern Astronomy. 2004. (Signature Lives Ser.). (Illus.). 112p. (J). 30.60 (978-0-7565-0812-8(6)) Compass Point Bks.

Space, Stars, & Planets (Gr. 3-4) 2003. (J). (978-1-58232-074-8(8)) Bryan Hse. Pubs., Inc.

Space; Stars; Battles, 3 vols., Set. 2001. 192p. (J). 25.95 (978-0-7525-5455-6(7)) Parragon, Inc.

Space Walks, 6 vols. (gr. 2-5). 36.95 (978-0-7368-4611-0(5)) Red Brick Learning.

Sparrow, Giles. Observing the Universe. 2006. (Illus.). 48p. (J). pap. (978-0-8368-7284-2(3)); lib. bdg. (978-0-8368-7277-4(0)) Stevens, Gareth Inc. (World Almanac Library).

Spinning Through Space, 8 bks., Set. Incl. Comets & Asteroids. Han, E. M. (gr. 3-4). 2001. lib. bdg. 25.69 (978-0-7398-2742-0(1)); Constellations. Hans, E. M. Sloan, Frank, ed. (gr. 3-4). 2001. lib. bdg. 25.69 (978-0-7398-2743-7(X)); Earth. Furniss, Tim. (gr. 2-4). 2000. lib. bdg. (978-0-7398-2737-6(5)); Moon. Furniss, Tim. (gr. 2-4). 2000. lib. bdg. 25.69 (978-0-7398-2738-3(3)); Solar System. Furniss, Tim. (gr. 2-4). 2000. lib. bdg. 25.69 (978-0-7398-2740-6(5)); Space Mysteries. Goldsmith, Mike. (gr. 2-4). 2001. lib. bdg. 25.69 (978-0-7398-2745-1(6)); Space Travel. Goldsmith, Mike. (gr. 2-4). 2001. lib. bdg. 25.69 (978-0-7398-2744-4(8)); Sun. Furniss, Tim. (gr. 2-4). 2000. lib. bdg. 25.69 (978-0-7398-2739-0(1)); 32p. (J). (Illus.). 2001. Set lib. bdg. 205.52 (978-0-7398-3007-9(4)) Raintree.

Spinning Through Space: Includes: Comets & Asteroid; Constellations; Space Mysteries; Space Travel, 4 bks., Set. 2001. (Illus.). (J). (gr. 2-4). 71.92 (978-0-7398-2746-8(4)) Raintree.

Steck-Vaughn Staff. Our Universe. 2000. pap., tchr. ed. (978-0-7398-3354-4(5)) Steck-Vaughn.

—Signals from Space: Chandra X. 1999. (J). pap., tchr. ed. (978-0-7398-2509-9(7)) Steck-Vaughn.

Steele, Philip. Galileo: The Genius Who Faced the Inquisition. 2005. (World History Biographies Ser.). (Illus.). 64p. (J). (gr. 3-7). 17.95 (978-0-7922-3656-6(4)); 27.90 (978-0-7922-3657-3(2)) National Geographic Society. (National Geographic Children's Bks.).

Stefoff, Rebecca, contrib. by. Blastoff! - Group 1, 5 bks., Set. 2002. (Illus.). (J). 142.50 (978-0-7614-1231-1(X)) Cavendish, Marshall Corp.

Storm, Dunlop. Atlas of the Night Sky. 2005. (Illus.). 224p. 29.95 (978-0-06-081891-3(3)) HarperCollins Pubs.

Stott, Carole. I Wonder Why Stars Twinkle: And Other Questions about Space. 2003. (J). lib. bdg. 14.10 (978-0-613-63164-8(1)) Tandem Library Bks.

—Kingfisher Pocket Guide to the Night Sky. 2006. (Illus.). 176p. (J). (gr. 5-9). pap. 6.95 (978-0-7534-5996-6(5) , Kingfisher) Houghton Mifflin Co. Trade & Reference Div.

—Space. 2008. 128p. (J). (gr. 3-6). 19.99 (***978-0-7566-3842-9(9)***) Dorling Kindersley Publishing, Inc.

—Stars & Planets. 2005. (Kingfisher Knowledge Ser.). (Illus.). 64p. (J). (gr. 5-9). 12.95 (978-0-7534-5865-5(9) , Kingfisher) Houghton Mifflin Co. Trade & Reference Div.

—The World of Astronomy. 2006. (World Of Ser.). (Illus.). 64p. (J). (gr. 4-6). pap. 8.95 (978-0-7534-6006-1(8) , Kingfisher) Houghton Mifflin Co. Trade & Reference Div.

Sweeney, Joan. Me & My Place in Space. 1999. (Dragonfly Bks.). (Illus.). 32p. (J). (gr. k-3). pap. 6.99 (978-0-517-88590-1(5) , Dragonfly Bks.) Random Hse. Children's Bks.

Thompson, C. E. Glow-in-the-Dark Constellations: A Field Guide for Young Stargazers. Chewning, Randy, illus. 1999. 32p. (J). (gr. 1-5). pap. 8.99 (978-0-448-41253-5(5) , Grosset & Dunlap) Penguin Group (USA) Inc.

—Glow-in-the-Dark Constellations: A Field Guide for Young Stargazers. 1999. (gr. 3-6). lib. bdg. 16.45 (978-0-613-72380-0(5)) Tandem Library Bks.

Tocci, Salvatore. Experiments with the Sun & the Moon. 2003. (True Book Ser.). (Illus.). 48p. (J). 25.00 (978-0-516-22605-7(3) , Children's Pr.) Scholastic Library Publishing.

Trueba, Jose Luis. Descubre... La Tierra y el Cosmos. Cortes, Osvaldo, illus. 2004. (Ser. Descubre). (SPA.). 96p. (J). (gr. 3-5). pap. 18.95 (978-970-29-0509-7(5)) Santillana USA Publishing Co., Inc.

Tweed, Matt. Compact Cosmos: A Journey Through Space & Time. 2005. (Wooden Books Ser.). (Illus.). 64p. 10.00 (978-0-8027-1455-8(2)) Walker & Co.

Van Order, Bill. The Wondrous Sky. Van Order, Barbara, illus. 2006. 32p. (J). per. 10.95 (***978-1-59879-187-7(7)***) Lifevest Publishing, Inc.

VanCleave, Janice Pratt. Janice VanCleaves A+ Projects in Astronomy: Winning Experiments for Science Fairs & Extra Credit. 2001. (Illus.). 224p. 32.50 (978-0-471-32816-2(2)); (VanCleave a+ Science Projects Ser.: Vol. 3). pap. 12.95 (978-0-471-32820-9(0)) Wiley, John & Sons, Inc. (Wiley).

Vekteris, Donna. Scholastic Atlas of Space. Wright, Kenneth, ed. 2005. (Illus.). 80p. (J). pap. 17.95 (978-0-439-67272-6(4) , Scholastic Reference) Scholastic, Inc.

Vickers, John C. & Wassilieff, Alex. Deep Space CCD Atlas North & South on CD-R Disk. 1999. (Illus.). 464p. cd-rom 38.75 (978-0-9740110-0-4(2)) Electronic Art & Publishing.

Vogt, Gregory L. Deep Space Astronomy. 1999. (Enthusiastic Astronomy Ser.). (Illus.). 80p. (gr. 5-8). lib. bdg. (978-0-7613-1369-4(9) , Millbrook Pr.) Lerner Publishing Group.

—The Milky Way. 2002. (Galaxy Ser.). (Illus.). 24p. (J). (gr. 2-3). lib. bdg. 18.60 (978-0-7368-1384-6(5) , Bridgestone Bks.) Capstone Pr., Inc.

—Stars & Constellations. 2000. (Our Universe Ser.). (Illus.). 48p. (J). (gr. 5-12). lib. bdg. 22.83 (978-0-7398-3115-1(1)) Raintree.

—Stars & Constellations. 2000. (Our Universe Ser.). (Illus.). (J). pap. (978-0-7398-3342-1(1)) Steck-Vaughn.

Wadsworth, Pamela. Golwg Gyntaf Ar Amser a Gofod. 2005. (WEL., Illus.). 24p. pap. (978-1-85596-248-4(9)) Dref Wen.

Warner, Gertrude. Star Stories for Little Folks. 2006. pap. 12.95 (***978-1-59605-906-1(0)*** , Cosimo Classics) Cosimo, Inc.

Wentz, Budd. Sky Challenger. Wentz, Budd, illus. 1999. (Illus.). 2p. (J). (gr. 3-8). 9.95 (978-0-924886-47-8(1)) Univ. of California, Berkeley, Lawrence Hall of Science.

West, Krista. Hands-On Projects about Earth & Space. 2002. (Great Earth Science Projects Ser.). (Illus.). 24p. (J). lib. bdg. 19.95 (978-0-8239-5843-6(4)) Rosen Publishing Group, Inc., The.

Where Are the Stars During the Day? (Discovery Readers Ser.). 48p. (J). pap. 3.95 (978-0-8249-5319-5(3) , Ideals Children's Bks.) Ideals Pubns.

Whitten, Wendy. Flumpa's World: Out of This World! 2000. 21p. (J). 14.95 incl. audio (978-1-886184-11-4(9)) Ion Imagination Publishing.

Willett, Edward. Comets, Stardust & Supernovas: The Science of Space. 1999. (Science @ Work Ser.). (Illus.). 48p. (J). (gr. 4-6). 27.12 (978-0-7398-0134-5(1)) Raintree.

Williams, Zella. Experiments about Planet Earth. 2007. (Do-It-Yourself Science Ser.). (Illus.). 24p. (J). (gr. 2-5). lib. bdg. 23.95 (978-1-4042-3662-2(7) , PowerKids Pr.) Rosen Publishing Group, Inc., The.

Wollard, K. El Porque de las Cosas. (SPA.). 224p. 16.00 (978-84-95456-69-4(9) , 87419) Ediciones Oniro S.A. ESP. *Dist:* Bilingual Pubns. Co., The, Lectorum Pubns., Inc., Libros Sin Fronteras.

Woodford, Chris. Time. 2005. (How Do We Measure ? Ser.). 32p. (J). (gr. 2-5). 23.70 (978-1-4103-0363-9(2) , Blackbirch Pr., Inc.) Thomson Gale.

World Book, contrib. by. Galaxies & the Universe. 2nd ed. 2006. (World Book's Solar System & Space Exploration Library). (Illus.). 64p. (J). (***978-0-7166-9513-4(8)***) World Bk., Inc.

Wright, Russell G. Asteroid! Investigations in Astronomy. (Event-Based Science Ser.). 32p. (gr. 5-9). pap., tchr.'s training gde. ed. 25.95 incl. VHS (978-0-201-49446-4(9)) Seymour, Dale Pubns.

ASTRONOMY, ANCIENT

Asimov, Isaac & Hantula, Richard. Astronomy in Ancient Times. 2005. (Isaac Asimov's 21st Century Library of the Universe). (Illus.). 32p. (J). lib. bdg. 24.67 (978-0-8368-3978-4(1)) Stevens, Gareth Inc.

ASTRONOMY—DICTIONARIES

Armentrout, David & Armentrout, Patricia. Space. 2003. (50 Words about Ser.). (Illus.). 32p. (gr. 2-4). 19.95 (978-1-58952-342-1(1)) Rourke Publishing, LLC.

ASTRONOMY—HISTORY

Atkinson, Mary. The Earth Is Flat! Science Facts & Fictions. 2007. (Shockwave: Science in Practice Ser.). (Illus.). 36p. (J). (gr. 4-6). lib. bdg. 25.00 (***978-0-531-17580-4(4)*** , Children's Pr.) Scholastic Library Publishing.

McCutcheon, Scott & McCutcheon, Bobbi. Space & Astronomy. 2005. (Pioneers in Science Ser.). (Illus.). 208p. (J). (gr. 6-12). 29.95 (978-0-8160-5467-1(3)) Facts On File, Inc.

Sakolsky, Josh. Copernicus & Modern Astronomy. 2004. (Primary Sources of Revolutionary Scientific Discoveries & Theories Ser.). (Illus.). 64p. (J). lib. bdg. 29.25 (978-1-4042-0305-1(2)) Rosen Publishing Group, Inc., The.

Solway, Andrew. Quantum Leaps & Big Bangs! A History of Astronomy. 2006. (Stargazers Guides Ser.). (Illus.). 48p. (J). 31.43 (978-1-4034-7712-5(4)); pap. 8.90 (978-1-4034-7719-4(1)) Heinemann Library.

Whiting, Jim. Galileo. 2007. (What's So Great About... ? Ser.). (J). lib. bdg. 25.70 (***978-1-58415-575-1(2)***) Mitchell Lane Pubs., Inc.

ASTRONOMY—VOCATIONAL GUIDANCE

Ghez, Andrea Mia & Cohen, Judith Love. You Can Be A Woman Astronomer. Katz, David Arthur, illus. l.t. ed. 40p. (J). 2006. pap. 12.95 incl. DVD (978-1-880599-77-8(5)); 2005. 17.95 incl. DVD (978-1-880599-78-5(3)) Cascade Pass, Inc.

Haydon, Julie. Astronomers. 2004. (J). lib. bdg. 27.10 (978-1-58340-541-3(0)) Smart Apple Media.

ASTROPHYSICS

Di Gesu, V., et al, eds. Data Analysis in Astronomy: Proceedings of the 5th Workshop Ettore Majorana Center for Scientific Culture, Erice, Italy, 27 October-3 November 1996. 1998. (Science & Culture Ser.). 440p. 86.00 (978-981-02-3171-2(7)) World Scientific Publishing Co., Inc.

Hodges, Susan. Up in Space. Barr, Marilynn G., illus. 1999. (Rhyme & Reason Workbook Ser.). 32p. (J). (ps-k). pap. 3.95 (978-1-57029-254-5(X) , WPH 01106, Totline Pubns.) Schaffer, Frank Pubns.

Kalz, Jill. Northern Lights. 2004. (Natural Wonders of the World Ser.). (Illus.). 32p. (J). lib. bdg. 18.95 (978-1-58341-326-5(X) , Creative Education) Creative Co., The.

ASWAN HIGH DAM

Parks, Peggy J. Aswan High Dam. (Building World Landmarks Ser.). (J). 2004. 26.19 (978-1-4103-0204-5(0)); 2003. (Illus.). 48p. 24.95 (978-1-56711-329-7(X)) Thomson Gale. (Blackbirch Pr., Inc.).

ATHENS (GREECE)

Curlee, Lynn. Parthenon. Curlee, Lynn, illus. 2004. (Illus.). 40p. (J). 17.95 (978-0-689-84490-4(5) , Atheneum) Simon & Schuster Children's Publishing.

Dargie, Richard. Look Around a Greek Temple. 2007. (J). (***978-1-84193-720-5(7)***) Smart Apple Media.

De Medeiros, James. Parthenon. 2007. (J). (***978-1-59036-727-8(8)); *978-1-59036-728-5(6)***) Weigl Pubs., Inc.

Harcourt School Publishers Staff. Living in Athens. 3rd ed. 2002. (Horizons Ser.). (Illus.). (J). pap. 3.70 (978-0-15-333196-1(8)) Harcourt Schl. Pubs.

Honan, Linda & Kosmer, Ellen. Spend the Day in Ancient Greece: Projects & Activities that Bring the Past to Life. 1998. (Spend the Day Ser.: Vol. 1). (Illus.). 128p. (gr. 3-7). pap. 12.95 (978-0-471-15454-9(7) , Wiley) Wiley, John & Sons, Inc.

Kotapish, Dawn. Daily Life in Ancient & Modern Athens. Moulder, Bob, illus. 2005. (Cities Through Time Ser.). 64p. (gr. 5-12). 25.26 (978-0-8225-3216-3(6)) Lerner Publishing Group.

Langley, Andrew. Athens. 2003. (Great Cities of the World Ser.). (Illus.). 48p. (J). (gr. 5 up). pap. 11.95 (978-0-8368-5181-6(1)); lib. bdg. 30.00 (978-0-8368-5021-5(1)) Stevens, Gareth Inc. (World Almanac Library).

Naden, Corinne J. & Blue, Rose. Ancient Greeks & the Parthenon. 2003. (J). (978-1-58417-314-4(9)); pap. (978-1-58417-315-1(7)) Lake Street Pubs.

Nardo, Don. The Parthenon of Ancient Greece. 1998. (Building History Ser.). (Illus.). 96p. (YA). (gr. 6-9). 27.45 (978-1-56006-431-2(5) , Lucent Bks.) Thomson Gale.

—Pericles: Great Leader of Ancient Athens. 2006. (Rulers of the Ancient World Ser.). (Illus.). 160p. (J). lib. bdg. 27.93 (978-0-7660-2561-5(6)) Enslow Pubs., Inc.

Shuter, Jane. Life in Ancient Athens. 2005. (Picture the Past Ser.). (Illus.). 32p. (J). (gr. 2-4). lib. bdg. 26.79 (978-1-4034-6443-9(X)); pap. (978-1-4034-6450-7(2)) Heinemann Library.

ATHENS (GREECE)—FICTION

Chappas, Bess. Kiki & the Red Shoes. 2007. (J). 17.99 (***978-1-60131-012-5(9)***) Big Tent Bks.

Denenburg, Barry. Pandora of Athens,399 B. C. 2004. (Life & Times Ser.). 176p. (J). (gr. 4-7). pap. 10.95 (978-0-439-64982-7(X)) Scholastic, Inc.

Harcourt School Publishers Staff. Greetings from Ancient Greece On Level. 3rd ed. 2002. (Trophies Reading Program Ser.). (Illus.). pap. 5.10 (978-0-15-323445-3(8)) Harcourt Schl. Pubs.

Lamb, Charles & Lamb, Mary. Tales from Shakespeare: "A Midsummer Night's Dream" Strang, Kay, ed. Andrews, Gary, illus. rev. ed. 2005. 40p. pap. 4.95 (978-0-9542905-3-5(4)) Capercaillie Bks., Ltd GBR. *Dist:* Wilson & Assocs.

Liggitt, Ed, Sr. Color Me Christian: A Greek Legionnaire's Story. 2004. 76p. pap. 14.95 (978-1-4137-1504-0(4)) PublishAmerica, Inc.

Literature Connections English: A Midsummer Night's Dream. 2004. (gr. 6-12). (978-0-395-77543-1(4) , 2-80112) McDougal Littell Inc.

A Midsummer Night's Dream. 2002. (Illus.). 48p. (YA). stu. ed., per. 17.95 (978-1-56254-616-8(3) , SP6163) Saddleback Educational Publishing.

Riggs, Sandy. Three Ancient Communities. 2005. (Navigators Ser.). (J). pap. 38.00 (***978-1-4108-5093-5(5)***) Benchmark Education Co.

Snedeker, Caroline Dale. Lysis Goes to the Play. Clark, Elizabeth Palmer, illus. 2003. 62p. (J). per. 8.95 (978-0-9667067-4-1(9)) American Home-School Publishing, LLC.

—Theras & His Town. 2002. 208p. (J). per. 13.95 (978-0-9667067-2-7(2)) American Home-School Publishing, LLC.

ATHENS (GREECE)—HISTORY

Conley, Kate A. Daily Life in Ancient Athens. 2005. (Life in Ancient Days: Greece Ser.). (J). (978-1-59197-868-8(8)) ABDO Publishing Co.

Harcourt School Publishers Staff. Democratic Athens: Take-Home Book. 2001. (Collections Ser.). (Illus.). (J). pap. 1.90 (978-0-15-319557-0(6)) Harcourt Schl. Pubs.

Kotapish, Dawn. Daily Life in Ancient & Modern Athens. Moulder, Bob, illus. 2005. (Cities Through Time Ser.). 64p. (gr. 5-12). 25.26 (978-0-8225-3216-3(6)) Lerner Publishing Group.

Kubiak, Mike, photos by. Everywhere You Turn: The Acropolis of Athens. 2002. cd-rom 11.75 (978-1-931792-18-9(6)) E-Digital Bks., LLC.

MacDonald, Fiona. Inside Ancient Athens. James, John et al, illus. 2005. (Inside... Ser.). 32p. (J). (gr. 5). 19.95 (978-1-59270-044-8(6)) Enchanted Lion Bks., LLC.

Mann, Elizabeth. The Parthenon: The Height of Greek Civilization. Lee, Yuan, illus. 2006. (Wonders of the World Book Ser.). 48p. (J). (gr. 4-8). 22.95 (978-1-931414-15-9(7)) Mikaya Pr.

Nardo, Don. Ancient Athens. 2002. (Traveler's Guide to Ser.). (Illus.). 112p. (J). (gr. 5). 28.70 (978-1-59018-016-7(X) , Lucent Bks.) Thomson Gale.

—Life in Ancient Athens. 1999. (Illus.). 112p. (YA). (gr. 4-12). 27.45 (978-1-56006-494-7(3) , LML00902-177857, Lucent Bks.) Thomson Gale.

Shuter, Jane. The Acropolis. 2002. (Visiting the Past Ser.). (Illus.). 32p. (J). (gr. 5-7). pap. 6.95 (978-1-58810-420-5(6) , 91178) Heinemann Library.

ATHLETES

see also African American Athletes

Abbey, Cherie D., ed. Biography Today: Profiles of People of Interest to Young Readers. (Sports Ser.: 10). (YA). 2003. lib. bdg. (978-0-7808-0655-9(7)); 2003. lib. bdg. (978-0-7808-0654-2(9)); 2002. 200p. lib. bdg. 44.00 (978-0-7808-0511-8(9)) Omnigraphics, Inc.

Adler, David A. America's Champion Swimmer: Gertrude Ederle. Widener, Terry, illus. 32p. (J). (gr. k-4). 2000. 16.00 (978-0-15-201969-3(3) , Gulliver Bks.); 2005. reprint ed. pap. 6.00 (978-0-15-205251-5(8) , Voyager Bks./Libros Viajeros) Harcourt Children's Bks.

—America's Champion Swimmer: Gertrude Ederle. 2000. (Illus.). 32p. (J). (gr. 1-4). 18.98 (978-0-7398-2197-8(0)) Raintree.

Amazing Athletes. 2005. (J). (978-1-59564-668-2(X)) Steps To Literacy, LLC.

Armentrout, David & Armentrout, Patricia. Marion Jones. 2005. (Discover the Life of a Sports Star Ser.). (Illus.). 24p. (gr. 1-4). 14.95 (978-1-59515-131-5(1)) Rourke Publishing, LLC.

Armentrout, David & Armentrout, Patricia, trs. Lance Armstrong. 2003. (Discover the Life of a Sports Star Ser.). (Illus.). 24p. (J). 20.64 (978-1-58952-651-8(1)) Rourke Publishing, LLC.

—Mia Hamm. 2003. (Discover the Life of a Sports Star Ser.). (Illus.). 24p. (J). 20.64 (978-1-58952-652-5(X)) Rourke Publishing, LLC.

Armstrong, Kristin. Lance Armstrong: The Race of His Life. Call, Ken, illus. 2000. (All Aboard Reading Ser.). 48p. (J). (gr. 2-3). 13.89 (978-0-448-42415-6(0)); (gr. 4-7). pap. 3.99 (978-0-448-42407-1(X)) Penguin Group (USA) Inc. (Grosset & Dunlap).

—Lance Armstrong: The Race of His Life. 2000. (All Aboard Reading Ser.). (J). (978-0-606-20267-1(6)); lib. bdg. 11.80 (978-0-613-31402-2(6)); (Illus.). (J). (978-0-606-20403-3(2)) Tandem Library Bks.

Awesome Athletes - Set II, Set. Incl. Anfernee Hardaway. Joseph, Paul. (gr. k-6). lib. bdg. 22.78 (978-1-56239-842-2(3)); Brett Favre. Wheeler, Jill C. (gr. k-6). lib. bdg. 22.78 (978-1-56239-844-6(X)); Grant Hill. Joseph, Paul. (gr. 3). lib. bdg. 22.78 (978-1-56239-843-9(1)); Sheryl Swoopes. Sehnert, Chris W. (gr. k-6). lib. bdg. 22.78 (978-1-56239-845-3(8)); Tara Lipinski. Wheeler, Jill C. (gr. k-6). lib. bdg. 22.78 (978-1-56239-846-0(6)); Tiger Woods. Joseph, Paul. (gr. k-6). lib. bdg. 22.78 (978-1-56239-841-5(5)); (J). 1998. (Illus.). 32p. 1998. Set lib. bdg. 136.68 (978-1-56239-942-9(X) , Checkerboard Library) ABDO Publishing Co.

Awesome Athletes Set 4. 2007. 136.68 (978-1-59928-303-6(4) , Checkerboard Library) ABDO Publishing Co.

Awesome Athletes Set III. 2004. (J). (gr. k-6). lib. bdg. 136.68 (978-1-59197-482-6(8) , Checkerboard Library) ABDO Publishing Co.

Bankston, John. Lance Armstrong. 2004. (Blue Banner Biography Ser.). (Illus.). 32p. (J). lib. bdg. (978-1-58415-334-4(2)) Mitchell Lane Pubs., Inc.

Barnhart, C. A. What Makes Great Athletes. 2005. (Illus.). 24p. (J). (***978-0-328-13561-5(5)*** , Scott Foresman) Addison-Wesley Educational Pubs., Inc.

Belval, Brian. Olympic Track & Field. 2007. (Great Moments in Olympic History Ser.). (Illus.). 48p. (J). (gr. 5-8). lib. bdg. 26.50 (***978-1-4042-0971-8(9)***) Rosen Publishing Group, Inc., The.

Benge, Janet. Eric Liddell: Something Greater Than Gold. 1998. (gr. 5-8). lib. bdg. 15.30 (978-0-613-83686-9(3)) Tandem Library Bks.

Benson, Michael. Lance Armstrong, Cyclist. 2003. (Ferguson Career Biographies Ser.). (Illus.). 144p. (J). (gr. 6-12). 25.00 (978-0-8160-5479-4(7) , Ferguson Publishing Co.) Facts On File, Inc.

Berman, Ron. Future Stars of America. 2005. (Illus.). 90p. (J). (***978-0-9741997-4-0(5)***) Scobre Pr. Corp.

Bernstein, Ross. Shaquille O'Neal. 2005. (Amazing Athletes Ser.). (Illus.). 32p. (gr. 3-4). lib. bdg. 22.60 (978-0-8225-3689-5(7)) Lerner Publishing Group.

Bjarkman, Peter C. Reggie Miller: Star Guard. 1999. (Sports Reports). (Illus.). 104p. (YA). (gr. 4-10). lib. bdg. 26.60 (978-0-7660-1082-6(1)) Enslow Pubs., Inc.

Bonner, Mike. Jeremy Mayfield. 1999. (Race Car Legends Ser.). (Illus.). 64p. (YA). (gr. 4-7). pap. 25.00 (978-0-7910-5678-3(3)); 25.00 (978-0-7910-5412-3(8)) Facts On File, Inc. (Chelsea Hse.).

—Jeremy Mayfield. 2000. (gr. 5-8). lib. bdg. 16.40 (978-0-613-20890-1(0)) Tandem Library Bks.

Bradley, Michael. Generation Next: Superstar Kids of Superstar Athletes. 2004. (J). 3.99 (978-1-930623-33-0(X)) Sports Illustrated For Kids.

—Yao Ming. 2003. (Illus.). 48p. (J). 27.07 (978-0-7614-1758-3(3) , Benchmark Bks.) Cavendish, Marshall Corp.

Branon, Dave. Undefeated: Catching Inspiration & Hope Thrown by Athletes of Integrity. 2006. 176p. (J). pap. 10.99 (978-0-7642-0293-3(6)) Bethany Hse. Pubs.

Braun, Eric. Jesse Owens. 2005. (Pebble Books). (Illus.). 24p. (J). (978-0-7368-4230-3(6) , Pebble Bks.) Capstone Pr., Inc.

Brennan, Kristine. Scott Hamilton: Figure Skater. 1999. (Overcoming Adversity Ser.). (Illus.). (YA). 128p. pap. 9.95 (978-0-7910-4945-7(0)); 112p. (gr. 5 up). 30.00 (978-0-7910-4944-0(2)) Facts On File, Inc. (Chelsea Hse.).

Brown, Don. Bright Path: Young Jim Thorpe. Brown, Don, illus. 2006. (Illus.). 40p. (J). 17.95 (978-1-59643-041-9(9)) Roaring Brook Pr.

—Bright Path: Young Jim Thorpe. 2008. (Illus.). 40p. (J). pap. 6.99 (***978-0-312-37748-9(7)***) Square Fish.

Bruchac, Joseph. Jim Thorpe, Original All-American. 2006. (Illus.). 288p. (J). (gr. 5). 16.99 (978-0-8037-3118-9(3) , Dial) Penguin Group (USA) Inc.

Burgan, Michael. Great Moments in the Olympics. 2002. (Great Moments in Sports Ser.). (Illus.). 48p. (J). (gr. 5 up). pap. 14.60 (978-0-8368-5362-9(8) , World Almanac Library) Stevens, Gareth Inc.

Cantwell, Lois & Smith, Pohla. Women Winners: Then & Now. 2005. (Sports Illustrated for Kids Bks.). (Illus.). 176p. (YA). (gr. 7-12). lib. bdg. 25.25 (978-0-8239-3695-3(3)) Rosen Publishing Group, Inc., The.

—Women Winners: Then & Now. (J). (gr. 3-9). pap. 3.99 (978-1-930623-09-5(7)) Sports Illustrated For Kids.

Caughey, Ellen. Eric Liddell: Gold Medal Missionary. (Heros of the Faith Ser.). 2006. 208p. pap. 2.97 (978-1-59789-115-8(0)); 2000. (Illus.). 224p. (J). (gr. 3-7). pap. 1.39 (978-1-57748-721-0(4)) Barbour Publishing, Inc.

Cayleff, Susan E. Babe Didrikson. 2000. (gr. 7-12). lib. bdg. 17.45 (978-0-613-27718-1(X)) Tandem Library Bks.

—Babe Didrikson: The Greatest All-Sport Athlete of All Time. 2000. (Barnard Biography Ser.: Vol. 4). (Illus.). 168p. (YA). (gr. 7-12). pap. 8.95 (978-1-57324-194-6(6) , Red Wheel) Red Wheel/Weiser.

Cheyney, Arnold B. Athletes of Purpose. 2004. (Illus.). 128p. pap. (978-0-673-58667-4(7)) Good Year Bks.

Childress, Boyd. 100 Most Popular Team Sports Heroes for Young Adults: Biographical Sketches & Professional Paths. 2003. (Profiles & Pathways Ser.). 500p. (978-1-56308-738-7(3)) Libraries Unlimited, Inc.

Christopher, Matt. On the Bike with... Lance Armstrong. 2003. (Illus.). 112p. (J). (gr. 5-8). pap. 4.99 (978-0-316-07549-7(3)) Little, Brown Bks. for Young Readers.

—On the Bike with... Lance Armstrong. 2003. (gr. 3-6). lib. bdg. 13.00 (978-0-613-71601-7(9)) Tandem Library Bks.

Cohen, Sasha. Sasha Cohen: Autobiography of a Champion Figure Skater. Goedeken, Kathy, illus. 2005. (J). (gr. 3 up). pap. 9.99 (978-0-06-072489-4(7)) HarperCollins Pubs.

Conroy, Tim. How to Become a Star Athlete. (Illus.). 88p. (Orig.). (YA). (978-0-9636706-7-0(0)) Coach Enterprises.

Conway, Hollis. Grasshopper: The Hollis Conway Story. 2004. 30p. (J). per. (978-1-59196-584-8(5)) Instantpublisher.com.

Cook, Brian & Tupper, Mark. Brian Cook: An Illini Legend. 2003. (Illus.). 96p. (J). pap. 5.95 (978-1-58261-731-2(7)) Sports Publishing, LLC.

Cooper, John. Rapid Ray: The Story of Ray Lewis. 2002. (Illus.). 160p. (J). (gr. 5-9). pap. 8.95 (978-0-88776-612-1(9)) Tundra Bks., Inc./Livres Toundra, Inc. CAN. *Dist:* Random Hse., Inc.

Dave Mirra. 2007. (J). pap. 5.95 (***978-0-8225-6597-0(8)*** , First Avenue Editions) Lerner Publishing Group.

Deportistas de Poder Series, Set. 2003. (Deportistas de Poder Ser.). (SPA & ENG., Illus.). (J). 103.50 (978-0-8239-7197-8(X)); lib. bdg. 103.50 (978-0-8239-7193-0(7)) Rosen Publishing Group, Inc., The. (Buenas Letra).

Dippold, Joel. Picabo Street: Downhill Dynamo. rev. ed. 1998. (J). 5.95 (978-0-8225-9839-8(6)) Lerner Publishing Group.

Ditchfield, Christin. Top 10 American Women's Olympic Gold Medalists. 2000. (Sports Top 10 Ser.). (Illus.). 48p. (YA). (gr. 4-10). lib. bdg. 23.93 (978-0-7660-1277-6(8)) Enslow Pubs., Inc.

Donkin, Andrew. Going for Gold! 1999. (Eyewitness Readers Ser.). (Illus.). 48p. (J). (gr. 2-4). lib. bdg. 10.79 (978-0-606-19382-5(0)); (gr. k-3). lib. bdg. 11.80 (978-0-613-21609-8(1)) Tandem Library Bks.

Donovan, Sandy. Lance Armstrong. 2005. (Amazing Athletes Ser.). (Illus.). 32p. (J). (gr. 3-4). lib. bdg. 23.93 (978-0-8225-3691-8(9)) Lerner Publishing Group.

Draw 50 Athletes. 2002. (Draw 50 Ser.). (Illus.). (J). 17.60 (978-0-7587-4160-8(X)) Book Wholesalers, Inc.

Dublin, Anne. Bobbie Rosenfeld: The Olympian Who Could Do Everything. 2005. (Illus.). 148p. (YA). pap. 11.95 (978-1-896764-82-5(7)) Second Story Pr. CAN. *Dist:* Orca Bk. Pubs. USA, Univ. of Toronto Pr.

DuPont, Lonnie H. Oksana Baiul. 1998. (Female Figure Skating Legends Ser.). (Illus.). 64p. (J). (gr. 4-7). lib. bdg. 18.65 (978-0-7910-4201-4(4) , Chelsea Hse.) Facts On File, Inc.

Dynamic Athletes & the Sports They Influenced, 6 bks. Incl. Dare to Be Different : Athletes Who Changed Sports. Herzog, Brad. 112p. lib. bdg. 27.95 (978-0-8239-3696-0(1)); Hoopmania : The Book of Basketball History & Trivia. Herzog, Brad. 176p. lib. bdg. 32.60 (978-0-8239-3697-7(X)); Top Teams Ever : Football, Baseball, Basketball & Hockey Winners. Ross, Dalton. 176p. lib. bdg. 27.95 (978-0-8239-3693-9(7)); Women Winners : Then & Now. Cantwell, Lois & Smith, Pohla. 176p. lib. bdg. 25.25 (978-0-8239-3695-3(3)); World of Soccer : A Complete Guide to the World's Most Popular Sport. Collie, Ashley Jude. 176p. lib. bdg. 27.95 (978-0-8239-3698-4(8)); 20 Greatest Athletes of the 20th Century. Herzog, Brad. 176p. lib. bdg. 27.95 (978-0-8239-3694-6(5)); (YA). (gr. 7-12). (Illus.). 176p. 2005. Set lib. bdg. 169.65 (978-0-8239-9733-6(2)) Rosen Publishing Group, Inc., The.

Eboch, Chris. Jesse Owens: Young Record Breaker. Henderson, Meryl, illus. 2008. (Childhood of Famous Americans Ser.). 208p. (J). pap. 5.99 (***978-1-4169-3922-1(9)*** , Aladdin) Simon & Schuster Children's Publishing.

Edelson, Paula. Nancy Kerrigan. 1999. (Female Figure Skating Legends Ser.). (Illus.). 64p. (YA). (gr. 2-5). lib. bdg. 18.65 (978-0-7910-5028-6(9) , Chelsea Hse.) Facts On File, Inc.

Egan, Christopher & Egan, Lorraine Hopping. Sports Hall of Fame. 2000. (Illus.). 40p. (J). (gr. 2-5). pap. 6.95 (978-1-57255-776-5(1)) Mondo Publishing.

Ellis. Becoming A Master Student Athlete Eleventh Edition Plus Meyer Briggs Type Indicator. 11th ed. 2005. (YA). pap., pap. 58.36 (978-0-618-72294-5(7) , 397243) Houghton Mifflin College Div.

—Becoming a Master Student Athlete Plus Portfolio Assessment Cd. 11th ed. 2005. (YA). pap., pap. 56.36 (978-0-618-72292-1(0) , 397241) Houghton Mifflin College Div.

Ellwood, Nancy. Lance Armstrong: With a Discussion of Determination. 2004. (Values in Action Ser.). (J). (978-1-59203-073-6(4)) Learning Challenge, Inc.

Fandel, Jennifer. Jim Thorpe: Greatest Athlete in the World. Whigham, Rod, illus. 2008. (J). (***978-1-4296-0152-8(3)***) Capstone Pr., Inc.

Feldman, Heather. Marion Jones: Individual Title Six-Packs. (On Deck Ser.). 24p. (gr. 4-5). 35.00 (978-0-7578-1001-5(2)) Rigby Education.

—Marion Jones, Atleta de Categoria Internacional. 2002. (Superestrellas del Deporte Ser.). (SPA & ENG., Illus.). 24p. (J). lib. bdg. 17.25 (978-0-8239-6123-8(0) , Buenas Letra) Rosen Publishing Group, Inc., The.

Ferrara, Cos. Babe Didrikson Zaharias: Outcast & Hero. 2004. (Girls Explore, Reach for the Stars Ser.). (Illus.). 109p. (J). 20.00 (978-0-9749456-2-0(5) , Girls Explore) Girls Explore LLC.

Fiske, Brian D. BMX Greats. 2004. (Edge Books BMX Extreme). (Illus.). 32p. (J). 16.95 (978-0-7368-2434-7(0)) Capstone Pr., Inc.

Ford, Michael. You Wouldn't Want to Be a Greek Athlete! 2004. (You Wouldn't Want to Ser.). (Illus.). 32p. (J). (gr. 2-5). pap. 9.95 (978-0-531-16394-8(6) , Watts, Franklin) Scholastic Library Publishing.

Frew, Katherine. Gladiators: Battling in the Arena. 2005. (Way of the Warrior Ser.). (Illus.). 48p. (J). 24.00 (978-0-516-25121-9(X)); (gr. 7-12). pap. 6.95 (978-0-516-25090-8(6)) Scholastic Library Publishing. (Children's Pr.).

Frey, Shellie M. Winning Spirit: An Inside Look at LDS Sports Heros. 1999. (Illus.). 120p. (J). pap. 9.95 (978-0-8425-2459-9(2)) Brigham Young Univ.

—Winning Spirit Vol. II: An Inside Look at LDS Sports Heros. 1998. (Illus.). 152p. (YA). (gr. 5-12). pap. 9.95 (978-0-8425-2460-5(6)) Brigham Young Univ.

Garcia, Kimberly. Lance Armstrong. 2002. (Real-Life Reader Biographies Ser.). (Illus.). 32p. (J). (gr. 3-8). lib. bdg. 15.95 (978-1-58415-125-8(0)) Mitchell Lane Pubs., Inc.

Gerstein, Mordicai. The Man Who Walked Between the Towers. Gerstein, Mordicai, illus. 2007. (Illus.). 40p. (J). pap. 6.95 (***978-0-312-36878-4(X)***) Square Fish.

Gifford, Clive. Drugs & Sports. 2003. (Face the Facts Ser.). (Illus.). 56p. pap. 8.95 (978-1-4109-0339-6(7)); (J). lib. bdg. 28.56 (978-0-7398-6849-2(7)) Raintree.

—Drugs & Sports. 2003. (gr. 5-8). lib. bdg. 17.60 (978-0-613-78304-0(2)) Tandem Library Bks.

Gikow, Louise. Extreme Sports: A Chapter Book. 2004. (True Tales Ser.). (J). 22.50 (978-0-516-23730-5(6) , Children's Pr.) Scholastic Library Publishing.

Goldman, David J. Jewish Jocks: Athletic Stars Past & Present. 2004. (General Jewish Interest Ser.). (Illus.). 96p. (J). (gr. 6 up). pap. (978-1-58013-085-1(2)) Kar-Ben Publishing.

—Jewish Sports Stars: Athletic Heroes Past & Present. 2006. (Illus.). 96p. (J). pap. 9.95 (978-1-58013-183-4(2)) Kar-Ben Publishing.

Goodman, Michael E. Famous Athletes. 1999. (Eyes on America Ser.). (Illus.). 29p. (J). (978-1-56156-710-2(8)) Kidsbooks, Inc.

Gordon, Jeff. Pierre Turgeon: The Playmaker. 1999. (Sport Snaps Ser.). (Illus.). 40p. pap. 9.95 (978-1-892920-03-4(4)) GHB Publishers, LLC.

—Pierre Turgeon: The Playmaker. 1999. (gr. 7-12). lib. bdg. 18.75 (978-0-613-32946-0(5)) Tandem Library Bks.

Grabowski, John F. Lance Armstrong. 2005. (People in the News Ser.). (Illus.). 112p. (J). (ps-7). lib. bdg. 32.45 (978-1-59018-711-1(3) , Lucent Bks.) Thomson Gale.

Gramling, Scott, ed. Mystery Athletes: Can You Guess the Mystery Athlete? 1998. 32p. (J). (gr. 3-8). pap. 3.95 (978-1-886749-49-8(3)) Sports Illustrated For Kids.

Gray, Valerie A. Jason Kidd: Star Guard. 2000. (Sports Reports). (Illus.). 104p. (YA). (gr. 4-10). lib. bdg. 20.95 (978-0-7660-1333-9(2)) Enslow Pubs., Inc.

Great Sporting Events: Individual Title Six-Packs. 32p. (gr. 4 up). 44.00 (978-0-7578-0610-0(4)) Rigby Education.

Great Sports Teams, 35 bks. , Set. (Illus.). (YA). (gr. 4-10). lib. bdg. 625.35 (978-0-89490-888-0(X)) Enslow Pubs., Inc.

Gutman, Bill. Marion Jones: The Fastest Woman in the World. 2000. (YA). (978-0-606-19499-0(1)) Tandem Library Bks.

—Queen of the Ice: Tara Lipinski. 1999. (978-0-606-17391-9(9)) Tandem Library Bks.

Gwilliam, Heather. Livewire Real Lives Cathy Freeman. 1999. (Livewires Ser.). 32p. (gr. 6-9). pap. 6.00 (978-0-521-78826-7(9)) Cambridge Univ. Pr.

Hanel, Rachael. Gladiators. 2007. (J). (978-1-58341-535-1(1) , Creative Education) Creative Co., The.

Harcourt School Publishers Staff. The Golden Runner On Level. 3rd ed. 2002. (Trophies Reading Program Ser.). (Illus.). pap. 5.10 (978-0-15-323254-1(4)) Harcourt Schl. Pubs.

Hasday, Judy L. Extraordinary Women Athletes. 2000. (Extraordinary People Ser.). (Illus.). 288p. (YA). (gr. 6 up). pap. 16.95 (978-0-516-27039-5(7) , Children's Pr.) Scholastic Library Publishing.

—Extraordinary Women Athletes. 2000. (gr. 7-12). lib. bdg. 26.85 (978-0-613-54473-3(0)) Tandem Library Bks.

Herzog, Brad. Dare to Be Different: Athletes Who Changed Sports. 2005. (Sports Illustrated for Kids Bks.). (Illus.). 112p. (YA). (gr. 7-12). lib. bdg. 27.95 (978-0-8239-3696-0(1)) Rosen Publishing Group, Inc., The.

—Dare to Be Different: Athletes Who Changed Sports. Goehner, Amy Lennard, ed. 2000. 96p. (J). (gr. 2-8). pap. 3.99 (978-1-886749-95-5(7)) Sports Illustrated For Kids.

—The 20 Greatest Athletes of the 20th Century. 2005. (Sports Illustrated for Kids Bks.). (Illus.). 176p. (YA). (gr. 7-12). lib. bdg. 27.95 (978-0-8239-3694-6(5)) Rosen Publishing Group, Inc., The.

Hill, Anne E. Ekatarina Gordeeva: Figure Skater. 1999. (Overcoming Adversity Ser.). (Illus.). (YA). (gr. 5 up). 128p. pap. 9.95 (978-0-7910-4949-5(3)); 112p. 30.00 (978-0-7910-4948-8(5)) Facts On File, Inc. (Chelsea Hse.).

—Michelle Kwan. 2004. (Sports Heroes & Legends Ser.). (Illus.). 112p. (J). (gr. 6-12). lib. bdg. 27.93 (978-0-8225-1795-5(7)) Lerner Publishing Group.

Horton, Ron. Awesome Athletes. 2003. (History Makers Ser.). (Illus.). 112p. (J). 29.95 (978-1-59018-307-6(X) , Lucent Bks.) Thomson Gale.

—Extreme Athletes. 2004. (History Makers Ser.). (Illus.). 112p. (J). (gr. 7-10). 29.95 (978-1-59018-519-3(6) , Lucent Bks.) Thomson Gale.

Hotchkiss, Ron. The Matchless Six: The Story of Canada's First Women's Olympic Team. 2006. (Illus.). 200p. (J). (gr. 6). pap. 16.95 (978-0-88776-738-8(9)) Tundra Bks., Inc./Livres Toundra, Inc. CAN. *Dist:* Random Hse., Inc.

Isenberg, Marc & Rhoads, Rick. The Real Athletes Guide: How to Succeed in Sports, School & Life. Conley, Sebastian, illus. 1998. 185p. (YA). (gr. 7 up). pap. 19.95 (978-0-9666764-0-2(8)) A-Game, LLC.

James Barter. A Roman Gladiator. 2004. lib. bdg. 27.45 (978-1-59018-479-0(3)) Thomson Gale.

Jones, Brenn. Learning about Resilience from the Life of Lance Armstrong. 2002. (Character Building Book Ser.). (Illus.). 24p. (J). (gr. 3). lib. bdg. 18.75 (978-0-8239-5779-8(9) , PowerKids Pr.) Rosen Publishing Group, Inc., The.

Jones, Veda Boyd. Nicole Bobek. 1999. (Female Figure Skating Legends Ser.). (Illus.). 64p. (YA). (ps up). lib. bdg. 18.65 (978-0-7910-5029-3(7) , Chelsea Hse.) Facts On File, Inc.

Kaminsky, Marty. Uncommon Champions. 2003. (gr. 7-12). lib. bdg. 18.75 (978-0-613-79872-3(4)) Tandem Library Bks.

—Uncommon Champions: Fifteen Athletes Who Battled Back. 152p. (YA). 2003. (gr. 6-9). pap. 10.95 (978-1-59078-005-3(1)); 2001. (Illus.). (gr. 4-7). 14.95 (978-1-56397-787-9(7)) Boyds Mills Pr.

Kaplan, Ben. Sports Illustrated for Kids Super Sports Stars: The Coolest Athletes in the World. Seik, Margaret, ed. 1999. 48p. (J). (gr. 2-8). pap. 4.99 (978-1-886749-72-6(8)) Sports Illustrated For Kids.

Kehoe, Stasia Ward. Tara Lipinski, Superstar Ice Skater. 2001. (Great Record Breakers in Sports Ser.). (Illus.). 24p. (J). lib. bdg. 18.75 (978-0-8239-5634-0(2) , PowerKids Pr.) Rosen Publishing Group, Inc., The.

Keiser, Howard. Superstars of Men's Swimming & Diving. 1999. (Male Sports Stars Ser.). (Illus.). 64p. (YA). (gr. 4-7). 18.65 (978-0-7910-4589-3(7) , Chelsea Hse.) Facts On File, Inc.

Kelly, Evelyn. Katarina Witt. 1999. (Female Figure Skating Legends Ser.). (Illus.). 64p. (YA). (gr. 2-5). lib. bdg. 18.65 (978-0-7910-5026-2(2) , Chelsea Hse.) Facts On File, Inc.

Kent, Deborah. Athletes with Disabilities. 2003. (Watts Library). (Illus.). 64p. (J). (gr. 5-7). pap. 8.95 (978-0-531-16664-2(3)); 25.50 (978-0-531-12019-4(8)) Scholastic Library Publishing. (Watts, Franklin).

Kidd, Bruce. Tom Longboat. (Illus.). 64p. (J). (gr. 5 up). pap. (978-1-55041-838-5(6)) Fitzhenry & Whiteside, Ltd.

Knapp, Ron. Sports Great Hakeem Olajuwon. rev. ed. 2000. (Sports Great Bks.). (Illus.). 64p. (YA). (gr. 4-10). lib. bdg. 22.60 (978-0-7660-1268-4(9)) Enslow Pubs., Inc.

—Top 10 American Men's Olympic Gold Medalists. 2000. (Sports Top 10 Ser.). (Illus.). 48p. (YA). (gr. 4-10). lib. bdg. 23.93 (978-0-7660-1274-5(3)) Enslow Pubs., Inc.

Knotts, Bob. Sports Superstars: 8 of Today's Hottest Athletes. 2005. (Sports Illustrated for Kids Bks.). (Illus.). 176p. (YA). (gr. 7-12). lib. bdg. 27.95 (978-0-8239-3692-2(9)) Rosen Publishing Group, Inc., The.

—Super Eight: Today's Hottest Sports Stars. Sieck, Margaret, ed. 1999. (Illus.). 95p. (Orig.). (J). (gr. 2-8). pap. 3.99 (978-1-886749-68-9(X)) Sports Illustrated For Kids.

Kovatch, Sarah. Record Breaking Woman. 2005. (Voices Reading Ser.). (Illus.). 16p. (J). (978-0-7367-2914-7(3)) Zaner-Bloser, Inc.

Kramer, Barbara. Lance Armstrong: Determined to Beat the Odds. 2005. (Awesome Values in Famous Lives Ser.). (Illus.). 48p. (J). (ps-7). lib. bdg. 23.93 (978-0-7660-2377-2(X) , Enslow Elementary) Enslow Pubs., Inc.

Krull, Kathleen. Lives of the Athletes: Thrills, Spills (And What the Neighbors Thought) 1998. (Lives of the... Ser.). (Illus.). 96p. (J). (gr. 3-8). lib. bdg. 20.98 (978-0-8172-4191-9(4)) Raintree.

—Wilma Sin Limites. 2000. Tr. of Wilma Unlimited. (978-0-606-18197-6(0)); (SPA.). (gr. 3-6). lib. bdg. 14.15 (978-0-613-27592-7(6)) Tandem Library Bks.

—Wilma Unlimited. 2000. (978-0-606-18198-3(9)) Tandem Library Bks.

Lance Armstrong. 2004. (J). 27.07 (978-0-7614-1761-3(3)) Cavendish, Marshall Corp.

Lee, Veronica. Field Hockey. 2003. (Sports Injuries Ser.). (Illus.). 64p. (J). lib. bdg. (978-1-59084-631-5(1)) Mason Crest Pubs.

Lehn, Barbara. What Is an Athlete? Krauss, Carol, photos by. 2002. (What Is...? Ser.). (Illus.). 32p. (gr. k-3). lib. bdg. 21.90 (978-0-7613-2258-0(2) , Millbrook Pr.) Lerner Publishing Group.

Lincoln Library of Sports Champions, 14 volumes, 14 volume set. 7th ed. 2004. (Illus.). 1800p. (J). lib. bdg. 498.00 (978-0-912168-19-7(6) , 800-516-2656, Lincoln Library) Lincoln Library Press, The.

Littlefield, Bill. Champions: Stories of Ten Remarkable Athletes. Fuchs, Bernie, illus. 1998. 144p. (J). (gr. 3-7). pap. 10.95 (978-0-316-55849-5(4)) Little Brown & Co.

—Champions: Stories of Ten Remarkable Athletes. 1998. (J). (978-0-606-13262-6(7)) Tandem Library Bks.

Lovitt, Chip. American Gymnasts: Gold Medal Dreams. 2000. (gr. 5-8). lib. bdg. 13.00 (978-0-613-73123-2(9)) Tandem Library Bks.

Lyons, Michele. Going for the Gold. 2003. (On the Job Ser.). (Illus.). 32p. (gr. 3-5). 23.00 (978-0-7910-7412-1(9) , Chelsea Hse.) Facts On File, Inc.

MacNab, Chris. Field. 2003. (Sports Injuries Ser.). (Illus.). 64p. (J). lib. bdg. (978-1-59084-639-1(7)) Mason Crest Pubs.

Mandell, Judith J. Super Sports Star Gary Payton. 2001. (Super Sports Star Ser.). (Illus.). 48p. (J). (gr. 1-4). lib. bdg. 23.93 (978-0-7660-1519-7(X)) Enslow Pubs., Inc.

Marcovitz, Hal. The Munich Olympics. 2002. (Great Disasters, Reforms & Ramifications Ser.). (Illus.). 112p. (J). 30.00 (978-0-7910-6737-6(8)); pap. 13.25 (978-0-7910-6911-0(7)) Facts On File, Inc. (Chelsea Hse.).

Marion Jones: Individual Title Six-Packs. (On Deck en Espanol Ser.). (SPA.). 24p. (gr. 4-5). 35.00 (978-0-7578-6384-4(1)) Rigby Education.

Martin, Michael. Gladiators. 2007. (Edge Books). (Illus.). 32p. (J). (gr. 3-6). 23.93 (***978-0-7368-6429-9(6)***) Capstone Pr., Inc.

Mason, Paul. Training for the Top: Nutrition & Exercise. 2005. (Illus.). 32p. (J). (978-1-4109-1964-9(1)); lib. bdg. (978-1-4109-1933-5(1)) Steck-Vaughn.

Maxwell, E. J. Xtreme Sports: Cutting Edge. 2003. (Xtreme Sports Ser.). (Illus.). 96p. (J). (gr. 3-6). pap. 4.99 (978-0-439-46854-1(X) , Scholastic Paperbacks) Scholastic, Inc.

—Xtreme Sports: Cutting Edge. 2003. (gr. 3-6). lib. bdg. 13.00 (978-0-613-71994-0(8)) Tandem Library Bks.

McDaniel, Melissa. Pushing the Limits: A Chapter Book. (True Tales Ser.). (Illus.). 48p. (J). 2005. (gr. 2-4). pap. 4.95 (978-0-516-24688-8(7)); 2004. 22.50 (978-0-516-23734-3(9)) Scholastic Library Publishing. (Children's Pr.).

McLeese, Don. Jim Thorpe. 2003. (Rourke Discovery Library). (Illus.). 24p. (gr. 2-5). 14.95 (978-1-58952-305-0(9)) Rourke Publishing, LLC.

McNeil, Niki, et al. HOCPP 1078 Gladiators. 2006. spiral bd. 19.50 (***978-1-60308-078-1(3)***) In the Hands of a Child.

Mello, Tara Baukus. Mark Martin. 1999. (Race Car Legends Ser.). (Illus.). 64p. (YA). (gr. 4-7). pap. (978-0-7910-5677-6(5)); 25.00 (978-0-7910-5411-6(X)) Facts On File, Inc. (Chelsea Hse.).

—Rusty Wallace. 1999. (Race Car Legends Ser.). (Illus.). 64p. (J). (gr. 2-5). 28.00 (978-0-7910-5023-1(8) , Chelsea Hse.) Facts On File, Inc.

Mia Hamm, 6 Packs. (On Deck en Espanol Ser.). (SPA.). 24p. (gr. 4-5). 35.00 (978-0-7578-6381-3(7)) Rigby Education.

Migliaccio, Eric. Track & Field: Easy Olympic Sports Reader. 2004. (U. S. Olympic Committee Easy Olympic Sports Readers Ser.). (Illus.). 16p. (J). pap. 2.99 (978-1-58000-115-1(7)) Griffin Publishing Group.

Molzahn, Arlene Bourgeois. Top 10 American Women Sprinters. 1998. (Sports Top 10 Ser.). (Illus.). 48p. (YA). (gr. 4-10). lib. bdg. 23.93 (978-0-7660-1011-6(2)) Enslow Pubs., Inc.

Monroe, Judy. Steroids, Sports, & Body Image: The Risks of Performance-Enhancing Drugs. 2004. (Issues in Focus Ser.). (Illus.). 128p. (J). lib. bdg. 26.60 (978-0-7660-2160-0(2)) Enslow Pubs., Inc.

Morgan, Terri. Gabrielle Reece: Volleyball's Model Athlete. 1999. (Sports Achievers Biographies Ser.). (Illus.). (YA). (gr. 4-9). 80p. lib. bdg. 22.60 (978-0-8225-3667-3(6)); 64p. pap. (978-0-8225-9828-2(0)) Lerner Publishing Group. (LernerSports).

—Gabrielle Reece: Volleyball's Model Athlete. 1999. (Illus.). (J). (978-0-606-18819-7(3)) Tandem Library Bks.

Morley, Jacqueline. How to Be an Ancient Greek Athlete. 2005. (How to Be Ser.). (Illus.). 32p. (J). (gr. 3-7). 14.95 (978-0-7922-7443-8(1) , National Geographic Children's Bks.) National Geographic Society.

Nichols, Catherine. Record Breakers: A Chapter Book. (True Tales Ser.). (J). 2005. (Illus.). 48p. (gr. 2-4). pap. 4.95 (978-0-516-24689-5(5)); 2004. 22.50 (978-0-516-23732-9(2)) Scholastic Library Publishing. (Children's Pr.).

O'Brien, Eileen. Starving to Win: Athletes & Eating Disorders. 1998. (Teen Health Library of Eating Disorder Prevention). (Illus.). 64p. (J). (gr. 4-6). lib. bdg. 26.50 (978-0-8239-2764-7(4) , EDATEA) Rosen Publishing Group, Inc., The.

O'Hearn, Michael. Jake Burton Carpenter & the Snowboard. Frenz, Ron & Barnett, Charles, illus. 2007. (Graphic Library). 32p. (J). (***978-0-7368-7516-5(6)***) Capstone Pr., Inc.

Otten, Jack. Atletismo. 2004. (Entrenamiento Deportivo Ser.). (SPA & ENG., Illus.). 24p. (J). lib. bdg. 17.25 (978-0-8239-6846-6(4) , Buenas Letra) Rosen Publishing Group, Inc., The.

Owens, Jesse, intro. The Lincoln Library of Sports Champions, 14 vols., Set. 8th ed. 2006. (Illus.). (J). (gr. 4 up). lib. bdg. 523.00 (978-0-912168-25-8(0) , 800-516-2656, Lincoln Library) Lincoln Library Press, The.

Packard, Mary. Beating the Odds: A Chapter Book. (True Tales Ser.). (J). 2005. (Illus.). 48p. (gr. 2-4). pap. 4.95 (978-0-516-24682-6(8)); 2004. 22.50 (978-0-516-23731-2(4)) Scholastic Library Publishing. (Children's Pr.).

Parham, Jerrill. Thrills & Spills: Fast Sports. 2007. (Shockwave: the Human Experience Ser.). 36p. (J). pap. 6.95 (***978-0-531-18796-8(9));*** (Illus.). (gr. 4-6). lib. bdg. 25.00 (***978-0-531-17762-4(9))*** Scholastic Library Publishing. (Children's Pr.).

Persico, Deborah A. Vernonia School District vs. Acton: Drug Testing in Schools. 1999. (Landmark Supreme Court Cases Ser.). (Illus.). 128p. (YA). (gr. 6-12). lib. bdg. 26.60 (978-0-7660-1087-1(2)) Enslow Pubs., Inc.

Piven, Hanoch. What Athletes Are Made Of. Piven, Hanoch, illus. 2006. (Illus.). 40p. (J). (gr. 1-5). 16.95 (978-1-4169-1002-2(6) , Atheneum) Simon & Schuster Children's Publishing.

Preller, James. Rock Solid. 2000. (gr. 5-8). lib. bdg. 12.40 (978-0-613-29503-1(X)) Tandem Library Bks.

Rappoport, Ken. Profiles in Sports Courage. 2006. (Illus.). 160p. (J). 15.95 (978-1-56145-368-9(4) , Peachtree Junior) Peachtree Pubs., Ltd.

Rau, Dana Meachen. Athletic Shoes. 2008. (J). lib. bdg. 25.26 (***978-1-60279-027-8(2)***) Cherry Lake Publishing.

Raum, Elizabeth. Famous Athletes. 2007. (J). (***978-1-4109-2973-0(6));*** pap. (***978-1-4109-2994-5(9)***) Steck-Vaughn.

Riddle, John. Professional Athlete & Sports Official. 2003. (Careers with Character Ser.). (Illus.). 96p. (J). (gr. 7 up). lib. bdg. 22.95 (978-1-59084-321-5(5)) Mason Crest Pubs.

Roberts, Robin. Basketball Year: What It's Like to Be a Woman Pro. 2000. (Get in the Game! with Robin Roberts Ser.). (Illus.). 48p. (gr. 4-8). lib. bdg. (978-0-7613-1406-6(7) , Millbrook Pr.) Lerner Publishing Group.

Rock. The Rock Says. 2000. (Illus.). 416p. (gr. 7-12). per. 16.45 (978-0-613-33610-9(0)) Tandem Library Bks.

Rosenthal. Michael Johnson: Sprinter Deluxe. 2000. (Sport Snaps Ser.). (J). (978-0-606-20158-2(0)) Tandem Library Bks.

Rutledge, Rachel. The Best of the Best in Track & Field. 1999. (Women of Sports Ser.: up). (Illus.). 64p. (gr. 5-8). pap. 7.95 (978-0-7613-0446-3(0) , Twenty-First Century Bks.) Lerner Publishing Group.

—The Best of the Best in Track & Field. 1999. (Women of Sports Ser.). (978-0-606-17030-7(8)) Tandem Library Bks.

Sandler, Michael. Jean Driscoll: Dream Big, Work Hard! 2007. (Defining Moments Ser.). (Illus.). 32p. (J). lib. bdg. 25.27 (978-1-59716-268-5(X)) Bearport Publishing Co., Inc.

Savage, Jeff. Carly Patterson. 2005. (Amazing Athletes Ser.). (Illus.). 32p. (J). (gr. 2-5). pap. 5.95 (978-0-8225-2640-7(9)) Lerner Publishing Group.

—Top 10 Physically Challenged Athletes. 2000. (Sports Top 10 Ser.). (Illus.). 48p. (J). (gr. 4-10). lib. bdg. 23.93 (978-0-7660-1272-1(7)) Enslow Pubs., Inc.

Scheppler, Bill. The Ironman Triathlon. 2002. (Ultra Sports Ser.). (Illus.). 64p. (YA). (gr. 5-8). lib. bdg. 26.50 (978-0-8239-3556-7(6) , Rosen Central) Rosen Publishing Group, Inc., The.

Schilling, Vincent. Native Athletes in Action! 2007. (Native Trailblazers Ser.). (Illus.). 128p. (J). (gr. 4-8). pap. 9.95 (***978-0-9779183-0-0(0)***) 7th Generation.

Shea, Pegi Deitz. Ekatarina Gordeeva. 1999. (Female Figure Skating Legends Ser.). (Illus.). 64p. (YA). (gr. 2-7). 12.95 (978-0-7910-5027-9(0) , Chelsea Hse.) Facts On File, Inc.

Smith, Michelle. Raise the Roof! 2001. (WNBA Ser.). (Illus.). 96p. (J). (gr. 3-7). pap. 4.99 (978-0-439-24112-0(X)) Scholastic, Inc.

Spirn, Michele. Against the Odds: The Jackie Joyner-Kersee Story. 2001. (YA). pap. (978-1-56765-063-1(5) , R692P) AMSCO Schl. Pubns., Inc.

Sports Heroes. Incl. Alex Rodriguez. Covert, Kim. 2002. lib. bdg. 21.26 (978-0-7368-1051-7(X)); Brett Favre. Nelson, Sharlene P. & Nelson, Ted. 2000. lib. bdg. 21.26 (978-0-7368-0576-6(1)); Derek Jeter. Covert, Kim. 2001. lib. bdg. 21.26 (978-0-7368-0777-7(2)); Jeff Gordon. Wallner, Rosemary. 2000. lib. bdg. 21.26 (978-0-7368-0577-3(X)); Ken Griffey, Jr. Schaefer, A. R. 2002. lib. bdg. 21.26 (978-0-7368-1294-8(6)); Kevin Garnett. Molzahn, Arlene Bourgeois. 2001. lib. bdg. 21.26 (978-0-7368-0778-4(0)); Kobe Bryant. Schaefer, A. R. 2002. lib. bdg. 21.26 (978-0-7368-1052-4(8)); Kurt Warner. Schaefer, A. R. 2002. lib. bdg. 21.26 (978-0-7368-1295-5(4)); Mark McGwire. Powell, Phelan. 2000. lib. bdg. 21.26 (978-0-7368-0578-0(8)); Mia Hamm. Latimer, Clay. 2000. lib. bdg. 21.26 (978-0-7368-0579-7(6)); Michelle Kwan. Wallner, Rosemary. 2001. lib. bdg. 21.26 (978-0-7368-0779-1(9)); Pedro Martinez. Schaefer, A. R. 2002. lib. bdg. 21.26 (978-0-7368-1296-2(2)); Randy Moss. Molzahn, Arlene Bourgeois. 2002. lib. bdg. 21.26 (978-0-7368-1053-1(6)); Sammy Sosa. Molzahn, Arlene Bourgeois. 2000. lib. bdg. 21.26 (978-0-7368-0580-3(X)); Serena & Venus Williams. Schaefer, A. R. 2002. lib. bdg. 21.26 (978-0-7368-1054-8(4)); Shaquille O'Neal. Schaefer, A. R. 2002. lib. bdg. 21.26 (978-0-7368-1297-9(0)); Sheryl Swoopes. Wallner, Rosemary. 2001. lib. bdg. 21.26 (978-0-7368-0780-7(2)); Tiger Woods. Sirimarco, Elizabeth. 2000. lib. bdg. 21.26 (978-0-7368-0581-0(8)); 48p. (J). (gr. 3-4). (Illus.). Set lib. bdg. 382.68 (978-0-7368-1298-6(9) , Capstone High-Interest Bks.) Capstone Pr., Inc.

Sports Heroes Classroom Library. (gr. 4 up). lib. bdg. 62.95 (978-0-7368-9280-3(X)) Red Brick Learning.

Sports Heroes Complete Unit. (gr. 4 up). 358.95 (978-0-7368-9281-0(8)) Red Brick Learning.

Sports Illustrated for Kids Books. 2005. (Illus.). 176p. (gr. 7-12). lib. bdg. 388.65 (978-0-8239-3925-1(1)) Rosen Publishing Group, Inc., The.

Stewart, Mark. Alex Rodriguez: Gunning for Greatness. 1999. (Baseball's New Wave Ser.: up). (Illus.). 48p. (gr. 4-7). pap. 6.95 (978-0-7613-1040-2(1) , Millbrook Pr.) Lerner Publishing Group.

—Alex Rodriguez: Gunning for Greatness. 1999. (Baseball's New Wave Ser.). (Illus.). (J). 13.75 (978-0-606-18277-5(2)) Tandem Library Bks.

—One Wild Ride: The Life of Skateboarding Superstar Tony Hawk. 2003. (Illus.). 64p. (gr. 6 up). pap. (978-0-7613-1689-3(2) , Twenty-First Century Bks.) Lerner Publishing Group.

—Sweet Victory: Lance Armstrong's Incredible Journey. 2000. 64p. (gr. 4-7). (Single Titles Ser.: up). pap. (978-0-7613-1387-8(7) , Millbrook Pr.); (Inspiring People Ser.). (Illus.). lib. bdg. 24.90 (978-0-7613-1861-3(5) , Twenty-First Century Bks.) Lerner Publishing Group.

—Sweet Victory: Lance Armstrong's Incredible Journey. 2000. (J). (978-0-606-19176-0(3)); (gr. 3-6). lib. bdg. 16.40 (978-0-613-27144-8(0)) Tandem Library Bks.

Stewart, Mark Alan. Andres Galarraga: The Big Cat. 1998. (Sports Stars Ser.). (J). pap. 5.95 (978-0-516-26289-5(0) , Children's Pr.) Scholastic Library Publishing.

—Eric Lindros: Power Player. 1998. (Sports Stars Ser.). (Illus.). 48p. (J). (gr. 3-4). pap. 5.95 (978-0-516-26052-5(9) , Children's Pr.) Scholastic Library Publishing.

—Randy Johnson: The Big Unit. Friedman, Mark, ed. 1998. (Sports Stars Ser.). (Illus.). 48p. (J). pap. 5.95 (978-0-516-26119-5(3) , Children's Pr.) Scholastic Library Publishing.

Strudwick, Leslie. Athletes. 1998. (Women in Profile Ser.). (Illus.). 48p. (J). (gr. 4). lib. bdg. (978-0-7787-0015-9(1)) Crabtree Publishing Co.

Superestrellas del Deporte Series, Set. 2003. (Superestrellas del Deporte Ser.). (Illus.). (J). (SPA & ENG.). 103.50 (978-0-8239-7198-5(8)); lib. bdg. 103.50 (978-0-8239-7194-7(5)) Rosen Publishing Group, Inc., The. (Buenas Letra).

Sutcliffe, Jane. Babe Didrikson Zaharias: All-Around Athlete. Reeves, Jeni, illus. (On My Own Biographies Ser.). 48p. 2005. (gr. 2-5). lib. bdg. 23.93 (978-1-57505-421-6(3)); 2000. (J). (gr. 1-3). pap. 5.95 (978-1-57505-447-6(7)) Lerner Publishing Group.

Thompson, John. Lance Armstrong. 2001. (Overcoming Adversity Ser.). (Illus.). (J). 100p. pap. 9.95 (978-0-7910-5880-0(8)); 112p. (gr. 5 up). 30.00 (978-0-7910-5879-4(4)) Facts On File, Inc. (Chelsea Hse.).

Thornley, Stew. Allen Iverson: Star Guard. 2001. (Sports Reports). (Illus.). 104p. (J). (gr. 4-10). lib. bdg. 26.60 (978-0-7660-1501-2(7)) Enslow Pubs., Inc.

—Super Sports Star Kevin Garnett. 2001. (Super Sports Star Ser.). (Illus.). 48p. (J). (gr. 1-4). lib. bdg. 23.93 (978-0-7660-1515-9(7)) Enslow Pubs., Inc.

—Super Sports Star Kobe Bryant. 2001. (Super Sports Star Ser.). (Illus.). 48p. (J). (gr. 1-4). lib. bdg. 23.93 (978-0-7660-1514-2(9)) Enslow Pubs., Inc.

—Super Sports Star Tim Duncan. 2001. (Super Sports Star Ser.). (Illus.). 48p. (J). (gr. 1-4). lib. bdg. 23.93 (978-0-7660-1513-5(0)) Enslow Pubs., Inc.

Time Out: Star Athletes Who Shine off the Field. (Illus.). 32p. (J). (gr. 3-9). pap. 3.99 (978-1-930623-19-4(4)) Sports Illustrated For Kids.

Tomlinson, Dylan B. How to Reach Your Favorite Sports Star. Woo, Dianne J., ed. 1999. (How to Reach Your Favorite Star Ser.: Vol. 4). (Illus.). 96p. (J). (gr. 3-7). pap. 5.95 (978-1-56565-702-1(0) , 07020W) Lowell Hse. Juvenile.

Torres, John Albert. Fitness Stars of Bodybuilding. 2000. (Legends of Health & Fitness Ser.). (Illus.). 96p. (gr. 6-10). lib. bdg. 25.70 (978-1-58415-051-0(3)) Mitchell Lane Pubs., Inc.

Upsets & Comebacks. 2006. (Upsets & Comebacks Ser.). (J). lib. bdg. 143.76 (978-1-59716-201-2(9)) Bearport Publishing Co., Inc.

Vickery, A. Lou. How to Be a Winner: The Young Athlete's Notebook. 1998. 176p. (YA). (gr. 5 up). pap. 12.95 (978-0-9654140-2-9(7)) Upword Pr.

Weihenmayer, Erik. Touch the Top of the World. 2002. (gr. 7-12). lib. bdg. 23.45 (978-0-613-56864-7(8)) Tandem Library Bks.

Wellman, Sam. Kristi Yamaguchi. 1999. (Female Figure Skating Legends Ser.). (Illus.). 64p. (YA). (gr. 2-5). 12.95 (978-0-7910-5025-5(4) , Chelsea Hse.) Facts On File, Inc.

Williams, Jean Kinney. Tiger Woods: Professional Golfer. 2001. (Career Biographies Ser.). (Illus.). 128p. (YA). (gr. 6-12). 25.00 (978-0-89434-371-1(8) , F414, Ferguson Publishing Co.) Facts On File, Inc.

Wilner, Barry. Girls Rule! The Glory & Spirit of Women in Sports. 2000. (Illus.). 160p. (J). pap. 22.95 (978-0-7407-1171-8(7)) Andrews McMeel Publishing.

—Tara Lipinski: Star Figure Skater. 2001. (Sports Reports). (Illus.). 104p. (J). (gr. 4-10). lib. bdg. 26.60 (978-0-7660-1505-0(X)) Enslow Pubs., Inc.

Wingate, Brian. Tony Hawk: Skateboarding Champion. 2005. (World of Skateboarding Ser.). (Illus.). 48p. (YA). (gr. 5-8). lib. bdg. 26.50 (978-0-8239-3651-9(1)) Rosen Publishing Group, Inc., The.

Wulffson, Don L. Pro Sports: How Did They Begin? Giuliani, Alfred, illus. 2000. 64p. (J). (gr. 2-5). pap. 5.95 (978-1-57255-814-4(8)) Mondo Publishing.

Young, Ian. Lance Armstrong: Champion for Life!, 6 vols. (gr. 4 up). 49.95 (978-0-7368-3868-9(6) , High Five) Red Brick Learning.

Young, Ian & Rasinski, Timothy V. Lance Armstrong: Champion for Life! 2004. (High Five Reading Ser.). (J). (978-0-7368-3850-4(3)); 23.93 (978-0-7368-3878-8(3)) Capstone Pr., Inc.

ATHLETES, AFRICAN AMERICAN

see African American Athletes

ATHLETICS

see also Coaching (Athletics); Gymnastics; Olympics; Physical Education and Training; Sports; Track Athletics
also names of specific athletic activities, e.g. Boxing; Rowing; etc.

Atletismo, 6 Pcks. (On Deck en Espanol Ser.). (SPA.). 24p. (gr. 4-5). 35.00 (978-0-7578-6388-2(4)) Rigby Education.

Bagley, Katie. Coaches. 2001. (Community Helpers Ser.). (Illus.). 24p. (J). (gr. 1-2). lib. bdg. 18.60 (978-0-7368-0807-1(8) , Bridgestone Bks.) Capstone Pr., Inc.

Barnhart, C. A. What Makes Great Athletes. 2005. (Illus.). 24p. (J). (*978-0-328-13561-5(5) , Scott Foresman) Addison-Wesley Educational Pubs., Inc.

Bartel, Blaine. Little Black Book for Athletes. 2004. 80p. pap. 4.99 (978-1-57794-622-9(7)) Harrison Hse., Inc.

Canizares, Susan & Chanko, Pamela. Ready, Set, Go. 1999. (ps-2). lib. bdg. 10.10 (978-0-613-22246-4(6)) Tandem Library Bks.

Dintiman, George Blough. Speed Improvement for Young Athletes: How to Sprint Faster in Your Sport in 30 Workouts. rev. ed. 2006. Vol. 2. (Illus.). 153p. pap. 17.95 (978-0-938074-26-7(1)) National Assn. of Speed & Explosion.

Frisch, Aaron. The Story of Nike. 2008. (Built for Success Ser.). (J). (*978-1-58341-608-2(0) , Creative Education) Creative Co., The.

Harcourt School Publishers Staff. The Golden Spike. 3rd ed. 2002. (Horizons Ser.). (Illus.). (J). pap. 7.30 (978-0-15-333581-5(5)) Harcourt Schl. Pubs.

Jackson, Colin. Jovenes Atletas. (SPA.). 32p. (YA). (gr. 2 up). 16.76 (978-84-272-4966-0(7)) Molino, Editorial ESP. *Dist:* Lectorum Pubns., Inc.

Knapp, Ron. Top 10 Stars of the NCAA Men's Basketball Tournament. 2001. (Sports Top 10 Ser.). (Illus.). 48p. (J). (gr. 4-10). lib. bdg. 23.93 (978-0-7660-1498-5(3)) Enslow Pubs., Inc.

Knotts, Bob. Weightlifting. 2000. (gr. 3-6). lib. bdg. 15.25 (978-0-613-53581-6(2)) Tandem Library Bks.

Lehn, Barbara. What Is an Athlete? Krauss, Carol, photos by. 2002. (What Is...? Ser.). (Illus.). 32p. (gr. k-3). lib. bdg. 21.90 (978-0-7613-2258-0(2) , Millbrook Pr.) Lerner Publishing Group.

Minden, Cecilia. Coaches. 2006. (Neighborhood Helpers Ser.). (Illus.). 32p. (J). (gr. k-4). 22.79 (978-1-59296-561-8(X)) Child's World, Inc.

Morley, Jacqueline. How to Be an Ancient Greek Athlete. 2005. (How to Be Ser.). (Illus.). 32p. (J). (gr. 3-7). 21.90 (978-0-7922-7495-7(4) , National Geographic Children's Bks.) National Geographic Society.

Perez, Herb. The Complete Tae Kwon Do for Kids. 1999. (Martial Arts Ser.). (Illus.). 128p. (J). (gr. 4-7). pap. 7.95 (978-1-56565-959-9(7) , 09597W, Roxbury Park) Lowell Hse.

Schindler, John. Triathlons. 2005. (Illus.). 24p. (J). pap. 5.95 (978-0-8368-4551-8(X)); (YA). lib. bdg. 22.00 (978-0-8368-4544-0(7)) Stevens, Gareth Inc.

ATHLETICS—FICTION

Anderson, Scoular. Stan the Dog & the Sneaky Snacks. 2006. (Read-It! Chapter Books). (J). 21.26 (978-1-4048-2742-4(0)) Picture Window Bks.

Arena, Felice & Kettle, Phil. Olympics. Cox, David, illus. 2004. (J). pap. (978-1-59336-374-1(5)) Mondo Publishing.

Boushell, Mike. Freshman Five. (J). pap. 9.99 (978-0-88092-602-7(3)) Royal Fireworks Publishing Co.

Brouwer, Sigmund. Hurricane Power. 2007. (Orca Sports Ser.). 176p. (YA). (gr. 5 up). pap. (*978-1-55143-865-8(8)) Orca Bk. Pubs.

Brown, Marc. Arthur & the Best Coach Ever. Brown, Marc, illus. 4th ed. 2001. (Arthur Good Sports Ser.: Bk. 4). (Illus.). 64p. (J). (gr. 2-4). 13.95 (978-0-316-11965-8(2)); pap. 4.25 (978-0-316-12117-0(7)) Little, Brown Bks. for Young Readers.

—Arthur & the Best Coach Ever. 2001. (Arthur Good Sports Ser.: Bk. 4). (gr. 3-6). lib. bdg. 11.80 (978-0-613-35627-5(6)); (Illus.). (J). 10.75 (978-0-606-21910-5(2)) Tandem Library Bks.

Crutcher, Chris. Ironman. 2004. 288p. (J). pap. 6.99 (978-0-06-059840-2(9) , HarperTeen) HarperCollins Pubs.

Downs, Mike. You See a Circus, I See... McGrory, Anik, illus. 2005. 32p. (J). 14.95 (978-1-58089-097-7(0)) Charlesbridge Publishing, Inc.

Flynn, Dale Bachm. A Very Special Athlete. Soltero, Emilio, illus. 2004. 32p. (J). lib. bdg. 14.95 (978-0-9741332-1-8(3)) Pearl Pr.

Gorman, Carol & Findley, Ron. The Stumptown Kid. 2005. 224p. (J). (gr. 3-7). 14.95 (978-1-56145-337-5(4)) Peachtree Pubs., Ltd.

Harcourt School Publishers Staff. I Can't Play Baseball: Take-Home Book. 2001. (Collections Ser.). (Illus.). (J). pap. 1.90 (978-0-15-319546-4(0)) Harcourt Schl. Pubs.

Harris, Richard. I'm Walking, I'm Running, I'm Jumping, I'm Hopping. Harris, R. Craig, illus. 2006. 32p. 16.95 (978-0-9704504-1-8(9)) CPG Publishing, Inc.

Klett, David E. Rachel & the Wizard of Lake Lure: The Lake Lure Chronicles - Book 2. 2006. (J). lib. bdg. 17.95 (*978-0-9779325-1-1(6)) Five Oaks Pr.

Linko, G. J. Holden's Heart. 2004. (Seekers Ser.). 5.99 (978-0-8066-4180-5(0) , Augsburg Bks.) Augsburg Fortress, Pubs.

Lion, Melissa. Swollen. 2006. 192p. (YA). pap. 6.50 (978-0-553-49408-2(2) , Laurel Leaf) Random Hse. Children's Bks.

Martin, Ann M. Karen's Field Day. 1999. (Baby-Sitters Little Sister Ser.: No. 108). 112p. (J). (gr. 3-7). pap. 3.99 (978-0-590-50060-9(0)) Scholastic, Inc.

McEwan, Jamie. Willy the Scrub. 2005. 64p. (J). pap. 4.99 (978-1-58196-020-4(4)) Darby Creek Publishing.

Nishiyama, Nuriko. Harlem Beat No.03. 2003. (gr. 7-12). lib. bdg. 18.75 (978-0-613-82608-2(6)) Tandem Library Bks.

Pearce, Richard & Story, Ken. Dorkman. 2006. (YA). mass mkt. 8.50 (*978-0-9753367-8-6(9)) Onstage Publishing, LLC.

Riordan, Rick. The Lightning Thief. 2005. (Percy Jackson & the Olympians: Bk. 1). 384p. (J). (gr. 5-17). 17.95 (978-0-7868-5629-9(7)) Hyperion Bks. for Children.

Spinelli, Jerry. Maniac Magee. 2002. (J). 13.15 (978-0-7587-0201-2(9)) Book Wholesalers, Inc.

—Maniac Magee. 1999. 192p. (J). (gr. 4-7). pap. 6.99 (978-0-316-80906-1(3)) Little Brown & Co.

—Maniac Magee. 1998. (Assessment Packs Ser.). 15p. pap., tchr.'s training gde. ed. 15.95 (978-1-58303-050-9(6)) Pathways Publishing.

—Maniac Magee. unabr. ed. 2004. 184p. (J). (gr. 4-7). pap. 36.00 incl. audio (978-0-8072-0667-6(9) , Listening Library) Random Hse. Audio Publishing Group.

Steindal, Yvonne L. D. Holden's Heart. ldr.'s ed. 2004. (Seekers Ser.). 3.99 (978-0-8066-4183-6(5)) Augsburg Fortress, Pubs.

Swan, William. Fast Finish. 1999. (gr. 7-12). lib. bdg. 13.55 (978-0-613-18217-1(0)) Tandem Library Bks.

Warner, Gertrude Chandler. Gymnastics Mystery. 2000. (gr. 3-6). lib. bdg. 11.80 (978-0-613-21664-7(4)) Tandem Library Bks.

Watson, Katy. Juice. 2000. 200p. (J). pap. 13.95 (978-1-86368-304-3(6)) Fremantle Pr. AUS. *Dist:* International Specialized Bk. Services.

—Juice. 2000. (gr. 7-12). lib. bdg. 23.40 (978-0-613-58398-5(1)) Tandem Library Bks.

Weeks, Jan. The Marathon Runner. Harrison, Paul, illus. 2006. (Read-It! Chapter Books). 64p. (J). (gr. 2-4). 19.95 (978-1-4048-1669-5(0)) Picture Window Bks.

Wooden, Thomas James, Jr. Four-Hundred Meter Champion. Winston, Dennis, illus. 2003. 103p. (J). mass mkt. 12.00 (978-0-9740195-0-5(X)) New Castle Publishing Co.

ATLANTA BRAVES (BASEBALL TEAM)

Epstein, Brad M. Atlanta Braves 101: My first Team-board-book. l.t. ed. 2007. (Illus.). 22p. (J). bds. 10.95 (*978-1-932530-74-2(6) , 101 Bk.) Michaelson Entertainment.

Goodman, Michael E. The History of the Atlanta Braves. 1998. (Baseball, the Great American Game Ser.). (Illus.). 32p. (YA). (gr. 3-12). pap. 21.30 (978-0-88682-898-1(8) , Creative Education) Creative Co., The.

Grabowski, John F. The Atlanta Braves. 2003. (Illus.). 112p. (J). 29.95 (978-1-59018-304-5(5) , Lucent Bks.) Thomson Gale.

Potts, Steve. Atlanta Braves. 2001. (Championship Teams Ser.). (Illus.). (J). (978-1-58340-089-0(3)) Smart Apple Media.

Robinson, Tom. Andruw Jones: All-Star on & off the Field. 2007. (Sports Stars with Heart Ser.). (Illus.). 128p. (J). (gr. 5). lib. bdg. 31.93 (*978-0-7660-2867-8(4)) Enslow Pubs., Inc.

Stewart, Mark. The Atlanta Braves. 2006. (Team Spirit Ser.). (Illus.). 48p. (J). lib. bdg. 25.27 (978-1-59953-000-0(7)) Norwood Hse. Pr.

Stewart, Mark. Atlanta Braves. 2008. 48p. pap. 9.95 (*978-1-60357-006-0(3)) Norwood Hse. Pr.

Stewart, Wayne. Atlanta Braves. 2002. (Baseball Ser.). (Illus.). 32p. (J). pap. (978-1-58341-200-8(X) , Creative Education); pap. 5.95 (978-0-89812-334-0(8) , Creative Paperbacks) Creative Co., The.

ATLANTIC COAST

Arnosky, Jim. Following the Coast. Arnosky, Jim, illus. 2004. (Illus.). 32p. (J). (gr. 3 up). 15.99 (978-0-688-17117-9(6)) HarperCollins Pubs.

Gibbons, Gail. Surrounded by Sea: Life on a New England Fishing Island. Gibbons, Gail, illus. (Illus.). 32p. (J). (ps-3). 2006. 6.95 (978-0-8234-2021-6(3)); 2005. 17.95 (978-0-8234-1941-8(X)) Holiday Hse., Inc.

Karas, G. Brian. Atlantic. Karas, G. Brian, illus. 2004. (Illus.). 32p. (J). (ps-2). reprint ed. pap. 6.99 (978-0-14-240027-2(0) , Puffin) Penguin Group (USA) Inc.

Moore, Robin. The Man with the Silver Oar. 2002. 192p. (J). (gr. 5 up). 15.89 (978-0-06-000048-6(1)) HarperCollins Pubs.

Prevost, John F. Atlantic Ocean. 2003. (Oceans & Seas Ser.). (Illus.). 24p. (J). (gr. k-6). lib. bdg. 21.35 (978-1-57765-092-8(1)) ABDO Publishing Co.

St. Antoine, Sara, ed. The North Atlantic Coast. 2004. (Stories from Where We Live Ser.). (Illus.). 288p. pap. 10.95 (978-1-57131-643-1(4)) Milkweed Editions.

—The South Atlantic Coast & Piedmont: A Literary Field Guide. Nicholson, Trudy, illus. 2006. (Stories from Where We Live Ser.). 256p. (J). pap. 10.95 (978-1-57131-664-6(7)) Milkweed Editions.

ATLANTIC STATES

Barr, Gary. The Mid-Atlantic. 2006. (Regions of the USA Ser.). (Illus.). 56p. (J). (978-1-4109-2307-3(X)); pap. (978-1-4109-2315-8(0)) Steck-Vaughn.

Dillon, Christine J., ed. Eastern United States. rev. ed. 1998. (My First Report Ser.). (Illus.). 58p. (J). (gr. 1-3). ring bd. 5.95 (978-1-57896-020-0(7) , 1996) Hewitt Research Foundation, Inc.

—Middle United States. rev. ed. 1998. (My First Report Ser.). (Illus.). 62p. (J). (gr. 1-3). ring bd. 5.95 (978-1-57896-021-7(5) , 1998) Hewitt Research Foundation, Inc.

Jameson, W. C. Buried Treasures of the Mid-Atlantic States: Legends of Island Treasure, Jewelry Caches & Secret Tunnels. 2001. (Buried Treasures Ser.). (Illus.). 192p. (J). (gr. 3-7). pap. 11.95 (978-0-87483-531-1(3)) August Hse. Pubs., Inc.

Kent, Deborah. In the Middle Colonies. 1999. (How We Lived Ser.). (Illus.). 72p. (J). (gr. 4-8). lib. bdg. 28.50 (978-0-7614-0907-6(6) , Benchmark Bks.) Cavendish, Marshall Corp.

Nelson, Sheila. The Northern Colonies. 2005. (How America Became America Ser.). (Illus.). 96p. (J). lib. bdg. (978-1-59084-901-9(9)) Mason Crest Pubs.

Ponte, June. Fun & Simple Mid-Atlantic State Crafts: New York, New Jersey, Pennsylvania, Delaware, Maryland, & Washington, D. C. 2008. (Fun & Simple State Crafts Ser.). (Illus.). 48p. (J). (gr. 3-4). lib. bdg. 23.93 (*978-0-7660-2933-0(6) , Enslow Elementary) Enslow Pubs., Inc.

Pryor, Joanne. I Spy... the Next Stop: Kids Camping the Coast from Maine to Georgia. 2004. (Illus.). 164p. (J). spiral bd. (978-0-9735907-1-5(8)) Destination Publishing.

Sagan, Miriam. The Middle Atlantic States. Date not set. (American Food Library). 48p. (J). (gr. 3-6). lib. bdg. 22.60 (978-0-86625-508-0(7)) Rourke Publishing, LLC.

ATLANTIS (LEGENDARY PLACE)

Balit, Christina. Atlantis: The Legend of the Lost City. rev. ed. 2000. (Illus.). 32p. (J). (ps-3). 17.95 (978-0-8050-6334-9(X) , Holt, Henry & Co. Bks. For Young Readers) Holt, Henry & Co.

DeMolay, Jack. Atlantis: The Mystery of the Lost City. 2007. (Jr. Graphic Mysteries Ser.). (Illus.). 24p. (J). (978-1-4042-2350-9(9)); pap. (978-1-4042-2160-4(3)); (gr. 2-6). lib. bdg. 21.25 (978-1-4042-3407-9(1)) Rosen Publishing Group, Inc., The. (PowerKids Pr.).

Donkin, Andrew. Atlantis: The Lost City. 2000. (Eyewitness Bks.). (Illus.). 48p. (J). (gr. 2-4). pap. 3.99 (978-0-7894-6682-2(1)) Dorling Kindersley Publishing, Inc.

—Atlantis: The Lost City. 2000. (gr. k-3). lib. bdg. 11.80 (978-0-613-32293-5(2)) Tandem Library Bks.

Donkin, Andrew & Dorling Kindersley Publishing Staff. Atlantis: The Lost City? 2000. (Eyewitness Bks.). (Illus.). 48p. (J). (gr. 2-4). 14.99 (978-0-7894-6681-5(3)) Dorling Kindersley Publishing, Inc.

Herbst, Judith. Lands of Mystery. (Unexplained Ser.). (Illus.). 48p. (J). 2005. lib. bdg. 26.60 (978-0-8225-1630-9(6)); 2004. pap. 7.95 (978-0-8225-2407-6(4)) Lerner Publishing Group.

Innes, Brian. Where Was Atlantis? 1999. (Unsolved Mysteries Ser.). (Illus.). 48p. (YA). (gr. 3 up). lib. bdg. 25.69 (978-0-8172-5476-6(5)) Raintree.

—Where Was Atlantis? 1998. (Unsolved Mysteries Ser.). (Illus.). 48p. (J). (gr. 3-7). pap. 8.05 (978-0-8172-4273-2(2)) Steck-Vaughn.

Lewis, Ann. Atlantis. 2005. (Unsolved Mysteries Ser.). (Illus.). 48p. (YA). (gr. 5-8). lib. bdg. 25.25 (978-0-8239-3559-8(0)) Rosen Publishing Group, Inc., The.

Martin, Michael. Atlantis. 2007. (Edge Books, the Unexplained). (Illus.). 32p. (J). (978-0-7368-6759-7(7)) Capstone Pr., Inc.

Nardo, Don. Atlantis. 2003. (Illus.). 112p. (J). 29.95 (978-1-59018-287-1(1) , Lucent Bks.) Thomson Gale.

Nuzzolo, Deborah. Journey to Atlantis Funbook. 2004. (Illus.). 22p. (J). act. bk. ed. 3.99 (978-1-893698-90-1(4) , A01) SeaWorld, Inc.

Roberts, Russell. The Lost Continent of Atlantis. 2006. (Natural Disasters Ser.). (Illus.). 32p. (J). (gr. 1-4). lib. bdg. 25.70 (978-1-58415-496-9(9)) Mitchell Lane Pubs., Inc.

Wallace, Holly. Mystery of Atlantis. 2001. (Can Science Solve? Ser.). (Illus.). (J). (978-0-606-21717-0(7)) Tandem Library Bks.

Wallace, Holly. The Mystery of Atlantis. (Can Science Solve? Ser.). 32p. (J). 2006. lib. bdg. 29.29 (*978-1-4034-8331-7(0)); 1999. (gr. 4-7). lib. bdg. 22.79 (978-1-57572-803-2(6)); 2nd ed. 2006. pap. 7.85 (*978-1-4034-8340-9(X)); Set 1. 2002. (Illus.). (gr. 4-7). pap. 7.50 (978-1-58810-307-9(2) , 91034) Heinemann Library.

A B

ATLANTIS (LEGENDARY PLACE)—FICTION

Artifact Group. My Trip to Atlantis: By SpongeBob SquarePants. 2007. (SpongeBob SquarePants Ser.). 32p. (J). pap. 3.99 ***(978-1-4169-3794-4(3)***, Simon Spotlight/Nickelodeon) Simon & Schuster Children's Publishing.

San Souci, Robert D. Child of Atlantis. Lattimore, Deborah Nourse, illus. 2002. (J). 14.99 (978-0-307-41176-1(1), Golden Bks.) Random Hse. Children's Bks.

Waring, Scott C. West's Time MacHine. 2007. 200p. 24.95 ***(978-0-595-88775-0(9)***; per. 14.95 ***(978-0-595-41887-9(2))*** iUniverse, Inc.

ATLASES

see also Bible—Geography

also names of countries, cities, etc. with the subdivision Maps, e.g. U. S.—Maps; etc.

AAA Staff. North American Atlas for Teens 2002. 2002. (Illus.). 160p. 24.95 (978-1-56251-744-1(9)) AAA.

Act-Two Staff. First Fun Atlas. (Illus.). 48p. (J). (gr. 3 up). lib. bdg. (978-1-59084-556-1(0)) Mason Crest Pubs.

Adams, Simon. Atlas of Exploration & Empires. 2007. (Kingfisher Atlas Ser.). 48p. (J). (gr. 3-5). 15.95 (978-0-7534-6033-7(5), Kingfisher) Houghton Mifflin Co. Trade & Reference Div.

Atlas Escolar. 2003. (SPA.). (J). 16.95 (978-84-670-0004-7(X)) Espasa Calpe, S.A. ESP. *Dist:* Planeta Publishing Corp.

Atlas Series, 2 vols., Set. 1999. (Atlas Ser.). 48p. (J). (gr. 3-8). 26.00 (978-0-7166-9604-9(5), 1531) World Bk., Inc.

Atlases of the Earth & Its Resources, 3 bks. Incl. Environment. lib. bdg. 34.00 (978-0-8368-5616-3(3)); Food & Nutrition. lib. bdg. 34.00 (978-0-8368-5617-0(1)); People & Their Quality of Life. lib. bdg. 34.00 (978-0-8368-5618-7(X)); 80p. (J). (gr. 5 up). (Illus.). 2004. Set lib. bdg. 102.00 (978-0-8368-5615-6(5), World Almanac Library) Stevens, Gareth Inc.

Axelrod-Contrada, Joan. A Historical Atlas of Colonial America. 2005. (United States, Historical Atlases of the Growth of a New Nation Ser.). (Illus.). 64p. (J). (gr. 7-12). lib. bdg. 30.60 (978-1-4042-0200-9(5)) Rosen Publishing Group, Inc., The.

Boyle, Bill & Hopkins, Dave. My First Atlas. (Illus.). (J). (FRE.). 21.99 (978-0-590-24520-3(1)); 48p. pap. 18.95 (978-0-590-24339-1(X)) Scholastic, Inc.

Brocklehurst, Ruth. Children's Picture Atlas. Edwards, Linda, illus. 2004. (Children's Picture Atlas Ser.). 48p. (J). 12.95 (978-0-7945-0640-7(2), Usborne) EDC Publishing.

—Mini Children's Picture Atlas. 2005. (Illus.). 48p. (J). 7.95 (978-0-7945-1112-8(0), Usborne) EDC Publishing.

Buckley, Susan. Places in Time: A New Atlas of American History. 2001. (gr. 3-6). lib. bdg. 15.25 (978-0-613-60829-9(1)) Tandem Library Bks.

Buckley, Susan & Leacock, Elspeth. Journeys in Time: A New Atlas of American History. Prato, Rodica, illus. 2003. 48p. (J). pap. 6.95 (978-0-618-31114-9(9)) Houghton Mifflin Co. Trade & Reference Div.

—Places in Time: A New Atlas of American History. Jones, Randy, illus. 2003. 48p. (J). pap. 6.95 (978-0-618-31113-2(0)) Houghton Mifflin Co. Trade & Reference Div.

Buckley, Susan, et al. Journeys in Time: A New Atlas of American History. Prato, Rodica, illus. 2001. 48p. (J). (gr. 4-6). tchr. ed. 15.00 (978-0-395-97956-3(0)) Houghton Mifflin Co. Trade & Reference Div.

—Places in Time: A New Atlas of American History. Jones, Randy, illus. 2001. 48p. (J). (gr. 4-6). tchr. ed. 15.00 (978-0-395-97958-7(7)) Houghton Mifflin Co. Trade & Reference Div.

Cambridge Educational, prod. An Electronic Atlas for Schools. 2000. (YA). cd-rom 89.95 (978-0-7365-3382-9(6)) Films Media Group.

Chancellor, Deborah. The Kingfisher First Picture Atlas. Kingfisher Publications, Inc. Staff, ed. Lewis, Anthony, illus. 2005. (Kingfisher First Ser.). 48p. (J). (gr. k-3). 10.95 (978-0-7534-5848-8(9), Kingfisher) Houghton Mifflin Co. Trade & Reference Div.

Children's Atlas. 2002. 64p. (J). pap. 9.98 (978-0-7525-6285-8(1)) Parragon, Inc.

Children's Atlas of the United States. 2003. (Illus.). 144p. (J). (gr. 3 up). lib. bdg. 34.00 (978-0-8368-3778-0(9)) Stevens, Gareth Inc.

Ciovacco, Justine, et al. State-by-State Atlas. 128p. (J). 2006. pap. 9.99 (978-0-7566-1828-5(2)); 2003. (Illus.). pap. 19.99 (978-0-7894-9257-9(1)) Dorling Kindersley Publishing, Inc.

Countries, Set. 2002. (J). (gr. k-6). lib. bdg. 227.80 (978-1-57765-838-2(8)) ABDO Publishing Co.

Cullen, David. My First Atlas. Leeks, David, illus. 2004. 48p. (J). 7.99 (978-1-85854-425-0(4)) Brimax Books Ltd. GBR. *Dist:* Byeway Bks.

Cullen, David & Williams, Simon. My First Atlas. Leeks, David, illus. 2004. 48p. (J). 5.99 (978-1-85854-709-1(1)) Brimax Books Ltd. GBR. *Dist:* Byeway Bks.

Dalby, Elizabeth. First Atlas - Internet Linked. 2004. (First Encyclopedias Ser.). 64p. (J). lib. bdg. 17.95 (978-1-58086-646-0(8), Usborne) EDC Publishing.

—First Atlas - Internet Linked. Rogers, Kirsteen, ed. 2004. (First Encyclopedias Ser.). (Illus.). 64p. (J). pap. 9.95 (978-0-7945-0660-5(7), Usborne) EDC Publishing.

De Luca, Daniela, illus. Meyers Bunter Weltatlas fuer Kinder. (GER.). 50p. (978-3-411-07781-6(6)) Bibliographisches Institut & F. A. Brockhaus AG DEU. *Dist:* i.b.d., Ltd.

Denne, Ben. Flags Sticker Atlas. 2004. (Sticker Atlas Ser.). (Illus.). 24p. (J). pap. 8.95 (978-0-7945-0669-8(0), Usborne) EDC Publishing.

DK Publishing. Abracadabra. 2008. 16p. (J). pap. 2.49 ***(978-0-7566-3315-8(X))*** Dorling Kindersley Publishing, Inc.

—My Amazing Picture Atlas. 2008. 32p. (J). (gr. 1-3). 19.99 ***(978-0-7566-3838-2(0))*** Dorling Kindersley Publishing, Inc.

—Student Atlas: 5th Edition. 2008. 160p. (J). (gr. 1). 19.95 ***(978-0-7566-3818-4(6))*** Dorling Kindersley Publishing, Inc.

DK Publishing Staff. School Atlas. 2007. 112p. (YA). (gr. 5-8). pap. 12.99 ***(978-0-7566-3270-0(6))*** Dorling Kindersley Publishing, Inc.

Dorling Kindersley Publishing Staff. First Atlas. 2004. (DK First Reference Ser.). 128p. (J). 15.99 (978-0-7566-0231-4(9)) Dorling Kindersley Publishing, Inc.

—Student Atlas. 4th ed. 2006. 160p. (J). 19.95 (978-0-7566-1875-9(4)) Dorling Kindersley Publishing, Inc.

Douglas, Vincent & School Specialty Publishing Staff. Notebook Reference Atlas & Fact Guide. 2002. (Notebook Reference Ser.). (Illus.). 128p. (J). (gr. 4-8). pap. 4.95 (978-1-57768-448-0(6)) School Specialty Publishing.

The Environment. 2004. (Atlases of the Earth & Its Resources Ser.). (Illus.). 80p. (J). (gr. 5 up). lib. bdg. 34.00 (978-0-8368-5616-3(3), World Almanac Library) Stevens, Gareth Inc.

Equipo Staff. Atlas Escolar 2000.Tr. of Student Atlas 2000. (SPA.). 148p. (J). (gr. 3-5). 4.76 (978-84-241-1224-0(5)) Everest de Ediciones y Distribucion, S.L. ESP. *Dist:* Lectorum Pubns., Inc.

Eyewitness, 4 bks. 2002. 64p. (J). (gr. 3-7). 49.00 (978-0-7166-2043-3(X), 0018) World Bk., Inc.

Facts on File, Inc. Staff. Geography on File, 2005 Update. 2005. (Geography on File Ser.). 36p. (gr. 9-12). ring bd. 55.00 (978-0-8160-5942-3(X)) Facts On File, Inc.

Farndon, John. Children's Atlas. 2003. (Illus.). 80p. (YA). (978-1-903954-54-6(1)) Chrysalis Children's Bks.

—Family Picture Atlas. 1999. (J). (978-1-84100-268-2(2)) Quadrillion Publishing.

Feldman, Thea & Hunter-Bone, Maureen. Discover Our World Globe Book. Disney Press Staff, ed. 2007. 32p. (gr. 1-4). 12.99 ***(978-1-4231-0250-2(9))*** Disney Pr.

Fevrier, Gilles. Atlas of World Facts. 2000. (Atlas of World Facts Ser.: Vol. 4). (Illus.). 60p. (YA). (gr. 4-7). lib. bdg. 25.30 (978-0-88682-944-5(5), Creative Education) Creative Co., The.

First Atlas. 64p. (J). 2003. (Illus.). 7.98 (978-1-4054-0518-8(X)); 2000. 9.98 (978-0-7525-3810-5(1)) Parragon, Inc.

Fonda, Suzanne Patrick, ed. National Geographic United States Atlas for Young Explorers. rev. ed. 2004. (Illus.). 176p. (gr. 3-7). 24.95 (978-0-7922-6840-6(7), National Geographic Children's Bks.) National Geographic Society.

Food & Nutrition. 2004. (Atlases of the Earth & Its Resources Ser.). (Illus.). 80p. (J). (gr. 5 up). lib. bdg. 34.00 (978-0-8368-5617-0(1), World Almanac Library) Stevens, Gareth Inc.

Gareth Stevens Atlas of the World. 2004. (Illus.). 200p. (J). (gr. 4 up). lib. bdg. 40.67 (978-0-8368-4091-9(7)) Stevens, Gareth Inc.

Gareth Stevens Publishing Staff. Children's Atlas of the World. 2006. (YA). (gr. 2 up). 36.67 (978-0-8368-4989-9(2)) Stevens, Gareth Inc.

Garton, Keith & Cutler, Nelida Gonzalez, eds. Time for Kids World Atlas. 2007. (Illus.). 176p. (J). reprint ed. pap. 11.00 ***(978-1-4223-6807-7(6))*** DIANE Publishing Co.

Hammond Inc. Staff, ed. Discovering Maps. rev. ed. 2007. 80p. pap. 9.95 ***(978-0-8437-0953-7(7))*** Hammond World Atlas Corp.

—Hammond Student World Atlas. rev. ed. 2007. 80p. (J). pap. 9.95 ***(978-0-8437-0956-8(1))*** Hammond World Atlas Corp.

—Hammond Sutdent's Notebook Atlas. 4th ed. 2007. 32p. (J). pap. 3.95 ***(978-0-8437-0949-0(9))*** Hammond World Atlas Corp.

Hammond World Atlas Corporation Staff. Intermediate World Atlas. 2000. (J). (gr. 5-9). pap. 8.95 (978-0-8437-7466-5(5)) Hammond World Atlas Corp.

—New Comparative World Atlas. 1999. (gr. 5 up). pap. 10.95 (978-0-8437-7100-8(3)) Hammond World Atlas Corp.

Hammond World Atlas Corporation Staff. World Almanac Notebook Atlas 2008. 2007. 56p. pap. 6.95 ***(978-0-8437-0951-3(0))*** Hammond World Atlas Corp.

Hanson III, Andrew C., et. ed. Ice Age Trail Atlas 2005. 2005. (Illus.). 100p. spiral bd. 25.00 (978-0-9627079-3-3(7)) Ice Age Park and Trail Foundation, Inc.

Harcourt School Publishers Staff. Horizons Desk Atlas. 2nd ed. 2003. (Harcourt Horizons Ser.). (SPA., Illus.). (gr. k-6). 8.00 incl. cd-rom (978-0-15-335865-4(3)) Harcourt Schl. Pubs.

—Horizons Interactive Atlas. 2nd ed. 2003. (Harcourt Horizons Ser.). (SPA., Illus.). (gr. k-6). 57.80 incl. cd-rom (978-0-15-336409-9(2)) Harcourt Schl. Pubs.

Harrison, James. Magic Atlas. Hutchinson, Tim & Watts, Richard, illus. 2005. (Magic Color Bks.). 12p. (J). 9.95 (978-1-4027-2059-8(9), Sterling/Pinwheel) Sterling Publishing Co., Inc.

Hook, Sue. Scholastic First Encyclopedia: A First Atlas. 2000. (978-0-606-18596-7(8)) Tandem Library Bks.

Illustrated Atlas. 2002. (Illus.). 288p. (J). (gr. 2-8). (978-0-7166-4039-4(2), 60057) World Bk., Inc.

Is the World Flat? An Atlas of Cool World Maps That Teach Twenty-First Century Kids New Ways of Seeing Our Changing Earth¿s History, People, Environment, & Wildlife. 2006. (Illus.). 32p. (J). 19.94 (978-0-9788138-1-9(2)) Nimble Bks. LLC.

Jones, Mary Varilla, ed. Scholastic Pocket World Atlas. 2005. (Scholastic Reference Ser.). (Illus.). 224p. pap. 8.95 (978-0-439-68193-3(6), Scholastic Reference) Scholastic, Inc.

Juvik, James O., et al. Student Atlas of Hawaii. 2000. (Illus.). 48p. (gr. 4-13). 9.95 (978-1-57306-049-3(6)) Bess Pr., Inc.

Kemp, Richard. Atlas Visual del Mundo. Delf, Brian, illus. (SPA.). 80p. (YA). (gr. 5-8). (978-84-216-1576-8(9), BU4606) Bruño, Editorial ESP. *Dist:* Lectorum Pubns., Inc.

King, C. Jigsaw World Atlas. 2004. 20p. (J). 14.95 (978-0-7945-0595-0(3)) EDC Publishing.

Kingfisher, ed. Kingfisher 1st Picture Atlas. 2007. (Illus.). 48p. (J). pap. 8.95 ***(978-0-7534-5941-6(8)***, Kingfisher) Houghton Mifflin Co. Trade & Reference Div.

Kingfisher Books Staff, ed. Kingfisher First Picture Atlas. 1999. (gr. 3-6). lib. bdg. 16.40 (978-0-613-21866-5(3)) Tandem Library Bks.

Kneib, Martha. A Historical Atlas of the American Revolution. 2005. (United States, Historical Atlases of the Growth of a New Nation Ser.). (Illus.). 64p. (J). (gr. 7-12). lib. bdg. 30.60 (978-1-4042-0204-7(8)) Rosen Publishing Group, Inc., The.

Larousse Gran Atlas Universal (Larousse Large Universal Atlas) 2000. (ENG & SPA.). 318p. (YA). (gr. 8-12). (978-970-607-800-1(2)) Larousse.

Leacock, Elspeth & Buckley, Susan. Places in Time: A New Atlas of American History. Jones, Randy, illus. 2006. 48p. (J). (gr. 4-8). reprint ed. 15.00 (978-1-4223-5555-8(1)) DIANE Publishing Co.

Lye. Atlas of the World. rev. ed. 2002. (Illus.). (J). pap. 10.30 (978-0-7398-5001-5(6)) Steck-Vaughn.

Lye, Keith. New Children's Illustrated Atlas of the World. 2000. (Illus.). 56p. (gr. 4-7). 9.98 (978-0-7624-0643-2(7), Courage Bks.) Running Pr. Bk. Pubs.

—Raintree Atlas of the World. 2002. (Illus.). 160p. (YA). (gr. 5-8). lib. bdg. 49.93 (978-0-7398-4891-3(7)) Raintree.

Los Mapas Del Mundo, 6 vols., Vol. 2. (Explorers. Exploradores Nonfiction Sets Ser.). (SPA.). 32p. (gr. 3-6). 44.95 (978-0-7699-0646-1(X)) Shortland Pubns. (U. S. A.) Inc.

Maps & Our World: Level O, 6 vols., Vol. 2. (Explorers Ser.). 32p. (gr. 3-6). 44.95 (978-0-7699-0610-2(9)) Shortland Pubns. (U. S. A.) Inc.

McGowan, Kristy. Rand Mcnally Kids' Road Atlas. 2003. (gr. 3-6). lib. bdg. 11.80 (978-0-613-90398-1(6)) Tandem Library Bks.

Merriam-Webster, ed. Merriam-Webster's Notebook Atlas. 2005. (Illus.). 68p. (gr. 5 up). pap. 4.95 (978-0-87779-652-7(1), MER-652) Merriam-Webster, Inc.

Miles Kelly Staff. Scholastic Atlas of the World. Scholastic, Inc. Staff, ed. 2001. (Core Reference Ser.). 224p. (J). (gr. 3 up). pap. 19.95 (978-0-439-08795-7(3), Scholastic Reference) Scholastic, Inc.

Moody, Richard. Atlas of the Evolving Earth. 2001. 75.00 (978-0-02-865632-8(6)) Thomson Gale.

Morris, Neil. Junior Atlas. 2003. (Knowledge Masters Ser.). (Illus.). 32p. (YA). pap. incl. cd-rom (978-1-903954-50-8(9)) Chrysalis Children's Bks.

—Wonders of the World Atlas. 2004. (Atlases Ser.). (Illus.). 48p. (gr. 3-6). (J). pap. 7.95 (978-1-58728-130-3(9)); 13.95 (978-1-58728-131-0(7)) T&N Children's Publishing. (Two Can Publishing).

—Wonders of the World Atlas, 2 vols., Set. 1999. (Illus.). 48p. (J). (gr. 3-8). (978-0-7166-9600-1(2)) World Bk., Inc.

My First Atlas. 2005. (My First Ser.). (Illus.). 128p. (978-0-7853-8371-0(9), 7183600) Publications International, Ltd.

Nardi, Adriano & Meucci, Antonella. The Children's World Pictorial Atlas of the World. 1998. (Illus.). 48p. (J). (gr. 2 up). 11.95 (978-0-7641-5062-3(6)) Barron's Educational Series, Inc.

National Geographic, creator. National Geographic World Atlas for Young Explorers. 3rd ed. 2007. (Illus.). 191p. (J). (gr. 3-7). 24.95 ***(978-1-4263-0088-2(3)***, National Geographic Children's Bks.) National Geographic Society.

National Geographic Society Staff. National Geographic Beginner's World Atlas. rev. ed. 2005. (Illus.). 64p. (J). (gr. k-3). 17.95 (978-0-7922-4205-5(X)); 27.90 (978-0-7922-4211-6(4)) National Geographic Society. (National Geographic Children's Bks.).

—National Geographic Student Atlas of the World. Fonda, Suzanne Patrick, ed. rev. exp. ed. 2005. (Illus.). 144p. (J). (gr. 6-9). pap. 12.95 (978-0-7922-7178-9(5), National Geographic Children's Bks.) National Geographic Society.

—National Geographic Student Atlas of the World. rev. exp. ed. 2005. (Illus.). 144p. (J). (gr. 6-9). 19.95 (978-0-7922-7168-0(8), National Geographic Children's Bks.) National Geographic Society.

—National Geographic United States Atlas for Young Explorers. rev. ed. 2004. (Illus.). 176p. (J). (gr. 3-7). 45.90 (978-0-7922-6981-6(0), National Geographic Children's Bks.) National Geographic Society.

The Nystrom Block Buddy Atlas. 1998. (J). (gr. 1). pap. 6.95 (978-0-7825-0657-0(7)) Nystrom.

The Nystrom Nystronaut Atlas. 1998. (J). (gr. 2). pap. 6.95 (978-0-7825-0662-4(3)) Nystrom.

Oceanor Staff. Fisica - Atlas Visual. 1999. (SPA.). (gr. 3-6). lib. bdg. 20.00 (978-0-613-80880-4(0)) Tandem Library Bks.

—Geologia - Atlas Visual. 1999. (SPA.). (gr. 3-6). lib. bdg. 20.00 (978-0-613-80882-8(7)) Tandem Library Bks.

Oleksy, Walter. Mapping the Seas. 2002. (Watts Library Ser.). (Illus.). 64p. (J). (gr. 5-7). pap. 25.50 (978-0-531-12030-9(9), Watts, Franklin) Scholastic Library Publishing.

—Mapping the Skies. (Watts Library). (Illus.). 64p. (J). (gr. 5-7). 2003. pap. 8.95 (978-0-531-16635-2(X)); 2002. pap. 25.50 (978-0-531-12031-6(7)) Scholastic Library Publishing. (Watts, Franklin).

—Mapping the World. (Watts Library). 64p. (J). (gr. 5-7). 2003. pap. 8.95 (978-0-531-16636-9(8)); 2002. (Illus.). pap. 25.50 (978-0-531-12029-3(5)) Scholastic Library Publishing. (Watts, Franklin).

Oxford University Press Staff, ed. Atlas of the World. 2003. 256p. (J). 12.98 (978-1-4054-1708-2(0)) Parragon, Inc.

Page, Jason & Pickering, Mel. Atlas: The Book & Disk That Work Together. 2000. (Interfact Reference Ser.). (Illus.). 48p. (J). (gr. 3-6). 19.95 incl. cd-rom (978-1-58728-471-7(5), Two Can Publishing) T&N Children's Publishing.

People & Their Quality of Life. 2004. (Atlases of the Earth & Its Resources Ser.). (Illus.). 80p. (J). (gr. 5 up). lib. bdg. 34.00 (978-0-8368-5618-7(X), World Almanac Library) Stevens, Gareth Inc.

Pickering, Mel. Atlas. 2004. (Picture Reference Ser.). (SPA., Illus.). 48p. (gr. 3-6). (J). pap. 7.95 (978-1-58728-651-3(3)); 13.95 (978-1-58728-655-1(6)) T&N Children's Publishing. (Two Can Publishing).

Picture Reference, 5 vols., Set. 1999. (Illus.). 240p. (J). (gr. 2-6). 79.00 (978-0-7166-9916-3(8), 30042) World Bk., Inc.

Pocket Atlas. 2000. 128p. (J). 9.98 (978-0-7525-3968-3(X)) Parragon, Inc.

Pocket Library, 3 vols., Set. 2000. (J). 29.95 (978-0-7525-3734-4(2)) Parragon, Inc.

Porter, Malcolm. The Cherrytree Children's Atlas. rev. ed. (Illus.). 96p. (J). (978-0-7451-5179-3(5), Cherrytree Books) Evans Publishing Group.

Priddy, Roger. My Picture Atlas: Essential Facts about Every Country in the World. rev. ed. 2003. (First Reference Ser.). 94p. (J). bds. 14.95 (978-0-312-49167-3(0), Priddy Bks.) St. Martin's Pr.

Rand McNally Staff. Atlas Schoolhouse Beginner's Workbook. 2005. 128p. (J). pap. 7.95 (978-0-528-93469-8(4)) Rand McNally.

—Atlas Schoolhouse Illustrated World Atlaas. 2005. 112p. (J). 9.95 (978-0-528-93458-2(9)) Rand McNally.

—Atlas Schoolhouse Intermediate World Atlas. 2005. 128p. (J). pap. 6.95 (978-0-528-93460-5(0)) Rand McNally.

—Atlas Scoolhouse Beginner's World Atlas. 2005. 48p. (J). pap. 5.95 (978-0-528-93463-6(5)) Rand McNally.

—Kids' Road Atlas. (Backseat Bks.). 80p. (J). pap. 3.95 (978-0-528-96544-9(1)) Rand McNally.

Rand McNally Staff, creator. Intermediate Geography & Map Activities. 2005. (Illus.). 128p. pap. 7.95 (978-0-528-93470-4(8)) Rand McNally.

Rodriguez, Jose Cruz. Mi Primer Atlas Everest. (SPA., Illus.). 48p. (J). (gr. 2-4). (978-84-241-1206-6(7), EV5438) Everest de Ediciones y Distribucion, S.L. ESP. *Dist:* Lectorum Pubns., Inc.

Rogers, Alisdair. The Illustrated World Atlas. 1998. (Illus.). 80p. (J). (gr. 3). (978-0-86505-897-2(0)); pap. (978-0-86505-911-5(X)) Crabtree Publishing Co.

—The Illustrated World Atlas. rev. ed. 2004. (Illus.). 80p. (J). (gr. 3-6). pap. (978-0-7787-0040-1(2)) Ryland Peters & Small.

Royston, Angela & Hook, Sue. A First Atlas. Pickering, M. & Norton, L., illus. 2000. (First Encyclopedia Ser.). 96p. (J). (ps-3). pap. 7.95 (978-0-590-47528-0(2)) Scholastic, Inc.

Rubel, David. Scholastic Atlas of the United States. 2000. (Illus.). 144p. (J). (gr. 4-7). pap. 19.95 (978-0-590-57562-0(9), Scholastic Reference) Scholastic, Inc.

—Scholastic Atlas of the United States. 2003. (gr. 3-6). lib. bdg. 18.75 (978-0-613-72002-1(4)) Tandem Library Bks.

Rubel, David, et al. Scholastic Atlas of the United States. 2003. (Illus.). 144p. (J). 10.95 (978-0-439-47436-8(1), Scholastic Reference) Scholastic, Inc.

Sacks, Janet. Magic Skeleton Book: Discover Hidden Worlds. Tomblin, Gill & Smith, Ian, illus. 2005. (Magic Color Bks.). 12p. (J). 9.95 (978-1-4027-2057-4(2), Sterling/Pinwheel) Sterling Publishing Co., Inc.

Scholastic, Inc. Staff. Scholastic Atlas of Oceans. Varilla, Mary, ed. 2004. (Illus.). 96p. (J). (gr. 2-5). pap. 18.95 (978-0-439-56128-0(0), Scholastic Reference) Scholastic, Inc.

—Scholastic Atlas of the World. 2003. (Illus.). 224p. (J). pap. 12.95 (978-0-439-52797-2(X), Scholastic Reference) Scholastic, Inc.

Solway, Andrew. Atlas. Pickering, Mel & Land, Jacqueline, illus. 2004. (Mis Primeros Conocimientos Ser.). (SPA.). 48p. (gr. 3-6). 13.95 (978-1-58728-661-2(0), Two Can Publishing) T&N Children's Publishing.

—Atlas. Creative Publishing international Editors, ed. Pickering, Mel & Land, Jacqueline, illus. 2004. (Mis Primeros Conocimientos Ser.). (SPA.). 48p. (J). (gr. 3-6). pap. 7.95 (978-1-58728-656-8(4), TWO8597, Two Can Publishing) T&N Children's Publishing.

Stace, Alexa. Atlas of Earth. 1999. (Illus.). 96p. (J). (gr. 5 up). lib. bdg. 34.00 (978-0-8368-2505-3(5)) Stevens, Gareth Inc.

Standard Publishing Staff. Standard Bible Atlas. 2006. 48p. pap. 12.99 (978-0-7847-1872-8(5)) Standard Publishing.

Steele, Philip. Children's Atlas of the World. 2001. (Reference Ser.). (Illus.). 128p. (J). (gr. 2-6). 37.00 (978-0-531-11775-0(8)); pap. 19.95 (978-0-531-16551-5(5)) Scholastic Library Publishing. (Watts, Franklin).

—Children's Atlas of the World. 2000. (Illus.). (J). 27.50 (978-0-606-20602-0(7)) Tandem Library Bks.

—Kingfisher Atlas of the World. 2001. (gr. 3-6). lib. bdg. 22.20 (978-0-613-90590-9(3)) Tandem Library Bks.

—The Kingfisher Young People's Atlas of the World. 2000. (Illus.). 94p. (YA). (gr. 6-9). reprint ed. 20.00 (978-0-7881-9450-4(X)) DIANE Publishing Co.

—Scholastic Atlas of the World. 2003. (gr. 3-6). lib. bdg. 22.20 (978-0-613-72248-3(5)) Tandem Library Bks.

Student Atlas. 1998. (J). (gr. k-10). 15.95 (978-0-7894-3110-3(6)) Dorling Kindersley Publishing, Inc.

Student Atlas of the World: A Comprehensive Reference for School & Home. 2001. (Illus.). (gr. 3-6). lib. bdg. 22.20 (978-0-613-49369-7(9)) Tandem Library Bks.

Thornford, Charles. The World Today. 1999. (Illus.). 48p. (J). (gr. 3-7). pap. 29.00 (978-0-7217-1074-7(3)) Schofield & Sims Ltd. GBR. *Dist:* State Mutual Bk. & Periodical Service, Ltd.

Time for Kids Editors. Time for Kids: World Atlas. rev. ed. 2007. 144p. (J). (gr. 2-8). pap. 10.99 (***978-1-933821-94-8(9)***) Time, Inc. Home Entertainment.

Time for Kids Editors. World Atlas. 2004. (Time for Kids Ser.). (Illus.). 176p. (J). pap. 10.99 (978-1-931933-72-8(3)) Time, Inc. Home Entertainment.

Turnbull, S. Essential Atlas of the World. 2004. (Geography Ser.). (Illus.). 112p. (J). 13.95 (978-0-7945-0614-8(3)) EDC Publishing.

Turnbull, Stephanie. Little school atlas - internet Linked. 2005. 112p. (J). 7.95 (978-0-7945-1082-4(5) , Usborne) EDC Publishing.

Turnbull, Stephanie & Helbrough, Emma. Children's World Atlas. 2004. (Geography Ser.). (Illus.). 144p. (J). 22.95 (978-0-7945-0318-5(7)); lib. bdg. 30.95 (978-1-58086-489-3(9)) EDC Publishing.

—Children's World Atlas - Internet Linked. 2005. 144p. (J). 14.99 (978-0-7945-1079-4(5) , Usborne) EDC Publishing.

Turnbull, Stephanie & Patchett, Fiona. Sticker Atlas of the World. 2005. (Sticker Atlases Ser.). 24p. (J). pap. 8.99 (978-0-7945-0911-8(8) , Usborne) EDC Publishing.

Two-Can Publishing Ltd. Staff, contrib. by. My First Trip Around the World: A Picture Atlas Adventure. 2004. (Illus.). 34p. 15.95 (978-1-58728-515-8(0) , Two Can Publishing) T&N Children's Publishing.

Ultimate Atlas of the World. 2002. 256p. (J). 12.98 (978-1-84084-990-5(8) , Dempsey Parr); 15.98 (978-1-84084-415-3(9) , Dempsey Parr); 25.95 (978-0-7525-8875-9(3)) Parragon, Inc.

The Usborne Picture Atlas. (Illus.). 32p. (J). (gr. 3-6). lib. bdg. 14.95 (978-0-88110-702-9(6)) EDC Publishing.

Van Rose, S. Atlas Visual de la Tierra. (Coleccion Atlas Visual). (SPA., Illus.). 310p. (YA). (gr. 5-8). (978-84-216-2574-3(8) , BU1496) Bruño, Editorial ESP. *Dist:* Lectorum Pubns., Inc.

Walrus Books. Kids' Canadian Atlas. (Illus.). 40p. (J). (gr. 1-9). 14.95 (978-1-55285-149-4(4)) Whitecap Bks., Ltd. CAN. *Dist:* Graphic Arts Ctr. Publishing Co.

Weber, Belinda. The Kingfisher Children's Atlas. 2004. (Illus.). 80p. (J). (gr. 3-5). 14.95 (978-0-7534-5774-0(1) , Kingfisher) Houghton Mifflin Co. Trade & Reference Div.

Webster's Dictionary & Thesaurus for Students with Full-Color World Atlas. 2006. (Illus.). 880p. pap. 9.98 (978-1-59695-017-7(X)) Federal Street Pr.

Weldon, Owen & Reader's Digest Editors. The Reader's Digest Children's Atlas of the World. 1998. (Illus.). 128p. (J). (gr. 3-8). 22.99 (978-1-57584-156-4(8) , Reader's Digest Children's Bks.) Reader's Digest Children's Publishing, Inc.

Wiegand, Patrick, ed. Oxford International Student Atlas. 2007. (Illus.). 120p. (YA). 19.95 (978-0-19-832165-1(1)) Oxford Univ. Pr., Inc.

Wilkinson, Philip. The Kingfisher Student Atlas. 2003. (Illus.). 128p. (J). (gr. 4-6). tchr. ed. 24.95 (978-0-7534-5589-0(7) , Kingfisher) Houghton Mifflin Co. Trade & Reference Div.

Willis, Shirley. The Watts Picture Atlas. Hewetson, Nicholas, illus. 2002. (Watts Reference Ser.). 64p. (J). (gr. 1-3). pap. 25.00 (978-0-531-14650-7(2) , Watts, Franklin) Scholastic Library Publishing.

—Watts Picture Atlas. 2003. (gr. k-3). lib. bdg. 30.35 (978-0-613-72677-1(4)) Tandem Library Bks.

World Atlas: A Resource for Students. rev. ed. 1999. 96p. (J). (gr. 5-9). pap. 7.95 (978-0-88463-480-5(9) , 9A90) Nystrom.

World Book, Inc. Staff. Illustrated Atlas. (Illus.). 288p. (J). 2001. (gr. 2-8). 36.00 incl. cd-rom (978-0-7166-4037-0(6)); 1999. (gr. 3-8). 29.95 (978-0-7166-4034-9(1)) World Bk., Inc.

The World Reference Maps & Forms. 2004. (J). per. 14.99 (978-1-55799-954-2(6) , EMC 3720) Evan-Moor Educational Pubs.

Wright & Potter. Mi Primera Atlas. 2000. (My First Encyclopedias Ser.).Tr. of My First Atlas. (SPA., Illus.). 48p. (J). 19.95 (978-84-488-0511-1(9)) Beascoa, Ediciones S.A. ESP. *Dist:* Distribooks, Inc.

Wright, David & Wright, Jill. Children's Atlas. rev. ed. 2000. (Atlas Ser.). (Illus.). 96p. (YA). (gr. 4-9). 18.95 (978-0-8160-4433-7(3) , Checkmark Bks.) Facts On File, Inc.

—The Facts on File Children's Atlas. 5th rev. ed. 96p. (gr. 4-9). 18.95 (978-0-8160-6711-4(2) , Checkmark Bks.) Facts On File, Inc.

Yorinks, Arthur. The Alphabet Atlas. Yorinks, Adrienne, illus. 1999. 64p. (J). (ps-3). 19.95 (978-1-890817-14-5(7)) Winslow Pr.

21st Century Atlas of the United States, Canada & the World. 2001. (Illus.). 200p. (J). (gr. 4 up). lib. bdg. 39.93 (978-0-8368-2919-8(0)) Stevens, Gareth Inc.

ATLASES, HISTORICAL

see Historical Geography—Maps

ATMOSPHERE

Here are entered works treating the body of air surrounding the earth as distinguished from the upper rarefied air. Works dealing with air as an element and of its chemical and physical properties are entered under Air.

see also Air; Meteorology

Aigner-Clark, Julie. Baby Galileo the World Around Me - Sky. Zaidi, Nadeem, illus. 2004. (Baby Einstein Ser.). 12p. (ps-17). 15.99 (978-0-7868-0941-7(8)) Hyperion Bks. for Children.

Banquieri, Eduardo. The Biosphere. 2005. (Our Planet Ser.). (Illus.). 32p. (J). (gr. 4-8). lib. bdg. 28.00 (978-0-7910-9008-4(6) , Chelsea Clubhouse) Facts On File, Inc.

Bergethon, Peter R. The Atmosphere: An Ocean of Air, Student Science Journal. 1999. (Illus.). 156p. (YA). (gr. 6-8). pap. (978-1-58447-065-6(8)) Symmetry Learning Systems.

La Capa Ozono. (Nuestro Mundo en Peligro Ser.). (SPA.). 32p. (YA). 10.50 (978-84-342-1930-4(1) , CAR1930) Parramon Ediciones S.A. ESP. *Dist:* Continental Bk. Co., Inc.

Carroll, Colleen. Elements: Earth, Air, Fire & Water. 1998. (How Artists See Ser.). (Illus.). 48p. (gr. 3 up). 12.95 (978-0-7892-0476-9(2)) Abbeville Pr., Inc.

Casper, Julie Kerr. Water & Atmosphere: The Lifeblood of Natural Systems. 2007. (Natural Resources Ser.). 224p. (J). (gr. 6-12). 39.50 (***978-0-8160-6359-8(1)*** , Chelsea Hse.) Facts On File, Inc.

Desonie, Dana. Atmosphere. 2007. (Our Fragile Planet Ser.). 208p. (gr. 6-12). 35.00 (***978-0-8160-6213-3(7)*** , Chelsea Hse.) Facts On File, Inc.

—Biosphere. 2007. (Our Fragile Planet Ser.). 232p. (J). (gr. 6-12). 35.00 (***978-0-8160-6219-5(6)*** , Chelsea Hse.) Facts On File, Inc.

El Efecto Invernadero. (Nuestro Mundo en Peligro Ser.). (SPA.). (J). 10.50 (978-84-342-1912-0(3) , CAR1912) Parramon Ediciones S.A. ESP. *Dist:* Continental Bk. Co., Inc., Distribuidora Norma, Inc.

Gallant, Roy A. Atmosphere: Sea of Air. 2002. (Earthworks Ser.). (Illus.). 80p. (J). 29.93 (978-0-7614-1366-0(9) , Benchmark Bks.) Cavendish, Marshall Corp.

Harman, Rebecca. Carbon-Oxygen & Nitrogen. 2005. (Heinemann Infosearch Ser.). (Illus.). 32p. (J). pap. (978-1-4034-7067-6(7)); lib. bdg. (978-1-4034-7060-7(X)) Heinemann Library.

Holt, Rinehart and Winston Staff. The Atmosphere: Chapter Resources: Tennessee Edition. 3rd ed. 2003. (Holt Science & Technology Ser.). pap. 11.40 (978-0-03-069147-8(8)) Holt, Rinehart & Winston.

—Environmental Science Chptr. 13: Atmosphere & Climate. 4th ed. Date not set. pap. 11.20 (978-0-03-068073-1(5)) Holt, Rinehart & Winston.

—Holt Science & Technology Chapter 15: Earth Science: The Atmosphere. 5th ed. 2004. (Illus.). pap. 12.86 (978-0-03-030322-7(2)) Holt, Rinehart & Winston.

—Holt Science Spectrum Chptr. 22: The Atmosphere. 4th ed. Date not set. pap. 11.20 (978-0-03-068061-8(1)) Holt, Rinehart & Winston.

Jennings, Terry. Atmosphere & Weather. 2005. (Illus.). 48p. (J). (gr. 6-9). lib. bdg. 29.95 (978-1-58340-725-7(1)) Smart Apple Media.

Joekay, Eliza, et al. Ellam Cai (Parts of the Sky) Joekay, Eliza, illus. l.t. ed. 1999. (ESK., Illus.). 12p. (J). (gr. k-3). pap. 6.00 (978-1-58084-098-9(1)) Lower Kuskokwim Schl. District.

—Illi Qilim (Parts of the Sky) Joekay, Eliza, illus. l.t. ed. 1999. (ESK., Illus.). 12p. (J). (gr. k-3). pap. 6.00 (978-1-58084-151-1(1)) Lower Kuskokwim Schl. District.

—Parts of the Sky. Joekay, Eliza, illus. l.t. ed. 1999. (Illus.). 12p. (J). (gr. k-3). pap. 6.00 (978-1-58084-097-2(3)) Lower Kuskokwim Schl. District.

Keeping Warm! Keeping Cool! 6 Each of 1 Student Book, 6 vols. (Sunshinetm Science Ser.). 24p. (gr. 1-2). 41.95 (978-0-7802-1410-1(2)) Wright Group, The.

Keeping Warm! Keeping Cool! Big Book. (Sunshinetm Science Ser.). 24p. (gr. 1-2). 37.50 (978-0-7802-1411-8(0)) Wright Group, The.

Miles, Elizabeth. Dew & Frost. 2004. (J). lib. bdg. 24.21 (978-1-4034-5576-5(7)) Heinemann Library.

Modules: Earth Science; Earth's Atmosphere TE. 2005. (gr. 6-12). (978-0-618-33416-2(5) , 2-01006) McDougal Littell Inc.

Nadeau, Isaac. Water in the Atmosphere. 2003. (Water Cycle Ser.). (Illus.). 24p. (J). lib. bdg. 18.75 (978-0-8239-6262-4(8) , PowerKids Pr.) Rosen Publishing Group, Inc., The.

Nardo, Don. Ozone. 2005. (Our Environment Ser.). (Illus.). 48p. (J). (gr. 3-8). lib. bdg. 26.20 (978-0-7377-2630-5(X) , Greenhaven Pr., Inc.) Thomson Gale.

Parker, Steve. The Science of Air: Projects & Experiments on Air & Flight. 2005. (Tabletop Scientist Ser.). (Illus.). 32p. (J). (gr. 4-7). lib. bdg. 27.79 (978-1-4034-7280-9(7)); (ps-6). pap. 7.95 (978-1-4034-7287-8(4)) Heinemann Library.

Pluckrose, Henry. Air. 2001. (Let's Explore Ser.). (Illus.). 32p. (J). (gr. 1 up). lib. bdg. 23.33 (978-0-8368-2957-0(3)) Stevens, Gareth Inc.

Pluckrose, Henry Arthur. Air. 2006. (Illus.). 32p. (J). (978-1-59771-033-6(4)) Sea-To-Sea Pubns.

Rodgers, Alan & Streluk, Angella. Wind & Air Pressure. 2002. (Illus.). 32p. (J). (gr. 3-5). pap. (978-1-4034-0130-4(6) , 91635); lib. bdg. 22.79 (978-1-58810-690-2(X)) Heinemann Library.

Sammis, Fran. Oceans & Skies. 1999. (Mapping Our World Ser.). (Illus.). 64p. (J). (gr. 4-8). lib. bdg. 27.07 (978-0-7614-0374-6(4) , Benchmark Bks.) Cavendish, Marshall Corp.

Staub, Frank. The Kids' Book of Clouds & Sky. 2005. (Illus.). 80p. (J). pap. 9.95 (978-1-4027-2806-8(9)) Sterling Publishing Co., Inc.

Time-Life Books Editors. Sky & Earth. 1999. (Illus.). 88p. (J). (gr. 1-4). 14.95 (978-0-8094-4837-1(8)) Time-Life, Inc.

Underwood, Deborah. The Northern Lights. 2004. (Illus.). 48p. (J). 26.20 (978-0-7377-2085-3(9) , Greenhaven Pr., Inc.) Thomson Gale.

Walker, Jane. The Ozone Hole. 2004. (J). lib. bdg. 27.10 (978-1-932799-09-5(5)) Stargazer Bks.

Ye, Ting-Xing. Share the Sky. Langlois, Suzane, illus. 1999. 32p. (J). (ps-2). lib. bdg. 17.95 (978-1-55037-579-4(2)) Annick Pr., Ltd. CAN. *Dist:* Firefly Bks., Ltd.

—Share the Sky. 1999. (gr. k-3). lib. bdg. 15.25 (978-0-613-26907-0(1)) Tandem Library Bks.

ATMOSPHERE—POLLUTION

see Air—Pollution

ATMOSPHERE, UPPER

see also Stratosphere

Donald, Rhonda Lucas. Ozone Layer. 2001. (gr. 3-6). lib. bdg. 15.25 (978-0-613-50354-9(6)) Tandem Library Bks.

ATOLLS

see Coral Reefs and Islands

ATOMIC BOMB

Allman, Toney. J. Robert Oppenheimer: Theoretical Physicist, Atomic Pioneer. 2005. (Giants of Science Ser.). (Illus.). 64p. (J). (gr. 5-7). 26.20 (978-1-56711-889-6(5) , Blackbirch Pr., Inc.) Thomson Gale.

Anderson, Dale. The Atom Bomb Project. 2004. (Landmark Events in American History Ser.). (Illus.). 48p. (J). (gr. 5 up). pap. 11.95 (978-0-8368-5413-8(6)); lib. bdg. 30.00 (978-0-8368-5385-8(7)) Stevens, Gareth Inc. (World Almanac Library).

Bankston, John. Edward Teller & the Development of the Hydrogen Bomb. l.t. ed. 2002. (Unlocking the Secrets of Science Ser.). (Illus.). 56p. (gr. 4-10). lib. bdg. 25.70 (978-1-58415-108-1(0)) Mitchell Lane Pubs., Inc.

Crewe, Sabrina & Anderson, Dale. The Atom Bomb Project. 2004. (Events That Shaped America Ser.). (Illus.). 32p. (J). lib. bdg. 24.67 (978-0-8368-3404-8(6)) Stevens, Gareth Inc.

Elish, Dan. The Manhattan Project. 2007. (Cornerstones of Freedom). (Illus.). 48p. (J). (gr. 4-6). 26.00 (978-0-516-23299-7(1) , Children's Pr.) Scholastic Library Publishing.

Gonzales, Doreen. The Manhattan Project & the Atomic Bomb in American History. 2000. (In American History Ser.). (Illus.). 128p. (YA). (gr. 5-12). lib. bdg. 26.60 (978-0-89490-879-8(0)) Enslow Pubs., Inc.

Harris, Nathaniel. Hiroshima. 2004. (Illus.). 56p. (J). 27.07 (978-1-4034-4872-9(8)); pap. (978-1-4034-6259-6(3)) Heinemann Library.

Hook, Jason. Hiroshima. 2002. (Days That Shook the World Ser.). 48p. (J). lib. bdg. 27.12 (978-0-7398-5234-7(5)) Raintree.

Lace, William W. The Atom Bomb. 2001. (Building History Ser.). (Illus.). 112p. (J). (gr. 6-9). 32.45 (978-1-56006-724-5(1) , Lucent Bks.) Thomson Gale.

Lawton, Clive A. Hiroshima. 60th anniv. ed. 2004. (Illus.). 48p. (J). (gr. 5 up). 18.99 (978-0-7636-2271-8(0)) Candlewick Pr.

Malam, John. The Bombing of Hiroshima. 2002. (Dates with History Ser.). (Illus.). 31p. (J). lib. bdg. 24.25 (978-1-58340-213-9(6)) Smart Apple Media.

Orr, Tamra. The Atom Bomb: Creating & Exploding the First Nuclear Weapon. 2004. (Library of Weapons of Mass Destruction). (Illus.). 64p. (J). lib. bdg. 26.50 (978-1-4042-0292-4(7)) Rosen Publishing Group, Inc., The.

Richard Tames. Hiroshima. 2nd ed. 2006. (Illus.). 32p. (J). pap. (***978-1-4034-9149-7(6)***) Heinemann Library.

Scherer, Glenn & Fletcher, Marty. J. Robert Oppenheimer: The Brain Behind the Bomb. 2007. (Inventors Who Changed the World Ser.). (Illus.). 128p. (J). lib. bdg. 33.27 (978-1-59845-050-7(6) , MyReportLinks.com Bks.) Enslow Pubs., Inc.

Sherrow, Victoria. The Making of the Atom Bomb. 1999. (World History Ser.). (Illus.). 128p. (YA). (gr. 8-11). 27.45 (978-1-56006-585-2(0) , LML00902-177940, Lucent Bks.) Thomson Gale.

Tames, Richard. Hiroshima: The Shadow of the Bomb. 2006. (Point of Impact Ser.). (Illus.). 32p. (YA). (gr. 5-8). lib. bdg. 29.29 (***978-1-4034-9140-4(2)***) Heinemann Library.

—Hiroshima: The Shadow of the Bomb. 2001. (Illus.). 32p. (J). (gr. 4-7). lib. bdg. 15.25 (978-0-613-36102-6(4)) Tandem Library Bks.

Tracy, Kathleen. Top Secret: The Story of the Manhattan Project. 2005. (Illus.). 48p. (YA). lib. bdg. (978-1-58415-399-3(7)) Mitchell Lane Pubs., Inc.

ATOMIC BOMB—FICTION

Bauld, Jane Scoggins. Hector Saves the Moon, Vol. 2. Laronde, Gary, illus. 7.95 (978-1-57168-312-0(7)) Eakin Pr.

Davies, Jacqueline. Where the Ground Meets the Sky. 2002. 224p. (YA). (gr. 5-9). 14.95 (978-0-7614-5105-1(6) , Cavendish Children's Bks.) Cavendish, Marshall Corp.

Reeder, Carolyn. The Secret Project Notebook. 2005. 247p. (J). (978-0-941232-33-3(6)) Los Alamos Historical Society.

Taylor, Theodore. The Bomb. 2007. (Illus.). 208p. (YA). pap. 6.95 (***978-0-15-206165-4(7)*** , Harcourt Paperbacks) Harcourt Children's Bks.

Zindel, Paul. The Gadget. 2003. (Illus.). 192p. (YA). (gr. 7). pap. 6.50 (978-0-440-22951-3(0) , Laurel Leaf) Random Hse. Children's Bks.

—The Gadget. 2003. (gr. 5-8). lib. bdg. 13.55 (978-0-613-62203-5(0)) Tandem Library Bks.

ATOMIC BOMB—PHYSIOLOGICAL EFFECT

Coerr, Eleanor. Sadako. Young, Ed, illus. 2002. (J). 24.55 (978-0-7587-3544-7(8)) Book Wholesalers, Inc.

—Sadako & the Thousand Paper Cranes. Himler, Ronald, illus. 2004. 80p. (gr. 8). pap. 5.99 (978-0-14-240113-2(7) , Puffin) Penguin Group (USA) Inc.

—Sadako & the Thousand Paper Cranes. Himler, Ronald, illus. 1999. 79p. (J). (ps-ps). lib. bdg. 13.00 (978-0-613-23029-2(9)) Tandem Library Bks.

—Sadako & the Thousand Paper Cranes. 1999. (978-0-606-17425-1(7)) Tandem Library Bks.

Himler, Ronald, illus. Sadako & the Thousand Paper Cranes. 2005. 80p. (J). pap. 3.99 (978-0-14-240440-9(3) , Puffin) Penguin Group (USA) Inc.

Sadako & the Thousand Paper Cranes. 1999. (J). 9.95 (978-1-56137-178-5(5)); 11.95 (978-1-56137-631-5(0)) Novel Units, Inc.

ATOMIC ENERGY

see Nuclear Energy

ATOMIC NUCLEI

see Nuclear Physics

ATOMIC PILES

see Nuclear Reactors

ATOMIC POWER

see Nuclear Energy

ATOMIC SUBMARINES

see Nuclear Submarines

ATOMS

see also Nuclear Physics

Claybourne, Anna. Microworlds: Unlocking the Secrets of Atoms & Molecules. 2008. (J). pap. (***978-1-60044-606-1(X)***) Rourke Publishing, LLC.

Clowes, Martin. Atoms & Molecules. 2004. (Routes of Science Ser.). (J). pap. 11.20 (978-1-4103-0324-0(1) , Blackbirch Pr., Inc.) Thomson Gale.

Dalton, Cindy Devine. Atoms. 2001. (How Can I Experiment With? Ser.). (Illus.). 32p. (J). (gr. 1-4). lib. bdg. 28.50 (978-1-58952-010-3(6)) Rourke Publishing, LLC.

Gallant, Roy A. The Ever Changing Atom. 2000. (Story of Science Ser.). (Illus.). 80p. (YA). (gr. 5 up). lib. bdg. 29.93 (978-0-7614-0961-8(0) , Benchmark Bks.) Cavendish, Marshall Corp.

Goldstein, Natalie. How Do We Know the Nature of the Atom? 2001. (Great Scientific Questions & the Scientists Who Answered Them Ser.). (Illus.). 112p. (YA). (gr. 4-6). lib. bdg. 26.50 (978-0-8239-3385-3(7)) Rosen Publishing Group, Inc., The.

Holt, Rinehart and Winston Staff. Holt Science & Technology Chapter 11: Physical Science: Introduction to Atoms. 5th ed. 2004. (Illus.). pap. 12.86 (978-0-03-030403-3(2)) Holt, Rinehart & Winston.

—Holt Science & Technology Chptr. 21: Introduction to Atoms: Chapter Resources - Tennessee Version. 3rd ed. 2003. (YA). pap. 11.40 (978-0-03-069154-6(0)) Holt, Rinehart & Winston.

Jones & Bartlett Publishers, prod. Atomic Orbitals. (YA). cd-rom 89.95 (978-0-7365-7149-4(3)) Films Media Group.

Manning, Phillip. Atoms, Molecules, & Compounds. 2007. (Essential Chemistry Ser.). 144p. (gr. 6-12). 35.00 (***978-0-7910-9534-8(7)*** , Chelsea Hse.) Facts On File, Inc.

Mebane, Robert C. & Rybolt, Thomas R. Adventures with Atoms & Molecules: Chemistry Experiments for Young People. 1998. (Adventures with Science Ser.). (Illus.). (YA). (gr. 4-9). Bk. I. 82p. pap. 11.93 (978-0-7660-1224-0(7)); Bk. II. 96p. pap. 11.93 (978-0-7660-1225-7(5)); Bk. III. 96p. pap. 11.93 (978-0-7660-1226-4(3)); Bk. IV. 96p. pap. 11.93 (978-0-7660-1227-1(1)); Bk. V. 96p. pap. 11.93 (978-0-7660-1228-8(X)) Enslow Pubs., Inc.

Morgan, Sally. From Greek Atoms to Quarks: Discovering Atoms. 2007. (Chain Reactions Ser.). (Illus.). 64p. (YA). (gr. 6-9). lib. bdg. 34.29 (***978-1-4034-9551-8(3)***) Heinemann Library.

Nardo, Don. Atoms. 2001. (Kidhaven Science Library). (Illus.). 48p. (J). (gr. 3-5). 23.70 (978-0-7377-0942-1(1) , LML00102-178579, Kidhaven) Thomson Gale.

Oxlade, Chris. Atoms. (Chemicals in Action Ser.). 48p. (J). (gr. 6-8). 2002. (Illus.). lib. bdg. 25.64 (978-1-58810-195-2(9)); 2nd ed. 2007. lib. bdg. 22.00 (***978-1-4329-0051-9(X)***) Heinemann Library.

Richardson, Hazel. How to Split the Atom. Anderson, Scoular, illus. 2001. (How to Ser.). 96p. (J). (gr. 5-7). 16.00 (978-0-531-14646-0(4)); pap. 4.95 (978-0-531-16202-6(8)) Scholastic Library Publishing. (Watts, Franklin).

Saunders, N. Atoms & Molecules. 2007. (J). lib. bdg. (***978-1-4042-3750-6(X)*** , Rosen Central) Rosen Publishing Group, Inc., The.

Science Kids Publishing Staff. What's the Matter? The Story of Atoms & Molecules. 1999. (J). (gr. 2-6). pap. 6.95 (978-1-891418-14-3(9)) Science Kids.

Slade, Suzanne. Atoms & Chemical Reactions. 2007. (Library of Physical Sciences). (Illus.). 24p. (J). (978-1-4042-2352-3(5)); pap. (978-1-4042-2162-8(X)); (gr. 3-6). lib. bdg. 21.25 (978-1-4042-3415-4(2)) Rosen Publishing Group, Inc., The. (PowerKids Pr.).

—Scientific Instruments for Studying Atoms & Molecules. 2007. (Library of Physical Sciences). (Illus.). 24p. (J). (978-1-4042-2356-1(8)); pap. (978-1-4042-2166-6(2)); lib. bdg. (978-1-4042-3419-2(5)) Rosen Publishing Group, Inc., The. (PowerKids Pr.).

—States of Matter. 2007. (Library of Physical Sciences). (J). (978-1-4042-2353-0(3)); (Illus.). 24p. pap. (978-1-4042-2163-5(8)) Rosen Publishing Group, Inc., The. (PowerKids Pr.).

Slade, Suzanne. The Structure of Atoms. 2007. (Illus.). 24p. (J). pap. (***978-1-4042-2161-1(1)*** , PowerKids Pr.) Rosen Publishing Group, Inc., The.

Solway, Andrew. A History of Super Science: Atoms & Elements. 2005. (Illus.). 32p. (J). (978-1-4109-1951-9(X)); (gr. 3-5). lib. bdg. 28.21 (978-1-4109-1920-5(X)) Steck-Vaughn.

Spilsbury, Louise & Spilsbury, Richard. Atoms & Molecules. 2007. (Illus.). 32p. (J). (978-1-4034-9341-5(3)); lib. bdg. (978-1-4034-9336-1(7)) Heinemann Library.

Stewart, Melissa. Atoms. 2003. (Simply Science Ser.). (Illus.). 32p. (J). (gr. 3 up). lib. bdg. 19.93 (978-0-7565-0441-0(4)) Compass Point Bks.

Stille, Darlene R. Atoms & Molecules: Building Blocks of the Universe. 2006. (Illus.). 48p. (J). (978-0-7565-1960-5(8)) Compass Point Bks.

Sussman, Art. Dr. Art's Guide to Science: Connecting Atoms, Galaxies & Everything in Between. 2006. (Illus.). 256p. 22.95 (978-0-7879-8326-0(8) , Jossey-Bass) Wiley, John & Sons, Inc.

Trumbauer, Lisa. What Are Atoms? 2005. (Rookie Read-About Science Ser.). (Illus.). 32p. (J). (gr. 1-2). pap. 4.95 (978-0-516-24665-9(8) , Children's Pr.) Scholastic Library Publishing.

Walker, Denise. Materials. 2007. (***978-1-58340-817-9(7)***) Smart Apple Media.

ATTENDANCE, SCHOOL

see School Attendance

ATTENTION DEFICIT DISORDERS

see Attention-Deficit Hyperactivity Disorder

ATTENTION-DEFICIT HYPERACTIVITY DISORDER

Arnold, Ellen. Brilliant Brain Banishes Boredom. Farber, Deborah, illus. 2001. (MI Strategies for Kids Ser.). 32p. (J). (gr. 1-5). pap. 7.00 (978-1-56976-115-1(9) , 1144, Zephyr Pr.) Chicago Review Pr., Inc.

Baldwin, Carol. Attention Deficit Disorder. 2003. (Health Matters Ser.). (Illus.). 32p. (J). (gr. 3-5). lib. bdg. 24.22 (978-1-4034-0249-3(3)) Heinemann Library.

Brinkerhoff, Shirley. Stuck on Fast Forward: Youth with Attention Deficit Hyper Activity Disorder. 2004. (Youth with Special Needs Ser.). (Illus.). 128p. (J). (978-1-59084-728-2(8)) Mason Crest Pubs.

Capaccio, George. ADD & ADHD. 2007. (Health Alert Ser.). 64p. (J). lib. bdg. 31.36 (***978-0-7614-2705-6(8)*** , Benchmark Bks.) Cavendish, Marshall Corp.

Chara, Kathleen A. & Chara, Paul J. Sensory Smarts: A Book for Kids with ADHD or Autism Spectrum Disorders Struggling with Sensory Integration Problems. Berns, Joel M., illus. 2004. 64p. (J). pap. (978-1-84310-783-5(X)) Kingsley, Jessica Ltd.

Connelly, Elizabeth Russell. Conduct Unbecoming: Hyperactivity, Attention Deficit & Disruptive Behavior Disorders. Nadelson, Carol C., ed. 1998. (Encyclopedia of Psychological Disorders Ser.). (Illus.). 104p. (gr. 4-7). 35.00 (978-0-7910-4895-5(0) , Chelsea Hse.) Facts On File, Inc.

Eshom, Dan. Lithium: What You Should Know. 1999. (Drug Abuse Prevention Library). (Illus.). 64p. (YA). (gr. 7-12). lib. bdg. 25.25 (978-0-8239-2828-6(4) , DRLITH) Rosen Publishing Group, Inc., The.

Gold, Susan Dudley. Attention Deficit Disorder. 2000. (Health Watch Ser.). (Illus.). 48p. (YA). (gr. 4-10). lib. bdg. 23.93 (978-0-7660-1657-6(9)) Enslow Pubs., Inc.

Kraus, Jeanne. Cory's Stories: A Kid's Book about Living with ADHD. Martin, Whitney, illus. 2005. 32p. (J). 11.95 (978-1-59147-148-6(6)); pap. 6.95 (978-1-59147-154-7(0)) American Psychological Assn. (Magination Pr.).

Moe, Barbara. Coping with Tourette's Syndrome & Other Tic Disorders. 2000. (Coping Ser.). (Illus.). 128p. (YA). (gr. 7-12). lib. bdg. 26.50 (978-0-8239-2976-4(0) , COTICS) Rosen Publishing Group, Inc., The.

Moe, Barbara A. Coping with Tourettes & Tics. rev. ed. 2005. (Coping Ser.). 192p. (J). (gr. 7-12). lib. bdg. 26.50 (978-0-8239-4089-9(6)) Rosen Publishing Group, Inc., The.

Morrison, Jaydene. Coping with ADD-ADHD: Attention Deficit Disorder - Attention Deficit Hyperactivity Disorder. 1998. (Coping Skills Library). (YA). (gr. 7-12). pap. 6.95 (978-1-56838-184-8(0) , 1156A) Hazelden Publishing & Educational Services.

—Coping with ADD/ADHD (Attention Deficit Disorder/ Attention Deficity Hyperactivity Disorder) rev. ed. 2005. (Coping Ser.). (Illus.). 192p. (YA). (gr. 7-12). lib. bdg. 26.50 (978-0-8239-3196-5(X) , COADDA) Rosen Publishing Group, Inc., The.

Nadeau, Kathleen G. & Dixon, Ellen B. Learning to Slow Down & Pay Attention: A Book for Kids about ADHD. Beyl, Charles, illus. 3rd ed. 2005. 96p. (J). 14.95 (978-1-59147-149-3(4)); pap. 9.95 (978-1-59147-155-4(9)) American Psychological Assn. (Magination Pr.).

Nemiroff, Marc A. & Annunziata, Jane. Help Is on the Way: A Child's Book about ADD. Scott, Margaret, illus. 1998. 64p. (J). (gr. k-4). 19.95 (978-1-55798-505-7(7) , 441-5057) American Psychological Assn.

Peacock, Judith. ADD & ADHD. 2000. (Perspectives on Mental Health Ser.). (Illus.). 64p. (J). (gr. 4-6). lib. bdg. 23.93 (978-0-7368-1029-6(3) , LifeMatters Bks.) Capstone Pr., Inc.

Petersen, Christine. Does Everyone Have ADHD? A Teen's Guide to Diagnosis & Treatment. 2006. (Health & Human Disease Ser.). (Illus.). 144p. (J). (gr. 9-12). 30.50 (978-0-531-16794-6(1) , Watts, Franklin) Scholastic Library Publishing.

Pigache, Philippa. ADHD. 2004. (Just the Facts Ser.). (Illus.). 56p. (J). lib. bdg. 27.07 (978-1-4034-5142-2(7)) Heinemann Library.

Pomere, Jonas. Frequently Asked Questions about ADD & ADHD. 2006. (FAQ Ser.). (Illus.). 64p. (YA). (gr. 7-12). lib. bdg. 27.95 (***978-1-4042-1970-0(6)***) Rosen Publishing Group, Inc., The.

Poremba, Mark, et al. Attention-Deficit/Hyperactivity Disorder (ADHD) 2007. (Psychological Disorders Ser.). 128p. (gr. 9). 37.50 (978-0-7910-8541-7(4) , Chelsea Hse.) Facts On File, Inc.

Quinn, Patricia O. & Stern, Judith M. Putting on the Brakes: Young People's Guide to Understanding Attention Deficit Hyperactivity Disorder. 2nd rev. ed. 2001. (Illus.). 80p. (J). (gr. 3-8). 14.95 (978-1-55798-832-4(3) , Magination Pr.) American Psychological Assn.

—Putting on the Brakes: Young People's Guide to Understanding Attention Deficit Hyperactivity Disorder. 2nd ed. 2001. (Illus.). 80p. (J). (gr. 3-8). pap. 9.95 (978-1-55798-795-2(5) , Magination Pr.) American Psychological Assn.

Quinn, Patricia O. & Stern, Judith M., eds. The Best of "Brakes" An Activity Book for Kids with ADD. Sternberg, Kate, illus. 2000. 94p. (J). (gr. 2-8). pap. (978-1-55798-661-0(4) , 441-6614, Magination Pr.) American Psychological Assn.

Rotner, Shelley & Kelly, Sheila M. The A. D. D. Book for Kids. Rotner, Shelley, photos by. 2000. (Illus.). (J). (ps-ps). lib. bdg. 16.40 (978-0-613-24076-5(6)) Tandem Library Bks.

Sheen, Barbara. Attention Deficit Disorder. 2000. (Diseases & Disorders Ser.). (Illus.). 96p. (YA). (gr. 6-9). 28.70 (978-1-56006-828-0(0) , Lucent Bks.) Thomson Gale.

Silverstein, Alvin, et al. The ADHD Update: Understanding Attention-Deficit/Hyperactivity Disorder. 2008. (Disease Update Ser.). (Illus.). 128p. (J). (gr. 5 up). lib. bdg. 31.93 (***978-0-7660-2800-5(3)***) Enslow Pubs., Inc.

Silverstein, Alvin, et al. Attention Deficit Disorder. 2001. (My Health Ser.). (Illus.). 48p. (J). (gr. 3-5). 25.50 (978-0-531-11778-1(2) , Watts, Franklin) Scholastic Library Publishing.

Trueit, Trudi Strain. ADHD. 2004. (Life Balance Ser.). (Illus.). 80p. (J). 20.50 (978-0-531-12261-7(1) , Watts, Franklin) Scholastic Library Publishing.

Walker, B. Girls' Guide to Ad/Hd. 2004. (Illus.). 174p. (J). pap. 17.95 (978-1-890627-56-0(9)) Woodbine Hse.

Weiner, Ellen. Taking A. D. D. to School: A Story about Attention Deficit Disorder. Gosselin, Kim, ed. Ravanelli, Terry, illus. 1999. (Special Kids in School Ser.: Vol. 4). 32p. (J). (gr. k-5). pap. 11.95 (978-1-891383-06-9(X)) JayJo Bks., LLC.

ATTENTION-DEFICIT HYPERACTIVITY DISORDER—FICTION

Beyer, Pamela J. & Bilbrey, Hilary. Little Jake Learns to Stop: A Heartwarming Tale about Determination & Succeeding with Attention Difficulties. Armstrong, Michelle Hartz, illus. 2006. (J). per. 9.99 (978-0-9787074-0-8(0)) Inspired By Family.

Cannon, Deborah Scott, illus. A. D. D. or XYZ. 1999. (J). (978-0-9671455-0-1(3)) Renaissance Publishing Co.

Carpenter, Phyllis & Ford, Marti. Sparky's Excellent Misadventures: My A. D. D. Journal by Me (Sparky) Horjas, Peter, illus. 1999. 32p. (J). (gr. k-6). pap. (978-1-55798-606-1(1) , 441-6061, Magination Pr.) American Psychological Assn.

Cheaney, J. B. The Middle of Somewhere. 2007. (Illus.). 224p. (J). (gr. 4-6). 15.99 (978-0-375-83790-6(6)); lib. bdg. 18.99 (978-0-375-93790-3(0)) Random Hse. Children's Bks. (Knopf Bks. for Young Readers).

Corman, Clifford L. & Trevino, Esther. Eukee the Jumpy Jumpy Elephant. DiMatteo, Richard A., illus. 2003. 24p. (J). (gr. 1-4). 15.00 (978-0-9621629-8-5(1)) Specialty Pr., Inc.

Crawford, Teresa. I'm Not Stupid! I'm ADHD! 2004. 23p. pap. 14.95 (978-1-4137-3249-8(6)) PublishAmerica, Inc.

Deans, Sis Boulos. Rainy. 2005. 208p. (J). (ps-7). 16.95 (978-0-8050-7831-2(2)) Holt, Henry & Co.

French, Jennifer. Fidgets. 2007. 132p. pap. 9.95 (***978-1-59663-531-9(2)*** , Castle Keep Pr.) Rock, James A. & Co. Pubs.

Galvin, Matthew. Otto Learns about His Medicine: A Story about Medication for Children with ADHD. Ferraro, Sandra, illus. 3rd ed. 2001. 32p. (J). (ps-3). 14.95 (978-1-55798-771-6(8)); pap. 8.95 (978-1-55798-772-3(6)) American Psychological Assn. (Magination Pr.).

Gantos, Jack. Joey Pigza Loses Control. braille ed. 2003. (J). (gr. 2). spiral bd. (978-0-616-15268-3(X)) Canadian National Institute for the Blind/Institut National Canadien pour les Aveugles.

—Joey Pigza Loses Control. 2000. (Joey Pigza Ser.). 208p. (J). (gr. 4-7). 16.00 (978-0-374-39989-4(1) , Farrar, Straus & Giroux (BYR)) Farrar, Straus & Giroux.

—Joey Pigza Loses Control. 2002. 208p. (J). (gr. 5 up). pap. 5.99 (978-0-06-441022-9(6) , Harper Trophy) HarperCollins Pubs.

—Joey Pigza Loses Control. unabr. ed. 2004. 195p. (J). (gr. 5-9). pap. 36.00 incl. audio (978-0-8072-8726-2(1) , LyA 248 SP, Listening Library) Random Hse. Audio Publishing Group.

—Joey Pigza Loses Control. 2002. (gr. 5-8). lib. bdg. 14.15 (978-0-613-49677-3(9)) Tandem Library Bks.

—Joey Pigza Loses Control. l.t. ed. 2001. 196p. (J). 22.95 (978-0-7862-3425-7(3)) Thorndike Pr.

—Joey Pigza Se Trago la Llave. (Torre de Papel Ser.). (SPA., Illus.). (YA). (gr. 6 up). 8.95 (978-958-04-5635-3(6) , NR30566) Norma S.A. COL. *Dist:* Distribuidora Norma, Inc., Lectorum Pubns., Inc.

—Joey Pigza Swallowed the Key. 1998. (Joey Pigza Ser.). (Illus.). 196p. (J). (gr. 4-7). 16.00 (978-0-374-33664-6(4) , Farrar, Straus & Giroux (BYR)) Farrar, Straus & Giroux.

—Joey Pigza Swallowed the Key. 2000. (J). pap., tchr. ed. (978-0-06-449267-6(2)); 160p. (gr. 5 up). pap. 5.99 (978-0-06-440833-2(7)) HarperCollins Pubs. (Harper Trophy).

—Joey Pigza Swallowed the Key. unabr. ed. 2004. 154p. (J). (gr. 5-9). pap. 29.00 incl. audio (978-0-8072-8166-6(2) , YA120SP, Listening Library) Random Hse. Audio Publishing Group.

—Joey Pigza Swallowed the Key. 2000. (Illus.). (J). 12.64 (978-0-606-18904-0(1)) Tandem Library Bks.

—Joey Pigza Swallowed the Key. l.t. ed. 2000. 174p. (J). 21.95 (978-0-7862-2912-3(8)) Thorndike Pr.

—What Would Joey Do? A Dazzling Conclusion to the Joey Pigza Trilogy! 2004. 240p. (J). (gr. 5-9). pap. 36.00 incl. audio (978-1-4000-9020-4(2) , Listening Library) Random Hse. Audio Publishing Group.

Guest, Jacqueline. Racing Fear. 2004. (SideStreets Ser.). 160p. (gr. 7-12). 7.95 (978-1-55028-838-4(5)); (***978-1-55028-839-1(3)***) Lorimer, James & Co., Ltd., Pubs. CAN. *Dist:* Casemate Pubs. & Bk. Distributors, LLC.

Harrar, George. Parents Wanted. Murphy, Dan, illus. 2001. (J). (gr. 3-8). 288p. 17.95 (978-1-57131-632-5(9)); 320p. pap. 6.95 (978-1-57131-633-2(7)) Milkweed Editions.

Little, Jean. Birdie for Now. 2002. (gr. 3-6). lib. bdg. 13.00 (978-0-613-53482-6(4)) Tandem Library Bks.

—Birdie for Now. Benoit, Renne, illus. 2002. 160p. (J). (gr. 3-6). pap. 5.95 (978-1-55143-203-8(X)) Orca Bk. Pubs. USA.

Moss, Deborah M. Shelley, the Hyperactive Turtle. Schwartz, Carol, illus. 2nd ed. 2006. 20p. (J). pap. (978-1-890627-75-1(5)) Woodbine Hse.

Myer, Ellen. Annie's Shoes. Simmons, Marcia, illus. 2002. (J). (ps-3). pap. 6.95 (978-0-9721586-0-2(X)) Family Treasures Publishing Co.

Penn, Audrey. A. D. D. Not B. A. D. Wyrick, Monica, illus. 2003. (New Child & Family Press Titles Ser.). 32p. pap. 9.95 (978-0-87868-849-4(8) , 8498, Child & Family Pr.) Child Welfare League of America, Inc.

Penn, Audrey & Wyrick, Monica. A.D.D. Not B.A.D. Penn, Audrey & Wyrick, Monica, illus. 2006. (Illus.). 32p. pap. 7.99 (978-0-9749303-7-4(7)) Tanglewood Pr.

Roberts, Barbara A. Phoebe's Best Best Friend. Sternberg, Kate, illus. 2000. (Phoebe Flower's Adventures Ser.). 70p. (J). pap. 5.95 (978-0-9660366-9-5(7)) National Bk. Network.

ATTILA, D. 453

Harvey, Bonnie. Attila the Hun. 2003. (Ancient World Leaders Ser.). (Illus.). 112p. (gr. 6-12). 30.00 (978-0-7910-7221-9(5)); pap. 30.00 (978-0-7910-7495-4(1)) Facts On File, Inc. (Chelsea Hse.).

Oliver, Marilyn Tower. Attila the Hun. 2005. (Heroes & Villains Ser.). (Illus.). 96-112p. (gr. 7-10). 29.95 (978-1-59018-638-1(9) , Blackbirch Pr., Inc.) Thomson Gale.

ATTITUDE (PSYCHOLOGY)

see also Public Opinion

Berry, Joy Wilt. A Book about Being Bossy. 2005. (Illus.). (J). (978-0-7172-8594-5(4)) Scholastic, Inc.

—A Book about Complaining. 2005. (Illus.). (J). (978-0-7172-8595-2(2)) Scholastic, Inc.

—A Book about Whining. 2005. (Illus.). (J). (978-0-7172-7898-5(0)) Scholastic, Inc.

de Vries, Dirk. Life Skills. 2000. (Attitude Ser.: Vol. 2). 136p. (YA). (gr. 7-12). pap. 14.95 (978-1-889108-43-8(X)) Living the Good News.

Irwin, Cait. Depression: Challenge the Beast Within Yourself & Win. Shaughnessy, Patrick S. et al, eds. 2nd rev. ed. 1998. (Illus.). 112p. (J). (gr. 6-12). pap. 12.95 (978-0-9663665-1-8(4)) AVI Communications, Inc.

Kalman, Bobbie. Thank You Animals. 2000. (Attitude of Gratitude Ser.). (Illus.). 32p. (J). (gr. 2-7). pap. (978-0-7787-0271-9(5)); (gr. 3-7). lib. bdg. (978-0-7787-0259-7(6)) Crabtree Publishing Co.

—Thank You Body. 2000. (Attitude of Gratitude Ser.). (Illus.). 32p. (J). (gr. 2-7). pap. (978-0-7787-0269-6(3)); (gr. 3-7). lib. bdg. (978-0-7787-0257-3(X)) Crabtree Publishing Co.

—Thank You Earth. 2000. (Attitude of Gratitude Ser.). (Illus.). 32p. (J). (gr. 2-7). pap. (978-0-7787-0268-9(5)); (gr. 3-7). lib. bdg. (978-0-7787-0256-6(1)) Crabtree Publishing Co.

—Thank You Oceans. 2000. (Attitude of Gratitude Ser.). (Illus.). 32p. (J). (gr. 2-7). pap. (978-0-7787-0270-2(7)); (gr. 3-7). lib. bdg. (978-0-7787-0258-0(8)) Crabtree Publishing Co.

—Thank You Plants. 2000. (Attitude of Gratitude Ser.). (Illus.). 32p. (J). (gr. 2-7). pap. (978-0-7787-0272-6(3)); (gr. 3-7). lib. bdg. (978-0-7787-0260-3(X)) Crabtree Publishing Co.

Wilbur, Regina, ed. Keys to Sucess: Getting Control of Mr. & Mrs. Attitude & Temper (A. T.) 2003. tchr. ed., spiral bd. 8.95 (978-0-9710925-1-8(6) , 0-9710925-1-6) EniCare Consulting, Inc.

The Winners. 2005. (YA). 14.95 (***978-0-9661256-4-1(9)***) Youth Communication - New York Center.

ATTORNEYS

see Lawyers

ATTUCKS, CRISPUS, D. 1770

Beier, Anne. Crispus Attucks: Hero of the Boston Massacre. (Primary Sources of Famous People in American History Ser.). (Illus.). 32p. 2004. (gr. 4-8). lib. bdg. 21.25 (978-0-8239-4106-3(X) , Rosen Central); 2004. (SPA & ENG., (gr. 4-8). lib. bdg. 21.25 (978-0-8239-4154-4(X) , Buenas Letra); 2003. (YA). pap. (978-0-8239-4178-0(7)) Rosen Publishing Group, Inc., The.

—Crispus Attucks: Heroe de la Masacre de Boston. 2004. (Grandes Personajes en la Historia de los Estados Unidos (Famous People in American History) Ser.). (SPA & ENG., Illus.). 32p. (gr. 4-8). lib. bdg. 21.25 (978-0-8239-4130-8(2) , Buenas Letra) Rosen Publishing Group, Inc., The.

Mattern, Joanne. The Cost of Freedom: Crispus Attucks & the Boston Massacre. 2004. (Great Moments in American History Ser.). (Illus.). 32p. (gr. 4-8). lib. bdg. 21.25 (978-0-8239-4341-8(0) , Rosen Central) Rosen Publishing Group, Inc., The.

McLeese, Don. Crispus Attucks. 2005. (Heroes of the American Revolution Ser.). (Illus.). 32p. (gr. 2-5). 19.95 (978-1-59515-218-3(0)) Rourke Publishing, LLC.

Rausch, Monica. Crispus Attucks. 2006. (Illus.). 24p. (J). pap. (***978-0-8368-7688-8(1)***); lib. bdg. (***978-0-8368-7681-9(4)***) Stevens, Gareth Inc. (Weekly Reader Early Learning Library).

AUCTIONS

Woog, Adam. Pierre M. Omidyar: Creator of Ebay. 2007. (Innovators Ser.). (Illus.). 64p. (J). (gr. 4-8). 24.95 (***978-0-7377-3864-3(2)*** , Kidhaven) Thomson Gale.

AUCTIONS—FICTION

Evans, Kristina. Cherish Today: A Celebration of Life's Moments. Collier, Bryan, illus. 2007. 32p. (ps-3). 15.99 (978-0-7868-0818-2(7) , Jump at the Sun) Hyperion Bks. for Children.

Hancock, Irving H. The High School Boys' Canoe Club or Dick. 2006. 78.99 (***978-1-4219-9899-2(8)***); pap. 72.99 (***978-1-4219-9890-9(4)***) IndyPublish.com.

Harrison, Troon. Wonderful Junk. Hocking, Geoff, illus. 1998. 32p. (J). (ps-3). pap. 7.95 (978-1-55037-520-6(2)); lib. bdg. 17.95 (978-1-55037-521-3(0)) Annick Pr., Ltd. CAN. *Dist:* Firefly Bks., Ltd.

Seymour, Tres. Auction! Smith, Cat Bowman, illus. 2005. 32p. (J). (gr. 1-4). 16.99 (978-0-7636-1242-9(1)) Candlewick Pr.

Warner, Gertrude Chandler. Disappearing Staircase Mystery. 2001. (gr. 3-6). lib. bdg. 11.80 (978-0-613-53176-4(0)) Tandem Library Bks.

AUDIO-VISUAL EDUCATION

Steck-Vaughn Staff. Interpreting Visual Information. 2004. pap. 5.00 (978-0-7398-9842-0(6)) Harcourt Schl. Pubs.

—Interpreting Visual Information 10-Pack. 2004. pap. 44.95 (978-0-7398-9923-6(6)) Harcourt Schl. Pubs.

AUDUBON, JOHN JAMES, 1785-1851

Armstrong, Jennifer. Audubon: Painter of Birds in the Wild Frontier. Smith, Joseph A., illus. 2003. 40p. (J). (gr. k-4). 17.95 (978-0-8109-4238-7(0)) Abrams, Harry N., Inc.

Brenner, Barbara. On the Frontier with Mr. Audubon. Lippincott, Gary, illus. 2003. 72p. (YA). (gr. 4-6). pap. 9.95 (978-1-56397-679-7(X)) Boyds Mills Pr.

Davies, Jacqueline. The Boy Who Drew Birds: A Story of John James Audubon. Sweet, Melissa, illus. 2004. 32p. (J). (gr. k-3). tchr. ed. 16.00 (978-0-618-24343-3(7)) Houghton Mifflin Co. Trade & Reference Div.

Mason, Miriam E. John Audubon: Young Naturalist. Underdown, Harold, ed. Morrison, Cathy, illus. 2nd rev. ed. 2006. (Young Patriots Ser.). 120p. (J). 15.95 (978-1-882859-51-1(0)); pap. 9.95 (978-1-882859-52-8(9)) Patria Pr., Inc. (Young Patriots Series).

AUGUSTINE, SAINT, BISHOP OF HIPPO, 354-430

Alex, Ben. St. Augustine. Rava, Giuseppe, illus. 1998. (Heroes of Faith & Courage Ser.). 50p. (gr. 3-12). reprint ed. pap. 7.99 (978-1-884543-19-7(7)) Authentic Media.

Magedanz, Stacy. CliffsNotes on St. Augustine's Confessions. 2004. 96p. pap. 5.99 (978-0-7645-4480-4(2) , Cliff Notes) Wiley, John & Sons, Inc.

AUGUSTUS, EMPEROR OF ROME, 63 B.C.-14 A.D.

Forsyth, Fiona. Augustus: The First Emperor. 2003. (Leaders of Ancient Rome Ser.). (Illus.). 112p. (YA). (gr. 5-8). lib. bdg. 31.95 (978-0-8239-3588-8(4) , Rosen Central) Rosen Publishing Group, Inc., The.

Greenblatt, Miriam. Augustus & Imperial Rome. 1999. (Rulers & Their Times Ser.). (Illus.). 80p. (J). (gr. 6 up). lib. bdg. 29.93 (978-0-7614-0912-0(2) , Benchmark Bks.) Cavendish, Marshall Corp.

Whiting, Jim. The Life & Times of Augustus Caesar. 2005. (Biography from Ancient Civilizations Ser.). (Illus.). 48p. (J). (ps-7). lib. bdg. 29.95 (978-1-58415-336-8(9)) Mitchell Lane Pubs., Inc.

AUNT EATER (FICTITIOUS CHARACTER)—FICTION

Cushman, Doug. Aunt Eater Loves a Mystery. Cushman, Doug, illus. 2002. (Aunt Eater Mysteries Ser.). (Illus.). (J). 12.30 (978-0-7587-5990-0(8)) Book Wholesalers, Inc.

—Aunt Eater's Mystery Christmas. Cushman, Doug, illus. 2002. (Aunt Eater Mysteries Ser.). (Illus.). (J). 12.30 (978-0-7587-5991-7(6)) Book Wholesalers, Inc.

—Aunt Eater's Mystery Halloween. Cushman, Doug, illus. 2002. (Aunt Eater Mysteries Ser.). (Illus.). (J). 11.91 (978-0-7587 5992-4(4)) Book Wholesalers, Inc.

—Aunt Eater's Mystery Halloween. Cushman, Doug, illus. 1999. (I Can Read Bks.). (Illus.). 64p. (J). (gr. k-3). pap. 3.99 (978-0-06-444266-4(7) , Harper Trophy) HarperCollins Pubs.

—Aunt Eater's Mystery Halloween. 1998. (I Can Read Bks.). (Illus.). (J). (gr. k-3). 64p. 14.95 (978-0-06-027803-8(X)); 40p. 14.89 (978-0-06-027804-5(8)) HarperCollins Pubs.

—Aunt Eater's Mystery Halloween. Cushman, Doug, illus. 1999. (I Can Read Bks.). 64p. lib. bdg. 10.79 (978-0-606-17301-8(3)) Tandem Library Bks.

—Aunt Eater's Mystery Halloween. 1999. (gr. k-3). lib. bdg. 11.80 (978-0-613-22814-5(6)) Tandem Library Bks.

—Aunt Eater's Mystery Vacation. Cushman, Doug, illus. 2002. (Aunt Eater Mysteries Ser.). (Illus.). (J). 12.30 (978-0-7587-5993-1(2)) Book Wholesalers, Inc.

AUSTEN, JANE, 1775-1817

Bloom, Harold. Jane Austen. 2002. (Bloom's BioCritiques Ser.). (Illus.). 112p. (gr. 9-13). 35.00 (978-0-7910-6184-8(1) , 000865, Chelsea Hse.) Facts On File, Inc.

Chapman, Lynne F. Jane Austen. 1999. (Illus.). 56p. (YA). (gr. 6 up). lib. bdg. 16.95 (978-0-88682-740-3(X) , Creative Education) Creative Co., The.

Kirk, Connie Ann. A Student's Guide to Jane Austen. 2007. (Understanding Literature Ser.). (Illus.). 160p. (YA). (gr. 6). lib. bdg. 27.93 (***978-0-7660-2439-7(5)***) Enslow Pubs., Inc.

Locke, Juliane. England's Jane: The Story of Jane Austen. 2006. (World Writers Ser.). (Illus.). 144p. (YA). lib. bdg. 26.95 (978-1-931798-82-2(6)) Reynolds, Morgan Inc.

Ruth, Amy. Jane Austen. 2005. (Biography Ser.). (Illus.). 112p. (J). (gr. 6-12). lib. bdg. 27.93 (978-0-8225-4992-5(1)) Lerner Publishing Group.

Wagner, Heather Lehr. Jane Austen. 2003. (Who Wrote That? Ser.). (Illus.). 112p. (gr. 6-12). 30.00 (978-0-7910-7623-1(7) , Chelsea Hse.) Facts On File, Inc.

AUSTIN, STEPHEN FULLER, 1793-1836

Roberts, Russell. The Life & Times of Stephen F. Austin. 2007. (Profiles in American History Ser.). (Illus.). 48p. (J). lib. bdg. 29.95 ***(978-1-58415-531-7(0))*** Mitchell Lane Pubs., Inc.

Ross, Dan. Steve Austin: Story of the Wrestler They Call "Stone Cold" 1999. (Pro Wrestling Legends Ser.). (Illus.). 64p. (YA). (gr. 3 up). 25.00 (978-0-7910-5403-1(9) , Chelsea Hse.) Facts On File, Inc.

AUSTIN FAMILY (FICTITIOUS CHARACTERS)—FICTION

L'Engle, Madeleine. Meet the Austins. 2002. (Austin Family Ser.: No. 1). (Illus.). (J). 13.94 (978-0-7587-8955-6(6)) Book Wholesalers, Inc.

AUSTRALASIA

Heinrichs, Ann. Australia. rev. ed. 2007. (Enchantment of the World, Second Ser.). (Illus.). 144p. (J). (gr. 5-9). 36.00 (978-0-516-24873-8(1) , Children's Pr.) Scholastic Library Publishing.

McClish, Bruce. Southeast Asia, Australia, & the Pacific Realm. 2007. (J). ***(978-1-4034-9900-4(4));*** pap. ***(978-1-4034-9909-7(8))*** Heinemann Library.

AUSTRALIA

Alter, Judy. Discovering Australia's Land, People, & Wildlife: A MyReportLinks. com Book. 2004. (Continents of the World Ser.). (Illus.). 48p. (J). lib. bdg. 25.26 (978-0-7660-5207-9(9) , MyReportLinks.com Bks.) Enslow Pubs., Inc.

Bagley, Katie. Australia. 2002. (Continents Ser.). (Illus.). 79p. (J). (gr. 1-2). 18.60 (978-0-7368-1417-1(5) , Bridgestone Bks.) Capstone Pr., Inc.

Banting, Erinn. Australia: The Culture. 2003. (gr. 3-6). lib. bdg. 16.40 (978-0-613-52805-4(0)) Tandem Library Bks.

—Australia: The Land. 2003. (gr. 3-6). lib. bdg. 16.40 (978-0-613-52806-1(9)) Tandem Library Bks.

—Australia: The People. 2003. (gr. 3-6). lib. bdg. 16.40 (978-0-613-52807-8(7)) Tandem Library Bks.

—Australia - The Culture. 2002. (Lands, Peoples & Cultures Ser.). (Illus.). 32p. (J). (gr. 4-5). (978-0-7787-9345-8(1)); pap. (978-0-7787-9713-5(9)) Crabtree Publishing Co.

—Australia - The Land. 2002. (Lands, Peoples & Cultures Ser.). (Illus.). 32p. (J). (gr. 4-5). (978-0-7787-9343-4(5)); pap. (978-0-7787-9711-1(2)) Crabtree Publishing Co.

—Australia - The People. 2002. (Lands, Peoples & Cultures Ser.). (Illus.). 32p. (J). (gr. 4-5). (978-0-7787-9344-1(3)); pap. (978-0-7787-9712-8(0)) Crabtree Publishing Co.

Bateman, Helen & Denshire, Jayne. Australia. 2006. (Illus.). 32p. (J). (978-1-58340-798-1(7)) Smart Apple Media.

Bell, Rachael. Australia. (Visit to Ser.). 32p. pap. 6.50 (978-1-4034-4143-0(X)); 1999. (J). lib. bdg. 21.36 (978-1-57572-850-6(8)) Heinemann Library.

Bell, Robin. My Adventure Discovering Australia. 2007. 44p. (J). 8.99 (978-1-59092-416-7(9) , Orchard Academy Pr.) Windstorm Creative.

—My Adventure Discovering Australia: Advanced My Adventure. 2007. 44p. (J). pap. 8.99 (978-1-59092-417-4(7) , Orchard Academy Pr.) Windstorm Creative.

Berendes, Mary. Australia. 2007. (Welcome to the World Ser.). 32p. (J). (gr. 1-5). 27.07 ***(978-1-59296-910-4(0))*** Child's World, Inc.

Bingham, Jane. Australia. 2006. (Exploring Continents Ser.). (Illus.). 32p. (978-1-4034-8244-0(6)); pap. (978-1-4034-8252-5(7)) Heinemann Library.

Bingham, Jane. World Cultures: Living in the Australian Outback. 2007. (J). ***(978-1-4109-2813-9(6)); (978-1-4109-2822-1(5))*** Steck-Vaughn.

Boast, Clare. Australia. 1998. (Next Stop! Ser.). 32p. (J). lib. bdg. 19.92 (978-1-57572-675-5(0)) Heinemann Library.

Boraas, Tracey. Australia. 2002. (Countries & Cultures Ser.). (Illus.). 64p. (J). (gr. 3-4). lib. bdg. 23.93 (978-0-7368-1075-3(7) , Bridgestone Bks.) Capstone Pr., Inc.

Bramwell, Martyn. Australia, the Pacific & Antarctica. 2001. (World in Maps Ser.). (Illus.). 40p. (J). (gr. 5-12). lib. bdg. 23.93 (978-0-8225-2917-0(3) , Lerner Pubns.) Lerner Publishing Group.

Cahir, Sandra. Livewire Investigates Aboriginal Studies Reconciliation. 2002. (Livewires Ser.). (Illus.). 32p. pap. 5.00 (978-0-521-52671-5(X)) Cambridge Univ. Pr.

Canizares, Susan. Australia. 1999. (J). 3.25 (978-0-439-04574-2(6)) Scholastic, Inc.

Carmi, Rebecca. Expedition down Under. 2002. (Magic School Bus Chapter Bks.: No. 10). (Illus.). 96p. (J). pap. 4.99 (978-0-439-20424-8(0) , Scholastic Paperbacks) Scholastic, Inc.

—Expedition down Under. 2001. (gr. 3-6). lib. bdg. 11.80 (978-0-613-50686-1(3)) Tandem Library Bks.

Cobb, Leigh Ann. Australia. 2002. (Steadwell Books World Tour). (Illus.). 48p. (J). 24.26 (978-0-7398-5751-9(7)) Raintree.

Collins, Alan. A Promised Land? 2001. 424p. (YA). pap. 18.95 (978-0-7022-3244-2(0)) Univ. of Queensland Pr. AUS. *Dist:* International Specialized Bk. Services.

Corwin, Jeff. Into Wild Australia. 2004. (Animal Planet Ser.). (Illus.). 48p. (J). 24.95 (978-1-4103-0239-7(3)); 11.20 (978-1-4103-0240-3(7)) Thomson Gale. (Blackbirch Pr., Inc.).

Currie, Stephen. Australia & the Pacific Islands. 2004. (J). (gr. 7-10). 29.95 (978-1-59018-496-7(3) , Lucent Bks.) Thomson Gale.

Darian-Smith, Kate. Australia, Antarctica, & the Pacific. (Continents of the World Ser.). 2006. (Illus.). 64p. (YA). (gr. 7-10). lib. bdg. 32.67 (978-0-8368-5912-6(X)); 2005. (J). (978-0-8368-5919-5(7)) Stevens, Gareth Inc. (World Almanac Library).

Davis, Kevin A. Look What Came from Australia. 1999. (J). (978-0-606-20142-1(4)); (gr. 3-6). lib. bdg. 15.25 (978-0-613-54742-0(X)) Tandem Library Bks.

Dolce, Laura. Australia. 1999. (Major World Nations Ser.). (Illus.). 144p. (YA). (gr. 4-7). 29.95 (978-0-7910-4731-6(8) , Chelsea Hse.) Facts On File, Inc.

Donaldson, Madeline. Australia. 2005. (Pull Ahead Bks.). (Illus.). 32p. (J). (gr. k-3). lib. bdg. 22.60 (978-0-8225-4718-1(X)) Lerner Publishing Group.

Einfeld, Jann. Life in the Australian Outback. 2002. (Way People Live Ser.). (Illus.). 112p. (J). (gr. 7-10). 29.95 (978-1-59018-014-3(3) , Lucent Bks.) Thomson Gale.

Encyclopaedia Britannica Publishers, Inc. Staff. Views of Asia & Australia. 2004. (Britannica Learning Library). (Illus.). (J). lib. bdg. 14.95 (978-1-59339-010-5(6)) Encyclopaedia Britannica, Inc.

Ewards, Yvonne, et al. Going for Kalta: Hunting for Sleepy Lizards at Yalata. 1999. (Illus.). 32p. 19.95 (978-0-949659-99-6(1)) IAD Pr. AUS. *Dist:* International Specialized Bk. Services.

Fowler, Allan. Australia. 2001. (Rookie Read-About Geography Ser.). (Illus.). 32p. (J). (gr. 1-2). pap. 5.95 (978-0-516-27298-6(5)); 20.50 (978-0-516-21670-6(8)) Scholastic Library Publishing. (Children's Pr.).

—Australia. 2001. (gr. k-3). lib. bdg. 14.10 (978-0-613-53940-1(0)) Tandem Library Bks.

Fox, Mary Virginia. Australia. (Heinemann First Library). (Illus.). 32p. (J). 2006. lib. bdg. 25.36 ***(978-1-4034-8542-7(9));*** 2001. lib. bdg. 21.36 (978-1-57572-449-2(9)) Heinemann Library.

Fox, Mary Virginia & Foster, Leila. Australia. 2002. (Continents Ser.). (Illus.). 32p. (J). (gr. k-2). pap. 6.95 (978-1-58810-948-4(8) , 91438) Heinemann Library.

Frost, Helen. A Look at Australia. Saunders-Smith, Gail, ed. 2002. (Our World Ser.). (Illus.). 24p. (J). (gr. k-1). lib. bdg. 15.93 (978-0-7368-1165-1(6) , Pebble Bks.) Capstone Pr., Inc.

—A Look at Australia. 2005. (One World, Many Cultures Ser.). 24p. (YA). (gr. k-3). pap. (978-0-7368-9360-2(1) , Pebble Bks.) Capstone Pr., Inc.

Germaine, Elizabeth & Burckhardt, Ann. Cooking the Australian Way. 2nd rev. ed. 2004. (Easy Menu Ethnic Cookbooks). (Illus.). 72p. (J). (gr. 5-12). 25.26 (978-0-8225-4101-1(7)) Lerner Publishing Group.

Gordon, Sharon. Australia. 2004. (Discovering Cultures Ser.). (J). 25.64 (978-0-7614-1791-0(5) , Benchmark Bks.) Cavendish, Marshall Corp.

Grabowski, John F. Australia. 2002. (Modern Nations of the World Ser.). (Illus.). 120p. (YA). (gr. 7-10). 27.45 (978-1-56006-566-1(4) , Lucent Bks.) Thomson Gale.

Gray, Shirley W. Australia. 2000. (First Reports). (Illus.). 48p. (J). (gr. 3 up). lib. bdg. 22.60 (978-0-7565-0026-9(5)) Compass Point Bks.

Griffiths, Diana. Australia. 1999. (Festivals of the World Ser.). (Illus.). 32p. (J). (gr. 3 up). lib. bdg. 24.67 (978-0-8368-2021-8(5)) Stevens, Gareth Inc.

Group/McGraw-Hill, Wright. Australia: Urban & Outback, 6 vols. (Book2WebTM Ser.). (J). (gr. 4-8). 36.50 (978-0-322-04446-3(4)) Wright Group, The.

Hatt, Christine. Sydney. 1999. (World Cities Ser.). (Illus.). 48p. (J). (gr. 2-6). lib. bdg. 16.95 (978-1-929298-26-6(9)) Chrysalis Education.

Haugen, Brenda & Compass Point Books Staff. Teens in Australia. 2006. (Global Connections Ser.). (Illus.). 96p. (J). (gr. 5-7). 31.93 ***(978-0-7565-2441-8(5))*** Compass Point Bks.

Heinrichs, Ann. Australia. 2nd ed. 1998. (Enchantment of the World, Second Ser.). (Illus.). 144p. (J). (gr. 5-9). 36.00 (978-0-516-20648-6(6) , Children's Pr.) Scholastic Library Publishing.

Hiemen, Sara. Australia ABCs: A Book about the People & Places of Australia. Avila, Antonio, illus. 2004. (Country ABCs Ser.). 32p. (gr. k-5). 23.93 (978-1-4048-0018-2(2)) Picture Window Bks.

Hill, Valerie. Australia. 2002. (Ask about Asia Ser.). (Illus.). 48p. (YA). (gr. 4 up). lib. bdg. (978-1-59084-208-9(1)) Mason Crest Pubs.

Hovanec, Erin M. An Online Visit to Australia. (Internet Field Trips Ser.). 24p. (J). 2002. lib. bdg. 18.75 (978-0-8239-6421-5(3)); 2001. (Illus.). (gr. 3). lib. bdg. 18.75 (978-0-8239-5653-1(9)) Rosen Publishing Group, Inc., The. (PowerKids Pr.).

Israel, Fred L. & Schlesinger, Arthur M., Jr., eds. Australia: The Unique Continent. 1999. (Cultural & Geographical Exploration Ser.). (Illus.). 144p. (YA). (gr. 5 up). 21.95 (978-0-7910-5441-3(1) , Chelsea Hse.) Facts On File, Inc.

—History of Third Parties: The Unique Continent. 2000. (Your Government Ser.). 64p. (J). (gr. 7-12). 25.00 (978-0-7910-5541-0(8) , Chelsea Hse.) Facts On File, Inc.

Italia, Bob. Australia. 2000. (Countries Ser.). (Illus.). 40p. (J). (gr. k-6). lib. bdg. 22.78 (978-1-57765-384-4(X) , Checkerboard Library) ABDO Publishing Co.

James, Otto. Focus on Australia. 2006. (Illus.). 64p. (J). pap. ***(978-0-8368-6744-2(0));*** lib. bdg. ***(978-0-8368-6737-4(8))*** Stevens, Gareth Inc. (World Almanac Library).

Jordan-Bychkov, Terry G. Australia. 2003. (Modern World Nations Ser.). (Illus.). 150p. (gr. 6-12). 30.00 (978-0-7910-7609-5(1) , Chelsea Hse.) Facts On File, Inc.

Kalman, Bobbie & Sjonger, Rebecca. Explore Australia & Oceania. 2007. (Explore the Continents Ser.). (Illus.). 32p. (J). (gr. 1-7). ***(978-0-7787-3073-6(5));*** pap. ***(978-0-7787-3087-3(5))*** Crabtree Publishing Co.

Kavanagh, James. Australian Birds: An Introduction to Familiar Species. Leung, Raymond, illus. 2001. (Pocket Traveller Ser.). 12p. pap. 5.95 (978-1-58355-036-6(4)) Waterford Pr., Ltd.

Kerns, Ann. Australia in Pictures. 2nd ed. 2004. (Visual Geography Series, Second Ser.). (Illus.). 80p. (J). (gr. 5-12). 27.93 (978-0-8225-0932-5(6)) Lerner Publishing Group.

Landau, Elaine. Australia & New Zealand. 2000. (True Bks.). (Illus.). 48p. (J). (gr. 3-5). pap. 6.95 (978-0-516-26573-5(3) , Children's Pr.) Scholastic Library Publishing.

—Australia & New Zealand. 1999. (gr. 3-6). lib. bdg. 15.25 (978-0-613-50269-6(8)) Tandem Library Bks.

Langeland, Deirdre. Kangaroo Island: A Story of An Australian Mallee Forest. Ordaz, Frank, illus. 1998. (Nature Conservancy Habitat Ser.). (J). (gr. 1-4). 32p. 15.95 (978-1-56899-543-4(1) , B7007); 32p. 19.95 incl. reel tape (978-1-56899-545-8(8) , BC7007); 32p. pap. 6.95 (978-1-56899-544-1(X)); 36p. pap. 10.95 incl. audio (978-1-56899-546-5(6)); Incl. toy. 36p. 26.95 (978-1-56899-547-2(4)); Incl. toy. 36p. 31.95 incl. audio (978-1-56899-549-6(0)); Incl. toy. 36p. pap. 19.95 incl. audio (978-1-56899-550-2(4)) Soundprints.

Leppman, Elizabeth J. Australia & the Pacific. 2005. (Modern World Cultures Ser.). (Illus.). 128p. (J). (gr. 6-12). 30.00 (978-0-7910-8150-1(8) , Chelsea Hse.) Facts On File, Inc.

A Look at Australia, 6 vols. (gr. k-2). 28.95 (978-0-7368-9361-9(X)) Red Brick Learning.

Lumb, Miriam. Australia: Listen Up! 2006. (Destination Detectives Ser.). (Illus.). 48p. (J). (978-1-4109-2336-3(3)); pap. (978-1-4109-2347-9(9)) Steck-Vaughn.

March, Michael. Guide to Australia. 1998. (World Guides Ser.). (Illus.). 32p. (J). (gr. 2-6). lib. bdg. 21.27 (978-1-884756-38-2(7)) Davidson Titles, Inc.

Marshall, Diana. Aboriginal Australians. 2004. (Indigenous Peoples Ser.). (J). pap. 7.95 (978-1-59036-156-6(3)); (Illus.). 32p. lib. bdg. 18.20 (978-1-59036-121-4(0)) Weigl Pubs., Inc.

Mary Virginia Fox. Australia. 2nd ed. 2006. (Heinemann First Library). (Illus.). 32p. (J). pap. ***(978-1-4034-8550-2(X))*** Heinemann Library.

Mason, Paul. Sydney. Bowden, Rob, photos by. 2007. (Global Cities Ser.). (Illus.). 64p. (J). (gr. 5-8). 30.00 (978-0-7910-8849-4(9) , Chelsea Hse.) Facts On File, Inc.

McAvoy, Jim. Mel Gibson. 2001. (People in the News Ser.). (Illus.). 112p. (J). (gr. 6-9). 32.45 (978-1-56006-980-5(5) , Lucent Bks.) Thomson Gale.

McCollum, Sean. Australia. (Country Explorers Ser.). 48p. (J). 2007. (gr. 2-4). lib. bdg. 27.93 ***(978-0-8225-7126-1(9)*** , Lerner Pubns.); 1999. (Illus.). (gr. k-2). 22.60 (978-1-57505-129-1(X) , Carolrhoda Bks.); 1999. (Illus.). (gr. 3-5). lib. bdg. 22.60 (978-1-57505-104-8(4) , Carolrhoda Bks.) Lerner Publishing Group.

McNeil, Niki, et al. HOCPP 1074 Australia. 2006. spiral bd. 24.00 ***(978-1-60308-074-3(0))*** In the Hands of a Child.

—HOCPP 1107 Steve Irwin. 2006. spiral bd. 21.00 ***(978-1-60308-107-8(0))*** In the Hands of a Child.

Moore, Jo Ellen. Australia. Evans, Marilyn, ed. Davis, Cindy & Winters, Keli, illus. 1999. (Geography Units Ser.). 80p. (J). (gr. 3-6). pap., tchr. ed. 12.95 (978-1-55799-712-8(8) , EMC 765) Evan-Moor Educational Pubs.

Morgan, Anne. The Glow Worm Cave. Kurczok, Belinda, illus. 1999. 31p. (J). (gr. 3-7). pap. 19.55 (978-0-85575-343-6(9)) Aboriginal Studies Pr. AUS. *Dist:* International Specialized Bk. Services.

Moss, Miriam. This Is the Coral Reef. Kennaway, Adrienne, illus. 2007. 32p. (J). (gr. k-4). 16.95 ***(978-1-84507-573-6(0))*** Lincoln, Frances Ltd. GBR. *Dist:* Perseus Distribution.

Needham, Peter & Whitecap Books Staff. Australia. 2000. (Investigate Ser.). (Illus.). 64p. (J). (gr. 1-7). pap. 3.95 (978-1-55285-154-8(0)) Whitecap Bks., Ltd. CAN. *Dist:* Firefly Bks., Ltd.

Niz, Xavier. Australia. 2006. (Illus.). 24p. (J). (978-0-7368-5428-3(2)) Capstone Pr., Inc.

North, Peter. Australia. 1998. (Countries of the World Ser.). (Illus.). 96p. (J). (gr. 6 up). lib. bdg. 30.00 (978-0-8368-2122-2(X)) Stevens, Gareth Inc.

North, Peter & McKay, Susan. Welcome to Australia. 1999. (Welcome to My Country Ser.). (Illus.). 48p. (J). (gr. 2 up). lib. bdg. 26.00 (978-0-8368-2393-6(1)) Stevens, Gareth Inc.

Olson, Nathan. Australia. 2005. (Fact Finders Ser.). (Illus.). 32p. (J). 22.60 (978-0-7368-3747-7(7)) Capstone Pr., Inc.

Park, Ted. Australia. 2000. (Taking Your Camera to Ser.). (Illus.). 32p. (J). (gr. 4-7). lib. bdg. 22.83 (978-0-7398-1810-7(4)) Raintree.

—Taking Your Camera To... Includes: Australia, Brazil, Canada, Egypt, France, Israel, Italy, Japan, Mexico, Panama, Russia, Spain, 12 bks., Set. 2000. (Taking Your Camera to Ser.). (Illus.). (J). (gr. 4-7). 273.96 (978-0-7398-3096-3(1)) Raintree.

—Taking Your Camera to Australia. 2001. (Illus.). pap. (978-0-7398-3331-5(6)) Steck-Vaughn.

Pelusey, Michael & Pelusey, Jane. Australia. 2004. (Continents Ser.). (Illus.). 32p. (J). (gr. 2-4). 23.00 (978-0-7910-8278-2(4) , Chelsea Hse.) Facts On File, Inc.

Petersen, David. Australia. Taft, James, ed. 1998. (True Bks.). (Illus.). 48p. (J). (gr. 3-5). pap. 6.95 (978-0-516-26372-4(2) , Children's Pr.) Scholastic Library Publishing.

—Australia. 1998. (Illus.). 47p. (J). (ps-ps). lib. bdg. 15.25 (978-0-613-37278-7(6)) Tandem Library Bks.

Popper, Garry. Kez in Australia. Johnson, Andi, illus. 2004. 36p. (ps-7). 4.00 (978-1-84161-055-9(0)) Ravette Publishing, Ltd. GBR. *Dist:* Parkwest Pubns., Inc.

Prosser, Robert. Australia. 2004. (Countries of the World Ser.). (Illus.). 64p. (J). (gr. 6-12). 30.00 (978-0-8160-5505-0(X)) Facts On File, Inc.

Rau, Dana Meachen. Australia. 2002. (Country Files Ser.). (Illus.). 32p. (J). lib. bdg. 24.25 (978-1-58340-206-1(3)) Smart Apple Media.

Richardson, Adele D. Australia. (Let's Investigate Ser.). (Illus.). 32p. (J). 2000. pap. 10.60 (978-0-89812-002-8(0) , Creative Paperbacks); 1998. lib. bdg. 19.95 (978-0-88682-341-2(2) , Creative Education) Creative Co., The.

Richardson, Margot. Australia. Fairclough, Chris, photos by. 2004. (Letters from Around the World Ser.). (J). lib. bdg. (978-1-84234-245-9(2) , Cherrytree Books) Evans Publishing Group.

—Australia. 2003. (Changing Face Of... Ser.). (Illus.). 48p. (J). lib. bdg. 28.56 (978-0-7398-5487-7(9)) Raintree.

Riggs, Sandy. Habitats of AUST. 2005. (Navigators Ser.). (J). pap. 38.00 ***(978-1-4108-5072-0(2))*** Benchmark Education Co.

Rose, Elizabeth. A Primary Source Guide to Australia. 2004. (Primary Sources of Countries of the World Ser.). (Illus.). 24p. (J). lib. bdg. 19.95 (978-0-8239-6730-8(1) , PowerKids Pr.) Rosen Publishing Group, Inc., The.

Ruth, Angie. My Adventure in Australia. 2007. 44p. (J). 8.99 (978-1-59092-423-5(1) , Orchard Academy Pr.) Windstorm Creative.

Sayre, April Pulley. Australia. 1998. (Seven Continents Ser.: 8). (Illus.). 64p. (gr. 5-8). lib. bdg. 25.90 (978-0-7613-3007-3(0) , Millbrook Pr.) Lerner Publishing Group.

—G'Day Australia! 2003. 32p. (J). (gr. 2-5). pap. 7.95 (978-0-7613-1987-0(5)); (Illus.). lib. bdg. 21.90 (978-0-7613-2122-4(5)) Lerner Publishing Group. (Millbrook Pr.).

Smith, Kate Darian. Australia. 2000. (Exploration Into... Ser.). (Illus.). 48p. (J). (gr. 4-7). 25.00 (978-0-7910-6020-9(9) , Chelsea Hse.) Facts On File, Inc.

Soffer, Ruth. Great Barrier Reef Coloring Book. 2007. 32p. pap. 3.95 ***(978-0-486-45689-8(7))*** Dover Pubns., Inc.

Somervill, Barbara A. Australia. 2003. (Continents Ser.). (Illus.). 32p. (J). (gr. 2-6). 27.07 (978-1-59296-063-7(4)) Child's World, Inc.

Steele, Philip. Sydney. 2004. (Great Cities of the World Ser.). (Illus.). 48p. (J). (gr. 5 up). pap. 11.95 (978-0-8368-5192-2(7)); lib. bdg. 30.00 (978-0-8368-5032-1(7)) Stevens, Gareth Inc. (World Almanac Library).

Stein, R. Conrad. Sydney. Downing, Joan, ed. 1998. (Cities of the World Ser.). (Illus.). 64p. (J). (gr. 4-9). pap. 9.95 (978-0-516-26328-1(5) , Children's Pr.) Scholastic Library Publishing.

Striveildi, Cheryl. Australia. 2003. (Continents Ser.). (Illus.). 32p. (J). (gr. k-4). lib. bdg. 22.78 (978-1-57765-961-7(9)) ABDO Publishing Co.

Walker, Kathryn. Melbourne. 2005. (Great Cities of the World Ser.). (J). pap. (978-0-8368-5212-7(5)); (Illus.). 48p. 30.00 (978-0-8368-5052-9(1)) Stevens, Gareth Inc. (World Almanac Library).

Wilkinson, Carole. Black Snake: The Daring of Ned Kelly. 2002. (Illus.). 144p. (J). pap. (978-1-876372-15-6(X)) Black Dog Bks.

Williams, Brian & Williams, Brenda. Australia. World Book, Inc. Staff, ed. 1998. (World Book Looks at Ser.). (Illus.). 64p. (J). (gr. 3-8). (978-0-7166-1814-0(1)) World Bk., Inc.

World Book, Inc. Staff. Christmas in Australia. 1999. (Christmas Around the World Ser.). (Illus.). 80p. (YA). (gr. 2-12). 19.00 (978-0-7166-0850-9(2)) World Bk., Inc.

Wunungmurra, Johnny. Djet & Nak Nak. Wunungmurra, Helen, illus. 2003. 32p. (J). pap. 9.95 (978-0-85575-398-6(6)) Aboriginal Studies Pr. AUS. *Dist:* International Specialized Bk. Services.

Wymarra, Elizabeth & Wymarra, Wandihnu. Wandihnu & the Old Dugong. 2007. 28p. pap. 17.00 ***(978-1-921248-18-4(1))*** Magabala Bks. AUS. *Dist:* International Specialized Bk. Services.

Young, Abby. Australia: A Primary Source Cultural Guide. 2005. (Primary Sources of World Cultures Ser.). (J). lib. bdg. (978-1-4042-0476-8(8)) Rosen Publishing Group, Inc., The.

AUSTRALIA—FICTION

Abdel-Fattah, Randa. Does My Head Look Big in This? 2007. 368p. (J). (gr. 7 up). pap. 16.99 ***(978-0-439-91947-0(9)*** , Orchard Bks.) Scholastic, Inc.

Abela, Deborah. In Search of the Time & Space Machine. Murphy, Jobi, illus. 2005. (Spy Force Ser.). vi, 248p. (Orig.). (J). 14.95 (978-1-74051-765-2(2) , Simon & Schuster Children's Publishing) Simon & Schuster Children's Publishing.

—Mission: In Search of the Time & Space Machine. O'Connor, George, illus. 2005. (Mission Ser.). 224p. (J). (gr. 4-7). 9.95 (978-0-689-87357-7(3) , Simon & Schuster Children's Publishing) Simon & Schuster Children's Publishing.

Applegate, Cathy. Red Sand, Blue Sky. 2002. (Girls First! Ser.). 144p. (gr. 4-7). pap. 13.50 (978-1-55861-278-5(5)) Feminist Pr. at The City Univ. of New York.

Arnold, Marsha D. The Pumpkin Runner. 1998. (Illus.). 32p. (J). (ps-3). 16.99 (978-0-8037-2124-1(2) , Dial) Penguin Group (USA) Inc.

Barwood, Lee. Klassic Koalas: Ancient Aboriginal Tales in New Retellings. 2007. (Illus.). 64p. (J). pap. 28.99 ***(978-0-9764698-1-0(2))*** Koala Jo Publishing.

Bastian, Greg. Great Secondhand Supper. 144p. pap. 11.95 (978-0-7022-2245-0(3)) Univ. of Queensland Pr. AUS. *Dist:* International Specialized Bk. Services.

Bateson, Catherine. Being Bee. 2007. 136p. (J). (gr. 3-7). 16.95 ***(978-0-8234-2104-6(X))*** Holiday Hse., Inc.

—The Boyfriend Rules of Good Behavior. 2006. 192p. (YA). 16.95 (978-0-8234-2026-1(4)) Holiday Hse., Inc.

—Rain May & Captain Daniel. 2002. 144p. (YA). pap. 15.50 (978-0-7022-3337-1(4)) Univ. of Queensland Pr. AUS. *Dist:* International Specialized Bk. Services.

Bateson, Catherine. Stranded in Boringsville. 144p. (gr. 5-9). (J). 16.95 (978-0-8234-1969-2(X)); 2007. (YA). pap. 6.95 ***(978-0-8234-2113-8(9))*** Holiday Hse., Inc.

Bernard, Virginia. Eliza down Under. 2000. (Going to Ser.). (Illus.). 121p. (J). (gr. 4-8). pap. 6.95 (978-1-893577-02-2(3)) Four Corners Publishing Co., Inc.

Boonstra, Jean Elizabeth. Going Home. 2004. 95p. (J). (978-0-8163-2019-6(5)) Pacific Pr. Publishing Assn.

—A New Life down Under. 2004. 95p. (J). (978-0-8163-2017-2(9)) Pacific Pr. Publishing Assn.
—Secrets & Friends. 2004. 95p. (J). (978-0-8163-2021-9(7)) Pacific Pr. Publishing Assn.
—A Wedding in Avondale. 2004. 95p. (J). (978-0-8163-2018-9(7)) Pacific Pr. Publishing Assn.
Bruce, Mary Grant. Back to Billabong. l.t. ed. 2006. 200p. pap. 15.99 (978-1-4264-2197-6(4)) BiblioBazaar.
—Mates at Billabong. l.t. ed. 2006. 186p. pap. 14.99 (978-1-4264-1061-1(1)) BiblioBazaar.
Brugman, Alyssa. Being Bindy. 2006. 208p. (YA). (gr. 7). 15.95 (978-0-385-73294-9(5)); lib. bdg. 17.99 (978-0-385-90315-8(4)) Random Hse. Children's Bks. (Delacorte Bks. for Young Readers).
—Finding Grace. 2004. 240p. (YA). (gr. 7). lib. bdg. 17.99 (978-0-385-90142-0(9) , Delacorte Bks. for Young Readers) Random Hse. Children's Bks.
Burton, Rebecca. Leaving Jetty Road. (YA). (gr. 7). 2008. 272p. mass mkt. 6.50 (***978-0-553-49505-8(4)*** , Laurel Leaf); 2006. 256p. 15.95 (978-0-375-83488-2(5) , Knopf Bks. for Young Readers); 2006. 256p. lib. bdg. 17.99 (978-0-375-93488-9(X) , Knopf Bks. for Young Readers) Random Hse. Children's Bks.
Carey, Peter. True History of the Kelly Gang. 2002. (gr. 7-12). lib. bdg. 23.45 (978-0-613-45844-3(3)) Tandem Library Bks.
Caswell, Brian & Chiem, David Phu An. The Full Story. 2002. 184p. pap. 17.50 (978-0-7022-3299-2(8)) Univ. of Queensland Pr. AUS. *Dist:* International Specialized Bk. Services.
Catran, Ken. Artists Are Crazy & Other Stories. (Takeaways Ser.). 160p. pap. (978-0-7344-0475-6(1) , Lothian Bks.) Hachette Livre Australia.
Chapman, Jean. Favourite Live Thing. (Illus.). 62p. pap. 10.95 (978-0-7022-2888-9(5)) Univ. of Queensland Pr. AUS. *Dist:* International Specialized Bk. Services.
Chase, Diana. Angel in a Gum Tree. 2006. 32p. pap. 13.50 (978-1-921064-77-7(3)) Fremantle Pr. AUS. *Dist:* International Specialized Bk. Services.
—Surf's Up. 1999. 200p. (J). pap. 12.95 (978-1-86368-250-3(3)) Fremantle Pr. AUS. *Dist:* International Specialized Bk. Services.
Clarke, Judith. Al Capsella & Watchdogs. 164p. pap. 9.95 (978-0-7022-2294-8(1)) Univ. of Queensland Pr. AUS. *Dist:* International Specialized Bk. Services.
—Kalpana's Dream. 2005. 168p. (J). 16.95 (978-1-932425-22-2(5) , Lemniscaat) Boyds Mills Pr.
—The Lost Day. rev. ed. 1999. 160p. (gr. 7-12). 16.95 (978-0-8050-6152-9(5) , Holt, Henry & Co. Bks. For Young Readers) Holt, Henry & Co.
—Night Train. 2007. (J). pap. 9.95 (***978-1-932425-92-5(6)*** , Front Street) Boyds Mills Pr.
—Night Train. 2000. 200p. (gr. 7-12). 16.95 (978-0-8050-6151-2(7) , Holt, Henry & Co. Bks. For Young Readers) Holt, Henry & Co.
Clarke, Judith. One Whole & Perfect Day. 2007. 250p. (YA). (gr. 7 up). 16.95 (***978-1-932425-95-6(0)*** , Front Street) Boyds Mills Pr.
Cleary, Jon. The Sundowners. (J). 25.95 (978-0-88411-467-3(8)) Amereon LTD.
Cohn, Rachel. The Steps. 144p. (J). 2003. (Illus.). (gr. 3-7). 15.95 (978-0-689-84549-9(9)); 2004. reprint ed. pap. 4.99 (978-0-689-87414-7(6) , Aladdin) Simon & Schuster Children's Publishing.
Cole, Linda J. Frank & Beans. 2003. pap. 7.95 (978-0-533-14328-3(4)) Vantage Pr., Inc.
Cole, Stephen. The Adventures of Mr. Bean. 2002. (Illus.). 64p. (J). pap. 6.99 (978-1-84222-657-5(6)) Carlton Bks., Ltd. GBR. *Dist:* Independent Pubs. Group.
Collins, Alan. Boys from Bondi. 160p. pap. 11.95 (978-0-7022-2084-5(1)) Univ. of Queensland Pr. AUS. *Dist:* International Specialized Bk. Services.
Conn, Bruce. The Curse of Durgan's Reef. 2004. 142p. (YA). 21.95 (978-0-595-66223-4(4)); pap. 11.95 (978-0-595-30935-1(6)) iUniverse, Inc.
Corbet, Robert. Fifteen Love. 2005. 192p. (YA). pap. 6.95 (978-0-8027-7714-0(7)) Walker & Co.
Crawford, Joanne. Bilby & the Bushfire. 2007. 28p. pap. 17.00 (***978-1-921248-30-6(0)***) Magabala Bks. AUS. *Dist:* International Specialized Bk. Services.
Crew, Gary. Mama's Babies: A Novel. 2002. 160p. (J). (gr. 5-9). pap. 6.95 (978-1-55037-724-8(8)); lib. bdg. 18.95 (978-1-55037-725-5(6)) Annick Pr., Ltd. CAN. *Dist:* Firefly Bks., Ltd.
—Mama's Babies: A Novel. 2002. (gr. 5-8). lib. bdg. 15.25 (978-0-613-58241-4(1)) Tandem Library Bks.
—The Watertower. 2000. 32p. (J). (gr. 2-9). pap. 7.95 (978-1-56656-331-4(3) , Crocodile Bks.) Interlink Publishing Group, Inc.
Curley, Marianne. El Circulo de Fuego. Puig, Fernando Gari, tr. 2001. (SPA.). 256p. (978-84-7888-710-1(5) , 1952) Emece Editores.
Dennard, Deborah. Koala Country: A Story of an Australian Eucalyptus Forest. 2005. (Soundprints' Wild Habitats Ser.). (Illus.). 32p. (J). (gr. 1-4). 8.95 incl. audio (978-1-59249-106-3(5) , SC7018) Soundprints.
Disher, Garry. The Divine Wind: A Love Story. 2004. 160p. (J). pap. 5.99 (978-0-439-36916-9(9)); 2002. 176p. (YA). (gr. 9 up). pap. 15.95 (978-0-439-36915-2(0)) Scholastic, Inc. (Levine, Arthur A. Bks.).
Dorling Kindersley Publishing Staff. Finding Nemo Sticker Book. 2003. (Ultimate Sticker Bks.). (Illus.). 16p. (J). pap. 6.99 (978-0-7894-9245-6(8)) Dorling Kindersley Publishing, Inc.
Dowswell, Paul. Prison Ship: Adventures of a Youn Sailor. 2006. 306p. 16.95 (***978-1-58237-674-5(3)***) Creative Thinkers, Inc.
—Prison Ship: Adventures of a Young Sailor. 2007. 320p. (YA). pap. 7.95 (***978-1-59990-156-5(0)*** , Bloomsbury Children) Bloomsbury Publishing.
Dubosarsky, Ursula. The Red Shoe. 2007. 192p. (J). (gr. 7 up). 16.95 (978-1-59643-265-9(9)) Roaring Brook Pr.
Earls, Nick. After Summer. 2005. 240p. (YA). (gr. 7). pap. 6.99 (978-0-618-45781-6(X) , Graphia) Houghton Mifflin Co. Trade & Reference Div.
—48 Shades of Brown. 2004. 288p. (YA). (gr. 7 up). pap. 6.99 (978-0-618-45295-8(8) , Graphia) Houghton Mifflin Co. Trade & Reference Div.
—48 Shades of Brown. 1999. 300p. (YA). pap. (978-0-14-028769-1(8)) Penguin Group (USA) Inc.
Eaton, Anthony. The Darkness. 2000. (Illus.). 192p. (J). pap. 15.95 (978-0-7022-3152-0(5)) Univ. of Queensland Pr. AUS. *Dist:* International Specialized Bk. Services.
—Nightpeople. 2005. (Darklands Trilogy Ser.: Bk. 1). 400p. (Orig.). (YA). pap. 18.95 (978-0-7022-3494-1(X)) Univ. of Queensland Pr. AUS. *Dist:* International Specialized Bk. Services.
Elliott, Louise. Mr. Hornbeams Treasure Hunt. (Illus.). 96p. pap. 10.95 (978-0-7022-2587-1(8)) Univ. of Queensland Pr. AUS. *Dist:* International Specialized Bk. Services.
Engineering is Elementary Team. A Reminder for Emily: An Electrical Engineering Story. 2006. (J). lib. bdg. 15.99 (***978-0-9774084-3-6(4)***) Museum of Science.
Evans, Alwyn. Walk in My Shoes. 2005. 360p. (J). pap. 14.00 (978-0-14-300231-4(7) , Penguin Global) Penguin Group (USA) Inc.
Fairbairn, John. Green Slime. Allen, Rosemary, illus. 96p. pap. 9.95 (978-0-7022-2488-1(X)) Univ. of Queensland Pr. AUS. *Dist:* International Specialized Bk. Services.
—Highgate Hill Mob. 96p. pap. 10.95 (978-0-7022-2590-1(8)) Univ. of Queensland Pr. AUS. *Dist:* International Specialized Bk. Services.
Fernandez, Nacho. La nueva era del sueno vol. 2: Los desiertos del Norte: The New Age of Dreams vol. 2: the Deserts of the North. 2007. (SPA.). 48p. 22.95 (***978-1-59497-398-7(9)***) Public Square Bks.
Fienberg, Anna. Big Big Big Book of Tashi. 2002. (gr. 3-6). lib. bdg. 21.05 (978-0-613-54979-0(1)) Tandem Library Bks.
Fienberg, Anna & Fienberg, Barbara. Tashi & the Big Stinker. Gamble, Kim, illus. 2001. (Tashi Ser.). 64p. (Orig.). (J). (gr. 2-4). pap. 5.95 (978-1-86508-350-6(X)) Allen & Unwin AUS. *Dist:* Independent Pubs. Group.
Fire! Individual Title Six-Packs. (Bookweb Ser.). 32p. (gr. 4 up). 34.00 (978-0-7635-3739-5(X)) Rigby Education.
French, Jackie. Josephine Wants to Dance. Whatley, Bruce, illus. 2007. 32p. (J). (ps-1). 15.95 (***978-0-8109-9431-7(3)*** , Abrams Bks. for Young Readers) Abrams, Harry N., Inc.
French, Simon. Where in the World. 2003. 208p. (J). (gr. 3-6). 14.95 (978-1-56145-292-7(0) , Q34443) Peachtree Pubs., Ltd.
Fry, Chris. Djomi Dream Child. Sarago-Kendrick, Delphine, illus. 2004. 28p. (J). pap. 17.00 (978-1-875641-82-6(3)) Magabala Bks. AUS. *Dist:* International Specialized Bk. Services.
Germein, Katrina. Big Rain Coming. Bancroft, Bronwyn, illus. 2000. 32p. (J). (gr. k-3). tchr. ed. 16.00 (978-0-618-08344-2(8) , Clarion Bks.) Houghton Mifflin Co. Trade & Reference Div.
Gilboues, Isabelle. Standing Up. Gillet, Anne-Marie, illus. 2005. 32p. (J). 14.95 (978-1-929132-71-3(9)) Kane/Miller Bk. Pubs., Inc.
Gleitzman, Morris. Misery Guts. l.t. ed. 2005. (Illus.). 184p. (J). pap. incl. audio (978-0-7540-7867-8(1) , CLP 456) BBC Audio.
—Toad Away. 208p. (J). (gr. 3-7). 2007. 4.99 (978-0-375-82767-9(6) , Yearling); 2006. 14.95 (978-0-375-82766-2(8) , Random Hse. Bks. for Young Readers); 2006. lib. bdg. 16.99 (978-0-375-92766-9(2) , Random Hse. Bks. for Young Readers) Random Hse. Children's Bks.
—Toad Heaven. 2006. 208p. (J). (gr. 3-7). reprint ed. 4.99 (978-0-375-82765-5(X) , Yearling) Random Hse. Children's Bks.
—Toad Rage. l.t. ed. 2005. (J). pap. (978-0-7540-7844-9(2) , CLP 434) BBC Audio.
Godwin, Jane. Falling from Grace. 2007. 204p. (YA). (gr. 6 up). 16.95 (***978-0-8234-2105-3(8)***) Holiday Hse., Inc.
Goode, Katherine. Jumping to Heaven: Stories about Refugee Children. 2004. 176p. (J). pap. 16.95 (978-1-86254-427-7(1)) Wakefield Pr. Pty, Ltd. AUS. *Dist:* Independent Pubs. Group.
Graham, Bob. Tales from the Waterhole. 2004. (Illus.). 64p. (J). (978-0-7445-6593-5(6)) Walker Bks., Ltd.
Gray, Luli. Falcon & the Charles Street Witch. 2002. 144p. (J). (gr. 5-9). 16.00 (978-0-618-16410-3(3)) Houghton Mifflin Co. Trade & Reference Div.
Greenburg, J. C. In the Desert. Gerardi, Jan, illus. 2008. (Andrew Lost: 17). 96p. (J). (***978-0-375-84667-0(0)***) Random Hse., Inc.
Greenburg, J. C. In the Jungle. Gerardi, Jan, illus. 2007. (Andrew Lost Ser.: Bk. 15). 96p. (J). (gr. 2-4). 3.99 (978-0-375-83564-3(4)); lib. bdg. 11.99 (978-0-375-93564-0(9)) Random Hse. Children's Bks. (Random Hse. Bks. for Young Readers).
Greenwood, Mark. The Legend of Lasseter's Reef. 2003. (Illus.). 32p. 22.50 (978-1-876268-99-2(9)) Univ. of Western Australia Pr. AUS. *Dist:* International Specialized Bk. Services.
—The Legend of Moondyne Joe. Lessac, Frane, illus. 2004. 32p. pap. 15.25 (978-1-920694-32-6(3)) Univ. of Western Australia Pr. AUS. *Dist:* International Specialized Bk. Services.
Greenwood, Mark & Lessac, Frane. The Legend of Moondyne Joe. 2002. (Illus.). 32p. (J). 22.45 (978-1-876268-70-1(0)) Univ. of Western Australia Pr. AUS. *Dist:* International Specialized Bk. Services.
Guo, Jing Jing. Grandpa's Mask. Wu, Di, illus. 2001. 32p. (J). (978-1-876615-05-5(2)) Benchmark Pubns. Pty, Ltd.
Hampshire, David. Living & Working in Australia: A Survival Handbook. 3rd ed. 2005. (Illus.). 560p. pap. 24.95 (978-1-901130-80-5(0)) Survival Bks. GBR. *Dist:* National Bk. Network.
Harrison, John. Fergal Onions. Harrison, John, illus. 2004. (Illus.). 36p. 17.50 (978-0-7022-3448-4(6)) Univ. of Queensland Pr. AUS. *Dist:* International Specialized Bk. Services.
Hartnett, Sonya. Stripes of Sidestep Wolf. 2007. (Illus.). 208p. (YA). (gr. 7). pap. 7.99 (***978-0-7636-3416-2(6)***) Candlewick Pr.
Hartnett, Sonya. Stripes of the Sidestep Wolf. 2005. 208p. (J). (gr. 7 up). 16.99 (978-0-7636-2644-0(9)) Candlewick Pr.
Henry, Patrick. The Spectacular Adventures of John Cross. 2005. (J). per. 8.99 (978-0-9773990-1-7(X)) Mother's Hse. Publishing.
Herrick, Steven. By the River. 2006. 240p. (YA). 16.95 (978-1-932425-72-7(1) , Lemniscaat) Boyds Mills Pr.
—Naked Bunyip Dancing. Norling, Beth, illus. 2008. (J). (***978-1-59078-499-0(5)*** , Front Street) Boyds Mills Pr.
Herrick, Steven. The Wolf. 2007. 214p. (YA). (gr. 7 up). 17.95 (978-1-932425-75-8(6) , Front Street) Boyds Mills Pr.
Hirsch, Odo. Have Courage, Hazel Green! (J). 2007. (Illus.). 256p. pap. 6.95 (978-1-59990-003-2(3)); 2006. 262p. 15.95 (978-1-58234-659-5(3)) Bloomsbury Publishing. (Bloomsbury Children).
—Hazel Green. (J). 2005. 190p. (gr. 3-6). pap. 5.95 (978-1-58234-940-4(1)); 2003. (Illus.). 188p. (gr. 2-6). 15.95 (978-1-58234-820-9(0)) Bloomsbury Publishing. (Bloomsbury Children).
—Hazel Green. 2004. 190p. (J). (gr. 3-7). lib. bdg. 13.60 (978-0-606-30296-8(4)) Tandem Library Bks.
Honey, Elizabeth. Don't Pat the Wombat! 2001. (Illus.). (J). 11.15 (978-0-606-21157-4(8)) Tandem Library Bks.
—Don't Pat the Wombat. 2001. (gr. 3-6). lib. bdg. 12.40 (978-0-613-36095-1(8)) Tandem Library Bks.
Hord, Donald. Shortcut & Friends Australian Outback. 2006. pap. 12.99 (***978-1-4259-6355-2(2)***) AuthorHouse.
Hunt, Elizabeth Singer. The Search for the Sunken Treasure. 2007. (Secret Agent Jack Stalwart Ser.). 128p. (J). (gr. 1-4). pap. 4.99 (***978-1-60286-002-5(5)***) Weinstein Bks.
Jeans, Peter. Stoker's Bay. 2003. (Illus.). 240p. (YA). pap. 13.50 (978-1-876268-97-8(2)) Univ. of Western Australia Pr. AUS. *Dist:* International Specialized Bk. Services.
Jenkins, Wendy. Big Game. 1999. 184p. (J). pap. 12.95 (978-1-86368-183-4(3)) Fremantle Pr. AUS. *Dist:* International Specialized Bk. Services.
Jinks, Catherine. Evil Genius. 2008. (Illus.). 512p. (YA). pap. 7.95 (***978-0-15-206185-2(1)*** , Harcourt Paperbacks) Harcourt Children's Bks.
—Evil Genius. 2007. (Illus.). 496p. (YA). (gr. 7 up). 17.00 (978-0-15-205988-0(1)); 486p. (J). (***978-1-4287-3510-1(0)***) Harcourt Trade Pubs.
Jonsberg, Barry. The Crimes & Punishments of Miss Payne. (gr. 7). 2006. 288p. (YA). pap. 8.95 (978-0-375-84022-7(2)); 2005. 272p. (J). 15.95 (978-0-375-83240-6(8)) Random Hse. Children's Bks. (Knopf Bks. for Young Readers).
Kroll, Virginia L. & Jones, Dawn L. Kingston's Flowering Forest. Maydak, Michael S., illus. 2001. (J). (978-0-9712840-5-0(9)) Boyds Collection Ltd., The.
Laguna, Sofie. Surviving Aunt Marsha. 2005. 208p. (J). pap. 15.95 (978-0-439-64485-3(2)) Scholastic, Inc.
Langeland, Deirdre. Kangaroo Island: A Story of an Australian Mallee Forest. 2005. (Soundprints' Wild Habitats Ser.). (Illus.). 32p. (J). (gr. 1-4). pap. 8.95 incl. reel tape (978-1-59249-095-0(6)) Soundprints.
Larbalestier, Justine. Magic Lessons. 2007. 304p. (YA). pap. 7.99 (978-1-59514-124-8(3) , Razorbill) Penguin Group (USA) Inc.
—Magic or Madness. (gr. 7-12). 2006. 304p. (YA). pap. 7.99 (978-1-59514-070-8(0)); 2005. 288p. (J). 16.99 (978-1-59514-022-7(0)) Penguin Group (USA) Inc. (Razorbill).
Lawrinson, Julia. Skating the Edge. 2002. 360p. pap. 14.95 (978-1-86368-379-1(8)) Fremantle Pr. AUS. *Dist:* International Specialized Bk. Services.
Lee, Julia Elizabeth. Seahorses Down Under. Weiser, Robert, ed. (Defenders of Wildlife Ser.). (Illus.). 50+p. (J). (gr. k-3). lib. bdg. 9.95 (978-0-9666857-0-1(9)) Dawn of Day Childrens Publishing Co., Inc.
Lester, Alison. Are We There Yet? A Journey Around Australia. Lester, Alison, illus. 2005. (Illus.). 32p. (J). 15.95 (978-1-929132-73-7(5)) Kane/Miller Bk. Pubs., Inc.
—The Quicksand Pony. 1998. (Illus.). 144p. (J). (gr. 5-9). tchr. ed. 15.00 (978-0-395-93749-5(3) , Walter Lorraine) Houghton Mifflin Co. Trade & Reference Div.
—The Snow Pony. 2003. (Illus.). 208p. (J). (gr. 5-9). tchr. ed. 15.00 (978-0-618-25404-0(8) , Walter Lorraine) Houghton Mifflin Co. Trade & Reference Div.
Lindsay, Norman. The Magic Pudding. 2006. (Illus.). 144p. (J). pap. 7.95 (978-0-486-45281-4(6)) Dover Pubns., Inc.
—The Magic Pudding. 2006. 77.99 (***978-1-4280-3115-9(4)***); 2005. (ENG.). pap. 70.99 (***978-1-4219-2134-1(0)***) IndyPublish.com.
—The Magic Pudding. 2004. reprint ed. pap. 15.95 (978-1-4191-7119-2(4)); pap. 1.99 (978-1-4192-7119-9(9)) Kessinger Publishing, LLC.
—The Magic Pudding. Lindsay, Norman, illus. 2004. (New York Review Children's Collection). (Illus.). 184p. (J). (gr. 3-6). pap. 16.95 (978-1-59017-101-1(2) , NYR Children's Collection) New York Review of Bks., Inc., The.
Litttle, Lorna. The Mark of the Wagarl. Lyndon, Janice, illus. 2004. 28p. (J). 20.75 (978-1-875641-97-0(1)) Magabala Bks. AUS. *Dist:* International Specialized Bk. Services.
Lowry, Brigid. Follow the Blue. 2004. 205p. (J). (gr. 7 up). tchr. ed. 16.95 (978-0-8234-1827-5(8)) Holiday Hse., Inc.
—Follow the Blue. 2006. 208p. (YA). pap. 8.95 (978-0-312-34297-5(7) , St. Martin's Griffin) St. Martin's Pr.
—Guitar Highway Rose. 2003. 208p. (J). (gr. 7 up). tchr. ed. 16.95 (978-0-8234-1790-2(5)) Holiday Hse., Inc.
—Guitar Highway Rose. 2006. 208p. (YA). reprint ed. pap. 8.95 (978-0-312-34296-8(9) , St. Martin's Griffin) St. Martin's Pr.
Lucashenko, Melissa. Killing D'arcy. 1998. 240p. (YA). (gr. 8-12). pap. 16.95 (978-0-7022-3041-7(3)) Univ. of Queensland Pr. AUS. *Dist:* International Specialized Bk. Services.
MacLeod, Doug. I'm Being Stalked by a Moonshadow. 2007. 212p. (YA). (gr. 8 up). 16.95 (***978-1-59078-501-0(0)*** , Front Street) Boyds Mills Pr.
Marchetta, Melina. Looking for Alibrandi. 2006. 320p. (YA). (gr. 7). lib. bdg. 17.99 (978-0-375-93694-4(7)); reprint ed. pap. 8.95 (978-0-375-83694-7(2)) Random Hse. Children's Bks. (Knopf Bks. for Young Readers).
—Looking for Alibrandi. 1999. 256p. (YA). (gr. 7-12). pap. 16.95 (978-0-531-30142-5(7)); lib. bdg. 17.99 (978-0-531-33142-2(3)) Scholastic, Inc. (Orchard Bks.).
—Saving Francesca. 2006. 256p. (YA). (gr. 7). reprint ed. pap. 8.95 (978-0-375-82983-3(0) , Knopf Bks. for Young Readers) Random Hse. Children's Bks.
Marsden, John. Burning for Revenge. 2000. 272p. (YA). (gr. 7-12). 16.00 (978-0-395-96054-7(1)) Houghton Mifflin Co. Trade & Reference Div.
—Darkness Be My Friend. 1999. 288p. (YA). (gr. 7-12). 16.00 (978-0-395-92274-3(7)) Houghton Mifflin Co. Trade & Reference Div.
—The Dead of Night. 2006. (Tomorrow Ser.: No. 2). 272p. (J). pap. 8.99 (978-0-439-82911-3(9) , Scholastic Paperbacks) Scholastic, Inc.
—The Dead of Night. 1999. (J). (978-0-606-16450-4(2)) Tandem Library Bks.
—A Killing Frost. 1998. 288p. (YA). (gr. 7-12). 16.00 (978-0-395-83735-1(9)) Houghton Mifflin Co. Trade & Reference Div.
—A Killing Frost. 2006. (Tomorrow Ser.: No. 3). 288p. (J). pap. 8.99 (978-0-439-82912-0(7) , Scholastic Paperbacks) Scholastic, Inc.
—The Night Is for Hunting. 2001. (Tomorrow Ser.). (Illus.). 256p. (YA). (gr. 7 up). 16.00 (978-0-618-07026-8(5)) Houghton Mifflin Co. Trade & Reference Div.
—The Night Is for Hunting. 2007. (Tomorrow Ser.: Vol. 6). 256p. (J). pap. 8.99 (978-0-439-85804-5(6) , Scholastic Paperbacks) Scholastic, Inc.
—The Other Side of Dawn. 2002. (Tomorrow Ser.). (Illus.). 352p. (YA). (gr. 7 up). 16.00 (978-0-618-07028-2(1)) Houghton Mifflin Co. Trade & Reference Div.
—Other Side of Dawn. 2007. (Tomorrow Ser.). 336p. (J). pap. 8.99 (978-0-439-85805-2(4) , Scholastic Paperbacks) Scholastic, Inc.
—Tomorrow, When the War Began. ed. 2006. (Tomorrow Ser.: No. 1). 304p. (J). pap. 8.99 (978-0-439-82910-6(0) , Scholastic Paperbacks) Scholastic, Inc.
Marsh, Carole. The Mystery on the Great Barrier Reef. 2006. 144p. (gr. 3-5). 14.95 (***978-0-635-06210-9(0)***); pap. 5.95 (***978-0-635-06206-2(2)***) Gallopade International.
Massey, Barbara & DeLoach, Sylvia. Darby down Under. Robinson, Amy Giles, illus. 2000. (Child Like Me Ser.: Vol. 4). (J). (gr. 2-5). 6.99 (978-1-56309-766-9(4)) New Hope Pubs.
Mathur-Kamat, Ambika. Miss Panda in Australia. 1998. (Illus.). 16p. (J). (gr. k-2). pap. 8.00 (978-0-8059-4316-0(1)) Dorrance Publishing Co., Inc.
May, Kyla. Introducing Kyla May Miss. Behaves. 2005. (Illus.). 64p. (J). (gr. 4-7). pap. 4.99 (978-0-8431-1370-9(7) , Price Stern Sloan) Penguin Group (USA) Inc.
McCann, Daryl & Forbes, Debbie. Wish You Weren't Here. 2000. 144p. (YA). pap. 14.95 (978-0-7022-3103-2(7)) Univ. of Queensland Pr. AUS. *Dist:* International Specialized Bk. Services.
McLeod, Kate & Dorling Kindersley Publishing Staff. Outback Adventure. 2004. (Dk Readers Ser.). (Illus.). 32p. (J). 12.99 (978-0-7566-0544-5(X)); pap. 3.99 (978-0-7566-0545-2(8)) Dorling Kindersley Publishing, Inc.
McVeity, Jen. On Different Shores. 1998. (Illus.). 167p. (YA). (gr. 5-9). 17.99 (978-0-531-33115-6(6)); pap. 16.95 (978-0-531-30115-9(X)) Scholastic, Inc. (Orchard Bks.).
Moloney, James. Touch Me. 2000. 256p. (YA). pap. 16.95 (978-0-7022-3151-3(7)) Univ. of Queensland Pr. AUS. *Dist:* International Specialized Bk. Services.
Moriarty, Jaclyn. The Murder of Bindy MacKenzie. (J). 2008. 496p. 8.99 (978-0-439-74052-4(5)); 2006. 352p. pap. 16.99 (978-0-439-74051-7(7)) Scholastic, Inc. (Levine, Arthur A. Bks.).
—The Spell Book of Listen Taylor. 2007. (YA). (***978-0-439-84679-0(X)*** , Levine, Arthur A. Bks.) Scholastic, Inc.
Moriarty, Jaclyn. The Year of Secret Assignments. (Illus.). 352p. 2004. (J). pap. 16.95 (978-0-439-49881-4(3) , Levine, Arthur A. Bks.); 2005. reprint ed. pap. 7.99 (978-0-439-49882-1(1) , Scholastic Paperbacks) Scholastic, Inc.
Murray, Kirsty. Bridie's Fire. 2005. 264p. (J). pap. 8.95 (978-1-86508-727-6(0)) Allen & Unwin AUS. *Dist:* Independent Pubs. Group.
Murray, Martine. The Slightly True Story of Cedar B. Hartley: (Who Planned to Live an Unusual Life) 2002. (Illus.). 204p. (J). (978-1-86508-623-1(1)) Allen & Unwin.
—Slightly True Story of Cedar B. Hartley: (Who Planned to Live an Unusual Life) 2004. (Illus.). 240p. (J). reprint ed. pap. 4.99 (978-0-439-48623-1(8) , Levine, Arthur A. Bks.) Scholastic, Inc.

A
B

Newton, Robert. Runner. 2007. 224p. (J). (gr. 5). lib. bdg. 18.99 (978-0-375-93744-6(7) , Knopf Bks. for Young Readers) Random Hse. Children's Bks.

Odgers, Sally. Boy down Under. 2004. (YA). mass mkt. 5.99 (978-0-8439-5453-1(1)) Dorchester Publishing Co., Inc.

Oliver, Narelle. The Best Beak in Boonaroo Bay. Oliver, Narelle, illus. (Illus.). 48p. (YA). pap. (978-0-85091-671-3(2) , Lothian Bks.) Hachette Livre Australia.

Ormerod, Jan. Lizzie Nonsense. Ormerod, Jan, illus. 2004. (Illus.). 40p. (J). (*978-1-877003-59-2(X)*) Little Hare Bks.

Ormerod, Jan. Lizzie Nonsense: A Story of Pioneer Days. 2005. (Illus.). 40p. (J). (gr. k-3). 15.00 (978-0-618-57493-3(X) , Clarion Bks.) Houghton Mifflin Co. Trade & Reference Div.

Orr, Wendy. Peeling the Onion. 1999. (Laurel-Leaf Bks.). 176p. (YA). (gr. 7-12). mass mkt. 5.50 (978-0-440-22773-1(9) , Laurel Leaf) Random Hse. Children's Bks.

—Peeling the Onion: A Gripping Story, Told with Honesty & Biting Humour. 1999. (978-0-606-15918-0(5)); (gr. 7-12). lib. bdg. 13.00 (978-0-613-15339-3(1)) Tandem Library Bks.

Osborne, Mary Pope. Dingoes at Dinnertime, Vol. 20. unabr. ed. 2004. (Magic Tree House Ser. : No. 20). 71p. (J). (gr. k-3). pap. 17.00 incl. audio (978-0-8072-0929-5(5) , S FTR 252 SP, Listening Library) Random Hse. Audio Publishing Group.

—Dingoes at Dinnertime. Murdocca, Sal, illus. 2000. (Magic Tree House Ser.: No. 20). 96p. (J). (gr. k-3). lib. bdg. 11.99 (978-0-679-99066-6(6)); pap. 3.99 (978-0-679-89066-9(1)) Random Hse. Children's Bks. (Random Hse. Bks. for Young Readers).

—Dingoes at Dinnertime. 2000. (Magic Tree House Ser. : No. 20). (J). (gr. k-3). lib. bdg. 11.80 (978-0-613-24836-5(8)); (Illus.). 10.79 (978-0-606-18491-5(0)) Tandem Library Bks.

Ottley, Reginald. By the Sandhills of Yamboorah. 2003. 224p. pap. 17.50 (978-0-7022-3350-0(1)) Univ. of Queensland Pr. AUS. *Dist:* International Specialized Bk. Services.

Overton, Max & Overton, Ariana. Glass House. 2003. 208p. 22.00 (978-1-59426-010-0(9) , gh-hc) Mundania Pr.

Perry, Glyn & Parry, Glyn. Invisible Girl. 2003. 160p. (YA). pap. 15.25 (978-1-920731-48-9(2)) Fremantle Pr. AUS. *Dist:* International Specialized Bk. Services.

Plourde, Josee. Un Colis pour l'Australie. 1999. (Premier Roman Ser.). (FRE., Illus.). 64p. (J). (gr. 2-5). pap. (978-2-89021-345-6(5)) Diffusion du livre Mirabel.

Ponko, Cindy A. Olive Fingers. 2006. (J). (978-0-9768230-0-1(4)) Some Kids I Know.

Porter, Annaliese & Bancroft, Bronwyn. The Outback. 2005. (Illus.). 28p. (J). 20.95 (978-1-875641-86-4(6)) Magabala Bks. AUS. *Dist:* International Specialized Bk. Services.

Porter, James G. Edge of the Rainforest. (Illus.). 180p. pap. 11.95 (978-0-7022-2350-1(6)) Univ. of Queensland Pr. AUS. *Dist:* International Specialized Bk. Services.

Rayner, Robert. Falling Star. 2007. (Sports Stories Ser.). 136p. (J). (gr. 3-8). 7.95 (*978-1-55028-970-1(5)*) Lorimer, James & Co., Ltd., Pubs. CAN. *Dist:* Casemate Pubs. & Bk. Distributors, LLC.

Robinson, David. The Australian Cowboy & the Big Storm. Plante, Alyson, illus. 2002. 20p. (J). pap. 7.95 (978-0-9718091-0-9(0)) Robinson Pubs.

Ross, Leanna. Julie Simone. 2004. 194p. (YA). pap. 14.95 (978-0-595-30376-2(5)) iUniverse, Inc.

Roth, Susan L. The Biggest Frog in Australia. 2000. (Illus.). (J). (978-0-606-21611-1(1)) Tandem Library Bks.

Russon, Penni. Breathe. 2007. (Illus.). 368p. (J). (gr. 9 up). 16.99 (978-0-06-079393-7(7)); lib. bdg. 17.89 (978-0-06-079394-4(5)) HarperCollins Pubs.

—Undine. 2006. (Illus.). 336p. (J). 16.99 (978-0-06-079389-0(9)); lib. bdg. 17.89 (978-0-06-079390-6(2)) HarperCollins Pubs.

Ryan, Emer & Newman, Clive, eds. From Two Islands: The Best of Irish-Australian Writers with New Fiction for Younger Readers. 2000. 180p. (J). pap. 12.95 (978-1-86368-282-4(1)) Fremantle Pr. AUS. *Dist:* International Specialized Bk. Services.

Scott, Mark. Nell of the Seas. Bayley, Ruth, illus. 2002. 160p. (YA). 32.50 (978-1-85776-680-6(6)) Book Guild, Ltd. GBR. *Dist:* Trans-Atlantic Pubns., Inc.

Scraper, Katherine. Save the Fairy Penguins. 2005. 40.00 (*978-1-4108-4214-5(2)*) Benchmark Education Co.

Shanahan, Lisa. The Sweet, Terrible, Glorious Year I Truly, Completely Lost It. 2007. 304p. (YA). (gr. 7-10). 15.99 (*978-0-385-73516-2(2)*); lib. bdg. 18.99 (*978-0-385-90505-3(X)*) Random Hse. Children's Bks. (Delacorte Bks. for Young Readers).

Singer, Marilyn. The Company of Crows: A Book of Poems. Saport, Linda, illus. 2002. 48p. (J). (gr. k-3). tchr. ed. 16.00 (978-0-618-08340-4(5) , Clarion Bks.) Houghton Mifflin Co. Trade & Reference Div.

Southall, Ivan. Ash Road. 2004. (Illus.). 192p. (J). pap. 7.95 (978-1-932425-11-6(X) , Lemniscaat) Boyds Mills Pr.

—Josh. 2005. 208p. (YA). pap. (978-1-932425-36-9(5) , Lemniscaat) Boyds Mills Pr.

Sparrow, Rebecca. The Year Nick McGowan Came to Stay. 2008. (YA). (*978-0-375-84570-3(4)*); lib. bdg. (*978-0-375-94570-0(9)*) Knopf, Alfred A. Inc.

Spence, Eleanor. Jamberoo Road. 2007. 198p. (YA). pap. 12.95 (*978-1-932350-17-3(9)*) Bethlehem Bks.

Spillman, David. Yellow-Eye. Wilson, Mark, illus. 2001. 32p. (J). (gr. 2-4). 15.95 (978-1-56656-410-6(7) , Crocodile Bks.) Interlink Publishing Group, Inc.

Stafford, Liliana. A Race Is Run. 2001. (Illus.). 128p. (YA). pap. 12.95 (978-1-876268-52-7(2)) Univ. of Western Australia Pr. AUS. *Dist:* International Specialized Bk. Services.

—Through the Starting Flags. 2001. (Chiko Ser. : Bk. 1). (Illus.). 171p. (YA). pap. 12.95 (978-1-876268-51-0(4)) Univ. of Western Australia Pr. AUS. *Dist:* International Specialized Bk. Services.

Stilton, Geronimo. Down & Out down under. 2007. (Geronimo Stilton Ser.: No. 29). (Illus.). 128p. (J). pap. 6.99 (978-0-439-84120-7(8) , Scholastic Paperbacks) Scholastic, Inc.

Svendsen, Mark. Poison under Their Lips. 2002. 160p. (YA). pap. (978-0-7344-0183-0(3) , Lothian Bks.) Hachette Livre Australia.

—Poison under Their Lips. 2001. (gr. 7-12). lib. bdg. 22.20 (978-0-613-90595-4(4)) Tandem Library Bks.

Thompson, Lisa. Sent to Sydney. Squire, Stan, illus. 2006. (Read-It! Chapter Books). 80p. (J). (gr. 2-4). 19.95 (978-1-4048-1671-8(2)) Picture Window Bks.

Turner, Ethel. Seven Little Australians. 2005. 27.95 (978-1-4218-0333-3(X)); 204p. pap. 12.95 (978-1-4218-0433-0(6)) 1st World Publishing, Inc. (1st World Library - Literary Society).

—Seven Little Australians. 2006. 142p. pap. 10.99 (978-1-4264-1638-5(5)) BiblioBazaar.

—Seven Little Australians. (ENG.). 2006. 25.99 (*978-1-4280-4145-5(1)*); 2004. pap. 35.99 (*978-1-4142-8241-1(9)*) IndyPublish.com.

—Seven Little Australians. 2004. reprint ed. pap. 20.95 (978-1-4191-4679-4(3)); pap. 1.99 (978-1-4192-4679-1(8)) Kessinger Publishing, LLC.

Wang, Gabrielle. El Jardin de la Emperatriz Casia. Holguin, Magdalena, tr. Cuellar, Olga, illus. 2004. (SPA.). 108p. (YA). 8.95 (978-958-04-7346-6(3)) Norma S.A. COL. *Dist:* Distribuidora Norma, Inc., Lectorum Pubns., Inc.

Ward, Helen. Old Shell, New Shell: A Coral. 2002. (Illus.). 40p. (gr. k-2). lib. bdg. 24.90 (978-0-7613-2708-0(8) , Millbrook Pr.) Lerner Publishing Group.

—Old Shell, New Shell: A Coral Reef Tale. 2002. (Illus.). 40p. (gr. k-2). (978-0-7613-1635-0(3) , Millbrook Pr.) Lerner Publishing Group.

Wels, Barbara. Finwood & Lisa. 144p. pap. 11.95 (978-0-7022-2502-4(9)) Univ. of Queensland Pr. AUS. *Dist:* International Specialized Bk. Services.

Wharton, Herb. Yumba Days. 1999. 144p. (J). pap. 13.95 (978-0-7022-3113-1(4)) Univ. of Queensland Pr. AUS. *Dist:* International Specialized Bk. Services.

Wignell, Edel. The Long Sticky Walk. Huxley, Dee, illus. 2003. 72p. (YA). pap. 11.95 (978-1-876268-81-7(6)) Univ. of Western Australia Pr. AUS. *Dist:* International Specialized Bk. Services.

Wignell, Edel & Argent, Leanne. I Wonder Who Lives Upstairs. (Illus.). 32p. 18.95 (978-1-875560-19-6(X)) Univ. of Western Australia Pr. AUS. *Dist:* International Specialized Bk. Services.

Wild, Margaret. Bobbie Dazzler. Dawson, Janine, illus. 2007. 32p. (J). (ps-1). 15.95 (*978-1-933605-46-3(4)*) Kane/Miller Bk. Pubs., Inc.

Yasas, Kathleen. Australian Fly. North Coleman Road Elementary School Staff, illus. 1998. 48p. (J). (gr. k-5). pap. 12.95 (978-0-9667146-0-9(1) , FLY001) Ivy Editorial Services, Inc.

Zann, Paul. The Aussie Six in Australia. 2004. (J). pap. (*978-0-88887-223-4(2)*) Borealis Pr.

Zindel, Paul. Reef of Death. 1998. (Illus.). 192p. (J). (gr. 3 up). 15.95 (978-0-06-024728-7(2)); (gr. 6-10). lib. bdg. 15.89 (978-0-06-024733-1(9)) HarperCollins Pubs.

—Reef of Death. 1999. (978-0-606-16669-0(6)) Tandem Library Bks.

AUSTRALIA—HISTORY

Arnold, Caroline. Uluru: Australia's Aboriginal Heart. Arnold, Arthur P., illus. 2003. 64p. (J). (gr. 5 up). tchr. ed. 16.00 (978-0-618-18181-0(4) , Clarion Bks.) Houghton Mifflin Co. Trade & Reference Div.

Costain, Meredith. You Wouldn't Want to Be an 18th-century British Convict! A Trip to Australia You'd Rather Not Take. 2006. (Illus.). 32p. (J). (gr. 2-5). 28.50 (*978-0-531-14973-7(0)*) Scholastic Library Publishing.

Cummins, Philip. Australia & Its People. 2001. (Cambridge Junior History Ser.). (Illus.). 48p. pap. 7.00 (978-0-521-77647-9(3)) Cambridge Univ. Pr.

Davis, Kevin A. Look What Came from Australia. 2000. (Look What Came from Ser.). (Illus.). 32p. (gr. 2-4). pap. 6.95 (978-0-531-16433-4(0) , Watts, Franklin) Scholastic Library Publishing.

Enderlein, Cheryl L. Celebrating Birthdays in Australia. 1998. (Birthdays Around the World Ser.). (Illus.). 24p. (J). (gr. k-3). lib. bdg. 14.00 (978-0-531-11544-2(5) , Watts, Franklin) Scholastic Library Publishing.

Goodrich, Samuel Griswol. Peter Parleys Tales about America & Au. 2006. pap. (*978-1-4068-3320-1(7)*) Echo Library.

Gritzner, Charles, ed. Australia. (Illus.). 144p. pap. 30.00 (978-0-7910-7771-9(3) , Chelsea Hse.) Facts On File, Inc.

Hampton, David. Australia. 2006. (Living In- Ser.). (Illus.). 32p. (J). (978-1-59771-041-1(5) , 1268834) Sea-To-Sea Pubns.

Harcourt School Publishers Staff. Saving Kakadu. 3rd ed. 2002. (Horizons Ser.). (Illus.). (J). pap. 7.30 (978-0-15-333642-3(0)) Harcourt Schl. Pubs.

Hudak, Heather C. Australia. 2005. (Illus.). 32p. (J). (ps-6). lib. bdg. 26.00 (978-1-59036-319-5(1)); pap. 7.95 (978-1-59036-326-3(4)) Weigl Pubs., Inc.

Kalman, Bobbie & Sjonger, Rebecca. Explora Australia y Oceanía. 2007. (SPA.). 32p. (gr. 6-10). pap. (*978-0-7787-8298-8(0)*) Crabtree Publishing Co.

Malbunka, Mary. When I Was Little, Like You. 2005. (Illus.). 32p. 19.95 (978-1-86508-903-4(6)) Allen & Unwin AUS. *Dist:* Independent Pubs. Group.

Nicholson, John. Building the Sydney Harbour Bridge. Nicholson, John, illus. 2000. (Illus.). 32p. (J). (978-1-86508-259-2(7)); mass mkt. (978-1-86508-258-5(9)) Allen & Unwin.

—The Mighty Murray. Nicholson, John, illus. 2002. (Illus.). 48p. (Orig.). (J). (978-1-86508-564-7(2)); mass mkt. (978-1-86508-565-4(0)) Allen & Unwin.

Papunya School Staff & Wheatley, Nadia. Papunya School Book of Country & History. Searle, Ken, illus. 2001. 48p. pap. 7.95 (978-1-86508-525-8(1)) Allen & Unwin AUS. *Dist:* Independent Pubs. Group.

Pickwell, Linda. Australia. 2004. (QEB Travel Through Ser.). (Illus.). 32p. (J). lib. bdg. 18.95 (978-1-59566-058-9(5)) QEB Publishing Inc.

Reynolds, Jan. Down Under: Vanishing Cultures. 2007. 32p. (J). (*978-1-60060-126-2(X)*); (*978-1-60060-141-5(3)*) Lee & Low Bks., Inc.

AUSTRALIA—NATIVE RACES

Ferry, Steven. Australian Aborigines. 1998. (Endangered Cultures Ser.). (Illus.). 32p. (YA). (gr. 4-7). lib. bdg. 16.95 (978-1-887068-73-4(2)) Smart Apple Media.

Finley, Carol. Aboriginal Art of Australia: Exploring Cultural Traditions. 1998. (Art Around the World Ser.). (Illus.). 56-64p. (gr. 4-8). 23.93 (978-0-8225-2076-4(1)) Lerner Publishing Group.

AUSTRALIAN FOOTBALL

Campbell, Melissa. Livewire Real Lives Ang Christou. 1998. (Livewires Ser.). (Illus.). 32p. pap. 5.95 (978-0-7336-0722-6(5)) Cambridge Univ. Pr.

AUSTRALIAN LITERATURE—COLLECTIONS

Kinsella, John, ed. Salt 11. 1998. (Illus.). 368p. pap. 16.95 (978-1-86368-229-9(5)) Fremantle Pr. AUS. *Dist:* International Specialized Bk. Services.

AUSTRIA

Ake, Anne. Austria. 2000. (Modern Nations of the World Ser.). (Illus.). 112p. (J). (gr. 7-10). 27.45 (978-1-56006-758-0(6) , Lucent Bks.) Thomson Gale.

Allport, Alan. Austria. 2002. (Modern World Nations Ser.). (Illus.). 150p. (gr. 6-12). 30.00 (978-0-7910-6775-8(0) , Chelsea Hse.) Facts On File, Inc.

Davis, Kevin A. Look What Came from Austria. 2003. (Look What Came from Ser.). (Illus.). 32p. (J). (gr. 2-4). pap. 6.95 (978-0-531-16627-7(9) , Watts, Franklin) Scholastic Library Publishing.

—Look What Came from Austria. 2002. (gr. 3-6). lib. bdg. 15.25 (978-0-613-59507-0(6)) Tandem Library Bks.

Grahame, Deborah A. Austria. 2006. (Discovering Cultures Ser.). (Illus.). 48p. (J). lib. bdg. 28.50 (978-0-7614-1984-6(5) , Benchmark Bks.) Cavendish, Marshall Corp.

Hughes, Helga. Cooking the Austrian Way. 2nd rev. ed. 2004. (Easy Menu Ethnic Cookbooks). (Illus.). 72p. (J). (gr. 5-12). 25.26 (978-0-8225-4102-8(5)) Lerner Publishing Group.

Mazdra, Marian. Austria. 2004. (J). lib. bdg. 30.00 (978-0-8368-3115-3(2)) Stevens, Gareth Inc.

Sanna, Jeanine. Austria. 2006. (European Union Ser.). (Illus.). 88p. (J). (gr. 5 up). lib. bdg. (978-1-4222-0039-1(6) , 1247981) Mason Crest Pubs.

Sheehan, Sean. Austria. 2nd ed. 2003. (Illus.). 144p. (gr. 5 up). lib. bdg. 37.07 (978-0-7614-1497-1(5) , Cavendish, Marshall Reference Bks.) Cavendish, Marshall Corp.

Stein, R. Conrad. Austria. 2000. (Enchantment of the World, Second Ser.). (Illus.). 144p. (YA). (gr. 5-9). 36.00 (978-0-516-21049-0(1) , Children's Pr.) Scholastic Library Publishing.

Tan, Ronald. Welcome to Austria. 2005. (Welcome to My Country Ser.). (Illus.). 48p. (J). lib. bdg. 26.00 (978-0-8368-3133-7(0)) Stevens, Gareth Inc.

Van Cleaf, Kristin. Austria. 2007. (Countries Set VI Ser.). (Illus.). 40p. (J). (gr. k-6). lib. bdg. 24.21 (*978-1-59928-779-9(X)* , Checkerboard Library) ABDO Publishing Co.

AUSTRIA—FICTION

Alllen, Katherine. Gloves down Under. Alllen, Katherine, illus. 2005. (Illus.). 32p. (J). 15.95 (978-0-9747278-9-9(X)) Diakonia Publishing.

Bell, Mary Reeves. Secret of Mezuzah. 1999. (J). (978-0-606-18974-3(2)) Tandem Library Bks.

Costanza, Stephen. Mozart Finds a Melody. rev. ed. 2004. (Illus.). 40p. (J). 17.95 (978-0-8050-6627-2(6) , Holt, Henry & Co. Bks. For Young Readers) Holt, Henry & Co.

Denenberg, Barry. One Eye Laughing, the Other Weeping: The Diary of Julie Weiss, Vienna, Austria to New York, 1938. 2000. (Dear America Ser.). (Illus.). 256p. (J). (gr. 4-9). pap. 12.95 (978-0-439-09518-1(2)) Scholastic, Inc.

Dunlop, Ed. Escape to Liechtenstein. 2003. 152p. (J). (gr. 4-7). 7.49 (978-1-59166-013-2(0)) Jones, Bob Univ. Pr.

Glatshteyn, Yankev. Emil & Karl. Shandler, Jeffrey, tr. from YID. 2006. 208p. (J). 17.95 (978-1-59643-119-5(9)) Roaring Brook Pr.

Ibbotson, Eva & Minneapolis Institute of Arts Staff, Minneapolis Institute of Arts. The Star of Kazan. Hawkes, Kevin, illus. 2004. 416p. (J). (gr. 5). 16.99 (978-0-525-47347-3(5) , Dutton Juvenile) Penguin Group (USA) Inc.

Koss, Amy Goldman. Stolen Words. 2001. (978-0-606-22775-9(X)) Tandem Library Bks.

Manners, Tyler. Continental Change of Heart. 2006. 65p. pap. 12.95 (978-1-4137-9483-0(1)) PublishAmerica, Inc.

Masson, Sophie. Sooner or Later. 115p. pap. 11.95 (978-0-7022-2336-5(0)) Univ. of Queensland Pr. AUS. *Dist:* International Specialized Bk. Services.

Orgel, Doris. Devil in Vienna. 2004. 256p. (YA). (gr. 3-6). pap. 6.99 (978-0-14-240236-8(2) , Puffin) Penguin Group (USA) Inc.

Walters, Celeste. The Last Race. 2000. (UQP Young Adult Fiction Ser.). 224p. (J). pap. 16.95 (978-0-7022-3172-8(X)) Univ. of Queensland Pr. AUS. *Dist:* International Specialized Bk. Services.

AUTHORS

see also African American Authors; Literature—Bio-Bibliography

also classes of writers (e.g. Novelists; Poets; etc.); and names of individual authors

Abbey, Cherie D., ed. Biography Today: Profiles of People of Interest to Young Readers. (Author Ser.: Vol. 15). 2004. (J). (gr. 3 up). lib. bdg. (978-0-7808-0707-5(3)); 2003. (YA). lib. bdg. 44.00 (978-0-7808-0652-8(2)); 2003. (YA). lib. bdg. 44.00 (978-0-7808-0651-1(4)); 2002. (YA). lib. bdg. 44.00 (978-0-7808-0610-8(7)); 2002. 200p. (YA). (gr. 8 up). lib. bdg. 44.00 (978-0-7808-0608-5(5)); 2002. 220p. (J). (gr. 4 up). lib. bdg. 44.00 (978-0-7808-0464-7(3)); 2001. 200p. (J). (gr. 4 up). lib. bdg. 44.00 (978-0-7808-0462-3(7)) Omnigraphics, Inc.

About the Author Set 3. (Illus.). (J). (gr. k-5). 112.50 (978-1-4042-3291-4(5)) Rosen Publishing Group, Inc., The.

Ada, Alma Flor. Under the Royal Palms: A Childhood in Cuba. 1998. (Illus.). 96p. (J). (gr. 3-7). 17.99 (978-0-689-80631-5(0) , Atheneum) Simon & Schuster Children's Publishing.

Aristizabal, Luis H. German Arciniegas -un joven de cien Años. 2005. 148p. pap. (978-958-30-1707-0(8)) Panamericana Editorial.

Authors & Artists for Young Adults. 1998. (Authors & Artists for Young Adults Ser.: Vol. 24). 250p. (gr. 8-12). 130.00 (978-0-7876-1971-8(X) , 00157487); 51. 2003. (Illus.). 250p. (YA). 130.00 (978-0-7876-5180-0(X) , UXL); Vol. 27. 1998. (Authors & Artists for Young Adults Ser.: Vol. 27). (Illus.). 250p. (gr. 8-12). 130.00 (978-0-7876-2070-7(X) , GML14099-111588); Vol. 28. 1999. (Authors & Artists for Young Adults Ser.: Vol. 28). (Illus.). 250p. (gr. 8-12). 130.00 (978-0-7876-2071-4(8) , GML14099-111589); Vol. 45. 2002. (Authors & Artists Ser.). 250p. 130.00 (978-0-7876-5174-9(5) , GML00502-173184); Vol. 49. 2003. (Illus.). 250p. (YA). 105.00 (978-0-7876-5178-7(8) , UXL); Vol. 50. 2003. (Illus.). 250p. (YA). 130.00 (978-0-7876-5179-4(6) , UXL); Vol. 52. 2003. (YA). 130.00 (978-0-7876-5181-7(8)); Vol. 55. 2004. (Authors & Artists for Young Adults Ser.). 130.00 (978-0-7876-6643-9(2)); Vol. 56. 2004. (Authors & Artists for Young Adults Ser.). 130.00 (978-0-7876-6644-6(0)); Vol. 57. 2004. (Authors & Artists for Young Adults Ser.). 130.00 (978-0-7876-6645-3(9)); Vol. 58. 2004. (Authors & Artists for Young Adults Ser.). 130.00 (978-0-7876-6646-0(7)) Thomson Gale.

Aykroyd, Clarissa. Savage Satire: The Story of Jonathan Swift. 2006. (World Writers Ser.). (Illus.). 160p. (J). (gr. 6-12). lib. bdg. 27.95 (978-1-59935-027-1(0)) Reynolds, Morgan Inc.

Ball, Heather. Remarkable Women Writers. 2006. (Illus.). 100p. (J). pap. 7.95 (978-1-897187-08-1(4)) Second Story Pr. CAN. *Dist:* Orca Bk. Pubs. USA.

Benatar, Raquel. Isabel Allende: Memories for a Story: Recuerdos para un Cuento / Isabel Allende. Petersen, Patricia, tr. Molinari, Fernando, illus. (SPA & ENG.). 32p. 15.95 (978-1-55885-379-9(0) , Piñata Books) Arte Publico Pr.

Benatar, Raquel & Torrecilla, Pablo. Isabel Allende: Recuerdos para un Cuento. Petersen, Patricia, tr. Benatar, Raquel & Torrecilla, Pablo, illus. 2004. (ENG & SPA.). (J). 14.95 (978-1-56492-341-7(X) , Piñata Books) Arte Publico Pr.

Bloom, Harold, et al. Bloom's Major Novelists. 2005. (Illus.). 80-144p. (J). pap. 894.60 (978-0-7910-7380-3(7)) Facts On File, Inc.

Bloom's Biocritiques. 2005. pap. 1645.00 (978-0-7910-9134-0(1) , Chelsea Hse.) Facts On File, Inc.

Bloom's BioCritiques Series, 28 vols., Set. Incl. Alice Walker. Bloom, Harold, ed. & intro. (Illus.). 2002. 35.00 (978-0-7910-6182-4(5) , 000863); Anton Chekhov. Bloom, Harold, ed. (Illus.). 2002. 35.00 (978-0-7910-6381-1(X) , 000886); Arthur Miller. Lommel, Cookie & Heims, Neil. Bloom, Harold, ed. (Illus.). 2002. 35.00 (978-0-7910-6188-6(4) , 000855); Bronte Sisters. Bloom, Harold, ed. & intro. (Illus.). 2002. 35.00 (978-0-7910-6187-9(6) , 000868); Charles Dickens. Bloom, Harold & Chin, Mei, eds. (Illus.). 2003. 35.00 (978-0-7910-6365-1(8) , 000870); Dante Allighieri. Bloom, Harold, ed. & intro. (Illus.). 2002. 35.00 (978-0-7910-6366-8(6) , 000871); Edgar Allan Poe. Bloom, Harold, ed. & intro. (Illus.). 2002. 35.00 (978-0-7910-6173-2(6) , 000853); Emily Dickinson. Bloom, Harold, ed. (Illus.). 2002. 35.00 (978-0-7910-6179-4(5) , 000860); Ernest Hemingway. Bloom, Harold, ed. & intro. (Illus.). 2001. 35.00 (978-0-7910-6174-9(4) , 000854); F. Scott Fitzgerald. Bloom, Harold, ed. & intro. (Illus.). 2001. 35.00 (978-0-7910-6176-3(0) , 000857); Geoffrey Chaucer. Bloom, Harold, ed. 2002. 35.00 (978-0-7910-6181-7(7) , 000862); J. D. Salinger. Bloom, Harold. (Illus.). 2002. 35.00 (978-0-7910-6175-6(2) , 000856); Jane Austen. Bloom, Harold. (Illus.). 2002. 35.00 (978-0-7910-6184-8(1) , 000865); John Milton. Bloom, Harold, ed. & intro. (Illus.). 2002. 35.00 (978-0-7910-6370-5(4) , 000875); John Steinbeck. Sanna, Ellyn & Price, Michael. Bloom, Harold, ed. (Illus.). 2003. 35.00 (978-0-7910-6172-5(8) , 000852); Joseph Conrad. Rupple, Richard & Sickles, Amy. Bloom, Harold, ed. (Illus.). 2003. 35.00 (978-0-7910-6371-2(2) , 000876); Langston Hughes. Bloom, Harold, ed. & intro. (Illus.). 2001. 35.00 (978-0-7910-6186-2(8) , 000867); Lord Byron. Wills, Karen & Pesta, Duke. Bloom, Harold, ed. (Illus.). 2003. 35.00 (978-0-7910-6367-5(4) , 000872); Mark Twain. Lutz, Norma Jean & Williams, Tenley. Bloom, Harold, ed. (Illus.). 2003. 35.00 (978-0-7910-6372-9(0) , 000877); Maya Angelou. Bloom, Harold, ed. & intro. (Illus.). 2002. 35.00 (978-0-7910-6177-0(9) , 000858); Robert Frost. Bloom, Harold, ed. (Illus.). 2002. 35.00 (978-0-7910-6183-1(3) , 000864); Stephen Crane. Bloom, Harold. (Illus.). 2002. 35.00 (978-0-7910-6375-0(5) , 000886); Stephen

King. Bloom, Harold. (Illus.). 2002. 35.00 (978-0-7910-6178-7(7) , 000859); Tennessee Williams. Lutz, Norma Jean & LaBrie, Aimee. Bloom, Harold, ed. (Illus.). 2002. 35.00 (978-0-7910-6185-5(X) , 000866); Toni Morrison. Bloom, Harold, ed. (Illus.). 2002. 35.00 (978-0-7910-6180-0(9) , 000861); Walt Whitman. Bloom, Harold, ed. (Illus.). 2002. 35.00 (978-0-7910-6377-4(1) , 000882); William Faulkner. Bloom, Harold. (Illus.). 2002. 35.00 (978-0-7910-6378-1(X) , 000883); William Shakespeare. Bloom, Harold, ed. (Illus.). 2002. 35.00 (978-0-7910-6171-8(X) , 000851); 112p. (gr. 9-13). 726.60 (978-0-7910-7192-2(8) , 000850S, Chelsea Hse.) Facts On File, Inc.

Bloom's Major Novelists Series, 25 vols., Set. Incl. Alice Walker. Bloom, Harold. (YA). (gr. 8 up). 1999. 31.95 (978-0-7910-5250-1(8) , 039951, Chelsea Hse.); Brontes. Bloom, Harold. (YA). (gr. 8 up). 1999. 31.95 (978-0-7910-5257-0(5) , 039958, Chelsea Hse.); Charles Dickens. Bloom, Harold, intro. (YA). (gr. 8 up). 1999. 31.95 (978-0-7910-5251-8(6) , 039952, Chelsea Hse.); D. H. Lawrence. Bloom, Harold, ed. & intro. (YA). (gr. 8 up). 2001. 31.95 (978-0-7910-6350-7(X) , 039968, Chelsea Hse.); Edith Wharton. Bloom, Harold, ed. & intro. (YA). (gr. 8 up). 2001. 31.95 (978-0-7910-6349-1(6) , 039970, Chelsea Hse.); Ernest Hemingway. Bloom, Harold, ed. (YA). (gr. 8 up). 1999. 31.95 (978-0-7910-5259-4(1) , 039960, Chelsea Hse.); F. Scott Fitzgerald. Bloom, Harold, ed. (YA). (gr. 8 up). 1999. 31.95 (978-0-7910-5254-9(0) , 039955, Chelsea Hse.); Franz Kafka. Bloom, Harold, ed. & intro. (Illus.). (gr. 9-13). 2002. 31.95 (978-0-7910-7028-4(X) , 039975, Chelsea Hse.); Fyodor Dostoevsky. Chang, Emmy. Bloom, Harold, ed. (Illus.). (gr. 9-13). 2002. 31.95 (978-0-7910-6346-0(1) , 039964, Chelsea Hse.); Henry James. Bloom, Harold, ed. & intro. (YA). (gr. 8 up). 2001. 31.95 (978-0-7910-6352-1(6) , 039966, Chelsea Hse.); Herman Melville. Piorkowski, Sue. Bloom, Harold, ed. (Illus.). (gr. 9-13). 2003. 31.95 (978-0-7910-7027-7(1) , 039976, Chelsea Hse.); James Joyce. Bloom, Harold, ed. & intro. (YA). (gr. 8 up). 2001. 31.95 (978-0-7910-6353-8(4) , 039967, Chelsea Hse.); Jane Austen. Bloom, Harold. (Illus.). (YA). (gr. 8 up). 1999. 31.95 (978-0-7910-5260-0(5) , 039961, Chelsea Hse.); John Steinbeck. Bloom, Harold. (YA). (gr. 8 up). 1999. 31.95 (978-0-7910-5252-5(4) , 039953, Chelsea Hse.); Leo Tolstoy. Bloom, Harold, ed. & intro. (YA). (gr. 8 up). 2001. 31.95 (978-0-7910-6347-7(X) , 039969, Chelsea Hse.); Marcel Proust. Bloom, Harold, ed. & intro. (YA). (gr. 8 up). 2002. 31.95 (978-0-7910-7029-1(8) , 039977); Mark Twain. Bloom, Harold. (YA). (gr. 8 up). 1999. 31.95 (978-0-7910-5256-3(7) , 039957, Chelsea Hse.); Nathaniel Hawthorne. Hawthorne, Nathaniel. Bloom, Harold, ed. (YA). (gr. 8 up). 1999. 31.95 (978-0-7910-5253-2(2) , 039954, Chelsea Hse.); Stendhal. Bloom, Harold, ed. & intro. (YA). (gr. 8 up). 2001. 31.95 (978-0-7910-6351-4(8) , 039972, Chelsea Hse.); Thomas Hardy. Marson, Janyce. Bloom, Harold, ed. (Illus.). (gr. 9-13). 2003. 31.95 (978-0-7910-6348-4(8) , 039965, Chelsea Hse.); Toni Morrison. Bloom, Harold. (YA). (gr. 8 up). 1999. 31.95 (978-0-7910-5258-7(3) , 039959, Chelsea Hse.); Virginia Woolf. Bloom, Harold, ed. & intro. (YA). (gr. 8 up). 2001. 31.95 (978-0-7910-6344-6(5) , 039971, Chelsea Hse.); Willa Cather. Bloom, Harold. (YA). (gr. 8 up). 1999. 31.95 (978-0-7910-5261-7(3) , 039962, Chelsea Hse.); William Faulkner. Bloom, Harold. (YA). (gr. 8 up). 1999. 31.95 (978-0-7910-5255-6(9) , 039956, Chelsea Hse.); 120p. 573.75 (978-0-7910-7197-7(9) , 039950S, Chelsea Hse.) Facts On File, Inc.

Bloom's Major Short Story Writers. 2005. pap. 926.55 (978-0-7910-9135-7(X) , Chelsea Hse.) Facts On File, Inc.

Brackett, Virginia. Restless Genius: The Story of Virginia Woolf. 2004. (World Writers Ser.). (Illus.). 144p. (YA). (gr. 6-12). 23.95 (978-1-931798-37-2(0)) Reynolds, Morgan Inc.

Briggs, Lucy. Kate DiCamillo. 2005. (My Favorite Writer Ser.). (Illus.). 32p. (J). (gr. k-7). lib. bdg. 26.00 (978-1-59036-283-9(7)) Weigl Pubs., Inc.

Burnett, Frances Hodgson. El Pequeño Lord. (SPA., Illus.). (YA). 11.95 (978-84-7281-059-4(3) , AF1059) Auriga, Ediciones S.A. ESP. *Dist:* Continental Bk. Co., Inc.

—El Pequeño Lord. (Coleccion Clasicos de la Juventud). (SPA., Illus.). 204p. (J). 12.95 (978-84-7189-096-2(8) , ORT315) Ortells, Alfredo Editorial S.L. ESP. *Dist:* Continental Bk. Co., Inc.

Children's Authors Set 4. 2007. 128.10 (978-1-59679-761-1(4) , Checkerboard Library) ABDO Publishing Co.

Collins, David R. Write a Book for Me: The Story of Marguerite Henry. 2004. (World Writers Ser.). (Illus.). 112p. (YA). (gr. 6-12). 23.95 (978-1-883846-39-8(0) , First Biographies) Reynolds, Morgan Inc.

Contemporary Authors. 2000. (Contemporary Authors Ser.: Vol. 181). 500p. (YA). (gr. 9-12). Vol. 181. 225.00 (978-0-7876-3241-0(4)); Vol. 182. 225.00 (978-0-7876-3242-7(2)); Vol. 183. 225.00 (978-0-7876-3243-4(0)); Vol. 184. 225.00 (978-0-7876-3244-1(9)); Vol. 185. 225.00 (978-0-7876-3245-8(7)) Thomson Gale. (UXL).

Daudet, Alphonse. Las Aventuras Prodigiosas de Tartarin de Tarascon. (Coleccion Clasicos de la Juventud). (SPA., Illus.). 204p. (J). 12.95 (978-84-7189-195-2(6) , ORT324) Ortells, Alfredo Editorial S.L. ESP. *Dist:* Continental Bk. Co., Inc.

Davenport, John C. Dante: Poet, Author & Proud Florentine. 2005. (Makers of the Middle Ages & Renaissance Ser.). (Illus.). 140p. (J). (gr. 4-8). lib. bdg. 30.00 (978-0-7910-8634-6(8) , Chelsea Hse.) Facts On File, Inc.

de Paola, Tomie. 26 Fairmount Avenue. de Paola, Tomie, illus. 2002. (Illus.). (J). 13.19 (978-0-7587-0230-2(2)) Book Wholesalers, Inc.

—26 Fairmount Avenue. 2001. (Twenty-Six Fairmount Avenue Bks.). (Illus.). 64p. (J). (gr. 2-5). pap. 6.99 (978-0-698-11864-5(2) , Putnam Juvenile) Penguin Group (USA) Inc.

—26 Fairmount Avenue. de Paola, Tomie, illus. 1999. (26 Fairmount Avenue Bks.). (Illus.). 32p. (J). (gr. 2-6). 13.99 (978-0-399-23246-6(X) , Putnam Juvenile) Penguin Group (USA) Inc.

—26 Fairmount Avenue, unabr. ed. 2004. (Fairmount Avenue Ser.: Vol. 1). 64p. (J). (gr. 2-5). pap. 17.00 incl. audio (978-0-8072-0654-6(7) , LFTR 245 SP, Listening Library) Random Hse. Audio Publishing Group.

—26 Fairmount Avenue. 2001. (J). (978-0-606-21010-2(5)); (gr. 3-6). lib. bdg. 14.15 (978-0-613-35892-7(9)) Tandem Library Bks.

Delano, Poli. When I Was a Boy Neruda Called Me Policarpo: A Memoir. Higgins, Sean, tr. from SPA. Monroy, Manuel, illus. 2006. 96p. (J). 15.95 (978-0-88899-726-5(4)) Groundwood Bks. CAN. *Dist:* Perseus Distribution.

Demi. Su Dongpo: Chinese Genius. 2006. (Illus.). 56p. (J). (gr. 2-5). 24.00 (978-1-58430-256-8(9)) Lee & Low Bks., Inc.

Downing, Sybil & Barker, Jane Valentine. Crown of Life: The Story of Mary Roberts Rinehart. 1999. (Illus.). 178p. (gr. 4-7). pap. 9.95 (978-1-879373-18-1(1)) Rinehart, Roberts Pubs.

Ehrlich, Amy. Willa: The Story of Willa Cather. Minor, Wendell, illus. 2006. (J). 16.99 (978-0-689-86573-2(2) , Simon & Schuster Children's Publishing) Simon & Schuster Children's Publishing.

Einarson, Earl. The Moccasins. Einarson, Earl, illus. 2005. (Illus.). 16p. (J). pap. 7.95 (978-1-894778-14-5(6)) Theytus Bks., Ltd. CAN. *Dist:* Orca Bk. Pubs. USA.

Eisemann, Henry. Salinas Streets, Steinbeck's Town Then & Now. Martin, J. C., illus. 1998. 48p. (J). (gr. 1-6). pap. 8.95 (978-0-938129-07-3(4)) Emprise Pubns.

Erlic, Lily. Lois Lowry. 2005. (My Favorite Writer Ser.). (Illus.). 32p. (J). (gr. k-7). lib. bdg. 26.00 (978-1-59036-286-0(1)); (gr. 2-6). pap. 7.95 (978-1-59036-292-1(6)) Weigl Pubs., Inc.

—Louis Sachar. 2005. (My Favorite Writer Ser.). (Illus.). 32p. (J). (gr. k-7). lib. bdg. 26.00 (978-1-59036-288-4(8)); pap. 7.95 (978-1-59036-294-5(2)) Weigl Pubs., Inc.

Favorite Children's Authors & Illustrators, 8 vols. 2nd ed. 2006. 368.00 ***(*978-1-59187-065-4(8))*** Tradition Publishing Co.

Gamble, Nikki. Favourite Classic Writers. (Illus.). 32p. pap. (978-0-7502-4286-8(8) , Hodder Wayland) Hodder Children's Division.

Great Life Stories: Writers & Poets. 2004. (Illus.). 88.50 (978-0-531-19296-2(2)) Scholastic Library Publishing.

Great Writers. 2005. (Illus.). 128p. (gr. 9-13). pap. 191.70 (978-0-7910-7842-6(6) , Chelsea Hse.) Facts On File, Inc.

Halliwell, Sarah. The Romantics: Artists, Writers & Composers. 1998. (Who & When Ser.: Vol. 4). (Illus.). 96p. (J). (gr. 7-12). lib. bdg. 29.97 (978-0-8172-4729-4(7)) Raintree.

—The 19th Century: Artists, Writers & Composers. 1998. (Who & When Ser.). (Illus.). 96p. (J). (gr. 7-12). lib. bdg. 29.97 (978-0-8172-4728-7(9)) Raintree.

—The 20th Century: Post-1945 - Artists, Writers & Composers. 1998. (Who & When Ser.). (Illus.). 96p. (J). (gr. 7-12). lib. bdg. 29.97 (978-0-8172-4732-4(7)) Raintree.

Harcourt School Publishers Staff. Vamos de Fiesta: Una Entrevista los Hermanos Grimm Take-Home Book. 2001. (SPA., Illus.). (J). (gr. 4). pap. 2.80 (978-0-15-321300-7(0)) Harcourt Schl. Pubs.

Harris, Laurie Lanzen, ed. Biography Today: Profiles of People of Interest to Young Readers. 1998. (Author Ser.: Vol. 4). (Illus.). 200p. (YA). (gr. 4-12). lib. bdg. 44.00 (978-0-7808-0363-3(9)) Omnigraphics, Inc.

Henry, W., et al. Bloom's BioCritiques. (J). 934.20 (978-0-7910-7379-7(3) , Chelsea Hse.) Facts On File, Inc.

Hill, Christine M. Ten Hispanic American Authors. 2002. (Collective Biographies Ser.). (Illus.). 112p. (J). (gr. 6-12). lib. bdg. 26.60 (978-0-7660-1541-8(6)) Enslow Pubs., Inc.

Hughes, Shirley. A Life Drawing. 2007. (Illus.). 208p. (J). (ps-k). 36.95 ***(*978-0-370-32605-4(9))*** Transworld Publishers Ltd. GBR. *Dist:* Independent Pubs. Group.

Hunter, Shaun. Writers. 1998. (Women in Profile Ser.). (Illus.). 48p. (J). (gr. 4). pap. (978-0-7787-0027-2(5)); lib. bdg. (978-0-7787-0005-0(4)) Crabtree Publishing Co.

—Writers. 1998. (Illus.). 48p. (J). (ps-11). lib. bdg. 17.60 (978-0-613-09123-7(X)) Tandem Library Bks.

Hurwitz, Johanna. A Dream Come True. Craine, Michael, photos by. 1998. (Meet the Author Ser.). (Illus.). 32p. (J). (gr. 2-5). 14.95 (978-1-57274-193-5(7) , 719) Owen, Richard C. Pubs., Inc.

Hyde, Margaret O. Robert Cormier. 2005. (Who Wrote That? Ser.). (Illus.). 102p. (YA). (gr. 6-12). lib. bdg. 30.00 (978-0-7910-8232-4(6) , Chelsea Hse.) Facts On File, Inc.

Jerome, Jerome K. Tres Hombres en una Barca. (Coleccion Clasicos de la Juventud). (SPA., Illus.). 208p. (J). 12.95 (978-84-7189-048-1(8) , ORT317) Ortells, Alfredo Editorial S.L. ESP. *Dist:* Continental Bk. Co., Inc.

Kjelle, Marylou Morano, et al. Who Wrote That?, 29 vols., Set. 2006. (Who Wrote That? Ser.). (gr. 6-12). 810.00 (978-0-7910-9328-3(X) , Chelsea Hse.) Facts On File, Inc.

Kovacs, Deborah & Preller, James. Meet the Authors & Illustrators. pap. 13.95 (978-0-590-24111-3(7)) Scholastic, Inc.

Lazaro, Georgina & Donoso, Marcela. Pablo. 2008. (J). ***(*978-1-933032-09-2(X))*** Lectorum Pubns., Inc.

Lazo, Caroline Evensen. Alice Walker: Freedom Writer. 2005. (Lerner Biographies Ser.). (Illus.). 128p. (gr. 6-12). 27.93 (978-0-8225-4960-4(3)) Lerner Publishing Group.

Levy, Nathan. Famous Authors. Kristensen, Renee & Sculthorp, Jeffrey A., eds. 2000. (Whose Clues? Ser.). 32p. (J). pap., tchr. ed. 5.99 (978-1-889319-43-8(0) , MindMotion) Trend Enterprises, Inc.

Library of Author Biographies, 6 bks. Incl. Gary Paulsen. Thomson, Sarah L. lib. bdg. 26.50 (978-0-8239-3773-8(9)); J. K. Rowling. Compson, William. lib. bdg. 26.50 (978-0-8239-3774-5(7)); Lois Lowry. Daniel, Susanna. lib. bdg. 26.50 (978-0-8239-3775-2(5)); Robert Cormier. Thomson, Sarah L. lib. bdg. 26.50 (978-0-8239-3776-9(3)); S. E. Hinton. Wilson, Antoine. lib. bdg. 26.50 (978-0-8239-3778-3(X)); Virginia Hamilton. Marinelli, Deborah A. lib. bdg. 26.50 (978-0-8239-3777-6(1)); 112p. (YA). (gr. 5-8). 2003. (Illus.). 2002. Set lib. bdg. 159.00 (978-0-8239-4053-0(5) , Rosen Central) Rosen Publishing Group, Inc., The.

The Library of Author Biographies, 1-4 bks., Set. 2005. (YA). (gr. 5-8). lib. bdg. 478.80 (978-1-4042-0501-7(2)) Rosen Publishing Group, Inc., The.

The Library of Author Biographies Set 5. (YA). (gr. 5-8). 159.00 (978-1-4042-0622-9(1) , Rosen Central) Rosen Publishing Group, Inc., The.

The Library of Author Biographies Set 6. (YA). (gr. 5-8). 159.00 (978-1-4042-0623-6(X) , Rosen Central) Rosen Publishing Group, Inc., The.

Ling, Bettina. Willa Cather: Author & Critic. 2003. (Great Life Stories: Writers & Poets Ser.). (Illus.). 112p. (J). 30.50 (978-0-531-12316-4(2) , Watts, Franklin) Scholastic Library Publishing.

Literary Lifelines, 10 vols., Set. 1998. (Illus.). (YA). (gr. 6). lib. bdg. 335.00 (978-0-7172-9211-0(8) , Grolier) Scholastic Library Publishing.

Lowry, Lois. Looking Back: A Book of Memories. 2000. (gr. 5-8). lib. bdg. 24.55 (978-0-613-28561-2(1)) Tandem Library Bks.

Lynch, Wendy. Dr. Suess, Set 1. 2002. (Lives & Times Ser.). (Illus.). 24p. (J). (gr. k-3). pap. 6.50 (978-1-58810-345-1(5) , 91105) Heinemann Library.

Marcus, Leonard S. Ways of Telling: Conversations on the Art of the Picture Book. 2005. (Illus.). 247p. reprint ed. 30.00 (978-0-7567-9704-1(7)) DIANE Publishing Co.

Martin, Carol. Catharine Parr Traill: Backwoods Pioneer. 2004. (Illus.). (YA). pap. (978-0-88899-495-0(8) , Libros Tigrillo) Groundwood Bks. CAN. *Dist:* Transition Vendor.

Millidge, Gary Spencer & Man, Smoky. Alan Moore: Portrait of an Extraordinary Gentleman. 2003. (Illus.). 352p. pap. 14.95 (978-0-946790-06-7(X)) Abiogenesis Pr. GBR. *Dist:* Diamond Bk. Distributors.

Mirriam-Goldberg, Caryn. Sandra Cisneros: Latina Writer & Activist. 1998. (Hispanic Biographies Ser.). (Illus.). 112p. (YA). (gr. 6-12). lib. bdg. 26.60 (978-0-7660-1045-1(7)) Enslow Pubs., Inc.

Molnar, Ferenc. Los Muchachos de la Calle Pal. (Coleccion Clasicos de la Juventud). (SPA., Illus.). 176p. (J). 12.95 (978-84-7189-021-4(6) , ORT303) Ortells, Alfredo Editorial S.L. ESP. *Dist:* Continental Bk. Co., Inc.

Musgrave, Susan. Certain Things about My Mother: Daughters Speak. 2003. (gr. 7-12). lib. bdg. 16.40 (978-0-613-78407-8(3)) Tandem Library Bks.

—You Be Me: Friendship in the Lives of Teen Girls. 2002. (gr. 7-12). lib. bdg. 16.40 (978-0-613-78373-6(5)) Tandem Library Bks.

Musgrave, Susan, ed. Certain Things about My Mother: Daughters Speak. 2003. 128p. (YA). (gr. 9-12). 18.95 (978-1-55037-813-9(9)); pap. 7.95 (978-1-55037-812-2(0)) Annick Pr., Ltd. CAN. *Dist:* Firefly Bks., Ltd.

—You Be Me: Friendship in the Lives of Teen Girls. 2002. 128p. (YA). (gr. 10 up). 18.95 (978-1-55037-739-2(6)); pap. 7.95 (978-1-55037-738-5(8)) Annick Pr., Ltd. CAN. *Dist:* Firefly Bks., Ltd.

Nixon, Joan Lowery. The Making of a Writer. 2003. (gr. 5-8). lib. bdg. 13.00 (978-0-613-70572-1(6)) Tandem Library Bks.

Paulsen, Gary. How Angel Peterson Got His Name. 2003. 128p. (gr. 5 up). 12.95 (978-0-385-72949-9(9) , Lamb, Wendy) Random Hse. Children's Bks.

Peters, Stephanie True. Gary Paulsen. Clark, Kimberley, ed. 1999. (Meet the Author Ser.). (Illus.). 112p. (J). (gr. 3-6). pap. 7.99 (978-0-88160-324-8(4) , LW-387, Learning Works, The) Creative Teaching Pr., Inc.

Poets & Playwrights, 5 vols., Set. Incl. Carl Sandburg. Murcia, Rebecca Thatcher. lib. bdg. 37.10 (978-1-58415-430-3(6)); Emily Dickinson. Griskey, Michele. lib. bdg. 37.10 (978-1-58415-429-7(2)); Langston Hughes. Gibson, Karen Bush. lib. bdg. 37.10 (978-1-58415-431-0(4)); Tennessee Williams. Tracy, Kathleen. lib. bdg. 37.10 (978-1-58415-427-3(6)); William Shakespeare. Whiting, Jim. lib. bdg. 37.10 (978-1-58415-426-6(8)); (Illus.). 112p. (YA). (gr. 6-12). 2006. 2007. Set lib. bdg. 185.50 ***(*978-1-58415-284-2(2))*** Mitchell Lane Pubs., Inc.

Primm, E. Russell, III. Barbara Park to Seymour Simon, Vol. 5. 2002. (Favorite Children's Authors & Illustrators Ser.). (Illus.). (J). (gr. 3-8). lib. bdg. (978-1-59187-022-7(4)) Tradition Publishing Co.

—Carmen Lomas Garza to Ursula K. Le Guin, Vol. 3. 2002. (Favorite Children's Authors & Illustrators Ser.). (Illus.). (J). lib. bdg. (978-1-59187-020-3(8)) Tradition Publishing Co.

—Edward Lear to Helen Oxenbury, Vol. 4. 2002. (Favorite Children's Authors & Illustrators Ser.). (Illus.). (J). lib. bdg. (978-1-59187-021-0(6)) Tradition Publishing Co.

—Joanna Cole to Jack Gantos, Vol. 2. 2002. (Favorite Children's Authors & Illustrators Ser.). (Illus.). (J). lib. bdg. (978-1-59187-019-7(4)) Tradition Publishing Co.

—Peter Sis to Gene Zion, Vol. 6. 2002. (Favorite Children's Authors & Illustrators Ser.). (Illus.). (J). (gr. 3-8). lib. bdg. (978-1-59187-023-4(2)) Tradition Publishing Co.

—Verna Aardema to Brock Cole, Vol. 1. 2002. (Favorite Children's Authors & Illustrators Ser.). (Illus.). (J). lib. bdg. (978-1-59187-018-0(6)) Tradition Publishing Co.

Quackenbush, Robert. Two Slapstick Biographies: Once upon a Time! A Story of the Brothers Grimm & Quick, Annie, Give Me a Catchy Line! A Story of Samuel F. B. Morse. 1999. (Two Slapstick Biographies Ser.: Vol. 1). (Illus.). 64p. (YA). (gr. 3 up). reprint ed. pap. 5.95 (978-0-9612518-1-9(6)) Quackenbush, Robert Studios.

Richardson, Gillian. Dan Gutman. 2005. (My Favorite Writer Ser.). (Illus.). 32p. (J). (gr. 2-6). lib. bdg. 26.00 (978-1-59036-284-6(5)) Weigl Pubs., Inc.

Salgari, Emilio. Los Pirates de Malasia. (Coleccion Clasicos de la Juventud). (SPA., Illus.). 200p. (J). 12.95 (978-84-7189-058-0(5) , ORT312) Ortells, Alfredo Editorial S.L. ESP. *Dist:* Continental Bk. Co., Inc.

—Los Tigres de Mom Pracem. (Coleccion Clasicos de la Juventud). (SPA., Illus.). 224p. (J). 12.95 (978-84-7189-056-6(9) , ORT318) Ortells, Alfredo Editorial S.L. ESP. *Dist:* Continental Bk. Co., Inc.

Sickels, Amy. Adrienne Rich. 2005. (Gay & Lesbian Writers Ser.). (Illus.). 144p. (YA). (gr. 9-13). 35.00 (978-0-7910-8223-2(7) , Chelsea Hse.) Facts On File, Inc.

Silverman, Erica. Sholom's Treasure: How Sholom Aleichem Became a Writer. Gerstein, Mordicai, illus. 2005. 40p. (J). 16.00 (978-0-374-38055-7(4) , Farrar, Straus & Giroux (BYR)) Farrar, Straus & Giroux.

Smith, Angela. Katherine Mansfield: A Literary Life. rev. ed. 2001. (Literary Lives Ser.). 183p. 79.95 (978-0-333-61877-6(7)) Palgrave Macmillan.

Speaker-Yuan, Margaret. Avi. 2005. (Who Wrote That? Ser.). (Illus.). 112p. (J). (gr. 6-12). lib. bdg. 30.00 (978-0-7910-8230-0(X) , Chelsea Hse.) Facts On File, Inc.

Steinbauer, Janine. Bronte Sisters. 1999. (Profiles Ser.). (Illus.). 56p. (YA). (gr. 6 up). lib. bdg. 16.95 (978-0-88682-739-7(6) , Creative Education) Creative Co., The.

—James Joyce. 1999. (Profiles Ser.). (Illus.). 56p. (YA). (gr. 6 up). lib. bdg. 16.95 (978-0-88682-819-6(8) , Creative Education) Creative Co., The.

Stout, William. William Stout - Tribute to Ray Harryhausen. 2003. (Illus.). 70p. (YA). per. 20.00 (978-0-9712716-9-2(0)) Stout, William Inc.

Szumski, Bonnie. Readings on "Tess of the D'Urbervilles" 2000. (Literary Companion to American Literature Ser.). (Illus.). 224p. (YA). (gr. 9-12). pap. (978-0-7377-0196-8(X) , Greenhaven Pr., Inc.) Thomson Gale.

Tolstoï, Lev Nikolaevich. El Prisonero del Caucaso. (Coleccion Clasicos de la Juventud). (SPA., Illus.). 232p. (J). 12.95 (978-84-7189-088-7(7) , ORT319) Ortells, Alfredo Editorial S.L. ESP. *Dist:* Continental Bk. Co., Inc.

Trachtenberg, Martha P. Anne McCaffrey: Science Fiction Storyteller. 2001. (People to Know Ser.). (Illus.). 112p. (YA). (gr. 6-12). lib. bdg. 26.60 (978-0-7660-1151-9(8)) Enslow Pubs., Inc.

Tracy, Kathleen. John Steinbeck. 2004. (Classic Storytellers Ser.). (Illus.). 48p. (J). (gr. 4-8). lib. bdg. 20.95 (978-1-58415-271-2(0)) Mitchell Lane Pubs., Inc.

Ward, S. About the Author, 6 bks. Incl. Meet A. A. Milne. 2001. lib. bdg. 18.75 (978-0-8239-5708-8(X)); Meet Beverly Cleary. 2001. lib. bdg. 18.75 (978-0-8239-5710-1(1)); Meet E. B. White. 2001. lib. bdg. 18.75 (978-0-8239-5713-2(6)); Meet J. K. Rowling. 2000. lib. bdg. 18.75 (978-0-8239-5711-8(X)); Meet Laura Ingalls Wilder. 2001. lib. bdg. 18.75 (978-0-8239-5712-5(8)); Meet Shel Silverstein. 2001. lib. bdg. 18.75 (978-0-8239-5709-5(8)); 24p. (J). (gr. 3). (Illus.). 2001. Set lib. bdg. 112.50 (978-0-8239-7061-2(2) , PowerKids Pr.) Rosen Publishing Group, Inc., The.

Whitelaw, Nancy. Bram Stoker: Author of Dracula. rev. exp. ed. 2004. (World Writers Ser.). (Illus.). 112p. (YA). (gr. 6-12). 23.95 (978-1-931798-33-4(8)) Reynolds, Morgan Inc.

Who Wrote That?, 6 vols., Set. (Illus.). 112p. (YA). (gr. 6-12). 137.70 (978-0-7910-6718-5(1) , Chelsea Hse.) Facts On File, Inc.

World Writers, 8 bks., Set. Incl. Best of Times : The Story of Charles Dickens. Caravantes, Peggy. 160p. (J). (gr. 3-7). 2005. lib. bdg. 26.95 (978-1-931798-68-6(0)); Dark Dreams : The Story of Stephen King. Whitelaw, Nancy. 128p. (YA). (gr. 5 up). 2005. lib. bdg. 26.95 (978-1-931798-77-8(X)); Deep Woods : The Story of Robert Frost. Caravantes, Peggy. 160p. (J). (gr. 6 up). 2006. lib. bdg. 26.95 (978-1-931798-92-1(3)); England's Jane : The Story of Jane Austen. Locke, Juliane. 144p. (YA). 2006. lib. bdg. 26.95 (978-1-931798-82-2(6)); Gift of Imagination : The Story of Roald Dahl. Gelletly, LeeAnne. 160p. (YA). (gr. 6-12). 2006. lib. bdg. 27.95 (978-1-59935-026-4(2)); Ralph Ellison : Author of Invisible Man. Rhynes, Martha E. 160p. (J). (gr. 5 up). 2006. lib. bdg. 26.95 (978-1-931798-69-3(9)); Savage Satire : The Story of Jonathan Swift. Aykroyd, Clarissa. 160p. (J). (gr. 6-12). 2006. lib. bdg. 27.95 (978-1-59935-027-1(0)); Writing Is My Business : The Story of O. Henry. Caravantes, Peggy. 160p. (J). (gr. 6-12). 2006. lib. bdg. 27.95 (978-1-59935-031-8(9)); (Illus.). 2007. Set lib. bdg. 223.60 ***(*978-1-59935-014-1(9))*** Reynolds, Morgan Inc.

Writers & Their Works, 5 bks., Set. Incl. Arthur Miller. Andersen, Richard. 144p. (978-0-7614-1946-4(2)); Charlotte Brontë. Reiff, Raychel Haugrud. 159p. (978-0-7614-1948-8(9)); F. Scott Fitzgerald. Boon, Kevin A. 142p. (978-0-7614-1947-1(0)); Mark Twain. McArthur, Debra. 158p. (978-0-7614-1950-1(0)); Toni Morrison. Andersen, Richard. 143p. (978-0-7614-1945-7(4)); (Illus.). (YA). 2005. 2005. (978-0-7614-1944-0(6) , Benchmark Bks.) Cavendish, Marshall Corp.

Wukovits, John F. Stephen King. 1999. (People in the News Ser.). (Illus.). 96p. (YA). (gr. 6-9). 27.45 (978-1-56006-562-3(1) , Lucent Bks.) Thomson Gale.

Zuluaga, Conrado. Gabriel García Marquez- el vicio incurable de Contar. 2005. 136p. pap. (978-958-30-1959-3(3)) Panamericana Editorial.

AUTHORS, AFRICAN AMERICAN

see African American Authors

AUTHORS, AMERICAN

Aaseng, Nathan. Michael Crichton. 2002. (Illus.). 104p. (YA). (gr. 4-12). 32.45 (978-1-59018-019-8(4) , Lucent Bks.) Thomson Gale.

Abrams, Dennis. Barbara Park. 2006. (Who Wrote That? Ser.). (Illus.). 138p. (J). 30.00 (978-0-7910-8969-9(X) , Chelsea Hse.) Facts On File, Inc.

Abrams, Dennis. Gary Soto. 2008. (Who Wrote That? Ser.). 128p. (gr. 6-12). 30.00 (*978-0-7910-9529-4(0) , Chelsea Hse.) Facts On File, Inc.

Adil, Janeen R. Dr. Seuss. 2004. (Robbie Reader Ser.). (Illus.). 32p. (J). (gr. 1-4). lib. bdg. 25.70 (978-1-58415-288-0(5)) Mitchell Lane Pubs., Inc.

Adler, David A. My Writing Day. Crews, Nina, photos by. 1999. (Meet the Author Ser.). (Illus.). 32p. (J). (gr. 2-5). 14.95 (978-1-57274-326-7(3) , 723) Owen, Richard C. Pubs., Inc.

—A Picture Book of Harriet Beecher Stowe. Bootman, Colin, illus. 2003. 32p. (J). (gr. k-3). 6.95 (978-0-8234-1878-7(2)); tchr. ed. 16.95 (978-0-8234-1646-2(1)) Holiday Hse., Inc.

Albert, Lisa Rondinelli. Lois Lowry: The Giver of Stories & Memories. 2007. (Authors Teens Love Ser.). (Illus.). 128p. (J). (gr. 6 up). lib. bdg. 31.93 (*978-0-7660-2722-0(8)) Enslow Pubs., Inc.

Alcott, Louisa May. The Girlhood Diary of Louisa May Alcott, 1843-1846: Writings of a Young Author. Graves, Kerry A., ed. 2000. (Blue Earth Books). (Illus.). 32p. (J). (gr. 3-4). lib. bdg. 22.60 (978-0-7368-0599-5(0) , Bridgestone Bks.) Capstone Pr., Inc.

Aller, Susan Bivin. Beyond Little Women: A Story about Louisa May Alcott. Wang, Qi Z., illus. 2004. (Creative Minds Biography Ser.). 64p. (J). (gr. 4-8). lib. bdg. 22.60 (978-1-57505-602-9(X)) Lerner Publishing Group.

—Mark Twain. (Just the Facts Biographies Ser.). (Illus.). 112p. (J). 2006. 27.93 (978-0-8225-3425-9(8)); 2006. pap. (*978-0-8225-5998-6(6)); 2001. (gr. 6-12). lib. bdg. 27.93 (978-0-8225-4994-9(8)) Lerner Publishing Group. (Lerner Pubns.).

Alter, Judy. Laura Ingalls Wilder: Pioneer & Author. 2003. (Spirit of America). (Illus.). 32p. (J). (gr. 2-6). 27.07 (978-1-59296-007-1(3)) Child's World, Inc.

Amper, Susan. Bloom's How to Write about Edgar Allan Poe. 2007. (Bloom's How to Write about Literature Ser.). 224p. (YA). (gr. 9 up). 45.00 (*978-0-7910-9488-4(X) , Chelsea Hse.) Facts On File, Inc.

Ancona, George. Self Portrait. Ancona, George, photos by. 2006. (Meet the Author Ser.). (Illus.). 32p. (J). 14.95 (978-1-57274-860-6(5) , 733, Meet the Author) Owen, Richard C. Pubs., Inc.

Anderson, William. Laura Ingalls Wilder: A Biography. 2007. (Little House Ser.). 256p. (J). pap. 6.99 (978-0-06-088552-6(1) , Harper Trophy) HarperCollins Pubs.

—Laura's Album: A Remembrance Scrapbook of Laura Ingalls Wilder. 1998. (Little House Ser.). (Illus.). 80p. (J). (gr. 3 up). 21.99 (978-0-06-027842-7(0)) HarperCollins Pubs.

Anderson, William T. Pioneer Girl: The Story of Laura Ingalls Wilder. Andreasen, Dan, illus. (Little House Ser.). 32p. (J). (gr. 2 up). 2000. pap. 6.99 (978-0-06-446234-1(X) , Harper Trophy); 1998. 15.89 (978-0-06-027244-9(9)) HarperCollins Pubs.

—Pioneer Girl: The Story of Laura Ingalls Wilder. 2000. (978-0-606-18712-1(X)) Tandem Library Bks.

Angel, Ann. Robert Cormier: Author of the Chocolate War. 2007. (Authors Teens Love Ser.). (Illus.). 104p. (J). (gr. 6 up). lib. bdg. 31.93 (978-0-7660-2719-0(8)) Enslow Pubs., Inc.

Appelt, Kathi. My Father's Summers: A Daughter's Memoir. rev. ed. 2004. (Illus.). 208p. (J). 15.95 (978-0-8050-7362-1(0) , Holt, Henry & Co. Bks. For Young Readers) Holt, Henry & Co.

Armentrout, David & Armentrout, Patricia. Laura Ingalls Wilder. 2004. (Discover the Life of an American Legend Ser.). (Illus.). 24p. (gr. 2-5). 14.95 (978-1-58952-663-1(5)) Rourke Publishing, LLC.

—Mark Twain. 2004. (Discover the Life of an American Legend Ser.). (Illus.). 24p. (gr. 2-5). 14.95 (978-1-58952-660-0(0)) Rourke Publishing, LLC.

Arnosky, James. Whole Days Outdoors: An Autobiographical Album. Arnosky, Deanna, photos by. 2006. (Meet the Author Ser.). (Illus.). 32p. (J). 14.95 (978-1-57274-859-0(1) , 734, Meet the Author) Owen, Richard C. Pubs., Inc.

Aykroyd, Clarissa. Julia Alvarez. 2007. (Twentieth Century Most Influential Hispanics Ser.). (Illus.). 128p. (gr. 7-10). 31.20 (*978-1-4205-0022-6(8) , Lucent Bks.) Thomson Gale.

Bagley, Val Chadwick. My Book about Me. (J). pap. 4.95 (978-1-57734-341-7(7) , 01113682) Covenant Communications, Inc.

Bankston, John. F. Scott Fitzgerald. 2004. (Classic Storytellers Ser.). (Illus.). 48p. (J). (gr. 4-8). lib. bdg. 20.95 (978-1-58415-249-1(4)) Mitchell Lane Pubs., Inc.

—Jack London. 2004. (Classic Storytellers Ser.). (Illus.). 48p. (J). (gr. 4-8). lib. bdg. 20.95 (978-1-58415-263-7(X)) Mitchell Lane Pubs., Inc.

Banting, Erinn. Mary Pope Osbourne. 2007. (My Favorite Writer Ser.). (978-1-59036-483-3(X)); lib. bdg. (978-1-59036-482-6(1)) Weigl Pubs., Inc.

Baptiste, Tracey. Jerry Spinelli. 2007. 128p. 30.00 (*978-0-7910-9572-0(X) , Chelsea Hse.) Facts On File, Inc.

—Madeleine L'Engle. 2007. 128p. 30.00 (*978-0-7910-9573-7(8) , Chelsea Hse.) Facts On File, Inc.

Behnke, Alison. Jack Kerouac. 2007. (Biography Ser.). 112p. (J). (gr. 6-12). 29.27 (978-0-8225-6614-4(1) , Twenty-First Century Bks.) Lerner Publishing Group.

Benson, Sonia & Straub, Deborah Gillan, eds. UXL Hispanic American Voices. 2nd ed. 2002. (Illus.). xxi, 294p. (J). 67.00 (978-0-7876-6603-3(3) , UXL) Thomson Gale.

Bernard, Catherine. E. B. White: Spinner of Webs & Tales. 2005. (Authors Teens Love Ser.). (Illus.). 104p. (J). (gr. 6-12). lib. bdg. 26.60 (978-0-7660-2350-5(8)) Enslow Pubs., Inc.

—Understanding to Kill a Mockingbird. 2003. (Understanding Great Literature Ser.). (Illus.). 112p. (J). 29.95 (978-1-56006-860-0(4) , Lucent Bks.) Thomson Gale.

Berne, Emma Carlson. Laura Ingalls Wilder. 2007. (Essential Lives Ser.). (ENG., Illus.). 112p. (J). (gr. 6-8). lib. bdg. 32.79 (*978-1-59928-843-7(5) , Essential Library) ABDO Publishing Co.

Bigmama's. 1998. (J). pap. 3.95 (978-0-439-04436-3(7)) Scholastic, Inc.

Black, Jean Blashfield. Toni Morrison. 2001. (Women of Achievement Ser.). (Illus.). 112p. (J). (gr. 8-12). pap. 30.00 (978-0-7910-5886-2(7)); 30.00 (978-0-7910-5885-5(9)) Facts On File, Inc. (Chelsea Hse.).

Blasingame, James B. Gary Paulsen. 2007. (Teen Reads: Student Companions to Young Adult Literature Ser.). 184p. (J). 45.00 (*978-0-313-33532-7(X) , GR3532, Greenwood Pr.) Greenwood Publishing Group, Inc.

Bloom, Harold, ed. & tr. The House on Mango Street. Bloom, Harold, tr. 2003. (Bloom's Guides Ser.). (Illus.). 80p. (gr. 9-13). 30.00 (978-0-7910-7565-4(6) , Chelsea Hse.) Facts On File, Inc.

Bodie, Idella. Carolina Girl: A Writer's Beginning. 1998. (Illus.). 225p. (J). pap. 12.95 (978-0-87844-140-2(9)) Sandlapper Publishing Co., Inc.

Boerst, William J. Edgar Rice Burroughs: Creator of Tarzan. 2004. (World Writers Ser.). (Illus.). 112p. (J). (gr. 6-12). 23.95 (978-1-883846-56-5(0) , First Biographies) Reynolds, Morgan Inc.

Boomhower, Ray E. The Sword & the Pen: A Life of Lew Wallace. 2005. (Illus.). x, 164p. (J). (978-0-87195-185-4(1)) Indiana Historical Society.

Boon, Kevin A. Ernest Hemingway: The Sun Also Rises & Other Works. 2007. (Writers & Their Works). 160p. (YA). (gr. 9 up). lib. bdg. 39.93 (978-0-7614-2590-8(X) , Benchmark Bks.) Cavendish, Marshall Corp.

Borden, Louise. The Journey That Saved Curious George: The True Wartime Escape of Margret & H. A. Rey. Drummond, Allan, illus. 2005. 80p. (J). (gr. 3-5). 17.00 (978-0-618-33924-2(8)) Houghton Mifflin Co. Trade & Reference Div.

Brackett, Virginia. A Home in the Heart: The Story of Sandra Cisneros. 2004. (World Writers Ser.). (Illus.). 112p. (J). (gr. 6-12). 23.95 (978-1-931798-42-6(7)) Reynolds, Morgan Inc.

Braun, Eric. Maurice Sendak. (First Biographies Ser.). 24p. (J). pap. 5.95 (978-0-7368-5092-6(9)) Capstone Pr., Inc.

—Tomie DePaola. 2005. (First Biographies Ser.). (Illus.). 24p. (J). 15.93 (978-0-7368-3641-8(1) , Pebble Bks.) Capstone Pr., Inc.

—Tomie DePaola. (First Biographies Ser.). 24p. (J). pap. 5.95 (978-0-7368-5093-3(7)) Capstone Pr., Inc.

Briggs, Lucy. Kate DiCamillo. 2005. (My Favorite Writer Ser.). (Illus.). 32p. (J). (gr. 2-6). pap. 7.95 (978-1-59036-289-1(6)) Weigl Pubs., Inc.

Brown, Don. American Boy: The Adventures of Mark Twain. 2003. (Illus.). 32p. (J). (gr. k-3). 16.00 (978-0-618-17997-8(6)) Houghton Mifflin Co. Trade & Reference Div.

Brown, Monica. My Name Is Gabito: Me llamo Gabito: la vida de Gabriel Garcia Marquez: the Life of Gabriel Garcia Marquez. Colón, Raul, illus. 2007. (ENG & SPA.). 32p. 15.95 (*978-0-87358-908-6(4) , Luna Rising) Northland Publishing.

—My Name Is Gabito: The Life of Gabriel Garcia Marquez. Colón, Raul, illus. 2007. 32p. 15.95 (*978-0-87358-934-5(3)) Northland Publishing.

Brown, Monica. My Name Is Gabriela/Me Llamo Gabriela: The Life of Gabriela Mistral/la Vida de Gabriela Mistral. Parra, John, illus. 2005. (SPA.). 32p. (gr. 3-7). 15.95 (978-0-87358-859-1(2) , Luna Rising) Northland Publishing.

Bruchac, Joseph. Bowman's Store: A Journey to Myself. 2001. (Illus.). 328p. (YA). (gr. 7 up). pap. 6.95 (978-1-58430-027-4(2)) Lee & Low Bks., Inc.

—Bowman's Store: A Journey to Myself. 2001. (gr. 3-6). lib. bdg. 15.25 (978-0-613-84717-9(2)) Tandem Library Bks.

—Seeing the Circle. Fine, John Christopher, photos by. 1999. (Meet the Author Ser.). (Illus.). 32p. (J). (gr. 2-5). 14.95 (978-1-57274-327-4(1) , 724) Owen, Richard C. Pubs., Inc.

Bryant, Philip S. Zora Neale Hurston. 2003. (African-American Biographies Ser.). (Illus.). 64p. (J). 28.56 (978-0-7398-6872-0(1)) Raintree.

Bulla, Clyde Robert. A Grain of Wheat: A Writer Begins. 2004. (Illus.). 56p. (J). pap. 10.95 (978-1-59078-333-7(6)) Boyds Mills Pr.

Buzzeo, Toni. Toni Buzzeo & You. 2005. (Author & You Ser.). (Illus.). 176p. pap. 35.00 (978-1-59158-211-3(3) , LU2113) Libraries Unlimited, Inc.

Cammarano, Rita. Betsy Byars. 2002. (Who Wrote That? Ser.). (Illus.). 112p. (gr. 6-12). 30.00 (978-0-7910-6720-8(3) , Chelsea Hse.) Facts On File, Inc.

Campbell, Kimberly. Richard Peck: A Spellbinding Storyteller. 2007. (Authors Teens Love Ser.). (Illus.). 112p. (J). (gr. 6 up). lib. bdg. 31.93 (*978-0-7660-2723-7(6)) Enslow Pubs., Inc.

Cannarella, Deborah. James Baldwin: African-American Writer & Activist. 2003. (Journey to Freedom Ser.). (Illus.). 40p. (J). (gr. 3-7). 28.50 (978-1-56766-531-4(4)) Child's World, Inc.

Caravantes, Peggy. Deep Woods: The Story of Robert Frost. 2006. (World Writers Ser.). (Illus.). 160p. (J). (gr. 6 up). lib. bdg. 26.95 (978-1-931798-92-1(3)) Reynolds, Morgan Inc.

—O. Henry: William Sidney Porter: Texas Cowboy Writer. 2003. (J). (978-1-57168-768-5(8) , Eakin Pr.) Eakin Pr.

—Writing Is My Business: The Story of O. Henry. 2006. (World Writers Ser.). (Illus.). 160p. (J). (gr. 6-12). lib. bdg. 27.95 (978-1-59935-031-8(9)) Reynolds, Morgan Inc.

Carbajal, Xavier Joseph. Edgar & Lenore: Edgar Allan Poe: A Love Story. Jodway, Sherry L., ed. 2001. (Edgar Allan Poe Ser.). 251p. (YA). (gr. 9 up). 24.95 (978-0-9654507-8-2(3) , 071540) New Future Publishing.

Carew-Miller, Anna. Mark Twain. Di Gennaro, Andrea, illus. 2003. (Great Names Ser.). (J). (978-957-745-414-0(3)) Mason Crest Pubs.

Carlson, Cheryl. Dr. Seuss. 2005. (First Biographies Ser.). (Illus.). 24p. (J). 15.93 (978-0-7368-3639-5(X) , Pebble Bks.) Capstone Pr., Inc.

—Dr Seuss. (First Biographies Ser.). 24p. (J). pap. 5.95 (978-0-7368-5091-9(0)) Capstone Pr., Inc.

Cherry, Lynne. Making a Difference in the World. Fine, John Christopher, photos by. 2000. (Meet the Author Ser.). (Illus.). 32p. (J). (gr. 2-5). 14.95 (978-1-57274-373-1(5)) Owen, Richard C. Pubs., Inc.

Cohen, Joel H. R. L. Stine. 1999. (People in the News Ser.). (Illus.). 96p. (YA). (gr. 6-9). 28.70 (978-1-56006-608-8(3) , Lucent Bks.) Thomson Gale.

Collier, James Lincoln. The Mark Twain You Never Knew. 2004. (You Never Knew Ser.). (Illus.). 80p. (J). 25.50 (978-0-516-24430-3(2) , Children's Pr.) Scholastic Library Publishing.

Collins, David R. Washington Irving: Storyteller for a New Nation. 2004. (World Writers Ser.). (Illus.). 112p. (YA). (gr. 6-12). 23.95 (978-1-883846-50-3(1) , First Biographies) Reynolds, Morgan Inc.

Colson, Mary. The Story Behind Toni Morrison's the Bluest Eye. 2006. (History in Literature Ser.). 56p. (J). (gr. 7 up). lib. bdg. 32.86 (978-1-4034-8212-9(8)) Heinemann Library.

Cook, Judy, et al. Natural Writer: A Story about Marjorie Kinnan Rawlings. Harden, Laurie, illus. 2001. (Creative Minds Biographies Ser.). 64p. (J). (gr. 3-6). lib. bdg. 22.60 (978-1-57505-468-1(X) , Carolrhoda Bks.) Lerner Publishing Group.

Craats, Rennay. E. B. White. 2002. (My Favorite Writer Ser.). (Illus.). 32p. (J). lib. bdg. 16.95 (978-1-59036-026-2(5)) Weigl Pubs., Inc.

Crews, Donald. Bigmama's. 2001. (J). (gr. k-3). pap. 16.90 incl. audio (978-0-8045-6840-1(5) , 6840) Spoken Arts, Inc.

Crompton, Samuel Willard. Thomas Merton. 2004. (Spiritual Leaders & Thinkers Ser.). (Illus.). 120p. (gr. 9-13). 30.00 (978-0-7910-7862-4(0) , Chelsea Hse.) Facts On File, Inc.

Crumbley, Paul & Gantt, Patricia. Student's Encyclopedia of Great American Writers. 2008. (Great American Writers Ser.). 448p. (gr. 6-12). 85.00 (*978-0-8160-6089-4(4)) Facts On File, Inc.

Crutcher, Chris. King of the Mild Frontier: An Ill-Advised Autobiography. (J). 2003. (Illus.). 208p. (gr. 7-12). 16.99 (978-0-06-050249-2(5)); 2004. 272p. reprint ed. pap. 6.99 (978-0-06-050251-5(7) , HarperTeen) HarperCollins Pubs.

Currie-McGhee, Leanne K. Mattie Stepanek: Inspirational Poet. 2007. (J). (gr. 4-8). 27.45 (*978-0-7377-3637-3(2) , Greenhaven Pr., Inc.) Thomson Gale.

Dailey, Donna. Tamora Pierce. 2006. (Who Wrote That? Ser.). (Illus.). 152p. (J). 30.00 (978-0-7910-8795-4(6) , Chelsea Hse.) Facts On File, Inc.

Daniel, Susanna. Karen Cushman. annot. ed. 2005. (Library of Author Biographies). (Illus.). 112p. (J). (ps-ps). lib. bdg. 26.50 (978-1-4042-0463-8(6)) Rosen Publishing Group, Inc., The.

—Lois Lowry. 2003. (Library of Author Biographies). (Illus.). 112p. (YA). (gr. 5-8). lib. bdg. 26.50 (978-0-8239-3775-2(5) , Rosen Central) Rosen Publishing Group, Inc., The.

Darraj, Susan Muaddi. Amy Tan. 2007. (Asian Americans of Achievement Ser.). 112p. (gr. 6-12). 30.00 (978-0-7910-9269-9(0) , Chelsea Hse.) Facts On File, Inc.

Datnow, Claire L. American Science Fiction & Fantasy Writers. 1999. (Collective Biographies Ser.). (Illus.). 128p. (YA). (gr. 6-12). lib. bdg. 26.60 (978-0-7660-1090-1(2)) Enslow Pubs., Inc.

de Paola, Tomie. Here We All Are. de Paola, Tomie, illus. 2002. 13.19 (978-1-4046-0935-8(0)) Book Wholesalers, Inc.

—Here We All Are. de Paola, Tomie, illus. 2001. (Illus.). 80p. (J). pap. 5.99 (978-0-698-11909-3(6) , Putnam Juvenile) Penguin Group (USA) Inc.

—Here We All Are. unabr. ed. 2004. (Fairmount Avenue Ser.: Vol. 2). 80p. (J). (gr. 2-5). pap. 17.00 incl. audio (978-0-8072-0655-3(5) , LDTR 246 SP, Listening Library) Random Hse. Audio Publishing Group.

—Here We All Are. 2001. 12.79 (978-0-606-22515-1(3)); (gr. 3-6). lib. bdg. 14.15 (978-0-613-44390-6(X)) Tandem Library Bks.

—Here We All Are: A 26 Fairmount Avenue Book. 2000. (26 Fairmount Avenue Bks.). (Illus.). 80p. (J). (gr. 2-6). 13.99 (978-0-399-23496-5(9) , Putnam Juvenile) Penguin Group (USA) Inc.

—I'm Still Scared: A 26 Fairmount Avenue Book. 2006. (Illus.). 96p. (J). (gr. 1-4). 13.99 (978-0-399-24502-2(2) , Putnam Juvenile) Penguin Group (USA) Inc.

—On My Way: A 26 Fairmount Avenue Book. (J). 2002. 80p. (gr. 2-5). pap. 5.99 (978-0-698-11948-2(7)); 2001. (Illus.). 1p. (gr. 4-7). 13.99 (978-0-399-23583-2(3)) Penguin Group (USA) Inc. (Putnam Juvenile).

—On My Way: A 26 Fairmount Avenue Book. 2002. (gr. 3-6). lib. bdg. 14.15 (978-0-613-45300-4(X)) Tandem Library Bks.

—On My Way Vol. 3: A 26 Fairmount Avenue Book. unabr. ed. 2004. (Fairmount Avenue Ser.: Vol. 3). 75p. (J). (gr. 2-5). pap. 17.00 incl. audio (978-0-8072-0656-0(3) , LFTR 247 SP, Listening Library) Random Hse. Audio Publishing Group.

—Things Will Never Be the Same: A 26 Fairmount Avenue Book. 2003. (Illus.). 96p. (J). (ps-5). 13.99 (978-0-399-23982-3(0) , Putnam Juvenile) Penguin Group (USA) Inc.

—What a Year. (26 Fairmount Avenue Book Ser.). (Illus.). 80p. (J). 2003. (gr. 2-5). pap. 5.99 (978-0-14-250158-0(1) , Puffin); 2002. 13.99 (978-0-399-23797-3(6) , Putnam Juvenile) Penguin Group (USA) Inc.

—What a Year, Vol. 4. 2004. (26 Fairmount Avenue Ser.). 75p. (J). (gr. 2-5). pap. 17.00 incl. audio (978-0-8072-0657-7(1) , Listening Library) Random Hse. Audio Publishing Group.

—Why? The War Years. 2007. (26 Fairmount Avenue Book Ser.). (Illus.). 96p. (J). (gr. 2-4). 14.99 (978-0-399-24692-0(4) , Putnam Juvenile) Penguin Group (USA) Inc.

—26 Fairmount Avenue. de Paola, Tomie, illus. 2005. (Illus.). 58p. (J). (gr. k-4). reprint ed. 14.00 (978-0-7567-8722-6(X)) DIANE Publishing Co.

Dean, Tanya. Theodor Geisel (Dr. Seuss) 2002. (Who Wrote That? Ser.). (Illus.). 112p. (gr. 6-12). 30.00 (978-0-7910-6724-6(6) , Chelsea Hse.) Facts On File, Inc.

DePaola, Tomie. I'm Still Scared: A 26 Fairmount Avenue Book. 2007. 96p. (J). (gr. 2-6). pap. 5.99 (978-0-14-240826-1(3) , Puffin) Penguin Group (USA) Inc.

Diorio, Mary Ann L. A Student's Guide to Nathaniel Hawthorne. 2004. (Understanding Literature Ser.). (Illus.). 160p. (YA). lib. bdg. 27.93 (978-0-7660-2283-6(8)) Enslow Pubs., Inc.

Ditchfield, Christin. Louisa May Alcott: Author of Little Women. 2005. (Great Life Stories Ser.). (Illus.). 111p. (J). (gr. 6-8). 30.50 (978-0-531-12403-1(7) , Watts, Franklin) Scholastic Library Publishing.

Dr. Suess. 2003. (Rookie Bios Pb Ser.). pap. 4.95 (978-0-516-24725-0(5) , Children's Pr.) Scholastic Library Publishing.

Drew, Bernard A. 100 More Popular Young Adult Authors: Biographical Sketches & Bibliographies. 2002. (Popular Authors Ser.). (Illus.). 500p. 65.00 (978-1-56308-920-6(3) , LU9203) Libraries Unlimited, Inc.

Dunkleberger, Amy. A Student's Guide to Arthur Miller. 2005. (Understanding Literature Ser.). (Illus.). 160p. (YA). (gr. 7-13). lib. bdg. 27.93 (978-0-7660-2432-8(6)) Enslow Pubs., Inc.

Dyer, Daniel. Jack London: A Biography. 2002. 240p. (J). pap. 5.99 (978-0-590-22217-4(1)) Scholastic, Inc.

Ehrlich, Amy, ed. When I Was Your Age Vol. 2: Original Stories about Growing Up. 2006. (Illus.). 187p. (YA). (gr. 8-11). reprint ed. 17.00 (978-1-4223-5199-4(8)) DIANE Publishing Co.

Elleman, Barbara. Virginia Lee Burton: A Life in Art. 2002. (Illus.). 144p. (J). (gr. 7 up). tchr. ed. 20.00 (978-0-618-00342-6(8)) Houghton Mifflin Co. Trade & Reference Div.

Ellsworth, Mary Ellen. Gertrude Chandler Warner & the Boxcar Children. 2002. (gr. 3-6). lib. bdg. 15.25 (978-0-613-75732-4(7)) Tandem Library Bks.

—Gertrude Chandler Warner & the Boxcar Children. DeJohn, Marie, illus. 2004. (Boxcar Children Ser.). 64p. (J). (gr. 2-7). pap. 6.95 (978-0-8075-2838-9(2)) Whitman, Albert & Co.

Emerson, Ralph Waldo. Emerson's Essays. 2006. (Bloom's Modern Critical Interpretations Ser.). 150p. 45.00 (978-0-7910-8118-1(4) , Chelsea Hse.) Facts On File, Inc.

Evans, Robert C. & Gantt, Patricia. Student's Encyclopedia of Great American Writers. 2008. (Great American Writers Ser.). 448p. (gr. 6-12). 85.00 (*978-0-8160-6090-0(8)) Facts On File, Inc.

Fine, Edith Hope. Gary Paulsen: Author & Wilderness Adventurer. 2000. (People to Know Ser.). (Illus.). 128p. (YA). (gr. 6-12). lib. bdg. 26.60 (978-0-7660-1146-5(1)) Enslow Pubs., Inc.

Fleming, Denise. Maker of Things. Bowers, Karen & Bowers, Karen, photos by. 2002. (Meet the Author Ser.). (Illus.). 32p. (J). (gr. 2-5). 14.95 (978-1-57274-596-4(7) , 729) Owen, Richard C. Pubs., Inc.

Florence, Donne. John Steinbeck: America's Author. 2000. (People to Know Ser.). (Illus.). 128p. (YA). (gr. 6-12). lib. bdg. 26.60 (978-0-7660-1150-2(X)) Enslow Pubs., Inc.

Florian, Douglas. See for Your Self. Florian, Douglas & Taplinger, Lee, photos by. 2005. (Meet the Author Ser.). (Illus.). 32p. (J). 14.95 (978-1-57274-821-7(4) , 731) Owen, Richard C. Pubs., Inc.

Foran, Jill. Dr. Seuss. 2002. (My Favorite Writer Ser.). (Illus.). 32p. (J). lib. bdg. 16.95 (978-1-59036-028-6(1)) Weigl Pubs., Inc.

Ford, Carin T. Dr. Seuss: Best-Loved Author. 2003. (People to Know Ser.). (Illus.). 128p. (J). (gr. 6-12). lib. bdg. 26.60 (978-0-7660-2106-8(8)) Enslow Pubs., Inc.

—Laura Ingalls Wilder: Real-Life Pioneer of the Little House Books. 2003. (People to Know Ser.). (Illus.). 112p. (J). lib. bdg. 26.60 (978-0-7660-2105-1(X)) Enslow Pubs., Inc.

Frampton, David. Mr. Ferlinghetti's Poem. 2006. (Illus.). 32p. (J). (gr. k-4). 18.00 (978-0-8028-5290-8(4) , Eerdmans Bks For Young Readers) Eerdmans, William B. Publishing Co.

Frisch, Aaron. Edgar Allan Poe. 2005. (Voices in Poetry Ser.). (Illus.). 48p. (gr. 5-9). 21.95 (978-1-58341-344-9(8) , Creative Education) Creative Co., The.

Fullen, Marilyn K. Great Black Writers. 2002. (Contributions Ser.). (Illus.). 64p. (J). 12.95 (978-0-940880-66-5(0)); pap. 6.95 (978-0-940880-67-2(9)) Open Hand Publishing, LLC.

Gaines, Ann. Christopher Paul Curtis. 2004. (Blue Banner Biography Ser.). (Illus.). 32p. (J). lib. bdg. (978-1-58415-330-6(X)) Mitchell Lane Pubs., Inc.

Gaines, Ann Graham. Christopher Paul Curtis. 2001. (Real-Life Reader Biography Ser.). (Illus.). 32p. (J). (gr. 3-8). lib. bdg. 15.95 (978-1-58415-076-3(9)) Mitchell Lane Pubs., Inc.

—Dr. Seuss. 2001. (Real-Life Reader Biography Ser.). (Illus.). 32p. (J). (gr. 3-8). lib. bdg. 15.95 (978-1-58415-074-9(2)) Mitchell Lane Pubs., Inc.

—Gary Paulsen. 2001. (Real-Life Reader Biography Ser.). (Illus.). 32p. (J). (gr. 3-8). lib. bdg. 15.95 (978-1-58415-077-0(7)) Mitchell Lane Pubs., Inc.

—Maurice Sendak. l.t. ed. 2001. (Real-Life Reader Biography Ser.). (Illus.). 32p. (gr. 3-8). lib. bdg. 24.95 (978-1-58415-079-4(3)) Mitchell Lane Pubs., Inc.

Gantt, Patricia. Student's Encyclopedia of Great American Writers. 2008. (Great American Writers Ser.). 448p. (gr. 6-12). 85.00 (***978-0-8160-6092-4(4)***) Facts On File, Inc.

—Student's Encyclopedia of Great American Writers Set, 5-Volumes. 2008. (Great American Writers Ser.). 2240p. (gr. 6-12). 425.00 (***978-0-8160-6087-0(8)***) Facts On File, Inc.

Giff, Patricia Reilly. Don't Tell the Girls: A Family Memoir. 2005. (Illus.). 144p. (J). 16.95 (978-0-8234-1813-8(8)) Holiday Hse., Inc.

Gillis, Jennifer Blizin. Mercy Otis Warren: Author & Historian. 2005. (Signature Lives Ser.). (Illus.). 112p. (J). (gr. 5-7). (978-0-7565-0982-8(3)) Compass Point Bks.

Goldsmith, Howard. Mark Twain at Work! Habbas, Frank, illus. 2003. (Ready-to-Read Childhood of the Famous Americans Ser.). 32p. (J). pap. 3.99 (978-0-689-85399-9(8) , Aladdin) Simon & Schuster Children's Publishing.

—Mark Twain at Work! 2003. (gr. k-3). lib. bdg. 11.80 (978-0-613-66461-5(2)) Tandem Library Bks.

Gormley, Beatrice. Laura Ingalls Wilder: Young Pioneer. Henderson, Meryl, illus. 2001. (Childhood of Famous Americans Ser.). 224p. (J). (gr. 3-7). pap. 5.99 (978-0-689-83924-5(3) , Aladdin) Simon & Schuster Children's Publishing.

—Laura Ingalls Wilder: Young Pioneer. 2001. (Childhood of Famous Americans Ser.). (Illus.). (J). (978-0-606-21290-8(6)) Tandem Library Bks.

Griskey, Michele. Emily Dickinson. 2006. (Poets & Playwrights Ser.). (Illus.). 112p. (YA). (gr. 6-12). lib. bdg. 37.10 (978-1-58415-429-7(2)) Mitchell Lane Pubs., Inc.

—Harriet Beecher Stowe. 2005. (Classic Storytellers Ser.). (Illus.). 48p. (J). lib. bdg. 29.95 (978-1-58415-375-7(X)) Mitchell Lane Pubs., Inc.

Grolier Educational Staff. Lives & Works: Young Adult Authors, 8 vols. 1999. (YA). lib. bdg. 265.00 (978-0-7172-9227-1(4) , Grolier) Scholastic Library Publishing.

Hamilton, John. The Golden Age & Beyond. 2007. (World of Science Fiction Ser.). (Illus.). 32p. 24.21 (978-1-59679-989-9(7)) ABDO Publishing Co.

—Modern Masters of Science Fiction. 2007. (World of Science Fiction Ser.). (Illus.). 32p. (J). (gr. 4-6). lib. bdg. 24.21 (978-1-59679-990-5(0) , ABDO & Daughters) ABDO Publishing Co.

—Pioneers of Science Fiction. 2007. (World of Science Fiction Ser.). 32p. 24.21 (978-1-59679-992-9(7)) ABDO Publishing Co.

Hamilton, Sue L. Masters of Horror. 2007. (ENG., Illus.). 32p. (YA). lib. bdg. 24.21 (***978-1-59928-770-6(6)*** , ABDO & Daughters) ABDO Publishing Co.

Harcourt School Publishers Staff. Autores Populares Estadounidenses de Cuentos Infantiles: On Level. 3rd ed. 2002. (Trofeos Ser.). (SPA., Illus.). pap. 6.80 (978-0-15-324274-8(4)) Harcourt Schl. Pubs.

Harkins, Susan and William. Walter Dean Myers. 2007. (YA). lib. bdg. (***978-1-58415-534-8(5)***) Mitchell Lane Pubs., Inc.

Harris, Laurie Lanzen. Biography for Beginners: All Authors. 2005. (Illus.). 300p. (978-1-931360-31-9(6)) Favorable Impressions.

Hart, Joyce. Native Son: The Story of Richard Wright. 2004. (World Writers Ser.). (Illus.). 128p. (YA). (gr. 6-12). 23.95 (978-1-931798-06-8(0)) Reynolds, Morgan Inc.

Haugen, Brenda. Harriet Beecher Stowe: Author & Advocate. 2004. (Signature Lives Ser.). (Illus.). 112p. (J). 30.60 (978-0-7565-0822-7(3) , 1240140) Compass Point Bks.

Herrera, Juan Felipe. Calling the Doves. 2001. Tr. of El Canto De Las Palomos. (SPA.). (gr. 3-6). lib. bdg. 16.40 (978-0-613-34098-4(1)) Tandem Library Bks.

—El Canto de las Palomas/Calling the Doves. ed. 2004. (ENG & SPA., Illus.). (J). (gr. 3-6). spiral bd. (978-0-616-14607-1(8)) Canadian National Institute for the Blind/Institut National Canadien pour les Aveugles.

Hill, Christine M. Ten Terrific Authors for Teens. 2000. (Collective Biographies Ser.). (Illus.). 128p. (J). (gr. 6-12). lib. bdg. 26.60 (978-0-7660-1380-3(4)) Enslow Pubs., Inc.

Hill, Mary. Harriet Beecher Stowe. 2003. (Welcome Book Ser.). (Illus.). 24p. (J). 18.00 (978-0-516-25865-2(6) , Children's Pr.) Scholastic Library Publishing.

Hillstrom, Laurie. Gabriel Garcia Marquez. 2007. (Twentieth Century Most Influential Hispanics Ser.). (Illus.). 128p. (J). (gr. 7-10). 31.20 (***978-1-4205-0020-2(1)*** , Lucent Bks.) Thomson Gale.

Hinton-Johnson, Kaavonia. Jacqueline Woodson. 2007. (Classic Storytellers Ser.). (Illus.). 48p. (J). lib. bdg. 29.95 (***978-1-58415-533-1(7)***) Mitchell Lane Pubs., Inc.

Hobby, Blake & Gantt, Patricia. Student's Encyclopedia of Great American Writers. 2008. (Great American Writers Ser.). 448p. (gr. 6-12). 85.00 (***978-0-8160-6091-7(6)***) Facts On File, Inc.

Holt, Rinehart and Winston Staff. The Endless Steppe. 3rd ed. 2002. pap., stu. ed. 13.20 (978-0-03-067528-7(6)) Holt, Rinehart & Winston.

—The Endless Steppe: With Connections. 3rd ed. 2002. 14.64 (978-0-03-067527-0(8)) Holt, Rinehart & Winston.

Houghton, Gillian. Mildred Taylor. 2004. (Library of Author Biographies). (Illus.). 112p. (YA). 26.50 (978-1-4042-0330-3(3)) Rosen Publishing, Inc.

Hurtig, Jennifer. Maurice Sendak. 2007. (My Favorite Writer Ser.). (J). (978-1-59036-485-7(6)) Weigl Pubs., Inc.

I Know Why the Caged Bird Sings. 1998. 44p. (YA). 11.95 (978-1-56137-634-6(5) , NU6345SP) Novel Units, Inc.

Ishizuka, Kathy. Asian-American Authors. 2000. (Collective Biographies Ser.). (Illus.). 128p. (YA). (gr. 6-12). lib. bdg. 26.60 (978-0-7660-1376-6(6)) Enslow Pubs., Inc.

—John Grisham: Best-Selling Author. 2003. (People to Know Ser.). (Illus.). 112p. (J). lib. bdg. 26.60 (978-0-7660-2102-0(5)) Enslow Pubs., Inc.

Jones, Brenn. Learning about Achievement from the Life of Maya Angelou. 2002. (Character Building Book Ser.). (Illus.). 24p. (J). (gr. 3). lib. bdg. 18.75 (978-0-8239-5780-4(2) , PowerKids Pr.) Rosen Publishing Group, Inc., The.

Jones, Jen. Judy Blume: Fearless Storyteller for Teens. 2008. (***978-0-7660-2960-6(3)***) Enslow Pubs., Inc.

Judson, Karen. Isaac Asimov: Master of Science Fiction. 1998. (People to Know Ser.). (Illus.). 112p. (YA). (gr. 6-12). lib. bdg. 26.60 (978-0-7660-1031-4(7)) Enslow Pubs., Inc.

Kehret, Peg. Five Pages a Day: A Writer's Journey. 2002. 192p. (J). (gr. 3-8). 15.95 (978-0-8075-8650-1(1)) Whitman, Albert & Co.

Kenschaft, Lori J. Lydia Maria Child: The Quest for Racial Justice. 2002. (Oxford Portraits Ser.). (Illus.). 128p. (YA). 28.00 (978-0-19-513257-1(2)) Oxford Univ. Pr., Inc.

Kent, Zachary. Edgar Allan Poe: Tragic Poet & Master of Mystery. 2001. (Historical American Biographies Ser.). (Illus.). 128p. (J). (gr. 6-12). lib. bdg. 26.60 (978-0-7660-1600-2(5)) Enslow Pubs., Inc.

Kimbrel, William. Bloom's How to Write about Ernest Hemingway. 2007. 256p. (gr. 9). 45.00 (***978-0-7910-9485-3(5)*** , Chelsea Hse.) Facts On File, Inc.

Kimmel, Eric A. Tuning Up: A Visit with Eric Kimmel. Childers, Basil, photos by. 2005. (Meet the Author Ser.). (Illus.). 32p. (J). 14.95 (978-1-57274-822-4(2) , 732) Owen, Richard C. Pubs., Inc.

Kite, L. Patricia. Maya Angelou. 2006. (Just the Facts Biographies Ser.). (Illus.). 112p. (J). 27.93 (978-0-8225-3426-6(6)); pap. (***978-0-8225-5997-9(8)***) Lerner Publishing Group. (Lerner Pubns.).

Kjelle, Marylou. Katherine Paterson. 2004. (Classic Storytellers Ser.). (Illus.). 48p. (J). (gr. 4-8). lib. bdg. 20.95 (978-1-58415-268-2(0)) Mitchell Lane Pubs., Inc.

Kjelle, Marylou Morano. Francis Scott Key. 2006. (What's So Great About... ? Ser.). (Illus.). 32p. (J). (gr. 1-4). lib. bdg. (978-1-58415-474-7(8)) Mitchell Lane Pubs., Inc.

Kjelle, Marylou Morano. S. E. Hinton: Author of the Outsiders. 2007. (Authors Teens Love Ser.). (Illus.). 112p. (J). (gr. 6). lib. bdg. 31.93 (***978-0-7660-2720-6(1)***) Enslow Pubs., Inc.

Krull, Kathleen. The Boy on Fairfield Street: How Ted Geisel Grew up to Become Dr. Seuss. Johnson, Steve & Fancher, Lou, illus. 2004. 48p. (J). (gr. 1-7). 16.95 (978-0-375-82298-8(4)); lib. bdg. 18.99 (978-0-375-92298-5(9)) Random Hse. Children's Bks. (Random Hse. Bks. for Young Readers).

Kudlinski, Kathleen. Dr. Seuss: Young Author & Artist. Henderson, Meryl, illus. 2005. 184p. (J). lib. bdg. 18.46 (***978-1-4242-2201-8(X)***) Fitzgerald Bks.

Kurtz, Jane. Jane Kurtz & You. 2007. (Author & YOU Ser.: No. 8). (Illus.). 204p. 35.00 (978-1-59158-295-3(4) , LU2954) Libraries Unlimited, Inc.

Lange, Brenda. Edward Stratemeyer. 2003. (Who Wrote That? Ser.). (Illus.). 112p. (gr. 6-12). 30.00 (978-0-7910-7621-7(0) , Chelsea Hse.) Facts On File, Inc.

Lappi, Megan. Will Hobbs. 2007. (My Favorite Writer Ser.). (J). pap. (978-1-59036-489-5(9)); lib. bdg. (978-1-59036-488-8(0)) Weigl Pubs., Inc.

Lasky, Kathryn. A Brilliant Streak: The Making of Mark Twain. Moser, Barry, illus. 1998. 48p. (J). (gr. 1-7). 18.00 (978-0-15-252110-3(0)) Harcourt Children's Bks.

Lazo, Caroline Evensen. F. Scott Fitzgerald: Voice of the Jazz Age. 2002. (Lerner Long Biographies Ser.). (Illus.). 128p. (J). lib. bdg. 27.93 (978-0-8225-0074-2(4) , Lerner Pubns.) Lerner Publishing Group.

Leonard, Tara. The Gift of Imagination: John Steinbeck's Childhood. Scott, Laura, illus. 2001. 32p. (J). (gr. 2-4). pap. 12.95 (978-1-57931-150-6(4)) ToucanEd Pubns.

Lester, Helen. Author: A True Story. Lester, Helen, illus. 2002. (Illus.). 32p. (J). (gr. k-3). pap. 5.95 (978-0-618-26010-2(2) , Walter Lorraine) Houghton Mifflin Co. Trade & Reference Div.

Levin, Judy & Draper, Allison Stark. Christopher Paul Curtis. annot. ed. 2005. (Library of Author Biographies). (Illus.). 112p. (YA). (ps-ps). lib. bdg. 26.50 (978-1-4042-0458-4(X)) Rosen Publishing Group, Inc., The.

Levine, Stuart P. Dr. Seuss. 2000. (Importance of Ser.). (Illus.). 112p. (J). (gr. 7-10). 32.45 (978-1-56006-748-1(9) , Lucent Bks.) Thomson Gale.

Litwin, Laura Baskes. E. B. White: Beyond Charlotte's Web & Stuart Little. 2003. (People to Know Ser.). (Illus.). 112p. (J). lib. bdg. 26.60 (978-0-7660-2107-5(6)) Enslow Pubs., Inc.

—Zora Neale Hurston: I Have Been in Sorrow's Kitchen. 2007. (African-American Biography Library). (Illus.). 128p. (YA). (gr. 6 up). lib. bdg. 31.93 (978-0-7660-2536-3(5)) Enslow Pubs., Inc.

London, Jonathan. Tell Me a Story. Shahan, Sherry, photos by. 1998. (Meet the Author Ser.). (Illus.). 32p. (J). (gr. 2-5). 14.95 (978-1-57274-194-2(5) , 720) Owen, Richard C. Pubs., Inc.

Lopez, Barry. About This Life: Journeys on the Threshold of Memory. 1999. (gr. 7-12). lib. bdg. 22.25 (978-0-613-24087-1(1)) Tandem Library Bks.

Lowry, Lois. Looking Back: A Book of Memories. 1998. (Illus.). 192p. (J). (gr. 4-6). tchr. ed. 17.00 (978-0-395-89543-6(X) , Walter Lorraine) Houghton Mifflin Co. Trade & Reference Div.

—Looking Back: A Book of Memories. 2000. (Illus.). 192p. (J). (gr. 4-7). pap. 14.95 (978-0-385-32699-5(8) , Delacorte Bks. for Young Readers) Random Hse. Children's Bks.

—Looking Back: A Book of Memories. 2000. (Illus.). (J). (978-0-606-18106-8(7)) Tandem Library Bks.

Ludwig, Elisa. Shel Silverstein. 2003. (Who Wrote That? Ser.). (Illus.). 112p. (gr. 6-12). 30.00 (978-0-7910-7624-8(5) , Chelsea Hse.) Facts On File, Inc.

Lynette, Rachel. Shel Silverstein. 2006. (Inventors & Creators Ser.). 48p. (gr. 4-8). 27.45 (978-0-7377-3555-0(4) , Greenhaven Pr., Inc.) Thomson Gale.

Lyon, George Ella & Soentpiet, Chris K. A Sign. 1998. (Illus.). 32p. (J). (gr. k-4). pap. 15.95 (978-0-531-30073-2(0) , Orchard Bks.) Scholastic, Inc.

Macken, JoAnn Early. Gary Paulsen: Voice of Adventure & Survival. 2007. (Authors Teens Love Ser.). (Illus.). 104p. (J). (gr. 6 up). lib. bdg. 31.93 (978-0-7660-2721-3(X)) Enslow Pubs., Inc.

MacLeod, Elizabeth. Mark Twain: An American Star. 2008. 32p. pap. (***978-1-55337-909-6(8)***) Kids Can Pr., Ltd.

Madison, Bob. American Horror Writers. 2001. (Collective Biographies Ser.). (Illus.). 104p. (YA). (gr. 6-12). lib. bdg. 26.60 (978-0-7660-1379-7(0)) Enslow Pubs., Inc.

Mangal, Melina. Mildred Taylor. 2004. (Classic Storytellers Ser.). (Illus.). 48p. (J). (gr. 4-8). lib. bdg. 20.95 (978-1-58415-311-5(3)) Mitchell Lane Pubs., Inc.

Mara, Wil. Laura Ingalls Wilder. 2003. (Rookie Biographies Ser.). (gr. 1-2). pap. 4.95 (978-0-516-27840-7(1)); (Illus.). 32p. (J). 20.50 (978-0-516-22855-6(2)) Scholastic Library Publishing. (Children's Pr.).

—Laura Ingalls Wilder. 2003. (YA). lib. bdg. 12.95 (978-0-613-67639-7(4)) Tandem Library Bks.

Marcovitz, Hal. Bruce Coville. 2005. (Who Wrote That? Ser.). (Illus.). 128p. (J). (gr. 6-12). 30.00 (978-0-7910-8656-8(9) , Chelsea Hse.) Facts On File, Inc.

—Lawrence Yep. 2008. (Who Wrote That? Ser.). 128p. (gr. 6-12). 30.00 (***978-0-7910-9527-0(4)*** , Chelsea Hse.) Facts On File, Inc.

—R. L. Stine. 2005. (Who Wrote That? Ser.). (Illus.). 134p. (YA). (gr. 6-12). lib. bdg. 30.00 (978-0-7910-8659-9(3) , Chelsea Hse.) Facts On File, Inc.

—Scott O'Dell. 2007. (Who Wrote That? Ser.). 112p. (J). (gr. 6-12). 30.00 (***978-0-7910-9526-3(6)*** , Chelsea Hse.) Facts On File, Inc.

Marcovitz, Hal. Will Hobbs. 2005. (Who Wrote That? Ser.). (Illus.). 124p. (J). (gr. 6-12). lib. bdg. 30.00 (978-0-7910-8657-5(7) , Chelsea Hse.) Facts On File, Inc.

Marcus, Leonard. Margaret Wise Brown: Awakened by the Moon. 1999. (gr. 7-12). lib. bdg. 24.55 (978-0-613-29289-4(8)) Tandem Library Bks.

Marcus, Leonard S. Side by Side: Five Favorite Picture-Book Teams Go to Work. (Illus.). 64p. (J). 2006. pap. 11.95 (978-0-8027-9616-5(8)); 2001. (gr. 3 up). 22.95 (978-0-8027-8778-1(9)) Walker & Co.

Marinelli, Deborah A. Virginia Hamilton. 2003. (Library of Author Biographies). (Illus.). 112p. (YA). (gr. 5-8). lib. bdg. 26.50 (978-0-8239-3777-6(1) , Rosen Central) Rosen Publishing Group, Inc., The.

Mass, Wendy. Great Authors of Children's Literature. 1999. (History Makers Ser.). (Illus.). 112p. (YA). (gr. 7-10). 28.70 (978-1-56006-589-0(3) , Lucent Bks.) Thomson Gale.

—Ray Bradbury: Master of Science Fiction & Fantasy. 2004. (Authors Teens Love Ser.). (Illus.). 104p. (J). lib. bdg. 26.60 (978-0-7660-2240-9(4)) Enslow Pubs., Inc.

McArthur, Debra. A Student's Guide to Edgar Allan Poe. 2006. (Understanding Literature Ser.). (Illus.). 160p. (J). lib. bdg. 27.93 (978-0-7660-2437-3(7)) Enslow Pubs., Inc.

McCarthy, Pat. Henry David Thoreau: Writer, Thinker, Naturalist. 2003. (Historical American Biographies Ser.). (Illus.). 128p. (J). (gr. 6-12). lib. bdg. 26.60 (978-0-7660-1978-2(0)) Enslow Pubs., Inc.

McElroy, Lisa Tucker & Cobb, Abby. Meet My Grandmother: She's a Children's Book Author. Benjamin, Joel, photos by. 2001. (Grandmothers at Work Ser.). (Illus.). 32p. (gr. 2-4). lib. bdg. 22.90 (978-0-7613-1972-6(7) , Millbrook Pr.) Lerner Publishing Group.

McGinty, Alice B. Meet Daniel Pinkwater. 2003. (About the Author Ser.). (Illus.). 24p. (J). lib. bdg. 18.75 (978-0-8239-6406-2(X)) Rosen Publishing Group, Inc., The.

—Meet Eve Bunting. 2003. (About the Author Ser.). (Illus.). 24p. (J). lib. bdg. 18.75 (978-0-8239-6411-6(6) , PowerKids Pr.) Rosen Publishing Group, Inc., The.

—Meet Gail Carson Levine. 2003. (About the Author Ser.). (Illus.). 24p. (J). lib. bdg. 18.75 (978-0-8239-6409-3(4) , PowerKids Pr.) Rosen Publishing Group, Inc., The.

—Meet Jane Yolen. 2003. (About the Author Ser.). (Illus.). 24p. (J). lib. bdg. 18.75 (978-0-8239-6407-9(8) , PowerKids Pr.) Rosen Publishing Group, Inc., The.

—Meet Jerry Spinelli. 2003. (About the Author Ser.). (Illus.). 24p. (J). lib. bdg. 18.75 (978-0-8239-6408-6(6) , PowerKids Pr.) Rosen Publishing Group, Inc., The.

—Meet Laurence Yep. 2003. (About the Author Ser.). (Illus.). 24p. (J). lib. bdg. 18.75 (978-0-8239-6410-9(8) , PowerKids Pr.) Rosen Publishing Group, Inc., The.

McKissack, Patricia C. & McKissack, Fredrick L. Zora Neale Hurston: Writer & Storyteller. rev. ed. 2002. (Great African Americans Ser.). (Illus.). 32p. (J). (gr. 1-4). lib. bdg. 18.60 (978-0-7660-1694-1(3)) Enslow Pubs., Inc.

Medina, Jane. Tomas Rivera. Martinez, Edward, illus. 2004. (Green Light Reader Ser., Level 2). 24p. (J). 12.95 (978-0-15-205146-4(5)); pap. 3.95 (978-0-15-205145-7(7)) Harcourt Children's Bks. (Green Light Readers).

Meehan, Elizabeth. Twentieth-Century American Writers. 2000. (History Makers Ser.). (Illus.). 112p. (YA). (gr. 7-10). 27.45 (978-1-56006-671-2(7) , Lucent Bks.) Thomson Gale.

Meister, Cari. Beverly Cleary. 2001. (Children's Authors Ser.). (Illus.). 24p. (J). (gr. k-6). lib. bdg. 21.35 (978-1-57765-480-3(3) , Checkerboard Library) ABDO Publishing Co.

—H. A. Rey. 2001. (Children's Authors Ser.). (Illus.). 24p. (J). (gr. k-6). lib. bdg. 21.35 (978-1-57765-481-0(1) , Checkerboard Library) ABDO Publishing Co.

—R. L. Stine. 2001. (Children's Authors Ser.). (Illus.). 24p. (J). (gr. k-6). lib. bdg. 21.35 (978-1-57765-484-1(6) , Checkerboard Library) ABDO Publishing Co.

—Shel Silverstein. 2001. (Children's Authors Ser.). (Illus.). 24p. (J). (gr. k-6). lib. bdg. 21.35 (978-1-57765-483-4(8) , Checkerboard Library) ABDO Publishing Co.

Meltzer, Milton. Edgar Allan Poe: A Biography. 2003. (Single Titles Ser.). (Illus.). 144p. (gr. 7 up). lib. bdg. 31.90 (978-0-7613-2910-7(2) , Twenty-First Century Bks.) Lerner Publishing Group.

—Henry David Thoreau: A Biography. 2007. (J). spiral bd. 31.93 (978-0-8225-5893-4(9) , Twenty-First Century Bks.) Lerner Publishing Group.

—Up Close: John Steinbeck: John Steinbeck. 2008. 208p. (YA). (gr. 6). 16.99 (***978-0-670-06139-6(5)*** , Viking Juvenile) Penguin Group (USA) Inc.

—Willa Cather: A Biography. 2008. (J). (***978-0-8225-7604-4(X)***) Twenty First Century Bks.

Micklos, John, Jr. Jerry Spinelli: Master Teller of Teen Tales. 2007. (Authors Teens Love Ser.). (Illus.). 104p. (J). (gr. 6 up). lib. bdg. 31.93 (978-0-7660-2718-3(X)) Enslow Pubs., Inc.

Middleton, Haydn. Mark Twain. 2001. (Creative Lives Ser.). (Illus.). 64p. (YA). (gr. 6-8). lib. bdg. 27.07 (978-1-58810-205-8(X)) Heinemann Library.

Miller, William. Zora Hurston y El Arbol Sonador. 2001. (Illus.). (J). (978-0-606-21545-9(X)) Tandem Library Bks.

—Zora Hurston Y el Arbol Sonador. 2001. (SPA.). (gr. k-3). lib. bdg. 15.25 (978-0-613-36034-0(6)) Tandem Library Bks.

Myers, Walter Dean. Bad Boy: A Memoir. l.t. ed. 2005. (Thorndike Press Large Print the Literacy Bridge Ser.). 269p. (978-0-7862-7537-3(5)) Thorndike Pr.

Nault, Jennifer. Judy Blume. 2002. (My Favorite Writer Ser.). (Illus.). 32p. (J). lib. bdg. 18.20 (978-1-59036-025-5(7)) Weigl Pubs., Inc.

Naylor, Phyllis Reynolds. How I Came to Be a Writer. 2000. (J). 11.64 (978-0-606-20087-5(8)) Tandem Library Bks.

North, Sterling. Rascal. 2004. (Illus.). 240p. (J). pap. 5.99 (978-0-14-240252-8(4) , Puffin) Penguin Group (USA) Inc.

—Rascal. unabr. ed. 1998. 189p. (J). (gr. 4-7). pap. 36.00 incl. audio (978-0-8072-7897-0(1) , 1124-AB, Listening Library) Random Hse. Audio Publishing Group.

—Rascal. unabr. ed. 1998. (YA). Class Set. 100.70 incl. audio (978-0-7887-2541-8(6) , 46711); Homework Set. (gr. 7). 43.24 incl. audio (978-0-7887-2236-3(0) , 40720) Recorded Bks., LLC.

—Rascal. 2001. (SPA.). (J). (978-0-606-20879-6(8)) Tandem Library Bks.

Numeroff, Laura Joffe. If You Give an Author a Pencil. Shahan, Sherry, illus. 2002. (Meet the Author Ser.). 32p. (J). (gr. 2-5). 14.95 (978-1-57274-595-7(9) , 727) Owen, Richard C. Pubs., Inc.

O'Hara, Megan, ed. The Girlhood Diary of Wanda Gag, 1908-1909: Portrait of a Young Artist. 2000. (Blue Earth Books). (Illus.). 32p. (J). (gr. 3-4). lib. bdg. 22.60 (978-0-7368-0598-8(2) , Bridgestone Bks.) Capstone Pr., Inc.

Pallotta, Jerry. Read a Zillion Books. 2002. (Illus.). 32p. (J). 14.95 (978-1-57274-597-1(5)) Owen, Richard C. Pubs., Inc.

Parish, James Robert. Stephen King—Author. 2004. (Ferguson Career Biographies Ser.). (Illus.). 144p. (J). (gr. 6-12). 25.00 (978-0-8160-5543-2(2) , Ferguson Publishing Co.) Facts On File, Inc.

Parker-Rock, Michelle. Bruce Coville: An Author Kids Love. 2008. (Authors Kids Love Ser.). (Illus.). 48p. (J). (gr. 3-4). lib. bdg. 23.93 (978-0-7660-2755-8(4) , Enslow Elementary) Enslow Pubs., Inc.

Parker-Rock, Michelle. Jack Gantos: An Author Kids Love. 2008. (Authors Kids Love Ser.). (Illus.). 48p. (J). (gr. 3-4). lib. bdg. 23.93 (***978-0-7660-2756-5(2)*** , Enslow Elementary) Enslow Pubs., Inc.

Patchett, Kaye. Laura Ingalls Wilder. 2005. (Inventors & Creators Ser.). (Illus.). 48p. (J). (gr. 4-8). 26.20 (978-0-7377-3159-0(1) , Greenhaven Pr., Inc.) Thomson Gale.

Paterra, Elizabeth. Gary Paulsen. 2002. (Who Wrote That? Ser.). (Illus.). 112p. (gr. 6-12). 30.00 (978-0-7910-6723-9(8) , Chelsea Hse.) Facts On File, Inc.

Paulsen, Gary. Beet Fields: Memories of a Sixteenth Summer. 2002. (gr. 7-12). lib. bdg. 14.15 (978-0-613-49391-8(5)) Tandem Library Bks.

—The Beet Fields: Memories of a Sixteenth Summer. 2002. 176p. (YA). (gr. 9 up). mass mkt. 5.99 (978-0-440-41557-2(8) , Laurel Leaf) Random Hse. Children's Bks.

—Caught by the Sea. l.t. ed. 2002. 104p. (J). 22.95 (978-0-7862-4160-6(8)) Thomson Gale.

—Caught by the Sea: My Life on Boats. (Illus.). 112p. (YA). 2003. (gr. 7). mass mkt. 5.50 (978-0-440-40716-4(8) , Laurel Leaf); 2001. (gr. 5 up). 15.95 (978-0-385-32645-2(9) , Delacorte Bks. for Young Readers) Random Hse. Children's Bks.

—Caught by the Sea: My Life on Boats. 2003. (gr. 7-12). lib. bdg. 13.55 (978-0-613-72185-1(3)) Tandem Library Bks.

—Guts. 2002. 160p. (YA). (gr. 7 up). pap. 5.99 (978-0-440-40712-6(5) , Laurel Leaf) Random Hse. Children's Bks.

—Guts: The True Stories Behind Hatchet & the Brian Books. l.t. ed. 2001. (YA). 22.95 (978-0-7862-3407-3(5)) Thorndike Pr.

—How Angel Peterson Got His Name. 2003. 128p. (gr. 5 up). 12.95 (978-0-385-72949-9(9) , Lamb, Wendy) Random Hse. Children's Bks.

—My Life in Dog Years. 1999. (Illus.). 144p. (J). (gr. 5-9). pap. 5.99 (978-0-440-41471-1(7) , Yearling) Random Hse. Children's Bks.

—My Life in Dog Years. 1999. (gr. 7-12). lib. bdg. 13.00 (978-0-613-18320-8(7)) Tandem Library Bks.

—My Life in Dog Years. l.t. ed. 2003. 176p. pap. 10.95 (978-0-7862-6188-8(9)) Thorndike Pr.

—My Life in Dog Years. Paulsen, Ruth Wright, illus. l.t. ed. 2000. (Juvenile Ser.). 176p. (J). (gr. 4-7). 21.95 (978-0-7862-2740-2(0)) Thorndike Pr.

Peltak, Jennifer. Edgar Allan Poe. 2003. (Who Wrote That? Ser.). (Illus.). 112p. (gr. 6-12). 30.00 (978-0-7910-7622-4(9) , Chelsea Hse.) Facts On File, Inc.

Pingelton, Timothy J. A Student's Guide to Ernest Hemingway. 2005. (Understanding Literature Ser.). (Illus.). 160p. (YA). (gr. 7-13). lib. bdg. 27.93 (978-0-7660-2431-1(8)) Enslow Pubs., Inc.

Prince, April Jones. Who Was Mark Twain? O'Brien, John & Harrison, Nancy, illus. 2004. (Who Was...? Ser.). 112p. (J). (gr. 3-7). pap. 4.99 (978-0-448-43319-6(2) , Grosset & Dunlap) Penguin Group (USA) Inc.

Purslow, Neil. R.L. Stine/Neil Purslow. 2007. (My Favorite Writer Ser.). (J). (978-1-59036-487-1(2)); lib. bdg. (978-1-59036-486-4(4)) Weigl Pubs., Inc.

Raatma, Lucia. Laura Ingalls Wilder: Teacher & Author. 2001. (Career Biographies Ser.). (Illus.). 128p. (J). (gr. 6-12). 25.00 (978-0-89434-375-9(0) , F418, Ferguson Publishing Co.) Facts On File, Inc.

—Maya Angelou: Author & Documentary Filmmaker. 2000. (Career Biographies Ser.). (Illus.). 128p. (J). (gr. 6-12). 25.00 (978-0-89434-336-0(X) , F406, Ferguson Publishing Co.) Facts On File, Inc.

Randolph, Ryan P. Harriet Beecher Stowe: Author & Abolitionist. 2005. (Library of American Lives & Times). (Illus.). 112p. (J). (gr. 4-8). lib. bdg. 31.95 (978-0-8239-6623-3(2)) Rosen Publishing Group, Inc., The.

Rasmussen, R. Kent. Mark Twain for Kids: His Life & Times, 21 Activities. 2004. (For Kids Ser.). (Illus.). 160p. (J). pap. 14.95 (978-1-55652-527-8(3)) Chicago Review Pr., Inc.

Reed, Arthea J. S. Norma Fox Mazer: A Writer's World. 2000. (Studies in Young Adult Literature : No. 3). (Illus.). 160p. 41.00 (978-0-8108-3814-7(1)) Scarecrow Pr., Inc.

Rhodes, Lisa Renee. Toni Morrison: Great American Writer. 2001. (Book Report Biographies Ser.). (Illus.). 100p. (YA). (gr. 6-8). pap. 6.95 (978-0-531-15555-4(2) , Watts, Franklin) Scholastic Library Publishing.

Richardson, Gillian. Dan Gutman. 2005. (My Favorite Writer Ser.). (Illus.). 32p. (J). (gr. 2-6). pap. 7.95 (978-1-59036-290-7(X)) Weigl Pubs., Inc.

Riggs, Kate. Ernest Hemingway. 2008. (***978-1-58341-661-7(7)** , Creative Education) Creative Co., The.

Ring, Susan. Beverly Cleary. 2002. (My Favorite Writer Ser.). (Illus.). 32p. (J). lib. bdg. 16.95 (978-1-59036-030-9(3)) Weigl Pubs., Inc.

Ruffin, Frances E. Meet Cynthia Rylant. 2006. (About the Author Ser.). (Illus.). 24p. (J). lib. bdg. (978-1-4042-3131-3(5) , PowerKids Pr.) Rosen Publishing Group, Inc., The.

—Meet Lois Lowry. 2006. (About the Author Ser.). (Illus.). 24p. (J). lib. bdg. (978-1-4042-3129-0(3) , PowerKids Pr.) Rosen Publishing Group, Inc., The.

—Meet Patricia MacLachlan. 2006. (About the Author Ser.). (Illus.). 24p. (J). (978-1-4042-3130-6(7) , PowerKids Pr.) Rosen Publishing Group, Inc., The.

—Meet Paula Danziger. 2006. (About the Author Ser.). (Illus.). 24p. (J). lib. bdg. (978-1-4042-3133-7(1) , PowerKids Pr.) Rosen Publishing Group, Inc., The.

—Meet Sid Fleischman. 2006. (About the Author Ser.). (Illus.). 24p. (J). lib. bdg. 18.75 (978-1-4042-3132-0(3) , PowerKids Pr.) Rosen Publishing Group, Inc., The.

Schelly, Bill. Words of Wonder: The Life & Times of Otto Binder. 2003. (978-0-9645669-9-6(0)) Hamster Pr.

Schoell, William. Mystery & Terror: The Story of Edgar Allan Poe. 2004. (Illus.). 128p. (YA). (gr. 6-12). 23.95 (978-1-931798-39-6(7)) Reynolds, Morgan Inc.

Sherman, Josepha. Mark Twain. 2005. (Classic Storytellers Ser.). (Illus.). 48p. (J). lib. bdg. 29.95 (978-1-58415-374-0(1)) Mitchell Lane Pubs., Inc.

Shields, Charles J. Amy Tan. 2001. (Women of Achievement Ser.). (Illus.). 116p. (J). pap. 30.00 (978-0-7910-5890-9(5)); 112p. (YA). (gr. 5 up). 30.00 (978-0-7910-5889-3(1)) Facts On File, Inc. (Chelsea Hse.).

Shirley, David. Alex Haley: Author. 2005. (Black Americans of Achievement Ser.). (Illus.). 112p. (J). (gr. 6-12). 30.00 (978-0-7910-8249-2(0)); pap. 13.25 (978-0-7910-8369-7(1)) Facts On File, Inc. (Chelsea Hse.).

Sickels, Amy. Laura Ingalls Wilder. 2007. (Who Wrote That? Ser.). 144p. (J). (gr. 6-12). 30.00 (***978-0-7910-9525-6(8)** , Chelsea Hse.) Facts On File, Inc.

—Richard Peck. 2007. 128p. 30.00 (***978-0-7910-9530-0(4)** , Chelsea Hse.) Facts On File, Inc.

Silverstein, Shel. Shel Silverstein Pop-up Treasury. Silverstein, Shel, illus. 2008. 16p. (J). 29.99 (***978-0-06-147269-5(7))** HarperCollins Pubs.

Silverthorne, Elizabeth. Louisa May Alcott. 2002. (Who Wrote That? Ser.). (Illus.). 112p. (gr. 6-12). 30.00 (978-0-7910-6721-5(1) , Chelsea Hse.) Facts On File, Inc.

Simon, Seymour. From Paper Airplanes to Outer Space. Crews, Nina, photos by. 2000. (Meet the Author Ser.). (Illus.). 32p. (J). (gr. 2-5). 14.95 (978-1-57274-374-8(3) , 725) Owen, Richard C. Pubs., Inc.

Sis, Peter. The Wall: Growing up Behind the Iron Curtain. 2007. (Illus.). 56p. (J). (gr. 3 up). 18.00 (978-0-374-34701-7(8) , Farrar, Straus & Giroux (BYR)) Farrar, Straus & Giroux.

Skarmeas, Nancy J., ed. Mark Twain. 1998. (Great American Ser.). (Illus.). 96p. (J). 17.95 (978-0-8249-4085-0(7)) Ideals Pubns.

Sommers, Michael A. Chris Crutcher. 2004. (Library of Author Biographies). (Illus.). 112p. (YA). lib. bdg. 26.50 (978-1-4042-0325-9(7)) Rosen Publishing Group, Inc., The.

Spinelli, Jerry. Knots in My Yo-Yo String: The Autobiography. 1998. (Illus.). 160p. (J). (gr. 5-8). pap. 10.95 (978-0-679-88791-1(1) , Knopf Bks. for Young Readers) Random Hse. Children's Bks.

—Knots in My Yo-Yo String: The Autobiography of a Kid. 1998. (J). (978-0-606-13553-5(7)) Tandem Library Bks.

—Knots in My Yo-Yo String: The Autobiography of a Kid. l.t. ed. 2000. (Illus.). 187p. (J). (gr. 8-12). 21.95 (978-0-7862-2973-4(X)) Thorndike Pr.

Spring, Albert. M. E. Kerr. annot. ed. 2005. (Library of Author Biographies). (Illus.). 112p. (J). (ps-ps). lib. bdg. 26.50 (978-1-4042-0465-2(2)) Rosen Publishing Group, Inc., The.

Stalcup, Ann & Politi, Leo. Leo Politi: Artist of the Angels. 2004. (J). 24.95 (978-1-893110-38-0(9)) Silver Moon Pr.

Steffof, Rebecca. Jack London: An American Original. 2002. (Portraits Ser.). (Illus.). 128p. (YA). 28.00 (978-0-19-512223-7(2)) Oxford Univ. Pr., Inc.

Steinbauer, Janine. Carson McCullers. 2002. (Profiles Ser.). (Illus.). 56p. (YA). (gr. 6 up). lib. bdg. 17.95 (978-0-88682-652-9(7) , Creative Education) Creative Co., The.

Stielau, Allison. F. Scott Fitzgerald. 2nd rev. ed. 2006. (Bloom's Modern Critical Views Ser.). viii, 261p. 45.00 (978-0-7910-8570-7(8) , Chelsea Hse.) Facts On File, Inc.

Streissguth, Thomas. Edgar Allan Poe. (Just the Facts Biographies Ser.). (J). 2007. 27.93 (978-0-8225-6800-1(4) , Lerner Pubns.); 2005. (Illus.). 112p. (gr. 6-12). lib. bdg. 27.93 (978-0-8225-4991-8(3)) Lerner Publishing Group.

Strudwick, Leslie. Laura Ingalls Wilder. 2002. (My Favorite Writer Ser.). (Illus.). 32p. (J). lib. bdg. 18.20 (978-1-59036-027-9(3)) Weigl Pubs., Inc.

Tait, Leia. Avi. 2007. (My Favorite Writer Ser.). (J). pap. (978-1-59036-479-6(1)); lib. bdg. (978-1-59036-478-9(3)) Weigl Pubs., Inc.

Tessitore, John. Extraordinary American Writers. 2004. (Extraordinary People Ser.). (Illus.). 288p. (J). 40.00 (978-0-516-22656-9(8) , Children's Pr.) Scholastic Library Publishing.

Thaler, Mike. Imagination. Shahan, Sherry & Shahan, Sherry, photos by. 2002. (Meet the Author Ser.). (Illus.). 32p. (J). (gr. 2-5). 14.95 (978-1-57274-598-8(3) , 728) Owen, Richard C. Pubs., Inc.

Thatcher Murcia, Rebecca. E. B. White. 2004. (Classic Storytellers Ser.). (Illus.). 48p. (J). (gr. 4-8). lib. bdg. 20.95 (978-1-58415-273-6(7)) Mitchell Lane Pubs., Inc.

Thomson, Sarah L. Robert Cormier. 2003. (Library of Author Biographies). (Illus.). 112p. (YA). (gr. 5-8). lib. bdg. 26.50 (978-0-8239-3776-9(3) , Rosen Central) Rosen Publishing Group, Inc., The.

Thoreau, Henry David. Henry David's House. Schnur, Steven, ed. Fiore, Peter, illus. 2007. (J). pap. 7.95 (***978-0-88106-117-8(4))** Charlesbridge Publishing, Inc.

Thoreau, Henry David, et al. Henry David's House. Schnur, Steven, ed. Fiore, Peter A., illus. 2002. (Writing & Thinking Ser.). 32p. (J). (ps-2). 16.95 (978-0-88106-116-1(6)) Charlesbridge Publishing, Inc.

Tinnemeyer, Andrea & Gantt, Patricia. Student's Encyclopedia of Great American Writers. 2008. (Great American Writers Ser.). 448p. (gr. 6-12). 85.00 (***978-0-8160-6088-7(6))** Facts On File, Inc.

Tracy, Kathleen. John Steinbeck. 2004. (Classic Storytellers Ser.). (Illus.). 48p. (J). (gr. 4-8). lib. bdg. 20.95 (978-1-58415-271-2(0)) Mitchell Lane Pubs., Inc.

Tracy, Kathleen. Matt Christopher. 2007. (Classic Storytellers Ser.). (J). lib. bdg. (***978-1-58415-535-5(3))** Mitchell Lane Pubs., Inc.

True-Peters, Stephanie. Gary Paulsen. 1999. (Meet the Author Ser.). (J). (978-0-606-16576-1(2)) Tandem Library Bks.

Van Leeuwen, Jean. Growing Ideas. Gavril, David, photos by. 1998. (Meet the Author Ser.). (Illus.). 32p. (J). (gr. 2-5). 14.95 (978-1-57274-195-9(3) , 721) Owen, Richard C. Pubs., Inc.

Wade, Mary Dodson. Joan Lowery Nixon: Masterful Mystery Writer. 2004. (Authors Teens Love Ser.). (Illus.). 128p. (J). lib. bdg. 26.60 (978-0-7660-2194-5(7)) Enslow Pubs., Inc.

Wadsworth, Ginger. Laura Ingalls Wilder. Haas, Shelly O., illus. (On My Own Biographies Ser.). 48p. (J). (gr. 1-3). 2003. pap. 5.95 (978-1-57505-423-0(X)); 1999. lib. bdg. 23.93 (978-1-57505-266-3(0) , Carolrhoda Bks.) Lerner Publishing Group.

—Laura Ingalls Wilder. 2000. (gr. 3-6). lib. bdg. 14.10 (978-0-613-68249-7(1)); (Illus.). (J). (978-0-606-21947-1(1)) Tandem Library Bks.

Walker, Pamela. Laura Ingalls Wilder. 2001. (Real People Ser.). (Illus.). 24p. (J). (ps-2). 17.00 (978-0-516-23435-9(8)); pap. 4.95 (978-0-516-23589-9(3)) Scholastic Library Publishing. (Children's Pr.).

—Laura Ingalls Wilder. 2001. (gr. k-3). lib. bdg. 12.95 (978-0-613-58846-1(0)) Tandem Library Bks.

Ward, S. Meet Beverly Cleary. 2001. (About the Author Ser.). (Illus.). 24p. (J). (gr. 3). lib. bdg. 18.75 (978-0-8239-5710-1(1) , PowerKids Pr.) Rosen Publishing Group, Inc., The.

—Meet E. B. White. 2001. (About the Author Ser.). (Illus.). 24p. (J). (gr. 3). lib. bdg. 18.75 (978-0-8239-5713-2(6) , PowerKids Pr.) Rosen Publishing Group, Inc., The.

—Meet Laura Ingalls Wilder. 2001. (About the Author Ser.). (Illus.). 24p. (J). (gr. 3). lib. bdg. 18.75 (978-0-8239-5712-5(8) , PowerKids Pr.) Rosen Publishing Group, Inc., The.

—Meet Shel Silverstein. 2001. (About the Author Ser.). (Illus.). 24p. (J). (gr. 3). lib. bdg. 18.75 (978-0-8239-5709-5(8) , PowerKids Pr.) Rosen Publishing Group, Inc., The.

Watson, Galadriel Findlay. Toni Morrison. 2005. (Great African American Women for Kids Ser.). (Illus.). 24p. (J). (ps-7). pap. 6.95 (978-1-59036-340-9(X)); lib. bdg. 26.00 (978-1-59036-334-8(5)) Weigl Pubs., Inc.

Watson, Michele Griskey. Beverly Cleary. 2006. (Classic Storytellers Ser.). (Illus.). 48p. (J). lib. bdg. 20.95 (978-1-58415-457-0(8) , 1259543) Mitchell Lane Pubs., Inc.

—Ray Bradbury. 2006. (Classic Storytellers Ser.). (Illus.). 48p. (J). lib. bdg. 20.95 (978-1-58415-455-6(1) , 1259542) Mitchell Lane Pubs., Inc.

Weidt, Maryann N. Oh, the Places He Went: A Story about Dr. Seuss - Theodore Seuss Geisel. 2000. (J). 9.95 (978-1-56137-653-7(1)) Novel Units, Inc.

Weisbrod, Eva. A Student's Guide to F. Scott Fitzgerald. 2004. (Understanding Literature Ser.). (Illus.). 160p. (J). lib. bdg. 27.93 (978-0-7660-2202-7(1)) Enslow Pubs., Inc.

Wheeler, Jill C. Barbara Park. 2007. (Children's Authors Ser.). (Illus.). 24p. (J). 21.35 (978-1-59679-766-6(5)) ABDO Publishing Co.

—Children's Authors Set III. 2005. (Children's Authors Set Iii Ser.). (J). (gr. k-6). lib. bdg. 128.10 (978-1-59197-737-7(1) , Checkerboard Library) ABDO Publishing Co.

—Christopher Paolini. 2007. (Children's Authors Ser.). (Illus.). 24p. (J). 21.35 (978-1-59679-765-9(7)) ABDO Publishing Co.

—Gertrude Chandler Warner. 2005. (Children's Authors Ser.). (Illus.). 24p. (J). (gr. k-6). lib. bdg. 21.35 (978-1-59197-609-7(X)) ABDO Publishing Co.

—Judy Blume. 2005. (Children's Authors Ser.). (Illus.). 24p. (J). (gr. k-6). lib. bdg. 21.35 (978-1-59197-604-2(9)) ABDO Publishing Co.

—Lemony Snicket. 2007. (Children's Authors Ser.). (Illus.). 24p. 21.35 (978-1-59679-767-3(3)) ABDO Publishing Co.

—Margaret Wise Brown. 2007. (Children's Authors Ser.). (Illus.). 24p. (J). 21.35 (978-1-59679-762-8(2)) ABDO Publishing Co.

—Marjorie Weinman Sharmat. 2005. (Children's Authors Ser.). (Illus.). 24p. (J). (gr. k-6). lib. bdg. 21.35 (978-1-59197-608-0(1)) ABDO Publishing Co.

—Mary Pope Osborne. 2007. (Children's Authors Ser.). (Illus.). 24p. (J). 21.35 (978-1-59679-764-2(9)) ABDO Publishing Co.

—Mercer Mayer. 2005. (Children's Authors Ser.). (Illus.). 24p. (J). (gr. k-6). lib. bdg. 21.35 (978-1-59197-606-6(5)) ABDO Publishing Co.

—Norman Bridwell. 2005. (Children's Authors Ser.). (Illus.). 24p. (J). (gr. k-6). lib. bdg. 21.35 (978-1-59197-605-9(7)) ABDO Publishing Co.

Whiting, Jim. Ernest Hemingway. 2005. (Classic Storytellers Ser.). (Illus.). 48p. (J). (gr. 6-8). lib. bdg. 29.95 (978-1-58415-376-4(8)) Mitchell Lane Pubs., Inc.

Wilder, Laura Ingalls. A Little House Reader: A Collection of Writings by Laura Ingalls Wilder. Anderson, William, ed. Andreasen, Dan, illus. 2005. (Little House Ser.). 208p. (J). (gr. 3 up). pap. 9.99 (978-0-06-058695-9(8) , Harper Trophy) HarperCollins Pubs.

Wilkinson, Brenda. African American Women Writers. Haskins, Jim, ed. 1999. (Black Stars Ser.). (Illus.). 176p. (gr. 5-9). 22.95 (978-0-471-17580-3(3) , Wiley) Wiley, John & Sons, Inc.

Willems, Mo. You Can Never Find a Rickshaw When It Monssons: The World on One Cartoon a Day. 2006. (Illus.). 408p. (YA). (gr. 8-17). pap. 12.99 (978-0-7868-3747-2(0)) Hyperion Pr.

Williams, Brian. The Story Behind John Steinbeck's of Mice & Men. 2006. (History in Literature Ser.). (Illus.). 56p. (YA). (gr. 6-9). lib. bdg. 32.86 (978-1-4034-8207-5(1)) Heinemann Library.

Wilson, Antoine. S. E. Hinton. 2003. (Library of Author Biographies). (Illus.). 112p. (YA). (gr. 5-8). lib. bdg. 26.50 (978-0-8239-3778-3(X) , Rosen Central) Rosen Publishing Group, Inc., The.

Wilson, Suzan. Stephen King: King of Thrillers & Horror. 2000. (People to Know Ser.). (Illus.). 128p. (YA). (gr. 6-12). lib. bdg. 26.60 (978-0-7660-1233-2(6)) Enslow Pubs., Inc.

Wong, Janet S. Before It Wriggles Away. Lindsay, Anne, photos by. 2006. (Meet the Author Ser.). (Illus.). 32p. (J). 14.95 (978-1-57274-861-3(3) , 735, Meet the Author) Owen, Richard C. Pubs., Inc.

Wooding, Sharon. Mark Twain in Nevada, a History Coloring Book for Children. l.t. ed. 2003. (Illus.). 25p. (J). (SPA.). pap. 5.95 (978-0-9727757-1-7(4)); pap. 5.95 (978-0-9727757-0-0(6)) Susy & Livy Pubns.

Woods, Mae. Dr. Seuss. 2000. (Children's Authors Ser.). (Illus.). 24p. (J). (gr. k-6). lib. bdg. 21.35 (978-1-57765-110-9(3) , Checkerboard Library) ABDO Publishing Co.

—Laura Ingalls Wilder. 2000. (Children's Authors Ser.). (Illus.). 24p. (J). (gr. k-6). lib. bdg. 21.35 (978-1-57765-113-0(8) , Checkerboard Library) ABDO Publishing Co.

—Marc Brown. 2001. (Children's Authors Ser.). (Illus.). 24p. (J). (gr. k-6). lib. bdg. 21.35 (978-1-57765-111-6(1) , Checkerboard Library) ABDO Publishing Co.

—Stan & Jan Berenstain. 2000. (Children's Authors Ser.). (Illus.). 24p. (J). (gr. k-6). lib. bdg. 21.35 (978-1-57765-115-4(4) , Checkerboard Library) ABDO Publishing Co.

Woog, Adam. E. B. White. 2005. (Inventors & Creators Ser.). (Illus.). 47p. (J). (gr. 4-8). 26.20 (978-0-7377-2612-1(1) , Greenhaven Pr., Inc.) Thomson Gale.

Wooten, Sara McIntosh. Robert Frost: The Life of America's Poet. 2006. (People to Know Today Ser.). (Illus.). 128p. (YA). lib. bdg. 31.93 (978-0-7660-2627-8(2)) Enslow Pubs., Inc.

—Willa Cather: Writer of the Prairie. 1998. (People to Know Ser.). (Illus.). 128p. (YA). (gr. 6-12). lib. bdg. 20.95 (978-0-89490-980-1(0)) Enslow Pubs., Inc.

Worth, Richard. Jack Kerouac: The Road Is Life. 2006. (American Rebels Ser.). (Illus.). 160p. (J). lib. bdg. 34.60 (978-0-7660-2448-9(2)) Enslow Pubs., Inc.

Wright, Richard. Black Boy. 2006. (Bloom's Modern Critical Interpretations Ser.). 150p. 45.00 (978-0-7910-8585-1(6) , Chelsea Hse.) Facts On File, Inc.

Yannuzzi, Della A. Ernest Hemingway: Writer & Adventurer. 1998. (People to Know Ser.). (Illus.). 112p. (YA). (gr. 6-12). lib. bdg. 26.60 (978-0-89490-979-5(7)) Enslow Pubs., Inc.

Youngblood, Wayne. Mark Twain along the Mississippi. 2006. (In the Footsteps of American Heroes Ser.). (Illus.). 64p. (J). pap. (978-0-8368-6435-9(2)); lib. bdg. 32.67 (978-0-8368-6430-4(1)) Stevens, Gareth Inc. (World Almanac Library).

Zimmer, Kyle, frwd. Jane Yolen. 2005. (Who Wrote That? Ser.). (Illus.). 126p. (J). (gr. 6-12). lib. bdg. 30.00 (978-0-7910-8660-5(7) , Chelsea Hse.) Facts On File, Inc.

AUTHORS, DANISH

Brust, Beth Wagner. The Amazing Paper Cuttings of Hans Christian Andersen. Seng, Terry & Andersen, Hans Christian, illus. 2003. 80p. (J). (gr. 5-6). pap. 9.95 (978-0-618-31109-5(2)) Houghton Mifflin Co. Trade & Reference Div.

—Amazing Paper Cuttings of Hans Christian Andersen. 2003. (gr. 5-8). lib. bdg. 18.75 (978-0-613-60760-5(0)) Tandem Library Bks.

Fradin, Dennis B. Tell Us a Tale, Hans! The Life of Hans Christian Andersen. Buhler, Cynthia von, illus. 2006. (J). (978-1-59336-681-0(7)); pap. (978-1-59336-682-7(5)) Mondo Publishing.

Leslie, Roger. Isak Dinesen: Gothic Storyteller. 2004. (World Writers Ser.). (Illus.). 128p. (YA). (gr. 6-12). 23.95 (978-1-931798-17-4(6)) Reynolds, Morgan Inc.

Varmer, Hjordis. Hans Christian Andersen: His Fairy Tale Life. Nunnally, Tiina, tr. from DAN. Brogger, Lilian, illus. 2005. 112p. (J). (gr. 5). 19.95 (978-0-88899-690-9(X)) Groundwood Bks. CAN. *Dist:* Perseus Distribution.

—Hans Christian Andersen: His Fairy Tale Life. Brogger, Lilian, illus. 2007. 112p. (J). pap. 12.95 (978-0-88899-798-2(1)) Groundwood Bks. CAN. *Dist:* Perseus Distribution.

Yolen, Jane. The Perfect Wizard: Hans Christian Andersen. Nolan, Dennis, illus. 2005. 32p. (J). (gr. 1). 16.99 (978-0-525-46955-1(9) , Dutton Juvenile) Penguin Group (USA) Inc.

AUTHORS, ENGLISH

Abrams, Dennis. Anthony Horowitz. 2006. (Who Wrote That? Ser.). (Illus.). 128p. (J). 30.00 (978-0-7910-8968-2(1) , Chelsea Hse.) Facts On File, Inc.

Aliki. William Shakespeare & the Globe. Aliki, illus. 1999. (Illus.). 48p. (J). (gr. 7 up). lib. bdg. 17.89 (978-0-06-027821-2(8)) HarperCollins Pubs.

Barber, Nicola & Lee-Browne, Patrick. Thomas Hardy. 2000. (Writers in Britain Ser.). (Illus.). 30p. (J). 24.99 (978-0-237-52117-2(2) , Evans Brothers, Limited) Evans Publishing Group GBR. *Dist:* Independent Pubs. Group.

Benge, Janet & Benge, Geoff. C. S. Lewis: Master Storyteller. 2007. (Christian Heroes: Then & Now Ser.). 191p. (J). (gr. 3-7). per. (***978-1-57658-385-2(6))** YWAM Publishing.

Boerst, William J. Generous Anger: The Story of George Orwell. 2004. (World Writers Ser.). (Illus.). 112p. (YA). (gr. 6-12). 23.95 (978-1-883846-74-9(9) , First Biographies) Reynolds, Morgan Inc.

Boothroyd, Jennifer. Roald Dahl: A Life of Imagination. 2008. (Pull Ahead Books-Biographies Ser.). (J). lib. bdg. 22.60 (***978-0-8225-8825-2(0)** , Lerner Pubns.) Lerner Publishing Group.

Brackett, Virginia. Restless Genius: The Story of Virginia Woolf. 2004. (World Writers Ser.). (Illus.). 144p. (YA). (gr. 6-12). 23.95 (978-1-931798-37-2(0)) Reynolds, Morgan Inc.

Brighton, Catherine. Brontes. 2004. (Illus.). 32p. (J). pap. 7.95 (978-1-84507-334-3(7)) Lincoln, Frances Ltd. GBR. *Dist:* Perseus Distribution.

Browne, Anthony. The Shape Game. Browne, Anthony, illus. 2003. (Illus.). 32p. (J). (gr. k up). 16.00 (978-0-374-36764-0(7) , Farrar, Straus & Giroux (BYR)) Farrar, Straus & Giroux.

Caravantes, Peggy. Best of Times: The Story of Charles Dickens. 2005. (World Writers Ser.). (Illus.). 160p. (J). (gr. 3-7). lib. bdg. 26.95 (978-1-931798-68-6(0)) Reynolds, Morgan Inc.

Carpenter, Angelica Shirley. Lewis Carroll: Through the Looking Glass. 2002. (Lerner Long Biographies Ser.). (Illus.). 128p. (J). 27.93 (978-0-8225-0073-5(6) , Lerner Pubns.) Lerner Publishing Group.

Champion, Neil. Charles Dickens. 2001. (Creative Lives Ser.). (Illus.). 64p. (YA). (gr. 6-8). lib. bdg. 27.07 (978-1-58810-207-2(6)) Heinemann Library.

Compson, William. J. K. Rowling. 2003. (Library of Author Biographies). (Illus.). 112p. (YA). (gr. 5-8). lib. bdg. 26.50 (978-0-8239-3774-5(7) , Rosen Central) Rosen Publishing Group, Inc., The.

Craats, Rennay. Roald Dahl. 2002. (My Favorite Writer Ser.). (Illus.). 32p. (J). lib. bdg. 18.20 (978-1-59036-029-3(X)) Weigl Pubs., Inc.

Dahl, Roald. Boy: Tales of Childhood. 1999. (Illus.). 176p. (J). (gr. 5-9). pap. 6.99 (978-0-14-130305-5(0) , Puffin) Penguin Group (USA) Inc.

—Going Solo. 1999. (Illus.). 224p. (gr. 7-12). pap. 6.99 (978-0-14-130310-9(7) , Puffin) Penguin Group (USA) Inc.

—Going Solo. 1998. (Illus.). 209p. (YA). (gr. 7-12). per. 15.30 (978-0-613-10109-7(X)) Tandem Library Bks.

Darrow, Sharon. Through the Tempests Dark & Wild: A Story of Mary Shelley, Creator of "Frankenstein" Barrett, Angela, illus. 2003. 40p. (J). (gr. 3-7). 18.99 (978-0-7636-0835-4(1)) Candlewick Pr.

Davenport, John. C. S. Lewis. 2003. (Who Wrote That? Ser.). (Illus.). 112p. (gr. 6-12). 30.00 (978-0-7910-7620-0(2) , Chelsea Hse.) Facts On File, Inc.

Dommermuth-Costa, Carol. William Shakespeare. 2001. (Biography Ser.). (Illus.). 112p. (J). (gr. 6-12). lib. bdg. 27.93 (978-0-8225-4996-3(4) , Lerner Pubns.) Lerner Publishing Group.

Foreman, Michael. War Boy. 2006. (Illus.). 96p. (J). pap. 16.99 (***978-1-84365-087-4(8)***) Anova Bks. GBR. *Dist:* Independent Pubs. Group.

Gaines, Ann Graham. J. K. Rowling. 2001. (Real-Life Reader Biography Ser.). (Illus.). 32p. (J). (gr. 3-8). lib. bdg. 15.95 (978-1-58415-078-7(5)) Mitchell Lane Pubs., Inc.

—Roald Dahl. 2001. (Real-Life Reader Biography Ser.). (Illus.). 32p. (J). (gr. 3-8). lib. bdg. 15.95 (978-1-58415-075-6(0)) Mitchell Lane Pubs., Inc.

Gelletly, LeeAnne. Gift of Imagination: The Story of Roald Dahl. 2006. (World Writers Ser.). (Illus.). 160p. (YA). (gr. 6-12). lib. bdg. 27.95 (978-1-59935-026-4(2)) Reynolds, Morgan Inc.

Gormley, Beatrice. C. S. Lewis: The Man Behind Narnia. 2nd ed. 2005. (Illus.). 180p. (YA). (gr. 8-12). pap. 12.00 (978-0-8028-5301-1(3) , Eerdmans Bks For Young Readers) Eerdmans, William B. Publishing Co.

Greenhill, Wendy & Wignall, Paul. Shakespeare: A Life. 2006. (Illus.). 32p. (978-1-4034-8609-7(3)) Heinemann Library.

—Shakespeare: Man of the Theater. 2000. (Illus.). 196p. (J). (gr. 8 up). lib. bdg. 28.50 (978-1-57572-282-5(8)) Heinemann Library.

Grolier Educational Staff. Lives & Works: Young Adult Authors, 8 vols. 1999. (YA). lib. bdg. 265.00 (978-0-7172-9227-1(4) , Grolier) Scholastic Library Publishing.

Hamilton, John. Pioneers of Science Fiction. 2007. (World of Science Fiction Ser.). 32p. 24.21 (978-1-59679-992-9(7)) ABDO Publishing Co.

Hamilton, Sue L. Masters of Horror. 2007. (ENG., Illus.). 32p. (YA). lib. bdg. 24.21 (***978-1-59928-770-6(6)*** , ABDO & Daughters) ABDO Publishing Co.

Harmin, Karen Leigh. J. K. Rowling: Author of Harry Potter. 2006. (People to Know Today Ser.). (Illus.). 128p. (J). lib. bdg. 31.93 (978-0-7660-1850-1(4)) Enslow Pubs., Inc.

Heims, Neil. J. R. R. Tolkien. 2004. (Great Writers Ser.). (Illus.). 128p. (YA). (gr. 9-13). 31.95 (978-0-7910-7847-1(7) , Chelsea Hse.) Facts On File, Inc.

Hill, Mary. J K Rowling. 2003. (gr. k-3). lib. bdg. 12.95 (978-0-613-67727-1(7)) Tandem Library Bks.

Hook, Jason. Roald Dahl. 2004. (Illus.). 48p. (J). lib. bdg. 28.56 (978-0-7398-6626-9(5)) Raintree.

Houle, Michelle M. Roald Dahl: Author of Charlie & the Chocolate Factory. 2006. (Authors Teens Love Ser.). (Illus.). 104p. (YA). lib. bdg. 31.93 (978-0-7660-2353-6(2)) Enslow Pubs., Inc.

Kenyon, Karen Smith. The Bronte Family: Passionate Literary Geniuses. 2005. (Lerner Biographies Ser.). (Illus.). 128p. (gr. 6-12). 27.93 (978-0-8225-0071-1(X)) Lerner Publishing Group.

King-Smith, Dick. Chewing the Cud: An Extraordinary Life Remembered by the Author of Babe: the Gallant Pig. Horse, Harry, illus. 2002. 208p. (J). (gr. 5 up). 16.95 (978-0-375-81459-4(0) , Knopf Bks. for Young Readers) Random Hse. Children's Bks.

Klaus, Gustav. James Kelmam. 2004. (Writers & Their Work Ser.). (Illus.). 128p. (978-0-7463-1064-9(1)); pap. (978-0-7463-0976-6(7)) Northcote Hse. Pubs., Ltd.

Klingel, Cynthia Fitterer & Court, Rob. Art of Early Africa. 2003. (Scribbles Institute : Art in Ancient Civilizations Ser.). (Illus.). 32p. (J). (gr. 1-5). 21.36 (978-1-56766-551-2(9) , 65519) Child's World, Inc.

Lappi, Megan. C. S. Lewis. 2005. (My Favorite Writer Ser.). (Illus.). 32p. (J). (ps-7). pap. 7.95 (978-1-59036-291-4(8)) Weigl Pubs., Inc.

Locke, Juliane. England's Jane: The Story of Jane Austen. 2006. (World Writers Ser.). (Illus.). 144p. (YA). lib. bdg. 26.95 (978-1-931798-82-2(6)) Reynolds, Morgan Inc.

McCarthy, Shaun. All about J. K. Rowling. 2003. (All About Ser.). (Illus.). 32p. (J). pap. 7.50 (978-1-4109-0719-6(8)); lib. bdg. 24.28 (978-1-4109-0718-9(X)) Raintree.

—All about J. K. Rowling. 2003. (gr. 3-6). lib. bdg. 15.90 (978-0-613-78210-4(0)) Tandem Library Bks.

Meister, Cari. J. K. Rowling. 2001. (Children's Authors Ser.). (Illus.). 24p. (J). (gr. k-6). lib. bdg. 21.35 (978-1-57765-482-7(X) , Checkerboard Library) ABDO Publishing Co.

Miller, Calvin Craig. Spirit Like a Storm: The Story of Mary Shelley. 2nd rev. ed. 2004. (World Writers Ser.). (Illus.). 144p. (YA). (gr. 6-12). 23.95 (978-1-931798-08-2(7)) Reynolds, Morgan Inc.

Mills, Cliff. Virginia Woolf. 2003. (Women in the Arts Ser.). (Illus.). 112p. (gr. 6-12). 30.00 (978-0-7910-7459-6(5) , Chelsea Hse.) Facts On File, Inc.

Mittelstaedt, Walt. A Student's Guide to William Shakespeare. 2005. (Understanding Literature Ser.). (Illus.). 192p. (J). lib. bdg. 27.93 (978-0-7660-2284-3(6)) Enslow Pubs., Inc.

Neimark, Anne E. Myth Maker: J. R. R. Tolkien. Newbold, Greg, illus. 1998. 128p. (J). (gr. 5-9). pap. 4.95 (978-0-688-15741-8(6) , Harper Trophy) HarperCollins Pubs.

—Myth Maker: J. R. R. Tolkien. 1998. (J). (978-0-606-13639-6(8)) Tandem Library Bks.

Nettleton, Pamela Hill. William Shakespeare: Playwright & Poet. 2004. (Signature Lives Ser.). (Illus.). 112p. (J). 30.60 (978-0-7565-0816-6(9) , 1240125) Compass Point Bks.

Nichols, Joan K. Mary Shelley: Frankenstein's Creator - The First Science Fiction Writer. 1998. (Barnard Biography Ser.: No. 3). (Illus.). 150p. (YA). (gr. 7-12). pap. 6.95 (978-1-57324-087-1(7) , Red Wheel) Red Wheel/Weiser.

Orme, David. The Brontes. 1999. (Writers in Britain Ser.). (Illus.). 32p. 24.99 (978-0-237-51744-1(2) , Evans Brothers, Limited) Evans Publishing Group GBR. *Dist:* Independent Pubs. Group.

Otfinoski, Steven. Bram Stoker: The Man Who Wrote Dracula. 2005. (Great Life Stories Ser.). (Illus.). 111p. (J). 30.50 (978-0-531-16750-2(X) , Watts, Franklin) Scholastic Library Publishing.

Parker, Victoria. C.S. Lewis. 2006. (Illus.). 48p. (J). pap. (978-1-4034-7339-4(0)); lib. bdg. (978-1-4034-7336-3(6)) Heinemann Library.

—J.R.R. Tolkien. 2006. (Illus.). 48p. (J). pap. (978-1-4034-7338-7(2)); lib. bdg. (978-1-4034-7335-6(8)) Heinemann Library.

Pezzi, Bryan. J. K. Rowling. 2005. (My Favorite Writer Ser.). (Illus.). 32p. (J). (gr. 2-6). pap. 7.95 (978-1-59036-293-8(4)) Weigl Pubs., Inc.

Powling, Chris. Dick King-Smith. (Illus.). 22p. (J). (978-0-237-51970-4(4) , Evans Brothers, Limited) Evans Publishing Group.

—Shirley Hughes. 1999. (Tell Me about Ser.). (Illus.). 22p. (J). 15.99 (978-0-237-52039-7(7) , Evans Brothers, Limited) Evans Publishing Group GBR. *Dist:* Independent Pubs. Group.

Price, Joan. J.K. Rowling. 2004. (Trailblazers of the Modern World Ser.). (Illus.). 48p. (J). pap. 11.95 (978-0-8368-5268-4(0)); (YA). lib. bdg. 30.00 (978-0-8368-5499-2(3)) Stevens, Gareth Inc. (World Almanac Library).

Rosen, Michael. Dickens: His Work & His World. Ingpen, Robert R., illus. 2005. 96p. (YA). (gr. 7-11). 19.99 (978-0-7636-2752-2(6)) Candlewick Pr.

—Shakespeare: His Work & His World. Ingpen, Robert R., illus. 2006. 96p. (J). (gr. 7-11). pap. 9.99 (978-0-7636-3201-4(5)) Candlewick Pr.

Ross, Stewart. William Shakespeare. 2004. (Illus.). 48p. (J). lib. bdg. 28.56 (978-0-7398-6630-6(3)) Raintree.

Ruffin, Frances E. Meet Roald Dahl. 2006. (About the Author Ser.). (Illus.). 24p. (J). lib. bdg. (978-1-4042-3134-4(X) , PowerKids Pr.) Rosen Publishing Group, Inc., The.

Ruth, Amy. Jane Austen. 2005. (Biography Ser.). (Illus.). 112p. (J). (gr. 6-12). lib. bdg. 27.93 (978-0-8225-4992-5(1)) Lerner Publishing Group.

Sexton, Colleen A. J.K. Rowling. (Biography ' Ser.). (J). 2007. lib. bdg. 30.60 (***978-0-8225-7949-6(9)***); 2006. (Illus.). 112p. 27.93 (978-0-8225-3423-5(1) , Lerner Pubns.) Lerner Publishing Group.

Sexton, Colleen A. & Cosgrove, Martha. J.K. Rowling. 2006. (Just the Facts Biographies Ser.). (Illus.). 112p. (J). pap. (***978-0-8225-5995-5(1)*** , Lerner Pubns.) Lerner Publishing Group.

Shapiro, Marc. J. K. Rowling: The Wizard Behind Harry Potter. 2007. 288p. pap. 6.99 (***978-0-312-37697-0(9)*** , St. Martin's Griffin) St. Martin's Pr.

—J. K. Rowling: The Wizard Behind Harry Potter. 2000. (J). (978-0-606-19640-6(4)) Tandem Library Bks.

—J. K. Rowling: The Wizard Behind Harry Potter. l.t. ed. 2001. (J). (gr. 8-12). 23.95 (978-0-7862-3225-3(0)) Thorndike Pr.

Shields, Charles J. Mythmaker: The Story of J. K. Rowling. 2002. (Who Wrote That? Ser.). (Illus.). 112p. (gr. 6-12). 30.00 (978-0-7910-6719-2(X) , Chelsea Hse.) Facts On File, Inc.

Speaker-Yuan, Margaret & Yuan, Margaret Speaker. Phillip Pullman. 2005. (Who Wrote That? Ser.). (Illus.). 118p. (J). (gr. 6-12). lib. bdg. 30.00 (978-0-7910-8658-2(5) , Chelsea Hse.) Facts On File, Inc.

Stanley, Diane & Vennema, Peter. Bard of Avon: The Story of William Shakespeare. Stanley, Diane, illus. 1998. (Illus.). (J). (ps-ps). lib. bdg. 15.30 (978-0-613-09937-0(0)) Tandem Library Bks.

Stone, Elaine Murray. C. S. Lewis: Creator of Narnia. Kelley, Patrick, illus. 2001. 144p. (gr. 4-9). 8.95 (978-0-8091-6672-5(0) , 6672-0) Paulist Pr.

Streissguth, Thomas. Legends of Dracula. 1998. (Biography Ser.). (Illus.). 112p. (gr. 6-12). lib. bdg. 27.93 (978-0-8225-4942-0(3)) Lerner Publishing Group.

Streissguth, Thomas & Streissguth, Tom. Legends of Dracula. 2003. (Biography Ser.). (Illus.). 112p. (YA). (gr. 6 up). pap. 7.95 (978-0-8225-9682-0(2) , Carolrhoda Bks.) Lerner Publishing Group.

Ward, S. Meet A. A. Milne. 2001. (About the Author Ser.). (Illus.). 24p. (J). (gr. 3). lib. bdg. 18.75 (978-0-8239-5708-8(X) , PowerKids Pr.) Rosen Publishing Group, Inc., The.

—Meet J. K. Rowling. (About the Author Ser.). 24p. (J). 2003. lib. bdg. 18.75 (978-0-8239-6808-4(1)); 2000. (Illus.). (gr. 3). lib. bdg. 18.75 (978-0-8239-5711-8(X)) Rosen Publishing Group, Inc., The. (PowerKids Pr.).

Webb, Ruth. Virginia Woolf. 2000. (British Library Writers' Lives). (Illus.). 128p. (978-0-7123-4616-0(3)) British Library Document Supply Ctr.

Wellman, Sam. C. S. Lewis: Author of Mere Christianity. 1999. (Heroes of the Faith Ser.). (Illus.). 208p. (YA). (gr. 4-7). lib. bdg. 17.95 (978-0-7910-5032-3(7) , Chelsea Hse.) Facts On File, Inc.

—John Bunyan: Author of The Pilgrim's Progress. 1999. (Heroes of the Faith Ser.). (Illus.). 208p. (YA). (gr. 4-7). 14.95 (978-0-7910-5035-4(1) , Chelsea Hse.) Facts On File, Inc.

Wheeler, Jill C. A. A. Milne. 2005. (Children's Authors Ser.). (Illus.). 24p. (J). (gr. k-6). lib. bdg. 21.35 (978-1-59197-607-3(3)) ABDO Publishing Co.

—Roald Dahl. 2007. (Children's Authors Ser.). (Illus.). 24p. (J). 21.35 (978-1-59679-763-5(0)) ABDO Publishing Co.

Willett, Edward. J. R. R. Tolkien: Master of Imaginary Worlds. 2004. (Authors Teens Love Ser.). (Illus.). 128p. (J). lib. bdg. 26.60 (978-0-7660-2246-1(3)) Enslow Pubs., Inc.

Winter, Jeanette. Beatrix: Various Episodes from the Life of Beatrix Potter. Winter, Jeanette, illus. 2003. (Illus.). 64p. (J). (gr. k-3). 15.00 (978-0-374-30655-7(9) , Farrar, Straus & Giroux (BYR)) Farrar, Straus & Giroux.

Woog, Adam. Roald Dahl. 2004. (Inventors & Creators Ser.). (Illus.). 48p. (J). (gr. 4-7). 26.20 (978-0-7377-2614-5(8) , Greenhaven Pr., Inc.) Thomson Gale.

AUTHORS, EUROPEAN

Gibbon, Monk. Pupil: A Memory of Love. 128p. 9.95 (978-0-905473-68-0(X)) Wolfhound Pr. IRL. *Dist:* Irish American Bk. Co.

AUTHORS—FICTION

Amesse, Susan. Kissing Brendan Callahan. 2005. 160p. (J). (gr. 5-8). 15.95 (978-1-59643-015-0(X)) Roaring Brook Pr.

Baker, Barbara. Anna's Book. O'Neil, Catherine, illus. 2004. 24p. (J). (ps). 8.99 (978-0-525-47231-5(2) , Dutton Juvenile) Penguin Group (USA) Inc.

Baratz-Logsted, Lauren. Secrets of My Suburban Life. 2008. 240p. (YA). pap. 7.99 (***978-1-4169-2525-5(2)*** , Simon Pulse) Simon & Schuster Children's Publishing.

Blume, Judy. Places I Never Meant to Be: Original Stories by Censored Writers. 2001. (gr. 7-12). lib. bdg. 18.80 (978-0-613-33720-5(4)); (Illus.). (J). (978-0-606-20855-0(0)) Tandem Library Bks.

Brown, Marc. Arthur Writes a Story. Brown, Marc, illus. 2002. (Arthur Adventure Ser.). (Illus.). (J). 13.15 (978-0-7587-1974-4(4)) Book Wholesalers, Inc.

—Arthur Writes a Story. ed. 2004. (Arthur Adventure Ser.). (J). (gr. k-3). spiral bd. (978-0-616-01604-6(2)); spiral bd. (978-0-616-01605-3(0)) Canadian National Institute for the Blind/Institut National Canadien pour les Aveugles.

—Arthur Writes a Story. 2003. (Arthur Adventure Ser.). (Illus.). 14.95 (978-1-59319-021-7(2)) LeapFrog Enterprises, Inc.

Dana, Barbara. Emily Dickinson: Fictionalized Biography. Date not set. (J). (gr. 3-7). 14.99 (978-0-06-028704-7(7)); 15.89 (978-0-06-028705-4(5)); mass mkt. 4.99 (978-0-06-440843-1(4)) HarperCollins Pubs.

Dawes, Claiborne. A Different Drummer: Thoreau & Will's Independence Day. Moyle, J. Stephen, illus. 1998. 32p. (J). (gr. 2-5). pap. 7.95 (978-1-57960-039-6(5)) History Compass, LLC.

DeVillers, Julia. How My Private, Personal Journal Became a Bestseller. 2004. 224p. (J). (gr. 5). 15.99 (978-0-525-47283-4(5) , Dutton Juvenile) Penguin Group (USA) Inc.

—How My Private Personal Journal Became a Bestseller. 2005. 224p. (J). (gr. 5). pap. 5.99 (978-0-14-240332-7(6) , Puffin) Penguin Group (USA) Inc.

Freire, Espido. La Ultima Batalla de Vincavec el Bandido. Ruano, Alfonso, illus. 2001. Tr. of Final Battle of Vincavec the Bandit. (SPA.). 238p. (978-84-348-7438-1(5)) SM Ediciones ESP. *Dist:* AIMS International Bks., Inc.

Garcia-Clairac, Santiago. El Libro Invisible (The Invisible Book) Flores, Enrique, illus. 10th ed. 2001. (SPA.). 140p. (J). (gr. 4-6). (978-84-348-6556-3(4)) SM Ediciones.

Givner, Joan. Ellen Fremedon: Journalist. 2006. 192p. pap. 6.95 (978-0-88899-691-6(8)) Groundwood Bks. CAN. *Dist:* Perseus Distribution.

Gormley, Beatrice. Laura Ingalls Wilder. 2001. (gr. 3-6). lib. bdg. 13.00 (978-0-613-63422-9(5)) Tandem Library Bks.

Hahn, Mary Downing. Janey & the Famous Author. Bush, Timothy, illus. 2005. 48p. (J). (gr. k-3). 15.00 (978-0-618-35408-5(5) , Clarion Bks.) Houghton Mifflin Co. Trade & Reference Div.

Harcourt School Publishers Staff. Silent Observer Level D: Reader. 2001. (Collections Ser.). (Illus.). (J). 5.90 (978-0-15-314376-2(2)) Harcourt Schl. Pubs.

Hausman, Gerald & Hausman, Loretta. A Mind with Wings: The Story of Henry David Thoreau. 2006. (Illus.). 160p. (YA). 15.95 (978-1-59030-228-6(1) , Trumpeter) Shambhala Pubns., Inc.

Hershenhorn, Esther. The Confession$ & $ecret$ of Howard J. Fingerhut. Long, Ethan, illus. 2002. 144p. (J). (gr. 4-6). tchr. ed. 16.95 (978-0-8234-1642-4(9)) Holiday Hse., Inc.

Howe, James. Bunnicula Meets Edgar Allan Crow. Fortune, Eric, illus. 2006. (Bunnicula Ser.). 160p. (J). 15.95 (978-1-4169-1458-7(7) , Ginne Seo Bks) Simon & Schuster Children's Publishing.

Kakugawa, Frances H. Wordsworth Dances the Waltz. DeSica, Melissa, illus. 2007. 32p. 10.95 (***978-0-9790647-3-9(2)***) Watermark Publishing, LLC.

Kristina Learns about Fishing. 2007. (J). (***978-0-9792728-0-6(7)***) Tracepaper Bks. Inc.

Maltby Jr., Richard. Miss Potter. 2006. 196p. (J). pap. 7.99 (978-0-7232-5899-5(6) , Warne) Penguin Group (USA) Inc.

McAlpine, Gordon. Mystery Box. 2003. 190p. (YA). 16.95 (978-0-8126-2680-3(X)) Cricket Bks.

Nance, Andrew. Daemon Hall. Polhemus, Coleman, illus. 2007. 272p. (YA). 16.95 (***978-0-8050-8171-8(2)***) Holt, Henry & Co.

Peckham, Howard & Schaaf, Martha E. Lew Wallace: Boy Writer. Underdown, Harold, ed. Morrison, Cathy, illus. 2nd ed. 2001. (Young Patriots Ser.: Vol. 3). 112p. (J). (gr. 3 up). pap. 9.95 (978-1-882859-06-1(5)); 15.95 (978-1-882859-05-4(7)) Patria Pr., Inc.

Prowse, Philip. Help! Level 1. 1999. (Cambridge English Readers Ser.). (Illus.). 32p. pap. 6.00 (978-0-521-65615-3(X)) Cambridge Univ. Pr.

Pulver, Robin. Author Day for Room 3T. Richards, Chuck, illus. 2005. 32p. (J). (gr. 3-5). 16.00 (978-0-618-35406-1(9) , Clarion Bks.) Houghton Mifflin Co. Trade & Reference Div.

Ross, Leanna. Julie Simone. 2004. 194p. (YA). pap. 14.95 (978-0-595-30376-2(5)) iUniverse, Inc.

Sargent, Dave & Sargent, Pat. Charcoal: (Charcoal Grey) Be Decisive, 25, 13. Lenoir, Jane, illus. 2001. (Saddle Up Ser.: 13). 36p. (J). pap. 6.95 (978-1-56763-606-2(3)); lib. bdg. 22.60 (978-1-56763-605-5(5)) Ozark Publishing.

Schaaf, Martha E. Lew Wallace, Boy Writer. 2001. (gr. 3-6). lib. bdg. 18.75 (978-0-613-80164-5(4)) Tandem Library Bks.

Sortland, Bjorn. The Story of the Search for the Story. Elling, Lars, illus. 2003. (Picture Bks.). 40p. (J). (ps-3). 15.95 (978-1-57505-375-2(6) , Carolrhoda Bks.) Lerner Publishing Group.

Tinder, Jeremy. Cry Yourself to Sleep. 2006. (Illus.). 88p. (YA). pap. 7.00 (978-1-891830-81-5(3)) Top Shelf Productions.

Trumbauer, Lisa. Mountain Manor Mystery. Hawkes, Kevin, illus. 2006. 96p. (J). pap. (978-1-59034-810-9(9)) Mondo Publishing.

Warner, Gertrude Chandler. The Vanishing Passenger. 2006. (Boxcar Children Mysteries Ser.: 106). (Illus.). 128p. (J). 14.95 (978-0-8075-1066-7(1)); pap. 4.50 (978-0-8075-1067-4(X)) Whitman, Albert & Co.

Wersba, Barbara. Walter: The Story of a Rat. Diamond, Donna, illus. 2005. 64p. (J). (gr. 4-8). 16.95 (978-1-932425-41-3(1) , Lemniscaat) Boyds Mills Pr.

Whelan, Gloria. The Pathless Woods: Ernest Hemingway's Sixteenth Summer in Northern Michigan. Wolff, Glenn, illus. 2nd rev. ed. 1998. (J). (gr. 6-10). 16.95 (978-1-882376-63-6(3)); 176p. (gr. 7-12). pap. 11.95 (978-1-882376-44-5(7)) Thunder Bay Pr.

Wiggin, Kate Douglas. Penelope's Postscripts. 2004. reprint ed. pap. 15.95 (978-1-4191-4073-0(6)); pap. 1.99 (978-1-4192-4073-7(0)) Kessinger Publishing, LLC.

Williams, Rozanne Lanczak. The Author with the Fancy Purple Pen. Maio, Barbara, ed. Richard, Ilene, illus. 2006. (Learn to Write Ser.). (J). 16p. pap. 2.99 (978-1-59198-299-9(5) , 6189); per. 6.99 (***978-1-59198-346-0(0)***) Creative Teaching Pr., Inc.

Wilson, Jacqueline. Secrets. l.t. ed. 2003. (Illus.). 208p. (J). 16.95 (978-0-7540-7854-8(X) , Galaxy Children's Large Print) BBC Audiobooks America.

AUTHORS, FRENCH

Bayer, Linda N. Elie Wiesel: Spokesman for Remembrance. 2005. (Holocaust Biographies Ser.). (Illus.). 112p. (J). (gr. 7-12). lib. bdg. 26.50 (978-0-8239-3306-8(7) , HB-WIES) Rosen Publishing Group, Inc., The.

—Elie Wiesel: Spokesman for Remembrance. 1999. (Illus.). 112p. (YA). per. 10.95 (978-1-56254-456-0(X) , SP456X) Saddleback Educational Publishing.

Broderick, Joe. Samuel Beckett -la tragicomedia de la Vida. 2005. 192p. pap. (978-958-30-1730-8(2)) Panamericana Editorial.

García Aguilar, Eduardo. Voltaire -el festín de la Inteligencia. 2005. 96p. pap. (978-958-30-1436-9(2)) Panamericana Editorial.

Houghton, Sarah. Elie Wiesel: A Holocaust Survivor Cries Out for Peace. 2003. (High Five Reading Ser.). (Illus.). (J). 64p. lib. bdg. 22.60 (978-0-7368-2792-8(7)); 48p. pap. 8.75 (978-0-7368-2833-8(8)) Capstone Pr., Inc.

—Elie Wiesel: A Holocaust Survivor Cries Out for Peace, 6 vols. (gr. 4 up). 49.95 (978-0-7368-2843-7(5) , High Five) Red Brick Learning.

Schoell, William. Remarkable Journeys: The Story of Jules Verne. 2004. (World Writers Ser.). (Illus.). 112p. (YA). (gr. 6-12). 23.95 (978-1-883846-92-3(7) , First Biographies) Reynolds, Morgan Inc.

Streissguth, Thomas. Science Fiction Pioneer: A Story about Jules Verne. Ramstad, Ralph L., illus. 2000. (Creative Minds Biographies Ser.). 64p. (J). (gr. 3-6). lib. bdg. 22.60 (978-1-57505-440-7(X) , Carolrhoda Bks.) Lerner Publishing Group.

Tracy, Sophia Okun. A Woman Ahead of Her Time: Christine de Pizan, Defender of Womankind. 2003. (Avisson Young Adult Ser.). (Illus.). 84p. (J). pap. (978-1-888105-57-5(7)) Avisson Pr., Inc.

AUTHORS, GERMAN

Harcourt School Publishers Staff. An Interview with the Brothers Grimm Below Level. 3rd ed. 2002. (Trophies Reading Program Ser.). (Illus.). pap. 5.10 (978-0-15-323239-8(0)) Harcourt Schl. Pubs.

Hettinga, Donald R. The Brothers Grimm: Two Lives, One Legacy. 2001. (Illus.). 192p. (J). (gr. 5-9). tchr. ed. 22.00 (978-0-618-05599-9(1) , Clarion Bks.) Houghton Mifflin Co. Trade & Reference Div.

Tomljanovic, Tatiana. Cornelia Funke: My Favorite Writer. 2007. (My Favorite Writer Ser.). (J). (978-1-59036-481-9(3)); lib. bdg. (978-1-59036-480-2(5)) Weigl Pubs., Inc.

AUTHORS, LATIN AMERICAN

Mora, Pat. A Library for Juana: The World of Sor Juana Ines. Vidal, Beatriz, illus. 2002. 40p. (J). (gr. k-3). 15.95 (978-0-375-80643-8(1) , Knopf Bks. for Young Readers) Random Hse. Children's Bks.

AUTHORS, RUSSIAN

Enrique, Luque Muñoz. Fiodor Dostoievski. 2005. 152p. pap. (978-958-30-1438-3(9)) Panamericana Editorial.

AUTHORS, SCOTTISH

Hein, Rolland. George MacDonald: Victorian Mythmaker. 2nd rev. ed. 1999. (Illus.). 406p. lib. bdg. 28.00 (978-1-881084-64-8(7)) Johannesen Printing & Publishing.

Hunsicker, Ranelda Mack. Sir Gibbie: A Guide for Teachers & Students. 2001. (Classics for Young Readers Ser.). 62p. (J). (gr. 3-6). pap., stu. ed. 6.99 (978-0-87552-730-7(2)) P & R Publishing.

AUTHORS, SPANISH

Parker, Barbara Keevil & Parker, Duane F. Miguel de Cervantes. 2003. (Great Hispanic Heritage Ser.). (Illus.). 112p. (J). (gr. 6-12). 30.00 (978-0-7910-7252-3(5) , Chelsea Hse.) Facts On File, Inc.

A B

AUTHORSHIP

see also Biography (As a Literary Form); Drama—Technique; Journalism; Report Writing; Versification

Grade 6. (J). pap., tchr.'s training gde. ed. (978-0-8136-1882-1(7)) Modern Curriculum Pr.

Adelman, Linda & Wright, Elena D. Writing & Thinking for Young Authors: Blue Level - Reproducible Student Resources. 2001. (978-1-57091-309-9(9)) Charlesbridge Publishing, Inc.

—Writing & Thinking for Young Authors: Tan Level - Reproducible Student Resources. 2001. (978-1-57091-310-5(2)) Charlesbridge Publishing, Inc.

Adler, David A. My Writing Day. Crews, Nina, photos by. 1999. (Meet the Author Ser.). (Illus.). 32p. (J). (gr. 2-5). 14.95 (978-1-57274-326-7(3) , 723) Owen, Richard C. Pubs., Inc.

Al-Marwani, Amatullah. Star Writers. 2006. (Illus.). vii, 167p. (J). (978-0-9767861-2-2(5)) Muslim Writers Publishing.

Angel, Ann. Robert Cormier: Author of the Chocolate War. 2007. (Authors Teens Love Ser.). (Illus.). 104p. (J). (gr. 6 up). lib. bdg. 31.93 (978-0-7660-2719-0(8)) Enslow Pubs., Inc.

Aranega, Merce. Quiero Escribir un Cuento. (SPA.). 32p. (J). (978-84-236-5722-3(1)) Edebé ESP. *Dist:* Lectorum Pubns., Inc.

Asher, Sandy. But That's Another Story: Favorite Authors Introduce Popular Genres. 1999. (J). (978-0-606-16876-2(1)) Tandem Library Bks.

Bankston, John. F. Scott Fitzgerald. 2004. (Classic Storytellers Ser.). (Illus.). 48p. (J). (gr. 4-8). lib. bdg. 20.95 (978-1-58415-249-1(4)) Mitchell Lane Pubs., Inc.

—Jack London. 2004. (Classic Storytellers Ser.). (Illus.). 48p. (J). (gr. 4-8). lib. bdg. 20.95 (978-1-58415-263-7(X)) Mitchell Lane Pubs., Inc.

Baptiste, Tracey. Jerry Spinelli. 2007. 128p. 30.00 (***978-0-7910-9572-0(X)*** , Chelsea Hse.) Facts On File, Inc.

Barker, Ray & Moorcroft, Christine. Write First. 2001. (J). (gr. 6-9). Bk. 1. 64p. pap., stu. ed. 16.95 (978-0-7487-6148-7(9)); Bk. 2. (Illus.). 80p. pap., stu. ed. 18.50 (978-0-7487-6153-1(5)); Bk. 3. (Illus.). 96p. pap., stu. ed. 18.50 (978-0-7487-6154-8(3)) Nelson Thornes Ltd. GBR. *Dist:* Trans-Atlantic Pubns., Inc.

Barrett, Shari & Barrett, Steve. Put That in Writing Level One: Answer Key & Test Bank. 2003. 32p. 7.50 (978-0-9728731-1-6(2)) Barrett's Bookshelf.

—Put That in Writing Level One: Mastering the Paragraph. 2003. 211p. spiral bd. 49.95 (978-0-9728731-0-9(4)) Barrett's Bookshelf.

Berne, Emma Carlson. Laura Ingalls Wilder. 2007. (Essential Lives Ser.). (ENG., Illus.). 112p. (J). (gr. 6-8). lib. bdg. 32.79 (***978-1-59928-843-7(5)*** , Essential Library) ABDO Publishing Co.

Bidini, Dave. For Those about to Write: How I Learned to Love Books & Why I Had to Write Them. 2007. 144p. (J). (gr. 5). pap. 9.95 (***978-0-88776-769-2(9)***) Tundra Bks., Inc./Livres Toundra, Inc. CAN. *Dist:* Random Hse., Inc.

Blasingame, James B. Gary Paulsen. 2007. (Teen Reads: Student Companions to Young Adult Literature Ser.). 184p. (J). 45.00 (***978-0-313-33532-7(X)*** , GR3532, Greenwood Pr.) Greenwood Publishing Group, Inc.

Bloom, Harold, intro. The Tale of Genji. 2003. (Bloom's Modern Critical Interpretations Ser.). (Illus.). 150p. (gr. 9-13). 45.00 (978-0-7910-7584-5(2) , Chelsea Hse.) Facts On File, Inc.

Boothroyd, Jennifer. Roald Dahl: A Life of Imagination. 2008. (Pull Ahead Books-Biographies Ser.). (J). lib. bdg. 22.60 (***978-0-8225-8825-2(0)*** , Lerner Pubns.) Lerner Publishing Group.

Borden, Louise. The Journey That Saved Curious George: The True Wartime Escape of Margret & H. A. Rey. Drummond, Allan, illus. 2005. 80p. (J). (gr. 3-5). 17.00 (978-0-618-33924-2(8)) Houghton Mifflin Co. Trade & Reference Div.

Bradman, Tony. So You Want to Write Fiction. (Illus.). 32p. (YA). (978-0-7502-3647-8(7) , Hodder Wayland) Hodder Children's Division.

Briggs, Lucy. Kate DiCamillo. 2005. (My Favorite Writer Ser.). (Illus.). 32p. (J). (gr. k-7). lib. bdg. 26.00 (978-1-59036-283-9(7)) Weigl Pubs., Inc.

Brocker, Susan. War Heroes: Level U, 6 vols. 128p. (gr. 6 up). 36.95 (978-0-322-05893-4(7)) Wright Group, The.

Burgess, Chris. English Skills: Creative Writing Module. 1999. (J). (gr. 4-8). pap. 35.00 (978-0-7217-0607-8(X)) Schofield & Sims Ltd. GBR. *Dist:* State Mutual Bk. & Periodical Service, Ltd.

Burkholder, Kelly. Diaries & Journals. 2000. (Artistic Adventures Ser.). (Illus.). 24p. (J). (gr. 2-6). lib. bdg. 23.93 (978-1-57103-352-9(1)) Rourke Publishing, LLC.

—Stories. 2000. (Artistic Adventures Ser.). (Illus.). 24p. (J). (gr. 2-6). lib. bdg. 23.93 (978-1-57103-356-7(4)) Rourke Publishing, LLC.

Cambridge Young Writers Staff. Tell You What! Cambridge Young Writers Award 2001. 2001. (Cambridge Reading Ser.). (Illus.). 80p. pap. 10.00 (978-0-521-00808-2(5)) Cambridge Univ. Pr.

Carroll, Joyce Armstrong. Dr. JAC's Guide to Writing With Depth. 2004. 192p. 23.95 (978-1-888842-40-1(7)) Absey & Co.

Center for Learning Network Staff. Writing 2: Becoming a Writer. 2000. (English Ser.). 252p. (YA). (gr. 10-11). spiral bd. 39.95 (978-1-56077-608-6(0)) Ctr. for Learning, The.

Charlesworth, Liza & Scholastic, Inc. Staff. Joyful Learning: Exciting Writing. 2001. (Joyful Learning Ser.). 72p. pap., tchr. ed. 8.95 (978-0-439-40815-8(6) , Teaching Resources) Scholastic, Inc.

Cherniss, Bonnie C. Creating Lifetime Mentor's Fun Children with Ghostwriting, 1. Dean, Diane C., illus. 2000. (YA). 10.00 (978-0-9700678-0-7(1)) Cherniss, Bonnie.

Chippendale, Lisa A. Triumph of the Imagination: The Story of Writer J. K. Rowling. 2001. (Overcoming Adversity Ser.). (Illus.). 112p. (J). (gr. 4-8). 30.00 (978-0-7910-6312-5(7) , Chelsea Hse.) Facts On File, Inc.

Clairday, Robynn. A Girl's Story: How to Write Your Autobiography. 2006. pap. 7.99 (978-0-9717119-5-2(X)) Consumer Pr., The.

Clish, Marian L. Solve a Mystery, Bk. 1. Crombie, Stephen, illus. unabr. ed. 1999. (J). (gr. k-5). pap. 8.95 incl. audio (978-1-928632-02-3(5)) Writers Marketplace:Consulting, Critiquing & Publishing.

Cohen, Joel H. R. L. Stine. 1999. (People in the News Ser.). (Illus.). 96p. (YA). (gr. 6-9). 28.70 (978-1-56006-608-8(3) , Lucent Bks.) Thomson Gale.

Coyle, Kathleen & Buckley, Annie. Once upon a Time: Creative Writing Fun for Kids. Law, Cathy, illus. 2004. 50p. (J). 14.95 (978-0-8118-4227-3(4)) Chronicle Bks. LLC.

Craats, Rennay. E. B. White. 2002. (My Favorite Writer Ser.). (Illus.). 32p. (J). lib. bdg. 16.95 (978-1-59036-026-2(5)) Weigl Pubs., Inc.

—Roald Dahl. 2002. (My Favorite Writer Ser.). (Illus.). 32p. (J). lib. bdg. 18.20 (978-1-59036-029-3(X)) Weigl Pubs., Inc.

Crutcher, Chris. King of the Mild Frontier: An Ill-Advised Autobiography. 2004. 272p. (J). reprint ed. pap. 6.99 (978-0-06-050251-5(7) , HarperTeen) HarperCollins Pubs.

Dahlstrom, Lorraine M. Writing down the Days: 365 Creative Journaling Ideas for Young People. 2nd rev. ed. 2004. (Illus.). 184p. (J). (gr. 7 up). pap. 14.95 (978-1-57542-086-8(4)) Free Spirit Publishing, Inc.

Dillon, Christine J. My First Report: Set of Fourteen Unit Studies. 1998. (Illus.). (J). (gr. 1-4). ring bd. 49.95 (978-1-57896-038-5(X) , 9212) Hewitt Research Foundation, Inc.

Douglas, Vincent & School Specialty Publishing Staff. Writer's Guide. Notebk Referenc, ed. 2nd rev. ed. 2006. (Notebook Reference Ser.). 144p. (J). pap. 3.95 (978-0-7696-4345-8(0) , American Education Publishing) School Specialty Publishing.

—Writing: Grade 4. 2001. (Spectrum Writing Ser.). (Illus.). 130p. (J). (gr. 4-4). pap., wbk. ed. 8.95 (978-1-57768-914-0(3) , Spectrum) School Specialty Publishing.

Dunkleberger, Amy. So You Want to Be a Film or TV Screenwriter? 2007. (Careers in Film & Television Ser.). (Illus.). 128p. (YA). (gr. 5-10). lib. bdg. 31.93 (978-0-7660-2645-2(0)) Enslow Pubs., Inc.

Dunn, Connie. Under the Wisdom Tree: Workshop on Developing Stories. 2002. (Illus.). 25p. pap. 25.00 (978-1-890641-07-8(3)) No Stress Pr.

Dwyer, Judy. Genre Writer. (Illus.). 60p. (J). (gr. 3-6). pap. (978-1-876367-34-3(2)) Wizard Bks.

Elleman, Barbara. Virginia Lee Burton: A Life in Art. 2002. (Illus.). 144p. (J). (gr. 7 up). tchr. ed. 20.00 (978-0-618-00342-6(8)) Houghton Mifflin Co. Trade & Reference Div.

Ellis, Sarah. The Young Writer's Companion. Fitzherbert, Juan, illus. 112p. (J). 2001. (gr. 4-7). pap. 7.95 (978-0-88899-411-0(7)); 1999. (gr. 5-9). pap. 12.95 (978-0-88899-371-7(4) , Libros Tigrillo) Groundwood Bks. CAN. *Dist:* Perseus Distribution.

Erlic, Lily. Lois Lowry. 2005. (My Favorite Writer Ser.). (Illus.). 32p. (J). (gr. k-7). lib. bdg. 26.00 (978-1-59036-286-0(1)); (gr. 2-6). pap. 7.95 (978-1-59036-292-1(6)) Weigl Pubs., Inc.

—Louis Sachar. 2005. (My Favorite Writer Ser.). (Illus.). 32p. (J). (gr. k-7). lib. bdg. 26.00 (978-1-59036-288-4(8)); pap. 7.95 (978-1-59036-294-5(2)) Weigl Pubs., Inc.

Every Page Perfect: A Full-Size Writer's Manual for Manuscript Format & Submission Protocol. 4th ed. 2001. 208p. (C). per. 19.95 (978-0-9710143-0-5(2)) Lynnx Ink.

Facts on File, Inc. Staff, contrib. by. Discovering Careers for Your Future. 2005. (Discovering Careers for Your Future Ser.). (Illus.). 96p. (J). (gr. 4-9). 21.95 (978-0-8160-5845-7(8) , Ferguson Publishing Co.) Facts On File, Inc.

Farrell, Tish. Write Your Own Adventure Story. 2006. (Write Your Own Ser.). (Illus.). 64p. (J). (gr. 5-7). 30.60 (978-0-7565-1638-3(2)) Compass Point Bks.

—Write Your Own Fantasy Story. 2006. (Write Your Own Ser.). (Illus.). 64p. (J). (gr. 5-7). 30.60 (978-0-7565-1639-0(0)) Compass Point Bks.

—Write Your Own Historical Fiction Story. 2006. (Write Your Own Ser.). (Illus.). 64p. (J). (gr. 5-7). 30.60 (978-0-7565-1640-6(4)) Compass Point Bks.

—Write Your Own Mystery Story. 2006. (Write Your Own Ser.). (Illus.). 64p. (J). (gr. 5-7). 30.60 (978-0-7565-1641-3(2)) Compass Point Bks.

—Write Your Own Realistic Fiction Story. 2006. (Write Your Own Ser.). (Illus.). 64p. (J). (gr. 5-7). 30.60 (978-0-7565-1642-0(0)) Compass Point Bks.

—Write Your Own Science Fiction Story. 2006. (Write Your Own Ser.). (Illus.). 64p. (J). (gr. 5-7). 30.60 (978-0-7565-1643-7(9)) Compass Point Bks.

Ferguson. Careers in Focus: Writing. 3rd rev. ed. 2007. (Careers in Focus Ser.). 224p. (J). (gr. 6-12). 29.95 (***978-0-8160-6596-7(9)*** , Ferguson Publishing Co.) Facts On File, Inc.

Fleischman, Sid. The Abracadabra Kid: A Writer's Life. 1998. 11.60 (978-0-606-13107-0(8)) Tandem Library Bks.

Fletcher, Ralph. How to Write Your Life Story. 2007. (J). 112p. 15.99 (***978-0-06-050770-1(5)***); 128p. pap. 5.99 (***978-0-06-050769-5(1)***) HarperCollins Pubs.

Fletcher, Ralph J. How Writers Work. 2000. (J). 11.79 (978-0-606-19977-3(2)); (gr. 3-6). lib. bdg. 13.00 (978-0-613-31337-7(2)) Tandem Library Bks.

—Live Writing: Breathing Life into Your Words. 1999. 144p. (J). (gr. 3-7). pap. 5.99 (978-0-380-79701-1(1) , Harper Trophy) HarperCollins Pubs.

—Poetry Matters: Writing a Poem from the Inside Out. 2002. (Illus.). 160p. (J). (gr. 3-7). pap. 5.99 (978-0-380-79703-5(8) , Harper Trophy) HarperCollins Pubs.

Francis, Barbara. Other People's Words: What Plagiarism Is & How to Avoid It. 2005. (Issues in Focus Today Ser.). (Illus.). 112p. (J). (gr. 6 up). lib. bdg. 31.93 (978-0-7660-2525-7(X)) Enslow Pubs., Inc.

Frank, Vivien & Jaffe, Deborah. Make a Book: Six Different Books to Make, Write, & Illustrate. 2004. (Illus.). 32p. (J). (gr. 2-8). reprint ed. pap. 15.00 (978-0-7567-7703-6(8)) DIANE Publishing Co.

Friedman, Lauri S. Pollution. 2007. (Writing the Critical Essay Ser.). (Illus.). 128p. (gr. 6-10). 29.95 (***978-0-7377-3198-9(2)*** , Greenhaven Pr., Inc.) Thomson Gale.

Fun to Write! Classroom Storybooks - Fiction. 2005. (J). spiral bd. 24.95 (978-1-58970-696-5(X)) Lakeshore Learning Materials.

Fun to Write! Classroom Storybooks - Non Fiction. 2005. (J). spiral bd. 24.95 (978-1-58970-697-2(8)) Lakeshore Learning Materials.

Gelletly, LeeAnne. Gift of Imagination: The Story of Roald Dahl. 2006. (World Writers Ser.). (Illus.). 160p. (YA). (gr. 6-12). lib. bdg. 27.95 (978-1-59935-026-4(2)) Reynolds, Morgan Inc.

Get in Shape to Write. 1998. (J). spiral bd. 14.00 (978-0-939564-22-4(X)) Pen Notes, Inc.

Gould, Judith S. & Burke, Mary F. Write Now! Mitchell, Judith, ed. Rasche, Shelly S., illus. 2005. 80p. (J). pap. 6.95 (978-1-57310-449-4(3)) Teaching & Learning Co.

Graham, Ann M. Write a Book or Just Have Fun with Writing! 1999. 100p. (J). pap. 12.99 (978-0-9655719-2-0(0)) KCDI Publishing.

Hall, Dorothy & Cunningham, Patricia. Reading/Writing Complex Rhymes: Rhymes with More Than One Spelling Pattern. 2003. (Four-Blocks Ser.). 88p. (J). per. 29.99 (978-0-88724-920-4(5)) Carson-Dellosa Publishing Co., Inc.

—Reading/Writing Simple Rhymes: Rhymes with One Spelling Pattern. 2003. (Four-Blocks Ser.). 88p. (J). per. 29.99 (978-0-88724-919-8(1)) Carson-Dellosa Publishing Co., Inc.

Hambleton, Vicki & Greenwood, Cathleen, eds. So, You Wanna Be a Writer? How to Write, Get Published, & Maybe Even Make It Big! Eldridge, Laura & Mistretta, Corey, illus. 2001. (So, You Wanna Be ... Ser.). 120p. (gr. 3-11). pap. (978-1-58270-043-4(5)) Beyond Words Publishing, Inc.

Hamley, Harold, ed. How to Write & Sell. 4th ed. 121p. (Orig.). (YA). (gr. 9-12). reprint ed. lib. bdg. 8.95 (978-0-9621758-0-0(3)) Raconteurs, Inc.

Harcourt School Publishers Staff. What Do Authors Do: Library Edition. 1999. (Collections Ser.). (Illus.). (J). 5.30 (978-0-15-314324-3(X)) Harcourt Schl. Pubs.

Haugen, Hayley Mitchell. Daniel Handler: The Real Lemony Snicket. 2005. (Inventors & Creators Ser.). (Illus.). 47p. (J). (ps-ps). lib. bdg. 26.20 (978-0-7377-3117-0(6) , Greenhaven Pr., Inc.) Thomson Gale.

Hennessy, Brendan. Essay to Write? 2nd ed. 2004. 93p. pap. 13.25 (978-1-85703-835-4(5)) How To Books GBR. *Dist:* Parkwest Pubns., Inc.

Hollenbeck, Kathleen M. Teaching with Favorite Leo Lionni Books: Creative Activities for Exploring Friendship, Self-Esteem, Cooperation & Other Themes in These Beloved Books. 1999. (Illus.). 64p. pap. 10.95 (978-0-439-04388-5(3)) Scholastic, Inc.

Hook, Dianne. Just for Journaling. 2005. 128p. (J). per. 19.99 (978-1-59441-314-8(2) , DJ-604013) Carson-Dellosa Publishing Co., Inc.

Hook, Jason. Roald Dahl. 2004. (Illus.). 48p. (J). lib. bdg. 28.56 (978-0-7398-6626-9(5)) Raintree.

Hulme, Joy N. & Guthrie, Donna. How to Write, Recite, & Delight in All Kinds of Poetry. 2003. (Single Titles Ser.: Vol. 8). 96p. (J). (gr. 3-6). pap. 9.95 (978-0-7613-1831-6(3) , Millbrook Pr.) Lerner Publishing Group.

Hurtig, Jennifer. Maurice Sendak. 2007. (My Favorite Writer Ser.). (J). (978-1-59036-485-7(6)); lib. bdg. (978-1-59036-484-0(8)) Weigl Pubs., Inc.

J. G. Ferguson Publishing Company Staff, contrib. by. Careers in Focus: Writing. 2nd ed. 2002. (Careers in Focus Ser.). (Illus.). 192p. (YA). (gr. 6-12). 22.95 (978-0-89434-439-8(0) , F507, Ferguson Publishing Co.) Facts On File, Inc.

J. G. Ferguson Publishing Company Staff, ed. Careers in Focus: Writing. 2000. (Careers in Focus Ser.). 188p. (J). (gr. 7 up). lib. bdg. (978-0-89434-318-6(1) , F507, Ferguson Publishing Co.) Facts On File, Inc.

Jazz up Your Journal Writing 1-2. 2004. 48p. (J). pap. 5.99 (978-0-88724-193-2(X) , CD-8066) Carson-Dellosa Publishing Co., Inc.

Jazz up Your Journal Writing 3-4. 2004. 48p. (J). pap. 5.99 (978-0-88724-194-9(8) , CD-8067) Carson-Dellosa Publishing Co., Inc.

Jazz up Your Journal Writing 5-6. 2004. 48p. (J). pap. 5.99 (978-0-88724-195-6(6) , CD-8068) Carson-Dellosa Publishing Co., Inc.

Jones, Jen. Judy Blume: Fearless Storyteller for Teens. 2008. (***978-0-7660-2960-6(3)***) Enslow Pubs., Inc.

Kapell, Dave & Steenland, Sally. The Kids' Magnetic Poetry Book & Creativity Kit. 1998. (Illus.). 64p. (J). (gr. 3-7). spiral bd. 16.95 (978-0-7611-1357-7(6) , 11357) Workman Publishing Co., Inc.

Kassirer, Sue. Learn to Write. Date not set. (J). (978-0-679-85297-1(2) , Random Hse. Bks. for Young Readers) Random Hse. Children's Bks.

Kemmerer, Susan. The Word Artist. 2005. per. 10.95 (978-0-9758543-5-8(6)) Schoolhouse Publishing.

Kemper, Dave, et al. Write Ahead: A Student Handbook. 2004. (YA). (978-0-669-50787-4(3)); (Illus.). x, 550p. pap. (978-0-669-50786-7(5)) Great Source Education Group, Inc.

Kilpatrick, Susan. Developing Young Authors 2-3: Using Favorite Literature to Create Text Innovations. Hamaguchi, Carla, ed. Yuh, Catherine, illus. 2001. 80p. pap. 10.99 (978-1-57471-782-2(0) , 2329) Creative Teaching Pr., Inc.

—Developing Young Authors Grades K-1: Using Favorite Literature to Creatie Text Innovations, 2328. Hamaguchi, Carla, ed. Yuh, Catherine, illus. 2001. 80p. pap. 10.99 (978-1-57471-781-5(2)) Creative Teaching Pr., Inc.

King-Smith, Dick. Chewing the Cud: An Extraordinary Life Remembered by the Author of Babe: the Gallant Pig. Horse, Harry, illus. 2002. 208p. (J). (gr. 5 up). 16.95 (978-0-375-81459-4(0) , Knopf Bks. for Young Readers) Random Hse. Children's Bks.

Kjelle, Marylou. Katherine Paterson. 2004. (Classic Storytellers Ser.). (Illus.). 48p. (J). (gr. 4-8). lib. bdg. 20.95 (978-1-58415-268-2(0)) Mitchell Lane Pubs., Inc.

Kjelle, Marylou Morano. S. E. Hinton: Author of the Outsiders. 2007. (Authors Teens Love Ser.). (Illus.). 112p. (J). (gr. 6). lib. bdg. 31.93 (***978-0-7660-2720-6(1)***) Enslow Pubs., Inc.

Krull, Kathleen. The Boy on Fairfield Street: How Ted Geisel Grew up to Become Dr. Seuss. Johnson, Steve & Fancher, Lou, illus. 2004. 48p. (J). (gr. 1-7). 16.95 (978-0-375-82298-8(4) , Random Hse. Bks. for Young Readers) Random Hse. Children's Bks.

Kunkel, Jeff. Jesus, This Is Your Life: Stories & Pictures by Kids. 2001. (Illus.). 48p. (gr. k-7). 12.99 (978-0-8066-4165-2(7) , Augsburg Bks.) Augsburg Fortress, Pubs.

Kuprin, Alexander. To Chekhov's Memory. 2004. reprint ed. pap. 15.95 (978-1-4191-9023-0(7)); pap. 1.99 (978-1-4192-9023-7(1)) Kessinger Publishing, LLC.

Kurtz, Jane. Jane Kurtz & You. 2007. (Author & YOU Ser.: No. 8). (Illus.). 204p. 35.00 (978-1-59158-295-3(4) , LU2954) Libraries Unlimited, Inc.

Laminack, Lester. Cracking Open the Author's Craft. 2007. 96p. pap. 29.99 (***978-0-439-91964-7(9)***) Scholastic, Inc.

Larson, Mark. Moe's Cafe. 2006. (Illus.). 128p. (YA). pap. (978-1-59647-088-0(7)) Good Year Bks.

Learning to Write: 4-Month Academic Access Version. 2003. (Illus.). (C). E-Book incl. cd-rom (978-0-9726808-1-3(0)) MEIER Enterprises Inc.

Lee, Marian. J. P. Landerz Solve a Mystery, Bk. 2. Crombie, Steven, illus. unabr. ed. 1999. (J). (gr. 3-5). reprint ed. 10.95 (978-0-516-01992-5(9)) Writers Marketplace:Consulting, Critiquing & Publishing.

Leedy, Loreen. Look at My Book: How Kids Can Write & Illustrate Terrific Books. 2005. (Illus.). 32p. (J). 6.95 (978-0-8234-1959-3(2)) Holiday Hse., Inc.

Lester, Helen. Author: A True Story. Lester, Helen, illus. 2002. (Illus.). 32p. (J). (gr. k-3). pap. 5.95 (978-0-618-26010-2(2) , Walter Lorraine) Houghton Mifflin Co. Trade & Reference Div.

Levine, Gail Carson. Writing Magic: Creating Stories That Fly. 2006. 176p. (J). (gr. 5 up). 16.99 (978-0-06-051961-2(4)); pap. 5.99 (978-0-06-051960-5(6)) HarperCollins Pubs. (Collins).

Levine, Stuart P. Dr. Seuss. 2000. (Importance of Ser.). (Illus.). 112p. (J). (gr. 7-10). 32.45 (978-1-56006-748-1(9) , Lucent Bks.) Thomson Gale.

Levithan, David, ed. You Are Here, This Is Now: The Best Young Writers & Artists in America. 2002. (Illus.). 272p. (J). pap. 6.99 (978-0-439-37618-1(1) , PUSH) Scholastic, Inc.

Lurie, Alison. Boys & Girls Forever. 2003. (gr. 7-12). lib. bdg. 24.60 (978-0-613-61607-2(3)) Tandem Library Bks.

Lynette, Rachel. Shel Silverstein. 2006. (Inventors & Creators Ser.). 48p. (gr. 4-8). 27.45 (978-0-7377-3555-0(4) , Greenhaven Pr., Inc.) Thomson Gale.

MacGregor, Cynthia. When I Grow up, I Want to Be a Writer. Flook, Helen, illus. 2001. (Millennium Generation). 100p. (J). pap. 9.95 (978-1-894222-42-6(3)) Lobster Pr. CAN. *Dist:* Univ. of Toronto Pr.

Macken, JoAnn Early. Gary Paulsen: Voice of Adventure & Survival. 2007. (Authors Teens Love Ser.). (Illus.). 104p. (J). (gr. 6 up). lib. bdg. 31.93 (978-0-7660-2721-3(X)) Enslow Pubs., Inc.

Marcovitz, Hal. R. L. Stine. 2005. (Who Wrote That? Ser.). (Illus.). 134p. (YA). (gr. 6-12). lib. bdg. 30.00 (978-0-7910-8659-9(3) , Chelsea Hse.) Facts On File, Inc.

Marcovitz, Hal. Scott O'Dell. 2007. (Who Wrote That? Ser.). 112p. (J). (gr. 6-12). 30.00 (***978-0-7910-9526-3(6)*** , Chelsea Hse.) Facts On File, Inc.

Marcus, Leonard S. Side by Side: Five Favorite Picture-Book Teams Go to Work. 2006. (Illus.). 64p. (J). pap. 11.95 (978-0-8027-9616-5(8)) Walker & Co.

McCarthy, Shaun. All about J. K. Rowling. 2003. (gr. 3-6). lib. bdg. 15.90 (978-0-613-78210-4(0)) Tandem Library Bks.

McGinty, Alice B. Meet Daniel Pinkwater. 2003. (About the Author Ser.). (Illus.). 24p. (J). lib. bdg. 18.75 (978-0-8239-6406-2(X)) Rosen Publishing Group, Inc., The.

—Meet Gail Carson Levine. 2003. (About the Author Ser.). (Illus.). 24p. (J). lib. bdg. 18.75 (978-0-8239-6409-3(4) , PowerKids Pr.) Rosen Publishing Group, Inc., The.

—Meet Jane Yolen. 2003. (About the Author Ser.). (Illus.). 24p. (J). lib. bdg. 18.75 (978-0-8239-6407-9(8) , PowerKids Pr.) Rosen Publishing Group, Inc., The.

—Meet Jerry Spinelli. 2003. (About the Author Ser.). (Illus.). 24p. (J). lib. bdg. 18.75 (978-0-8239-6408-6(6) , PowerKids Pr.) Rosen Publishing Group, Inc., The.

—Meet Laurence Yep. 2003. (About the Author Ser.). (Illus.). 24p. (J). lib. bdg. 18.75 (978-0-8239-6410-9(8) , PowerKids Pr.) Rosen Publishing Group, Inc., The.

Meltzer, Milton. Milton Meltzer: Writing Matters. 2004. (Single Title - Bios Ser.). (Illus.). 160p. (J). 29.00 (978-0-531-12257-0(3) , Watts, Franklin) Scholastic Library Publishing.

Micklos, John, Jr. Jerry Spinelli: Master Teller of Teen Tales. 2007. (Authors Teens Love Ser.). (Illus.). 104p. (J). (gr. 6 up). lib. bdg. 31.93 (978-0-7660-2718-3(X)) Enslow Pubs., Inc.

Miles, Lisa, ed. Starting to Write. 1998. (Sticker Learning Bks.). (SPA., Illus.). 18p. (J). (ps-3). pap. 6.95 (978-0-7460-3108-7(4)) EDC Publishing.

Milliken, Linda. My Story Book: Primary. Rogers, Kathy, ed. Fuller, Janelle, illus. 1998. 32p. (J). pap., stu. ed., wbk. ed. 1.99 (978-1-56472-145-7(0) , EP145) Edupress, Inc.

—My Story Book: Upper Grade. Rogers, Kathy, ed. Fuller, Janelle, illus. 1998. 32p. (J). pap. 1.99 (978-1-56472-146-4(9)) Edupress, Inc.

Moore, Jo Ellen. Making Books with Beginning Writers. Evans, Marilyn, ed. Larsen, Jo, illus. 1999. (How to Make Books with Children Ser.). 160p. (J). (gr. k-2). pap., tchr. ed. 16.95 (978-1-55799-730-2(6) , EMC 776) Evan-Moor Educational Pubs.

Morina, Barbara. Me, Myself & My Personal Journal. Morina, Barbara, ed. 2001. (Write It down Ser.). (Illus.). 202p. 19.95 (978-1-892033-35-2(6)) Journals Unlimited, Inc.

Moses, Brian & Bradman, Tony. So You Want to Write Poetry. Date not set. (Illus.). 32p. pap. 13.00 (978-0-7502-3858-8(5) , Hodder & Stoughton) Hodder General Publishing Division GBR. *Dist:* Trafalgar Square Publishing.

Murray, Jennifer. 'Twas a Dark & Stormy Night... Why Writers Write. 2007. (Shockwave: Life Stories Ser.). (Illus.). 36p. (J). (gr. 4-6). lib. bdg. 25.00 (***978-0-531-17773-0(4)*** , Children's Pr.) Scholastic Library Publishing.

Myers, Walter Dean. Bad Boy: A Memoir. l.t. ed. 2005. (Thorndike Press Large Print the Literacy Bridge Ser.). 269p. (978-0-7862-7537-3(5)) Thorndike Pr.

Nault, Jennifer. Judy Blume. 2002. (My Favorite Writer Ser.). (Illus.). 32p. (J). lib. bdg. 18.20 (978-1-59036-025-5(7)) Weigl Pubs., Inc.

Naylor, Phyllis Reynolds. How I Came to Be a Writer. rev. ed. 2001. (Illus.). 144p. (J). (gr. 4). pap. 5.99 (978-0-689-83887-3(5) , Aladdin) Simon & Schuster Children's Publishing.

—How I Came to Be a Writer. 2001. (gr. 3-6). lib. bdg. 13.00 (978-0-613-29979-4(5)); 2000. (J). 11.64 (978-0-606-20087-5(8)) Tandem Library Bks.

Numeroff, Laura Joffe. If You Give an Author a Pencil. Shahan, Sherry, illus. 2002. (Meet the Author Ser.). 32p. (J). (gr. 2-5). 14.95 (978-1-57274-595-7(9) , 727) Owen, Richard C. Pubs., Inc.

O'Conner, Patricia T. Words Fail Me: What Everyone Who Writes Should Know about Writing. 2000. (gr. 7-12). lib. bdg. 21.10 (978-0-613-65854-6(X)) Tandem Library Bks.

Oguhebe, Festus. God Bless the USA: Continuing Testimony Stressing the Neighborly Spirit of America & Her Love Poems. 2002. (YA). per. (978-0-9636510-5-1(6)) Hebe's International Pubs.

—The "How to Write" Book. (YA). (978-0-9636510-0-6(5)) Hebe's International Pubs.

O'Neil, Dennis. Dc Comics Guide to Writing Comics. 2001. (gr. 7-12). lib. bdg. 30.35 (978-0-613-51137-7(9)) Tandem Library Bks.

Orr, Tamra. Extraordinary Essays. 2006. 128p. (YA). (gr. 8-12). pap. 9.95 (978-0-531-17576-7(6) , Watts, Franklin) Scholastic Library Publishing.

Orr, Tamra B. Extraordinary Essays. 2005. (F.W. Prep Ser.). (Illus.). 127p. (YA). (gr. 8-13). 30.50 (978-0-531-16761-8(5) , Watts, Franklin) Scholastic Library Publishing.

Otfinoski, Steven. Extraordinary Short Story Writing. (F.W. Prep Ser.). (Illus.). 128p. (YA). (gr. 8-12). 2006. pap. 9.95 (978-0-531-17578-1(2)); 2005. 30.50 (978-0-531-16760-1(7)) Scholastic Library Publishing. (Watts, Franklin).

Pallotta, Jerry. Read a Zillion Books. 2002. (Illus.). 32p. (J). 14.95 (978-1-57274-597-1(5)) Owen, Richard C. Pubs., Inc.

Panman, Sandra & Panman, Richard. Short Stories: Reading - Thinking - Writing. 2000. (Illus.). 192p. (YA). (gr. 7 up). pap. 22.00 (978-0-912813-26-4(1)) Active Learning Corp.

Parker-Rock, Michelle. Bruce Coville: An Author Kids Love. 2008. (Authors Kids Love Ser.). (Illus.). 48p. (J). (gr. 3-4). lib. bdg. 23.93 (978-0-7660-2755-8(4) , Enslow Elementary) Enslow Pubs., Inc.

Parks, Peggy J. Writer. 2003. (Illus.). 48p. (J). 26.20 (978-0-7377-2069-3(7) , Greenhaven Pr., Inc.) Thomson Gale.

Pascal, Francine. Haciendo Novelas. Orig. Title: Playing Hockey. (SPA.). 120p. (J). 6.95 (978-84-272-3790-2(1)) Molino, Editorial ESP. *Dist:* AIMS International Bks., Inc.

Patterson, Ella. How to Research & Write Your Book. Sherman, Mary Ann, photos by. 2000. (Write-to-Publish Ser.: Vol. 1). (Illus.). (J). lib. bdg. 25.00 (978-1-884331-19-0(X) , KCES) Knowledge Concepts Pubns.

Paulsen, Gary. Guts. 2002. 160p. (YA). (gr. 7 up). pap. 5.99 (978-0-440-40712-6(5) , Laurel Leaf) Random Hse. Children's Bks.

—Guts: The True Stories Behind Hatchet & the Brian Books. l.t. ed. 2001. (YA). 22.95 (978-0-7862-3407-3(5)) Thorndike Pr.

Pearce, Querida L. Story Starters: Mysteries. 1999. (Gifted & Talented Ser.). (Illus.). 64p. (J). (gr. 1-3). pap. 5.95 (978-0-7373-0204-2(6)) Lowell Hse.

Pearson, Craig, et al. Writing: Grade 6. 2001. (Spectrum Writing Ser.). (Illus.). 130p. (J). (gr. 6-6). pap., wbk. ed. 8.95 (978-1-57768-916-4(X) , Spectrum) School Specialty Publishing.

Pearson, Kim. You Can Be an Author, Even If You're Not A Writer: The 1-2-3 of Creating a Book. 2005. 64p. pap. 6.95 (978-1-881849-06-3(6)) Primary Sources.

Pellegrino, Victor C. A Writer's Guide to Powerful Paragraphs. Magee, Christopher, illus. 2003. 187p. (YA). (gr. 7 up). pap. 18.95 (978-0-945045-05-2(0)) Maui Arthoughts Co.

Peterson, Shelley & Griwkowsky, Chris. Becoming Better Writers, Vol. 1. 1999. (Illus.). 182p. (YA). (gr. 4-9). pap. 15.95 (978-0-9699619-0-1(1)) FP Hendriks Publishing, Ltd. CAN. *Dist:* Baker & Taylor Bks.

Pezzi, Bryan. J. K. Rowling. 2005. (My Favorite Writer Ser.). (Illus.). 32p. (J). (gr. 2-6). lib. bdg. 26.00 (978-1-59036-287-7(X)) Weigl Pubs., Inc.

Pierce, Mark & Jennings, Karen. Wright Fright: A Guide to Writing Scary Stories. 2004. 88p. pap. (978-0-673-58655-1(3)) Good Year Bks.

Price, Joan. J.K. Rowling. 2004. (Trailblazers of the Modern World Ser.). (Illus.). 48p. (J). pap. 11.95 (978-0-8368-5268-4(0)); (YA). lib. bdg. 30.00 (978-0-8368-5499-2(3)) Stevens, Gareth Inc. (World Almanac Library).

Rea, Dean. Write Stuff Adventure: Exploring the Art of Writing. 1999. 208p. (YA). (gr. 7-10). pap. 19.99 (978-1-883934-04-0(4)) Great Expectations Bk. Co.

Realtime Associates and Mazer Corporation Staff & LeapFrog Staff, compiled by. Identify the Climax of a Story. 2002. (J). (gr. 5). 66.75 (978-1-58605-486-1(4) , LeapFrog Schl. Hse.) LeapFrog Enterprises, Inc.

—Judge the Support for an Author's Statement. 2002. (J). (gr. 5). 66.75 (978-1-58605-483-0(X) , LeapFrog Schl. Hse.) LeapFrog Enterprises, Inc.

Reeves, Diane Lindsey. Career Ideas for Kids Who Like Writing. 2nd rev. ed. (Career Ideas for Kids Ser.). 200p. (J). (gr. 4-9). pap. 16.95 (***978-0-8160-6556-1(X)*** , Checkmark Bks.); 2007. 32.95 (***978-0-8160-6555-4(1)*** , Ferguson Publishing Co.) Facts On File, Inc.

Reeves, Diane Lindsey, ed. Career Ideas for Kids Who Like Writing. Bond, Nancy, illus. 1998. (Career Ideas for Kids Ser.). 166p. (J). (gr. 4-8). pap. 12.95 (978-0-8160-3691-2(8)) Facts On File, Inc.

Reeves, Diane Lindsey & Karlitz, Gail. Virtual Apprentice: Author. 2007. (Virtual Apprentice Ser.). 64p. (J). (gr. 6-12). 29.95 (***978-0-8160-6756-5(2)*** , Ferguson Publishing Co.) Facts On File, Inc.

Rhatigan, Joe. In Print! 40 Cool Publishing Projects for Kids. 2004. (Illus.). 128p. (YA). 20.00 (978-0-7567-8235-1(X)) DIANE Publishing Co.

Richardson, Gillian. Dan Gutman. 2005. (My Favorite Writer Ser.). (Illus.). 32p. (J). (gr. 2-6). lib. bdg. 26.00 (978-1-59036-284-6(5)) Weigl Pubs., Inc.

Rigby. Creative Writing Prompts. 2001. pap. (978-0-7635-7819-0(3)) Steck-Vaughn.

Ring, Susan. Beverly Cleary. 2002. (My Favorite Writer Ser.). (Illus.). 32p. (J). lib. bdg. 16.95 (978-1-59036-030-9(3)) Weigl Pubs., Inc.

Roets, Lois F. Writing Fiction. 2000. 56p. (YA). (gr. 3-12). pap. 12.00 (978-0-911943-69-6(2)) Leadership Pub., Inc.

Rosenberg, Mandie. Mastering Writing Skills. 2002. lib. bdg. 22.20 (978-0-613-52142-0(0)) Tandem Library Bks.

Rosinsky, Natalie M. Write Your Own Myth. 2007. (J). lib. bdg. (***978-0-7565-3372-4(4)***) Compass Point Bks.

Roy, Jennifer Rozines. You Can Write a Story or Narrative. 2003. (You Can Write Ser.). (Illus.). 64p. (J). (gr. 6-12). lib. bdg. 22.60 (978-0-7660-2085-6(1)) Enslow Pubs., Inc.

Roy, Jennifer Rozines & Haney, Johannah. You Can Write an Essay. 2004. (You Can Write Ser.). (Illus.). 64p. (J). lib. bdg. 22.60 (978-0-7660-2091-7(6)) Enslow Pubs., Inc.

Ruffin, Frances E. Meet Patricia MacLachlan. 2006. (About the Author Ser.). (Illus.). 24p. (J). (978-1-4042-3130-6(7) , PowerKids Pr.) Rosen Publishing Group, Inc., The.

School Newspaper: Individual Title Six-Packs. (On Deck Ser.). 24p. (gr. 4-5). 35.00 (978-0-7578 1023 7(3)) Rigby Education.

Schwiebert. Reading & Writing from Literature Ap Version. 2002. (YA). (gr. 6-12). stu. ed. 74.36 (978-0-618-21889-9(0) , 349693) Houghton Mifflin College Div.

Shapiro, Marc. J. K. Rowling: The Wizard Behind Harry Potter. 2007. 288p. pap. 6.99 (***978-0-312-37697-0(9)*** , St. Martin's Griffin) St. Martin's Pr.

Shawntel, Ashley. The Heart's Flames. 2005. (Fresh Voices Ser.). 163p. (J). (gr. 8-17). pap. 5.95 (978-1-932802-99-3(1) , Holy Macro! Bks.) MrExcel.com Publishing.

Shields, Charles J. Mythmaker: The Story of J. K. Rowling. 2002. (Who Wrote That? Ser.). (Illus.). 112p. (gr. 6-12). 30.00 (978-0-7910-6719-2(X) , Chelsea Hse.) Facts On File, Inc.

Sickels, Amy. Richard Peck. 2007. 128p. 30.00 (***978-0-7910-9530-0(4)*** , Chelsea Hse.) Facts On File, Inc.

Silverstein, Shel. Shel Silverstein Pop-up Treasury. Silverstein, Shel, illus. 2008. 16p. (J). 29.99 (***978-0-06-147269-5(7)***) HarperCollins Pubs.

Skills for Young Writers: Helping Students Make Good Stories Great. 48p. (gr. 1 up). 5.99 (978-1-56822-582-1(2) , IF5140) School Specialty Publishing.

So, Meilo, illus. Read a Rhyme, Write a Rhyme. 2005. 32p. (J). (gr. k-3). 16.95 (978-0-375-82286-5(0)); lib. bdg. 18.99 (978-0-375-92286-2(5)) Random Hse. Children's Bks. (Knopf Bks. for Young Readers).

Spectrum Writing Grade 3. 2001. (Spectrum Writing Ser.). (Illus.). 130p. (J). (gr. 3-3). pap., wbk. ed. 8.95 (978-1-57768-913-3(5) , Spectrum) School Specialty Publishing.

Spilsbury, Richard. Comics & Graphic Novels. 2006. (Art off the Wall Ser.). (Illus.). 56p. (978-1-4034-8286-0(1)) Heinemann Library.

Steck-Vaughn Staff. Answer Key Soaring Score Map Communication Arts Level G. 2002. (J). pap. (978-0-7398-5633-8(2)) Steck-Vaughn.

—Answer Key Soaring Score Map Communication Arts Level K: High School Edition. 2002. (YA). pap. (978-0-7398-5645-1(6)) Steck-Vaughn.

—Introduction to Journal Writing. 1998. (Illus.). (J). (gr. 1). pap. (978-0-8172-5797-2(7)); (gr. 2). pap. (978-0-8172-5798-9(5)); (gr. 3). pap. (978-0-8172-5799-6(3)) Steck-Vaughn.

—Reading & Writing Exercises: High School. 2001. (YA). pap. (978-0-7398-3958-4(6)) Steck-Vaughn.

—Write to the Top Grade 3: California Edition. 2002. (gr. 3). tchr. ed. 21.95 (978-0-7398-5764-9(9)) Steck-Vaughn.

—Write to the Top Grade 4: California Edition. 2002. (J). (gr. 4). tchr. ed. 21.95 (978-0-7398-5765-6(7)) Steck-Vaughn.

—Write to the Top Grade 5: California Editon. 2002. (J). (gr. 5). tchr. ed. 21.95 (978-0-7398-5766-3(5)) Steck-Vaughn.

—Write to the Top Grade 6: California Edition. 2002. (J). (gr. 6). tchr. ed. 21.95 (978-0-7398-5767-0(3)) Steck-Vaughn.

—Write to the Top Grade 7: California Edition. 2002. (YA). (gr. 7). tchr. ed. 21.95 (978-0-7398-5768-7(1)) Steck-Vaughn.

Stockland, Patricia M., tr. The Free & the Brave: A Collection of Poems about the United States. 2004. (Poet's Toolbox Ser.). (Illus.). 32p. (J). (gr. 3 up). 22.60 (978-0-7565-0563-9(1)) Compass Point Bks.

Storm, Wilda. Write up A Storm! ¿ Practice for Proficiency: Student Handbook 3rd Grade. 2007. ring bd. (***978-0-9772935-8-2(0)***) DoveTail Hse., Inc.

—Write up A Storm! ¿ Practice for Proficiency: Student Handbook 4th Grade. 2007. ring bd. (***978-0-9772935-9-9(9)***) DoveTail Hse., Inc.

—Write up A Storm! ¿ Writing Tools: A Student Guide ¿ Grade 2-3. 2007. ring bd. (***978-0-9772935-5-1(6)***) DoveTail Hse., Inc.

—Write up A Storm! Take Rewarding Revisions by Storm. 2007. ring bd. (***978-0-9772935-2-0(1)***) DoveTail Hse., Inc.

Stux, Erica. Writing for Freedom: A Story about Lydia Maria Child. Young, Mary O'Keefe, illus. 2000. (Creative Minds Biographies Ser.). 64p. (J). (gr. 3-6). lib. bdg. 22.60 (978-1-57505-439-1(6) , Carolrhoda Bks.) Lerner Publishing Group.

Sweeney, Alyse. All about Me Write & Read Books: 15 Fun-Shaped Book Patterns with Motivating Prompts to Get Kids Excited about Writing. 2000. (Illus.). 64p. (J). (gr. 1-2). pap. 10.95 (978-0-439-10616-0(8)) Scholastic, Inc.

Tait, Leia. Avi. 2007. (My Favorite Writer Ser.). (J). pap. (978-1-59036-479-6(1)); lib. bdg. (978-1-59036-478-9(3)) Weigl Pubs., Inc.

Teitelbaum, Michael & Bender, Howard. Making Comic Books. 2006. (Boys Rock! Ser.). (Illus.). 32p. (J). (gr. 1-5). 24.21 (978-1-59296-733-9(7)) Child's World, Inc.

Think Aloud Trade Book Package. 2003. 165.50 (978-0-673-75203-1(8)) Modern Curriculum Pr.

Thomas, Marian. Comedy Writer. (Illus.). 48p. (J). (gr. 3-6). pap. (978-1-875739-84-4(X)) Wizard Bks.

—Fantasy Writer. (Illus.). (J). (gr. 3-6). pap. (978-1-876367-11-4(3)) Wizard Bks.

—Mystery Writer. (Illus.). 48p. (J). (gr. 4-6). pap. (978-1-876367-00-8(8)) Wizard Bks.

Thompson, Kristin & Grigsby, Ann, creators. Creating a Legacy: Leave More Than Money. 2003. 20p. per. 6.00 (978-0-9745923-0-5(7)) Editorial Resources, Inc.

Tomljanovic, Tatiana. Cornelia Funke: My Favorite Writer. 2007. (My Favorite Writer Ser.). (J). (978-1-59036-481-9(3)); lib. bdg. (978-1-59036-480-2(5)) Weigl Pubs., Inc.

Tracy, Kathleen. John Steinbeck. 2004. (Classic Storytellers Ser.). (Illus.). 48p. (J). (gr. 4-8). lib. bdg. 20.95 (978-1-58415-271-2(0)) Mitchell Lane Pubs., Inc.

Tracy, Kathleen. Matt Christopher. 2007. (Classic Storytellers Ser.). (J). lib. bdg. (***978-1-58415-535-5(3)***) Mitchell Lane Pubs., Inc.

Trimmer. The Riverside Reader: AP Version. 7th ed. 2002. (YA). (gr. 6-12). stu. ed. 56.36 (978-0-618-26233-5(4) , 356188) Houghton Mifflin College Div.

Tucker, Shelley. Painting the Sky. 2nd ed. 2006. 160p. pap. (978-1-59647-012-5(7)) Good Year Bks.

Turrell, Linda. Everyday Writing - How to Master Basic Writing Skills Student Activities Book. Matthews, Douglas L., ed. 2003. (Illus.). stu. ed., wbk. ed. (978-1-931680-83-7(3) , Expert Systems for Teachers) Teaching Point, Inc.

—Writing Good Stories: Mastering Language Arts Series. Matthews, Douglas L., ed. 2003. (Illus.). stu. ed., wbk. ed., act. bk. ed. (978-1-931680-85-1(X) , Expert Systems for Teachers) Teaching Point, Inc.

Varikyan, Arpine & Wallace, Dejuanna. From the Inside Out. 2004. (ENG.). 80p. (YA). per. (978-0-595-33149-9(1)) iUniverse, Inc.

Venolia, Jan. Kids Write Right! 2000. (978-0-606-20316-6(8)) Tandem Library Bks.

Ventresca, Yvonne. Publishing. 2005. (Careers for the Twenty-First Century Ser.). (Illus.). 112p. (J). (gr. k-8). per. 29.95 (978-1-59018-298-7(7) , Lucent Bks.) Thomson Gale.

Ward, S. Meet Shel Silverstein. 2001. (About the Author Ser.). (Illus.). 24p. (J). (gr. 3). lib. bdg. 18.75 (978-0-8239-5709-5(8) , PowerKids Pr.) Rosen Publishing Group, Inc., The.

Watson, Michele Griskey. Ray Bradbury. 2006. (Classic Storytellers Ser.). (Illus.). 48p. (J). lib. bdg. 20.95 (978-1-58415-455-6(1) , 1259542) Mitchell Lane Pubs., Inc.

Wheeler, Jill C. Gertrude Chandler Warner. 2005. (Children's Authors Ser.). (Illus.). 24p. (J). (gr. k-6). lib. bdg. 21.35 (978-1-59197-609-7(X)) ABDO Publishing Co.

—Judy Blume. 2005. (Children's Authors Ser.). (Illus.). 24p. (J). (gr. k-6). lib. bdg. 21.35 (978-1-59197-604-2(9)) ABDO Publishing Co.

—Lemony Snicket. 2007. (Children's Authors Ser.). (Illus.). 24p. 21.35 (978-1-59679-767-3(3)) ABDO Publishing Co.

—Mercer Mayer. 2005. (Children's Authors Ser.). (Illus.). 24p. (J). (gr. k-6). lib. bdg. 21.35 (978-1-59197-606-6(5)) ABDO Publishing Co.

—Norman Bridwell. 2005. (Children's Authors Ser.). (Illus.). 24p. (J). (gr. k-6). lib. bdg. 21.35 (978-1-59197-605-9(7)) ABDO Publishing Co.

Willhoff, Jude. Interviews with Your Favorite Romance Authors. 2004. Orig. Title: Stories to Inspire Your Writing. 212p. (YA). per. 19.95 (978-1-932344-71-4(3)) Thornton Publishing.

Williams, Rozanne Lanczak. This Is My Story. Maio, Barbara & Faulkner, Stacey, eds. Burris, Priscilla, illus. 2006. (J). per. 4.99 (***978-1-59198-331-6(2)***) Creative Teaching Pr., Inc.

—Two Stories, Two Friends. Maio, Barbara, ed. Allen, Joy, illus. 2006. (J). per. 6.99 (***978-1-59198-343-9(6)***) Creative Teaching Pr., Inc.

—When You Go Walking. Maio, Barbara, ed. Briles, Patty, illus. 2006. (J). per. 6.99 (***978-1-59198-345-3(2)***) Creative Teaching Pr., Inc.

—Writing about Books. Maio, Barbara & Faulkner, Stacey, eds. Schneider, Christine, illus. 2006. (J). per. 4.99 (***978-1-59198-340-8(1)***) Creative Teaching Pr., Inc.

—Writing Dino-mite Poems. Maio, Barbara & Faulkner, Stacey, eds. Adnet, Bernard, illus. 2006. (J). per. 4.99 (***978-1-59198-336-1(3)***) Creative Teaching Pr., Inc.

Wong, Janet S. You Have to Write. Flavin, Teresa, illus. 2002. 40p. (J). (gr. 4 up). 17.00 (978-0-689-83409-7(8) , McElderry, Margaret K.) Simon & Schuster Children's Publishing.

Writer's Companion. 2001. (YA). (gr. 6-12). stu. ed. 24.97 (978-0-13-815556-8(9)) Prentice Hall PTR.

Writing. 2004. (Practice Makes Perfect Ser.). 24p. (J). (gr. k-2). 4.99 (978-1-85997-980-8(7)) Byeway Bks.

Writing. 2002. (My First Sticker Bks.). 16p. (J). (ps-k). pap. 2.98 (978-1-84273-838-2(0) , Exclusive Editions) Parragon, Inc.

Yates, Irene. How to Be a Wizard at Writing Stories. 48p. (J). (gr. 3-6). pap. (978-1-875739-67-7(X)) Wizard Bks.

Young, Judy. R Is for Rhyme: A Poetry Alphabet. Juhasz, Victor, illus. rev. ed. 2006. 48p. (J). (gr. k-5). 17.95 (978-1-58536-240-0(9)) Sleeping Bear Pr.

Zoltan, Melanie Barton. A Kid's Guide to Getting Published. 2001. 144p. (J). (gr. 2-10). pap. 12.95 (978-0-940159-66-2(X)) Camino Bks., Inc.

AUTHORSHIP—FICTION

Amato, Mary. Please Write in This Book. Brace, Eric, illus. 2006. 112p. (J). (gr. 2-5). 16.95 (978-0-8234-1932-6(0)) Holiday Hse., Inc.

Auch, Mary Jane. The Plot Chickens. 2008. (J). (***978-0-8234-2087-2(6)***) Holiday Hse., Inc.

Avi. A Beginning, a Muddle, & an End: The Return of the End of the Beginning. Tusa, Tricia, illus. 2008. 176p. (J). 14.95 (***978-0-15-205555-4(X)***) Harcourt Trade Pubs.

Baker, Barbara. Anna's Book. O'Neil, Catherine, illus. 2004. 24p. (J). (ps). 8.99 (978-0-525-47231-5(2) , Dutton Juvenile) Penguin Group (USA) Inc.

Banks, Lynne Reid. Alice-by-Accident. 2000. (Avon Camelot Bks.). 144p. (J). (gr. 4-7). 14.95 (978-0-380-97865-6(2)) HarperCollins Pubs.

Bastian, Greg. Great Secondhand Supper. 144p. pap. 11.95 (978-0-7022-2245-0(3)) Univ. of Queensland Pr. AUS. *Dist:* International Specialized Bk. Services.

Blegvad, Lenore. Kitty & Mr. Kipling: Neighbors in Vermont. Blegvad, Erik, illus. 2005. 144p. (J). (gr. 3-5). 16.95 (978-0-689-87363-8(8) , McElderry, Margaret K.) Simon & Schuster Children's Publishing.

Block, Francesca Lia. Violet & Claire. 2000. (J). (978-0-606-20003-5(7)) Tandem Library Bks.

Borden, Louise & Gustavson, Adam. The Day Eddie Met the Author. 2004. (Illus.). 44p. (J). pap. 6.99 (978-0-689-86720-0(4) , Aladdin) Simon & Schuster Children's Publishing.

Bradbury, Ray. Death Is a Lonely Business. 1999. (gr. 7-12). lib. bdg. 22.20 (978-0-613-17166-3(7)) Tandem Library Bks.

Brown, Marc. Arthur & the Poetry Contest. Brown, Marc, illus. 18th ed. 1999. (Arthur Chapter Bks. : Bk. 18). (Illus.). 64p. (J). (gr. 2-4). pap. 4.25 (978-0-316-12295-5(5)) Little, Brown Bks. for Young Readers.

—Arthur Writes a Story. Brown, Marc, illus. rev. ed. 2007. (Arthur Adventure Ser.). (Illus.). 32p. (J). (ps-1). pap. 10.99 incl. audio compact disk (***978-0-316-11865-1(6)***) Little, Brown Bks. for Young Readers.

Brown, Marc. Arturo Escribe un Cuento. Sarfatti, Esther, tr. 2001. (SPA.). (J). pap. 6.95 (978-1-880507-95-7(1) , 6468) Lectorum Pubns., Inc.

—Arturo Escribe un Cuento. 2001. (SPA.). (gr. k-3). lib. bdg. 15.25 (978-0-613-35899-6(6)); (Illus.). (J). 13.75 (978-0-606-21043-0(1)) Tandem Library Bks.

Bulion, Leslie. Uncharted Waters. 2006. 155p. (J). 14.95 (978-1-56145-365-8(X) , Peachtree Junior) Peachtree Pubs., Ltd.

Butler, Dori Hillestad. Tank Talbott's Guide to Girls. 2006. (Illus.). 135p. (J). 15.95 (978-0-8075-7761-5(8)) Whitman, Albert & Co.

—Trading Places with Tank Talbott. 2003. 136p. (J). (gr. 3-6). 15.95 (978-0-8075-1708-6(9)) Whitman, Albert & Co.

Child, Lauren. Clarice Bean Spells Trouble. Child, Lauren, illus. 2006. (Clarice Bean Ser.). 192p. (J). (gr. 3-6). pap. 5.99 (978-0-7636-2903-8(0)) Candlewick Pr.

Clarke, Nicole & Henderson, Mel. Write Here, Right Now, No. 1. 2006. (Flirt Ser.: No. 1). 224p. (J). (gr. 7-10). pap. 6.99 (978-0-448-44263-1(9), Grosset & Dunlap) Penguin Group (USA) Inc.

Clements, Andrew. Lunch Money. Selznick, Brian, illus. 2007. 240p. (J). (gr. 3-7). pap. 5.99 (***978-0-689-86685-2(2)***, Aladdin) Simon & Schuster Children's Publishing.

Clements, Andrew. The School Story. unabr. ed. 2004. (Middle Grade Cassette Librariestm Ser.). 224p. (J). (gr. 3-7). pap. 29.00 incl. audio (978-0-8072-1000-0(5), S YA 352 SP, Listening Library) Random Hse. Audio Publishing Group.

—The School Story. Selznick, Brian, illus. (J). 2002. 224p. pap. 5.99 (978-0-689-85186-5(3), Aladdin); 2001. 160p. (gr. 4-6). 16.00 (978-0-689-82594-1(3)) Simon & Schuster Children's Publishing.

—The School Story. 2002. (gr. 3-6). lib. bdg. 13.00 (978-0-613-54852-6(3)) Tandem Library Bks.

Codell, Esmé Raji. Sahara Special. 2003. (Illus.). 192p. (gr. 3-7). 15.99 (978-0-7868-0793-2(8)) Hyperion Bks. for Children.

Cornwell, Autumn. Carpe Diem. 2007. 368p. (YA). (gr. 7 up). 16.95 (***978-0-312-36792-3(9)***) Feiwel & Friends.

Craft, Elizabeth & Fain, Sarah. Bass Ackwards & Belly Up. 2006. 240p. (J). (gr. 7-17). 16.99 (978-0-316-05793-6(2)) Little Brown & Co.

—Bass Ackwards & Belly Up. 2007. 404p. (J). (gr. 10 up). pap. 8.99 (***978-0-316-05794-3(0)***, Poppy) Little, Brown Bks. for Young Readers.

Davis, Terry. If Rock & Roll Were a Machine: A Novel. 2003. 174p. (YA). pap. 15.95 (978-0-910055-86-4(6)) Eastern Washington Univ. Pr.

Dee, Barbara. Just Another Day in My Insanely Real Life. 2007. 256p. (J). pap. 5.99 (***978-1-4169-4739-4(6)***) Kaplan Bks.

—Just Another Day in My Insanely Real Life. 2006. (Illus.). 256p. (J). 15.95 (978-1-4169-0861-6(7), McElderry, Margaret K.) Simon & Schuster Children's Publishing.

DiSalvo-Ryan, DyAnne. The Sloppy Copy Slipup. 2005. (Illus.). 128p. (J). 16.95 (978-0-8234-1947-0(9)) Holiday Hse., Inc.

D'Lacey, Chris. Fire Star. 560p. (J). 2008. pap. 7.99 (978-0-439-90185-7(5)); 2007. (gr. 4-7). pap. 15.99 (978-0-439-84582-3(3)) Scholastic, Inc. (Orchard Bks.).

—The Fire Within. 2007. 352p. (J). pap. 7.99 (978-0-439-67244-3(9), Orchard Bks.) Scholastic, Inc.

Durant, Alan. That's Not Right. McEwen, Katharine, illus. 2004. (Flying Foxes Ser.). 48p. (J). (978-0-7787-1486-6(1)); pap. (978-0-7787-1532-0(9)) Crabtree Publishing Co.

Fine, Anne. Jennifer's Diary. Aldous, Kate, illus. 2007. 64p. (J). (gr. 2-5). 15.00 (978-0-374-33673-8(3), Farrar, Straus & Giroux (BYR)) Farrar, Straus & Giroux.

Funke, Cornelia. Inkheart. 2008. (Inkheart Movie Ser.). 576p. (J). 9.99 (***978-0-545-04626-8(2)***, Scholastic) Scholastic, Inc.

—Inkheart. Bell, Anthea, tr. 2005. (Illus.). 560p. (ps-7). pap. 8.99 (978-0-439-70910-1(5)) Scholastic, Inc.

—Inkheart. 2003. 544p. (J). 60.00 (978-0-439-61671-3(9), Chicken Hse., The) Scholastic, Inc.

—Inkheart. Bell, Anthea, tr. from GER. 2003. (Illus.). 544p. (J). (gr. 3-6). pap. 19.95 (978-0-439-53164-1(0), Chicken Hse., The) Scholastic, Inc.

—Inkheart. Bell, Anthea, tr. 2005. 550p. (J). (ps-7). lib. bdg. 15.04 (978-0-606-33803-5(9)) Tandem Library Bks.

—Inkheart. l.t. ed. 2006. 709p. (YA). pap. 10.95 (978-0-7862-8363-7(7)) Thorndike Pr.

—Inkheart. Bell, Anthea, tr. l.t. ed. 2005. (Illus.). 709p. (J). (gr. 3-7). 23.95 (978-0-7862-8041-4(7), Large Print Pr.) Thorndike Pr.

—Inkspell. l.t. ed. 2006. 779p. (YA). 23.95 (978-0-7862-8040-7(9)) Thorndike Pr.

Gantos, Jack. Jack's Black Book. 1999. (Jack Henry Ser.). (Illus.). 176p. (J). (gr. 5-9). pap. 6.95 (978-0-374-43716-9(5), Sunburst) Farrar, Straus & Giroux.

—Jack's Black Book. 1999. (J). 12.60 (978-0-606-17353-7(6)); (gr. 5-8). lib. bdg. 14.10 (978-0-613-22879-4(0)) Tandem Library Bks.

Greenwald, Sheila. Rosy Cole's Memoir Explosion: A Heartbreaking Story about Losing Friends, Annoying Family, & Ruining Romance. 2006. (Rosie Cole Ser.). (Illus.). 112p. (J). 16.00 (978-0-374-36347-5(1)) Farrar, Straus & Giroux.

Grimes, Nikki. Jazmin's Notebook. 2002. (Illus.). (J). 12.34 (978-0-7587-0368-2(6)) Book Wholesalers, Inc.

—Jazmin's Notebook. 112p. (J). 1998. (gr. 8-12). 15.99 (978-0-8037-2224-8(9), Dial); 2000. (gr. 5-9). reprint ed. pap. 5.99 (978-0-14-130702-2(1), Puffin) Penguin Group (USA) Inc.

—Jazmin's Notebook. 2000. (gr. 7-12). lib. bdg. 14.15 (978-0-613-23623-2(8)); (Illus.). (J). 12.64 (978-0-606-18414-4(7)) Tandem Library Bks.

Grindley, Sally. Bravo, Max! Ross, Tony, illus. 2007. 160p. (J). (gr. 1-4). 15.99 (978-1-4169-0393-2(3), McElderry, Margaret K.); pap. 4.99 (978-1-4169-3645-9(9), Aladdin) Simon & Schuster Children's Publishing.

—Dear Max. Ross, Tony, illus. 144p. (J). 2007. pap. 4.99 (978-1-4169-3443-1(X), Aladdin); 2006. (gr. 1-4). 14.95 (978-1-4169-0392-5(5), McElderry, Margaret K.) Simon & Schuster Children's Publishing.

Haddix, Margaret Peterson. Dexter the Tough. Elliott, Mark, illus. 2007. 144p. (J). (gr. 2-5). 15.99 (978-1-4169-1159-3(6)) Simon & Schuster Children's Publishing.

Hinton, S. E. Taming the Star Runner. 1999. (YA). 22.00 (978-0-8446-7027-0(8)) Smith, Peter Pub., Inc.

Howe, James. Bud Barkin, Private Eye. Helquist, Brett, illus. (Tales from the House of Bunnicula Ser.). (J). 2004. 112p. pap. 3.99 (978-0-689-86989-1(4), Aladdin); 2003. 96p. 9.95 (978-0-689-85632-7(6), Atheneum) Simon & Schuster Children's Publishing.

—Howie Monroe & the Doghouse of Doom. Helquist, Brett, illus. 2002. (Tales from the House of Bunnicula Ser.). 96p. (J). 9.95 (978-0-689-83951-1(0), Atheneum) Simon & Schuster Children's Publishing.

—Howie Monroe & the Doghouse of Doom. 2002. (Tales from the House of Bunnicula Ser.). (Illus.). 90p. (J). (gr. 3-6). 9.95 (978-0-689-88395-8(1), Atheneum) Simon & Schuster Children's Publishing.

—Howie Monroe & the Doghouse of Doom. Helquist, Brett, illus. 2003. (Tales from the House of Bunnicula Ser.). 112p. (J). pap. 3.99 (978-0-689-83952-8(9), Aladdin) Simon & Schuster Children's Publishing.

—Howie Monroe & the Doghouse of Doom. 2004. (Tales from the House of Bunnicula Ser.). 85p. (J). (gr. 3-6). pap. 17.00 incl. audio (978-1-4000-8634-4(5), Listening Library) Random Hse. Audio Publishing Group.

—Invasion of the Mind Swappers from Asteroid 6! 2004. (Tales from the House of Bunnicula Ser.). 112p. (J). (gr. 3-6). pap. 17.00 incl. audio (978-1-4000-8633-7(7), Listening Library) Random Hse. Audio Publishing Group.

—Invasion of the Mind Swappers from Asteroid 6! Helquist, Brett, illus. (Tales from the House of Bunnicula Ser.). (J). 2003. 112p. pap. 3.99 (978-0-689-83950-4(2), Aladdin); 2002. 96p. (gr. 2-4). 9.95 (978-0-689-83949-8(9), Atheneum) Simon & Schuster Children's Publishing.

—Invasion of the Mind Swappers from Asteroid 6! 2003. (Tales from the House of Bunnicula Ser.). (gr. 3-6). lib. bdg. 11.80 (978-0-613-66414-1(0)) Tandem Library Bks.

—It Came from Beneath the Bed! Helquist, Brett, illus. 2002. (Tales from the House of Bunnicula Ser.). 96p. (J). (gr. 2-4). 9.95 (978-0-689-83947-4(2), Atheneum) Simon & Schuster Children's Publishing.

—It Came from Beneath the Bed! 2003. (Tales from the House of Bunnicula Ser.). (gr. 3-6). lib. bdg. 11.80 (978-0-613-66415-8(9)) Tandem Library Bks.

—It Came from Beneath the Bed! 2004. (Tales from the House of Bunnicula Ser.). 112p. (J). (gr. 3-6). pap. 17.00 incl. audio (978-1-4000-8632-0(9), Listening Library) Random Hse. Audio Publishing Group.

—The Odorous Adventures of Stinky Dog. Helquist, Brett, illus. 2003. (Tales from the House of Bunnicula Ser.). 112p. (J). bds. 9.95 (978-0-689-85633-4(4), Atheneum) Simon & Schuster Children's Publishing.

—Screaming Mummies of the Pharaoh's Tomb II. Helquist, Brett, illus. 2003. (Tales from the House of Bunnicula Ser.). 112p. (J). 9.95 (978-0-689-83953-5(7), Atheneum) Simon & Schuster Children's Publishing.

Jack Gantos. Jack's Black Book. l.t. ed. 2006. 160p. (J). 23.95 (978-0-7862-9033-8(1)) Thorndike Pr.

Jenkins, Jerry B. & Fabry, Chris. Phantom Writer. 2005. (Red Rock Mysteries Ser.). 256p. (J). pap. 5.99 (978-1-4143-0145-7(6)) Tyndale Hse. Pubs.

Jewett, Sarah Orne. The Country of the Pointed Firs & Other Stories. 2000. (gr. 7-12). lib. bdg. 11.80 (978-0-613-27778-5(3)) Tandem Library Bks.

Johnson, D. B. Henry Works. 2004. (Illus.). 32p. (J). (gr. k-3). tchr. ed. 15.00 (978-0-618-42003-2(7)) Houghton Mifflin Co. Trade & Reference Div.

Joseph, Lynn. The Color of My Words. 2002. 144p. (J). (gr. 5 up). pap. 5.99 (978-0-06-447204-3(3), Harper Trophy) HarperCollins Pubs.

Jung, Reinhardt. Bambert's Book of Missing Stories. 2006. 128p. (J). (gr. 4-7). pap. 5.50 (978-0-440-42045-3(8), Yearling) Random Hse. Children's Bks.

Kanninen, Barbara J. A Story with Pictures. Reed, Lynn Rowe, illus. 2007. 32p. (J). (ps-3). 16.95 (***978-0-8234-2049-0(3)***) Holiday Hse., Inc.

Kimmel, Elizabeth Cody. Lily B. on the Brink of Cool. 2003. 256p. (J). (gr. 3-7). 15.99 (978-0-06-000586-3(6)) HarperCollins Pubs.

—Lily B. on the Brink of Love. (J). 2006. 208p. pap. 5.99 (978-0-06-075545-4(8), Harper Trophy); 2005. 224p. 15.99 (978-0-06-075541-6(5)); 2005. 192p. lib. bdg. 16.89 (978-0-06-075543-0(1)) HarperCollins Pubs.

Kirk, Daniel. Library Mouse. 2007. (Illus.). 32p. (J). (ps-3). 15.95 (***978-0-8109-9346-4(5)***, Abrams Bks. for Young Readers) Abrams, Harry N., Inc.

Kline, Lisa Williams. The Princesses of Atlantis. 2002. (Illus.). 192p. (J). 16.95 (978-0-8126-2855-5(1)) Cricket Bks.

Klinger, Shula. The Kingdom of Strange. 2008. (YA). (***978-0-7614-5395-6(4)***) Cavendish, Marshall Corp.

Koertge, Ronald. Shakespeare Bats Clean-Up. 2003. 128p. (YA). (gr. 7). 15.99 (978-0-7636-2116-2(1)) Candlewick Pr.

Kroll, Steven. Patches Lost & Found. Gott, Barry, illus. 2005. 32p. (J). pap. 5.95 (978-0-7614-5217-1(6)) Cavendish, Marshall Corp.

—Patches Lost & Found. Gott, Barry, illus. 2001. 40p. (J). (gr. k-3). 15.95 (978-1-890817-53-4(8)) Winslow Pr.

—Patches Lost & Found. Gott, Barry, illus. 2005. 32p. (J). (gr. k-4). lib. bdg. 13.15 (978-0-606-33744-1(X)) Tandem Library Bks.

Lisle, Janet Taylor. How I Became a Writer & Oggie Learned to Drive. 2003. (Illus.). 160p. (YA). (ps-17). pap. 5.99 (978-0-14-250167-2(0), Puffin) Penguin Group (USA) Inc.

Lubar, David. Sleeping Freshmen Never Lie. (YA). 2007. 288p. pap. 6.99 (978-0-14-240780-6(1), Puffin); 2005. 160p. (gr. 6-10). 16.99 (978-0-525-47311-4(4), Dutton Juvenile) Penguin Group (USA) Inc.

Mackall, Dandi. Larger-Than-Life Lara. 2006. 195p. (J). (gr. 5). 16.99 (978-0-525-47726-6(8), Dutton Juvenile) Penguin Group (USA) Inc.

Michaels, Jamie. Kiss My Book. 2007. 288p. (YA). (gr. 7). pap. 7.99 (***978-0-385-73499-8(9)***); lib. bdg. 10.99 (***978-0-385-90493-3(2)***) Random Hse. Children's Bks. (Delacorte Bks. for Young Readers).

Muntean, Michaela. Do Not Open This Book! Lemaitre, Pascal, illus. 2006. 40p. (J). (ps-3). pap. 16.99 (978-0-439-69839-9(1), Scholastic Pr.) Scholastic, Inc.

Nelson, Theresa. Ruby Electric. 272p. (J). 2003. (Illus.). 16.95 (978-0-689-83852-1(2), Atheneum/Richard Jackson Bks.); 2004. reprint ed. pap. 5.99 (978-0-689-87146-7(5), Aladdin) Simon & Schuster Children's Publishing.

O'Malley, Kevin. Once upon a Cool Motorcycle Dude. O'Malley, Kevin et al, illus. 2005. 32p. (J). 16.95 (978-0-8027-8947-1(1)) Walker & Co.

Park, Linda Sue. Project Mulberry. 2005. 240p. (J). (gr. 5-9). 16.00 (978-0-618-47786-9(1), Clarion Bks.) Houghton Mifflin Co. Trade & Reference Div.

—Project Mulberry. 2007. 240p. (J). (gr. 4-7). pap. 6.50 (978-0-440-42163-4(2), Yearling) Random Hse. Children's Bks.

Rau, Dana Meachen. My Book by Me. Rau, Dana Meachen, illus. (Rookie Reader Skill Set Ser.). (Illus.). (J). 2001. 32p. (gr. k-2). pap. 4.95 (978-0-516-27082-1(6)); 2000. 31p. (gr. 1-2). 19.50 (978-0-516-22032-1(2)) Scholastic Library Publishing. (Children's Pr.).

—My Book by Me. 2000. (gr. k-3). lib. bdg. 12.95 (978-0-613-54618-8(0)) Tandem Library Bks.

Reece, Colleen L. Thursday Trials. 1998. (Juli Scott, Super Sleuth Ser.: Bk. 4). 176p. (J). (gr. 4-10). pap. 2.97 (978-1-57748-180-5(1)) Barbour Publishing, Inc.

—Thursday Trials. l.t. ed. 2001. (Juli Scott, Super Sleuth Ser.). (Illus.). 204p. (J). 23.95 (978-0-7862-3201-7(3)) Thorndike Pr.

Reiche, Dietlof & Brownjohn, John. The Haunting of Freddy. Cepeda, Joe, illus. 2006. (Golden Hamster Saga Ser.: Bk. 4). 320p. (J). pap. 16.99 (978-0-439-53159-7(4), Scholastic Pr.) Scholastic, Inc.

Rylant, Cynthia. Mr. Putter & Tabby Write the Book. Howard, Arthur, illus. 2004. (Mr. Putter & Tabby Ser.). 44p. (J). 14.00 (978-0-15-200241-1(3)) Harcourt Children's Bks.

—Mr. Putter & Tabby Write the Book. Howard, Arthur, illus. 2005. (Mr. Putter & Tabby Ser.). 44p. (J). (ps). pap., pap. 5.95 (978-0-15-200242-8(1)) Harcourt Trade Pubs.

Salisbury, Linda G. The Mysterious Jamestown Suitcase: A Bailey Fish Adventure. Grotke, Christopher, illus. 2007. 192p. (J). per. 8.95 (978-1-881539-43-8(1)) Tabby Hse. Bks.

Schwartz, Virginia Frances. 4 Kids in 5E & 1 Crazy Year. 2006. 208p. (J). 16.95 (978-0-8234-1946-3(0)) Holiday Hse., Inc.

Snyder, Zilpha Keatley. The Bronze Pen. 2008. 208p. (J). 16.99 (***978-1-4169-4201-6(7)***) Simon & Schuster Children's Publishing.

Spizman, Robyn Freedman & Johnston, Mark. Secret Agent. 240p. (J). 2006. (gr. 4-7). pap. 5.99 (978-1-4169-1862-2(0), Aladdin); 2005. 16.95 (978-0-689-87044-6(2), Atheneum) Simon & Schuster Children's Publishing.

Stine, R. L. It Came from Ohio! My Life As a Writer. 1998. (978-0-606-13528-3(6)) Tandem Library Bks.

The Storybook. 2004. 224p. per. 6.95 (978-0-9703729-3-2(0)) Missing Piece Pr.

Sturtevant, Katherine. A True & Faithful Narrative. 2006. 256p. (YA). 17.00 (978-0-374-37809-7(6)) Farrar, Straus & Giroux.

—A True & Faithful Narrative. l.t. ed. 2006. 289p. (YA). 21.95 (978-0-7862-9081-9(1)) Thorndike Pr.

Tripp, Valerie. Changes for Kit: A Winter Story 1934. Rane, Walter & McAliley, Susan, illus. 2001. 64p. (J). (gr. 3-6). lib. bdg. 14.10 (978-0-613-44636-5(4)) Tandem Library Bks.

Vaughan, Christina, et al. The Tale of Artie's Tale. 2000. (Artie Stories Ser.). 32p. (J). (gr. 1-5). spiral bd. 18.95 (978-0-9641697-3-9(8), You-Draw-It Bks.) Castlebrook Pubns.

Ware-Holmes, Barbara. Letters to Julia. 1999. (J). (978-0-606-17466-4(4)) Tandem Library Bks.

Williams, Dell. If I Forget, You Remember. 1999. (J). 11.64 (978-0-606-16171-8(6)) Tandem Library Bks.

Williams, Rozanne Lanczak. My Picture Story. Maio, Barbara & Faulkner, Stacey, eds. Mahan, Benton, illus. 2006. (Learn to Write Ser.). (J). 8p. pap. 1.99 (978-1-59198-281-4(2), 6175); per. 4.99 (***978-1-59198-332-3(0)***) Creative Teaching Pr., Inc.

—Special Memories. Maio, Barbara, ed. Nobens, C. A., illus. 2006. (Learn to Write Ser.). (J). 16p. pap. 2.99 (978-1-59198-302-6(9), 6196); per. 6.99 (***978-1-59198-360-6(6)***) Creative Teaching Pr., Inc.

Wittlinger, Ellen. Hard Love. 2001. (Illus.). 240p. (YA). (gr. 8-12). reprint ed. pap. 8.99 (978-0-689-84154-5(X), Simon Pulse) Simon & Schuster Children's Publishing.

Wittlinger, Ellen. Love & Lies: Marisol's Story. 2008. 256p. (YA). (***978-1-4169-1623-9(7)***, Simon & Schuster Children's Publishing) Simon & Schuster Children's Publishing.

Wizner, Jake. Spanking Shakespeare. 2007. (YA). (***978-0-375-84086-9(9)***) Random Hse. Children's Bks.

—Spanking Shakespeare. Ewing, Richard, illus. 2007. 287p. (YA). (gr. 9-11). lib. bdg. 18.99 (***978-0-375-94085-9(5)***); 15.99 (***978-0-375-84085-2(0)***) Random Hse. Children's Bks. (Random Hse. Bks. for Young Readers).

AUTISM

Autism & PDD Expanding Social Options. 2003. (YA). per. 21.95 (978-0-7606-0499-1(1)) LinguiSystems, Inc.

Baker, Jed. The Social Skills Picture Book: For High School & Beyond. 2006. (Illus.). 177p. (J). (gr. 4-7). per. 39.95 (***978-1-932565-35-5(3)***) Future Horizons, Inc.

Baldwin, Carol. Autism. 2003. (Health Matters Ser.). (Illus.). 32p. (J). (gr. 3-5). lib. bdg. 24.22 (978-1-4034-0250-9(7)) Heinemann Library.

Bardhan-Quallen, Sudipta. Autism. 2005. (Understanding Diseases & Disorders Ser.). (Illus.). 48p. (J). (gr. 4-8). 26.20 (978-0-7377-2167-6(7), Greenhaven Pr., Inc.) Thomson Gale.

Barrette, Melanie. Welcome to School: Helping Friends with Autism. James, Colin, ed. Crestan, David, illus. James, Colin & Newton, Jennifer, photos by. 2005. 16p. (J). (gr. k-6). pap. 12.00 (978-1-928598-11-4(0)) Pyramid Educational Products, Inc.

Bonnice, Sherry. The Hidden Child: Youth with Autism. 2004. (Youth with Special Needs Ser.). (Illus.). 128p. (J). (978-1-59084-736-7(9)) Mason Crest Pubs.

Brill, Marlene Targ. Autism. 2007. (Health Alert Ser.). 64p. (J). lib. bdg. 31.36 (***978-0-7614-2700-1(7)***, Benchmark Bks.) Cavendish, Marshall Corp.

Buron, Kari Dunn. When My Autism Gets Too Big! A Relaxation Book for Children with Autism Spectrum Disorders. Buron, Kari Dunn, illus. 2003. (Illus.). 44p. (gr. k-3). pap. 15.95 (978-1-931282-51-2(X), 9935) Autism Asperger Publishing Co.

Chastain, Zachary & Livingston, Phyllis. Youth with Asperger's Syndrome: A Different Drummer. 2008. (J). (978-1-4222-0137-4(6)) Mason Crest Pubs.

Crissey, Pat. Personal Hygiene? What's That Got to Do with Me? Crissey, Noah, illus. 2005. 94p. (J). pap. (978-1-84310-796-5(1)) Kingsley, Jessica Ltd.

Edwards, Michele Engel. Autism. 2001. (Diseases & Disorders Ser.). (Illus.). 120p. (YA). (gr. 6-9). 32.45 (978-1-56006-829-7(9), GML12001-178161, Lucent Bks.) Thomson Gale.

Elder. Planet Autism. 2007. (Illus.). 48p. (J). pap. (***978-1-84310-842-9(9)***) Kingsley, Jessica Ltd.

Elder, Jennifer. Different Like Me: My Book of Autism Heroes. 2005. (Illus.). 6p. (J). (978-1-84310-815-3(1)) Kingsley, Jessica Ltd.

Fredericks, Carrie. Autism. 2007. (Perspectives on Diseases & Disorders Ser.). (Illus.). (gr. 10-12). 32.45 (***978-0-7377-3869-8(3)***, Greenhaven Pr., Inc.) Thomson Gale.

Gast, Christy & Krug, Jane. Caring for Myself: A Social Skills Storybook. Laackman, Kotoe, photos by. 2007. (Illus.). 96p. (J). (***978-1-84310-872-6(0)***) Kingsley, Jessica Ltd.

Jaffe, Amy V. & Gardner, Luci. My Book Full of Feelings: HT Control & React to the SIZE of Your Emotions - an Interactive Workbook for Parents, Professionals & Children. 2006. (J). spiral bd. 26.95 (***978-1-931282-83-3(8)***) Autism Asperger Publishing Co.

Keating-Velasco, Joanna. A Is for Autism F Is for Friend: A Kid's Book for Making Friends with a Child Who Has Autism. 2007. (J). pap. 12.95 (***978-1-931282-43-7(9)***) Autism Asperger Publishing Co.

Landau, Elaine. Autism. 2001. (Single Title - Science Ser.). (Illus.). 128p. (J). (gr. 8-12). 26.00 (978-0-531-11780-4(4), Watts, Franklin) Scholastic Library Publishing.

Larson, Elaine Larson. The Kaleidoscope Kid: Focusing on the Strengths of Children with Asperger Syndrome & High-Functioning Autism. 2007. (J). 17.95 (***978-1-931282-41-3(2)***) Autism Asperger Publishing Co.

Lazar, Michelle & Jensen, Jeremy. Tuned in to Learning Vol. 1: Social Skills & Pragmatics for Autism & Related Needs, 11 vols. 2005. (J). spiral bd. 59.95 incl. audio compact disk (978-0-9768881-3-0(0)) Tuned in to Learning.

Lennard-Brown, Sarah. Autism. 2003. (Health Issues Ser.). (Illus.). 64p. (J). lib. bdg. 28.56 (978-0-7398-6422-7(X)) Raintree.

Lowell, Jamie & Tuchel, Tara. My Best Friend Will. 2005. 37p. 21.95 (978-1-931282-75-8(7), 9947) Autism Asperger Publishing Co.

Manasco, Hunter. The Way to A: Empowering Children with Autism Spectrum & Other Neurological Disorders to Monitor & Replace Aggression & Tantrum Behavior. Manasco, Katherine, illus. 2006. (J). spiral bd., wbk. ed. 18.95 (978-1-931282-87-1(0)) Autism Asperger Publishing Co.

Mccracken, Heather. That's What's Different about Me! Helping Children Understand Autism Spectrum Disorders - Story & Coloring BK. Robbins, Kathryn, illus. 2006. (J). pap. 3.00 (***978-1-931282-97-0(8)***) Autism Asperger Publishing Co.

McKracken, Heather. That's What's Different about Me: Helping Children Understand Autism Spectrum Disorders. Robbins, Kathryn, illus. 2006. (J). pap. 59.95 (***978-1-931282-96-3(X)***) Autism Asperger Publishing Co.

Messner, Abby Ward. Captain Tommy. Belliveau, Kim Harris, illus. 1999. 28p. (J). (gr. 1-4). 9.95 (978-1-885477-58-3(9)) Future Horizons, Inc.

Mulstay, Linda Muratore. Autism & PDD Answering Questions, Level 1. 2006. (J). per. 29.95 (978-0-7606-0673-5(0)) LinguiSystems, Inc.

Muratore, Linda Mulstay. Autism & PDD Answering Questions, Level 2. 2006. (J). per. 29.95 (978-0-7606-0674-2(9)) LinguiSystems, Inc.

Reese, Pam Britton & Challenner, Nena. Autism & PDD Intermediate Communication. 2002. (J). per. 21.95 (978-0-7606-0415-1(0)) LinguiSystems, Inc.

Respess, Beth. Autism & PDD Opposites Buddy Bear & Bonnie Bear. 2004. (J). spiral bd. (978-0-7606-0579-0(3)) LinguiSystems, Inc.

—Autism & PDD Opposites Buddy Bear's Animals. 2004. (J). spiral bd. (978-0-7606-0576-9(9)) LinguiSystems, Inc.

—Autism & PDD Opposites Buddy Bear's Clothes. 2004. (J). spiral bd. (978-0-7606-0575-2(0)) LinguiSystems, Inc.

—Autism & PDD Opposites Buddy Bear's Food. 2004. (J). spiral bd. (978-0-7606-0578-3(5)) LinguiSystems, Inc.

—Autism & PDD Opposites Buddy Bear's Toys. 2004. (J). spiral bd. (978-0-7606-0577-6(7)) LinguiSystems, Inc.

Respess, Beth, et al. Autism & PDD Concepts What Shape Is it, Becca Bunny? 2004. (J). spiral bd. (978-0-7606-0591-2(2)) LinguiSystems, Inc.

Respess, Beth W. Autism & PDD Associations Buddy Bear Gets Ready for School. 2004. (J). spiral bd. (978-0-7606-0567-7(X)) LinguiSystems, Inc.

—Autism & PDD Associations Buddy Bear Goes on a Picnic. 2004. (J). spiral bd. (978-0-7606-0569-1(6)) LinguiSystems, Inc.

—Autism & PDD Associations Buddy Bear Has Fun. 2004. (J). spiral bd. (978-0-7606-0566-0(1)) LinguiSystems, Inc.

—Autism & PDD Associations Buddy Bear Helps Mama Bear. 2004. (J). spiral bd. (978-0-7606-0568-4(8)) LinguiSystems, Inc.

—Autism & PDD Associations Buddy Bear Likes Animals. 2004. (J). spiral bd. (978-0-7606-0565-3(3)) LinguiSystems, Inc.

—Autism & PDD Categories Buddy Bear in the House. 2004. (J). spiral bd. (978-0-7606-0560-8(2)) LinguiSystems, Inc.

—Autism & PDD Categories Buddy Bear in the Kitchen. 2004. (J). spiral bd. (978-0-7606-0562-2(9)) LinguiSystems, Inc.

—Autism & PDD Categories Buddy Bear in the Yard. 2004. (J). spiral bd. (978-0-7606-0561-5(0)) LinguiSystems, Inc.

—Autism & PDD Categories Buddy Bear on Vacation. 2004. (J). spiral bd. (978-0-7606-0563-9(7)) LinguiSystems, Inc.

—Autism & PDD Categories Buddy Bear Plays. 2004. (J). spiral bd. (978-0-7606-0564-6(5)) LinguiSystems, Inc.

—Autism & PDD Comparatives/Superlatives What Buddy Bear Does. 2004. (J). spiral bd. (978-0-7606-0572-1(6)) LinguiSystems, Inc.

—Autism & PDD Comparatives/Superlatives What Buddy Bear Finds. 2004. (J). spiral bd. (978-0-7606-0571-4(8)) LinguiSystems, Inc.

—Autism & PDD Comparatives/Superlatives What Buddy Bear Has. 2004. (J). spiral bd. (978-0-7606-0570-7(X)) LinguiSystems, Inc.

—Autism & PDD Comparatives/Superlatives What Buddy Bear Likes. 2004. (J). spiral bd. (978-0-7606-0574-5(2)) LinguiSystems, Inc.

—Autism & PDD Comparatives/Superlatives What Buddy Bear Sees. 2004. (J). spiral bd. (978-0-7606-0573-8(4)) LinguiSystems, Inc.

—Autism & PDD Yes/No Questions Buddy Bear at Home. 2004. (J). spiral bd. (978-0-7606-0557-8(2)) LinguiSystems, Inc.

—Autism & PDD Yes/No Questions Buddy Bear at School. 2004. (J). spiral bd. (978-0-7606-0555-4(6)) LinguiSystems, Inc.

—Autism & PDD Yes/No Questions Buddy Bear at the Beach. 2004. (J). (978-0-7606-0556-1(4)) LinguiSystems, Inc.

—Autism & PDD Yes/No Questions Buddy Bear at the Grocery Store. 2004. (J). spiral bd. (978-0-7606-0558-5(0)) LinguiSystems, Inc.

—Autism & PDD Yes/No Questions Buddy Bear at the Park. 2004. (J). spiral bd. (978-0-7606-0554-7(8)) LinguiSystems, Inc.

Rosaler, Maxine. Coping with Asperger Syndrome. 2005. (Coping Ser.). 192p. (J). (gr. 7-12). lib. bdg. 26.50 (978-0-8239-4482-8(4)) Rosen Publishing Group, Inc., The.

Rosenberg, Marsha Sarah. Coping When a Brother or Sister Is Autistic. 2005. (Coping Ser.). (Illus.). 192p. (YA). (gr. 7-12). lib. bdg. 26.50 (978-0-8239-3194-1(3)) Rosen Publishing Group, Inc., The.

—Everything You Need to Know When a Brother or Sister Is Autistic. 2005. (Need to Know Library). (Illus.). 64p. (YA). (gr. 7-12). lib. bdg. 25.25 (978-0-8239-3123-1(4) , NTAUTI) Rosen Publishing Group, Inc., The.

Sanders, Robert S., Jr. Overcoming Asperger's: Personal Experience & Insight. Enticknap, Martin A., ed. Enticknap, Martin A. & Matthews, Brian, illus. 2002. 164p. (J). pap. 14.95 (978-1-928798-05-7(5)) Armstrong Valley Publishing Co.

Shanta, N. D. He's My Brother. 2006. 24p. (J). 19.95 (***978-1-58909-380-5(1)***) Bookstand Publishing.

Stontz, Karen & Malone, Kelly. Autism & PDD Concepts How Many, Becca Bunny. 2004. (J). spiral bd. (978-0-7606-0593-6(9)) LinguiSystems, Inc.

—Autism & PDD Concepts What Time Is it, Becca Bunny. 2004. (J). spiral bd. (978-0-7606-0592-9(0)) LinguiSystems, Inc.

—Autism & PDD Concepts Where are they Hiding, Becca Bunny? 2004. (J). spiral bd. (978-0-7606-0595-0(5)) LinguiSystems, Inc.

Sullivan, Connor. I Love My Brother! A Preschooler's View of Living with a Brother Who Has Autism. Sullivan, Danielle, ed. Griffin, Christopher, illus. 2001. 28p. (J). (ps-1). 14.95 (978-0-9706581-1-7(7)) Phat Art 4.

Tyree, Debi. Jessica's Little Sister: A Story about Autism. 2004. 35p. pap. 17.95 (978-1-4137-1724-2(1)) PublishAmerica, Inc.

VanDerTuuk-Perkins, Jennifer E. Life with Gabriel. VanDerTuuk-Perkins, Jennifer E. & Perkins, Rodney R., illus. l.t. ed. 2004. 22p. (J). per. 9.95 (978-0-9749862-0-3(8)) Theragogy.com.

What It Is to Be Me! An Asperger Kid Book. 2005. (J). 9.95 (978-1-59352-199-8(5)) Christian Services Publishing.

AUTISM—FICTION

Choldenko, Gennifer. Al Capone Does My Shirts. 240p. 2004. (Illus.). (YA). (gr. 4-6). 16.99 (978-0-399-23861-1(1) , Putnam Juvenile); 2006. (J). (gr. 5). reprint ed. pap. 6.99 (978-0-14-240370-9(9) , Puffin) Penguin Group (USA) Inc.

—Al Capone Does My Shirts. l.t. ed. 2005. 299p. (YA). 22.95 (978-0-7862-8043-8(3)) Thorndike Pr.

Clark, Joan. Ann Drew Jackson. 2007. (J). pap. 17.95 (***978-1-931282-45-1(5)***) Autism Asperger Publishing Co.

Day, Alexandra. The Flight of a Dove. 2004. (Illus.). 32p. (J). 16.00 (978-0-374-39952-8(2) , Farrar, Straus & Giroux (BYR)) Farrar, Straus & Giroux.

Duane, Diane. A Wizard Alone. (Young Wizards Ser.: Bk. 6). (YA). 2003. 352p. pap. 6.95 (978-0-15-204911-9(8) , Magic Carpet Bks.); 2002. (Illus.). 336p. (gr. 7 up). 17.00 (978-0-15-204562-3(7)) Harcourt Children's Bks.

Edwards, Andreanna. Taking Autism to School. Dineen, Tom, illus. 2001. (Special Kids in School Ser.: Vol. 10). 32p. (J). pap. 11.95 (978-1-891383-13-7(2)) JayJo Bks., LLC.

Edwards, Becky. My Brother Sammy. 2000. (Illus.). 25p. (J). 19.99 (978-0-7475-3996-4(0)) Bloomsbury Publishing Plc GBR. *Dist:* Independent Pubs. Group.

—My Brother Sammy. Newton, Jill, illus. 2000. 32p. pap. 9.99 (978-0-7475-4654-2(1)) Bloomsbury Publishing Plc GBR. *Dist:* Trafalgar Square Publishing.

—My Brother Sammy. Armitage, David, illus. 1999. 32p. (gr. k-3). lib. bdg. 23.90 (978-0-7613-1417-2(2) , Millbrook Pr.) Lerner Publishing Group.

Ellis, Marvie. Keisha's Doors Bk. 1: An Autism Story. l.t. ed. 2005. Tr. of Las Puertas de Keisha. (SPA., Illus.). 32p. (J). per. 16.95 (978-1-933319-00-1(3)) Speech Kids Texas Pr.

—Tacos Anyone? Bk. 2: An Autism Story Book. l.t. ed. 2005. Tr. of ¿Alguien quiere Tacos?. (SPA., Illus.). 32p. (J). per. 16.95 (978-1-933319-01-8(1)) Speech Kids Texas Pr.

Ely, Lesley. Looking after Louis. Dunbar, Polly, tr. Dunbar, Polly, illus. 2004. 32p. (J). (gr. 2-5). 15.95 (978-0-8075-4746-5(8)) Whitman, Albert & Co.

Flowers, Natasha. Sammy the Snail. 2006. 10.00 (978-0-8059-9158-1(1)) Dorrance Publishing Co., Inc.

Gagnon, Elisa & Myles, Brenda Smith. Esto es el Sindrome de Asperger. Tahara, Sachi, illus. 2004. (SPA.). 14.95 (978-1-931282-27-7(7) , 9620) Autism Asperger Publishing Co.

Kochka. The Boy Who Ate Stars. Adams, Sarah, tr. from FRE. 2006. 112p. (J). 12.95 (978-1-4169-0038-2(1)) Simon & Schuster Children's Publishing.

Lears, Laurie. Ian's Walk: A Story about Autism. 2003. (gr. k-3). lib. bdg. 15.25 (978-0-613-75728-7(9)) Tandem Library Bks.

—Ian's Walk: A Story about Autism. Ritz, Karen, illus. 2004. 32p. (J). (gr. 1-4). pap. 6.95 (978-0-8075-3481-6(1)) Whitman, Albert & Co.

Lord, Cynthia. Rules. 2006. 208p. (J). (gr. 4-7). pap. 15.99 (978-0-439-44382-1(2) , Scholastic Pr.) Scholastic, Inc.

—Rules. rev. l.t. ed. 2007. 200p. (YA). 23.95 (***978-0-7862-9559-3(7)***) Thorndike Pr.

Luchsinger, Dena. Playing by the Rules: A Story about Autism. Olson, Julie, illus. 2007. (Special Needs Collection). 36p. (J). (ps-3). 16.95 (***978-1-890627-83-6(6)***) Woodbine Hse.

Maguire, Arlene. Special People, Special Ways. Bailey, Sheila, illus. 2000. 28p. (gr. k-5). per. 14.95 (978-1-885477-65-1(1)) Future Horizons, Inc.

Mammay, Judith. It's Time. Fargo, Todd, illus. l.t. ed. 2007. 32p. (J). pap. 9.95 (***978-0-944727-20-1(4)***); lib. bdg. 15.95 (***978-0-944727-21-8(2)***) Jason & Nordic Pubs. (Turtle Bks.).

—Knowing Joseph. 2008. (Illus.). 256p. (YA). (gr. 2-7). 16.95 (***978-1-933831-05-3(7)***) Blooming Tree Pr.

Mandarino, Gene. What's Autism? 2006. pap. 25.00 (978-0-9786795-0-7(4)) Charlie's Gift.

Matlin, Marlee & Cooney, Doug. Nobody's Perfect. 2006. (Illus.). 240p. (J). (gr. 3-7). 15.95 (978-0-689-86986-0(X) , Simon & Schuster Children's Publishing) Simon & Schuster Children's Publishing.

Mitchell, Lesli. Party Train. Gil, Ramon, illus. 2001. 32p. (J). (ps-5). 16.95 (978-0-9665266-1-5(9)) DRL Bk., Inc.

Murrell, Diane. Friends Learn about Tobin. Kock, W.K., tr. Murrell, Diane, illus. 2007. (Illus.). 29p. (J). (ps-3). pap. 16.95 (***978-1-932565-41-6(8)***) Future Horizons, Inc.

Murrell, Diane. Tobin Learns to Make Friends. 2001. (Illus.). (J). (ps-3). per. 16.95 (978-1-885477-79-8(1)) Future Horizons, Inc.

Peck, Lisa J. A Challenge for Brittany. 1999. (Choose the Right Ser.: Bk. 2). 60p. (J). pap. (978-1-57008-664-9(8)) Scribbulations LLC.

Peck, Lisa J. A Challenge for Brittany: CTR Club - Book One, 4 bks. 2005. (J). pap. 6.95 (***978-0-9749241-5-1(6)***) Golden Wings Enterprises.

Reish, Kathleen. Matthew's Box. Leonhard, Herb, illus. 2005. 48p. (J). 21.95 (978-0-9762664-0-2(7) , 3000) KBR Mutti's Pubns.

Rozanski, Bonnie. Borderline. 2007. 224p. (YA). pap. 22.95 (***978-0-88984-293-9(0)***) Porcupine's Quill, Inc. CAN. *Dist:* Univ. of Toronto Pr.

Werlin, Nancy. Are You Alone on Purpose? 2007. 208p. (YA). (gr. 7). pap. 7.99 (978-0-14-240777-6(1) , Puffin) Penguin Group (USA) Inc.

Yamanaka, Lois-Ann. The Heart's Language. Jasinski, Aaron, illus. 2005. 32p. (ps-3). 15.99 (978-0-7868-1848-8(4)) Hyperion Bks. for Children.

AUTO COURTS

see Hotels, Motels, etc.

AUTOBIOGRAPHIES

Al-Windawi, Thura. Thura's Diary. 2004. (Illus.). 144p. (J). (gr. 3-7). 15.99 (978-0-670-05886-0(6) , Viking Juvenile) Penguin Group (USA) Inc.

Are We There Yet? Stories of Trips, Travels & Journeys by San Francisco Youth, 2 vols., 2. 2000. (Illus.). 168p. (J). spiral bd. 15.00 (978-0-9646977-8-2(5)) Streetside Stories, Inc.

Are We There Yet? Stories of Trips, Travels & Journeys by San Francisco Youth, 2 vols. 2000. (Illus.). 206p. (J). spiral bd. 15.00 (978-0-9646977-7-5(7)) Streetside Stories, Inc.

Borg, Mary. Writing Your Life: Autobiographical Writing Activities for Young People. 3rd rev. ed. 1998. (Illus.). 62p. (J). (gr. 5-12). pap. 15.95 (978-1-877673-09-2(9) , WLT-BWK03) Cottonwood Pr., Inc.

Burkholder, Kelly. Diaries & Journals. 2000. (Artistic Adventures Ser.). (Illus.). 24p. (J). (gr. 2-6). lib. bdg. 23.93 (978-1-57103-352-9(1)) Rourke Publishing, LLC.

Capacchione, Lucia. The Creative Journal for Teens: Making Friends with Yourself. 2nd ed. 2001. (Illus.). 192p. pap. 14.99 (978-1-56414-572-7(7) , New Page Bks.) Career Pr., Inc.

Chobanian, Elizabeth, ed. Coco-Notes: A Book of Notes to Tear & Share. Lukatz, Casey, illus. 2003. (Coconut Ser.). 80p. pap. 5.95 (978-1-58485-798-3(6)) American Girl Publishing, Inc.

Corrigan, Eireann. You Remind Me of You: A Poetry Memoir. 2002. 128p. (J). (gr. 8 up). 6.99 (978-0-439-29771-4(0) , PUSH) Scholastic, Inc.

Dormer, Cindy. Hold That Thought for Kids: Capturing Precious Memories Through Fun Questions, Images & Conversations. 2005. (Hold that Thought Keepsake Conversation Journals). (Illus.). 145p. (J). 19.95 (978-0-9743720-0-6(5)) Brightside Co.

Dumont, Ninda, ed. My Heart 2 Heart Diary: Broccoli Edition. Franklin, Linda C., illus. 1998. 128p. (J). 11.95 (978-0-9640713-9-1(8)) Fine Print Publishing Co.

—My Heart 2 Heart Diary: Indigo Puppy Edition. Franklin, Linda C., illus. 1998. 64p. (J). 11.95 (978-0-9640713-8-4(X)) Fine Print Publishing Co.

—My Heart 2 Heart Travel Diary. Franklin, Linda C., illus. 1998. 64p. (J). pap. 11.95 (978-0-9640713-7-7(1)) Fine Print Publishing Co.

Edwards, Judith & Comport, Sally Wern. The Great Expedition of Lewis & Clark: By Private Reubin Field, Member of the Corps of Discovery. Comport, Sally Wern, illus. 2003. (Illus.). 40p. (J). 17.00 (978-0-374-38039-7(2) , Farrar, Straus & Giroux (BYR)) Farrar, Straus & Giroux.

Finn, Perdita. Teaching Memoir Writing: 20 Easy Mini-lessons & Thought-Provoking Activities That Inspire Kids. 1999. (Illus.). 48p. pap. 10.95 (978-0-439-04390-8(5)) Scholastic, Inc.

Goetsch, Lory M. My Memory Box Journal. 1998. (J). spiral bd. 19.95 (978-0-9663436-0-1(3)) Grote Publishing.

Jernegan, Laura. A Whaling Captain's Daughter: The Diary of Laura Jernegan, 1868-1871. O'Hara, Megan, ed. 2000. (Blue Earth Books). (Illus.). 32p. (J). (gr. 3-4). lib. bdg. 22.60 (978-0-7368-0346-5(7) , Bridgestone Bks.) Capstone Pr., Inc.

Kranz, Linda. More about Me: Another Keepsake Journal for Kids. 1998. (Keepsakes Ser.). (Illus.). 128p. (J). (gr. 3-6). 12.95 (978-0-87358-716-7(2) , Rising Moon Bks. for Young Readers) Northland Publishing.

—Through My Eyes: A Journal for Teens. 1998. (Keepsakes Ser.). (Illus.). 128p. (YA). (gr. 7-12). 12.95 (978-0-87358-715-0(4) , Rising Moon Bks. for Young Readers) Northland Publishing.

Morina, Barbara. Me, Myself & My Personal Journal. Morina, Barbara, ed. 2001. (Write It down Ser.). (Illus.). 202p. 19.95 (978-1-892033-35-2(6)) Journals Unlimited, Inc.

Perlow, Ann. The Story of Me. Perlow, Ann & Pacheco, Gabe, eds. Pacheco, Gabe, illus. 2001. 36p. (J). (ps-6). 14.95 (978-0-9714999-0-4(X)) Gabann Enterprises.

Roberts, Candace. The Diary of Candace Roberts, 1801-1806. Leach, Gail, ed. 2001. (Illus.). 63p. (YA). (gr. 9-12). pap. 14.00 (978-0-9715501-0-0(7)) Bristol Historical Society.

Roop, Peter & Roop, Connie. Take Command, Captain Farragut! McCurdy, Michael, illus. 2002. 48p. (J). (gr. 3-5). 16.00 (978-0-689-83022-8(X) , Atheneum) Simon & Schuster Children's Publishing.

Roper, Ingrid. Dream Time Journal. Sampson, Nancy, illus. 2002. 128p. (J). (gr. 3 up). pap. 9.99 (978-0-439-39997-5(1) , Tangerine Pr.) Scholastic, Inc.

Stern, Zoe. Protect This Girl's Journal. Meisse, Michelle, illus. 2004. 96p. (gr. 4-7). 12.95 (978-1-58246-015-4(9) , Tricycle Pr.) Ten Speed Pr.

Townsley, Janet Howe. Dakota Dreams: Fannie Sabra Howe's Own Story, 1881-1884. 2003. (Illus.). 77p. (J). 19.95 (978-0-9715171-4-1(2)) South Dakota State Historical Society.

Wilber, Jessica. The Absolutely True, Positively Awesome Book about... Me!!! By Me!!! (With Help from Jessica Wilber) 1999. (Illus.). 128p. (J). (gr. 1-5). pap. 9.95 (978-1-57542-061-5(9)) Free Spirit Publishing, Inc.

Young, Jay, creator. Secret Ziga Zaga. 2003. (Ziga Zaga Ser.). 192p. (YA). (978-1-84347-034-2(9)) Chrysalis Children's Bks.

AUTOMATIC COMPUTERS

see Computers

AUTOMATIC CONTROL

see also Automation; Cybernetics

Biggs, Andy, et al. Systems & Control Technology. 2nd rev. ed. 2002. (Illus.). 152p. (YA). pap. 27.50 (978-0-7487-6080-0(6)) Nelson Thornes Ltd. GBR. *Dist:* Trans-Atlantic Pubns., Inc.

AUTOMATIC DATA PROCESSING

see Electronic Data Processing

AUTOMATIC INFORMATION RETRIEVAL

see Information Storage and Retrieval Systems

AUTOMATION

Espejo, Roman. What Is the Impact of Automation? 2007. (At Issue Ser.). (Illus.). 128p. (gr. 10-12). 29.95 (***978-0-7377-3944-2(4)***); pap. 21.20 (***978-0-7377-3945-9(2)***) Thomson Gale. (Greenhaven Pr., Inc.).

AUTOMOBILE ACCIDENTS

see Traffic Accidents

AUTOMOBILE DRIVERS

Allen, Kenny. Kurt Busch. 2007. (NASCAR Champions Ser.). (Illus.). 24p. (J). lib. bdg. (978-1-4042-3457-4(8) , PowerKids Pr.) Rosen Publishing Group, Inc., The.

Anderson, Wayne A. Tony Stewart: NASCAR Driver. 2006. (Illus.). 48p. (J). (gr. 5-8). lib. bdg. 26.50 (978-1-4042-0984-8(0)) Rosen Publishing Group, Inc., The.

Armentrout, David & Armentrout, Patricia. Dale Earnhardt, Jr. 2005. (Rourke Discovery Library). (Illus.). 24p. (gr. 1-4). 14.95 (978-1-59515-132-2(X)) Rourke Publishing, LLC.

—Dale Jarrett: In the Fast Lane. 2007. (In the Fast Lane Ser.). (Illus.). 24p. (J). (978-1-60044-216-2(1)) Rourke Publishing, LLC.

—Kurt Busch: In the Fast Lane. 2007. (In the Fast Lane Ser.). (J). (978-1-60044-218-6(8)) Rourke Publishing, LLC.

—Matt Kenseth: In the Fast Lane. 2007. (Illus.). 24p. (J). (978-1-60044-219-3(6)) Rourke Publishing, LLC.

—Rusty Wallace: In the Fast Lane. 2007. (In the Fast Lane Ser.). (Illus.). 24p. (J). (978-1-60044-220-9(X)) Rourke Publishing, LLC.

—Tony Stewart: In the Fast Lane. 2007. (In the Fast Lane Ser.). (Illus.). 24p. (J). (978-1-60044-221-6(8)) Rourke Publishing, LLC.

Barber, Phil. Bill Elliott; The Fastest Man Alive. 2003. (World of Nascar Ser.). (Illus.). 32p. (J). (gr. 2-6). 25.64 (978-1-59187-037-1(2)) Child's World, Inc.

Basen, Ryan. Tony Stewart: Rocket on the Racetrack. 2008. (Heroes of Racing Ser.). 128p. (J). (gr. 5-9). lib. bdg. 31.93 (***978-0-7660-2998-9(0)***) Enslow Pubs., Inc.

Benson, Michael. Dale Earnhardt Scrapbook. 2002. (Celebrity Ser.). pap. 6.99 (978-0-88013-050-9(4)) Profile Entertainment, Inc.

Biking Safely: Fourth Grade Guided Comprehension Level K. (On Our Way to English Ser.). (gr. 4 up). 34.50 (978-0-7578-7149-8(6)) Rigby Education.

Braidich, Victoria. Dale Earnhardt. 2007. (NASCAR Champions Ser.). (Illus.). 24p. (J). lib. bdg. (978-1-4042-3512-0(4) , PowerKids Pr.) Rosen Publishing Group, Inc., The.

Bridges, Sarah. I Drive an Ambulance. Alderman, Derrick & Shea, Denise, illus. 2004. (Working Wheels Ser.). 24p. (C). (gr. k-2). 22.60 (978-1-4048-0618-4(0)) Picture Window Bks.

Buckley, James. Nascar. 2005. (Eyewitness Books). (Illus.). 72p. (J). 15.99 (978-0-7566-1194-1(6)); lib. bdg. 19.99 (978-0-7566-1193-4(8)) Dorling Kindersley Publishing, Inc.

Cain, Woody. Drivers Series: Jeff Gordon. 2002. (NASCAR Wonder Boy Collector's Ser.). (Illus.). 48p. (J). pap. 7.99 (978-1-57243-523-0(2)) Triumph Bks.

Calcar Staff. Sport Driving Vol. 3: 4X4 Xpert Guide. 2000. (Sport Xpert Tips Ser.). (Illus.). 38p. (YA). (gr. 11 up). pap. 7.95 (978-0-9705167-2-5(X) , 1000133) Calcar, Inc.

Christopher, Matt. Dale Earnhardt Sr. 2007. (Matt Christopher Legends in Sports Ser.). (Illus.). 128p. (J). (gr. 3-7). pap. 4.99 (***978-0-316-01114-3(2)***) Little Brown & Co.

Crisp, Dan. Let's Help. 2006. (Illus.). 14p. 7.99 (978-1-904550-95-2(9)) Child's Play-International.

—Let's Rescue. 2006. (Illus.). 14p. 7.99 (978-1-904550-97-6(5)) Child's Play-International.

—Let's Ride. 2006. (Illus.). 14p. 7.99 (978-1-904550-96-9(7)) Child's Play-International.

Croft, Andy & Basic Skills Agency Staff. Michael Schumacher. 2005. 32p. pap. 8.50 (978-0-340-84882-1(0)) Cambridge Univ. Pr.

Dutton, Monte. Jeff Gordon: The Racer. 2000. (gr. 7-12). lib. bdg. 22.20 (978-0-613-32714-5(4)) Tandem Library Bks.

Fleischman, Bill. Dale Earnhardt JR. collector's ed. 2005. (Race Car Legends Ser.). (Illus.). 67p. (J). (gr. 4-8). lib. bdg. 25.00 (978-0-7910-8671-1(2) , Chelsea Hse.) Facts On File, Inc.

Gaines, Ann Graham. Kenny Irwin Jr. rev. collector's ed. 2005. (Race Car Legends Ser.). (Illus.). 64p. (J). (gr. 4-8). lib. bdg. 25.00 (978-0-7910-8766-4(2) , Chelsea Hse.) Facts On File, Inc.

Garfield, Ken. Dale Earnhardt, Jr: Born to Race. 2005. (Sports Leaders Ser.). (Illus.). 104p. (J). (gr. k-13). lib. bdg. 26.60 (978-0-7660-2424-3(5)) Enslow Pubs., Inc.

Gerdes, Louise I., ed. Drunk Driving. 2001. (Contemporary Issues Companion Ser.). 138p. (YA). (gr. 9 up). lib. bdg. 32.45 (978-0-7377-0460-0(8)); (Illus.). (gr. 10 up). pap. 21.20 (978-0-7377-0459-4(4)) Thomson Gale. (Greenhaven Pr., Inc.).

Gillis, Jennifer Blizin. Jobs on Wheels. 2007. (978-1-60044-202-5(1)) Rourke Publishing, LLC.

Gitlin, Marty. Jeff Gordon: Racing's Brightest Star. 2008. (Heroes of Racing Ser.). (Illus.). 128p. (J). (gr. 5-9). lib. bdg. 31.93 (***978-0-7660-2997-2(2)***) Enslow Pubs., Inc.

—Jimmie Johnson: Racing Champ. 2008. (Heroes of Racing Ser.). 128p. (J). (gr. 5-9). lib. bdg. 31.93 (***978-0-7660-2999-6(9)***) Enslow Pubs., Inc.

Goddard, Jennifer S. On the Road: The Savvy Girl's Guide to Cars. 2006. (Illus.). 49p. (J). pap. (***978-0-88441-701-9(8)***) Girl Scouts of the USA.

Gravelle, Karen. The Driving Book: Everything New Drivers Need to Know but Don't Know to Ask. Flook, Helen, illus. 2005. 160p. 16.95 (978-0-8027-8933-4(1)) Walker & Co.

A B

Grosshandler, Janet. Drugs & Driving. rev. ed. 2005. (Drug Abuse Prevention Library). (Illus.). 64p. (YA). (gr. 7-12). lib. bdg. 25.25 (978-0-8239-3459-1(4)) Rosen Publishing Group, Inc., The.

Horn, Geoffrey M. Dale Earnhardt, Jr. 2006. (Today's Superstars). (Illus.). 32p. (YA). (gr. 5 up). lib. bdg. 23.93 (978-0-8368-6182-2(5)) Stevens, Gareth Inc.

Hubbard-Brown, Janet. The Labonte Brothers. rev. collector's ed. 2005. (Race Car Legends Ser.). (Illus.). 72p. (J). (gr. 4-8). lib. bdg. 25.00 (978-0-7910-8767-1(0), Chelsea Hse.) Facts On File, Inc.

James, Lincoln. Dale Jarrett. 2007. (NASCAR Champions Ser.). (Illus.). 24p. (J). lib. bdg. (978-1-4042-3459-8(4), PowerKids Pr.) Rosen Publishing Group, Inc., The.

Leebrick, Kristal. Jeff Gordon. 2004. (Edge Books NASCAR Racing). (Illus.). 32p. (J). 16.95 (978-0-7368-2424-8(3)) Capstone Pr., Inc.

—Tony Stewart. 2004. (Edge Books NASCAR Racing). (Illus.). 32p. (J). 16.95 (978-0-7368-2425-5(1)) Capstone Pr., Inc.

Levy, Janey. Kurt Busch. 2007. (Illus.). 48p. (J). pap. (978-0-531-18714-2(4)) Children's Pr., Ltd.

—Kurt Busch. 2006. (Illus.). 48p. (J). (978-0-531-16806-6(9), Children's Pr.) Scholastic Library Publishing.

MacDonald, James. Dale Earnhardt, Jr: Racing's Living Legacy. 2008. (Heroes of Racing Ser.). (Illus.). 128p. (J). (gr. 5-9). lib. bdg. 31.93 (***978-0-7660-2996-5(4)***) Enslow Pubs., Inc.

Mattern, Joanne. Big Bucks. 2006. (Illus.). 48p. (J). (978-0-531-16807-3(7), Children's Pr.) Scholastic Library Publishing.

—Big Bucks: The Fast Cash of Stock Car Racing. 2007. (Illus.). 48p. (J). pap. (978-0-531-18715-9(2), Children's Pr.) Scholastic Library Publishing.

Mello, Tara Baukus. Rusty Wallace. rev. collector's ed. 2005. (Race Car Legends Ser.). (Illus.). 70p. (J). (gr. 4-7). lib. bdg. 25.00 (978-0-7910-8669-8(0), Chelsea Hse.) Facts On File, Inc.

Mitchell, Jason. Drivers Series Tony Stewart. 2002. (NASCAR Wonder Boy Collector's Ser.). (Illus.). 48p. (J). pap. 7.99 (978-1-57243-524-7(0)) Triumph Bks.

Mitchell, Joyce Slayton. Tractor-Trailer Trucker: A Powerful Truck Book. Borns, Steven, photos by. 2005. (Illus.). 40p. (J). (ps-k). pap. 7.95 (978-1-58246-155-7(4), Tricycle Pr.) Ten Speed Pr.

Payment, Simone. Ryan Newman: NASCAR Driver. 2006. (Behind the Wheel Ser.). (Illus.). 48p. (J). (gr. 5-8). lib. bdg. 26.50 (978-1-4042-0983-1(2)) Rosen Publishing Group, Inc., The.

Poolos, J. Jeff Gordon: NASCAR Driver. 2006. (Behind the Wheel Ser.). (Illus.). 48p. (J). (gr. 5-8). lib. bdg. 26.50 (978-1-4042-0980-0(8)) Rosen Publishing Group, Inc., The.

Race Car Legends: Collector's Edition. collector's ed. 2005. (Illus.). 64p. (gr. 4-8). pap. 375.00 (978-0-7910-9065-7(5), Chelsea Hse.) Facts On File, Inc.

Rau, Dana Meachen. Driving. 2006. (On the Move Ser.). (ENG & SPA., Illus.). 24p. (J). lib. bdg. 22.79 (978-0-7614-2316-4(8), Benchmark Bks.) Cavendish, Marshall Corp.

Robinson, Tom. Mark Martin: Master Behind the Wheel. 2008. (Heroes of Racing Ser.). 128p. (J). (gr. 5-9). lib. bdg. 31.93 (***978-0-7660-3001-5(6)***) Enslow Pubs., Inc.

Roselius, J. Chris. Matt Kenseth: Speeding to Victory. 2008. (Heroes of Racing Ser.). 128p. (J). (gr. 5-9). lib. bdg. 31.93 (***978-0-7660-3000-8(8)***) Enslow Pubs., Inc.

Roza, Greg. Dale Earnhardt Jr. NASCAR Driver. 2006. (Behind the Wheel Ser.). (Illus.). 48p. (J). (gr. 5-8). lib. bdg. 26.50 (978-1-4042-0979-4(4)) Rosen Publishing Group, Inc., The.

Savage, Jeff. Dale Earnhardt Jr. 2005. (Illus.). 32p. (J). (gr. 4-7). pap. 5.95 (978-0-8225-2953-8(X)) Lerner Publishing Group.

—Danica Patrick. 2006. (Amazing Athletes Ser.). (Illus.). 32p. (J). pap. 5.95 (978-0-8225-6012-8(7), First Avenue Editions) Lerner Publishing Group.

Savage Jeff. James Stewart. 2007. (Amazing Athletes Ser.). (J). pap. 6.95 (***978-0-8225-7662-4(7)***, First Avenue Editions) Lerner Publishing Group.

Schaefer, A. R. Dale Earnhardt. 2006. (Edge Books NASCAR Racing). (Illus.). 32p. (J). (978-0-7368-4377-5(9)) Capstone Pr., Inc.

—Richard Petty. 2006. (Edge Books NASCAR Racing). (Illus.). 32p. (J). (978-0-7368-4378-2(7)) Capstone Pr., Inc.

Seivert, Terri. James Stewart. 2005. (Illus.). 32p. (J). (gr. 2 up). lib. bdg. 22.60 (978-0-7368-4365-2(5)) Capstone Pr., Inc.

Sherman, Josepha. Dale Earnhardt, Jr. 2005. (Robbie Reader Ser.). (Illus.). 32p. (J). (gr. 1-4). lib. bdg. (978-1-58415-360-3(1)) Mitchell Lane Pubs., Inc.

Stewart, Mark. Jeff Gordon: Rainbow Warrior. 2000. (Auto Racing's New Wave Ser.: up). (Illus.). 48p. (gr. 4-7). pap. (978-0-7613-1385-4(0), Millbrook Pr.) Lerner Publishing Group.

Teitelbaum, Michael. Tony Stewart. 2007. (World's Greatest Athletes Ser.). 32p. (J). (gr. 1-5). 27.07 (978-1-59296-792-6(2)) Child's World, Inc.

Thompson, Gary. What Every Teen Should Know Before Getting Behind the Wheel Alone: A Guide to Increasing Your Child's Safety While Reducing Your Auto Repair Expenses. 2004. 131p. (YA). per. 9.95 (978-0-9749763-1-0(8)) Guiding Horizons.

Walker, Pam. Car Rides. 2000. (gr. k-3). lib. bdg. 12.95 (978-0-613-51999-1(X)) Tandem Library Bks.

Winters, Adam. Everything You Need to Know about Being a Teen Driver. 2005. (Need to Know Library). (Illus.). 64p. (YA). (gr. 7-12). 25.25 (978-0-8239-3287-0(7), NTTEDR) Rosen Publishing Group, Inc., The.

AUTOMOBILE DRIVERS—FICTION

Bauer, Joan. Rules of the Road. 208p. (gr. 7). 2005. (YA). pap. 7.99 (978-0-14-240425-6(X), Puffin); 1998. (J). 16.99 (978-0-399-23140-7(4), Putnam Juvenile) Penguin Group (USA) Inc.

—Rules of the Road. 2000. (YA). (978-0-606-20252-7(8)); 201p. (gr. 7-12). lib. bdg. 13.64 (978-0-606-20370-8(2)) Tandem Library Bks.

Brown, Joe. The Flights of Marceau: Week One. 2007. (Illus.). 56p. (J). 22.50 (***978-0-9797495-0-6(6)***) Majestic Eagle Publishing.

Cooney, Caroline B. Driver's Ed. 2004. 192p. (YA). (gr. 7). lib. bdg. 17.99 (978-0-385-90236-6(0), Delacorte Bks. for Young Readers) Random Hse. Children's Bks.

Coy, John. Night Driving. McCarty, Peter, illus. rev. ed. 2001. 32p. (J). (ps-3). pap. 7.95 (978-0-8050-6708-8(6), Holt, Henry & Co. Bks. For Young Readers) Holt, Henry & Co.

—Night Driving. 2001. (gr. k-3). lib. bdg. 15.25 (978-0-613-75371-5(2)) Tandem Library Bks.

Fienberg, Anna. Minton Goes Driving. Gamble, Kim, illus. 2001. (Minton Ser.). 32p. (J). (ps-1). pap. 6.95 (978-1-86448-594-3(9)) Allen & Unwin AUS. *Dist:* Independent Pubs. Group.

Hall, Kirsten. Zoom Zoom Zoom. Garofoli, Viviana, illus. 2004. (My First Reader Ser.). 32p. (J). (gr. k-1). pap. 3.95 (978-0-516-25509-5(6), Children's Pr.) Scholastic Library Publishing.

Hill, David. Coming Back. 2007. 189p. pap. 18.95 (***978-0-9542330-2-0(6)***) Aurora Metro Pubns. Ltd. GBR. *Dist:* Consortium Bk. Sales & Distribution.

Nick Drives the Car. Date not set. (J). pap. (978-1-58453-040-4(5)) Pioneer Valley Educational Pr., Inc.

Perlman, Rhea. Born to Drive. Santat, Dan, illus. 2006. (Otto Undercover Ser.). 128p. (J). 14.99 (978-0-06-075496-9(6)); pap. 3.99 (978-0-06-075495-2(8)) HarperCollins Pubs. (Tegen, Katherine Bks).

—Toxic Taffy Takeover. Santat, Dan, illus. 2006. (Otto Undercover Ser.). 128p. (J). 14.99 (978-0-06-075502-7(4), Tegen, Katherine Bks); pap. 3.99 (978-0-06-075501-0(6), Harper Trophy) HarperCollins Pubs.

—Water Balloon Doom. Santat, Dan, illus. 2006. (Otto Undercover Ser.: No. 3). 128p. (J). (gr. 3-5). 14.99 (978-0-06-075500-3(8), Tegen, Katherine Bks); pap. 3.99 (978-0-06-075499-0(0), Harper Trophy) HarperCollins Pubs.

Powell, Richard. Formula Bunny. Holt, Emma, illus. 2003. (Whizzy Wheels Bks.). 20p. (J). bds. 4.95 (978-0-7641-5590-1(3)) Barron's Educational Series, Inc.

—GTI Kitten. Holt, Emma, illus. 2003. (Whizzy Wheels Bks.). 20p. (J). bds. 4.95 (978-0-7641-5588-8(1)) Barron's Educational Series, Inc.

—Race Bear. Holt, Emma, illus. 2003. (Whizzy Wheels Bks.). 20p. (J). bds. 4.95 (978-0-7641-5587-1(3)) Barron's Educational Series, Inc.

—Team Pig. Holt, Emma, illus. 2003. (Whizzy Wheels Bks.). 20p. (J). bds. 4.95 (978-0-7641-5586-4(5)) Barron's Educational Series, Inc.

Scott, Jerry. Zits Vol. 7: Carretera y Manta. 2007. (SPA., Illus.). 128p. reprint ed. pap. 19.95 (***978-1-59497-337-6(7)***) Public Square Bks.

Tali Drives His Car. (Pebble Soup Explorations Ser.). 16p. (ps up). 31.00 (978-0-7578-1663-5(0)) Rigby Education.

Tali Drives His Car: Small Book. (Pebble Soup Explorations Ser.). 16p. (ps up). 5.00 (978-0-7578-1703-8(3)) Rigby Education.

Teitelbaum, Michael. If I Could Drive an Ambulance! Mones, Marc & Mones, Isidre, illus. 2003. (Tonka Ser.). 24p. (J). (ps-2). pap. 3.50 (978-0-439-43433-1(5)) Scholastic, Inc.

—If I Could Drive an Ambulance! 2003. (gr. k-3). lib. bdg. 11.25 (978-0-613-67095-1(7)) Tandem Library Bks.

Wood, Jakki. Bumper to Bumper: A Traffic Jam. Wood, Jakki, illus. 1999. (Illus.). 32p. (J). (ps-k). pap. (978-0-7112-1031-8(4)) Lincoln, Frances Ltd. GBR. *Dist:* Transition Vendor.

AUTOMOBILE DRIVING

see Automobile Drivers

AUTOMOBILE ENGINES

see Automobiles—Engines

AUTOMOBILE INDUSTRY AND TRADE

Bell, Lonnie. The Story of the Ford Motor Company. 2003. (Built for Success Ser.). (Illus.). 48p. (J). 28.50 (978-1-58340-293-1(4)) Smart Apple Media.

Brown, Jonatha A. Henry Ford. 2005. (People to Know Ser.). (Illus.). 24p. (J). pap. (978-0-8368-4473-3(4)); (YA). lib. bdg. 19.33 (978-0-8368-4466-5(1), Weekly Reader Early Learning Library) Stevens, Gareth Inc.

Burgan, Michael. Henry Ford. 2002. (Trailblazers of the Modern World Ser.). (Illus.). 48p. (J). (gr. 5 up). pap. 14.95 (978-0-8368-5230-1(3)); lib. bdg. 30.00 (978-0-8368-5070-3(X)) Stevens, Gareth Inc. (World Almanac Library).

—Henry Ford. 2002. (gr. 3-6). lib. bdg. 16.40 (978-0-613-76803-0(5)) Tandem Library Bks.

—Henry Ford: Industrialist. 2001. (Career Biographies Ser.). (Illus.). 128p. (J). (gr. 6-12). 25.00 (978-0-89434-369-8(6), F412, Ferguson Publishing Co.) Facts On File, Inc.

Cars of the Past: Individual Title Six-Packs. (On Deck Ser.). 24p. (gr. 4-5). 35.00 (978-0-7578-1048-0(9)) Rigby Education.

Ford, Carin T. Henry Ford: The Car Man. 2003. (Famous Inventors Ser.). (Illus.). 32p. (J). (gr. 1-4). lib. bdg. 22.60 (978-0-7660-2179-2(3)) Enslow Pubs., Inc.

Green, Robert. Cars. 2008. (J). lib. bdg. 25.26 (***978-1-60279-028-5(0)***) Cherry Lake Publishing.

Kaminski, Edward S. The Magor Car Corporation. 2000. 200p. (J). 55.00 (978-1-930013-04-9(3)) Signature Pr.

Kulling, Monica. Eat My Dust! Henry Ford's First Race. Walz, Richard, illus. 2004. (Step into Reading Ser.). 48p. (J). (gr. 1-3). pap. 3.99 (978-0-375-81510-2(4), Random Hse. Bks. for Young Readers) Random Hse. Children's Bks.

Mara, Wil. Henry Ford. (Rookie Biographies Ser.). (Illus.). (J). 2004. 31p. (gr. 1-2). pap. 4.95 (978-0-516-27917-6(3)); 2003. 32p. 20.50 (978-0-516-25863-8(X)) Scholastic Library Publishing. (Children's Pr.).

Musolf, Nell. The Story of Ford. 2008. (J). (***978-1-58341-604-4(8)***, Creative Education) Creative Co., The.

Schaefer, Lola M. Famous People in Transportation, 4 bks. Incl. Henry Ford. Saunders-Smith, Gail, ed. lib. bdg. 15.93 (978-0-7368-0546-9(X)); Robert Fulton. lib. bdg. 15.93 (978-0-7368-0547-6(8)); Robert Goddard. lib. bdg. 15.93 (978-0-7368-0548-3(6)); Wright Brothers. lib. bdg. 15.93 (978-0-7368-0549-0(4)); 24p. (J). (gr. k-1). (Illus.). 2000. Set lib. bdg. 63.72 (978-0-7368-0563-6(X), Pebble Bks.) Capstone Pr., Inc.

Shuter, Jane. Henry Ford. 2000. (Lives & Times Ser.). (Illus.). 24p. (J). lib. bdg. 19.92 (978-1-57572-229-0(1)) Heinemann Library.

Wyborny, Sheila. Henry Ford. 2002. (Inventors & Creators Ser.). (Illus.). 48p. (J). (gr. 3-5). 23.70 (978-0-7377-1286-5(4), LML00902-181325, Kidhaven) Thomson Gale.

Young, Jeff C. Henry Ford: Genius Behind the Affordable Car. 2007. (Inventors Who Changed the World Ser.). (Illus.). 128p. (J). (gr. 5). lib. bdg. 33.27 (***978-1-59845-053-8(0)***, MyReportLinks.com Bks.) Enslow Pubs., Inc.

Zuehlke, Jeffrey. Henry Ford. 2007. (History Maker Bios Ser.). (J). 26.60 (978-0-8225-6583-3(8), Lerner Pubns.) Lerner Publishing Group.

AUTOMOBILE INDUSTRY AND TRADE—HISTORY

Malam, John. Henry Ford. 2001. (Profiles Ser.). (Illus.). 56p. (J). (gr. 4-6). lib. bdg. 24.22 (978-1-58810-058-0(8)) Heinemann Library.

Rivera, Sheila. Thunderbird. 2004. (Ultimate Cars Ser.). (Illus.). 27p. (J). (gr. 3-8). lib. bdg. 24.21 (978-1-59197-583-0(2)) ABDO Publishing Co.

AUTOMOBILE RACING

see also Karts and Karting

Aloian, Molly & Kalman, Bobbie. Racecars: Start Your Engines! 2007. (Vehicles on the Move Ser.). (Illus.). 32p. (J). (gr. 1-5). (***978-0-7787-3043-9(3)***); pap. (***978-0-7787-3057-6(3)***) Crabtree Publishing Co.

Armentrout, David & Armentrout, Patricia. Dale Earnhardt, Jr. 2005. (Rourke Discovery Library). (Illus.). 24p. (gr. 1-4). 14.95 (978-1-59515-132-2(5)) Rourke Publishing, LLC.

Armentrout, David & Armentrout, Patricia, trs. Jeff Gordon. 2003. (Discover the Life of a Sports Star Ser.). (Illus.). 24p. (J). 20.64 (978-1-58952-653-2(8)) Rourke Publishing, LLC.

Balloon. Vroom Vroom: Sports Cars. 1998. (J). 9.95 (978-0-8069-9555-7(6)) Sterling Publishing Co., Inc.

Barber, Phil. Dale Earnhardt: The Likeable Intimidator. 2002. (World of NASCAR Ser.). (Illus.). 32p. (J). (gr. 2-6). 25.64 (978-1-59187-001-2(1)) Child's World, Inc.

—From Finish to Start: A Week in the Life of a NASCAR Racing Team. 2003. (World of NASCAR Ser.). (Illus.). 32p. (J). (gr. 2-6). 25.64 (978-1-59187-030-2(5)) Child's World, Inc.

—Stock Car's Greatest Race: The First & the Fastest. 2002. (World of NASCAR Ser.). (Illus.). 32p. (J). (gr. 2-6). 25.64 (978-1-59187-003-6(8)) Child's World, Inc.

Bechtel, Mark. NASCAR Race Day: Behind the Scenes. 2003. (J). 3.99 (978-1-930623-28-6(3)) Sports Illustrated For Kids.

Bensimon, Perla. Super Racing. 2002. (Cool Cars Ser.). (Illus.). 12p. (J). (gr. k-4). 12.95 (978-1-57145-732-5(1), Silver Dolphin Bks.) Advantage Pubs. Group.

Benson, Michael. Dale Earnhardt Scrapbook. 2002. (Celebrity Ser.). pap. 6.99 (978-0-88013-050-9(4)) Profile Entertainment, Inc.

Bentley, Dawn. Speedy Little Race Cars. Cahoon, Heather, illus. 2004. 20p. 10.99 (978-0-9755195-1-6(4)) MEL-JAMES, Inc.

Blackwood, Gary L. The Great Race: Around the World by Automobile. 2008. 144p. (J). 19.95 (***978-0-8109-9489-8(5)***) Abrams, Harry N., Inc.

Bledsoe, Glen & Bledsoe, Karen. The World's Fastest Dragsters. 2003. (Built for Speed Ser.). (Illus.). 48p. (J). (gr. 3-4). lib. bdg. 21.26 (978-0-7368-1500-0(7), Capstone High-Interest Bks.) Capstone Pr., Inc.

—The World's Fastest Indy Cars. 2003. (Built for Speed Ser.). (Illus.). 48p. (J). (gr. 3-4). lib. bdg. 21.26 (978-0-7368-1501-7(5), Capstone High-Interest Bks.) Capstone Pr., Inc.

—The World's Fastest Trucks. 2002. (Built for Speed Ser.). (Illus.). 48p. (J). (gr. 3-4). lib. bdg. 21.26 (978-0-7368-1062-3(5), Capstone High-Interest Bks.) Capstone Pr., Inc.

Braulick, Carrie A. Rally Cars. 2007. (Illus.). 32p. (J). (978-0-7368-6784-9(8)) Capstone Pr., Inc.

Buckley, James, Jr. Life in the Pits: Twenty Seconds That Make the Difference. 2002. (World of NASCAR Ser.). (Illus.). 32p. (J). (gr. 2-6). 25.64 (978-1-59187-008-1(9)) Child's World, Inc.

Buckley, James. Nascar. 2005. (Eyewitness Books). (Illus.). 72p. (J). 15.99 (978-0-7566-1194-1(6)); lib. bdg. 19.99 (978-0-7566-1193-4(8)) Dorling Kindersley Publishing, Inc.

Bullard, Lisa. Stock Cars. 2004. (Pull Ahead Bks.). (Illus.). 32p. (J). (gr. k-2). lib. bdg. 22.60 (978-0-8225-0694-2(7)) Lerner Publishing Group.

Burnin' Rubber. 1998. (Hot Wheels Ser.). (Illus.). 32p. (J). (ps-1). pap. (978-0-7666-0100-0(5), Honey Bear Bks.) Modern Publishing.

Caldwell, Dave. Speed Show: How NASCAR Won the Heart of America. 2006. (New York Times Ser.). (Illus.). 128p. (J). (gr. 5). 16.95 (978-0-7534-6011-5(4), Kingfisher) Houghton Mifflin Co. Trade & Reference Div.

Car Race. 2004. (Illus.). (J). (978-1-59577-012-7(7)) Starfall Education.

Car Racing. (J). (978-0-8118-4879-4(5)) Chronicle Bks. LLC.

Cavin, Curt. Race Day: The Fastest Show on Earth. 2002. (World of NASCAR Ser.). (Illus.). 32p. (J). (gr. 2-6). 25.64 (978-1-59187-009-8(7)) Child's World, Inc.

—Terrific Tracks: The Coolest Places to Race. 2003. (World of NASCAR Ser.). (Illus.). 32p. (J). (gr. 2-6). 25.64 (978-1-59187-033-3(X)) Child's World, Inc.

—Under the Helmet: Inside the Mind of a Driver. 2003. (World of NASCAR Ser.). (Illus.). 32p. (J). (gr. 2-6). 25.64 (978-1-59187-036-4(4)) Child's World, Inc.

Cefrey, Holly. Race Car Drivers: Life on the Fast Track. 2005. (Extreme Careers Ser.). (Illus.). 64p. (YA). (gr. 5-8). 26.50 (978-0-8239-3367-9(9)) Rosen Publishing Group, Inc., The.

—Stock Car. 2001. (Built for Speed Ser.). (Illus.). 48p. (J). (gr. 7-12). 24.00 (978-0-516-23164-8(2), Children's Pr.) Scholastic Library Publishing.

—Stock Car. 2001. (gr. 7-12). lib. bdg. 15.25 (978-0-613-52191-8(9)) Tandem Library Bks.

Ching, Jacqueline. Adventure Racing. 2002. (Ultra Sports Ser.). (Illus.). 64p. (YA). (gr. 5-8). lib. bdg. 26.50 (978-0-8239-3555-0(8), Rosen Central) Rosen Publishing Group, Inc., The.

Clemson, Wendy, et al. Win a Grand Prix. 2004. (Mathworks!). (Illus.). 31p. (J). lib. bdg. 24.67 (978-0-8368-4214-2(6)) Stevens, Gareth Inc.

Cook, Nick. The World's Fastest Cars. 2000. (Built for Speed Ser.). (Illus.). 48p. (J). (gr. 3-4). lib. bdg. 21.26 (978-0-7368-0570-4(2), Capstone High-Interest Bks.) Capstone Pr., Inc.

Dahl, Michael. One Checkered Flag: A Counting Book about Racing. Aldermand, Derrick & Shea, Denise, illus. 2004. (Know Your Numbers Ser.). 24p. (J). (gr. k-3). 22.60 (978-1-4048-0576-7(1), 1229522) Picture Window Bks.

Dalmatian Press Staff. NASCAR Racers Get on Track. 2000. (Illus.). (J). pap. 2.99 (978-1-57759-298-3(0)) Dalmatian Pr.

—NASCAR Racers Maximum Performance. 2000. (Illus.). (J). pap. 2.99 (978-1-57759-299-0(9)) Dalmatian Pr.

—NASCAR Racers Road Thunder. 2000. (Illus.). (J). pap. 2.50 (978-1-57759-344-7(8)) Dalmatian Pr.

David, Jack. Go Kart Racing. 2008. (Illus.). 24p. (J). lib. bdg. 19.95 (978-1-60014-123-2(4)) Bellwether Media.

—Indy Cars. 2008. (Illus.). 24p. (J). lib. bdg. 19.95 (***978-1-60014-148-5(X)***) Bellwether Media.

—Moto-X Freestyle. 2007. (Torque: Action Sports Ser.). (Illus.). 24p. (J). (gr. 3-7). lib. bdg. 20.00 (***978-0-531-18492-9(7)***, Children's Pr.) Scholastic Library Publishing.

—Motocross Racing. 2007. (Torque: Action Sports Ser.). (Illus.). 24p. (J). (gr. 3-7). lib. bdg. 20.00 (***978-0-531-18491-2(9)***, Children's Pr.) Scholastic Library Publishing.

—Stock Cars. 2008. (Illus.). 24p. (J). lib. bdg. 19.95 (***978-1-60014-153-9(6)***) Bellwether Media.

Deady, Kathleen W. Dragsters. 2001. (Wild Rides! Ser.). (Illus.). 32p. (J). (gr. 3-4). lib. bdg. 21.26 (978-0-7368-0926-9(0), Capstone High-Interest Bks.) Capstone Pr., Inc.

DK Publishing Staff. My Terrific Race Car Book. 2007. 14p. (J). (ps-3). 12.99 (***978-0-7566-3184-0(X)***) Dorling Kindersley Publishing, Inc.

Doeden, Matt. At the Races. 2008. (***978-1-4296-0083-5(7)***) Capstone Pr., Inc.

—Behind the Wheel. 2008. (J). (***978-1-4296-0084-2(5)***) Capstone Pr., Inc.

—Dragsters. 2004. (Horsepower Ser.). (Illus.). 32p. (J). lib. bdg. 19.93 (978-0-7368-2735-5(8)) Capstone Pr., Inc.

—NASCAR's Wildest Wrecks. 2005. (NASCAR Racing Ser.). (Illus.). 32p. (J). 22.60 (978-0-7368-3775-0(2)) Capstone Pr., Inc.

—Stock Cars. 2005. (Blazers—Horsepower Ser.). (Illus.). 32p. (J). 19.93 (978-0-7368-3792-7(2)) Capstone Pr., Inc.

—Stock Cars. 2007. (Motor Mania Ser.). (Illus.). 48p. (J). (gr. 4-7). 26.60 (978-0-8225-3530-0(0)) Lerner Publishing Group.

Doeden, Matt. Under the Hood. 2008. (J). (***978-1-4296-0085-9(3)***) Capstone Pr., Inc.

Dooling, Michael. The Great Horseless Carriage Race. Dooling, Michael, illus. 2005. (Illus.). 32p. (J). (gr. k-3). tchr. ed. 16.95 (978-0-8234-1640-0(2)) Holiday Hse., Inc.

Dorling Kindersley Publishing Staff. Race Car. 2000. (978-0-606-17811-2(2)) Tandem Library Bks.

—Racing Car. 1998. (Wheelies Ser.). (Illus.). 12p. (J). (ps-3). bds. 5.99 (978-0-7894-3712-9(0)) Dorling Kindersley Publishing, Inc.

Dragsters. (Horsepower Ser.). 32p. (YA). 7.95 (978-0-7368-5217-3(4)) Capstone Pr., Inc.

Dubois, Muriel L. Pro Stock Cars. 2001. (Wild Rides! Ser.). (Illus.). 32p. (J). (gr. 3-4). lib. bdg. 21.26 (978-0-7368-0931-3(7), Capstone High-Interest Bks.) Capstone Pr., Inc.

Dune Buggy. 2004. (Illus.). (J). (978-1-59577-010-3(0)) Starfall Education.

Eagen, Rachel. Nascar. 2006. (Automania! Ser.). (Illus.). 32p. (J). (978-0-7787-3007-1(7)); (gr. 4-5). pap. (978-0-7787-3029-3(8)) Crabtree Publishing Co.

Egan, Erin. Hottest Race Cars. 2007. (Wild Wheels! Ser.). (Illus.). 48p. (J). (gr. 4-10). lib. bdg. 23.93 (***978-0-7660-2871-5(2)***) Enslow Pubs., Inc.

Ethan, Eric. Brickyard 400. Cameras in Action Staff, photos by. 1999. (NASCAR! Ser.). (Illus.). 24p. (J). (gr. 1 up). lib. bdg. 19.93 (978-0-8368-2136-9(X)) Stevens, Gareth Inc.

—Coca-Cola 600. Cameras in Action Staff, photos by. 1999. (NASCAR! Ser.). (Illus.). 24p. (J). (gr. 1 up). lib. bdg. 19.93 (978-0-8368-2137-6(8)) Stevens, Gareth Inc.

—Daytona 500. Cameras in Action Staff, photos by. 1999. (NASCAR! Ser.). (Illus.). 24p. (J). (gr. 1 up). lib. bdg. 19.93 (978-0-8368-2138-3(6)) Stevens, Gareth Inc.

—Miller 400. Cameras in Action Staff, photos by. 1999. (NASCAR! Ser.). (Illus.). 24p. (J). (gr. 1 up). lib. bdg. 19.93 (978-0-8368-2139-0(4)) Stevens, Gareth Inc.

—Nascar, 6 bks. Cameras in Action Staff, photos by. Incl. Brickyard 400. lib. bdg. 19.93 (978-0-8368-2136-9(X)); Coca-Cola 600. lib. bdg. 19.93 (978-0-8368-2137-6(8)); Daytona 500. lib. bdg. 19.93 (978-0-8368-2138-3(6)); Miller 400. lib. bdg. 19.93 (978-0-8368-2139-0(4)); Southern 500. lib. bdg. 19.93 (978-0-8368-2140-6(8)); Winston 500. lib. bdg. 19.93 (978-0-8368-2141-3(6)); 24p. (J). (gr. 1 up). 1999. (Illus.). 1999. Set lib. bdg. 119.60 (978-0-8368-2135-2(1)) Stevens, Gareth Inc.

—Southern 500. Cameras in Action Staff, photos by. 1999. (NASCAR! Ser.). (Illus.). 24p. (J). (gr. 1 up). lib. bdg. 19.93 (978-0-8368-2140-6(8)) Stevens, Gareth Inc.

—Winston 500. Cameras in Action Staff, photos by. 1999. (NASCAR! Ser.). (Illus.). 24p. (J). (gr. 1 up). lib. bdg. 19.93 (978-0-8368-2141-3(6)) Stevens, Gareth Inc.

Evans, Huw. The Cars of Gran Turismo. 2003. (Illus.). 96p. (YA). pap. 14.95 (978-0-7603-1495-1(0)) MBI Publishing Co. LLC.

Extreme Racing. 1998. (Hot Wheels Ser.). (Illus.). 32p. (J). (ps-1). pap. (978-0-7666-0101-7(3) , Honey Bear Bks.) Modern Publishing.

Fish, Bruce. Indy Car Racing. (Race Car Legends Ser.). (Illus.). (J). 2001. pap. 7.95 (978-0-7910-5846-6(8)); 2000. 64p. (gr. 4-7). 25.00 (978-0-7910-5845-9(X)) Facts On File, Inc. (Chelsea Hse.).

Foley, Cate. Let's Go to a Car Race. 2001. (gr. k-3). lib. bdg. 12.95 (978-0-613-58985-7(8)) Tandem Library Bks.

Fox, Martha Capwell. Car Racing. 2003. (History of Sports Ser.). (Illus.). 112p. (J). 29.95 (978-1-59018-354-0(1) , Lucent Bks.) Thomson Gale.

Gaines, Ann Graham. Famous Finishes. (Race Car Legends Ser.). (Illus.). 64p. 1999. (YA). (ps up). 28.00 (978-0-7910-5017-0(3)); 2005. (J). (gr. 4-8). lib. bdg. 25.00 (978-0-7910-8758-9(1)) Facts On File, Inc. (Chelsea Hse.).

Gifford, C. Racing Cars. rev. ed. 2005. 32p. (J). pap. 6.99 (978-0-7945-0838-8(3) , Usborne) EDC Publishing.

Gigliotti, Jim. Dale Jarrett: It Was Worth the Wait. 2002. (World of NASCAR Ser.). (Illus.). 32p. (J). (gr. 2-6). 25.64 (978-1-59187-002-9(X)) Child's World, Inc.

—Fantastic Finishes: NASCAR's Great Races. 2003. (World of NASCAR Ser.). (Illus.). 32p. (J). (gr. 2-6). 25.64 (978-1-59187-029-6(1)) Child's World, Inc.

Gigliotti, Jim. Hottest Dragsters & Funny Cars. 2007. (Wild Wheels! Ser.). (Illus.). 48p. (J). (gr. 4-10). lib. bdg. 23.93 (***978-0-7660-2870-8(4))** Enslow Pubs., Inc.

Gigliotti, Jim & Kelley, K. C. Authorized Handbook. 2004. (Nascar Ser.). (Illus.). 48p. (J). pap. 5.99 (978-0-7944-0414-7(6) , Reader's Digest Children's Bks.) Reader's Digest Children's Publishing, Inc.

Gilden, Mel. Chain Reaction. 2001. (NASCAR Racers Ser.: No. 6). (Illus.). 112p. (J). (gr. 2-6). pap. 4.50 (978-0-06-107200-0(1)) HarperCollins Pubs.

—NASCAR Racers: Lightning Pace. 2001. (NASCAR Racers Ser.). 40p. (J). (gr. 1-5). pap. 12.99 (978-0-06-107192-8(7) , Harper Entertainment) HarperCollins Pubs.

Gould, Robert. Racers. Gould, Robert, photos by. 2005. (Big Stuff Ser.). (Illus.). 16p. (J). bds. 7.95 (978-1-929945-52-8(3)) Big Guy Bks., Inc.

Graham, Ian. The Best Book of Speed Machines. 2002. (Best Book of... Ser.). (Illus.). 32p. (J). (gr. k-3). tchr. ed. 12.95 (978-0-7534-5436-7(X) , Kingfisher) Houghton Mifflin Co. Trade & Reference Div.

—Race Cars. 2003. (Designed for Success Ser.). 32p. pap. 7.50 (978-1-4034-3359-6(3)); (Illus.). (J). 24.22 (978-1-4034-0771-9(1)) Heinemann Library.

—The Search for the Ultimate Race Car. 2005. (Science Quest Ser.). (Illus.). 32p. (J). lib. bdg. 24.67 (978-0-8368-4558-7(7)) Stevens, Gareth Inc.

Gunn, Richard. Racing Cars. 2006. (Cool Wheels Ser.). (Illus.). 32p. (J). lib. bdg. (978-0-8368-6829-6(3)) Stevens, Gareth Inc.

Gutelle, Andrew. Stock Car Kings. 2001. (gr. 3-6). lib. bdg. 11.80 (978-0-613-35623-7(3)) Tandem Library Bks.

Healy, Nick. Enduro Racing. 2005. (Illus.). 32p. (J). (gr. 2 up). lib. bdg. 22.60 (978-0-7368-4364-5(7)) Capstone Pr., Inc.

Herran, Joe & Thomas, Ron. Formula One Car Racing. 2002. (Action Sports Ser.). (Illus.). 32p. (gr. 4-8). 28.00 (978-0-7910-7000-0(X) , Chelsea Hse.) Facts On File, Inc.

Herzog, Brad. R Is for Race: A Stock Car Alphabet. Bready, Jane Gilltrap, illus. 2006. 40p. (J). (gr. k-5). 16.95 (978-1-58536-272-1(7)) Sleeping Bear Pr.

Hodges, David W. Classic Racing Cars, Vol. 2. 1999. (Encyclopedia of Custom & Classic Transportation Ser.). (Illus.). 112p. (YA). 31.95 (978-0-7910-4999-0(X) , Chelsea Hse.) Facts On File, Inc.

Hofer, Charles. Race Cars. 2008. (J). lib. bdg. (***978-1-4042-4175-6(2)** , PowerKids Pr.) Rosen Publishing Group, Inc., The.

Huff, Richard M. Demolition Derby. 1999. (Race Car Legends Ser.). (Illus.). 64p. (YA). (gr. 4-7). 25.00 (978-0-7910-5416-1(0)); pap. 25.00 (978-0-7910-5682-0(1)) Facts On File, Inc. (Chelsea Hse.).

—Demolition Derby. 2000. (J). (978-0-606-19344-3(8)); (gr. 5-8). lib. bdg. 16.40 (978-0-613-20806-2(4)) Tandem Library Bks.

—History of Nascar. 1999. (Race Car Legends Ser.). (Illus.). 64p. (YA). (gr. 4-7). 25.00 (978-0-7910-5414-7(4) , Chelsea Hse.) Facts On File, Inc.

Indy Cars. (Horsepower Ser.). 32p. (YA). 7.95 (978-0-7368-6171-7(8)) Capstone Pr., Inc.

Jefferis. Race Cars, 6 bks., Set. 2003. mass mkt. 48.30 (978-1-4109-0276-4(5)) Raintree.

—Racing Cars. 2004. (Mean Machines Ser.). (Illus.). 64p. (J). 32.79 (978-1-4109-0556-7(X)); pap. 8.95 (978-1-4109-0830-8(5)) Harcourt Schl. Pubs.

—Racing Cars 6-Pack. 2004. (Illus.). (J). pap. 48.35 (978-1-4109-0835-3(6)) Harcourt Schl. Pubs.

Jefferis, David. Race Cars. 2003. (gr. 3-6). lib. bdg. 16.40 (978-0-613-78222-7(4)) Tandem Library Bks.

—Racing Cars. 2001. (Monster Machines Ser.). (Illus.). 32p. (J). (ps-3). lib. bdg. 25.69 (978-0-7398-2880-9(0)) Raintree.

Jeffries. Race Cars. 2003. (Monster Machines Ser.). (Illus.). 32p. (J). pap. 7.95 (978-1-4109-0057-9(6)) Raintree.

Johnstone, Michael. NASCAR. 2005. (Need for Speed Ser.). (Illus.). 32p. (gr. 3-5). lib. bdg. 23.93 (978-0-8225-0389-7(1)) Lerner Publishing Group.

—NASCAR. 2002. (gr. 5-8). lib. bdg. 16.40 (978-0-613-46155-9(X)) Tandem Library Bks.

—Nascar. 2003. (Need for Speed Ser.). (Illus.). 32p. (YA). (gr. 3-6). 7.95 (978-0-8225-0392-7(1) , Carolrhoda Bks.) Lerner Publishing Group.

Kalman, Bobbie & Crossingham, John. Extreme Motocross. 2003. (Extreme Sports - No Limits Ser.). (Illus.). 32p. (J). pap. (978-0-7787-1716-4(X)) Crabtree Publishing Co.

Kelley, K. C. Hottest NASCAR Machines. 2007. (Wild Wheels! Ser.). (Illus.). 48p. (J). (gr. 4-10). lib. bdg. 23.93 (***978-0-7660-2869-2(0))** Enslow Pubs., Inc.

Kelley, K. C. Racing to the Finish: Teamwork at 200 Mph! 2005. (NASCAR Reader Book - Level 2 Ser.). (Illus.). 32p. (J). pap. 3.99 (978-0-7944-0603-5(3) , Reader's Digest Children's Bks.) Reader's Digest Children's Publishing, Inc.

Kulling, Monica. Eat My Dust! Henry Ford's First Race. Walz, Richard, illus. 2004. (Step into Reading Ser.). 48p. (gr. 1-3). (J). pap. 3.99 (978-0-375-81510-2(4)); (YA). lib. bdg. 11.99 (978-0-375-91510-9(9)) Random Hse. Children's Bks. (Random Hse. Bks. for Young Readers).

LaDow, William. Conversations with a Winner — the Ray Nichels Story. 2004. 54.95 (978-0-9723623-0-6(4)) LaDow Publishing.

Latham, Donna. Superfast Trucks. 2006. (Ultimate Speed Ser.). (Illus.). 32p. (J). lib. bdg. 25.27 (978-1-59716-253-1(1)) Bearport Publishing Co., Inc.

Levy, Janey. Dale Earnhardt Jr. 2007. 48p. (J). (978-0-531-16805-9(0)) Children's Pr., Ltd.

—Dale Earnhardt, Jr. 2007. 48p. (J). pap. (978-0-531-18713-5(6)) Children's Pr., Ltd.

—Racing Through History. 2006. (High Interest Books). (Illus.). 48p. (J). (978-0-531-16808-0(5) , Children's Pr.) Scholastic Library Publishing.

—Racing Through History: Stock Cars Then to Now. 2007. (High Interest Books). (Illus.). 48p. (J). (***978-1-4287-2914-8(3))** Children's Pr., Ltd.

—Racing Through History: Stock Cars Then to Now. 2007. (High Interest Books). (Illus.). 48p. (J). pap. (978-0-531-18716-6(0) , Children's Pr.) Scholastic Library Publishing.

Mara, W. P. Pro Stock Car Racing. 1998. (MotorSports Ser.). (Illus.). 48p. (J). (gr. 3-4). lib. bdg. 21.26 (978-0-7368-0025-9(5) , Capstone High-Interest Bks.) Capstone Pr., Inc.

Martin, Michael. The World's Fastest Cars. 2006. (Edge Books, the World's Top Ten). (Illus.). 32p. (J). (978-0-7368-5455-9(X)) Capstone Pr., Inc.

Mattern, Joanne. Behind Every Great Driver: Stock Car Teams. 2007. (Illus.). 48p. (J). pap. (978-0-531-18712-8(8) , Children's Pr.) Scholastic Library Publishing.

Mattern Joanne. Behind Every Great Driver Stock Car Teams. 2006. (Illus.). 48p. (J). (978-0-531-16804-2(2) , Children's Pr.) Scholastic Library Publishing.

Mattern, Joanne. Big Bucks. 2006. (Illus.). 48p. (J). (978-0-531-16807-3(7) , Children's Pr.) Scholastic Library Publishing.

—Big Bucks: The Fast Cash of Stock Car Racing. 2007. (Illus.). 48p. (J). pap. (978-0-531-18715-9(2) , Children's Pr.) Scholastic Library Publishing.

—Track Trucks. 2007. (Stock Car Racing Ser.). (Illus.). 48p. (J). pap. (978-0-531-18717-3(9)); (***978-1-4287-2959-9(3))** Children's Pr., Ltd.

—Track Trucks. 2006. (High Interest Books). (Illus.). 48p. (J). (978-0-531-16809-7(3) , Children's Pr.) Scholastic Library Publishing.

Maurer, Tracy. NASCAR Racers. 2003. (Illus.). 48p. (J). 29.93 (978-1-58952-751-5(8)) Rourke Publishing, LLC.

McGuire, Anne. Burnin' Rubber: Behind the Scenes in Stock Car Racing. 2000. (Illus.). (J). 15.75 (978-0-606-18280-5(2)) Tandem Library Bks.

—History of NASCAR. 1999. (Race Car Legends Ser.). (Illus.). 64p. (YA). (gr. 3 up). pap. 25.00 (978-0-7910-5680-6(5) , Chelsea Hse.) Facts On File, Inc.

—History of NASCAR. 2000. (Illus.). (J). (978-0-606-18034-4(6)) Tandem Library Bks.

Mead, Sue. Off-Road Racing. 2000. (Race Car Legends Ser.). (Illus.). 64p. (J). (gr. 4-7). 28.00 (978-0-7910-5851-0(4) , Chelsea Hse.) Facts On File, Inc.

—Off Road Racing. rev. collector's ed. 2005. (Race Car Legends Ser.). (Illus.). 72p. (J). (gr. 4-8). lib. bdg. 25.00 (978-0-7910-8690-2(9) , Chelsea Hse.) Facts On File, Inc.

Mello, T. The Pit Crew. rev. ed. 2007. (Race Car Legends Ser.). 72p. (J). (gr. 5-8). 25.00 (978-0-7910-8665-0(8) , Chelsea Hse.) Facts On File, Inc.

Mello, Tara Baukus. Need for Speed. 2000. (Race Car Legends Ser.). (Illus.). 64p. (J). (gr. 4-7). 25.00 (978-0-7910-6015-5(2) , Chelsea Hse.) Facts On File, Inc.

Mezzanotte, Jim. Flat Track. 2006. (Illus.). 24p. (J). lib. bdg. 22.00 (978-0-8368-6421-2(2)) Stevens, Gareth Inc.

—Hillclimb. 2006. (Illus.). 24p. (J). lib. bdg. 22.00 (978-0-8368-6422-9(0)) Stevens, Gareth Inc.

Miller, Timothy. Vroom! Motoring into the Wild World of Racing. 2006. (Illus.). 58p. (YA). (gr. 4 up). pap. 17.95 (978-0-88776-755-5(9)) Tundra Bks., Inc./Livres Toundra, Inc. CAN. *Dist:* Random Hse., Inc.

Moore, Davey, et al. Create 'n' Race Masterbuilders. abr. ed. 2000. (LEGO Masterbuilders Ser.). (Illus.). 64p. (J). pap. 19.99 (978-1-903276-19-8(5)) Lego Media International, Inc.

Mountain Bike Mania: Individual Title Six-Packs. (Action Packs Ser.). 104p. (gr. 3-5). 44.00 (978-0-7635-2999-4(0)) Rigby Education.

My Racing Car. 2002. (Chunky Vehicle Shaped Boards Ser.). (J). bds. 4.98 (978-0-7525-4772-5(0)) Parragon, Inc.

NASCAR Micro Cars: Start Your Engines! 2002. 18p. (J). (978-0-439-45567-1(7)) Scholastic, Inc.

NASCAR Racing. 2005. (Illus.). (J). (gr. 3-4). lib. bdg. 180.80 (978-0-7368-3822-1(8)) Capstone Pr., Inc.

Norman, Tony. Auto Racing. 2006. (Illus.). 32p. (J). 24.67 (978-0-8368-6365-9(8)) Stevens, Gareth Inc.

Off-Road Truck Racing, 6 vols. (gr. 4 up). 39.95 (978-0-7368-8962-9(0)) Red Brick Learning.

One Checkered Flag. (Know Your Numbers Ser.). 24p. (J). 7.95 (978-1-4048-1121-8(4)) Picture Window Bks.

Orme, David. Formula One. 2007. (Trailblazers Ser.). (Illus.). 36p. pap. 7.95 (***978-1-84167-428-5(1))** Ransom Publishing Ltd. GBR. *Dist:* International Publishers Marketing.

Owens, Thomas S. Collecting Stock Car Racing Memorabilia. 2001. (Illus.). 80p. (gr. 5-8). lib. bdg. 26.90 (978-0-7613-1853-8(4) , Millbrook Pr.) Lerner Publishing Group.

Owens, Tom. Stock Car Racing. 2000. (Game Plan Ser.). (Illus.). 64p. (J). (gr. 5-8). lib. bdg. 26.90 (978-0-7613-1374-8(5) , Twenty-First Century Bks.) Lerner Publishing Group.

Oxlade, Chris. This Is My Racing Car. 2007. (J). (***978-1-59771-107-4(1))** Sea-To-Sea Pubns.

Parr, Ann. The Allisons. 2007. (Race Car Legends Ser.). 80p. (J). (gr. 5-8). 25.00 (978-0-7910-8694-0(1) , Chelsea Hse.) Facts On File, Inc.

—Lowriders. rev. collector's ed. 2005. (Race Car Legends Ser.). (Illus.). 64p. (J). (gr. 4-7). lib. bdg. 25.00 (978-0-7910-8673-5(9) , Chelsea Hse.) Facts On File, Inc.

Parsont, Meg. Race Car. Curti, Anna, illus. 1999. (Go Bks.). 12p. (ps-k). 5.95 (978-0-7892-0545-2(9)) Abbeville Pr., Inc.

Pearce, Al. Famous Tracks. collector's ed. 2005. (Race Car Legends Ser.). (Illus.). 77p. (J). (gr. 4-8). lib. bdg. 25.00 (978-0-7910-8692-6(5) , Chelsea Hse.) Facts On File, Inc.

Performance Racing Car. 2004. (Press-Out & Build Ser.). (Illus.). 24p. (J). per. (978-1-84229-722-3(8)) Top That! Publishing PLC.

Peterson, Brian C. Mark Martin: Perennial Contender. 2003. (World of NASCAR Ser.). (Illus.). 32p. (J). (gr. 2-6). 25.64 (978-1-59187-031-9(3)) Child's World, Inc.

Piehl, Janet. Formula One Race Cars. (Motor Mania Ser.). (Illus.). (J). 2007. 48p. (gr. 4-7). 26.60 (978-0-8225-5929-0(3) , Lerner Pubns.); 2004. 32p. (gr. k-2). lib. bdg. 22.60 (978-0-8225-0693-5(9)) Lerner Publishing Group.

Pimm, Nancy Roe. Indy 500: the Inside Track. 2005. (Illus.). 64p. (J). (gr. 4-12). pap. 8.95 (978-1-58196-023-5(9)) Darby Creek Publishing.

Pitt, Matthew. Drag Racer. 2001. (gr. 7-12). lib. bdg. 15.25 (978-0-613-52021-8(1)) Tandem Library Bks.

—Formula One. 2001. (Built for Speed Ser.). (Illus.). 48p. (gr. 7-12). (J). 23.00 (978-0-516-23160-0(X)); (YA). pap. 6.95 (978-0-516-23263-8(0)) Scholastic Library Publishing. (Children's Pr.).

—Formula One. 2001. (gr. 7-12). lib. bdg. 15.25 (978-0-613-52056-0(4)) Tandem Library Bks.

Poolos, J. Travis Pastrana. 2005. (Illus.). 64p. (J). (gr. 5-8). lib. bdg. 26.50 (978-1-4042-0071-5(1)) Rosen Publishing Group, Inc., The.

Poolos, Jamie. Wild about Dragsters. 2007. (J). lib. bdg. (***978-1-4042-3792-6(5)** , PowerKids Pr.) Rosen Publishing Group, Inc., The.

—Wild about Lowriders. 2008. (J). lib. bdg. (***978-1-4042-3789-6(5)** , PowerKids Pr.) Rosen Publishing Group, Inc., The.

Pro Stock Car Racing, 6 vols. (gr. 4 up). 39.95 (978-0-7368-8964-3(7)) Red Brick Learning.

Raby, Philip. Racing Cars. (Need for Speed Ser.). (Illus.). 32p. (gr. 3-6). 2003. (J). pap. 7.95 (978-0-8225-9853-4(1)); 1999. lib. bdg. 23.93 (978-0-8225-2487-8(2)) Lerner Publishing Group.

—Racing Cars. 1999. (gr. 5-8). lib. bdg. 16.40 (978-0-613-81319-8(7)) Tandem Library Bks.

Race Cars: Individual Title Six-Packs. (Sails Literacy Ser.). (gr. 1-2). 36.00 (978-0-7578-4024-1(8)) Rigby Education.

Rex, Michael. My Race Car. rev. ed. 2000. (Illus.). 32p. (J). (ps-2). 16.95 (978-0-8050-6101-7(0) , Holt, Henry & Co. Bks. For Young Readers) Holt, Henry & Co.

Richards, Jon, text. Race Cars. 2003. (Microfacts Ser.). (Illus.). 48p. (J). (978-0-439-62757-3(5)) Scholastic, Inc.

A Ride, 6 Packs. (Sails Literacy Ser.). 16p. (gr. k up). 27.00 (978-0-7635-4386-0(1)) Rigby Education.

Riley, Gail Blasser. NASCAR Rules. 2008. (J). (***978-1-4296-1288-3(6))** Capstone Pr., Inc.

Savage, Jeff. Dale Earnhardt Jr. 2005. (Illus.). 32p. (J). (gr. 4-7). pap. 5.95 (978-0-8225-2953-8(X)) Lerner Publishing Group.

—Danica Patrick. 2006. (Amazing Athletes Ser.). (Illus.). 32p. (J). pap. 5.95 (978-0-8225-6012-8(7) , First Avenue Editions) Lerner Publishing Group.

—Demolition Derby Cars. 2003. (Wild Rides! Ser.). (Illus.). 32p. (J). (gr. 3-4). lib. bdg. 21.26 (978-0-7368-1516-1(3) , Capstone High-Interest Bks.) Capstone Pr., Inc.

—Rally Cars. 2004. (Wild Rides! Ser.). (Illus.). 32p. (J). lib. bdg. 16.95 (978-0-7368-2431-6(6)) Capstone Pr., Inc.

—Travis Pastrana. 2006. (Amazing Athletes Ser.). (Illus.). 32p. (J). 22.60 (978-0-8225-3428-0(2) , Lerner Pubns.) Lerner Publishing Group.

—The World's Fastest Stock Cars. 2003. (Built for Speed Ser.). (Illus.). 48p. (J). (gr. 3-4). lib. bdg. 21.26 (978-0-7368-1503-1(1) , Capstone High-Interest Bks.) Capstone Pr., Inc.

Schaefer, A. R. The Brickyard 400. 2004. (Edge Books NASCAR Racing). (Illus.). 32p. (J). 16.95 (978-0-7368-2422-4(7)) Capstone Pr., Inc.

—Bristol Motor Speedway. 2007. (Edge Books NASCAR Racing). (Illus.). 32p. (J). 23.93 (978-0-7368-4376-8(0)) Capstone Pr., Inc.

—Dale Earnhardt. 2006. (Edge Books NASCAR Racing). (Illus.). 32p. (J). (978-0-7368-4377-5(9)) Capstone Pr., Inc.

—The Daytona 500. 2004. (Edge Books NASCAR Racing). (Illus.). 32p. (J). 16.95 (978-0-7368-2423-1(5)) Capstone Pr., Inc.

—Formula One Cars. 2004. (Wild Rides! Ser.). (Illus.). 32p. (J). lib. bdg. 22.60 (978-0-7368-2724-9(2)) Capstone Pr., Inc.

—The History of NASCAR. 2005. (NASCAR Racing Ser.). (Illus.). 32p. (J). 22.60 (978-0-7368-3774-3(4)) Capstone Pr., Inc.

—Sprint Cars. 2004. (Wild Rides! Ser.). (Illus.). 32p. (J). lib. bdg. 22.60 (978-0-7368-2727-0(7)) Capstone Pr., Inc.

—Talladega Superspeedway. 2007. (Edge Books NASCAR Racing). (Illus.). 32p. (J). 23.93 (978-0-7368-4379-9(5)) Capstone Pr., Inc.

Schaefer, Adam R. Racing with the Pit Crew. 2005. (NASCAR Racing Ser.). (Illus.). 32p. (J). (ps-9). lib. bdg. 22.60 (978-0-7368-3776-7(0)) Capstone Pr., Inc.

Schuette, Sarah L. Formula One Cars. 2007. (Blazers—Horsepower Ser.). (Illus.). 32p. (J). 19.93 (978-0-7368-6448-0(2)) Capstone Pr., Inc.

Seate, Mike. Streetbike Extreme. 2002. (gr. 7-12). lib. bdg. 30.35 (978-0-613-60620-2(5)) Tandem Library Bks.

Seivert, Terri. James Stewart. 2005. (Illus.). 32p. (J). (gr. 2 up). lib. bdg. 22.60 (978-0-7368-4365-2(5)) Capstone Pr., Inc.

Sessler, Peter & Sessler, N. Drag Cars. 1999. (Illus.). 24p. (J). (gr. 2-6). lib. bdg. 25.64 (978-1-57103-280-5(0)) Rourke Publishing, LLC.

—Sprint Cars. 1999. (Off to the Races Ser.). (Illus.). 24p. (J). (gr. 2-6). lib. bdg. 25.64 (978-1-57103-283-6(5)) Rourke Publishing, LLC.

—Stock Cars. 1999. (Illus.). 24p. (J). (gr. 2-6). lib. bdg. 25.64 (978-1-57103-284-3(3)) Rourke Publishing, LLC.

Sexton, Susan. Stock Car Racing: Running with the Big Boys. 2003. (Cover-To-Cover Books). (Illus.). 64p. (J). pap. (978-0-7891-5922-9(8)); (gr. 4-7). lib. bdg. 17.95 (978-0-7569-1189-8(3)) Perfection Learning Corp.

Shifter Karts: High-Speed Go-Karts. (Horsepower Ser.). 32p. (YA). 7.95 (978-0-7368-5213-5(1)) Capstone Pr., Inc.

Simon and Schuster Staff. NASCAR Jeff Gordon: Stock Car Superstar. 2005. (Nascar Ser.). (J). 59.94 (978-0-7944-0344-7(1)); 59.94 (978-0-7944-0345-4(X)) Reader's Digest Children's Publishing, Inc. (Reader's Digest Children's Bks.).

—NASCAR Tony Stewart: Racing to Victory Lane. 2005. (Nascar Ser.). (J). 59.95 (978-0-7944-0346-1(8)); 59.95 (978-0-7944-0347-8(6)) Reader's Digest Children's Publishing, Inc. (Reader's Digest Children's Bks.).

Sports Illustrated for Kids Editors. Race Day: Behind the Scenes at NASCAR. 2004. (Sports Illustrated for Kids Ser.). (Illus.). 96p. pap. 9.99 (978-1-931933-65-0(0)) Time, Inc. Home Entertainment.

Starke, John. Speed Machines: Mission Xtreme 3D. 2004. (Mission Xtreme 3D Ser.). (Illus.). 18p. (J). pap. 5.95 (978-1-902626-50-5(8)) Red Bird Publishing GBR. *Dist:* Weatherhill, Inc.

Stewart, Mark. The Indy 500. Kennedy, Mike, ed. 2003. (Watts History of Sports Ser.). (Illus.). 128p. (J). 34.50 (978-0-531-11954-9(8) , Watts, Franklin) Scholastic Library Publishing.

Stewart, Mark & Kennedy, Mike. Behind the Wheel. 2008. (Science of NASCAR Ser.). (J). lib. bdg. 27.93 (***978-0-8225-8737-8(8)** , Lerner Pubns.) Lerner Publishing Group.

Stille, Darlene R. Race Cars. 2001. (Transportation Ser.). (Illus.). 32p. (J). (gr. 1 up). lib. bdg. 19.93 (978-0-7565-0149-5(0)) Compass Point Bks.

Stock Car Racing, 6 vols. 2006. (Illus.). (YA). (gr. 7-12). 144.00 (***978-0-531-12472-7(X))** Scholastic Library Publishing.

Stock Cars. (Illus.). 24p. (978-2-7643-0250-7(9)) Phidal Publishing, Inc./Editions Phidal, Inc.

Sullivan, George. Burnin' Rubber: Behind the Scenes in Stock Car Racing. (Illus.). 48p. (gr. 5-9). 2000. (Single Titles Ser.: 8). pap. (978-0-7613-1348-9(6)); 1998. lib. bdg. 22.90 (978-0-7613-1256-7(0)) Lerner Publishing Group. (Millbrook Pr.).

Teitelbaum, Michael. Motorsphere to the Max. 2000. (NASCAR Racers Ser.). (J). (gr. 1-5). pap. 7.95 (978-0-06-107193-5(5) , Harper Entertainment) HarperCollins Pubs.

Thompson, Luke. Sprint Car. 2001. (gr. 7-12). lib. bdg. 15.25 (978-0-613-52186-4(2)) Tandem Library Bks.

Werther, Scott P. Dragsters. 2002. (Reading Power Ser.). (Illus.). 24p. (J). (gr. 1). lib. bdg. 17.25 (978-0-8239-5953-2(8) , PowerKids Pr.) Rosen Publishing Group, Inc., The.

—Dragsters: Individual Title Six-Packs. (On Deck Ser.). 24p. (gr. 4-5). 35.00 (978-0-7578-1045-9(4)) Rigby Education.

West, David. Why Things Don't Work. 2006. (Illus.). 32p. (J). (978-1-4109-2555-8(2)) Steck-Vaughn.

Whitecap Books Staff. Racing Cars. 2000. (Investigate Ser.). (Illus.). 64p. (J). (gr. 1-7). pap. 3.95 (978-1-55285-067-1(6)) Whitecap Bks., Ltd. CAN. *Dist:* Firefly Bks., Ltd.

Whiting, Sue & Book Company Staff. The Great Race. Mosley, Dudley, illus. 2002. (Button Bks.). 12p. (J). bds. (978-1-74047-163-3(6)) Book Co. Publishing Pty, Ltd., The.

Woods, Bob. Dirt Track Daredevils: The History of NASCAR. 2002. (World of NASCAR Ser.). (Illus.). 32p. (J). (gr. 2-6). 25.64 (978-1-59187-004-3(6)) Child's World, Inc.

—Earning a Ride: How to Become a NASCAR Driver. 2003. (World of NASCAR Ser.). (Illus.). 32p. (J). (gr. 2-6). 25.64 (978-1-59187-028-9(3)) Child's World, Inc.

—Hottest Motorcycles. 2007. (Wild Wheels! Ser.). (Illus.). 48p. (J). (gr. 4-10). lib. bdg. 23.93 ***(978-0-7660-2874-6(7))*** Enslow Pubs., Inc.

—Hottest Sports Cars. 2007. (Wild Wheels! Ser.). (Illus.). 48p. (J). (gr. 4-10). lib. bdg. 23.93 ***(978-0-7660-2873-9(9))*** Enslow Pubs., Inc.

Woods, Bob. Live from the Racetrack: NASCAR on TV. 2003. (World of NASCAR Ser.). (Illus.). 32p. (J). (gr. 2-6). 25.64 (978-1-59187-035-7(6)) Child's World, Inc.

Wukovits, John F. Auto Racing. 1999. (Composite Guide Ser.). (Illus.). 64p. (YA). (gr. 4-7). 28.00 (978-0-7910-4722-4(9) , Chelsea Hse.) Facts On File, Inc.

Youngblood, Ed. Superbike Racing. 2000. (Motorcycles Ser.). (Illus.). 48p. (J). (gr. 3-4). lib. bdg. 21.26 (978-0-7368-0478-3(1) , Capstone High-Interest Bks.) Capstone Pr., Inc.

Zuehlke, Jeffrey. Drag Racers. 2008. (Motor Mania Ser.). (J). lib. bdg. 26.60 ***(978-0-8225-7287-9(7)*** , Lerner Pubns.) Lerner Publishing Group.

—Supercross. 2008. (Motor Mania Ser.). (J). lib. bdg. 26.60 ***(978-0-8225-7286-2(9))*** Lerner Publishing Group.

AUTOMOBILE RACING—BIOGRAPHY

Allen, Kenny. Kurt Busch. 2007. (NASCAR Champions Ser.). (Illus.). 24p. (J). lib. bdg. (978-1-4042-3457-4(8) , PowerKids Pr.) Rosen Publishing Group, Inc., The.

Anderson, Wayne A. Tony Stewart: NASCAR Driver. 2006. (Illus.). 48p. (J). (gr. 5-8). lib. bdg. 26.50 (978-1-4042-0984-8(0)) Rosen Publishing Group, Inc., The.

Armentrout, David & Armentrout, Patricia. Dale Jarrett: In the Fast Lane. 2007. (In the Fast Lane Ser.). (Illus.). 24p. (J). (978-1-60044-216-2(1)) Rourke Publishing, LLC.

—Kurt Busch: In the Fast Lane. 2007. (In the Fast Lane Ser.). (J). (978-1-60044-218-6(8)) Rourke Publishing, LLC.

—Matt Kenseth: In the Fast Lane. 2007. (Illus.). 24p. (J). (978-1-60044-219-3(6)) Rourke Publishing, LLC.

Armentrout, David & Armentrout, Patricia, trs. Jeff Gordon. 2003. (Discover the Life of a Sports Star Ser.). (Illus.). 24p. (J). 20.64 (978-1-58952-653-2(8)) Rourke Publishing, LLC.

Bach, Julie S. Jeff Gordon. (Illus.). 32p. 2001. (gr. 3). pap. 8.95 (978-0-89812-324-1(0) , Creative Paperbacks); 2000. (J). pap. 10.60 (978-0-89812-025-7(X) , Creative Paperbacks); 1998. (YA). (gr. 4-7). pap. (978-0-88682-939-1(9) , Creative Education) Creative Co., The.

Basen, Ryan. Tony Stewart: Rocket on the Racetrack. 2008. (Heroes of Racing Ser.). 128p. (J). (gr. 5-9). lib. bdg. 31.93 ***(978-0-7660-2998-9(0))*** Enslow Pubs., Inc.

Benson, Michael. Dale Earnhardt. 1999. (Race Car Legends Ser.). (Illus.). 64p. (J). (gr. 4-7). pap. 25.00 (978-0-7910-5756-8(9) , Chelsea Hse.) Facts On File, Inc.

Bentley, Karen & Gluck, Jeff, texts. The Unsers. rev. collector's ed. 2005. (Race Car Legends Ser.). (Illus.). 72p. (J). (gr. 4-7). lib. bdg. 25.00 (978-0-7910-8764-0(6) , Chelsea Hse.) Facts On File, Inc.

Book & Car. 2004. (Nascar Ser.). 24p. (J). 9.99 (978-0-7944-0410-9(3)); 9.99 (978-0-7944-0409-3(X)) Reader's Digest Children's Publishing, Inc. (Reader's Digest Children's Bks.).

Brock, Ted. Fast Families: Racing Together Through Life. 2002. (World of NASCAR Ser.). (Illus.). 32p. (J). (gr. 2-6). 25.64 (978-1-59187-005-0(4)) Child's World, Inc.

Buckley, James. The Starting Line: Life As a NASCAR Rookie. 2003. (World of NASCAR Ser.). (Illus.). 32p. (J). (gr. 2-6). 25.64 (978-1-59187-034-0(8)) Child's World, Inc.

Christopher, Matt. On the Track with... Jeff Gordon. 2001. (Matt Christopher Sports Biographies Ser.). (Illus.). 128p. (J). (gr. 3-7). pap. 4.99 (978-0-316-13469-9(4)) Little, Brown Bks. for Young Readers.

—On the Track with... Jeff Gordon. (Matt Christopher Sports Biographies Ser.). 2001. (Illus.). (J). (978-0-606-21367-7(8)); 2000. (gr. 3-6). lib. bdg. 12.95 (978-0-613-35647-3(0)) Tandem Library Bks.

de Leon, Mauricio Velazquez, tr. Dale Earnhardt, Jr., Piloto de Nascar. 2002. (Coleccion Power Kids). (SPA & ENG., Illus.). 24p. (J). (gr. k-2). lib. bdg. 17.25 (978-0-8239-6146-7(X) , RN31315, Buenas Letra) Rosen Publishing Group, Inc., The.

Doeden, Matt. Dale Earnhardt Jr. 2005. (Sports Heroes & Legends Ser.). (Illus.). 106p. (J). (gr. 3-7). 27.93 (978-0-8225-3067-1(8) , Lerner Pubns.) Lerner Publishing Group.

Doeden, Matt. NASCAR's Greatest Moments. 2008. (J). ***(978-1-4296-0086-6(1))*** Capstone Pr., Inc.

Dutton, Monte. Jeff Gordon: The Racer. 2000. (gr. 7-12). lib. bdg. 22.20 (978-0-613-32714-5(4)) Tandem Library Bks.

Farmer, Emily. Jimmie Johnson: NASCAR Driver. 2006. (Behind the Wheel Ser.). (Illus.). 48p. (YA). (gr. 5-8). lib. bdg. 26.50 (978-1-4042-0981-7(6)) Rosen Publishing Group, Inc., The.

Figorito, Marcus. Matt Kenseth. 2006. (NASCAR Champions Ser.). (Illus.). 24p. (J). lib. bdg. (978-1-4042-3458-1(6) , PowerKids Pr.) Rosen Publishing Group, Inc., The.

Fleischman, Bill. Jimmie Johnson. collector's ed. 2005. (Race Car Legends Ser.). (Illus.). 64p. (J). (gr. 4-8). lib. bdg. 25.00 (978-0-7910-8672-8(0) , Chelsea Hse.) Facts On File, Inc.

Ford, June. Jeff Burton. 2000. (Race Car Legends Ser.). (Illus.). 64p. (J). (gr. 4-7). 28.00 (978-0-7910-5847-3(6) , Chelsea Hse.) Facts On File, Inc.

Gaines, Ann Graham. Famous Finishes. 1999. (Race Car Legends Ser.). (Illus.). 64p. (YA). (ps up). 28.00 (978-0-7910-5017-0(3) , Chelsea Hse.) Facts On File, Inc.

Gigliotti, Jim. Dale Earnhardt, Jr: Tragedy & Triumph. 2003. (World of NASCAR Ser.). (Illus.). 32p. (J). (gr. 2-6). 25.64 (978-1-59187-027-2(5)) Child's World, Inc.

Gitlin, Marty. Jimmie Johnson: Racing Champ. 2008. (Heroes of Racing Ser.). (Illus.). 128p. (J). (gr. 5-9). lib. bdg. 31.93 ***(978-0-7660-2999-6(9))*** Enslow Pubs., Inc.

Gluck, Jeff, text. Jeff Burton. rev. collector's ed. 2005. (Race Car Legends Ser.). (Illus.). 64p. (J). (gr. 4-8). lib. bdg. 25.00 (978-0-7910-8699-5(2) , Chelsea Hse.) Facts On File, Inc.

Hand, Jimmie, told to. Jimmy Spencer: Don't Ever Quit! 2004. (YA). pap. 19.95 (978-0-9754755-0-8(9)) Strong Corner Publishing, LCC.

Hubbard-Brown, Janet. The Labonte Brothers. (Race Car Legends Ser.). (Illus.). 64p. (YA). 1999. (gr. 2-5). 28.00 (978-0-7910-5019-4(X)); 1998. (gr. 3 up). pap. 7.95 (978-0-7910-5758-2(5)) Facts On File, Inc. (Chelsea Hse.).

Huff, Richard M. The Jarretts. 1998. (Race Car Legends Ser.). (Illus.). 64p. (YA). (gr. 3 up). pap. 7.95 (978-0-7910-5759-9(3) , Chelsea Hse.) Facts On File, Inc.

James, Lincoln. Dale Jarrett. 2007. (NASCAR Champions Ser.). (Illus.). 24p. (J). lib. bdg. (978-1-4042-3459-8(4) , PowerKids Pr.) Rosen Publishing Group, Inc., The.

Kirkpatrick, Rob. Dale Earnhardt, Jr. NASCAR Road Racer. 2000. (Reading Power Ser.). (Illus.). 24p. (J). (gr. 1). lib. bdg. 17.25 (978-0-8239-5545-9(1) , PKDAEA, PowerKids Pr.) Rosen Publishing Group, Inc., The.

—Dale Earnhardt Jr: NASCAR Road Racer. rev. ed. 2003. (Buenas Letras Bilingual Ser.). 24p. (J). lib. bdg. 17.25 (978-0-8239-7540-2(1) , Buenas Letra) Rosen Publishing Group, Inc., The.

—Dale Earnhardt, Jr., Piloto de Nascar. 2002. (Grandes Idoles Ser.). (SPA & ENG., Illus.). 24p. (J). lib. bdg. 17.25 (978-0-8239-6128-3(1) , Buenas Letra) Rosen Publishing Group, Inc., The.

—Jeff Gordon: NASCAR Champion. 2000. (Reading Power Ser.). (Illus.). 24p. (J). (gr. 1). lib. bdg. 17.25 (978-0-8239-5544-2(3) , PKJEGO, PowerKids Pr.) Rosen Publishing Group, Inc., The.

—Jeff Gordon, Campeon de NASCAR. 2002. (Coleccion Power Kids). (SPA & ENG., Illus.). 24p. (J). (gr. k-2). lib. bdg. 17.25 (978-0-8239-6147-4(8) , N31303, Buenas Letra) Rosen Publishing Group, Inc., The.

Leebrick, Kristal. Jeff Gordon. 2004. (Edge Books NASCAR Racing). (Illus.). 32p. (J). 16.95 (978-0-7368-2424-8(3)) Capstone Pr., Inc.

—Tony Stewart. 2004. (Edge Books NASCAR Racing). (Illus.). 32p. (J). 16.95 (978-0-7368-2425-5(1)) Capstone Pr., Inc.

Levy, Janey. Dale Earnhardt Jr. 2007. 48p. (J). (978-0-531-16805-9(0)) Children's Pr., Ltd.

—Dale Earnhardt, Jr. 2007. 48p. (J). pap. (978-0-531-18713-5(6)) Children's Pr., Ltd.

—Kurt Busch. 2007. (Illus.). 48p. (J). pap. (978-0-531-18714-2(4)) Children's Pr., Ltd.

—Kurt Busch. 2006. (Illus.). 48p. (J). (978-0-531-16806-6(9) , Children's Pr.) Scholastic Library Publishing.

Macnow, Glen. Sports Great Jeff Gordon. 2001. (Sports Great Bks.). (Illus.). 64p. (YA). (gr. 4-10). lib. bdg. 22.60 (978-0-7660-1469-5(X)) Enslow Pubs., Inc.

Mantell, Paul. Dale Earnhardt: Young Race Car Driver. Henderson, Meryl, illus. 2006. 216p. (J). lib. bdg. 18.46 ***(978-1-4242-2205-6(2))*** Fitzgerald Bks.

—Dale Earnhardt: Young Race Car Driver. Henderson, Meryl, illus. 2006. (Childhood of Famous Americans Ser.). 192p. (J). pap. 5.99 (978-1-4169-1266-8(5) , Aladdin) Simon & Schuster Children's Publishing.

Maruszewski, Kelley. Matt Kenseth: Midwest Racing Sensation. 2003. (Racing Superstar Ser.). (Illus.). 93p. mass mkt. 4.95 (978-1-58261-653-7(1)) Sports Publishing, LLC.

Mello, T. The Need for Speed. rev. ed. 2007. (Race Car Legends Ser.). 72p. (J). (gr. 5-8). 25.00 (978-0-7910-8667-4(4) , Chelsea Hse.) Facts On File, Inc.

Mello, Tara Baukus. Danica Patrick. 2007. (Race Car Legends: Ser.). 72p. (J). (gr. 5-8). 25.00 ***(978-0-7910-9126-5(0)*** , Chelsea Hse.) Facts On File, Inc.

—Mark Martin. rev. ed. 2007. (Race Car Legends: Ser.). 72p. (J). (gr. 5-8). 25.00 (978-0-7910-8664-3(X) , Chelsea Hse.) Facts On File, Inc.

—Rusty Wallace. 1999. (Race Car Legends Ser.). (Illus.). 64p. (J). (gr. 2-5). 28.00 (978-0-7910-5023-1(8) , Chelsea Hse.) Facts On File, Inc.

—Rusty Wallace. 2000. (gr. 5-8). lib. bdg. 16.40 (978-0-613-20976-2(1)) Tandem Library Bks.

—Tony Stewart. rev. collector's ed. 2005. (Race Car Legends Ser.). (Illus.). 64p. (J). (gr. 4-8). lib. bdg. 25.00 (978-0-7910-8670-4(4) , Chelsea Hse.) Facts On File, Inc.

Mitchell, Jason. Drivers Series Tony Stewart. 2002. (NASCAR Wonder Boy Collector's Ser.). (Illus.). 48p. (J). pap. 7.99 (978-1-57243-524-7(0)) Triumph Bks.

Ovations Series, 2 vols., Set. Incl. Jeff Gordon. Bach, Julie S. pap. 10.60 (978-0-89812-025-7(X)); Shaquille O'Neal. Goodman, Michael E. pap. 10.60 (978-0-89812-026-4(8)); (J). 2000. (Illus.). 32p. Set pap. 21.20 (978-0-89812-010-3(1) , Creative Paperbacks) Creative Co., The.

Persinger, Kathy. Mark Martin: Ozark Original. 2004. (Illus.). 96p. (J). (gr. 4-7). per. 5.95 (978-1-58261-654-4(X)) Sports Publishing, LLC.

Peterson, Brian C. Rusty Wallace: Short Track to Success. 2003. (World of NASCAR Ser.). (Illus.). 32p. (J). (gr. 2-6). 25.64 (978-1-59187-032-6(1)) Child's World, Inc.

Poole, David. Drivers Series: Dale Earnhardt Jr. 2002. 48p. pap. 7.99 (978-1-57243-525-4(9)) Triumph Bks.

Porterfield, Jason. Kurt Busch: NASCAR Driver. 2006. (Behind the Wheel Ser.). (Illus.). 48p. (YA). (gr. 5-8). lib. bdg. 26.50 (978-1-4042-0982-4(4)) Rosen Publishing Group, Inc., The.

Prentzas, G. S. A. J. Foyt. rev. ed. 2007. (Race Car Legends Ser.). 72p. (J). (gr. 5-8). 25.00 (978-0-7910-8759-6(X) , Chelsea Hse.) Facts On File, Inc.

Prentzas, S. Mario Andretti. rev. ed. 2007. (Race Car Legends Ser.). 80p. (J). (gr. 5-8). 25.00 (978-0-7910-8755-8(7) , Chelsea Hse.) Facts On File, Inc.

Race Car Legends. 2005. pap. 375.00 (978-0-7910-9143-2(0) , Chelsea Hse.) Facts On File, Inc.

Riley, Gail Blasser. NASCAR Greats. 2008. (J). ***(978-1-4296-1287-6(8))*** Capstone Pr., Inc.

—NASCAR Technology. 2008. (J). ***(978-1-4296-1289-0(4))*** Capstone Pr., Inc.

Robinson, Tom. Mark Martin: Master Behind the Wheel. 2008. (Heroes of Racing Ser.). 128p. (J). (gr. 5-9). lib. bdg. 31.93 ***(978-0-7660-3001-5(6))*** Enslow Pubs., Inc.

Roselius, J. Chris. Matt Kenseth: Speeding to Victory. 2008. (Heroes of Racing Ser.). 128p. (J). (gr. 5-9). lib. bdg. 31.93 ***(978-0-7660-3000-8(8))*** Enslow Pubs., Inc.

Savage, Jeff. Dale Earnhardt, JR. 2006. (Amazing Athletes Ser.). (Illus.). 32p. (J). (gr. 3-7). 23.93 (978-0-8225-2946-0(7) , Lerner Pubns.) Lerner Publishing Group.

—Danica Patrick. 2007. (Amazing Athletes Ser.). (Illus.). 32p. (J). 23.93 (978-0-8225-5954-2(4) , Lerner Pubns.) Lerner Publishing Group.

—Jeff Gordon. (Amazing Athletes Ser.). 2007. (J). pap. 5.95 (978-0-8225-6802-5(0) , Lerner Pubns.); 2005. (Illus.). 32p. (gr. 3-4). lib. bdg. 22.60 (978-0-8225-1339-1(0)) Lerner Publishing Group.

—Jeff Gordon: Racing's Superstar. 2000. (Sports Achievers Biographies Ser.). (Illus.). 64p. (YA). (gr. 4-9). pap. (978-0-8225-9859-6(0)); lib. bdg. (978-0-8225-3679-6(X)) Lerner Publishing Group. (LernerSports).

—Jeff Gordon: Racing's Superstar. 2000. (Illus.). (J). (978-0-606-18820-3(7)) Tandem Library Bks.

—Travis Pastrana. 2006. (Amazing Athletes Ser.). (Illus.). 32p. (J). 22.60 (978-0-8225-3428-0(2) , Lerner Pubns.) Lerner Publishing Group.

Schaefer, A. R. Dale Earnhardt, Jr. 2005. (NASCAR Racing Ser.). (Illus.). 32p. (J). 22.60 (978-0-7368-3773-6(6)) Capstone Pr., Inc.

Sherman, Josepha. Jeff Gordon. 2001. (Sports Files Ser.). (Illus.). 32p. (J). (gr. 1-3). lib. bdg. (978-1-58810-111-2(8)) Heinemann Library.

Steenkamer, Paul. Dale Earnhardt: Star Race Car Driver. 2000. (Sports Reports). (Illus.). 104p. (YA). (gr. 4-10). lib. bdg. 26.60 (978-0-7660-1335-3(9)) Enslow Pubs., Inc.

—Jeff Gordon: Star Race Car Driver. 1999. (Sports Reports). (Illus.). 104p. (YA). (gr. 4-10). lib. bdg. 26.60 (978-0-7660-1083-3(X)) Enslow Pubs., Inc.

Stewart, Mark. Dale Earnhardt, Jr. Driven by Destiny. 2003. (Auto Racing's New Wave Ser.: up). (Illus.). 48p. (gr. 4 up). lib. bdg. 22.90 (978-0-7613-2908-4(0) , Millbrook Pr.) Lerner Publishing Group.

—Jeff Gordon: Rainbow Warrior. 2000. (Illus.). 48p. (gr. 4 up). (New Wave Ser.). lib. bdg. 22.90 (978-0-7613-1871-2(2)); (Auto Racing's New Wave Ser.: up). pap. (978-0-7613-1385-4(0)) Lerner Publishing Group. (Millbrook Pr.).

—Jeff Gordon: Rainbow Warrior. 2000. (gr. 3-6). lib. bdg. 15.25 (978-0-613-25797-8(9)) Tandem Library Bks.

Teitelbaum, Michael. Richard Petty: "The King" 2002. (World of NASCAR Ser.). (Illus.). 32p. (J). (gr. 2-6). 25.64 (978-1-59187-010-4(0)) Child's World, Inc.

—Tony Stewart: Instant Superstar! 2002. (World of NASCAR Ser.). (Illus.). 32p. (J). (gr. 2-6). 25.64 (978-1-59187-011-1(9)) Child's World, Inc.

Triumph Books Staff. Dale Earnhardt: Forever in Our Hearts. 2002. 176p. 24.95 (978-1-57243-495-0(3)) Triumph Bks.

Velazquez, Mauricio, tr. Jeff Gordon, Campeon de NASCAR. 2002. (Power Kids Coleccion). (SPA.). 24p. (J). (gr. 2-3). lib. bdg. 17.25 (978-0-8239-6129-0(X) , RN30777, Buenas Letra) Rosen Publishing Group, Inc., The.

Wallner, Rosemary. Jeff Gordon. 2000. (Sports Heroes Ser.). (Illus.). 48p. (J). (gr. 3-4). lib. bdg. 21.26 (978-0-7368-0577-3(X) , Capstone High-Interest Bks.) Capstone Pr., Inc.

Weber, Terri Smith. Jeff Gordon: Racing to Win. 2003. (J). pap. (978-0-9740180-2-7(3)); lib. bdg. (978-0-9740180-0-3(7)) Panda Publishing, L.L.C. (Bios for Kids).

Woods, Bob. Hot Wheels: The Newest Stock Car Stars. 2002. (World of NASCAR Ser.). (Illus.). 32p. (J). (gr. 2-6). 25.64 (978-1-59187-006-7(2)) Child's World, Inc.

—Racer Girls. 2006. (Girls Rock! Ser.). (Illus.). 32p. (J). (gr. 1-5). 24.21 (978-1-59296-742-1(6)) Child's World, Inc.

AUTOMOBILE RACING—FICTION

Arena, Felice & Kettle, Phil. Race Car Dreamers. Cox, David, illus. 2004. (J). pap. (978-1-59336-375-8(3)) Mondo Publishing.

Bright, J. E. All or Nothing. 2000. (NASCAR Racers Ser.: Vol. 5). 144p. (J). (gr. 4-7). pap. 4.50 (978-0-06-107197-3(8)) HarperCollins Pubs.

—High Stakes. 2001. (NASCAR Racers Ser.: No. 8). 144p. (J). (gr. 2-6). 4.50 (978-0-06-107202-4(8) , Harper Entertainment) HarperCollins Pubs.

Bryant, Raymond. At the Races. 2004. (Funtime Rhymes Ser.). (Illus.). 10p. (J). bds. 4.95 (978-0-7641-5717-2(5)) Barron's Educational Series, Inc.

Cooper, Ann Goode. Zebordee Goes to the Races. Jessee, Diana, illus. 2005. 30p. (J). (978-1-933251-01-1(8)) Parkway Pubs., Inc.

Disney Pixar Staff, creator. Cars. 2006. (Illus.). pap. 7.99 (978-1-59816-481-7(3) , Tokyopop Kids) TOKYOPOP, Inc.

—Cars Jr Cine Manga. 2006. (Illus.). 24p. pap. 3.99 (978-1-59816-483-1(X) , Tokyopop Kids) TOKYOPOP, Inc.

Disney Storybook Artists Staff, et al, illus. Cars. 2006. (Little Golden Book Ser.). 24p. (J). (gr. k-k). 2.99 (978-0-7364-2347-2(8) , Golden/Disney) Random Hse. Children's Bks.

Dixon, Franklin W. Double Jeopardy. 2003. (Hardy Boys Ser.: No. 181). 160p. (J). pap. 4.99 (978-0-689-85780-5(2) , Aladdin) Simon & Schuster Children's Publishing.

—Double Jeopardy. 2003. 150p. (J). (gr. 3-7). per. 13.00 (978-0-613-89000-7(0)) Tandem Library Bks.

Donovan, Kyle. CurBee Races the NasBee 500: The Do'Bees. 2007. (J). 15.95 net. ***(978-0-9767670-2-2(3))*** WannaBees Media LLC.

Early Bird Books Staff. The Race. Date not set. (J). 1.95 (978-0-394-86703-8(3) , Random Hse. Bks. for Young Readers) Random Hse. Children's Bks.

Elliott, Craig. Racer Buddies-Opening Day at Daytona. William, Harper, illus. 2004. 40p. (J). per. 12.95 (978-0-9746445-0-9(1) , 1234022) Powerband, LLC.

Esckilsen, Erik E. Outside Groove. 2006. 272p. (J). (gr. 5). 16.00 (978-0-618-66854-0(3)) Houghton Mifflin Co.

Finn, Mitch. NASCAR: Cat Racer's Race Day. Reiter, Cheryl, ed. Hogan, Jayne, illus. 2000. 12p. (J). (ps). mass mkt. 9.99 (978-1-887327-45-9(2)) Ertl Co., Inc.

Floca, Brian. The Racecar Alphabet. Floca, Brian, illus. 2003. (Illus.). 40p. (J). 17.99 (978-0-689-85091-2(3) , Atheneum/Richard Jackson Bks.) Simon & Schuster Children's Publishing.

Gutelle, Andrew. Stock Car Kings. Snyder, Joel, illus. 2001. (All Aboard Reading Ser.). 1p. (J). (ps-3). pap. 3.99 (978-0-448-42489-7(4) , Grosset & Dunlap) Penguin Group (USA) Inc.

Hampshire, Anthony. Fast Track. 2004. (Redline Racing Ser.: Bk. 1). (Illus.). 104p. (YA). pap. 3.99 (978-1-55305-007-0(X)) Cygnet Publishing Group, Inc./Coolreading.com CAN. *Dist:* Orca Bk. Pubs. USA.

—Fast Track. 2005. (Redline Racing Ser.: Bk. 1). (Illus.). 138p. (YA). (gr. 6 up). pap. ***(978-1-55041-570-4(0))*** Fitzhenry & Whiteside, Ltd.

—Full Throttle. 2004. (Redline Racing Ser.: Bk. 2). (Illus.). 108p. (YA). pap. 3.99 (978-1-55305-008-7(8)) Cygnet Publishing Group, Inc./Coolreading.com CAN. *Dist:* Orca Bk. Pubs. USA.

—Full Throttle. 2005. (Redline Racing Ser.: Bk. 2). (Illus.). 138p. (YA). (gr. 6 up). pap. ***(978-1-55041-564-3(6))*** Fitzhenry & Whiteside, Ltd.

—G-Force. 2007. (Redline Racing Ser.: Bk. 4). 184p. (YA). (gr. 6 up). pap. ***(978-1-55455-027-2(0))*** Fitzhenry & Whiteside, Ltd.

—On the Limit. 2004. (Redline Racing Ser.: Bk. 3). 144p. (YA). pap. 3.99 (978-1-55305-025-4(8)) Cygnet Publishing Group, Inc./Coolreading.com CAN. *Dist:* Orca Bk. Pubs. USA.

—On the Limit. 2006. (Redline Racing Ser.: Bk. 3). (Illus.). 138p. (YA). (gr. 6 up). pap. ***(978-1-55041-568-1(9))*** Fitzhenry & Whiteside, Ltd.

Hampshire, Anthony. Title Run. 2004. (Redline Racing Ser.: Bk. 4). 148p. (YA). pap. 3.99 (978-1-55305-026-1(6)) Cygnet Publishing Group, Inc./Coolreading.com CAN. *Dist:* Orca Bk. Pubs. USA.

Harcourt School Publishers Staff. The Derby On Level. 3rd ed. 2002. (Trophies Reading Program Ser.). (Illus.). pap. 5.10 (978-0-15-323165-0(3)) Harcourt Schl. Pubs.

Harville, Shawn T. Tell a Story Stock Car Coloring Book. Harville, Shawn T., illus. 1999. (Illus.). 64p. (J). (gr. k-4). mass mkt. 3.95 (978-1-893691-00-1(4) , 20001) Sundown Publishing Co.

Hobbs, Valerie. How Far Would You Have Gotten If I Hadn't Called You Back? 2003. 320p. (J). pap. 5.99 (978-0-439-58396-1(9) , Scholastic Paperbacks) Scholastic, Inc.

Keith, Don. White Lightning. 1999. (gr. 7-12). lib. bdg. 14.15 (978-0-613-17594-4(8)) Tandem Library Bks.

Keylocke, Andrew, illus. Whizzy Woof. 2004. (Crazy Racers Ser.). 12p. (J). bds. 4.95 (978-0-7641-5748-6(5)) Barron's Educational Series, Inc.

Kolar, Bob. Racer Dogs. Kolar, Bob, illus. 2003. (Illus.). 32p. (J). (ps-2). 15.99 (978-0-525-45939-2(1) , Dutton Juvenile) Penguin Group (USA) Inc.

Maddox, Jake. Speedway Switch. Tiffany, Sean, illus. 2007. (J). 72p. ***(978-1-59889-321-2(1)***); 65p. pap. ***(978-1-59889-416-5(1))*** Stone Arch Bks.

Marsoli, Lisa Ann & Random House Disney Staff. Cars. Disney Storybook Artists Staff, illus. 2006. (Read-Aloud Storybook Ser.). 72p. (J). (ps-3). 8.99 (978-0-7364-2338-0(9) , RH/Disney) Random Hse. Children's Bks.

McMorrine, David. Tim, Sherri & Formula One. 2003. 140p. (YA). pap. 7.95 (978-0-9639940-4-2(2)) Morgan Publishing Co.

Mills, Marylin. Little Flagger at the Races. 2005. (ENG., Illus.). 40p. (J). (ps-7). per. 23.00 (978-1-4208-0980-0(6)) AuthorHouse.

Miranda, Anne. Vroom, Chugga, Vroom-Vroom. 2000. (ps-2). lib. bdg. 16.40 (978-0-613-28127-0(6)) Tandem Library Bks.

Montgomery, R. A. Behind the Wheel. 2008. (Choose Your Own Adventure Ser.: No. 26). (Illus.). 144p. (J). per. 5.99 (***978-1-933390-26-0(3)***) Chooseco LLC.

Montgomery, R. A. Race Forever. 2006. (Choose Your Own Adventure Ser.: No. 7). (Illus.). 144p. (J). mass mkt. 5.99 (978-1-933390-07-9(7) , CHCL07) Chooseco LLC.

—Race Forever. 2005. (Illus.). 122p. (J). (***978-0-7608-9695-2(X)***) Sundance/Newbridge Educational Publishing.

Murawski, Kevin, illus. Harold & the Purple Crayon: Race Car. 2004. 32p. (J). (ps-ps). lib. bdg. 10.79 (978-0-606-29918-3(1)) Tandem Library Bks.

My Racing Car. 2002. (Chunky Vehicle Shaped Boards Ser.). (J). bds. 1.98 (978-0-7525-7050-1(1)) Parragon, Inc.

Peck, Richard. Here Lies the Librarian. 160p. (J). (gr. 5 up). 2007. 6.99 (***978-0-14-240908-4(1)*** , Puffin); 2006. 16.99 (978-0-8037-3080-9(2) , Dial) Penguin Group (USA) Inc.

—Here Lies the Librarian. rev. ed. 175p. 23.95 (***978-0-7862-9183-0(4)***) Thorndike Pr.

Perlman, Rhea. Brain Freeze. Santat, Dan, illus. 2007. (Otto Undercover Ser.: No. 6). 128p. (J). (gr. 2-6). pap. 3.99 (***978-0-06-075505-8(9)*** , Harper Trophy) HarperCollins Pubs.

Perlman, Rhea. The Brink of Ex-stink-tion. Santat, Dan, illus. 2007. (Otto Undercover Ser.: No. 5). 128p. (J). pap. 3.99 (978-0-06-075503-4(2) , Harper Trophy) HarperCollins Pubs.

The Race Car: Individual Title Six-Packs. (Sails Literacy Ser.). 16p. (gr. k up). 27.00 (978-0-7635-4438-6(8)) Rigby Education.

Random House Disney Staff. Cars: Join the Pit Crew. 2006. (Illus.). 12p. (J). (ps-2). bds. 9.99 (978-0-7364-2349-6(4) , RH/Disney) Random Hse. Children's Bks.

—Cars: The Junior Novelization. 2006. (Junior Novel Ser.). (Illus.). 128p. (J). (gr. 3-7). 4.99 (978-0-7364-2291-8(9) , RH/Disney) Random Hse. Children's Bks.

—Let's Cruise. 2006. (Friendship Box Ser.). (Illus.). 12p. (J). (gr. k-k). bds. 9.99 (978-0-7364-2391-5(5) , RH/Disney) Random Hse. Children's Bks.

—The Race Is On! 2006. (Illus.). 24p. (J). (ps-2). pap. 5.99 (978-0-7364-2438-7(5) , RH/Disney) Random Hse. Children's Bks.

Reilly, Matthew. Full Throttle. Raimondi, Pablo, illus. 2006. (Hover Car Racer Ser.). 224p. (J). pap. 5.99 (978-1-4169-0228-7(7) , Aladdin) Simon & Schuster Children's Publishing.

Rissi, Anica Mrose. Cars Supercharged. Disney Press Staff, ed. 2007. 14p. (ps-2). 12.99 (***978-1-4231-0820-7(5)***) Disney Pr.

Shigeno, Shuichi. Initial-D. 2002. (Illus.). 224p. 1. pap. 9.99 (978-1-931514-98-9(4)); Vol. 2. pap. 9.99 (978-1-59182-035-2(9)); Vol. 3. pap. 9.99 (978-1-59182-036-9(7)) TOKYOPOP, Inc. (Tokyopop Adult).

Shigeno, Shuichi, illus. & creator. Initial D, Vol. 22. Shigeno, Shuichi, creator. 22nd rev. ed. 2006. 240p. pap. 9.99 (978-1-59182-998-0(4) , Tokyopop Adult) TOKYOPOP, Inc.

Sporteller Staff. Race to Win (Auto Racing) 64p. (YA). (gr. 6-12). pap. 10.95 (978-0-8224-6479-2(9)) Globe Fearon Educational Publishing.

Trimble, Irene. Faster Than Fast. Disney Storybook Artists Staff, illus. 2006. (Stepping Stone Bks.). 80p. (J). (gr. 2-5). pap. 3.99 (978-0-7364-2346-5(X) , RH/Disney) Random Hse. Children's Bks.

Weaver, Will. Saturday Night Dirt. 2008. (Motor Novel Ser.). 176p. (YA). 14.95 (***978-0-374-35060-4(4)***) Farrar, Straus & Giroux.

Welling, Peter J. Justin Potemkin & the 500-Mile Race. Welling, Peter J., illus. 2004. (Illus.). 32p. (J). pap. 15.95 (978-1-58980-149-3(0)) Pelican Publishing Co., Inc.

Wheeler, Chase. Challenge of the Masked Racer #2. 2008. 144p. (J). (gr. 2-5). 6.99 (***978-0-448-44805-3(X)*** , Grosset & Dunlap) Penguin Group (USA) Inc.

—The Great Plan #1. 2008. 144p. (J). (gr. 2-5). 6.99 (***978-0-448-44804-6(1)*** , Grosset & Dunlap) Penguin Group (USA) Inc.

—The Race Against the Mammoth Car #4. 2008. 144p. (J). (gr. 2-5). 6.99 (***978-0-448-44807-7(6)*** , Grosset & Dunlap) Penguin Group (USA) Inc.

—Race for Revenge #6. 2008. 144p. (J). (gr. 2-5). 6.99 (***978-0-448-44809-1(2)*** , Grosset & Dunlap) Penguin Group (USA) Inc.

—The Secret Engine #3. 2008. 144p. (J). (gr. 2-5). 6.99 (***978-0-448-44806-0(8)*** , Grosset & Dunlap) Penguin Group (USA) Inc.

White, Megan Tara. Left in the Dust. 2005. 207p. pap. 19.95 (978-1-4137-6672-1(2)) PublishAmerica, Inc.

Wielkiewicz, Richard M. Okay, Riders, Set 'Em Up: A Nate Walker BMX Adventure. Dwyer, Corinne et al, illus. 2005. 140p. (J). pap. 12.95 (978-0-9774129-0-7(3)) Main Event Pr.

Zane, Alex & Zacks, Lewis. The Wheels on the Race Car. Warhola, James, illus. 2005. 32p. (J). pap. 14.95 (978-0-439-59080-8(9) , Orchard Bks.) Scholastic, Inc.

Zucker, Jonny. Inside the Game. Smith, Pete, illus. 2007. 33p. (J). pap. (***978-1-59889-426-4(9)***); 40p. (YA). (gr. 5-9). lib. bdg. 21.26 (***978-1-59889-330-4(0)***) Stone Arch Bks.

AUTOMOBILE TOURING

see Automobile Travel

AUTOMOBILE TRAILERS

see Automobiles—Trailers

AUTOMOBILE TRAVEL

see also Games for Travelers

Ashley, Susan. Going by Bus. 2003. (Going Places Ser.). (Illus.). 24p. (YA). (gr. 2 up). lib. bdg. 19.33 (978-0-8368-3729-2(0) , Weekly Reader Early Learning Library) Stevens, Gareth Inc.

—Going by Car. 2003. (Going Places Ser.). (Illus.). 24p. (gr. 2 up). (YA). lib. bdg. 19.33 (978-0-8368-3730-8(4)); (J). pap. 5.95 (978-0-8368-3835-0(1)) Stevens, Gareth Inc. (Weekly Reader Early Learning Library).

Brown, Don. Alice Ramsey's Grand Adventure. 2000. (YA). 12.75 (978-0-606-19423-5(1)) Tandem Library Bks.

Gordon, Wendy. I'm Safe! In the Car. Gordon, Paul, illus. 2001. (I'm Safe! Ser.). 24p. (J). (ps-2). pap., act. bk. ed. 2.95 (978-1-891596-15-5(2)) BackYard Bks.

Hanson, Anders. Let's Go by Car. 2007. (Let's Go! Ser.). (ENG., Illus.). 24p. (J). (ps-3). lib. bdg. 19.93 (***978-1-59928-897-0(4)*** , SandCastle) ABDO Publishing Co.

LaRochelle, David. The Mighty Big BookTM of Travel Mysteries. 2002. (Illus.). 288p. (J). (gr. 3-7). mass mkt. 5.99 (978-0-8431-7734-3(9) , Price Stern Sloan) Penguin Group (USA) Inc.

Morris, Juddi. Route 66: Main Street of America. 2006. (J). pap. (978-1-59336-716-9(3)) Mondo Publishing.

Price, Sean. Route 66: America's Road. 2007. (J). (***978-1-4109-2697-5(4)***); pap. (***978-1-4109-2708-8(3)***) Steck-Vaughn.

Schlesinger, Arthur M., Jr. & Israel, Fred L., eds. Touring America Seventy-Five Years Ago. 1999. (Cultural & Geographical Exploration Ser.). (Illus.). x, 122p. (J). (gr. 4-7). lib. bdg. 21.95 (978-0-7910-5098-9(X) , Chelsea Hse.) Facts On File, Inc.

AUTOMOBILE TRAVEL—FICTION

Arnold, Tedd. Fly High, Fly Guy! 2008. (Fly Guy Ser.). 32p. (J). 5.99 (***978-0-545-00722-1(4)***) Scholastic, Inc.

Balan, Bruce. Cows Going Past. Nash, Scott, illus. 2005. 32p. (J). (ps-ps). 9.99 (978-0-8037-2902-5(2)) Penguin Group (USA) Inc.

Behrens, Andy. All the Way. 2006. 256p. (YA). (gr. 9). 16.99 (978-0-525-47761-7(6) , Dutton Juvenile) Penguin Group (USA) Inc.

Berenstain, Stan & Berenstain, Jan. The Berenstain Bears & the Big Spelling Bee, No. 6. Berenstain, Jan, illus. 2007. (Berenstain Bears Ser.). (Illus.). 32p. (J). 3.99 (***978-0-06-057386-7(4)*** , Harper Festival) HarperCollins Pubs.

—The Berenstain Bears & Too Much Car Trip. 2006. (Berenstain Bears Ser.). (Illus.). 32p. (J). (ps-2). 8.99 (978-0-06-057400-0(3)); pap. 3.99 (978-0-06-057384-3(8)) HarperCollins Pubs. (Harper Festival).

—The Berenstain Bears Hug & Make Up. 2006. (Berenstain Bears Ser.). (Illus.). 32p. (J). pap. 3.99 (978-0-06-057385-0(6) , Harper Festival) HarperCollins Pubs.

—The Berenstain Bears Hug & Make Up, No. 5. Berenstain, Stan & Berenstain, Jan, illus. 2006. (Berenstain Bears Ser.). (Illus.). 32p. (J). 8.99 (978-0-06-057401-7(1) , Harper Festival) HarperCollins Pubs.

Cheaney, J. B. The Middle of Somewhere. 2007. (Illus.). 224p. (J). (gr. 4-6). 15.99 (978-0-375-83790-6(6)); lib. bdg. 18.99 (978-0-375-93790-3(0)) Random Hse. Children's Bks. (Knopf Bks. for Young Readers).

Cooney, Caroline B. Hit the Road. 2006. 192p. (gr. 7). (J). lib. bdg. 17.99 (978-0-385-90174-1(7)); (YA). 15.95 (978-0-385-72944-4(8)) Random Hse. Children's Bks. (Delacorte Bks. for Young Readers).

Driscoll, Laura. Super Specs. Gott, Barry, illus. 2005. 32p. (J). lib. bdg. 20.00 (***978-1-4242-1074-9(7)***) Fitzgerald Bks.

—Super Specs. Adams, Lynn, illus. 2005. (Math Matters Ser.). 32p. (J). pap. 4.95 (978-1-57565-145-3(9)) Kane Pr., The.

Elya, Susan Middleton. Oh No, Gotta Go! Karas, G. Brian, illus. 2005. 29p. (J). (gr. k-4). reprint ed. 15.00 (978-0-7567-8946-6(X)) DIANE Publishing Co.

Eschbacher, Roger. Road Trip! Wickstrom, Thor, illus. 2006. 32p. (J). (ps). 16.99 (978-0-8037-2927-8(8) , Dial) Penguin Group (USA) Inc.

Fleming, Ian. Chitty Chitty Bang Bang. l.t. ed. 2002. (Illus.). 80p. (J). 16.95 (978-0-7540-7831-9(0) , Galaxy Children's Large Print) BBC Audiobooks America.

—Chitty Chitty Bang Bang. Selznick, Brian, illus. 2005. 160p. (J). (gr. 3). 5.99 (978-0-375-83283-3(1) , Random Hse. Bks. for Young Readers) Random Hse. Children's Bks.

Hergenrader, Christina. Dangerous Roads. 2004. 224p. (J). 6.99 (978-0-7586-0715-7(6)) Concordia Publishing Hse.

Homel, David. Travels with My Family. Gay, Marie-Louise, illus. 2007. 120p. (J). pap. 7.95 (***978-0-88899-833-0(3)***) Groundwood Bks. CAN. *Dist:* Perseus Distribution.

Lumley, Jemima. The Journey Home from Grandpa's. Fatus, Sophie, illus. 2006. 24p. (J). (978-1-905236-37-4(9)) Barefoot Bks., Inc.

McCarthy, Maureen. Rose by Any Other Name. 2008. 336p. (YA). 16.95 (***978-1-59643-372-4(8)***) Roaring Brook Pr.

McKay, Sindy. We Both Read-My Car Trip. Johnson, Meredith, illus. 2005. (J). (***978-1-4156-3785-2(7)***) Book Wholesalers, Inc.

—We Both Read-My Car Trip. Johnson, Meredith, illus. 2005. (We Both Read Ser.). 44p. (J). (gr. k up). 7.99 (978-1-891327-63-6(1)); pap. 3.99 (978-1-891327-64-3(X)) Treasure Bay, Inc.

Moss, Marissa. Amelia's Are-We-There-yet Longest Ever Car Trip. Moss, Marissa, illus. 2006. (Amelia's Notebooks). (Illus.). 40p. (J). 9.95 (978-1-4169-0906-4(0) , Simon & Schuster/Paula Wiseman Bks.) Simon & Schuster Children's Publishing.

Mr. Meow. Mr. Meow's Amazing Alphabet Adventure. Crawford, Gregory, illus. 2004. 32p. (J). pap. (978-1-58394-098-3(7) , Frog Ltd.) North Atlantic Bks.

Murphy, Stuart J. Tally O'Malley. Jabar, Cynthia, illus. 2004. (MathStart Ser.). 40p. (J). (gr. 1 up). 15.99 (978-0-06-053162-1(2)); pap. 5.99 (978-0-06-053164-5(9)) HarperCollins Pubs.

Penrose, Margaret. The Motor Girls on a Tour. 2006. pap. (***978-1-84702-440-4(8)***) Echo Library.

Ponti, Claude. En El Coche. 2003. (SPA.). 32p. 15.95 (978-84-95150-08-0(5)) Corimbo, Editorial S.L. ESP. *Dist:* Distribooks, Inc.

Rosen, Michael J. A Drive in the Country. Burckhardt, Marc, illus. 2007. 32p. (J). (gr. k-5). 16.99 (***978-0-7636-2140-7(4)***) Candlewick Pr.

Rugrats. 2007. (J). 128.10 (***978-1-59961-354-3(9)***) Spotlight.

Sanchez, Alex. Rainbow Road. 2007. 272p. (YA). pap. 8.99 (978-1-4169-1191-3(X) , Simon Pulse) Simon & Schuster Children's Publishing.

Sanchez, Alex & Louth, Jack. Rainbow Road. 2005. 256p. (J). 16.95 (978-0-689-86565-7(1)) Simon & Schuster Children's Publishing.

Scott, Janine. Sunny Sunday Drive. Forss, Ian, illus. 2006. 32p. (J). (gr. k-2). 22.60 (978-1-4048-1696-1(8)) Picture Window Bks.

St. Pierre, Stephanie. Rugrats Blast Off. 2007. 24p. (J). 21.35 (***978-1-59961-358-1(1)***) Spotlight.

The Trolley Ride: 6 Small Books. (gr. k-3). 24.00 (978-0-7635-6233-5(5)) Rigby Education.

Walters, Virginia. Are We There Yet, Daddy? 2002. (gr. k-3). lib. bdg. 15.30 (978-0-613-83552-7(2)) Tandem Library Bks.

—Are We There yet, Daddy? Schindler, S. D., illus. 2005. 27p. (J). (gr. k-4). reprint ed. 16.00 (978-0-7567-9708-9(X)) DIANE Publishing Co.

Winfield, Arthur M. Rover Boys on A Tour or Last Days at Bri. 2006. pap. 31.95 (***978-1-4286-4389-5(3)***) Kessinger Publishing, LLC.

AUTOMOBILE TRUCKS

see Trucks

AUTOMOBILES

see also Buses; Trucks

also names of automobiles, e.g. Ford Automobile

Allen, Francesca, illus. Cars. 2005. 10p. (J). 4.95 (978-0-7945-0855-5(3) , Usborne) EDC Publishing.

Allman, Toney. From Boxfish Bodies to Bionic Cars. 2006. (Imitating Nature Ser.). 32p. (J). (gr. 3-6). 24.95 (978-0-7377-3609-0(7) , Greenhaven Pr., Inc.) Thomson Gale.

Amato, William. High-Tech Vehicles, 6 bks. Incl. Aircraft Carriers. lib. bdg. 17.25 (978-0-8239-6012-5(9)); Bullet Trains. lib. bdg. 17.25 (978-0-8239-6008-8(0)); Cruise Ships. lib. bdg. 17.25 (978-0-8239-6010-1(2)); Nuclear Submarines. lib. bdg. 17.25 (978-0-8239-6011-8(0)); Space Shuttle. lib. bdg. 17.25 (978-0-8239-6007-1(2)); Supersonic Jets. lib. bdg. 17.25 (978-0-8239-6009-5(9)); 24p. (J). (gr. 2). 2002. (Illus.). 2001. Set lib. bdg. 96.00 (978-0-8239-7177-0(5) , PowerKids Pr.) Rosen Publishing Group, Inc., The.

Around & Around: Individual Title Six-Packs. (Sails Literacy Ser.). (gr. 1-2). 36.00 (978-0-7578-4028-9(0)) Rigby Education.

Ashley, Susan. En Carro. Coffey, Colleen & Carrillo, Consuelo, trs. 2003. (Weekly Reader Early Learning Library). (SPA., Illus.). 24p. (J). (gr. 2 up). lib. bdg. 19.33 (978-0-8368-3735-3(5) , Weekly Reader Early Learning Library) Stevens, Gareth Inc.

—En Carro. 2003. (Weekly Reader Early Learning Library). (SPA., Illus.). 24p. (J). (gr. 2 up). pap. (978-0-8368-3840-4(8) , Weekly Reader Early Learning Library) Stevens, Gareth Inc.

—Going by Car. 2003. (Going Places Ser.). (Illus.). 24p. (YA). (gr. 2 up). lib. bdg. 19.33 (978-0-8368-3730-8(4) , Weekly Reader Early Learning Library) Stevens, Gareth Inc.

Augarde, Steve. Garage: A Pop-up Book. Augarde, Steve, illus. 2005. (Illus.). 10p. (J). (gr. k-4). reprint ed. 15.00 (978-0-7567-9299-2(1)) DIANE Publishing Co.

Auto Mechanics. (Community Helpers Ser.). 24p. (J). 6.95 (978-0-7368-8451-8(3)) Capstone Pr., Inc.

Autos del Pasado: Individual Title Six-Packs. (On Deck en Espanol Ser.).Tr. of Cars of the Past. (SPA.). 24p. (gr. 4-5). 35.00 (978-0-7578-6423-0(6)) Rigby Education.

Aylmore, Angela. I Like Cars. 2007. (Illus.). 24p. (J). (978-1-4034-9277-7(8)); lib. bdg. 21.36 (978-1-4034-9268-5(9)) Heinemann Library.

Bailer, Darice. Dump It! Ellis, Art, illus. 2004. (Matchbox Ser.). 16p. (J). bds. 6.99 (978-0-689-87316-4(6) , Little Simon) Simon & Schuster Children's Publishing.

Bailey, Katharine. Muscle Cars. 2006. (Automania! Ser.). (Illus.). 32p. (J). (978-0-7787-3010-1(7)); (gr. 4-5). pap. (978-0-7787-3032-3(8)) Crabtree Publishing Co.

—Sweet Rides. 2006. (Automania! Ser.). (Illus.). 32p. (J). (978-0-7787-3008-8(5)); (gr. 4-5). pap. (978-0-7787-3030-9(1)) Crabtree Publishing Co.

Ball, Jacqueline A. Start the Car. 2003. (Step Back Science Ser.). (Illus.). 48p. (J). 24.95 (978-1-56711-678-6(7) , Blackbirch Pr., Inc.) Thomson Gale.

Beck, Paul, et al. Uncover a Race Car: Take a Three Dimensioanl Look Inside a Race Car. 2003. (Uncover Ser.). (Illus.). 16p. (J). 18.95 (978-1-57145-791-2(7)) Advantage Pubs. Group.

Bender, Lionel. Cars & Motorcycles. 2006. (J). (978-1-59389-262-3(4)) Chrysalis Education.

Beylon, Cathy. Little Cars Stickers. 2000. (Illus.). 4p. (J). pap. 1.50 (978-0-486-40975-7(9)) Dover Pubns., Inc.

Blathwayt, Benedict. Ben's Big Book of Cars. 2003. (Illus.). 28p. (J). pap. 9.99 (978-0-09-940472-9(9) , Hutchinson) Random Hse. GBR. *Dist:* Independent Pubs. Group.

Bradley, Michael. The Corvette. 2008. (J). (***978-0-7614-2976-0(X)***) Cavendish, Marshall Bks., Ltd.

Braulick, Carrie A. Indy Cars. 2006. (Blazers—Horsepower Ser.). (Illus.). 32p. (J). 19.93 (978-0-7368-4390-4(6)) Capstone Pr., Inc.

Braun, Eric. Hot Rods. 2007. (Motor Mania Ser.). (Illus.). 48p. (J). (gr. 4-7). 26.60 (978-0-8225-3531-7(9)) Lerner Publishing Group.

Bryant, Raymond. On the Road. 2003. (Funtime Rhymes Ser.). (Illus.). 10p. (J). bds. 4.95 (978-0-7641-2660-4(1)) Barron's Educational Series, Inc.

Built for Speed: World's Fastest Boats; Cars; Helicopters; Military Airplanes; Superbikes; Trains; Trucks; Wildest Roller Coasters, 8 bks. (Illus.). (J). (gr. 3-4). lib. bdg. 170.08 (978-0-7368-1081-4(1) , Capstone High-Interest Bks.) Capstone Pr., Inc.

Bullard, Lisa. Chevrolet Corvette. 2008. (J). (***978-1-4296-0098-9(5)***) Capstone Pr., Inc.

—Ferrari. 2008. (J). (***978-1-4296-0099-6(3)***) Capstone Pr., Inc.

—Lowriders. 2007. (J). (Illus.). 32p. pap. 5.95 (***978-0-8225-6423-2(8)*** , First Avenue Editions); 22.60 (978-0-8225-6379-2(7) , Lerner Pubns.) Lerner Publishing Group.

—Porsche. 2008. (J). (***978-1-4296-0104-7(3)***) Capstone Publishing.

Burch, Lynda S. Wicky Wacky Things that Go! Automobiles 1. Burch, Lynda S. & Roberts, MarySue, photos by. 2004. (Illus.). 30p. (J). E-Book 9.95 incl. cd-rom (978-1-933090-12-2(X)) Guardian Angel Publishing, Inc.

Burgan, Michael. The Automobile. 2005. (Great Inventions Ser.). (Illus.). 48p. (YA). lib. bdg. 30.00 (978-0-8368-5800-6(X) , World Almanac Library) Stevens, Gareth Inc.

Burton, Margie, et al. How Many Are Left? Adams, Alison, ed. 1999. (Early Connections Ser.). 16p. (J). (gr. k-2). pap. 4.50 (978-1-58344-066-7(6)) Benchmark Education Co.

Car. (Blank Books for Young Authors Ser.). (gr. k-3). 1.99 (978-0-7424-0382-6(3) , IF78) School Specialty Publishing.

Cars. 2005. (Transportation Ser.). (YA). (gr. k-3). (978-1-56065-966-2(1) , Pebble Bks.) Capstone Pr., Inc.

Cars: Third Grade Newcomer Books. (On Our Way to English Ser.). (gr. 3 up). 29.50 (978-0-7578-7249-5(2)) Rigby Education.

Cars & Trucks. Date not set. (Illus.). (J). bds. 9.98 (978-0-7525-9892-5(9)) Parragon, Inc.

Cars in America, 6 vols. (Book2WebTM Ser.). (gr. 4-8). 36.50 (978-0-322-02992-7(9)) Wright Group, The.

Chari, Sheela. Car Smarts. 2002. (Smarts Ser.). (Illus.). 48p. (J). (gr. 7-12). pap. 23.00 (978-0-516-23927-9(9) , Children's Pr.) Scholastic Library Publishing.

—Car Smarts. 2002. (gr. 7-12). lib. bdg. 15.25 (978-0-613-58690-0(5)) Tandem Library Bks.

Collier, James Lincoln. The Automobile. 2005. (Great Inventions Ser.). (Illus.). 112p. (J). (gr. 3-7). lib. bdg. (978-0-7614-1877-1(6) , Benchmark Bks.) Cavendish, Marshall Corp.

¿Como Funciona un Auto? (SPA.). (J). (gr. 1-3). pap. (978-950-724-554-1(5) , LMA8231) Lumen ARG. *Dist:* Lectorum Pubns., Inc.

Cooper, Sharon Katz. Whose Vehicle Is This? A Look at Vehicles Workers Drive—Fast, Loud, & Bright. Muehlenhardt, Amy Bailey, illus. 2006. (Whose Is It? Ser.). 24p. (J). (ps-2). 22.60 (978-1-4048-1603-9(8) , 1253206) Picture Window Bks.

Cooper, Wade. On the Road. 2008. (Scholastic Reader Level 1 Ser.). 32p. (J). pap. 3.99 (***978-0-545-00720-7(8)*** , Cartwheel Bks.) Scholastic, Inc.

Court, Rob. How to Draw Cars & Trucks. 2007. (Doodle Bks.). 32p. (J). 21.36 (***978-1-59296-804-6(X)***) Child's World, Inc.

D'Amelio, Dennis P. Colored Cars. D'Amelio, Dennis P., illus. 1998. (Right Track Bks.: Vol. 4). (Illus.). 24p. (J). (ps-3). pap. (978-1-891528-66-8(1)) Telescopic Pr.

—Counting Cars. D'Amelio, Dennis P., illus. 1998. (Right Track Bks.: Vol. 1). (Illus.). (J). (ps). pap. (978-1-891528-50-7(5)) Telescopic Pr.

Dan's Old Van: Set B Individual Title Six-Packs. (gr. k-3). 29.00 (978-0-7635-0537-0(4)) Rigby Education.

David, Jack. Lowriders. 2008. (Illus.). 24p. (J). lib. bdg. 19.95 (***978-1-60014-150-8(1)***) Bellwether Media.

—Tuner Cars. 2008. (Illus.). 24p. (J). lib. bdg. 19.95 (***978-1-60014-154-6(4)***) Bellwether Media.

Daynes, Katie. Cars. Larkum, A., illus. 2005. 64p. (J). (gr. 2 up). pap. 5.95 (978-0-7945-0999-6(1) , Usborne) EDC Publishing.

DeGezelle, Terri. Tow Trucks. 2006. (Pebble Plus Ser.). (Illus.). 24p. (J). (978-0-7368-5359-0(6)) Capstone Pr., Inc.

Dirt Bikes, 6 vols. (gr. 4 up). 39.95 (978-0-7368-9290-2(7)) Red Brick Learning.

Doeden, Matt. Crazy Cars. 2007. (Motor Mania Ser.). 48p. (J). (gr. 4-7). 26.60 (978-0-8225-6565-9(X) , Lerner Pubns.) Lerner Publishing Group.

—Custom Cars. 2008. (Motor Mania Ser.). (J). lib. bdg. 26.60 (***978-0-8225-7289-3(3)*** , Lerner Pubns.) Lerner Publishing Group.

—Lowriders. 2005. (Blazers—Horsepower Ser.). (Illus.). 149p. (J). 19.93 (978-0-7368-3789-7(2)) Capstone Pr., Inc.

—Lowriders. 2007. (Motor Mania Ser.). (Illus.). 48p. (J). (gr. 4-7). 26.60 (978-0-8225-6042-5(9) , Lerner Pubns.) Lerner Publishing Group.

—Sports Cars. 2004. (Blazers—Horsepower Ser.). (Illus.). 32p. (J). lib. bdg. 19.93 (978-0-7368-2734-8(X)) Capstone Pr., Inc.

—Stock Cars. 2007. (Motor Mania Ser.). (Illus.). 48p. (J). (gr. 4-7). 26.60 (978-0-8225-3530-0(0)) Lerner Publishing Group.

Donovan, Sandra. Sports Cars. 2007. (Motor Mania Ser.). (Illus.). 48p. (J). (gr. 4-7). 26.60 (978-0-8225-5928-3(5) , Lerner Pubns.) Lerner Publishing Group.

Dorling Kindersley Publishing Staff. The Cars: The Ultimate Guide. 2006. 48p. (J). 12.99 (978-0-7566-1462-1(7)) Dorling Kindersley Publishing, Inc.

—The Fun Car. 1999. (Wheelies Ser.). (Illus.). 10p. (J). (gr. k-2). bds. 5.99 (978-0-7894-4732-6(0)) Dorling Kindersley Publishing, Inc.

—In My Car. 2006. (Keep Me Busy! Ser.). (Illus.). 12p. (J). bds. 12.99 (978-0-7566-1513-0(5)) Dorling Kindersley Publishing, Inc.

—Sports Car. 2003. (Wheelies Ser.). (Illus.). 12p. (J). bds. 6.99 (978-0-7894-9711-6(5)) Dorling Kindersley Publishing, Inc.

—Sudden Impact. 2003. (Wheelies Ser.). (Illus.). 12p. (J). bds. 6.99 (978-0-7894-9874-8(X)) Dorling Kindersley Publishing, Inc.

Dorling Kindersley Publishing Staff, ed. Do Cars Fly? 2005. (DK See Through Ser.). (Illus.). 21p. (J). 6.99 (978-0-7566-0774-6(4)) Dorling Kindersley Publishing, Inc.

Dragsters. (Horsepower Ser.). 32p. (YA). 7.95 (978-0-7368-5217-3(4)) Capstone Pr., Inc.

Dragsters, 6 vols. (gr. 4 up). 39.95 (978-0-7368-9289-6(3)) Red Brick Learning.

Draw 50 Cars, Trucks, & Motorcycles. 2002. (Draw 50 Ser.). (Illus.). (J). 17.60 (978-0-7587-0011-7(3)) Book Wholesalers, Inc.

DuBosque, Doug. Draw Cars, Vol. 12. rev. ed. 2000. (Learn to Draw Ser.). (Illus.). 64p. (J). (gr. 6-9). pap. 8.99 (978-0-939217-29-8(5)) Peel Productions, Inc.

Dubowski, Mark. Superfast Cars. 2005. (Ultimate Speed Ser.). (Illus.). 32p. (J). lib. bdg. 25.27 (978-1-59716-080-3(6)) Bearport Publishing Co., Inc.

Eckold, David. The Ultimate Car Kit. 2005. 1p. (J). 29.99 (978-0-7566-1421-8(X)) Dorling Kindersley Publishing, Inc.

Edmonston, Phil. Car Smarts: Hot Tips for the Car Crazy. 2003. (gr. 5-8). lib. bdg. 25.70 (978-0-613-77313-3(6)) Tandem Library Bks.

Edmonston, Phil & Sawa, Maureen. Car Smarts: Hot Tips for the Car Crazy. Sauve, Gordon, illus. 2003. 80p. (J). (gr. 4-9). pap. 15.95 (978-0-88776-646-6(3)) Tundra Bks., Inc./Livres Toundra, Inc. CAN. *Dist:* Random Hse., Inc.

Ehrlich, Fred. Does a Giraffe Drive? Bolam, Emily, illus. 2007. 28p. (ps-1). pap. 5.95 (***978-1-59354-615-1(7)***) Blue Apple Bks.

—Does a Giraffe Drive? Bolam, Emily, illus. 2007. 32p. 13.50 (***978-1-59354-614-4(9)***) Handprint Bks.

Erne, Andrea. Que? Como? Por que?: Autos y Camiones: What? How? Why?: Cars & Trucks, Spanish-Language Edition. 2007. (Illus.). 16p. (J). 9.95 (***978-970-718-490-9(6)*** , Silver Dolphin en Español) Advanced Marketing, S. de R. L. de C. V. MEX. *Dist:* Perseus Distribution.

Ethan, Eric. Great American Muscle Cars, 6 bks. Incl. Camaros. lib. bdg. 20.67 (978-0-8368-1742-3(7)); Cobras. lib. bdg. 20.67 (978-0-8368-1743-0(5)); Corvettes. lib. bdg. 20.67 (978-0-8368-1744-7(3)); Firebirds. lib. bdg. 20.67 (978-0-8368-1745-4(1)); GTOs. lib. bdg. 20.67 (978-0-8368-1746-1(X)); Mustangs. lib. bdg. 20.67 (978-0-8368-1747-8(8)); 24p. (J). (gr. 1 up). 1998. (Illus.). Set lib. bdg. 124.02 (978-0-8368-1741-6(9)) Stevens, Gareth Inc.

Fast Machines. 2001. 12p. (J). bds. 11.95 (978-0-7525-5263-7(5)) Parragon, Inc.

Faulkner, Keith & Chesterman, Adrian. Extreme Machines. 2005. (Illus.). 12p. (J). bds. 8.99 (978-0-7641-5836-0(8)) Barron's Educational Series, Inc.

Fechert, Sarah & Kespert, Deborah, contrib. by. De Aqui para Alla: On the Move. 2004. (Ladders—Spanish Ser.). (SPA., Illus.). 32p. (J). pap. 9.95 (978-1-58728-444-1(8)); 12.95 (978-1-58728-163-1(5)) T&N Children's Publishing. (Two Can Publishing).

Figorito, Christine. Go Far in the Car: Learning the AR Sound. (PowerPhonics Ser.). (Illus.). (J). 2002. 24p. (gr. 1). lib. bdg. 18.50 (978-0-8239-5938-9(4)); 2001. 23p. pap. 26.40 (978-0-8239-8283-7(1)) Rosen Publishing Group, Inc., The. (PowerKids Pr.).

Flammang, James M. Cars. 2001. (Transportation & Communication Ser.). (Illus.). 48p. (J). (gr. 1-4). lib. bdg. 23.93 (978-0-7660-1646-0(3)) Enslow Pubs., Inc.

Flanagan, Alice K. Mr. Yee Fixes Cars. Rau, Dana, ed. Flanagan, Romie, illus. 1998. (Our Neighborhood Ser.). 32p. (J). (gr. 1-2). pap. 6.95 (978-0-516-26297-0(1) , Children's Pr.) Scholastic Library Publishing.

Fontes, Justine & Petruccio, Steven James. At the Auto Repair Center. 1999. (Tonka Ser.). (J). (ps-2). pap. 3.50 (978-0-439-04286-4(0) , Cartwheel Bks.) Scholastic, Inc.

Foster, Walter, ed. Cars & Trucks: Step by Step Instructions for 28 Different Vehicles. Shelly, Jeff, illus. 2004. (Draw & Color Ser.). 40p. pap. 4.95 (978-1-56010-819-1(3)) Foster, Walter Publishing, Inc.

Franks, Pete. Ice Cream: (With Sundae Driver) S. I. International Staff, illus. 2005. (Matchbox Ser.). 16p. (J). bds. 6.99 (978-1-4169-0253-9(8) , Little Simon) Simon & Schuster Children's Publishing.

Gerth, Melanie. Mi Primer Gran Libro de los Vehiculos. 2004. (Mi primer gran libro de ... Ser.). (SPA., Illus.). 10p. 16.95 (978-84-7864-821-4(6)) Combel Editorial, S.A. ESP. *Dist:* Independent Pubs. Group.

Gibbs, Lynne & Morris, Neil. Mega Book of Cars. 2003. (Illus.). 32p. (YA). pap. 12.99 (978-1-903954-56-0(8)) Chrysalis Children's Bks.

Glencoe McGraw-Hill Staff. Automotive Excellence, Vol. 1. 2nd ed. 2003. (gr. 6-12). stu. ed. 66.64 (978-0-07-860572-7(5) , 9780078605727) Glencoe/McGraw-Hill.

—Automotive Excellence Vol. 2: Student Package. 2nd ed. 2003. (gr. 6-12). 66.64 (978-0-07-860573-4(3) , 9780078605734) Glencoe/McGraw-Hill.

Graham, Ian. Amazing Vehicles: Foldout Book. 2005. (Illus.). 14p. (J). (gr. k-4). reprint ed. 10.00 (978-0-7567-8777-6(7)) DIANE Publishing Co.

—The Best Book of Speed Machines. 2008. (Best Book of... Ser.). (Illus.). 32p. (J). pap. 6.95 (***978-0-7534-6168-6(4)*** , Kingfisher) Houghton Mifflin Co. Trade & Reference Div.

—Build Your Own Cool Cars. 2004. (Illus.). 48p. (***978-0-439-67662-5(2)***) Scholastic, Inc.

—Cars. 1999. (Built for Speed Ser.). (Illus.). 32p. (J). (gr. 3-7). lib. bdg. 25.69 (978-0-8172-4222-0(8)) Raintree.

—Cars. 2000. (Fast Forward Ser.). (Illus.). 32p. (J). (gr. 4-8). pap. 9.95 (978-0-531-16442-6(X) , Watts, Franklin) Scholastic Library Publishing.

—Cars. 2006. (Mighty Machines Ser.). (Illus.). 31p. (J). (978-1-58340-917-6(3)) Smart Apple Media.

—Cars. Connell, Tom, illus. 1998. (Built for Speed Ser.). 32p. (J). (gr. 3-7). pap. 7.95 (978-0-8172-8073-4(1)) Steck-Vaughn.

—Cars. 2000. (J). (978-0-606-19780-9(X)); (gr. 3-6). lib. bdg. 18.75 (978-0-613-34634-4(3)) Tandem Library Bks.

—Cars & Bikes: Machines at Work. 2007. (J). lib. bdg. 19.95 (978-1-59566-317-7(7)) QEB Publishing Inc.

—Race Cars. 2005. (World's Greatest Ser.). (Illus.). 32p. (J). (978-1-4109-2085-0(2)); (gr. 6-9). pap. 7.85 (978-1-4109-2092-8(5)) Steck-Vaughn.

—Sports Cars. 2003. (Designed for Success Ser.). 32p. pap. 7.50 (978-1-4034-3360-2(7)); (Illus.). (J). 24.22 (978-1-4034-0772-6(X)) Heinemann Library.

Graham, Ian & Salariya, David. Cars. Bergin, Mark, illus. 2000. (Fast Forward Ser.). 32p. (J). (gr. 4-8). 29.00 (978-0-531-11876-4(2) , Watts, Franklin) Scholastic Library Publishing.

Great Machines. 2001. 12p. (J). bds. 11.95 (978-0-7525-5264-4(3)) Parragon, Inc.

Group/McGraw-Hill, Wright. On the Move: Level H, 6 vols. (First Explorers Ser.). 24p. (gr. 1-2). 29.95 (978-0-7699-1449-7(7)) Shortland Pubns. (U. S. A.) Inc.

Gutelle, Andrew. Stock Car Kings. Snyder, Joel, illus. 2001. (All Aboard Reading Ser.). 1p. (J). (ps-3). pap. 3.99 (978-0-448-42489-7(4) , Grosset & Dunlap) Penguin Group (USA) Inc.

—Stock Car Kings. 2001. (All Aboard Reading Ser.). (Illus.). (J). (978-0-606-21467-4(4)) Tandem Library Bks.

Harpster, Steve. Cars & Trucks. 2006. (Pencil, Paper, Draw! Ser.). (Illus.). 64p. (J). pap., pap., spiral bd. 5.95 (978-1-4027-2975-1(8)) Sterling Publishing Co., Inc.

Harrison, Peter. Cars. 2001. (Investigations Ser.). (Illus.). 64p. (gr. 4-7). 14.95 (978-0-7548-0628-8(6) , Lorenz Bks.) Anness Publishing GBR. *Dist:* National Bk. Network.

Harrison, Peter, et al. Car & Road, Train & Track: Discover How Modern Land-Based Vehicles Changed Our World, How They Have Evolved & How They Work. 2004. (Illus.). 128p. pap. 17.99 (978-1-84476-004-6(9) , Southwater) Anness Publishing GBR. *Dist:* National Bk. Network.

Hart, Simon. Vamos, Vamos, Coches! 2006. 10p. (J). (ps-ps). bds. 4.99 (978-0-8431-2106-3(8) , Price Stern Sloan) Penguin Group (USA) Inc.

Hawley, Rebecca. Corvette. 2007. (Superfast Cars Ser.). (Illus.). 24p. (J). (gr. 3-5). lib. bdg. 21.25 (978-1-4042-3643-1(0) , PowerKids Pr.) Rosen Publishing Group, Inc., The.

—Lamborghini. 2007. (Superfast Cars Ser.). (Illus.). 24p. (J). (gr. 3-5). lib. bdg. 21.25 (978-1-4042-3642-4(2) , PowerKids Pr.) Rosen Publishing Group, Inc., The.

—Mustang. 2007. (Superfast Cars Ser.). (Illus.). 24p. (J). (gr. 3-5). lib. bdg. 21.25 (***978-1-4042-3645-5(7)***) Rosen Publishing Group, Inc., The.

—Porsche. 2007. (Superfast Cars Ser.). (Illus.). 24p. (J). (gr. 3-5). lib. bdg. 21.25 (978-1-4042-3641-7(4) , PowerKids Pr.) Rosen Publishing Group, Inc., The.

—Superfast Cars, 6 bks., Set. Incl. Corvette. lib. bdg. 21.25 (978-1-4042-3643-1(0) , PowerKids Pr.); Ferrari. lib. bdg. 21.25 (978-1-4042-3640-0(6) , PowerKids Pr.); Lamborghini. lib. bdg. 21.25 (978-1-4042-3642-4(2) , PowerKids Pr.); Mustang. lib. bdg. 21.25 (***978-1-4042-3645-5(7)***); Porsche. lib. bdg. 21.25 (978-1-4042-3641-7(4) , PowerKids Pr.); Viper. lib. bdg. 21.25 (978-1-4042-3644-8(9) , PowerKids Pr.); (Illus.). 24p. (J). (gr. 3-5). 2007. 2007. Set lib. bdg. 127.50 (***978-1-4042-3602-8(3)***) Rosen Publishing Group, Inc., The.

Hawley, Rebecca. Viper. 2007. (Superfast Cars Ser.). (Illus.). 24p. (J). (gr. 3-5). lib. bdg. 21.25 (978-1-4042-3644-8(9) , PowerKids Pr.) Rosen Publishing Group, Inc., The.

Henderson, Kathy & Hard, Charlotte. Cars Cars Cars. 2004. (Illus.). 32p. (J). pap. 7.95 (978-1-84507-176-9(X)) Lincoln, Frances Ltd. GBR. *Dist:* Perseus Distribution.

Hewitt, Sally. Cars. 2006. (Illus.). 24p. (YA). (gr. 1 up). lib. bdg. 22.80 (978-1-931983-55-6(0)) Chrysalis Education.

High Performance, 4 bks. Incl. Corvettes. Gronvall, Kal. lib. bdg. 21.26 (978-1-56065-391-2(4)); Jaguars. Green, Michael. lib. bdg. 21.26 (978-1-56065-393-6(0)); Lamborghinis. Green, Michael. lib. bdg. 21.26 (978-1-56065-394-3(9)); Mustangs. Gillespie, Lorrine. lib. bdg. 21.26 (978-1-56065-392-9(2)); 48p. (J). (gr. 3-4). 1996. (Illus.). Set lib. bdg. 85.04 (978-1-56065-647-0(6) , Capstone High-Interest Bks.) Capstone Pr., Inc.

Hill, Randal C. Aston Martin. 2008. (J). (***978-1-4296-0097-2(7)***) Capstone Pr., Inc.

—Lamborghini. 2008. (J). (***978-1-4296-0102-3(7)***) Capstone Pr., Inc.

Hill, Susanna Leonard. Taxi! With Checker Taxi. S. I. International Illustrators, illus. 2005. (Matchbox Ser.). 16p. (J). bds. 6.99 (978-1-4169-0254-6(6) , Little Simon) Simon & Schuster Children's Publishing.

Hinkler Books. Emergency: Let's Help! 2006. (Illus.). 8p. (J). (gr. 3-7). bds. 7.95 (978-1-74157-576-7(1)) Hinkler Bks. Pty, Ltd. AUS. *Dist:* Penton Overseas, Inc.

Hirst, Mike. Monster Machines. Veres, Laszlo, illus. 2005. (Twenty4Sevens Ser.). 48p. (J). pap. (978-0-439-78529-7(4)) Scholastic, Inc.

Holub, Joan. Cars & Trucks. 2002. (gr. k-3). lib. bdg. 14.15 (978-0-613-82376-0(1)) Tandem Library Bks.

Hosley, Maria. Cars. 2007. (Illus.). 24p. (J). 21.35 (***978-1-59679-800-7(9)***) ABDO Publishing Co.

Hot Animation Staff, Animation & Redmond, Diane. El Cumpleaños de Bob. Ziegler, Argentina Palacios, tr. 2004. (Bob the Builder Ser.).Tr. of Bob's Birthday. (SPA., Illus.). 24p. (J). 3.99 (978-0-689-86975-4(4)) Simon & Schuster Children's Publishing.

Hot Wheels Sticker. 2004. (J). act. bk. ed. (978-0-7666-0817-7(4) , 69670) Modern Publishing.

Hot Wheels Sticker Activity Books. 2004. (J). act. bk. ed. (978-0-7666-0818-4(2) , 69670) Modern Publishing.

How things Work: Level Q, 6 vols., Vol. 3. (Explorers Ser.). 32p. (gr. 3-6). 44.95 (978-0-7699-0620-1(6)) Shortland Pubns. (U. S. A.) Inc.

Hubbard-Brown, Janet. The Labonte Brothers. (Race Car Legends Ser.). (Illus.). 64p. (YA). 1999. (gr. 2-5). 28.00 (978-0-7910-5019-4(X)); 1998. (gr. 3 up). pap. 7.95 (978-0-7910-5758-2(5)) Facts On File, Inc. (Chelsea Hse.).

Hubbell, Joan. Corvette Pop-Up. 1999. (Illus.). 8.99 (978-0-525-46037-4(3) , Dutton Juvenile) Penguin Group (USA) Inc.

—Mustang Pop-Up. 1999. (Illus.). 8.99 (978-0-525-46038-1(1) , Dutton Juvenile) Penguin Group (USA) Inc.

Jefferis, David. Cars. 2007. (J). (***978-1-59920-040-8(6)***) Smart Apple Media.

Jeffries. Race Cars. 2003. (Monster Machines Ser.). (Illus.). 32p. (J). pap. 7.95 (978-1-4109-0057-9(6)) Raintree.

Johnstone, Michael. Cars. (Illus.). 32p. (J). mass mkt. 8.99 (978-0-590-24423-7(X)) Scholastic, Inc.

Kaelberer, Angie Peterson. Funny Cars. 2006. (Blazers—Horsepower Ser.). (Illus.). 32p. (J). (978-0-7368-4389-8(2)) Capstone Pr., Inc.

Kerrod, Robin. Transportation. 2004. (21st Century Science Ser.). (Illus.). 44p. (J). lib. bdg. 28.50 (978-1-58340-507-9(0)) Smart Apple Media.

Kilby, Don. In the City. 2005. (Wheels at Work Ser.). (Illus.). 24p. (J). (ps-2). (978-1-55337-471-8(1)) Kids Can Pr., Ltd.

Kimber, David. Auto-Mania! 2003. (Vehicle-Mania! Ser.). (Illus.). 32p. (J). (gr. 2 up). lib. bdg. 23.33 (978-0-8368-3781-0(9)) Stevens, Gareth Inc.

Klutz Press Staff. The Solar Car Book. 2001. (Illus.). 48p. (J). spiral bd. 21.95 (978-1-57054-646-4(0)) Klutz.

Kniffke, Sophie. El Coche. (Coleccion Mundo Maravilloso). (SPA., Illus.). 40p. (J). (gr. 2-4). (978-84-348-3472-9(3) , SM5465) SM Ediciones ESP. *Dist:* Lectorum Pubns., Inc.

LaFontaine, Bruce. American Muscle Cars, 1960-1975. 2001. (Pictorial Archive Ser.). (Illus.). 48p. (J). pap. 3.95 (978-0-486-41863-6(4)) Dover Pubns., Inc.

—Classic Cars Coloring Book. 2007. 112p. pap. 7.95 (***978-0-486-46067-3(3)***) Dover Pubns., Inc.

—Luxury Cars Coloring Book. 2005. (Illus.). 32p. (gr. 3). pap. 3.95 (978-0-486-44436-9(8)) Dover Pubns., Inc.

—Shiny Fast Cars. 2004. (Shiny Stickers Ser.). (Illus.). 2p. (J). (ps-5). 1.50 (978-0-486-43535-0(0)) Dover Pubns., Inc.

LaPenta, Marilyn. My Little Wipe-off Car Fun. Valdivia, Rochelle, illus. 2000. (My Little Wipe-Off Ser.). 8p. (J). (ps-1). bds. 4.99 (978-0-7681-0225-3(1) , 35016, McClanahan Bk.) Learning Horizons, Inc.

Lattimer, Jule-Ann. The Little Book of Street Rods. Lattimer, Jule-Ann, photos by. 2000. (Books for Young Learners). 12p. (J). pap. 5.00 (978-1-57274-393-9(X)) Owen, Richard C. Pubs., Inc.

Lee, Debra. Sylvia's Garage. Jabar, Cynthia, illus. Evans, Douglas, photos by. 2001. (Doors to Discovery Ser.). 8p. (J). pap. 7.76 (978-0-322-04831-7(1)) Wright Group, The.

Lee Stacy. BMW. 2004. (Hot Cars Ser.). 32p. pap. 6.95 (978-1-59515-343-2(8)) Rourke Publishing, LLC.

—Corvette. 2004. (Hot Cars Ser.). 32p. pap. 6.95 (978-1-59515-344-9(6)) Rourke Publishing, LLC.

—Ferrari. 2004. (Hot Cars Ser.). 32p. pap. 6.95 (978-1-59515-345-6(4)) Rourke Publishing, LLC.

—Mercedes Benz. 2004. (Hot Cars Ser.). 32p. pap. 6.95 (978-1-59515-347-0(0)) Rourke Publishing, LLC.

—Porsche. 2004. (Hot Cars Ser.). 32p. pap. 6.95 (978-1-59515-348-7(9)) Rourke Publishing, LLC.

Levin, Freddie. 1-2-3 Draw Cars, Trucks, & Other Vehicles: A Step-by-Step Guide. 2001. (1-2-3 Draw Ser.). (Illus.). 64p. (J). (gr. 1-7). pap. 8.99 (978-0-939217-44-1(9) , 32065) Peel Productions, Inc.

Lichtenheld, Tom. Everything I Know about Cars: A Collection of Made-Up Facts, Educated Guesses, & Silly Pictures about Cars, Trucks, & Other Zoomy Things. Lichtenheld, Tom, illus. 2005. (Illus.). 40p. (J). 16.95 (978-0-689-84382-2(8) , Simon & Schuster Children's Publishing) Simon & Schuster Children's Publishing.

Lindeen, Carol K. Ambulances. 2005. (Pebble Plus: Mighty Machines Ser.). (Illus.). 24p. (J). 19.93 (978-0-7368-3652-4(7) , Pebble Bks.) Capstone Pr., Inc.

Longhurst, Terry. I Can Draw Cars & Trucks. 2002. (I Can Draw Ser.). 32p. (J). 9.95 (978-0-7525-7282-6(2)) Parragon, Inc.

Loves, June. Cars. 2001. (Database Transportation Ser.). (Illus.). 32p. (J). (gr. 4 up). 22.95 (978-0-7910-6589-1(8) , 010503, Chelsea Hse.) Facts On File, Inc.

Lowriders. (Horsepower Ser.). 32p. (YA). 7.95 (978-0-7368-5212-8(3)) Capstone Pr., Inc.

Marx, Mandy. Demolition Derby Cars. 2006. (Blazers—Horsepower Ser.). (Illus.). 32p. (J). (978-0-7368-5472-6(X) , 1252778) Capstone Pr., Inc.

Mattern, Joanne. Staying Safe in the Car. 2006. (J). (ENG & SPA.). pap. (***978-0-8368-8065-6(X)***); (ENG & SPA.). lib. bdg. (***978-0-8368-8058-8(7)***); (Illus.). 24p. pap. (***978-0-8368-7800-4(0)***); (Illus.). 24p. lib. bdg. (***978-0-8368-7793-9(4)***) Stevens, Gareth Inc. (Weekly Reader Early Learning Library).

Matthews, Derek, illus. Escucha y Aprende: Trafico. 2005. (Escucha y Aprende Ser.). (SPA.). 10p. (J). (ps-7). 12.95 (978-970-718-297-4(0) , Silver Dolphin en Español) Advanced Marketing, S. de R. L. de C. V. MEX. *Dist:* Perseus Distribution.

Maurer, Tracy. Bugatti. 2008. (J). (***978-1-60044-570-5(5)***) Rourke Publishing, LLC.

—Jeep. 2007. (Illus.). 32p. (J). (978-1-60044-223-0(4)) Rourke Publishing, LLC.

—Lamborghini. 2007. (J). (978-1-60044-224-7(2)) Rourke Publishing, LLC.

—Limousines. 2003. (Illus.). 48p. (J). 29.93 (978-1-58952-747-8(X)) Rourke Publishing, LLC.

—Lotus. 2007. (J). (978-1-60044-226-1(9)) Rourke Publishing, LLC.

—Lowriders. 2003. (Roaring Rides Ser.). (Illus.). 48p. (J). 29.93 (978-1-58952-748-5(8)) Rourke Publishing, LLC.

—Mini Cooper. 2008. (J). (***978-1-60044-575-0(6)***) Rourke Publishing, LLC.

—Muscle Cars. 2003. (Illus.). 48p. (J). 29.93 (978-1-58952-750-8(X)) Rourke Publishing, LLC.

—Mustang. 2007. (J). (978-1-60044-227-8(7)) Rourke Publishing, LLC.

—PT Cruiser. 2008. (J). (***978-1-60044-576-7(4)***) Rourke Publishing, LLC.

—Tesla Roadster. 2008. (J). (***978-1-60044-577-4(2)***) Rourke Publishing, LLC.

Maurer, Tracy. VW Beetle: Full Throttle. 2007. (J). (978-1-60044-229-2(3)) Rourke Publishing, LLC.

Mayer, Cassie. By Car. 2006. (Illus.). 24p. (J). (978-1-4034-8394-2(9)); pap. (978-1-4034-8401-7(5)) Heinemann Library.

—En Automovil. 2006. (ENG & SPA., Illus.). 24p. (J). (978-1-4034-8635-6(2)); pap. (978-1-4034-8642-4(5)) Heinemann Library.

Maynard, Christopher. Racing Cars. 1999. (Supreme Machines Ser.). (Illus.). 48p. (J). (gr. 3-7). 14.95 (978-0-7641-5195-8(9)) Barron's Educational Series, Inc.

Mayo, Margaret. Dig Dig Digging. Ayliffe, Alex, illus. 2006. 24p. (J). bds. 5.95 (978-0-8050-7985-2(8) , Holt, Henry & Co. Bks. For Young Readers) Holt, Henry & Co.

McKenna, A. T. Corvette. 2000. (Ultimate Cars Ser.). (Illus.). 32p. (J). (gr. 3-8). lib. bdg. 24.21 (978-1-57765-127-7(8) , ABDO & Daughters) ABDO Publishing Co.

—Ferrari. 2000. (Ultimate Cars Ser.). (Illus.). 32p. (J). (gr. 3-8). lib. bdg. 24.21 (978-1-57765-123-9(5) , ABDO & Daughters) ABDO Publishing Co.

—Mustang. 2000. (Ultimate Cars Ser.). (Illus.). 32p. (J). (gr. 3-8). lib. bdg. 24.21 (978-1-57765-126-0(X) , ABDO & Daughters) ABDO Publishing Co.

—Porsche. 2000. (Ultimate Cars Ser.). (Illus.). 32p. (J). (gr. 3-8). lib. bdg. 24.21 (978-1-57765-124-6(3) , ABDO & Daughters) ABDO Publishing Co.

Mellet, Peter, et al, trs. All about Cars. 2004. (All About-...Ser.). (Illus.). 64p. pap. 7.99 (978-1-84215-893-7(7) , Southwater) Anness Publishing GBR. *Dist:* National Bk. Network.

Merrell, Patrick. Everything Kids' Racecars Puzzle & Activity Book: Put the pedal to the metal for laps & laps of Fun! 2008. 144p. pap. 7.95 (***978-1-59869-243-3(7)***) Adams Media Corp.

Mezzanotte, Jim. The Story of Ferrari. 2005. (Classic Cars Ser.). (Illus.). 24p. (YA). lib. bdg. 22.00 (978-0-8368-4533-4(1)) Stevens, Gareth Inc.

—The Story of the Ford Mustang. 2005. (Classic Cars Ser.). (Illus.). 24p. (YA). lib. bdg. 22.00 (978-0-8368-4534-1(X)) Stevens, Gareth Inc.

Miller, Gary. Auto Mania. 2005. (Real Deal-Red Plus Ser.). (Illus.). 32p. (gr. 4-8). 19.00 (978-0-7910-8894-4(4)) Facts On File, Inc.

Miller, Heather. Carros. 2003. (Ruedas, Alas y Agua Ser.).Tr. of Cars. (SPA., 24p. (J). Illus.). lib. bdg. 18.50 (978-1-4034-0917-1(X)); pap. 5.25 (978-1-4034-3532-3(4)) Heinemann Library.

—Cars. 2003. (Wheels, Wings, & Water Ser.). (Illus.). 24p. (J). lib. bdg. 18.50 (978-1-4034-0880-8(7)); pap. (978-1-4034-3619-1(3)) Heinemann Library.

—Cars. 2003. (gr. k-3). lib. bdg. 13.30 (978-0-613-67396-9(4)) Tandem Library Bks.

Minden, Cecilia & Minden-Zins, Mary. Auto Mechanics. 2006. (Neighborhood Helpers Ser.). (Illus.). 32p. (J). (gr. k-4). 22.79 (978-1-59296-560-1(1)) Child's World, Inc.

Mitchell, Joyce Slayton. Crashed, Smashed, & Mashed: A Trip to Junkyard Heaven. Borns, Steven, photos by. 2005. (Illus.). 32p. (J). (ps-3). pap. 7.95 (978-1-58246-156-4(2) , Tricycle Pr.) Ten Speed Pr.

Mitton, Tony. Cool Cars. Parker, Ant, illus. 2005. (Amazing Machines Ser.). 24p. (J). (ps-k). 9.95 (978-0-7534-5802-0(0) , Kingfisher) Houghton Mifflin Co. Trade & Reference Div.

Morganelli, Adrianna. Formula One. 2006. (Automania! Ser.). (Illus.). 32p. (J). (gr. 4-6). pap. (978-0-7787-3031-6(X)); lib. bdg. (978-0-7787-3009-5(3)) Crabtree Publishing Co.

Morse, Jenifer Corr. Cars. 2001. (Speed! Ser.). (Illus.). 24p. (J). (gr. 3-6). 21.20 (978-1-56711-467-6(9) , Blackbirch Pr., Inc.) Thomson Gale.

Multimedia Auto Shop Safety. (Shop Safety Ser.). (YA). cd-rom 69.95 (978-0-7365-9989-4(4)) Films Media Group.

Murawski, Laura. How to Draw Cars. 2001. (Kid's Guide to Drawing Ser.). (Illus.). 24p. (J). (gr. 3). lib. bdg. 21.25 (978-0-8239-5548-0(6) , PowerKids Pr.) Rosen Publishing Group, Inc., The.

Murphy. Beep Beep, Vroom Vroom. 2002. (Illus.). pap. (978-0-7398-6783-9(0)) Steck-Vaughn.

Murphy, Stuart J. Beep Beep, Vroom Vroom! Demarest, Chris L., illus. 2000. (MathStart Ser.). 40p. (J). (ps up). pap. 5.99 (978-0-06-446728-5(7) , Harper Trophy) HarperCollins Pubs.

Murphy, Stuart J. & Murphy, Stuart J. Beep Beep, Vroom Vroom! Demarest, Chris L., illus. 2000. 33p. (J). (ps-ps). lib. bdg. 13.00 (978-0-613-21188-8(X)) Tandem Library Bks.

My First Car. 1999. (Illus.). pap. 16.99 (978-0-525-46030-5(6) , Dutton Juvenile) Penguin Group (USA) Inc.

NASCAR. NASCAR Learn to Draw Race Cars. 2006. (NASCAR Ser.). 32p. (J). (gr. 3-5). pap. 5.95 (978-1-56010-782-8(0)) Foster, Walter Publishing, Inc.

NASCAR Micro Cars: Start Your Engines! 2002. 18p. (J). (978-0-439-45567-1(7)) Scholastic, Inc.

Newhouse, Maxwell. Let's Go for a Ride. 2006. (Illus.). 24p. (J). (ps-2). 16.95 (978-0-88776-748-7(6)) Tundra Bks., Inc./Livres Toundra, Inc. CAN. *Dist:* Random Hse., Inc.

Off-Road Racers. (Mighty MacHines Ser.). 16p. (J). (978-2-7643-0173-9(1)) Phidal Publishing, Inc./Editions Phidal, Inc.

Oldham, Donald L. Drive for Your Life. 2000. (gr. 7-12). lib. bdg. 21.60 (978-0-613-74614-4(7)) Tandem Library Bks.

Otfinoski, Steven. Here We Go!, 4 bks., Set, Group 1. Incl. Behind the Wheel : Cars Then & Now. lib. bdg. 22.79 (978-0-7614-0403-3(1)); Into the Wind : Sailboats Then & Now. lib. bdg. 22.79 (978-0-7614-0405-7(8)); Pedaling Along : Bikes Then & Now. lib. bdg. 22.79 (978-0-7614-0402-6(3)); Taking Off : Planes Then & Now. lib. bdg. 22.79 (978-0-7614-0407-1(4)); 32p. (J). (gr. 1-12). 1996. (Illus.). lib. bdg. (978-0-7614-0401-9(5) , Benchmark Bks.) Cavendish, Marshall Corp.

Out & About: Level Q, 6 vols., Vol. 2. (Explorers Ser.). 32p. (gr. 3-6). 44.95 (978-0-7699-0608-9(7)) Shortland Pubns. (U. S. A.) Inc.

Oxlade, Chris. Car. 2002. (Take It Apart Ser.). (Illus.). 32p. (J). (gr. 4-6). lib. bdg. 24.25 (978-1-930643-94-9(2)) Chrysalis Education.

—Cars. 2000. (Transportation Around the World Ser.). (Illus.). 32p. (J). (gr. k-2). lib. bdg. 21.36 (978-1-57572-302-0(6)) Heinemann Library.

—Sports Cars. 2004. (Mean Machines Ser.). (Illus.). 32p. (J). 32.79 (978-1-4109-1084-4(9)); pap. 8.95 (978-1-4109-1199-5(3)) Harcourt Schl. Pubs.

—Sports Cars 6-Pack. 2004. (Mean Machines Ser.). (Illus.). (J). pap. 48.30 (978-1-4109-1204-6(3)) Harcourt Schl. Pubs.

Parker, Steve. Cars. Sweet, Stephen, illus. 2005. (Twenty4Sevens Ser.). 48p. (J). pap. (978-0-439-78528-0(6)) Scholastic, Inc.

—The Inside & Out Guide to Speed Machines. 2006. (Illus.). 32p. (J). (978-1-4034-9089-6(9)); pap. (978-1-4034-9096-4(1)) Heinemann Library.

Parr, Ann. Low Riders. 2000. (Race Car Legends Ser.). (Illus.). 64p. (J). (gr. 4-7). 28.00 (978-0-7910-5849-7(2)); pap. 5.95 (978-0-7910-5850-3(6)) Facts On File, Inc. (Chelsea Hse.).

Parr, Danny. Lowriders. 2001. (Wild Rides! Ser.). (Illus.). 32p. (J). (gr. 3-4). lib. bdg. 21.26 (978-0-7368-0928-3(7) , Capstone High-Interest Bks.) Capstone Pr., Inc.

Parsons, Jayne, ed. Diggers & Dumpers. 2005. (Ultimate sticker Bks.). 16p. (J). pap. 6.99 (978-0-7566-0974-0(7)) Dorling Kindersley Publishing, Inc.

Pearson, Debora. Rough Tough Wheels. McLeod, Chum, illus. 2000. (Mighty Wheels Ser.). 24p. (J). (gr. k-ps). pap. 5.95 (978-1-55037-636-4(5)) Annick Pr., Ltd. CAN. *Dist:* Firefly Bks., Ltd.

—Rough, Tough Wheels. McLeod, Chum, illus. 2000. (Mighty Wheels Ser.). 24p. (J). (gr. k-ps). lib. bdg. 17.95 (978-1-55037-637-1(3)) Annick Pr., Ltd. CAN. *Dist:* Firefly Bks., Ltd.

Pedal to the Metal: A History of Cars. 2005. (Book Treks Ser.). (J). 37.95 (978-0-7652-3249-6(9)) Celebration Pr.

Petty, Kate. The Encyclopedia of Awesome Machines. Watton, Ross & Moore, Jo, illus. 2003. 112p. (J). (gr. 4-8). reprint ed. 15.00 (978-0-7567-6963-5(9)) DIANE Publishing Co.

Piehl, Janet. Indy Race Cars. 2007. (Motor Mania Ser.). 48p. (J). (gr. 4-7). 26.60 (978-0-8225-6566-6(8) , Lerner Pubns.) Lerner Publishing Group.

Pipe, Jim. Cars. 2006. (Illus.). 24p. (J). (978-1-59604-116-5(1)) Stargazer Bks.

Poiley, Joel. Cool Cars: Lean, Mean, Racing Machines. 2000. (Illus.). 32p. (J). pap. 3.99 (978-1-930623-05-7(4)) Sports Illustrated For Kids.

Police Cars, 6 vols. (gr. k-2). 28.95 (978-0-7368-8128-9(X)) Red Brick Learning.

Poolos, Jamie. Hot Rods. 2008. (J). lib. bdg. ***(978-1-4042-3790-2(9)*** , PowerKids Pr.) Rosen Publishing Group, Inc., The.

—Muscle Cars. 2008. (J). lib. bdg. ***(978-1-4042-3788-9(7)*** , PowerKids Pr.) Rosen Publishing Group, Inc., The.

Povey, Karen D. Hybrid Cars. 2006. (Our Environment Ser.). 48p. (J). (gr. 4-8). 26.20 (978-0-7377-3484-3(1) , Greenhaven Pr., Inc.) Thomson Gale.

Priddy Books Staff & Priddy, Roger. Happy Baby: Things That Go. 2004. (Illus.). 28p. (J). bds. 8.95 (978-0-312-49198-7(0) , Priddy Bks.) St. Martin's Pr.

—Wipe Clean Things That Go: Things That Go 26 Wipe-Clean Pages of Early Learning Fun. rev. ed. 2004. (Wipe Clean Ser.). (Illus.). 28p. (J). bds. 8.95 (978-0-312-49400-1(9) , Priddy Bks.) St. Martin's Pr.

Priddy, Roger. Picture Pops Machines. 2005. (Illus.). 18p. (J). (ps-7). 12.95 (978-0-312-49466-7(1) , Priddy Bks.) St. Martin's Pr.

—Soft-to-Touch Slipcase 1: Things,Words & Animals. 2004. 84p. (J). bds. 22.95 (978-0-312-49422-3(X) , Priddy Bks.) St. Martin's Pr.

Pro Stock Cars, 6 vols. (gr. 4 up). 39.95 (978-0-7368-9294-0(X)) Red Brick Learning.

Randolph, Joanne. Tow Trucks. 2008. lib. bdg. ***(978-1-4042-4154-1(X)*** , PowerKids Pr.) Rosen Publishing Group, Inc., The.

Random House Disney Staff. The Fast Lane. Disney Storybook Artists Staff, illus. 2006. (Deluxe Coloring Book Ser.). 64p. (J). (ps-2). pap. 3.99 (978-0-375-83377-9(3) , Golden/Disney) Random Hse. Children's Bks.

—Welcome to Radiator Springs. Disney Storybook Artists Staff, illus. 2006. (Paint Box Book Ser.). 32p. (J). (ps-2). pap. 3.99 (978-0-375-83378-6(1) , Golden/Disney) Random Hse. Children's Bks.

Rau, Dana Meachen. Driving. 2006. (On the Move Ser.). (ENG & SPA., Illus.). 24p. (J). lib. bdg. 22.79 (978-0-7614-2316-4(8) , Benchmark Bks.) Cavendish, Marshall Corp.

Robertson, Brian. Pop-up Planes, Trains & Automobiles. Robertson, Brian & King, Chris, illus. 2005. 10p. (J). (gr. k-4). reprint ed. 17.00 (978-0-7567-9255-8(X)) DIANE Publishing Co.

Robertson, Scott. How to Draw Cars the Hot Wheels Way. rev. ed. 2004. (Illus.). 144p. (J). pap., pap. 21.95 (978-0-7603-1480-7(2)) MBI Distribution Services.

Rockwell, Anne F. Cars. 1999. (J). (ps-2). lib. bdg. 14.15 (978-0-8085-7279-4(2)) Tandem Library Bks.

Rowe, Barry & Doyle, Garry. Atmosphere & Light: The Automotive Paintings of Barry Rowe. 2004. (Illus.). 224p. 125.00 (978-1-893618-34-3(X)) Bull, David Publishing, Inc.

Sacks, Janet. Mini Magic Color Book: Cars. Rinaldo, Luana, illus. 2007. 10p. (J). 3.95 (978-1-4027-4592-8(3) , Sterling/Pinwheel) Sterling Publishing Co., Inc.

Sandler, Martin W. Driving Around the USA: Automobiles in American Life. 2003. (Transportation in America Ser.). (Illus.). 64p. (YA). 21.95 (978-0-19-513230-4(0)) Oxford Univ. Pr., Inc.

Saunders-Smith, Gail. Cars. 1998. (J). pap. 13.25 (978-0-516-21226-5(5) , Children's Pr.) Scholastic Library Publishing.

Sautter, Aaron. How to Draw Incredible Cars. Bascle, Brian, illus. 2008. (J). ***(978-1-4296-0077-4(2))*** Capstone Pr., Inc.

Scarry, Richard. Cars & Trucks & Things That Go. 1998. (Richard Scarry's Ser.). (Illus.). 72p. (J). (ps-3). 14.99 (978-0-307-15785-0(7) , 15785, Golden Bks.) Random Hse. Children's Bks.

Schaefer, A. R. Sprint Cars. 2004. (Wild Rides! Ser.). (Illus.). 32p. (J). lib. bdg. 22.60 (978-0-7368-2727-0(7)) Capstone Pr., Inc.

Schlesinger, Willy. Scooter Mania! Fun Tricks & Cool Tips for Today's Hottest Ride. 2000. (gr. 7-12). lib. bdg. 16.40 (978-0-613-84834-3(9)) Tandem Library Bks.

Schoberle, Cecile. Storm Chaser! Huxtable, John, illus. 2004. (Matchbox Ser.). 32p. (J). pap. 3.99 (978-0-689-87338-6(7) , Little Simon) Simon & Schuster Children's Publishing.

Scholastic, Inc. Staff. Cars & Trucks. 2008. (Littlest Pet Shop Ser.). 24p. (J). pap. 5.99 ***(978-0-545-00141-0(2)*** , Scholastic Reference) Scholastic, Inc.

Scholastic, Inc. Staff. Design It Yourself Supercars. Araujo, Paige Krul, ed. 2005. (J). 9.99 (978-0-439-71607-9(1)) Scholastic, Inc.

Scholastic, Inc. Staff & Kelly, Alex. Cars & Trucks. 2008. (How I Survived Middle School Ser.). 24p. (J). pap. 3.99 ***(978-0-545-00793-1(3))*** Scholastic, Inc.

School Specialty Publishing. Car. 1999. (Blank Books for Young Authors Ser.). 16p. (J). (gr. k-3). pap. 16.99 (978-0-7424-0383-3(1) , IF78B) School Specialty Publishing.

Schuette, Sarah L. Drift Cars. 2008. ***(978-1-4296-0826-8(9))*** Capstone Pr., Inc.

—Hot Rods. 2007. (Blazers—Horsepower Ser.). (Illus.). 32p. (J). (978-0-7368-6781-8(3) , 1264927) Capstone Pr., Inc.

—Sprint Cars. 2007. (Blazers—Horsepower Ser.). (Illus.). 32p. 19.93 (978-0-7368-6452-7(0)) Capstone Pr., Inc.

—Tuner Cars. 2006. (Blazers—Horsepower Ser.). (Illus.). 32p. (J). (978-0-7368-5475-7(4)) Capstone Pr., Inc.

Seelig, Tina L. Games for Your Brain: Cars. 2007. (Illus.). 61p. (J). 9.95 (978-0-8118-5707-9(7)) Chronicle Bks. LLC.

Shulman, Mark. Car & Truck Show. Small, Phillip, illus. 2005. (Storytime Stickers Ser.). 16p. (J). pap. 4.95 (978-1-4027-1807-6(1)) Sterling Publishing Co., Inc.

Simon, Seymour. Cool Cars. 2003. (See More Readers). (Illus.). 32p. (J). 14.50 (978-1-58717-236-6(4)); (gr. 1-3). pap. 3.95 (978-1-58717-237-3(2)) Chronicle Bks. LLC. (SeaStar Bks.).

Sinclair, Julie L. The Automobile, 6 vols. (gr. 2-5). 36.95 (978-0-7368-4613-4(1)) Red Brick Learning.

Sloan, Peter. Car That Stopped. 2000. (gr. k-3). lib. bdg. 11.80 (978-0-613-30305-7(9)) Tandem Library Bks.

—Making a Car. 1999. (gr. k-3). lib. bdg. 11.55 (978-0-613-30583-9(3)) Tandem Library Bks.

Sports Cars. (Horsepower Ser.). 32p. (YA). 7.95 (978-0-7368-5219-7(0)) Capstone Pr., Inc.

Stacy, Lee. Ferrari. 2005. (Hot Cars Ser.). (Illus.). 32p. (gr. 4-8). 19.95 (978-1-59515-210-7(5)) Rourke Publishing, LLC.

—Mercedes. 2005. (Hot Cars Ser.). (Illus.). 32p. (gr. 4-8). 19.95 (978-1-59515-212-1(1)) Rourke Publishing, LLC.

—Porsche. 2005. (Hot Cars Ser.). (Illus.). 32p. (gr. 4-8). 19.95 (978-1-59515-213-8(X)) Rourke Publishing, LLC.

Stevens, Ian. Extreme Machines. 2005. (Top Tens Ser.). (Illus.). 32p. (J). (gr. 4-7). lib. bdg. 25.27 (978-1-59716-065-0(2)) Bearport Publishing Co., Inc.

Stickland, Paul. Cars. 2004. (By Air, Sea, & Land Ser.). (Illus.). 24p. (J). pap. 3.99 (978-0-7696-3373-2(0) , Waterbird Bks.) School Specialty Publishing.

—Cars. Stickland, Paul, illus. 1998. (On the Move Ser.). (Illus.). 16p. (J). (ps up). lib. bdg. 19.93 (978-0-8368-2152-9(1)) Stevens, Gareth Inc.

Stock Cars. (Horsepower Ser.). 32p. (YA). 7.95 (978-0-7368-5215-9(8)) Capstone Pr., Inc.

Strickland, Paul. On the Move: Boats; Cars; Planes; Trains, 4 bks. Strickland, Paul, illus. 2002. (Illus.). (J). (ps up). pap. (978-0-8368-3333-1(3) , Weekly Reader Early Learning Library) Stevens, Gareth Inc.

Sundance, ed. What a Car Has. 2000. (ps-2). lib. bdg. 11.65 (978-0-613-37634-1(X)) Tandem Library Bks.

Tallarico, Tony. A-Maze-Ing Cool Cars. 2002. (Illus.). 96p. (J). (978-1-58865-037-5(5)) Kidsbooks, Inc.

Tatge, Cathy. Cars. 2007. (J). (978-1-58341-527-6(0) , Creative Education) Creative Co., The.

Teitelbaum, Michael. Hot Wheels Stock Cars Book & Toy Set. 2003. (Illus.). 64p. 6.95 (978-0-7603-1507-1(8)) MBI Publishing Co. LLC.

Tiner, John Hudson. Cars. (Illus.). 32p. 2004. pap. 8.95 (978-0-89812-388-3(7) , Creative Paperbacks); 2003. (J). lib. bdg. 18.95 (978-1-58341-256-5(5) , Creative Education) Creative Co., The.

Top That Publishing Staff, ed. Fast Cars. 2005. (Illus.). 24p. (978-1-84510-536-5(2)) Top That! Publishing PLC.

Trucks & Cars. 2003. 32p. 12.98 (978-1-4054-2006-8(5)) Parragon, Inc.

Turk, Steve, illus. Race Cars. 2001. (Sticker Stories Ser.). 20p. (J). (ps-3). pap. 4.99 (978-0-448-42194-0(1) , Grosset & Dunlap) Penguin Group (USA) Inc.

Turney, William J. & Chek-Chart Staff. Automotive Steering, Suspension, & Wheel Alignment. 2nd ed. 1999. (Illus.). (J). (978-1-57932-151-2(8)) Keller, J.J. & Assocs., Inc.

The Ultimate History of Ferrari. 2002. 192p. (YA). 39.95 (978-0-7525-8873-5(7)) Parragon, Inc.

The Ultimate History of Porsche. 2003. 192p. (YA). 39.95 (978-0-7525-8874-2(5)) Parragon, Inc.

Volke, Gordon. Crazy Cars. Chauhan, Manhar, illus. 2006. 14p. (J). 8.99 (978-0-439-85674-4(4)) Scholastic, Inc.

Walker, Pamela. Car Rides. 2000. (Welcome Bks.). (Illus.). 24p. (J). (ps-2). pap. 4.95 (978-0-516-23025-2(5) , Children's Pr.) Scholastic Library Publishing.

Walsh, Patricia. Cars. 2002. (Draw It! Ser.). (Illus.). 32p. (J). (gr. 3-6). pap. 7.50 (978-1-58810-292-8(0) , 91042) Heinemann Library.

Walsh, Patricia & Westerfield, David. Cars. 2000. (Draw It! Ser.). (Illus.). 32p. (J). (gr. 3-5). lib. bdg. 22.79 (978-1-57572-348-8(4)) Heinemann Library.

Watt, Fiona. That's Not My Car. Wells, Rachel, illus. 2004. (Touchy-Feely Board Books Ser.). 10p. (J). 7.95 (978-0-7945-0636-0(4) , Usborne) EDC Publishing.

Weiss, Ellen. Math in the Car. 2007. (Scholastic News Nonfiction Readers: Everyday Math—NEW SUBSET Ser.). 24p. (J). pap. 6.95 ***(978-0-531-18783-8(7));*** (Illus.). (gr. 1-2). lib. bdg. 20.00 ***(978-0-531-18530-8(3))*** Scholastic Library Publishing. (Children's Pr.).

Werther, Scott P. Big Rigs: Individual Title Six-Packs. (On Deck Ser.). 24p. (gr. 4-5). 35.00 (978-0-7578-1043-5(8)) Rigby Education.

—Dragsters. 2004. (Maquinas Extremas Ser.). (SPA & ENG., Illus.). 24p. (J). (gr. 3-6). lib. bdg. 17.25 (978-0-8239-6886-2(3) , Buenas Letra) Rosen Publishing Group, Inc., The.

—Limosinas Largas: Individual Title Six-Packs. (On Deck en Espanol Ser.).Tr. of Long Limousines. (SPA.). 24p. (gr. 4-5). 35.00 (978-0-7578-6422-3(8)) Rigby Education.

—Long Limousines. 2002. (Reading Power Ser.). (Illus.). 24p. (J). (gr. 1). lib. bdg. 17.25 (978-0-8239-5958-7(9) , PowerKids Pr.) Rosen Publishing Group, Inc., The.

—Long Limousines: Individual Title Six-Packs. (On Deck Ser.). 24p. (gr. 4-5). 35.00 (978-0-7578-1047-3(0)) Rigby Education.

—Low Riders. 2002. (Reading Power Ser.). (Illus.). 24p. (J). (gr. 1). lib. bdg. 17.25 (978-0-8239-5954-9(6) , PowerKids Pr.) Rosen Publishing Group, Inc., The.

—Low Riders: Autos Low Rider. 2004. (Reading Power Ser.). (ENG & SPA., Illus.). 24p. (J). (gr. 3-6). lib. bdg. 17.25 (978 0 8239-6888-6(X) , PowerKids Pr.) Rosen Publishing Group, Inc., The.

—Low Riders: Individual Title Six-Packs. (On Deck Ser.). 24p. (gr. 4-5). 35.00 (978-0-7578-1046-6(2)) Rigby Education.

Wick, Walter. Can You See What I See? Trucks & Cars. 2007. (J). bds. 4.99 (978-0-439-86230-1(2) , Cartwheel Bks.) Scholastic, Inc.

Wild Rides! BMX Bikes; Dirt Bikes; Dragsters; Lowriders; Monster Trucks; Motocross Cycles; Pro Stock Cars; Snowmobiles, 8 bks. (Illus.). (J). (gr. 3-4). lib. bdg. 170.08 (978-0-7368-1006-7(4) , Capstone High-Interest Bks.) Capstone Pr., Inc.

Wilkinson, Philip, et al. On the Move; Minipedia. 2002. (Illus.). 144p. (J). pap. (978-0-439-38192-5(4)) Scholastic, Inc.

Willson, Quentin. Classic Cars of the World. Lucas, Sharon, ed. (YA). pap. 39.95 (978-0-7894-5097-5(6)) Dorling Kindersley Publishing, Inc.

Winget, Mary. Taxis. 2007. (Illus.). 32p. (J). pap. 5.95 ***(978-0-8225-6425-6(4)*** , First Avenue Editions) Lerner Publishing Group.

Winget, Mary & Winget, W. Bryan. Tow Trucks. 2007. (Pull Ahead Books). (J). 22.60 (978-0-8225-6006-7(2) , Lerner Pubns.) Lerner Publishing Group.

Woods, Bob. Hottest Muscle Cars. 2007. (Wild Wheels! Ser.). (Illus.). 48p. (J). (gr. 4-10). lib. bdg. 23.93 ***(978-0-7660-2872-2(0))*** Enslow Pubs., Inc.

The World's Fastest Cars, 6 vols. (gr. 4 up). 39.95 (978-0-7368-8948-3(5)) Red Brick Learning.

Zronik, John Paul. Street Cred. 2006. (Automania! Ser.). (Illus.). 32p. (J). (gr. 4-6). pap. (978-0-7787-3028-6(X)); lib. bdg. (978-0-7787-3006-4(9)) Crabtree Publishing Co.

Zuehlke, Jeffrey. Concept Cars. 2007. (Motor Mania Ser.). 48p. (J). (gr. 4-7). 26.60 (978-0-8225-6568-0(4) , Lerner Pubns.) Lerner Publishing Group.

—Muscle Cars. 2007. (Motor Mania Ser.). (Illus.). 48p. (J). (gr. 4-7). 26.60 (978-0-8225-5927-6(7) , Lerner Pubns.) Lerner Publishing Group.

AUTOMOBILES—ACCIDENTS

see Traffic Accidents

AUTOMOBILES—DESIGN AND CONSTRUCTION

Anderson, Jenna. How It Happens at the Truck Plant. Wolfe, Bob & Wolfe, Diane, photos by. 2002. (How It Happens Ser.). (Illus.). 32p. (J). (gr. 2-5). lib. bdg. 19.95 (978-1-881508-93-9(5)) Oliver Pr., Inc.

Banting, Erinn. Inventing the Automobile. 2006. (Breakthrough Inventions Ser.). (Illus.). 32p. (J). (gr. 3-9). pap. (978-0-7787-2834-4(X)); (978-0-7787-2812-2(9)) Crabtree Publishing Co.

De Angelis, George, et al. The Ford Model A - As Henry Built It: A Color, Upholstery & Production Facts Book. De Angelis, George, ed. 5th ed. 2001. (Illus.). 246p. (gr. 10 up). reprint ed. pap. 33.50 (978-0-9712668-0-3(8)) DeA Publishing Co., G.

DeBoard, Will. Building a Stock Car: The Need for More Speed. 2002. (World of NASCAR Ser.). (Illus.). 32p. (J). (gr. 2-6). 25.64 (978-1-59187-000-5(3)) Child's World, Inc.

DK Publishing Staff. Pinewood Derby Design Secrets. 2007. 12.95 ***(978-0-7566-3262-5(5))*** Dorling Kindersley Publishing, Inc.

Green, Robert. Cars. 2008. (J). lib. bdg. 25.26 ***(978-1-60279-028-5(0))*** Cherry Lake Publishing.

Zemlicka, Shannon. From Iron to Car. 2004. (Start to Finish Ser.). (Illus.). 24p. (J). 18.60 (978-0-8225-0943-1(1) , Lerner Pubns.) Lerner Publishing Group.

AUTOMOBILES—DRIVING

see Automobile Drivers

AUTOMOBILES—ENGINES

Bankston, John. Karl Benz & the Single Cylinder Engine. 2004. (Uncharted, Unexplored, & Unexplained Ser.). (Illus.). 48p. (J). (gr. 4-8). lib. bdg. 29.95 (978-1-58415-244-6(3)) Mitchell Lane Pubs., Inc.

AUTOMOBILES—FICTION

Appleton, Victor. Tom Swift & His Electric Runabout or T. 2006. pap. ***(978-1-4065-0901-4(9))*** Dodo Pr.

Aroner, Miriam. Clink, Clank, Clunk. Catalano, Dominic, illus. 2006. 32p. (J). 15.95 (978-1-59078-270-5(4)) Boyds Mills Pr.

Awdry, Wilbert V. Engines & Animals. Yee, Josie, illus. 2005. (Thomas & Friends Ser.). 12p. (J). (gr. k-k). bds. 4.99 (978-0-375-83162-1(2) , Random Hse. Bks. for Young Readers) Random Hse. Children's Bks.

Banscherus, Jurgen & Baron, Daniel C. Clues in the Car Wash. Butschkow, Ralf, illus. 2007. (J). 40p. ***(978-1-59889-337-3(8));*** 67p. pap. ***(978-1-59889-432-5(3))*** Stone Arch Bks.

Barbot, Daniel. El Auto del Sr. Pulga. Mas, Maribel, illus. 2004. (SPA.). 28p. (J). pap. 6.99 (978-980-257-260-1(8)) Ekare, Ediciones VEN. *Dist:* Lectorum Pubns., Inc.

Barrows, Will. A Car Followed Us. O'Malley, Kathleen, illus. 2000. (Books for Young Learners). 8p. (J). pap. 5.00 (978-1-57274-251-2(8)) Owen, Richard C. Pubs., Inc.

Barton, Byron. My Car. Barton, Byron, illus. (J). (ps-1). 2003. (Illus.). 36p. bds. 6.99 (978-0-06-056045-4(2)); 2001. (Illus.). 40p. 15.99 (978-0-06-029624-7(0)); 2001. (Illus.). 40p. lib. bdg. 16.89 (978-0-06-029625-4(9)); 2004. 40p. reprint ed. pap. 6.99 (978-0-06-058940-0(X) , Harper Trophy) HarperCollins Pubs.

Base, Graeme. Truckdogs: A Novel in Four Bites. (J). (gr. 3-7). 2005. 160p. pap. 7.95 (978-0-8109-8789-0(9)); 2004. (Illus.). 158p. 16.95 (978-0-8109-5031-3(6)) Abrams, Harry N. , Inc.

Baxter, Nicola. Little Red Car. Ladybird Books Staff, ed. 1998. (Little Vehicle Stories Ser.). (Illus.). 32p. (J). 2.50 (978-0-7214-1931-2(3) , Dutton Juvenile) Penguin Group (USA) Inc.

Beautiful Book Staff. Hello PistenBully! 2006. (PistonBully Ser.). (Illus.). 24p. pap. 8.95 (978-0-9549476-9-9(X)) Beautiful Bks. GBR. *Dist:* International Publishers Marketing.

Berenstain, Stan & Berenstain, Jan. The Berenstain Bears Red Roadster. Torgerson, Dell & Reyner, Mark, eds. 2000. 10p. (J). (ps). mass mkt. 9.99 (978-1-887327-36-7(3)) CT Co., Inc.

Beresford, Elisabeth. Wombles Buggy Trouble. (Illus.). 15p. (J). (gr. k-6). pap. (978-0-340-74670-7(X) , Hodder & Stoughton) Hodder General Publishing Division.

Blake, Quentin. Mrs. Armitage: Queen of the Road. Blake, Quentin, illus. 2003. (Illus.). 32p. (J). (gr. k-3). 15.95 (978-1-56145-287-3(4)) Peachtree Pubs., Ltd.

—Mrs. Armitage Queen of the Road. 2003. (Illus.). 32p. (978-0-224-06472-9(X) , Jonathan Cape) Random Hse. Children's Bks. GBR. *Dist:* Random Hse. of Canada, Ltd.

Bonnell, Kris. We Ride. 2005. (J). 3.75 (978-1-933727-19-6(5)) Reading Reading Bks., LLC.

Boyce, Frank Cottrell, ed. Framed. 2006. 320p. (J). 16.99 (978-0-06-073402-2(7)); lib. bdg. 17.89 (978-0-06-073403-9(5)) HarperCollins Pubs.

Brouillette, Peter. The Adventures of Old Henry: Nobody Cares. Lee, Williams, illus. 2004. (J). per. 19.99 (978-0-9760419-3-1(6)) ThatsMyLife Co.

Brovelli, Tito Alberto. Hare que los Autos Vuelen! Cuentos Bilingues. 2001. Tr. of I'll Make the Cars Fly!: Bilingual Stories. (SPA & ENG., Illus.). 32p. (J). (gr. k up). pap. 10.95 (978-0-9673032-4-6(9)) Sweet Dreams Bilingual Pubs.

The Bumper Cars: First Wave Satellite Individual Title, 6 pack. (Sails Literacy Ser.). 16p. (gr. k up). 27.00 (978-0-7578-6870-2(3)) Rigby Education.

Car Trouble: Individual Title Six-Packs. 16p. (gr. 2 up). 35.00 (978-0-7635-9380-3(X)) Rigby Education.

Carey, Craig Robert. Driving Force: Pure Power. Mones, Marc & Mones, Isidre, illus. 2005. (Tonka Ser.: No. 1). 24p. (J). (ps-ps). pap. 3.50 (978-0-439-74678-6(7)) Scholastic, Inc.

—Driving Force: Super Size. Mones, Isidre, illus. 2005. (Tonka Ser.: No. 3). 24p. (J). (ps-k). pap. 3.50 (978-0-439-74680-9(9)) Scholastic, Inc.

—High Speed. Mones, Isidre, illus. 2005. (Tonka Ser.: No. 2). 24p. (J). (ps-ps). pap. 3.50 (978-0-439-74679-3(5)) Scholastic, Inc.

—Run Wild: Driving Force. Mones, Isidre & Vazquez, Ivan, illus. 2005. (Tonka Ser.). 24p. (J). (ps-k). pap. 3.50 (978-0-439-74681-6(7)) Scholastic, Inc.

Chouette, ed. Caillou Things That Go! rev. ed. 2006. (Caillou Board Bks.). (ENG & FRE., Illus.). 24p. (J). pap. 7.95 (*978-2-89450-592-2(2)) Chouette Publishing CAN. *Dist:* Independent Pubs. Group.

Christelow, Eileen. Five Little Monkeys Wash the Car. (Illus.). 40p. (J). (ps-1). 2004. 5.95 (978-0-618-48602-1(X)); 2000. tchr. ed. 15.00 (978-0-395-92566-9(5)) Houghton Mifflin Co. Trade & Reference Div. (Clarion Bks.).

Clark, Betsy Huhn. Lizzie's Extraordinary Adventure. 2006. (Illus.). 24p. (J). 9.99 (978-1-4276-0116-2(X)) Aardvark Global Publishing.

Cottrell Boyce, Frank. Framed. 2008. 320p. (J). pap. 6.99 (*978-0-06-073404-6(3) , Harper Trophy) HarperCollins Pubs.

Dann, Penny. The Wheels on the Bus. 1999. (Toddler Bks.). (Illus.). 20p. (J). pap. 4.95 (978-0-7641-0856-3(5)) Barron's Educational Series, Inc.

Danner-Walls, Carolyn. Richard Scarry's: Ma Pig's New Car. Reiter, Cheryl, ed. 2000. (Illus.). 10p. (J). (ps). mass mkt. 9.99 (978-1-887327-40-4(1)) Ertl Co., Inc.

d'Aulaire, Ingri & D'Aulaire, Edgar Parin. The Two Cars. 2007. (Illus.). 32p. (J). (ps-1). 14.95 (*978-1-59017-234-6(5) , NYR Children's Collection) New York Review of Bks., Inc., The.

David, Mark. Crazy Cars. David, Mark, illus. 2006. (Illus.). 32p. (J). pap. 7.95 (978-1-933605-05-0(7)) Kane/Miller Bk. Pubs., Inc.

DePrisco, Dorothea. Willie & Buster Take the Train. Ansley, Frank, illus. 2003. (Stories to Share Ser.). 10p. (J). 10.95 (978-1-58117-183-9(8) , Intervisual/Piggy Toes) Dalmatian Pr.

Disney. Cars & Superstars. 2007. (Hannah Montana Cinemanga Ser.: Vol. 4). 96p. pap. 7.99 (*978-1-4278-0786-1(8) , Tokyopop Kids) TOKYOPOP, Inc.

Disney Press, ed. Disney/Pixar Cars Storybook & CD. rev. ed. 2007. 48p. (ps-1). 12.99 (*978-1-4231-0480-3(3)) Disney Pr.

Disney Storybook Artists Staff, illus. Cars: Out for a Spin. 2006. 10p. (ps-17). 12.99 (978-0-7868-3596-6(6)) Disney Pr.

Doherty, Paula. Going Places-Car. Doherty, Paula, illus. 2005. (Going Places Board Bks.). (Illus.). 10p. (J). bds. 4.99 (978-0-7641-5885-8(6)) Barron's Educational Series, Inc.

—Going Places-Plane. Doherty, Paula, illus. 2005. (Going Places Board Bks.). (Illus.). 10p. (J). bds. 4.99 (978-0-7641-5886-5(4)) Barron's Educational Series, Inc.

—Going Places-Train. Doherty, Paula, illus. 2005. (Going Places Board Bks.). (Illus.). 10p. (J). bds. 4.95 (978-0-7641-5888-9(0)) Barron's Educational Series, Inc.

Donahue, Jill L. Car Shopping. Jensen, Brian, illus. 2006. (Read-It! Readers Ser.). (J). 19.93 (978-1-4048-2406-5(5)) Picture Window Bks.

Dower, Laura. Red to the Rescue. 2007. (Firehouse Tales Ser.). (J). bds. 5.99 (978-0-439-89462-3(X)) Scholastic, Inc.

Drummond, Alan H. Cars, Cars, Cars. 2008. 32p. (J). 16.95 (978-0-374-32000-3(4) , Farrar, Straus & Giroux (BYR)) Farrar, Straus & Giroux.

Dunn, Opal. Little Car. Paterson, Bettina, illus. rev. ed. 2000. (Track-Me-Back Board Bks.). 12p. (J). (ps-k). 5.95 (978-0-8050-6417-9(6) , Holt, Henry & Co. Bks. For Young Readers) Holt, Henry & Co.

DuPrau, Jeanne. Car Trouble. 288p. (J). 2006. pap. 6.99 (978-0-06-073675-0(5) , HarperTeen); 2005. 15.99 (978-0-06-073672-9(0)); 2005. lib. bdg. 16.89 (978-0-06-073674-3(7)) HarperCollins Pubs.

Durk, Jim, et al, illus. Billy the Bus, 8 vols., Vol. 8. (J). bds. (978-0-7853-3644-0(3)) Publications International, Ltd.

—Buster Bulldozer, 8 vols., Vol. 7. (J). bds. (978-0-7853-3643-3(5)) Publications International, Ltd.

—Little Chug, 8 vols., Vol. 5. (J). bds. (978-0-7853-3642-6(7)) Publications International, Ltd.

—Little Jet, 8 vols., Vol. 1. (J). bds. (978-0-7853-3640-2(0)) Publications International, Ltd.

—Rookie Fire Truck, 8 vols., Vol. 3. (J). bds. (978-0-7853-3641-9(9)) Publications International, Ltd.

—Things That Go!, 8 vols., Vol. 6. (J). bds. (978-0-7853-3645-7(1)) Publications International, Ltd.

—Things That Go! 8 Shaped Board Books, 8 vols. Incl. Vol. 1. Little Jet. bds. (978-0-7853-3640-2(0)); Vol. 2. Tiny Tug. bds. (978-0-7853-3638-9(9)); Vol. 3. Rookie Fire Truck. bds. (978-0-7853-3641-9(9)); Vol. 4. Trusty Trooper. bds. (978-0-7853-3639-6(7)); Vol. 5. Little Chug. bds. (978-0-7853-3642-6(7)); Vol. 6. Things That Go! bds. (978-0-7853-3645-7(1)); Vol. 7. Buster Bulldozer. bds. (978-0-7853-3643-3(5)); Vol. 8. Billy the Bus. bds. (978-0-7853-3644-0(3)); (J). (Illus.). bds. (978-0-7853-3637-2(0)) Publications International, Ltd.

—Tiny Tug, 8 vols., Vol. 2. (J). bds. (978-0-7853-3638-9(9)) Publications International, Ltd.

—Trusty Trooper, 8 vols., Vol. 4. (J). bds. (978-0-7853-3639-6(7)) Publications International, Ltd.

Elya, Susan Middleton. Oh No, Gotta Go! Karas, G. Brian, illus. 32p. (J). 2006. pap. 5.99 (978-0-14-240334-1(2) , Puffin); 2003. (SPA.). 15.99 (978-0-399-23493-4(4) , Putnam Juvenile) Penguin Group (USA) Inc.

Ernst, Lisa Campbell, illus. This Is the Van That Dad Cleaned. 2005. 40p. (J). 15.95 (978-0-689-86190-1(7) , Simon & Schuster Children's Publishing) Simon & Schuster Children's Publishing.

Estes, Don. Willy: The Little Jeep Who Wanted to Be a Fire Truck. Garrison, Sue, illus. 2003. (J). lib. bdg. 14.95 (978-1-883551-47-6(1) , ASP-471, Attic Studio Pr.) Attic Studio Publishing Hse.

—Willy & Friends traveling through the Seasons: The continuing story of Willy the little fire Jeep. Glass, Eric, illus. 2006. (J). (978-1-883551-75-9(7) , Maple Corners Press) Attic Studio Publishing Hse.

Evolution. 1998. (Hot Wheels Ser.: Vol. 1). (Illus.). (J). (978-0-7666-0246-5(X) , 19600) Modern Publishing.

Evolution. 2004. (gr. 7 up). 99.95 incl. DVD (978-1-57807-856-1(3) , WG35469) WGBH Boston Video.

Ewing, Lynne. Drive-By. 1998. (Harper Trophy Bks.). (J). 11.79 (978-0-606-12926-8(X)) Tandem Library Bks.

Feldman, Thea. Things That Go. 2006. 3p. 5.99 (978-1-932915-31-0(1)) Sandvik Publishing.

Fienberg, Anna. Minton Goes Driving. Gamble, Kim, illus. 2001. (Minton Ser.). 32p. (J). (ps-1). pap. 6.95 (978-1-86448-594-3(9)) Allen & Unwin AUS. *Dist:* Independent Pubs. Group.

Finkelstein, Chaim. The Burksfield Bike Club, Book 2: Lost & Found. Jennings, R. W., illus. 2007. 224p. (J). 15.95 (978-1-932443-69-1(X) , BBC1H) Judaica Pr., Inc., The.

Fishman, Cathy Goldberg. Car Wash Kid. Gott, Barry, illus. 2003. (Rookie Reader Skill Set Ser.). (J). (gr. k-2). pap. 4.95 (978-0-516-27811-7(8) , Children's Pr.) Scholastic Library Publishing.

—Car Wash Kid. 2003. (gr. k-3). lib. bdg. 12.95 (978-0-613-67601-4(7)) Tandem Library Bks.

Fleming, Ian. Chitty Chitty Bang Bang. Date not set. 159p. (J). (gr. 5-6). reprint ed. lib. bdg. 19.95 (978-0-88411-983-8(1) , Aeonian Pr.) Amereon LTD.

—Chitty Chitty Bang Bang. Selznick, Brian, illus. 2003. 160p. (J). (gr. 3-7). 15.95 (978-0-375-82591-0(6)); lib. bdg. 17.99 (978-0-375-92591-7(0)) Random Hse. Children's Bks. (Random Hse. Bks. for Young Readers).

Follow That Car. 2002. (Illus.). (J). pap. (978-0-7398-5066-4(0)) Steck-Vaughn.

Galvin, Matthew. Otto Learns about His Medicine: A Story about Medication for Children with ADHD. Ferraro, Sandra, illus. 3rd ed. 2001. 32p. (J). (ps-3). 14.95 (978-1-55798-771-6(8)); pap. 8.95 (978-1-55798-772-3(6)) American Psychological Assn. (Magination Pr.).

Garis, Howard Roger. Uncle Wiggily's Automobile. Date not set. 192p. (J). 20.95 (978-0-8488-2276-7(5)) Amereon LTD.

Gaydos, Nora. Innovative Kids Readers: the Long Ride. Sharp, Chris, illus. 2007. 24p. (J). (gr. k-2). pap. 6.99 (978-1-58476-544-8(5)) Innovative Kids.

Gibbons, Faye. Mama & Me & the Model T. 1999. (Illus.). 40p. (J). (ps-3). 15.89 (978-0-688-15299-4(6)) HarperCollins Pubs.

—Mama & Me & the Model T. Rand, Ted, illus. 1999. 40p. (J). (ps-3). 16.95 (978-0-688-15298-7(8)) HarperCollins Pubs.

Gill, Janie S. Cheap Jeep: A Predictable Word Book. 1998. (Illus.). 24p. (ps-3). 5.95 (978-0-89868-361-5(0)) ARO Publishing Co.

Gould, Robert. Big Rigs. 2004. (Big Stuff Ser.). (Illus.). 16p. (J). bds. 7.95 (978-1-929945-41-2(8)) Big Guy Bks., Inc.

—Giant Earth Movers. 2004. (Big Stuff Ser.). (Illus.). 16p. (J). bds. 7.95 (978-1-929945-42-9(6)) Big Guy Bks., Inc.

Guest, Jacqueline. Dream Racer. 2006. (SideStreets Ser.). 136p. (YA). (gr. 7-12). (*978-1-55028-945-9(4)); 7.95 (*978-1-55028-942-8(X)) Lorimer, James & Co., Ltd., Pubs. CAN. *Dist:* Casemate Pubs. & Bk. Distributors, LLC.

Haesche, Richard P., Sr. The Littlest Matador. Klein, Elizabeth, illus. aut. ed. 2000. 204p. (J). pap. 11.99 (978-1-929381-65-4(4) , Third Millennium Publishing) Sci Fi-Arizona, Inc.

Hagen, Carol. Night Henry Ford Met Santa. Faulkner, Matt, illus. 2006. 32p. (J). 17.95 (978-1-58536-132-8(1)) Sleeping Bear Pr.

Hall, Kirsten. Zoom, Zoom, Zoom. Garofoli, Viviana, tr. Garofoli, Viviana, illus. 2004. (My First Reader (Revised) Ser.). 31p. (J). 18.50 (978-0-516-24414-3(0) , Children's Pr.) Scholastic Library Publishing.

Harville, Shawn T. Tell a Story Stock Car Coloring Book. Harville, Shawn T., illus. 1999. (Illus.). 64p. (J). (gr. k-4). mass mkt. 3.95 (978-1-893691-00-1(4) , 20001) Sundown Publishing Co.

Haynes, Max. In the Driver's Seat. 1999. (J). lib. bdg. (978-0-606-16582-2(7)) Tandem Library Bks.

Hempel, Linda K. Have Fries - Will Travel! The Adventures of a Veggie-Powered Car & an Eco-Rap Star. Dotson, Kathy, illus. 2005. 72p. (J). (ps-7). (978-0-86571-549-3(1)) New Society Pubs., Ltd.

Henderson, Kathy. Cars, Cars, Cars. Hard, Charlotte, illus. 2001. 32p. (J). (ps-3). pap. 8.99 (978-0-7112-1382-1(8)) Lincoln, Frances Ltd. GBR. *Dist:* Transition Vendor.

Hillert, Margaret. The Birthday Car. 2002. (Illus.). (J). 15.00 (978-1-4046-0064-5(7)) Book Wholesalers, Inc.

—The Birthday Car. Oechsli, Kelly, illus. rev. exp. ed. 2007. (Beginning to Read Ser.). 32p. (J). lib. bdg. (978-1-59953-043-7(0)) Norwood Hse. Pr.

Holland, Robert. The Purple Car. 1998. (Books Boys Want to Read Ser.). 163p. (YA). (gr. 6-12). pap. 10.95 (978-0-9658523-3-3(4)) Frost Hollow Pubs., LLC.

Horton, Chris, ed. From Cadillac to Duesenburg, 7 vols., Set. 1998. (Encyclopedia of Cars Ser.: Vol. 2). (Illus.). 112p. (gr. 4-7). 29.95 (978-0-7910-4866-5(7) , Chelsea Hse.) Facts On File, Inc.

Hubbard, Sharron/Y. Rosie's New Bike. Schleihs, Kristin, illus. 2006. (J). bds. 7.95 (*978-0-9762434-1-0(5)) Link & Rosie Pr.

Hubbard, Suzanna. Lady Who Lived in a Car. 2007. (Illus.). 24p. (J). pap. 6.99 (*978-1-84458-055-2(5)) Anova Bks. GBR. *Dist:* Independent Pubs. Group.

Hubbell, Patricia. Cars: Rushing! Honking! Zooming! Halsey, Megan & Addy, Sean, illus. 2006. 32p. (J). 14.99 (978-0-7614-5296-6(6)) Cavendish, Marshall Corp.

Hurd, Thacher. Zoom City. 1998. (Growing Tree Ser.). (Illus.). 8p. (J). (ps up). 6.99 (978-0-694-01057-8(X) , Harper Festival) HarperCollins Pubs.

Jacobs, Paul DuBois & Swender, Jennifer. My Taxi Ride. Alko, Selina, illus. 2006. 32p. (J). 15.95 (978-1-4236-0073-2(8)) Gibbs Smith, Publisher.

Jeffery, Peter. Beep. Lanting, Norm, illus. 2001. 27p. (J). pap. (978-1-894400-10-7(0)) Joshua Pr., Inc.

Jennings, Sharon. Franklin & the Scooter. Gagnon, Celeste et al, illus. 2004. 32p. (J). lib. bdg. 15.38 (*978-1-4242-1169-2(7)) Fitzgerald Bks.

Keylocke, Andrew, illus. Hasty Hetty. 2004. (Crazy Racers Ser.). 12p. (J). bds. 4.95 (978-0-7641-5746-2(9)) Barron's Educational Series, Inc.

—Lazy Larry. 2004. (Crazy Racers Ser.). 12p. (J). bds. 4.95 (978-0-7641-5747-9(7)) Barron's Educational Series, Inc.

Kirk, David. Miss Spider's New Car. Kirk, David, illus. 1999. (Miss Spider Ser.). (Illus.). 32p. (J). (ps-2). bds. 8.95 (978-0-439-04675-6(0)) Scholastic, Inc.

Labatt, Mary. Sam Gets Lost. Sarrazin, Marisol, illus. 2004. 32p. (J). lib. bdg. 15.38 (*978-1-4242-1159-3(X)) Fitzgerald Bks.

LeapFrog Staff & HIT Entertainment Staff, compiled by. Bob & Lofty Save the Day. 2002. (J). (ps-2). 14.95 (978-1-58605-748-0(0)) LeapFrog Enterprises, Inc.

Lenski, Lois. Little Auto. 2000. (Illus.). 48p. (J). 16.95 (978-0-8488-2764-9(3)) Amereon LTD.

Leonard, Nellie M. Grand Daddy Whiskers, M. D. 2004. reprint ed. pap. 15.95 (978-1-4191-2227-9(4)); pap. 1.99 (978-1-4192-2227-6(9)) Kessinger Publishing, LLC.

Martin, LaJoyce. The Silver Ghost. 2004. (Illus.). 161p. (J). pap. 9.99 (978-1-56722-643-0(4)) Word Aflame Pr.

Marzollo, Jean. I Spy Little Wheels. Wick, Walter, illus. 1998. (I Spy Bks.). 26p. (J). (ps). bds. 6.99 (978-0-590-04706-7(X) , Cartwheel Bks.) Scholastic, Inc.

McCormick, Shawn R. Zoey & the Zones: A Story for Children with Asthma. 2003. per. 8.95 (978-0-9718120-8-6(X)); 2002. (Illus.). (J). per. 8.95 (978-0-9740697-3-9(6)) HealthSprings, LLC.

McCormick, Shawn R. & Trevino, Ginny. Zoey & the Zones: A Story for Children with Asthma. 2002. (J). per. 8.95 (978-0-9718120-0-0(4) , ZC-2004) HealthSprings, LLC.

McEwen, James. Westley, the Big Truck. 2004. 32p. (J). 10.99 (978-0-89051-410-8(0)) Master Bks.

McKay, Sindy. We Both Read-the Big Tan Van. Johnson, Meredith, illus. 2001. (We Both Read Ser.). 44p. (J). (gr. 1 up). 7.99 (978-1-891327-35-3(6)); pap. 3.99 (978-1-891327-36-0(4)) Treasure Bay, Inc.

Milliron, Kerry. Great Race. 2000. (ps-2). lib. bdg. 11.80 (978-0-613-32615-5(6)) Tandem Library Bks.

Miranda, Anne. Beep! Beep! 2000. (ps-2). lib. bdg. 16.40 (978-0-613-27731-0(7)) Tandem Library Bks.

—Beep! Beep! A Vehicle Imagination Book. Murphy, David, illus. 2000. 32p. (J). (ps up). pap. 7.95 (978-1-890515-20-1(5)) Turtle Bks.

Moloney, James. Black Taxi. 2005. 272p. (J). (gr. 7 up). 15.99 (978-0-06-055937-3(3)); lib. bdg. 16.89 (978-0-06-055938-0(1)) HarperCollins Pubs.

Mr. Frumble's Pickle Car. 1998. (Richard Scarry's on the Go Bks.). 12p. (J). 11.99 (978-0-689-82487-6(4) , Simon Spotlight) Simon & Schuster Children's Publishing.

My Visit to the Car Factory. 2004. (J). ring bd. 4.50 (978-0-9762740-7-0(8) , Flat Kids) Smart Smiles Co., The.

Nugent, Cynthia. Francesca & the Magic Bike Teacher Guide. 2005. 4p. (J). pap. (978-1-55192-825-8(6)) Raincoast Bk. Distribution CAN. *Dist:* Transition Vendor.

Ostby, Kristin & Piper, Watty. Ride along with the Little Engine That Could. Ong, Cristina & Artful Doodlers Limited Staff, illus. 2005. (Little Engine That Could Ser.). 10p. (J). (ps). bds. 6.99 (978-0-448-43845-0(3) , Grosset & Dunlap) Penguin Group (USA) Inc.

Oxenbury, Helen. En El Auto.Tr. of In the Car. (SPA.). 24p. (J). 7.50 (978-84-261-2000-7(8)) Juventud, Editorial ESP. *Dist:* AIMS International Bks., Inc.

P., Michael. Daniel's Ride: Bilingual Edition. 2nd ed. 2005. (Illus.). 32p. 18.95 (978-0-86719-641-2(6)) Last Gasp of San Francisco.

Parvensky Barwell, Catherine A. Tommi Goes Camping, 4 vols. Barwell, Matthew W. et al, eds. Parvensky Barwell, Catherine A., illus. 2006. (Illus.). 40p. (J). 14.95 (978-0-9774409-3-1(1) , TL004) ILT Publishing.

—Tommi Goes to the Beach, 4 vols. Barwell, Matthew W. & Parvensky, Mary T., eds. 2006. (Illus.). 40p. (J). (978-0-9774409-2-4(3) , TL003) ILT Publishing.

—Tommi Lance Grows Up, 4 vols. 2006. (Illus.). 30p. (J). (978-0-9774409-0-0(7) , TL001) ILT Publishing.

—Tommi's First Snowfall, 4 vols. 2006. (Illus.). 32p. (J). (978-0-9774409-1-7(5) , TL002) ILT Publishing.

Paulsen, Gary. The Car. 2006. (Illus.). 192p. (YA). pap. 5.95 (978-0-15-205827-2(3) , Harcourt Paperbacks) Harcourt Children's Bks.

Peck, Richard. Here Lies the Librarian. 160p. (J). (gr. 5 up). 2007. 6.99 (*978-0-14-240908-4(1) , Puffin); 2006. 16.99 (978-0-8037-3080-9(2) , Dial) Penguin Group (USA) Inc.

—Here Lies the Librarian. rev. ed. 175p. 23.95 (*978-0-7862-9183-0(4)) Thorndike Pr.

Penrose, Margaret. The Motor Girls on Cedar Lake, or the He. 2006. 63.99 (*978-1-4219-9401-7(1)); pap. 56.99 (*978-1-4219-9422-2(4)) IndyPublish.com.

Perera, Hilda. El Automovil de Mi Abuelo. Rosillo, Carlos Rodriguez, illus. 2000. (SPA.). 32p. (J). 12.95 (978-84-241-3332-0(3)) Everest de Ediciones y Distribucion, S.L. ESP. *Dist:* Lectorum Pubns., Inc.

Perlman, Rhea. Canyon Catastrophe. Santat, Dan, illus. 2006. (Otto Undercover Ser.). 128p. (J). 14.99 (978-0-06-075498-3(2)); pap. 3.99 (978-0-06-075497-6(4)) HarperCollins Pubs.

Perry, Michael. Daniel's Ride. Ballard, Lee, illus. 2001. 32p. (J). (gr. 2-5). 16.00 (978-0-9701771-9-3(4)) Free Will Pr.

The Pillow Sale: KinderWords Individual Title Six-Packs. (Kinderstarters Ser.). 8p. (ps-1). 21.00 (978-0-7635-8707-9(9)) Rigby Education.

Piper, Watty. The Little Engine That Could & the Snowy, Blowy Christmas. Ong, Cristina, illus. 2005. (Little Engine That Could Ser.). 12p. (J). (ps-1). bds. 6.99 (978-0-448-43919-8(0) , Grosset & Dunlap) Penguin Group (USA) Inc.

Pomaska, Anna. Invisible Cars & Trucks Magic. 1998. (Illus.). 16p. (J). (ps-2). pap. 1.50 (978-0-486-40236-9(3) , 881924Q) Dover Pubns., Inc.

Posner-Sanchez, Andrea. Tales from the Track. Random House Disney Staff, illus. 2007. (Toddler Board Bks.). 30p. (J). (gr. k-k). bds. 11.99 (*978-0-7364-2510-0(1) , RH/Disney) Random Hse. Children's Bks.

Powell, Richard. Zoom's Finest Hour. Hawksley, Gerald, illus. 2004. (Softy Wheels Ser.). 18p. (J). bds. 8.95 (978-0-7641-7789-7(3)) Barron's Educational Series, Inc.

Price, Mathew. In the Snow. Augarde, Steve, illus. 2000. (Little Red Car Bks.). 10p. (J). (ps-1). pap. 6.95 (978-0-7892-0674-9(9) , Abbeville Kids) Abbeville Pr., Inc.

—Little Red Car Has an Accident. Augarde, Steve, illus. 2000. (Little Red Car Bks.). 10p. (J). (ps-1). pap. 6.95 (978-0-7892-0673-2(0) , Abbeville Kids) Abbeville Pr., Inc.

—Little Red Car Plays Taxi. Augarde, Steve, illus. 2000. (Little Red Car Bks.). 10p. (J). (ps-1). pap. 6.95 (978-0-7892-0675-6(7) , Abbeville Kids) Abbeville Pr., Inc.

Price, Matthew. Little Red Car Gets in Trouble. Augarde, Steve, illus. 2000. (Little Red Car Bks.). 10p. (J). (ps-1). pap. 6.95 (978-0-7892-0676-3(5) , Abbeville Kids) Abbeville Pr., Inc.

Priddy, Roger. Bright Baby Noisy Car. 2007. 24p. (J). bds. 8.95 (*978-0-312-50016-0(5) , Priddy Bks.) St. Martin's Pr.

Pruett, Scott & Pruett, Judy. Twelve Little Race Cars. Eytchison, Glen, ed. Dietz, Mike & Toft, Kevin, illus. 1999. 32p. (J). (ps-3). 12.95 (978-0-9670600-0-2(1)) Word Weaver Bks., Inc.

Pulver, Robin. Axle Annie. Arnold, Tedd, illus. 2001. 32p. (J). pap. 5.99 (978-0-14-230014-5(4) , Puffin) Penguin Group (USA) Inc.

—Axle Annie. 2001. (gr. k-3). lib. bdg. 14.15 (978-0-613-44187-2(7)) Tandem Library Bks.

Puzzle Track Staff, ed. Red Car Ride. 2007. (Puzzle Track Ser.). 20p. (J). bds. 18.95 (*978-0-7696-5579-6(3)) School Specialty Publishing.

Raintree Steck-Vaughn Staff. What Was It Like Before Cars? 2000. (Read All about It Ser.). (Illus.). (J). pap. 4.95 (978-0-8114-3787-5(6)) Steck-Vaughn.

—Wheels, Wheels, Wheels. 2000. (Read All about It Ser.). (Illus.). (J). pap. 4.95 (978-0-8114-3772-1(8)) Steck-Vaughn.

Random House Disney Staff. Cars. 2006. (Read-Aloud Board Book Ser.). (Illus.). 24p. (J). (gr. k-k). bds. 4.99 (978-0-7364-2293-2(5) , RH/Disney) Random Hse. Children's Bks.

—Disney/Pixar Fun Kit. 2007. (Fun Kit Ser.). (Illus.). 48p. (J). (ps-2). pap. 9.99 (*978-0-7364-2492-9(X) , Golden/Disney) Random Hse. Children's Bks.

—Lightning Fast. 2007. (Color Plus Chunky Crayons Ser.). (Illus.). 48p. (J). (ps-2). pap. 3.99 (978-0-375-83980-1(1) , Golden/Disney) Random Hse. Children's Bks.

—Old, New, Red, Blue! 2006. (Step into Reading Ser.). (Illus.). 32p. (J). (ps-2). pap. 3.99 (978-0-7364-2410-3(5)); lib. bdg. 11.99 (978-0-7364-8050-5(1)) Random Hse. Children's Bks. (RH/Disney).

—Thunder & Lightning. 2006. (Random House Pictureback Book Ser.). (Illus.). 24p. (J). (ps-2). pap. 3.99 (978-0-7364-2321-2(4) , RH/Disney) Random Hse. Children's Bks.

Richter, Dana. Arthur's Road Trip. Moroney, Christopher, illus. 2001. (J). (978-0-7853-4859-7(X)) Publications International, Ltd.

Rindone, Nancy. Cars, Trains, Planes, & Trucks. S. I. Artists Staff, illus. 2004. (Fisher-Price Little People Flip & Learn Ser.). 10p. (J). bds. 8.99 (978-0-7944-0443-7(X) , Reader's Digest Children's Bks.) Reader's Digest Children's Publishing, Inc.

Root, Phyllis. Rattletrap Car. Barton, Jill, illus. 40p. (J). (ps-3). 2001. 15.99 (978-0-7636-0919-1(6)); 2004. reprint ed. pap. 6.99 (978-0-7636-2007-3(6)) Candlewick Pr.

Ross, Diana. The Little Red Engine & the Rocket. 1999. (Illus.). 32p. (J). 16.00 (978-0-233-99405-5(X)) Andre Deutsch GBR. *Dist:* Independent Pubs. Group.

—The Little Red Engine Goes to Town. 1999. (Illus.). 32p. (J). 16.00 (978-0-233-99404-8(1)) Andre Deutsch GBR. *Dist:* Independent Pubs. Group.

Ross, K. K. The Little Red Car. Alley, R. W., illus. (Jellybean Bks.). 24p. (J). (ps-k). 2000. 2.99 (978-0-375-80142-6(1)); 1999. lib. bdg. 7.99 (978-0-375-90142-3(6)) Random Hse. Children's Bks. (Random Hse. Bks. for Young Readers).

Sargent, Dave & Sargent, Pat. Goober: (Silver Dapple) Appreciate Others, 30 vols., Vol. 29. Lenoir, Jane, illus. 2003. (Saddle Up Ser.: Vol. 29). 42p. (J). lib. bdg. 22.60 (978-1-56763-689-5(6)) Ozark Publishing.

—Goober: (Sliver Dapple) Appreciate Others, 30 vols., Vol. 29. Lenoir, Jane, illus. 2004. (Saddle Up Ser.: Vol. 29). 42p. (J). pap. 6.95 (978-1-56763-690-1(X)) Ozark Publishing.

Sargent, Dave, et al. Grubby: (Smutty Olive Grullo) Have a Good Disposition, 30, 31. 2003. (Saddle Up Ser.: Vol. 31). (Illus.). 42p. (J). pap. 6.95 (978-1-56763-692-5(6)) Ozark Publishing.

Schaefer, Lola M. Mittens. Hartung, Susan Kathleen, illus. 2006. (My First I Can Read Book Ser.). 32p. (J). 14.99 (978-0-06-054659-5(X)); lib. bdg. 15.89 (978-0-06-054660-1(3)) HarperCollins Pubs.

Silver Dolphin en Español Staff. Figuras magicas: Cars: Magical Magnets: Cars, Spanish-Language Edition. 2006. (Illus.). 8p. (J). bds. 12.95 (978-970-718-388-9(8) , Silver Dolphin en Español) Advanced Marketing, S. de R. L. de C. V. MEX. *Dist:* Perseus Distribution.

Silver Dolphin en Español Staff, ed. Cine en casa: Cars: Movie Theater: Cars. 2007. (Cine en casa Disney Ser.). (Illus.). 46p. (J). 24.95 (*978-970-718-508-1(2) , Silver Dolphin en Español) Advanced Marketing, S. de R. L. de C. V. MEX. *Dist:* Perseus Distribution.

Simon, Seymour. Seemore Emergency Vehicles. 2006. (Illus.). 32p. (J). 14.50 (978-0-8118-5406-1(X)) Chronicle Bks. LLC.

Soto, Gary. My Little Car. Sawaya, Linda Dalal & Paparone, Pamela, illus. 2006. Tr. of Mi Carrito. (ENG & SPA.). 32p. (J). (ps-3). 15.99 (978-0-399-23220-6(6) , Putnam Juvenile) Penguin Group (USA) Inc.

Spanyol, Jessica. Come on, Bugs! Let's Have Some Fun! Spanyol, Jessica, illus. 2006. (Illus.). 32p. (J). (gr. k-k). 15.99 (978-0-7636-3055-3(1)) Candlewick Pr.

Standish, Burt L. Frank Merriwell's Auto. Rudman, Jack, ed. 2003. (Frank Merriwell Ser.). 29.95 (978-0-8373-9350-6(7)); pap. 9.95 (978-0-8373-9050-5(8)) Merriwell, Frank Inc.

Stanford, Don. The Red Car. 2000. (Illus.). 256p. (J). reprint ed. 31.95 (978-1-56849-731-0(8)) Buccaneer Bks., Inc.

Stanley, George. The Case of the Dirty Clue: Third-Grade Detectives. Murdocca, Salvatore, illus. 2005. (Ready-for-Chapters Ser.). (J). lib. bdg. 15.00 (978-1-59054-898-1(1)) Fitzgerald Bks.

Stein, Erin K. Sam's New Car. Staples, Val, illus. 2007. (Transformers Ser.). 24p. (J). pap. 3.99 (*978-0-06-088823-7(7) , Harper Entertainment) HarperCollins Pubs.

Stellinga, Mark. Buster Boogernose & the Boxcar. 2007. (J). per. 9.95 (*978-0-9796421-1-1(6)) Stellinga, Mark.

Stierle, Cynthia & Disney Pixar Artists. Disney Pixar Cars Movie Theater Storybook & Movie Projector. 2006. (RD Innovative Book & Player Format Ser.). 48p. (J). (ps-3). 24.99 (978-0-7944-1269-2(6)) Reader's Digest Assn., Inc., The.

Stine, R. L. The Haunted Car. 1999. (Goosebumps Series 2000: No. 21). (Illus.). (J). (gr. 3-7). (978-0-606-18552-3(6)) Tandem Library Bks.

Stokes, Katherine. The Motor Maids in Fair Japan. 2006. 78.99 (*978-1-4280-1270-7(2)); pap. 71.99 (*978-1-4280-1264-6(8)) IndyPublish.com.

Super Stunt Show. 1998. (Hot Wheels Ser.: Vol. 2). (Illus.). (J). (978-0-7666-0245-8(1) , 19600) Modern Publishing.

Swan, Michelle, illus. Wheels on the Bus. 2006. 12p. (J). bds. 5.99 (978-0-439-83982-2(3) , Cartwheel Bks.) Scholastic, Inc.

Taylor, Mildred D. The Gold Cadillac. Hays, Michael & Ginsberg, Max, illus. 1998. 48p. (YA). (gr. 2-6). pap. 4.99 (978-0-14-038963-0(6) , Puffin) Penguin Group (USA) Inc.

—The Gold Cadillac. 1998. 11.79 (978-0-606-13433-0(6)) Tandem Library Bks.

Teitelbaum, Michael. If I Could Drive a Er! 2001. (ps-2). lib. bdg. 11.80 (978-0-613-54568-6(0)) Tandem Library Bks.

—If I Could Drive a Loader! 2001. (ps-2). lib. bdg. 11.25 (978-0-613-54567-9(2)) Tandem Library Bks.

Timmers, Leo. Who Is Driving? Timmers, Leo, illus. 2007. (Illus.). 32p. (J). (ps-k). 12.95 (978-1-59990-021-6(1) , Bloomsbury Children) Bloomsbury Publishing.

Toy Box Innovations, creator. Disney/Pixar 2: Volume 2. abr. ed. 2006. (Disney's Read along Collection Ser.). (J). (ps-3). pap. 14.99 incl. audio compact disk (978-0-7634-2181-6(2)) Walt Disney Records.

ToyBox Innovations, creator. Disney Cars. 2006. (Disney's Read Along Ser.). (Illus.). 24p. (J). (ps-3). audio compact disk, audio compact disk 7.99 (978-0-7634-2169-4(3)) Walt Disney Records.

Trueman, Terry. No Right Turn. 2006. 176p. (J). 16.99 (978-0-06-057491-8(7)); lib. bdg. 16.89 (978-0-06-057492-5(5)) HarperCollins Pubs. (HarperTeen).

Turbo Powers! Individual Title Six-Packs. (Bookweb Ser.). 32p. (gr. 6 up). 34.00 (978-0-7578-0903-3(0)) Rigby Education.

Valat, Pierre-Marie. Things That Go. 2002. (First Discovery Look-Inside Board Bks.). (Illus.). 10p. (J). bds. 4.95 (978-0-439-35593-3(1) , Cartwheel Bks.) Scholastic, Inc.

The Van. 2005. (J). (978-1-932570-40-3(3)) Literacy Footprints Inc.

Van Dusen, Chris. If I Built a Car. Van Dusen, Chris, illus. (J). (gr. k). 2007. 40p. pap. 6.99 (978-0-14-240825-4(5) , Puffin); 2005. (Illus.). 32p. 15.99 (978-0-525-47400-5(5) , Dutton Juvenile) Penguin Group (USA) Inc.

Walt & Wells. Este No Es Mi Tren. 2004. (Touchy-Feely Board Bks.).Tr. of That's Not My Train. (SPA., Illus.). 12p. (J). (ps up). 7.95 (978-0-7460-5073-6(9)) EDC Publishing.

Ward, Frank. Moville. 1999. (Illus.). 32p. (J). (ps). 11.95 (978-0-9667475-0-8(X)) Renaissance-Atlantic Films.

The Wheel Deal. 1998. (Hot Wheels Ser.). (Illus.). 96p. (J). (ps-1). pap. (978-0-7666-0103-1(X) , Honey Bear Bks.) Modern Publishing.

Whitehead, Pete, illus. Scooters. 2006. (I'm Going to Read Ser.). 32p. (J). pap. 3.95 (978-1-4027-3077-1(2)) Sterling Publishing Co., Inc.

Woodbury, Mary. The Ghost in the Machine. 2005. 222p. (J). (gr. 6-9). pap. 7.95 (978-1-55050-227-5(1)) Coteau Bks. CAN. *Dist:* Fitzhenry & Whiteside, Ltd.

Woolley, Bryan. Mr. Green's Magnificent Machine. Arbuckle, Scott, illus. 2003. 32p. 15.95 (978-1-57168-606-0(1)) Eakin Pr.

Wyre, Yvonne. The Further Adventures of Cuthbert the Coal Lorry & all His Friends. 2007. (Illus.). 204p. pap. (*978-1-84401-801-7(6)) Athena Pr.

AUTOMOBILES—HISTORY

Abraham, Philip. Cars. 2004. (High Interest Bks.). (Illus.). 48p. (J). (gr. 7-12). pap. 6.95 (978-0-516-25944-4(X) , Children's Pr.) Scholastic Library Publishing.

Banting, Erinn. Inventing the Automobile. 2006. (Breakthrough Inventions Ser.). (Illus.). 32p. (J). (gr. 3-9). pap. (978-0-7787-2834-4(X)); (978-0-7787-2812-2(9)) Crabtree Publishing Co.

Beyer, Mark. Autos Del Pasado. 2004. (Transporte Ayer y Hoy Ser.). (SPA & ENG., Illus.). 24p. (J). (gr. 3-6). lib. bdg. 17.25 (978-0-8239-6851-0(0) , Buenas Letra) Rosen Publishing Group, Inc., The.

—Cars of the Past. 2002. (Reading Power Ser.). (Illus.). 24p. (J). (gr. 1). lib. bdg. 17.25 (978-0-8239-5983-9(X) , PowerKids Pr.) Rosen Publishing Group, Inc., The.

Cheetham, Craig. American Cars Before 1950. 2006. (Illus.). 32p. lib. bdg. (*978-0-8368-7723-6(3)) Stevens, Gareth Inc.

—American Cars of the 1950's. 2006. (Illus.). 32p. lib. bdg. (*978-0-8368-7724-3(1)) Stevens, Gareth Inc.

—American Cars of the 1960s. 2006. (Illus.). 32p. lib. bdg. (*978-0-8368-7725-0(X)) Stevens, Gareth Inc.

—American Cars of the 1970's. 2006. (Illus.). 32p. lib. bdg. (*978-0-8368-7726-7(8)) Stevens, Gareth Inc.

—American Cars of the 1980's. 2006. (Illus.). 32p. lib. bdg. (*978-0-8368-7727-4(6)) Stevens, Gareth Inc.

—American Cars of the 1990s & Today. 2006. (Illus.). 32p. lib. bdg. (*978-0-8368-7728-1(4)) Stevens, Gareth Inc.

Conley, Robyn. The Automobile. 2005. (Inventions That Shaped the World Ser.). (Illus.). 80p. (J). (gr. 5-8). pap. 9.95 (978-0-531-16719-9(4)); 30.50 (978-0-531-12333-1(2)) Scholastic Library Publishing. (Watts, Franklin).

Corbett, David. Automobiles. 1999. (History Ser.). (Illus.). 31p. (J). (gr. 5 up). pap. 5.95 (978-0-7641-0644-6(9)) Barron's Educational Series, Inc.

—A History of Cars. 2006. (From Past to Present Ser.). (Illus.). 36p. (J). lib. bdg. 24.67 (978-0-8368-6286-7(4)) Stevens, Gareth Inc.

Cowdery, Ray. All American Wonder, Vol 2, Vol. II. 4th ed. 2003. (Illus.). 144p. pap. 29.95 (978-0-9700567-3-3(7)) Victory WW 2 Publishing Ltd.

Dooling, Michael. The Great Horseless Carriage Race. Dooling, Michael, illus. 2005. (Illus.). 32p. (J). (gr. k-3). tchr. ed. 16.95 (978-0-8234-1640-0(2)) Holiday Hse., Inc.

Fitzpatrick, Anne. The Automobile. 2003. 24p. (J). lib. bdg. 21.35 (978-1-58340-319-8(1)) Smart Apple Media.

Fletcher, Robert A. Jeeps at War. Naples, Thomas R. et al, eds. Fletcher, Robert A., illus. 2007. (Illus.). 36p. (J). 19.95 (*978-0-9722961-3-5(5)) Iron Mountain Pr.

Genat, Robert. Mopar Muscle: Fifty Years. Newhardt, David, photos by. 2004. (Illus.). 352p. 50.00 (978-0-7603-2016-7(0) , Motorbooks) MBI Publishing Co. LLC.

Georgano, G. N. Cars of the Seventies & Eighties: Hatchbacks for the Sportsman. 2002. (World of Wheels Ser.). (Illus.). 104,132p. (YA). (gr. 7 up). lib. bdg. (978-1-59084-488-5(2)) Mason Crest Pubs.

Gibbs, Lynne. Mega Book of Motorcycles. 2003. (Illus.). 32p. (YA). pap. (978-1-903954-57-7(6)) Chrysalis Children's Bks.

Gibbs, Lynne & Morris, Neil. Mega Book of Cars. 2003. (Illus.). 32p. (YA). pap. (978-1-903954-56-0(8)) Chrysalis Children's Bks.

Hawley, Rebecca. Ferrari. 2007. (Superfast Cars Ser.). (Illus.). 24p. (J). (gr. 3-5). lib. bdg. 21.25 (978-1-4042-3640-0(6) , PowerKids Pr.) Rosen Publishing Group, Inc., The.

Horton, Chris, ed. From Abath to Buick, 7 vols., Set. 1998. (Encyclopedia of Cars Ser.: Vol. 1). (Illus.). 112p. (gr. 4-7). 29.95 (978-0-7910-4865-8(9) , Chelsea Hse.) Facts On File, Inc.

—From Dupont to Hudson, 7 vols., Set. 1998. (Encyclopedia of Cars Ser.: Vol. 3). (Illus.). 112p. (gr. 4-7). 29.95 (978-0-7910-4867-2(5) , Chelsea Hse.) Facts On File, Inc.

—From Humber to Maserati, 7 vols., Set. 1998. (Encyclopedia of Cars Ser.: Vol. 4). (Illus.). 112p. (gr. 4-7). 29.95 (978-0-7910-4868-9(3) , Chelsea Hse.) Facts On File, Inc.

—From Mathis to Panhard, 7 vols., Set. 1998. (Encyclopedia of Cars Ser.: Vol. 5). (Illus.). 112p. (gr. 4-7). 29.95 (978-0-7910-4869-6(1) , Chelsea Hse.) Facts On File, Inc.

—From Singer to Wolsley, 7 vols., Set. 1998. (Encyclopedia of Cars Ser.: Vol. 7). (Illus.). 112p. (gr. 4-7). 29.95 (978-0-7910-4871-9(3) , Chelsea Hse.) Facts On File, Inc.

Lally, Linda Jean. The Volkswagen Beetle. 1999. (On the Road Ser.). (Illus.). 48p. (J). (gr. 3-4). lib. bdg. 21.26 (978-0-7368-0185-0(5) , Capstone High-Interest Bks.) Capstone Pr., Inc.

Levinson, Nancy Smiler. Cars: A Holiday House Reader, Level 2. Rogers, Jacqueline, tr. Rogers, Jacqueline, illus. 32p. (J). (gr. k-3). tchr. ed. 14.95 (978-0-8234-1614-1(3)) Holiday Hse., Inc.

Maurer, Tracy. Maserati. 2008. (J). (*978-1-60044-573-6(X)) Rourke Publishing, LLC.

—Mazda. 2008. (J). (*978-1-60044-574-3(8)) Rourke Publishing, LLC.

Maurer, Tracy. Viper: Full Throttle. 2007. (J). (978-1-60044-228-5(5)) Rourke Publishing, LLC.

Mezzanotte, Jim. The Story of the Cadillac Eldorado. 2005. (Classic Cars Ser.). (Illus.). 24p. (YA). lib. bdg. 22.00 (978-0-8368-4532-7(3)) Stevens, Gareth Inc.

Morris, Neil. Cars. (Past & Present Ser.). (Illus.). 32p. lib. bdg. 24.25 (978-1-931983-36-5(4)) Chrysalis Education.

Mort, Norm. Classic Cars: 1931-1980. 2007. (Illus.). 32p. (J). (gr. 2-9). (*978-0-7787-3012-5(3)); pap. (*978-0-7787-3034-7(4)) Crabtree Publishing Co.

Nielsen, L. Michelle. Vintage Cars. 2006. (Automania! Ser.). (Illus.). 32p. (J). (gr. 4-6). pap. (978-0-7787-3033-0(6)); lib. bdg. (978-0-7787-3011-8(5)) Crabtree Publishing Co.

Raum, Elizabeth. The History of the Car. 2007. (J). (*978-1-4034-9648-5(X)); pap. (*978-1-4034-9654-6(4)) Heinemann Library.

Schlesinger, Arthur M., Jr. & Israel, Fred L., eds. Touring America Seventy-Five Years Ago. 1999. (Cultural & Geographical Exploration Ser.). (Illus.). x, 122p. (J). (gr. 4-7). lib. bdg. 21.95 (978-0-7910-5098-9(X) , Chelsea Hse.) Facts On File, Inc.

Sinclair, Julie. The Automobile. 2003. (Fact Finders Ser.). (Illus.). 32p. (J). lib. bdg. 22.60 (978-0-7368-2214-5(3)) Capstone Pr., Inc.

Somervill, Barbara A. The History of the Automobile. 2004. (Timeline Library Ser.). 32p. (J). (gr. 2-6). 27.07 (978-1-59296-344-7(7)) Child's World, Inc.

Volkswagen History to Hobby: All the Facts - All the Fun. 2005. (YA). lib. bdg. 24.99 net. (978-0-9765261-0-0(7)) Jersey Classic Publishing.

Wheeler, Jill C. Beetle. 2004. (Ultimate Cars Ser.). (Illus.). 27p. (J). (gr. 3-8). lib. bdg. 24.21 (978-1-59197-578-6(6)) ABDO Publishing Co.

—Camaro. 2004. (Ultimate Cars Ser.). (J). (gr. 3-8). lib. bdg. 24.21 (978-1-59197-579-3(4)) ABDO Publishing Co.

—Maserati. 2004. (Ultimate Cars Ser.). (Illus.). 26p. (J). (gr. 3-8). lib. bdg. 24.21 (978-1-59197-580-9(8) , ABDO & Daughters) ABDO Publishing Co.

—Mercedes-Benz. 2004. (Ultimate Cars Ser.). (Illus.). 27p. (J). (gr. 3-8). lib. bdg. 24.21 (978-1-59197-581-6(6)) ABDO Publishing Co.

—Rolls Royce. 2004. (Ultimate Cars Ser.). (Illus.). 26p. (J). (gr. 3-8). lib. bdg. 24.21 (978-1-59197-582-3(4)) ABDO Publishing Co.

—Ultimate Cars Set II, 6 vols. 2004. (Illus.). (J). (gr. 3-8). lib. bdg. 145.26 (978-1-59197-577-9(8) , ABDO & Daughters) ABDO Publishing Co.

Wright, David. Classic Cars, 6 bks. Incl. Story of Chevy Corvettes. lib. bdg. 22.00 (978-0-8368-3189-4(6)); Story of Chevy Impalas. lib. bdg. 22.00 (978-0-8368-3190-0(X)); Story of Ford Thunderbirds. lib. bdg. 22.00 (978-0-8368-3191-7(8)); Story of Model T Fords. lib. bdg. 22.00 (978-0-8368-3192-4(6)); Story of Porsches. lib. bdg. 22.00 (978-0-8368-3193-1(4)); Story of Volkswagen Beetles. lib. bdg. 22.00 (978-0-8368-3194-8(2)); 24p. (YA). (gr. 2 up). 2002. (Illus.). 2002. Set lib. bdg. 127.60 (978-0-8368-3188-7(8)) Stevens, Gareth Inc.

—The Story of Chevy Corvettes. 2002. (Classic Cars Ser.). (Illus.). 24p. (YA). (gr. 2 up). lib. bdg. 22.00 (978-0-8368-3189-4(6)) Stevens, Gareth Inc.

—The Story of Chevy Impalas. 2002. (Classic Cars Ser.). (Illus.). 24p. (YA). (gr. 2 up). lib. bdg. 22.00 (978-0-8368-3190-0(X)) Stevens, Gareth Inc.

—The Story of Ford Thunderbirds. 2002. (Classic Cars Ser.). (Illus.). 24p. (YA). (gr. 2 up). lib. bdg. 22.00 (978-0-8368-3191-7(8)) Stevens, Gareth Inc.

—The Story of Model T Fords. 2002. (Classic Cars Ser.). (Illus.). 24p. (YA). (gr. 2 up). lib. bdg. 22.00 (978-0-8368-3192-4(6)) Stevens, Gareth Inc.

—The Story of Porsches. 2002. (Classic Cars Ser.). (Illus.). 24p. (YA). (gr. 2 up). lib. bdg. 22.00 (978-0-8368-3193-1(4)) Stevens, Gareth Inc.

—The Story of Volkswagen Beetles. 2002. (Classic Cars Ser.). (Illus.). 24p. (YA). (gr. 2 up). lib. bdg. 22.00 (978-0-8368-3194-8(2)) Stevens, Gareth Inc.

AUTOMOBILES—MODELS

Balloon. Vroom Vroom: Sports Cars. 1998. (J). 9.95 (978-0-8069-9555-7(6)) Sterling Publishing Co., Inc.

Beyer, Julie. Miniature Cars. 2000. (High Interest Bks.). (Illus.). 48p. (YA). (gr. 7-12). 24.00 (978-0-516-23332-1(7)); pap. 6.95 (978-0-516-23532-5(X)) Scholastic Library Publishing. (Children's Pr.).

Burgan, Michael. The Pontiac Firebird. 1999. (On the Road Ser.). (Illus.). 48p. (J). (gr. 3-4). lib. bdg. 21.26 (978-0-7368-0182-9(0) , Capstone High-Interest Bks.) Capstone Pr., Inc.

—The Porsche 911. 1999. (On the Road Ser.). (Illus.). 48p. (J). (gr. 3-4). lib. bdg. 21.26 (978-0-7368-0183-6(9) , Capstone High-Interest Bks.) Capstone Pr., Inc.

—The Toyota Land Cruiser. 1999. (On the Road Ser.). (Illus.). 48p. (J). (gr. 3-4). lib. bdg. 21.26 (978-0-7368-0184-3(7) , Capstone High-Interest Bks.) Capstone Pr., Inc.

Carre, Kathy & Ansary, Mir Tamim. Model Cars. 1998. (Cool Collections). (J). 18.50 (978-1-57572-116-3(3)) Heinemann Library.

DK Publishing Staff. Pinewood Derby Design Secrets. 2007. 12.95 (*978-0-7566-3262-5(5)) Dorling Kindersley Publishing, Inc.

Lego Staff. Cool Cars. 2000. (LEGO Creator Brick Tricks Ser.). (Illus.). 24p. (J). spiral bd. 7.99 (978-1-903276-09-9(8)) Lego Media International, Inc.

Moore, Davey, et al. Create 'n' Race Masterbuilders. abr. ed. 2000. (LEGO Masterbuilders Ser.). (Illus.). 64p. (J). pap. 19.99 (978-1-903276-19-8(5)) Lego Media International, Inc.

Resch, Kurt M. The Collector's Guide to Bus Toys & Models. 2002. (Schiffer Book for Collectors Ser.). (Illus.). 176p. (gr. 10-13). pap. 29.95 (978-0-7643-1631-9(1)) Schiffer Publishing, Ltd.

Rigsby, Mike. Amazing Rubber Band Cars: Easy-To-Build Wind-Up Racers, Models, & Toys. 2007. 128p. (J). (gr. 4 up). pap. 12.95 (*978-1-55652-736-4(5)) Chicago Review Pr., Inc.

Sadler, Wendy. Toy Cars. 2005. (Heinemann First Library). (Illus.). 32p. (J). (978-1-4034-6825-3(7)); pap. (978-1-4034-6831-4(1)) Heinemann Library.

AUTOMOBILES—MOTORS

see Automobiles—Engines

AUTOMOBILES—RACING

see Automobile Racing

AUTOMOBILES—REPAIRING

Brett, Jane. Noisy Garage. Thatcher, Frances, illus. 2000. (Little Helpers Ser.). (J). (978-0-439-21516-9(1)) Scholastic, Inc.

Sundance, ed. At the Gas Station. 2000. (ps-2). lib. bdg. 11.65 (978-0-613-37620-4(X)) Tandem Library Bks.

Thompson, Gary. What Every Teen Should Know Before Getting Behind the Wheel Alone: A Guide to Increasing Your Child's Safety While Reducing Your Auto Repair Expenses. 2004. 131p. (YA). per. 9.95 (978-0-9749763-1-0(8)) Guiding Horizons.

AUTOMOBILES—REPAIRING—VOCATIONAL GUIDANCE

Augarde, Steve. Garage. Augarde, Steve, illus. 2002. (Illus.). 10p. (J). (ps-2). 14.95 (978-1-57091-507-9(5)) Charlesbridge Publishing, Inc.

Boraas, Tracey. Auto Mechanics. 1999. (Community Helpers Ser.). (Illus.). 24p. (J). lib. bdg. 18.60 (978-0-7368-0072-3(7) , Bridgestone Bks.) Capstone Pr., Inc.

Frost, Helen. We Need Auto Mechanics. 2004. (Helpers in Our Community Ser.). (Illus.). 24p. (J). lib. bdg. 15.93 (978-0-7368-2574-0(6) , Pebble Bks.) Capstone Pr., Inc.

AUTOMOBILES—SERVICE STATIONS

see Service Stations

AUTOMOBILES—TOURING

see Automobile Travel

AUTOMOBILES—TRAILERS

Bender, Lionel. Trucks & Trailers. 2006. (J). (978-1-59389-270-8(5)) Chrysalis Education.

Hanson, Anders. Let's Go by RV. 2007. (Let's Go! Ser.). (ENG., Illus.). 24p. (J). (ps-3). lib. bdg. 19.93 (*978-1-59928-902-1(4) , SandCastle) ABDO Publishing Co.

Horton, Chris, ed. From Cadillac to Duesenburg, 7 vols., Set. 1998. (Encyclopedia of Cars Ser.: Vol. 2). (Illus.). 112p. (gr. 4-7). 29.95 (978-0-7910-4866-5(7) , Chelsea Hse.) Facts On File, Inc.

Ransom, Candice F. & Brill, Marlene Targ. Big Rigs. 2005. (Pull Ahead Bks.). (Illus.). 32p. (J). (gr. k-2). lib. bdg. 22.60 (978-0-8225-1537-1(7)) Lerner Publishing Group.

AUTUMN

Autumn, 6 vols. (gr. k-2). 28.95 (978-0-7368-8014-5(3)) Red Brick Learning.

Brode, Robyn. September. 2003. (Illus.). 24p. (J). pap. (978-0-8368-3620-2(0)); lib. bdg. 19.33 (978-0-8368-3584-7(0) , Weekly Reader Early Learning Library) Stevens, Gareth Inc.

Bryant, Margaret A., et al. Learning about Fall with Children's Literature: Cross-Curricular Units Based on the Works of Eric Carle, Robert Kalan, Ludwig Bemelmans & More. 2006. 160p. (J). pap. 14.95 (978-1-56976-204-2(X) , Zephyr Pr.) Chicago Review Pr., Inc.

Burton, Jane & Taylor, Kim. The Nature & Science of Autumn. Burton, Jane & Taylor, Kim, photos by. 1999. (Exploring the Science of Nature Ser.). (Illus.). 32p. (J). (gr. 3 up). lib. bdg. 24.67 (978-0-8368-2190-1(4)) Stevens, Gareth Inc.

Busch, Phyllis S. Autumn. Halsey, Megan, illus. 2000. (Nature Projects for Every Season Ser.). 48p. (J). (gr. 2 up). lib. bdg. 24.21 (978-0-7614-0988-5(2) , Benchmark Bks.) Cavendish, Marshall Corp.

Butterworth Moira. Fall. James, Helen, illus. 2005. 32p. (J). (gr. 2-5). lib. bdg. 27.10 (978-1-58340-616-8(6)) Smart Apple Media.

Claybourne, Anna. Autumn. 2001. (Seasons Ser.). (Illus.). 32p. (J). lib. bdg. 24.25 (978-1-930643-05-5(5)) Chrysalis Education.

Davis, Rebecca Fjelland. Falling Leaves & Footballs: A Fall Counting Book. 2006. (A+ Books). (Illus.). 32p. (J). (978-0-7368-5376-7(6)) Capstone Pr., Inc.

—Footballs & Falling Leaves: A Fall Counting Book. 2006. (J). (978-0-7368-6889-1(5)) Capstone Pr., Inc.

DeGezelle, Terri. Autumn. 2002. (Bridgestone Science Library). (Illus.). 24p. (J). (gr. 1-2). lib. bdg. 18.60 (978-0-7368-1409-6(4) , Bridgestone Bks.) Capstone Pr., Inc.

Fall Seasons. 2006. (Illus.). 24p. (J). (gr. k-2). 18.50 (*978-0-531-17885-0(4)) Scholastic Library Publishing.

Figorito, Christine. How Leaves Change Color. 2002. (Reading Room Collection). (Illus.). 24p. (J). pap. (978-0-8239-8154-0(1)); lib. bdg. 18.75 (978-0-8239-3717-2(8)) Rosen Publishing Group, Inc., The.

Finnegan, Mary Pat. Autumn: Signs of the Season Around North America. Thomas, Eric, illus. 2004. (Through the Seasons Ser.). 24p. (C). (gr. k-1). 22.60 (978-1-4048-0000-7(X)) Picture Window Bks.

George, Jean Craighead. Autumn Moon. 2001. (gr. 3-6). lib. bdg. 14.10 (978-0-613-50407-2(0)) Tandem Library Bks.

Green, Emily K. Fall. 2006. (Blastoff! Readers Ser.). (Illus.). 24p. (J). lib. bdg. 16.95 (978-1-60014-033-4(5)) Bellwether Media.

Harcourt School Publishers Staff. Fall Colors. 3rd ed. 2002. (Trophies English Language Learners Ser.). (Illus.). pap. 5.10 (978-0-15-327632-3(0)) Harcourt Schl. Pubs.

Here Comes Fall! 2003. (J). per. (978-1-57657-970-1(0)) Paradise Pr., Inc.

Jackson, Ellen B. The Autumn Equinox: Celebrating the Harvest. 2003. (Illus.). 32p. (J). (gr. 3-6). pap. 7.95 (978-0-7613-1984-9(0) , Millbrook Pr.) Lerner Publishing Group.

—The Autumn Equinox: Celebrating the Harvest. Ellis, Jan Davey, illus. 2000. 32p. (gr. 2-4). (978-0-7613-1442-4(3) , Millbrook Pr.) Lerner Publishing Group.

—The Autumn Equinox: Celebrating the Harvest. Ellis, Jan Davey, illus. 2000. (Traditions of the Seasons Ser.). 32p. (gr. 2-4). lib. bdg. (978-0-7613-1354-0(0) , Millbrook Pr.) Lerner Publishing Group.

Kalz, Jill. Fall. 2005. (Illus.). 24p. (gr. k-3). 15.95 (978-1-58341-362-3(6) , Creative Education) Creative Co., The.

Latta, Sara L. What Happens in Fall? 2006. (I Like the Seasons! Ser.). (Illus.). 24p. (J). lib. bdg. 21.26 (978-0-7660-2417-5(2) , Enslow Elementary) Enslow Pubs., Inc.

Macken, JoAnn Early. Autumn. 2006. (Illus.). 16p. (J). pap. 4.50 (978-0-8368-6358-1(5)); lib. bdg. 16.67 (978-0-8368-6353-6(4)) Stevens, Gareth Inc.

—Autumn: Otoño. 2006. (ENG & SPA., Illus.). 16p. (J). pap. (978-0-8368-6537-0(5)); lib. bdg. 16.67 (978-0-8368-6532-5(4)) Stevens, Gareth Inc.

Maestro, Betsy. Why Do Leaves Change Color? 2001. 24.75 (978-0-06-000333-3(2)) HarperCollins Pubs.

Maurer, Tracy. Autumn. 2006. (to Z Ser.). (Illus.). 32p. (gr. k-2). 20.95 (978-1-58952-196-4(X)) Rourke Publishing, LLC.

Meyer, Mary L. Fall. 2002. (J). 21.35 (978-1-58340-141-5(5)) Smart Apple Media.

Parker, Victoria. Days In... Fall. 2004. (Raintree Sprouts Ser.). (Illus.). 24p. (J). pap. 5.50 (978-1-4109-0743-1(0)); lib. bdg. 18.56 (978-1-4109-0738-7(4)) Raintree.

Pfeffer, Wendy. We Gather Together. Bleck, Linda, illus. 2006. 40p. (J). (gr. 1). 17.99 (978-0-525-47669-6(5) , Dutton Juvenile) Penguin Group (USA) Inc.

Rius, Maria. Las Cuatro Estaciones: El Otono. 1999. (Four Seasons Ser.).Tr. of Four Seasons. (SPA., Illus.). 32p. (J). (ps-k). pap. 6.95 (978-0-7641-0892-1(1)) Barron's Educational Series, Inc.

—Four Seasons: Fall. 1998. (Four Seasons Ser.). (Illus.). 32p. (J). (ps-k). pap. 6.95 (978-0-7641-0552-4(3)) Barron's Educational Series, Inc.

Roca, Nuria. Fall. 2004. (Four Seasons Ser.). (Illus.). 36p. (J). pap. 6.95 (978-0-7641-2729-8(2)) Barron's Educational Series, Inc.

—El Otono. 2004. (Cuatro Estaciones Ser.).Tr. of Autumn. (SPA., Illus.). 36p. (J). pap. 6.95 (978-0-7641-2730-4(6)) Barron's Educational Series, Inc.

Ross, Kathy. Crafts to Make in the Fall. Enright, Vicky, illus. 1998. (Crafts for All Seasons Ser.). 64p. (J). (gr. k-3). pap. 9.95 (978-0-7613-0335-0(9) , First Avenue Editions) Lerner Publishing Group.

—Crafts to Make in the Fall. 1998. (gr. k-3). lib. bdg. 18.75 (978-0-613-90452-0(4)) Tandem Library Bks.

Rustad, Martha E. H. Animals in Fall. 2008. (J). ***978-1-4296-0022-4(5)*** Capstone Pr., Inc.

—People in Fall. 2008. ***978-1-4296-0025-5(X)*** Capstone Pr., Inc.

Rylant, Cynthia. In November. Kastner, Jill, illus. 2000. 32p. (J). (ps-2). 17.00 (978-0-15-201076-8(9)) Harcourt Children's Bks.

Saunders, Gail. Autumn. 1998. (Seasons Ser.). (Illus.). 24p. (J). (ps-3). pap. 13.25 (978-0-516-21326-2(1) , Children's Pr.) Scholastic Library Publishing.

Saunders-Smith, Gail. Animals in the Fall. 1998. (J). pap. 13.25 (978-0-516-21248-7(6) , Children's Pr.) Scholastic Library Publishing.

—Autumn, Vol. 4. 2005. (Our Seasons & Weather Ser.). 24p. (YA). (gr. k-3). pap. (978-1-56065-846-7(0) , Pebble Bks.) Capstone Pr., Inc.

Schaefer, Lola M. Fall Fun, 4 bks. 1998. (978-0-516-29822-1(4) , Children's Pr.) Scholastic Library Publishing.

Schuette, Sarah L. Let's Look at Fall. 2007. (Pebble Plus Ser.). (Illus.). 24p. (J). (978-0-7368-6705-4(8) , 1264871) Capstone Pr., Inc.

Senisi, Ellen B. Fall Changes. 2001. (Illus.). (J). (978-0-439-24094-9(8)) Scholastic, Inc.

Thayer, Tanya. Fall. 2005. (First Step Nonfiction Ser.). (Illus.). 24p. (gr. k-2). lib. bdg. 17.27 (978-0-8225-1987-4(9)) Lerner Publishing Group.

—Fall. 2001. (gr. k-3). lib. bdg. 11.80 (978-0-613-76624-1(5)) Tandem Library Bks.

Whitehouse, Patricia. Fall. (Seasons Ser.). (Illus.). 24p. (J). (ps-1). 2003. lib. bdg. 17.08 (978-1-58810-892-0(9)); 2002. pap. 5.25 (978-1-4034-0536-4(0)) Heinemann Library.

—Otono. 2002. (Las Estaciones (Seasons) Ser.). (ENG & SPA., Illus.). 24p. (J). pap. 5.25 (978-1-4034-0546-3(8)) Heinemann Library.

Zoehfeld, Kathleen Weidner. Fall Leaves Change Color. 2001. (Scholastic Science Readers Ser.). 32p. (J). (978-0-439-26986-5(5)) Scholastic, Inc.

AUTUMN—POETRY

London, Jonathan. Park Beat: Rhymin' Through the Seasons. 2001. (Illus.). 32p. (J). (ps-3). 15.89 (978-0-688-13995-7(7)) HarperCollins Pubs.

Salas, Laura Purdie. Shrinking Days, Frosty Nights: Poems about Fall. 2008. ***978-1-4296-1205-0(3)*** Capstone Pr., Inc.

AVALANCHES

Dokey, Cameron. Washington Avalanche 1910. 2000. (978-0-606-17952-2(6)) Tandem Library Bks.

Drohan, Michele Ingber. Avalanches. 1999. (Natural Disasters Ser.). (Illus.). 24p. (J). (gr. k-4). lib. bdg. 19.95 (978-0-8239-5283-0(5) , PowerKids Pr.) Rosen Publishing Group, Inc., The.

Duden, Jane. Avalanche! The Deadly Slide. 2000. (Cover-to-Cover Bks.). (Illus.). 56p. (J). 15.95 (978-0-7807-9008-7(1)); pap. 8.95 (978-0-7891-5031-8(X)) Perfection Learning Corp.

Hamilton, John. Avalanches. 2006. (Illus.). 32p. (J). (gr. 3-8). lib. bdg. 24.21 (978-1-59679-328-6(7) , ABDO & Daughters) ABDO Publishing Co.

Jennings, Terry. Landslides & Avalanches. 1999. (Natural Disasters Ser.). (Illus.). 32p. (J). lib. bdg. 16.95 (978-1-929298-44-0(7)) Chrysalis Education.

O'Shei, Tim. Disaster in the Mountains! Colby Coombs' Story of Survival. 2007. (Illus.). 32p. (J). ***978-0-7368-6778-8(3)*** Capstone Pr., Inc.

Redmond, Jim & Redmond, Ronda. Landslides & Avalanches. 2001. (Nature on the Rampage Ser.). (Illus.). 32p. (J). (ps-3). lib. bdg. 22.83 (978-0-7398-4704-6(X)) Raintree.

Shone, Rob. Avalanches & Landslides. 2007. (Graphic Natural Disasters Ser.). (Illus.). 48p. (J). (gr. 5-8). lib. bdg. 29.25 ***978-1-4042-1992-2(7)*** Rosen Publishing Group, Inc., The.

—Avalanches & Mudslides. 2007. (J). ***978-1-4042-1984-7(6));*** (Illus.). 48p. pap. ***978-1-4042-1983-0(8)*** Rosen Publishing Group, Inc., The.

Spilsbury, Louise & Spilsbury, Richard. Crushing Avalanches. 2003. (Illus.). 32p. (J). pap. (978-1-4034-4230-7(4)); lib. bdg. 24.22 (978-1-4034-3721-1(1)) Heinemann Library.

Walker, Vanessa. Avalanche & Landslide Alert! 2004. (Disaster Alert! Ser.). (Illus.). 32p. (J). (978-0-7787-1576-4(0) , 1234689); pap. (978-0-7787-1608-2(2) , 1234689) Crabtree Publishing Co.

Woods, Michael & Woods, Mary B. Avalanches. 2007. (Disasters up Close Ser.). (J). 27.93 (978-0-8225-6577-2(3) , Lerner Pubns.) Lerner Publishing Group.

Yivisaker, Anne. Avalanches. 2003. (Natural Disasters Ser.). (Illus.). 48p. (J). (gr. 3-4). lib. bdg. 21.26 (978-0-7368-1504-8(X) , Capstone High-Interest Bks.) Capstone Pr., Inc.

AVIATION

see Aeronautics

AVIATORS

see Air Pilots

AYLWARD, GLADYS, 1902-1970

Benge, Janet Hazel & Benge, Geoffrey Francis. Gladys Aylward: The Adventure of a Lifetime. 1998. (Christian Heroes Ser.). (Illus.). 208p. (gr. 5-9). pap. 8.99 (978-1-57658-019-6(9)) YWAM Publishing.

AZTECS

see Indians of Mexico—Aztecs

B

BABAR (FICTITIOUS CHARACTER)—FICTION

Abrams. Babar Bedtime. 2004. (Illus.). 10p. (J). (ps-ps). bds. 5.95 (978-0-8109-5038-2(3)) Abrams, Harry N. , Inc.

de Brunhoff, Jean. Babar & Father Christmas. Haas, Merle, tr. from FRE. 2001. Tr. of Babar et le Pere Noel. (Illus.). 48p. (J). (ps-2). 15.95 (978-0-375-81444-0(2) , Random Hse. Bks. for Young Readers) Random Hse. Children's Bks.

—Babar und der Weihnachtsmann. Serusclat-Bruett, Francoise, tr. from FRE. 1999. Orig. Title: Babar et le Pere Noel. (GER.). 40p. (J). (978-3-257-00729-9(9)) Diogenes Verlag AG CHE. *Dist:* International Bk. Import Service, Inc.

—Bonjour, Babar! The Six Unabridged Classics by the Creator of Babar. Schulman, Janet, ed. Haas, Merle, tr. unabr. ed. 2000. (Babar Ser.). (Illus.). 280p. (J). (gr. k-3). 29.95 (978-0-375-81060-2(9) , Random Hse. Bks. for Young Readers) Random Hse. Children's Bks.

—Histoire de Babar: Le Petit Elephant. 2001. (Babar Ser.).Tr. of Story of Babar, the Little Elephant. (FRE., Illus.). (J). (ps-3). 13.95 (978-2-01-002519-8(9)) Istra FRA. *Dist:* Distribooks, Inc.

—Les Vacances de Zephir. 2000. (Babar Ser.). (FRE., Illus.). (J). 13.95 (978-2-01-003571-5(2)) Istra FRA. *Dist:* Distribooks, Inc.

—Le Voyage de Babar. 1999. (Babar Ser.). (FRE., Illus.). (J). (ps-3). 13.95 (978-2-01-002518-1(0)) Istra FRA. *Dist:* Distribooks, Inc.

de Brunhoff, Jean & de Brunhoff, Laurent. Babar en Famille. 1999. (Babar Ser.).Tr. of Babar & His Children. (FRE., Illus.). (J). (ps-3). 15.95 (978-2-01-002516-7(4)) Distribooks, Inc.

—Babar y Sus Amigos Van de Viaje. 2001. Tr. of Babar & Friends Go on a Trip. (978-84-7546-677-4(X)) Beascoa, Ediciones S.A.

de Brunhoff, Laurent. L' Anniversaire de Babar. (Babar Ser.). (FRE., Illus.). (J). (ps-3). pap. (978-2-01-002551-8(2)) Hachette Groupe Livre.

—Babar a New York. 1999. (Babar Ser.). (FRE., Illus.). (J). (ps-3). (978-2-01-002552-5(0)) Istra.

—Babar & the Succotash Bird. 2000. (Babar Ser.). (Illus.). 38p. (J). (ps-3). 16.95 (978-0-8109-5700-8(0)) Abrams, Harry N. , Inc.

—Babar dans l'Ile aux Oiseaux.Tr. of Babar in the Jungle. (FRE., Illus.). (J). pap. 16.95 ***978-2-211-09806-9(1)*** Archimede Editions FRA. *Dist:* Distribooks, Inc.

—Babar dans l'Ile aux Oiseaux. (Babar Ser.).Tr. of Babar in the Jungle. (FRE., Illus.). 29p. (J). (ps-3). 15.95 (978-0-7859-0681-0(9) , F2002) French & European Pubns., Inc.

—Babar dans l'Ile aux Oiseaux. 1999. (Babar Ser.).Tr. of Babar in the Jungle. (FRE., Illus.). (J). (ps-3). (978-2-01-002547-1(4)) Istra.

—Babar en Amerique. 1999. (Babar Ser.).Tr. of Babar in America. (FRE., Illus.). (J). (ps-3). 13.95 (978-2-01-002553-2(9)) Istra FRA. *Dist:* Distribooks, Inc.

—Babar et la Vieille Dame. (Babar Ser.). (FRE., Illus.). (J). (ps-3). pap. 15.95 (978-0-7859-0614-8(2) , FC254) French & European Pubns., Inc.

—Babar et le Pere Noel. 1999. (Babar Ser.).Tr. of Babar & Father Christmas. (FRE., Illus.). (J). (ps-3). (978-2-01-002549-5(0)) Istra.

—Babar et le Professeur Grifaton. 1999. (Babar Ser.). (FRE., Illus.). (J). (ps-3). (978-2-01-002550-1(4)) Istra.

—Babar et le Wouly-Wouly. (Babar Ser.).Tr. of Babar & the Wully-Wully. (FRE., Illus.). 26p. (J). (ps-3). 15.95 (978-0-7859-0682-7(7) , M11805) French & European Pubns., Inc.

—Babar et le Wouly-Wouly. 1999. (Babar Ser.).Tr. of Babar & the Wully-Wully. (FRE., Illus.). (J). (ps-3). (978-2-01-004209-6(3)) Istra.

—Babar et ses Amis a la Ferme. (Babar Ser.). (FRE., Illus.). 48p. (J). (ps-3). 19.95 (978-0-7859-8805-2(X)) French & European Pubns., Inc.

—Babar et ses Amis a la Fete. (Babar Ser.). (FRE., Illus.). 48p. (J). (ps-3). 19.95 (978-0-7859-8806-9(8)) French & European Pubns., Inc.

—Babar et ses Amis a la Maison. (Babar Ser.). (FRE., Illus.). 48p. (J). (ps-3). 19.95 (978-0-7859-8804-5(1)) French & European Pubns., Inc.

—Babar et ses Amis a la Ville. (Babar Ser.). (FRE., Illus.). 48p. (J). (ps-3). 19.95 (978-0-7859-8809-0(2)) French & European Pubns., Inc.

—Babar et ses Amis a L'Ecole. (Babar Ser.). (FRE., Illus.). 48p. (J). (ps-3). 19.95 (978-0-7859-8802-1(5)) French & European Pubns., Inc.

—Babar et ses Amis au Spectacle. (Babar Ser.). (FRE., Illus.). 48p. (J). (ps-3). 19.95 (978-0-7859-8803-8(3)) French & European Pubns., Inc.

—Babar et ses Amis en Foret. (Babar Ser.). (FRE., Illus.). 48p. (J). (ps-3). 19.95 (978-0-7859-8811-3(4)) French & European Pubns., Inc.

—Babar et ses Amis en Vacances. (Babar Ser.). (FRE., Illus.). 48p. (J). (ps-3). 19.95 (978-0-7859-8808-3(4)) French & European Pubns., Inc.

—Babar et ses Amis Font les Courses. (Babar Ser.). (FRE., Illus.). 48p. (J). (ps-3). 19.95 (978-0-7859-8810-6(6)) French & European Pubns., Inc.

—Babar et ses Amis Visitent le Royaume. (Babar Ser.). (FRE., Illus.). 48p. (J). (ps-3). 19.95 (978-0-7859-8807-6(6)) French & European Pubns., Inc.

—Babar les 500 Premiers Mots. (Babar Ser.). (FRE., Illus.). 48p. (J). (ps-3). 19.95 (978-0-7859-8812-0(2)) French & European Pubns., Inc.

—Babar pour Chaque Soir de la Semaine. 15.95 (978-2-01-223932-6(3)) Hachette Groupe Livre FRA. *Dist:* Distribooks, Inc.

—Babar Raconte Flore Reporter. (Babar Ser.). (FRE., Illus.). 48p. (J). (ps-3). 19.95 (978-0-7859-8813-7(0)) French & European Pubns., Inc.

—Babar Raconte Halte a la Pollution. (Babar Ser.). (FRE., Illus.). 48p. (J). (ps-3). 19.95 (978-0-7859-8816-8(5)) French & European Pubns., Inc.

—Babar Raconte la Course a la Lune. (Babar Ser.). (FRE., Illus.). 48p. (J). (ps-3). 19.95 (978-0-7859-8820-5(3)) French & European Pubns., Inc.

—Babar Raconte l'Affaire de la Couronne. (Babar Ser.). (FRE., Illus.). 48p. (J). (ps-3). 19.95 (978-0-7859-8818-2(1)) French & European Pubns., Inc.

—Babar Raconte l'Arrivee du Bebe Elephant. (Babar Ser.). (FRE., Illus.). 48p. (J). (ps-3). 19.95 (978-0-7859-8815-1(7)) French & European Pubns., Inc.

—Babar Raconte le Fantome. (Babar Ser.). (FRE., Illus.). 48p. (J). (ps-3). 19.95 (978-0-7859-8819-9(X)) French & European Pubns., Inc.

—Babar Raconte le Meilleur Ami des Elephants. (Babar Ser.). (FRE., Illus.). 48p. (J). (ps-3). 19.95 (978-0-7859-8823-6(8)) French & European Pubns., Inc.

—Babar Raconte le Pianiste. (Babar Ser.). (FRE., Illus.). 48p. (J). (ps-3). 19.95 (978-0-7859-8822-9(X)) French & European Pubns., Inc.

—Babar Raconte le Plus Beau Cadeau du Monde. (Babar Ser.). (FRE., Illus.). 48p. (J). (ps-3). 19.95 (978-0-7859-8821-2(1)) French & European Pubns., Inc.

—Babar Raconte Que la Fete Continue. (Babar Ser.). (FRE., Illus.). 48p. (J). (ps-3). 19.95 (978-0-7859-8824-3(6)) French & European Pubns., Inc.

—Babar Raconte un Diner Chez Rataxes. (Babar Ser.). (FRE., Illus.). 48p. (J). (ps-3). 19.95 (978-0-7859-8817-5(3)) French & European Pubns., Inc.

—Babar Raconte Zephir Fait le Singe. (Babar Ser.). (FRE., Illus.). 48p. (J). (ps-3). 19.95 (978-0-7859-8814-4(9)) French & European Pubns., Inc.

—Babar sur la Planete Molle. 2000. (Babar Ser.). (FRE., Illus.). (J). (ps-3). 13.95 (978-2-01-006867-6(X)) Istra FRA. *Dist:* Distribooks, Inc.

—Babar Visits Another Planet. 2003. (Illus.). 32p. (J). (ps-3). 16.95 (978-0-8109-4244-8(5)) Abrams, Harry N. , Inc.

—Babar y Sus Amigos: Letras y Numeros. l.t. ed. 2000. (Babar Ser.).Tr. of Babar & His Friends: Letters & Numbers. (SPA., Illus.). 48p. (J). 15.95 (978-84-7546-912-6(4)) Beascoa, Ediciones S.A. ESP. *Dist:* Distribooks, Inc.

—Babar y Sus Amigos de Vacaciones. l.t. ed. 2000. (Babar Ser.).Tr. of Babar & His Friends on Vacation. (SPA., Illus.). 48p. (J). 15.95 (978-84-7546-535-7(8)) Beascoa, Ediciones S.A. ESP. *Dist:* Distribooks, Inc.

—Babar's Book of Color. 2004. (Illus.). 32p. (J). (ps-1). 17.95 (978-0-8109-4840-2(0)) Abrams, Harry N. , Inc.

—Babar's Counting Book. 2003. (Illus.). 32p. (J). (ps-k). 16.95 (978-0-8109-4243-1(7)) Abrams, Harry N. , Inc.

—Babar's Museum of Art. 2003. (Illus.). 48p. (J). (ps-17). 17.95 (978-0-8109-4597-5(5)) Abrams, Harry N. , Inc.

—Babar's Mystery. ed. 2004. (Illus.). 30p. (J). (ps-3). 16.95 (978-0-8109-5033-7(2)) Abrams, Harry N. , Inc.

—Babar's Rescue. 2004. (Illus.). 32p. (J). (ps-3). 16.95 (978-0-8109-4839-6(7)) Abrams, Harry N. , Inc.

—Le Chateau de Babar. 1999. (Babar Ser.).Tr. of Babar's House. (FRE., Illus.). (J). (ps-3). pap. (978-2-01-002515-0(6)) Hachette Groupe Livre.

—Meet Babar & His Family. (Babar Ser.). (Illus.). 32p. (J). (ps-3). Random Hse. Children's Bks.

—Las Primeras Palabras de Babar. l.t. ed. 2000. (Babar Ser.).Tr. of Babar's First Words. (SPA., Illus.). 48p. (J). 15.95 (978-84-7546-828-0(4)) Beascoa, Ediciones S.A. ESP. *Dist:* Distribooks, Inc.

—Il Re Babar. pap. 12.95 (978-88-04-44195-3(X)) Mondadori ITA. *Dist:* Distribooks, Inc.

—Le Roi Babar. 1999. (Babar Ser.).Tr. of Babar the King. (FRE., Illus.). (J). (ps up). pap. 19.95 (978-2-01-002517-4(2)) Hachette Groupe Livre FRA. *Dist:* Distribooks, Inc.

—Storia de Babar l'elefantino. pap. 12.95 (978-88-04-44508-1(4)) Mondadori ITA. *Dist:* Distribooks, Inc.

de Brunhoff, Laurent & de Brunhoff, Jean. Babar Goes to School. 2003. (Illus.). 32p. (J). (ps-1). 9.95 (978-0-8109-4582-1(7)) Abrams, Harry N. , Inc.

de Brunhoff, Laurent & Weiss, Ellen. Babar & the Runaway Egg. Gibert, Jean Claude & Gray, Judith, illus. 2004. 24p. (J). (ps-1). 9.95 (978-0-8109-4838-9(9)) Abrams, Harry N. , Inc.

Viagem de Babar. pap. 19.95 (978-85-85466-78-7(2)) Companhia das Letras BRA. *Dist:* Distribooks, Inc.

Weiss, Ellen & de Brunhoff, Laurent. Babar: A Gift for Mother. Gibert, Jean Claude & Gray, Judith, illus. 2004. 24p. (J). (ps-1). 9.95 (978-0-8109-4837-2(0)) Abrams, Harry N. , Inc.

BABBITT, SPENCER (FICTITIOUS CHARACTER)—FICTION

Abbott, Tony. Stinky Business. 2000. (Don't Touch That Remote Ser.: No. 3). 160p. (J). (gr. 3-6). pap. 3.99 (978-0-671-02783-4(2) , Aladdin) Simon & Schuster Children's Publishing.

BABIES

see Infants

BABOONS

Grolier Educational Staff, contrib. by. Baboons. 2001. (Nature's Children Ser.). (Illus.). 48p. (J). (978-0-7172-5533-7(6) , Grolier) Scholastic Library Publishing.

Holmes, Kevin J. Baboons. 2000. (Animals Ser.). (Illus.). 24p. (J). (gr. 2-3). lib. bdg. 18.60 (978-0-7368-0494-3(3) , Bridgestone Bks.) Capstone Pr., Inc.

Horak, Steven A. Baboons & Other Old World Monkeys, Vol. 1. World Book, Inc. Staff, ed. 2002. (World Book's Animals of the World Ser.: Set 3). (Illus.). 64p. (J). (978-0-7166-1224-7(0)) World Bk., Inc.

Murray, Julie. Baboons. 2002. (Animal Kingdom Ser.). (Illus.). 24p. (J). (ps-3). lib. bdg. 21.35 (978-1-57765-711-8(X)) ABDO Publishing Co.

Murray, Peter & Lockwood, Sophie. Baboons. 2005. (World of Mammals Ser.). (Illus.). 40p. (J). (gr. 2-6). 29.93 (978-1-59296-497-0(4)) Child's World, Inc.

Richardson, Adele D. Baboons: Life in the Troop. 2001. (Wild World of Animals Ser.). (Illus.). 24p. (J). (gr. 1-2). lib. bdg. 18.60 (978-0-7368-0961-0(9) , Bridgestone Bks.) Capstone Pr., Inc.

Rigby Education Staff. Baboon Troops. (Sails Literacy Ser.). (Illus.). 16p. (gr. 2-3). 27.00 (978-0-7635-9955-3(7) , 699557C99) Rigby Education.

Stewart, Melissa. Baboons. 2007. (Nature Watch Ser.). (Illus.). 48p. (J). 25.26 (978-1-57505-868-9(5) , Lerner Pubns.) Lerner Publishing Group.

Suen, Anastasia. A Baboon Grows Up. Denman, Michael L. & Huiett, William J., illus. 2005. (Wild Animals Ser.). 24p. (J). (ps). lib. bdg. 23.93 (978-1-4048-0983-3(X)) Picture Window Bks.

Tagliaferro, Linda. Baboons & Their Infants. 2004. (Animal Offspring Ser.). (Illus.). 24p. (J). 13.95 (978-0-7368-2386-9(7) , Pebble Bks.) Capstone Pr., Inc.

Wilsdon, Christina. Baboons. 2007. (J). ***978-1-59939-124-3(4)*** , Reader's Digest Young Families, Inc.) Reader's Digest Children's Publishing, Inc.

BABY ANIMALS

see Animals—Infancy

BABY SITTERS

see Babysitters

BABYLONIA

Bryant, Tamera. The Life & Times of Hammurabi. 2005. (Biography from Ancient Civilizations Ser.). (Illus.). 48p. (J). (ps-7). lib. bdg. 29.95 (978-1-58415-338-2(5) , 1244807) Mitchell Lane Pubs., Inc.

Gambino, Elena. Ancient Mesopotamians. 2001. (Myths & Civilization Ser.). (Illus.). 48p. (J). (gr. 3 up). 16.95 (978-0-87226-593-6(5) , 65935B, Bedrick, Peter Bks.) School Specialty Publishing.

BABYLONIA—FICTION

Howard, Annabelle. Hammurabi's Law & Order. 2005. 40.00 (***978-1-4108-4233-6(9)***) Benchmark Education Co.

Kerr, P. B. Blue Djinn of Baby. 2006. (Children of the Lamp Ser.: No. 2). 384p. (J). pap. 6.99 (978-0-439-67022-7(5)) Scholastic, Inc.

Lattimore, Deborah Nourse. Winged Cat: And Other Tales of Ancient Civilization. 2002. (Illus.). 80p. (J). pap. 4.25 (978-0-06-442154-6(6) , Harper Trophy) HarperCollins Pubs.

BABYSITTERS

American Academy of Pediatrics Staff, contrib. by. Babysitter Lessons & Safety Training. 2nd rev. ed. 2006. (Illus.). 75p. pap. 5.95 (978-0-7637-3516-6(7)) Jones & Bartlett Pubs., Inc.

American Red Cross Staff. American Red Cross Babysitter's Handbook. 1998. (J). 9.75 (978-0-8151-3685-9(4)) Mosby, Inc.

Babysitting 101. . . Your Complete Guide to Becoming the Best Babysitter! 2003. (YA). stu. ed. (978-0-9729706-2-4(2)); (978-0-9729706-1-7(4)) Production 101, Inc.

Buckley, Annie. Be a Better Babysitter. 2006. (Girls Rock! Ser.). (Illus.). 32p. (J). (gr. 1-5). 24.21 (978-1-59296-740-7(X)) Child's World, Inc.

Dayee, Frances S. Babysitting. Graf, Heidi, illus. rev. ed. 2000. (Single Titles Ser.). 160p. (YA). (gr. 9-12). 24.00 (978-0-531-11745-3(6) , Watts, Franklin) Scholastic Library Publishing.

—Babysitting. rev. ed. 2000. (gr. 7-12). lib. bdg. 17.60 (978-0-613-34066-3(3)) Tandem Library Bks.

Fine, Jil. Baby-Sitting Smarts. 2002. (High Interest Bks.). (Illus.). 48p. (YA). (gr. 7-12). pap. 6.95 (978-0-516-24011-4(0) , Children's Pr.) Scholastic Library Publishing.

—Baby-Sitting Smarts. 2002. (gr. 7-12). lib. bdg. 15.25 (978-0-613-58688-7(3)) Tandem Library Bks.

Hunter, Dette. 38 Ways to Entertain Your Babysitter. MacEachern, Stephen, illus. 2003. 48p. (J). (ps-4). pap., act. bk. ed. 9.95 (978-1-55037-794-1(9)); lib. bdg., act. bk. ed. 19.95 (978-1-55037-795-8(7)) Annick Pr., Ltd. CAN. *Dist:* Firefly Bks., Ltd.

Laker, Leah Browning. Babysitting Rules: A Guide for When You're in Charge. 2007. (Babysitting Ser.). (Illus.). 32p. (J). (gr. 4-6). lib. bdg. 25.26 (978-0-7368-6464-0(4)) Capstone Pr., Inc.

Martin, Ann M. Dawn on the Coast. (Baby-Sitters Club Ser.: No. 23). 10p. (J). (gr. 3-7). pap. 3.95 (978-0-590-42007-5(0)) Scholastic, Inc.

Mattox, Wendy Ann. Babysitting Activities: Fun with Kids of All Ages. 2007. (Snap Books). (Illus.). 32p. (J). 25.26 (978-0-7368-6461-9(X)) Capstone Pr., Inc.

Mehlman, Barbara. Babysitting Safety: Preventing Accidents & Injuries. 2007. (Snap Books). (Illus.). 32p. (J). 25.26 (978-0-7368-6465-7(2)) Capstone Pr., Inc.

Raatma, Lucia. Safety for Babysitters. 2004. (Living Well Ser.). 32p. (J). (gr. 2-6). 27.07 (978-1-59296-239-6(4)) Child's World, Inc.

Weintraub, Aileen. Everything You Need to Know about Being a Babysitter: A Teen's Guide to Responsible Child Care. (Need to Know Library). (Illus.). 64p. (gr. 4-6). 2000. (J). lib. bdg. 25.25 (978-0-8239-3085-2(8) , NTBASI); 2005. (YA). lib. bdg. 25.25 (978-0-8239-3770-7(4)) Rosen Publishing Group, Inc., The.

BABYSITTERS—FICTION

Alexander's First Babysitter. 2004. (J). 5.00 (978-1-882541-38-6(3)) Food Allergy & Anaphylaxis Network.

Amelia Bedelia & the Baby. 2002. (Amelia Bedelia Ser.). (Illus.). (J). 12.34 (978-0-7587-0422-1(4)) Book Wholesalers, Inc.

Archer, Mike. Looking after Little Ellie. Archer, Dosh, illus. 2005. 300p. (J). 15.95 (978-1-58234-971-8(1)) Bloomsbury Publishing.

Austin, M. O, Boy Named Joe. 2006. pap. 12.99 (***978-1-4259-6217-3(3)***) AuthorHouse.

The Babysitter. 1999. 19.95 (978-0-517-76278-3(1) , Random Hse. Bks. for Young Readers) Random Hse. Children's Bks.

Benjamin, A. H. Baa! Moo! What Will We Do? Chapman, Jane, tr. Chapman, Jane, illus. 2003. 32p. (J). pap. 6.95 (978-1-58925-381-0(7) , tiger tales) ME Media LLC.

Bergen, Lara & Bergen, Lara. Angelica, Island Princess: The Rugrats Meet the Wild Thornberrys. 2003. (gr. 3-6). lib. bdg. 11.80 (978-0-613-66347-2(0)) Tandem Library Bks.

Berk, Sheryl. Barney's Little Lessons: The New Babysitter. Yingling, Kathryn, illus. 2003. (Barney Ser.). 224p. (J). (ps-1). bds. 5.99 (978-1-58668-302-3(0)) Scholastic, Inc.

Bourgeois, Paulette. Franklin & the Baby-Sitter. ed. 2004. (Illus.). (J). (gr. k-3). spiral bd. (978-0-616-11097-3(9)); spiral bd. (978-0-616-11098-0(7)) Canadian National Institute for the Blind/Institut National Canadien pour les Aveugles.

—Franklin & the Baby-Sitter. Clark, Brenda, illus. 2002. (Franklin TV-Tie In Ser.: No. 10). 32p. (J). (ps-2). per. 4.50 (978-0-439-24431-2(5) , Cartwheel Bks.) Scholastic, Inc.

Brand, Christianna. Nurse Matilda: The Collected Tales. Ardizzone, Edward, illus. ed. 2005. 300p. (J). 16.95 (978-1-58234-670-0(4)) Bloomsbury Publishing.

Brown, Harriet. Babysitter's Business Kit. 2007. 64p. (J). pap. 12.95 (***978-1-59369-186-8(6)*** , Pleasant Co.) American Girl Publishing, Inc.

Brown, Marc. Arthur & the Babysitter. 2004. 32p. (J). 15.95 (978-0-316-12128-6(2)) Little Brown & Co.

—Arthur's Mystery Babysitter. Brown, Marc, illus. 2004. (Arthur's 8 x 8 Bks.). (Illus.). 24p. (J). (ps-3). pap. 3.99 (978-0-316-73394-6(6) , Tingley, Megan Bks.) Little, Brown Bks. for Young Readers.

—Arturo y los Terribles Gemelos. 2000. (SPA.). (gr. k-3). lib. bdg. 15.25 (978-0-613-18086-3(0)) Tandem Library Bks.

Child, Lauren. Clarice Bean, Guess Who's Babysitting? Child, Lauren, illus. 2001. (Illus.). 32p. (J). (gr. 1-5). 16.99 (978-0-7636-1373-0(8)) Candlewick Pr.

Christopher, Matt. Operation Baby-Sitter. 2001. (978-0-606-22564-9(1)) Tandem Library Bks.

Cullen, Lynn. The Three Lives of Harris Harper. 1998. 160p. (J). pap. 3.99 (978-0-380-72901-2(6) , Harper Trophy) HarperCollins Pubs.

Cuscuna, Susan. Molly & Me & Manny Magee. 2007. (J). (***978-0-7666-2839-7(6)***) Modern Publishing.

Day, Alexandra. Carl Goes to Daycare. Day, Alexandra, illus. 2002. (Illus.). (J). 22.13 (978-0-7587-2192-1(7)) Book Wholesalers, Inc.

de Paola, Tomie. La Hermanita de Tommy. 2000. Tr. of Baby Sister. (978-0-606-22409-3(2)) Tandem Library Bks.

Delton, Judy. Angel in Charge. 1999. (Illus.). 160p. (J). (gr. 4-6). pap. 5.95 (978-0-395-96061-5(4)) Houghton Mifflin Co. Trade & Reference Div.

—Angel in Charge. 1999. (gr. 3-6). lib. bdg. 12.95 (978-0-613-18232-4(4)); (Illus.). (J). 11.60 (978-0-606-18206-5(3)) Tandem Library Bks.

DK Publishing Staff. Staying with A Babysitter. 2007. 12p. (J). (ps-2). bds. 6.99 (***978-0-7566-3105-5(X)***) Dorling Kindersley Publishing, Inc.

Gilson, Kristin. A Baby-Sitter's Nightmare: Tales Too Scary to Be True. 1998. (Illus.). 112p. (J). (gr. 3-7). pap. 4.95 (978-0-06-440700-7(4)) HarperCollins Pubs.

Gorbachev, Valeri. Ms. Turtle the Babysitter. Gorbachev, Valeri, illus. 2005. (I Can Read Bks.). (Illus.). 64p. (J). (gr. k-3). 15.99 (978-0-06-058073-5(9)); lib. bdg. 16.89 (978-0-06-058074-2(7)) HarperCollins Pubs.

Gray, Kes. Nelly the Monstersitter. Ross, Tony, illus. 2006. 48p. (J). lib. bdg. (***978-1-4048-3124-7(X)***) Picture Window Bks.

Gregory, Valiska. Shirley's Wonderful Baby. Degen, Bruce, illus. 32p. (ps-2). 2002. (J). 14.99 (978-0-06-028132-8(4)); 1999. pap. 5.95 (978-0-06-443513-0(X)) HarperCollins Pubs.

Griffin, Adele. My Almost Epic Summer. 2008. 176p. (YA). (gr. 7). pap. 6.99 (***978-0-14-240805-6(0)*** , Puffin); 2006. 192p. (J). (gr. 4). 15.99 (978-0-399-23784-3(4) , Putnam Juvenile) Penguin Group (USA) Inc.

Griffin, Adele. My Almost Epic Summer (Splashproof Ed.) 2007. 1p. (YA). (gr. 7). pap. 6.99 (978-0-14-240860-5(3) , Puffin) Penguin Group (USA) Inc.

Hapka, Cathy & Titlebaum, Ellen. How Not to Babysit Your Brother. Palen, Debbie, illus. 2005. (Step into Reading Ser.). 48p. (J). (gr. 2-4). pap. 3.99 (978-0-375-82856-0(7) , Random Hse. Bks. for Young Readers) Random Hse. Children's Bks.

Harris, Robie H. Don't Forget to Come Back! Bliss, Harry, illus. 2004. 40p. (J). (ps up). 15.99 (978-0-7636-1782-0(2)) Candlewick Pr.

Hastings, Suanne. Many Moods of Maddie. 2006. 24p. pap. 12.95 (978-0-9769348-0-6(9)) Tastica, Suanne Creations Inc.

Hearne, Betsy. Who's in the Hall? A Mystery in Four Chapters. 2000. (Illus.). 32p. (J). (gr. 2 up). 16.89 (978-0-688-16262-7(2)) HarperCollins Pubs.

Hershenhorn, Esther. Chicken Soup by Heart. Litzinger, Rosanne, illus. 2002. 32p. (J). (gr. k-3). 16.95 (978-0-689-82665-8(6)) Simon & Schuster Children's Publishing.

Horvath, Polly. The Trolls. 2001. (Sunburst Bks.). (Illus.). 144p. (J). (gr. 3-7). reprint ed. pap. 5.95 (978-0-374-47991-6(7) , Sunburst) Farrar, Straus & Giroux.

Hudson, Charlotte. Who Will Sing My Puff-a-Bye? McQuillan, Mary, illus. 2005. 32p. (J). pap. 9.99 (978-0-09-943946-2(8) , Red Fox) Random Hse. Children's Bks. GBR. *Dist:* Trafalgar Square Publishing.

James, Simon. Jake & the Babysitter. 2002. (gr. 3-6). lib. bdg. 13.00 (978-0-613-53738-4(6)) Tandem Library Bks.

Jennings, Sharon, et al. Franklin & the Baby-Sitter. Southern, Shelley et al, illus. 2001. (Franklin TV Storybook Ser.). 32p. (J). (ps-3). (978-1-55074-916-8(1)) Kids Can Pr., Ltd.

Johnson, Marion. Caillou Watches Rosie. rev. ed. 2008. (Playtime Ser.). (Illus.). 20p. (J). pap. 4.95 (***978-2-89450-635-6(X)***) Chouette Publishing CAN. *Dist:* Independent Pubs. Group.

Jones, Christianne C. The Babysitter. Trover, Zachary, illus. 2005. (Read-It! Readers Ser.). 24p. (J). (ps-ps). lib. bdg. 18.60 (978-1-4048-1187-4(7)) Picture Window Bks.

Keller, Holly. Geraldine & Mrs. Duffy. 2000. (Illus.). (J). (gr. k-3). 24p. 15.95 (978-0-688-16887-2(6)); 32p. 15.89 (978-0-688-16888-9(4)) HarperCollins Pubs.

Kenney, Peterson, et al. The Snooze Brothers: A Lesson in Responsibility. Big Idea Design Staff, illus. 2006. (VeggieTown Values Ser.: Bk. 6). 32p. (J). pap. 3.99 (978-0-310-70739-4(0)) Zonderkidz.

Kindig, Tess Eileen. Muggsy Makes an Assist. 2000. (Slam Dunk Ser.: Vol. 3). 96p. (J). (gr. 1-4). Vol. 3, (Illus.). 4.99 (978-0-570-07018-4(X)); Vol. 4. 4.99 (978-0-570-07019-1(8)) Concordia Publishing Hse.

—Muggsy Makes an Assist. 2000. (gr. k-3). lib. bdg. 13.00 (978-0-613-72906-2(4)) Tandem Library Bks.

Konigsburg, E. L. Silent to the Bone. unabr. ed. 2004. (Middle Grade Cassette Librariestm Ser.). 272p. (J). (gr. 5-9). pap. 38.00 incl. audio (978-0-8072-8741-5(5) , S YA 253 SP, Listening Library) Random Hse. Audio Publishing Group.

—Silent to the Bone. 272p. 2004. (YA). mass mkt. 5.99 (978-0-689-86715-6(8) , Simon Pulse); 2002. pap. 5.99 (978-0-689-83602-2(3) , Aladdin) Simon & Schuster Children's Publishing.

—Silent to the Bone. Konigsburg, E. L., illus. 2000. (Jean Karl Bks.). (Illus.). 272p. (J). (gr. 5-9). 16.00 (978-0-689-83601-5(5) , Atheneum) Simon & Schuster Children's Publishing.

—Silent to the Bone. 2002. (gr. 5-8). lib. bdg. 14.15 (978-0-613-45102-4(3)) Tandem Library Bks.

—Silent to the Bone. l.t. ed. 2001. 271p. (J). (gr. 4-7). 23.95 (978-0-7862-3169-0(6)) Thorndike Pr.

Kromhout, Rindert. Little Donkey & the Babysitter. Martens, Marianne, tr. from DUT. Van Haeringen, Annemarie, illus. 2006. 32p. (J). 15.95 (978-0-7358-2057-9(0)) North-South Bks., Inc.

Kubler, Annie. Baby-Sitter. 2000. (All in a Day Boardbooks Ser.). (Illus.). 14p. (J). (ps-k). bds. 3.99 (978-0-85953-588-5(6)) Child's Play-International.

Levin, Betty. That'll Do, Moss. 2002. (Illus.). 128p. (J). (gr. 3 up). 15.89 (978-0-06-000532-0(7)) HarperCollins Pubs.

Long, Melinda. Pirates Don't Change Diapers. Shannon, David, illus. 2007. 44p. (J). (ps-2). 16.00 (978-0-15-205353-6(0)) Harcourt Trade Pubs.

Martin, Ann M. Abby & the Best Kid Ever. 1998. (Baby-Sitters Club Ser.: No. 116). (J). (gr. 3-7). pap. 3.99 (978-0-590-05994-7(7)) Scholastic, Inc.

—Abby & the Best Kid Ever. 1998. (Baby-Sitters Club Ser.: No. 116). (J). (gr. 3-7). (978-0-606-13160-5(4)) Tandem Library Bks.

—Abby & the Notorious Neighbor. 1998. (Baby-Sitters Club Mystery Ser.: No. 35). (Illus.). (J). (gr. 3-7). pap. 3.99 (978-0-590-05975-6(0) , Scholastic Paperbacks) Scholastic, Inc.

—Abby in Wonderland. 1998. (Baby-Sitters Club Ser.: No. 121). (J). (gr. 3-7). pap. 4.50 (978-0-590-50063-0(5) , Scholastic Paperbacks) Scholastic, Inc.

—Abby in Wonderland. 1998. (Baby-Sitters Club Ser.: No. 121). (J). (gr. 3-7). (978-0-606-13165-0(5)) Tandem Library Bks.

—Baby-Sitters' European Vacation. 1998. (Baby-Sitters Club Super Special Ser.: No. 15). (J). (gr. 3-7). pap. 4.50 (978-0-590-06000-4(7)) Scholastic, Inc.

—Bsls Box Set, No. 9. 2003. (J). 11.80 (978-0-590-66716-6(5)) Scholastic, Inc.

—Claudia & Crazy Peaches. 1999. (Baby-Sitters Club Ser.: No. 78). 138p. (J). (gr. 3-7). pap. 3.99 (978-0-590-92610-2(1)) Scholastic, Inc.

—Claudia & the Little Liar. 1999. (Baby-Sitters Club Ser.: No. 128). 114p. (J). (gr. 3-7). pap. 4.50 (978-0-590-50351-8(0)) Scholastic, Inc.

—Claudia & the Middle School Mystery. collector's ed. 1998. (Baby-Sitters Club Ser.: No. 40). (Illus.). 135p. (J). (gr. 3-7). pap. 3.99 (978-0-590-73452-3(0)) Scholastic, Inc.

—Claudia & the Terrible Truth. 1998. (Baby-Sitters Club Ser.: No. 117). (J). (gr. 3-7). pap. 4.50 (978-0-590-05995-4(5) , Scholastic Paperbacks) Scholastic, Inc.

—Claudia & the Terrible Truth. 1998. (Baby-Sitters Club Ser.: No. 117). (J). (gr. 3-7). (978-0-606-13161-2(2)) Tandem Library Bks.

—Dawn on the Coast. (Baby-Sitters Club Ser.: No. 23). 10p. (J). (gr. 3-7). pap. 3.95 (978-0-590-42007-5(0)) Scholastic, Inc.

—Everything Changes. 1999. (Baby-Sitters Club Friends Forever Special Ser.: No. 1). (J). (gr. 3-7). pap. 4.50 (978-0-590-50391-4(X)) Scholastic, Inc.

—Graduation Day. 2000. (Baby-Sitters Club Friends Forever Special Ser.: No. 2). 192p. (J). (gr. 3-7). pap. 4.50 (978-0-439-21918-1(3)) Scholastic, Inc.

—Gran Idea de Kristy. 2002. (Baby-Sitters Club Ser.).Tr. of Kristy's Great Idea. (SPA.). 168p. (J). 11.95 (978-84-272-3651-6(4)) Molino, Editorial ESP. *Dist:* AIMS International Bks., Inc.

—Karen's Book. 1998. (Baby-Sitters Little Sister Ser.: No. 100). (J). (gr. 3-7). pap. 4.50 (978-0-590-50051-7(1) , Scholastic Paperbacks) Scholastic, Inc.

—Karen's Chain Letter. 1998. (Baby-Sitters Little Sister Ser.: No. 101). (J). (gr. 3-7). (978-0-606-13168-1(X)) Tandem Library Bks.

—Karen's Christmas Carol. 1998. (Baby-Sitters Little Sister Ser.: No. 104). 112p. (J). (gr. 3-7). pap. 3.50 (978-0-590-50056-2(2)) Scholastic, Inc.

—Karen's Copycat. 1999. (Baby-Sitters Little Sister Ser.: No. 107). 112p. (J). (gr. 3-7). pap. 3.99 (978-0-590-50059-3(7)) Scholastic, Inc.

—Karen's Field Day. 1999. (Baby-Sitters Little Sister Ser.: No. 108). 112p. (J). (gr. 3-7). pap. 3.99 (978-0-590-50060-9(0)) Scholastic, Inc.

—Karen's Hurricane. 1999. (Baby-Sitters Little Sister Ser.: No. 113). (Illus.). 106p. (J). (gr. 3-7). pap. 3.99 (978-0-590-52379-0(1)) Scholastic, Inc.

—Karen's Movie Star. 1998. (Baby-Sitters Little Sister Ser.: No. 103). 112p. (J). (gr. 3-7). pap. 3.99 (978-0-590-50055-5(4)) Scholastic, Inc.

—Karen's Promise. 1998. (Baby-Sitters Little Sister Ser.: No. 95). (J). (gr. 3-7). pap. 3.99 (978-0-590-06593-1(9) , Scholastic Paperbacks) Scholastic, Inc.

—Karen's Promise. 1998. (Baby-Sitters Little Sister Ser.: No. 95). (J). (gr. 3-7). (978-0-606-13171-1(X)) Tandem Library Bks.

—Karen's Snow Princess. 1998. (Baby-Sitters Little Sister Ser.: No. 94). (J). (gr. 3-7). pap. 3.99 (978-0-590-06592-4(0)) Scholastic, Inc.

—Karen's Spy Mystery. 1999. (Babysitters Little Sister Ser.: No. 111). (Illus.). 109p. (J). (gr. 3-7). pap. 3.99 (978-0-590-52356-1(2)) Scholastic, Inc.

—Karen's Yo-Yo. 2000. (Baby-Sitters Little Sister Ser.: No. 119). (Illus.). 144p. (J). (gr. 3-7). pap. 3.99 (978-0-590-52511-4(5)) Scholastic, Inc.

—Kristy & the Cat Burglar. 1998. (Baby-Sitters Club Mystery Ser.: No. 36). (J). (gr. 3-7). pap. 3.99 (978-0-590-05976-3(9) , Scholastic Paperbacks) Scholastic, Inc.

—Kristy in Charge. 1998. (Baby-Sitters Club Ser.: No. 122). (J). (gr. 3-7). pap. 3.99 (978-0-590-50064-7(3)) Scholastic, Inc.

—Kristy in Charge. 1998. (Baby-Sitters Club Ser.: No. 122). (J). (gr. 3-7). (978-0-606-13166-7(3)) Tandem Library Bks.

—Kristy Thomas, Dog Trainer. 1998. (Baby-Sitters Club Ser.: No. 118). (J). (gr. 3-7). pap. 3.99 (978-0-590-05996-1(3) , Scholastic Paperbacks) Scholastic, Inc.

—Kristy Thomas, Dog Trainer. 1998. (Baby-Sitters Club Ser.: No. 118). (J). (gr. 3-7). (978-0-606-13162-9(0)) Tandem Library Bks.

—Mary Anne & Miss Priss. 2001. (Baby-Sitters Club Ser.: No. 73). (J). (gr. 3-7). pap. 3.99 (978-0-590-92604-1(7)) Scholastic, Inc.

—Mary Anne & the Haunted Bookstore. 1998. (Baby-Sitters Club Mystery Ser.: No. 34). (J). (gr. 3-7). pap. 3.99 (978-0-590-05974-9(2) , Scholastic Paperbacks) Scholastic, Inc.

—Mary Anne & the Playground Fight. 1998. (Baby-Sitters Club Ser.: No. 120). (J). (gr. 3-7). pap. 3.99 (978-0-590-05998-5(X) , Scholastic Paperbacks) Scholastic, Inc.

—Mary Anne & the Playground Fight. 1998. (Baby-Sitters Club Ser.: No. 120). (J). (gr. 3-7). (978-0-606-13164-3(7)) Tandem Library Bks.

—Mary Anne in the Middle. 1998. (Baby-Sitters Club Ser.: No. 125). (Illus.). 121p. (J). (gr. 3-7). pap. 3.99 (978-0-590-50179-8(8)) Scholastic, Inc.

—Mary Anne y la Gran Boda. 2001. (Baby-Sitters Club Ser.).Tr. of Mary Anne & the Great Rom.... (SPA.). 152p. (YA). 11.95 (978-84-272-3680-6(8)) Molino, Editorial ESP. *Dist:* AIMS International Bks., Inc.

—Stacey & the Stolen Hearts. 1998. (Baby-Sitters Club Mystery Ser.: No. 33). (J). (gr. 3-7). pap. 3.99 (978-0-590-05973-2(4)) Scholastic, Inc.

—Stacey McGill... Matchmaker? 1998. (Baby-Sitters Club Ser.: No. 124). 160p. (J). (gr. 3-7). pap. 3.99 (978-0-590-50175-0(5)) Scholastic, Inc.

—Stacey's Ex-Boyfriend. 1998. (Baby-Sitters Club Ser.: No. 119). (J). (gr. 3-7). pap. 3.99 (978-0-590-05997-8(1)) Scholastic, Inc.

—Stacey's Ex-Boyfriend. 1998. (Baby-Sitters Club Ser.: No. 119). (J). (gr. 3-7). (978-0-606-13163-6(9)) Tandem Library Bks.

—The Truth about Stacey. 2006. (Baby-Sitters Club Ser.: No. 3). (Illus.). 144p. (J). (gr. 3-7). pap. 8.99 (978-0-439-73936-8(5)); pap. 16.99 (978-0-439-86724-5(X)) Scholastic, Inc. (Graphix).

Mayer, Mercer. Just Me & My Babysitter. Mayer, Mercer, illus. 1998. (Little Critter Ser.). (Illus.). 24p. (J). (gr. k-k). pap. 3.99 (978-0-307-11945-2(9) , 11945, Random Hse. Bks. for Young Readers) Random Hse. Children's Bks.

Mazer, Anne. Out of Sight, Out of Mind. 2002. (Amazing Days of Abby Hayes Ser.: No. 9). (Illus.). 144p. (J). (gr. 1-4). pap. 4.99 (978-0-439-35368-7(8)) Scholastic, Inc.

—Out of Sight, Out of Mind. 2002. (Amazing Days of Abby Hayes Ser.: No. 9). (gr. 3-6). lib. bdg. 12.40 (978-0-613-59859-0(8)) Tandem Library Bks.

McAllister, Angela & Archbold, Tim. Be Good Gordon. 2002. (Illus.). 32p. (J). pap. 10.99 (978-0-7475-5580-3(X)) Bloomsbury Publishing Plc GBR. *Dist:* Independent Pubs. Group.

Mccoy, Mimi. Babysitting Wars. 2007. (Candy Apple Ser.). 176p. (J). pap. 4.99 (***978-0-439-92954-7(7)***) Scholastic, Inc.

McNaughton, Colin. Captain Abdul's Little Treasure. McNaughton, Colin, illus. 2006. (Illus.). 48p. (J). (gr. k). 14.99 (978-0-7636-3045-4(4)) Candlewick Pr.

Mills, Claudia. You're a Brave Man, Julius Zimmerman. 2001. 160p. (gr. 3-7). pap. 5.99 (978-0-7868-1448-0(9)) Hyperion Bks. for Children.

Minsky, Terri, creator. When Moms Attack & Misadventures in Babysitt, 4 vols., Vol. 3. 2003. (Lizzie McGuire Ser.: Vol. 3). (Illus.). 192p. pap. 7.99 (978-1-59182-245-5(9) , Tokyopop Kids) TOKYOPOP, Inc.

Morton, Elizabeth. Anne's Baby Sitting Blues: The Animated Series. 2001. 96p. (J). (gr. 2-5). pap. 4.99 (978-0-06-442159-1(7) , Avon) HarperCollins Pubs.

Moss, Miriam. A Babysitter for Billy Bear. Currey, Anna, illus. 2008. 32p. (J). (ps). 16.99 (***978-0-8037-3269-8(4)*** , Dial) Penguin Group (USA) Inc.

Muldrow, Diane. Measure of Thanks. Pollack, Barbara, illus. 2007. (Dish Ser.: Vol. 10). 160p. (J). (gr. 4-7). pap. 4.99 (***978-0-448-44662-2(6)*** , Grosset & Dunlap) Penguin Group (USA) Inc.

Murail, Marie-Aude. Baby-Sitter Blues. 2000. (la Orilla Del Viento Ser.). (SPA., Illus.). 100p. (J). (ps-ps). pap. 7.99 (978-968-16-6070-3(6) , 126) Fondo de Cultura Economica USA.

Ostrow, Kim. Up All Night. Saunders, Zina, illus. 2004. (Ready-to-Read Ser.: Vol. 1). 32p. (J). pap. 3.99 (978-0-689-86320-2(9) , Simon Spotlight/Nickelodeon) Simon & Schuster Children's Publishing.

—Up All Night. 2004. (gr. k-3). lib. bdg. 11.80 (978-0-613-73459-2(9)) Tandem Library Bks.

Parish, Herman. Amelia Bedelia under Construction. Sweat, Lynn, illus. (I Can Read Bks.). 64p. (J). 2007. pap. 3.99 (***978-0-06-084346-5(2)*** , Harper Trophy); 2006. 15.99 (978-0-06-084344-1(6)); 2006. lib. bdg. 16.89 (978-0-06-084345-8(4)) HarperCollins Pubs.

Play Time. 2002. (978-0-9720825-0-1(6)) Toy Box Pr., The.

Posner-Sanchez, Andrea & Random House Disney Staff. Jack-Jack Attack. Disney Storybook Artists Staff, illus. 2006. 24p. (J). (gr. k-k). 2.99 (978-0-7364-2377-9(X) , Golden/Disney) Random Hse. Children's Bks.

Prince, Sarah. Rosie Moon. 2001. (gr. k-3). lib. bdg. 11.80 (978-0-613-33422-8(1)) Tandem Library Bks.

Proysen, Alf. Mrs. Pepperpot Minds the Baby. 2006. (Illus.). 24p. (J). pap. 8.99 (***978-0-09-945156-3(5)*** , Red Fox) Random Hse. Children's Bks. GBR. *Dist:* Independent Pubs. Group.

Rigby Education Staff. Miss Grimble. (Sails Literacy Ser.). (Illus.). 16p. (gr. 1-2). 27.00 (978-0-7635-9925-6(5) , 699255C99) Rigby Education.

Robbins, Beth. Tom, Ally & the Babysitter. Stuart, Jon, illus. 2001. (It's OK! Ser.). 24p. (J). (ps-k). pap. 3.95 (978-0-7894-7426-1(3) , D K Ink) Dorling Kindersley Publishing, Inc.

Ross, Pat. M & M & the Bad News Babies. 1999. (Illus.). (J). (gr. 3-6). lib. bdg. 13.00 (978-0-8085-3696-3(6)) Tandem Library Bks.

Rylant, Cynthia. Henry & Mudge. Stevenson, Sucie, illus. 2002. (Henry & Mudge Ser.). (J). 11.91 (978-0-7587-1269-1(3)) Book Wholesalers, Inc.

—Henry & Mudge & Mrs. Hopper's House. Bracken, Carolyn, illus. 2003. (Henry & Mudge Ser.). 40p. (J). pap. 3.99 (978-0-689-83446-2(2) , Aladdin); 14.95 (978-0-689-81153-1(5)) Simon & Schuster Children's Publishing.

—Henry & Mudge & Mrs. Hopper's House. 2006. (Henry & Mudge Ser.). (J). (gr. 1-6). 24.21 (978-1-59961-084-9(1)) Spotlight.

Siburt, Ruth. The Trouble with Alex. 1998. 93p. (J). (gr. k-9). pap. 9.99 (978-0-88092-366-8(0) , 3660) Royal Fireworks Publishing Co.

Silent to the Bone. 2004. 261p. (J). (gr. 5-9). lib. bdg. 14.15 (978-0-613-73424-0(6)) Tandem Library Bks.

Smith, Jane Denitz. Fairy Dust. (J). Date not set. (gr. 3-7). mass mkt. 4.99 (978-0-06-440961-2(9)); 2002. (Illus.). 160p. 15.89 (978-0-06-029280-5(6)) HarperCollins Pubs.

Sumerak, Mark. Misadventures in Babysitting. 2006. (Illus.). (J). (gr. 2-6). 21.35 (978-1-59961-034-4(5)) Spotlight.

Tomasi, Joseph. Miss Wheezer Comes to Stay. 2006. 48p. pap. 12.95 (978-1-4241-3703-9(9)) PublishAmerica, Inc.

Travers, Pamela L. Mary Poppins. 202p. (J). (gr. 3-5). pap. 6.00 (978-0-8072-1536-4(8) , Listening Library) Random Hse. Audio Publishing Group.

Venn, Cecilia. On with the Show! Handelman, Dorothy, photos by. 1998. (Real Kids Readers Ser.). (Illus.). 48p. (gr. 1-3). lib. bdg. 18.90 (978-0-7613-2011-1(3)); 32p. (J). (gr. 2-4). pap. 4.99 (978-0-7613-2036-4(9)) Lerner Publishing Group. (Millbrook Pr.).

Ward, Nick. Don't Eat the Babysitter. 2006. 32p. (J). (gr. k-3). 9.95 (978-0-385-75062-2(5) , Fickling, David Bks.) Random Hse. Children's Bks.

Wax, Wendy. For Love or Money. Piluso, Piero, illus. 2006. 32p. (J). lib. bdg. 9.00 (***978-1-4242-0955-2(2)***) Fitzgerald Bks.

Wells, Rosemary. Shy Charles. 2001. (ps-2). lib. bdg. 14.15 (978-0-613-36076-0(1)) Tandem Library Bks.

Wilson, Pauline Hutchens & Dengler, Sandy. The Case of the Monster in the Creek. 2001. (New Sugar Creek Gang Ser.: Vol. 6). 144p. (J). 5.99 (978-0-8024-8666-0(5)) Moody Pubs.

Wolff, Virginia Euwer. Make Lemonade. 2006. 208p. (YA). pap. 6.95 (978-0-8050-8070-4(8) , Holt, Henry & Co. Bks. For Young Readers) Holt, Henry & Co.

—Make Lemonade. unabr. ed. 2004. (Young Adult Cassette Librariestm Ser.). 200p. (J). (gr. 7 up). pap. 36.00 incl. audio (978-0-8072-0793-2(4) , S YA 348 SP, Listening Library) Random Hse. Audio Publishing Group.

—Make Lemonade. l.t. ed. 2004. 257p. pap. 10.95 (978-0-7862-6358-5(X)) Thorndike Pr.

Wollman, Jessica. Bunches of Fun. MacNeil, Chris, illus. 2006. 149p. (J). (***978-1-4156-5003-5(9)*** , Aladdin) Simon & Schuster Children's Publishing.

Zoehfeld, Kathleen Weidner. Roo's New Babysitter. 1999. (My Very First Winnie the Pooh Ser.). (Illus.). 32p. (J). (ps-k). 11.99 (978-0-7868-3215-6(0)) Disney Pr.

BACH, JOHANN SEBASTIAN, 1685-1750

Boughton, Rutland. Bach, the Master, a New Interpretation of His Genius. 2001. 303p. (YA). reprint ed. 98.00 (978-0-7222-6313-6(9)) Library Reprints, Inc.

Catucci, Stefano. Bach & Baroque Music. 1998. (Masters of Music Ser.). (Illus.). 64p. (YA). (gr. 6-12). 14.95 (978-0-7641-5130-9(4)) Barron's Educational Series, Inc.

Celenza, Anna Harwell. Bach's Goldberg Variations. Kitchel, JoAnn E., illus. 2005. 32p. (J). 19.95 incl. audio compact disk (978-1-57091-510-9(5)) Charlesbridge Publishing, Inc.

Cencetti, Greta. Bach. 2002. (Classic Composers Ser.). (Illus.). 40p. (J). incl. audio compact disk (978-1-59069-092-5(3) , T2102) Studio Mouse LLC.

—Bach: Getting to Know Your Classical Composers. 2002. (Classic Composers Ser.). (Illus.). 32p. (978-1-59069-025-3(7) , T2002) Studio Mouse LLC.

du Bouchet, Paule. Johann Sebastian Bach. 2007. (Descubrimos a los Musicos Ser.). (Illus.). 24p. (J). 14.95 (***978-84-9825-162-3(1)***) Combel Editorial, S.A. ESP. *Dist:* Independent Pubs. Group.

Ekker, Ernst A. Johann Sebastian Bach: Un Album Musical. Eisenburger, Doris, illus. 2002. (Coleccion Joven Musica).Tr. of Johann Sebastian Bach: A Musical Picture Book. (SPA.). 24p. (YA). (gr. 5 up). 20.76 incl. audio compact disk (978-84-89804-48-7(6)) Loguez Ediciones ESP. *Dist:* Lectorum Pubns., Inc.

Getzinger, Donna & Felsenfeld, Daniel. Johann Sebastian Bach & the Art of Baroque Music. 2004. (Classical Composers Ser.). (Illus.). 144p. (YA). (gr. 6-12). 26.95 (978-1-931798-22-8(2)) Reynolds, Morgan Inc.

Pancella, Peggy. Johann Sebastian Bach. 2005. (J). pap. (978-1-4034-6753-9(6)); (Illus.). 32p. (978-1-4034-6745-4(5)) Heinemann Library.

Parry, Charles H. H. Life of J. S. Bach. 2001. (YA). reprint ed. 150.00 (978-0-7222-5315-1(X)) Library Reprints, Inc.

Rachlin, Ann. Bach. 2002. (Ninos Famosos Ser.). (ENG & SPA.). 24p. pap. 6.95 (978-85-7416-079-5(2)) Callis Editora Ltda BRA. *Dist:* Independent Pubs. Group.

Summerer, Eric Michael. Johann Sebastian Bach. 2006. (Primary Source Library of Famous Composers). (Illus.). 32p. (J). 21.95 (978-1-4042-2770-5(9) , PowerKids Pr.) Rosen Publishing Group, Inc., The.

Venezia, Mike. Johann Sebastian Bach. 1998. (Getting to Know the World's Greatest Composers Ser.). (Illus.). 32p. (J). (gr. 3-4). pap. 6.95 (978-0-516-26352-6(8)); 27.00 (978-0-516-20760-5(1)) Scholastic Library Publishing. (Children's Pr.).

Vernon, Roland. Bach: Introducing. 2000. (Introducing Composers Ser.). (Illus.). 32p. (J). (gr. 4-7). 21.95 (978-0-7910-6037-7(3) , Chelsea Hse.) Facts On File, Inc.

Wilcox, Judy. Sebastian Bach the Boy from Thuringia Study Guide. 2005. (Illus.). 32p. (J). 4.95 (978-0-9746505-2-4(8) , 4354) Zeezok Publishing.

Winter, Jeanette. Sebastian: A Book about Bach. 1999. (Illus.). 40p. (J). 16.00 (978-0-15-200629-7(X) , Silver Whistle) Harcourt Trade Pubs.

—Sebastian: A Book about Bach. 1999. (Illus.). 40p. (gr. 4-7). (978-0-8172-3772-1(0)) Raintree.

BACILLI

see Bacteriology

BACON'S REBELLION, 1676

Powell, Phelan. Sir William Berkeley. 2000. (Colonial Leaders Ser.). (Illus.). 80p. (J). (gr. 4-7). pap. 31.00 (978-0-7910-6117-6(5)); 27.50 (978-0-7910-6116-9(7)) Facts On File, Inc. (Chelsea Hse.).

—Sir William Berkeley. 2001. (gr. 5-8). lib. bdg. 17.60 (978-0-613-33059-6(5)) Tandem Library Bks.

BACTERIA

see also Bacteriology

Bacteria. 2003. (Discovery Channel School Science Ser.). (Illus.). 32p. (J). (gr. 5 up). lib. bdg. 24.67 (978-0-8368-3366-9(X)) Stevens, Gareth Inc.

Day, Nancy. Killer Superbugs: The Story of Drug-Resistant Diseases. 2001. (Issues in Focus Ser.). (Illus.). 128p. (YA). (gr. 6-12). lib. bdg. 26.60 (978-0-7660-1588-3(2)) Enslow Pubs., Inc.

Gray, Shirley W. Cleanliness for Good Health. 2003. (Living Well). (Illus.). 32p. (J). (gr. 2-6). 27.07 (978-1-59296-084-2(7)) Child's World, Inc.

Heinlen, Marieka, illus. Germs Are Not for Sharing. 2006. (Best Behavior Ser.). 40p. (J). (ps-2). pap. 11.95 (978-1-57542-197-1(6)) Free Spirit Publishing, Inc.

—Germs Are Not for Sharing Board Book. 2006. (Best Behavior Ser.). 24p. (J). (ps). 7.95 (978-1-57542-196-4(8)) Free Spirit Publishing, Inc.

Holley, Dennis. Viruses & Bacteria: Hands-on & Minds-on Investigations for Middle to High School. 2000. (Illus.). 82p. (YA). (gr. 7-12). pap. 15.99 (978-0-89455-717-0(3) , MP6201) Critical Thinking Bks. & Software.

Holt, Rinehart and Winston Staff. Bacteria & Viruses: Chapter Resources: Tennessee Edition. 3rd ed. 2003. (Holt Science & Technology Ser.). pap. 11.40 (978-0-03-069134-8(6)) Holt, Rinehart & Winston.

—Holt Science & Technology Chapter 10: Life Science: Bacteria & Viruses. 5th ed. 2004. (Illus.). pap. 12.86 (978-0-03-030206-0(4)) Holt, Rinehart & Winston.

Kornberg, Arthur. Germ Stories. Alaniz, Adam, illus. Kolter, Roberto, photos by. 2007. (J). (gr. 1-7). 22.50 (***978-1-891389-51-1(3)***) University Science Bks.

Latta, Sara L. The Good, the Bad, the Slimy: The Secret Life of Microbes. 2006. (Prime Ser.). (Illus.). 128p. (J). (gr. 4-9). lib. bdg. 31.93 (978-0-7660-1294-3(8)) Enslow Pubs., Inc.

Miller, Connie Colwell. Disgusting Places. 2007. (J). (978-0-7368-6801-3(1)) Capstone Pr., Inc.

Moore, Eva. The Giant Germ. 2001. (Magic School Bus Chapter Bks.). (Illus.). (J). 11.79 (978-0-606-21310-3(4)) Tandem Library Bks.

Romanek, Trudee. Achoo! The Most Interesting Book You'll Ever Read about Germs. Cowles, Rose, illus. 2004. (Mysterious You Ser.). 40p. (J). (gr. 4-6). (978-1-55337-451-0(7)); (978-1-55337-450-3(9)) Kids Can Pr., Ltd.

Simione, Ruth. Mike the Microbe. Simione, Allen, illus. Date not set. 38p. (J). (gr. 4-8). pap. 14.70 (978-1-877960-23-9(3)) Kemtec Educational Corp.

Smith, Tara C. Streptococcus (Group B) 2007. (Deadly Diseases & Epidemics Ser.). 88p. (gr. 9). 31.95 (***978-0-7910-9243-9(7)*** , Chelsea Hse.) Facts On File, Inc.

Thomas, Peggy. Bacteria & Viruses. 2004. (Lucent Library of Science & Technology). (Illus.). 112p. (J). (gr. 7-10). 29.95 (978-1-59018-438-7(6) , Lucent Bks.) Thomson Gale.

BACTERIOLOGY

see also Immunity; Microorganisms

McNeil, Niki, et al. HOCPP 1140 Germs. 2007. spiral bd. 16.00 (***978-1-60308-140-5(2)***) In the Hands of a Child.

Nadler, Beth. The Magic School Bus Inside Ralphie: A Book about Germs. Duchesne, Lucie, tr. (Magic School Bus Ser.). (FRE., Illus.). 32p. (J). (gr. 1-4). pap. 5.99 (978-0-590-24658-3(5)) Scholastic, Inc.

Pascoe, Elaine. Slime, Molds & Fungi. Kuhn, Dwight, photos by. 1998. (Nature Close-Up Ser.). (Illus.). 48p. (J). (gr. 4-8). 23.70 (978-1-56711-182-8(3) , Blackbirch Pr., Inc.) Thomson Gale.

BAD DREAMS

see Nightmares

BADGERS

Delano, Poli. El Tejon Traicionero. 2002. (SPA., Illus.). 24p. (J). (978-968-494-123-6(4)) Centro de Informacion y Desarrollo de la Comunicacion y la Literatura.

Howard, Fran. Badgers: Active at Night. 2004. (Wild World of Animals Ser.). (Illus.). 24p. (J). lib. bdg. 21.26 (978-0-7368-2612-9(2) , Bridgestone Bks.) Capstone Pr., Inc.

Klobuchar, Lisa. Badgers & Other Mustelids. 2005. (World Book's Animals of the World Ser.). (Illus.). 64p. (J). (978-0-7166-1265-0(8)) World Bk., Inc.

Leach, Michael. Badger. 2006. (Illus.). (J). (gr. 3-4). pap. 11.99 (978-0-7502-4771-9(1) , Hodder & Stoughton) Hodder General Publishing Division GBR. *Dist:* Trafalgar Square Publishing.

Murphy, Patricia J. Badgers. Saunders-Smith, Gail, ed. 2004. (Grassland Animals Ser.). (Illus.). 24p. (J). (gr. k-1). lib. bdg. 15.93 (978-0-7368-2071-4(X) , Pebble Bks.) Capstone Pr., Inc.

Taylor, Bonnie Highsmith. Amos: An American Badger. 2001. (Animal Adventures Ser.). (Illus.). (J). 54p. pap. (978-0-7891-5238-1(X)); 56p. (gr. 1-4). lib. bdg. 16.95 (978-0-7807-9648-5(9)) Perfection Learning Corp.

BADGERS—FICTION

Baglio, Ben M. The Badger in the Basement, Vol. 6. McNicholas, Shelagh, illus. 1998. (Animal Ark Ser.: No. 7). (J). (gr. 3-5). pap. 3.99 (978-0-590-18754-1(6) , Scholastic Paperbacks) Scholastic, Inc.

Bailey, Norman. Fight for Freedom. 2006. pap. (***978-1-84375-267-7(0)***) Universal Publishing Solutions Online, Limited (UPSO).

Bunting, Eve. Can You Do This, Old Badger? Pham, LeUyen, illus. 2004. (Badger Bks.). 32p. (J). pap. 6.00 (978-0-15-204603-3(8)) Harcourt Children's Bks.

—Can You Do This, Old Badger? Pham, LeUyen, illus. 2004. 26p. (J). (ps-ps). lib. bdg. 12.80 (978-0-606-30397-2(9)) Tandem Library Bks.

—Little Badger, Terror of the Seven Seas. Pham, LeUyen, illus. 2006. (Badger Bks.). 32p. (J). pap. 6.00 (978-0-15-205702-2(1) , Voyager Bks./Libros Viajeros) Harcourt Children's Bks.

Díaz, Katacha. Badger at Sandy Ridge Road. Kest, Kristin, illus. 2005. (Smithsonian's Backyard Ser.). 32p. (J). (ps-2). 15.95 (978-1-59249-420-0(X) , B5028); 4.95 (978-1-59249-421-7(8) , B5078); pap. 6.95 (978-1-59249-422-4(6) , S5028) Soundprints.

Diaz, Katacha. Badger at Sandy Ridge Road. Kest, Kristin, illus. 2005. (Smith Sonian's Backyard Ser.). 32p. (J). (gr. 2-2). pap. 8.95 (978-1-59249-423-1(4) , SC5028) Soundprints.

Hamley, Dennis. Badger's Fate. 2006. (ENG., Illus.). 112p. per. (***978-1-904529-19-4(4)*** , Back to Front) Solidus.

Hiscock, Bruce. Coyote & Badger: Desert Hunters of the Southwest. 2003. (Illus.). 32p. (J). (gr. 2-4). 15.95 (978-1-56397-848-7(2)) Boyds Mills Pr.

Hoban, Russell. A Bargain for Frances. Hoban, Lillian, illus. 1999. (I Can Read Bks.). 64p. (J). (ps-3). 12.95 (978-0-694-01295-4(5) , Harper Festival) HarperCollins Pubs.

—Bedtime for Frances. 1999. (J). pap. 1.95 (978-0-590-09887-8(X)) Scholastic, Inc.

—Best Friends for Frances. braille ed. 2004. (Illus.). (J). (gr. k-3). spiral bd. (978-0-616-01674-9(3)) Canadian National Institute for the Blind/Institut National Canadien pour les Aveugles.

—A Birthday for Frances. 2000. (J). pap. 3.95 (978-0-590-04360-1(9)) Scholastic, Inc.

—El Gran Negocio de Francisca. Hoban, Lillian, illus. 2006. (I Can Read Bks.).Tr. of Bargain for Frances. (SPA.). 64p. (J). pap. 3.99 (978-0-06-088703-2(6)) HarperCollins Pubs.

Hunter, Erin. Twilight. 2006. (Warriors Ser.: Bk. 5). (Illus.). 336p. (J). 16.99 (978-0-06-082764-9(5)); lib. bdg. 16.89 (978-0-06-082766-3(1)) HarperCollins Pubs.

Jacques, Brian. Eulalia! 2007. (Redwall Ser.). 400p. (J). (gr. 5). 23.99 (***978-0-399-24209-0(0)*** , Philomel) Penguin Group (USA) Inc.

Jacques, Brian. Lord Brocktree. Fangorn, illus. 2005. (Redwall Ser.). 384p. (YA). (gr. 7). pap. 7.99 (978-0-14-250110-8(7) , Puffin) Penguin Group (USA) Inc.

—Lord Brocktree. 2000. (Redwall Ser.). (Illus.). 384p. (J). (gr. 4-8). 23.99 (978-0-399-23590-0(6) , Philomel) Penguin Group (USA) Inc.

—Lord Brocktree. 2001. (Redwall Ser.). (gr. 5-8). lib. bdg. 15.30 (978-0-613-44230-5(X)) Tandem Library Bks.

Kasza, Keiko. Badger's Fancy Meal. Kasza, Keiko, illus. 2007. (Illus.). 32p. (J). (gr. k-2). 16.99 (978-0-399-24603-6(7) , Putnam Juvenile) Penguin Group (USA) Inc.

Kulling, Monica. Edgar Badger's Fishing Day. Twinem, Nancy, illus. 1999. 48p. (J). (gr. 1-5). pap. 4.50 (978-1-57255-603-4(X)) Mondo Publishing.

—Edgar Badger's Fishing Day. 1999. (gr. 3-6). lib. bdg. 12.40 (978-0-613-17198-4(5)) Tandem Library Bks.

Oram, Hiawyn. Badger's Bad Mood. Varley, Susan, illus. 32p. (J). (ps-3). 2002. pap. 5.99 (978-0-590-21693-7(7)); 1998. pap. 15.95 (978-0-590-18920-0(4)) Scholastic, Inc.

Parry, Alan. Badger's Easter Surprise. Parry, Linda, illus. 2004. (Oaktree Wood Ser.). 16p. (ps-3). 15.00 (978-0-687-04813-7(3)) Abingdon Pr.

—Badger's Lovely Day. Parry, Linda, illus. 2004. (Oaktree Wood Ser.). (ps-3). 5.00 (978-0-687-09712-8(6)) Abingdon Pr.

Pham, LeUyen. Can You Do This, Old Badger? 2004. (ps-2). lib. bdg. 14.15 (978-0-613-83873-3(4)) Tandem Library Bks.

Sargent, Dave & Sargent, Pat. Buddy Badger: I'm a Little Bully, 15 vols., Vol. 17. Huff, Jeane, illus. 2nd rev. ed. 2003. (Animal Pride Ser.: 17). 42p. (J). pap. 6.95 (978-1-56763-792-2(2)); lib. bdg. 19.95 (978-1-56763-791-5(4)) Ozark Publishing.

Schuurmans, Hilde. Sidney Won't Swim. Schuurmans, Hilde, illus. 2001. (Illus.). 32p. (J). (ps-3). 15.95 (978-1-57091-476-8(1)) Charlesbridge Publishing, Inc.

Varley, Susan. Badger's Parting Gifts. (Illus.). 32p. (J). (ps-3). (ENG, URD, ARA, VIE & CHI.). (978-1-85430-527-5(1)); (BEN, ENG, URD, ARA & VIE., (978-1-85430-528-2(X)) Magi Pubns.

Wells, Rosemary. Practice Makes Perfect. 2002. (gr. k-3). lib. bdg. 11.80 (978-0-613-74979-4(0)) Tandem Library Bks.

BADGES OF HONOR

see Decorations of Honor

BADMINTON

Kalman, Bobbie. Badminton in Action. 2003. (gr. 3-6). lib. bdg. 15.25 (978-0-613-59052-5(X)) Tandem Library Bks.

BAGGINS, BILBO (FICTITIOUS CHARACTER)—FICTION

Tolkien, J. R. R. The Hobbit. 2002. 16.60 (978-0-7587-7961-8(5)) Book Wholesalers, Inc.

—The Hobbit. 1999. (YA). 9.95 (978-1-56137-253-9(6)) Novel Units, Inc.

—El Hobbit. 2003. (Lord of the Rings Ser.). (SPA.). 320p. (YA). 17.95 (978-84-450-7141-0(6) , MQ9001) Minotauro Ediciones ESP. *Dist:* Distribooks, Inc., Lectorum Pubns., Inc., Planeta Publishing Corp.

—The Hobbit. adapted ed. 2001. (J). 23.50 (978-0-606-21234-2(5)) Tandem Library Bks.

—The Hobbit: Or There & Back Again. 2002. (Illus.). 365p. (YA). (gr. 5). pap. 10.00 (978-0-618-26030-0(7)) Houghton Mifflin Co. Trade & Reference Div.

—The Hobbit: Or There & Back Again. Sis, Peter, illus. 2001. 320p. (YA). (gr. 7 up). pap. 10.00 (978-0-618-15082-3(X)) Houghton Mifflin Co. Trade & Reference Div.

—The Hobbit: Or There & Back Again. 1999. (Illus.). 320p. pap. 12.00 (978-0-618-00221-4(9)) Houghton Mifflin Co. Trade & Reference Div.

—The Hobbit: Or, There & Back Again. 2001. (Illus.). 330p. (YA). (gr. 7 up). 18.00 (978-0-618-16221-5(6)) Houghton Mifflin Co. Trade & Reference Div.

BAGGINS, FRODO (FICTITIOUS CHARACTER)—FICTION

Tolkien, J. R. R. The Lord of the Rings. unabr. ed. 2000. 1216p. (YA). pap. 80.00 incl. audio (978-0-8072-8344-8(4) , LL0187, Listening Library) Random Hse. Audio Publishing Group.

—The Return of the King. 2002. (J). 16.60 (978-0-7587-5212-3(1)) Book Wholesalers, Inc.

—Senhor dos Aneis. pap. 36.95 (978-85-336-1337-9(7)) Livraria Martins Editora BRA. *Dist:* Distribooks, Inc.

BAGGS, BILLY (FICTITIOUS CHARACTER)—FICTION

Weaver, Will. Farm Team. 1999. 288p. (J). (gr. 6 up). pap. 7.99 (978-0-06-447118-3(7) , Harper Trophy) HarperCollins Pubs.

—Farm Team. 1999. (J). 12.64 (978-0-606-15860-2(X)); (gr. 5-8). lib. bdg. 14.10 (978-0-613-11530-8(9)) Tandem Library Bks.

—Hard Ball. (gr. 6 up). 1999. 256p. (J). pap. 5.99 (978-0-06-447208-1(6) , Harper Trophy); 1998. 240p. (YA). 15.89 (978-0-06-027122-0(1)); 1998. 240p. (YA). 15.95 (978-0-06-027121-3(3)) HarperCollins Pubs.

—Hard Ball. 1999. (J). 12.64 (978-0-606-16706-2(4)); (gr. 7-12). lib. bdg. 14.15 (978-0-613-18254-6(5)) Tandem Library Bks.

—Hard Ball: A Billy Baggs Novel. l.t. ed. 2000. (Illus.). 270p. (YA). (gr. 8-12). 20.95 (978-0-7862-2752-5(4)) Thorndike Pr.

BAHAI FAITH

Sage, Ana. I Am Bahai. 1999. (Religions of the World Ser.). 24p. (J). (gr. k-4). lib. bdg. 18.75 (978-0-8239-5262-5(2) , PowerKids Pr.) Rosen Publishing Group, Inc., The.

BAHAISM

see Bahai Faith

BAHAMAS

Barlas, Robert. Bahamas. 2000. (Cultures of the World Ser.). (Illus.). 128p. (gr. 5-12). lib. bdg. 37.07 (978-0-7614-0992-2(0) , Benchmark Bks.) Cavendish, Marshall Corp.

Temple, Bob. The Bahamas. 2003. (Countries: Faces & Places Ser.). (Illus.). 32p. (J). (gr. 1-5). 25.64 (978-1-56766-904-6(2)) Child's World, Inc.

Williams, Colleen Madonna Flood. The Bahamas. 2003. (Discovering the Caribbean Ser.). (Illus.). 64p. (J). (gr. 5 up). lib. bdg. (978-1-59084-296-6(0)) Mason Crest Pubs.

BAHAMAS—FICTION

Baglio, Ben M. Riding the Storm. 2002. (Dolphin Diaries: No. 3). 176p. (J). pap. 4.99 (978-0-439-31949-2(8)) Scholastic, Inc.

—Riding the Storm. 2002. (gr. 3-6). lib. bdg. 12.40 (978-0-613-72055-7(5)) Tandem Library Bks.

—Under the Stars. 2002. (gr. 3-6). lib. bdg. 12.40 (978-0-613-58139-4(3)) Tandem Library Bks.

Cooper, Susan. Green Boy. (Illus.). 208p. (J). 2003. pap. 5.99 (978-0-689-84760-8(2) , Aladdin); 2002. (gr. 4-6). 16.00 (978-0-689-84751-6(3) , McElderry, Margaret K.) Simon & Schuster Children's Publishing.

Dorris, Michael. Morning Girl. rev. ed. 1999. 80p. (gr. 4-17). pap. 4.99 (978-0-7868-1358-2(X)) Hyperion Pr.

Grover, Wayne. Dolphin Freedom. Fowler, Jim, illus. 1999. 112p. (J). (gr. 3-7). 15.00 (978-0-688-16010-4(7)) HarperCollins Pubs.

—Dolphin Freedom. 2000. (gr. 3-6). lib. bdg. 12.95 (978-0-613-24880-8(5)); (Illus.). (J). 11.75 (978-0-606-18900-2(9)) Tandem Library Bks.

Higson, Charlie. Silverfin: A James Bond Adventure. l.t. ed. 2005. 514p. (YA). 22.95 (978-0-7862-7910-4(9)) Thorndike Pr.

Robertson, Barbara. Rosemary & the Island Treasure: Back to 1947. 2001. (Hourglass Adventures Ser.: Bk. 4). (Illus.). 128p. (J). (gr. 3-5). pap. 4.95 (978-1-890817-58-9(9)) Winslow Pr.

Shaw, Cynthia. Grouper Moon. 1999. (Illus.). ix, 151p. (J). pap. 9.95 (978-0-9670595-2-5(6)) Aurelia Pr.

Wohlford, Martha Crikelair. Splash: The Staniel Cay Cat. 2006. (J). per. 21.95 (***978-0-9787981-0-9(4)***) Serenity Pr.

BAILEY CITY MONSTERS (FICTITIOUS CHARACTERS)—FICTION

Dadey, Debbie & Jones, Marcia Thornton. Frankenstein Doesn't Start Food Fights. Gurney, John Steven, illus. 2003. (Adventures of the Bailey School Kids Ser.: No. 47). 80p. (J). 3.99 (978-0-439-55999-7(5) , Scholastic Paperbacks) Scholastic, Inc.

—Frankenstein Doesn't Start Food Fights. 2003. (gr. 3-6). lib. bdg. 11.80 (978-0-613-82754-6(6)) Tandem Library Bks.

Jones, Marcia Thornton & Dadey, Debbie. Double Trouble Monsters. 1999. (Bailey City Monsters Ser.: No. 5). (Illus.). 80p. (J). (gr. 2-4). pap. 3.99 (978-0-439-05870-4(8)) Scholastic, Inc.

—Double Trouble Monsters. 1999. (Bailey City Monsters Ser.: No. 5). (J). (gr. 2-4). (978-0-606-16604-1(1)) Tandem Library Bks.

—The Hauntlys' Hairy Surprise. 1999. (Bailey City Monsters Super Special Ser.: No. 1). (Illus.). 112p. (J). (gr. 2-4). pap. 3.99 (978-0-590-04302-1(1)) Scholastic, Inc.

—The Hauntlys' Hairy Surprise. 1999. (Bailey City Monsters Super Special Ser.: No. 1). (J). (gr. 2-4). (978-0-606-19911-7(X)) Tandem Library Bks.

—Howling at the Hauntlys' Gurney, John Steven, illus. 1998. (Bailey City Monsters Ser.: No.2). (J). (gr. 2-4). pap. 3.99 (978-0-590-10845-4(X)) Scholastic, Inc.

—Kilmer's Pet Monster. 1999. (Bailey City Monsters Ser.: No. 4). (Illus.). 72p. (J). (gr. 2-4). pap. 3.99 (978-0-590-10847-8(6)) Scholastic, Inc.

—The Monsters Next Door. Gurney, John Steven, illus. 1998. (Bailey City Monsters Ser.: No. 1). 71p. (J). (gr. 2-4). pap. 3.99 (978-0-590-10787-7(9)) Scholastic, Inc.

—Snow Monster Mystery. 1999. (Bailey City Monsters Ser.: No. 8). (Illus.). (J). (gr. 2-4). (978-0-606-18514-1(3)) Tandem Library Bks.

—Spooky Spells. 1999. (Bailey City Monsters Ser.: No. 6). (Illus.). 80p. (J). (gr. 2-4). pap. 3.99 (978-0-439-05871-1(6)) Scholastic, Inc.

—Spooky Spells. 1999. (Bailey City Monsters Ser.: No. 6). (J). (gr. 2-4). (978-0-606-16656-0(4)) Tandem Library Bks.

—Vampire Baby. 1999. (Bailey City Monsters Ser.: No. 7). (Illus.). 80p. (J). (gr. 2-4). pap. 3.99 (978-0-439-05872-8(4)) Scholastic, Inc.

—Vampire Baby. 1999. (Bailey City Monsters Ser.: No. 7). (J). (gr. 2-4). (978-0-606-17059-8(6)) Tandem Library Bks.

—Vampire Trouble. 1998. (Bailey City Monsters Ser.: No. 3). (Illus.). 80p. (J). (gr. 2-4). pap. 3.99 (978-0-590-10846-1(8)) Scholastic, Inc.

BAILEY SCHOOL KIDS (FICTITIOUS CHARACTERS)—FICTION

The Abominable Snowman Doesn't Roast Marshmallows, 6 bks., Pack. 2005. 96p. (J). pap. 3.99 (978-0-439-86573-9(5)) Scholastic, Inc.

Dadey, Debbie & Jones, Marcia Thornton. The Abominable Snowman Doesn't Roast Marshmallows. Gurney, John Steven, illus. 2005. (Little Apple Ser.). 73p. (J). (978-1-4155-8202-2(5)) Scholastic, Inc.

—The Abominable Snowman Doesn't Roast Marshmallows. Gurney, John Steven, illus. 2005. 73p. (J). (ps-k). lib. bdg. 10.79 (978-0-606-33290-3(1)) Tandem Library Bks.

—The Bride of Frankenstein Doesn't Bake Cookies. 2000. (gr. 3-6). lib. bdg. 11.80 (978-0-613-32344-4(0)) Tandem Library Bks.

—Dracula Doesn't Rock & Roll. Gurney, John Steven, illus. 2000. (Adventures of the Bailey School Kids Ser.: No 39). 80p. (J). (gr. 2-4). mass mkt. 3.99 (978-0-439-04399-1(9) , Scholastic Paperbacks) Scholastic, Inc.

—Dracula Doesn't Rock & Roll. 2000. (Adventures of the Bailey School Kids Ser.: No. 39). (Illus.). (J). (gr. 2-4). 10.79 (978-0-606-18537-0(2)); 1999. (gr. 3-6). lib. bdg. 11.80 (978-0-613-21464-3(1)) Tandem Library Bks.

—Dragons Don't Throw Snowballs. 2006. (Little Apple Ser.). (Illus.). 80p. (J). pap. 3.99 (978-0-439-79337-7(8) , Scholastic Paperbacks) Scholastic, Inc.

—Dragons Don't Throw Snowballs. Gurney, John Steven, illus. 2006. (Little Apple Ser.). 75p. (J). (978-1-4156-4913-8(8)) Scholastic, Inc.

—Frankenstein Doesn't Slam Hockey Pucks. Gurney, John Steven, illus. 1999. (Adventures of the Bailey School Kids Ser.: No. 34). 80p. (J). (gr. 2-4). pap. 3.99 (978-0-590-18984-2(0)) Scholastic, Inc.

—Genies Don't Ride Bicycles. (Adventures of the Bailey School Kids Ser.: No. 8). (FRE., Illus.). (J). (gr. 2-4). pap. 5.99 (978-0-590-24377-3(2)) Scholastic, Inc.

—Ghosts Don't Eat Potato Chips. (Adventures of the Bailey School Kids Ser.: No. 5). (FRE.). (J). (gr. 2-4). pap. 5.99 (978-0-590-74836-0(X)) Scholastic, Inc.

—Ghouls Don't Scoop Ice Cream. 1998. (Adventures of the Bailey School Kids Ser.: No. 31). (J). (gr. 2-4). 10.79 (978-0-606-13426-2(3)) Tandem Library Bks.

—Goblins Don't Play Video Games. Gurney, John Steven, illus. 1999. (Adventures of the Bailey School Kids Ser.: No. 37). 96p. (J). (gr. 2-4). pap. 3.99 (978-0-439-04397-7(2)) Scholastic, Inc.

—Goblins Don't Play Video Games. 1999. (Adventures of the Bailey School Kids Ser.: No. 37). (J). (gr. 2-4). 10.79 (978-0-606-17276-9(9)) Tandem Library Bks.

—Hercules Doesn't Pull Teeth. Gurney, John Steven, illus. 1998. (Adventures of the Bailey School Kids Ser.: No. 30). 80p. (J). (gr. 2-4). pap. 3.99 (978-0-590-25809-8(5) , Scholastic Paperbacks) Scholastic, Inc.

—Hercules Doesn't Pull Teeth. 1998. (Adventures of the Bailey School Kids Ser.: No. 30). (J). (gr. 2-4). 10.79 (978-0-606-13475-0(1)) Tandem Library Bks.

—Leprechauns Don't Play Fetch. 2003. (Bailey School Kids Holiday Special Ser.). (Illus.). 96p. (J). (gr. 2-4). pap. 3.99 (978-0-439-40833-2(4) , Scholastic Paperbacks) Scholastic, Inc.

—Leprechauns Don't Play Fetch. 2002. (Bailey School Kids Holiday Special Ser.). (gr. 3-6). lib. bdg. 11.80 (978-0-613-63312-3(1)) Tandem Library Bks.

—Monsters Don't Scuba Dive. (Adventures of the Bailey School Kids Ser.: No. 14). (FRE., Illus.). 80p. (J). (gr. 2-4). pap. 5.99 (978-0-590-24550-0(3)) Scholastic, Inc.

—Mrs. Jeepers in Outer Space. 1999. (Adventures of the Bailey School Kids Super Special Ser.: No. 4). (J). (gr. 2-4). (978-0-606-19912-4(8)) Tandem Library Bks.

—Mrs. Jeepers' Monster Class Trip. 2001. (Adventures of the Bailey School Kids Super Special Ser.: No. 5). (J). (gr. 2-4). (978-0-606-19930-8(6)) Tandem Library Bks.

—Mrs. Jeepers on Vampire Island. Gurney, John Steven, illus. 2002. (Bailey School Kids Ser.: No. 6). 128p. mass mkt. 3.99 (978-0-439-30641-6(8) , Scholastic Paperbacks) Scholastic, Inc.

—Mrs. Jeepers' Secret Cave. Gurney, John Steven, illus. 1998. (Adventures of the Bailey School Kids Super Special Ser.: No. 3). 128p. (J). (gr. 2-4). pap. 4.99 (978-0-590-11712-8(2) , Scholastic Paperbacks) Scholastic, Inc.

—Ninjas Don't Bake Pumpkin Pies. Gurney, John Steven, illus. 1999. (Adventures of the Bailey School Kids Ser.: No. 38). 80p. (J). (gr. 2-4). 3.99 (978-0-439-04398-4(0)) Scholastic, Inc.

—Ninjas Don't Bake Pumpkin Pies. 1999. (gr. 3-6). lib. bdg. 11.80 (978-0-613-22101-6(X)); (Adventures of the Bailey School Kids Ser.: No. 38). (J). (gr. 2-4). (978-0-606-18588-2(7)) Tandem Library Bks.

—Ogres Don't Hunt Easter Eggs. 2004. (Adventures of the Bailey School Kids Ser.). 96p. (J). pap. 3.99 (978-0-439-40834-9(2) , Scholastic Paperbacks) Scholastic, Inc.

—Phantoms Don't Drive Sports Cars. Gurney, John Steven, illus. 1998. (Adventures of the Bailey School Kids Ser.: No. 32). 80p. (J). (gr. 2-4). pap. 3.99 (978-0-590-18982-8(4) , Scholastic Paperbacks) Scholastic, Inc.

—Phantoms Don't Drive Sports Cars. 1998. (Adventures of the Bailey School Kids Ser.: No. 32). (J). (gr. 2-4). (978-0-606-13702-7(5)) Tandem Library Bks.

—Sea Monsters Don't Ride Motorcycles. Gurney, John Steven, illus. 2000. (Adventures of the Bailey School Kids Ser.: No. 40). 80p. (J). (gr. 2-4). pap. 3.99 (978-0-439-04401-1(4) , Scholastic Paperbacks) Scholastic, Inc.

—Sea Monsters Don't Ride Motorcycles. 2000. (Adventures of the Bailey School Kids Ser.: No. 40). (J). (gr. 2-4). (978-0-606-18601-8(8)); (Bailey School Kids Ser.: No.40). (gr. 3-6). lib. bdg. 11.80 (978-0-613-26864-6(4)) Tandem Library Bks.

—Sea Serpents Don't Juggle Water Balloons. Gurney, John Steven, illus. 2002. (Bailey School Kids Ser.: Bk. 46). 80p. (J). 3.99 (978-0-439-36805-6(7) , Scholastic Paperbacks) Scholastic, Inc.

—Sea Serpents Don't Juggle Water Balloons. 2002. (gr. 3-6). lib. bdg. 11.80 (978-0-613-50498-0(4)) Tandem Library Bks.

—Sorciers N'Ont Pas Besoin d'Ordinateurs. (Adventures of the Bailey School Kids Ser.). (FRE., Illus.). 88p. (J). pap. 5.99 (978-0-590-16024-7(9)) Scholastic, Inc.

—Trolls Don't Ride Roller Coasters. Gurney, John Steven, illus. 1999. (Adventures of the Bailey School Kids Ser.: No. 35). 80p. (J). (gr. 2-4). 3.99 (978-0-590-18985-9(9) , Scholastic Paperbacks) Scholastic, Inc.

—Trolls Don't Ride Roller Coasters. 1999. (Adventures of the Bailey School Kids Ser.: No. 35). (J). (gr. 2-4). (978-0-606-16587-7(8)); (gr. 3-6). lib. bdg. 11.80 (978-0-613-17030-7(X)) Tandem Library Bks.

—Wolfmen Don't Hula Dance. 1999. (Adventures of the Bailey School Kids Ser.: No. 36). (J). (gr. 2-4). (978-0-606-16938-7(5)) Tandem Library Bks.

Dadey, Debbie, et al. The Abominable Snowman Doesn't Roast Marshmallows. 2005. (Bailey School Kids Ser.). (Illus.). 96p. (J). pap. 3.99 (978-0-439-65037-3(2) , Scholastic Paperbacks) Scholastic, Inc.

—Ghouls Don't Scoop Ice Cream. Gurney, John Steven, illus. 1998. (Adventures of the Bailey School Kids Ser.: No. 31). 80p. (J). (gr. 2-4). 3.99 (978-0-590-25819-7(2) , Scholastic Paperbacks) Scholastic, Inc.

Jones, Marcia Thornton & Dadey, Debbie. Werewolves Don't Run for President. Gurney, John Steven, illus. 2004. (Baily School Kids Ser.). 96p. (J). (gr. 2-5). pap. 3.99 (978-0-439-65036-6(4) , Scholastic Paperbacks) Scholastic, Inc.

BAIRD, JOHN LOGIE, 1888-1945

Reid, Struan. John Logie Baird. 2000. (Groundbreakers Ser.). (Illus.). 48p. (J). (gr. 5-7). lib. bdg. 25.64 (978-1-57572-372-3(7)) Heinemann Library.

BAJA CALIFORNIA (MEXICO : PENINSULA)—FICTION

Alegria, Malin. Sofi Mendoza's Guide to Getting Lost in Mexico. 2007. 304p. (YA). (gr. 9 up). 15.99 (978-0-689-87811-4(7)) Simon & Schuster Children's Publishing.

Cruz, Maria Colleen. Border Crossing. 128p. (YA). pap. 9.95 (978-1-55885-405-5(3) , Piñata Books) Arte Publico Pr.

—Border Crossing. 2003. (gr. 7-12). lib. bdg. 18.75 (978-0-613-90255-7(6)) Tandem Library Bks.

Gill, Shelley. Big Blue. Barrow, Ann, illus. 32p. (J). (ps-6). 2005. pap. 6.95 (978-1-57091-667-0(5)); 2004. 15.95 (978-1-57091-352-5(8)) Charlesbridge Publishing, Inc.

BAKERS AND BAKERIES

Anderson, Catherine. Bread Bakery. 2004. (Field Trip! Ser.). (Illus.). 24p. (J). pap. 5.75 (978-1-4034-6167-4(8)); lib. bdg. 20.64 (978-1-4034-6161-2(9)) Heinemann Library.

Bakers. (Community Helpers Ser.). 24p. (J). 6.95 (978-0-7368-8034-3(8)) Capstone Pr., Inc.

Bakers, 6 vols. (gr. 2-5). 36.95 (978-0-7368-8048-0(8)) Red Brick Learning.

Hughes, Sarah. My Grandfather Works in a Bakery. 2001. (Welcome Bks.). (Illus.). 24p. (J). (ps-2). pap. 4.95 (978-0-516-29575-6(6)); lib. bdg. 13.50 (978-0-516-23282-9(7)) Scholastic Library Publishing. (Children's Pr.).

—My Grandfather Works in a Bakery. 2001. (Illus.). 24p. (J). (ps-3). lib. bdg. 12.95 (978-0-613-58864-5(9)) Tandem Library Bks.

Klinting, Lars. Castor Pastelero. 1998. Tr. of Beaver the Baker. (SPA., Illus.). 32p. (J). (ps-k). 18.95 (978-84-89675-07-0(4) , LEC5074) Zendrera Zariquiey, Editorial ESP. *Dist:* AIMS International Bks., Inc.

McConnell, Sharon. What a Baker Makes: Learning the Long A Sound. 2002. (PowerPhonics Ser.). (Illus.). (J). 23p. lib. bdg. (978-0-8239-8262-2(9)); 24p. (gr. 1). lib. bdg. 18.50 (978-0-8239-5917-4(1)) Rosen Publishing Group, Inc., The. (PowerKids Pr.).

Myers, Edward. The Adventures of Forri the Baker. 1999. 92p. (J). (gr. 3-6). pap. 6.00 (978-0-9674477-0-4(4) , M-9900-01) Montemayor Pr.

Pohl, Kathleen. What Happens at a Bakery? 2006. (Illus.). 24p. (J). pap. (978-0-8368-6891-3(9)); lib. bdg. (978-0-8368-6884-5(6)) Stevens, Gareth Inc.

BAKING

see also Bread; Cake; Pastry

Beech, Linda Ward. The Magic School Bus Gets Baked in a Cake: A Book about Kitchen Chemistry. Duchesne, Lucie, tr. from ENG. Degen, Bruce, illus. (Magic School Bus Ser.). (FRE.). 32p. (J). (gr. 1-4). pap. 5.99 (978-0-590-24660-6(7)) Scholastic, Inc.

Berofsky, Adrienne. Disney Bakery Cookbook. 2000. 64p. (J). (gr. 1-5). 14.99 (978-0-7868-3246-0(0)) Disney Pr.

Bull, Jane. The Baking Book. 2005. (Illus.). 48p. (J). (ps-3). 12.99 (978-0-7566-1373-0(6)) Dorling Kindersley Publishing, Inc.

Bush, Timothy, illus. All in Just One Cookie. 2006. 32p. (J). lib. bdg. 17.89 (978-0-06-009093-7(6)) HarperCollins Pubs.

Cohen, Elaine. Super-Duper Cupcakes: Kids' Creations from the Cupcake Caboose. 2006. (Illus.). 96p. (J). 9.95 (978-1-4027-2174-8(9)) Sterling Publishing Co., Inc.

Cole, Joanna. The Magic School Bus Gets Baked in a Cake: A Book about Kitchen Chemistry. 2002. (Magic School Bus Ser.). (Illus.). (J). 11.45 (978-0-7587-6701-1(3)) Book Wholesalers, Inc.

Collister, Linda. Baking with Kids. Wreford, Polly, photos by. 2006. (Illus.). 128p. (J). (978-1-84597-220-2(1)) Ryland Peters & Small.

Contini, Mary. Easy Peasy Sweetie Pie: Truly Scrumptious Treats for Kids Who Love to Bake. 2000. (Illus.). 128p. 24.99 (978-0-09-187787-3(3) , Ebury Pr.) Ebury Publishing GBR. *Dist:* Independent Pubs. Group.

DK Publishing Staff. First Baking Activity Book. 2006. 48p. (J). 9.99 (978-0-7566-2578-8(5)) Dorling Kindersley Publishing, Inc.

Dodge, Abigail Johnson. Williams-Sonoma Kids Baking. Williams, Chuck, ed. rev. ed. 2003. (Illus.). 128p. spiral bd. 19.95 (978-0-8487-2780-2(0) , 130054) Oxmoor Hse., Inc.

Ericsson, Jennifer A. Out & About at the Bakery. McMullen, Anne, illus. 2004. (Field Trips Ser.). 24p. (C). (gr. k-3). 23.93 (978-1-4048-0037-3(9)) Picture Window Bks.

From Father to Son: 6 Small Books. (Greetings Ser.: Vol. 1). 24p. (gr. 3-5). 31.00 (978-0-7635-1748-9(8)) Rigby Education.

From Father to Son: Big Book. (Greetings Ser.: Vol. 1). 24p. (gr. 3-5). 31.00 (978-0-7635-3135-5(9)) Rigby Education.

G and R Publishing Staff. Gifts in a Jar, for Kids. 2002. (Illus.). 128p. (J). pap. 10.00 (978-1-56383-135-5(X)) G&R Publishing.

Goodman, Susan E. All in Just One Cookie. Bush, Timothy, illus. 2006. 32p. (J). 16.99 (978-0-06-009092-0(8)) HarperCollins Pubs.

Harbison, Elizabeth M. Loaves of Fun: A History of Bread with Activities & Recipes from Around the World. Harbison, John, illus. 1999. 108p. (J). (gr. 1-7). pap. 14.95 (978-1-55652-311-3(4)) Chicago Review Pr., Inc.

Hill, Mary. Let's Make Cookies. 2002. (Welcome Bks.). (Illus.). 24p. (J). (ps-2). pap. 4.95 (978-0-516-24019-0(6) , Children's Pr.) Scholastic Library Publishing.

—Let's Make Cookies. 2002. (gr. k-3). lib. bdg. 12.95 (978-0-613-58784-6(7)) Tandem Library Bks.

Innovative Cooking Enterprises Staff. Electric Bread for Kids: A Bread Machine Activity Book. McKay, D. John, ed. Tilly, Jim, illus. Parshin, Oleg, photos by. 1998. 176p. (J). (gr. 1-9). 29.95 (978-1-891705-00-7(8)) Innovative Cooking Enterprises - ICE, Inc.

Kleven, Elisa. Sun Bread. 2004. (Illus.). 32p. (J). reprint ed. pap. 6.99 (978-0-14-240073-9(4) , Puffin) Penguin Group (USA) Inc.

MacLeod, Elizabeth. Bake & Make Amazing Cakes. Bradford, June, illus. unabr. ed. 2001. (Kids Can Do It Ser.). 40p. (J). (gr. 4-6). (978-1-55074-848-2(3)); (978-1-55074-849-9(1)) Kids Can Pr., Ltd.

—Bake & Make Amazing Cakes. 2001. (gr. 3-6). lib. bdg. 14.10 (978-0-613-50769-1(X)); (Illus.). (J). (978-0-606-21049-2(0)) Tandem Library Bks.

Midnight Bakery: Individual Title Six-Packs. (Bookweb Ser.). 32p. (gr. 5 up). 34.00 (978-0-7635-3793-7(4)) Rigby Education.

Patchett, Fiona. Children's Bk of Baking. 2007. 96p. (J). 17.99 (978-0-7945-1438-9(3) , Usborne) EDC Publishing.

Picture Window Books, contrib. by. Out & about at the Bakery. (Field Trips Ser.). 24p. (J). pap. 8.95 (978-1-4048-0165-3(0)) Picture Window Bks.

Pohl, Kathleen. What Happens at a Bakery? 2006. (Illus.). 24p. (J). pap. (978-0-8368-6891-3(9)); lib. bdg. (978-0-8368-6884-5(6)) Stevens, Gareth Inc.

—What Happens at a Bakery: Qué Pasa en una Panadera? 2006. (ENG & SPA., Illus.). 24p. (J). pap. (978-0-8368-7392-4(0)); lib. bdg. (978-0-8368-7385-6(8)) Stevens, Gareth Inc. (Weekly Reader Early Learning Library).

Rau, Dana Meachen. Baker. 2007. (Jobs in Town Ser.). 24p. (J). lib. bdg. 22.79 (***978-0-7614-2623-3(X)*** , Benchmark Bks.) Cavendish, Marshall Corp.

Sloan, Peter. Baking a Cake. 1999. (gr. k-3). lib. bdg. 11.80 (978-0-613-30254-8(0)) Tandem Library Bks.

Williamson, Sarah A. Bake the Best-Ever Cookies! Ernst, Tom, illus. 2001. (Quick Starts for Kids! Ser.). 64p. (J). (gr. 4 up). pap. 8.95 (978-1-885593-56-6(2) , Williamson Bks.) Ideals Pubns.

BAKING—FICTION

Andreasen, Dan. The Baker's Dozen: A Counting Book. 2007. (Illus.). 32p. (J). (ps-1). 16.95 (***978-0-8050-7809-1(6)***) Holt, Henry & Co.

Armas, Teresa. Remembering Grandma / Recordando a Abuela. Baeza Ventura, Gabriela, tr. from ENG. Rodriguez Howard, Pauline, illus. 2003. (ENG & SPA.). 32p. (J). 14.95 (978-1-55885-344-7(8) , Piñata Books) Arte Publico Pr.

Beck, Ana. Elliot Bakes a Cake. 1999. (gr. k-3). lib. bdg. 14.10 (978-0-613-33361-0(6)) Tandem Library Bks.

Beck, Andrea. Elliot Bakes a Cake. Beck, Andrea, illus. 2004. (Elliot Moose Ser.). (Illus.). 32p. (J). (gr. k-3). (978-1-55074-696-9(0)) Kids Can Pr., Ltd.

—Elliot Bakes a Cake. 2004. (Elliot Moose Ser.). (Illus.). 32p. (J). (gr. k-3). (978-1-55074-443-9(7)) Kids Can Pr., Ltd.

—Elliot Bakes a Cake. 2000. (J). (978-0-606-19014-5(7)) Tandem Library Bks.

Billings, David Joseph. Road Trip with Rabbit & Squash. Billings, David Joseph, illus. 2006. (Illus.). 48p. (J). per. (978-0-9789036-0-2(9)) Billings, David J.

Brett, Jan. Gingerbread Baby. Brett, Jan, illus. 2003. (Illus.). 36p. (J). bds. 7.99 (978-0-399-24166-6(3) , Putnam Juvenile) Penguin Group (USA) Inc.

—Gingerbread Baby. 1999. (Illus.). 32p. (J). (ps-3). 16.99 (978-0-399-23444-6(6) , Putnam Juvenile) Penguin Group (USA) Inc.

Brimner, Larry Dane. Country Bear's Good Neighbor. 2003. (Illus.). 32p. (J). (ps up). pap. 9.95 (978-1-56397-786-2(9)) Boyds Mills Pr.

Carle, Eric. Pancakes, Pancakes! Carle, Eric, illus. 2004. (Classic Board Bks.). (Illus.). 32p. (J). bds. 7.99 (978-0-689-87148-1(1) , Little Simon) Simon & Schuster Children's Publishing.

—Walter the Baker. Carle, Eric, illus. 2002. (Illus.). (J). 14.47 (978-0-7587-3919-3(2)) Book Wholesalers, Inc.

—Walter the Baker. Carle, Eric, illus. 1998. (Illus.). 40p. (J). (ps-3). 7.99 (978-0-689-82088-5(7) , Aladdin) Simon & Schuster Children's Publishing.

—Walter the Baker. 1998. (J). (978-0-606-13888-8(9)) Tandem Library Bks.

Carlson, Nancy. Harriet & George's Christmas Treat. Carlson, Nancy, illus. 2005. (Picture Bks.). (Illus.). 32p. (J). (gr. k-2). 15.95 (978-1-57505-506-0(6)) Lerner Publishing Group.

—Harriet & George's Christmas Treat. 2003. (Illus.). 32p. (J). (gr. k-2). pap. (978-1-57505-639-5(9)) Lerner Publishing Group.

—Harriet & George's Christmas Treat. 2001. (gr. k-3). lib. bdg. 15.25 (978-0-613-68088-2(X)) Tandem Library Bks.

Christelow, Eileen. Five Little Monkeys Bake a Birthday Cake. 2005. (Illus.). 28p. (J). (ps-ps). pap 5.95 (978 0 618-49648-8(3) , Clarion Bks.) Houghton Mifflin Co. Trade & Reference Div.

Dahl, Roald. Charlie & the Chocolate Factory. Blake, Quentin, illus. 2002. 155p. (J). (ps-7). per. 14.45 (978-0-88103-333-5(2)) Tandem Library Bks.

Dunbar, Fiona. The Truth Cookie. 2005. 224p. (J). (gr. 4-7). pap. 15.99 (978-0-439-74022-7(3) , Orchard Bks.) Scholastic, Inc.

Elya, Susan Middleton. Eight Animals Bake a Cake. Chapman, Lee, illus. 2002. (ENG & SPA.). 32p. (J). (ps-3). 15.99 (978-0-399-23468-2(3) , Putnam Juvenile) Penguin Group (USA) Inc.

Fontes, Justine. Conoce a Strawberry Shortcake. Molinero, Nuria, tr. Workman, Lisa, illus. 2005. (Strawberry Shortcake Ser.). 32p. (J). (ps-2). pap. 3.99 (978-0-448-43958-7(1) , Grosset & Dunlap) Penguin Group (USA) Inc.

Gershator, David. Bread Is for Eating. 1998. Tr. of Spanish). 13.75 (978-0-606-13225-1(2)) Tandem Library Bks.

Gershator, David & Gershator, Phillis. Bread Is for Eating. Shaw-Smith, Emma, illus. 2003. Tr. of Spanish). (ENG & SPA.). 25p. (J). (gr. k-4). reprint ed. 16.00 (978-0-7567-9033-2(6)) DIANE Publishing Co.

—Bread Is for Eating. Shaw-Smith, Emma, illus. rev. ed. 1998. Tr. of Spanish). 32p. (J). pap. 7.95 (978-0-8050-5798-0(6) , Holt, Henry & Co. Bks. For Young Readers) Holt, Henry & Co.

Gwynne, Phillip. Bites: Crazy for Cake! Can Rick bake the best Cake? Gordon, Gus, illus. 2007. 108p. (J). pap. 3.95 (***978-0-7624-2923-3(2)*** , Running Pr. Kids) Running Pr. Bk. Pubs.

Harcourt School Publishers Staff. Birthday Cookies Below Level. 3rd ed. 2002. (Trophies Reading Program Ser.). (Illus.). pap. 5.10 (978-0-15-323049-3(5)) Harcourt Schl. Pubs.

A B

—Ingredientes Secretos On Level. 3rd ed. 2002. (Trofeos Ser.).Tr. of Secret Ingredients. (SPA., Illus.). pap. 6.80 (978-0-15-324176-5(4)) Harcourt Schl. Pubs.

—Little Red Hen Bakes a Cake: Independent Reader. 3rd ed. 2002. (Trophies Reading Program Ser.). (Illus.). (J). pap. 2.90 (978-0-15-325490-1(4)) Harcourt Schl. Pubs.

—Mr. Football Bakes: Take-Home Book. 1999. (Signatures Ser.). (Illus.). (J). pap. 1.90 (978-0-15-313956-7(0)) Harcourt Schl. Pubs.

Hawkins, Colin. Foxy Bakes a Cake. 2001. (Illus.). 25p. (J). pap. 8.99 (978-0-00-664757-7(X) , HarperSport) HarperCollins Pubs. Ltd. GBR. *Dist:* Independent Pubs. Group.

Hill, Eric. Spot Bakes a Cake. Hill, Eric, illus. 2003. (Illus.). 22p. (J). (ps-1). bds. 7.99 (978-0-399-24013-3(6) , Putnam Juvenile) Penguin Group (USA) Inc.

Kempf, Molly. The Sweet Treats Carnival. MJ Illustration Staff, illus. 2007. 16p. (J). pap. 4.99 (978-0-448-44456-7(9) , Grosset & Dunlap) Penguin Group (USA) Inc.

Ketteman, Helen. The Great Cake Bake. Collins, Matt, illus. 2005. 32p. (J). 16.95 (978-0-8027-8950-1(1)) Walker & Co.

King, Anthony. The Little Cupcakes. 2005. (J). 15.95 (978-0-9752786-1-1(4)) Cupcake Pubns.

Kline, Suzy. Horrible Harry Takes the Cake. Remkiewicz, Frank, illus. 2006. (Horrible Harry Ser.). 64p. (J). (gr. 2-6). 13.99 (978-0-670-06075-7(5) , Viking Juvenile) Penguin Group (USA) Inc.

Klinting, Lars. Harvey the Baker. 2005. (Handy Harvey Ser.). (Illus.). 40p. (J). (ps-k). pap., pap. 4.95 (978-0-7534-5913-3(2) , Kingfisher) Houghton Mifflin Co. Trade & Reference Div.

London, Jonathan. Froggy Bakes a Cake. Remkiewicz, Frank, illus. 2000. (Reading Railroad Bks.). 32p. (J). (ps-3). pap. 3.99 (978-0-448-42153-7(4) , Grosset & Dunlap) Penguin Group (USA) Inc.

—Froggy Bakes a Cake. 2000. (ps-2). lib. bdg. 11.25 (978-0-613-25269-0(1)); (Illus.). (J). 10.29 (978-0-606-21801-6(7)) Tandem Library Bks.

Mackinnon, Mairi. Runaway Pancake. Provantini, Silvia, illus. 2006. 48p. (J). 8.99 (978-0-7945-1276-7(3) , Usborne) EDC Publishing.

Masurel, Claire. Happy Thanksgiving, Emily! Calitri, Susan, illus. 2004. (Emily Ser.). 16p. (J). pap. 6.99 (978-0-14-240201-6(X) , Puffin) Penguin Group (USA) Inc.

McKissack, Patricia C. Messy Bessey's Holidays. 1999. (gr. k-3). lib. bdg. 12.95 (978-0-613-37457-6(6)) Tandem Library Bks.

McKissack, Patricia C. & McKissack, Fredrick L. Messy Bessey's Holidays. Regan, Dana, illus. 1999. (Rookie Readers Ser.). 32p. (J). (gr. 1-2). 19.50 (978-0-516-20829-9(2) , Children's Pr.) Scholastic Library Publishing.

McOmber, Rachel B., ed. McOmber Phonics Storybooks: The Cake. rev. ed. (Illus.). (J). (978-0-944991-44-2(0)) Swift Learning Resources.

Millen, C. M. Blue Bowl Down: An Appalachian Rhyme. Meade, Holly, illus. 2004. 32p. (J). (gr. k-k). 16.99 (978-0-7636-1817-9(9)) Candlewick Pr.

Mills, Claudia. Gus & Grandpa & the Christmas Cookies. 2000. (J). (978-0-606-20133-9(5)) Tandem Library Bks.

Mills, Susan & Shara, Diana. Frankie & Her Little Pals - Stir It Up. 2007. (J). 7.95 ***(*978-0-9790690-0-0(9))*** Lucky Red Pr., LLC.

Mora, Pat. The Bakery Lady/la señora de la Panadería. Mora, Pat & Ventura, Gabriela Baeza, trs. Torrecilla, Pablo, illus. Tr. of Señora de la Panadería. (ENG & SPA.). 32p. (J). (ps-3). 15.95 (978-1-55885-343-0(X) , Piñata Books) Arte Publico Pr.

Mullican, Judy. Mary & Marsha Make Cookies. Storch, Ellen N., illus. l.t. ed. 2005. 18p. (J). (ps-k). pap. 10.95 (978-1-57332-346-8(2)) HighReach Learning, Inc.

Nicholson, Doris. A Day with Grandma. 2006. 9.00 (978-0-8059-9914-3(0)) Dorrance Publishing Co., Inc.

Numeroff, Laura Joffe. The Best Mouse Cookie. Bond, Felicia, illus. 2006. (If You Give... Ser.). 24p. (J). 9.99 (978-0-06-113760-0(X) , Geringer, Laura Book) HarperCollins Pubs.

Ogburn, Jacqueline K. The Bake Shop Ghost. Priceman, Marjorie, illus. 2005. 32p. (J). (gr. k-3). 16.00 (978-0-618-44557-8(9)) Houghton Mifflin Co. Trade & Reference Div.

El pan de Urraca: Individual Title Six-Packs. (Coleccion Pm Ser.).Tr. of Magpie's baking day. (SPA.). 16p. (gr. 1 up). 26.00 (978-0-7578-3009-9(9)) Rigby Education.

Paulson, Michael William. The Baker Street Bunch & the Missing Pie Mystery. 2005. (J). per. (978-0-9754241-9-3(X)) MiMar Publishing.

Pinkwater, Daniel M. Rainy Morning. Pinkwater, Jill, illus. 1999. (Pinkwater Ser.: Vol. 1). 32p. (J). (gr. k-3). 16.00 (978-0-689-81143-2(8) , Atheneum) Simon & Schuster Children's Publishing.

Remkiewicz, Frank, illus. Froggy Bakes a Cake. 2002. (Froggy Ser.). (J). 11.06 (978-0-7587-5541-4(4)) Book Wholesalers, Inc.

RH Disney. The Fairy Berry Bake-off. 2008. (Step into Reading Ser.). 48p. (J). (gr. k-3). pap. 3.99 ***(*978-0-7364-2525-4(X));*** lib. bdg. 11.99 ***(*978-0-7364-8061-1(7))*** Random Hse. Children's Bks. (RH/Disney).

Roche, Hannah. My Sister Is Super. 1998. (Science Made Simple Ser.). (Illus.). 24p. (J). (ps-k). pap. (978-1-84089-015-0(0) , 868238Q, Zero to Ten, Limited) Evans Publishing Group.

Rosenthal, Betsy R. It's Not Worth Making a Tzimmes Over! Rivers, Ruth, illus. 2006. 32p. (J). 15.95 (978-0-8075-3677-3(6)) Whitman, Albert & Co.

Rylant, Cynthia. Mr. Putter & Tabby Bake the Cake. 2000. (Mr. Putter & Tabby Ser.). (J). (gr. 1 up). pap., stu. ed. 30.00 incl. audio (978-0-7887-4342-9(2) , 41136) Recorded Bks., LLC.

Salas, Macarena, ed. Let's Bake Cookies, Pinocchio!/vamos A Hornear Galletas, Pinocho! 2005. (Disney Bil Ser.). (SPA.). 10p. (J). bds. 3.99 (978-0-439-66366-3(0) , Scholastic en Espanol) Scholastic, Inc.

Santillo, LuAnn. Jane. Santillo, LuAnn, ed. 2003. (Half-Pint Kids Readers Ser.). (Illus.). 7p. (J). (ps-1). pap. (978-1-59256-099-8(7)) Half-Pint Kids, Inc.

Shulman, Goldie. Way Too Much Challah Dough. 2006. (Illus.). 30p. (J). 12.95 (978-1-929628-23-0(4)) Hachai Publishing.

Simmonds, Posy. Baker Cat. (Illus.). 32p. (J). pap. 8.99 ***(*978-0-09-945596-7(X)*** , Red Fox) Random Hse. Children's Bks. GBR. *Dist:* Trafalgar Square Publishing.

Skead, Robert. Elves Can't Kick. 2005. 84p. per. 7.99 (978-1-929478-66-8(6)) Cross Training Publishing.

Slater, David Michael. Flour Girl: A Recipe for Disaster. Brooks, S. G., illus. 2007. (Missy Swiss & More Ser.). 32p. (J). (ps-4). lib. bdg. 27.07 ***(*978-1-60270-009-3(5)*** , Looking Glass Library) Magic Wagon.

Smalls, Irene. My Pop Pop & Me. Johnson, Cathy Ann, illus. 2006. 24p. (J). (ps-3). 15.99 (978-0-316-73422-6(5)) Little Brown & Co.

Smith, Linda. Mrs. Biddlebox: Her Bad Day... And What She Did about It! Frazee, Marla, illus. 2007. 32p. (J). (ps-2). 15.00 ***(*978-0-15-206349-8(8))*** Harcourt Trade Pubs.

Smothers, Ethel Footman. Auntee Edna. Clay, Wil, illus. 2004. 32p. (J). pap. 8.00 (978-0-8028-5246-5(7)); 16.00 (978-0-8028-5154-3(1)) Eerdmans, William B. Publishing Co.

—Auntee Edna. 2002. (gr. k-3). lib. bdg. 16.45 (978-0-613-75338-8(0)) Tandem Library Bks.

Stadler, Alexander. Beverly Billingsly Takes the Cake. 2005. (Gulliver Books). (Illus.). 32p. (J). 16.00 (978-0-15-205357-4(3)) Harcourt Trade Pubs.

Stanley, George Edward. The Battle of the Bakers. Graves, Linda Dockey, illus. 2000. (Katie Lynn Cookie Company Ser. : Vol. 3). (J). (978-0-606-19900-1(4)) Tandem Library Bks.

Stephens, Monique Z. The Berrylicious Bake-off: A Scratch-and-Sniff Story. S. I. Artists Staff, illus. 2003. (Strawberry Shortcake Ser.). 16p. (J). (ps-2). mass mkt. 4.99 (978-0-448-43186-4(6) , Grosset & Dunlap) Penguin Group (USA) Inc.

Stevens, Janet & Crummel, Susan Stevens. Cook-a-Doodle-Doo! Stevens, Janet, illus. 1999. (Illus.). 48p. (J). (ps-3). 17.00 (978-0-15-201924-2(3)) Harcourt Children's Bks.

Stock, Catherine, illus. Gus & Grandpa & the Christmas Cookies. 2002. (Gus & Grandpa Ser.). (J). 22.19 (978-0-7587-1233-2(2)) Book Wholesalers, Inc.

Teevin, Toni. What to Do? What to Do? Pedersen, Janet, illus. 2006. 32p. (J). (gr. k-3). 16.00 (978-0-618-44632-2(X) , Clarion Bks.) Houghton Mifflin Co. Trade & Reference Div.

Tierno, Susan F. El Mejor Dia. Alvarado, Ana María, tr. Ramirez, Michael, illus. 2000. (Think-Kids Book Collection).Tr. of Best-Ever Day. (SPA.). 16p. (J). (gr. 1). pap. 2.95 (978-1-58237-045-3(1)) Creative Thinkers, Inc.

Wells, Rosemary. Bunny Cakes. Wells, Rosemary, illus. 2002. (Max the Bunny Ser.). (Illus.). (J). 13.19 (978-0-7587-5445-5(0)) Book Wholesalers, Inc.

—Bunny Cakes. 1999. (Max & Ruby Ser.). (Illus.). 32p. (J). (gr. k-2). 15.99 (978-0-670-88686-9(6) , Viking Juvenile) Penguin Group (USA) Inc.

Wurzburg, Robert. Who Took the Cake? 2006. (I'm Going to Read Ser.). (Illus.). 24p. (J). pap. 3.95 (978-1-4027-3344-4(5)) Sterling Publishing Co., Inc.

Yamada, Utako. The Story of Cherry the Pig. Yamada, Utako, illus. 2007. (Illus.). 32p. (J). 15.95 (978-1-933605-25-8(1) , 05258) Kane/Miller Bk. Pubs., Inc.

BALANCE OF NATURE

see Ecology

BALBOA, VASCO NUNEZ DE, 1475-1519

Marcovitz, Hal. Vasco Nuanez de Balboa & the Discovery of the South Sea. 2001. (Explorers of New Worlds Ser.). (Illus.). (J). 63p. pap. 25.00 (978-0-7910-6429-0(8)); 64p. 25.00 (978-0-7910-6428-3(X)) Facts On File, Inc. (Chelsea Hse.).

Molzahn, Arlene Bourgeois. Vasco Nunez de Balboa: Explorer to the Pacific Ocean. 2004. (Explorers! Ser.). (Illus.). 48p. (J). lib. bdg. 23.93 (978-0-7660-2142-6(4)) Enslow Pubs., Inc.

Otfinoski, Steven. Vasco Nunez de Balboa: Explorer of the Pacific. 2004. (Great Explorations Ser.). (Illus.). 79p. (J). 29.93 (978-0-7614-1609-8(9) , Benchmark Bks.) Cavendish, Marshall Corp.

Petrie, Kristin. Vasco Nuñez de Balboa. 2007. (Illus.). 32p. (J). 22.78 (978-1-59679-740-6(1)) ABDO Publishing Co.

BALI (ISLAND)

Grant, Gaia. Journey to Bali Coloring Book. 2005. (Illus.). 16p. pap. 6.95 (978-0-7946-0333-5(5)) Tuttle Publishing.

BALINOR (IMAGINARY PLACE)—FICTION

Stanton, Mary. By Moonlight, by Fire. 1999. (Unicorns of Balinor Ser.: No. 4). 144p. (J). (gr. 3-7). pap. 4.50 (978-0-439-06283-1(7)) Scholastic, Inc.

—Night of the Shifter's Moon. 2000. (Unicorns of Balinor Ser.: Vol. 7). (Illus.). 144p. (J). (gr. 3-7). pap. 4.50 (978-0-439-16786-4(8)) Scholastic, Inc.

—The Road to Balinor. 1999. (Unicorns of Balinor Ser.: No. 1). (978-0-606-17550-0(4)) Tandem Library Bks.

—Shadows over Balinor. 2000. (Unicorns of Balinor Ser.: Bk. 8). (Illus.). 128p. (J). (gr. 4-7). pap. 4.50 (978-0-439-16787-1(6)) Scholastic, Inc.

—Sunchaser's Quest. 1999. (Unicorns of Balinor Ser.: No. 2). 160p. (J). (gr. 3-7). pap. 4.50 (978-0-439-06281-7(0)) Scholastic, Inc.

—Sunchaser's Quest. 1999. (Unicorns of Balinor Ser.: No. 2). (978-0-606-17551-7(2)) Tandem Library Bks.

—Valley of Fear. 1999. (Unicorns of Balinor Ser.: No. 3). 144p. (J). (gr. 3-7). pap. 4.50 (978-0-439-06282-4(9)) Scholastic, Inc.

—Valley of Fear. 1999. (Unicorns of Balinor Ser.: No. 3). (978-0-606-17552-4(0)) Tandem Library Bks.

BALKAN PENINSULA

Adams, Simon. The Balkans. 2005. (Illus.). 44p. (J). (gr. 6-9). lib. bdg. 29.95 (978-1-58340-603-8(4)) Smart Apple Media.

Docalavich, Heather. Slovakia. 2006. (European Union Ser.). (Illus.). 88p. (YA). (gr. 5 up). lib. bdg. (978-1-4222-0060-5(4)) Mason Crest Pubs.

—Slovenia. 2006. (European Union Ser.). (Illus.). 88p. (J). (gr. 5 up). lib. bdg. (978-1-4222-0061-2(2)) Mason Crest Pubs.

The European Union: Political, Social, & Economic Cooperation, 26 vols., Set. Incl. Austria. Sanna, Jeanine. (J). 2006. lib. bdg. (978-1-4222-0039-1(6) , 1247981); Belgium. Walker, Ida. (J). 2006. lib. bdg. (978-1-4222-0040-7(X) , 1247982); Cyprus. Etingoff, Kim. (YA). 2006. lib. bdg. (978-1-4222-0041-4(8) , 1247983); Czech Republic. Docalavich, Heather. (YA). 2006. lib. bdg. (978-1-4222-0042-1(6)); Denmark. Docalavich, Heather. (YA). 2006. lib. bdg. (978-1-4222-0043-8(4)); Estonia. Libal, Autumn. (J). 2006. lib. bdg. (978-1-4222-0044-5(2) , 1247996); European Union : Facts & Figures. Stafford, James. (YA). 2007. lib. bdg. (978-1-4222-0045-2(0)); Finland. Sia, Nicole. (J). 2006. lib. bdg. (978-1-4222-0046-9(9) , 1247998); France. Sanna, Jeanine. (J). 2006. lib. bdg. (978-1-4222-0047-6(7) , 1247999); Germany. Walker, Ida. (J). 2006. lib. bdg. (978-1-4222-0048-3(5) , 1248000); Greece. Etingoff, Kim. (J). 2006. lib. bdg. (978-1-4222-0049-0(3)); Hungary. Docalavich, Heather. (J). 2006. lib. bdg. (978-1-4222-0050-6(7) , 1248003); Ireland. Walker, Ida. (YA). 2006. lib. bdg. (978-1-4222-0051-3(5)); Italy. Sadik, Ademola O. (J). 2006. lib. bdg. (978-1-4222-0052-0(3)); Latvia. Docalavich, Heather. (J). 2006. lib. bdg. (978-1-4222-0053-7(1)); Lithuania. Docalavich, Heather. (YA). 2006. lib. bdg. (978-1-4222-0054-4(X)); Luxembourg. Simons, Rae. (J). 2006. lib. bdg. (978-1-4222-0055-1(8)); Malta. Stafford, James. (J). 2006. lib. bdg. (978-1-4222-0056-8(6)); Netherlands. Docalavich, Heather. (YA). 2006. lib. bdg. (978-1-4222-0057-5(4)); Poland. Docalavich, Heather. (YA). 2006. lib. bdg. (978-1-4222-0058-2(2)); Portugal. Etingoff, Kim. (J). 2006. lib. bdg. (978-1-4222-0059-9(0)); Slovakia. Docalavich, Heather. (YA). 2006. lib. bdg. (978-1-4222-0060-5(4)); Slovenia. Docalavich, Heather. (J). 2006. lib. bdg. (978-1-4222-0061-2(2)); Spain. Simons, Rae. (J). 2006. lib. bdg. (978-1-4222-0062-9(0)); Sweden. Docalavich, Heather. (J). 2006. lib. bdg. (978-1-4222-0063-6(9)); United Kingdom. Simons, Rae. (YA). 2006. lib. bdg. (978-1-4222-0064-3(7)); (gr. 5 up). (Illus.). 88p. 2006. lib. bdg. (978-1-4222-0038-4(8) , 1247983) Mason Crest Pubs.

Hintz, Martin. Croatia. 2004. (Enchantment of the World, Second Ser.). (Illus.). 144p. (YA). (gr. 5-9). 36.00 (978-0-516-24253-8(9) , Children's Pr.) Scholastic Library Publishing.

Marcovitz, Hal. The Balkans: People in Conflict. 2002. (People at Odds Ser.). (Illus.). 112p. (J). (gr. 5 up). 30.00 (978-0-7910-6710-9(6) , Chelsea Hse.) Facts On File, Inc.

Orr, Tamra. Slovenia. 2004. (Enchantment of the World, Second Ser.). (Illus.). 144p. (YA). (gr. 5-9). 36.00 (978-0-516-24249-1(0) , Children's Pr.) Scholastic Library Publishing.

Pavlovic, Zoran. Croatia. 2002. (Modern World Nations Ser.). (Illus.). 150p. (gr. 6-12). 30.00 (978-0-7910-7210-3(X) , Chelsea Hse.) Facts On File, Inc.

BALKAN PENINSULA—FICTION

Hayes, W. Clair. The Boy Allies in the Balkan Campaign or. 2006. 78.99 ***(*978-1-4219-9904-3(8));*** pap. 72.99 ***(*978-1-4219-9919-7(6))*** IndyPublish.com.

Uncle Markie. Piglettё & Bobo Winter in Zagreb. 2003. (YA). ring bd. 9.95 (978-1-933129-11-2(5)) Studio 403.

BALL GAMES

see names of games, e.g. Baseball; Soccer

Bourassa, Barbara. Ball Sports. 2007. (J). lib. bdg. 18.95 ***(*978-1-59566-349-8(5))*** QEB Publishing Inc.

Cohen, Santiago, illus. Play Ball! 2008. (J). ***(*978-0-7614-5451-9(9))*** Cavendish, Marshall Corp.

Juegos de Pelota 6 Packs. Individual Title. (Coleccion Pm Ser.: Vol. 2). Tr. of Ball games. (SPA.). 16p. (gr. k-1). 26.00 (978-0-7578-0683-4(X)) Rigby Education.

Play Ball! (Illus.). 32p. (J). (gr. 3 up). lib. bdg. (978-1-59084-195-2(6)) Mason Crest Pubs.

Play Ball! Level O, 6 vols., Vol. 3. (Explorers Ser.). 32p. (gr. 3-6). 44.95 (978-0-7699-0624-9(9)) Shortland Pubns. (U. S. A.) Inc.

Reiser, Lynn. Play Ball with Me. 2006. (Illus.). 28p. (J). (gr. k-ps). 9.95 (978-0-375-83244-4(0) , Knopf Bks. for Young Readers) Random Hse. Children's Bks.

Royston, Angela. Wood: Let's Look at a Sports Bat. 2005. (J). (978-1-4109-1819-2(X)); pap. (978-1-4109-1828-4(9)) Steck-Vaughn.

Stillinger, Doug. Ball Games. 2005. (Illus.). 52p. (J). (gr. 1 up). spiral bd. 14.95 (978-1-57054-254-1(6)) Klutz.

BALLADS

see also Folk Songs

Delessert, Etienne, illus. Who Killed Cock Robin? 2004. 32p. (gr. k-4). 17.95 (978-1-56846-191-5(7) , Creative Editions) Creative Co., The.

Guest, Ann Hutchinson. The Adventures of Klig & Gop: In Rotation-Land. 2001. (Illus.). 84p. (J). (ps-6). pap. (978-1-930798-05-2(9)) National Dance Education Organization.

—The Adventures of Klig & Gop: In Spring-Up-Land. 2001. 59p. (J). (ps-6). pap. (978-1-930798-06-9(7)) National Dance Education Organization.

—The Adventures of Klig & Gop: In Support-Land. 2001. 54p. (J). (ps-6). pap. (978-1-930798-07-6(5)) National Dance Education Organization.

Guest, Ann Hutchinson, et al. The Adventures of Klig & Gop No. 2: Parent & Teacher Guide. 2001. (Illus.). 76p. (J). (ps-6). pap. (978-1-930798-04-5(0)) National Dance Education Organization.

Simpson, Harold B. A Century of Ballads, 1810-1910: Their Composers & Singers. 2001. 349p. (YA). reprint ed. 98.00 (978-0-7222-6219-1(1)) Library Reprints, Inc.

BALLET

Augustyn, Frank & Tanaka, Shelley. Footnotes: Dancing Ballets. 2001. (Women at War Ser.). (Illus.). 96p. (gr. 5 up). lib. bdg. 24.90 (978-0-7613-2323-5(6) , Twenty-First Century Bks.) Lerner Publishing Group.

—Footnotes: Dancing fhe World's Best-Loved Ballets. 2002. 96p. (J). (gr. 5-10). 17.95 (978-0-7613-1646-6(9) , Twenty-First Century Bks.) Lerner Publishing Group.

—Footnotes: Dancing the World's Best-Loved Ballets. 2001. (Illus.). 96p. (J). 24.95 (978-1-55263-285-7(7)) Key Porter Bks. CAN. *Dist:* Firefly Bks., Ltd.

Ballerina. 2003. (Illus.). 32p. (J). 12.98 (978-1-4054-1296-4(8)) Parragon, Inc.

Ballerina Belle. 2002. (Dolly Board Book Ser.). bds. 4.98 (978-0-7525-8278-8(X)) Parragon, Inc.

Barringer, Janice & Schlesinger, Sarah. The Pointe Book: Shoes, Training & Technique. rev. ed. 1998. 208p. (gr. 7-12). pap. 18.95 (978-0-87127-204-1(0)) Princeton Bk. Co. Pubs.

Bicknell, Joanna & Page, Nick. Look at Me! I'm a Ballerina! Snaith, Andy, photos by. 2005. (Illus.). 23p. (J). (ps-3). 12.95 incl. audio (978-1-905051-72-4(7)) Make Believe Ideas GBR. *Dist:* Ingram Pub. Services.

Blackledge, Annabel. I Want to Be a Ballerina. 2005. (Dk Readers Ser.). 32p. (J). pap. 3.99 (978-0-7566-1696-0(4)); (Illus.). 12.99 (978-0-7566-1695-3(6)); (Illus.). (978-1-4156-4653-3(8)) Dorling Kindersley Publishing, Inc.

Bowes, Deborah. The Ballet Book: A Young Person's Guide to Classical Dance. Pawelak, Lydia, photos by. 1999. (Illus.). 143p. (YA). (gr. 4-7). reprint ed. pap. 17.00 (978-0-7567-5498-3(4)) DIANE Publishing Co.

Bussell, Darcey. The Ballet Book. 2006. (Illus.). 72p. (J). pap. 6.99 (978-0-7566-1933-6(5)) Dorling Kindersley Publishing, Inc.

Bussell, Darcey & Linton, Patricia. The Ballet Book. 2006. (Illus.). 64p. (J). ***(*978-1-4156-6607-4(5))*** Dorling Kindersley Publishing, Inc.

Castle, Kate. Ballet. 2002. (gr. 3-6). lib. bdg. 19.90 (978-0-613-90904-4(6)) Tandem Library Bks.

—My First Ballet Book: From Barres & Ballet Shoes to Plies & Performances. 2006. (My First Book Ser.). (Illus.). 48p. (J). (gr. k-3). 9.95 (978-0-7534-6026-9(2) , Kingfisher) Houghton Mifflin Co. Trade & Reference Div.

—The World of Ballet. 2005. (World Of Ser.). (Illus.). 64p. (J). (gr. 4-6). pap. 8.95 (978-0-7534-5833-4(0) , Kingfisher) Houghton Mifflin Co. Trade & Reference Div.

Castor, Harriet. Ballet Magic, Vol. 1. Fisher, Chris, illus. 64p. (J). pap. 7.95 (978-0-14-038479-6(0)) Penguin Group (USA) Inc.

Clibbon, Meg. Imagine You're a Ballerina. Clibbon, Lucy, illus. 2006. (Imagine This! Ser.). 32p. (J). (ps-4). 19.95 (978-1-55451-020-7(1)); pap. 8.95 (978-1-55451-019-1(8)) Annick Pr., Ltd. CAN. *Dist:* Firefly Bks., Ltd.

Davidson, Susanna & Daynes, Katie. Little Ballet Treasury. 2006. 96p. (J). 7.99 (978-0-7945-1441-9(3) , Usborne) EDC Publishing.

Daynes, Katie & Davidson, Susannah. Ballet Treasury. 2005. (Ballet Treasury Ser.). 96p. (J). 19.95 (978-0-7945-0936-1(3) , Usborne) EDC Publishing.

Degas, Edgar, illus. I Dreamed I Was A Ballerina. 2001. (J). (978-0-87099-988-8(5)) Metropolitan Museum of Art, The.

Dillman, Lisa. Ballet. 2004. (Get Going! Hobbies Ser.). (Illus.). 32p. (J). pap. (978-1-4034-6122-3(8)); (gr. 4-6). lib. bdg. 27.79 (978-1-4034-6115-5(5)) Heinemann Library.

Dorling Kindersley Publishing Staff. Ballerina for a Day. 2005. (Illus.). 12p. (J). bds. 12.99 (978-0-7566-1118-7(0)) Dorling Kindersley Publishing, Inc.

—Ballet. 2004. (Ultimate Sticker Bks.). 16p. (J). pap. 6.99 (978-0-7566-0233-8(5)) Dorling Kindersley Publishing, Inc.

—Ballet School. 2003. (Illus.). 48p. (J). 12.99 (978-0-7894-9228-9(8)) Dorling Kindersley Publishing, Inc.

Dorling Kindersley Publishing Staff, contrib. by. Ballerina. 2005. (Glitter Stickers Ser.). (Illus.). 16p. (J). (ps-3). pap. 6.99 (978-0-7566-1414-0(7)) Dorling Kindersley Publishing, Inc.

Dorling Kindersley Publishing Staff, ed. Sparkly Ballerina. 2005. (Illus.). 10p. (J). bds. 5.99 (978-0-7566-0995-5(X)) Dorling Kindersley Publishing, Inc.

Dorling Kindersley Publishing Staff & Newman, Barbara. Illustrated Ballet Stories. Tomblin, Gill, illus. 2000. (Read & Listen Ser.). 64p. (J). (gr. 4-7). pap. 9.99 (978-0-7894-5466-9(1)) Dorling Kindersley Publishing, Inc.

Dowd, Olympia. A Young Dancer's Apprenticeship: On Tour with the Moscow City Ballet. 2003. (Single Titles Ser.). (Illus.). 128p. (gr. 7 up). lib. bdg. 24.90 (978-0-7613-2917-6(X) , Twenty-First Century Bks.) Lerner Publishing Group.

—A Young Dancer's Apprenticeship: On Tour with the Moscow City Ballet. 2002. (Illus.). 96p. (J). (978-1-55192-558-5(3)) Raincoast Bk. Distribution.

—A Young Dancer's Odyssey. 2001. (Illus.). 50p. (YA). (gr. 5 up). pap. (978-1-55192-326-0(2)) Raincoast Bk. Distribution.

Edom, H. & Katrak, N. Starting Ballet. 32p. (J). lib. bdg. 12.95 (978-1-58086-815-0(0) , Usborne) EDC Publishing.

Edom, Helen. Starting Ballet. 2001. (gr. k-3). lib. bdg. 12.95 (978-0-613-90706-4(X)) Tandem Library Bks.

Frith, Margaret. Hooray for Ballet! 2003. (gr. k-3). lib. bdg. 14.15 (978-0-613-61628-7(6)) Tandem Library Bks.

Frith, Margaret & Haley, Amanda. Hooray for Ballet! 2003. (Smart about Art Ser.). (Illus.). 32p. (J). (gr. 1-4). pap. 5.99 (978-0-448-42884-0(9) , Grosset & Dunlap) Penguin Group (USA) Inc.

Geras, Adaele & McNicholas, Shelagh. Tilly Tutu. McNicholas, Shelagh, illus. 2004. (ESP & SPA., Illus.). 28p. (J). 14.99 (978-84-8488-091-2(5)) Serres, Ediciones, S. L. ESP. *Dist:* Lectorum Pubns., Inc.

Geras, Adele & Clark, Emma Chichester. The Nutcracker. 2001. (Magic of Ballet Ser.). (Illus.). 32p. (J). (gr. 1-4). 10.95 (978-1-86233-236-2(3)) David & Charles Children's Bks. GBR. *Dist:* Sterling Publishing Co., Inc.

Gibbs, Lynne. The Ultimate Ballerina Sticker Book. 2004. (Barbie Sticker Books Ser.). (Illus.). 20p. (J). pap. 6.99 (978-0-7566-0572-8(5)) Dorling Kindersley Publishing, Inc.

Goodman, Joan E. Ballet Bunnies: Written & Illustrated by Joan Elizabeth Goodman. 2008. (J). ***(978-0-7614-5392-5(X))*** Cavendish, Marshall Corp.

Gourley, Catherine. Who Is Maria Tallchief? Taylor, Val Paul & Harrison, Nancy, illus. 2002. (Who Was...? Ser.). 112p. (J). mass mkt. 4.99 (978-0-448-42675-4(7) , Grosset & Dunlap) Penguin Group (USA) Inc.

—Who Is Maria Tallchief? 2002. (gr. 3-6). lib. bdg. 13.00 (978-0-613-45330-1(1)) Tandem Library Bks.

Graham, Debbie. Graham Crackers' Nutcracker. Snyder, Lesley & Snyder, Tim, illus. 2000. 26p. (J). (ps-3). 12.99 (978-0-615-11409-5(1)) Graham Cracker Kids.

Graves, Karen Marie. Ballet Dance. 2008. ***(978-1-4296-0119-1(1))*** Capstone Pr., Inc.

Grigorovich, Yuri & Kamova, Sania D. The Golden Age: A Three-Act Ballet. Coey, Tim, tr. Pchalkin, Vladimir, photos by. 1999. (Illus.). 127p. (YA). (gr. 6-12). reprint ed. 20.00 (978-0-7881-6414-9(7)) DIANE Publishing Co.

Grigorovich, Yuri, et al. The Authorized Bolshoi Ballet Book of Romeo & Juliet. 2006. (Illus.). 95p. (YA). (gr. 4-8). reprint ed. 22.00 (978-1-4223-5261-8(7)) DIANE Publishing Co.

Grindley, Sally. The Little Ballerina. 1999. (Eyewitness Readers). (Illus.). 32p. (J). (gr. 1-3). pap. 3.99 (978-0-7894-4004-4(0)) Dorling Kindersley Publishing, Inc.

—The Little Ballerina. 1999. (Illus.). 32p. (J). (gr. 1-3). lib. bdg. 11.19 (978-0-606-18990-3(4)); (ps-ps). lib. bdg. 11.80 (978-0-613-17346-9(5)) Tandem Library Bks.

Grindley, Sally & Dorling Kindersley Publishing Staff. The Little Ballerina. 1999. (Eyewitness Readers). (Illus.). 32p. (J). (ps-4). 14.99 (978-0-7894-4005-1(9)) Dorling Kindersley Publishing, Inc.

Harcourt School Publishers Staff. Toe Shoes & Tutus: Take-Home Book. 2001. (Collections Ser.). (Illus.). (J). pap. 1.90 (978-0-15-319532-7(0)) Harcourt Schl. Pubs.

—Toe Shoes & Tutus Below Level. 3rd ed. 2002. (Trophies Reading Program Ser.). (Illus.). pap. 5.10 (978-0-15-323330-2(3)) Harcourt Schl. Pubs.

—Vamos de Fiesta: Zapatos para Balet y Tutus Take-Home Book. 2001. (SPA., Illus.). (J). pap. 2.80 (978-0-15-321313-7(2)) Harcourt Schl. Pubs.

Hayward, Linda & Dorling Kindersley Publishing Staff. Jobs People Do: A Day in the Life of a Dancer. 2001. (Readers Ser.). (Illus.). 32p. (J). (ps-3). 12.95 (978-0-7894-7370-7(4)); pap. 3.99 (978-0-7894-7369-1(0)) Dorling Kindersley Publishing, Inc.

Holabird, Katharine. My First Ballet Class. Craig, Helen, illus. 2007. (Angelina Ballerina Ser.). 32p. (J). 9.99 (978-0-448-44507-6(7) , Grosset & Dunlap) Penguin Group (USA) Inc.

Isadora, Rachel. On Your Toes: A Ballet ABC. 2006. pap. (978-0-06-050242-3(8)) HarperCollins Canada, Ltd.

—On Your Toes: A Ballet ABC. Isadora, Rachel, illus. 2003. (Illus.). 40p. (J). 17.99 (978-0-06-050238-6(X)) HarperCollins Pubs.

Jaffe, Susan. Becoming a Ballerina. Ellison, Nancy, photos by. 2003. (Illus.). 96p. (J). 19.95 (978-0-7893-0976-1(9)) Universe Publishing.

Junor, Amy. My First Ballet Recital. 2008. (Dk Readers Ser.). 48p. (J). (gr. 2-3). 14.99 ***(978-0-7566-3826-9(7));*** pap. 3.99 ***(978-0-7566-3827-6(5))*** Dorling Kindersley Publishing, Inc.

Kuklin, Susan. Reaching for Dreams: A Ballet from Rehearsal to Opening Night. 2001. (gr. 7-12). lib. bdg. 23.40 (978-0-613-90805-4(8)) Tandem Library Bks.

—Reaching for Dreams: A Ballet from Rehearsal to Opening Night. 2001. (Illus.). 136p. (gr. 7-11). pap. 13.95 (978-0-595-17081-4(1)) iUniverse, Inc.

Lawrenson, Diana. Inside the Australian Ballet. 1999. (Illus.). 39p. (J). (978-1-86448-959-0(6)); mass mkt. (978-1-86448-958-3(8)) Allen & Unwin.

Lee, Laura. A Child's Introduction to Ballet: The Stories, Music & Magic of Classical Dance. Hamilton, Meredith, illus. 2007. 96p. (J). (gr. 3 up). 19.95 incl. audio compact disk (978-1-57912-699-5(5)) Black Dog & Leventhal Pubs., Inc.

Loibl, Marianne. Little Ballerina Book & Tutu. Suetens, Clara, illus. 2007. 48p. (J). (ps). 17.95 ***(978-0-7358-2148-4(8))*** North-South Bks., Inc.

Meredith, S. Ballet. 2006. 32p. (J). 12.99 ***(978-1-58086-928-7(9))*** EDC Publishing.

Meredith, Sue. Ballet (Level 2) - Internet Referenced. 2006. (Illus.). 32p. (J). 4.99 (978-0-7945-1343-6(3) , Usborne) EDC Publishing.

Morris, Ann. Dancing to America. Kolnik, Paul, photos by. 2004. (Illus.). 40p. (YA). (gr. 7-10). 16.00 (978-0-7567-7577-3(9)) DIANE Publishing Co.

Newmann, Barbara, et al. Illustrated Book of Ballet Stories. Tomblin, Gill, illus. 2000. (Read & Listen Ser.). 64p. (J). pap. 9.99 incl. audio compact disk (978-0-7894-6097-4(1)) Dorling Kindersley Publishing, Inc.

Pavlova, Anna. I Dreamed I Was A Ballerina. Degas, Edgar, illus. 2001. 32p. (J). (gr. k-2). 16.00 (978-0-689-84676-2(2) , Atheneum) Simon & Schuster Children's Publishing.

Rinaldi, Robin. Ballet. (World of Dance Ser.). (Illus.). (gr. 9-13). 2004. 112p. pap. 30.00 (978-0-7910-7773-3(X)); 2003. 120p. 30.00 (978-0-7910-7640-8(7)) Facts On File, Inc. (Chelsea Hse.).

Schoberle, Cecile. Prima Ballerina. Apperley, Dawn, illus. 2005. 16p. (J). pap. 4.99 (978-0-689-87101-6(5) , Little Simon) Simon & Schuster Children's Publishing.

Spatt, Leslie E. The Sleeping Beauty: Behind the Scenes at the Ballet. (Illus.). (J). pap. 19.99 (978-0-590-24536-4(8)) Scholastic, Inc.

Tallchief, Maria & Well, Rosemary. Tallchief: America's Prima Ballerina. Kelley, Gary, illus. 2001. 28p. (J). (gr. k-4). lib. bdg. 15.30 (978-0-613-44420-0(5)) Tandem Library Bks.

Tallchief, Maria & Wells, Rosemary. Tallchief: America's Prima Ballerina. Kelley, Gary, illus. 1999. 32p. (J). (gr. k-4). 16.99 (978-0-670-88756-9(0) , Viking Juvenile) Penguin Group (USA) Inc.

Tatchell, Judy. Internet-Linked World of Ballet. Safarewicz, E. & Smith, G., illus. Date not set. 64p. (J). 39.95 (978-0-7460-1693-0(X)) EDC Publishing.

—World of Ballet. 2004. (Kid Kits Ser.). (Illus.). 64p. (J). pap. 9.95 (978-0-7945-0403-8(5)); lib. bdg. 17.95 (978-1-58086-514-2(3)) EDC Publishing.

Tatchell, Judy. World of Ballet - Internet Linked. rev. ed. 2007. (World of Ballet Ser.). 64p. (J). pap. 9.99 ***(978-0-7945-1060-2(4)*** , Usborne) EDC Publishing.

Thomas, Mark. Ballet Dancing. 2001. (Welcome Bks.). (Illus.). 24p. (J). (ps-2). pap. 4.95 (978-0-516-23067-2(0)); 17.00 (978-0-516-23142-6(1)) Scholastic Library Publishing. (Children's Pr.).

—Ballet Dancing. 2001. (gr. k-3). lib. bdg. 12.95 (978-0-613-51979-3(5)) Tandem Library Bks.

Tobey, Cheryl. Ballet Dancing. 2001. (After School Ser.). (Illus.). 48p. (YA). (gr. 7-12). 23.00 (978-0-516-23147-1(2) , Children's Pr.) Scholastic Library Publishing.

—Ballet Dancing. 2001. (gr. 7-12). lib. bdg. 15.25 (978-0-613-58689-4(1)) Tandem Library Bks.

Uralskaia, Valeria, et al. Tales of Classical Ballet, Talmi, Mary, ed. Loutchinina, Ekaterina, tr. from RUS. Dmitriev, Sergei, illus. 2004. 40p. (J). (978-0-9743082-1-0(8) , Moscow Ballet) Sports Marketing International, Inc.

Watt, Fiona. Little Ballerina Dancing Book. Lo Cascio, Maria Cristina, illus. 2007. 12p. (YA). bds. 15.99 incl. audio compact disk (978-0-7945-1520-1(7) , Usborne) EDC Publishing.

Wenzel, Angela. Edgar Degas: Dance Like a Butterfly. Jackson, Rosie, tr. from GER. 2002. (Adventures in Art Ser.). (Illus.). 30p. (gr. 4-6). 14.95 (978-3-7913-2736-5(4)) Prestel Publishing.

White, Diana. Ballerina Dreams, Level 3. Rogers, Jacqueline, illus. 1998. (Hello Reader! Ser.). 48p. (J). (gr. 1-3). pap. 3.99 (978-0-590-37233-6(5)) Scholastic, Inc.

Wilkes, Angela. The Best Book of Ballet. (Best Book of... Ser.). (Illus.). 32p. (J). 2007. pap. 6.95 ***(978-0-7534-6091-7(2));*** 2000. tchr. ed. 12.95 (978-0-7534-5275-2(8)) Houghton Mifflin Co. Trade & Reference Div. (Kingfisher).

BALLET—FICTION

Aggs, Patrice, illus. The Kingfisher Treasury of Ballet Stories. 2003. (Kingfisher Treasury of Stories Ser.). 160p. (J). (gr. k-3). pap. 5.95 (978-0-7534-5630-9(3) , Kingfisher) Houghton Mifflin Co. Trade & Reference Div.

Allen, Debbie. Dancing in the Wings. Nelson, Kadir A., illus. (J). (gr. k-2). 2003. 32p. pap. 6.99 (978-0-14-250141-2(7) , Puffin); 2000. 1p. 16.99 (978-0-8037-2501-0(9) , Dial) Penguin Group (USA) Inc.

—Dancing in the Wings. 2003. (gr. k-3). lib. bdg. 15.30 (978-0-613-86700-9(9)) Tandem Library Bks.

Ballerina Magic Shoes. 2003. (Illus.). 32p. (J). 5.98 (978-1-4054-1144-8(9)) Parragon, Inc.

Bennet, Elizabeth. Ballet: A Dancer's Diary. 2007. 32p. (J). (gr. 1). pap. 6.99 ***(978-1-58476-631-5(X)*** , IKIDS) Innovative Kids.

Bloss, Janet A. Ballet Bunny. Bloss, Janet A., illus. 1998. (Illus.). 24p. (J). (gr. k-3). reprint ed. pap. 1.99 (978-0-87406-374-5(4) , Willowisp Pr.) Darby Creek Publishing.

Bottner, Barbara. Bootsie Barker Ballerina. Karas, G. Brian, illus. 1998. (I Can Read Bks.). 48p. (J). (gr. k-3). pap. 3.99 (978-0-06-444241-1(1)) HarperCollins Pubs.

Bradley, Kimberly Brubaker. Ballerino Nate. Alley, R. W., illus. 2006. 32p. (J). (ps). 16.99 (978-0-8037-2954-4(5) , Dial) Penguin Group (USA) Inc.

Brandenberg, Alexa. Ballerina Flying. 2002. (Illus.). 40p. (J). (ps-1). (ENG & FRE.). 15.95 (978-0-06-029549-3(X)); 15.89 (978-0-06-029550-9(3)) HarperCollins Pubs.

Brownrigg, Sheri. All Tutus Should Be Pink. Johnson, Meredith, illus. 2004. 32p. (J). lib. bdg. 15.00 (978-1-59054-371-9(8)) Fitzgerald Bks.

—Best Friends Wear Pink Tutus. Johnson, Meredith, illus. 2004. 32p. (J). lib. bdg. 15.00 (978-1-59054-377-1(7)) Fitzgerald Bks.

Bryant, Ann. Ballet Magic (Combined Volume) 2007. (Ballerina Dreams Ser.). 336p. (J). pap. 7.99 ***(978-0-7945-1740-3(4)*** , Usborne) EDC Publishing.

—Christmas Nutcracker. 2006. 192p. (J). pap. 4.99 (978-0-7945-1369-6(7) , Usborne) EDC Publishing.

—Dancing Forever. Benton, Tim, illus. 2006. 112p. (J). pap. 4.99 (978-0-7945-1299-6(2) , Usborne) EDC Publishing.

—Dancing Friends (Combined Volume) 2007. (Ballerina Dreams Ser.). 336p. (J). pap. 7.99 ***(978-0-7945-1741-0(2)*** , Usborne) EDC Publishing.

—Dancing Princess. Benton, Tim, illus. 2006. 112p. (J). pap. 4.99 (978-0-7945-1297-2(6) , Usborne) EDC Publishing.

—Dancing with the Stars. Benton, Tim, illus. 2006. 112p. (J). pap. 4.99 (978-0-7945-1298-9(4) , Usborne) EDC Publishing.

Bunting, Eve. The Day Before Christmas. 2000. (gr. k-3). lib. bdg. 14.10 (978-0-613-29920-6(5)) Tandem Library Bks.

Carlson, Nancy. Harriet's Recital. 2006. (J). pap. 6.95 (978-1-57505-929-7(0) , First Avenue Editions) Lerner Publishing Group.

Carlson, Nancy L. Harriet's Recital. 2006. (Illus.). (J). 15.95 (978-1-57505-898-6(7) , Carolrhoda Bks.) Lerner Publishing Group.

Carr, Jan. Ballet Party! 1998. (You're Invited to Mary-Kate & Ashley's Ser.). (Illus.). 48p. (J). (gr. 2-4). pap. 3.99 (978-0-590-29399-0(0)) Scholastic, Inc.

Christian, Posey. Tina Ballerina's Ballet Class. 2006. 14p. (J). bds. 12.99 (978-0-439-74653-3(1) , Cartwheel Bks.) Scholastic, Inc.

Cirrone, Dorian. Dancing in Red Shoes Will Kill You. 2006. 224p. (J). pap. 7.99 (978-0-06-055703-4(6) , Harper Trophy) HarperCollins Pubs.

Cleary, Beverly. Ellen Tebbits. 160p. (J). (gr. 2-4). pap. 4.99 (978-0-8072-1397-1(7) , Listening Library) Random Hse. Audio Publishing Group.

Conway, Celeste. The Melting Season. 2008. 224p. (YA). (gr. 7). mass mkt. 6.50 ***(978-0-440-23953-6(2)*** , Laurel Leaf) Random Hse. Children's Bks.

Corey, Shana. Ballerina Bear. Paparone, Pamela, illus. (Jellybean Bks.). 24p. (J). (ps-k). 2000. 2.99 (978-0-375-80098-6(0)); 1999. lib. bdg. 7.99 (978-0-375-90098-3(5)) Random Hse. Children's Bks. (Random Hse. Bks. for Young Readers).

Coulman, Valerie. I Am a Ballerina. Lamb, Sandra, illus. 2004. 32p. (J). 15.95 (978-1-894222-91-4(1)) Lobster Pr. CAN. *Dist:* Univ. of Toronto Pr.

Coulman, Valerie. Je Suis Ballerine! Duchesne, Christiane, tr. from ENG. Lamb, Sandra, illus. (FRE.). 32p. (J). pap. 6.95 ***(978-2-922435-05-4(9))*** Editions Homard CAN. *Dist:* Univ. of Toronto Pr.

Cristaldi, Kathryn. Baseball Ballerina. Carter, Abby, illus. 2002. (J). 11.91 (978-0-7587-0907-3(2)) Book Wholesalers, Inc.

Davidson, Susanna. Nutcracker. Luraschi, Anna, illus. 2007. 24p. (J). 9.99 (978-0-7945-1515-7(0) , Usborne) EDC Publishing.

DePalma, Mary Newell. The Nutcracker Doll. (J). 2008. (978-0-439-80243-7(1)); 2007. 32p. pap. 16.99 (978-0-439-80242-0(3)) Scholastic, Inc. (Levine, Arthur A. Bks.).

Edwards, Pamela Duncan. Honk! The Story of a Prima Swanerina. Cole, Henry, illus. 2000. 32p. (gr. k-4). pap. 5.99 (978-0-7868-1298-1(2)) Disney Pr.

Edwards, Pat. A Visit to Cousin Boris. Selway, Martina, illus. 1999. 24p. (J). (978-0-7608-3196-0(3)) Sundance/Newbridge Educational Publishing.

Faulkner, Keith. Rainbow's End. 2003. (Illus.). 10p. (J). 9.95 (978-0-7641-5641-0(1)) Barron's Educational Series, Inc.

Feldman, Thea. My Day of Ballet: Magnix Imagination. 2007. 6p. bds. 5.99 ***(978-1-932915-41-9(9))*** Sandvik Innovations, LLC.

Ford, Bernette. Ballet Kitty. Williams, Sam, illus. 2007. 32p. (J). (ps-1). 14.95 ***(978-1-905417-56-8(X))*** Boxer Bks., Ltd. GBR. *Dist:* Sterling Publishing Co., Inc.

French, Jackie. Josephine Wants to Dance. Whatley, Bruce, illus. 2007. 32p. (J). (ps-1). 15.95 ***(978-0-8109-9431-7(3)*** , Abrams Bks. for Young Readers) Abrams, Harry N., Inc.

Garn, Laura Aimee. Bella Basset Ballerina. Sokolova, Valerie, illus. 2006. 32p. (J). (ps-3). 15.95 (978-0-9759378-0-8(4)) Pretty Please Pr., Inc.

Gauch, Patricia Lee. Baila, Tanya. Ichikawa, Satomi, illus. 2002. Tr. of Dance, Tanya. (SPA.). 32p. (J). (ps-3). 16.99 (978-84-8488-032-5(X) , RR31515) Serres, Ediciones, S. L. ESP. *Dist:* Lectorum Pubns., Inc.

—Bravo, Tanya. Ichikawa, Satomi, illus. 2002. (SPA.). 32p. (J). (ps-3). 14.95 (978-84-8488-034-9(6)) Serres, Ediciones, S. L. ESP. *Dist:* Lectorum Pubns., Inc.

—Tanya & the Red Shoes. Ichikawa, Satomi, illus. 2002. 40p. (J). 16.99 (978-0-399-23314-2(8) , Philomel) Penguin Group (USA) Inc.

Geras, Adele. Good Luck, Louisa, Vol. 6. Popham, Karen, illus. 2002. 62p. pap. (978-0-09-940944-1(5) , Red Fox) Random Hse. Children's Bks. GBR. *Dist:* Trafalgar Square Publishing.

Geras, Adèle. Like a Real Ballerina. McNicholas, Shelagh, illus. 2008. 32p. (J). (ps). 16.99 ***(978-0-8037-3237-7(6)*** , Dial) Penguin Group (USA) Inc.

Geras, Adele. Time for Ballet. McNicholas, Shelagh, tr. McNicholas, Shelagh, illus. 2004. 32p. (J). (gr. k-1). 16.99 (978-0-8037-2978-0(2) , Dial) Penguin Group (USA) Inc.

Giff, Patricia Reilly. A Glass Slipper for Rosie. Durrell, Julie, illus. 1998. (Ballet Slippers Ser.: Vol. 5). 80p. (J). (gr. 2-5). pap. 4.99 (978-0-14-130159-4(7) , Puffin) Penguin Group (USA) Inc.

—Not-So-Perfect Rosie, No. 4. Durrell, Julie, illus. 1998. (Ballet Slippers Ser.: Vol. 4). 80p. (J). (gr. 2-5). pap. 4.99 (978-0-14-130060-3(4) , Puffin) Penguin Group (USA) Inc.

—Starring Rosie. Durrel, Julie, illus. 1998. (Ballet Slippers Ser.: Vol. 3). 80p. (J). (gr. 2-5). pap. 4.99 (978-0-14-038967-8(9) , Puffin) Penguin Group (USA) Inc.

Golds, Cassandra. Clair de Lune. Blackall, Sophie, illus. 2006. 208p. (J). (gr. 5). 15.95 (978-0-375-83395-3(1)); lib. bdg. 17.99 (978-0-375-93395-0(6)) Random Hse. Children's Bks. (Knopf Bks. for Young Readers).

—Clair de Lune. Blackall, Sophie, illus. 2007. 208p. (J). (gr. 4-7). 5.99 (978-0-440-42089-7(X) , Yearling) Random Hse. Children's Bks.

Gollub, Matthew. Gobble, Quack, Moon. Love, Judy, illus. 2002. 32p. (J). (ps-3). 18.95 incl. audio compact disk (978-1-889910-20-8(1)) Tortuga Pr.

Grover, Lorie Ann. On Pointe. 2004. 320p. (J). 17.99 (978-0-689-86525-1(2) , McElderry, Margaret K.) Simon & Schuster Children's Publishing.

Gruska, Denise Eliana. The Only Boy in Ballet Class. Wummer, Amy, illus. 2007. 32p. (J). (ps-3). 15.95 ***(978-1-4236-0220-0(X))*** Gibbs Smith, Publisher.

Hall, Kirsten. Ballerina Girl. 2004. (My First Reader Ser.). (J). (gr. k-1). pap. 3.95 (978-0-516-24623-9(2) , Children's Pr.) Scholastic Library Publishing.

Hampshire, Susan. Rosie's Ballet Slippers. Meloni, Maria T., illus. 1998. (Trophy Picture Bk.). 32p. (J). (ps-2). pap. 5.95 (978-0-06-443488-1(5) , Harper Trophy) HarperCollins Pubs.

Harcourt School Publishers Staff. Darci's Ballet Dream Advanced Level. 3rd ed. 2002. (Trophies Reading Program Ser.). (Illus.). pap. 5.10 (978-0-15-323194-0(7)) Harcourt Schl. Pubs.

Hartry, Nancy. Jocelyn & the Ballerina. Hendry, Linda, illus. (J). (ps-k). 2000. 36p. (978-1-55041-649-7(9)); 2nd ed. 32p. pap. (978-1-55041-803-3(3)) Fitzhenry & Whiteside, Ltd.

Hewett, Lorri. Dancer. 2001. (J). 12.64 (978-0-606-20620-4(5)); 2000. (gr. 7-12). lib. bdg. 14.15 (978-0-613-33689-5(5)) Tandem Library Bks.

—Dancer: Everybody Has a Dream. 2001. 224p. (YA). (gr. 8-12). pap. 5.99 (978-0-14-131085-5(5) , Puffin) Penguin Group (USA) Inc.

Holabird, Katharine. All Dancers on Deck. Craig, Helen, illus. 2006. (Angelina Ballerina Ser.). 32p. (J). (ps-1). 3.99 (978-0-448-44388-1(0) , Grosset & Dunlap) Penguin Group (USA) Inc.

—Angelina & the Princess. Craig, Helen, illus. 2006. 32p. (J). (ps). 13.99 (978-0-670-06085-6(2) , Viking Juvenile) Penguin Group (USA) Inc.

—Angelina & the Rag Doll. Craig, Helen, illus. 2006. (Angelina Ballerina Ser.). 24p. (J). (ps-1). 3.99 (978-0-448-44331-7(7) , Grosset & Dunlap) Penguin Group (USA) Inc.

—Angelina Ballerina. Craig, Helen, illus. 2006. (Angelina Ballerina Ser.). 32p. (J). (ps). 13.99 (978-0-670-06026-9(7) , Viking Juvenile) Penguin Group (USA) Inc.

—Angelina Has the Hiccups! Craig, Helen, illus. 2006. (Angelina Ballerina Ser.). 32p. (J). (ps-1). pap. 3.99 (978-0-448-44389-8(9) , Grosset & Dunlap) Penguin Group (USA) Inc.

—Angelina in the Wings. Craig, Helen, illus. 2006. (Angelina Ballerina Ser.). 24p. (J). (ps-1). 3.99 (978-0-448-44471-0(2) , Grosset & Dunlap) Penguin Group (USA) Inc.

—Angelina's Ballet Class. Craig, Helen, illus. 2006. (Angelina Ballerina Ser.). 24p. (J). (ps-2). pap. 5.99 (978-0-448-44013-2(X) , Grosset & Dunlap) Penguin Group (USA) Inc.

—Angelina's Diary. Craig, Helen, illus. 2006. (Angelina Ballerina Ser.). 80p. (J). (gr. 1-3). 3.99 (978-0-448-44016-3(4) , Grosset & Dunlap) Penguin Group (USA) Inc.

—Angelina's Lucky Penny. Craig, Helen, illus. 2006. (Angelina Ballerina Ser.). 24p. (J). (ps-1). 3.99 (978-0-448-44449-9(6) , Grosset & Dunlap) Penguin Group (USA) Inc.

—Christmas in Mouseland. Craig, Helen, illus. 2007. (Angelina Ballerina Ser.). 24p. (J). (ps-1). 6.99 ***(978-0-448-44663-9(4)*** , Grosset & Dunlap) Penguin Group (USA) Inc.

—The Silver Locket. Craig, Helen, illus. 2006. (Angelina Ballerina Ser.). 24p. (J). (ps-1). 3.99 (978-0-448-44472-7(0) , Grosset & Dunlap) Penguin Group (USA) Inc.

—A Very Special Secret: Angelina Young Readers. Craig, Helen, illus. 2006. (Angelina Ballerina Ser.: No. 3). 80p. (J). (gr. 1-3). 3.99 (978-0-448-44332-4(5) , Grosset & Dunlap) Penguin Group (USA) Inc.

Holabird, Katharine & Mason, James. Dance of Friendship. Craig, Helen, illus. 2006. (Angelina Ballerina Ser.). 24p. (J). (ps-2). 3.99 (978-0-448-44115-3(2) , Grosset & Dunlap) Penguin Group (USA) Inc.

Holmes, Sally, illus. Ballet Stories. 2003. (Red Hot Reads Ser.). 224p. (J). (gr. 4-8). pap. 6.95 (978-0-7534-5674-3(5) , Kingfisher) Houghton Mifflin Co. Trade & Reference Div.

Isadora, Rachel. Lili at Ballet. Isadora, Rachel, illus. 2002. (Illus.). (J). 14.04 (978-0-7587-2986-6(3)) Book Wholesalers, Inc.

—Lili Backstage. Isadora, Rachel, illus. 2002. (Illus.). (J). 13.19 (978-0-7587-2987-3(1)) Book Wholesalers, Inc.

—Lili on Stage. Isadora, Rachel, illus. 2002. (Illus.). (J). 14.04 (978-0-7587-2988-0(X)) Book Wholesalers, Inc.

Jacobson, Jennifer. Winnie (Dancing) on Her Own. Geis, Alissa Imre, illus. 2003. 112p. (J). (gr. 3-5). pap. 5.95 (978-0-618-36921-8(X)) Houghton Mifflin Co. Trade & Reference Div.

Jacobson, Jennifer Richard. Winnie Dancing on Her Own. 2003. (gr. 3-6). lib. bdg. 14.10 (978-0-613-90720-0(5)) Tandem Library Bks.

James, Annabelle. Abigail's Ballet Class. Beckes, Shirley, illus. 2004. 10p. (J). (ps-k). 12.49 (978-1-883043-54-4(9)) Straight Edge Pr., The.

Jane, Pamela. Noelle of the Nutcracker. Brett, Jan, illus. 2003. 64p. (J). (gr. 4-6). pap. 5.95 (978-0-618-36922-5(8)) Houghton Mifflin Co. Trade & Reference Div.

Johnson, Sarah. Time to Dance. Lew, Willie, illus. Lew, Willie, photos by. 2003. (J). 16.98 (978-0-7853-8811-1(7)) Publications International, Ltd.

Jordan, Apple & Random House Staff. Barbie: On Your Toes. Wolcott, Karen, illus. 2005. (Step into Reading Ser.: No. 1). 32p. (ps-1). pap. 3.99 (978-0-375-83142-3(8) , Random Hse. Bks. for Young Readers) Random Hse. Children's Bks.

Kanter, Angela. My Ballerina Sister. 2002. (Illus.). 64p. pap. 8.99 (978-0-09-941702-6(2)) Random Hse. GBR. *Dist:* Trafalgar Square Publishing.

—My Ballerina Sister on Stage. 2002. (Illus.). 64p. (J). pap. 8.99 (978-0-09-941703-3(0)) Random Hse. GBR. *Dist:* Independent Pubs. Group.

Karas, G. Brian, illus. Bootsie Barker Ballerina. 2002. (Bootsie Barker Ser.). (J). 11.91 (978-0-7587-6034-0(5)) Book Wholesalers, Inc.

Keene, Carolyn. The Cinderella Ballet Mystery. 2007. (Nancy Drew & the Clue Crew Ser.). 96p. (J). (gr. 2-4). 24.21 (***978-1-59961-345-1(X)***) Spotlight.

Krash, Elizabeth D. Hannah's Ballerina Dreams. Vansant, Wayne, illus. 1999. iii, 37p. (J). (ps-6). 15.95 (978-1-928719-00-7(7)) Quadre Enterprises, Ltd.

Lagonegro, Melissa & Random House Disney Staff. Ballerina Princess. 2007. (Step into Reading Ser.). (Illus.). 32p. (J). (ps-2). lib. bdg. 11.99 (978-0-7364-8051-2(X) , RH/Disney) Random Hse. Children's Bks.

—Ballerina Princess. Harding, Niall, illus. 2007. (Step into Reading Ser.). 32p. (J). (ps-2). pap. 3.99 (978-0-7364-2428-8(8) , RH/Disney) Random Hse. Children's Bks.

Lima, Chely. El Credito Que Amaba el Ballet. Rodriguez, Juan, illus. (SPA.). (J). pap. (978-980-01-1035-5(6)) Monte Avila Editores Latinoamericana CA VEN. *Dist:* Lectorum Pubns., Inc.

Luna, Rachel Nickerson. Nutcracker Magic. Luna, Rachel Nickerson, illus. 2002. (Illus.). 20p. (J). (ps-3). pap. 10.95 (978-1-886551-04-6(9)) Howard, Emma Bks.

Malcolm, Jahnna N. Drat! We're Rats! 2000. (Bad News Ballet Ser.). Orig. Title: The Terrible Tryouts. 160p. (J). (gr. 4-6). pap. 3.95 (978-0-9700164-0-9(9)) Starcatcher Pr.

Marzollo, Jean. Shanna's Ballerina Show. Evans, Shane, illus. 2003. 24p. (ps-2). pap. 3.50 (978-0-7868-1758-0(5)) Hyperion Bks. for Children.

—Shanna's Ballerina Show. 2003. (gr. k-3). lib. bdg. 11.25 (978-0-613-68386-9(2)) Tandem Library Bks.

Masurel, Claire. Emily's Ballet Box: A Book & Doll Set. Calitri, Susan, illus. gif. ed. 2001. (Boxed Sets Ser.). 16p. (J). 15.99 (978-0-14-230052-7(7) , Puffin) Penguin Group (USA) Inc.

McKinlay, Penny. Elephants Don't Do Ballet. (Illus.). 25p. (J). pap. (978-0-7112-1130-8(2)) Lincoln, Frances Ltd. GBR. *Dist:* Transition Vendor.

Meyer, Carolyn. Marie, Dancing. 2005. (Illus.). 272p. (YA). (gr. 7). 17.00 (978-0-15-205116-7(3) , Gulliver Bks.) Harcourt Children's Bks.

Mills, Elaine. Marinetta at the Ballet. Mills, Elaine, illus. 2001. (Illus.). 27p. (J). (gr. k-2). pap. 9.99 (978-1-84270-000-6(6)) Andersen GBR. *Dist:* Trafalgar Square Publishing.

Mitchard, Jacquelyn. Starring Prima! The Mouse of the Ballet Jolie. Tusa, Tricia, illus. 2004. 160p. (J). (gr. 3 up). 15.99 (978-0-06-057356-0(2)); 16.89 (978-0-06-057357-7(0)) HarperCollins Pubs.

Moss, Alexandra. Ellie's Chance to Dance, No. 1. 2005. (Royal Ballet School Diaries Ser.: Bk. 1). 144p. (J). (gr. 4-8). mass mkt. 4.99 (978-0-448-43535-0(7) , Grosset & Dunlap) Penguin Group (USA) Inc.

—Lara's Perfect Performance, Vol. 2. 2005. (Royal Ballet School Diaries Ser.: Bk. 2). 144p. (J). (gr. 4-8). mass mkt. 4.99 (978-0-448-43536-7(5) , Grosset & Dunlap) Penguin Group (USA) Inc.

—Sophie's Flight of Fancy, No. 4. 2005. (Royal Ballet School Diaries: No. 4). 144p. (gr. 3-5). mass mkt. 4.99 (978-0-448-43770-5(8) , Grosset & Dunlap) Penguin Group (USA) Inc.

Munoz, Claudio, illus. Dream Dancer. 2002. 32p. (J). (ps-3). 15.95 (978-0-06-000932-8(2)) HarperCollins Pubs.

Napoli, Donna Jo. One Leap Forward. 1999. (Angelwings Ser.: No. 4). (Illus.). 96p. (J). (gr. 2-5). pap. 7.95 (978-0-689-82986-4(8) , Aladdin) Simon & Schuster Children's Publishing.

—One Leap Forward. 1999. (Angelwings Ser.: No. 4). (Illus.). (J). (978-0-606-17907-2(0)) Tandem Library Bks.

Newsome, Jill. Dream Dancer. 2002. (Illus.). 32p. (J). (ps-3). 15.89 (978-0-06-001322-6(2)) HarperCollins Pubs.

Ormerod, Jan. Ballet Sisters No. 1: The Duckling & the Swan. 2007. (Scholastic Reader Ser.). 32p. (J). (gr. k-2). pap. 5.99 (978-0-439-82281-7(5)) Scholastic, Inc.

Ormerod, Jan. The Newest Dancer. 2008. (Ballet Sisters Ser.: No. 2). 32p. (J). pap. 5.99 (***978-0-439-82282-4(3)***) Scholastic, Inc.

Peters, Stephanie & Hoffmann, E. My First Nutcracker. Bronson, Linda, illus. 2007. 32p. (J). (ps). 16.99 (978-0-525-47687-0(3) , Dutton Juvenile) Penguin Group (USA) Inc.

Piggy Toes Press. Our Ballet Recital. Maddocks, Maria, illus. 2005. 12p. (J). (ps-ps). 12.95 (978-1-58117-425-0(X) , Intervisual/Piggy Toes) Dalmatian Pr.

Pinkwater, Daniel M. Dancing Larry. Pinkwater, Daniel M. & Pinkwater, Jill, illus. 2006. 32p. (J). 16.95 (978-0-7614-5220-1(6)) Cavendish, Marshall Corp.

Rogers, Stan K. Molly Takes Ballet. Cooper, Steve, illus. 2000. 34p. (J). (gr. k-5). pap. 9.95 (978-0-9704665-0-1(1)) Cedar Chest Publishing, Inc.

S. I. Artists Staff, illus. Strawberry Shortcake's Ballet Recital: Sticker Stories. 2005. (Strawberry Shortcake Ser.). 16p. (J). (ps-1). pap. 4.99 (978-0-448-43573-2(X) , Grosset & Dunlap) Penguin Group (USA) Inc.

Scholastic, Inc. Staff. Ballet Party, 8. 1998. (J). 103.60 (978-0-590-95520-1(9)) Scholastic, Inc.

Shulman, Lisa. Over in the Meadow at the Big Ballet. Massini, Sarah, illus. 2007. 32p. (J). (gr. k). 16.99 (978-0-399-24289-2(9)) Penguin Group (USA) Inc.

Shure Ballet Designers Fashion Doll Creativity Set: Incl. Art Materials & Paper Dolls. 1998. (Illus.). 8p. (J). (gr. k up). 9.95 (978-1-58286-552-2(3)) Shure Products, Inc.

Shure Ballet Make-Up Studio Creativity Set: Incl. Art Materials & Paper Dolls. 1998. (Illus.). 12p. (J). (gr. k up). 22.00 (978-1-58286-507-2(8)) Shure Products, Inc.

Shure Cinderella Ballet Backpack Creativity Set: Incl. Art Materials & Paper Dolls. 1998. (Illus.). 8p. (J). (gr. k up). 24.99 (978-1-58286-570-6(1)) Shure Products, Inc.

Shure Cinderella Ballet Jewelry Box Creativity Set: Incl. Art Materials & Paper Dolls. 2nd rev. ed. 1998. (Illus.). 8p. (J). (gr. k up). reprint ed. 15.00 (978-1-58286-540-9(X)) Shure Products, Inc.

Shure Cinderella Ballet Tutu Creativity Set: Incl. Art Materials & Paper Dolls. 1998. (Illus.). 8p. (J). (gr. k up). 29.99 (978-1-58286-580-5(9)) Shure Products, Inc.

Shure Cinderella's Balloon Dance Fashion Doll Creativity Set: Incl. Art Materials & Paper Dolls. 1998. (Illus.). 8p. (J). (gr. k up). 9.95 (978-1-58286-551-5(5)) Shure Products, Inc.

Shure Nutcracker Ballet Creativity Art Set: Incl. Art Materials & Paper Dolls. 1998. (Illus.). 16p. (J). (gr. k up). 30.00 (978-1-58286-503-4(5)) Shure Products, Inc.

Shure Sleeping Beauty Ballet Backpack Creativity Set: Incl. Art Materials & Paper Dolls. 1998. (Illus.). 8p. (J). (gr. k up). 24.99 (978-1-58286-571-3(X)) Shure Products, Inc.

Shure Sugarplum Fairy Ballet Tutu Creativity Set: Incl. Art Materials & Paper Dolls. 1998. (Illus.). 8p. (J). (gr. k up). 29.99 (978-1-58286-582-9(5)) Shure Products, Inc.

Shure Sugarplum Land of Sweets Fashion Doll Creativity Set: Incl. Art Materials & Paper Dolls. 1998. (Illus.). 8p. (J). (gr. k up). 9.95 (978-1-58286-550-8(7)) Shure Products, Inc.

Sis, Peter. Ballerina! 2005. (Illus.). 30p. (J). (ps-ps). bds. 6.99 (978-0-06-075966-7(6) , Harper Festival) HarperCollins Pubs.

—Ballerina! Sis, Peter, illus. 2001. (Illus.). 24p. (J). (ps-1). 15.99 (978-0-688-17944-1(4)) HarperCollins Pubs.

Southgate, Martha. Another Way to Dance. 1998. (978-0-606-12878-0(6)) Tandem Library Bks.

Stadler, Alexander. Lila Bloom. 2004. (Illus.). 40p. (J). 16.00 (978-0-374-34474-0(4) , Farrar, Straus & Giroux (BYR)) Farrar, Straus & Giroux.

Sweeney, Joan. Bijou, Bonbon, & Beau: The Kittens Who Danced for Degas. Wu, Leslie, illus. 2002. 26p. (J). pap. 6.95 (978-0-8118-3486-5(7)) Chronicle Bks. LLC.

Thomassie, Tynia. Mimi's Tutu. Gilchrist, Jan Spivey, illus. 2002. 32p. (J). (gr. k-2). pap. 5.99 (978-0-590-44021-9(7) , Scholastic Pr.) Scholastic, Inc.

—Mimi's Tutu. 2001. (978-0-606-22267-9(7)) Tandem Library Bks.

Ure, Jean. Dazzling Danny. 2003. (Illus.). 96p. (J). pap. 7.99 (978-0-00-713370-3(7)) HarperCollins Pubs. Ltd. GBR. *Dist:* Independent Pubs. Group.

Vail, Rachel. Please, Please, Please. (Friendship Ring Ser.: No. 2). 240p. (J). (gr. 4-8). 1999. pap. 3.99 (978-0-439-08762-9(7)); 1998. pap. 14.95 (978-0-590-00327-8(5)); 1998. pap. 4.99 (978-0-590-37452-1(4)) Scholastic, Inc.

Van Scoyoc, Pam. The Ballerina with Webbed Feet/la Bailarina Palmipeda. Teichman, Diane E., tr. Lewis, R. J., illus. l.t. ed. 2004. (ENG & SPA.). 40p. (J). (gr. k-2). lib. bdg. 16.98 (978-0-9663629-2-3(6)) By Grace Enterprises.

Weeks, Sarah. Ella, of Course! Cushman, Doug, illus. 2007. 32p. (J). (ps). 16.00 (978-0-15-204943-0(6)) Harcourt Trade Pubs.

Willson, Sarah. Up & Away, Reptar! Rillo, Cary, illus. 1999. (Ready-to-Read Ser.). 32p. (J). (ps-3). pap. 3.99 (978-0-689-82631-3(1) , 076714003996, Simon Spotlight/Nickelodeon) Simon & Schuster Children's Publishing.

Yep, Laurence. The Amah. 2001. (gr. 7-12). lib. bdg. 14.15 (978-0-613-35896-5(1)) Tandem Library Bks.

—Angelfish. 2001. 1p. (J). (gr. 5 up). 16.99 (978-0-399-23041-7(6) , Putnam Juvenile) Penguin Group (USA) Inc.

Young, Amy. Belinda Begins Ballet. Young, Amy, illus. 2008. 32p. (J). (ps). 15.99 (***978-0-670-06244-7(8)*** , Viking Juvenile) Penguin Group (USA) Inc.

Young, Amy. Belinda, the Ballerina. 2003. (Illus.). 32p. (J). (gr. k-2). 15.99 (978-0-670-03549-6(1) , Viking Juvenile) Penguin Group (USA) Inc.

Ziefert, Harriet & Ehrlich, H. M. Dancing Class. Rader, Laura, illus. 2001. 32p. (J). (ps-1). pap. 12.95 (978-0-531-30300-9(4) , Orchard Bks.) Scholastic, Inc.

BALLETS—STORIES, PLOTS, ETC.

Barber, Antonia. Tales from the Ballet. 1999. (gr. 3-6). lib. bdg. 21.05 (978-0-613-88636-9(4)) Tandem Library Bks.

Dewhurst, Carin. The Nutcracker. Howland, Naomi, illus. 2006. 24p. (J). (gr. 4-8). reprint ed. 20.00 (978-1-4223-5524-4(1)) DIANE Publishing Co.

Frith, Margaret. Hooray for Ballet! 2003. (gr. k-3). lib. bdg. 14.15 (978-0-613-61628-7(6)) Tandem Library Bks.

Frith, Margaret & Haley, Amanda. Hooray for Ballet! 2003. (Smart about Art Ser.). (Illus.). 32p. (J). (gr. 1-4). pap. 5.99 (978-0-448-42884-0(9) , Grosset & Dunlap) Penguin Group (USA) Inc.

Geras, Adele & Clark, Emma Chichester. Giselle. 2001. (Magic of Ballet Ser.). (Illus.). 32p. (J). (gr. 1-4). 10.95 (978-1-86233-226-3(6)) David & Charles Children's Bks. GBR. *Dist:* Sterling Publishing Co., Inc.

—Sleeping Beauty. 2001. (Magic of Ballet Ser.). (Illus.). 32p. (J). (gr. 1-4). 10.95 (978-1-86233-246-1(0)) David & Charles Children's Bks. GBR. *Dist:* Sterling Publishing Co., Inc.

—Swan Lake. 2001. (Magic of Ballet Ser.). (Illus.). 32p. (J). (gr. 1-4). 10.95 (978-1-86233-231-7(2)) David & Charles Children's Bks. GBR. *Dist:* Sterling Publishing Co., Inc.

Herman, Mark & Apter, Ronnie, trs. from RUS. Moscow Ballet Great Russian Nutcracker. Fedorov, Valentin, illus. 2003. 32p. (J). (978-0-9743082-0-3(X)) Sports Marketing International, Inc.

Kain, Karen. The Nutcracker. Kupesic, Rajka, illus. 2005. 32p. (J). (ps-7). 18.95 (978-0-88776-696-1(X)) Tundra Bks., Inc./Livres Toundra, Inc. CAN. *Dist:* Random Hse., Inc.

Mahoney, Jean. The Nutcracker Ballet Theatre. Seddon, Viola Anne, illus. 2004. 12p. (J). (gr. k up). 22.99 (978-0-7636-2453-8(5)) Candlewick Pr.

Mahoney, Jean. The Sleeping Beauty Ballet Theatre. Seddon, Viola Anne, illus. 2007. 32p. (J). (gr. 1). 24.99 (***978-0-7636-3467-4(0)***) Candlewick Pr.

Newman, Barbara. The Illustrated Book of Ballet Stories. Tomblin, Gill, illus. 2005. 64p. (J). (ps-7). 19.99 incl. audio compact disk (978-0-7566-1372-3(8)) Dorling Kindersley Publishing, Inc.

Yolen, Jane & Stemple, Heidi. The Barefoot Book of Ballet Stories. Guay, Rebecca, illus. 2004. 96p. (J). 19.99 (978-1-84148-229-3(3)) Barefoot Bks., Inc.

BALLOONS

see also Aeronautics

Balloon Sculpting Made Easy: Learn How to Make Balloon Animals & More. 2nd ed. 2001. cd-rom 9.99 (978-0-9661745-1-9(8)) Conceptions.

The Balloons: First Wave Satellite Individual Title Six-Packs. (Sails Literacy Ser.). 16p. (gr. k up). 27.00 (978-0-7578-6862-7(2)) Rigby Education.

Beak, Nick Huckleberry. Balloon Ideas. 2001. (Illus.). 64p. (gr. 3-7). pap. 6.95 (978-1-84215-479-3(6) , Southwater) Anness Publishing GBR. *Dist:* National Bk. Network.

Bledsoe, Glen & Bledsoe, Karen. Ballooning Adventures. 2000. (Dangerous Adventures Ser.). (Illus.). 48p. (J). (gr. 3-4). lib. bdg. 21.26 (978-0-7368-0574-2(5) , Capstone High-Interest Bks.) Capstone Pr., Inc.

Brighter Vision Publishing Staff. Balloons. 1999. (Stick'n Learn Stories Ser.). (Illus.). (J). (ps-1). pap. 2.50 (978-1-55254-069-5(3)) Brighter Vision Pubns.

Burch, Lynda S. Wicky Wacky Things that Go! Hot Air Balloons. Roberts, MarySue, photos by. 2004. (Illus.). 28p. (J). E-Book 9.95 incl. cd-rom (978-1-933090-08-5(1)) Guardian Angel Publishing, Inc.

Crazy Creatures Balloon Modeling. 2004. (Fun Kits Ser.). (Illus.). 48p. (J). (978-1-84229-732-2(5)) Top That! Publishing PLC.

Harcourt School Publishers Staff. Floating Around the World. 3rd ed. 2002. (Trophies English Language Learners Ser.). (Illus.). pap. 5.10 (978-0-15-327881-5(1)) Harcourt Schl. Pubs.

Hinkler Books Staff. Balloon Animals. 2004. (Illus.). 48p. (J). 6.95 (978-1-86515-644-6(2)) Hinkler Bks. Pty, Ltd. AUS. *Dist:* Penton Overseas, Inc.

Loves, June. Balloons, Kites, Airships & Gliders. 2001. (Flight Ser.). (Illus.). (J). (gr. 5 up). 27.00 (978-0-7910-6563-1(4) , 010302, Chelsea Hse.) Facts On File, Inc.

O'Brien, Joan. Hot Air Balloons Stickers. 2006. 4p. pap. 1.50 (978-0-486-44855-8(X)) Dover Pubns., Inc.

Obrochta, Dale. Faces, Faces, Balloon Faces. 2003. (Illus.). 32p. (YA). (978-0-9728793-0-9(7)) DEO Consulting, Inc.

Outrageous Monster Balloons. 2004. (How 2 Kits Ser.). (Illus.). 48p. (J). (978-1-84229-960-9(3)) Top That! Publishing PLC.

Priceman, Marjorie. Hot Air: The (Mostly) True Story of the First Hot-Air Balloon Ride. Priceman, Marjorie, illus. 2005. (Illus.). 40p. (J). (ps). 16.95 (978-0-689-82642-9(7) , Atheneum) Simon & Schuster Children's Publishing.

Really Cool Balloon Modeling. 2004. (How 2 Kits Ser.). (Illus.). 48p. (J). (978-1-84229-937-1(9)) Top That! Publishing PLC.

Small, B. Crafty Birthday Balloons. 1999. (Illus.). 16p. (978-1-874735-57-1(3)) B Small Publishing.

Thompson, Gare. My Balloon Ride. 2002. (Windows on Literacy Ser.). (Illus.). 24p. (J). (978-0-7922-8501-4(8)) National Geographic Society.

Top That Publishing Staff, ed. Brilliant Balloon Modeling. 2004. (Fun Kits Ser.). (Illus.). 48p. (J). (978-1-84510-247-0(9)) Top That! Publishing PLC.

Tremaine, Jon. Balloons. 2002. 64p. (J). pap. 9.98 (978-0-7525-6286-5(X)) Parragon, Inc.

Warren, Jean. Balloons. Cubley, Kathleen, ed. 1998. (Sticker Book Ser.). (Illus.). 32p. (J). (ps). pap. 3.95 (978-1-57029-211-8(6) , WPH 3701, Totline Pubns.) Schaffer, Frank Pubns.

Whiter, Barbara. Balloon Animals. 2002. 32p. mass mkt. 4.95 (978-0-689-02456-6(8)) Meadowbrook Pr.

Willard, Keith, et al. Ballooning. 2000. (World of Sports Ser.). (Illus.). 32p. (J). (gr. 5 up). lib. bdg. 16.95 (978-1-887068-51-2(1)) Smart Apple Media.

BALLOONS, DIRIGIBLE

see Airships

BALLOONS—FICTION

Alborough, Jez. Balloon. 1999. (Illus.). 30p. (J). pap. 11.00 (978-0-00-664624-2(7)) HarperCollins Pubs. Ltd. GBR. *Dist:* Independent Pubs. Group.

Allen, Quincy. The Outdoor Chums on the Gulf or Rescuin. 2006. 77.99 (***978-1-4280-1998-0(7)***) IndyPublish.com.

Awdry, Wilbert V. James & the Red Balloon. 2005. (Book & CD Ser.). (Illus.). 24p. (J). (ps-2). 9.95 (978-0-375-83026-6(X) , Random Hse. Bks. for Young Readers) Random Hse. Children's Bks.

The Balloon Ride, 6, Pack. (Sails Literacy Ser.). 16p. (gr. k up). 27.00 (978-0-7635-4427-0(2)) Rigby Education.

The Balloon Ride: KinderConcepts Individual Title Six-Packs. (Kinderstarters Ser.). 8p. (ps-1). 21.00 (978-0-7635-8736-9(2)) Rigby Education.

Balloons. Date not set. 5.95 (978-0-89868-343-1(2)) ARO Publishing Co.

Bird, Helen. The Balloon Launch, Level 2. Dimitri, Simona, illus. 2005. (Lightning Readers Ser.). 32p. (J). (gr. k-1). pap., pap. 3.95 (978-0-7696-4220-8(9) , Gingham Dog Pr.) School Specialty Publishing.

—La Suelta de Globos, Level 2. Dimitri, Simona, illus. 2005. (Lightning Readers Ser.). 32p. (J). (gr. k-1). pap., pap. 3.95 (978-0-7696-4240-6(3) , Gingham Dog Pr.) School Specialty Publishing.

Bird/Dimitri, Helen/Simona. The Balloon Launch. 2005. (Illus.). 32p. (J). lib. bdg. 9.00 (***978-1-4242-0887-6(4)***) Fitzgerald Bks.

Bonners, Susan. The Silver Balloon. Bonners, Susan, illus. 1999. (Illus.). 80p. (J). (gr. 2-4). pap. 5.95 (978-0-374-46647-3(5) , Sunburst) Farrar, Straus & Giroux.

Burke, Ellinor Rozecki. Susana Worrywart & the Magical Teddy Bear Balloon. Perciopelo, illus. 2003. 32p. (J). 17.99 (978-0-9741586-3-1(1)) Comfort Tales, LLC.

—Susana Worrywart & the Magical Teddy Bear Balloon: With CD for Relaxation. Perciopelo, illus. 2003. 32p. (J). 27.00 incl. audio compact disk (978-0-9741586-0-0(7)) Comfort Tales, LLC.

Bynum, Janie. Altoona Baboona. 2002. (Illus.). 36p. (J). (ps-2). pap. 7.00 (978-0-15-216404-1(9) , Voyager Bks./Libros Viajeros) Harcourt Children's Bks.

Conboy, Fiona. Mr. Mombo's Balloon Flight. Holmes, Steve, illus. 1998. (J). 15.99 (978-1-884628-62-7(1) , Flying Frog Publishing) Allied Publishing.

Curtis, Jamie Lee. Where Do Balloons Go? An Uplifting Mystery. 2001. (J). 135.60 (978-0-06-623707-7(6)) HarperCollins Pubs.

—Where Do Balloons Go? An Uplifting Mystery. Cornell, Laura, illus. 2000. 36p. (J). (ps-3). 16.89 (978-0-06-027981-3(8)); 16.99 (978-0-06-027980-6(X) , Cotler, Joanna Books) HarperCollins Pubs.

Das, Christina. The Red Spotted Balloon. l.t. ed. 2005. (Illus.). 32p. (J). 15.95 (978-0-9763082-3-2(1) , A JuneOne Production) JuneOne Publishing Hub.

Davis, Daylelynn. Balloon Catcher. 1998. pap. 5.95 (978-0-9652894-3-6(5)) GA Publishing.

Davis, Elena. Where Do the Balloons Go? Jurinich, Anna, illus. 2004. 32p. (ps-3). 16.95 (978-0-9714372-3-4(8)) National Bk. Network.

De Beer, Hans. Little Polar Bear & the Big Balloon. Lanning, Rosemary, tr. from GER. De Beer, Hans, illus. 2006. (Illus.). 22p. (J). (gr. k-4). reprint ed. 16.00 (978-0-7567-9875-8(2)) DIANE Publishing Co.

Dematons, Charlotte. Yellow Balloon. 2004. (Illus.). 32p. (J). 15.95 (978-1-932425-01-7(2) , Lemniscaat) Boyds Mills Pr.

Drake, David. The Great Balloon Adventure. 2002. (Cricket of Dew Drop Dell Ser.). (Illus.). 32p. (J). 3.49 (978-1-885631-62-6(6) , Family Of Man Pr., The) Hutchison, G.F. Pr.

Du Bois, William Pene. Twenty-One Balloons. Du Bois, William Pene, illus. 2005. (Illus.). 180p. (J). lib. bdg. 15.00 (***978-1-4242-2270-4(2)***) Fitzgerald Bks.

du Bois, William Pène, illus. The Twenty-One Balloons. 2005. (Puffin Modern Classics Ser.). 179p. (J). (***978-1-4155-8330-2(7)*** , Puffin) Penguin Group (USA) Inc.

Dubois, William Pene. The Twenty-One Balloons. 2000. (J). pap., tchr. ed., wbk. ed. (978-1-56137-376-5(1)) Novel Units, Inc.

Faine, Edward Allan. The Balloon Galloon. Waites, Joan C., illus. 2001. 24p. (J). (ps-3). pap. 3.95 (978-0-9654651-8-2(7)) IM Pr.

Garber, Linda. My Balloon at the Zoo. Garber, Linda, illus. 2nd l.t. ed. 1999. (Illus.). 21p. (J). (gr. 1-4). spiral bd. 9.95 (978-1-892218-05-6(4)) Murlin Pubns.

Gathorne-Hardy, Jonathan. Jane's Adventures: Jane's Adventures in & Out of the Book, Jane's Adventures on the Island of Peeg, & Jane's Adventures in a Balloon. 2006. (Illus.). 588p. (J). 27.95 (978-1-58567-798-6(1)) Overlook Pr., The.

Gilman, Phoebe. The Balloon Tree. ed. 2004. (J). (gr. k-3). spiral bd. (978-0-616-01650-3(6)) Canadian National Institute for the Blind/Institut National Canadien pour les Aveugles.

—The Balloon Tree. (Tell Me a Story Ser.). (FRE., Illus.). (J). 13.99 (978-0-590-24399-5(3)) Scholastic, Inc.

Gummelt, Donna & Melchiorre, Dondino. I'm All Blown Up. Wall, Randy Hugh, ed. Varela, Juan D., tr. Varela, Juan D., illus. 2006. Tr. of Ya Creci. (SPA.). 34p. (J). 14.95 (978-0-9764798-4-0(2)) Story Store Collection Publishing.

Harcourt School Publishers Staff. The Balloon Popper: Take-Home Book. 2001. (Collections Ser.). (Illus.). (J). (gr. 6). pap. 1.90 (978-0-15-319543-3(6)) Harcourt Schl. Pubs.

Hincher, Theresa B. Baldy the Balloon. 2005. 16p. (J). (ps). per. 13.95 (978-0-933767-06-5(4)) Pex Publishing Co.

Hinkler Books Staff, reader. Barney's Big Balloon. 2004. 32p. (J). 9.99 incl. audio compact disk (978-1-86515-997-3(2)) Hinkler Bks. Pty, Ltd. AUS. *Dist:* Penton Overseas, Inc.

Hooray for Boys & Girls! ed. 2006. (J). 15.95 (978-0-9776837-0-3(2)) West Woods Pr.

Kellogg, Steven. Tallyho Pinkerton. 2002. lib. bdg. 15.30 (978-0-613-43643-4(1)) Tandem Library Bks.

Lillegard, Dee. Balloons, Balloons, Balloons. Pons, Bernadette, illus. 2007. 32p. (J). (ps-1). 16.99 (978-0-525-45940-8(5) , Dutton Juvenile) Penguin Group (USA) Inc.

Masters, Anthony. Hot Air. Perkins, Mike, illus. 2007. (Graphic Trax Ser.). 66p. (J). (gr. 4-8). lib. bdg. 19.93 (978-1-59889-086-0(7)) Stone Arch Bks.

Milgrim, David. See Pip Point. Milgrim, David, illus. 2004. (Adventures of Otto Ser.). (Illus.). 32p. (J). pap. 3.99 (978-0-689-85140-7(5) , Aladdin) Simon & Schuster Children's Publishing.

Nolen, Jerdine. Harvey Potter's Balloon Farm. Buehner, Mark, illus. 1998. 32p. (J). (ps-3). pap. 6.99 (978-0-688-15845-3(5) , Harper Trophy) HarperCollins Pubs.
—Harvey Potter's Balloon Farm. 1998. (J). 12.75 (978-0-606-13100-1(0)) Tandem Library Bks.
Nora, David, Jr. Happy Balloon to You. 2005. 9.00 (978-0-8059-9870-2(5)) Dorrance Publishing Co., Inc.
Orloff, Erica. Balloonatiks: The 1st Goopy, Goofy, Loopy Adventure. 2002. 128p. (J). pap. 5.95 (978-0-9703338-1-0(1) , 174-001) Animagic Entertainment Group, Inc.
Pene Du Bois, William & Pene DuBois, William. The Twenty-One Balloons. Pene Du Bois, William, illus. 2005. (Puffin Modern Classics Ser.). (Illus.). 192p. (J). (ps-7). pap. 5.99 (978-0-14-240330-3(X) , Puffin) Penguin Group (USA) Inc.
Rau, Dana Meachen. Lots of Balloons, Level A. 2001. (Early Reader Ser.). (Illus.). 24p. (J). (gr. k up). lib. bdg. 18.60 (978-0-7565-0117-4(2)) Compass Point Bks.
The Red Balloons: Kindergarten Guided Reading Level B. (On Our Way to English Ser.). (gr. k up). 27.75 (978-0-7578-7008-8(2)) Rigby Education.
Redbank, Tennant. Walk, Don't Walk. Mathieu, Joe, illus. 1999. (Between the Lions Ser.). (J). (ps-k). lib. bdg. 11.99 (978-0-307-36507-1(7) , Golden Bks.) Random Hse. Children's Bks.
Rey, Margret & Rey, H. A. Curious George & the Hot Air Balloon. 1998. (Curious George Ser.). (Illus.). 24p. (J). (gr. k-3). tchr. ed. 12.95 (978-0-395-91918-7(5)) Houghton Mifflin Co. Trade & Reference Div.
Rigby Education Staff. A Job for Clown. (Sails Literacy Ser.). (Illus.). 16p. (gr. 1-2). 27.00 (978-0-7635-9907-2(7) , 699077C99) Rigby Education.
Robbins, Sandra. No Balloons Today: A Zoo Story. Garzon, Alfredo, illus. 2001. 32p. (J). (ps-3). pap. 11.95 incl. audio (978-1-882601-29-5(7)); pap. 6.95 (978-1-882601-30-1(0)) See-More's Workshop.
Rogers, Alan. Rhino Rouge. 2000. (FRE., Illus.). 16p. (J). (ps-k). 5.95 (978-1-58728-174-7(0) , Two Can Publishing) T&N Children's Publishing.
Ross, Dev. We Both Read-Frank & the Balloon. Reinhart, Larry, illus. 2008. (We Both Read Ser.). 44p. (J). 7.99 (***978-1-60115-011-0(3));*** pap. 3.99 (***978-1-60115-012-7(1))*** Treasure Bay, Inc.
Rozek, Kathy. Rudy & the Magical Twin Balloons. 2002. 32p. (J). 15.95 (978-0-9720871-0-0(9)) Brookline Merrimac Pubs.
Rylant, Cynthia. The Case of the Troublesome Turtle. Karas, G. Brian, illus. 2003. (High-Rise Private Eyes Ser.: No. 4). (J). (gr. k-3). 25.95 incl. audio (978-1-59112-202-9(3)) Live Oak Media.
Sakai, Komako. Emily's Balloon. 2006. (Illus.). 44p. (J). 14.95 (978-0-8118-5219-7(9)) Chronicle Bks. LLC.
Sandhaus, Ellen. The Runaway Balloon (El Globo Que Se Escapo) Blanco, Osvaldo J., tr. unabr. ed. 1999. (SPA & ENG., Illus.). 24p. (J). (gr. k-4). pap. 4.95 (978-1-893266-01-8(X)) Sandhaus, Paul Assocs., Inc.
—Where Do Lost Balloons Go? (Adonde Van los Globos Perdidos?) Blanco, Osvaldo J., tr. unabr. ed. 1999. (ENG & SPA., Illus.). 24p. (J). (gr. k-4). pap. 4.95 (978-1-893266-00-1(1)) Sandhaus, Paul Assocs., Inc.
Scholastic, Inc. Staff. Balloon Beasts, 1. 1999. (Illus.). (J). (gr. 3-7). 6.95 (978-0-590-66240-6(6)) Scholastic, Inc.
Smith, Alexander McCall. Max & Maddy & the Bursting Balloons Mystery. Pamintuan, Macky, illus. 2007. 128p. (J). (gr. 2-4). 9.95 (978-1-59990-035-3(1) , Bloomsbury Children) Bloomsbury Publishing.
Stamper, Judith Bauer. Up, up, & Away! Ramsey, Marcy Dunn, illus. 2000. (Scholastic At-Home Phonics Reading Program Ser.: Vol. 55). 24p. (J). (978-0-590-68857-4(X)) Scholastic, Inc.
Van Leeuwen, Jean. The Amazing Air Balloon: To Soar Like a Bird. Ventura, Marco, illus. 2003. 32p. (J). (gr. k). 16.99 (978-0-8037-2258-3(3) , Dial) Penguin Group (USA) Inc.
Weitzman, Jacqueline Preiss. You Can't Take a Balloon into the Metropolitan Museum. Bonnell, J., ed. Glasser, Robin Preiss, illus. 2001. 40p. (J). (ps-3). pap. 6.99 (978-0-14-056816-5(6) , Puffin) Penguin Group (USA) Inc.
—You Can't Take a Balloon into the Metropolitan Museum. Glasser, Robin, illus. 1998. 40p. (J). (gr. k-3). 18.99 (978-0-8037-2301-6(6) , Dial) Penguin Group (USA) Inc.
—You Can't Take a Balloon into the Metropolitan Museum. 2001. (Illus.). (J). (978-0-606-21004-1(0)); 2000. lib. bdg. 15.30 (978-0-613-33742-7(5)) Tandem Library Bks.
—You Can't Take a Balloon into the Museum of Fine Arts. Glasser, Robin Preiss, illus. 2002. 40p. (J). (gr. k-4). 18.99 (978-0-8037-2570-6(1) , Dial) Penguin Group (USA) Inc.
—You Can't Take a Balloon into the National Gallery. Glasser, Robin Preiss, illus. 2002. 40p. (J). pap. 7.99 (978-0-14-230131-9(0) , Puffin) Penguin Group (USA) Inc.
—You Can't Take a Balloon into the National Gallery. 2002. (ps-2). lib. bdg. 16.45 (978-0-613-83550-3(6)) Tandem Library Bks.
Wood, Audrey. Balloonia. Wood, Audrey, illus. 2005. (Illus.). 32p. (J). pap. 7.99 (978-1-904550-49-5(5)) Child's Play-International.
Ziefert, Harriet. Buzzy's Balloon. Bolam, Emily, illus. 2007. 28p. (J). 9.95 (978-1-59354-603-8(3)) Blue Apple Bks.

BALLOT

see Elections

BALLROOM DANCING

Freese, Joan. Ballroom Dancing. 2008. (J). (***978-1-4296-0123-8(X))*** Capstone Pr., Inc.
Gillis, Jennifer Blizin. Ballroom Dancing for Fun! 2007. (J). lib. bdg. (***978-0-7565-3285-7(X))*** Compass Point Bks.

BALTIMORE (MD.)

Dell, Pamela. The National Anthem. 2004. (Let's See Library). (Illus.). 24p. (J). (gr. 1 up). lib. bdg. 19.93 (978-0-7565-0619-3(0)) Compass Point Bks.
Ingram, Scott. The Writing of "The Star-Spangled Banner" 2004. (Landmark Events in American History Ser.). (Illus.). 48p. (J). (gr. 5 up). pap. 11.95 (978-0-8368-5418-3(7)); lib. bdg. 30.00 (978-0-8368-5390-2(3)) Stevens, Gareth Inc. (World Almanac Library).
Landau, Elaine. The National Anthem. 2007. (True Bks.). (Illus.). 48p. (J). (gr. 3-5). lib. bdg. 26.00 (***978-0-531-12633-2(1)*** , Children's Pr.) Scholastic Library Publishing.
Marsh, Carole. The Mystery of Biltmore House. 2002. (Illus.). 160p. (J). (gr. 2-8). pap. 5.95 (978-0-635-01347-7(9) , 13479) Gallopade International.
Pingry, Patricia. O Little Town of Bethlehem. 2005. (Illus.). 16p. (J). bds. 12.99 (978-0-8249-6566-2(3)) Ideals Pubns.

BALTIMORE (MD.)—FICTION

Bode, N. E. The Slippery Map. 2007. 288p. (J). lib. bdg. 17.89 (***978-0-06-079109-4(8))*** HarperCollins Pubs.
—The Slippery Map. Dorman, Brandon, illus. 2007. 288p. (J). (gr. 3-7). 16.99 (***978-0-06-079108-7(X))*** HarperCollins Pubs.
Chronicle Books LLC Staff. Football Heroes. 2008. (J). 14.95 (978-0-8118-5661-4(5)) Chronicle Bks. LLC.
Dans, Peter E. Perry's Baltimore Adventure: A Bird's-Eye View of Charm City. Harrell, Kim, illus. 2007. (J). 14.95 (***978-1-933822-08-2(2))*** Camino Bks., Inc.
—Perry's Baltimore Adventure: A Bird's-Eye View of Charm City. Harrell, Kim, illus. 2003. 30p. (J). 11.95 (978-0-87033-540-2(5) , Tidewater Pubs.) Cornell Maritime Pr., Inc.
Fuqua, Jonathon Scott. Reappearance of Sam Webber. 1999. (Illus.). 232p. (YA). pap. 23.95 (978-1-890862-03-9(7)) Bancroft Pr.
—The Reappearance of Sam Webber. 2001. (Illus.). 288p. (J). (gr. 5). reprint ed. pap. 9.99 (978-0-7636-1424-9(6)) Candlewick Pr.
Hahn, Mary Downing. Anna All Year Round. deGroat, Diane, illus. 2001. 144p. (J). (gr. 4-7). pap. 4.95 (978-0-380-73317-0(X) , Harper Trophy) HarperCollins Pubs.
—Anna All Year Round. 2001. (Illus.). (J). (978-0-606-21037-9(7)) Tandem Library Bks.
—Anna All Year Round. deGroat, Diane, illus. 1999. 144p. (J). (gr. 4-6). tchr. ed. 15.00 (978-0-395-86975-8(7) , Clarion Bks.) Houghton Mifflin Co. Trade & Reference Div.
Howard, Elizabeth Fitzgerald. Aunt Flossie's Hats (and Crab Cakes Later) Ransome, James E., illus. 10th anniv. ed. 2001. 40p. (J). (gr. k-3). tchr. ed. 16.00 (978-0-618-12038-3(6) , Clarion Bks.) Houghton Mifflin Co. Trade & Reference Div.
Jackson, Kamichi. You're Too Much, Reggie Brown. Goldberg, Jeff A., illus. l.t. ed. 2000. 110p. (J). (gr. 2-5). pap. 5.95 (978-0-615-11287-9(0)) Pen Poised Pr.
Klam, Cheryl. The Pretty One. 2008. 288p. (YA). (gr. 7). pap. 9.99 (***978-0-385-73373-1(9));*** lib. bdg. 12.99 (***978-0-385-90388-2(X))*** Random Hse. Children's Bks. (Delacorte Bks. for Young Readers).
Reeder, Carolyn. Before the Creeks Ran Red. 2003. 384p. (J). (gr. 5 up). 16.99 (978-0-06-623615-5(0)) HarperCollins Pubs.
Sternberg, Libby. Finding the Forger. 2004. 192p. (YA). 19.95 (978-1-890862-32-9(0)); pap. 14.95 (978-1-890862-37-4(1)) Bancroft Pr.
—Finding the Forger. 2006. (YA). mass mkt. 5.99 (978-0-8439-5503-3(1) , SMOOCH) Dorchester Publishing Co., Inc.

BALTIMORE ORIOLES (BASEBALL TEAM)

Nichols, John. Baltimore Orioles. 2002. (Baseball Ser.). (Illus.). 32p. (J). (978-1-58341-201-5(8) , Creative Education) Creative Co., The.
—The History of the Baltimore Orioles. 2002. (Illus.). 32p. (J). pap. 5.95 (978-0-89812-335-7(6) , Creative Paperbacks) Creative Co., The.
Omoth, Tyler. The Story of the Baltimore Orioles. 2007. (J). (***978-1-58341-480-4(0)*** , Creative Education) Creative Co., The.
Pietrusza, David. The Baltimore Orioles Baseball Team. 2000. (Great Sports Teams Ser.). (Illus.). 48p. (YA). (gr. 4-10). lib. bdg. 23.93 (978-0-7660-1283-7(2)) Enslow Pubs., Inc.
Rambeck, Richard. The History of the Baltimore Orioles. 1998. (Baseball, the Great American Game Ser.). (Illus.). 32p. (YA). (gr. 3-12). pap. 21.30 (978-0-88682-899-8(6) , Creative Education) Creative Co., The.
Ripken, Cal. The Longest Season: The Story of the Orioles' 1988 Losing Streak. Mazellan, Ron, illus. 2007. 32p. (J). (gr. 1). 16.99 (978-0-399-24492-6(1) , Philomel) Penguin Group (USA) Inc.
Ripken, Cal, Jr. & Bryan, Mike. Cal Ripken, Jr. Play Ball! 1999. (Puffin Easy-to-Read Ser.). (J). 10.79 (978-0-606-16825-0(7)) Tandem Library Bks.
Stewart, Mark. The Baltimore Orioles. 2007. (Team Spirit Ser.). (Illus.). 48p. (J). lib. bdg. 25.27 (***978-1-59953-092-5(9))*** Norwood Hse. Pr.
Young, Robert. A Personal Tour of Camden Yards. 1999. (How It Was Ser.). (Illus.). 64p. (J). (gr. 4-6). lib. bdg. (978-0-8225-3578-2(5) , Lerner Pubns.) Lerner Publishing Group.

BAMBI (FICTITIOUS CHARACTER)—FICTION

Bambi: A Little Spring Shower. unabr. ed. Date not set. (My First Read Along Ser.). (Illus.). 18p. (J). 7.99 incl. audio (978-1-55723-749-1(2)) Walt Disney Records.
Cooke, Marjorie Benton. Bambi. 2004. reprint ed. pap. 27.95 (978-1-4191-0885-3(9)); pap. 1.99 (978-1-4192-0885-0(3)) Kessinger Publishing, LLC.
Dalmatian Press Staff. Disney Bambi. rev. ed. 2006. 72p. (J). 9.99 (978-1-4037-2186-0(6)) Dalmatian Pr.
Dalmatian Press Staff, ed. Bambi. rev. ed. 2006. 24p. pap. 3.50 (978-1-4037-2889-0(5)) Dalmatian Pr.
Disney Staff. Bambi. (FRE.). 96p. (J). (gr. k-5). pap. 9.95 (978-0-7859-8850-2(5)) French & European Pubns., Inc.
Mouse Works Staff. The Jungle Book/Bambi, 2 vols. 75th anniv. ed. 1998. (978-0-7364-0090-9(7)) Mouse Works.
Random House Disney Staff. Bambi. (FRE.). (J). (gr. 3-8). 13.95 (978-0-7859-0613-1(4) , S26622) French & European Pubns., Inc.
—Bambi. 2001. (978-84-305-7629-6(0)) Lectorum Pubns., Inc.
—Bambi. unabr. ed. (Read-Along Ser.). (J). 7.99 incl. audio (978-1-55723-008-9(0)) Walt Disney Records.
Salten, Felix. Bambi - Life in the Woods. (J). 20.95 (978-0-8488-1467-0(3)) Amereon LTD.
Walt Disney's Bambi. 2002. (J). pap. (978-0-9720651-0-8(5)) Story Reader, Inc.

BANANA

Bananas: From Farm to Home Set E, 6 vols. (Phonics Readers Ser.). (gr. k-2). 28.95 (978-0-7368-4068-2(0)) Red Brick Learning.
Bananas on My Table: Kindergarten Guided Reading Level B. (On Our Way to English Ser.). (gr. k up). 27.75 (978-0-7578-7015-6(5)) Rigby Education.
Blue Bananas. 2005. (J). (978-1-59564-735-1(X)) Steps To Literacy, LLC.
Farmer, Jacqueline. Bananas! 1999. (gr. k-3). lib. bdg. 15.25 (978-0-613-24034-5(0)) Tandem Library Bks.
Gleason, Carrie & Eagen, Rachel. The Biography of Bananas. 2005. (How Did That Get Here? Ser.). (Illus.). 32p. (J). (gr. 3-9). pap. (978-0-7787-2483-4(2)); pap. (978-0-7787-2519-0(7)) Crabtree Publishing Co.
Landau, Elaine. Bananas. 1999. (True Bks.). (Illus.). 48p. (J). (gr. 3-5). 25.00 (978-0-516-21025-4(4) , Children's Pr.) Scholastic Library Publishing.
—Bananas. 1999. (gr. 3-6). lib. bdg. 15.25 (978-0-613-37282-4(4)) Tandem Library Bks.
Spilsbury, Louise. Bananas. (Food Ser.). 32p. pap. 6.95 (978-1-4034-4046-4(8)); 2003. (Illus.). (J). lib. bdg. 22.79 (978-1-58810-615-5(2)) Heinemann Library.
—El Platano. 2003. (Alimentos Ser.).Tr. of Bananas. (SPA & ENG., Illus.). 32p. (J). lib. bdg. 22.79 (978-1-4034-3734-1(3)) Heinemann Library.
—El Platano. 2003. Tr. of Bananas. (SPA.). (gr. k-3). lib. bdg. 14.75 (978-0-613-67113-2(9)) Tandem Library Bks.
—El Platano. 2003. (Alimentos Ser.). (ENG & SPA.). 32p. (J). pap. 6.50 (978-1-4034-3740-2(8)) Heinemann Library.

BANDITS

see Robbers and Outlaws

BANDMASTERS

see Conductors (Music)

BANDS (MUSIC)

Band: Individual Title Six-Packs. (On Deck Ser.). 24p. (gr. 4-5). 35.00 (978-0-7578-1020-6(9)) Rigby Education.
Banda: Individual Title Six-Packs. (On Deck en Espanol Ser.).Tr. of Band. (SPA.). 24p. (gr. 4-5). 35.00 (978-0-7578-6399-8(X)) Rigby Education.
Bullock, Jack & Maiello, Anthony. Belwin 21st Century Band Method, Vol. 3. 1999. (J). (gr. 3). 10.95 incl. audio compact disk (978-0-7692-9349-3(2) , Warner Bros. Pubns.) Alfred Publishing Co., Inc.
—Belwin 21st Century Band Method: Combo Percussion, Level 2. 1999. 64p. (J). (gr. 2). 8.95 (978-0-7692-8631-0(3) , Warner Bros. Pubns.) Alfred Publishing Co., Inc.
Clo, David. You're in the Band Bk. 2: Unplugged. l.t. ed. 2001. 32p. (YA). (978-0-87718-085-2(7)) Willis Music Co.
Emmer, Rae. Band. 2002. (Reading Power Ser.). (Illus.). 24p. (J). (gr. 1). lib. bdg. 17.25 (978-0-8239-5969-3(4) , PowerKids Pr.) Rosen Publishing Group, Inc., The.
Farmer, Henry George. Memoirs of the Royal Artillery Band. 2001. (YA). reprint ed. 150.00 (978-0-7222-5179-9(3)) Library Reprints, Inc.
Garty, Judy. Marching Band Competition. 2003. (Let's Go Team Ser.). (Illus.). 64p. (J). (gr. 5 up). lib. bdg. (978-1-59084-539-4(0)) Mason Crest Pubs.
Harvey, M. A. Wannabes Pop Diva: For Girls Who Know What They Want to Be. 2004. (Illus.). 128p. (J). pap. (978-1-84458-049-1(0)) Chrysalis Children's Bks.
Hoggarth, Janet E. Create Your Own Girl Band. 2001. (Illus.). 160p. (J). pap. 4.99 (978-0-439-29651-9(X) , Chicken Hse., The) Scholastic, Inc.
Hooks, Kristine. School Band. 2001. (After School Ser.). (Illus.). 48p. (YA). (gr. 7-12). 23.00 (978-0-516-23153-2(7) , Children's Pr.) Scholastic Library Publishing.
—School Band. 2001. (High Interest Bks.). (Illus.). 48p. (YA). (gr. 7-12). pap. 6.95 (978-0-516-29557-2(8) , Children's Pr.) Scholastic Library Publishing.
McCarraher, James. The Sailor Story: A Glass of Champagne: the Official Sailor Story. 2nd rev. ed. 2005. (Illus.). 384p. per. 22.99 (978-1-905363-30-8(3) , Exposure Publishing) Meadow Bks. GBR. *Dist:* Ingram Bk. Co.
Miller, George J. The Military Band. 2001. 106p. (YA). reprint ed. 88.00 (978-0-7222-5878-1(X)) Library Reprints, Inc.
Sloan, Karyn. Techniques of Color Guard. 2003. (Let's Go Team Ser.). (Illus.). 64p. (J). (gr. 5 up). lib. bdg. (978-1-59084-536-3(6)) Mason Crest Pubs.
Techniques of Marching Bands. (Illus.). 64p. (YA). (gr. 5-9). lib. bdg. (978-1-59084-538-7(2)) Mason Crest Pubs.
Usilton, Theresa A. Let's Go team: Cheer, Dance, & March, 12 vols., Set. 2003. (Let's Go Team Ser.). (Illus.). 64p. (YA). (gr. 5 up). lib. bdg. (978-1-59084-529-5(3)) Mason Crest Pubs.

BANDS (MUSIC)—FICTION

Anderson, Peggy Perry. Chuck's Band. 2008. 32p. (J). 16.00 (***978-0-618-96506-9(8))*** Houghton Mifflin Co.
Arena, Felice & Kettle, Phil. Rock Star. Gordon, Gus, illus. 2004. (J). pap. (978-1-59336-368-0(0)) Mondo Publishing.
Arterburn, Stephen & Hunt, Angela Elwell. Taz. 2004. (Young Believer on Tour Ser.). (J). pap. 3.99 (978-0-8423-8340-0(9)) Tyndale Hse. Pubs.
Benator, Eileen. A Marching Band for Bears. Benator, Seth, illus. 2004. 32p. (J). lib. bdg. 15.95 (978-0-9748478-5-6(2)) Lion's Tale Press, L.L.C.
Bernstein, Margery. Stop That Noise! Handelman, Dorothy, photos by. 1999. (Real Kids Readers Ser.). (Illus.). 48p. (gr. 1-3). lib. bdg. 18.90 (978-0-7613-2060-9(1)); 32p. (J). (gr. 2-4). pap. 4.99 (978-0-7613-2085-2(7)) Lerner Publishing Group. (Millbrook Pr.).
—Stop That Noise! 1999. (J). (978-0-606-19174-6(7)); (gr. 3-6). lib. bdg. 11.80 (978-0-613-16851-9(8)) Tandem Library Bks.
Carlson, Melody. Road Trip, No. 7. 2003. (Diary of a Teenage Girl Ser.). 304p. pap. 12.99 (978-1-59052-142-7(0) , Multnomah) WaterBrook Pr.
—Sold Out. 2003. (gr. 7-12). lib. bdg. 22.25 (978-0-613-86368-1(2)) Tandem Library Bks.
—Sold Out: Diary Number 6. 2003. (Diary of a Teenage Girl Series, Book Six Ser.). 288p. pap. 12.99 (978-1-59052-141-0(2) , Multnomah) WaterBrook Pr.
Carlson, Nancy. Loudmouth George & the Cornet. rev. ed. 2004. (Carolrhoda Picture Books Ser.). (Illus.). 32p. (J). (gr. k-2). pap. 6.95 (978-1-57505-725-5(5)) Lerner Publishing Group.
Coxe, Molly. Fox Trot. 1999. (Road to Reading Ser.). (J). lib. bdg. (978-0-03-074629-1(9) , Saunders) Elsevier - Health Sciences Division.
Curry, Kenneth. Fuzzy & the All Bear Band. 2007. (Illus.). 22p. (J). 10.95 (***978-0-9798364-8-0(4))*** Curry Brothers Publishing.
Denman, K. L. Battle of the Bands. 2006. (Orca Soundings Ser.). 112p. (YA). (gr. 7 up). pap. 8.95 (978-1-55143-540-4(3)); lib. bdg. 14.95 (978-1-55143-674-6(4)) Orca Bk. Pubs. USA.
deRubertis, Barbara. Bouncy Mouse. Cockrille, Eva V., illus. 1998. (Let's Read Together Ser.). 32p. (J). (ps-3). pap. 4.95 (978-1-57565-043-2(6)) Kane Pr., The.
Dessen, Sarah. This Lullaby. 2002. 304p. (J). 16.99 (978-0-670-03530-4(0) , Viking Juvenile) Penguin Group (USA) Inc.
Dodd, Quentin. The Princess of Neptune. 2004. 224p. (J). 17.00 (978-0-374-36119-8(3) , Farrar, Straus & Giroux (BYR)) Farrar, Straus & Giroux.
Donahue, Jill L. The Zoo Band. 2007. (Illus.). 24p. (J). (***978-1-4048-2381-5(6))*** Picture Window Bks.
—The Zoo Band. Eroglu, Aysin D., illus. 2006. 24p. (J). (***978-1-4048-3165-0(7))*** Picture Window Bks.
Driggs, Scout. Pony Pop Stars. Fletcher, Lynn, illus. 2005. (J). (***978-1-4156-1609-3(4)*** , Harper Festival) HarperCollins Pubs.
Dunlap, Maggie, illus. The Four Dog Blues Band, or, How Chester, Boy, Dog in the Fog, & Diva Took the Big City by Storm. 2007. (J). (***978-1-887422-13-0(7))*** Mississippi Museum of Art.
Ellis, Kathryn. Joey Jeremiah. 2006. (Degrassi Junior High Ser.). 184p. (YA). (gr. 5-10). 7.95 (978-1-55028-924-4(1)) Lorimer, James & Co., Ltd., Pubs. CAN. *Dist:* Casemate Pubs. & Bk. Distributors, LLC.
G Studios & Crouch, Cheryl. Double-Booked. 2007. (Chosen Girls' Ser.). 144p. (J). pap. 6.99 (978-0-310-71268-8(8)) Zonderkidz.
—Solo Act. 2007. (Chosen Girls' Ser.). 144p. (J). pap. 6.99 (978-0-310-71270-1(X)) Zonderkidz.
—Unplugged. 2007. (Chosen Girls' Ser.). 144p. (J). pap. 6.99 (978-0-310-71269-5(6)) Zonderkidz.
Garfinkle, Debra. The Band: Trading Guys: Trading Guys. 2007. 256p. (YA). (gr. 12). pap. 9.99 (***978-0-425-21513-5(X)*** , Berkley Trade) Penguin Group (USA) Inc.
Gershenson, Harold P. Freddy Flamingo & the Kindertown Five. Mills, Christopher, illus. 2005. 27p. (J). (978-1-58987-070-3(0)) Kindermusik International.
Harcourt School Publishers Staff. The Bang-on-a-Can Band. 3rd ed. 2002. (Trophies English Language Learners Ser.). (Illus.). pap. 5.10 (978-0-15-327871-6(4)) Harcourt Schl. Pubs.
Harranth, Wolf. The Flute Concert. Candea, Romulus, illus. 1998. Tr. of Flotenkonzert. 32p. (J). (ps-3). 23.69 (978-1-56711-803-2(8) , Blackbirch Pr., Inc.) Thomson Gale.
Hillerman, Tony. Buster Mesquite's Cowboy Band. Franklin, Ernest, illus. 2001. 32p. (J). 19.95 (978-0-914001-11-9(6)) Sidewinder Publishing LLC.
Hoobler, Dorothy & Hoobler, Thomas. The 1950's: Music. Hoffman, Robin, illus. 2001. (Century Kids Ser.). 160p. (J). (gr. 5-8). lib. bdg. 22.90 (978-0-7613-1605-3(1) , Twenty-First Century Bks.) Lerner Publishing Group.
Hurd, Thacher. Mama Don't Allow. Hurd, Thacher, illus. 2001. (Illus.). pap. 33.95 incl. audio (978-0-87499-745-3(3)); pap. 35.95 incl. audio compact disk (978-1-59112-605-8(3)); (J). pap. 18.95 incl. audio compact disk (978-1-59112-135-0(3)) Live Oak Media.
Johnson, Angela. Violet's Music. Huliska-Beith, Laura, illus. 2004. 32p. (J). (ps-3). 16.99 (978-0-8037-2740-3(2) , Dial) Penguin Group (USA) Inc.
Korman, Gordon. Born to Rock. 2008. 272p. pap. 8.99 (***978-0-7868-0921-9(3))*** Hyperion Bks. for Children.
London, Jonathan. Froggy Plays in the Band. Remkiewicz, Frank, illus. (Froggy Ser.). 32p. (J). 2004. pap. 5.99 (978-0-14-240051-7(3) , Puffin); 2002. 15.99 (978-0-670-03532-8(7) , Viking Juvenile) Penguin Group (USA) Inc.

A B

Lurie, April. The Latent Powers of Dylan Fontaine. 2008. 224p. (YA). (gr. 9). 15.99 (***978-0-385-73125-6(6)*** , Delacorte Bks. for Young Readers) Random Hse. Children's Bks.

Millman, M. C. Cheery Bim Band No. 7: Stage Fright. Frank, Connie, illus. (Cheery Bim Band Ser.: Vol. 7). 143p. (J). (gr. 5-6). 13.95 (978-1-56062-272-7(5) , CJR148H) CIS Communications, Inc.

Mitchell, Robin & Steedman, Judith. Sunny. 2003. (Illus.). 40p. 15.95 (978-0-9688768-5-5(4)) Simply Read Bks. CAN. *Dist:* Perseus Distribution.

Moss, Lloyd. Our Marching Band. Bluthenthal, Diana Cain, illus. 2001. 1p. (J). (ps-3). 15.99 (978-0-399-23335-7(0) , Putnam Juvenile) Penguin Group (USA) Inc.

Nelson, Blake. Rock Star, Superstar. 2004. 224p. (J). (gr. 7). 16.99 (978-0-670-05933-1(1) , Viking Juvenile) Penguin Group (USA) Inc.

—Rock Star Superstar Blake Nelson. 2006. 256p. (YA). (gr. 7). reprint ed. pap. 6.99 (978-0-14-240574-1(4) , Puffin) Penguin Group (USA) Inc.

Norman, Tony. Nervous. Savage, Paul, illus. 2006. 40p. (J). (gr. 2-3). lib. bdg. (978-1-59889-018-1(2)) Stone Arch Bks.

Nygaard, Elizabeth. Snake Alley Band. 1999. (978-0-606-16731-4(5)) Tandem Library Bks.

Petrucha, Stefan & Pendleton, Thomas. Torn. 2007. (Wicked Dead Ser.: No. 2). 224p. (YA). (gr. 7 up). pap. 7.99 (***978-0-06-113850-8(9)*** , HarperTeen) HarperCollins Pubs.

Pinkwater, Daniel M. Rainy Morning. Pinkwater, Jill, illus. 1999. (Pinkwater Ser.: Vol. 1). 32p. (J). (gr. k-3). 16.00 (978-0-689-81143-2(8) , Atheneum) Simon & Schuster Children's Publishing.

Piper, Watty. The Little Engine That Could Saves the Thanksgiving Day Parade. Ong, Cristina, illus. 2002. (Reading Railroad Bks.). 32p. (J). pap. 3.49 (978-0-448-42861-1(X) , Grosset & Dunlap) Penguin Group (USA) Inc.

Schaap, Martine & De Wolf, Alex. Mop's Backyard Concert. 2003. (Mop & Family Ser.). (Illus.). 32p. (J). (ps-3). 12.95 (978-1-57768-892-1(9) , Cricket) School Specialty Publishing.

Scholastic, Inc. Staff. Rock & Bop. 2007. (Doodlebops Ser.). 16p. (J). pap. 4.99 (***978-0-545-00059-8(9)***) Scholastic, Inc.

Steele, Michael Anthony. Battle of the Bands, Bk. 2. 2008. (Naked Brothers Band Ser.). 96p. (J). pap. 4.99 (***978-0-545-03921-5(5)***) Scholastic, Inc.

Stuchner, Joan Betty. The Kugel Valley Klezmer Band. Row, Richard, illus. 2005. 30p. (J). (gr. 2-6). reprint ed. 16.00 (978-0-7567-8605-2(3)) DIANE Publishing Co.

—The Kugel Valley Klezmer Band. Bow, Richard, illus. 2001. 32p. (J). (ps-3). 15.95 (978-1-56656-430-4(1) , Crocodile Bks.) Interlink Publishing Group, Inc.

Tarlow, Ellen. Beat It! Arroyo, Fian, illus. 2002. 16p. (J). (978-0-439-35084-6(0)) Scholastic, Inc.

Westerfeld, Scott. The Last Days. 2007. 304p. (YA). (gr. 9-12). pap. 8.99 (978-1-59514-128-6(6) , Razorbill) Penguin Group (USA) Inc.

Weyn, Suzanne & Gonzalez, Diana. South Beach Sizzle. 2005. 249p. (YA). (gr. 9-12). per. 14.45 (978-1-4176-6059-9(7)) Tandem Library Bks.

Wilson, Jacqueline. Mr. Cool. Lewis, Stephen, illus. 2004. (I Am Reading Ser.). 48p. (J). (gr. 1-3). pap. 3.95 (978-0-7534-5822-8(5) , Kingfisher) Houghton Mifflin Co. Trade & Reference Div.

Yolen, Jane & Stemple, Adam. Pay the Piper: A Rock 'n' Roll Fairy Tale. 2006. 192p. (J). 5.99 (978-0-7653-5041-1(6) , Starscape) Doherty, Tom Assocs., LLC.

BANGLADESH

Barker, Amanda. Bangladesh. 1998. (Worldfocus Ser.). (Illus.). 32p. (J). (978-1-57572-031-9(0)) Heinemann Library.

—Bangladesh. (World Focus Ser.). (Illus.). 32p. pap. 3.99 (978-0-431-07257-9(4)) Oxfam Publishing GBR. *Dist:* Stylus Publishing, LLC.

Bowden, Rob. The Ganges. 2003. (River Journey Ser.). (Illus.). 48p. (J). lib. bdg. 28.56 (978-0-7398-6070-0(4)) Raintree.

Brooks, Susie. Bangladesh. 2005. (Our Lives, Our World Ser.). (Illus.). 32p. (J). (gr. 3-7). lib. bdg. 27.10 (978-1-59389-231-9(4)) Chrysalis Education.

Cumming, David. Bangladesh. Davies, Howard, photos by. 2004. (Letters from Around the World Ser.). (Illus.). 32p. (J). (978-1-84234-255-8(X) , Cherrytree Books) Evans Publishing Group.

—Bangladesh. 1999. (Country Fact Files Ser.). (Illus.). 48p. (J). (gr. 4-8). lib. bdg. 27.12 (978-0-8172-5405-6(6)) Raintree.

Harcourt School Publishers Staff. Social Studies: Bangladesh. 2000. (Harcourt Brace Social Studies). (Illus.). (gr. k-7). pap. 33.90 (978-0-15-317434-6(X)) Harcourt Schl. Pubs.

Khoo, Eileen. Welcome to Bangladesh. 2005. (Welcome to My Country Ser.). 48p. (J). lib. bdg. 26.00 (978-0-8368-3125-2(X)) Stevens, Gareth Inc.

London, Ellen. Bangladesh. 2004. (Countries of the World Ser.). (Illus.). 96p. (J). (gr. 6 up). lib. bdg. 30.00 (978-0-8368-3107-8(1)) Stevens, Gareth Inc.

March, Michael. Bangladesh. 2004. (Country File Ser.). (Illus.). 32p. (J). lib. bdg. 27.10 (978-1-58340-496-6(1)) Smart Apple Media.

Orr, Tamra. Bangladesh. 2007. (Enchantment of the World, Second Ser.). (Illus.). 144p. (J). (gr. 5-9). 36.00 (978-0-516-25012-0(4) , Children's Pr.) Scholastic Library Publishing.

Phillips, Douglas A. & Gritzner, Charles F. Bangladesh. 2007. (Modern World Nations Ser.). (Illus.). 112p. (gr. 6-12). 30.00 (***978-0-7910-9251-4(8)*** , Chelsea Hse.) Facts On File, Inc.

Rosenau, Kimberly. Trip to Where? A: 5-Day Series about Bangladesh for School-Age Children. 2000. (Illus.). 51p. (J). 9.95 (978-1-888796-19-3(7)) ABWE Publishing.

Thomson, Ruth. Bangladesh. 2006. (Living In- Ser.). (Illus.). 32p. (978-1-59771-045-9(8)) Sea-To-Sea Pubns.

Valliant, Doris. Bangladesh. 2005. (Growth & Influence of Islam in the Nations of Asia & Central Asia Ser.). (Illus.). 128p. (J). lib. bdg. 25.95 (978-1-59084-879-1(9)) Mason Crest Pubs.

Whyte, Mariam. Bangladesh. 1999. (Cultures of the World Ser.). (Illus.). 128p. (gr. 5-12). lib. bdg. 37.07 (978-0-7614-0869-7(X) , Benchmark Bks.) Cavendish, Marshall Corp.

BANKING

see Banks and Banking

BANKS AND BANKING

see also Credit; Investments; Money

Allman, Barbara. Banking. 2006. (How Economics Works). (Illus.). 48p. (J). (ps-7). 25.26 (978-0-8225-2148-8(2) , Lerner Pubns.) Lerner Publishing Group.

Andrade, J. Jack. Mom, Dad, Tell Me about Money: A Primer. 2004. 68p. (YA). per. 19.95 (978-0-9759494-0-5(3) , 2004-money01) Thundermist Consulting and Research Co.

Apel, Melanie Ann. The Federal Reserve ACT: Making the American Banking System Stronger. 2004. (Progressive Movement, 1900-1920 Ser.). (Illus.). 32p. (J). lib. bdg. (978-1-4042-0196-5(3)) Rosen Publishing Group, Inc., The.

Attebury, Nancy Garhan. Out & about at the Bank. Trover, Zachary, illus. 2005. (Field Trips Ser.). 24p. (J). (ps). lib. bdg. 23.93 (978-1-4048-1147-8(8)) Picture Window Bks.

Basel, Roberta. What Do Banks Do? 2006. (First Facts Ser.). (Illus.). 24p. (J). (978-0-7368-5398-9(7)) Capstone Pr., Inc.

Brown, Lisa. Baby Do My Banking. 2006. 12p. 6.95 (978-1-932416-55-8(2)) McSweeney's Publishing.

Cooper, Jason. Keeping Money Safe. 2003. (Rourke Discovery Library). (Illus.). 24p. (J). (gr. 3-6). 14.95 (978-1-58952-214-5(1)) Rourke Publishing, LLC.

Crompton, Samuel Willard & McNeese, Tim. McCulloch V. Maryland: Implied Powers of the Federal Government. 2007. (Great Supreme Court Decisions Ser.). 136p. (J). (gr. 5-8). 30.00 (978-0-7910-9262-0(3) , Chelsea Hse.) Facts On File, Inc.

Giesecke, Ernestine. Everyday Banking: Consumer Banking. 2003. (Everyday Economics Ser.). (Illus.). 48p. (J). (gr. 3-5). lib. bdg. 27.07 (978-1-58810-489-2(3)) Heinemann Library.

—Everyday Banking: Consumer Banking. 2003. (gr. 3-6). lib. bdg. 16.40 (978-0-613-45748-4(X)) Tandem Library Bks.

—Money Business: Banks & Banking. 2003. (Everyday Economics Ser.). (Illus.). 48p. (J). (gr. 3-5). lib. bdg. 27.07 (978-1-58810-490-8(7)) Heinemann Library.

Giesecke, Ernestine. Everyday Banking: Consumer Banking. 2002. (Everyday Economics Ser.). 48p. (J). (gr. 3-5). pap. 8.50 (978-1-58810-952-1(6) , 91585) Heinemann Library.

—Money Business: Banks & Banking. 2002. (Everyday Economics Ser.). 48p. (J). (gr. 3-5). pap. 8.50 (978-1-58810-953-8(4) , 91587) Heinemann Library.

Godfrey, Neale S. Check It Out: The Book about Banking: Classroom Set. 2003. (One & Only Common Sense/ents Ser.). 486.95 (978-0-7652-0811-8(3)) Modern Curriculum Pr.

Goldman, Phyllis B., ed. Monkeyshines on Math, Money & Banking. 2002. (Illus.). 183p. (J). pap. 32.95 (978-1-888325-21-8(6)) Allosaurus Pubs.

Hall, Margaret. Banks. 2007. (J). (***978-1-4034-9814-4(8));*** pap. (***978-1-4034-9819-9(9)***) Heinemann Library.

Hall, Margaret C. Banks. (Earning, Saving, Spending Ser.). 32p. (J). (gr. 1-4). 2002. pap. 7.50 (978-1-58810-337-6(4) , 91083); 2000. (Illus.). lib. bdg. 21.36 (978-1-57572-231-3(3)) Heinemann Library.

Hammonds, Heather. Banking. 2006. (Illus.). 32p. (J). (978-1-58340-783-7(9)) Smart Apple Media.

Johnston, Marianne. Let's Visit the Bank. 2000. (Our Community Ser.). (Illus.). 24p. (J). (gr. 3). lib. bdg. 18.75 (978-0-8239-5432-2(3) , PowerKids Pr.) Rosen Publishing Group, Inc., The.

Leonard, Barry, ed. The Story of the Federal Reserve System. 2005. (Illus.). 138p. (YA). (gr. 4-8). reprint ed. pap. 20.00 (978-1-4223-0294-1(6)) DIANE Publishing Co.

Loewen, Nancy. In the Money: A Book about Banking. Fitzpatrick, Brad, illus. (Money Matters Ser.). (J). (ps). 2005. 24p. lib. bdg. 22.60 (978-1-4048-1156-0(7)); 2004. (978-1-4048-0950-5(3)) Picture Window Bks.

McAlpine, Margaret. Working in Banking & Finance. 2005. (My Future Career Ser.). (Illus.). 64p. (J). lib. bdg. 26.00 (978-0-8368-4772-7(5)) Stevens, Gareth Inc.

Money & Banks, 6 Vols. 115.98 (978-0-8368-4867-0(5)) Stevens, Gareth Inc.

Parker, Lewis K. J. Pierpont Morgan & Wall Street. 2003. (Reading Power Ser.). (Illus.). 24p. (J). lib. bdg. 17.25 (978-0-8239-6449-9(3) , PowerKids Pr.) Rosen Publishing Group, Inc., The.

Pettifor, Bonnie & Petit, Charles E. McCulloch V. Maryland: When State & Federal Powers Conflict. 2004. (Landmark Supreme Court Cases Ser.). (Illus.). 128p. (J). lib. bdg. 26.60 (978-0-7660-1887-7(3)) Enslow Pubs., Inc.

Rau, Dana Meachen. What Is a Bank? 2005. (Money & Banks Ser.). (Illus.). 24p. (J). pap. (978-0-8368-4880-9(2)); lib. bdg. 19.33 (978-0-8368-4873-1(X)) Stevens, Gareth Inc.

Schwartz, Stuart B. & Conley, Craig. Opening a Bank Account. 1998. (Career Books). (Illus.). 32p. (J). (gr. 3-4). lib. bdg. 21.26 (978-0-7368-0047-1(6) , LifeMatters Bks.) Capstone Pr., Inc.

Tattersall, Clare. The Young Zillionaire's Guide to Money & Banking. 2000. (Be a Zillionaire Ser.). (Illus.). 48p. (YA). (gr. 5-8). lib. bdg. 23.95 (978-0-8239-3262-7(1) , ZIMOBA, Rosen Central) Rosen Publishing Group, Inc., The.

BANKS AND BANKING—FICTION

Bain, Michelle. The Adventures of Thumbs up Johnnie: Banker Bill's Guide to Common Cents. Lizana, Lorenzo, illus. 2007. (J). 14.95 (***978-0-9761421-9-5(8)***) Pixie Stuff LLC.

First Bank Community Writers Staff. Fir$t Kid$ Bank - $aving Is Fun. Freeman, Troy, illus. l.t. ed. 1998. (Kids! Ser.: No. 38). 70p. (J). (gr. 2-4). pap. 3.95 (978-1-57635-020-1(7)) WeWrite LLC.

Morgan, Allen. Matthew & the Midnight Bank. Martchenko, Michael, illus. 2001. (Matthew's Midnight Adventures Ser.). 32p. (J). (ps-3). 6.99 (978-0-7737-6134-6(9)) Stoddart Kids CAN. *Dist:* Fitzhenry & Whiteside, Ltd.

Webster, Frank V. Dick the Bank Boy. 2007. (ENG.). 184p. per. 11.95 (***978-1-4218-3331-6(X)***) 1st World Publishing, Inc.

Webster, V. Frank. Dick the Bank Boy or A Missing Fortune. 2006. 95.99 (***978-1-4280-4992-5(4)***); pap. 88.99 (***978-1-4280-4991-8(6)***) IndyPublish.com.

BANKS AND BANKING—VOCATIONAL GUIDANCE

Bagley, Katie. Bank Tellers. 2001. (Community Helpers Ser.). (Illus.). 92p. (J). (gr. 1-2). 18.60 (978-0-7368-0805-7(1) , Bridgestone Bks.) Capstone Pr., Inc.

Haddock, Patricia. Careers in Banking & Finance. rev. ed. 2005. (Career Resource Library). (Illus.). 192p. (YA). (gr. 7-12). lib. bdg. 26.50 (978-0-8239-3446-1(2)) Rosen Publishing Group, Inc., The.

Simpson, Carolyn. Choosing a Career in Banking & Finance. rev. ed. 1999. (World of Work Ser.). (Illus.). 64p. (YA). (gr. 7-12). lib. bdg. 25.25 (978-0-8239-3016-6(5) , WWBAFI) Rosen Publishing Group, Inc., The.

BANNEKER, BENJAMIN, 1731-1806

Bednarz, Robert, et al. TIME for Kids Readers: Benjamin Banneker. 3rd ed. 2002. (Harcourt Horizons Ser.). (gr. k-7). pap. 38.10 (978-0-15-335272-0(8)) Harcourt Schl. Pubs.

Benjamin Banneker 24: Leveled Books. 2001. (McGraw-Hill. Lectura Ser.). (ENG & SPA.). (gr. 1 up). (978-0-02-188001-0(8)) Macmillan/McGraw-Hill Schl. Div.

Blue, Rose & Naden, Corinne J. Benjamin Banneker: Mathematician & Stargazer. 2001. (Gateway Biography Ser.). (Illus.). 48p. (gr. 2-4). lib. bdg. 23.90 (978-0-7613-1805-7(4) , Millbrook Pr.) Lerner Publishing Group.

Braun, Eric. Benjamin Banneker. 2005. (Pebble Books). (Illus.). 24p. (J). (978-0-7368-4233-4(0) , Pebble Bks.) Capstone Pr., Inc.

Burke, Rick. Benjamin Banneker. 2003. (American Lives Ser.). (Illus.). 32p. (J). lib. bdg. 24.22 (978-1-4034-0725-2(8)); pap. 6.50 (978-1-4034-3100-4(0)) Heinemann Library.

Harcourt School Publishers Staff. Dear Benjamin... Reader's Choice Book. 2001. (Collections Ser.). (Illus.). (J). 4.70 (978-0-15-314396-0(7)) Harcourt Schl. Pubs.

Hinman, Bonnie. Benjamin Banneker. 1999. (Colonial Leaders Ser.). (Illus.). 79p. (J). (gr. 3 up). pap. 8.95 (978-0-7910-5691-2(0) , Chelsea Hse.) Facts On File, Inc.

—Benjamin Banneker: American Mathematician & Astronomer. 2000. (Colonial Leaders Ser.). (Illus.). 80p. (J). (gr. 3 up). 27.50 (978-0-7910-5348-5(2) , Chelsea Hse.) Facts On File, Inc.

Lassieur, Allison. Benjamin Banneker: Astronomer & Mathematician. 2006. (Fact Finders Ser.). (Illus.). 32p. (J). (978-0-7368-5432-0(0)) Capstone Pr., Inc.

Litwin, Laura Baskes. Benjamin Banneker: Astronomer & Mathematician. 1999. (African-American Biographies Ser.). (Illus.). 112p. (YA). (gr. 6-12). lib. bdg. 26.60 (978-0-7660-1208-0(5)) Enslow Pubs., Inc.

Pinkney, Andrea Davis. Dear Benjamin Banneker. Pinkney, Brian, illus. 1998. 32p. (J). (gr. 1-5). pap. 7.00 (978-0-15-201892-4(1) , Harcourt Paperbacks) Harcourt Children's Bks.

—Dear Benjamin Banneker. 1998. 12.80 (978-0-606-13324-1(0)) Tandem Library Bks.

Wadsworth, Ginger. Benjamin Banneker: Pioneering Scientist. Orback, Craig, illus. 2003. (On My Own Biographies Ser.). 48p. (J). (gr. 1-3). 5.95 (978-0-87614-104-5(1) , Carolrhoda Bks.); (gr. 2-5). 25.26 (978-0-87614-916-4(6)) Lerner Publishing Group.

—Benjamin Banneker: Pioneering Scientist. 2003. (gr. 3-6). lib. bdg. 14.10 (978-0-613-58889-8(4)) Tandem Library Bks.

Weatherly, Myra. Benjamin Banneker: American Scientific Pioneer. 2006. (Signature Lives Ser.). (Illus.). 112p. (J). (gr. 5-7). 30.60 (978-0-7565-1579-9(3)) Compass Point Bks.

Welch, Catherine A. Benjamin Banneker. 2008. (History Maker Biographies Ser.). (J). lib. bdg. 26.60 (***978-0-8225-7167-4(6)*** , Lerner Pubns.) Lerner Publishing Group.

BANNERS

see Flags

BANTING, FREDERICK GRANT, SIR, 1891-1941

Bankston, John. Frederick Banting & the Discovery of Insulin. 2002. (Unlocking the Secrets of Science Ser.). (Illus.). 56p. (gr. 4-10). lib. bdg. 25.70 (978-1-58415-094-7(7)) Mitchell Lane Pubs., Inc.

BAPTISM

Baptism in the Holy Spirit. 2003. (YA). 1.50 (978-0-9673342-4-0(1)) Saints Of Glory Church.

Bowman, Peg. Welcomed by Name: Our Child's Baptism. 2004. (978-0-8294-1798-2(2)) Loyola Pr.

Cannon, Elaine. Baptized & Confirmed: Your Lifeline to Heaven. 2001. 96p. (J). pap. 9.95 (978-1-57345-915-0(1) , SKU 4128992, Bookcraft, Inc.) Deseret Bk. Co.

Clawson, Jan. Baptism—My Promise to Jesus: Girl. 1998. (Illus.). 24p. pap. 5.98 (978-0-88290-617-1(8) , 1301G) Horizon Pubs. & Distributors, Inc.

Consuegra, Claudio & Consuegra, Pamela. Making Jesus My Best Friend: Baptism Preparation for Younger Children (Ages 8-10) 2005. (Illus.). 95p. (J). (gr. 4-7). pap. 8.99 (978-0-8280-1836-4(7)) Review & Herald Publishing Assn.

Daybell, Chad G. Baptism: Entering the Path to Eternal Life. 2004. 72p. (J). pap. 7.95 (978-1-932898-18-7(2) , 98182) Spring Creek Bk. Co.

Donahue, Laurie. God's Plan My Response. Rittenhouse, Ralph, ed. 2003. (Illus.). 100p. pap. 9.99 (978-0-9718306-0-8(6)) LifeSong Pubs.

Donahue, Laurie & Rittenhouse, Ralph. God... Should I Be Baptized? 2003. (Illus.). 96p. pap. 10.99 (978-0-9718306-1-5(4)) LifeSong Pubs.

Durrant, George D. Seven Years Old & Preparing for Baptism. 2007. (Illus.). 68p. (J). pap. 7.95 (***978-1-932898-74-3(3)***) Spring Creek Bk. Co.

Fitzgerald, Tony. ChristWise Discipleship Guide for Teens: Especiallty for Ages 13-15. 2002. 128p. (YA). pap. (978-0-8280-1711-4(5) , 033-783) Review & Herald Publishing Assn.

—ChristWise Discipleship Guide for Youth: Especially for Ages 15-18. 2002. 144p. (YA). pap. 5.99 (978-0-8280-1712-1(3) , 033-784) Review & Herald Publishing Assn.

—ChristWise Leader's Guide for Juniors, Teens, & Youth: Especially for Ages 9-12. 2002. 326p. (J). pap. 12.99 (978-0-8280-1713-8(1) , 033-781) Review & Herald Publishing Assn.

Hanna, Heather. Daniel Asks about Baptism & Communion. 2005. (Illus.). 32p. (J). (978-0-8163-2083-7(7)) Pacific Pr. Publishing Assn.

Jolly, Judy. Happy Baptism Day. 2004. (Illus.). 24p. 11.00 (978-0-687-03064-4(1)) Abingdon Pr.

Memories of My Baptism, Boy. 1998. (gr. 3). 9.95 (978-1-57734-271-7(2) , 01113313) Covenant Communications, Inc.

Milton, Bev. My Baptism. Kyle, Margaret, illus. 1998. 24p. (J). 23.95 (978-1-55145-296-8(0)) Wood Lake Bks., Inc. CAN. *Dist:* Logos Productions, Inc.

Muggli, Glorianne. Baptism. 2003. (YA). pap. 7.95 (978-1-57665-085-1(5)) Muggli Graphics.

Murdock, S. Reed. Gideon's Baptism: A Day to Always Remember. Savage, Ben, illus. 2002. 32p. (J). (gr. 1-6). 11.95 (978-1-930980-76-1(0) , 80760) Granite Publishing & Distribution.

Murrie, Diana. My Baptism Book (hardback) A child's guide to Baptism. Cameron, Craig, illus. 2006. 32p. 13.00 (***978-0-7151-4076-5(0)***) Church Hse. Pubng. GBR. *Dist:* Church Publishing, Inc.

—My Baptism Book (paperback) A Child's Guide to Baptism. Cameron, Craig, illus. 2006. 32p. pap. 10.00 (***978-0-7151-4091-8(4)***) Church Hse. Pubng. GBR. *Dist:* Church Publishing, Inc.

Olive, Phyllis Carol. Baptism, the Key to Heaven. unabr. ed. 2001. (Illus.). 25p. (J). (ps-3). 12.95 (978-1-930980-22-8(1) , 80221) Granite Publishing & Distribution.

—The Gift of the Holy Ghost. Olive, Phyllis Carol, illus. unabr. ed. 2003. (Illus.). 25p. (J). (gr. k-4). 12.95 (978-1-932280-08-1(1) , 80081) Granite Publishing & Distribution.

Perry, Marilyn. Our Baby's Being Baptized. Date not set. (Illus.). 16p. (J). pap. 3.95 (978-0-929032-70-2(5)) Wood Lake Bks., Inc. CAN. *Dist:* Logos Productions, Inc.

Piper, Sophie. My Baptism Book. Kolanovic, Dubravka, illus. 2007. 64p. 14.95 (978-1-55725-535-8(0)) Paraclete Pr., Inc.

Reed. What Is Baptism? 2006. 32p. pap. 2.00 (978-0-687-49327-2(7)) Abingdon Pr.

Robinson, Timothy M. A Fountain of Pure Water: A Nephite Baptism Story. Madsen, Jim, illus. 2001. 32p. (J). 15.95 (978-1-57345-840-5(6) , SKU 4024631, Bookcraft, Inc.) Deseret Bk. Co.

Setzer, Lee Ann. I Am Ready for Baptism. 2006. 30p. (J). 4.99 (978-1-55517-944-1(4) , Cedar Fort, Inc.) Cedar Fort, Inc./CFI Distribution.

Spear, Kevin. What's a Bathtub Doing in My Church? Fifteen Questions Kids Ask about Baptism, Salvation & Snorkels. 2006. 32p. pap. 5.99 (978-1-59317-155-1(2)) Warner Pr. Pubs.

Stanton, Sue. Child's Guide to Baptism. Blake, Anne Catharine, illus. 2006. 32p. (J). 9.95 (978-0-8091-6728-9(X) , 6728-x) Paulist Pr.

Walker, Joni. Holy Baptism. Walker, Joni, illus. 2005. (Follow & Do Ser.). (Illus.). 32p. (J). 6.99 (978-0-7586-0800-0(4)) Concordia Publishing Hse.

Wittenback, Janet. God Makes Me His Child in Baptism. McDonnell, Janet, illus. rev. ed. 2007. (ENG.). 32p. (J). 5.99 (***978-0-7586-1305-9(9)***) Concordia Publishing Hse.

Wood Lake Books Staff & Novalis Staff. Your Child's Baptism: Protestant. 1998. 16p. (J). pap. 2.50 (978-0-919599-54-3(0)) Wood Lake Bks., Inc. CAN. *Dist:* Words Distributing Co.

—Your Child's Baptism: Roman Catholic. Date not set. 16p. (Orig.). (J). pap. 2.50 (978-2-89088-669-8(7)) Logos Productions, Inc.

BAPTISTS

see also Mennonites

Allison, Amy. Roger Williams: Founder of Rhode Island. 2000. (Colonial Leaders Ser.). (Illus.). 80p. (J). (gr. 8-12). 27.50 (978-0-7910-5964-7(2) , Chelsea Hse.) Facts On File, Inc.

Bader, Bonnie. Who Was Martin Luther King Jr. Harrison, Nancy & Wolf, Elizaabeth, illus. 2007. (Who Was... ? Ser.). 112p. (J). (gr. 2-5). 4.99 (***978-0-448-44723-0(1)*** , Grosset & Dunlap) Penguin Group (USA) Inc.

Bolden, Tonya. M. L. K. The Journey of a King. Adelman, Bob, ed. 2007. 128p. (J). (gr. 5-9). 19.95 (978-0-8109-5476-2(1) , Abrams Bks. for Young Readers) Abrams, Harry N. , Inc.

Boyd, Herb. Martin Luther King, Jr. Marcos, Pablo, illus. 2005. (Heroes of America Ser.). 240p. (J). (gr. 3-8). lib. bdg. 21.35 (978-1-59679-258-6(2)) ABDO Publishing Co.

Brown, Jonatha A. Martin Luther King, Jr. 2005. (Illus.). 24p. (ENG & SPA.). (J). pap. (978-0-8368-4590-7(0)); (J). lib. bdg. (978-0-8368-4474-0(2)); (ENG & SPA., (J). lib. bdg. 19.33 (978-0-8368-4583-9(8)); (YA). lib. bdg. 19.33 (978-0-8368-4467-2(X) , Weekly Reader Early Learning Library) Stevens, Gareth Inc.

Burgan, Michael. Roger Williams: Founder of Rhode Island. 2006. (Signature Lives Ser.). (Illus.). 112p. (J). (gr. 5-7). 30.60 (978-0-7565-1596-6(3)) Compass Point Bks.

Fandel, Jennifer. Martin Luther King, Jr. 2005. (Genius Ser.). (Illus.). 48p. (gr. 5-9). 21.95 (978-1-58341-329-6(4) , Creative Education) Creative Co., The.

—Martin Luther King, Jr: Great Civil Rights Leader. 2007. (Graphic Library). (Illus.). 32p. (J). (978-0-7368-6498-5(9)) Capstone Pr., Inc.

Feinstein, Stephen. Lee sobre Martin Luther King, Jr./Read about Martin Luther King, Jr. 2006. (I Like Biographies! Bilingual Ser.). (ENG & SPA., Illus.). 24p. (J). (gr. 1-3). lib. bdg. 21.26 (978-0-7660-2745-9(7) , Enslow Elementary) Enslow Pubs., Inc.

—Read about Martin Luther King, Jr. 2004. (I Like Biographies Ser.!). (Illus.). 24p. (J). lib. bdg. 24.95 (978-0-7660-2300-0(1)) Enslow Pubs., Inc.

Fine, Edith Hope. Martin Luther King, Jr: Champion of Civil Rights. 2006. (Heroes of American History Ser.). (Illus.). 32p. (J). lib. bdg. 22.60 (978-0-7660-2466-3(0) , Enslow Elementary) Enslow Pubs., Inc.

Fleming, Alice Mulcahey. Martin Luther King, Jr. A Dream of Hope. 2008. (Sterling Biographies Ser.). (Illus.). 128p. (J). pap. 5.95 (***978-1-4027-4439-6(0)***) Sterling Publishing Co., Inc.

Gaustad, Edwin S. Roger Williams: Prophet of Liberty. 2001. (Oxford Portraits Ser.). (Illus.). 144p. (YA). (gr. 9 up). 28.00 (978-0-19-513000-3(6)) Oxford Univ. Pr., Inc.

Gotsch, Patrice. Martin Luther King, Jr: Changing Lives. Arreola, Gil, illus. 2005. 19p. (J). pap. (***978-1-55501-779-8(7)***) Ballard & Tighe Pubs.

Harrington, Patricia. I Am Baptist. 1999. (Religions of the World Ser.). 24p. (J). (gr. k-4). lib. bdg. 18.75 (978-0-8239-5261-8(4)) Rosen Publishing Group, Inc., The.

Hatt, Christine. Martin Luther King, Jr. 2004. (Judge for Yourself Ser.). (Illus.). 64p. (J). pap. (978-0-8368-5565-4(5)); (gr. 5 up). lib. bdg. 30.00 (978-0-8368-5562-3(0)) Stevens, Gareth Inc. (World Almanac Library).

Jakoubek, Robert E. Martin Luther King, Jr. Civil Rights Leader. (Black Americans of Achievement Ser.). (Illus.). 112p. (gr. 6-12). 2005. pap. 13.25 (978-0-7910-8335-2(7)); 2004. 30.00 (978-0-7910-8161-7(3)) Facts On File, Inc. (Chelsea Hse.).

Jeffrey, Gary. Martin Luther King, Jr: The Life of a Civil Rights Leader. Riley, Terry, illus. 2006. (Graphic Biographies Ser.). 48p. (J). lib. bdg. 29.95 (978-1-4042-0858-2(5)) Rosen Publishing Group, Inc., The.

—Martin Luther King Jr: The Life of a Civil Rights Leader. Forsey, Christopher, illus. 2006. 48p. (J). (978-1-4042-0920-6(4)); pap. (978-1-4042-0921-3(2)) Rosen Publishing Group, Inc., The.

Jones, Rob Lloyd. Martin Luther King, Jr. 2006. (Illus.). 62p. (J). pap. (***978-0-439-02299-6(1)***) Scholastic, Inc.

Linney, Susan. Martin Luther King, Jr: With a Discussion of Responsibility. 2004. (Values in Action Ser.). (J). (978-1-59203-069-9(6)) Learning Challenge, Inc.

The Lottie & Annie Upside-down Book. 2003. 8.99 (978-1-56309-627-3(7)) Woman's Missionary Union.

Lowery, Linda. Martin Luther King Jr Day. 2004. (gr. k-3). lib. bdg. 14.10 (978-0-613-79212-7(2)) Tandem Library Bks.

Lynch, Emma, et al. Martin Luther King, Jr. 2005. (Illus.). 32p. (J). (978-1-4034-6351-7(4)); pap. (978-1-4034-6365-4(4)) Heinemann Library.

MacMillan, Dianne M. Martin Luther King, Jr. Day. 2nd ed. 2008. (Best Holiday Books Ser.). 48p. (J). (gr. 3-4). lib. bdg. 23.93 (***978-0-7660-3043-5(1)***) Enslow Pubs., Inc.

Manheimer, Ann S. Martin Luther King Jr: Dreaming of Equality. 2005. (Trailblazer Biography Ser.). (Illus.). 112p. (J). 30.60 (978-1-57505-627-2(5) , Carolrhoda Bks.) Lerner Publishing Group.

Martin's Big Words. 2004. pap. 38.75 incl. audio compact disk (978-1-55592-637-3(1)); pap. 32.75 incl. audio (978-1-55592-367-9(4)); pap. 14.95 incl. audio (978-1-55592-169-9(8)) Weston Woods Studios, Inc.

Murcia, Rebecca Thatcher. The Civil Rights Movement. 2005. (Monumental Milestones Ser.). (Illus.). 48p. (YA). (ps-7). lib. bdg. (978-1-58415-401-3(2)) Mitchell Lane Pubs., Inc.

Rappaport, Doreen. Martin's Big Words: The Life of Dr. Martin Luther King Jr. Collier, Bryan, illus. 2001. 40p. (gr. k-4). 15.99 (978-0-7868-0714-7(8)) Hyperion Bks. for Children.

Rappaport, Doreen. Martin's Big Words: The Life of Dr. Martin Luther King Jr. Collier, Bryan, illus. rev. ed. 2007. 40p. (ps-17). pap. 6.99 (***978-1-4231-0635-7(0)*** , Jump at the Sun) Hyperion Bks. for Children.

Raum, Elizabeth. Roger Williams. 2004. (Illus.). 32p. (J). pap. 7.50 (978-1-4034-5969-5(X)); lib. bdg. 25.64 (978-1-4034-5961-9(4)) Heinemann Library.

Rivera, Sheila. Martin Luther King Jr. A Life of Determination. 2006. (Pull Ahead Books). (Illus.). 32p. (J). 22.60 (978-0-8225-3477-8(0) , Lerner Pubns.) Lerner Publishing Group.

Schraff, Anne E. Martin Luther King, JR: We Shall Overcome. 2005. (African-American Biography Library). (Illus.). 128p. (J). (gr. 6-13). lib. bdg. 31.93 (978-0-7660-1774-0(5)) Enslow Pubs., Inc.

Schuldt, Lori Meek. Martin Luther King, Jr: With Profiles of Mohandas K. Gandhi & Nelson Mandela. 2006. (Biographical Connections Ser.). (Illus.). 112p. (J). (978-0-7166-1822-5(2)) World Bk., Inc.

The Story of Martin Luther King, Jr. 2001. (Illus.). 24p. (J). (ps-k). 6.95 (978-0-8249-4144-4(6)) Ideals Pubns.

Walsh, Kieran. Roger Williams. 2005. (Discover the Life of a Colonial American Ser.). 24p. (gr. 2-5). 14.95 (978-1-59515-140-7(0)) Rourke Publishing, LLC.

Wellman, Sam. T. D. Jakes: Religious Leader. (Black Americans of Achievement Ser.). (Illus.). (J). 2000. 112p. (gr. 4-7). 30.00 (978-0-7910-5362-1(8)); 1999. 103p. (gr. 5 up). pap. 30.00 (978-0-7910-5363-8(6)) Facts On File, Inc. (Chelsea Hse.).

Winget, Mary. Martin Luther King, Jr. 2003. (History Maker Bios Ser.). (Illus.). 47p. (J). 26.60 (978-0-8225-4674-0(4) , Lerner Pubns.) Lerner Publishing Group.

—Martin Luther King, Jr. 2004. (History Maker Bios Ser.). (Illus.). 48p. (J). pap. (978-0-8225-4804-1(6) , Lerner Pubns.) Lerner Publishing Group.

BAR

see Lawyers

BARBADOS

Elias, Marie Louise. Barbados. 2000. (Cultures of the World Ser.). (Illus.). 128p. (gr. 5-12). lib. bdg. 37.07 (978-0-7614-0976-2(9) , Benchmark Bks.) Cavendish, Marshall Corp.

Orr, Tamra. Barbados. 2003. (Discovering Latin America Ser.). (Illus.). 64p. (J). (gr. 5 up). lib. bdg. (978-1-59084-306-2(1)) Mason Crest Pubs.

BARBADOS—FICTION

Headley, Lester "Zoom". Smiley B. 2006. (ENG., Illus.). 48p. per. 20.95 (***978-1-59800-548-6(0)***) Outskirts Press, Inc.

Literature Connections English: The Witch of Blackbird Pond. 2004. (gr. 6-12). (978-0-395-78592-8(8) , 2-70293) McDougal Littell Inc.

Matthews, Annette. Mischievous Molly. 2006. (Illus.). x, 48p. pap. (***978-1-4120-9693-5(6)***) Trafford Publishing.

BARBARY CORSAIRS

see Pirates

BARBARY STATES

see Africa, North

BARBECUE COOKING

see Outdoor Cookery

BARBIE (FICTITIOUS CHARACTER)—FICTION

Aber, Linda Williams. The Clue in the Castle Wall. 2004. (Barbie Mystery Ser.: No. 6). 48p. (J). pap. 3.99 (978-0-439-55709-2(7) , Scholastic Paperbacks) Scholastic, Inc.

—The Haunted Mansion Mystery. 2002. (Barbie Mystery Files Ser.: No. 1). 64p. (J). (gr. 1-4). pap. 3.99 (978-0-439-37204-6(6)) Scholastic, Inc.

—The Mystery of the Jeweled Mask. 2002. (Barbie Mystery Files Ser.: No. 2). (Illus.). 80p. (J). (gr. 1-3). pap. 3.99 (978-0-439-37205-3(4)) Scholastic, Inc.

—The Mystery of the Lost Valentine. 2004. (Barbie Mystery Ser.). 48p. (J). pap. 3.99 (978-0-439-55708-5(9) , Scholastic Paperbacks) Scholastic, Inc.

—The Mystery of the Missing Stallion. 2003. (Barbie Mystery Files Ser.: No. 4). 80p. (J). pap. 3.99 (978-0-439-37207-7(0)) Scholastic, Inc.

Aber, Linda Williams, adapted by. Barbie of Swan Lake: A Junior Novelization. 2003. (Barbie Ser.). (Illus.). 64p. (J). pap. 3.99 (978-0-439-54523-5(4) , Scholastic Paperbacks) Scholastic, Inc.

Alberto, Daisy. Barbie as the Island Princess. 2007. (Step into Reading Ser.). (Illus.). 32p. (J). (ps-2). 3.99 (***978-0-375-84353-2(1));*** lib. bdg. 11.99 (***978-0-375-94353-9(6)***) Random Hse. Children's Bks. (Random Hse. Bks. for Young Readers).

Barbie As Rapunzel, Vol. 1. 7.99 (978-1-59532-717-8(7)) TOKYOPOP, Inc.

Barbie First Play a Sound Barb. pap. 7.98 (978-0-7853-3332-6(0)) Publications International, Ltd.

Barbie Learn 'N' Tell Sticker Workbooks. 2004. (J). wbk. ed. (978-0-7666-0700-2(3) , 49890); wbk. ed. (978-0-7666-0701-9(1) , 49890); wbk. ed. (978-0-7666-0702-6(X) , 49890); wbk. ed. (978-0-7666-0703-3(8) , 49890) Modern Publishing.

Barbie of Swan Lake. 10p. 9.98 (978-0-7853-9372-6(2)) Publications International, Ltd.

Barbie Preschool Educational. 2004. (J). (978-0-7666-1353-9(4) , 64065) Modern Publishing.

Burr, Daniela. Barbie Fairytopia: Mermaidia. Schutz, Samatha, ed. 2006. (Illus.). 80p. (J). pap. 3.99 (978-0-439-85636-2(1)) Scholastic, Inc.

Cane, Rochelle. Barbie Glitter Fun. 2006. (Style Bks.). 12p. (J). bds. 12.99 (978-0-7944-0943-2(1)) Reader's Digest Assn., Inc., The.

Capozzi, Suzy. Barbie: On the Road. Wolcott, Karen, illus. 2004. (Steeping into Reading Ser.: Vol. 2). 32p. (J). (ps-2). pap. 3.99 (978-0-375-82861-4(3) , Random Hse. Bks. for Young Readers) Random Hse. Children's Bks.

Frazer, Rebecca. Barbie Loves Cheerleading. Wolcott, Karen, illus. 2007. 24p. (J). (ps-2). 3.99 (978-0-375-87485-7(2) , Golden Bks.) Random Hse. Children's Bks.

Frazer, Rebecca. Barbie Loves Pets. An, Jiyoung, illus. 2007. (Pictureback(R) Ser.). 16p. (J). (ps-1). pap. 3.99 (***978-0-375-84797-4(9)*** , Golden Bks.) Random Hse., Inc.

Gikow, Louise. Barbie Rules #3: No Teasing Allowed. 2003. (Barbie Rules Ser.). (Illus.). 24p. (J). (gr. k-3). pap. 3.25 (978-0-307-10357-4(9) , Golden Bks.) Random Hse. Children's Bks.

Golden Books Staff. Animal Magic. 2007. (Paint Box Book Ser.). (Illus.). 48p. (J). (ps-2). 3.99 (***978-0-375-84466-9(X)*** , Golden Bks.) Random Hse. Children's Bks.

—Barbie As Ballerina. 2001. (Illus.). (J). (ps-2). pap. 1.00 (978-0-307-20016-7(7) , Golden Bks.) Random Hse. Children's Bks.

—Barbie Fairytopia: Mermaidia Board Book. 2007. 24p. (J). (gr. k-k). bds. 4.99 (978-0-375-83851-4(1) , Golden Bks.) Random Hse. Children's Bks.

—Barbie in the 12 Dancing Princesses Make Your Own Little Golden Book. 2006. (Illus.). 16p. (J). (gr. k-k). 5.99 (978-0-375-83866-8(X) , Golden Bks.) Random Hse. Children's Bks.

—Barbie with Gold Earrings. 1999. (Illus.). 70p. (J). pap. 0.99 (978-0-307-20020-4(5) , Golden Bks.) Random Hse. Children's Bks.

—Barbie with Pets. 1999. (Illus.). 70p. (J). pap. 0.99 (978-0-307-20019-8(1) , Golden Bks.) Random Hse. Children's Bks.

—Fashion Show. 2000. (Illus.). 128p. (J). (ps-2). pap. 0.99 (978-0-307-44332-8(9) , Golden Bks.) Random Hse. Children's Bks.

—Princess Stories: A Collection to Color. 2007. (Jumbo Coloring Book Ser.). (Illus.). 224p. (J). (ps-2). 4.99 (978-0-375-83971-9(2) , Golden Bks.) Random Hse. Children's Bks.

—Rising Stars. Duarte, Pamela, illus. 2004. (Barbie Ser.). 64p. (J). (ps-2). 2.99 (978-0-375-82649-8(1) , Golden Bks.) Random Hse. Children's Bks.

—Spring into Fashion. 2004. (Barbie Ser.). (Illus.). 12p. (J). (ps-2). pap. 3.99 (978-0-375-82648-1(3) , Golden Bks.) Random Hse. Children's Bks.

—The Story of Cinderella. 2007. (Color Plus Chunky Crayons Ser.). (Illus.). 48p. (J). (ps-2). 3.99 (978-0-375-83972-6(0) , Golden Bks.) Random Hse. Children's Bks.

—Welcome to Fairytopia. Harchy, Atelier Philippe, illus. 2005. 32p. (J). (ps-2). pap. 2.99 (978-0-375-83186-7(X) , Golden Bks.) Random Hse. Children's Bks.

Goldowsky, Jill & Reader's Digest Staff. Barbie Magical Moments Storybook & DVD. 2007. (Readers Book & DVD Ser.). 32p. (J). 17.99 (***978-0-7944-1296-8(3)***) Reader's Digest Assn., Inc., The.

Hamilton, Tisha, adapted by. Barbie Fairytopia: A Junior Novelization. 2005. (Illus.). 74p. (J). pap. (***978-0-439-74086-9(X)***) Scholastic, Inc.

Inches, Alison. Barbie: Super Spy. Wolcott, Karen, illus. 2005. (Starring Barbie Ser.: Vol. 4). (J). (***978-1-4155-7688-5(2)*** , Golden Bks.) Random Hse. Children's Bks.

Katschke, Judy. Barbie As the Island Princess. 2007. 80p. (J). pap. 3.99 (***978-0-439-02548-5(6)***) Scholastic, Inc.

Landolf, Diane Wright. Barbie: Fairytopia. 2006. (Step into Reading Ser.). (Illus.). 32p. (J). (ps-2). pap. 3.99 (978-0-375-83696-1(9)); lib. bdg. 11.99 (978-0-375-93696-8(3)) Random Hse. Children's Bks. (Random Hse. Bks. for Young Readers).

Lou Weber Staff, ed. Barbie Princess & Pauper Little Sound Bk. 2004. 10p. (J). bds. 9.98 (978-1-4127-3125-6(9) , 7231200) Publications International, Ltd.

Man-Kong, Mary. Barbie & the Magic of Pegasus. 2006. (Illus.). 22p. (J). (gr. k-ps). bds. 4.99 (978-0-375-83539-1(3) , Golden Bks.) Random Hse. Children's Bks.

—Barbie as the Island Princess. Tormey, Carlotta, illus. 2007. (Picture Book Ser.). 32p. (J). (ps-2). 8.99 (***978-0-375-84217-7(9)*** , Golden Bks.) Random Hse. Children's Bks.

—Barbie as the Island Princess: A Storybook. 2007. (Pictureback(R) Ser.). (Illus.). 24p. (J). (ps-2). 3.99 (***978-0-375-84218-4(7)*** , Random Hse. Bks. for Young Readers) Random Hse. Children's Bks.

—Barbie as the Island Princess:MYOLG. 2007. (Make Your Own LGB Ser.). (Illus.). 16p. (J). (ps-2). 5.99 (***978-0-375-84219-1(5)*** , Golden Bks.) Random Hse. Children's Bks.

—Barbie Fairytopia: The Magic of the Rainbow: A Storybook. 2007. (Pictureback(R) Ser.). (Illus.). 16p. (J). (ps-2). 3.99 (978-0-375-83985-6(2) , Golden Bks.) Random Hse. Children's Bks.

—Barbie Loves Weddings. 2004. (Illus.). 16p. (J). (ps-2). pap. 3.99 (978-0-375-82742-6(0) , Golden Bks.) Random Hse. Children's Bks.

—Barbie: Mariposa. 2008. (Pictureback(R) Ser.). 16p. (J). (ps-1). pap. 3.99 (***978-0-375-84798-1(7)*** , Golden Bks.) Random Hse., Inc.

—Fairytopia. 2006. (Board Books). (Illus.). 22p. (J). (gr. k-ps). bds. 4.99 (978-0-375-83538-4(5) , Golden Bks.) Random Hse. Children's Bks.

Man-Kong, Mary. The Magic of the Rainbow. 2008. 24p. (J). (gr. k-k). bds. 4.99 (***978-0-375-84796-7(0)*** , Golden Bks.) Random Hse., Inc.

Man-Kong, Mary & Golden Books Staff. Amazing Makeover. Wolcott, Karen, illus. 2006. 12p. (J). (ps-1). 10.95 (978-0-375-83552-0(0) , Golden Bks.) Random Hse. Children's Bks.

—Barbie in the Twelve Dancing Princesses. 2006. (Illus.). 24p. (J). (ps-2). pap. 3.99 (978-0-375-83762-3(0) , Golden Bks.) Random Hse. Children's Bks.

—Barbie in the Twelve Dancing Princesses. Tormey, Carlotta, illus. 2006. 32p. (J). (ps-2). 8.99 (978-0-375-83748-7(5) , Golden Bks.) Random Hse. Children's Bks.

Man-Kong, Mary & Posner-Sanchez, Andrea. Barbie of Swan Lake. movie tie-in ed. 2003. (Barbie Ser.). (Illus.). 24p. (J). (ps-2). pap. 3.99 (978-0-375-82640-5(8) , Golden Bks.) Random Hse. Children's Bks.

Man-Kong, Mary & Roberts, Angela. Barbie Loves Ballet. Wolcott, Karen, illus. 2005. (Barbie Ser.). 24p. (J). (ps-2). pap. 3.99 (978-0-375-82756-3(0) , Golden Bks.) Random Hse. Children's Bks.

Miller, Sara Swan. Barbie Super Fun. O'Brien, Jeff & Yuh, Ramona, photos by. 2001. (Barbie Friendship Craft Kit Ser.). (Illus.). (J). (gr. 1-3). (978-1-57584-812-9(0)) Reader's Digest Children's Publishing, Inc.

North, Merry, adapted by. Barbie Movie Theater Storybook & Movie Projector. 2005. (RD Innovative Book & Player Format Ser.). (Illus.). 48p. (J). (ps). 24.99 (978-0-7944-0682-0(3)) Reader's Digest Assn., Inc., The.

O'Neill, Cynthia, ed. Mujer Profesional. 2004. (SPA.). 48p. (J). pap. 6.99 (978-0-7566-0448-6(6)) Dorling Kindersley Publishing, Inc.

Parker, Jessie, et al. Barbie: A Dress-up Day. S. I. International Staff, illus. 2003. (Step into Reading Ser.: Vol. 1). 32p. (J). (ps-1). pap. 3.99 (978-0-375-82501-9(0) , Random Hse. Bks. for Young Readers) Random Hse. Children's Bks.

Posner-Sanchez, Andrea & Man-Kong, Mary. Barbie & the Magic of Pegasus: A Storybook. 2005. (Random House Pictureback Book Ser.). (Illus.). (J). (***978-1-4156-2366-4(X)***) Random Hse. Children's Bks.

Pugliano-Martin, Carol. BarbieTM: A Day at the Fair. S. I. International Staff, illus. 2003. (Step into Reading Ser.). 32p. (J). (ps-1). pap. 3.99 (978-0-375-82368-8(9) , Random Hse. Bks. for Young Readers) Random Hse. Children's Bks.

Pugliano-Martin, Carol & Gordh, Bill. Barbie Story Collection. Wolcott, Karen, illus. 2006. (Step into Reading Ser.). 192p. (J). (ps-3). pap. 8.99 (978-0-375-84124-8(5) , Random Hse. Bks. for Young Readers) Random Hse. Children's Bks.

Random House Staff & Golden Books Staff. The Swan Princess. Duarte, Pamela, illus. 2003. 64p. (J). (ps-2). pap. 3.99 (978-0-375-82535-4(5) , Golden Bks.) Random Hse. Children's Bks.

Reader's Digest Editors. Barbie & the Twelve Dancing Princess. 2006. 12p. (J). bds. 9.99 (978-0-7944-1108-4(8)) Reader's Digest Assn., Inc., The.

—Barbie Fairytopia (board book) the Magic of the Rainbow. 2007. 10p. (J). bds. 9.99 (978-0-7944-1214-2(9)) Reader's Digest Assn., Inc., The.

—Barbie Fairytopia (panorama sticker book) the Magic of the Rainbow. 2007. 16p. (J). bds. 7.99 (978-0-7944-1215-9(7)) Reader's Digest Assn., Inc., The.

Reader's Digest Staff. Barbie & the Twelve Dancing Princess Panorama Sticker Storybook. 2006. (Barbie Movie Tie-in Ser.). 16p. (J). 7.99 (978-0-7944-1109-1(6)) Reader's Digest Assn., Inc., The.

Reader's Digest Staff & Katschke, Judy. Barbie Pretty Hairstyle Revised. 2006. (Style Bks.). 12p. (J). bds. 12.99 (978-0-7944-1009-4(X)) Reader's Digest Assn., Inc., The.

Reader's Digest Staff & Mattel Photo Studio. Barbie the Island Princess. 2007. 10p. (J). bds. 9.99 (***978-0-7944-1298-2(X)***) Reader's Digest Assn., Inc., The.

—Barbie the island princess sticker panorama Book. 2007. 16p. (J). 7.99 (***978-0-7944-1299-9(8)***) Reader's Digest Assn., Inc., The.

Redbank, Tennant & Golden Books Staff. Barbie in the Twelve Dancing Princesses. 2006. (Step into Reading Ser.: No. 2). (Illus.). 32p. (J). (ps-2). pap. 3.99 (978-0-375-83780-7(9) , Random Hse. Bks. for Young Readers) Random Hse. Children's Bks.

Rogers, Beth. Barbie As Rapunzel. 2006. 16p. (J). 7.99 (978-0-7944-0945-6(8)) Reader's Digest Assn., Inc., The.

Saunders, Catherine. The Essential Guide. 2005. (Illus.). 48p. (J). (ps-7). 12.99 (978-0-7566-1333-4(7)) Dorling Kindersley Publishing, Inc.

Saunders, Catherine & Dorling Kindersley Publishing Staff. Barbie Princess Tales. 2005. (Ultimate sticker Bks.). (Illus.). 16p. (J). (ps-7). pap. 6.99 (978-0-7566-1332-7(9)) Dorling Kindersley Publishing, Inc.

Schutz, Samantha & Burr, Daniela. Barbie in the Twelve Dancing Princesses. 2006. (Illus.). 80p. (J). pap. 3.99 (978-0-439-87003-0(8) , Scholastic Paperbacks) Scholastic, Inc.

Wax, Wendy & Mattel Photo Studio. The Barbie Diaries. 2006. 64p. (J). bds. 14.99 (978-0-7944-1145-9(2)) Reader's Digest Assn., Inc., The.

Weber, Lou, ed. Barbie 123 Wipe off Book. 2004. 16p. (J). spiral bd., bds. 10.98 (978-1-4127-0561-5(4) , 7222200) Publications International, Ltd.

—Barbie ABC Wipe off Book. 2004. 16p. (J). spiral bd., bds. 10.98 (978-1-4127-0560-8(6) , 7222100) Publications International, Ltd.

—Magic Wand Barbie. 2005. 14p. (J). bds. 15.98 (978-1-4127-3538-4(6) , 7264600) Publications International, Ltd.

Webster, Christy. Barbie Mariposa. 2008. (Step into Reading Ser.). (Illus.). 32p. (J). (ps-1). lib. bdg. 11.99 (***978-0-375-95198-5(9));*** pap. 3.99 (***978-0-375-85198-8(4)***) Random Hse. Children's Bks. (Random Hse. Bks. for Young Readers).

Weinberger, Kimberly. Barbie As Rapunzel. 2002. (Junior Chapter Bk.). 48p. (J). (ps-3). pap. 3.99 (978-0-439-44295-4(8)) Scholastic, Inc.

BARCELONA (SPAIN)

Cormand, Bernat. Barcelona, Tell Us about Gaudi. Kliczkowski, H., ed. Rifa, Fina, illus. 80p. (978-84-89439-29-0(X)) Asppan, A., S.L. Distribuidora Internacional de Libros y Revistas.

—Barcelona, Tell Us about Yourself. (SPA., Illus.). 80p. (978-84-96048-36-2(5)) Asppan, A., S.L. Distribuidora Internacional de Libros y Revistas.

A B

BARNABY (FICTITIOUS CHARACTER : HOLDER)—FICTION

Rouillard, Wendy W. Barnaby-Seasons in the Park. Rouillard, Wendy W., ed. 2000. (Barnaby Ser.: Vol. 5). (Illus.). 32p. (J). 15.95 (978-0-9642836-9-5(7)) Barnaby & Co.

—Barnaby's Kite Ride. Rouillard, Wendy W., illus. l.t. ed. 1998. (Illus.). 32p. (J). (gr. 1-3). 15.95 (978-0-9642836-6-4(2)) Barnaby & Co.

BARNARD, CHRISTIAAN, 1922-2001

Bankston, John. Christiaan Barnard & the Story of the First Heart Transplant. l.t. ed. 2002. (Unlocking the Secrets of Science Ser.). (Illus.). 56p. (gr. 4-10). lib. bdg. 25.70 (978-1-58415-120-3(X)) Mitchell Lane Pubs., Inc.

BARNAVELT, LEWIS (FICTITIOUS CHARACTER)—FICTION

Bellairs, John. The Figure in the Shadows. Mayer, Mercer, illus. 2004. (Lewis Barnavelt Ser.). 160p. (J). pap. 5.99 (978-0-14-240260-3(5) , Puffin) Penguin Group (USA) Inc.

—The Figure in the Shadows. 1999. (J). (gr. 3 up). 21.75 (978-0-8446-7009-6(X)) Smith, Peter Pub., Inc.

—The House with a Clock in Its Walls. Gorey, Edward, illus. 2004. (Lewis Barnavelt Ser.). 192p. (J). pap. 5.99 (978-0-14-240257-3(5) , Puffin) Penguin Group (USA) Inc.

—The House with a Clock in Its Walls. 179p. (J). (gr. 4-6). pap. 4.50 (978-0-8072-1423-7(X) , Listening Library) Random Hse. Audio Publishing Group.

BARNEY (FICTITIOUS CHARACTER)—FICTION

Amaral, Gayla. Barney's Color Train Readalong. Hernandez, Joseph, illus. 2000. 24p. (J). (ps-2). 6.95 (978-1-57064-713-0(5) , 97964) Scholastic, Inc.

—Hooray for Mommies! Babies & BarneyTM. Full, Dennis, photos by. 2002. (Barney Ser.). (Illus.). 22p. (J). (ps-k). bds. 5.99 (978-1-58668-220-0(2)) Scholastic, Inc.

Amaral, Gayla, ed. Barney, Let's Discover. McKee, Darren, illus. 2001. (Barney Ser.). 32p. (J). (ps-3). pap. 0.99 (978-1-58668-134-0(6)) Scholastic, Inc.

Amaral, Gayla & Lyrick Publishing Staff. Barney's C Is for Christmas. Yingling, Kathryn, illus. 2001. (Barney Ser.). 16p. (J). (ps-k). bds. 6.99 (978-1-57064-726-0(7)) Scholastic, Inc.

Barney: My First Telephone Book. 2000. (Illus.). (J). 16.98 (978-0-7853-4538-1(8)) Publications International, Ltd.

Barney & BJ Go to the Police Station. 2002. (Barney's Go to Ser.). 32p. (J). (ps-k). bds. 5.95 (978-1-58668-231-6(8)) Lyrick Studios.

Barney Goes to the Dentist. 2002. (Barney's Go to Ser.). 32p. (J). (ps-k). bds. 5.95 (978-1-58668-248-4(2)) Scholastic, Inc.

Barney Let's Go to the Zoo. 2001. (Barney Ser.). (Illus.). 60p. (J). (ps-k). 1.99 (978-1-57064-940-0(5)) Scholastic, Inc.

Barney Meets the New Baby. 2002. (Barney Ser.). 32p. (J). (ps-k). bds. 5.95 (978-1-58668-246-0(6)) Scholastic, Inc.

Barney Plays Piano. 2002. (Illus.). (J). 16.98 (978-0-7853-5234-1(1)) Publications International, Ltd.

Barney Publishing Staff & Bernthal, Mark S. Barney's Book of Colors. McKee, Darren, illus. 1999. (Barney Ser.). 22p. (J). (ps-3). bds. 5.99 (978-1-57064-454-2(3)) Scholastic, Inc.

Barney's ABC Animals! 1999. (Barney Ser.). (Illus.). 32p. (J). (ps-k). 6.95 (978-1-57064-624-9(4)) Scholastic, Inc.

Berger, Ellie. Barney's I Love Nursery Rhymes! Amaral, Gayla, ed. McKee, Darren, illus. 2001. (Barney Ser.). 64p. (J). (ps-3). 1.99 (978-1-58668-132-6(X)) Scholastic, Inc.

Berk, Sheryl. Barney's Little Lessons: Be My Friend! Valentine-Ruppe, June, illus. 2002. (Barney Ser.). 8p. (J). (ps-1). bds. 5.99 (978-1-58668-293-4(8)) Scholastic, Inc.

—Barney's Little Lessons: The New Babysitter. Yingling, Kathryn, illus. 2003. (Barney Ser.). 224p. (J). (ps-1). bds. 5.99 (978-1-58668-302-3(0)) Scholastic, Inc.

Bernstein, Lee. Barney's Sing-Along Stories: I Love You. Valentine-Ruppe, June, illus. 2003. (Barney Ser.). 24p. (J). (ps-1). pap. 3.50 (978-1-58668-299-6(7)) Scholastic, Inc.

Bernthal, Mark S. Barney's 12 Days of Christmas. 1998. (Barney Ser.). 26p. (J). (ps-k). bds. 13.95 (978-1-57064-241-8(9)) Scholastic, Inc.

Bernthal, Mark S. & Lyrick Publishing Staff. Barney & BJ Go to the Zoo. Full, Dennis, photos by. 1999. (Barney's Go to Ser.). (Illus.). 24p. (J). (ps-k). pap. 3.50 (978-1-57064-446-7(2)) Scholastic, Inc.

—Barney's Book of Shapes. 1998. (Barney Ser.). (Illus.). 22p. (J). (ps). bds. 5.95 (978-1-57064-242-5(7)) Scholastic, Inc.

Bernthal, Mark S. & Scholastic, Inc. Staff. Barney's ABC Animals! Baker, Darrell, illus. 1999. (Barney Ser.). 32p. (J). (ps-k). pap. 3.50 (978-1-57064-453-5(5)) Scholastic, Inc.

Cooner, Donna D. Barney Makes Music. Davis, Guy, ed. 1999. (Barney Ser.). (Illus.). 24p. (J). (ps-k). 4.95 (978-1-57064-461-0(6)) Scholastic, Inc.

—Barney's Toolbox. Hernandez, Joseph, illus. 1998. (Barney Ser.). 14p. (J). (ps-k). 5.95 (978-1-57064-244-9(3)) Scholastic, Inc.

Davis, Guy. Barney Says "Night-Night" McKee, Darren, illus. 1998. (Barney Ser.). 12p. (J). (ps-k). 6.95 (978-1-57064-455-9(1)) Scholastic, Inc.

—Barney's ABC, 123 & More. McKee, Darren, illus. 1999. (Barney Ser.). 14p. (J). (ps-k). bds. 9.99 (978-1-57064-243-2(5)) Scholastic, Inc.

—Barney's Musical Castle. Full, Dennis, illus. 2001. (Barney Ser.). 24p. (J). (ps-k). pap. 3.50 (978-1-57064-710-9(0)) Scholastic, Inc.

—Barney's Neighborhood. Davis, Guy, illus. Dipold, Jane, photos by. 1999. (Barney Ser.). (Illus.). 18p. (J). (ps-k). 6.95 (978-1-57064-463-4(2)) Scholastic, Inc.

—Freddi Fish & the Pirate's Treasure. Winslow, Becky, illus. 2001. (Humongous Ser.). 12p. (J). bds. 9.99 incl. cd-rom (978-1-58668-066-4(8)) Lyrick Studios.

Davis, Guy, ed. Barney's We Wish You a Merry Christmas. 1999. (Barney Ser.). (Illus.). 14p. (J). (ps-k). pap. 5.95 (978-1-57064-750-5(X)) Scholastic, Inc.

Davis, Guy & Valentine-Ruppe, June. Baby Bop's Blankey. 1999. (Barney Ser.). (Illus.). 14p. (J). (ps-k). 5.95 (978-1-57064-613-3(9)) Scholastic, Inc.

Dudko, Mary Ann & Larsen, Margie. Barney's in, Out & All Around. Full, Dennis, illus. 1999. (Barney Ser.). 24p. (J). (ps-k). bds. 4.99 (978-1-57064-445-0(4)) Scholastic, Inc.

Full, Dennis, photos by. Barney's Favorite Farm Animals. 2001. (Barney Ser.). (Illus.). 10p. (J). (ps-k). bds. 3.99 (978-1-58668-129-6(X)) Scholastic, Inc.

Goodnight Barney. 2001. (Illus.). (J). 7.95 (978-0-7853-4752-1(6)) Publications International, Ltd.

Halfmann, Janet. Barney's Four Seasons. Davis, Guy, ed. Sharp, Chris, illus. 1999. 80p. (J). (ps-3). 1.99 (978-1-57064-465-8(9)) Scholastic, Inc.

Halfmann, Janet & Scholastic, Inc. Staff. Barney's Christmas Fun: A Dino-Mite Color & Activity Book. Davis, Guy, ed. Valentine-Ruppe, June, illus. 1999. (Barney Ser.). 80p. (J). (ps-k). 1.99 (978-1-57064-466-5(7)) Scholastic, Inc.

Halfmann, Janet, et al. Barney's Favorite Songs. Davis, Guy, ed. Valentine-Ruppe, June, illus. 1999. (Barney Ser.). 112p. (J). (ps-k). act. bk. ed. 2.99 (978-1-57064-457-3(8)) Scholastic, Inc.

Harris, Annmarie, ed. Land of Make Believe: Sticker Storybook. 2005. (Barney Ser.). 20p. (J). pap. 5.99 (978-0-439-69156-7(7)) Scholastic, Inc.

Hinkler Books Staff, reader. Barney Says "Play Safely" 2004. 32p. (J). 9.99 incl. audio compact disk (978-1-86515-998-0(0)) Hinkler Bks. Pty, Ltd. AUS. *Dist:* Penton Overseas, Inc.

—Barney's Big Balloon. 2004. 32p. (J). 9.99 incl. audio compact disk (978-1-86515-997-3(2)) Hinkler Bks. Pty, Ltd. AUS. *Dist:* Penton Overseas, Inc.

—Barney's Outer Space Adventure. 2004. (J). 9.99 incl. audio compact disk (978-1-86515-996-6(4)) Hinkler Bks. Pty, Ltd. AUS. *Dist:* Penton Overseas, Inc.

—Come on over Barneys House. 2004. 32p. (J). 9.99 incl. audio compact disk (978-1-86515-999-7(9)) Hinkler Bks. Pty, Ltd. AUS. *Dist:* Penton Overseas, Inc.

Kearns, Kimberly & Amaral, Gayla. BJ's Rub a Dub Dub. Davis, Guy, ed. Johnson, Jay B., illus. 1999. (Barney Ser.). 14p. (J). (ps-k). 5.95 (978-1-57064-612-6(0)) Scholastic, Inc.

Larsen, Margie & Dudko, Mary Ann. Barney's "Let's Learn" Boxed Set, Set. Full, Dennis, photos by. 1998. (Barney Ser.). (Illus.). (J). (ps-k). 9.99 (978-1-57064-517-4(5)) Scholastic, Inc.

Lee, Quinlan B. Barney: Ready, Set, Go! Albrecht, Jeff, illus. 2005. (Barney Ser.). 5p. (J). pap. 7.99 (978-0-439-69155-0(9)) Scholastic, Inc.

—I See Barney! McKee, Darren, illus. 2005. (Barney Ser.). 5p. (J). bds. 6.99 (978-0-439-69154-3(0)) Scholastic, Inc.

Lyrick Studios Staff. Barney's Count to 10. 1999. (Barney Ser.). (Illus.). 24p. (J). (ps-k). 6.95 (978-1-57064-623-2(6)) Scholastic, Inc.

McAdam, Christine. Barney's Shapes. McKee, Darren, illus. 1999. (Barney Ser.). 22p. (J). (ps-k). 5.95 (978-1-57064-651-5(1)) Scholastic, Inc.

McKee, Darren. Barney Visits the Zoo. Brower, Howard, illus. 2003. (Barney Ser.). 64p. (J). (ps). 2.99 (978-1-58668-313-9(6) , Levine, Arthur A. Bks.) Scholastic, Inc.

McKee, Darren, illus. Barney's Musical Fun Fair. 2004. (Deluxe Jukebox Ser.). 24p. (J). bds. (978-0-7853-9958-2(5) , 7209200) Publications International, Ltd.

Mckee, Darren, illus. Clean Up! 2004. (Barney Ser.). 24p. (J). pap. 3.50 (978-0-439-63978-1(6)) Scholastic, Inc.

Mody, Monica. Barney's Easter Party! Baker, Darrell, illus. 2000. (Barney Ser.). 22p. (J). (ps-k). pap. 5.99 (978-1-57064-714-7(3)) Scholastic, Inc.

Moore, Gay. Barney & the Missing Shoes. 2006. (ENG.). 28p. per. 19.99 (***978-1-4259-0147-9(6)***) AuthorHouse.

Neusner, Dena Wallenstein. Barney Is Sooo Big! McKee, Darren, illus. 2003. (Barney Ser.). 5p. (J). bds. 6.99 (978-1-58668-301-6(2)) Scholastic, Inc.

Nickel, Scott. Barney's World of Trucks. Full, Dennis, photos by. 2001. (Barney Ser.). (Illus.). 40p. (J). (ps-k). pap. 6.99 (978-1-58668-135-7(4)) Scholastic, Inc.

Parent, Nancy. Barney's Book of Clothes. Johnson, Jay, illus. 2004. 8p. (J). pap. 5.99 (978-1-58668-309-2(8)) Lyrick Publishing.

—Barney's Book of Clothes. Johnson, Jay, illus. 2004. (Barney Ser.). 8p. (J). bds. 5.99 (978-0-439-63981-1(6)) Scholastic, Inc.

—Barney's Zoo Friends. Yee, Josie, illus. 2001. (Barney Ser.). 12p. (J). (ps-1). bds. 9.99 (978-1-58668-233-0(4)) Scholastic, Inc.

Ryan, Lisa & Scholastic, Inc. Staff. The Wheels on Barney's Bus. Winslow, Becky, illus. 2002. (Barney Ser.). 6p. (J). (ps-1). pap. 9.99 (978-1-58668-292-7(X)) Scholastic, Inc.

Sander, Sonia. Getting Ready for 123 Fun. McKee, Darren, illus. 2003. (Barney Ser.). 64p. (J). pap. 2.99 (978-1-58668-310-8(1)) Scholastic, Inc.

Scholastic, Inc. Staff. Barney Play Time! Swendsen, Silje, ed. 2004. (Barney Ser.). 144p. (J). pap. 3.99 (978-0-439-60700-1(0)) Scholastic, Inc.

—Barney's Christmas Countdown. 2007. (Barney Ser.). 12p. (J). bds. 3.99 (***978-0-545-00061-1(0)***) Scholastic, Inc.

—Barney's Favorite Easter Stories, 2 vols., Set. Amaral, Gayla, ed. Sharp, Chris & Valentine-Ruppe, June, illus. 2001. (Barney Ser.). 48p. (J). (ps-k). pap. 4.99 (978-1-58668-072-5(2)) Scholastic, Inc.

—Barney's Paint & Play. Amaral, Gayla, ed. McKee, Darren & Winslow, Becky, illus. 2001. (Barney Ser.). 32p. (J). (ps-1). pap., act. bk. ed. 2.99 (978-1-58668-142-5(7)) Scholastic, Inc.

—Barney's Sing-Along Stories: If You're Happy & You Know It! McKee, Darren, illus. 2004. (Barney Ser.). 24p. (J). pap. 3.50 (978-0-439-45862-7(5)) Scholastic, Inc.

—I Love Animals. Amaral, Gayla, ed. McKee, Darren, illus. 2001. (Barney Ser.). 96p. (J). 2.99 (978-1-58668-131-9(1)) Scholastic, Inc.

—Merry Christmas! Neusner, Dena, ed. 2003. (Barney Ser.). 80p. (J). pap. 2.99 (978-0-439-52451-3(2)) Scholastic, Inc.

Scholastic, Inc. Staff, et al. Barney's Colorful World. McKee, Darren, illus. 2003. (Barney Ser.). 32p. (J). pap. 3.99 (978-0-439-56881-4(1)) Scholastic, Inc.

Sing along Barney: Story Reader. 2004. 26p. (J). spiral bd. (978-1-4127-3229-1(8) , 7237200) Publications International, Ltd.

Valvassori, Maureen M. My Day with Barney. Hill, Nelson, illus. 2001. (Barney Ser.). 12p. (J). bds. 5.99 (978-1-58668-139-5(7)) Scholastic, Inc.

Valvassori, Maureen M. & Scholastic, Inc. Staff. What Will I Be When I Grow Up? Alvord, R. & Greenfield, Nelson, illus. 2000. (Barney Ser.). 16p. (J). (ps). pap. 5.99 (978-1-57064-712-3(7) , 97963) Scholastic, Inc.

White, Stephen. Barney's Storybook Treasury. Sharp, Chris & McGlothin, David, illus. 1999. (Barney Ser.). 176p. (J). (ps-k). pap. 10.95 (978-1-57064-579-2(5)) Scholastic, Inc.

White, Stephen & Scholastic, Inc. Staff. Barney's Night Before Christmas. Davis, Guy, ed. Grayson, Rick, illus. 1999. (Barney Ser.). 24p. (J). (ps-k). pap. 3.50 (978-1-57064-462-7(4)) Scholastic, Inc.

BARNUM, P. T. (PHINEAS TAYLOR), 1810-1891

Warrick, Karen Clemens. P. T. Barnum: Genius of the Three-Ring Circus. 2001. (Historical American Biographies Ser.). (Illus.). 128p. (YA). (gr. 6-12). lib. bdg. 26.60 (978-0-7660-1447-3(9)) Enslow Pubs., Inc.

BARRISTERS

see Lawyers

BARTH, SEBASTIAN (FICTITIOUS CHARACTER)—FICTION

Howe, James. Dew Drop Dead. 2000. (Sebastian Barth Mysteries Ser.). 160p. (J). (gr. 3-7). pap. 5.99 (978-0-689-80760-2(0) , Aladdin) Simon & Schuster Children's Publishing.

—Dew Drop Dead: A Sebastian Barth Mystery. 2000. (J). 11.64 (978-0-606-17314-8(5)) Tandem Library Bks.

BARTHOLDI, FREDERIC AUGUSTE, 1834-1904

Curlee, Lynn. Liberty. Curlee, Lynn, illus. 2003. (Illus.). 48p. (J). (gr. 2-7). pap. 6.99 (978-0-689-85683-9(0) , Aladdin) Simon & Schuster Children's Publishing.

—Liberty. 2000. (Illus.). 48p. (J). (gr. 2-7). 18.95 (978-0-689-82823-2(3) , Atheneum) Simon & Schuster Children's Publishing.

—Liberty. 2003. (gr. 3-6). lib. bdg. 15.30 (978-0-613-61638-6(3)) Tandem Library Bks.

Fandel, Jennifer. The Statue of Liberty. 2005. (What in the World? Ser.). (Illus.). 48p. (gr. 5-9). 21.95 (978-1-58341-377-7(4) , Creative Education) Creative Co., The.

Marcovitz, Hal. The Statue of Liberty. 2002. (American Symbols & Their Meanings Ser.). (Illus.). 48p. (YA). (gr. 4 up). lib. bdg. (978-1-59084-022-1(4)) Mason Crest Pubs.

BARTON, CLARA, 1821-1912

Benge, Janet & Benge, Geoff. Clara Barton: Courage under Fire. 2003. 192p. pap. 8.99 (978-1-883002-50-3(8)) Emerald Bks.

Clara Barton. 2005. (First Biographies Ser.). (YA). (gr. k-3). (978-0-7368-9410-4(1) , Pebble Bks.) Capstone Pr., Inc.

Collier, James Lincoln. The Clara Barton You Never Knew. (You Never Knew Ser.). (Illus.). 80p. (J). 2004. (gr. 4-6). pap. 6.95 (978-0-516-25838-6(9)); 2003. 25.50 (978-0-516-24346-7(2)) Scholastic Library Publishing. (Children's Pr.).

Collins, David R. Clara Barton. Landgraf, Ken, illus. 1999. (Young Reader's Christian Library). 224p. (J). (gr. 4-7). pap. 1.39 (978-1-57748-601-5(3)) Barbour Publishing, Inc.

Ditchfield, Christin. Clara Barton: Founder of the American Red Cross. 2004. (Great Life Stories Ser.). (Illus.). 111p. (J). 30.50 (978-0-531-12276-1(X) , Watts, Franklin) Scholastic Library Publishing.

Dubowski, Cathy East. Clara Barton: I Want to Help! 2005. (Defining Moments Ser.). (Illus.). 31p. (J). (gr. 3-7). lib. bdg. 25.27 (978-1-59716-075-9(X)) Bearport Publishing Co., Inc.

Ford, Carin T. Clara Barton: Brave Nurse. 2006. (Heroes of American History Ser.). (Illus.). 32p. (J). lib. bdg. 22.60 (978-0-7660-2602-5(7) , Enslow Elementary) Enslow Pubs., Inc.

Francis, Dorothy Brenner. Clara Barton: Founder of the American Red Cross. 2002. (Gateway Biography Ser.). (Illus.). 48p. (gr. 2-4). lib. bdg. 23.90 (978-0-7613-2621-2(9) , Millbrook Pr.) Lerner Publishing Group.

Klingel, Cynthia Fitterer & Noyed, Robert B. Clara Barton: Founder of the American Red Cross. 2002. (Spirit of America: Our People Ser.). (Illus.). 32p. (J). (gr. 2-6). 27.07 (978-1-56766-172-9(6)) Child's World, Inc.

Koestler-Grack, Rachel A. The Story of Clara Barton. 2003. (Breakthrough Biographies Ser.). (Illus.). 32p. (gr. 3-5). 23.00 (978-0-7910-7312-4(2) , Chelsea Hse.) Facts On File, Inc.

Kramer, Candice. Clara Barton: Angel of the Battlefield. ed. 2004. (Reader's Theater Ser.). (J). pap. 22.00 (978-1-4108-1136-3(0)) Benchmark Education Co.

Lakin, Patricia. Clara Barton: Spirit of the American Red Cross. Sullivan, Simon, illus. 2004. (Ready-to-Read Stories of Famous Americans Ser.). 48p. (J). pap. 3.99 (978-0-689-86513-8(9) , Aladdin) Simon & Schuster Children's Publishing.

—Clara Barton Spirit of the American Red Cross. Sullivan, Simon, illus. ed. 2005. (Ready-to-Read Ser. Level 3). 48p. (J). lib. bdg. 15.00 (978-1-59054-958-2(9)) Fitzgerald Bks.

Lassieur, Allison. Clara Barton: Angel of the Battlefield. Bascle, Brian, illus. 2005. (Graphic Library). 32p. (J). (gr. 3-7). lib. bdg. 25.27 (978-0-7368-4632-5(8)) Capstone Pr., Inc.

Mara, Wil. Clara Barton. (Rookie Biographies Ser.). (Illus.). 32p. (J). (gr. 1-2). 2003. pap. 4.95 (978-0-516-27339-6(6)); 2002. 20.50 (978-0-516-22523-4(5)) Scholastic Library Publishing. (Children's Pr.).

—Clara Barton. 2002. (gr. k-3). lib. bdg. 12.95 (978-0-613-59459-2(2)) Tandem Library Bks.

Marko, Eve. Clara Barton & the American Red Cross. Marcos, Pablo, illus. 2005. (Heroes of America Ser.). 240p. (J). (gr. 3-8). lib. bdg. 21.35 (978-1-59679-255-5(8)) ABDO Publishing Co.

Meloche, Renee. Clara Barton: Heroes for Young Readers. 2005. (Illus.). 32p. (J). 6.99 (978-1-932096-33-0(7)) Emerald Bks.

Nardo, Don. Clara Barton: "Face Danger, but Never Fear It" 2008. (Americans-the Spirit of a Nation Ser.). 128p. (J). (gr. 5 up). lib. bdg. 31.93 (***978-0-7660-3024-4(5)***) Enslow Pubs., Inc.

Ransom, Candice F. Clara Barton. 2003. (History Maker Bios Ser.). (Illus.). 48p. (J). (gr. 3-5). lib. bdg. 26.60 (978-0-8225-4677-1(9)) Lerner Publishing Group.

Raum, Elizabeth. Clara Barton. 2004. (Illus.). 32p. (J). pap. 6.95 (978-1-4034-5704-2(2)); lib. bdg. (978-1-4034-4993-1(7)) Heinemann Library.

Ruffin, Frances E. Clara Barton. 2002. (American Legends Ser.). (Illus.). 24p. (J). (gr. 3). lib. bdg. 18.75 (978-0-8239-5825-2(6) , PowerKids Pr.) Rosen Publishing Group, Inc., The.

Schaefer, Lola M. Clara Barton. Saunders-Smith, Gail, ed. 2002. (First Biographies Ser.). (Illus.). 24p. (J). (gr. k-1). lib. bdg. 15.93 (978-0-7368-1434-8(5) , Pebble Bks.) Capstone Pr., Inc.

Somervill, Barbara A. Clara Barton: Founder of the American Red Cross. (Illus.). 112p. (J). 2007. pap. (***978-0-7565-2199-8(8));*** 2006. (978-0-7565-1888-2(1)) Compass Point Bks.

Time for Kids Editors. Clara Barton: Angel of the Battlefield. 2008. (Time for Kids Ser.). (Illus.). 48p. (J). 15.99 (***978-0-06-057623-3(5));*** pap. 3.99 (***978-0-06-057622-6(7))*** HarperCollins Pubs.

Wheeler, Jill C. Clara Barton. 2002. (Breaking Barriers Ser.). (Illus.). 64p. (J). (gr. 3-8). lib. bdg. 25.65 (978-1-57765-317-2(3) , ABDO & Daughters) ABDO Publishing Co.

BARTON, CLARA, 1821-1912—FICTION

Osborne, Mary Pope. Civil War on Sunday, Vol. 21. unabr. ed. 2004. (Magic Tree House Ser. : No. 21). 76p. (J). (gr. k-3). pap. 17.00 incl. audio (978-0-8072-0930-1(9) , S FTR 253 SP, Listening Library) Random Hse. Audio Publishing Group.

—Civil War on Sunday. Murdocca, Sal, illus. 2000. (Magic Tree House Ser.: No. 21). 96p. (J). (gr. k-3). lib. bdg. 11.99 (978-0-679-99067-3(4)); mass mkt. 3.99 (978-0-679-89067-6(X)) Random Hse. Children's Bks. (Random Hse. Bks. for Young Readers).

—Civil War on Sunday. 2000. (Magic Tree House Ser. : No. 21). (J). (gr. k-3). lib. bdg. 11.80 (978-0-613-24596-8(2)); (Illus.). 10.79 (978-0-606-18852-4(5)) Tandem Library Bks.

BARTRAM, JOHN, 1699-1777

Ray, Deborah Kogan. The Flower Hunter: William Bartram, America's First Naturalist. Ray, Deborah Kogan, illus. 2004. (Illus.). 40p. (J). 17.00 (978-0-374-34589-1(9) , Farrar, Straus & Giroux (BYR)) Farrar, Straus & Giroux.

BARTRAM, WILLIAM, 1739-1823

Ray, Deborah Kogan. The Flower Hunter: William Bartram, America's First Naturalist. Ray, Deborah Kogan, illus. 2004. (Illus.). 40p. (J). 17.00 (978-0-374-34589-1(9) , Farrar, Straus & Giroux (BYR)) Farrar, Straus & Giroux.

BASEBALL

see also Little League Baseball; Softball

Abrams, Dennis. Ty Cobb. 2007. (Baseball Superstars Ser.). 136p. (J). (gr. 6-12). 30.00 (***978-0-7910-9439-6(1)*** , Chelsea Hse.) Facts On File, Inc.

Adelson, Bruce. Grand Slam Trivia. Pulver, Harry, illus. 1998. (Sports Trivia Ser.). 64p. (gr. 5-9). (J). pap. (978-0-8225-9803-9(5)); (YA). lib. bdg. (978-0-8225-3314-6(6)) Lerner Publishing Group. (Lerner Pubns.).

Adler, David A. Lou Gehrig: The Luckiest Man. 2001. (gr. k-3). lib. bdg. 14.15 (978-0-613-35534-6(2)) Tandem Library Bks.

Banks, Kerry. Old-Time Baseball Trivia: The Stormy Years 1969-89. 2003. (Illus.). pap. 9.95 (978-1-55054-673-6(2)) Sterling Publishing Co., Inc.

Baseball: Individual Title Six-Packs. (On Deck Ser.). 24p. (gr. 4-5). 35.00 (978-0-7578-1006-0(3)) Rigby Education.

Baseball for Fun! (For Fun Ser.). 48p. (YA). 8.95 (978-0-7565-1150-0(X)) Compass Point Bks.

Beisbol, 6 Packs. (On Deck en Espanol Ser.). (SPA.). 24p. (gr. 4-5). 35.00 (978-0-7578-6389-9(2)) Rigby Education.

Benjamin, Lisa. Baseball Dreams: The Story of Roberto Clemente. (Voices Reading Ser.). (Illus.). 32p. (J). (978-0-7367-2912-3(7)) Zaner-Bloser, Inc.

Blackall, Bernie. Baseball. 1999. (J). (gr. 4-6). 21.36 (978-1-57572-839-1(7)) Heinemann Library.

Bratton, Deboral B. & Bratton, Ashley D. Record-a-Sport Baseball & Softball Organizer. Bratton, Deboral B. & Bratton, Ashley D., eds. Bratton, Deboral B. & Bratton, Ashley D., illus. 2003. (Illus.). (gr. 1 up). 18.95 (978-1-931746-03-8(6)) Sport Your Stuff Corp.

Briand, Kevin. The Baseball Book: A Young Player's Guide to Baseball. 2003. (Illus.). 120p. (J). (gr. 4). 19.95 (978-1-55297-708-8(0)) ; pap. 12.95 (978-1-55297-690-6(4)) Firefly Bks., Ltd.

—Baseball Book: A Young Player's Guide to Baseball. 2003. (gr. k-3). lib. bdg. 22.20 (978-0-613-78609-6(2)) Tandem Library Bks.

Brill, Marlene Targ. Baseball & Softball. 2001. (Winning Women in Sports Ser.). (Illus.). 104p. (YA). (gr. 4 up). lib. bdg. 14.95 (978-1-56674-306-8(0)) Forest Hse. Publishing Co., Inc.

Brown, Jim. A Bridge to Cross. 2003. 234p. (YA). 25.95 (978-0-595-74894-5(5)); pap. 15.95 (978-0-595-28773-4(5)) iUniverse, Inc.

Brown, Jonatha A. Baseball. 2004. (J). pap. (978-0-8368-4344-6(4)); lib. bdg. 19.33 (978-0-8368-4337-8(1)) Stevens, Gareth Inc.

Buckley, James, Jr. American League East. 2005. (Major League Baseball Ser.). (Illus.). 48p. (J). (gr. 1-5). 27.07 (978-1-59296-359-1(5)) Child's World, Inc.

Buckley, James. A Bat Boy's Day. 2005. (Dk Readers Ser.). (Illus.). 32p. (J). (gr. 2-3). pap. 3.99 (978-0-7566-1207-8(1)) Dorling Kindersley Publishing, Inc.

Buckley, James, Jr. A Batboy's Day. 2005. 32p. (J). (ps-3). lib. bdg. 11.19 (978-0-606-34046-5(7)) Tandem Library Bks.

Buckley, James. Home Run Heroes. 2001. (gr. k-3). lib. bdg. 11.80 (978-0-613-35143-0(6)) Tandem Library Bks.

—Let's Go to the Ballpark. 2005. (Dk Readers Ser.). (Illus.). 32p. (J). 14.99 (978-0-7566-1208-5(X)); (gr. 2-3). pap. 3.99 (978-0-7566-1209-2(8)) Dorling Kindersley Publishing, Inc.

—MLB Strikeout Kings. 2001. (gr. k-3). lib. bdg. 11.80 (978-0-613-35243-7(2)) Tandem Library Bks.

—MLB Super Shortstops. 2001. (gr. k-3). lib. bdg. 11.80 (978-0-613-35245-1(9)) Tandem Library Bks.

Buckley, James, Jr. MLB World Series Sticker Book. 2003. (Major League Baseball Ser.). (Illus.). 16p. (J). pap. 6.99 (978-0-7894-9254-8(7)) Dorling Kindersley Publishing, Inc.

—Play Ball! The Official Major League Baseball Guide for Young Players. Eliason, Mike, photos by. 2002. (Illus.). 48p. (J). (gr. 3 up). 12.99 (978-0-7894-8509-0(5)) Dorling Kindersley Publishing, Inc.

—Strikeout Kings. 2001. (Eyewitness Readers Ser.). (Illus.). (J). (978-0-606-20930-4(1)) Tandem Library Bks.

—The Ultimate All-star Sticker Book. 2003. (Major League Baseball Ser.). (Illus.). 16p. (J). pap. 6.99 (978-0-7894-9906-6(1)) Dorling Kindersley Publishing, Inc.

—The World of Baseball. 2003. (Major League Baseball Readers Ser.). (Illus.). 48p. (J). pap. 3.99 (978-0-7894-9845-8(6)) Dorling Kindersley Publishing, Inc.

Buckley, James, Jr. & Dorling Kindersley Publishing Staff. At the Ballpark. 2003. (Major League Baseball Ser.). (Illus.). 16p. (J). pap. 6.99 (978-0-7894-9846-5(4)) Dorling Kindersley Publishing, Inc.

—Baseball 1-2-3. 2001. (Illus.). 24p. (J). (gr. 4-7). bds. 6.99 (978-0-7894-7339-4(9)) Dorling Kindersley Publishing, Inc.

—Baseball ABC. 2001. (Illus.). 24p. (J). (ps-k). bds. 6.99 (978-0-7894-7338-7(0)) Dorling Kindersley Publishing, Inc.

Burke, Bob & Parr, Royse. Allie Reynolds: Super Chief. Campbell, Gini Moore, ed. 2002. (Oklahoma Trackmaker Ser.). (Illus.). 302p. 24.95 (978-1-885596-27-7(8)) Oklahoma Heritage Assn.

Cheripko, Jan. Get Ready to Play Tee Ball. Cheripko, Jan, photos by. 2003. (Illus.). 32p. (J). (gr. k-2). pap. 7.95 (978-1-56397-716-9(8)) Boyds Mills Pr.

—Get Ready to Play Tee Ball. 1999. 14.75 (978-0-606-17660-6(8)); lib. bdg. 16.40 (978-0-613-16689-8(2)) Tandem Library Bks.

Christopher, Matt. At the Plate with... Ichiro. 2003. (Illus.). 112p. (J). (gr. 5-8). pap. 4.99 (978-0-316-13679-2(4)) Little, Brown Bks. for Young Readers.

Christopher, Matt. The World Series: The Greatest Moments of the Most Exciting Games. 2007. (Legendary Sports Events Ser.). 128p. (J). (gr. 2-7). pap. 4.99 (*978-0-316-01117-4(7)) Little, Brown Bks. for Young Readers.

Clendening, John. American League West. 2005. (Major League Baseball Ser.). 48p. (J). (gr. 1-5). 27.07 (978-1-59296-360-7(9)) Child's World, Inc.

Cohen, Joel H. Odd Moments in Baseball. 2000. (Odd Sports Stories Ser.: Vol. 1). (Illus.). 96p. (J). (gr. 3-6). pap. 4.50 (978-0-590-37066-0(9)) Scholastic, Inc.

Cook, Sally & Charlton, James. Hey Batta Batta Swing! The Wild Old Days of Baseball. MacDonald, Ross, illus. 2007. 56p. (J). 17.99 (978-1-4169-1207-1(X) , McElderry, Margaret K.) Simon & Schuster Children's Publishing.

Cooper, Elisha. Ballpark. Cooper, Elisha, illus. 1998. (Illus.). 40p. (J). (gr. k-3). 15.00 (978-0-688-15755-5(6)) HarperCollins Pubs.

Coupe, Robert. Play Ball! 1999. (Explorers Ser.). (Illus.). 32p. (J). (978-0-7699-0500-6(5)) Shortland Pubns. (U. S. A.) Inc.

Craats, Rennay. For the Love of Baseball. 2003. (gr. 3-6). lib. bdg. 15.25 (978-0-613-79821-1(X)) Tandem Library Bks.

—For the Love of Baseball. Craats, Rennay & Kissock, Heather, eds. 2003. (For the Love of Sports Ser.). (Illus.). 32p. (J). pap. 6.95 (978-1-59036-068-2(0)) Weigl Pubs., Inc.

—For the Love of Baseball. Craats, Rennay, ed. 2001. (For the Love of Sports Ser.). (Illus.). 24p. (J). (gr. k-3). lib. bdg. 15.95 (978-1-930954-00-7(X)) Weigl Pubs., Inc.

Crossingham, John. Baseball in Action. 2000. (Sports in Action Ser.). (J). 13.75 (978-0-606-18049-8(4)) Tandem Library Bks.

Curlee, Lynn. Ballpark: The Story of America's Baseball Fields. Curlee, Lynn, illus. 2005. (Illus.). 48p. (J). 18.99 (978-0-689-86742-2(5) , Atheneum) Simon & Schuster Children's Publishing.

Curt Schilling. 2007. (J). pap. 5.95 (978-0-8225-3596-6(3) , First Avenue Editions) Lerner Publishing Group.

Dann, Sarah & Crossingham, John. Baseball in Action. 1999. (Sports in Action Ser.). (Illus.). 32p. (J). (gr. 3-4). pap. (978-0-7787-0175-0(1)); lib. bdg. (978-0-7787-0163-7(8)) Crabtree Publishing Co.

—Béisbol en Accion. 2005. (Illus.). 32p. (SPA.). pap. (978-0-7787-8617-7(X)); (FRE & SPA., (J). pap. (978-0-7787-8571-2(8)) Crabtree Publishing Co.

DeGezelle, Terri. Let's Play Baseball! 2006. (Pebble Plus Ser.). (Illus.). 24p. (J). (978-0-7368-5361-3(8)) Capstone Pr., Inc.

DeWerth, Ann Farry & Jeter, Derek. Derek Jeter's You're a Star. Suutala, Jeff, ed. 2002. (Illus.). 32p. (978-1-878843-35-7(4) , IMP Publishing) International Management Group (International Merchandising Corporation).

Dorling Kindersley Publishing Staff. Baseball. 2005. (Eyewitness Bks.). (Illus.). 72p. (J). 15.99 (978-0-7566-1061-6(3)) Dorling Kindersley Publishing, Inc.

—Baseball Top Ten. 2004. 96p. (J). pap. 9.99 (978-0-7566-0320-5(X)) Dorling Kindersley Publishing, Inc.

—DK Readers: Record Breakers. 2003. (gr. k-3). lib. bdg. 11.80 (978-0-613-75177-3(9)) Tandem Library Bks.

—Major League Baseball. 2003. (Major League Baseball Ser.). (Illus.). 12p. (J). bds. 6.99 (978-0-7894-9253-1(9)) Dorling Kindersley Publishing, Inc.

—My Baseball Book. Dorling Kindersley Publishing Staff, illus. 2002. (Illus.). 18p. (J). bds. 7.99 (978-0-7894-8508-3(7)) Dorling Kindersley Publishing, Inc.

Dorling Kindersley Publishing Staff, ed. October Magic. 2004. (Dk Readers Ser.). (Illus.). 48p. (J). pap. 3.99 (978-0-7566-0839-2(2)) Dorling Kindersley Publishing, Inc.

—October Magic: All the Best World Series! 2004. (Dk Readers Ser.). (Illus.). 48p. (J). (gr. 8). 12.99 (978-0-7566-0836-1(8)) Dorling Kindersley Publishing, Inc.

Driscoll, Laura. Negro Leagues: All Black Baseball. 2002. (gr. k-3). lib. bdg. 14.15 (978-0-613-45298-4(4)) Tandem Library Bks.

Eckart, Edana. I Can Play Baseball. 2002. (Welcome Bks.). (Illus.). 24p. (J). (ps-2). pap. 4.95 (978-0-516-24030-5(7) , Children's Pr.) Scholastic Library Publishing.

—I Can Play Baseball. 2002. (gr. k-3). lib. bdg. 12.95 (978-0-613-58841-6(X)) Tandem Library Bks.

Egan, Terry. The Good Guys of Baseball: Seventeen True Sports Stories. 2000. (Illus.). (J). (978-0-606-17920-1(8)) Tandem Library Bks.

Elismith, Benjamin. Batter Up! The Ultimate Baseball Scorekeeper. Man, Art, illus. 2004. 128p. (YA). (gr. 6-10). reprint ed. ring bd. 15.00 (978-0-7567-8070-8(5)) DIANE Publishing Co.

Epstein, Brad M. Auburn Tigers 123: My first counting Book. l.t. ed. 2006. (Illus.). 22p. (J). bds. 14.95 (*978-1-932530-44-5(4) , 123 Bk.) Michaelson Entertainment.

—Michigan State University Spartans 123: My first counting Book. l.t. ed. 2006. (Illus.). 22p. (J). bds. 14.95 (*978-1-932530-50-6(9) , 123 Bk.) Michaelson Entertainment.

—The Ohio State University Buckeyes 123: My first counting Book. l.t. ed. 2006. (Illus.). 22p. (J). bds. 15.95 (*978-1-932530-55-1(X) , 123 Bk.) Michaelson Entertainment.

—Oklahoma State University 101: My First Text-Board-Book. l.t. ed. 2007. (101—My First Text-Board Books). (Illus.). 20p. (J). bds. 10.95 (*978-1-932530-27-8(4) , 101 Bk.) Michaelson Entertainment.

—Texas A&M Aggies 123: My first counting Book. l.t. ed. 2006. (Illus.). 22p. (J). bds. 14.95 (*978-1-932530-53-7(3) , 123 Bk.) Michaelson Entertainment.

—UCLA Bruins 123: My first counting Book. l.t. ed. 2006. (Illus.). 22p. (J). bds. 14.95 (*978-1-932530-45-2(2) , 123 Bk.) Michaelson Entertainment.

—University of Alabama Crimson Tide 123: My first counting Book. l.t. ed. 2006. (Illus.). 22p. (J). bds. 14.95 (*978-1-932530-43-8(6) , 123 Bk.) Michaelson Entertainment.

—University of Arkansas 101: My First Text-Board-Book. l.t. ed. 2007. (101—My First Text-Board Books). (Illus.). 20p. (J). bds. 10.95 (*978-1-932530-58-2(4) , 101 Bk.) Michaelson Entertainment.

—University of Georgia Bulldogs 123: My first counting Book. l.t. ed. 2006. (Illus.). 22p. (J). bds. 14.95 (*978-1-932530-46-9(0) , 123 Bk.) Michaelson Entertainment.

—University of Illinois Fighting Illini 123: My first counting Book. l.t. ed. 2006. (Illus.). 22p. (J). bds. 14.95 (*978-1-932530-47-6(9) , 123 Bk.) Michaelson Entertainment.

Fauchald, Nick. Nice Hit! You Can Play Baseball. Dickson, Bill, illus. 2004. (Game Day Ser.). 24p. (J). (gr. k-3). 22.60 (978-1-4048-0259-9(2) , 1229516) Picture Window Bks.

Feldman, Heather. Derek Jeter: Estrella del Beisbol. 2002. (Superestrellas del Deporte Ser.).Tr. of Derek Jeter: Baseball Star. (SPA.). 24p. (J). lib. bdg. 17.25 (978-0-8239-6116-0(8) , Buenas Letra) Rosen Publishing Group, Inc., The.

—My Day at the Baseball Game: A Book about a Special Day. 2000. (PowerKids Readers Ser.). (Illus.). 24p. (J). (gr. 1). lib. bdg. 16.00 (978-0-8239-5525-1(7) , PK-MYBA, PowerKids Pr.) Rosen Publishing Group, Inc., The.

Fischer, David. American League Central. 2005. (Major League Baseball Ser.). (Illus.). 48p. (J). (gr. 1-5). 27.07 (978-1-59296-358-4(7)) Child's World, Inc.

—Grand Slam Baseball Quiz Book: What Is Your Baseball IQ? 2000. (J). (gr. 3-9). pap. 2.99 (978-1-930623-16-3(X)) Sports Illustrated For Kids.

Fishback, John R. Where's the Play?': Teaches Kids Baseball Smarts. 2001. (J). (gr. 3-6). cd-rom 24.95 (978-0-9726029-1-4(7)) P&P Studios, Inc.

Fitzgerald, Ron. Baseball: Becoming A Great Hitter. 2000. (gr. 7-12). lib. bdg. 15.25 (978-0-613-51981-6(7)) Tandem Library Bks.

—Baseball: Fielding Ground Balls. 2000. (High Interest Bks.). (Illus.). 48p. (YA). (gr. 7-12). 23.00 (978-0-516-23360-4(2) , Children's Pr.) Scholastic Library Publishing.

Forker, Dom. Baseball Brain Teasers: Major League Puzzlers. Hoffman, Sandy, illus. 2003. 128p. (gr. 5-9). pap. 6.95 (978-0-8069-6284-9(4)) Sterling Publishing Co., Inc.

Forker, Dom, et al. Baffling Baseball Trivia. 2004. 288p. 6.98 (978-1-4027-1338-5(X)) Sterling Publishing Co., Inc.

Franchino, Vicky. Roberto Clemente. 2008. (J). lib. bdg. 26.00 (*978-1-60279-073-5(6)) Cherry Lake Publishing.

Franks, Katie. I Want to Be a Baseball Star. 2007. (Dream Jobs Ser.). (Illus.). 24p. (J). (gr. 3-5). lib. bdg. 21.25 (978-1-4042-3622-6(8) , PowerKids Pr.) Rosen Publishing Group, Inc., The.

Fuerst, Jeffrey B. The Kids' Baseball Workout: How to Get in Shape & Improve Your Game. Green, Anne Canevari, illus. 2002. 80p. (gr. 4 up). lib. bdg. 24.90 (978-0-7613-2307-5(4) , Millbrook Pr.) Lerner Publishing Group.

Gagne, Eric & Brown, Greg. Eric Gagne: Break Barriers. 2004. (Illus.). 48p. (J). 15.95 (978-0-9634650-6-1(6)) Positively for Kids, Inc.

Geng, Don. Play-by-Play Baseball. 2001. (gr. 5-8). lib. bdg. 16.40 (978-0-613-32954-5(6)) Tandem Library Bks.

Geng, Don & King, Andy. Baseball. 2003. (Play-By-Play Ser.). (Illus.). 80p. (J). (gr. 5 up). pap. 7.95 (978-0-8225-9880-0(9)) Lerner Publishing Group.

Get Inside Series. Incl. Baseball. Almonte, Paul. 80p. 14.95 (978-1-881889-55-7(6)); Ranch. Morgenroth, Barbara. 64p. 14.95 (978-1-881889-56-4(4)); (Illus.). (J). 1994. 29.90 (978-1-881889-79-3(3)) Silver Moon Pr.

Gibbons, Gail. My Baseball Book. Gibbons, Gail, illus. 2000. (Illus.). 24p. (J). (ps-2). 5.99 (978-0-688-17137-7(0)) HarperCollins Pubs.

Gigliotti, Jim. National League West. 2005. (Major League Baseball Ser.). (Illus.). 48p. (J). (gr. 1-5). 27.07 (978-1-59296-363-8(3)) Child's World, Inc.

Gigliotti, Jim & Dorling Kindersley Publishing Staff. 1,001 Facts about Pitchers. 2004. (Illus.). 168p. (J). pap. 8.99 (978-0-7566-0493-6(1)) Dorling Kindersley Publishing, Inc.

Goodman, Michael E. The History of the Houston Astros. 1998. (Baseball, the Great American Game Ser.). (Illus.). 32p. (YA). (gr. 3-12). pap. 21.30 (978-0-88682-910-0(0) , Creative Education) Creative Co., The.

—The History of the Montreal Expos. 1998. (Baseball, the Great American Game Ser.). (Illus.). 32p. (YA). (gr. 3-12). pap. 21.30 (978-0-88682-915-5(1) , Creative Education) Creative Co., The.

—The History of the Seattle Mariners. 1998. (Baseball, the Great American Game Ser.). (Illus.). 32p. (YA). (gr. 3-12). pap. 21.30 (978-0-88682-925-4(9) , Creative Education) Creative Co., The.

Grant, Elaine Y. & Elliott, Sharon M. The Little Book of Baseball. 2003. (Illus.). 168p. (J). spiral bd. 12.95 (978-0-9729676-0-0(5) , LBOB) Presence Publishing.

Gregory, Paul. Baseball & Softball. 3rd ed. 1999. (Play the Game Ser.). (Illus.). 80p. (J). (gr. 3-7). pap. 10.95 (978-0-7063-7713-2(3)) Ward Lock GBR. *Dist:* Sterling Publishing Co., Inc.

Gutman, Bill. Baseball Bloopers. 1998. (gr. 3-6). lib. bdg. 11.80 (978-0-613-76295-3(9)) Tandem Library Bks.

Gutman, Dan. Jackie Robinson & the Big Game. Garvin, Elaine, illus. 2006. 32p. (J). lib. bdg. 15.00 (*978-1-4242-0957-6(9)) Fitzgerald Bks.

Harcourt School Publishers Staff. Baseball & the Barrios: Reader's Choice Book. 2001. (Collections Ser.). (Illus.). (J). 5.90 (978-0-15-314390-8(8)) Harcourt Schl. Pubs.

—Rounders Advanced Level. 3rd ed. 2002. (Trophies Reading Program Ser.). (Illus.). pap. 5.10 (978-0-15-323284-8(6)) Harcourt Schl. Pubs.

Harrison, Peggy. We Love Baseball! 2003. (Random House Pictureback Book Ser.). (Illus.). 24p. (J). (ps-2). pap. 3.25 (978-0-375-81442-6(6) , Random Hse. Bks. for Young Readers) Random Hse. Children's Bks.

—We Love Baseball! 2003. (gr. k-3). lib. bdg. 10.95 (978-0-613-86256-1(2)) Tandem Library Bks.

Henderson, Carolyn. Horse & Pony Book: A Practical Guide to Caring for a Horse or Pony. Grabham, Sue, ed. 2002. (Illus.). 160p. (J). 19.99 (978-0-7894-8511-3(7)) Dorling Kindersley Publishing, Inc.

Herzog, Brad. H Is for Home Run: A Baseball Alphabet. Rose, Melanie, illus. 2004. 40p. (J). 16.95 (978-1-58536-219-6(0)) Sleeping Bear Pr.

—Seventh-Inning Stretch: Time-Out for Baseball Trivia. Wolf, Catherine, ed. 2000. (Sports Illustrated for Kids Bks.). 48p. (J). (gr. 2-8). pap. 2.99 (978-1-886749-88-7(4)) Sports Illustrated For Kids.

Hill, Mary. Let's Go to a Baseball Game. 2004. (Weekend Fun Ser.). (Illus.). 24p. (J). 18.00 (978-0-516-23997-2(X)); pap. 4.95 (978-0-516-25916-1(4)) Scholastic Library Publishing. (Children's Pr.).

Hoskins, Barbara. Birthday Magic - Baseball Fans, Level 2. 2000. (Let's Go Readers Ser.). (Illus.). 30p. (J). 7.25 (978-0-19-436456-0(9)) Oxford Univ. Pr., Inc.

Hughes, Morgan. Baseball. 2005. (Junior Sports Ser.). (Illus.). 32p. (J). (gr. 2-4). 19.95 (978-1-59515-188-9(5)) Rourke Publishing, LLC.

Isadora, Rachel. Nick Plays Baseball. Isadora, Rachel, illus. 2004. (Illus.). 30p. (J). (gr. 2-6). reprint ed. 16.00 (978-0-7567-7254-3(0)) DIANE Publishing Co.

—Nick Plays Baseball. Isadora, Rachel, illus. (Illus.). (J). (ps-3). 2003. 32p. pap. 6.99 (978-0-698-11989-5(4)); 2001. 1p. 15.99 (978-0-399-23231-2(1)) Penguin Group (USA) Inc. (Putnam Juvenile).

—Nick Plays Baseball. 2003. (Illus.). (J). (ps-3). lib. bdg. 15.30 (978-0-613-61647-8(2)) Tandem Library Bks.

Jacobs, Greg. The Everything Kids' Baseball Book, with Scores of Updated Stats. 4th ed. 2006. (Everything Ser.). (Illus.). 176p. (J). pap. 7.95 (978-1-59337-614-7(6)) Adams Media Corp.

January, Brendan. A Baseball All-Star. 2004. (Making of a Champion Ser.). (YA). 29.93 (978-1-4034-5362-4(4)); pap. 8.50 (978-1-4034-5546-8(5)) Heinemann Library.

Jennison, Christopher. Baseball Math: Grandslam Activities & Projects. 3rd ed. 2005. (Illus.). 112p. (J). pap. (978-1-59647-007-1(0)) Good Year Bks.

Jeter, Derek & DeWerth, Ann Farry. Derek Jeter's All-Star Manual. IMG Creative Staff, illus. 2002. 28p. (YA). pap. (978-1-878843-34-0(6) , IMP Publishing) International Management Group (International Merchandising Corporation).

Jordan, Godfrey P. The Official Kids' Book of Baseball. 1999. (Illus.). 144p. (YA). (gr. 6-11). reprint ed. pap. 10.00 (978-0-7881-6571-9(2)) DIANE Publishing Co.

Kalman, Bobbie. Baseball in Action. 2000. (gr. 3-6). lib. bdg. 14.10 (978-0-613-21172-7(3)) Tandem Library Bks.

Kalman, Bobbie & Dyer, Hadley. Batter up Baseball. 2007. (Illus.). 32p. (J). (gr. 1-5). (*978-0-7787-3136-8(7)); pap. (*978-0-7787-3168-9(5)) Crabtree Publishing Co.

Kelley, James & Dorling Kindersley Publishing Staff. Baseball. 2005. (Eyewitness Books). (Illus.). 72p. (J). (ps-7). lib. bdg. 19.99 (978-0-7566-1062-3(1)) Dorling Kindersley Publishing, Inc.

Kennedy, Mike. Baseball. 2002. (True Book Ser.). (Illus.). 48p. (J). (gr. 3-5). pap. 25.00 (978-0-516-22334-6(8) , Children's Pr.) Scholastic Library Publishing.

—Baseball. 2002. (gr. 3-6). lib. bdg. 15.25 (978-0-613-59449-3(5)) Tandem Library Bks.

Krasner, Steven. Play Ball Like the Hall of Famers: Tips for Kids from 19 Baseball Greats. Neely, Keith, illus. 2005. 208p. (J). pap. 14.95 (978-1-56145-339-9(0)) Peachtree Pubs., Ltd.

Ladd, Patricia. Beyond Baseball. 2002. (Illus.). (YA). (gr. 5-10). 56.00 (978-1-57336-373-0(1) , 3013) Interaction Pubs., Inc.

Little League's Official How-to-Play Baseball. 2007. 210p. 39.95 incl. DVD (*978-1-55919-997-1(0)) MasterVision.

Lloyd, Bryant. Beisbo: El Campo y el Equipo. 2002. (Juega Como un Profesional Ser.). (SPA.). (J). 23.93 (978-1-58952-446-0(2)) Rourke Publishing, LLC.

—Beisbol: Las Reglas del Juego. 2002. (Juega Como un Profesional Ser.). (SPA.). (J). 23.93 (978-1-58952-447-7(0)) Rourke Publishing, LLC.

Macht, Norman L. Baseball. 1999. (Composite Guide Ser.). (Illus.). 64p. (YA). (gr. 4-7). 28.00 (978-0-7910-4723-1(7) , Chelsea Hse.) Facts On File, Inc.

Mackin, Bob. Record-Breaking Baseball Trivia: Games, Puzzles, Quizzes. 2003. (Illus.). 128p. pap. 6.95 (978-1-55054-757-3(7) , Greystone Bks.) Douglas & McIntyre, Ltd. CAN. *Dist:* Transition Vendor.

Mandel, Peter. Say Hey! A Song of Willie Mays. Tate, Don, illus. 2004. 30p. (J). (gr. k-2). reprint ed. 16.00 (978-0-7567-8162-0(0)) DIANE Publishing Co.

Mangiat, Jeff. Baseball. Mangiat, Jeff, illus. 2008. (Sticker Stories Ser.). 16p. (J). (ps-1). 4.99 (*978-0-448-44724-7(X) , Grosset & Dunlap) Penguin Group (USA) Inc.

Mattern, Joanne. I Use Math at the Game. 2005. (Illus.). 24p. (J). pap. (978-0-8368-4862-5(4)); lib. bdg. 19.33 (978-0-8368-4855-7(1)) Stevens, Gareth Inc.

—I Use Math at the Game: Uso Las Matematicas el Juego de Pelota. 2005. (SPA., Illus.). 24p. (J). pap. (978-0-8368-6007-8(1)); lib. bdg. 19.33 (978-0-8368-6000-9(4)) Stevens, Gareth Inc.

McGrath, Barbara Barbieri. The Baseball Counting Book. Shaw, Brian, illus. 1999. 32p. (J). (ps-3). 15.95 (978-0-88106-332-5(0)); pap. 6.95 (978-0-88106-333-2(9)) Charlesbridge Publishing, Inc.

—The Baseball Counting Book. Shaw, Brian, illus. 1999. (J). (ps-ps). lib. bdg. 15.25 (978-0-613-16324-8(9)) Tandem Library Bks.

McGrath, Barbara Barbieri & Shaw, Brian. Cuenta con el Beisbol. Canetti, Yanitzia, tr. from SPA. Shaw, Brian, illus. 2005. (Illus.). 32p. (J). pap. 7.95 (978-1-57091-608-3(X)) Charlesbridge Publishing, Inc.

Meister, Cari. El Dia Del Partido. 2001. (SPA.). (gr. k-3). lib. bdg. 12.95 (978-0-613-54194-7(4)) Tandem Library Bks.

Migliaccio, Eric. Baseball & Softball Easy Olympic Sports Reader. 2004. (U. S. Olympic Committee Easy Olympic Sports Readers Ser.). (Illus.). 16p. (J). pap. 2.99 (978-1-58000-110-6(6)) Griffin Publishing Group.

Monteleone, John J. & Gola, Mark. Little League Baseball Guide to Correcting the 25 Most Common Mistakes: Recognizing & Repairing the Mistakes Young Playaers Make. 2003. (Little League Baseball Guides Ser.). (Illus.). 144p. pap. 14.95 (978-0-07-140887-5(8) , 9780071408875) McGraw-Hill Cos., The.

Murray, Jim, intro. Today's Stars. 1998. (Illus.). 64p. (gr. 3). 220.35 (978-0-7910-4503-9(X) , Chelsea Hse.) Facts On File, Inc.

Nevius, Carol. Baseball Hour. Thomson, Bill, illus. 2008. 32p. (J). 16.99 (***978-0-7614-5380-2(6)***) Cavendish, Marshall Corp.

New Kids Media Staff. Bible Baseball. 1998. (Bible Fun Ser.). (Illus.). (J). (gr. 1-4). pap. 9.99 (978-0-8010-0250-2(8) , New Kids Media) Baker Bks.

Nichols, John. The History of the Florida Marlins. 1998. (Baseball, the Great American Game Ser.). (Illus.). 32p. (YA). (gr. 3-12). pap. 21.30 (978-0-88682-909-4(7) , Creative Education) Creative Co., The.

Norworth, Jack. Take Me Out to the Ballgame. Gillman, Alec, illus. 1999. 40p. (J). (ps-3). 6.99 (978-0-689-82433-3(5) , Aladdin) Simon & Schuster Children's Publishing.

—Take Me Out to the Ballgame. Gillman, Alec, illus. 1999. 30p. (J). (ps-3). lib. bdg. 15.30 (978-0-613-73244-4(8)) Tandem Library Bks.

Otten, Jack. Baseball. 2002. (Reading Power Ser.). (Illus.). 24p. (J). lib. bdg. 17.25 (978-0-8239-5971-6(6) , PowerKids Pr.) Rosen Publishing Group, Inc., The.

—Beisbol. 2004. (Entrenamiento Deportivo Ser.). (SPA & ENG., Illus.). 24p. (J). lib. bdg. 17.25 (978-0-8239-6845-9(6) , Buenas Letra) Rosen Publishing Group, Inc., The.

Ovations. Incl. Barry Bonds. Goodman, Michael E. lib. bdg. 21.30 (978-0-88682-694-9(2)); Grant Hill. Goodman, Michael E. lib. bdg. (978-0-88682-831-8(7)); Hillary Rodham Clinton. Loewen, Nancy. lib. bdg. (978-0-88682-636-9(5)); Jeff Gordon. Bach, Julie S. pap. (978-0-88682-939-1(9)); Monica Seles. Goodman, Michael E. lib. bdg. 21.30 (978-0-88682-699-4(3)); Shaquille O'Neal. Goodman, Michael E. lib. bdg. (978-0-88682-633-8(0)); Spike Lee. Chapman, Ferguson. lib. bdg. (978-0-88682-697-0(7)); Whoopi Goldberg. DeBoer, Andy. 21.30 (978-0-88682-696-3(9)); (Illus.). 32p. (YA). (gr. 4-7). 1998. 59.80 (978-0-88682-693-2(4) , Creative Education) Creative Co., The.

Owens, Thomas & Helmer, Diana Star. Baseball. 1999. (Game Plan Ser.). (Illus.). 64p. (J). (gr. 5-8). lib. bdg. (978-0-7613-1373-1(7) , Twenty-First Century Bks.) Lerner Publishing Group.

Owens, Thomas S. Baseball Parks. 2001. (Sports Palaces Ser.). (Illus.). 64p. (gr. 6-8). lib. bdg. 25.90 (978-0-7613-1765-4(1) , Millbrook Pr.) Lerner Publishing Group.

Panamericana Staff. Reglamento de Beisbol. (SPA.). 244p. (J). 6.95 (978-958-30-0068-3(X)) Panamericana Editorial COL. *Dist:* AIMS International Bks., Inc.

Patrick, Denise Lewis. Jackie Robinson Strong Inside & Out. 2005. 44p. (J). lib. bdg. 15.00 (***978-1-4242-0850-0(5)***) Fitzgerald Bks.

Patrick, Jean L. S. The Girl Who Struck Out Babe Ruth. 2000. (gr. 3-6). lib. bdg. 14.10 (978-0-613-53509-0(X)) Tandem Library Bks.

Pellowski, Michael J. The Little Giant Book of Baseball Facts. 2007. (Illus.). 352p. (J). pap. 6.95 (978-1-4027-4273-6(8)) Sterling Publishing Co., Inc.

Picture Window Books, contrib. by. Nice Hit! (Game Day Ser.). 24p. (J). pap. 7.95 (978-1-4048-0510-1(9)) Picture Window Bks.

Polzer, Tim. Quarterback Power. 2004. (NFL Reader Ser.: No. 01). (Illus.). 32p. (J). pap. 3.99 (978-0-439-69179-6(6)) Scholastic, Inc.

Porterfield, Jason. Baseball: Rules, Tips, Strategy, & Safety. 2006. (Sports from Coast to Coast Ser.). (Illus.). 48p. (J). (gr. 5-8). lib. bdg. 26.50 (978-1-4042-0991-6(3)) Rosen Publishing Group, Inc., The.

Preller, James. Major League Baseball Card Collector's Kit 2003. 2003. 48p. (J). pap. 9.99 (978-0-439-54525-9(0) , Tangerine Pr.) Scholastic, Inc.

Puckett & Gutelle. K Puckett's Baseball Game. 2004. pap. 111.60 (978-0-7611-0494-0(1) , 20494) Algonquin Bks. of Chapel Hill.

Rambeck, Richard. The History of the Anaheim Angels. 1998. (Baseball, the Great American Game Ser.). (Illus.). 32p. (YA). (gr. 3-12). lib. bdg. 21.30 (978-0-88682-901-8(1) , Creative Education) Creative Co., The.

—The History of the Kansas City Royals. 1998. (Baseball, the Great American Game Ser.). (Illus.). 32p. (YA). (gr. 3-12). pap. 21.30 (978-0-88682-911-7(9) , Creative Education) Creative Co., The.

—The History of the Minnesota Twins. 1998. (Baseball, the Great American Game Ser.). (Illus.). 32p. (J). (gr. 3-12). pap. 21.30 (978-0-88682-914-8(3) , Creative Education) Creative Co., The.

Ritter, Lawrence S. The Story of Baseball. 3rd ed. 1999. 208p. (YA). pap. 7.95 (978-0-688-16265-8(7) , Harper Trophy) HarperCollins Pubs.

Roberts, Kelly. Baseball Book for Kids. 2006. 24.95 (978-0-9777764-4-3(1)) Arbor Bks.

Roberts, Russell. 100 Baseball Legends Who Shaped Sports History. 2003. (gr. 7-12). lib. bdg. 16.40 (978-0-613-67109-5(0)) Tandem Library Bks.

Rodda, Bob. For the Fun of It: The Story of the 2001 Wooster, Ohio, Williamsport Little League Team's Tournament Run to the State Playoffs. 2003. 152p. (YA). pap. 14.00 (978-1-59098-190-0(1)) Wooster Bk. Co., The.

Royston, Angela. Madera: Miremos un Bate Deportivo. 2006. (Heinemann Lee y Aprende Ser.). (Illus.). 24p. (J). (SPA & ENG.). (978-1-4034-7549-7(0)); (ENG & SPA., pap. (978-1-4034-7558-9(X)) Heinemann Library.

—Wood: Let's Look at a Baseball Bat. 2005. (Illus.). 24p. (J). (978-1-4034-7672-2(1)); pap. (978-1-4034-7681-4(0)) Heinemann Library.

Rozner, Barry. Mark Grace Winning with Grace. 1999. (gr. 3-6). lib. bdg. 12.95 (978-0-613-84720-9(2)) Tandem Library Bks.

Rumaner, Marc. Play Ball! Incl. 2 1/2" Baseball. (Illus.). 12p. (J). (ps-1). bds. (978-1-56021-372-7(8) , 219) W.J. Fantasy, Inc.

Saiyan Saga 99 Cent Booster Pack. 2000. (Saiyan Saga Ser.). (YA). (gr. 6 up). 0.99 (978-1-888392-20-3(7)) Donruss Playoff, L.P.

Santella, Andrew. Baseball. 1998. (Successful Sports Ser.). 32p. (J). lib. bdg. 21.36 (978-1-57572-068-5(X)) Heinemann Library.

Savage, Jeff. David Ortiz. 2006. (Illus.). (J). pap. 5.95 (978-0-8225-3594-2(7) , First Avenue Editions) Lerner Publishing Group.

Scher, Jon. Record Breakers. 2003. (DK Readers Ser.). (Illus.). 48p. (J). pap. 3.99 (978-0-7894-9842-7(1)) Dorling Kindersley Publishing, Inc.

Schwarz, Alan. Baseball All-Stars: Today's Greatest Players. 2005. (Sports Illustrated for Kids Bks.). (Illus.). 176p. (YA). (gr. 7-12). lib. bdg. 27.95 (978-0-8239-3688-5(0)) Rosen Publishing Group, Inc., The.

—Rising Stars: 10 Best Young Players in Baseball. Rolfe, John, ed. 2000. (Illus.). 96p. (J). (gr. 2-8). pap. 3.99 (978-1-886749-82-5(5)) Sports Illustrated For Kids.

—Sports Illustrated for Kids Baseball All-Stars. Gramling, Scott, ed. 1999. (Illus.). 96p. (J). (gr. 2-8). pap. 3.99 (978-1-886749-73-3(6)) Sports Illustrated For Kids.

—Sports Illustrated for Kids Baseball's Best. Northrop, Michael & Gramling, Scott, eds. 1999. 32p. (J). (gr. 2-8). pap. 3.99 (978-1-886749-71-9(X)) Sports Illustrated For Kids.

Schwarz, Alan & Bradley, Michael. Head-to-Head Baseball: Mark McGuire & Sammy Sosa. Goehner, Amy Lennard, ed. 2000. 96p. (J). (gr. 2-8). pap. 3.99 (978-1-886749-89-4(2)) Sports Illustrated For Kids.

Shalin, Michael. Mo Vaughn Angel on a Mission. 1999. (gr. 3-6). lib. bdg. 12.95 (978-0-613-85263-0(X)) Tandem Library Bks.

Silbaugh, Johnq. National League Central. 2005. (Major League Baseball Ser.). (Illus.). 48p. (J). (gr. 1-5). 27.07 (978-1-59296-361-4(7)) Child's World, Inc.

Silverstone, Michael. Latino Legends: Hispanics in Major League Baseball, 6 vols. (gr. 4 up). 49.95 (978-0-7368-2842-0(7) , High Five) Red Brick Learning.

Smith Jr., Charles R. Diamond Life: Baseball Sights, Sounds, & Swings. 2004. 32p. (J). pap. 15.95 (978-0-439-43180-4(8)) Scholastic, Inc.

Sports Illustrated: The World Series. 1999. 224p. (YA). (gr. 7 up). 29.95 (978-1-883013-52-3(6)) Time, Inc. Home Entertainment.

Stewart, John. The Baseball Clinic: A Handbook for Players & Coaches. 2004. (Illus.). 146p. (J). (gr. 4-8). reprint ed. 20.00 (978-0-7567-7637-4(6)) DIANE Publishing Co.

Stewart, Mark. Ichiro Suzuki: The Best in the West. 2002. (New Wave Ser.). (Illus.). 48p. (gr. 4 up). lib. bdg. 22.90 (978-0-7613-2616-8(2) , Millbrook Pr.) Lerner Publishing Group.

—Los Mejores Bateadores del Beisbol Latino. 2003. Tr. of Latino Baseball's Hottest Hitters. (SPA.). (gr. 5-8). lib. bdg. 18.75 (978-0-613-90692-0(6)) Tandem Library Bks.

—Las Mejores Estrellas del Beisbol Latino: Los Guantes. 2003. Tr. of Latino Baseball's Finest. (SPA.). (gr. 5-8). lib. bdg. 18.75 (978-0-613-91017-0(6)) Tandem Library Bks.

Stewart, Mark & Kennedy, Mike. Long Ball: The Legend & Lore of the Home Run. 2006. (Illus.). 64p. (J). 22.60 (978-0-7613-2779-0(7)) Lerner Publishing Group.

Stewart, Wayne. Baseball Oddities: Bizarre Plays & Other Funny Stuff. 1998. (Illus.). 96p. (gr. 4-7). 14.95 (978-0-8069-0709-3(6)) Sterling Publishing Co., Inc.

Stewart, Wayne, et al. The Big Book of Baseball Brainteasers. 2004. 288p. 6.98 (978-1-4027-1337-8(1) , Sterling/Main St.) Sterling Publishing Co., Inc.

Strazzabosco, Jeanne M. Cal Ripken. rev. ed. 1999. (Character Building Book Ser.). (Illus.). 24p. (J). lib. bdg. 18.75 (978-0-8239-3028-9(9) , PowerKids Pr.) Rosen Publishing Group, Inc., The.

Sullivan, George. Don't Step on the Foul Line: Sports Superstitions. 2000. (gr. 3-6). lib. bdg. 17.60 (978-0-613-55824-2(3)) Tandem Library Bks.

Sweeny, Sheila. Wacky Baseball Facts to Bat Around. Sieck, Margaret, ed. 1998. (Illus.). 32p. (J). (gr. k-3). pap. 3.50 (978-1-886749-41-2(8)) Sports Illustrated For Kids.

Teitelbaum, Michael. National League East. 2005. (Major League Baseball Ser.). (Illus.). 48p. (J). (gr. 1-5). 27.07 (978-1-59296-362-1(5)) Child's World, Inc.

Thomas, Keltie. How Baseball Works. Hall, Greg, illus. (How Sports Work Ser.). 64p. (J). 2008. 22.95 (***978-1-897349-20-5(3)***); 2008. pap. 10.95 (***978-1-897349-21-2(1)***); 2004. (gr. 3-7). 19.95 (978-1-894379-60-1(8)) Maple Tree Pr. CAN. *Dist:* Perseus Distribution, Firefly Bks., Ltd.

Thomas, Ron & Herran, Joe. Getting into Baseball. Porcellato, Nives & Craig, Andy, illus. 2005. (Getting into Sports Ser.). 32p. (J). (gr. 2-4). lib. bdg. 28.00 (978-0-7910-8808-1(1) , Chelsea Clubhouse) Facts On File, Inc.

Tramontano, Anthony P. The Official Book of Baseball Dreams & Memories. Tramontano, Melissa A., ed. 1998. (Illus.). v, 40p. (J). (gr. 6). 15.95 (978-0-9663140-0-7(X)) SMC Publishing (Strategic Marketing Concepts).

Vigue, Jim, ed. Peak Power Baseball: How to Turn Your Little League Dream into Major League Reality. 2003. (Illus.). 238p. (YA). (gr. 7 up). pap. 17.95 (978-0-9724194-0-6(3)) Power Pubns., Inc.

Wark, Laurie & Ritchie, Scot. Baseball. (FRE., Illus.). (J). pap. 5.99 (978-0-590-24305-6(5)) Scholastic, Inc.

Weaver, Earl. Baseball Legends, 6 bks., Set. 1999. (Illus.). 64p. (gr. 3). 101.70 (978-0-7910-5222-8(2) , Chelsea Hse.) Facts On File, Inc.

West, David Anthony. Baseball: Secrets of the Know 'n Go Game. l.t. ed. 2006. (Illus.). 224p. (J). per. 17.95 (978-0-9769478-5-1(4)) Aztec 5 Publishing.

Will, Sandra. Baseball for Fun. 2003. (Sports for Fun Ser.). (Illus.). 48p. (J). (gr. 3 up). lib. bdg. 21.26 (978-0-7565-0428-1(7)) Compass Point Bks.

Wright, John. Baseball. 2003. (Sports Injuries Ser.). (Illus.). 64p. (J). lib. bdg. (978-1-59084-626-1(5)) Mason Crest Pubs.

YMCA of the USA Staff. Playing YMCA Baseball & Softball: Bronze Edition. 2000. (Illus.). 48p. (J). pap. 6.00 (978-0-7360-3040-3(9) , YMCA of the U.S.A.) Human Kinetics Pubs.

—Playing YMCA Baseball & Softball: Gold Edition. 2000. (Illus.). 48p. (J). pap. 6.00 (978-0-7360-3042-7(5) , YMCA of the U.S.A.) Human Kinetics Pubs.

—Playing YMCA Baseball & Softball: Silver Edition. 2000. (Illus.). 48p. (J). pap. 6.00 (978-0-7360-3041-0(7) , YMCA of the U.S.A.) Human Kinetics Pubs.

Zuehlke, Jeffrey. Curt Schilling. 2007. (Amazing Athletes Ser.). (Illus.). 32p. (J). 23.93 (978-0-8225-3431-0(2) , Lerner Pubns.) Lerner Publishing Group.

BASEBALL—BIOGRAPHY

Aaseng, Nathan. Jose Canseco: Baseball's Forty-Forty Man. 1999. 56p. (YA). (gr. 4-9). pap. 4.95 (978-0-8225-9586-1(9) , Lerner Pubns.) Lerner Publishing Group.

Abraham, Philip. Jackie Robinson. 2002. (Wel-Real People Ser.). (Illus.). 24p. (J). (ps-2). 18.00 (978-0-516-23950-7(3)); pap. 4.95 (978-0-516-23605-6(9)) Scholastic Library Publishing. (Children's Pr.).

—Jackie Robinson. 2002. (gr. k-3). lib. bdg. 12.95 (978-0-613-58845-4(2)) Tandem Library Bks.

Acosta, Tatiana & Gutierrez, Guillermo, trs. Jackie Robinson. 2004. (Gente Que Hay Que Conocer Ser.). (SPA., Illus.). 24p. (J). lib. bdg. 19.33 (978-0-8368-4353-8(3)) Stevens, Gareth Inc.

Adler, David A. Campy: The Story of Roy Campanella. James, Gordon C., illus. 2007. 40p. (J). (gr. 1-4). 15.99 (978-0-670-06041-2(0) , Viking Adult) Penguin Group (USA) Inc.

—Lou Gehrig: The Luckiest Man. 2001. (978-0-606-21307-3(4)) Tandem Library Bks.

—Satchel Paige: Don't Look Back. Widener, Terry, illus. 2007. 32p. (J). 16.00 (978-0-15-205585-1(1)) Harcourt Trade Pubs.

Albert Pujols. 2007. (J). pap. 5.95 (***978-0-8225-6850-6(0)*** , First Avenue Editions) Lerner Publishing Group.

Anderson, Ken. Nolan Ryan: Fastball to Cooperstown. 1999. (Illus.). 160p. 16.95 (978-1-57168-350-2(X)); 5.95 (978-1-57168-349-6(5)) Eakin Pr.

Anderson, Sheila. Roberto Clemente: A Life of Generosity. 2008. (Pull Ahead Books-Biographies Ser.). (J). lib. bdg. 22.60 (***978-0-8225-8586-2(3)*** , Lerner Pubns.) Lerner Publishing Group.

Armentrout, David & Armentrout, Patricia, trs. Alex Rodriguez. 2003. (Discover the Life of a Sports Star Ser.). (Illus.). 24p. (J). 20.64 (978-1-58952-654-9(6)) Rourke Publishing, LLC.

Barrymore, Drew. Sammy Sosa. 1999. (Overcoming Adversity Ser.). (Illus.). 128p. (YA). (gr. 5 up). pap. 9.95 (978-0-7910-5301-0(6) , Chelsea Hse.) Facts On File, Inc.

Baseball Hall of Famers of the Negro Leagues, 6 bks. Incl. Buck Leonard. Payment, Simone. lib. bdg. 29.25 (978-0-8239-3473-7(X)); Cool Papa Bell. McCormack, Shaun. lib. bdg. 29.25 (978-0-8239-3474-4(8)); Josh Gibson. Twemlow, Nick. lib. bdg. 29.25 (978-0-8239-3475-1(6)); Judy Johnson. Billus, Kathleen. lib. bdg. 29.25 (978-0-8239-3476-8(4)); Monte Irvin. Haegele, Katie. lib. bdg. 29.25 (978-0-8239-3477-5(2)); Satchel Paige. Schmidt, Julie. lib. bdg. 29.25 (978-0-8239-3478-2(0)); 112p. (YA). (gr. 5-8). (Illus.). 2002. Set lib. bdg. 175.50 (978-0-8239-9686-5(7) , Rosen Central) Rosen Publishing Group, Inc., The.

Benjamin, Lisa. Jackie Robinson: Changing the Game. 2005. (Voices Reading Ser.). (Illus.). 32p. (J). (978-0-7367-2937-6(2)) Zaner-Bloser, Inc.

Benson, Michael. Hank Aaron, Baseball Player. 2004. (Ferguson Career Biographies Ser.). (Illus.). 128p. (J). (gr. 6-12). 25.00 (978-0-8160-5349-0(9) , Ferguson Publishing Co.) Facts On File, Inc.

Berkow, Ira. Hank Greenberg: Hall-of-Fame Slugger. Ellison, Mick, illus. 2000. 108p. pap. 9.95 (978-0-8276-0685-2(0)) Jewish Pubn. Society.

Bernstein, Ross. Barry Bonds. 2004. (Sports Heroes & Legends Ser.). (Illus.). 112p. (J). (gr. 6-12). lib. bdg. 27.93 (978-0-8225-1791-7(4)) Lerner Publishing Group.

Billus, Kathleen. Judy Johnson. 2002. (Baseball Hall of Famers of the Negro League Ser.). (Illus.). 112p. (YA). (gr. 5-8). lib. bdg. 29.25 (978-0-8239-3476-8(4) , Rosen Central) Rosen Publishing Group, Inc., The.

Bloom, Barry. Sandy & Roberto Alomar: Baseball Brothers. Rains, Rob, ed. 2000. (Superstar Ser.). (Illus.). 96p. (J). (gr. 4-7). per. 14.95 (978-1-58261-054-2(1)) Sports Publishing, LLC.

—Tony Gwynn: Mr. Padre. Rains, Rob, ed. 1999. (Superstar Ser.). (Illus.). 112p. (J). (gr. 4-7). per. 4.95 (978-1-58261-049-8(5)) Sports Publishing, LLC.

Boothroyd, Jennifer. Lou Gehrig: A Life of Dedication. 2008. (Pull Ahead Books-Biographies Ser.). (J). lib. bdg. 22.60 (***978-0-8225-8587-9(1)*** , Lerner Pubns.) Lerner Publishing Group.

Brenner, Richard J. Mark McGwire. 1999. (Illus.). 32p. (YA). (gr. 1 up). pap. 4.50 (978-0-688-17085-1(4) , Harper Trophy) HarperCollins Pubs.

—Mark McGwire. 1999. (J). (978-0-606-17075-8(8)) Tandem Library Bks.

—Sammy Sosa. 1999. (Illus.). 32p. (J). (gr. 1-4). pap. 4.50 (978-0-688-17084-4(6)) HarperCollins Pubs.

—Sammy Sosa. 1999. (978-0-606-17082-6(0)) Tandem Library Bks.

—Superstars Album, 1999: Baseball. 1999. (Illus.). 48p. (J). (gr. 4-7). pap. 4.95 (978-0-688-16589-5(3) , Harper Trophy) HarperCollins Pubs.

Brooks, Aaron & Brown, Greg. Aaron Brooks: Rise Above. 2004. (Illus.). 48p. (J). 15.95 (978-0-9634650-9-2(0)) Positively for Kids, Inc.

Brown, Jonatha A. & Raatma, Lucia. Jackie Robinson. 2004. (Illus.). 24p. (J). pap. (978-0-8368-4318-7(5)); (YA). lib. bdg. 19.33 (978-0-8368-4311-8(8)) Stevens, Gareth Inc.

Buckley, James, Jr. Home Run Heroes: Big Mac, Sammy & Junior. 2004. (Illus.). 48p. (J). (gr. k-4). reprint ed. pap. 10.00 (978-0-7567-7273-4(7)) DIANE Publishing Co.

—Home Run Heroes: Big Mac, Sammy & Junior. 2001. (Eyewitness Readers Ser.). (Illus.). (J). 10.79 (978-0-606-20707-2(4)) Tandem Library Bks.

—Roberto Clemente. 2001. (Eyewitness Readers Ser.). (Illus.). (J). (978-0-606-20888-8(7)); (SPA., (978-0-606-20889-5(5)) Tandem Library Bks.

—Super Shortstops: Jeter, A-Rod, & Jeter. 2001. (Major League Baseball Readers Ser.). (Illus.). 48p. (J). (gr. 2-4). pap. 3.99 (978-0-7894-7348-6(8)) Dorling Kindersley Publishing, Inc.

—Super Shortstops: Jeter, Nomar & A-Rod. 2001. (Eyewitness Readers Ser.). (Illus.). (J). (978-0-606-20933-5(6)) Tandem Library Bks.

Buckley, James. World Series Heroes. 2003. (gr. k-3). lib. bdg. 11.80 (978-0-613-62439-8(4)) Tandem Library Bks.

Buckley, James, Jr. World Series Heroes. 2003. (Major League Baseball Ser.). (Illus.). 48p. pap. 3.99 (978-0-7894-9252-4(0)) Dorling Kindersley Publishing, Inc.

Buckley, James, Jr. & Dorling Kindersley Publishing Staff. Home Run Heroes: Big Mac, Sammy & Junior. 2001. (Readers Ser.). (Illus.). 48p. (J). (ps-3). pap. 3.99 (978-0-7894-7340-0(2)) Dorling Kindersley Publishing, Inc.

—Roberto Clemente. 2001. (Readers Ser.). (Illus.). 48p. (J). (ps-3). pap. 3.99 (978-0-7894-7342-4(9)); (SPA., pap. 3.99 (978-0-7894-7344-8(5)) Dorling Kindersley Publishing, Inc.

—Strikeout Kings. 2001. (Major League Baseball Readers Ser.). (Illus.). 48p. (J). (gr. 2-4). pap. 3.99 (978-0-7894-7346-2(1)); (gr. 4-7). 12.95 (978-0-7894-7347-9(X)) Dorling Kindersley Publishing, Inc.

Buckley, James & Dorling Kindersley Publishing Staff. World Series Heroes. 2003. (Major League Baseball Ser.). (Illus.). 48p. (J). 12.99 (978-0-7894-9546-4(5)) Dorling Kindersley Publishing, Inc.

Buckman, Virginia. Baseball Stars. 2006. (Sports Stars Ser.). (Illus.). 48p. (J). (978-0-531-12583-0(1)) Children's Pr., Ltd.

—Baseball Stars. 2007. (Sports Stars Ser.). (Illus.). 48p. (J). pap. (978-0-531-18700-5(4)) Children's Pr., Ltd.

Burke, Rick. Sammy Sosa. 2001. (Sports Files Ser.). (Illus.). 32p. (J). (gr. 1-3). lib. bdg. (978-1-58810-113-6(4)) Heinemann Library.

Burleigh, Robert. Stealing Home: Jackie Robinson: Against the Odds. Wimmer, Mike, illus. 2007. 32p. (J). (gr. 1-4). 16.99 (978-0-689-86276-2(8) , Simon & Schuster Children's Publishing) Simon & Schuster Children's Publishing.

Cameron, Mike & Brown, Greg. Mike Cameron: It Takes a Team. 2002. (Illus.). 48p. (J). 15.95 (978-1-57243-502-5(X) , Benchmark Pr.) Triumph Bks.

Canter, Len. Babe Ruth. Marcos, Pablo, illus. 2005. (Heroes of America Ser.). 240p. (J). (gr. 3-8). lib. bdg. 21.35 (978-1-59679-261-6(2)) ABDO Publishing Co.

Carr-Hurtt, L. Denise. Buck O'Neil & I. Carr, Monica M., ed. Roland, Lesley Michael, illus. Thomas, Frederick Douglas, photos by. 2000. 75p. (YA). pap. 14.95 (978-0-9700224-0-0(9)) Greene Pubns.

Castle, George. Sammy Sosa: Slammin' Sammy. Rains, Rob, ed. 2003. (Superstar Ser.). (Illus.). 96p. (J). (gr. 4-7). pap. 4.95 (978-1-58261-029-0(0)) Sports Publishing, LLC.

—Sammy Sosa: Slammin' Sammy. 1999. (gr. 3-6). lib. bdg. 12.95 (978-0-613-17732-0(0)) Tandem Library Bks.

Christensen, Joe. Alex Rodriguez. 2004. (Awesome Athletes Ser.). (Illus.). 32p. (J). (gr. k-6). lib. bdg. 22.78 (978-1-59197-485-7(2)) ABDO Publishing Co.

Christopher, Matt. At the Plate with... Mark McGwire. 1999. 11.64 (978-0-606-17501-2(6)) Tandem Library Bks.

—At the Plate with... Sammy Sosa. 1999. 11.64 (978-0-606-17502-9(4)); (gr. 3-6). lib. bdg. 12.95 (978-0-613-21143-7(X)) Tandem Library Bks.

—En el Campo de Juego con Alex Rodriguez. 2005. (Illus.). 134p. (J). (ps-7). per. 11.64 (978-0-606-33453-2(X)) Tandem Library Bks.

—En el Campo de Juego con Derek Jeter. 2005. (Illus.). 138p. (J). (ps-7). per. 11.64 (978-0-606-33452-5(1)) Tandem Library Bks.

—On the Field with... Alex Rodriguez. 2002. (#1 Sports Series for Kids). (Illus.). 128p. (J). (gr. 4-6). pap. 4.99 (978-0-316-14483-4(5)) Little, Brown Bks. for Young Readers.

—On the Field with... Derek Jeter. 2000. (Illus.). 128p. (J). (gr. 3-7). pap. 4.99 (978-0-316-13508-5(9)) Little Brown & Co.

—On the Field with... Derek Jeter. 2000. (J). (978-0-606-19840-0(7)) Tandem Library Bks.

—On the Mound with... Randy Johnson. 2003. (Illus.). 160p. (J). (gr. 3-7). pap. 4.99 (978-0-316-75167-4(7)) Little, Brown Bks. for Young Readers.

Christopher, Matt & Stout, Glenn. At the Plate with... Sammy Sosa. 1999. (Illus.). 128p. (J). (gr. 3-7). pap. 4.99 (978-0-316-13477-4(5)) Little Brown & Co.

—On the Mound with... Curt Schilling. 2004. (Illus.). 112p. (J). (gr. 4-7). pap. 4.99 (978-0-316-60736-0(3)) Little Brown & Co.

Cline-Ransome, Lesa. Satchel Paige. Ransome, James E., illus. 2004. 31p. (J). (gr. k-4). reprint ed. pap. 7.00 (978-0-7567-7799-9(2)) DIANE Publishing Co.

—Satchel Paige. Ransome, James E., illus. 40p. (J). (gr. 1-5). 2003. 6.99 (978-0-689-85681-5(4) , Aladdin); 2000. 17.99 (978-0-689-81151-7(9)) Simon & Schuster Children's Publishing.

—Satchel Paige. 2003. (gr. 3-6). lib. bdg. 15.30 (978-0-613-55361-2(6)) Tandem Library Bks.

Cockcroft, James D. Latinos in Beisbol. 2004. (Illus.). 207p. (J). (gr. 4-9). reprint ed. pap. 10.00 (978-0-7567-7347-2(4)) DIANE Publishing Co.

Copley, Robert E. The Tall Mexican: The Life of Hank Aguirre All-Star Pitcher, Businessman, Humanitarian. 2000. (J). (978-0-606-19189-0(5)); (gr. 7-12). lib. bdg. 18.75 (978-0-613-28666-4(9)) Tandem Library Bks.

Covert, Kim. Alex Rodriguez. 2002. (Sports Heroes Ser.). (Illus.). 48p. (J). (gr. 3-4). lib. bdg. 21.26 (978-0-7368-1051-7(X) , Capstone High-Interest Bks.) Capstone Pr., Inc.

—Derek Jeter. 2001. (Sports Heroes Ser.). (Illus.). 48p. (J). (gr. 3-4). lib. bdg. 21.26 (978-0-7368-0777-7(2) , Capstone High-Interest Bks.) Capstone Pr., Inc.

Darraj, Susan Muaddi. Jackie Robinson. 2007. (Baseball Superstars Ser.). 128p. (gr. 6-12). 30.00 (***978-0-7910-9442-6(1)*** , Chelsea Hse.) Facts On File, Inc.

de Leon, Mauricio Velázquez, tr. Derek Jeter, Estrella del Beisbol. 2002. (Coleccion Power Kids). (SPA & ENG., Illus.). 24p. (J). (gr. k-2). lib. bdg. 17.25 (978-0-8239-6134-4(6) , RN31301, Buenas Letra) Rosen Publishing Group, Inc., The.

Deane, Bill. Sports Great Frank Thomas. 2000. (Sports Great Bks.). (Illus.). 64p. (YA). (gr. 4-10). lib. bdg. 22.60 (978-0-7660-1269-1(7)) Enslow Pubs., Inc.

—Top 10 Baseball Shortstops. 1999. (Sports Top 10 Ser.). (Illus.). 48p. (YA). (gr. 4-10). lib. bdg. 23.93 (978-0-7660-1128-1(3)) Enslow Pubs., Inc.

Deangelis, Gina. Jackie Robinson. 2001. (gr. 5-8). lib. bdg. 18.75 (978-0-613-32699-5(7)) Tandem Library Bks.

DeMarco, Tony. Larry Walker: Canadian Rocky. Rains, Rob, ed. 1999. (Superstar Ser.). (Illus.). 112p. (J). (gr. 4-7). per. 4.95 (978-1-58261-052-8(5)) Sports Publishing, LLC.

—Vinny Castilla. 2000. (Latinos in Baseball Ser.). (Illus.). 64p. (YA). (gr. 5-9). lib. bdg. 18.95 (978-1-58415-008-4(4)) Mitchell Lane Pubs., Inc.

Doeden, Matt. Sandy Koufax. 2007. (Sports Heroes & Legends Ser.). (J). 27.93 (978-0-8225-5961-0(7) , Twenty-First Century Bks.) Lerner Publishing Group.

Donovan, Sandy. Derek Jeter. 2004. (Amazing Athletes Ser.). (Illus.). 32p. (J). (gr. 3-4). lib. bdg. 23.93 (978-0-8225-3674-1(9)) Lerner Publishing Group.

—Derek Jeter. 2004. (Illus.). 32p. (J). (ps-7). lib. bdg. 12.75 (978-0-606-30542-6(4)) Tandem Library Bks.

Dorling Kindersley Publishing Staff. DK Readers: The World of Baseball. 2003. (gr. k-3). lib. bdg. 11.80 (978-0-613-75178-0(7)) Tandem Library Bks.

Dougherty, Terri. Barry Bonds. 2002. (Jam Session Ser.). (Illus.). 32p. (J). (gr. 3-8). lib. bdg. 24.21 (978-1-57765-675-3(X) , ABDO & Daughters) ABDO Publishing Co.

—Derek Jeter. 2000. (Jam Session Ser.). (Illus.). 32p. (J). (gr. 3-8). lib. bdg. 24.21 (978-1-57765-366-0(1) , ABDO & Daughters) ABDO Publishing Co.

—Ichiro Suzuki. 2004. (Awesome Athletes Ser.). (Illus.). 32p. (J). (gr. k-6). lib. bdg. 22.78 (978-1-59197-483-3(6)) ABDO Publishing Co.

—Ken Griffey, Jr. 2001. (Jam Session Ser.). (Illus.). 32p. (J). (gr. 3-8). lib. bdg. 24.21 (978-1-57765-472-8(2) , ABDO & Daughters) ABDO Publishing Co.

—Mark McGwire. 1999. (Jam Session Ser.). (Illus.). 32p. (J). (gr. 3-8). lib. bdg. 24.21 (978-1-57765-349-3(1) , ABDO & Daughters) ABDO Publishing Co.

—Sammy Sosa. 1999. (Jam Session Ser.). (Illus.). 32p. (J). (gr. 3-8). lib. bdg. 24.21 (978-1-57765-348-6(3) , ABDO & Daughters) ABDO Publishing Co.

Driscoll, Laura. The Negro Leagues: All-Black Baseball. Mitchell, Tracy, illus. 2002. (Smart about History Ser.). 32p. (J). pap. 5.99 (978-0-448-42684-6(6) , Grosset & Dunlap) Penguin Group (USA) Inc.

—Sammy Sosa: Home Run Hero. Call, Ken, illus. 1999. (All Aboard Reading Ser.). 48p. (J). (gr. 2-3). pap. 3.99 (978-0-448-42067-7(8) , Grosset & Dunlap) Penguin Group (USA) Inc.

—Sammy Sosa: Home-Run Hero. 1999. (gr. k-3). lib. bdg. 11.80 (978-0-613-15129-0(1)) Tandem Library Bks.

Dunn, Herb. Jackie Robinson: Young Sports Trailblazer. Henderson, Meryl, illus. 1999. (Childhood of Famous Americans Ser.). 192p. (J). (gr. 3-7). pap. 5.99 (978-0-689-82453-1(X) , Aladdin) Simon & Schuster Children's Publishing.

—Jackie Robinson: Young Sports Trailblazer. 1999. (Childhood of Famous Americans Ser.). (J). 11.64 (978-0-606-16287-6(9)); (gr. 3-6). lib. bdg. 13.00 (978-0-613-15849-7(0)) Tandem Library Bks.

—Joe DiMaggio: Young Sports Hero. 1999. (Childhood of Famous Americans Ser.). (Illus.). 208p. (J). (gr. 3-7). mass mkt. 5.99 (978-0-689-83186-7(2) , Aladdin) Simon & Schuster Children's Publishing.

—Joe DiMaggio: Young Sports Hero. 1999. 11.64 (978-0-606-17509-8(1)) Tandem Library Bks.

—Joe Dimaggio: Young Sports Hero. 1999. (gr. 3-6). lib. bdg. 13.00 (978-0-613-21813-9(2)) Tandem Library Bks.

Dunn, Joe. Jackie Robinson. Espinosa, Rod, illus. 2007. (Bio-Graphics Ser.). 32p. (J). (gr. 3-6). lib. bdg. 27.07 (***978-1-60270-068-0(0)*** , Graphic Planet) Magic Wagon.

Edwards, Sarah & Salman, Jacqueline. Kevin Brown: Kevin with a "K" Rains, Rob, ed. 1999. (Superstar Ser.: Vol. 11). (Illus.). 112p. (J). (gr. 4-7). per. 4.95 (978-1-58261-050-4(9)) Sports Publishing, LLC.

Eisenstark, Reyna. Baseball's Stars: The Negro League. 2005. (Voices Reading Ser.). (Illus.). 16p. (J). (978-0-7367-2927-7(5)) Zaner-Bloser, Inc.

Eldridge, Grant & Bush, Karen Elizabeth. Willie Horton: Detroit's Own "Willie the Wonder" 2001. (Detroit Biography Series for Young Readers). (Illus.). 160p. (J). (gr. 5). 27.95 (978-0-8143-3013-5(4)); pap. 16.00 (978-0-8143-3025-8(8)) Wayne State Univ. Pr.

Elish, Dan. Jackie Robinson. 2005. (Cornerstones of Freedom Ser.). (Illus.). 48p. (J). (ps-6). 26.00 (978-0-516-23635-3(0) , Children's Pr.) Scholastic Library Publishing.

Feinstein, Stephen. Read about Jackie Robinson. 2005. (I Like Biographies! Ser.). (Illus.). 24p. (J). lib. bdg. 21.26 (978-0-7660-2592-9(6) , Enslow Elementary) Enslow Pubs., Inc.

Feldman, Heather. Derek Jeter: Baseball's Best. 2001. (Reading Power Ser.). (Illus.). 24p. (J). (gr. 1). lib. bdg. 17.25 (978-0-8239-5719-4(5) , PKDEJE, PowerKids Pr.) Rosen Publishing Group, Inc., The.

Fischer, David. Albert Pujols. 2006. (World's Greatest Athletes Ser.). (Illus.). 32p. (J). (gr. 1-5). 27.07 (978-1-59296-753-7(1)) Child's World, Inc.

—Alex Rodriguez. 2007. (World's Greatest Athletes Ser.). 32p. (J). (gr. 1-5). 27.07 (978-1-59296-787-2(6)) Child's World, Inc.

—Roberto Clemente. 2004. (Trailblazers of the Modern World Ser.). (J). pap. 11.95 (978-0-8368-5264-6(8)); (Illus.). 48p. (YA). lib. bdg. 30.00 (978-0-8368-5495-4(0)) Stevens, Gareth Inc. (World Almanac Library).

Ford, Carin T. Jackie Robinson: All I Ask Is That You Respect Me as a Human Being. 2005. (African-American Biography Library). (Illus.). 128p. (J). (gr. 6-12). lib. bdg. 31.93 (978-0-7660-2461-8(X)) Enslow Pubs., Inc.

—Jackie Robinson: Hero of Baseball. 2006. (Heroes of American History Ser.). (Illus.). 32p. (J). (ps-3). lib. bdg. 22.60 (978-0-7660-2600-1(0) , Enslow Elementary) Enslow Pubs., Inc.

—Roberto Clemente: Baseball Legend. 2005. (Latino Biography Library). (Illus.). 128p. (J). (gr. 6-12). lib. bdg. 31.93 (978-0-7660-2485-4(7)) Enslow Pubs., Inc.

Friedman, Nick. Mike Piazza. 2007. (Baseball Superstars Ser.). 136p. (gr. 6-12). 30.00 (***978-0-7910-9493-8(6)***) Facts On File, Inc.

Frisch, Aaron. Derek Jeter. 2003. (Ovations Ser.). (Illus.). 32p. (J). pap. (978-1-58341-247-3(6) , Creative Education) Creative Co., The.

Gallagher, Jim. Alex Rodriguez. 2000. (Latinos in Baseball Ser.). (Illus.). 64p. (YA). (gr. 5-9). lib. bdg. 18.95 (978-1-58415-010-7(6)) Mitchell Lane Pubs., Inc.

—Mark McGwire. 1999. (Real-Life Reader Biography Ser.). (Illus.). 32p. (gr. 3-8). lib. bdg. 15.95 (978-1-58415-017-6(3)) Mitchell Lane Pubs., Inc.

—Pedro Martinez. 1999. (Latinos in Baseball Ser.). (Illus.). 72p. (gr. 4-10). lib. bdg. 18.95 (978-1-883845-85-8(8)) Mitchell Lane Pubs., Inc.

—Ramon Martinez. 2000. (Latinos in Baseball Ser.). (Illus.). 64p. (YA). (gr. 5-12). lib. bdg. 18.95 (978-1-58415-009-1(2)) Mitchell Lane Pubs., Inc.

Garcia, Kimberly. Roberto Clemente. l.t. ed. 2002. (Real Life Reader Biography Ser.). (Illus.). 32p. (gr. 3-8). lib. bdg. 24.95 (978-1-58415-127-2(7)) Mitchell Lane Pubs., Inc.

Gigliotti, Jim. Power Pitchers. 2007. (Boys Rock! Ser.). 32p. (J). (gr. 1-5). 24.21 (***978-1-59296-860-2(0)***) Child's World, Inc.

Gilbert, Thomas W. Damn Yankees: Casey, Yogi, Whitey & the Mick. 1998. (J). pap. 9.95 (978-0-531-15879-1(9) , Watts, Franklin) Scholastic Library Publishing.

Glaser, Jason. Jackie Robinson: Baseball's Great Pioneer. Lentz, Bob, illus. 2005. (Graphic Library). 32p. (J). (gr. 3-7). lib. bdg. 25.26 (978-0-7368-4633-2(6)) Capstone Pr., Inc.

Golenbock, Peter. Teammates. 1998. (Illus.). 32p. (ps-3). 16.98 (978-0-8172-4092-9(6)) Raintree.

Gomez, Rebecca. Jackie Robinson. 2003. (First Biographies Ser.). (Illus.). 32p. (J). (gr. k-4). lib. bdg. 22.78 (978-1-57765-949-5(X)) ABDO Publishing Co.

Goodman, Michael E. Barry Bonds. 1998. (Ovations Ser.). (Illus.). 32p. (YA). (gr. 4-7). lib. bdg. 21.30 (978-0-88682-694-9(2) , Creative Education) Creative Co., The.

Grant, Evan. Juan González: Juan Gone! Rains, Rob, ed. 1999. (Superstar Ser.). (Illus.). 112p. (J). (gr. 4-7). per. 4.95 (978-1-58261-048-1(7)) Sports Publishing, LLC.

Green Berg, Doreen & Geenberg, Michael. A Drive to Win: The Story of Nancy Lieberman-Cline. 2003. (Anything You Can Do. . .Ser.; Vol. 1). (Illus.). 112p. (J). (gr. 2-5). pap. 9.95 (978-1-930546-40-0(8)) Wish Publishing.

Green, Michelle Y. A Strong Right Arm: The Story of Mamie "Peanut" Johnson. Nelson, Kadir, illus. 2002. 128p. (J). (gr. 4-7). 15.99 (978-0-8037-2661-1(9) , Dial) Penguin Group (USA) Inc.

—A Strong Right Arm: The Story of Mamie "Peanut" Johnson. 2004. (gr. 5-8). lib. bdg. 14.15 (978-0-613-83004-1(0)) Tandem Library Bks.

Greenberg, Keith Elliot. Derek Jeter. 2005. (Sports Heroes & Legends Ser.). (Illus.). 106p. (J). (gr. 3-7). 27.93 (978-0-8225-3068-8(6) , Lerner Pubns.) Lerner Publishing Group.

Gutman, Bill. Greg Maddux: Master on the Mound. 1999. (Millbrook Sports World Ser.). (Illus.). 48p. (gr. 3-6). lib. bdg. 22.90 (978-0-7613-1454-7(7) , Millbrook Pr.) Lerner Publishing Group.

—Ken Griffey, Jr. A Biography. 1998. (J). (978-0-606-13550-4(2)) Tandem Library Bks.

—Ken Griffey, Jr. Baseball's Best. 1998. (Millbrook Sports World Ser.). (Illus.). 48p. (gr. 3-6). lib. bdg. 22.90 (978-0-7613-0415-9(0) , Millbrook Pr.) Lerner Publishing Group.

Gutman, Dan. Jackie Robinson & the Big Game. Garvin, Elaine, illus. 2006. (Ready-to-Read Cofa Ser.). 32p. (J). lib. bdg. 11.89 (978-0-689-86240-3(7) , Aladdin Library) Simon & Schuster Children's Publishing.

Haegele, Katie. Monte Irvin. 2002. (Baseball Hall of Famers of the Negro League Ser.). (Illus.). 112p. (YA). (gr. 5-8). lib. bdg. 29.25 (978-0-8239-3477-5(2) , Rosen Central) Rosen Publishing Group, Inc., The.

Hagen, Paul. Curt Schilling Phillie Phire! Rains, Rob, ed. 1999. (Superstar Ser.). (Illus.). 112p. (J). (gr. 4-7). per. 4.95 (978-1-58261-055-9(X)) Sports Publishing, LLC.

Hanft, Joshua E. Jackie Robinson. Marcos, Pablo, illus. 2005. (Heroes of America Ser.). 240p. (J). (gr. 3-8). lib. bdg. 21.35 (978-1-59679-259-3(0)) ABDO Publishing Co.

Harcourt School Publishers Staff. The Pride of Puerto Rico. 3rd ed. 2002. (Horizons Ser.). (Illus.). (J). pap. 7.30 (978-0-15-333591-4(2)) Harcourt Schl. Pubs.

Healy, Nick. Roberto Clemente: Baseball Legend. 2006. (Fact Finders Ser.). (Illus.). 32p. (J). (978-0-7368-5442-9(8)) Capstone Pr., Inc.

Higgins, Christopher. Arizona Diamondbacks (Great Sports Teams) 2003. (Illus.). 112p. (J). 29.95 (978-1-59018-303-8(7) , Lucent Bks.) Thomson Gale.

Hoffman, Mary Ann. Alex Rodriguez: Baseball Star. 2007. (Sports Superstars Ser.). (Illus.). 24p. (J). lib. bdg. (***978-1-4042-3533-5(7)***) Rosen Publishing Group, Inc., The.

—Alex Rodriguez: Baseball Star = Estrella Del Béisbol. 2007. (Illus.). 24p. (J). (***978-1-4042-7598-0(3)*** , PowerKids Pr.) Rosen Publishing Group, Inc., The.

Hoffman, Mary Ann. David Ortiz: Baseball Star. 2006. (Sports Superstars Ser.). (Illus.). 24p. (J). lib. bdg. (978-1-4042-3534-2(5)) Rosen Publishing Group, Inc., The.

Holder, Sherie, ed. The Great Home Run Chase. 1998. 32p. (J). (gr. 1-9). pap. 4.99 (978-1-886749-57-3(4)) Sports Illustrated For Kids.

Horn, Geoffrey M. Albert Pujols. 2006. (Today's Superstars). (Illus.). 32p. (YA). (gr. 5 up). lib. bdg. 23.93 (978-0-8368-6185-3(X)) Stevens, Gareth Inc.

Hubbard, Crystal. Catching the Moon: The Story of a Young Girl's Baseball Dream. DuBurke, Randy, illus. 2005. 32p. (J). 16.95 (978-1-58430-243-8(7)) Lee & Low Bks., Inc.

Jackie Robinson. 1999. (SmartReader Ser.). (J). Level 1. pap., tchr. ed. 19.95 incl. audio (978-0-7887-1156-5(3) , 79417T3); Level 2. pap., tchr. ed. 19.95 incl. audio (978-0-7887-0280-8(7) , 79320T3) Recorded Bks., LLC.

Jensen, Luke. Joltin' Joe Baseball Hero: The Amazing True Story of Joe DiMaggio. 1999. (J). (978-0-606-18666-7(2)) Tandem Library Bks.

Joe Mauer. 2008. (Amazing Athletes Ser.). (J). 23.93 (***978-0-8225-8835-1(8)*** , Lerner Pubns.); pap. 6.95 (***978-0-8225-8976-1(1)*** , First Avenue Editions) Lerner Publishing Group.

Johan Santana. 2007. (J). pap. 5.95 (***978-0-8225-6596-3(X)*** , First Avenue Editions) Lerner Publishing Group.

Kappes, Serena. Alex Rodriguez. 2006. (Sports Heroes & Legends Ser.). 106p. (J). 27.93 (978-0-8225-5963-4(3) , Lerner Pubns.) Lerner Publishing Group.

Kellogg, David. True Stories of Baseball's Hall of Famers. 2000. (Illus.). 144p. (J). 8.95 (978-0-912517-41-4(7)) Bluewood Bks.

—True Stories of Baseball's Hall of Famers. 2000. (gr. 7-12). lib. bdg. 17.60 (978-0-613-90829-0(5)) Tandem Library Bks.

Kennedy, Mike & Stewart, Mark. Latino Baseball's Finest Fielders/Las Mejores Estrellas del Beisbol Latino. Kalmanovitz, Manuel, tr. 2002. (En Fuego Ser.). (SPA & ENG., Illus.). 64p. (gr. 5 up). lib. bdg. 26.90 (978-0-7613-2566-6(2) , Twenty-First Century Bks.) Lerner Publishing Group.

—Latino Baseball's Hottest Hitters/Los Mejores Bateadores del Beisbol Latino. Kalmanovitz, Manuel, tr. 2002. (En Fuego Ser.). (ENG & SPA., Illus.). 64p. (gr. 5 up). lib. bdg. 26.90 (978-0-7613-2567-3(0) , Twenty-First Century Bks.) Lerner Publishing Group.

Kernan, Kevin. Bernie Williams: Quiet Superstar. Rains, Rob, ed. 1999. (Superstar Ser.). (Illus.). 112p. (J). (gr. 4-7). per. 4.95 (978-1-58261-044-3(4)) Sports Publishing, LLC.

—Roger Clemens Rocket Man. Rains, Rob, ed. 1999. (Superstar Ser.: Vol. 19). 96p. (J). (gr. 4-7). per. 4.95 (978-1-58261-128-0(9)) Sports Publishing, LLC.

Kirkpatrick, Rob. Mark McGwire. 2001. (Great Record Breakers in Sports Ser.). (Illus.). 24p. (J). lib. bdg. 18.75 (978-0-8239-5630-2(X) , PowerKids Pr.) Rosen Publishing Group, Inc., The.

—Mark McGwire: Record Breaker. 2000. (Reading Power Ser.). (Illus.). 24p. (J). (gr. 1). lib. bdg. 17.25 (978-0-8239-5535-0(4) , PowerKids Pr.) Rosen Publishing Group, Inc., The.

—Mark Mcgwire: Record Breaker. 2002. (Deportistas de Poder Ser.). (SPA.). 24p. (J). lib. bdg. 17.25 (978-0-8239-6115-3(X) , Buenas Letra) Rosen Publishing Group, Inc., The.

—Mark McGwire, Rompe Records. 2002. (Coleccion Power Kids). (SPA & ENG., Illus.). 24p. (J). (gr. k-2). lib. bdg. 17.25 (978-0-8239-6133-7(8) , RN31304, Buenas Letra) Rosen Publishing Group, Inc., The.

—Sammy Sosa: Home Run Hitter. 2002. (Reading Power Ser.). (Illus.). 24p. (J). (gr. 1). lib. bdg. 17.25 (978-0-8239-5534-3(6) , PowerKids Pr.) Rosen Publishing Group, Inc., The.

—Sammy Sosa, Bateador de Home Runs. 2002. (Coleccion Power Kids). (SPA & ENG., Illus.). 24p. (J). (gr. k-2). lib. bdg. 17.25 (978-0-8239-6132-0(X) , RN31299, Buenas Letra) Rosen Publishing Group, Inc., The.

—Sammy Sosa, Batedor de Home Runs. 2002. (Deportistas de Poder Ser.). (SPA & ENG., Illus.). 24p. (J). lib. bdg. 17.25 (978-0-8239-6114-6(1) , Buenas Letra) Rosen Publishing Group, Inc., The.

Kisseloff, Jeff. Who Is Baseball's Greatest Pitcher? 2003. (Marcato Book Ser.). (Illus.). 160p. (J). (gr. 5-7). 15.95 (978-0-8126-2685-8(0)) Cricket Bks.

Kjelle, Marylou Morano. Alex Rodriguez: Professional Baseball Player. 2005. (Robbie Reader Ser.). (Illus.). 32p. (J). (gr. 1-4). lib. bdg. (978-1-58415-394-8(6)) Mitchell Lane Pubs., Inc.

Klingel, Cynthia Fitterer & Noyed, Robert B. Jackie Robinson. 2001. (Wonder Books Level 2: Biographies Ser.). (Illus.). 24p. (J). (ps-3). 22.79 (978-1-56766-953-4(0)) Child's World, Inc.

Knox, Barbara. Jackie Robinson. 2003. (Photo-Illustrated Biographies Ser.). (Illus.). 24p. (J). lib. bdg. 19.93 (978-0-7368-2224-4(0) , Bridgestone Bks.) Capstone Pr., Inc.

Koestler-Grack, Rachel A. Kirby Puckett. 2007. (Baseball Superstars Ser.). 128p. (J). (gr. 6-12). 30.00 (***978-0-7910-9497-6(9)*** , Chelsea Hse.) Facts On File, Inc.

Korman, Susan. Sammy Sosa. 2001. (Latinos in the Limelight Ser.). (Illus.). 64p. (J). (gr. 4-7). 27.50 (978-0-7910-6474-0(3) , Chelsea Hse.) Facts On File, Inc.

Kramer, Sydelle A. Baseball's Greatest Hitters. Campbell, Jim, illus. rev. ed. 2000. (Step into Reading Step 4 Bks.). 48p. (J). (gr. 2-5). pap. 3.99 (978-0-375-80583-7(4) , Random Hse. Bks. for Young Readers) Random Hse. Children's Bks.

—Baseball's Greatest Hitters. 2000. (Illus.). (J). 10.79 (978-0-606-18484-7(8)) Tandem Library Bks.

Krasner, Steven. Pedro Martinez. 2001. (Latinos in the Limelight Ser.). (Illus.). 64p. (J). (gr. 4-7). 27.50 (978-0-7910-6480-1(8) , Chelsea Hse.) Facts On File, Inc.

—Play Ball Like the Pros: Tips for Kids from 20 Big League Stars. 2002. (Illus.). 160p. (J). (gr. 4-7). pap. 12.95 (978-1-56145-261-3(0)) Peachtree Pubs., Ltd.

—Play Ball Like the Pros: Tips for Kids from 20 Big League Stars. 2002. (gr. 3-6). lib. bdg. 22.20 (978-0-613-84739-1(3)) Tandem Library Bks.

Lashnits, Tom. Pedro Martinez. 2006. (Great Hispanic Heritage Ser.). (Illus.). 136p. (J). 30.00 (978-0-7910-8840-1(5) , Chelsea Hse.) Facts On File, Inc.

Latinos in Baseball: Sammy Sosa; Roberto Alomar; Tino Martinez; Moises Alou; Pedro Martinez; Bobby Bonilla; Alex Rodriguez; Bernie Williams; Manny Ramirez; Vinny Castilla; Ivan Rodriguez; Ramon Martinez, 12 vols. 2000. (Illus.). 768p. (YA). (gr. 5 up). lib. bdg. 227.40 (978-1-58415-053-4(X)) Mitchell Lane Pubs., Inc.

Layden, Joe. Heroe del Jonron: La Historia de Sammy Sosa, 1 vol. 1998. (SPA., Illus.). 58p. (J). (gr. 2-9). pap. 3.99 (978-0-439-07758-3(3)) Scholastic, Inc.

Lazenby, Roland. Ichiro: The Making of an American Hero. 2005. (Illus.). 51p. (YA). reprint ed. 13.00 (978-0-7567-8238-2(4)) DIANE Publishing Co.

Leigh, David S. Ichiro Suzuki. 2004. (Sports Heroes & Legends Ser.). (Illus.). 112p. (J). (gr. 6-12). lib. bdg. 27.93 (978-0-8225-1792-4(2)) Lerner Publishing Group.

Levin, Judith. Ichiro Suzuki. 2007. (Baseball Superstars Ser.). 144p. (J). (gr. 6-12). 30.00 (***978-0-7910-9440-2(5)*** , Chelsea Hse.) Facts On File, Inc.

Lewis, Gregg. Dave Dravecky. 2002. (gr. 3-6). lib. bdg. 13.00 (978-0-613-71674-1(4)) Tandem Library Bks.

Littleton, Mark. Baseball. 2002. (gr. 3-6). lib. bdg. 14.15 (978-0-613-71665-9(5)) Tandem Library Bks.

—Baseball. 2002. (Illus.). 112p. (J). pap. 5.99 (978-0-310-70291-7(7)) Zonderkidz.

Macht, Norman L. Roberto Alomar. 1999. (Latinos in Baseball Ser.). (Illus.). 72p. (gr. 4-10). lib. bdg. 18.95 (978-1-883845-84-1(X)) Mitchell Lane Pubs., Inc.

—Roger Clemens. 1999. (Baseball Legends Ser.). 64p. (gr. 4-7). pap. 10.60 (978-0-7910-5455-0(1) , Chelsea Hse.) Facts On File, Inc.

—Roger Clemens. 1999. (gr. 5-8). lib. bdg. 16.40 (978-0-613-26779-3(6)) Tandem Library Bks.

MacLean, Caleb. Sammy Sosa: Cubs Clubber. 1999. (gr. 3-6). lib. bdg. 14.10 (978-0-613-62314-8(2)) Tandem Library Bks.

Macnow, Glen. Sports Great Alex Rodriguez. 2002. (Sports Great Books). (Illus.). 64p. (J). (gr. 4-10). lib. bdg. 22.60 (978-0-7660-1845-7(8)) Enslow Pubs., Inc.

—Sports Great Deion Sanders. 1999. (Sports Great Bks.). (Illus.). 64p. (YA). (gr. 4-10). lib. bdg. 22.60 (978-0-7660-1068-0(6)) Enslow Pubs., Inc.

—Sports Great Kevin Garnett. 2000. (Sports Great Bks.). (Illus.). 64p. (YA). (gr. 4-10). lib. bdg. 17.95 (978-0-7660-1263-9(8)) Enslow Pubs., Inc.

Malone, Julio. Sammy Sosa en 9 Innings. 2nd exp. ed. 2004. (SPA.). (YA). pap. 12.95 net. (978-0-9671705-0-3(8)) Editorial Miglo.

—Sammy Sosa in 9 Innings. 2004. (YA). pap. 12.95 (978-0-9671705-1-0(6)) Editorial Miglo.

Manoloff, Dennis. Omar Vizquel: The Man with the Golden Glove. Rains, Rob, ed. 2003. (Super Star Ser.). (Illus.). 96p. (J). (gr. 4-7). pap. 4.95 (978-1-58261-045-0(2)) Sports Publishing, LLC.

Mara, Wil. Jackie Robinson. 2003. (Rookie Biographies Ser.). (Illus.). 32p. (J). (gr. 1-2). pap. 4.95 (978-0-516-27336-5(1) , Children's Pr.) Scholastic Library Publishing.

—Jackie Robinson. 2003. (Illus.). 31p. (J). (ps-3). lib. bdg. 12.95 (978-0-613-59501-8(7)) Tandem Library Bks.

Marsh, Carole. Jackie Robinson. 2002. (One Thousand Readers Ser.). (Illus.). 12p. (J). (gr. k-4). 2.95 (978-0-635-01529-7(3) , 15293) Gallopade International.

Mattern, Joanne. David Ortiz. 2007. (Blue Banner Biography Ser.). (Illus.). 32p. (J). (gr. 4-8). lib. bdg. 25.70 (***978-1-58415-620-8(1)***) Mitchell Lane Pubs., Inc.

Mattern, Joanne. Miguel Tejada. 2006. (Blue Banner Biography Ser.). (Illus.). 32p. (J). (gr. 4-8). lib. bdg. 25.70 (978-1-58415-505-8(1)) Mitchell Lane Pubs., Inc.

McCormack, Shaun. Cool Papa Bell. 2002. (Baseball Hall of Famers of the Negro League Ser.). (Illus.). 112p. (YA). (gr. 5-8). lib. bdg. 29.25 (978-0-8239-3474-4(8) , Rosen Central) Rosen Publishing Group, Inc., The.

McDonough, Yona Zeldis. Hammerin' Hank: The Life of Hank Greenberg. Zeldis, Malcah, illus. 2006. 32p. (J). 17.85 (978-0-8027-8998-3(6)); 16.95 (978-0-8027-8997-6(8)) Walker & Co.

McLeese, Don. Babe Ruth. 4th ed. 2003. (Rourke Discovery Library). (Illus.). 24p. (gr. 2-5). 14.95 (978-1-58952-304-3(0)) Rourke Publishing, LLC.

—Jackie Robinson. 2002. (Illus.). 24p. (J). (ps-3). lib. bdg. 20.64 (978-1-58952-288-6(5)) Rourke Publishing, LLC.

Merz, Robert L. Ryan Howard: King of Swing. 2007. 120p. per. 9.95 ***978-0-9765868-2-1(7))** Values of America Co.

Miller, Raymond H. Barry Bonds. 2002. (Stars of Sports Ser.). (Illus.). 48p. (J). 26.20 (978-0-7377-1393-0(3) , Greenhaven Pr., Inc.) Thomson Gale.

Mills, Clifford W. Bernie Williams. 2007. (Baseball Superstars Ser.). 128p. (YA). (gr. 6-12). 30.00 ***(*978-0-7910-9468-6(5)*** , Chelsea Hse.) Facts On File, Inc.

—Curt Schilling. 2008. (Baseball Superstars Ser.). (gr. 6-12). 30.00 ***(*978-0-7910-9635-2(1)*** , Chelsea Hse.) Facts On File, Inc.

—Derek Jeter. 2007. (Baseball Superstars Ser.). 128p. (J). (gr. 6-12). 30.00 ***(*978-0-7910-9422-8(7)*** , Chelsea Hse.) Facts On File, Inc.

Molzahn, Arlene Bourgeois. Sammy Sosa. 2000. (Sports Heroes Ser.). (Illus.). 48p. (J). (gr. 3-4). lib. bdg. 21.26 (978-0-7368-0580-3(X) , Capstone High-Interest Bks.) Capstone Pr., Inc.

Morris, Roz. Henry Aaron: Dream Chaser. 2002. (Alabama Roots Biography Ser.). (Illus.). 120p. (J). per. 7.95 (978-1-878561-94-7(4)) Seacoast Publishing, Inc.

Morrison, John. Sammy Sosa. 2006. (Great Hispanic Heritage Ser.). (Illus.). 112p. (J). 30.00 (978-0-7910-8845-6(6) , Chelsea Hse.) Facts On File, Inc.

Murphy, Frank. Babe Ruth Saves Baseball. Walz, Richard, illus. 2005. (Step into Reading Ser.). 48p. (J). (gr. 1-3). lib. bdg. 11.99 (978-0-375-93048-5(5) , Random Hse. Bks. for Young Readers) Random Hse. Children's Bks.

—Babe Ruth Saves Baseball! Walz, Richard, illus. 2005. (Step into Reading Ser.: Vol. 3). 48p. (J). (gr. 1-3). pap. 3.99 (978-0-375-83048-8(0) , Random Hse. Bks. for Young Readers) Random Hse. Children's Bks.

Murphy, Frank. Babe Ruth Saves Baseball Book & CD. Walz, Richard, illus. 2008. (Book & CD Ser.). 48p. (J). (gr. 1-3). 9.99 ***(*978-0-375-84184-2(9)*** , Random Hse. Bks. for Young Readers) Random Hse. Children's Bks.

Murray, Jim, intro. Chipper Jones. 1999. (Baseball Legends Ser.). (Illus.). 64p. (YA). (gr. 3-8). 12.95 (978-0-7910-5157-3(9) , Chelsea Hse.) Facts On File, Inc.

—Larry Walker. 1999. (Baseball Legends Ser.). (Illus.). 64p. (YA). (gr. 3-7). 18.65 (978-0-7910-5159-7(5) , Chelsea Hse.) Facts On File, Inc.

—Mark McGwire. 1999. (Baseball Legends Ser.). (Illus.). 64p. (YA). (gr. 3-7). 18.65 (978-0-7910-5155-9(2) , Chelsea Hse.) Facts On File, Inc.

—Randy Johnson. 1999. (Baseball Legends Ser.). (Illus.). 64p. (YA). (gr. 3-7). pap. 18.65 (978-0-7910-5158-0(7) , Chelsea Hse.) Facts On File, Inc.

—Roger Clemens. 1999. (Baseball Legends Ser.). (Illus.). 64p. (YA). (gr. 3-7). pap. 18.65 (978-0-7910-5156-6(0) , Chelsea Hse.) Facts On File, Inc.

Muskat, Carrie. Mark McGwire. 1999. (Baseball Legends Ser.). (Illus.). 64p. (gr. 4-7). pap. 7.95 (978-0-7910-5491-8(8) , Chelsea Hse.) Facts On File, Inc.

—Mark McGwire. 1999. (Baseball Legends Ser.). (978-0-606-18036-8(2)); (gr. 5-8). lib. bdg. 16.40 (978-0-613-26135-7(6)) Tandem Library Bks.

—Moises Alou. 1999. (Latinos in Baseball Ser.). (Illus.). 72p. (gr. 4-10). lib. bdg. 18.95 (978-1-883845-86-5(6)) Mitchell Lane Pubs., Inc.

—Sammy Sosa. 2000. (Overcoming Adversity Ser.). (Illus.). 112p. (YA). 30.00 (978-0-7910-5300-3(8) , Chelsea Hse.) Facts On File, Inc.

—Sammy Sosa. 1999. (Latinos in Baseball Ser.). (Illus.). 72p. (gr. 4-10). lib. bdg. 18.95 (978-1-883845-92-6(0)); 32p. (gr. 3-8). lib. bdg. 15.95 (978-1-883845-96-4(3)) Mitchell Lane Pubs., Inc.

Needham, Tom. Albert Pujols: MVP on & off the Field. 2007. (Sports Stars with Heart Ser.). (Illus.). 128p. (J). (gr. 5). lib. bdg. 31.93 ***(*978-0-7660-2866-1(6))*** Enslow Pubs., Inc.

Nicholson, Lois. From Maryland to Cooperstown: Seven Maryland Natives in Baseball's Hall of Fame. 1998. (Illus.). 144p. (J). (gr. 4-8). 19.95 (978-0-87033-494-8(8) , Tidewater Pubs.) Cornell Maritime Pr., Inc.

Noble, Marty. Mike Piazza: Mike & the Mets. Rains, Rob, ed. 2003. (Superstar Ser.). (Illus.). 96p. (J). (gr. 4-7). pap. 4.95 (978-1-58261-051-1(7)) Sports Publishing, LLC.

O'Connell, Jack. Derek Jeter: The Yankee Kid. Rains, Rob, ed. 2003. (Super Star Ser.). 96p. (J). pap. 4.95 (978-1-58261-043-6(6)) Sports Publishing, LLC.

O'Hern, Kerri & Raatma, Lucia. Jackie Robinson. 2006. (Illus.). 31p. (J). pap. (978-0-8368-6250-8(3) , World Almanac Library) Stevens, Gareth Inc.

Patrick, Denise Lewis & Time for Kids Editors. Jackie Robinson: Strong Inside & Out. 2005. (Time for Kids Ser.). (Illus.). 48p. (J). 15.99 (978-0-06-057601-1(4)); pap. 3.99 (978-0-06-057600-4(6)) HarperCollins Pubs.

Patrick, Jean L. S. The Girl Who Struck Out Babe Ruth. Reeves, Jeni, illus. (On My Own History Ser.). 48p. (J). (gr. 1-3). 2003. pap. 5.95 (978-1-57505-455-1(8)); 2000. lib. bdg. 23.93 (978-1-57505-397-4(7) , Carolrhoda Bks.) Lerner Publishing Group.

—The Girl Who Struck Out Babe Ruth. 2000. (J). (978-0-606-19443-3(6)) Tandem Library Bks.

Payment, Simone. Buck Leonard. 2002. (Baseball Hall of Famers of the Negro League Ser.). (Illus.). 112p. (YA). (gr. 5-8). lib. bdg. 29.25 (978-0-8239-3473-7(X) , Rosen Central) Rosen Publishing Group, Inc., The.

Pellowski, Michael. Super Sports Star Mike Piazza. 2004. (Super Sports Star Ser.). (Illus.). 48p. (J). lib. bdg. 23.93 (978-0-7660-2159-4(9)) Enslow Pubs., Inc.

Pietrusza, David. Top 10 Baseball Managers. 1999. (Sports Top 10 Ser.). (Illus.). 48p. (YA). (gr. 4-10). lib. bdg. 23.93 (978-0-7660-1076-5(7)) Enslow Pubs., Inc.

Powell, Phelan. Mark McGwire. 2000. (Sports Heroes Ser.). (Illus.). 48p. (J). (gr. 3-4). lib. bdg. 21.26 (978-0-7368-0578-0(8) , Capstone High-Interest Bks.) Capstone Pr., Inc.

Preller, James. McGwire & Sosa: A Season to Remember. 1998. (Illus.). 32p. (J). (ps up). pap. 5.99 (978-0-689-82871-3(3) , Simon Pulse) Simon & Schuster Children's Publishing.

Prince, April Jones. Jackie Robinson: He Led the Way. Casilla, Robert, illus. 2007. (All Aboard Reading Ser.). 48p. (J). (gr. 1-3). pap. 3.99 ***(*978-0-448-44721-6(5)*** , Grosset & Dunlap) Penguin Group (USA) Inc.

Raatma, Kerri & Raatma, Lucia. Jackie Robinson. Campbell, Alex & Spay, Anthony, illus. 2006. (Graphic Biographies Ser.). 32p. (J). (gr. 3-5). lib. bdg. 26.00 (978-0-8368-6198-3(1) , World Almanac Library) Stevens, Gareth Inc.

Rains, Rob. Mark McGwire: "Mac Attack!" 1998. (Superstar Ser.). (Illus.). 100p. (YA). (gr. 7-10). per. 5.95 (978-1-58261-004-7(5)) Sports Publishing, LLC.

—Mark McGwire: Slugger! Sporting News Staff, ed. 1998. (Illus.). 50p. (J). (gr. 1-6). 15.95 (978-1-58261-005-4(3)) Sports Publishing, LLC.

Rappoport, Ken. Super Sports Star Alex Rodriguez. 2004. (Super Sports Star Ser.). (Illus.). 48p. (J). lib. bdg. 23.93 (978-0-7660-2138-9(6)) Enslow Pubs., Inc.

—Super Sports Star Derek Jeter. 2004. (Super Sports Star Ser.). (Illus.). 48p. (J). lib. bdg. 23.93 (978-0-7660-2139-6(4)) Enslow Pubs., Inc.

—Super Sports Star Ichiro Suzuki. 2004. (Super Sports Star Ser.). (Illus.). 48p. (J). lib. bdg. 23.93 (978-0-7660-2137-2(8)) Enslow Pubs., Inc.

Ripken, Cal, Jr. & Bryan, Mike. Cal Ripken, Jr. Play Ball! Silver, Stan, illus. 1999. 96p. (J). (ps-3). pap. 3.99 (978-0-14-130184-6(8) , Puffin) Penguin Group (USA) Inc.

—Cal Ripken, Jr. Play Ball! 1999. (Puffin Easy-to-Read Ser.). (J). 10.79 (978-0-606-16825-0(7)) Tandem Library Bks.

Roberts, Jerry. Roberto Clemente: Baseball Player. 2005. (Ferguson Career Biographies Ser.). (Illus.). 128p. (J). (gr. 6-12). 25.00 (978-0-8160-6072-6(X) , Ferguson Publishing Co.) Facts On File, Inc.

Robinson, Tom. Andruw Jones: All-Star on & off the Field. 2007. (Sports Stars with Heart Ser.). (Illus.). 128p. (J). (gr. 5). lib. bdg. 31.93 ***(*978-0-7660-2867-8(4))*** Enslow Pubs., Inc.

Rodriguez, Alex. Hit a Grand Slam. 1998. 40p. 14.95 (978-0-87833-997-6(3)) Taylor Trade Publishing.

Rolfe, John, et al. Ken Griffey, Jr. 2000. 112p. (J). pap. 3.99 (978-1-930623-07-1(0)) Sports Illustrated For Kids.

—Ken Griffey, Jr. Superstar Centerfielder. 2005. (Sports Illustrated for Kids Bks.). (Illus.). 176p. (YA). (gr. 7-12). lib. bdg. 30.50 (978-0-8239-3687-8(2)) Rosen Publishing Group, Inc., The.

Rolte, John & Ross, Dalton. Ken Griffey, Jr. 1999. (Sports Illustrated for Kids Bks.). 112p. (J). (gr. 4-6). pap. 3.99 (978-1-886749-58-0(2)) Sports Illustrated For Kids.

Rosewater, Amy, ed. Jim Thome: Lefty Launcher. 2000. (Baseball Superstar Ser.: Vol. 23). (Illus.). 96p. (J). (gr. 4-7). per. 4.95 (978-1-58261-251-5(X)) Sports Publishing, LLC.

Rozner, Barry. Mark Grace: Winning with Grace. Rains, Rob, ed. 1999. (Superstar Ser.: Vol. 16). (Illus.). 112p. (J). (gr. 4-7). per. 4.95 (978-1-58261-056-6(8)) Sports Publishing, LLC.

Ryan Howard. 2008. (Amazing Athletes Ser.). (J). pap. 6.95 ***(*978-0-8225-8978-5(8)*** , First Avenue Editions) Lerner Publishing Group.

Sammy Sosa, 6 vols. (gr. 4 up). 39.95 (978-0-7368-9277-3(X)) Red Brick Learning.

Savage, Jeff. Albert Pujols. 2007. (Amazing Athletes Ser.). (J). 23.93 (978-0-8225-6849-0(7) , Lerner Pubns.) Lerner Publishing Group.

—Barry Bonds. 2004. (Amazing Athletes Ser.). (Illus.). 32p. (J). (gr. 3-4). lib. bdg. 23.93 (978-0-8225-3688-8(9)) Lerner Publishing Group.

—Barry Bonds: Record Breaker. 2nd rev. ed. 2003. (Sports Achievers Biographies Ser.). (Illus.). 64p. (J). (gr. 4-9). 5.95 (978-0-8225-0472-6(3) , Carolrhoda Bks.) Lerner Publishing Group.

—David Ortiz. 2006. (Amazing Athletes Ser.). (Illus.). 32p. (J). 22.60 (978-0-8225-3429-7(0) , Lerner Pubns.) Lerner Publishing Group.

—Home Run Kings. 1999. (Illus.). 48p. (YA). (gr. 3-7). (978-0-7398-0216-8(X)) Raintree.

—Home Run Kings. 1999. (Illus.). 48p. (J). (gr. 3-7). pap. 6.95 (978-0-7398-0215-1(1)) Steck-Vaughn.

—Ichiro Suzuki. 2007. (J). pap. 5.95 (978-0-8225-7266-4(4) , Lerner Pubns.); 2005. (Illus.). 32p. (gr. 3-4). lib. bdg. 22.60 (978-0-8225-1344-5(7)) Lerner Publishing Group.

—Mark McGwire: Home Run King. (Sports Achievers Biographies Ser.). (Illus.). (YA). (gr. 4-9). 2003. 64p. pap. 5.95 (978-0-8225-9845-9(0) , Carolrhoda Bks.); 1999. 80p. lib. bdg. 22.60 (978-0-8225-3675-8(7) , Lerner-Sports) Lerner Publishing Group.

—Ryan Howard. 2008. (Amazing Athletes Ser.). (J). lib. bdg. 23.93 ***(*978-0-8225-8833-7(1)*** , Lerner Pubns.) Lerner Publishing Group.

—Sammy Sosa. (Amazing Athletes Ser.). (J). 2006. (Illus.). (gr. 3-4). 23.93 (978-0-8225-3672-7(2)); 2005. 32p. (gr. 2-5). pap. 5.95 (978-0-8225-2041-2(9)) Lerner Publishing Group.

—Sammy Sosa: Heroe del Jonron. 2000. Tr. of Sammy Sosa: Home Run Hero. (978-0-606-18825-8(8)) Tandem Library Bks.

—Sammy Sosa: Home Run Hero. (Sports Achievers Biographies Ser.). (Illus.). 2005. (SPA.). 80p. (gr. 7-12). lib. bdg. 22.60 (978-0-8225-3681-9(1)); 2003. 64p. (J). (gr. 4-9). 5.95 (978-0-8225-9858-9(2) , Carolrhoda Bks.); 2000. (SPA., 64p. (YA). (gr. 4-9). pap. 5.95 (978-0-8225-9861-9(2) , LernerSports) Lerner Publishing Group.

—Sammy Sosa: Home Run Hero. 2000. (SPA.). (gr. 5-8). lib. bdg. 14.10 (978-0-613-84488-8(2)) Tandem Library Bks.

Schaefer, A. R. Ken Griffey, Jr. 2002. (Sports Heroes Ser.). (Illus.). 48p. (J). (gr. 3-4). lib. bdg. 21.26 (978-0-7368-1294-8(6) , Capstone High-Interest Bks.) Capstone Pr., Inc.

—Pedro Martinez. 2002. (Sports Heroes Ser.). (Illus.). 48p. (J). (gr. 3-4). lib. bdg. 21.26 (978-0-7368-1296-2(2) , Capstone High-Interest Bks.) Capstone Pr., Inc.

Scher, Jon. Baseball's Best Sluggers: Today's Hottest Hitters. 2000. (Illus.). 48p. (J). (gr. 2-8). pap. 2.99 (978-1-886749-85-6(X)) Sports Illustrated For Kids.

Schnakenberg, Robert E. Derek Jeter: Surefire Shortstop. (Sports Achievers Biographies Ser.). (Illus.). 1999. 80p. (gr. 7-12). lib. bdg. 22.60 (978-0-8225-3671-0(4)); 1998. 64p. (YA). (gr. 4-9). pap. (978-0-8225-9838-1(8) , LernerSports) Lerner Publishing Group.

Schwarz, Alan. Baseball All-Stars. Gramling, Scott, ed. 1999. 96p. (J). (gr. 2-8). pap. 3.99 (978-1-886749-69-6(8)) Sports Illustrated For Kids.

—Rising Stars: The 10 Best Young Players in Baseball. 2005. (Sports Illustrated for Kids Bks.). (Illus.). 176p. (YA). (gr. 7-12). lib. bdg. 32.00 (978-0-8239-3576-5(0)) Rosen Publishing Group, Inc., The.

Sexton, Colleen. Jackie Robinson: A Life of Determination. 2007. (Illus.). 24p. (J). lib. bdg. 19.95 (978-1-60014-089-1(0)) Bellwether Media.

Shalin, Mike. Alex Rodriguez: A-Plus Shortstop. Rains, Rob, ed. 1999. (Superstar Ser.). 96p. (J). (gr. 4-7). per. 4.95 (978-1-58261-104-4(1)) Sports Publishing, LLC.

—Mo Vaughn: Angel on a Mission. Rains, Rob, ed. 1999. (Superstar Ser.: Vol. 7). (Illus.). 112p. (J). (gr. 4-7). per. 4.95 (978-1-58261-046-7(0)) Sports Publishing, LLC.

—Nomar Garciaparra: High 5! Rains, Rob, ed. 2003. (Superstar Ser.). (Illus.). 96p. (J). (gr. 4-7). pap. 4.95 (978-1-58261-053-5(3)) Sports Publishing, LLC.

—Pedro Martinez: Throwing Strikes. Rains, Rob, ed. 2003. (Superstar Ser.). (Illus.). 96p. (J). (gr. 4-7). pap. 4.95 (978-1-58261-047-4(9)) Sports Publishing, LLC.

Silverstone, Michael. Latino Legends: Hispanics in Major League Baseball. 2003. (High Five Reading Ser.). (Illus.). (J). 64p. lib. bdg. 22.60 (978-0-7368-2791-1(9)); 48p. pap. 23.93 (978-0-7368-2832-1(X)) Capstone Pr., Inc.

Smithwicks, John. Meet Alex Rodriguez: Baseball's Lightning Rod. 2007. (All-Star Players Ser.). (Illus.). 32p. (J). (gr. 4-6). lib. bdg. 23.95 (978-1-4042-3636-3(8) , PowerKids Pr.) Rosen Publishing Group, Inc., The.

—Meet David Ortiz: Baseball's Top Slugger. 2007. (All-Star Players Ser.). (Illus.). 32p. (J). (gr. 4-6). lib. bdg. 23.95 (978-1-4042-3637-0(6) , PowerKids Pr.) Rosen Publishing Group, Inc., The.

STATS, Inc. Staff. STATS Baseball's Terrific 20. 1999. 48p. (J). (gr. 2-7). pap. 9.95 (978-1-884064-70-8(1)) S T A T S Publishing.

Stewart, Mark. Alex Rodriguez: Gunning for Greatness. 1999. (New Wave Ser.). (Illus.). 48p. (gr. 4 up). lib. bdg. 22.90 (978-0-7613-1515-5(2) , Millbrook Pr.) Lerner Publishing Group.

—Andruw Jones: Love That Glove. 2001. (New Wave Ser.). (Illus.). 48p. (gr. 4 up). lib. bdg. 22.90 (978-0-7613-1967-2(0) , Millbrook Pr.) Lerner Publishing Group.

—Derek Jeter: Substance & Style. 1999. (New Wave Ser.). (Illus.). 48p. (gr. 4 up). lib. bdg. 22.90 (978-0-7613-1516-2(0) , Millbrook Pr.) Lerner Publishing Group.

—Ivan Rodriguez: Armed & Dangerous. 1999. (gr. 3-6). lib. bdg. 14.10 (978-0-613-62297-4(9)) Tandem Library Bks.

—Ken Griffey, Jr. 1999. (gr. 3-6). lib. bdg. 14.10 (978-0-613-90736-1(1)) Tandem Library Bks.

—Nomar Garciaparra: Non-Stop Shortstop. 2000. (New Wave Ser.). (Illus.). 48p. (gr. 4 up). lib. bdg. 22.90 (978-0-7613-1520-9(9) , Millbrook Pr.) Lerner Publishing Group.

—Pedro Martinez: Pitcher Perfect. 2000. (gr. 3-6). lib. bdg. 14.10 (978-0-613-62308-7(8)) Tandem Library Bks.

Stewart, Mark. Sammy Sosa: Touching All the Bases. 2004. (American Literary Greats Ser.). (Illus.). 64p. (J). (gr. 5 up). lib. bdg. (978-0-7613-2778-3(9) , Millbrook Pr.) Lerner Publishing Group.

Stewart, Mark. Todd Helton: The Hits Keep Coming. 2001. (New Wave Ser.). (Illus.). 48p. (gr. 4 up). lib. bdg. 22.90 (978-0-7613-2271-9(X) , Millbrook Pr.) Lerner Publishing Group.

Stewart, Mark & Kennedy, Mike. Latino Baseball's Finest Fielders/Las Mas Destacados Guantes del Beisbol Latino. Kalmanovitz, Manuel, tr. 2003. (En Fuego Ser.). (ENG & SPA., Illus.). 48p. (J). (gr. 5 up). pap. 9.95 (978-0-7613-1749-4(X) , Twenty-First Century Bks.) Lerner Publishing Group.

—Latino Baseball's Hottest Hitters. Kalmanovitz, Manuel, tr. 2003. (En Fuego Ser.). (SPA & ENG., Illus.). 48p. (J). (gr. 5 up). pap. 9.95 (978-0-7613-1775-3(9) , Twenty-First Century Bks.) Lerner Publishing Group.

Stewart, Mark Alan. Mark McGwire: Home Run King. 1999. (Sports Stars Ser.). 48p. (gr. 3-4). pap. 5.95 (978-0-516-26512-4(1) , Children's Pr.) Scholastic Library Publishing.

—Nomar Garciaparra: Non-Stop Shortstop. 2000. (Baseball's New Wave Ser.: up). (Illus.). 48p. (gr. 4-7). pap. (978-0-7613-1335-9(4) , Millbrook Pr.) Lerner Publishing Group.

—Nomar Garciaparra: Non-Stop Shortstop. 2000. (J). (978-0-606-19167-8(4)) Tandem Library Bks.

Sullivan, George. Baseball's Boneheads, Bad Boys & Just Plain Crazy. 2003. (Single Titles Ser.). (Illus.). 64p. (gr. 5-8). lib. bdg. 23.90 (978-0-7613-2321-1(X) , Millbrook Pr.) Lerner Publishing Group.

Sullivan, George E. Sluggers: Twenty-Seven of Baseball's Greatest. 1999. (978-0-606-15947-0(9)) Tandem Library Bks.

Sweet, Kimberly. Hank Aaron: The Life of the Home Run King. 2001. (J). (gr. 4-7). pap. 7.95 (978-1-58838-022-7(X)) NewSouth, Inc.

Thornley, Stew. Alex Rodriguez: Slugging Shortstop. 1998. (Sports Achievers Biographies Ser.). (Illus.). 64p. (gr. 4-9). lib. bdg. (978-0-8225-3663-5(3) , LernerSports) Lerner Publishing Group.

—Derek Jeter: Daring to Dream. 2004. (Sports Leaders Ser.). (Illus.). 104p. (J). lib. bdg. 26.60 (978-0-7660-2035-1(5)) Enslow Pubs., Inc.

—Mark McGwire: Star Home Run Hitter. 1999. (Sports Reports). (Illus.). 104p. (YA). (gr. 4-10). lib. bdg. 20.95 (978-0-7660-1329-2(4)) Enslow Pubs., Inc.

—Roberto Alomar: Star Second Baseman. 1999. (Sports Reports). (Illus.). 104p. (YA). (gr. 4-10). lib. bdg. 26.60 (978-0-7660-1079-6(1)) Enslow Pubs., Inc.

—Roberto Clemente. 2007. (Sports Heroes & Legends Ser.). (Illus.). 106p. (J). 27.93 (978-0-8225-5962-7(5) , Lerner Pubns.) Lerner Publishing Group.

—Super Sports Star Barry Bonds. 2004. (Super Sports Star Ser.). (Illus.). 48p. (J). lib. bdg. 23.93 (978-0-7660-2132-7(7)) Enslow Pubs., Inc.

—Super Sports Star Chipper Jones. 2004. (Super Sports Star Ser.). (Illus.). 48p. (J). lib. bdg. 23.93 (978-0-7660-2134-1(3)) Enslow Pubs., Inc.

—Super Sports Star Ken Griffey, Jr. 2004. (Super Sports Star Ser.). (Illus.). 48p. (J). lib. bdg. 23.93 (978-0-7660-2133-4(5)) Enslow Pubs., Inc.

Todd, Anne M. Roger Maris. 2008. (Baseball Superstars Ser.). (gr. 6-12). 30.00 ***(*978-0-7910-9734-2(X)*** , Chelsea Hse.) Facts On File, Inc.

Torres, John Albert. Bobby Bonilla. 1999. (Latinos in Baseball Ser.). (Illus.). 64p. (YA). (gr. 4-7). lib. bdg. 18.95 (978-1-883845-83-4(1)) Mitchell Lane Pubs., Inc.

—Derek Jeter. 2000. (Real-Life Reader Biography Ser.). (Illus.). 32p. (J). (gr. 3-8). lib. bdg. 15.95 (978-1-58415-031-2(9)) Mitchell Lane Pubs., Inc.

—Sports Great Sammy Sosa. 2003. (Sports Great Books). (Illus.). 64p. (J). (gr. 4-10). lib. bdg. 22.60 (978-0-7660-2065-8(7)) Enslow Pubs., Inc.

—Tino Martinez. 1999. (Latinos in Baseball Ser.). (Illus.). 72p. (gr. 4-10). lib. bdg. 18.95 (978-1-883845-82-7(3)) Mitchell Lane Pubs., Inc.

—Top 10 Baseball Legends. 2001. (Sports Top 10 Ser.). (Illus.). 48p. (YA). (gr. 4-10). lib. bdg. 23.93 (978-0-7660-1493-0(2)) Enslow Pubs., Inc.

Twemlow, Nick. Josh Gibson. 2002. (Baseball Hall of Famers of the Negro League Ser.). (Illus.). 112p. (YA). (gr. 5-8). lib. bdg. 29.25 (978-0-8239-3475-1(6) , Rosen Central) Rosen Publishing Group, Inc., The.

Villegas, Jose Luis, illus. & photos by. Home Is Everything: The Latino Baseball Story: from the Barrio to the Major Leagues. Villegas, Jose Luis, photos by. 2003. Tr. of Homes Es Todo. (ENG & SPA.). 148p. (YA). pap. 25.95 (978-0-938317-70-8(9)) Cinco Puntos Pr.

Viola, Kevin. Joe Dimaggio. 2006. (Sports Heroes & Legends Ser.). (Illus.). 106p. (J). (gr. 3-7). 27.93 (978-0-8225-3081-7(3) , Lerner Pubns.) Lerner Publishing Group.

Vizquel, Omar & Dyer, Bob. Omar! My Life on & off the Field. 2003. (Illus.). 272p. pap. 13.95 (978-1-886228-59-7(0)) Gray & Co., Pubs.

Walker, Sally M. Jackie Robinson. Pate, Rodney S., illus. 2005. (Yo Solo (On My Own) Ser.). (SPA & ENG.). 48p. (J). (gr. 2-5). lib. bdg. 23.93 (978-0-8225-3126-5(7) , Ediciones Lerner) Lerner Publishing Group.

—Jackie Robinson. Pate, Rodney, illus. 2002. (On My Own Biographies Ser.). 48p. (J). lib. bdg. 23.93 (978-0-87614-599-9(3) , Carolrhoda Bks.) Lerner Publishing Group.

—Jackie Robinson. Pate, Rodney S., illus. 2002. 48p. (J). (ps-3). lib. bdg. 14.10 (978-0-613-52412-4(8)) Tandem Library Bks.

Weber, Bruce & LaPadula, Tom. Mark McGwire: The Home-run King. 1999. (J). 3.99 (978-0-439-09905-9(6)) Scholastic, Inc.

Weber, Terri Smith. Alex Rodrigues: Improving His Game. 2004. (J). pap. (978-1-932724-19-6(2) , Bios for Kids) Panda Publishing, L.L.C.

—Alex Rodriguez: Improving His Game. 2004. (J). lib. bdg. (978-1-932724-18-9(4) , Bios for Kids) Panda Publishing, L.L.C.

—Alex Rodriguez: Mejorando Su Juego. 2003. (SPA.). (J). pap. (978-0-9740180-6-5(6)); lib. bdg. (978-0-9740180-5-8(8)) Panda Publishing, L.L.C. (Bios for Kids).

Wilmore, Kathy. Jackie Robinson: With a Discussion of Respect. 2004. (Values in Action Ser.). (J). (978-1-59203-071-2(8)) Learning Challenge, Inc.

Winter, Jonah. Beisbol! Latino Baseball Pioneers & Legends. 2001. (SPA., Illus.). 32p. (J). (gr. 1 up). pap. 13.56 (978-1-58430-012-0(4)) Lee & Low Bks., Inc.

—Beisbol: Pioneros y Leyendas Del Beisbol Latino. 2002. (SPA., Illus.). (J). pap. 16.95 (978-1-58430-035-9(3)) Lee & Low Bks., Inc.

—Beisbol: Pioneros y Leyendas Del Beisbol Latino. Del Risco, Enrique, tr. 2002. (SPA., Illus.). 32p. (J). (gr. 1-5). pap. 6.95 (978-1-58430-036-6(1)) Lee & Low Bks., Inc.

—Fair Ball! 14 Great Stars from Baseball's Negro Leagues. 2002. (J). pap. 5.99 (978-0-590-39465-9(7) , Levine, Arthur A. Bks.); 32p. (gr. 2-5). pap. 5.99 (978-0-439-37604-4(1)) Scholastic, Inc.

—Fair Ball! 14 Great Stars from Baseball's Negro Leagues. Winter, Jonah, illus. 1999. (Illus.). 32p. (J). (gr. 2-5). pap. 15.95 (978-0-590-39464-2(9)) Scholastic, Inc.

Wise, Bill. Louis Sockalexis: Native American Baseball Pioneer. Farnsworth, Bill, illus. 2007. (J). (978-1-58430-269-8(0)) Lee & Low Bks., Inc.

Wittenmyer, Gordon. Randy Johnson. 1999. (Baseball Legends Ser.). (Illus.). 64p. (J). (gr. 4-7). pap. 7.95 (978-0-7910-5454-3(3) , Chelsea Hse.) Facts On File, Inc.

Wukovitz, John F. Jackie Robinson & the Integration of Baseball. 2006. (Lucent Library of Black History). 112p. (YA). (gr. 5-8). lib. bdg. 32.45 (978-1-59018-913-9(2) , Lucent Bks.) Thomson Gale.

Young, Jeff C. Top 10 World Series MVPs. 2001. (Sports Top 10 Ser.). (Illus.). 48p. (YA). (gr. 4-10). lib. bdg. 23.93 (978-0-7660-1497-8(5)) Enslow Pubs., Inc.

Zuehlke, Jeffrey. Alex Rodriguez. 2005. (Amazing Athletes Ser.). (Illus.). 32p. (J). (gr. 2-5). pap. 5.95 (978-0-8225-2311-6(6)); (gr. 3-4). 23.93 (978-0-8225-2427-4(9)) Lerner Publishing Group.

—Johan Santana. 2007. (Amazing Athletes Ser.). (J). 23.93 (978-0-8225-6592-5(7) , Lerner Pubns.) Lerner Publishing Group.

BASEBALL—COLLECTIBLES

Owens, Thomas S. Collecting Baseball Cards. 21st ed. 2000. (Single Titles Ser.: up). (Illus.). 80p. (gr. 4-7). pap. 9.95 (978-0-7613-1478-3(4) , Millbrook Pr.) Lerner Publishing Group.

—Collecting Baseball Cards: 21st Century Edition. 2001. (Sports Palaces Ser.). (Illus.). 80p. (gr. 5-8). lib. bdg. 26.90 (978-0-7613-1708-1(2) , Millbrook Pr.) Lerner Publishing Group.

Preller, James. The Major League Baseball Card Collector's Kit. 2002. (Illus.). 48p. (J). (gr. 4-7). pap. 9.99 (978-0-439-23887-8(0)) Scholastic, Inc.

—Major League Baseball Card Collectors's Kit. 2002. (Illus.). 48p. (J). (gr. 2-7). pap. 9.99 (978-0-439-40786-1(9)) Scholastic, Inc.

Wong, Stephen. Baseball Treasures. Einstein, Susan, illus. 2007. 64p. (J). (gr. 1-6). 16.99 (***978-0-06-114464-6(9)***) HarperCollins Pubs.

—Baseball Treasures. 2007. (Illus.). 58p. (J). (gr. 1-6). lib. bdg. 17.89 (***978-0-06-114473-8(8)***) HarperCollins Pubs.

BASEBALL—DICTIONARIES

Trust, Richard. Baseball Pictionary. 2005. 48p. (J). (978-0-7868-0064-3(X)) Hyperion Pr.

BASEBALL—FICTION

Adler, David A. The Babe & I. Widener, Terry, illus. 1999. 32p. (J). (gr. k-4). 17.00 (978-0-15-201378-3(4) , Gulliver Bks.) Harcourt Children's Bks.

—The Babe & I. Widener, Terry, illus. 2004. 32p. (J). reprint ed. pap. 6.00 (978-0-15-205026-9(4) , Voyager Bks./Libros Viajeros) Harcourt Children's Bks.

—Cam Jansen & the Mystery of the Babe Ruth Baseball. Natti, Susanna, illus. 2004. (Cam Jansen Ser.: No. 6). 64p. (J). (gr. 2-4). pap. 3.99 (978-0-14-240015-9(7) , Puffin) Penguin Group (USA) Inc.

—Cam Jansen & the Mystery of the Babe Ruth Baseball. 1998. (Cam Jansen Ser.: No. 6). (J). 3.50 (978-0-439-04442-4(1)) Scholastic, Inc.

—Mama Played Baseball. O'Leary, Chris, illus. 2003. 32p. (J). 16.00 (978-0-15-202196-2(5) , Gulliver Bks.) Harcourt Children's Bks.

—Young Cam Jansen & the Baseball Mystery. Moore, Lisa, ed. Natti, Susanna, illus. 2001. (Young Cam Jansen Ser.: No. 5). 32p. (J). pap. 3.99 (978-0-14-131106-7(1) , Puffin) Penguin Group (USA) Inc.

—Young Cam Jansen & the Baseball Mystery. Natti, Susanna, illus. 1999. (Young Cam Jansen Ser.: No. 5). 32p. (J). (gr. k-3). 14.99 (978-0-670-88481-0(2) , Viking Juvenile) Penguin Group (USA) Inc.

—Young Cam Jansen & the Baseball Mystery. 2001. (Young Cam Jansen Ser.: No. 5). (gr. 3-6). lib. bdg. 11.80 (978-0-613-35625-1(X)); (Illus.). (J). (978-0-606-21540-4(9)) Tandem Library Bks.

Advantage Publishers Group & Rojany Buccieri, Lisa. Let's Make Noise at the Ballpark. 2007. (Illus.). 10p. (J). 12.95 (978-1-59223-642-8(1) , Silver Dolphin Bks.) Advantage Pubs. Group.

Albee, Sarah. Take Us Out to the Ball Game. 2003. (J). pap. 3.25 (978-0-375-81587-4(2) , Random Hse. Bks. for Young Readers) Random Hse. Children's Bks.

Alcorn, Randy & Ben-Ami, Doran. Wait until Then. 2007. (Illus.). 32p. (J). 14.99 (978-1-4143-1041-1(2) , Tyndale Kids) Tyndale Hse. Pubs.

Aryal, Aimee. Let's Go White Sox! 2007. (J). 14.95 (***978-1-932888-87-4(X)***) Mascot Bks., Inc.

Barron, Marietta. Two Worlds. 1999. 94p. (J). (gr. 3-6). 9.99 (978-0-88092-120-6(X) , 120-X) Royal Fireworks Publishing Co.

Beam, Matt. Getting to First Base with Danalda Chase. 2007. (Illus.). 192p. (J). (gr. 5-8). 16.99 (978-0-525-47578-1(8) , Dutton Juvenile) Penguin Group (USA) Inc.

Bee, Clair. Clutch Hitter. (J). 17.95 (978-0-8488-1246-1(8)) Amereon LTD.

—Clutch Hitter, Vol. 4. Farley, Cynthia B. & Farley, Randall K., eds. rev. ed. 1998. (Chip Hilton Ser.: Vol. 4). 195p. (J). pap. 5.99 (978-0-8054-1817-0(2)) B&H Publishing Grp.

—Dugout Jinx. (J). 17.95 (978-0-8488-1247-8(6)) Amereon LTD.

—Dugout Jinx, Vol. 8. 1999. (Chip Hilton Sports Ser.: Vol. 8). x, 207p. (J). reprint ed. pap. 5.99 (978-0-8054-1990-0(X)) B&H Publishing Grp.

—Home Run Feud, Vol. 22. 2002. (Chip Hilton Sports Ser.: Vol. 22). 208p. (J). pap. 5.99 (978-0-8054-2124-8(6)) B&H Publishing Grp.

—Hungry Hurler Vol. 23: The Homecoming. 2002. (Chip Hilton Sports Ser.: Vol. 23). (Illus.). 208p. (J). pap. 5.99 (978-0-8054-2125-5(4)) B&H Publishing Grp.

—No-Hitter, Vol. 17. 2001. (Chip Hilton Sports Ser.). x, 197p. (J). pap. 5.99 (978-0-8054-2096-8(7)) B&H Publishing Grp.

—Pay-Off Pitch, Vol. 16. rev. ed. 2000. (Chip Hilton Sports Ser.: No. 16). (Illus.). xi, 187p. (J). pap. 5.99 (978-0-8054-2095-1(9)) B&H Publishing Grp.

—Pitchers Duel, Vol. 7. 1999. (Chip Hilton Sports Ser.: Vol. 7). (Illus.). x, 213p. (J). reprint ed. pap. 5.99 (978-0-8054-1989-4(6)) B&H Publishing Grp.

—Strike Three, Vol. 3. Farley, Cynthia B. & Farley, Randall K., eds. rev. ed. 1998. (Chip Hilton Ser.: Vol. 3). 211p. (J). pap. 5.99 (978-0-8054-1816-3(4)) B&H Publishing Grp.

Beeuwsaert, Matt. I Got Game. Beeuwsaert, Matt, illus. 2003. (Illus.). 176p. per. 14.95 (978-0-9724358-0-2(8)) Beex Art Bks.

Berenstain, Michael, et al. The Berenstain Bears Say Their Prayers. 2008. (J). pap. (***978-0-310-71246-6(7)***) Zonderkidz.

Berenstain, Stan & Berenstain, Jan. The Berenstain Bears Play Ball. l.t. ed. 1998. (Berenstain Bears Ser.). (Illus.). 48p. (J). (ps-3). pap. 10.95 (978-0-590-94732-9(X)) Scholastic, Inc.

Berra, Yogi. Let's Go Yankees! Moore, Danny, illus. 2006. (J). 17.95 (***978-1-932888-81-2(0)***) Mascot Bks., Inc.

Best, Cari. Last Licks: A Spaldeen Story. 2000. (Illus.). 40p. (J). pap. 5.95 (978-0-7894-2656-7(0) , D K Ink) Dorling Kindersley Publishing, Inc.

Bildner, Phil. Playing the Field. 2006. (Illus.). 192p. (YA). 15.95 (978-1-4169-0284-3(8)) Simon & Schuster Children's Publishing.

—Shoeless Joe & Black Betsy. Payne, C. F., illus. 40p. (J). 2002. (gr. 1-5). 17.00 (978-0-689-82913-0(2)); 2006. reprint ed. pap. 6.99 (978-0-689-87437-6(5) , Aladdin) Simon & Schuster Children's Publishing.

Bildner, Phil & Long, Loren. Game 1. Long, Loren, illus. 2007. (Barnstormers Ser.). (Illus.). 144p. (J). (gr. 2-5). 9.99 (978-1-4169-1863-9(9)) Simon & Schuster Children's Publishing.

—Game 2. Long, Loren, illus. 2007. (Barnstormers Ser.). (Illus.). 195p. (J). (gr. 2-5). 10.99 (978-1-4169-1864-6(7)) Simon & Schuster Children's Publishing.

Blumenthal, Scott & Hodus, Brett. The Road to the Majors. 2002. 147p. 9.95 (978-0-9708992-0-0(3)) Scobre Pr. Corp.

Bogart, Mike. Meet the Henderson Twins: Matt & Mike. 2005. 93p. pap. 14.95 (978-1-4137-8233-2(7)) PublishAmerica, Inc.

Boock, Paula. Home Run. 1999. 115p. pap. 13.00 (978-1-877135-27-9(5)) Longacre Pr. NZL. *Dist:* Pacific Island Bks.

Bourgeois, Paulette. Franklin's Music Lessons. 2002. (gr. k-3). lib. bdg. 11.80 (978-0-613-50568-0(9)) Tandem Library Bks.

Bowen, Fred. Winners Take All. Casale, Paul, illus. 2000. (All-Star Sport Story Ser.). 104p. (J). (gr. 3-7). pap. 4.95 (978-1-56145-229-3(7) , Q26776) Peachtree Pubs., Ltd.

—Winners Take All. 2000. (J). (978-0-606-19863-9(6)); (gr. 3-6). lib. bdg. 12.95 (978-0-613-36750-9(2)) Tandem Library Bks.

Brandon, Cecile V. The Murderer Wore New Shoes. 2002. 155p. pap. 9.95 (978-0-595-23789-0(4) , Writers Advantage Pr.) iUniverse, Inc.

Brooks, Bruce. Throwing Smoke. 2000. (Illus.). 144p. (J). (gr. 5 up). 15.95 (978-0-06-028972-0(4) , Geringer, Laura Book) HarperCollins Pubs.

—Throwing Smoke. 2002. (gr. 3-6). lib. bdg. 14.10 (978-0-613-68470-5(2)) Tandem Library Bks.

Brooks, Walter R. Freddy & the Baseball Team from Mars. Wiese, Kurt, illus. 1999. 256p. (J). (gr. 3-7). 23.95 (978-0-87951-942-1(8)) Overlook Pr., The.

—Freddy & the Baseball Team from Mars. 2000. (J). pap. 67.95 incl. audio (978-0-7887-4461-7(5) , 41150) Recorded Bks., LLC.

Brophy, Mary-Beth. The Last Stop Before Home. 2004. 166p. (YA). pap. 12.95 (978-0-595-30436-3(2)) iUniverse, Inc.

Brown, Marc. Arthur & the Seventh-Inning Stretcher. Brown, Marc, illus. 2nd ed. 2001. (Arthur Good Sports Ser.: Bk. 2). (Illus.). 64p. (J). (gr. 2-4). 13.95 (978-0-316-11861-3(3)) Little, Brown Bks. for Young Readers.

—Arthur & the Seventh-Inning Stretcher. 2001. (Arthur Good Sports Ser.: Bk. 2). (Illus.). (J). 11.05 (978-0-606-21042-3(3)) Tandem Library Bks.

Burgoyne, Tom. The Adventures of Super Phanatic. Epstein, Len, illus. 2007. 32p. (***978-0-9705804-7-4(9)***) Middle Atlantic Pr.

—Phillie Phanatic's Christmas Wish, Vols. 4. Epstein, Len, illus. 2005. 32p. (J). 5.95 (978-0-9754419-0-9(6)) Middle Atlantic Pr.

—The Phillie Phanatics Moving Day. Epstein, Len, illus. 2005. 32p. (J). pap. (978-0-9705804-8-1(7)) Middle Atlantic Pr.

Burleigh, Robert. Home Run: The Story of Babe Ruth. 1998. (J). 16.00 (978-0-15-202115-3(9)) Harcourt Trade Pubs.

—Home Run: The Story of Babe Ruth. Wimmer, Mike, illus. 1998. 32p. (J). (gr. k-5). 16.00 (978-0-15-200970-0(1) , Silver Whistle) Harcourt Trade Pubs.

—Home Run: The Story of Babe Ruth. Wimmer, Mike, illus. 2003. (J). (ps-7). lib. bdg. 14.15 (978-0-613-59899-6(7)) Tandem Library Bks.

—Home Run: The Story of Babe Ruth. Wimmer, Mike, illus. 2003. 32p. (J). pap. 7.00 (978-0-15-204599-9(6) , Voyager Bks./Libros Viajeros) Harcourt Children's Bks.

Butcher, Kristin. Cairo Kelly & the Mann. 2002. 176p. (J). (gr. 3-7). pap. 6.95 (978-1-55143-211-3(0)) Orca Bk. Pubs. USA.

Butler, Dori Hillestad. Sliding into Home. 2005. 192p. (J). pap. 5.95 (978-1-56145-341-2(2)) Peachtree Pubs., Ltd.

—Sliding into Home. Casale, Paul, illus. 2003. (Peachtree Junior Publication Ser.). 192p. (J). 14.95 (978-1-56145-222-4(X)) Peachtree Pubs., Ltd.

Bylsma, Dan & Bylsma, Jay M. Pitcher's Hands Is Out! 2001. 256p. (YA). (gr. 4-9). 15.95 (978-0-938682-65-3(2)) River Road Pubns., Inc.

Carlson, Ron. The Speed of Light. 2003. (Illus.). 288p. (J). 15.99 (978-0-380-97837-3(7)); 16.89 (978-0-06-029825-8(1)) HarperCollins Pubs. (HarperTeen).

Carrier, Roch. The Longest Home Run. Fischman, Sheila, tr. from FRE. Cohen, Sheldon, illus. 2001. Orig. Title: Le Plus Long Circuit. 24p. (J). (gr. 3). pap. 7.95 (978-0-88776-312-0(X)) Tundra Bks., Inc./Livres Toundra, Inc. CAN. *Dist:* Random Hse., Inc.

—Le Plus Long Circuit. Cohen, Sheldon, illus. 2001. (FRE & SPA.). 24p. (J). (gr. 3). pap. 7.95 (978-0-88776-313-7(8) , Livres Toundra) Tundra Bks., Inc./Livres Toundra, Inc. CAN. *Dist:* Random Hse., Inc.

Cebulash, Mel. Ruth Marini, Dodger Ace. 2000. (Ruth Marini on the Mound Ser.). 144p. (gr. 4-7). pap. 10.95 (978-0-595-09093-8(1)) iUniverse, Inc.

—Ruth Marini of the Dodgers. 2000. (Ruth Marini on the Mound Ser.). 144p. (gr. 4-7). pap. 10.95 (978-0-595-09094-5(X)) iUniverse, Inc.

—Ruth Marini World Series Star. 2000. (Ruth Marini on the Mound Ser.). 148p. (YA). (gr. 4-7). pap. 10.95 (978-0-595-09095-2(8) , Backinprint.com) iUniverse, Inc.

Cervasio, Mark. Life's a Ball with Billy the Baseball. 2007. (J). 12.95 (***978-1-59526-758-0(1)***) Media Creations, Inc.

Chabon, Michael. Summerland. 2004. (gr. 3-6). lib. bdg. 17.60 (978-0-613-90441-4(9)) Tandem Library Bks.

—Summerland. l.t. ed. 2003. 615p. (J). 25.95 (978-0-7862-5143-8(3)) Thorndike Pr.

—Summerland: A Novel. 2004. 512p. (J). (ps-17). reprint ed. pap. 8.95 (978-0-7868-1615-6(5)) Miramax Bks.

The Chosen. 2004. (Literature Connections Ser.). (gr. 6-12). (978-0-395-88145-3(5) , 2-70858) McDougal Littell Inc.

Christopher, Matt. Baseball, 4 bks., Set. 2003. (Illus.). 512p. (J). (gr. 3-7). pap., pap. 17.99 (978-0-316-73605-3(8)) Little Brown & Co.

—Baseball Turnaround. ed. 2005. (Sports Classics I Ser.). 123p. (J). lib. bdg. 15.00 (978-1-59054-747-2(0)) Fitzgerald Bks.

—The Catcher's Mask: A Peach Street Mudders Story. Dodson, Bert, illus. 1998. (Peach Street Mudders Story Ser.). 64p. (J). (gr. 2-4). 13.95 (978-0-316-14186-4(0)) Little Brown & Co.

—Challenge at Second Base. Ramsey, Marcy, illus. ed. 2005. (Sports Classics I Ser.). 114p. (J). lib. bdg. 15.00 (978-1-59054-750-2(0)) Fitzgerald Bks.

—Double Play at Short. ed. 2005. (Sports Classics I Ser.). 137p. (J). lib. bdg. 15.00 (978-1-59054-754-0(3)) Fitzgerald Bks.

—The Kid Who Only Hit Homers. 2007. 127p. (J). lib. bdg. (***978-1-59953-107-6(0)***) Norwood Hse. Pr.

—The Lucky Baseball Bat: 50th Anniversary Commemorative Edition. Henneberger, Robert, illus. anniv. ed. 2004. 128p. (J). (gr. 2-4). pap. 4.99 (978-0-316-01012-2(X)) Little Brown & Co.

—El Muchacho Que Bateaba Solo Jonrones. 2004. Tr. of Kid Who Only Hit Homers. (SPA., Illus.). 176p. (J). 15.95 (978-0-316-73767-8(4)) Little Brown & Co.

—El Muchacho Que Bateaba Solo Jonrones.Tr. of Kid Who Only Hit Homers. 145p. (J). (gr. 3-5). pap. 145.00 (978-0-8072-1464-0(7) , Listening Library) Random Hse. Audio Publishing Group.

—Prime-Time Pitcher. ed. 2005. (Sports Classics I Ser.). 142p. (J). lib. bdg. 15.00 (978-1-59054-765-6(9)) Fitzgerald Bks.

—Prime-Time Pitcher. 1998. (Matt Christopher Sports Classics Ser.). 160p. (J). (gr. 3-7). 15.95 (978-0-316-14215-1(8)) Little, Brown Bks. for Young Readers.

—Prime-Time Pitcher, No. 59. 1998. (Matt Christopher Sports Classics Ser.). (978-0-606-13722-5(X)) Tandem Library Bks.

—Return of the Home Run Kid. ed. 2005. (Sports Classics I Ser.). 152p. (J). lib. bdg. 15.00 (978-1-59054-766-3(7)) Fitzgerald Bks.

—Stealing Home. 2004. 144p. (J). (gr. 4-7). pap. 4.99 (978-0-316-60742-1(8)) Hachette Bk. Group.

—Stranger in Right Field. 2000. (978-0-606-18266-9(7)) Tandem Library Bks.

—Stranger in Right Field: A Peach Street Mudders Story. Dodson, Bert, illus. 2000. (Peach Street Mudders Story Ser.). 64p. (J). (gr. 2-4). pap. 4.50 (978-0-316-10677-1(1)) Little Brown & Co.

—Striker Courage. 2001. (J). (978-0-316-13729-4(4)) Little Brown & Co.

—The Submarine Pitch. ed. 2005. (Sports Classics I Ser.). 124p. (J). lib. bdg. 15.00 (978-1-59054-775-5(6)) Fitzgerald Bks.

Chronicle Books LLC Staff. Baseball Heroes. 2008. (J). 15.99 (978-0-8118-5662-1(3)) Chronicle Bks. LLC.

Clausen, Andrew. In the Year of the Boar & Jackie Robinson. 1999. 66p. (J). (gr. 4-6). stu. ed., ring bd. 12.99 (978-1-58609-135-4(2)) Progeny Pr.

Cole, Joanna. The Magic School Bus Plays Ball: A Book about Forces. 2002. (Magic School Bus Ser.). (Illus.). (J). 11.45 (978-0-7587-6703-5(X)) Book Wholesalers, Inc.

Cooney, Doug. I Know Who Likes You. Bernardin, James, illus. 2005. 224p. (J). pap. 4.99 (978-1-4169-0261-4(9) , Aladdin) Simon & Schuster Children's Publishing.

Corbett, Sue. Free Baseball. 2008. 160p. (J). (gr. 3). 5.99 (***978-0-14-241080-6(2)*** , Puffin) Penguin Group (USA) Inc.

Corey, Shana. Players in Pigtails. 2006. 40p. (J). pap. 6.99 (978-0-439-18306-2(5) , Scholastic Paperbacks) Scholastic, Inc.

—Players in Pigtails. Gibbon, Rebecca, illus. 2003. 40p. (J). pap. 16.95 (978-0-439-18305-5(7)) Scholastic, Inc.

Cosby, Bill. Hooray for the Dandelion Warriors! Honeywood, Varnette P., illus. 1999. (Little Bill Books for Beginning Readers Ser.: No. 11). 40p. (J). (gr. 1-5). pap. 3.99 (978-0-590-52194-9(2) , Cartwheel Bks.) Scholastic, Inc.

Cristaldi, Kathryn. Baseball Ballerina. Carter, Abby, illus. 2002. (J). 11.91 (978-0-7587-0907-3(2)) Book Wholesalers, Inc.

—Baseball Ballerina Strikes Out. Carter, Abby, illus. 2002. (YA). 11.91 (978-0-7587-9516-8(5)) Book Wholesalers, Inc.

Curtis, Gavin. The Bat Boy & His Violin. Lewis, Earl, illus. 2002. (J). 26.13 (978-0-7587-0338-5(4)) Book Wholesalers, Inc.

—The Bat Boy & His Violin. Lewis, Earl, illus. (J). (ps-3). 2001. 32p. 7.99 (978-0-689-84115-6(9) , Aladdin); 1999. mass mkt. 6.99 (978-0-689-83012-9(2) , Aladdin); 1998. 32p. 16.95 (978-0-689-80099-3(1)) Simon & Schuster Children's Publishing.

—The Bat Boy & His Violin. 2001. (Illus.). (J). 13.79 (978-0-606-20563-4(2)) Tandem Library Bks.

—Bat Boy & His Violin. 2001. (gr. 3-6). lib. bdg. 15.30 (978-0-613-33669-7(0)) Tandem Library Bks.

Delaney, Ned. Two Strikes, Four Eyes. Date not set. (J). pap. (978-0-679-84172-2(5)); lib. bdg. (978-0-679-94172-9(X)) Random Hse. Children's Bks. (Random Hse. Bks. for Young Readers).

Deuker, Carl. Heart of a Champion. 2007. 208p. (YA). (gr. 7-17). pap. 7.99 (***978-0-316-06726-3(1)***) Little, Brown Bks. for Young Readers.

Deuker, Carl. High Heat. 2005. 352p. (J). (gr. 7 up). pap. 6.99 (978-0-06-057248-8(5) , Harper Trophy) HarperCollins Pubs.

—High Heat. 2003. 288p. (J). (gr. 7-9). tchr. ed. 16.00 (978-0-618-31117-0(3)) Houghton Mifflin Co. Trade & Reference Div.

Disney Staff. Team Player. 2001. (Jersey Ser.). (Illus.). (J). (978-0-606-21263-2(9)) Tandem Library Bks.

Driscoll, Laura, et al. Curious George at the Baseball Game. Hines, Anna Grossnickle, illus. 2006. 24p. (J). (ps-k). 12.95 (978-0-618-66374-3(6)); pap. 3.95 (978-0-618-66375-0(4)) Houghton Mifflin Co.

Dunrea, Olivier. Peedie. 2008. (Illus.). 32p. (J). (ps-k). bds. 6.95 (***978-0-618-75506-6(3)***) Houghton Mifflin Co. Trade & Reference Div.

Eaton, Deborah. The Rainy Day Grump. Handelman, Dorothy, photos by. 1998. (Real Kids Readers Ser.). (Illus.). 32p. (gr. k-2). (J). pap. 4.99 (978-0-7613-2043-2(1)); lib. bdg. 18.90 (978-0-7613-2018-0(0)) Lerner Publishing Group. (Millbrook Pr.).

Egan, Tim. Roasted Peanuts. 2006. (Illus.). 32p. (J). (gr. k-3). 16.00 (978-0-618-33718-7(0)) Houghton Mifflin Co.

Elster, Jean Alicia. Just Call Me Joe Joe. Tadgell, Nicole, illus. 2001. (Joe Joe in the City Ser.). 32p. (gr. 1-5). 12.00 (978-0-8170-1398-1(9)) Judson Pr.

English, Travis. Knights of Paris. 2004. (J). per. 11.95 (978-0-9759903-1-5(4)) Blue Tiger Publishing.

Farley, Colby King. A Warm Familiar Feeling. 2nd ed. 2003. (YA). per. 13.50 (978-0-943864-48-8(8)) Davenport, May Pubs.

Farrell, Mame. Bradley & the Billboard. 2002. 224p. (J). pap. 5.95 (978-0-374-40912-8(9) , Sunburst) Farrar, Straus & Giroux.

—Bradley & the Billboard. 1999. (YA). pap., stu. ed. 58.00 incl. audio (978-0-7887-3060-3(6) , 40894) Recorded Bks., LLC.

Fehler, Gene. Beanball. 2008. 128p. (J). (gr. 7 up). 16.00 (***978-0-618-84348-0(5)*** , Clarion Bks.) Houghton Mifflin Co. Trade & Reference Div.

Ferguson, Donald. Chums of Scranton High or Hugh Morgans U. 2006. 94.99 (***978-1-4280-3997-1(X)***); pap. 88.99 (***978-1-4280-4008-3(0)***) IndyPublish.com.

Fidler, Mark. Signed Ball. 2002. 146p. (J). pap. 11.95 (978-0-595-21780-9(X) , Writers Club Pr.) iUniverse, Inc.

Finnegan, Evelyn M. My Little Friend Goes to a Baseball Game. Houghton, Diane R., illus. 2006. 32p. (J). (ps-3). reprint ed. pap. 7.00 (978-1-4223-5403-2(2)) DIANE Publishing Co.

Forbes, Graham. The Boys of Columbia High. 2002. 244p. pap. 29.95 (978-1-932080-50-6(3)) Ross & Perry, Inc.

Ford, Linda. The Santa Season. 2002. 93p. (J). (978-0-439-43532-1(3)) Scholastic, Inc.

Forsyth, C. A. Power Hitter. 2001. (Sports Stories Ser.). 96p. (gr. 3-8). (J). (***978-1-55028-733-2(8)***); (Illus.). 7.95 (978-1-55028-732-5(X)) Lorimer, James & Co., Ltd., Pubs. CAN. *Dist:* Casemate Pubs. & Bk. Distributors, LLC.

Fox, Jason. The Game of a Lifetime. 2005. 57p. pap. 12.95 (978-1-4137-6379-9(0)) PublishAmerica, Inc.

Fromm, Pete. How All This Started: A Novel. 2001. (gr. 7-12). lib. bdg. 23.45 (978-0-613-45189-5(9)) Tandem Library Bks.

Funari Willever, Lisa. Nicky Fifth on 32 Dandelion Court. 2003. 160p. 5.95 (978-0-9679227-7-5(1) , 329-008) Franklin Mason Pr.

Gaetz, Dayle Campbell. No Problem. (Orca Soundings Ser.). 2006. 112p. (YA). lib. bdg. 14.95 (978-1-55143-556-5(X)); 2003. 96p. (J). (gr. 7-12). pap. 7.95 (978-1-55143-231-1(5)) Orca Bk. Pubs. USA.

—No Problem. 2003. (gr. 7-12). lib. bdg. 16.40 (978-0-613-62976-8(0)) Tandem Library Bks.

Gantos, Jack. Joey Pigza Loses Control. braille ed. 2003. (J). (gr. 2). spiral bd. (978-0-616-15268-3(X)) Canadian National Institute for the Blind/Institut National Canadien pour les Aveugles.

—Joey Pigza Loses Control. 2000. (Joey Pigza Ser.). 208p. (J). (gr. 4-7). 16.00 (978-0-374-39989-4(1) , Farrar, Straus & Giroux (BYR)) Farrar, Straus & Giroux.

—Joey Pigza Loses Control. 2002. 208p. (J). (gr. 5 up). pap. 5.99 (978-0-06-441022-9(6) , Harper Trophy) HarperCollins Pubs.

—Joey Pigza Loses Control. unabr. ed. 2004. 195p. (J). (gr. 5-9). pap. 36.00 incl. audio (978-0-8072-8726-2(1) , LyA 248 SP, Listening Library) Random Hse. Audio Publishing Group.

—Joey Pigza Loses Control. 2002. (gr. 5-8). lib. bdg. 14.15 (978-0-613-49677-3(9)) Tandem Library Bks.

—Joey Pigza Loses Control. l.t. ed. 2001. 196p. (J). 22.95 (978-0-7862-3425-7(3)) Thorndike Pr.

Garfield, Henry. Tartabull's Throw. 2001. (Illus.). 272p. (J). (gr. 7 up). 16.00 (978-0-689-83840-8(9) , Atheneum/Richard Jackson Bks.) Simon & Schuster Children's Publishing.

—Tartabull's Throw. 2003. (gr. 7-12). lib. bdg. 14.15 (978-0-613-61823-6(8)) Tandem Library Bks.

Giff, Patricia Reilly. Ronald Morgan Goes to Bat. Natti, Susanna, illus. 2002. (J). 13.19 (978-0-7587-3528-7(6)) Book Wholesalers, Inc.

Gill, Amber. Joseph's Summer. 2006. 71p. pap. 14.95 (978-1-4241-0122-1(0)) PublishAmerica, Inc.

Golding, Theresa Martin. The Truth about Twelve. 2004. (Illus.). 176p. (J). (gr. 4-6). pap. 16.95 (978-1-59078-291-0(7)) Boyds Mills Pr.

Golenbock, Peter. Companeros de Equipo. Ada, Alma Flor & Campoy, F. Isabel, trs. Bacon, Paul, illus. 2002. Tr. of Teammates. (SPA.). 32p. (J). pap. 7.00 (978-0-15-216390-7(5) , Voyager Bks./Libros Viajeros) Harcourt Children's Bks.

—Companeros de Equipo. 2002. Tr. of Teammates. (SPA.). (gr. k-3). lib. bdg. 15.30 (978-0-613-82224-4(2)) Tandem Library Bks.

Gordon, Amy. The Gorillas of Gill Park. 2003. 256p. (J). (gr. 4-6). tchr. ed. 16.95 (978-0-8234-1751-3(4)) Holiday Hse., Inc.

Gorman, Carol & Findley, Ron. The Stumptown Kid. 2005. 224p. (J). (gr. 3-7). 14.95 (978-1-56145-337-5(4)) Peachtree Pubs., Ltd.

Gratz, Alan. Samurai Shortstop. 2006. 288p. (J). (gr. 6 up). 17.99 (978-0-8037-3075-5(6) , Dial) Penguin Group (USA) Inc.

Gratz, Alan M. Samurai Shortstop. 2008. 288p. (YA). (gr. 6). pap. 7.99 (*978-0-14-241099-8(3) , Puffin) Penguin Group (USA) Inc.

Greenburg, Dan. My Grandma, Major League Slugger. Davis, Jack E., illus. 2001. (Zack Files Ser.: No. 24). 64p. (J). (gr. 2-5). pap. 4.99 (978-0-448-42550-4(5) , Grosset & Dunlap) Penguin Group (USA) Inc.

—My Grandma, Major League Slugger. 2001. (gr. 3-6). lib. bdg. 13.00 (978-0-613-58376-3(0)) Tandem Library Bks.

Grey, Zane. The Redheaded Outfield. 302p. (J). reprint ed. lib. bdg. 22.95 (978-0-89190-759-6(9) , Rivercity Pr.) Amereon LTD.

—The Young Pitcher. Exams Unlimited, Inc. Staff, ed. 2002. (Illus.). 185p. (C). reprint ed. cd-rom 8.95 (978-1-59132-087-6(9)) Exams Unlimited, Inc.

Griffiths, Sara. Thrown a Curve: A Novel. 2007. 151p. (YA). (gr. 6-10). pap. 12.95 (*978-1-890862-49-7(5)); 16.95 (*978-1-890862-48-0(7)) Bancroft Pr.

Gutman, Dan. Abner & Me. (Baseball Card Adventures Ser.). 176p. (J). 2007. pap. 5.99 (978-0-06-053445-5(1) , Harper Trophy); 2005. (Illus.). 16.99 (978-0-06-053443-1(5)); 2005. (Illus.). lib. bdg. 17.89 (978-0-06-053444-8(3)) HarperCollins Pubs.

—Babe & Me. 2002. (Baseball Card Adventures Ser.). (Illus.). 176p. (J). (gr. 3-7). pap. 5.99 (978-0-380-80504-4(9) , Harper Trophy) HarperCollins Pubs.

—Babe & Me. 2002. (Baseball Card Adventures Ser.). (gr. 3-6). lib. bdg. 14.15 (978-0-613-53793-3(9)) Tandem Library Bks.

—Babe & Me: A Baseball Card Adventure. 2000. (Baseball Card Adventures Ser.). (Illus.). 176p. (J). (gr. 5 up). 16.99 (978-0-380-97739-0(7)) HarperCollins Pubs.

—Babe Ruth & the Ice Cream Mess. Garvin, Elaine, illus. ed. 2005. (Ready-to-Read Ser. Level 2). 32p. (J). lib. bdg. 15.00 (978-1-59054-940-7(6)) Fitzgerald Bks.

—Honus & Me. 1999. (Baseball Card Adventures Ser.). (Illus.). 144p. (J). (gr. 4-7). pap. 5.99 (978-0-380-78878-1(0) , Harper Trophy) HarperCollins Pubs.

—Jackie & Me. 2005. (Baseball Card Adventures Ser.). (Illus.). 145p. (YA). (gr. 4-8). reprint ed. 20.00 (978-0-7567-9569-6(9)) DIANE Publishing Co.

—Jackie & Me. 2000. (Baseball Card Adventures Ser.). (gr. 5-8). lib. bdg. 14.15 (978-0-613-27912-3(3)) Tandem Library Bks.

—Mickey & Me. 2004. (Baseball Card Adventures Ser.). (Illus.). 160p. (J). pap. 5.99 (978-0-06-447258-6(2) , Harper Trophy) HarperCollins Pubs.

—Satch & Me. 2006. (Baseball Card Adventures Ser.). (Illus.). 192p. (J). 15.99 (978-0-06-059491-6(8)); lib. bdg. 16.89 (978-0-06-059492-3(6)) HarperCollins Pubs.

Hafer, Todd. Stealing Home. 2004. (Spirit of the Game, Sports Fiction Ser.). 144p. (J). pap. 4.99 (978-0-310-70671-7(8)) Zonderkidz.

Hall, Donald. When Willard Met Babe Ruth. 2001. (J). (978-0-606-21521-3(2)) Tandem Library Bks.

Ham, David A. & Sibley, Janice B. Magic Baseball Cap. Bostick, Blair, illus. 2006. 48p. (J). 16.95 (978-0-9746920-2-9(6)) CRM Pubs., LLC.

Hammond, John, as told by. Lucky in Life. 2003. 150p. (YA). per. 13.95 (978-1-885631-76-3(6)) Hutchison, G.F. Pr.

Hancock, H. Irving. The Grammar School Boys in Summer Athlet. rev. ed. 2006. 216p. 27.95 (978-1-4218-1748-4(9)); pap. 12.95 (978-1-4218-1848-1(5)) 1st World Publishing, Inc. (1st World Library - Literary Society).

—The High School Pitcher. rev. ed. 2006. 212p. 27.95 (978-1-4218-1743-9(8)); pap. 12.95 (978-1-4218-1843-6(4)) 1st World Publishing, Inc. (1st World Library - Literary Society).

Hancock, Irving H. The Grammar School Boys in Summer Athlet. 2006. 78.99 (*978-1-4219-9869-5(6)); pap. 72.99 (*978-1-4219-9873-2(4)) IndyPublish.com.

—The High School Pitcher or Dick & Co. on. 2006. 78.99 (*978-1-4219-9918-0(8)); pap. 72.99 (*978-1-4219-9929-6(3)) IndyPublish.com.

Harcourt School Publishers Staff. A Big Day for Nicodemus: Take-Home Book. 2001. (Collections Ser.). (Illus.). (J). pap. 1.90 (978-0-15-319540-2(1)) Harcourt Schl. Pubs.

—A Big Day in Nicodemus' Life Below Level. 3rd ed. 2002. (Trophies Reading Program Ser.). (Illus.). pap. 5.10 (978-0-15-323340-1(0)) Harcourt Schl. Pubs.

—Buen Deportista Advanced Level. 3rd ed. 2002. (Trofeos Ser.). (SPA., Illus.). pap. 6.80 (978-0-15-324114-7(4)) Harcourt Schl. Pubs.

—Can We Play Now: Take-Home Book. 1999. (Collections Ser.). (Illus.). (J). pap. 1.90 (978-0-15-317206-9(1)) Harcourt Schl. Pubs.

—Cross-Country Champ Below Level. 3rd ed. 2002. (Trophies Reading Program Ser.). (Illus.). pap. 5.10 (978-0-15-323404-0(0)) Harcourt Schl. Pubs.

—Full Count Advanced Level. 3rd ed. 2002. (Trophies Reading Program Ser.). (Illus.). pap. 5.10 (978-0-15-323481-1(4)) Harcourt Schl. Pubs.

—The Helping Hands Baseball Team On Level. 3rd ed. 2002. (Trophies Reading Program Ser.). (Illus.). pap. 5.10 (978-0-15-323346-3(X)) Harcourt Schl. Pubs.

—I've Got Your Number: Take-Home Book. 2001. (Collections Ser.). (Illus.). (J). pap. 1.90 (978-0-15-319536-5(3)) Harcourt Schl. Pubs.

—The Kid from Brighton Beach Below Level. 3rd ed. 2002. (Trophies Reading Program Ser.). (Illus.). pap. 5.10 (978-0-15-323224-4(2)) Harcourt Schl. Pubs.

—The Kid of Brighton Beach: Take-Home Book. 2001. (Collections Ser.). (Illus.). (J). pap. 1.90 (978-0-15-319486-3(3)) Harcourt Schl. Pubs.

—Left Out. 2001. (Reader's Choice Bks.). (Illus.). (gr. 6). pap. 13.20 (978-0-15-314419-6(X)) Harcourt Schl. Pubs.

—Making the Right Moves Below Level. 3rd ed. 2002. (Trophies Reading Program Ser.). (Illus.). (gr. 3). pap. 5.10 (978-0-15-323143-8(2)) Harcourt Schl. Pubs.

—Play Ball! 3rd ed. 2002. (Trophies English Language Learners Ser.). (Illus.). pap. 5.10 (978-0-15-327653-8(3)); pap. 5.10 (978-0-15-327872-3(2)) Harcourt Schl. Pubs.

—Play Ball! Below Level. 3rd ed. 2002. (Trophies Reading Program Ser.). (Illus.). (J). pap. 3.20 (978-0-15-322942-8(X)) Harcourt Schl. Pubs.

—Stealing Home: Reader's Choice Book. 2001. (Collections Ser.). (Illus.). pap. 13.20 (978-0-15-314365-6(7)) Harcourt Schl. Pubs.

—The Subway Series On Level. 3rd ed. 2002. (Trophies Reading Program Ser.). (Illus.). pap. 5.10 (978-0-15-323174-2(2)) Harcourt Schl. Pubs.

—Trofeos On Level: La Serie de los Subterraneos. 3rd ed. 2002. (SPA., Illus.). pap. 6.80 (978-0-15-324085-0(7)) Harcourt Schl. Pubs.

Haven, Paul. Two Hot Dogs with Everything. Ferguson, Peter, illus. 2007. 320p. (J). (gr. 4-7). 6.50 (978-0-375-83349-6(8) , Yearling) Random Hse. Children's Bks.

—Two Hot Dogs with Everything. 2006. (J). lib. bdg. (978-0-375-93350-9(6)) Random Hse. Children's Bks.

—Two Hot Dogs with Everything. Ferguson, Peter & Jessell, Tim, illus. 2006. 320p. (J). (gr. 3-7). 15.95 (978-0-375-83348-9(X) , Random Hse. Bks. for Young Readers) Random Hse. Children's Bks.

—Two Hot Dogs with Everything. Ferguson, Peter, illus. 2006. 320p. (J). (gr. 3-7). lib. bdg. 17.99 (978-0-375-93348-6(4) , Random Hse. Bks. for Young Readers) Random Hse. Children's Bks.

Heller, Pete. Peppy Learns to Play Baseball. Kinsey, Thomas D., ed. Schaeffer, Bob, illus. (Peppy Learns to Play Ser.). 32p. (J). (gr. k-5). pap. 3.95 (978-0-932423-00-9(0)) Summa Bks.

Hello, Phillie Phanatic! 2007. (J). 17.95 (*978-1-932888-85-0(3)) Mascot Bks., Inc.

Hennessy, James. Shane's Game. 2003. 184p. 23.95 (978-0-595-74739-9(6)); pap. 13.95 (978-0-595-28112-1(5)) iUniverse, Inc.

Henry. Biode. 2008. (J). (*978-0-374-30802-5(0)) Farrar, Straus & Giroux.

Hernandez, Keith. First-Base Hero: A Lift-the-Flap Pop-up Book. Manders, John, illus. 2005. 12p. (J). (gr. k-4). reprint ed. 13.00 (978-0-7567-8543-7(X)) DIANE Publishing Co.

Hoff, Syd. The Littlest Leaguer. Hoff, Syd, illus. 2008. (I Can Read Bks.). 48p. (J). pap. 3.99 (*978-0-06-053774-6(4) , Harper Trophy); (Illus.). 16.99 (*978-0-06-053772-2(8)) HarperCollins Pubs.

Holohan, Maureen. Everybody's Favorite. 2000. (Broadway Ballplayers Ser.). (Illus.). (J). (978-0-606-20653-2(1)) Tandem Library Bks.

—Left Out: By Rosie. 2001. (Broadway Ballplayers Ser.). (Illus.). (J). (978-0-606-21292-2(2)) Tandem Library Bks.

Honeywood, Varnette P., illus. Hooray for the Dandelion Warriors! 2002. (Little Bill Ser.). (J). 11.91 (978-0-7587-1286-8(3)) Book Wholesalers, Inc.

Honsinger, Laura. Mike's New Friends. 2005. 35p. (J). pap. 5.92 (978-1-4116-3070-3(X)) Lulu.com.

Hopkinson, Deborah. Girl Wonder. Widener, Terry, illus. 2003. 40p. (J). (gr. k-3). 16.95 (978-0-689-83300-7(8) , Atheneum/Anne Schwartz Bks.) Simon & Schuster Children's Publishing.

—Girl Wonder: A Baseball Story in Nine Innings. Widener, Terry, illus. 2004. 31p. (J). (gr. k-4). 17.00 (978-0-7567-7801-9(8)) DIANE Publishing Co.

—Girl Wonder: A Baseball Story in Nine Innings. Widener, Terry, illus. 2006. 40p. (J). reprint ed. pap. 6.99 (978-1-4169-1393-1(9) , Aladdin) Simon & Schuster Children's Publishing.

Hughes, Dean. Bases Loaded. 1999. (Scrappers Ser.: No. 5). (J). (gr. 3-7). (978-0-606-16298-2(4)) Tandem Library Bks.

—Brad & Butter Play Ball! 1998. (Stepping Stone Bks.). (J). (978-0-606-13957-1(5)) Tandem Library Bks.

—Home Run Hero. 1999. (Scrappers Ser.: No. 2). (J). (gr. 3-7). (978-0-606-16289-0(5)) Tandem Library Bks.

—No Easy Out. 1999. (Scrappers Ser.: No. 6). (J). (gr. 3-7). (978-0-606-16299-9(2)) Tandem Library Bks.

—Now We're Talking. 1999. (Scrappers Ser.: No. 4). (J). (gr. 3-7). (978-0-606-16297-5(6)) Tandem Library Bks.

—Play Ball! 1999. (Scrappers Ser.: No. 1). (J). (gr. 3-7). (978-0-606-16288-3(7)) Tandem Library Bks.

—Take Your Base. 1999. (Scrappers Ser.: No. 7). 120p. (J). (gr. 3-7). pap. 3.99 (978-0-689-81940-7(4) , 076714003996, Simon Pulse) Simon & Schuster Children's Publishing.

—Take Your Base. 1999. (Scrappers Ser.: No. 7). (J). (gr. 3-7). (978-0-606-16300-2(X)) Tandem Library Bks.

—Team Player. 1999. (Scrappers Ser.: No. 3). (J). (gr. 3-7). (978-0-606-16290-6(9)) Tandem Library Bks.

Hunter, Dawn. Hit & Run. 1999. (gr. 3-6). lib. bdg. 13.55 (978-0-613-29639-7(7)) Tandem Library Bks.

Hunter, Dawn & Hunter, Karen. Hit & Run. 1999. (Sports Stories Ser.). 92p. (gr. 3-8). (J). (*978-1-55028-673-1(0)); 7.95 (978-1-55028-672-4(2)) Lorimer, James & Co., Ltd., Pubs. CAN. *Dist:* Casemate Pubs. & Bk. Distributors, LLC.

Hurwitz, Johanna. Baseball Fever. 2000. (Illus.). 128p. (J). (gr. 3-7). pap. 4.99 (978-0-380-73255-5(6) , Harper Trophy) HarperCollins Pubs.

—Baseball Fever. 2000. (Illus.). (J). 11.79 (978-0-606-17959-1(3)) Tandem Library Bks.

In the Year of the Boar & Jackie Robinson. 1999. (J). 9.95 (978-1-56137-344-4(3)) Novel Units, Inc.

Isadora, Rachel. Luke Goes to Bat. Isadora, Rachel, illus. 2005. (Illus.). 32p. (J). (ps-3). 15.99 (978-0-399-23604-4(X) , Putnam Juvenile) Penguin Group (USA) Inc.

—Max. Isadora, Rachel, illus. 2002. (Illus.). (J). 13.40 (978-0-7587-6689-2(0)) Book Wholesalers, Inc.

Jaimie Hope, Jaimie. Adventures of Baby Jaimie. 2006. pap. 12.99 (*978-1-4259-5947-0(4)) AuthorHouse.

Jennings, Patrick. Out Standing in My Field. 176p. (J). 2006. pap. 5.99 (978-0-439-48749-8(8) , Scholastic Paperbacks); 2005. (Illus.). pap. 16.95 (978-0-439-46581-6(8)) Scholastic, Inc.

Johnson, Angela. Just Like Josh Gibson. Peck, Beth, illus. 32p. (J). 2004. 15.95 (978-0-689-82628-3(1)); 2007. reprint ed. 6.99 (978-1-4169-2728-0(X) , Aladdin) Simon & Schuster Children's Publishing.

Johnson, Sandi. Baseball Billy. Johnson, Britt, ed. Nadaskay, Lori, illus. l.t. ed. 2003. 12p. (J). (gr. k-5). spiral bd. 5.99 (978-1-929063-30-7(X) , 320) Moons & Stars Publishing For Children.

Johnson, Scott. Safe at Second. 2001. 256p. (YA). pap. 6.99 (978-0-698-11877-5(4) , Putnam Juvenile) Penguin Group (USA) Inc.

—Safe at Second. 2001. (J). (978-0-606-21407-0(0)); (gr. 5-8). lib. bdg. 14.15 (978-0-613-36009-8(5)) Tandem Library Bks.

Johnson, Tim. Never So Green. 2002. 240p. (YA). 18.00 (978-0-374-35509-8(6) , Farrar, Straus & Giroux (BYR)) Farrar, Straus & Giroux.

Jones, Jennifer B. Dear Mrs. Ryan, You're Ruining My Life. 2004. 144p. (J). pap. 5.95 (978-0-8027-7653-2(1)) Walker & Co.

Jordan, Deloris & Jordan, Michael. Michael's Golden Rules. Nelson, Kadir, illus. 2007. 32p. (J). 16.99 (978-0-689-87016-3(7) , Simon & Schuster/Paula Wiseman Bks.) Simon & Schuster Children's Publishing.

Jordan's Catch: Individual Title, 6 packs. 16p. (gr. 2 up). 35.00 (978-0-7635-9240-0(4)) Rigby Education.

Joyce, William. Baseball Bob. Joyce, William, illus. 1999. (Illus.). 10p. (J). (ps-k). 6.95 (978-0-694-01180-3(0) , Harper Festival) HarperCollins Pubs.

—Dinosaur Bob & His Adventures with the Family Lazardo. Joyce, William, illus. ltd. ed. (Laura Geringer Bks.). (Illus.). 48p. (J). (ps-3). 1998. 150.00 (978-0-06-025429-2(7)); 1999. pap. 4.95 (978-0-06-443247-4(5) , Harper Trophy) HarperCollins Pubs.

Karen & Kary. Little Wizard. 2004. 21p. pap. 14.95 (978-1-4137-2956-6(8)) PublishAmerica, Inc.

Keathley, Sarah. Ben's Baseball Excitement. 2002. (J). pap. 8.00 (978-0-8059-5250-6(0)) Dorrance Publishing Co., Inc.

Keene, Carolyn. Strike-Out Scare. Jones, Jan Naimo, illus. 2005. 70p. (J). (978-1-4155-7741-7(2) , Aladdin) Simon & Schuster Children's Publishing.

Kessler, Leonard. Here Comes the Strikeout! Kessler, Leonard, illus. 2002. (Illus.). (J). 12.34 (978-0-7587-6136-1(8)) Book Wholesalers, Inc.

King, Charles. Billy Baseball. 2006. (J). pap. 7.95 (978-0-533-14820-2(0)) Vantage Pr., Inc.

Kleinhenz, Sydine. Bats in My Attic. Stromoski, Rick, illus. 2005. (Rookie Reader Ser.). 31p. (J). (ps-ps). 19.50 (978-0-516-24865-3(0) , Children's Pr.) Scholastic Library Publishing.

Kloepfer, Marguerite. In a Pickle. 2003. (YA). 12.95 (978-1-932173-02-4(1)) Stephens Pr. LLC.

Koertge, Ronald. Shakespeare Bats Clean-Up. 2003. 128p. (YA). (gr. 7). 15.99 (978-0-7636-2116-2(1)) Candlewick Pr.

—Shakespeare Bats Cleanup. 2006. 128p. (YA). (gr. 7). reprint ed. pap. 5.99 (978-0-7636-2939-7(1)) Candlewick Pr.

Korba, Joanna. Cindy Eller Plays Ball: A Modern-Day Cinderella Tale. 2006. 42.00 (*978-1-4108-6164-1(3)) Benchmark Education Co.

Korman, Susan. Brother's Keeper: Take Me Out of the Ball Game! 1999. (gr. 3-6). lib. bdg. 11.80 (978-0-613-88657-4(7)) Tandem Library Bks.

Kovalski, Maryann. Take Me Out to the Ball Game. 2004. (Illus.). 32p. (J). (gr. k-2). (978-1-55041-897-2(1)) Fitzhenry & Whiteside, Ltd.

—Take Me Out to the Ball Game. 2006. (Illus.). 32p. (J). pap. 7.95 (978-1-55041-899-6(8)) Fitzhenry & Whiteside, Ltd. CAN. *Dist:* F & W Pubns., Inc.

Kramer, Jennifer E. Good Luck, Charlie. Moores, Jeff, illus. 2004. (Rookie Reader Ser.). 31p. (J). 19.50 (978-0-516-21722-2(4) , Children's Pr.) Scholastic Library Publishing.

Krensky, Stephen. Arthur Makes the Team. 1998. (Arthur Chapter Bks. : Bk. 3). (J). (gr. 3-6). pap. 3.95 (978-0-316-10536-1(8)); (Illus.). 64p. (gr. 2-4). pap. 4.25 (978-0-316-11551-3(7)) Little, Brown Bks. for Young Readers.

—Arthur Makes the Team. 1998. (Arthur Chapter Bks.: Bk. 3). (J). (gr. 3-6). 11.05 (978-0-606-13152-0(3)) Tandem Library Bks.

Krensky, Stephen & LeapFrog Staff. Arthur Makes the Team. 2001. (Arthur Chapter Bks. : Bk. 3). (J). (ps-2). spiral bd. 14.99 (978-1-58605-130-3(X)) LeapFrog Enterprises, Inc.

LaBate, Jim. Mickey Mantle Day in Amsterdam: Another Novella by Jim LaBate. Batemen, Brian, illus. 1999. 61p. (YA). (gr. 7-12). pap. 7.95 (978-0-9662100-7-1(7)) Mohawk River Pr.

Lamote, Lisa Edman. Don't Judge a Book by Its Cover. 2006. (J). 15.99 (978-1-933673-01-1(X) , BookMann Pr.) Mann Publishing Group.

Leaney, Cindy. On the Beach. Whitehouse, Patty, ed. King, Sue & Wilks, Peter, illus. 2004. (Friendly Phonics Ser.). 24p. (J). lib. bdg. 14.95 (978-1-59054-108-1(1)) Fitzgerald Bks.

Lengel, Reed. A Ballplayer's Choice. 2001. (Illus.). 144p. (YA). (gr. 5-10). pap. 14.95 (978-0-9672533-2-9(2)) Kichita Productions.

Lester, Helen. Batter up Wombat. Munsinger, Lynn, illus. 2006. 32p. (J). (*978-1-4287-0160-1(5)) Houghton Mifflin Co.

—Batter up Wombat. Munsinger, Lynn M., illus. 2006. 32p. (J). (gr. k-3). 16.00 (978-0-618-73784-0(7) , Walter Lorraine) Houghton Mifflin Co. Trade & Reference Div.

Lilienstein, Jennel. First Ball Game/Sports! 2003. 36p. (J). 8.99 (978-0-9741215-2-9(5)) Stories of My Life, The.

Lloyd, Emily. Home Run Has-Been: The Case of the Slugfish Slugger. 1998. (Kinetic City Super Crew Ser.: No. 11). (Illus.). 160p. (C). (gr. 4-7). pap. 4.25 (978-0-07-007066-0(0) , 9780070070660) McGraw-Hill Cos., The.

London, Jonathan. When the Fireflies Come. Widener, Terry, illus. 2003. 32p. (J). (ps). 15.99 (978-0-525-45404-5(7) , Dutton Juvenile) Penguin Group (USA) Inc.

Lorbiecki, Marybeth. Jackie's Bat. Pinkney, Brian, illus. 2006. 40p. (J). (gr. k-3). 15.95 (978-0-689-84102-6(7)) Simon & Schuster Children's Publishing.

Lupica, Mike. The Big Field. 2008. 288p. (YA). (gr. 5). 17.99 (*978-0-399-24625-8(8) , Philomel) Penguin Group (USA) Inc.

Lupica, Mike. Heat. 2006. 220p. (YA). (gr. 5). 16.99 (978-0-399-24301-1(1) , Philomel) Penguin Group (USA) Inc.

Lyga, Barry. Boy Toy. 2007. 416p. (YA). (gr. 7). 16.95 (*978-0-618-72393-5(5)) Houghton Mifflin Co.

Lynch, Chris. Gold Dust. 2002. 208p. (J). (gr. 5 up). pap. 7.99 (978-0-06-447201-2(9)) HarperCollins Pubs.

—Gold Dust. 2002. (gr. 5-8). lib. bdg. 14.10 (978-0-613-67089-0(2)) Tandem Library Bks.

Lytle, Robert A. A Pitch in Time. Williams, Bill, illus. 2002. 368p. (YA). pap. 12.95 (978-0-9712692-5-5(4)) EDCO Publishing, Inc.

Mackel, Kathy. A Season of Comebacks. 1998. (J). (978-0-606-13767-6(X)) Tandem Library Bks.

MacLachlan, Patricia. Edward's Eyes. 2007. 128p. (J). (gr. 3-7). 15.99 (*978-1-4169-2743-3(3) , Atheneum) Simon & Schuster Children's Publishing.

Madison, Alan. Pecorino Plays Ball. Cantone, Annalaura, illus. 2006. 40p. (J). (ps-3). 15.95 (978-0-689-86522-0(8) , Atheneum/Anne Schwartz Bks.) Simon & Schuster Children's Publishing.

Maizel, Karen, illus. Jake Plays Ball. 2007. (I Can Read!). 32p. (J). pap. 3.99 (*978-0-310-71455-2(9)) Zonderkidz.

Maloney, Peter & Zekauskas, Felicia. Saved by the Ball. 2003. (Just Schoolin' Around Ser.). (Illus.). 32p. (J). (978-0-439-39521-2(6)) Scholastic, Inc.

Mammano, Julie. Rhinos Who Play Baseball. Mammano, Julie, illus. 2006. (Illus.). 24p. (J). (gr. k-4). reprint ed. 14.00 (978-0-7567-9995-3(3)) DIANE Publishing Co.

Marsh, Carole. The Baseball Bully. 2006. 64p. (gr. 2-4). 14.95 (*978-0-635-06221-5(6)); pap. (*978-0-635-06215-4(1)) Gallopade International.

Marzollo, Jean. Baseball Brothers. Kelley, True, illus. 1999. (Hello Reader! Ser.). 32p. (J). pap. 3.99 (978-0-590-38398-1(1)) Scholastic, Inc.

—Baseball Brothers. 1999. (Hello Reader! Ser.). (J). 10.30 (978-0-606-16599-0(1)); lib. bdg. 11.25 (978-0-613-16897-7(6)) Tandem Library Bks.

Marzollo, Jean, et al. Baseball Brothers. Kelley, True, illus. 2004. 32p. (J). lib. bdg. 15.00 (978-1-59054-418-1(8)) Fitzgerald Bks.

McCormick, Patricia. My Brother's Keeper. 2005. 192p. (gr. 5-17). 15.99 (978-0-7868-5173-7(2)) Hyperion Bks. for Children.

—My Brother's Keeper. 2006. 192p. (gr. 5-17). reprint ed. pap. 5.99 (978-0-7868-5174-4(0)) Hyperion Pr.

McCully, Emily Arnold. Mouse Practice. 1999. (J). (Illus.). pap. 16.95 (978-0-590-68267-1(9)); (978-0-439-07055-3(4)) Scholastic, Inc.

McFarlane, Brian. The Baseball Thief. 8th ed. 2007. (Mitchell Brothers Ser.: Bk. 8). 200p. (J). (gr. 3-7). pap. 6.95 (***978-1-55168-276-1(1)***) Key Porter Bks. CAN. *Dist:* Perseus Distribution.

—Daredevil over Niagara. 7th ed. 2007. (Mitchell Brothers Ser.). 200p. (J). (gr. 3-7). pap. 6.99 (***978-1-55168-275-4(3)***) Key Porter Bks. CAN. *Dist:* Perseus Distribution.

McKay, Sindy & Johnson, Meredith. We Both Read-Baseball Fever. 2003. (Illus.). 44p. (J). (gr. 1-2). 7.99 (978-1-891327-45-2(3)) Treasure Bay, Inc.

McKeon, Kathryn Cristaldi. Baseball Ballerina Strikes Out. 2000. (Illus.). (J). (978-0-606-18483-0(X)) Tandem Library Bks.

McKissack, Patricia C. Miami Makes the Play. 2001. (gr. k-3). lib. bdg. 11.80 (978-0-613-43071-5(9)) Tandem Library Bks.

McKissack, Patricia C. & McKissack, Fredrick L. Miami Jackson Makes the Play. Chesworth, Michael, illus. 2004. (Road to Reading Ser.). 96p. (J). (gr. k-3). pap. 3.99 (978-0-307-26505-0(6) , Random Hse. Bks. for Young Readers) Random Hse. Children's Bks.

—Miami Makes the Play. Chesworth, Michael, illus. 2004. 92p. (J). (gr. 4-7). lib. bdg. 11.19 (978-0-606-32802-9(5)) Tandem Library Bks.

McOmber, Rachel B., ed. McOmber Phonics Storybooks: Everyone Knows a Pitcher. rev. ed. (Illus.). (J). (978-0-944991-79-4(3)) Swift Learning Resources.

Meister, Cari. Game Day: Level A. Hicks, Mark A., illus. 2001. (Rookie Readers Ser.). 24p. (J). (gr. k-1). 19.50 (978-0-516-22262-2(7) , Children's Pr.) Scholastic Library Publishing.

Michaelson, Richard. Across the Alley. Lewis, E. B., illus. 2006. 32p. (J). (ps-3). 16.99 (978-0-399-23970-0(7) , Putnam Juvenile) Penguin Group (USA) Inc.

Mochizuki, Ken. Baseball Saved Us. Lee, Dom, illus. (Picture Book Readalong Ser.). 28.95 incl. audio compact disk (978-1-59112-916-5(8)); pap. 39.95 incl. audio compact disk (978-1-59112-917-2(6)) Live Oak Media.

—Baseball Saved Us. 2005. (Picture Book Readalong Ser.). (Illus.). (J). pap. 18.95 incl. audio compact disk (978-1-59112-915-8(X)); pap. 16.95 incl. audio (978-1-59112-455-9(7)) Live Oak Media.

—Baseball Saved Us. Lee, Dom, illus. 2004. (Picture Book Readalong Ser.). (J). (ps-ps). audio 25.95 (978-1-59112-456-6(5)) Live Oak Media.

—El Beisbol Nos Salvo. ed. 2004. (SPA., Illus.). (J). (gr. k-4). spiral bd. (978-0-616-03090-5(8)) Canadian National Institute for the Blind/Institut National Canadien pour les Aveugles.

Morrison, Kevin. Stitches. Nixon, John, illus. 2003. 32p. (J). 12.95 (978-1-929039-15-9(8)) Ambassador Bks., Inc.

Mullen, Paul Michael. The Day I Hit a Home Run at Great American Ball Park. 2007. (J). (***978-1-933197-29-6(3)***) Orange Frazer Pr.

Munro, Ken. The Mysterious Baseball Scorecard. 2005. (Sammy & Brian Mystery Ser.: 17). pap. 5.95 (978-1-932864-31-1(8)) Masthof Pr.

Murphy, Claire Rudolf. Free Radical. 2002. 208p. (YA). (gr. 7). 15.00 (978-0-618-11134-3(4) , Clarion Bks.) Houghton Mifflin Co. Trade & Reference Div.

Myers, Walter Dean. The Journal of Biddy Owens: The Negro Leagues, Birmingham, Alabama 1948. 2001. (978-0-606-22807-7(1)) Tandem Library Bks.

Naylor, Phyllis Reynolds. Boys in Control. 2005. (Boy/Girl Battle Ser.). 160p. (J). (gr. 4-7). pap. 5.50 (978-0-440-41681-4(7) , Yearling) Random Hse. Children's Bks.

Negron, Ray. The Boy of Steel: A Baseball Dream Come True. Seeley, Laura, illus. 2006. 48p. (J). 19.95 (978-0-06-089870-0(4) , ReganBooks) HarperCollins Pubs.

Nelson, Vaunda Micheaux. Mayfield Crossing. 2002. (gr. 3-6). lib. bdg. 14.15 (978-0-613-43634-2(2)) Tandem Library Bks.

Norworth, Jack. Take Me Out to the Ball Game. Stadler, John, illus. 2005. 16p. (J). 12.95 (978-0-689-85917-5(1) , Little Simon) Simon & Schuster Children's Publishing

Nussbaum, Ben, ed. Take Me Out to the Ballgame. Pamintuan, Macky, illus. 2006. 32p. (J). pap. 8.95 incl. audio compact disk (978-1-59249-593-1(1)); 14.95 incl. audio compact disk (978-1-59249-572-6(9)) Soundprints.

Nye, Penny. Batter Up! Nye, Penny, illus. 1999. (Bookmates Ser.). (Illus.). 16p. (J). (ps-5). pap. 12.00 (978-1-890703-14-1(1)) Penny Laine Papers, Inc.

O'Connell, Fabian. Alpha's Baseball Field. 2004. 42p. pap. 19.95 (978-1-4137-0301-6(1)) PublishAmerica, Inc.

Okimoto, Jean Davies. Dear Ichiro. Keith, Doug, illus. 2006. 29p. (J). (gr. 4-8). reprint ed. 17.00 (***978-1-4223-5803-0(8)***) DIANE Publishing Co.

—Dear Ichiro. Keith, Doug, illus. 2002. 32p. (J). 16.95 (978-1-57061-373-9(7)) Sasquatch Bks.

Olker, Constance. The Punctuation Pals Go to the Baseball Park. 2005. (Illus.). (J). 44p. per. 18.95 (978-1-933449-15-9(2)); 22p. per. 17.95 (978-0-9761289-8-4(5)) Nightengale Pr.

O'Malley, Kevin. My Lucky Hat. O'Malley, Kevin, illus. 1999. (Illus.). 32p. (J). (gr. k-4). 15.95 (978-1-57255-710-9(9)) Mondo Publishing.

Papademetriou, Lisa. Lucky Me! 1999. (Real Kids Readers Ser.). (Illus.). 32p. (J). (gr. 2-4). pap. 4.99 (978-0-7613-2096-8(2) , Millbrook Pr.) Lerner Publishing Group.

—Lucky Me! Handelman, Dorothy, photos by. 1999. (Real Kids Readers Ser.). (Illus.). 48p. (gr. 1-3). lib. bdg. 18.90 (978-0-7613-2071-5(7) , Millbrook Pr.) Lerner Publishing Group.

—Lucky Me! 1999. (J). (978-0-606-19160-9(7)); lib. bdg. 11.80 (978-0-613-18160-0(3)) Tandem Library Bks.

—Lucky Me! Handelman, Dorothy, photos by. 1999. (978-1-58824-805-3(4)) ipicturebooks, LLC.

Pastel, JoAnne & Fitzsimmons, Kakie. Bur Bur Throws Out the First Pitch. VanDeWeghe, Lindsay, illus. 2007. (J). (***978-0-9777121-4-4(1)***) Interface Publishing.

Patneaude, David. Haunting at Home Plate. 2000. (gr. 3-6). lib. bdg. 15.25 (978-0-613-61848-9(3)) Tandem Library Bks.

—Haunting at Home Plate. 2000. 192p. (J). (gr. 4-8). 15.95 (978-0-8075-3181-5(2)); pap. 6.95 (978-0-8075-3182-2(0)) Whitman, Albert & Co.

Paxton, Tom. The Jungle Baseball Game. Schmidt, Karen L., illus. 1999. 40p. (ps-3). (J). 15.89 (978-0-688-13980-3(9)); (YA). 16.00 (978-0-688-13979-7(5)) HarperCollins Pubs.

Peck, Robert Newton. Extra Innings. 2001. 192p. (J). (gr. 7 up). 16.99 (978-0-06-028867-9(1)) HarperCollins Pubs.

—Extra Innings. 2003. (gr. 5-8). lib. bdg. 14.15 (978-0-613-61762-8(2)) Tandem Library Bks.

The Phillie Phanatic's Phantastic Journey. 2005. (J). (978-0-9705804-9-8(5)) Middle Atlantic Pr.

Play Ball, Amelia Bedelia. 2002. (Amelia Bedelia Ser.). (Illus.). (J). 12.34 (978-0-7587-6239-9(9)) Book Wholesalers, Inc.

Players in Pigtails. 2004. 29.95 incl. cd-rom (978-0-7882-0518-7(8)); 24.95 incl. audio (978-0-7882-0517-0(X)) Weston Woods Studios, Inc.

Posada, Jorge. Play Ball! Colon, Raul, illus. 2006. 32p. (J). (gr. 1-5). 16.95 (978-1-4169-0687-2(8)) Simon & Schuster Children's Publishing.

—Sí, puedes (Play Ball!) Colon, Raul, illus. 2006. (SPA.). 32p. (J). 16.95 (978-1-4169-1476-1(5)) Simon & Schuster Children's Publishing.

Powell, Randy. Dean Duffy. 2003. 176p. (YA). pap. 7.95 (978-0-374-41698-0(2) , Sunburst) Farrar, Straus & Giroux.

Preller, James. Six Innings: A Game in the Life. 2008. 160p. (J). 16.95 (***978-0-312-36763-3(5)***) Feiwel & Friends.

Puffin, Usa. Casey at the Bat. 1999. 32p. (J). pap. 5.99 (978-0-14-055886-9(1) , Puffin) Penguin Group (USA) Inc.

Purciello, Gerard. The Year They Won: A Tale of the Boston Red Sox. 2005. 112p. (YA). pap. (978-0-9746481-5-6(9)) Brown Barn Bks.

Raintree Steck-Vaughn Staff. Béisbol Campestre. 1999. (Coleccion en Parejas). (SPA.). (J). pap., stu. ed. 21.50 (978-0-7398-0824-5(9)) Steck-Vaughn.

Rallison, Janette. Playing the Field. 172p. (J). 2004. pap. 6.95 (978-0-8027-7697-6(3)); 2002. (gr. 5-8). 16.95 (978-0-8027-8804-7(1)) Walker & Co.

Rappaport, Doreen. Dirt on Their Skirts: The Story of the Young Women Who Won the World Championship. Callan, Lyndall & Lewis, Earl, illus. 2000. 32p. (J). (ps-3). 16.99 (978-0-8037-2042-8(4) , Dial) Penguin Group (USA) Inc.

Raven, Margot Theis. Let Them Play. Ellison, Chris, illus. 2005. 40p. (J). 16.95 (978-1-58536-260-8(3)) Sleeping Bear Pr.

Remy, Jerry. Hello, Wally! Moore, Danny, illus. 2006. (J). 17.95 (***978-1-932888-80-5(2)***) Mascot Bks., Inc.

—Wally's Journey Through Red Sox Nation! 2007. (J). 14.95 (***978-1-932888-89-8(6)***) Mascot Bks., Inc.

Rickis, Andrew. The Magic Oak: (A Baseball Story) A Novel for Young Adults. 2003. 114p. pap. 16.95 (978-1-4137-0665-9(7)) PublishAmerica, Inc.

Rinn, Miriam. The Saturday Secret. 1999. (Illus.). 144p. (J). (gr. 4-7). pap. 7.95 (978-1-881283-26-3(7)) Alef Design Group.

Ritter, John H. The Boy Who Saved Baseball. 224p. 2005. (J). (gr. 4). pap. 6.99 (978-0-14-240286-3(9) , Puffin); 2003. (Illus.). (YA). (gr. 5-7). 17.99 (978-0-399-23622-8(8) , Philomel) Penguin Group (USA) Inc.

—The Boy Who Saved Baseball. 2005. 216p. (J). (ps-7). per. 12.64 (978-0-606-33116-6(6)) Tandem Library Bks.

—Choosing up Sides. 1998. 176p. (J). (gr. 4-9). 18.99 (978-0-399-23185-8(4) , Philomel) Penguin Group (USA) Inc.

—Over the Wall. 2002. (gr. 5-8). lib. bdg. 15.30 (978-0-613-67112-5(0)) Tandem Library Bks.

Roberts, Kelly. Baseball Boy. 2007. 17.95 (***978-0-9792147-0-7(X)***) Beau Francis Pr.

Roberts, Ken. Thumb on a Diamond. Franson, Leanne, illus. 128p. (J). 2007. (gr. 4-7). pap. 7.95 (978-0-88899-705-0(1)); 2006. 15.95 (978-0-88899-629-9(2)) Groundwood Bks. CAN. *Dist:* Perseus Distribution.

Roberts, Kristi. My Thirteenth Season. rev. ed. 2005. (Illus.). 160p. (J). 15.95 (978-0-8050-7495-6(3) , Holt, Henry & Co. Bks. For Young Readers) Holt, Henry & Co.

Robins, Eleanor. The Right Kind of Win. 2003. (Illus.). 48p. (YA). per. 3.95 (978-1-56254-691-5(0) , SP6910) Saddleback Educational Publishing.

Robinson, Sharon. Safe at Home. 160p. (J). 2007. (gr. 4-7). pap. 4.99 (***978-0-439-67198-9(1)*** , Scholastic Paperbacks); 2006. pap. 16.99 (978-0-439-67197-2(3) , Scholastic) Scholastic, Inc.

Rocky the Mudhen: We're Talkin' Baseball. 2004. (J). lib. bdg. 14.95 (978-0-9748922-0-7(3)) Rabbit Ears Pr. & Co.

Rodriguez, Alex. Jonron! Morrison, Frank, illus. 2007. (SPA.). 32p. (J). (ps-3). 16.99 (978-0-06-115197-2(1) , Rayo) HarperCollins Pubs.

—Out of the Ballpark. Morrison, Frank, illus. 2007. 32p. (J). lib. bdg. 17.89 (978-0-06-115195-8(5)); 16.99 (978-0-06-115194-1(7)) HarperCollins Pubs.

Rosenfeld, Dina. On the Ball. Nodel, Norman, illus. 1998. (Yossi & Laibel Ser.). (J). 9.95 (978-0-922613-83-0(4)) Hachai Publishing.

Roy, Ron. The Unwilling Umpire. Gurney, John Steven, illus. 2004. (A to Z Mysteries Ser.: No. 21). 112p. (J). (gr. 1-4). lib. bdg. 11.99 (978-0-375-91370-9(X) , Random Hse. Bks. for Young Readers) Random Hse. Children's Bks.

—The Unwilling Umpire. Gurney, John Steven, illus. 2004. (A to Z Mysteries Ser.: No. 21). (J). (gr. k-3). lib. bdg. 11.80 (978-0-613-82496-5(2)) Tandem Library Bks.

—The Unwilling Umpire: A to Z Mysteries. Gurney, John Steven, illus. 2004. (A to Z Mysteries Ser.: No. 21). 112p. (J). (gr. 1-4). pap. 3.99 (978-0-375-81370-2(5) , Random Hse. Bks. for Young Readers) Random Hse. Children's Bks.

Russell, Nancy L. M. So Long, Jackie Robinson. rev. ed. 2007. 224p. (gr. 7 up). pap. 7.95 (***978-1-55263-863-7(4)***) Key Porter Bks. CAN. *Dist:* Perseus Distribution.

Schade, Susan. Baseball Camp on the Planet of the Eyeballs. Buller, Jon, illus. 1998. (Step into Reading Step 3 Bks.). (J). (gr. 2-3). (978-0-606-13950-2(8)) Tandem Library Bks.

—Cat at Bat. 2000. (gr. k-3). lib. bdg. 11.80 (978-0-613-27765-5(1)) Tandem Library Bks.

Schade, Susan & Buller, Jon. Cat at Bat. 2000. (Road to Reading Ser.). (Illus.). 32p. (J). (ps-1). pap. 3.99 (978-0-307-26211-0(1) , Random Hse. Bks. for Young Readers) Random Hse. Children's Bks.

Schnur, Steven. The Koufax Dilemma. Treatner, Meryl, illus. 2001. 196p. (YA). pap. 14.95 (978-0-595-19998-3(4) , Backinprint.com) iUniverse, Inc.

—Koufax Dilemma. 2001. (gr. 3-6). lib. bdg. 24.55 (978-0-613-85103-9(X)) Tandem Library Bks.

Schraff, Anne. Hunter. 2001. (gr. 7-12). lib. bdg. 11.80 (978-0-613-32659-9(8)) Tandem Library Bks.

—Planet Doom. 2001. (PageTurner Adventure Ser.). 80p. (YA). per. 3.95 (978-1-56254-184-2(6) , SP 1846) Saddleback Educational Publishing.

—Planet Doom. 2001. (gr. 7-12). lib. bdg. 11.80 (978-0-613-32953-8(8)) Tandem Library Bks.

Schultz, Jessica. Jack Plays the Violin. D'Augusta, Luisa, illus. 2002. 16p. (J). (978-0-439-35070-9(0)) Scholastic, Inc.

Schulz, Charles M. It's a Home Run, Charlie Brown! LoBianco, Peter & LoBianco, Nick, illus. 2002. (Ready-to-Read Ser.). 32p. (J). (gr. 1-4). pap. 3.99 (978-0-689-84939-8(7) , Little Simon) Simon & Schuster Children's Publishing.

Schulz, Charles M. Peanuts: Snoopy at Bat. 2008. 10p. (J). pap. 7.95 (***978-0-7624-3235-6(7)*** , Running Pr.) Running Pr. Bk. Pubs.

Schulz, Charles M., illus. It's a Home Run, Charlie Brown! 2002. (gr. k-3). lib. bdg. 11.80 (978-0-613-61780-2(0)) Tandem Library Bks.

Schwartz, Ellen. Stealing Home. 2006. 224p. (J). (gr. 4-7). pap. 8.95 (978-0-88776-765-4(6)) Tundra Bks., Inc./ Livres Toundra, Inc. CAN. *Dist:* Random Hse., Inc.

Seymour's Soaring Red Sox: A Bird's-Eye View of the 2004 World Series. 2005. (J). kivar 19.95 (978-0-9761820-1-6(7)) Cassiopeia Pr.

Shane, Sam. Rocky the Mudhen: Baseball & Humble Pie. 2006. (Illus.). (J). lib. bdg. 15.95 (978-0-9748922-1-4(1)) Rabbit Ears Pr. & Co.

Shanks, Melanie. The Squints. 2007. 116p. per. 10.95 (***978-0-595-44849-4(6)***) iUniverse, Inc.

Shannon, David. How Georgie Radbourn Saved Baseball. 2000. (Illus.). (J). (978-0-606-18562-2(3)) Tandem Library Bks.

Sheets, Scott & Vanover, Howard. A Day at the Ball Park-Book 1 of the Wannabe Kids Series. 2007. 16p. (J). per. 9.99 (***978-1-59886-792-3(X)***) Tate Publishing & Enterprises, L.L.C.

Sherman, Harold M. Strike Him Out. 2005. pap. 26.95 (978-1-4191-1422-9(0)) Kessinger Publishing, LLC.

Siemiatycki, Jack & Slodovnick, Avi. The Baseball Card. Watson, Laura, illus. 2005. 32p. (J). (ps-4). 15.95 (978-1-894222-95-2(4)) Lobster Pr. CAN. *Dist:* Univ. of Toronto Pr.

—La Estampa de Beisbol. Watson, Laura, illus. 2005. (SPA.). 28p. pap. (978-2-922435-07-8(5)) Lobster Pr.

Silver Dolphin en Español Editors. Magical Magnets: Chicken Little. 2006. (SPA., Illus.). 8p. (J). bds. 12.95 (978-970-718-318-6(7)) Advantage Pubs. Group.

Skead, Robert. Hitting Glory: A Baseball Bat Adventure. 2001. 120p. (YA). per. 6.99 (978-1-929478-30-9(5)) Cross Training Publishing.

Smith, Charles R. Let's Play Baseball! Widener, Terry, illus. 2006. (Super Sturdy Picture Book Ser.). 24p. (J). (gr. k-ps). 8.99 (978-0-7636-1646-5(X)) Candlewick Pr.

Smith, Jennifer E. The Comeback Season. 2008. 256p. (YA). 15.99 (***978-1-4169-3847-7(8)*** , Simon & Schuster Children's Publishing) Simon & Schuster Children's Publishing.

Smith, Ozzie. Hello, Fredbird! de Angel, Miguel, illus. 2006. 30p. (J). 17.95 (***978-1-932888-83-6(7)***) Mascot Bks., Inc.

Speck, Nancy. Secret of the Hidden Room. Thomas, Jerry D., ed. Ford, Mark, illus. 1999. (Shoebox Kids Ser.: Vol. 9). 93p. (J). pap. 6.99 (978-0-8163-1682-3(1)) Pacific Pr. Publishing Assn.

Spence, Tom. Tough Day at the Plate. 2004. 39p. (J). per. 5.95 (978-1-59453-241-2(9) , 1734) Airleaf Publishing & Bookselling.

Standish, Burt L. Frank Merriwell's Baseball Victories. Rudman, Jack, ed. 2003. (Frank Merriwell Ser.). 29.95 (978-0-8373-9348-3(5)); pap. 9.95 (978-0-8373-9048-2(6)) Merriwell, Frank Inc.

Staub, Rusty. Hello, Mr. Met! Moore, Danny, illus. 2006. (J). 17.95 (***978-1-932888-82-9(9)***) Mascot Bks., Inc.

Steele, Michael Anthony. Forgotten Heroes. l.t. ed. 2000. (Wishbone Mysteries Ser.: No. 12). (Illus.). 139p. (J). (gr. 4 up). lib. bdg. 23.33 (978-0-8368-2695-1(7)) Stevens, Gareth Inc.

Strike Two (Baseball) 64p. (YA). (gr. 6-12). pap. 10.95 (978-0-8224-6481-5(0)) Globe Fearon Educational Publishing.

Superstar Charlie. 2006. 16p. (J). pap. 1.99 (978-0-7847-1707-3(9) , 04168) Standard Publishing.

Swango, Lynn. No Baseball in Fairview. 2003. (Illus.). (J). per. 12.95 (978-1-878044-95-2(8)) Mayhaven Publishing.

Tavares, Matt. Mudball. Tavares, Matt, illus. 2005. (Illus.). 32p. (J). (gr. 1-5). 15.99 (978-0-7636-2387-6(3)) Candlewick Pr.

—Oliver's Game. Tavares, Matt, illus. 2004. (Illus.). 32p. (J). (gr. 1-5). 15.99 (978-0-7636-1852-0(7)) Candlewick Pr.

—Zachary's Ball. Tavares, Matt, illus. (Illus.). 32p. (J). 2005. (gr. 1-4). pap. 6.99 (978-0-7636-2918-2(9)); 2000. (gr. 2-7). 15.99 (978-0-7636-0730-2(4)) Candlewick Pr.

Taylor, Jeannie St. John. Out at Home: A Novel. 2004. 144p. (J). pap. 6.99 (978-0-8254-3724-3(5)) Kregel Pubns.

Teague, Mark. Field Beyond the Outfield. 2006. (Illus.). 40p. (J). pap. 5.99 (978-0-439-81215-3(1) , Scholastic Pr.) Scholastic, Inc.

Teitelbaum, Michael. Wild Pitch #1. Zalme, Ron, illus. 2008. 80p. (J). (gr. 1-3). 3.99 (***978-0-448-44711-7(8)*** , Grosset & Dunlap) Penguin Group (USA) Inc.

Testa, Maria. Becoming Joe Dimaggio. Hunt, Scott, illus. 2002. 64p. (J). (gr. 5-9). 14.99 (978-0-7636-1537-6(4)) Candlewick Pr.

—Becoming Joe DiMaggio. Hunt, Scott, illus. 2005. 64p. (J). (gr. 5-9). reprint ed. pap. 5.99 (978-0-7636-2444-6(6)) Candlewick Pr.

—Some Kind of Pride. 2003. 128p. (gr. 3-7). 4.99 (978-0-440-41669-2(8) , Yearling) Random Hse. Children's Bks.

—Some Kind of Pride. 2003. (gr. 3-6). lib. bdg. 13.00 (978-0-613-62119-9(0)) Tandem Library Bks.

The Throwing Smoke. 2000. (J). (978-0-06-029064-1(1)) HarperCollins Pubs.

Tocher, Timothy. Chief Sunrise, John McGraw, & Me. 2004. 168p. (J). 16.95 (978-0-8126-2711-4(3)) Cricket Bks.

Torrey, Richard L. Beans Baker, Num. 5. Torrey, Richard L., illus. 2001. (Road to Reading Ser.). (Illus.). 48p. (J). (gr. 1-3). pap. 3.99 (978-0-307-26335-3(5) , Random Hse. Bks. for Young Readers) Random Hse. Children's Bks.

—Beans Baker, No. 5. 2001. (gr. k-3). lib. bdg. 11.80 (978-0-613-42993-1(1)); (Illus.). (J). 10.79 (978-0-606-20564-1(0)) Tandem Library Bks.

Troughton, Joanna. The Great Ball Play. 2000. (Illus.). 32p. (J). (ps-3). 13.95 (978-1-899248-37-7(4)); pap. 5.95 (978-1-899248-32-2(3)) Happy Cat Bks. GBR. *Dist:* Star Bright Bks., Inc.

Trueman, Terry. 7 Days at the Hot Corner, No. 2. 2007. 160p. (J). (gr. 7 up). 15.99 (978-0-06-057494-9(1)); lib. bdg. 16.89 (978-0-06-057495-6(X)) HarperCollins Pubs. (HarperTeen).

Tunis, John R. Keystone Kids. 2006. (Illus.). 252p. (J). pap. 5.95 (978-0-15-205634-6(3) , Odyssey Classics) Harcourt Children's Bks.

Tunis, John R. & Koelsch, Michael. The Kid from Tomkinsville. 2006. (Illus.). 300p. (J). pap. 5.95 (978-0-15-205641-4(6) , Odyssey Classics) Harcourt Children's Bks.

—Rookie of the Year. 2006. (Illus.). 240p. (J). pap. 5.95 (978-0-15-205648-3(3) , Odyssey Classics) Harcourt Children's Bks.

Turner, Ann. Hard Hit. l.t. ed. 2006. (YA). 21.95 (978-0-7862-8745-1(4)) Thorndike Pr.

Turner, Ann Warren. Hard Hit. 2006. 128p. (J). (gr. 7 up). pap. 16.99 (978-0-439-29680-9(3)) Scholastic, Inc.

Uhlberg, Myron. Dad, Jackie, & Me. Bootman, Colin, illus. 2005. 32p. (J). (ps-3). 16.95 (978-1-56145-329-0(3)) Peachtree Pubs., Ltd.

Waldman, Neil. Say-Hey & the Babe: Two Mostly-True Baseball Stories. Waldman, Neil, illus. 2005. (Illus.). 40p. (J). (gr. 1-5). 16.95 (978-0-8234-1857-2(X)) Holiday Hse., Inc.

Wallace, Rich. Curveball. (Winning Season Ser.). 128p. (J). 2007. 14.99 (978-0-670-06119-8(0) , Viking Juvenile); No. 9. 2008. (gr. 3). 4.99 (***978-0-14-241092-9(6)*** , Puffin) Penguin Group (USA) Inc.

—Southpaw. 2006. 105p. (J). lib. bdg. 15.38 (***978-1-4242-2166-0(8)***) Fitzgerald Bks.

—Southpaw. (Winning Season Ser.: Vol. 6). 128p. (J). 2007. pap. 4.99 (978-0-14-240785-1(2) , Puffin); 2006. (gr. 4). 14.99 (978-0-670-06053-5(4) , Viking Juvenile) Penguin Group (USA) Inc.

Warner, Gertrude Chandler. Home Run Mystery. 2000. (gr. 3-6). lib. bdg. 11.80 (978-0-613-27879-9(8)) Tandem Library Bks.

—The Homerun Mystery. 2000. (Boxcar Children Special Ser.: No. 14). (J). (gr. 2-5). 10.60 (978-0-606-18772-5(3)) Tandem Library Bks.

Warner, Gertrude Chandler, creator. The Boxcar Children Summer Special. 2007. (Boxcar Children Mysteries Ser.). 376p. (J). pap. 7.95 (***978-0-8075-0885-5(3)***) Whitman, Albert & Co.

Warner, Gertrude Chandler, creator. The Homerun Mystery. (Boxcar Children Special Ser.: No. 14). (Illus.). 120p. (J). (gr. 2-5). 2000. lib. bdg. 13.95 (978-0-8075-3368-0(8)); Vol. 14. 2004. pap. 4.50 (978-0-8075-3369-7(6)) Whitman, Albert & Co.

Weatherford, Carole Boston. Champions on the Bench: The Cannon Street YMCA All-Stars. Jenkins, Leonard, illus. 2007. 32p. (J). (gr. 1-4). 16.99 (978-0-8037-2987-2(1) , Dial) Penguin Group (USA) Inc.

Weaver, Will. Farm Team. 1999. 288p. (J). (gr. 6 up). pap. 7.99 (978-0-06-447118-3(7) , Harper Trophy) HarperCollins Pubs.

—Farm Team. 1999. (J). 12.64 (978-0-606-15860-2(X)); (gr. 5-8). lib. bdg. 14.10 (978-0-613-11530-8(9)) Tandem Library Bks.

—Hard Ball. (gr. 6 up). 1999. 256p. (J). pap. 5.99 (978-0-06-447208-1(6) , Harper Trophy); 1998. 240p. (YA). 15.89 (978-0-06-027122-0(1)); 1998. 240p. (YA). 15.95 (978-0-06-027121-3(3)) HarperCollins Pubs.

—Hard Ball. 1999. (J). 12.64 (978-0-606-16706-2(4)); (gr. 7-12). lib. bdg. 14.15 (978-0-613-18254-6(5)) Tandem Library Bks.

—Hard Ball: A Billy Baggs Novel. l.t. ed. 2000. (Illus.). 270p. (YA). (gr. 8-12). 20.95 (978-0-7862-2752-5(4)) Thorndike Pr.

Wiles, Deborah. The Aurora County All-Stars. 2007. (Illus.). 256p. (J). (gr. 5 up). 16.00 (***978-0-15-206068-8(5)***) Harcourt Children's Bks.

Wooldridge, Frosty. Strike Three! Take Your Base. Petri, Freeman, illus. 2001. 160p. (YA). (gr. 6-12). pap. 6.95 (978-1-930093-07-2(1)) Brookfield Reader, Inc., The.

—Strike Three! Take Your Base. Freeman, Pietri, illus. 2001. 160p. (YA). (gr. 6-12). 16.95 (978-1-930093-01-0(2)) Brookfield Reader, Inc., The.

Yavin, T. S. All-Star Season. Orback, Craig, illus. 2007. 160p. (J). (gr. 4-6). spiral bd. 15.95 (978-1-58013-211-4(1)) Kar-Ben Publishing.

Zagwyn, Deborah Turney. Apple Batter. 2004. (Illus.). 32p. (J). (gr. 1-3). 14.95 (978-1-883672-92-8(9) , Tricycle Pr.) Ten Speed Pr.

Zinnen, Linda. Holding at Third. 2006. 160p. (YA). (gr. 4). pap. 5.99 (978-0-14-240554-3(X) , Puffin) Penguin Group (USA) Inc.

86 Years: The Legend of the Boston Red Sox. 2005. (J). 18.95 (978-0-9767938-0-9(6)) Brown Hse. Bks.

BASEBALL—HISTORY

Baseball: The Great American Game, 30 bks. (Illus.). (J). 478.50 (978-0-88682-929-2(1) , Creative Education) Creative Co., The.

Bildner, Phil. The Shot Heard 'Round the World. Payne, C. F., illus. 2005. 32p. (J). 16.95 (978-0-689-86273-1(3)) Simon & Schuster Children's Publishing.

Burgan, Michael. Great Moments in Baseball. 2002. (Great Moments in Sports Ser.). (Illus.). 48p. (J). (gr. 5 up). pap. 14.60 (978-0-8368-5358-2(X)); lib. bdg. 30.00 (978-0-8368-5344-5(X)) Stevens, Gareth Inc. (World Almanac Library).

Burke, Jim & Norworth, Jack. Take Me Out to the Ballgame: The Sensational Baseball Song. 2006. (Illus.). 32p. (J). (ps-1). 16.99 (978-0-316-75819-2(1)) Little Brown & Co.

Campbell, Peter A. Old Time Baseball & the First. 2002. (Illus.). 48p. (gr. 3-6). lib. bdg. 24.90 (978-0-7613-2466-9(6) , Millbrook Pr.) Lerner Publishing Group.

Cho, Alan. World Series. 2007. (J). (***978-1-59036-699-8(9)); (*978-1-59036-700-1(6)***) Weigl Pubs., Inc.

Cockcroft, James D. Latinos in Beisbol. 2004. (Illus.). 207p. (J). (gr. 4-9). reprint ed. pap. 10.00 (978-0-7567-7347-2(4)) DIANE Publishing Co.

Coleman, Janet Wyman & Warren, Elizabeth V. Baseball for Everyone: Stories from the Great Game. 2003. (Illus.). 48p. (J). (gr. 3-7). 16.95 (978-0-8109-4580-7(0)) Abrams, Harry N. , Inc.

—Baseball for Everyone: Stories from the Great Game. 2006. (Illus.). 51p. (J). (gr. 4-8). reprint ed. 17.00 (978-0-7567-9972-4(4)) DIANE Publishing Co.

Collins, Ace & Hillman, John. Blackball Superstars: Legendary Players of the Negro Baseball Leagues. 1999. (Illus.). 141p. (J). (gr. 6-12). lib. bdg. 19.95 (978-1-888105-38-4(0)) Avisson Pr., Inc.

Fischer, David. The Story of the New York Yankees. 2003. (Major League Baseball Ser.). (Illus.). 48p. pap. 3.99 (978-0-7894-9251-7(2)) Dorling Kindersley Publishing, Inc.

—Story of the New York Yankees. 2003. (gr. k-3). lib. bdg. 11.80 (978-0-613-62437-4(8)) Tandem Library Bks.

Fischer, David & Dorling Kindersley Publishing Staff. The Story of the New York Yankees. 2003. (Major League Baseball Ser.). (Illus.). 48p. (J). 12.99 (978-0-7894-9545-7(7)) Dorling Kindersley Publishing, Inc.

Frisch, Aaron. Boston Red Sox. 2002. 32p. (J). pap. 5.95 (978-0-89812-336-4(4) , Creative Paperbacks); (Illus.). (978-1-58341-202-2(6) , Creative Education) Creative Co., The.

—Chicago Cubs. 2002. (J). pap. 5.95 (978-0-89812-337-1(2) , Creative Paperbacks); (Illus.). 32p. (978-1-58341-203-9(4) , Creative Education) Creative Co., The.

—Milwaukee Brewers. 2002. (Baseball Ser.). (Illus.). 32p. (J). (978-1-58341-213-8(1) , Creative Education); pap. 5.95 (978-0-89812-347-0(X) , Creative Paperbacks) Creative Co., The.

—Minnesota Twins. 2002. 32p. (J). pap. 5.95 (978-0-89812-348-7(8) , Creative Paperbacks); (Illus.). (978-1-58341-214-5(X) , Creative Education) Creative Co., The.

—Oakland Athletics. 2002. 32p. (J). pap. 5.95 (978-0-89812-352-4(6) , Creative Paperbacks); (Illus.). (978-1-58341-218-3(2) , Creative Education) Creative Co., The.

—San Francisco Giants. 2002. 32p. (J). pap. 5.95 (978-0-89812-357-9(7) , Creative Paperbacks); (Illus.). (978-1-58341-223-7(9) , Creative Education) Creative Co., The.

—Texas Rangers. 2002. (Baseball Ser.). (Illus.). 32p. (J). (978-1-58341-226-8(3) , Creative Education); pap. 5.95 (978-0-89812-360-9(7) , Creative Paperbacks) Creative Co., The.

Frystak, Timothy D. Jackie Robinson: With Profiles of Satchel Paige & & Branch Rickey. 2006. (Biographical Connections Ser.). (Illus.). 112p. (J). (978-0-7166-1828-7(1)) World Bk., Inc.

Goodman, Michael E. The History of the Houston Astros. 1998. (Baseball, the Great American Game Ser.). (Illus.). 32p. (YA). (gr. 3-12). pap. 21.30 (978-0-88682-910-0(0) , Creative Education) Creative Co., The.

—The History of the Montreal Expos. 1998. (Baseball, the Great American Game Ser.). (Illus.). 32p. (YA). (gr. 3-12). pap. 21.30 (978-0-88682-915-5(1) , Creative Education) Creative Co., The.

—The History of the Seattle Mariners. 1998. (Baseball, the Great American Game Ser.). (Illus.). 32p. (YA). (gr. 3-12). pap. 21.30 (978-0-88682-925-4(9) , Creative Education) Creative Co., The.

—Montreal Expos. 2002. (Baseball Ser.). (Illus.). 32p. (J). (978-1-58341-215-2(8) , Creative Education); pap. 5.95 (978-0-89812-349-4(6) , Creative Paperbacks) Creative Co., The.

—New York Mets. 2002. 32p. (J). pap. 5.95 (978-0-89812-350-0(X) , Creative Paperbacks); (Illus.). (978-1-58341-216-9(6)) Creative Co., The.

—New York Yankees. 2002. (Baseball Ser.). (Illus.). 32p. (J). (978-1-58341-217-6(4) , Creative Education) Creative Co., The.

—Philadelphia Phillies. 2002. 32p. (J). pap. 5.95 (978-0-89812-353-1(4) , Creative Paperbacks); (Illus.). (978-1-58341-219-0(0) , Creative Education) Creative Co., The.

—San Diego Padres. 2002. (J). pap. 5.95 (978-0-89812-356-2(9) , Creative Paperbacks); (Illus.). 32p. (978-1-58341-222-0(0) , Creative Education) Creative Co., The.

—Seattle Mariners. 2002. 32p. (J). pap. 5.95 (978-0-89812-358-6(5) , Creative Paperbacks); (Illus.). (978-1-58341-224-4(7) , Creative Education) Creative Co., The.

—St. Louis Cardinals. 2002. 32p. (J). pap. 5.95 (978-0-89812-355-5(0) , Creative Paperbacks); (Illus.). (978-1-58341-221-3(2)) Creative Co., The.

—Toronto Blue Jays. 2002. (Baseball Ser.). (Illus.). 32p. (J). (978-1-58341-227-5(1) , Creative Education); pap. 5.95 (978-0-89812-361-6(5) , Creative Paperbacks) Creative Co., The.

Grabowski, John F. The Atlanta Braves. 2003. (Illus.). 112p. (J). 29.95 (978-1-59018-304-5(5) , Lucent Bks.) Thomson Gale.

—Baseball. 2000. (History of Sports Ser.). (Illus.). 112p. (YA). (gr. 6-9). 28.70 (978-1-56006-677-4(6) , Lucent Bks.) Thomson Gale.

—The Boston Red Sox Baseball Team. 2001. (Great Sports Teams Ser.). (Illus.). 48p. (YA). (gr. 4-10). lib. bdg. 23.93 (978-0-7660-1488-6(6)) Enslow Pubs., Inc.

—Chicago White Sox. 2002. (Illus.). 112p. (J). 29.95 (978-1-56006-938-6(4) , Lucent Bks.) Thomson Gale.

Gutman, Dan. World Series Classics (1912-1991) 2001. (Illus.). 240p. (J). (gr. 5-7). reprint ed. 15.00 (978-0-7881-9988-2(9)) DIANE Publishing Co.

Harcourt School Publishers Staff. All-Americans: Take-Home Book. 2001. (Collections Ser.). (Illus.). (J). pap. 1.90 (978-0-15-319545-7(2)) Harcourt Schl. Pubs.

—All-Americans Below Level. 3rd ed. 2002. (Trophies Reading Program Ser.). (Illus.). pap. 5.10 (978-0-15-323403-3(2)) Harcourt Schl. Pubs.

—A Soaking to Satchel Advanced Level. 3rd ed. 2002. (Trophies Reading Program Ser.). (Illus.). pap. 5.10 (978-0-15-323376-0(1)) Harcourt Schl. Pubs.

Helmer, Diana Star & Owens, Tom. The History of Baseball. 2000. (Sports Throughout History Ser.). 24p. (J). (gr. k-4). lib. bdg. 18.75 (978-0-8239-5469-8(2) , PowerKids Pr.) Rosen Publishing Group, Inc., The.

La Historia del Beisbol: Individual Title Six-Packs. (On Deck en Espanol Ser.).Tr. of Story of Baseball. (SPA.). 24p. (gr. 4-5). 35.00 (978-0-7578-6395-0(7)) Rigby Education.

Kennedy, Mike & Stewart, Mark. Latino Baseball's Finest Fielders/Las Mejores Estrellas del Beisbol Latino. Kalmanovitz, Manuel, tr. 2002. (En Fuego Ser.). (SPA & ENG., Illus.). 64p. (gr. 5 up). lib. bdg. 26.90 (978-0-7613-2566-6(2) , Twenty-First Century Bks.) Lerner Publishing Group.

—Latino Baseball's Hottest Hitters/Los Mejores Bateadores del Beisbol Latino. Kalmanovitz, Manuel, tr. 2002. (En Fuego Ser.). (ENG & SPA., Illus.). 64p. (gr. 5 up). lib. bdg. 26.90 (978-0-7613-2567-3(0) , Twenty-First Century Bks.) Lerner Publishing Group.

Mackin, Bob. Off the Wall Baseball Trivia: Games - Puzzles - Quizzes. 2003. (Illus.). pap. 6.95 (978-1-55054-821-1(2)) Douglas & McIntyre, Ltd. CAN. *Dist:* Transition Vendor.

McKissack, Patricia C. Black Diamond: The Story of the Negro Baseball Leagues. 1998. (gr. 5-8). lib. bdg. 14.15 (978-0-613-70493-9(2)) Tandem Library Bks.

McKissack, Patricia C. & McKissack, Frederick. Black Diamond: The Story of the Negro Baseball Leagues. 1998. 192p. (J). pap. 5.99 (978-0-590-68213-8(X)) Scholastic, Inc.

Morelli, Jack. Heroes of the Negro Leagues. 2007. 128p. 19.95 (***978-0-8109-9434-8(8)***) Abrams, Harry N. , Inc.

Moss, Marissa. Mighty Jackie: The Strike-Out Queen. Payne, C. F., tr. Payne, C. F., illus. 2004. 32p. (J). 16.95 (978-0-689-86329-5(2) , Simon & Schuster/Paula Wiseman Bks.) Simon & Schuster Children's Publishing.

Murphy, Frank. Babe Ruth Saves Baseball. Walz, Richard, illus. 2005. (Step into Reading Ser.). 48p. (J). (gr. 1-3). lib. bdg. 11.99 (978-0-375-93048-5(5) , Random Hse. Bks. for Young Readers) Random Hse. Children's Bks.

—Babe Ruth Saves Baseball! Walz, Richard, illus. 2005. (Step into Reading Ser.: Vol. 3). 48p. (J). (gr. 1-3). pap. 3.99 (978-0-375-83048-8(0) , Random Hse. Bks. for Young Readers) Random Hse. Children's Bks.

Murphy, Frank. Babe Ruth Saves Baseball Book & CD. Walz, Richard, illus. 2008. (Book & CD Ser.). 48p. (J). (gr. 1-3). 9.99 (***978-0-375-84184-2(9)*** , Random Hse. Bks. for Young Readers) Random Hse. Children's Bks.

Murray, Jim, intro. Life in the Minor Leagues. 1999. (Baseball Legends Ser.). (Illus.). 64p. (YA). (gr. 3-7). 18.65 (978-0-7910-5160-3(9) , Chelsea Hse.) Facts On File, Inc.

Nichols, John. Arizona Diamondbacks. 2002. (Baseball Ser.). (Illus.). 32p. (J). pap. (978-1-58341-199-5(2) , Creative Education); pap. 5.95 (978-0-89812-333-3(X) , Creative Paperbacks) Creative Co., The.

—Florida Marlins. 2002. (Baseball Ser.). (Illus.). 32p. (J). (978-1-58341-209-1(3) , Creative Education); pap. 5.95 (978-0-89812-343-2(7) , Creative Paperbacks) Creative Co., The.

—The History of the Arizona Diamondbacks. 1999. (Baseball Ser.). (Illus.). 32p. (YA). (gr. 4-7). pap. 21.30 (978-0-88682-896-7(1) , Creative Education) Creative Co., The.

—Tampa Bay Devil Rays. 2002. (Baseball Ser.). (Illus.). 32p. (J). (978-1-58341-225-1(5) , Creative Education); pap. 5.95 (978-0-89812-359-3(3) , Creative Paperbacks) Creative Co., The.

Obojski, Robert. Baseball's Zaniest Moments. 1999. (gr. 3-6). lib. bdg. 15.25 (978-0-613-75471-2(9)) Tandem Library Bks.

Patrick Jean L. S. La niña que poncho a Babe Ruth (the Girl Who Struck Out Babe Ruth) Reeves, Jeni, illus. 2007. (Yo solo Historia (on My Own History) Ser.). (J). pap. 6.95 (***978-0-8225-7788-1(7)*** , Ediciones Lerner) Lerner Publishing Group.

Patrick, Jean L. S. La Niña Que Poncho a Babe Ruth (The Girl Who Struck Out Babe Ruth) Reeves, Jeni, illus. 2007. (Yo Solo - Historia (on My Own - History) Ser.). (SPA.). 48p. (J). (gr. 2-4). 25.26 (***978-0-8225-7785-0(2)*** , Ediciones Lerner) Lerner Publishing Group.

Pellowski, Michael. The Chicago Black Sox Baseball Scandal. 2003. (Headline Court Cases Ser.). (Illus.). 128p. (J). (gr. 6-12). lib. bdg. 26.60 (978-0-7660-2044-3(4)) Enslow Pubs., Inc.

Pietrusza, David. The Baltimore Orioles Baseball Team. 2000. (Great Sports Teams Ser.). (Illus.). 48p. (YA). (gr. 4-10). lib. bdg. 23.93 (978-0-7660-1283-7(2)) Enslow Pubs., Inc.

—The Cleveland Indians Baseball Team. 2001. (Great Sports Teams Ser.). (Illus.). 48p. (YA). (gr. 4-10). lib. bdg. 23.93 (978-0-7660-1491-6(6)) Enslow Pubs., Inc.

—The Los Angeles Dodgers Baseball Team. 1999. (Great Sports Teams Ser.). (Illus.). 48p. (YA). (gr. 4-10). lib. bdg. 23.93 (978-0-7660-1097-0(X)) Enslow Pubs., Inc.

—The New York Yankees Baseball Team. 1998. (Great Sports Teams Ser.). (Illus.). 48p. (YA). (gr. 4-10). lib. bdg. 23.93 (978-0-7660-1018-5(X)) Enslow Pubs., Inc.

—The San Francisco Giants Baseball Team. 2000. (Great Sports Teams Ser.). (Illus.). 48p. (YA). (gr. 4-10). lib. bdg. 23.93 (978-0-7660-1284-4(0)) Enslow Pubs., Inc.

—The St. Louis Cardinals Baseball Team. 2001. (Great Sports Teams Ser.). (Illus.). 48p. (YA). (gr. 4-10). lib. bdg. 23.93 (978-0-7660-1490-9(8)) Enslow Pubs., Inc.

Potts, Steve. Atlanta Braves. 2001. (Championship Teams Ser.). (Illus.). (J). (978-1-58340-089-0(3)) Smart Apple Media.

—New York Yankees. 2001. (Championship Teams Ser.). (Illus.). (J). (978-1-58340-085-2(0)) Smart Apple Media.

Rambeck, Richard. The History of the Anaheim Angels. 1998. (Baseball, the Great American Game Ser.). (Illus.). 32p. (YA). (gr. 3-12). lib. bdg. 21.30 (978-0-88682-901-8(1) , Creative Education) Creative Co., The.

—The History of the Kansas City Royals. 1998. (Baseball, the Great American Game Ser.). (Illus.). 32p. (YA). (gr. 3-12). pap. 21.30 (978-0-88682-911-7(9) , Creative Education) Creative Co., The.

—The History of the Milwaukee Brewers. 1998. (Baseball, the Great American Game Ser.). (Illus.). 32p. (YA). (gr. 3-12). pap. 21.30 (978-0-88682-913-1(5) , Creative Education) Creative Co., The.

—The History of the Minnesota Twins. 1998. (Baseball, the Great American Game Ser.). (Illus.). 32p. (J). (gr. 3-12). pap. 21.30 (978-0-88682-914-8(3) , Creative Education) Creative Co., The.

—The History of the New York Yankees. 1998. (Baseball, the Great American Game Ser.). (Illus.). 32p. (YA). (gr. 3-12). pap. 21.30 (978-0-88682-918-6(6) , Creative Education) Creative Co., The.

—The History of the Oakland Athletics. 1998. (Baseball, the Great American Game Ser.). (Illus.). 32p. (YA). (gr. 3-12). pap. 21.30 (978-0-88682-919-3(4) , Creative Education) Creative Co., The.

—The History of the Texas Rangers. 1998. (Baseball, the Great American Game Ser.). (Illus.). 32p. (YA). (gr. 3-12). pap. 21.30 (978-0-88682-927-8(5) , Creative Education) Creative Co., The.

—The History of the Toronto Blue Jays. 1998. (Baseball, the Great American Game Ser.). (Illus.). 32p. (YA). (gr. 3-12). pap. 21.30 (978-0-88682-928-5(3) , Creative Education) Creative Co., The.

Ritter, Lawrence S. Leagues Apart: The Men & Times of the Negro Baseball Leagues. Merkin, Richard, illus. 2004. 35p. (J). (gr. k-4). reprint ed. pap. 12.00 (978-0-7567-7714-2(3)) DIANE Publishing Co.

—Leagues Apart: The Men & Times of the Negro Baseball Leagues. Merkin, Richard, illus. 1999. (J). (ps-ps). lib. bdg. 16.45 (978-0-613-18183-9(2)) Tandem Library Bks.

—The Story of Baseball. 1999. (Illus.). (J). (978-0-606-21763-7(0)) Tandem Library Bks.

Ruzich, Christian. World Series Stars & Stats. McClusky, Mark, ed. 1999. 32p. (Orig.). (J). pap. 3.99 (978-1-886749-66-5(3)) Sports Illustrated For Kids.

Shaughnessy, Dan. The Legend of the Curse of the Bambino. Payne, C. F., illus. 2005. 32p. (J). 16.95 (978-0-689-87235-8(6) , Simon & Schuster Children's Publishing) Simon & Schuster Children's Publishing.

Stewart, Mark. Minnesota Twins. 2006. (Team Spirit Ser.). (Illus.). 48p. (J). lib. bdg. (978-1-59953-058-1(9)) Norwood Hse. Pr.

Stewart, Mark & Kennedy, Mike. Latino Baseball's Finest Fielders/Las Mas Destacados Guantes del Beisbol Latino. Kalmanovitz, Manuel, tr. 2003. (En Fuego Ser.). (ENG & SPA., Illus.). 48p. (J). (gr. 5 up). pap. 9.95 (978-0-7613-1749-4(X) , Twenty-First Century Bks.) Lerner Publishing Group.

Stewart, Mark Alan. Baseball: A History of the National Pastime. 1998. (History of Sports Ser.). (Illus.). 160p. (YA). (gr. 5-8). 34.50 (978-0-531-11455-1(4) , Watts, Franklin) Scholastic Library Publishing.

Stewart, Wayne. Anaheim Angels. 2002. (Baseball Ser.). (Illus.). 32p. (J). pap. (978-1-58341-198-8(4) , Creative Education); pap. 5.95 (978-0-89812-332-6(1) , Creative Paperbacks) Creative Co., The.

—Los Angeles Dodgers. 2002. 32p. (J). pap. 5.95 (978-0-89812-346-3(1) , Creative Paperbacks); (Illus.). (978-1-58341-212-1(3) , Creative Education) Creative Co., The.

—Chicago White Sox. 2002. 32p. (J). pap. 5.95 (978-0-89812-338-8(0) , Creative Paperbacks); (Illus.). (978-1-58341-204-6(2) , Creative Education) Creative Co., The.

—Cincinnati Reds. 2002. (Baseball Ser.). (Illus.). 32p. (J). (978-1-58341-205-3(0) , Creative Education); pap. 5.95 (978-0-89812-339-5(9) , Creative Paperbacks) Creative Co., The.

—Cleveland Indians. 2002. (Baseball Ser.). (Illus.). 32p. (J). (978-1-58341-206-0(9) , Creative Education); pap. 5.95 (978-0-89812-340-1(2) , Creative Paperbacks) Creative Co., The.

—Colorado Rockies. 2002. 32p. (J). pap. 5.95 (978-0-89812-341-8(0) , Creative Paperbacks); (Illus.). (978-1-58341-207-7(7) , Creative Education) Creative Co., The.

—Detroit Tigers. 2002. 32p. (J). pap. 5.95 (978-0-89812-342-5(9) , Creative Paperbacks); (Illus.). (978-1-58341-208-4(5)) Creative Co., The.

—Kansas City Royals. 2002. (Baseball Ser.). (Illus.). 32p. (J). (978-1-58341-211-4(5) , Creative Education); pap. 5.95 (978-0-89812-345-6(3) , Creative Paperbacks) Creative Co., The.

—Pittsburgh Pirates. 2002. 32p. (J). pap. 5.95 (978-0-89812-354-8(2) , Creative Paperbacks); (Illus.). (978-1-58341-220-6(4) , Creative Education) Creative Co., The.

The Story of Baseball, 6 Pack. (On Deck Ser.). 24p. (gr. 4-5). 35.00 (978-0-7578-1012-1(8)) Rigby Education.

Suen, Anastasia. La Historia del Beisbol. Spanish Educational Publishers Staff, tr. 2004. (Historia de los Deportes Ser.). (SPA.). 24p. (J). (gr. 3-6). lib. bdg. 17.25 (978-0-8239-6873-2(1) , Buenas Letra) Rosen Publishing Group, Inc., The.

—The Story of Baseball. 2002. (Reading Power Ser.). (Illus.). 24p. (J). (gr. 2). lib. bdg. 17.25 (978-0-8239-6000-2(5) , PowerKids Pr.) Rosen Publishing Group, Inc., The.

Sullivan, George. Baseball's Boneheads, Bad Boys & Just Plain Crazy. 2003. (Single Titles Ser.). (Illus.). 64p. (gr. 5-8). lib. bdg. 23.90 (978-0-7613-2321-1(X) , Millbrook Pr.) Lerner Publishing Group.

—Baseball's Boneheads, Bad Boys, & Just Plain Crazy Guys. Green, Anne Canevari, illus. 2003. 64p. (J). (gr. 5-8). pap. 8.95 (978-0-7613-1928-3(X) , Millbrook Pr.) Lerner Publishing Group.

Ward, Geoffrey C., et al. Who Invented the Game? Baseball: the American Epic. 2004. (Illus.). 80p. (J). (gr. 6-10). reprint ed. 15.00 (978-0-7567-7571-1(X)) DIANE Publishing Co.

Weatherford, Carole Boston. A Negro League Scrapbook. 2004. (Illus.). 48p. (YA). 19.95 (978-1-59078-091-6(4)) Boyds Mills Pr.

Windwalker, Stephen. The 100 Greatest Baseball Games of All Time: Box Scores & Game Stories of Baseball's Unforgettable Moments. 2003. 160p. per. 21.95 (978-0-9715778-1-7(1) , Harvard Perspectives in American Sports) Harvard Perspectives Pr.

Winter, Jonah. Fair Ball! 14 Great Stars from Baseball's Negro Leagues. 2002. (J). pap. 5.99 (978-0-590-39465-9(7) , Levine, Arthur A. Bks.); 32p. (gr. 2-5). pap. 5.99 (978-0-439-37604-4(1)) Scholastic, Inc.

—Fair Ball! 14 Great Stars from Baseball's Negro Leagues. Winter, Jonah, illus. 1999. (Illus.). 32p. (J). (gr. 2-5). pap. 15.95 (978-0-590-39464-2(9)) Scholastic, Inc.

Wong, Stephen. Baseball Treasures. Einstein, Susan, illus. 2007. 64p. (J). (gr. 1-6). 16.99 (***978-0-06-114464-6(9)***) HarperCollins Pubs.

—Baseball Treasures. 2007. (Illus.). 58p. (J). (gr. 1-6). lib. bdg. 17.89 (***978-0-06-114473-8(8)***) HarperCollins Pubs.

Wukovits, John F. Life in the Negro Baseball. 2004. (Way People Live Ser.). (Illus.). 112p. (J). 29.95 (978-1-59018-273-4(1) , Lucent Bks.) Thomson Gale.

BASEBALL—POETRY

Lewis, J. Patrick. Tulip at Bat. Hirao, Amiko, illus. 2007. 32p. (J). (gr. k-3). 16.99 (978-0-316-61280-7(4)) Little Brown & Co.

Shane, Bill. Hey Batter Batter: A Collection of Baseball Poems for Kids. 2003. (Illus.). 88p. (J). (gr. k-9). pap. 7.95 (978-1-931643-20-7(2)) Seven Locks Pr.

—Hey Batter Batter: A Collection of Baseball Poems for Kids. 2003. (gr. 3-6). lib. bdg. 16.40 (978-0-613-89868-3(0)) Tandem Library Bks.

Thayer, Ernest Lawrence. Casey at the Bat: A Ballad of the Republic Sung in the Year 1888. Payne, C. F., illus. 2003. 40p. (J). 16.95 (978-0-689-85494-1(3)) Simon & Schuster Children's Publishing.

Thayer, Ernest Lawrence & Bing, Christopher H. Casey at the Bat: A Ballad of the Republic Sung in the Year 1888. 2000. (Illus.). 32p. (J). (gr. 3-7). 17.95 (978-1-929766-00-0(9)) Handprint Bks.

BASEBALL CLUBS

see Baseball Teams

BASEBALL TEAMS

Buckley Jr., James. American League East. 2007. (Behind the Plate Ser.). 48p. (J). (gr. 1-5). 28.50 (***978-1-59296-838-1(4)***) Child's World, Inc.

Christopher, Matt. On the Field with... Alex Rodriguez. 2002. (gr. 3-6). lib. bdg. 12.95 (978-0-613-70948-4(9)) Tandem Library Bks.

—On the Field with... Derek Jeter. 2000. (gr. 3-6). lib. bdg. 13.00 (978-0-613-30646-1(5)) Tandem Library Bks.

Clendening, John. American League West. 2007. (Behind the Plate Ser.). 48p. (J). (gr. 1-5). 28.50 (***978-1-59296-839-8(2)***) Child's World, Inc.

Fischer, David. American League Central. 2007. (Behind the Plate Ser.). 48p. (J). (gr. 1-5). 28.50 (***978-1-59296-837-4(6)*** Child's World, Inc.

Fried, Mark. Great Teams in Baseball. 2005. (Great Teams Ser.). (Illus.). 48p. (J). 29.29 (978-1-4109-1484-2(4)); pap. 8.50 (978-1-4109-1491-0(7)) Raintree.

Frisch, Aaron. Minnesota Twins. 2002. 32p. (J). pap. 5.95 (978-0-89812-348-7(8) , Creative Paperbacks); (Illus.). (978-1-58341-214-5(X) , Creative Education) Creative Co., The.

Gigliotti, Jim. National League West. 2007. (Behind the Plate Ser.). 48p. (J). (gr. 1-5). 28.50 (***978-1-59296-842-8(2)*** Child's World, Inc.

Gilbert, Sara. The Story of the Arizona Diamondbacks. 2007. (J). (***978-1-58341-478-1(9)*** , Creative Education) Creative Co., The.

—The Story of the Kansas City Royals. 2007. (J). (***978-1-58341-490-3(8)*** , Creative Education) Creative Co., The.

—The Story of the Los Angeles Angels of Anaheim. 2007. (J). (***978-1-58341-477-4(0)*** , Creative Education) Creative Co., The.

Goodman, Michael E. The History of the Montreal Expos. 1998. (Baseball, the Great American Game Ser.). (Illus.). 32p. (YA). (gr. 3-12). pap. 21.30 (978-0-88682-915-5(1) , Creative Education) Creative Co., The.

—The History of the Seattle Mariners. 1998. (Baseball, the Great American Game Ser.). (Illus.). 32p. (YA). (gr. 3-12). pap. 21.30 (978-0-88682-925-4(9) , Creative Education) Creative Co., The.

—Houston Astros. 2002. (Baseball Ser.). (Illus.). 32p. (J). (978-1-58341-210-7(7) , Creative Education); pap. 5.95 (978-0-89812-344-9(5) , Creative Paperbacks) Creative Co., The.

—Montreal Expos. 2002. (Baseball Ser.). (Illus.). 32p. (J). (978-1-58341-215-2(8) , Creative Education); pap. 5.95 (978-0-89812-349-4(6) , Creative Paperbacks) Creative Co., The.

—Seattle Mariners. 2002. 32p. (J). pap. 5.95 (978-0-89812-358-6(5) , Creative Paperbacks); (Illus.). (978-1-58341-224-4(7) , Creative Education) Creative Co., The.

Hawkes, Brian. The Story of the Washington Nationals. 2007. (J). (***978-1-58341-553-5(X)*** , Creative Education) Creative Co., The.

LeBoutillier, Nate. The Story of the Minnesota Twins. 2007. (J). (978-1-58341-493-4(2) , Creative Education) Creative Co., The.

Morelli, Jack. Heroes of the Negro Leagues. 2007. 128p. 19.95 (***978-0-8109-9434-8(8))*** Abrams, Harry N. , Inc.

Nichols, John. The History of the Colorado Rockies. rev. ed. 1998. (Baseball, the Great American Game Ser.). (Illus.). 32p. (J). (gr. 3-12). pap. 21.30 (978-0-88682-907-0(0) , Creative Education) Creative Co., The.

—The History of the Tampa Bay Devil Rays. 1999. (Baseball Ser.). (Illus.). 32p. (YA). (gr. 4-7). pap. 21.30 (978-0-88682-926-1(7) , Creative Education) Creative Co., The.

Omoth, Tyler. The Story of the Colorado Rockies. 2007. (J). (***978-1-58341-486-6(X)*** , Creative Education) Creative Co., The.

Peterson, Sheryl. The Story of the Florida Marlins. 2007. (J). (***978-1-58341-480-0(6)*** , Creative Education) Creative Co., The.

—The Story of the Seattle Mariners. 2007. (J). (***978-1-58341-500-9(9)*** , Creative Education) Creative Co., The.

Rambeck, Richard. The History of the Kansas City Royals. 1998. (Baseball, the Great American Game Ser.). (Illus.). 32p. (YA). (gr. 3-12). pap. 21.30 (978-0-88682-911-7(9) , Creative Education) Creative Co., The.

—The History of the Minnesota Twins. 1998. (Baseball, the Great American Game Ser.). (Illus.). 32p. (J). (gr. 3-12). pap. 21.30 (978-0-88682-914-8(3) , Creative Education) Creative Co., The.

—The History of the Texas Rangers. 1998. (Baseball, the Great American Game Ser.). (Illus.). 32p. (YA). (gr. 3-12). pap. 21.30 (978-0-88682-927-8(5) , Creative Education) Creative Co., The.

—The History of the Toronto Blue Jays. 1998. (Baseball, the Great American Game Ser.). (Illus.). 32p. (YA). (gr. 3-12). pap. 21.30 (978-0-88682-928-5(3) , Creative Education) Creative Co., The.

Richardson, Adele. The Story of the Texas Rangers. 2007. (J). (***978-1-58341-502-3(5)*** , Creative Education) Creative Co., The.

Ross, Dalton. The Top Teams Ever: Football, Baseball, Basketball & Hockey Winners. 2005. (Sports Illustrated for Kids Bks.). (Illus.). 176p. (YA). (gr. 7-12). lib. bdg. 27.95 (978-0-8239-3693-9(7)) Rosen Publishing Group, Inc., The.

Shofner, Shawndra. The Story of the Tampa Bay Devil Rays. 2007. (J). (***978-1-58341-501-6(7)*** , Creative Education) Creative Co., The.

—The Story of the Toronto Blue Jays. 2007. (J). (***978-1-58341-503-0(3)*** , Creative Education) Creative Co., The.

Silbaugh, John. National League Central. 2007. (Behind the Plate Ser.). 48p. (J). (gr. 1-5). 28.50 (***978-1-59296-840-4(6))*** Child's World, Inc.

Stewart, Mark. The Houston Astros. 2007. (Team Spirit Ser.). (Illus.). 48p. (J). lib. bdg. 25.27 (***978-1-59953-094-9(5))*** Norwood Hse. Pr.

—Minnesota Twins. 2008. 48p. pap. 9.95 (***978-1-60357-009-1(8))*** Norwood Hse. Pr.

—The Seattle Mariners. 2007. (Team Spirit Ser.). (Illus.). 48p. (J). lib. bdg. 25.27 (***978-1-59953-097-0(X))*** Norwood Hse. Pr.

Teitelbaum, Michael. National League East. 2007. (Behind the Plate Ser.). 48p. (J). (gr. 1-5). 28.50 (***978-1-59296-841-1(4))*** Child's World, Inc.

Thornley, Stew. Minnesota Twins: The First 40 Years. 2001. (Illus.). (J). (978-0-8225-3699-4(4)) Lerner Publishing Group.

BASHFULNESS

Braithwaite, Althea. Feeling Shy. Jude, Conny, illus. Best, Charlie, photos by. 1998. (Exploring Emotions Ser.). 32p. (J). (gr. 3 up). lib. bdg. 23.33 (978-0-8368-2119-2(X)) Stevens, Gareth Inc.

Bryant-Mole, Karen. I Feel Shy. 1999. (gr. k-3). lib. bdg. 14.45 (978-0-613-30497-9(7)) Tandem Library Bks.

Carducci, Bernardo J. & Fields, Teesue H. Shyness Workbook for Teens. 2006. xii, 143p. (YA). pap. 16.95 (978-0-87822-583-5(8) , 5286) Research Pr.

Clement, Claude & Daly, Melissa. Don't Be Shy: How to Fit in, Make Friends, & Have Fun-Even If You Weren't Born Outgoing. Quennehen, Christian, illus. 2005. (Sunscreen Ser.). 112p. (J). (gr. 5-9). pap. 9.95 (978-0-8109-5860-9(0)) Abrams, Harry N. , Inc.

Johnston, Marianne. Let's Talk about Being Shy. 1998. (PowerKids Ser.). 24p. (J). (gr. k-3). reprint ed. pap. 6.95 (978-1-56838-222-7(7)) Hazelden Publishing & Educational Services.

Medina, Sarah. Shy. Brooker, Jo, illus. 2007. (J). (***978-1-4034-9795-6(8)***); pap. (***978-1-4034-9802-1(4))*** Heinemann Library.

Moore-Mallinos, Jennifer & Roca, Nuria. Eres Timido? Are You Shy?, Spanish Edition. Fabrega, Marta, illus. 2006. (Let's Talk about It Bks.). (SPA.). 32p. (J). pap. 6.99 (978-0-7641-3509-5(0)) Barron's Educational Series, Inc.

Roca, Nuria. Are You Shy? Fabrega, Marta, illus. 2006. (Let's Talk about It Bks.). 32p. (J). (ps-2). pap. 6.99 (978-0-7641-3508-8(2)) Barron's Educational Series, Inc.

BASHFULNESS—FICTION

Asquith, Ros. Boo. 2004. (Illus.). 32p. (J). pap. 11.00 (978-0-00-711267-8(X)) HarperCollins Pubs. Ltd. GBR. *Dist:* Independent Pubs. Group.

Best, Cari. Shrinking Violet. Potter, Giselle, illus. 2002. (J). 25.45 (978-0-7587-9811-4(3)) Book Wholesalers, Inc.

—Shrinking Violet. Potter, Giselle, illus. 2000. (J). (978-0-7894-6531-3(0)) Dorling Kindersley Publishing, Inc.

—Shrinking Violet. Potter, Giselle, illus. 2001. 40p. (J). (gr. 9-13). 16.50 (978-0-374-36882-1(1) , Farrar, Straus & Giroux (BYR)) Farrar, Straus & Giroux.

Cain, Barbara S. I Don't Know Why... I Guess I'm Shy. Smith-Moore, J. J., illus. 1999. 32p. (J). (ps-3). (978-1-55798-596-5(0) , 441-5960, Magination Pr.) American Psychological Assn.

Cooper, Ilene. Lucy on the Loose. Harvey, Amanda, illus. 2000. (Road to Reading Ser.). 80p. (J). (gr. 2-5). 11.99 (978-0-307-46508-5(X)); pap. 3.99 (978-0-307-26508-1(0)) Random Hse. Children's Bks. (Golden Bks.).

—Lucy on the Loose. 2000. (J). (978-0-606-18929-3(7)) Tandem Library Bks.

Gibbs, Lynne. Quiet as a Mouse. Mitchell, Melanie, illus. 2003. (Growing Pains Ser.). 32p. (J). pap. 4.95 (978-1-57768-928-7(3)); 12.95 (978-1-57768-481-7(8)) School Specialty Publishing. (Gingham Dog Pr.).

Inserra, Rose. Wedding Day Disaster. Hill, Trish, illus. 1999. (Supa Doopers Ser.). 64p. (J). (978-0-7608-3288-2(9)) Sundance/Newbridge Educational Publishing.

Jackson, J. S. Shyness Isn't a Minus: How to Turn Bashfulness into a Plus! Alley, R. W., illus. 2006. (J). per. 7.95 (***978-0-87029-403-7(2))*** Abbey Pr.

Johnson, Jane. Tiger. 2003. (Illus.). 32p. (J). pap. 7.95 (978-1-84270-244-4(0)) Andersen GBR. *Dist:* Independent Pubs. Group.

Lacombe, Benjamin. Cherry & Olive. 2007. (J). (***978-0-8027-9708-7(3))*** Walker & Co.

—Cherry & Olive. Lacombe, Benjamin, illus. 2007. (Illus.). 32p. (J). (ps-2). 16.95 (***978-0-8027-9707-0(5))*** Walker & Co.

Lipp, Frederick J. Bread Song. Gaillard, Jason, tr. Gaillard, Jason, illus. 2004. (J). 15.95 (978-1-59336-000-9(2)); pap. (978-1-59336-001-6(0)) Mondo Publishing.

Little, Jean. Emma's Magic Winter. Plecas, Jennifer, illus. (I Can Read Bks.). 64p. (J). (ps-3). 2000. pap. 3.99 (978-0-06-443706-6(X) , Harper Trophy); 1998. 15.95 (978-0-06-025389-9(4)); 1998. 15.89 (978-0-06-025390-5(8)) HarperCollins Pubs.

—Emma's Magic Winter. 2000. (gr. k-3). lib. bdg. 11.80 (978-0-613-27805-8(4)) Tandem Library Bks.

Longo, Sharon. My Friend Daniel Doesn't Talk: A Story for Children with Social Anxiety & the Friends Who Care about Them. (Illus.). 28p. pap. (978-0-86388-562-4(4) , 002-5288) Speechmark Publishing Ltd.

Lucas, David. Halibut Jackson. 2005. (Illus.). 32p. pap. (978-1-84270-371-7(4)) Andersen.

—Halibut Jackson. 2004. (Illus.). 32p. (J). (ps-3). 16.95 (978-0-375-82690-0(4) , Knopf Bks. for Young Readers) Random Hse. Children's Bks.

Mack, David. The Shy Creatures. 2007. (Illus.). 48p. (J). (gr. k-2). 16.95 (***978-0-312-36794-7(5))*** Feiwel & Friends.

Poydar, Nancy. Brave Santa. 2004. (Illus.). 32p. (J). (gr. k-3). tchr. ed. 16.95 (978-0-8234-1821-3(9)) Holiday Hse., Inc.

Puttock, Simon. Here I Am! Said Smedley. 2002. (gr. k-3). lib. bdg. 12.95 (978-0-613-52852-8(2)) Tandem Library Bks.

Roberts, Diane. Puppet Pandemonium. 128p. (J). (gr. 3-7). 2007. 5.99 (***978-0-440-42096-5(2)*** , Yearling); 2006. 15.95 (978-0-385-73309-0(7) , Delacorte Bks. for Young Readers); 2006. lib. bdg. 17.99 (978-0-385-90328-8(6) , Delacorte Bks. for Young Readers) Random Hse. Children's Bks.

Schreiber, Ellen. Comedy Girl. 2004. (Illus.). 288p. (J). (gr. 7 up). 15.99 (978-0-06-009338-9(2) , Tegen, Katherine Bks) HarperCollins Pubs.

Sempé, Jean-Jacques. Martin Pebble. Bell, Anthea, tr. from FRE. rev. ed. 2006. (Illus.). 120p. 19.95 (978-0-7148-4714-6(3)) Phaidon Pr., Inc.

Shrinking Violet. 2004. 29.95 incl. cd-rom (978-1-55592-497-3(2)) Weston Woods Studios, Inc.

Skinner, Daphne. Almost Invisible Irene. Smath, Jerry, illus. 2003. (Science Solves It! Ser.). 32p. (J). 4.99 (978-1-57565-129-3(7)) Kane Pr., The.

—Almost Invisible Irene. 2003. (gr. k-3). lib. bdg. 13.00 (978-0-613-79277-6(7)) Tandem Library Bks.

Wells, Rosemary. Shy Charles. 2001. (Illus.). 32p. (J). (ps-3). reprint ed. pap. 5.99 (978-0-14-056843-1(3) , Puffin) Penguin Group (USA) Inc.

—Shy Charles. 2001. (ps-2). lib. bdg. 14.15 (978-0-613-36076-0(1)) Tandem Library Bks.

Williams, Tara. Benji Martin Is Bashful. Lenoir, Jane, illus. 2001. 36p. (J). (gr. 1-6). lib. bdg. 14.95 (978-0-9705727-1-4(9)) Coastal Publishing Carolina, Inc.

Wilson, Karma. Bear's New Friend. Chapman, Jane, illus. 2006. 40p. (J). (ps-2). 16.95 (978-0-689-85984-7(8) , McElderry, Margaret K.) Simon & Schuster Children's Publishing.

BASKET MAKING

Cherrington, Janelle. Native American Baskets. 2003. (Compass Point Phonics Readers Ser.). (Illus.). 16p. (J). (gr. 1 up). 13.26 (978-0-7565-0514-1(3)) Compass Point Bks.

Doney, Meryl. Baskets. 1998. (World Crafts Ser.). (Illus.). 32p. (J). (gr. 3-5). pap. 6.95 (978-0-531-15328-4(2) , Watts, Franklin) Scholastic Library Publishing.

BASKETBALL

Aaseng, Nathan. Sports Great David Robinson. rev. ed. 1998. (Sports Great Bks.). (Illus.). 64p. (YA). (gr. 4-10). lib. bdg. 22.60 (978-0-7660-1077-2(5)) Enslow Pubs., Inc.

Adams, Sean. Tim Duncan. 2004. (Sports Heroes & Legends Ser.). (Illus.). 112p. (J). (gr. 6-12). lib. bdg. 27.93 (978-0-8225-1793-1(0)) Lerner Publishing Group.

Adelson, Bruce. Slam Dunk Trivia. Pulver, Harry, illus. 1998. (Sports Trivia Ser.). 64p. (J). (gr. 5-9). pap. (978-0-8225-9804-6(3)); lib. bdg. (978-0-8225-3313-9(8)) Lerner Publishing Group. (Lerner Pubns.).

Aryal, Aimee. Hello Testudo! Goh, Tai Hwa, illus. 2003. (J). 18.95 (978-0-9743442-1-8(4)) Mascot Bks., Inc.

Baloncesto: Individual Title Six-Packs. (On Deck en Espanol Ser.).Tr. of Basketball. (SPA.). 24p. (gr. 4-5). 35.00 (978-0-7578-6387-5(6)) Rigby Education.

Basketball: Individual Title Six-Packs. (On Deck Ser.). 24p. (gr. 4-5). 35.00 (978-0-7578-1004-6(7)) Rigby Education.

Basketball: The Mental Truth. 2000. (Illus.). (YA). spiral bd. (978-0-9744047-0-7(5)) Mental Truth Inc.

Bennett, Frank. The Illustrated Rules of Basketball. Zuehlke, Paul, illus. 2001. 32p. (J). (ps-3). pap. 5.95 (978-0-8249-5418-5(1) , Ideals Children's Bks.) Ideals Pubns.

Bernards, Neal. All Out: The Kentucky Wildcats Story. 1999. (College Sports Today Ser.). (Illus.). 32p. (J). (gr. 4-7). pap. 21.30 (978-0-88682-992-6(5) , Creative Education) Creative Co., The.

Berry, Skip. Kid's Book of Basketball. 2002. (Illus.). 192p. pap. 10.95 (978-0-8065-2238-8(0) , Citadel Pr.) Kensington Publishing Corp.

Bird, Sue & Brown, Greg. Sue Bird: Be Yourself. 2004. (Illus.). 48p. (J). 15.95 (978-0-9634650-5-4(8)) Positively for Kids, Inc.

Blake, Jennifer. Raising the Roof: WNBA Action on the Court & Behind the Scenes. 2002. (Read 180 Ser.). (Illus.). 40p. (J). pap. (978-0-439-12338-9(0)) Scholastic, Inc.

Blatt, Howard. The NBA's 10 Greatest Teams Ever: Fast Breaks. 1999. (J). (978-0-606-16617-1(3)) Tandem Library Bks.

Bradley, Michael. Yao Ming. 2003. (Illus.). 48p. (J). 27.07 (978-0-7614-1758-3(3) , Benchmark Bks.) Cavendish, Marshall Corp.

Bratton, Deboral B. & Bratton, Ashley D. Record-a-Sport Basketball Sport Organizer. Bratton, Deboral B. & Bratton, Ashley D., eds. 2003. (Illus.). (gr. 1 up). 18.95 (978-1-931746-02-1(8)) Sport Your Stuff Corp.

Brenner, Richard J. Superstars Album 1999: Basketball. 1998. (Illus.). 48p. (J). (gr. 4-7). pap. 4.50 (978-0-688-16230-6(4)) HarperCollins Pubs.

Brill, Marlene Targ. Basketball. 2001. (Winning Women in Sports Ser.). (Illus.). 104p. (YA). (gr. 4 up). lib. bdg. 14.95 (978-1-56674-307-5(9)) Forest Hse. Publishing Co., Inc.

Brown, James E. Maximum Performance Basketball: In-Season Workout Book for Players 7th Grade ¿ 12th Grade. 2006. 60p. per. 10.00 (***978-1-59824-368-0(3))*** E-BookTime LLC.

Brown, Jonatha A. Basketball. 2004. (J). pap. (978-0-8368-4345-3(2)); lib. bdg. 19.33 (978-0-8368-4338-5(X)) Stevens, Gareth Inc.

Buckley, James. NBA All Time Super Scorers. 2001. (gr. 3-6). lib. bdg. 11.80 (978-0-613-43854-4(X)) Tandem Library Bks.

Butler, Robbie. The Harlem Globetrotters: Clown Princes of Basketball, 6 vols. (gr. 4 up). 49.95 (978-0-7368-9511-8(6) , High Five) Red Brick Learning.

—The Harlem Globetrotters: The Clown Princes of Basketball. 2001. (Illus.). 64p. (J). pap. (978-0-7368-9501-9(9)); (gr. 4-5). lib. bdg. 22.60 (978-0-7368-4001-9(X) , Capstone High-Interest Bks.) Capstone Pr., Inc.

Carrier, Roch. Le Joueur de Basket-ball. Cohen, Sheldon, illus. 2001. (FRE & SPA.). 24p. (J). (gr. 3). pap. 7.95 (978-0-88776-554-4(8) , Livres Toundra) Tundra Bks., Inc./Livres Toundra, Inc. CAN. *Dist:* Random Hse., Inc.

Coleman, Lori. Girls' Basketball: Making Your Mark on the Court. 2007. (Girls Got Game Ser.). (Illus.). 32p. (J). (gr. 3-6). lib. bdg. 25.26 (978-0-7368-6821-1(6)) Capstone Pr., Inc.

Compass Point Books, contrib. by. Basketball for Fun! (For Fun Ser.). 32p. (YA). pap. 8.95 (978-0-7565-1151-7(8)) Compass Point Bks.

Cooper, Floyd. Jump! From the Life of Michael Jordan. Cooper, Floyd, illus. 2004. (Illus.). 40p. (J). (gr. 1-5). 15.99 (978-0-399-24230-4(9) , Philomel) Penguin Group (USA) Inc.

Craats, Rennay. For the Love of Basketball. Craats, Rennay, illus. 2001. (For the Love of Sports Ser.). (Illus.). 24p. (J). (gr. 1-3). lib. bdg. 15.95 (978-1-930954-05-2(0)) Weigl Pubs., Inc.

Crossingham, John. Basketball in Action. 2000. (Sports in Action Ser.). (Illus.). (J). 12.75 (978-0-606-18050-4(8)) Tandem Library Bks.

Crossingham, John & Dann, Sarah. Basketball in Action. 1999. (Sports in Action Ser.). (Illus.). 32p. (J). (gr. 3-4). (978-0-7787-0162-0(X)); pap. (978-0-7787-0174-3(3)) Crabtree Publishing Co.

—Basketball in Action. 1999. (Illus.). 32p. (J). (ps-ps). lib. bdg. 14.10 (978-0-613-21174-1(X)) Tandem Library Bks.

—Basquetbol en Accion. 2005. (Deportes en Accion Ser.). (Illus.). 32p. (J). (SPA.). (gr. 6-9). pap. (978-0-7787-8618-4(8)); (FRE & SPA., (978-0-7787-8572-9(6)) Crabtree Publishing Co.

Daly, Chuck, intro. Antoine Walker. 1999. (Basketball Legends Ser.). (Illus.). 64p. (YA). (gr. 2-5). 12.95 (978-0-7910-5008-8(4) , Chelsea Hse.) Facts On File, Inc.

—Chris Webber. 1999. (Basketball Legends Ser.). (Illus.). 64p. (YA). (gr. 2-5). 12.95 (978-0-7910-5010-1(6) , Chelsea Hse.) Facts On File, Inc.

—Keith Van Horn. 1999. (Basketball Legends Ser.). (Illus.). 64p. (YA). (gr. 2-5). 12.95 (978-0-7910-5009-5(2) , Chelsea Hse.) Facts On File, Inc.

—Kevin Garnett. 1999. (Basketball Legends Ser.). (Illus.). 64p. (YA). (gr. 2-5). 12.95 (978-0-7910-5006-4(8) , Chelsea Hse.) Facts On File, Inc.

Dixon, Tamecka & Cohen, Judith. You Can Be a Woman Basketball Player. 1999. (Illus.). 40p. (J). (gr. 4-8). 14.95 incl. audio compact disk (978-1-880599-39-6(2)); pap. 7.00 (978-1-880599-38-9(4)) Cascade Pass, Inc.

Dixon, Tamecka & Cohen, Judith Love. You Can Be a Woman Basketball Player. 1999. (Illus.). (J). (gr. 4-8). 13.95 (978-1-880599-40-2(6)) Cascade Pass, Inc.

Dorling Kindersley Publishing Staff. Basketball. 2005. (Eyewitness Books). 72p. (J). 15.99 (978-0-7566-1063-0(X)); (Illus.). lib. bdg. 19.99 (978-0-7566-1064-7(8)) Dorling Kindersley Publishing, Inc.

—My Basketball. 2005. (Lift-the-Flap Bks.). (Illus.). 12p. (J). bds. 9.99 (978-0-7566-1222-1(5)) Dorling Kindersley Publishing, Inc.

—My Basketball Touch & Feel. 2006. (Touch & Feel (New York, N.Y.) Ser.). (Illus.). 12p. (J). bds. 9.99 (978-0-7566-1475-1(9)) Dorling Kindersley Publishing, Inc.

Dougherty, Terri. Kobe Bryant. 2000. (Jam Session Ser.). (Illus.). 32p. (J). (gr. 3-8). lib. bdg. 24.21 (978-1-57765-427-8(7) , ABDO & Daughters) ABDO Publishing Co.

Drewett, Jim. How to Improve at Basketball. 2007. 48p. (J). (gr. 3-9). pap. (***978-0-7787-3588-5(5))*** Crabtree Publishing Co.

Epstein, Brad M. LSU Tigers 123: My first counting Book. l.t. ed. 2006. (Illus.). 22p. (J). bds. 14.95 (***978-1-932530-49-0(5)*** , 123 Bk.) Michaelson Entertainment.

Eule, Brian. Basketball for Fun. 2003. (Sports for Fun Ser.). (Illus.). 48p. (J). (gr. 3 up). lib. bdg. 21.26 (978-0-7565-0429-8(5)) Compass Point Bks.

Fauchald, Nick. Jump Ball! You Can Play Basketball. Dickson, Bill, illus. 2004. (Game Day Ser.). 24p. (J). (gr. k-3). 22.60 (978-1-4048-0261-2(4) , 1229515) Picture Window Bks.

Fawaz, John. Megastars, 2008. 2008. (Nba Ser.). 32p. (J). pap. 5.99 (***978-0-545-00654-5(6)*** , Scholastic) Scholastic, Inc.

Franks, Katie. I Want to Be a Basketball Player. 2007. (Dream Jobs Ser.). (Illus.). 24p. (J). (gr. 3-5). lib. bdg. 21.25 (978-1-4042-3621-9(X)) Rosen Publishing Group, Inc., The.

Gettelman, Elizabeth. Competitive Basketball for Girls. 2005. (SportsGirl Ser.). (Illus.). 64p. (YA). (gr. 5-8). lib. bdg. 26.50 (978-0-8239-3402-7(0)) Rosen Publishing Group, Inc., The.

Gibbons, Gail. My Basketball Book. Gibbons, Gail, illus. 2000. (Illus.). 24p. (J). (ps-2). 5.99 (978-0-688-17140-7(0)) HarperCollins Pubs.

Giggons, Gail. My Basketball Book. 2000. (J). 5.89 (978-0-06-029224-9(5)) HarperCollins Pubs.

Gordon, Randy. NBA Ultimate Sticker Book. 2002. (NBA Ser.). 36p. (J). pap. 7.99 (978-0-439-44303-6(2)) Scholastic, Inc.

Griffin, Gwen. The Kansas Jayhawks Story. 1999. (College Sports Today Ser.). (Illus.). 32p. (J). (gr. 4-7). pap. 21.30 (978-0-88682-991-9(7) , Creative Education) Creative Co., The.

Guest, Jacqueline. Free Throw. 1999. (Sports Stories Ser.: Vol. 34). 128p. (gr. 3-8). 7.95 (978-1-55028-664-9(1)) Lorimer, James & Co., Ltd., Pubs. CAN. *Dist:* Casemate Pubs. & Bk. Distributors, LLC.

Haidle, Helen & Jacobson, Matt. Bobby Basketball. Haidle, David & Ochsner, Dennis, illus. 1998. (GoodSports Ser.). 16p. (J). (ps-3). bds. 6.99 (978-1-57673-361-5(0) , Multnomah) WaterBrook Pr.

Hareas, John. Ultimate Basketball. Dorling Kindersley Publishing Staff, ed. 2004. (Illus.). 160p. 30.00 (978-0-7894-9652-2(6)) Dorling Kindersley Publishing, Inc.

Hareas, John & Dorling Kindersley Publishing Staff. Basketball Top 10. 2004. (Illus.). 96p. (J). pap. 9.99 (978-0-7566-0321-2(8)) Dorling Kindersley Publishing, Inc.

Helmer, Diana Star. The History of Basketball. 2000. (Sports Throughout History Ser.). 24p. (J). (gr. k-4). lib. bdg. 18.75 (978-0-8239-5470-4(6) , PowerKids Pr.) Rosen Publishing Group, Inc., The.

Hirschberg, Dan. Tim Hardaway. 1999. (Basketball Legends Ser.). (Illus.). 64p. (YA). (gr. 2-5). lib. bdg. 18.65 (978-0-7910-5007-1(6) , Chelsea Hse.) Facts On File, Inc.

A
B

La Historia del Baloncesto: Individual Title Six-Packs. (On Deck en Espanol Ser.).Tr. of Story of Basketball. (SPA.). 24p. (gr. 4-5). 35.00 (978-0-7578-6393-6(0)) Rigby Education.

Hughes, Morgan. Basketball. 2005. (Junior Sports Ser.). (Illus.). 32p. (gr. 2-4). 19.95 (978-1-59515-189-6(3)) Rourke Publishing, LLC.

Ingram, Scott. A Basketball All-Star. (Making of a Champion Ser.). 48p. (J). 2005. pap. 8.50 (978-1-4034-5547-5(3)); 2004. lib. bdg. 29.93 (978-1-4034-5363-1(2)) Heinemann Library.

Kalman, Bobbie & Crossingham, John. Slam Dunk Basketball. 2007. (Illus.). 32p. (J). (gr. 1-5). ***(978-0-7787-3139-9(1))***; pap. ***(978-0-7787-3171-9(5))*** Crabtree Publishing Co.

Keith, Harold. Brief Garland: Ponytails, Basketball & Nothing but Net. 1999. (Illus.). 318p. 18.95 (978-1-57168-334-2(8)) Eakin Pr.

Kelley, Brent. Lisa Leslie. 2000. (Illus.). 64p. (J). (gr. 4-7). lib. bdg. 17.60 (978-0-613-32788-6(8)) Tandem Library Bks.

Kennedy, Mike. Basketball. 2002. (True Book Ser.). (Illus.). 48p. (J). (gr. 3-5). pap. 25.00 (978-0-516-22335-3(6), Children's Pr.) Scholastic Library Publishing.

—Basketball. 2002. (gr. 3-6). lib. bdg. 15.25 (978-0-613-59450-9(9)) Tandem Library Bks.

Kirkpatrick, Rob. Grant Hill, Estrella del Basketball. 2002. (Coleccion Power Kids). (SPA & ENG., Illus.). 24p. (J). lib. bdg. 17.25 (978-0-8239-6143-6(5), RN31312, Buenas Letra) Rosen Publishing Group, Inc., The.

Knapp, Ron. Top 10 Professional Basketball Coaches. 1998. (Sports Top 10 Ser.). (Illus.). 48p. (YA). (gr. 4-10). lib. bdg. 23.93 (978-0-7660-1008-6(2)) Enslow Pubs., Inc.

—Top 10 Stars of the NCAA Men's Basketball Tournament. 2001. (Sports Top 10 Ser.). (Illus.). 48p. (J). (gr. 4-10). lib. bdg. 23.93 (978-0-7660-1498-5(3)) Enslow Pubs., Inc.

Ladewski, Paul. Nba: Playbook with Marker: Playbook with Marker. 2008. 32p. pap. 5.99 ***(978-0-545-00666-8(X)***, Scholastic) Scholastic, Inc.

Ladewski, Paul. Super Guards. 2007. (NBA Reader Ser.). 32p. (J). pap. 3.99 (978-0-439-91239-6(3)) Scholastic, Inc.

Layden, Joe. Rising Stars: Profiles of the up & Coming Stars. 2000. (NBA Ser.: No. 1). (Illus.). 32p. (J). (gr. 2-5). pap. 5.99 (978-0-439-14069-0(2)) Scholastic, Inc.

Lindeen, Carol K. Let's Play Basketball! 2006. (Pebble Plus Ser.). (Illus.). 24p. (J). (978-0-7368-5362-0(6)) Capstone Pr., Inc.

Macnow, Glen. Sports Great Charles Barkley. rev. ed. 1998. (Sports Great Bks.). (Illus.). 64p. (YA). (gr. 4-10). lib. bdg. 17.95 (978-0-7660-1004-8(X)) Enslow Pubs., Inc.

Marcovitz, Hal. LeBron James. 2007. (J). ***(978-1-4222-0205-0(4))*** Mason Crest Pubs.

Martin, Clare. An Insider's Guide to the WNBA. 2002. (Wnba Sticker Book Ser.). 24p. (J). pap. 7.99 (978-0-439-38013-3(8)) Scholastic, Inc.

Milito, John. Basketball Puzzles. 2001. (Champion Sport Word Game Ser.). 120p. (J). pap. (978-1-894622-05-9(7)) Warwick Publishing.

Miller, Faye Young & Coffey, Wayne. Winning Basketball for Girls. 3rd ed. (Winning Sports for Girls Ser.). (Illus.). 176p. (YA). (gr. 9-12). pap. 16.95 (978-0-8160-4674-4(3), Checkmark Bks.); 2002. (J). (gr. 6-12). 35.00 (978-0-8160-4673-7(5)) Facts On File, Inc.

Moore, David. Dynamic Duos. 1998. (Fast Breaks Ser.: Vol. 3). (J). (gr. 2-4). pap. 3.50 (978-0-590-12079-1(4)) Scholastic, Inc.

Mullin, Chris. Jovenes Jugadores de Baloncesto. (SPA.). 46p. (YA). (gr. 2 up). 16.76 (978-84-272-4985-1(3)) Molino, Editorial ESP. *Dist:* Lectorum Pubns., Inc.

NBA Play Book. 2001. (gr. 3-6). lib. bdg. 16.45 (978-0-613-32874-6(4)) Tandem Library Bks.

Nba, Reader & Ladewski, Paul. Nba Reader: Fast Forwards: Fast Forwards. 2008. 32p. pap. 3.99 ***(978-0-545-00664-4(3)***, Scholastic) Scholastic, Inc.

Nichols, John. Tobacco Road: The North Carolina Tar Heels Story. 1999. (College Sports Today Ser.). (Illus.). 32p. (J). (gr. 4-7). pap. 21.30 (978-0-88682-994-0(1), Creative Education) Creative Co., The.

Otten, Jack. Baloncesto. 2004. (Entrenamiento Deportivo Ser.). (SPA & ENG., Illus.). 24p. (J). lib. bdg. 17.25 (978-0-8239-6849-7(9), Buenas Letra) Rosen Publishing Group, Inc., The.

—Basketball. 2002. (Reading Power Ser.). (Illus.). 24p. (J). (gr. 1). lib. bdg. 17.25 (978-0-8239-5974-7(0), PowerKids Pr.) Rosen Publishing Group, Inc., The.

Owens, Thomas S. Basketball Arenas. 2002. (Sports Palaces Ser.). (Illus.). 64p. (gr. 6-8). lib. bdg. 25.90 (978-0-7613-1766-1(X), Millbrook Pr.) Lerner Publishing Group.

Owens, Tom & Helmer, Diana Star. Basketball. 1999. (Game Plan Ser.). (Illus.). 64p. (YA). (gr. 5-8). lib. bdg. 25.40 (978-0-7613-3234-3(0), Twenty-First Century Bks.) Lerner Publishing Group.

—The Charlotte Sting: Teamwork. 1999. (Women's Professional Basketball Ser.). 24p. (J). lib. bdg. 18.75 (978-0-8239-5242-7(8), PowerKids Pr.) Rosen Publishing Group, Inc., The.

—The Cleveland Rockers: Teamwork. 1999. (Women's Professional Basketball Ser.). 24p. (J). lib. bdg. 18.75 (978-0-8239-5241-0(X), PowerKids Pr.) Rosen Publishing Group, Inc., The.

—The Los Angeles Sparks: Teamwork. 1999. (Women's Professional Basketball Ser.). 24p. (J). lib. bdg. 18.75 (978-0-8239-5240-3(1), PowerKids Pr.) Rosen Publishing Group, Inc., The.

—The New York Liberty: Teamwork. 1999. (Women's Professional Basketball Ser.). 24p. (J). lib. bdg. 18.75 (978-0-8239-5239-7(8), PowerKids Pr.) Rosen Publishing Group, Inc., The.

—Teamwork, the Phoenix Mercury in Action. 1999. (Women's Professional Basketball Ser.). 24p. (J). lib. bdg. 18.75 (978-0-8239-5243-4(6), PowerKids Pr.) Rosen Publishing Group, Inc., The.

Panamericana Staff. Reglamento de Baloncesto. (SPA.). 176p. (J). 7.50 (978-958-30-0013-3(2)) Panamericana Editorial COL. *Dist:* AIMS International Bks., Inc.

Parselle, Matt. Basketball. 2004. (Sports Club Ser.). (SPA., Illus.). 32p. (J). (gr. 3-6). pap. 5.95 (978-1-58728-002-3(7), Two Can Publishing) T&N Children's Publishing.

—Basketball. Pickering, Mel, illus. rev. ed. 2004. (Sports Club Ser.). (SPA.). 32p. (gr. 3-6). 9.95 (978-1-58728-000-9(0), Two Can Publishing) T&N Children's Publishing.

Picture Window Books, contrib. by. Jump Ball! (Game Day Ser.). 24p. (J). pap. 7.95 (978-1-4048-0512-5(5)) Picture Window Bks.

Preller, James. The NBA Book of Opposites. 2000. (NBA Ser.). (Illus.). 32p. (J). (ps-2). pap. 3.50 (978-0-439-14075-1(7)) Scholastic, Inc.

Raber, Thomas R. Michael Jordan: Returning Champion. 2002. (gr. 5-8). lib. bdg. 14.10 (978-0-613-46151-1(7)) Tandem Library Bks.

Ramen, Fred. Basketball: Rules, Tips, Strategy, & Safety. 2006. (Sports from Coast to Coast Ser.). (Illus.). 48p. (YA). (gr. 5-8). lib. bdg. 26.50 (978-1-4042-0992-3(1)) Rosen Publishing Group, Inc., The.

Rappoport, Ken. Sheryl Swoopes: Star Forward. 2002. (Sports Reports). (Illus.). 112p. (J). (gr. 4-10). lib. bdg. 26.60 (978-0-7660-1827-3(X)) Enslow Pubs., Inc.

Rekela, George R. Karl Malone: Star Forward. 1998. (Sports Reports). (Illus.). 104p. (YA). (gr. 4-10). lib. bdg. 26.60 (978-0-89490-931-3(2)) Enslow Pubs., Inc.

Richmond, Sandra. Shoot to Score. 1999. (Sports Stories Ser.). 92p. (gr. 3-8). (J). ***(978-1-55028-643-4(9))***; 7.95 (978-1-55028-642-7(0)) Lorimer, James & Co., Ltd., Pubs. CAN. *Dist:* Casemate Pubs. & Bk. Distributors, LLC.

Roberts, Robin. Basketball, the Right Way. 2000. (Get in the Game! with Robin Roberts Ser.). (Illus.). 48p. (gr. 4-8). lib. bdg. (978-0-7613-1409-7(1), Millbrook Pr.) Lerner Publishing Group.

Robertson, Oscar & O'Daniel, Michael. The Art of Basketball: A Guide to Self-Improvement in the Fundamentals of the Game. 1998. (Illus.). 96p. (YA). (gr. 5 up). pap. 12.95 (978-0-9662483-0-2(9)) Robertson, Oscar Media Ventures.

Rolte, John & Gramling, Scott. Grant Hill. Sielk, Margaret, ed. rev. ed. Date not set. (Sports Illustrated for Kids Bks.). 112p. (J). (gr. 4-6). pap. 3.99 (978-1-886749-59-7(0)) Sports Illustrated For Kids.

Ross, Dalton. The Top Teams Ever: Football, Baseball, Basketball & Hockey Winners. 2005. (Sports Illustrated for Kids Bks.). (Illus.). 176p. (YA). (gr. 7-12). lib. bdg. 27.95 (978-0-8239-3693-9(7)) Rosen Publishing Group, Inc., The.

Ross, Jesse. All-Star Sports Puzzles: Basketball: Games, Trivia, Puzzles & More! 2007. 64p. pap. 7.95 ***(978-1-55192-822-7(1))*** Raincoast Bk. Distribution CAN. *Dist:* Perseus Distribution.

Roussa, Nick. Basketball Legends of All Times, Vol. 2. 1999. (Sports Legends Ser.). (Illus.). 216p. lib. bdg. 24.95 (978-1-56674-283-2(8)) Forest Hse. Publishing Co., Inc.

Rutledge, Rachel. The Best of the Best in Basketball. 1998. (Women of Sports Ser.). (Illus.). 64p. (gr. 5 up). lib. bdg. 24.90 (978-0-7613-1301-4(X), Twenty-First Century Bks.) Lerner Publishing Group.

Sampler, Robert. Mind Mastery for Basketball. 2000. 115p. (YA). (gr. 6 up). pap. 29.95 (978-0-9653920-5-1(8)) Aries International (U.B.T.O.).

Savage, Jeff. LeBron James. 2005. (Illus.). 32p. (J). (gr. 3-7). pap. 5.95 (978-0-8225-2954-5(8)) Lerner Publishing Group.

Schrackenberg, Robert E. Kobe Bryant. 1999. (Basketball Legends Ser.). (Illus.). 64p. (YA). (gr. 2-5). 12.95 (978-0-7910-5005-7(X), Chelsea Hse.) Facts On File, Inc.

Smith, Charles. Rimshots: Baketball Pix, Rolls, & Rhythm. 2000. (gr. 3-6). lib. bdg. 15.30 (978-0-613-23758-1(7)) Tandem Library Bks.

Smith, Charles R. Rimshots: Basketball Pix, Rolls & Rhythms. 2000. (Illus.). 32p. (J). (gr. 4-7). pap. 6.99 (978-0-14-056678-9(3), Puffin) Penguin Group (USA) Inc.

Smith, Michelle. Stars of the WNBA. 2002. (gr. 3-6). lib. bdg. 11.80 (978-0-613-55905-8(3)) Tandem Library Bks.

Smith, Stewart & Kolb, Joe. Get Fit Now for High School Basketball: Strength & Conditioning for Ultimate Performance on the Court. Peck, Peter Field, photos by. 2002. (Illus.). 264p. (YA). (gr. 7-13). 15.95 (978-1-57826-094-2(9), Hatherleigh Pr.) Hatherleigh Co., Ltd., The.

Stewart, Mark. Los Heat de Miami. Kalmanovitz, Manuel, tr. from ENG. 2007. (Team Spirit Ser.). (SPA.). (J). lib. bdg. 25.27 ***(978-1-59953-102-1(X))*** Norwood Hse. Pr.

—Los Lakers de Los Angeles. Kalmanovtiz, Manuel, tr. from ENG. 2007. (Team Spirit Ser.). (SPA.). (J). lib. bdg. 25.27 ***(978-1-59953-100-7(3))*** Norwood Hse. Pr.

Stewart, Mark. The NBA Finals. Kennedy, Mike, ed. 2003. (Watts History of Sports Ser.). (Illus.). 128p. (J). 34.50 (978-0-531-11955-6(6), Watts, Franklin) Scholastic Library Publishing.

Stewart, Wayne. A Little Giant Book: Basketball Facts. 2007. (Illus.). 360p. (J). pap. 6.95 ***(978-1-4027-4978-0(3))*** Sterling Publishing Co., Inc.

Stone, Lynn M. Power Forwards. 2008. (J). ***(978-1-60044-595-8(0))*** Rourke Publishing, LLC.

Sweeny, Sheila. Wacky Basketball Facts to Bounce Around. Wolf, Cathrine, ed. rev. ed. Date not set. (Illus.). 32p. (J). (gr. k-3). pap. 2.50 (978-1-886749-38-2(8)) Sports Illustrated For Kids.

Thomas, Keltie. How Basketball Works. Hall, Greg, illus. 2005. 64p. 21.95 (978-1-897066-18-8(X)); pap. 6.95 (978-1-897066-19-5(8)) Maple Tree Pr. CAN. *Dist:* Perseus Distribution.

Thomas, Ron & Herran, Joe. Getting into Basketball. 2005. (Getting Into Ser.). (Illus.). 32p. (J). (ps-8). lib. bdg. 28.00 (978-0-7910-8809-8(X), Chelsea Clubhouse) Facts On File, Inc.

Torres, John Albert. Kobe Bryant. 2000. (Real-Life Reader Biography Ser.). (Illus.). 32p. (J). (gr. 3-8). lib. bdg. 24.95 (978-1-58415-030-5(0)) Mitchell Lane Pubs., Inc.

—Sports Great Jason Kidd. 1998. (Sports Great Bks.). (Illus.). 64p. (YA). (gr. 4-10). lib. bdg. 22.60 (978-0-7660-1001-7(5)) Enslow Pubs., Inc.

—Sports Great Tim Duncan. 2002. (Sports Great Bks.). (Illus.). 64p. (J). (gr. 4-10). lib. bdg. 22.60 (978-0-7660-1766-5(4)) Enslow Pubs., Inc.

—Top 10 NBA Finals Most Valuable Players. 2000. (Sports Top 10 Ser.). (Illus.). 48p. (YA). (gr. 4-10). lib. bdg. 23.93 (978-0-7660-1276-9(X)) Enslow Pubs., Inc.

Tuttle, Dennis R. Basketball. 1999. (Composite Guides Ser.). (Illus.). 64p. (YA). (gr. 4-7). lib. bdg. 18.65 (978-0-7910-4724-8(5), Chelsea Hse.) Facts On File, Inc.

Ulmer, Michael. A Basketball Alphabet. rev. ed. 2007. 40p. pap. 7.95 ***(978-1-58536-338-4(3))*** Sleeping Bear Pr.

Ulmer, Michael. J Is for Jump Shot: A Basketball Alphabet. Braught, Mark, illus. 2005. (Sports Alphabet Ser.). 40p. (J). (gr. k-5). 16.95 (978-1-58536-229-5(8)) Sleeping Bear Pr.

Ultimate Sports Force Staff. Super Squad: Basketball's Superstars. 2003. (Illus.). 56p. (J). pap. 7.95 (978-1-57243-601-5(8)) Triumph Bks.

Van Gundy, Bill. Basketball: Man-to-Man Defense. 2000. (High Interest Bks.). (Illus.). 48p. (J). (gr. 7-12). 23.00 (978-0-516-23362-8(9), Children's Pr.) Scholastic Library Publishing.

—Basketball: Outside Shooting. 2000. (High Interest Bks.). (Illus.). 48p. (J). (gr. 7-12). 23.00 (978-0-516-23363-5(7), Children's Pr.) Scholastic Library Publishing.

—Basketball: Outside Shooting. 2000. (gr. 7-12). lib. bdg. 15.25 (978-0-613-51984-7(1)) Tandem Library Bks.

Vander Hook, Sue. Cameron Crazies: The Duke Bluedevils Story. 1999. (College Sports Today Ser.). (Illus.). 32p. (J). (gr. 4-7). pap. 21.30 (978-0-88682-988-9(7), Creative Education) Creative Co., The.

—Hail Hoosiers! The Indiana Hoosiers Story. 1999. (College Sports Today Ser.). (Illus.). 32p. (J). (gr. 4-7). pap. 21.30 (978-0-88682-990-2(9), Creative Education) Creative Co., The.

Vanderlinden, Kathy. Basketball Challenge: Puzzles, Quizzes, Games & Other Cool Stuff for Young Slam Fans. 2003. (Illus.). (gr. 3 up). pap. (978-1-55054-753-5(4), Greystone Bks.) Douglas & McIntyre, Ltd.

Weatherspoon, Teresa. Teresa Weatherspoon's Basketball for Girls: A Pro Superstar Teaches You the Game. 1999. (Illus.). 120p. (J). (ps-7). per. 24.55 (978-0-613-16562-4(4)) Tandem Library Bks.

Weatherspoon, Teresa, et al. Teresa Weatherspoon's Basketball for Girls. 1999. (Illus.). 128p. (gr. 3-7). pap. 15.95 (978-0-471-31784-5(5), Wiley-Interscience) Wiley, John & Sons, Inc.

Weber, Bruce. NBA Awesome Dynamic Duos Poster Book. 2002. (NBA Ser.). 32p. (J). pap. 5.99 (978-0-439-44300-5(8)) Scholastic, Inc.

—NBA Megastars 2001. 2001. (gr. 3-6). lib. bdg. 14.15 (978-0-613-32873-9(6)) Tandem Library Bks.

—NBA Megastars '98. 1998. (J). pap. 7.99 (978-0-590-60005-7(2)) Scholastic, Inc.

Weierbach, Jane & Phillips-Hershey, Elizabeth. Mind over Basketball: Coach Yourself to Handle Stress. Beyl, Charles, illus. 2007. 48p. (J). (gr. 3-7). 14.95 ***(978-1-4338-0135-8(3)***, 4418006); pap. 8.95 ***(978-1-4338-0136-5(1)***, 4418007) American Psychological Assn. (Magination Pr.).

We're a Team! Individual Title Six-Packs. (ps-2). 27.00 (978-0-7635-9482-4(2)) Rigby Education.

Wright, John. Basketball. 2003. (Sports Injuries Ser.). (Illus.). 64p. (J). lib. bdg. (978-1-59084-627-8(3)) Mason Crest Pubs.

Wrobel, Scott. Wizards of Westwood: The UCLA Bruins Story. 1999. (College Sports Today Ser.). (Illus.). 32p. (J). (gr. 4-7). pap. 21.30 (978-0-88682-997-1(6), Creative Education) Creative Co., The.

YMCA of the USA Staff. Playing YMCA Basketball: Bronze Edition. 2000. (Illus.). 48p. (J). pap. 6.00 (978-0-7360-3043-4(3), YMCA of the U.S.A.) Human Kinetics Pubs.

—Playing YMCA Basketball: Gold Edition. 2000. (Illus.). 48p. (J). pap. 6.00 (978-0-7360-3045-8(X), YMCA of the U.S.A.) Human Kinetics Pubs.

—Playing YMCA Basketball: Silver Edition. 2000. (Illus.). 48p. (J). pap. 6.00 (978-0-7360-3044-1(1), YMCA of the U.S.A.) Human Kinetics Pubs.

Yoder, Lou Gearhart. A Ball, a Ball, a Basketball. Trobaugh, Barb, illus. 2000. 36p. (J). (gr. 2-8). pap. (978-0-9703986-0-4(3)) Yoder, Lou A.

Young, Jeff C. Burning up the Court: the Miami Heat. 2007. (Sensational Sports Teams Ser.). (Illus.). 128p. (J). (gr. 5). lib. bdg. 33.27 ***(978-1-59845-049-1(2)***, MyReportLinks.com Bks.) Enslow Pubs., Inc.

Young, Jeff C. Top 10 Basketball Shot-Blockers. 2000. (Sports Top 10 Ser.). (Illus.). 48p. (YA). (gr. 4-10). lib. bdg. 23.93 (978-0-7660-1275-2(1)) Enslow Pubs., Inc.

Zuehlke, Jeffrey. Kevin Garnett. 2005. (Amazing Athletes Ser.). (Illus.). 32p. (J). (gr. 3-4). lib. bdg. 23.93 (978-0-8225-2429-8(5)) Lerner Publishing Group.

BASKETBALL—BIOGRAPHY

Aaseng, Nathan. Sports Great David Robinson. rev. ed. 1998. (Sports Great Bks.). (Illus.). 64p. (YA). (gr. 4-10). lib. bdg. 22.60 (978-0-7660-1077-2(5)) Enslow Pubs., Inc.

Anderson, Joan. Rookie: A First Year with the WNBA. 2000. (YA). (978-0-606-19506-5(8)) Tandem Library Bks.

Aschburner, Steve. Kevin Garnett Story. 2001. (NBA Reader Ser.). (Illus.). 40p. (J). pap. 3.99 (978-0-439-34305-3(4)) Scholastic, Inc.

—NBA All-Star Kevin Garnett. 2001. (gr. 3-6). lib. bdg. 11.80 (978-0-613-43840-7(X)) Tandem Library Bks.

Bailey, Peter. Superstar Steve Nash. 2007. 104p. pap. 12.95 ***(978-1-55168-319-5(9))*** Fenn, H. B. & Co., Ltd. CAN. *Dist:* Transition Vendor.

Basen, Ryan. Steve Nash: Leader on & off the Court. 2007. (Sports Stars with Heart Ser.). (Illus.). 128p. (J). (gr. 5). lib. bdg. 31.93 ***(978-0-7660-2868-5(2))*** Enslow Pubs., Inc.

Basketball Hall of Famers, 8 bks. Incl. Bill Bradley. Buckley, James, Jr. lib. bdg. 29.25 (978-0-8239-3479-9(9)); Bill Russell. Hayhurst, Chris. lib. bdg. 29.25 (978-0-8239-3480-5(2)); Bob Cousy. Kirkpatrick, Rob. lib. bdg. 29.25 (978-0-8239-3481-2(0)); Jerry West. Ramen, Fred. lib. bdg. 29.25 (978-0-8239-3482-9(9)); Kareem Abdul-Jabbar. Kneib, Martha. lib. bdg. 29.25 (978-0-8239-3483-6(7)); Larry Bird. Beyer, Mark. lib. bdg. 29.25 (978-0-8239-3484-3(5)); Oscar Robertson. Cohen, Joel H. lib. bdg. 29.25 (978-0-8239-3485-0(3)); Wilt Chamberlain. Greenberger, Robert. lib. bdg. 29.25 (978-0-8239-3486-7(1)); 112p. (YA). (gr. 5-8). (Illus.). 2002. Set lib. bdg. 234.00 (978-0-8239-9687-2(5), Rosen Central) Rosen Publishing Group, Inc., The.

Bayne, Bijan C. Sky Kings: Black Pioneers of Professional Basketball. 1998. (African-American Experience Ser.). 144p. (J). (gr. 8-12). pap. 9.95 (978-0-531-15900-2(0), Watts, Franklin) Scholastic Library Publishing.

Bednar, Chuck. The San Antonio Spurs. 2003. (Great Sports Teams Ser.). (Illus.). 112p. (J). 29.95 (978-1-59018-242-0(1), Lucent Bks.) Thomson Gale.

Bell, Sara. Basketball Saturday. 2000. (Illus.). 56p. (J). pap. 10.00 (978-0-8059-4836-3(8)) Dorrance Publishing Co., Inc.

Bernstein, Ross. Kevin Garnett: Star Forward. 2002. (Sports Reports). (Illus.). 104p. (J). (gr. 4-10). lib. bdg. 26.60 (978-0-7660-1829-7(6)) Enslow Pubs., Inc.

Beyer, Mark. Larry Bird. 2002. (Basketball Hall of Famers Ser.). (Illus.). 112p. (YA). (gr. 5-8). lib. bdg. 29.25 (978-0-8239-3484-3(5), Rosen Central) Rosen Publishing Group, Inc., The.

Bradshaw, Douglas. Shaquille O'Neal: Man of Steel. 2001. (All Aboard Reading Ser.). (Illus.). 48p. (J). (ps-3). pap. 3.99 (978-0-448-42552-8(1), Grosset & Dunlap) Penguin Group (USA) Inc.

—Shaquille O'Neal: Man of Steel. 2001. (gr. k-3). lib. bdg. 11.80 (978-0-613-31685-9(1)) Tandem Library Bks.

Brenner, Richard. Kobe Bryant. 1999. (gr. k-3). lib. bdg. 11.80 (978-0-613-16733-8(3)) Tandem Library Bks.

Brenner, Richard J. Kobe Bryant. 1999. 32p. (J). (978-0-688-16584-0(2)); (Illus.). (gr. 1-4). pap. 3.95 (978-0-688-16585-7(0)) HarperCollins Pubs.

—Kobe Bryant. 1999. (J). (978-0-606-16676-8(9)) Tandem Library Bks.

—Michael Jordan. (J). 2000. 25.01 (978-0-688-16586-4(9)); 1999. (Illus.). 32p. pap. 3.95 (978-0-688-16587-1(7)) HarperCollins Pubs.

—Michael Jordan. 1999. (978-0-606-17077-2(4)) Tandem Library Bks.

—Superstars Album 1999: Basketball. 1998. (Illus.). 48p. (J). (gr. 4-7). pap. 4.50 (978-0-688-16230-6(4)) HarperCollins Pubs.

Buckley, James, Jr. Super Scorers. 2001. (NBA Reader Ser.: Vol. 4). (Illus.). 48p. (J). pap. 3.99 (978-0-439-34306-0(2)) Scholastic, Inc.

Burgan, Michael. Sheryl Swoopes. 2000. (Women Who Win Ser.). (Illus.). 64p. (J). (gr. 4-7). pap. 25.00 (978-0-7910-6155-8(8)); 25.00 (978-0-7910-5795-7(X)) Facts On File, Inc. (Chelsea Hse.).

—Sheryl Swoopes. 2001. (gr. 3-6). lib. bdg. 17.60 (978-0-613-33051-0(X)) Tandem Library Bks.

Byman, Jeremy. Tim Duncan. 2004. (Great Athletes Ser.). (Illus.). 64p. (YA). (gr. 5 up). 18.95 (978-1-883846-43-5(9), First Biographies) Reynolds, Morgan Inc.

Christopher, Matt. On the Court with... Kobe Bryant. 2001. (978-0-606-22562-5(5)); (gr. 3-6). lib. bdg. 13.00 (978-0-613-44172-8(9)) Tandem Library Bks.

—On the Court with... Lisa Leslie. 1998. (Matt Christopher Sports Biographies Ser.). 128p. (J). (gr. 3-7). pap. 4.99 (978-0-316-14216-8(6)) Little, Brown Bks. for Young Readers.

—On the Court with... Shaquille O'Neil. 2003. (Illus.). 128p. (J). (gr. 3-7). pap. 4.99 (978-0-316-16473-3(9)) Little Brown & Co.

—On the Court with... Yao Ming. 2004. (Matt Christopher Sports Biographies Ser.). (Illus.). 112p. (J). (gr. 5-8). pap. 4.99 (978-0-316-73574-2(4), Tingley, Megan Bks.) Little, Brown Bks. for Young Readers.

Coffey, Wayne. The Kobe Bryant Story. 1999. (Fast Breaks Ser.). (Illus.). 64p. (J). (gr. 2-5). pap. 4.99 (978-0-590-05234-4(9)) Scholastic, Inc.

Cohen, Joel H. Oscar Robertson. 2002. (Basketball Hall of Famers Ser.). (Illus.). 112p. (YA). (gr. 5-8). lib. bdg. 29.25 (978-0-8239-3485-0(3), Rosen Central) Rosen Publishing Group, Inc., The.

Cook, Brian & Tupper, Mark. Brian Cook: An Illini Legend. 2003. (Illus.). 96p. (J). pap. 5.95 (978-1-58261-731-2(7)) Sports Publishing, LLC.

Cornelius, Kay. Chamique Holdsclaw. 2000. (Women Who Win Ser.). (Illus.). 64p. (J). (gr. 4-7). pap. 25.00 (978-0-7910-6153-4(1)); (gr. 3 up). 25.00 (978-0-7910-5793-3(3)) Facts On File, Inc. (Chelsea Hse.).

—Chamique Holdsclaw. 2001. (gr. 3-6). lib. bdg. 17.60 (978-0-613-32387-1(4)) Tandem Library Bks.

Daly, Chuck, intro. Allen Iverson. 1999. (Basketball Legends Ser.). (Illus.). 64p. (J). (gr. 4-7). 12.95 (978-0-7910-4852-8(7), Chelsea Hse.) Facts On File, Inc.

—Alonzo Mourning. 1999. (Basketball Legends Ser.). (Illus.). 64p. (YA). (gr. 4-7). 12.95 (978-0-7910-4577-0(3) , Chelsea Hse.) Facts On File, Inc.
—Gary Payton. 1999. (Basketball Legends Ser.). (Illus.). 64p. (YA). (gr. 4-7). 12.95 (978-0-7910-4578-7(1) , Chelsea Hse.) Facts On File, Inc.
—The Head Coaches. 1999. (Basketball Legends Ser.). (Illus.). 64p. (YA). (gr. 4-7). lib. bdg. 18.65 (978-0-7910-4580-0(3) , Chelsea Hse.) Facts On File, Inc.
—John Stockton. 1999. (Basketball Legends Ser.). (Illus.). 64p. (YA). (gr. 4-7). lib. bdg. 18.65 (978-0-7910-4579-4(X) , Chelsea Hse.) Facts On File, Inc.
—Juwan Howard. 1999. (Basketball Legends Ser.). (Illus.). 64p. (YA). (gr. 4-7). lib. bdg. 18.65 (978-0-7910-4575-6(7) , Chelsea Hse.) Facts On File, Inc.
Damon - Beyond the Glory. l.t. ed. 2003. (Illus.). 152p. per. 14.95 (978-0-9724033-2-0(9)) Backroads Pr.
Dougherty, Denis. Michael Jordan. 1999. (Jam Session Ser.). (Illus.). 32p. (J). (gr. 3-8). lib. bdg. 24.21 (978-1-57765-038-6(7) , ABDO & Daughters) ABDO Publishing Co.
Dougherty, Terri. Kevin Garnett. 1999. (Jam Session Ser.). (Illus.). 32p. (J). (gr. 3-8). lib. bdg. 24.21 (978-1-57765-039-3(5) , ABDO & Daughters) ABDO Publishing Co.
—Lisa Leslie. 1999. (Jam Session Ser.). (Illus.). 32p. (J). (gr. 3-8). lib. bdg. 24.21 (978-1-57765-313-4(0) , ABDO & Daughters) ABDO Publishing Co.
—Shaquille O'Neal. 2001. (Jam Session Ser.). (Illus.). 32p. (J). (gr. 3-8). lib. bdg. 24.21 (978-1-57765-471-1(4) , ABDO & Daughters) ABDO Publishing Co.
Egan, Erin & SI for Kids Staff, eds. SI for Kids Extra It's Showtime: With Kobe Bryant. 1998. (Illus.). 16p. (J). (gr. 3-8). reprint ed. pap. 0.75 (978-1-886749-50-4(7)) Sports Illustrated For Kids.
Ekstrand, Chris. Team USA 2000. 2000. (gr. 3-6). lib. bdg. 14.15 (978-0-613-27183-7(1)) Tandem Library Bks.
Fawaz, John. Highflying Stars. 2007. (NBA Reader Ser.). 32p. (J). pap. 5.99 (978-0-439-91240-2(7)) Scholastic, Inc.
Fried, Mark. Great Teams in Basketball. 2005. (Great Teams Ser.). (Illus.). 48p. (J). 29.29 (978-1-4109-1485-9(2)); pap. 8.50 (978-1-4109-1492-7(5)) Raintree.
—Great Teams in Basketball 6-Pack. 2005. pap. 51.00 (978-1-4109-1499-6(2)) Raintree.
—Great Teams in College Basketball. 2005. (Great Teams Ser.). (Illus.). 48p. (J). 27.79 (978-1-4109-1488-0(7)); pap. 8.50 (978-1-4109-1495-8(X)) Raintree.
Frisaro, Joe. Reggie Miller: From Downtown. 2003. (Superstar Ser.: Vol. 6). (Illus.). 96p. (gr. 4-7). pap. 4.95 (978-1-58261-180-8(7)) Sports Publishing, LLC.
Gaines, Ann Graham. Allen Iverson. l.t. ed. 2002. (Real Life Reader Biographies Ser.). (Illus.). 32p. (gr. 3-8). lib. bdg. 15.95 (978-1-58415-134-0(X)) Mitchell Lane Pubs., Inc.
Gilliam, Nancy, creator. LeBron James: King of the Court Companion Study Guide. 2005. (YA). pap. 10.00 (978-0-9771113-0-5(X)) Forest Hill Publishing, LLC.
Goodman, Michael E. Grant Hill. 1998. (Ovations Ser.). (Illus.). 32p. (YA). (gr. 4-7). lib. bdg. (978-0-88682-831-8(7) , Creative Education) Creative Co., The.
—Kobe Bryant. 2003. (Ovations Ser.). (Illus.). 32p. (J). lib. bdg. (978-1-58341-248-0(4) , Creative Education) Creative Co., The.
—Shaquille O'Neal. (Ovations Ser.). (Illus.). 2001. 31p. (J). (gr. 3). pap. 8.95 (978-0-89812-323-4(2) , Creative Paperbacks); 2000. 32p. (J). pap. 10.60 (978-0-89812-026-4(8) , Creative Paperbacks); 1998. 32p. (YA). (gr. 4-7). lib. bdg. (978-0-88682-633-8(0) , Creative Education) Creative Co., The.
Gottfried, Ted. Earvin "Magic" Johnson: Champion & Crusader. 2001. (Book Report Biographies Ser.). (Illus.). 100p. (YA). (gr. 6-8). pap. 6.95 (978-0-531-15550-9(1) , Watts, Franklin) Scholastic Library Publishing.
Grody, Carl W. Sports Great Keith Van Horn. 2001. (Sports Great Bks.). (Illus.). 64p. (J). (gr. 4-10). lib. bdg. 22.60 (978-0-7660-1471-8(1)) Enslow Pubs., Inc.
—Sports Great Mitch Richmond. 1999. (Sports Great Bks.). (Illus.). 64p. (YA). (gr. 4-10). lib. bdg. 17.95 (978-0-7660-1070-3(8)) Enslow Pubs., Inc.
Gutman, Bill. Michael Jordan & Scottie Pippen. 1998. (Teammates Ser.). (Illus.). 112p. (gr. 4-6). lib. bdg. 23.90 (978-0-7613-0420-3(7) , Millbrook Pr.) Lerner Publishing Group.
Harcourt School Publishers Staff. Tiny, Terrific Debbie Black Below Level. 3rd ed. 2002. (Trophies Reading Program Ser.). (Illus.). pap. 5.10 (978-0-15-323134-6(3)) Harcourt Schl. Pubs.
Hareas, John. All-Star Allen Iverson. 2003. (NBA Reader Ser.). 40p. (J). pap. 3.99 (978-0-439-44301-2(6)) Scholastic, Inc.
—All-Star Allen Iverson. 2003. (gr. k-3). lib. bdg. 11.80 (978-0-613-72200-1(0)) Tandem Library Bks.
—NBA Slam Dunk 3-D. 2006. (J). pap. (***978-0-439-78814-4(5)***) Scholastic, Inc.
—NBA's Greatest. 2003. (Illus.). 160p. 30.00 (978-0-7894-9977-6(0)) Dorling Kindersley Publishing, Inc.
—Yao Ming. 2003. (N B A Ser.). 40p. (J). pap. 3.99 (978-0-439-59108-9(2)) Scholastic, Inc.
—Yao Ming. 2003. (gr. 3-6). lib. bdg. 11.80 (978-0-613-85396-5(2)) Tandem Library Bks.
Hayhurst, Chris. Bill Russell. 2002. (Basketball Hall of Famers Ser.). (Illus.). 112p. (YA). (gr. 5-8). lib. bdg. 29.25 (978-0-8239-3480-5(2) , Rosen Central) Rosen Publishing Group, Inc., The.
Healy, Nick. Bill Russell. 2003. (Illus.). 64p. (J). lib. bdg. 28.56 (978-0-7398-7034-1(3)) Raintree.
—Bill Russell. 2003. (gr. 3-6). lib. bdg. 18.20 (978-0-613-78179-4(1)) Tandem Library Bks.
Hoffman, Mary Ann. Dwyane Wade: Basketball Star. 2006. (Sports Superstars Ser.). (Illus.). 24p. (J). lib. bdg. (978-1-4042-3536-6(1) , PowerKids Pr.) Rosen Publishing Group, Inc., The.
—LeBron James: Basketball Star. 2006. (Sports Superstars Ser.). (J). lib. bdg. (978-1-4042-3535-9(3)) Rosen Publishing Group, Inc., The.
Houghton, Sarah. Michael Jordan: The Best Ever. 2001. (Illus.). 64p. (J). pap. (978-0-7368-9502-6(7)); (gr. 4-5). lib. bdg. 22.60 (978-0-7368-4002-6(8) , Capstone High-Interest Bks.) Capstone Pr., Inc.
Jackel, Molly. WNBA Superstars: Leslie, Lobo & Swoopes. 1998. (Fast Breaks Ser.: Vol. 4). (Illus.). 88p. (J). (gr. 2-4). pap. 3.99 (978-0-590-12081-4(6)) Scholastic, Inc.
—WNBA Superstars: Leslie, Lobo & Swoopes, 4. 1998. (Fast Breaks Ser.). (J). (978-0-606-13378-4(X)) Tandem Library Bks.
Keith, Ted. Kevin Garnett. 2007. (World's Greatest Athletes Ser.). 32p. (J). (gr. 1-5). 27.07 (978-1-59296-790-2(6)) Child's World, Inc.
Kelley, Brent P. Lisa Leslie. 2000. (Women Who Win Ser.). (Illus.). 64p. (gr. 4-7). (J). pap. 25.00 (978-0-7910-6154-1(X)); (YA). 25.00 (978-0-7910-5794-0(1)) Facts On File, Inc. (Chelsea Hse.).
Kennedy, Nick. Kobe Bryant: Star Guard. 2002. (Sports Reports). (Illus.). 104p. (J). (gr. 4-10). lib. bdg. 26.60 (978-0-7660-1828-0(8)) Enslow Pubs., Inc.
Kernan, Kevin. Tim Duncan: Slam Duncan. 2000. (SuperStar Ser.: Vol. 5). (Illus.). 96p. (J). (gr. 4-7). per. 4.95 (978-1-58261-179-2(3)) Sports Publishing, LLC.
Kevin Garnett, 6 vols. (gr. 4 up). 39.95 (978-0-7368-9273-5(7)) Red Brick Learning.
Kirkpatrick, Rob. Bob Cousy. 2002. (Basketball Hall of Famers Ser.). (Illus.). 112p. (YA). (gr. 5-8). lib. bdg. 29.25 (978-0-8239-3481-2(0) , Rosen Central) Rosen Publishing Group, Inc., The.
—Grant Hill: Basketball All-Star. 2003. (Reading Power Ser.). (Illus.). 24p. (J). (gr. 1). lib. bdg. 17.25 (978-0-8239-5538-1(9) , PowerKids Pr.) Rosen Publishing Group, Inc., The.
—Kobe Bryant: "Slam Dunk" Champion. 2000. (Reading Power Ser.). (Illus.). 24p. (J). (gr. 1). lib. bdg. 17.25 (978-0-8239-5539-8(7) , PowerKids Pr.) Rosen Publishing Group, Inc., The.
—Kobe Bryant, Campeon del "Slam Dunk" 2002. (Deportistas de Poder Ser.). (SPA & ENG., Illus.). 24p. (J). lib. bdg. 17.25 (978-0-8239-6124-5(9)); lib. bdg. 17.25 (978-0-8239-6142-9(7) , RN31311) Rosen Publishing Group, Inc., The. (Buenas Letra).
Kirkpatrick, Rob, et al, contrib. by. Michael Jordan, Basketball Superstar: Rob Kirkpatrick. 2001. (Great Record Breakers in Sports Ser.). (Illus.). 24p. (J). lib. bdg. 18.75 (978-0-8239-5633-3(4) , PowerKids Pr.) Rosen Publishing Group, Inc., The.
Knapp, Ron. Top 10 Professional Basketball Coaches. 1998. (Sports Top 10 Ser.). (Illus.). 48p. (YA). (gr. 4-10). lib. bdg. 23.93 (978-0-7660-1008-6(2)) Enslow Pubs., Inc.
Kneib, Martha. Kareem Abdul-Jabbar. 2002. (Basketball Hall of Famers Ser.). (Illus.). 112p. (YA). (gr. 5-8). lib. bdg. 29.25 (978-0-8239-3483-6(7) , Rosen Central) Rosen Publishing Group, Inc., The.
Krawiec, Richard. Yao Ming: Gentle Giant of Basketball. 2003. (Avisson Young Adult Ser.). (Illus.). 108p. (J). 19.95 (978-1-888105-63-6(1)) Avisson Pr., Inc.
Layden, Joe. NBA Hot Shots. 1999. (Illus.). 24p. (ps-2). pap. 3.50 (978-0-590-06056-1(2)) Scholastic, Inc.
Lebrecque, Ellen. Magic Johnson. 2008. (J). lib. bdg. 26.00 (***978-1-60279-071-1(X)***) Cherry Lake Publishing.
Lovitt, Chip. Michael Jordan. (Scholastic Biography Ser.). (Illus.). (gr. 4-9). 2nd rev. ed. 1998. 213p. (YA). pap. 4.50 (978-0-590-59644-2(6)); 3rd rev. ed. 1999. 224p. (J). pap. 4.50 (978-0-439-12961-9(3)) Scholastic, Inc.
—Michael Jordan. 1999. (978-0-606-17877-8(5)) Tandem Library Bks.
Macnow, Glen. Sports Great Allen Iverson. 2003. (Sports Great Books). (Illus.). 64p. (J). (gr. 4-10). lib. bdg. 22.60 (978-0-7660-2063-4(0)) Enslow Pubs., Inc.
—Sports Great Chris Webber. 1999. (Sports Great Bks.). (Illus.). 64p. (YA). (gr. 4-10). lib. bdg. 17.95 (978-0-7660-1069-7(4)) Enslow Pubs., Inc.
—Sports Great Kobe Bryant. 2000. (Sports Great Bks.). (Illus.). 64p. (YA). (gr. 4-10). lib. bdg. 22.60 (978-0-7660-1264-6(6)) Enslow Pubs., Inc.
Mattern, Joanne. Basketball Greats. 2002. (History Makers Ser.). (Illus.). 112p. (J). (gr. 7-10). 29.95 (978-1-59018-228-4(6) , Lucent Bks.) Thomson Gale.
—LeBron James. 2004. (Robbie Reader Ser.). (Illus.). 32p. (J). (gr. 1-4). lib. bdg. 25.70 (978-1-58415-293-4(1)) Mitchell Lane Pubs., Inc.
McCormick, Lisa Wade. Michael Jordan. 2006. (Illus.). 31p. (J). (978-0-516-29843-6(7)) Children's Pr., Ltd.
Miller, Ray. Shaquille O'Neal. 2002. (Stars of Sports Ser.). (Illus.). 48p. (J). 26.20 (978-0-7377-1422-7(0) , Kidhaven) Thomson Gale.
Miller, Raymond H. Kobe Bryant. 2003. (Stars of Sports Ser.). (Illus.). 48p. (J). 26.20 (978-0-7377-1538-5(3) , Greenhaven Pr., Inc.) Thomson Gale.
Molzahn, Arlene Bourgeois. Kevin Garnett. 2001. (Sports Heroes Ser.). (Illus.). 48p. (J). (gr. 3-4). lib. bdg. 21.26 (978-0-7368-0778-4(0) , Capstone High-Interest Bks.) Capstone Pr., Inc.
Murdico, Suzanne J. Hakeem Olajuwon. 1998. (Overcoming the Odds Ser.). (Illus.). 48p. (J). (gr. 3-8). lib. bdg. (978-0-8172-4131-5(0)) Raintree.
—Hakeem Olajuwon. 1998. (Overcoming the Odds Ser.). (Illus.). 48p. (J). (gr. 4-7). pap. 7.95 (978-0-8172-8002-4(2)) Steck-Vaughn.
NBA, creator. Greatest Stars of the NBA 2004: Jason Kidd, 4 vols., Vol. 3. 2005. (Illus.). 96p. pap. 7.99 (978-1-59532-183-1(7) , Tokyopop Kids) TOKYOPOP, Inc.
—Greatest Stars of the NBA 2004: Kevin Garnett, 4 vols., Vol. 4. 2005. (Illus.). 96p. pap. 7.99 (978-1-59532-184-8(5) , Tokyopop Kids) TOKYOPOP, Inc.
—Greatest Stars of the NBA 2004: Shaquille O'Neal, 4 vols. 2004. (Illus.). 96p. pap. 7.99 (978-1-59532-181-7(0) , Tokyopop Kids) TOKYOPOP, Inc.
—Greatest Stars of the NBA 2004: Tim Duncan, 4 vols., Vol. 2. 2004. (Illus.). 96p. pap. 7.99 (978-1-59532-182-4(9) , Tokyopop Kids) TOKYOPOP, Inc.
Nba, Reader & Hareas, John. Nba Reader: Steve Nash: Steve Nash. 2008. 32p. pap. 3.99 (***978-0-545-03411-1(6)*** , Scholastic) Scholastic, Inc.
Nelson, Glenn, et al. Rising Stars: The Ten Best Young Players in the NBA. 2005. (Sports Illustrated for Kids Bks.). (Illus.). 176p. (YA). (gr. 7-12). lib. bdg. 32.00 (978-0-8239-3574-1(4)) Rosen Publishing Group, Inc., The.
Nelson, Kristi. WNBA: The Chamique Holdsclaw Story. 2000. 11.79 (978-0-606-18616-2(6)) Tandem Library Bks.
Ovations Series, 2 vols., Set. Incl. Jeff Gordon. Bach, Julie S. pap. 10.60 (978-0-89812-025-7(X)); Shaquille O'Neal. Goodman, Michael E. pap. 10.60 (978-0-89812-026-4(8)); (J). 2000. (Illus.). 32p. Set pap. 21.20 (978-0-89812-010-3(1) , Creative Paperbacks) Creative Co., The.
Owens, Tom & Helmer, Diana Star. Teamwork, the Houston Comets in Action. 1999. (Women's Professional Basketball Ser.). 24p. (J). lib. bdg. 18.75 (978-0-8239-5246-5(0) , PowerKids Pr.) Rosen Publishing Group, Inc., The.
—Teamwork, the Sacramento Monarchs in Action. 1999. (Women's Professional Basketball Ser.). 24p. (J). lib. bdg. 18.75 (978-0-8239-5245-8(2) , PowerKids Pr.) Rosen Publishing Group, Inc., The.
Paul, Alan & Kramer, Jon. Basketball All-Stars. 2000. 64p. (J). pap. 3.99 (978-1-930623-08-8(9)) Sports Illustrated For Kids.
—Basketball All-Stars: The NBA's Best. 2005. (Sports Illustrated for Kids Bks.). (Illus.). 176p. (YA). (gr. 7-12). lib. bdg. 25.25 (978-0-8239-3689-2(9)) Rosen Publishing Group, Inc., The.
Pellowski, Michael J. Super Sports Star Latrell Sprewell. 2002. (Super Sports Star Ser.). (Illus.). 48p. (J). (gr. 1-4). lib. bdg. 23.93 (978-0-7660-1811-2(3)) Enslow Pubs., Inc.
Plum-Ucci, Carol. Super Sports Star Stephon Marbury. 2002. (Super Sports Star Ser.). (Illus.). 48p. (J). (gr. 1-4). lib. bdg. 23.93 (978-0-7660-1810-5(5)) Enslow Pubs., Inc.
Ponti, James. WNBA: Stars of Women's Basketball. 1999. (J). (978-0-606-19505-8(X)) Tandem Library Bks.
Pyle, Lydia. Kobe Bryant. 2004. (Awesome Athletes Ser.). (Illus.). 32p. (J). (gr. k-6). lib. bdg. 22.78 (978-1-59197-488-8(7)) ABDO Publishing Co.
—Yao Ming. 2004. (Awesome Athletes Ser.). (J). (gr. k-6). lib. bdg. 22.78 (978-1-59197-484-0(4)) ABDO Publishing Co.
Raber, Thomas R. Michael Jordan: Basketball Skywalker. 3rd rev. exp. ed. 1999. (Sports Achievers Biographies Ser.). (Illus.). 80p. (gr. 4-9). (978-0-8225-9846-6(9) , LernerSports) Lerner Publishing Group.
—Michael Jordan: Returning Champion. 4th rev. ed. 2005. (Sports Achievers Biographies Ser.). (Illus.). 80p. (gr. 7-12). 22.60 (978-0-8225-0473-3(1)) Lerner Publishing Group.
Ramen, Fred. Jerry West. 2002. (Basketball Hall of Famers Ser.). (Illus.). 112p. (YA). (gr. 5-8). lib. bdg. 29.25 (978-0-8239-3482-9(9) , Rosen Central) Rosen Publishing Group, Inc., The.
Rapoport, Ken. Jason Kidd: Leader on the Court. 2004. (Sports Leaders Ser.). (Illus.). 104p. (J). lib. bdg. 26.60 (978-0-7660-2214-0(5)) Enslow Pubs., Inc.
Rappoport, Ken. LeBron James: King on & off the Court. 2006. (Sports Stars with Heart Ser.). (Illus.). 128p. (J). lib. bdg. 31.93 (978-0-7660-2420-5(2)) Enslow Pubs., Inc.
—Scottie Pippen: Star Forward. 1999. (Sports Reports). (Illus.). 104p. (YA). (gr. 4-10). lib. bdg. 20.95 (978-0-7660-1080-2(5)) Enslow Pubs., Inc.
—Super Sports Star Glen Rice. 2002. (Super Sports Star Ser.). (Illus.). 48p. (J). (gr. 1-4) lib. bdg. 23.93 (978-0-7660-1808-2(3)) Enslow Pubs., Inc.
Rekela, George R. Karl Malone: Star Forward. 1998. (Sports Reports). (Illus.). 104p. (YA). (gr. 4-10). lib. bdg. 26.60 (978-0-89490-931-3(2)) Enslow Pubs., Inc.
Roberts, Robin. Basketball Year: What It's Like to Be a Woman Pro. 2000. (Get in the Game! with Robin Roberts Ser.). (Illus.). 48p. (gr. 4-8). lib. bdg. (978-0-7613-1406-6(7) , Millbrook Pr.) Lerner Publishing Group.
Robinson, B. J. LeBron James: King of the Court. 2005. (YA). pap. 15.00 (978-0-9759251-5-7(6)) Forest Hill Publishing, LLC.
Robinson, Tom. Shaquille O'Neal: Giant on & off the Court. 2006. (Sports Stars with Heart Ser.). (Illus.). 128p. (J). lib. bdg. 31.93 (978-0-7660-2823-4(2)) Enslow Pubs., Inc.
Rolfe, John & Ross, Dalton. Grant Hill: Superstar Forward. 2005. (Sports Illustrated for Kids Bks.). (Illus.). 176p. (YA). (gr. 7-12). lib. bdg. 30.50 (978-0-8239-3578-9(7)) Rosen Publishing Group, Inc., The.
Roselius, J. Chris. Kevin Garnett: All-Star on & off the Court. 2007. (Sports Stars with Heart Ser.). (Illus.). 128p. (J). (gr. 5). lib. bdg. 31.93 (***978-0-7660-2863-0(1)***) Enslow Pubs., Inc.
Roselius, J. Chris. Tim Duncan: Champion on & off the Court. 2006. (Sports Stars with Heart Ser.). (Illus.). 128p. (J). lib. bdg. 31.93 (978-0-7660-2821-0(6)) Enslow Pubs., Inc.
Rosenthal, Bert. Anfernee Hardaway: Star Guard. 1999. (Sports Reports). (Illus.). 104p. (YA). (gr. 4-10). lib. bdg. 20.95 (978-0-7660-1234-9(4)) Enslow Pubs., Inc.
Rutledge, Rachel. The Best of the Best in Basketball. 1998. (Women of Sports Ser.). (Illus.). 64p. (gr. 5 up). lib. bdg. 24.90 (978-0-7613-1301-4(X) , Twenty-First Century Bks.) Lerner Publishing Group.
Sandler, Michael. Basketball: The Return of Bernard King. 2006. (Upsets & Comebacks Ser.). (Illus.). 32p. (J). lib. bdg. 25.27 (978-1-59716-166-4(7)) Bearport Publishing Co., Inc.
Savage, Jeff. Dwyane Wade. (Amazing Athletes Ser.). (J). 2007. 23.93 (978-0-8225-5955-9(2) , Lerner Pubns.); 2006. (Illus.). 32p. pap. 5.95 (978-0-8225-6013-5(5) , First Avenue Editions) Lerner Publishing Group.
—Kobe Bryant. 2005. (Amazing Athletes Ser.). (Illus.). 32p. (gr. 3-4). lib. bdg. 22.60 (978-0-8225-1300-1(5)) Lerner Publishing Group.
—Kobe Bryant: Basketball Big Shot. (Sports Achievers Biographies Ser.). (Illus.). 2005. 80p. (gr. 7-12). lib. bdg. 22.60 (978-0-8225-3680-2(3)); 2003. 64p. (J). (gr. 4-9). pap. 5.95 (978-0-8225-9860-2(4)) Lerner Publishing Group.
—Kobe Bryant: Basketball Big Shot. 2001. (gr. 5-8). lib. bdg. 14.10 (978-0-613-39481-9(X)) Tandem Library Bks.
—LeBron James. 2006. (Amazing Athletes Ser.). (Illus.). 32p. (J). (gr. 3-7). 23.93 (978-0-8225-2947-7(5) , Lerner Pubns.) Lerner Publishing Group.
—Lisa Leslie: Slam Dunk Queen. 2005. (Sports Leaders Ser.). (Illus.). 104p. (J). lib. bdg. 26.60 (978-0-7660-2423-6(7)) Enslow Pubs., Inc.
—Sports Great Juwan Howard. 1999. (Sports Great Bks.). (Illus.). 64p. (YA). (gr. 4-10). lib. bdg. 22.60 (978-0-7660-1065-9(1)) Enslow Pubs., Inc.
—Sports Great Rebecca Lobo. 2001. (Sports Great Bks.). (Illus.). 64p. (J). (gr. 4-10). lib. bdg. 22.60 (978-0-7660-1466-4(5)) Enslow Pubs., Inc.
—Sports Great Vince Carter. 2002. (Sports Great Bks.). (Illus.). 64p. (J). (gr. 4-10). lib. bdg. 22.60 (978-0-7660-1767-2(2)) Enslow Pubs., Inc.
—Steve Nash. (Amazing Athletes Ser.). (Illus.). 32p. (J). 2007. 23.93 (978-0-8225-5956-6(0) , Lerner Pubns.); 2006. pap. 5.95 (978-0-8225-6014-2(3) , First Avenue Editions) Lerner Publishing Group.
—Terrell Davis: TD! 1999. (Sports Achievers Biographies Ser.). (Illus.). 80p. (gr. 7-12). lib. bdg. 22.60 (978-0-8225-3676-5(5)) Lerner Publishing Group.
—Top 10 Women's Basketball Stars. 2001. (Sports Top 10 Ser.). (Illus.). 48p. (YA). (gr. 4-10). lib. bdg. 23.93 (978-0-7660-1496-1(7)) Enslow Pubs., Inc.
—Yao Ming. (Amazing Athletes Ser.). (Illus.). 32p. (J). 2005. (gr. 3-4). lib. bdg. 23.93 (978-0-8225-2432-8(5)); 2004. (gr. 2-5). pap. 5.95 (978-0-8225-2225-6(X)) Lerner Publishing Group.
Schaefer, A. R. Kobe Bryant. 2002. (Sports Heroes Ser.). (Illus.). 48p. (J). (gr. 3-4). lib. bdg. 21.26 (978-0-7368-1052-4(8) , Capstone High-Interest Bks.) Capstone Pr., Inc.
—Shaquille O'Neal. 2002. (Sports Heroes Ser.). (Illus.). 48p. (J). (gr. 3-4). lib. bdg. 21.26 (978-0-7368-1297-9(0) , Capstone High-Interest Bks.) Capstone Pr., Inc.
Schnakenberg, Robert. Cynthia Cooper. 2000. (Illus.). 64p. (J). (gr. 4-7). lib. bdg. 17.60 (978-0-613-32432-8(3)) Tandem Library Bks.
Schnakenberg, Robert E. Cynthia Cooper. 2000. (Women Who Win Ser.). (Illus.). 64p. (gr. 4-7). (YA). pap. 25.00 (978-0-7910-6156-5(6)); (J). 25.00 (978-0-7910-5796-4(8)) Facts On File, Inc. (Chelsea Hse.).
—Teammates: Karl Malone & John Stockton. 1998. (Teammates Ser.). (Illus.). 96p. (gr. 4-6). lib. bdg. 23.90 (978-0-7613-0300-8(6) , Millbrook Pr.) Lerner Publishing Group.
Schwarz, Alan. Basketball Big Shots. Goehner, Amy Lennard, ed. 2000. (Illus.). 24p. (J). (gr. 2-8). pap. 2.99 (978-1-886749-80-1(9)) Sports Illustrated For Kids.
—Basketball Big Shots. Goehner, Amy L., ed. 1999. 32p. (J). (gr. 2-7). pap. 3.99 (978-1-886749-52-8(3)) Sports Illustrated For Kids.
Sharp, Anne Wallace. Lebron James. 2007. (People in the News Ser.). (Illus.). 128p. (gr. 7-10). 31.20 (***978-1-4205-0014-1(7)*** , Lucent Bks.) Thomson Gale.
Shea, Therese. Basketball Stars. 2007. (Sports Stars Ser.). (Illus.). 48p. (J). (978-0-531-12584-7(X)) Children's Pr., Ltd.
—Yao Ming: International Basketball Star. 2006. (Tony Stead Nonfiction Independent Reading Collection). (J). pap. (978-1-4042-5538-8(9)) Rosen Publishing Group, Inc., The.
Sherman, Josepha. Shaquille O'Neal. 2005. (Robbie Reader Ser.). (Illus.). 32p. (J). (gr. 1-4). lib. bdg. (978-1-58415-361-0(X)) Mitchell Lane Pubs., Inc.
Sibila, Tom. LeBron James: King of the Court. 2005. (High Five Reading Ser.). (Illus.). 64p. (J). (gr. 4-5). lib. bdg. incl. audio (978-0-7368-5757-4(5)) Capstone Pr., Inc.
Sibila, Tom & Rasinski, Timothy V. LeBron James: King of the Court. 2005. (High Five Reading Ser.). (Illus.). 48p. (J). (978-0-7368-5747-5(8)); (978-0-7368-5737-6(0)) Capstone Pr., Inc.
Simpson, Fiona, ed. NBA: Superstars 2006. 2006. 32p. (J). pap. 5.99 (978-0-439-78805-2(6)) Scholastic, Inc.
—NBA Reader: Tracy Mcgrady. 2006. (Illus.). 32p. (J). pap. 3.99 (978-0-439-78803-8(X)) Scholastic, Inc.
Smallwood. NBA - Yesterday's Heroes: A Journey Through the History of African-American Superstars in the NBA. 2000. (J). (978-0-606-19933-9(0)) Tandem Library Bks.
Smallwood, John. Dwyane Wade. 2007. (NBA Reader Ser.). 32p. (J). pap. 3.99 (978-0-439-91237-2(7)) Scholastic, Inc.
—Superstars. 2005. 32p. (J). pap. 5.99 (978-0-439-70400-7(6)) Scholastic, Inc.
Smallwood, John, Jr. Yesterday's Heroes: A Journey Through the History of African-American Superstars in the NBA. 2001. (NBA Ser.). (Illus.). 80p. (J). (gr. 3-7). pap. 4.99 (978-0-439-24110-6(3)) Scholastic, Inc.
Smith, Doug. The Vince Carter Story. 2001. (NBA Ser.). (Illus.). 88p. (J). (gr. 3-7). pap. 4.99 (978-0-439-24106-9(5)) Scholastic, Inc.

A
B

Smith, Michelle. Megastars. 2003. (WNBA Ser.). (Illus.). 48p. (J). pap. 3.99 (978-0-439-45602-9(9)) Scholastic, Inc.

—She's Got Game: Stars of the WNBA. 1999. (WNBA Ser.). (Illus.). 93p. (J). (gr. 3-7). pap. 4.99 (978-0-439-07804-7(0)) Scholastic, Inc.

Smith, Pohla & Wilson, Steve. Shaquille O'Neal: Superhero at Center. 2005. (Sports Illustrated for Kids Bks.). (Illus.). 176p. (YA). (gr. 7-12). lib. bdg. 25.25 (978-0-8239-3577-2(9)) Rosen Publishing Group, Inc., The.

Smithwicks, John. Meet Dwyane Wade: Basketball's Rising Star. 2007. (All-Star Players Ser.). (Illus.). 32p. (J). (gr. 4-6). lib. bdg. 23.95 (978-1-4042-3639-4(2) , PowerKids Pr.) Rosen Publishing Group, Inc., The.

—Meet LeBron James: Basketball's King James. 2007. (All-Star Players Ser.). (Illus.). 32p. (J). (gr. 4-6). lib. bdg. 23.95 (978-1-4042-3638-7(4) , PowerKids Pr.) Rosen Publishing Group, Inc., The.

Steen, Sandra. Take It to the Hoop: 100 Years of Women's Basketball. 2003. (Single Titles Ser.). (Illus.). 144p. (gr. 6 up). lib. bdg. 25.90 (978-0-7613-2470-6(4) , Twenty-First Century Bks.) Lerner Publishing Group.

Stewart-Jones, Mark. Vince Carter: The Fire Burns Bright. 2001. (978-0-606-22379-9(7)) Tandem Library Bks.

Stewart, Mark. Allen Iverson: Motion & Emotion. 2001. (New Wave Ser.). (Illus.). 48p. (gr. 4 up). lib. bdg. 22.90 (978-0-7613-1958-0(1) , Millbrook Pr.) Lerner Publishing Group.

—Chamique Holdsclaw: Driving Force. 2000. (New Wave Ser.). (Illus.). 48p. (gr. 4 up). lib. bdg. 22.90 (978-0-7613-1801-9(1) , Millbrook Pr.) Lerner Publishing Group.

—Jackie Stiles: Gym Dandy. 2002. (New Wave Ser.). (Illus.). 48p. (gr. 4 up). lib. bdg. 22.90 (978-0-7613-2614-4(6) , Millbrook Pr.) Lerner Publishing Group.

—Kevin Garnett/Shake up the Game. 2002. (New Wave Ser.). (Illus.). 48p. (gr. 4 up). lib. bdg. 22.90 (978-0-7613-2615-1(4) , Millbrook Pr.) Lerner Publishing Group.

—Kobe Bryant: Hard to the Hoop. 2000. (J). (978-0-606-20194-0(7)) Tandem Library Bks.

—Lisa Leslie. 1998. (gr. 3-6). lib. bdg. 14.10 (978-0-613-90733-0(7)) Tandem Library Bks.

—Tim Duncan: Tower of Power. 1999. (New Wave Ser.). (Illus.). 48p. (gr. 4 up). lib. bdg. 22.90 (978-0-7613-1513-1(6) , Millbrook Pr.) Lerner Publishing Group.

—Tim Duncan: Tower of Power. 1999. (gr. 3-6). lib. bdg. 15.25 (978-0-613-27255-1(2)) Tandem Library Bks.

—Vince Carter: The Fire Burns Bright. 2001. (New Wave Ser.). (Illus.). 48p. (gr. 4 up). lib. bdg. 22.90 (978-0-7613-2270-2(1) , Millbrook Pr.) Lerner Publishing Group.

—Vince Carter: The Fire Burns Bright. 2001. (gr. 3-6). lib. bdg. 16.40 (978-0-613-45235-9(6)) Tandem Library Bks.

Stewart, Mark Alan. Lisa Leslie: Queen of the Court. 1998. (Sports Stars Ser.). (Illus.). 48p. (J). (gr. 3-4). 19.50 (978-0-516-20585-4(4) , Children's Pr.) Scholastic Library Publishing.

—Tim Duncan: Tower of Power. 2000. (J). (978-0-606-19177-7(1)) Tandem Library Bks.

Sullivan, Michael J. Sports Great Shaquille O'Neal. rev. ed. 1998. (Sports Great Bks.). (Illus.). 64p. (YA). (gr. 4-10). lib. bdg. 22.60 (978-0-7660-1003-1(1)) Enslow Pubs., Inc.

Thomas, William. Pete Thompson & the Long Road Home. 2003. 80p. pap. 14.95 (978-1-4137-1620-7(2)) PublishAmerica, Inc.

Thornley, Stew. Grant Hill: Star Forward. 1999. (Sports Reports). (Illus.). 104p. (YA). (gr. 4-10). lib. bdg. 20.95 (978-0-7660-1078-9(3)) Enslow Pubs., Inc.

—Super Sports Star Chris Webber. 2002. (Super Sports Star Ser.). (Illus.). 48p. (J). (gr. 1-4). lib. bdg. 23.93 (978-0-7660-1807-5(5)) Enslow Pubs., Inc.

—Super Sports Star Jason Kidd. 2002. (Super Sports Star Ser.). (Illus.). 48p. (J). (gr. 1-4). lib. bdg. 23.93 (978-0-7660-1806-8(7)) Enslow Pubs., Inc.

—Super Sports Star Kobe Bryant. 2001. (Super Sports Star Ser.). (Illus.). 48p. (J). (gr. 1-4). lib. bdg. 23.93 (978-0-7660-1514-2(9)) Enslow Pubs., Inc.

—Super Sports Star Vince Carter. 2002. (Super Sports Star Ser.). (Illus.). 48p. (J). (gr. 1-4). lib. bdg. 23.93 (978-0-7660-1805-1(9)) Enslow Pubs., Inc.

Torres, John Albert. Allen Iverson: Never Give Up. 2004. (Sports Leaders Ser.). (Illus.). 104p. (J). lib. bdg. 26.60 (978-0-7660-2174-7(2)) Enslow Pubs., Inc.

—Kevin Garnett: "Da Kid" (Sports Achievers Biographies Ser.). (Illus.). 2003. 64p. (J). (gr. 4-9). pap. 5.95 (978-0-8225-9843-5(4) , Carolrhoda Bks.); 1999. 80p. (gr. 7-12). lib. bdg. 22.60 (978-0-8225-3673-4(0)) Lerner Publishing Group.

—Shaquille O'Neal: Gentle Giant. 2004. (Sports Leaders Ser.). (Illus.). 104p. (J). lib. bdg. 26.60 (978-0-7660-2175-4(0)) Enslow Pubs., Inc.

—Sheryl Swoopes. 2001. (Real-Life Reader Biography Ser.). (Illus.). 32p. (gr. 3-8). lib. bdg. 15.95 (978-1-58415-068-8(8)) Mitchell Lane Pubs., Inc.

—Sports Great Dikembe Mutombo. 2000. (Sports Great Bks.). (Illus.). 64p. (YA). (gr. 4-10). lib. bdg. 22.60 (978-0-7660-1267-7(0)) Enslow Pubs., Inc.

—Top 10 Basketball Three-Point Shooters. 1999. (Sports Top 10 Ser.). (Illus.). 48p. (YA). (gr. 4-10). lib. bdg. 23.93 (978-0-7660-1071-0(6)) Enslow Pubs., Inc.

—Vince Carter: Slam Dunk Artist. 2004. (Sports Leaders Ser.). (Illus.). 104p. (J). lib. bdg. 26.60 (978-0-7660-2173-0(4)) Enslow Pubs., Inc.

Townsend, Brad. Shaquille O'Neal: Center of Attention. 3rd rev. ed. 1998. (Sports Achievers Biographies Ser.). (Illus.). 64p. (YA). (gr. 4-9). pap. (978-0-8225-9818-3(3) , LernerSports) Lerner Publishing Group.

—Shaquille O'Neal, Center of Attention. 1998. (Achievers Ser.). (J). lib. bdg. 19.93 (978-0-8225-3665-9(X)) Lerner Publishing Group.

Triumph Books Staff. Allen Iverson. 2002. 48p. 12.95 (978-1-57243-492-9(9)) Triumph Bks.

Velazquez, Mauricio, tr. Grant Hill, Estrella del Basketball. 2002. (Power Kids Coleccion). (SPA.). 24p. (J). (gr. 2-3). lib. bdg. 17.25 (978-0-8239-6125-2(7) , RN30764, Buenas Letra) Rosen Publishing Group, Inc., The.

Wallner, Rosemary. Sheryl Swoopes. 2001. (Sports Heroes Ser.). (Illus.). 48p. (J). (gr. 3-4). lib. bdg. 21.26 (978-0-7368-0780-7(2) , Capstone High-Interest Bks.) Capstone Pr., Inc.

Walters, John. LeBron James. 2006. (World's Greatest Athletes Ser.). (Illus.). 32p. (J). (gr. 1-5). 27.07 (978-1-59296-756-8(6)) Child's World, Inc.

—Tim Duncan. 2006. (World's Greatest Athletes Ser.). (Illus.). 32p. (J). (gr. 1-5). 27.07 (978-1-59296-759-9(0)) Child's World, Inc.

Weber, Bruce. NBA Megastars 99. 1999. (Illus.). 32p. (J). (gr. 2-5). pap. 7.99 (978-0-590-05468-3(6)) Scholastic, Inc.

Weber, Terri Smith. Lebron James: Rising Star. 2004. (J). pap. (978-1-932724-23-3(0)); lib. bdg. (978-1-932724-22-6(2)) Panda Publishing, L.L.C. (Bios for Kids).

Weiss, Allan. Young Guns: Meet the Future Stars of the NHL. 2002. (gr. 3-6). lib. bdg. 15.30 (978-0-613-72428-9(3)) Tandem Library Bks.

Wheeler, Jill C. Lebron James. 2007. (Awesome Athletes Ser.). (Illus.). 32p. (J). 22.78 (978-1-59928-306-7(9)) ABDO Publishing Co.

Wilson, Glenn, et al. Rising Stars: The 10 Best Young Players in the NBA. Berler, Ron, ed. 1999. (Rising Stars Ser.). (Illus.). 95p. (J). (gr. 2-8). pap. 3.99 (978-1-886749-81-8(7)) Sports Illustrated For Kids.

Wilson, Steve & Smith, Pohla. Shaquille O'Neal. 2000. (Illus.). 64p. (J). (gr. 3-9). pap. 3.99 (978-1-930623-13-2(5)) Sports Illustrated For Kids.

Xiao, Chunfei. Yao Ming: The Road to the NBA. 2004. 254p. 18.95 (978-1-59265-002-6(3) , YAMIRO) Long River Pr.

Young, Jeff C. Yao Ming: Basketball's Big Man. 2005. (Sports Leaders Ser.). (Illus.). 104p. (J). lib. bdg. 26.60 (978-0-7660-2422-9(9)) Enslow Pubs., Inc.

Zuehlke Jeffrey. Dirk Nowitzki. 2007. (Amazing Athletes Ser.). (J). pap. 6.95 (***978-0-8225-7666-2(X)*** , First Avenue Editions) Lerner Publishing Group.

BASKETBALL—FICTION

Alphin, Elaine Marie. The Perfect Shot. 2005. 360p. (YA). (gr. 7-13). per. 16.95 (978-1-57505-862-7(6) , Carolrhoda Bks.) Lerner Publishing Group.

Andracki, Zenon. Dear Ashley: A Middle Grade Novel. 2006. (ENG.). 84p. per. 14.95 (***978-1-4241-6168-3(1)***) PublishAmerica, Inc.

Angerman, Liane. Season of Haze. 2006. 13.00 (***978-0-8059-9197-0(2)***) Dorrance Publishing Co., Inc.

Arena, Felice & Kettle, Phil. Basketball Buddies. Gordon, Gus, illus. 2004. (J). pap. (978-1-59336-369-7(9)) Mondo Publishing.

Arena, Jacqueline. Basketball Showdown. Foye, Lloyd, illus. 2005. (Girlz Rock! Ser.). (J). pap. (978-1-59336-704-6(X)) Mondo Publishing.

Armstrong, Robb. Got Game? Smith, Bruce, illus. 1998. (Patrick's Pals Ser.: No. 3). 96p. (J). (gr. 2-7). mass mkt. 3.99 (978-0-06-107069-3(6) , Harper Entertainment) HarperCollins Pubs.

—Runnin' with the Big Dawgs. Smith, Bruce, illus. 1998. (Patrick's Pals Ser.: No. 1). 96p. (J). (gr. 2-7). mass mkt. 3.99 (978-0-06-107067-9(X) , Harper Entertainment) HarperCollins Pubs.

Arterburn, Stephen & Hunt, Angela Elwell. Shane. 2004. (Young Believer on Tour Ser.). (J). pap. 3.99 (978-0-8423-8339-4(5)) Tyndale Hse. Pubs.

Aryal, Aimee. Let's Go Pistons! 2007. (YA). 14.95 (***978-1-932888-71-3(3)***) Mascot Bks., Inc.

Barber, Barbara E. Allie's Basketball Dream. Ligasan, Darryl, illus. 1998. 32p. (J). (ps-5). 6.95 (978-1-880000-72-4(5)) Lee & Low Bks., Inc.

Baskin, Nora Raleigh. Basketball (or Something Like It) 176p. (J). 2007. (gr. 4-7). pap. 5.99 (978-0-06-059612-5(0) , Harper Trophy); 2005. 15.99 (978-0-06-059610-1(4)); 2005. lib. bdg. 16.89 (978-0-06-059611-8(2)) HarperCollins Pubs.

Bateman, Teresa. The Princesses Have a Ball. Cravath, Lynne W., illus. 2002. 32p. (J). (gr. 2-5). 16.95 (978-0-8075-6626-8(8)) Whitman, Albert & Co.

—The Princesses Have a Ball. Cravath, Lynne, illus. 2005. (Albert Whitman Prairie Bks.). 32p. (J). (gr. 2-5). reprint ed. pap. 6.95 (978-0-8075-6628-2(4)) Whitman, Albert & Co.

Bates, Cynthia. Shooting Star. 2001. (Sports Stories Ser.). 102p. (gr. 3-8). (J). (***978-1-55028-727-1(3));*** (Illus.). 7.95 (978-1-55028-726-4(5)) Lorimer, James & Co., Ltd., Pubs. CAN. *Dist:* Casemate Pubs. & Bk. Distributors, LLC.

Bee, Clair. Backcourt Ace, Vol. 19. 2001. (Chip Hilton Sports Ser.: No. 19). x, 177p. (J). (gr. 3-8). pap. 5.99 (978-0-8054-2098-2(3)) B&H Publishing Grp.

—Buzzer Basket, Vol. 20. 2001. (Chip Hilton Sports Ser.: Vol. 20). xi, 177p. (J). pap. 5.99 (978-0-8054-2099-9(1)) B&H Publishing Grp.

—Championship Ball, Vol. 2. Farley, Cynthia B. & Farley, Randall, eds. rev. ed. 1998. (Chip Hilton Ser.: Vol. 2). (Illus.). 194p. (J). pap. 5.99 (978-0-8054-1815-6(6)) B&H Publishing Grp.

—Championship Ball. 1998. (gr. 5-8). lib. bdg. 14.15 (978-0-613-90137-6(1)) Tandem Library Bks.

—Comeback Cagers, Vol. 21. 2001. (Chip Hilton Sports Ser.). 208p. (J). pap. 5.99 (978-0-8054-2100-2(9)) B&H Publishing Grp.

—Hoop Crazy!, Vol. 6. 1999. (Chip Hilton Sports Ser.: Vol. 6). xi, 209p. (J). reprint ed. pap. 5.99 (978-0-8054-1988-7(8)) B&H Publishing Grp.

Bennett, James. The Squared Circle. 2002. 256p. (YA). (gr. 9 up). pap. 4.99 (978-0-590-48672-9(1) , Scholastic Paperbacks) Scholastic, Inc.

Bennett, James W. Blue Star Rapture. 2001. (J). (978-0-606-20574-0(8)) Tandem Library Bks.

—Squared Circle. 2002. (978-0-606-22265-5(0)) Tandem Library Bks.

Berenstain, Stan & Berenstain, Jan. The Wrong Crowd. 2001. (Berenstain Bears Ser.). (Illus.). (J). (gr. k-3). (978-0-606-21060-7(1)) Tandem Library Bks.

Bledsoe, Lucy Jane. Hoop Girlz. 2002. (Illus.). 128p. (J). (gr. 4-6). tchr. ed. 16.95 (978-0-8234-1691-2(7)) Holiday Hse., Inc.

Blumenthal, Scott & Hodus, Brett. Hoop City. 2002. 138p. 9.95 (978-0-9708992-1-7(1)) Scobre Pr. Corp.

Bly, Stephen A. Danger at Deception Pass. 1998. (gr. 7-12). lib. bdg. 13.00 (978-0-613-77372-0(1)) Tandem Library Bks.

Bossley, Michele Martin. Queen of the Court. 2000. (Sports Stories Ser.). (Illus.). 89p. (gr. 3-8). (J). (***978-1-55028-703-5(6));*** 7.95 (978-1-55028-702-8(8)) Lorimer, James & Co., Ltd., Pubs. CAN. *Dist:* Casemate Pubs. & Bk. Distributors, LLC.

—Queen of the Court. 2001. (gr. 5-8). lib. bdg. 13.55 (978-0-613-78314-9(X)) Tandem Library Bks.

Bowen, Fred. The Final Cut. Barrow, Ann, illus. 1999. (All-Star Sport Story Ser.). 112p. (J). (gr. 3-7). pap. 4.95 (978-1-56145-192-0(4) , Q23844) Peachtree Pubs., Ltd.

—The Final Cut. 1999. (Allstar Sportstory Ser.). (J). 11.75 (978-0-606-16914-1(8)) Tandem Library Bks.

—Final Cut. 1999. (gr. 3-6). lib. bdg. 12.95 (978-0-613-23227-2(5)) Tandem Library Bks.

—Full Court Fever. Barrow, Ann, illus. 1998. (All-Star Sport Story Ser.). 103p. (J). (gr. 4-7). pap. 4.95 (978-1-56145-160-9(6)) Peachtree Pubs., Ltd.

—Off the Rim. Barrow, Ann, illus. 1998. (All-Star Sport Story Ser.). 112p. (J). (gr. 3-7). pap. 4.95 (978-1-56145-161-6(4)) Peachtree Pubs., Ltd.

Brooks, Bruce. The Moves Make the Man. (J). pap., stu. ed. (978-0-13-017518-2(8)) Prentice Hall (Schl. Div.).

—Prince. 1998. (Wolfbay Wings Ser.: No. 5). (Illus.). 144p. (J). (gr. 4-7). pap. 4.50 (978-0-06-440600-0(8)) HarperCollins Pubs.

—Prince. 1998. (Wolfbay Wings Ser.: No. 5). (J). (gr. 4-7). (978-0-606-13925-0(7)) Tandem Library Bks.

Brouwer, Sigmund. Titan Clash. 2007. (Orca Sports Ser.). 176p. (YA). (gr. 5 up). pap. (***978-1-55143-721-7(X)***) Orca Bk. Pubs.

Brown, Marc. Arthur & the Pen-Pal Playoff. 2002. (Arthur Good Sports Ser.: Bk. 6). (Illus.). (J). 11.70 (978-0-7587-6863-6(X)) Book Wholesalers, Inc.

—Arthur & the Pen-Pal Playoff. Brown, Marc, illus. 6th ed. 2001. (Arthur Good Sports Ser.: Bk. 6). (Illus.). 64p. (J). (gr. 2-4). 14.95 (978-0-316-12054-8(5)); pap. 4.25 (978-0-316-12170-5(3)) Little, Brown Bks. for Young Readers.

—Arthur & the Pen-Pal Playoff. 2001. (Arthur Good Sports Ser.: Bk. 6). (ps-3). (Illus.). 55p. (J). lib. bdg. 12.10 (978-0-613-44165-0(6)); 11.05 (978-0-606-22556-4(0)) Tandem Library Bks.

Capeci, Anne. The Maltese Dog. l.t. ed. 1999. (Wishbone Mysteries Ser.: No. 6). 144p. (J). (gr. 4 up). lib. bdg. 23.33 (978-0-8368-2387-5(7)) Stevens, Gareth Inc.

Carbone, Elisa. Sarah & the Naked Truth. 2005. (J). per. 10.95 (978-0-9769404-8-7(5) , 0-9769404-8-5) Cloonfad Pr.

Carrier, Roch. The Basketball Player. Fischman, Sheila, tr. from FRE. Cohen, Sheldon, illus. 2001. 24p. (J). (gr. 3). pap. 7.95 (978-0-88776-553-7(X)) Tundra Bks., Inc./ Livres Toundra, Inc. CAN. *Dist:* Random Hse., Inc.

Casey, C. A. Top of the Key. 2006. 120p. (J). 20.95 (978-0-9759555-3-6(5)); per. 8.95 (978-0-9759555-4-3(3)) Bedazzled Ink Publishing Co.

Cheripko, Jan. Rat. (Illus.). 208p. (YA). 2004. pap. 9.95 (978-1-59078-349-8(2)); 2003. (gr. 6-9). 16.95 (978-1-59078-034-3(5)) Boyds Mills Pr.

Christopher, Matt. Center Court Sting. 1998. 160p. (J). (gr. 3-7). pap. 4.99 (978-0-316-14205-2(0)) Little Brown & Co.

—Center Court Sting. 1998. 140p. (J). (ps-7). per. 12.40 (978-0-613-11395-3(0)) Tandem Library Bks.

—Johnny Long Legs. ed. 2005. (Sports Classics II Ser.). 117p. (J). lib. bdg. 15.00 (978-1-59054-760-1(8)) Fitzgerald Bks.

—Long Shot for Paul. ed. 2005. (Sports Classics II Ser.). 130p. (J). lib. bdg. 15.00 (978-1-59054-762-5(4)) Fitzgerald Bks.

—Nothin but Net. 2003. (Matt Christopher Sports Ser.). 144p. (J). (gr. 3-7). pap. 4.99 (978-0-316-13344-9(2)) Little Brown & Co.

—Slam Dunk. 2004. (Illus.). 128p. (J). (gr. 4-7). pap. 4.99 (978-0-316-60762-9(2)) Little Brown & Co.

—Wheel Wizards. 2000. 132p. (J). (gr. 3-7). 15.95 (978-0-316-13611-2(5)) Little Brown & Co.

Christopher, Matt & #1 Sports Writer for Kids Staff. Center Court Sting. 1998. 160p. (J). (gr. 3-7). 15.95 (978-0-316-14278-6(6)) Little Brown & Co.

Coburn, Jake. Lovesick. 2007. 240p. (YA). pap. 7.99 (978-0-14-240802-5(6) , Puffin) Penguin Group (USA) Inc.

Coy, John. Around the World. Reonegro, Antonio & Lynch, Tom, illus. 2005. 32p. (J). (gr. 1-4). 17.95 (978-1-58430-244-5(5)) Lee & Low Bks., Inc.

—Strong to the Hoop. Jean-Bart, Leslie, illus. 32p. (J). 2003. 6.95 (978-1-58430-178-3(3)); 1999. (gr. 1 up). 16.95 (978-1-880000-80-9(6)) Lee & Low Bks., Inc.

Coy, John, et al. Directo Al Aro. Jean-Bart, Leslie, illus. 2002. (SPA & ENG.). (J). 16.95 (978-1-58430-082-3(5)); pap. 6.95 (978-1-58430-083-0(3)) Lee & Low Bks., Inc.

de La Pena, Matt. Ball Don't Lie. 2005. 288p. (YA). (gr. 8-12). lib. bdg. 18.99 (978-0-385-90258-8(1)); (gr. 9-12). 16.95 (978-0-385-73232-1(5)) Random Hse. Children's Bks. (Delacorte Bks. for Young Readers).

de la Pena, Matt. Ball Don't Lie. 2007. 288p. (YA). (gr. 9). pap. 7.99 (978-0-385-73425-7(5) , Delacorte Bks. for Young Readers) Random Hse. Children's Bks.

Deuker, Carl. Night Hoops. 2001. 256p. (gr. 7 up). pap. 6.99 (978-0-06-447275-3(2) , Harper Trophy) HarperCollins Pubs.

—Night Hoops. 2000. (Illus.). 224p. (J). (gr. 7-12). tchr. ed. 15.00 (978-0-395-97936-5(6)) Houghton Mifflin Co. Trade & Reference Div.

—Night Hoops. 2001. (978-0-606-22927-2(2)); 250p. (gr. 7-12). lib. bdg. 14.15 (978-0-613-61919-6(6)) Tandem Library Bks.

Diersch, Sandra. Home Court Advantage. 2001. (Sports Stories Ser.). 128p. (gr. 3-8). (J). (***978-1-55028-749-3(4));*** 7.95 (978-1-55028-748-6(6)) Lorimer, James & Co., Ltd., Pubs. CAN. *Dist:* Casemate Pubs. & Bk. Distributors, LLC.

Dominguez, Carlos. El Hombre de Otra Galaxia. 2001. Tr. of Men from Another Galaxy. (SPA.). 112p. (J). 7.95 (978-84-348-2709-7(3)) SM Ediciones ESP. *Dist:* AIMS International Bks., Inc.

Einspruch, Andrew. Dunkin' Dazza's Daring Dribble. Foster, Peter, illus. 1999. (Supa Doopers Ser.). 64p. (J). (978-0-7608-3290-5(0)) Sundance/Newbridge Educational Publishing.

—Dunkin' Dazza's Daring Dribble. 1999. (gr. 3-6). lib. bdg. 12.60 (978-0-613-30370-5(9)) Tandem Library Bks.

Feinstein, John. Last Shot: A Final Four Mystery. (J). (gr. 6-10). 2005. 256p. 16.95 (978-0-375-83168-3(1) , Knopf Bks. for Young Readers); 2006. 272p. reprint ed. pap. 6.50 (978-0-553-49460-0(0) , Yearling) Random Hse. Children's Bks.

Ferriell, Phil. Bernie Bocks Makes the Team. 2007. 86p. 14.95 (***978-1-4241-4991-9(6)***) PublishAmerica, Inc.

Foley, John. Hoops of Steel. 2007. 240p. (J). (gr. 9 up). pap. 8.95 (978-0-7387-0981-9(6) , Flux) Llewellyn Pubns.

Forrey, B. J. Basketball's My Favorite. 2004. 20p. pap. 14.95 (978-1-4137-2991-7(6)) PublishAmerica, Inc.

Fowler, Marie. Long Shot. 2003. (Dream Series Ser.). 160p. 9.95 (978-0-9708992-6-2(2)) Scobre Pr. Corp.

Furr, L. David. Hoops & Me. Simonton, Tom, illus. 2005. 16p. (J). pap. 5.00 (978-1-57274-751-7(X) , 2746, Bks. for Young Learners) Owen, Richard C. Pubs., Inc.

Garland, Michael. Hooray Jose! 2007. (Illus.). 32p. (J). 14.99 (***978-0-7614-5345-1(8)***) Cavendish, Marshall Corp.

Garland, Michael, illus. Hooray José! 2007. (J). (***978-1-4287-3591-0(7)*** , Cavendish Children's Bks.) Cavendish, Marshall Corp.

Gelsey, James. Scooby-Doo! & the Hoopster Horror. 2005. (Illus.). 61p. (J). lib. bdg. 15.00 (***978-1-4242-0305-5(8)***) Fitzgerald Bks.

Gershon, Dann & Full Force. Slam Dunk. Gershon, David, illus. 1999. (Hangin' with the Hombeez Ser.: Vol. 6). 40p. (J). (gr. k-6). 9.95 (978-0-9656985-8-0(0)) Noware Bks.

Greene, Janice. Blood & Basketball. 2004. (Illus.). 32p. (YA). 2.95 (978-1-56254-739-4(9) , SP7399) Saddleback Educational Publishing.

Griffeth, Rodger W. The Reluctant Star. 2000. 108p. (YA). (gr. 4-7). pap. 9.95 (978-0-595-13025-2(9)) iUniverse, Inc.

Gunnery, Sylvia. Personal Best. 2005. (Sports Stories Ser.). 112p. (J). (gr. 3-8). 7.95 (978-1-55028-896-4(2)); (***978-1-55028-897-1(0)***) Lorimer, James & Co., Ltd., Pubs. CAN. *Dist:* Casemate Pubs. & Bk. Distributors, LLC.

Gutman, Dan. The Million Dollar Shot. 2nd ed. 2006. 128p. (gr. 3-7). pap. 5.99 (978-1-4231-0084-3(0)) Hyperion Pr.

Hafer, Todd. Full Court Press. 2004. (Spirit of the Game, Sports Fiction Ser.). 144p. (J). (gr. 3-6). pap. 4.99 (978-0-310-70668-7(8)) Zonderkidz.

—Goal-Line Stand. Lucado, Max, ed. 2004. (Spirit of the Game, Sports Fiction Ser.). 144p. (J). (gr. 3-6). pap. 4.99 (978-0-310-70669-4(6)) Zonderkidz.

—Three-Point Play. 2005. (Spirit of the Game, Sports Fiction Ser.). 144p. (J). (ps-7). pap. 4.99 (978-0-310-70795-0(1)) Zonderkidz.

Hale, Jane. Heartland. 1999. (Illus.). 288p. (J). (gr. 8-12). pap. 12.95 (978-0-934426-91-6(0)) NAPSAC Reproductions.

Hallem, J. The Super Electrics. Dale, Rae, illus. 2006. (Read-It! Chapter Books). 64p. (J). (gr. 2-4). 19.95 (978-1-4048-1663-3(1)) Picture Window Bks.

Hallinan, P. K. Let's Play As a Team. 2003. (Illus.). 28p. (J). 7.95 (978-0-8249-5452-9(1)) Ideals Pubns.

Harcourt School Publishers Staff. Basement Basketball On Level. 3rd ed. 2002. (Trophies Reading Program Ser.). (Illus.). pap. 5.10 (978-0-15-323164-3(5)) Harcourt Schl. Pubs.

—Basement Basketball 5-Pack, On Level. 3rd ed. 2002. (Trophies Reading Program Ser.). (Illus.). (gr. 3). pap. 25.60 (978-0-15-327020-8(9)) Harcourt Schl. Pubs.

Harkrader, L. D. Airball: My Life in Briefs. 2005. 208p. (J). (ps-7). 16.95 (978-1-59643-060-0(5)) Roaring Brook Pr.

—Airball: My Life in Briefs. 2008. 224p. (J). pap. 6.99 (***978-0-312-37382-5(1)***) Square Fish.

Harris, Dorthy. Angela's Basketball Triumph. 2005. 67p. pap. 14.95 (978-1-4137-7547-1(0)) PublishAmerica, Inc.

Heldring, Thatcher. Toby Wheeler: Eighth-Grade Benchwarmer. 2007. 224p. (J). (gr. 4-7). 14.99 (***978-0-385-73390-8(9)***); lib. bdg. 17.99 (***978-0-385-90405-6(3)***) Random Hse. Children's Bks. (Delacorte Bks. for Young Readers).

Herman, Gail. Just Like Mike. 2001. (978-0-606-21277-9(9)) Tandem Library Bks.

Hicks, Betty. Basketball Bats. McCauley, Adam, illus. 2008. 64p. (J). 14.95 (***978-1-59643-243-7(8)***) Roaring Brook Pr.

Higgins, Richard P. Basketballs & Babysteps. 2001. 192p. (YA). pap. 13.95 (978-0-595-20051-1(6) , Authors Choice Pr.) iUniverse, Inc.

Holbrook, Bill. Dancing on the Basketball Court No. 2: Safe Havens. 2000. (Illus.). 152p. (YA). pap. 12.95 (978-1-929462-16-2(6)) Plan Nine Publishing, Inc.

Holohan, Maureen. Sideline Blues. 2001. (Broadway Ballplayers Ser.). (Illus.). (J). (978-0-606-21433-9(X)) Tandem Library Bks.

I Can't Play Basketball, I'm Only Four Feet Tall. 2003. (J). 10.95 (978-0-9745798-1-8(5)) Pen & Sword Publishing Co., The.

Jean-Bart, Leslie. Strong to the Hoop. 2003. (gr. k-3). lib. bdg. 15.25 (978-0-613-86394-0(1)) Tandem Library Bks.

Jordan, Deloris. Salt in His Shoes: Michael Jordan in Pursuit of a Dream. Nelson, Kadir A., illus. 2002. 32p. (J). mass mkt. 1.00 (978-0-689-85524-5(9) , Simon & Schuster Children's Publishing) Simon & Schuster Children's Publishing.

—Salt in His Shoes: Michael Jordan in Pursuit of a Dream. Nelson, Kadir A., illus. 2003. lib. bdg. 15.30 (978-0-613-89001-4(9)) Tandem Library Bks.

Jordan, Deloris & Jordan, Roslyn M. Salt in His Shoes: Michael Jordan in Pursuit of a Dream. Nelson, Kadir A., illus. 32p. (J). 2003. pap. 7.99 (978-0-689-83419-6(5) , Aladdin); 2000. (gr. 2-4). 16.95 (978-0-689-83371-7(7)) Simon & Schuster Children's Publishing.

Kesler, J. Billie. 2006. 304p. pap. 24.95 (978-1-4241-3457-1(9)) PublishAmerica, Inc.

Kim, Kenneth H. Half & Half. 2000. (gr. 7-12). lib. bdg. 11.80 (978-0-613-51051-6(8)) Tandem Library Bks.

Kindig, Tess Eileen. Camp Bee-A-Champ. 2001. (gr. k-3). lib. bdg. 13.00 (978-0-613-72852-2(1)) Tandem Library Bks.

—Double Whammy. 2001. (gr. k-3). lib. bdg. 13.00 (978-0-613-72853-9(X)) Tandem Library Bks.

—Double Whammy!, Vol. 8. 2001. (Slam Dunk Ser.: Vol. 8). 96p. (J). (gr. 1-4). 4.99 (978-0-570-07142-6(9)) Concordia Publishing Hse.

—Gimme an "A", Vol. 5. 2000. (Slam Dunk Ser.: Vol. 5). (Illus.). 96p. (J). (gr. 1-4). 4.99 (978-0-570-07091-7(0)) Concordia Publishing Hse.

—March Mania, Vol. 6. 2000. (Slam Dunk Ser.: Vol. 6). 96p. (J). (gr. 1-4). 4.99 (978-0-570-07092-4(9)) Concordia Publishing Hse.

—March Mania. 2000. (gr. k-3). lib. bdg. 13.00 (978-0-613-72796-9(7)) Tandem Library Bks.

—Muggsy Makes an Assist. 2000. (Slam Dunk Ser.: Vol. 3). 96p. (J). (gr. 1-4). Vol. 3. (Illus.). 4.99 (978-0-570-07018-4(X)); Vol. 4. 4.99 (978-0-570-07019-1(8)) Concordia Publishing Hse.

—Muggsy Makes an Assist. 2000. (gr. k-3). lib. bdg. 13.00 (978-0-613-72906-2(4)) Tandem Library Bks.

—Sixth Man Switch. 2000. (Slam Dunk Ser.: Vol. 1). 96p. (J). (gr. 1-4). 4.99 (978-0-570-07016-0(3)) Concordia Publishing Hse.

—Sixth Man Switch. 2000. (gr. k-3). lib. bdg. 13.00 (978-0-613-72839-3(4)) Tandem Library Bks.

—Slam Dunk Set, 8 vols. (Slam Dunk Ser.). (J). 38.99 (978-0-7586-0014-1(3)) Concordia Publishing Hse.

—Spider Mcghee & the Hoopla. 2000. (gr. k-3). lib. bdg. 13.00 (978-0-613-72840-9(8)) Tandem Library Bks.

—Spider McGhee & the Hoopla, Vol. 2. 2000. (Slam Dunk Ser.: Vol. 2). (Illus.). 96p. (J). (gr. 1-4). 4.99 (978-0-570-07017-7(1)) Concordia Publishing Hse.

—Zip, Zero, Zilch. 2000. (gr. k-3). lib. bdg. 13.00 (978-0-613-72905-5(6)) Tandem Library Bks.

Kindig, Tess Eileen & Van Severen, Joe. Double Whammy!, Vol. 7. 2001. (Slam Dunk Ser.: Vol. 7). (Illus.). 96p. (J). (gr. 1-4). 4.99 (978-0-570-07143-3(7)) Concordia Publishing Hse.

King, Donna. Slam Dunk. 2007. 160p. (J). (gr. 4-7). pap. 5.95 (***978-0-7534-6155-6(2)*** , Kingfisher) Houghton Mifflin Co. Trade & Reference Div.

Klass, David. Danger Zone. 1998. (J). 11.64 (978-0-606-13080-6(2)) Tandem Library Bks.

Kline, Suzy. Orp Goes to the Hoop. 2000. (978-0-606-18442-7(2)) Tandem Library Bks.

Kline, Trish & Donev, Mary. Hoops in the Coop: KA Reader 7. 2007. (Illus.). 32p. (J). per. 20.00 (***978-1-934307-00-7(9)***) Ghost Hunter Productions.

Kolb, Joseph J. Reservation Dreams. 2004. 185p. pap. 19.95 (978-1-4137-3054-8(X)) PublishAmerica, Inc.

Korman, Gordon. Nick's a Chick. 2000. (gr. 3-6). lib. bdg. 13.00 (978-0-613-31525-8(1)) Tandem Library Bks.

Krech, Bob. Rebound. 2006. 272p. (J). (gr. 9 up). 16.99 (978-0-7614-5319-2(9)) Cavendish, Marshall Corp.

Lanier, Bob. It's All in the Name. 2003. (gr. k-3). lib. bdg. 11.80 (978-0-613-66643-5(7)) Tandem Library Bks.

—Out of Bounds. 2003. (gr. k-3). lib. bdg. 11.80 (978-0-613-85123-7(4)) Tandem Library Bks.

—Stuck in the Middle. 2003. (gr. k-3). lib. bdg. 11.80 (978-0-613-84844-2(6)) Tandem Library Bks.

—Take the Court. 2003. (gr. k-3). lib. bdg. 11.80 (978-0-613-66673-2(9)) Tandem Library Bks.

Lanier, Bob & Goodyear, Heather. It's All in the Name. 2003. (Hey L'il D! Ser.: No. 1). (Illus.). 96p. (J). pap. 3.99 (978-0-439-40899-8(7) , Scholastic Paperbacks) Scholastic, Inc.

—Out of Bounds. 2003. (Hey L'il D! Ser.: No. 4). (Illus.). 80p. (J). pap. 3.99 (978-0-439-40902-5(0) , Scholastic Paperbacks) Scholastic, Inc.

—Stuck in the Middle. Grover, Desire, illus. 2003. (Hey L'il D! Ser.: No. 3). 80p. (J). pap. 3.99 (978-0-439-40901-8(2) , Scholastic Paperbacks) Scholastic, Inc.

—Take the Court. 2003. (Hey L'il D! Ser.: No. 2). (Illus.). 80p. (J). pap. 3.99 (978-0-439-40900-1(4) , Scholastic Paperbacks) Scholastic, Inc.

Lavette, Lavaille. The Adventures of Roopster Roux: Escape from Vulture's Roost. Mitchell, Louis H., illus. 1998. (Adventures of Roopster Roux Ser.). 32p. (J). (ps-3). pap. 5.95 (978-1-56554-360-7(2)) Pelican Publishing Co., Inc.

—The Adventures of Roopster Roux: Slammin' Slime. Mitchell, Louis H., illus. 1998. (Adventures of Roopster Roux Ser.). 32p. (J). (ps-3). pap. 5.95 (978-1-56554-359-1(9)) Pelican Publishing Co., Inc.

—The Adventures of Roopster Roux: Surfing the Net. Mitchell, Louis H., illus. 1998. (Adventures of Roopster Roux Ser.). 32p. (J). (ps-3). pap. 5.95 (978-1-56554-361-4(0)) Pelican Publishing Co., Inc.

—The Adventures of Roopster Roux: The Monster All-Stars. Mitchell, Louis H., illus. 1998. (Adventures of Roopster Roux Ser.). 32p. (J). (ps-3). pap. 5.95 (978-1-56554-362-1(9)) Pelican Publishing Co., Inc.

Like Mike. novel ed. 2002. 112p. (J). pap. 4.99 (978-0-439-44527-6(2)) Scholastic, Inc.

Lupica, Mike. Hot Hand. 2007. (Mike Lupica's Comeback Kids Ser.). 165p. (J). (gr. 4-7). 9.99 (***978-0-399-24714-9(9)*** , Philomel) Penguin Group (USA) Inc.

—Miracle on 49th Street. 256p. (gr. 5). 2007. (J). pap. 7.99 (***978-0-14-240942-8(1)*** , Puffin); 2006. (YA). 17.99 (978-0-399-24488-9(3) , Philomel) Penguin Group (USA) Inc.

—Summer Ball. 2007. 256p. (YA). (gr. 4 up). 17.99 (978-0-399-24487-2(5) , Philomel) Penguin Group (USA) Inc.

—Travel Team. 288p. (YA). 2005. (gr. 5-8). pap. 7.99 (978-0-14-240462-1(4) , Puffin); 2004. (gr. 3-8). 16.99 (978-0-399-24150-5(7) , Philomel) Penguin Group (USA) Inc.

—Travel Team. l.t. ed. 2005. 400p. (J). (ps-7). lib. bdg. 23.95 (978-0-7862-7415-4(8)) Thorndike Pr.

Maddox, Jake. Free Throw. Tiffany, Sean, illus. 2007. (Jake Maddox Sports Story Ser.). 65p. (J). (gr. 4-8). lib. bdg. 21.26 (978-1-59889-060-0(3)) Stone Arch Bks.

Maddox, Jake. Slam Dunk Shoes. Tiffany, Sean, illus. 2008. (J). (***978-1-59889-842-2(6)***); pap. (***978-1-59889-894-1(9)***) Stone Arch Bks.

Marbury, Stephon & Dean, Marshall. The Adventures of Young Starbury: Practice Makes Perfect. Nakai, Ryan, illus. 2007. 36p. (J). 12.99 (***978-0-9798250-0-2(8)***) Godspeed Pr.

Marsh, Carole. The Baskerville Basketball. 2006. 64p. (gr. 2-4). 14.95 (***978-0-635-06222-2(4)***); pap. 3.99 (***978-0-635-06216-1(X)***) Gallopade International.

Martin, Bill. Swish! 2000. (gr. 3-6). lib. bdg. 15.25 (978-0-613-31778-8(5)) Tandem Library Bks.

Marzollo, Jean & Marzollo, Dan. Basketball Buddies, Level 3. Kelley, True, illus. 1998. (Hello Reader! Ser.). 32p. (J). (gr. 1-3). pap. (978-0-590-38401-8(5)) Scholastic, Inc.

McDonald, Megan. Meet Julie. McAliley, Susan & Hunt, Robert, illus. 2007. 104p. (YA). (gr. 3 up). pap. 6.95 (***978-1-59369-257-5(9)***) American Girl Publishing, Inc.

—Meet Julie. McAliley, Susan. 2007. 104p. (YA). (gr. 3 up). 12.95 (***978-1-59369-287-2(0)***) American Girl Publishing, Inc.

McGirr, Randel W. Bible Camp. 2007. 176p. per. 13.95 (***978-0-595-44663-6(9)***) iUniverse, Inc.

Mercer, Adrienne. Rebound. 2002. (Sports Stories Ser.). 128p. (gr. 3-8). (J). (***978-1-55028-761-5(3)***); 7.95 (978-1-55028-760-8(5)) Lorimer, James & Co., Ltd., Pubs. CAN. *Dist:* Casemate Pubs. & Bk. Distributors, LLC.

—Rebound. 2002. (gr. 3-6). lib. bdg. 13.55 (978-0-613-78322-4(0)) Tandem Library Bks.

Meunier, Brian & Edgerton, Perky. Bravo, Tavo! 2007. (Illus.). 32p. (J). (gr. k-3). 16.99 (978-0-525-47478-4(1) , Dutton Juvenile) Penguin Group (USA) Inc.

Miller, Tom. Full Court Press: Tom Miller. Hier, Marjorie A., illus. 2000. 70p. (J). pap. 7.50 (978-0-931209-91-8(9)) Mid-Prairie Bks.

Mills, Claudia. Gus & Grandpa at Basketball. Stock, Catherine, illus. 2001. (Gus & Grandpa Ser.). 48p. (J). (gr. 1-3). 15.00 (978-0-374-32818-4(8) , Farrar, Straus & Giroux (BYR)) Farrar, Straus & Giroux.

Moore-Mallinos, Jennifer. It's OK to Be Me: Just Like You, I Can Do Almost Anything. Fabrega, Marta, illus. 2007. (Live & Learn Ser.). 36p. (J). (gr. k-2). pap. 6.99 (978-0-7641-3584-2(8)) Barron's Educational Series, Inc.

—Que bien es ser yo Mismo: Puedo hacer casi todo lo que me de la Gana! Fabrega, Marta, illus. 2007. (Live & Learn Ser.). 36p. (J). (gr. k-2). pap. 6.99 (978-0-7641-3585-9(6)) Barron's Educational Series, Inc.

Myers, Bill. My Life As a Busted-Up Basketball Backboard, Vol. 18. 2000. (Incredible Worlds of Wally McDoogle Ser.: No. 18). 128p. (J). (gr. 3-7). pap. 6.99 (978-0-8499-4027-9(3)) Nelson, Thomas Inc.

Myers, Walter Dean. Game. 2008. 240p. (J). 16.99 (***978-0-06-058294-4(4)***); lib. bdg. 17.89 (***978-0-06-058295-1(2)***) HarperCollins Pubs. (HarperTeen).

—Hoops. 2002. (Illus.). (J). 13.94 (978-0-7587-4823-2(X)) Book Wholesalers, Inc.

—Slam! 1998. (Point Signature Ser.). 272p. (YA). (gr. 7-12). 5.99 (978-0-590-48668-2(3) , Scholastic Paperbacks) Scholastic, Inc.

Myers, Walter Dean & Myers, Walter Dean. Slam! 1998. 266p. (YA). (gr. 7-12). lib. bdg. 14.15 (978-0-613-12111-8(2)) Tandem Library Bks.

Noble, Trinka Hakes. Jimmy's Boa & the Bungee Jump Slam Dunk. Kellogg, Steven, illus. 2003. 32p. (J). (ps). 16.99 (978-0-8037-2600-0(7) , Dial) Penguin Group (USA) Inc.

—Jimmy's Boa & the Bungee Jump Slam Dunk. Kellogg, Steven, illus. 2005. 32p. (J). pap. 5.99 (978-0-14-240453-9(5) , Puffin) Penguin Group (USA) Inc.

Ocorr, Dave. Matt & Shawn: Backcourt Duo. 1998. (Coach's Choice Ser.). 155p. (J). (gr. 4-9). pap. 8.95 (978-0-9660758-2-3(X)) Perth Pubns., Ltd.

O'Malley, Kevin. Mount Olympus Basketball. O'Malley, Kevin, illus. (Illus.). 32p. (J). 2005. (gr. 1-4). pap., pap. 6.95 (978-0-8027-7728-7(7)); 2004. (gr. 2-6). 15.95 (978-0-8027-8844-3(0)) Walker & Co.

—Mount Olympus Basketball. 2004. (Illus.). 32p. (J). (gr. 2-6). 16.85 (978-0-8027-8845-0(9)) Walker & Co.

Parker, Robert Andrew. Edenville Owls. 2008. 208p. (YA). (gr. 4-6). pap. 7.99 (***978-0-14-241161-2(2)*** , Puffin) Penguin Group (USA) Inc.

Patneaude, David. Deadly Drive. 184p. (J). 2007. pap. 6.95 (***978-0-8075-0845-9(4)***); 2005. (gr. 6-8). 15.95 (978-0-8075-0844-2(6)) Whitman, Albert & Co.

Pavlik, Al. Battles in the Backcourt. 2003. 120p. (J). per. 9.97 (978-0-9722906-2-3(1)) AP Publishing.

Pee-Wee Basketball. 2003. (J). per. (978-1-57657-939-8(5)) Paradise Pr., Inc.

Perry, Phyllis Jean. The Alien, the Giant, & Rocketman. Francis, Guy, illus. 2006. (J). pap. (978-1-59336-723-7(6)) Mondo Publishing.

Pippenger, Jack G. The Young Rebel. 2007. 292p. 27.95 (***978-0-595-86314-3(0)***); per. 17.95 (***978-0-595-41077-4(4)***) iUniverse, Inc.

Prescott, Duncan. The Wave. 2004. 226p. pap. 19.95 (978-1-4137-1006-9(9)) PublishAmerica, Inc.

Rallison, Janette. Life, Love, & the Pursuit of Free Throws. 2006. 192p. (J). pap. 6.95 (978-0-8027-8898-6(X)); 2004. 176p. (YA). 16.95 (978-0-8027-8927-3(7)) Walker & Co.

Richardson, Charisse. The Real Slam Dunk (SE) 2005. 80p. (J). pap. 3.99 (978-0-14-240442-3(X) , Puffin) Penguin Group (USA) Inc.

Richardson, Charisse K. The Real Lucky Charm. Velasquez, Eric, illus. 2005. 80p. (J). (gr. 2-5). 16.99 (978-0-8037-3105-9(1) , Dial); pap. 4.99 (978-0-14-240431-7(4) , Puffin) Penguin Group (USA) Inc.

Ritter, John H. Over the Wall. 2002. 320p. (J). pap. 6.99 (978-0-698-11931-4(2) , Putnam Juvenile) Penguin Group (USA) Inc.

Robins, Eleanor. The Easy Way. 2003. (Illus.). 48p. (YA). per. (978-1-56254-683-0(X) , SP683X) Saddleback Educational Publishing.

Robinson, Sharon. Slam Dunk! 2007. 160p. (J). (gr. 4-7). pap. 16.99 (***978-0-439-67199-6(X)*** , Scholastic Pr.) Scholastic, Inc.

Rockwell, Anne F. Brendan & Belinda & the Slam Dunk. Meisel, Paul, illus. 2007. (Good Sports Ser.). 40p. (J). lib. bdg. 16.89 (978-0-06-028447-3(1)); 15.99 (978-0-06-028443-5(9)) HarperCollins Pubs.

Rud, Jeff. In the Paint: South Side Sports. 2005. (Illus.). 176p. (J). (gr. 3-7). pap. 7.95 (978-1-55143-337-0(0)) Orca Bk. Pubs. USA.

Sasturain, Juan. Brooklin y Medio. (SPA.). (YA). 9.95 (978-958-04-6876-9(1)) Norma S.A. COL. *Dist:* Distribuidora Norma, Inc.

Selman, Marty. Nick's a Chick. Weizman, Daniel, ed. 2000. (Jersey Ser.: 3). (Illus.). 128p. (gr. 3-7). pap. 4.99 (978-0-7868-4423-4(X)) Disney Pr.

—Nick's a Chick. 2000. (Jersey Ser.). (Illus.). (J). (978-0-606-20738-6(4)) Tandem Library Bks.

Shackelford, Jim. Totally Responsible & Totally Wild. 2002. 104p. per. 8.00 (978-0-9720125-0-8(8)) Frozen Field Pr.

Sharing Turf. 2004. (Illus.). (YA). mass mkt. 19.95 (978-0-9753663-0-1(0)) Ballad Productions.

Shaskan, Trisha Speed. Camden's Game. 2007. (Illus.). 24p. (J). (***978-1-4048-1226-0(1)***) Picture Window Bks.

—Camden's Game. Yilmaz, Necdet, illus. 2006. 24p. (J). (***978-1-4048-3136-0(3)***) Picture Window Bks.

Sitomer, Alan Lawrence. The Hoopster: Read-Along/Homework Pack. unabr. ed. 2005. (YA). 65.74 incl. audio (978-1-4025-7027-8(9) , 41853) Recorded Bks., LLC.

Smith, Charles R. Let's Play Basketball! Widener, Terry, illus. 2004. (Super Sturdy Picture Books). 24p. (J). (gr. k-ps). 8.99 (978-0-7636-1691-5(5)) Candlewick Pr.

Smith, Stephen & Caldwell, Lise. Full Court Pressure. 2006. (Game on for Girls Ser.). 128p. (J). pap. 5.99 (978-0-7847-1730-1(3) , 42147) Standard Publishing.

Suen, Anastasia. Loose Tooth. 2003. (gr. k-3). lib. bdg. 11.80 (978-0-613-67459-1(6)) Tandem Library Bks.

—The Loose Tooth. Eitzen, Allan, illus. 2003. (Easy-to-Read Ser.). 32p. (J). (gr. k-2). pap. 3.99 (978-0-14-250064-4(X) , Puffin) Penguin Group (USA) Inc.

Sweeney, Joyce. Players. 2000. 222p. (J). (gr. 7-12). 16.95 (978-1-890817-54-1(6)) Winslow Pr.

Tang, Charles, illus. The Basketball Mystery, Vol. 68. 1999. (Boxcar Children Ser.: No. 68). 128p. (J). (gr. 2-5). pap. 3.95 (978-0-8075-0576-2(5)) Whitman, Albert & Co.

Taylor, Thomas. Superstar Coach. 2004. (Sport Story Ser.: 1). 202p. (J). 9.95 (978-0-9702216-0-5(6)) Sport Story Publishing.

Tocher, Timothy. Long Shot. 2001. (J). 137p. (978-0-88166-395-2(6)); 144p. pap. 4.95 (978-0-689-84331-0(3)) Meadowbrook Pr.

Trueman, Terry. Cruise Control. 2004. 160p. (J). 15.99 (978-0-06-623960-6(5)); lib. bdg. 16.89 (978-0-06-623961-3(3)) HarperCollins Pubs.

Volponi, Paul. Black & White. 2005. 192p. (YA). (gr. 7). 15.99 (978-0-670-06006-1(2) , Viking Adult) Penguin Group (USA) Inc.

—Rucker Park Setup. 2007. 208p. (J). 15.99 (978-0-670-06130-3(1) , Viking Juvenile) Penguin Group (USA) Inc.

Wallace, Rich. Dunk under Pressure, Vol. 7. 2007. 120p. (J). pap. 4.99 (978-0-14-240858-2(1) , Puffin) Penguin Group (USA) Inc.

—Dunk under Pressure: Winning Season 7. 2006. (Winning Season Ser.). 128p. (J). (gr. 4-6). 14.99 (978-0-670-06095-5(X) , Viking Juvenile) Penguin Group (USA) Inc.

—Losing Is Not an Option. 2005. 144p. (YA). (gr. 7 up). pap. 5.99 (978-0-440-23844-7(7) , Laurel Leaf) Random Hse. Children's Bks.

—Playing Without the Ball. 2002. 224p. (YA). (gr. 9 up). pap. 5.99 (978-0-440-22972-8(3) , Laurel Leaf) Random Hse. Children's Bks.

—Second String Center. 2007. (Winning Season Ser.). 128p. (J). (gr. 4). 14.99 (***978-0-670-06150-1(6)*** , Viking Juvenile) Penguin Group (USA) Inc.

Wallace, Rich. Technical Foul: Winning Season. 2005. (Winning Season Ser.: Bk. 2). 128p. (YA). (gr. 3). pap. 4.99 (978-0-14-240444-7(6) , Puffin) Penguin Group (USA) Inc.

Walters, Eric. Hoop Crazy! 2001. (Young Reader Ser.). (Illus.). 144p. (J). (gr. 3-6). pap. 5.95 (978-1-55143-184-0(X)) Orca Bk. Pubs. USA.

—Hoop Crazy! 2001. (gr. 3-6). lib. bdg. 13.00 (978-0-613-50205-4(1)) Tandem Library Bks.

—Long Shot. 2002. (Illus.). 140p. (J). (gr. 4-7). per. 13.00 (978-0-613-62793-1(8)) Tandem Library Bks.

—Off Season. 2003. (Orca Young Readers Ser.). (Illus.). 144p. (J). (gr. 3-6). pap. 4.99 (978-1-55143-237-3(4)) Orca Bk. Pubs. USA.

—Rebound. 2001. 262p. (gr. 5-9). mass mkt. 6.95 (978-0-7736-7485-1(3)); (YA). 15.95 (978-0-7737-3303-9(5)) Stoddart Kids CAN. *Dist:* Fitzhenry & Whiteside, Ltd.

—Rebound. 2000. (gr. 3-6). lib. bdg. 15.25 (978-0-613-50233-7(7)) Tandem Library Bks.

—Road Trip. 2002. (Orca Young Readers Ser.). (Illus.). 160p. (J). (gr. 3-6). pap. 4.99 (978-1-55143-201-4(3)) Orca Bk. Pubs. USA.

—Road Trip. 2002. (gr. 3-6). lib. bdg. 13.00 (978-0-613-62828-0(4)) Tandem Library Bks.

—Three on Three. 1999. (Young Reader Ser.). (J). (978-0-606-19479-2(7)) Tandem Library Bks.

—Underdog. 2004. (Orca Young Readers Ser.). (Illus.). 144p. (J). (gr. 3-6). pap., tchr. ed. 4.99 (978-1-55143-302-8(8) , 1234544) Orca Bk. Pubs. USA.

Walters, Eric & Mantha, John. Long Shot. 2002. (Orca Young Readers Ser.). (Illus.). 160p. (J). (gr. 3-6). pap. 5.95 (978-1-55143-216-8(1)) Orca Bk. Pubs. USA.

Walters, Eric & Williams, Jerome. Triple Threat. 2004. (Orca Young Readers Ser.). (Illus.). 144p. (J). (gr. 3-6). pap. 5.95 (978-1-55143-359-2(1)) Orca Bk. Pubs. USA.

Waltman, Kevin. Learning the Game. 224p. (J). 2006. pap. 7.99 (978-0-439-67611-3(8)); 2005. (gr. 7 up). pap. 16.95 (978-0-439-73109-6(7)) Scholastic, Inc. (Scholastic Pr.).

Warner, Gertrude Chandler. Basketball Mystery. 1999. (gr. 3-6). lib. bdg. 11.80 (978-0-613-11312-0(8)) Tandem Library Bks.

Warner, Gertrude Chandler, creator. The Basketball Mystery. 1999. (Boxcar Children Ser.: No. 68). (J). (gr. 2-5). 10.60 (978-0-606-17179-3(7)) Tandem Library Bks.

—The Basketball Mystery. 1999. (Boxcar Children Ser.: No. 68). (Illus.). 128p. (J). (gr. 2-5). lib. bdg. 13.95 (978-0-8075-0575-5(7)) Whitman, Albert & Co.

Watson, Pat. Slam! Durst, Shirley J., ed. 2000. (YA). 9.95 (978-1-58130-640-8(7)); 11.95 (978-1-58130-641-5(5)) Novel Units, Inc.

Wilhelm, Doug. Falling. 2007. 256p. (YA). (gr. 9 up). 17.00 (978-0-374-32251-9(1)) Farrar, Straus & Giroux.

Yarnell, Duane. The Winning Basket. 2005. pap. 26.95 (978-1-4191-5930-5(5)) Kessinger Publishing, LLC.

Yee, Lisa. Stanford Wong Flunks Big Time. (Illus.). (J). 2007. 320p. pap. 5.99 (978-0-439-62248-6(4)); 2005. 304p. (gr. 5-7). pap. 16.99 (978-0-439-62247-9(6)) Scholastic, Inc. (Levine, Arthur A. Bks.).

Zucker, Jonny. Basketball War. Savage, Paul, illus. 2006. 40p. (J). (gr. 2-3). lib. bdg. (978-1-59889-009-9(3)) Stone Arch Bks.

BASKETBALL—HISTORY

Aretha, David. The Detroit Pistons Basketball Team. 2001. (Great Sports Teams Ser.). (Illus.). 48p. (YA). (gr. 4-10). lib. bdg. 23.93 (978-0-7660-1487-9(8)) Enslow Pubs., Inc.

—The Seattle SuperSonics Basketball Team. (Great Sports Teams Ser.). (Illus.). 48p. (YA). (gr. 4-10). 2000. pap. 11.93 (978-0-7660-1754-2(0)); 1999. lib. bdg. 23.93 (978-0-7660-1102-1(X)) Enslow Pubs., Inc.

Bayne, Bijan C. Sky Kings: Black Pioneers of Professional Basketball. 1998. (African-American Experience Ser.). 144p. (J). (gr. 8-12). pap. 9.95 (978-0-531-15900-2(0) , Watts, Franklin) Scholastic Library Publishing.

Burgan, Michael. Great Moments in Basketball. 2002. (Great Moments in Sports Ser.). (Illus.). 48p. (J). (gr. 5 up). pap. 14.60 (978-0-8368-5359-9(8)); lib. bdg. 30.00 (978-0-8368-5345-2(8)) Stevens, Gareth Inc. (World Almanac Library).

De Medeiros, Michael. NBA Finals. 2007. (J). (***978-1-59036-691-2(3)***); (***978-1-59036-692-9(1)***) Weigl Pubs., Inc.

Frisch, Aaron. The History of the Dallas Mavericks. (Pro Basketball Today Ser.). 32p. 2006. 18.95 (978-1-58341-404-0(5)); 2001. (Illus.). (J). (978-1-58341-095-0(3)) Creative Co., The. (Creative Education).

—The History of the Denver Nuggets. 2001. (Pro Basketball Today Ser.). (Illus.). 32p. (J). (978-1-58341-096-7(1) , Creative Education) Creative Co., The.

—The History of the Detroit Pistons. 2001. (Pro Basketball Today Ser.). (Illus.). 32p. (J). (978-1-58341-097-4(X) , Creative Education) Creative Co., The.

—The History of the Golden State Warriors. 2001. (Pro Basketball Today Ser.). (Illus.). 32p. (J). (978-1-58341-098-1(8) , Creative Education) Creative Co., The.

—The History of the Houston Rockets. 2001. (Pro Basketball Today Ser.). (Illus.). 32p. (J). (978-1-58341-099-8(6) , Creative Education) Creative Co., The.

—The History of the Indiana Pacers. (Pro Basketball Today Ser.). (Illus.). 32p. 2006. 18.95 (978-1-58341-409-5(6)); 2001. (J). (978-1-58341-100-1(3)) Creative Co., The. (Creative Education).

—The History of the Los Angeles Clippers. (Pro Basketball Today Ser.). (Illus.). 32p. 2006. 18.95 (978-1-58341-410-1(X)); 2001. (J). (978-1-58341-101-8(1)) Creative Co., The. (Creative Education).

—The History of the Los Angeles Lakers. 2001. (Pro Basketball Today Ser.). (Illus.). 32p. (J). (978-1-58341-102-5(X) , Creative Education) Creative Co., The.

—The History of the Memphis Grizzlies. 2001. (Pro Basketball Today Ser.). (Illus.). 32p. (J). (978-1-58341-117-9(8) , Creative Education) Creative Co., The.

—The History of the Milwaukee Bucks. 2001. (Pro Basketball Today Ser.). (Illus.). 32p. (J). (978-1-58341-104-9(6) , Creative Education) Creative Co., The.

—The History of the New Jersey Nets. 2001. (Pro Basketball Today Ser.). (Illus.). 32p. (J). lib. bdg. (978-1-58341-106-3(2) , Creative Education) Creative Co., The.

—The History of the New York Knicks. 2001. (Pro Basketball Today Ser.). (Illus.). 32p. (J). lib. bdg. (978-1-58341-107-0(0) , Creative Education) Creative Co., The.

—The History of the Philadelphia 76ers. 2001. (Pro Basketball Today Ser.). (Illus.). 32p. (J). (978-1-58341-109-4(7) , Creative Education) Creative Co., The.

—The History of the Phoenix Suns. (Pro Basketball Today Ser.). (Illus.). 32p. (J). 2006. 18.95 (978-1-58341-421-7(5)); 2001. lib. bdg. (978-1-58341-110-0(0)) Creative Co., The. (Creative Education).

—The History of the Portland Trail Blazers. (Pro Basketball Today Ser.). (Illus.). 32p. 2006. 18.95 (978-1-58341-422-4(3)); 2001. (J). (978-1-58341-111-7(9)) Creative Co., The. (Creative Education).

—The History of the Sacramento Kings. 2001. (Pro Basketball Today Ser.). (Illus.). 32p. (J). lib. bdg. (978-1-58341-112-4(7) , Creative Education) Creative Co., The.

—The History of the San Antonio Spurs. 2001. (Pro Basketball Today Ser.). (Illus.). 32p. (J). lib. bdg. (978-1-58341-113-1(5) , Creative Education) Creative Co., The.

—The History of the Seattle Supersonics. 2001. (Pro Basketball Today Ser.). (Illus.). 32p. (J). lib. bdg. (978-1-58341-114-8(3) , Creative Education) Creative Co., The.

—The History of the Toronto Raptors. 2001. (Pro Basketball Today Ser.). (Illus.). 32p. (J). lib. bdg. (978-1-58341-115-5(1) , Creative Education) Creative Co., The.

—The History of the Utah Jazz. 2001. (Pro Basketball Today Ser.). (Illus.). 32p. (J). lib. bdg. (978-1-58341-116-2(X) , Creative Education) Creative Co., The.

—The History of the Washington Wizards. 2001. (Pro Basketball Today Ser.). (Illus.). 32p. (J). lib. bdg. (978-1-58341-118-6(6) , Creative Education) Creative Co., The.

—The Story of the Washington Wizards. 2006. (NBA—A History of Hoops Ser.). (Illus.). 32p. 18.95 (978-1-58341-428-6(2) , Creative Education) Creative Co., The.

Gigliotti, Jim & Schnakenberg, Robert. The Southeast Division. 2006. (Above the Rim Ser.). (Illus.). 48p. (J). (gr. 1-5). 28.50 (978-1-59296-558-8(X)) Child's World, Inc.

Gilbert, Sara. The History of the Memphis Grizzlies. 2006. (Pro Basketball Today Ser.). (Illus.). 32p. 18.95 (978-1-58341-412-5(6) , Creative Education) Creative Co., The.

—The History of the Miami Heat. 2006. (Pro Basketball Today Ser.). (Illus.). 32p. 18.95 (978-1-58341-413-2(4) , Creative Education) Creative Co., The.

—The History of the Minnesota Timberwolves. 2006. (Pro Basketball Today Ser.). (Illus.). 32p. 18.95 (978-1-58341-415-6(0) , Creative Education) Creative Co., The.

—The History of the New Orleans Hornets. 2006. (Pro Basketball Today Ser.). (Illus.). 32p. 18.95 (978-1-58341-417-0(7) , Creative Education) Creative Co., The.

—The History of the Orlando Magic. 2006. (Pro Basketball Today Ser.). (Illus.). 32p. 18.95 (978-1-58341-419-4(3) , Creative Education) Creative Co., The.

—The History of the Toronto Raptors. 2006. (Pro Basketball Today Ser.). (Illus.). 32p. 18.95 (978-1-58341-426-2(6) , Creative Education) Creative Co., The.

Grabowski, John F. Basketball. 2000. (History of Sports Ser.). (Illus.). 96p. (YA). (gr. 6-9). 28.70 (978-1-56006-742-9(X) , Lucent Bks.) Thomson Gale.

—The Boston Celtics. 2002. (Illus.). 112p. (J). 29.95 (978-1-56006-936-2(8) , Lucent Bks.) Thomson Gale.

—New York Knicks Basketball. 2003. (Great Sports Teams in History Ser.). (Illus.). 104p. (J). 29.95 (978-1-56006-944-7(9) , Lucent Bks.) Thomson Gale.

Hareas, John. NBA's Greatest. 2003. (Illus.). 160p. 30.00 (978-0-7894-9977-6(0)) Dorling Kindersley Publishing, Inc.

Herzog, Brad. Hoopmania: The Book of Basketball History & Trivia. 2005. (Sports Illustrated for Kids Bks.). (Illus.). 176p. (YA). (gr. 7-12). lib. bdg. 32.60 (978-0-8239-3697-7(X)) Rosen Publishing Group, Inc., The.

Herzog, Brad & Palmer, Christopher. Hoopmania! The Jam-Packed Book of Basketball Trivia. rev. ed. 1999. (Sports Illustrated for Kids Bks.). 144p. (J). (gr. 4-6). pap. 3.99 (978-1-886749-61-0(2)) Sports Illustrated For Kids.

Hofstetter, Adam B. Olympic Basketball. 2007. (Great Moments in Olympic History Ser.). (Illus.). 48p. (J). (gr. 5-8). lib. bdg. 26.50 (***978-1-4042-0967-1(0)***) Rosen Publishing Group, Inc., The.

Klein, Fredrick C. For the Love of the Cubs: An A-to-Z Primer for Cubs Fans of All Ages. Anderson, Mark, illus. 2005. 48p. 16.95 (978-1-57243-795-1(2)) Triumph Bks.

Lace, William W. The Houston Rockets Basketball Team. 2000. (Great Sports Teams Ser.). (Illus.). 48p. (YA). (gr. 4-10). pap. 11.93 (978-0-7660-1749-8(4)) Enslow Pubs., Inc.

—The Los Angeles Lakers Basketball Team. 2000. (Great Sports Teams Ser.). (Illus.). 48p. (YA). (gr. 4-10). pap. 11.93 (978-0-7660-1750-4(8)) Enslow Pubs., Inc.

Lannin, Joanne. A History of Basketball for Girls & Women: From Bloomers to Big Leagues. (Sports Legacy Ser.). (Illus.). 144p. (gr. 7-12). 2005. lib. bdg. 26.63 (978-0-8225-3331-3(6)); 2003. (J). pap. 9.95 (978-0-8225-9863-3(9)) Lerner Publishing Group.

LeBoutillier, Nat. The Story of the San Antonio Spurs. 2006. (NBA—A History of Hoops Ser.). (Illus.). 32p. 18.95 (978-1-58341-424-8(X) , Creative Education) Creative Co., The.

LeBoutillier, Nate. The History of the Atlanta Hawks. 2006. (Pro Basketball Today Ser.). (Illus.). 32p. (J). 18.95 (978-1-58341-399-9(5) , Creative Education) Creative Co., The.

—The History of the Boston Celtics. 2006. (Pro Basketball Today Ser.). (Illus.). 32p. (J). 18.95 (978-1-58341-400-2(2) , Creative Education) Creative Co., The.

—The History of the Chicago Bulls. 2006. (Pro Basketball Today Ser.). (Illus.). 32p. (J). 18.95 (978-1-58341-402-6(9) , Creative Education) Creative Co., The.

—The History of the Cleveland Cavaliers. 2006. (Pro Basketball Today Ser.). (Illus.). 32p. (J). 18.95 (978-1-58341-403-3(7) , Creative Education) Creative Co., The.

—The History of the Denver Nuggets. 2006. (Pro Basketball Today Ser.). 32p. 18.95 (978-1-58341-405-7(3) , Creative Education) Creative Co., The.

—The History of the Detroit Pistons. 2006. (Pro Basketball Today Ser.). (Illus.). 32p. 18.95 (978-1-58341-406-4(1) , Creative Education) Creative Co., The.

—The History of the Golden State Warriors. 2006. (Pro Basketball Today Ser.). (Illus.). 32p. 18.95 (978-1-58341-407-1(X) , Creative Education) Creative Co., The.

—The History of the Houston Rockets. 2006. (Pro Basketball Today Ser.). (Illus.). 32p. (J). 18.95 (978-1-58341-408-8(8) , Creative Education) Creative Co., The.

—The History of the Los Angeles Lakers. 2006. (Pro Basketball Today Ser.). (Illus.). 32p. (J). 18.95 (978-1-58341-411-8(8) , Creative Education) Creative Co., The.

—The History of the Milwaukee Bucks. 2006. (Pro Basketball Today Ser.). (Illus.). 32p. 18.95 (978-1-58341-414-9(2) , Creative Education) Creative Co., The.

—The History of the New Jersey Nets. 2006. (Pro Basketball Today Ser.). (Illus.). 32p. 18.95 (978-1-58341-416-3(9) , Creative Education) Creative Co., The.

—The History of the New York Knicks. 2006. (Pro Basketball Today Ser.). (Illus.). 32p. 18.95 (978-1-58341-418-7(5) , Creative Education) Creative Co., The.

—The History of the Philadelphia 76ers. 2006. (Pro Basketball Today Ser.). (Illus.). 32p. (J). 18.95 (978-1-58341-420-0(7) , Creative Education) Creative Co., The.

—The History of the Sacramento Kings. 2006. (Pro Basketball Today Ser.). (Illus.). 32p. (J). 18.95 (978-1-58341-423-1(1) , Creative Education) Creative Co., The.

—The History of the Utah Jazz. 2006. (Pro Basketball Today Ser.). (Illus.). 32p. 18.95 (978-1-58341-427-9(4) , Creative Education) Creative Co., The.

—The Story of the Seattle Supersonics. 2006. (NBA—A History of Hoops Ser.). (Illus.). 32p. 18.95 (978-1-58341-425-5(8) , Creative Education) Creative Co., The.

Macnow, Glen. The Philadelphia 76ers Basketball Team. (Great Sports Teams Ser.). (Illus.). 48p. (YA). (gr. 4-10). 2000. pap. 11.93 (978-0-7660-1751-1(6)); 1998. lib. bdg. 23.93 (978-0-7660-1063-5(5)) Enslow Pubs., Inc.

Nichols, John. The History of the Atlanta Hawks. 2001. (Pro Basketball Today Ser.). (Illus.). 32p. (J). (978-1-58341-090-5(2) , Creative Education) Creative Co., The.

—The History of the Boston Celtics. 2001. (Pro Basketball Today Ser.). (Illus.). 32p. (J). (978-1-58341-091-2(0) , Creative Education) Creative Co., The.

—The History of the Charlotte Bobcats. 2006. (Pro Basketball Today Ser.). (Illus.). 32p. 18.95 (978-1-58341-401-9(0) , Creative Education) Creative Co., The.

—The History of the Charlotte Hornets. 2001. (Pro Basketball Today Ser.). (Illus.). 32p. (J). (978-1-58341-092-9(9) , Creative Education) Creative Co., The.

—The History of the Chicago Bulls. 2001. (Pro Basketball Today Ser.). (Illus.). 32p. (J). (978-1-58341-093-6(7) , Creative Education) Creative Co., The.

—The History of the Cleveland Cavaliers. 2001. (Pro Basketball Today Ser.). (Illus.). 32p. (J). (978-1-58341-094-3(5) , Creative Education) Creative Co., The.

—The History of the Miami Heat. 2001. (Pro Basketball Today Ser.). (Illus.). 32p. (J). (978-1-58341-103-2(8) , Creative Education) Creative Co., The.

—The History of the Minnesota Timberwolves. 2001. (Pro Basketball Today Ser.). (Illus.). 32p. (J). (978-1-58341-105-6(4) , Creative Education) Creative Co., The.

—The History of the Orlando Magic. 2001. (Pro Basketball Today Ser.). (Illus.). 32p. (J). lib. bdg. (978-1-58341-108-7(9) , Creative Education) Creative Co., The.

—Toronto Raptors. 1998. (NBA Today Ser.). 32p. (YA). (gr. 3-12). lib. bdg. 21.30 (978-0-88682-894-3(5) , Creative Education) Creative Co., The.

—Vancouver Grizzlies. 1998. (NBA Today Ser.). 32p. (YA). (gr. 3-12). lib. bdg. 21.30 (978-0-88682-895-0(3) , Creative Education) Creative Co., The.

O'Shei, Tim. The Duke Blue Devils Men's Basketball Team. 1999. (Great Sports Teams Ser.). (Illus.). 48p. (YA). (gr. 4-10). lib. bdg. 23.93 (978-0-7660-1213-4(1)) Enslow Pubs., Inc.

Owens, Thomas S. The Chicago Bulls Basketball Team. 2000. (Great Sports Teams Ser.). (Illus.). 48p. (YA). (gr. 4-10). pap. 11.93 (978-0-7660-1748-1(6)) Enslow Pubs., Inc.

Owens, Tom & Helmer, Diana Star. The Utah Starzz: Teamwork. 1999. (Women's Professional Basketball Ser.). 24p. (J). lib. bdg. 18.75 (978-0-8239-5244-1(4) , PowerKids Pr.) Rosen Publishing Group, Inc., The.

Pietrusza, David. The Boston Celtics Basketball Team. (Great Sports Teams Ser.). (Illus.). 48p. (YA). (gr. 4-10). 2000. pap. 9.95 (978-0-7660-1747-4(8)); 1998. lib. bdg. 23.93 (978-0-7660-1019-2(8)) Enslow Pubs., Inc.

—The Phoenix Suns Basketball Team. 2000. (Great Sports Teams Ser.). (Illus.). 48p. (YA). (gr. 4-10). pap. 11.93 (978-0-7660-1752-8(4)) Enslow Pubs., Inc.

Potts, Steve. Chicago Bulls. 2001. (Championship Teams Ser.). (Illus.). (J). (978-1-58340-088-3(5)) Smart Apple Media.

— Los Angeles Lakers. 2001. (Championship Teams Ser.). (Illus.). (J). (978-1-58340-087-6(7)) Smart Apple Media.

Rappoport, Ken. Tim Duncan: Star Forward. 2000. (Sports Reports). (Illus.). 112p. (YA). (gr. 4-10). lib. bdg. 20.95 (978-0-7660-1334-6(0)) Enslow Pubs., Inc.

Reiser, Howard. The Georgetown University Hoyas Men's Basketball Team. 1999. (Great Sports Teams Ser.). (Illus.). 48p. (YA). (gr. 4-10). lib. bdg. 23.93 (978-0-7660-1160-1(7)) Enslow Pubs., Inc.

Rogers, Glenn. The San Antonio Spurs Basketball Team. 2000. (Great Sports Teams Ser.). (Illus.). 48p. (YA). (gr. 4-10). pap. 9.95 (978-0-7660-1753-5(2)) Enslow Pubs., Inc.

Rud, Jeff. Steve Nash: The Making of an MVPWith a foreword by Steve Nash. 2007. 240p. (J). (gr. 3). 5.99 (***978-0-14-241014-1(4)*** , Puffin) Penguin Group (USA) Inc.

Schultz, Randy. The New York Knicks Basketball Team. 2000. (Great Sports Teams Ser.). (Illus.). 48p. (YA). (gr. 4-10). lib. bdg. 23.93 (978-0-7660-1281-3(6)) Enslow Pubs., Inc.

Simpson, Fiona, ed. Hardwood Heroes: Multi-Player. 2006. (Illus.). 32p. (J). pap. 3.99 (978-0-439-78804-5(8)) Scholastic, Inc.

Stewart, Mark. Los Angeles Lakers. 48p. 2007. pap. 9.95 (***978-1-60357-003-9(9)); 2006. (Illus.). (J). lib. bdg. 25.27 (978-1-59953-068-0(6)) Norwood Hse. Pr.

—The Chicago Bulls. 2007. (J). (***978-1-59953-129-8(1)***) Norwood Hse. Pr.

—Dallas Mavericks. 2006. (Team Spirit Ser.). (Illus.). 48p. (J). lib. bdg. 25.27 (978-1-59953-067-3(8)) Norwood Hse. Pr.

—The Detroit Pistons. 2006. (Team Spirit Ser.). (Illus.). 48p. (J). lib. bdg. 25.27 (978-1-59953-008-6(2)) Norwood Hse. Pr.

—The Miami Heat. 2006. (Team Spirit Ser.). (Illus.). 48p. (J). (gr. 4-7). lib. bdg. 25.27 (978-1-59953-009-3(0)) Norwood Hse. Pr.

—Miami Heat. 2007. 48p. pap. 9.95 (***978-1-60357-004-6(7)***) Norwood Hse. Pr.

—Milwaukee Bucks. 2006. (Team Spirit Ser.). (Illus.). 48p. (J). lib. bdg. 25.27 (978-1-59953-062-8(7)) Norwood Hse. Pr.

—New York Knicks. 2006. (Team Spirit Ser.). (Illus.). 48p. (J). lib. bdg. 25.27 (978-1-59953-069-7(4)) Norwood Hse. Pr.

—The Phoenix Suns. 2006. (Team Spirit Ser.). (Illus.). 48p. (J). lib. bdg. 25.27 (978-1-59953-010-9(4)) Norwood Hse. Pr.

Stewart, Mark & Zeysing, Matt. The Charlotte Bobcats. 2007. (J). lib. bdg. (***978-1-59953-123-6(2)***) Norwood Hse. Pr.

—The Indiana Pacers. 2007. (J). (***978-1-59953-122-9(4)***) Norwood Hse. Pr.

—The New Jersey Nets. 2007. (J). (***978-1-59953-124-3(0)***) Norwood Hse. Pr.

—The Philadelphia 76ers. 2008. (J). lib. bdg. (***978-1-59953-125-0(9)***) Norwood Hse. Pr.

—The Portland Trail Blazers. 2008. (J). lib. bdg. (***978-1-59953-126-7(7)***) Norwood Hse. Pr.

—The San Antonio Spurs. 2006. (Team Spirit Ser.). (Illus.). 48p. (J). lib. bdg. 25.27 (978-1-59953-011-6(2)) Norwood Hse. Pr.

Stewart, Mark & Zeysing, Matt. The Utah Jazz. 2007. (J). (***978-1-59953-127-4(5)***) Norwood Hse. Pr.

Stewart, Mark Alan. Basketball: A History of Hoops. 1998. (History of Sports Ser.). (Illus.). 160p. (YA). (gr. 5-8). 34.50 (978-0-531-11492-6(9) , Watts, Franklin) Scholastic Library Publishing.

The Story of Basketball, 6 Pack. (On Deck Ser.). 24p. (gr. 4-5). 35.00 (978-0-7578-1010-7(1)) Rigby Education.

Suen, Anastasia. Historia Del Baloncesto. 2004. (Historia de los Deportes Ser.). (SPA & ENG., Illus.). 24p. (J). (gr. 3-6). lib. bdg. 17.25 (978-0-8239-6868-8(5) , Buenas Letra) Rosen Publishing Group, Inc., The.

—The Story of Basketball. 2002. (Reading Power Ser.). (Illus.). 24p. (J). (gr. 2). lib. bdg. 17.25 (978-0-8239-5995-2(3) , PowerKids Pr.) Rosen Publishing Group, Inc., The.

Trogdon, Wendell. Who Killed Hoosier Hysteria? Sport Survives amid Fading Fervor. Lt. ed. 2004. (Illus.). 168p. (YA). pap. (978-0-9724033-3-7(7)) Backroads Pr.

Walters, John & Schnakenberg, Robert. The Southwest Division. 2006. (Above the Rim Ser.). (Illus.). 48p. (J). (gr. 1-5). 28.50 (978-1-59296-559-5(8)) Child's World, Inc.

Weber, Bruce. Greatest Moments of the NBA. 2000. (NBA Ser.). (Illus.). 32p. (J). (gr. 2-5). pap. 5.99 (978-0-439-14072-0(2)) Scholastic, Inc.

—Greatest Moments of the NBA. 2000. (Illus.). (J). (978-0-606-18553-0(4)) Tandem Library Bks.

Wyckoff, Edwin Brit. The Man Who Invented Basketball: James Naismith & His Amazing Game. 2007. (Genius at Work! Great Inventor Biographies Ser.). (Illus.). 32p. (J). (gr. 3-4). lib. bdg. 22.60 (978-0-7660-2846-3(1) , Enslow Elementary) Enslow Pubs., Inc.

BASKETBALL CLUBS

Aretha, David. The Detroit Pistons Basketball Team. 2001. (Great Sports Teams Ser.). (Illus.). 48p. (YA). (gr. 4-10). lib. bdg. 23.93 (978-0-7660-1487-9(8)) Enslow Pubs., Inc.

Cleverley, James, et al. The Spirit of a Buckeye: Brutus Buckeye's Lessons for Life. 1999. 28p. (J). pap. (978-0-9675664-0-5(1)) Cleverley Created, Ltd.

Fried, Mark. Great Teams in College Basketball 6-Pack. 2005. pap. 51.00 (978-1-4109-1502-3(6)) Raintree.

Macnow, Glen. The Philadelphia 76ers Basketball Team. 1998. (Great Sports Teams Ser.). (Illus.). 48p. (YA). (gr. 4-10). lib. bdg. 23.93 (978-0-7660-1063-5(5)) Enslow Pubs., Inc.

Owens, Tom & Helmer, Diana Star. The Utah Starzz: Teamwork. 1999. (Women's Professional Basketball Ser.). 24p. (J). lib. bdg. 18.75 (978-0-8239-5244-1(4) , PowerKids Pr.) Rosen Publishing Group, Inc., The.

Pietrusza, David. The Boston Celtics Basketball Team. 1998. (Great Sports Teams Ser.). (Illus.). 48p. (YA). (gr. 4-10). lib. bdg. 23.93 (978-0-7660-1019-2(8)) Enslow Pubs., Inc.

BAT

see Bats

BATES, KATHARINE LEE, 1859-1929

Ouren, Todd, illus. America the Beautiful. 2004. (Patriotic Songs Ser.). 24p. (J). (ps-4). 22.60 (978-1-4048-0172-1(3)) Picture Window Bks.

Younger, Barbara. Purple Mountain Majesties: The Story of Katharine Lee Bates & America the Beautiful. Schuett, Stacey, illus. 2005. 29p. (J). reprint ed. 16.00 (978-0-7567-8984-8(2)) DIANE Publishing Co.

—Purple Mountain Majesty. 2002. (gr. k-3). lib. bdg. 15.30 (978-0-613-45305-9(0)) Tandem Library Bks.

BATHS—FICTION

The Bath: Set C Individual Title Six-Packs. (Smart Start Ser.). (gr. k-1). 23.00 (978-0-7635-0431-1(9)) Rigby Education.

Beck, Ana. Elliot's Bath. 2001. lib. bdg. 14.10 (978-0-613-36327-3(2)) Tandem Library Bks.

Boynton. Bath Time! 2007. 10p. pap. 7.95 (***978-0-7611-4780-0(2)***) Workman Publishing Co., Inc.

Boza, Eduardo Robles. Mi Amigo - Banarse (My Friend Doesn't Like - Baths) (SPA.). (J). 4.95 (978-970-05-0209-0(0)) Grijalbo, Editorial MEX. *Dist:* AIMS International Bks., Inc.

Brouillard, Anne. The Bathtub Prima Donna. Brouillard, Anne, illus. 2004. (Illus.). 24p. (J). (gr. k-4). reprint ed. 13.00 (978-0-7567-7755-5(0)) DIANE Publishing Co.

Capucilli, Alyssa Satin. Bathtime for Biscuit. 1999. (gr. k-3). lib. bdg. 11.80 (978-0-613-22819-0(7)) Tandem Library Bks.

Conrad, Pam. The Tub People. Egielski, Richard, illus. 1999. (Laura Geringer Bks.). 32p. (J). (ps-3). 15.95 (978-0-06-021340-4(X) , Geringer, Laura Book) HarperCollins Pubs.

Dad's Bathtime: Individual Title Six-Packs. (Literatura 2000 Ser.). (gr. 1-2). 28.00 (978-0-7635-0128-0(X)) Rigby Education.

Danis, Naomi. Splish-Splash, into the Bath! Kreloff, Elliot, illus. 2007. 16p. (J). (***978-1-59354-609-0(2)***) Handprint Bks.

Dannenbring-Eichstadt, Lana. Bubble. Harvey, Kathleen, illus. 2004. 24p. (J). (978-1-57579-282-8(6)) Pine Hill Pr., Inc.

DePrisco, Dorothea & Burnett, Alex. Tub-a-Tub: A Bath Book. 2006. (Illus.). 10p. (J). pap. 9.95 (978-1-58117-463-2(2) , Intervisual/Piggy Toes) Dalmatian Pr.

Dorling Kindersley Publishing Staff. Bathtime Peekaboo! 2005. (Illus.). 12p. (J). bds. 6.99 (978-0-7566-1145-3(8)) Dorling Kindersley Publishing, Inc.

Dougherty, Terri. The Bath. Yi, Hye Won, illus. 2006. (Read-It! Readers Ser.). 32p. (J). (ps-3). 18.60 (978-1-4048-1576-6(7)) Picture Window Bks.

Dreidemy, Joelle, illus. Bath Time, Beth! 2006. 24p. 9.99 (978-1-84643-024-4(0)) Child's Play-International.

Edwards, Frank B. Mortimer Mooner Stopped Taking a Bath. 2000. (978-0-606-22925-8(6)) Tandem Library Bks.

Edwards, Frank B. & Bianchi, John. Mortimer Mooner Stopped Taking a Bath. 2000. (Mooner Ser.). (Illus.). 24p. (J). (ps-2). pap. 4.95 (978-1-894323-21-5(1)) Pokeweed Pr. CAN. *Dist:* Fitzhenry & Whiteside, Ltd.

Ehrlich, Fred. Does an Elephant Take a Bath? Bolam, Emily, illus. 2005. (Early Experiences Ser.). 32p. (J). (ps-k). 13.50 (978-1-59354-111-8(2)) Blue Apple Bks.

Esbaum, Jill. Estelle Takes a Bath. DePalma, Mary Newell, illus. rev. ed. 2006. 32p. (J). 16.95 (978-0-8050-7741-4(3)) Holt, Henry & Co.

Ficocelli, Elizabeth. Kid Tea. Dibley, Glin, illus. 2007. 40p. (J). (ps-2). 14.99 (978-0-7614-5333-8(4)) Cavendish, Marshall Corp.

Gerver, Jane E. Bath Time. Ovresat, Laura, illus. (My First Reader Ser.). (J). (gr. k-1). 2005. 32p. pap. 3.95 (978-0-516-25111-0(2)); 2004. 31p. 18.50 (978-0-516-24677-2(1)) Scholastic Library Publishing. (Children's Pr.).

Gillespie, Jane. Happy Honu Takes a Bath. Cabanting, Ruth, illus. 2004. 10p. (J). 6.95 (978-1-933067-03-2(9)) Beachhouse Publishing, LLC.

Goodman, Joan Elizabeth. Bernard's Bath. 2000. (gr. k-3). lib. bdg. 16.40 (978-0-613-28754-8(1)) Tandem Library Bks.

Gurney, Stella. Sailor Sally. Worsley, Belinda, illus. 2006. 32p. (J). lib. bdg. 9.00 (***978-1-4242-0883-8(1)***) Fitzgerald Bks.

—Sailor Sally, Level P. Worsley, Belinda, illus. 2006. (Lightning Readers Ser.). 32p. (J). pap. 3.95 (978-0-7696-4185-0(7) , Gingham Dog Pr.) School Specialty Publishing.

Haley, Amanda, illus. A Bath for a Princess. 2007. (I'm Going to Read Ser.). 32p. (J). (gr. 1-2). pap. 3.95 (***978-1-4027-4297-2(5)***) Sterling Publishing Co., Inc.

Hall, John. How to Get a Gorilla Out of Your Bathtub. Gilpin, Stephen, illus. 2006. 48p. (J). 14.99 (978-1-59379-070-7(8)) White Stone Bks.

Harcourt School Publishers Staff. Trofeos Below Level: Las Botas/Dodi. 3rd ed. 2002. (SPA., Illus.). (J). pap. 3.50 (978-0-15-323857-4(7)) Harcourt Schl. Pubs.

Harper, Jamie. Splish Splash, Baby Bundt: A Recipe for Bath Time. Harper, Jamie, illus. 2007. (Illus.). 24p. (J). (gr. k-ps). bds. 6.99 (***978-0-7636-3240-3(6)***) Candlewick Pr.

Have You Ever Seen a Moose Taking a Bath? 2000. (J). pap. 12.95 (978-0-9709533-0-8(5)) JAFS, Inc.

Hawkins, Karen. Splish, Splash, Splish, Splash. 2002. 15.00 (978-0-8059-5578-1(X)) Dorrance Publishing Co., Inc.

Hines, Thomas, illus. The Bubble Machine. l.t. ed. 2003. 26p. (J). per. (978-1-887636-02-5(1)) Creative Writing & Publishing Co.

Howard-Parham, Pam. When I Take a Bath. Gillen, Lisa P., illus. 2005. (J). bds. (978-1-57332-364-2(0)) HighReach Learning, Inc.

Hughes, Frieda. Thing in the Sink Storybook. Riddell, Chris, illus. 48p. (J). pap. 9.99 (978-0-340-86579-8(2) , Hodder & Stoughton) Hodder General Publishing Division GBR. *Dist:* Trafalgar Square Publishing.

Jackson, Chris. Edmund & Washable: A Tale from China Plate Farm. 2000. (Illus.). 24p. (J). 12.00 (978-0-00-224558-6(2)) HarperCollins Pubs.

Janison, Kevin D. Deputy Dorkface: How Stinkville Got Cleaned Up. Doty, Eldon, illus. 2007. 32p. (J). (ps-1). 16.95 (***978-1-932173-82-6(X)***) Stephens Pr. LLC.

Jarman, Julia. Big Red Tub. Reynolds, Adrian, illus. 2004. (Clifford Big Red Reader Ser.). 32p. (J). pap. 14.95 (978-0-439-67232-0(5) , Orchard Bks.) Scholastic, Inc.

Jonell, Lynne. Mommy Go Away! 2000. (Illus.). (J). (978-0-606-22033-0(X)) Tandem Library Bks.

Jones, Sylvie. Who's in the Tub? Constantin, Pascale, illus. 2007. 38p. (ps-3). 15.95 (***978-1-59354-612-0(2)***) Handprint Bks.

Kalin, Julia. Brady's Bath: A Reader Illustrated Storybook. unabr. ed. 1999. (Picture-It Storybook Ser.). 16p. (J). (ps-6). pap. 12.95 (978-0-9672430-1-6(7) , 9802) Stay, Play & Learn.

Kay, Julia. Gulliver Snip & the Clipper Ship. 2008. 32p. (J). 16.95 (***978-0-8050-7992-0(0)***) Holt, Henry & Co.

Kennedy, Fran. The Pickle Patch Bathtub. Aldridge, Sheila, illus. 2004. 32p. (J). 14.95 (978-1-58246-112-0(0) , Tricycle Pr.) Ten Speed Pr.

Kilpatrick, Irene. Blue Takes a Dip! Craig, Karen, illus. 2007. (Blue's Clues Ser.). 6p. (J). 5.99 (978-1-4169-3667-1(X) , Simon Spotlight/Nickelodeon) Simon & Schuster Children's Publishing.

Kitamura, Satoshi. El Bano de Gato. 2001. (SPA.). 114p. (J). (978-84-207-8949-1(6)) Grupo Anaya, S.A. ESP. *Dist:* Lectorum Pubns., Inc.

Krosoczka, Jarrett J. Bubble Bath Pirates. 2003. (Illus.). 40p. (J). (ps-k). 15.99 (978-0-670-03599-1(8) , Viking Juvenile) Penguin Group (USA) Inc.

Kubler, Annie. Save Humpy. 1999. (Real Sound Bath Bks Ser.). (Illus.). 10p. (ps-k). pap. 9.99 (978-0-85953-611-0(4)) Child's Play International Ltd. GBR. *Dist:* Child's Play-International.

L'Heureux, Christine. Caillou Time for a Bath. Lambert, Carole, illus. 2004. (Carousel Ser.). 24p. (J). bds. 5.95 (978-2-89450-413-0(6)) Chouette Publishing CAN. *Dist:* Perseus Distribution.

Lindahl, Inger. Bertil & the Bathroom Elephants. Dysseggaard, Elisabeth Kallick, tr. Lindstrom, Eva, illus. 2003. 28p. (J). 15.00 (978-91-29-65944-3(2)) R & S Bks. SWE. *Dist:* Macmillan.

Lock, Brian. There's a Hippo in My Bathtub. 2007. (ENG.). 76p. per. 14.95 (***978-1-4241-7331-0(0)***) PublishAmerica, Inc.

Lynne, Rustyna. Derrick & Sierra Take Baths. Lawrence, Mary, illus. l.t. ed. 2002. 15p. (J). (gr. k-2). spiral bd. 11.95 (978-0-9719657-0-6(6)) Red Carpet Publishing.

—Derrick & Sierra Take Baths: Special Needs Version. Lawrence, Mary, illus. l.t. ed. 2002. 15p. (YA). (gr. 3-8). spiral bd. 11.95 (978-0-9719657-1-3(4)) Red Carpet Publishing.

Maccarone, Grace. Magic Matt & the Skunk in the Tub. Bridwell, Norman, illus. 2003. (Reader Ser.). 32p. (J). pap. 3.99 (978-0-439-40570-6(X) , Cartwheel Bks.) Scholastic, Inc.

Matsuoka, Kyoko. I Love to Take a Bath. Hayashi, Akiko, illus. 2006. 32p. (J). 17.95 (978-1-74126-023-6(X)) R.I.C. Pubns. AUS. *Dist:* SCB Distributors.

Miller, Shannon Terry & Warner, Timothy. Tub Toys. Calderon, Lee, illus. 2007. 32p. (J). pap. 6.95 (***978-1-58246-235-6(6)*** , Tricycle Pr.) Ten Speed Pr.

Mitzo Thompson, Kim & Mitzo Hilderbrand, Karen. Sleep, My Little One. 2006. (Read & Sing along Board Books with CDs Ser.). 18p. (J). bds. 7.49 (978-0-7696-4589-6(5)) School Specialty Publishing.

Neubecker, Robert. Beasty Bath. 2005. (Illus.). 32p. (J). (ps-1). pap. 14.99 (978-0-439-64000-8(8) , Orchard Bks.) Scholastic, Inc.

Pallotta, Jerry. Dory Story. Biedrzycki, David, illus. 2004. (J). (ps-ps). lib. bdg. 14.50 (978-0-606-30230-2(1)) Tandem Library Bks.

Pelletier, Andrew. The Amazing Adventures of Bathman. Elwell, Peter, illus. 2007. 32p. (J). (ps). pap. 5.99 (978-0-14-240776-9(3) , Puffin) Penguin Group (USA) Inc.

Philip, Neil. The Fish Is Me! Bathtime Rhymes. Henley, Claire, illus. 2002. 32p. (J). (gr. k-3). tchr. ed. 16.00 (978-0-618-15939-0(8) , Clarion Bks.) Houghton Mifflin Co. Trade & Reference Div.

Priddy, Roger. Baby Gund Mirror Bathtime. rev. ed. 2006. 12p. (J). bds. 6.95 (978-0-312-49708-8(3) , Priddy Bks.) St. Martin's Pr.

Rodriguez, Edarissa. The Girl Who Took a Shower. Santiago, Claribel, ed. Rodriguez, Edarissa, illus. 2003. (J). pap. 13.99 (978-0-9744726-0-7(3)) Santiago, Claribel.

Ross, Tony. Hora de Dormir. 2006. (Little Princess Ser.).Tr. of Bedtime. (SPA.). (J). (ps-k). bds. 7.95 (978-968-19-1488-2(0) , AT33282) Lectorum Pubns., Inc.

Rylant, Cynthia. Puppy Mudge Takes a Bath. 2004. (Puppy Mudge Ser.). (ps-2). lib. bdg. 11.80 (978-0-613-90714-9(0)) Tandem Library Bks.

Rylant, Cynthia & Mones, Isidre. Puppy Mudge Takes a Bath. (Puppy Mudge Ser.). (Illus.). 32p. (J). 2004. pap. 3.99 (978-0-689-86621-0(6) , Aladdin); 2002. 14.95 (978-0-689-83980-1(4)) Simon & Schuster Children's Publishing.

Sarrazin, Marisol, illus. Peppy, Patch, & the Bath. 2005. (Read-It! Readers Ser.). 32p. (C). (gr. k-3). 18.60 (978-1-4048-1032-7(3)) Picture Window Bks.

Sarrazin, Marisol & Homel, David. Peppy, Phlox & the Bath. 2000. (Illus.). 32p. (J). (gr. 1-4). pap. (978-1-894363-42-6(6)) Dominique & Friends.

Schafer, Milton. Bath Time for Baby Strawberry. S. I. Artists Staff, illus. 2006. (Strawberry Shortcake Baby Ser.). 6p. (J). (ps-ps). bds. 4.99 (978-0-448-44357-7(0) , Grosset & Dunlap) Penguin Group (USA) Inc.

Schories, Pat, illus. Bathtime for Biscuit. 2002. (Biscuit Ser.). (J). 11.91 (978-0-7587-6003-6(5)) Book Wholesalers, Inc.

Sexton, Brenda. Busy Bath. Maccarone, Grace, ed. 2006. (Illus.). 8p. (J). 8.99 (978-0-439-83652-4(2) , Cartwheel Bks.) Scholastic, Inc.

—Elephants in the Bathtub & Other Silly Riddles. Mills, Liz, ed. 2006. (Illus.). 12p. (J). pap. 5.99 (978-0-439-82312-8(9) , Cartwheel Bks.) Scholastic, Inc.

Shannon, Terry Miller & Warner, Tim. Tub Toys. Calderon, Lee, illus. 2004. 30p. (J). (gr. k-2). 14.95 (978-1-58246-066-6(3) , Tricycle Pr.) Ten Speed Pr.

Smalls-Hector, Irene. I Can't Take a Bath. Boyd, Aaron, illus. 2004. (Just for You! Ser.). 32p. (J). pap. 3.99 (978-0-439-56852-4(8)) Scholastic, Inc.

Smith, Janice Lee. Jess & the Stinky Cowboys. Thiesing, Lisa, illus. 2004. (Dial Easy-to-Read Ser.). 48p. (J). (gr. k-3). 14.99 (978-0-8037-2641-3(4) , Dial) Penguin Group (USA) Inc.

Spinelli, Eileen. Bath Time. Pedersen, Janet, illus. 2003. 32p. (J). 14.95 (978-0-7614-5117-4(X)) Cavendish, Marshall Corp.

Thompson, Kay. Eloise Takes a Bawth. Knight, Hilary, illus. ltd. ed. 2002. (Eloise Ser.). 300.00 (978-0-689-84694-6(0) , Simon & Schuster Children's Publishing) Simon & Schuster Children's Publishing.

Thompson, Kay & Crowley, Mart. Eloise Takes a Bawth. Knight, Hilary, illus. 2002. (Eloise Ser.). 80p. (J). (ps-3). 17.95 (978-0-689-84288-7(0)) Simon & Schuster Children's Publishing.

Tuxworth, Nicola. Splish, Splash: A Very First Picture Book. 1999. (Pictures & Words Ser.). (Illus.). 24p. (J). (ps up). lib. bdg. 22.00 (978-0-8368-2433-9(4)) Stevens, Gareth Inc.

Warnes, Tim & Sykes, Julie. Bathtime, Little Tiger! Warnes, Tim, illus. 2003. (Little Tiger Lift-the-Flap Ser.). (Illus.). 12p. (J). 5.95 (978-1-58925-693-4(X) , tiger tales) ME Media LLC.

Weiss, Ellen. Twins Take a Bath. Williams, Sam, illus. 2003. (Ready-to-Read Ser.). 24p. (J). pap. 3.99 (978-0-689-85740-9(3) , Aladdin) Simon & Schuster Children's Publishing.

—Twins Take a Bath. Williams, Sam, illus. ed. 2005. (Ready-to-Read Ser. PreLevel 1). 22p. (J). lib. bdg. 15.00 (978-1-59054-964-3(3)) Fitzgerald Bks.

When Bath Time Comes. 2004. (J). per. (978-1-57657-470-6(9)) Paradise Pr., Inc.

Wood, Audrey. King Bidgood's in the Bathtub. Wood, Don, illus. 2005. 32p. (J). (ps-ps). 17.95 (978-0-15-205578-3(9)) Harcourt Children's Bks.

Yablonsky, Buster. Where Is Slippery Soap? A Bath Book with Magic Ink. Johnson, Traci Paige, illus. 2001. (Blue's Clues Ser.). 8p. (J). (ps-k). 5.99 (978-0-689-82948-2(5) , Simon Spotlight/Nickelodeon) Simon & Schuster Children's Publishing.

BATHYSCAPHE

Weeks, Sarah. Splish, Splash, Splash! Wolff, Ashley, illus. 1999. (My First I Can Read Bks.). 32p. (J). (ps up). 12.89 (978-0-06-027893-9(5)) HarperCollins Pubs.

BATMAN (FICTITIOUS CHARACTER)—FICTION

Aptekar, Devan. The Batman: Above the Law. Armstrong, Jason et al, illus. 2005. (Batman Ser.). 80p. (J). 2.99 (978-0-439-72784-6(7)) Scholastic, Inc.

—Frostbite. 2006. (Batman Ser.: No. 1). (Illus.). 32p. (J). pap. 3.99 (978-0-439-78951-6(6)) Scholastic, Inc.

—Hot & Cold. 2005. (Batman Ser.). (Illus.). 104p. (J). (ps-k). pap. 4.99 (978-0-439-72781-5(2)) Scholastic, Inc.

—Maximum Justice. 2005. (Batman Ser.). (Illus.). 104p. (J). 4.99 (978-0-439-72778-5(2)) Scholastic, Inc.

—Severe Gear. Levins, Tim, illus. 2005. (Batman Ser.). 80p. (J). 2.99 (978-0-439-72785-3(5)) Scholastic, Inc.

Augustyn, Brian. The One-Man Justice League: 8x8 Storybook. Rousseau, Craig, illus. 2003. (Justice League Ser.). 24p. (J). per. 2.99 (978-1-4037-0297-5(7)) Dalmatian Pr.

Beatty, Scott. Batman Begins: The Visual Guide. 2005. (Illus.). 64p. (J). (ps-7). 19.99 (978-0-7566-1233-7(0)) Dorling Kindersley Publishing, Inc.

—The BatmanTM Handbook: The Ultimate Training Manual. Hahn, David, illus. 2005. 192p. pap. 15.95 (978-1-59474-023-7(2)) Quirk Bks.

Burchett, Rick, illus. The Batman: Going Batty. 2005. (Batman Ser.). 24p. (J). 3.99 (978-0-439-72777-8(4)) Scholastic, Inc.

Byrne, John A. Generations: An Imaginary Tale. Crain, Dale, ed. Byrne, John, illus. rev. ed. 2000. (Superman/Batman Ser.). 208p. pap. 17.95 (978-1-56389-605-7(2)) DC Comics.

Cosentino, Ralph. Batman. 2008. 40p. (J). (ps). 15.99 (***978-0-670-06255-3(3)*** , Viking Juvenile) Penguin Group (USA) Inc.

DC Comics Staff. Batman Big Color & Activity Book: With Stickers. Meredith Books Staff & Forlini, Victoria, eds. 2005. 64p. (J). pap., act. bk. ed. 2.99 (978-0-696-22721-9(5)) Meredith Bks.

—Batman Jumbo Color & Activity Book. Meredith Books Staff et al, eds. 2005. 400p. (J). pap. 5.99 (978-0-696-22722-6(3)) Meredith Bks.

DC Comics Staff, ed. Batman Classic Book with Activity Kit. 2008. 32p. (J). pap. 14.99 (***978-0-696-23961-8(2)***) Meredith Bks.

DC Comics Staff & Simonson, Louise. Superman Returns: Strange Visitor. 2nd novel rev. ed. 2006. 144p. (J). (ps-17). pap. 4.99 (978-0-316-17799-3(7)) Little, Brown Bks. for Young Readers.

Dorling Kindersley Publishing Staff. Batman. 2001. (Ultimate Sticker Bks.). 16p. (J). pap. 6.99 (978-0-7894-7866-5(8)) Dorling Kindersley Publishing, Inc.

Fisch, Sholly. Batman Beyond: Grounded. Delaney, John et al, illus. 2002. (Pictureback Ser.). 24p. (J). (ps-3). pap. 3.25 (978-0-375-80655-1(5) , Random Hse. Bks. for Young Readers) Random Hse. Children's Bks.

Forlini, Victoria, ed. Batman Begins Audio Pack. 2005. (ENG., Illus.). 22p. (J). (ps-ps). 15.95 (978-0-696-22390-7(2)) Meredith Bks.

—Batman Begins Color & Activity Book with Crayons: Gotham's Guardian. Raimondi, Pablo & DeCarlo, Mike, illus. 2005. 32p. (J). (ps-ps). pap., act. bk. ed. 3.99 (978-0-696-22393-8(7)) Meredith Bks.

—Batman Begins Sticker Storybook: Swinging into Action. 2005. (Illus.). 16p. (J). (ps-ps). pap. 3.99 (978-0-696-22505-5(0)) Meredith Bks.

Grayson, Devin. Batman: The Copycat Crime. 2003. (gr. k-3). lib. bdg. 11.80 (978-0-613-71996-4(3)) Tandem Library Bks.

Grayson, Devin, et al. Batman No. 2: The Copycat Crime. 2003. (Reader Ser.). (Illus.). 40p. (J). pap. 3.99 (978-0-439-47097-1(8) , Cartwheel Bks.) Scholastic, Inc.

Harper, Ben. The Batman: In the Shadows. 2005. (Batman Ser.). 32p. (J). 3.99 (978-0-439-72786-0(3)) Scholastic, Inc.

—The Batman: Night Vision. 2006. 32p. (J). 4.99 (978-0-439-78953-0(2)) Scholastic, Inc.

—The Cave of Wonders. 2005. (Batman Ser.: No. 4). 32p. (J). 3.99 (978-0-439-72788-4(X)) Scholastic, Inc.

Harris, Ann Marie, ed. Top Secret Files. 2006. 48p. (J). pap. 9.99 (978-0-439-80349-6(7)) Scholastic, Inc.

Hunt, Brian. Joker's Wild. DC Comics Staff, illus. 2006. (Batman Ser.: No. 2). 24p. (J). pap. 3.50 (978-0-439-78950-9(8)) Scholastic, Inc.

McCann, Jesse Leon. Batman: Four Adventure Stories. Byrne, John, illus. 2005. (Reader Collection). 160p. (J). 6.99 (978-0-439-76312-7(6) , Cartwheel Bks.) Scholastic, Inc.

McCann, Jesse Leon, et al. Batman No. 1: Time Thaw. Byrne, John, illus. 2003. (Scholastic Reader Ser.). 40p. (J). pap. 3.99 (978-0-439-47096-4(X) , Cartwheel Bks.) Scholastic, Inc.

Meredith Books Staff, ed. Batman Sticker Storybook. 2008. 16p. pap. 5.99 (***978-0-696-23960-1(4)***) Meredith Bks.

—Heads or Tails. 2008. 24p. pap. 3.99 (***978-0-696-23959-5(0)***) Meredith Bks.

—Race Against Crime. 2008. 24p. pap. 3.99 (***978-0-696-23958-8(2)***) Meredith Bks.

Miller, Frank. Batman: The Dark Knight Returns. Miller, Frank, illus. 2002. (Illus.). 22.40 (978-1-4046-2249-4(7)) Book Wholesalers, Inc.

Peterson, Scott. Batman: The Story of Batman. 2006. (Scholastic Reader Ser.). (Illus.). 40p. (J). pap. 3.99 (978-0-439-47104-6(4) , Cartwheel Bks.) Scholastic, Inc.

—Batman Beyond: New Hero in Town. Kruse, Brandon et al, illus. 2000. (Pictureback Ser.). 24p. (J). (ps-3). pap. 3.99 (978-0-375-80653-7(9) , Random Hse. Bks. for Young Readers) Random Hse. Children's Bks.

Puckett, Kelley. Batman's Dark Secret. 2000. (Hello Reader! Ser.). (Illus.). (J). 10.79 (978-0-606-18517-2(8)) Tandem Library Bks.

Scholastic, Inc. Staff & Muntz, Percival. Batman Reader No. 4: The Birthday Bash. Burchett, Rick, illus. 2004. (Batman Ser.: No. 5). 40p. (J). (ps-3). pap. 3.99 (978-0-439-47099-5(4) , Cartwheel Bks.) Scholastic, Inc.

Slavkovic, Sibin & Lee, Stan. Just Imagine Stan Lee's Batman. Kubert, Joe, illus. rev. ed. 2001. 48p. pap. 5.95 (978-1-56389-822-8(5)) DC Comics.

Snider, Brandon T. Cry of the Penguin: Deluxe Sound Storybook. Forlini, Victoria, ed. Staton, Joe & DeCarlo, Mike, illus. 2005. (Batman Ser.). 22p. (J). (ps-3). 15.95 (978-0-696-22736-3(3)) Meredith Bks.

Steele, Michael Anthony. The Book of Crooks. Armstrong, Jason, illus. 2005. (Batman Ser.). 64p. (J). (ps-k). pap. 5.99 (978-0-439-72780-8(4)) Scholastic, Inc.

—Cool Cat. 2006. (Batman Ser.). (Illus.). 32p. (J). pap. 3.99 (978-0-439-83002-7(8)) Scholastic, Inc.

Teitelbaum, Michael. Batman Beyond: The Return of the Joker. 2000. 144p. (J). (gr. 4-7). pap. 4.99 (978-0-439-20769-0(X)) Scholastic, Inc.

Waid, Mark. Jla: Tower of Babel. 2001. (gr. 5-8). lib. bdg. 22.20 (978-0-613-60569-4(1)) Tandem Library Bks.

Wells, Conrad. The Batman: How to Draw. Albano, Ursula, illus. 2005. (Batman Ser.). 32p. (J). (ps-k). 4.99 (978-0-439-72782-2(0)) Scholastic, Inc.

BATS

Appelt, Kathi. Bats Around the Clock. Sweet, Melissa, illus. 2000. 32p. (J). (gr. k-5). 16.99 (978-0-688-16469-0(2)) HarperCollins Pubs.

Ball, Jacqueline A. Migrating Animals of the Air. 2007. (J). pap. (***978-0-8368-8422-7(1));*** 24p. (gr. 2-4). lib. bdg. 19.93 (***978-0-8368-8417-3(5)***) Stevens, Gareth Inc. (Weekly Reader Early Learning Library).

Bats. (Animals Ser.). 32p. (J). 6.95 (978-0-7368-8069-5(0)) Capstone Pr., Inc.

Bats. (Nature's Friends Ser.). 32p. (J). 7.95 (978-0-7565-1224-8(7)) Compass Point Bks.

Bats, 6 vols. (gr. 2-5). 36.95 (978-0-7368-8179-1(4)) Red Brick Learning.

Bats, 6 Packs. 16p. (gr. 2 up). 36.00 (978-0-7635-9395-7(8)) Rigby Education.

Bats, Bats, Bats. (Rosen Real Readers Big Bookstm Ser.). 8p. (J). (gr. k-1). 27.95 (978-1-4042-6207-2(5)) Rosen Publishing Group, Inc., The.

Bats Set B, 6 vols. (Phonics Readers Ser.). (gr. k-2). 17.50 (978-0-7368-3199-4(1)) Red Brick Learning.

Bats Set II. 2006. (J). (gr. k-6). 128.10 (978-1-59679-319-4(8) , Checkerboard Library) ABDO Publishing Co.

Bauman, Amy & Lundberg, Kathryn T. The Wonder of Bats. 2000. (Animal Wonders Ser.). (Illus.). 48p. (J). (gr. 1 up). lib. bdg. 26.00 (978-0-8368-2660-9(4)) Stevens, Gareth Inc.

Berger, Melvin. How Do Bats See in the Dark? Questions & Answers about Night Creatures. 2001. 12.75 (978-0-606-22153-5(0)) Tandem Library Bks.

Berger, Melvin & Berger, Gilda. How Do Bats See in the Dark? Questions & Answers about Night Creatures. Effler, Jim, illus. (Question & Answer Ser.). (J). 2001. 48p. (gr. 2-4). pap. 5.95 (978-0-439-22904-3(9) , Scholastic Reference); 2000. (978-0-439-19374-0(5)) Scholastic, Inc.

—Screech! A Book about Bats. 2000. (Hello Reader! Ser.). (978-0-606-18600-1(X)) Tandem Library Bks.

Berger, Melvin, et al. How Do Bats See in the Dark? Questions & Answers about Night Creatures. 2000. (Question & Answer Ser.). (Illus.). (J). pap. (978-0-439-19375-7(3)) Scholastic, Inc.

Berman, Ruth. Squeaking Bats. 1998. (Pull Ahead Bks.). (Illus.). 32p. (J). (gr. k-2). pap. 5.95 (978-0-8225-3608-6(0)); lib. bdg. 22.60 (978-0-8225-3602-4(1) , Lerner Pubns.) Lerner Publishing Group.

—Squeaking Bats. 1998. (Illus.). 32p. (J). (gr. k-2). lib. bdg. 14.10 (978-0-613-43895-7(7)) Tandem Library Bks.

Bernard, Robin. Bats. 1998. 32p. pap. 8.95 (978-0-590-10617-7(1)) Scholastic, Inc.

Boynton, Bibi. Bats. 2003. (Compass Point Phonics Readers Ser.). (Illus.). 16p. (J). (gr. 1 up). 13.26 (978-0-7565-0505-9(4)) Compass Point Bks.

Bradley, James V. The Bat. 2006. (Nature Walk Ser.). (Illus.). 64p. (J). 28.00 (978-0-7910-9117-3(1) , Chelsea Hse.) Facts On File, Inc.

Braun, Eric & Donovan, Sandy. Bats. 2001. (Animals of the Rain Forest Ser.). (Illus.). 32p. (YA). lib. bdg. 22.83 (978-0-7398-4679-7(5)) Raintree.

Brenner, Barbara, et al. Where's That Bat? 1999. (Hide & Seek Science Ser.). (Illus.). (J). (978-0-590-12819-3(1)) Scholastic, Inc.

Cole, Joanna & Moore, Eva. The Truth about Bats. 1999. (Magic School Bus Chapter Bks.: No. 1). (J). (gr. 1-4). (978-0-606-18574-5(7)) Tandem Library Bks.

Cooper, Ann C. Bats: Swift Shadows in the Twilight. Denver Museum of Art Staff, illus. 1999. (Wonder Ser.). 64p. (gr. 3-7). pap. 7.95 (978-1-879373-52-5(1)) Rinehart, Roberts Pubs.

Coste, Marion. The Hawaiian Bat: Ope'ape'a. Maxner, Pearl, illus. 2005. 30p. (J). (gr. 4 up). 12.95 (978-0-8248-2797-7(X)) Univ. of Hawaii Pr.

Crowther, Robert. Deep down under Ground: A Pop-up Book of Amazing Facts & Feats. Crowther, Robert, illus. 2004. (Illus.). 18p. (J). (gr. 3-8). reprint ed. pap. 22.00 (978-0-7567-7179-9(X)) DIANE Publishing Co.

Dittrich, Tina & Morrison, Kathryn. Stellaluna: An Study of Birds & Bats. 2005. pap. 10.95 (***978-1-931334-85-3(4)***) Pieces of Learning.

Donovan, Sandy. A Bat in Its Cave. 2003. (Where Do Animals Live? Ser.). (J). lib. bdg. (978-1-58417-188-1(X)) Lake Street Pubs.

Dornfeld, Margaret. Bats. 2004. (Animals, Animals Ser.). (Illus.). 46p. (J). 25.64 (978-0-7614-1754-5(0) , Benchmark Bks.) Cavendish, Marshall Corp.

Franco, Betsy. Word Family Tales -At: A Bat Named Pat. Weissman, Bart, illus. 2002. (Word Family Tales Ser.). 16p. (ps-2). pap. 2.95 (978-0-439-26266-8(6)) Scholastic, Inc.

Gallimard Jeunesse Publishing Staff. Night Creatures. Perols, Sylvaine, illus. 1998. (First Discovery Book Ser.). 24p. (J). (ps-2). 12.95 (978-0-590-11765-4(3)) Scholastic, Inc.

Generazzo, Roger. Bats! Know It Alls. Harris, Greg, illus. 2000. (Know-It-Alls Ser.). 24p. (J). (ps-3). mass mkt. 2.79 (978-0-7681-0209-3(X) , 57007, McClanahan Bk.) Learning Horizons, Inc.

George, Michael. Bats. 2006. (New Naturebooks). (Illus.). 32p. (J). (gr. 1-5). 27.07 (978-1-59296-631-8(4)) Child's World, Inc.

Gibbons, Gail. Bats. Gibbons, Gail, illus. 1999. (Illus.). 32p. (J). (gr. k-3). pap. 6.95 (978-0-8234-1637-0(2)); tchr. ed. 16.95 (978-0-8234-1457-4(4)) Holiday Hse., Inc.

Gibson, Deborah C. Bats & Their Homes. 1999. (Animal Habitats Ser.). (Illus.). 24p. (J). (gr. k-4). lib. bdg. 18.75 (978-0-8239-5312-7(2) , PowerKids Pr.) Rosen Publishing Group, Inc., The.

Gilpin, Daniel. Bats. Hersey, Bob, illus. 2004. (Scary Creatures Ser.). (J). 22.50 (978-0-531-12375-1(8)); 32p. (gr. 2-4). pap. 6.95 (978-0-531-16746-5(1)) Scholastic Library Publishing. (Watts, Franklin).

Glaser, Linda. Beautiful Bats. Holm, Sharon Lane, illus. 1998. 3. 32p. (J). (gr. k-3). pap. 8.95 (978-0-7613-0340-4(5) , Millbrook Pr.) Lerner Publishing Group.

Goldberger, Andrew. Bats. 2002. 16p. (J). (978-0-439-35092-1(1)) Scholastic, Inc.

Greenaway, Theresa. Bats. 2002. (Secret World Of... Ser.). (Illus.). 48p. (J). lib. bdg. 27.12 (978-0-7398-4982-8(4)) Raintree.

Hanging Around Bats. 2005. (Book Treks Ser.). (J). (gr. 3 up). stu. ed. 34.95 (978-0-673-62834-3(5)) Celebration Pr.

Harcourt School Publishers Staff. Bats: Phonics Practice Reader. 1999. (Collections Ser.). (Illus.). (J). pap. 2.60 (978-0-15-312917-9(4)) Harcourt Schl. Pubs.

Heinrichs, Ann. Bats. 2004. (Illus.). 32p. (J). (gr. 2 up). lib. bdg. 21.26 (978-0-7565-0591-2(7)) Compass Point Bks.

Iorio, Nicole. Bats! 2005. 32p. (J). lib. bdg. 13.85 ***(978-1-4242-0856-2(4))*** Fitzgerald Bks.

Kalman, Bobbie. What Is a Bat? (Science of Living Things Ser.). (J). 1999. (Illus.). 32p. (gr. 2-3). (978-0-86505-883-5(0)); 1999. (Illus.). 32p. (gr. 2-3). pap. (978-0-86505-895-8(4)); 1998. (gr. 4-7). pap. (978-0-86560-895-5(4)) Crabtree Publishing Co.

—What Is a Bat? 1998. (gr. 3-6). lib. bdg. 14.10 (978-0-613-89151-6(1)) Tandem Library Bks.

Kalman, Bobbie & Levigne, Heather. Les Chauves-Souris. 2003. (FRE., Illus.). 32p. (J). pap. (978-2-920660-83-0(7)) Crabtree Publishing Co.

—Qué Son los Murciélagos? 2005. (Ciencia de los Seres Vivos Ser.). (SPA., Illus.). 32p. (J). (gr. 3-4). pap. (978-0-7787-8809-6(1)); (978-0-7787-8763-1(X)) Crabtree Publishing Co.

—What Is a Bat? 1998. (Illus.). 32p. (J). (ps-7). lib. bdg. 14.10 (978-0-613-12259-7(3)) Tandem Library Bks.

Kalman, Bobbie & Lundblad, Kristina. Endangered Bats. 2006. (Illus.). 32p. (J). (gr. 2-8). pap. (978-0-7787-1912-0(X)); (978-0-7787-1866-6(2)) Crabtree Publishing Co.

Kovacs. Noises in the Night. 1999. (Illus.). (J). pap. (978-0-7398-2472-6(4)) Steck-Vaughn.

Kovacs, Deborah. Noises in the Night: The Habits of Bats. 1999. (Rain Forest Pilot Ser.). (Illus.). 48p. (J). (gr. 4-6). 18.98 (978-0-7398-2218-0(7)) Raintree.

—Noises in the Night: The Habits of Bats. 2000. (Turnstone Rain Forest Pilot Book Ser.). (Illus.). 48p. (J). (gr. 4-6). pap. 7.95 (978-0-7398-2227-2(6)) Steck-Vaughn.

Labella, Susan. Bats & Other Animals with Amazing Ears. 2005. (Scholastic News Nonfiction Readers Ser.). (Illus.). 24p. (J). (gr. 1-2). 19.00 (978-0-516-24926-1(6) , Children's Pr.) Scholastic Library Publishing.

Landau, Elaine. Bats: Hunters of the Night. 2007. (Animals after Dark Ser.). (Illus.). 32p. (J). (gr. 2-4). lib. bdg. 22.60 (978-0-7660-2772-5(4) , Enslow Elementary) Enslow Pubs., Inc.

Lockwood, Sophie. Bats. 2008. (World of Mammals Ser.). 40p. (J). (gr. 2-6). 29.93 ***(978-1-59296-926-5(7))*** Child's World, Inc.

Lunde, Darrin. Hello, Bumblebee Bat. Wynne, Patricia J., illus. 2007. (J). (ps-1). 32p. 15.95 (978-1-57091-374-7(9)); 28p. pap. 6.95 ***(978-1-57091-464-5(8))*** Charlesbridge Publishing, Inc.

Macken, JoAnn Early. The Life Cycle of a Bat. 2006. (Illus.). 24p. (J). pap. (978-0-8368-6386-4(0)); lib. bdg. 19.33 (978-0-8368-6379-6(8)) Stevens, Gareth Inc.

Markle, Sandra. Little Lost Bat. Marks, Alan, illus. 2006. 32p. (J). (gr. 1-4). 15.95 (978-1-57091-656-4(X)) Charlesbridge Publishing, Inc.

—Outside & Inside Bats. 2004. (Illus.). 40p. (J). pap. 7.95 (978-0-8027-7713-3(9)) Walker & Co.

Mason, Adrienne. Bats. Ogle, Nancy Gray, illus. 2004. (Kids Can Press Wildlife Ser.). 32p. (J). (gr. k-3). (978-1-55337-525-8(4)); (978-1-55337-524-1(6)) Kids Can Pr., Ltd.

Mattern, Joanne. Bats Are Night Animals. 2006. (Illus.). 24p. (J). pap. ***(978-0-8368-7852-3(3));*** lib. bdg. ***(978-0-8368-7845-5(0))*** Stevens, Gareth Inc. (Weekly Reader Early Learning Library).

—Bats Are Night Animals: Los Murciélagos Son Animales Nocturnos. 2006. (ENG & SPA., Illus.). 24p. pap. ***(978-0-8368-8049-6(8));*** lib. bdg. ***(978-0-8368-8042-7(0))*** Stevens, Gareth Inc. (Weekly Reader Early Learning Library).

McMorrow, Annalisa. Bats: A Science Discovery Book. Chalk, Philip, illus. 1999. 48p. (J). (gr. 3-6). pap. 7.95 (978-1-57612-076-7(7) , MM2090) Monday Morning Bks., Inc.

Moore, Eva. The Truth about Bats. Enik, Ted, illus. 2000. (Magic School Bus Chapter Bks.: No. 1). 80p. (J). (gr. 1-4). pap. 4.99 (978-0-439-10798-3(9)) Scholastic, Inc.

—Truth about Bats. 1999. (gr. 3-6). lib. bdg. 11.80 (978-0-613-22531-1(7)) Tandem Library Bks.

Morris, Ting. Bat. 2005. (Illus.). 32p. (YA). (gr. 3 up). lib. bdg. 27.10 (978-1-58340-524-6(0)) Smart Apple Media.

Los Murcielagos. (Fascinante Mundo de... Ser.).Tr. of Fascinating World of Bats. (Illus.). 8.95 (978-958-04-3230-2(9)) Norma S.A. COL. *Dist:* Distribuidora Norma, Inc.

Murray, Julie. Vampire Bats. 2005. (Animal Kingdom Set Ii Ser.). (Illus.). 24p. (J). (gr. k-4). lib. bdg. 21.35 (978-1-59197-313-3(9)) ABDO Publishing Co.

—Wrinkle-Faced Bats. 2002. (Animal Kingdom Ser.). (Illus.). 24p. (J). (gr. k-4). lib. bdg. 21.35 (978-1-57765-710-1(1)) ABDO Publishing Co.

O'Donnell, Kerri. Bats. 2006. (Ugly Animals Ser.). (Illus.). 24p. (J). (gr. k-2). lib. bdg. 21.25 (978-1-4042-3525-0(6) , PowerKids Pr.) Rosen Publishing Group, Inc., The.

Perry, Phyllis J. Bats: The Amazing Upside-Downers. 1998. (First Bks.). 64p. (J). 23.00 (978-0-531-20342-2(5) , Watts, Franklin) Scholastic Library Publishing.

Piper, Molly. ET My Bat. 1999. 56p. (J). pap. 7.95 (978-1-891360-04-6(3)) Little Deer Pr.

Preszler, June. Bats. 2006. (Illus.). 24p. (J). (978-0-7368-5415-3(0)) Capstone Pr., Inc.

Prims, Marta & Roca, Nuria. I Am a Little Bat. 2001. (Barron's Little Animal Ser.). (Illus.). 24p. (J). (ps-k). 9.95 (978-0-7641-5346-4(3)) Barron's Educational Series, Inc.

Pringle, Laurence P. Bats! Strange & Wonderful. Henderson, Meryl, illus. 2003. 32p. (J). (gr. 2-4). 15.95 (978-1-56397-327-7(8)) Boyds Mills Pr.

Prior, Jennifer Overend. Bats. Hale, Janet A., ed. Hedges, Bruce, illus. 1999. (Thematic Units Ser.). 80p. (J). pap., tchr. ed. 9.99 (978-1-57690-376-6(1) , TCA2376) Teacher Created Materials, Inc.

Raabe, Emily. Bulldog Bats. 2003. (Library of Bats Ser.). (Illus.). 24p. (J). lib. bdg. 18.75 (978-0-8239-6326-3(8) , PowerKids Pr.) Rosen Publishing Group, Inc., The.

—Flying Foxes. 2003. (Library of Bats Ser.). (Illus.). 24p. (J). lib. bdg. 18.75 (978-0-8239-6324-9(1) , PowerKids Pr.) Rosen Publishing Group, Inc., The.

—Free-Tailed Bats. 2003. (Library of Bats Ser.). (Illus.). 24p. (J). lib. bdg. 18.75 (978-0-8239-6325-6(X) , PowerKids Pr.) Rosen Publishing Group, Inc., The.

—Horseshoe Bats. 2003. (Library of Bats Ser.). (Illus.). 24p. (J). lib. bdg. 18.75 (978-0-8239-6327-0(6) , PowerKids Pr.) Rosen Publishing Group, Inc., The.

—Plain-Nosed Bats. 2003. (Library of Bats Ser.). (Illus.). 24p. (J). lib. bdg. 18.75 (978-0-8239-6323-2(3) , PowerKids Pr.) Rosen Publishing Group, Inc., The.

—Vampire Bats. 2003. (Library of Bats Ser.). (Illus.). 24p. (J). lib. bdg. 18.75 (978-0-8239-6322-5(5) , PowerKids Pr.) Rosen Publishing Group, Inc., The.

Rigby Education Staff. Upside Down. (Sails Literacy Ser.). (Illus.). 16p. (gr. k-1). 27.00 (978-0-7635-9863-1(1) , 698631C99) Rigby Education.

Riley, Joelle. Bats. 2005. (Early Bird Nature Bks.). (Illus.). (J). (gr. 2-4). lib. bdg. 25.26 (978-0-8225-2416-8(3)) Lerner Publishing Group.

Robb, Jackie & Stringle, Berny. The Story of Bat. Duncan, Karen & Stringle, Sam, illus. 2003. (Bang on the Door Ser.). 32p. (YA). pap. (978-1-85602-316-0(8)) Chrysalis Children's Bks.

Ruff, Sue & Wilson, Don E. Bats. 2000. (Animal Ways Ser.). (Illus.). 104p. (J). (gr. 5 up). lib. bdg. 31.36 (978-0-7614-1137-6(2) , Benchmark Bks.) Cavendish, Marshall Corp.

Salzmann, Mary Elizabeth. What Has Wings? 2007. (Creature Features Ser.). (ENG., Illus.). 24p. (J). (ps-3). lib. bdg. 24.21 ***(978-1-59928-876-5(1)*** , Super SandCastle) ABDO Publishing Co.

Shaw, Nancy. Bats. 1998. (Let's Investigate Ser.: Vol. 12). (Illus.). 32p. (J). (ps-3). lib. bdg. 19.95 (978-0-88682-958-2(5) , Creative Education) Creative Co., The.

Shaw, Nancy J. Bats. (Illus.). 32p. pap. 8.95 (978-0-89812-318-0(6)); 2000. (J). pap. 10.60 (978-0-89812-003-5(9) , Creative Paperbacks) Creative Co., The.

Silverman, Buffy. El Paseo Nocturno Del Murcielago. de la Vega, Eida, tr. Buskirk, Judith Prowse, illus. 2001. (Books for Young Learners).Tr. of Bat's Night Out. (SPA.). 16p. (J). (gr. k-2). pap. 5.00 (978-1-57274-449-3(9) , 2888) Owen, Richard C. Pubs., Inc.

Sjonger, Rebecca & Kalman, Bobbie. The Life Cycle of a Bat. 2005. (Bobbie Kalman Book Ser.). (Illus.). 32p. (J). (gr. k-6). (978-0-7787-0671-7(0)); pap. (978-0-7787-0701-1(6)) Crabtree Publishing Co.

Somervill, Barbara A. Vampire Bats: Feasting on Blood. 2008. (J). lib. bdg. ***(978-1-4042-3804-6(2)*** , PowerKids Pr.) Rosen Publishing Group, Inc., The.

Steck-Vaughn Staff. Noises in the Night: Teacher's Resource Binder. 1999. (J). pap., tchr. ed. (978-0-7398-2475-7(9)) Steck-Vaughn.

Stewart, Melissa. How Do Bats Fly in the Dark? 2008. (J). ***(978-0-7614-2924-1(7))*** Cavendish, Marshall Bks., Ltd.

Swanson, Diane. Bats. 2003. (Welcome to the World of Animals Ser.). (Illus.). 32p. (J). (gr. 3 up). lib. bdg. 23.33 (978-0-8368-3559-5(X)) Stevens, Gareth Inc.

—Bats. 2003. (gr. k-3). lib. bdg. 14.10 (978-0-613-78494-8(4)) Tandem Library Bks.

Sway, Marlene. Bats: Mammals That Fly. 1999. (Animals in Order Ser.). (Illus.). 48p. (J). (gr. 4-6). pap. 6.95 (978-0-531-15943-9(4)); 26.50 (978-0-531-11449-0(X)) Scholastic Library Publishing. (Watts, Franklin).

—Bats: Mammals That Fly. 1999. (gr. 3-6). lib. bdg. 15.25 (978-0-613-34602-3(5)) Tandem Library Bks.

Taylor, Barbara. Birds & Other Flying Animals. 2002. (J). 24.95 (978-1-57768-965-2(8) , Bedrick, Peter Bks.) School Specialty Publishing.

Taylor, Bonnie Highsmith. Zelda: A Little Brown Bat. 2001. (Animal Adventures Ser.). (Illus.). (J). 54p. pap. (978-0-7891-5158-2(8)); 56p. (gr. 1-4). lib. bdg. 16.95 (978-0-7807-9322-4(6)) Perfection Learning Corp.

Theodorou, Rod. Gray Bat. (Animals in Danger Ser.). (Illus.). 32p. (J). (gr. k-2). 2002. pap. 6.95 (978-1-58810-445-8(1) , 91152); 2001. lib. bdg. 21.36 (978-1-57572-270-2(4)) Heinemann Library.

Tiffault, Benette W. Ghost Bat in a Gum Tree. Grosshauser, Peter, illus. 1998. 32p. (ps-3). pap. 9.95 (978-1-56044-618-7(8) , Falcon) Globe Pequot Pr., The.

Time for Kids Editors. Bats! 2005. (Time for Kids Ser.). (Illus.). 32p. (J). 14.99 (978-0-06-057639-4(1)); pap. 3.99 (978-0-06-057638-7(3) , Harper Trophy) HarperCollins Pubs.

Tuttle, Merlin D. Discover Bats! The Multi-Media Education Kit about Bats. Tyburec, Janet & McCabe, Sara, eds. Chapman, David, illus. 1998. 270p. (J). (gr. 4-8). pap. 54.95 incl. VHS (978-0-9638248-1-3(3)) Bat Conservation International, Inc.

Vogel, Julia. Bats. Recher, Andrew, illus. 2007. (Our Wild World Ser.). 48p. (J). (gr. 3-6). 10.95 (978-1-55971-968-1(0)); pap. 7.95 (978-1-55971-969-8(9)) T&N Children's Publishing. (NorthWord Bks. for Young Readers).

Welsbacher, Anne. Vampire Bats. 2001. (Predators in the Wild Ser.). (Illus.). 48p. (J). (gr. 3-4). lib. bdg. 21.26 (978-0-7368-0787-6(X) , Capstone High-Interest Bks.) Capstone Pr., Inc.

What Is Bat?, 6 Packs. (Literatura 2000 Ser.). (gr. 1-2). 28.00 (978-0-7635-0118-1(2)) Rigby Education.

Wheeler, Jill C. Bumblebee Bats. 2006. (Checkerboard Animal Library). (Illus.). 24p. (J). (gr. k-6). 21.35 (978-1-59679-320-0(1) , Checkerboard Library) ABDO Publishing Co.

—Fringe-Lipped Bats. 2006. (Checkerboard Animal Library). (Illus.). 24p. (J). (gr. k-6). 21.35 (978-1-59679-321-7(X) , Checkerboard Library) ABDO Publishing Co.

—Ghost-Faced Bats. 2006. (Checkerboard Animal Library). (Illus.). 24p. (J). (gr. k-6). 21.35 (978-1-59679-322-4(8) , Checkerboard Library) ABDO Publishing Co.

—Honduran White Bats. 2006. (Checkerboard Animal Library). (Illus.). 24p. (J). (gr. k-6). 21.35 (978-1-59679-324-8(4) , Checkerboard Library) ABDO Publishing Co.

—Slit-Faced Bats. 2006. (Checkerboard Animal Library). (Illus.). 24p. (J). (gr. k-6). 21.35 (978-1-59679-323-1(6) , Checkerboard Library) ABDO Publishing Co.

Whitehouse, Patricia. Bats. 2003. (What's Awake? Ser.). (Illus.). 24p. (J). (ps-1). lib. bdg. 17.08 (978-1-58810-878-4(3)); pap. (978-1-4034-0625-5(1)) Heinemann Library.

—El Murcielago. 2003. (Que Esta Despierto? (What's Awake?) Ser.).Tr. of Bats. (SPA.). 24p. (J). lib. bdg. 17.08 (978-1-4034-0393-3(7)); (Illus.). pap. 5.25 (978-1-4034-0634-7(0)) Heinemann Library.

Wildlife Education, Ltd. Staff, et al. Bats. 1999. (Zoobooks Ser.). (Illus.). 18p. (J). pap. 2.95 (978-0-937934-59-3(3)) Wildlife Education, Ltd.

Williams, Kimberly Joan & Stoops, Erik Daniel. Bat Basics. 2001. (Young Explorer Ser.). (Illus.). 32p. (J). lib. bdg. 4.85 net. (978-1-890475-12-3(2)) Faulkner's Publishing Group.

—Bat Conservation, 6 vols., Set. 2001. (Young Explorer Ser.). (Illus.). 32p. (J). (gr. 3-7). lib. bdg. 4.85 net. (978-1-890475-13-0(0)) Faulkner's Publishing Group.

—Bats That Drink Nectar, 6 vols., Set. 2001. (Young Explorer Ser.). (Illus.). 32p. (J). (gr. 3-7). lib. bdg. 4.85 net. (978-1-890475-16-1(5)) Faulkner's Publishing Group.

—Bats That Eat Fruit, 6 vols., Set. 2001. (Young Explorer Ser.). (Illus.). 32p. (J). (gr. 3-7). lib. bdg. 4.85 net. (978-1-890475-14-7(9)) Faulkner's Publishing Group.

—Bats That Eat Insects, 6 vols., Set. 2001. (Young Explorer Ser.). (Illus.). 32p. (J). (gr. 3-7). lib. bdg. 4.85 net. (978-1-890475-15-4(7)) Faulkner's Publishing Group.

—Vampire Bats, 6 vols., Set. 2001. (Young Explorer Ser.). (Illus.). 32p. (J). (gr. 3-7). lib. bdg. 4.85 net. (978-1-890475-17-8(3)) Faulkner's Publishing Group.

Windsor, Jo. Bat & Parrot: Emergent Level Satellite Individual Title Six-Packs. Storey, Jim, illus. (Sails Literacy Ser.). (gr. k-1). 27.00 (978-0-7578-7917-3(9)) Rigby Education.

—Bats in Blankets: Early Level Satellite Individual Title Six-Packs. (Sails Literacy Ser.). 16p. (gr. 1-2). 27.00 (978-0-7578-2939-0(2)) Rigby Education.

Wood, Lily. Bats. 2001. (Scholastic Science Readers Ser.). (Illus.). 32p. (J). (gr. k-1). pap. 3.99 (978-0-439-29582-6(3) , Scholastic Reference) Scholastic, Inc.

—Bats. Scholastic, Inc. Staff, ed. 2000. (Science Readers Ser.). (Illus.). 32p. (J). (978-0-439-16293-7(9)) Scholastic, Inc.

—Bats. 2001. (gr. k-3). lib. bdg. 11.80 (978-0-613-36204-7(7)); (Illus.). (J). 10.79 (978-0-606-21414-8(3)) Tandem Library Bks.

Wood, Linda C. & Rink, Deane. Bats. 2001. (Zoobooks Ser.). (Illus.). 24p. (J). (gr. 1-6). 15.95 (978-1-888153-48-4(2)) Wildlife Education, Ltd.

World Book, Inc. Staff, contrib. by. Flying Foxes & Other Bats. 2005. (World Book's Animals of the World Ser.). (Illus.). 64p. (J). (978-0-7166-1262-9(3)) World Bk., Inc.

BATS—FICTION

Appelt, Kathi. Bat Jamboree. Sweet, Melissa, illus. 1998. 32p. (J). (ps-3). pap. 6.99 (978-0-688-16167-5(7) , Harper Trophy) HarperCollins Pubs.

Badgley, Catherine. Pippa's First Summer. Miljour, Bonnie, illus. (J). 2006. pap. 8.95 (978-1-58726-313-2(0)); 2005. 112p. 14.95 (978-1-58726-281-4(9)) Ann Arbor Media Group, LLC. (Mitten Pr.).

Bat's Band. (Early Intervention Levels Ser.). 21.30 (978-0-7362-0383-8(4)) Hampton-Brown Bks.

Bauld, Jane Scoggins. Hector Saves the Moon, Vol. 2. Laronde, Gary, illus. 7.95 (978-1-57168-312-0(7)) Eakin Pr.

Brouillet, Chrystine. Chauve-Souris Qui Pleurait d'Etre Trop Belle. 2000. (Illus.). 24p. (YA). (ps up). pap. (978-2-89021-331-9(5)) Diffusion du livre Mirabel.

Butcher, Ginger & Broadhurst, Beth. Adventure of Echo the Bat. 2001. (Illus.). 24p. (J). (gr. k-4). pap. 8.00 (978-0-16-050684-0(0)) United States Government Printing Office.

—The Adventure of Echo the Bat. Butcher, Ginger, illus. 2005. (Illus.). 22p. (J). (gr. k-4). reprint ed. pap. 20.00 (978-0-7567-4761-9(9)) DIANE Publishing Co.

Cannon, Janell. Stellaluna. Cannon, Janell, illus. 2002. (Illus.). (J). 23.40 (978-0-7587-3703-8(3)) Book Wholesalers, Inc.

Cannon, Janell. Stellaluna. 2007. (Illus.). 42p. (J). (ps). bds. 7.95 ***(978-0-15-206287-3(4)*** , Red Wagon Bks.) Harcourt Children's Bks.

Cole, Kathryn. Pawluk. 2004. 48p. pap. 12.95 (978-1-4137-5477-3(5)) PublishAmerica, Inc.

Danziger, Paula. There's a Bat in Bunk Five. 2002. tchr. ed. (978-1-56137-669-8(8)) Novel Units, Inc.

—There's a Bat in Bunk Five. 160p. (J). pap. 160.00 (978-0-8072-1369-8(1) , Listening Library) Random Hse. Audio Publishing Group.

—There's a Bat in Bunk Five. 1998. (978-0-606-13094-3(2)) Tandem Library Bks.

Davies, Nicola. Bat Loves the Night. Fox-Davies, Sarah, illus. (Read & Wonder Ser.). 32p. (J). (gr. k-3). 2004. pap. 6.99 (978-0-7636-2438-5(1)); 2001. 15.99 (978-0-7636-1202-3(2)) Candlewick Pr.

Davis, Mike. Pirates, Bats, & Dragons. Simpson, William, illus. 2004. 174p. (J). 15.95 (978-0-9747078-2-2(1)) Perceval Pr.

Dragonwagon, Crescent. Bat in the Dining Room. Schindler, S. D., illus. 2005. 32p. (J). pap. 5.95 (978-0-7614-5146-4(3)) Cavendish, Marshall Corp.

Edwards, Pamela. Ms. Bitsy Bat's Kindergarten. Cole, Henry, illus. 2005. 32p. (ps-2). 15.99 (978-0-7868-0669-0(9)) Hyperion Bks. for Children.

Edwards, Pamela Duncan. Ms. Bitsy Bat's Kindergarten. Cole, Henry, illus. 2005. (J). ***(978-1-4156-2782-2(7))*** Hyperion Bks. for Children.

Fruit Bat's Feast. 2002. (Animal's Around the World Mini Bks.). (Illus.). 32p. (J). (978-1-59069-169-4(5) , H4005) Studio Mouse LLC.

Gilson, Jamie. It Goes Eeeeeeeeeeee! 2001. (gr. 3-6). lib. bdg. 12.95 (978-0-613-35528-5(8)) Tandem Library Bks.

Goss, Michael Anthony. The Bat Who Wore Glasses. Longabough, Kristen, illus. 2005. (J). pap. (978-1-933156-13-2(9)); per. (978-1-933156-06-4(6)) GSVQ Publishing. (VisionQuest Kids).

Greenburg, J. C. With the Bats. Gerardi, Jan, illus. 2006. (Andrew Lost Ser.: Bk. 14). 96p. (J). (gr. 2-4). 3.99 (978-0-375-83563-6(6)); No. 14. lib. bdg. 11.99 (978-0-375-93563-3(0)) Random Hse. Children's Bks. (Random Hse. Bks. for Young Readers).

Gresham, P. A. Anything Could Be Any Thing. 2005. 128p. pap. 12.95 (978-1-4116-4353-6(4)) Lulu.com.

Halfmann, Janet. Red Bat at Sleep Hollow Lane. Stegos, Daniel, illus. 2005. 32p. (J). (ps-2). 19.95 incl. audio (978-1-59249-343-2(2) , BC5027); 8.95 incl. reel tape (978-1-59249-344-9(0) , SC5027); 15.95 (978-1-59249-340-1(8) , B5027); 4.95 (978-1-59249-342-5(4) , B5077); pap. 6.95 (978-1-59249-341-8(6) , S5027) Soundprints.

—Red Bat at Sleep Hollow Lane. Buchs, Thomas, illus. 2004. 32p. (J). (ps-2). 9.95 (978-1-59249-345-6(9) , PB5027) Soundprints.

Hall, Kirsten. Going Batty. Burnett, Lindy, illus. 2001. (Hello Reader! Ser.). (J). pap. (978-0-439-31706-1(1)) Scholastic, Inc.

Harris, Ann Marie, ed. Top Secret Files. 2006. 48p. (J). pap. 9.99 (978-0-439-80349-6(7)) Scholastic, Inc.

Hotaling, Billie. Be Like the Bats. 2002. (gr. 7-12). lib. bdg. 25.70 (978-0-613-78097-1(3)) Tandem Library Bks.

Irbinskas, Heather. Pauly the Adventurous Pallid Bat. Anthis, Brian, illus. Tuttle, Merlin D., photos by. 2003. 32p. (J). pap. 7.95 (978-1-58369-032-1(8)) Western National Parks Assn.

Jarvis, Robin. Oaken Throne. 2005. (Illus.). 384p. (J). 17.95 (978-1-58717-277-9(1) , SeaStar Bks.) Chronicle Bks. LLC.

Jennings, Sharon. Bats in the Garbage. Mardon, John, illus. 2002. (First Flight Reader Ser.). 64p. (J). (gr. 2-5). pap. (978-1-55041-723-4(1)) Fitzhenry & Whiteside, Ltd.

—Bats in the Garbage. 2003. (gr. 3-6). lib. bdg. 12.95 (978-0-613-87468-7(4)) Tandem Library Bks.

Johnston, Tony. Desert Song. Young, Ed, illus. 2000. 32p. (J). (gr. k-4). reprint ed. 16.95 (978-0-87156-491-7(2)) Gibbs Smith, Publisher.

Kleinhenz, Sydine. Bats in My Attic. Stromoski, Rick, illus. 2005. (Rookie Reader Ser.). 31p. (J). (ps-ps). 19.50 (978-0-516-24865-3(0) , Children's Pr.) Scholastic Library Publishing.

Kleinhenz, Sydnie Meltzer. Bats in My Attic. Stromoski, Rick, illus. 2006. 32p. (J). (gr. k-2). pap. 4.95 (978-0-516-25022-9(1) , Children's Pr.) Scholastic Library Publishing.

Knudson, Michelle. The Case of Vampire Vivian. Wummer, Amy, illus. 2003. (Science Solves It! Ser.). 32p. (J). 4.99 (978-1-57565-127-9(0)) Kane Pr., The.

Landry, Leo. Fat Bat & Swoop. rev. ed. 2005. (Illus.). 64p. (J). (gr. 1-3). 15.95 (978-0-8050-7003-3(6) , Holt, Henry & Co. Bks. For Young Readers) Holt, Henry & Co.

Laronde, Gary, illus. Hector Visits His Country Cousin, Vol. 3. 2002. 25p. 14.95 (978-1-57168-601-5(0)); 7.95 (978-1-57168-676-3(2)) Eakin Pr.

Laschutza, Susanne. Nat the Bat. Laschutza, Susanne, illus. 2003. (Illus.). 24p. (J). (gr. 1 up). lib. bdg. 23.33 (978-0-8368-3573-1(5)) Stevens, Gareth Inc.

Lies, Brian. Bats at the Beach. 2006. (Illus.). 32p. (J). (gr. k-3). 16.00 (978-0-618-55744-8(X)) Houghton Mifflin Co.

Marsh, Carole. Dear Bats: The Creepy Cave Caper. 2007. (Postcard Mysteries Ser.). 128p. (J). (gr. 2-9). 14.95 ***(978-0-635-06398-4(0)*** , Marsh, Carole Family CD-Rom); pap. 5.99 ***(978-0-635-06342-7(5))*** Gallopade International.

Mayr, Diane. Littlebat's Halloween Story. Kendall, Gideon, illus. 2001. 32p. (J). (ps-2). 15.95 (978-0-8075-7629-8(8)) Whitman, Albert & Co.

Metzger, Steve. Five Little Bats Flying in the Night. Bryant, Laura, illus. 2006. 32p. (J). pap. 3.99 (978-0-439-77592-2(2) , Cartwheel Bks.) Scholastic, Inc.

Mitchard, Jacquelyn. Baby Bat's Lullaby. Noonan, Julia, illus. 2004. 32p. (J). (ps-1). 15.99 (978-0-06-050760-2(8)); lib. bdg. 16.89 (978-0-06-050761-9(6)) HarperCollins Pubs.

Navarro, Laura. Don Sabino, el Murciélago de la Ciudad: Don Sabino, the City Bat. Sebastian, Juan, illus. 2000. (ENG & SPA.). 45p. (J). (ps-3). pap. 8.95 (978-0-292-75569-7(4)) Univ. of Texas Pr.

—Semillas de Barbarita, la Murciélaga (Seeds from Little Barbara, the Bat) Sebastian, Juan, illus. 2002. (ENG & SPA.). 45p. pap. 8.95 (978-0-9638248-9-9(9)) Univ. of Texas Pr.

Naylor, Phyllis Reynolds. Bernie Magruder & the Bats in the Belfry. 2004. (Bernie Magruder Ser.). (Illus.). 144p. (J). pap. 5.99 (978-0-689-85067-7(0) , Aladdin) Simon & Schuster Children's Publishing.

—Bernie Magruder & the Bats in the Belfry. DiTerlizzi, Tony, illus. 2003. (Bernie Magruder Ser.). 144p. (J). (gr. 4-7). 16.95 (978-0-689-85066-0(2) , Atheneum) Simon & Schuster Children's Publishing.

—Bernie Magruder & the Bats in the Belfry. l.t. ed. 2003. (Bernie Magruder Ser.). 139p. (J). 22.95 (978-0-7862-5739-3(3)) Thorndike Pr.

Newton, Richard. One Bat - Two Bats. 2007. (J). per. 8.99 ***(978-1-59886-866-1(7))*** Tate Publishing & Enterprises, L.L.C.

Nickel, Scott. Billions of Bats: A Buzz Beaker Brainstorm. Smith, Andy J., illus. 2007. 33p. (J). pap. ***(978-1-59889-408-0(0))*** Stone Arch Bks.

Nickel, Scott & Stone Arch Books (Firm : Afton, Minn.) Staff. Billions of Bats: A Buzz Beaker Brainstorm. Smith, Andy J., illus. 2007. (Buzz Beaker Brainstorm Ser.). 40p. (J). (gr. k-4). lib. bdg. 21.26 ***(978-1-59889-313-7(0))*** Stone Arch Bks.

Oppel, Kenneth. Darkwing. Thompson, Keith, illus. 2007. 432p. (J). (gr. 5 up). 16.99 ***(978-0-06-085054-8(X));*** lib. bdg. 17.89 ***(978-0-06-085055-5(8))*** HarperCollins Pubs. (Eos).

—Firewing. (J). 2008. 320p. pap. 6.99 ***(978-1-4169-4999-2(2)*** , Aladdin); 2003. (Illus.). 272p. (gr. 3-7). 16.95 (978-0-689-84993-0(1)); 2004. 300p. reprint ed. pap. 5.99 (978-0-689-86988-4(6) , Aladdin) Simon & Schuster Children's Publishing.

—Firewing. l.t. ed. 2003. 459p. (J). 23.95 (978-0-7862-5986-1(8)) Thorndike Pr.

—Silverwing. braille ed. 2003. (J). (gr. 2). spiral bd. (978-0-616-15274-4(4)) Canadian National Institute for the Blind/Institut National Canadien pour les Aveugles.

—Silverwing. 2007. 224p. (J). pap. 6.99 ***(978-1-4169-4998-5(4)*** , Aladdin) Simon & Schuster Children's Publishing.

—Silverwing. 1999. (978-0-606-16312-5(3)); (gr. 3-6). lib. bdg. 13.00 (978-0-613-15978-4(0)) Tandem Library Bks.

—Sunwing. 320p. (J). 2008. pap. 6.99 ***(978-1-4169-4997-8(6));*** 2001. (gr. 3-7). pap. 5.99 (978-0-689-83287-1(7)) Simon & Schuster Children's Publishing. (Aladdin).

—Sunwing. 2001. (J). (978-0-606-21473-5(9)); (gr. 3-6). lib. bdg. 13.00 (978-0-613-62080-2(1)) Tandem Library Bks.

Ortiz, Gilberto Rendon. Tuiiiiii el Murcielago. (Barril Sin Fondo Ser.). (SPA.). (J). (gr. 3-5). pap. (978-968-6465-22-8(7)) Casa de Estudios de Literatura y Talleres Artisticos Amaquemecan A.C. MEX. *Dist:* Lectorum Pubns., Inc.

Posner, Fran. Halloween Makes Me Batty! 2007. (Illus.). 12p. (J). (gr. k-k). bds. 3.99 ***(978-0-7364-2458-5(X)*** , Golden Bks.) Random Hse. Children's Bks.

Pottie, Marjolein & Auzary-Luton, Sylvie. Going Batty! Special Glow-in-the-Dark Surprise Pictures. Auzary-Luton, Sylvie, illus. 2005. (Illus.). 32p. (J). 15.95 (978-0-689-04635-3(9) , Milk & Cookies) ibooks, Inc.

Quackenbush, Robert. Batbaby Finds a Home. 2001. (Step into Reading Ser.). (Illus.). (J). 10.79 (978-0-606-21050-8(4)) Tandem Library Bks.

Raintree Steck-Vaughn Staff, contrib. by. Stellaluna. 1999. (J). (ps-3). 16.00 (978-0-8172-9782-4(0)); pap. 22.00 (978-0-8172-9784-8(7)) Steck-Vaughn.

Raye, Rebekah. The Very Best Bed. Raye, Rebekah, illus. 2006. (Illus.). 32p. (J). (ps-3). 16.95 (978-0-88448-284-0(7)) Tilbury Hse. Pubs.

Ricci, Christine. Puppy Takes a Bath. Mangano, Tom, illus. 2006. (Ready-To-Read Ser.). 24p. (J). pap. 3.99 (978-1-4169-1483-9(8) , Simon Spotlight/Nickelodeon) Simon & Schuster Children's Publishing.

Ross, Tony & Willis, Jeanne. Daft Bat. 2007. (Illus.). 32p. (J). (gr. k-2). 16.95 ***(978-1-84270-476-9(1))*** Transworld Publishers Ltd. GBR. *Dist:* Independent Pubs. Group.

Sander, Sonia. Sagwa: Sagwa's Lucky Bat. George, Chris, illus. 2003. (Sagwa, the Chinese Siamese Cat Ser.). 64p. (J). (ps-3). 2.99 (978-0-439-45181-9(7)) Scholastic, Inc.

Sargemt, Dave & Sargent, Pat. Batley Needs Glasses, 10, 12. Robinson, Laura, illus. 2004. (Learn to Read Ser.: 10). 18p. (J). lib. bdg. 19.95 (978-1-56763-819-6(8)) Ozark Publishing.

Sargent, Dave & Sargent, Pat. Batley Needs Glasses, 10, 12. Robinson, Laura, illus. 2004. (Learn to Read Ser.: 10). Tr. of Batley Necesita Anteojos. 18p. (J). pap. 9.95 (978-1-56763-820-2(1)) Ozark Publishing.

—Ding Bat: Accuracy, 56 vols., 44. Lenoir, Jane, illus. 2001. (Cherokee Indian Legend Ser.: Vol. 44). 36p. (J). lib. bdg. 19.95 (978-1-56763-529-4(6)) Ozark Publishing.

—Ding Bat: Accuracy, 17 bks, 44. Huff, Jan Lirley, illus. 2000. (Animal Pride Ser.: 44). 42p. (J). pap. 6.95 (978-1-56763-530-0(X)) Ozark Publishing.

Silverman, Buffy. Bat's Night Out. Buskirk, Judith Prowse, illus. 1999. (Books for Young Learners). 16p. (J). (gr. k-2). pap. 5.00 (978-1-57274-247-5(X) , A2428) Owen, Richard C. Pubs., Inc.

Simon, Seymour. Amazing Bats. 2005. (Illus.). 40p. (J). pap. 3.95 (978-1-58717-262-5(3) , SeaStar Bks.) Chronicle Bks. LLC.

—Amazing Bats. 2005. (Illus.). 40p. (J). 14.50 (978-1-58717-261-8(5) , SeaStar Bks.) Chronicle Bks. LLC.

Skurzynski, Gloria. Running Scared. 2002. (gr. 3-6). lib. bdg. 14.10 (978-0-613-62832-7(2)) Tandem Library Bks.

Skurzynski, Gloria & Ferguson, Alane. Running Scared. 2002. (Mysteries in Our National Parks Ser.: Vol. 11). 160p. (J). (gr. 3-7). pap. 5.95 (978-0-7922-6948-9(9) , National Geographic Children's Bks.) National Geographic Society.

Stellaluna. (Literature Notes Ser.). (gr. k-6). 2.99 (978-0-7682-0745-3(2) , FS128207) Schaffer, Frank Pubns.

Stellaluna. 1998. (J). 3.95 (978-0-439-04432-5(4)) Scholastic, Inc.

Sullivan, William J. About Black Bat. 2003. (Illus.). 32p. (J). per. 7.95 (978-0-9708066-7-3(1)) Painted Horse Pubns., Inc.

Thomas-Christensen, Sheelagh & Thomas, Dylan. Morus Yr Ystlum. 2005. (WEL., Illus.). 36p. pap. (978-0-86243-396-3(7)) Y Lolfa.

Williams, Paul. How the Bat Got Its Wings & Young Bear's Lesson: Two Cherokee Stories. 2003. (J). per. 14.95 (978-0-9630310-6-8(6)) Will Hall Bks.

Zindel, Paul. Night of the Bat. 144p. (gr. 5-9). 2003. pap. 5.99 (978-0-7868-1226-4(5)); 2001. 15.99 (978-0-7868-0340-8(1)) Hyperion Bks. for Children.

BATTLE OF BRITAIN, 1940

see Britain, Battle of, 1940

BATTLE SHIPS

see Warships

BATTLES

see also Naval Battles

also names of wars with the subdivision Campaigns and Battles, e.g. World War, 1939-1945—Campaigns and Battles; and names of individual battles, e.g. Ardennes, Battle of the, 1944-1945

Allison, Emily & Powers, Fiona. Battles. 2005. (10 Minute Histories Ser.). (Illus.). 14p. (J). pap. ***(978-1-85074-927-1(2))*** English Heritage.

Atlas of Conflicts. 64p. 196.02 (978-0-8368-5664-4(3)) Stevens, Gareth Inc.

La Batalla de 5 de Mayo. 2005. (SPA.). (J). pap. 9.95 (978-968-7381-12-1(4)) Tecolote, Ediciones, S.A. de C.V. MEX. *Dist:* Iaconi, Mariuccia Bk. Imports.

Chapman, Caroline. Battles & Weapons: Exploring History Through Art. 2007. (Picture That! Ser.). 64p. (gr. 3-7). 19.95 ***(978-1-58728-588-2(6)*** , Two Can Publishing) T&N Children's Publishing.

Crompton, Samuel Willard. Tenochtitan. (Battles That Changed the World Ser.). (J). pap. 13.25 (978-0-7910-7166-3(9) , Chelsea Hse.) Facts On File, Inc.

Doeden, Matt. The Battle of the Alamo. (Graphic History Ser.). 32p. (YA). pap. 7.95 (978-0-7368-5242-5(5)) Capstone Pr., Inc.

Englar, Mary. The Battle of Bunker Hill. 2007. (J). lib. bdg. ***(978-0-7565-2461-6(X))*** Compass Point Bks.

Hamilton, John. Battles of World War I. 2004. (World War I Ser.). (Illus.). 32p. (J). lib. bdg. 24.21 (978-1-57765-913-6(9)) ABDO Publishing Co.

Hansen, Ole Steen. Great Battles of World War II. 2001. (World Wars Ser.). (Illus.). 64p. (J). (gr. 5). lib. bdg. 27.12 (978-0-7398-2757-4(X)) Raintree.

Pollard, Josephine. Battles of America, Vol. 2. 1998. (Illus.). 256p. (J). reprint ed. 15.00 (978-1-889128-43-6(0)) Mantle Ministries.

Sordu, John R. & Dean, Robert. Big Battles for Little Hands: Wargaming Source Book for Children. Palmer, Chris, photos by. 2002. (Illus.). 141p. (YA). 25.00 (978-1-889584-10-2(X) , 071102) LMW Works.

Waldman, Scott P. The Battle of Monmouth. 2003. (Atlas of Famous Battles of the American Revolution Ser.). (Illus.). 24p. (J). lib. bdg. 21.25 (978-0-8239-6330-0(6) , PowerKids Pr.) Rosen Publishing Group, Inc., The.

Wilkinson, Philip. Lift the Lid on Gladiators No. 2: Enter the Roman Colosseum & Prepare Your Gladiator for Combat! 2002. (Illus.). 32p. (J). pap. 21.95 (978-0-7624-1338-6(7) , Running Pr. Kids) Running Pr. Bk. Pubs.

BATTLESHIPS

see Warships

BAY OF PIGS INVASION

see Cuba—History

BAYEUX TAPESTRY

Lemaresquier, D. & Pivard, G. Story of a Conquest: The Bayeux Tapestry Narrated to Children. 2007. (Illus.). 48p. 23.95 ***(978-2-915762-15-0(5))*** OREP Edition & Communication FRA. *Dist:* Casemate Pubs. & Bk. Distributors, LLC.

El tapiz de Bayeux 9: Leveled Books. 2001. (McGraw-Hill Lectura Ser.). (ENG & SPA.). (gr. 5 up). (978-0-02-188281-6(9)) Macmillan/McGraw-Hill Schl. Div.

BAZAARS

see Fairs

BEACHES

see Seashore

BEACONSFIELD, BENJAMIN DISRAELI, 1ST EARL OF, 1804-1881

see Disraeli, Benjamin, Earl of Beaconsfield, 1804-1881

BEADWORK

Baker, Diane. Make Your Own Hairwear: Beaded Barrettes, Clips, Dangles & Headbands. Michaels, Alexandra, illus. 2001. (Quick Starts for Kids! Ser.). 64p. (J). (gr. 3 up). pap. 8.95 (978-1-885593-63-4(5) , Williamson Bks.) Ideals Pubns.

Bhatt, Sonal. Beaded Critters. (Illus.). 80p. 2006. (J). pap. 9.95 (978-1-4027-4043-5(3)); 2005. 19.95 (978-1-4027-0416-1(X)) Sterling Publishing Co., Inc.

Boase, Petra. Beads & Bracelets. 2002. (Fun Factory Ser.). (Illus.). 64p. (J). (gr. 3-7). pap. 6.95 (978-1-84215-609-4(8) , Southwater) Anness Publishing GBR. *Dist:* National Bk. Network.

Boonyadhistarn, Thiranut. Beading: Bracelets, Barrettes, & Beyond. 2007. (Snap Books Craft Ser.). (Illus.). 32p. (J). (gr. 4-8). 25.26 (978-0-7368-6472-5(5)) Capstone Pr., Inc.

Brillant Beads & Bracelets. 2006. (Creative Studio Ser.). (Illus.). 48p. (YA). (978-1-905359-85-1(3)) Top That! Publishing PLC.

Burgan, Michael. Beadwork. 2003. (Step-by-Step Ser.). 32p. (J). pap. 7.95 (978-1-4034-0715-3(0)) Heinemann Library.

Collings, Julie. Creaturas. 2005. (SPA., Illus.). 92p. (J). spiral bd. 20.95 (978-968-5528-01-6(2)) Klutz Latino MEX. *Dist:* Independent Pubs. Group.

Collings, Julie & Elton, Candice. Beadlings. 2000. (Illus.). 92p. (J). (gr. 4-7). spiral bd. 16.95 (978-1-57054-476-7(X)) Klutz.

Conner, Wendy Simpson. The Children's Beading Book: Techniques for Little Beadlovers. 2002. (Beading Bks.: Vol. 8). (Illus.). 52p. (J). 11.95 (978-0-9645957-6-7(1)) Interstellar Publishing Co.

Delhaye, Nathalie. Beads, Buttons, & Bijoux: 58 Original Designs for Making Rings, Necklaces, & Bracelets. 2006. (Illus.). 144p. 25.95 (978-0-307-34572-1(6) , Potter Craft) Crown Publishing Group.

Dorling Kindersley Publishing Staff. Beading. 2007. (DK CREATE & MAKE Ser.). 224p. (J). 20.00 (978-0-7566-1776-9(6)) Dorling Kindersley Publishing, Inc.

Fabulous Footwear. 2006. (Creative Studio Ser.). (Illus.). 48p. (YA). (978-1-905359-84-4(5)) Top That! Publishing PLC.

Fantastic Beads. 2004. (Whizz Kits Ser.). (Illus.). 48p. (J). (978-1-84229-948-7(4)) Top That! Publishing PLC.

Fujimoto, Naomi. Cool Jewels: Beading Projects for Teens. 2007. (Illus.). 96p. (YA). pap. 19.95 ***(978-0-87116-247-2(4))*** Kalmbach Publishing Co., Bks. Div.

Green, Marilyn. Beaded Bobby Pins. 1999. (Illus.). 48p. (YA). (gr. 4-7). 14.95 (978-1-57054-401-9(8)) Klutz.

Hirschmann, Kris. Hello Kitty Beads Activity Book. 2002. (Hello Kitty & Her Friends Crafts Club Ser.). (Illus.). 44p. (J). (978-0-439-32845-6(4)) Scholastic, Inc.

Johnson, Anne Akers. Bead Rings. 1999. (Illus.). 64p. (YA). (gr. 4-7). spiral bd. 12.95 (978-1-57054-397-5(6)) Klutz.

—Pulseras Rusticas. 2004. (SPA., Illus.). 32p. (J). (gr. 1). spiral bd. 17.95 (978-968-5528-11-5(X)) Klutz Latino MEX. *Dist:* Independent Pubs. Group.

Llimos Plomer, Anna. Easy Bead Crafts in 5 Steps. 2008. (Easy Crafts in 5 Steps Ser.). 32p. (J). (gr. 3-4). lib. bdg. 22.60 ***(978-0-7660-3082-4(2))*** Enslow Pubs., Inc.

Miles, L. Hair Braiding Kid Kit. rev. ed. 2005. 32p. (J). 10.99 (978-1-58086-858-7(4) , Usborne) EDC Publishing.

Murray, Patricia. Make It & Pray It: The Rosary Kit Gift Edition. Murray, Patricia, illus. 2005. (Illus.). 110p. (J). (gr. 3-7). spiral bd. 19.95 (978-0-88489-895-5(4)) St. Mary's Pr.

My Bead Box. 2002. 64p. (J). pap. 9.98 (978-0-7525-6288-9(6)) Parragon, Inc.

Powell, Michelle. Beadwork. 2003. (Step-by-Step Ser.). (Illus.). 32p. (J). (gr. 3-5). lib. bdg. 25.64 (978-1-4034-0696-5(0)) Heinemann Library.

—Beadwork. 2002. (Step-by-Step Children's Crafts Ser.). (Illus.). 32p. pap. 7.95 (978-0-85532-979-2(3) , 9793) Search Pr., Ltd. GBR. *Dist:* Independent Pubs. Group.

Running Press Staff & Nicholson, Sue. Funky Jewelry: Fun Stuff to Unlock & Share. 2001. (Quarto Children's Book Ser.). (Illus.). 32p. (J). pap. 9.95 (978-0-7624-1062-0(0) , Running Pr. Kids) Running Pr. Bk. Pubs.

Sadler, Judy Ann. Beads.Tr. of Perles. (FRE., Illus.). (J). pap. 7.99 (978-0-590-24194-6(X)) Scholastic, Inc.

—Hemp Jewelry. Bradford, June, illus. 2005. (Kids Can Do It Ser.). 40p. (YA). (gr. 3 up). (978-1-55337-775-7(3)); (978-1-55337-774-0(5)) Kids Can Pr., Ltd.

Scheunemann, Pam. Cool Beaded Jewelry. 2005. (Cool Crafts Ser.). (Illus.). 32p. (J). (gr. k-6). lib. bdg. 22.78 (978-1-59197-739-1(8)) ABDO Publishing Co.

Souter, Gillian. Beads 'n' Badges. Watson, Clare, illus. Martin, Andre, photos by. 2001. (Handy Crafts Ser.). 48p. (J). (gr. 2 up). lib. bdg. 24.67 (978-0-8368-2819-1(4)) Stevens, Gareth Inc.

Tandy, Rachel, ed. Pop Bead Critters. 2005. (Chicken Socks). (Illus.). 20p. (J). 12.95 (978-1-59174-365-1(6)) Klutz.

BEAGLE (DOG BREED)

Gray, Susan H. Beagles. 2008. (Domestic Dogs Ser.). 32p. (J). (gr. k-4). 27.07 ***(978-1-59296-961-6(5))*** Child's World, Inc.

Stone, Lynn M. Beagles. 2003. (Eye to Eye with Dogs Ser.). (Illus.). 24p. (gr. 2-5). 17.95 (978-1-58952-325-8(3)) Rourke Publishing, LLC.

—Eye to Eye with Dogs. 2003. (Eye to Eye with Dogs Ser.). (gr. 2-5). 394.90 (978-1-58952-324-1(5)) Rourke Publishing, LLC.

BEAGLE EXPEDITION (1831-1836)

MacDonald, Fiona. Inside the Beagle with Charles Darwin. 2005. (Illus.). 48p. (J). (gr. 4-6). 19.95 (978-1-59270-041-7(1)) Enchanted Lion Bks., LLC.

Weaver, Anne H. The Voyage of the Beetle: A Journey Around the World with Charles Darwin & the Search for the Solution to the Mystery of Mysteries, As Narrated by Rosie, an Articulate Beetle. Lawrence, George, illus. 2007. 80p. (YA). (gr. 5 up). 16.95 ***(978-0-8263-4304-8(X))*** Univ. of New Mexico Pr.

BEAGLE EXPEDITION (1831-1836)—FICTION

Weaver, Anne H. The Voyage of the Beetle: A Journey Around the World with Charles Darwin & the Search for the Solution to the Mystery of Mysteries, as Narrated by Rosie, an Articulate Beetle. Lawrence, George, tr. Lawrence, George, illus. 2004. (Roman Mysteries Ser.). 80p. (J). (gr. 5-8). lib. bdg. 26.90 (978-0-7613-2923-7(4) , Millbrook Pr.) Lerner Publishing Group.

BEAGLES (DOGS)

see Beagle (Dog Breed)

BEAR (SHIP)

Hatkoff, Isabella, et al. Knut: How One Little Polar Bear Captivated the World. 2007. (Knut Ser.). 40p. (J). pap. 16.99 ***(978-0-545-04716-6(1)*** , Scholastic Pr.) Scholastic, Inc.

BEARS

All Kinds of Bears, 6 vols. (Book2WebTM Ser.). (gr. 4-8). 36.50 (978-0-322-02972-9(4)) Wright Group, The.

Anderson, Jill. Polar Bears. 2007. 24p. (J). pap. ***(978-1-55971-975-9(3)); (978-1-55971-974-2(5))*** T&N Children's Publishing. (NorthWord Bks. for Young Readers).

Animal Lives: Bears. 2006. pap. 4.99 (978-1-4206-8159-8(1)) Teacher Created Materials, Inc.

Author Of The Life O Staff. The Life of a Bear: His Birth, Education & Adventure. 2004. reprint ed. pap. 27.95 (978-1-4179-4276-3(2)) Kessinger Publishing, LLC.

Baines, Rebecca. Arctic Tale. 2007. 32p. (J). (gr. k-4). lib. bdg. 22.90 (978-1-4263-0085-1(9) , National Geographic Children's Bks.) National Geographic Society.

Baines, Rebecca & Fifield, Donnali. Arctic Tale. 2007. 32p. (J). (gr. k-4). 5.95 (978-1-4263-0084-4(0) , National Geographic Children's Bks.) National Geographic Society.

Barbaresi, Nina. Bears Stickers. 2004. (Stickers Ser.). (Illus.). 4p. (J). (ps-5). pap. 1.50 (978-0-486-43306-6(4)) Dover Pubns., Inc.

Barghusen, Laura. The Bear. 1999. (Endangered Animals & Habitats Ser.). (Illus.). 96p. (YA). (gr. 4-12). 27.45 (978-1-56006-394-0(7) , Lucent Bks.) Thomson Gale.

Barnes, Julia. The Secret Lives of Brown Bears. 2006. (Illus.). 32p. (J). lib. bdg. ***(978-0-8368-7655-0(5))*** Stevens, Gareth Inc.

Barnes, Julia. 101 Facts about Polar Bears. 2004. (One Hundred One Facts about Predators Ser.). (Illus.). 32p. (J). (gr. 3 up). lib. bdg. 23.33 (978-0-8368-4038-4(0)) Stevens, Gareth Inc.

Barry, Holly. Wisdom of Bear. 2006. 64p. pap. 6.95 (978-1-882190-50-8(5)) Polar Bear & Co.

Bears. (Eyes on Nature Ser.). 32p. (J). (gr. 1). pap. (978-1-882210-75-6(1)) Action Publishing, Inc.

Bears, Vol. 4. 2005. (Animals, Animals, Animals Ser.). (YA). (gr. k-3). 118.80 (978-0-7368-4210-5(1) , Pebble Bks.) Capstone Pr., Inc.

The Bears: Individual Title Six-Packs. (Sails Literacy Ser.). 16p. (gr. k up). 27.00 (978-0-7635-4433-1(7)) Rigby Education.

Bears & Their Dens. (Animal Homes Ser.). 24p. (J). 6.95 (978-0-7368-5121-3(6)) Capstone Pr., Inc.

Bears Have Cubs. (Animals & Their Young Ser.). 24p. (J). 7.95 (978-0-7565-1235-4(2)) Compass Point Bks.

Bear's House. Date not set. (Illus.). (J). bds. 4.98 (978-1-4054-0784-7(0)) Parragon, Inc.

Bears Set. (gr. k-2). 114.95 (978-0-7368-9042-7(4)) Red Brick Learning.

Becker, John. Grizzly Bears. 2003. (Returning Wildlife Ser.). (Illus.). 48p. (J). (gr. 3-5). 23.70 (978-0-7377-1534-7(0) , Kidhaven) Thomson Gale.

Beers, Jack. Bears, Ten by Ten. 2000. (Metro Math Readers Yellow Level Ser.). (J). (gr. 1-2). 3.75 (978-1-58120-407-0(8)) Metropolitan Teaching & Learning Co.

Bender, Lionel. Polar Bear. 2005. (Illus.). 32p. (J). 18.95 (978-1-59389-194-7(6)) Chrysalis Education.

Berger, Melvin. Grunidos! Un Libro Sobre Osos. 1999. (Coleccion "Hola, Lector" Ser.). (SPA., Illus.). 40p. (J). (gr. 1-3). pap. 3.99 (978-0-439-16307-1(2) , SO8026, Cartwheel Bks.) Scholastic, Inc.

Berger, Melvin & Berger, Gilda. Bears. 2002. (Scholastic Readers Ser.). (Illus.). (J). (978-0-439-44533-7(7)) Scholastic, Inc.

—Growl! A Book about Bears. 2005. (Illus.). 40p. (J). (978-0-439-80183-6(4)) Scholastic, Inc.

—Polar Bears Live on Ice. 2003. (Scholastic Time-To-Discover Readers Ser.). (Illus.). (J). (978-0-439-47181-7(8)) Scholastic, Inc.

Berman, Ruth. Fishing Bears. Stone, Lynn M., photos by. 1998. (Pull Ahead Bks.). (Illus.). 32p. (gr. k-2). (J). pap. 5.95 (978-0-8225-3607-9(2)); lib. bdg. 22.60 (978-0-8225-3601-7(3)) Lerner Publishing Group.

Biel, Timothy Levi. Osos Polares. Rountree, Monica, tr. 2003. (Zoobooks). Orig. Title: Polar Bears. (SPA., Illus.). 24p. (J). (gr. k-6). lib. bdg. 15.95 (978-1-888153-77-4(6)) Wildlife Education, Ltd.

Black Bears, Vol. 4. 2005. (Animals, Animals, Animals Ser.). (YA). (gr. k-3). (978-0-7368-8097-8(6) , Pebble Bks.) Capstone Pr., Inc.

Black Bears, 6 vols. (gr. k-2). 28.95 (978-0-7368-8121-0(2)) Red Brick Learning.

Black, Sonia W. & MacCombie, Turi. Follow the Polar Bears. 2000. (Hello Reader! Science Ser.). (Illus.). (J). (ps-3). pap. 3.99 (978-0-439-20641-9(3)) Scholastic, Inc.

A B

Bright, Michael. Bears. 2002. (Illus.). 64p. pap. 7.95 (978-1-84215-625-4(X)) Anness Publishing GBR. *Dist:* National Bk. Network.

—Bears & Pandas, 3 vols. Anness Publishing Staff, ed. 1999. (Nature Watch Ser.). (Illus.). 64p. (gr. 3-7). 12.95 (978-1-85967-642-4(1) , Lorenz Bks.) Anness Publishing GBR. *Dist:* National Bk. Network.

Brisville, J. C. Invierno en Vid - Grand Oso (Winter - Life of Big Bear) (SPA.). 32p. (J). 17.50 (978-84-305-6104-9(8)) Susaeta Ediciones, S.A. ESP. *Dist:* AIMS International Bks., Inc.

Brown Bears, Vol. 4. 2005. (Animals, Animals, Animals Ser.). (YA). (gr. k-3). (978-0-7368-8098-5(4) , Pebble Bks.) Capstone Pr., Inc.

Brown Bears, 6 vols. (gr. k-2). 28.95 (978-0-7368-8122-7(0)) Red Brick Learning.

Camm, Martin, illus. Meyers Buch der Baeren. (GER.). 48p. (978-3-411-07461-7(2)) Bibliographisches Institut & F. A. Brockhaus AG DEU. *Dist:* i.b.d., Ltd.

Canizares, Susan, et al. Polar Bears. 1998. (Science Emergent Readers Ser.). (Illus.). 128p. (J). pap. 3.50 (978-0-590-76153-6(6)) Scholastic, Inc.

Christian, Peggy. Chocolate, a Glacier Grizzly. Cottone-Kolthoff, Carol, illus. (Humane Society of the United States Animal Tales Ser.). 32p. (J). (gr. 1-5). 34.95 incl. audio (978-1-882728-64-0(5)); pap. 9.95 incl. audio (978-1-882728-67-1(X)); pap. 19.95 incl. audio (978-1-882728-69-5(6)) Benefactory, Inc., The.

Cole & Leeson. El Oso Pardo. 2002. (Osos Salvajes Serie).Tr. of Wild Bears: The Grizzly Bear. (SPA.). 24p. (J). (gr. 3-5). 24.94 (978-1-4103-0000-3(5) , Blackbirch Pr., Inc.) Thomson Gale.

Cooper, Jason. Cub to Grizzly. 2003. (Illus.). 24p. (J). 20.64 (978-1-58952-691-4(0)) Rourke Publishing, LLC.

Cotton, Jacqueline S. Polar Bears. 2004. (Pull Ahead Books Ser.). (J). 22.60 (978-0-8225-3776-2(1) , Carolrhoda Bks.); 32p. pap. 5.95 (978-0-8225-9890-9(6)) Lerner Publishing Group.

Crawford, Tracey. Bears. 2006. 24p. (J). (978-1-4034-8454-3(6)); pap. (978-1-4034-8461-1(9)) Heinemann Library.

Creative Publishing international Editors. Forest Animals. 2004. (Our Wild World Ser.). (Illus.). 192p. (J). (gr. 2-5). ring bd. 16.95 (978-1-55971-708-3(4) , NorthWord Bks. for Young Readers) T&N Children's Publishing.

Davies, Nicola. Ice Bear: In the Steps of the Polar Bear. Blythe, Gary, illus. 2005. 32p. (J). (gr. k-3). 16.99 (978-0-7636-2759-1(3)) Candlewick Pr.

Deady, Kathleen W. Grizzly Bears. 2002. (Predators in the Wild Ser.). (Illus.). 32p. (J). (gr. 3-4). lib. bdg. 21.26 (978-0-7368-1063-0(3) , Capstone High-Interest Bks.) Capstone Pr., Inc.

Dineen, Jacqueline. Grizzly Bears. 2003. (Amazing Animals Ser.). (Illus.). 24p. (J). lib. bdg. 21.35 (978-1-58340-229-0(2)) Weigl Pubs., Inc.

Do Bears Buzz? (Animals All Around Ser.). 24p. (J). 7.95 (978-1-4048-0370-1(X)) Picture Window Bks.

Doherty, James G., contrib. by. Endangered!, 6 bks., Set, Group 1. Incl. Apes. Horton, Casey. lib. bdg. 25.64 (978-0-7614-0212-1(8)); Bears. Horton, Casey. lib. bdg. 25.64 (978-0-7614-0211-4(X)); Dolphins. Horton, Casey. lib. bdg. 22.79 (978-0-7614-0216-9(0)); Eagles. Horton, Casey. lib. bdg. 25.64 (978-0-7614-0214-5(4)); Tigers. Harman, Amanda. lib. bdg. 22.79 (978-0-7614-0215-2(2)); Wolves. Horton, Casey. lib. bdg. 25.64 (978-0-7614-0213-8(6)); 32p. (J). (gr. 3-5). 1995. (Illus.). Set lib. bdg. 136.71 (978-0-7614-0210-7(1) , Benchmark Bks.) Cavendish, Marshall Corp.

—Endangered - Group 4, 4 bks., Set. Incl. Butterflies. Green, Jen. lib. bdg. 25.64 (978-0-7614-0321-0(3)); Cheetahs. Grimbly, Shona. lib. bdg. 25.64 (978-0-7614-0319-7(1)); Crocodiles & Alligators. Woodward, John. lib. bdg. 25.64 (978-0-7614-0322-7(1)); Zebras. Grimbly, Shona. lib. bdg. 25.64 (978-0-7614-0320-3(5)); 32p. (J). (gr. 3-5). (Illus.). 1999. Set lib. bdg. 102.57 (978-0-7614-0318-0(3) , Benchmark Bks.) Cavendish, Marshall Corp.

Dorling Kindersley Publishing Staff. Bear. 2004. (Watch Me Grow Ser.). (Illus.). 24p. (J). 7.99 (978-0-7566-0194-2(0)) Dorling Kindersley Publishing, Inc.

—Butterfly. 2004. (Watch Me Grow Ser.). (Illus.). 24p. (J). 7.99 (978-0-7566-0193-5(2)) Dorling Kindersley Publishing, Inc.

Englar, Mary. Why Do Bears Sleep All Winter? A Book about Hibernation. 2007. (First Facts Ser.). (Illus.). 24p. (J). 21.26 (978-0-7368-6379-7(6)) Capstone Pr., Inc.

Feeney, Kathy. Black Bears. McGee, John F., photos by. 2004. (Our Wild World Ser.). (Illus.). 48p. (J). (gr. 2-5). pap. 7.95 (978-1-55971-742-7(4) , NorthWord Bks. for Young Readers) T&N Children's Publishing.

Feeny, Kathy. Black Bears. 2000. (gr. 3-6). lib. bdg. 16.40 (978-0-613-24376-6(5)) Tandem Library Bks.

Fifield, Donnali. Arctic Tale: Official Companion to the Major Motion Picture. 2007. (Illus.). 160p. 30.00 (978-1-4262-0065-6(X) , National Geographic) National Geographic Society.

Fogle, Jennifer, photos by. Bears: And Other Top Predators, 6 issues. 2000. 48p. 6.95 (978-0-9759110-6-8(6)) High Desert Publishing.

Foreman, Michael. The Panda. 1999. (Illus.). 64p. (J). (gr. 5 up). pap. 14.99 (978-1-86205-290-1(5) , Pavilion Bks., Ltd.) Anova Bks. GBR. *Dist:* Independent Pubs. Group.

Fraggalosch, Audrey. Great Grizzly Wilderness: A Story of the Pacific Rain Forest. Eberhart, Donald G., illus. 2000. (Habitat Ser.). 32p. (J). (ps-3). pap. 5.95 (978-1-56899-839-8(2)) Soundprints.

Freeman, Marcia S. Black Bears. Saunders-Smith, Gail, ed. 1998. (Bears Ser.). (Illus.). 24p. (J). (gr. k-1). lib. bdg. 14.60 (978-0-7368-0096-9(4) , Pebble Bks.) Capstone Pr., Inc.

—Black Bears. 1998. (J). lib. bdg. 13.25 (978-0-516-21484-9(5) , Children's Pr.) Scholastic Library Publishing.

—Brown Bears. Saunders-Smith, Gail, ed. 1998. (Bears Ser.). (Illus.). 24p. (J). (gr. k-1). lib. bdg. 14.60 (978-0-7368-0097-6(2) , Pebble Bks.) Capstone Pr., Inc.

—Polar Bears. Saunders-Smith, Gail, ed. 1998. (Bears Ser.). (Illus.). 24p. (J). (gr. k-1). lib. bdg. 14.60 (978-0-7368-0099-0(9) , Pebble Bks.) Capstone Pr., Inc.

Gaines, Richard Marshall. When Bears Attack! 2006. (When Wild Animals Attack! Ser.). (Illus.). 48p. (J). (gr. 4-10). lib. bdg. 23.93 (978-0-7660-2669-8(8)) Enslow Pubs., Inc.

Gareth Stevens Publishing Staff, contrib. by. Polar Bear. 2004. (All about Wild Animals Ser.). (J). lib. bdg. 23.33 (978-0-8368-4187-9(5)) Stevens, Gareth Inc.

George, Jean Craighead. Winter Moon. 2003. (J). (gr. 3-7). 20.75 (978-0-8446-7244-1(0)) Smith, Peter Pub., Inc.

Gibbons, Gail. Grizzly Bears. Gibbons, Gail, illus. 2003. (Illus.). 32p. (J). (gr. k-3). tchr. ed. 16.95 (978-0-8234-1793-3(X)) Holiday Hse., Inc.

—Polar Bears. Gibbons, Gail, illus. (Illus.). (J). (gr. k-3). 2005. 32p. 6.95 (978-0-8234-1768-1(9)); 2001. 36p. tchr. ed. 16.95 (978-0-8234-1593-9(7)) Holiday Hse., Inc.

Gish, Melissa. Brown Bears. 2000. (Northern Trek Ser.). (Illus.). 24p. (J). (gr. 2-7). lib. bdg. 15.95 (978-1-58340-032-6(X)) Smart Apple Media.

Goecke, Michael P. Short-Faced Bear. 2004. (Prehistoric Animals Set II Ser.). (Illus.). 23p. (J). (gr. k-4). lib. bdg. 21.35 (978-1-57765-976-1(7)) ABDO Publishing Co.

Gorbachev, Valeri. Ricitos de Oro y los Tres Osos. 2003. Tr. of Goldilocks & the Three Bears. (SPA.). (gr. 7-12). lib. bdg. 15.25 (978-0-613-81368-6(5)) Tandem Library Bks.

Grambo, Rebecca. Borealis: A Polar Bear Cub's First Year. Cox, Daniel J., photos by. 2003. (Wild Beginnings Ser.). (Illus.). 48p. (J). (ps-3). pap. 9.95 (978-1-55285-465-5(5)) Whitecap Bks., Ltd. CAN. *Dist:* Firefly Bks., Ltd.

Greene, Jacqueline/D. Grizzly Bears: Saving the Silvertip. 2008. (J). lib. bdg. 25.27 ***(978-1-59716-533-4(6))*** Bearport Publishing Co., Inc.

The Grizzly Bear. (Wildlife of North America Ser.). 48p. (YA). 7.95 (978-0-7368-8486-0(6)) Capstone Pr., Inc.

The Grizzly Bear, 6 vols. (gr. 4 up). 39.95 (978-0-7368-8498-3(X)) Red Brick Learning.

Group/McGraw-Hill, Wright. Bears: Magazine Anthology: Level 5, 6 vols. (Comprehension Strand Ser.). (gr. 4-8). 54.00 (978-0-322-09855-8(6)) Wright Group, The.

Guidoux, Valérie. Little Bears. 2007. (Born to Be Wild Ser.). (Illus.). 22p. (J). lib. bdg. ***(978-0-8368-6696-4(7))*** Stevens, Gareth Inc.

Guidoux, Valerie. Little Polar Bears. 2005. (Born to Be Wild Ser.). (Illus.). 24p. (J). (ps). lib. bdg. 22.00 (978-0-8368-4739-0(3)) Stevens, Gareth Inc.

Hamaguchi, Carla, ed. Bears Stickety-Splits, 12 vols., 0642. Schamber, Kimberly, illus. 2002. 10p. pap. 6.99 (978-1-57471-891-1(6)) Creative Teaching Pr., Inc.

Harcourt School Publishers Staff. All about Bears: Take-Home Book. 1999. (Collections Ser.). (Illus.). (J). pap. 1.90 (978-0-15-317205-2(3)) Harcourt Schl. Pubs.

—Bears Are Big, 5 No., Pack. 3rd ed. 2002. (Trophies Reading Program Ser.). (Illus.). (gr. 1). pap. 20.10 (978-0-15-326813-7(1)) Harcourt Schl. Pubs.

—Bears Are Big: Below Level. 3rd ed. 2002. (Trophies Reading Program Ser.). (Illus.). (J). pap. 4.10 (978-0-15-322963-3(2)) Harcourt Schl. Pubs.

—Trofeos Below Level: Los Osos. 3rd ed. 2002. (SPA., Illus.). pap. 5.50 (978-0-15-323874-1(7)) Harcourt Schl. Pubs.

Harkrader, Lisa. The Grizzly Bear: A Myreportlinks. com Book. 2005. (Endangered & Threatened Animals Ser.). (Illus.). 48p. (J). (ps-10). lib. bdg. 25.26 (978-0-7660-5066-2(1) , MyReportLinks.com Bks.) Enslow Pubs., Inc.

Harvey, Bev. The Bear Family. 2003. (Animal Families Ser.). (Illus.). 32p. (gr. 2-4). 23.00 (978-0-7910-7540-1(0) , Chelsea Hse.) Facts On File, Inc.

Hatkoff, Isabella. Knut: How One Little Polar Bear Captivated the World. 2007. (J). pap. 16.99 ***(978-0-545-04717-3(X)*** , Scholastic Pr.) Scholastic, Inc.

Head, Honor. What's It Like to Be a Baby Polar Bear? Nichols, Matthew, illus. 1998. (Baby Animals Ser.). 32p. (gr. k-3). lib. bdg. 20.90 (978-0-7613-1255-0(2) , Millbrook Pr.) Lerner Publishing Group.

Helbrough, Emma. Bears (Level 1) - Internet Referenced. 2006. 32p. (J). 4.99 (978-0-7945-1393-1(X) , Usborne) EDC Publishing.

Hemstock, Annie. The Polar Bear. 1998. (Wildlife of North America Ser.). (Illus.). 48p. (J). (gr. 3-4). lib. bdg. 21.26 (978-0-7368-0031-0(X) , Capstone High-Interest Bks.) Capstone Pr., Inc.

Hirschi, Ron. Searching for Grizzlies. Mangelsen, Thomas D. & Cooper, Deborah, illus. Mangelsen, Thomas D., photos by. 2005. (J). (978-1-4156-2797-6(5)) Boyds Mills Pr.

Hirschi, Ron & Mangelsen, Thomas. Searching for Grizzlies. 2005. (Illus.). 32p. (J). 15.95 (978-1-59078-014-5(0)) Boyds Mills Pr.

Hodge, Deborah. Bears: Polar Bears, Black Bears & Grizzly Bears. Stephens, Pat, illus. unabr. ed. 2004. (Kids Can Press Wildlife Ser.). 32p. (J). (gr. k-3). (978-1-55074-355-5(4)) Kids Can Pr., Ltd.

—Bears: Polar Bears, Black Bears & Grizzly Bears. Stephens, Pat, illus. 1999. 32p. (J). (ps-ps). lib. bdg. 14.10 (978-0-613-16326-2(5)) Tandem Library Bks.

Hoff, Mary King. Polar Bears. 2005. (Illus.). 32p. (gr. 2-5). 18.95 (978-1-58341-353-1(7) , Creative Education) Creative Co., The.

Hunt, Joni Phelps & London Town Press Staff. A Band of Bears: The Rambling Life of a Lovable Loner. Leon, Vicki, ed. 2nd ed. 2006. (Jean-Michel Cousteau Presents Ser.). (Illus.). 48p. (J). pap. 8.95 ***(978-0-9766134-5-9(X))*** London Town Pr.

Instructional Fair. Bear. 1999. (Blank Books for Young Authors Ser.). 16p. (J). (gr. k-3). pap. 1.49 (978-0-7424-0376-5(9) , IF75); pap. 16.99 (978-0-7424-0377-2(7) , IF75B) School Specialty Publishing.

Iorio, Nicole. Bears! 2005. 32p. (J). lib. bdg. 13.85 ***(978-1-4242-0857-9(2))*** Fitzgerald Bks.

Jaffe, Elizabeth Dana. Bears Have Cubs. 2002. (Animals & Their Young Ser.). (Illus.). 24p. (J). (gr. 1 up). lib. bdg. 18.60 (978-0-7565-0168-6(7)) Compass Point Bks.

Jarrow, Gail. Bears. 2003. (Animal Attacks Ser.). (Illus.). 48p. (J). 26.20 (978-0-7377-1525-5(1) , Greenhaven Pr., Inc.) Thomson Gale.

Johnson, Jinny. Polar Bear. 2006. (Illus.). 31p. (J). (978-1-58340-901-5(7)) Smart Apple Media.

Kaeser, Sophia. Our Family Adventures with Bears. 2005. pap. 7.95 (978-0-533-15054-0(X)) Vantage Pr., Inc.

Kalman, Bobbie. What Is a Bear? 2001. (gr. 3-6). lib. bdg. 14.10 (978-0-613-43524-6(9)) Tandem Library Bks.

Kalman, Bobbie & Burns, Kylie. Endangered Bears. 2007. (Earth's Endangered Animals Ser.). (Illus.). 32p. (J). (gr. 1-7). ***(978-0-7787-1861-1(1));*** pap. ***(978-0-7787-1907-6(3))*** Crabtree Publishing Co.

Kalman, Bobbie & Crossingham, John. Les Ours. 2003. (FRE., Illus.). 32p. (J). pap. (978-2-89579-007-5(8)) Crabtree Publishing Co.

—What Is a Bear? 2001. (Science of Living Things Ser.). (Illus.). 32p. (J). (gr. 2-3). (978-0-86505-983-2(7)); pap. (978-0-86505-960-3(8)) Crabtree Publishing Co.

Kendell, Patricia. Grizzly Bears. 2003. (In the Wild Ser.). (Illus.). 32p. (J). lib. bdg. 25.70 (978-0-7398-5499-0(2)) Raintree.

—Polar Bears. 2002. (In the Wild Ser.). (Illus.). 32p. (J). lib. bdg. 25.69 (978-0-7398-4908-8(5)) Raintree.

Lang, Aubrey. The Adventures of Baby Bear. Lynch, Wayne, photos by. 2001. (Nature Babies Ser.). (Illus.). 36p. (gr. k-3). pap. 5.95 (978-1-894004-71-8(X)) Fifth Hse. Pubs. CAN. *Dist:* Fitzhenry & Whiteside, Ltd.

—The Adventures of Baby Bear. Lynch, Wayne, photos by. 2001. (Nature Babies Ser.). (Illus.). 36p. (J). (gr. k-3). (978-1-55041-670-1(7)) Fitzhenry & Whiteside, Ltd.

—Baby Grizzly. Lynch, Wayne, photos by. 2005. (Nature Babies Ser.). (Illus.). 36p. (J). (gr. k-3). (978-1-55041-577-3(8)) Fitzhenry & Whiteside, Ltd.

—Baby Grizzly. Lynch, Wayne, photos by. 2006. (Nature Babies Ser.). (Illus.). 36p. (J). (gr. k-3). pap. 6.95 (978-1-55041-579-7(4)) Fitzhenry & Whiteside, Ltd. CAN. *Dist:* F & W Pubns., Inc.

Leach, Michael. Grizzly Bear: Habitats, Life Cycles, Food Chains, Threats. 2001. (Natural World Ser.). (Illus.). 48p. (J). (gr. 3-7). lib. bdg. 27.12 (978-0-7398-2768-0(5)) Raintree.

Leathers, Dan. Polar Bears on the Hudson Bay. 2007. (On the Verge of Extinction Ser.). (Illus.). 32p. (J). (gr. 1-4). lib. bdg. 25.70 ***(978-1-58415-586-7(8))*** Mitchell Lane Pubs., Inc.

Leeson, Cole. El Oso Negro. 2002. (Osos Salvajes Serie).Tr. of Wild Bears: The Black Bear. (SPA.). 24p. (J). (gr. 3-5). 24.94 (978-1-56711-959-6(X) , Blackbirch Pr., Inc.) Thomson Gale.

—El Oso Polar. 2002. (Osos Salvajes Serie).Tr. of Wild Bears: The Polar Bear. (SPA.). 24p. (J). (gr. 3-5). 24.94 (978-1-56711-963-3(8) , Blackbirch Pr., Inc.) Thomson Gale.

Legg, Gerald. Bears. Bergin, Mark, illus. 2002. (Scary Creatures Ser.). (J). (gr. 2-4). 31p. pap. 6.95 (978-0-531-14847-1(5)); 32p. pap. 22.50 (978-0-531-14667-5(7)) Scholastic Library Publishing. (Watts, Franklin).

—Bears. 2002. (gr. 3-6). lib. bdg. 15.25 (978-0-613-53953-1(2)) Tandem Library Bks.

Levin, Amy. A Bear's Year. 2003. (Compass Point Phonics Readers Ser.). (Illus.). 16p. (J). (gr. 1 up). 13.26 (978-0-7565-0500-4(3)) Compass Point Bks.

Lockwood, Sophie. Polar Bears. 2005. (World of Mammals Ser.). 40p. (J). (gr. 2-6). 29.93 (978-1-59296-501-4(6)) Child's World, Inc.

Lukas, Catherine. Bears. 2006. (J). 7.99 (978-1-59939-036-9(1) , Reader's Digest Young Families, Inc.) Reader's Digest Children's Publishing, Inc.

Lynch, Wayne. Bears, Bears, Bears. Lynch, Wayne, photos by. 2003. (Illus.). 64p. (J). (gr. 5-7). pap. 9.95 (978-1-895565-69-0(3)) Firefly Bks., Ltd.

Macken, JoAnn Early. Bears. 2002. (Animals I See at the Zoo Ser.). (Illus.). 24p. (J). (ps up). lib. bdg. 19.33 (978-0-8368-3266-2(3)); pap. 5.95 (978-0-8368-3279-2(5)) Stevens, Gareth Inc. (Weekly Reader Early Learning Library).

—Bears/Los Osos. Coffey, Colleen & Carrillo, Consuelo, trs. from ENG. 2003. (Weekly Reader Early Learning Library). (ENG & SPA., Illus.). 24p. (J). (ps up). lib. bdg. 19.33 (978-0-8368-3998-2(6) , Weekly Reader Early Learning Library) Stevens, Gareth Inc.

—Bears/Los Osos. 2003. (Weekly Reader Early Learning Library). (ENG & SPA., Illus.). 24p. (J). (ps up). pap. 5.95 (978-0-8368-4003-2(8) , Weekly Reader Early Learning Library) Stevens, Gareth Inc.

—Black Bears. 2005. (Illus.). 24p. (J). pap. (978-0-8368-4487-0(4)); (YA). lib. bdg. 19.33 (978-0-8368-4480-1(7)) Stevens, Gareth Inc.

Mackley, Carter, ed. Bears: And Other Top Predators, 6 issues. Bailey, Carol, photos by. 2000. 48p. 6.95 (978-0-9759110-4-4(X)) High Desert Publishing.

—Bears: And Other Top Predators, 6 issues. Ward, Kennan et al, photos by. 2000. 48p. 6.95 (978-0-9759110-5-1(8)) High Desert Publishing.

Markle, Sandra. Polar Bears. (Animal Predators Ser.). 40p. (J). 2005. (gr. 4-6). pap. 7.95 (978-1-57505-746-0(8)); 2004. (Illus.). (gr. 3-6). lib. bdg. 25.26 (978-1-57505-730-9(1)) Lerner Publishing Group.

Martinucci, Suzanne. Where There Was Smoke. 2002. (Illus.). 16p. (J). (978-0-439-35115-7(4)) Scholastic, Inc.

McBratney, Sam. Todos Son Mis Favoritos. Jeram, Anita, illus. 2004. Tr. of You're All My Favorites. (SPA.). 32p. (J). 16.99 (978-84-88342-67-6(5)) S.A. Kokinos ESP. *Dist:* Lectorum Pubns., Inc.

Middleton, Don. Polar Bears. 2001. (Untamed World Ser.). (Illus.). 64p. (J). lib. bdg. 28.54 (978-0-8172-4578-8(2)) Raintree.

Miles, Elizabeth. Watching Grizzly Bears in North America. 2006. (Heinemann First Library). (Illus.). 32p. (J). pap. (978-1-4034-7240-3(8)); lib. bdg. (978-1-4034-7227-4(0)) Heinemann Library.

Miller, Debbie S. A Polar Bear Journey. Van Zyle, Jon, illus. 2005. 32p. pap. 7.95 (978-0-8027-7715-7(5)) Walker & Co.

Minarik, Else Holmelund. Little Bear Makes a Mask. 2003. (gr. k-3). lib. bdg. 11.80 (978-0-613-69140-6(7)) Tandem Library Bks.

—The Little Bear Treasury: Little Bear; Little Bear's Friend; Little Bear's Visit. Sendak, Maurice, illus. (I Can Read Bks.). 190p. (J). (978-0-06-027398-9(4)) HarperCollins Pubs.

Molter, Carey. Bears. l.t. ed. 2001. (Zoo Animals Ser.). (Illus.). 24p. (J). (ps-3). lib. bdg. 19.93 (978-1-57765-558-9(3) , SandCastle) ABDO Publishing Co.

Morgan, Sally. Bears. 2004. (QEB Animal Lives Ser.). (Illus.). 32p. (J). lib. bdg. 18.95 (978-1-59566-033-6(X)) QEB Publishing Inc.

Murray, Julie. Black Bears. 2005. (Animal Kingdom Set Ii Ser.). (Illus.). 24p. (J). (gr. k-4). lib. bdg. 21.35 (978-1-59197-302-7(3)) ABDO Publishing Co.

—Grizzly Bears. 2002. (Animal Kingdom Ser.). (Illus.). 24p. (J). (gr. k-4). lib. bdg. 21.35 (978-1-57765-715-6(2)) ABDO Publishing Co.

—Polar Bears. 2005. (Animal Kingdom Set Ii Ser.). (Illus.). 24p. (J). (gr. k-4). lib. bdg. 21.35 (978-1-59197-332-4(5)) ABDO Publishing Co.

Nagda, Ann Whitehead & Bickel, Cindy. Polar Bear Math: Learning about Fractions from Klondike & Snow. 2007. (Illus.). 32p. (J). pap. 7.99 ***(978-0-312-37749-6(5))*** Square Fish.

Nault, Jennifer. Project Polar Bear. 2003. (gr. 3-6). lib. bdg. 15.25 (978-0-613-79814-3(7)) Tandem Library Bks.

—Project Polar Bear. Kissock, Heather & Marshall, Diana, eds. 2003. (Zoo Life Ser.). (Illus.). 24p. (J). pap. 6.95 (978-1-59036-060-6(5)) Weigl Pubs., Inc.

—Project Polar Bear. 2002. (Zoo Babies Ser.). (Illus.). 24p. (J). lib. bdg. 15.15 (978-1-59036-014-9(1)) Weigl Pubs., Inc.

Neal, Chuck. Grizzlies in the Mist. 2003. (Illus.). 160p. pap. 14.95 (978-0-943972-75-6(2) , 75-2) Homestead Publishing.

Nicholas, Christopher. Bears! Know It Alls. Gonzales, Pedro, illus. 2000. (Know-It-Alls Ser.). 24p. (J). (ps-3). mass mkt. 2.79 (978-0-7681-0210-9(3) , 57008, McClanahan Bk.) Learning Horizons, Inc.

Niebergall, Jane Sutherland. Bears to Barely Bears. 2005. (Cross-Curricular/Thematic Studies). (gr. 6 up). 9.95 (978-1-878051-12-7(1)) Circumpolar Pr.

Olson, Donald. Bears. 2001. (Nature's Wild Ser.). (J). lib. bdg. (978-1-58952-201-5(X)) Rourke Publishing, LLC.

Orme, Helen. Polar Bears in Danger. 2007. (Wildlife Survival Ser.). (Illus.). 32p. (J). lib. bdg. 25.27 (978-1-59716-264-7(7)) Bearport Publishing Co., Inc.

Los Osos. (Fascinante Mundo de... Ser.). 8.95 (978-958-04-3229-6(5)) Norma S.A. COL. *Dist:* Distribuidora Norma, Inc.

Parker, Janice. Grizzly Bears. 2000. (gr. 5-8). lib. bdg. 19.90 (978-0-613-74061-6(0)) Tandem Library Bks.

Patent, Dorothy Hinshaw. Garden of the Spirit Bear: Life in the Great Northern Rainforest. Milton, Deborah Jane, illus. 2004. 40p. (J). (gr. 3-5). tchr. ed. 16.00 (978-0-618-21259-0(0) , Clarion Bks.) Houghton Mifflin Co. Trade & Reference Div.

—Great Ice Bear: The Polar Bear & the Eskimo. 1999. (Illus.). 40p. (J). (gr. 2 up). 16.00 (978-0-688-13767-0(9)); 15.89 (978-0-688-13768-7(7)) HarperCollins Pubs.

—A Polar Bear Biologist at Work. 2002. (Wildlife Conservation Society Bks.). (Illus.). 48p. (J). (gr. 4-6). pap. 6.95 (978-0-531-16569-0(8) , Watts, Franklin) Scholastic Library Publishing.

—Polar Bears. Munoz, William, photos by. 2000. (Nature Watch Ser.). (Illus.). 48p. (J). (gr. 3-6). lib. bdg. 25.26 (978-1-57505-020-1(X) , Carolrhoda Bks.) Lerner Publishing Group.

Pearson, Debora. Polar Bear Alert. 2007. (Dk Readers Ser.). 48p. (J). (gr. 2-3). 14.99 ***(978-0-7566-3143-7(2))*** Dorling Kindersley Publishing, Inc.

—Polar Bear Capital. 2007. (Dk Readers Ser.). 48p. (J). (gr. 2-3). pap. 3.99 ***(978-0-7566-3140-6(8))*** Dorling Kindersley Publishing, Inc.

Penny, Malcolm. Polar Bear: Habitats, Life Cycles, Food Chains, Threats. 2000. (Natural World Ser.). (Illus.). 48p. (J). (gr. 4-7). lib. bdg. 27.12 (978-0-7398-1060-6(X)) Raintree.

Perry, Malcolm. Polar Bear. 2000. (Natural World Ser.). (Illus.). 48p. (J). (gr. 4-7). pap. 9.95 (978-0-7398-1816-9(3)) Steck-Vaughn.

Petersen, Shirley A. Grizzlies & Other Bears, Vol. 6. World Book, Inc. Staff, ed. 2001. (World Book's Animals of the World Ser.: Set 2). (Illus.). 64p. (J). (978-0-7166-1212-4(7)) World Bk., Inc.

Petty, Kate. Bears. 2004. (J). lib. bdg. 22.80 (978-1-932799-40-8(0)) Stargazer Bks.

Pighin, Marcel. Tickles the Bear, 1 bk. Pighin, Marcel & Daggett, Irma, illus. 2005. 92p. (J). per. 7.99 (978-0-9717947-5-7(8)) MP2ME Enterprise.

The Polar Bear. (Wildlife of North America Ser.). 48p. (YA). 7.95 (978-0-7368-8489-1(0)) Capstone Pr., Inc.

The Polar Bear, 6 vols. (gr. 4 up). 39.95 (978-0-7368-8501-0(3)) Red Brick Learning.

Polar Bears, 6 Packs. 16p. (gr. 3 up). 36.00 (978-0-7635-9687-3(6)) Rigby Education.

Polar Bears: Individual Title Six-Packs. (Story Steps Ser.). (gr. k-2). 32.00 (978-0-7635-9612-5(4)) Rigby Education.

Polar Bears: Level M, 6 vols. (Wonder Worldtm Ser.). 16p. 34.95 (978-0-7802-4593-8(8)); 26.50 (978-0-7802-7006-0(1)) Wright Group, The.

Pollack, Pam. Bear Cub. 2001. (gr. k-3). lib. bdg. 11.80 (978-0-613-64395-5(X)) Tandem Library Bks.

Pollack, Pam & Belviso, Meg. Bear Cub. Twinem, Neecy, illus. 2001. (All Aboard Reading Ser.). 48p. (J). pap. 3.99 (978-0-448-42523-8(8) , Grosset & Dunlap) Penguin Group (USA) Inc.

Preston-Mafham, Rod. Bears. 2002. (Secret World Of... Ser.). (Illus.). 48p. (J). lib. bdg. 27.12 (978-0-7398-4983-5(2)) Raintree.

Price, Susan. Goldilocks & the Three Bears Big Book: American English Edition. Beardshaw, Rosalind, illus. 2000. (Cambridge Reading Ser.). 16p. pap. 29.00 (978-0-521-79523-4(0)) Cambridge Univ. Pr.

Priddy, Roger. B Is for Bear. 2007. 26p. (J). bds. 12.95 (978-0-312-49918-1(3) , Priddy Bks.) St. Martin's Pr.

—Cloth Book: Snowy Bear. rev. ed. 2005. 10p. (J). 8.95 (978-0-312-49535-0(8) , Priddy Bks.) St. Martin's Pr.

Raintree Steck-Vaughn Staff. Bear Facts. 2000. (Illus.). (J). pap. 19.24 (978-0-8172-6451-2(5)) Steck-Vaughn.

—Grizzly Bears. 2000. (Untamed World Ser.). (Illus.). 64p. (J). (gr. 5-9). pap. 10.95 (978-0-7398-1682-0(9)) Steck-Vaughn.

Riehecky, Janet. Cave Bear: Ursus Spelaeus. 2008. ***(978-1-4296-0113-9(2))*** Capstone Pr., Inc.

Ring, Susan. Polar Babies. McCue, Lisa, illus. 2000. (Step into Reading Ser.). (J). (978-0-606-19904-9(7)) Tandem Library Bks.

Robinson, Claire. Bears. (In the Wild Ser.). (Illus.). 24p. (gr. k-2). 2002. (J). pap. 6.95 (978-1-57572-463-8(4) , 90453); 1998. lib. bdg. 21.36 (978-1-57572-134-7(1)) Heinemann Library.

—Bears. 2001. (In the Wild Ser.). (Illus.). 24p. (J). (ps-3). lib. bdg. 13.30 (978-0-606-21979-2(X)) Tandem Library Bks.

Robinson, Sandra Chisholm. The Everywhere Bear. 1999. (Wonder Ser.). (Illus.). 64p. (ps up). pap. 7.95 (978-1-879373-07-5(6)) Rinehart, Roberts Pubs.

Rocket Bear. (Buggy Buddies with Flaps Ser.). (Illus.). (YA). bds. 3.00 net. (978-1-56021-392-5(2)) W.J. Fantasy, Inc.

Rockwell, Anne F. Backyard Bear. Halsey, Megan, illus. 2006. 32p. (J). (gr. k-3). 15.95 (978-0-8027-9573-1(0)); 16.85 (978-0-8027-9574-8(9)) Walker & Co.

Ryder, Joanne. A Pair of Polar Bears: Twin Cubs Find a Home at the San Diego Zoo. World-Famous San Diego Zoo Staff, photos by. 2006. (Illus.). 32p. (J). (ps-3). 16.95 (978-0-689-85871-0(X)) Simon & Schuster Children's Publishing.

Sartore, Joel. Face to Face with Grizzlies. Sartore, Joel, illus. 2007. (Face to Face with Animals Ser.). (Illus.). 32p. (J). (gr. 2-6). 16.95 (978-1-4263-0050-9(6)); lib. bdg. 25.90 (978-1-4263-0051-6(4)) National Geographic Society. (National Geographic Children's Bks.).

Schaefer, Lola M. Bears: Paws, Claws & Jaws. 2001. (Wild World of Animals Ser.). (Illus.). 24p. (J). (gr. 1-2). lib. bdg. 18.60 (978-0-7368-0823-1(X) , Bridgestone Bks.) Capstone Pr., Inc.

Schwabacher, Martin. Bears. 2000. (Animals Animals Ser.). (Illus.). 48p. (J). (gr. 3-5). lib. bdg. 25.64 (978-0-7614-1169-7(0) , Benchmark Bks.) Cavendish, Marshall Corp.

Schwaeber, Barbie Heit. Alphabet of Bears. Nelson, Will, illus. 2007. 40p. 15.95 ***(978-1-59249-689-1(X))*** Soundprints.

Shea, Therese. Bears. 2006. (Big Bad Biters Ser.). (Illus.). 24p. (J). (ps-2). lib. bdg. 19.95 (978-1-4042-3524-3(8) , PowerKids Pr.) Rosen Publishing Group, Inc., The.

Shively, Julie. Baby Polar Bear. Johnson, Meredith, illus. 2005. (San Diego Zoo Animal Library: Vol. 10). 24p. (J). bds. 6.95 (978-0-8249-6576-1(0)) Ideals Pubns.

Shores, Erika L. Polar Bears. 2005. (World of Mammals Ser.). (Illus.). 24p. (J). (ps-7). lib. bdg. 21.26 (978-0-7368-4312-6(4)) Capstone Pr., Inc.

Simon, Seymour. Wild Bears. 2002. (See More Readers Ser.). (Illus.). 32p. (J). (gr. k-4). pap. 3.95 (978-1-58717-144-4(9) , SeaStar Bks.) Chronicle Bks. LLC.

—Wild Bears. 2002. (gr. 3-6). lib. bdg. 11.80 (978-0-613-58448-7(1)) Tandem Library Bks.

Sjonger, Rebecca & Kalman, Bobbie. The Life Cycle of a Polar Bear. 2005. (Life Cycle Ser.). (Illus.). 32p. (J). (gr. k-6). (978-0-7787-0668-7(0)); pap. (978-0-7787-0698-4(2)) Crabtree Publishing Co.

Sjonger, Rebecca & Kalman, Bobbie. Les Ours Polaires. 2007. (FRE.). 32p. pap. 8.95 ***(978-2-89579-163-8(5))*** Editions Banjo CAN. *Dist:* Crabtree Publishing Co.

Smithsonian Institution Staff. Bear on His Own. 2000. (Let's Go to the Zoo! Ser.). (Illus.). 16p. (J). (ps-k). bds. 5.95 (978-1-56899-913-5(5) , B9008) Soundprints.

Soffer, Ruth. Learning about Bears. 2004. (Illus.). 16p. (J). pap. 1.50 (978-0-486-43317-2(X)) Dover Pubns., Inc.

Spezialy, Millie. Bears of Alaska: A Natural History Coloring & Activity Book. 2001. (Illus.). 32p. 5.95 (978-1-890692-05-6(0)) Wizard Works.

—Binky's Trophy. (J). 14.95 (978-0-9654200-2-0(7)) Six Suns Publishing.

Squire, Ann. Polar Bears. 2006. (True Book Ser.). (Illus.). 47p. (J). (978-0-516-25473-9(1)) Children's Pr., Ltd.

—Polar Bears. 2006. (True Book Ser.). (Illus.). 47p. (J). (978-0-516-22826-6(9) , Children's Pr.) Scholastic Library Publishing.

Steck-Vaughn Staff. In Land of Polar Bear (Arctic) 1999. (Take Me Home Ser.). (Illus.). (J). pap. (978-0-7398-2591-4(7)) Steck-Vaughn.

Steele, Christy. Malayan Sun Bears. 2003. (Animals of the Rain Forest Ser.). (Illus.). 32p. (J). lib. bdg. 24.28 (978-0-7398-6838-6(1)) Raintree.

Stefoff, Rebecca. Bears. 2001. (Animalways Ser.). (Illus.). 112p. (J). (gr. 5 up). lib. bdg. 31.36 (978-0-7614-1268-7(9) , Benchmark Bks.) Cavendish, Marshall Corp.

Stevenson, Katherine. Grizzly Bears. 2007. (New Naturebooks Ser.). 32p. (J). (gr. 1-5). 27.07 ***(978-1-59296-847-3(3))*** Child's World, Inc.

Stirling, Ian, ed. Bears. rev. ed. 2000. (Illus.). 240p. (J). reprint ed. 40.00 (978-1-875137-88-6(2)) Weldon Owen, Inc.

Stone, Jason, et al. Polar Bear. 2000. (Wild Bears! Ser.). (Illus.). 24p. (J). (gr. 3-6). 24.94 (978-1-56711-344-0(3) , Blackbirch Pr., Inc.) Thomson Gale.

Stone, Lynn M. Brown Bears. 1998. (Early Bird Nature Bks.). (Illus.). 48p. (gr. 2-4). lib. bdg. 25.26 (978-0-8225-3029-9(5)) Lerner Publishing Group.

Stone, Lynn M., photos by. Grizzlies. 2007. (Nature Watch Ser.). (Illus.). 48p. (J). 25.26 (978-0-8225-6601-4(X) , Lerner Pubns.) Lerner Publishing Group.

Stone, Tanya Lee. Polar Bears. 2003. (Wild Wild World Ser.). 24p. (YA). 24.94 (978-1-56711-820-9(8) , Blackbirch Pr., Inc.) Thomson Gale.

Stonehouse, Bernard. Bears: A Visual Introduction to Bears. Camm, Martin, illus. (Animal Watch Ser.). 48p. (J). (gr. 4-9). 16.95 (978-0-8160-3923-4(2) , Checkmark Bks.) Facts On File, Inc.

Swanson, Diane. Bears. 1998. (Welcome to the World of Animals Ser.). (Illus.). 32p. (J). (gr. 3 up). lib. bdg. 23.33 (978-0-8368-2213-7(7)) Stevens, Gareth Inc.

Swanson, Diane. Welcome to the World of the Spirit Bears. 2007. (Welcome to the World Ser.). (Illus.). 28p. (J). (ps-2). pap. 5.95 ***(978-1-55285-847-9(2)*** , Walrus Bks.) Whitecap Bks., Ltd. CAN. *Dist:* Firefly Bks., Ltd.

Swinburne, Stephen R. Black Bear: North America's Bear. 2003. (Illus.). 32p. (YA). (gr. 4-6). 15.95 (978-1-59078-023-7(X)) Boyds Mills Pr.

Tagliaferro, Linda. Bears & Their Cubs. 2004. (Animal Offspring Ser.). (Illus.). 24p. (J). 13.95 (978-0-7368-2387-6(5) , Pebble Bks.) Capstone Pr., Inc.

—Bears & Their Dens. 2004. (Pebble Plus, Animal Homes Ser.). (Illus.). 24p. (J). 13.95 (978-0-7368-2381-4(6)) Capstone Pr., Inc.

—Polar Bears. McGee, John F., illus. 2004. (Our Wild World Ser.). 48p. (J). (gr. 2-5). ring bd. 10.95 (978-1-55971-829-5(3)); pap. 7.95 (978-1-55971-828-8(5)) T&N Children's Publishing. (NorthWord Bks. for Young Readers).

—Polar Bears. McGee, John F., illus. 2002. 47p. (J). (ps-3). lib. bdg. 16.40 (978-0-613-55884-6(7)) Tandem Library Bks.

Tara, Stephanie/Tara. Snowy White World. Walton, Alex, illus. 2007. (J). 16.95 ***(978-1-933285-89-4(3))*** Brown Bks. Publishing Group.

Taylor, Barbara. Grizzly Bears. 2003. (Predators Ser.). (Illus.). 32p. (J). lib. bdg. 25.70 (978-0-7398-6600-9(1)) Raintree.

—Why Don't Polar Bears Have Stripes? 2004. (Animal Puzzlers Ser.). (Illus.). 32p. (J). 12.95 (978-1-57768-946-1(1) , Waterbird Bks.) School Specialty Publishing.

Tessier, Tess & Tessier, Grandma. White Spirit Bear. 2000. (Illus.). 48p. pap. 12.95 (978-0-88839-475-0(6)) Hancock Hse. Pubs.

—White Spirit Bear. Miller, Nancy, ed. 2nd ed. 2000. (Illus.). 48p. (J). (gr. k-7). 17.95 (978-0-88839-462-0(4)) Hancock Hse. Pubs.

Theodorou, Rod. Polar Bear. (Animals in Danger Ser.). (Illus.). 32p. (J). (gr. k-2). 2002. pap. 6.95 (978-1-58810-364-2(1) , 91078); 2001. lib. bdg. 21.36 (978-1-57572-273-3(9)) Heinemann Library.

Thomas, Isabel. Polar Bear vs. Grizzly Bear. 2006. (Illus.). 32p. (J). pap. (978-1-4109-2401-8(7)); lib. bdg. (978-1-4109-2394-3(0)) Steck-Vaughn.

Thomas, Keltie. Bear Rescue: Changing the Future for Endangered Wildlife. 2006. (Firefly Animal Rescue Ser.). (Illus.). 64p. (J). (gr. 5-12). pap. 9.95 (978-1-55297-921-1(0)); lib. bdg. 19.95 (978-1-55297-922-8(9)) Firefly Bks., Ltd.

Thompson. Theme Pack: Bears. 2002. (Pair-It Bks.). (J). pap. (978-0-7398-6370-1(3)) Steck-Vaughn.

Time for Kids Editors. Bears! 2005. (Time for Kids Ser.). (Illus.). 32p. (J). pap. 3.99 (978-0-06-078196-5(3) , Harper Trophy) HarperCollins Pubs.

Time for Kids Editors & Iorio, Nicole. Bears! 2005. (Time for Kids Ser.). (Illus.). 32p. (J). 14.99 (978-0-06-078201-6(3)) HarperCollins Pubs.

Townsend, Emily Rose. Polar Bears. Saunders-Smith, Gail, ed. 2004. (Polar Animals Ser.). (Illus.). 24p. (J). (gr. k-1). lib. bdg. 15.93 (978-0-7368-2358-6(1) , Pebble Bks.) Capstone Pr., Inc.

Tracqui, Valerie. The Brown Bear: Giant of the Mountains. Bios Agency Staff, photos by. 1998. (Animal Close-Ups Ser.). (Illus.). 28p. (J). (ps-3). pap. 6.95 (978-0-88106-439-1(4)) Charlesbridge Publishing, Inc.

—The Brown Bear: Giant of the Mountains. 1998. (Animal Close-Ups Ser.). (978-0-606-13230-5(9)) Tandem Library Bks.

Trapani, Iza. Row Row Row Your Boat. Trapani, Iza, illus. 2000. (Extended Nursery Rhymes Ser.). (Illus.). 32p. (J). (ps up). lib. bdg. 23.33 (978-0-8368-2668-5(X)) Stevens, Gareth Inc.

—Sing along with Iza & Friends: Row Row Row Your Boat. Trapani, Iza, illus. 2004. (Illus.). 32p. (J). pap. 9.95 incl. audio compact disk (978-1-58089-102-8(0)) Charlesbridge Publishing, Inc.

Twine, Alice. Bears. 2008. (J). lib. bdg. ***(978-1-4042-3770-4(4)*** , PowerKids Pr.) Rosen Publishing Group, Inc., The.

Varela, Barry. Arctic Tale (Junior Novelization) 2007. 128p. (J). (gr. 2-5). lib. bdg. 21.90 (978-1-4263-0107-0(3)); (Illus.). pap. 4.99 (978-1-4263-0106-3(5)) National Geographic Society. (National Geographic Children's Bks.).

Vogel, Julia. Polar Animals. McGee, John F., illus. 2004. (Our Wild World Ser.). 192p. (J). (gr. 2-5). ring bd. 16.95 (978-1-55971-832-5(3) , NorthWord Bks. for Young Readers) T&N Children's Publishing.

Ward, Kennan & Johnson, Johnny, photos by. Bears: And Other Top Predators, 6 vols., Vol. 6. 1999. 300p. 29.95 (978-0-9759110-0-6(7)) High Desert Publishing.

Watt, Fiona. Este No Es Mi Orso. 2007. 10p. (J). bds. 7.99 ***(978-0-7460-8350-5(5)*** , Usborne) EDC Publishing.

Welvaert, Scott R. A Bear in Its Den. 2003. (Where Do Animals Live? Ser.). (J). (978-1-58417-184-3(7)); pap. (978-1-58417-185-0(5)) Lake Street Pubs.

Wexo, John Bonnett. Bears. 2001. (Zoobooks Ser.). (Illus.). 24p. (J). (gr. 1-6). 15.95 (978-1-888153-36-1(9)) Wildlife Education, Ltd.

—Bears. French, Lisa, illus. 2001. (Zoobooks Ser.). 18p. (J). (gr. 1-6). reprint ed. pap. 2.95 (978-0-937934-07-4(0)) Wildlife Education, Ltd.

—Bears. rev. ed. 2003. (Illus.). 24p. (J). (gr. 1-12). 10.95 (978-1-888153-90-3(3) , Zoo Bks.) Wildlife Education, Ltd.

—Osos. Rountree, Monica, tr. 2003. (Zoobooks). Orig. Title: Bears. (SPA., Illus.). 24p. (J). (gr. 1-7). lib. bdg. 15.95 (978-1-888153-73-6(3)) Wildlife Education, Ltd.

Whitehouse, Patricia. Brown Bear. 2003. (Zoo Animals Ser.). (Illus.). 24p. (ps-1). (J). lib. bdg. 17.09 (978-1-58810-888-3(0)); pap. 5.25 (978-1-4034-0537-1(9)) Heinemann Library.

—El Oso Cafe. 2003. (Animales del Zoologico Ser.). (SPA.). 24p. pap. 5.25 (978-1-4034-0547-0(6)) Heinemann Library.

—El Oso Pardo. 2003. (Animales del Zoologico (Zoo Animals) Ser.). (SPA., Illus.). 24p. (J). (ps-1). lib. bdg. 17.08 (978-1-4034-0329-2(5)) Heinemann Library.

Wildlife Education, Ltd. Staff & Levibiel, Timothy. Polar Bears. Woods, Michael & Stuart, Walter, illus. 2001. (Zoobooks Ser.). 24p. (J). 15.95 (978-0-937934-85-2(2)) Wildlife Education, Ltd.

Wilsdon, Christina. Polar Bears. 2006. (J). ***(978-1-59939-116-8(3)*** , Reader's Digest Young Families, Inc.) Reader's Digest Children's Publishing, Inc.

Wood, Ted. Bear Dogs: Canines with a Mission. 2001. (Illus.). 32p. (J). (gr. 8-12). 16.95 (978-0-8027-8758-3(4)) Walker & Co.

Ziefert, Harriet. Bear Gets Dressed: A Guessing Game Story. Capucilli, Alyssa, illus. 2004. 16p. (J). 9.95 (978-1-4027-1705-5(9)) Sterling Publishing Co., Inc.

Zollman, Pam. A Bear Cub Grows Up. 2005. (Scholastic News Nonfiction Readers Ser.). (Illus.). 24p. (J). (gr. 1-2). 19.00 (978-0-516-24943-8(6) , Children's Pr.) Scholastic Library Publishing.

BEARS—FICTION

Ackerman, Peter. My Favorite Bear. Cox, Rhonda, photos by. 1999. (Books for Young Learners). (Illus.). 12p. (J). (gr. k-2). pap. 5.00 (978-1-57274-336-6(0) , A2759) Owen, Richard C. Pubs., Inc.

Adams, Georgie. Three Bears on Vacation. Young, Selina, illus. 2003. 28p. (J). (gr. k-1). pap. 6.95 (978-0-7696-3154-7(1) , Gingham Dog Pr.) School Specialty Publishing.

Adelson, Leone. The Mystery Bear: A Purim Story. Howland, Naomi, illus. 2004. 32p. (J). (gr. k-3). tchr. ed. 15.00 (978-0-618-33725-5(3) , Clarion Bks.) Houghton Mifflin Co. Trade & Reference Div.

—The Mystery Bear: A Purim Story. Howland, Naomi, tr. Howland, Naomi, illus. 2004. 32p. (J). (ps-2). 15.00 (978-0-618-33727-9(X) , Clarion Bks.) Houghton Mifflin Co. Trade & Reference Div.

Adventures of Buster Bear. 2000. mass mkt. 3.99 (978-1-55902-948-3(X) , Aerie) Doherty, Tom Assocs., LLC.

Agee, Jon. The Bear in the Hat. Agee, Jon, illus. 2000. (Michael di Capua Bks.). (Illus.). 32p. (J). lib. bdg. 15.89 (978-0-06-205188-2(1)); 15.95 (978-0-06-205187-5(3)) HarperCollins Pubs.

Alborough, Jez. It's the Bear! Alborough, Jez, illus. 2002. (Illus.). (J). 13.83 (978-0-7587-2879-1(4)) Book Wholesalers, Inc.

—It's the Bear! Alborough, Jez, illus. 2004. (Illus.). 30p. (J). (gr. k-ps). bds. 6.99 (978-0-7636-2316-6(4)) Candlewick Pr.

—My Friend Bear. Alborough, Jez, illus. 2002. (Illus.). (J). 24.36 (978-0-7587-4189-9(8)) Book Wholesalers, Inc.

—My Friend Bear. Alborough, Jez, illus. (Illus.). (J). (gr. k-ps). 2003. 28p. bds. 6.99 (978-0-7636-2017-2(3)); 2001. 32p. pap. 5.99 (978-0-7636-1414-0(9)) Candlewick Pr.

—My Friend Bear. 2001. (ps-2). lib. bdg. 14.15 (978-0-613-74722-6(4)); (Illus.). (J). (978-0-606-21341-7(4)) Tandem Library Bks.

—Where's My Teddy? Alborough, Jez, illus. 2002. (Illus.). 24p. (J). (gr. k-ps). bds. 6.99 (978-0-7636-1868-1(3)) Candlewick Pr.

Alderson, Sue Ann. Wherever Bears Be. Johnson, Arden, illus. 2003. 32p. (J). (ps-3). 14.95 (978-1-883672-77-5(5) , Tricycle Pr.) Ten Speed Pr.

Alerson, Sue Ann. Wherever Bears Be: A Story for Two Voices. Johnson, Arden, illus. 1999. 30p. (J). (ps-3). (978-1-896580-18-0(1)) Tradewind Bks.

Alex Toys Staff. Alex Toys Finger Puppet Storybooks: Goldilocks & the Three Bears. McDonald, Jill, illus. 4th rev. ed. 2006. 8p. (J). (ps-1). 11.99 (978-0-316-15395-9(8)) Little Brown & Co.

Alexander, Martha. Blackboard Bear. Alexander, Martha, illus. 2002. (Blackboard Bear Ser.). (Illus.). (J). 20.53 (978-0-7587-4198-1(7)) Book Wholesalers, Inc.

—I Sure Am Glad to See You, Blackboard Bear. Alexander, Martha, illus. 2nd rev. ed. 2004. (Illus.). 30p. (J). (gr. k-3). reprint ed. 11.00 (978-0-7567-7153-9(6)) DIANE Publishing Co.

—I'll Never Share You, Blackboard Bear. Alexander, Martha, illus. 2003. (Illus.). 32p. (J). (ps-1). 13.99 (978-0-7636-1590-1(0)) Candlewick Pr.

Allan-Meyer, Kathleen. Little Bear at Big School. Garvin, Elaine, illus. 2000. (Little Bear Adventure Ser.: Vol. 4). 28p. (J). (ps-1). pap. 6.49 (978-1-57924-398-2(3)) Jones, Bob Univ. Pr.

—Little Bear's Big Adventure. Garvin, Elaine, illus. 1998. 32p. (J). (ps-1). pap. 6.49 (978-1-57924-060-8(7)) Jones, Bob Univ. Pr.

—Little Bear's Crunch-a-Roo Cookies. Garvin, Elaine, illus. 2000. (Little Bear Adventure Ser.: Vol. 5). 27p. (J). (ps-1). pap. 6.49 (978-1-57924-438-5(6)) Jones, Bob Univ. Pr.

—Little Bear's Secret. Garvin, Elaine, illus. 2000. 32p. (J). (ps-1). pap. 6.49 (978-1-57924-358-6(4)) Jones, Bob Univ. Pr.

—Little Bear's Surprise. Garvin, Elaine, illus. 1999. 32p. (J). (ps-1). pap. 6.49 (978-1-57924-066-0(6)) Jones, Bob Univ. Pr.

—Little Bear's Surprise. 1999. (ps-2). lib. bdg. 13.55 (978-0-613-83923-5(4)) Tandem Library Bks.

—Play Fair, Little Bear. Garvin, Elaine, illus. (J). (ps-1). pap. 6.49 (978-1-57924-887-1(X)) Jones, Bob Univ. Pr.

Aloha Bear - Footprint Detective. 2002. (J). pap. 8.99 (978-0-89610-290-3(4)) Island Heritage Publishing.

Amato, Carol A. On the Trail of the Grizzly, Vol. 9. O'Brien, Patrick & Wenzel, David, illus. 1998. (Young Reader Ser.: No. 9). 48p. (J). (gr. 3-6). lib. bdg. 13.45 (978-1-56674-240-5(4)) Forest Hse. Publishing Co., Inc.

Ambrosio, Michael. It Takes a Lot of Love. Awes, Jennifer, illus. 2007. 32p. (J). 14.95 ***(978-0-9716085-4-2(7))*** LionX Publishing.

Amery, H. & Cartwright, S. Goldilocks & the Three Bears. 2004. (First Stories Ser.). 16p. (J). pap. 4.99 (978-0-7945-0608-7(9)) EDC Publishing.

Amery, H. & Cartwright, Stephen. Goldilocks & the Three Bears. 16p. (J). lib. bdg. 12.95 (978-1-58086-619-4(0) , Usborne) EDC Publishing.

Anderson, Derek. Romeo & Lou Blast Off. Anderson, Derek, illus. 2007. 32p. (J). (ps-3). 15.99 ***(978-1-4169-3784-5(6)*** , Simon & Schuster Children's Publishing) Simon & Schuster Children's Publishing.

Anderson, Jeannine. Nightlight. Johnson, Nikki, illus. 2004. 32p. (J). pap. 7.95 (978-0-89317-057-8(7) , WW-0577); lib. bdg. 16.95 (978-0-89317-056-1(9) , WW-0569) Finney Co., Inc. (Windward Publishing).

Anderson, Wayne R. Paula's Perilous Adventure. 2006. 48p. (YA). 12.95 (978-0-9773478-0-3(X)); 19.95 incl. DVD (978-0-9773478-2-7(6)) IMAGECRAFTERS.

Andreae, Giles. Heaven Is Having You. Cabban, Vanessa, illus. (J). (ps-k). 2007. 24p. bds. 7.95 ***(978-1-58925-820-4(7));*** 2002. 32p. tchr. ed. 15.95 (978-1-58925-016-1(8)); 2004. 32p. reprint ed. pap. 6.95 (978-1-58925-388-9(4)) ME Media LLC. (tiger tales).

Andreae, Giles. Love Is a Handful of Honey. Cabban, Vanessa, illus. 1999. 32p. (J). (ps-2). 14.95 (978-1-888444-58-2(4)) Little Tiger Pr.

—Love Is a Handful of Honey. Cabban, Vanessa, illus. 2004. 32p. (J). (ps-k). 5.95 (978-1-58925-353-7(1)); tchr. ed. 15.95 (978-1-58925-003-1(6)) ME Media LLC. (tiger tales).

—Love Is a Handful of Honey. 2001. (ps-2). lib. bdg. 14.10 (978-0-613-57645-1(4)) Tandem Library Bks.

Anglund, Joan Walsh. Cowboy & His Friend. 2002. (Illus.). 40p. 6.95 (978-0-7407-2211-0(5)) Andrews McMeel Publishing.

Appelt, Kathi. Where, Where Is Swamp Bear? Halsey, Megan, illus. 2002. 32p. (J). (ps-2). 15.95 (978-0-688-17102-5(8)); lib. bdg. 15.89 (978-0-688-17103-2(6)) HarperCollins Pubs.

Arnosky, Jim. Every Autumn Comes the Bear. Arnosky, Jim, illus. 2002. (Illus.). (J). 13.19 (978-0-7587-2468-7(3)) Book Wholesalers, Inc.

Aruego, Jose. Splash! 2001. (gr. k-3). lib. bdg. 11.80 (978-0-613-66386-1(1)) Tandem Library Bks.

Aruego, Jose & Dewey, Ariane. Splash! 2003. (Green Light Readers Level 2 Ser.). (Illus.). 32p. (J). 11.95 (978-0-15-204872-3(3)); pap. 3.95 (978-0-15-204832-7(4)) Harcourt Children's Bks. (Green Light Readers).

Asato, Dennis. A Dolphin Day in Hawaii. 2001. (Illus.). 50p. (J). (ps-1). pap. 9.95 (978-0-9702618-2-3(9)) Anoai Pr.

—A Dolphin Day in Hawaii. Asato, Dennis, illus. l.t. ed. 1999. (Illus.). 50p. (J). (ps-1). 12.00 (978-0-9653971-8-6(1)) Anoai Pr.

Asch, Frank. Good Night, Baby Bear. Asch, Frank, illus. 2001. (Illus.). 32p. (J). (ps-k). pap. 7.00 (978-0-15-216368-6(9) , Voyager Bks./Libros Viajeros) Harcourt Children's Bks.

—Good Night, Baby Bear. 2001. 12.80 (978-0-606-22600-4(1)); lib. bdg. 14.15 (978-0-613-53034-7(9)) Tandem Library Bks.

—Happy Birthday, Moon. Asch, Frank, illus. 2002. (Moonbear Ser.). (Illus.). (J). 15.53 (978-0-7587-2686-5(4)) Book Wholesalers, Inc.

—Happy Birthday, Moon. Asch, Frank, illus. (Stories to Go! Ser.). (Illus.). 32p. (J). 2005. 4.99 (978-1-4169-0307-9(0)); 2000. pap. 6.99 (978-0-689-83544-5(2)) Simon & Schuster Children's Publishing. (Aladdin).

—Happy Birthday, Moon. 2005. (Stories to Go! Ser.). (Illus.). (J). ***(978-1-4156-0411-3(8)*** , Aladdin) Simon & Schuster Children's Publishing.

—Moonbear's Bargain. Asch, Frank, illus. 2002. (Moonbear Ser.). (Illus.). (YA). 14.47 (978-1-4046-0166-6(X)) Book Wholesalers, Inc.

A

B

—Moonbear's Bargain. (Moonbear Ser.). (ps-k). 2000. (J). (978-0-606-18624-7(7)); 1999. lib. bdg. 14.15 (978-0-8335-2711-0(8)) Tandem Library Bks.

—Moonbear's Dream. Asch, Frank, illus. 2002. (Illus.). 32p. (J). (ps-1). pap. 6.99 (978-0-689-85310-4(6) , Aladdin) Simon & Schuster Children's Publishing.

—Moonbear's Pet. Asch, Frank, illus. 2002. (Moonbear Ser.). (Illus.). (J). 14.47 (978-1-4046-0167-3(8)) Book Wholesalers, Inc.

—Moonbear's Shadow. Asch, Frank, illus. 2002. (Moonbear Ser.). (Illus.). (J). 14.47 (978-0-7587-6647-2(5)) Book Wholesalers, Inc.

—Moonbear's Shadow. Asch, Frank, illus. 2000. (Moonbear Ser.). 32p. (J). (ps-k). 6.99 (978-0-689-83519-3(1) , Aladdin) Simon & Schuster Children's Publishing.

—Moonbear's Shadow. 2000. (978-0-606-18625-4(5)); 1999. lib. bdg. 15.30 (978-0-8335-2452-2(6)) Tandem Library Bks.

—Mooncake. Asch, Frank, illus. 2002. (Moonbear Ser.). (Illus.). (J). 14.47 (978-0-7587-6749-3(8)) Book Wholesalers, Inc.

—Mooncake. Asch, Frank, illus. 2000. (Moonbear Ser.). 32p. (J). (ps-k). 6.99 (978-0-689-83517-9(5) , Aladdin) Simon & Schuster Children's Publishing.

—Mooncake. 1999. (ps-2). lib. bdg. 15.30 (978-0-613-37191-9(7)) Tandem Library Bks.

—Moondance. Asch, Frank, illus. 2002. (Moonbear Ser.). (Illus.). 13.83 (978-1-4046-0169-7(4)) Book Wholesalers, Inc.

—Moongame. Asch, Frank, illus. 2002. (Moonbear Ser.). (Illus.). (J). 14.47 (978-0-7587-6424-9(3)) Book Wholesalers, Inc.

—Moongame. Asch, Frank, illus. 2000. (Moonbear Ser.). (Illus.). 32p. (J). (ps-k). 6.99 (978-0-689-83518-6(3) , Aladdin) Simon & Schuster Children's Publishing.

—Moongame. (Moonbear Ser.). (ps-k). 2000. (J). (978-0-606-18896-8(7)); 1999. lib. bdg. 15.30 (978-0-613-60907-4(7)) Tandem Library Bks.

Asch, Frank & Asch, Frank. Happy Birthday, Moon. 1999. (Illus.). 28p. (J). (ps-3). lib. bdg. 15.30 (978-0-613-63293-5(1)) Tandem Library Bks.

Ash, Jo Ann Clark. Yule, the Great Christmas Bear. 2000. (Illus.). 28p. (J). (ps-5). pap. 8.00 (978-0-9715835-0-4(1)) Clark, Jo Ann.

Ashby, Lenore. The Magic of the Bear. 2003. (Illus.). 162p. (YA). per. 7.95 (978-0-9728535-0-7(2) , 853502) Grandma Chubby's Bks.

Ashforth, Camilla. Willow on the River. Ashforth, Camilla, illus. 2002. (Illus.). 32p. (J). (ps-2). 12.00 (978-0-7636-1088-3(7)) Candlewick Pr.

Ashworth, Camilla. La Cama de Horacio. (Picture Books Collection). (SPA., Illus.). 32p. (J). (gr. k-3). pap. 10.95 (978-1-56014-581-3(1)) Santillana USA Publishing Co., Inc.

Atkinson, Ruth & Atkinson, Brett. Story Templates. Atkinson, Ruth & Atkinson, Brett, illus. (Illus.). (J). (gr. k-2). pap. (978-1-875739-73-8(4)) Wizard Bks.

Austin, Margot. A Friend for Growl Bear. 2001. (J). pap. (978-0-06-443745-5(0) , Harper Trophy) HarperCollins Pubs.

Austin, Margot & McPhail, David M. A Friend for Growl Bear Board Book. 1999. (Illus.). 32p. (J). (ps-k). 6.95 (978-0-694-01257-2(2) , Harper Festival) HarperCollins Pubs.

Azordegan, Kambiz. The Bear's Den: Bear's Family. Sajem, Johnny, illus. abr. l.t. ed. 1998. (Tootee's Magical Stories Ser.: Vol. 5). 40p. (J). 9.95 (978-1-890571-29-0(6)) Positive Children's Programming Corp.

Baby Bear's Toys. (Early Intervention Levels Ser.). 21.30 (978-0-7362-0361-6(3)) Hampton-Brown Bks.

Baby Looney Tunes. 2001. (J). (978-1-58805-128-8(5)) DS-Max USA, Inc.

Baby Looney Tunes Box Set with Coloring Books. 2000. (J). (978-1-58805-130-1(7)) DS-Max USA, Inc.

Baglio, Ben M. Bears in the Barn. 2001. (Animal Ark Ser.: No. 23). 144p. (J). pap. 3.99 (978-0-439-23022-3(5) , Scholastic Paperbacks) Scholastic, Inc.

Baicker, Karen & Williams, Sam. Yum Tummy Tickly! 2004. (Illus.). 5p. (J). bds. 6.95 (978-1-59354-037-1(X)) Handprint Bks.

Bailey, Arthur Scott. Sleepy-Time Tales: The Tale of Cuffy Bea. 2006. (Illus.). pap. (***978-1-4065-0448-4(3)***) Dodo Pr.

Bailey, Elinor Peace. Brunhilde, the Mother Bear. Bailey, Elinor Peace, illus. 2002. (J). 9.50 (978-0-9716586-8-4(4)) Fairfield Processing Corp.

Baker, Barbara. One Saturday Evening: By Barbara Baker: Pictures by Kate Duke. Duke, Kate, illus. 2007. (J). (***978-0-525-47850-8(7)*** , Dutton Juvenile) Penguin Group (USA) Inc.

Balaban, Mariah, ed. Easter Egg Hunt. 2007. (Care Bears Ser.). (J). bds. 5.99 (978-0-439-89465-4(4)) Scholastic, Inc.

Baldwin, Sherry. Beecher Bear Plays Here & There. Stowe, Becky, illus. 2001. 32p. (J). (ps). 16.00 (978-0-9700870-0-3(4)) Read-It-To-Me Publishing.

Ball, Lynda Anne. Kwanzaa Teddy, The Curious Bear. Johnson, Larry, illus. 2004. (Adventures of KT). 32p. (J). (ps-2). per. 6.95 (978-1-889383-11-8(2)) Angel Pubns.

Bamboo & Friends. (C). 180.80 (978-1-4048-1528-5(7)) Picture Window Bks.

Barcita, Pamela. The Dancing Bears. 2007. (J). (ps up). 19.95 (***978-1-933982-00-7(4)*** , TDB) Bumble Bee Publishing.

Barlow, Ben. Mimi's Bears. 2006. 24p. 13.76 (978-1-4116-7984-9(9)) Lulu.com.

Barnhart, Shelby. I Can't Wait Any Longer. 2003. 45p. pap. 17.95 (978-1-59286-930-5(0)) PublishAmerica, Inc.

Baronian, Jean-Baptiste. Con Todo Mi Corazon. 2000. (SPA., Illus.). 12p. (J). 16.95 (978-84-488-0686-6(7) , BS8814) Beascoa, Ediciones S.A. ESP. *Dist:* Lectorum Pubns., Inc.

Barske, Dianne. Two Bears There: The Story of Alpun & Oreo. 2005. 14.95 (978-1-888125-49-8(7)) Publication Consultants.

Bart, Kathleen. Town Teddy Country Bear. 2004. 32p. (J). (978-1-932485-19-6(8)) Reverie Publishing Co.

Barton, Byron. The Three Bears. 1999. 32p. (J). (ps-1). pap. 4.95 (978-0-06-443365-5(X)) HarperCollins Pubs.

Bastedo, Jamie. Tracking Triple Seven: Grizzly on the Tundra. 2004. 216p. (YA). (gr. 5 up). pap., tchr. ed. 9.95 (978-0-88995-238-6(8)) Red Deer Pr. CAN. *Dist:* Fitzhenry & Whiteside, Ltd.

—Tracking Triple Seven: Grizzly on the Tundra. 2002. (gr. 5-8). lib. bdg. 18.75 (978-0-613-63357-4(1)) Tandem Library Bks.

Bauer, Marion Dane. Baby Bear Discovers the World. Tekiela, Stan, photos by. 2006. 68p. 14.95 (978-1-59193-165-2(7)) Adventure Pubns., Inc.

—A Bear Named Trouble. 2005. 128p. (J). (gr. 3-5). 14.00 (978-0-618-51738-1(3) , Clarion Bks.) Houghton Mifflin Co. Trade & Reference Div.

—A Bear Named Trouble. 2006. 128p. (J). (gr. 4-7). pap. 5.99 (978-0-440-42132-0(2) , Yearling) Random Hse. Children's Bks.

Be Kind, Be Friendly, Be Thankful: The Adventures of Brisky Bear & Trooper Dog. 2007. Orig. Title: Friends for Always. (J). pap. 7.95 incl. audio compact disk (***978-0-9795127-0-4(0)***) Glory Be Collectibles.

Be Nice to Pooh. 1999. (J). pap. 2.99 (978-0-307-08598-6(8) , 08598, Golden Bks.) Random Hse. Children's Bks.

The Bear & the Trolls, 6 Packs. 32p. (gr. 3 up). 37.00 (978-0-7635-9678-1(7)) Rigby Education.

A Bear for All Seasons. 1999. (Disney Ser.). (Illus.). 70p. (J). (ps-3). pap. 2.29 (978-0-307-08542-9(2) , 08542, Golden Bks.) Random Hse. Children's Bks.

Bear Hugs. 2000. (Daybreaks Ser.). (Illus.). 368p. (J). spiral bd. 9.99 (978-0-310-98400-9(9)) Zondervan.

Bear Hunt: Individual Title Six-Pack Pouch - Level H. (Lighthouse Ser.). 16p. (gr. 1 up). 26.00 (978-0-7578-0841-8(7)) Rigby Education.

Bear in Trouble, 6 Packs. (Sails Literacy Ser.). (gr. 1-2). 36.00 (978-0-7578-4010-4(8)) Rigby Education.

The Bear Lake Mystery. 2001. 200p. mass mkt. 5.99 (978-0-9708721-0-4(0)) Palmtree Publishing.

Bear Story Board Books 800655, 5. 2005. (J). bds. (978-1-59794-007-8(0)) Environments, Inc.

The Bear Who Learned to Read. 1998. (J). (ps). 9.95 (978-0-7894-2986-5(1)) Dorling Kindersley Publishing, Inc.

Bears, Bears, Bears, 6 Packs. (Story Steps Ser.). (gr. k-2). 23.00 (978-0-7635-9608-8(6)) Rigby Education.

Bear's Diet, 6 Packs. 16p. (gr. 2 up). 35.00 (978-0-7635-9373-5(7)) Rigby Education.

A Bear's Year Set C, 6 vols. (Phonics Readers Ser.). (gr. k-2). 17.50 (978-0-7368-3200-7(9)) Red Brick Learning.

Beck, Ian. Getting Dressed. 2004. (Little Brown Bear Ser.). (Illus.). 12p. (J). bds. 4.99 (978-1-85854-650-6(8)) Brimax Books Ltd. GBR. *Dist:* Byeway Bks.

—Let's Pretend. 2004. (Little Brown Bear Ser.). (Illus.). 12p. (J). bds. 4.99 (978-1-85854-649-0(4)) Brimax Books Ltd. GBR. *Dist:* Byeway Bks.

—Perdido en la Nieve. 2001. (SPA., Illus.). 32p. (J). (gr. k-2). (978-84-261-3103-4(4) , JV4196) Juventud, Editorial ESP. *Dist:* Lectorum Pubns., Inc.

—Playtime. 2004. (Little Brown Bear Ser.). (Illus.). 12p. (J). bds. 4.99 (978-1-85854-648-3(6)) Brimax Books Ltd. GBR. *Dist:* Byeway Bks.

Becker, Bonny. A Visitor for Bear. Denton, Kady MacDonald, illus. 2008. (J). (***978-0-7636-2807-9(7)***) Candlewick Pr.

Bedford & Worthington. Big! 2006. (Illus.). 12p. (J). 9.95 (978-0-7624-2784-0(1)) Running Pr. Bk. Pubs.

Bedford, David. Bedtime for Little Bears! Pedler, Caroline, illus. 2007. 28p. (J). (ps-2). 16.95 (***978-1-56148-587-1(X)***) Good Bks.

—Big Bear Little Bear. Chapman, Jane, illus. 2005. 16p. (J). (ps). bds. 6.95 (978-1-58925-770-2(7) , tiger tales) ME Media LLC.

—Big Bears Can! Hansen, Gaby, illus. (J). (ps-k). 2007. 18p. bds. 6.95 (***978-1-58925-826-6(6)*** , tiger tales); 2001. 32p. tchr. ed. 14.95 (978-1-58925-006-2(0)) ME Media LLC.

—I've Seen Santa! Warnes, Tim, illus. 2006. 32p. (J). 15.95 (978-1-58925-058-1(3) , tiger tales) ME Media LLC.

—Pues Claro Que Si! Hansen, Gaby, illus. 2002. (SPA.). 202p. (J). (978-84-488-1095-5(3) , BS30458) Beascoa, Ediciones S.A. ESP. *Dist:* Lectorum Pubns., Inc.

—Touch the Sky, My Little Bear. Chapman, Jane, illus. 2001. 32p. (J). (ps-k). 15.95 (978-1-929766-20-8(3)) Handprint Bks.

Beer, Hans. Kleiner eisbar wohin fahrst Du. pap. 17.95 (978-3-423-07954-9(1)) Deutscher Taschenbuch Verlag GmbH & Co KG DEU. *Dist:* Distribooks, Inc.

Bell, A. L. The Adventures of Captain Zero: I'm the Hero (Special Edition Cover) 2005. 45p. 17.00 (978-1-4116-3732-0(1)) Lulu.com.

Benator, Eileen. A Marching Band for Bears. Benator, Seth, illus. 2004. 32p. (J). lib. bdg. 15.95 (978-0-9748478-5-6(2)) Lion's Tale Press, L.L.C.

Bengts, Mandy. The Tale of the Greedy Raven & the Hungry Bear. Bennington, Michael, illus. 2002. 24p. pap. 7.95 (978-1-894303-17-0(2)) RRP Pubs.

Bennett, David. The Lost Teddy. 2004. (Ben & Friends Ser.). (Illus.). 24p. (J). pap. 4.99 (978-1-85854-691-9(5)) Brimax Books Ltd. GBR. *Dist:* Byeway Bks.

Bentley, Dawn. Fuzzy Bear: A Getting Dressed Book. Nagy, Krisztina, illus. 1998. (Fuzzy Bear Ser.). 10p. (J). (ps-k). 10.95 (978-1-58117-011-5(4) , Intervisual/Piggy Toes) Dalmatian Pr.

—Fuzzy Bear Goes to School. Nagy, Krisztina, illus. 2005. (Fuzzy Bear Ser.). 10p. (J). 10.95 (978-1-58117-124-2(2) , Intervisual/Piggy Toes) Dalmatian Pr.

—Fuzzy Bear's Christmas. Nagy, Krisztina, illus. 2000. (Fuzzy Bear Ser.). 10p. (J). (ps-3). 11.95 (978-1-58117-105-1(6) , Intervisual/Piggy Toes) Dalmatian Pr.

—Goodnight Bear: A Book & Night Light. Couri, Kathryn A., illus. 2005. (Stories to Share Ser.). 12p. (J). 12.95 (978-1-58117-034-4(3) , Intervisual/Piggy Toes) Dalmatian Pr.

—Wake up, Black Bear! Stover, Beth, illus. 2003. (Read-and-Discover Atlantic Wilderness Adventures Ser.). 32p. (J). (ps-17). pap. 3.95 (978-1-59249-007-3(7) , S2020) Soundprints.

Berardy, Lloyd, 1st. A Tropical Bear in Hawaii Goes Underwater. 2006. (J). 12.95 (978-1-4276-0212-1(3)) Aardvark Global Publishing.

Berenstain, Jan. The Berenstain Bears' Baby Easter Bunny. Berenstain, Jan, illus. 2008. (Berenstain Bears Ser.). 16p. (J). 6.99 (***978-0-06-057420-8(8)*** , Harper Festival) HarperCollins Pubs.

Berenstain, Jan & Berenstain, Michael. The Berenstain Bears' Big Bedtime Book. 2008. (Berenstain Bears Ser.). 48p. (J). 12.99 (***978-0-06-057434-5(8)***); lib. bdg. 13.89 (***978-0-06-057435-2(6)***) HarperCollins Pubs.

Berenstain, Jan & Berenstain, Stan. The Berenstain Bears Trim the Tree. Berenstain, Jan, illus. 2007. (Berenstain Bears Ser.). 16p. (J). (ps-1). 6.99 (***978-0-06-057417-8(8)*** , Harper Festival) HarperCollins Pubs.

Berenstain, Jan, et al. The Berenstain Bears Save Christmas. Berenstain, Michael, illus. 2003. (Berenstain Bears Ser.). 48p. (J). (ps-3). 12.99 (978-0-06-052670-2(X)) HarperCollins Pubs.

Berenstain, Michael, et al. The Berenstain Bears & the Golden Rule. 2008. (J). pap. (***978-0-310-71247-3(5)***) Zonderkidz.

—The Berenstain Bears Go to Sunday School. 2008. (J). pap. (***978-0-310-71248-0(3)***) Zonderkidz.

—The Berenstain Bears Say Their Prayers. 2008. (J). pap. (***978-0-310-71246-6(7)***) Zonderkidz.

Berenstain, Stan & Berenstain, Jan. Bears in the Night. Berenstain, Stan & Berenstain, Jan, illus. 2002. (Berenstain Bears Bright & Early Bks.). (Illus.). (J). 16.70 (978-0-7587-0922-6(6)) Book Wholesalers, Inc.

—The Bears' Picnic. Berenstain, Stan & Berenstain, Jan, illus. 2002. (Berenstain Bears Beginner Bks.). (Illus.). (J). (gr. k-3). 15.74 (978-0-7587-0924-0(2)) Book Wholesalers, Inc.

—The Berenstain Bear Scouts & the Coughing Catfish. 1998. (Berenstain Bear Scouts Ser.). (Illus.). 32p. (J). (gr. 3-8). pap. 3.50 (978-0-590-60384-3(1)) Scholastic, Inc.

—The Berenstain Bear Scouts & the Evil Eye. 1998. (Berenstain Bear Scouts Ser.). (J). (gr. 3-6). pap. 3.99 (978-0-590-94488-5(6) , Scholastic Paperbacks) Scholastic, Inc.

—The Berenstain Bear Scouts & the Evil Eye. 1998. (Berenstain Bear Scouts Ser.). (J). (gr. 3-6). (978-0-606-13190-2(6)) Tandem Library Bks.

—The Berenstain Bear Scouts & the Missing Merit Badges. 1998. (Berenstain Bear Scouts Ser.). (Illus.). 32p. (J). (gr. 3-6). pap. 3.50 (978-0-590-56390-1(4)) Scholastic, Inc.

—The Berenstain Bear Scouts & the Missing Merit Badges. 1998. (Berenstain Bear Scouts Ser.). (J). (gr. 3-6). (978-0-606-13191-9(4)) Tandem Library Bks.

—The Berenstain Bear Scouts & the Really Big Disaster. 1998. (Berenstain Bear Scouts Ser.). (Illus.). 32p. (J). (gr. 3-6). pap. 3.99 (978-0-590-94481-6(9) , Scholastic Paperbacks) Scholastic, Inc.

—The Berenstain Bear Scouts & the Really Big Disaster. 1998. (Berenstain Bear Scouts Ser.). (J). (gr. 3-6). (978-0-606-13192-6(2)) Tandem Library Bks.

—The Berenstain Bear Scouts & the Ripoff Queen. 1998. (Berenstain Bear Scouts Ser.). (Illus.). 112p. (J). (gr. 3-6). pap. 3.99 (978-0-590-94493-9(2)) Scholastic, Inc.

—The Berenstain Bear Scouts & the Search for Naughty Ned. 1998. (Berenstain Bear Scouts Ser.). (Illus.). 32p. (J). (gr. 3-6). pap. 3.50 (978-0-590-56509-7(5)) Scholastic, Inc.

—The Berenstain Bear Scouts & the Search for Naughty Ned. 1998. (Berenstain Bear Scouts Ser.). (J). (gr. 3-6). (978-0-606-13193-3(0)) Tandem Library Bks.

—The Berenstain Bear Scouts & the Stinky Milk Mystery. 1999. (Berenstain Bear Scouts Ser.). (Illus.). 32p. (J). (gr. 3-6). pap. 3.50 (978-0-590-56524-0(9) , Cartwheel Bks.) Scholastic, Inc.

—The Berenstain Bear Scouts & the Stinky Milk Mystery. 1999. (Berenstain Bear Scouts Ser.). (J). (gr. 3-6). (978-0-606-16597-6(5)) Tandem Library Bks.

—The Berenstain Bear Scouts & the White-Water Mystery. 1999. (Berenstain Bear Scouts Ser.). 32p. (J). (gr. 3-6). pap. 3.50 (978-0-590-56522-6(2)) Scholastic, Inc.

—The Berenstain Bear Scouts & the White-Water Mystery. 1999. (Berenstain Bear Scouts Ser.). (J). (gr. 3-6). (978-0-606-16598-3(3)) Tandem Library Bks.

—The Berenstain Bear Scouts Scream Their Heads Off. 1998. (Berenstain Bear Scouts Ser.). (Illus.). 32p. (J). (gr. 3-6). pap. 3.99 (978-0-590-94484-7(3) , Scholastic Paperbacks) Scholastic, Inc.

—The Berenstain Bear Scouts Scream Their Heads Off. 1998. (Berenstain Bear Scouts Ser.). (J). (gr. 3-6). (978-0-606-13194-0(9)) Tandem Library Bks.

—The Berenstain Bears, 7 vols., Date not set. (Early Childhood First Bks.). (Illus.). (J). (ps-2). lib. bdg. 97.65 (978-1-56674-942-8(5)) Forest Hse. Publishing Co., Inc.

—The Berenstain Bears & Baby Makes Five. 2000. (Berenstain Bears First Time Bks.). (Illus.). 32p. (J). (gr. k-1). pap. 3.25 (978-0-679-88960-1(4) , Random Hse. Bks. for Young Readers) Random Hse. Children's Bks.

—The Berenstain Bears & Baby Makes Five. 2000. (Berenstain Bears First Time Bks.). (J). (ps-2). lib. bdg. 10.95 (978-0-613-24332-2(3)); (Illus.). 10.05 (978-0-606-18485-4(6)) Tandem Library Bks.

—The Berenstain Bears & Mama's New Job. Berenstain, Stan & Berenstain, Jan, illus. 2002. (Berenstain Bears First Time Bks.). (Illus.). (J). 11.19 (978-0-7587-0953-0(6)) Book Wholesalers, Inc.

—The Berenstain Bears & Mama's New Job. 1999. (Berenstain Bears First Time Bks.). (Illus.). (J). (gr. k-2). pap. 10.25 (978-0-88103-144-7(5)) Tandem Library Bks.

—The Berenstain Bears & No Guns Allowed. 2000. (Berenstain Bears Big Chapter Bks.). (Illus.). (J). (gr. 3-6). 10.79 (978-0-606-18486-1(4)) Tandem Library Bks.

—The Berenstain Bears & the Baby Chipmunk. Berenstain, Stan, illus. 2005. (Berenstain Bears Ser.). 32p. (J). lib. bdg. 13.85 (***978-1-4242-0817-3(3)***) Fitzgerald Bks.

—The Berenstain Bears & the Baby Chipmunk. Berenstain, Stan & Berenstain, Jan, illus. 2005. (Berenstain Bears Ser.). (Illus.). 32p. (J). pap. 3.99 (978-0-06-058413-9(0)); 15.99 (978-0-06-058412-2(2)) HarperCollins Pubs.

—The Berenstain Bears & the Bad Dream. Berenstain, Stan & Berenstain, Jan, illus. 2002. (Berenstain Bears First Time Bks.). (Illus.). (J). 11.19 (978-0-7587-0957-8(9)) Book Wholesalers, Inc.

—The Berenstain Bears & the Bad Dream. ed. 2004. (Berenstain Bears First Time Bks.). (J). (ps-2). spiral bd. (978-0-616-01555-1(0)); spiral bd. (978-0-616-01556-8(9)) Canadian National Institute for the Blind/Institut National Canadien pour les Aveugles.

—The Berenstain Bears & the Bad Habit. Berenstain, Jan, illus. 2002. (Berenstain Bears First Time Bks.). (Illus.). (J). (gr. k-3). 11.19 (978-0-7587-0949-3(8)) Book Wholesalers, Inc.

—The Berenstain Bears & the Big Blooper. ed. 2004. (Berenstain Bears First Time Bks.). (J). (gr. k-3). spiral bd. (978-0-616-07216-5(3)); spiral bd. (978-0-616-07217-2(1)) Canadian National Institute for the Blind/Institut National Canadien pour les Aveugles.

—The Berenstain Bears & the Big Blooper. Klimo, Kate, ed. 2000. (Berenstain Bears First Time Bks.). (Illus.). 32p. (J). (gr. k-3). pap. 3.25 (978-0-679-88962-5(0) , Random Hse. Bks. for Young Readers) Random Hse. Children's Bks.

—The Berenstain Bears & the Big Blooper. 2000. (Berenstain Bears First Time Bks.). (J). (gr. k-2). 10.15 (978-0-606-19887-5(3)); lib. bdg. 10.95 (978-0-613-32320-8(3)) Tandem Library Bks.

—The Berenstain Bears & the Big Date. 1998. (Berenstain Bears Big Chapter Bks.). (J). (gr. 2-6). (978-0-606-13951-9(6)) Tandem Library Bks.

—The Berenstain Bears & the Big Question. 1999. (Berenstain Bears First Time Bks.). (Illus.). 32p. (J). (gr. k-3). 3.99 (978-0-679-88961-8(2) , Random Hse. Bks. for Young Readers) Random Hse. Children's Bks.

—The Berenstain Bears & the Big Question. 1999. (Berenstain Bears First Time Bks.). (J). (gr. k-3). lib. bdg. 10.95 (978-0-613-86658-3(4)) Tandem Library Bks.

—The Berenstain Bears & the Big Road Race. Berenstain, Stan & Berenstain, Jan, illus. 2002. (Berenstain Bears First Time Bks.). (Illus.). (J). 11.19 (978-0-7587-0938-7(2)) Book Wholesalers, Inc.

—The Berenstain Bears & the Big Spelling Bee, No. 6. Berenstain, Jan, illus. 2007. (Berenstain Bears Ser.). (Illus.). 32p. (J). 3.99 (***978-0-06-057386-7(4)*** , Harper Festival) HarperCollins Pubs.

—The Berenstain Bears & the Blame Game. Berenstain, Stan & Berenstain, Jan, illus. 2002. (Berenstain Bears First Time Bks.). (Illus.). (J). 11.19 (978-0-7587-0965-3(X)) Book Wholesalers, Inc.

—The Berenstain Bears & the Blame Game. ed. 2004. (Berenstain Bears First Time Bks.). (Illus.). (J). (gr. k-3). spiral bd. (978-0-616-14559-3(4)); spiral bd. (978-0-616-14560-9(8)) Canadian National Institute for the Blind/Institut National Canadien pour les Aveugles.

—The Berenstain Bears & the Bully. Berenstain, Stan & Berenstain, Jan, illus. 2002. (Berenstain Bears First Time Bks.). (Illus.). (J). 11.19 (978-0-7587-0947-9(1)) Book Wholesalers, Inc.

—The Berenstain Bears & the Double Dare. Berenstain, Stan & Berenstain, Jan, illus. 2002. (Berenstain Bears First Time Bks.). (Illus.). (J). 11.19 (978-0-7587-0956-1(0)) Book Wholesalers, Inc.

—The Berenstain Bears & the Dress Code. Berenstain, Stan & Berenstain, Jan, illus. 2002. (Berenstain Bears Big Chapter Bks.). (Illus.). (J). 11.91 (978-0-7587-0444-3(5)) Book Wholesalers, Inc.

—The Berenstain Bears & the Drug Free Zone. Berenstain, Stan & Berenstain, Jan, illus. 2002. (Berenstain Bears Big Chapter Bks.). (Illus.). (J). (gr. 2-6). 11.91 (978-0-7587-0941-7(2)) Book Wholesalers, Inc.

—The Berenstain Bears & the Escape of the Bogg Brothers. 2000. (Berenstain Bears Ser.). (J). (gr. k-3). (978-0-606-20272-5(2)) Tandem Library Bks.

—The Berenstain Bears & the G-Rex Bones. 2001. (Berenstain Bears Big Chapter Bks.). (J). (gr. 2-6). lib. bdg. 11.99 (978-0-679-98949-3(8) , Random Hse. Bks. for Young Readers) Random Hse. Children's Bks.

—The Berenstain Bears & the G-Rex Bones. 1999. (Berenstain Bears Big Chapter Bks.). (J). (978-0-606-16863-2(X)) Tandem Library Bks.

—The Berenstain Bears & the Great Ant Attack. 2000. (Berenstain Bears Big Chapter Bks.). (Illus.). (J). (gr. 2-6). (978-0-606-18487-8(2)) Tandem Library Bks.

—The Berenstain Bears & the Green-Eyed Monster. Berenstain, Stan & Berenstain, Jan, illus. 2002. (Berenstain Bears First Time Bks.). (Illus.). (J). 11.19 (978-0-7587-0946-2(3)) Book Wholesalers, Inc.

—The Berenstain Bears & the Homework Hassle. Berenstain, Stan & Berenstain, Jan, illus. 2002. (Berenstain Bears First Time Bks.). (Illus.). (J). 11.19 (978-0-7587-0966-0(8)) Book Wholesalers, Inc.

—The Berenstain Bears & the Love Match. 1998. (Berenstain Bears Big Chapter Bks.). (J). (gr. 2-6). (978-0-606-13952-6(4)) Tandem Library Bks.

—The Berenstain Bears & the Mama's Day Surprise. 2004. (Berenstain Bears First Time Bks.). (Illus.). 32p. (J). (gr. k-3). pap. 3.99 (978-0-375-81132-6(X)); lib. bdg. 10.99 (978-0-375-91132-3(4)) Random Hse. Children's Bks. (Random Hse. Bks. for Young Readers).

—The Berenstain Bears & the Messy Room Book & CD. 2005. (Berenstain Bears First Time Bks.). (Illus.). 32p. (J). (ps-2). 9.95 (978-0-375-83412-7(5) , Random Hse. Bks. for Young Readers) Random Hse. Children's Bks.

—The Berenstain Bears & the Missing Dinosaur Bone. Berenstain, Stan & Berenstain, Jan, illus. 2002. (Berenstain Bears Beginner Bks.). (Illus.). (J). (gr. k-3). 16.70 (978-0-7587-0962-2(5)) Book Wholesalers, Inc.

—The Berenstain Bears & the Missing Honey. Berenstain, Stan & Berenstain, Jan, illus. 2002. (Berenstain Bears First Time Bks.). (Illus.). (J). (gr. k-3). 11.19 (978-0-7587-0445-0(3)) Book Wholesalers, Inc.

—The Berenstain Bears & the Missing Watermelon Money. 2001. (Berenstain Bears Ser.). (Illus.). 48p. (J). (gr. 1-3). 11.99 (978-0-679-99230-1(8)); pap. 3.99 (978-0-679-89230-4(3)) Random Hse. Children's Bks. (Random Hse. Bks. for Young Readers).

—The Berenstain Bears & the Missing Watermelon Money. 2001. (Berenstain Bears Ser.). (J). (gr. k-3). lib. bdg. 11.80 (978-0-613-35600-8(4)); (Illus.). 10.79 (978-0-606-21056-0(3)) Tandem Library Bks.

—The Berenstain Bears & the Papa's Day Roast. 2003. (Illus.). 32p. (J). (gr. k-3). lib. bdg. 8.99 (978-0-375-91129-3(4) , Random Hse. Bks. for Young Readers) Random Hse. Children's Bks.

—The Berenstain Bears & the Papa's Day Surprise. 2003. (Berenstain Bears First Time Bks.). (Illus.). 32p. (J). (gr. k-3). pap. 3.99 (978-0-375-81129-6(X) , Random Hse. Bks. for Young Readers) Random Hse. Children's Bks.

—The Berenstain Bears & the Papa's Day Surprise. 2003. (Berenstain Bears First Time Bks.). (J). (gr. k-3). lib. bdg. 10.95 (978-0-613-64152-4(3)) Tandem Library Bks.

—The Berenstain Bears & the Phantom of the Gymnasium. 2000. (Illus.). (J). pap. 3.99 (978-0-679-88949-6(3) , Random Hse. Bks. for Young Readers) Random Hse. Children's Bks.

—The Berenstain Bears & the Prize Pumpkin. Berenstain, Stan & Berenstain, Jan, illus. 2002. (Berenstain Bears First Time Bks.). (Illus.). (J). 11.19 (978-0-7587-0959-2(5)) Book Wholesalers, Inc.

—The Berenstain Bears & the Real Easter Eggs. Berenstain, Stan & Berenstain, Jan, illus. 2002. (Berenstain Bears Ser.). (Illus.). (J). 11.19 (978-0-7587-8978-5(5)) Book Wholesalers, Inc.

—The Berenstain Bears & the Real Easter Eggs. 2002. (Berenstain Bears Ser.). (Illus.). 32p. (J). (gr. k-3). pap. 3.99 (978-0-375-81133-3(8) , Random Hse. Bks. for Young Readers) Random Hse. Children's Bks.

—The Berenstain Bears & the Real Easter Eggs. 2002. (gr. k-3). lib. bdg. 10.95 (978-0-613-64153-1(1)) Tandem Library Bks.

—The Berenstain Bears & the Sitter. Berenstain, Stan & Berenstain, Jan, illus. 2002. (Berenstain Bears First Time Bks.). (Illus.). (J). 11.19 (978-0-7587-0942-4(0)) Book Wholesalers, Inc.

—The Berenstain Bears & the Tic-Tac-Toe Mystery. (Berenstain Bears Ser.). (Illus.). 48p. (J). (gr. k-3). 2003. lib. bdg. 11.99 (978-0-679-99229-5(4)); 2001. pap. 3.99 (978-0-679-89229-8(X)) Random Hse. Children's Bks. (Random Hse. Bks. for Young Readers).

—The Berenstain Bears & the Trouble with Chores. 2005. (Berenstain Bears Ser.). (Illus.). 32p. (J). (ps-2). 8.99 (978-0-06-057398-0(8)); pap. 3.99 (978-0-06-057382-9(1)) HarperCollins Pubs. (Harper Festival).

—The Berenstain Bears & the Trouble with Grownups. Berenstain, Stan & Berenstain, Jan, illus. 2002. (Berenstain Bears First Time Bks.). (Illus.). (J). 11.19 (978-0-7587-0958-5(7)) Book Wholesalers, Inc.

—The Berenstain Bears & the Truth. Berenstain, Stan & Berenstain, Jan, illus. 2002. (Berenstain Bears First Time Bks.). (Illus.). (J). 11.19 (978-0-7587-4345-9(9)) Book Wholesalers, Inc.

—The Berenstain Bears & the Wax Museum. 1999. (Berenstain Bears Big Chapter Bks.). (J). (gr. 2-6). (978-0-606-16943-1(1)) Tandem Library Bks.

—The Berenstain Bears & the Week at Grandma's. Berenstain, Stan & Berenstain, Jan, illus. 2002. (Berenstain Bears First Time Bks.). (Illus.). (J). 11.19 (978-0-7587-6632-8(7)) Book Wholesalers, Inc.

—The Berenstain Bears & the Wishing Star. Berenstain, Stan & Berenstain, Jan, illus. 2005. (Berenstain Bears Ser.). (Illus.). 32p. (J). pap. 3.99 (978-0-06-058347-7(9)); 15.99 (978-0-06-058346-0(0)) HarperCollins Pubs.

—The Berenstain Bears & Too Much Birthday. Berenstain, Stan & Berenstain, Jan, illus. 2002. (Berenstain Bears First Time Bks.). (Illus.). (J). 11.19 (978-0-7587-6422-5(7)) Book Wholesalers, Inc.

—The Berenstain Bears & Too Much Car Trip. 2006. (Berenstain Bears Ser.). (Illus.). 32p. (J). (ps-2). 8.99 (978-0-06-057400-0(3)); pap. 3.99 (978-0-06-057384-3(8)) HarperCollins Pubs. (Harper Festival).

—The Berenstain Bears & Too Much Junk Food. 1999. (Berenstain Bears First Time Bks.). (Illus.). (J). (ps-2). lib. bdg. 10.95 (978-0-8085-3551-5(X)) Tandem Library Bks.

—The Berenstain Bears & Too Much TV. Berenstain, Stan & Berenstain, Jan, illus. 2002. (Berenstain Bears First Time Bks.). (Illus.). (J). 11.19 (978-0-7587-0943-1(9)) Book Wholesalers, Inc.

—The Berenstain Bears & Too Much Vacation. Berenstain, Stan & Berenstain, Jan, illus. 2002. (Berenstain Bears First Time Bks.). (Illus.). (J). 11.19 (978-0-7587-0954-7(4)) Book Wholesalers, Inc.

—The Berenstain Bears' Bedtime Battle. Berenstain, Stan & Berenstain, Jan, illus. 2005. (Berenstain Bears Ser.). (Illus.). 32p. (J). (ps-2). 3.99 (978-0-06-057381-2(3) , Harper Festival) HarperCollins Pubs.

—The Berenstain Bears Big Bear Small Bear. 1998. (Berenstain Bears Ser.). (Illus.). 32p. (J). (gr. k). lib. bdg. 11.99 (978-0-679-98717-8(7)); pap. 3.99 (978-0-679-88717-1(2)) Random Hse. Children's Bks. (Random Hse. Bks. for Young Readers).

—The Berenstain Bears Blaze a Trail. Berenstain, Stan & Berenstain, Jan, illus. 2002. (Berenstain Bears First Time Bks.). (Illus.). (J). 11.19 (978-0-7587-0950-9(1)) Book Wholesalers, Inc.

—The Berenstain Bears by the Sea. Berenstain, Stan & Berenstain, Jan, illus. 2002. (Berenstain Bears Ser.). (Illus.). (J). (gr. k-3). 11.91 (978-0-7587-0969-1(2)) Book Wholesalers, Inc.

—The Berenstain Bears by the Sea. 1998. (Berenstain Bears Ser.). (Illus.). 32p. (ps-2). (J). pap. 3.99 (978-0-679-88719-5(9)); lib. bdg. 11.99 (978-0-679-98719-2(3)) Random Hse. Children's Bks. (Random Hse. Bks. for Young Readers).

—The Berenstain Bears by the Sea. 1998. (Berenstain Bears Ser.). (J). (ps-3). 10.79 (978-0-606-13954-0(0)); (Illus.). lib. bdg. 11.80 (978-0-613-07341-7(X)) Tandem Library Bks.

—The Berenstain Bears Catch the Bus. Berenstain, Stan & Berenstain, Jan, illus. 2002. (Berenstain Bears Ser.). (Illus.). (J). (gr. k-3). 11.91 (978-0-7587-0977-6(3)) Book Wholesalers, Inc.

—The Berenstain Bears Catch the Bus. 1999. (Berenstain Bears Ser.). (Illus.). 32p. (J). (ps-3). lib. bdg. 11.99 (978-0-679-99227-1(8)); pap. 3.99 (978-0-679-89227-4(3)) Random Hse. Children's Bks. (Random Hse. Bks. for Young Readers).

—The Berenstain Bears Catch the Bus. 1999. (Berenstain Bears Ser.). (J). (ps). (Illus.). 32p. lib. bdg. 11.80 (978-0-613-16056-8(8)); 10.79 (978-0-606-16944-8(X)) Tandem Library Bks.

—The Berenstain Bears Clean House. 2005. (Illus.). 30p. (J). lib. bdg. 9.00 (***978-1-4242-0815-9(7)***) Fitzgerald Bks.

—The Berenstain Bears Clean House. 2005. (Berenstain Bears Ser.). (Illus.). 32p. (J). (gr. k-3). 15.99 (978-0-06-058334-7(7)) HarperCollins Pubs.

—The Berenstain Bears Clean House. Berenstain, Stan, illus. 2005. (Berenstain Bears Ser.). (Illus.). 32p. (J). (gr. k-3). pap. 3.99 (978-0-06-058335-4(5)) HarperCollins Pubs.

—The Berenstain Bears' Dollars & Sense. 2001. (Berenstain Bears First Time Bks.). (Illus.). 32p. (J). (gr. k-3). pap. 3.99 (978-0-375-81124-1(9) , Random Hse. Bks. for Young Readers) Random Hse. Children's Bks.

—The Berenstain Bears' Dollars & Sense. 2001. (Berenstain Bears First Time Bks.). (J). (gr. k-3). 10.79 (978-0-606-22793-3(8)); (gr. 3-6). lib. bdg. 10.95 (978-0-613-32322-2(X)) Tandem Library Bks.

—The Berenstain Bears Don't Pollute (Anymore) 1999. (Berenstain Bears First Time Bks.). (Illus.). (J). (ps-2). lib. bdg. 10.95 (978-0-8335-6545-7(1)) Tandem Library Bks.

—The Berenstain Bears down on the Farm. Berenstain, Stan & Berenstain, Jan, illus. 2006. (Berenstain Bears Ser.). (Illus.). 32p. (J). 15.99 (978-0-06-058350-7(9)) HarperCollins Pubs.

—The Berenstain Bears down on the Farm. 2006. (Berenstain Bears Ser.). (Illus.). 32p. (J). pap. 3.99 (978-0-06-058351-4(7) , Harper Trophy); (***978-1-4156-8342-2(5)***) HarperCollins Pubs.

—The Berenstain Bears' Easter Surprise. l.t. ed. 1998. (Berenstain Bears Ser.). (Illus.). 48p. (J). (ps-3). pap. 10.95 (978-0-590-94730-5(3)) Scholastic, Inc.

—The Berenstain Bears Forget Their Manners. Berenstain, Stan & Berenstain, Jan, illus. 2002. (Berenstain Bears First Time Bks.). (Illus.). (J). (gr. k-3). 11.19 (978-0-7587-3684-0(3)) Book Wholesalers, Inc.

—The Berenstain Bears' Funny Valentine. 2002. (Berenstain Bears First Time Bks.). (Illus.). 32p. (J). (gr. k-3). pap. 3.99 (978-0-375-81126-5(5) , Random Hse. Bks. for Young Readers) Random Hse. Children's Bks.

—The Berenstain Bears' Funny Valentine. 2003. (Berenstain Bears First Time Bks.). (J). (ps-2). lib. bdg. 10.95 (978-0-613-57494-5(X)) Tandem Library Bks.

—The Berenstain Bears Get in a Fight. Berenstain, Stan & Berenstain, Jan, illus. 2002. (Berenstain Bears First Time Bks.). (Illus.). (J). (gr. k-3). 11.19 (978-0-7587-4124-0(3)) Book Wholesalers, Inc.

—The Berenstain Bears Get the Gimmies. Berenstain, Stan & Berenstain, Jan, illus. 2002. (Berenstain Bears First Time Bks.). (Illus.). (J). 11.19 (978-0-7587-0955-4(2)) Book Wholesalers, Inc.

—The Berenstain Bears Get the Scaredies. Berenstain, Stan & Berenstain, Jan, illus. 1999. (Berenstain Bears Ser.). (Illus.). 24p. (J). (ps-3). lib. bdg. 7.99 (978-0-679-99323-0(1) , Random Hse. Bks. for Young Readers) Random Hse. Children's Bks.

—The Berenstain Bears Get Their Kicks. 1998. (Berenstain Bears First Time Bks.). (Illus.). 32p. (J). (gr. k-3). pap. 3.25 (978-0-679-88955-7(8) , Random Hse. Bks. for Young Readers) Random Hse. Children's Bks.

—The Berenstain Bears Get Their Kicks. 1998. (Berenstain Bears First Time Bks.). (J). (gr. k-2). 10.05 (978-0-606-13955-7(9)) Tandem Library Bks.

—The Berenstain Bears Go Back to School. Berenstain, Michael, illus. 2005. (Berenstain Bears Ser.). 32p. (J). (ps-3). 9.99 (978-0-06-052673-3(4)); lib. bdg. 14.89 (978-0-06-052674-0(2)) HarperCollins Pubs.

—The Berenstain Bears Go Hollywood. 1999. (Berenstain Bears Big Chapter Bks.). (J). (gr. 2-6). (978-0-606-17264-6(5)) Tandem Library Bks.

—The Berenstain Bears Go in & Out. 2000. (Berenstain Bears Ser.). (Illus.). (J). (gr. k-3). (978-0-606-18488-5(0)) Tandem Library Bks.

—The Berenstain Bears Go on a Ghost Walk. 2005. (Berenstain Bears Ser.). (Illus.). 32p. (J). (ps-2). 8.99 (978-0-06-057399-7(6)); pap. 3.99 (978-0-06-057383-6(X)) HarperCollins Pubs. (Harper Festival).

—The Berenstain Bears Go on Vacation. 2006. (Berenstain Bears Ser.: No. 1). (Illus.). 32p. (J). 9.99 (978-0-06-057431-4(3)); Bk. 1. lib. bdg. 15.89 (978-0-06-057432-1(1)) HarperCollins Pubs.

—The Berenstain Bears Go to Camp. Berenstain, Stan & Berenstain, Jan, illus. 2002. (Berenstain Bears First Time Bks.). (Illus.). (J). 11.19 (978-0-7587-0944-8(7)) Book Wholesalers, Inc.

—The Berenstain Bears Go to School. Berenstain, Stan & Berenstain, Jan, illus. 2002. (Berenstain Bears First Time Bks.). (Illus.). (J). (gr. k-3). 11.19 (978-0-7587-4125-7(1)) Book Wholesalers, Inc.

—The Berenstain Bears Go to School. ed. 2004. (Berenstain Bears First Time Bks.). (J). (gr. k-3). spiral bd. (978-0-616-01551-3(8)); spiral bd. (978-0-616-01552-0(6)) Canadian National Institute for the Blind/Institut National Canadien pour les Aveugles.

—The Berenstain Bears Go to the Doctor. Berenstain, Stan & Berenstain, Jan, illus. 2002. (Berenstain Bears First Time Bks.). (Illus.). (J). 11.19 (978-0-7587-0945-5(5)) Book Wholesalers, Inc.

—The Berenstain Bears Go up & Down: A Math Reader. 1999. (Berenstain Bears Ser.). (Illus.). 32p. (J). (gr. k-3). lib. bdg. 11.99 (978-0-679-98720-8(7) , Random Hse. Bks. for Young Readers) Random Hse. Children's Bks.

—The Berenstain Bears Go up & Down: A Math Reader. 1999. (Berenstain Bears Ser.). (J). (ps-k). lib. bdg. (978-0-606-15895-4(2)) Tandem Library Bks.

—The Berenstain Bears Hug & Make Up. 2006. (Berenstain Bears Ser.). (Illus.). 32p. (J). pap. 3.99 (978-0-06-057385-0(6) , Harper Festival) HarperCollins Pubs.

—The Berenstain Bears Hug & Make Up, No. 5. Berenstain, Stan & Berenstain, Jan, illus. 2006. (Berenstain Bears Ser.). (Illus.). 32p. (J). 8.99 (978-0-06-057401-7(1) , Harper Festival) HarperCollins Pubs.

—The Berenstain Bears in the Dark. Berenstain, Stan & Berenstain, Jan, illus. 2002. (Berenstain Bears First Time Bks.). (Illus.). (J). 11.19 (978-0-7587-0937-0(4)) Book Wholesalers, Inc.

—The Berenstain Bears in the House of Mirrors. Berenstain, Stan & Berenstain, Jan, illus. 2002. (Berenstain Bears Ser.). (Illus.). (J). (gr. k-3). 11.91 (978-0-7587-0974-5(9)) Book Wholesalers, Inc.

—The Berenstain Bears in the House of Mirrors. 1999. (Berenstain Bears Ser.). (J). (ps-k). 10.79 (978-0-606-16837-3(0)) Tandem Library Bks.

—The Berenstain Bears Learn about Strangers. Berenstain, Stan & Berenstain, Jan, illus. 2002. (Berenstain Bears First Time Bks.). (Illus.). (J). 11.19 (978-0-7587-4126-4(X)) Book Wholesalers, Inc.

—The Berenstain Bears Lend a Helping Hand. 1998. (Berenstain Bears First Time Bks.). (Illus.). 32p. (J). (gr. k-3). pap. 3.99 (978-0-679-88956-4(6) , Random Hse. Bks. for Young Readers) Random Hse. Children's Bks.

—The Berenstain Bears Lose a Friend. Berenstain, Stan & Berenstain, Jan, illus. 2007. (Berenstain Bears Ser.). 32p. (J). (ps-2). 8.99 (***978-0-06-057405-5(4)*** , Harper Festival) HarperCollins Pubs.

—The Berenstain Bears Lost in Cyberspace. 1999. (Berenstain Bears Big Chapter Bks.). (J). (gr. 2-6). (978-0-606-16839-7(7)) Tandem Library Bks.

—The Berenstain Bears' Mad, Mad, Mad Toy Craze. 1999. (Berenstain Bears First Time Bks.). (Illus.). 32p. (J). (gr. k-3). pap. 3.25 (978-0-679-88958-8(2) , Random Hse. Bks. for Young Readers) Random Hse. Children's Bks.

—The Berenstain Bears' Mad, Mad, Mad Toy Craze. 1999. (Berenstain Bears First Time Bks.). (J). (gr. k-2). 10.05 (978-0-606-15979-1(7)); lib. bdg. 10.95 (978-0-613-16060-5(6)) Tandem Library Bks.

—The Berenstain Bears' Moving Day. Berenstain, Stan & Berenstain, Jan, illus. 2002. (Berenstain Bears First Time Bks.). (Illus.). (J). (gr. k-3). 11.19 (978-0-7587-4127-1(8)) Book Wholesalers, Inc.

—The Berenstain Bears' New Kitten. Berenstain, Stan, illus. 2007. (I Can Read Bks.). 32p. (J). 15.99 (***978-0-06-058356-9(8));*** pap. 3.99 (***978-0-06-058357-6(6)*** , Harper Trophy) HarperCollins Pubs.

—The Berenstain Bears' New Pup. Berenstain, Stan & Berenstain, Jan, illus. 2005. (Berenstain Bears Ser.). (Illus.). 32p. (J). (gr. k-3). 15.99 (978-0-06-058343-9(6)) HarperCollins Pubs.

—The Berenstain Bears' New Pup. 2005. (Berenstain Bears Ser.). (Illus.). 32p. (J). (gr. k-3). pap. 3.99 (978-0-06-058344-6(4)) HarperCollins Pubs.

—The Berenstain Bears' New Pup. Berenstain, Stan & Berenstain, Jan, illus. 2005. (Berenstain Bears Ser.). (Illus.). 32p. (J). (ps-3). lib. bdg. 11.19 (978-0-606-33614-7(1)) Tandem Library Bks.

—The Berenstain Bears Out West. Berenstain, Stan & Berenstain, Jan, illus. 2006. (Berenstain Bears Ser.). (Illus.). 32p. (J). 15.99 (978-0-06-058353-8(3)) HarperCollins Pubs.

—The Berenstain Bears Play Ball. l.t. ed. 1998. (Berenstain Bears Ser.). (Illus.). 48p. (J). (ps-3). pap. 10.95 (978-0-590-94732-9(X)) Scholastic, Inc.

—The Berenstain Bears Play T-Ball. Berenstain, Stan & Berenstain, Jan, illus. Berenstain, Michael, illus. 2005. (Berenstain Bears Ser.). 32p. (J). (gr. k-3). 15.99 (978-0-06-058337-8(1)); pap. 3.99 (978-0-06-058338-5(X)) HarperCollins Pubs.

—The Berenstain Bears Play T-Ball. 2005. (Berenstain Bears Ser.). (Illus.). 32p. (J). (ps-3). lib. bdg. 11.19 (978-0-606-33323-8(1)) Tandem Library Bks.

—The Berenstain Bears Red Roadster. Torgerson, Dell & Reyner, Mark, eds. 2000. 10p. (J). (ps). mass mkt. 9.99 (978-1-887327-36-7(3)) Ertl Co., Inc.

—The Berenstain Bears' Report Card Trouble. ed. 2004. (Berenstain Bears First Time Bks.). (J). (gr. k-3). spiral bd. (978-0-616-11095-9(2)); spiral bd. (978-0-616-11096-6(0)) Canadian National Institute for the Blind/Institut National Canadien pour les Aveugles.

—The Berenstain Bears' Report Card Trouble. 2002. (Berenstain Bears First Time Bks.). (Illus.). 32p. (J). (gr. k-3). pap. 3.99 (978-0-375-81127-2(3) , Random Hse. Bks. for Young Readers) Random Hse. Children's Bks.

—The Berenstain Bears' Report Card Trouble. 2002. (Berenstain Bears First Time Bks.). (J). (gr. k-3). lib. bdg. 3.80 (978-0-613-70585-1(8)) Tandem Library Bks.

—The Berenstain Bears Ride the Thunderbolt. 1998. (Berenstain Bears Ser.). (Illus.). 32p. (J). (ps-1). pap. 3.99 (978-0-679-88718-8(0) , Random Hse. Bks. for Young Readers) Random Hse. Children's Bks.

—The Berenstain Bears Ride the Thunderbolt. 1998. (Early Step into Reading Ser.). (J). (ps-k). 10.79 (978-0-606-13956-4(7)) Tandem Library Bks.

—The Berenstain Bears Save Christmas. Berenstain, Michael, illus. 2005. (Berenstain Bears Ser.). 48p. (J). (ps-3). pap. 6.99 (978-0-06-052672-6(6)) HarperCollins Pubs.

—The Berenstain Bears' Seashore Treasure. Berenstain, Stan, illus. 2005. (Illus.). 30p. (J). lib. bdg. 13.85 (***978-1-4242-0814-2(9)***) Fitzgerald Bks.

—The Berenstain Bears' Seashore Treasure. Berenstain, Stan & Berenstain, Jan, illus. 2005. (Berenstain Bears Ser.). (Illus.). 32p. (J). (gr. k-3). 15.99 (978-0-06-058340-8(1) , Harper Festival) HarperCollins Pubs.

—The Berenstain Bears' Seashore Treasure. 2005. (Berenstain Bears Ser.). (Illus.). 32p. (J). (ps). pap. 3.99 (978-0-06-058341-5(X) , Harper Festival) HarperCollins Pubs.

—The Berenstain Bears Think of Those in Need. 1999. (Berenstain Bears First Time Bks.). (Illus.). 32p. (J). (gr. k-3). pap. 3.99 (978-0-679-88957-1(4) , Random Hse. Bks. for Young Readers) Random Hse. Children's Bks.

—The Berenstain Bears Think of Those in Need. 1999. (Berenstain Bears First Time Bks.). (J). (ps-2). lib. bdg. 10.95 (978-0-613-16061-2(4)); (Illus.). 10.05 (978-0-606-20465-1(2)) Tandem Library Bks.

—The Berenstain Bears' Trouble at School. Berenstain, Stan & Berenstain, Jan, illus. 2002. (Berenstain Bears First Time Bks.). (Illus.). (J). 11.19 (978-0-7587-4349-7(1)) Book Wholesalers, Inc.

—The Berenstain Bears Visit the Dentist. Berenstain, Stan & Berenstain, Jan, illus. 2002. (Berenstain Bears First Time Bks.). (Illus.). (J). 11.19 (978-0-7587-4350-3(5)) Book Wholesalers, Inc.

—The Berenstain Bears We Like Kites. 2004. (Berenstain Bears Ser.). (Illus.). 32p. (J). (ps-1). pap. 3.99 (978-0-679-89231-1(1) , Random Hse. Bks. for Young Readers) Random Hse. Children's Bks.

—The Berenstain Bears We Like Kites. 2004. (Berenstain Bears Ser.). (J). (ps-2). lib. bdg. 11.80 (978-0-613-87779-4(9)) Tandem Library Bks.

—Big Book of the Berenstain Bears. 2007. (Illus.). 160p. (J). (gr. k-1). 10.99 (***978-0-375-84214-6(4)*** , Random Hse. Bks. for Young Readers) Random Hse. Children's Bks.

—The Big Honey Hunt. Berenstain, Stan & Berenstain, Jan, illus. 2002. (Berenstain Bears Beginner Bks.). (Illus.). (J). (gr. k-3). 16.70 (978-0-7587-0993-6(5)) Book Wholesalers, Inc.

—The Bike Lesson. Berenstain, Stan & Berenstain, Jan, illus. 2002. (Berenstain Bears Beginner Bks.). (Illus.). (J). (gr. k-3). 15.74 (978-0-7587-0998-1(6)) Book Wholesalers, Inc.

—The Birds, the Bees, & the Berenstain Bears. 2000. (Berenstain Bears First Time Bks.). (Illus.). 32p. (J). (gr. k-3). pap. 3.99 (978-0-679-88959-5(0) , Random Hse. Bks. for Young Readers) Random Hse. Children's Bks.

—The Birds, the Bees, & the Berenstain Bears. 1999. (Berenstain Bears First Time Bks.). (J). (gr. k-2). (978-0-679 88971-7(X)) Random Hse., Inc.

—The Birds, the Bees, & the Berenstain Bears. 2000. (Berenstain Bears First Time Bks.). (J). (gr. k-3). 10.05 (978-0-606-17523-4(7)); lib. bdg. 10.95 (978-0-613-21223-6(1)) Tandem Library Bks.

—The Haunted Lighthouse. 2001. (Berenstain Bears Ser.). (J). (gr. k-3). lib. bdg. 11.80 (978-0-613-33814-1(6)); (Illus.). 10.79 (978-0-606-21058-4(X)) Tandem Library Bks.

—Inside, Outside, Upside Down. 2000. (Berenstain Bears Bright & Early Bks.). (J). (ps-3). 7.99 (978-0-375-80253-9(3)) Random Hse., Inc.

—Los Osos Berenstain y Demasiada Fiesta. ed. 2004. Tr. of Berenstain Bears & Too Much Birthday. (SPA., Illus.). (J). (gr. k-3). spiral bd. (978-0-616-14610-1(8)) Canadian National Institute for the Blind/Institut National Canadien pour les Aveugles.

—Los Osos Scouts Berenstain y el Desastre Colosal. 1998. (Berenstain Bear Scouts Ser.).Tr. of Berenstain Bear Scouts & the Really Big Disaster. (SPA.). (J). (gr. 3-6). pap. 3.50 (978-0-590-94482-3(7) , Scholastic Paperbacks) Scholastic, Inc.

—The Runamuck Dog Show. 2001. (Berenstain Bears Ser.). (Illus.). (J). (gr. k-3). 10.79 (978-0-606-21059-1(8)) Tandem Library Bks.

—The Wrong Crowd. 2001. (Berenstain Bears Ser.). (Illus.). (J). (gr. k-3). (978-0-606-21060-7(1)) Tandem Library Bks.

Berenstain, Stan, et al. The Berenstain Bears Save Christmas. Berenstain, Stan et al, illus. 2003. (Berenstain Bears Ser.). (J). (gr. k-3). 129.90 (978-0-06-056995-2(6)) HarperCollins Pubs.

Bergren, Lisa Tawn. God Gave Us Christmas. Hohn, David, illus. 2006. 40p. (J). 9.99 (978-1-4000-7175-3(5) , WaterBrook Pr.) WaterBrook Pr.

—God Gave Us Two. Bryant, Laura J., illus. 2001. 40p. (J). 9.99 (978-1-57856-507-8(3) , WaterBrook Pr.) WaterBrook Pr.

—God Gave Us You. Bryant, Laura J., illus. 2000. 40p. (J). (ps-k). 10.99 (978-1-57856-323-4(2) , WaterBrook Pr.) WaterBrook Pr.

Berkner, Laurie. Victor Vito & Freddie Vasco. 2007. 40p. (J). pap. 5.99 (***978-0-439-91529-8(5)*** , Cartwheel Bks.) Scholastic, Inc.

Bernthal, Mark & Exclaim Entertainment Staff. Boz/Good Morning Boz. Jeffords, Brandon, illus. 2006. (BOZ#8482; Ser.). 14p. (J). 4.99 (978-0-310-71207-7(6)) Zondervan.

—Boz/Good Night Boz. Jeffords, Brandon, illus. 2006. (BOZ#8482; Ser.). 14p. (J). 4.99 (978-0-310-71206-0(8)) Zondervan.

—God Loves Your Nose. McKee, Darren, illus. 2006. (BOZ#8482; Ser.). 12p. (J). 5.99 (978-0-310-71152-0(5)) Zonderkidz.

Betancourt, Jeanne. Pony & the Bear. Bachem, Paul, illus. 1999. (Pony Pals Ser.: No. 23). 85p. (J). (gr. 2-5). pap. 3.99 (978-0-439-06489-7(9)) Scholastic, Inc.

—Pony & the Bear. 1999. (Pony Pals Ser.: No. 23). (J). (gr. 2-5). (978-0-606-19601-7(3)) Tandem Library Bks.

Betz, Adrienne. A Deal Is a Deal. Andriani, Vincent, illus. 1999. (Scholastic At-Home Phonics Reading Program Ser.: Vol. 33). 24p. (J). pap. (978-0-590-68782-9(4)) Scholastic, Inc.

Bieber, Hartmut. Busy Bear Around the House. 2003. (Loveable Busy Bear Is Back in Two New Adventures! Ser.). (Illus.). 14p. (J). 5.99 (978-1-59384-005-1(5)) Parklane Publishing.

—Busy Bear Celebrates Christmas. 2003. (Illus.). (J). 5.99 (978-1-59384-006-8(3)) Parklane Publishing.

—Busy Bear Goes to Kindergarten. 2004. (Illus.). 14p. (J). 5.99 (978-1-59384-049-5(7)) Parklane Publishing.

—Busy Bear Goes to the Beach. 2004. (Illus.). 14p. (J). 5.99 (978-1-59384-050-1(0)) Parklane Publishing.

Billings, David Joseph. Road Trip with Rabbit & Squash. Billings, David Joseph, illus. 2006. (Illus.). 48p. (J). per. (978-0-9789036-0-2(9)) Billings, David J.

Bishop, Gavin. Stay Awake, Bear! Bishop, Gavin, illus. 2000. (Illus.). 32p. (J). (ps-1). 16.99 (978-0-531-33249-8(7)); pap. 15.95 (978-0-531-30249-1(0)) Scholastic, Inc. (Orchard Bks.).

Bittner, Wolfgang. Wake up, Grizzly! 1999. (gr. k-3). lib. bdg. 15.25 (978-0-613-78764-2(1)) Tandem Library Bks.

Black Bear's Tree. 2002. (Wild Heritage Collection Mini Bks.). (Illus.). 32p. (J). (978-1-59069-159-5(8) , H3003) Studio Mouse LLC.

Blackaby, Susan. Rembrandt's Hat. DePalma, Mary Newell, illus. 2002. 32p. (J). (gr. k-3). 15.00 (978-0-618-11452-8(1)) Houghton Mifflin Co. Trade & Reference Div.

Blackman, Malorie. Sinclair, Wonder Bear. Allwright, Deborah, illus. 2005. (Blue Go Bananas Ser.). 48p. (J). pap. (978-0-7787-2653-1(3)) Crabtree Publishing Co.

Blackstone, Stella. Bear about Town. Harter, Debbie, illus. 24p. (J). (ps-k). 2001. bds. 6.99 (978-1-84148-373-3(7)); 2001. 5.99 (978-1-84148-152-4(1)); 2000. 13.95 (978-1-902283-57-9(0)); 2000. reprint ed. pap. 5.99 (978-1-902283-69-2(4)) Barefoot Bks., Inc.

—Bear about Town. 2001. (J). 12.79 (978-0-606-20027-1(4)) Tandem Library Bks.

—Bear at Home. Harter, Debbie, illus. 24p. (J). 2006. pap. 5.99 (978-1-84148-701-4(5)); 2002. bds. 6.99 (978-1-84148-925-4(5)); 2001. 14.99 (978-1-84148-436-5(9)) Barefoot Bks., Inc.

—Bear in a Square. Harter, Debbie, illus. 2000. 24p. (J). (ps-1). pap. 5.99 (978-1-84148-120-3(3)); reprint ed. bds. 6.99 (978-1-84148-287-3(0)) Barefoot Bks., Inc.

—Bear in a Square. 2000. (J). 12.79 (978-0-606-19702-1(8)); lib. bdg. 14.15 (978-0-613-23133-6(3)) Tandem Library Bks.

—Bear in Sunshine. Harter, Debbie, illus. 24p. (J). pap. 5.99 (978-1-84148-700-7(7)); 2002. bds. 6.99 (978-1-84148-923-0(9)); 2001. 14.99 (978-1-84148-321-4(4)) Barefoot Bks., Inc.

—Bear on a Bike. Harter, Debbie, illus. (J). (ps-k). 2001. 24p. bds. 6.99 (978-1-84148-375-7(3)); 2000. 32p. pap. 5.99 (978-1-84148-121-0(1)); 1999. 32p. 13.95 (978-1-901223-49-1(3)) Barefoot Bks., Inc.

—Bear on a Bike. 2000. (J). 12.79 (978-0-606-19701-4(X)) Tandem Library Bks.

—Bear's Busy Family. Harter, Debbie, illus. 2000. (Bear Ser.). 24p. (J). (ps-k). 13.95 (978-1-902283-90-6(2)) Barefoot Bks., Inc.

—Bear's Busy Family. 1999. (Illus.). 24p. (J). (978-1-902283-89-0(9)) Barefoot Bks., Inc.

—Bear's Busy Family. Harter, Debbie, illus. 24p. (J). (ps-1). reprint ed. 2001. pap. 5.99 (978-1-84148-153-1(X)); 2000. bds. 6.99 (978-1-84148-391-7(5)) Barefoot Bks., Inc.

—Bear's Busy Family. 2000. (ps-2). lib. bdg. 14.15 (978-0-613-33672-7(0)) Tandem Library Bks.

—Bear's Busy Family. Harter, Debbie, illus. 2000. (J). 12.79 (978-0-606-19748-9(6)) Tandem Library Bks.

—La Familia Activa de Oso. 2003. (SPA.). (gr. k-3). lib. bdg. 14.15 (978-0-613-65691-7(1)) Tandem Library Bks.

—La Familia activa de Oso (Bear's Busy Family) Sarfatti, Esther, tr. Harter, Debbie, illus. 2003. (Bear Ser.). (SPA.). 24p. (J). 5.99 (978-1-84148-777-9(5)) Barefoot Bks., Inc.

—Oso Bajo el Sol. 2003. (SPA.). (gr. k-3). lib. bdg. 14.15 (978-0-613-65704-4(7)) Tandem Library Bks.

—Oso bajo el sol (Bear in Sunshine) Sarfatti, Esther, tr. Harter, Debbie, illus. 2003. (Bear Ser.). (SPA.). 24p. (J). 5.99 (978-1-84148-778-6(3)) Barefoot Bks., Inc.

—Oso en Bicicleta. 2003. (SPA.). (gr. k-3). lib. bdg. 14.15 (978-0-613-65705-1(5)) Tandem Library Bks.

—Oso en bicicleta (Bear on a Bike) Sarfatti, Esther, tr. Harter, Debbie, illus. 2003. (Bear Ser.). (SPA.). 32p. (J). 5.99 (978-1-84148-775-5(9)) Barefoot Bks., Inc.

—Oso en Casa. 2003. (SPA.). (gr. k-3). lib. bdg. 14.15 (978-0-613-65706-8(3)) Tandem Library Bks.

—Oso en casa (Bear at Home) Sarfatti, Esther, tr. Harter, Debbie, illus. 2003. (Bear Ser.). (SPA.). 24p. (J). 5.99 (978-1-84148-779-3(1)) Barefoot Bks., Inc.

—Oso en la Ciudad. 2003. (gr. k-3). lib. bdg. 14.15 (978-0-613-65707-5(1)) Tandem Library Bks.

—Oso en la ciudad (Bear About Town) Sarfatti, Esther, tr. Harter, Debbie, illus. 2003. (Bear Ser.). (SPA.). 24p. (J). 5.99 (978-1-84148-776-2(7)) Barefoot Bks., Inc.

—Oso en un Cuadrado. 2003. (SPA.). (gr. k-3). lib. bdg. 14.15 (978-0-613-65708-2(X)) Tandem Library Bks.

—Oso en un cuadrado (Bear in a Square) Sarfatti, Esther, tr. Harter, Debbie, illus. 2003. (Bear Ser.). (SPA.). 24p. (J). 5.99 (978-1-84148-774-8(0)) Barefoot Bks., Inc.

Bland, Steve. Bedtime Bear. 2001. (Phone Friends Ser.). (Illus.). 12p. (J). bds. 4.95 (978-0-7641-5380-8(3)) Barron's Educational Series, Inc.

Bloom, Suzanne. Splendid Friend Indeed Big BK. 2007. (Illus.). 32p. pap. 24.95 (***978-1-59078-532-4(0)***) Boyds Mills Pr.

—Treasure. 2007. (Illus.). 32p. (J). (ps-1). 15.95 (***978-1-59078-457-0(X)***) Boyds Mills Pr.

Bloom, Suzanne, illus. A Splendid Friend, Indeed. 2007. 32p. (J). 15.95 (978-1-59078-286-6(0)) Boyds Mills Pr.

Blueberries for Sal. 2004. (J). 24.95 incl. audio (978-0-89719-860-8(3)); pap. 18.95 incl. audio compact disk (978-1-55592-799-8(8)); pap. 18.95 incl. audio compact disk (978-1-55592-767-7(X)); pap. 38.75 incl. audio compact disk (978-1-55592-816-2(1)); pap. 38.75 incl. audio compact disk (978-1-55592-782-0(3)) Weston Woods Studios, Inc.

Boase, Wendy. Los Tres Osos. Bull, Carolyn, illus. (Primeros Cuentos Ser.). (SPA.). 28p. (J). (gr. k-3). pap. 7.95 (978-1-56014-475-5(0)) Santillana USA Publishing Co., Inc.

Bodnar, Judit Z. Tale of a Tail. Sandford, John B., illus. 1998. 40p. (J). (ps-3). 15.95 (978-0-688-12174-7(8)); 15.89 (978-0-688-12175-4(6)) HarperCollins Pubs.

Boehm, Arlene P. Jack in Search of Art. Boehm, Arlene P., illus. (Illus.). 32p. (ps-3). 2001. pap. 7.95 (978-1-57098-234-7(1)); 1998. 16.95 (978-1-57098-244-6(9)) Rinehart, Roberts Pubs.

Boelts, Maribeth. Looking for Sleepy. Pons, Bernadette, illus. 2004. 24p. (J). (ps-1). 14.95 (978-0-8075-0447-5(5)) Whitman, Albert & Co.

Bolte, Mary. Brown Bear, Brown Bear, What Do You See? Palinay, Agi & Wall, Jethro, illus. 1999. (Literature Units Ser.). 48p. pap., tchr. ed. 7.99 (978-1-57690-625-5(6) , TCA2625) Teacher Created Materials, Inc.

Bombay, Cal & Sharpe, Margaret. Slave, Brave & Free, 10 bks. 2003. 256p. (J). per. 12.99 (978-1-929125-41-8(0) , Multnomah) WaterBrook Pr.

Bond, Michael. A Bear Called Paddington. Fortnum, Peggy, illus. rev. ed. 1998. (Paddington Ser.). (SPA.). 144p. (J). (gr. 4-6). 15.00 (978-0-395-92951-3(2)) Houghton Mifflin Co. Trade & Reference Div.

—My Scrapbook. Alley, R. W., illus. 1999. (Paddington Ser.). 20p. (J). (ps-3). 12.95 (978-0-694-00886-5(9) , Harper Festival) HarperCollins Pubs.

—Paddington at Large. Fortnum, Peggy, illus. rev. ed. 2002. (Paddington Bear Ser.). 144p. (J). (gr. 4-6). pap. 4.95 (978-0-618-19678-4(1)) Houghton Mifflin Co. Trade & Reference Div.

—Paddington at Work. Fortnum, Peggy, illus. 144p. (J). (gr. 4-6). 2003. pap. 4.95 (978-0-618-31105-7(X)); 2001. 15.00 (978-0-618-11577-8(3)) Houghton Mifflin Co. Trade & Reference Div.

—Paddington at Work. 2003. (gr. 3-6). lib. bdg. 12.95 (978-0-613-62980-5(9)) Tandem Library Bks.

—Paddington Bear. Alley, R. W., illus. rev. ed. 1998. (Paddington Ser.). 40p. (J). (ps-3). 15.99 (978-0-06-027854-0(4)) HarperCollins Pubs.

—Paddington Bear All Day. braille ed. 2004. (Illus.). (J). (gr. 1). spiral bd., bds. (978-0-616-01860-6(6)) Canadian National Institute for the Blind/Institut National Canadien pour les Aveugles.

—Paddington Bear All Day. Alley, R. W., illus. 1998. (Paddington Ser.). 7p. (J). (ps up). 5.95 (978-0-694-00893-3(1) , Harper Festival) HarperCollins Pubs.

—Paddington Bear All Day. Alley, R. W., illus. 2004. (VIE, GUJ, SOM, CHI & ARA.). 12p. (J). (978-1-85269-443-2(2)); (978-1-85269-444-9(0)); (978-1-85269-445-6(9)); (978-1-85269-456-2(4)); (978-1-85269-442-5(4)) Mantra Publishing, Ltd.

—Paddington Bear & the Busy Bee Carnival. Alley, R. W., illus. 1998. (Paddington Ser.). 40p. (J). (ps-3). 13.95 (978-0-06-027765-9(3)) HarperCollins Pubs.

—Paddington Bear & the Busy Bee Carnival. 2000. (Paddington Ser.). (J). (ps-3). (978-0-606-18710-7(3)) Tandem Library Bks.

—Paddington Bear & the Christmas Surprise. 1999. (ps-2). lib. bdg. 14.10 (978-0-613-22917-3(7)); (J). (978-0-606-17305-6(6)) Tandem Library Bks.

—Paddington Bear at the Circus. Alley, R. W., illus. 2000. (Paddington Ser.). 40p. (J). (ps-3). 15.99 (978-0-06-028213-4(4)) HarperCollins Pubs.

—Paddington Bear Board Book & Rattle Paddington Bear All Day. Alley, R. W., illus. 1999. (Paddington Bear Ser.). 14p. (J). (ps up). 15.95 (978-0-694-00887-2(7) , Harper Festival) HarperCollins Pubs.

—Paddington Bear Goes to Market. Alley, R. W., illus. 1998. (Paddington Ser.). 7p. (J). (ps up). 5.95 (978-0-694-00891-9(5) , Harper Festival) HarperCollins Pubs.

—Paddington Bear Goes to Market. Alley, R. W., illus. 2004. (VIE, GUJ, SOM, CHI & ARA.). 12p. (J). (978-1-85269-455-5(6)); (978-1-85269-451-7(3)) Mantra Publishing, Ltd.

—Paddington Bear in the Garden. Alley, R. W., illus. 2002. (Paddington Bear Ser.). 40p. (J). (ps-3). 15.99 (978-0-06-029696-4(8)) HarperCollins Pubs.

—Paddington Goes to Town. Fortnum, Peggy, illus. 144p. (J). (gr. 4-6). 2003. pap. 4.95 (978-0-618-31104-0(1)); 2001. 15.00 (978-0-618-08307-7(3)) Houghton Mifflin Co. Trade & Reference Div.

—Paddington Goes to Town. 2001. (gr. 3-6). lib. bdg. 12.95 (978-0-613-62981-2(7)) Tandem Library Bks.

—Paddington Helps Out. Fortnum, Peggy, illus. rev. ed. (Paddington Bear Ser.). 144p. (J). (gr. 4-6). 2002. pap. 4.95 (978-0-618-19679-1(X)); 1999. 15.00 (978-0-395-96037-0(1)) Houghton Mifflin Co. Trade & Reference Div.

—Paddington on Top. Fortnum, Peggy, illus. rev. ed. 2002. (Paddington Bear Ser.). 144p. (J). (gr. 4-6). pap. 4.95 (978-0-618-25072-1(7)) Houghton Mifflin Co. Trade & Reference Div.

—Paddington Takes the Test. Fortnum, Peggy, illus. 2002. (Paddington Bear Ser.). 144p. (J). (gr. 4-6). 15.00 (978-0-618-18384-5(1)) Houghton Mifflin Co. Trade & Reference Div.

—Paddington Takes to TV. Fortnum, Peggy, illus. rev. ed. (Paddington Bear Ser.). 144p. (J). (gr. 4-6). 2002. pap. 4.95 (978-0-618-25071-4(9)); 2000. 15.00 (978-0-395-91370-3(5)) Houghton Mifflin Co. Trade & Reference Div.

—Paddington Treasury. Fortnum, Peggy & Nuttall-Smith, Caroline, illus. 1999. (Paddington Ser.). 384p. (J). (gr. 4-6). 29.95 (978-0-395-90507-4(9)) Houghton Mifflin Co. Trade & Reference Div.

—Paddington's First Word Book. Lobban, John, illus. 1998. (Paddington Ser.). (J). (ps-3). (978-0-606-13692-1(4)) Tandem Library Bks.

Bond, Michael & Jankel, Karen. Paddington Bear Goes to the Hospital. Alley, R. W., illus. 2001. (Paddington Ser.). 40p. (J). (ps-3). 12.95 (978-0-694-01563-4(6)) HarperCollins Pubs.

Boniface, William. The Treasure Hunter. Harris, Jim, illus. 1998. 32p. (J). 15.99 (978-0-939251-97-1(3)) Accord Publishing, Ltd.

—The Treasure Hunter. Harris, Jim, illus. 2007. 28p. bds. 9.99 (***978-1-57939-354-0(3)***) Andrews McMeel Publishing.

Bonnell, Kris. Where Is a Bear? 2007. (J). 3.95 (***978-1-933727-63-9(2)***) Reading Reading Bks., LLC.

Book Buddy: Polar Bear with Story Book. Orig. Title: Child's Play. (Illus.). 10p. (J). (ps-3). reprint ed. (978-1-881469-48-3(4)) Safari, Ltd.

Book Company Staff. Catch That Hat! 2002. (Magical World of Teddies Ser.). 14p. (J). bds. 12.95 (978-1-74047-162-6(8)) Book Co. Publishing Pty, Ltd., The AUS. *Dist:* Penton Overseas, Inc.

—Teddy Mini Box Set. 2002. (Pop-up Books Mini Ser.). 14p. (J). 15.95 (978-1-74047-209-8(8)) Book Co. Publishing Pty, Ltd., The AUS. *Dist:* Penton Overseas, Inc.

Books, Fernleigh. Snow Bear. 2007. 32p. (J). pap. 4.99 (***978-0-439-92533-4(9)*** , Cartwheel Bks.) Scholastic, Inc.

Bookworks Staff. Prayertime Bear. 2002. (Baby Blessings Ser.). 6p. 12.99 (978-0-7847-1360-0(X) , 04021) Standard Publishing.

Boucles d'Or et les Trois Ours.Tr. of Goldilocks & the Three Bears. (FRE.). 48p. pap. 12.95 incl. audio compact disk (978-2-89558-061-4(8)) Coffragants CAN. *Dist:* Penton Overseas, Inc.

Bour, Daniele. Petit ours brun aime Noel. pap. 12.95 (978-2-227-70915-7(4)) Bayard Editions FRA. *Dist:* Distribooks, Inc.

—Petit ours brun fait un Cauche. pap. 12.95 (978-2-227-70921-8(9)) Bayard Editions FRA. *Dist:* Distribooks, Inc.

—Petit ours brun repond au Teleph. pap. 12.95 (978-2-227-74805-7(2)) Bayard Editions FRA. *Dist:* Distribooks, Inc.

Bourgeois, Paulette & Clark, Brenda. Franklin Has a Sleepover. 1999. (Franklin Ser.). (Illus.). 168p. (J). (ps-3). (978-1-55074-664-8(2)) Kids Can Pr., Ltd.

Bourgeois, Paulette & Clark, Brenda, creators. Franklin & the Baby. 1999. (Illus.). (J). (978-0-439-12065-4(9)) Scholastic, Inc.

Bourne, C. L. Sam the Big Blue Bear, Vol. 1. Bourne, C. L., illus. Date not set. (Illus.). 24p. (J). (gr. k-4). pap. (978-0-9651281-4-8(8)) Beach Front Bks.

Boyle, Alison. Twinkle, Twinkle, Little Star. Pichon, Liz, illus. 2000. (Finger Puppet Bks.). 16p. (J). (ps-k). 10.95 (978-1-86233-111-2(1)) Sterling Publishing Co., Inc.

Bramble Bear; Can I Help. 2006. (Alphabet & Counting Ser.). (J). per. 3.99 (978-1-934004-10-4(3)) Byeway Bks.

Bramble Bear; I Wish I Was... 2006. (J). per. 3.99 (978-1-934004-11-1(1)) Byeway Bks.

Bramble Bear; Pretends to Be... 2006. (J). per. 3.99 (978-1-934004-13-5(8)) Byeway Bks.

Bramble bear; the Missing Necklace. 2006. (J). per. 3.99 (978-1-934004-12-8(X)) Byeway Bks.

Brandon, Taylor. The Bear Who Couldn't Hibernate! (Sleep) Sandow, Paris, illus. 1999. (World's Greatest Children's Bks.). 48p. (J). (gr. k-5). 14.99 (978-1-889945-57-6(9)) Imperius.

Brandon, Wendy. Cinderbear: (Imagination in a Box) Winter, Janet, illus. 2004. 10p. (J). bds. 17.99 (978-1-883043-50-6(6) , 6020) Straight Edge Pr., The.

Brandt-Taylor, Diane. The Bunny, the Bear, the Bug & the Bee. Brandt, Michael, illus. 2005. (J). cd-rom 9.88 (978-0-9773236-0-9(9)) TaySysCo Publishing.

Braun, Sebastien. I Love My Daddy. Braun, Sebastien, illus. 2004. (Illus.). 32p. (J). (ps-2). 12.99 (978-0-06-054311-2(6)) HarperCollins Pubs.

Bravery Soup. 2002. (Albert Whitman Prairie Bks.). (Illus.). 32p. (J). (ps-2). pap. 6.95 (978-0-8075-0871-8(3)) Whitman, Albert & Co.

Braybrooks, Ann. Hunny, Funny, Sunny Day. 1999. (Disney Ser.). 24p. (ps-3). pap. 3.29 (978-0-307-13148-5(3) , Golden Bks.) Random Hse. Children's Bks.

—Pooh Bedtime Stories: Two Tigger Tales. 2000. (Disney Ser.: Vol. 1). (Illus.). 24p. (J). (ps-3). pap. 3.29 (978-0-307-13196-6(3) , Golden Bks.) Random Hse. Children's Bks.

—Pooh's Best Friend Book & Friendship Bracelet. Jones, Tim, illus. 1998. (Disney's Pooh Ser.). 32p. (J). (gr. 1-4). pap. 7.95 (978-0-7868-3152-4(9)) Disney Pr.

—Tiggers Hate to Lose. 1999. (Winnie the Pooh First Readers Ser.: No. 8). (Illus.). 40p. (J). (gr. k-3). pap. 3.99 (978-0-7868-4266-7(0)) Disney Pr.

Brennan, Martin. Three Lessons for Astair the Bear. Huntington, Amy, illus. 2007. 40p. (J). 18.95 (***978-1-58726-435-1(8)*** , Mitten Pr.) Ann Arbor Media Group, LLC.

Brett, Jan. The Three Snow Bears. Brett, Jan, illus. 2007. 32p. (J). (ps-3). 16.99 (***978-0-399-24792-7(0)*** , Putnam Juvenile) Penguin Group (USA) Inc.

Brian, Janeen. Where Does Thursday Go? King, Stephen Michael, illus. 2002. 32p. (J). (gr. k-3). 14.00 (978-0-618-21264-4(7) , Clarion Bks.) Houghton Mifflin Co. Trade & Reference Div.

Bright, J. E. Care Bears: What Makes You Happy? Stein, David, illus. 2003. (Care Bears 8x8 Ser.). 24p. (J). (ps-1). pap. 3.50 (978-0-439-45543-5(X)) Scholastic, Inc.

—Care Bears: What Makes You Happy? 2003. (ps-2). lib. bdg. 11.25 (978-0-613-72172-1(1)) Tandem Library Bks.

Brimner, Larry Dane. Country Bear's Good Neighbor. 2003. (Illus.). 32p. (J). (ps up). pap. 9.95 (978-1-56397-786-2(9)) Boyds Mills Pr.

—Country Bear's Good Neighbor. 2001. (ps-2). lib. bdg. 16.40 (978-0-613-58407-4(4)) Tandem Library Bks.

—Country Bear's Surprise. Cooncell, Ruth T., illus. 2003. 32p. (J). (ps up). pap. 7.95 (978-1-56397-674-2(9)) Boyds Mills Pr.

Broekstra, Lorette. Baby Bbear Goes to the Farm. 2004. (Baby-Bear Ser.). (Illus.). 32p. (J). 5.99 (978-1-85854-488-5(2)) Brimax Books Ltd. GBR. *Dist:* Byeway Bks.

—Baby Bear Goes Camping. 2004. (Baby Bear Ser.). (Illus.). 32p. (J). 5.99 (978-1-85854-408-3(4)) Brimax Books Ltd. GBR. *Dist:* Byeway Bks.

Brook, Jasmine. Top to Tail Bear. 1998. (Illus.). 12p. (J). (ps). 7.95 (978-0-7641-5072-2(3)) Barron's Educational Series, Inc.

Brooke, Samantha. Oopsy Does It. 2007. (Care Bears 8x8 Ser.). 24p. (J). pap. 3.99 (***978-0-439-02676-5(8)***) Scholastic, Inc.

Brooks, Erik. The Practically Perfect Pajamas. Brooks, Erik, illus. 2000. (Illus.). 40p. (J). (ps-3). 16.95 (978-1-890817-22-0(8)) Winslow Pr.

Broutin & Stehr. Baldomero Va A la Escuela. (SPA.). 26p. (978-84-95150-47-9(6)) Corimbo, Editorial S.L.

Brown Bear Cub. 2002. (Baby Animals Ser.). (Illus.). (978-1-59069-058-1(3) , 1-1005) Studio Mouse LLC.

Brown, Margaret. Little Fur Family. Williams, Garth, illus. 2005. 32p. (J). (ps-1). 6.99 (978-0-06-075960-5(7) , Harper Festival) HarperCollins Pubs.

Brown, Margaret Wise. Goodnight Bear. 2006. 24p. 12.99 (978-1-4037-2704-6(X)); 12p. 5.99 (978-1-4037-2706-0(6)) Dalmatian Pr.

—Love Songs of the Little Bear. 2020. (Illus.). 32p. (J). pap. 4.99 (978-0-7868-1361-2(X)) Hyperion Paperbacks for Children.

Browne, Anthony. Bear Goes to Town. (Illus.). 32p. (J). 17.95 (978-0-241-10817-8(9) , Hamilton, Hamish) Penguin Bks., Ltd. GBR. *Dist:* Trafalgar Square Publishing.

Bruchac, Joseph. Bearwalker. Comport, Sally Wern, illus. 2007. 224p. (J). (gr. 5-8). 15.99 (***978-0-06-112309-2(9)***); lib. bdg. 16.89 (***978-0-06-112311-5(0)***) HarperCollins Pubs.

Bruhac, Joseph. How Chipmunk Got His Stripes. 2001. (gr. k-3). lib. bdg. 15.30 (978-0-613-61631-7(6)) Tandem Library Bks.

Bruna, Dick. Boris & Barbara. 2004. (Illus.). 24p. (J). 7.99 (978-1-59226-027-0(6)) Big Tent Entertainment, Inc.

Brundage, Frances, illus. The Three Bears. 2004. 16p. (J). (ps-3). 9.95 (978-1-883211-94-3(8)) Laughing Elephant.

Bryan, Sean. A Bear & His Boy. Murphy, Tom, illus. rev. ed. 2007. 32p. (J). (ps-1). 14.99 (***978-1-55970-838-8(7)***) Arcade Publishing, Inc.

Buchholz, Quint. Sleep Well, Little Bear. 2004. (Illus.). pap. (978-0-374-46709-8(9)) Farrar, Straus & Giroux.

Buddy Bears Feelings. 2000. (J). (978-1-931312-21-9(4)) SoftPlay, Inc.

Buddy Bear's Feelings. 2000. (Illus.). (J). (978-1-56156-832-1(5)) Kidsbooks, Inc.

Buehner, Caralyn & Buehner, Mark. Goldilocks & the Three Bears. 2007. (Illus.). 32p. (J). (ps). 16.99 (978-0-8037-2939-1(1) , Dial) Penguin Group (USA) Inc.

Bugsilocks & the Three Bears. 1999. (McGraw-Hill Junior Academic Ser.). (Illus.). 16p. (J). (gr. k-2). pap. 3.99 (978-1-57768-215-8(7)) School Specialty Publishing.

Buller, Jon. Growling Grizzly. 2002. (gr. k-3). lib. bdg. 11.80 (978-0-613-72092-2(X)) Tandem Library Bks.

Bunting, Eve. Little Bear's Little Boat. Carpenter, Nancy, illus. 2003. 32p. (J). (gr. k-ps). tchr. ed. 12.00 (978-0-395-97462-9(3) , Clarion Bks.) Houghton Mifflin Co. Trade & Reference Div.

Burchett, Loni R. Bear & Katie in a Day at Nestlenook Farm. l.t. ed. 2004. (Illus.). 76p. (J). per. 11.95 (978-0-9742815-1-3(4)) Black Lab Publishing LLC.

—Bear & Katie in a Day with Friends, Vol. 3. l.t. ed. 2005. (Illus.). 68p. (J). per. 11.95 (978-0-9742815-2-0(2) , bk003) Black Lab Publishing LLC.

—Bear & Katie in the Great Searsport Caper. l.t. ed. 2004. (Illus.). 81p. (J). pap. 12.95 (978-0-9742815-0-6(6)) Black Lab Publishing LLC.

Burfoot, Ella. Bear & Me. 2007. (Illus.). 32p. (J). (ps-k). pap. 9.95 (978-1-84270-485-1(0)) Andersen GBR. *Dist:* Independent Pubs. Group.

Burgess, Thornton W. The Adventures of Buster Bear. (J). 19.95 (978-0-8488-0354-4(X)) Amereon LTD.

—Big Book of Animal Stories. 2001. (Illus.). 208p. (J). (gr. 4-7). pap. 7.95 (978-0-486-41980-0(0)) Dover Pubns., Inc.

—Buster Bear's Twins. (J). 19.95 (978-0-8488-0396-4(5)) Amereon LTD.

—Buster Bear's Twins. 1999. (Dover Children's Thrift Classics Ser.). 80p. (J). (gr. 3-6). pap. 1.50 (978-0-486-40790-6(X)) Dover Pubns., Inc.

Burke, David. Goldilocks (English to German - Level 2) Learn GERMAN Through Fairy Tales. 2007. (Learn German Through Fairy Tales Ser.). (ENG & GER., Illus.). (J). per. 14.95 incl. audio compact disk (*978-1-891888-83-0(8)) Slangman Publishing.

—Goldilocks (English to Italian - Level 2) Learn ITALIAN Through Fairy Tales. 2007. (Learn Italian Through Fairy Tales Ser.). (ENG & ITA., Illus.). (J). per. 14.95 incl. audio compact disk (*978-1-891888-82-3(X)) Slangman Publishing.

—Goldilocks (English to Spanish - Level 2) Learn SPANISH Through Fairy Tales. 2007. (Learn Spanish Through Fairy Tales Ser.). (ENG & SPA., Illus.). (J). per. 14.95 incl. audio compact disk (*978-1-891888-80-9(3)) Slangman Publishing.

Burke, David, adapted by. GOLDILOCKS (English to Chinese - Level 2) Learn MANDARIN CHINESE Through Fairy Tales. 2007. (Learn Chinese Through Fairy Tales Ser.). (ENG & CHI., Illus.). (J). per. 14.95 incl. audio compact disk (*978-1-891888-85-4(4)) Slangman Publishing.

—Goldilocks (English to French - Level 2) Learn FRENCH Through Fairy Tales. 2007. (Learn French Through Fairy Tales Ser.). (ENG & FRE., Illus.). (J). per. 14.95 incl. audio compact disk (*978-1-891888-81-6(1)) Slangman Publishing.

Bushey, Jeanne. The Polar Bear's Gift. Krykorka, Vladyana Langer, illus. 2004. (Northern Lights Books for Children Ser.). 32p. (J). (ps-3). pap. 16.95 (978-0-88995-220-1(5)) Red Deer Pr. CAN. *Dist:* Fitzhenry & Whiteside, Ltd.

Busy Bear Book Set 800938, 4 vols. 2005. (J). bds. (978-1-59794-097-9(6)) Environments, Inc.

Butler, Dorothy. My Brown Bear Barney. 2000. pap. 4.95 (978-0-688-17723-2(9)) HarperCollins Pubs.

Butler, M. Christina. Snow Friends. Macnaughton, Tina, illus. 2005. 28p. (J). (ps-2). 16.00 (978-1-56148-485-0(7)) Good Bks.

—Who's Been Eating My Porridge? Howarth, Daniel, illus. 2004. 32p. (J). (ps). tchr. ed. 15.95 (978-1-58925-040-6(0) , tiger tales) ME Media LLC.

Buzzati, Dino & Lobb, Frances. The Bears' Famous Invasion of Sicily. 2003. (New York Review Children's Collection). (Illus.). 152p. (J). 18.95 (978-1-59017-076-2(8) , NYR Children's Collection) New York Review of Bks., Inc., The.

Buzzati, Dino & Snicket, Lemony. The Bears' Famous Invasion of Sicily. Buzzati, Dino, illus. 2005. (Illus.). 192p. (J). pap. 5.99 (978-0-06-072608-9(3)) HarperCollins Pubs.

Buzzy Bear: Shaky Sound Book. 2003. (J). (978-1-59292-019-8(5)) SoftPlay, Inc.

Cabrera, Jane. Bear's Good Night. Cabrera, Jane, illus. 2002. (J). (gr. k-k). (Illus.). 12p. bds. 4.99 (978-0-7636-1796-7(2)); bds. 4.99 Candlewick Pr.

Caffrey-Kira, Albina. The Bear Who Loves Apples. 2006. 25.00 (978-0-8059-9128-4(X)) Dorrance Publishing Co., Inc.

Callahan, Cornelius P. The Ringbear. Verrill, Chad, illus. 2001. 36p. (J). (gr. 1-6). 14.95 (978-0-9658769-2-6(6)) Sextant Pr., Inc.

Callahan, Sean. The Bear Hug. Bryant, Laura, illus. 2006. 24p. (J). 15.95 (978-0-8075-0596-0(X)) Whitman, Albert & Co.

Candlewick. My Little Bear Library. 2004. (J). 4.50 (978-0-7636-2808-6(5)) Candlewick Pr.

Candlewick Press Staff. Bordrs Little Bear Stories. 2001. (J). 4.00 (978-0-7636-1754-7(7)) Candlewick Pr.

Capriola, Arlene & Swenson, Rigmor. The Three Bears. Mastry, Cherisse, ed. Burns, Kathy, illus. 1998. (Once upon a Time Ser.). (J). (gr. k-2). pap., wbk. ed. 12.95 incl. audio (978-1-57022-177-4(4)) ECS Learning Systems, Inc.

Capucilli, Alyssa Satin. Bear Hugs. Ishii, Jim, illus. 2000. (Road to Reading Ser.). 32p. (J). (ps-1). pap. 3.99 (978-0-307-26113-7(1) , Random Hse. Bks. for Young Readers) Random Hse. Children's Bks.

—Bear Hugs. Ishi, Jim, illus. 2000. (J). (ps-ps). lib. bdg. 11.80 (978-0-613-32316-1(5)) Tandem Library Bks.

—Bear Hugs. 2000. (J). 10.79 (978-0-606-18921-7(1)) Tandem Library Bks.

Carle, Eric. Ours Blanc Dis Moi. pap. 15.95 (978-2-87142-190-0(0)) Mijade Editions BEL. *Dist:* Distribooks, Inc.

Carlstrom, Nancy White. Climb the Family Tree, Jesse Bear! Degen, Bruce, illus. 2004. (Jesse Bear Ser.). 32p. (J). 15.95 (978-0-689-80701-5(5)) Simon & Schuster Children's Publishing.

—Guess Who's Coming, Jesse Bear. Degen, Bruce, illus. 2002. (Jesse Bear Ser.). 32p. (J). 6.99 (978-0-689-84820-9(X) , Aladdin) Simon & Schuster Children's Publishing.

—Guess Who's Coming, Jesse Bear. 2002. (ps-2). lib. bdg. 15.30 (978-0-613-45053-9(1)) Tandem Library Bks.

—Happy Birthday, Jesse Bear! 2000. (Illus.). (J). 13.79 (978-0-606-17922-5(4)) Tandem Library Bks.

—Jesse Bear, What Will You Wear? braille ed. 2004. (Illus.). (J). (gr. 1). spiral bd., bds. (978-0-616-01861-3(4)) Canadian National Institute for the Blind/Institut National Canadien pour les Aveugles.

—Jesse Bear, What Will You Wear? Degen, Bruce, illus. 2nd ed. 2005. (Stories to Go! Ser.). (J). 32p. 4.99 (978-1-4169-0834-0(X)); (*978-1-4156-3022-8(4)) Simon & Schuster Children's Publishing. (Aladdin).

—Let's Count It Out Jesse Bear. 2001. (Illus.). (J). (978-0-606-20763-8(5)) Tandem Library Bks.

—What a Scare. Degen, Bruce, illus. 2002. (Jesse Bear Ser.). 32p. (J). 6.99 (978-0-689-85190-2(1) , Aladdin) Simon & Schuster Children's Publishing.

—What a Scare, Jesse Bear. 2002. (ps-2). lib. bdg. 15.30 (978-0-613-90790-3(6)) Tandem Library Bks.

—Where Is Christmas, Jesse Bear? 2003. (ps-2). lib. bdg. 15.30 (978-0-613-88993-3(2)) Tandem Library Bks.

Carrick, Carol. The Polar Bears Are Hungry. ed. 2004. (Illus.). (J). (ps-3). spiral bd. (978-0-616-14567-8(5)) Canadian National Institute for the Blind/Institut National Canadien pour les Aveugles.

—The Polar Bears Are Hungry. Carrick, Paul, illus. 2002. 32p. (J). (gr. k-3). tchr. ed. 14.00 (978-0-618-15962-8(2) , Clarion Bks.) Houghton Mifflin Co. Trade & Reference Div.

Castle, Caroline. The Big Fuzzy. 2007. (J). lib. bdg. 16.95 (*978-1-59566-368-9(1)) QEB Publishing Inc.

Catalano, Dominic. Santa & the Three Bears. Catalano, Dominic, illus. 2001. (Illus.). 32p. (YA). (gr. k-2). 15.95 (978-1-56397-864-7(4)) Boyds Mills Pr.

Caviezel, Giovanni. Sleep Tight, Little Bear. Pagnoni, Roberta, illus. 2006. 12p. (J). bds. 6.99 (978-1-4169-1383-2(1) , Little Simon) Simon & Schuster Children's Publishing.

Chaconas, Doris J. Goodnight, Dewberry Bear. 2003. (Illus.). 32p. 17.00 (978-0-687-02691-3(1)) Abingdon Pr.

Chalk, Gary. The Forebears: 1000 Years of Bearly Factual History 1999. (Illus.). (J). (978-0-7894-4937-5(4)) Dorling Kindersley Publishing, Inc.

Chandler, Pauline. Mr. Rabbit the Farmer. Smith, Eric, illus. 2005. 24p. (J). lib. bdg. 22.65 (*978-1-59646-736-1(3)) Dingles & Co.

Chaney Fritz, Kathleen, illus. Tears of Mother Bear. 2004. (ENG.). (J). 17.95 (978-0-9749145-0-3(9)) Mackinac Island Pr., Inc.

Chapman, Jane, illus. Bear Wants More. unabr. ed. 2006. (J). (ps-2). 24.95 incl. audio (*978-0-439-90572-5(9)); 29.95 incl. audio compact disk (*978-0-439-90578-7(8)) Weston Woods Studios, Inc.

Chapman, Jason. Ted, Bo, & Diz: The First Adventure. 2007. 28p. (J). (ps-2). 16.00 (*978-1-56148-592-5(6)) Good Bks.

Cheer Bear: Three Cheers for You. (Care Bearstm Ser.). (J). bds. 9.99 (978-1-4037-0557-0(7)) Dalmatian Pr.

Chen, Chih-Yuan. The Best Christmas Ever. 2006. (Illus.). 48p. (J). 15.95 (978-0-9762056-2-3(9)) Heryin Publishing Corp.

Cherrington, Janelle. Mystery at the Big Blue House. 2000. (gr. k-3). lib. bdg. 11.25 (978-0-613-26334-4(0)) Tandem Library Bks.

Cherrington, Janelle & Strader, P. Kevin. Mystery at the Big Blue House. Brannon, Tom, illus. 2000. (Bear in the Big Blue House Ser.). 24p. (J). pap. (978-0-7434-0843-1(8) , Simon & Schuster Children's Publishing) Simon & Schuster Children's Publishing.

Cherrinton, Janelle. Welcome to the Big Blue House. 1998. (J). bds. 7.99 (978-0-689-82401-2(7) , Simon Spotlight/ Nickelodeon) Simon & Schuster Children's Publishing.

Christmas in Beartown. 2003. (J). bds. 4.99 (978-1-59384-010-5(1)) Book Club of America.

Ciardi, John. Someone Could Win a Polar Bear. Gorey, Edward, illus. 2003. 64p. (J). (gr. 2-4). 9.95 (978-1-59078-012-1(4)) Boyds Mills Pr.

—Someone Could Win a Polar Bear. 2002. (ps-2). lib. bdg. 18.75 (978-0-613-56614-8(9)) Tandem Library Bks.

Clark, Brenda, illus. Franklin & the Baby. 2002. (Franklin Ser.). (J). 12.40 (978-0-7587-0012-4(1)) Book Wholesalers, Inc.

—Franklin & the Baby-Sitter. 2002. (Franklin Ser.). (J). 12.40 (978-1-4046-0124-6(4)) Book Wholesalers, Inc.

—Franklin & the Big Kid. 2002. (Franklin Ser.). (J). 12.40 (978-1-4046-2017-9(6)) Book Wholesalers, Inc.

—Franklin & the Hero. 2002. (Franklin Ser.). 12.40 (978-1-4046-0309-7(3)) Book Wholesalers, Inc.

—Franklin & the Magic Show. 2002. (Franklin Ser.). (J). 12.40 (978-1-4046-1980-7(1)) Book Wholesalers, Inc.

—Franklin & the Thunderstorm. 2002. (Franklin Ser.). 12.40 (978-1-4046-0310-3(7)) Book Wholesalers, Inc.

—Franklin Has a Sleepover. 2002. (Franklin Ser.). (J). 12.40 (978-1-4046-0313-4(1)) Book Wholesalers, Inc.

Clark, Maxine. Build-a-Bear Workshop Furry Friends Hall of Fame: The Official Collector's Guide. 2005. (Illus.). 160p. (J). (gr. 4-7). (978-1-59258-142-9(0)) Hylas Publishing.

Claycomb, Patty & Bittinger, Gayle. The Best of Totline Bear Hugs. Cubley, Kathleen, ed. Ekberg, Marion H., illus. 1999. (Best of Totline Ser.). 160p. (J). (ps-k). pap. 14.95 (978-1-57029-238-5(8) , WPH 02603, Totline Pubns.) Schaffer, Frank Pubns.

Clement, Rebecca Irvin. Bears in the Berry Patch: Alaska Adventures Bears. 2001. (Alaska Adventure Bears Ser.). (Illus.). 16p. (gr. k-1). 9.95 (978-1-888125-78-8(0)) Publication Consultants.

Clements, Becky. A Picnic with Friends: Alaska Adventure Bears. 2003. (Alaska Adventure Bears Ser.), 16p. pap. 9.95 (978-1-888125-87-0(X)) Publication Consultants.

Cole, Joanna & Van Horn, William. Ca C'est Chez Moi.Tr. of This is the Place for Me. (FRE.). (J). 6.99 (978-0-590-71919-3(X)) Scholastic, Inc.

Colors All Day. (J). 26.20 (978-0-8136-8399-7(8)); 59.50 (978-0-8136-7918-1(4)); 1998. pap. (978-0-8136-8292-1(4)) Modern Curriculum Pr.

Conrad, Liz, illus. Bedtime Bear. 1999. 20p. (J). reprint ed. 16.95 (978-1-892374-28-8(5)) Weldon Owen, Inc.

Coombs, Bob. Ted P Bear - A Bitter Tale. 2005. 83p. (YA). pap. 8.69 (978-1-4116-4260-7(0)) Lulu.com.

Cooper, Elisha. Bear Dreams. Cooper, Elisha, illus. 2006. (Illus.). 40p. (J). 16.99 (978-0-06-087428-5(7) , Greenwillow Bks.); lib. bdg. 17.89 (978-0-06-087429-2(5)) HarperCollins Pubs.

Corey, Shana. Ballerina Bear. Paparone, Pamela, illus. (Jellybean Bks.). 24p. (J). (ps-k). 2000. 2.99 (978-0-375-80098-6(0)); 1999. lib. bdg. 7.99 (978-0-375-90098-3(5)) Random Hse. Children's Bks. (Random Hse. Bks. for Young Readers).

Corke, Estelle. Goldilocks & the Three Bears. 2004. (Flip up Fairy Tales Ser.). (Illus.). 24p. (J). 7.99 (978-0-85953-608-0(4)) Child's Play-International.

Corke, Estelle, illus. Goldilocks & the Three Bears. 2005. 24p. pap. (978-1-904550-19-8(3)) Child's Play-International.

Costain, Meredith. Polar Bears. 2000. (gr. k-3). lib. bdg. 11.80 (978-0-613-30680-5(5)) Tandem Library Bks.

Costantino, Eric. Beeboo Bear Dreamed A Dream. 2004. 31p. pap. 17.95 (978-1-4137-3649-6(1)) PublishAmerica, Inc.

Cottringer, Anne. Bruna. McClure, Gillian, illus. 2003. 32p. (J). 16.95 (978-0-58234-836-0(7) , Bloomsbury Children) Bloomsbury Publishing.

Couri, Kathryn A., illus. Goodnight Bear! A Book & Night Light. 1999. 12p. (J). (ps-k). 10.95 (978-1-58117-059-7(9) , Intervisual/Piggy Toes) Dalmatian Pr.

Couri, Kathy. Goodnight Bear! Bentley, Dawn, illus. 1999. 12p. (J). bds. 10.98 (978-1-58048-063-5(2)) Sandvik Publishing.

Coutu, Raymond. Duke's First Case: Jessie & the Missing Yarn. Graef, Renee, illus. 2001. (J). (978-0-9712840-6-7(7) , Bear & Co.) Bear & Co.

Coutu, Raymond & Jones, Dawn L. Babette & the Apple Bandit. Graef, Renee, illus. 2001. (J). (978-0-9712840-8-1(3)) Boyds Collection Ltd., The.

—Poker & the Cupcake Chase. Graef, Renee, illus. 2001. (J). pap. (978-0-9712840-7-4(5)) Boyds Collection Ltd., The.

Cowan, Charlotte. Katie Caught a Cold. 2008. (Illus.). 32p. 17.95 (978-0-9753516-3-5(X)) Hippocratic Pr., The.

Cox, Phil Roxbee & Cartwright, S. Ted in a Red Bed. 2004. (Phonics Board Bks.). 10p. (J). 4.95 (978-0-7945-0061-0(7) , Usborne) EDC Publishing.

Craig, Helen. This Is the Bear. 2003. (ps-2). lib. bdg. 11.80 (978-0-613-74748-6(8)) Tandem Library Bks.

Crane Johnson, Amy. Cinnamon & the April Shower/Canela y el aquacero de Abril: A Solomon Raven Story/un cuento del cuervo Salomon, 4 vols. de la Vega, Eida, tr. Mommaerts, Robb, illus. 2003. (Solomon Raven Ser. : 3). Tr. of Canela y el aguacero de abril:un cuento del cuervo Salomon. (SPA & ENG.). 32p. (J). (gr. k-3). 16.95 (978-0-9720192-2-4(7) , 626999) Raven Tree Pr.

Cratzius, Barbara & Thonissen, Uta. Good Morning, Sunshine. 2004. (Illus.). 16p. (J). 5.99 (978-1-59384-041-9(1)) Parklane Publishing.

Crum, Shutta. Click! Beder, John, tr. Beder, John, illus. 2003. 24p. (J). (978-1-55005-074-5(5)) Fitzhenry & Whiteside, Ltd.

Curry, Don, ed. Goldilocks & the Three Bears. 2006. (My Turn! Your Turn! Ser.). (ENG., Illus.). 24p. (J). pap. 3.99 (978-0-696-22854-4(8)) Meredith Bks.

Curry, Kenneth. Fuzzy & the All Bear Band. 2007. (Illus.). 22p. (J). 10.95 (*978-0-9798364-8-0(4)) Curry Brothers Publishing.

Curwood, James Oliver. The Bear. 2005. (Medallion Edition Ser.). Orig. Title: The Grizzly King. (Illus.). 208p. (YA). (ps-7). pap. 5.95 (978-1-55704-131-9(8)) Newmarket Pr.

Daher, Anita. Flight from Bear Canyon. 2004. (Orca Young Readers Ser.). (Illus.). 144p. (J). (gr. 3-6). pap. 4.99 (978 1 55143-326-4(5)) Orca Bk. Pubs. USA.

Daigneault, Sylvie. Bruno Falls Asleep. 2000. (Bruno Book Ser.). (Illus.). 32p. (J). (ps-2). 16.00 (978-0-00-224557-9(4)) HarperCollins Pubs.

Daley Mackall, Dandi. I Love You Daddy. Lee Schmidt, Karen, illus. 2006. (I Love You Ser.). 20p. (J). bds. 7.99 (978-0-7847-1816-2(4) , 04138) Standard Publishing.

—I Love You Mommy. Lee Schmidt, Karen, illus. 2005. (I Love You Ser.). 20p. (J). bds. 7.99 (978-0-7847-1815-5(6) , 04137) Standard Publishing.

D'Allance, Mireille. No, No Y No! (SPA.). 88p. (978-84-8470-034-0(8)) Corimbo, Editorial S.L.

Dalmatian Press Staff. Bear Baby: Soft Spot Board Book. 2002. (Soft Spot Bks.). (Illus.). 10p. (J). bds. 3.99 (978-1-57759-625-7(0)) Dalmatian Pr.

—Goldilocks & the Three Bears: Best Loved Stories Collection. 2004. (Illus.). 160p. (J). 5.99 (978-1-4037-0749-9(9)) Dalmatian Pr.

Dalmatian Press Staff, ed. Bedtime Bear: Sweet Dreams. (Care Bearstm Ser.). 6p. (J). bds. 9.99 (978-1-4037-0556-3(9)) Dalmatian Pr.

—Funshine Bear: Let the Fun Shine In. (Care Bearstm Ser.). 8p. (J). bds. 9.99 (978-1-4037-0558-7(5)) Dalmatian Pr.

Daly, Catherine. Best Friends. 2000. (gr. k-3). lib. bdg. 11.25 (978-0-613-30993-6(6)) Tandem Library Bks.

Daly-Weir, Catherine. Love Is All You Need. 2000. (gr. k-3). lib. bdg. 14.15 (978-0-613-21934-1(1)) Tandem Library Bks.

D'Amelio, Dennis P. The Last Bear. D'Amelio, Dennis P., illus. 1998. (Illus.). 26p. (J). pap. (978-1-891528-71-2(8)) Telescopic Pr.

Damon, Emma, illus. Milo in a Mess. 2006. (Read-It! Chapter Books). 48p. (J). (gr. 2-4). 19.95 (978-1-4048-1679-4(8)) Picture Window Bks.

Darling, Abigail. The Teddy Bear's Picnic Cookbook. Day, Alexandra, illus. rev. ed. 2003. 32p. (J). (gr. 3-7). 14.50 (978-1-883211-60-8(3) , Green Tiger Pr.) Laughing Elephant.

Davidson, Susanna. Goldilocks & the three Bears. Gordon, Mike, illus. 2007. (First Reading Level 4 Ser.). 48p. (J). 8.99 (*978-0-7945-1708-3(0) , Usborne) EDC Publishing.

Davis, Lee. Good Morning: Bear Shaped Board Books. 2001. (Pajama Bedtime Bear Ser.). (Illus.). 12p. (J). bds. 6.95 (978-0-7894-3731-0(7) , D K Ink) Dorling Kindersley Publishing, Inc.

—P. B. Bear's Wonderful Word Book. 2001. (Illus.). 24p. (J). (ps). pap. 12.95 (978-0-7894-3109-7(2) , D K Ink) Dorling Kindersley Publishing, Inc.

—PB Bear Goes to School. 1998. (Illus.). 24p. (J). (ps). pap. 12.95 (978-0-7894-1172-3(5) , D K Ink) Dorling Kindersley Publishing, Inc.

Day, Marie. Quennu & the Cave Bear. Day, Marie, illus. 1999. (Illus.). 32p. (J). (gr. 2-7). (978-1-895688-86-3(8)); pap. 6.95 (978-1-895688-87-0(6)) Maple Tree Pr. CAN. (Owl Bks.). *Dist:* Firefly Bks., Ltd.

—Quennu & the Cave Bear. 1999. (978-0-606-17092-5(8)) Tandem Library Bks.

—Quennu & the Cave Bear: A Prehistoric Tale. 1999. (gr. k-3). lib. bdg. 15.25 (978-0-613-26686-4(2)) Tandem Library Bks.

Daykin, Louise, illus. Goldilocks & the Three Bears. 2004. 32p. (J). (ENG & ALB.). (978-1-84444-035-1(4)); (ENG & ARA.). (978-1-84444-036-8(2)); (ENG & BEN.). (978-1-84444-037-5(0)); (ENG & CHI.). (978-1-84444-038-2(9)); (ENG & PER.). (978-1-84444-039-9(7)); (ENG & FRE.). (978-1-84444-040-5(0)); (ENG & GER.). (978-1-84444-041-2(9)); (ENG & GUJ.). (978-1-84444-042-9(7)); (ENG & PAN.). (978-1-84444-043-6(5)); (POR & ENG.). (978-1-84444-044-3(3)); (ENG & SOM.). (978-1-84444-045-0(1)); (ENG & SPA.). (978-1-84444-046-7(X)); (ENG & TUR.). (978-1-84444-047-4(8)); (ENG & URD.). (978-1-84444-048-1(6)); (CZE & ENG.). (978-1-84444-049-8(4)); (ENG & ITA.). (978-1-84444-050-4(8)); (ENG & POL.). (978-1-84444-051-1(6)); (RUS & ENG.). (978-1-84444-052-8(4)); (SBC, ENG & SER.). (978-1-84444-053-5(2)); (TAM & ENG.). (978-1-84444-054-2(0)); (ENG & HIN.). (978-1-84444-059-7(1)) Mantra Publishing, Ltd.

Daykin, Louise, tr. & illus. Goldilocks & the Three Bears. Daykin, Louise, illus. 2004. (J). (ENG & VIE.). 32p. (978-1-84444-055-9(9)); 31p. (978-1-84444-057-3(5)) Mantra Publishing, Ltd.

de Beer, Hans. Donde Vas Osito Polar. 1998. (SPA.). 28p. (ps-3). 11.00 (978-84-264-3611-5(0)) Lectorum Pubns., Inc.

—Just Like Father! 2004. (Little Polar Bear Story Ser.). (Illus.). 22p. (J). bds. 3.95 (978-1-4027-1289-0(8)) Sterling Publishing Co., Inc.

—Lars & His Friends: Board Book & Doll. 2004. (Little Polar Bear Story Ser.). (Illus.). 22p. 9.95 (978-1-4027-1341-5(X)) Sterling Publishing Co., Inc.

—Lars & the Egg. 2004. (Little Polar Bear Story Ser.). (Illus.). 24p. pap. 3.95 (978-1-4027-1299-9(5)) Sterling Publishing Co., Inc.

—Little Polar Bear. 1999. (Illus.). 14p. (J). (ps). bds. 6.95 (978-0-7358-1080-8(X)) North-South Bks., Inc.

—Little Polar Bear. de Beer, Hans, illus. enl. ed. 1999. (Little Polar Bear Ser.). (Illus.). 28p. (J). (gr. k-3). pap. 19.95 (978-0-7358-1216-1(0)) North-South Bks., Inc.

de, Beer Hans. Little Polar Bear & Reindeer. de, Beer Hans, illus. 2007. (Illus.). 0032p. pap. 6.95 (*978-0-7358-2139-2(9)) North-South Bks., Inc.

de Beer, Hans. Little Polar Bear & the Big Balloon. Lanning, Rosemary, tr. from GER. de Beer, Hans, illus. 2002. (Illus.). 32p. (J). (gr. k-3). 16.50 (978-0-7358-1533-9(X)) North-South Bks., Inc.

De Beer, Hans. Little Polar Bear & the Big Balloon. Lanning, Rosemary, tr. from GER. De Beer, Hans, illus. 2006. (Illus.). 22p. (J). (gr. k-4). reprint ed. 16.00 (978-0-7567-9875-8(2)) DIANE Publishing Co.

de Beer, Hans. Little Polar Bear & the Brave Little Hare. 2000. (Illus.). 32p. (J). (gr. k-3). pap. 6.95 (978-0-7358-1332-8(9)) North-South Bks., Inc.

—Little Polar Bear & the Brave Little Hare. de Beer, Hans, illus. 1998. (Illus.). 32p. (J). (gr. k-3). 15.95 (978-0-7358-1011-2(7)) North-South Bks., Inc.

—Little Polar Bear & the Brave Little Hare. 2000. (gr. k-3). lib. bdg. 15.25 (978-0-613-30007-0(6)) Tandem Library Bks.

—Little Polar Bear & the Husky Pup. de Beer, Hans, illus. (Illus.). 32p. (J). (ps-3). 2004. pap. 6.95 (978-0-7358-1904-7(1)); 1999. 15.95 (978-0-7358-1154-6(7)) North-South Bks., Inc.

—Little Polar Bear & the Reindeer. 2005. (Illus.). 28p. (J). (ps up). 15.95 (978-0-7358-2029-6(5)) North-South Bks., Inc.

—Little Polar Bear, Take Me Home! Lanning, Rosemary, tr. from GER. 2001. (Little Polar Bear Ser.). (Illus.). 32p. (J). pap. 6.95 (978-0-7358-1497-4(X)) North-South Bks., Inc.

—Little Polar Bear, Take Me Home! 2001. (ps-2). lib. bdg. 15.25 (978-0-613-44363-0(2)) Tandem Library Bks.

—Llevame a Casa, Osito Polar! Gambolini, Gerardo, tr. from GER. 2001. (SPA & ENG., Illus.). 32p. (J). (gr. k-3). pap. 6.95 (978-0-7358-1500-1(3) , NS30711) North-South Bks., Inc.

—Llevame a Casa, Osito Polar! 2001. (gr. k-3). (SPA.). lib. bdg. 15.25 (978-0-613-73576-6(5)); (978-0-606-22735-3(0)) Tandem Library Bks.

—Oh No, Ono! 2006. (Illus.). 32p. (J). pap. 6.95 (978-0-7358-2036-4(8)) North-South Bks., Inc.

—Osito Pardo, Que Suenas? 2001. (SPA.). 28p. (J). (gr. k-3). 14.36 (978-84-264-3691-7(9)) Editorial Lumen ESP. *Dist:* Lectorum Pubns., Inc.

—El Osito Polar y el Conejito Valiente. 2000. (SPA.). (gr. k-3). lib. bdg. 15.25 (978-0-613-32923-1(6)) Tandem Library Bks.

—The Secret Hideout. 2004. (Little Polar Bear Story Ser.). (Illus.). 24p. pap. 3.95 (978-1-4027-1340-8(1)) Sterling Publishing Co., Inc.

—You Can Do It! 2004. (Little Polar Bear Story Ser.). (Illus.). 24p. pap. 3.95 (978-1-4027-1339-2(8)) Sterling Publishing Co., Inc.

de Beer, Hans, illus. Little Polar Bear Sticker Book. 2001. 12p. (J). pap. 4.99 (978-1-59014-033-8(8)) North-South Bks., Inc.

de Beers, Hans. Little Polar Bear & Big Balloo. 2006. (Illus.). 32p. (J). 6.95 (978-0-7358-2077-7(5)) North-South Bks., Inc.

—Osito Polar y el Gran Globo. 2006. (SPA., Illus.). 32p. (J). pap. 6.95 (978-0-7358-1739-5(1)) North-South Bks., Inc.

Dean, Carol S. The Live Bale of Hay: A Real Maine Adventure. Dunn, Sandra, illus. 2005. 32p. (ps-ps). 15.95 (978-0-89272-674-5(1)) Down East Bks.

Degen, Bruce, illus. Better Not Get Wet, Jesse Bear. 2002. (Jesse Bear Ser.). (J). 14.47 (978-0-7587-2083-2(1)) Book Wholesalers, Inc.

—Happy Birthday, Jesse Bear! 2002. (J). 14.47 (978-0-7587-2685-8(6)) Book Wholesalers, Inc.

—How Do You Say It Today, Jesse Bear? 2002. (Jesse Bear Ser.). (J). 14.47 (978-0-7587-2760-2(7)) Book Wholesalers, Inc.

—It's about Time, Jesse Bear: And Other Rhymes. 2002. (Jesse Bear Ser.). (J). 14.47 (978-0-7587-2875-3(1)) Book Wholesalers, Inc.

—Jesse Bear, What Will You Wear? 2002. (Jesse Bear Ser.). (J). 15.53 (978-0-7587-2900-2(6)) Book Wholesalers, Inc.

Delval, Marie He. Voici les trois freres Ours. (FRE.). pap. 14.95 (978-2-227-75607-6(1)) Bayard Editions FRA. *Dist:* Distribooks, Inc.

Delval, Marie-Helene. Los Tres Hermanos Osos. Courtin, Thierry, illus. 2002. (Palabras Menudas Ser.).Tr. of Three Brother Bears. (SPA.). 14p. (ps). 4.95 (978-84-7864-513-8(6)) Combel Editorial, S.A. ESP. *Dist:* Independent Pubs. Group.

Dennis, Murray Marjorie. Dont Wake up Bear. Wittmann, Patricia, illus. 2006. 32p. 5.99 (978-0-7614-5330-7(X)) Cavendish, Marshall Corp.

DePrisco, Dorothea. Mini Snowbears Winter Day. 2006. 10p. (J). 4.95 (978-1-58117-506-6(X) , Intervisual/Piggy Toes) Dalmatian Pr.

—Snowbear's Winter Day: A Winter Wonder Book. Fehlau, Dagmar, illus. 2005. 18p. (J). (ps). 9.95 (978-1-58117-133-4(1) , Intervisual/Piggy Toes) Dalmatian Pr.

Derrick, Patricia. Beaser the Rocky Mountain Bear. 2007. 18.95 (978-1-933818-09-2(3)) Animalations.

—Rickity & Snickity at the Balloon Fiesta. 2007. 32p. 18.95 (978-1-933818-11-5(5)) Animalations.

Devine, Monica. Hanna Bear's Christmas. Cassidy, Sean, illus. 2007. 32p. (J). (ps-1). ***(978-1-55041-585-8(9))*** Fitzhenry & Whiteside, Ltd.

Dewey, Ariane. Splash! 2001. (Green Light Readers Ser.). (Illus.). (J). (978-0-606-21448-3(8)) Tandem Library Bks.

DeWitt, Dawn Davis. Searching for Blue Bears. Rolando, Cecilia, tr. Rolando, Cecilia, illus. 2003. (J). (978-0-9677057-5-0(4)) Raven Productions, Inc.

deYonge, Sandra. The Last Bit Bear: A Fable. Meloy, Ellen D., illus. 20th anniv. ed. 2004. 48p. pap. 7.95 (978-1-57098-431-0(X)) Rinehart, Roberts Pubs.

Dickens, Ned. By a Thread. Ross, Graham, illus. 2005. 32p. (J). (ps-2). 16.95 (978-1-55143-325-7(7)) Orca Bk. Pubs. USA.

Disney Press Staff. Easter Bear? 2003. (gr. k-3). lib. bdg. 10.95 (978-0-613-73671-8(0)) Tandem Library Bks.

Disney Staff. Follow the Leader. Disney Staff, illus. 1999. (Pooh's Learn & Grow Ser.: Vol. 2). (Illus.). 12p. (J). 3.49 (978-1-57973-036-9(1)) Advance Pubs. LLC.

—Hunting for Honey. 1999. (Disney Ser.). (Illus.). 84p. (J). (ps-3). pap. 2.99 (978-0-307-25700-0(2) , 25700, Golden Bks.) Random Hse. Children's Bks.

—Peek-a-Boo, Pooh! Disney Staff, illus. 1999. (Pooh's Learn & Grow Ser.: Vol. 7). (Illus.). 12p. (J). 3.49 (978-1-57973-041-3(8)) Advance Pubs. LLC.

—Pooh Plays Doctor. 1999. (Learn & Grow Ser.). (Illus.). 32p. (J). (ps-3). 11.99 (978-0-7364-0144-9(X)) Mouse Works.

—Pooh's Garden. 1999. (Pooh's Learn & Grow Ser.: Vol. 11). (Illus.). 12p. (J). 3.49 (978-1-57973-045-1(0)) Advance Pubs. LLC.

—Pooh's Hero Party, No. 12. 1999. (Winnie the Pooh First Readers Ser.: No. 12). (Illus.). 37p. (J). (gr. k-3). pap. 3.99 (978-0-7868-4270-4(9)) Disney Pr.

—Pooh's Rainy Day. Disney Staff, illus. 1999. (Pooh's Learn & Grow Ser.: Vol. 10). (Illus.). 12p. (J). 3.49 (978-1-57973-044-4(2)) Advance Pubs. LLC.

—Pooh's Sunny Day. Disney Staff, illus. 1999. (Pooh's Learn & Grow Ser.: Vol. 3). (Illus.). 12p. (J). 3.49 (978-1-57973-037-6(X)) Advance Pubs. LLC.

—Spring Cleaning: Color by Numbers. 2000. (Disney Ser.). (Illus.). 40p. (J). (ps-3). pap. 1.19 (978-0-307-16414-8(4) , Golden Bks.) Random Hse. Children's Bks.

DK Publishing. Goldilocks & the Three Bears: Read-along Paperbacks. 2007. 16p. (J). (ps-5). pap. 4.99 ***(978-0-7566-3456-8(3))*** Dorling Kindersley Publishing, Inc.

D'Lacey, Chris. Fire Star. 560p. (J). 2008. pap. 7.99 (978-0-439-90185-7(5)); 2007. (gr. 4-7). pap. 15.99 (978-0-439-84582-3(3)) Scholastic, Inc. (Orchard Bks.).

—Franklin's Bear. Taylor, Thomas, illus. 2005. (Red Go Bananas Ser.). 48p. (J). pap. (978-0-7787-2696-8(7)) Crabtree Publishing Co.

—Icefire. 432p. (J). 2007. pap. 7.99 (978-0-439-67246-7(5)); 2006. pap. 14.99 (978-0-439-67245-0(7)) Scholastic, Inc. (Orchard Bks.).

Docan, Cristina C. A Secret Promise. 2007. (Illus.). 24p. (J). 16.95 ***(978-1-905636-01-3(6))*** Beautiful Bks. GBR. *Dist:* International Publishers Marketing.

Dodd, Emma. Just Like You. 2008. 24p. (J). (ps). 10.99 ***(978-0-525-47933-8(3)*** , Dutton Juvenile) Penguin Group (USA) Inc.

Dodd, Lynley. Wake up, Bear. Dodd, Lynley, illus. 2001. (Gold Star First Readers Ser.). (Illus.). 32p. (J). (gr. 1 up). lib. bdg. 22.00 (978-0-8368-2786-6(4)) Stevens, Gareth Inc.

Donaki & Rosenberry, Donald. Spectacular Journey. Rosenberry, Akiko & Rosenberry, Susan, illus. 2006. (J). per. 20.00 ***(978-0-9771482-6-4(2)*** , Ithaca Pr.) Authors & Artists Publishers of New York, Inc.

Donaldson, Julia. One Ted Falls Out of Bed. Currey, Anna, illus. 2006. 32p. (J). 15.95 (978-0-8050-7787-2(1)) Holt, Henry & Co.

Donovan, Kevin. Billy & His Friends Rescue a Baby Bear. 2003. (Illus.). 32p. 10.95 (978-0-9641338-4-6(9)) Billy the Bear & His Friends, Inc.

—Billy & His Friends Rescue Betsy Bear. 2003. (Illus.). 28p. 10.95 (978-0-9641338-3-9(0)) Billy the Bear & His Friends, Inc.

Dorling Kindersley Publishing Staff. Pajama Bedtime Bear Stroller Book: Hello, PB Bear! 2002. (Stroller Books Ser.). (Illus.). 16p. (J). bds. 4.95 (978-0-7894-6278-7(8) , D K Ink) Dorling Kindersley Publishing, Inc.

—Pajama Bedtime Bear Stroller Book: PB Bear's Friends. 2002. (Stroller Books Ser.). (Illus.). 16p. (J). bds. 4.99 (978-0-7894-6366-1(0) , D K Ink) Dorling Kindersley Publishing, Inc.

—Pajama Bedtime Bear Touch-and-Feel: Meet My Friends. 2002. (Touch & Feel Ser.). (Illus.). 12p. (J). bds. 6.95 (978-0-7894-6277-0(X) , D K Ink) Dorling Kindersley Publishing, Inc.

—Pajama Bedtime Bear's Magic Surprise: A Lift-the-Flap Book. 2002. (Lift-the-Flap Books Ser.). (Illus.). 12p. (J). pap. 6.95 (978-0-7894-6276-3(1) , D K Ink) Dorling Kindersley Publishing, Inc.

—Winnie the Pooh. 2004. (Ultimate Sticker Bks.). 16p. (J). pap. 6.99 (978-0-7894-9996-7(7)) Dorling Kindersley Publishing, Inc.

Douglas, Vincent. The Big Honeypot Rescue. 2001. (Disney Parent & Child Read Together Ser.). (Illus.). 40p. (ps-k). 4.99 (978-1-57768-732-0(9)) School Specialty Publishing.

—The Honey Tree. 2001. (Disney Parent & Child Read Together Ser.). (Illus.). 40p. (ps-k). 4.99 (978-1-57768-733-7(7)) School Specialty Publishing.

Downey, Glen. Ice Journey. Brucker, Glenn, illus. 2007. 48p. (J). lib. bdg. 23.08 ***(978-1-4242-1618-5(4))*** Fitzgerald Bks.

DPWW. Many Adventures of Winnie the Pooh. 1998. 192p. (J). 19.95 (978-0-7868-3224-8(X)) Disney Pr.

Dunrea, Olivier. Bear Noel. Dunrea, Olivier, illus. (Illus.). 32p. (J). 2006. pap. 5.95 (978-0-374-40001-9(6)); 2000. 16.00 (978-0-374-39990-0(5)) Farrar, Straus & Giroux. (Farrar, Straus & Giroux (BYR)).

—Pupper! 2001. (Illus.). (J). (978-0-618-06766-4(3)) Houghton Mifflin Co.

Duplaix, Georges. The Big Brown Bear. 2001. (978-0-606-22794-0(6)) Tandem Library Bks.

Duval, Kathy. The Three Bears' Christmas. Meisel, Paul, illus. 32p. (J). 6.95 (978-0-8234-2039-1(6)); 16.95 (978-0-8234-1871-8(5)) Holiday Hse., Inc.

—The Three Bears' Halloween. Meisel, Paul, illus. 2007. 32p. (J). (ps-1). 16.95 (978-0-8234-2032-2(9)) Holiday Hse., Inc.

Dyer, Howard Wayne. The Itty Bitty Bear. 2006. 11.00 ***(978-0-9760691-0-2(5))*** Itty Bitty Bks.

Dziekan, Jennifer Ellen. The Wishing Bear. l.t. ed. 2006. (Illus.). 40p. (J). per. 7.50 (978-0-9772231-0-7(8)) Kidstory Pr.

Eagle, Golden. You've Got to Know When to Lead. 2005. (Illus.). 20p. (J). per. 9.99 (978-1-59879-025-2(0)) Lifevest Publishing, Inc.

Eaton, Seymour. Teddy Bears Traveling Adventures. Akmon, Nancy, ed. Akmon, Roni, illus. 2004. 46p. (J). (gr. k-4). reprint ed. 15.00 (978-0-7567-8171-2(X)) DIANE Publishing Co.

Edgar, Amy. Winnie the Pooh's Bedtime Hummables. 2000. (Winnie the Pooh Ser.). (Illus.). 16p. (J). (ps-k). bds. 7.99 (978-0-7364-1020-5(1) , RH/Disney) Random Hse. Children's Bks.

Edgell, Ernest. The Cowbears of Texas: The Hero. Haycraft, Marilynn J., illus. 2004. 25p. pap. 14.95 (978-1-4137-3507-9(X)) PublishAmerica, Inc.

Edwards, Richard. Copy Me, Copycub. 1999. 32p. (J). (ps-2). pap. 5.95 (978-0-06-443603-8(9)) HarperCollins Pubs.

—Where Are You Hiding Copycub? Winter, Susan, illus. 2005. 32p. (J). pap. 7.95 (978-1-84507-362-6(2)) Lincoln, Frances Ltd. GBR. *Dist:* Perseus Distribution.

Ekaitis, Joe. Collinsfort Village. 2005. (Illus.). 161p. (J). per. 9.95 (978-1-886249-21-9(0)) WindRiver Publishing.

Elboz, Stephen. Temmi & Flying Bears. l.t. ed. 1999. (Illus.). 164p. (J). pap. (978-0-7540-6043-7(8) , CLP 245) BBC Audio.

—Temmi & the Flying Bears. unabr. l.t. ed. 2003. (Read-Along Ser.). (J). pap. 24.95 incl. audio (978-0-7540-6208-0(2) , Galaxy Children's Large Print) BBC Audiobooks America.

Elwell, Peter. A Most Remarkable Bear. Elwell, Peter, illus. Date not set. (Illus.). 32p. (J). (gr. k-3). 15.95 (978-0-7614-5008-5(4) , Benchmark Bks.) Cavendish, Marshall Corp.

Erlbruch, Wolf. El Milagro Del Oso. 2002. (SPA., Illus.). 32p. (978-84-89804-51-7(6)) Loguez Ediciones ESP. *Dist:* Lectorum Pubns., Inc.

—The Miracle of the Bears. Reynolds, Michael, tr. from GER. 2006. (Illus.). 32p. pap. 14.95 (978-1-933372-21-1(4)) Europa Editions, Inc.

Ernest & Celestine. 2004. (J). pap. 14.95 incl. audio (978-1-56008-039-8(6)) Weston Woods Studios, Inc.

Ernest & Celestine's Picnic. 2004. 24.95 incl. audio (978-1-56008-198-2(8)); (J). pap. 14.95 incl. audio (978-1-56008-199-9(6)) Weston Woods Studios, Inc.

Ernst, Lisa Campbell. Goldilocks Returns. Ernst, Lisa Campbell, illus. (Illus.). 40p. (J). (gr. k-3). 2003. pap. 7.99 (978-0-689-85705-8(5) , Aladdin); 2000. 16.95 (978-0-689-82537-8(4)) Simon & Schuster Children's Publishing.

—Goldilocks Returns. 2001. (J). (gr. k-3). 26.95 incl. audio (978-0-8045-6874-6(X) , 6874) Spoken Arts, Inc.

—Goldilocks Returns. 2003. (gr. k-3). lib. bdg. 15.30 (978-0-613-66409-7(4)) Tandem Library Bks.

Eubank, Patti Reeder. Count Your Blessings! 2004. (Illus.). 14p. (J). bds. 9.95 (978-0-8249-6544-0(2)) Ideals Pubns.

Evans, Hubert. Bear Stories. LaFave, Kim, illus. unabr. ed. 32p. (Orig.). (J). (978-0-88971-153-2(4)) Harbour Publishing Co., Ltd.

Exclaim Entertainment. It's Fun to Share. 2007. (BOZ#8482; Ser.). 14p. (J). 4.99 ***(978-0-310-71405-7(2))*** Zonderkidz.

Exclaim Entertainment Staff. I Love My Family. 2007. (BOZ#8482; Ser.). 14p. (J). 4.99 ***(978-0-310-71404-0(4))*** Zonderkidz.

Famous, Howard B. Bobby Bear & Other Stories. 2005. reprint ed. pap. 19.95 (978-1-4179-3376-1(3)) Kessinger Publishing, LLC.

Fanger, Rolf & Moltgen, Ulrike. Moonbeam Bear. 2004. (Illus.). 32p. (J). 10.99 (978-1-59384-015-0(2)) Parklane Publishing.

Farnsworth, Frances. Cubby in Wonderland. 2005. pap. 20.95 (978-1-4179-8778-8(2)) Kessinger Publishing, LLC.

Farnsworth, Frances Joyce. Tike & Tiny in the Tetons. 2007. (Illus.). 172p. (J). pap. 14.95 ***(978-0-943972-79-4(5))*** Homestead Publishing.

Fast, Suellen M. Golden-Brown Baby Bear & the Three Sisters. Serman, Gina L., ed. 30p. (Orig.). (J). (ps up). pap. 4.00 (978-0-935281-11-8(8)) Daughter Culture Pubns.

Fearnley, Jan. Mr. Wolf & the Three Bears. 2002. (Illus.). 32p. (J). (ps-2). 16.00 (978-0-15-216423-2(5)) Harcourt Children's Bks.

Ferguson, Don. Winnie the Pooh's A to ZZZZ. Wakeman, Bill & Langley, Diana, illus. 2020. 32p. (J). (ps-2). pap. 4.99 (978-0-7868-4094-6(3)) Disney Pr.

Ferrell, Annie K. Benny the Burro Bears His Burden. 2004. 24p. pap. 14.95 (978-1-4137-2495-0(7)) PublishAmerica, Inc.

Ferri, Francesca, illus. Good Night, Teddy. 2003. 8p. (J). 14.95 (978-0-7641-2595-9(8)) Barron's Educational Series, Inc.

—Little Polar Bear. 2003. 8p. (J). pap. 12.95 (978-0-7641-2596-6(6)) Barron's Educational Series, Inc.

Fireman Bear: New Heroes Backpack Story. 2002. (J). (978-1-931312-58-5(3)) SoftPlay, Inc.

Firth, Barbara, illus. Can't You Sleep, Little Bear? 2002. (Little Bear Picture Bks.). (J). 13.83 (978-0-7587-2185-3(4)) Book Wholesalers, Inc.

—Good Job, Little Bear. 2002. (Little Bear Picture Bks.). (J). 23.40 (978-0-7587-2616-2(3)) Book Wholesalers, Inc.

—Let's Go Home, Little Bear. 2002. (Little Bear Picture Bks.). (J). 13.83 (978-0-7587-2976-7(6)) Book Wholesalers, Inc.

—You & Me, Little Bear. 2002. (Little Bear Picture Bks.). (J). 14.79 (978-0-7587-4058-8(1)) Book Wholesalers, Inc.

Fleming, Sheila G. A Very Berra Holiday. 2002. 108p. pap. 9.95 (978-0-595-25600-6(7) , Weekly Reader Teacher's Pr) iUniverse, Inc.

Floate, Helen, illus. Goldilocks & the Three Bears: Puppet Theater. 2004. 11p. (J). (gr. k-4). reprint ed. 17.00 (978-0-7567-8020-3(9)) DIANE Publishing Co.

Floyd, Madeleine. Cold Paws, Warm Heart. 2005. (Illus.). 32p. (J). (ps-3). 15.99 (978-0-7636-2761-4(5)) Candlewick Pr.

Flynn, Claire K. Saving B Bear. Woods, S. Gail, illus. 2001. 34p. (J). (ps-5). pap. 9.95 (978-1-930653-03-0(4)) For Kids' Sake Pr.

Foley, Greg. Don't Worry Bear. Foley, Greg, illus. 2008. 32p. (J). (ps). 15.99 ***(978-0-670-06245-4(6)*** , Viking Juvenile) Penguin Group (USA) Inc.

Foley, Greg. Thank You Bear. Foley, Greg, illus. 2007. (Illus.). 32p. (J). (ps-1). 15.99 (978-0-670-06165-5(4) , Viking Juvenile) Penguin Group (USA) Inc.

Fontes, Justine. Christmas Cub. 1999. (gr. k-3). lib. bdg. 11.80 (978-0-613-32403-8(X)) Tandem Library Bks.

—The Easter Cub. McQueen, Lucinda, illus. 2003. (Hello Reader! Ser.). 32p. (J). (gr. k-2). pap. 3.99 (978-0-439-44340-1(7) , Cartwheel Bks.) Scholastic, Inc.

Forbush, Kyle. Who Is Alaska's Favorite Bear? Forbush, Lisa, illus. 2003. (J). bds. 6.95 (978-1-57833-211-3(7)) Todd Communications.

Ford, Miela. Mom & Me. Ford, Miela, photos by. 1998. (Illus.). 24p. (J). (ps-3). 15.00 (978-0-688-15889-7(7)) HarperCollins Pubs.

—On My Own. 1999. (Illus.). 16p. (J). (ps-k). pap. 5.95 (978-0-688-16452-2(8)) HarperCollins Pubs.

Foreman, Michael. Hello World. Foreman, Michael, illus. 2003. (Illus.). 48p. (J). (ps). 16.99 (978-0-7636-2112-4(9)) Candlewick Pr.

—The Panda. 1999. (Illus.). 64p. (J). (gr. 5 up). pap. 14.99 (978-1-86205-290-1(5) , Pavilion Bks., Ltd.) Anova Bks. GBR. *Dist:* Independent Pubs. Group.

Foust, Cindy G. Benny Bear: Having A Baby Sister Isn't Fair. Revoir, Joyce, illus. 2004. (J). 12.95 (978-0-9749220-1-0(3)) Alpha-kidZ.

Fox, Frances Margaret. Little Bear at Work & at Play. 2004. reprint ed. pap. 15.95 (978-1-4191-3071-7(4)); pap. 1.99 (978-1-4192-3071-4(9)) Kessinger Publishing, LLC.

Fox, Mem. Sleepy Bears. 2002. (Illus.). (J). 13.19 (978-1-4046-4374-1(5)) Book Wholesalers, Inc.

—Sleepy Bears. ed. 2004. (Illus.). (J). (ps-2). spiral bd. (978-0-616-03033-2(9)); spiral bd. (978-0-616-04554-1(9)) Canadian National Institute for the Blind/Institut National Canadien pour les Aveugles.

—Sleepy Bears. Argent, Kerry, illus. 32p. (J). (gr. k-2). 2002. pap. 7.00 (978-0-15-216542-0(8) , Voyager Bks./Libros Viajeros); 1999. 16.00 (978-0-15-202016-3(0)) Harcourt Children's Bks.

—Sleepy Bears. 2002. (ps-2). lib. bdg. 14.15 (978-0-613-86526-5(X)) Tandem Library Bks.

Fraggalosch, Audrey. Grizzly Bear Family. 2005. (Soundprints' Amazing Animal Adventures! Ser.). (Illus.). 36p. (J). (ps-2). 19.95 incl. audio (978-1-59249-394-4(7) , BC7103) Soundprints.

—Grizzly Bear Family. 2003. (gr. k-3). lib. bdg. 15.25 (978-0-613-71037-4(1)) Tandem Library Bks.

—Grizzly Bear Family. Eberhart, Donald, illus. 2005. (Soundprints' Amazing Animal Adventures! Ser.). (J). (ps-2). 30p. 2.95 (978-1-59249-050-9(6) , S7153); 36p. 9.95 (978-1-59249-059-2(X) , PS7153) Soundprints.

Fraggalosch, Audrey & Eberhart, Donald G. Grizzly Bear Family. 2005. (Amazing Animal Adventures Ser.). (Illus.). 36p. (J). (ps-2). 15.95 (978-1-59249-048-6(4) , B7103); pap. 6.95 (978-1-59249-049-3(2) , S7103) Soundprints.

Freedman, Claire. Follow That Bear If You Dare! Edgson, Alison, illus. 2008. (J). ***(978-1-56148-588-8(8))*** Good Bks.

—Good Night, Sleep Tight. Tyger, Rory, illus. 2003. 32p. (J). (ps-1). 14.95 (978-0-8109-4513-5(4)) Abrams, Harry N. , Inc.

Freedman, Claire. Good Night, Sleep Tight! Tyger, Rory, illus. 2007. 32p. (J). pap. 6.95 ***(978-1-58925-405-3(8)*** , tiger tales) ME Media LLC.

Freeman, Claire. One Magical Morning. Ho, Louise, illus. 2005. 28p. (J). 16.00 (978-1-56148-472-0(5)) Good Bks.

Freeman, Don. All about Corduroy. 2002. (Illus.). 9.98 (978-0-670-03624-0(2) , Viking Adult) Penguin Group (USA) Inc.

—Un Bolsillo para Corduroy & A Pocket for Corduroy, 2 bks. Freeman, Don, illus. unabr. ed. 1999. (Corduroy Ser.). (SPA & ENG., Illus.). (J). (gr. k-3). pap. 33.95 incl. audio (978-0-87499-565-7(5)) Live Oak Media.

—Corduroy, 2 vols., Set. Freeman, Don, illus. unabr. ed. 1999. (Corduroy Ser.). (SPA & ENG., Illus.). (J). (gr. k-1). pap. 33.95 incl. audio (978-0-87499-566-4(3)) Live Oak Media.

—Corduroy Goes to the Doctor. McCue, Lisa, illus. 2005. 14p. (J). (ps-ps). pap. 5.99 (978-0-670-06031-3(3) , Viking Juvenile) Penguin Group (USA) Inc.

—Corduroy's Christmas Surprise. McCue, Lisa, illus. 2000. (Corduroy Ser.). 32p. (J). (gr. k-1). pap. 3.99 (978-0-448-42191-9(7) , Grosset & Dunlap) Penguin Group (USA) Inc.

—Corduroy's Christmas Surprise. 2000. (gr. k-3). lib. bdg. 11.25 (978-0-613-31090-1(X)) Tandem Library Bks.

—Corduroy's Day. McCue, Lisa, illus. 2005. 14p. (J). bds. 5.99 (978-0-670-06030-6(5) , Viking Juvenile) Penguin Group (USA) Inc.

—Corduroy's Easter. McCue, Lisa, illus. 1999. (Corduroy Ser.). 8p. (J). (gr. k-1). 11.99 (978-0-670-88101-7(5) , Viking Juvenile) Penguin Group (USA) Inc.

—Corduroy's Easter Party. McCue, Lisa, illus. 2000. (Corduroy Ser.). 32p. (J). (gr. k-1). pap. 3.49 (978-0-448-42154-4(2) , Grosset & Dunlap) Penguin Group (USA) Inc.

—Corduroy's Easter Party. 2000. (ps-2). lib. bdg. 11.25 (978-0-613-24691-0(8)) Tandem Library Bks.

—Corduroy's Merry Christmas. McCue, Lisa, illus. 2002. 16p. (J). bds. 5.99 (978-0-670-03579-3(3) , Viking Juvenile) Penguin Group (USA) Inc.

—Corduroy's Party. McCue, Lisa, illus. 2005. 14p. (J). (ps-ps). pap. 5.99 (978-0-670-05995-9(1) , Viking Juvenile) Penguin Group (USA) Inc.

—Happy Easter, Corduroy. McCue, Lisa, illus. 2004. 16p. (J). (ps-ps). bds. 5.99 (978-0-670-03677-6(3) , Viking Juvenile) Penguin Group (USA) Inc.

Fremont, Eleanor. Just Be Nice... And Not to Rough. 1999. (Disney Ser.). (Illus.). 24p. (J). (ps-k). pap. 3.29 (978-0-307-10011-5(1) , 10011, Golden Bks.) Random Hse. Children's Bks.

Fronte, Kathy. Bella's Bow Tie Bears: Three Magnificent Tales of Adventure, Dreams & Magic. 2006. (Illus.). 36p. (J). pap. 12.95 (978-0-9727725-0-1(2)) Fronte, Kathy.

Fuchs, Menucha. Now Dovy Bear Can Wait. Rappaport, Aviva, tr. 2002. (HEB., Illus.). 32p. (J). 9.95 (978-1-880582-29-9(5)) Judaica Pr., Inc., The.

Fuge, Charles. My Dad! (Illus.). (J). 2005. 22p. bds. 5.95 (978-1-4027-2191-5(9)); 2003. 24p. 12.95 (978-1-4027-0707-0(X)) Sterling Publishing Co., Inc.

Gabriel, Andrea. My Favorite Bear. Gabriel, Andrea, illus. 2004. (Illus.). 32p. (J). pap. 6.95 (978-1-58089-039-7(3)) Charlesbridge Publishing, Inc.

—My Favorite Bear. 2003. (Illus.). 32p. (J). 15.95 (978-1-58089-038-0(5)) Charlesbridge Publishing, Inc.

Gabriel, Ashala. Night Night Toes: A Lift-the-Flap Story. Porter, Sue, illus. 2002. 24p. (J). (ps-k). 12.95 (978-0-689-85089-9(1) , Little Simon) Simon & Schuster Children's Publishing.

Gaines, Isabel. Be Quiet, Pooh! 1999. 40p. (J). pap. 3.99 (978-0-7868-4385-5(3)) Disney Pr.

—Happy Birthday, Eeyore! 1998. (Winnie the Pooh First Readers Ser.). (Illus.). 48p. (J). (ps-3). pap. 3.95 (978-0-7868-4183-7(4)) Disney Pr.

—Happy Valentine's Day, Pooh. 2000. (Winnie the Pooh Ser.: Vol. 25). (Illus.). 37p. (J). pap. 3.99 (978-0-7868-4372-5(1)) Disney Pr.

—Pooh Gets Stuck, No. 1. 1998. (Winnie the Pooh First Readers Ser.). (Illus.). 48p. (J). (ps-3). pap. 3.95 (978-0-7868-4184-4(2)) Disney Pr.

—Pooh's Christmas Gift. 1999. 40p. (J). pap. 3.99 (978-0-7868-4402-9(7)) Disney Pr.

—Pooh's Fall Harvest. 2000. (Winnie the Pooh First Readers Ser.: No. 23). (Illus.). 35p. (J). (ps-3). pap. 3.99 (978-0-7868-4370-1(5)) Disney Pr.

—Pooh's Graduation. 22nd ed. 2000. (Winnie the Pooh Ser.). (Illus.). 37p. (J). (gr. k-3). pap. 3.99 (978-0-7868-4369-5(1)) Disney Pr.

—Pooh's Hero Party. 1999. (978-0-606-18111-2(3)) Tandem Library Bks.

—Pooh's Honey Tree, No. 5. 1998. (Winnie the Pooh First Readers Ser.: No. 3). (Illus.). 40p. (J). (ps-3). pap. 3.95 (978-0-7868-4253-7(9)) Disney Pr.

—Pooh's Pumpkin. 1998. (Winnie the Pooh First Readers Ser.: No. 6). (Illus.). 32p. (J). (ps-3). pap. 3.99 (978-0-7868-4256-8(3)) Disney Pr.

—Pooh's Pumpkin School Market Edition. 1998. (Winnie the Pooh First Readers Ser.: No. 3). (Illus.). 48p. (J). (gr. k-2). pap. 3.95 (978-0-7868-4304-6(7)) Disney Pr.

—Pooh's Sled Ride. 2000. (Winnie the Pooh First Readers Ser.: No. 24). (Illus.). 34p. (J). (ps-3). pap. 3.99 (978-0-7868-4371-8(3)) Disney Pr.

Gaines, Isabel, et al. The Giving Bear. Yee, Josie, illus. 1999. (Winnie the Pooh First Readers Ser.: No. 9). 37p. (J). (gr. k-3). pap. 3.99 (978-0-7868-4267-4(9)) Disney Pr.

Galdone, Paul. The Three Bears. Galdone, Paul, illus. 2002. (Illus.). (J). 14.74 (978-0-7587-3796-0(3)) Book Wholesalers, Inc.

—The Three Bears. 2001. (Carry-Along Book & Cassette Favorites Ser.). (Illus.). 32p. (J). (gr. k-3). pap. 9.95 incl. audio (978-0-618-11746-8(6) , Clarion Bks.) Houghton Mifflin Co. Trade & Reference Div.

—Los Tres Osos. Mlawer, Teresa, tr. (SPA., Illus.). (J). (gr. k-3). pap. 8.99 (978-1-880507-71-1(4) , LC6060) Lectorum Pubns., Inc.

—Los Tres Osos. Mlawer, Teresa, tr. 2004. (Illus.). 32p. (J). (ps-3). lib. bdg. 14.15 (978-0-606-30090-2(2)) Tandem Library Bks.

—Los Tres Osos. 2001. (SPA.). (J). (gr. k-3). lib. bdg. 15.25 (978-0-613-36043-2(5)) Tandem Library Bks.

Gansle, Sherry. Oops, a Curious Horse Big Book. Light, Carol, illus. 2003. 56p. (J). (978-0-9745803-6-4(8)) Little Big Tomes.

—Oops, a Curious Horse Little Book. Light, Carol, illus. 2003. 52p. (J). (978-0-9745803-7-1(6)) Little Big Tomes.

Gantschev, Ivan. The Rabbit & the Bear: A Christmas Tale. Gantschev, Ivan, illus. 2007. (Illus.). 32p. (J). (ps). 16.95 ***978-0-7358-2145-3(3))** North-South Bks., Inc.

Garber, Linda. The Polar Bear Who Hated Snow. Feig, Harriet, illus. 1998. 55p. (J). (gr. 2-5). pap. 9.95 (978-1-892218-00-1(3)) Murlin Pubns.

Geist, Ken, ed. Carebears: 4 Easy-to-Read Stories. 2005. (Scholastic Reader Collection Level 2 Ser.). 144p. (J). (ps-ps). pap. 6.99 (978-0-439-76310-3(X) , Cartwheel Bks.) Scholastic, Inc.

Genechten, Guido van. Because I Love You So Much. 2004. (Illus.). 32p. (J). tchr. ed. 15.95 (978-1-58925-039-0(7) , tiger tales) ME Media LLC.

—Porque Te Quiero Tanto. 2003. (SPA., Illus.). 28p. (J). (gr. k-3). 15.95 (978-970-29-0912-5(0)) Santillana USA Publishing Co., Inc.

—Snowy's Special Secret. 2005. (Illus.). 32p. (J). (ps-ps). 15.95 (978-1-58925-049-9(4) , tiger tales) ME Media LLC.

George, Jean Craighead. Snow Bear. 2003. (gr. k-3). lib. bdg. 14.15 (978-0-613-75033-2(0)) Tandem Library Bks.

Gerver, Jane E. The Big Red Sled. Burris, Priscilla, illus. 2001. (Hello Reader! Ser.). 32p. (J). (ps-1). 3.99 (978-0-439-20434-7(8) , Cartwheel Bks.) Scholastic, Inc.

—The Big Red Sled. Burris, Priscilla, illus. 2001. (J). (ps-3). lib. bdg. 11.80 (978-0-613-43797-4(7)) Tandem Library Bks.

—The Big Red Sled. 2001. 10.79 (978-0-606-22227-3(8)) Tandem Library Bks.

Ghost Bear. 2001. (Illus.). 32p. (J). (gr. 2-5). pap. 10.00 (978-0-9713219-1-5(4)) Jumping Jack Holidays.

Giesler, Dagmar. Max juega en la Arena. 2004. (Coleccion Max Max Ser.). (SPA.). (J). bds. 11.95 (978-84-261-3295-6(2)) Juventud, Editorial ESP. *Dist:* Distribooks, Inc., Lectorum Pubns., Inc.

Gili, Phillida. The Lost Ears. 25th annot. anniv. ed. 2006. (Illus.). 32p. (J). (ps-1). 12.95 (978-1-905417-18-6(7)) Boxer Bks., Ltd. GBR. *Dist:* Sterling Publishing Co., Inc.

Ginsburg, Mirra. Two Greedy Bears: Adapted from a Hungarian Folktale. Aruego, Jose & Dewey, Ariane, illus. 1999. (J). pap., tchr. ed. 33.95 incl. audio (978-0-87499-505-3(1)); pap. 16.95 incl. audio (978-0-87499-503-9(5)) Live Oak Media.

—Two Greedy Bears: Adapted from a Hungarian Folktale. 1998. (J). (978-0-606-13881-9(1)) Tandem Library Bks.

Gipson, Morrell. Mr. Bear Squash-You-All-Flat. Angela, illus. 2000. 48p. (J). 15.00 (978-1-930900-04-2(X)) Purple Hse. Pr.

Gizard, W. J. Hector Bear's Homecoming. 1999. (Hickabob Farm Ser.). (Illus.). (J). pap. 5.95 (978-1-57167-433-3(0)) Sagamore Publishing, L.L.C.

Glicksman, Caroline. Eric the Math Bear. 2003. (Illus.). 32p. (J). (ps-2). lib. bdg. 17.99 (978-0-375-92432-3(9) , Knopf Bks. for Young Readers) Random Hse. Children's Bks.

—Eric the Red. (Illus.). 32p. 2004. 19.99 (978-0-370-32626-9(1)); 2003. (J). pap. 8.99 (978-0-09-943923-3(9) , Arrow Bks., Ltd.) Random Hse. GBR. *Dist:* Independent Pubs. Group.

Gliori, Debi. Little Bear & the Wish Fish. (Illus.). 32p. (J). (ps-2). pap. 9.99 (978-0-7112-0986-2(3)) Lincoln, Frances Ltd. GBR. *Dist:* Transition Vendor.

—Mr. Bear to the Rescue. Gliori, Debi, illus. 2000. (Illus.). 32p. (J). (ps-1). pap. 15.95 (978-0-531-30276-7(8) , Orchard Bks.) Scholastic, Inc.

—Mr. Bear's Vacation. Gliori, Debi, illus. 2000. (Illus.). 32p. (J). (ps-1). pap. 15.95 (978-0-531-30255-2(5) , Orchard Bks.) Scholastic, Inc.

—Un Sueno Magico. Eroles, Elena, tr. Gliori, Debi, illus. 2001. (SPA., Illus.). (J). (gr. k-2). 12.95 (978-84-480-1670-8(X) , TM30442) Timun Mas, Editorial S.A. ESP. *Dist:* Planeta Publishing Corp.

Golden Books Staff. First Words. 2001. (Step Ahead Ser.). 54p. (J). (ps-3). 2.99 (978-0-307-24957-9(3) , Golden Bks.) Random Hse. Children's Bks.

—Pooh & the Dragon. 2000. (Little Golden Bks.). (Illus.). 24p. (J). (ps-k). bds. 2.99 (978-0-307-98798-3(1) , 98798, Golden Bks.) Random Hse. Children's Bks.

—The Three Bears. Hefferan, Rob, illus. 2003. (Little Golden Book Ser.). 24p. (J). (gr. k-k). 2.99 (978-0-375-82576-7(2) , Golden Bks.) Random Hse. Children's Bks.

Golden Books Staff & Scott, Evelyn. The Fourteen Bears in Summer & Winter. 2005. (Illus.). 64p. (J). (gr. k-k). lib. bdg. 16.99 (978-0-375-93279-3(8) , Golden Bks.) Random Hse. Children's Bks.

Goldilocks. 2004. (J). pap. 14.95 incl. audio (978-0-7882-0688-7(5)) Weston Woods Studios, Inc.

Goldilocks: 6 Small Books. (gr. k-2). 23.00 (978-0-7635-8512-9(2)) Rigby Education.

Goldilocks & the Three Bears. 2004. (My First Fairy Tales Ser.). (Illus.). 24p. (J). pap. 3.99 (978-1-85854-686-5(9)) Brimax Books Ltd. GBR. *Dist:* Byeway Bks.

Goldilocks & the Three Bears. 2002. (Puppy Tales Ser.). (Illus.). 24p. (J). (gr. k-3). 1.49 (978-1-57759-219-8(0)); pap. 2.99 (978-1-57759-479-6(7)) Dalmatian Pr.

Goldilocks & the Three Bears. 2005. (J). bds. 3.99 (978-1-933200-09-5(X)) Family Bks. at Home.

Goldilocks & the Three Bears. (Ladybird Bks.). (ARA., Illus.). 52p. (J). 12.95 incl. audio (978-0-86685-254-8(9) , LDL109C) International Bk. Ctr., Inc.

Goldilocks & the Three Bears. 2005. (Emergent Library: Vol. 2). (YA). (ps-1). 23.94 (978-0-8215-8930-4(X)) Sadlier, William H. Inc.

Goldilocks & the Three Bears: Take-Home Book. 2005. (Emergent Library: Vol. 2). (YA). (ps-1). 12.60 (978-0-8215-7260-3(1)) Sadlier, William H. Inc.

Goldilocks & the Three Bears Read 'n Play Set. 1998. (Illus.). 8p. (J). (ps). 40.00 (978-1-888074-77-2(9)) Pockets of Learning.

GoldilocksThree Bears. 2004. (J). E-Book incl. cd-rom (978-1-84444-460-1(0)) Mantra Publishing, Ltd.

Goodnight Pooh. 2001. (Illus.). (J). 7.98 (978-0-7853-4788-0(7)) Publications International, Ltd.

Graf, Rosanna. Beary Beary Quite Contrary. Lawson, Laura, illus. l.t. ed. 1998. 24p. (Orig.). (J). (gr. 2-5). pap. 7.50 (978-1-882788-02-6(8)) Vangar Pubs./Baltimore.

Gravett, Emily. Orange Pear Apple Bear. Gravett, Emily, illus. 2007. 32p. (J). (ps). 12.99 (978-1-4169-3999-3(7)) Simon & Schuster Children's Publishing.

Gray, Nigel. Little Bear's Grandad. Cabban, Vanessa, illus. 2001. 28p. (J). (ps-k). tchr. ed. 14.95 (978-1-58925-008-6(7) , tiger tales) ME Media LLC.

—Osito y Su Abuelo. Cabban, Vanessa, illus. 2001. (SPA.). 32p. (J). (gr. k-2). (978-84-480-1630-2(0) , TM5011) Timun Mas, Editorial S.A. ESP. *Dist:* Lectorum Pubns., Inc.

Greene, Carol. The Cat & the Bear. 2005. 32p. (J). pap. (978-0-7868-1175-5(7)) Hyperion Bks. for Children.

Greene, Rhonda Gowler. Firebears, the Rescue Team. Andreasen, Dan, illus. rev. ed. 2005. 32p. (J). 15.95 (978-0-8050-7010-1(9) , Holt, Henry & Co. Bks. For Young Readers) Holt, Henry & Co.

Gregorich, Barbara. Waltur Buys a Pig in a Poke & Other Stories. Sorra, Kristin, illus. 2006. 64p. (J). (gr. 3-5). 15.00 (978-0-618-47306-9(8)) Houghton Mifflin Co.

Gregorich, Barbara & Sorra, Kristin. Waltur Paints Himself into a Corner & Other Stories. Gregorich, Barbara & Sorra, Kristin, illus. 2007. (Illus.). 48p. (J). (gr. k-3). 15.00 ***978-0-618-74796-2(6))** Houghton Mifflin Co.

Grey, Mini. Biscuit Bear. 2004. (Illus.). 32p. (J). (978-0-224-06496-5(7) , Jonathan Cape) Random Hse. Children's Bks.

Grigg, Carol. The Singing Snowbear. Grigg, Carol, illus. 1999. (Illus.). 32p. (J). (gr. k-3). tchr. ed. 15.00 (978-0-395-94223-9(3)) Houghton Mifflin Co. Trade & Reference Div.

Grindley, Sally. A Little Bit of Trouble. Taylor, Eleanor, illus. 2004. 32p. (J). 16.95 (978-1-58234-882-7(0) , Bloomsbury Children) Bloomsbury Publishing.

—No Trouble at All. 2004. (Illus.). 32p. (J). reprint ed. pap. 6.95 (978-1-58234-894-0(4) , Bloomsbury Children) Bloomsbury Publishing.

—Polar Star. Butler, John, illus. 1998. 32p. (J). (ps-3). 15.95 (978-1-56145-181-4(9) , Q26655) Peachtree Pubs., Ltd.

—What Are Friends For? Dann, Penny, illus. 1998. 18p. (J). pap. 11.98 (978-1-58048-053-6(5)) Sandvik Publishing.

—Will You Forgive Me? Dann, Penny, illus. 2001. 32p. (J). (ps-k). tchr. ed. 15.95 (978-0-7534-5295-0(2) , Kingfisher) Houghton Mifflin Co. Trade & Reference Div.

Griz Attack 2001. 2002. pap. 19.95 (978-1-56037-221-9(4)) Farcountry Pr.

Grooms, Molly. We Are Bears. 2002. (Illus.). 32p. (J). (ps-2). pap. 7.95 (978-1-55971-836-3(6) , NorthWord Bks. for Young Readers) T&N Children's Publishing.

—We Are Bears. 2000. (ps-2). lib. bdg. 16.40 (978-0-613-55921-8(5)) Tandem Library Bks.

Groth, Lynn. Buttons' Bouquet of Flowers. 2003. (Illus.). (J). pap. 5.99 (978-0-8100-1334-6(7)) Northwestern Publishing Hse.

—Buttons in the Dark. 2003. (Illus.). pap. 5.99 (978-0-8100-1333-9(9)) Northwestern Publishing Hse.

—Buttons' Picnic. 2003. (Illus.). (J). pap. 5.99 (978-0-8100-1331-5(2)) Northwestern Publishing Hse.

—Buttons Visits Grandma. 2003. (Illus.). pap. 5.99 (978-0-8100-1332-2(0)) Northwestern Publishing Hse.

Grumpy Bear: 3-in-1 Package. (Sails Literacy Ser.). 24p. (gr. k up). 57.00 (978-0-7578-3196-6(6)) Rigby Education.

Grumpy Bear: 6 Small Books. (Sails Literacy Ser.). 24p. (gr. k up). 25.00 (978-0-7578-3172-0(9)) Rigby Education.

Grumpy Bear: Big Book Only. (Sails Literacy Ser.). 24p. (gr. k up). 27.00 (978-0-7635-6988-4(7)) Rigby Education.

Gutman, Anne. Penelope in the Winter. Hallensleben, Georg, illus. 2005. 12p. (J). (ps-k). pap. 9.99 (978-0-439-67360-0(7) , Cartwheel Bks.) Scholastic, Inc.

—Penelope Says Good Night. Hallensleben, Georg, illus. 2006. 12p. (J). pap. 9.99 (978-0-439-67359-4(3) , Cartwheel Bks.) Scholastic, Inc.

Guy, Glen. The Adventure Fire: Adventures of Dusty Sourdough. 2005. 9.95 (978-1-59433-006-3(9)) Publication Consultants.

Gwent (Wales), Staff Development Unit Staff & Acen Staff, contrib. by. Nos Da, Arthur. 2005. (WEL., Illus.). 8p. (978-1-874049-31-9(9)) Acen Limited.

Haddon, Mark. The Ice Bear's Cave. Axtell, David, illus. 2002. 30p. (J). (gr. k-2). pap. 9.99 (978-0-00-664628-0(X)) HarperCollins Pubs. Ltd. GBR. *Dist:* Trafalgar Square Publishing.

Hague, Kathleen. Alphabears: An ABC Book. Hague, Michael, illus. rev. ed. 1999. 28p. (J). (ps-k). bds. 6.95 (978-0-8050-6208-3(4) , Holt, Henry & Co. Bks. For Young Readers) Holt, Henry & Co.

—Numbears: A Counting Book. Hague, Michael, illus. rev. ed. 1999. 28p. (J). (ps-k). bds. 6.95 (978-0-8050-6207-6(6) , Holt, Henry & Co. Bks. For Young Readers) Holt, Henry & Co.

—Ten Little Bears. Hague, Michael, illus. 1999. 24p. (J). (ps-k). 16.00 (978-0-688-16383-9(1)); 15.89 (978-0-688-16732-5(2)) HarperCollins Pubs.

Haider, Sajjad S. Time Bears Witness. 1999. (Illus.). (J). pap. 14.95 (978-1-871031-92-8(3)) Abjad Bk. Designers & Builders.

Hal Leonard Corporation Staff. Winnie the Pooh. 1998. (Style Collections). 40p. (ps-3). pap. 10.95 (978-0-7935-8754-4(9) , 0793587549) Leonard, Hal Corp.

Halfman, Janet. Polar Bear Horizon. Chesterman, Adrian, illus. 2006. (Smithsonian Oceanic Collection). 32p. (J). 19.95 incl. audio (978-1-59249-568-9(0)); 9.95 (978-1-59249-570-2(2)) Soundprints.

Halfmann, Janet. Polar Bear Horizon. Chesterman, Adrian, illus. 2006. 32p. pap. 8.95 incl. reel tape (978-1-59249-569-6(9)); (J). 15.95 (978-1-59249-565-8(6)); (J). pap. 4.95 (978-1-59249-567-2(2)); (J). mass mkt. 6.95 (978-1-59249-566-5(4)) Soundprints.

Hall, Kirsten. A Bear for You. Rosa, Iole, illus. (My First Reader Ser.). (J). (gr. k-1). 2005. 32p. pap. 3.95 (978-0-516-25112-7(0)); 2004. 31p. 18.50 (978-0-516-24675-8(5)) Scholastic Library Publishing. (Children's Pr.).

Hamilton, Elizabeth L. Cubby Bear's Big Responsibility. 2004. (Character Critters Ser.: No. 8). (Illus.). 32p. (J). per. 5.95 (978-0-9754629-4-2(6) , Character-in-Action) Quiet Impact, Inc.

Hao, K. T. One Pizza, One Penny. Feldman, Roxanne Hsu, tr. from CHI. Ferri, Giuliano, illus. 2003. 32p. 15.95 (978-0-8126-2702-2(4)) Cricket Bks.

Hapka, Catherine. Ballerina Bear. Valeri, Jim & Valeri, Kara, illus. 2004. (Build-A-Bear Workshop Ser.). 24p. (J). (ps-1). 3.50 (978-0-06-075284-2(X) , Harper Festival) HarperCollins Pubs.

Happy Birthday, Moon. 2004. (J). 24.95 incl. audio (978-1-56008-031-2(0)) Weston Woods Studios, Inc.

Happy Birthday Moon. 2004. 29.95 incl. cd-rom (978-1-55592-842-1(0)); pap. 32.75 incl. audio (978-1-55592-236-8(8)); (J). pap. 18.95 incl. audio compact disk (978-1-55592-805-6(6)); (J). pap. 18.95 incl. audio compact disk (978-1-55592-773-8(4)); (J). pap. 38.75 incl. audio compact disk (978-1-55592-822-3(6)); (J). pap. 38.75 incl. audio compact disk (978-1-55592-788-2(2)); (J). pap. 32.75 incl. audio (978-1-55592-237-5(6)); (J). pap. 14.95 incl. audio (978-1-55592-657-1(6)) Weston Woods Studios, Inc.

Happy Birthday Paddington. 1998. (Illus.). 4p. (J). pap. 17.98 (978-1-58048-046-8(2)) Sandvik Publishing.

Harbo, Gary. The Northern Woods Adventure: Early Reader. Harbo, Gary, illus. l.t. ed. 2004. (If You Want to Succeed, You Need to Read! Ser.: 6). (Illus.). 33p. (J). 10.95 (978-1-884149-16-0(2)) Kutie Kari Bks., Inc.

Harcourt School Publishers Staff. Are You There, Baby Bear: Library Book. 3rd ed. 2002. (Trophies Reading Program Ser.). (Illus.). pap. 13.50 (978-0-15-326529-7(9)) Harcourt Schl. Pubs.

—Are You There, Bear. 99th ed. 1998. (Signatures Ser.). (Illus.). (gr. k-1). pap. 60.70 (978-0-15-310893-8(2)) Harcourt Schl. Pubs.

—The Bear Facts Advanced Level. 3rd ed. 2002. (Trophies Reading Program Ser.). (Illus.). pap. 5.10 (978-0-15-323031-8(2)) Harcourt Schl. Pubs.

—Bear Pie: Take-Home Book. 1999. (Signatures Ser.). (Illus.). (J). pap. 1.90 (978-0-15-313915-4(3)) Harcourt Schl. Pubs.

—Collections: Two Bear Cubs: Grade Level Library. 1999. (Illus.). (J). pap. 4.70 (978-0-15-315203-0(6)) Harcourt Schl. Pubs.

—Counting Bears: On Level. 3rd ed. 2002. (Trophies Reading Program Ser.). (Illus.). pap. 5.10 (978-0-15-323001-1(0)) Harcourt Schl. Pubs.

—Goldy & the Three Bears: Below Level. 3rd ed. 2002. (Trophies Reading Program Ser.). (Illus.). (J). pap. 4.10 (978-0-15-322970-1(5)) Harcourt Schl. Pubs.

—Lester & the Bear: Take-Home Book. 1999. (Signatures Ser.). (Illus.). (J). (gr. 6). pap. 1.90 (978-0-15-313953-6(6)) Harcourt Schl. Pubs.

—One of My Bears: Take-Home Book. 1999. (Collections Ser.). (Illus.). (J). pap. 1.90 (978-0-15-317236-6(3)) Harcourt Schl. Pubs.

—Pack Your Pajamas. 3rd ed. 2002. (Trophies English Language Learners Ser.). (Illus.). pap. 5.10 (978-0-15-327646-0(0)) Harcourt Schl. Pubs.

—The Polar Bear & the Brave Hare: Library Edition. 1999. (Collections Ser.). (Illus.). (J). 4.70 (978-0-15-314306-9(1)) Harcourt Schl. Pubs.

—The Three Bears: Phonics Practice Reader. 1999. (Collections Ser.). (Illus.). (J). pap. 2.60 (978-0-15-312941-4(7)) Harcourt Schl. Pubs.

—Trofeos Advanced Level: Osos de Verdad. 3rd ed. 2002. (SPA., Illus.). (gr. 1). pap. 6.80 (978-0-15-323942-7(5)) Harcourt Schl. Pubs.

Harley, Bill. Bear's All-Night Party. Ferreira, Melissa, illus. 2001. 32p. (J). (ps-2). 15.95 (978-0-87483-572-4(0)) August Hse. Pubs., Inc.

Harper, Piers. Snow Bear. Black, Sonia, ed. Harper, Piers, illus. 2003. (Illus.). 32p. (J). lthr. 15.95 (978-0-439-54426-9(2) , Cartwheel Bks.) Scholastic, Inc.

Harper, Piers, illus. Snow Bear's Surprise. 2004. 32p. (J). (978-1-4050-4883-5(2)) Macmillan Publishers Ltd.

Harris, Joel Chandler. Tar Baby: Tales of Brer Rabbit. Deryk, Thomas, illus. 2000. (Classic Portables Ser.). 160p. (J). reprint ed. 10.95 (978-1-84068-020-1(2)) Creation Bks. GBR. *Dist:* Subterranean Co.

Harvey, M. A. The Riddle of Bear Cave: Dare to Take the Test. 2004. (Illus.). 128p. (J). pap. (978-1-84458-146-7(2)) Chrysalis Children's Bks.

Haseley, Dennis. A Story for Bear. LaMarche, Jim, illus. 2002. 32p. (J). (gr. k-3). 16.00 (978-0-15-200239-8(1) , Silver Whistle) Harcourt Trade Pubs.

Hats: Individual Title Six-Packs. (Sails Literacy Ser.). 16p. (gr. k up). 27.00 (978-0-7635-4443-0(4)) Rigby Education.

Hayes, Geoffrey. Patrick & the Big Bully. 2001. (Illus.). (J). lib. bdg. 16.49 (978-0-7868-2594-3(4)) Hyperion Pr.

Hayes, Geoffrey, illus. & text. Patrick at the Circus. Hayes, Geoffrey, text. 2002. (J). lib. bdg. (978-0-7868-2595-0(2)) Hyperion Bks. for Children.

Hayes, Karel. The Winter Visitors. 2007. 32p. (ps-3). 16.95 ***978-0-89272-750-6(0))** Down East Bks.

Hayes, Sarah. El Solo y la Merienda. 2000. (Easy Readers Ser.).Tr. of Bear & the Snack. (SPA., Illus.). 32p. (J). 11.95 (978-84-207-3401-9(2)) Grupo Anaya, S.A. ESP. *Dist:* Distribooks, Inc.

—This Is the Bear. Craig, Helen, illus. 1999. (Read & Share Ser.). 24p. (J). (ps). pap. 3.99 (978-0-7636-0867-5(X)) Candlewick Pr.

Heap, Sue. Espera y Veras. (SPA.). pap. 7.95 (978-950-07-2025-0(6)) Editorial Sudamericana S.A. ARG. *Dist:* Distribooks, Inc.

—Four Friends in the Garden. Heap, Sue, illus. 2004. (Illus.). 32p. (J). (gr. k-ps). 15.99 (978-0-7636-2371-5(7)) Candlewick Pr.

Hegarty, Sue. Barnaby & Thor. Shaw, Alice, illus. 2002. (J). 16.95 (978-0-939549-53-5(0)) ZON International Publishing Co.

Heinz, Brian J. Nanuk, Lord of the Ice. Manchess, Gregory, illus. 2005. (J). (978-0-936335-13-1(0)); pap. (978-0-936335-14-8(9)) Ballyhoo BookWorks, Inc.

Heling, Kathryn & Hembrook, Deborah. Bear's Big Ideas. Walz, Richard, illus. 2005. (Step into Reading Ser.: Vol. 2). 32p. (J). (ps-2). pap. 3.99 (978-0-375-83391-5(9) , Random Hse. Bks. for Young Readers) Random Hse. Children's Bks.

Helmrath, M. O. & Bartlett, J. L. Bobby Bear Series, 18 bks. (Illus.). (J). (ps-1). lib. bdg. 189.60 (978-0-87783-163-1(7)); Set. 63.52 (978-0-87783-181-5(5)) Oddo Publishing, Inc.

Hendrickson, Jean A. A Fun Day with Angelbear. 2001. (Angell Ser.). (Illus.). 32p. (J). (ps up). pap. (978-1-929953-01-1(1)) Gates & Bridges Inc.

Hest, Amy. Un Beso de Buenas Noches. Rubio, Esther, tr. Jeram, Anita, illus. (SPA.). (J). 16.00 (978-1-930332-04-1(1) , LC3294) Lectorum Pubns., Inc.

—Don't You Feel Well, Sam? Jeram, Anita, illus. 32p. (J). (ps). 2007. pap. 4.99 (978-0-7636-2408-8(X)); 2002. 15.99 (978-0-7636-1009-8(7)) Candlewick Pr.

—Kiss Good Night. Jeram, Anita, illus. (J). (ps). 2006. 32p. pap. 4.99 (978-0-7636-2114-8(5)); 2004. 30p. bds. 6.99 (978-0-7636-2094-3(7)); 2001. 32p. 15.99 (978-0-7636-0780-7(0)) Candlewick Pr.

—Kiss Good Night: With Plush. Jeram, Anita, illus. gif. ed. 2004. 30p. (J). 12.99 (978-0-7636-2524-5(8)) Candlewick Pr.

—You Can Do It, Sam. Jeram, Anita, illus. (Sam Bks.). 32p. (J). (ps). 2007. pap. 4.99 ***978-0-7636-3688-3(6));** 2003. 15.99 (978-0-7636-1934-3(5)) Candlewick Pr.

Heuck, Sidgrid. Poni/Oso/Estrella. 2002. Tr. of Pony/Bear & Star. (SPA., Illus.). 32p. (J). 11.95 (978-84-261-2270-4(1)) Juventud, Editorial ESP. *Dist:* AIMS International Bks., Inc.

Hill, Eric. Spot's Little Book of Fun at Home. Hill, Eric, illus. 2003. (Spots Little Book of Fun Ser.). (Illus.). 10p. (J). (ps-k). 5.99 (978-0-399-23895-6(6) , Putnam Juvenile) Penguin Group (USA) Inc.

Hillert, Margaret. The Three Bears. Wilde, Irma, illus. rev. ed. 2006. (Beginning to Read Ser.). 30p. (J). lib. bdg. 18.60 (978-1-59953-026-0(0)) Norwood Hse. Pr.

Hissey, Jane. Old Bear Tales. (Illus.). (J). (978-0-399-21829-3(7) , Philomel) Penguin Group (USA) Inc.

—Los Pantalones del Osito. 2001. (SPA., Illus.). 32p. (J). (gr. k-2). (978-84-89675-56-8(2) , ZZ0592) Zendrera Zariquiey, Editorial ESP. *Dist:* Lectorum Pubns., Inc.

Hoban, Russell. Bedtime for Frances. 1999. (J). pap. 1.95 (978-0-590-09887-8(X)) Scholastic, Inc.

Hobbs, Carolyn. The Adventures of Honey Bear. Beard, Larry, illus. 2000. (Aunt Carolyn's Collection). 17p. (J). (gr. k-6). pap. 8.95 incl. audio (978-0-929291-61-1(1)); pap. 6.95 (978-0-929291-60-4(3)) Gospel Projects Pr.

Hobbs, Will. Beardance. 2004. (Illus.). 197p. (J). (gr. 4-7). lib. bdg. 12.04 (978-0-606-32685-8(5)) Tandem Library Bks.

—Beardream. 2000. (gr. k-3). lib. bdg. 15.30 (978-0-613-28414-1(3)) Tandem Library Bks.

Hofmann, Ginnie. Who Wants an Old Teddy Bear?, 5 vols. Hofmann, Ginnie, illus. 2003. (Illus.). 32p. (J). pap. 5.95 (978-1-932485-00-4(7)) Reverie Publishing Co.

Hogan, Mary. Pooh's Pumpkin Surprise. 1999. (Learn & Grow Ser.). (Illus.). 10p. (J). (ps). 4.99 (978-0-7364-0158-6(X)) Mouse Works.

Holburn, Sandra. The Angel & the Bear. 2006. (ENG.). 28p. per. 15.30 (***978-1-4259-4994-5(0)***) AuthorHouse.

Holub, Joan. Lost & Found in Jumpstart Town. del Sur, Duendes, illus. 2000. (Jumpstart Workbooks). 32p. (J). (ps-k). pap. 3.99 (978-0-439-08789-6(9)) Scholastic, Inc.

—Silly Bears. Burris, Priscilla, illus. 2001. (My First Hello Reader! Ser.). (J). pap. (978-0-439-32473-1(4)) Scholastic, Inc.

Hope, Laura Lee. The Story of a Plush Bear. 2006. pap. 87.99 (***978-1-4219-7489-7(4)***) IndyPublish.com.

Horowitz, Jeanine. Latch Key Kid. 2006. 75p. (YA). lib. bdg. 12.99 (***978-1-934190-10-4(1)***) Ocean Front Bk. Publishing, Inc.

Howell, Theresa. I Don't See Any Bears Do You? A Yellowstone, Grand Teton, Glacier Adventure. Jones, Larry, illus. 2004. 12p. (J). reprint ed. bds. 7.95 (978-0-87358-886-7(X) , Rising Moon Bks. for Young Readers) Northland Publishing.

Howland, Deborah. Polar Bear. Howland, Deborah, illus. 2002. (Illus.). (J). bds. (978-1-59069-258-5(6) , HS3004) Studio Mouse LLC.

Hull, Maureen. Rainy Days with Bear. Franson, Leanne, illus. 2005. 32p. pap. (978-1-897073-34-6(8)) Lobster Pr.

Hungry Bear, 6 Packs. (Chiquilibros Ser.). (gr. k-1). 23.00 (978-0-7635-0424-3(6)) Rigby Education.

Hutchins, Hazel J. It's Raining, Yancy & Bear. Ohi, Ruth, illus. 1998. 32p. (J). (ps-2). pap. 5.95 (978-1-55037-528-2(8)); lib. bdg. 15.95 (978-1-55037-529-9(6)) Annick Pr., Ltd. CAN. *Dist:* Firefly Bks., Ltd.

—It's Raining, Yancy & Bear. ed. 2004. (Illus.). (J). (gr. k-3). spiral bd. (978-0-616-01678-7(6)); spiral bd. (978-0-616-01679-4(4)) Canadian National Institute for the Blind/Institut National Canadien pour les Aveugles.

—Robyn Looks for Bears. Cathcart, Yvonne, illus. 2000. (New First Novels Ser.: Vol. 16). 58p. (gr. 1-5). (J). (978-0-88780-497-7(7)); 4.95 (978-0-88780-496-0(9)) Formac Publishing Co., Ltd. CAN. *Dist:* Casemate Pubs. & Bk. Distributors, LLC.

I Lost My Bear. 2004. 24.95 incl. audio (978-1-55592-694-6(0)); 29.95 incl. audio compact disk (978-1-55592-704-2(1)); pap. 18.95 incl. audio compact disk (978-1-55592-707-3(6)); pap. 14.95 incl. audio (978-1-55592-698-4(3)) Weston Woods Studios, Inc.

Ilagan, Roland Mechael B. Baba the Bear. Ilagan, Roland Mechael B., illus. 5000th ed. 2005. (Illus.). 32p. (J). (978-0-9773809-0-9(4)) Wonderbooks Publishing.

Inkpen, Mick. Bear. (Illus.). 34p. (J). (ps-2). (BEN, ENG, URD, VIE & SPA.). (978-1-85430-546-6(8)); (ENG, URD, VIE, SPA & CHI., (978-1-85430-550-3(6)) Magi Pubns.

Inteli, Nancy. Tutter Family Reunion. 2001. (gr. k-3). lib. bdg. 14.15 (978-0-613-51327-2(4)) Tandem Library Bks.

Irwin, Daniel. The Adventures of Tylor Bear & Mana. 2004. 144p. pap. 19.95 (978-1-4137-5580-0(1)) PublishAmerica, Inc.

Jackson, Teresa Jean. Huggable Harry. 2004. 21p. pap. 14.95 (978-1-4137-1102-8(2)) PublishAmerica, Inc.

Jacquemain, Patti. Journey of the Great Bear: Through California's Golden Past. Jacquemain, Patti, illus. 2006. (J). (978-0-929702-10-0(7)) Mission Creek Studios.

Jacques, Brian. The Tale of Urso Brunov: Little Father of All Bears. Natchev, Alexi, illus. 2003. 45p. (J). (ps-3). 16.99 (978-0-399-23762-1(3) , Philomel) Penguin Group (USA) Inc.

—The Tale of Urso Brunov: Little Father of All Bears. Natchev, Alexi, illus. 2006. 48p. (J). (gr. k). reprint ed. pap. 6.99 (978-0-14-240723-3(2) , Puffin) Penguin Group (USA) Inc.

James, Annabelle. Goldilocks & the Three Bears Story in a Box. Winter, Janet, illus. 2002. (Story in a Box Ser.). 12p. (J). bds. 8.99 (978-1-883043-37-7(9)) Straight Edge Pr., The.

James, D. W. Chase. 2003. 108p. pap. 13.95 (978-1-59286-450-8(3)) PublishAmerica, Inc.

James, Elizabeth. The Woman Who Married a Bear. Atanas, illus. 2007. 40p. (J). (gr. k up). 16.95 (***978-1-894965-49-1(3)***) Simply Read Bks. CAN. *Dist:* Perseus Distribution.

James, Susan. This Is My Dance: Sing, Dance & Read with Me, Read-Along with Big Book & Cassette. 2000. 16p. (J). (ps-3). pap. 14.95 incl. audio (978-1-931127-32-5(8) , 986-011) Kindermusik International.

Janosch. Yo Te Curare, Dijo el Pequeno Oso, Level 3.5. 2001. (SPA.). 48p. (J). 10.95 (978-84-204-4807-7(9)) Alfaguara, Ediciones, S.A.- Grupo Santillana ESP. *Dist:* Santillana USA Publishing Co., Inc.

—Yo Te Curare, Dijo el Pequeno Oso. Janosch, illus. 2003. (SPA., Illus.). 48p. (J). (gr. k-3). pap. 8.95 (978-958-24-0110-8(9)) Santillana USA Publishing Co., Inc.

Jeffs, Stephanie. Christopher Bear Makes Friends. Thomas, Jacqui, illus. 2004. (Christopher Bear Ser.). 32p. 5.99 (978-0-8066-4401-1(X) , Augsburg Bks.) Augsburg Fortress, Pubs.

Jennings, Patrick. The Pup Tent: An Ike & Mem Story. O'Neill, Catharine, illus. 2005. (J). (978-0-8234-1938-8(X)) Holiday Hse., Inc.

Jennings, Patti, illus. Fleecy Bear. 2003. (Fleecy Friends Ser.). 10p. (J). (ps). 9.99 (978-0-8431-0525-4(9) , Price Stern Sloan) Penguin Group (USA) Inc.

Jennings, Sharon & Watt, Melanie. Bearcub & mama. 2005. (Illus.). 32p. (J). (ps-2). (978-1-55337-566-1(1)) Kids Can Pr., Ltd.

Jennings, Sharon, et al. Franklin Snoops. Jeffrey, Sean, illus. 2003. (Franklin TV Storybook Ser.). 32p. (J). (ps-3). (978-1-55337-364-3(2)) Kids Can Pr., Ltd.

Jeram, Anita. You're All My Favorites Book & Toy Gift Set. Jeram, Anita, illus. 2004. (Illus.). 32p. (J). (ps-2). 15.99 (978-0-7636-2442-2(X)) Candlewick Pr.

Jim Henson Staff. Bear Breakfast Treat. 2000. (Illus.). 32p. (J). (gr. k-3). pap. 3.99 (978-0-7434-0837-0(3) , Simon & Schuster Children's Publishing) Simon & Schuster Children's Publishing.

—Bear Loves Weather. 2000. (Bearbigblue). (Illus.). 20p. (J). (gr. k-3). per. 4.99 (978-0-671-77446-2(8) , Simon & Schuster Children's Publishing) Simon & Schuster Children's Publishing.

—Tutters Tiny Trip. 2000. (Bear in the Big Blue House Ser.). (Illus.). 32p. (J). per. (978-0-7434-0836-3(5) , Simon & Schuster Children's Publishing) Simon & Schuster Children's Publishing.

Job. Yakari & the Grizzly. Jeffrey, Erica, tr. from FRE. Derib, illus. 2007. 48p. pap. 9.99 (***978-1-905460-16-8(3)***) CineBook GBR. *Dist:* Biblio Distribution.

Johnson, D. B. Henry Hikes to Fitchburg. 2006. (Illus.). 32p. (J). (gr. k-3). reprint ed. 6.95 (978-0-618-73749-9(9)) Houghton Mifflin Co. Trade & Reference Div.

—Henry Works. 2004. (Illus.). 32p. (J). (gr. k-3). tchr. ed. 15.00 (978-0-618-42003-2(7)) Houghton Mifflin Co. Trade & Reference Div.

Johnson, Donald B. Henry Hikes to Fitchburg. 2002. (Illus.). (J). 24.04 (978-0-7587-4606-1(7)) Book Wholesalers, Inc.

—Henry Hikes to Fitchburg. 2000. (Illus.). 32p. (J). (gr. k-3). tchr. ed. 15.00 (978-0-395-96867-3(4)) Houghton Mifflin Co. Trade & Reference Div.

Jones, Carolyn. Theodora Bear. Spurll, Barbara, illus. 2007. (Orca Echoes Ser.). 64p. (J). (gr. 2-4). pap. (***978-1-55143-496-4(2)***) Orca Bk. Pubs.

Jones, Christianne C. Busy Bear. 2007. (Illus.). 24p. (J). (***978-1-4048-2426-3(X)***) Picture Window Bks.

—Busy Bear. Jensen, Brian, illus. 2006. 24p. (J). lib. bdg. (***978-1-4048-2396-9(4)***) Picture Window Bks.

Jones, Maurice. Welcome Home Little Bear. Currey, Anna, illus. 1998. 28p. (J). (ps-1). 13.95 (978-0-7641-5081-4(2)) Barron's Educational Series, Inc.

Joosse, Barbara M. Nikolai, the Only Bear. Liwska, Renata, illus. 2005. 32p. (J). (ps-3). 16.99 (978-0-399-23884-0(0) , Philomel) Penguin Group (USA) Inc.

The Journals of Punkin Bear Volume One. 2006. (J). per. 12.00 (***978-0-9778471-0-5(1)***) Bayliss, Erin.

Jukes, Mavis. You're a Bear. Johnson, Steve & Fancher, Lou, illus. 2003. 40p. (J). (gr. k-3). 16.95 (978-0-375-80267-6(3)); lib. bdg. 18.99 (978-0-375-90267-3(8)) Random Hse. Children's Bks. (Knopf Bks. for Young Readers)

Jules, Jacqueline. Once upon a Shabbos. Kahn, Katherine Janus, illus. 1998. 32p. (J). (ps-3). 15.95 (978-1-58013-020-2(8)); pap. 6.95 (978-1-58013-021-9(6)) Kar-Ben Publishing.

Julietta, Melinda & Groom, Molly. We Are Bears. Guamotta, Lucia, photos by. 2000. (Illus.). 31p. (J). (ps-k). 12.95 (978-1-55971-747-2(5) , NorthWord Bks. for Young Readers) T&N Children's Publishing.

Kacer, Kathy. The Secret of Gabi's Dresser. 2005. (Illus.). 128p. (YA). (gr. 3-6). pap. 4.95 (978-1-896764-15-3(0)) Second Story Pr. CAN. *Dist:* Orca Bk. Pubs. USA, Univ. of Toronto Pr.

Kalz, Jill. Bears on Ice. Olin, Troy, illus. 2006. (Read-It! Readers Ser.). 32p. (J). (ps-3). 18.60 (978-1-4048-1577-3(5)) Picture Window Bks.

Kanter, Stephen. The Bear & the Blackberry. Kanter, Dory, illus. 1999. 6p. (J). (ps-7). 15.00 (978-0-9675888-0-3(4)) Kantourian Pr.

Kasza, Keiko. The Mightiest. 2003. (Picture Puffin Ser.). (Illus.). 32p. (J). pap. 5.99 (978-0-14-250185-6(9) , Puffin) Penguin Group (USA) Inc.

—The Mightiest. Kasza, Keiko, illus. 2001. (Illus.). 32p. (J). 16.99 (978-0-399-23586-3(8) , Putnam Juvenile) Penguin Group (USA) Inc.

—Mightiest. 2003. (ps-2). lib. bdg. 14.15 (978-0-613-89797-6(8)) Tandem Library Bks.

—No Te Rias, Pepe. (Buenas Noches Coleccion). (SPA.). (J). (gr. k-3). 8.95 (978-958-04-3623-2(1)) Norma S.A. COL. *Dist:* Distribuidora Norma, Inc., Lectorum Pubns., Inc.

Kelly, Mary. Becky & Bear. 2006. (Illus.). 31p. (J). pap. 9.95 (***978-1-930596-64-1(2)***) Amherst Pr.

Kenneth, Caroline. Just Be Nice... To Your Little Friends. 2000. (Disney Ser.). (Illus.). 24p. (J). (ps-k). pap. 3.29 (978-0-307-10100-6(2) , 10100, Golden Bks.) Random Hse. Children's Bks.

Kenyon, Tony. Oops! It's Olly Bear. 2003. (Illus.). 32p. (J). 18.00 (978-1-85881-899-3(0)) Orion Bks. Ltd. GBR. *Dist:* Trafalgar Square Publishing.

Kern, Noris. I Love You with All My Heart. 2002. (Illus.). 26p. (J). bds. 6.95 (978-0-8118-3622-7(3)) Chronicle Bks. LLC.

Kern, Noris & Baronian, Jean-Baptiste. I Love You with All My Heart. 1998. (Illus.). 32p. (J). (ps-1). 15.95 (978-0-8118-2031-8(9)) Chronicle Bks. LLC.

Keselman, Gabriela. Cuando Viene Papa? Gusti, illus. 2000. (Tren Azul Ser.).Tr. of When Will Dad Be Back?. (SPA.). 32p. (J). (ps-2). (978-84-236-5493-2(1)) Edebé ESP. *Dist:* Baker & Taylor Bks.

Keylock, Joanna Murray. Pupazzo's Colorful World. Pelayo, Ruben, tr. Murray, Paula, illus. 2006. Tr. of colorido mundo de Pupazzo. (J). 10.00 (978-1-889289-62-5(0)) Ye Olde Font Shoppe.

Kideckel, Marsha. The Too Big Bear. Macaulay, Kitty, illus. 2003. (Annikins Ser.: Vol. 13). 12p. (Orig.). (J). (ps-2). pap. 0.99 (978-1-55037-347-9(1)) Annick Pr., Ltd. CAN. *Dist:* Firefly Bks., Ltd.

Kimpton, Diana. Un Osito para Maddie. Roffe, Mercedes, tr. Kiernan, Anna, illus. 2001. (SPA.). 32p. (J). (gr. k-1). pap. 4.00 (978-0-439-31740-5(1) , SO30907, Cartwheel Bks.) Scholastic, Inc.

King, Deborah. Bears Dream Picture Book. 2002. (Illus.). 30p. pap. 8.99 (978-0-00-664679-2(4)) Zondervan.

King, Jamie R. Barry the Bear Meets the Mother of All Bears. Lemmon, David, illus. 1999. (Zoooo Stories Ser.). (J). (978-1-893993-00-6(0)) Medias & Co., Inc.

Kinney, Kendall. Tiger Tails. 2004. 68p. (J). per. 10.95 (978-1-932196-21-4(8)) WordWright.biz, Inc.

Kliros, Thea, illus. The Three Bears. 2003. 22p. (J). (ps-1). 5.99 (978-0-06-008238-3(0)) HarperCollins Pubs.

Kolar, Marsha. Little Brave Bear. Di Marco, Audrey, illus. 2005. 17p. (J). per. (978-0-9766804-0-6(8)) CottonWood Publishing Co.

Kovalski, Maryann. Omar on Ice. ed. 2004. (J). (gr. k-3). spiral bd. (978-0-616-01690-9(5)); spiral bd. (978-0-616-01691-6(3)) Canadian National Institute for the Blind/Institut National Canadien pour les Aveugles.

—Omar on Ice. Kovalski, Maryann, illus. (First Flight Ser.). (Illus.). (J). (gr. 1-3). 40p. lib. bdg. (978-1-55041-409-7(7)); 2002. 32p. pap. (978-1-55041-783-8(5)) Fitzhenry & Whiteside, Ltd.

—Omar on Ice. 1999. (First Flight Ser.). (Illus.). 32p. (J). (gr. k-3). (978-1-55041-507-0(7)) Fitzhenry & Whiteside, Ltd.

—Omar on Ice. Kovalski, Maryann, illus. 1999. (First Flight Ser.). (Illus.). 38p. (J). (gr. 1-3). pap. (978-1-55041-407-3(0)) Fitzhenry & Whiteside, Ltd.

Kovalski, Maryann. Omar's Halloween. 2007. (Illus.). 32p. (J). (ps-3). per. (***978-1-55455-049-4(1)***) Fitzhenry & Whiteside, Ltd.

Krasner, Steven. Have a Nice Nap, Humphrey. Griffis, Sandy, illus. 1998. 36p. (J). (gr. k-5). pap. 12.95 (978-0-9642721-2-5(1)) Gorilla Productions.

Krauss, Ruth. Bears. Sendak, Maurice, illus. 2005. 24p. (J). 14.95 (978-0-06-027994-3(X)) HarperCollins Pubs.

Kreloff, Elliot. Harry Bear & Friends: Opposites. 2007. (Illus.). 18p. (J). bds. 7.95 (978-1-59354-601-4(7)) Blue Apple Bks.

Kreloff, Elliot. Harry Bear & Friends Count Fish. 2007. (Illus.). 16p. (ps-k). bds. 7.95 (***978-1-59354-619-9(X)***) Handprint Bks.

Krulik, Nancy E. Puzzlers. 1999. (My Very First Winnie the Pooh Ser.). (Illus.). 64p. (J). (ps-1). pap. 4.99 (978-0-7868-4344-2(6)) Disney Pr.

Kulling, Monica. Edgar Badger's Fishing Day. Twinem, Nancy, illus. 1999. 48p. (J). (gr. 1-5). pap. 4.50 (978-1-57255-603-4(X)) Mondo Publishing.

—Edgar Badger's Fishing Day. 1999. (gr. 3-6). lib. bdg. 12.40 (978-0-613-17198-4(5)) Tandem Library Bks.

Kunkel, Mike. Herobear & the Kid Vol. 1: The Inheritance. 2003. (Illus.). 208p. pap. 19.95 (978-0-9721259-1-8(4)) Astonish Comics.

—Inheritance. 2003. (gr. k-3). lib. bdg. 30.35 (978-0-613-77882-4(0)) Tandem Library Bks.

Kurgas, Ann B. Just As the Sun Came Peeking over the Banyan Trees: A Color & Keep Book. Kurgas, Ann B., illus. 1998. (Illus.). iv, 80p. (J). (gr. 1-6). pap. 14.95 (978-0-9665060-0-6(6) , K-9801-A) Le Jam Bks.

Kurtz, Carmen. Brun. (SPA.). 128p. (YA). (gr. 5-8). (978-84-279-3367-5(3)) Noguer y Caralt Editores, S. A. ESP. *Dist:* Lectorum Pubns., Inc.

—Brun. 2001. (SPA.). (gr. 7-12). lib. bdg. 16.40 (978-0-613-84207-5(3)) Tandem Library Bks.

Kurtz, John. Goldilocks & the Three Bears. Kurtz, John, illus. 2004. (Illus.). 24p. (J). lib. bdg. 8.00 (***978-1-4242-0635-3(9)***) Fitzgerald Bks.

Kurtz, John, illus. Goldilocks & the Three Bears. 2004. (Jump at the Sun Fairy-Tale Classics Ser.). 24p. (ps-2). pap. 3.50 (978-0-7868-0952-3(3)) Hyperion Bks. for Children.

Kvasnosky, Laura McGee. Frank & Izzy Set Sail. Kvasnosky, Laura McGee, illus. 2004. (Illus.). 32p. (J). (gr. k-4). 15.99 (978-0-7636-2146-9(3)) Candlewick Pr.

La Fon-Cox, Angelique. A Tale of Kooshla & Saboo: in Heavenly Castles. 2006. (ENG.). 48p. per. 19.99 (***978-1-4259-7997-3(1)***) AuthorHouse.

Ladd, Frances Ann. All for You! Johnson, Jay, illus. 2004. (Care Bears Ser.). 16p. (J). 5.99 (978-0-439-62493-0(2)) Scholastic, Inc.

—Where Are You? Johnson, Jay, illus. 2004. (Care Bears Ser.). 16p. (J). 5.99 (978-0-439-62491-6(6)) Scholastic, Inc.

Lamb, Albert. Woolly Winter Hat. McPhail, David, illus. 2006. 32p. (J). pap. 6.99 (978-0-439-79304-9(1)) Scholastic, Inc.

Landa, Norbert. Little Bear & the Wishing Tree. Mendez, Simon, illus. 2007. 28p. (J). (ps-2). 16.95 (***978-1-56148-566-6(7)***) Good Bks.

Landa, Norbert. The Little Bear's Christmas. Scharff-Kniemeyer, Marlis, illus. 1999. 32p. (J). (ps-3). 14.95 (978-1-888444-60-5(6)) Little Tiger Pr.

Lang, Tom. Bear. 2002. 64p. per. 5.00 (978-0-9649742-6-5(6)) Boudelang Pr.

Lange, Nikki Bataille. Cheer up! a Care Bears Feeling Book: A Plush Face Book with Flocking. Moore, Saxton, illus. 2009. (Care Bears Ser.). 10p. (J). ring bd. 11.95 (***978-1-57791-301-6(9)***) Brighter Minds Children's Publishing.

Lansky, Vicki. No Es Tu Culpa, Koko Oso. Prince, Jane, illus. 1999. (Lansky, Vicki Ser.).Tr. of It's Not Your Fault, Koko Bear. (SPA.). 32p. (ps-2). pap. 7.99 (978-0-916773-45-8(0)) Book Peddlers.

Larsen, Beverly Jean. Bessy Bear at the Zoo. Causton, Linda, illus. 2000. 34p. (J). (ps-2). 12.95 (978-0-9649922-7-6(2)) DeForest Pr.

—Bessy Bear's Winter Dreams. McWaters, Karen, illus. 2000. 34p. (Orig.). (J). (gr. 3-8). pap. 13.95 (978-1-58275-053-8(X)) Black Forest Pr.

Larson, Verna. Bernie's Forest Adventure: A Case for Secular Humanism. Jones, Sharon, ed. Tagnetti, Nikki, illus. 2nd rev. ed. 1999. (Bearables of Bernie Bear Ser.: No. 1). 24p. (J). (ps-k). 8.95 (978-1-56550-085-3(7)) Vision Bks. International.

Lavelle, Sheila. Ursula at the Zoo. (Illus.). 32p. (J). 13.95 (978-0-241-11728-6(3) , Hamilton, Hamish) Penguin Bks., Ltd. GBR. *Dist:* Trafalgar Square Publishing.

Lawson, Julie. Bear on the Train. Deines, Brian, illus. 1999. 32p. (J). (gr. k-3). pap. 6.95 (978-1-55074-560-3(3)) Kids Can Pr., Ltd.

—Bear on the train. Deines, Brian, illus. 2001. 32p. (J). (gr. k-3). (978-1-55337-068-0(6)) Kids Can Pr., Ltd.

Layton, Neal. Bartholomew & the Bug. 2006. (Illus.). (J). (ps). 14.99 (978-0-340-87328-1(0)); pap. 9.99 (978-0-340-87329-8(9)) Hodder General Publishing Division GBR. (Hodder & Stoughton). *Dist:* Trafalgar Square Publishing.

LeapFrog Staff, compiled by. Pooh's Honey Tree: MFLP. 2001. (J). (ps-2). spiral bd. 12.99 (978-1-58605-111-2(3)) LeapFrog Enterprises, Inc.

LeBear, Clair. The Adventures of Old Bear. Avati, Debbie, illus. 2001. (Clair's Story Book Video Ser.: Vol. 1). (J). (ps-3). pap. 24.95 incl. VHS (978-0-9706321-7-3(7) , SBV001) Cozy Cottage Entertainment.

LeBlanc, Anne & Sterling Publishing Company Staff. Benjamin Finds a Friend. 1999. (Adventures with Benjamin Bear Ser.). (Illus.). 20p. (J). (ps-k). 4.95 (978-0-8069-1923-2(X)) Sterling Publishing Co., Inc.

—Benjamin in the Snow. 1999. (Adventures with Benjamin Bear Ser.). (Illus.). 20p. (ps-k). 4.95 (978-0-8069-1931-7(0)) Sterling Publishing Co., Inc.

—Benjamin Takes Care of Mommy. 1999. (Adventures with Benjamin Bear Ser.). (Illus.). 20p. (ps-k). 4.95 (978-0-8069-1933-1(7)) Sterling Publishing Co., Inc.

—Benjamin's Busy Day. 1999. (Adventures with Benjamin Bear Ser.). (Illus.). 20p. (J). (ps-k). 4.95 (978-0-8069-1935-5(3)) Sterling Publishing Co., Inc.

Lee, Jamie. Washaka: The Bear Dreamer. 2007. 226p. pap. 12.95 (978-0-9729002-4-9(1)) Many Kites Pr.

Lee, Quilan B. Ositos Cariosos: Special Delivery. 2004. (Care Bears Ser.). 24p. (J). pap. 3.50 (978-0-439-61713-0(8) , Scholastic en Espanol) Scholastic, Inc.

Lee, Quinlan B. Care Bears: Easter Egg Hunt. Johnson, Jay, illus. 2005. (Care Bears Ser.). 24p. (J). 3.50 (978-0-439-69161-1(3)) Scholastic, Inc.

—Giving Thanks. Johnson, Jay, illus. 2005. (Care Bears Ser.). 24p. (J). (ps-k). pap. 3.50 (978-0-439-74415-7(6)) Scholastic, Inc.

—Special Delivery. Johnson, Jay, illus. 2004. (Care Bears Ser.). 24p. (J). pap. 3.50 (978-0-439-60318-8(8) , Scholastic Paperbacks) Scholastic, Inc.

—Wish upon a Star. Johnson, Jay, illus. 2005. (Care Bears Ser.). 5p. (J). bds. 6.99 (978-0-439-69597-8(X)) Scholastic, Inc.

Leman, Kevin & Leman, Kevin, II. My Only Child, There's No One Like You. 2005. (Illus.). 32p. (J). (ps). 12.99 (978-0-8007-1864-0(X)) Revell.

Lemieux, Michele. What's That Noise? ed. 2004. (J). (gr. k-3). spiral bd. (978-0-616-01698-5(0)); spiral bd. (978-0-616-01699-2(9)) Canadian National Institute for the Blind/Institut National Canadien pour les Aveugles.

Lepp, Royden. Barnabas Goes Swimming. 2008. 32p. (J). pap. 3.99 (***978-0-310-71584-9(9)***) Zondervan.

—Barnabas Helps a Friend. 2008. 32p. (J). pap. 3.99 (***978-0-310-71585-6(7)***) Zondervan.

—God Loves You Barnbas. 2008. 32p. (J). pap. 3.99 (***978-0-310-71587-0(3)***) Zondervan.

—Happy Birthday Barnabas. 2008. 32p. (J). pap. 3.99 (***978-0-310-71586-3(5)***) Zondervan.

Levert, Mireille. Molly Counts. Levert, Mireille, illus. 1998. (Molly Bear Bks.: No. 5). (Illus.). 16p. (J). (gr. k-ps). bds. 4.95 (978-1-55037-547-3(4)) Annick Pr., Ltd. CAN. *Dist:* Firefly Bks., Ltd.

—Molly Draws. Levert, Mireille, illus. 1998. (Molly Bear Bks.: No. 6). (Illus.). 16p. (J). (gr. k-ps). bds. 4.95 (978-1-55037-546-6(6)) Annick Pr., Ltd. CAN. *Dist:* Firefly Bks., Ltd.

Levin, Betty. The Banished. 1999. (Illus.). 160p. (J). (gr. 5 up). 16.00 (978-0-688-16602-1(4)) HarperCollins Pubs.

Lewis, Anne Margaret. Sleeping Bear. Grant, Sarah, illus. 2007. 32p. (J). 16.95 (***978-1-934133-15-6(9)***) Mackinac Island Pr., Inc.

Lewis, Carolyn & DeVince, James. The Hairy Beary Adventure Series, 3 bks. DeVince, James, ed. Porcheron, Tammy, illus. 2005. 122p. (J). pap. 24.95 (978-0-9712641-3-7(9)) J M D's Business Services.

—Hairy Beary Book Three: The Blue Ribbon Hero, 3 bks., Vol. 3. DeVince, James, ed. Porcheron, Tammy, illus. 2003. (Hairy Beary Ser.: 3). 46p. (J). pap. 9.95 (978-0-9712641-2-0(0)) J M D's Business Services.

Lewis, Gill. The Most Precious Thing. Ho, Louise, illus. 2006. (J). 16.00 (978-1-56148-534-5(9)) Good Bks.

Lewis, Paeony. I'll Always Love You. Ives, Penny, illus. 2004. 32p. (J). pap. 5.95 (978-1-58925-360-5(4) , tiger tales) ME Media LLC.

—I'll Always Love You. 2002. (ps-2). lib. bdg. 14.10 (978-0-613-52270-0(2)) Tandem Library Bks.

Lewis, Paul Owen. P. Bear's New Year's Party: A Counting Book. 2004. (Illus.). 32p. (J). (ps-1). 6.95 (978-1-883672-99-7(6)) ; 13.95 (978-1-58246-002-4(7)) Ten Speed Pr. (Tricycle Pr.).

—P Bear's New Year's Party: A Counting Book. 1999. (ps-2). lib. bdg. 15.25 (978-0-613-86794-8(7)) Tandem Library Bks.

Lewis, Randolph. Alanis Obomsawin: The Vision of a Native Filmmaker. 2006. (American Indian Lives Ser.). (Illus.). 262p. 45.00 (978-0-8032-2963-1(1)) Univ. of Nebraska Pr.

Lewis, Rob. Bye-Bye Bozwell Bear. 2002. (Illus.). 32p. (J). pap. 8.99 ***(978-0-09-940869-7(4))*** Transworld Publishers Ltd. GBR. *Dist:* Independent Pubs. Group.

—Grandpa at the Beach. Lewis, Rob, illus. 1998. (Mondo Ser.). (Illus.). 48p. (J). (gr. 1-5). pap. 4.50 (978-1-57255-552-5(1)) Mondo Publishing.

—Too Much Trouble for Grandpa. 1998. (Mondo Ser.). (Illus.). 48p. (J). (gr. 1-5). pap. 4.50 (978-1-57255-551-8(3)) Mondo Publishing.

Library Bear. Date not set. 9.95 (978-0-89868-293-9(2)); pap. 0.95 (978-0-89868-292-2(4)) ARO Publishing Co.

Libster, Bernard. The Bonsai Bear. Cheung, Aries, illus. 2006. 31p. (J). (gr. k-4). reprint ed. 16.00 ***(978-1-4223-5857-3(7))*** DIANE Publishing Co.

—The Bonsai Bear. Cheung, Aries, illus. 1999. 32p. (ps-3). 15.95 (978-0-935699-15-9(5)) Illumination Arts Publishing Co., Inc.

Lichfield, Walter C. Fanciful Bear Stories for Little Kids & Factual Bear Stories for Big Kids. 2006. 124p. per. 12.95 (978-1-59453-967-1(7) , Airleaf Publishing) Airleaf Publishing & Bookselling.

—Fanciful Bear Stories for Small Kids & Factual Bear Stories for Big Kids. 2003. (Illus.). 84p. per. (978-1-931456-47-0(X)) Athena Pr.

Lieshout, Elle van & Os, Erik van. The Nothing King. Gerritsen, Paula, illus. 2004. 32p. (J). (gr. k-3). 15.95 (978-1-932425-14-7(4) , Lemniscaat) Boyds Mills Pr.

Light, Carol. Chickensing Big Book. Light, Carol, illus. 2003. (Illus.). (J). (978-0-9745803-2-6(5)) Little Big Tomes.

Lincoln, Hazel. Little Snow Bear. Lincoln, Hazel, illus. 2004. (Illus.). 32p. (J). pap. 17.95 (978-0-86315-454-6(9)) Floris Bks. GBR. *Dist:* SteinerBooks, Inc.

Linderman, Frank, et al. Big Jinny: The Story of a Grizzly Bear. 2005. 130p. pap. 15.00 (978-0-8032-8044-1(0) , LINBIX, A Bison Original) Univ. of Nebraska Pr.

Lite, Lori. A Boy & a Bear: The Children's Relaxation Book. Hartigan, Meg, illus. 2003. 32p. (J). (ps-5). pap. 11.00 (978-1-886941-07-6(6) , 0941) Specialty Pr., Inc.

Little Bear. 2003. (Goodnight Mr. Moon Ser.). (Illus.). (J). bds. 2.98 (978-0-7525-4740-4(2)) Parragon, Inc.

Little Bear. 1999. (I Can Read Bks.). (J). (ps-1). pap. 1.95 (978-0-590-31967-6(1)) Scholastic, Inc.

The Little Prayer Bear. 2004. lib. bdg. 12.95 (978-0-9748558-0-6(4)) Rainbow Valley Publishing Co.

Lobel, Gillian. Little Bear's Special Wish. Hansen, Gaby, illus. (J). (ps). 2005. 16p. bds. 6.95 (978-1-58925-769-6(3)); 2004. 32p. tchr. ed. 16.95 (978-1-58925-034-5(6)) ME Media LLC. (tiger tales).

—Little Honey Bear & the Smiley Moon. Warnes, Tim, illus. 2006. 28p. (J). 16.00 (978-1-56148-533-8(0)) Good Bks.

Lodge, Yvette. Love You Lots! A Heart-Shaped Pop-up Book. 2009. (Care Bears Ser.). (Illus.). 10p. (J). pap. 13.95 ***(978-1-57791-302-3(7))*** Brighter Minds Children's Publishing.

LoisKeffer. God Is There Little Bear. 2007. (Sleepytime Stories Ser.). 24p. (J). bds. 6.99 (978-0-7814-4351-7(2) , 0781443512) Cook, David C. Publishing Co.

Lomando, Suzanne. My, Buddy Bear, Tales: Buddy Bear's, First Storybook. 2005. 10.00 (978-0-8059-9755-2(5)) Dorrance Publishing Co., Inc.

Lomba, Ana. Easy Spanish Storybook: Goldilocks & the Three Bears. 2005. (ENG & SPA., Illus.). 41p. 14.95 incl. cd-rom (978-0-07-146170-2(1) , 9780071461702) McGraw-Hill Cos., The.

—EasyFrench Storybook: Goldilocks & the Three Bears. 2005. (ENG & FRE., Illus.). 41p. 14.95 incl. cd-rom (978-0-07-146173-3(6) , 9780071461733) McGraw-Hill Cos., The.

London, Jonathan. Count the Ways, Little Bear. 2003. (gr. k-3). lib. bdg. 15.30 (978-0-613-82997-7(2)) Tandem Library Bks.

—Count the Ways, Little Brown Bear. Moore, Margie, illus. 2004. 32p. (J). (ps-3). lib. bdg. 14.19 (978-0-606-30362-0(6)) Tandem Library Bks.

—Honey Paw & Lightfoot. Van Zyle, Jon, illus. 1998. 40p. (J). (ps-3). pap. 7.95 (978-0-8118-2037-0(8)) Chronicle Bks. LLC.

—Honey Paw & Lightfoot. Van Zyle, Jon, illus. 1998. (J). (ps-ps). lib. bdg. 15.25 (978-0-613-10133-2(2)) Tandem Library Bks.

London, Jonathan & Moore, Margie. Do Your ABCs, Little Brown Bear. 2007. 32p. (J). pap. 5.99 (978-0-14-240713-4(5) , Puffin) Penguin Group (USA) Inc.

Long, Ben. Great Montana Bear Stories. 2002. (gr. 5-8). lib. bdg. 22.20 (978-0-613-61489-4(5)) Tandem Library Bks.

Lopez, Horacio. La Funcion de Teatro. Wright, Douglas, illus. 2003. (SPA.). 38p. (J). (gr. k-3). pap. 8.95 (978-950-511-622-5(5)) Santillana USA Publishing Co., Inc.

Loupy, Christophe. Little Polar Bear/Little Reind. 2005. (Illus.). 32p. (J). (ps up). 16.50 (978-0-7358-2030-2(9)) North-South Bks., Inc.

Love, Pamela. A Cub Explores. Sykes, Shannon, illus. 2004. 32p. (gr. k-2). 15.95 (978-0-89272-593-9(1)) Down East Bks.

Lumry, Amanda. Polar Bear Puzzle. 2007. (Adventures of Riley Ser.). 36p. (ps-3). 18.95 ***(978-1-60040-005-6(1)); 15.95 (978-1-60040-004-9(3))*** Eaglemont Pr.

Luther, Jacqueline. Black Bear Cub. Trachock, Cathy, illus. 2006. 32p. (J). pap. 3.95 (978-1-59249-587-0(7)) Soundprints.

—Grizzly Bear Cub. Nelson, Will, illus. 2006. (Soundprints' Read-And-Discover Ser.). 32p. (J). pap. 3.95 (978-1-59249-583-2(4)) Soundprints.

—Polar Bear Cub. Trachock, Cathy, illus. 2006. 32p. (J). pap. 3.95 (978-1-59249-589-4(3)) Soundprints.

MacDonald, Alan. Beware of the Bears! Williamson, Gwyneth, illus. 1999. 32p. (J). (ps up). pap. 5.95 (978-1-58431-008-2(1)) Little Tiger Pr.

—Beware of the Bears! Williamson, Gwyneth, illus. 2nd ed. 2001. 32p. (J). pap. 5.95 (978-1-58925-359-9(0) , tiger tales) ME Media LLC.

MacDonald, Alan & Williamson, Gwyneth. Beware of the Bears! 1998. (Illus.). 32p. (J). (ps-2). 14.95 (978-1-888444-28-5(2) , 21026) Little Tiger Pr.

MacDonald, Steven. Just Clowning Around: Two Stories. McPhail, David, illus. 2003. 20p. (J). (ps-3). lib. bdg. 11.80 (978-0-613-66362-5(4)) Tandem Library Bks.

—Just Clowning Around: Two Stories. 2000. (Illus.). (J). (978-0-606-18180-8(6)) Tandem Library Bks.

—Just Clowning Around: Two Stories. McPhail, David M., illus. 2003. (Green Light Readers Level 1 Ser.). 24p. (J). 11.95 (978-0-15-204816-7(2)); pap. 3.95 (978-0-15-204856-3(1)) Harcourt Children's Bks. (Green Light Readers).

Mace, Ann. Looking for Bears. Buskirk, Judith Prowse, illus. 1999. (Books for Young Learners). 12p. (J). (gr. k-2). pap. 5.00 (978-1-57274-268-0(2) , A2468) Owen, Richard C. Pubs., Inc.

Machas, Dimi, illus. Tsaani: The Grizzly Bear Story. 2nd ed. 2005. 28p. (YA). 15.00 (978-0-9767217-0-3(8)) Chickaloon Village Publishing.

Mack. The Legend of the Lonesome Bear: Level O, 6 vols. (Take-Twostm Ser.). 32p. 38.95 (978-0-322-04486-9(3)) Wright Group, The.

Mackall, Dandi Daley. Merry Creature Christmas. 2006. 24p. (J). bds. 9.99 (978-1-4003-0823-1(2)) Nelson, Thomas Inc.

Magoun, James. There's a Bear in My Chair. Magnuson, Diana, illus. 2004. 20p. (J). (gr. k-3). pap. 4.95 (978-1-57874-080-2(0)) Kaeden Corp.

Maguire, Thomas Aquinas. A Growling Place. 2007. (Illus.). 32p. (J). (gr. k up). 16.95 ***(978-1-894965-74-3(4))*** Simply Read Bks. CAN. *Dist:* Perseus Distribution.

Mahoney, Daniel J. A Really Good Snowman. 2005. (Illus.). 32p. (J). (gr. k-3). 15.00 (978-0-618-47554-4(0) , Clarion Bks.) Houghton Mifflin Co. Trade & Reference Div.

Mahto, Jamison C. The Misadventures of Bonehead Bear. 2002. (Illus.). 24p. (J). (ps-3). 14.95 (978-1-889401-10-2(2)); pap. 7.95 (978-1-889401-11-9(0)) Spirit Bear.

Major, Charles. Bears of Blue River. reprint ed. lib. bdg. 23.95 (978-0-88411-094-1(X)) Amereon LTD.

—The Bears of Blue River. 1998. (gr. 4-7). reprint ed. 35.95 (978-1-56849-716-7(4)) Buccaneer Bks., Inc.

Major, Roberta Olsen. The Prince in the Flower Bed. 2001. 147p. (YA). pap. 13.95 (978-1-59088-977-0(0)) Wings ePress, Inc.

Majors, Ursula. The Bear. Spengler, Kenneth J., illus. 2002. 32p. (J). pap. 15.95 (978-1-59034-182-7(1)) Mondo Publishing.

Malak, Annabel, illus. Goldilocks & the Three Bears. (Classic Stories Ser.). 48p. (J). audio, audio compact disk (978-2-921997-84-3(3)) Coffragants.

Mallat, Kathy. Brave Bear. (Illus.). 24p. (J). (ps-k). 2004. 15.95 (978-0-8027-8704-0(5)); 2004. pap. 6.95 (978-0-8027-7613-6(2)); 1999. lib. bdg. 15.85 (978-0-8027-8705-7(3)) Walker & Co.

Mangan, Anne. The Smallest Bear. Moss, Joanne, illus. 1998. 32p. (J). (ps-3). 14.95 (978-1-56656-266-9(X) , Crocodile Bks.) Interlink Publishing Group, Inc.

Marcus, Marcelina A. Arca: The Clear Bear. 1998. (Illus.). 16p. (J). (gr. k-2). pap. 6.00 (978-0-8059-4357-3(9)) Dorrance Publishing Co., Inc.

Marshall, Hallie. Disney's Winnie the Pooh's Telling Time: Book & Watch Set. 2000. (Illus.). 24p. (J). (ps-3). 9.99 (978-0-7364-1028-1(7)) Mouse Works.

Marshall, James. Goldilocks & the Three Bears. Marshall, James, illus. 2002. (Illus.). (J). 14.04 (978-0-7587-2613-1(9)) Book Wholesalers, Inc.

—Goldilocks & the Three Bears. 1998. (J). 13.79 (978-0-606-12946-6(4)) Tandem Library Bks.

Martin, Bill, Jr. Baby Bear, Baby Bear, What Do You See? Carle, Eric, illus. 2007. 32p. (J). (ps-3). 16.95 ***(978-0-8050-8336-1(7)*** , Holt, Henry & Co. Bks. For Young Readers) Holt, Henry & Co.

—The Brown Bear & Friends Gift Set. Carle, Eric, illus. rev. ed. 2004. 32p. (J). 49.95 (978-0-8050-7628-8(X) , Holt, Henry & Co. Bks. For Young Readers) Holt, Henry & Co.

—Brown Bear, Brown Bear, What Do You See? Date not set. (J). bds. 12.95 (978-0-8050-7209-9(8) , Holt, Henry & Co. Bks. For Young Readers) Holt, Henry & Co.

—Brown Bear, Brown Bear, What Do You See? Carle, Eric, illus. 2004. (J). (ENG & ARA.). pap. (978-1-84444-116-7(4)); (ENG & CHI.). pap. (978-1-84444-118-1(0)); (ENG & PER.). pap. (978-1-84444-120-4(2)); (ENG & GUJ.). pap. (978-1-84444-121-1(0)); (ENG & HIN.). pap. (978-1-84444-122-8(9)); (ENG & PAN.). pap. (978-1-84444-123-5(7)); (ENG & ALB.). 26p. pap. (978-1-84444-115-0(6)); (ENG & VIE.). pap. (978-1-84444-124-2(5)); (TAM & ENG.). pap. (978-1-84444-126-6(1)); (ENG & TUR.). 27p. pap. (978-1-84444-127-3(X)); (ENG & URD.). pap. (978-1-84444-128-0(8)); (YOR & ENG.). 25p. pap. (978-1-84444-129-7(6)); (KUR & ENG.). 26p. pap. (978-1-84444-158-7(X)); (POR & ENG.). 27p. pap. (978-1-84444-159-4(8)); (ENG & SOM.). 27p. pap. (978-1-84444-125-9(3)) Mantra Publishing, Ltd.

—Oso Pardo, Oso Pardo, Que Ves Ahi? Mlawer, Terresa, tr. Carle, Eric, illus. rev. ed. 1998. (SPA.). 32p. (J). (ps-k). 17.95 (978-0-8050-5967-0(9) , Holt, Henry & Co. Bks. For Young Readers) Holt, Henry & Co.

Martin, David. Three Little Bears. Gutierrez, Akemi, illus. 2004. (Brand New Readers Ser.). 48p. (J). (ps-2). pap. 5.99 (978-0-7636-2350-0(4)) Candlewick Pr.

Martin, Joy. Bear Story: A Rhyme from A to Zzzz's. Cartwright, Shannon, illus. 2001. 32p. 15.95 (978-0-936425-69-6(5)); 9.95 (978-0-936425-70-2(9)) Greatland Graphics.

Mason, Chad. Wake up, Bertha Bear! Wallace, Chad, illus. 2006. 32p. 15.95 (978-0-89272-655-4(5)) Down East Bks.

Mason, Jane B. Stella & the Berry Thief. Koopmans, Loek, tr. Koopmans, Loek, illus. 2004. 32p. (J). 16.95 (978-0-7614-5123-5(4)) Cavendish, Marshall Corp.

Mattern, Joanne. The Tricky Garden. 2005. 22.00 ***(978-1-4108-4191-9(X))*** Benchmark Education Co.

Mayhew, James & Morris, Jackie. Can You See a Little Bear? 2005. (Illus.). 32p. (J). (ps-1). 16.95 (978-1-84507-298-8(7)) Lincoln, Frances Ltd. GBR. *Dist:* Perseus Distribution.

Mazzeo Zocchi, Judy. Paulie & Sasha: Circus or Not. Vannozzi, Don, illus. 2001. (Adventures of Paulie & Sasha Ser.). 32p. (J). (gr. k-4). 15.95 (978-1-891997-00-6(9) , Treehouse Court) Dingles & Co.

McAllister, Angela. Brave Bitsy & the Bear. Beeke, Tiphanie, illus. 2006. 32p. (J). (ps-k). 16.00 (978-0-618-63994-6(2) , Clarion Bks.) Houghton Mifflin Co. Trade & Reference Div.

McCain, Steve. The Storybook Bear. l.t. ed. 2002. (Illus.). 40p. (J). per. 9.95 (978-1-932344-08-0(X)) Thornton Publishing.

McClintock, Barbara, illus. Goldilocks & the Three Bears. 2003. 32p. (J). (ps-2). pap. 15.95 (978-0-439-39545-8(3) , Scholastic Pr.) Scholastic, Inc.

McCloskey, Robert. Blue Berries for Sal. McCloskey, Robert, illus. 2004. (Illus.). 52p. (J). (gr. k-4). reprint ed. pap. 14.00 (978-0-7567-7105-8(6)) DIANE Publishing Co.

—Blueberries for Sal. McCloskey, Robert, illus. 2002. (Illus.). (J). 14.04 (978-0-7587-0097-1(0)) Book Wholesalers, Inc.

—Blueberries for Sal. 2000. (J). pap. 19.97 incl. audio (978-0-7366-9193-2(6)) Books on Tape, Inc.

—Blueberries for Sal. (J). (ps-k). pap. 12.95 incl. audio Weston Woods Studios, Inc.

McCourt, Lisa. My Forever Valentine. Bryant, Laura J., illus. 2008. (J). ***(978-0-439-75058-5(X))*** Scholastic, Inc.

McCreary, Laura. Stickers 'n Shapes. 2002. (Bear in the Big Blue House Ser.: Bk. 7). (Illus.). 16p. (J). mass mkt. 3.99 (978-0-689-84023-4(3) , Simon Spotlight) Simon & Schuster Children's Publishing.

McCue, Lisa, illus. Corduroy's Thanksgiving. 2006. 16p. (J). (ps). bds. 5.99 (978-0-670-06108-2(5) , Viking Juvenile) Penguin Group (USA) Inc.

McDonald, Diane. Treasure Chest. Halicky, Sandi, illus. 2002. 34p. (J). spiral bd. 12.95 (978-0-9721681-0-6(9)) McDonald, Diane.

McPhail, David. Big Brown Bear/El gran oso Pardo. Campoy, F. Isabel & Ada, Alma Flor, trs. from ENG. 2007. (Green Light Readers Level 1 Ser.). (ENG & SPA., Illus.). 28p. (J). 12.95 (978-0-15-205965-1(2)); pap. 3.95 (978-0-15-205970-5(9)) Harcourt Trade Pubs.

—Big Brown Bear's Birthday Surprise. O'Connor, John, illus. 2007. (Big Brown Bear Ser.). 32p. (J). (ps-2). 16.00 (978-0-15-206098-5(7)) Harcourt Trade Pubs.

—Big Brown Bear's up & down Day. 2006. (Illus.). 48p. (J). pap. 6.00 (978-0-15-205684-1(X) , Voyager Bks./Libros Viajeros) Harcourt Children's Bks.

McPhail, David. Rick Is Sick. McPhail, David, illus. 2004. (Illus.). 24p. (J). lib. bdg. 10.00 ***(978-1-4242-0183-9(7))*** Fitzgerald Bks.

McPhail, David M. Big Brown Bear. McPhail, David M., illus. 2002. (Illus.). (J). 11.45 (978-0-7587-0990-5(0)) Book Wholesalers, Inc.

—Big Brown Bear. 2003. (Green Light Readers Level 1 Ser.). (Illus.). 24p. (J). 11.95 (978-0-15-204817-4(0)); pap. 3.95 (978-0-15-204858-7(8)) Harcourt Children's Bks. (Green Light Readers).

—Big Brown Bear. 1999. (J). (978-0-606-16509-9(6)); lib. bdg. 11.80 (978-0-613-64462-4(X)) Tandem Library Bks.

—Big Brown Bear Goes to Town. O'Connor, John, illus. 2006. 40p. (J). 16.00 (978-0-15-205317-8(4)) Harcourt Trade Pubs.

—Big Brown Bear's up & down Day. McPhail, David M., illus. 2005. (Illus.). 42p. (J). (ps-3). reprint ed. 16.00 (978-0-7567-8542-0(1)) DIANE Publishing Co.

—Big Brown Bear's up & down Day. McPhail, David M., illus. 2003. (Illus.). 48p. (J). 16.00 (978-0-15-216407-2(3)) Harcourt Trade Pubs.

—A Bug, a Bear & a Boy. 1998. (Hello Reader! Ser.). (Illus.). 32p. (J). (ps-1). pap. 3.99 (978-0-590-14904-4(0)) Scholastic, Inc.

—A Bug, a Bear & a Boy. 1998. (Hello Reader! Ser.). (J). (ps-1). 10.79 (978-0-606-13231-2(7)) Tandem Library Bks.

—A Bug, a Bear & a Boy Go to School. 1999. (Illus.). (J). 10.79 (978-0-606-20469-9(5)) Tandem Library Bks.

—A Bug, a Bear, & a Boy Go to School. 2004. 32p. (J). lib. bdg. 15.00 (978-1-59054-668-0(7)) Fitzgerald Bks.

—Drawing Lessons from a Bear. McPhail, David M., illus. 2000. (Illus.). 32p. (J). (ps-3). 15.99 (978-0-316-56345-1(5)) Little Brown & Co.

—Fix It. McPhail, David M., illus. 2002. (Illus.). (J). 12.34 (978-0-7587-2515-8(9)) Book Wholesalers, Inc.

—Rick Is Sick. 2004. (Green Light Readers Level 1 Ser.). (Illus.). 24p. (J). 12.95 (978-0-15-205091-7(4)); pap. 3.95 (978-0-15-205092-4(2)) Harcourt Children's Bks. (Green Light Readers).

—Tinker & Tom & the Star Baby. 2000. (Illus.). 32p. (J). (ps-3). pap. 5.95 (978-0-316-56389-5(7)) Little Brown & Co.

—Tinker & Tom & the Star Baby. McPhail, David M., illus. 1998. (Illus.). 32p. (J). (ps-3). 14.95 (978-0-316-56349-9(8)) Little Brown & Co.

Mercer, Lynn. Schubert's Snowflakes. 2002. (Illus.). 32p. (J). (gr. k-3). pap. 12.95 (978-0-9535413-6-2(3)) iynx publishing GBR. *Dist:* Dufour Editions, Inc.

Meredith Books Staff. Cheer Bear's Circus Adventure: Deluxe Sound Storybook. Forlini, Victoria, ed. 2004. (Care Bears Ser.). (ENG., Illus.). 22p. (J). (gr. k-3). 15.95 (978-0-696-22297-9(3)) Meredith Bks.

Meredith Books Staff & Forlini, Victoria, eds. Bedtime Bear's Caring Dreams: Deluxe Sound Storybook. 2004. (Care Bears Ser.). (ENG., Illus.). 22p. (gr. k-3). 15.95 (978-0-696-22296-2(5)) Meredith Bks.

Meyer, Brigit. Merry Christmas, Little Bear. Mussenbrock, Anne, illus. 2004. 10p. (J). bds. 5.99 (978-1-59384-062-4(4)) Parklane Publishing.

Meyers, Cindy. Rolling along with Goldilocks & the Three Bears. Morgan, Carol, illus. 1999. 27p. (J). (ps-2). 14.95 (978-1-890627-12-6(7)) Woodbine Hse.

Miel para Osito Marcos, 6 vols., Pack. (Coleccion Pm Ser.).Tr. of Honey for baby bear. (SPA.). 16p. (gr. 1 up). 26.00 (978-0-7578-3011-2(0)) Rigby Education.

Miles, Victoria. Old Mother Bear. Bang, Molly Garrett, illus. 2007. 48p. (J). (ps-3). 16.95 (978-0-8118-5033-9(1) , SeaStar Bks.) Chronicle Bks. LLC.

Milios, Rita. Bears, Bears, Everywhere. Motoyama, Keiko, illus. rev. ed. 2003. (Rookie Reader Espanol Ser.). (J). (gr. k-2). pap. 4.95 (978-0-516-27830-8(4) , Children's Pr.) Scholastic Library Publishing.

—Osos, Osos por Todas Partes. Motoyama, Keiko, illus. rev. ed. 2003. (Rookie Reader Espanol Ser.). (SPA.). (J). 19.50 (978-0-516-25886-7(9) , Children's Pr.) Scholastic Library Publishing.

Miller, Edward. 3 Tales Retold & Illustrated: The Three Little Pigs, Goldilocks & the Three Bears, Three Billy Goats Gruff. Miller, Edward, illus. 2007. (Illus.). 48p. (J). (ps-2). 17.95 (978-0-8050-7916-6(5)) Holt, Henry & Co.

Miller, Jennifer. Run, Rasputin, Run! Trials & Friendships (Book 2) 2006. (ENG., Illus.). 172p. per. ***(978-1-4120-8494-9(6))*** Trafford Publishing.

Miller, Ruth. The Bear on the Bed. Slavin, Bill, illus. 32p. (J). (gr. k-3). 2004. (978-1-55337-687-3(0)); 2002. (978-1-55337-036-9(8)) Kids Can Pr., Ltd.

Miller, Virginia. On Your Potty. Miller, Virginia, illus. 1998. (George & Ba Ser.). (Illus.). 32p. (J). (gr. k-k). pap. 5.99 (978-0-7636-0694-7(4)) Candlewick Pr.

—Ten Red Apples: A Bartholomew Bear Counting Book. 2002. (Illus.). 32p. (J). (ps-k). 13.99 (978-0-7445-9280-1(1)) Candlewick Pr.

Milne, A. A. The Complete Tales of Winnie the Pooh. 70th ed. 1999. (Illus.). 368p. (J). (gr. 4-7). 40.00 (978-0-525-45060-3(2) , Dutton Juvenile) Penguin Group (USA) Inc.

—The House at Pooh Corner, Set. Shepard, Ernest H., illus. (J). incl. audio (978-1-57375-653-2(9) , 71524) Audioscope.

—The Magical Pop-Up World of Winnie-the-Pooh. Shepard, Ernest H., illus. deluxe ed. 2003. 5p. (J). (ps). 24.99 (978-0-525-47141-7(3) , Dutton Juvenile) Penguin Group (USA) Inc.

—Pooh. Shepard, Ernest H., illus. 1999. 10p. (J). (ps-k). bds. 7.99 (978-0-525-46232-3(5) , Dutton Juvenile) Penguin Group (USA) Inc.

—Pooh Loves You. 1999. (Pooh Friendly Tale Ser.). (Illus.). 10p. (J). (ps-k). 6.99 (978-0-7364-0102-9(4)) Mouse Works.

—Pooh Touch & Feel: A Pooh Texture Book. abr. ed. 1998. (Illus.). 12p. (J). (ps). 9.99 (978-0-525-45830-2(1) , Dutton Juvenile) Penguin Group (USA) Inc.

—Pooh's First Clock. Shepard, Ernest H., illus. 1998. 12p. (J). (ps-3). bds. 12.99 (978-0-525-45983-5(9) , Dutton Juvenile) Penguin Group (USA) Inc.

—Winnie Puh. (ITA., Illus.). pap. 29.95 (978-88-7782-278-9(3)) Salani ITA. *Dist:* Distribooks, Inc.

—Winnie the Pooh: Touch & Feel. Shepard, Ernest H., illus. 2002. 10p. (J). 12.99 (978-0-525-47007-6(7) , Dutton Juvenile) Penguin Group (USA) Inc.

—Winnie the Pooh & When We Were Young, Boxed set. Shepard, Ernest H., illus. 32p. (J). pap. incl. audio compact disk (978-1-57375-583-2(4) , 71512) Audioscope.

—Winnie the Pooh at Pooh Corner & Now We Are Six, Set. 1998. (J). 29.98 incl. audio Audioscope.

—Winny de Puh. Shepard, Ernest H., illus. 2000. (SPA.). 176p. (J). (gr. 3 up). 15.99 (978-0-525-44986-7(8) , DT1541, Dutton Juvenile) Penguin Group (USA) Inc.

Milne, A. A. & Krensky, Stephen. Pooh Goes Visiting, Vol. 2. Shepard, Ernest H., illus. 2002. (Puffin-Easy-to-Read Ser.). 48p. (J). pap. 3.99 (978-0-14-230184-5(1) , Puffin) Penguin Group (USA) Inc.

Minarik, Else Holmelund. The Adventures of Little Bear. 1998. (Illus.). (J). 12.95 (978-0-06-028044-4(1)) HarperCollins Pubs.

—Un Beso para Osito. Sendak, Maurice, illus. 2003. (SPA.). 36p. (J). (gr. k-3). 11.95 (978-84-204-3050-8(1) , AF1633) Alfaguara, Ediciones, S.A.- Grupo Santillana ESP. *Dist:* Lectorum Pubns., Inc., Santillana USA Publishing Co., Inc.

—Un Beso para Osito. Sendak, Maurice, tr. Sendak, Maurice, illus. (SPA.). 34p. (J). (gr. k-3). pap. 8.95 (978-84-204-4827-5(3)) Santillana USA Publishing Co., Inc.

—The Cricket Who Came to Dinner. Hahner, Chris, illus. 2004. 32p. (ps). lib. bdg. 11.19 (978-0-606-29910-7(6)) Tandem Library Bks.

—I Miss You, Father Bear. 2002. (gr. k-3). lib. bdg. 11.80 (978-0-613-70862-3(8)) Tandem Library Bks.

—Little Bear & the Missing Pie. 2002. (gr. k-3). lib. bdg. 11.80 (978-0-613-62523-4(4)) Tandem Library Bks.

—Little Bear's Bad Day. 2003. (gr. k-3). lib. bdg. 11.80 (978-0-613-69141-3(5)) Tandem Library Bks.

—Little Bear's Friends - Los Amigos de Osito. (SPA.). 64p. (J). 7.95 (978-84-204-3049-2(8)) Santillana USA Publishing Co., Inc.

—Little Bear's Loose Tooth. Hahner, Chris, illus. 2002. (Maurice Sendak's Little Bear Ser.). 32p. (J). (ps-2). pap. 3.95 (978-0-694-01713-3(2) , Harper Festival) HarperCollins Pubs.

—Little Bear's Loose Tooth. 2002. (gr. k-3). lib. bdg. 11.80 (978-0-613-62524-1(2)) Tandem Library Bks.

—Little Bear's Visit. Sendak, Maurice, illus. (J). pap. 12.95 incl. audio Weston Woods Studios, Inc.

—Lost in Little Bear's Room. Wenzel, David T., illus. 2004. (Festival Reader Ser.). 32p. (J). (ps-2). pap. 3.99 (978-0-694-01706-5(X) , Harper Festival) HarperCollins Pubs.

—Maurice Sendak's Little Bear: Little Bear's Bad Day. Wenzel, David T., illus. 2003. (Festival Reader Ser.). 32p. (J). (ps-2). pap. 4.95 (978-0-06-053546-9(6) , Harper Festival) HarperCollins Pubs.

—Maurice Sendak's Little Bear: Lost in Little Bear's Room. 2004. (ps-2). lib. bdg. 11.80 (978-0-613-73429-5(7)) Tandem Library Bks.

—Maurice Sendak's Little Bear: Lucky Little Bear. 2004. (ps-2). lib. bdg. 11.80 (978-0-613-73428-8(9)) Tandem Library Bks.

—Osito. Sendak, Maurice, illus. 2003. (SPA.). 60p. (J). (gr. k-3). pap. 8.95 (978-84-204-3044-7(7) , AF1346) Santillana USA Publishing Co., Inc.

—Papa Oso Vuele a Casa. 2003. (Osito Ser.). (SPA., Illus.). (J). (ps-3). pap. (978-84-204-3048-5(X) , AF1359) Alfaguara, Ediciones, S.A.- Grupo Santillana ESP. *Dist:* Santillana USA Publishing Co., Inc.

—Present for Mother Bear. 2002. (gr. k-3). lib. bdg. 11.80 (978-0-613-62535-7(8)) Tandem Library Bks.

—La Visita de Osito. Sendak, Maurice, illus. 2003. (Osito Ser.). (SPA.). 64p. (J). (gr. k-3). pap. 11.95 (978-968-19-0623-8(3) , AF1060) Santillana USA Publishing Co., Inc.

Minarik, Else Holmelund & Sendak, Maurice. Baiser pour Petit Ours. 2000. Tr. of Kiss for Little Bear. (FRE.). (J). pap. 17.95 (978-2-211-01767-1(3)) Archimede Editions FRA. *Dist:* Distribooks, Inc.

—Papa Ours Revient. 2000. Tr. of Papa Bear Returns. (FRE.). (J). pap. 23.95 (978-2-211-01759-6(2)) Archimede Editions FRA. *Dist:* Distribooks, Inc.

—Petit Ours. 2000. Tr. of Little Bear. (FRE.). (J). pap. 23.95 (978-2-211-01716-9(9)) Archimede Editions FRA. *Dist:* Distribooks, Inc.

Minarik, Else Holmelund & Tashlin, Frank. El Oso Que No lo Era. Sendak, Maurice, illus. 2003. (SPA.). 62p. (J). (gr. k-3). pap. 8.95 (978-958-24-0002-6(1)) Santillana USA Publishing Co., Inc.

Mishica, Clare. Is Your Pail Full? Hickman, Estella L., illus. 2000. 12p. (J). (gr. k-2). pap. 3.75 (978-1-58323-000-8(9) , Seedling Pubns.) Continental Pr., Inc.

Moerbeck, Kees, illus. & des. Goldilocks. Moerbeck, Kees, des. 2006. 9.99 (978-1-84643-017-6(8)) Child's Play-International.

Monkman, Olga. Dos Perros y una Abuela. Calderon, Marcela, illus. 2003. (SPA.). 31p. (J). (gr. k-3). pap. 9.95 (978-950-511-642-3(X)) Santillana USA Publishing Co., Inc.

Moody-Luther, Jacqueline. Bear & the pizza tree - word World. 2007. 12p. (J). 12.95 (***978-1-59764-297-2(5)***) New Line Bks.

Moore, Bonnie S. Honey Bear & the Honey Horde: Bear Tales. 2007. (J). per. 6.00 (***978-1-59872-823-1(7)***) Instantpublisher.com.

Morey, Walt. Gentle Ben. Schoenherr, John, illus. l.t. ed. 2004. (LRS Large Print Cornerstone Ser.). 264p. (J). lib. bdg. 33.95 (978-1-58118-119-7(1)) LRS.

—Gentle Ben. Schoenherr, John, illus. 2006. 192p. (J). (gr. 3). pap. 6.99 (978-0-14-240551-2(5) , Puffin) Penguin Group (USA) Inc.

Morpurgo, Michael. The Rainbow Bear. 1999. (Illus.). 32p. (J). (978-0-385-60017-0(8) , Corgi) Transworld Publishers Ltd.

—The Rainbow Bear. 2000. (Illus.). 32p. (J). (gr. k-3). pap. 11.99 (978-0-552-54640-9(2) , Corgi) Transworld Publishers Ltd. GBR. *Dist:* Independent Pubs. Group.

Morris, Clarine. The Obstinate Bear. Bamford, Daneen, illus. 2000. 12p. (J). pap. 3.00 (978-0-9650312-8-8(4)) Cosmo Starr Bks.

Morris, Deborah. Bear Attack & Other True Stories. 2003. (J). 21.95 (978-0-7862-5173-5(5)) Thorndike Pr.

Morton, Christine. No Te Preocupes, Guille. McMullen, Nigel, illus. (Buenas Noches Coleccion). (SPA.). 26p. (J). (gr. k-3). 8.95 (978-958-04-5088-7(9)) Norma S.A. COL. *Dist:* Distribuidora Norma, Inc., Lectorum Pubns., Inc.

Morton-Shaw, Christine & Shaw, Greg. Wake up, Sleepy Bear. 2006. 32p. (J). (ps). 12.99 (978-0-670-06175-4(1) , Viking Juvenile) Penguin Group (USA) Inc.

Moss, Miriam. A Babysitter for Billy Bear. Currey, Anna, illus. 2008. 32p. (J). (ps). 16.99 (***978-0-8037-3269-8(4)*** , Dial) Penguin Group (USA) Inc.

—Bare Bear. McQuillan, Mary, illus. 2005. 32p. (J). 16.95 (978-0-8234-1934-0(7)) Holiday Hse., Inc.

—Don't Forget I Love You. Currey, Anna, illus. 32p. (J). 2005. pap. 5.99 (978-0-14-240548-2(5) , Puffin); 2003. 15.99 (978-0-8037-2920-9(0) , Dial) Penguin Group (USA) Inc.

—The Snow Bear. Kneen, Maggie, illus. 2001. 32p. (J). (ps-3). 15.99 (978-0-525-46658-1(4) , Dutton Juvenile) Penguin Group (USA) Inc.

Mouse Works Staff. Happy Easter, Pooh! Friendly Tales. 2000. (Winnie the Pooh Ser.). (Illus.). 10p. (J). (ps-k). bds. 6.99 (978-0-7364-1056-4(2)) Hyperion Pr.

—Happy Graduation, Pooh! Friendly Tales. 2000. (Winnie the Pooh Ser.). (Illus.). 10p. (J). (ps-k). bds. 6.99 (978-0-7364-1057-1(0)) Hyperion Pr.

—I Love You, Pooh! 2000. (Keepsake Photo Storybooks Ser.). (Illus.). 10p. (J). (ps-3). bds. 6.99 (978-0-7364-0190-6(3)) Mouse Works.

—Many Adventures of Winnie the Pooh. 1998. (Classic Storybook Ser.). (Illus.). 96p. (J). 7.98 (978-1-57082-804-1(0)) Mouse Works.

—Merry Xmas from Pooh to You Santa Roo. 1998. 10p. (J). 13.97 (978-0-7364-0054-1(0)) Mouse Works.

—Pooh. 1999. (My Very First Cloth Book Ser.). (J). 6.99 (978-0-7364-0177-7(6)) Disney Pr.

—Pooh. 1998. 10p. (J). 6.99 (978-0-7364-0019-0(2)) Mouse Works.

—Pooh: Tigger Friendly Tales. 1998. 10p. (J). 6.99 (978-0-7364-0020-6(6)) Mouse Works.

—Pooh Friendly Tales. 1999. (J). 27.96 (978-0-7364-0041-1(9)) Mouse Works.

—Pooh Loves Christmas! A Winnie the Pooh Photo Album & Storybook. 2000. (Keepsake Photo Storybooks Ser.). (Illus.). 10p. (J). (ps-3). 6.99 (978-0-7364-0191-3(1)) Mouse Works.

—Santa Pooh. 1998. (Winnie the Pooh Ser.). (Illus.). 10p. (J). (ps-k). 6.99 (978-1-57082-858-4(X)) Mouse Works.

—Who's Our Mommy Pooh? Discovery Lift the Flap. 2000. 14p. (J). 5.99 (978-0-7364-1059-5(7)) Little Brown & Co.

—Winnie the Pooh Spanish Read. 1999. 48p. (J). pap. 4.99 (978-0-7364-0108-1(3)) Mouse Works.

—Winnie the Pooh's Friendly Adventures. 1999. (Disney's Read-Aloud Storybooks Ser.). (Illus.). 72p. (J). (ps-2). 8.99 (978-0-7364-0107-4(5) , RH/Disney) Random Hse. Children's Bks.

—Winnie the Pooh's Touch & Feel Book. 2nd ed. 2005. 10p. (J). 6.99 (978-0-7364-1021-2(X)) Hyperion Pr.

Mozelle, Shirley. The Bear Upstairs. Cushman, Doug, illus. 2005. 32p. (J). 16.95 (978-0-8050-6820-7(1) , Holt, Henry & Co. Bks. For Young Readers) Holt, Henry & Co.

Mullen, Susan. Buggy Bear. Dinsmore, Beverly Baker, illus. 1998. 24p. (J). (ps-3). 16.95 (978-0-9668658-0-6(4)) Family Buggy Publishing.

Murphy, Jill. Peace at Last. Murphy, Jill, illus. 2002. (Illus.). (J). 13.19 (978-0-7587-3382-5(8)) Book Wholesalers, Inc.

Murray, Marjorie D. Don't Wake up the Bear! Wittmann, Patricia, illus. 2003. 32p. (J). 14.95 (978-0-7614-5107-5(2)) Cavendish, Marshall Corp.

Muth, Jon J. Zen Shorts. Muth, Jon J., illus. 2005. (Illus.). 40p. (J). pap. 16.95 (978-0-439-33911-7(1)) Scholastic, Inc.

Nagy, Krisztina. Fuzzy Bear: A Getting Dressed Book. enl. ed. 2000. (Illus.). 10p. (J). 16.95 (978-1-58117-050-4(5) , Intervisual/Piggy Toes) Dalmatian Pr.

Nagy, Krisztina, illus. Sleepy Bear: A Bedtime Touch-and-Learn Pop-Up Book. enl. ed. 2000. 10p. (J). 16.95 (978-1-58117-052-8(1) , Intervisual/Piggy Toes) Dalmatian Pr.

Namm, Diane. Little Bear. 2004. (My First Reader Ser.). (J). (gr. k-1). pap. 3.95 (978-0-516-24633-8(X) , Children's Pr.) Scholastic Library Publishing.

—Little Bear. McCue, Lisa, illus. 2003. (My First Reader Ser.). 32p. (J). 18.50 (978-0-516-22931-7(1) , Children's Pr.) Scholastic Library Publishing.

Napp, Daniel. Professor Bumble & the Monster of the Deep. 2008. 32p. (J). 15.95 (***978-0-8109-9484-3(4)*** , Abrams Bks. for Young Readers) Abrams, Harry N., Inc.

Neebe, Charles A. The Cave Monster. DiSalvo, Len, illus. 2007. (J). 15.95 (***978-1-933872-32-2(2)***) Lima Bear Pr LLC, The.

Neebe, Charles A. How Back-Back Got His Name. 2007. (J). 15.95 (978-1-933872-20-9(9)) Lima Bear Pr LLC, The.

Nelson, Marilen. Bed Bear's Adventure to the Land of Lost Things. LeRoy, Doreene, illus. l.t. ed. 2002. 40p. (J). cd-rom 11.95 (978-1-59208-003-8(0) , 775-846-1185) JetKor.

Newman, Leslea. Where Is Bear? Gorbachev, Valeri, illus. 2004. 44p. (J). 16.00 (978-0-15-204936-2(3) , Gulliver Bks.) Harcourt Children's Bks.

Newman, Leslea & Gorbachev, Valeri. Where Is Bear? 2006. (Illus.). 44p. (J). pap. 6.00 (978-0-15-205918-7(0) , Voyager Bks./Libros Viajeros) Harcourt Children's Bks.

Nivens, Karen. Benjamin P. Blizzard: Welcome to Christmastown. Grisham, Jason, illus. 2007. 48p. (J). per. (***978-0-9798154-1-6(X)***) Living Waters Publishing Co.

Nolan, J. & Moffatt, J. Floaties: Teddy Bear Teddy Bear. 2003. (J). 9.95 (978-1-929766-60-4(2)) Handprint Bks.

Nolan, Janet. A Father's Day Thank You. Ember, Kathi, illus. 2007. 32p. (J). 15.95 (978-0-8075-2291-2(0)) Whitman, Albert & Co.

Nolte, Nancy. The Gingerbread Man. Scarry, Richard, illus. 2004. 32p. (J). (gr. k-k). 8.99 (978-0-375-82589-7(4)); lib. bdg. 10.99 (978-0-375-92589-4(9)) Random Hse. Children's Bks. (Golden Bks.).

North American Bear Co., Inc. Staff. A Charmed Life by Muffy Vander Bear. Drake, Heather, illus. 1998. 32p. (J). (ps-6). 14.95 (978-0-9665277-0-4(4)) North American Bear.

Northeast, Brenda V. Auguste con Amor. 2000. (CAT., Illus.). 32p. (J). (gr. k-2). 14.95 (978-84-95040-54-1(9)) Serres, Ediciones, S. L. ESP. *Dist:* Lectorum Pubns., Inc.

Novak, Matt. Jazzbo, Vol. 3. 2001. 32p. (J). (ps-17). 12.99 (978-0-7868-0591-4(9)) Hyperion Bks. for Children.

—Jazzbo, Vol. 4. 2007. 32p. (J). (ps-17). 12.99 (978-0-7868-0592-1(7)) Hyperion Pr.

Numeroff, Laura Joffe. If You Give a Bear a Brownie. Date not set. 32p. (J). (ps-2). 15.99 (978-0-06-027571-6(5)); lib. bdg. 16.89 (978-0-06-027572-3(3)) HarperCollins Pubs.

—If You Give a Bear a Brownie: Book & Doll. Bond, Felicia, illus. Date not set. (J). 19.99 (978-0-694-01423-1(0)) HarperCollins Pubs.

Ocean Front Books. Coloring Book. l.t. ed. 2006. (J). lib. bdg. (***978-1-934190-02-9(0)***) Ocean Front Bk. Publishing, Inc.

Offerman, Lynn. Little Teddy Bear's Happy Face, Sad Face: A First Book about Feelings. 1999. (Illus.). 12p. (ps-k). 9.95 (978-0-7613-0983-3(7) , Millbrook Pr.) Lerner Publishing Group.

—Little Teddy Bear's Happy Face, Sad Face: A First Book about Feelings. Moroney, Tracey, illus. 1998. 4p. (J). bds. 12.98 (978-1-58048-035-2(7)) Sandvik Publishing.

Oke, Janette. Trouble in a Fur Coat. Munger, Nancy, illus. rev. ed. 2001. (Janette Oke's Animal Friends Ser.). 80p. (Orig.). (J). (gr. 1-5). pap. 6.99 (978-0-7642-2456-0(5)) Bethany Hse. Pubs.

—Trouble in a Fur Coat. 2001. (Orig.). (gr. 3-6). lib. bdg. 14.15 (978-0-613-85067-4(X)) Tandem Library Bks.

Once upon a Time Spanish Version-the Three Bears. 2005. (J). (978-1-57022-563-5(X)) ECS Learning Systems, Inc.

Ondrias, Rachel. Kolby, the Skatin Bear from Kalamazoo! 2006. (Illus.). 28p. (J). 16.95 (***978-1-933660-00-4(7)*** , Tadpole Pr. 4 Kids) Smooth Sailing Pr.

—Kolby, the Skating Bear: A Kalamazoo Christmas. Scarborough, Casey, illus. 2007. (J). 16.95 (***978-1-933660-29-5(5)*** , Tadpole Pr. 4 Kids) Smooth Sailing Pr.

Oppenheim, Joanne. Could It Be? Schindler, S. D., illus. 1998. (Bank Street Reader Collection). 48p. (J). (gr. 1-3). lib. bdg. 22.60 (978-0-8368-1770-6(2)) Stevens, Gareth Inc.

Optic, Oliver. Bear & Forbear: Getting Along. unabr. ed. 1998. (Lakeshore Ser.: Vol. 6). (Illus.). 312p. reprint ed. 15.00 (978-1-889128-55-9(4)) Mantle Ministries.

Oram, Hiawyn. Busy Busy Bears. Joos, Frederic, illus. 2004. 32p. (J). 17.99 (978-1-84270-245-1(9)) Andersen GBR. *Dist:* Independent Pubs. Group.

—Not-So-Grizzly Bear Stories. Warnes, Tim, illus. 1998. 96p. (J). (gr. k-4). 16.95 (978-1-888444-41-4(X)) Little Tiger Pr.

Ordal, Stina Langlo. Princess Aasta. 2002. (Illus.). 32p. (J). (ps-3). 16.95 (978-1-58234-783-7(2) , Bloomsbury Children) Bloomsbury Publishing.

Ordiway, Clipper Zane. There's a Bear on the Porch & There's a Bear on the Hill! 2004. 51p. (J). pap. 12.95 (978-1-4137-3121-7(X)) PublishAmerica, Inc.

O'ryan, Ellie. Christmas Wishes. 2006. (Care Bears Ser.). (Illus.). 24p. (J). pap. 3.50 (978-0-439-78541-9(3)) Scholastic, Inc.

Osborne, Mary Pope. Polar Bears Past Bedtime, Vol. 12. unabr. ed. 2004. (Magic Tree House Ser. : No. 12). 71p. (J). (gr. k-3). pap. 17.00 incl. audio (978-0-8072-0537-2(0) , Listening Library) Random Hse. Audio Publishing Group.

Osito Marcos quiere Pescar: Individual Title Six-Packs. (Coleccion Pm Ser.).Tr. of Baby Bear goes fishing. (SPA.). 16p. (gr. 1 up). 26.00 (978-0-7578-2988-8(0)) Rigby Education.

Un Oso con Hambre, 6 Packs. (Chiquilibros Ser.). (SPA.). (gr. k-1). 23.00 (978-0-7635-8598-3(X)) Rigby Education.

Ostrow, Kim. Bear in the Big Blue House. (Ready-to-Read Ser.: Vol. 2). (Illus.). (J). 2003. mass mkt. 3.99 (978-0-689-83814-9(X)); 1999. mass mkt. 3.99 (978-0-689-83813-2(1)) Simon & Schuster Children's Publishing. (Little Simon).

Ottolenghi, Carol. Ben the Postbear. Campanella, Marco, illus. 2005. 24p. (J). (ps-ps). 10.95 (978-0-7696-4301-4(9) , Gingham Dog Pr.) School Specialty Publishing.

Our Best Bear, Bo. 2002. (J). per. (978-1-931456-08-1(9)) Athena Pr.

Our Old Friend, Bear, 6 Packs. (gr. 3 up). 35.00 (978-0-7635-9670-5(1)) Rigby Education.

Oxenbury, Helen, illus. We're Going on a Bear Hunt. 2004. 33p. (J). (TAM, CZE, VIE, GUJ & PER.). (978-1-85269-707-5(5)); (TAM, CZE, VIE, GUJ & PER.). (978-1-85269-708-2(3)); (TAM, CZE, VIE, GUJ & PER.). (978-1-85269-709-9(1)); (TAM, CZE, VIE, GUJ & PER.). (978-1-85269-713-6(X)); (TAM, CZE, VIE, GUJ & PER.). (978-1-85269-714-3(8)); (CZE, TAM, VIE, GUJ & PER.). (978-1-85269-719-8(9)); (TAM, CZE, VIE, GUJ & PER.). (978-1-85269-721-1(0)) Mantra Publishing, Ltd.

Oxenbury, Helen & Rosen, Michael. Vamos a Cazar un Oso. Oxenbury, Helen, illus. 1999. (SPA., Illus.). 36p. (J). (gr. 2-4). 17.99 (978-980-257-107-9(5) , EK5539) Ekare, Ediciones VEN. *Dist:* AIMS International Bks., Inc., Kane/Miller Bk. Pubs., Inc., Lectorum Pubns., Inc.

P. B. Bear's Bedtime Book. 1998. (P. B. Bear Ser.). (Illus.). 32p. (J). (ps). 12.95 (978-0-7894-2870-7(9)) Dorling Kindersley Publishing, Inc.

Paddington Bear. Childhood Memories. l.t. unabr. ed. 1999. 212p. (J). 21.95 (978-1-85089-456-8(6) , 894566) ISIS Large Print Bks. GBR. *Dist:* Transaction Pubs.

Page, Josephine. Bye-Bye Bear. Beasley, Roberta, illus. 2005. 8p. (J). (gr. 7). 7.99 (978-0-439-72514-9(3) , Cartwheel Bks.) Scholastic, Inc.

Page, Nick & Page, Claire. Goldilocks & the Three Bears. 2007. (Ready to Read: Level 1 (Make Believe Ideas) Ser.). (Illus.). 31p. (J). (gr. k-2). 3.99 (***978-1-84610-440-4(8)***) Make Believe Ideas GBR. *Dist:* Ingram Pub. Services.

Page, Rhonda G. The Most Important Thing to Have. 2003. pap. 8.00 (978-0-8059-5438-8(4)) Dorrance Publishing Co., Inc.

Pajama Bedtime Bear Picture Books Set. (P. B. Bear Picture Books Ser.). (J). pap. 29.95 (978-0-7894-2198-2(4)) Dorling Kindersley Publishing, Inc.

Papa Oso y los Peces: Individual Title Six-Packs. (Coleccion Pm Ser.).Tr. of Father Bear goes fishing. (SPA.). 16p. (gr. 1 up). 26.00 (978-0-7578-2973-4(2)) Rigby Education.

Parent, Nancy. Care Bears: Caring Contest. Stein, David, illus. 2003. (Care Bears 8x8 Ser.). 24p. (J). (ps-1). pap. 3.50 (978-0-439-45158-1(2)) Scholastic, Inc.

—Pooh Says Boo. 1998. (Pooh Ser.). (Illus.). 10p. (J). (ps). 4.99 (978-1-57082-752-5(4)) Mouse Works.

Parry, Linda. Bramble Forgets. Parry, Alan, illus. 1998. (Honey Bear Ser.). 28p. (J). pap. 4.99 (978-0-8054-1791-3(5)) B&H Publishing Grp.

—Where's Pipkin? Parry, Alan, illus. 1998. (Honey Bear Ser.). 28p. (J). pap. 4.99 (978-0-8054-1788-3(5)) B&H Publishing Grp.

Parry, Linda & Parry, Alan. Christmastime with Mr Bear. 2006. 12p. (J). bds. 11.99 (978-0-7847-1469-0(X) , 04389) Standard Publishing.

Pattou, Edith. East. (YA). 2005. 516p. pap. 8.95 (978-0-15-205221-8(6) , Magic Carpet Bks.); 2003. 512p. (gr. 6 up). 18.00 (978-0-15-204563-0(5)) Harcourt Children's Bks.

—East. 2005. 507p. (YA). (gr. 7-12). per. 14.60 (978-0-606-33423-5(8)) Tandem Library Bks.

Paulsen, Gary. Brian's Hunt. 2005. 112p. (J). (gr. 5). pap. 5.99 (978-0-553-49415-0(5) , Laurel Leaf) Random Hse. Children's Bks.

—Brian's Hunt: A Novel. 2005. 103p. (YA). (gr. 4-8). reprint ed. 15.00 (978-0-7567-9570-2(2)) DIANE Publishing Co.

Pavekla, Joe. Ned: The Story of Bear Six Nine Three. 2007. (Illus.). 32p. (J). (ps-1). 21.95 (***978-1-894765-95-4(8)***) Rocky Mountain Bks. CAN. *Dist:* Midpoint Trade Bks., Inc.

Paver, Michelle. Hermano Lobo: Cronicas de la Prehistoria. Anton de vez, Patricia, tr. 2005. (Illus.). 222p. 17.25 (978-84-7888-933-4(7)) Emece Editores ESP. *Dist:* Ediciones Universal.

—Wolf Brother. Taylor, Geoff, illus. 2005. (Chronicles of Ancient Darkness). 304p. (J). (gr. 5 up). lib. bdg. 17.89 (978-0-06-072826-7(4)) HarperCollins Pubs.

—Wolf Brother. 2005. (Chronicles of Ancient Darkness: Bk. 1). (Illus.). 304p. (J). (gr. 5 up). 16.99 (978-0-06-072825-0(6)) HarperCollins Pubs.

—Wolf Brother. Taylor, Geoff, illus. 2006. (Chronicles of Ancient Darkness). 320p. (J). reprint ed. pap. 6.99 (978-0-06-072827-4(2) , Harper Trophy) HarperCollins Pubs.

PC Treasures, prod. Goldilocks & the Three Bears. 2007. (J). (***978-1-60072-034-5(X)***) PC Treasures, Inc.

—Little Red Riding Hood. 2007. (J). (***978-1-60072-031-4(5)***) PC Treasures, Inc.

PEEF Bears. (J). 7.95 (978-0-931674-38-9(7)); 12.95 (978-0-931674-54-9(9)); 11.95 (978-0-931674-34-1(4)) Waldman Hse. Pr., Inc.

Peltzman, Adam. It's Spring, Blue! Pontillo, Jenine, illus. 2000. (Blue's Clues Ser.). 16p. (J). (ps-k). pap. 3.99 (978-0-689-83097-6(1) , Simon Spotlight/Nickelodeon) Simon & Schuster Children's Publishing.

Percy, Graham, illus. Goldilocks & the Three Bears. l.t. ed. 2001. (SPA.). 28p. (ps-3). incl. audio compact disk (978-84-8214-087-2(6) , 1622) Peralt Montagut.

—Goldilocks & the Three Bears. l.t. ed. 2001. 28p. (J). (ps-3). 8.99 incl. audio (978-84-86154-91-2(X)) Peralt Montagut ESP. *Dist:* imaJen, Inc.

Peris, Carme. Goldilocks & the Three Bears. 1998. (Fairy Tale Theater Ser.). (Illus.). 32p. (J). (gr. k-3). pap. 8.95 (978-0-7641-5116-3(9)) Barron's Educational Series, Inc.

Peters, Andrew. Bear & Turtle & the Great Winter Race. Edgson, Alison, illus. 2006. 32p. pap. 7.99 (978-1-904550-91-4(6)) Child's Play-International.

Peters, Lisa Westberg. Sleepyhead Bear. Schoenherr, Ian, illus. 2006. (J). 32p. 16.99 (978-0-06-059675-0(9)); 40p. lib. bdg. 17.89 (978-0-06-059676-7(7)) HarperCollins Pubs.

Phillips, Jan. Just for Today. Shapiro, Alison Bonds, illus. 2005. 32p. (J). (ps-5). 15.95 (978-1-932073-07-2(8)) Kramer, H.J. Inc.

Picture Me Cuddly as a Bunny Mini. 2002. (Baby Costume Minis Ser.). 10p. (J). (ps up). bds. 2.99 (978-1-57151-553-7(4)) Playhouse Publishing.

Pighin, Marcel. Tickles the Bear Goes on a Cruise, 1 bk. Mitchell, Hazel, illus. 2006. 48p. (J). per. 10.49 (***978-0-9776679-7-0(9)***) MP2ME Enterprise.

Pillaha, Randell Lane. Tommy T the Railroad Bear. 2003. pap. 6.95 (978-0-533-14307-8(1)) Vantage Pr., Inc.

Pinkwater, Daniel M. At the Hotel Larry. Pinkwater, Jill, illus. 2005. 32p. (J). pap. 5.95 (978-0-7614-5178-5(1)) Cavendish, Marshall Corp.

—Bad Bears & a Bunny. Pinkwater, Jill, illus. 2005. (Irving & Muktuk Story Ser.). 32p. (J). (gr. k-3). 16.00 (978-0-618-33926-6(4)) Houghton Mifflin Co. Trade & Reference Div.

—Bad Bears Go Visiting. Pinkwater, Jill, illus. 2007. 32p. (J). (gr. k-3). 16.00 (978-0-618-43126-7(8)) Houghton Mifflin Co.

—Bad Bears in the Big City: An Irving & Muktuk Story. Pinkwater, Jill, illus. 2006. 32p. (J). (gr. k-3). pap. 6.95 (978-0-618-68952-1(4)) Houghton Mifflin Co.

—Bear's Picture. Johnson, D. B., illus. 2008. 32p. (J). (gr. 3-5). 16.00 (***978-0-618-75923-1(9)***) Houghton Mifflin Co.

—Bongo Larry. Pinkwater, Jill, illus. 1998. (Accelerated Reader Bks.). 32p. (J). (ps up). 14.95 (978-0-7614-5020-7(3) , Cavendish Children's Bks.) Cavendish, Marshall Corp.

—Dancing Larry. Pinkwater, Daniel M. & Pinkwater, Jill, illus. 2006. 32p. (J). 16.95 (978-0-7614-5220-1(6)) Cavendish, Marshall Corp.

—Ice Cream Larry. Pinkwater, Jill, illus. 1999. (Accelerated Reader Bks.). 32p. (J). (ps up). 15.95 (978-0-7614-5043-6(2) , Cavendish Children's Bks.) Cavendish, Marshall Corp.

—Irving & Muktuk: Two Bad Bears. Pinkwater, Jill, illus. 2003. 32p. (J). (gr. k-3). 5.95 (978-0-618-35404-7(2)) Houghton Mifflin Co. Trade & Reference Div.

—Irving & Muktuk: Two Bad Bears. Pinkwater, Jill, illus. 2003. (J). (ps-3). lib. bdg. 14.10 (978-0-613-88664-2(X)) Tandem Library Bks.

—Irving & Muktuk: Two Bad Bears. Pinkwater, Jill & Pinkwater, Daniel M., illus. 2001. 32p. (J). (gr. k-3). tchr. ed. 15.00 (978-0-618-09334-2(6)) Houghton Mifflin Co. Trade & Reference Div.

—Irving & Muktuk: Two Bad Bears. ed. 2004. (Illus.). (J). (gr. k-3). spiral bd. (978-0-616-11136-9(3)); spiral bd. (978-0-616-11137-6(1)) Canadian National Institute for the Blind/Institut National Canadien pour les Aveugles.

—Sleepover Larry. 2007. (Illus.). 32p. 16.99 (***978-0-7614-5335-2(0)***) Cavendish, Marshall Corp.

—Sleepover Larry. Pinkwater, Jill, illus. 2006. 32p. (J). (ps-3). 16.99 (978-0-7614-5314-7(8)) Cavendish, Marshall Corp.

—Young Larry. Pinkwater, Jill, illus. 2005. 32p. (J). pap. 5.95 (978-0-7614-5177-8(3)) Cavendish, Marshall Corp.

Pinkwater, Daniel M. & Pinkwater, Jill. Bongo Larry. 2005. (Illus.). 32p. (J). pap. 5.95 (978-0-7614-5189-1(7)) Cavendish, Marshall Corp.

—Ice Cream Larry. 2005. (Illus.). 32p. (J). pap. 5.95 (978-0-7614-5186-0(2)) Cavendish, Marshall Corp.

Pinkwater, Daniel M. & Pinkwater, Jill, illus. Bad Bear Detectives: An Irving & Muktuk Story. 2006. 32p. (J). (gr. k-3). 16.00 (978-0-618-43125-0(X)) Houghton Mifflin Co.

—Bad Bears Go Visiting: An Irving & Muktuk Story. 2007. (J). (***978-1-4287-3949-9(1)***) Houghton Mifflin Co.

Pinkwater, Daniel M. & Pinkwater, Jill, illus. Bad Bears in the Big City: An Irving & Muktuk Story. 2004. 32p. (J). (gr. k-3). tchr. ed. 16.00 (978-0-618-25208-4(8)) Houghton Mifflin Co. Trade & Reference Div.

Pinwheel, ed. Little Green Bear in the Backyard. 2001. (Rattle Bear Bks.). (Illus.). 12p. (J). bds. 3.95 (978-0-8069-8085-0(0)) Sterling Publishing Co., Inc.

—Wake Up, Sleepy Bear. 2001. (Changing Faces Ser.). (Illus.). 12p. (J). bds. 4.95 (978-0-8069-8092-8(3)) Sterling Publishing Co., Inc.

Pisarik, Michael E. Ursus: A Bear's Story. 2005. (YA). per. (978-1-59872-564-3(5)) Instantpublisher.com.

Pitcher, Caroline. Are You Spring? 2000. (J). (978-0-606-20115-5(7)) Tandem Library Bks.

Pokornik, Brigitte. Busy Bears. Leberer, Sigrid, illus. 2001. (Funny Fingers Ser.). 16p. 6.95 (978-0-7892-0724-1(9)) Abbeville Pr., Inc.

Polar Bear's Cubs. 2002. (Wild Heritage Collection Mini Bks.). (Illus.). 32p. (J). (978-1-59069-158-8(X) , H3002) Studio Mouse LLC.

Pooh & Piglet Snow Globe. 1999. (Winnie the Pooh Ser.). (J). (978-1-57082-891-1(1)) Mouse Works.

Pooh Play a Song Juegos y Fiestas. 2001. (SPA., Illus.). 8p. (J). 7.98 (978-0-7853-5228-0(7)) Publications International, Ltd.

Pooh's Perfect Day. 2000. (Giant Pooh Book Ends Ser.). (Illus.). 10p. (J). (ps). (978-1-57584-807-5(4)) Reader's Digest Children's Publishing, Inc.

Posner, Renee & Quinton, Sasha. Suzy Season Loves Spring. D'Argo, Laura, illus. (Be Mine Bears Ser.). (J). bds. 4.99 (978-1-58209-350-5(4)) Books Are Fun, Ltd.

—Suzy Season Loves Summer. D'Argo, Laura, illus. (Be Mine Bears Ser.). (J). bds. 4.99 (978-1-58209-351-2(2)) Books Are Fun, Ltd.

Potter, Tony. Let's Find Teddy. 1998. (Illus.). 8p. (J). (ps). 9.95 (978-1-902553-00-9(4)) Grimond FRA. *Dist:* Continental Enterprises Group, Inc. (CEG).

Powell, Richard. I See a Teddy. Davis, Caroline, illus. 2003. (Plastic Shapes Ser.). 12p. (J). bds. 5.95 (978-0-7641-5648-9(9)) Barron's Educational Series, Inc.

—Race Bear. Holt, Emma, illus. 2003. (Whizzy Wheels Bks.). 20p. (J). bds. 4.95 (978-0-7641-5587-1(3)) Barron's Educational Series, Inc.

Prap, Lila. 1001 Stories. Prap, Lila, illus. 2006. (Illus.). 32p. (J). 15.95 (978-1-929132-92-8(1)) Kane/Miller Bk. Pubs., Inc.

Prater, John. Hold Tight! 2003. (Illus.). 32p. (J). (ps). pap. 5.95 (978-0-7641-2304-7(1)) Barron's Educational Series, Inc.

—Is It Christmas? Prater, John, illus. 2003. (Illus.). 32p. (J). 13.95 (978-0-7641-5668-7(3)) Barron's Educational Series, Inc.

—Number One, Tickle Your Tum. 1999. (Baby Bear Ser.). (Illus.). 24p. (J). 6.95 (978-0-7641-5185-9(1)) Barron's Educational Series, Inc.

—¡Otra Vez! 2000. Tr. of Again!. (SPA.). 28p. (J). 16.95 (978-980-257-252-6(7)) Ekare, Ediciones VEN. *Dist:* Lectorum Pubns., Inc.

Prayer Bear Pillow Book. 2003. (J). (978-1-59292-026-6(8)) SoftPlay, Inc.

Preller, James. Case of the Race Against Time. 2003. (gr. 3-6). lib. bdg. 11.80 (978-0-613-63389-5(X)) Tandem Library Bks.

—Wake Me in Spring. Scherer, Jeffrey, illus. 2004. 32p. (J). lib. bdg. 15.00 (978-1-59054-397-9(1)) Fitzgerald Bks.

Price, Mathew. Don't Worry, Alfie. Clark, Emma Chichester, illus. 1999. 14p. (J). (ps-k). pap. 9.95 (978-0-531-30127-2(3) , Orchard Bks.) Scholastic, Inc.

Pruett, Candace. A Visit with My Uncle Ted. 2003. (J). per. 16.95 (978-1-930859-68-5(6)) Elderberry Press, Inc.

Pryor, Bonnie. Grandpa Bear's Christmas. 1999. (Illus.). 32p. (J). (ps-3). pap. 4.95 (978-0-688-17066-0(8)) HarperCollins Pubs.

—Grandpa Bear's Christmas. 1999. (J). (978-0-606-17245-5(9)) Tandem Library Bks.

Pugliano-Martin, Carol. See You in Spring! 2006. (Early Explorers Ser.). (J). 34.00 (***978-1-4108-6105-4(8)***) Benchmark Education Co.

Quintart, Natalie. Mama Bear. Blanchart, Stephanie, illus. 2005. 32p. (J). (ps-ps). 6.95 (978-1-58925-394-0(9) , tiger tales) ME Media LLC.

Raintree Steck-Vaughn Staff. Bear Escape. 2000. (Illus.). (J). pap. 19.24 (978-0-8172-6450-5(7)); pap. 20.45 (978-0-8172-6600-4(3)) Steck-Vaughn.

Random House Disney Staff & Braybrooks, Ann. The Easter Bear? Yee, Josie, illus. 2003. 24p. (J). (gr. k-3). pap. 3.99 (978-0-7364-1298-8(0) , RH/Disney) Random Hse. Children's Bks.

Ransom, Candice. Goldilocks & the Three Bears. Bryant, Laura J., illus. 2007. 22p. (J). (ps-k). bds. 12.95 (***978-0-7696-5272-6(7)*** , Gingham Dog Pr.) School Specialty Publishing.

Ransom, Candice F. Goldilocks & the Three Bears. Bryant, Laura J., illus. 2002. (Brighter Child Keepsake Stories Ser.). 32p. (J). (ps-3). pap. 3.99 (978-1-57768-178-6(9) , Brighter Child) School Specialty Publishing.

—Goldilocks & the Three Bears: Ricitos de Oro y los Tres Osos. Lyon, Tammie, illus. 2005. (Keepsake Stories Ser.). (ENG & SPA.). 32p. (J). (gr. k-3). pap. 3.99 (978-0-7696-3815-7(5) , Brighter Child) School Specialty Publishing.

Ratoff, Michael. Silent Noisy Spring, 3 vols. Painter, Laurie, illus. l.t. ed. 2001. (Every Thing in an Empty Box Ser.). 56p. (J). (ps-3). lib. bdg. 9.95 (978-0-9627986-4-1(9)) Rebel Butterfly Pr.

—Silver & Shiny, 3 vols. Painter, Laurie, illus. 2nd l.t. ed. 2001. (Every Thing in an Empty Box Ser.). 56p. (J). (ps-3). lib. bdg. 9.95 (978-0-9627986-2-7(2)) Rebel Butterfly Pr.

Rawlinson, Julia. Fred & the Little Egg. Massey, Jane, illus. 2005. 28p. (J). 16.00 (978-1-56148-468-3(7)) Good Bks.

Raye, Rebekah. The Very Best Bed. Raye, Rebekah, illus. 2006. (Illus.). 32p. (J). (ps-3). 16.95 (978-0-88448-284-0(7)) Tilbury Hse. Pubs.

Redenbaugh, Vicki. Skar's Picnic ... A Bear's Tale. Redenbaugh, Vicki, illus. 2005. (Illus.). (J). 14.95 (978-1-59091-034-4(6)) Eastern National.

Reece, Stephen. The Bear in the Air Scare. 1998. (Illus.). 12p. (J). (ps-3). pap. 2.95 (978-1-892388-00-1(6)) Little Trucker Bks.

Relf, Adam, illus. The Biggest Bear. 2006. 28p. (J). 15.99 (978-0-439-84015-6(5) , Cartwheel Bks.) Scholastic, Inc.

Repp, Janelle. Little Bear & the Springwood Spinners. Garvin, Elaine, illus. 2000. (Little Bear Adventure Ser.: Vol. 6). 32p. (J). (ps-1). pap. 6.49 (978-1-57924-439-2(4)) Jones, Bob Univ. Pr.

—Little Bear & the Springwood Spinners. 2001. (ps-2). lib. bdg. 13.55 (978-0-613-85511-2(6)) Tandem Library Bks.

Reynolds, Adrian. Pete & Polo's Farmyard Adventure. Reynolds, Adrian, illus. 2002. (Illus.). 32p. (J). (ps-1). pap. 16.95 (978-0-439-30913-4(1) , Orchard Bks.) Scholastic, Inc.

Rhodes, Tim W. The Story of the Bed Bear. 2007. (Illus.). (J). 14.95 (***978-1-60131-009-5(9)***) Big Tent Bks.

Richards. Magic Sky Board Book. 2007. (Illus.). 22p. (J). (ps-k). 7.99 (***978-1-4052-2441-3(X)***) Egmont Bks., Ltd. GBR. *Dist:* Independent Pubs. Group.

Richards, Helene. Disney Winnie the Pooh Music Play Storybook. 2005. (RD Innovative Book & Player Format Ser.). (Illus.). 40p. (J). 24.99 (978-0-7944-0768-1(4)) Reader's Digest Assn., Inc., The.

Richards, Lucy. The Magic Sky. (Illus.). 32p. (J). 2008. pap. 14.00 (***978-1-4052-3045-2(2)***); 2004. pap. 8.99 (978-1-4052-1335-6(3)) Egmont Bks., Ltd. GBR. *Dist:* Independent Pubs. Group.

Richter, Bernd & Richter, Susan. Goodnight Alaska - Goodnight Little Bear. 2002. 14p. bds. 6.95 (978-1-931353-06-9(9)) Saddle Pal Creations, Inc.

—The Little Bear Who Didn't Want to Hibernate. Green, Sue, illus. 2003. 42p. pap. 9.95 (978-1-931353-10-6(7)) Saddle Pal Creations, Inc.

Ricitos de Oro y los Tres Osos. 2001. (SPA.). (978-968-6347-34-0(8)) Larousse, Ediciones, S. A. de C. V.

Ricitos de Oro y los tres osos/Goldilocks & the Three Bears. 2005. (Libros en Espanol Para Ninos Ser.). (SPA.). (YA). (ps-1). 11.97 (978-0-8215-0995-1(0)); 15.75 (978-0-8215-1205-0(6)) Sadlier, William H. Inc.

Rigby Education Staff. Goldilocks: Jumbled Tumble. (gr. k-2). 26.00 (978-0-7635-2418-0(2)) Rigby Education.

—Honey, Honey. (Sails Literacy Ser.). (Illus.). 16p. (gr. k-1). 27.00 (978-0-7635-9872-3(0)) Rigby Education.

—A Place to Sleep. (Sails Literacy Ser.). (Illus.). 16p. (gr. k-1). 27.00 (978-0-7635-9869-3(0) , 698690C99) Rigby Education.

Rissman, Angelica. Julius & the Lost Letter to Santa. 2003. (J). 7.99 (978-1-59384-019-8(5)) Parklane Publishing.

Ritchie, Alison. Me & My Dad! Edgson, Alison, illus. 2007. 28p. (J). (ps-2). 16.95 (***978-1-56148-565-9(9)***) Good Bks.

Ritchie, Alison. What Bear Likes Best! Kolanovic, Dubravka, illus. 2005. 28p. (J). 16.00 (978-1-56148-473-7(3)) Good Bks.

Rives. If I Were a Polar Bear. Rives, illus. 2001. (Illus.). 12p. (J). (ps-k). 16.95 (978-1-58117-046-7(7) , Intervisual/Piggy Toes) Dalmatian Pr.

Roberts, Dannel. Me & Uncle Mike & the 3-Toed Bear. Tapia, Lonnie C., illus. l.t. ed. 1999. (Me & Uncle Mike Children's Book Ser.: Bk. 1). 36p. (J). (gr. k-5). per. 14.95 (978-1-893459-00-7(4)) Lions & Tigers & Bears Publishing, Inc.

Roberts, Tom. Goldilocks. Kubinyi, Laszlo, illus. 2006. (J). (gr. 2-6). 25.65 (978-1-59197-748-3(7)) Spotlight.

Robinson, Rachaell. Princess Karakul: The Runaway Bear. 2003. 22.00 (978-0-8059-6188-1(7)) Dorrance Publishing Co., Inc.

Robinson, Sandra Chisholm. Last Bit Bear: A Fable. Meloy, Ellen D., illus. 7th ed. 2000. 49p. (ps up). pap. 5.95 (978-0-911797-09-1(2)) Rinehart, Roberts Pubs.

Rockhill, Dennis. Polar Slumber. Rockhill, Dennis, illus. 2006. 32p. (J). (gr. k-3). pap. 16.95 (978-0-9741992-8-3(1)) Raven Tree Pr.

—Polar Slumber/Sueño Polar. Raven Tree Press Staff, ed. de la Vega, Eida, tr. Rockhill, Dennis, illus. 2004. Tr. of Sueño Polar. (SPA & ENG., Illus.). 32p. (J). (ps-3). 16.95 (978-0-9724973-1-2(5) , 1234791) Raven Tree Pr.

Rockwell, Anne F. Morgan Plays Soccer. Meisel, Paul, illus. 1999. 32p. (J). (ps-1). pap. 5.95 (978-0-06-446739-1(2)) HarperCollins Pubs.

Rodriguez, AJ. Theodore Da Baer Ii: A New Beginning. 2006. 207p. pap. 19.95 (978-1-4241-1125-1(0)) PublishAmerica, Inc.

Rogers, Alan. Green Bear. 2004. (Little Giants Ser.). (Illus.). 16p. (ps-k). (J). pap. 3.95 (978-1-58728-159-4(7)); 5.95 (978-1-58728-152-5(X)) T&N Children's Publishing. (Two Can Publishing).

—El Oso Verde. 2004. (Pequenos Gigantes Ser.).Tr. of Green Bear. (SPA., Illus.). 16p. (ps-k). (J). pap. 3.95 (978-1-58728-957-6(1)); 5.95 (978-1-58728-143-3(0)) T&N Children's Publishing. (Two Can Publishing).

—El Oso Verde. Rogers, Alan, illus. 2000. (Pequenos Gigantes Ser.).Tr. of Green Bear. (Illus.). 15p. (J). (ps-ps). lib. bdg. 10.75 (978-0-606-20836-9(4)) Tandem Library Bks.

—Ours Vert. 2003. (Little Giants Ser.). (SPA., Illus.). 16p. (J). (ps-k). 5.95 (978-1-58728-180-8(5) , Two Can Publishing) T&N Children's Publishing.

Rogers, Gregory. Midsummer Knight. Rogers, Gregory, illus. 2007. (Illus.). 32p. (J). (gr. 1-4). 16.95 (***978-1-59643-183-6(0)***) Roaring Brook Pr.

Roosa, Bertha. The Hobert Bears' Great Ideas. 2007. (Illus.). 80p. (J). (***978-0-9639391-2-8(2)***) Pine Hill Pr., Inc.

Root, Phyllis. Oliver Finds His Way. Denise, Christopher, illus. 2002. 40p. (J). (ps-1). 14.99 (978-0-7636-1383-9(5)) Candlewick Pr.

Rosado, Maria. Bear Rescue! 2002. (gr. 3-6). lib. bdg. 11.80 (978-0-613-51291-6(X)) Tandem Library Bks.

Rosala Osa. 2001. (SPA.). (J). 6.49 (978-1-57924-567-2(6) , 180281) Jones, Bob Univ. Pr.

Rosales, Melodye. Leola & the Honeybears. 1999. (Illus.). (J). 95.70 (978-0-439-11756-2(9)) Scholastic, Inc.

Rosen, Michael. Bear's Day Out. Reynolds, Adrian, illus. 2007. 32p. (J). (ps-3). 16.95 (***978-1-59990-007-0(6)***) Bloomsbury Publishing.

—Vamos a Cazar un Oso. Oxenbury, Helen, illus. 2000. (SPA.). 36p. (J). (gr. 2-4). bds. 10.95 (978-980-257-225-0(X) , EK4034) Ekare, Ediciones VEN. *Dist:* Lectorum Pubns., Inc.

—We're Going on a Bear Hunt. Oxenbury, Helen, illus. 2003. 36p. (J). pap. 7.99 (978-0-689-85349-4(1) , Aladdin) Simon & Schuster Children's Publishing.

—We're Going on a Bear Hunt. 2003. (gr. k-3). lib. bdg. 16.45 (978-0-613-61665-2(0)) Tandem Library Bks.

Rosen, Michael & Oxenbury, Helen. We're Going on a Bear Hunt. 2004. (POR, TAM, CZE, VIE & CHI., Illus.). 32p. (J). (978-1-85269-706-8(7)); (978-1-85269-710-5(5)); (978-1-85269-711-2(3)); (978-1-85269-716-7(4)); (978-1-85269-718-1(0)); (978-1-85269-720-4(2)) Mantra Publishing, Ltd.

Rosen, Michael J. Three Feet Small. Gorbachev, Valeri, illus. 2005. 32p. (J). 16.00 (978-0-15-204938-6(X) , Gulliver Bks.) Harcourt Children's Bks.

—We're Going on a Bear Hunt. Oxenbury, Helen, illus. gif. ed. 2002. 40p. (J). 9.99 (978-0-7636-1979-4(5)) Candlewick Pr.

Ross, Michael Elsohn. Baby Bear Isn't Hungry. Powell, Consie, illus. 2006. 24p. (J). lib. bdg. 9.95 (978-1-930238-24-4(X)) Yosemite Assn.

Ross, Tony. Big Bad Barney Bear. 2002. (Illus.). 32p. (J). pap. 8.99 (978-1-84270-058-7(8)) Random Hse. GBR. *Dist:* Independent Pubs. Group.

Rouillard, Wendy W. Barnaby-Seasons in the Park. Rouillard, Wendy W., ed. 2000. (Barnaby Ser.: Vol. 5). (Illus.). 32p. (J). 15.95 (978-0-9642836-9-5(7)) Barnaby & Co.

—Barnaby's Kite Ride. Rouillard, Wendy W., illus. l.t. ed. 1998. (Illus.). 32p. (J). (gr. 1-3). 15.95 (978-0-9642836-6-4(2)) Barnaby & Co.

Roxbee-Cox, Phil. Find the Teddy. 2007. (Find-its Board Bks). 12p. (J). bds. 6.99 (***978-0-7945-1805-9(2)*** , Usborne) EDC Publishing.

Rubio, Gabriela. Terrible Terrible. 2006. (SPA., Illus.). 32p. (J). (978-84-933060-7-6(X)) Ekare, Ediciones.

Rucki, Ani. When the Earth Wakes. 1998. (Illus.). 32p. (J). (ps-2). pap. 15.95 (978-0-590-05951-0(3)) Scholastic, Inc.

Ryder, Joanne. Bear of My Heart. Moore, Margie, illus. 32p. (J). 2010. bds. 8.99 (***978-1-4169-5472-9(4)*** , Little Simon Inspirations); 2006. 12.95 (978-0-689-85947-2(3) , Simon & Schuster Children's Publishing) Simon & Schuster Children's Publishing.

Ryder, Joanne. Big Bear Ball. Kellogg, Steven, illus. 2002. 32p. (J). (ps-1). 15.95 (978-0-06-027955-4(9)) HarperCollins Pubs.

Sadler, Marilyn. Honey Bunny's Honey Bear. Bollen, Roger, illus. 2008. (Step into Reading Ser.). (J). (978-0-375-84326-6(4)); lib. bdg. 11.99 (978-0-375-94326-3(9)) Random Hse. Children's Bks.

Saltzman, Ruth E. Poppy Bear: The Garden That Overslept. Deeter, Catherine, illus. 2001. 32p. (J). (gr. k-2). 16.95 (978-1-58270-042-7(7)) Beyond Words Publishing, Inc.

Sandage, Charley. ALL AROUND ARKANSAS Big Book. 2005. (J). pap. (***978-0-9794044-2-9(8)***) Archeological Assessments, Inc.

—ALL AROUND ARKANSAS student Edition. 2005. (J). pap. (***978-0-9638956-5-3(6)***) Archeological Assessments, Inc.

—Big Bear's Arkansas ABCs. Przybylek, Leslie, illus. 2004. 56p. (J). (gr. k-2). pap. 14.95 (978-0-9638956-9-1(9)) Archeological Assessments, Inc.

—Big Bear's Arkansas ABCs Big Book. 2005. (J). pap. (***978-0-9794044-1-2(X)***) Archeological Assessments, Inc.

—I can tell you stories, if you gather round Big Book. 2005. (J). pap. (***978-0-9794044-3-6(6)***) Archeological Assessments, Inc.

Sander, Sonia. Busy, Busy, Sunny Day. Stein, David, illus. 2003. (Care Bears Ser.). 24p. (J). pap. 3.50 (978-0-439-53196-2(9)) Scholastic, Inc.

—Care Bears: Find That Rainbow! Sticker Storybook. del Sur, Duendes, illus. 2003. (Care Bears Ser.). 16p. (J). (ps-2). pap. 5.99 (978-0-439-45176-5(0)) Scholastic, Inc.

—Care Bears: Find That Rainbow! Sticker Storybook. 2003. (ps-2). lib. bdg. 14.15 (978-0-613-72161-5(6)) Tandem Library Bks.

—The Care Bears' Big Wish. Johnson, Jay, illus. 2005. (Care Bears Ser.). 48p. (J). (ps-k). pap. 7.99 (978-0-439-74416-4(4)) Scholastic, Inc.

—Care Bears Love Is All Around. Moore, Saxton, illus. 2006. 24p. (J). pap. 3.50 (978-0-439-78930-1(3)) Scholastic, Inc.

—Care BearsTM: Caring Rainbow. Johnson, Jay, illus. 2003. (Care Bears Ser.). 8p. (J). (ps). bds. 5.99 (978-0-439-45178-9(7)) Scholastic, Inc.

—Christmas Cheer. 2007. (Care Bears Ser.). 24p. (J). pap. 3.99 (***978-0-439-89511-8(1)***) Scholastic, Inc.

—Oopsy Saves the Day. 2007. (Care Bears Movie Reader Ser.). 32p. (J). pap. 3.99 (***978-0-439-02675-8(X)***) Scholastic, Inc.

Sander, Sonia. Wish Bear's Promise. Johnson, Jay, illus. 2005. (Care Bears Ser.). 32p. (J). (ps-k). pap. 3.99 (978-0-439-74414-0(8)) Scholastic, Inc.

Sanschagrin, Joceline. El Osito de Peluche. 2004. (Caillou Osa Menor Ser.).Tr. of Where's Teddy?. (SPA., Illus.). 24p. (J). (ps up). bds. 5.95 (978-1-58728-404-5(9) , Creative Publishing International) Quayside.

Sargent, Dave & Sargent, David, Jr. Pinkie Flamingo: Leaving Home, 19, 15. Lenoir, Jane, illus. 2003. (Feather Tales Ser.: 15). 42p. (J). pap. 6.95 (978-1-56763-748-9(5)) Ozark Publishing.

Sargent, Dave & Sargent, Pat. Brutus the Bear: Show Respect, 15 vols., Vol. 4. Huff, Jeane, illus. 2nd rev. ed. 2003. (Animal Pride Ser.: 4). 42p. (J). pap. 6.95 (978-1-56763-766-3(3)); lib. bdg. 19.95 (978-1-56763-765-6(5)) Ozark Publishing.

—Young Brutus: Show Respect!, 4. Woodward, Elaine, illus. 2003. (Young Animal Pride Ser.: 4). 24p. (J). pap. 6.95 (978-1-56763-870-7(8)); lib. bdg. 19.95 (978-1-56763-869-1(4)) Ozark Publishing.

Sargent, Pat L. The Grizzly, 6, vol. 1. Lenoir, Jane, illus. 2004. (Barney the Bear Killer Ser.: No. 1). 129p. (YA). pap. 9.95 (978-1-56763-964-3(X)) Ozark Publishing.

Scarry, Patricia M. The Sweet Smell of Christmas. Miller, J. P., illus. 2003. 36p. (J). (gr. k-k). 8.99 (978-0-375-82643-6(2) , Golden Bks.) Random Hse. Children's Bks.

Scarry, Patsy. Good Night, Little Bear. Scarry, Richard, illus. (J). (gr. k-k). 2004. 26p. bds. 4.99 (978-0-375-82840-9(0)); 2001. 24p. 2.99 (978-0-307-98624-5(1)) Random Hse. Children's Bks. (Golden Bks.).

Schaaf, Ron. BearClaw: Finding Courage Within. 2007. (J). (***978-0-9787555-1-5(0)***) Hickory Tales Publishing.

Schertle, Alice. Very Hairy Bear. Phelan, Matt, illus. 2007. 32p. (J). (ps-2). 16.00 (978-0-15-216568-0(1)) Harcourt Trade Pubs.

Scheunemann, Pam. Bear Claws. Chawla, Neena, illus. 2006. (Fact & Fiction Ser.). 24p. (J). pap. (978-1-59679-926-4(9)); (gr. 1-3). 21.35 (978-1-59679-925-7(0) , Sand-Castle) ABDO Publishing Co.

Schlachter, Rita. The Bear's Tale. Sloat, Teri, illus. 1999. (Books for Young Learners). 12p. (J). (gr. k-2). pap. 5.00 (978-1-57274-146-1(5) , A2429) Owen, Richard C. Pubs., Inc.

Schneider, Antonie. The Birthday Bear. 2000. (J). 12.75 (978-0-606-19469-3(X)) Tandem Library Bks.

Scholastic, Inc. Staff. Five Little Care Bears. 2006. (Care Bears Ser.). 3p. (J). bds. 12.99 (978-0-439-82954-0(2)) Scholastic, Inc.

—Murphy & Myrtle Beanbag. 2002. (Sidekicks Ser.). (J). 9.99 (978-0-439-40397-9(9) , Sidekicks TM) Scholastic, Inc.

Schuler, Karen. The Backyard Bears Present the Story of Christmas: A Nativity Play. Necaise, Jimmy, photos by. 2004. (Illus.). 32p. 14.99 (978-1-58169-148-1(3) , Evergreen Pr.) Genesis Communications, Inc.

Schwartz, Staci J. New Bear on the Block. 2006. (J). pap. (978-0-9766889-2-1(1)) ComteQ Publishing.

Scott, Evelyn & Golden Books Staff. The Fourteen Bears in Summer & Winter. Parsons, Virginia, illus. 2005. 64p. (J). (gr. k-k). reprint ed. 14.95 (978-0-375-83279-6(3) , Golden Bks.) Random Hse. Children's Bks.

Scripture Teachers: Solomon & Friends Learn about Being Wonderfully Made. 2003. pap. (***978-0-9712894-3-7(3)***) Lighthouse Christian Products Co.

A B

Scripture Teachers: Solomon & Friends Learn about Forgiveness. 2003. pap. (*978-0-9712894-1-3(7)) Lighthouse Christian Products Co.

Scripture Teachers: Solomon & Friends Learn about Prayer. 2003. pap. (*978-0-9712894-0-6(9)) Lighthouse Christian Products Co.

Scripture Teachers: Solomon & Friends Learn about the Christmas Story. 2003. pap. (*978-0-9712894-4-4(1)) Lighthouse Christian Products Co.

Scripture Teachers: Solomon & Friends Learn about Trusting God. 2003. pap. (*978-0-9712894-2-0(5)) Lighthouse Christian Products Co.

Searcy, Margaret Zehmer. The Charm of the Bearclaw Necklace. Brough, Hazel, illus. 80p. (J). (gr. 3-7). pap. 7.95 (978-1-56554-777-3(2)) Pelican Publishing Co., Inc.

Seeger, Laura Vaccaro. Dog & Bear. Seeger, Laura Vaccaro, illus. 2007. (Illus.). 32p. (J). (ps-3). 12.95 (978-1-59643-053-2(2)) Roaring Brook Pr.

Seltzer, Eric. Doodle Dog. ed. 2005. (Illus.). 32p. (J). lib. bdg. 15.00 (978-1-59054-979-7(1)) Fitzgerald Bks.

—Granny Doodle Day. Seltzer, Eric, illus. 2006. (Ready-to-Reads Ser.). (Illus.). 32p. (J). pap. 3.99 (978-0-689-85911-3(2), Aladdin) Simon & Schuster Children's Publishing.

Sendak, Maurice, illus. Father Bear Comes Home. 2002. (Little Bear Ser.). (J). 12.34 (978-0-7587-6089-0(2)) Book Wholesalers, Inc.

—A Kiss for Little Bear. 2002. (Little Bear Ser.). (J). 12.34 (978-0-7587-6175-0(9)) Book Wholesalers, Inc.

—Little Bear's Friend. 2002. (Little Bear Ser.). (J). 12.34 (978-0-7587-6185-9(6)) Book Wholesalers, Inc.

—Little Bear's Visit. 2002. (Little Bear Ser.). (J). 12.34 (978-0-7587-6186-6(4)) Book Wholesalers, Inc.

Senshu, Noriko. Sonny's Dream. Senshu, Noriko, illus. 2001. (Illus.). 40p. (J). (ps up). 16.95 (978-1-57174-215-5(8)) Hampton Roads Publishing Co., Inc.

Seton, Ernest Thompson. Biography of A Grizzly. 2007. pap. 87.99 (*978-1-4280-5279-6(8)) IndyPublish.com.

—Johnny Bear. 2004. reprint ed. pap. 1.99 (978-1-4192-2787-5(4)) Kessinger Publishing, LLC.

—Monarch: The Big Bear of Tallac. 2004. reprint ed. pap. 1.99 (978-1-4192-3486-6(2)) Kessinger Publishing, LLC.

Sewell-Shaw, Eve. Every Day Will Be Saturday When You Find a Friend. 1999. (Illus.). 50p. (J). 9.95 (978-0-7541-0786-6(8)) Minerva Pr. GBR. *Dist:* Unity Distribution.

Shahan, Sherry. In Eisiger Kalte. 2002. (GER.). 160p. pap. 15.00 (978-1-4000-3957-9(6), New Media German Language) Random House Foreign Language Publishing.

Shannon, George. La Cancion del Lagarto. Aruego, Jose & Dewey, Ariane, illus. unabr. ed. 2005. (SPA.). (J). (gr. 2-4). pap. 16.95 incl. audio (978-0-87499-349-3(0), LK6492) Live Oak Media.

Shotwell, Mary. Summer Expedition. 2007. (J). per. 6.99 (*978-1-59886-921-7(3)) Tate Publishing & Enterprises, L.L.C.

Silsbe, Brenda. The Bears We Know. Ritchie, Scot, illus. 2003. (Annikins Ser.: Vol. 8). 12p. (Orig.). (J). (ps-2). pap. 0.99 (978-1-55037-048-5(0)) Annick Pr., Ltd. CAN. *Dist:* Firefly Bks., Ltd.

Simon-Kerr, Julia. Best Buddies. 2006. (Open Season Ser.). 24p. (J). pap. 3.99 (978-0-06-084602-2(X)) HarperCollins Pubs.

Simon, Mary Manz. Bear Obeys. Clearwater, Linda & Couri, Kathy, illus. 2006. (First Virtues for Toddlers Ser.). 20p. (J). 5.99 (978-0-7847-1416-4(9), 04068) Standard Publishing.

Sister Bear. 2001. 12.99 (978-0-310-98508-2(0)) Zondervan.

Skead, Robert. Elves Can't Kick. 2005. 84p. per. 7.99 (978-1-929478-66-8(6)) Cross Training Publishing.

Skiing: KinderConcepts Individual Title Six-Packs. (Kinderstarters Ser.). 8p. (ps-1). 21.00 (978-0-7635-8718-5(4)) Rigby Education.

Skurzynski, Gloria. The Hunted. 2001. 12.60 (978-0-606-22147-4(6)); (gr. 3-6). lib. bdg. 14.10 (978-0-613-62422-0(X)) Tandem Library Bks.

Skurzynski, Gloria & Ferguson, Alane. The Hunted. (National Parks Mysteries Ser.: No. 5). 160p. (J). (gr. 3-7). 2000. (Illus.). 15.95 (978-0-7922-7053-9(3)); 5th ed. 2001. pap. 5.95 (978-0-7922-7665-4(5)) National Geographic Society. (National Geographic Children's Bks.).

—Night of the Black Bear: A Mystery in Great Smoky Mountains National Park. 2007. (Mysteries in Our National Park Ser.). (Illus.). 160p. (J). (gr. 3-7). 4.99 (978-1-4263-0094-3(8)); 18.90 (978-1-4263-0105-6(7)) National Geographic Society. (National Geographic Children's Bks.).

Slater, David Michael. The Ring Bear. Brooks, S. G., illus. 2004. 32p. (J). 15.95 (978-0-9729225-1-7(2), 1231960) Flashlight Pr.

Slater, Teddy. Goldilocks & the Three Bears: Pop-up Storybook Theater. Yerkes, Lane, illus. 2004. 10p. (J). (gr. k-4). reprint ed. 17.00 (978-0-7567-8224-5(4)) DIANE Publishing Co.

Slingsby, Janet. Bear's Dream. Morris, Tony, illus. 2000. 32p. (J). (ps-1). pap. 4.99 (978-0-439-19096-1(7)) Scholastic, Inc.

Smart, Jamie. Bear: Immortal. 2004. (Illus.). 144p. pap. 14.95 (978-1-59362-001-1(2)) Slave Labor Bks.

Smee, Nicola. Funny Face. 2006. (Illus.). 24p. (J). 8.95 (978-1-58234-710-3(7), Bloomsbury Children) Bloomsbury Publishing.

Smiley, Lucy Ireland. Bass-Fishing Bears. 2006. (J). pap. 8.00 (978-0-8059-7017-3(7)) Dorrance Publishing Co., Inc.

Smith, Laura Rountree. Snubby Nose & Tippy Toes. 2004. reprint ed. pap. 15.95 (978-1-4191-4792-0(7)); pap. 1.99 (978-1-4192-4792-7(1)) Kessinger Publishing, LLC.

Smith, Rountree Laur. Snubby Nose & Tippy Toes. 2006. pap. 87.99 (*978-1-4219-7387-6(1)) IndyPublish.com.

Smythe, Theresa. Snowbear's Christmas Countdown, YOU. Ottaviano, Christy, ed. rev. ed. 2004. (Illus.). 40p. (J). 14.95 (978-0-8050-7244-0(6), Holt, Henry & Co. Bks. For Young Readers) Holt, Henry & Co.

Snyder, George. Stubby the Baby Bear. Tackett, Steve, illus. 1999. 26p. (J). (ps-6). pap. 5.95 (978-1-928597-00-1(9)) PaPa Fuzz Pubns.

Solis, Valerie. Pink for Polar Bear. Solis, Valerie, illus. (Illus.). 32p. (J). 13.95 (978-0-241-00250-6(8), Hamilton, Hamish) Penguin Bks., Ltd. GBR. *Dist:* Trafalgar Square Publishing.

Sommer, Carl. Can You Help Me Find My Smile? 2003. (Another Sommer-Time Story Ser.). (Illus.). 48p. (J). (gr. k-4). lib. bdg. 23.95 incl. audio compact disk (978-1-57537-707-0(1)); (gr. k-4). lib. bdg. 23.95 incl. audio (978-1-57537-757-5(8)); (gr. 1-4). 16.95 incl. audio (978-1-57537-556-4(7)); (gr. 1-4). 16.95 incl. audio compact disk (978-1-57537-507-6(9)) Advance Publishing, Inc.

La sorpresa de Papa Oso: Individual Title Six-Packs. (Coleccion Pm Ser.).Tr. of Father Bear's surprise. (SPA.). 16p. (gr. 1 up). 26.00 (978-0-7578-3046-4(3)) Rigby Education.

Southey, Robert. Goldilocks & the Three Bears. 2005. (Classics Illustrated Junior Ser.). 32p. 5.99 (978-1-894998-21-5(9)) Lake, Jack Productions, Inc. CAN. *Dist:* Hushion Hse. Publishing, Ltd.

Spelman, Cornelia Maude. Mama & Daddy Bear's Divorce. 2001. (gr. k-3). lib. bdg. 15.25 (978-0-613-70954-5(3)) Tandem Library Bks.

—Mama & Daddy Bear's Divorce. Parkinson, Kathy, illus. 2004. (Concept Book Ser.). 24p. (J). (ps-1). pap. 6.95 (978-0-8075-5222-3(4)) Whitman, Albert & Co.

—When I Care about Others. Parkinson, Kathy, illus. 2002. (Way I Feel Bks.). 24p. (J). (ps-1). 15.95 (978-0-8075-8889-5(X)); pap. 6.95 (978-0-8075-8898-7(9)) Whitman, Albert & Co.

—When I Feel Jealous. Parkinson, Kathy, illus. (Way I Feel Bks.). 24p. (J). 2005. (gr. 3-6). pap. 6.95 (978-0-8075-8902-1(0)); 2003. (ps-1). 15.95 (978-0-8075-8886-4(5)) Whitman, Albert & Co.

Spelvin, Justin. Care Bears: Most Valuable Bear. Johnson, Jay, illus. 2005. (Care Bears Ser.). 32p. (J). pap. 3.99 (978-0-439-66958-0(8)) Scholastic, Inc.

Spengler, Kenneth J. The Bear: An American Folk Song. Spengler, Kenneth J., illus. 2002. (Illus.). 32p. (J). (ps-3). 15.95 (978-1-59034-190-2(2)) Mondo Publishing.

Spitzer, Linda. A Friend in Freezeville. 2005. 23p. (J). 10.95 (978-1-4116-4968-2(0)) Lulu.com.

Sprecher, John. Zoe & the Very Unmerry Bear. Forrest, James, illus. l.t. ed. Date not set. (Special Kids "Special Message" Book Ser.). 32p. (J). (gr. k-4). pap. 10.00 (978-1-892186-03-4(9), SKPB4) Anythings Possible, Inc.

Staenberg, Bonnie. A Present for Mama Bear. Bratun, Katy, illus. 1999. (Hello Reader! Ser.). 32p. (J). (gr. 1-3). pap. 3.99 (978-0-590-28154-6(2)) Scholastic, Inc.

—Present for Mama Bear. 1999. (Hello Reader! Ser.). (978-0-606-16633-1(5)) Tandem Library Bks.

Stafford, Liliana. Snow Bear. Davis, Lambert, illus. 32p. (J). pap. (978-0-88899-441-7(9)) Groundwood Bks.

—Snow Bear. Davis, Lambert, illus. 2001. 32p. (J). (gr. 1-3). 15.95 (978-0-439-26977-3(6)) Scholastic, Inc.

Stagnaro, Louis R. Fred the Teddy Bear. 2004. pap. 7.95 (978-0-533-14717-5(4)) Vantage Pr., Inc.

Stanley, Diane. Goldie & the Three Bears. Stanley, Diane, illus. 40p. (J). 2007. pap. 6.99 (978-0-06-113611-5(5), Harper Trophy); 2003. (Illus.). 15.99 (978-0-06-000008-0(2)); 2003. (Illus.). lib. bdg. 17.89 (978-0-06-000009-7(0)) HarperCollins Pubs.

Stanley, Elizabeth. The Deliverance of Dancing Bears. Stanley, Elizabeth, illus. 2003. (Illus.). 40p. (J). (gr. k-4). 15.95 (978-1-929132-41-6(7)) Kane/Miller Bk. Pubs., Inc.

—The Deliverance of Dancing Bears. 2003. (Illus.). 40p. (J). reprint ed. 24.95 (978-1-875560-37-0(8)) Univ. of Western Australia Pr. AUS. *Dist:* International Specialized Bk. Services.

Steele, Michael Anthony. Boz/Boz Says Wiggle Your Ears BB. Johnson, Jay, illus. 2007. (BOZ#8482; Ser.). 20p. (J). 6.99 (978-0-310-71400-2(1)) Zondervan.

Steele, Michael Anthony & Exclaim Entertainment Staff. God Gives You Friends: With Boz the Bear. McKee, Darren, illus. 2006. (Boz Ser.). 12p. (J). 5.99 (978-0-310-71153-7(3)) Zonderkidz.

Stein, David Ezra. Leaves. Stein, David Ezra, illus. 2007. (Illus.). 32p. (J). (ps-2). 15.99 (978-0-399-24636-4(3), Putnam Juvenile) Penguin Group (USA) Inc.

Steinberg, David. The Snow Ball. Conrad, Liz, illus. 2007. 10p. (J). (ps-k). bds. 6.99 (*978-0-8431-2680-8(9), Price Stern Sloan) Penguin Group (USA) Inc.

Steiner, Jorg. The Bear Who Wanted to Be a Bear. Mueller, Jorg, illus. 2007. 44p. (J). 16.95 (*978-0-9787550-1-0(4)) Heryin Publishing Corp.

Stellinga, Mark. Buster Boogernose & the Grizzly Bear. 2007. (J). per. 9.95 (*978-0-9796421-4-2(0)) Stellinga, Mark.

Sterling, Amber. Little Mud Bear. 2006. (Illus.). 44p. (J). per. (*978-0-9803058-1-4(0)) Carpe Diem Publishing.

Sterling Publishing Co., Inc. & Fernleigh Books Staff. Goldilocks: A Magic 3-Dimensional Fairy-Tale World. 2006. (Step Inside Ser.). (Illus.). 12p. (J). 9.95 (978-1-4027-3657-5(6)) Sterling Publishing Co., Inc.

Sterling Publishing Company Staff. Benjamin Helps Mommy Bear. 1999. (Adventures with Benjamin Bear Ser.). (Illus.). 18p. (ps-k). 4.95 (978-0-8069-3764-9(5)) Sterling Publishing Co., Inc.

Stevenson, James. Zampano y Su Oso. (Coleccion el Faro Azul). (SPA., Illus.). (J). 8.95 (978-84-348-1571-1(0), SM004) SM Ediciones ESP. *Dist:* Continental Bk. Co., Inc.

Stickers N Shapes, Cherrington, et al. The Ojo Lympics. 2000. (Bear in the Big Blue House Ser.). (Illus.). 32p. (J). per. (978-0-7434-0839-4(X), Simon & Schuster Children's Publishing) Simon & Schuster Children's Publishing.

Stimson, Joan. Oscar Needs a Friend. Rutherford, Meg, illus. 1998. 32p. (J). (ps-1). pap. 5.95 (978-0-7641-0746-7(1)) Barron's Educational Series, Inc.

Stone-Spedden, Daisy Corning. Polar the Titanic Bear. McGaw, Laurie, illus. 2001. 64p. (J). (gr. 3-7). pap. 10.99 (978-0-316-80909-2(8)) Little, Brown Bks. for Young Readers.

Stowe, Dorothy Bye. Bearly Bigger. Stowe, Dorothy Bye, illus. 2002. (Illus.). 32p. (J). (ps-2). (978-0-9704586-1-2(4)) Verse-a-Tale Pr.

Strauch, Kendrick. Hello, Mole Bear! Style Guide Staff, illus. 2007. (Land of Milk & Honey Ser.). 8p. (J). 11.99 (978-1-4169-3648-0(3), Little Simon Inspirations) Simon & Schuster Children's Publishing.

Sutherland, Paul H. Mani & Pitouee: The True Legend of Sleeping Bear Dunes. Gibbons, Timothy, illus. 2005. 36p. (J). 20.00 (978-0-9661060-3-9(2)) Utopia Pr.

Swanson, Maggie, illus. Goldilocks & the Three Bears: A Tale about Respecting Others. 2006. (J). 6.99 (978-1-59939-006-2(X), Reader's Digest Young Families, Inc.) Reader's Digest Children's Publishing, Inc.

Swinburne, Stephen R. Moon in Bear's Eyes. Forest, Crista, illus. 2004. 32p. (YA). pap. 9.95 (978-1-59078-330-6(1)) Boyds Mills Pr.

Tafuri, Nancy. Mama's Little Bears. 2004. (J). bds. 7.99 (978-0-439-57357-3(2)) Scholastic, Inc.

Talkington, Bruce. Disney's: Winnie the Pooh's - Easter. 1998. 32p. (J). 5.95 (978-0-7868-3202-6(9)) Hyperion Bks. for Children.

—Winnie the Pooh & the Bumble Bee Chase. rev. ed. 1998. 14p. (J). 11.95 (978-0-7868-3228-6(2)) Disney Pr.

—Winnie the Pooh's Valentine Mini. 1998. (Illus.). 32p. (J). 11.95 (978-0-7868-3201-9(0)) Disney Pr.

Tattum, Stephan. Bear Cub. 2005. (J). 4.95 (978-1-59792-008-7(8)) F.A.S.T. Learning LLLC.

Taylor, Bonnie Highsmith. Eli: A Black Bear. 1999. (Animal Adventures Ser.). (Illus.). (J). 54p. pap. (978-0-7891-2937-6(X)); 56p. (gr. 1-4). lib. bdg. 16.95 (978-0-7807-8967-8(9)) Perfection Learning Corp.

Taylor, Theodore. The Weirdo. 2006. (Illus.). 304p. (J). pap. 6.95 (978-0-15-205666-7(1), Harcourt Paperbacks) Harcourt Children's Bks.

Teckentrup, Britta. Big Smelly Bear. 2007. (Illus.). 32p. (J). (ps-1). 12.95 (978-1-905417-37-7(3)) Boxer Bks., Ltd. GBR. *Dist:* Sterling Publishing Co., Inc.

Ted in a Red Bed Kid Kit. (Kid Kits Ser.). (Illus.). 10p. (J). 11.95 (978-1-58086-416-9(3)); 2004. bds. 9.95 (978-1-58086-404-6(X)) EDC Publishing.

Templar Publishing Staff. Winnie the Pooh: Winnie's Hologram Book. 2005. (Illus.). 32p. (J). pap. 11.99 (978-0-7868-4162-2(1)) Disney Pr.

Tétro, Marc. I Can Skate. 2005. (Illus.). (978-1-55278-542-3(4)) McArthur & Co. CAN. *Dist:* National Bk. Network.

There's a Bear in God's Woods! 1999. (Peek-In Board Book Ser.). (Illus.). 10p. (J). (ps-k). bds. 4.99 (978-0-7847-1080-7(5), 04286, Bean Sprouts) Standard Publishing.

Thomas, Deborah E. The Bramble Thicket. l.t. ed. 2004. (Illus.). 88p. (J). 27.95 (978-0-9742805-0-9(X)) Gypsy Hill Publishing Co.

Thomas, Frances. Mr Bear & the Bear. Brown, Ruth, illus. 2003. 32p. (J). pap. 8.99 (978-1-84270-226-0(2)) Andersen GBR. *Dist:* Independent Pubs. Group.

Thompson, Lauren. Polar Bear Night. Savage, Stephen, illus. 2004. 32p. (J). pap. 15.95 (978-0-439-49524-0(5), Scholastic Pr.) Scholastic, Inc.

Thong, Roseanne. Cuddly Bear Cubs Carnival. 2006. 12p. 14.95 (978-1-58117-478-6(0), Intervisual/Piggy Toes) Dalmatian Pr.

Thorpe, Kiki. Big Blue House Call. 2000. (gr. k-3). lib. bdg. 11.25 (978-0-613-21212-0(6)) Tandem Library Bks.

—Raiders of the Lost Cheese. 2000. (gr. k-3). lib. bdg. 14.15 (978-0-613-21623-1(1)) Tandem Library Bks.

—Spring Has Sprung! 2000. (gr. k-3). lib. bdg. 11.25 (978-0-613-22429-1(9)) Tandem Library Bks.

The Three Bears. 2004. (J). (978-1-58453-275-0(0)) Pioneer Valley Educational Pr., Inc.

The Three Bears: Individual Title Six-Pack Pouch - Level C. (Lighthouse Ser.). 12p. (gr. k-1). 24.00 (978-0-7578-0829-6(8)) Rigby Education.

Timbers, James. Salmon & Fuzz in Helping a Friend. 2004. 30p. pap. 14.95 (978-1-4137-2602-2(X)) PublishAmerica, Inc.

Tokuda, Wendy. Samson the Hot Tub Bear: A True Story. Millis, Lokken, illus. 1998. 30p. (ps-3). 15.95 (978-1-57098-090-9(X)) Rinehart, Roberts Pubs.

—Samson the Hot Tub Bear: A True Story. 2005. 32p. pap. 9.95 (978-1-58979-215-9(7)) Taylor Trade Publishing.

Top That Publishing Staff, ed. Goldilocks & Three Bears. 2006. (Illus.). 10p. bds. (978-1-905359-93-6(4)) Top That! Publishing PLC.

Torres, Laura & Milne, A. A. Clay Modeling with Pooh. Rigol, Francese, illus. 1999. (Learn & Grow Ser.). 23p. (J). (ps-3). 11.99 (978-0-7868-3223-1(1)) Disney Pr.

Toy Box Productions Staff, Box, creator. Disney's Instant Classics: Chicken Little/Lilo & Stitch/Brother Bear. unabr. abr. ed. 2005. (Disney's Read along Collection). (Illus.). (J). audio compact disk 14.99 (978-0-7634-1148-0(5)) Walt Disney Records.

The Treasure Hunt. 2008. (J). 19.95 (978-1-933872-25-4(X)) Lima Bear Pr LLC, The.

Tripp, Jenny. Pete & Fremont. Manders, John, illus. 2007. 192p. (J). (gr. 2-4). 16.00 (978-0-15-205629-2(7)) Harcourt Trade Pubs.

Tripp, Patricia. The Bears That Lived in Evergreen Forest. 2006. 18p. (J). spiral bd. 10.76 (978-1-4116-5835-6(3)) Lulu.com.

A Tropical Bear in Hawaii. 2005. (Illus.). 32p. (J). (gr. 1-2). 12.95 (978-1-59779-002-4(8)) Reece, Kim Taylor Prodns. LLC.

A Tropical Bear Learns to Surf. 2005. 32p. (J). (gr. 1-2). 12.95 (978-1-59779-003-1(6)) Reece, Kim Taylor Prodns. LLC.

Trudel, Sylvain. Yan Contre Max Denferre. 2000. (Premier Roman Ser.). (FRE.). 64p. (J). (gr. 2-5). pap. (978-2-89021-400-2(1)) Diffusion du livre Mirabel.

Tugman, Etta. Smokey Mountain Bears. 2006. 9.00 (978-0-8059-8189-6(6)) Dorrance Publishing Co., Inc.

Tunison, Dick. Marley & the Big Stone Castle. Carrel, Dolores W., illus. l.t. ed. 2001. 40p. (J). (gr. k-5). pap. 7.95 (978-0-9707015-0-3(0)) Emmaus Pr.

Turner, Barbara F. Charles T. Bear & the Christmas Snow. Turner, Barbara F., illus. 1998. (Illus.). (J). (ps-3). pap. 6.00 (978-1-892614-07-0(3), SC-CTB-2) Briarwood Pubns.

Tym, Kate. Bear Hugs. 2000. (Illus.). 128p. (J). (gr. 2-4). pap. 4.95 (978-1-902618-01-2(7)) Element Children's Bks.

Tyrrell, Frances. Woodland Christmas: Twelve Days of Christmas in the North Woods. 2000. (J). 5.99 (978-0-590-86368-1(1)) Scholastic, Inc.

Umansky, Kaye. A Chair for Baby Bear. Fisher, Chris, illus. 2004. 32p. (J). 12.95 (978-0-7641-5789-9(2)) Barron's Educational Series, Inc.

V., Patti. My Na Na Stories. 2005. 18.00 (978-0-8059-9806-1(3)) Dorrance Publishing Co., Inc.

Valliere, Connie. Billy the Builder Bear Builds a House. Quick, Bob, illus. 1998. 32p. (J). (gr. k-6). pap. 6.95 (978-1-890394-22-6(X), Sage Creek Pr.) Rhodes & Easton.

Van Dusen, Chris. A Camping Spree with Mr. Magee. 2003. (Illus.). 36p. (J). 14.95 (978-0-8118-3603-6(7)) Chronicle Bks. LLC.

van Genechten, Guido. Because I Love you So Much: A Pop-up Book. van Genechten, Guido, illus. 2006. (Illus.). 12p. (J). 15.95 (978-1-58925-794-8(4), tiger tales) ME Media LLC.

van Kampen, Vlasta. Bear Tales: Three Treasured Stories. 2000. lib. bdg. 15.25 (978-0-613-53139-9(6)) Tandem Library Bks.

van Kampen, Vlasta, illus. & retold by. Bear Tales: Three Treasured Stories. van Kampen, Vlasta, retold by. 2000. (Folk Tales Ser.). 40p. (J). (gr. k-3). pap. 6.95 (978-1-55037-618-0(7)); lib. bdg. 18.95 (978-1-55037-619-7(5)) Annick Pr., Ltd. CAN. *Dist:* Firefly Bks., Ltd.

Van Lieshout, Elle & Van Os, Erik. Nice Party. 1998. (Illus.). 32p. (J). 15.95 (978-1-886910-89-8(8), Lemniscaat) Boyds Mills Pr.

Vercz, Carol A. The Coat That Became a Teddy Bear. 1998. (Illus.). (J). (gr. k-4). pap. 7.95 (978-0-910119-52-8(X)) S.O.C.O. Pubns.

Volpp, Rosemary Paul. The Happy-est Bear: A Biography. 2001. 51p. 24.95 (978-1-58275-061-3(0)) Black Forest Pr.

Vorndran, Judith Clay. Mr. Bear Lives There. l.t. ed. 2005. (Illus.). 11p. (J). pap. 7.98 (978-0-9772439-0-7(7)) Vorndran, Judith Clay.

Waddell, Martin. Can't You Sleep, Little Bear? Firth, Barbara, illus. 10th anniv. ed. 2002. 32p. (J). (ps-2). 15.99 (978-0-7636-1929-9(9)) Candlewick Pr.

—Can't You Sleep, Little Bear? (CHI & ENG., Illus.). 32p. (J). (978-1-85430-315-8(5), 93445) Magi Pubns.

—Good Job, Little Bear. Firth, Barbara, illus. 2002. (Little Bear Ser.). 32p. (J). (ps-1). pap. 5.99 (978-0-7636-1709-7(1)) Candlewick Pr.

—Good Job, Little Bear. 2002. (ps-2). lib. bdg. 14.15 (978-0-613-74781-3(X)) Tandem Library Bks.

—Let's Go Home, Little Bear. ed. 2004. (Illus.). (J). (gr. k-3). spiral bd. (978-0-616-01804-0(5)); spiral bd. (978-0-616-01805-7(3)) Canadian National Institute for the Blind/Institut National Canadien pour les Aveugles.

—Muy Bien, Osito. 2003. Tr. of Good. (SPA., Illus.). (J). (978-84-88342-26-3(8), KK5127) S.A. Kokinos ESP. *Dist:* Lectorum Pubns., Inc.

—Non Dormi Piccolo Orso. pap. 19.95 (978-88-7782-378-6(X)) Salani ITA. *Dist:* Distribooks, Inc.

—Sleep Tight, Little Bear. Firth, Barbara, illus. 2005. 32p. (J). (ps-1). 15.99 (978-0-7636-2439-2(X)) Candlewick Pr.

—Small Bear Lost. 1998. (978-0-606-13778-2(5)) Tandem Library Bks.

—Snow Bears. Fox-Davies, Sarah, illus. 2002. 32p. (J). (ps-1). 14.99 (978-0-7636-1906-0(X)) Candlewick Pr.

—Snow Bears. Fox-Davies, Sarah, illus. 2004. 24p. (J). (gr. k-ps). bds. 6.99 (978-0-7636-2441-5(1)) Candlewick Pr.

—Tu Ne Dors Pas, Petit Ours? 1999. (FRE.). (J). (ps-3). pap. 15.95 (978-2-211-07902-0(4)) Distribooks, Inc.

—When the Teddy Bears Came. 1998. (J). (978-0-606-13908-3(7)) Tandem Library Bks.

—You & Me, Little Bear. ed. 2004. (Illus.). (J). (ps-2). spiral bd. (978-0-616-01802-6(9)); spiral bd. (978-0-616-01803-3(7)) Canadian National Institute for the Blind/Institut National Canadien pour les Aveugles.

Waechter, Philip. Me! Franceschelli, Christopher, tr. from GER. 2005. (Illus.). 64p. (J). (gr. k-3). 9.95 (978-1-59354-087-6(6)) Handprint Bks.

Wahl, Jan. Humphrey's Bear. Joyce, William & Joyce, William, illus. 2005. 32p. (J). (ps-ps). 16.95 (978-0-8050-7812-1(6), Holt, Henry & Co. Bks. For Young Readers) Holt, Henry & Co.

Wallace, Bill. Eye of the Great Bear. 1999. 176p. (J). (gr. 3-6). pap. 9.95 (978-0-671-02502-1(3) , Aladdin) Simon & Schuster Children's Publishing.

—Eye of the Great Bear. 1999. (J). 11.64 (978-0-606-19050-3(3)); (gr. 3-6). lib. bdg. 13.00 (978-0-613-21509-1(5)) Tandem Library Bks.

Wallace, Nancy Elizabeth. Leaves! Leaves! Leaves! 2003. (Illus.). 40p. (J). 16.95 (978-0-7614-5140-2(4)) Cavendish, Marshall Corp.

—Seeds! Seeds! Seeds! 2004. (Illus.). 40p. (J). 16.95 (978-0-7614-5159-4(5)) Cavendish, Marshall Corp.

—Seeds Seeds Seeds. 2007. 32p. 5.99 ***(978-0-7614-5366-6(0))*** Cavendish, Marshall Corp.

Wallace, Nancy Elizabeth. A Taste of Honey. Wallace, Nancy Elizabeth, illus. 2004. 32p. (J). pap. 5.95 (978-0-7614-5181-5(1)) Cavendish, Marshall Corp.

—A Taste of Honey. 2001. (Illus.). 40p. (J). (ps-3). 15.95 (978-1-890817-51-0(1)) Winslow Pr.

Wallace, Nancy Elizabeth, illus. Shells! Shells! Shells! 2006. 32p. (J). 16.99 (978-0-7614-5332-1(6)) Cavendish, Marshall Corp.

—A Taste of Honey. 2005. 32p. (J). pap. 5.95 (978-0-7614-5215-7(X)) Cavendish, Marshall Corp.

Wallen, Ila. The Moon in My Room. Sauber, Robert, illus. 2002. (Willowbe Woods Campfire Stories Ser.: Bk. 1). 32p. (J). (ps-3). 16.95 (978-0-9710627-0-2(6)) Bent Willow Publishing.

Wallen, Virginia. Boo Boo Bear. 2005. 17.00 (978-0-8059-9886-3(1)) Dorrance Publishing Co., Inc.

Walter, Nadine. Apolline & Her Bear. 1999. (Magical Library). (J). (ps-3). (978-1-894155-00-7(9)) Cethial & Bossche Co.

Walton, Rick. Bear Came over to My House. 2003. (gr. k-3). lib. bdg. 15.30 (978-0-613-61601-0(4)) Tandem Library Bks.

Ward, Nick. Who's Been Eating MY Porridge? 2003. (Illus.). (J). (978-0-439-58732-7(8)) Scholastic, Inc.

Wardlaw, Lee. The Chair Where Bear Sits. Benfanti, Russell, illus. 2001. 56p. (ps-2). 23.00 (978-1-890817-85-5(6)) Winslow Pr.

Wargin, Kathy-Jo. The Legend of Sleeping Bear. van Frankenhuyzen, Gijsbert, illus. 1998. (Great Lakes Legend Ser.). 48p. (J). (ps-3). 17.95 (978-1-886947-35-1(X)) Sleeping Bear Pr.

Washakie, John. Yuse: The Bully & the Bear. Cox, Jon, illus. 2nd ed. 2004. 47p. (J). 14.95 (978-0-9759806-0-6(2)) Painted Pony, Inc.

Watson, Rick. Up a Tree. Bergum, Constance Rummel, illus. 2002. 16p. (J). (978-0-439-35102-7(2)) Scholastic, Inc.

Watt, Fiona & Wells, R. That's Not My Bear. 2004. 10p. (J). 7.99 (978-0-7945-0363-5(2)) EDC Publishing.

Weare, Tim. Sweet Dreams, Honey Bear. 2001. (Hand Puppet Board Bks.). (Illus.). 10p. (J). bds. 14.95 (978-0-439-29720-2(6) , Cartwheel Bks.) Scholastic, Inc.

Weber, Lou, ed. Build a Bear Ballerina Dress up Sticker Fun. 2005. 16p. (J). spiral bd., bds. 10.98 (978-1-4127-3459-2(2) , 7259800) Publications International, Ltd.

—Build a Bear Sew Fun. 2005. 16p. (J). spiral bd., bds. 10.98 (978-1-4127-3468-4(1) , 7260100) Publications International, Ltd.

Weigelt, Udo. Bear's Last Journey. Kazeroid, Sibylle, tr. from GER. Kadmon, Cristina, illus. 2003. 32p. (J). (gr. k-3). 15.95 (978-0-7358-1799-9(5)) North-South Bks., Inc.

Weigelt, Udo. Bears Last Journey. Kadmon, Christina, illus. 2007. 0032p. pap. 6.95 ***(978-0-7358-2155-2(0))*** North-South Bks., Inc.

Weinberg, Larry. The Forgetful Bears Help Santa. Wolff, Jason, illus. 2001. 40p. (J). (gr. k-2). 9.95 (978-0-307-10684-1(5) , Golden Bks.) Random Hse. Children's Bks.

Weirdo. 2002. stu. ed. (978-1-56137-815-9(1)) Novel Units, Inc.

Weiss, Ellen. Welcome to the Big Blue House! Ewers, Joe, illus. 1999. (Bear in the Big Blue House Ser.). 12p. (J). (ps-k). bds. 5.99 (978-0-689-82386-2(X) , 076714004993, Simon Spotlight) Simon & Schuster Children's Publishing.

Weiss, Nicki. Where Does the Brown Bear Go. Date not set. (Illus.). 32p. (J). 5.95 (978-0-06-051534-8(1)) HarperCollins Pubs.

Wells, Rosemary. The Bear Went over the Mountain. Wells, Rosemary, illus. 2007. (Bruno & Boots Book Ser.). (Illus.). 18p. (J). bds. 5.99 (978-0-590-02910-0(X)) Scholastic, Inc.

—Eduardo: Cumpleanos en la Piscina. 2003. Orig. Title: Edward's Big Splash. (SPA., Illus.). 22p. (J). (ps-k). 12.95 (978-1-56014-664-3(8)) Santillana USA Publishing Co., Inc.

—Eduardo: El Primer Dia de Colegio. 2003. Orig. Title: Edward's First Day at School. (SPA., Illus.). 22p. (J). (ps-k). 12.95 (978-1-56014-620-9(6)) Santillana USA Publishing Co., Inc.

—Only You. 2003. (SPA., Illus.). 24p. (J). (ps). 14.99 (978-0-670-03634-9(X) , Viking Juvenile) Penguin Group (USA) Inc.

Weninger, Brigitte. Ragged Bear. 1998. (ps-2). lib. bdg. 15.25 (978-0-613-81230-6(1)) Tandem Library Bks.

Wensell & Scheffler. Quien Quiere a Mi Hermanita? 2002. (SPA.). 32p. (J). (978-84-261-3235-2(9)) Juventud, Editorial.

Wheeler, Lisa. One Dark Night. Bates, Ivan, illus. 2006. 32p. (J). reprint ed. pap. 6.00 (978-0-15-205888-3(5) , Voyager Bks./Libros Viajeros) Harcourt Children's Bks.

Whelan, Gloria. Jam & Jelly by Holly & Nellie. van Frankenhuyzen, Gijsbert, illus. 2002. 48p. (J). (ps-5). 17.95 (978-1-58536-109-0(7)) Sleeping Bear Pr.

White-Carlstrom, Nancy. How Do You Say it Today, Jesse Bear? 1999. (J). (978-0-606-16941-7(5)) Tandem Library Bks.

White, Carolyn. The Adventure of Louey & Frank. Dronzek, Laura, illus. 2001. 24p. (J). (ps). 14.95 (978-0-688-16503-1(6)) HarperCollins Pubs.

White, Marsha. Bear's New Classes. White, Marsha, illus. (Illus.). 16p. (J). 10.95 (978-1-58117-294-2(X) , Intervisual/Piggy Toes) Dalmatian Pr.

Whitfield, Peter. Zen Tails No Presents Please. Bevington, Nancy, illus. 2005. (Zen Tails Ser.). 28p. (J). (gr. 2-17). 15.95 (978-1-894965-23-1(X)) Simply Read Bks. CAN. *Dist:* Perseus Distribution.

Whittington, Gisella. Pump the Bear. Crisalli, Joseph, illus. 2001. 26p. (J). (gr. k-7). 14.95 (978-0-9706038-0-7(0)) Whittington, Gisella.

Wickett, Violet E. About Nubs & Me. Wickett, Violet E., illus. 2000. (Illus.). 48p. (J). (ps-2). 24.95 (978-0-9673120-0-2(0)) Uluquim Bks.

Wilhelm, Hans. Anook: The Snow Princess. 2003. (Illus.). 36p. (J). 12.95 (978-0-7641-5600-7(4)) Barron's Educational Series, Inc.

—With Lots of Love. 2004. (Illus.). 32p. (J). 12.95 (978-0-7641-5767-7(1)) Barron's Educational Series, Inc.

Willert, Michael. Wanted Billy the Bear. 2007. (ENG., Illus.). 24p. (J). per. 11.95 ***(978-1-59800-808-1(0))*** Outskirts Press, Inc.

Willey, Margaret. North Woods Three Bears. Solomon, Heather, illus. 2008. 40p. (J). ***(978-1-4169-2494-4(9))*** Simon & Schuster Children's Publishing.

Williams, Paul. How the Bat Got Its Wings & Young Bear's Lesson: Two Cherokee Stories. 2003. (J). per. 14.95 (978-0-9630310-6-8(6)) Will Hall Bks.

Williams, Rozanne Lanczak. All about Real Bears. Maio, Barbara & Faulkner, Stacey, eds. Christensen, David, illus. 2006. (Learn to Write Ser.). (J). 8p. pap. 1.99 (978-1-59198-288-3(X) , 6182); per. 4.99 ***(978-1-59198-339-2(8))*** Creative Teaching Pr., Inc.

—Postcards from Barney Bear. Maio, Barbara & Faulkner, Stacey, eds. Thelen, Mary, illus. 2006. (Learn to Write Ser.). 8p. (J). pap. 1.99 (978-1-59198-287-6(1) , 6181) Creative Teaching Pr., Inc.

Willis, Jeanne. El Nino y los Osos de Peluche. (SPA.). (J). 8.95 (978-958-04-7344-2(7)) Norma S.A. COL. *Dist:* Distribuidora Norma, Inc.

Wilson, Gina. Grandma's Bears. Howard, Paul, illus. 2004. 40p. (J). (ps-1). 15.99 (978-0-7636-2518-4(3)) Candlewick Pr.

Wilson, Karma. Bear Feels Sick. Chapman, Jane, illus. 2007. 40p. (J). (ps-2). 16.99 (978-0-689-85985-4(6) , McElderry, Margaret K.) Simon & Schuster Children's Publishing.

—Bear Snores On. Chapman, Jane, illus. 2002. (J). 25.11 (978-0-7587-9751-3(6)) Book Wholesalers, Inc.

—Bear Snores On. Chapman, Jane, illus. (Classic Board Bks.). (J). 2005. 34p. bds. 7.99 (978-1-4169-0272-0(4) , Little Simon); 2002. 40p. 16.95 (978-0-689-83187-4(0) , McElderry, Margaret K.) Simon & Schuster Children's Publishing.

—Bear Snores On. 2005. (J). (ps-2). 29.95 incl. audio compact disk (978-0-439-76664-7(8) , WHCD666); 24.95 incl. audio (978-0-439-76660-9(5) , WHRA666) Weston Woods Studios, Inc.

—Bear Stays up for Christmas. Chapman, Jane, illus. 2004. 40p. (J). (ps-2). 16.95 (978-0-689-85278-7(9) , McElderry, Margaret K.) Simon & Schuster Children's Publishing.

—Bear Wants More. Chapman, Jane, illus. (Classic Board Bks.). (J). 2008. 34p. 7.99 ***(978-1-4169-4922-0(4)*** , Little Simon); 2003. 40p. 16.95 (978-0-689-84509-3(X) , McElderry, Margaret K.) Simon & Schuster Children's Publishing.

Wilson, Karma. Bear's New Friend. Chapman, Jane, illus. 2006. 40p. (J). (ps-2). 16.95 (978-0-689-85984-7(8) , McElderry, Margaret K.) Simon & Schuster Children's Publishing.

Winnie the Pooh. (Sing-Along Ser.). (J). 11.99 incl. audio (978-1-55723-933-4(9)) Walt Disney Records.

Winnie the Pooh & a Day for Eeyore, (Read-Along Ser.). (J). 7.99 incl. audio (978-1-55723-176-5(1)) Walt Disney Records.

Winnie the Pooh & the Hanukkah Dreidel. 1998. (Winnie the Pooh Ser.). (Illus.). 8p. (J). (ps-1). pap. 2.99 (978-1-57082-994-9(2)) Mouse Works.

Wiseman, Bernard. Morris & Boris at the Circus. Wiseman, Bernard, illus. 2002. (Illus.). (J). 12.34 (978-0-7587-5557-5(0)) Book Wholesalers, Inc.

Wish Bear: Let's Make a Wish Cake. (Care Bearstm Ser.). (J). bds. 9.99 (978-1-4037-0559-4(3)) Dalmatian Pr.

Wojtowycz, David, illus. What Will You Wear, Claude? 2004. 10p. (J). (ps-3). reprint ed. 8.00 (978-0-7567-8259-7(7)) DIANE Publishing Co.

Wolf, Erica. I Love You Just the Same. Wolf, Erica, illus. rev. ed. 2003. (Illus.). 32p. (J). 16.95 (978-0-8050-7128-3(8) , Holt, Henry & Co. Bks. For Young Readers) Holt, Henry & Co.

Wolfbear, Jessie. Tales of Bear & Deer: Native American Teaching Stories for Children of All Age. 2001. (gr. k-3). lib. bdg. 24.55 (978-0-613-74718-9(6)) Tandem Library Bks.

Wolff, Ferida. Watch Out for Bears! The Adventures of Henry & Bruno. 1999. (Step into Reading Ser.). (978-0-606-16893-9(1)) Tandem Library Bks.

Wood, Audrey. A Book for Honey Bear. Wood, Audrey, illus. 2001. (Illus.). 24p. (J). 7.99 (978-0-689-84347-1(X) , Little Simon) Simon & Schuster Children's Publishing.

—A Book for Honey Bear: Reading Keeps the Sighs Away. 2001. 16p. mass mkt. 1.25 (978-0-689-84660-1(6) , Little Simon) Simon & Schuster Children's Publishing.

—Box of Horrors. 2001. (Illus.). 24p. (J). (gr. 1-4). 15.95 (978-0-85953-842-8(7)) Child's Play-International.

—Oh My Baby Bear! 1999. (978-0-15-202169-6(8)) Harcourt Trade Pubs.

Wood, Audrey & Wood, Don. The Little Mouse, the Red Ripe Strawberry & the Big Hungry Bear. Wood, Don, illus. 1998. (Illus.). 24p. (J). (ps-1). bds. 6.99 (978-0-85953-659-2(9)) Child's Play-International.

Wood, David. Under the Bed. Fowler, Richard, illus. 2006. 18p. (J). 9.99 (978-0-7641-5926-8(7)) Barron's Educational Series, Inc.

Wood, Debra. William Warrior Bear. Blake, Joshua Aaron, illus. l.t. ed. 2005. 30p. (J). per. 12.95 (978-1-59879-001-6(3)) Lifevest Publishing, Inc.

Wood, Don & Wood, Audrey. Merry Christmas: Big Hungry Bear! Wood, Don, illus. 2002. (Illus.). 48p. (J). (gr. k-2). pap. 15.95 (978-0-439-32092-4(5) , Blue Sky Pr., The) Scholastic, Inc.

Woods, Shirley. Tooga Story of Polar Bear. Wood, Muriel, illus. 2004. 96p. (J). (978-1-55041-898-9(X)) Fitzhenry & Whiteside, Ltd.

Woodward, Susan. Seldovia Sam & Blueberry Bear, Vol. 4. Meissner, Amy, illus. 2005. 64p. (J). pap. 6.95 (978-0-88240-603-9(5) , Alaska Northwest Bks.) Graphic Arts Ctr. Publishing Co.

Wright, Cliff. Bear & Ball. 2005. (Illus.). 16p. (J). bds. 5.95 (978-0-8118-4819-0(1)) Chronicle Bks. LLC.

—Bear & Kite. 2005. (Illus.). 16p. (J). bds. 5.95 (978-0-8118-4820-6(5)) Chronicle Bks. LLC.

Wright, Dale. Edith & Mr Bear: A Lonely Doll Story. 2000. (gr. k-3). lib. bdg. 15.25 (978-0-613-27801-0(1)) Tandem Library Bks.

Wright, Dare. Edith & Mr. Bear. 2000. (Lonely Doll Story Ser.). (Illus.). 64p. (J). (gr. k-3). tchr. ed. 16.00 (978-0-618-00332-7(0)); pap. 6.95 (978-0-618-04253-1(9)) Houghton Mifflin Co. Trade & Reference Div.

Wurtz, K. D. Digby Finds a Friend. Carrier, Tracey Dahle, illus. 2001. (Digby in Disguise Ser.: Vol. 2). (J). (978-0-9712840-2-9(4) , Bear & Co.) Bear & Co.

—Digby in Disguise. Carrier, Tracey Dahle, illus. 2001. (Digby in Disguise Ser.: Vol. 1). (J). (978-0-9712840-1-2(6)) Boyds Collection Ltd., The.

Yang, Stella, illus. Our Day, 6, Pack. (Sails Literacy Ser.). 16p. (gr. k up). 27.00 (978-0-7635-4435-5(3)) Rigby Education.

Yektai, Niki. Bears at the Beach: Counting 10 to 20. 2001. (Single Titles Ser.: 2). (Illus.). 32p. (J). (gr. k-2). pap. 7.95 (978-0-7613-1483-7(0) , Millbrook Pr.) Lerner Publishing Group.

Yolen, Jane. Baby Bear's Big Dreams. Sweet, Melissa, illus. 2007. 40p. (J). (ps-k). 16.00 (978-0-15-205291-1(7)) Harcourt Trade Pubs.

—Baby Bear's Books. Sweet, Melissa, illus. 2006. 40p. (J). 16.00 (978-0-15-205290-4(9)) Harcourt Trade Pubs.

—Baby Bear's Chairs. Sweet, Melissa, illus. 2005. 40p. (J). (ps). 16.00 (978-0-15-205114-3(7)) Harcourt Children's Bks.

Yoon, Salina. Count My Blessings 1 Through 10. Yoon, Salina, illus. 2008. 24p. (J). (ps-ps). bds. 6.99 ***(978-0-399-25069-9(7)*** , Putnam Juvenile) Penguin Group (USA) Inc.

Young, Ruth. Golden Bear. Isadora, Rachel, illus. 2002. (J). 14.04 (978-0-7587-2611-7(2)) Book Wholesalers, Inc.

Zaugh, Robert. Teddy Bear Goes to the Moon. Peterson, Mary, illus. 1998. 32p. (J). (gr. k-3). pap. 7.95 (978-1-892071-00-2(2)) Dillingham Publishing.

Zehler, Antonia. Two Fine Ladies: Tea for Three. 2002. (ps-2). lib. bdg. 11.80 (978-0-613-84579-3(X)) Tandem Library Bks.

Ziefert, Harriet. Bear All Year: A Guessing Game Story. 2005. (Illus.). 16p. 9.95 (978-1-4027-1942-4(6)); pap. 5.95 (978-1-4027-1946-2(9)) Sterling Publishing Co., Inc.

—Bear Gets Dressed: A Guessing Game Story. Lobel, Arnold & Capucilli, Alyssa, illus. 2004. 16p. (J). pap. 5.95 (978-1-4027-1795-6(4)) Sterling Publishing Co., Inc.

—Bear Goes Shopping: A Guessing Game Story. 2005. (Illus.). 16p. (J). 9.95 (978-1-4027-1941-7(8)); pap. 5.95 (978-1-4027-1945-5(0)) Sterling Publishing Co., Inc.

—Bear's Busy Morning: A Guessing Game Story. Capucilli, Alyssa, illus. 2004. 16p. (J). 9.95 (978-1-4027-1706-2(7)) Sterling Publishing Co., Inc.

—Bear's Busy Morning: A Guessing Game Story. Lobel, Arnold & Capucilli, Alyssa, illus. 2004. 16p. (J). pap. 5.95 (978-1-4027-1796-3(2)) Sterling Publishing Co., Inc.

—A Polar Bear Can Swim. Bolam, Emily, illus. 1998. (Puffin-Easy-to-Read Ser.). 32p. (J). (gr. k-3). pap. 3.99 (978-0-14-038692-9(0) , Puffin) Penguin Group (USA) Inc.

Zimnik, Reiner. The Bear & the People. Ignatowicz, Nina, tr. from GER. Zimnik, Reiner, illus. 2005. (New York Review Children's Collection). (Illus.). 84p. (J). pap. 16.95 (978-1-59017-049-6(0) , NYR Children's Collection) New York Review of Bks., Inc., The.

Zobel, Allia. Count Your Blessings. 2004. bds. 12.99 (978-0-8254-5511-7(1)) Kregel Pubns.

Zocchi, Judy. Paulie & Sasha: Circus or Not. Vannozzi, Don, illus. 2001. (Paulie & Sasha Ser.). 32p. (J). lib. bdg. 23.00 (978-1-891997-17-4(3)) Dingles & Co.

—Paulie & Sasha: The Rescue. Vannozzi, Don, illus. 2001. (Paulie & Sasha Ser.). 32p. (J). lib. bdg. 23.00 (978-1-891997-15-0(7)) Dingles & Co.

Zoehfeld, Kathleen Weidner. Be Patient, Pooh. 2000. (Illus.). 32p. (J). (ps-k). 12.99 (978-0-7868-3250-7(9)) Disney Pr.

—Can You Find the Easter Eggs, Pooh? 2000. (Winnie the Pooh Ser.). (Illus.). 14p. (J). (ps-3). 5.99 (978-0-7364-0052-7(4)) Mouse Works.

—Don't Talk to Strangers, Pooh! 2000. (My Very First Winnie the Pooh Ser.). (Illus.). 32p. (J). (ps-k). pap. 4.99 (978-0-7868-4378-7(0)) Disney Pr.

—Have You Seen My Pot of Honey? 1999. (Learn & Grow Ser.). (Illus.). 12p. (J). (ps-3). 5.99 (978-0-7364-0099-2(0)) Mouse Works.

—Is It Christmas Yet, Pooh? 2000. 14p. (J). 5.99 (978-0-7364-1058-8(9)) Mouse Works.

—Pooh Plays Doctor. 1999. (My Very First Winnie the Pooh Ser.). (Illus.). 32p. (J). (ps-k). pap. 4.99 (978-0-7868-4341-1(1)) Disney Pr.

—Pooh Welcomes Winter. 1999. (My Very First Winnie the Pooh Ser.). (Illus.). 32p. (J). (ps-k). pap. 4.99 (978-0-7868-4355-8(1)) Disney Pr.

—Pooh Welcomes Winter. 1999. (978-0-606-17535-7(0)) Tandem Library Bks.

—Pooh's Birthday Surprise: Learn & Grow. 2000. (Lift the Flaps Bks.). 14p. (J). (ps-3). 5.99 (978-0-7364-1007-6(4)) Mouse Works.

—Pooh's First Day of School. Cuddy, Robbin, illus. 1999. (My Very First Winnie the Pooh Ser.). 32p. (J). (ps-k). pap. 4.99 (978-0-7868-4348-0(9)) Disney Pr.

—Pooh's Jingle Bells. (Illus.). 32p. (J). (ps-k). 2000. pap. 4.99 (978-0-7868-4419-7(1)); 1998. 11.95 (978-0-7868-3204-0(5)) Disney Pr.

—Pooh's Neighborhood. 1999. (My Very First Winnie the Pooh Ser.). (Illus.). 32p. (J). (ps-k). pap. 4.99 (978-0-7868-4340-4(3)) Disney Pr.

—Pooh's Neighborhood. 1999. (978-0-606-18112-9(1)) Tandem Library Bks.

—Roo's New Babysitter. 1999. (My Very First Winnie the Pooh Ser.). (Illus.). 32p. (J). (ps-k). 11.99 (978-0-7868-3215-6(0)) Disney Pr.

Zoehfeld, Kathleen Weidner & Milne, A. A. Don't Talk to Strangers, Pooh! Cuddy, Robbin, illus. 1998. (My Very First Winnie the Pooh Ser.). 32p. (J). (ps). pap. 11.95 (978-0-7868-3145-6(6)) Disney Pr.

Zoehfeld, Kathleen Weidner & Random House Disney Staff. Time for School, Pooh. Cuddy, Robbin, illus. 2001. 24p. (J). (gr. k-3). pap. 3.25 (978-0-7364-1179-0(8) , RH/Disney) Random Hse. Children's Bks.

Zolotow, Charlotte. Growing up Stories for 5-6 Year Olds. 2020. 114p. (J). (ps-17). 19.99 (978-0-7868-0519-8(6)) Disney Pr.

Zolty, H. Calli the Bear: the Story of a Little Bear Who Explores California & Helps Children Learn about the Golden State. 2006. 56p. pap. 19.98 (978-1-4116-4889-0(7)) Lulu.com.

—Calli the Bear: the Story of a Little Bear Who Teaches Children about the Power of Friendship. 2005. 36p. 16.19 (978-1-4116-7135-5(X)) Lulu.com.

BEARS—PICTORIAL WORKS

Freeman, Marcia S. Bears, 4 bks., Set. 1998. (J). 53.00 (978-0-516-29819-1(4) , Children's Pr.) Scholastic Library Publishing.

—Brown Bears. 1998. (J). lib. bdg. 13.25 (978-0-516-21485-6(3) , Children's Pr.) Scholastic Library Publishing.

—Polar Bears. 1998. (J). lib. bdg. 13.25 (978-0-516-21487-0(X) , Children's Pr.) Scholastic Library Publishing.

Hairston, Kennard. World's Best Recreational Activity Bears. 2003. (Illus.). 24p. (J). (gr. 2-4). spiral bd. 7.00 (978-0-8059-4498-3(2)) Dorrance Publishing Co., Inc.

Howe, Deborah. Teddy Bear's Scrapbook. 2001. (gr. k-3). lib. bdg. 11.80 (978-0-613-90197-0(5)) Tandem Library Bks.

Howe, Deborah & Howe, James. Teddy Bear's Scrapbook. 2001. (Illus.). (J). (978-0-606-21483-4(6)) Tandem Library Bks.

Keller, Holly. Jacob's Tree. 1999. (Illus.). 24p. (J). (ps-3). 15.00 (978-0-688-15995-5(8)) HarperCollins Pubs.

Tracqui, Valerie & Charlesbridge Publishing. The Brown Bear: Giant of the Mountains. Bios Agency, photos by. 1998. (Illus.). (J). (ps-ps). lib. bdg. 15.25 (978-0-613-07410-0(6)) Tandem Library Bks.

BEARS—POETRY

Appelt, Kathi. Bats on Parade. Sweet, Melissa, illus. 1999. 32p. (J). (ps-3). 15.95 (978-0-688-15665-7(7)); 15.89 (978-0-688-15666-4(5)) HarperCollins Pubs.

BEASTS

see Animals

BEATLES

Beatles. Date not set. 384p. (J). 5.98 (978-1-4054-0716-8(6)) Parragon, Inc.

Brassey, Richard. The Beatles. (Illus.). 24p. (J). pap. 8.99 (978-1-84255-229-2(5)) Dolphin Paperbacks GBR. *Dist:* Trafalgar Square Publishing.

Burgan, Michael. The Beatles. 2002. (Trailblazers of the Modern World Ser.). (Illus.). 48p. (J). (gr. 5 up). pap. 14.95 (978-0-8368-5228-8(1)); lib. bdg. 30.00 (978-0-8368-5068-0(8)) Stevens, Gareth Inc. (World Almanac Library).

—Beatles. 2002. (gr. 3-6). lib. bdg. 24.55 (978-0-613-76810-8(8)) Tandem Library Bks.

Edgers, Geoff. Who Were the Beatles? Tageau, Jerry, illus. 2006. (Who Was— ? Ser.). 106p. (J). (978-0-448-43907-5(7) , Grosset & Dunlap) Penguin Group (USA) Inc.

—Who Were the Beatles? Tugeau, Jeremy, illus. 2006. (Who Was... ? Ser.). 112p. (J). (gr. 2-5). pap. 4.99 (978-0-448-43906-8(9) , Grosset & Dunlap) Penguin Group (USA) Inc.

Gallagher, Jim. The Beatles. 2008. (J). ***(978-1-4222-0186-2(4))*** Mason Crest Pubs.

Lalani, Zane. Teenagers Guide to the Beatles. 2005. (Illus.). 216p. (YA). 24.95 (978-0-9658740-7-6(9)) AverStream Pr.

Little Monster Records, et al. All Together Now. 2006. (Illus.). (J). bds. 13.98 incl. audio compact disk ***(978-1-4243-1410-2(0))*** Independent Publisher Services.

Roberts, Jeremy. The Beatles. (Biography Ser.). (Illus.). 112p. (J). (gr. 6-12). 2005. lib. bdg. 27.93 (978-0-8225-4998-7(0)); 2003. pap. 7.95 (978-0-8225-5002-0(4)) Lerner Publishing Group.

Sierra I Fabra, Jordi. John Lennon - Imagina que esto fue Real. 2005. 168p. pap. (978-958-30-1702-5(7)) Panamericana Editorial.

Spitz, Robert. Yeah! Yeah! Yeah! the Beatles. 2007. 240p. (gr. 3-7). 18.99 ***(978-0-316-11555-1(X))*** Little, Brown Bks. for Young Readers.

Wentzel, Jim. The Beatles. 2006. (Rock & Roll Hall of Famers Ser.). (Illus.). 112p. (YA). (gr. 5-8). lib. bdg. 29.25 (978-0-8239-3526-0(4)) Rosen Publishing Group, Inc., The.

Wimmer, Teresa. The Beatles' Sgt. Pepper's Lonely Hearts Club Band. 2008. (J). ***(978-1-58341-651-8(X)*** , Creative Education) Creative Co., The.

BEAUTY, PERSONAL

see also Cosmetics; Costume; Hair

Barkan, Joanne. Looking Good. 2005. (Real Deal - Green Plus Ser.). (Illus.). 32p. (gr. 4-8). 19.00 (978-0-7910-8902-6(9)) Facts On File, Inc.

Beautiful Nail & Body Art. 2004. (How 2 Kits Ser.). (Illus.). 32p. (J). (978-1-84229-932-6(8)) Top That! Publishing PLC.

Beker, Jeanne. The Big Night Out. Dion, Nathalie, illus. 2005. 80p. (J). (gr. 4). pap. 15.95 (978-0-88776-719-7(2)) Tundra Bks., Inc./Livres Toundra, Inc. CAN. *Dist:* Random Hse., Inc.

Bell, Alison. Your Beauty, Your Health, Yourself. 2000. (Your Body, Your Self Bks.). (Illus.). 144p. (J). (gr. 4-8). pap. 8.95 (978-0-7373-0350-6(6) , 03506W) Lowell Hse. Juvenile.

Body Art. 2004. (Formula Fun Ser.). (Illus.). 48p. (J). (978-1-84229-585-4(3)); 128p. (978-1-84229-983-8(2)) Top That! Publishing PLC.

Body Crayons. 2004. (Whizz Kits Ser.). (Illus.). 48p. (J). (978-1-84229-942-5(5)) Top That! Publishing PLC.

Boleman-Herring, Elizabeth. The First of Everso. 2005. (Illus.). (J). pap. (978-0-9759042-0-6(5)) Literate Chigger Pr., Inc., The.

Bonnell, Jennifer. Stylin' Salon 'n' Spa: Spa Tips, Beauty Tricks, & Recipes for Feelin' Good! 2003. (Bratz Ser.). (Illus.). 1p. pap. 8.40 (978-0-14-131750-2(7) , Putnam Juvenile) Penguin Group (USA) Inc.

Boraas, Tracey. Cosmetologist. 2000. (Career Exploration Ser.). (Illus.). 48p. (J). (gr. 3-4). lib. bdg. 21.26 (978-0-7368-0592-6(3) , LifeMatters Bks.) Capstone Pr., Inc.

Bordenkercher, S. A. How to Win Your Crown: A Teen's Guide to Pageant Competition. 2nd rev. ed. 1998. (ENG., Illus.). 88p. (YA). pap. 12.95 (978-0-9661771-0-7(X) , 07508) Abby Publishing.

Boritzer, Etan. What Is Beautiful? Forrest, Nancy, illus. 2004. 32p. (ps-5). 14.95 (978-0-9637597-6-4(0)); 6.95 (978-0-9637597-7-1(9)) Lane, Veronica Bks.

—What Is Beautiful? 2002. (gr. 3-6). lib. bdg. 15.25 (978-0-613-77790-2(5)) Tandem Library Bks.

Bratz Fashion Funktivity Books. 2004. (J). 1.49 (978-0-7666-1222-8(8) , 99215); 1.49 (978-0-7666-1223-5(6) , 99215); 1.49 (978-0-7666-1224-2(4) , 99215) Modern Publishing.

Brown, Bobbi & Iverson, Annemarie. Bobbi Brown Teenage Beauty: Everything You Need to Look Pretty, Natural, Sexy & Awesome. 2000. (Illus.). 224p. (gr. 7-12). 25.00 (978-0-06-019636-3(X)) HarperCollins Pubs.

Byrd, Sandra. The Inside-Out Beauty Book: Tips & Tools for Girls Like You. 2002. (Girls Like You Ser.: Vol. 2). (Illus.). 128p. (gr. 4-7). pap. 7.99 (978-0-7642-2493-5(X)) Bethany Hse. Pubs.

Currie-McGhee, L. K. Tattoos & Body Piercing. 2005. (Overview Ser.). (Illus.). 112p. (J). (gr. 7-10). per. 29.95 (978-1-59018-749-4(0) , 1244601, Lucent Bks.) Thomson Gale.

Design your own Body Art. 2004. (How 2 Kits Ser.). (Illus.). 48p. (J). (978-1-84229-926-5(3)) Top That! Publishing PLC.

Douglas, Ann & Douglas, Julie. Body Talk: The Straight Facts on Fitness, Nutrition, & Feeling Great about Yourself! Davila, Claudia, illus. 2nd ed. 2006. (Girl Zone Ser.). 64p. (J). 19.95 (978-1-897066-62-1(7)); pap. 9.95 (978-1-897066-61-4(9)) Maple Tree Pr. CAN. *Dist:* Perseus Distribution.

Esherick, Joan. Clothing, Cosmetic, & Self-Esteem Tips: Making the Most of the Body You Have. 2005. (Obesity Ser.). (Illus.). 104p. (J). (ps-7). (978-1-59084-951-4(5)) Mason Crest Pubs.

Everett, Felicity. Makeup. rev. ed. 1998. (Usborne Fashion Guides Ser.). (Illus.). 32p. (gr. 6-12). (J). lib. bdg. 14.95 (978-1-58086-035-2(4)); (YA). pap. 6.95 (978-0-7460-3111-7(4)) EDC Publishing.

Fabulous Hair & Groovy Nails. 2004. (How 2 Kits Ser.). (Illus.). 48p. (J). (978-1-84229-958-6(1)) Top That! Publishing PLC.

Finger, Shari & Tumblety, Susan. Fabulous Nails. 2000. (Funtastic Kits Ser.). (Illus.). 48p. (J). 12.98 (978-0-7853-3869-7(1)) Publications International, Ltd.

Flaunt It! 2004. (Bratz). (J). (978-0-7666-1226-6(0) , 65030); (978-0-7666-1227-3(9) , 65030) Modern Publishing.

Friends & Trends. 2004. (Bratz). (J). 2.49 (978-0-7666-1303-4(8) , 49315) Modern Publishing.

Funky Body Crayons. 2004. (Fun Kits Ser.). (Illus.). 48p. (J). (978-1-84229-860-2(7)) Top That! Publishing PLC.

Gelman, Amy. The Buzz on Beauty: A Girl's Guide to Looking & Feeling Your Best. 1999. (Girls' Guides). (Illus.). 48p. (YA). (gr. 5-8). lib. bdg. 23.95 (978-0-8239-2986-3(8) , GGBUBE) Rosen Publishing Group, Inc., The.

Girls Club & Nicholson, Sue. Hair Magic: Fun Stuff to Unlock & Share. 2001. (Girls Club Ser.). (Illus.). 32p. (J). (gr. 4-7). pap. 9.95 (978-0-7624-0952-5(5) , Running Pr. Kids) Running Pr. Bk. Pubs.

—Nail Magic. 2001. (Girls Club Ser.). (Illus.). 32p. (J). (gr. 4-7). pap. 9.95 (978-0-7624-0949-5(5) , Courage Bks.) Running Pr. Bk. Pubs.

Gonzalez, Michelle. Face & Body Painting with Michelle Gonzalez. Faulkner, Pamela, ed. Gonzalez, Michelle, illus. Rix, Barbara, photos by. 1998. (Illus.). 23p. (YA). (gr. 2 up). pap. 12.95 (978-0-615-11689-1(2)) Michelle Designs.

Grabis, Bettina, et al. Nail Decorating. 2004. (Illus.). 62p. pap. ***(978-1-59412-033-6(1))*** Mud Puddle, Inc.

Graydon, Shari. In Your Face: The Culture of Beauty & You. 2004. (Illus.). 176p. (J). (gr. 6). 24.95 (978-1-55037-857-3(0)); pap. 14.95 (978-1-55037-856-6(2)) Annick Pr., Ltd. CAN. *Dist:* Firefly Bks., Ltd.

Haab, Sherri. Unas Divertidas. 2005. (SPA., Illus.). 58p. (J). (gr. 4-7). spiral bd. 23.95 (978-968-5528-12-2(8)) Klutz Latino MEX. *Dist:* Independent Pubs. Group.

Haberman, Lia. About Face: Beauty Tricks & Tips. 2005. (Illus.). 48p. (J). ***(978-0-439-80297-0(0))*** Scholastic, Inc.

Hair Designer. 2004. (Whizz Kits Ser.). (Illus.). 48p. (J). (978-1-84229-941-8(7)); pap. (978-1-84229-584-7(5)) Top That! Publishing PLC.

Hangin' with the Girls! 2004. (Bratz). (J). (978-0-7666-1304-1(6) , 49315) Modern Publishing.

Harper, Charise Mericle. Flush: The Scoop on Poop Throughout the Ages. 2007. (Illus.). 26p. (J). (ps-1). 15.99 (978-0-316-01064-1(2)) Little Brown & Co.

Harris, Destiny. Beauty Secrets for Girls: Beauty Secrets for Girls. 2004. (J). per. (978-0-9754380-2-2(6) , 100) Harris, Pleshette Communications Inc. Publishing.

Harrison, Emma. From Head to Toe: The Girls' Life Guide to Taking Care of You. Montagna, Frank, illus. 2004. 124p. (J). (978-0-439-44983-0(9)) Scholastic, Inc.

Hoobler, Dorothy & Hoobler, Thomas. Vanity Rules: A History of American Fashion & Beauty. 2000. (Single Titles Ser.). (Illus.). 160p. (gr. 7 up). lib. bdg. 28.90 (978-0-7613-1258-1(7) , Millbrook Pr.) Lerner Publishing Group.

Hurley, Jo. Every Girl Can Be a Princess Kit. Saunders, Zina, illus. 2004. 32p. (J). (gr. 2 up). spiral bd. 8.99 (978-0-439-63244-7(7)) Scholastic, Inc.

Inspire Kids Got Style. 2000. (Illus.). 112p. (J). 29.95 (978-1-928986-01-0(3)) Intra America Beauty Network.

Irons, Diane. Teen Beauty Secrets. 2002. (gr. 5-8). lib. bdg. 24.55 (978-0-613-57147-0(9)) Tandem Library Bks.

Johnson, Anne Akers. The Body Book: Recipes for Natural Body Care. 2001. (Illus.). 80p. (YA). (gr. 7 up). 21.95 (978-1-57054-590-0(1)) Klutz.

Katschke, Judy. Beautiful Makeup Book. Chapmanworks Staff, illus. 2000. (Barbie Ser.). 12p. (J). (gr. k-3). bds. 12.99 (978-1-57584-650-7(0) , Reader's Digest Children's Bks.) Reader's Digest Children's Publishing, Inc.

Kauchak, Therese. Real Beauty: 101 Ways to Feel Great about You. Yoshizumi, Carol, illus. 2004. (American Girl Library(R) Ser.). 120p. (J). pap. 9.95 (978-1-58485-908-6(3)) American Girl Publishing, Inc.

Kinch, Michael P. Warts. 2000. (gr. 3-6). lib. bdg. 15.25 (978-0-613-31878-5(1)) Tandem Library Bks.

Krulik, Nancy E. & Ladybird Books Staff. Jade: Xtreme Kool! 2003. (Bratz Ser.). (Illus.). 32p. pap. 2.99 (978-1-84422-188-2(1) , Putnam Juvenile) Penguin Group (USA) Inc.

—Sasha: Hip-Hop Hot! 2003. (Bratz Ser.). (Illus.). 32p. pap. 2.99 (978-1-84422-187-5(3) , Putnam Juvenile) Penguin Group (USA) Inc.

Libal, Autumn. Can I Change the Way I Look? A Teen's Guide to the Health Implications of Cosmetic Surgery, Makeovers, & Beyond. 2004. (Science of Health Ser.). (Illus.). 128p. (J). (978-1-59084-843-2(8)) Mason Crest Pubs.

Llewellyn, Claire. Your Hair. 2007. (J). ***(978-1-59771-097-8(0))*** Sea-To-Sea Pubns.

Mason, Linda. Teen Makeup: Looks to Match Your Every Mood. 2004. (Illus.). 144p. (YA). (gr. 7-12). pap. 16.95 (978-0-8230-2980-8(8)) Watson-Guptill Pubns., Inc.

Mayall, Beth. Galaxy Girl. 2002. (Get the Look Ser.). (Illus.). 32p. (J). (978-0-439-32894-4(2)) Scholastic, Inc.

—Glamour Girl. 2002. (Get the Look Ser.). (Illus.). 31p. (J). (978-0-439-32896-8(9)) Scholastic, Inc.

My Beauty Box. 2002. 64p. (J). pap. 9.98 (978-0-7525-6287-2(8)) Parragon, Inc.

Naylor, Caroline. Beauty Trix for Cool Chix: Easy-to-Make Lotions, Potions, & Spells to Bring out a Beautiful You. 2003. (Cool Chix Ser.). (Illus.). 96p. (gr. 5 up). pap. 9.95 (978-0-8230-6957-6(5)) Watson-Guptill Pubns., Inc.

Petty, Kate. Hair (World Show-and-Tell) 2006. (Illus.). 32p. 14.95 (978-1-58728-531-8(2) , Two Can Publishing) T&N Children's Publishing.

Pinkney, Sandra L. & Pinkney, Myles C. I Am Latino: The Beauty in Me. 2007. (Illus.). 32p. (J). (ps-1). 16.99 (978-0-316-16009-4(1)) Little Brown & Co.

Platt, Richard. They Wore What?! The Weird History of Fashion & Beauty. 2007. (J). pap. ***(978-1-58728-584-4(3)); 48p. (978-1-58728-582-0(7))*** T&N Children's Publishing. (Two Can Publishing).

Quinlan, Kathryn A. Makeup Artist. 1999. (Careers Without College Ser.). (Illus.). 48p. (J). (gr. 3-4). lib. bdg. 21.26 (978-0-7368-0175-1(8) , LifeMatters Bks.) Capstone Pr., Inc.

Reynolds, Helen. Makeup & Body Decorations. 2003. (Fashionable History of Costume Ser.). (Illus.). 32p. (J). lib. bdg. 25.70 (978-1-4109-0028-9(2)) Raintree.

Rue, Nancy N. & Rue, Marijean. Beauty Lab. 2007. (Faithgirlz!#8482; Ser.). 144p. (J). pap. 7.99 (978-0-310-71276-3(9)) Zonderkidz.

Schaefer, Valorie. The Care & Keeping of You: The Body Book for Girls. Bendell, Norm, illus. 1998. (American Girl Library). 104p. (J). (gr. 3 up). pap. 9.95 (978-1-56247-666-3(1) , American Girl) American Girl Publishing, Inc.

Scholastic, Inc. Staff. Body Crystals. Im, Angela, ed. 2002. (Fun Pack Ser.). 48p. (J). pap. 7.99 (978-0-439-43453-9(X) , Tangerine Pr.) Scholastic, Inc.

Silver, Patricia. Face Painting. Phillips, Louise, illus. 2004. (Kids Can Do It Ser.). 134p. (J). (gr. 4-6). (978-1-55074-689-1(8)) Kids Can Pr., Ltd.

—Face Painting. 2000. (gr. 3-6). lib. bdg. 14.10 (978-0-613-30394-1(6)) Tandem Library Bks.

Silver, Patricia & Phillips, Louise. Face Painting. 2004. (Kids Can Do It Ser.). (Illus.). 338p. (J). (gr. 4-6). (978-1-55074-845-1(9)) Kids Can Pr., Ltd.

Small, Mary. Fairness Is. Ouren, Todd, illus. 2004. (J). (978-1-4048-0276-6(2)) Picture Window Bks.

Smithee, Allan. Beauty Bizz. 2002. (J). 14.95 (978-1-58728-446-5(4)); pap. 7.95 (978-1-58728-506-6(1)) T&N Children's Publishing. (Two Can Publishing).

Sommers, Annie Leah. Everything You Need to Know about Looking & Feeling Your Best: A Guide for Girls. 2005. (Need to Know Library). (Illus.). 64p. (YA). (gr. 7-12). lib. bdg. 25.25 (978-0-8239-3079-1(3) , NTGUWO) Rosen Publishing Group, Inc., The.

Sommers, Michael A. Everything You Need to Know about Looking & Feeling Your Best: A Guide for Guys. 2005. (Need to Know Library). (Illus.). 64p. (YA). (gr. 7-12). lib. bdg. 25.25 (978-0-8239-3080-7(7) , NTGUGU) Rosen Publishing Group, Inc., The.

Southwater Staff. Outrageously Cool Hair Braids & Beads. 2002. (Illus.). 96p. (gr. 3-7). pap. 9.95 (978-1-84215-611-7(X) , Southwater) Anness Publishing GBR. *Dist:* National Bk. Network.

Temporary Tattoos. 2004. (Whizz Kits Ser.). (Illus.). 48p. (J). (978-1-84229-947-0(6)) Top That! Publishing PLC.

Top That Publishing Staff, ed. Fabulous Facials. 2004. (Cachet Ser.). (Illus.). 48p. (YA). (978-1-84510-330-9(0)) Top That! Publishing PLC.

Twardowski, Lynda. Face Facts: How to Bring Out the Beautiful You. 2001. (Among Teens Ser.). (Illus.). 110p. (J). (978-0-439-27217-9(3)) Scholastic, Inc.

Tym, Kate. Totally You! Every Girl's Guide to Looking Good. 1999. (Illus.). 160p. (YA). (gr. 7-9). pap. 5.95 (978-1-902618-44-9(0)) Element Children's Bks.

Weiss, Stefanie Iris. Coping with the Beauty Myth: A Guide for Real Girls. (Coping Ser.). (Illus.). (YA). (gr. 7-12). 2005. 192p. lib. bdg. 26.50 (978-0-8239-3757-8(7)); 2000. 112p. lib. bdg. 25.25 (978-0-8239-3033-3(5) , COBEAU) Rosen Publishing Group, Inc., The.

—Everything You Need to Know about Mehndi, Temporary Tattoos & Other Body Arts. 2000. (Need to Know Library). (Illus.). 64p. (J). (gr. 4-6). lib. bdg. 25.25 (978-0-8239-3086-9(6) , NTMEND) Rosen Publishing Group, Inc., The.

Wingate, Philippa. Hair & Makeup. 2000. (gr. 7-12). lib. bdg. 19.90 (978-0-613-88054-1(4)) Tandem Library Bks.

—The Usborne Book of Hair. rev. ed. 2000. (Usborne Fashion Guides Ser.). (Illus.). 32p. (J). (gr. 4-7). lib. bdg. 15.95 (978-1-58086-225-7(X)) EDC Publishing.

Winkler, Kathleen. Tattooing & Body Piercing: Understanding the Risks. 2002. (Teen Issues Ser.). (Illus.). 64p. (YA). (gr. 6-12). lib. bdg. 22.60 (978-0-7660-1668-2(4)) Enslow Pubs., Inc.

You Glow, Girl! Beauty Basics for Teens Journal. 2001. pap. 20.00 (978-0-9706688-0-6(5)) York-Goldman Enterprises, Inc.

Youngs, Jennifer Leigh. Feeling Great, Looking Hot, & Loving Yourself! Health Fitness & Beauty for Teen. 2000. (gr. 7-12). lib. bdg. 24.55 (978-0-613-90258-8(0)) Tandem Library Bks.

BEAUTY CONTESTS—FICTION

Barry, Maureen. Miss Fairfield's Beauty Pageant. 2006. (J). pap. 20.00 net. ***(978-1-60402-176-9(4))*** Independent Pub.

Bradman, Tony. It Came from Outer Space. Wright, Carol, illus. 2004. 25p. (J). (VIE, ARA, CHI, GUJ & ENG.). (978-1-85269-336-7(3)); (CHI, ARA, VIE, GUJ & ENG.). (978-1-85269-393-0(2)) Mantra Publishing, Ltd.

Dockray, Tracy. My Life Story. Dockray, Tracy, illus. 2003. (Illus.). 40p. (J). lib. bdg. 15.95 (978-1-58717-218-2(6) , SeaStar Bks.) Chronicle Bks. LLC.

Dodd, Quentin. The Princess of Neptune. 2004. 224p. (J). 17.00 (978-0-374-36119-8(3) , Farrar, Straus & Giroux (BYR)) Farrar, Straus & Giroux.

Echols, Jennifer. Major Crush. 2006. (Romantic Comedies Ser.). 304p. (YA). pap. 6.99 (978-1-4169-1830-1(2) , Simon Pulse) Simon & Schuster Children's Publishing.

Juby, Susan. Miss Smithers. 2004. (Illus.). 336p. (J). 15.99 (978-0-06-051546-1(5)); lib. bdg. 16.89 (978-0-06-051547-8(3)) HarperCollins Pubs. (HarperTeen).

Levine, Gail Carson. Fairest. 2006. 336p. (J). (gr. 3-9). 16.99 (978-0-06-073408-4(6)); lib. bdg. 17.89 (978-0-06-073409-1(4)) HarperCollins Pubs.

Michael, Todd. Texas State Bird Beauty Pageant. Randall, Lee Brandt, illus. 2005. 32p. (J). (ps-3). 16.95 (978-1-893062-75-7(9)) Quail Ridge Pr., Inc.

Quinn, Stephanie. The Miss Medieval Beauty Pageant. 2008. (J). per. 6.99 ***(978-0-9773099-3-1(2))*** Quinn Entertainment.

Vision, David & Vision, Mutiya Sahar. What Makes Me Beautiful? Alcantara, Ignacio, illus. 2005. 24p. (J). 16.00 (978-0-9659538-4-9(X)) Soul Vision Works Publishing.

Zuckerman, Lilla & Zuckerman, Nora. Beauty Queen Blowout. 2003. (Miss Adventures Ser.: Bk. 2). 240p. pap. 9.95 (978-0-7432-3846-5(X) , Fireside) Simon & Schuster.

BEAUTY SHOPS

Hair Stylists. 2000. (My Ancestors—My Heroes Ser.: Vol. 46). (J). (gr. 3-4). (978-1-893091-45-0(7)) Parker Publishing Co.

BEAVERS

Bauman, Amy & Corrigan, Patricia. The Wonder of Beavers. 2000. (Animal Wonders Ser.). (Illus.). 48p. (J). (gr. 1 up). lib. bdg. 26.00 (978-0-8368-2661-6(2)) Stevens, Gareth Inc.

Beavers & Their Lodges. (Animal Homes Ser.). 24p. (J). 6.95 (978-0-7368-5126-8(7)) Capstone Pr., Inc.

Crewe, Sabrina. Life Cycle of the Beaver. 1999. (Life Cycles Ser.). (Illus.). 32p. (gr. 2-5). pap. 6.95 (978-0-8172-4249-7(X)) Steck-Vaughn.

Donovan, Sandy. A Beaver in Its Lodge. 2003. (Where Do Animals Live? Ser.). (J). pap. (978-1-58417-183-6(9)); lib. bdg. (978-1-58417-182-9(0)) Lake Street Pubs.

Frisch, Aaron. Beavers. 2000. (Northern Trek Ser.). (Illus.). 24p. (J). (gr. 2-7). lib. bdg. 15.95 (978-1-58340-030-2(3)) Smart Apple Media.

Gibson, Deborah C. Beavers & Their Homes. 1999. (Animal Habitats Ser.). (Illus.). 24p. (J). (gr. k-4). lib. bdg. 18.75 (978-0-8239-5307-3(6) , PowerKids Pr.) Rosen Publishing Group, Inc., The.

Goldish, Meish. Beavers & Other Rodents, Vol. 2. World Book, Inc. Staff, ed. 2002. (World Book's Animals of the World Ser.). (Illus.). 64p. (J). (978-0-7166-1225-4(9)) World Bk., Inc.

Hall, Margaret. Beavers. Saunders-Smith, Gail, ed. 2004. (Wetland Animals Ser.). (Illus.). 24p. (J). (gr. k-1). lib. bdg. 15.93 (978-0-7368-2063-9(9) , Pebble Bks.) Capstone Pr., Inc.

Hodge, Deborah. Beavers. Stephens, Pat, illus. (Kids Can Press Wildlife Ser.). 32p. (J). (gr. k-3). 2004. (978-1-55074-679-2(0)); 1998. (978-1-55074-429-3(1)) Kids Can Pr., Ltd.

—Beavers. 1999. (J). 12.75 (978-0-606-19011-4(2)) Tandem Library Bks.

Jacobs, Lee. Beaver. 2003. (Wild America Ser.). (Illus.). 24p. (J). 24.94 (978-1-56711-566-6(7) , Blackbirch Pr., Inc.) Thomson Gale.

James, Kathleen. Building Beavers. 2000. (gr. k-3). lib. bdg. 14.10 (978-0-613-43801-8(9)) Tandem Library Bks.

Kalman, Bobbie. The Life Cycle of a Beaver. 2006. (Life Cycle Ser.). (Illus.). 32p. (J). (gr. 2-3). pap. (978-0-7787-0702-8(4)); lib. bdg. (978-0-7787-0628-1(1)) Crabtree Publishing Co.

Klinting, Lars. Castor Carpintero. 1998. Tr. of Beaver the Builder. (SPA., Illus.). 32p. (J). (ps-3). 18.95 (978-84-89675-05-6(8) , LEC5058) Zendrera Zariquiey, Editorial ESP. *Dist:* AIMS International Bks., Inc.

Mara, Wil. Beavers. 2007. (Animals Animals Ser.). (Illus.). 48p. (J). (gr. 4-7). lib. bdg. 28.50 (978-0-7614-2524-3(1) , Benchmark Bks.) Cavendish, Marshall Corp.

Marie, Christian. Little Beavers. 2005. (Born to Be Wild Ser.). (Illus.). 24p. (J). (ps-17). lib. bdg. 22.00 (978-0-8368-4734-5(2)) Stevens, Gareth Inc.

Martin-James, Kathleen. Building Beavers. (Pull Ahead Bks.). (Illus.). 32p. (gr. k-2). 2003. (J). pap. 5.95 (978-0-8225-3632-1(3)); 1999. lib. bdg. 22.60 (978-0-8225-3628-4(5)) Lerner Publishing Group.

O'Sullivan, Elizabeth. Beavers. 2007. (Early Bird Nature Books). (J). 25.26 (978-0-8225-6465-2(3) , Lerner Pubns.) Lerner Publishing Group.

Rounds, Glen. The Beaver. 1999. (Illus.). 32p. (J). (gr. k-3). tchr. ed. 16.95 (978-0-8234-1440-6(X)) Holiday Hse., Inc.

Rue, Leonard Lee, III, photos by & text. Beavers. Rue, Leonard Lee, III, text. rev. ed. 2002. (WorldLife Library). (Illus.). 72p. pap. 17.95 (978-0-89658-548-5(4)) Voyageur Pr., Inc.

Stone, Lynn M. Beaver. 2003. (Animals in U.S. History Ser.). (Illus.). 24p. (J). 25.64 (978-1-58952-697-6(X)) Rourke Publishing, LLC.

Sullivan, Jody. Beavers: Big-Toothed Builders. 2002. (Wild World of Animals Ser.). (Illus.). 24p. (J). (gr. 1). lib. bdg. 18.60 (978-0-7368-1392-1(6) , Bridgestone Bks.) Capstone Pr., Inc.

Swanson, Diane. Beavers. 2003. (Welcome to the World of Animals Ser.). (Illus.). 32p. (J). (gr. 3 up). lib. bdg. 23.33 (978-0-8368-3560-1(3)) Stevens, Gareth Inc.

Turner, Matt. Beavers. 2003. (Secret World Of... Ser.). (Illus.). 48p. (J). lib. bdg. 27.14 (978-0-7398-7018-1(1)) Raintree.

BEAVERS—FICTION

Bailey, Arthur Scott. Sleepy-Time Tales: The Tale of Brownie B. 2006. (Illus.). pap. ***(978-1-4065-0447-7(5))*** Dodo Pr.

Beechen, Adam. Best Valentine. 2001. (gr. k-3). lib. bdg. 11.25 (978-0-613-43917-6(1)) Tandem Library Bks.

Bell, David M. The Adventures of Ecomunk: Mr. Beaver Builds a Dam. 1998. (Illus.). 68p. (J). (gr. 3-6). pap. 9.95 (978-1-893120-01-3(5) , EM-01) Glamorgan Bks.

Bentley, Dawn. Busy Little Beaver. Stover, Beth, illus. 2005. (Read-and-Discover Atlantic Wilderness Adventures Ser.). 32p. (J). (ps-1). pap. 3.95 (978-1-59249-011-0(5) , S2029) Soundprints.

Bowman, Andy. Bobby Beaver Learns a Lesson. Travis, Stephanie, illus. 26p. (J). (gr. k-5). pap. 6.95 (978-1-931650-10-6(1)); lib. bdg. 14.95 (978-1-931650-11-3(X)) Coastal Publishing Carolina, Inc.

Brenner, Barbara. Beavers Beware! McCully, Emily Arnold, illus. 1998. (Bank Street Reader Collection). 48p. (J). (gr. 1-3). lib. bdg. 22.60 (978-0-8368-1769-0(9)) Stevens, Gareth Inc.

Burgess, Thornton W. The Adventures of Paddy the Beaver. (J). 18.95 (978-0-8488-0379-7(5)) Amereon LTD.

—The Adventures of Paddy the Beaver. 2000. (Dover Children's Thrift Classics Ser.). (Illus.). 80p. (J). (gr. 3-6). pap. 2.00 (978-0-486-41305-1(5)) Dover Pubns., Inc.

—The Adventures of Paddy the Beaver. 2004. reprint ed. pap. 15.95 (978-1-4191-5156-9(8)); pap. 1.99 (978-1-4192-5156-6(2)) Kessinger Publishing, LLC.

Burgess, W. Thornton. Adventures of Paddy Beaver. 2007. pap. 33.99 ***(978-1-4280-5109-6(0))*** IndyPublish.com.

Crimi, Carolyn. Get Busy, Beaver! Bynum, Janie, illus. 2004. 32p. (J). (ps-3). pap. 15.95 (978-0-439-54866-3(7) , Orchard Bks.) Scholastic, Inc.

Dalrymple, Marilyn. Bartholomew's Buttons. 2006. 18p. (J). 9.73 (978-1-4116-9200-8(4)) Lulu.com.

deRubertis, Barbara. Perky Otter. Cockrille, Eva V., illus. 1998. (Let's Read Together Ser.). 32p. (J). (ps-3). pap. 4.95 (978-1-57565-045-6(2)) Kane Pr., The.

George, William T. Beaver at Long Pond. 2000. (Illus.). (J). (978-0-606-18677-3(8)) Tandem Library Bks.

Harper, Charise Mericle. When Randolph Turned Rotten. 2007. 40p. (J). (gr. k-3). 16.99 (***978-0-375-84071-5(0)***); lib. bdg. 19.99 (***978-0-375-94071-2(5)***) Random Hse. Children's Bks. (Knopf Bks. for Young Readers).

Job. Yakari & the Beavers. 2007. 48p. pap. 9.99 (***978-1-905460-09-0(0)***) CineBook GBR. *Dist:* Biblio Distribution.

Johnson, Amy Crane. Mason Moves Away/Mason se Muda: A Solomon Raven Story: un cuento del cuervo Salomon, 4 vols. de la Vega, Eida, tr. Mommaerts, Robb, illus. 2004. (Solomon Raven Ser. : 4). Tr. of Mason se Muda. (SPA & ENG.). 32p. (J). (gr. k-3). 16.95 (978-0-9720192-3-1(5) , 626999) Raven Tree Pr.

Jordan, Christopher & Boey, Stephanie. The Little Beaver. 2008. (Illus.). 24p. 15.95 (***978-1-55168-249-5(4)***) Key Porter Bks. CAN. *Dist:* Perseus Distribution.

Kline, Trish & Donev, Mary. Coming Home: KA Reader 8. 2007. (Illus.). 32p. (J). per. 20.00 (***978-1-934307-01-4(7)***) Ghost Hunter Productions.

Klinting, Lars. Beaver the Tailor: A How-to Picture Book. Klinting, Lars, illus. 2004. Orig. Title: Castor Syr.. (Illus.). 32p. (J). (gr. k-3). reprint ed. 17.00 (978-0-7567-7213-0(3)) DIANE Publishing Co.

—Harvey the Baker. 2005. (Handy Harvey Ser.). (Illus.). 40p. (J). (ps-k). pap., pap. 4.95 (978-0-7534-5913-3(2) , Kingfisher) Houghton Mifflin Co. Trade & Reference Div.

Law, Felicia. Rumble Meets Buddy Beaver. 2005. (Read-It! Readers Ser.). (Illus.). 32p. (J). (ps-k). lib. bdg. 18.60 (978-1-4048-1287-1(3)) Picture Window Bks.

LeGrand, Hank, 3rd. Paddle Tail's First Winter Adventure. Fair, Patricia Lynn, illus. 2006. (J). per. 7.95 (978-1-59466-082-5(4) , Growing Years) Port Town Publishing.

MacDonald, Amy. Little Beaver & the Echo. Fox-Davies, Sarah, illus. 1998. 32p. (J). (ps-3). pap. 6.99 (978-0-698-11628-3(3) , Putnam Juvenile) Penguin Group (USA) Inc.

Markowitz, Susan Meredith. Bitsy el castor & Bitsy the Beaver. 2005. spiral bd. 66.00 (***978-1-4108-5646-3(1)***) Benchmark Education Co.

Martinez, Jill F. Rio de Castor. (SPA.). 128p. (J). (978-84-279-3123-7(9) , NG0617) Noguer y Caralt Editores, S. A. ESP. *Dist:* Lectorum Pubns., Inc.

Meredith-Markowitz, Susan. Bitsy the Beaver. ed. 2003. (Early Connections Ser.). (J). pap. 33.00 (978-1-4108-1364-0(9)) Benchmark Education Co.

Morneau, Robert F. A Tale from Paleface Creek. Mau, Marjorie M., illus. 2001. 32p. (J). (ps-3). 9.95 (978-0-8091-6678-7(X) , 6678-x) Paulist Pr.

Nitto, Tomio. The Red Rock. 2006. (Illus.). 32p. (J). 15.95 (978-0-88899-669-5(1)) Groundwood Bks. CAN. *Dist:* Perseus Distribution.

Northey, Neil W. Paddletail the Beaver & His Neighbors. 1998. (Illus.). 182p. (J). (gr. 4-7). pap. 6.95 (978-1-881545-84-2(9)) A B Publishing.

Sargent, Dave & Sargent, Pat. Billy Beaver: A New Beginning, 15 vols., Vol. 2. Huff, Jeane, illus. 2nd rev. ed. 2003. (Animal Pride Ser.: 2). 42p. (J). pap. 6.95 (978-1-56763-762-5(0)); lib. bdg. 19.95 (978-1-56763-761-8(2)) Ozark Publishing.

Scott, James. The Sign of the Beaver: Reproducible Teaching Unit. 1999. 38p. (YA). (gr. 7-12). ring bd. 29.50 (978-1-58049-099-3(9) , TU95) Prestwick Hse., Inc.

Sign of the Beaver. 1999. (J). stu. ed. 11.95 (978-1-56137-495-3(4)) Novel Units, Inc.

Speare, Elizabeth George. The Sign of the Beaver. 2002. (Illus.). (J). 14.47 (978-0-7587-0311-8(2)) Book Wholesalers, Inc.

—The Sign of the Beaver. 135p. (J). (gr. 4-6). pap. 4.99 (978-0-8072-1517-3(1)); 1998. pap. 29.00 incl. audio (978-0-8072-7960-1(9) , YA950 SP) Random Hse. Audio Publishing Group. (Listening Library).

—The Sign of the Beaver. 1998. (J). (gr. 5). pap. 3.95 (978-0-439-04475-2(8)) Scholastic, Inc.

Vischer, Phil. 47 Beavers in the Big Blue Sea. 2007. (Illus.). 48p. (J). 15.99 (978-1-4003-0836-1(4)) Nelson, Thomas Inc.

Watson, Patrick. Ahmek. Thomson, Tracy, illus. 1999. 164p. (J). (gr. 3-7). 14.95 (978-0-7737-3145-5(8)) Stoddart Kids CAN. *Dist:* Fitzhenry & Whiteside, Ltd.

Wells, Rosemary. Doris's Dinosaur. Wheeler, Jody & Nez, John, illus. 2001. (Yoko & Friends School Days Ser.: No. 4). 32p. (gr. k-2). 9.99 (978-0-7868-0726-0(1) , Volo) Hyperion Bks. for Children.

—Doris's Dinosaur. 2001. (J). 10.79 (978-0-606-22550-2(1)) Tandem Library Bks.

Williams, G. Walton. The Beavers Build a Dam. Kollock, John, ed. unabr. ed. 2000. (Illus.). 64p. (Orig.). (J). pap. 6.95 (978-0-9703570-0-7(1)) Barksdale Hse. Pr.

Woods, Shirley E. Jack: The Story of a Beaver. Godkin, Celia, illus. 2003. 96p. (J). pap. (978-1-55041-735-7(5)) Fitzhenry & Whiteside, Ltd.

BECKWOURTH, JAMES PIERSON, 1798-1867

Burke, Rick. James Beckwourth. 2003. (American Lives Ser.). 32p. pap. 6.95 (978-1-4034-4199-7(5)) Heinemann Library.

Demund, Tom. From Slave to Superstar of the Wild West: The Awesome Story of Jim Beckwourth. 2007. 160p. (YA). 18.95 (***978-0-9786904-0-3(0)***) Legends of the West Publishing Co.

Manheimer, Ann S. James Beckwourth: Legendary Mountain Man. 2006. (Trailblazer Biography Ser.). (Illus.). 112p. (J). (ps-7). 30.60 (978-1-57505-892-4(8) , Twenty-First Century Bks.) Lerner Publishing Group.

BEDELIA, AMELIA (FICTITIOUS CHARACTER)—FICTION

see Amelia-Bedelia (Fictitious Character)—Fiction

BEDOUINS

Losleben, Elizabeth. The Bedouin of the Middle East. 2005. (First Peoples Ser.). (Illus.). 48p. (gr. 4-8). lib. bdg. 23.95 (978-0-8225-0663-8(7)) Lerner Publishing Group.

BEDOUINS—FICTION

Ivey, Jean. Wadduda of the Desert: A Legend of the Arabian War Mare. Dorwin, Judy Frazier, illus. 1998. 230p. (J). (gr. 4-12). pap. 9.95 (978-0-9658891-3-1(0)) Elan Pr.

Temple, Frances. The Beduins' Gazelle. Bowers, David, illus. 1998. (Harper Trophy Bks.). 160p. (J). (gr. 7 up). pap. 5.99 (978-0-06-440669-7(5) , Harper Trophy) HarperCollins Pubs.

BEDTIME

Ackroyd, Dorothea. Bedtime Board Book. 1999. (Baby's World Ser.). (Illus.). 12p. (ps-k). 3.95 (978-1-58185-201-1(0)) Quadrillion Media LLC.

Acredolo, Linda. Baby Signs for Bedtime. Gentieu, Penny, illus. 2003. 24p. (J). (ps up). 6.99 (978-0-06-009076-0(6) , Harper Entertainment) HarperCollins Pubs.

Bailey, Debbie. Buenas Noches. Huszar, Susan, photos by. 2001. (Hablemos Ser.). (SPA., Illus.). 14p. (J). (gr. k-ps). bds. 5.95 (978-1-55037-710-1(8)) Annick Pr., Ltd. CAN. *Dist:* Firefly Bks., Ltd.

—Good Night. Huszar, Susan, photos by. 2001. (Talk-about-Books). (Illus.). 14p. (J). (gr. k-ps). bds. 5.95 (978-1-55037-698-2(5)) Annick Pr., Ltd. CAN. *Dist:* Firefly Bks., Ltd.

Beaton, Clare, illus. Mrs. Moon: Lullabies for Bedtime. 2003. 48p. (J). 19.99 incl. audio compact disk (978-1-84148-176-0(9)) Barefoot Bks., Inc.

Berry, Joy Wilt. Teach Me about Bedtime: A Special Times Book. Fitzpatrick, Roey, illus. rev. ed. 1999. (Teach Me about Ser. : Vol. 3). 32p. (J). (ps). bds. 5.95 (978-1-58634-002-5(6) , 01-0101-03) Goldstar Publishing, Inc.

Berry, Ron & Sharp, Chris. It's Bedtime. Sharp, Chris & Currant, Gary, illus. 2003. (It's Time to Ser.). 14p. (J). (ps-k). bds. 6.95 (978-1-891100-61-1(0)) Smart Kids Publishing.

Boynton, Sandra. Buenas Noches a Todos. Boynton, Sandra, illus. 2004. Tr. of Going to Bed Book. (SPA., Illus.). 14p. (J). bds. 5.99 (978-0-689-86652-4(6) , Libros Para Ninos) Simon & Schuster Children's Publishing.

Deschamps, Nicola, ed. Bedtime. 2001. (Touch & Feel Ser.). (Illus.). 12p. (J). (ps-3). bds. 6.99 (978-0-7894-7418-6(2)) Dorling Kindersley Publishing, Inc.

Dorling Kindersley Publishing Staff, ed. Buenas Noches, Bebe! / Good Night, Baby! 2004. (SPA & ENG., Illus.). 18p. (J). bds. 4.99 (978-0-7566-0438-7(9)) Dorling Kindersley Publishing, Inc.

Feldman, Heather. My Bedtime: A Book about Getting Ready for Bed. 2000. (PowerKids Readers Ser.). (Illus.). 24p. (J). (gr. 1). lib. bdg. 16.00 (978-0-8239-5522-0(2) , PKMYBE, PowerKids Pr.) Rosen Publishing Group, Inc., The.

Finney, Amy J. Bedtime. Mets, Marilyn, illus. 2001. (Books for Young Learners). 8p. (J). pap. 5.00 (978-1-57274-521-6(5) , 2124) Owen, Richard C. Pubs., Inc.

Kent, Susan. Let's Talk about When You Have Trouble Going to Sleep. 2000. (Let's Talk Library). (Illus.). 24p. (J). (gr. 3). lib. bdg. 18.75 (978-0-8239-5424-7(2) , PowerKids Pr.) Rosen Publishing Group, Inc., The.

Litchfield, Jo. Bedtime. Litchfield, Jo, illus. 2007. 12p. (J). bds. 12.99 (978-0-7945-1461-7(8) , Usborne) EDC Publishing.

McKee, Darren, illus. Barney's Dreamtime Songs. 2003. (Musical Nightlight Bks.). (J). bds. (978-0-7853-7983-6(5)) Publications International, Ltd.

Smart Kids Publishing Staff. Its Bedtime. 2000. (Time to... Board Books Ser.). 16p. (J). bds. 6.95 (978-1-58015-248-4(6)) Penton Overseas, Inc.

Smart Kids Publishing Staff. My Snuggle up Bedtime Book. Smart Kids Publishing Staff, illus. 2007. 16p. 14.99 (***978-0-8249-6695-9(3)***) Ideals Pubns.

Stohs, Anita Reith. Hush, Little One: A Lullaby for God's Children. Kanzler, John, tr. Kanzler, John, illus. 2004. 32p. (J). 12.99 (978-0-570-07144-0(5)) Concordia Publishing Hse.

Swain, Gwenyth. Bedtime! 2003. (Illus.). 24p. (J). (ps-2). pap. 6.95 (978-1-57505-162-8(1)) Lerner Publishing Group.

—Bedtime! 2002. (gr. k-3). lib. bdg. 15.25 (978-0-613-46049-1(9)) Tandem Library Bks.

BEDTIME—FICTION

Adams, Michael. The Little King & the Honeybee. 2005. (J). per. 9.95 (978-1-58597-327-9(0)) Leathers Publishing.

Adelman, Nechama Dina. Bedtime. Blau, Nicole, illus. (J). 9.95 (978-1-929628-12-4(9)) Hachai Publishing.

Aigner-Clark, Julie. Sweet Dreams, Mimi. Zaidi, Nadeem, illus. 2004. (Baby Einstein Ser.). 16p. (J). (ps-17). bds. 5.99 (978-0-7868-5115-7(5)) Hyperion Bks. for Children.

Aignier-Clark, Julie. Nighttime Lullaby. 2008. 10p. 9.99 (***978-1-4231-0861-0(2)***) Hyperion Bks. for Children.

Albee, Sarah. Off to Bed. Ebert, Len, illus. 2006. (Step-By-Step Readers Ser.). (J). pap. (978-1-59939-060-4(4) , Reader's Digest Young Families, Inc.) Reader's Digest Children's Publishing, Inc.

Allen, Lisa & Sharp, Julis. Time for Bed - The Secret of Shadows: Shadow Theater Inside. Johnson, Vickie, illus. 26p. (J). (ps-2). pap. (978-1-56021-355-0(8) , 206) W.J. Fantasy, Inc.

Allison, Christine, et al. 365 Bedtime Stories. 1998. (Illus.). 448p. (J). (ps-5). 22.95 (978-0-7679-0096-6(0) , Broadway) Broadway Bks.

Alvord, David Myron. Albert & His Journey Through the Mountains. 2006. 76p. pap. 14.95 (***978-1-4241-2423-7(9)***) PublishAmerica, Inc.

Anders, Bill. Becoming Noah. 2004. 114p. (J). pap. 7.95 (978-0-9762059-0-6(4)) Leaping Antelope Productions.

Andreae, Giles. Keep Love in Your Heart, Little One. Vulliamy, Clara, illus. 2007. 32p. (J). (ps-2). 15.95 (***978-1-58925-066-6(4)***, tiger tales) ME Media LLC.

Anything Is Possible. 2006. (J). 12.00 (***978-0-9769827-1-5(4)***) Wren Song Pr.

Appelt, Kathi. Bubba & Beau Go Night-Night. Howard, Arthur, illus. 2003. (Bubba & Beau Ser.). 32p. (J). 16.00 (978-0-15-204593-7(7)) Harcourt Children's Bks.

—Bubba & Beau Go Night-Night. Howard, Arthur, illus. 2006. (Bubba & Beau Ser.). 32p. (J). pap. 6.00 (978-0-15-205815-9(X) , Voyager Bks./Libros Viajeros) Harcourt Children's Bks.

Apperley, Dawn. Good Night, Sleep Tight, Little Bunnies. Apperley, Dawn, illus. 2002. (Illus.). 32p. (J). (ps-k). pap. 9.95 (978-0-439-22525-0(6) , Cartwheel Bks.) Scholastic, Inc.

Asch, Frank. Good Night, Baby Bear. Asch, Frank, illus. 2001. (Illus.). 32p. (J). (ps-k). pap. 7.00 (978-0-15-216368-6(9) , Voyager Bks./Libros Viajeros) Harcourt Children's Bks.

—Good Night, Baby Bear. 2001. 12.80 (978-0-606-22600-4(1)); lib. bdg. 14.15 (978-0-613-53034-7(9)) Tandem Library Bks.

Ashman, Linda. How to Make a Night. Tusa, Tricia, illus. (J). (ps-3). Date not set. 32p. pap. 5.99 (978-0-06-443699-1(3)); 2004. 40p. 15.99 (978-0-06-029032-0(3)) HarperCollins Pubs.

—Starry Safari. Mack, Jeff, illus. 2005. 40p. (J). 16.00 (978-0-15-204766-5(2)) Harcourt Children's Bks.

Ashworth, Camilla. La Cama de Horacio. (Picture Books Collection). (SPA., Illus.). 32p. (J). (gr. k-3). pap. 10.95 (978-1-56014-581-3(1)) Santillana USA Publishing Co., Inc.

Aston, Dianna Hutts. Bless This Mouse: A Soft-to-Touch Book. 2004. (Illus.). 24p. (J). 14.95 (978-1-59354-050-0(7)) Handprint Bks.

Averbeck, Jim. In a Blue Room. Tusa, Tricia, illus. 2008. 32p. (J). 16.00 (***978-0-15-205992-7(X)***) Harcourt Trade Pubs.

Awdry, Wilbert V. & Random House Staff. Thomas & the Shooting Star. Stubbs, Tommy, illus. 2002. (Thomas & Friends Ser.). 32p. (J). (ps-2). 8.99 (978-0-375-81523-2(6) , Random Hse. Bks. for Young Readers) Random Hse. Children's Bks.

Aylesworth, Jim. Teddy Bear Tears. 2000. (gr. k-3). lib. bdg. 14.15 (978-0-613-28667-1(7)) Tandem Library Bks.

Baby's Bedtime Stories. 2002. (J). spiral bd. (978-0-9720158-2-0(5)) Story Reader, Inc.

Baicker, Karen. Snuggle Me Snuggly! 2004. (Illus.). 5p. (J). bds. 6.95 (978-1-59354-038-8(8)) Handprint Bks.

Bailey, Arthur Scott. Sleepy Time Tales the Tale of Fatty Coon. 2004. reprint ed. pap. 15.95 (978-1-4191-4779-1(X)); pap. 1.99 (978-1-4192-4779-8(4)) Kessinger Publishing, LLC.

Bailey, Linda. Goodnight, Sweet Pig. Masse, Josée, illus. 2007. 32p. (J). (ps-k). (***978-1-55337-844-0(X)***) Kids Can Pr., Ltd.

Bajaj, Varsha. How Many Kisses Do You Want Tonight? Bates, Ivan, illus. 2004. 28p. (J). (ps-3). 15.99 (978-0-316-82381-4(3)) Little, Brown Bks. for Young Readers.

Bajaj, Varsha. How Many Kisses Do You Want Tonight? Bates, Ivan, illus. 2007. 26p. (J). bds. 6.99 (***978-0-316-06735-5(0)***) Little, Brown Bks. for Young Readers.

Banks, Kate. And If the Moon Could Talk. Hallensleben, Georg, illus. 2002. (J). 24.36 (978-0-7587-1943-0(4)) Book Wholesalers, Inc.

—And If the Moon Could Talk. Hallensleben, Georg, illus. 2001. (J). (gr. k-2). 25.95 incl. audio (978-0-8045-6867-8(7) , 6867) Spoken Arts, Inc.

Barger, Jan. Bedtime, Nelly! Barger, Jan, illus. 2004. (Illus.). 32p. (J). 14.95 (978-1-58089-094-6(6) , 1234820) Charlesbridge Publishing, Inc.

Bauer, Marion Dane. Sleep, Little One, Sleep. Stammen, JoEllen McAllister, illus. 2002. 32p. (J). (ps). pap. 6.99 (978-0-689-85269-5(X) , Aladdin) Simon & Schuster Children's Publishing.

—Sleep, Little One, Sleep. 2002. (gr. k-3). lib. bdg. 15.30 (978-0-613-57328-3(5)) Tandem Library Bks.

Baum, Louis. The Mouse Who Braved Bedtime. Hellard, Sue, illus. 2006. 32p. (J). 16.95 (978-1-58234-691-5(7) , Bloomsbury Children) Bloomsbury Publishing.

Baver, Marion Dane. Sleep, Little One, Sleep. Stammen, JoEllen McAllister, illus. 2005. 29p. (J). (gr. k-3). reprint ed. 16.00 (978-0-7567-9641-9(5)) DIANE Publishing Co.

Bea, Holly. Bless Your Heart. Howard, Kim, illus. 2001. 32p. (J). (ps-1). 16.00 (978-0-915811-94-6(4)) Kramer, H.J. Inc.

Beaudoin, Beau. The Url King. 2006. (Illus.). 56p. (J). per. 15.95 (***978-0-9788401-0-5(0)***) Red Ink Pr.

Beaumont, Karen. Baby Danced the Polka. Plecas, Jennifer, illus. 2004. 32p. (J). (ps). 12.99 (978-0-8037-2587-4(6) , Dial) Penguin Group (USA) Inc.

Bedford, David. Bedtime for Little Bears! Pedler, Caroline, illus. 2007. 28p. (J). (ps-2). 16.95 (***978-1-56148-587-1(X)***) Good Bks.

Bedtime for Bunny. 2001. (J). (978-1-931312-00-4(1)) Soft-Play, Inc.

Bedtime Tales. (3-Minute Treasury Ser.). 160p. (J). (978-0-7853-6329-3(7) , 7162200) Publications International, Ltd.

Bedtime with Mothergoose. 2005. (J). bds. (978-1-4194-0089-6(4)) Paradise Pr., Inc.

Beinstein, Phoebe. Dora's Bedtime Wishes. Roper, Robert, illus. 2003. (Dora the Explorer Ser.). 14p. (J). bds. 11.95 (978-0-689-85499-6(4) , Simon Spotlight/Nickelodeon) Simon & Schuster Children's Publishing.

Bennetts, Nancy. Bed Head. 2003. (Illus.). 48p. (J). 16.95 (978-0-9726004-1-5(8)) Big Valley Publishing.

Bentley, Dawn. Fuzzy Bear's Bedtime. Nagy, Krisztina, illus. 2005. (Fuzzy Bear Ser.). 10p. (J). (ps-k). act. bk. ed. 10.95 (978-1-58117-055-9(6) , Intervisual/Piggy Toes) Dalmatian Pr.

—Goodnight Bear: A Book & Night Light. Couri, Kathryn A., illus. 2005. (Stories to Share Ser.). 12p. (J). 12.95 (978-1-58117-034-4(3) , Intervisual/Piggy Toes) Dalmatian Pr.

Bercowetz, Cynthia. Grandpa Herman¿s Petting Zoo. 2007. (Illus.). 48p. (J). per. 14.95 (***978-0-9708430-9-8(7)***) Uitti, Daniel.

Berenstain, Stan & Berenstain, Jan. The Berenstain Bears' Bedtime Battle. Berenstain, Stan & Berenstain, Jan, illus. 2005. (Berenstain Bears Ser.). (Illus.). 32p. (J). (ps-2). 3.99 (978-0-06-057381-2(3) , Harper Festival) HarperCollins Pubs.

Berg, Ray. Sailing Duck. 2005. 15p. (J). 9.33 (978-1-4116-3554-8(X)) Lulu.com.

Bergman, Mara. Oliver Who Would Not Sleep! Maland, Nick, illus. 2007. (J). (***978-0-439-92827-4(3)***); 40p. pap. 16.99 (***978-0-439-92826-7(5)***) Scholastic, Inc. (Levine, Arthur A. Bks.).

Bernthal, Mark & Exclaim Entertainment Staff. Boz/Good Night Boz. Jeffords, Brandon, illus. 2006. (BOZ#8482; Ser.). 14p. (J). 4.99 (978-0-310-71206-0(8)) Zondervan.

Bilgrami, Shaheen. Icy Antics. Chambers, Sally & Ratie, Patricia, illus. 2003. (Curious Creatures Bks.). 12p. (J). bds. 12.95 (978-1-4027-0820-6(3) , Sterling/Pinwheel) Sterling Publishing Co., Inc.

Bjorkman, Steve. Good Night, Little One. Bjorkman, Steve, illus. 1999. (Illus.). 40p. (J). (ps-3). 9.99 (978-1-57856-275-6(9) , WaterBrook Pr.) WaterBrook Pr.

Blake, Chris & Charismalife. Hover Get's His Wings. 2004. 24p. (J). (gr. k-3). 9.99 (978-1-59185-452-4(0) , Charisma Kids) Strang Communications Co.

Blake, Michel. Off to Bed. Gant, Trish, illus. 2005. 16p. (J). (gr. k-ps). bds. 5.99 (978-0-7636-2766-9(6)) Candlewick Pr.

Bland, Steve. Bedtime Bear. 2001. (Phone Friends Ser.). (Illus.). 12p. (J). bds. 4.95 (978-0-7641-5380-8(3)) Barron's Educational Series, Inc.

Blase, Dean. There's an Octopus under My Bed. Ross, D., illus. 2007. 32p. (J). 16.99 (***978-0-9777651-1-9(3)***) Shake It.

Blitz, Shmuel. Bedtime Stories of Jewish Values. 1998. 48p. 14.99 (978-1-57819-195-6(5) , BEDV) Mesorah Pubns., Ltd.

—Bedtime Stories of Torah Values. 1999. 48p. 14.99 (978-1-57819-498-8(9) , BEDB) Mesorah Pubns., Ltd.

—Bedtime Stories to Make You Smile. 2003. 14.99 (978-1-57819-745-3(7) , BEDS) Mesorah Pubns., Ltd.

—A Treasury of Shabbos Bedtime Stories. 2004. (ArtScroll Youth Ser.). (Illus.). 48p. (J). 14.99 (978-1-57819-431-5(8) , BESH) Mesorah Pubns., Ltd.

Blue's Clues: Goodnight Blue. 2002. (J). pap. 9.98 incl. audio compact disk (978-0-7379-0055-2(5) , 75840) Rhino Entertainment Co, A Warner Music Group Co.

Blyton, Enid. Enid Blyton Bedtime Stories. (Bright Light Ser.). (Illus.). 224p. (J). (ps-7). 18.95 (978-1-904668-97-8(6)) Mercury Bks. Ltd. GBR. *Dist:* International Publishers Marketing.

Boelts, Maribeth. Looking for Sleepy. Pons, Bernadette, illus. 2004. 24p. (J). (ps-1). 14.95 (978-0-8075-0447-5(5)) Whitman, Albert & Co.

—Starlight Lullaby. Sarrazin, Marisol, illus. 2006. 12p. (J). 9.99 (978-1-4169-0633-9(9) , Little Simon) Simon & Schuster Children's Publishing.

Bogan, Paulette. Goodnight Lulu. 2005. 32p. (YA). pap. 6.95 (978-1-58234-983-1(5) , Bloomsbury Children) Bloomsbury Publishing.

—Goodnight Lulu. Bogan, Paulette, illus. 2003. (Illus.). 32p. (J). (ps-1). 15.95 (978-1-58234-803-2(0) , Bloomsbury Children) Bloomsbury Publishing.

Bond, Katherine Grace. Sleepy-Time Dance. 2002. 12p. 5.99 (978-0-310-70252-8(6)) Zondervan.

Bonnell, Kris. Bedtime for Carl. 2006. (J). 3.75 (***978-1-933727-26-4(8)***) Reading Reading Bks., LLC.

Bonnett-Rampersaud, Louise. Bubble & Squeak. Banta, Susan, illus. 2006. 24p. (J). 14.99 (978-0-7614-5310-9(5)) Cavendish, Marshall Corp.

Book Company Staff. Little Treasures. Francour, Kathleen, illus. 2003. (Stationery Ser.). (J). 14.95 (978-1-74047-311-8(6)) Book Co. Publishing Pty, Ltd., The AUS. *Dist:* Penton Overseas, Inc.

Bourgeois, Paulette. La Manta de Franklin. Varela, Alejandra Lopez, tr. Clark, Brenda, illus. (SPA.). (J). (gr. k-2). pap. 5.95 (978-1-880507-98-6(6) , LC30178); ring bd. 10.95 (978-1-880507-99-5(4) , LC30179) Lectorum Pubns., Inc.

Boyle, Alison. Twinkle, Twinkle, Little Star. Pichon, Liz, illus. 2000. (Finger Puppet Bks.). 16p. (J). (ps-k). 10.95 (978-1-86233-111-2(1)) Sterling Publishing Co., Inc.

Boynton, Sandra. Dinosaur's Binkit. 1998. (Illus.). 14p. (J). (ps-k). bds. 10.95 (978-0-689-82203-2(0) , Little Simon) Simon & Schuster Children's Publishing.

—The Going to Bed Book. Boynton, Sandra, illus. 14p. (J). 2006. 12.95 (978-1-4169-2794-5(8) , Little Simon); 2001. (Illus.). 4.99 (978-0-689-83623-7(6) , Simon & Schuster Children's Publishing) Simon & Schuster Children's Publishing.

—Pajama Time! 2000. (Illus.). 24p. (J). (ps). bds. 6.95 (978-0-7611-1975-3(2) , 11975) Workman Publishing Co., Inc.

—Snoozers: 7 Short Short Bedtime Stories for Lively Little Kids. 2001. (J). bds. 7.99 (978-0-689-83617-6(1) , Simon & Schuster Children's Publishing) Simon & Schuster Children's Publishing.

Boza, Eduardo Robles. Mi Amigo Se Hace Pipi... (My Friends Wets His Bed) (SPA.). (J). 4.95 (978-968-419-812-8(4)) Grijalbo, Editorial MEX. *Dist:* AIMS International Bks., Inc.

Brachfeld, Aaron & Choate, Mary. Picnics in the Wood & Other Bedtime Stories. Brachfeld, Aaron & Choate, Mary, illus. 2006. (J). im. lthr. (978-0-9785944-1-1(X)) Coastalfields.

Bradbury, Ray. Switch on the Night. Dillon, Leo & Dillon, Diane, illus. 40p. (J). (gr. k-2). 2000. 14.95 (978-0-375-80608-7(3) , Knopf Bks. for Young Readers); 2004. reprint ed. pap. 6.99 (978-0-553-11244-3(9) , Dragonfly Bks.) Random Hse. Children's Bks.

Bradford, William. Jeremy Mcbright Was Afraid of the Night. 2006. (Illus.). 36p. (J). lib. bdg. 13.95 (978-0-9672585-2-2(9)) CyPress Pubns.

Branford, Henrietta. Little Pig Figwort Can't Get to Sleep. Munoz, Claudio, illus. 2002. 32p. (J). (gr. k-3). 14.00 (978-0-618-15968-0(1) , Clarion Bks.) Houghton Mifflin Co. Trade & Reference Div.

—Six Chicks. Elfezzani, Thierry, illus. 2005. 24p. (J). pap. 8.99 (978-0-00-664767-6(7)) HarperCollins Pubs. Ltd. GBR. *Dist:* Trafalgar Square Publishing.

Bridwell, Norman. Clifford's Bedtime. (Naked Brothers Band Ser.). (J). 2008. 10p. pap. 6.99 (***978-0-545-03513-2(9)*** , Cartwheel Bks.); 2003. (SPA., Illus.). 7p. pap. 3.95 (978-0-439-54568-6(4) , Scholastic en Espanol) Scholastic, Inc.

Brown, Margaret Wise. Boa Noite Lua. pap. 19.95 (978-85-336-0713-2(X)) Livraria Martins Editora BRA. *Dist:* Distribooks, Inc.

—Bonsoir Lune.Tr. of Goodnight Moon. (FRE.). (J). pap. 21.95 (***978-2-211-01028-3(8)***) Archimede Editions FRA. *Dist:* Distribooks, Inc.

—Buenas Noches, Luna. Hurd, Clement, illus. 2002. (SPA.). 34p. (J). (ps up). bds. 8.99 (978-0-694-01651-8(9) , HC8997) HarperCollins Pubs.

—A Child's Good Night Book. 2002. (Illus.). (J). 22.91 (978-0-7587-0101-5(2)) Book Wholesalers, Inc.

—A Child's Good Night Book. (J). 12.89 (978-0-201-09155-7(0)) HarperCollins Pubs.

—Goodnight Bear. 2006. 24p. 12.99 (978-1-4037-2704-6(X)); 12p. 5.99 (978-1-4037-2706-0(6)) Dalmatian Pr.

—Goodnight Bunny. 2006. (J). 11p. 12.99 (978-1-4037-2549-3(7)); 24p. 12.99 (978-1-4037-2703-9(1)); 12p. 5.99 (978-1-4037-2705-3(8)) Dalmatian Pr.

—Goodnight Moon. 2002. (Illus.). 14.47 (978-0-7587-0015-5(6)) Book Wholesalers, Inc.

—Goodnight Moon. Hurd, Clement, illus. (J). 2005. 32p. lib. bdg. 17.89 (978-0-06-077586-5(6)); 2001. 34p. 12.99 (978-0-694-01675-4(6) , Harper Festival); 2001. 16p. 15.99 (978-0-694-01638-9(1) , Harper Festival); 60th anniv. ed. 2005. 32p. 16.99 (978-0-06-077585-8(8)) HarperCollins Pubs.

—Goodnight Moon. Hurd, Clement, illus. (J). pap. 32.75 incl. audio. 24.95 incl. audio. 2004. pap. 14.95 incl. audio (978-0-89719-775-5(5) , PRA298) Weston Woods Studios, Inc.

—Goodnight Moon: Board Book & Baby Socks. Hurd, Clement, illus. 2002. 34p. (J). (ps up). 12.99 (978-0-06-009427-0(3) , Harper Festival) HarperCollins Pubs.

—Goodnight Moon 123: A Counting Book. Hurd, Clement, illus. 2007. 32p. (J). lib. bdg. 17.89 (978-0-06-112594-2(6)); 16.99 (978-0-06-112593-5(8)) HarperCollins Pubs.

—Goodnight Moon 123/Buenas Noches, Luna 123: A Counting Book/Un Libro para Contar. Hurd, Clement, illus. 2007. (ENG & SPA.). 32p. (J). (ps-k). 16.99 (***978-0-06-117325-7(8)*** , Rayo) HarperCollins Pubs.

—Goodnight Moon Big Book. Hurd, Clement, illus. 2007. 32p. (J). pap. 24.99 (***978-0-06-111977-4(6)*** , Harper Festival) HarperCollins Pubs.

—Goodnight Moon Board Book & Bunny. Hurd, Clement, illus. 2005. 34p. (J). (ps up). bds. 14.99 (978-0-06-076027-4(3) , Harper Festival) HarperCollins Pubs.

—Goodnight Moon Board Book & Nightlight. Hurd, Clement, illus. 2003. 34p. (J). (ps up). 12.99 (978-0-06-054179-8(2) , Harper Festival) HarperCollins Pubs.

Brown, Margaret Wise. Goodnight Moon Board Book & Slippers. Hurd, Clement, illus. 2007. 34p. (J). 19.99 (***978-0-06-123902-1(X)*** , Harper Festival) HarperCollins Pubs.

Brown, Margaret Wise & Hurd, Clement. Goodnight Moon. unabr. ed. 2000. (J). pap. 7.98 incl. audio Random Hse. Audio Publishing Group.

Brown, Margaret Wise & Kahn, Si. Goodnight Moon. Hurd, Clement, illus. unabr. abr. ed. 1998. (Share a Story Ser.). (J). (ps up). 9.95 (978-0-694-70094-3(0)) HarperCollins Pubs.

Brown, Margaret Wise & Wiggins, Beth Foster. Buenas noches Conejito. 2006. 24p. (J). 12.95 (978-1-882077-63-2(6)) Sweetwater Pr.

—Buenas noches Oso. 2006. 24p. (J). 12.95 (978-1-882077-61-8(X)) Sweetwater Pr.

Brunelle, Nicholas. Snow Moon. 2005. (Illus.). 36p. (J). 15.99 (978-0-670-06024-5(0) , Viking Juvenile) Penguin Group (USA) Inc.

Brutschy, Jennifer. Just One More Story. Smith, Cat Bowman, illus. 2000. (J). lib. bdg. (978-0-531-30296-5(2) , Orchard Bks.) Scholastic, Inc.

Bryan, Jennifer. The Different Dragon. Hosler, Danamarie, illus. 2006. (J). pap. 10.95 (978-0-9674468-6-8(4)) Two Lives Publishing.

Buchholz, Quint. Duerme Bien, Pequeño Oso. 2nd ed. 2003. (Rosa y Manzana Ser.). (SPA., Illus.). 208p. 15.16 (978-84-89804-10-4(9)) Loguez Ediciones ESP. *Dist:* Lectorum Pubns., Inc.

Bullard, Lisa. Not Enough Beds. Oeltjenbruns, Joni, illus. 2004. (Carolrhoda Picture Books Ser.). 32p. (J). (ps-3). pap. 6.95 (978-1-57505-797-2(2)) Lerner Publishing Group.

—Not Enough Beds! A Christmas Alphabet Book. Oeltjenbruns, Joni, illus. 2004. (Picture Bks.). 32p. (J). (ps-3). 15.95 (978-1-57505-356-1(X) , Carolrhoda Bks.) Lerner Publishing Group.

—Not Enough Beds: A Christmas Alphabet Book. Oeltjenbruns, Joni, illus. 2004. 26p. (J). (ps-ps). lib. bdg. 13.75 (978-0-606-30541-9(6)) Tandem Library Bks.

Buller, Jon & Schade, Susan. I Love You, Good Night. Pons, Bernadette, illus. 2005. 28p. (J). 7.99 (978-0-689-86212-0(1) , Little Simon) Simon & Schuster Children's Publishing.

Bumpy Slide Books Staff. Blue's Bedtime. Nickelodeon/ Viacom International Staff, ed. 2000. (Blue's Clues: No. 10). (Illus.). 32p. (J). (ps-1). 3.49 (978-1-57973-076-5(0)) Advance Pubs. LLC.

Burke, Tina. La Cama Grande de Sofía. Burke, Tina, illus. 2008. (SPA., Illus.). 24p. (J). pap. 4.99 (***978-1-933605-78-4(2)***) Kane/Miller Bk. Pubs., Inc.

—Sophie's Big Bed. Burke, Tina, illus. 2007. (Illus.). 24p. (Orig.). (J). (ps). pap. 4.99 (***978-1-933605-48-7(0)***) Kane/Miller Bk. Pubs., Inc.

Burrows, Terry. Chiquitines Cuentos de las Bunas Noches. 2002. (Toddler's Ser.).Tr. of Stories for Bedtime. (SPA., Illus.). 78p. (J). (978-968-5308-38-0(1) , Silver Dolphin en Español) Advanced Marketing, S. de R. L. de C. V.

Butler, John. Can You Growl Like a Bear? Butler, John, illus. 2007. (Illus.). 40p. (J). (ps-1). pap. 15.95 (***978-1-56145-396-2(X)*** , Peachtree Junior) Peachtree Pubs., Ltd.

Butler, John. Hush, Little Ones. Butler, John, illus. 2002. (Illus.). 32p. (J). (ps-k). 15.95 (978-1-56145-269-9(6)) Peachtree Pubs., Ltd.

Butterworth, MyLinda. The Monster Run. Day, Linda S., ed. Mercer, Matthew, illus. l.t. ed. 2004. 32p. (J). (ps-3). 14.95 (978-1-890905-23-1(2)) Day to Day Enterprises.

Cabal, Graciela Beatriz. Cosquillas en el Ombligo. 2002. (SPA.). 64p. (J). pap. (978-1-4000-0013-5(0)) Editorial Sudamericana S.A.

Cabrera, Jane. Bear's Good Night. Cabrera, Jane, illus. 2002. (J). (gr. k-k). (Illus.). 12p. bds. 4.99 (978-0-7636-1796-7(2)); bds. 4.99 Candlewick Pr.

Candlewick Press Staff. Ghmily Ams Ed. 2002. (J). bds. 12.99 (978-0-7636-1820-9(9)) Candlewick Pr.

Captain, Cliff. Fables by the Sea, 2 vols. 2005. 145p. (J). Vol. 1. pap. (978-0-9766401-0-3(4)); Vol. 2. pap. (978-0-9766401-1-0(2)) Aenor Trust, The.

Capucilli, Alyssa Satin. Bizcocho. Mlawer, Teresa, tr. Schories, Pat, illus. 2nd ed. 2001. (Coleccion Ya Se Leer). (SPA.). 32p. (J). (ps up). pap. 4.99 (978-0-06-444310-4(8) , HC30732) HarperCollins Pubs.

—Bizcocho. 2001. (SPA.). (ps-2). lib. bdg. 12.95 (978-0-613-35909-2(7)) Tandem Library Bks.

Carlson, Nancy. Henry's Show & Tell. 2004. (Illus.). 32p. (J). (ps-1). 15.99 (978-0-670-03695-0(1) , Viking Juvenile) Penguin Group (USA) Inc.

Carlson, Nancy & Inkpen, Mick. It's bedtime, Wibbly Pig! Inkpen, Mick, illus. 2004. (Illus.). 32p. (J). (ps-1). 15.99 (978-0-670-05880-8(7) , Viking Juvenile) Penguin Group (USA) Inc.

Chaconas, Doris J. Goodnight, Dewberry Bear. 2003. (Illus.). 32p. 17.00 (978-0-687-02691-3(1)) Abingdon Pr.

Charlip, Remy. Baby Hearts & Baby Flowers. 2001. (Illus.). 24p. (J). (ps-3). 15.89 (978-0-06-029592-9(9)) HarperCollins Pubs.

Child, Lauren. I Am Not Sleepy & I Will Not Go to Bed. ed. 2004. (J). (gr. k-3). spiral bd. (978-0-616-11105-5(3)); spiral bd. (978-0-616-11104-8(5)) Canadian National Institute for the Blind/Institut National Canadien pour les Aveugles.

—I Am Not Sleepy & I Will Not Go to Bed. Child, Lauren, illus. 2001. (Illus.). 32p. (J). (ps-3). 16.99 (978-0-7636-1570-3(6)) Candlewick Pr.

—My Dream Bed. 2002. (Illus.). 18p. (J). (ps-2). pap. 15.95 (978-0-439-30912-7(3) , Levine, Arthur A. Bks.) Scholastic, Inc.

—No Tengo Sueno y No Quiero Irme a la Cama. 2002. (Illus.). (J). (gr. k-3). (CAT.). 25p. 17.95 (978-84-8488-014-1(1)); (SPA., 312p. 17.95 (978-84-8488-010-3(9) , RR0510) Serres, Ediciones, S. L. ESP. *Dist:* Lectorum Pubns., Inc.

Child, Lauren, illus. I Am Not Sleepy & I Will Not Go to Bed. 2005. (Charlie & Lola Ser.). 32p. (J). (ps-1). reprint ed. pap. 6.99 (978-0-7636-2970-0(7)) Candlewick Pr.

Chima, Ahiru & Misu, Max. Ellena__- Ellen meets Frog King - 2005. 32p. pap. 14.99 (978-1-4116-4050-4(0)) Lulu.com.

Chouette. Caillou Is Sick. rev. ed. 2005. (Abracadabra Ser.).Tr. of Caillou est Malade. (Illus.). 24p. (J). (ps-1). pap. 4.95 (978-2-89450-547-2(7)) Chouette Publishing CAN. *Dist:* Independent Pubs. Group.

Christelow, Eileen. Five Little Monkeys Play Hide-and-Seek. 2004. (Illus.). 40p. (J). (ps-k). tchr. ed. 16.00 (978-0-618-40949-5(1) , Clarion Bks.) Houghton Mifflin Co. Trade & Reference Div.

Christen, Thiel. Night & Day. 2003. (Illus.). 14p. (J). 4.95 (978-1-59466-010-8(7) , Little Ones) Port Town Publishing.

Christensen, Nancy. Good Night, Little Kitten. 2004. (My First Reader Ser.). (Illus.). 29p. (J). (gr. k-1). pap. 3.95 (978-0-516-24628-4(3) , Children's Pr.) Scholastic Library Publishing.

—Good Night, Little Kitten. Hockerman, Dennis, illus. 2003. (My First Reader Ser.). 32p. (J). 18.50 (978-0-516-22926-3(5) , Children's Pr.) Scholastic Library Publishing.

Chronicle Books LLC Staff. Paul Frank Picturebook 1. 2008. (J). 12.95 (978-0-8118-6024-6(8)) Chronicle Bks. LLC.

Clark, Matthew. SongrrrLines: A Beastie Bedtime Dreaming, & Coloring Book. 2005. 26p. (J). pap. 8.95 net. (978-1-59975-106-1(2)) Independent Pub.

Conover, David & Conover, Patricia. Humphrey the Hugganite. Acker, I. M., illus. 2000. 32p. (J). (ps-3). pap. 7.99 (978-0-9677987-0-7(1)) Hugganite Publishing.

—Humphrey the Hugganite: Book/Toy Edition. Acker, I. M., illus. 2nd ed. 2000. 32p. (J). (ps-3). pap. 19.98 (978-0-9677987-2-1(8)) Hugganite Publishing.

Conrad, Liz, illus. Bedtime Bear. 1999. (J). (978-1-892374-26-4(9)) Weldon Owen, Inc.

—Bedtime Bear. 1999. 20p. (J). reprint ed. 16.95 (978-1-892374-28-8(5)) Weldon Owen, Inc.

Cook, Sally. Good Night Pillow Fight. Cornell, Laura, illus. 2004. 32p. (J). lib. bdg. 16.89 (978-0-06-205190-5(3) , Cotler, Joanna Books) HarperCollins Pubs.

Cooley, Judy. I Love You More. 2007. 32p. 9.95 (***978-1-59038-758-0(9)***); 2005. (Illus.). 29p. (J). 17.95 (978-1-59038-432-9(6)) Deseret Bk. Co. (Shadow Mountain).

Cooper, Elisha. A Good Night Walk. 2005. (Illus.). 40p. (J). pap. 16.99 (978-0-439-68783-6(7) , Orchard Bks.) Scholastic, Inc.

Cooper, Helen. Boy Who Wouldn't Go to Bed. 2000. (gr. k-3). lib. bdg. 14.15 (978-0-613-33679-6(8)) Tandem Library Bks.

—The Boy Who Wouldn't Go to Bed: Pictures & Story. Cooper, Helen, illus. 2000. (Illus.). 32p. (J). (ps-2). pap. 5.99 (978-0-14-056771-7(2) , Puffin) Penguin Group (USA) Inc.

Cosby, Bill. One Dark & Scary Night. 1999. (Little Bill Books for Beginning Readers Ser.). (J). (gr. k-3). pap. 47.88 (978-0-439-04655-8(6) , Cartwheel Bks.) Scholastic, Inc.

—One Dark & Scary Night. 1999. (Little Bill Books for Beginning Readers Ser.). (J). (gr. k-3). (978-0-606-15831-2(6)) Tandem Library Bks.

—One Dark & Scary Night: Level. 3. Honeywood, Varnette P., illus. 1999. (Little Bill Books for Beginning Readers Ser.: No. 7). 40p. (J). (gr. k-3). pap. 3.99 (978-0-590-51476-7(8) , Cartwheel Bks.) Scholastic, Inc.

Cosby, Bill & Honeywood, Varnette P. One Dark & Scary Night. 1999. (Little Bill Books for Beginning Readers Ser.). (Illus.). (J). (gr. k-3). pap. 13.95 (978-0-590-51475-0(X)) Scholastic, Inc.

Costales, Amy. Hello Night: Hola Noche. McDonald, Mercedes, illus. 2007. (ENG & SPA.). 24p. 12.95 (***978-0-87358-927-7(0)*** , Luna Rising) Northland Publishing.

Cousins, Lucy. Bedtime. 1999. (gr. k-3). lib. bdg. 11.00 (978-0-613-21186-4(3)) Tandem Library Bks.

—Maisy Goes to Bed. Cousins, Lucy, illus. ed. 2006. 14p. (J). (ps). 4.99 (978-0-7636-3123-9(X)) Candlewick Pr.

—Maisy's Bedtime. Cousins, Lucy, illus. 1999. (Maisy Bks.). (Illus.). 24p. (J). pap. 3.99 (978-0-7636-0908-5(0)) Candlewick Pr.

Cowley, Joy. The Bedtime Train. Odone, Jamison, illus. 2008. (J). (***978-1-59078-493-8(6)*** , Front Street) Boyds Mills Pr.

Cox, Phil Roxbee & Cartwright, S. Sam Sheep Can't Sleep. 2004. (Phonics Board Bks.). 10p. (J). 4.99 (978-0-7945-0060-3(9) , Usborne) EDC Publishing.

Cratzius, Barbara & Thonissen, Uta. Good Night, Sleep Tight! 2004. (Illus.). 16p. (J). bds. 5.99 (978-1-59384-040-2(3)) Parklane Publishing.

Crelin, Bob. There Once Was Sky Full of Stars. 2006. 232p. pap. 17.95 (978-1-931559-37-9(6)) Sky Publishing.

Croll, Carolyn & Maday, Jane, illus. Bedtime Hugs. 2001. (My First Treasury Ser.). 38p. (J). bds. 7.98 (978-0-7853-4858-0(1) , 7131200) Publications International, Ltd.

Curtis, Susan. Baa Baa Bedtime. Samuel, Janet, illus. 2007. 24p. (J). 14.99 (978-1-4169-3836-1(2) , Little Simon) Simon & Schuster Children's Publishing.

Daddo, Andrew. Goodnight, Me. Quay, Emma, illus. 2007. 32p. (J). (ps). 11.95 (***978-1-59990-153-4(6)***) Bloomsbury Publishing.

Dale, Penny. Ten in the Bed. Dale, Penny, illus. 2007. (Illus.). 24p. (J). (gr. k-ps). bds. 5.99 (***978-0-7636-3514-5(6)***) Candlewick Pr.

Dalmatian Press Staff. Best Loved Bedtime Stories: Keepsake Treasury. 2004. (Keepsake Treasuries Ser.). (Illus.). 224p. (J). 10.99 (978-1-4037-0771-0(5)) Dalmatian Pr.

Dalmatian Press Staff, ed. Bedtime Bear: Sweet Dreams. (Care Bearstm Ser.). 6p. (J). bds. 9.99 (978-1-4037-0556-3(9)) Dalmatian Pr.

—Sleep Tight. Prebenna, David, illus. rev. ed. 2006. 24p. (J). pap. 3.50 (978-1-4037-2184-6(X)) Dalmatian Pr.

Danis, Naomi. Splish-Splash, into the Bath! Kreloff, Elliot, illus. 2007. 16p. (J). (***978-1-59354-609-0(2)***) Handprint Bks.

Davis, Buddy. Whale of a Story: Adventures on the High Seas. 2003. 40p. (J). 14.99 (978-0-89051-390-3(2)) Master Bks.

de Vries, Maggie. How Sleep Found Tabitha. Lott, Sheena, illus. 2002. 32p. (J). (ps-2). 16.95 (978-1-55143-193-2(9)) Orca Bk. Pubs. USA.

Dealey, Erin. Little Bo Peep Can't Get to Sleep. Wakiyama, Hanako, illus. 2005. 40p. (J). 15.95 (978-0-689-84099-9(3) , Atheneum) Simon & Schuster Children's Publishing.

DeJohnette-Harvin, Yvonne. Bed Time Blues. 2003. pap. 14.00 (978-0-8059-6014-3(7)) Dorrance Publishing Co., Inc.

Demers, Dominique. Every Single Night. Debon, Nicolas, illus. 2006. 32p. (J). 17.95 (978-0-88899-699-2(3)) Groundwood Bks. CAN. *Dist:* Perseus Distribution.

Denton, P. J. The Trouble with Brothers. Denos, Julia, illus. 2007. (Sleepover Squad Ser.). 96p. (J). (gr. 1-4). pap. 3.99 (***978-1-4169-2800-3(6)*** , Aladdin) Simon & Schuster Children's Publishing.

DePrisco, Dorothea & Barnard, Lucy. Lullaby & Good Night. 2006. 12.95 (978-1-58117-450-2(0) , Intervisual/ Piggy Toes) Dalmatian Pr.

Devernois, Elsa. Una Vez Mas. Gay, Michel, illus. (SPA.). 32p. (J). 7.16 (978-84-95150-32-5(8)) Corimbo, Editorial S.L. ESP. *Dist:* Lectorum Pubns., Inc.

Dewan, Ted. Bing: Bed Time. 2004. 24p. (J). (gr. k-ps). 5.99 (978-0-385-75045-5(5) , Fickling, David Bks.) Random Hse. Children's Bks.

DiPucchio, Kelly S. Bed Hogs. Fine, Howard, illus. 2004. 32p. (ps-k). 15.99 (978-0-7868-1884-6(0)) Hyperion Bks. for Children.

Disney Press, ed. Disney Bedtime Favorites. rev. ed. 2007. 304p. (gr. k-17). 15.99 (***978-1-4231-0440-7(4)***) Disney Pr.

Ditchfield, Christin. Cowlick! Beardshaw, Rosalind, illus. 2007. (Deluxe Golden Book Ser.). 40p. (J). (ps-k). 14.99 (978-0-375-83540-7(7) , Golden Bks.) Random Hse. Children's Bks.

DK Publishing Staff. Lullaby & Goodnight. 2007. 12p. (J). (ps-2). 12.99 (***978-0-7566-3092-8(4)***) Dorling Kindersley Publishing, Inc.

Dodds, Dayle Ann. The Prince Won't Go to Bed. Brooker, Kyrsten, illus. 2007. 32p. (J). (ps-1). 16.00 (978-0-374-36108-2(8)) Farrar, Straus & Giroux.

Donald, Diana. My Special Angel: A Bedtime Story. Polito, Mike, illus. 31p. incl. audio compact disk (978-1-894290-01-2(1)) Heart of the Matter Publishing.

Doyle, Malachy. One, Two, Three O'Leary. Hillenbrand, Will, tr. Hillenbrand, Will, illus. 2004. 32p. (J). 15.95 (978-0-689-85513-9(3) , McElderry, Margaret K.) Simon & Schuster Children's Publishing.

Dragonwagon, Crescent. Is This a Sack of Potatoes? Stock, Catherine, illus. 2002. 32p. (J). (ps-k). 15.95 (978-0-7614-5089-4(0)) Cavendish, Marshall Corp.

Dubow, Jeremy. Margaret. Dubow, Jeremy, illus. 2006. (Illus.). 32p. 12.95 (978-1-888045-18-5(3)) Action Publishing, LLC.

Dulaney, Kim L. My Lost Dream. 1999. (Fuzzy-Feeling Bks.). (J). pap. 8.25 (978-1-891636-07-3(3)) Unique Expression.

Dunbar, Joyce. Tell Me Something Happy Before I Go to Sleep, Set. Gliori, Debi, illus. gif. ed. 2003. (Lullaby Lights Ser.). 32p. (J). 16.95 (978-0-15-204756-6(5) , Red Wagon Bks.) Harcourt Children's Bks.

Duncan, Lois. I Walk at Night. Johnson, Steve & Fancher, Lou, illus. 2002. 32p. (J). (gr. k-3). pap. 6.99 (978-0-14-230090-9(X) , Puffin) Penguin Group (USA) Inc.

Dunnick, Regan. Sweet Dreams Douglas. Dunnick, Regan, illus. 2002. (Illus.). (J). (ps-2). 16.95 (978-0-9632421-3-6(X)) Junior League of Houston, Inc.

Dwyer, Mindy. Just Close Your Eyes. 2005. (J). (978-0-88240-592-6(6)); pap. (978-0-88240-593-3(4)) Graphic Arts Ctr. Publishing Co. (Alaska Northwest Bks.).

Dyer, Heather. The GIRL with the BROKEN WIND. 2007. 160p. (J). pap. 4.99 (***978-0-439-74828-5(3)*** , Scholastic Paperbacks) Scholastic, Inc.

Edvall, Lilian. The Rabbit Who Didn't Want to Go to Sleep. Dyssegaard, Elisabeth Kallick, tr. from SWE. Gimbergsson, Sara, illus. 2004. 32p. (J). 15.00 (978-91-29-66001-2(7)) R & S Bks. SWE. *Dist:* Macmillan.

Edwards, Frank B. Nightgown Countdown. 1999. (gr. k-3). lib. bdg. 12.95 (978-0-613-37019-6(8)) Tandem Library Bks.

Edwards, Helen L. Clara's Imagination. Doggett, Al, illus. 2005. 19.95 (978-0-9765414-0-0(8)) Bad Publishing.

Edwards, Nicola. Goodnight Baxter. 2004. (Illus.). 28p. (J). (ps-3). 12.95 (978-0-7624-1725-4(0) , Running Pr. Kids) Running Pr. Bk. Pubs.

Ellis, Kiersten. Do Planets Hang on Strings? 2006. 24p. (J). per. 11.99 (***978-1-59886-688-9(5)***); 14.99 (***978-1-59886-992-7(2)***) Tate Publishing & Enterprises, L.L.C.

Ells, Marcia Louise. Glips, Snodagers & Wallywogs. Ells, Marcia Louise, illus. l.t. ed. 2006. (Illus.). 44p. (J). 6.99 (978-0-9777359-0-7(7)) Marcia's Menagerie.

Elsohn, Michael & Long, Sylvia. Snug as a Bug. 2004. (Illus.). 32p. (J). 13.95 (978-0-8118-4245-7(2)) Chronicle Bks. LLC.

Emberley, Ed. Go Away, Big Green Monster! Make the Monster Disappear! 2005. 32p. (J). 10.99 (978-0-316-01104-4(5)) Little Brown & Co.

Emmons, Katherine M. & Roman, Claire. Oh, Brother! Disney Storybook Artists Staff, illus. 2007. 24p. (J). (ps-2). pap. 3.99 (978-0-7364-2432-5(6) , RH/Disney) Random Hse. Children's Bks.

England, Brooke. Guardian Fairies. 2006. 17p. 12.00 (978-1-4116-7923-8(7)) Lulu.com.

Englemann-Berner, Beth. The Good Knight Night Book: A Picture Riddle Book. Riggs, Jenna, illus. 2005. 10p. (J). (ps-7). 9.95 (978-1-58117-420-5(9) , Intervisual/Piggy Toes) Dalmatian Pr.

Entara Ltd. Staff, photos by. Time for Bed. 2006. (Jakers! Ser.). 24p. (J). pap. 3.99 (978-0-689-87737-7(4) , Simon Spotlight) Simon & Schuster Children's Publishing.

Faith, Susan. Purple Puppy. Offner, Naomi, illus. 2005. 32p. (J). 19.95 (978-0-9707793-0-4(5)) Purple People, Inc.

Fancher, Lou. Star Climbing. Johnson, Steve, illus. 2006. 32p. (J). 15.99 (978-0-06-073901-0(0)); lib. bdg. 16.89 (978-0-06-073902-7(9)) HarperCollins Pubs. (Geringer, Laura Book).

Faris, Debi. Kaya & Nannas First Excellent Adventur. 2006. pap. 18.99 (***978-1-4259-7780-1(4)***) AuthorHouse.

Faulkner, Keith. The Scared Little Bear: A Not Too Scary Pop up Book. Lambert, Jonathan, illus. 2000. 16p. (J). (ps-2). bds. 9.95 (978-0-531-30267-5(9) , Orchard Bks.) Scholastic, Inc.

Fernandes, Eugenie. Sleepy Little Mouse. Ferandes, Kim, illus. unabr. ed. 2002. (Little Mice Ser.). 24p. (J). (ps-k). (978-1-55074-703-4(7)) Kids Can Pr., Ltd.

—Sleepy Little Mouse. 2002. (ps-2). lib. bdg. 14.10 (978-0-613-81789-9(3)) Tandem Library Bks.

Ferreri, Della Ross. How Will I Ever Sleep in This Bed? Mazille, Capucine, illus. 2007. 24p. (J). bds. 5.95 (978-1-4027-4324-5(6)); 2005. 32p. 12.95 (978-1-4027-1492-4(0)) Sterling Publishing Co., Inc.

Ferreri, Della Ross. Huggle Wuggle Bedtime Snuggle. 2008. (J). 14.95 (***978-0-87358-937-6(8)***) Northland Publishing.

Ferri, Francesca, illus. Good Night, Teddy. 2003. 8p. (J). 14.95 (978-0-7641-2595-9(8)) Barron's Educational Series, Inc.

Fields, Sherry. Molly Magrew & the Pencil Crew. Horn, Isaac, illus. 1999. 12p. (J). 8.95 (978-1-930482-00-5(0)) Fields Enterprises, Inc.

Firth, Barbara, illus. Can't You Sleep, Little Bear? 2002. (Little Bear Picture Bks.). (J). 13.83 (978-0-7587-2185-3(4)) Book Wholesalers, Inc.

Fleming, Maria. Word Family Tales -Eep: To Sleep, Count Sheep. Pillo, Cary, illus. 2002. (Word Family Tales Ser.). 16p. (ps-2). pap. 2.95 (978-0-439-26268-2(2)) Scholastic, Inc.

Fore, S. J. Tiger Can't Sleep. Alley, R. W., illus. 2006. 32p. (J). 15.99 (978-0-670-06078-8(X) , Viking Juvenile) Penguin Group (USA) Inc.

Forgas, Christine. After Dark. Forgas-Davis, Mellssa, illus. 2004. 17p. (J). (gr. 1-6). pap. (978-1-930200-27-2(7)) Martell Publishing Co.

Fowles, Shelley. Climbing Rosa. 2006. (Illus.). 32p. (J). 15.95 (978-1-84507-079-3(8)) Lincoln, Frances Ltd. GBR. *Dist:* Perseus Distribution.

Fox, Diane, et al. Goodnight PiggyWiggy: A Pull-the-Page Book. Fox, Christyan, illus. 2000. 24p. (J). (ps-k). 12.95 (978-1-929766-06-2(8)) Handprint Bks.

Fox, Mem. Time for Bed. 2002. (Illus.). (J). 23.40 (978-0-7587-3813-4(7)) Book Wholesalers, Inc.

—Time for Bed. braille ed. 2004. (Illus.). (J). (gr. 1). spiral bd., bds. (978-0-616-01863-7(0)) Canadian National Institute for the Blind/Institut National Canadien pour les Aveugles.

—Time for Bed. Dyer, Jane, illus. 2005. 28p. (J). bds. 10.95 (978-0-15-205349-9(2) , Red Wagon Bks.) Harcourt Children's Bks.

—Time for Bed. 2003. (J). 12.99 (978-0-15-204964-5(9)) Harcourt Trade Pubs.

—Where the Giant Sleeps. Radunsky, Vladimir, illus. 2007. 32p. (J). (ps-2). 16.00 (978-0-15-205785-5(4)) Harcourt Trade Pubs.

Fox, Sabrina. Who Can Help Me Sleep? Rothan, Ann, illus. 2004. 32p. (ps-3). 16.95 (978-1-885394-36-1(5)) Amber Lotus Publishing.

Frazee, Marla. Hush, Little Baby: A Folk Song with Pictures. 2003. (Illus.). 40p. (J). (ps-ps). pap., pap. 6.00 (978-0-15-204761-0(1) , Voyager Bks./Libros Viajeros) Harcourt Children's Bks.

Frazier, Craig. There Is a Monkey in My Drawers! 2003. (Illus.). 24p. (J). (ps-k). 14.95 (978-1-932026-10-8(X)) Graphis, U.S., Inc.

Frederick, Heather Vogel. Calamity Wayne at the O.K. Corral. Brown, Kathryn, illus. 2007. (J). (978-0-15-205789-3(7)) Harcourt Trade Pubs.

Freedman, Claire. Good Night, Sleep Tight. Tyger, Rory, illus. 2003. 32p. (J). (ps-1). 14.95 (978-0-8109-4513-5(4)) Abrams, Harry N. , Inc.

—Good Night, Sleep Tight! Tyger, Rory, illus. 2007. 32p. (J). pap. 6.95 (***978-1-58925-405-3(8)*** , tiger tales) ME Media LLC.

—Hushabye Lily. Bendall-Brunello, John, illus. 2003. 32p. (J). (ps-1). pap. 15.95 (978-0-439-47106-0(0) , Orchard Bks.) Scholastic, Inc.

—Night-Night, Emily! Massey, Jane, illus. 2005. 32p. (J). 6.95 (978-1-58925-390-2(6) , tiger tales) ME Media LLC.

—Night-Night, Emily! Massey, Jane, tr. Massey, Jane, illus. 2003. 32p. (J). (ps-1). tchr. ed. 15.95 (978-1-58925-032-1(X) , tiger tales) ME Media LLC.

Freedman, Claire. Snuggle up, Sleepy Ones. Macnaughton, Tina, illus. 28p. (J). (ps). 2007. bds. 8.95 (***978-1-56148-562-8(4));*** 2005. 16.00 (978-1-56148-475-1(X)) Good Bks.

French, Vivian. The Daddy Goose Treasury. Collins, Ross, illus. 2006. 96p. (J). pap. 18.99 (978-0-439-79608-8(3) , Chicken Hse., The) Scholastic, Inc.

Friedman, Rainey L. Monsters in Your Bed... Monsters in Your Head. Dill, Betsy, illus. 1999. 32p. (J). 15.95 (978-0-9666199-1-(9)) DreamDog Pr.

Funke, Cornelia. The Wildest Brother. Latsch, Oliver, tr. from GER. Meyer, Kerstin, illus. 2006. 32p. (J). pap. 16.99 (978-0-439-82862-8(7) , Chicken Hse., The) Scholastic, Inc.

Gabriel, Andrea. My Favorite Bear. Gabriel, Andrea, illus. 2004. (Illus.). 32p. (J). pap. 6.95 (978-1-58089-039-7(3)) Charlesbridge Publishing, Inc.

—My Favorite Bear. 2003. (Illus.). 32p. (J). 15.95 (978-1-58089-038-0(5)) Charlesbridge Publishing, Inc.

Gabriel, Ashala. Night Night Toes: A Lift-the-Flap Story. Porter, Sue, illus. 2002. 24p. (J). (ps-k). 12.95 (978-0-689-85089-9(1) , Little Simon) Simon & Schuster Children's Publishing.

Gaines, Simon Ludvigsen. Good Night, Sleep Tight. 2007. (Little Scholastic Ser.). (Illus.). 24p. (J). (ps). bds. 9.99 (***978-0-439-86726-9(6)*** , Cartwheel Bks.) Scholastic, Inc.

Gallardo, Miguel & Bermejo, Victoria. Cuentos para Contar en 1 Minuto. 2001. (SPA., Illus.). 96p. 17.95 (978-84-7901-724-8(4) , 8100) RBA Libros, S.A. ESP. *Dist:* Santillana USA Publishing Co., Inc.

Gamble, Adam. Good Night Arizona. Hansen, Red, illus. 2008. (Good Night Our World Ser.). 20p. (J). bds. 9.95 (***978-1-60219-000-9(3))*** Our World of Books.

—Good Night California. Kelly, Cooper, illus. 2008. (Good Night Our World Ser.). 24p. (J). bds. 9.95 (***978-1-60219-021-4(6))*** Our World of Books.

—Good Night Tennessee. Veno, Joe, illus. 2007. (Good Night Our World Ser.). 20p. (J). bds. 9.95 (***978-1-60219-019-1(4))*** Our World of Books.

—Good Night Texas. Hansen, Red, illus. 2007. (Good Night Our World Ser.). 20p. (J). bds. 9.95 (***978-1-60219-015-3(1))*** Our World of Books.

Garis, Howard Roger. The Curlytops on Star Island. 2005. 26.95 (978-1-4218-1467-4(6)); 192p. pap. 11.95 (978-1-4218-1567-1(2)) 1st World Publishing, Inc. (1st World Library - Literary Society).

—The Curlytops on Star Island. 2004. reprint ed. pap. 1.99 (978-1-4192-5843-5(5)) Kessinger Publishing, LLC.

—Listen & Read Uncle Wiggily Stories. 1998. (Illus.). 66p. (gr. 3-6). pap. 7.95 (978-0-486-40102-7(2)) Dover Pubns., Inc.

Garis, Howard Roger. Lulu Alice & Jimmie Wibblewobble. 2006. 77.99 (***978-1-4280-3866-0(3));*** pap. 71.99 (***978-1-4280-3854-7(X))*** IndyPublish.com.

Gassett, John D. Little John - The Webb City Kid. Skrzeczkoski, Jeanne & Andrews, Erica, illus. 1999. 125p. (J). (gr. 1-8). pap. (978-0-9671895-0-5(0)) Gassett, John D.

Gay, Marie-Louise. Estela, Princesa de la Noche. 2006. Tr. of Stella Princess of the Sky. (SPA.). (J). (gr. 1-2). 10.99 (978-980-257-304-2(3) , EK33231) Ekare, Ediciones VEN. *Dist:* Lectorum Pubns., Inc.

—Good Night, Sam. 2003. (Stella Ser.). (Illus.). 24p. (J). 14.95 (978-0-88899-530-8(X)) Groundwood Bks. CAN. *Dist:* Perseus Distribution.

Gay, Michel. Zee Is Not Scared. Mianowski, Marie, tr. from FRE. 2004. (Illus.). 32p. (J). (gr. k-ps). tchr. ed. 15.00 (978-0-618-43931-7(5) , Clarion Bks.) Houghton Mifflin Co. Trade & Reference Div.

Geiger, Lorraine Lynch. A Wild & Woolly Night. Vargo, Sharon, illus. 2007. (J). (***978-1-891795-25-1(2))*** RGU Group, The.

Geisert, Arthur. Lights Out. 2005. (Illus.). 32p. (J). (gr. k-3). 16.00 (978-0-618-47892-7(2) , Walter Lorraine) Houghton Mifflin Co. Trade & Reference Div.

Gerber, Carole. Baa Baa Black Sheep. Husted, Marty, illus. 2004. 26p. (J). bds. 6.95 (978-1-58089-089-2(X)) Charlesbridge Publishing, Inc.

—Blizzard. Husted, Marty, illus. 2001. (J). pap. (978-1-58089-065-6(2)); 15.95 (978-1-58089-064-9(4)) Charlesbridge Publishing, Inc.

—Firefly Night. Husted, Marty, illus. 2000. 32p. (J). (ps-1). 16.95 (978-1-58089-051-9(2)); pap. 6.95 (978-1-58089-066-3(0)) Charlesbridge Publishing, Inc.

—Firefly Night. Husted, Marty, illus. 2000. (J). (ps-3). lib. bdg. 15.25 (978-0-613-35117-1(7)) Tandem Library Bks.

—Firefly Night. 2000. (J). (978-0-606-19687-1(0)) Tandem Library Bks.

Gil, Alejandra & Magnasco, Carlos. Mystery in the Depth of My Bed. 2005. (Illus.). 28p. (J). (ps-ps). 12.95 (978-9974-7896-2-3(1)) Hardenville SA URY. *Dist:* Independent Pubs. Group.

Ginsburg, Mirra. The Sun's Asleep Behind the Hill. 2000. (J). (978-0-606-20297-8(8)) Tandem Library Bks.

Glass, Julie. Counting Sheep. 2000. (Illus.). (J). 11.99 (978-0-375-90658-9(4)); 32p. pap. 3.99 Random Hse. Children's Bks.

—Counting Sheep. Wohnoutka, Mike, illus. 2000. (Step into Reading Ser.). (J). 10.79 (978-0-606-19890-5(3)) Tandem Library Bks.

Gliori, Debi. Bedtime Stories. 2005. (Illus.). 80p. (J). 19.99 (978-0-7566-1466-9(X)) Dorling Kindersley Publishing, Inc.

—Flora's Blanket. Gliori, Debi, illus. 2001. (Illus.). 32p. (J). (ps-1). pap. 15.95 (978-0-531-30305-4(5) , Orchard Bks.) Scholastic, Inc.

—Siempre Te Querre. 2001. (SPA., Illus.). 32p. (J). (gr. k-2). (978-84-480-1632-6(7) , TM7120) Timun Mas, Editorial S.A. ESP. *Dist:* Lectorum Pubns., Inc.

—Un Sueno Magico. Eroles, Elena, tr. Gliori, Debi, illus. 2001. (SPA., Illus.). (J). (gr. k-2). 12.95 (978-84-480-1670-8(X) , TM30442) Timun Mas, Editorial S.A. ESP. *Dist:* Planeta Publishing Corp.

Glitz, Angelika. A Monster under Alex's Bed. Kerntke, Felix, tr. from GER. Sonnichsen, Imke, illus. 2002. 32p. (J). pap. 5.95 (978-1-58925-373-5(6) , tiger tales) ME Media LLC.

—Monster under Alex's Bed. 2002. (gr. k-3). lib. bdg. 14.10 (978-0-613-62803-7(9)) Tandem Library Bks.

Going to Bed: First Wave Satellite Individual Title Six-Packs. (Sails Literacy Ser.). 16p. (gr. k up). 27.00 (978-0-7578-6854-2(1)) Rigby Education.

Golden Books Staff. Sleepytime Tales. 2006. (Little Golden Book Treasury Ser.). (Illus.). 224p. (J). (gr. k-k). 10.95 (978-0-375-83848-4(1) , Golden Bks.) Random Hse. Children's Bks.

Good night, baby - tummy Time. 2007. 8p. (J). 12.95 (***978-1-59764-295-8(9))*** New Line Bks.

Good Night Elmo. 2001. (Illus.). (J). 7.98 (978-0-7853-4795-8(X)) Publications International, Ltd.

Goodbye to Bedtime Fears. 2006. (978-0-9777203-3-0(0)) Brenner Publishing, LLC.

Goodnight Barney. 2001. (Illus.). (J). 7.95 (978-0-7853-4752-1(6)) Publications International, Ltd.

Goodnight, I Wish You Goodnight. (Illus.). (J). (978-1-930948-82-2(4)) Apple Pie Pubs.

Goodnight Moon. 2004. (J). 24.95 incl. audio (978-0-89719-774-8(7)); pap. 32.75 incl. audio (978-1-55592-233-7(3)); pap. 32.75 incl. audio (978-1-55592-234-4(1)) Weston Woods Studios, Inc.

Goodnight Pooh. 2001. (Illus.). (J). 7.98 (978-0-7853-4788-0(7)) Publications International, Ltd.

Gordon, Jeffie Ross. Two Badd Babies. Demarest, Chris L., illus. 2003. 32p. (J). (gr. k-2). pap. 8.95 (978-1-56397-895-1(4)) Boyds Mills Pr.

Gordon, Lynn. 52 Series: Sleepytime Rituals. Johnson, Karen, illus. 2005. 6.95 (978-0-8118-4484-0(6)) Chronicle Bks. LLC.

Got, Yves. Sweet Dreams, Sam. 2000. (Illus.). 14p. (J). (ps). 9.95 (978-0-8118-2985-4(5)) Chronicle Bks. LLC.

Grayson, Barry/Scott. Twisted Yarns: Bedtime Stories for Hip Kids. 2007. (Illus.). 40p. (J). pap. (***978-0-9774357-1-5(7))*** Grayson, Kate.

Greenstein, Elaine. Dreaming. 2000. (Illus.). 32p. (J). (ps-k). pap. 15.95 (978-0-439-06302-9(7) , Levine, Arthur A. Bks.) Scholastic, Inc.

—One Child Dreaming. 2000. (Illus.). (J). (978-0-439-06303-6(5)) Itsy Bitsy Entertainment Co.

Grosset and Dunlap Staff. Night-Night, Baby: A Touch & Feel Book. Hathon, Elizabeth, photos by. 2000. (Illus.). 12p. (J). (ps-k). bds. 6.99 (978-0-448-42296-1(4) , Grosset & Dunlap) Penguin Group (USA) Inc.

Gutman, Anne. Penelope Says Good Night. Hallensleben, Georg, illus. 2006. 12p. (J). pap. 9.99 (978-0-439-67359-4(3) , Cartwheel Bks.) Scholastic, Inc.

Guy, Ginger Foglesong. Go Back to Bed! Bernardin, James, illus. 2006. (J). 15.95 (978-1-57505-750-7(6) , Carolrhoda Bks.) Lerner Publishing Group.

Gwent (Wales), Staff Development Unit Staff & Acen Staff, contrib. by. Nos Da, Arthur. 2005. (WEL., Illus.). 8p. (978-1-874049-31-9(9)) Acen Limited.

Hachler, Bruno. What Does My Teddy Bear Do All Night? Muller, Birte, illus. 2005. 32p. (J). (ps-2). 14.99 (978-0-698-40029-0(1) , Minedition) Penguin Group (USA) Inc.

Hague, Kathleen. Good Night, Fairies. Hague, Michael, illus. 2002. 40p. (J). (ps-2). 16.99 (978-1-58717-134-5(1) , SeaStar Bks.) Chronicle Bks. LLC.

—Good Night Fairies. Hague, Michael, illus. 2006. 40p. (J). pap. 6.95 (978-0-8118-5762-8(X)) Chronicle Bks. LLC.

Hall, Rohan. The Little Boy. 2005. (Illus.). 34p. (J). 14.95 (978-0-9729187-7-0(9)) Eye Contact Media.

Hang Around Bedtime Stories. (Bedtime Stories Ser.). 6p. (J). bds. (978-2-89393-981-0(3)); bds. (978-2-89393-983-4(X)) Phidal Publishing, Inc./Editions Phidal, Inc.

Harper, Jamie. Night Night, Baby Bundt: A Recipe for Bedtime. Harper, Jamie, illus. 2007. (Illus.). 24p. (J). (gr. k-ps). bds. 6.99 (***978-0-7636-3239-7(2))*** Candlewick Pr.

Harris, Emma. Bedtime, Little Monsters! Cherrill, Paul, illus. 2002. 20p. (J). tchr. ed. 14.95 (978-1-58925-689-7(1) , tiger tales) ME Media LLC.

Harris, Robie H. I'm Not Sleepy! Hollander, Nicole, illus. 2005. (Just Being Me Ser.: Vol. 2). 32p. (J). (ps-1). 7.99 (978-0-316-10941-3(X)) Little Brown & Co.

Harris, Robie H. Maybe a Bear Ate It! Emberley, Michael, illus. 2008. (Jewel Fairies Ser.). 40p. (J). pap. 15.99 (***978-0-439-92961-5(X)*** , Orchard Bks.) Scholastic, Inc.

Harry Hamster & his Bedtime. 2004. (Play Pals Ser.). (Illus.). 12p. (J). bds. (978-1-84229-645-5(0)) Top That! Publishing PLC.

Hartinger, Brent. Dreamquest: Tales of Slumberia. 2007. 160p. (J). (gr. 8 up). 16.95 (***978-0-7653-1397-3(9)*** , Starscape) Doherty, Tom Assocs., LLC.

Hawley, Greg. Don't Let the Bedbugs Bite. Regan, Dana, illus. 2004. (J). (978-0-9657612-7-7(4)) Paddle Wheel Publishing.

Hayes, Geoffrey. A Night-Light for Bunny. Date not set. 32p. (J). (ps-3). pap. 5.99 (978-0-06-443728-8(0)) HarperCollins Pubs.

—A Night-Light for Bunny. Hayes, Geoffrey, illus. 2004. (Illus.). 32p. (J). (ps-3). 14.99 (978-0-06-029163-1(X)) HarperCollins Pubs.

Hemingway, Edward. Bump in the Night. 2008. 32p. (J). (ps-k). 15.99 (***978-0-399-24761-3(0)*** , Putnam Juvenile) Penguin Group (USA) Inc.

Henderson, Kathy. 15 Ways to Go to Bed. 1999. (Illus.). 32p. (J). (ps-3). pap. (978-0-7112-0589-5(2)) Lincoln, Frances Ltd. GBR. *Dist:* Transition Vendor.

Henderson, Kathy, ed. The Bedtime Book. Ives, Penny, illus. 2004. 72p. (J). pap. 10.95 (978-1-84507-139-4(5)) Lincoln, Frances Ltd. GBR. *Dist:* Perseus Distribution.

Hendry, Diana. Very Noisy Night. 2001. (gr. k-3). lib. bdg. 14.15 (978-0-613-44427-9(2)) Tandem Library Bks.

Henry, Sandy. A Child's Bedtime Companion. Pavlova, Vera, illus. 2005. 26p. (J). (ps-2). per. 12.95 (978-1-929039-31-9(X)) Ambassador Bks., Inc.

Hest, Amy. Un Beso de Buenas Noches. Rubio, Esther, tr. Jeram, Anita, illus. (SPA.). (J). 16.00 (978-1-930332-04-1(1) , LC3294) Lectorum Pubns., Inc.

—Kiss Good Night. Jeram, Anita, illus. (J). (ps). 2006. 32p. pap. 4.99 (978-0-7636-2114-8(5)); 2004. 30p. bds. 6.99 (978-0-7636-2094-3(7)); 2001. 32p. 15.99 (978-0-7636-0780-7(0)) Candlewick Pr.

—Kiss Good Night: With Plush. Jeram, Anita, illus. gif. ed. 2004. 30p. (J). 12.99 (978-0-7636-2524-5(8)) Candlewick Pr.

Hetzer, Michael. Footprints on the Ceiling: Your Child's Footprint Completes the Story. Clayton, Kim, illus. 2nd ed. 2005. 32p. (J). 18.95 (978-0-9728222-2-0(4)) Webster Henrietta Publishing.

Hill, Eric. Good Night Spot. 2004. (Illus.). 14p. (J). (ps-1). bds. 3.99 (978-0-399-24319-6(4) , Putnam Juvenile) Penguin Group (USA) Inc.

Hill, Susan. Backyard Bedtime. Root, Barry, illus. 2001. (Growing Tree Ser.). 24p. (J). (ps up). 7.99 (978-0-694-01317-3(X) , Harper Festival) HarperCollins Pubs.

Hindley, Judy. Sleepy Places. Freeman, Tor, illus. 2006. 32p. (J). (ps-1). 15.99 (978-0-7636-2983-0(9)) Candlewick Pr.

Hines, Anna Grossnickle. My Own Big Bed. Watson, Mary, illus. 1998. 24p. (J). (ps-3). 16.99 (978-0-688-15599-5(5)) HarperCollins Pubs.

Hodge, Marie. Are You Sleepy Yet, Petey? Graef, Renee, illus. 2006. 24p. (J). bds. 5.95 (978-1-4027-4025-1(5)) Sterling Publishing Co., Inc.

Hodges, Lynn, et al. Count Yourself to Sleep. 2005. (Song of God's Love Ser.). (Illus.). 32p. (J). 14.99 (978-0-310-70717-2(X)) Zonderkidz.

Hodgkins, Fran. If You Were My Baby. Bryant, Laura J., illus. 2007. 26p. (J). (ps-ps). bds. 7.95 (***978-1-58469-090-0(9))*** Dawn Pubns.

Hodgkins, Fran. If You Were My Baby: A Wildlife Lullaby. Bryant, Laura J., illus. 2005. (Sharing Nature with Children Book Ser.). 32p. (J). (ps-2). pap. 8.95 (978-1-58469-075-7(5)); 16.95 (978-1-58469-074-0(7)) Dawn Pubns.

Hodgson, Mona Gansberg. Bedtime in the Southwest. Graef, Renee, illus. 2004. 32p. 14.95 (978-0-87358-871-3(1) , Rising Moon Bks. for Young Readers) Northland Publishing.

Hood, Karen Jean Matsko. Goodnight, I Wish You Goodnight. 2005. (Illus.). 32p. (J). 15.95 (978-1-930948-83-9(2)) Whispering Pine Pr., Inc.

—Goodnight, I Wish You Goodnight. Keyama, Hiroshi Hata, illus. 2005. 32p. (J). 24.95 (978-1-930948-97-6(2)) Whispering Pine Pr., Inc.

—Goodnight, I Wish You Goodnight. 2002. (J). per. 15.95 (978-1-59210-500-7(9)) Whispering Pine Pr., Inc.

Hood, Susan. Time for Bed? 1999. (Real Kids Readers Ser.: 2). (Illus.). 32p. (J). (gr. k-2). pap. 4.99 (978-0-7613-2094-4(6) , Millbrook Pr.) Lerner Publishing Group.

—Time for Bed? Handelman, Dorothy, photos by. 1999. (Real Kids Readers Ser.). (Illus.). 32p. (gr. k-2). lib. bdg. 18.90 (978-0-7613-2069-2(5) , Millbrook Pr.) Lerner Publishing Group.

—Time for Bed? 1999. (J). (978-0-606-19178-4(X)); lib. bdg. 11.80 (978-0-613-18165-5(4)) Tandem Library Bks.

Horn, Peter. Cuando Sea Grande... Kadmon, Cristina, illus. 2001. (SPA.). 32p. (J). (gr. k-3). pap. 6.95 (978-0-7358-1435-6(X) , NS30340) North-South Bks., Inc.

—When I Grow Up... Cuando Sea Grande. Almohar, Ariel, tr. from GER. Kadmon, Cristina, illus. 2001. 32p. (J). (ps-3). pap. 6.95 (978-0-7358-1418-9(X)) North-South Bks., Inc.

Horvath, Polly. The Trolls. unabr. ed. 2004. 144p. (J). (gr. 3-7). pap. 29.00 incl. audio (978-0-8072-8372-1(X) , Listening Library) Random Hse. Audio Publishing Group.

—The Trolls. 2001. (Illus.). (J). (978-0-606-20955-7(7)) Tandem Library Bks.

Hunter, Julius K. Absurd Alphabedtime Stories. Bauman, Todd, illus. 2nd rev. l.t. ed. 2004. 32p. (J). 16.95 (978-0-9761422-0-1(1)) J.K.H. Enterprises.

Hupp, Sarah M. A Sneaky Snake's Bedtime Prank. Adnet, Bernard, illus. 2003. 12p. (J). 6.99 (978-0-310-70568-0(1)) Zonderkidz.

Hurd, Thacher. Sleepy Cadillac: A Bedtime Drive. Hurd, Thacher, illus. 2005. (Illus.). 32p. (J). 15.99 (978-0-06-073020-8(X)); lib. bdg. 16.89 (978-0-06-073021-5(8)) HarperCollins Pubs.

Hurst, Rich. The Goodnight Thing. 2006. 10.99 (***978-0-9763770-1-6(2))*** Red Door Pr.

Hutchins, Pat. Little Pink Pig. 2000. (Illus.). 32p. (J). (ps-3). pap. 5.95 (978-0-688-17516-0(3) , Harper Trophy) HarperCollins Pubs.

—Little Pink Pig. 2000. (Illus.). (J). (978-0-606-18703-9(0)) Tandem Library Bks.

Imai, Ayano. The 108th Sheep. Imai, Ayano, illus. 2007. (Illus.). 32p. (J). (ps-2). 15.95 (978-1-58925-063-5(X) , tiger tales) ME Media LLC.

Imbody, Amy E. Snug As a Bug. Gordon, Mike, illus. (Mothers of Preschoolers Ser.). (J). 2004. 28p. pap. 4.99 (978-0-310-70819-3(2)); 2001. 32p. 7.99 (978-0-310-70063-0(9)) Zonderkidz.

In My Bed: Individual Title, 6 Packs. (Literatura 2000 Ser.). (gr. k-1). 28.00 (978-0-7635-0007-8(0)) Rigby Education.

In My Room: Individual Title Six-Packs. (Literatura 2000 Ser.). (gr. k-1). 28.00 (978-0-7635-0032-0(1)) Rigby Education.

Inches, Alison. The Stuffed Animals Get Ready for Bed. Langdo, Bryan, illus. 2006. 32p. (J). 16.00 (978-0-15-216466-9(9)) Harcourt Children's Bks.

Inkpen, Mick. Kipper. Inkpen, Mick, illus. 2002. (Illus.). (J). 13.15 (978-0-7587-6464-5(2)) Book Wholesalers, Inc.

—Kipper. (ENG & FRE., Illus.). 32p. (J). (978-1-85430-330-1(9) , 93450); (978-1-85430-333-2(3) , 93451) Magi Pubns.

—Kipper. 1999. (978-0-606-17487-9(7)) Tandem Library Bks.

Isadora, Rachel. Mr. Moon. Date not set. (J). 15.99 (978-0-06-029821-0(9)); lib. bdg. 16.89 (978-0-06-029822-7(7)) HarperCollins Pubs.

Isadora, Rachel. Peekaboo Bedtime. Isadora, Rachel, illus. 2008. 32p. (J). (ps-k). 16.99 (***978-0-399-24384-4(4)*** , Putnam Juvenile) Penguin Group (USA) Inc.

It's Time for Bed. 2002. 12p. (J). bds. 7.95 (978-1-84250-496-3(7) , Bright Sparks) Parragon, Inc.

Ives, Penny. Rabbit Pie. 2006. (Illus.). 32p. (J). (ps-1). 15.99 (978-0-670-05951-5(X) , Viking Adult) Penguin Group (USA) Inc.

Jam, Teddy. Night Cars. Beddows, Eric, illus. 2006. 32p. 9.95 (978-0-88899-748-7(5)) Groundwood Bks. CAN. *Dist:* Perseus Distribution.

Janik, Dan. Sourdough Scott's Bedtime Fairy Tales from Alaska. 2005. (J). per. 12.95 net. (978-1-59433-031-5(X)) Publication Consultants.

Jasper, Mark. Good Night Charleston. Kelly, Cooper, illus. 2007. (Good Night Our World Ser.). 20p. (J). bds. 9.95 (***978-1-60219-022-1(4))*** Our World of Books.

—Good Night Florida Keys. Rosen, Anne, illus. 2008. (Good Night Our World Ser.). 20p. (J). bds. 9.95 (***978-1-60219-020-7(8)***) Our World of Books.

Jennings, Sharon. No Monsters Here. Ohi, Ruth, illus. 2004. 32p. (J). (gr. k-1). (978-1-55041-787-6(8)) Fitzhenry & Whiteside, Ltd.

—Sleep Tight, Mrs. Ming. ed. 2004. (Illus.). (J). (ps-3). spiral bd. (978-0-616-01683-1(2)) Canadian National Institute for the Blind/Institut National Canadien pour les Aveugles.

Jenny in Bed: Individual Title Six-Pack Pouch - Level G. (Lighthouse Ser.). 12p. (gr. 1 up). 26.00 (978-0-7578-0837-1(9)) Rigby Education.

Johnson, Andi. Little Molly Yo-Yo. 2004. (Illus.). 16p. 9.00 (978-1-84161-114-3(X)) Ravette Publishing, Ltd. GBR. *Dist:* Parkwest Pubns., Inc.

Johnson, Jane. Are You Ready for Bed? Hansen, Gaby, illus. 2004. 32p. (J). tchr. ed. 14.95 (978-1-58925-017-8(6), tiger tales) ME Media LLC.

—Little Bunny's Bedtime. Hansen, Gaby, illus. 2006. Orig. Title: Are You Ready for Bed?. 16p. (J). bds. 6.95 (978-1-58925-773-3(1), tiger tales) ME Media LLC.

Johnson, Vickey L. The Monster Mix-Up. 2003. (Illus.). (J). pap. 9.00 (978-0-8059-6125-6(9)) Dorrance Publishing Co., Inc.

Jones, Christianne C. Room to Share. Trover, Zachary, illus. 2005. (Read-It! Readers Ser.). 24p. (J). (ps). lib. bdg. 18.60 (978-1-4048-1185-0(0)) Picture Window Bks.

Jones, T. L. Santa Takes a Holiday! 2005. (Santa Chronicles Ser.: Bk. 1). (Illus.). 100p. (J). per. 12.00 (978-0-9707594-4-3(4), 00001) Mercury/Hula Babe Productions.

Jones, Terry & Newman, Nanette. Bedtime Stories. Foreman, Michael, illus. 2007. 192p. (J). pap. 16.99 (***978-1-84458-477-2(1)***) Anova Bks. GBR. *Dist:* Independent Pubs. Group.

Jonsberg, Barry. Dreamrider. 2008. 256p. (J). (gr. 9). lib. bdg. 18.99 (***978-0-375-94457-4(5)***, Knopf Bks. for Young Readers) Random Hse. Children's Bks.

Joyce, William. Sleepy Time Olie. Joyce, William, illus. 2001. (Rolie Polie Olie Ser.). (Illus.). 40p. (J). (ps-3). 15.95 (978-0-06-029613-1(5), Geringer, Laura Book) HarperCollins Pubs.

—Sleepy Time Olie. 2001. (Rolie Polie Olie Ser.). (Illus.). 40p. (J). (ps-3). 15.89 (978-0-06-029614-8(3), Geringer, Laura Book) HarperCollins Pubs.

—Sleepy Time Olie. Joyce, William, illus. 2006. (Rolie Polie Olie Ser.). 40p. (J). pap. 6.99 (978-0-06-084222-2(9), Harper Trophy) HarperCollins Pubs.

Just As Well Really! 2000. (Sweet Dreams Ser.). 32p. (J). 9.95 (978-1-84250-160-3(7), Bright Sparks) Parragon, Inc.

Kaldor, Connie & Campagne, Carmen. Lullaby Berceuse: A Warm Prairie Night. Deines, Brian, illus. 2006. 40p. (J). 16.95 incl. audio compact disk (978-2-923163-22-2(2)) La Montagne Secrete CAN. *Dist:* National Bk. Network.

Kalz, Jill. Mike's Nightlight. Spence, Tom, illus. 2006. (Read-It! Readers Ser.). 32p. (J). (ps-3). 18.60 (978-1-4048-1726-5(3)) Picture Window Bks.

Kanevsky, Polly. Sleepy Boy. Anderson, Stephanie, illus. 2006. 32p. (J). (ps-k). 15.95 (978-0-689-86735-4(2), Atheneum) Simon & Schuster Children's Publishing.

Kenney, Cindy. Where Is God When I'm Scared? 2004. (Illus.). 22p. bds. 4.99 (978-0-310-70784-4(6)) Zonderkidz.

Kirk, David. Bedtime Story. 2006. (Miss Spider Ser.). (Illus.). 32p. (J). 6.99 (978-0-448-44367-6(8)) Penguin Group (USA) Inc.

Kirk, David. Bedtime Story/David Kirk. 2006. (Illus.). 32p. (J). (***978-1-4156-8869-4(9)***; (***978-0-448-44514-4(X)***) Penguin Group (USA) Inc.

Kitchens, Jennifer. Who Made the Stars? A Collection of Bedtime Stories. 2005. 57p. per. (978-1-59196-978-5(6)) Instantpublisher.com.

Klein, Abby. Help! A Vampire's Coming. McKinley, John, illus. 2005. (Ready, Freddy! Ser.). 96p. (J). pap. 3.99 (978-0-439-55606-4(6), Blue Sky Pr., The) Scholastic, Inc.

—Worst Nightmare. McKinley, John, illus. 2005. (J). (978-0-439-55605-7(8), Blue Sky Pr., The) Scholastic, Inc.

Kleven, Elisa, illus. Angels Watching over Me. 2007. 32p. (J). (ps-k). 16.99 (978-0-689-86252-6(0)) Simon & Schuster Children's Publishing.

Klinting, Lars. What Do You Want? Lundin, Maria, tr. from SWE. 2006. (Illus.). 36p. (J). 15.95 (978-0-88899-636-7(5)) Groundwood Bks. CAN. *Dist:* Perseus Distribution.

Kloske, Geoffrey. Once upon a Time, the End: Asleep in 60 Seconds. 2007. (Illus.). 27p. (J). 16.00 (***978-1-4223-6591-5(3)***) DIANE Publishing Co.

—Once upon a Time, the End: Asleep in 60 Seconds. Blitt, Barry, illus. 2005. 40p. (J). (gr. k-2). 15.95 (978-0-689-86619-7(4), Atheneum) Simon & Schuster Children's Publishing.

Kono, Erin Eitter. Hula Lullaby. 2005. (Illus.). 32p. (J). (ps-1). 15.99 (978-0-316-73591-9(4)) Little Brown & Co.

Kraushaar, Sabine. Good Night Baby. 2007. (Illus.). (J). bds. 3.99 (978-0-7358-2120-0(8)) North-South Bks., Inc.

Kreischer, Elsie Karr. Bigger Than a Button. Brandenburg, Claire, illus. 2002. 28p. (J). 14.95 (978-0-9708940-4-5(X)) Gently Worded Bks., LLC.

Krensky, Stephen. Fraidy Cats. Lewin, Betsy, illus. 2004. 32p. (J). lib. bdg. 15.00 (978-1-59054-383-2(1)) Fitzgerald Bks.

Krosoczka, Jarrett J. Good Night, Monkey Boy. Krosoczka, Jarrett J., illus. 2003. (Illus.). 40p. (J). (gr. k-k). pap. 6.99 (978-0-440-41798-9(8), Dragonfly Bks.) Random Hse. Children's Bks.

Kurty, G. Thomas the Treemaker: a Short Story about a Tall Tale. 2007. (ENG.). 76p. per. 14.95 (***978-1-4241-6219-2(X)***) PublishAmerica, Inc.

Landry, Leo. Space Boy. 2007. 32p. (J). (gr. k-3). 16.00 (***978-0-618-60568-2(1)***) Houghton Mifflin Co.

Layne, Steven L. Thomas' Sheep & the Great Geography Test. Board, Perry, illus. 1998. 32p. (J). (ps-3). 15.95 (978-1-56554-274-7(6)) Pelican Publishing Co., Inc.

Lee, Nancy. Hoover's Summer Tale. 2004. (J). spiral bd. 8.95 (978-0-9748087-6-5(8)) Journey Pubns., LLC.

Leithart, Peters. Wise Words: Family Stories That Bring the Proverbs to Life. 2006. cd-rom 20.00 (***978-1-59128-585-4(2)***) Canon Pr.

Leuck, Laura. Goodnight Baby Monster. Date not set. 32p. (J). (ps-1). pap. 4.99 (978-0-06-443723-3(X)) HarperCollins Pubs.

—Goodnight, Baby Monster. 2002. (Illus.). 32p. (J). (ps-1). 14.99 (978-0-06-029151-8(6)); 16.89 (978-0-06-029152-5(4)) HarperCollins Pubs.

Lewis, Kim. Good Night Harry. Lewis, Kim, illus. 2004. (Illus.). 32p. (J). (ps-1). 15.99 (978-0-7636-2206-0(0)) Candlewick Pr.

Lewis, Paeony. No More Yawning! Granstrom, Brita, illus. 2008. 32p. (J). pap. 16.99 (***978-0-545-02957-5(0)***, Chicken Hse., The) Scholastic, Inc.

L'Heureux, Christine. Buenas Noches! 2004. (Caillou Estrella Polar Ser.). (SPA., Illus.). 24p. (J). (ps up). pap. 3.95 (978-1-58728-345-1(X), Creative Publishing International) Quayside.

—Caillou Time for Bed. Lambert, Carole, illus. 2004. (Carousel Ser.). 24p. (J). 5.95 (978-2-89450-412-3(8)) Chouette Publishing CAN. *Dist:* Perseus Distribution.

Lignell, Kirk. Listen to the Raindrops W/cd. 2007. 32p. 17.95 (***978-1-932399-15-8(1)***) Huron River Pr.

Lily, Aunt. The Mystical Garden Path. Dove, Auntie, illus. 2001. 30p. (J). pap. 12.95 (978-0-9701704-2-2(4), Diversified Productions) Williams Publishing Co.

Lipniacka, Ewa. To Bed... or Else! Bogdonowicz, Basia, illus. 2000. 32p. (J). (ps-3). pap. 7.95 (978-1-56656-214-0(7), Crocodile Bks.) Interlink Publishing Group, Inc.

Listening with Zachary. (J). pap. 13.75 (978-0-8136-4655-8(3)) Modern Curriculum Pr.

Lloyd-Jones, Sally. Sweet Dreams. 2004. (Illus.). (J). bds. 8.99 (978-0-8423-7740-9(9)) Tyndale Hse. Pubs.

—Time to Say Goodnight. Chapman, Jane, illus. 2006. 32p. (J). 15.99 (978-0-06-054328-0(0)); lib. bdg. 16.89 (978-0-06-054329-7(9)) HarperCollins Pubs.

LoisKeffer. God Is There Little Bear. 2007. (Sleepytime Stories Ser.). 24p. (J). bds. 6.99 (978-0-7814-4351-7(2), 0781443512) Cook, David C. Publishing Co.

London, Jonathan. Froggy Goes to Bed. Remkiewicz, Frank, illus. (Froggy Ser.). 32p. (J). (gr. k-3). 2002. pap. 5.99 (978-0-14-056657-4(0), Puffin); 2000. 15.99 (978-0-670-88860-3(5), Viking Juvenile) Penguin Group (USA) Inc.

—Froggy Goes to Bed. 2002. (gr. k-3). lib. bdg. 14.15 (978-0-613-45265-6(8)) Tandem Library Bks.

Lou Weber Staff, ed. 5-Minute Good Night Stories. 2004. (Illus.). 320p. 15.98 (978-0-7853-7661-3(5), 3934402) Publications International, Ltd.

Loye, David. Grandfather's Garden: Bedtime Stories for Little & Big Folk. 2008. (J). pap. 18.95 (***978-0-9795257-7-3(2)***) Benjamin Franklin Pr.

Lum, Kate. What! Cried Granny. 2002. (ps-2). lib. bdg. 15.30 (978-0-613-49647-6(7)) Tandem Library Bks.

Lum, Kate & Johnson, Adrian. What! Cried Granny. 1999. (Illus.). 32p. (J). pap. (978-0-7475-4178-3(7)) Bloomsbury Publishing Plc.

Lundgren, Mary Beth. Seven Scary Monsters. Fine, Howard, illus. 2003. 32p. (J). (gr. k-3). tchr. ed. 15.00 (978-0-395-88913-8(8), Clarion Bks.) Houghton Mifflin Co. Trade & Reference Div.

Lurie, Dana. It's Time for Bed Sleepyhead. Gordon, Shari & Maltz, Brenda, illus. 2005. (J). mass mkt. 12.95 (978-0-9768012-0-7(5)) Tomgirlz Enterprises LLC.

Lyly, Olivia, illus. Bedtime for Baby. 2005. 8p. (J). 6.95 (978-0-7641-7848-1(2)) Barron's Educational Series, Inc.

Macedo, Blanca, illus. Cuentos Clasicos Infantiles. 2005. (SPA.). 159p. pap. 8.90 (978-968-7748-16-0(8)) LD Bks., Inc.

Madame M. Eerie Little Bedtime Stories. 2006. (J). 12.99 (978-0-9777972-0-2(1)) Blue Tie Publishing.

Madden, Gloria. Grandmother's Bedtime Stories. 2005. 57p. pap. 12.95 (978-1-4137-6489-5(4)) PublishAmerica, Inc.

Magsamen, Sandra. Goodnight, Little One. 2007. (Messages from the Heart Ser.). (Illus.). 6p. (J). (ps). 10.99 (***978-0-316-06594-8(3)***) Little, Brown Bks. for Young Readers.

Maizel, Karen, illus. Jake's Brave Night. 2007. (I Can Read!). 32p. (J). pap. 3.99 (***978-0-310-71456-9(7)***) Zonderkidz.

Mammola-Koravos, Beth Ann. Good Night God, Love Olivia. Bebirian, Helena, illus. l.t. ed. 2006. 25p. (J). 15.95 (978-1-59879-110-5(9)); per. 10.95 (978-1-59879-091-7(9)) Lifevest Publishing, Inc.

Marcus, John V. Birdy Bird & the Plane. 2007. 9.00 (***978-0-8059-7312-9(5)***) Dorrance Publishing Co., Inc.

Markes, Julie. Shhhhh! Everybody's Sleeping. Parkins, David, illus. 2005. 32p. (J). (ps-1). 14.99 (978-0-06-053790-6(6)); lib. bdg. 16.89 (978-0-06-053791-3(4)) HarperCollins Pubs.

Martin, David. Pillow Fight. 2000. (Illus.). (J). (978-0-7636-1330-3(4)) Candlewick Pr.

Masurel, Claire. Bonne Nuit! 2000. Tr. of Good Night!. (FRE.). (J). pap. 13.95 (978-2-211-02616-1(8)) Archimede Editions FRA. *Dist:* Distribooks, Inc.

Matsuda, Christine. Goodnight Little One: Bedtime Around the World. Ishida, Jui, illus. 2008. (J). 15.95 (***978-0-87358-925-3(4)***, Rising Moon Bks. for Young Readers) Northland Publishing.

Matthews, Derek. Happy Snappy Easter Egg Hunt. 2006. (Happy Snappy Bks.). (Illus.). 10p. (J). 4.95 (978-1-59223-565-0(4), Silver Dolphin Bks.) Advantage Pubs. Group.

Maxwell, Mimi. Monster Mash. 1998. (J). pap. 6.99 (978-0-9680678-8-8(3)) Tumbleweed Pr.

Mayer, Mercer. Just Go to Bed. 2001. mass mkt. 3.29 (978-0-307-81940-6(X), Golden Bks.) Random Hse. Children's Bks.

—There's a Nightmare in My Closet. Mayer, Mercer, illus. 2002. (Illus.). (J). 14.04 (978-0-7587-3783-0(1)) Book Wholesalers, Inc.

McBratney, Sam. The Caterpillow Fight. 2002. (Illus.). (J). 11.23 (978-0-7587-2207-2(9)) Book Wholesalers, Inc.

—Guess How Much I Love You. Jeram, Anita, illus. 2005. 34p. (J). bds. 19.95 (978-0-9769313-1-7(1)) BrailleInk.

—Guess How Much I Love You. Jeram, Anita, illus. 10th anniv. ed. 2004. 32p. (J). 20.00 (978-0-7636-2435-4(7)) Candlewick Pr.

—Guess How Much I Love You & Story Time DVD. Jeram, Anita, illus. 2006. 32p. (J). (ps-3). 15.99 incl. DVD (978-0-7636-3503-9(0)) Candlewick Pr.

McBratney, Sam. Tell Me a Story Before I Go to Bed. Braun, Sebastien, illus. 2007. 32p. (J). pap. (***978-0-00-714180-7(7)***) HarperCollins Canada, Ltd.

McClure, Nikki. Awake to Nap. 2006. (Illus.). 16p. (J). bds. 9.95 (978-1-57061-507-8(1)) Sasquatch Bks.

McCue, Lisa & Falken, L. C. Snuggle Bunnies. McCue, Lisa, illus. 2003. (Illus.). 11p. (J). bds. 6.99 (978-0-7944-0040-8(X)) Reader's Digest Assn., Inc., The.

McCullough, Pierce. Bunbun at Bedtime. 2002. (Bunbun Ser.). (Illus.). 24p. (J). (gr. k-2). bds. 6.99 (978-1-84148-379-5(6)) Barefoot Bks., Inc.

McCullough, Sharon Pierce. Bunbun at Bedtime. McCullough, Sharon Pierce, illus. 2001. (Illus.). 24p. (J). (ps-2). 14.99 (978-1-84148-438-9(5)) Barefoot Bks., Inc.

McDonald, Megan. Bedbugs. Johnson, Paul Brett, illus. 1999. 32p. (J). (ps-1). 16.99 (978-0-531-33193-4(8), Orchard Bks.) Scholastic, Inc.

McKay, Hilary. There's a Dragon Downstairs. Harvey, Amanda, tr. Harvey, Amanda, illus. 2005. 32p. (J). 16.95 (978-0-689-86774-3(3), McElderry, Margaret K.) Simon & Schuster Children's Publishing.

McKay, Sindy. New Red Bed. 1999. (gr. k-3). lib. bdg. 11.80 (978-0-613-82080-6(0)) Tandem Library Bks.

McMullan, Kate. If You Were My Bunny. McPhail, David M., illus. 2002. 15.70 (978-0-7587-2831-9(X)) Book Wholesalers, Inc.

—If You Were My Bunny. McPhail, David M., illus. 1998. (Hello Reader! Ser.). 26p. (J). reprint ed. bds. 6.99 (978-0-590-34126-4(X)) Scholastic, Inc.

McPhail, David M. Night Night, Baby. 2007. 24p. (J). (ps). bds. 7.99 (***978-0-689-85028-8(X)***, Little Simon) Simon & Schuster Children's Publishing.

Meade, Holly. A Place to Sleep. 2001. (Illus.). 32p. (J). (ps-1). 15.95 (978-0-7614-5096-2(3), Cavendish Children's Bks.) Cavendish, Marshall Corp.

Medearis, Angela Shelf. Lights Out! Tadgell, Nicole, illus. 2004. 32p. (J). lib. bdg. 15.00 (***978-1-4242-0221-8(3)***) Fitzgerald Bks.

Medearis, Angela Shelf. Snug in Mama's Arms. Sandford, John, illus. 2004. 32p. (J). 14.95 (978-1-57768-430-5(3), Gingham Dog Pr.) School Specialty Publishing.

Melling, David. The Kiss That Missed. 2007. 32p. (J). (gr. k-2). pap. 7.99 (978-0-7641-3624-5(0)) Barron's Educational Series, Inc.

Miley, Berry. Christmas Village Chronicles & Other Short Stories. 2005. 63p. pap. 8.95 (978-1-4116-2617-1(6)) Lulu.com.

Miller-Gill, Angela. There Are No Blankets on the Moon. Kellem-Kellner, Blynda, illus. 2004. 32p. (J). 16.00 (978-0-9716442-2-9(5)) Jackson Publishing.

Mills, Dorothy. Big Beds & Little Beds. 2003. (Illus.). (J). per. 14.25 (978-1-932301-48-9(8), 1275) Airleaf Publishing & Bookselling.

Milne, A. A. Bedtime with Winnie-the-Pooh. Shepard, Ernest H., illus. 2003. 22p. (J). (ps). 9.99 (978-0-525-47148-6(0), Dutton Juvenile) Penguin Group (USA) Inc.

Mitchard, Jacquelyn. Baby Bat's Lullaby. Noonan, Julia, illus. 2004. 32p. (J). (ps-1). 15.99 (978-0-06-050760-2(8)); lib. bdg. 16.89 (978-0-06-050761-9(6)) HarperCollins Pubs.

Mitchell, Melanie, illus. Good Morning, Good Night Bilingual: Buenos Dias! Buenas Noches! 2005. (ENG & SPA.). 12p. (J). 9.95 (978-1-58117-389-5(X), Intervisual/Piggy Toes) Dalmatian Pr.

Mitzo Thompson, Kim & Mitzo Hilderbrand, Karen. Bedtime Stories, 2 Packs. Edelson, Wendy & Schwartz, Carol, illus. 2006. 36p. (J). bds. 14.98 (978-0-7696-4965-3(3)) School Specialty Publishing.

—It's Night-Night Time. 2006. (Read & Sing along Board Books with CDs Ser.). 18p. (J). bds. 7.49 (978-0-7696-4588-9(7)) School Specialty Publishing.

—Sleep, My Little One. 2006. (Read & Sing along Board Books with CDs Ser.). 18p. (J). bds. 7.49 (978-0-7696-4589-6(5)) School Specialty Publishing.

Modaressi, Mitra. Stay Awake, Sally. Modaressi, Mitra, illus. 2007. 32p. (J). 16.99 (***978-0-399-24545-9(6)***, Putnam Juvenile) Penguin Group (USA) Inc.

Moeller-Masel, Christy A. Eerie Little Bedtime Stories. 2001. (Madame M Presents Ser.: Vol. 2). (Illus.). 128p. (J). per. 18.95 (978-0-9704159-1-2(5)) Creepy Little Productions.

Mola, Astrid & Khakdan, Wahed. The Good-Night Kiss. 2004. (Illus.). 32p. (J). 10.99 (978-1-59384-046-4(2)) Parklane Publishing.

Morales, Yuyi. Little Night. 2007. (Illus.). 32p. (J). (ps-3). 16.95 (978-1-59643-088-4(5)) Roaring Brook Pr.

Morales, Yuyi. Nochecita. 2007. (SPA., Illus.). 32p. (J). (ps-3). 16.95 (***978-1-59643-232-1(2)***) Roaring Brook Pr.

Morgan, Allen. Nicole's Boat. Marton, Jirina, illus. rev. ed. 2000. 24p. (J). (gr. k-ps). pap. 5.95 (978-1-55037-630-2(6)); lib. bdg. 15.95 (978-1-55037-631-9(4)) Annick Pr., Ltd. CAN. *Dist:* Firefly Bks., Ltd.

Morgan, Mary. Sleep Tight, Little Mouse. Morgan, Mary, illus. 2003. (Illus.). 32p. (J). (ps-1). 12.95 (978-0-375-82308-4(5)); lib. bdg. 14.99 (978-0-375-92308-1(X)) Random Hse. Children's Bks. (Knopf Bks. for Young Readers).

Morrissey, Dean. The Crimson Comet. Morrissey, Dean, illus. 2006. (Illus.). 32p. (J). lib. bdg. 17.89 (978-0-06-008070-9(1)) HarperCollins Pubs.

Morrissey, Dean & Krensky, Stephen. The Crimson Comet. Morrissey, Dean, illus. 2006. (Illus.). 32p. (J). 16.99 (978-0-06-008068-6(X)) HarperCollins Pubs.

Mortensen, Denise Dowling. Good Night Engines. Iwai, Melissa, illus. 2003. 32p. (J). (gr. k-3). 15.00 (978-0-618-13537-0(5), Clarion Bks.) Houghton Mifflin Co. Trade & Reference Div.

Morton, Lone & Risk, Mary. Goodnight Everyone. Bougard, Marie-Therese, tr. Wood, Jakki, photos by. 1998. (I Can Read Bks.).Tr. of Bonne Nuit a Tous. (ENG & FRE.). (J). (ps up). 9.95 incl. audio (978-0-7641-7188-8(7)) Barron's Educational Series, Inc.

Mr. Cheesehead Goes for a Ride... 2nd rev. ed. 2005. (Illus.). 32p. (J). 12.99 (978-0-9764463-1-6(6)) Vertigo Publishing.

Muller, Ann. The Elfree Stories. 2002. (Illus.). 64p. (J). (gr. 1-5). pap. 8.95 (978-1-903464-05-2(6)) Collins Pr., The IRL. *Dist:* Dufour Editions, Inc.

Munsch, Robert. Get Out of Bed! ed. 2004. (Illus.). (J). (gr. k-3). spiral bd. (978-0-616-04557-2(3)); spiral bd. (978-0-616-03049-3(5)) Canadian National Institute for the Blind/Institut National Canadien pour les Aveugles.

—Love You Forever. McGraw, Sheila, illus. gif. ed. 2000. 32p. (J). (ps-1). 19.95 (978-1-55209-109-8(0)) Firefly Bks., Ltd.

Munsch, Robert, et al. Get Out of Bed! Daniel, Alan & Daniel, Lea, illus. 2002. 32p. (J). pap. 3.99 (978-0-439-38851-1(1)) Scholastic, Inc.

Munsch, Robert N. Mortimer. Martchenko, Michael, illus. 2007. Tr. of Mortimer. (SPA.). 24p. (J). (ps-2). pap. 5.95 (***978-1-55451-109-9(7)***) Annick Pr., Ltd. CAN. *Dist:* Firefly Bks., Ltd.

Musgrave, Susan. Dreams Are More Real Than Bathtubs. braille ed. 2004. (Illus.). (J). (gr. k-3). spiral bd. (978-0-616-01748-7(0)) Canadian National Institute for the Blind/Institut National Canadien pour les Aveugles.

—Dreams Are More Real Than Bathtubs. Gay, Marie-Louise, illus. 1999. 32p. (J). (ps-2). 14.95 (978-1-55143-107-9(6)) Orca Bk. Pubs. USA.

Muttini, Pablo. Monstruos en la Noche. 2005. (SPA., Illus.). 28p. (J). 14.95 (978-9974-7799-4-5(4), nicanitas) Hardenville SA URY. *Dist:* Independent Pubs. Group.

My First Book of Bedtime Stories. 2003. (J). 8.99 (978-1-59384-013-6(6)) Parklane Publishing.

Nakamura, Katherine Riley. Song of Night: It's Time to Go to Bed. Riley, Linnea Asplind, illus. 2002. 40p. (J). (ps-3). pap. 15.95 (978-0-439-26678-9(5), Blue Sky Pr., The) Scholastic, Inc.

Német, Andreas. Five Little Sleepyheads. Schmidt, Hans-Christian, illus. 2007. 12p. (J). 8.95 (***978-0-7358-2138-5(0)***) North-South Bks., Inc.

Newcomer, Martha. Runaway Bed. Donato, Angela, illus. 2004. 32p. 14.95 (978-1-893224-46-9(5), New Millennium Pr.) New Millennium Entertainment.

Night Night Baby. 2005. (J). bds. 6.99 (978-0-9753127-2-8(3)) Family Bks. at Home.

No Longer Will I Hide the Stranger in My Bed. 2003. (YA). per. 15.95 (978-0-9740081-0-3(9)) RAPHA, Inc.

Novak, Matt. Rock-A-Bye Christmas. 2007. (Illus.). 16p. (J). (ps-1). 7.95 (***978-1-59643-187-4(3)***) Roaring Brook Pr.

Numeroff, Laura Joffe. When Sheep Sleep. McPhail, David, illus. 2006. 24p. (J). (ps-3). 15.95 (978-0-8109-5469-4(9)) Abrams, Harry N., Inc.

Ochiltree, Dianne. Lull-a-Bye, Little One. Takahashi, Hideko, illus. 2006. 32p. (J). (gr. 1-ps). 16.99 (978-0-399-24305-9(4)) Penguin Group (USA) Inc.

Ohi, Ruth. Pants off First! 2001. (Illus.). 22p. (J). (ps-k). bds. (978-1-55041-667-1(7)) Fitzhenry & Whiteside, Ltd.

O'Leary, Sara. When You Were Small. Morstad, Julie, illus. 2006. 32p. (J). 16.95 (978-1-894965-36-1(1)) Simply Read Bks. CAN. *Dist:* Perseus Distribution.

Olsen, Madeline. Baby's Bedtime. Rutten, Nicole, illus. 2001. (Starring Me! Ser.). 10p. (J). bds. 7.95 (978-1-57145-465-2(9), Silver Dolphin Bks.) Advantage Pubs. Group.

Olvera, Jillann. Christian's Lullaby. 2006. 29p. pap. 14.95 (978-1-4241-1909-7(X)) PublishAmerica, Inc.

Oppenheim, Joanne. The Prince's Bedtime. Latimer, Miriam, illus. 2005. 32p. (J). 16.99 (978-1-84148-597-3(7)) Barefoot Bks., Inc.

Ormerod, Jan. Moonlight. 2005. (Illus.). 32p. pap. 14.95 (978-1-84507-391-6(6)) Lincoln, Frances Ltd. GBR. *Dist:* Transition Vendor.

Ostrow, Kim. Up All Night. Saunders, Zina, illus. 2004. (Ready-to-Read Ser.: Vol. 1). 32p. (J). pap. 3.99 (978-0-689-86320-2(9), Simon Spotlight/Nickelodeon) Simon & Schuster Children's Publishing.

—Up All Night. 2004. (gr. k-3). lib. bdg. 11.80 (978-0-613-73459-2(9)) Tandem Library Bks.

Ottolenghi, Carol. Father Loves His Little One. Campanella, Marco, illus. 2006. (Tell Me a Story Ser.). 36p. (J). (gr. k-k). bds. 14.95 (978-0-7696-4813-2(4), Gingham Dog Pr.) School Specialty Publishing.

—Grandparents Love Their Little Ones. Campanella, Marco, illus. 2006. (Tell Me a Story Ser.). 36p. (J). (gr. k-k). bds. 14.95 (978-0-7696-4815-6(0), Gingham Dog Pr.) School Specialty Publishing.

—I Love You, My Little One! Campanella, Marco, illus. 2006. (Tell Me a Story Ser.). 36p. (J). (gr. k-k). bds. 14.95 (978-0-7696-4814-9(2) , Gingham Dog Pr.) School Specialty Publishing.

—Mother Loves Her Little One. Campanella, Marco, illus. 2006. (Tell Me a Story Ser.). 36p. (J). (gr. k-k). bds. 14.95 (978-0-7696-4812-5(6) , Gingham Dog Pr.) School Specialty Publishing.

—Tip the Mouse Can't Sleep. Campanella, Marco, illus. 2005. (Tip the Mouse Ser.). 32p. (J). (ps-ps). 10.95 (978-0-7696-4299-4(3) , Gingham Dog Pr.) School Specialty Publishing.

Owens, Mary Beth. Panda Whispers. 2007. (Illus.). 32p. (J). (ps-2). 16.99 (978-0-525-47171-4(5) , Dutton Juvenile) Penguin Group (USA) Inc.

Pajama Bedtime Bear Picture Books Set. (P. B. Bear Picture Books Ser.). (J). pap. 29.95 (978-0-7894-2198-2(4)) Dorling Kindersley Publishing, Inc.

Palatini, Margie. Tub-Boo-Boo. ed. 2004. (Illus.). (J). (gr. k-3). spiral bd. (978-0-616-11132-1(0)); spiral bd. (978-0-616-11133-8(9)) Canadian National Institute for the Blind/Institut National Canadien pour les Aveugles.

Pape, Gordon & Kerbel, Deborah. Family Quizmas: Christmas Bedtime Stories & Trivia Fun. 2006. (Illus.). 192p. pap. 13.00 (978-0-452-28780-8(4) , Plume) Penguin Group (USA) Inc.

Parr, Todd. Otto Goes to Bed. 2003. (Illus.). 24p. (J). (ps-3). 9.95 (978-0-316-73873-6(5) , Tingley, Megan Bks.) Little, Brown Bks. for Young Readers.

Parry, Alan. Mouse Can't Sleep. Parry, Linda, illus. 2004. (Oaktree Wood Ser.). (ps-3). 5.00 (978-0-687-09711-1(8)) Abingdon Pr.

Paul, Ann Whitford. Hasta Manana, Monito. (SPA.). (J). 8.95 (978-958-04-7073-1(1)) Norma S.A. COL. *Dist:* Distribuidora Norma, Inc.

Paul, Ann Whitford. Snail's Good Night. Litzinger, Rosanne, illus. 2008. (J). ***978-0-8234-1912-8(6))** Holiday Hse., Inc.

Paul, Ann Whitford & Walker, David. Little Monkey Says Good Night. 2003. (Illus.). 32p. (J). 16.00 (978-0-374-34609-6(7) , Farrar, Straus & Giroux (BYR)) Farrar, Straus & Giroux.

Peck, Jan. Way up High in a Tall Green Tree. Petrone, Valeria, illus. 2005. 32p. (J). (ps-ps). 15.95 (978-1-4169-0071-9(3)) Simon & Schuster Children's Publishing.

Peck, Richard. Monster Night at Grandma's House. Freeman, Don, illus. 2003. 32p. (J). (gr. k-3). reprint ed. 12.99 (978-0-8037-2904-9(9) , Dial) Penguin Group (USA) Inc.

Peek, Merle. ¡Dénse Vuelta!/Roll Over! 2008. (ENG & SPA., Illus.). 24p. (J). (gr. k-ps). bds. 5.95 (***978-0-618-89420-8(9)** , Clarion Bks.) Houghton Mifflin Co. Trade & Reference Div.

Penner, Lucille Recht. Lights Out. 2000. (Math Matters Ser.). (Illus.). (J). (978-0-606-18220-1(9)) Tandem Library Bks.

—Lights Out! Smath, Jerry, illus. 2000. (Math Matters Ser.). 32p. (J). (ps-3). pap. 4.95 (978-1-57565-092-0(4)) Kane Pr., The.

—Lights Out! 2000. (gr. k-3). lib. bdg. 12.95 (978-0-613-27940-6(9)) Tandem Library Bks.

Penton Overseas, Inc. Staff. The Moon in My Room. 2004. 16p. (J). (gr. 2-5). 9.95 (978-1-59125-468-3(X) , Penton Kids) Penton Overseas, Inc.

Penton Overseas, Inc. Staff, ed. It's Bed Time: Building Early Childhood Sleep Skills! rev. ed. 2006. (Illus.). 8p. (J). (gr. 2-4). 7.95 (978-1-59125-743-1(3) , Smart Kids) Penton Overseas, Inc.

Perl, Erica S. Chicken Bedtime Is Really Early. Bates, George, illus. 2005. 32p. (J). (ps-1). 14.95 (978-0-8109-4926-3(1)) Abrams, Harry N. , Inc.

Perry, Robert. Down at the Seaweed Cafe. Guzek, Greta, illus. 2006. 32p. (J). pap. 7.95 (978-1-55192-865-4(5)) Raincoast Bk. Distribution CAN. *Dist:* Perseus Distribution.

Peter, Rutherford. Ready for Bed. 2006. (Illus.). 32p. (J). (ps). 12.95 (978-1-904613-95-4(0) , Buster Bks.) O'Mara, Michael Bks., Ltd. GBR. *Dist:* Independent Pubs. Group.

Piggy Toes Press Staff. Baby Tweety's Bedtime. 2000. (Lovable Huggable Baby Looney Tunes Cloth Bks.). (Illus.). 6p. (J). (ps up). 14.95 (978-1-58117-077-1(7) , Intervisual/Piggy Toes) Dalmatian Pr.

Piggy Toes Press Staff & Haskamp, Steve. Good Morning, Good Night! 2006. (Illus.). 12p. (J). 12.95 (978-1-58117-461-8(6) , Intervisual/Piggy Toes) Dalmatian Pr.

Piper, Noel. Most of All Jesus Loves You. Anderson, Debby, illus. 2005. 24p. (J). 9.99 (978-1-58134-630-5(1) , Crossway Bibles) Crossway Bks.

Pledger, Maurice. Pledger sounds of wild Nighttime. 2007. (Illus.). 16p. (J). 16.95 (***978-1-59223-471-4(2)** , Silver Dolphin Bks.) Advantage Pubs. Group.

Plourde, Lynn. Wild Child. Couch, Greg, illus. 2003. 32p. (J). pap. 7.99 (978-0-689-86349-3(7) , Aladdin) Simon & Schuster Children's Publishing.

Postgate, Daniel. Engelbert Sneem & His Dream Vacuum Machine. Postgate, Daniel, illus. 2007. (Illus.). 32p. (J). (ps). 16.95 (***978-0-7358-2151-4(8))** North-South Bks., Inc.

Potter, Author Tina M. The Horse Story. 2005. 36p. (J). pap. 9.65 (978-1-4116-5761-8(6)) Lulu.com.

Potter, Beatrix. Peter Rabbit Bathtime Fun. 2007. (Illus.). 8p. (J). 4.99 (978-0-7232-5926-8(7) , Warne) Penguin Group (USA) Inc.

—Sleep Tight, Peter Rabbit. 2007. (Illus.). 12p. (J). pap. 12.99 (978-0-7232-5809-4(0) , Warne) Penguin Group (USA) Inc.

Potter, George. The Wisemen of Bountiful. Harmon, Glenn, illus. 2005. per. 11.99 (978-1-55517-814-7(6) , Cedar Fort, Inc.) Cedar Fort, Inc./CFI Distribution.

Pow, Tom. Tell Me One Thing, Dad. Andrew, Ian, illus. 2004. 32p. (J). (ps-k). 15.99 (978-0-7636-2474-3(8)) Candlewick Pr.

Priddy, Roger. Baby Gund Mirror Bedtime. rev. ed. 2006. 12p. (J). bds. 6.95 (978-0-312-49707-1(5) , Priddy Bks.) St. Martin's Pr.

Provost, Elizabeth. Ten Little Sleepyheads. Saaf, Donald, illus. 2005. 32p. (J). 16.95 (978-1-58234-838-4(3)) Bloomsbury Publishing.

The Puffin Book of Bedtime Stories. 2006. 184p. (J). pap. 16.00 (978-0-670-05841-9(6) , Penguin Global) Penguin Group (USA) Inc.

Pumphrey, Jerome & Pumphrey, Jarrett. Creepy Things Are Scaring Me! Litzinger, Rosanne, illus. 2003. 32p. (J). (ps-3). lib. bdg. 15.89 (978-0-06-028963-8(5)) HarperCollins Pubs.

Pumphrey, W. Jerome. Creepy Things Are Scaring Me! (Illus.). 32p. (J). (ps-3). 5.99 (978-0-06-443680-9(2)) HarperCollins Pubs.

Puttock, Simon. Earth to Stella! Hopman, Philip, illus. 2006. 32p. (J). (ps-k). 16.00 (978-0-618-58535-9(4) , Clarion Bks.) Houghton Mifflin Co. Trade & Reference Div.

Quintart, Natalie. Mama Bear. Blanchart, Stephanie, illus. 2005. 32p. (J). (ps-ps). 6.95 (978-1-58925-394-0(9) , tiger tales) ME Media LLC.

Ramos, Mario. A La Cama, Monstruito! (SPA.). 32p. (J). 16.95 (978-84-8470-007-4(0)) Corimbo, Editorial S.L. ESP. *Dist:* Distribooks, Inc., Lectorum Pubns., Inc.

Random House Disney Staff. My Best Friend Is a Princess: A Princess Friendship Treasury. 2007. (Toddler Board Bks.). 30p. (J). (gr. k-k). bds. 11.99 (***978-0-7364-2505-6(5)** , RH/Disney) Random Hse. Children's Bks.

Raschka, Chris. Can't Sleep. Raschka, Chris, illus. 1999. (Illus.). (J). (ps-1). 32p. 15.99 (978-0-531-08779-4(4)); 16p. bds. 6.95 (978-0-531-30201-9(6)); 32p. pap. 14.95 (978-0-531-09479-2(0)) Scholastic, Inc. (Orchard Bks.).

Rathmann, Peggy. Faltan 10 Minutos Para Dormir. 2003. (SPA.). (gr. k-3). lib. bdg. 15.25 (978-0-613-81125-5(9)) Tandem Library Bks.

—Good Night, Gorilla. Rathmann, Peggy, illus. 2002. (Illus.). (J). 13.19 (978-0-7587-2619-3(8)) Book Wholesalers, Inc.

—Good Night, Gorilla. Rathmann, Peggy, illus. (Illus.). (J). (ps-1). 2004. 34p. bds. 12.99 (978-0-399-24260-1(0) , Putnam Juvenile); 2002. bds. 9.99 (978-0-399-23994-6(4)); 2000. (SPA., 40p. reprint ed. pap. 5.99 (978-0-698-11649-8(6) , Putnam Juvenile) Penguin Group (USA) Inc.

—Good Night, Gorilla. 2000. (gr. k-3). lib. bdg. 14.15 (978-0-613-28500-1(X)); (Illus.). (J). 12.79 (978-0-606-18837-1(1)) Tandem Library Bks.

—10 Minutes till Bedtime. 2004. (Illus.). 48p. (J). (ps-k). pap. 6.99 (978-0-14-240024-1(6) , Puffin) Penguin Group (USA) Inc.

—10 Minutes till Bedtime. Rathmann, Peggy, illus. (Illus.). (J). (ps-2). 2001. 21p. bds. 7.99 (978-0-399-23770-6(4)); 1998. 48p. 16.99 (978-0-399-23103-2(X)) Penguin Group (USA) Inc. (Putnam Juvenile).

—10 Minutes till Bedtime. 2004. (gr. k-3). lib. bdg. 15.30 (978-0-613-82995-3(6)) Tandem Library Bks.

—10 Minutes Till Bedtime. Rathmann, Peggy, illus. 2002. (Illus.). (J). 23.64 (978-0-7587-1888-4(8)) Book Wholesalers, Inc.

—10 Minutos Antes de Dormir. 2004. (SPA.). 46p. (J). (gr. k up). pap. 6.99 (978-980-257-276-2(4)) Ekare, Ediciones VEN. *Dist:* Lectorum Pubns., Inc., Iaconi, Mariuccia Bk. Imports.

—10 Minutos y a la Cama. Rathmann, Peggy, illus. 2005. 16p. (J). (ps-1). bds. 8.99 (978-0-399-24359-2(3) , Putnam Juvenile) Penguin Group (USA) Inc.

Ray, Mary Lyn. My Carousel Horse. Taxali, Gary, illus. 2000. (J). 13.95 (978-0-15-200023-3(2)) Harcourt Trade Pubs.

Read Along Bedtime Stories. 2001. (Illus.). (J). 15.95 (978-0-7853-5345-4(3)) Publications International, Ltd.

Reichert, Amy. While Mama Had a Quick Little Chat. Boiger, Alexandra, illus. 2005. 40p. (J). 15.95 (978-0-689-85170-4(7) , Atheneum) Simon & Schuster Children's Publishing.

Remkiewicz, Frank, illus. Froggy Goes to Bed. 2002. (Froggy Ser.). (J). 13.19 (978-1-4046-0751-4(X)) Book Wholesalers, Inc.

Rettore, Kenny E. My Baby Goodnight. Lyly, Olivia, illus. 2006. 2p. (J). 12.99 (978-0-7641-7922-8(5)) Barron's Educational Series, Inc.

Rex, Michael. Goodnight Goon. 2008. 32p. (J). (ps-k). 14.99 (***978-0-399-24534-3(0)** , Putnam Juvenile) Penguin Group (USA) Inc.

Rey, H. A. & Rey, Margret. Curious George Good Night Book: A Tabbed Board Book. 2007. (Illus.). 14p. (J). (gr. k-ps). bds. 7.99 (***978-0-618-77711-2(3))** Houghton Mifflin Co. Trade & Reference Div.

Ricci, Christine. Buenas Noches, Dora! Cuento Para Levantar la Tapita. Hall, Susan, illus. 2004. (Dora the Explorer Ser.).Tr. of Good Night, Dora!. (SPA.). 16p. (J). pap. 5.99 (978-0-689-86648-7(8) , Libros Para Ninos) Simon & Schuster Children's Publishing.

—Good Night, Dora! A Lift-the-Flap Story. Hall, Susan, illus. 2002. (Dora the Explorer Ser.).Tr. of Good Night, Dora!. 16p. (J). (ps-1). pap. 5.99 (978-0-689-84774-5(2) , Simon Spotlight/Nickelodeon) Simon & Schuster Children's Publishing.

Rich, Scharlotte. I Love My Daddy. 2001. 96p. (J). 7.99 (978-0-310-70104-0(X)) Zondervan.

—I Love My Mommy. 2001. 96p. (J). 7.99 (978-0-310-70103-3(1)) Zondervan.

Rickards, Lynne. Jack's Bed. Beardshaw, Rosalind, illus. 2006. (Green Bananas Ser.). 48p. (J). (gr. k-2). pap. (978-0-7787-1044-8(0)) Crabtree Publishing Co.

Ritchie, Alison. I Don't Want to Sleep Alone! Gale, Cathy, illus. 2002. 32p. (J). 5.95 (978-1-58925-372-8(8) , tiger tales) ME Media LLC.

—I Don't Want to Sleep Alone! 2002. (gr. k-3). lib. bdg. 14.10 (978-0-613-56427-4(8)) Tandem Library Bks.

Robbins, Beth. Tom Is Afraid of the Dark. Stuart, Jon, illus. 2001. (It's OK! Ser.). 24p. (J). (ps-k). pap. 3.95 (978-0-7894-7420-9(4) , D K Ink) Dorling Kindersley Publishing, Inc.

Robbins, Maria Polushkin. Mother, Mother, I Want Another. Goodell, Jon, illus. 2005. 32p. (J). (ps-1). 14.95 (978-0-375-82588-0(6)); lib. bdg. 16.99 (978-0-375-92588-7(0)) Random Hse. Children's Bks. (Knopf Bks. for Young Readers).

Roberts, Phyllis. Teeny Tiny Star. 2007. (Illus.). 30p. (J). lib. bdg. 19.95 (***978-1-933732-40-4(7)** , Bear Hug Bks.) MidAmerica Publishing Co.

Robinson, Laura. William & the Christmas Moon: A Shadow Casting Bedtime Story. 2000. (Illus.). 32p. (J). (gr. k up). spiral bd. 32.00 (978-0-87846-596-5(0)) Museum of Fine Arts, Boston.

Rock, Lois. I Wish Tonight. Wilson, Anne, illus. 2001. 28p. (J). (ps-3). 16.00 (978-1-56148-315-0(X)) Good Bks.

Rockwell, Anne F. Here Comes the Night. 2006. (Illus.). 32p. (J). (***978-0-7522-7663-2(8)**); 16.95 (978-0-8050-7663-9(8)) Holt, Henry & Co.

Roep, Nada. Kisses. Cate, Marijke Ten, illus. 1998. 32p. (J). 15.95 (978-1-886910-85-0(5) , Lemniscaat) Boyds Mills Pr.

Rohmann, Eric. Clara & Asha. Rohmann, Eric, illus. 2005. (Illus.). 40p. (J). (ps-ps). 16.95 (978-1-59643-031-0(1)) Roaring Brook Pr.

Root, Phyllis. Ten Sleepy Sheep. Gaber, Susan, illus. 2004. 32p. (J). (gr. k-k). 15.99 (978-0-7636-1545-1(5)) Candlewick Pr.

Rosenberg, Liz. Eli's Night-Light. Yardley, Joanna, illus. 2001. 32p. (J). (ps-1). pap. 15.95 (978-0-531-30316-0(0) , Orchard Bks.) Scholastic, Inc.

Rosenberg, Liz & Yardley, Joanna. Eli's Night-Light. 2001. (Illus.). (J). lib. bdg. (978-0-531-33316-7(7) , Orchard Bks.) Scholastic, Inc.

Ross, Tony. Hora de Dormir. 2006. (Little Princess Ser.).Tr. of Bedtime. (SPA.). (J). (ps-k). bds. 7.95 (978-968-19-1488-2(0) , AT33282) Lectorum Pubns., Inc.

—I Don't Want to Go to Bed. Ross, Tony, illus. 2004. (Illus.). 28p. (J). pap. 4.95 (978-1-929132-66-9(2)) Kane/Miller Bk. Pubs., Inc.

Roth, Carol. Who Will Tuck Me in Tonight? 2006. (Illus.). 32p. (J). pap. 6.95 (978-0-7358-1976-4(9)) North-South Bks., Inc.

—Who Will Tuck Me in Tonight? Gorbachev, Valeri, illus. 2003. 32p. (J). 15.95 (978-0-7358-1772-2(3)); 16.50 (978-0-7358-1773-9(1)) North-South Bks., Inc.

—Who Will Tuck Me in Tonight Sp. 2007. (J). 16.50 (978-0-7358-2108-8(9)); (Illus.). pap. 6.95 (978-0-7358-2107-1(0)) North-South Bks., Inc.

Rothstein, Gloria L. Sheep Asleep. Date not set. 224p. (J). (ps-1). pap. 4.99 (978-0-06-443717-2(5)) HarperCollins Pubs.

Rowe, Papa. Itchy Lee & Itchy Dee Mcgee. Wilkins, Kevan & Mason, Shannon, eds. Shortell, Stephen, illus. ed. 2006. (J). 15.99 (978-0-9778858-0-0(1)) WowZee Works Inc.

Runnells, Treesha. Ten Wishing Stars: A Countdown to Bedtime Book. Dillard, Sarah, illus. 2005. 22p. (J). 9.95 (978-1-58117-187-7(0) , Intervisual/Piggy Toes) Dalmatian Pr.

Rusackas, Francesca. Daddy All Day Long. Burris, Priscilla, tr. Burris, Priscilla, illus. 2004. 32p. (J). (ps-k). lib. bdg. 13.89 (978-0-06-050285-0(1)) HarperCollins Pubs.

Russo, Marisabina. The Bunnies Are Not in Their Beds. Russo, Marisabina, illus. 2007. 40p. (J). (ps-2). lib. bdg. 17.99 (978-0-375-93961-7(X)); (Illus.). 15.99 (978-0-375-83961-0(5)) Random Hse. Children's Bks. (Schwartz & Wade Bks.).

Rydell, Katy. Wind Says Good Night. Jorgensen, David, illus. 2000. 32p. (J). (gr. k-3). pap. 5.95 (978-0-618-08585-9(8)) Houghton Mifflin Co. Trade & Reference Div.

—Wind Says Good Night. Jorgensen, David, illus. 2000. (ps-ps). lib. bdg. 14.10 (978-0-613-30193-0(5)) Tandem Library Bks.

—Wind Says Good Night. 2000. (Illus.). (J). (978-0-606-21735-4(5)) Tandem Library Bks.

Salas, Macarena, ed. Dopey's Bedtime/Tontin Se Va la Cama: A Book about Routines/Un Libro Sobre Rutinas. 2005. (SPA.). 6p. (J). bds. 3.99 (978-0-439-66360-1(1) , Scholastic en Espanol) Scholastic, Inc.

Saltzberg, Barney. Cornelius P. Mud, Are You Ready for Bed? Saltzberg, Barney, illus. (Illus.). (J). (gr. k-ps). 2007. 26p. bds. 6.99 (978-0-7636-3303-5(8)); 2005. 32p. 15.99 (978-0-7636-2399-9(7)) Candlewick Pr.

—Goodnight Kisses. 2006. (Illus.). 14p. (J). bds., bds. 8.95 (978-0-15-205647-6(5) , Red Wagon Bks.) Harcourt Children's Bks.

Sanroman, Susana. Senora Reganona: A Mexican Bedtime Story. Domi, illus. 2006. 20p. (J). (gr. k-4). reprint ed. 15.00 (978-1-4223-5466-7(0)) DIANE Publishing Co.

Santomero, Angela C. Buenas Noches, Blue. Pontillo, Jenine, illus. 2003. (Blue's Clues Ser.). (SPA.). 22p. (J). bds. 4.99 (978-0-689-86309-7(8) , Libros Para Ninos) Simon & Schuster Children's Publishing.

—Good Night Blue. Pontillo, Jenine, illus. 1999. (Blue's Clues Ser.). 10p. (J). (ps-k). bds. 4.99 (978-0-689-82950-5(7) , Simon Spotlight/Nickelodeon) Simon & Schuster Children's Publishing.

Sanzo, Stephen. Cranky Pants. Whitlock, Matt, illus. 2005. 32p. 16.95 (978-0-9759627-0-1(1)) Cranky Pants Publishing, LLC.

Sauer, Cat. Flip Flop & Hoot. Jankowski, Dan, illus. l.t. ed. 2003. (Brown Bag Bedtime Bks.: 1). 35p. (YA). spiral bd. 16.95 (978-0-9704460-6-0(3)) Writer's Ink. Studios, Inc.

—A Possum in the Roses. Jankowski, Dan, illus. l.t. ed. 2003. (Brown Bag Bedtime Bks.: 1). 27p. (YA). spiral bd. 16.95 (978-0-9704460-7-7(1)) Writer's Ink. Studios, Inc.

—What's a Jaybird to Do? Jankowski, Dan, illus. l.t. ed. 2003. (Brown Bag Bedtime Bks.: 1). 31p. (YA). spiral bd. 16.95 (978-0-9704460-8-4(X)) Writer's Ink. Studios, Inc.

Saunders, Helen. Good Night Little Man. Groshelle, Dave, illus. 2006. (J). (978-0-9763143-4-9(7)) Happy Heart Kids Publishing.

Sauro, Joan. Does God Ever Sleep? Sauro, Joan, photos by. 2005. (Illus.). 32p. (J). (ps-3). 8.99 (978-1-59473-110-5(1)) SkyLight Paths Publishing.

Scarry, Patsy. Good Night, Little Bear. Scarry, Richard, illus. (J). (gr. k-k). 2004. 26p. bds. 4.99 (978-0-375-82840-9(0)); 2001. 24p. 2.99 (978-0-307-98624-5(1)) Random Hse. Children's Bks. (Golden Bks.).

Schaefer, Carole Lexa. Down in the Woods at Sleepytime. Cabban, Vanessa, illus. 2000. 32p. (J). (gr. k-k). 15.99 (978-0-7636-0843-9(2)) Candlewick Pr.

—Down in the Woods at Sleepytime. Cabban, Vanessa, illus. 2004. 24p. (J). (gr. k-ps). bds. 6.99 (978-0-7636-2566-5(3)) Candlewick Pr.

—Someone Says. Morgan, Pierr, illus. 2003. 32p. (J). (gr. k-2). 15.99 (978-0-670-03664-6(1) , Viking Juvenile) Penguin Group (USA) Inc.

Schaefer, Lola M. Out of the Night. Gilbert, Rob, illus. 1999. 32p. (ps-k). pap. 6.95 (978-1-58089-023-6(7)) Charlesbridge Publishing, Inc.

Schimel, Lawrence. Little Pirate Goes to Bed. Perez, Sara Rojo, illus. 2007. 12p. (J). (ps-k). bds. 6.99 (978-1-58476-546-2(1)) Innovative Kids.

Scholastic, Inc. Staff. Bedtime Storybook Collection. 2007. (Sweet Dreams Ser.). 96p. (J). pap. 7.99 (***978-0-439-93403-9(6)** , Cartwheel Bks.) Scholastic, Inc.

Scholastic, Inc. Staff, et al. Lights Out! Tadgell, Nicole, illus. 2004. (Just for You! Ser.). 32p. (J). (gr. k-1). pap. 3.99 (978-0-439-56868-5(4) , Teaching Resources) Scholastic, Inc.

Schories, Pat, illus. Biscuit. 2002. (Biscuit Ser.). (J). 12.34 (978-0-7587-0002-5(4)) Book Wholesalers, Inc.

Schroeder, Lisa. Baby Can't Sleep. Garofoli, Viviana, illus. 2005. 32p. (J). (ps). 12.95 (978-1-4027-2171-7(4)) Sterling Publishing Co., Inc.

Schubert, Ingrid & Schubert, Dieter. There's a Crocodile Under My Bed. 2nd ed. 2005. (Illus.). 32p. (J). (ps-1). 15.95 (978-1-932425-48-2(9) , Lemniscaat) Boyds Mills Pr.

Schwartz, Amy. Some Babies. Schwartz, Amy, illus. 2000. (Illus.). 32p. (J). (ps-k). 16.99 (978-0-531-33287-0(X) , Orchard Bks.) Scholastic, Inc.

Scillian, Devin. Cosmo's Moon. Braught, Mark, illus. 2003. 40p. (J). (gr. k-5). 15.95 (978-1-58536-123-6(2)) Sleeping Bear Pr.

Scotton, Rob. Go to Sleep, Russell the Sheep. Scotton, Rob, illus. 2007. 16p. (J). 9.99 (***978-0-06-128434-2(3))** HarperCollins Pubs.

Scotton, Rob. Russell the Sheep. 2005. (Illus.). 40p. (J). (ps-2). 15.99 (978-0-06-059848-8(4)) HarperCollins Pubs.

—Russell the Sheep. Scotton, Rob, illus. 2005. (Illus.). 40p. (J). (ps-ps). lib. bdg. 17.89 (978-0-06-059849-5(2)) HarperCollins Pubs.

Seelen, Christopher. Daddy Is That the Best You Got? Moen, Tyler, illus. 2005. 36p. (J). 5.97 (978-0-9776385-0-5(2)) JoBen Bks., LLC.

Shulevitz, Uri. The Moon in My Room. Shulevitz, Uri, illus. 2003. (Illus.). 32p. (J). reprint ed. pap. 5.95 (978-0-374-45314-5(4) , Sunburst) Farrar, Straus & Giroux.

Shulman, Mark. Nutsy the Robot Goes to Bed. Boyce, Katie, illus. 2006. (Nutsy the Robot Ser.). 10p. (J). bds. 15.95 (978-0-7696-4605-3(0) , Brighter Child) School Specialty Publishing.

Shultz, Lucy. Goodnight Faces. 2007. (Illus.). 12p. (J). (ps). bds. 5.99 (***978-1-58476-672-8(7)** , IKIDS) Innovative Kids.

Sidle, Christian. Murphy Dog Bedtime Story. Lynn, Dianne, illus. l.t. ed. 2001. 48p. (J). (ps-3). per. 12.50 (978-0-9708053-3-1(0)) Authors & Artists Publishers of New York, Inc.

Siegel, Terri. Goodnight Princess Scharazad. 2005. (J). lib. bdg. 19.95 (***978-0-9754728-5-9(2)** , Bear Hug Bks.) MidAmerica Publishing Co.

Slater, Teddy. Llamas in Pajamas. Kindert, Jennifer, illus. 2006. 32p. (J). (ps-ps). 6.95 (978-1-4027-2021-5(1)) Sterling Publishing Co., Inc.

Sleepytime Monsters Pop-up Boggle Eyes. 2001. (Illus.). 10p. (J). (ps-k). 2.99 (978-0-307-20042-6(6) , Golden Bks.) Random Hse. Children's Bks.

Smallfield, Jane. The Bedtime Treasury of Real Fairy Tales. Smallfield, Graeme, illus. 2005. 96p. 17.95 (978-0-689-03923-2(9) , Milk & Cookies) ibooks, Inc.

Smee, Nicola. No Bed Without Ted. 2005. (Illus.). 24p. (J). (ps-ps). 14.95 (978-1-58234-963-3(0)) Bloomsbury Publishing.

Smith, Jane. Starlight Starbright. 2006. 12p. 12.95 (978-1-58117-495-3(0) , Intervisual/Piggy Toes) Dalmatian Pr.

Smucker, Anna. Outside the Window. Schuett, Stacey, illus. 2005. 32p. (J). reprint ed. per. 7.95 (978-1-891852-40-4(X)) Quarrier Pr.

Sobel, June. The Goodnight Train. Huliska-Beith, Laura, illus. 2006. 32p. (J). 16.00 (978-0-15-205436-6(7)) Harcourt Trade Pubs.

Spencely, Annabel, illus. The Kingfisher Treasury of Bedtime Stories. 2003. (Kingfisher Treasury of Stories Ser.: Vol. 9). 160p. (J). (gr. k-3). pap. 5.95 (978-0-7534-5669-9(9) , Kingfisher) Houghton Mifflin Co. Trade & Reference Div.

Spinelli, Eileen. Kittycat Lullaby. Mortimer, Anne, illus. 2001. 32p. (J). 13.49 (978-0-7868-2400-7(X)) Disney Pr.

—Kittycat Lullaby. Mortimer, Anne, illus. 2001. 32p. (ps-1). 14.99 (978-0-7868-0458-0(0)) Hyperion Bks. for Children.

—When Mama Comes Home Tonight. Dyer, Jane, illus. (Classic Board Bks.). (J). (ps-k). 2001. 30p. bds. 7.99 (978-0-689-84220-7(1) , Little Simon); 1999. 30p. bds. 14.00 (978-0-689-82714-3(8) , Simon & Schuster Children's Publishing); 1998. 32p. 14.00 (978-0-689-81065-7(2)); 2002. 32p. reprint ed. 6.99 (978-0-689-84897-1(8) , Aladdin) Simon & Schuster Children's Publishing.

—When Mama Comes Home Tonight. 2002. (gr. k-3). lib. bdg. 15.30 (978-0-613-62881-5(0)) Tandem Library Bks.

Spinner, Stephanie. It's a Miracle! A Hanukkah Storybook. 2007. (Illus.). 40p. (J). (ps-3). 6.99 (***978-1-4169-5001-1(X)*** , Aladdin) Simon & Schuster Children's Publishing.

Sproule, Gail. Singing in Dark. Lott, Sheena, illus. 2006. 32p. pap. 7.95 (978-1-55041-348-9(1)) Fitzhenry & Whiteside, Ltd. CAN. *Dist:* F & W Pubns., Inc.

St-Aubin, Bruno. My Favorite Monster. 2005. (Read-It! Readers Ser.). (Illus.). 32p. (J). (gr. k-3). 18.60 (978-1-4048-1029-7(3)) Picture Window Bks.

Steck-Vaughn Staff. I Was Just about to Go to Bed. 1999. (Illus.). pap. 1.20 (978-0-8172-8726-9(4)) Steck-Vaughn.

Steinbrenner, Jessica. My Sleepy Room. 2004. (Illus.). 32p. (J). 15.95 (978-1-59354-007-4(8)) Handprint Bks.

Strickland, Brad & MacHale, D. J. The Storm, No. 4. 2006. (Flight 29 Down Ser.: Vol. 4). 224p. (J). (gr. 4-7). pap. 5.99 (978-0-448-44130-6(6) , Grosset & Dunlap) Penguin Group (USA) Inc.

Style Guide Staff, illus. Blue's Bedtime: A Cloth Book to Touch & Feel. 2001. (Blue's Clues Ser.). 8p. (J). 12.95 (978-0-689-84041-8(1) , Simon Spotlight/Nickelodeon) Simon & Schuster Children's Publishing.

Su, Lucy, illus. Goodnight, Little Leprechaun. 2003. 16p. 10.95 (978-0-7171-3612-4(4)) Gill & MacMillan, Ltd. IRL. *Dist:* Irish Bks. & Media, Inc.

Syatt, Steve. Close Your Eyes. Caruso, Frank, illus. 2007. 32p. (J). 10.95 (***978-0-312-37381-8(3)***) St. Martin's Pr.

Sykes, Julie. A Dormir, Tigrito. Warnes, Tim, illus. 2002. (Little Tiger Board Book Ser.). (SPA.). 88p. 8.95 (978-84-488-0928-7(9) , BS7936) Beascoa, Ediciones S.A. ESP. *Dist:* Lectorum Pubns., Inc.

—I Don't Want to Go to Bed! Warnes, Tim, illus. 1998. 14p. (J). (ps-2). bds. 6.95 (978-1-888444-33-9(9) , 21301) Little Tiger Pr.

—I Don't Want to Go to Bed! Warnes, Tim, illus. 2001. (J). 32p. 5.95 (978-1-58925-350-6(7)); 26p. tchr. ed. 14.95 (978-1-58925-001-7(X)) ME Media LLC. (tiger tales).

—I Don't Want to Go to Bed! Warnes, Tim, illus. 1998. (ENG, URD, SPA, VIE & CHI.). 32p. (J). (978-1-85430-535-0(2)); (978-1-85430-537-4(9)); (978-1-85430-539-8(5)); (978-1-85430-538-1(7)); (978-1-85430-536-7(0)) Magi Pubns.

—Time for Bed, Little Tiger. Warnes, Tim, illus. 2000. 12p. (J). (ps-k). bds. 5.95 (978-1-58431-018-1(9)) Little Tiger Pr.

—Time for Bed, Little Tiger. Warnes, Tim, illus. 2001. (Little Tiger Lift-the-Flap Ser.). 14p. (J). (ps-k). bds. 5.95 (978-1-58925-654-5(9) , tiger tales) ME Media LLC.

Sykes, Marsha F. The Village of Spence Hill: A Multicultural Bedtime Story. Sykes, Johnnie F., illus. 2002. 20p. (J). (ps-6). pap. 6.00 (978-0-9720816-0-3(7)) M & JP Publishing.

Szekeres, Cyndy. Buenas Noches, Rapo. 2005. (Collection Ternura Bedtime Stories Ser.).Tr. of Good Night, Little Fox. (SPA.). (J). (gr. k-2). pap. 4.95 (978-950-11-0574-2(1)) Sigmar ARG. *Dist:* Iaconi, Mariuccia Bk. Imports.

—A Comer! 2005. (Collection Ternura Bedtime Stories Ser.).Tr. of Time to Eat!. (SPA.). (J). (gr. k-2). pap. 4.95 (978-950-11-0576-6(8)) Sigmar ARG. *Dist:* Iaconi, Mariuccia Bk. Imports.

—Las Cuentas Osito. 2005. (Collection Ternura Bedtime Stories Ser.).Tr. of Little Bear Counts. (SPA.). (J). (gr. k-2). pap. 4.95 (978-950-11-0634-3(9)) Sigmar ARG. *Dist:* Iaconi, Mariuccia Bk. Imports.

—Un Dia Muy Especial. 2005. (Collection Ternura Bedtime Stories Ser.).Tr. of Very Special Day. (SPA.). (J). (gr. k-2). pap. 4.95 (978-950-11-0632-9(2)) Sigmar ARG. *Dist:* Iaconi, Mariuccia Bk. Imports.

—El Juego de Las Escondidas. 2005. (Collection Ternura Bedtime Stories Ser.).Tr. of Hide & Go Seek. (SPA.). (J). (gr. k-2). pap. 4.95 (978-950-11-0577-3(6)) Sigmar ARG. *Dist:* Iaconi, Mariuccia Bk. Imports.

—La Mudanza de la Ratita. 2005. (Collection Ternura Bedtime Stories Ser.).Tr. of Little Mouse Moves. (SPA.). (J). (gr. k-2). pap. 4.95 (978-950-11-0635-0(7)) Sigmar ARG. *Dist:* Iaconi, Mariuccia Bk. Imports.

—Nada Que Hacer. 2005. (Collection Ternura Bedtime Stories Ser.).Tr. of Nothing To Do. (SPA.). (J). (gr. k-2). pap. 4.95 (978-950-11-0573-5(3)) Sigmar ARG. *Dist:* Iaconi, Mariuccia Bk. Imports.

—El Perrito Perdido. 2005. (Collection Ternura Bedtime Stories Ser.). (SPA.). (J). (gr. k-2). pap. 4.95 (978-950-11-0633-6(0)) Sigmar ARG. *Dist:* Iaconi, Mariuccia Bk. Imports.

Tabby, Abigail. Baby Tickle Shakes: Book & Rattle Gift Set. Beeke, Tiphanie, illus. 2007. (Little Simon Baby Ser.). 16p. (J). bds. 9.99 (978-1-4169-1900-1(7) , Little Simon) Simon & Schuster Children's Publishing.

Tafuri, Nancy. Goodnight, My Duckling. 2005. (Illus.). 32p. (J). pap. 16.95 (978-0-439-39881-7(9)) Scholastic, Inc.

Tarbox, A. D. Already Asleep. Olson, Julie, illus. 2006. 32p. 12.95 (978-0-9766805-6-7(4) , Moo Pr.) Keene Publishing.

They Might Be Giants Staff, et al. Bed, Bed, Bed. Ozama, Marcel, illus. 2003. 48p. (ps-5). 16.95 incl. audio compact disk (978-0-7432-5024-5(9)) Simon & Schuster.

Thomas, Shelley Moore. Good Night, Good Knight. Plecas, Jennifer, illus. 2002. 11.49 (978-1-4046-1571-7(7)) Book Wholesalers, Inc.

—Good Night, Good Knight. Plecas, Jennifer, illus. 2000. 48p. (J). (ps-2). 13.99 (978-0-525-46326-9(7) , Dutton Juvenile) Penguin Group (USA) Inc.

Thomas, Shelley Moore & Plecas, Jennifer. Good Night, Good Knight. 2002. (Easy-to-Read Ser.). (Illus.). 48p. (J). pap. 3.99 (978-0-14-230201-9(5) , Puffin) Penguin Group (USA) Inc.

Thompson, Lauren. Little Quack's Bedtime. Anderson, Derek, illus. 2005. 32p. (J). 14.95 (978-0-689-86894-8(4)) Simon & Schuster Children's Publishing.

Thompson, Richard. Foo. Fernandes, Eugenie, illus. 2000. (Annikins Ser.). 24p. (J). (ps-k). pap. 1.25 (978-1-55037-641-8(1)) Annick Pr., Ltd. CAN. *Dist:* Firefly Bks., Ltd.

Thomson, Sarah L. Imagine a Night. Gonsalves, Rob, illus. 2003. 40p. (J). 18.99 (978-0-689-85218-3(5) , Atheneum) Simon & Schuster Children's Publishing.

Tibo, Gilles. Noches de Papel. (Barril Sin Fondo Ser.). (SPA.). (J). (gr. 3-5). pap. (978-968-6465-32-7(4)) Casa de Estudios de Literatura y Talleres Artisticos Amaquemecan A.C. MEX. *Dist:* Lectorum Pubns., Inc.

Tildes, Phyllis L. Billy's Big-Boy Bed. Tildes, Phyllis L., illus. 2003. 32p. pap. 6.95 (978-1-57091-606-9(3)) Charlesbridge Publishing, Inc.

—Billy's Big-Boy Bed. 2003. (gr. k-3). lib. bdg. 15.25 (978-0-613-70803-6(2)) Tandem Library Bks.

Tocco, Nicole. Toothbrush, Jammies, Man in the Moon—Why Is It Bedtime So Soon? 2006. (J). (978-0-7666-2463-4(3)) Modern Publishing.

Torrel, Wendy. Guardian of Dreams: A Bedtime Story, Klingbeil, Kendall, illus. l.t. ed. 2004. 32p. (J). 14.95 (978-0-9746890-0-5(9)); pap. 10.95 (978-0-9746890-1-2(7)) White Tulip Publishing.

Train, Mary. Time for the Fair. Hayes, Karel, illus. 2005. (ps). 15.95 (978-0-89272-694-3(6)) Down East Bks.

Tresh, Doreene. Elephants, Aren't They Great? 2003. (Illus.). 28p. (J). per. 9.95 (978-1-59405-028-2(7)) New Age World Publishing.

Twinkle, Twinkle Little Star Pillow Book. 2003. (J). (978-1-59292-027-3(6)) SoftPlay, Inc.

Uncle Anup's Bedtime Stories with a Moral. 2001. (YA). per. 11.99 (978-0-9657083-3-3(0)) ANUP Research & Multimedia LP.

Under the Bed: Individual Title-Six Packs. (Chiquilibros Ser.). (gr. k-1). 23.00 (978-0-7635-0449-6(1)) Rigby Education.

Verlander, Susan. Goodnight Country. 2004. (Illus.). 28p. (J). 13.95 (978-0-8118-4172-6(3)) Chronicle Bks. LLC.

Vestergaard, Hope. Hillside Lullaby. Moore, Margie, tr. Moore, Margie, illus. 2006. 32p. (J). (ps). 15.99 (978-0-525-47215-5(0) , Dutton Juvenile) Penguin Group (USA) Inc.

Villarreal, Carlos C. The Light Beneath the Shadow: Sharing God's Love with Your Child as You Read Together: A Bedtime Story Intended to Awaken Your Parental Christian Spirit. 2006. 48p. pap. 12.95 (978-1-4241-1247-0(8)) PublishAmerica, Inc.

Villaseñor, Victor. Goodnight, Papito Dios/Buenas Noches, Papito Dios. Ramírez, José, illus. 2007. (SPA & ENG.). 32p. (J). (ps-2). 15.95 (***978-1-55885-467-3(3)*** , Piñata Books) Arte Publico Pr.

Waddell, Martin. Who Do You Love. Ashforth, Camilla, illus. 2004. 24p. (J). (gr. k-ps). bds. 6.99 (978-0-7636-2565-8(5)) Candlewick Pr.

Wahl, Jan. Elf Night. Weevers, Peter, illus. 2005. (Picture Bks.). 32p. (gr. k-2). 15.25 (978-1-57505-512-1(0)) Lerner Publishing Group.

—Humphrey's Bear. Joyce, William, illus. 2005. 32p. (J). pap. 6.95 (978-0-8050-7887-9(8) , Holt, Henry & Co. Bks. For Young Readers) Holt, Henry & Co.

Walsh, Joanna. All Asleep. rev. ed. 2008. 24p. (J). (ps). bds. 6.99 (***978-0-316-11871-2(0)***) Little, Brown Bks. for Young Readers.

Walton, Rick. So Many Bunnies: A Bedtime ABC & Counting Book. Miglio, Paige, illus. 32p. (J). (ps-3). 2002. pap. 5.95 (978-0-06-443751-6(5) , Harper Trophy); 2000. 6.99 (978-0-688-17364-7(0) , Harper Festival) HarperCollins Pubs.

—So Many Bunnies: A Bedtime ABC & Counting Book. 1998. (Illus.). 32p. (J). (ps-1). 15.89 (978-0-688-13657-4(5)) HarperCollins Pubs.

—So Many Bunnies: A Bedtime ABC & Counting Book. Miglio, Paige, illus. 1998. 32p. (J). (ps-3). 17.99 (978-0-688-13656-7(7)) HarperCollins Pubs.

Wang, Dorothea DePrisco & Imperato, Teresa. All the Ways I Love You. Downing, Julie, illus. 2005. 10p. (J). 8.95 (978-1-58117-190-7(0) , Intervisual/Piggy Toes) Dalmatian Pr.

Ward, Nick. Don't Eat the Babysitter. 2006. 32p. (J). (gr. k-3). 9.95 (978-0-385-75062-2(5) , Fickling, David Bks.) Random Hse. Children's Bks.

Warner, Rex. Men & Gods: Myths & Legends of the Ancient Greeks. Gorey, Ward, illus. 2008. 296p. (J). 16.95 (***978-1-59017-263-6(9)*** , NYR Children's Collection) New York Review of Bks., Inc., The.

Warnes, Tim. Can't You Sleep, Dotty? Warnes, Tim, illus. 2003. (Illus.). 32p. (J). pap. 5.95 (978-1-58925-376-6(0) , tiger tales) ME Media LLC.

—Can't You Sleep, Dotty? 2001. (Illus.). 28p. (J). tchr. ed. 14.95 (978-1-58925-010-9(9) , tiger tales) ME Media LLC.

—Can't You Sleep, Dotty? 2003. (ps-2). lib. bdg. 14.10 (978-0-613-84706-3(7)) Tandem Library Bks.

Watt, Fiona. Sleepy Baby Board Bk. Mackinnon, Catherine-Anne, illus. 2006. 10p. (J). bds. 8.99 (978-0-7945-1071-8(X) , Usborne) EDC Publishing.

Watt, Fiona & Wells, Rachel. Baby's Bedtime. 2004. (Baby's World Ser.). (Illus.). 16p. (J). (ps up). pap. 4.95 (978-0-7460-3374-6(5)) EDC Publishing.

Watters, Mark. Bedtime Snories for Children, Volume One. 2005. 48p. (J). pap. 13.50 (978-1-4116-4995-8(8)) Lulu.com.

Weber, Lou, ed. Bedtime Higs Musical Treasury. 2005. 40p. (J). bds. 12.98 (978-1-4127-3478-3(9) , 7259500) Publications International, Ltd.

—Bedtime Stories Carry Case. 2005. 48p. (J). bds. 7.98 (978-1-4127-3450-9(9) , 7251800) Publications International, Ltd.

Weedn, Flavia M. & Weedn, Lisa. I Feel Happy: Bedtime Magic for Baby's Sweet Dreams. 1999. (Flavia Children's Board Bks.). (Illus.). 26p. (ps up). pap. 7.95 (978-0-7683-2065-7(8)) CEDCO Publishing.

Weeks, Sarah. Counting Ovejas. Diaz, David, illus. 2006. (ENG & SPA.). 40p. (J). (ps-1). 17.99 (978-0-689-86750-7(6) , Atheneum) Simon & Schuster Children's Publishing.

Weiss, Ellen & Weiss, Ellen. Twins Go to Bed. 2004. (Ready-to-Read Ser.). (Illus.). 24p. (J). pap. 3.99 (978-0-689-86517-6(1) , Aladdin) Simon & Schuster Children's Publishing.

Wells, Rosemary. Goodnight Max. Wells, Rosemary, illus. 2000. (Max & Ruby Ser.). (Illus.). 14p. (J). (gr. k-2). pap. 11.99 (978-0-670-88707-1(2) , Viking Juvenile) Penguin Group (USA) Inc.

Weninger, Brigitte. Good Night, Nori. Bishop, Kathryn, tr. from GER. Yonezu, Yusuke, illus. 2007. 32p. (J). (ps-2). 15.99 (***978-0-698-40065-8(8)*** , Minedition) Penguin Group (USA) Inc.

Whoozit? Goodnight Board Book. 2000. (J). bds. (978-0-9676292-1-6(7)) Manhattan Toy.

Whoozit? Goodnight Book. 2000. (J). bds. (978-0-9676292-0-9(9)) Manhattan Toy.

Whoozit Goodnight Book & Puppet Set. 2000. (J). bds. (978-0-9676292-2-3(5)) Manhattan Toy.

Whybrow, Ian. The Noisy Way to Bed. Beeke, Tiphanie, tr. Beeke, Tiphanie, illus. 2004. (J). (978-0-439-55690-3(2) , Levine, Arthur A. Bks.) Scholastic, Inc.

—Noisy Way to Bed. Beeke, Tiphanie, tr. Beeke, Tiphanie, illus. 2004. 32p. (J). 16.95 (978-0-439-55689-7(9) , Levine, Arthur A. Bks.) Scholastic, Inc.

Wiede, Edie. Pinky & Bluey Explore the Sky. 1999. (J). (gr. k-3). pap. 6.95 (978-0-533-13148-8(0)) Vantage Pr., Inc.

Wilcoxen, Chuck. Niccolini's Song. Buehner, Mark, illus. 2004. 40p. (J). (ps). 16.99 (978-0-525-46805-9(6) , Dutton Juvenile) Penguin Group (USA) Inc.

—Niccolini's Song. Buehner, Mark, illus. 2006. 40p. (J). (ps). pap. 6.99 (978-0-14-240710-3(0) , Puffin) Penguin Group (USA) Inc.

Wild, Margaret. Nighty Night! Argent, Kerry, illus. 2001. 32p. (J). (ps-1). 15.95 (978-1-56145-246-0(7)); (978-0-7333-0590-0(3)) Peachtree Pubs., Ltd.

Willems, Mo. Don't Let the Pigeon Stay up Late! 2006. (Illus.). 40p. (ps-1). 12.99 (978-0-7868-3746-5(2)) Hyperion Bks. for Children.

Williamgoldenpen. Quacker's Bedtime Stories. 2006. 49p. pap. 12.95 (978-1-4241-2236-3(8)) PublishAmerica, Inc.

Williamgoldenpen. Quacker's Bedtime Stories... Continued. 2007. (ENG.). 68p. per. 12.95 (***978-1-4241-7448-5(1)***) PublishAmerica, Inc.

Williams, Regina. What If... Keith, Doug, illus. l.t. ed. 2001. 32p. (J). (ps up). 15.95 (978-0-935699-22-7(8)) Illumination Arts Publishing Co., Inc.

Willis, Jeanne. Monster Bed. 1999. (J). (978-0-606-17392-6(7)) Tandem Library Bks.

Willis, Jeanne & Varley, Susan. The Monster Bed. 1999. (Illus.). 32p. (J). (ps-3). mass mkt. 5.95 (978-0-688-16707-3(1) , Harper Trophy) HarperCollins Pubs.

Willson, Sarah. Dora's Backpack. Roper, Robert, illus. 2002. (Dora the Explorer Ser.). 24p. (J). pap. 3.50 (978-0-689-84720-2(3) , Simon Spotlight/Nickelodeon) Simon & Schuster Children's Publishing.

—Dora's Backpack. 2002. (ps-2). lib. bdg. 11.25 (978-0-613-73315-1(0)) Tandem Library Bks.

Wilson, Karma. Sleepyhead. Segal, John, illus. 2006. 32p. (J). (ps-2). 15.95 (978-1-4169-1241-5(X) , McElderry, Margaret K.) Simon & Schuster Children's Publishing.

Wing, Natasha. Go to Bed, Monster! Kantorovitz, Sylvie, illus. 2007. 40p. (J). (ps-2). 16.00 (978-0-15-205775-6(7)) Harcourt Trade Pubs.

Winthrop, Elizabeth. Maggie & the Monster. DePaola, Tomie, illus. 2007. 32p. (J). 16.99 (978-0-399-24711-8(4) , Putnam Juvenile) Penguin Group (USA) Inc.

Wisnewski, Andrea, illus. & retold by. Little Red Riding Hood. Wisnewski, Andrea, retold by. 2007. 32p. (J). (ps-3). 18.95 (978-1-56792-303-2(8)) Godine, David R. Pub.

Wolf, Jackie. Picture Me Peek-A-Boo Bedtime. 2001. (Picture Me Ser.). (Illus.). 10p. (J). (ps up). bds. 4.99 (978-1-57151-592-6(5)) Playhouse Publishing.

Wood, A. & Hawkins, Emily A. Amazing Baby Night-Night, Baby! Jolley, Mike, illus. 2007. (Amazing Baby Ser.). 16p. (J). bds. 5.95 (***978-1-59223-802-6(5)*** , Silver Dolphin Bks.) Advantage Pubs. Group.

Wood, Audrey. Cerditos. Campoy, F. Isabel, tr. Wood, Don, illus. 2006. 34p. (J). bds. 6.95 (978-0-15-205731-2(5) , Voyager Bks./Libros Viajeros) Harcourt Children's Bks.

—The Napping House. Wood, Don, illus. 2005. 32p. (J). bds. 10.95 (978-0-15-205620-9(3) , Red Wagon Bks.) Harcourt Children's Bks.

Wood, Audrey & Wood, Don. Piggies: Book & Musical CD. 2006. (Illus.). 32p. (J). 17.95 (978-0-15-205667-4(X)) Harcourt Children's Bks.

—Piggies: Lap-Sized Board Book. 2005. (Illus.). 32p. (J). (gr. 17-ps). bds. 10.95 (978-0-15-205632-2(7) , Red Wagon Bks.) Harcourt Children's Bks.

Woodward, Kay. La Cuenta Regresiva Level P. AMIT, Ofra, illus. 2006. (Lightning Readers Ser.). 32p. (J). pap. 3.95 (978-0-7696-4205-5(5) , Gingham Dog Pr.) School Specialty Publishing.

Wright, Lynn F. Grandma, Tell Me a Story. Pagliughi, Debbie, illus. 1999. (J). 13.95 (978-1-881519-10-2(4)); pap. 6.95 (978-1-881519-11-9(2)) WorryWart Publishing Co.

The Wrong Side of the Bed. 2003. (J). lib. bdg. 16.95 (978-1-931650-20-5(9)) Coastal Publishing Carolina, Inc.

Yaccarino, Dan. Good Night, Mr. Night. 2004. (Illus.). 26p. (J). bds. 6.95 (978-0-15-205351-2(4) , Red Wagon Bks.) Harcourt Children's Bks.

—Good Night, Mr. Night. Yaccarino, Dan, illus. 2001. (Illus.). 32p. (J). (ps-k). pap. 6.00 (978-0-15-216386-0(7) , Voyager Bks./Libros Viajeros) Harcourt Children's Bks.

—Good Night, Mr. Night. 2001. 12.80 (978-0-606-22601-1(X)) Tandem Library Bks.

Yolen, Jane. Baby Bear's Chairs. Sweet, Melissa, illus. 2005. 40p. (J). (ps). 16.00 (978-0-15-205114-3(7)) Harcourt Children's Bks.

—How Do Dinosaurs Say Good Night? Teague, Mark, illus. 2000. 40p. (J). (ps up). pap. 15.95 (978-0-590-31681-1(8) , Blue Sky Pr., The) Scholastic, Inc.

—How Do Dinosaurs Say Good Night? Book & Plush Set. 2002. (Illus.). (J). 25.04 (978-0-7587-2759-6(3)) Book Wholesalers, Inc.

—How Do Dinosaurs Say Good Night? Book & Plush Set. 2004. (J). (ps-1). 24.95 incl. audio (978-1-55592-099-9(3)) Weston Woods Studios, Inc.

Yolen, Jane & Stemple, Heidi E. Y. Sleep, Black Bear, Sleep. Dyer, Brooke, illus. 2007. 32p. (J). (ps-1). 15.99 (978-0-06-081560-8(4) , HarperCollins); lib. bdg. 16.89 (978-0-06-081561-5(2)) HarperCollins Pubs.

Yoon, Salina. Count My Blessings, One Through Ten. Yoon, Salina, illus. 2006. (Illus.). 32p. (J). (ps-k). 9.99 (978-0-399-24660-9(6) , Putnam Juvenile) Penguin Group (USA) Inc.

—Good Night, Little One. 2005. (Illus.). 16p. (J). pap. 6.99 (978-0-439-66373-1(3) , Cartwheel Bks.) Scholastic, Inc.

—My Little Shimmery Time for Bed. Yoon, Salina, illus. 2002. (Illus.). 12p. (J). bds. 5.95 (978-1-58117-089-4(0) , Intervisual/Piggy Toes) Dalmatian Pr.

Yoyo Books Staff. Bedtime: Learning Words Series. 2004. 12p. bds. 12.95 (978-90-5843-607-8(1)) YoYo Bks. BEL. *Dist:* National Bk. Network.

Zafra, Jose. Historias de Sergio. (SPA.). 160p. (J). (978-84-216-2870-6(4) , BU6937) Bruño, Editorial ESP. *Dist:* Lectorum Pubns., Inc.

Zemeckis, Robert, et al. The Polar Express Movie Shadowbook: An Interactive Shadow-Casting Bedtime Story. Allsburg, ChrisVan, illus. 2006. 12p. (J). (gr. 4 up). reprint ed. 13.00 (978-1-4223-5172-7(6)) DIANE Publishing Co.

Ziefert, Harriet. Buzzy's Big Bedtime Book. Bolam, Emily, illus. 2004. 40p. 9.95 (978-1-59354-059-3(0)) Blue Apple Bks.

—Clara Ann Cookie, Go to Bed! Bolam, Emily, illus. 2000. 32p. (J). (gr. k-3). tchr. ed. 15.00 (978-0-395-97381-3(3) , Walter Lorraine) Houghton Mifflin Co. Trade & Reference Div.

—Mommy, I Want to Sleep in Your Bed! Kreloff, Elliot, illus. 2005. 40p. 15.95 (978-1-59354-103-3(1)) Handprint Bks.

5 Minute Bedtime Stories: Sleepy Time Stories. 2001. (SPA.). (J). (978-1-58805-137-0(4)) DS-Max USA, Inc.

12 Bedtime Stories. pap. 10.98 (978-0-7853-7921-8(5)) Publications International, Ltd.

86 Years: The Legend of the Boston Red Sox. 2005. (J). 18.95 (978-0-9767938-0-9(6)) Brown Hse. Bks.

BEE

see Bees

BEES

see also Honey

Allen, Judy. Are You a Bee? Humphries, Tudor, illus. 2004. (Backyard Bks.). 32p. (J). (ps up). pap. 5.95 (978-0-7534-5804-4(7) , Kingfisher) Houghton Mifflin Co. Trade & Reference Div.

Allen, Judy, et al. Are You a Bee? 2001. (Backyard Bks.). (Illus.). 32p. (J). (gr. k-3). tchr. ed. 9.95 (978-0-7534-5345-2(2) , Kingfisher) Houghton Mifflin Co. Trade & Reference Div.

Ashley, Susan. Bees. 2004. (Weekly Reader Early Learning Library). (Illus.). 24p. (gr. 1 up). (J). pap. 5.95 (978-0-8368-4058-2(5)); (YA). lib. bdg. 19.93 (978-0-8368-4051-3(8)) Stevens, Gareth Inc. (Weekly Reader Early Learning Library).

Barraclough, Sue. Bees. 2005. (Creepy Creatures Ser.). (Illus.). 24p. (J). (978-1-4109-1504-7(2)); pap. (978-1-4109-1509-2(3)) Steck-Vaughn.

The Beekeeper, 6 Packs. (Literatura 2000 Ser.). (gr. 2-3). 33.00 (978-0-7635-0161-7(1)) Rigby Education.

Bees. (Animals Ser.). 32p. (J). 6.95 (978-0-7368-8062-6(3)) Capstone Pr., Inc.

Bees. (Nature's Friends Ser.). 32p. (J). 7.95 (978-0-7565-1225-5(5)) Compass Point Bks.

Bees, 6 vols. (gr. 2-5). 36.95 (978-0-7368-8174-6(3)) Red Brick Learning.

Bees & Their Hives. (Animal Homes Ser.). 24p. (J). 6.95 (978-0-7368-5122-0(4)) Capstone Pr., Inc.

Bees & Wasps, 6 Packs. (Sails Literacy Ser.). (gr. 1-2). 36.00 (978-0-7578-4019-7(1)) Rigby Education.

Bentley, Dawn. Buzz-Buzz, Busy Bees: An Animal Sounds Book. Cahoon, Heather, illus. ed. 2006. 14p. (J). 5.99 (978-1-4169-1388-7(2) , Little Simon) Simon & Schuster Children's Publishing.

Berger, Melvin & Berger, Gilda. Bees Live in Hives. 2003. (Scholastic Time-To Discover Readers Ser.). (Illus.). (J). pap. (978-0-439-47179-4(6)) Scholastic, Inc.

Birch. Bees. 2004. (Raintree Perspectives Ser.). (Illus.). 32p. (J). pap. 7.50 (978-1-4109-1145-2(4)) Harcourt Schl. Pubs.

Birch, Robin. Bees. 2004. (J). pap. (978-1-4109-1152-0(7)); (Illus.). 32p. 26.36 (978-1-4109-1138-4(1)) Harcourt Schl. Pubs.

Booth, Reed. Confessions of the Killer Bee Guy, 2nd l.t. ed. 2002. (Illus.). 84p. spiral bd. 20.00 (978-0-9722462-0-0(7)) Reed's Apiary.

Bumble Bees. (Bugs, Bugs, Bugs! Ser.). 24p. (J). 6.95 (978-0-7368-5100-8(3)); 2005. (YA). (978-0-7368-8207-1(3) , Pebble Bks.) Capstone Pr., Inc.

Bumble Bees, 6 vols. (gr. k-2). 28.95 (978-0-7368-8247-7(2)) Red Brick Learning.

Busy Buzzers. (Backyard Bugs Ser.). 24p. (J). 7.95 (978-1-4048-0445-6(5)) Picture Window Bks.

Claybourne, Anna. Bees & Wasps. (Illus.). 32p. (YA). (gr. 3 up). lib. bdg. 27.10 (978-1-932799-56-9(7)) Stargazer Bks.

Cole, Joanna. The Magic School Bus Inside a Beehive. Degen, Bruce, illus. (Magic School Bus Ser.). 56p. (J). (gr. 1-4). (SPA.). pap. 4.95 (978-0-590-37042-4(1)); pap. 4.95 (978-0-590-44685-3(1)) Scholastic, Inc.

—The Magic School Bus Inside a Beehive. Degen, Bruce, illus. 1998. (Magic School Bus Ser.). (J). (gr. 1-4). (978-0-606-12989-3(8)) Tandem Library Bks.

¿Como Hacen Miel las Abejas? (Coleccion Primeros Pasos en la Ciencia). (SPA., Illus.). (J). (gr. 1-3). pap. (978-950-724-691-3(6) , LMA8232) Lumen ARG. *Dist:* Lectorum Pubns., Inc.

Cooper, Jason. Honeybee. 2003. (Life Cycles II Ser.). (Illus.). 24p. (J). 25.64 (978-1-58952-705-8(4)) Rourke Publishing, LLC.

Coughlan, Cheryl. Bumble Bees. Saunders-Smith, Gail, ed. 1999. (Insects Ser.). (Illus.). 24p. (J). (gr. k-1). lib. bdg. 15.93 (978-0-7368-0236-9(3) , Pebble Bks.) Capstone Pr., Inc.

Diary of a Honeybee: Individual Title Six-Packs. (Literatura 2000 Ser.). (gr. 2-3). 33.00 (978-0-7635-0164-8(6)) Rigby Education.

Do Bees Make Butter? (Animals All Around Ser.). 24p. (J). 7.95 (978-1-4048-0377-0(7)) Picture Window Bks.

Echols, Jean C. Buzzing a Hive. Bergman, Lincoln & Fairwell, Kay, eds. Baker, Lisa H., illus. Curtis, Elizabeth et al, photos by. 1999. (Great Explorations in Math & Science Ser.). 146p. (J). pap., tchr. ed. 16.00 (978-0-924886-39-3(0) , GEMS) Univ. of California, Berkeley, Lawrence Hall of Science.

Facklam, Margery. What's the Buzz: The Secret Lives of Bees. 1999. (Rain Forest Pilot Ser.). (Illus.). 48p. (J). (gr. 4-6). 18.98 (978-0-7398-2219-7(5)) Raintree.

—What's the Buzz: The Secret Lives of Bees. 2000. (Turnstone Rain Forest Pilot Book Ser.). (Illus.). 48p. (J). (gr. 4-6). pap. 7.95 (978-0-7398-2228-9(4)) Steck-Vaughn.

—What's the Buzz? The Secret Lives of Bees. 1999. (J). pap. (978-0-7398-2476-4(7)) Steck-Vaughn.

Flanagan, Alice K. & Osinski, Christine. Learning about Bees from Mr. Krebs. 2000. (Our Neighborhood Ser.). (Illus.). 32p. (J). (gr. 1-2). pap. 6.95 (978-0-516-26539-1(3) , Children's Pr.) Scholastic Library Publishing.

Franks, Katie. Bees up Close. 2008. (J). lib. bdg. (***978-1-4042-4137-4(X)*** , PowerKids Pr.) Rosen Publishing Group, Inc., The.

Furgang, Kathy. Let's Take a Trip to a Beehive. 2000. (Neighborhoods in Nature Ser.). (Illus.). 24p. (J). (gr. 3-5). lib. bdg. 18.75 (978-0-8239-5443-8(9) , PowerKids Pr.) Rosen Publishing Group, Inc., The.

Galvin, Laura Gates. Bumblebee at Apple Tree Lane. 2005. (Smithsonian's Backyard Ser.). (Illus.). 32p. (J). (ps-2). 19.95 incl. audio (978-1-56899-822-0(8) , BC5019) Soundprints.

—Bumblebee at Apple Tree Lane. Kest, Kristin, illus. (Smithsonian's Backyard Ser.). 32p. (J). (ps-2). 2005. 6.95 (978-1-931465-41-0(X) , S5019); 2000. incl. audio (978-1-56899-828-2(7)) Soundprints.

—Bumblee at Apple Tree Lane. Kest, Kristin, illus. 2005. (Smithsonian's Backyard Ser.: Vol. 19). 32p. (J). (ps-2). 15.95 (978-1-56899-820-6(1) , B5019) Soundprints.

—Bumblee at Apple Tree Lane: Includes Toy. Kest, Kristin, illus. 2000. (Smithsonian's Backyard Ser.: Vol. 19). 32p. (J). (ps-2). 29.95 (978-1-56899-824-4(4)) Soundprints.

—Bumblee at Apple Tree Lane: Micro Toy Included. Kest, Kristin, illus. 2005. (Smithsonian's Backyard Ser.: Vol. 19). 32p. (J). (ps-2). 9.95 (978-1-56899-825-1(2) , PB5069) Soundprints.

Galvin, Laura Gates & Kest, Kristin, illus. Bumblebee at Apple Tree Lane. 2005. (Smithsonian's Backyard Ser.: Vol. 19). 32p. (J). (ps-2). 4.95 (978-1-56899-821-3(X) , B5069) Soundprints.

Garver, Lorie. Killer Bees. 2004. (Animals Attack Ser.). (J). 26.20 (978-0-7377-1541-5(3) , Greenhaven Pr., Inc.) Thomson Gale.

Ghione, Yvette. This Is Daniel Cook Making Honey. Gagnon, Céleste, illus. 2007. (This Is Daniel Cook Ser.). 24p. (J). (ps-1). (***978-1-55453-086-1(5)); (978-1-55453-085-4(7))*** Kids Can Pr., Ltd.

Gibbons, Gail. The Honey Makers. 2000. (Illus.). (J). (978-0-606-18694-0(8)) Tandem Library Bks.

Glaser, Linda. Brilliant Bees. Holland, Gay W., illus. 2003. 32p. lib. bdg. 22.90 (978-0-7613-2670-0(7) , Millbrook Pr.) Lerner Publishing Group.

—Brilliant Bees. 2003. (Illus.). 32p. (J). (gr. k-3). pap. 8.95 (978-0-7613-1943-6(3) , Millbrook Pr.) Lerner Publishing Group.

Green, Emily K. Bumblebees. 2006. (Blastoff! Readers Ser.). (Illus.). 24p. (J). lib. bdg. 16.95 (978-1-60014-009-9(2)) Bellwether Media.

—Bumblebees. 2006. (Blastoff! Readers Ser.). (Illus.). 24p. (J). (gr. k-2). 18.50 (***978-0-531-17859-1(5)***) Scholastic Library Publishing.

Green, Jen. Ants, Bees, Wasps & Termites. 2004. (Illus.). 64p. pap. 8.99 (978-1-84215-977-4(1) , Southwater) Anness Publishing GBR. *Dist:* National Bk. Network.

Haag, Ruth. Honeybees Make Honey. 2002. Tr. of Abejas de Miel Producen la Miel. (SPA.). 22p. pap. 6.00 (978-0-9665497-5-1(9)) Haag Pr.

Harcourt School Publishers Staff. A Honey of a Story Advanced Level. 3rd ed. 2002. (Trophies Reading Program Ser.). (Illus.). (gr. 1). pap. 5.10 (978-0-15-323032-5(0)) Harcourt Schl. Pubs.

—Trofeos Below Level: Que Ven/Abejas? 3rd ed. 2002. (SPA., Illus.). pap. 5.50 (978-0-15-323875-8(5)) Harcourt Schl. Pubs.

—What a Bee Can See: Below Level. 3rd ed. 2002. (Trophies Reading Program Ser.). (Illus.). (J). pap. 4.10 (978-0-15-322964-0(0)) Harcourt Schl. Pubs.

—What a Bee Can See 5-Pack, Below Level. 3rd ed. 2002. (Trophies Reading Program Ser.). (Illus.). (gr. 1). pap. 20.10 (978-0-15-326814-4(X)) Harcourt Schl. Pubs.

Hartley, Karen. Bee. 2002. (Bug Bks.). (Illus.). 32p. (J). (gr. k-2). pap. 6.95 (978-1-57572-457-7(X) , 90447) Heinemann Library.

Hartley, Karen & Macro, Chris. Bee. 2006. (Illus.). 32p. (J). (***978-1-4034-8293-8(4));*** 2nd ed. pap. (***978-1-4034-8306-5(X)***) Heinemann Library.

Heiligman, Deborah. Honeybees. Golembe, Carla, illus. 2007. (Jump into Science Ser.). 32p. (J). (ps-3). 6.95 (978-1-4263-0157-5(X) , National Geographic Children's Bks.) National Geographic Society.

Heinrichs, Ann. Bees. 2002. (Nature's Friends Ser.). (Illus.). 32p. (J). (gr. 2 up). lib. bdg. 21.26 (978-0-7565-0165-5(2)) Compass Point Bks.

High, Linda Oatman. Beekeepers. 2003. (Illus.). 32p. (J). (gr. 2-4). 15.95 (978-1-56397-486-1(X)) Boyds Mills Pr.

—Beekeepers. Chayka, Doug, illus. 2003. 32p. (J). (gr. 2-4). pap. 9.95 (978-1-59078-046-6(9)) Boyds Mills Pr.

Hodge, Deborah. Bees. Bees. Mulock, Julian, illus. 2004. (Denver Museum of Nature & Science Bks.). 32p. (J). (gr. k-3). (978-1-55337-656-9(0)); (978-1-55337-065-9(1)) Kids Can Pr., Ltd.

Honey Bees, Vol. 4. 2005. (Bugs, Bugs, Bugs Ser.). (YA). (gr. k-3). 118.80 (978-0-7368-4206-8(3) , Pebble Bks.) Capstone Pr., Inc.

Honey Bees, 6 vols. (gr. k-2). 28.95 (978-0-7368-8242-2(1)) Red Brick Learning.

Honey Bees & Flowers, 6 vols. (gr. k-2). 28.95 (978-0-7368-8243-9(X)) Red Brick Learning.

Honey Bees & Hives, 6 vols. (gr. k-2). 28.95 (978-0-7368-8241-5(3)) Red Brick Learning.

Honey Bees & Honey, 6 vols. (gr. k-2). 28.95 (978-0-7368-8244-6(8)) Red Brick Learning.

Honey Bees Set. (gr. k-2). 114.95 (978-0-7368-9039-7(4)) Red Brick Learning.

Hosler, Jay. Clan Apis, 1 vols. 3rd ed. 2000. (Illus.). 152p. pap. 15.00 (978-0-9677255-0-5(X)) Active Synapse.

—Clan Apis. Hosler, Jay, illus. 2002. (Illus.). 26.60 (978-1-4046-1367-6(6)) Book Wholesalers, Inc.

Houghton, Gillian. Bee. 2004. (Getting into Nature Ser.). (Illus.). 32p. (J). lib. bdg. 21.25 (978-0-8239-4204-6(X)) Rosen Publishing Group, Inc., The.

Hovanec, Erin M. I Wonder What It's Like to Be a Bee. 2000. (Life Science Wonder Bks.). (Illus.). 24p. (J). (gr. k-4). lib. bdg. 18.75 (978-0-8239-5450-6(1) , PowerKids Pr.) Rosen Publishing Group, Inc., The.

Howard, Fran. Bumblebees. 2005. (Pebble Plus: Bugs, Bugs, Bugs! Ser.). 24p. (J). 19.93 (978-0-7368-3642-5(X)) Capstone Pr., Inc.

Hughes, Sarah. My Mom Is a Beekeeper. 2000. (My Family at Work Ser.). (Illus.). 24p. (J). lib. bdg. (978-0-516-23284-3(3) , Children's Pr.) Scholastic Library Publishing.

Jango-Cohen, Judith. Bees. 2006. (Animals Animals Ser.). (Illus.). 48p. (J). lib. bdg. 28.50 (978-0-7614-2235-8(8) , Benchmark Bks.) Cavendish, Marshall Corp.

Johnson, Guinevere. Cotton. 1999. (Let's Investigate Ser.). (Illus.). 32p. (J). (gr. 1-4). lib. bdg. (978-0-88682-959-9(3) , Creative Education) Creative Co., The.

Kalman, Bobbie. The Life Cycle of a Honeybee. 2004. (Life Cycle Ser.). (Illus.). 32p. (J). (978-0-7787-0664-9(8)); pap. (978-0-7787-0694-6(X)) Crabtree Publishing Co.

Kalman, Bobbie & Brière, Marie-Josée. Les Abeilles: Life Cycle of a Honeybee. 2006. (FRE., Illus.). 32p. pap. (978-2-89579-079-2(5)) Crabtree Publishing Co.

Kerby, Mona. Cockroaches & Friendly Bees, Ferocious Bees. 2000. (Illus.). 164p. (gr. 4-7). pap. 11.95 (978-0-595-14664-2(3) , Backinprint.com) iUniverse, Inc.

Landau, Elaine. Killer Bees. 2003. (Fearsome, Scary, & Creepy Animals Ser.). (Illus.). 48p. (J). (gr. 1-4). lib. bdg. 23.93 (978-0-7660-2061-0(4)) Enslow Pubs., Inc.

Lazourenko, S. Bee. 2000. (Babies Bks.). (Illus.). 8p. (J). (ps-k). 10.95 (978-0-7641-5234-4(3)) Barron's Educational Series, Inc.

Lockwood, Sophie. Bees. 2007. (World of Insects Ser.). 40p. (J). (gr. 2-6). 29.93 (***978-1-59296-818-3(X)***) Child's World, Inc.

Loewen, Nancy. Busy Buzzers: Bees in Your Backyard. Reibeling, Brandon, illus. 2004. (Backyard Bugs Ser.). 24p. (C). (gr. k-3). 22.60 (978-1-4048-0143-1(X)) Picture Window Bks.

Markle, Sandra. Outside & Inside Killer Bees. 2004. (Illus.). 40p. (J). 17.95 (978-0-8027-8906-8(4)) Walker & Co.

McDonald, Mary Ann. Bees. 2003. (Naturebooks: Creepy Crawlers Ser.). (Illus.). 32p. (J). (gr. 1-5). 25.64 (978-1-56766-611-3(6)) Child's World, Inc.

McNeil, Niki, et al. HOCPP 1127 Bees. 2006. spiral bd. (***978-1-60308-127-6(5)***) In the Hands of a Child.

Milton, Joyce. Honeybees. Mueller, Peter, illus. 2003. (All Aboard Science Reader Station Stop Ser.). 48p. (J). (gr. 1-3). pap. 3.99 (978-0-448-42846-8(6) , Grosset & Dunlap) Penguin Group (USA) Inc.

—Honeybees, Vol. 2. Mueller, Pete, illus. 2003. (All Aboard Science Reader Station Stop Ser.: No. 2). 48p. (J). (gr. 1-3). 13.89 (978-0-448-43142-0(4) , Grosset & Dunlap) Penguin Group (USA) Inc.

—Honeybees. 2003. (gr. k-3). lib. bdg. 11.80 (978-0-613-64410-5(7)) Tandem Library Bks.

Morgan, Sally. Ants, Bees, & Wasps. 2001. (Illus.). 32p. (J). lib. bdg. 24.25 (978-1-930643-10-9(1)) Chrysalis Education.

—Bees. 2007. (QEB Down on the Farm Ser.). (J). lib. bdg. 15.95 (***978-1-59566-386-3(X)***) QEB Publishing Inc.

Morgan, Sally. Bees & Wasps. 2006. (Illus.). 32p. (J). lib. bdg. 19.95 (978-1-59566-202-6(2)) QEB Publishing Inc.

Morris, Neil & Morris, Ting. Bee. 2003. (Illus.). 32p. (J). lib. bdg. (978-1-58340-378-5(7)) Smart Apple Media.

Mullican, Judy. It's a Bee! Ruminski, Jeff, illus. l.t. ed. 2003. (HRL Big Book Ser.). 8p. (Orig.). (J). (ps-k). pap. 10.95 (978-1-57332-259-1(8)); pap. 10.95 (978-1-57332-260-7(1)) HighReach Learning, Inc.

Murray, Julie. Bees. (Life Cycles Ser.). 24p. (J). (gr. k-4). 2007. lib. bdg. 21.35 (***978-1-59928-703-4(X)*** , Buddy Bks.); 2002. (Illus.). lib. bdg. 21.35 (978-1-57765-717-0(9)) ABDO Publishing Co.

Nelson, Robin. From Flower to Honey. (From Start to Finish Ser.). (J). (gr. k-2). 2003. (Illus.). 24p. lib. bdg. 18.60 (978-0-8225-0717-8(X)); 2002. pap. 4.95 (978-0-8225-0667-6(X)) Lerner Publishing Group.

Neye, Emily. Honeybees. Leonard, Tom, illus. 2002. (Road to Reading Ser.). 32p. (J). (gr. 2-4). pap. 3.99 (978-0-307-26217-2(0) , Random Hse. Bks. for Young Readers) Random Hse. Children's Bks.

—Honeybees. Leonard, Thomas, illus. 2002. 32p. (J). (ps-3). lib. bdg. 11.80 (978-0-613-50204-7(3)) Tandem Library Bks.

Park, Frances & Park, Ginger. The Royal Bee. Zhang, Christopher Zhong-Yuan, illus. 2003. 32p. (J). (gr. k-2). pap. 9.95 (978-1-56397-867-8(9)) Boyds Mills Pr.

Patrick, Steve. Bees & Honey: KinderFacts Individual Title Six-Packs. (Kinderstarters Ser.). 8p. (ps-1). 21.00 (978-0-7635-8740-6(0)) Rigby Education.

Penny, Malcolm. Bees. 2003. (Secret World Of... Ser.). (Illus.). 48p. (J). lib. bdg. 27.14 (978-0-7398-7019-8(X)) Raintree.

Prischmann, Deirdre A. Bees. 2005. (Illus.). 24p. (J). (ps-7). lib. bdg. 21.26 (978-0-7368-4334-8(5)) Capstone Pr., Inc.

Pugliano-Martin, Carol. Discover the Life Cycle of Bees. 2006. (English Explorers Ser.). (J). pap. 39.00 (***978-1-4108-6471-0(5)***) Benchmark Education Co.

—The Life Cycle of Bees. 2006. (English Explorers Ser.). (J). pap. 39.00 (***978-1-4108-6468-0(5)***) Benchmark Education Co.

Rau, Dana Meachen. Buzz, Bee, Buzz! 2007. (Go, Critter, Go! Ser.). (Illus.). 23p. (J). (ps-3). lib. bdg. 22.79 (***978-0-7614-2648-6(5)*** , Benchmark Bks.) Cavendish, Marshall Corp.

—Buzz, Bee, Buzz!/¡Zumba Abeja, Zumba! 2007. (Go, Critter, Go!/¡Vamos Criaturita, Vamos! Ser.). (SPA & ENG.). 24p. (J). lib. bdg. 22.79 (***978-0-7614-2813-8(5)*** , Benchmark Bks.) Cavendish, Marshall Corp.

—Guess Who Stings. 2008. (J). (***978-0-7614-2973-9(5)***) Cavendish, Marshall Bks., Ltd.

—¡Zumba, Abeja, Zumba! 2007. (¡Vamos Criaturita, Vamos! Ser.). (SPA.). 24p. (J). lib. bdg. 22.79 (***978-0-7614-2789-6(9)*** , Benchmark Bks.) Cavendish, Marshall Corp.

Riley, Joelle. Buzzing Bumblebees. 2003. (Pull Ahead Bks.). (Illus.). 32p. (J). (gr. k-3). lib. bdg. 22.60 (978-0-8225-4668-9(X)) Lerner Publishing Group.

—Buzzing Bumblebees. 2003. (gr. k-3). lib. bdg. 14.10 (978-0-613-58891-1(6)) Tandem Library Bks.

Robinson, W. Wright. How Insects Build Their Amazing Homes. Iverson, Carlyn, illus. 1999. (Animal Architects Ser.). 64p. (J). (gr. 5-9). 24.95 (978-1-56711-375-4(3) , Blackbirch Pr., Inc.) Thomson Gale.

Robson, Pam. Honey. Robson, Paul, ed. 1998. (What's for Lunch? Ser.). (Illus.). 32p. (J). (gr. k-2). pap., stu. ed. 6.95 (978-0-516-26220-8(3) , Children's Pr.) Scholastic Library Publishing.

Rockwell, Anne. Honey in a Hive. Schindler, S. D., illus. 2005. (Let's-Read-and-Find-Out Science Ser.). 40p. (J). (ps-ps). 15.99 (978-0-06-028566-1(4)) HarperCollins Pubs.

Rockwell, Anne F. Honey in a Hive. Schindler, S. D., illus. 2005. (Let's-Read-and-Find-Out Science Ser.). 40p. (J). (gr. k-4). pap. 5.99 (978-0-06-445204-5(2)); lib. bdg. 16.89 (978-0-06-028567-8(2)) HarperCollins Pubs.

Rustad, Martha E. H. Honey Bees. 2003. (Insects Ser.). (Illus.). 24p. (J). (gr. k-1). lib. bdg. 15.93 (978-0-7368-1666-3(6) , Pebble Bks.) Capstone Pr., Inc.

—Honey Bees, Vol. 2. 2005. (Bugs, Bugs, Bugs Ser.). 24p. (YA). (gr. k-3). pap. (978-0-7368-3388-2(9) , Pebble Bks.) Capstone Pr., Inc.

Sayre, April Pulley. The Bumblebee Queen. Wynne, Patricia J., illus. 32p. (J). 2006. pap. 6.95 (978-1-57091-363-1(3)); 2005. 14.95 (978-1-57091-362-4(5)) Charlesbridge Publishing, Inc.

Schaefer, Lola M. Honey Bees. Saunders-Smith, Gail, ed. 1999. (Honey Bees Ser.). (Illus.). 24p. (J). (gr. k-1). lib. bdg. 14.60 (978-0-7368-0231-4(2) , Pebble Bks.) Capstone Pr., Inc.

—Honey Bees, 4 bks. Saunders-Smith, Gail, ed. Incl. lib. bdg. 14.60 (978-0-7368-0231-4(2)); Honey Bees & Flowers. lib. bdg. 14.60 (978-0-7368-0232-1(0)); Honey Bees & Hives. lib. bdg. 14.60 (978-0-7368-0230-7(4)); Honey Bees & Honey. lib. bdg. 14.60 (978-0-7368-0233-8(9)); 24p. (J). (gr. k-1). 1999. (Illus.). Set lib. bdg. 58.40 (978-0-7368-0264-2(9) , Pebble Bks.) Capstone Pr., Inc.

—Honey Bees, Vol. 4. 2005. (Bugs, Bugs, Bugs Ser.). 24p. (YA). (gr. k-3). pap. (978-0-7368-8202-6(2) , Pebble Bks.) Capstone Pr., Inc.

—Honey Bees & Flowers. Saunders-Smith, Gail, ed. 1999. (Honey Bees Ser.). (Illus.). 24p. (J). (gr. k-1). lib. bdg. 14.60 (978-0-7368-0232-1(0) , Pebble Bks.) Capstone Pr., Inc.

—Honey Bees & Flowers, Vol. 4. 2005. (Bugs, Bugs, Bugs Ser.). 24p. (YA). (gr. k-3). pap. (978-0-7368-8203-3(0) , Pebble Bks.) Capstone Pr., Inc.

—Honey Bees & Hives. Saunders-Smith, Gail, ed. 1999. (Honey Bees Ser.). (Illus.). 24p. (J). (gr. k-1). lib. bdg. 14.60 (978-0-7368-0230-7(4) , Pebble Bks.) Capstone Pr., Inc.

—Honey Bees & Hives, Vol. 4. 2005. (Bugs, Bugs, Bugs Ser.). 24p. (YA). (gr. k-3). pap. (978-0-7368-8201-9(4) , Pebble Bks.) Capstone Pr., Inc.

—Honey Bees & Honey. Saunders-Smith, Gail, ed. 1999. (Honey Bees Ser.). (Illus.). 24p. (J). (gr. k-1). lib. bdg. 14.60 (978-0-7368-0233-8(9) , Pebble Bks.) Capstone Pr., Inc.

—Honey Bees & Honey, Vol. 4. 2005. (Bugs, Bugs, Bugs Ser.). 24p. (YA). (gr. k-3). pap. (978-0-7368-8204-0(9) , Pebble Bks.) Capstone Pr., Inc.

Schaub, Michelle. Honeybees Help Flowers. 2006. (Early Explorers Ser.). (J). 36.00 (***978-1-4108-6122-1(8)***) Benchmark Education Co.

Schwabacher, Martin. Bees. 2002. (Animalways Ser.). (Illus.). 112p. (J). 31.36 (978-0-7614-1392-9(8) , Benchmark Bks.) Cavendish, Marshall Corp.

Sexton, Colleen. Honey Bees. 2007. (Illus.). 24p. (J). lib. bdg. 16.95 (978-1-60014-052-5(1)) Bellwether Media.

—Honey Bees. 2007. (Blastoff! Readers Ser.). 24p. (J). (gr. k-2). 18.50 (***978-0-531-17568-2(5)*** , Children's Pr.) Scholastic Library Publishing.

Somervill, Barbara. Africanized Honeybee. 2008. (J). lib. bdg. 25.26 (***978-1-60279-117-6(1)***) Cherry Lake Publishing.

Spilsbury, Louise & Spilsbury, Richard. A Colony of Bees. 2004. (Animal Groups Ser.). (Illus.). 32p. (J). lib. bdg. (978-1-4034-4688-6(1)) Heinemann Library.

Spilsbury, Richard. A Colony of Bees. 2004. (Animal Groups Ser.). (Illus.). 32p. (J). pap. 7.50 (978-1-4034-5414-0(0)) Heinemann Library.

Starosta, Paul. The Bee. 2005. (J). pap. (978-1-57091-623-6(3)) Charlesbridge Publishing, Inc.

—The Bee: Friend of the Flowers. 2005. (Animal Close-Ups Ser.). (Illus.). 28p. (J). (ps-ps). pap. 6.95 (978-1-57091-629-8(2)) Charlesbridge Publishing, Inc.

Stewart, Melissa. How Do Bees Make Honey? 2008. (J). (***978-0-7614-2923-4(9)***) Cavendish, Marshall Bks., Ltd.

Stone, Lynn M. Honey Farms. 1999. (Funky Farms Ser.). (Illus.). 24p. (J). (gr. 1-4). lib. bdg. 19.27 (978-0-86593-540-2(8)) Rourke Publishing, LLC.

Tagliaferro, Linda. Bees & Their Hives. 2004. (Pebble Plus, Animal Homes Ser.). (Illus.). 24p. (J). 13.95 (978-0-7368-2382-1(4)) Capstone Pr., Inc.

Thomson, Ruth. Honeybee. 2007. (J). lib. bdg. (***978-1-4042-3713-1(5)*** , PowerKids Pr.) Rosen Publishing Group, Inc., The.

Time for Kids Editors. Bees. 2005. (Time for Kids Science Scoops Ser.). (Illus.). 32p. (J). pap. 3.99 (978-0-06-057642-4(1)) HarperCollins Pubs.

—Bees! 2005. (Time for Kids Science Scoops Ser.). (Illus.). 32p. (J). 14.99 (978-0-06-057643-1(X)) HarperCollins Pubs.

Trumbauer, Lisa. The Life Cycle of a Bee. 2002. (Life Cycles Ser.). (Illus.). 24p. (J). (gr. k-1). lib. bdg. 15.95 (978-0-7368-1450-8(7) , Pebble Bks.) Capstone Pr., Inc.

Twist, Clint. Honeybees. 2006. (Illus.). 32p. (J). lib. bdg. 23.33 (978-0-8368-6376 5(3)) Stevens, Gareth Inc.

Unstead, Sue. The Beautiful Bee Book. Tomblin, Gill, illus. 2006. (Beautiful Bug Ser.). 24p. (J). (gr. k-2). spiral bd. 17.95 (978-0-7696-4428-8(7)) School Specialty Publishing.

Van Dyck, Sara. Bumblebees. 2005. (Early Bird Nature Bks.). (Illus.). 47p. (J). (gr. 2-4). lib. bdg. 25.26 (978-0-8225-2498-4(8)) Lerner Publishing Group.

Wallace, Karen. Busy Buzzy Bee. 1999. (Eyewitness Readers). (Illus.). 32p. (J). (ps-3). pap. 3.99 (978-0-7894-4758-6(4)) Dorling Kindersley Publishing, Inc.

—Busy Buzzy Bee. 1999. (gr. k-3). lib. bdg. 11.80 (978-0-613-21270-0(3)); (Illus.). (J). 10.79 (978-0-606-18115-0(6)) Tandem Library Bks.

Wallace, Karen & Dorling Kindersley Publishing Staff. Busy, Buzzy Bee. 1999. (Eyewitness Readers). (Illus.). 32p. (J). (ps-3). 14.99 (978-0-7894-4759-3(2)) Dorling Kindersley Publishing, Inc.

Watts, Barrie. Bee. 2004. (J). lib. bdg. 27.10 (978-1-58340-502-4(X)) Smart Apple Media.

Weingartz, Jill. Beehives. 2001. (Created Environments Ser.). (Illus.). 24p. (J). 21.35 (978-1-58340-105-7(9)) Smart Apple Media.

Wimmer, Teresa. Bees. 2006. (My First Look at Insects Ser.). 24p. (J). (gr. k-2). lib. bdg. 15.95 (978-1-58341-454-5(1) , Creative Education) Creative Co., The.

Winchester, Elizabeth. Bees! 2005. 32p. (J). lib. bdg. 13.85 (***978-1-4242-0858-6(0)***) Fitzgerald Bks.

BEES—FICTION

Bailey, Scott Arthur. The Tale of Buster Bumblebee. 2006. pap. 33.99 (***978-1-4280-4091-5(9)***) IndyPublish.com.

The Baker Street Bunch & the Missing Honeybees Mystery. 2005. (J). per. (978-0-9754241-5-5(7)) MiMar Publishing.

Barcita, Pamela, illus. Ruby Lee the Bumble Bee Promotional Coloring Book. 2005. 16p. (J). 4.95 (978-0-9754342-3-9(3)) Bumble Bee Publishing.

Bea's Own Good: Evaluation Guide. 2006. (J). (978-1-55942-401-1(X)) Marsh Media.

Beatty, Susi. Angie the Ant & the Bumblebee Tree. 2006. (J). 19.95 (978-0-9773653-0-2(1)) Susi B. Marketing, Inc.

The Beeman: Early Level Satellite, 6 Packs. (Sails Literacy Ser.). 16p. (gr. 1-2). 27.00 (978-0-7578-2921-5(X)) Rigby Education.

Berner, Beth Engleman & Gevry, Claudine. Follow that Bee. 2006. (Illus.). 10p. (J). 9.95 (978-1-58117-447-2(0), Intervisual/Piggy Toes) Dalmatian Pr.

Bonnell, Kris. A Flower for a Bee. 2006. (J). 3.95 (*978-1-933727-23-3(3)) Reading Reading Bks., LLC.

Boyle, Alison. How Bees Be. Hambleton, Laura, illus. 2003. 28p. (J). pap. 7.95 (978-1-84059-332-7(6)) Milet Publishing.

Boynton, Cara. Sam's Secret World. 2006. (ENG.). 48p. per. 12.95 (*978-1-4241-4529-4(5)) PublishAmerica, Inc.

Brandt-Taylor, Diane. The Bunny, the Bear, the Bug & the Bee. Brandt, Michael, illus. 2005. (J). cd-rom 9.88 (978-0-9773236-0-9(9)) TaySysCo Publishing.

Brennan-Nelson, Denise. Buzzy the Bumblebee. Monroe, Michael Glenn, illus. 32p. (J). (gr. k-3). 2003. pap. 6.95 (978-1-58536-166-3(6)); 1999. 15.00 (978-1-886947-82-5(1)) Sleeping Bear Pr.

—Buzzy the Bumblebee. 2003. (gr. k-3). lib. bdg. 15.25 (978-0-613-79710-8(8)) Tandem Library Bks.

Brown, J. A. Busy Bee. Knight, Paula, illus. 2003. (Funny Faces Ser.). 10p. (J). bds. 3.95 (978-1-58925-715-3(4), tiger tales) ME Media LLC.

Brown, Margaret Wise. Bumble Bee. Raymond, Victoria, illus. 1999. (Growing Tree Ser.). 14p. (J). (ps up). 5.95 (978-0-694-01749-2(3), Harper Festival) HarperCollins Pubs.

Buchmann, Stephen L. & Cohn, Diana. The Bee Tree. Mirocha, Paul, illus. 2007. 40p. (J). (gr. 2-6). 17.95 (*978-0-938317-98-2(9)) Cinco Puntos Pr.

Bumble Bee Helps Out. 2002. (My First Tab Story Ser.). (J). bds. 3.98 (978-0-7525-8954-1(7)) Parragon, Inc.

Bumblebee at Apple Tree Lane. 2005. (Smithsonian's Backyard Ser.). (Illus.). 32p. (J). (ps-2). 8.95 incl. reel tape (978-1-59249-071-4(9), SC5019) Soundprints.

The Busy Bumblebee. 2002. (Backyard Mini Bks.). (Illus.). 32p. (J). (978-1-59069-021-5(4), H2010) Studio Mouse LLC.

Carle, Eric. The Honeybee & the Robber. Carle, Eric, illus. rev. ed. 2001. (Illus.). 1p. (J). (ps-1). 18.99 (978-0-399-23731-7(3), Philomel) Penguin Group (USA) Inc.

Carroll, Jennifer. Bigsbee's Unbee-lievable Journey to Fly. Doty, Eldon, illus. 2005. 132p. per. 9.99 (978-0-9758570-5-2(3)) Morgan James Publishing, LLC.

Chambers, Kelli. Tiny the Bee. Chambers, Lynne, illus. 2002. 40p. (J). (ps-k). pap. 5.95 (978-1-928777-13-7(9), BOW Bks.) Blessing Our World, Inc.

Cheng, Andrea. When the Bees Fly Home. McFadden, Joline, illus. 2005. 32p. (J). (gr. 3-6). 16.95 (978-0-88448-238-3(3)) Tilbury Hse. Pubs.

Cogburn, Debra. Bobby Bumblebee Learns to Fly. Pitts, Kenetha, illus. 1998. 32p. (Orig.). (J). (ps-4). pap. (978-0-9644825-0-0(9)) Cogburn Enterprises.

Courtney, Richard, illus. James Goes Buzz, Buzz. 2004. (Step into Reading Ser.). 32p. (J). (ps-2). pap. 3.99 (978-0-375-82860-7(5), Random Hse. Bks. for Young Readers) Random Hse. Children's Bks.

Crabtree, Sally & Wallace, John. Ten Buzzy Bees. 2000. (Finger Puppet Bks.). (Illus.). 24p. (J). (ps-k). 10.95 (978-1-86233-162-4(6)) Sterling Publishing Co., Inc.

Daigneault, Sylvie. Bruno & the Bees. 2000. (Illus.). 32p. (J). pap. 6.99 (978-0-00-648145-4(0)) HarperCollins Pubs.

Davies, Rocky. Harvey Happy Bee. 2005. (Bee Attitude Board Books). (Illus.). (J). (978-1-59156-775-2(0)) Covenant Communications.

Davis, Michael Dale. Bumperly Bumper Bee. 2007. (Illus.). 20p. (J). 15.95 (*978-0-9791785-0-4(9)) Luna Publishing.

El diario de mis Abejas: Individual Title, 6 packs. (Literatura 2000 Ser.). (SPA.). (gr. 2-3). 33.00 (978-0-7635-1647-5(3)) Rigby Education.

Discovery Bee: A Play & Discover Book. 2002. (J). (978-1-931312-53-0(2)) SoftPlay, Inc.

DK Publishing. Bee Movie: A Guide to the Sweet Life. 2007. (Bee Movie Ser.). (Illus.). 47p. (J). (gr. 1-6). 12.99 (*978-0-7566-3210-6(2)) Dorling Kindersley Publishing, Inc.

Donovan, Kyle. HoniBee Loses Her Voice: The Do'Bees. 2007. (J). 15.95 net. (*978-0-9767670-3-9(1)) WannaBees Media LLC.

—Introducing the Do'Bees. 2007. (J). 15.95 net. (*978-0-9767670-1-5(5)) WannaBees Media LLC.

Driggs, Scout. Barry's Day Out. 2007. (Bee Movie Ser.). (Illus.). 24p. (J). (ps-2). pap. 3.99 (*978-0-06-125175-7(5), Harper Entertainment) HarperCollins Pubs.

—Bee Movie: Bee Meets Girl. 2007. (Bee Movie Ser.: No.2). (Illus.). 24p. (J). (ps-2). pap. 3.99 (*978-0-06-125174-0(7), Harper Entertainment) HarperCollins Pubs.

Duplaix, Georges. The Big Brown Bear. 2001. (978-0-606-22794-0(6)) Tandem Library Bks.

Eggleton, Jill. Beeman Interview, 6 Packs. Storey, Jim, illus. (Sails Literacy Ser.). 16p. (gr. 2-3). 27.00 (978-0-7578-0708-4(9)) Rigby Education.

—The Rock Boss: Early Level Satellite Individual Title Six-Packs. (Sails Literacy Ser.). 16p. (gr. 1-2). 27.00 (978-0-7578-2934-5(1)) Rigby Education.

Fairchild, Simone. The Queen Bee Mystery Trilogy, 33 vols. Key, Pamela, illus. 2007. 126p. (J). per. 49.95 (978-0-9788985-6-4(7)) A Better Be Write Pub.

Fornof, John. Tad Meets the Grumbly Grumblebee. Adnet, Bernard, illus. 2004. (Ribbits Ser.). 24p. (J). 9.99 (978-0-310-70716-5(1)) Zonderkidz.

Frantz, Jennifer. Barry's Buzzy World. 2007. (Bee Movie Ser.: No.1). 32p. (J). pap. 3.99 (*978-0-06-125169-6(0), Harper Trophy) HarperCollins Pubs.

—Bee Movie: The Junior Novel. 2007. (I Can Read Bks.: No.2). 32p. (J). pap. 3.99 (*978-0-06-125166-5(6), Harper Trophy) HarperCollins Pubs.

Gaines, Isabel. Pooh's Honey Tree, No. 5. 1998. (Winnie the Pooh First Readers Ser.: No. 3). (Illus.). 40p. (J). (ps-3). pap. 3.95 (978-0-7868-4253-7(9)) Disney Pr.

Galjanic, Lisa. When Bees Win. Hope, Michelle, illus. 2007. (J). 9.95 (978-1-933532-04-2(1)) LSG Pubns.

Galjanic, Lisa. When Series 6 Volume Set, 6, 6. 2007. (Illus.). 100p. (J). 34.95 (*978-1-933532-06-6(8)) LSG Pubns.

Gershon, Dann. Beez in Toyland. Robinson, David, illus. 1999. (Hangin' with the Hombeez Ser.: Vol. 2). 40p. (J). (gr. k-6). 9.95 (978-0-9656985-4-2(8)) Noware Bks.

—Extra Large. Robinson, David, illus. 1999. (Hangin' with the Hombeez Ser.: Vol. 3). 40p. (J). (gr. k-6). 14.95 (978-0-9656985-5-9(6)) Noware Bks.

—Goldstinger. Robinson, David, illus. 1999. (Hangin' with the Hombeez Ser.: Vol. 4). 40p. (J). (gr. k-6). 9.95 (978-0-9656985-6-6(4)) Noware Bks.

—The Spelling Bee. Robinson, David, illus. 1998. (Hangin' with the Hombeez Ser.: Vol. 1). 40p. (J). (gr. k-6). 14.95 (978-0-9656985-3-5(X)) Noware Bks.

Gershon, Dann & Full Force. Slam Dunk. Gershon, David, illus. 1999. (Hangin' with the Hombeez Ser.: Vol. 6). 40p. (J). (gr. k-6). 9.95 (978-0-9656985-8-0(0)) Noware Bks.

Gershon, Dann & Gershon, Gina. Hollyhive Hunnie. Robinson, David, illus. 2000. (Hangin' with the Hombeez Ser.: Vol. 5). 40p. (J). (gr. k-6). 9.95 (978-0-9656985-7-3(2)) Noware Bks.

Gibbons, Gail. The Honey Makers. Gibbons, Gail, illus. 2000. (Illus.). 32p. (J). (ps-3). pap. 6.99 (978-0-688-17531-3(7), Harper Trophy) HarperCollins Pubs.

Good Bee-Havior Good Behavior Rewards. 2003. (J). 8.95 (978-0-439-43743-1(1)) Scholastic, Inc.

Gran, Julia. Big Bug Surprise. 2007. 32p. (J). (ps-3). pap. 12.99 (978-0-439-67609-0(6), Scholastic Pr.) Scholastic, Inc.

Graver, Elizabeth. Honey Thief. 2000. (gr. 7-12). lib. bdg. 22.25 (978-0-613-36404-1(X)) Tandem Library Bks.

Grimm, Lana & Bloch, Tania. How Butterbees Came to Bee! 2001. (Illus.). (J). (978-0-9662048-2-7(4)) Bee Unlimited, Inc.

—How Butterbees Came to Bee! Michener, David, illus. 2nd ed. 2001. 48p. 19.95 (978-0-9662048-3-4(2)) Bee Unlimited, Inc.

Groves. Bee & the Sea, Bk. 9. Date not set. (Illus.). 32p. (J). pap. 129.15 (978-0-582-18770-2(2)) Addison-Wesley Longman, Ltd. GBR. *Dist:* Trans-Atlantic Pubns., Inc.

Gudino Kieffer, E. Giraluna (Moonflower) (J). 22.50 (978-950-04-1280-3(2)) Emecé Editores S.A. ARG. *Dist:* AIMS International Bks., Inc.

Gummelt, Donna & Melchiorre, Dondino. Don't Get My Honey... . HONEY. Wall, Randy Hugh, ed. Varela, Juan D., tr. Varela, Juan D., illus. 2006. (SPA.). 34p. (J). 14.95 (978-0-9764798-5-7(0)) Story Store Collection Publishing.

Harley Bill. Sarahs Story. Aldridge Eve, illus. 2006. 32p. (J). 6.95 (978-1-58246-178-6(3), Tricycle Pr.) Ten Speed Pr.

Harrah, Madge. Honey Girl. 2001. (Illus.). 120p. (J). (gr. 3-6). reprint ed. pap. 7.95 (978-0-9709152-1-4(7)) Trailway Bks.

High, Linda Oatman. Beekeepers. 2003. (Illus.). 32p. (J). (gr. 2-4). 15.95 (978-1-56397-486-1(X)) Boyds Mills Pr.

Hofmeister, Alan, et al. The Bee. (Reading for All Learners Ser.). (Illus.). (J). pap. (978-1-56861-124-2(2)) Swift Learning Resources.

ImageBooks Staff. Finger Puppet Friends: Little Duck, Little Ladybug, Little Lamb, & Little Bee. 2007. (Illus.). 48p. (J). (ps). bds. 22.95 (978-0-8118-5805-2(7)) Chronicle Bks. LLC.

Inches, Alison. Diego's Buzzing Bee Adventure. Zalme, Ron, illus. 2008. (Go, Diego, Go! Ser.). 24p. (J). pap. 3.99 (*978-1-4169-4776-9(0), Simon Spotlight/Nickelodeon) Simon & Schuster Children's Publishing.

Introducing the WanaBees (not Published) 2005. (J). 15.95 (978-0-9767670-0-8(7)) WannaBees Media LLC.

Jacobs, John. I Wanna Be. 2006. (Illus.). 144p. 9.95 (978-0-9774659-6-5(9)) Cameo Pubns., LLC.

Johnson, Emily Rhoads. Write Me If You Dare! 2000. (Illus.). 176p. (J). (gr. 3-6). 15.95 (978-0-8126-2944-6(2)) Cricket Bks.

Katschke, Judy. Buzz & the Bubble Planet Level 3, Vol. 1: Toy Story. 1998. (Disney's First Readers Ser.: No. 8). (Illus.). 40p. (J). (gr. 2-4). pap. 3.50 (978-0-7868-4168-4(0)) Disney Pr.

Katschke, Judy. What's the Buzz? 2007. (Bee Movie Ser.). 64p. (J). (gr. 2-5). pap. 4.99 (*978-0-06-125177-1(1), Harper Entertainment) HarperCollins Pubs.

Kelly, Mij. I Hate Everyone. Palmer, Ruth, illus. 2003. 32p. (YA). (978-1-85602-362-7(1)) Chrysalis Children's Bks.

Kessler, Cristina. The Best Beekeeper of Lalibela: A Tale from Africa. Jenkins, Leonard, illus. 2006. 32p. (J). 16.95 (978-0-8234-1858-9(8)) Holiday Hse., Inc.

Kingsley, Carmen. Ten Little Puppies. Cassidy, Sean, illus. 2001. 32p. (J). (ps-k). bds. (978-1-55041-654-1(5)) Fitzhenry & Whiteside, Ltd.

Kirk, David. The Prince, the Princess, & the Bee. 2008. 32p. (J). (ps-2). 17.99 (*978-0-448-44690-5(1)) Penguin Group (USA) Inc.

Kline, Trish & Donev, Mary. Where Can Lost Bee Be? KA Reader 6. 2007. (Illus.). 32p. (J). per. 20.00 (*978-0-9717234-9-8(4)) Ghost Hunter Productions.

Koja, Kathe. Kissing the Bee. 2007. 128p. (YA). (gr. 9 up). 16.00 (*978-0-374-39938-2(7), Farrar, Straus & Giroux (BYR)) Farrar, Straus & Giroux.

Korman, Susan. Bee Movie: The Junior Novel. 2007. (Bee Movie Ser.). 144p. (J). (gr. 3-7). pap. 4.99 (*978-0-06-125178-8(X), Harper Entertainment) HarperCollins Pubs.

—Bee Movie: The Movie Storybook. Mccraig, Dave, illus. 2007. (Bee Movie Ser.). 48p. (J). (ps-2). pap. 8.99 (*978-0-06-125179-5(8), Harper Entertainment) HarperCollins Pubs.

Krensky, Stephen. Winnie the Pooh & Some Bees. 2001. (978-0-606-22513-7(7)) Tandem Library Bks.

Krings, Antoon. Mireille L Abeille. (FRE.). pap. 18.95 (978-2-07-058440-6(2)) Gallimard, Editions FRA. *Dist:* Distribooks, Inc.

Lally, Soinbhe. A Hive for the Honeybee. Brewster, Patience, illus. 1999. 240p. (J). (gr. 5-9). pap. 16.95 (978-0-590-51038-7(X), Levine, Arthur A. Bks.) Scholastic, Inc.

—A Hive for the Honeybee. 2001. (Illus.). (J). 11.64 (978-0-606-21233-5(7)) Tandem Library Bks.

Larson, Verna. Bernie's Forest Adventure: A Case for Secular Humanism. Jones, Sharon, ed. Tagnetti, Nikki, illus. 2nd rev. ed. 1999. (Bearables of Bernie Bear Ser.: No. 1). 24p. (J). (ps-k). 8.95 (978-1-56550-085-3(7)) Vision Bks. International.

Lewison, Wendy Cheyette. Buzz Said the Bee. Wilhelm, Hans, illus. 2004. 32p. (J). lib. bdg. 15.00 (978-1-59054-589-8(3)) Fitzgerald Bks.

El Libro de la Abeja: Grand y Pequeno. 2000. Tr. of Big & Little. (SPA., Illus.). 10p. (J). (ps-k). 8.95 (978-84-488-0860-0(6)) Beascoa, Ediciones S.A. ESP. *Dist:* Distribooks, Inc.

Litchmore, Michael. The MB Force: Heroes at the Best! 2007. 56p. pap. 9.00 (*978-0-8059-7399-0(0)) Dorrance Publishing Co., Inc.

Lobel, Arnold. Sopa de Raton. 2004. (SPA., Illus.). 66p. (J). (gr. 1-3). pap. 7.99 (978-980-257-286-1(1)) Ekare, Ediciones VEN. *Dist:* Lectorum Pubns., Inc., Iaconi, Mariuccia Bk. Imports.

Losordo, Stephen. Cow Moo Me. Conteh-Morgan, Jane, illus. 1998. (Growing Tree Ser.). 16p. (J). (ps up). 5.95 (978-0-694-01108-7(8), Harper Festival) HarperCollins Pubs.

Lucado, Max. Buzby & the Grumble Bees. 2007. (Max Lucado's Hermie & Friends Ser.). 38p. (J). bds. 12.99 (*978-1-4003-0913-9(1)) Nelson, Thomas Inc.

Lucado, Max. Buzby, the Misbehaving Bee. 2005. (Hermie & Friends Ser.: No. 4). (Illus.). 48p. (J). 12.99 (978-1-4003-0510-0(1)) Nelson, Thomas Inc.

Lucado, Max & Schmidt, Troy. Buzby, the Misbehaving Bee. 2005. 32p. (J). pap. 3.99 (978-1-4003-0666-4(3)) Nelson, Thomas Inc.

Lyon, David. Flight of the Buzby Bee. Lyon, David, illus. 2005. (Illus.). 32p. (J). 16.95 (978-0-9741328-0-8(2)) Lyon, Ernest Media Productions.

MacLennan, Cathy. Chicky Chicky Chook Chook. MacLennan, Cathy, illus. 2007. (Illus.). 32p. (J). (ps-1). 12.95 (978-1-905417-40-7(3)) Boxer Bks., Ltd. GBR. *Dist:* Sterling Publishing Co., Inc.

Matheson, Dawn. Ruby Lee the Bumble Bee: A Bee's Bit of Wisdom. Cindy, Huffman, ed. Barcita, Pamela, illus. 2004. 40p. (J). 17.95 (978-0-9754342-0-8(9)) Bumble Bee Publishing.

—Ruby Lee the Bumble Bee: A Bee's Bit of Wisdom ~ Special Tribute Edition Benefiting Cancer Research. Huffman, Cndy, ed. Barcita, Pamela, illus. 2005. 40p. (J). (ps-ps). 17.95 (978-0-9754342-1-5(7)) Bumble Bee Publishing.

—Ruby Lee the Bumble Bee Critter Count Search & Find Game. Huffman, Cindy, ed. Barcita, Pamela, illus. 2005. 6p. (J). 4.95 (978-0-9754342-4-6(1)) Bumble Bee Publishing.

—Ruby Lee the Bumble Bee ~ A Bee of Possibility: Book & Plush Toy Bundle. Huffman, Cindy, ed. Barcita, Pam, illus. 2006. 40p. (J). 24.90 (978-0-9754342-2-2(5)) Bumble Bee Publishing.

McDonald, Megan & Payne, Tom. Ant & Honey Bee: What a Pair! Karas, G. Brian, illus. 2005. 32p. (J). (gr. k-3). 13.99 (978-0-7636-1265-8(0)) Candlewick Pr.

McKay, Sharon E. A Bee in Karley's Bonnet. 2001. (Welcome to Truck Town Ser.). (Illus.). 40p. (J). pap. 6.95 (978-1-894454-05-6(7)) Balmur Entertainment, Ltd. CAN. *Dist:* General Distribution Services, Inc.

McOmber, Rachel B., ed. McOmber Phonics Storybooks: Me & the Bee. rev. ed. (Illus.). (J). (978-0-944991-46-6(7)) Swift Learning Resources.

Milgrim, David. See Pip Point. Milgrim, David, illus. 2004. (Adventures of Otto Ser.). (Illus.). 32p. (J). pap. 3.99 (978-0-689-85140-7(5), Aladdin) Simon & Schuster Children's Publishing.

Montgomery, Mary Ann. Bonnie, the Baby Bumble Bee. Norby, Carey, illus. 2001. 32p. (J). (ps-3). pap. 7.50 (978-1-884083-74-7(9)) Maval Publishing, Inc.

Pando, Nancy J. I Don't Want to Go to School: Helping Children Cope with Separation Anxiety. Voerg, Kathy, illus. 2005. (Let's Talk Ser.). 48p. (J). pap. 8.95 (978-0-88282-254-9(3)) New Horizon Pr. Pubs., Inc.

Park, Frances & Park, Ginger. The Royal Bee. Zhang, Christopher Zhong-Yuan, photos by. 2003. (Illus.). 32p. (J). (gr. k-2). 16.95 (978-1-56397-614-8(5)) Boyds Mills Pr.

Petty, J. T. The Scrivener Bees. Friend, David Michael, illus. 2007. (Clemency Pogue Ser.). 176p. (J). (gr. 3-7). 11.99 (978-1-4169-0769-5(6), Simon & Schuster Children's Publishing) Simon & Schuster Children's Publishing.

Pin, Isabel. Bumblebee Blues. James, J. Alison, tr. from GER. 2003. (Illus.). 32p. (J). (gr. k-3). 15.95 (978-0-7358-1813-2(4)); lib. bdg. 16.50 (978-0-7358-1814-9(2)) North-South Bks., Inc. (Michael Neugebauer Bks.).

Polacco, Patricia. The Bee Tree. Polacco, Patricia, illus. 1998. (Illus.). 32p. (J). (ps-3). pap. 7.99 (978-0-698-11696-2(8), Putnam Juvenile) Penguin Group (USA) Inc.

—The Bee Tree. 1998. (J). 13.79 (978-0-606-13187-2(6)) Tandem Library Bks.

Polacco, Patricia & Polacco, Patricia. The Bee Tree. 1998. (Illus.). (J). (ps-ps). lib. bdg. 15.30 (978-0-613-07325-7(8)) Tandem Library Bks.

Price, Mary Ellizabeth. Wallbaby Bumblebees. 2004. (Illus.). 40p. (J). per. 15.75 (978-0-9715402-2-4(5), 410-707-6686) Barnhardt & Ashe Publishing, Inc.

Prude, Marsha A. C. C. bee moves to honey town & the adventures of grampa Bumble. 2007. pap. 7.95 (*978-0-533-15345-9(X)) Vantage Pr., Inc.

Rinaldo, Luana, illus. Clackers: BEE. 2008. (Clackers Ser.). 14p. (J). (gr. k-ps). bds. 4.99 (*978-0-375-84229-0(2), Robin Corey Bks.) Random Hse. Children's Bks.

Rojas, O. Un Dia Una Abeja. 2004. (SPA.). 32p. 6.95 (978-1-4000-9288-8(4)) Editorial Sudamericana S.A. ARG. *Dist:* Random Hse., Inc.

Rojas, Oscar. Un Dia, Una Abeja. (SPA.). pap. 8.95 (978-950-07-1986-5(X)) Editorial Sudamericana S.A. ARG. *Dist:* Distribooks, Inc.

Ruby Lee the Bumble Bee ~ A Bee of Possibility. 2006. (J). (978-0-9754342-6-0(8)) Bumble Bee Publishing.

Santillo, LuAnn. Bee. Santillo, LuAnn, ed. 2003. (Half-Pint Kids Readers Ser.). (Illus.). 7p. (J). (ps-1). pap. (978-1-59256-108-7(X)) Half-Pint Kids, Inc.

Sargent, Dave & Sargent, Pat. Young Brutus: Show Respect!, 4. Woodward, Elaine, illus. 2003. (Young Animal Pride Ser.: 4). 24p. (J). pap. 6.95 (978-1-56763-870-7(8)); lib. bdg. 19.95 (978-1-56763-869-1(4)) Ozark Publishing.

Sauers, Charlotte. The Bee in Bonnie Bondelle's Bow. 2008. (J). 16.95 (*978-1-60131-014-9(5)) Big Tent Bks.

Schaub, Michelle. The Bee Puzzle. 2006. (Early Explorers Ser.). (J). 36.00 (*978-1-4108-6123-8(6)) Benchmark Education Co.

Scheunemann, Pam. Spelling Bee. Nobens, C. A., illus. 2007. (Fact & Fiction Ser.). 24p. (J). pap. (978-1-59928-473-6(1)); 21.35 (978-1-59928-472-9(3)) ABDO Publishing Co.

Schwartz, Roslyn. The Mole Sisters & the Busy Bees. Schwartz, Roslyn, illus. 2000. (Mole Sisters Ser.). (Illus.). 32p. (J). (ps-k). pap. 4.95 (978-1-55037-662-3(4)); lib. bdg. 14.95 (978-1-55037-663-0(2)) Annick Pr., Ltd. CAN. *Dist:* Firefly Bks., Ltd.

—Mole Sisters & the Busy Bees. 2000. (ps-2). lib. bdg. 12.95 (978-0-613-78377-4(8)) Tandem Library Bks.

Shen, Michele. The Spider & the Bee. Shen, Michele, illus. 2002. (Illus.). 32p. (J). 4.95 (978-1-929132-25-6(5)) Kane/Miller Bk. Pubs., Inc.

Shreeve, Elizabeth. Hector Finds a Fortune. Levy, Pamela R., illus. 2004. (Ready-for-Chapters Ser.). 64p. (J). pap. 3.99 (978-0-689-86415-5(9), Aladdin) Simon & Schuster Children's Publishing.

—Hector Finds a Fortune. 2004. (gr. k-3). lib. bdg. 11.80 (978-0-613-86966-9(4)) Tandem Library Bks.

Siegel, Rv. A Bee Called Kangaroo. 2005. 81p. pap. 9.16 (978-1-4116-2890-8(X)) Lulu.com.

Smith, Tim. The Work Bees Go on Strike. 2006. (Buck Wilder's Adventure Ser.: 2). (Illus.). 60p. (J). pap. (978-1-934133-06-4(X)) Mackinac Island Pr., Inc.

Snell Jr., Mark "Jonathan". The Bee & the Magic Mirror: la Abela y el Espejo M+?gico. 2006. (ENG.). 32p. per. 13.24 (*978-1-4259-7214-1(4)) AuthorHouse.

So-Buzy Bee. 2004. (Plush Pals Board Bks.). (Illus.). (J). (gr. k-1). bds. (978-0-7666-0560-2(4), 39395) Modern Publishing.

Sommer, Carl. It's Not Fair! 2003. (Another Sommer-Time Story Ser.). (Illus.). 48p. (J). (gr. k-4). lib. bdg. 23.95 incl. audio compact disk (978-1-57537-720-9(9)); 16.95 incl. audio (978-1-57537-569-4(9)); (gr. 1-4). 16.95 incl. audio compact disk (978-1-57537-520-5(6)) Advance Publishing, Inc.

—It's Not Fair! Budwine, Greg, illus. 2003. (J). 9.95 (978-1-57537-021-7(2)); lib. bdg. 16.95 (978-1-57537-070-5(0)) Advance Publishing, Inc.

Sommer, Carl, narrated by. It's Not Fair! 2003. (Another Sommer-Time Story Ser.). (Illus.). 48p. (J). (gr. k-4). lib. bdg. 23.95 incl. audio (978-1-57537-770-4(5)) Advance Publishing, Inc.

Spelling Bee. 2003. (J). per. (978-1-57657-954-1(9)) Paradise Pr., Inc.

Steck-Vaughn Staff. Take a Peek/Baby Bee. 1999. (Take Me Home Ser.). (Illus.). (J). pap. (978-0-7398-2681-2(6)) Steck-Vaughn.

Stine, R. L. Goosebumps: Why I'm Afraid of Bees. 2005. (Goosebumps Ser.). 144p. (J). 4.99 (978-0-439-69354-7(3), Scholastic Paperbacks) Scholastic, Inc.

—Mutacion Fatal. 2003. (SPA.). pap. (978-0-590-01798-5(5)) Scholastic GBR. *Dist:* Lectorum Pubns., Inc.

—Why I'm Afraid of Bees. 2005. 117p. (J). (gr. 2-5). lib. bdg. 12.04 (978-0-606-33300-9(2)) Tandem Library Bks.

Stockton, Frank Richard. The Bee-Man of Orn. Lynch, P. J., illus. 2006. 44p. (J). (gr. k-4). reprint ed. 18.00 (978-1-4223-5505-3(5)) DIANE Publishing Co.

—The Bee-Man of Orn. Sendak, Maurice, illus. 2005. (Sendak Reissues Ser.). 56p. (ps up). 15.95 (978-0-06-029729-9(8)) HarperCollins Pubs.

—The Bee Man of Orn. 1999. (Notable American Authors Ser.). reprint ed. lib. bdg. 125.00 (978-0-7812-8927-6(0)) Reprint Services Co.

Sullivan, Jenny. Sion & the Bargain Bee. Jones, Jac, illus. 1998. (J). pap. 12.95 (978-0-8464-4912-6(9)) Beekman Bks., Inc.

Sypolt, Carl W. Adventures of David the Honeybee. 2003. 51p. pap. 9.95 (978-0-7414-1526-4(7)) Infinity Publishing.

The Book Company. Learn to Count: Bee's School Bus. 2005. (Illus.). 22p. (J). (gr. 2-4). bds. 5.95 (978-1-74047-626-3(3)) Book Co. Publishing Pty, Ltd., The AUS. *Dist:* Penton Overseas, Inc.

Thomas, Peter. The Adventures of Billy Bee Vol. 3: Colors of Love. Mahomet, John, illus. 2000. 48p. (J). (gr. k-4). 18.95 (978-1-886919-11-2(9)) Billy Bee Productions.

To Fly on a Bee. 2006. (J). (978-0-9763798-1-2(3)) Lion's Crest Pr.

Van Per Put, Klaartje. Little Bee: Finger Puppet Book. 2006. (Illus.). 12p. (J). bds., bds. 6.95 (978-0-8118-5236-4(9)) Chronicle Bks. LLC.

Vincent, Annie. Adventures at Honeybee Hive: Trouble in the New Forest. 2004. 69p. pap. 14.95 (978-1-4137-4676-1(4)) PublishAmerica, Inc.

Wait for Me, Bumblebee. 2004. (J). (978-0-9767179-7-3(2)) ABC Development, Inc.

WannaBees Media LLC, creator. HoniBee Loses Her Voice (paperback) The Do'Bees. 2007. (Illus.). 28p. (J). pap. 9.99 ***(978-0-9767670-4-6(X))*** WannaBees Media LLC.

Warner, Gertrude Chandler. Honeybee Mystery. 2000. (gr. 3-6). lib. bdg. 11.80 (978-0-613-30477-1(2)) Tandem Library Bks.

Wishinsky, Frieda. A Bee in Your Ear. Laliberte, Louise-Andree, illus. 2004. 64p. (J). lib. bdg. 20.00 ***(978-1-4242-1255-2(3))*** Fitzgerald Bks.

Wong, Janet S. Buzz. Chodos-Irvine, Margaret, illus. 2002. (YA). 13.19 (978-1-4046-1968-5(2)) Book Wholesalers, Inc.

—Buzz. Chodos-Irvine, Margaret, illus. 2002. 32p. (J). (ps-2). pap. 7.00 (978-0-15-216323-5(9) , Voyager Bks./Libros Viajeros) Harcourt Children's Bks.

—Buzz. Chodos-Irvine, Margaret, illus. 2002. (J). (ps-3). lib. bdg. 14.15 (978-0-613-53799-5(8)) Tandem Library Bks.

Yorinks, Arthur. Happy Bees! Armstrong-Ellis, Carey, illus. 2005. 24p. (J). (ps-1). 15.95 (978-0-8109-5866-1(X)) Abrams, Harry N. , Inc.

BEETHOVEN, LUDWIG VAN, 1770-1827

Beethoven, Ludwig van. Beethoven, the Man & the Artist, As Revealed in His Own Words. 2001. 110p. (YA). reprint ed. 88.00 (978-0-7222-5326-7(5)) Library Reprints, Inc.

Bekker, Paul. Beethoven. 2001. 391p. (YA). reprint ed. 98.00 (978-0-7222-5204-8(8)) Library Reprints, Inc.

Carew-Miller, Anna. Ludwig Van Beethoven: Great Composer. 2002. (Great Names Ser.). (Illus.). 32p. (J). (gr. 3 up). lib. bdg. (978-1-59084-148-8(4)) Mason Crest Pubs.

Cencetti, Greta. Beethoven. 2002. (Classic Composers Ser.). (Illus.). 40p. (J). incl. audio compact disk (978-1-59069-091-8(5) , T2101) Studio Mouse LLC.

—Beethoven: Getting to Know Your Classical Composers. 2002. (Classic Composers Ser.). (Illus.). 32p. (978-1-59069-024-6(9) , T2001) Studio Mouse LLC.

Crowest, Frederick J. Beethoven: Illustrations & Portraits. 2001. 319p. (YA). reprint ed. 98.00 (978-0-7222-5327-4(3)) Library Reprints, Inc.

Diehl, Alice M. The Life of Beethoven. 2001. 376p. (YA). reprint ed. 98.00 (978-0-7222-5328-1(1)) Library Reprints, Inc.

Ernest, Brother. A Story of Beethoven. 2005. (J). 17.95 (978-0-911845-02-0(X)) Neumann Pr., The.

Fandel, Jennifer. Beethoven's Fifth Symphony. 2006. (What in the World? Ser.). (Illus.). 48p. (J). 21.95 (978-1-58341-429-3(0) , Creative Education) Creative Co., The.

Grace, Harvey. Ludwig Van Beethoven. 2001. 326p. (YA). reprint ed. 98.00 (978-0-7222-6314-3(7)) Library Reprints, Inc.

Graeme, Elliot. Beethoven. 2001. 184p. (YA). reprint ed. 88.00 (978-0-7222-5332-8(X)) Library Reprints, Inc.

Indy, Vincent D'. Beethoven: A Critical Biography. 2001. 127p. (YA). reprint ed. 88.00 (978-0-7222-5336-6(2)) Library Reprints, Inc.

January, Brendan. Ludwig Van Beethoven: Musical Genius. 2004. (Book Report Biographies Ser.). (Illus.). 111p. (J). 30.50 (978-0-531-11909-9(2) , Watts, Franklin) Scholastic Library Publishing.

Josephson, Judith Pinkerton. Ludwig Van Beethoven. Kiwak, Barbara, illus. 2007. (Creative Minds Biography Ser.). 64p. (J). spiral bd. 22.60 (978-0-8225-5987-0(0)) Lerner Publishing Group.

Mayer-Skumanz, Lene. Ludwig von Beethoven. Opgenoorth, Winfried, illus. 2007. 40p. (J). (gr. 1). 20.00 ***(978-0-7358-2123-1(2))*** North-South Bks., Inc.

Myers, Carrie Mieko. What If You'd Met Beethoven? 2004. (Illus.). 16p. (J). (978-0-439-69713-2(1)) Scholastic, Inc.

Nohl, Ludwig. Beethoven Depicted by His Contemporaries. 2001. 374p. (YA). reprint ed. 98.00 (978-0-7222-5341-0(9)) Library Reprints, Inc.

—An Unrequited Love: Episode in Life of Beethoven. 2001. (YA). reprint ed. 150.00 (978-0-7222-5343-4(5)) Library Reprints, Inc.

Pancella, Peggy. Ludwig Van Beethoven. 2005. (J). pap. (978-1-4034-6754-6(4)); (Illus.). 32p. (978-1-4034-6746-1(3)) Heinemann Library.

Pinkwater, Daniel M. Rainy Morning. Pinkwater, Jill, illus. 1999. (Pinkwater Ser.: Vol. 1). 32p. (J). (gr. k-3). 16.00 (978-0-689-81143-2(8) , Atheneum) Simon & Schuster Children's Publishing.

Rolland, Romain. Beethoven. 2001. 244p. (YA). reprint ed. 98.00 (978-0-7222-5344-1(3)); 6th ed. 98.00 (978-0-7222-6305-1(8)) Library Reprints, Inc.

Ross, Stewart. The Story of Ludwig von Beethoven. 2002. (Lifetimes Ser.). (Illus.). 48p. (J). lib. bdg. 28.50 (978-1-931983-15-0(1)) Chrysalis Education.

Summerer, Eric Michael. Ludwig Van Beethoven. 2006. (Primary Source Library of Famous Composers). (Illus.). 32p. (J). 21.95 (978-1-4042-2771-2(7) , PowerKids Pr.) Rosen Publishing Group, Inc., The.

Thayer, Alexander W. Life of Beethoven, 2 vols., set. 2001. (YA). reprint ed. 250.00 (978-0-7222-5349-6(4)) Library Reprints, Inc.

Turner, Barrie Carson. Beethoven. 2003. (Famous Childhoods Ser.). (Illus.). (J). lib. bdg. 24.25 (978-1-59389-112-1(1)) Chrysalis Education.

Vernon, Roland. Beethoven: Introducing. 2000. (Introducing Composers Ser.). (Illus.). 32p. (J). (gr. 4-7). 21.95 (978-0-7910-6038-4(1) , Chelsea Hse.) Facts On File, Inc.

Wagner, Richard. Beethoven: A Supplement from the Philosophical Works of Arthur Schopenhauer. 2001. 177p. (YA). reprint ed. 88.00 (978-0-7222-5350-2(8)) Library Reprints, Inc.

Walcker, Yann. Ludwig Van Beethoven. 2007. (Descubrimos a los Musicos Ser.). (Illus.). 24p. (J). 14.95 ***(978-84-7864-959-4(X))*** Combel Editorial, S.A. ESP. *Dist:* Independent Pubs. Group.

Walker, Ernest. Beethoven. 2001. 195p. (YA). reprint ed. 88.00 (978-0-7222-5351-9(6)) Library Reprints, Inc.

BEETLES

Advantage Publishers Group & Pledger, Maurice. All about Bugs & Beetles. 2007. (All About Ser.). (Illus.). 80p. (J). 12.95 (978-1-59223-459-2(3) , Silver Dolphin Bks.) Advantage Pubs. Group.

Allman, Toney. From Jewel Beetles to Fire Sensors. 2006. (Imitating Nature Ser.). (Illus.). 32p. (gr. 3-6). 24.95 (978-0-7377-3626-7(7) , 1256743, Kidhaven) Thomson Gale.

Aloian, Molly & Kalman, Bobbie. El Ciclo de vida del Escarabajo. 2006. (SPA., Illus.). 32p. (gr. 2-3). pap. (978-0-7787-8715-0(X)) Crabtree Publishing Co.

—The Life Cycle of a Beetle. 2003. (Life Cycle Ser.). (Illus.). 32p. (J). (978-0-7787-0662-5(1)); pap. (978-0-7787-0692-2(3)) Crabtree Publishing Co.

Beetles, 6 vols. (gr. k-2). 28.95 (978-0-7368-8246-0(4)) Red Brick Learning.

Chanell, Jim & Greenaway, Theresa. Beetles. 1999. (Minipets Ser.). (Illus.). 32p. (J). (gr. 1-5). lib. bdg. 25.69 (978-0-8172-5586-2(9)) Raintree.

Claybourne, Anna. Beetles & Other Bugs. 2004. (Awesome Bugs Ser.). (J). lib. bdg. 27.10 (978-1-932799-54-5(0)) Stargazer Bks.

Coughlan, Cheryl. Beetles. 2005. (Bugs, Bugs, Bugs Ser.). 24p. (YA). (gr. k-3). pap. (978-0-7368-8206-4(5) , Pebble Bks.) Capstone Pr., Inc.

Derzipilski, Kathleen. Beetles. 2004. (Animals, Animals Ser.). (Illus.). 46p. (J). 25.64 (978-0-7614-1751-4(6) , Benchmark Bks.) Cavendish, Marshall Corp.

Donovan. Beetles. 2002. pap. (978-0-7398-5806-6(8)) Steck-Vaughn.

Donovan, Sandy. Beetles. 2002. (Animals of the Rain Forest Ser.). (Illus.). 32p. (YA). lib. bdg. 22.83 (978-0-7398-5368-9(6)) Raintree.

Eckart, Edana. Beetles. 2003. (gr. k-3). lib. bdg. 12.95 (978-0-613-67692-2(0)) Tandem Library Bks.

Greenaway, Theresa. Beetles. 1999. (Minipets Ser.). (Illus.). 32p. (J). (gr. 1-5). pap. 5.95 (978-0-7398-1384-3(6)) Steck-Vaughn.

—Beetles. 1999. (gr. 3-6). lib. bdg. 37.00 (978-0-613-76458-2(7)) Tandem Library Bks.

Grolier Educational Staff, contrib. by. Beetles. 2001. (Nature's Children Ser.). (Illus.). 48p. (J). (978-0-7172-5534-4(4) , Grolier) Scholastic Library Publishing.

Hall, Margaret. Beetles. 2006. (Pebble Plus: Bugs, Bugs, Bugs! Ser.). (J). (978-0-7368-4251-8(9)) Capstone Pr., Inc.

Hartley, Karen, et al, contrib. by. Beetle. 2000. (Bug Books Ser.). (Illus.). 32p. (J). (gr. k-2). lib. bdg. 21.36 (978-1-57572-546-8(0)) Heinemann Library.

Hartley, Karen, et al. Beetle. (Bug Bks.). 32p. pap. 6.95 (978-1-4034-3321-3(6)) Heinemann Library.

Helget, Nicole Lea. Beetles. 2007. (J). (978-1-58341-539-9(4) , Creative Education) Creative Co., The.

Hipp, Andrew. Dung Beetles. 2003. (Really Wild Life Of... Ser.). (Illus.). 24p. (J). lib. bdg. 18.75 (978-0-8239-6238-9(5) , PowerKids Pr.) Rosen Publishing Group, Inc., The.

Julivert, Maria Angels. Beetles. Arridondo, E. & Marcel Socias Studio Staff, illus. 1998. (Fascinating World of-...Ser.). 32p. (J). (gr. 2-6). lib. bdg. 14.95 (978-1-56674-246-7(3)) Forest Hse. Publishing Co., Inc.

Krul Araujo, Paige, ed. Beetles. 2006. (Real Thing Ser.). 48p. (J). pap. 8.99 (978-0-439-78792-5(0) , Tangerine Pr.) Scholastic, Inc.

Lockwood, Sophie. Beetles. 2007. (World of Insects Ser.). 40p. (J). (gr. 2-6). 29.93 ***(978-1-59296-819-0(8))*** Child's World, Inc.

Marie, Christian. La Mariquita. 2005. (Quien eres tu? Ser.). 24p. (J). 7.95 (978-84-7864-235-9(8)) Combel Editorial, S.A. ESP. *Dist:* Independent Pubs. Group.

Markle, Sandra. Diving Beetles: Underwater Insect Predators. 2008. (Insect World Ser.). (J). lib. bdg. 27.93 ***(978-0-8225-7295-4(8)*** , Lerner Pubns.) Lerner Publishing Group.

Marsico, Katie. A Ladybug Larva Grows Up. 2007. (Scholastic News Nonfiction Readers Ser.). (Illus.). 24p. (J). (gr. 1-2). 19.00 (978-0-531-17478-4(6) , Children's Pr.) Scholastic Library Publishing.

McEvey, Shane F. Beetles. 2001. (Insects & Spiders Ser.). (Illus.). 32p. (J). (gr. 4 up). 28.00 (978-0-7910-6600-3(2) , 010551, Chelsea Hse.) Facts On File, Inc.

Miller, Sara Swan. Beetles: The Most Common Insects. 2001. (gr. 3-6). lib. bdg. 15.25 (978-0-613-37286-2(7)) Tandem Library Bks.

Morgan, Sally. Ladybugs & Beetles. 2000. (Looking at Minibeasts Ser.). (Illus.). 32p. (J). (gr. 1-4). lib. bdg. 16.95 (978-1-929298-79-2(X)) Chrysalis Education.

Mudd, Maria M. The Beetle. Smith-Griswold, Wendy, illus. 2000. (Giant Look at Little Bugs Ser.). 14p. (J). (ps-k). 12.95 (978-1-58117-095-5(5) , Intervisual/Piggy Toes) Dalmatian Pr.

Murray, Peter. Beetles. 2003. (Naturebooks: Creepy Crawlers Ser.). (Illus.). 32p. (J). (gr. 1-5). 25.64 (978-1-56766-976-3(X)) Child's World, Inc.

Otfinoski, Steven. Ladybugs & Other Beetles, Vol. 7. World Book, Inc. Staff, ed. 2002. (World Book's Animals of the World Ser.: Set 1). 64p. (J). (978-0-7166-1244-5(5)) World Bk., Inc.

Packard, Mary. Goliath Beetle: One of the World's Heaviest Insects. 2007. (SuperSized! Ser.). (Illus.). 24p. (J). lib. bdg. 21.28 (978-1-59716-388-0(0) , 1265933) Bearport Publishing Co., Inc.

Pallotta, Jerry. The Beetle Alphabet Book. Biedrzycki, David, illus. 2004. 32p. (J). 16.95 (978-1-57091-551-2(2)) Charlesbridge Publishing, Inc.

—The Beetle Alphabet Book. Biedrzycki, David, tr. Biedrzycki, David, illus. 2004. 32p. (J). pap. 7.95 (978-1-57091-552-9(0)) Charlesbridge Publishing, Inc.

—Beetle Alphabet Book. 2004. (gr. k-3). lib. bdg. 16.40 (978-0-613-88752-6(2)) Tandem Library Bks.

Penny, Malcolm. Beetles. 2003. (Secret World Of... Ser.). (Illus.). 48p. (J). lib. bdg. 27.14 (978-0-7398-7020-4(3)) Raintree.

Prischmann, Deirdre A. Beetles. 2005. (Illus.). 24p. (J). 21.26 (978-0-7368-3706-4(X)) Capstone Pr., Inc.

Prishmann, Deirdre A. Poop-Eaters: Dung Beetles in the Food Chain. 2008. (J). ***(978-1-4296-1265-4(7)*** , Fact Finders) Capstone Pr., Inc.

Richardson, Adele D. Beetles. 1998. (Bugs Ser.). (Illus.). 32p. (YA). (gr. 3-12). lib. bdg. 16.95 (978-1-887068-30-7(9)) Smart Apple Media.

Robinson, Fay. Creepy Beetles. 2001. (Hello Reader! Ser.). (Illus.). (J). 10.79 (978-0-606-21129-1(2)) Tandem Library Bks.

—Creepy Beetles! Cassels, Jean, illus. 2001. 32p. (J). (ps-ps). lib. bdg. 11.80 (978-0-613-35498-1(2)) Tandem Library Bks.

Robinson, Fay & Cassels, Jean. Creepy Beetles. Cassels, Jean, illus. 2001. (Hello Reader! Ser.). (Illus.). 32p. (J). (gr. k-2). pap. 3.99 (978-0-439-06754-6(5)) Scholastic, Inc.

Sexton, Colleen. Beetles. 2007. (Blastoff! Readers Ser.). (Illus.). 24p. (J). lib. bdg. 16.95 (978-1-60014-050-1(5)) Bellwether Media.

—Beetles. 2007. (Blastoff! Readers Ser.). 24p. (J). (gr. k-2). 18.50 ***(978-0-531-17566-8(9)*** , Children's Pr.) Scholastic Library Publishing.

Spotted Beetles. (Backyard Bugs Ser.). 24p. (J). 7.95 (978-1-4048-0444-9(7)) Picture Window Bks.

Squire, Ann O. Beetles. (True Bks.). (J). 2004. 47p. (gr. 3-5). pap. 6.95 (978-0-516-29358-5(3)); 2003. (Illus.). 48p. 25.00 (978-0-516-22658-3(4)) Scholastic Library Publishing. (Children's Pr.).

Twist, Clint. Dung Beetles. 2006. (Illus.). 32p. (J). lib. bdg. 23.33 (978-0-8368-6374-1(7)) Stevens, Gareth Inc.

Unstead, Sue. The Beautiful Beetle Book. Tomblin, Gill, illus. 2005. (Beautiful Bug Ser.). 24p. (J). (ps-ps). spiral bd. 17.95 (978-0-7696-4150-8(4)) School Specialty Publishing.

Watts, Barrie. Beetles. (Illus.). 32p. (YA). (gr. 2 up). lib. bdg. 27.10 (978-1-932889-16-1(7)) Sea-To-Sea Pubns.

Windsor, Jo. Beetles: Early Level Satellite Individual Title Six-Packs. (Sails Literacy Ser.). 16p. (gr. 1-2). 27.00 (978-0-7578-2925-3(2)) Rigby Education.

Zabludoff, Marc. Beetles. 2007. (Animalways Ser.). 112p. (J). lib. bdg. 34.21 ***(978-0-7614-2532-8(2)*** , Benchmark Bks.) Cavendish, Marshall Corp.

Ziefert, Harriet. Bugs, Beetles, & Butterflies. Flather, Lisa, illus. 1998. (Easy-to-Read Ser.). 32p. (J). (ps-2). pap. 3.99 (978-0-14-038691-2(2) , Puffin) Penguin Group (USA) Inc.

—Bugs, Beetles, & Butterflies. Flather, Lisa, illus. 1998. (Puffin Easy-to-Read Ser.). 32p. (J). (ps-2). lib. bdg. 10.79 (978-0-606-20458-3(X)); lib. bdg. 11.80 (978-0-613-11368-7(3)) Tandem Library Bks.

BEHAVIOR

see also Christian Life; Courage; Courtesy; Ethics; Etiquette; Friendship; Interpersonal Relations; Love; Patriotism; Self-Control; Self-Culture; Social Adjustment; Spiritual Life; Truthfulness and Falsehood

Agassi, Martine. Hands Are Not for Hitting. Heinlen, Marieka, illus. (Best Behavior Ser.). 24p. (J). 2006. 7.95 (978-1-57542-200-8(X)); 2002. bds. 7.95 (978-1-57542-112-4(7)) Free Spirit Publishing, Inc.

Amos, Janine. Don't Do That! Spenceley, Annabel, illus. 2002. (Courteous Kids Ser.). 32p. (J). (ps up). lib. bdg. 23.33 (978-0-8368-3605-9(7)) Stevens, Gareth Inc.

—Don't Say That! Spenceley, Annabel, illus. 2002. (Courteous Kids Ser.). 32p. (J). (ps up). lib. bdg. 23.33 (978-0-8368-3606-6(5)) Stevens, Gareth Inc.

—Go Away! Spenceley, Annabel, illus. 2002. (Courteous Kids Ser.). 32p. (J). (ps up). lib. bdg. 23.33 (978-0-8368-3607-3(3)) Stevens, Gareth Inc.

—It Won't Work! Spenceley, Annabel, illus. 2002. (Courteous Kids Ser.). 32p. (J). (ps up). lib. bdg. 23.33 (978-0-8368-3608-0(1)) Stevens, Gareth Inc.

—It's Mine! Spenceley, Annabel, illus. 2002. (Courteous Kids Ser.). 32p. (J). (ps up). lib. bdg. 23.33 (978-0-8368-3609-7(X)) Stevens, Gareth Inc.

—Move Over! Spenceley, Annabel, illus. 2002. (Courteous Kids Ser.). 32p. (J). (ps up). lib. bdg. 23.33 (978-0-8368-3610-3(3)) Stevens, Gareth Inc.

Anderson, David A. What You Can See, You Can Be! Jones, Don, illus. 2003. 48p. (gr. 3-8). 13.95 (978-0-87516-603-2(2) , Devorss Pubns.) DeVorss & Co.

Bender, Marie. Caring Counts. 2003. (Character Counts Ser.). (Illus.). 32p. (J). (gr. k-6). lib. bdg. 22.78 (978-1-57765-869-6(8)) ABDO Publishing Co.

—Respect Counts. 2003. (Character Counts Ser.). (Illus.). 32p. (J). (gr. k-6). lib. bdg. 22.78 (978-1-57765-873-3(6)) ABDO Publishing Co.

Benson, Edmund F. & Benson, Susan. If I Could Start Life Over... 1999. (Illus.). 16p. (J). (gr. 3-4). pap. 1.95 (978-1-58614-087-6(6)) Arise Foundation.

—Mama Said. 1999. (Illus.). 16p. (J). (gr. 3-4). pap. 1.95 (978-1-58614-095-1(7)) Arise Foundation.

—Trapped: 67 Reasons to Wait for Sex. 1999. (Illus.). 16p. (J). (gr. 3-4). pap. 1.95 (978-1-58614-096-0(5)) Arise Foundation.

Bode, Janet. Kids Still Having Kids: People Talk about Teen Pregnancy. rev. ed. 1999. (Single Titles-Teen Issues Ser.). (Illus.). 160p. (YA). (gr. 8-12). pap. 9.95 (978-0-531-15973-6(6) , Watts, Franklin) Scholastic Library Publishing.

Bolden, Tonya. 33 Things Every Girl Should Know: Stories, Songs, Poems, & Smart Talk by 33 Extraordinary Women. 1998. (Illus.). 160p. (YA). (gr. 7-10). pap. 13.00 (978-0-517-70936-8(8) , Crown Books For Young Readers) Random Hse. Children's Bks.

Book of Life: English Book of Life Youth Version. 1998. (Illus.). 64p. (YA). (gr. 7-13). mass mkt. 1.00 (978-1-890525-06-4(5)) Book of Hope International.

Bunnell, Jean. You Decide! Making Responsible Choices. 1999. (Middle School Teacher Resource Book Ser.). (Illus.). 128p. (J). (gr. 5-8). pap. 13.99 (978-1-56822-427-5(3) , IF2543) School Specialty Publishing.

Burton, Margie, et al. One for You & One for Me. Adams, Alison, ed. 1999. (Early Connections Ser.). 16p. (gr. k-2). pap. 4.50 (978-1-58344-075-9(5)) Benchmark Education Co.

—Rules. Adams, Alison, ed. 1999. (Early Connections Ser.). 16p. (J). (gr. k-2). pap. 4.50 (978-1-58344-081-0(X)) Benchmark Education Co.

—Working Together. Evento, Susan, ed. 1998. (Early Connections Ser.). 16p. (J). (gr. k-2). pap. 4.25 (978-1-892393-47-0(6)) Benchmark Education Co.

Bussard, Paula. Bug Beepers for Promise Keepers: Critter County Activity Book. 1998. (Nineteen Ninety-Nine 50-Day Spiritual Adventure Ser.). (Illus.). 64p. (J). pap. 7.00 (978-1-57849-109-4(6)) Mainstay Church Resources.

Canizares, Susan & Betsey, Chessen. Two Can Do It! 1999. (ps-2). lib. bdg. 10.10 (978-0-613-22540-3(6)) Tandem Library Bks.

Canizares, Susan & Chessen, Betsey. Two Can Do It! 1999. (Social Studies Emergent Readers). (J). 2.50 (978-0-439-04559-9(2)) Scholastic, Inc.

Carroll, Jacqueline. Reality Check. 2001. (Turning Seventeen Ser.: No. 10). 208p. (YA). (gr. 7 up). pap. 4.95 (978-0-06-447344-6(9) , Harper Trophy) HarperCollins Pubs.

Covey, Sean. The 7 Habits of Highly Effective Teens. 1999. (YA). pap., wbk. ed. 5.00 (978-1-929494-17-0(3)) Franklin Covey Co.

—The 7 Habits of Highly Effective Teens. 2003. (Miniature Editions Ser.). (Illus.). 108p. (YA). 4.95 (978-0-7624-1474-1(X) , Running Pr. Minature Editions) Running Pr. Bk. Pubs.

—The 7 Habits of Highly Effective Teens: The Ultimate Teenage Success Guide. 1998. (Illus.). 288p. pap. 14.95 (978-0-684-85609-4(3) , Fireside) Simon & Schuster.

—The 7 Habits of Highly Effective Teens Personal Workbook. 2004. (Illus.). 240p. pap., wbk. ed. 14.95 (978-0-7432-5098-6(2) , Fireside) Simon & Schuster.

Cress, Eric. Your Potential Is Huge! Roberts, Cathy et al, eds. Ross, Lorenzo, illus. 1999. 24p. (YA). (gr. 7-10). pap. 2.95 (978-1-929488-19-3(X)) Cress Co., The.

Criswell, Patti Kelley. What Would You Do? Quizzes About Real-Life Problems. Bendell, Norm, illus. 2004. (Americangirl Library(R) Ser.). 64p. (J). pap. 8.95 (978-1-58485-874-4(5)) American Girl Publishing, Inc.

—What Would You Do? Quizzes About Real-Life Problems. 2004. (gr. 3-6). lib. bdg. 17.60 (978-0-613-83321-9(X)) Tandem Library Bks.

Davis, Anthony C. & Jackson, Jeffrey. Yo, Little Brother: Basic Rules of Survival for Young African-American Males. 1998. 145p. (gr. 4-7). pap. 14.95 (978-0-913543-58-0(6)) African American Images.

DeGezelle, Terri. Manners on the Playground. 2004. (First Facts Ser.). (Illus.). 24p. (J). (gr. k-2). lib. bdg. 21.26 (978-0-7368-2647-1(5) , First Facts) Capstone Pr., Inc.

DeMeyer, Patricia. Little Horsey Little Lessons: A Young Girl & Her Special Horse Help Teach Skills for Life. Christie, Terri, illus. 1999. 40p. (J). (gr. 1-6). pap. 9.95 (978-0-9666433-0-5(5)) Saddle Tree Pr.

Doyle, Alfreda C. Teaching You about Self Sufficiency with Stories That Rhyme. Doyle, Alfreda C., illus. 1998. (Illus.). 30p. (J). (gr. 5-9). 9.95 (978-1-56820-384-3(5)) Story Time Stories That Rhyme.

Dromgoole, Glenn. What Puppies Teach Us: Life's Lessons Learned from Our Little Friends. 2003. (Illus.). 32p. tchr. ed. 12.95 (978-1-57223-684-4(1) , 6841) Willow Creek Pr., Inc.

Dumas, Glenda F. Respect You Draw & Color Book Bk. 1: Respect. 1999. 34p. (J). (ps-2). mass mkt. 9.99 (978-1-930457-00-3(6)) Glenda's Place.

—Respect You Draw & Color Book Bk. 2: Do unto Others as You Would Have Them Do unto You. 1999. 36p. (J). (ps-2). mass mkt. 9.99 (978-1-930457-02-7(2)) Glenda's Place.

—Respeto Tu Libro para Dibujar y Colorear Libro 1: Respeto. 1999. Tr. of Respect You Drawing & Coloring Book. (SPA.). 34p. (J). (ps-2). mass mkt. 9.99 (978-1-930457-01-0(4)) Glenda's Place.

Edens, Cooper. Remember the Night Rainbow. 2002. (Illus.). 40p. 10.95 (978-0-8118-3511-4(1)) Chronicle Bks. LLC.

Erlbach, Arlene. Real Kids Taking the Right Risks: Plus, How You Can, Too! 1998. Orig. Title: Worth the Risk: True Sories about Risk Takers: Plus How You Can Be One, Too. (Illus.). 136p. (YA). (gr. 5-10). pap. 12.95 (978-1-57542-051-6(1)) Free Spirit Publishing, Inc.

Espeland, Pamela & Verdick, Elizabeth. Making Every Day Count: Daily Readings for Young People on Solving Problems, Setting Goals & Feeling Good about Yourself. 1998. 408p. (YA). (gr. 6 up). pap. 10.95 (978-1-57542-047-9(3)) Free Spirit Publishing, Inc.

Face the Facts, 7 bks. 2003. 199.92 (978-0-7398-6437-1(8)); Set 3. 2004. (Illus.). 171.36 (978-1-4109-1073-8(3)); Sets 1&2. 2003. (Illus.). pap. 56.35 (978-1-4109-0433-1(4)) Raintree.

Fairview Press Staff, ed. How We Made Our World a Better Place: Kids & Teens Write on How They Changed Their Corner of the World. 1998. 256p. (ps up). pap. 9.95 (978-1-57749-079-1(7)) Fairview Pr.

—Teens Write Through It: Essays from Teens Who've Triumphed over Trouble. annual 1998. 256p. (ps up). pap. 9.95 (978-1-57749-083-8(5)) Fairview Pr.

Fister, Susan, et al. Cool Kids: A Proactive Approach to Social Responsibility. 1998. (Illus.). 228p. (J). pap. 39.50 incl. audio (978-1-57035-134-1(1), 47COOL) Sopris West Educational Services.

—Cool Kids - A Proactive Approach to Social Responsibility Level I: Reproducibles. Weber, Philip A., Jr., illus. 1998. 114p. (J). (gr. k-3). pap. 25.00 (978-1-57035-156-3(2)) Sopris West Educational Services.

—Cool Kids - A Proactive Approach to Social Responsibility Level II: Reproducibles. Weber, Philip A., Jr., illus. 1998. 124p. (J). (gr. 3-8). pap. 25.00 (978-1-57035-157-0(0)) Sopris West Educational Services.

Forrest, Donna B. 180 Days of Character. Madden, Elizabeth, illus. 1998. 180p. (J). (gr. k-12). pap. 8.95 (978-1-889636-10-8(X), B002) Youthlight, Inc.

Frank, Kim T. & Smith-Rex, Susan J. Getting with It! A Kid's Guide to Forming Good Relationships & Fitting In. Jackson, Ruth A. & Elliott, Jan H., illus. 1998. 200p. (J). (gr. k-5). pap. 9.95 (978-0-932796-77-6(X)) Educational Media Corp.

Frank, Norma. Sailing New Seas: Helping Students in Grades 1-4 Cope with Moving. Deppenschmidt, Kurt, illus. 1999. 93p. (J). (gr. 1-4). pap. 14.95 (978-1-57543-070-6(3)) MAR*CO Products, Inc.

Gaissert, Anna Jean. Opening Doors to the Future: A 12-Session Suport Group for Middle & High School Students Who Are at Risk. Deppenschmidt, Kurt, illus. 1999. 40p. (YA). (gr. 6-12). pap. 8.95 (978-1-57543-072-0(X)) MAR*CO Products, Inc.

Gareth Stevens Publishing Staff. No Funciona! 2003. (SPA.). (gr. k-3). lib. bdg. 14.10 (978-0-613-76726-2(8)) Tandem Library Bks.

Gellman, Marc. "Always Wear Clean Underwear!" And Other Ways Parents Say "I Love You" 2000. (Illus.). (J). 11.79 (978-0-606-22049-1(6)) Tandem Library Bks.

—Always Wear Clean Underwear! And Other Ways Parents Say I Love You. Tilley, Debbie, illus. 2000. 112p. (J). (gr. 3-7). pap. 4.99 (978-0-688-17112-4(5), Harper Trophy) HarperCollins Pubs.

Golomb, Ruth Goldfinger & Vavrichek, Sherri Mansfield. The Hair Pulling Habit & You: How to Solve the Trichotillomania Puzzle. Yokel, Uri & Condon-Douglas, Emily, illus. rev. ed. 2000. 147p. (gr. 5-12). pap. 28.95 (978-0-9673050-2-8(0)) Writers' Cooperative of Greater Washington.

Goobie, Beth. Sticks & Stones. 2002. (Orca Soundings Ser.). 96p. (J). (gr. 7-12). pap. 7.95 (978-1-55143-213-7(7)) Orca Bk. Pubs. USA.

—Sticks & Stones. 2002. (gr. 7-12). lib. bdg. 16.40 (978-0-613-60618-9(3)) Tandem Library Bks.

Gouss, Deva Joy. A Tool Box for You: Activities for Helping Kids Cope with Serious Illness. Fairview Press Staff, ed. 1998. 32p. (gr. 2-6). pap. 6.95 (978-1-57749-086-9(X)) Fairview Pr.

Gulotta, Charles. Learn This! Stuff You Need to Know, & Mistakes You Need to Stop Making, Before You Step Foot into High School. 3rd rev. ed. 2005. (Illus.). 64p. (YA). (978-0-9653263-5-3(7)) Mostly Bright Ideas.

Harman, Chuck. Clean up That Mess! 2000. (Adventures of Artie the Airplane & His Friends Ser.). (Illus.). 32p. (J). (ps-6). pap. 6.95 (978-1-891736-11-7(6)) Studio Five/Fourteen.

—I Didn't Think It Would Hurt Anyone. 2000. (Adventures of Artie the Airplane & His Friends Ser.). 32p. (J). (ps-6). pap. 6.95 (978-1-891736-04-9(3)) Studio Five/Fourteen.

Hendersen. Aliens Took My Daughter. Hendersen, illus. 1998. (Illus.). 32p. (J). (gr. k-2). 14.95 (978-1-890453-13-8(7)) Little Friend Pr.

Hovanec, Erin M. Learning about Creativity from the Life of Steven Spielberg. 1999. (Character Building Book Ser.). (Illus.). 24p. (J). (gr. 3). lib. bdg. 18.75 (978-0-8239-5349-3(1), PowerKids Pr.) Rosen Publishing Group, Inc., The.

Howard, Patrick. Serving Others. Cannizzo, Karen A., ed. 1999. (Conversations with Teens Ser.). 16p. (YA). pap. 7.95 (978-0-937997-63-5(3), 3828) Pflaum Publishing Group.

Humphrey, Sandra McLeod. It's up to You... What Do You Do? Strassburg, Brian, illus. 1999. (Young Readers Ser.). 114p. (gr. 1 up). pap. 14.00 (978-1-57392-263-0(3), Pyr Bks.) Prometheus Bks., Pubs.

Jensen, Hay R. Home with Honor Vol. 1: A Vietnam P.O.W. Tells How to Conquer Adversity Through Courage, Honor & Faith. (Illus.). 171p. (Orig.). (YA). pap. 14.95 (978-1-877898-15-0(5)) P.O.W. (Pubns. of Worth).

Johnston, Marianne. Dealing with Anger. 1998. (Conflict Resolution Library). (Illus.). 24p. (J). (gr. k-4). pap. 6.95 (978-1-56838-265-4(0)) Hazelden Publishing & Educational Services.

—Let's Talk about Being Shy. 1998. (PowerKids Ser.). 24p. (J). (gr. k-3). reprint ed. pap. 6.95 (978-1-56838-222-7(7)) Hazelden Publishing & Educational Services.

Kahaner, Ellen. Everything You Need to Know about Growing Up Female. rev. ed. 2001. (Need to Know Library). (Illus.). 64p. (YA). (gr. 4-6). lib. bdg. 25.25 (978-0-8239-3463-8(2)) Rosen Publishing Group, Inc., The.

Klingel, Cynthia Fitterer, et al. Cooperation. 2002. (Wonder Books Level 3: Values Ser.). (Illus.). 32p. (J). (ps-3). 22.79 (978-1-56766-086-9(X)) Child's World, Inc.

—Fairness. 2002. (Wonder Books Level 3: Values Ser.). (Illus.). 32p. (J). (ps-3). 22.79 (978-1-56766-087-6(8)) Child's World, Inc.

—Sharing. 2002. (Wonder Books Level 3: Values Ser.). (Illus.). 32p. (J). (ps-3). 22.79 (978-1-56766-093-7(2)) Child's World, Inc.

Knapp, Toni. Ordinary Splendors: Tales of Virtues & Wisdom. Sohl, Kevin, illus. 2000. 43p. (YA). (gr. 5-7). reprint ed. 16.00 (978-0-7881-6845-1(2)) DIANE Publishing Co.

Knight, K. R. What Do You See? Lift-a-Flap Board Book. Santalucia, Francesco & Santalucia, Francesco, illus. 2002. (Lift-a-Flap Board Bks.). 10p. (J). 8.99 (978-1-57759-786-5(9)) Dalmatian Pr.

Krishnamurti, Jiddu. What Are You Doing with Your Life? Carlson, Dale, ed. Nicklaus, Carol, illus. 2002. (Books on Living for Teens Ser.: Vol. 1). 272p. (gr. 8-12). pap. 14.95 (978-1-888004-24-3(X)) Krishnamurti Pubns. of America.

Lagorio-Anthony, Jeanne. Everyday Heroes: Secrets Shared by Those with L. D. Design Scapes Studio Staff, illus. 1998. 80p. (YA). (gr. 5 up). pap. 8.95 (978-0-9633195-5-5(8)) Empowerment in Action.

Lee, Quinlan B. Hello Day! McKee, Darren, illus. 2004. (Barney Ser.). 6p. (J). bds. 5.99 (978-0-439-62497-8(5)) Scholastic, Inc.

Leigh, Susan K. God, I Need to Talk to You About Bad Manners. 2005. (J). 5.99 (978-0-7586-0813-0(6)) Concordia Publishing Hse.

—God, I Need to Talk to You about Bad Words. Clark, Bill, illus. 2005. (ENG.). 16p. (J). pap. 0.99 (978-0-7586-0793-5(8)) Concordia Publishing Hse.

Lerman, Laura. Supermax. Weiner, Ann, illus. 1998. (J). 11.99 (978-0-679-88659-4(1)); lib. bdg. 13.99 (978-0-679-98659-1(6)) Random Hse., Inc.

Lewis, Barbara A. Being Your Best: Character Building for Kids 7-10. 2004. (Laugh & Learn Ser.). (Illus.). 172p. (J). (gr. 4-7). pap. 14.95 (978-1-57542-063-9(5)) Free Spirit Publishing, Inc.

Lindros, Eric. Pursue Your Goals. 1999. (Positively for Kids Ser.). (Illus.). 40p. (gr. 3-7). 14.95 (978-0-87833-167-3(0)) Taylor Trade Publishing.

Lindsay, Jeanne Warren. Teenage Couples - Expectations & Reality: Teens' Views on Living Together, Roles, Work, Children, Jealousy, & Partner Abuse. 2003. (Teen Pregnancy & Parenting Series Ser.). (Illus.). 192p. (J). (gr. 7-12). pap. 14.95 (978-0-930934-98-9(9)) Morning Glory Pr., Inc.

Lindsay, Jeanne Warren & McCullough, Sally. Discipline from Birth to Three: How Teen Parents Can Prevent & Deal with Discipline Problems with Babies & Toddlers. Crawford, David, photos by. 3rd ed. 2004. (Teen Pregnancy & Parenting Series Ser.). 224p. (J). 18.95 (978-1-932538-10-6(0)); pap. 12.95 (978-1-932538-09-0(7)) Morning Glory Pr., Inc.

Lovitt, Chip. Sharing. 1999. (Doing the Right Thing Ser.). (Illus.). 32p. (J). (gr. k-3). lib. bdg. 26.60 (978-1-55916-236-4(8)) Rourke Publishing, LLC.

Mandino, Og. Og Mandino's Great Trilogy: The Greatest Salesman in the World, the Greatest Secret in the World & the Greatest Miracle in the World. 2008. 420p. (J). (978-0-8119-0428-5(8)) Lifetime Bks.

Martin, Dawn. Fast Girls Finish Last: A Girl's Guide to Becoming a Virgin with Attitude! 2nd rev. ed. 2006. (Illus.). 248p. (YA). (gr. 7-13). per. 19.95 (978-0-9668718-0-7(4)) Eos Publishing.

Martin, Donald R. "Rick". God Created You: A Guide to Temperament Therapy. 2004. 232p. per. 19.95 (978-0-9726996-2-4(7), GCY) Cook Communication.

Mastering Life Starter Kit Plus. (YA). (gr. 7-12). 39.95 (978-1-928726-01-2(1)) Positive Productions.

Matlock, Mark. Avoiding Stupidity: The Art & Science of Decision-Making. 1998. (Wise Guides Ser.). 48p. (YA). pap. 5.95 (978-1-888237-20-7(1)) Baxter Pr.

McCourt, Lisa, et al. Attitude: Tips to Help You Deal, Feel, & Be Real. 2000. (Attitude Ser.). (Illus.). 96p. (J). (gr. 3-7). pap. 6.95 (978-0-7373-0336-0(0), 03360W, Roxbury Park Juvenile) Lowell Hse. Juvenile.

McIntyre, Thomas. The Behavior Survival Guide for Kids: How to Make Good Choices & Stay Out of Trouble. 2004. (Illus.). 176p. (YA). (gr. 4-9). pap. 14.95 (978-1-57542-132-2(1)) Free Spirit Publishing, Inc.

Meiners, Cheri J. Be Polite & Kind. 2004. (Learning to Get Along Ser.). (Illus.). 40p. (J). (ps-3). pap. 10.95 (978-1-57542-151-3(8)) Free Spirit Publishing, Inc.

—Try & Stick with It. Johnson, Meredith, illus. 2004. (Learning to Get Along Ser.). 40p. (J). (ps-3). pap. 10.95 (978-1-57542-159-9(3)) Free Spirit Publishing, Inc.

Middleton, Don. Dealing with Feeling Left Out. 1998. (Conflict Resolution Library). (Illus.). 24p. (J). (gr. k-4). pap. 6.95 (978-1-56838-270-8(7)) Hazelden Publishing & Educational Services.

—Dealing with Secrets. 1998. (Conflict Resolution Library). (Illus.). 24p. (J). (gr. k-4). pap. 6.95 (978-1-56838-271-5(5)) Hazelden Publishing & Educational Services.

—Dealing with Secrets. 1999. (Conflict Resolution Library). 24p. (J). lib. bdg. 18.75 (978-0-8239-5265-6(7), PowerKids Pr.) Rosen Publishing Group, Inc., The.

—Dealing with Someone Who Is Selfish. 1999. (Conflict Resolution Library). 24p. (J). lib. bdg. 18.75 (978-0-8239-5268-7(1), PowerKids Pr.) Rosen Publishing Group, Inc., The.

—Dealing with Tattling. 1999. (Conflict Resolution Library). 24p. (J). lib. bdg. 18.75 (978-0-8239-5266-3(5), PowerKids Pr.) Rosen Publishing Group, Inc., The.

Miller, Maryann. Coping with Weapons & Violence at School & on Your Streets. rev. ed. 1999. (Coping Ser.). (Illus.). 189p. (YA). (gr. 7-12). lib. bdg. 26.50 (978-0-8239-2968-9(X), COWESC) Rosen Publishing Group, Inc., The.

Morris, Marilyn. Teens, Sex & Choices. McEowen, Shannan, illus. 2000. 210p. (YA). (gr. 6 up). pap. 13.95 (978-0-9648113-6-2(7), 0723) Charles Rivers Publishing Co.

Mosatche, Harriet S. Girls: What's So Bad about Being Good? 2001. 240p. pap. 13.95 (978-0-7615-3289-7(7), Three Rivers Pr.) Crown Publishing Group.

Mosatche, Harriet S. & Unger, Karen. Too Old for This, Too Young for That! Your Survival Guide for the Middle-School Years. Gordon, Mike, illus. 2004. 200p. (YA). (gr. 5-9). pap. 14.95 (978-1-57542-067-7(8)) Free Spirit Publishing, Inc.

Nathan, Amy. Everything You Need to Know about Conflict Resolution. rev. ed. 1999. (Need to Know Library). (Illus.). 64p. (YA). (gr. 7-12). lib. bdg. 25.25 (978-0-8239-2955-9(8), NTCORE) Rosen Publishing Group, Inc., The.

The Need to Know Library: Teens Taking Charge of Their Lives, 8 bks. Incl. Everything You Need to Know about AIDS & HIV. Draimin, Barbara Hermie. lib. bdg. 25.25 (978-0-8239-3314-3(8), NTAIHI); Everything You Need to Know about Chemotherapy. Alagna, Magdalena. lib. bdg. 25.25 (978-0-8239-3394-5(6)); Everything You Need to Know about Depression. Ayer, Eleanor H. lib. bdg. 25.25 (978-0-8239-3439-3(X)); Everything You Need to Know about Dyslexia. Goldish, Meish. lib. bdg. 25.25 (978-0-8239-3462-1(4)); Everything You Need to Know about Falling in Love. Spencer, Lauren. lib. bdg. 25.25 (978-0-8239-3395-2(4)); Everything You Need to Know about Food Poisoning. Isle, Mick. lib. bdg. 25.25 (978-0-8239-3396-9(2)); Everything You Need to Know about Growing Up Female. Kahaner, Ellen. lib. bdg. 25.25 (978-0-8239-3463-8(2)); Everything You Need to Know about Human Papillomavirus. Carter, Elizabeth. lib. bdg. 25.25 (978-0-8239-3397-6(0)); 64p. (YA). (gr. 4-6). 2001. (Illus.). Set lib. bdg. 202.00 (978-0-8239-9432-8(5)) Rosen Publishing Group, Inc., The.

Noonan, Rosalind. Just Trust Me. 2001. (Turning Seventeen Ser.: No. 9). 208p. (YA). (gr. 7 up). pap. 4.95 (978-0-06-447343-9(0), Harper Trophy) HarperCollins Pubs.

Olkowski, Mary. Life's a Cinch with Just One Inch. Olkowski, Mary, illus. unabr. ed. 1999. (Illus.). (gr. 4 up). 68p. bds. 14.95 (978-0-9668781-3-4(2), 1004); 100p. (YA). 19.95 (978-0-9668781-2-7(4), 1003-1004) Limpid Butterfly Productions, The.

Pardo, Michael Jerome. You Are One Too! A Book for All Children. 1998. 32p. (J). (gr. 1-8). 15.00 (978-0-9666633-3-4(0), 9807001) Universal Way, The.

Parsley, Bonnie M. Intelligent Living: Activity Book. Burgess, Molly, illus. 1998. 97p. (J). 39.95 (978-0-9650838-2-9(9)) StarBright Pubs.

Peacock, Judith & Stutman, Suzanne. Anger Management. 2000. (Perspectives on Mental Health Ser.). (Illus.). 64p. (J). (gr. 4-6). lib. bdg. 23.93 (978-0-7368-0433-2(1), LifeMatters Bks.) Capstone Pr., Inc.

Post, Peggy & Senning, Cindy Post. The Guide to Good Manners for Kids. Bjorkman, Steve, illus. 2006. 144p. (J). (gr. 4-8). reprint ed. 16.00 (978-1-4223-5621-0(3)) DIANE Publishing Co.

Radcliffe, Rebecca R. About to Burst: Handling Stress & Ending Violence—A Message for Youth. 1999. (Illus.). 208p. (YA). (gr. 7-12). pap. 15.00 (978-0-9636607-4-9(8)) EASE.

Reiss, Johanna. El Viaje de Vuelta. 1998. (SPA., Illus.). 240p. (gr. 5-8). (978-84-239-2784-5(9), EC2754) Espasa Calpe, S.A. ESP. *Dist:* Lectorum Pubns., Inc.

Rondeau, Amanda. Justice. 2003. (United We Stand Ser.). (Illus.). 24p. (J). (ps-3). lib. bdg. 19.93 (978-1-57765-879-5(5)) ABDO Publishing Co.

Rondina, Catherine. Gossip: Before Word Gets Around. Workman, Dan, illus. 2004. (Deal with It Ser.). 32p. (J). (gr. 4-8). pap. 12.95 (978-1-55028-821-6(0)) Lorimer, James & Co., Ltd., Pubs. CAN. *Dist:* Casemate Pubs. & Bk. Distributors, LLC.

Salzmann, Mary Elizabeth. I Am Caring. 2003. (Building Character Ser.). (Illus.). 24p. (J). (ps-3). lib. bdg. 19.93 (978-1-57765-827-6(2)) ABDO Publishing Co.

—I Am Respectful. 2003. (Building Character Ser.). (Illus.). 24p. (J). (ps-3). lib. bdg. 19.93 (978-1-57765-829-0(9)) ABDO Publishing Co.

Schab, Lisa M. The Stop, Relax & Think Workbook. 2002. (J). (gr. 1-6). per. 17.95 (978-1-58815-053-0(4), 61503) Childswork/Childsplay.

Schietinger-Cachina, Daryl A. How to Be Responsible. 1999. (Illus.). 10p. (J). (gr. k-8). pap. 5.00 (978-1-928641-06-3(7)) Daryl Ann Pubns.

Scholastic, Inc. Staff. Great Job! 1999. (J). pap. 3.95 (978-0-439-07232-8(8)) Scholastic, Inc.

Schuette, Sarah L. I Am Caring. Saunders-Smith, Gail, ed. 2002. (Character Values Ser.). (Illus.). 24p. (J). (gr. k-1). lib. bdg. 15.93 (978-0-7368-1438-6(8), Pebble Bks.) Capstone Pr., Inc.

—I Am Cooperative. Saunders-Smith, Gail, ed. 2002. (Character Values Ser.). (Illus.). 24p. (J). (gr. k-1). lib. bdg. 15.93 (978-0-7368-1439-3(6), Pebble Bks.) Capstone Pr., Inc.

Schwartz, Stuart B. Building Self-Confidence. 1998. (J). lib. bdg. (978-0-516-21295-1(8), Children's Pr.) Scholastic Library Publishing.

—Improving Work Habits. 1998. (Life Skills Ser.). 32p. (J). lib. bdg. (978-0-516-21296-8(6), Children's Pr.) Scholastic Library Publishing.

Schwartz, Stuart B., told to. Life Skills. 1998. (J). (gr. 5-12). (978-0-516-29735-4(X), Children's Pr.) Scholastic Library Publishing.

Schwartz, Stuart B. & Conley, Craig. Life Skills - Career Books, 8 bks. Incl. Budgeting Your Money. lib. bdg. 21.26 (978-0-7368-0044-0(1)); Building Self-Confidence. lib. bdg. 21.26 (978-1-56065-720-0(0)); Buying Insurance. lib. bdg. 21.26 (978-0-7368-0045-7(X)); Finding an Apartment. lib. bdg. 21.26 (978-0-7368-0046-4(8)); Improving Work Habits. lib. bdg. 21.26 (978-1-56065-721-7(9)); Living on Your Own. lib. bdg. 21.26 (978-1-56065-719-4(7)); Opening a Bank Account. lib. bdg. 21.26 (978-0-7368-0047-1(6)); Setting Career Goals. lib. bdg. 21.26 (978-1-56065-722-4(7)); 32p. (J). (gr. 3-4). 1998. (Illus.). Set lib. bdg. 170.08 (978-0-7368-0131-7(6), LifeMatters Bks.) Capstone Pr., Inc.

Senning, Cindy Post & Post, Emily. Emily Post's the Guide to Good Manners for Kids. Bjorkman, Steve, illus. 2004. 144p. (J). 16.99 (978-0-06-057196-2(9)) HarperCollins Pubs.

Seto, Alex. What do you See? 2006. 14p. pap. 6.95 (978-0-9734496-4-8(0)) ADVAN Pr., Inc. CAN. *Dist:* Biblio Distribution.

Sharing. 2002. (Precious Moments Ser.). (Illus.). 11p. (J). bds. 4.99 (978-1-57759-379-9(0)) Dalmatian Pr.

Sheindlin, Judy. Win or Lose by How You Choose! Tore, Bob, illus. 2000. 80p. (J). (gr. 2-7). 14.89 (978-0-06-028474-9(9)) HarperCollins Pubs.

Sieh, Ron. Moving at the Speed of Life: A Youth Survival Handbook. 2002. (Illus.). 140p. (YA). (gr. 7 up). pap. (978-1-58394-013-6(8), Frog Ltd.) North Atlantic Bks.

Siomades, Lorianne. A Place to Bloom. 2003. (Illus.). 32p. (J). (ps up). 9.95 (978-1-56397-656-8(0)) Boyds Mills Pr.

Small, Mary. Being Fair: A Book about Fairness. Previn, Stacey, illus. 2005. (Way to Be! Ser.). 24p. (J). (gr. k-2). lib. bdg. 22.60 (978-1-4048-1051-8(X)) Picture Window Bks.

—Being Trustworthy: A Book about Trustworthiness. Previn, Stacey, illus. 2005. (Way to Be! Ser.). 24p. (J). (gr. k-2). lib. bdg. 22.60 (978-1-4048-1054-9(4)) Picture Window Bks.

Sprague, Jeff & Golly, Annemieke. Best Behavior: Building Positive Behavior Support in Schools. 2004. (Illus.). 254p. per. (978-1-59318-071-3(3), 230BEST) Sopris West Educational Services.

Sprick, Randall S. The Solution Book. (Solution Book Ser.). (gr. k-8). 99.90 (978-0-07-568978-2(2)) SRA/McGraw-Hill.

Stacy, Lori Moore. Discover Yourself! 2000. (All about You Ser.). 112p. (J). (gr. 4-7). pap. 4.50 (978-0-439-15529-8(0)) Scholastic, Inc.

Steinhorst, Steff. Thrills & Skills: An Innovative Life Skills Course for Grades 6-9. 2000. 128p. (J). pap. 39.95 (978-0-89390-499-9(6)) Resource Pubns., Inc.

Storm, Rory. The Extreme Survival Guide: Real Survival Stories, Survival Skills, Fantasy Survival Tests. 1999. (Illus.). 128p. (J). (gr. 4-7). pap. 4.95 (978-1-902618-33-3(5)) Element Children's Bks.

Sutherland, Charles & Rhee, Jhoon. Character for Champions. 2002. 124p. (J). (gr. 4-7). pap. (978-1-931135-01-6(0)) MVM Bks.

Teen Issues, 26 bks., Set. (Illus.). (YA). (gr. 6-12). lib. bdg. 344.10 (978-0-89490-887-3(1)) Enslow Pubs., Inc.

Trainer, Chaim. Shalom Secrets: How to Live in Peace with Friends & Family, a Children's Guide. 2001. (Illus.). 128p. (gr. 4-7). pap., wbk. ed. 13.99 (978-1-930640-05-4(6)) Inner Learning.

—Shalom Secrets: How to Live in Peace with Friends & Family, A Children's Guide. 2005. (YID., Illus.). 121p. (J). (gr. 4-7). pap. 13.95 (978-1-930640-06-1(4)) Inner Learning.

Vander Zee, Ruth. Discover Your Gifts: And Learn How to Use Them. 1999. (Discover Ser.). 32p. stu. ed. 4.75 (978-1-56212-366-6(1), 120400); 40p. 9.50 (978-1-56212-365-9(3), 120405) CRC Pubns. (Faith Alive Christian Resources).

Verdick, Elizabeth. Feet Are Not for Kicking. Heinlen, Marieka, illus. 2004. (Best Behavior Ser.). 24p. (J). 7.95 (978-1-57542-158-2(5)) Free Spirit Publishing, Inc.

—Tails Are Not for Pulling. Heinlen, Marieka, illus. 2005. (Best Behavior Ser.: Bk. 3). 24p. (J). (ps). 7.95 (978-1-57542-180-3(1)) Free Spirit Publishing, Inc.

—Teeth Are Not for Biting. Heinlen, Marieka, illus. 2003. (Best Behavior Ser.). 24p. (J). 7.95 (978-1-57542-128-5(3)) Free Spirit Publishing, Inc.

—Words Are Not for Hurting. Heinlen, Marieka, illus. 2004. (Best Behavior Ser.). 24p. (J). 7.95 (978-1-57542-155-1(0)) Free Spirit Publishing, Inc.

Vogel, Elizabeth. Dealing with Showoffs. 2000. (Conflict Resolution Library). (Illus.). 24p. (J). (gr. 3). lib. bdg. 18.75 (978-0-8239-5412-4(9), PowerKids Pr.) Rosen Publishing Group, Inc., The.

West, Patricia E. The Common Sense Book of Change. 3rd rev. ed. 2000. Orig. Title: Aquarium Book of Change. 190p. (YA). (gr. 5 up). pap. 7.50 (978-0-9670063-1-4(7)) +A Positive Action Pr.

Weston, Carol. For Girls Only: Wise Words, Good Advice. 2004. 208p. (J). (gr. 5 up). pap. 8.99 (978-0-06-058318-7(5), Harper Trophy) HarperCollins Pubs.

—For Girls Only: Wise Words, Good Advice. 1998. (978-0-606-13396-8(8)) Tandem Library Bks.

Wheelwright, Henry C., ed. Rules of Civility for the 21st Century: From Cub & Boy Scouts Across America. Wallner, John C., illus. 2000. 144p. (YA). (gr. 5-11). pap. 15.00 (978-0-913276-62-4(6)) Stone Wall Pr., Inc.

Willker, Joshua D. G. Everything You Need to Know about Sports Gambling. 2005. (Need to Know Library). (Illus.). 64p. (YA). (gr. 7-12). lib. bdg. 25.25 (978-0-8239-3229-0(X), NTSPGA) Rosen Publishing Group, Inc., The.

Winkler, Kathleen. Bullying: How to Deal with Taunting, Teasing, & Tormenting. 2005. (Issues in Focus Today). (Illus.). 104p. (J). (gr. 6-10). lib. bdg. 31.93 (978-0-7660-2355-0(9)) Enslow Pubs., Inc.

Wisniewski, David. The Secret Knowledge of Grown-ups. 1998. (Illus.). 48p. (J). (gr. 2 up). 17.89 (978-0-688-15340-3(2)) HarperCollins Pubs.

Woods, Len. The Unoffical Guide to Life after High School. 2000. (Illus.). 96p. (gr. 11-13). pap. 5.99 (978-0-8010-6208-7(X)) Baker Bks.

Yorks, Julia. The Kid's Guide to New Hope. 1999. (Illus.). 40p. 5.95 (978-0-9671987-0-5(4)) Simply Kid's Publishing.

Youth Specialties Staff. Cheap Thrills. 1998. pap. 6.00 (978-0-310-67944-8(3)) HarperCollins Pubs.

BEHAVIOR—FICTION

Ada, Alma Flor. It Wasn't Me... 2000. (Stories the Year 'Round Ser.). (Illus.). 16p. (J). (gr. k-3). 8.95 (978-1-58105-222-0(7)) Santillana USA Publishing Co., Inc.

—Me Gustaria Tener. (Libros para Contar Ser.). (SPA., Illus.). 16p. (J). (gr. k-3). pap. 6.95 (978-1-58105-194-0(8)) Santillana USA Publishing Co., Inc.

Adiran, Laurelle. Kita & the Sames: Understand & Respect Others' Differences. 2001. (Kita Kollection Ser.). (Illus.). 50p. (J). (gr. 2-5). 15.95 (978-0-9701301-0-5(4)) KITA Pubns.

Adler, David A. Parachuting Hamsters & Andy Russell. Hillenbrand, Will, illus. 2001. (Andy Russell Ser.). 128p. (YA). (gr. 2-5). pap. 5.95 (978-0-15-216414-0(6), Gulliver Bks.) Harcourt Children's Bks.

Adshead, Paul S. Incredible Reversing Peppermints. 1999. (Child's Play Library). (Illus.). 120p. (J). (gr. k-7). 5.99 (978-0-85953-629-5(7)) Child's Play-International.

Alberto, Daisy. No Rules for Rex! Smath, Jerry, illus. 2005. 32p. (J). lib. bdg. 20.00 (***978-1-4242-1112-8(3)***) Fitzgerald Bks.

—No Rules for Rex! Smath, Jerry, illus. 2005. (Social Studies Connects). 32p. (J). pap. 4.99 (978-1-57565-146-0(7)) Kane Pr., The.

Alexander, Lloyd. How the Cat Swallowed Thunder. Schachner, Judith B., illus. 2003. 40p. (J). (gr. k-4). pap. 6.99 (978-0-14-250003-3(8) , Puffin) Penguin Group (USA) Inc.

—How the Cat Swallowed Thunder. 2003. (gr. k-3). lib. bdg. 15.30 (978-0-613-61632-4(4)) Tandem Library Bks.

Allan-Meyer, Kathleen. Little Bear's Big Adventure. Garvin, Elaine, illus. 1998. 32p. (J). (ps-1). pap. 6.49 (978-1-57924-060-8(7)) Jones, Bob Univ. Pr.

Allard, Harry. Miss Nelson Is Missing. Marshall, James, illus. 2007. 32p. (J). (gr. k-3). pap. 9.95 incl. audio compact disk (***978-0-618-85281-9(6)***) Houghton Mifflin Co. Trade & Reference Div.

Aloha Potter! Evaluation Guide: Evaluation Guide. 2006. (J). (978-1-55942-397-7(8)) Marsh Media.

Amedick, Deborah. A Cat Named Wellington: His Lessons for Christmas. 1998. (Animal Ser.). (Illus.). 36p. (J). (ps-1). pap. 4.95 (978-1-891210-79-2(3) , CNWXM1) Bartlett Publishing.

Amery, H. The Naughty Sheep. 2004. (Keyring Pack Ser.). 16p. (J). pap. 6.95 (978-0-7945-0067-2(6) , Usborne) EDC Publishing.

Amery, H. & Cartwright, Stephen. The Naughty Sheep. 16p. (J). lib. bdg. 13.95 (978-1-58086-720-7(0) , Usborne) EDC Publishing.

Andersen, Hans Christian. The Emperor's New Clothes. Burton, Virginia Lee, illus. 2004. 48p. (J). (gr. k-3). tchr. ed. 16.00 (978-0-618-34421-5(7)); pap. 6.95 (978-0-618-34420-8(9)) Houghton Mifflin Co. Trade & Reference Div.

Applegate, Katherine. Aaron Lets Go, No. 14. 1999. (Making Out Ser.: No. 14). 176p. (YA). (gr. 7 up). pap. 3.99 (978-0-380-80870-0(6)) HarperCollins Pubs.

—Elfangor's Secret. 1999. (Animorphs Ser.: No. 3). (J). (gr. 3-7). 12.64 (978-0-606-16619-5(X)) Tandem Library Bks.

Arnold, Tedd. No Jumping on the Bed! Arnold, Tedd, illus. 2002. (Illus.). (J). 14.04 (978-0-7587-3265-1(1)) Book Wholesalers, Inc.

—No Jumping on the Bed! Arnold, Tedd, illus. 2004. (Illus.). 32p. (J). (ps). 6.99 (978-0-8037-3044-1(6) , Dial) Penguin Group (USA) Inc.

—No More Water in the Tub! Sequel to No Jumping on the Bed! Buehner, Mark, illus. 1998. (Picture Puffin Ser.). 32p. (J). (ps-3). pap. 6.99 (978-0-14-056430-3(6) , Puffin) Penguin Group (USA) Inc.

Asch, Frank. Moonbear's Dream. Asch, Frank, illus. 2002. (Illus.). 32p. (J). (ps-1). pap. 6.99 (978-0-689-85310-4(6) , Aladdin) Simon & Schuster Children's Publishing.

Ashley, Bernard. Justin & the Big Fight. (Illus.). 96p. (J). 7.95 (978-0-14-038386-7(7)) Penguin Bks., Ltd. GBR. *Dist:* Trafalgar Square Publishing.

Ashman, Linda. Desmond & the Naughtybugs. McGrory, Anik, illus. 2006. 32p. (J). (gr. k-3). 15.99 (978-0-525-47203-2(7) , Dutton Juvenile) Penguin Group (USA) Inc.

Atkins, Catherine. Alt Ed. 2004. 208p. (J). (gr. 8-12). reprint ed. pap. 6.99 (978-0-14-240235-1(4) , Puffin) Penguin Group (USA) Inc.

Atwell, Debby. The Warthog's Tail. 2005. (Illus.). 32p. (J). (gr. k-3). 16.00 (978-0-618-50781-8(7) , Walter Lorraine) Houghton Mifflin Co. Trade & Reference Div.

Atwood, Margaret. Rude Ramsay & the Roaring Radishes. Petricic, Dusan, illus. 2004. 32p. (J). 16.95 (978-1-58234-950-3(9) , Bloomsbury Children) Bloomsbury Publishing.

Auch, Mary Jane. Poultrygeist. Jane, Mary & Auch, Herm, illus. 32p. (J). (gr. k-3). reprint ed. 6.95 (978-0-8234-1876-3(6)) Holiday Hse., Inc.

Avi. The Fighting Ground. 152p. (J). pap. 4.95 (978-0-8072-1378-0(0) , Listening Library) Random Hse. Audio Publishing Group.

—Perloo the Bold. unabr. ed. 2000. (YA). (gr. 7 up). pap., stu. ed. 58.24 incl. audio (978-0-7887-3651-3(5) , 41016X4) Recorded Bks., LLC.

—Perloo the Bold. 1999. (978-0-606-17444-2(3)); (gr. 5-8). lib. bdg. 13.00 (978-0-613-23025-4(6)) Tandem Library Bks.

Aylesworth, Jim. Naughty Little Monkeys. Cole, Henry, illus. (J). (ps). 2003. 40p. 16.99 (978-0-525-46940-7(0) , Dutton Juvenile); 2006. 32p. reprint ed. pap. 6.99 (978-0-14-240562-8(0) , Puffin) Penguin Group (USA) Inc.

Baek, Matthew J. Be Gentle with the Dog, Dear. 2008. 32p. (J). (ps-k). 14.99 (***978-0-8037-3250-6(3)*** , Dial) Penguin Group (USA) Inc.

Baggette, Susan K. The Night the Moon Slept. Saunders, Ward, illus. 2000. 32p. (J). (ps-3). (978-0-9660172-8-1(5)) Brookfield Reader, Inc., The.

Banks, Lynne Reid. Angela & Diabola. 163p. (J). (gr. 4-6). pap. 4.50 (978-0-8072-1515-9(5) , Listening Library) Random Hse. Audio Publishing Group.

—Angela & Diabola. 1998. (J). (978-0-606-13124-7(8)) Tandem Library Bks.

Barbaresi, Nina, illus. The Tale of Tom Kitten: A Story about Good Behavior. 2006. (J). 6.99 (978-1-59939-002-4(7)) Reader's Digest Young Families, Inc.

Barber, Antonia. Lessons for Lucy. (Illus.). 96p. (J). 5.95 (978-0-14-038681-3(5)) Penguin Group (USA) Inc.

Basye, Dale E. Heck: Where the Bad Kids Go. Dob, Bob, illus. 2008. (J). (***978-0-375-84075-3(3)***); pap. (***978-0-375-84076-0(1)***); lib. bdg. (***978-0-375-94075-0(8)***) Random Hse., Inc.

Bauer, Marion Dane. On My Honor. Bauer, Marion Dane, illus. 2002. (Illus.). (J). 13.40 (978-0-7587-0300-2(7)) Book Wholesalers, Inc.

—On My Honor. 90p. (J). (gr. 5-6). pap. 4.50 (978-0-8072-1455-8(8) , Listening Library) Random Hse. Audio Publishing Group.

Be Nice to Pooh. 1999. (J). pap. 2.99 (978-0-307-08598-6(8) , 08598, Golden Bks.) Random Hse. Children's Bks.

Bee, Clair. Championship Ball, Vol. 2. Farley, Cynthia B. & Farley, Randall, eds. rev. ed. 1998. (Chip Hilton Ser.: Vol. 2). (Illus.). 194p. (J). pap. 5.99 (978-0-8054-1815-6(6)) B&H Publishing Grp.

—Championship Ball. 1998. (gr. 5-8). lib. bdg. 14.15 (978-0-613-90137-6(1)) Tandem Library Bks.

—Clutch Hitter. (J). 17.95 (978-0-8488-1246-1(8)) Amereon LTD.

—Clutch Hitter, Vol. 4. Farley, Cynthia B. & Farley, Randall K., eds. rev. ed. 1998. (Chip Hilton Ser.: Vol. 4). 195p. (J). pap. 5.99 (978-0-8054-1817-0(2)) B&H Publishing Grp.

—Strike Three, Vol. 3. Farley, Cynthia B. & Farley, Randall K., eds. rev. ed. 1998. (Chip Hilton Ser.: Vol. 3). 211p. (J). pap. 5.99 (978-0-8054-1816-3(4)) B&H Publishing Grp.

—Touchdown Pass. Farley, Cynthia B. & Farley, Randall, eds. rev. ed. 1998. (Chip Hilton Ser.: Vol. 1). 198p. (J). 5.99 (978-0-8054-1686-2(2)) B&H Publishing Grp.

Beil, Karen Magnuson. Mooove Over! A Book about Counting by Twos. Meisel, Paul, tr. Meisel, Paul, illus. 2004. 32p. (J). (gr. k-3). tchr. ed. 16.95 (978-0-8234-1736-0(0)) Holiday Hse., Inc.

Bellingham, Brenda. Lilly in the Middle. Owen, Elizabeth, illus. 2003. (First Novel Ser.). 64p. (J). (gr. 1-5). 4.95 (978-0-88780-589-9(2)); (***978-0-88780-590-5(6)***) Formac Publishing Co., Ltd. CAN. *Dist:* Casemate Pubs. & Bk. Distributors, LLC.

—Lilly Makes a Friend. MacDonald, Clarke, illus. 2004. 62p. (J). lib. bdg. 12.00 (***978-1-4242-1221-7(9)***) Fitzgerald Bks.

Bellingham, Brenda. Lilly Plays Her Part. Owen, Elizabeth & Kaulbach, Kathy R., illus. 2000. (New First Novels Ser.: Vol. 12). 58p. (J). (gr. 1-5). (978-0-88780-501-1(9)) Formac Publishing Co., Ltd. CAN. *Dist:* Casemate Pubs. & Bk. Distributors, LLC.

—Lilly Plays Her Part. Owen, Elizabeth, illus. 2000. (New First Novels Ser.: Vol. 12). 58p. (gr. 1-5). 4.95 (978-0-88780-500-4(0)) Formac Publishing Co., Ltd. CAN. *Dist:* Casemate Pubs. & Bk. Distributors, LLC.

Berenstain, Stan & Berenstain, Jan. The Berenstain Bears & the Blame Game. Berenstain, Stan & Berenstain, Jan, illus. 2002. (Berenstain Bears First Time Bks.). (Illus.). (J). 11.19 (978-0-7587-0965-3(X)) Book Wholesalers, Inc.

—The Berenstain Bears & the Blame Game. ed. 2004. (Berenstain Bears First Time Bks.). (Illus.). (J). (gr. k-3). spiral bd. (978-0-616-14559-3(4)); spiral bd. (978-0-616-14560-9(8)) Canadian National Institute for the Blind/Institut National Canadien pour les Aveugles.

—The Berenstain Bears Get the Scaredies. Berenstain, Stan & Berenstain, Jan, illus. 1999. (Berenstain Bears Ser.). (Illus.). 24p. (J). (ps-3). lib. bdg. 7.99 (978-0-679-99323-0(1) , Random Hse. Bks. for Young Readers) Random Hse. Children's Bks.

Bernstein, Susan H. N. E. Pominonous Epstein & Trouble. 2001. (E. Pominonous Epstein Ser.). 20p. (J). (ps-3). pap. 8.95 (978-0-9706596-1-3(X)) Bernstein, Susan.

Big Bad Bully. 2005. 32p. (J). 12.99 (978-0-9758709-1-4(2) , A.W.A. Gang) Journey Stone Creations, LLC.

Birchall, Mark. Rabbit's Wooly Sweater. Birchall, Mark, illus. 2003. (Picture Bks.). (Illus.). 32p. (J). (ps-3). 15.95 (978-1-57505-465-0(5) , Carolrhoda Bks.) Lerner Publishing Group.

Birney, Betty. Oh, Bother! Someone Won't Share. Stevenson, Nancy, illus. 2000. (Oh, Bother! Ser.). 24p. (J). (ps-3). pap. 3.29 (978-0-307-12766-2(4) , 12766, Golden Bks.) Random Hse. Children's Bks.

—Oh, Bother! Someone's Messy. Stevenson, Nancy, illus. 1999. (Look-Look Bks.). 24p. (J). (ps-3). pap. 3.29 (978-0-307-12690-0(0) , 12690, Golden Bks.) Random Hse. Children's Bks.

Birney, Betty & Fulton, Mary J. Someone's Fighting. Baker, Darrell, illus. 2000. (Look-Look Bks.). 24p. (J). (ps-3). pap. 3.29 (978-0-307-12635-1(8) , 12635, Golden Bks.) Random Hse. Children's Bks.

Blake, Jan. Give Me My Yam. Melnyczuk, Peter, illus. 1999. (Reading Together Ser.). 32p. (J). (ps). pap. 3.99 (978-0-7636-0873-6(4)) Candlewick Pr.

Blazek, Frank. Phil & His Fabulous Feathers. Thomas, Wes, illus. 2005. 32p. (J). (gr. 4-7). 15.95 (978-1-58980-280-3(2)) Pelican Publishing Co., Inc.

Blobel, Brigitte. Red Rage. Ward, Rachel, tr. from GER. 2007. 224p. (YA). (gr. 8-12). 21.95 (***978-1-55451-102-0(X)***); pap. 10.95 (***978-1-55451-101-3(1)***) Annick Pr., Ltd. CAN. *Dist:* Firefly Bks., Ltd.

Bloom, Becky. Leo & Lester. Biet, Pascal, illus. 2003. (J). 32p. 15.95 (978-1-59034-582-5(7)); 33p. pap. (978-1-59034-583-2(5)) Mondo Publishing.

Blume, Judy. Otherwise Known As Sheila the Great. 2004. (Fudge Ser.). 160p. (gr. 12). mass mkt. 5.99 (978-0-425-19380-8(2) , Berkley) Penguin Group (USA) Inc.

—Tales of a Fourth Grade Nothing. 2002. (Fudge Ser.). (Illus.). 128p. (J). 15.99 (978-0-525-46931-5(1) , Dutton Juvenile) Penguin Group (USA) Inc.

—Tales of a Fourth Grade Nothing. (Fudge Ser.). 120p. (J). (gr. 3-5). pap. 4.99 (978-0-8072-1496-1(5) , Listening Library) Random Hse. Audio Publishing Group.

Blumenthal, Deborah. The Chocolate-Covered-Cookie Tantrum. Stevenson, Harvey, illus. 1999. 32p. (J). (gr. k-3). pap. 6.95 (978-0-395-70028-0(0) , Clarion Bks.) Houghton Mifflin Co. Trade & Reference Div.

Blyton, Enid. The Naughtiest Girl Again. (Illus.). 192p. (J). mass mkt. 6.95 (978-0-09-915911-7(2)) Random Hse. GBR. *Dist:* Trafalgar Square Publishing.

—The Naughtiest Girl in the School. (Illus.). 160p. (J). 6.95 (978-0-09-945500-4(5)) Random Hse. GBR. *Dist:* Trafalgar Square Publishing.

Boelts, Maribeth. When It's the Last Day of School. Wakiyama, Hanako, illus. 2004. 32p. (J). (ps-3). 15.99 (978-0-399-23498-9(5) , Putnam Juvenile) Penguin Group (USA) Inc.

Borchard, Therese Johnson. Whitney Climbs the Tower of Babel & Learns What Happens to Snobs. VanNest, Wendy, illus. 2001. (Emerald Bible Collection). 80p. (J). (gr. 3-7). 5.95 (978-0-8091-6675-6(5) , 6675-5) Paulist Pr.

Bottner, Barbara. You Have to be Nice to Someone on Their Birthday. Mai-Wyss, Tatjana, illus. 2007. 32p. (J). 15.99 (978-0-399-24295-3(3) , Putnam Juvenile) Penguin Group (USA) Inc.

Boulden, Jim & Boulden, Joan. Tall Paul. Tate, Susan, ed. Drengenberg, Heiko, illus. 1999. 24p. (YA). (gr. 6-9). pap. 5.95 (978-1-892421-12-8(7) , 12-7ab) Boulden Publishing.

Bourgeois, Paulette. Franklin Es un Mandon. Lopez Varela, Alejandra, tr. from ENG. Clark, Brenda, illus. 1998. (Franklin Ser.). (SPA.). 32p. (J). (ps-3). pap. 5.95 (978-1-880507-42-1(0) , LC7795) Lectorum Pubns., Inc.

—Franklin Is Bossy. Clark, Brenda, illus. 1998. (Franklin Ser.). 30p. (J). (ps-3). 19.95 (978-0-590-25764-0(1)) Scholastic, Inc.

Bowdish, Lynea. How to Be Nice— & Other Lessons I Didn't Learn. Gray, Leslie, illus. 2006. 47p. (J). pap. (978-1-59336-726-8(0)) Mondo Publishing.

Boyce, Julia G. Not Very Messy, Unless... Durney, Ryan, illus. 1998. 8p. (J). (gr. k-2). pap. 3.75 (978-1-880612-79-8(8) , Seedling Pubns.) Continental Pr., Inc.

Boynton, Sandra. What's Wrong, Little Pookie? 2007. (Illus.). 18p. (J). (ps). bds. 5.99 (***978-0-375-84552-9(6)*** , Robin Corey Bks.) Random Hse. Children's Bks.

Bradley, Kimberly Brubaker. Leap of Faith. 2007. 192p. (J). (gr. 5 up). 16.99 (978-0-8037-3127-1(2) , Dial) Penguin Group (USA) Inc.

—Pop! A Book about Bubbles. Miller, Margaret, illus. 2001. (Let's-Read-and-Find-Out Science Ser.). 40p. (J). (ps-1). 15.95 (978-0-06-028700-9(4)) HarperCollins Pubs.

Bradman, Tony. Bad Boys. 2003. 169p. (YA). (gr. 7). pap. 9.99 (978-0-552-54761-1(1) , Corgi) Transworld Publishers Ltd. GBR. *Dist:* Independent Pubs. Group.

Bramwell, Wendie & Normand, Bridgid. Rhymitis. Kim, Julie J., tr. Kim, Julie J., illus. 2003. 32p. (J). pap. (978-0-9741388-6-6(6)) Committee for Children.

Bramwell, Wendie, et al. The Friendship Alphabet. Ziegler, Michael, illus. Ziegler, Michael, photos by. 2003. 32p. (J). pap. (978-0-9741388-3-1(5)) Committee for Children.

Brand, Christianna. Nurse Matilda: The Collected Tales. Ardizzone, Edward, illus. ed. 2005. 300p. (J). 16.95 (978-1-58234-670-0(4)) Bloomsbury Publishing.

Bray, Jeannine D. Superfro. Kenyatta, Imani, ed. Mitchell, Denise B., illus. 1998. 72p. (J). (gr. k-6). 14.95 (978-1-886580-10-7(3)) Pinnacle-Syatt Pubns.

Brennan, Martin. Three Lessons for Astair the Bear. Huntington, Amy, illus. 2007. 40p. (J). 18.95 (***978-1-58726-435-1(8)*** , Mitten Pr.) Ann Arbor Media Group, LLC.

Brewer, Gary. Servants of the Mist. Dobson, David, ed. 1998. 190p. (J). 6.95 (978-1-57895-058-4(9)) Bridge Resources.

Brewster, Jim. Wild League on Ice. 1998. (J). pap. 5.95 (978-0-9683303-4-0(7)) Tumbleweed Pr.

Brimner, Larry Dane. Lightning Liz. Floca, Brian, illus. 1998. (Rookie Readers Ser.). 32p. (J). (gr. 1-2). 19.50 (978-0-516-20753-7(9) , Children's Pr.) Scholastic Library Publishing.

—School Rules. Tripp, Christine, illus. 2002. (Rookie Choices Ser.). 32p. (J). (gr. 1-2). pap. 5.95 (978-0-516-27389-1(2) , Children's Pr.) Scholastic Library Publishing.

—School Rules. 2002. (gr. k-3). lib. bdg. 14.10 (978-0-613-50237-5(X)) Tandem Library Bks.

Brown, Marc. Arthur & the Perfect Brother. ed. 2000. (Arthur Chapter Bks. : Bk. 21). (J). pap. 3.95 (978-0-316-12108-8(8)) Little, Brown Bks. for Young Readers.

—Arthur & the Perfect Brother. Brown, Marc, illus. 21st ed. 2000. (Arthur Chapter Bks. : Bk. 21). (Illus.). 64p. (J). (gr. 2-4). pap. 4.25 (978-0-316-12226-9(2)) Little, Brown Bks. for Young Readers.

—Arthur & the Perfect Brother. 2000. (Illus.). (J). 54p. (ps-ps). lib. bdg. 11.80 (978-0-613-24245-5(9)); (Arthur Chapter Bks.: Bk. 21). (gr. 3-6). 10.75 (978-0-606-18252-2(7)) Tandem Library Bks.

—Arthur & the Popularity Test. (Arthur Chapter Bks. : Bk. 12). (J). 1999. (gr. 3-6). pap. 3.95 (978-0-316-11999-3(7)); 12th ed. 1998. (Illus.). 64p. (gr. 2-4). pap. 4.25 (978-0-316-11545-2(2)) Little, Brown Bks. for Young Readers.

—Arthur & the Popularity Test. (Arthur Chapter Bks.: Bk. 12). 58p. (J). (gr. 3-6). pap. 3.95 (978-0-8072-1308-7(X)); 2004. (gr. 2-4). pap. 17.00 incl. audio (978-0-8072-0413-9(7) , FTR204SP) Random Hse. Audio Publishing Group. (Listening Library).

—Arthur, Clean Your Room! 2003. (Arthur Ser.). (Illus.). 24p. (gr. k-3). lib. bdg. 11.99 (978-0-679-98467-2(4) , Random Hse. Bks. for Young Readers) Random Hse. Children's Bks.

—Arthur, Clean Your Room! 1999. (Arthur Ser.). (gr. k-3). lib. bdg. 11.80 (978-0-613-23105-3(8)) Tandem Library Bks.

—Arthur's Computer Disaster. 1999. (Arthur Adventure Ser.). (J). (gr. k-3). pap. 5.95 (978-0-316-12373-0(0)) Little, Brown Bks. for Young Readers.

—Arthur's Computer Disaster. Brown, Marc, illus. 1999. (Arthur Adventure Ser.). (Illus.). 32p. (J). (ps-3). pap. 6.99 (978-0-316-10534-7(1)) Little, Brown Bks. for Young Readers.

—D. W. All Wet. Brown, Marc, illus. 2002. (D. W. Ser.). (Illus.). (J). 13.15 (978-0-7587-2325-3(3)) Book Wholesalers, Inc.

—D. W. Flips! Brown, Marc, illus. 2002. (D. W. Ser.). (Illus.). (J). 13.15 (978-0-7587-2326-0(1)) Book Wholesalers, Inc.

—D. W., Go to Your Room! Brown, Marc, illus. 2001. (D. W. Ser.). (Illus.). 24p. (J). (ps-1). pap. 5.99 (978-0-316-10670-2(4)) Little, Brown Bks. for Young Readers.

—D. W. 's Guide to Perfect Manners. 2006. (D. W. Ser.). (Illus.). 32p. (J). (ps-3). 15.99 (978-0-316-12106-4(1)) Little Brown & Co.

—D. W. Thinks Big. Brown, Marc, illus. 2002. (D. W. Ser.). (Illus.). (J). 13.15 (978-0-7587-2329-1(6)) Book Wholesalers, Inc.

—Francine, Believe It or Not! ed. 1999. (Arthur Chapter Bks. : Bk. 14). (J). (gr. 3-6). pap. 3.95 (978-0-316-10463-0(9)) Little, Brown Bks. for Young Readers.

—Francine the Superstar. Brown, Marc, illus. 22nd ed. 2000. (Arthur Chapter Bks. : Bk. 22). (Illus.). 64p. (J). (gr. 2-4). 13.95 (978-0-316-12227-6(0)) Little, Brown Bks. for Young Readers.

—Francine the Superstar. Krensky, Stephen, tr. Brown, Marc, illus. 22nd ed. 2000. (Arthur Chapter Bks. : Bk. 22). (Illus.). 64p. (J). (gr. 2-4). pap. 4.25 (978-0-316-12250-4(5)) Little, Brown Bks. for Young Readers.

—Francine the Superstar. 2000. (Arthur Chapter Bks.: Bk. 22). (Illus.). (J). 57p. (ps). lib. bdg. 11.80 (978-0-613-25249-2(7)); (gr. 3-6). 10.75 (978-0-606-18253-9(5)) Tandem Library Bks.

Bruel, Nick. Bad Kitty. Bruel, Nick, illus. 2005. (Illus.). 40p. (J). (ps-3). 15.95 (978-1-59643-069-3(9)) Roaring Brook Pr.

Brun-Cosme, Nadine. No, I Want Daddy! Backes, Michel, illus. 2004. 32p. (J). (ps-k). tchr. ed. 14.00 (978-0-618-38157-9(0) , Clarion Bks.) Houghton Mifflin Co. Trade & Reference Div.

Bruna, Dick. Good Morning, Miffy. 1998. (Miffy Ser.). (Illus.). 12p. (J). (ps-k). 4.95 (978-1-56836-264-9(1)) Kodansha America, Inc.

—Miffy Helps at Home. 1998. (Illus.). 12p. (J). (ps-k). 4.95 (978-1-56836-265-6(X)) Kodansha America, Inc.

—Miffy Likes to Ride. 1998. (Miffy Ser.). (Illus.). 8p. (J). (ps-k). 8.95 (978-1-56836-268-7(4)) Kodansha America, Inc.

Buchanan, Paul & Randall, Rod. The Monopoly, Vol. 10. 1998. (Misadventures of Willie Plummett Ser.: Vol. 10). 128p. (J). (gr. 3-7). 5.99 (978-0-570-05089-6(8)) Concordia Publishing Hse.

—Shooting Stars, Vol. 8. 1998. (Misadventures of Willie Plummett Ser.: Vol. 8). (Illus.). 128p. (J). (gr. 3-7). 5.99 (978-0-570-05087-2(1)) Concordia Publishing Hse.

Buehner, Caralyn. I Did It, I'm Sorry. Buehner, Mark, illus. 2000. (Picture Puffin Ser.). 40p. (J). (ps-3). pap. 6.99 (978-0-14-056722-9(4) , Puffin) Penguin Group (USA) Inc.

—I Did It, I'm Sorry. Buehner, Mark, illus. 2000. (J). (ps). lib. bdg. 14.15 (978-0-613-25622-3(0)) Tandem Library Bks.

—I Did It, I'm Sorry. 2000. (Illus.). (J). (978-0-606-18838-8(X)) Tandem Library Bks.

—It's a Spoon Not a Shovel. Buehner, Mark, illus. 1998. 40p. (J). (ps-3). pap. 6.99 (978-0-14-056427-3(6) , Puffin) Penguin Group (USA) Inc.

Buffie, Margaret. Angels Turn Their Backs. 1998. (Margaret Buffie Ser.). 240p. (YA). (gr. 13 up). (978-1-55074-415-6(1)) Kids Can Pr., Ltd.

Bulla, Clyde Robert. Shoeshine Girl. 1999. (Illus.). (J). (gr. 3-6). lib. bdg. 13.00 (978-0-8335-2660-1(X)) Tandem Library Bks.

Bunting, Eve. Jumping the Nail. unabr. ed. 2000. (YA). pap., stu. ed. 43.25 incl. audio (978-0-7887-3009-2(6) , 40891X4) Recorded Bks., LLC.

—My Backpack. Cocca-Leffler, Maryann, illus. 2004. 32p. (J). (gr. k-2). 16.95 (978-1-56397-433-5(9)) Boyds Mills Pr.

Burnett, Karen Gedig. Simon's Hook: A Story about Teases & Put-Downs. Barrows, Laurie, illus. 1999. (Grandma Rose Story). 40p. (J). (gr. 1-4). 14.95 (978-0-9668530-0-1(8)); pap. 8.95 (978-0-9668530-1-8(6)) GR Publishing.

Burningham, John. Edwardo: The Horriblest Boy in the Whole Wide World. 2007. (Illus.). 32p. (J). (ps-3). 16.99 (978-0-375-84053-1(2)); lib. bdg. 19.99 (978-0-375-94053-8(7)) Random Hse. Children's Bks. (Knopf Bks. for Young Readers).

But You Promised! A Book about Keeping Your Word. 1998. (Big Comfy Couch Ser.). (Illus.). 32p. (J). 5.95 (978-0-7370-1001-5(0)) Time-Life Inc.

Cain, Barbara S. I Don't Know Why... I Guess I'm Shy. Smith-Moore, J. J., illus. 1999. 32p. (J). (ps-3). (978-1-55798-596-5(0) , 441-5960, Magination Pr.) American Psychological Assn.

Calvert, Patricia. Picking up the Pieces. 1999. (978-0-606-15922-7(3)) Tandem Library Bks.

Campbell, Joanna. Christina's Courage. 1998. (Thoroughbred Ser.: No. 27). 176p. (gr. 4-7). mass mkt. 4.99 (978-0-06-106529-3(3)) HarperCollins Pubs.

Canady, Pat. Upside - Downside, Downside - Upside. Zawiki, Neil, illus. 2000. 42p. (J). (ps-4). pap. 10.00 (978-1-929889-00-6(3)) Canady SW Publishing.

Cannon, Janell. Trupp: A Fuzzhead Tale. 1998. (Illus.). 48p. (J). pap. 7.00 (978-0-15-201695-1(3) , Harcourt Paperbacks) Harcourt Children's Bks.

—Trupp: A Fuzzhead Tale. 1998. (J). (978-0-606-13876-5(5)) Tandem Library Bks.

Capucilli, Alyssa Satin. Little Spotted Cat. Andreasen, Dan, illus. 2005. 32p. (J). (ps-ps). 14.99 (978-0-8037-2692-5(9) , Dial) Penguin Group (USA) Inc.

Carle, Eric. The Grouchy Ladybug. Carle, Eric, illus. 1999. (Illus.). 44p. (J). (ps-k). bds. 7.99 (978-0-694-01320-3(X) , Harper Festival) HarperCollins Pubs.

—The Very Clumsy Click Beetle. Carle, Eric, illus. 1999. (Illus.). 32p. (J). (ps-3). 21.99 (978-0-399-23201-5(X) , Philomel) Penguin Group (USA) Inc.

Carlson, Melody. Charlene's Grumpy Day: A Scoozie Tale about Patience. Fincher, Kathryn Andrews, illus. Date not set. 32p. (J). 9.99 (978-0-7369-0734-7(3)) Harvest Hse. Pubs.

—Forgive Others. Reagan, Susan Joy, illus. 2004. (Just Like Jesus Said Ser.). 32p. (J). (ps-5). 12.99 (978-0-8054-2385-3(0)) B&H Publishing Grp.

—Grover Tells a Whopper: A Scoozie Tale about Honesty. Fincher, Kathryn Andrews, illus. Date not set. 32p. (J). 9.99 (978-0-7369-0733-0(5)) Harvest Hse. Pubs.

—Love Your Neighbor. Reagan, Susan Joy, illus. 2004. (Just Like Jesus Said Ser.). 32p. (J). (ps-5). 12.99 (978-0-8054-2383-9(4)) B&H Publishing Grp.

Carlson, Nancy. Sit Still! 1998. (978-0-606-13776-8(9)) Tandem Library Bks.

Carlsson-Paige, Nancy. Best Day of the Week. 2004. (Illus.). 32p. (J). (ps-1). pap. 10.95 (978-1-884834-52-3(3) , 7070) Redleaf Pr.

Carr, Karen. Clumsy Wally the Handyman. Volodka, Aras, illus. 2000. 32p. (J). pap. (978-0-9701450-9-3(8)) Long Hill Productions, Inc.

Carter, Alden R. Bull Catcher. 2000. (Illus.). 288p. (YA). (gr. 7 up). pap. 4.99 (978-0-590-50959-6(4) , Scholastic Reference) Scholastic, Inc.

—Bull Catcher. 2000. (978-0-606-17876-1(7)) Tandem Library Bks.

Caseley, Judith. Bully. Caseley, Judith, illus. 2001. (Illus.). 32p. (J). (gr. 5 up). lib. bdg. 16.89 (978-0-688-17868-0(5)); (ps-3). 16.99 (978-0-688-17867-3(7)) HarperCollins Pubs.

Cassidy, Anne. Naughty Nancy. Guicciardini, Desideria, illus. 2004. (Read-It! Readers Ser.). 32p. (J). (gr. k-3). 18.60 (978-1-4048-0558-3(3)) Picture Window Bks.

Castle, Kathryn. Cool Junk. Ahers-Johnson, Patrizia, illus. 1998. (Think-Kids Book Collection). 16p. (J). (gr. 1-4). pap. 2.95 (978-1-58237-014-9(1)) Creative Thinkers, Inc.

Castor, Harriet. Milly's Golden Goal. (Illus.). 96p. (J). 7.95 (978-0-14-038478-9(2)) Penguin Bks., Ltd. GBR. *Dist:* Trafalgar Square Publishing.

Changed Behavior! Individual Title Six-Packs. (Bookweb Ser.). 32p. (gr. 6 up). 34.00 (978-0-7578-0892-0(1)) Rigby Education.

Chardiet, Bernice & Maccarone, Grace. We Scream for Ice Cream. Karas, G. Brian, illus. 1998. (Hello Reader! Ser.). (J). (978-0-590-63395-6(3)) Scholastic, Inc.

Charlie's Be Kind Day. 2006. 16p. (J). pap. 1.99 (978-0-7847-1689-2(7) , 02991) Standard Publishing.

Chartrand, Lili. Taming Horrible Harry. Ouriou, Susan, tr. from FRE. Rogé, illus. 2006. 32p. (J). (ps-3). 16.95 (978-0-88776-772-2(9)) Tundra Bks., Inc./Livres Toundra, Inc. CAN. *Dist:* Random Hse., Inc.

Chartrand, Micheline & Desputeaux, Helene. Caillou Knows How. Chartrand, Micheline & Desputeaux, Helene, illus. 1998. (Illus.). 4p. (J). bds. 4.49 (978-1-58048-033-8(0)) Sandvik Publishing.

Cherrington, Janelle. Drawing the Line. Goldberg, Barry, illus. 2000. (Wild Thornberrys Ready-to-Read Ser. : Vol. 2). 32p. (J). (gr. 4-6). pap. 3.99 (978-0-689-83231-4(1) , Simon Spotlight/Nickelodeon) Simon & Schuster Children's Publishing.

—Drawing the Line. 2000. (gr. k-3). lib. bdg. 11.80 (978-0-613-24899-0(6)) Tandem Library Bks.

Childrens Press Staff, ed. Messy Bessey. 2005. (Rookie Reader Ser.). 96p. (J). (ps-2). pap. 9.95 (978-0-516-25328-2(X) , Children's Pr.) Scholastic Library Publishing.

Chrismer, Melanie. Phoebe Clappsaddle & The Tumbleweed Gang. Roeder, Virginia M., illus. 2002. 32p. (J). 14.95 (978-1-56554-966-1(X)) Pelican Publishing Co., Inc.

Christopher, Matt. Center Court Sting. 1998. 160p. (J). (gr. 3-7). pap. 4.99 (978-0-316-14205-2(0)) Little Brown & Co.

—Center Court Sting. 1998. 140p. (J). (ps-7). per. 12.40 (978-0-613-11395-3(0)) Tandem Library Bks.

Christopher, Matt & #1 Sports Writer for Kids Staff. Center Court Sting. 1998. 160p. (J). (gr. 3-7). 15.95 (978-0-316-14278-6(6)) Little Brown & Co.

Cibula, Matt S. What's up with You, Taquandra Fu? Strassburg, Brian J., illus. 1998. 40p. (J). (ps-3). 16.95 (978-1-55933-212-5(3)) Zino Pr. Children's Bks.

Clairday, Robynn. Expect the Unexpected. 2000. (Illus.). 112p. (J). (gr. 4-7). pap. 4.50 (978-0-439-21581-7(1)) Scholastic, Inc.

Clark, Brenda, illus. Franklin Is Bossy. 2002. (Franklin Ser.). 12.40 (978-1-4046-0316-5(6)) Book Wholesalers, Inc.

Clark, Emma Chichester. It Was You, Blue Kangaroo! Clark, Emma Chichester, illus. 2004. 32p. (J). (gr. k-k). pap. 6.99 (978-0-553-11280-1(5) , Dragonfly Bks.) Random Hse. Children's Bks.

—It Was You, Blue Kangaroo. Clark, Emma Chichester, illus. 2002. (Illus.). 32p. (J). (gr. k-k). 15.95 (978-0-385-74623-6(7) , Doubleday Bks. for Young Readers) Random Hse. Children's Bks.

Clark, Will. School Bells & Broken Tales: Exploring with Jack & Jill. Witherspoon, P. J., illus. 1998. 176p. (J). (gr. 3-6). pap. 14.95 (978-0-9661993-5-2(9)) Motivation Basics.

Clarke, Nicole. Model Behavior, No. 10. 2007. 224p. (J). pap. 6.99 (978-0-448-44562-5(X) , Grosset & Dunlap) Penguin Group (USA) Inc.

Clements, Andrew. No Talking. Elliott, Mark, illus. 2007. 160p. (J). (gr. 3-7). 15.99 ***(978-1-4169-0983-5(4))*** Simon & Schuster Children's Publishing.

Clyde, Addie Mae. Charlie the Chair. 2006. (J). per. 10.95 ***(978-1-59872-694-7(3))*** Instantpublisher.com.

Cohen, Miriam. Eddy's Dream. Cohen, Adam, photos by. l.t. ed. 2000. (Illus.). 32p. (J). (gr. k-2). 16.95 (978-1-887734-57-8(0)) Star Bright Bks., Inc.

Cole, Babette. Una Nina Mal Educada. 2000. (SPA., Illus.). 32p. (J). (gr. 1-3). 16.95 (978-84-233-3037-9(0) , Dial) Penguin Group (USA) Inc.

—Princess Smartypants. ed. 2004. (J). (gr. k-2). spiral bd. (978-0-616-01619-0(0)); spiral bd. (978-0-616-01620-6(4)) Canadian National Institute for the Blind/Institut National Canadien pour les Aveugles.

—The Sprog Owner's Manual. 2005. (Illus.). 32p. (J). (ps-3). pap., pap. 9.99 (978-0-09-944765-8(7) , Red Fox) Random Hse. Children's Bks. GBR. *Dist:* Trafalgar Square Publishing.

Collicott, Sharleen. Toestomper & the Bad Butterflies. 2003. (Illus.). 32p. (J). (gr. k-3). tchr. ed. 15.00 (978-0-618-14092-3(1)) Houghton Mifflin Co. Trade & Reference Div.

—Toestomper & the Caterpillars. 2002. (Illus.). 32p. (J). (gr. k-3). pap. 5.95 (978-0-618-19675-3(7)) Houghton Mifflin Co. Trade & Reference Div.

—Toestomper & the Caterpillars. Collicott, Sharleen, illus. 1999. (Illus.). 32p. (J). (gr. k-3). tchr. ed. 15.00 (978-0-395-91168-6(0)) Houghton Mifflin Co. Trade & Reference Div.

—Toestomper & the Caterpillars. 2002. (gr. k-3). lib. bdg. 14.10 (978-0-613-90726-2(4)) Tandem Library Bks.

Conover, Chris. The Lion's Share. ed. 2004. (J). (gr. k-3). spiral bd. (978-0-616-07222-6(8)); spiral bd. (978-0-616-07223-3(6)) Canadian National Institute for the Blind/Institut National Canadien pour les Aveugles.

Cookson, Catherine. Solace of Sin. 2000. 416p. pap. 13.99 (978-0-552-14583-1(1) , Corgi) Transworld Publishers Ltd. GBR. *Dist:* Trafalgar Square Publishing.

Coomer, Gerald. Summer I Was Seventeen. 2002. (gr. 7-12). lib. bdg. 32.70 (978-0-613-77565-6(1)) Tandem Library Bks.

Cooper, Ilene. The Annoying Team. Paine, Colin, illus. 2005. (Stepping Stones Ser.). 80p. (J). (gr. 2-5). pap. 3.99 (978-0-307-26512-8(9) , Random Hse. Bks. for Young Readers) Random Hse. Children's Bks.

Corey, Shana. First Graders from Mars. Teague, Mark, illus. 2003. (First Graders from Mars Ser.: No. 4). 32p. (J). pap. 4.99 (978-0-439-45219-9(8) , Scholastic Pr.) Scholastic, Inc.

Corey, Shana & Teague, Mark. Tera, Star Student. 2003. (First Graders from Mars Ser.: No. 4). (Illus.). 32p. (J). pap. 15.95 (978-0-439-26634-5(3) , Scholastic Pr.) Scholastic, Inc.

Cory, Kim Delmar. Lilly's Way. Austin, Jane G., ed. 1998. 187p. (YA). (gr. 4-6). 9.99 (978-0-88092-363-7(6) , 3636) Royal Fireworks Publishing Co.

Cosby, Bill. Money Troubles. Honeywood, Varnette P., illus. 1998. (Little Bill Books for Beginning Readers Ser.). 40p. (J). (gr. k-3). pap. 13.95 (978-0-590-16402-3(3)) Scholastic, Inc.

—Money Troubles. Honeywood, Varnette P., illus. 1998. (Little Bill Books for Beginning Readers Ser.). (J). (gr. k-3). (978-0-606-13615-0(0)) Tandem Library Bks.

—Money Troubles, Level. 3. Honeywood, Varnette P., illus. 1998. (Little Bill Books for Beginning Readers Ser.: No. 6). 40p. (J). (gr. k-3). pap. 3.99 (978-0-590-95623-9(X)) Scholastic, Inc.

—The Worst Day of My Life. Honeywood, Varnette P., illus. 1999. (Little Bill Books for Beginning Readers Ser.). 40p. (J). (gr. k-3). pap. 3.99 (978-0-590-52175-8(6) , Cartwheel Bks.) Scholastic, Inc.

—The Worst Day of My Life. 1999. (Little Bill Books for Beginning Readers Ser.). (J). (gr. k-3). (978-0-606-18618-6(2)) Tandem Library Bks.

—Worst Day of My Life. 1999. (gr. k-3). lib. bdg. 11.80 (978-0-613-17951-5(X)) Tandem Library Bks.

Cosgrove, Stephen. Crabby Gabby. James, Robin, illus. rev. ed. 2001. (Serendipity Bks.). 1p. (J). pap. 4.99 (978-0-8431-7663-6(6) , Price Stern Sloan) Penguin Group (USA) Inc.

—Crabby Gabby. 2001. (gr. k-3). lib. bdg. 13.00 (978-0-613-87208-9(8)) Tandem Library Bks.

—Gabby. James, Robin, illus. 2003. (Serendipity Bks.). 32p. (J). (gr. k-5). pap. 4.99 (978-0-8431-0595-7(X) , Price Stern Sloan) Penguin Group (USA) Inc.

—Gabby. 2003. (gr. k-3). lib. bdg. 13.00 (978-0-613-81297-9(2)) Tandem Library Bks.

Costello, Emily. Calling the Shots. 1999. (Soccer Stars Ser.: No. 7). (J). (gr. 3-7). (978-0-606-17152-6(5)) Tandem Library Bks.

—Teaming Up. 1999. (Soccer Stars Ser.: No. 8). (J). (gr. 3-7). (978-0-606-17749-8(3)) Tandem Library Bks.

Cotner, June. Amazing Graces: Prayers & Poems for Children. Palmer, Jan, illus. 2001. 64p. (J). (ps-4). 12.95 (978-0-688-15566-7(9)) HarperCollins Pubs.

Cowell, Cressida. Don't Do That Kitty Kilroy! Cowell, Cressida, illus. 2000. (Illus.). 32p. (J). (ps-2). 15.95 (978-0-531-30209-5(1) , Orchard Bks.) Scholastic, Inc.

Cowley, Joy. Mrs. Wishy-Washy. Fuller, Elizabeth, illus. 1999. 16p. (J). (ps-k). bds. 5.99 (978-0-399-23391-3(1) , Philomel) Penguin Group (USA) Inc.

Coxe, Molly. Bookworm. 2000. (J). (978-0-606-18920-0(3)) Tandem Library Bks.

Craner, Kathy. Nibbles the Rabbit Has a Good Habit. 1998. (Illus.). (J). (ps-2). pap. 12.95 (978-0-7880-1404-8(8) , Fairway Pr.) CSS Publishing Co.

Crassy the Crude Beastie. 2001. (Beastie Buddies Ser.). (Illus.). 32p. (J). 6.95 (978-1-891100-86-4(6)) Smart Kids Publishing.

Crawford, Mary C. Suspicion of Arson. 2001. 125p. (J). (gr. 3-6). 9.99 (978-0-88092-550-1(7) , 550-7) Royal Fireworks Publishing Co.

Crimi, Carolyn. No Necesito Amigos. 2004. (SPA.). 32p. (978-84-7720-798-6(4)) Obelisco, Ediciones S.A.

Crutcher, Chris. Staying Fat for Sarah Byrnes. 2003. 304p. (J). (ps-3). pap. 6.99 (978-0-06-009489-8(3)) HarperCollins Pubs.

Cuneo, Diane. Mary Louise Loses Her Manners. Davis, Jack E., illus. 2000. (J). (978-0-606-20019-6(3)) Tandem Library Bks.

Current, Sharon S. McQuillken Finds His Purpose. Holloway, Pam, illus. l.t. ed. 1998. 24p. (J). (gr. k-2). pap. 9.95 (978-0-9668072-0-2(0)) Sunshine Pr., LLC.

Curtis, Jamie Lee. Tell Me Again about the Night I Was Born. Cornell, Laura, illus. 1999. (Joanna Cotler Bks.). 32p. (J). (ps-k). 7.99 (978-0-694-01215-2(7) , Harper Festival) HarperCollins Pubs.

Cutler, Jane. Rats! 1998. (978-0-606-13727-0(0)) Tandem Library Bks.

—Rats! Pearson, Tracey Campbell, illus. 1998. 114p. (J). (ps-k). per. 14.10 (978-0-613-08620-2(1)) Tandem Library Bks.

Cuyler, Margery. Kindness Is Cooler, Mrs. Ruler. Yoshikawa, Sachiko, illus. 2007. 50p. (J). (gr. k-2). 16.99 (978-0-689-87344-7(1) , Simon & Schuster Children's Publishing) Simon & Schuster Children's Publishing.

—Please Play Safe! Penguin's Guide to Playground Safety. Hillenbrand, Will, illus. 2006. 32p. (J). pap. 15.99 (978-0-439-52832-0(1) , Scholastic Pr.) Scholastic, Inc.

—Please Say Please! Penguin's Guide to Manners. Hillenbrand, Will, illus. 2005. (J). ***(978-0-439-67874-2(9))*** Scholastic, Inc.

—Please Say Please! Penguin's Guide to Manners. Hillenbrand, Will, tr. Hillenbrand, Will, illus. 2004. 32p. (J). pap. 15.95 (978-0-590-29224-5(2)) Scholastic, Inc.

—That's Good! That's Bad! Catrow, David, illus. 2002. (J). 15.49 (978-0-7587-3780-9(7)) Book Wholesalers, Inc.

Dahl, Roald. Charlie & the Chocolate Factory. movie tie-in ed. Date not set. 174p. (J). 19.95 (978-0-8488-2241-5(2)) Amereon LTD.

—Charlie & the Chocolate Factory. Blake, Quentin, illus. 176p. 2007. (J). (gr. 2). 6.99 ***(978-0-14-241031-8(4));*** 2005. (gr. 3-6). 6.99 (978-0-14-240388-4(1)) Penguin Group (USA) Inc. (Puffin).

—Charlie & the Chocolate Factory. movie tie-in ed. 2005. 176p. (J). (gr. 3-7). lib. bdg. 16.99 (978-0-375-93460-5(X) , Knopf Bks. for Young Readers) Random Hse. Children's Bks.

—Charlie & the Chocolate Factory. Blake, Quentin, illus. movie tie-in ed. 176p. (J). (gr. 3-7). 2005. 14.95 (978-0-375-83460-8(5)); 2001. 15.95 (978-0-375-81526-3(0)); 2001. lib. bdg. 17.99 (978-0-375-91526-0(5)) Random Hse. Children's Bks. (Knopf Bks. for Young Readers).

Danziger, Paula. The Cat Ate My Gymsuit. 2004. (Puffin Modern Classics Ser.). 160p. (J). (gr. 5). pap. 5.99 (978-0-14-240250-4(8) , Puffin); 30th anniv. ed. (gr. 2-6). 15.99 (978-0-399-24307-3(0) , Putnam Juvenile) Penguin Group (USA) Inc.

—The Cat Ate My Gymsuit. 128p. (J). (gr. 3-5). pap. 3.99 (978-0-8072-1368-1(3) , Listening Library) Random Hse. Audio Publishing Group.

—Earth to Matthew. 1998. (Matthew Martin Ser.: No. 3). 154p. (J). (gr. 3-7). pap. 5.99 (978-0-698-11692-4(5) , Putnam Juvenile) Penguin Group (USA) Inc.

David, Lawrence. The Good Little Girl. 1999. (YA). pap., wbk. ed. 100.70 incl. audio (978-0-7887-3021-4(5) , 46838) Recorded Bks., LLC.

Davidson, Ellen Dee. Princess Justina Albertina: A Cautionary Tale. Chesworth, Michael, illus. 2007. (J). (ps-2). 15.95 (978-1-57091-652-6(7)) Charlesbridge Publishing, Inc.

Davies, Simon. Pucker up, Buttercup. 2000. (Books for Valentine's Day). (Illus.). 16p. (J). (gr. k-4). 12.95 (978-0-7613-1286-4(2) , Millbrook Pr.) Lerner Publishing Group.

Davoll, Barbara. A Sunday Surprise. Hockerman, Dennis, illus. 1999. (Christopher Churchmouse Classics Ser.). 24p. (J). (ps-3). 7.99 (978-0-8024-4935-1(2)) Moody Pubs.

Dawe, Bruce. Luke & Lulu: Lulu Likes to Always Do Things Luke Doesn't Want Her To! 2006. (Bites Ser.). (Illus.). 86p. (J). (gr. 2-5). pap. 3.95 (978-0-7624-2623-2(3) , Running Pr. Kids) Running Pr. Bk. Pubs.

Day, Lauren. Where Do You Belong? 2000. (Rockett's World Ser.: No. 5). (Illus.). 128p. (J). (gr. 4-7). pap. 3.99 (978-0-439-08694-3(9)) Scholastic, Inc.

—Where Do You Belong? 2000. (Rockett's World Ser.: No. 5). (J). (gr. 4-7). (978-0-606-18887-6(8)) Tandem Library Bks.

de Paola, Tomie. Jamie O'Rourke & the Pooka. Frith, Margaret, ed. de Paola, Tomie, illus. 2000. (Illus.). 32p. (J). (ps-3). 16.99 (978-0-399-23467-5(5) , Putnam Juvenile) Penguin Group (USA) Inc.

—Trouble in the Barkers' Class. de Paola, Tomie, illus. 2003. (Barker Twins Ser.). (Illus.). 32p. (J). (ps-3). 14.99 (978-0-399-24164-2(7) , Putnam Juvenile) Penguin Group (USA) Inc.

De Vries, Anke. Bruises. Knecht, Stacey, tr. 2004. 176p. (YA). pap. 7.95 (978-1-886910-09-6(X) , Lemniscaat) Boyds Mills Pr.

—Bruises. 2003. (gr. 7-12). lib. bdg. 16.40 (978-0-613-80329-8(9)) Tandem Library Bks.

DeClements, Barthe. Five-Finger Discount. 2000. 144p. (gr. 4-7). pap. 10.95 (978-0-595-00780-6(5) , Backinprint.com) iUniverse, Inc.

—Liar, Liar. 1998. (Accelerated Reader Bks.). 144p. (J). (gr. 3-7). lib. bdg. 14.95 (978-0-7614-5021-4(1) , Cavendish Children's Bks.) Cavendish, Marshall Corp.

DePaola, Tomie. Trouble in the Barkers' Class. DePaola, Tomie, illus. 2006. (Barker Twins Ser.). (Illus.). 32p. (J). (ps). reprint ed. pap. 5.99 (978-0-14-240585-7(X) , Puffin) Penguin Group (USA) Inc.

deRubertis, Barbara. Wally Walrus. Pyk, Jan, illus. 1998. (Let's Read Together Ser.). 32p. (J). (ps-3). pap. 4.95 (978-1-57565-046-3(0)) Kane Pr., The.

Deuker, Carl. Night Hoops. 2001. 256p. (gr. 7 up). pap. 6.99 (978-0-06-447275-3(2) , Harper Trophy) HarperCollins Pubs.

—Night Hoops. 2000. (Illus.). 224p. (J). (gr. 7-12). tchr. ed. 15.00 (978-0-395-97936-5(6)) Houghton Mifflin Co. Trade & Reference Div.

—Night Hoops. 2001. (978-0-606-22927-2(2)); 250p. (gr. 7-12). lib. bdg. 14.15 (978-0-613-61919-6(6)) Tandem Library Bks.

Devlin, Wende. Kiss for a Warthog. Devlin, Harry, illus. 1999. 48p. (J). (gr. 1-3). 14.00 (978-1-892657-01-5(5)) Town Bk. Pr. The.

Dewji, Fatemah H. Where Have You Come From: By Nahal, the Bee. Dewji, Fatemah H., illus. 2000. (Illus.). 28p. (J). (gr. 1-5). bds. 16.00 (978-1-879402-68-3(8)) Tahrike Tarsile Quran, Inc.

Dieterle', Nathalie. I Am the King! American Edition. Dieterle', Nathalie, illus. 2001. (Illus.). 32p. (J). (ps-k). pap. 15.95 (978-0-531-30324-5(1) , Orchard Bks.) Scholastic, Inc.

Diggins, Matthew. Andrew & the Secret Gallery. Diggins, Matthew, illus. 2007. 32p. (J). (gr. 1-5). 15.95 ***(978-1-60108-016-5(6))*** Red Cygnet Pr.

Donnelly, Jennifer & Gammell, Stephen. Humble Pie. 2002. (Illus.). 32p. (J). (gr. k-2). 16.95 (978-0-689-84435-5(2) , Atheneum/Richard Jackson Bks.) Simon & Schuster Children's Publishing.

Douthwaite, Wendy. The Orange Pony. 2003. (Illus.). 86p. (J). (gr. 2-7). mass mkt. 6.99 (978-0-330-33631-4(2) , Pan) Pan Macmillan GBR. *Dist:* Trafalgar Square Publishing.

Downey, Lynn. The Tattletale. Paparone, Pam, illus. rev. ed. 2006. 32p. (J). 16.95 (978-0-8050-7152-8(0) , Holt, Henry & Co. Bks. For Young Readers) Holt, Henry & Co.

Dube, Jasmine. Fais un Voeu, Nazaire! 2001. (Premier Roman Ser.). (FRE.). 64p. (J). (gr. 2-5). pap. (978-2-89021-215-2(7)) Diffusion du livre Mirabel.

Dubé, Pierrette. Sticks & Stones! Jolin, Dominique, illus. 1998. 24p. (J). (gr. k-3). pap. 4.95 (978-1-55209-234-7(8)) Firefly Bks., Ltd.

Dubowski, Cathy East. Gift of Gab. 2000. (gr. 3-6). lib. bdg. 11.80 (978-0-613-31240-0(6)) Tandem Library Bks.

Dunbar, Joyce. Pomegranate Seeds. Craig, Helen, illus. 1998. (Panda & Gander Stories Ser.). (J). pap. (978-0-7636-0707-4(X)) Candlewick Pr.

Duncan, Jane. Janet Reachfar & Chickabird. 2002. (gr. k-3). lib. bdg. 16.40 (978-0-613-79940-9(2)) Tandem Library Bks.

Earhart, Kristin. Patch. 2008. (Stablemates Ser.). 48p. (J). pap. 3.99 ***(978-0-439-72240-7(3)*** , Cartwheel Bks.) Scholastic, Inc.

—Patch. Papp, Lisa, illus. 2006. (Breyer Stablemates Ser.). 48p. (J). pap. 4.99 (978-0-439-72236-0(5) , Cartwheel Bks.) Scholastic, Inc.

Edens, Cooper & Day, Alexandra. Special Deliveries. Day, Alexandra, illus. 2001. (Michael di Capua Bks.). (Illus.). 32p. (J). (gr. k-3). 15.95 (978-0-06-205151-6(2)) HarperCollins Pubs.

Edwards, Pamela Duncan. The Grumpy Morning. ed. 2004. (Illus.). (J). (gr. k up). spiral bd. (978-0-616-03030-1(4)); spiral bd. (978-0-616-04552-7(2)) Canadian National Institute for the Blind/Institut National Canadien pour les Aveugles.

—The Grumpy Morning. 2000. 32p. (J). pap. 4.99 (978-0-7868-1434-3(9)) Hyperion Bks. for Children.

—Why the Stomach Growls. Taylor, Bridget Starr, illus. 2006. 32p. (J). 15.95 (978-1-58536-298-1(0)) Sleeping Bear Pr.

Edwards, Pamela Duncan & Nascimbeni, Barbara. Rude Mule. 2002. (Illus.). 32p. (J). (ps-3). 15.95 (978-0-8050-7007-1(9)), Holt, Henry & Co. Bks. For Young Readers) Holt, Henry & Co.

Edwards, Pat. What's That? 1999. (gr. k-3). lib. bdg. 10.95 (978-0-613-30867-0(0)) Tandem Library Bks.

Egbufoama, Caius. Showbar Kingdom: My Wishes. 1998. 16p. (J). (gr. k-3). pap. 6.00 (978-0-8059-4235-4(1)) Dorrance Publishing Co., Inc.

Ehrmantraut, Brenda. I Want One Too! Short, Robbie, illus. 2003. (J). lib. bdg. 16.95 (978-0-9729833-1-0(7)); per. 9.95 (978-0-9729833-0-3(9)) Bubble Gum Pr.

Elgar, Rebecca. Sshh! Everyone is Sleeping. 1999. (Illus.). 10p. 6.95 (978-1-899607-12-9(9)) Sterling Publishing Co., Inc.

Elish, Dan. Born Too Short: The Confessions of an Eighth-Grade Basket Case. (Illus.). 160p. (YA). 2003. mass mkt. 5.99 (978-0-689-86213-7(X), Simon Pulse); 2002. (gr. 7-9). 16.95 (978-0-689-84386-0(0), Atheneum/Richard Jackson Bks.) Simon & Schuster Children's Publishing.

—Born Too Short: The Confessions of an Eighth-Grade Basket Case. 2003. (gr. 7-12). lib. bdg. 13.00 (978-0-613-73461-5(0)) Tandem Library Bks.

—Born Too Short: The Confessions of an Eighth-Grade Basket Case. l.t. ed. 2005. 157p. (J). 21.95 (978-0-7862-7536-6(7)) Thorndike Pr.

Elliott, Laura Malone. Hunter's Best Friend at School. Munsinger, Lynn, illus. 2002. 32p. (J). (ps-2). 16.99 (978-0-06-000230-5(1)); 17.89 (978-0-06-000231-2(X)) HarperCollins Pubs.

Emberley, Rebecca. Three Cool Kids. 1998. (J). (978-0-606-13847-5(1)) Tandem Library Bks.

Emerson, Charlotte. Amy's True Prize. 1999. (Little Women Journals Ser.). (J). (978-0-606-16348-4(4)) Tandem Library Bks.

—Meg's Dearest Wish. 1999. (Little Women Journals). (J). (978-0-606-16350-7(6)) Tandem Library Bks.

Emerson, Charlotte & Alcott, Louisa May. Amy's True Prize. Wasden, Kevin, illus. 1999. (Little Women Journals). 128p. (J). (gr. 3-7). mass mkt. 3.99 (978-0-380-79706-6(2)) HarperCollins Pubs.

—Jo's Troubled Heart. Wasden, Kevin, illus. 1999. (Little Women Journals). 128p. (J). (gr. 3-7). pap. 3.99 (978-0-380-79669-4(4)) HarperCollins Pubs.

—Meg's Dearest Wish. Wasden, Kevin, illus. 1999. (Little Women Journals). 128p. (J). (gr. 3-7). pap. 3.99 (978-0-380-79705-9(4)) HarperCollins Pubs.

Emesse, Tea. Yumi Talks the Talk. 2006. (Star Sisterztm Ser.: Bk. 6). 144p. (YA). pap. 4.99 (978-0-7869-3992-3(3), Mirrorstone) Wizards of the Coast.

Enderle, Judith R. What's the Matter, Kelly Beans? 1998. (J). (978-0-606-13906-9(0)) Tandem Library Bks.

Ernst, Lisa Campbell. Sylvia Jean, the Drama Queen. 2005. (Illus.). 32p. (J). (ps). 16.99 (978-0-525-46962-9(1), Dutton Juvenile) Penguin Group (USA) Inc.

Esbensen, Barbara Juster. Jumping Day. Cocca-Leffler, Maryann, illus. 1999. 24p. (J). (ps-1). 9.95 (978-1-56397-709-1(5)) Boyds Mills Pr.

Escott, Colin. The Big Bag Mistake. 2003. (Illus.). 16p. (C). pap. 9.00 (978-0-582-50498-1(8)) Pearson ESL.

Esham, Barbaraa. Mrs. Gorski, I Think I Have the Wiggle Fidgets. Gordon, Mike, illus. 2007. (ENG, SPA & FRE.). 32p. (J). 16.99 ***(978-1-60336-469-0(2))*** Mainstream Connections, Inc.

Evans, Douglas. Mouth Moths: And More Classroom Tales. Di Fiori, Lawrence, illus. 2006. 112p. (J). 15.95 (978-1-932425-23-9(3), Lemniscaat) Boyds Mills Pr.

Evans, Richard Paul. The Christmas Candle. Collins, Jacob, illus. 1998. 32p. (J). (ps-3). 16.95 (978-0-689-82319-0(3)) Simon & Schuster Children's Publishing.

Evrard, Jackie. It's Great to Be Me! A Special Story & Activity Book. l.t. ed. 1998. (Illus.). 24p. (J). (gr. 1-5). pap. 11.95 (978-0-9666317-0-8(6)) Rainbow Write! Publishing.

Eyles, Heather & Ross, Tony. Well, I Never! 1998. (Illus.). 32p. (J). (ps-1). pap. 9.95 (978-0-86264-787-2(8)) Andersen GBR. *Dist:* Trafalgar Square Publishing.

Falconer, Ian. Olivia. Falconer, Ian, illus. 2002. (Olivia Ser.). (YA). 26.13 (978-1-4046-0034-8(5)) Book Wholesalers, Inc.

—Olivia. ed. 2004. (Olivia Ser.). (J). (gr. k-3). (FRE., Illus.). spiral bd. (978-0-616-14599-9(3)); spiral bd. (978-0-616-07232-5(5)); spiral bd. (978-0-616-07233-2(3)) Canadian National Institute for the Blind/Institut National Canadien pour les Aveugles.

—Olivia. Mlawer, Teresa, tr. (Olivia Ser.). (SPA., Illus.). (J). (gr. k-2). 16.00 (978-1-930332-20-1(3), LC5675); 2002. 30p. 16.00 (978-1-930332-08-9(4), LC30181) Lectorum Pubns., Inc.

—Olivia. 2001. (Olivia Ser.). (Illus.). (J). (SPA.). 146p. (978-84-8488-016-5(8)); (CAT., 40p. (978-84-8488-017-2(6)) Serres, Ediciones, S. L. ESP. *Dist:* Lectorum Pubns., Inc.

—Olivia. Falconer, Ian, illus. 2000. (Olivia Ser.). (Illus.). 40p. (J). (ps-3). 16.95 (978-0-689-82953-6(1), Atheneum/Anne Schwartz Bks.) Simon & Schuster Children's Publishing.

Farber, Erica. Ooey Gooey. 1998. (Step into Reading Step 1 Bks.). (J). (ps-1). (978-0-606-13966-3(4)) Tandem Library Bks.

Fearnley, Jan. Mr. Wolf & the Three Bears. 2002. (Illus.). 32p. (J). (ps-2). 16.00 (978-0-15-216423-2(5)) Harcourt Children's Bks.

—The Search for the Perfect Child. Fearnley, Jan, illus. 2006. (Illus.). 40p. (J). (ps-1). 15.99 (978-0-7636-3231-1(7)) Candlewick Pr.

—Watch Out! Fearnley, Jan, illus. 2004. (Illus.). 40p. (J). (ps-2). 15.99 (978-0-7636-2318-0(0)) Candlewick Pr.

Feiffer, Jules. I'm Not Bobby! Feiffer, Jules, illus. 2006. (Illus.). 28p. (J). (gr. k-4). reprint ed. 16.00 (978-0-7567-9853-6(1)) DIANE Publishing Co.

Fenner, Carol. Yolonda's Genius. 1998. (J). pap. 4.50 (978-0-87628-346-2(6)) Ctr. for Applied Research in Education, The.

Ferguson, Suzanie P. Ferris Give Thanks. Date not set. (Illus.). 12p. (J). (ps-k). (978-0-9658745-0-2(8)) Ferguson, Suzanie Pamela.

Fernandes, Eugenie. A Difficult Day. Fernandes, Eugenie, illus. unabr. ed. 1999. (Illus.). 32p. (J). (gr. k-3). (978-0-921103-17-2(4)) Kids Can Pr., Ltd.

—A Difficult Day. (FRE.). (J). pap. 5.99 (978-0-590-71827-1(4)) Scholastic, Inc.

Ferris, Jean. Bad. 2001. 192p. (YA). pap. 5.95 (978-0-374-40475-8(5), Aerial) Farrar, Straus & Giroux.

—Bad. 2001. (gr. 5-8). lib. bdg. 14.10 (978-0-613-49390-1(7)) Tandem Library Bks.

The Fight for Right. 2002. (Illus.). (J). pap. (978-0-7398-5105-0(5)) Steck-Vaughn.

Fine, Anne. The Tulip Touch. l.t. ed. 2000. (Illus.). 228p. (J). pap. (978-0-7540-6091-8(8), CLP 288) BBC Audio.

—The Tulip Touch. unabr. l.t. ed. 2003. (Read-Along Ser.). 200p. (J). pap. 29.95 incl. audio (978-0-7540-6227-1(9), RA028, Galaxy Children's Large Print) BBC Audiobooks America.

—The Tulip Touch. 1999. (978-0-606-16711-6(0)) Tandem Library Bks.

Fleetwood, Tamela. Nellie Jelly & the Jelly Well, No. 1. 2000. 32p. (J). lib. bdg. 10.95 (978-0-9702128-0-1(1)) Odditeas, Inc.

Fleming, Candace. The Fabled Fourth Graders of Aesop Elementary School. 2007. 192p. (J). (gr. 2-6). lib. bdg. 18.99 ***(978-0-375-93672-2(6)***, Schwartz & Wade Bks.) Random Hse. Children's Bks.

Flinn, Alex. Breathing Underwater. 272p. (J). 2002. (gr. 5 up). pap. 8.99 (978-0-06-447257-9(4)); 2001. (Illus.). (gr. 8 up). 18.99 (978-0-06-029198-3(2)) HarperCollins Pubs.

—Breathing Underwater. unabr. ed. 2004. (Young Adult Cassette Librariestm Ser.). 272p. (J). (gr. 7 up). pap. 36.00 incl. audio (978-0-8072-0992-9(9), S YA 346 SP, Listening Library) Random Hse. Audio Publishing Group.

—Breathing Underwater. 2002. (gr. 7-12). lib. bdg. 16.45 (978-0-613-60383-6(4)) Tandem Library Bks.

Floca, Brian. The Frightful Story of Harry Walfish. Floca, Brian, illus. 2004. (Illus.). 26p. (J). (gr. k-4). reprint ed. pap. (978-0-7567-7852-1(2)) DIANE Publishing Co.

Foggo, Cheryl. One Thing That's True. unabr. ed. 128p. (YA). (gr. 13 up). 2002. (Illus.). (978-1-55074-377-7(5)); 1998. (978-1-55074-411-8(9)) Kids Can Pr., Ltd.

—Sam Finds a Monster. Sarrazin, Marisol, illus. 2004. (Kids Can Read! Ser.). 32p. (J). (gr. k-3). (978-1-55337-351-3(0)) Kids Can Pr., Ltd.

Fontes, Justine. Rude Ralph. Jordan, Charles, tr. Jordan, Charles, illus. 2004. (Rookie Reader Ser.). 31p. (J). 19.50 (978-0-516-24567-6(8), Children's Pr.) Scholastic Library Publishing.

Ford, Bernette. Don't Hit Me! Grier, Gary, illus. 2004. 32p. (J). lib. bdg. 15.00 ***(*978-1-4242-0218-8(3))*** Fitzgerald Bks.

Ford, Bernette G. Hurry Up! Kindert, Jennifer C., illus. 2004. (Just for You! Ser.). 32p. pap. 3.99 (978-0-439-56849-4(8), Teaching Resources) Scholastic, Inc.

Fox, Mem. Harriet, You'll Drive Me Wild! ed. 2004. (Illus.). (J). (gr. k-3). spiral bd. (978-0-616-07236-3(8)); spiral bd. (978-0-616-07237-0(6)) Canadian National Institute for the Blind/Institut National Canadien pour les Aveugles.

—Harriet, You'll Drive Me Wild! Frazee, Marla, illus. 2000. 32p. (J). (ps-2). 16.00 (978-0-15-201977-8(4)) Harcourt Children's Bks.

—Tough Boris. Brown, Kathryn, illus. 1998. 32p. (J). (ps-3). pap. 7.00 (978-0-15-201891-7(3), Harcourt Paperbacks) Harcourt Children's Bks.

Fox, Mem & Frazee, Marla. Harriet, You'll Drive Me Wild! 2003. (Illus.). 32p. (J). pap. 6.00 (978-0-15-204598-2(8), Voyager Bks./Libros Viajeros) Harcourt Children's Bks.

Francen, Mike. A Miracle in Your Mouth. rev. ed. 1998. (Illus.). 94p. (J). (gr. 7). pap. 6.00 (978-1-888079-16-6(9)) Francen World Outreach.

Freedman, Claire. Where's Your Smile, Crocodile? Julian, Sean, illus. 2001. 32p. (J). (ps-k). 16.95 (978-1-56145-251-4(3)) Peachtree Pubs., Ltd.

Freeman, Don. Quiet! There's a Canary in the Library. Freeman, Don, illus. 2007. 48p. (J). (ps). 15.99 ***(*978-0-670-06230-0(8)***, Viking Juvenile) Penguin Group (USA) Inc.

Freeman, Martha. The Polyester Grandpa. 1998. 160p. (J). (gr. 4-7). tchr. ed. 15.95 (978-0-8234-1398-0(5)) Holiday Hse., Inc.

Fuchs, Menucha. Hand in Hand: Stories about You & Me. Goldfield, Zelda, tr. from HEB. Gershtein, Yonathan, illus. 1999. (Children's Learning Ser.: Vol. 2). 48p. (J). (gr. 1-4). pap. 4.95 (978-1-880582-43-5(0)) Judaica Pr., Inc., The.

Fuchshuber, Annegert. Carly. Howe, Florence & Kirk, Heidi, trs. from ENG. 2004. (Illus.). 28p. (ps-3). 16.95 (978-1-55861-177-1(0)) Feminist Pr. at The City Univ. of New York.

Gaffney, Linda. My Daddy Does GOOD Things, Too! Dabney, Undra & Goettling, Nickalas, illus. 2006. 55p. per. 10.99 ***(*978-0-9787501-0-7(1))*** Gaffney, Linda.

Galante, Roberta. Missy's & Daisy's Lessons of Life. 2000. (Illus.). 70p. (YA). (gr. 7-12). pap. 9.95 (978-0-9705235-0-1(5)) Prestige Publishing.

Gantos, Jack. Back to School for Rotten Ralph. Rubel, Nicole, illus. (Rotten Ralph Ser.). 40p. (J). (ps-3). 2000. pap. 6.99 (978-0-06-443705-9(1), Harper Trophy); Bk. 1. 1998. 14.89 (978-0-06-027532-7(4)) HarperCollins Pubs.

—Back to School for Rotten Ralph. 2000. 12.75 (978-0-606-22184-9(0)); (gr. 3-6). lib. bdg. 14.10 (978-0-613-30974-5(X)) Tandem Library Bks.

—Wedding Bells for Rotten Ralph. Rubel, Nicole, illus. 1999. (Rotten Ralph Ser.: Vol. 2). (J). (ps-3). 40p. 15.99 (978-0-06-027533-4(2)); Bk. 2. 32p. 14.89 (978-0-06-027534-1(0)) HarperCollins Pubs.

Gardner, Sally. Boolar's Big Day Out. 2003. (Tales from the Box Ser.: Vol. 2). (Illus.). 128p. (J). 14.95 (978-1-58234-833-9(2), Bloomsbury Children) Bloomsbury Publishing.

—The Countess's Calamity: Tales from the Box. Gardner, Sally, illus. 2003. (Tales from the Box Ser.). (Illus.). 160p. (J). (gr. 1-6). 14.95 (978-1-58234-812-4(X)); pap. 6.95 (978-1-58234-855-1(3)) Bloomsbury Publishing. (Bloomsbury Children).

Gauch, Patricia Lee. Christina Katerina & the Box. 1998. (J). (978-0-606-13272-5(4)) Tandem Library Bks.

Gauthier, Gilles. Pas de Chausson dans Mon Salon. 1998. (La Courte Echelle Premier Roman Ser.). (FRE., Illus.). 64p. (J). (gr. 2-5). pap. (978-2-89021-339-5(0)) Diffusion du livre Mirabel.

Gedovius, Juan. Trucas. 1998. (Los Especiales de A la Orilla Del Viento Ser.).Tr. of Truca. (SPA., Illus.). 26p. (J). (ps-ps). reprint ed. 13.99 (978-968-16-5410-8(2), FC4102) Fondo de Cultura Economica USA.

Gehret, Jeanne. Eagle Eyes: A Child's Guide to Paying Attention. Covert, Susan, illus. 3rd rev. ed. 2003. 40p. (J). (gr. 1-5). pap. 9.95 (978-1-884281-11-2(7)) Verbal Images Pr.

Geldart, Thomas. Emilie the Peacemaker. 2004. reprint ed. pap. 15.95 (978-1-4191-1769-5(6)); pap. 1.99 (978-1-4192-1769-2(0)) Kessinger Publishing, LLC.

Gene, Barbara. Lamar Montgomery & the Freaky Faces Club. 2006. (J). per. 14.95 (978-1-889743-50-9(X)) Robbie Dean Pr.

Gentle Ben. 1999. (J). 9.95 (978-1-56137-076-4(2)) Novel Units, Inc.

George, Marjorie. Doing the Right Thing. Brunk, Cara, illus. l.t. ed. 2000. 8p. (J). (gr. k-3). pap. 6.00 (978-1-58084-214-3(3)); 6.00 (978-1-58084-212-9(7)) Lower Kuskokwim Schl. District.

—Elluallriamek Cucukiyaraq. Brunk, Cara, illus. l.t. ed. 2000. Tr. of Doing the Right Thing. (ESK.). 8p. (J). (gr. k-3). pap. 6.00 (978-1-58084-213-6(5)) Lower Kuskokwim Schl. District.

George, Michele Naylor. The Rainbow of Respect & Responsibility. 1999. (J). (978-0-9672049-0-1(9)) Grace & Mercy Publishing.

Geras, Adele. Watching the Roses. 1998. (Egerton Hall Trilogy). (978-0-606-13890-1(0)) Tandem Library Bks.

Gershator, Phyllis. Sambalena Show-Off. Jenkins, Leonard, ed. 1999. (Illus.). 20p. (J). (ps-2). reprint ed. 15.00 (978-0-7881-6696-9(4)) DIANE Publishing Co.

Gibson, Kari Smalley. Mooki & the Too-Proud Peacock. 2002. 40p. 12.99 (978-0-310-70303-7(4)) Zondervan.

Gifaldi, David. Gregory, Maw & the Mean One. 2000. (Illus.). 148p. (J). (gr. 4-7). pap. 10.95 (978-0-595-14504-1(3), Backinprint.com) iUniverse, Inc.

—Toby Scudder, King of the School. 2005. 208p. (J). (gr. 4-6). pap. 5.95 (978-0-618-55158-3(1), Clarion Bks.) Houghton Mifflin Co. Trade & Reference Div.

Giff, Patricia Reilly. Poopsie Pomerantz, Pick up Your Feet. 1998. (978-0-606-13715-7(7)) Tandem Library Bks.

Gifford, Peggy Elizabeth. Moxy Maxwell Does Not Love Writing Thank-You Notes. Fisher, Valorie, illus. Fisher, Valorie, photos by. 2008. (J). ***(*978-0-375-84270-2(5)); (*978-0-375-94552-6(0))*** Random Hse. Children's Bks. (Schwartz & Wade Bks.).

Gillis, Jennifer B. What Do You Say? 2006. (Reader's Clubhouse Set B Ser.). (Illus.). 24p. (J). pap. 3.99 (978-0-7641-3298-8(9)) Barron's Educational Series, Inc.

Gilson, Jamie. Gotcha! Wummer, Amy, illus. 2006. 80p. (J). (gr. k-3). 15.00 (978-0-618-54356-4(2), Clarion Bks.) Houghton Mifflin Co. Trade & Reference Div.

Ginsburg, Mirra. The Chinese Mirror. 2002. (Illus.). (J). 14.21 (978-0-7587-9538-0(6)) Book Wholesalers, Inc.

Girling, Brough. Granddad's Dinosaur. Dell, Stephen, illus. 2005. (I Am Reading Ser.). 48p. (J). (gr. k-3). pap. 3.95 (978-0-7534-5897-6(7), Kingfisher) Houghton Mifflin Co. Trade & Reference Div.

Gleitzman, Morris. Misery Guts. l.t. ed. 2005. (Illus.). 184p. (J). pap. incl. audio (978-0-7540-7867-8(1), CLP 456) BBC Audio.

Glumby the Grumbling Beastie. 2001. (Beastie Buddies Ser.). (Illus.). 32p. (J). 6.95 (978-1-891100-85-7(8)) Smart Kids Publishing.

Goldblatt, Stacey. Stray. 2007. 288p. (YA). (gr. 7-10). 15.99 (978-0-385-73443-1(3)); lib. bdg. 18.99 (978-0-385-90448-3(7)) Random Hse. Children's Bks. (Delacorte Bks. for Young Readers).

Golden Books Staff. Play It Cool! 2001. 12p. pap. 4.99 (978-0-307-20059-4(0), Golden Bks.) Random Hse. Children's Bks.

Gorman, Carol. Dork in Disguise. 2000. (Harper Trophy Bks.). (Illus.). 176p. (J). (gr. 3-7). pap. 5.99 (978-0-06-440891-2(4), Harper Trophy) HarperCollins Pubs.

—Dork in Disguise. 2000. (gr. 3-6). lib. bdg. 14.15 (978-0-613-30359-0(8)) Tandem Library Bks.

Goscinny, René. Nicholas & the Gang. 2007. (Illus.). 120p. (J). 19.95 ***(*978-0-7148-4788-7(7))*** Phaidon Pr., Inc.

Gosney, Joy. Hey Scruffy! 2001. (Illus.). 32p. (YA). (ps up). 16.95 (978-0-7475-4877-5(3)) Bloomsbury Publishing Plc GBR. *Dist:* Trafalgar Square Publishing.

—Naughty Parents. 2000. (Illus.). 32p. (ps-1). lib. bdg. 21.90 (978-0-7613-1823-1(2), Millbrook Pr.) Lerner Publishing Group.

Graf, Rosanna. Beary Beary Quite Contrary. Lawson, Laura, illus. l.t. ed. 1998. 24p. (Orig.). (J). (gr. 2-5). pap. 7.50 (978-1-882788-02-6(8)) Vangar Pubs./Baltimore.

Graham, Christine. Three Little Robbers. Boase, Susan, illus. 2007. 64p. (J). (gr. 2-5). 16.95 ***(*978-0-8050-8094-0(5))*** Holt, Henry & Co.

Gray, Kes. Nelly the Monstersitter. Ross, Tony, illus. 2006. 48p. (J). lib. bdg. ***(*978-1-4048-3124-7(X))*** Picture Window Bks.

Griffin, Claire Janosik. Kidding Around. Wright, Jane Chambless, illus. 2000. (Rollicking Rhymes Ser.). 20p. (J). (gr. k-1). 3.99 (978-1-56822-978-2(X), IF40212-E4, Instructional Fair) Schaffer, Frank Pubns.

Griffin, Kitty & Combs, Kathy. The Foot-Stomping Adventures of Clementine Sweet. Wohnoutka, Mike, tr. Wohnoutka, Mike, illus. 2004. 32p. (J). (gr. k-3). tchr. ed. 15.00 (978-0-618-24746-2(7), Clarion Bks.) Houghton Mifflin Co. Trade & Reference Div.

—Stinker & the Onion Princess. Manders, John, illus. 2005. (J). (978-0-8037-2976-6(6), Dial) Penguin Group (USA) Inc.

Griffiths, Andy. Just Stupid! Denton, Terry, illus. 2004. 160p. (J). pap. 4.99 (978-0-439-42474-5(7)) Scholastic, Inc.

Grindley, Sally. The Sulky Vulture. Terry, Michael, illus. 2003. 32p. (J). (gr. k-3). 15.95 (978-1-58234-794-3(8), Bloomsbury Children) Bloomsbury Publishing.

Groves. Snatch & Grab. Date not set. (Illus.). 32p. (J). pap. 129.15 (978-0-582-18303-2(0)) Addison-Wesley Longman, Ltd. GBR. *Dist:* Trans-Atlantic Pubns., Inc.

Gunnery, Sylvia. Menace & Mischief. l.t. ed. 1999. 104p. (J). (gr. 3-7). mass mkt. 5.95 (978-0-7736-7477-6(2)) Stoddart Kids CAN. *Dist:* Fitzhenry & Whiteside, Ltd.

Gutman, Anne. Gaspard & Lisa's Rainy Day. Hallensleben, Georg, illus. 2003. (Misadventures of Gaspard & Lisa Ser.). 32p. (J). (ps-3). 9.95 (978-0-375-82252-0(6), Knopf Bks. for Young Readers) Random Hse. Children's Bks.

Hacker, Marie. The Cute & Curious Cleo. 1998. (Illus.). 40p. (J). (gr. k-3). pap. 8.00 (978-0-8059-4408-2(7)) Dorrance Publishing Co., Inc.

Haddix, Margaret Peterson. Say What? 2004. 91p. (J). lib. bdg. 15.00 ***(*978-1-4242-0915-6(3))*** Fitzgerald Bks.

—Say What? Bernardin, James, illus. (Ready-for-Chapters Ser.). 96p. (J). 2005. pap. 3.99 (978-0-689-86256-4(3), Aladdin); 2004. (gr. 2-4). 14.99 (978-0-689-86255-7(5)) Simon & Schuster Children's Publishing.

Hahn, Mary Downing. As Ever, Gordy. 1998. 192p. (YA). (gr. 7-9). tchr. ed. 15.00 (978-0-395-83627-9(1), Clarion Bks.) Houghton Mifflin Co. Trade & Reference Div.

—As Ever, Gordy. 2000. (gr. 5-8). lib. bdg. 14.15 (978-0-613-28405-9(4)) Tandem Library Bks.

Hall, Kirsten & Flaxma, Jessica. Who Says? 2004. (My First Reader Ser.). (J). (gr. k-1). pap. 3.95 (978-0-516-24642-0(9), Children's Pr.) Scholastic Library Publishing.

Hall, Margaret & Jones, Dawn L. Sebastian in Egypt. Wenzel, David, illus. 2001. (Suitcase Bear Adventures Ser.). (J). (978-0-9713174-2-0(9), Bear & Co.) Bear & Co.

Hallinan, P. K. Heartprints. 24p. (J). 7.95 (978-0-8249-5358-4(4), Ideals) Ideals Pubns.

—Let's Care about Sharing! 2001. (Illus.). 24p. (J). (ps-3). pap. 3.25 (978-0-8249-5399-7(1), Ideals) Ideals Pubns.

—Let's Learn All We Can! (J). 2004. (Illus.). 48p. pap. 9.95 (978-0-8249-5491-8(2)); 2002. 24p. 7.95 (978-0-8249-5307-2(X), Ideals) Ideals Pubns.

—A Rainbow of Friends. 2006. 32p. pap. 3.95 (978-0-8249-5519-9(6), Ideals Children's Bks.); 2002. (Illus.). 24p. (J). 5.95 (978-0-8249-5395-9(9)) Ideals Pubns.

Hallinan, P. K., illus. A Rainbow of Friends. 2001. 24p. (J). (ps-3). 7.95 (978-0-8249-5394-2(0), Ideals) Ideals Pubns.

The Ham Who Cried Wolf. 2001. 32p. (YA). (gr. 6-12). pap. (978-0-8224-6536-2(1)) Globe Fearon Educational Publishing.

Hamilton, Richard. Let's Take over the Kindergarten. Heap, Sue, illus. 2007. 32p. (J). (ps-1). 15.95 (978-1-58234-707-3(7)) Bloomsbury Publishing.

Handy, Libby & Newnham, Jack. Boss for a Week.Tr. of C'Est Moi Qui Mene. (FRE., Illus.). (J). 13.99 incl. audio (978-0-590-73908-5(5)) Scholastic, Inc.

Hansen, Joyce. One True Friend. Giblin, James Cross, ed. 2001. 160p. (J). (gr. 5-9). tchr. ed. 14.00 (978-0-395-84983-5(7), Clarion Bks.) Houghton Mifflin Co. Trade & Reference Div.

Hanson, Anders. Monkey Business. Chawla, Neena, illus. 2006. (Fact & Fiction Ser.). 24p. (J). 21.35 (978-1-59679-951-6(X), SandCastle); pap. (978-1-59679-952-3(8)) ABDO Publishing Co.

Hargreaves, Roger. Little Miss Bossy. 1998. (Mr. Men & Little Miss Ser.). (Illus.). 32p. (J). (gr. k up). pap. 3.99 (978-0-8431-7423-6(4), Price Stern Sloan) Penguin Group (USA) Inc.

—Little Miss Chatterbox. 1999. (Mr. Men & Little Miss Ser.). (Illus.). 32p. (J). (gr. k up). pap. 3.99 (978-0-8431-7479-3(X), Price Stern Sloan) Penguin Group (USA) Inc.

—Little Miss Helpful. rev. ed. 1999. (Little Miss Bks.). (Illus.). 32p. (J). (gr. k-3). pap. 3.99 (978-0-8431-7503-5(6), Price Stern Sloan) Penguin Group (USA) Inc.

—Little Miss Magic. Hargreaves, Roger, illus. rev. ed. 2000. (Mr. Men & Little Miss Ser.). (Illus.). 32p. (J). (gr. k-3). pap. 3.99 (978-0-8431-7565-3(6), Price Stern Sloan) Penguin Group (USA) Inc.

—Little Miss Magic. 2000. (ps-2). lib. bdg. 10.65 (978-0-613-26028-2(7)) Tandem Library Bks.

—Little Miss Shy. 1998. (Mr. Men & Little Miss Ser.). (Illus.). 32p. (J). (gr. k up). pap. 3.99 (978-0-8431-7425-0(0), Price Stern Sloan) Penguin Group (USA) Inc.

A B

—Little Miss Stubborn. Hargreaves, Roger, illus. 2001. (Mr. Men & Little Miss Ser.). (Illus.). 32p. (J). pap. 3.99 (978-0-8431-7672-8(5) , Price Stern Sloan) Penguin Group (USA) Inc.

—Little Miss Trouble. 1998. (Mr. Men & Little Miss Ser.). (Illus.). 32p. (J). (gr. k-3). pap. 3.99 (978-0-8431-7426-7(9) , Price Stern Sloan) Penguin Group (USA) Inc.

—Mr. Busy. Hargreaves, Roger, illus. 2000. (Mr. Men & Little Miss Ser.). (Illus.). 32p. (J). (ps-3). pap. 3.99 (978-0-8431-7600-1(8) , Price Stern Sloan) Penguin Group (USA) Inc.

—Mr. Clumsy. Hargreaves, Roger, illus. rev. ed. 2000. (Mr. Men & Little Miss Ser.). (Illus.). 32p. (J). (ps-3). pap. 3.99 (978-0-8431-7617-9(2) , Price Stern Sloan) Penguin Group (USA) Inc.

—Mr. Daydream. Hargreaves, Roger, illus. rev. ed. 2000. (Mr. Men & Little Miss Ser.). (Illus.). 32p. (J). (gr. k-3). pap. 3.99 (978-0-8431-7563-9(X) , Price Stern Sloan) Penguin Group (USA) Inc.

—Mr. Forgetful. 1998. (Mr. Men & Little Miss Ser.). (Illus.). 32p. (gr. k-3). pap. 3.99 (978-0-8431-7419-9(6) , Price Stern Sloan) Penguin Group (USA) Inc.

—Mr. Grumpy. rev. ed. 1999. (Mr. Men & Little Miss Ser.). (Illus.). 32p. (J). (gr. k-3). pap. 3.99 (978-0-8431-7477-9(3) , Price Stern Sloan) Penguin Group (USA) Inc.

—Mr. Impossible. 1998. (Mr. Men & Little Miss Ser.). (Illus.). 32p. (J). (gr. k up). pap. 3.99 (978-0-8431-7420-5(X) , Price Stern Sloan) Penguin Group (USA) Inc.

—Mr. Mischief. Hargreaves, Roger, illus. 2001. (Mr. Men & Little Miss Ser.). (Illus.). 32p. (J). (ps-3). pap. 3.99 (978-0-8431-7653-7(9) , Price Stern Sloan) Penguin Group (USA) Inc.

—Mr. Nosey. 1999. (Mr. Men & Little Miss Ser.). (Illus.). 32p. (J). (gr. k up). pap. 3.99 (978-0-8431-7478-6(1) , Price Stern Sloan) Penguin Group (USA) Inc.

—Mr. Slow. Hargreaves, Roger, illus. 2000. (Mr. Men & Little Miss Ser.). (Illus.). 32p. (J). (ps-3). pap. 3.99 (978-0-8431-7601-8(6) , Price Stern Sloan) Penguin Group (USA) Inc.

—Mr. Strong. 1999. (Mr. Men & Little Miss Ser.). 32p. (J). pap. 3.99 (978-0-8431-7501-1(X) , Price Stern Sloan) Penguin Group (USA) Inc.

—Mr. Topsy-Turvy. Hargreaves, Roger, illus. 2001. (Mr. Men & Little Miss Ser.). (Illus.). 32p. (J). (ps-3). pap. 3.99 (978-0-8431-7654-4(7) , Price Stern Sloan) Penguin Group (USA) Inc.

Harley, Bill. Dear Santa: The Letters of James B. Dobbins. Alley, R. W., illus. 2005. 32p. (J). 15.99 (978-0-06-623778-7(5)); lib. bdg. 16.89 (978-0-06-623779-4(3)) HarperCollins Pubs.

Harman, Chuck. Clean up That Mess! 2000. (Adventures of Artie the Airplane & His Friends Ser.). (Illus.). 32p. (J). (ps-6). pap. 6.95 (978-1-891736-11-7(6)) Studio Five/ Fourteen.

—I Didn't Think It Would Hurt Anyone. 2000. (Adventures of Artie the Airplane & His Friends Ser.). 32p. (J). (ps-6). pap. 6.95 (978-1-891736-04-9(3)) Studio Five/ Fourteen.

Harold, Gwyneth. Bad Girls in School. 2006. 148p. (YA). pap. (978-0-435-21517-0(5)) Heinemann.

Harper, Charise Mericle. When Randolph Turned Rotten. 2007. 40p. (J). (gr. k-3). 16.99 (***978-0-375-84071-5(0)***); lib. bdg. 19.99 (***978-0-375-94071-2(5)***) Random Hse. Children's Bks. (Knopf Bks. for Young Readers).

Harper, Jessica. Lizzy's Do's & Don'ts. Dupont, Lindsay Harper, illus. 2002. 32p. (J). (ps-3). 15.95 (978-0-06-623860-9(9)); lib. bdg. 15.89 (978-0-06-623861-6(7)) HarperCollins Pubs.

Harris, Peter. Perfect Prudence. Allwright, Deborah, illus. 2003. 32p. (J). (gr. k-3). 15.95 (978-1-57768-437-4(0) , Gingham Dog Pr.) School Specialty Publishing.

Harris, Robie H. I'm So Mad! Hollander, Nicole, illus. 2005. (Just Being Me Ser.: Vol. 1). 32p. (J). (ps-1). 7.99 (978-0-316-10939-0(8)) Little Brown & Co.

Harrison, Jim. The Boy Who Ran to the Woods. Pohrt, Tom, illus. 2000. 32p. (J). (gr. 4-7). 18.95 (978-0-87113-822-4(0) , Atlantic Monthly Pr.) Grove/Atlantic, Inc.

Harshman, Terry Webb. Bessie's Bed. Vargo, Sharon Hawkins, illus. 2003. (Silly Millies Ser.). 32p. lib. bdg. 17.90 (978-0-7613-2742-4(8) , Millbrook Pr.) Lerner Publishing Group.

Hart, Tessa & Sergi, Frank. The Snarth Goes to School. Freeman, Pietri, illus. 2000. 48p. (J). (gr. k-5). 18.95 (978-0-9660172-0-5(X)) Brookfield Reader, Inc., The.

Have a Nice Life. 2001. (978-0-14-270022-8(3) , Putnam Juvenile) Penguin Group (USA) Inc.

Hayes, Sarah. The Grumpalump: Level Two, Yellow. Firth, Barbara, illus. 1999. (Reading Together Ser.). (J). pap. (978-0-7636-0861-3(0)) Candlewick Pr.

Hazen, Barbara Shook. The New Dog. 2000. (Illus.). (J). pap. (978-0-14-056531-7(0) , Puffin) Penguin Group (USA) Inc.

—That Toad Is Mine! Floca, Brian & Manning, Jane, illus. 1998. (Growing Tree Ser.). 24p. (J). (ps up). 9.95 (978-0-694-01035-6(9) , Harper Festival) HarperCollins Pubs.

Health Communications Staff, et al. Chicken Soup for the Soul Family Storybook Collection. 1998. (Chicken Soup for the Soul Ser.). 98p. (J). (ps-3). pap., tchr. ed. 12.95 (978-1-55874-642-8(0)) Health Communications, Inc.

Heartprints. (Illus.). 22p. (J). 5.95 (978-0-8249-5450-5(5)) Ideals Pubns.

Hebert, Marie-Francine. John's Day. Hamel, Caroline, illus. 2005. (Read-It! Readers Ser.). 32p. (C). (gr. k-3). 18.60 (978-1-4048-1071-6(4)) Picture Window Bks.

Helakoski, Leslie. Woolbur. Harper, Lee, illus. 2008. 32p. (J). 16.99 (***978-0-06-084726-5(3)***) HarperCollins Pubs.

Henig, Sherry. Sara Makes Her Mother Proud & Learns Good Behavior: A Children's Book. 2nd ed. 2006. per. 6.95 (978-0-9777203-2-3(2)) Brenner Publishing, LLC.

Henkes, Kevin. Lilly's Purple Plastic Purse. 2000. (Illus.). (J). (gr. k-3). pap. 25.95 incl. audio (978-0-87499-687-6(2)) BBC Audiobooks America.

—Lilly's Purple Plastic Purse. braille ed. 2004. (J). (gr. k-3). spiral bd. (978-0-616-01673-2(5)) Canadian National Institute for the Blind/Institut National Canadien pour les Aveugles.

Henrietta: Not Everybody Wears Horseshoes. 2004. (Illus.). 32p. (J). 6.99 (978-0-9744520-1-2(7)) Glitter Creek, Inc.

Hermes, Patricia. Calling Me Home. 1999. 448p. (J). pap. 3.99 (978-0-380-79100-2(5) , Harper Trophy) HarperCollins Pubs.

Hicks, Betty. Busted ! 2008. 192p. (J). pap. 6.99 (***978-0-312-38053-3(4)***) Square Fish.

Hidier, Tanuja Desai. Born Confused. 2003. 512p. mass mkt. 7.99 (978-0-439-51011-0(2) , PUSH) Scholastic, Inc.

Higginson, Sheila. Look Before You Leap! Disney Storybook Artists Staff, illus. 2007. 24p. (ps-k). pap. 3.99 (***978-1-4231-0646-3(6)***) Disney Pr.

Hillcrest, Dayne. Letena, Forever A-Flutter. 1999. (J). (gr. k-4). pap. 6.95 (978-0-533-12757-3(2)) Vantage Pr., Inc.

Hobbie, Holly. The New Friend. 2004. (Illus.). 32p. (J). (ps-3). 16.99 (978-0-316-36636-6(6) , Tingley, Megan Bks.) Little, Brown Bks. for Young Readers.

Hodgson, Mona Gansberg. Crabby Critters. 2000. (Desert Critter Friends Ser.: Vol. 11). (Illus.). 48p. (J). (ps-2). 4.99 (978-0-570-07074-0(0)) Concordia Publishing Hse.

—Crabby Critters. 2000. (ps-2). lib. bdg. 13.00 (978-0-613-72793-8(2)) Tandem Library Bks.

—Smelly Tales. Sharp, Chris, illus. 1998. (Desert Critter Friends Ser.: Vol. 4). 48p. (J). (ps-2). 4.99 (978-0-570-05071-1(5) , 56-1895) Concordia Publishing Hse.

—Smelly Tales. 1998. (ps-2). lib. bdg. 13.00 (978-0-613-72807-2(6)) Tandem Library Bks.

—Spelling Bees. 2000. (Desert Critter Friends Ser.: Vol. 12). (Illus.). 48p. (J). (ps-2). 4.99 (978-0-570-07075-7(9)) Concordia Publishing Hse.

—Spelling Bees. 2000. (ps-2). lib. bdg. 13.00 (978-0-613-72788-4(6)) Tandem Library Bks.

Hoffman, Henry & Hoffmann, Heinrich. Slovenly Betsy. Hayn, Walter, illus. 2004. (Wee Books for Wee Folks). 96p. (J). (gr. 4-7). 7.95 (978-1-55709-408-7(X)) Applewood Bks.

Hofmeister, Alan, et al. The Bad Men. (Reading for All Learners Ser.). (Illus.). (J). pap. (978-1-56861-117-4(X)) Swift Learning Resources.

—See Me. (Reading for All Learners Ser.). (Illus.). (J). pap. (978-1-56861-076-4(9)) Swift Learning Resources.

—Sid & the Mess. (Reading for All Learners Ser.). (Illus.). (J). pap. (978-1-56861-090-0(4)) Swift Learning Resources.

Honeywood, Varnette P., illus. The Meanest Thing to Say. 2002. (Little Bill Ser.). (J). 11.91 (978-0-7587-1432-9(7)) Book Wholesalers, Inc.

Hood, Susan. I Am Mad! Handelman, Dorothy, photos by. 1999. (Real Kids Readers Ser.). (Illus.). 32p. (gr. k-1). (J). pap. 4.99 (978-0-7613-2086-9(5)); lib. bdg. 18.90 (978-0-7613-2061-6(X)) Lerner Publishing Group. (Millbrook Pr.).

—I Am Mad! 1999. (J). 11.79 (978-0-606-19155-5(0)); lib. bdg. 13.00 (978-0-613-18156-3(5)) Tandem Library Bks.

—The New Kid. Handelman, Dorothy, photos by. 1998. (Real Kids Readers Ser.). (Illus.). 32p. (ps-1). lib. bdg. 18.90 (978-0-7613-2014-2(8)); (J). pap. 4.99 (978-0-7613-2039-5(3)) Lerner Publishing Group. (Millbrook Pr.).

Hooks, William H. Little Poss & Horrible Hound. Newsom, Carol, illus. 1998. (Bank Street Reader Collection). 48p. (J). (gr. 2-4). lib. bdg. 22.60 (978-0-8368-1773-7(7)) Stevens, Gareth Inc.

Hopkins, Cathy. Brat Princess. 2007. (Zodiac Girls Ser.). 192p. (J). (gr. 4-7). pap. 5.95 (***978-0-7534-6132-7(3)*** , Kingfisher) Houghton Mifflin Co. Trade & Reference Div.

Horse, Harry, illus. Little Rabbit Goes to School. 2004. 32p. (J). 15.95 (978-1-56145-320-7(X)) Peachtree Pubs., Ltd.

Hunt, Angela Elwell. Sleeping Rose. Gillies, Chuck, illus. 1998. 32p. (J). (ps-3). 14.99 (978-0-8499-5847-2(4)) Nelson, Thomas Inc.

Hurwitz, Johanna. Busybody Nora. Tilley, Debbie, illus. 2001. (Riverside Kids Ser.). 96p. (J). (gr. 1-4). pap. 4.99 (978-0-06-442143-0(0) , Harper Trophy) HarperCollins Pubs.

—Busybody Nora. 2001. (gr. 3-6). lib. bdg. 12.10 (978-0-613-34624-5(6)) Tandem Library Bks.

Jacobson, Jennifer Richard. Andy Shane & the Very Bossy Dolores Starbuckle. Carter, Abby, illus. 64p. (J). (gr. k-3). 2006. 4.99 (978-0-7636-3044-7(6)); 2005. 13.99 (978-0-7636-1940-4(X)) Candlewick Pr.

James, Simon. Jake & His Cousin Sidney. 2002. (gr. 3-6). lib. bdg. 13.00 (978-0-613-53737-7(8)) Tandem Library Bks.

—Jake & the Babysitter. 2002. (gr. 3-6). lib. bdg. 13.00 (978-0-613-53738-4(6)) Tandem Library Bks.

Jeffs, Stephanie. A Bad Day for Christopher Bear. Thomas, Jacqui, illus. 2004. (Christopher Bear Ser.). 30p. 5.99 (978-0-8066-4367-0(6) , Augsburg Bks.) Augsburg Fortress, Pubs.

Jennings, Linda. Buster. 1998. (ENG, CHI, URD, VIE & BEN., Illus.). 40p. (J). (978-1-85430-541-1(7)) Magi Pubns.

Jensen, Patricia. The Mess. 2004. (My First Reader Ser.). (Illus.). 32p. (J). (gr. k-1). pap. 3.95 (978-0-516-24634-5(8) , Children's Pr.) Scholastic Library Publishing.

Johnson, Adrian. That's Not Funny! Johnson, Adrian, illus. 2005. (Illus.). 32p. (J). (ps-ps). 16.95 (978-1-58234-966-4(5)) Bloomsbury Publishing.

Johnson, Steve & Fancher, Lou. The Quest for the One Big Thing: A Counting Book. 1998. (Illus.). 32p. (J). (gr. k-4). 10.95 (978-0-7868-3198-2(7)) Disney Pr.

Jonell, Lynne. Mommy Go Away! 2000. (Illus.). (J). (978-0-606-22033-0(X)) Tandem Library Bks.

Jones, Andrea. The Spitting Twins. Kulka, Joe, illus. 2004. 32p. (J). (978-1-58394-095-2(2) , Frog Ltd.) North Atlantic Bks.

Jones, Christianne C. Eric Won't Do It. Demski, James, illus. 2005. (Read It! Readers Ser.). 24p. (J). (ps). lib. bdg. 18.60 (978-1-4048-1188-1(5)) Picture Window Bks.

—Nate the Dinosaur. Epstein, Len, illus. 2006. (Read-It! Readers Ser.). 24p. (J). (ps-3). 18.60 (978-1-4048-1728-9(X)) Picture Window Bks.

Jones, Julie. The Problem at Pepperpine Zoo. Jones, Julie, illus. l.t. ed. 2004. (Illus.). 24p. (J). pap. 7.95 (978-0-9745553-0-0(4)) Greenwood Street Publishing. GSP.

Jones, Marguerite A. Strangers. 1998. (Illus.). 16p. (J). (gr. k-3). pap. 7.00 (978-0-8059-4531-7(8)) Dorrance Publishing Co., Inc.

Joyce, Eunice. Jack & the Silly Hat. Joyce, Eunice, ed. Joyce, Derrick, illus. 2001. 19p. (Orig.). (J). pap. 18.99 (978-0-9712932-0-5(1)) Four Sons Publishing, Inc.

Kalish, Ginny. Rachel Rude Rowdy. 2001. (Illus.). 128p. (J). pap. 15.95 (978-1-56976-127-4(2) , 1148, Zephyr Pr.) Chicago Review Pr., Inc.

Karas, G. Brian, illus. Bootsie Barker Bites. 2002. (J). 13.19 (978-0-7587-2135-8(8)) Book Wholesalers, Inc.

Kasza, Keiko. Don't Laugh, Joe! Kasza, Keiko, illus. 2000. (Illus.). 32p. (J). (ps-3). reprint ed. pap. 5.99 (978-0-698-11794-5(8) , Putnam Juvenile) Penguin Group (USA) Inc.

Keffer, Lois. Fancy the Filly's Not Selfish or Silly. 1999. (J). 9.99 (978-1-57673-442-1(0)) Zondervan.

—Mercury Mouse Slows down in the House. 1999. (J). 9.99 (978-1-57673-437-7(4)) Zondervan.

Keller, Holly. That's Mine, Horace. Keller, Holly, illus. 2000. (Illus.). 24p. (J). (ps up). 16.99 (978-0-688-17159-9(1)) HarperCollins Pubs.

Kelley, Marty. The Rules. Kelley, Marty, illus. 2000. (Illus.). 32p. (J). (ps-4). 12.95 (978-1-55933-284-2(0)) Zino Pr. Children's Bks.

Kellogg, Steven. Three Sillies. 2004. (Illus.). 40p. (J). (ps-3). reprint ed. pap. 6.99 (978-0-7636-1056-2(9)) Candlewick Pr.

Kennedy, A. L. So I Am Glad: A Novel. 2001. 288p. pap. 13.00 (978-0-375-70724-7(7) , Vintage) Knopf Publishing Group.

Kenney, Cindy. Madame Blueberry Learns to Be Thankful. 2004. (Illus.). 22p. bds. 4.99 (978-0-310-70782-0(X)) Zonderkidz.

Kerr, Judith. Mog's Bad Things. 2000. (Illus.). 32p. (J). (ps). 17.99 (978-0-00-198385-4(7)) HarperCollins Pubs. Ltd. GBR. *Dist:* Independent Pubs. Group.

Kerr, M. E. "Hello," I Lied. 1998. (978-0-606-13472-9(7)) Tandem Library Bks.

Khan, Rukhsana. Bedtime Ba-a-a-lk. Frost, Kristi, illus. 1998. 32p. (J). (ps-3). 13.95 (978-0-7737-3068-7(0)) Stoddart Kids CAN. *Dist:* Fitzhenry & Whiteside, Ltd.

Kienzle, Patricia Taylor. Good Morning! Good Morning? Individual Differences. Coffey, Peg, illus. 1999. 24p. (J). (ps-2). pap. 4.95 (978-1-890798-10-9(X)) Kienzle, Patricia Taylor.

King, Robert A. The Song of the Temple Stones. Vandervoort, Gene, illus. 1999. 16p. (J). (gr. 1-4). pap. 4.95 (978-0-8198-7017-9(X)) Pauline Bks. & Media.

King-Smith, Dick. Lady Lollipop. Barton, Jill, illus. 128p. (J). (gr. 2-5). 2003. pap. 6.99 (978-0-7636-2181-0(1)); 2001. 15.99 (978-0-7636-1269-6(3)) Candlewick Pr.

—Lady Lollipop. 2001. (gr. 3-6). lib. bdg. 14.15 (978-0-613-66589-6(9)) Tandem Library Bks.

Kirwan, Wednesday. Nobody Notices Minerva. 2007. (Illus.). 32p. (J). (ps up). 14.95 (***978-1-4027-4728-1(4)***) Sterling Publishing Co., Inc.

Klass, David. You Don't Know Me. 2001. 272p. (YA). (gr. 7 up). 18.00 (978-0-374-38706-8(0) , Farrar, Straus & Giroux (BYR)) Farrar, Straus & Giroux.

—You Don't Know Me. 2002. 352p. (J). (gr. 5 up). pap. 7.99 (978-0-06-447378-1(3) , HarperTeen) HarperCollins Pubs.

—You Don't Know Me. 2002. (gr. 7-12). lib. bdg. 15.30 (978-0-613-53336-2(4)) Tandem Library Bks.

Klein, Abby. The Pumpkin Elf Mystery. McKinley, John, illus. 2007. (Ready, Freddy! Ser.: No. 11). 96p. (J). pap. 3.99 (***978-0-439-89591-0(X)*** , Blue Sky Pr., The) Scholastic, Inc.

Kleven, Sandy. The Right Touch: A Read-Aloud Story to Help Prevent Child Sexual Abuse. Bergsma, Jody Lynn, illus. 1998. (Jody Bergsma Collection). 32p. (ps-3). 15.95 (978-0-935699-10-4(4)) Illumination Arts Publishing Co., Inc.

Kline, Suzy. Horrible Harry & the Dungeon. 1998. (Horrible Harry Ser.: No. 7). (Illus.). 64p. (J). (gr. 2-4). pap. 3.99 (978-0-14-038620-2(3) , Puffin) Penguin Group (USA) Inc.

Knowlton, Laurie Lazzaro. Why Cowgirls Are Such Sweet Talkers. Rice, James, illus. 2000. 31p. (ps-3). 15.95 (978-1-56554-698-1(9)) Pelican Publishing Co., Inc.

Koller, Jackie French. Bouncing on the Bed. Hines, Anna Grossnickle, illus. 1999. 32p. (J). (ps-k). 16.99 (978-0-531-33138-5(5)); pap. 15.95 (978-0-531-30138-8(9)) Scholastic, Inc. (Orchard Bks.).

—If I Had One Wish. 2000. 172p. (J). (gr. 4-7). pap. 11.95 (978-0-595-09317-5(5) , Backinprint.com) iUniverse, Inc.

Kollmorgan, Loreen M. Animal Patrol. l.t. ed. 2005. (Illus.). 69p. (J) (ps-7). per. 12.95 (978-1-59453-169-9(2) , 1810) Airleaf Publishing & Bookselling.

Kooser, Diane S. Potter Pig in Control: Four Stories on Anger Management. Norcross, Harry, illus. 2000. 64p. (J). (gr. 1-3). pap. 12.95 (978-1-57543-084-3(3)) MAR*CO Products, Inc.

Kopelke, Lisa. Excuse Me! Kopelke, Lisa, illus. 2003. (Illus.). 32p. (J). (gr. k-3). 16.95 (978-0-689-85111-7(1)) Simon & Schuster Children's Publishing.

—Tissue, Please! Kopelke, Lisa, illus. 2004. (Illus.). 32p. (J). 15.95 (978-0-689-86248-9(2)) Simon & Schuster Children's Publishing.

Korman, Gordon. Liar, Liar, Pants on Fire. Adinolfi, JoAnn, illus. 1999. 96p. (J). (gr. 2-4). pap. 4.99 (978-0-590-27141-7(5)) Scholastic, Inc.

—Liar, Liar, Pants on Fire. 1999. (J). (978-0-606-15612-7(7)) Tandem Library Bks.

Koss, Amy Goldman. The Ashwater Experiment. l.t. ed. 2000. 188p. (YA). (gr. 8-12). 20.95 (978-0-7862-2686-3(2)) Thorndike Pr.

—The Cheat. 2004. 176p. (J). (gr. 5 up). pap. 5.99 (978-0-14-240128-6(5) , Puffin) Penguin Group (USA) Inc.

—The Girls. 128p. (J). 2002. pap. 5.99 (978-0-14-230033-6(0) , Puffin); 2000. (Illus.). (gr. 5-9). 16.99 (978-0-8037-2494-5(2) , Dial) Penguin Group (USA) Inc.

Kraus, Jeanne R. Annie's Plan: Taking Charge of Schoolwork & Homework. Beyl, Charles, illus. 2006. 48p. (J). (gr. 2-5). 14.95 (978-1-59147-481-4(7)); pap. 8.95 (978-1-59147-482-1(5)) American Psychological Assn. (Magination Pr.).

Krauss, Ronnie. Responsibility. 1998. (Captain Kangaroo Ser.). 16p. (J). 0.35 (978-0-06-107144-7(7)) HarperCollins Pubs.

—Sharing & Caring. 1998. (Captain Kangaroo Ser.). (Illus.). 16p. (J). pap. 3.99 (978-0-06-107142-3(0)) HarperCollins Pubs.

Krensky, Stephen. Arthur & the Crunch Cereal Contest. 1998. (Arthur Chapter Bks.: Bk. 4). (J). (gr. 3-6). 11.05 (978-0-606-13150-6(7)) Tandem Library Bks.

—Louise Goes Wild. 2001. (Illus.). (J). (978-0-606-21308-0(2)) Tandem Library Bks.

Krischanitz, Raoul. Nobody Likes Me! 2001. (Illus.). 32p. (J). (gr. k-2). pap. 6.95 (978-0-7358-1488-2(0)) North-South Bks., Inc.

Kroll, Steven. That Makes Me Mad! Davenier, Christine, illus. 2002. 32p. (J). (ps-1). 16.50 (978-1-58717-184-0(8)); 15.95 (978-1-58717-183-3(X)) Chronicle Bks. LLC. (SeaStar Bks.).

Kroll, Virginia L. Good Neighbor Nicholas. Cote, Nancy, illus. 2006. (Way I ACT Books: Vol. 5). 24p. (J). (gr. 1-3). 15.95 (978-0-8075-2998-0(2)) Whitman, Albert & Co.

Krosoczka, Jarrett J. Good Night, Monkey Boy. Krosoczka, Jarrett J., illus. 2003. (Illus.). 40p. (J). (gr. k-k). pap. 6.99 (978-0-440-41798-9(8) , Dragonfly Bks.) Random Hse. Children's Bks.

Krulik, Nancy E. I Hate Rules, No. 5. 2003. (Katie Kazoo, Switcheroo Ser.: No. 5). (Illus.). 80p. (J). (gr. 2-6). pap. 3.99 (978-0-448-43100-0(9) , Grosset & Dunlap) Penguin Group (USA) Inc.

—No Bones about It, No. 12. John and Wendy Staff, illus. 2004. (Katie Kazoo, Switcheroo Ser.: No. 12). 80p. (J). (gr. 2-6). pap. 3.99 (978-0-448-43358-5(3) , Grosset & Dunlap) Penguin Group (USA) Inc.

—No Messin' with My Lesson, No. 11. John and Wendy Staff, illus. 2004. (Katie Kazoo, Switcheroo Ser.: No.. 11). 80p. (J). (gr. 2-6). pap. 3.99 (978-0-448-43357-8(5) , Grosset & Dunlap) Penguin Group (USA) Inc.

Kurtz, Jane. Rain Romp: Stomping Away a Grouchy Day. Wolcott, Dyanna, illus. 2002. 32p. (J). (ps up). 16.99 (978-0-06-029805-0(7)) HarperCollins Pubs.

Kyi, Tanya Lloyd. Truth. 2003. (Orca Soundings Ser.). 96p. (J). (gr. 7-12). pap. 7.95 (978-1-55143-265-6(X)) Orca Bk. Pubs. USA.

Lachtman, Ofelia Dumas, et al. Pepita Takes Time (Pepita, Siempre Tarde) 2000. (SPA & ENG., Illus.). 32p. (J). (ps-2). 14.95 (978-1-55885-304-1(9) , Piñata Books) Arte Publico Pr.

Laguna, Sofie. Bad Buster: Being Bad Is Not Just for the Dogs! Hobbs, Leigh, illus. 2006. (Nibbles Ser.). 72p. (J). (gr. 1-4). pap. 3.95 (978-0-7624-2626-3(8) , Running Pr. Kids) Running Pr. Bk. Pubs.

—Too Loud Lily. Argent, Kerry, illus. 2004. 32p. (J). pap. 14.95 (978-0-439-57913-1(9)) Scholastic, Inc.

Landon, Letitia Elizabeth. Traits & Trials of Early Life. 1999. (Scholars' Facsimiles & Reprints Ser.: Vol. 523). 342p. reprint ed. 75.00 (978-0-8201-1523-8(1)) Scholars' Facsimiles & Reprints.

Lansky, Vicki. No Es Tu Culpa, Koko Oso. Prince, Jane, illus. 1999. (Lansky, Vicki Ser.).Tr. of It's Not Your Fault, Koko Bear. (SPA.). 32p. (ps-2). pap. 7.99 (978-0-916773-45-8(0)) Book Peddlers.

Lavigne, Guy. L' Obsession de Jerome Delisle. 2003. (Roman Plus Ser.). (FRE., Illus.). 160p. (YA). (gr. 8 up). pap. (978-2-89021-190-2(8)) Diffusion du livre Mirabel.

Lawrence, David. Good Little Girl. 2000. (Illus.). (J). (978-0-606-18784-8(7)) Tandem Library Bks.

Lawson, Polly. Sam Luckless. (Illus.). 32p. (J). pap. 14.95 (978-0-86315-126-2(4) , 1470) Floris Bks. GBR. *Dist:* SteinerBooks, Inc.

Laxman, Kamala. The Thama Stories. Laxman, R. K., illus. 120p. (J). pap. (978-0-14-037812-2(X) , Puffin) Penguin Group (USA) Inc.

Leblanc, Louise. Maddie Tries to Be Good. Cummins, Sarah, tr. Gay, Marie-Louise, illus. 1999. (First Novel Ser.). 61p. (gr. 1-5). 4.95 (978-0-88780-482-3(9)) Formac Publishing Co., Ltd. CAN. *Dist:* Casemate Pubs. & Bk. Distributors, LLC.

Lee, Marie G. Necessary Roughness. 1998. 240p. (J). (gr. 7 up). pap. 6.50 (978-0-06-447169-5(1) , Harper Trophy) HarperCollins Pubs.

—Necessary Roughness. 1998. (J). (978-0-606-13000-4(4)) Tandem Library Bks.

Leitich Smith, Cynthia & Leitich Smith, Greg. Santa Knows. Bjorkman, Steve, illus. 2006. 32p. (J). pap. 16.99 (978-0-525-47757-0(8) , Dutton Juvenile) Penguin Group (USA) Inc.

Leonard, Marcia. I Like Mess. Handelman, Dorothy, photos by. 1998. (Real Kids Readers Ser.). (Illus.). 32p. (ps-1). lib. bdg. 18.90 (978-0-7613-2002-9(4)); (J). pap. 4.99 (978-0-7613-2027-2(X)) Lerner Publishing Group. (Millbrook Pr.).

Lester, Helen. Hurty Feelings. Munsinger, Lynn M., illus. 32p. (J). (gr. k-3). 2007. 6.95 (***978-0-618-84062-5(1));** 2004. tchr. ed. 16.00 (978-0-618-41082-8(1)) Houghton Mifflin Co. Trade & Reference Div. (Walter Lorraine).

—Me First. Munsinger, Lynn, illus. 2002. (J). 14.72 (978-0-7587-3116-6(7)) Book Wholesalers, Inc.

—El Pinguino Taky. Munsinger, Lynn, illus. 2001. (SPA.). 32p. (J). (gr. k-3). pap. 5.95 (978-0-618-12531-9(0) , HM30384); tchr. ed. 15.00 (978-0-618-12530-2(2) , HM30383) Houghton Mifflin Co. Trade & Reference Div.

—Three Cheers for Tacky. Munsinger, Lynn, illus. 2002. (J). 13.79 (978-0-7587-3801-1(3)) Book Wholesalers, Inc.

Let's Learn All We Can! (Illus.). 24p. (J). 5.95 (978-0-8249-5449-9(1)) Ideals Pubns.

LeVert, Mireille. Eddie Longpants. 2005. (Illus.). 32p. (gr. k-1). 16.95 (978-0-88899-671-8(3)) Groundwood Bks. CAN. *Dist:* Perseus Distribution.

Levin, Bridget. Rules of the Wild: An Unruly Book of Manners. Shepherd, Amanda, illus. 2004. 36p. (J). 14.95 (978-0-8118-4226-6(6)) Chronicle Bks. LLC.

Levy, Elizabeth. Take Two, They're Small. Elliott, Mark, illus. 2002. 96p. (J). 14.99 (978-0-06-028592-0(3)) HarperCollins Pubs.

Lewin, Ted. Something Special. 1999. (Illus.). 80p. (J). (gr. 4 up). 15.00 (978-0-688-14109-7(9)) HarperCollins Pubs.

Lindgren, Astrid. Lotta on Troublemaker Street. Glasser, Robin Preiss, illus. 2001. (Ready-for-Chapters Ser.). 64p. (J). pap. 7.95 (978-0-689-84673-1(8) , Aladdin) Simon & Schuster Children's Publishing.

Lindquist, Susan Hart. Wander. 2000. (978-0-606-18792-3(8)) Tandem Library Bks.

Lish, Ted. Ese No Es Mi Trabajo. Jordan, Charles, illus. 2002. (J). lib. bdg. 15.95 (978-0-7940-0011-0(8)) Munchweiler Pr.

—It's Not My Job! Jordan, Charles, illus. 2002. 24p. (J). 14.95 (978-0-7940-0004-2(5)); lib. bdg. 15.95 (978-0-7940-0005-9(3)) Munchweiler Pr.

Loftis, Chris & Lowenthal, Gary T. I Want It Now! Helping Children Cope with Frustration & Disappointment. Moore, Darryl, illus. 2003. (Let's Talk Ser.). 48p. (J). pap. 12.95 (978-0-88282-237-2(3) , Small Horizons) New Horizon Pr. Pubs., Inc.

The Lonely One. 2001. 32p. (YA). (gr. 6-12). pap. (978-0-8224-3769-7(4)) Globe Fearon Educational Publishing.

Long, John Arthur & Meyer, Chet. The Tooth Fairy Legend: The Touch of Kindness. 2002. (Illus.). 56p. (J). audio compact disk 24.95 (978-0-9710749-0-3(9)) L & M Creations.

Lord of the Flies. 1998. 40p. (YA). 11.95 (978-1-56137-384-0(2) , NU3842SP) Novel Units, Inc.

Lowrey, Janette Sebring. The Poky Little Puppy. Tenggren, Gustaf, illus. 2003. (Big Little Golden Bks.). 32p. (J). (gr. k-k). reprint ed. 8.99 (978-0-307-10328-4(5) , Golden Bks.) Random Hse. Children's Bks.

Lowry, Lois. Stay! Keeper's Story. 1999. (978-0-606-16584-6(3)) Tandem Library Bks.

—Stay Keeper's Story. annual Kelley, True, illus. 1999. 128p. (J). (gr. 4-7). 5.50 (978-0-440-41524-4(1) , Yearling) Random Hse. Children's Bks.

Lucado, Max. Buzby & the Grumble Bees. 2007. (Max Lucado's Hermie & Friends Ser.). 38p. (J). bds. 12.99 (***978-1-4003-0913-9(1)***) Nelson, Thomas Inc.

Lucado, Max. Buzby, the Misbehaving Bee. 2005. (Hermie & Friends Ser.: No. 4). (Illus.). 48p. (J). 12.99 (978-1-4003-0510-0(1)) Nelson, Thomas Inc.

Ludwig, Trudy. Big Mouth. Prevost, Mikela, illus. 2007. (J). (***978-1-58246-240-0(2)*** , Tricycle Pr) Ten Speed Pr.

Ludy, Mark. The Grump. Brunner, Pat, ed. Ludy, Mark, illus. 2000. (Illus.). 32p. (J). (gr. 4 up). 16.95 (978-0-9664276-1-5(0)) Green Pastures Publishing, Inc.

Lynch, Clam. Ruby Gloom's Keys to Happiness. Hsu, Martin, illus. 2004. 48p. (J). (gr. 5-9). 12.95 (978-0-8109-5036-8(7)) Abrams, Harry N. , Inc.

MacDonald, Alan. Beware of the Bears! Williamson, Gwyneth, illus. 1999. 32p. (J). (ps up). pap. 5.95 (978-1-58431-008-2(1)) Little Tiger Pr.

—Beware of the Bears! Williamson, Gwyneth, illus. 2nd ed. 2001. 32p. (J). pap. 5.95 (978-1-58925-359-9(0) , tiger tales) ME Media LLC.

MacDonald, Amy. No More Nasty. Smith, Cat Bowman, illus. 2001. (J). (978-0-7894-2676-5(5)) Dorling Kindersley Publishing, Inc.

—No More Nice. 1998. (Illus.). 144p. (J). (gr. 3-7). pap. 4.95 (978-0-380-73055-1(3) , Harper Trophy) HarperCollins Pubs.

MacDonald, Betty. Hello, Mrs. Piggle-Wiggle. Boiger, Alexandra, illus. 2007. 192p. (J). lib. bdg. 16.89 (***978-0-06-125124-5(0)***) HarperCollins Pubs.

—Mrs. Piggle-Wiggle. Boiger, Alexandra, illus. 2007. 192p. (J). lib. bdg. 16.89 (***978-0-06-125123-8(2)***) HarperCollins Pubs.

MacDonald, Betty Bard. Hello, Mrs. Piggle-Wiggle. 2000. (YA). pap. 40.20 incl. audio (978-0-7887-4171-5(3) , 41089) Recorded Bks., LLC.

—Mrs. Piggle-Wiggle. Knight, Hilary, illus. 2002. (J). 13.40 (978-0-7587-6605-2(X)) Book Wholesalers, Inc.

—The Won't-Pick-up-Toys Cure. Whatley, Bruce, illus. 1998. (Mrs. Piggle-Wiggle Adventure Ser.). (J). lib. bdg. (978-0-06-027629-4(0)) HarperCollins Pubs.

—The Won't-Take-a-Bath-Cure. Whatley, Bruce, illus. 1998. (Mrs. Piggle-Wiggle Adventure Ser.). 40p. (J). (ps-2). lib. bdg. 14.89 (978-0-06-027631-7(2)) HarperCollins Pubs.

MacDonald, Betty Bard, ed. Mrs. Piggle-Wiggle's Bad Table-Manners Cure. Whatley, Bruce, illus. 2000. (Mrs. Piggle-Wiggle Adventure Ser.). (J). 12.95 (978-0-06-027632-4(0)); 12.89 (978-0-06-027633-1(9)) HarperCollins Pubs.

MacDonald, Betty Bard & Canham, Anne Macdonald. Mrs. Piggle-Wiggle. Boiger, Alexandra, illus. 2007. 208p. (J). lib. bdg. 16.89 (***978-0-06-072813-7(2)***) HarperCollins Pubs.

MacDonald, George. The Wise Woman. 1998. (George MacDonald Original Works Ser.: Series III). (Illus.). 384p. reprint ed. 22.00 (978-1-881084-17-4(5)) Johannesen Printing & Publishing.

MacHado, Ana Maria. Me in the Middle. Unger, David, tr. from POR. Merola, Caroline, illus. 2002. 96p. (J). (gr. 2-6). 14.95 (978-0-88899-463-9(X)) Groundwood Bks. CAN. *Dist:* Perseus Distribution.

MacHado, Ana Maria & Merola, Caroline. Me in the Middle. Unger, David, tr. from POR. 2003. (Illus.). 112p. (J). (gr. 3-6). pap. 4.95 (978-0-88899-467-7(2)) Groundwood Bks. CAN. *Dist:* Perseus Distribution.

MacKall, Dandi Daley. Gift Horse. 2003. (Winnie the Horse Gentler Ser.). (Illus.). 224p. (J). mass mkt. 5.99 (978-0-8423-5547-6(2)) Tyndale Hse. Pubs.

MacRae, Tom. The Opposite. Odriozola, Elena, illus. 2006. 32p. (J). 15.95 (978-1-56145-371-9(4) , Peachtree Junior) Peachtree Pubs., Ltd.

Maddox, Tony. Spike's Best Nest. 1998. (Illus.). 32p. (J). pap. 5.95 (978-0-7641-0548-7(5)) Barron's Educational Series, Inc.

Madonna. Goodbye, Grace? Fulvimari, Jeffrey, illus. 2007. (English Roses Ser.). 124p. (J). (gr. 3-7). 9.99 (***978-0-14-240883-4(2)*** , Puffin) Penguin Group (USA) Inc.

Mahoney, Daniel J. The Saturday Escape. 2002. (Illus.). 32p. (J). (gr. k-3). 14.00 (978-0-618-13326-0(7) , Clarion Bks.) Houghton Mifflin Co. Trade & Reference Div.

Maisner, Heather. It's My Turn! Stephenson, Kristina, illus. 2005. (First Time Stories Ser.). 24p. (J). (gr. k-ps). pap. 3.95 (978-0-7534-5740-5(7) , Kingfisher) Houghton Mifflin Co. Trade & Reference Div.

Malcolm, Jahnna N. Blubberina: Names Can Never Hurt Me! 2001. (Bad News Ballet Ser.: Vol. 5). 135p. (J). (gr. 3-7). pap. 3.95 (978-0-9700164-4-7(1)) Starcatcher Pr.

Mangan, Anne. The Monkey Who Wanted the Moon. Walters, Catherine, illus. 2000. 32p. (J). (gr. k-3). 15.95 (978-1-56656-376-5(3)) Interlink Publishing Group, Inc.

Manning, Sarra. Let's Get Lost. 2006. 320p. (YA). (gr. 9). 16.99 (978-0-525-47666-5(0) , Dutton Juvenile) Penguin Group (USA) Inc.

Marijanovic, Stanislav. A Manual of House Monsters II. 2000. (Illus.). (J). pap. 15.95 (978-1-58653-181-2(6)) Mondo Publishing.

—A Manual of House Monsters II. Marijanovic, Stanislav, illus. 2000. (Manual of House Monsters Ser.: Vol. 2). (Illus.). 32p. (J). (gr. 2-6). 15.95 (978-1-58653-171-3(9)) Mondo Publishing.

Marshall, James. Someone Is Talking about Hortense. 2000. (Illus.). 32p. (J). (gr. k-3). tchr. ed. 5.95 (978-0-618-07318-4(3)) Houghton Mifflin Co. Trade & Reference Div.

Martenz, Arden. Glenda: A Story about Cooperation & Caring. Garafano, Marie, illus. 2001. 16p. (J). (gr. 1-4). pap. 6.95 (978-1-57543-088-1(6)) MAR*CO Products, Inc.

Martin, Ann M. Claudia & the Terrible Truth. 1998. (Baby-Sitters Club Ser.: No. 117). (J). (gr. 3-7). pap. 4.50 (978-0-590-05995-4(5) , Scholastic Paperbacks) Scholastic, Inc.

—Claudia & the Terrible Truth. 1998. (Baby-Sitters Club Ser.: No. 117). (J). (gr. 3-7). (978-0-606-13161-2(2)) Tandem Library Bks.

—Jessi's Horrible Prank. 2001. (Baby-Sitters Club Ser.: No. 75). (J). (gr. 3-7). pap. 3.99 (978-0-590-92607-2(1)) Scholastic, Inc.

—Karen's Chain Letter. 1998. (Baby-Sitters Little Sister Ser.: No. 101). (J). (gr. 3-7). pap. 3.99 (978-0-590-50053-1(8)) Scholastic, Inc.

—Karen's Promise. 1998. (Baby-Sitters Little Sister Ser.: No. 95). (J). (gr. 3-7). pap. 3.99 (978-0-590-06593-1(9) , Scholastic Paperbacks) Scholastic, Inc.

—Karen's Promise. 1998. (Baby-Sitters Little Sister Ser.: No. 95). (J). (gr. 3-7). (978-0-606-13171-1(X)) Tandem Library Bks.

—Mary Anne & the Playground Fight. 1998. (Baby-Sitters Club Ser.: No. 120). (J). (gr. 3-7). pap. 3.99 (978-0-590-05998-5(X) , Scholastic Paperbacks) Scholastic, Inc.

—Mary Anne & the Playground Fight. 1998. (Baby-Sitters Club Ser.: No. 120). (J). (gr. 3-7). (978-0-606-13164-3(7)) Tandem Library Bks.

—Mary Anne's Revenge. 2000. (Baby-Sitters Club Friends Forever Ser.: No. 8). (Illus.). 144p. (J). (gr. 3-7). pap. 4.50 (978-0-590-52340-0(6)) Scholastic, Inc.

Martin, S. R. Talk to Me. 1999. (Insomniacs Ser.: No. 3). (Illus.). 80p. (YA). (gr. 7-12). pap. 2.99 (978-0-590-69142-0(2)) Scholastic, Inc.

Martin, Steve & Chast, Roz. The Alphabet from A to Y, with Bonus Letter Z! 2007. (Illus.). 64p. (J). 17.95 (***978-0-385-51662-4(2)***); lib. bdg. 17.95 (***978-0-385-52377-6(7)***) Doubleday Publishing. (Flying Dolphin Pr.).

Matt Otra Vez en Problemas! Podra Ayudarlo la Consejera de la Escuela? 2001. 22p. (J). pap. 8.95 (978-0-9713839-2-0(8)) MarLin Bks.

Maxwell, Corey. The Big Little Lie. Vitale, Steve & Turnbaugh, Paul, illus. 1999. 32p. (J). (gr. k-3). 12.95 (978-1-890145-04-0(1) , Paw Island Entertainment, Inc.) PetCare, Inc.

Mayer, Mercer. All by Myself. Mayer, Mercer, illus. 2001. (Little Critter Ser.). (Illus.). 24p. (J). (gr. k-k). reprint ed. pap. 3.99 (978-0-307-11938-4(6) , 11938, Random Hse. Bks. for Young Readers) Random Hse. Children's Bks.

—I Just Forgot. Mayer, Mercer, illus. 1999. (Little Critter Ser.). (Illus.). 24p. (J). (gr. k-k). pap. 3.99 (978-0-307-11975-9(0) , 11975, Random Hse. Bks. for Young Readers) Random Hse. Children's Bks.

—What a Bad Dream. Mayer, Mercer, illus. 1999. (Little Critter Ser.). (Illus.). 24p. (J). (gr. k-k). pap. 3.99 (978-0-307-12685-6(4) , 12685, Random Hse. Bks. for Young Readers) Random Hse. Children's Bks.

McBratney, Sam. I'm Sorry. Eachus, Jennifer, illus. 40p. (J). 2006. pap. 6.99 (978-0-06-079927-4(7) , Harper Trophy); 2000. 15.99 (978-0-06-028686-6(5)) HarperCollins Pubs.

McCafferty, Catherine. Just Be Nice... And Say You're Sorry! Baker, Darrell, illus. 1998. (Disney Ser.). 24p. (J). (ps-k). pap. 3.29 (978-0-307-10343-7(9) , 10343, Golden Bks.) Random Hse. Children's Bks.

Mccann, Clare. Runaway Pickpocket. 2005. 182p. pap. 19.95 (978-1-4137-5908-2(4)) PublishAmerica, Inc.

McClements, George. Baron Von Baddie Wins. 2008. (J). (***978-0-15-206138-8(X)***) Harcourt Trade Pubs.

—Night of the Veggie Monster. 2008. (Illus.). 32p. (J). 15.85 (***978-1-59990-234-0(6)***) Bloomsbury Publishing.

—Night of the Veggie Monster. McClements, George, illus. 2008. (Illus.). 32p. (J). 14.95 (***978-1-59990-061-2(0)***) Bloomsbury Publishing.

McDaniel, Becky Bring. Kathy lo Hizo. Hoit, Richard, illus. rev. ed. 2003. (Rookie Reader Espanol Ser.). (SPA & ENG.). 31p. (J). 19.50 (978-0-516-25891-1(5) , Children's Pr.) Scholastic Library Publishing.

—Katie Did It. Hoit, Richard, illus. rev. ed. 2003. (Rookie Reader Espanol Ser.). (J). (gr. k-2). pap. 4.95 (978-0-516-27832-2(0) , Children's Pr.) Scholastic Library Publishing.

—Katie Did It. 2003. (gr. k-3). lib. bdg. 12.95 (978-0-613-66363-2(2)) Tandem Library Bks.

McDaniel, Lurlene. No Time to Cry. 2005. (Dawn Rochelle Ser.: No. 4). (Illus.). 160p. (gr. 6-12). reprint ed. pap. 4.99 (978-1-58196-006-8(9)) Lerner Publishing Group.

—No Time to Cry. 2003. (Dawn Rochelle Ser.: No. 4). (gr. 7-12). lib. bdg. 13.00 (978-0-613-84939-5(6)) Tandem Library Bks.

McDonald, Joyce. Comfort Creek. 1998. 10.64 (978-0-606-13289-3(9)) Tandem Library Bks.

McGee, Marni & Williams, Sam. Wake Up, Me! Salvadier, Elivia, illus. 2002. 40p. (J). (ps-k). 17.00 (978-0-689-83163-8(3)) Simon & Schuster Children's Publishing.

McGuinness-Kelly, Tracy-Lee. Bad Cat. McGuinness-Kelly, Tracy-Lee, illus. 2006. (Illus.). 29p. (J). (gr. k-4). reprint ed. 16.00 (978-0-7567-9823-9(X)) DIANE Publishing Co.

McHenry, E. B. Poodlena. McHenry, E. B., illus. 2005. (Illus.). 32p. (J). (ps-3). pap. 6.95 (978-1-58234-698-4(4) , Bloomsbury Children) Bloomsbury Publishing.

—Poodlena. 2004. (Illus.). (J). (978-1-58234-962-6(2)); 32p. (gr. 1 up). 16.95 (978-1-58234-824-7(3) , Bloomsbury Children) Bloomsbury Publishing.

McKenna, Colleen O'Shaughnessy. Third Grade Stinks! Roth, Stephanie, illus. 2001. 104p. (J). (gr. 4-6). tchr. ed. 15.95 (978-0-8234-1595-3(3)) Holiday Hse., Inc.

McKeowen, Sean. Anything but a Shot. Maval Publishing Inc. Staff, illus. 2001. 32p. (J). (ps-3). pap. 7.50 (978-1-884083-67-9(6)) Maval Publishing, Inc.

McKissack, Patricia C. Messy Bessey. rev. ed. 1999. (gr. k-3). lib. bdg. 12.95 (978-0-613-37455-2(X)) Tandem Library Bks.

McKissack, Patricia C. & McKissack, Fredrick. Messy Bessey. Regan, Dana, illus. rev. ed. 1999. (Rookie Readers Ser.). 32p. (J). (gr. 1-2). 19.50 (978-0-516-21650-8(3) , Children's Pr.) Scholastic Library Publishing.

—Messy Bessey, Vol. 2. 2006. 96p. (J). (gr. 1-2). 8.95 (978-0-516-25301-5(8) , Children's Pr.) Scholastic Library Publishing.

McKissack, Patricia C. & McKissack, Fredrick L. Messy Bessey. Regan, Dana, illus. rev. ed. 2000. (Rookie Reader Espanol Ser.). 32p. (J). (gr. k-2). pap. 4.95 (978-0-516-27003-6(6) , Children's Pr.) Scholastic Library Publishing.

—Messy Bessey's School Desk. Regan, Dana, illus. 1998. (Rookie Readers Ser.). 32p. (J). (gr. 1-2). 19.50 (978-0-516-20827-5(6) , Children's Pr.) Scholastic Library Publishing.

Meddaugh, Susan. The Best Place. Meddaugh, Susan, illus. 1999. (Illus.). 32p. (J). (gr. k-3). tchr. ed. 15.00 (978-0-395-97994-5(3) , Walter Lorraine) Houghton Mifflin Co. Trade & Reference Div.

—The Best Place. 2004. (Illus.). 32p. (J). (gr. k-3). reprint ed. pap. 5.95 (978-0-618-44882-1(9) , Walter Lorraine) Houghton Mifflin Co. Trade & Reference Div.

Medlyn, Lynda Lee & Staudenmier, Kelley Anne. The Best Belcher. 2007. (Illus.). 32p. (J). lib. bdg. 15.95 (***978-0-9793738-0-0(8)***) Window Box Pr. LLC.

Melling, David. The Scallywags. 2006. 32p. (J). (ps-2). 14.99 (978-0-7641-5991-6(7)) Barron's Educational Series, Inc.

Metzger, Steve. Five Spooky Ghosts Playing Tricks at School. Harrald-Pilz, Marilee, illus. 2005. (J). (***978-0-439-80381-6(0)***) Scholastic, Inc.

—I'm the Boss! Wilhelm, Hans, illus. 1998. (Dinofours Ser.: No. 6). 32p. (J). (ps-1). pap. 3.25 (978-0-590-37458-3(3)) Scholastic, Inc.

—It's Thanksgiving! Wilhelm, Hans, illus. 2001. (Dinofours Ser.). (J). (ps-1). 3.25 (978-0-439-29570-3(X)) Scholastic, Inc.

—My Bossy Dolly. Demarest, Chris L., illus. 2006. 24p. (J). pap. 3.50 (978-0-439-74055-5(X) , Cartwheel Bks.) Scholastic, Inc.

Miglis Sandvik, Jenny. Who Are You Calling Ugly? Karl, Linda, illus. 2004. (Shrek 2 Ser.). 32p. (J). act. bk. ed. 3.99 (978-0-439-57632-1(6)) Scholastic, Inc.

Miles, Betty. Just the Beginning. 2000. 160p. (gr. 4-7). pap. 10.95 (978-0-595-00736-3(8) , Backinprint.com) iUniverse, Inc.

Miller, Jayna. Too Much Trick or Treat. Thatch, Nancy, ed. Miller, Jayna, illus. 2005. (Illus.). 29p. (J). per. 19.95 (978-0-933849-83-9(4)) Landmark Editions, Inc.

Mills, Claudia. Alex Ryan, Stop That! 2003. 160p. (J). 16.00 (978-0-374-34655-3(0) , Farrar, Straus & Giroux (BYR)) Farrar, Straus & Giroux.

Mills, Lauren A. The Dog Prince. Mills, Lauren A. & Nolan, Dennis, illus. 2001. 32p. (J). (gr. 1-3). 15.95 (978-0-316-57417-4(1)) Little, Brown Bks. for Young Readers.

Mochizuki, Chiemi. The Promise. Randle, Walt R., ed. Mochizuki, Chiemi, illus. 2003. (Illus.). 38p. (J). (gr. 3-6). 16.99 (978-0-9720691-0-6(0)) Berkeley Major Publishing.

Morton, Lone. All about Me. Church, Caroline Jayne, illus. 1999. 24p. pap. (978-1-874735-07-6(7)) B Small Publishing.

Moss, Deborah M. Shelley, the Hyperactive Turtle. Schwartz, Carol, illus. 2nd ed. 2006. 20p. (J). pap. (978-1-890627-75-1(5)) Woodbine Hse.

Moss, Marissa. Amelia's Boredom Survival Guide. Moss, Marissa, illus. 2006. (Amelia's Notebooks). (Illus.). 64p. (J). 9.95 (978-1-4169-0916-3(8)) Simon & Schuster Children's Publishing.

Moss, Miriam. Bad Hare Day. Chapman, Lynne, illus. 2003. 32p. (J). (gr. k-3). 15.95 (978-1-58234-785-1(9) , Bloomsbury Children) Bloomsbury Publishing.

Most, Bernard. The Very Boastful Kangaroo. 2003. (Green Light Readers Level 2 Ser.). (Illus.). 24p. (J). 11.95 (978-0-15-204880-8(4)); pap. 3.95 (978-0-15-204840-2(5)) Harcourt Children's Bks. (Green Light Readers).

Mould, Wendy. Ants in My Pants. Mould, Wendy, illus. 2001. (Illus.). 32p. (J). (gr. k-3). tchr. ed. 15.00 (978-0-618-09640-4(X) , Clarion Bks.) Houghton Mifflin Co. Trade & Reference Div.

Mouse Works Staff. The Lady & the Tramp: We're All Different. 1999. (Illus.). (J). 2.99 (978-0-7364-0044-2(3)) Mouse Works.

Munsch, Robert. Get Out of Bed! Daniel, Alan & Daniel, Lea, illus. 1998. 32p. (J). (ps-1). pap. 10.95 (978-0-590-76977-8(4) , Cartwheel Bks.) Scholastic, Inc.

—Get Out of Bed! 1999. (Illus.). (J). 10.79 (978-0-606-18550-9(X)) Tandem Library Bks.

—We Share Everything. Martchenko, Michael, illus. 1999. 32p. (J). (ps-1). 11.95 (978-0-590-89600-9(8) , Cartwheel Bks.) Scholastic, Inc.

Murphy, Jill. Five Minutes' Peace. Murphy, Jill, illus. 2002. (Illus.). (J). 14.04 (978-0-7587-4111-0(1)) Book Wholesalers, Inc.

—Five Minutes' Peace. 1999. (Illus.). 32p. (J). (ps-3). pap. 6.99 (978-0-698-11787-7(5) , Putnam Juvenile) Penguin Group (USA) Inc.

—Five Minutes' Peace. 1999. (gr. k-3). lib. bdg. 15.30 (978-0-613-14722-4(7)) Tandem Library Bks.

Murray, Carol. Hurry Up! Garbot, Dave, illus. 2003. (Rookie Reader Ser.). 32p. (J). 19.50 (978-0-516-22585-2(5) , Children's Pr.) Scholastic Library Publishing.

Myers, Bill. My Life as a Computer Cockroach, Vol. 17. 1999. (Incredible Worlds of Wally McDoogle Ser.: No. 17). 128p. (J). (gr. 3-7). pap. 6.99 (978-0-8499-4026-2(5)) Nelson, Thomas Inc.

—Phantom of the Haunted Church. 1998. (Bloodhounds, Inc. Ser.: Vol. 3). (Illus.). 128p. (J). (gr. 3-8). pap. 5.99 (978-1-55661-892-5(1)) Bethany Hse. Pubs.

Napoli, Donna Jo. Running Away. 2000. (Angelwings Ser.: No. 10). 96p. (J). (gr. 2-6). pap. 7.95 (978-0-689-83210-9(9) , Aladdin) Simon & Schuster Children's Publishing.

—Running Away. 2000. (Angelwings Ser.: No. 10). (Illus.). (J). (978-0-606-20384-5(2)) Tandem Library Bks.

Naylor, Phyllis Reynolds. The Girls Get Even. 2002. 144p. (gr. 4-7). mass mkt. 5.50 (978-0-440-41842-9(9) , Yearling) Random Hse. Children's Bks.

—The Girls Get Even. 2002. (Juvenile Ser.). (Illus.). (J). 23.95 (978-0-7862-4854-4(8)) Thorndike Pr.

—I Can't Take You Anywhere! Kaminsky, Jef, illus. 2001. 32p. (J). (ps-3). 6.99 (978-0-689-84116-3(7) , Aladdin) Simon & Schuster Children's Publishing.

Nelson, Ray & Mohr-Hansen, Julie. I Am Hercules. McLane, Mike, ed. Holveck, Kyle et al, illus. 2000. (Farmer Bob Ser.). 32p. (J). (gr. 1-3). pap. 12.00 (978-1-883772-16-1(8)) Flying Rhinoceros, Inc.

—I Am Jenny. Holveck, Kyle et al, illus. 2000. (Farmer Bob Ser.). 32p. (J). (gr. 1-3). pap. 12.00 (978-1-883772-18-5(4)) Flying Rhinoceros, Inc.

—I Am Porkchop. Holveck, Kyle & Peeples, Aaron, illus. 2000. (Farmer Bob Ser.). 32p. (J). (gr. 1-2). pap. 12.00 (978-1-883772-17-8(6)) Flying Rhinoceros, Inc.

—I Am Sam. McLane, Mike et al, eds. Holveck, Kyle et al, illus. 2000. (Farmer Bob Ser.). 32p. (J). (gr. 1-3). pap. 12.00 (978-1-883772-15-4(X)) Flying Rhinoceros, Inc.

—Today I Will Moo. Holveck, Kyle & Peeples, Aaron, illus. 2000. (Farmer Bob Ser.). 32p. (J). (gr. 1-3). pap. 12.00 (978-1-883772-19-2(2)) Flying Rhinoceros, Inc.

Nelson, Ray, et al. The Battle Against Boredom. 2000. (Illus.). 48p. (J). (gr. 3-6). 18.00 (978-1-883772-20-8(6)) Flying Rhinoceros, Inc.

Neri, G. Chess Rumble. Watson, Jesse Joshua, illus. 2007. 64p. (J). (gr. 3-7). 18.95 (***978-1-58430-279-7(8)***) Lee & Low Bks., Inc.

Nodelman, Perry. Behaving Bradley. 2000. (Illus.). (J). (978-0-606-17911-9(9)) Tandem Library Bks.

A
B

—Behaving Bradley. l.t. ed. 2002. 272p. (J). 22.95 (978-0-7862-4779-0(7)) Thorndike Pr.

Noyes, Deborah. It's Vladimir! Mills, Christophe, illus. 2000. 32p. (J). (gr. k-3). 15.95 (978-0-7614-5071-9(8)), Cavendish Children's Bks.) Cavendish, Marshall Corp.

Nye, Naomi S. Sitti's Secrets. 1998. (J). pap. 5.99 (978-0-87628-371-4(7)) Ctr. for Applied Research in Education, The.

Oates, Joyce Carol. Big Mouth & Ugly Girl. 2003. 288p. pap. 7.99 (978-0-06-447347-7(3)) HarperCollins Pubs.

—Naughty Cherie. Graham, Mark, illus. 2008. (J). 40p. 17.89 (978-0-06-074359-8(X)); 32p. 16.99 (978-0-06-074358-1(1)) HarperCollins Pubs.

O'Connor, Edwin. Benjy: A Ferocious Fairy Tale. O'Neill, Catharine, illus. 2006. 96p. (J). reprint ed. pap. 12.00 (978-1-4223-5421-6(0)) DIANE Publishing Co.

O'Dea, Kendra. The Stolen Sleigh. McGovern, Sarah, illus. 2006. (J). pap. (978-0-922993-53-6(X)) Marquette Bks., LLC.

Offill, Jenny. Twenty Things I'm Not Allowed to Do Anymore. Carpenter, Nancy, illus. 2004. (J). 16.00 (978-0-689-85158-2(8), Atheneum/Anne Schwartz Bks.) Simon & Schuster Children's Publishing.

—17 Things I'm Not Allowed to Do Anymore. Carpenter, Nancy, illus. 2006. 32p. (J). (ps-3). 15.99 (978-0-375-83596-4(2)); lib. bdg. 17.99 (978-0-375-93596-1(7)) Random Hse. Children's Bks. (Schwartz & Wade Bks.).

Ogden, Charles. Mischief Manual. Carton, Rick, illus. 2007. (Edgar & Ellen Ser.). 112p. (J). pap. 7.99 (978-1-4169-3935-1(0), Aladdin) Simon & Schuster Children's Publishing.

O'Loughlin, Larry. Is Anybody Listening? 2002. 176p. (J). pap. 7.95 (978-0-86327-721-4(7)) Interlink Publishing Group, Inc.

Olson, Gretchen. Joyride. 2003. 184p. (YA). (gr. 6-9). 9.95 (978-1-56397-758-9(3)) Boyds Mills Pr.

—Joyride. 1999. (gr. 7-12). lib. bdg. 18.75 (978-0-613-17688-0(X)) Tandem Library Bks.

Once upon a Time Spanish Version-the Boy Who Cried Wolf. 2005. (J). (978-1-57022-557-4(5)) ECS Learning Systems, Inc.

O'Neill, Alexis. Loud Emily. 2001. (gr. k-3). lib. bdg. 15.30 (978-0-613-73313-7(4)) Tandem Library Bks.

O'Neill, Alexis & Carpenter, Nancy. Loud Emily. 2001. (Illus.). 40p. (J). pap. 6.99 (978-0-689-84669-4(X), Aladdin) Simon & Schuster Children's Publishing.

Oppenheim, Shulamith Levey. Ali & the Magic Stew. Pels, Winslow, illus. 2003. 32p. (YA). (gr. k-2). 15.95 (978-1-56397-869-2(5)) Boyds Mills Pr.

Orwell, George. Animal Farm. 2002. 14.00 (978-0-7587-7843-7(0)) Book Wholesalers, Inc.

Orwell, George, et al. Animal Farm. 1999. (Literature Made Easy Ser.). (Illus.). 96p. pap. 6.99 (978-0-7641-0819-8(0)) Barron's Educational Series, Inc.

Otfinoski, Steven. Time to Share. 2000. (gr. 3-6). lib. bdg. 11.80 (978-0-613-31820-4(X)) Tandem Library Bks.

Otte, Kathleen. I Can Show Good Manners. 2006. (J). pap., tchr. ed. (978-1-57332-438-0(8)); pap. (978-1-57332-439-7(6)) HighReach Learning, Inc.

Ottolenghi, Carol. Tip the Mouse Runs Away. Campanella, Marco, illus. 2005. (Tip the Mouse Ser.). 32p. (J). (ps-ps). 10.95 (978-0-7696-4298-7(5), Gingham Dog Pr.) School Specialty Publishing.

Palatini, Margie. Goldie Is Mad. Palatini, Margie, illus. 2001. (Illus.). 32p. (ps-k). 15.49 (978-0-7868-2490-8(5)); 14.99 (978-0-7868-0565-5(X)) Hyperion Bks. for Children.

Pansy (Isabella M. Alden). Tip Lewis & His Lamp. 2006. 112p. pap. (978-1-84702-198-4(0)) Echo Library.

Papademetriou, Lisa. You're in Big Trouble, Brad! Handelman, Dorothy, photos by. 1998. (Real Kids Readers Ser.). (Illus.). 48p. (gr. 1-3). lib. bdg. 18.90 (978-0-7613-2022-7(9)); 32p. (J). (gr. 2-4). pap. 4.99 (978-0-7613-2047-0(4)) Lerner Publishing Group. (Millbrook Pr.).

Park, Barbara. Junie B. Jones & Some Sneaky Peeky Spying. Brunkus, Denise, illus. 2005. (Junie B. Jones Ser.: No. 4). (SPA.). 80p. (J). (gr. k-3). pap. 3.99 (978-0-439-42515-5(8), Scholastic en Espanol) Scholastic, Inc.

—Junie B. Jones Is Not a Crook. unabr. ed. 2004. (Junie B. Jones Ser.: No. 9). 67p. (J). (gr. k-3). pap. 17.00 incl. audio (978-0-8072-0530-3(3), Listening Library) Random Hse. Audio Publishing Group.

Parr, Todd. Do's & Don'ts. 2004. (Illus.). 24p. (J). (ps-ps). bds. 6.99 (978-0-316-90808-5(8)) Little, Brown Bks. for Young Readers.

Parry, Linda. Bramble Forgets. Parry, Alan, illus. 1998. (Honey Bear Ser.). 28p. (J). pap. 4.99 (978-0-8054-1791-3(5)) B&H Publishing Grp.

Paul, Ann Whitford. Hasta Manana, Monito. (SPA.). (J). 8.95 (978-958-04-7073-1(1)) Norma S.A. COL. *Dist:* Distribuidora Norma, Inc.

—Manana, Iguana. Long, Ethan, tr. Long, Ethan, illus. 2005. 32p. (J). tchr. ed. 16.95 (978-0-8234-1808-4(1)) Holiday Hse., Inc.

Pearce, Emily Smith. Isabel & the Miracle Baby. 2007. 144p. (YA). (gr. 3 up). 15.95 (***978-1-932425-44-4(6)***, Front Street) Boyds Mills Pr.

Pennington, Krista & Pennington, Anna. Bartholomew's Blunder. Browne, James, illus. 1998. 32p. (J). (gr. k-4). pap. 9.99 (978-0-9659654-1-5(4)) Terpsichore Pubns.

Penton Overseas, Inc. Staff. Hogger the Hoarding Beastie. 2001. (Beastie Buddies Ser.). (Illus.). 32p. (J). 6.95 (978-1-891100-83-3(1)) Smart Kids Publishing.

—Moogie the Messy Beastie. 2001. (Beastie Buddies Ser.). (Illus.). 32p. (J). 6.95 (978-1-891100-84-0(X)) Smart Kids Publishing.

Perry, Dennis. Yakabou Must Choose. 2000. (J). pap. 8.99 (978-1-58374-024-8(4)) Chicago Spectrum Pr.

Peters, Julie Anne. Revenge of the Snob Squad. 2000. (978-0-606-17868-6(6)) Tandem Library Bks.

—Romance of the Snob Squad. 2000. (978-0-606-20369-2(9)) Tandem Library Bks.

Pfister, Marcus. How Leo Learned to Be King. 1998. (Illus.). 32p. (J). (ps-3). 15.95 (978-1-55858-913-1(9)) North-South Bks., Inc.

Pielle, Sue. T'aal: The One Who Takes Bad Children. Guzek, Greta, illus. unabr. ed. 1998. 28p. (J). (978-1-55017-180-8(1)) Harbour Publishing Co., Ltd.

Pinkwater, Daniel M. Bad Bears & a Bunny. Pinkwater, Jill, illus. 2005. (Irving & Muktuk Story Ser.). 32p. (J). (gr. k-3). 16.00 (978-0-618-33926-6(4)) Houghton Mifflin Co. Trade & Reference Div.

Piper, Watty. The Little Engine That Could: A Storybook & Wind-up Train/Dutton Motorbook. Bernal, Richard, illus. 1998. 8p. (J). (ps-2). pap. 21.99 (978-0-525-46029-9(2), Dutton Juvenile) Penguin Group (USA) Inc.

Poindexter, Sidney. Cobrina & Mongoose-Ra. 1998. (Illus.). 40p. (J). (gr. 3-6). pap. 9.00 (978-0-8059-4391-7(9)) Dorrance Publishing Co., Inc.

Polacco, Patricia. Thank You, Mr. Falker. Polacco, Patricia, illus. gif. ed. 2001. (Illus.). 1p. (J). (gr. k up). 18.99 (978-0-399-23732-4(1), Philomel) Penguin Group (USA) Inc.

Popov, Nikolai. Why? 1998. (Illus.). 48p. (J). (gr. k-3). pap. 6.95 (978-1-55858-996-4(1)) North-South Bks., Inc.

Potter, Beatrix. The Tale of Jemima Puddle-Duck. Potter, Beatrix, illus. 2002. (Illus.). (J). 15.23 (978-0-7587-4500-2(1)) Book Wholesalers, Inc.

—The Tale of Jemima Puddle-Duck. 2002. (Illus.). 64p. (J). 6.99 (978-0-7232-4778-4(1), Warne) Penguin Group (USA) Inc.

—The Tale of Jemima Puddle-Duck. (Illus.). 12p. 4.95 (978-1-58989-274-3(7)) Thurman Hse., LLC.

—The Tale of Jemima Puddle-Duck: Adapted from the Original. 2003. (Illus.). 32p. (J). (ps). 3.99 (978-0-7232-4719-7(6), Warne) Penguin Group (USA) Inc.

Powell, Anna. Don't Say That, Willy Nilly! Roberts, David, illus. 2005. 28p. (J). (gr. k-2). 16.00 (978-1-56148-488-1(1)) Good Bks.

Poydar, Nancy. Bunny Business. 2003. (Illus.). 32p. (J). (gr. k-3). tchr. ed. 16.95 (978-0-8234-1771-1(9)) Holiday Hse., Inc.

Pullman, Philip. I Was a Rat! Hawkes, Kevin, illus. 2002. 176p. (gr. 5). 5.99 (978-0-440-41661-6(2), Yearling) Random Hse. Children's Bks.

Puttock, Simon. Big Bad Wolf Is Good. Chapman, Lynne, illus. 2002. 32p. (J). (ps-2). 12.95 (978-0-8069-0027-8(X)) Sterling Publishing Co., Inc.

—"Here I Am!" Said Smedley. Chatterton, Martin & Chatterton, Ann, illus. 2001. (Blue Bananas Ser.). 48p. (J). (gr. 1-2). (978-0-7787-0838-4(1)); pap. (978-0-7787-0884-1(5)) Crabtree Publishing Co.

Ramirez, Linda M. & Salcines, Maria Luisa. Maggie's Visit to the Playroom. Llendler, Christine, illus. l.t. ed. 2000. 16p. (Orig.). (J). pap. 6.95 (978-0-945199-22-9(8), 956-668-1516) MarLin Bks.

Ramirez, Linda Manning & Salcines, Maria Luisa. Matt's in Trouble... Again! Can the School Counselor Help? Cartee-Cox, Amy, illus. 2001. 20p. pap. 8.95 (978-0-9713839-1-3(X)) MarLin Bks.

Random House Disney Staff & Winkelman, Barbara Gaines. Pinocchio's Nose Grows. 2002. (Step into Reading Bks.). (Illus.). 32p. (J). (ps-1). lib. bdg. 11.99 (978-0-7364-8001-7(3), RH/Disney) Random Hse. Children's Bks.

Rankin, Laura. Ruthie & the (Not So) Teeny Tiny Lie. Rankin, Laura, illus. 2007. (Illus.). 32p. (J). (ps-2). 15.95 (978-1-59990-010-0(6)) Bloomsbury Publishing.

Ransom, Jeanie Franz. What Do Parents Do When You're Not Home. Moore, Cyd, illus. 2007. 32p. (J). (gr. k-2). 16.95 (978-1-56145-409-9(5), Peachtree Junior) Peachtree Pubs., Ltd.

Rasmussen, Anne & Nemiroff, Marc. The Very Lonely Bathtub. Flanagan, Kate, illus. 1999. 32p. (J). (ps-2). (978-1-55798-607-8(X), 441-6070, Magination Pr.) American Psychological Assn.

Rathmann, Peggy, et al. Ruby, Mono Ve, Mono Hace. 2003. (Mariposa Ser.). (SPA., Illus.). 32p. (J). (ps-k). pap. 4.95 (978-0-590-50211-5(5), Scholastic en Espanol) Scholastic, Inc.

Rau, Dana Meachen. My Special Space. 2004. (Rookie Reader Espanol Ser.). (Illus.). 31p. (J). (gr. k-2). pap. 4.95 (978-0-516-27788-2(X), Children's Pr.) Scholastic Library Publishing.

—My Special Space. Kim, Julie J., illus. 2003. (Rookie Reader - Level C Ser.). 32p. (J). 19.50 (978-0-516-22881-5(1), Children's Pr.) Scholastic Library Publishing.

Redfield, James & Lillegard, Dee. The Song of Celestine. Morrissey, Dean, illus. 1998. 48p. (J). (ps-3). 14.95 (978-0-316-73923-8(5)) Little Brown & Co.

Reeder, Carolyn. Captain Kate. 1999. (Avon Camelot Bks.). 224p. (J). (gr. 4-7). 15.00 (978-0-380-97628-7(5)) HarperCollins Pubs.

Reger, Rob & Parker, Buzz. Emily the Strange, Vol. 1. 2006. (SPA., Illus.). 64p. 19.95 (978-1-59497-188-4(9)) Public Square Bks.

—Emily the Strange Vol. 2: El libro Secreto de Las Cosas Extrañas. 2006. (SPA., Illus.). 64p. reprint ed. 19.95 (978-1-59497-189-1(7)) Public Square Bks.

Reider, Katja. Snail Started It! Von Roehl, Angela, illus. 1999. 32p. (J). (gr. k-3). pap. 6.95 (978-0-7358-1142-3(3)) North-South Bks., Inc.

—Snail Started It! 1999. (gr. k-3). lib. bdg. 15.25 (978-0-613-29073-9(9)) Tandem Library Bks.

—Todo Empezo Con Caracol. 1999. (SPA.). (gr. k-3). lib. bdg. 15.25 (978-0-613-29109-5(3)) Tandem Library Bks.

Reider, Katja & Von Roehl, Angela. Todo Empezo Con Caracol. 1999. (978-0-606-17757-3(4)) Tandem Library Bks.

Reiss, Kathryn. Dreadful Sorry. 2004. 352p. (YA). pap. 6.95 (978-0-15-205087-0(6), Harcourt Paperbacks) Harcourt Children's Bks.

Rey, H. A. & Rey, Margret. The Original Curious George. Rey, H. A., illus. 1998. (Curious George Ser.). (Illus.). 64p. (J). (gr. k-3). tchr. ed. 25.00 (978-0-395-92272-9(0)) Houghton Mifflin Co. Trade & Reference Div.

Rey, Margret & Rey, H. A. Curious George & the Puppies. 1998. (Curious George Ser.). (Illus.). 24p. (J). (gr. k-3). pap. 3.95 (978-0-395-91215-7(6)) Houghton Mifflin Co. Trade & Reference Div.

—Curious George's Dream. Vipah Interactive Staff, illus. 1998. (Curious George Ser.). 24p. (J). (gr. k-3). pap. 3.95 (978-0-395-91911-8(8)) Houghton Mifflin Co. Trade & Reference Div.

Reynolds, Cynthia Furlong. Rascal Makes Mischief on Mackinac Island. Brege, Darrin, illus. 2006. (J). (ps-3). 17.95 (978-1-58726-312-5(2), Mitten Pr.) Ann Arbor Media Group, LLC.

Reynolds, Peter. The Best Kid in the World. 2006. (Illus.). (J). (***978-1-4156-9188-5(6)***) Simon & Schuster Children's Publishing.

Reynolds, Peter H. The Best Kid in the World: A SugarLoaf Book. Reynolds, Peter H., illus. 2006. (Illus.). 48p. (J). (ps-2). 15.95 (978-0-689-87624-0(6)) Simon & Schuster Children's Publishing.

Ribke, Simone T. I'll Do It Later. White, Lee, illus. (J). (gr. k-2). 2006. 32p. pap. 4.95 (978-0-516-25019-9(1)); 2005. 31p. 19.50 (978-0-516-24861-5(8)) Scholastic Library Publishing. (Children's Pr.).

Rice, David L. Because Brian Hugged His Mother. 2004. (Sharing Nature with Children Book Ser.). (Illus.). 32p. (YA). (ps-3). 16.95 (978-1-883220-90-7(4)); pap. 7.95 (978-1-883220-89-1(0)) Dawn Pubns.

Robberecht, Thierry. Angry Dragon. Goossens, Philippe, illus. 2004. 32p. (J). (gr. k-3). tchr. ed. 15.00 (978-0-618-47430-1(7), Clarion Bks.) Houghton Mifflin Co. Trade & Reference Div.

Roberts, Barbara A. Phoebe Flower's Adventures: That's What Kids Are For. Sternberg, Kate, illus. 1998. (Phoebe Flower's Adventures Ser.). 68p. (J). (gr. 2-4). pap. 5.95 (978-0-9660366-2-6(X)) Advantage Bks., LLC.

Roberts, David. Pee-Ew! Is That You, Bertie? 2004. (Illus.). 28p. (J). (ps-3). 14.95 (978-0-8109-5014-6(6)) Abrams, Harry N., Inc.

Roberts, Laura Peyton. Get a Life. 1998. (Clearwater Crossing Ser.: No. 1). (YA). (gr. 5-8). (978-0-606-13282-4(1)) Tandem Library Bks.

—Reality Check. 1998. (Clearwater Crossing Ser.: No. 2). (YA). (gr. 5-8). (978-0-606-13283-1(X)) Tandem Library Bks.

Rochelle, Belinda. Jewels. 2000. 32p. (J). pap. (978-0-14-038178-8(3), Puffin) Penguin Group (USA) Inc.

Rochman, Hazel. Leaving Home: Stories. McCampbell, Darlene Z., illus. 1998. 240p. (J). (gr. 7 up). pap. 11.99 (978-0-06-440706-9(3), Harper Trophy) HarperCollins Pubs.

Rockwell, Thomas. How to Fight a Girl. 112p. (J). (gr. 3-5). pap. 3.99 (978-0-8072-1452-7(3), Listening Library) Random Hse. Audio Publishing Group.

Rogers, Karen M. Hand over Hand. Taylor, Piper, illus. 1998. (Think-Kids Book Collection). 16p. (J). (gr. 1-4). pap. 2.95 (978-1-58237-007-1(9)) Creative Thinkers, Inc.

—Let's Find Out. Ramirez, Michael, illus. 1998. (Think-Kids Book Collection). 16p. (J). (gr. 1-4). pap. 2.95 (978-1-58237-003-3(6)) Creative Thinkers, Inc.

—Patterns in My Head. Ramirez, Michael, illus. 1998. (Think-Kids Book Collection). 16p. (J). (gr. 1-4). pap. 2.95 (978-1-58237-019-4(2)) Creative Thinkers, Inc.

—What I Do Best! Taylor, Piper, illus. 1998. (Think-Kids Book Collection). 16p. (J). (gr. 1-4). pap. 2.95 (978-1-58237-001-9(X)) Creative Thinkers, Inc.

Rogers, Karen M. & Rucker, Neima. Can I Try? 1998. (Think-Kids Book Collection). (Illus.). 16p. (J). (gr. 1-4). pap. 2.95 (978-1-58237-016-3(8)) Creative Thinkers, Inc.

Roman, Kathy Blankley, illus. Dume's Roar. unabr. ed. 1998. 14p. (J). (ps-3). 14.95 (978-0-7737-3003-8(6)) Stoddart Kids CAN. *Dist:* Fitzhenry & Whiteside, Ltd.

Root, Phyllis. Aunt Nancy & Old Man Trouble. ed. 2000. (J). (gr. 2). spiral bd. (978-0-616-01775-3(8)) Canadian National Institute for the Blind/Institut National Canadien pour les Aveugles.

Rosenthal, Marc. Phooey! Rosenthal, Marc, illus. 2007. 40p. (J). (ps-3). 16.99 (978-0-06-075248-4(3)); lib. bdg. 17.89 (978-0-06-075249-1(1)) HarperCollins Pubs. (Cotler, Joanna Books).

Rosoff, Meg. Meet Wild Boars. Blackall, Sophie, illus. rev. ed. 2005. 40p. (J). 15.95 (978-0-8050-7488-8(0), Holt, Henry & Co. Bks. For Young Readers) Holt, Henry & Co.

Ross, Pat. M & M & the Bad News Babies. 1999. (Illus.). (J). (gr. 3-6). lib. bdg. 13.00 (978-0-8085-3696-3(6)) Tandem Library Bks.

Ross, Tony. Oscar Got the Blame. Date not set. (Illus.). 24p. (J). pap. (978-0-05-004405-6(2)) Addison-Wesley Longman, Inc.

—Oscar Got the Blame. (Illus.). 32p. (J). pap. 9.99 (978-1-84270-359-5(5)) Andersen GBR. *Dist:* Trafalgar Square Publishing.

—Super Dooper Jezebel. (Illus.). 32p. (J). pap. 9.99 (978-1-84270-096-9(0)) Andersen GBR. *Dist:* Trafalgar Square Publishing.

Rouss, Sylvia A. No Rules for Michael. Simon, Susan, illus. 2003. 24p. (J). (ps-1). pap. 6.95 (978-1-58013-044-8(5)) Kar-Ben Publishing.

Rue, Nancy N. The Trap. 1998. (Christian Heritage Ser.). 208p. (J). (gr. 3-7). pap. (978-1-56179-567-3(4)) Focus on the Family Publishing.

Sanschagrin, Joceline. Eso es Mio! 2004. (Caillou Osa Menor Ser.).Tr. of It's Mine. (SPA & ENG., Illus.). 24p. (J). (ps up). bds. 5.95 (978-1-58728-292-8(5), Creative Publishing International) Quayside.

Sargent, Dave. Hoot Owl. Lenoir, Jane, illus. 2000. (J). lib. bdg. 19.95 (978-1-56763-449-5(4)) Ozark Publishing.

Sargent, Dave & Sargent, Julie. Billy Goat: Don't Brag on Yourself, 56 vols., Vol. 23. Huff, Jeane, illus. 2001. (Animal Pride Ser.: Vol. 23). 36p. (J). lib. bdg. 19.95 (978-1-56763-362-7(5)) Ozark Publishing.

Sargent, Dave & Sargent, Pat. Annie Antelope: Don't Worry, 56 vols. Huff, Jeane, illus. 2001. (Animal Pride Ser.: 21). 36p. (J). lib. bdg. 19.95 (978-1-56763-358-0(7)) Ozark Publishing.

—Chip Chipmunk: Tattletale, 56 vols., 25. Huff, Jeane, illus. 2001. (Animal Pride Ser.: Vol. 25). 36p. (J). lib. bdg. 19.95 (978-1-56763-366-5(8)) Ozark Publishing.

—Cody Coyote: Don't Play Tricks, 56 vols., 26. Huff, Jeane, illus. 2001. (Animal Pride Ser.: Vol. 26). 36p. (J). lib. bdg. 19.95 (978-1-56763-368-9(4)) Ozark Publishing.

—Eli the Elk: I Can! You Can't!, 6 vols., 27. Huff, Jeane, illus. 2001. (Animal Pride Ser.: Vol. 27). 36p. (J). pap. 19.95 (978-1-56763-371-9(4)) Ozark Publishing.

—Fancy Fannie: Show Off!, 56 vols., 28. Huff, Jeane, illus. 2001. (Animal Pride Ser.: Vol. 28). 36p. (J). pap. 19.95 (978-1-56763-373-3(0)) Ozark Publishing.

—Jack Moose: I Need Help, 56 vols., 29. Huff, Jeane, illus. 2001. (Animal Pride Ser.: Vol. 29). 36p. (J). lib. bdg. 19.95 (978-1-56763-374-0(9)) Ozark Publishing.

—Kitty Cougar, 60 vols. Huff, Jeane, illus. 2001. (Animal Pride Ser.: Vol. 30). 36p. (J). pap. 19.95 (978-1-56763-377-1(3)) Ozark Publishing.

—Lennie Leopard: Making New Friends, 56 vols., 50. Lenoir, Jane, illus. 2001. (Animal Pride Ser.: Vol. 50). 36p. (J). lib. bdg. 19.95 (978-1-56763-543-0(1)) Ozark Publishing.

—Leo Lion: Responsibility, 56 vols., 51. Lenoir, Jane, illus. 2001. (Animal Pride Ser.: Vol. 51). 36p. (J). lib. bdg. 19.95 (978-1-56763-541-6(5)) Ozark Publishing.

—Marty Mule: Stubborn Ole Mule!, 56 vols., 31. Huff, Jeane, illus. 2001. (Animal Pride Ser.: Vol. 31). 36p. (J). pap. 6.95 (978-1-56763-379-5(X)) Ozark Publishing.

—Odi Otter: Cheater! Cheater!, 38 vols., 32. Huff, Jeane, illus. 2001. (Animal Pride Ser.: Vol. 32). 36p. (J). pap. 6.95 (978-1-56763-381-8(1)) Ozark Publishing.

—Pansy Packrat: But I Want It!, 56 vols., 33. Huff, Jean Lirley, illus. 2001. (Animal Pride Ser.: Vol. 33). 36p. (J). lib. bdg. 19.95 (978-1-56763-382-5(X)) Ozark Publishing.

—Patty Panda: Disposition, 56 vols., 54. Lenoir, Jane, illus. 2000. (Cherokee Indian Legend Ser.: Vol. 54). 36p. (J). lib. bdg. 19.95 (978-1-56763-549-2(0)) Ozark Publishing.

—Prater the Prairie Dog: I'm a Worrywart!, 36 vols., 34. Huff, Jeane, illus. 2001. (Animal Pride Ser.: Vol. 34). 36p. (J). pap. 6.95 (978-1-56763-385-6(4)) Ozark Publishing.

—Robbie Razorback: Meanie! Meanie!, 56 vols., 35. Huff, Jeane, illus. 2001. (Animal Pride Ser.: 35). 36p. (J). lib. bdg. 19.95 (978-1-56763-386-3(2)) Ozark Publishing.

—Satan the Bull: I Don't Trust Anyone!, 56 vols., 37. Huff, Jeane, illus. 2001. (Animal Pride Ser.: Vol. 37). 36p. (J). lib. bdg. 19.95 (978-1-56763-390-0(0)) Ozark Publishing.

Sargent, Dave, et al. Lennie Leopard: Making New Friends, 17. 50. 2000. (Animal Pride Ser.). (Illus.). 42p. (J). pap. 6.95 (978-1-56763-544-7(X)) Ozark Publishing.

—Leo Lion: Responsibility, 17, 51. 2000. (Animal Pride Ser.: 51). (Illus.). 42p. (J). pap. 6.95 (978-1-56763-542-3(3)) Ozark Publishing.

Schafer, Randy & Schafer, Kathy. Beware of Larry. 2006. 116p. per. 6.99 (978-1-59453-770-7(4), Airleaf Publishing) Airleaf Publishing & Bookselling.

Schembri, Pamela & Catalanotto, Peter. No More Pumpkins. 2007. (Second Grade Friends Ser.). (Illus.). 64p. (J). (gr. 2-5). 15.95 (978-0-8050-7839-8(8)) Holt, Henry & Co.

Schlegel, Paige. What a Mess. Maval Publishing Inc. Staff, illus. 2001. 32p. (J). (ps-3). pap. 7.50 (978-1-884083-90-7(0)) Maval Publishing, Inc.

Schlessinger, Laura. But I Waaannt It! McFeeley, Daniel, illus. 2000. 40p. (J). (ps-2). 15.89 (978-0-06-028958-4(9)); 15.95 (978-0-06-028775-7(6)) HarperCollins Pubs.

Schneider, David. Dillan Mcmillan, Please Eat Your Peas. Shelly, Jeff, Sr., illus. 2007. 36p. (J). pap. 14.95 (***978-0-9744446-4-2(2)***) All About Kids Publishing.

Schneider, Josh. You'll Be Sorry. Schneider, Josh, illus. 2007. (Illus.). 32p. (J). (ps-1). 15.00 (***978-0-618-81932-4(0)***, Clarion Bks.) Houghton Mifflin Co. Trade & Reference Div.

Scholastic, Inc. Staff. Diaper David Plush Diaper David. 2005. (Diaper David Plush Ser.). (J). 9.99 (978-0-439-72696-2(4), Sidekicks TM) Scholastic, Inc.

—No, David! 2005. (No, David! Bookmark Ser.). (J). 6.99 (978-0-439-72689-4(1), Sidekicks TM) Scholastic, Inc.

Scholastic, Inc. Staff & Ford, Bernette G. Don't Hit Me! Grier, Gary, illus. 2004. (Just for You! Ser.). 32p. (gr. k-1). pap. 3.99 (978-0-439-56860-9(9), Teaching Resources) Scholastic, Inc.

Schuette, Sarah L. Soy Bondadosa (I Am Caring) 2003. (Character Values Bilingual Ser.). (ENG & SPA., Illus.). 24p. (J). lib. bdg. 15.93 (978-0-7368-2301-2(8)) Capstone Pr., Inc.

—Soy Cooperativa (I Am Cooperative) 2003. (Character Values Bilingual Ser.). (ENG & SPA., Illus.). 24p. (J). lib. bdg. 15.93 (978-0-7368-2302-9(6)) Capstone Pr., Inc.

—Soy Paciente (I Am Patient) 2003. (Character Values Bilingual Ser.). (ENG & SPA., Illus.). 24p. (J). lib. bdg. 15.93 (978-0-7368-2304-3(2)) Capstone Pr., Inc.

—Soy Respetuoso (I Am Respectful) 2003. (Character Values Bilingual Ser.). (ENG & SPA., Illus.). 24p. (J). lib. bdg. 15.93 (978-0-7368-2305-0(0)) Capstone Pr., Inc.

—Soy Responsable (I Am Responsible) 2003. (Character Values Bilingual Ser.). (ENG & SPA., Illus.). 24p. (J). lib. bdg. 15.93 (978-0-7368-2306-7(9)) Capstone Pr., Inc.

Schwiebert, Pat & DeKlyen, Chuck. Tear Soup: A Recipe for Healing after Loss. Bills, Taylor, illus. 2nd rev. l.t. ed. 2004. 56p. reprint ed. 19.95 (978-0-9615197-6-6(2) , 798) Perinatal Loss.

Scraper, Katherine. The Boy Who Cried Wolf: An Aesop's Fable. 2006. 42.00 (*978-1-4108-6166-5(X)) Benchmark Education Co.

Sebring Lowrey, Janette. The Poky Little Puppy. Tenggren, Gustaf, illus. 2007. 26p. (J). (gr. k-ps). bds. 4.99 (978-0-375-83925-2(9) , Golden Bks.) Random Hse. Children's Bks.

Sebring Lowrey, Janette. The Poky Little Puppy Special Anniversary Edition LGB. Tenggren, Gustaf, illus. 2007. (Special Edition LGB Ser.). 52p. (J). (gr. k-k). 8.99 (*978-0-375-83920-7(8) , Golden Bks.) Random Hse. Children's Bks.

Segal, Lore. Why Mole Shouted & Other Stories. Ruzzier, Sergio, illus. 2004. 40p. (J). 16.00 (978-0-374-38417-3(7) , Farrar, Straus & Giroux (BYR)) Farrar, Straus & Giroux.

Seidler, Tor. Mean Margaret. Agee, Jon, illus. 2001. 176p. (J). (gr. 3 up). pap. 8.99 (978-0-06-441039-7(0) , Harper Trophy) HarperCollins Pubs.

—Mean Margaret. 2001. (gr. 3-6). lib. bdg. 15.25 (978-0-613-44402-6(7)) Tandem Library Bks.

Selway, Martina, illus. The Visitor. 1999. (J). (978-0-7608-3194-6(7)) Sundance/Newbridge Educational Publishing.

—What's That? 1999. (J). (978-0-7608-3195-3(5)) Sundance/Newbridge Educational Publishing.

Seuling, Barbara. Robert Goes to Camp. Brewer, Paul, illus. 2007. (Robert Bks.). 160p. (J). (gr. 2-4). 16.95 (*978-0-8126-2753-4(9)) Cricket Bks.

Seuss, Dr. ¡El Gato con Sombrero Viene de Nuevo! Canetti, Yanitzia, tr. from ENG. 2004. (SPA., Illus.). 63p. (ps-1). 8.99 (978-1-930332-43-0(2)) Lectorum Pubns., Inc.

—The Grinch Meets His Max. 1998. (J). (ps-3). lib. bdg. 11.99 (978-0-679-98836-6(X) , Random Hse. Bks. for Young Readers) Random Hse. Children's Bks.

—How the Grinch Stole Christmas! 1999. (J). 12.99 (978-0-679-89270-0(2) , Random Hse. Bks. for Young Readers) Random Hse. Children's Bks.

Seymour, Tres. The Revelation of Saint Bruce. 1998. (Illus.). 128p. (YA). (gr. 7-12). pap. 16.95 (978-0-531-30109-8(5) , Orchard Bks.) Scholastic, Inc.

Shannon, David. A Bad Case of Stripes. 1998. (Illus.). 32p. (J). (gr. k-4). pap. 16.95 (978-0-590-92997-4(6) , Blue Sky Pr., The) Scholastic, Inc.

—David Gets in Trouble. Shannon, David, illus. 2002. (Illus.). 32p. (J). (ps-1). pap. 15.95 (978-0-439-05022-7(7) , Blue Sky Pr., The) Scholastic, Inc.

—David Gets in Trouble: David Se Mete en Lios. 2004. 32p. (J). pap. 3.99 (978-0-439-54561-7(7)) Scholastic, Inc.

—David Se Mete en Lios. 2003. (SPA.). 32p. (J). 13.95 (978-84-241-8661-6(3)) Everest de Ediciones y Distribucion, S.L. ESP. *Dist:* Lectorum Pubns., Inc.

—David Va Al Colegio. 1999. (SPA.). (gr. k-3). lib. bdg. 16.40 (978-0-613-64483-9(2)) Tandem Library Bks.

—No, David! Shannon, David, illus. 2002. (Illus.). (J). 25.06 (978-0-7587-0132-9(2)) Book Wholesalers, Inc.

—No, David! Mlawer, Teresa, tr. 2002. (SPA., Illus.). (J). pap. 6.95 (978-84-241-8114-7(X) , EV1688) Everest de Ediciones y Distribucion, S.L. ESP. *Dist:* Lectorum Pubns., Inc.

—No, David! 1999. (SPA., Illus.). 32p. (J). (ps-k). 12.95 (978-84-241-5885-9(7) , EV5753) Everest de Ediciones y Distribucion, S.L. ESP. *Dist:* Lectorum Pubns., Inc.

—No, David! Shannon, David, illus. 1998. (Illus.). 36p. (J). (ps-1). 15.95 (978-0-590-93002-4(8) , Blue Sky Pr., The) Scholastic, Inc.

—Oh, David! A Diaper David Book. Shannon, David, illus. 2005. (Oh, David! Ser.). (Illus.). 12p. (J). (gr. 8-10). bds. 6.99 (978-0-439-68881-9(7) , Blue Sky Pr., The) Scholastic, Inc.

—Oh, David: David en Panales. Shannon, David, illus. 2005. (Oh, David! Ser.). (SPA., Illus.). 12p. (J). 6.99 (978-0-439-70973-6(3) , Scholastic en Espanol) Scholastic, Inc.

—The Rain Came Down. Shannon, David, illus. 2000. (Illus.). 32p. (J). (ps-3). pap. 16.95 (978-0-439-05021-0(9)) Scholastic, Inc.

Shaw, Mary. Brady Brady & the Twirlin' Torpedo, 11 vols. Temple, Chuck, illus. l.t. ed. 2004. 32p. (J). per. (978-0-9735557-2-1(6)) Brady Brady, Inc.

—Brady Brady & the Twirlin' Torpedo. Temple, Chuck, illus. 2002. 32p. (ps-3). 4.95 (978-0-7737-6271-8(X)) Stoddart Kids CAN. *Dist:* Fitzhenry & Whiteside, Ltd.

Shea, Pegi Deitz, et al. The Boy & the Spell. Riglietti, Serena, illus. 2007. (Musical Stories Ser.). 36p. (J). (ps-3). 16.95 (978-0-9646010-4-8(4)) Pumpkin Hse., Ltd.

Short, Robbie, illus. I Want One Too! 2003. 32p. (J). lib. bdg. 12.95 (978-0-9729833-2-7(5)) Bubble Gum Pr.

Shubert Sees the Best. 2004. (J). 9.00 (978-1-889609-23-2(4)) Loving Guidance, Inc.

Siegel, Phil. Simon the Daredevil Centipede: He Learned to Skate - & Much, Much More. Caiarelli, Alisa, illus. 1998. 28p. (J). pap. 8.95 (978-0-932991-58-4(0) , Different Bks.) Place In The Woods, The.

Sierra, Judy. 'Twas the Fright Before Christmas. Hillenbrand, Will, illus. 2002. 32p. (J). (gr. k-2). 16.00 (978-0-15-201805-4(0) , Gulliver Bks.) Harcourt Children's Bks.

Silverman, Erica. When the Chickens Went on Strike. Trueman, Matthew, illus. 2005. 32p. (J). pap. 6.99 (978-0-14-240279-5(6) , Puffin) Penguin Group (USA) Inc.

Silverstein, Shel. The Giving Tree. (Illus.). 95.94 (978-0-06-056897-9(6)); 2004. 64p. (J). 18.99 incl. audio compact disk (978-0-06-058675-1(3)) HarperCollins Pubs.

Simmons, Jane. Daisy Says Coo! 2000. (Illus.). 8p. (J). (ps). bds. 5.95 (978-0-316-79764-1(2)) Little Brown & Co.

—Daisy's Favorite Things. Simmons, Jane, illus. 1999. (Illus.). 8p. (J). (ps). bds. 5.95 (978-0-316-79762-7(6)) Little Brown & Co.

Simon, Charnan. A Busy Guy. Bialke, Gary, illus. 1998. (Rookie Readers Ser.). 32p. (J). (gr. 1-2). 19.50 (978-0-516-20396-6(7) , Children's Pr.) Scholastic Library Publishing.

—The Good Bad Day. Handelman, Dorothy, photos by. 1998. (Real Kids Readers Ser.). (Illus.). 32p. (gr. k-2). (J). pap. 4.99 (978-0-7613-2042-5(3)); lib. bdg. 18.90 (978-0-7613-2017-3(2)) Lerner Publishing Group. (Millbrook Pr.).

—A Greedy Little Pig. Ramsey, Marcy Dunn, illus. 2006. (Magic Door to Learning Ser.). 24p. (J). (gr. 1-3). 21.36 (978-1-59296-622-6(5)) Child's World, Inc.

Simpson, Dorothy. A Lesson for Janie. Date not set. 190p. (J). 20.95 (978-0-8488-2617-8(5)) Amereon LTD.

—Matter of Pride. Date not set. 192p. (J). 20.95 (978-0-8488-2619-2(1)) Amereon LTD.

Singer, Marilyn. Solomon Sneezes. 1999. (Growing Tree Ser.). (Illus.). 24p. (J). (ps-3). 9.95 (978-0-694-01748-5(5)) HarperCollins Pubs.

Smith, Jane D. Charlie Is a Chicken. 2000. (Illus.). 176p. (J). (gr. 3-7). pap. 4.95 (978-0-06-440824-0(8)) HarperCollins Pubs.

—Charlie Is a Chicken. 2000. (Illus.). (J). (978-0-606-18682-7(4)) Tandem Library Bks.

Smith, Ronn, adapted by. Nothing but the Truth. 104p. (YA). 6.25 (978-1-58342-084-3(3) , N51) Dramatic Publishing Co.

Sommer, Carl. Miserable Millie. Vignolo, Enrique, illus. (J). 2006. (*978-1-57537-022-4(0)); 2005. (978-1-57537-071-2(9)) Advance Publishing, Inc.

—No Longer a Dilly Dally, 1 bk. 2003. (Another Sommer-Time Story Ser.). (Illus.). 48p. (J). 16.95 incl. audio (978-1-57537-550-2(8)); (gr. 1-4). 16.95 incl. audio compact disk (978-1-57537-501-4(X)) Advance Publishing, Inc.

—Spike the Rebel. Vignolo, Enrique, illus. 2007. (J). (*978-1-57537-023-1(9)); lib. bdg. (*978-1-57537-072-9(7)) Advance Publishing, Inc.

Sommer, Carl. Tied up in Knots. 2003. (Another Sommer-Time Story Ser.). (Illus.). 48p. (J). 14.95 incl. audio compact disk (978-1-57537-503-8(6)); (gr. 1-4). 16.95 incl. audio (978-1-57537-552-6(4)) Advance Publishing, Inc.

Spaht-Gill, Janie. Pigouts. Reese, Bob, illus. 1998. 24p. (J). (ps-3). 5.95 (978-0-89868-317-2(3)) ARO Publishing Co.

Spinelli, Jerry. Blue Ribbon Blues. 1998. (Tooter Tale Ser.). 10.79 (978-0-606-13053-0(5)) Tandem Library Bks.

Stanley, Mandy, illus. My Favorite Things. 1998. 5p. (J). pap. 4.99 (978-1-58048-050-5(0)) Sandvik Publishing.

Staunton, Ted. Morgan's Secret. Slavin, Bill, illus. 2000. (First Novels Ser.: Vol. 15). 58p. (J). (gr. 1-5). (978-0-88780-495-3(0)) Formac Publishing Co., Ltd. CAN. *Dist:* Casemate Pubs. & Bk. Distributors, LLC.

Stein, David Ezra. Ned's New Friend. Stein, David Ezra, illus. 2007. (Cowboy Ned & Andy Ser.). 32p. (J). (ps-1). 14.99 (978-1-4169-2490-6(6) , Simon & Schuster Children's Publishing) Simon & Schuster Children's Publishing.

Stephens, Helen. Poochie-Poo. 2003. (Illus.). 32p. (J). (ps-3). 14.95 (978-0-385-75012-7(9) , Fickling, David Bks.) Random Hse. Children's Bks.

Stevenson, James. Don't Make Me Laugh. 2003. (ps-2). lib. bdg. 14.10 (978-0-613-59603-9(X)) Tandem Library Bks.

—No Laughing, No Smiling, No Giggling: Is That Understood? 2004. (Illus.). 32p. (J). 16.00 (978-0-374-31829-1(8) , Farrar, Straus & Giroux (BYR)) Farrar, Straus & Giroux.

Stevenson, Nancy, illus. The Zubble-Wump! 1999. (Jellybean Bks.). 24p. (J). (ps-k). 1.99 (978-0-375-80233-1(9) , Random Hse. Bks. for Young Readers) Random Hse. Children's Bks.

—The Zumble-Wump! 1999. (Jellybean Bks.). 24p. (J). (ps-k). lib. bdg. 7.99 (978-0-375-90233-8(3) , Random Hse. Bks. for Young Readers) Random Hse. Children's Bks.

Stewart, Colina. Wild Flower. 2004. (Illus.). 56p. (J). (gr. 3-8). 5.95 (978-1-57197-235-4(8)) Pentland Pr., Inc.

Stewart, Kymberly M. Play It Again, Rachel. 2003. 74p. (J). pap. 10.95 (978-0-9740653-0-4(7)) Neema's Children Literature Assn., Inc.

Stine, R.L. Stepsister. 2005. 165p. (J). lib. bdg. 13.00 (*978-1-4242-0998-9(6)) Fitzgerald Bks.

Stolls, Amy. Palms to the Ground. 2005. 256p. (YA). 17.00 (978-0-374-35731-3(5) , Farrar, Straus & Giroux (BYR)) Farrar, Straus & Giroux.

Suen, Anastasia. Cutting in Line Isn't Fair! Ebbeler, Jeffrey, illus. 2007. (Main Street School - Kids with Character Ser.). 32p. (J). (ps-4). lib. bdg. 27.07 (*978-1-60270-029-1(X) , Looking Glass Library) Magic Wagon.

—Show Some Respect. Ebbeler, Jeffrey, illus. 2007. (Main Street School - Kids with Character Ser.). 32p. (J). (ps-4). lib. bdg. 27.07 (*978-1-60270-033-8(8) , Looking Glass Library) Magic Wagon.

Svendsen, Mark. Circus Carnivore. Redlich, Ben, illus. 2006. 40p. (J). (gr. 3-5). 16.00 (978-0-618-56328-9(8)) Houghton Mifflin Co. Trade & Reference Div.

Sydor, Colleen. Smarty Pants. Pavanel, Jane, ed. Langlois, Suzane, illus. 1999. 24p. (J). (ps-3). (978-1-894222-06-8(7)) Lobster Pr.

Sykes, Julie. I Don't Want to Take a Bath! Warnes, Tim, illus. 1998. (J). (ps-2). 32p. pap. 5.95 (978-1-888444-36-0(3) , 21036); 14p. bds. 6.95 (978-1-888444-34-6(7) , 21300) Little Tiger Pr.

Tada, Joni Eareckson. I'll Be with You Always. Nelson, Craig, illus. 2004. 32p. (gr. 8-12). 14.99 (978-1-58134-000-6(1)) Crossway Bks.

Talley, Linda. Aloha Potter! - hardcover Book. Chase, Andra, illus. 2004. 30p. (J). (978-1-55942-200-0(9)) Marsh Media.

Tashjian, Janet. Multiple Choice. 1999. (J). (gr. 5-10). 16.95 (978-0-8050-6114-7(2) , Holt, Henry & Co. Bks. For Young Readers) Holt, Henry & Co.

—Multiple Choice. 2001. 192p. (YA). (gr. 5-9). pap. 4.99 (978-0-439-17484-8(8)) Scholastic, Inc.

Taylor, Thomas. The Loudest Roar. 2003. (Illus.). (J). pap. (978-0-439-50131-6(8) , Levine, Arthur A. Bks.) Scholastic, Inc.

Taylor, Thomas, illus. The Loudest Roar. 2003. 32p. (J). 15.95 (978-0-439-50130-9(X) , Levine, Arthur A. Bks.) Scholastic, Inc.

Teal, Joyce Willard. The Point System. 1998. (Illus.). (J). pap. 8.80 (978-1-56763-399-3(4)); lib. bdg. 25.25 (978-1-56763-398-6(6)) Ozark Publishing.

That's the Way It Crumbles, Cookie. (Full House Ser.). 96p. (J). (gr. 4-6). pap. 2.95 (978-0-938753-77-3(0) , PP5) Parachute Publishing, LLC.

Think-Kids Book Collection. 1998. (Illus.). 16p. (J). (gr. 1-4). pap. 2.95 (978-1-58237-000-2(1)) Creative Thinkers, Inc.

Thomassie, Tynia. Feliciana Feydra LeRoux Meets d'Loup Garou: A Cajun Tall Tale. Smith, Cat Bowman, illus. 1998. 32p. (J). (ps-3). 15.95 (978-0-316-84133-7(1)) Little Brown & Co.

—Feliciana Meets D'Loup Garou: A Cajun Tall Tale. Bowman Smith, Cat, illus. 2005. 32p. (J). (ps-3). 15.95 (978-1-58980-287-2(X)) Pelican Publishing Co., Inc.

Thompson, Kay. Eloise: The Absolutely Essential. Knight, Hilary, illus. 50th anniv. ed. 2005. (Eloise Ser.). 80p. (J). (ps-3). 19.95 (978-1-4169-0823-4(4)) Simon & Schuster Children's Publishing.

Thoughts Staff. Lucky Clayman's Story. 2005. 16p. 9.99 (978-1-4116-2217-3(0)) Lulu.com.

Tierno, Susan F. The Best-Ever Day. Ramirez, Michael, illus. 1998. (Think-Kids Book Collection). 16p. (J). (gr. 1-4). pap. 2.95 (978-1-58237-009-5(5)) Creative Thinkers, Inc.

—It Was Just Another Problem. Ramirez, Michael, illus. 1998. (Think-Kids Book Collection). 16p. (J). (gr. 1-4). pap. 2.95 (978-1-58237-008-8(7)) Creative Thinkers, Inc.

—The Plan. Ramirez, Michael, illus. 1998. (Think-Kids Book Collection). 16p. (J). (gr. 1-4). pap. 2.95 (978-1-58237-006-4(0)) Creative Thinkers, Inc.

—That's a Tough Team to Beat! Ramirez, Michael, illus. 1998. (Think-Kids Book Collection). 16p. (J). (gr. 1-4). pap. 2.95 (978-1-58237-018-7(4)) Creative Thinkers, Inc.

Tough Choices. 2002. (Illus.). (J). pap. (978-0-7398-5107-4(1)) Steck-Vaughn.

Trent, John T. The Treasure Tree: Helping Kids Get along & Enjoy Each Other. 1998. (Illus.). 112p. (J). (ps-3). 15.99 (978-0-8499-5849-6(0)) Nelson, Thomas Inc.

Trouble in the Barkers' Class. 2005. (J). 27.95 incl. audio (978-0-8045-6935-4(5)); 29.95 incl. audio compact disk (978-0-8045-4134-3(5)) Spoken Arts, Inc.

Trudel, Sylvain. Une Saison au Paradis. 2002. (Premier Roman Ser.). (Illus.). 64p. (J). (gr. 2-5). pap. (978-2-89021-353-1(6)) Diffusion du livre Mirabel.

Trupin/Nascimbeni, Nick/Barbara. Sorry Sam. 2006. (Illus.). 32p. (J). lib. bdg. 9.00 (*978-1-4242-0884-5(X)) Fitzgerald Bks.

Tuchman, Gail. Simba's Pouncing Lessons, Level 2. 1998. (Disney's First Readers Ser.: No. 14). (Illus.). 32p. (J). (gr. 1-3). pap. 2.95 (978-0-7868-4228-5(8)) Disney Pr.

Turner, Nancy Byrd. When Young Melissa Sweeps. Santini, Debrah L., illus. 1998. 30p. (J). (ps-3). 15.95 (978-1-56145-157-9(6)) Peachtree Pubs., Ltd.

Turpin, Nick. Samuel, lo siento, Level P. NASCIMBENI, Barbara, illus. 2006. (Lightning Readers Ser.). 32p. (J). pap. 3.95 (978-0-7696-4216-1(0) , Gingham Dog Pr.) School Specialty Publishing.

Tuttle, Cameron. Be a Bad Girl Journal. Bettag, Susannah, illus. 2001. 144p. 12.95 (978-0-8118-3191-8(4)) Chronicle Bks. LLC.

Twain, Mark. The Spelling Bee. Bates, Amy, illus. 2007. (Adventures of Tom Sawyer Ser.: Bk. 4). 32p. (J). pap. 3.95 (978-1-4027-4269-9(X)) Sterling Publishing Co., Inc.

Tyrrell, Melissa. Pinocchio. McMullen, Nigel, illus. 2005. (Fairytale Friends Ser.: Vol. 7). 12p. (J). (ps-k). bds. 5.95 (978-1-58117-151-8(X) , Intervisual/Piggy Toes) Dalmatian Pr.

Ungerer, Tomi. Christmas Eve at the Mellops' Ungerer, Tomi, illus. 1998. (Illus.). 32p. (J). (gr. k-4). pap. 5.95 (978-1-57098-227-9(9)) Rinehart, Roberts Pubs.

—Keine Kuss fur Mutler. 2000. Tr. of No Kiss for Mother. (GER.). (J). pap. 15.95 (978-3-257-25018-3(5)) Diogenes Verlag AG CHE. *Dist:* Distribooks, Inc.

—No Kiss for Mother. 1998. (Illus.). 40p. (J). (ps-3). pap. 5.95 (978-1-57098-208-8(2)) Rinehart, Roberts Pubs.

Vail, Rachel. The Horrible Play Date. Bjorkman, Steve, illus. 2002. (Mama Rex & T Ser.). 32p. (J). pap. 14.95 (978-0-439-40627-7(7)); pap. 4.99 (978-0-439-28335-9(3)) Scholastic, Inc. (Orchard Bks.).

Van Laan, Nancy. Tickle Tum! Pons, Bernadette, illus. 2005. (Stories to Go! Ser.). 32p. (J). 4.99 (978-1-4169-0836-4(6) , Aladdin) Simon & Schuster Children's Publishing.

Vande Velde, Vivian. Three Good Deeds. (Illus.). 160p. 2007. (YA). pap. 5.95 (*978-0-15-205455-7(3) , Magic Carpet Bks.); 2005. (J). (gr. 3-7). 16.00 (978-0-15-205382-6(4)) Harcourt Children's Bks.

Viorst, Judith. Alexander, Who's Not (Do You Hear Me? I Mean It!) Going to Move. 1999. (Alexander Ser.). (J). (gr. k-3). pap. 23.24 incl. audio (978-0-7887-3789-3(9) , 41033) Recorded Bks., LLC.

—Alexander, Who's Not (Do You Hear Me? I Mean It!) Going to Move. Glasser, Robin Preiss, illus. 1998. (Alexander Ser.). (J). (gr. k-3). 12.79 (978-0-606-14146-8(4)) Tandem Library Bks.

Viorst, Judith. Nobody Here but Me. Davenier, Christine, illus. 2008. (J). (*978-0-374-35540-1(1)) Farrar, Straus & Giroux.

Wang, Margaret C. When I Grow Up: A Touch & Feel Book. Gevry, Claudine, illus. 2005. 12p. (J). bds. 10.95 (978-1-58117-423-6(3) , Intervisual/Piggy Toes) Dalmatian Pr.

Wangerin, Walter, Jr. The Crying for a Vision: A Novel. 2003. 346p. 16.95 (978-1-55725-342-2(0)) Paraclete Pr., Inc.

Wardlaw, Lee. 101 Ways to Bug Your Parents. (gr. k-3). 2005. 208p. pap. 5.99 (978-0-14-240340-2(7) , Puffin); 2002. 160p. (J). pap. (978-0-14-038739-1(0) , Putnam Juvenile) Penguin Group (USA) Inc.

—101 Ways to Bug Your Parents. 1998. (J). (978-0-606-13076-9(4)) Tandem Library Bks.

—101 Ways to Bug Your Teacher. 256p. 2005. (gr. 5-7). pap. 6.99 (978-0-14-240331-0(8) , Puffin); 2004. (Illus.). (J). (gr. 4). 16.99 (978-0-8037-2658-1(9) , Dial) Penguin Group (USA) Inc.

Warner, Gertrude Chandler. Sam Makes Trouble. 2002. (gr. k-3). lib. bdg. 11.80 (978-0-613-70863-0(6)) Tandem Library Bks.

—Sam Makes Trouble, Vol. 9. Life, Kay, illus. 2004. (Adventures of Benny & Watch: Vol. 9). 32p. (J). (ps-2). pap. 3.95 (978-0-8075-0646-2(X)) Whitman, Albert & Co.

Watson, Richard Jesse. The Boy Who Went Ape. Watson, Benjamin James, illus. 2008. (J). pap. (*978-0-590-47966-0(0)) Blue Sky Pr.

Watson, Stephanie. Elvis & Olive. 2008. 240p. (J). 15.99 (*978-0-545-03183-7(4) , Scholastic) Scholastic, Inc.

Weeks, Sarah. If I Were a Lion. Solomon, Heather M., illus. 2004. 40p. (J). 16.99 (978-0-689-84836-0(6) , Atheneum) Simon & Schuster Children's Publishing.

Wells, Rosemary. Bubble Gum Radar. Wheeler, Jody & Nez, John, illus. 2002. (Yoko & Friends School Days Ser.: Bk. 9). 32p. (J). (gr. k-2). pap. 3.99 (978-0-7868-1528-9(0) , Volo) Hyperion Bks. for Children.

—Julieta, Estate Quieta! (SPA.). 43p. (J). 5.50 (978-84-372-1523-5(4)) Santillana USA Publishing Co., Inc.

—Leave Well Enough Alone. 2002. 224p. (J). pap. 5.99 (978-0-14-230149-4(3) , Puffin) Penguin Group (USA) Inc.

—Noisy Nora. 2000. (gr. k-3). lib. bdg. 15.30 (978-0-8085-3632-1(X)) Tandem Library Bks.

—When No One Was Looking. 2000. (Illus.). 224p. (YA). (gr. 5-9). pap. 5.99 (978-0-14-130973-6(3) , Puffin) Penguin Group (USA) Inc.

—When No One Was Looking. 2001. (YA). 21.75 (978-0-8446-7193-2(2)) Smith, Peter Pub., Inc.

—When No One Was Looking. 2000. (978-0-606-20380-7(X)) Tandem Library Bks.

Welsh, David J. The Boy Who Burned Too Brightly: A Modern Allegory. Bolt, Brandon, illus. 2001. 67p. 19.95 (978-0-9656442-0-4(0)) Alisam Pr.

Weninger, Brigitte. Dany, Mira lo Que Has Hecho! 1999. (gr. k-3). (SPA.). lib. bdg. 15.25 (978-0-613-81373-0(1)); 13.75 (978-0-606-17631-6(4)) Tandem Library Bks.

—What Have You Done, Davy? 1999. (gr. k-3). lib. bdg. 15.25 (978-0-613-37172-8(0)) Tandem Library Bks.

Weston, Carrie. If a Chicken Stayed for Supper. Fatus, Sophie, illus. 2007. 32p. (J). (ps-3). 16.95 (978-0-8234-2067-4(1)) Holiday Hse., Inc.

Weyland, Jack. Ashley & Jen. 2000. (Illus.). 287p. (YA). 16.95 (978-1-57345-803-0(1)) Deseret Bk. Co.

Weyn, Suzanne. The Grouchiest Lovey. Brannon, Tom, illus. 1999. pap. 3.25 (978-0-375-80134-1(0) , Random Hse. Bks. for Young Readers) Random Hse. Children's Bks.

—Happy Grouchy Day. Lund, John, illus. 1999. (J). lib. bdg. 8.99 (978-0-375-90133-1(7) , Random Hse. Bks. for Young Readers) Random Hse. Children's Bks.

Wheeler, Lisa. Old Cricket. Goembel, Ponder, illus. 2006. 32p. (J). reprint ed. pap. 6.99 (978-1-4169-1855-4(8) , Aladdin) Simon & Schuster Children's Publishing.

Wheeler, Lisa & Goembel, Ponder. Old Cricket. 2003. (Illus.). 32p. (J). (ps-2). 17.99 (978-0-689-84510-9(3) , Atheneum/Richard Jackson Bks.) Simon & Schuster Children's Publishing.

Whybrow, Ian. Badness for Beginners: A Little Wolf & Smellybreff Adventure. 2005. (Illus.). 32p. (J). (ps-ps). 16.95 (978-1-57505-861-0(8) , Carolrhoda Bks.) Lerner Publishing Group.

—Little Wolf's Book of Badness. Ross, Tony, illus. (Middle Grade Fiction Ser.). 132p. (gr. 3-6). 2005. 14.95 (978-1-57505-410-0(8)); 2003. (J). pap. 6.95 (978-1-57505-550-3(3)) Lerner Publishing Group.

—Little Wolf's Book of Badness. 2000. (gr. 3-6). lib. bdg. 15.25 (978-0-613-68104-9(5)) Tandem Library Bks.

—Lobito Aprende a Ser Malo (Little Wolf's Book of Badness) Azaola, Miguel, tr. Ross, Tony, illus. 2007. (Ediciones Lerner Single Titles Ser.). (SPA.). (J). (gr. 3-7). pap. 6.95 (*978-0-8225-8644-9(4) , Ediciones Lerner) Lerner Publishing Group.

Whybrow, Ian. Whiff! 1999. (Illus.). 32p. (J). (978-0-385-41023-6(9) , Corgi) Transworld Publishers Ltd.

Wikler, Linda. Alfonse, Where Are You? 1998. (J). (978-0-606-13113-1(2)) Tandem Library Bks.

Willey, Margaret. North Woods Three Bears. Solomon, Heather, illus. 2008. 40p. (J). (***978-1-4169-2494-4(9))*** Simon & Schuster Children's Publishing.

Williams, Carol Ann. Loud Lily. Mai-Wyss, Tatjana, illus. 2008. 32p. (J). (ps-3). 16.99 (978-0-399-24277-9(5) , Putnam Juvenile) Penguin Group (USA) Inc.

Williams, Heather. Nellie Oleson Meets Laura Ingalls. 2007. (Little House Ser.). 240p. (J). lib. bdg. 16.89 (***978-0-06-124249-6(7));*** (gr. 3-7). 15.99 (***978-0-06-124248-9(9))*** HarperCollins Pubs.

Williams, Karen Lynn. One Thing I'm Good At. Date not set. (J). (gr. 3-7). pap. 4.99 (978-0-380-73276-0(9)) HarperCollins Pubs.

Willis, Jeanne. Be Gentle, Python! Birchall, Mark, illus. 2005. (Picture Bks.). 28p. (J). (gr. k-2). 7.95 (978-1-57505-508-4(2)) Lerner Publishing Group.

—Be Quiet, Parrot! Birchall, Mark, illus. 2005. (Picture Bks.). 32p. (J). (gr. k-2). 7.25 (978-1-57505-492-6(2)) Lerner Publishing Group.

—No Biting, Puma! Birchall, Mark, illus. 2005. (Picture Bks.). 28p. (J). (gr. k-2). 7.25 (978-1-57505-509-1(0)) Lerner Publishing Group.

Willner-Pardo, Gina. Spider Storch's Music Mess. Sharratt, Nick, illus. 1998. 80p. (J). (gr. 2-5). pap. 3.95 (978-0-8075-7584-0(4)); lib. bdg. 11.95 (978-0-8075-7583-3(6)) Whitman, Albert & Co.

Winkler, Henry & Oliver, Lin. My Secret Life as a Ping-Pong Wizard. 2006. (Hank Zipzer Ser.: No. 9). (J). (gr. 3-8). 24.21 (978-1-59961-110-5(4)) Spotlight.

Wisler, G. Clifton. Caleb's Choice. 1998. (Puffin Novel Ser.). 160p. (J). (gr. 5-9). pap. 4.99 (978-0-14-038256-3(9) , Puffin) Penguin Group (USA) Inc.

Wojtowycz, David. Dudley Helps Out! 2000. (Illus.). 14p. (J). (ps-3). pap. 7.95 (978-1-888444-71-1(1)) Little Tiger Pr.

Wolff, Virginia Euwer. Make Lemonade. unabr. ed. 2004. (Young Adult Cassette Librariestm Ser.). 200p. (J). (gr. 7 up). pap. 36.00 incl. audio (978-0-8072-0793-2(4) , S YA 348 SP, Listening Library) Random Hse. Audio Publishing Group.

Wood, Audrey. Silly Sally. Wood, Audrey, illus. 2002. (Illus.). (J). 23.40 (978-0-7587-3621-5(5)) Book Wholesalers, Inc.

—Silly Sally. braille ed. 2004. (J). (gr. 1). spiral bd., bds. (978-0-616-01864-4(9)) Canadian National Institute for the Blind/Institut National Canadien pour les Aveugles.

—Silly Sally. 1999. (Illus.). 30p. (J). (ps). bds. 6.95 (978-0-15-201990-7(1) , Red Wagon Bks.) Harcourt Children's Bks.

Woods, Cindy Smith. Once Inside A Storybook... Good Morals in Short Stories to Encourage Correct Behavior in the Little Ones in Your Life. 2006. 59p. pap. 12.95 (978-1-4241-2905-8(2)) PublishAmerica, Inc.

Wooldridge, Frosty. Strike Three! Take Your Base. Petri, Freeman, illus. 2001. 160p. (YA). (gr. 6-12). pap. 6.95 (978-1-930093-07-2(1)) Brookfield Reader, Inc., The.

—Strike Three! Take Your Base. Freeman, Pietri, illus. 2001. 160p. (YA). (gr. 6-12). 16.95 (978-1-930093-01-0(2)) Brookfield Reader, Inc., The.

Wynne-Jones, Tim. Last Piece of Sky. (J). pap. 5.99 (978-0-88899-181-2(9)) Groundwood Bks. CAN. *Dist:* Transition Vendor.

Yokococo. Be Good Girls! 2005. (Illus.). 32p. (J). (gr. k-k). 15.95 (978-0-7696-4434-9(1) , Gingham Dog Pr.) School Specialty Publishing.

Yolen, Jane. How Do Dinosaurs Go to School? Teague, Mark, illus. 2007. 40p. (J). (ps-2). 16.99 (***978-0-439-02081-7(6))*** Scholastic, Inc.

—How Do Dinosaurs Play with Their Friends? Teague, Mark, illus. 2006. 12p. (J). bds. 6.99 (978-0-439-85654-6(X) , Blue Sky Pr., The) Scholastic, Inc.

—How Do Dinosaurs Play with Their Friends (Como Juegan los Dinosaurios con Sus Amigos) 2006. 12p. (J). bds. 6.99 (978-0-439-87193-8(X) , Scholastic en Espanol) Scholastic, Inc.

—How Do Dinosaurs Say Good Night? Teague, Mark, illus. 2000. 40p. (J). (ps up). pap. 15.95 (978-0-590-31681-1(8) , Blue Sky Pr., The) Scholastic, Inc.

—How Do Dinosaurs Say Good Night? Book & Plush Set. 2002. (Illus.). (J). 25.04 (978-0-7587-2759-6(3)) Book Wholesalers, Inc.

—How Do Dinosaurs Say Good Night? Book & Plush Set. 2004. (J). (ps-1). 24.95 incl. audio (978-1-55592-099-9(3)) Weston Woods Studios, Inc.

Zarzour, Kim. Schoolyard Bully: How to Cope with Conflict & Raise an Assertive Child. 1999. 270p. (J). pap. (978-0-00-638519-6(2)) HarperCollins Canada, Ltd.

Ziefert, Harriet. There Was a Little Girl, She Had a Little Curl. 2006. (Illus.). 36p. (J). 15.95 (978-1-59354-161-3(9)) Blue Apple Bks.

Ziefert, Harriet & Bolam, Emily. Time Out, Buzzy. 2006. (Illus.). 32p. (J). 9.95 (978-1-59354-167-5(8)) Blue Apple Bks.

Zoehfeld, Kathleen Weidner. Be Patient, Pooh. 2000. (Illus.). 32p. (J). (ps-k). 12.99 (978-0-7868-3250-7(9)) Disney Pr.

BEHAVIOR PROBLEMS IN CHILDREN

see Problem Children

BEIJING (CHINA)

Barber, Nicola. Beijing. 2004. (Great Cities of the World Ser.). (Illus.). 48p. (J). (gr. 5 up). pap. 11.95 (978-0-8368-5188-5(9)); lib. bdg. 30.00 (978-0-8368-5028-4(9)) Stevens, Gareth Inc. (World Almanac Library).

Furstinger, Nancy. Beijing. 2005. (Cities Ser.). (Illus.). 32p. (J). (gr. k-6). lib. bdg. 22.78 (978-1-59197-853-4(X)) ABDO Publishing Co.

Hodge, Susie. The Forbidden City. 2005. (Places in History Ser.). (Illus.). 48p. (J). pap. (978-0-8368-5817-4(4)); lib. bdg. 30.00 (978-0-8368-5810-5(7)) Stevens, Gareth Inc. (World Almanac Library).

Holmes, Burton. Peking. Schlesinger, Arthur M., Jr. & Isreal, Fred L., eds. 1999. (World 100 Years Ago Ser.). (Illus.). 144p. (YA). (gr. 4-7). lib. bdg. 29.95 (978-0-7910-4666-1(4) , Chelsea Hse.) Facts On File, Inc.

—Peking. Israel, Fred L. & Schlesinger, Arthur M., Jr., eds. 1998. (World 100 Years Ago Ser.). (Illus.). 132p. (YA). (gr. 5 up). lib. bdg. 19.95 (978-0-7910-4667-8(2) , Chelsea Hse.) Facts On File, Inc.

Knox, Barbara. Forbidden City: China's Imperial Palace. 2006. (Castles, Palaces, & Tombs Ser.). (Illus.). 32p. (J). lib. bdg. 25.27 (978-1-59716-070-4(9) , 1251394) Bearport Publishing Co., Inc.

Morley, Jacqueline. You Wouldn't Want to Be in the Forbidden City! A Sheltered Life You'd Rather Avoid. (You Wouldn't Want to... : History of the World Ser.). 32p. (J). 2008. pap. 9.95 (***978-0-531-16901-8(4)*** , Watts, Franklin); 2007. spiral bd. 29.00 (***978-0-531-18749-4(7)*** , Children's Pr.) Scholastic Library Publishing.

Pellegrini, Nancy. Beijing. Cooper, Adrian, photos by. 2007. (Global Cities Ser.). (Illus.). 64p. (J). (gr. 5-8). 30.00 (978-0-7910-8848-7(0) , Chelsea Hse.) Facts On File, Inc.

BELDEN, TRIXIE (FICTITIOUS CHARACTER)—FICTION

Campbell, Julie. Mystery in Arizona, Vol. 6. Stevens, Mary, illus. 2004. (Trixie Belden Ser.: No. 6). 272p. (J). (gr. 3-7). 6.99 (978-0-375-82741-9(2) , Random Hse. Bks. for Young Readers) Random Hse. Children's Bks.

—The Red Trailer Mystery. Stevens, Mary, illus. 2003. (Trixie Belden Ser.: No. 2). 272p. (J). (gr. 3-7). 6.99 (978-0-375-82411-1(0) , Random Hse. Bks. for Young Readers) Random Hse. Children's Bks.

—The Secret of the Mansion. Stevens, Mary, illus. 2003. (Trixie Belden Ser.: No. 1). 272p. (J). (gr. 3-7). 6.99 (978-0-375-82412-8(X) , Random Hse. Bks. for Young Readers) Random Hse. Children's Bks.

Kenny, Kathryn. The Black Jacket Mystery. 2004. (Trixie Belden Ser.: Vol. 8). (Illus.). 272p. (gr. 3-7). lib. bdg. 9.99 (978-0-375-92979-3(7) , Random Hse. Bks. for Young Readers) Random Hse. Children's Bks.

—The Black Jacket Mystery. Frame, Paul, illus. 2004. (Trixie Belden Ser.: Vol. 8). 272p. (J). (gr. 3-7). 6.99 (978-0-375-82979-6(2) , Random Hse. Bks. for Young Readers) Random Hse. Children's Bks.

—The Mysterious Code. 2004. (Trixie Belden Ser.: No. 7). (Illus.). 272p. (J). (gr. 3-7). lib. bdg. 9.99 (978-0-375-92978-6(9) , Random Hse. Bks. for Young Readers) Random Hse. Children's Bks.

—The Mysterious Code, Vol. 7. Frame, Paul, illus. 2004. (Trixie Belden Ser.: Vol. 7). 272p. (J). (gr. 3-7). 6.99 (978-0-375-82978-9(4) , Random Hse. Bks. for Young Readers) Random Hse. Children's Bks.

—The Mystery on the Mississippi. 2006. (Illus.). 256p. (J). (gr. 3-7). lib. bdg. 9.99 (978-0-375-93055-3(8)); (Trixie Belden Ser.: No. 15). 6.99 (978-0-375-83055-6(3)) Random Hse. Children's Bks. (Random Hse. Bks. for Young Readers).

BELGIAN CONGO

see Congo (Democratic Republic)

BELGIUM

Burgan, Michael. Belgium. 2000. (Enchantment of the World, Second Ser.). (Illus.). 144p. (J). (gr. 5-9). 36.00 (978-0-516-21006-3(8) , Children's Pr.) Scholastic Library Publishing.

Mason, Antony. Top 10 Brussels & Antwerp Bruges, Ghent. 2004. (Eyewitness Travel Guides). (Illus.). 144p. (gr. 12). pap. 12.00 (978-0-7566-0029-7(4)) Dorling Kindersley Publishing, Inc.

Pateman, Robert & Elliot, Mark. Belgium. 2nd ed. 2006. (Cultures of the World Ser.). 144p. (J). lib. bdg. 39.93 (978-0-7614-2059-0(2) , Benchmark Bks.) Cavendish, Marshall Corp.

Van Cleaf, Kristin. Belgium. 2007. (Countries Set VI Ser.). (Illus.). 40p. (J). (gr. k-6). lib. bdg. 24.21 (***978-1-59928-780-5(3)*** , Checkerboard Library) ABDO Publishing Co.

Walker, Ida. Belgium. 2006. (European Union Ser.). (Illus.). 88p. (J). (gr. 5 up). lib. bdg. (978-1-4222-0040-7(X) , 1247982) Mason Crest Pubs.

World Book, Inc. Staff, contrib. by. Christmas in Belgium. 2004. (Christmas Around the World from World Book Ser.). (Illus.). 1760p. (gr. 2-8). 24.95 (978-0-7166-0864-6(2) , 20114) World Bk., Inc.

BELGIUM—FICTION

Brandeis, Madeline. Little Philippe of Belgium. 2005. reprint ed. pap. 22.95 (978-1-4179-3302-0(X)) Kessinger Publishing, LLC.

Breslin, Theresa. Remembrance. 2004. 304p. (YA). (gr. 7). mass mkt. 6.50 (978-0-440-23778-5(5) , Laurel Leaf) Random Hse. Children's Bks.

De La Rame, Louisa. Dog of Flanders. 2007. pap. 87.99 (***978-1-4280-5277-2(1))*** IndyPublish.com.

Farenhorst, Christine. A Cup of Cold Water: The Compassion of Nurse Edith Cavell. 2007. (J). pap. (***978-1-59638-026-4(8))*** P & R Publishing.

Goscinny, René. Asterix in Belgium. Uderzo, Albert, illus. 2005. 48p. pap. 9.95 (978-0-7528-6650-5(8)) Orion Bks. Ltd. GBR. *Dist:* Sterling Publishing Co., Inc.

Moeyaert, Bart. Brothers: The Oldest, the Quietest, the Realest, the Farthest, the Nicest, the Fastest, & I. Boeke, Wanda, tr. from DUT. 2005. (Illus.). 164p. (YA). (gr. 3-7). 16.95 (978-1-932425-18-5(7) , Lemniscaat) Boyds Mills Pr.

Ouida. A Dog of Flanders. 2000. (J). 19.95 (978-0-8488-2957-5(3)) Amereon LTD.

Perkins, Lucy Fitch. The Belgian Twins. 2004. reprint ed. pap. 15.95 (978-1-4191-5388-4(9)); pap. 1.99 (978-1-4192-5388-1(3)) Kessinger Publishing, LLC.

Simoen, Jan. What about Anna? Nieuwenhuizen, John, tr. from DUT. 2002. (Illus.). 264p. (YA). (gr. 7 up). 16.95 (978-0-8027-8808-5(4)) Walker & Co.

Van Heerde, Gerrit. The Man with the Red Beard. Van Bergen, Jantien, illus. 2002. (J). (978-0-9579517-0-9(1)) Inheritance Pubns.

BELIEF AND DOUBT

Byers, Carla Rae. Finding My Dream! The Magic of Believing. Kepler, Kit, ed. 2000. Vol. 5. (Illus.). 18p. (gr. 3 up). 7.95 (978-1-930910-00-3(2)) Heyokah Publishing Co.

Custom Curricul Staff. Can I Know What to Believe? 2004. (Custom Curriculum Ser.). 256p. pap., pap. 19.99 (978-0-7814-4089-9(0) , 0781440890) Cook, David C. Publishing Co.

Plantingo, Cornelius, Jr. A Sure Thing: What We Believe & Why. 2001. (Discover Ser.). 174p. (gr. 8-10). tchr. ed. 17.25 (978-1-56212-780-0(2) , 120315, Faith Alive Christian Resources) CRC Pubns.

Zizek, Slavoj. On Belief. 2001. (Thinking in Action Ser.). (Illus.). 176p. 19.95 (978-0-415-25532-5(5)) Routledge.

BELL, ALEXANDER GRAHAM, 1847-1922

Alexander Graham Bell, 6 vols. (gr. 2-5). 36.95 (978-0-7368-8434-1(3)) Red Brick Learning.

Auch, Allison. Personalidades electrizantes & Electrifying Personalities. 2005. spiral bd. 84.00 (***978-1-4108-5713-2(1))*** Benchmark Education Co.

Bankston, John. Alexander Graham Bell & the Story of the Telephone. 2004. (Uncharted, Unexplored, & Unexplained Ser.). (Illus.). 48p. (J). (gr. 4-8). lib. bdg. 29.95 (978-1-58415-243-9(5)) Mitchell Lane Pubs., Inc.

Berger, Melvin & Berger, Gilda. Did You Invent the Phone All Alone, Alexander Graham Bell? 2007. (Scholastic Science Supergiants Ser.). 48p. (J). pap. 4.99 (978-0-439-83381-3(7) , Scholastic Nonfiction) Scholastic, Inc.

Carson, Mary Kay. Sterling Biographies: Alexander Graham Bell: Giving Voice to the World. 2007. (Sterling Biographies Ser.). (Illus.). 128p. (J). 12.95 (***978-1-4027-4951-3(1));*** pap. 5.95 (***978-1-4027-3230-0(9))*** Sterling Publishing Co., Inc.

Cefrey, Holly. The Inventions of Alexander Graham Bell: The Telephone. 2003. (19th Century American Inventors Ser.). (Illus.). 24p. (J). lib. bdg. 17.25 (978-0-8239-6441-3(8) , PowerKids Pr.) Rosen Publishing Group, Inc., The.

Fandel, Jennifer. Alexander Graham Bell & the Telephone. Tucker, Keith & Barnett, Charles, illus. 2007. (Graphic Library). 32p. (J). 25.26 (978-0-7368-6478-7(4)) Capstone Pr., Inc.

Feinstein, Stephen. Alexander Graham Bell: Genius Behind the Bell. 2008. (Inventors Who Changed the World Ser.). 128p. (gr. 6 up). lib. bdg. 33.27 (***978-1-59845-055-2(7)*** , MyReportLinks.com Bks.) Enslow Pubs., Inc.

Ford, Carin T. Alexander Graham Bell: Inventor of the Telephone. 2002. (Meeting Famous People Ser.). (Illus.). 32p. (J). (gr. 1-4). lib. bdg. 22.60 (978-0-7660-1858-7(X)) Enslow Pubs., Inc.

Gaines, Ann Graham. Alexander Graham Bell. 2001. (Discover the Life of an Inventor Ser.). (Illus.). 24p. (J). (gr. 1-4). lib. bdg. 20.64 (978-1-58952-117-9(X)) Rourke Publishing, LLC.

—Alexander Graham Bell. Sarfatti, Esther & de la Vega, Eida, trs. 2001. (Inventores Famosos Ser.). (SPA & ENG., Illus.). 24p. (J). (gr. 1-4). lib. bdg. 19.27 (978-1-58952-173-5(0) , RK5266) Rourke Publishing, LLC.

—Alexander Graham Bell. 2002. (SPA.). (gr. k-3). lib. bdg. 14.10 (978-0-613-79408-4(7)) Tandem Library Bks.

—Alexander Graham Bell. Sarfatti, Esther & de la Vega, Eida, trs. 2002. (Inventores Famosos Ser.). (SPA., Illus.). 24p. (J). mass mkt. 5.95 (978-1-58952-233-6(8) , RK31450) Rourke Publishing, LLC.

Ganeri, Anita. Alexander Graham Bell. 2000. (What Would You Ask...? Ser.). (Illus.). 32p. (J). (gr. 2-6). lib. bdg. 16.95 (978-1-929298-76-1(5)) Chrysalis Education.

Garmon, Anita. Alexander Graham Bell Invents. 2007. (History Chapters Ser.). 48p. (J). (gr. 1-4). lib. bdg. 17.90 (***978-1-4263-0189-6(8)*** , National Geographic Children's Bks.) National Geographic Society.

Harcourt School Publishers Staff. Alexander Graham Bell: Take-Home Book. 1999. (Signatures Ser.). (Illus.). (J). pap. 1.90 (978-0-15-313920-8(X)) Harcourt Schl. Pubs.

Haven, Kendall F. Alexander Graham Bell: Inventor & Visionary. 2003. (Great Life Stories: Inventors & Scientists Ser.). (Illus.). 128p. (J). 30.50 (978-0-531-12314-0(6) , Watts, Franklin) Scholastic Library Publishing.

Klingel, Cynthia Fitterer. Alexander Graham Bell: Inventor. 2003. (Spirit of America: Our People Ser.). (Illus.). 32p. (J). (gr. 2-6). 27.07 (978-1-56766-367-9(2)) Child's World, Inc.

Kulling, Monica. Listen Up! Alexander Graham Bell's Talking Machine. Walz, Richard, illus. 2007. (Step into Reading Ser.). 48p. (J). (gr. 1-3). pap. 3.99 (978-0-375-83115-7(0)); lib. bdg. 11.99 (978-0-375-93115-4(5)) Random Hse. Children's Bks. (Random Hse. Bks. for Young Readers).

Linder, Greg. Alexander Graham Bell. 1999. (Photo-Illustrated Biographies Ser.). (Illus.). 24p. (J). (gr. 2-3). lib. bdg. 18.60 (978-0-7368-0202-4(9) , Bridgestone Bks.) Capstone Pr., Inc.

MacLeod, Elizabeth. Alexander Graham Bell. Krystoforski, Andrej, illus. 2007. 32p. pap. (***978-1-55453-002-1(4))*** Kids Can Pr., Ltd.

MacLeod, Elizabeth. Alexander Graham Bell: An Inventive Life. unabr. ed. 2004. (Snapshots Ser.). (Illus.). 32p. (J). (gr. 4-6). (978-1-55074-458-3(5)); (978-1-55074-456-9(9)) Kids Can Pr., Ltd.

—Alexander Graham Bell: An Inventive Life. 1999. (J). 12.75 (978-0-606-16545-7(2)); (gr. 3-6). lib. bdg. 14.10 (978-0-613-16313-2(3)) Tandem Library Bks.

Mara, Wil. Alexander Graham Bell. (Rookie Biographies Ser.). (Illus.). 32p. (J). (gr. 1-2). 2003. pap. 4.95 (978-0-516-27340-2(X)); 2002. 20.50 (978-0-516-22524-1(3)) Scholastic Library Publishing. (Children's Pr.).

—Alexander Graham Bell. 2002. (gr. k-3). lib. bdg. 12.95 (978-0-613-59444-8(4)) Tandem Library Bks.

Martin, Justin. Easy Reader Biographies: Alexander Graham Bell: A Famous Inventor. 2007. 16p. pap. 2.99 (***978-0-439-77415-4(2)*** , Teaching Resources) Scholastic, Inc.

Matthews, Tom L. Always Inventing: A Photobiography of Alexander Graham Bell. 64p. (J). 2006. (gr. 5). pap. 17.95 (978-0-7922-5932-9(7)); 1999. (Illus.). (gr. 3-13). 17.95 (978-0-7922-7391-2(5)) National Geographic Society. (National Geographic Children's Bks.).

McPherson, Stephanie Sammartino. Alexander Graham Bell. Butler, Tad, illus. 2007. (History Maker Biographies Ser.). (J). 26.60 (***978-0-8225-7606-8(6)*** , Lerner Pubns.) Lerner Publishing Group.

Micklos, John. Alexander Graham Bell Inventor of the Telephone. 2006. 44p. (J). lib. bdg. 15.00 (***978-1-4242-0686-5(3))*** Fitzgerald Bks.

Petrie, A. Roy. Alexander Graham Bell. 1999. (Canadians Ser.). (Illus.). 64p. (J). (978-1-55041-463-9(1)) Fitzhenry & Whiteside, Ltd.

—Alexander Graham Bell. 1999. (gr. 3-6). lib. bdg. 15.25 (978-0-613-84293-8(6)) Tandem Library Bks.

Pollard, Michael. Alexander Graham Bell: Father of Modern Communication. 2000. (Giants of Science Ser.). (Illus.). 64p. (J). (gr. 5-8). 27.44 (978-1-56711-334-1(6) , Blackbirch Pr., Inc.) Thomson Gale.

Raatma, Lucia. Alexander Graham Bell. 2004. (Compass Point Early Biographies Ser.). (Illus.). 32p. (J). (gr. 2 up). lib. bdg. 21.26 (978-0-7565-0569-1(0)) Compass Point Bks.

Reid, Struan. Alexander Graham Bell. (Groundbreakers Ser.). (Illus.). 48p. (J). (gr. 5-7). 2002. pap. 8.50 (978-1-58810-989-7(5) , 91464); 2000. lib. bdg. 25.64 (978-1-57572-366-2(2)) Heinemann Library.

Rivera, Sheila. Alexander Graham Bell: A Life of Helpfulness. 2007. (Pull Ahead Books-Biographies Ser.). (J). 22.60 (978-0-8225-6463-8(7) , Lerner Pubns.) Lerner Publishing Group.

Ross, Stewart. Alexander Graham Bell. 2001. (Scientists Who Made History Ser.). (Illus.). 48p. (J). lib. bdg. 27.12 (978-0-7398-4415-1(6)) Raintree.

Schaefer, Lola M. Alexander Graham Bell. 2005. (First Biographies Ser.). 24p. (YA). (gr. k-3). pap. (978-0-7368-3378-3(1) , Pebble Bks.) Capstone Pr., Inc.

—Alexander Graham Bell. Saunders-Smith, Gail, ed. 2003. (First Biographies Ser.). (Illus.). 24p. (J). (gr. k-1). lib. bdg. 15.93 (978-0-7368-1644-1(5) , Pebble Bks.) Capstone Pr., Inc.

Schuman, Michael A. Alexander Graham Bell: Inventor & Teacher. 1999. (Historical American Biographies Ser.). (Illus.). 128p. (YA). (gr. 6-12). lib. bdg. 20.95 (978-0-7660-1096-3(1)) Enslow Pubs., Inc.

Sherrow, Victoria. Alexander Graham Bell. Verstraete, Elaine, illus. (On My Own Biographies Ser.). 48p. 2005. (gr. 2-5). lib. bdg. 23.93 (978-1-57505-460-5(4)); 2003. (J). (gr. 1-3). 5.95 (978-1-57505-533-6(3)) Lerner Publishing Group.

—Alexander Graham Bell. 2001. (gr. 3-6). lib. bdg. 14.10 (978-0-613-79235-6(1)) Tandem Library Bks.

Shuter, Jane. Alexander Graham Bell. 2000. (Lives & Times Ser.). (Illus.). 24p. (J). (gr. k-2). lib. bdg. 19.92 (978-1-57572-228-3(3)) Heinemann Library.

Time for Kids Editors. Alexander Graham Bell. 2006. (Time for Kids Ser.). (Illus.). 48p. (J). 14.99 (978-0-06-057619-6(7)); pap. 3.99 (978-0-06-057618-9(9) , Harper Trophy) HarperCollins Pubs.

Webster, Christine. Alexander Graham Bell & the Telephone. 2004. (Cornerstones of Freedom Ser.). (Illus.). 48p. (J). 26.00 (978-0-516-24227-9(X) , Children's Pr.) Scholastic Library Publishing.

Williams, Brian. Bell & the Science of the Telephone. Antram, David, illus. 2006. (Explosion Zone Ser.). 32p. (J). 12.99 (978-0-7641-5972-5(0)) Barron's Educational Series, Inc.

BELLS

Rice, William G. Carillon Music & the Singing Towers of the Old World & the New. rev. ed. 2001. 474p. (YA). reprint ed. 98.00 (978-0-7222-5132-4(7)) Library Reprints, Inc.

BEN-GURION, DAVID, 1886-1973

St. John, Robert. Ben-Gurion: Builder of Israel. 1998. (J). 19.95 (978-0-9613262-4-1(7)) London Publishing Co.

World Book, Inc Staff, contrib. by. Golda Meir: With Profiles of David Ben-Gurion & Yitzhak Rabin. 2006. (Biographical Connections Ser.). (Illus.). 112p. (J). (978-0-7166-1829-4(X)) World Bk., Inc.

BENEDICT, SAINT, ABBOT OF MONTE CASSINO

Norris, Kathleen. The Holy Twins: Benedict & Scholastica. de Paola, Tomie, illus. 2004. 35p. (J). (gr. k-4). reprint ed. 17.00 (978-0-7567-7705-0(4)) DIANE Publishing Co.

—The Holy Twins: Benedict & Scholastica. de Paola, Tomie, illus. 2001. 32p. (J). (ps-3). 18.99 (978-0-399-23424-8(1) , Putnam Juvenile) Penguin Group (USA) Inc.

BENNET, ELIZABETH (FICTITIOUS CHARACTER)—FICTION

Austen, Jane. Pride & Prejudice. 1999. (YA). 11.95 (978-1-56137-767-1(8)) Novel Units, Inc.

—Pride & Prejudice. 2002. (gr. 7-12). lib. bdg. 16.45 (978-0-613-64095-4(0)) Tandem Library Bks.

—Pride & Prejudice: Penguin Readers Level 5. 1998. (Illus.). 80p. pap. 7.00 (978-0-14-081507-8(4)) Penguin Group (USA) Inc.

BEOWULF

Crossley-Holland, Kevin, tr. from ANG. Beowulf. Keeping, Charles, illus. 1999. 48p. (YA). 12.95 (978-0-19-272369-7(3)) Oxford Univ. Pr., Inc.

Down, Alan, illus. Beowulf: An Anglo-Saxon Epic. 2004. (J). (ENG & ALB.). 32p. pap. (978-1-84444-022-1(2)); (ENG & ARA.). 32p. pap. (978-1-84444-023-8(0)); (ENG & BEN.). 30p. pap. (978-1-84444-024-5(9)); (ENG & CHI.). 30p. pap. (978-1-84444-025-2(7)); (ENG & PER.). 30p. pap. (978-1-84444-026-9(5)); (ENG & FRE.). 30p. pap. (978-1-84444-027-6(3)); (ENG & GUJ.). 30p. pap. (978-1-84444-028-3(1)); (ENG & PAN.). 30p. pap. (978-1-84444-029-0(X)); (POR & ENG.). 30p. pap. (978-1-84444-030-6(3)); (ENG & SOM.). 32p. pap. (978-1-84444-031-3(1)); (ENG & SPA.). 30p. pap. (978-1-84444-032-0(X)); (ENG & TUR.). 30p. pap. (978-1-84444-033-7(8)); (ENG & URD.). 32p. pap. (978-1-84444-034-4(6)); (ENG & GER.). 30p. pap. (978-1-84444-109-9(1)); (ENG & ITA.). 30p. pap. (978-1-84444-110-5(5)); (SBC, ENG & SER.). 30p. pap. (978-1-84444-112-9(1)); (TAM & ENG.). 30p. pap. (978-1-84444-113-6(X)); (CZE & ENG.). 30p. pap. (978-1-84444-114-3(8)) Mantra Publishing, Ltd.

Kimmel, Eric A. The Hero Beowulf. Fisher, Leonard Everett, illus. 2005. 32p. (J). 16.00 (978-0-374-30671-7(0) , Farrar, Straus & Giroux (BYR)) Farrar, Straus & Giroux.

Nye, Robert. Beowulf. l.t. ed. 2005. 168p. (J). pap. (978-0-7540-6125-0(6) , CLP 322) BBC Audio.

—Beowulf. 2nd ed. 2004. (Illus.). 96p. (YA). pap. 9.95 ***(978-1-85881-076-8(0))*** Orion Publishing Group, Ltd. GBR. *Dist:* Independent Pubs. Group.

Potter, Tessa. Beowulf & the Dragon. 1998. (Myths & Legends Ser.). (Illus.). 24p. (J). 14.60 (978-1-57572-017-3(5)) Heinemann Library.

Rumford, James. Beowulf: A Hero's Tale Retold. 2007. (Illus.). 48p. (J). (gr. 5-8). 17.00 ***(978-0-618-75637-7(X))*** Houghton Mifflin Co.

Streissguth, Thomas. Beowulf. 2003. (Understanding Great Literature Ser.). (Illus.). 112p. (J). 29.95 (978-1-56006-861-7(2) , Lucent Bks.) Thomson Gale.

BERENSTAIN BEARS (FICTITIOUS CHARACTERS)—FICTION

Berenstain, Jan, et al. The Berenstain Bears Save Christmas. Berenstain, Michael, illus. 2003. (Berenstain Bears Ser.). 48p. (J). (ps-3). 12.99 (978-0-06-052670-2(X)) HarperCollins Pubs.

Berenstain, Stan. The Berenstain Bears & the Excuse Note. 2001. (Berenstain Bears First Time Bks.). (J). (gr. k-3). lib. bdg. 10.95 (978-0-613-64151-7(5)) Tandem Library Bks.

—The Berenstain Bears & the Tic-Tac-Toe Mystery. 2001. (Berenstain Bears Ser.). (J). (gr. k-3). lib. bdg. 11.80 (978-0-613-33791-5(3)) Tandem Library Bks.

Berenstain, Stan & Berenstain, Jan. Bears in the Night. Berenstain, Stan & Berenstain, Jan, illus. 2002. (Berenstain Bears Bright & Early Bks.). (Illus.). (J). 16.70 (978-0-7587-0922-6(6)) Book Wholesalers, Inc.

—The Bears' Picnic. Berenstain, Stan & Berenstain, Jan, illus. 2002. (Berenstain Bears Beginner Bks.). (Illus.). (J). (gr. k-3). 15.74 (978-0-7587-0924-0(2)) Book Wholesalers, Inc.

—The Berenstain Bear Scouts & the Coughing Catfish. 1998. (Berenstain Bear Scouts Ser.). (Illus.). 32p. (J). (gr. 3-8). pap. 3.50 (978-0-590-60384-3(1)) Scholastic, Inc.

—The Berenstain Bear Scouts & the Evil Eye. 1998. (Berenstain Bear Scouts Ser.). (J). (gr. 3-6). pap. 3.99 (978-0-590-94488-5(6) , Scholastic Paperbacks) Scholastic, Inc.

—The Berenstain Bear Scouts & the Missing Merit Badges. 1998. (Berenstain Bear Scouts Ser.). (Illus.). 32p. (J). (gr. 3-6). pap. 3.50 (978-0-590-56390-1(4)) Scholastic, Inc.

—The Berenstain Bear Scouts & the Missing Merit Badges. 1998. (Berenstain Bear Scouts Ser.). (J). (gr. 3-6). (978-0-606-13191-9(4)) Tandem Library Bks.

—The Berenstain Bear Scouts & the Really Big Disaster. 1998. (Berenstain Bear Scouts Ser.). (Illus.). 32p. (J). (gr. 3-6). pap. 3.99 (978-0-590-94481-6(9) , Scholastic Paperbacks) Scholastic, Inc.

—The Berenstain Bear Scouts & the Ripoff Queen. 1998. (Berenstain Bear Scouts Ser.). (Illus.). 112p. (J). (gr. 3-6). pap. 3.99 (978-0-590-94493-9(2)) Scholastic, Inc.

—The Berenstain Bear Scouts & the Search for Naughty Ned. 1998. (Berenstain Bear Scouts Ser.). (Illus.). 32p. (J). (gr. 3-6). pap. 3.50 (978-0-590-56509-7(5)) Scholastic, Inc.

—The Berenstain Bear Scouts & the Search for Naughty Ned. 1998. (Berenstain Bear Scouts Ser.). (J). (gr. 3-6). (978-0-606-13193-3(0)) Tandem Library Bks.

—The Berenstain Bear Scouts & the Stinky Milk Mystery. 1999. (Berenstain Bear Scouts Ser.). (Illus.). 32p. (J). (gr. 3-6). pap. 3.50 (978-0-590-56524-0(9) , Cartwheel Bks.) Scholastic, Inc.

—The Berenstain Bear Scouts & the White-Water Mystery. 1999. (Berenstain Bear Scouts Ser.). 32p. (J). (gr. 3-6). pap. 3.50 (978-0-590-56522-6(2)) Scholastic, Inc.

—The Berenstain Bear Scouts & the White-Water Mystery. 1999. (Berenstain Bear Scouts Ser.). (J). (gr. 3-6). (978-0-606-16598-3(3)) Tandem Library Bks.

—The Berenstain Bear Scouts Scream Their Heads Off. 1998. (Berenstain Bear Scouts Ser.). (Illus.). 32p. (J). (gr. 3-6). pap. 3.99 (978-0-590-94484-7(3) , Scholastic Paperbacks) Scholastic, Inc.

—The Berenstain Bear Scouts Scream Their Heads Off. 1998. (Berenstain Bear Scouts Ser.). (J). (gr. 3-6). (978-0-606-13194-0(9)) Tandem Library Bks.

—The Berenstain Bears, 7 vols., Date not set. (Early Childhood First Bks.). (Illus.). (J). (ps-2). lib. bdg. 97.65 (978-1-56674-942-8(5)) Forest Hse. Publishing Co., Inc.

—The Berenstain Bears & Baby Makes Five. 2000. (Berenstain Bears First Time Bks.). (Illus.). 32p. (J). (gr. k-1). pap. 3.25 (978-0-679-88960-1(4) , Random Hse. Bks. for Young Readers) Random Hse. Children's Bks.

—The Berenstain Bears & Baby Makes Five. 2000. (Berenstain Bears First Time Bks.). (J). (ps-2). lib. bdg. 10.95 (978-0-613-24332-2(3)); (Illus.). 10.05 (978-0-606-18485-4(6)) Tandem Library Bks.

—The Berenstain Bears & Mama's New Job. 1999. (Berenstain Bears First Time Bks.). (Illus.). (J). (gr. k-2). pap. 10.25 (978-0-88103-144-7(5)) Tandem Library Bks.

—The Berenstain Bears & No Guns Allowed. 2000. (Berenstain Bears Big Chapter Bks.). (Illus.). (J). (gr. 3-6). 10.79 (978-0-606-18486-1(4)) Tandem Library Bks.

—The Berenstain Bears & the Baby Chipmunk. Berenstain, Stan & Berenstain, Jan, illus. 2005. (Berenstain Bears Ser.). (Illus.). 32p. (J). pap. 3.99 (978-0-06-058413-9(0)); 15.99 (978-0-06-058412-2(2)) HarperCollins Pubs.

—The Berenstain Bears & the Bad Dream. Berenstain, Stan & Berenstain, Jan, illus. 2002. (Berenstain Bears First Time Bks.). (Illus.). (J). 11.19 (978-0-7587-0957-8(9)) Book Wholesalers, Inc.

—The Berenstain Bears & the Bad Dream. ed. 2004. (Berenstain Bears First Time Bks.). (J). (ps-2). spiral bd. (978-0-616-01555-1(0)); spiral bd. (978-0-616-01556-8(9)) Canadian National Institute for the Blind/Institut National Canadien pour les Aveugles.

—The Berenstain Bears & the Bad Habit. Berenstain, Jan, illus. 2002. (Berenstain Bears First Time Bks.). (Illus.). (J). (gr. k-3). 11.19 (978-0-7587-0949-3(8)) Book Wholesalers, Inc.

—The Berenstain Bears & the Big Blooper. Klimo, Kate, ed. 2000. (Berenstain Bears First Time Bks.). (Illus.). 32p. (J). (gr. k-3). pap. 3.25 (978-0-679-88962-5(0) , Random Hse. Bks. for Young Readers) Random Hse. Children's Bks.

—The Berenstain Bears & the Big Blooper. 2000. (Berenstain Bears First Time Bks.). (J). (gr. k-2). 10.05 (978-0-606-19887-5(3)); lib. bdg. 10.95 (978-0-613-32320-8(3)) Tandem Library Bks.

—The Berenstain Bears & the Big Date. 1998. (Berenstain Bears Big Chapter Bks.). (J). (gr. 2-6). (978-0-606-13951-9(6)) Tandem Library Bks.

—The Berenstain Bears & the Big Question. 1999. (Berenstain Bears First Time Bks.). (Illus.). 32p. (J). (gr. k-3). 3.99 (978-0-679-88961-8(2) , Random Hse. Bks. for Young Readers) Random Hse. Children's Bks.

—The Berenstain Bears & the Big Question. 1999. (Berenstain Bears First Time Bks.). (J). (gr. k-3). lib. bdg. 10.95 (978-0-613-86658-3(4)) Tandem Library Bks.

—The Berenstain Bears & the Blame Game. Berenstain, Stan & Berenstain, Jan, illus. 2002. (Berenstain Bears First Time Bks.). (Illus.). (J). 11.19 (978-0-7587-0965-3(X)) Book Wholesalers, Inc.

—The Berenstain Bears & the Blame Game. ed. 2004. (Berenstain Bears First Time Bks.). (Illus.). (J). (gr. k-3). spiral bd. (978-0-616-14559-3(4)); spiral bd. (978-0-616-14560-9(8)) Canadian National Institute for the Blind/Institut National Canadien pour les Aveugles.

—The Berenstain Bears & the Bully. Berenstain, Stan & Berenstain, Jan, illus. 2002. (Berenstain Bears First Time Bks.). (Illus.). (J). 11.19 (978-0-7587-0947-9(1)) Book Wholesalers, Inc.

—The Berenstain Bears & the Double Dare. Berenstain, Stan & Berenstain, Jan, illus. 2002. (Berenstain Bears First Time Bks.). (Illus.). (J). 11.19 (978-0-7587-0956-1(0)) Book Wholesalers, Inc.

—The Berenstain Bears & the Dress Code. Berenstain, Stan & Berenstain, Jan, illus. 2002. (Berenstain Bears Big Chapter Bks.). (Illus.). (J). 11.91 (978-0-7587-0444-3(5)) Book Wholesalers, Inc.

—The Berenstain Bears & the Drug Free Zone. Berenstain, Stan & Berenstain, Jan, illus. 2002. (Berenstain Bears Big Chapter Bks.). (Illus.). (J). (gr. 2-6). 11.91 (978-0-7587-0941-7(2)) Book Wholesalers, Inc.

—The Berenstain Bears & the Escape of the Bogg Brothers. 2000. (Berenstain Bears Ser.). (J). (gr. k-3). (978-0-606-20272-5(2)) Tandem Library Bks.

—The Berenstain Bears & the Excuse Note. Berenstain, Stan & Berenstain, Jan, illus. 2002. (Berenstain Bears First Time Bks.). (Illus.). (J). (gr. k-3). 11.19 (978-0-7587-6916-9(4)) Book Wholesalers, Inc.

—The Berenstain Bears & the Excuse Note. 2001. (Berenstain Bears First Time Bks.). (Illus.). 32p. (J). (gr. k-3). 3.99 (978-0-375-81125-8(7)); lib. bdg. 8.99 (978-0-375-91125-5(1)) Random Hse. Children's Bks. (Random Hse. Bks. for Young Readers).

—The Berenstain Bears & the Excuse Note. 2001. (Berenstain Bears First Time Bks.). (J). (gr. k-3). 10.05 (978-0-606-22387-4(8)) Tandem Library Bks.

—The Berenstain Bears & the G-Rex Bones. 2001. (Berenstain Bears Big Chapter Bks.). (J). (gr. 2-6). lib. bdg. 11.99 (978-0-679-98949-3(8) , Random Hse. Bks. for Young Readers) Random Hse. Children's Bks.

—The Berenstain Bears & the Great Ant Attack. 2000. (Berenstain Bears Big Chapter Bks.). (Illus.). (J). (gr. 2-6). (978-0-606-18487-8(2)) Tandem Library Bks.

—The Berenstain Bears & the Green-Eyed Monster. Berenstain, Stan & Berenstain, Jan, illus. 2002. (Berenstain Bears First Time Bks.). (Illus.). (J). 11.19 (978-0-7587-0946-2(3)) Book Wholesalers, Inc.

—The Berenstain Bears & the Homework Hassle. Berenstain, Stan & Berenstain, Jan, illus. 2002. (Berenstain Bears First Time Bks.). (Illus.). (J). 11.19 (978-0-7587-0966-0(8)) Book Wholesalers, Inc.

—The Berenstain Bears & the In-Crowd. Berenstain, Stan & Berenstain, Jan, illus. 2002. (Berenstain Bears First Time Bks.). (Illus.). (J). 11.19 (978-0-7587-0940-0(4)) Book Wholesalers, Inc.

—The Berenstain Bears & the Love Match. 1998. (Berenstain Bears Big Chapter Bks.). (J). (gr. 2-6). (978-0-606-13952-6(4)) Tandem Library Bks.

—The Berenstain Bears & the Missing Dinosaur Bone. Berenstain, Stan & Berenstain, Jan, illus. 2002. (Berenstain Bears Beginner Bks.). (Illus.). (J). (gr. k-3). 16.70 (978-0-7587-0962-2(5)) Book Wholesalers, Inc.

—The Berenstain Bears & the Missing Watermelon Money. 2001. (Berenstain Bears Ser.). (Illus.). 48p. (J). (gr. 1-3). 11.99 (978-0-679-99230-1(8)); pap. 3.99 (978-0-679-89230-4(3)) Random Hse. Children's Bks. (Random Hse. Bks. for Young Readers).

—The Berenstain Bears & the Missing Watermelon Money. 2001. (Berenstain Bears Ser.). (J). (gr. k-3). lib. bdg. 11.80 (978-0-613-35600-8(4)); (Illus.). 10.79 (978-0-606-21056-0(3)) Tandem Library Bks.

—The Berenstain Bears & the Papa's Day Roast. 2003. (Illus.). 32p. (J). (gr. k-3). lib. bdg. 8.99 (978-0-375-91129-3(4) , Random Hse. Bks. for Young Readers) Random Hse. Children's Bks.

—The Berenstain Bears & the Papa's Day Surprise. 2003. (Berenstain Bears First Time Bks.). (Illus.). 32p. (J). (gr. k-3). pap. 3.99 (978-0-375-81129-6(X) , Random Hse. Bks. for Young Readers) Random Hse. Children's Bks.

—The Berenstain Bears & the Phantom of the Gymnasium. 2000. (Illus.). (J). pap. 3.99 (978-0-679-88949-6(3) , Random Hse. Bks. for Young Readers) Random Hse. Children's Bks.

—The Berenstain Bears & the Prize Pumpkin. Berenstain, Stan & Berenstain, Jan, illus. 2002. (Berenstain Bears First Time Bks.). (Illus.). (J). 11.19 (978-0-7587-0959-2(5)) Book Wholesalers, Inc.

—The Berenstain Bears & the Real Easter Eggs. Berenstain, Stan & Berenstain, Jan, illus. 2002. (Berenstain Bears Ser.). (Illus.). (J). 11.19 (978-0-7587-8978-5(5)) Book Wholesalers, Inc.

—The Berenstain Bears & the Real Easter Eggs. 2002. (Berenstain Bears Ser.). (Illus.). 32p. (J). (gr. k-3). pap. 3.99 (978-0-375-81133-3(8) , Random Hse. Bks. for Young Readers) Random Hse. Children's Bks.

—The Berenstain Bears & the Real Easter Eggs. 2002. (gr. k-3). lib. bdg. 10.95 (978-0-613-64153-1(1)) Tandem Library Bks.

—The Berenstain Bears & the Tic-Tac-Toe Mystery. (Berenstain Bears Ser.). (Illus.). 48p. (J). (gr. k-3). 2003. lib. bdg. 11.99 (978-0-679-99229-5(4)); 2001. pap. 3.99 (978-0-679-89229-8(X)) Random Hse. Children's Bks. (Random Hse. Bks. for Young Readers).

—The Berenstain Bears & the Tic-Tac-Toe Mystery. 2001. (Berenstain Bears Ser.). (Illus.). (J). (gr. k-3). 10.79 (978-0-606-20569-6(1)) Tandem Library Bks.

—The Berenstain Bears & the Trouble with Chores. 2005. (Berenstain Bears Ser.). (Illus.). 32p. (J). (ps-2). 8.99 (978-0-06-057398-0(8)); pap. 3.99 (978-0-06-057382-9(1)) HarperCollins Pubs. (Harper Festival).

—The Berenstain Bears & the Trouble with Commercials. Berenstain, Stan, illus. 2007. (Berenstain Bears Ser.). 32p. (J). 8.99 (978-0-06-057403-1(8)); pap. 3.99 (978-0-06-057387-4(2)) HarperCollins Pubs. (Harper Festival).

—The Berenstain Bears & the Trouble with Grownups. Berenstain, Stan & Berenstain, Jan, illus. 2002. (Berenstain Bears First Time Bks.). (Illus.). (J). 11.19 (978-0-7587-0958-5(7)) Book Wholesalers, Inc.

—The Berenstain Bears & the Wax Museum. 1999. (Berenstain Bears Big Chapter Bks.). (J). (gr. 2-6). (978-0-606-16943-1(1)) Tandem Library Bks.

—The Berenstain Bears & the Week at Grandma's. Berenstain, Stan & Berenstain, Jan, illus. 2002. (Berenstain Bears First Time Bks.). (Illus.). (J). 11.19 (978-0-7587-6632-8(7)) Book Wholesalers, Inc.

—Berenstain Bears & the Wishing Star. 2005. (Illus.). 32p. (J). lib. bdg. 13.85 ***(978-1-4242-0813-5(0))*** Fitzgerald Bks.

—The Berenstain Bears & Too Much Junk Food. 1999. (Berenstain Bears First Time Bks.). (Illus.). (J). (ps-2). lib. bdg. 10.95 (978-0-8085-3551-5(X)) Tandem Library Bks.

—The Berenstain Bears & Too Much TV. Berenstain, Stan & Berenstain, Jan, illus. 2002. (Berenstain Bears First Time Bks.). (Illus.). (J). 11.19 (978-0-7587-0943-1(9)) Book Wholesalers, Inc.

—The Berenstain Bears & Too Much Vacation. Berenstain, Stan & Berenstain, Jan, illus. 2002. (Berenstain Bears First Time Bks.). (Illus.). (J). 11.19 (978-0-7587-0954-7(4)) Book Wholesalers, Inc.

—The Berenstain Bears' Bedtime Battle. Berenstain, Stan & Berenstain, Jan, illus. 2005. (Berenstain Bears Ser.). (Illus.). 32p. (J). (ps-2). 3.99 (978-0-06-057381-2(3) , Harper Festival) HarperCollins Pubs.

—The Berenstain Bears Big Bear Small Bear. 1998. (Berenstain Bears Ser.). (Illus.). 32p. (J). (gr. k). lib. bdg. 11.99 (978-0-679-98717-8(7)); pap. 3.99 (978-0-679-88717-1(2)) Random Hse. Children's Bks. (Random Hse. Bks. for Young Readers).

—The Berenstain Bears by the Sea. Berenstain, Stan & Berenstain, Jan, illus. 2002. (Berenstain Bears Ser.). (Illus.). (J). (gr. k-3). 11.91 (978-0-7587-0969-1(2)) Book Wholesalers, Inc.

—The Berenstain Bears by the Sea. 1998. (Berenstain Bears Ser.). (Illus.). 32p. (ps-2). (J). pap. 3.99 (978-0-679-88719-5(9)); lib. bdg. 11.99 (978-0-679-98719-2(3)) Random Hse. Children's Bks. (Random Hse. Bks. for Young Readers).

—The Berenstain Bears by the Sea. 1998. (Berenstain Bears Ser.). (Illus.). (J). (gr. k-3). lib. bdg. 11.80 (978-0-613-07341-7(X)) Tandem Library Bks.

—The Berenstain Bears Catch the Bus. Berenstain, Stan & Berenstain, Jan, illus. 2002. (Berenstain Bears Ser.). (Illus.). (J). (gr. k-3). 11.91 (978-0-7587-0977-6(3)) Book Wholesalers, Inc.

—The Berenstain Bears Catch the Bus. 1999. (Berenstain Bears Ser.). (Illus.). 32p. (J). (ps-3). lib. bdg. 11.99 (978-0-679-99227-1(8)); pap. 3.99 (978-0-679-89227-4(3)) Random Hse. Children's Bks. (Random Hse. Bks. for Young Readers).

—The Berenstain Bears Catch the Bus. 1999. (Berenstain Bears Ser.). (J). (ps). (Illus.). 32p. lib. bdg. 11.80 (978-0-613-16056-8(8)); 10.79 (978-0-606-16944-8(X)) Tandem Library Bks.

—The Berenstain Bears Clean House. 2005. (Berenstain Bears Ser.). (Illus.). 32p. (J). (gr. k-3). 15.99 (978-0-06-058334-7(7)) HarperCollins Pubs.

—The Berenstain Bears Clean House. Berenstain, Stan, illus. 2005. (Berenstain Bears Ser.). (Illus.). 32p. (J). (gr. k-3). pap. 3.99 (978-0-06-058335-4(5)) HarperCollins Pubs.

—The Berenstain Bears' Dinosaur Coloring Adventure. 2005. (Berenstain Bears Ser.). (Illus.). 32p. (J). pap. 3.99 (978-0-06-057413-0(5) , Harper Festival) HarperCollins Pubs.

—The Berenstain Bears' Dollars & Sense. 2001. (Berenstain Bears First Time Bks.). (Illus.). 32p. (J). (gr. k-3). pap. 3.99 (978-0-375-81124-1(9) , Random Hse. Bks. for Young Readers) Random Hse. Children's Bks.

—The Berenstain Bears' Dollars & Sense. 2001. (Berenstain Bears First Time Bks.). (J). (gr. k-3). 10.79 (978-0-606-22793-3(8)); (gr. 3-6). lib. bdg. 10.95 (978-0-613-32322-2(X)) Tandem Library Bks.

—The Berenstain Bears Don't Pollute (Anymore) 1999. (Berenstain Bears First Time Bks.). (Illus.). (J). (ps-2). lib. bdg. 10.95 (978-0-8335-6545-7(1)) Tandem Library Bks.

—The Berenstain Bears down on the Farm. 2006. (I Can Read Bks.). (Illus.). 32p. (J). ***(978-1-4156-8342-2(5))*** HarperCollins Pubs.

—Berenstain Bears down on the Farm. 2006. (Illus.). 32p. (J). lib. bdg. 15.00 ***(978-1-4242-1537-9(4))*** Fitzgerald Bks.

—The Berenstain Bears' Easter Surprise. l.t. ed. 1998. (Berenstain Bears Ser.). (Illus.). 48p. (J). (ps-3). pap. 10.95 (978-0-590-94730-5(3)) Scholastic, Inc.

—The Berenstain Bears Get the Gimmies. Berenstain, Stan & Berenstain, Jan, illus. 2002. (Berenstain Bears First Time Bks.). (Illus.). (J). 11.19 (978-0-7587-0955-4(2)) Book Wholesalers, Inc.

—The Berenstain Bears Get the Scaredies. Berenstain, Stan & Berenstain, Jan, illus. 1999. (Berenstain Bears Ser.). (Illus.). 24p. (J). (ps-3). lib. bdg. 7.99 (978-0-679-99323-0(1) , Random Hse. Bks. for Young Readers) Random Hse. Children's Bks.

—The Berenstain Bears Get Their Kicks. 1998. (Berenstain Bears First Time Bks.). (Illus.). 32p. (J). (gr. k-3). pap. 3.25 (978-0-679-88955-7(8) , Random Hse. Bks. for Young Readers) Random Hse. Children's Bks.

—The Berenstain Bears Get Their Kicks. 1998. (Berenstain Bears First Time Bks.). (J). (gr. k-2). 10.05 (978-0-606-13955-7(9)) Tandem Library Bks.

—The Berenstain Bears Go Back to School. Berenstain, Michael, illus. 2005. (Berenstain Bears Ser.). 32p. (J). (ps-3). 9.99 (978-0-06-052673-3(4)); lib. bdg. 14.89 (978-0-06-052674-0(2)) HarperCollins Pubs.

—The Berenstain Bears Go Hollywood. 1999. (Berenstain Bears Big Chapter Bks.). (J). (gr. 2-6). (978-0-606-17264-6(5)) Tandem Library Bks.

—The Berenstain Bears Go in & Out. 2000. (Berenstain Bears Ser.). (Illus.). (J). (gr. k-3). (978-0-606-18488-5(0)) Tandem Library Bks.

—The Berenstain Bears Go up & Down: A Math Reader. 1999. (Berenstain Bears Ser.). (Illus.). 32p. (J). (gr. k-3). lib. bdg. 11.99 (978-0-679-98720-8(7) , Random Hse. Bks. for Young Readers) Random Hse. Children's Bks.

—The Berenstain Bears Go up & Down: A Math Reader. 1999. (Berenstain Bears Ser.). (J). (ps-k). lib. bdg. (978-0-606-15895-4(2)) Tandem Library Bks.

—The Berenstain Bears in the House of Mirrors. Berenstain, Stan & Berenstain, Jan, illus. 2002. (Berenstain Bears Ser.). (Illus.). (J). (gr. k 3). 11.91 (978-0-7587-0974-5(9)) Book Wholesalers, Inc.

—The Berenstain Bears in the House of Mirrors. 1999. (Berenstain Bears Ser.). (J). (ps-k). 10.79 (978-0-606-16837-3(0)) Tandem Library Bks.

—The Berenstain Bears Lend a Helping Hand. 1998. (Berenstain Bears First Time Bks.). (Illus.). 32p. (J). (gr. k-3). pap. 3.99 (978-0-679-88956-4(6) , Random Hse. Bks. for Young Readers) Random Hse. Children's Bks.

—The Berenstain Bears Lose a Friend. Berenstain, Stan & Berenstain, Jan, illus. 2007. (Berenstain Bears Ser.). 32p. (J). (ps-2). pap. 3.99 ***(978-0-06-057389-8(9)*** , Harper Festival) HarperCollins Pubs.

—The Berenstain Bears' Mad, Mad, Mad Toy Craze. 1999. (Berenstain Bears First Time Bks.). (Illus.). 32p. (J). (gr. k-3). pap. 3.25 (978-0-679-88958-8(2) , Random Hse. Bks. for Young Readers) Random Hse. Children's Bks.

—The Berenstain Bears' Mad, Mad, Mad Toy Craze. 1999. (Berenstain Bears First Time Bks.). (J). (gr. k-2). 10.05 (978-0-606-15979-1(7)); lib. bdg. 10.95 (978-0-613-16060-5(6)) Tandem Library Bks.

—The Berenstain Bears' New Kitten. Berenstain, Stan, illus. 2007. (I Can Read Bks.). 32p. (J). 15.99 ***(978-0-06-058356-9(8));*** pap. 3.99 ***(978-0-06-058357-6(6)*** , Harper Trophy) HarperCollins Pubs.

—The Berenstain Bears' New Pup. Berenstain, Stan & Berenstain, Jan, illus. 2005. (Berenstain Bears Ser.). (Illus.). 32p. (J). (gr. k-3). 15.99 (978-0-06-058343-9(6)) HarperCollins Pubs.

—The Berenstain Bears' New Pup. 2005. (Berenstain Bears Ser.). (Illus.). 32p. (J). (gr. k-3). pap. 3.99 (978-0-06-058344-6(4)) HarperCollins Pubs.

—Berenstain Bears' New Pup. Berenstain, Stan, illus. 2005. (Illus.). 32p. (J). lib. bdg. 13.85 ***(978-1-4242-0816-6(5))*** Fitzgerald Bks.

A
B

—The Berenstain Bears Out West. Berenstain, Stan & Berenstain, Jan, illus. 2006. (I Can Read Bks.). (Illus.). 32p. (J). pap. 3.99 (978-0-06-058354-5(1) , Harper Trophy) HarperCollins Pubs.

—The Berenstain Bears Phenom in the Family. 2000. (Berenstain Bears Big Chapter Bks.). (J). (gr. 2-6). 10.64 (978-0-606-19888-2(1)) Tandem Library Bks.

—The Berenstain Bears Play Ball. l.t. ed. 1998. (Berenstain Bears Ser.). (Illus.). 48p. (J). (ps-3). pap. 10.95 (978-0-590-94732-9(X)) Scholastic, Inc.

—Berenstain Bears Play T-Ball. Berenstain, Stan, illus. 2005. (Illus.). 32p. (J). lib. bdg. 9.00 ***(978-1-4242-0818-0(1))*** Fitzgerald Bks.

—The Berenstain Bears Ride the Thunderbolt. 1998. (Berenstain Bears Ser.). (Illus.). 32p. (ps-1). (J). pap. 3.99 (978-0-679-88718-8(0)); lib. bdg. 11.99 (978-0-679-98718-5(5)) Random Hse. Children's Bks. (Random Hse. Bks. for Young Readers).

—The Berenstain Bears Ride the Thunderbolt. 1998. (Early Step into Reading Ser.). (J). (ps-k). 10.79 (978-0-606-13956-4(7)) Tandem Library Bks.

—The Berenstain Bears Think of Those in Need. 1999. (Berenstain Bears First Time Bks.). (Illus.). 32p. (J). (gr. k-3). pap. 3.99 (978-0-679-88957-1(4) , Random Hse. Bks. for Young Readers) Random Hse. Children's Bks.

—The Berenstain Bears Think of Those in Need. 1999. (Berenstain Bears First Time Bks.). (J). (ps-2). lib. bdg. 10.95 (978-0-613-16061-2(4)); (Illus.). 10.05 (978-0-606-20465-1(2)) Tandem Library Bks.

—The Big Honey Hunt. Berenstain, Stan & Berenstain, Jan, illus. 2002. (Berenstain Bears Beginner Bks.). (Illus.). (J). (gr. k-3). 16.70 (978-0-7587-0993-6(5)) Book Wholesalers, Inc.

—The Bike Lesson. Berenstain, Stan & Berenstain, Jan, illus. 2002. (Berenstain Bears Beginner Bks.). (Illus.). (J). (gr. k-3). 15.74 (978-0-7587-0998-1(6)) Book Wholesalers, Inc.

—The Birds, the Bees, & the Berenstain Bears. 2000. (Berenstain Bears First Time Bks.). (Illus.). 32p. (J). (gr. k-3). pap. 3.99 (978-0-679-88959-5(0) , Random Hse. Bks. for Young Readers) Random Hse. Children's Bks.

—The Birds, the Bees, & the Berenstain Bears. 1999. (Berenstain Bears First Time Bks.). (J). (gr. k-2). (978-0-679-88971-7(X)) Random Hse., Inc.

—The Birds, the Bees, & the Berenstain Bears. 2000. (Berenstain Bears First Time Bks.). (J). (gr. k-3). 10.05 (978-0-606-17523-4(7)) Tandem Library Bks.

—The Goofy, Goony Guy. 2001. (Berenstain Bears Ser.). (Illus.). (J). (gr. k-3). (978-0-606-21057-7(1)) Tandem Library Bks.

—The Haunted Lighthouse. 2001. (Berenstain Bears Ser.). (J). (gr. k-3). lib. bdg. 11.80 (978-0-613-33814-1(6)); (Illus.). 10.79 (978-0-606-21058-4(X)) Tandem Library Bks.

—He Bear, She Bear. Berenstain, Stan & Berenstain, Jan, illus. 2002. (Berenstain Bears Bright & Early Bks.). (Illus.). (J). 16.70 (978-0-7587-1253-0(7)) Book Wholesalers, Inc.

—He Bear, She Bear. 1999. (Berenstain Bears Bright & Early Bks.). (Illus.). 24p. (J). (gr. k). bds. 4.99 (978-0-679-89426-1(8) , Random Hse. Bks. for Young Readers) Random Hse. Children's Bks.

—Inside, Outside, Upside Down. 2000. (Berenstain Bears Bright & Early Bks.). (J). (ps-3). 7.99 (978-0-375-80253-9(3)) Random Hse., Inc.

—Los Osos Berenstain y Demasiada Fiesta. ed. 2004. Tr. of Berenstain Bears & Too Much Birthday. (SPA., Illus.). (J). (gr. k-3). spiral bd. (978-0-616-14610-1(8)) Canadian National Institute for the Blind/Institut National Canadien pour les Aveugles.

—Los Osos Scouts Berenstain y el Desastre Colosal. 1998. (Berenstain Bear Scouts Ser.).Tr. of Berenstain Bear Scouts & the Really Big Disaster. (SPA.). (J). (gr. 3-6). pap. 3.50 (978-0-590-94482-3(7) , Scholastic Paperbacks) Scholastic, Inc.

—The Runamuck Dog Show. 2001. (Berenstain Bears Ser.). (Illus.). (J). (gr. k-3). 10.79 (978-0-606-21059-1(8)) Tandem Library Bks.

—The Wrong Crowd. 2001. (Berenstain Bears Ser.). (Illus.). (J). (gr. k-3). (978-0-606-21060-7(1)) Tandem Library Bks.

Berenstain, Stan, et al. The Berenstain Bears Save Christmas. Berenstain, Stan et al, illus. 2003. (Berenstain Bears Ser.). (J). (gr. k-3). 129.90 (978-0-06-056995-2(6)) HarperCollins Pubs.

BERLIN, IRVING, 1888-1989

Furstinger, Nancy. Say It with Music: The Story of Irving Berlin. 2004. (Masters of Music Ser.). (Illus.). 128p. (YA). (gr. 6-12). 23.95 (978-1-931798-12-9(5)) Reynolds, Morgan Inc.

Gillis, Jennifer Blizin. Irving Berlin: America's Songwriter. 2005. (J). pap. (978-1-4034-6758-4(7)); (Illus.). 32p. (978-1-4034-6750-8(1)) Heinemann Library.

BERLIN (GERMANY)

Barber, Nicola. Berlin. 2005. (Great Cities of the World Ser.). (Illus.). 48p. (J). pap. (978-0-8368-5203-5(6)); (YA). lib. bdg. 30.00 (978-0-8368-5043-7(2)) Stevens, Gareth Inc. (World Almanac Library).

Burgan, Michael. The Berlin Airlift. 2006. 48p. (J). (gr. 4-7). lib. bdg. (978-0-7565-2024-3(X)) Compass Point Bks.

Cartlidge, Cherese & Clark, Charles. Life in Berlin. 2001. (Way People Live Ser.). (Illus.). 96p. (YA). (gr. 7-10). 28.70 (978-1-56006-870-9(1) , LML00902-178194, Lucent Bks.) Thomson Gale.

Garner, Simon. Berlin. 2007. (Global Cities Ser.). (Illus.). 64p. (J). (gr. 5-8). 30.00 (978-0-7910-8846-3(4) , Chelsea Hse.) Facts On File, Inc.

Grant, R. G. The Berlin Wall. 1998. (New Perspectives Ser.). (Illus.). 64p. (J). (gr. 4-7). lib. bdg. 28.54 (978-0-8172-5017-1(4)) Raintree.

Hatt, Christine. Berlin. 1999. (World Cities Ser.). (Illus.). 48p. (J). (gr. 2-6). lib. bdg. 16.95 (978-1-929298-27-3(7)) Chrysalis Education.

Holmes, Burton. Berlin. Schlesinger, Arthur M., Jr. & Isreal, Fred L., eds. 1999. (World 100 Years Ago Ser.). (Illus.). 144p. (YA). (ps-3). 29.95 (978-0-7910-4664-7(8) , Chelsea Hse.) Facts On File, Inc.

Swanson, Diane. The Balloon Sailors. Lipka-Sztarballo, Krystyna, illus. 2003. 24p. (J). (gr. k-3). lib. bdg. 15.95 (978-1-55037-809-2(0)) Annick Pr., Ltd. CAN. *Dist:* Firefly Bks., Ltd.

BERLIN (GERMANY)—FICTION

Boyne, John. The Boy in the Striped Pyjamas. l.t. ed. 2007. (Isis Softcover Ser.). 208p. 27.99 ***(978-0-7531-7651-1(3))*** ISIS Large Print Bks. GBR. *Dist:* Ulverscroft Large Print Bks., Ltd.

—The Boy in the Striped Pyjamas. 2006. 224p. (J). ***(978-0-385-60940-1(X)*** , David Fickling Books) Random Hse. Children's Bks.

Dahlberg, Maurine F. Escape to West Berlin. 2004. 192p. (J). 16.00 (978-0-374-30959-6(0) , Farrar, Straus & Giroux (BYR)) Farrar, Straus & Giroux.

Erik & Isabelle Senior Year at Foresthill High. 2007. (YA). per. 12.00 ***(978-0-9755848-3-5(9))*** Foglight Pr.

Hoobler, Dorothy & Hoobler, Thomas. The 1930s: Directions. Hoffman, Robin, illus. 2000. (Century Kids Ser.). 160p. (J). (gr. 5-8). lib. bdg. 22.90 (978-0-7613-1603-9(5) , Twenty-First Century Bks.) Lerner Publishing Group.

Rahlens, Holly-Jane. Prince William, Maximilian Minsky, & Me. (YA). (gr. 7-11). 2007. 320p. pap. 7.99 ***(978-0-7636-3299-1(6));*** 2005. 160p. 16.99 (978-0-7636-2704-1(6)) Candlewick Pr.

BERLIN WALL, BERLIN, GERMANY, 1961-1989

Brager, Bruce L. The Iron Curtain: The Cold War in Europe. 2004. (Arbitrary Borders Ser.). (Illus.). 112p. (gr. 9-13). 35.00 (978-0-7910-7832-7(9) , Chelsea Hse.) Facts On File, Inc.

Burgan, Michael. The Berlin Wall: Barrier to Freedom. 2007. (J). lib. bdg. ***(978-0-7565-3330-4(9))*** Compass Point Bks.

Downey, Glen. Escape from East Berlin. Lingas, Leo, illus. 2007. 48p. (J). lib. bdg. 23.08 ***(978-1-4242-1635-2(4))*** Fitzgerald Bks.

Grant, R. G. The Berlin Wall. 1998. (New Perspectives Ser.). (Illus.). 64p. (J). (gr. 4-7). lib. bdg. 28.54 (978-0-8172-5017-1(4)) Raintree.

Kelly, Nigel. The Fall of the Berlin Wall: The Cold War Ends. 2006. (Point of Impact Ser.). (Illus.). 32p. (J). ***(978-1-4034-9139-8(9))*** Heinemann Library.

Kelly, Nigel. The Fall of the Berlin Wall Set 1: The Cold War Ends. 2002. (Point of Impact Ser.). (Illus.). 32p. (J). (gr. 5-7). pap. 7.50 (978-1-58810-355-0(2) , 91114) Heinemann Library.

Levy, Patricia. The Fall of the Berlin Wall, November 9, 1989. 2002. (Days That Shook the World Ser.). (Illus.). 48p. (J). lib. bdg. 27.12 (978-0-7398-5233-0(7)) Raintree.

Richard Tames. The Fall of the Berlin Wall. 2nd ed. 2006. (Point of Impact Ser.). (Illus.). 32p. (J). ***(978-1-4034-9148-0(8))*** Heinemann Library.

Smith, Jeremy. The Fall of the Berlin Wall. 2004. (Days That Changed the World Ser.). (Illus.). 48p. (J). (gr. 5 up). pap. 11.95 (978-0-8368-5576-0(0)); lib. bdg. 30.00 (978-0-8368-5569-2(8)) Stevens, Gareth Inc. (World Almanac Library).

Swanson, Diane. The Balloon Sailors. Lipka-Sztarballo, Krystyna, illus. 2003. 24p. (J). (gr. k-3). lib. bdg. 15.95 (978-1-55037-809-2(0)) Annick Pr., Ltd. CAN. *Dist:* Firefly Bks., Ltd.

Tracy, Kathleen. The Fall of the Berlin Wall. 2005. (Illus.). 48p. (J). lib. bdg. 29.95 (978-1-58415-405-1(5)) Mitchell Lane Pubs., Inc.

Williams, Brian. The Fall of the Berlin Wall. 2003. (Dates with History Ser.). 45p. (J). lib. bdg. 28.50 (978-1-58340-409-6(0)) Smart Apple Media.

Woods, Jessica. The Berlin Wall. 2004. (Building World Landmarks Ser.). (Illus.). 48p. (J). (gr. 4-7). 24.95 (978-1-4103-0137-6(0) , Blackbirch Pr., Inc.) Thomson Gale.

BERLIN WALL, BERLIN, GERMANY, 1961-1989—FICTION

Buenas Nuevas Para Los Ninos Club Biblico. 2002. (J). (gr. 1-6). 39.95 (978-0-633-01743-9(4)) LifeWay Christian Resources.

Nelson, Suzanne. The Sound of Munich. Henderson, Jeanine, illus. 2006. (S. A. S. S. (Students Across the Seven Seas) Ser.). 224p. (J). (gr. 7). pap. 6.99 (978-0-14-240576-5(0) , Puffin) Penguin Group (USA) Inc.

Schneider, Peter. Mauerspringer. (GER.). pap. 18.95 (978-3-499-13532-3(9)) Rowohlt Taschenbuch Verlag GmbH DEU. *Dist:* Distribooks, Inc.

BERLIOZ, HECTOR, 1803-1869

Berlioz, Hector. Life & Letters of Hector Berlioz. 2001. 305p. (YA). reprint ed. 98.00 (978-0-7222-5356-4(7)) Library Reprints, Inc.

Thompson, Sydney R. Hector Berlioz: A Critical Monograph. 2001. (YA). reprint ed. 150.00 (978-0-7222-5357-1(5)) Library Reprints, Inc.

Whiting, Jim. The Life & Times of Hector Berlioz. 2004. (Masters of Music Ser.). (Illus.). 48p. (gr. 4-8). lib. bdg. 20.95 (978-1-58415-259-0(1)) Mitchell Lane Pubs., Inc.

BERMUDA ISLANDS

Crooker, Richard A. Bermuda. 2005. (Modern World Nations Ser.). 150p. (J). 30.00 (978-0-7910-8663-6(1) , Chelsea Hse.) Facts On File, Inc.

BERMUDA ISLANDS—FICTION

Weise, Selene H. C. Gold for a Boat. 2001. (Illus.). 68p. (J). (gr. 1-6). 5.95 (978-1-57249-270-7(8) , Burd Street Pr.) White Mane Publishing Co., Inc.

BERMUDA TRIANGLE

Aaseng, Nathan. The Bermuda Triangle. 2000. (Mystery Library). (Illus.). 96p. (YA). (gr. 4-12). 27.45 (978-1-56006-769-6(1) , Lucent Bks.) Thomson Gale.

DeMolay, Jack. The Bermuda Triangle: The Disappearance of Flight 19. 2007. (Graphic Mysteries Ser.). (J). (978-1-4042-2347-9(9)); pap. (978-1-4042-2157-4(3)); (gr. 2-6). lib. bdg. 21.25 (978-1-4042-3404-8(7)) Rosen Publishing Group, Inc., The. (PowerKids Pr.).

Donkin, Andrew. Bermuda Triangle, Vol. 3. 2000. (Eyewitness Readers). (Illus.). 48p. (J). (gr. 5-3). pap. 3.99 (978-0-7894-5415-7(7)) Dorling Kindersley Publishing, Inc.

—Bermuda Triangle. 2000. (Illus.). 48p. lib. bdg. 10.79 (978-0-606-18113-6(X)); lib. bdg. 11.80 (978-0-613-24337-7(4)) Tandem Library Bks.

Donkin, Andrew & Dorling Kindersley Publishing Staff. Bermuda Triangle. 2000. (Eyewitness Readers). (Illus.). 48p. (J). (gr. 2-3). 12.99 (978-0-7894-5416-4(5)) Dorling Kindersley Publishing, Inc.

Gorman, Jacqueline Laks. The Bermuda Triangle. 2002. (X Science Ser.). (Illus.). 24p. (YA). (gr. 2 up). lib. bdg. 22.00 (978-0-8368-3196-2(9)) Stevens, Gareth Inc.

Hamilton, Sue L. The Bermuda Triangle. 2007. (Unsolved Mysteries Ser.). (ENG., Illus.). 32p. (J). (gr. 4-8). lib. bdg. 25.65 ***(978-1-59928-834-5(6)*** , ABDO & Daughters) ABDO Publishing Co.

Innes, Brian. The Bermuda Triangle. 1999. (Unsolved Mysteries Ser.). (Illus.). 48p. (YA). (gr. 3 up). lib. bdg. (978-0-8172-5485-8(4)) Raintree.

—The Bermuda Triangle. 1999. (Unsolved Mysteries Ser.). (Illus.). 48p. (J). (gr. 3-7). pap. 8.05 (978-0-8172-5847-4(7)) Steck-Vaughn.

Jackson, Kay. The Bermuda Triangle 1945. 2006. (Natural Disasters Ser.). (Illus.). 32p. (J). (gr. 1-4). lib. bdg. (978-1-58415-497-6(7)) Mitchell Lane Pubs., Inc.

The Legend of the Bermuda Triangle. 1999. (SmartReader Ser.). (J). Level 1. pap., tchr. ed. 19.95 incl. audio (978-0-7887-0758-2(2) , 79346T3); Level 2. pap., tchr. ed. 19.95 incl. audio (978-0-7887-0113-9(4) , 79301T3) Recorded Bks., LLC.

Oxlade, Chris. The Mystery of the Bermuda Triangle. 2006. (Can Science Solve? Ser.). (Illus.). 32p. (978-1-4034-8336-2(1)) Heinemann Library.

—Mystery of the Bermuda Triangle. 2001. (Can Science Solve? Ser.). (Illus.). (J). (978-0-606-21718-7(5)) Tandem Library Bks.

—The Mystery of the Bermuda Triangle. (Can Science Solve? Ser.). (Illus.). 32p. 2nd ed. 2006. pap. (978-1-4034-8345-4(0)); Set 1. 2002. (J). (gr. 4-7). pap. 7.50 (978-1-58810-313-0(7) , 91038) Heinemann Library.

Rosenberg, Aaron. The Bermuda Triangle. 2005. (Unsolved Mysteries Ser.). (Illus.). 48p. (YA). (gr. 5-8). lib. bdg. 25.25 (978-0-8239-3560-4(4)) Rosen Publishing Group, Inc., The.

Rudolph, Aaron L. The Bermuda Triangle. 2004. (Unexplained Ser.). (Illus.). 32p. (J). lib. bdg. 22.60 (978-0-7368-2718-8(8)) Capstone Pr., Inc.

West, David. The Bermuda Triangle. Lacey, Mike, illus. 2005. (Graphic Mysteries Ser.). 48p. (J). pap. (978-1-4042-0806-3(2)) Rosen Publishing Group, Inc., The.

—The Bermuda Triangle: Strange Happenings at Sea. Lacey, Mike, illus. 2005. (Graphic Mysteries Ser.). 48p. (J). (gr. 5-8). lib. bdg. 29.95 (978-1-4042-0795-0(3)) Rosen Publishing Group, Inc., The.

BERNSTEIN, LEONARD, 1918-1990

Blashfield, Jean F. Leonard Bernstein: Conductor & Composer. 2000. (Career Biographies Ser.). (Illus.). 128p. (YA). (gr. 6-12). 25.00 (978-0-89434-337-7(8) , F404, Ferguson Publishing Co.) Facts On File, Inc.

Lazo, Caroline Evensen. Leonard Bernstein: In Love with Music. 128p. (J). (gr. 6 up). 18.95 (978-1-58013-105-6(0)) Kar-Ben Publishing.

—Leonard Bernstein: In Love with Music. 2002. (Lerner Biographies Ser.). (Illus.). 128p. (J). (gr. 6-12). lib. bdg. 27.93 (978-0-8225-0072-8(8) , Lerner Pubns.) Lerner Publishing Group.

Venezia, Mike. Leonard Bernstein. 1998. (Getting to Know the World's Greatest Composers Ser.). (Illus.). 32p. (J). (gr. 3-4). pap. 6.95 (978-0-516-26244-4(0) , Children's Pr.) Scholastic Library Publishing.

BERRIES

Burns, Diane L. Berries, Nuts & Seeds. Garrow, Linda, illus. 2000. (Young Naturalist Field Guides Ser.). 40p. (J). (gr. 3 up). lib. bdg. 24.67 (978-0-8368-2144-4(0)) Stevens, Gareth Inc.

Julius, Jennifer. I Like Berries. 2001. (gr. k-3). lib. bdg. 12.95 (978-0-613-52082-9(3)) Tandem Library Bks.

Snyder, Inez. Cranberries. 2004. (Harvesttime Ser.). (Illus.). 24p. (J). 18.00 (978-0-516-27592-5(5)); pap. 4.95 (978-0-516-25912-3(1)) Scholastic Library Publishing. (Children's Pr.).

BEST BOOKS

Buckley, William F., Jr. The National Review Treasury of Classic Children's Literature, Vol. II. 2004. 528p. (J). 29.95 (978-0-9627841-7-0(6)) ISI Bks.

Buckley, William F., Jr., selected by. The National Review Treasury of Classic Children's Literature. 2003. 523p. (J). 29.95 (978-0-9627841-5-6(X)) National Review, Inc.

Dibner, Ellen J. & Gustafson, Ronald. The Book Finders for Kids. Dibner, Ellen J. & Gustafson, Ronald, illus. 1998. (Illus.). 16p. (Orig.). (J). (gr. 2-8). pap. 3.95 (978-0-9620888-0-3(3)) Point Pubns.

Gillespie, John T. Best Books for Young Teen Readers: Grades 7-10. 2000. (Best Books for Young Teen Readers Ser.). 1066p. (YA). (gr. 7-10). 75.00 (978-0-8352-4264-6(1) , BOBBYTR) Greenwood Publishing Group, Inc.

Jweid, Rosann & Rizzo, Margaret. Building Character Through Literature: A Guide for Middle School Readers. 2001. (Illus.). 240p. (gr. 7-8). 39.50 (978-0-8108-3951-9(2)) Scarecrow Pr., Inc.

Odean, Kathleen. Great Books about Things That Kids Love. 2001. (Illus.). (J). 20.65 (978-0-606-21218-2(3)) Tandem Library Bks.

Random House Staff. The Sisterhood of the Traveling Pants: The Official Scrapbook. movie tie-in ed. 2005. (Illus.). 160p. (YA). (gr. 7). pap. 9.95 (978-0-553-37607-4(1) , Delacorte Bks. for Young Readers) Random Hse. Children's Bks.

Silvey, Anita. 500 Great Books for Teens. 2006. 416p. 26.00 (978-0-618-61296-3(3)) Houghton Mifflin Co.

Williams, Rozanne Lanczak. Itty Bitty Carrying Case, 36 bks. Briles, Patty, illus. 2002. (Itty Bitty Phonics Readers Ser.). (J). (gr. k-1). pap. 35.99 (978-1-57471-981-9(5) , 3261) Creative Teaching Pr., Inc.

BETHUNE, MARY MCLEOD, 1875-1955

Broadwater, Andrea. Mary McLeod Bethune: Educator & Activist. 2003. (African-American Biographies Ser.). (Illus.). 112p. (YA). (gr. 6-12). lib. bdg. 26.60 (978-0-7660-1771-9(0)) Enslow Pubs., Inc.

Dare to Be. . . Mary McLeod Bethune Children's Book. 2003. 3.99 (978-0-915960-55-2(9)) Ebon Research Systems Publishing, LLC.

Domblewski, Carol. Citizens Who Made a Difference. 2005. (Navigators Ser.). (J). pap. 38.00 ***(978-1-4108-5097-3(8))*** Benchmark Education Co.

Donovan, Sandy. Mary McLeod Bethune. 2003. (African-American Biographies Ser.). 64p. (YA). pap. 8.95 (978-1-4109-0039-5(8)); (Illus.). (J). lib. bdg. 28.56 (978-0-7398-6868-3(3)) Raintree.

Evento, Susan. Mary McLeod Bethune. 2004. (Rookie Biographies Ser.). (Illus.). 31p. (J). 20.50 (978-0-516-21720-8(8) , Children's Pr.) Scholastic Library Publishing.

—Mary Mcleod Bethune. 2004. (Rookie Biographies Ser.). 32p. (J). (gr. 1-2). pap. 4.95 (978-0-516-25830-0(3) , Children's Pr.) Scholastic Library Publishing.

Hanson, Joyce Ann. Mary McLeod Bethune & Black Women's Political Activism. 2003. (Illus.). 256p. 32.50 (978-0-8262-1451-5(7)) Univ. of Missouri Pr.

Johnston, Lissa Jones. Mary McLeod Bethune: Empowering Educator. 2006. (Fact Finders Ser.). (Illus.). 32p. (J). 22.60 (978-0-7368-6421-3(0)) Capstone Pr., Inc.

Kelso, Richard. Building a Dream: Mary Bethune's School. 2001. (Nonfiction Bookbag Ser.). (J). (gr. 3-4). per. 8.45 (978-1-58830-201-4(6)) Metropolitan Teaching & Learning Co.

Mary Mcleod Bethune. (Photo Illustrated Biographies Ser.). 24p. (J). 6.95 (978-0-7368-4471-0(6)) Capstone Pr., Inc.

Mary Mcleod Bethune, 6 vols. (gr. 2-5). 36.95 (978-0-7368-4563-2(1)) Red Brick Learning.

McKissack, Patricia C. & McKissack, Fredrick L. Mary McLeod Bethune: A Great American Educator. rev. ed. 2001. (Great African Americans Ser.). (Illus.). 32p. (J). (gr. 1-4). lib. bdg. 18.60 (978-0-7660-1680-4(3)) Enslow Pubs., Inc.

Somervill, Barbara A. Mary McLeod Bethune: African-American Educator. 2003. (Spirit of America). (Illus.). 32p. (J). (gr. 2-6). 27.07 (978-1-59296-008-8(1)) Child's World, Inc.

Sterling, Kristin. Mary McLeod Bethune: A Life of Resourcefulness. 2008. (Pull Ahead Books-Biographies Ser.). (J). lib. bdg. 22.60 ***(978-0-8225-8588-6(X)*** , Lerner Pubns.) Lerner Publishing Group.

BEVERAGES

Albrecht, John, Jr. Chocolate Milk Likes Me. Ashby, Chris, illus. 2006. 16p. (J). pap. 8.99 (978-0-9778586-3-7(4) , CRP004); pap. 8.99 (978-0-9778586-2-0(6) , CRP0003) Crooked River Pr. (Blue Jay Bks.).

Bell, Lonnie. The Story of Coca-Cola. 2003. (Built for Success Ser.). (Illus.). 48p. (J). 28.50 (978-1-58340-292-4(6)) Smart Apple Media.

Dunnington, Rose. Delicious Drinks to Sip, Slurp, Gulp & Guzzle. 2006. (Illus.). 112p. (J). 9.95 (978-1-57990-779-2(2) , 1252097) Lark Bks.

Frankeny, Hellmich & Hellmich, Mittie. Mini Bar: Rum. Stojanovic, Laura, photos by. 2007. (Illus.). 80p. 7.95 (978-0-8118-5438-2(8)) Chronicle Bks. LLC.

Hellmich, Mittie. Mini Bar: Gin. Frankeny, Frankie & Stojanovic, Laura, photos by. 2007. (Illus.). 80p. 7.95 (978-0-8118-5424-5(8)) Chronicle Bks. LLC.

—Mini Bar: Tequila. Frankeny, Frankie & Stojanovic, Laura, photos by. 2007. (Illus.). 80p. 7.95 (978-0-8118-5436-8(1)) Chronicle Bks. LLC.

Julius, Jennifer. I Like Juice. 2001. (gr. k-3). lib. bdg. 12.95 (978-0-613-52088-1(2)) Tandem Library Bks.

Martineau, Susan. Healthy Eating. 2006. (Illus.). 32p. (J). (978-1-58340-898-8(3) , 1262654) Smart Apple Media.

McClellan, Marilyn. The Big Deal about Alcohol: What Teens Need to Know about Drinking. 2004. (Issues in Focus Ser.). (Illus.). 128p. (J). lib. bdg. 26.60 (978-0-7660-2163-1(7)) Enslow Pubs., Inc.

Primm & Petelinsek. Food/Comida. 2004. (Talking Hands, Listening Eyes Ser.). (ENG & SPA., Illus.). 24p. (J). (ps-3). 21.36 (978-1-59296-020-0(0)) Child's World, Inc.

Raintree Steck-Vaughn Staff. Strawberry Crush & Other Recipes. 2000. (Read All about It Ser.). (Illus.). (J). pap. 4.95 (978-0-8114-3774-5(4)) Steck-Vaughn.

Rybolt, Thomas R. Soda Pop Science Projects: Experiments with Carbonated Soft Drinks. 2004. (Science Fair Success Ser.). (Illus.). 104p. (J). lib. bdg. 26.60 (978-0-7660-2089-4(4)) Enslow Pubs., Inc.

Trumbauer, Lisa. The Story of Orange Juice. 2005. (Yellow Umbrella Ser.). (J). (978-0-7368-5268-5(9)); (Illus.). 16p. (978-0-7368-5304-0(9)) Capstone Pr., Inc.

BIAFRA

see Nigeria

BIBLE

AB

Elkins, Stephen. Bible Blessings. Colton, Ellie, illus. 2003. (Lulla-Bible Series for Little Ones). 32p. (J). 9.99 incl. audio compact disk (978-0-8054-2761-5(9)) B&H Publishing Grp.

—Bible Promises. Colton, Ellie, illus. 2003. (Lulla-Bible Series for Little Ones). 32p. (J). 9.99 incl. audio compact disk (978-0-8054-2756-1(2)) B&H Publishing Grp.

—First Steps in the Bible. Colton, Ellie, illus. 2006. (First Steps Ser.). 32p. (J). 9.99 (978-0-8054-2672-4(8)) B&H Publishing Grp.

—My LullaBible A to Z Promise Book: Baby's First A to Z Collection of Bible Promises. Colton, Ellie, illus. 2007. 36p. (J). 14.99 (978-0-8054-2657-1(4)) B&H Publishing Grp.

—The Word & Song Bible. O'Connor, Tim, illus. 2004. 448p. (J). (ps-5). 19.99 (978-0-8054-1689-3(7)) B&H Publishing Grp.

—The Word & Song Bible. 1999. (Illus.). 448p. (J). (ps-5). 34.99 incl. audio (978-0-8054-1691-6(9)) B&H Publishing Grp.

—The Word & Song Songbook Vol. 1: The Old Testament. 2004. (Illus.). 64p. (J). 12.99 incl. audio (978-0-8054-1694-7(3)) B&H Publishing Grp.

Ellis, Gwen. My Little Learner Bible. 2005. 525p. (J). 14.99 (978-1-4003-0582-7(9)) Nelson, Thomas Inc.

Equipo Tecnico, Susaeta. Santa Biblia. 2001. Tr. of Holy Bible. (SPA.). 176p. (978-84-305-0875-4(9)) Lectorum Pubns., Inc.

EvangeCube Children Bible Study Leader¿s Guide. 2005. (J). 6.00 (978-1-933383-46-0(1)) E3 Resources.

Evans, Gwydion, et al. Gemau Gwirion! 2005. (WEL.). 107p. (978-1-85994-035-8(8)) Cyhoeddiadau'r Gair.

Exodus, Be Redeemed & Delivered. 2004. (YA). spiral bd. 14.00 (978-0-9729477-2-5(8)) Morningstar Christian Chapel.

The Explorer's Bible for Kids: Explore & Live God's Word. 2004. (Illus.). 1,744p. (J). 24.99 (978-0-7180-0694-5(1)) Nelson, Thomas Inc.

Extreme Faith Compact Youth Bible. 2000. (J). pap. 5.00 (978-1-58516-168-3(3)) American Bible Society.

Extreme Teen Bible. rev. ed. 2006. 1664p. (YA). 29.99 (978-0-7180-1610-4(6)) Nelson, Thomas Inc.

Extreme Teen Bible: Revised & Updated. 2006. (YA). 1600p. 29.99 (978-0-7180-1613-5(0)); 1600p. pap. 19.99 (978-0-7180-1612-8(2)); 1664p. pap. 19.99 (978-0-7180-1609-8(2)); 1664p. im. lthr. 39.99 (978-0-7180-1611-1(4)); 1600p. im. lthr. 39.99 (978-0-7180-1614-2(9)) Nelson, Thomas Inc.

Favorite Bible Verses. 2006. 28p. (J). pap. 3.49 (978-0-7847-1021-0(X) , 22085) Standard Publishing.

Feiler, Bruce S. Walking the Bible: An Illustrated Journey for Kids Through the Greatest Stories Ever Told. Meret, Sasha, illus. ed. 2005. 112p. (J). pap. 7.99 (978-0-06-051119-7(2) , Harper Trophy) HarperCollins Pubs.

Feldick, Les. Questions & Answers from the Bible. 2004. 364p. 12.00 (978-1-885344-99-1(6)) Feldick, Les Ministries.

Fill-in-the-Blank Bible Fun 4-6. 2004. 32p. (J). pap. 3.99 (978-0-88724-222-9(7) , CD-2043) Carson-Dellosa Publishing Co., Inc.

First Communion Bible - St. Joseph Edition (Girls) - New American Bible. 1998. (Illus.). 1676p. (J). (gr. 2-12). pap. 18.95 (978-0-89942-956-4(4) , 609-22FCG) Catholic Bk. Publishing Corp.

Fiske, Dwight. Without Music. 2005. reprint ed. pap. 22.95 (978-1-4191-7126-0(7)) Kessinger Publishing, LLC.

Fittro, Pat, ed. Standard Christmas Program Book: 2000 Edition. 2000. 48p. (J). pap. 4.99 (978-0-7847-1167-5(4) , 08650) Standard Publishing.

Fleetwood, Jenni. While Shepherds Watched. Melnyczuk, Peter, illus. 1999. 28p. (J). (ps-2). 12.99 (978-0-8054-2036-4(3)) B&H Publishing Grp.

Flegal, Daphna. Play & Say It: Bible Verses for Children. 2001. (Illus.). 48p. (J). (ps-3). 12.00 (978-0-687-01679-2(7)) Abingdon Pr.

—Sign & Say Bible Verses for Children. 2004. (Illus.). 48p. (ps-3). 13.00 (978-0-687-07442-6(8)) Abingdon Pr.

Flegal, Daphna & Augustine, Peg. Bible Says. Easter, Paige, illus. 2000. 16p. (J). (ps-k). 8.00 (978-0-687-01477-4(8)) Abingdon Pr.

Foce, Natalia, tr. from ENG. Jesus el Milagroso. Anderson, Jeff, illus. l.t. ed. 2004. Orig. Title: Jesus the Miracle Worker. (SPA.). 24p. (J). 2.99 (978-1-932789-28-7(6)) Editorial Sendas Antiguas, LLC.

—Jesus Maestro. Anderson, Jeff, illus. l.t. ed. 2004. Orig. Title: Jesus the Teacher. (SPA.). 24p. (J). 2.99 (978-1-932789-26-3(X)) Editorial Sendas Antiguas, LLC.

—Jesus Niño. Anderson, Jeff, illus. l.t. ed. 2004. Orig. Title: Jesus the Child. (SPA.). 24p. (J). 2.99 (978-1-932789-24-9(3)) Editorial Sendas Antiguas, LLC.

Forlini, Victoria, ed. Bible Big Color & Activity Book with Stickers. 2005. (ENG.). 64p. (J). pap. 2.99 (978-0-696-22824-7(6)) Meredith Bks.

—Bible Ultimate Color & Activity Book with Paints. 2005. (ENG.). 32p. (J). pap. 2.99 (978-0-696-22823-0(8)) Meredith Bks.

Francen, Mike. Vision, Passion, & the Pursuit of God. rev. ed. 1998. (Illus.). 72p. (YA). (gr. 7 up). pap. 6.00 (978-1-888079-15-9(0)) Francen World Outreach.

Freedman, Claire. My First Book of Bible Prayers. 2004. 32p. 10.99 (978-0-8254-7296-1(2)) Kregel Pubns.

Freeman, Kaye. Bible Covenants. 2005. 79p. (YA). pap. 7.99 (978-0-9703069-6-8(2)) Train-Up A Child, LLC.

Fryar, Jane L., ed. My Christmas Bible. 2004. (J). 0.99 (978-0-9747923-1-6(4)) C T A, Inc.

—My Christmas Bible: King James Version. 2004. (J). 0.99 (978-0-9747923-3-0(0)) C T A, Inc.

Gastaldi, Sylvia. People of the Bible: Life & Customs. Musatti, Claire, illus. 2001. 112p. (J). pap. 15.95 (978-0-86716-468-8(9)) St. Anthony Messenger Pr. & Franciscan Communications.

GNT Children's Bible with Deuterocanonical & Apocryphal Books. 2004. 1888p. lthr. 15.00 (978-1-58516-009-9(1)) American Bible Society.

GOD'S WORD for Boys. 2004. 1713p. 27.99 (978-1-932587-52-4(7)) Green Key Bks.

GOD'S WORD for Girls. 2004. 1714p. im. lthr. 27.99 (978-1-932587-53-1(5)) Green Key Bks.

Golden Books Staff. Jumbo Bible Coloring Book, Bk. C&A. 2006. (Illus.). 320p. (J). (ps-2). pap. 4.99 (978-0-375-83625-1(X) , Golden Inspirational) Random Hse. Children's Bks.

Gospel Light Publications Staff. Big Book of Bible Puzzles. 2000. (Big Book Ser.). (Illus.). 216p. pap. 17.99 (978-0-8307-2542-7(3) , Gospel Light) Gospel Light Pubns.

Graves, Sue. What Is the Bible? 2003. (Illus.). 62p. (J). 12.95 (978-0-8198-8306-3(9) , 332-414) Pauline Bks. & Media.

Gray, Charlotte. Traveling Through the Bible with Bible Folks. Henderson, Liz, illus. (J). spiral bd. 14.99 (978-0-89098-265-5(1)) Twentieth Century Christian Bks.

Greendyk, William, tr. Los DOS Osos. l.t. ed. 2004. (SPA.). 152p. (J). pap. 5.99 (978-1-932789-02-7(2) , R009N) Editorial Sendas Antiguas, LLC.

—La Hierba Mala. l.t. ed. 2004. Tr. of Hierba Mala. (SPA.). 156p. (J). pap. 5.99 (978-1-932789-01-0(4) , X002N) Editorial Sendas Antiguas, LLC.

—Los Niños de la Biblia. l.t. ed. 2004. (SPA.). 94p. (J). pap. 3.99 (978-1-932789-03-4(0) , X003N) Editorial Sendas Antiguas, LLC.

—Primeras Impresiones de Dios. l.t. ed. 2004. Tr. of Primeras Impresiones de Dios. (SPA.). 94p. (J). pap. 3.99 (978-1-932789-04-1(9) , W001N) Editorial Sendas Antiguas, LLC.

Grimm, Gary & Allison, Virginia. Bible Jingo. Schwab, Vanessa, illus. 1999. 32p. (YA). (gr. 3 up). 12.95 (978-1-56490-126-2(2)) Grim, Gary & Assocs.

Grispino, Joseph A., et al, contrib. by. The Golden Children's Bible. 1999. (Illus.). 512p. (J). (gr. 3-8). 17.99 (978-0-307-16520-6(5) , 16835, Golden Inspirational) Random Hse. Children's Bks.

Groome, Thomas H., et al. Acercandote al Amor de Dios (Coming to God's Love) 1998. (Acercandote a la Fe Ser.). (SPA & ENG., Illus.). 304p. (J). (gr. 4). pap. 12.36 net. (978-0-8215-4464-8(0)) Sadlier, William H. Inc.

Group Publishing Staff. Holyword, Preschool Student Books. 2000. (Illus.). (J). pap., stu. ed. 2.99 (978-0-7644-2182-2(4)) Group Publishing, Inc.

Group Publishing Staff & Tyndale House Publishers Staff, prods. Hands-on Bible. 2004. 1440p. (J). 24.99 (978-0-8423-8759-0(5)); per. 19.99 (978-0-8423-8760-6(9)) Tyndale Hse. Pubs.

Guetov, Dimitar D., des. Bulgarian Orthodox Bible: (Pravoslavna Biblia) 2nd ed. 2004. (BUL.). 820p. per. 24.99 (978-0-9753970-0-8(1)) Capricorn Publishing.

Gunderson, Vivian D. The Bible Is the Best Book. Why? Mowery, Linda Williams & Murphy, Emmy Lou, illus. 36p. (J). (gr. 4-8). pap., wbk. ed. 2.00 (978-0-915374-00-7(5)) Rapids Christian Pr., Inc.

Hahn, Samuel J. Learning from the Lizard: Bible Animal Object Lessons. 2000. (J). (ps-3). pap. 8.75 (978-0-7880-1593-9(1)) CSS Publishing Co.

The Hail Mary. Date not set. bds. 3.95 (978-0-88271-561-2(5) , 12011) Regina Pr., Malhame & Co.

Hakowski, Maryann. ScriptureWalk Junior High: Bible Themes. 2003. (ScriptureWalk Ser.). 104p. (YA). (gr. 8-12). pap. 19.95 (978-0-88489-607-4(2)) St. Mary's Pr.

Halley, Henry H. Halley's Bible Kidnotes. 2003. (NIrV Kid Reference Library). (Illus.). 448p. (J). 14.99 (978-0-310-70117-0(1)) Zonderkidz.

Ham Ken & Taylor Jonathan. My Creation Bible With. 2006. 11p. 11.99 (978-0-89051-462-7(3)) Master Bks.

Hands-On Bible Curriculum Director Manual: Fall 2000-Summer 2001. 1999. (Hands-On Bible Curriculum Ser.). (J). (ps-6). pap. 15.99 (978-0-7644-0226-5(9)) Group Publishing, Inc.

Harrast, Tracy. My Bible ABCs. Munger, Nancy, illus. 1998. 32p. (J). (ps). 4.99 (978-0-310-91778-6(6)) Zondervan.

—Not-So-Quiet Times Vol. 1: 240 Family Devotions Based on the Words of Jesus. Caldwell, Lise, ed. 2000. (Illus.). 272p. (J). (gr. 1-6). 12.99 (978-0-7847-1041-8(4) , 04297, Bean Sprouts) Standard Publishing.

—Peek-a-Bible Collection: A Lift-the-Flap Storybook, Set. 2003. (Illus.). 96p. (J). 12.99 (978-0-310-70450-8(2)) Zonderkidz.

Harrast, Tracy & Moore, Carl. The Christmas Story. Moore, Carl, illus. 1998. (Peek-a-Bible Ser.). (Illus.). 18p. (J). (ps-1). 6.99 (978-0-310-97585-4(9)) Zonderkidz.

Harrison, James, et al. My Very First Bible. 2005. (My very first Bks.). (Illus.). 80p. (J). 12.99 (978-0-7566-0983-2(6)) Dorling Kindersley Publishing, Inc.

Hastings, Selina. Children's Illustrated Bible. Thomas, Eric, illus. 2004. 320p. (J). (gr. 8). 22.99 (978-0-7566-0261-1(0)) Dorling Kindersley Publishing, Inc.

—The Illustrated Jewish Bible for Children. Thomas, Eric & Burch, Amy, illus. 2002. 192p. (J). (gr. 4-7). reprint ed. 19.00 (978-0-7567-5335-1(X)) DIANE Publishing Co.

Hathersmith, June. From Akebu to Zapotec: A Book of Bibleless Peoples. Roder, Alice, illus. 2002. 31p. (J). pap. (978-0-938978-28-2(4)) Wycliffe Bible Translators.

Haywood, H. L. Bible. 2004. 1152p. 35.00 (978-0-00-718952-6(4)) HarperCollins Pubs. Ltd. GBR. *Dist:* Independent Pubs. Group.

Head, Heno, Jr. God Made the Ocean. Ring, Laura, ed. Fletcher, Rusty, illus. 2000. (Happy Day Bks.). 24p. (J). (ps-2). 2.49 (978-0-7847-1100-2(3) , 04305, Bean Sprouts) Standard Publishing.

—God's World of Weather. Ring, Laura, ed. Fletcher, Rusty, illus. 2000. (Happy Day Bks.). 24p. (J). (ps-2). 2.49 (978-0-7847-1101-9(1) , 04306, Bean Sprouts) Standard Publishing.

Hendrickson, Julie. Carefree Play, Summer Day: A Bible Verse & Rhyme Book. Burris, Priscilla, illus. 1998. 32p. (J). (ps-1). 6.99 (978-0-570-05048-3(0) , 56-1872GJ) Concordia Publishing Hse.

Henley, Karyn. Day by Day Devotions 2. 2005. (Illus.). 368p. (J). (ps-ps). per. 12.99 (978-0-8423-7486-6(8) , Tyndale Fiction) Tyndale Hse. Pubs.

Her First Bible/Little Ones. 2002. 16.98 (978-0-310-60054-1(5)) Zondervan.

Hill, Karen. The Real Me Only God Can See (Pink) A Diary. 2003. 96p. (J). spiral bd. 14.99 (978-1-4003-0233-8(1)) Nelson, Thomas Inc.

Hollingsworth, Mary. The Amazing Expedition Bible. 1999. (Bible Basics Ser.). (Illus.). (J). (gr. 4-6). pap. 9.99 (978-0-8010-0275-5(3) , New Kids Media) Baker Bks.

Holmes, Andy. If You Give a Girl a Bible. 2004. (YA). pap. 11.99 (978-0-8254-5518-6(9)) Kregel Pubns.

Hoth, Iva. La Biblia Ilustrada. 2nd ed. 2003. Tr. of Picture Bible. (SPA.). 800p. 18.99 (978-0-8254-1998-0(0) , Editorial Portavoz) Kregel Pubns.

Howdeshell, Gary. Genesis to Revelation: A Bible Coloring Book. 1999. (Illus.). 48p. (J). pap. 5.95 (978-0-934426-92-3(9)) NAPSAC Reproductions.

Hunt, Susan. My ABC Bible Verses: Hiding God's Word in Little Hearts. 1998. (Illus.). 64p. (ps-2). 14.99 (978-1-58134-005-1(2) , Crossway Bibles) Crossway Bks.

Hutchings, Noah W. God, the Master Mathematician. 2002. (gr. 7-12). lib. bdg. 19.90 (978-0-613-64723-6(8)) Tandem Library Bks.

IBS Staff & Zondervan. NVI Biblia Aventura. 2004. (SPA.). 792p. pap. 24.99 (978-0-8297-3231-3(4)) Vida Pubs.

ICB Translation Staff, ed. ICB Holy Bible. 2005. 1508p. (J). pap. 21.99 (978-1-4003-0726-5(0)) Nelson, Thomas Inc.

Intermediate Bible Class: Winter, 2006/2007. 2006. (YA). pap. (978-1-59843-039-4(4)) Inc. Trustees of the Gospel Worker Society, The.

Intermediate Bible Class Vol. 3: Summer 2006. 2006. (YA). pap. (978-1-59843-037-0(8)) Inc. Trustees of the Gospel Worker Society, The.

Intermediate Bible Class Vol. 4: Fall 2006. 2006. (YA). pap. (978-1-59843-038-7(6)) Inc. Trustees of the Gospel Worker Society, The.

The International Student Bible for Catholics. 2001. 1664p. (YA). stu. ed. 21.99 (978-0-7180-0063-9(3)) Nelson, Thomas Inc.

Isbell, Charles D. God's Scribes Vol. 3: How the Bible Became the Bible. Gosline, Sheldon Lee & Ness, Lester, eds. 1999. (Marco Polo Monographs: Vol. 3). (ENG & HEB., Illus.). 270p. (C). pap. 31.00 (978-0-9677201-3-5(3)) Shangri-La Pubns.

Jackman, David. I Believe in the Bible. 2001. (Illus.). 240p. (J). pap. (978-0-340-74574-8(6) , Hodder & Stoughton Religious) Hodder Religious Division.

Jahns, Susan & Jahns, Randall. Pocket Promises for Kids: Verses to Learn from A to Z. Bryer, Debbie, illus. 2000. (Pocketpac Books Ser.). (ps-3). pap. 2.99 (978-0-87788-657-0(1) , Shaw) WaterBrook Pr.

James, Steven. Believe It! Bible Basics That Won't Break Your Brain. Lee, Jared D., illus. 2006. 76p. (YA). pap. 11.99 (978-0-7847-1393-8(6) , 42171) Standard Publishing.

Jesus Company Bible Time Grade. 2004. (gr. 6 up). tchr. ed. 15.99 (978-0-570-00685-5(6)); stu. ed. 7.99 (978-0-570-00684-8(8)) Concordia Publishing Hse.

John, Hatchard. Hedge of Thorns. 2004. 12.00 (978-1-58474-011-7(6)) Cornerstone Family Ministries/Lamplighter Publishing.

Jones, Sally Lloyd. How Big Is God's Love? A Soft-Edges Photo Frame Book. MacLean, Moira, illus. 2000. (Baby Blessings Ser.). 12p. (J). (ps-k). bds. 6.99 (978-0-7847-1136-1(4) , 04316, Bean Sprouts) Standard Publishing.

Joslin, Mary. God Is Love: Classic Bible Verses for Children. Saeker, Tom, illus. 2004. 24p. (ps up). 15.95 (978-0-8294-1487-5(8)) Loyola Pr.

Junior Bible Class: Winter 2006. 2006. (J). pap. (978-1-59843-031-8(9)) Inc. Trustees of the Gospel Worker Society, The.

Junior Bible Class Vol. 2: Spring 2006. 2006. (J). pap. (978-1-59843-028-8(9)) Inc. Trustees of the Gospel Worker Society, The.

Junior Bible Class Vol. 3: Summer 2006. 2006. (J). pap. (978-1-59843-029-5(7)) Inc. Trustees of the Gospel Worker Society, The.

Junior Bible Class Vol. 4: Fall 2006. 2006. (J). pap. (978-1-59843-030-1(0)) Inc. Trustees of the Gospel Worker Society, The.

Keels, Steve. NLT TruthQuest Inductive Student Bible. 2004. (TruthQuest Family Ser.). (Illus.). 1506p. 19.99 (978-1-55819-929-3(2)) B&H Publishing Grp.

Keels, Steve, et al. Truth Quest Inductive Student Bible. 2004. (TruthQuest Family Ser.). (Illus.). 1506p. 19.99 (978-1-55819-848-7(2)) B&H Publishing Grp.

Kids Devotional Staff. The Kid's Devotional Bible. 1999. (J). pap. 15.99 (978-0-310-90877-7(9)) Zondervan.

Kuhn, Pamela J. Bible Crafts on a Shoestring Budget: Boxes & Containers. 2004. 96p. (J). pap. 11.95 (978-1-58411-000-2(7)) Rainbow Pubs. & Legacy Pr.

—Bible Crafts on a Shoestring Budget: Craft Sticks & Clothespins. 2004. 96p. (J). pap. 11.95 (978-1-58411-001-9(5)) Rainbow Pubs. & Legacy Pr.

—Bible Crafts on a Shoestring Budget: Paper Plates & Cups. 2004. 96p. (J). pap. 11.95 (978-1-58411-002-6(3)) Rainbow Pubs. & Legacy Pr.

—Bible Crafts on a Shoestring Budget: Paper Sacks & Cardboard Tubes. 2004. 96p. (J). pap. 11.95 (978-1-58411-003-3(1)) Rainbow Pubs. & Legacy Pr.

Larsen, Carolyn. GOD'S WORD for Little Ones. Incrocci, Rick, illus. 2004. 374p. 19.99 (978-1-932587-41-8(1)) Green Key Bks.

—Little Boys Activity Bible for Toddlers. Turk, Caron, illus. 2002. 256p. (J). (ps). 12.99 (978-0-8010-4497-7(9) , New Kids Media) Baker Bks.

—Little Girls Activity Bible for Toddlers. Turk, Caron, illus. 2002. 256p. (J). (ps). 12.99 (978-0-8010-4496-0(0) , New Kids Media) Baker Bks.

—Little Girl's Bible Storybook for Fathers & Daughters. Turk, Caron, illus. 2000. 360p. (J). (gr. 1-4). 16.99 (978-0-8010-4469-4(3) , New Kids Media) Baker Bks.

Larson, Elsie. Bombus Creativity Book. Haidle, Elizabeth, illus. 1998. 40p. (J). (ps-3). pap. 4.99 (978-0-89051-241-8(8)) Master Bks.

LaTreill, Donna. The Vinedresser: Two Keys to Reaping the Best Harvest from Your Spiritual & Physical Vineyards. 2004. 64p. per. 19.95 (978-0-9718838-1-9(5)) Word-wright Communications.

Law, Jennifer. Thank You God for My Bible. Reeves, Rhonda, ed. Robinson, Timothy, illus. 1999. (Missions & Me Ser.). 16p. (J). (ps-k). 7.99 (978-1-56309-284-8(0)) Woman's Missionary Union.

Learning Lab: Fall 2001. 2001. (Hands-On Bible Curriculum Ser.). (J). (gr. 3-4). 44.99 incl. audio compact disk (978-0-7644-0258-6(7)) Group Publishing, Inc.

Lee, Witness. Eating the Lord. 2000. 44p. (J). (gr. 6). per. 5.25 (978-0-7363-1036-9(3) , 13-901-001) Living Stream Ministry.

Lepp, Royden. How to Draw Big Bad Bible Beasts. 2007. (2:52 Ser.). (Illus.). 48p. (J). pap. 6.99 (978-0-310-71336-4(6)) Zonderkidz.

—How to Draw Good, Bad & Ugly Bible Guys. 2007. (2:52 Ser.). (Illus.). 48p. (J). pap. 6.99 (978-0-310-71337-1(4)) Zonderkidz.

Life Publishers International Staff, tr. from ENG. Junior Bible Quiz 2, 2 vols, Vol. 2. 2002. (RUS.). 57p. (J). (978-0-7361-0325-1(2)) Life Pubs. International.

Lifepac Bible, Complete Set. 2004. (gr. 5). 47.95 (978-1-58095-614-7(9) , BIB0515, Lifepac) Alpha Omega Pubns., Inc.

Lifetrak Bible Studies for Older Youth. (J). 2005. (gr. 10-12). 29.95 (978-0-633-19487-1(5)); 2005. (gr. 10-12). 29.95 (978-0-633-19488-8(3)); 2004. 29.95 (978-0-633-19484-0(0)); 2004. (gr. 9-12). 29.95 (978-0-633-19390-4(9)); 2004. (gr. 9-12). 29.95 (978-0-633-09046-3(8)); 2004. (gr. 9-12). 29.95 (978-0-633-09045-6(X)); 2003. (gr. 9-12). 29.95 (978-0-633-09044-9(1)); 2003. (gr. 10-12). 29.95 (978-0-633-09026-5(3)); 2003. (gr. 10-12). 29.95 (978-0-633-02209-9(8)); 2003. (gr. 10-12). 29.95 (978-0-633-02208-2(X)); 2002. (gr. 10-12). 29.95 (978-0-633-02207-5(1)); 2002. (gr. 10-12). 29.95 (978-0-633-02278-5(0)) LifeWay Christian Resources.

Lifetrak Bible Studies for Younger Youth. (J). (gr. 7-9). 2005. 29.95 (978-0-633-19485-7(9)); 2005. 29.95 (978-0-633-19486-4(7)); 2004. 29.95 (978-0-633-19489-5(1)); 2004. 29.95 (978-0-633-19483-3(2)); 2004. 29.95 (978-0-633-09294-8(0)); 2004. 29.95 (978-0-633-09293-1(2)); 2003. 29.95 (978-0-633-09292-4(4)); 2003. 29.95 (978-0-633-09047-0(6)); 2003. 29.95 (978-0-633-02213-6(6)); 2003. 29.95 (978-0-633-02212-9(8)); 2002. 29.95 (978-0-633-02211-2(X)); 2002. 29.95 (978-0-633-02210-5(1)) LifeWay Christian Resources.

Lifetrak for Older Youth. (J). (gr. 10-12). 2002. 29.95 (978-0-633-01439-1(7)); 2002. 29.95 (978-0-633-01438-4(9)); 2001. 29.95 (978-0-633-01437-7(0)); 2001. 29.95 (978-0-633-01436-0(2)); 2001. 29.95 (978-0-633-00428-6(6)); 2001. 29.95 (978-0-633-00427-9(8)); 2001. 29.95 (978-0-633-05106-8(3)); 2000. 29.95 (978-0-633-00426-2(X)) LifeWay Christian Resources.

Lifetrak for Younger Youth. (J). (gr. 7-9). 2002. 29.95 (978-0-633-01443-8(5)); 2002. 29.95 (978-0-633-01442-1(7)); 2001. 29.95 (978-0-633-01441-4(9)); 2001. 29.95 (978-0-633-01440-7(0)); 2001. 29.95 (978-0-633-00424-8(3)); 2001. 29.95 (978-0-633-00423-1(5)); 2000. 29.95 (978-0-633-00422-4(7)) LifeWay Christian Resources.

Lingo, Susan. Basic Bible Skills. 2006. 112p. (YA). 15.99 (978-0-7847-1605-2(6) , 42020) Standard Publishing.

—Preschool Bible Message Make-N-Takes. 2006. 112p. (J). 14.99 (978-0-7847-1429-4(0) , 02523) Standard Publishing.

Lingo, Susan L. Disciple Makers: 13 Fun Filled Bible Lessons about Following Jesus. Barr, Marilynn G. & Jeffery, Megan E., illus. 2000. (Power Builders Ser.). 128p. (J). (gr. 1-5). 15.99 (978-0-7847-1148-4(8) , 42114) Standard Publishing.

—Faith Finders: 13 Fun Filled Bible Lessons about Faith. Barr, Marilynn G. & Jeffery, Megan E., illus. 2000. (Power Builders Ser.). 128p. (J). (gr. 1-5). 15.99 (978-0-7847-1146-0(1) , 42112) Standard Publishing.

—God's Friends. Ring, Laura, ed. Parks, Kathy, illus. 2000. (My Good Night Bible Doorknob Bks.). 10p. (J). (ps up). bds. 4.99 (978-0-7847-1057-9(0) , 03550, Bean Sprouts) Standard Publishing.

—My Little Good Night Bible. Parks, Kathy, illus. 2006. (My Good Night Collection). 108p. (J). 6.99 (978-0-7847-1228-3(X) , 04061) Standard Publishing.

—Servant Leaders: 13 Fun Filled Bible Lessons about Serving God. Barr, Marilynn G. & Jeffery, Megan E., illus. 2000. (Power Builders Ser.). 128p. (J). (gr. 1-5). 15.99 (978-0-7847-1147-7(X) , 42113) Standard Publishing.

—Value Seekers: 13 Fun Filled Bible Lessons about Values. Barr, Marilynn G. & Jeffery, Megan E., illus. 2000. (Power Builders Ser.). 128p. (J). (gr. 1-5). 15.99 (978-0-7847-1145-3(3) , 42111) Standard Publishing.

Little KidsTime 1: Bible Story Pictures. 2004. 104p. 19.99 (978-0-8307-2773-5(6) , Gospel Light) Gospel Light Pubns.

Littleton, Mark & Littleton, Jeanette Gardner. What's in the Bible for... Teens: The Bible Made Easy! 2000. (What's in the Bible For... Ser.). (Illus.). 352p. (gr. 7-12). pap. 16.95 (978-1-892016-05-8(2)) Starburst Pubs.

Live Wire Take Home Fall 2002. 2002. pap. 14.99 (978-1-59185-013-7(4)) CharismaLife Pubs.

Live Wire Winter 2002-03. 2002. pap. 14.99 (978-1-59185-100-4(9)) CharismaLife Pubs.

Livingstone Corporation Staff. Revolution. 2003. 1664p. 44.99 (978-0-310-92822-5(2)) Zondervan.

Livingstone Corporation Staff & Zondervan. Revolution: The Bible for Teen Guys. 2003. 1664p. (YA). pap. 22.99 (978-0-310-92820-1(6)); (Illus.). 27.99 (978-0-310-92819-5(2)) Zondervan.

—True Images: The Bible for Teen Girls. 2003. 1696p. (YA). 44.99 (978-0-310-92818-8(4)); pap. 22.99 (978-0-310-92816-4(8)); (Illus.). 27.99 (978-0-310-92815-7(X)) Zondervan.

Lloyd-Jones, Sally. Lift-the-Flap Bible. Moroney, Tracey, illus. 2000. 20p. (J). (ps-k). bds. 12.99 (978-0-7847-0965-8(3) , 03539) Standard Publishing.

Long, Laurie. Valuable Bible Characters - New Testament Math Puzzle Grade 1-2. Jackson, Cindy, illus. l.t. ed. 1999. 20p. (J). (gr. 1-2). pap. 4.50 (978-1-878669-75-9(3) , 3513) Creative Teaching Assocs.

—Valuable Bible Characters - New Testament Math Puzzles Grade 3-4. Jackson, Cindy, illus. l.t. ed. 1999. 20p. (J). (gr. 3-4). pap. 4.50 (978-1-878669-76-6(1) , 3514) Creative Teaching Assocs.

—Valuable Bible Characters - Old Testament Math Puzzles Grades 3-4. Jackson, Cindy, illus. l.t. ed. 1999. 20p. (J). (gr. 3-4). pap. 4.50 (978-1-878669-73-5(7) , 3511) Creative Teaching Assocs.

—Valuable Bible Characters Math Puzzle Book. Jackson, Cindy, illus. l.t. ed. 1998. 20p. (J). (gr. 1-2). 4.50 (978-1-878669-72-8(9) , CRE3510) Creative Teaching Assocs.

Loth, Paul J. My First Study Bible: Exploring God's Word on My Own! 2006. 528p. (J). 14.99 (978-1-4003-0887-3(9)) Nelson, Thomas Inc.

Lovasik, Lawrence G. St. Joseph Catholic Children's Bible. (Illus.). 96p. (J). 6.50 (978-0-89942-144-5(X) , 145/122, Resurrection Pr.) Catholic Bk. Publishing Corp.

Lowenfield, Tricia. S Is for Shepherd. 2004. (Illus.). 32p. (J). per. 17.99 incl. audio compact disk (978-0-9747367-0-9(8)) Pumpkins Pansies Bunnies & Bears.

Lucado, Max. Children's Daily Devotional Bible. 2006. 1504p. (J). 24.99 (978-1-4003-0821-7(6)); pap. 19.99 (978-1-4003-0827-9(5)); im. lthr. 29.99 (978-1-4003-0828-6(3)) Nelson, Thomas Inc.

Lucado, Max. God's Great Big Love for Me: A 3:16 Book. 2008. 12p. (J). 9.99 ***(978-1-4003-1106-4(3))*** Nelson, Thomas Inc.

Lucas, Daryl, ed. The Treasure Study Bible. 1998. (J). 24.95 incl. cd-rom (978-0-88707-353-3(0) , 213) Kirkbride, B.B. Bible Co., Inc.

Lucy Show Bible, Vol. 3. 2005. (Illus.). 48p. pap., stu. ed. 7.99 (978-0-9765142-3-7(0)) Entertainment Ministry, The.

MacArthur, John, ed. MacArthur Student Bible - Personal Size. 2006. 1856p. (YA). 29.99 (978-0-7180-1688-3(2)); im. lthr. 44.99 (978-0-7180-1689-0(0)) Nelson, Thomas Inc.

Mackall, Dandi Daley. Jesus Said, Go Tell the World, So I've Got a Job to Do. Harris, Jenny B., illus. 2005. 36p. (J). (ps-7). 9.99 (978-0-7847-1652-6(8) , 04073) Standard Publishing.

MacKenzie, Carine. Daniel Colouring Book. 16p. (J). pap., act. bk. ed. 1.50 (978-1-85792-825-9(3) , Christian Focus) Christian Focus Pubns. GBR. *Dist:* Riverside.

Mackenzie, Carine. Little Hands Story Bible P/b. (Illus.). 144p. (J). pap. 5.99 (978-1-85792-697-2(8) , Christian Focus) Christian Focus Pubns. GBR. *Dist:* Riverside.

—My First Book of Bible Promises. 2005. (Illus.). 64p. (J). (ps-ps). pap. (978-1-84550-039-9(3) , Christian Focus) Christian Focus Pubns.

MacKenzie, Carine. Noah: Rescue Plan. 1999. (Illus.). 32p. (J). (gr. 1-5). pap. (978-1-85792-466-4(5) , Christian Focus) Christian Focus Pubns.

MacLean, Moira. Baby's First Bible Songs. 2000. (Baby's First Bible Collection). (Illus.). 20p. (ps). 12.99 (978-0-7847-0966-5(1) , 03540, Bean Sprouts) Standard Publishing.

Manz, Simon Mary. My First Read & Learn: Favorite Bible Verses: Favorite Bible Verses. 2008. 40p. pap. 9.99 ***(978-0-545-02509-6(5)*** , Scholastic) Scholastic, Inc.

Marson, Janyce & Bloom, Harold. The Bible. 2nd rev. ed. 2006. (Bloom's Modern Critical Views Ser.). 320p. (gr. 9). 45.00 (978-0-7910-8137-2(0) , Chelsea Hse.) Facts On File, Inc.

McCallum, Jodi. Fun with Bible Friends. 1999. (Illus.). 48p. (J). (ps-2). 2.99 (978-0-7847-0760-9(X) , Bean Sprouts) Standard Publishing.

—God Made Me! 1999. (Illus.). 48p. (J). (ps-2). pap. 2.49 (978-0-7847-0981-8(5) , 22051, Bean Sprouts) Standard Publishing.

McCarthy, Michael. The Story of Daniel in the Lions' Den. Ferri, Giuliano, illus. 2003. 32p. (J). (gr. 1-3). 16.99 (978-1-84148-209-5(9)) Barefoot Bks., Inc.

McDowell, Josh & Johnson, Kevin. The Great Treasure Quest: Discovering the Purpose of the Bible. 2006. 160p. (J). pap. 10.99 (978-1-932587-85-2(3)) Green Key Bks.

McKinney, Karl & McKinney, Kellie. Relatively Loving: Family Dynamics in the Bible. 1999. (Generation Why Ser.: Vol. 4.8). 42p. (YA). (gr. 9-12). pap. 14.95 (978-0-87303-288-9(8)) Faith & Life Pr.

Memory Verse Mysteries Grade 1-3. 2002. (Christian Product Ser.). 32p. pap. 3.99 (978-0-88724-798-9(9) , CD-2020) Carson-Dellosa Publishing Co., Inc.

Memory Verse Mysteries Grade 4-6. 2002. (Christian Product Ser.). 32p. pap. 3.99 (978-0-88724-799-6(7) , CD-2021) Carson-Dellosa Publishing Co., Inc.

Memory Verse Mysteries Pre-K. 2002. (Christian Product Ser.). 32p. pap. 3.99 (978-0-88724-797-2(0) , CD-2019) Carson-Dellosa Publishing Co., Inc.

Mer, illus. Mary Jones & Her Bible. 160p. (J). mass mkt. 5.99 (978-1-85792-568-5(8) , Christian Heritage) Christian Focus Pubns. GBR. *Dist:* Riverside.

Mi Dios es Creador (My God Is Creator) Quarter 1, Level 1. (Caminando con Jesus (Walking with Jesus) Series A). (SPA.). (J). (ps-k). stu. ed. 3.50 (978-0-570-05107-7(X) , 16-1811) Concordia Publishing Hse.

Mi Dios es Grande (My God Is Big) Quarter 3, Level 1. (Caminando con Jesus (Walking with Jesus) Series A). (SPA.). (J). (ps-k). stu. ed. 3.50 (978-0-570-05109-1(6) , 16-1813) Concordia Publishing Hse.

Mi Primera Biblia. 2000. Tr. of My First Bible. (SPA., Illus.). 40p. (J). 19.98 (978-970-607-710-3(3)) Larousse, Ediciones, S. A. de C. V. MEX. *Dist:* Distribooks, Inc., Giron Bks.

Miller, Janet. Cut, Color & Paste: Bible Workers. 2004. 96p. (J). (ps-2). 11.95 (978-1-885358-82-0(2)) Rainbow Pubs. & Legacy Pr.

Minges, Barbara. Investigator's Notebook: Faith for Life2 Course Seven Student Book. Janssen, Patricia E., ed. 2nd ed. 2003. Orig. Title: Faith for Life Course Seven. (YA). stu. ed., spiral bd. 14.99 (978-0-9727146-2-4(6)) LOGOS System Assocs.

Moises: Serie para Ninos Amigos de la Vida. 2000. pap. (978-1-57697-789-7(7)) United Bible Societies/ Americas Service Ctr.

Moore, Karen. Dear God, Let's Talk about YOU. Wummer, Amy, illus. 2006. 128p. (YA). pap. 8.99 (978-0-7847-1247-4(6) , 42174) Standard Publishing.

More Time for Bible Puzzles & Games. (Illus.). 32p. (YA). (gr. 5 up). pap. 2.25 (978-0-87162-664-6(0) , E9706) Warner Pr. Pubs.

Moser, Cora. Illustrated Bible for Children. 2000. (Illus.). (J). 25.00 (978-0-689-80576-9(4) , Simon & Schuster Children's Publishing) Simon & Schuster Children's Publishing.

Mouser, William E. & Mouser, Barbara K. Five Aspects of Masculinity for Young Men: A Biblical Theology of Manhood, 1. 2003. (YA). spiral bd. (978-1-929656-10-3(6)) International Council for Gender Studies.

My Bible Hugs: Fall 2001. 2001. (Faith Weaver Ser.). (J). (ps). pap., stu. ed. 3.99 (978-0-7644-1185-4(3)) Group Publishing, Inc.

My Bible Words. 2006. 16p. (J). pap. 1.99 (978-0-7847-1388-4(X) , 22126) Standard Publishing.

My First Bible Sticker Dictionary. 2000. (Illus.). 48p. (J). (ps-3). pap. 4.99 (978-0-570-05580-8(6)) Concordia Publishing Hse.

My First Bible Sticker Questions & Answers. 2000. 48p. (J). (ps-3). pap. 4.99 (978-0-570-05579-2(2)) Concordia Publishing Hse.

My First Picture Bible. Date not set. (J). 8.95 (978-0-88271-532-2(1) , 10520) Regina Pr., Malhame & Co.

My Good Night Bible Songs. 2000. (My Good Night Bible Collection). (Illus.). 24p. (J). (ps up). bds. 16.99 (978-0-7847-1149-1(6) , 04008) Standard Publishing.

Nappa, Tony & Nappa, Mike. Lunch Box Trivia: Over 75 Tear-Out Fun Facts about the Bible & Other Cool Stuff. 2000. (Illus.). 160p. (J). (gr. k-6). pap. 7.99 (978-0-7847-1180-4(1) , 04325) Standard Publishing.

Neely, Keith. The Illustrated Bible: Joshua / Judges / Ruth. 2007. 128p. (J). pap. 6.99 ***(978-1-4003-1105-7(5))*** Nelson, Thomas Inc.

Neely, Keith. The Illustrated Bible: John. 2006. 112p. (J). pap. 6.99 (978-1-4003-0811-8(9)) Nelson, Thomas Inc.

Neely, Keith, illus. The Illustrated Bible: Exodus. 2007. 128p. (J). pap. 6.99 ***(978-1-4003-1038-8(5))*** Nelson, Thomas Inc.

—The Illustrated Bible: Genesis. 2007. 160p. (J). pap. 6.99 ***(978-1-4003-1037-1(7))*** Nelson, Thomas Inc.

—The Illustrated Bible: Luke. 2006. 128p. (J). pap. 6.99 (978-1-4003-0841-5(0)) Nelson, Thomas Inc.

—The Illustrated Bible: Mark. 2006. 96p. (J). pap. 6.99 (978-1-4003-0840-8(2)) Nelson, Thomas Inc.

Nelson Bibles Staff, contrib. by. La Biblia Extreme del Joven Radical. 2002. (SPA.). 1,750p. (YA). 34.99 (978-0-89922-614-9(0)) Grupo Nelson.

—Extreme Word: Study Bible for Young Adults. 2002. 1600p. 24.99 (978-0-7180-0168-1(0)) Nelson, Thomas Inc.

—International Children's Bible: Gift & Award Bible. 2002. (Illus.). 976p. (J). lthr. 9.99 (978-0-7180-0100-1(1)) Nelson, Thomas Inc.

Nelson Word Publishing Group Staff. Precious Moments Baby Bible for Catholics. 1999. (Illus.). 1624p. (YA). (ps up). 19.99 (978-0-7852-0083-5(5)) Nelson, Thomas Inc.

Ninos y Mujeres en la Biblia (Children & Women in the Bible) Quarter 2, Level 2. (Caminando con Jesus (Walking with Jesus) Series A). (SPA.). (J). (gr. 1-2). stu. ed. 3.50 (978-0-570-05133-6(9) , 16-2812) Concordia Publishing Hse.

Noller & Taylor. Mis Primeras Palabras de la Biblia (My First Bible Words) 2000. (My First... Ser.). (SPA.). (J). 10.99 (978-0-7899-0682-3(1) , 494617) Editorial Unilit.

Nothnagel, Juliana. My Very Own Bible for Toddlers. 1999. 228p. (J). (978-0-86997-635-7(4)) Lux Verbi.

Una Nueva Vida (A New Life) Quarter 3, Level 2. (Caminando con Jesus (Walking with Jesus) Series B). (SPA.). (J). (gr. 1-2). stu. ed. 3.50 (978-0-570-05137-4(1) , 16-2913) Concordia Publishing Hse.

Osborne, Rick & Bowler, Kathryn C. I Want to Know about the Bible: What Is the Bible, Why It's Important, & What It Tells Me. 1998. (I Want to Know Ser.). (Illus.). 32p. (J). (gr. 2-5). 9.99 (978-0-310-22089-3(0)) Zonderkidz.

Osborne, Rick & Strauss, Ed. The Ultimate Battle & Bible Prophecy. 2004. (Illus.). 112p. (J). pap. 7.99 (978-0-310-70776-9(5)) Zonderkidz.

Osborne, Rick & Zondervan. The Boys Bible: Your Ultimate Manual. 2002. (Illus.). 1696p. (J). 26.99 (978-0-310-70320-4(4)) Zonderkidz.

Osborne, Rick, et al. Weird & Gross Bible Stuff. Carpenter, Anthony, illus. 2003. (2:52 Soul Gear Ser.). 112p. (J). pap. 7.99 (978-0-310-70484-3(7)) Zondervan.

Ottaviani, Ettorina. My First Bible. 2000. 30p. 11.95 (978-0-8198-4827-7(1) , 332-218) Pauline Bks. & Media.

The Our Father. Date not set. bds. 3.95 (978-0-88271-562-9(3) , 12012) Regina Pr., Malhame & Co.

Parker, Victoria. Children's Illustrated Bible: Classic Stories Set in Religious & Historical Context. 2001. (Illus.). 512p. (gr. 3 up). 40.00 (978-0-7548-0648-6(0)) Anness Publishing, Inc.

—The Childrens Illustrated Bible: The New Testament. 2000. (Illus.). 256p. (J). (gr. 4-7). (978-1-84215-347-5(1) , Southwater) Anness Publishing.

Parker, Victoria & Dyson, Janet. Jesus on the Cross. 2003. (Bible Discoverers Ser.). (Illus.). 64p. (gr. 3-7). pap. 7.99 (978-1-84215-739-8(6) , Southwater) Anness Publishing GBR. *Dist:* National Bk. Network.

Parry, Alan. The Bible Made Easy: A Pop-Up, Pull-Out, Interactive Bible Adventure. Parry, Linda, illus. (J). 14.99 (978-1-85608-399-7(3)) Hunt, John Publishing Ltd. GBR. *Dist:* O. M. Literature.

Pawlitz, Carol J. & Pawlitz, Gary. Gospel Talks 1, 2, 3. 2000. (Illus.). 64p. (ps-2). 9.99 (978-0-570-05238-8(6)) Concordia Publishing Hse.

Peters-Pries, Pam. Go for Broke: Using the Gifts God Gave You. 1999. (Generation Why Ser.: Vol. 4.5). 34p. (YA). (gr. 9-12). pap. 12.95 (978-0-87303-285-8(3)) Faith & Life Pr.

Petersen, Randy. Bible Fun Stuff. 2000. 448p. per. 10.99 (978-0-8423-3618-5(4)) Tyndale Hse. Pubs.

Peterson, Eugene H. My First Message: A Devotional Bible for Kids. Corley, Rob & Bancroft, Tom, illus. 2007. (J). ***(978-1-57683-448-0(4))*** NavPress Publishing Group.

Petrie, H. D., photos by. All God's Creatures; Jesus Loves Me. ed. 2005. 32p. (J). spiral bd. (978-0-9774115-0-4(8)) AGC Outreach Ministry.

Petrusic, Anthony A. A Prayerful Journey with Mary - Lift up Your Hearts. Parker, Sue H., ed. D'Onofrio, Kathi, illus. 1999. 7.95 (978-0-937739-43-3(X) , 10041) Roman, Inc.

Por que era valiente David ? Serie para ninos Historias maravillosas. 2000. pap. (978-1-57697-800-9(1)) United Bible Societies/Americas Service Ctr.

Precious Moments Bible: Small Hands Edition. 1999. (Illus.). 1104p. (J). (ps-3). im. lthr. 19.97 (978-0-7852-0045-1(2)) Nelson, Thomas Inc.

Precious Moments Bible: Small Hands Edition. 1999. (Illus.). 1104p. (J). (ps-3). im. lthr. 19.97 (978-0-7852-0044-4(4)) Nelson, Thomas Inc.

Precious Moments Bible: Small Hands Edition. 1999. (Illus.). 1088p. (J). (ps-3). im. lthr. 24.99 (978-0-7852-0042-0(8)) Nelson, Thomas Inc.

Precious Moments Bible: Small Hands Edition. 1999. (J). 19.99 (978-0-7852-0047-5(9)); 19.99 (978-0-7852-0046-8(0)) Nelson, Thomas Inc.

Precious Moments New Testament Small Hands Catholic Edition: Precious Moments for Little Girls! 2004. (Illus.). 706p. (J). 15.99 (978-0-7180-0632-7(1)) Nelson, Thomas Inc.

Prenzlau, Sheryl. The Jewish Children's Bible, 5 vols., Set. Smekhov, Zely, illus. 1999. (Jewish Storyteller Ser.). 300p. (J). (gr. 1-4). pap. 94.95 (978-0-943706-36-8(X)) Pitspopany Pr.

Preschool Bible Puzzlers Grade. 2004. pap. 9.95 (978-0-7647-0499-4(0)) School Specialty Publishing.

Press Abingdon. Finding Your Way Through the B. 2007. 175p. pap. 5.75 ***(978-0-687-64547-3(6))*** Abingdon Pr.

Prestofillipo, Mary Nazarene, tr. The Bible for Little Ones. Flamini, Lorella, illus. 2004. 38p. (J). 9.95 (978-0-8198-1166-0(1) , 332-029) Pauline Bks. & Media.

Primary Bible Learner: Fall 2006. 2006. (J). pap. (978-1-59843-014-1(9)) Inc. Trustees of the Gospel Worker Society, The.

Primary Bible Learner: Spring 2006, Vol. 2. 2006. (J). pap. (978-1-59843-012-7(2)) Inc. Trustees of the Gospel Worker Society, The.

Primary Bible Learner: Summer 2006, Vol. 3. 2006. (J). pap. (978-1-59843-013-4(0)) Inc. Trustees of the Gospel Worker Society, The.

Primary Bible Learner: Winter, 2006/2007. 2006. (J). pap. (978-1-59843-015-8(7)) Inc. Trustees of the Gospel Worker Society, The.

Primetime Take Home Papers. 2004. pap. 2.99 (978-0-8307-3043-8(5)) Gospel Light Pubns.

Pulley, Kelly, illus. The Beginner's Bible: Timeless Bible Stories. 2005. 511p. (J). 16.99 (978-0-310-70962-6(8)) Zonderkidz.

Rainbow Studies, Inc Staff. Ultimate Catholic Student Bible. 2003. (gr. 7-12). lib. bdg. 36.20 (978-0-613-79425-1(7)) Tandem Library Bks.

Reed, Judy. His Word in My Life: Exploring the Bible. 2004. (Faith Rules Ser.). 96p. (J). pap. 4.99 (978-0-7424-2827-0(3) , In Celebration) Schaffer, Frank Pubns.

Reeves, Eira. My First Picture Bible. 1998. (Illus.). 128p. (J). (ps-3). 9.99 (978-0-8024-6023-3(2)) Moody Pubs.

Regina Press Staff. Beginner's Bible, Book Block, 12 bks. 1999. (J). 19.95 (978-0-88271-750-0(2)) Regina Pr., Malhame & Co.

—Beginner's Bible First Catholic Prayers. 1999. (J). 5.95 (978-0-88271-723-4(5)) Regina Pr., Malhame & Co.

—Catholic Baby's First Bible. 1999. (J). (ps-k). 10.99 (978-0-88271-714-2(6)) Regina Pr., Malhame & Co.

Regina Press Staff, ed. Catholic Bible. 2000. (Illus.). (J). (ps-k). bds. 9.99 (978-0-88271-751-7(0)) Regina Pr., Malhame & Co.

Remembering God's Awesome Acts. 2005. stu. ed. 20.00 (978-1-931292-50-4(7)); Vol. 1 (set) 35.00 (978-1-931292-52-8(3)) Eagle's Wings Educational Materials.

Reminders of Faith. Boy Scripture Theme. gif. ed. 2004. 7p. pap. 8.99 (978-0-9763691-1-0(7)) Reminders Of Faith, Inc.

—Girl Scripture Theme Pack. gif. ed. 2004. 7p. pap. 8.99 (978-0-9763691-2-7(5)) Reminders Of Faith, Inc.

—Mom Scripture Theme Pack. gif. ed. 2004. 7p. pap. 8.99 (978-0-9763691-0-3(9)) Reminders Of Faith, Inc.

Rettino, Ernie & Rettino, Debby. Psalty's Kids Bible. rev. ed. 2002. 1600p. (J). pap. 19.99 (978-0-310-70319-8(0)) Zondervan.

Rettino, Ernie, et al. Psalty's Kids Bible. rev. ed. 2002. 1600p. (J). 24.99 (978-0-310-70318-1(2)) Zonderkidz.

Revolve 2007 , NCV: The Complete New Testament. 2006. 400p. (YA). pap. 16.99 (978-0-7180-1648-7(3)) Nelson, Thomas Inc.

Rhodes, Karen. Numeros en la Biblia. 2004. (SPA., Illus.). 16p. (J). pap. 1.89 ***(978-1-59317-062-2(9))*** Warner Pr. Pubs.

Ricci, Regolo. The Lord Is My Shepherd. 2007. (Illus.). 24p. (J). 18.95 ***(978-0-88776-776-0(1))*** Tundra Bks. of Northern New York.

Robb, Andy. Catastrophic Kings. 2004. (Holy Happenings Ser.). (Illus.). 128p. pap. 6.50 (978-0-687-02306-6(8)) Abingdon Pr.

Rodgers, Barbara. Bible Outreach Activities: Ages 4-5. 2004. (Illus.). 96p. pap. 11.95 (978-1-58411-040-8(6)) Rainbow Pubs. & Legacy Pr.

—Bible Outreach Activities: Grades 1-2. 2004. (Illus.). 96p. pap. 11.95 (978-1-58411-041-5(4)) Rainbow Pubs. & Legacy Pr.

—Bible Outreach Activities: Grades 3-4. 2004. (Illus.). 96p. pap. 11.95 (978-1-58411-042-2(2)) Rainbow Pubs. & Legacy Pr.

Ruckman, Kathleen. God's Amazing Book. 2007. (Illus.). 28p. (J). 10.99 ***(978-1-59317-201-5(X))*** Warner Pr. Pubs.

Rue, Nancy. Faithgirlz Bible. 2006. (Faithgirlz!#8482; Ser.). 1504p. (J). 26.99 (978-0-310-71002-8(2)) Zondervan.

Sage, Angie, illus. Where Is Little Lamb? 2000. (Baby Blessings Ser.). 6p. (ps-3). 10.99 (978-0-7847-1132-3(1) , 04312) Standard Publishing.

Saint Mary's Press Staff, contrib. by. Breakthrough! The Bible for Young Catholics: Good News Translation. 2006. (Illus.). xx, 1908p. (J). 25.95 (978-0-88489-884-9(9)); pap. 18.95 (978-0-88489-862-7(8)) St. Mary's Pr.

Sanders, Nancy I. Old Testament Days: An Activity Guide. 1999. (Illus.). 144p. (J). (gr. k-7). pap. 16.95 (978-1-55652-354-0(8)) Chicago Review Pr., Inc.

Sasso, Sandy Eisenberg. Adam & Eve's New Day. Rothenberg, Joani Keller, illus. 2006. 24p. (J). bds. 7.99 (978-1-59473-205-8(1)) SkyLight Paths Publishing.

Sattgast, Linda J. The Rhyme Bible Storybook. 2000. (Bible Storybooks Ser.). 448p. (J). 17.99 (978-0-310-70197-2(X)) Zonderkidz.

—Toddler Rhyme Bible. 2002. (Illus.). 256p. (J). (ps-k). 16.99 (978-1-57673-319-6(X) , Multnomah) Water-Brook Pr.

Save, Ken. Jumbo Bible Coloring Fun, Vol. 3. Save, Ken, illus. 1998. (Jumbo Bible Activity Fun Ser.). (Illus.). 384p. (J). (ps-2). pap. 4.97 (978-1-57748-358-8(8)) Barbour Publishing, Inc.

Save, Ken & Save, Vickie. Bible Activities for Kids, Vols. 3 & 4. Save, Ken & Save, Vickie, illus. 1998. (Kid's Stuff Ser.). (Illus.). 224p. (J). (gr. 2-7). pap. 2.97 (978-1-57748-356-4(1)) Barbour Publishing, Inc.

Sawyer, Greg. What Is the Bible? 16p. stu. ed. 3.45 (978-0-570-00644-2(9) , 22-2765); 24p. 4.45 (978-0-570-00645-9(7) , 22-2766) Concordia Publishing Hse.

Schneider, Elaine. 52 Children's Moments: A Treasure for Every Week of the Year. 2003. (YA). per. 14.95 (978-0-7443-0720-7(1)) SynergEbks.

School Specialty Publishing. All Through the Bible. 2004. (In Celebration Coloring & Activity Book Ser.). 32p. (J). (gr. k-2). pap. 1.99 (978-0-7647-1012-4(5) , In Celebration) Schaffer, Frank Pubns.

—Biblical Men. 2004. (Flip-Flashtm Ser.). 160p. (J). (gr. k up). 7.99 (978-0-7424-2864-5(8)) School Specialty Publishing.

—Big Book of Bible Crafts. 2001. 160p. (J). pap. 14.99 (978-0-7647-0504-5(0)) School Specialty Publishing.

School Specialty Publishing Staff. A to Z Bible Activities. 2004. 96p. (J). (gr. k-2). pap. 9.99 (978-0-7647-0991-3(7) , In Celebration) Schaffer, Frank Pubns.

Schuller, Robert H. Dr. Robert Schuller's Children's Daily Devotional Bible: With Positive Thoughts for Each Day. 2005. 432p. (J). 16.99 (978-1-4003-0597-1(7)) Nelson, Thomas Inc.

Search & Find Bible Memory Game. 2001. (J). 6.99 (978-0-8254-7221-3(0)) Kregel Pubns.

Senker, Cath. Everyday Life in the Bible Lands. 2005. (Uncovering History Ser.). (Illus.). 46p. (J). (gr. 6-9). lib. bdg. 29.95 (978-1-58340-711-0(1)) Smart Apple Media.

Sharon, Berry. Decision Quest, Student Edition. 2002. (J). (gr. 1-6). 9.95 (978-0-633-07345-9(8)) LifeWay Christian Resources.

Shellenberger, Susie. Young Women of Faith Bible. 2002. (Ywof Library). (Illus.). 1664p. (J). lthr. 29.99 (978-0-310-70485-0(5)) Zonderkidz.

Shellenberger, Susie & Zondervan. Young Women of Faith Bible. 2002. (YWOF Library). (Illus.). 1664p. (J). 29.99 (978-0-310-70486-7(3)) Zondervan.

Shouting in the Hush Arbor Preschool/Kindergarten Bible Story Leader. 7.00 (978-0-687-32682-2(6)) Abingdon Pr.

Shouting in the Hush Arbor Student Handbook Preschool/ Kindergarten. 2.50 (978-0-687-32612-9(5)) Abingdon Pr.

Singer-Towns, Brian, ed. The Catholic Youth Bible. gif. ed. 2003. 1772p. (J). lthr. 47.95 (978-0-88489-797-2(4)) St. Mary's Pr.

—Catholic Youth Bible: New American Bible Translation. 2003. (Illus.). 1772p. (J). per. 27.95 (978-0-88489-744-6(3)) St. Mary's Pr.

—Catholic Youth Bible: Pray It, Study It, Live It. rev. ed. 2003. (Illus.). 1576p. (YA). (gr. 7-12). 37.95 (978-0-88489-667-8(6)); pap. 27.95 (978-0-88489-489-6(4)) St. Mary's Pr.

—New American Bible the Catholic Youth Bible: Pray It, Study It, Live It (Illus.). 1772p. (J). 2003. 37.95 (978-0-88489-745-3(1)); 2002. lthr. 47.95 (978-0-88489-746-0(X)) St. Mary's Pr.

Small. Kids' Collection. 1999. (J). 12.99 (978-0-310-97775-9(4)) Zonderkidz.

Smith, Kathie Billingslea. Bible Wipe-Off Activity Book. Nation, Tate, illus. 2002. 22p. (J). 6.99 (978-0-8254-5502-5(2)) Kregel Pubns.

Snellenberger, Earl & Snellenberger, Bonita. God Created the Animals. 1998. (God Created Ser.: Vol. 6). (Illus.). 32p. (J). pap. 4.95 (978-0-89051-154-1(3)) Master Bks.

—God Created the Insects. 1998. (God Created Ser.: Vol. 7). (Illus.). 32p. (J). pap. 4.95 (978-0-89051-155-8(1)) Master Bks.

—God Created the People. 1998. (God Created Ser.: Vol. 8). (Illus.). 32p. (J). pap. 4.95 (978-0-89051-157-2(8)) Master Bks.

—God Created the Plants & Trees. 1998. (God Created Ser.: Vol. 2). (Illus.). 32p. (J). pap. 4.95 (978-0-89051-150-3(0)) Master Bks.

Sp Little Girls Bible. 2000. 14.99 (978-0-7899-0792-9(5)) Editorial Unilit.

Spanish House Inc. Staff. Sp Little Bible Reader. 2003. 14.99 (978-0-7899-0214-6(1)) Editorial Unilit.

Spanish Kingsley's Meadow: No te Rinda (Hang In There) (SPA.). 32p. pap., act. bk. ed. 2.95 (978-1-58516-563-6(8)) American Bible Society.

Spirit-filled Life Student Bible: Growing in the Power of the Word. 2005. 1792p. (YA). 29.99 (978-0-7180-1513-8(4)); pap. 21.99 (978-0-7180-1514-5(2)) Nelson, Thomas Inc.

Spirit Press, creator. The Ultimate Bible Fun Book. 2005. (Illus.). 400p. (J). (ps-ps). pap. 5.99 (978-1-4037-1230-1(1) , Spirit Pr.) Dalmatian Pr.

Squint Free Holy Bible for Kids. lt. ed. 2000. (J). 1952p. (gr. 4-7). lthr. 17.99 (978-0-7852-5676-2(8)); 1728p. (gr. 8-12). lthr. 17.99 (978-0-7852-5674-8(1)) Nelson, Thomas Inc.

St. Pierre, Stephanie. Bible People Books Nativity Set, 2 vols. Lyon, Tammie Speer, illus. 2002. 14p. 16.99 (978-0-7847-1242-9(5)) Standard Publishing.

Standke, Linda. Play & Learn Bible Games: 16 Reproducible Games to Help Children Grow in Their Faith. 2003. 160p. (J). per. 10.99 (978-0-88724-873-3(X)) Carson-Dellosa Publishing Co., Inc.

Starburst Publishers. The Bible for Teens. 2001. (Learn the Word Ser.). 272p. pap. 14.99 (978-1-892016-51-5(6)) Starburst Pubs.

Starks, Bob & Starks, Judy. Busy Bible. 2002. (Illus.). 12p. (ps-5). 39.95 (978-0-9712022-0-7(6)) Busy Bibles, Inc.

Stephens, Andrea. Bible B. A. B. E. S: The Inside Dish on Divine Divas. 2005. (B. A. B. E. Book Ser.). 208p. (J). (ps-7). pap. 12.99 (978-0-8007-5969-8(9)) Revell.

Stevenson, Jennifer. Little Hands Story Bible. 16p. (J). pap., act. bk. ed. 1.50 (978-1-85792-431-2(2)); pap., act. bk. ed. 1.50 (978-1-85792-455-8(X) , Christian Focus); Vol. 2. pap., act. bk. ed. 1.50 (978-1-85792-432-9(0)); Vol. 2. pap., act. bk. ed. 1.50 (978-1-85792-456-5(8) , Christian Focus); Vol. 3. pap., act. bk. ed. 1.50 (978-1-85792-433-6(9)); Vol. 3. pap., act. bk. ed. 1.50 (978-1-85792-457-2(6) , Christian Focus); Vol. 4. pap., act. bk. ed. 1.50 (978-1-85792-434-3(7)); Vol. 4. pap., act. bk. ed. 1.50 (978-1-85792-458-9(4) , Christian Focus) Christian Focus Pubns. GBR. *Dist:* Riverside.

Stoddard, Sandol. A Child's First Bible Storybook. 1998. (Illus.). 96p. (J). (gr. k-1). 9.99 (978-0-88486-215-4(1) , Arrowood Pr.) BBS Publishing Corp.

Stoner, Marcia. Signs of Faith: Bible Verses for Teens. 2004. 48p. (gr. 4-7). 13.00 (978-0-687-09927-6(7)) Abingdon Pr.

Storch, Emilie M. I Love God's Word. Coffee, Jacque, illus. 2002. (J). spiral bd. (978-0-9715225-0-3(2)) Resting Place Pubns.

Stowell, Charlotte & Stowell, Gordon. God Gave. 1998. (ENG., Illus.). 22p. (J). (ps-2). bds. 2.99 (978-0-570-05495-5(8) , 56-1958GJ) Concordia Publishing Hse.

—God Understands. 1998. (Illus.). 24p. (J). (ps). bds. 2.99 (978-0-570-05494-8(X) , 56-1957GJ) Concordia Publishing Hse.

Strang Communications Company Staff, ed. Ages 4-5 Resource Summer 2002. 2002. (J). pap., tchr. ed. 5.49 (978-1-57405-970-0(X)) CharismaLife Pubs.

—Ages 4-5 Resources: Spring 2002. 2002. (J). (ps-k). pap. 12.99 (978-1-57405-930-4(0)) CharismaLife Pubs.

—Ages 4-5 Resources: Summer 2002. 2002. (J). (ps-k). pap. 12.99 (978-1-57405-968-7(8)) CharismaLife Pubs.

—Ages 4-5 Take Home Papers: Spring 2002. 2002. (J). (ps-k). pap. 14.99 (978-1-57405-931-1(9)) CharismaLife Pubs.

—Ages 4-5 Take Home Papers: Summer 2002. 2002. (J). (ps-k). pap. 14.99 (978-1-57405-969-4(6)) CharismaLife Pubs.

—Picture Lesson Cards & Albums: Summer 2002. 2002. (J). pap. 2.29 (978-1-57405-961-8(0)) CharismaLife Pubs.

Strauss, Ed. Seriously Sick Bible Stuff. Haya, Erwin, illus. 2007. (2:52 Ser.). 116p. (J). (gr. 3-7). per. 7.99 ***(978-0-310-71310-4(2))*** Zonderkidz.

Strickler, LeeDell. Super Simple Bible Lessons: 60 Ready-to-Use Bible Activities for Ages 3-5. 2005. 128p. pap. 14.00 (978-0-687-49770-6(1)) Abingdon Pr.

—Super Simple Bible Lessons: 60 Ready-to-Use Bible Activities for Ages 6-8. 2005. 128p. pap. 14.00 (978-0-687-49780-5(9)) Abingdon Pr.

Strobel, Lee, et al. NIrV Gift & Award Bible. 2006. 1024p. (J). pap. 7.99 (978-0-310-71298-5(X)); pap. 7.99 (978-0-310-71299-2(8)); pap. 7.99 (978-0-310-71297-8(1)) Zondervan.

Student Activity Workbook for Breakthrough! the Bible for Young Catholics: An Introduction to People of Faith. 2006. (YA). pap. 9.95 (978-0-88489-938-9(1)) St. Mary's Pr.

Student Activity Workbook for Breakthrough! the Bible for Young Catholics: Getting to Know Jesus. 2007. (J). pap. 6.95 ***(978-0-88489-978-5(0))*** St. Mary's Pr.

Syswerda, Jean E. The Super Heroes Bible: The Quest for Good over Evil. Jones, Dennis G., illus. 2002. 1504p. (J). 26.99 (978-0-310-70202-3(X)) Zonderkidz.

Takes, Toon, ed. Peel 'n Play Bible Adventures: Adventure Scene Activity Book. Reagan, Dawn, illus. 1999. 20p. (J). (ps-4). pap. 15.50 (978-1-929456-02-4(6)) Myrtle-Seal Publishing.

Taylor, Beverly. Back in the Days of Peter & Paul Vol. 5: New Testament Homilies for Children. DeVries, Dirk, ed. 1998. (Illus.). 96p. (ps-3). pap. 3.95 (978-1-889108-20-9(0)) Living the Good News.

Taylor, Kenneth N. A Child's First Bible. 2000. (Illus.). (J). 262p. 12.99 (978-0-8423-3174-6(3)); 19.99 (978-0-8423-3879-0(9)) Tyndale Hse. Pubs.

—A Child's First Bible. Wickenden, Nadine & Catchpole, Diana, illus. 2000. 262p. (J). 16.99 (978-0-8423-3199-9(9)) Tyndale Hse. Pubs.

—Mi Primera Biblia. 1999. (My First... Ser.). (SPA., Illus.). (J). (ps-3). 9.99 (978-0-7899-0573-4(6)); 9.99 (978-0-7899-0574-1(4)) Editorial Unilit.

—The New Bible in Pictures for Little Eyes. Spenceley, Annabel, illus. gif. ed. 2004. (Leading Young Hearts & Minds to God Ser.). 384p. (J). 24.99 (978-0-8024-3078-6(3)) Moody Pubs.

—The Picture Bible for Little People. 2004. 256p. (J). 15.99 (978-0-8423-8735-4(8)); (Illus.). 12.99 (978-0-8423-8734-7(X)) Tyndale Hse. Pubs.

Taylor, Kenneth N., ed. Mi Primera Biblia. (Biblias para Ninos Ser.). (SPA.). (J). (ps-3). 1999. 13.99 (978-1-56063-674-8(2) , 490282); 1998. (Illus.). 7.99 (978-0-7899-0571-0(X) , 490294) Editorial Unilit.

Taylor, Minnie. My S Book: Daily Words of Strength to Break Through Barriers. 2002. 72p. per. 12.95 (978-1-930908-18-5(0)) AGB Publishing.

Teen Bible Study: Low Cost Edition. 2004. (YA). lthr. (978-0-310-92838-6(9)) Zondervan.

Teller, Hanoch. The Mini Midrash & a Maaseh: An Anthology of Insights & Commentaries for Youngsters on the Weekly Torah Reading: Including Stories & Illustrations, 2 vols. 1998. 36.99 (978-1-881939-12-2(X)) New York City Publishing Co.

Tesoros Escondidos Vol. 1: Interactivo para Ninos. 2001. cd-rom (978-1-930564-95-4(3)) United Bible Societies/ Americas Service Ctr.

Tesoros Escondidos Vol. 2: Interactivo para Ninos. 2001. cd-rom (978-1-930564-96-1(1)) United Bible Societies/ Americas Service Ctr.

Tesoros Escondidos Vol. 2: Libro para ninos. 2000. (SPA.). pap. (978-1-57697-933-4(4)) United Bible Societies/ Americas Service Ctr.

Tesoros Escondidos Vol. 4: Libro para ninos. 2000. (SPA.). pap. (978-1-57697-935-8(0)) United Bible Societies/ Americas Service Ctr.

Tesoros Escondidos Vol. 5: Libro para ninos. 2000. (SPA.). pap. (978-1-57697-938-9(5)) United Bible Societies/ Americas Service Ctr.

Tesoros Escondidos Vol. 6: Libro para ninos. 2000. (SPA.). pap. (978-1-57697-939-6(3)) United Bible Societies/ Americas Service Ctr.

Tesoros Escondidos Vol. 8: Libro para ninos. 2001. (SPA.). pap. (978-1-57697-914-3(8)) United Bible Societies/ Americas Service Ctr.

Tesoros Escondidos Vol. 9: Libro para ninos. 2001. (SPA.). pap. (978-1-57697-915-0(6)) United Bible Societies/ Americas Service Ctr.

Theisen, Michael. Ready-to-Go Game Shows (That Teach Serious Stuff) Catholic Teachings & Practices Edition. 2003. (Illus.). 144p. (YA). 19.95 (978-0-88489-757-6(5)) St. Mary's Pr.

Thomas, Isaiah, creator. Curious Hieroglyphick Bible. 2005. (Illus.). 160p. (J). (gr. 4-7). 19.95 (978-1-55709-958-7(8)) Applewood Bks.

Thomas, Mack. Bible Tells Me So. Werner, Jerry, illus. 2001. 448p. (J). (gr. k-5). 14.99 (978-0-945564-20-1(1) , Multnomah) WaterBrook Pr.

Thomas Nelson. Early Readers Bible. 2006. 1664p. (J). 19.99 (978-0-7180-1330-1(1)) Nelson, Thomas Inc.

Thomas Nelson Publishing Staff. Bible NRSV Noahs ARK. 2005. 1,216p. (J). 24.99 (978-0-529-12092-2(5)) Nelson, Thomas Inc.

—ICB Princess Bible. 2007. 1504p. (J). im. lthr. 22.99 ***(978-1-4003-0987-0(5))*** Nelson, Thomas Inc.

—ICB Small Hands Bible: Boy. 2005. 1184p. (J). 16.99 (978-1-4003-0595-7(0)) Nelson, Thomas Inc.

—ICB Small Hands Bible: Girl. 2005. 1184p. (J). 16.99 (978-1-4003-0594-0(2)) Nelson, Thomas Inc.

—Small Hands Bible: Blastin' Bubble Blue. 2006. 1504p. (J). im. lthr. 17.99 (978-1-4003-0824-8(0)) Nelson, Thomas Inc.

—Small Hands Bible: Bubblegum Berry. 2006. 1504p. (J). im. lthr. 17.99 (978-1-4003-0820-0(8)) Nelson, Thomas Inc.

—Small Hands Bible: Grasshopper Glittergreen. 2006. 1504p. (J). im. lthr. 17.99 (978-1-4003-0814-9(3)) Nelson, Thomas Inc.

—Small Hands Bible: Powerpunch Purple. 2006. 1504p. (J). im. lthr. 17.99 (978-1-4003-0813-2(5)) Nelson, Thomas Inc.

Thorpe, Erick E. The Chozen-4: Coloring Book. Thorpe, Erick E., illus. 2001. (Illus.). 48p. (J). (ps-3). pap. 5.50 (978-0-9713096-0-9(4) , Fresch Fruitz) Got2Bfunki Artworks.

Time for Bible Puzzles & Games. (Illus.). 32p. (YA). (gr. 5 up). pap. 2.25 (978-0-87162-662-2(4) , E9705) Warner Pr. Pubs.

Time for Learning Bible. 2005. (Illus.). 96p. (978-0-7853-6323-1(8) , 7161600) Publications International, Ltd.

Treasures of the Bible. 1998. (Illus.). 580p. (J). (gr. 4-7). 24.95 (978-2-215-04276-1(1)) Continental Enterprises Group, Inc. (CEG).

Tween Biblezine for Boys. 2006. 400p. (J). pap. 16.99 (978-0-7180-1525-1(8)) Nelson, Thomas Inc.

Tyndale, creator. The One Year Bible Compact Edition NLT: Connect. 2006. 1440p. (YA). 14.99 (978-1-4143-1457-0(4)) Tyndale Hse. Pubs.

Tyndale House Publishers Staff. Book for Teens: Find Immediate Answers to Tough Questions. 1999. (gr. 7-12). lib. bdg. 24.60 (978-0-613-76793-4(4)) Tandem Library Bks.

Tyndale House Publishers Staff, contrib. by. The Jesus Bible. 2002. 1728p. (YA). pap. 24.99 (978-0-8423-5565-0(0)) Tyndale Hse. Pubs.

Tyndale House Publishers Staff, creator. Metal Bible (Connect) 2005. 1104p. (YA). 29.99 (978-1-4143-0770-1(5)) Tyndale Hse. Pubs.

—Student's Life Application Study Bible Personal Size NLT. 2006. 1440p. (YA). 26.99 (978-1-4143-0965-1(1)); per. 19.99 (978-1-4143-0964-4(3)); im. lthr. 39.99 (978-1-4143-0967-5(8)); im. lthr. 39.99 (978-1-4143-0966-8(X)) Tyndale Hse. Pubs.

Tyndale House Publishers Staff, ed. The One Year Bible for Kids: Challenge Edition. 2004. 496p. (J). per. 14.99 (978-0-8423-8517-6(7)) Tyndale Hse. Pubs.

Tyndale House Publishers Staff, prod. Metal Bible NLT: Silver Cross. 2002. 1104p. (YA). 29.99 (978-0-8423-7232-9(6)) Tyndale Hse. Pubs.

—Metal Bible NLT: Silver Thirsty. 2002. 1056p. (YA). 29.99 (978-0-8423-7233-6(4)) Tyndale Hse. Pubs.

Tyndale House Publishers Staff & Group Publishing Staff, creators. Hands-on New Testament-NLT. 2005. (Illus.). 464p. (J). (ps-7). pap. 8.99 (978-1-4143-0786-2(1)) Tyndale Hse. Pubs.

Tyndale House Publishers Staff & Livingstone, creators. Girls Life Application Study Bible NLT. 2006. 1568p. (J). im. lthr. 36.99 (978-1-4143-0266-9(5)) Tyndale Hse. Pubs.

—Girls Life Application Study Bible NLT. 2006. 1568p. (J). 26.99 (978-1-4143-0646-9(6)); per. 19.99 (978-1-4143-0645-2(8)) Tyndale Hse. Pubs.

Under the Baobab Tree: Claiming Roots, Kindling Hope, Spreading God's Love. 7.00 (978-0-687-08079-3(7)); 7.00 (978-0-687-08089-2(4)); 7.00 (978-0-687-08099-1(1)); 7.00 (978-0-687-08109-7(2)); 5.00 (978-0-687-08751-8(1)); 3.00 (978-0-687-08771-6(6)); 4.00 (978-0-687-08781-5(3)); 30.00 (978-0-687-08811-9(9)); 15.00 (978-0-687-09994-8(3)); pap. 14.00 (978-0-687-08069-4(X)) Abingdon Pr.

Under the Baobab Tree: Keep the Faith, Raise up Hope, Tell of God's Love: Decorating Resource Kit. pap. 20.00 (978-0-687-00738-7(0)) Abingdon Pr.

Van Dyken, Harry. Covenantal Catechism Bk. 5: The Acts. 2000. 143p. (J). (gr. 4-7). pap. 6.95 (978-0-9705251-5-4(X)) Line of Promise Pr.

Vida Publishers Staff, ed. Promesas de Dios para Ninos. 2000. (Bible Promises Ser.). (SPA.). 160p. (J). pap. 3.99 (978-0-8297-2370-0(6)) Vida Pubs.

VonSeggen, Liz. Choose Your Pardner. 2001. (J). spiral bd. 50.00 incl. audio compact disk (978-1-58302-198-9(1)) One Way St., Inc.

Vv. Biblia para los Mas Jovenes, Vol. 6.Tr. of Bible for Teenagers. (SPA.). 264p. (YA). 33.48 (978-84-305-9777-2(8)) Susaeta Ediciones, S.A. ESP. *Dist:* AIMS International Bks., Inc., Giron Bks.

Wagner, Kathi & Wagner, Aubrey. The Everything Kids' Bible Trivia Book: Stump Your Friends & Family with Your Bible Knowledge! 2004. (Illus.). 138p. (J). 6.95 (978-1-59337-031-2(8)) Adams Media Corp.

Washington, Linda & Dall, Jeanette. Favorite Bible Children: Ages 2 & 3. 2004. (Illus.). 96p. (J). pap. 11.95 (978-1-885358-75-2(X)) Rainbow Pubs. & Legacy Pr.

Weekly Bible Reader Fall 2002. 2002. pap. 14.99 (978-1-59185-022-9(3)) CharismaLife Pubs.

Weekly Bible Reader Winter 2002-03. 2002. pap. 14.99 (978-1-59185-109-7(2)) CharismaLife Pubs.

Wegener, Bill, illus. & des. The Bible Game - New Testament: The Bible Game - New Testament. Wegener, Bill, des. 2004. (YA). bds. 34.95 (978-0-9753620-1-3(1)) IMAGINEX, LLC.

Weinke, Sandra Ann. The Bible 6 Booklets: Discovering Its Meaning for Catholics. 1998. (Illus.). (YA). (gr. 9-13). pap., stu. ed. 7.45 (978-0-89837-155-0(4)) Pflaum Publishing Group.

Welborn, Amy, ed. Prove It! The Catholic Teen Bible. 2004. 1,600p. (YA). per. 14.95 (978-1-59276-078-7(3)) Our Sunday Visitor, Publishing Div.

Wenig, Laurin J. Understanding the Bible, 6 booklets. 1998. (Illus.). (YA). (gr. 7-10). pap., stu. ed. 7.45 (978-0-89837-205-2(4)) Pflaum Publishing Group.

White Stone Books Staff. The Bible Almanac for Kids: A Journey of Discovery into the Wild, Incredible, & Mysterious Facts & Trival of the Bible! 2004. (Illus.). 256p. (J). (gr. 3-6). pap. 12.99 (978-1-59379-018-9(X)) White Stone Bks.

Wilger, Jennifer Root. Wiggle Worms Learn the Psalms. 2003. (Godprints Bible Funstuff Ser.). 112p. pap., pap. 16.99 (978-0-7814-3960-2(4) , 0781439604) Cook, David C. Publishing Co.

Williams, Derek. What's What in the Bible. Thomas, Jacqui, illus. 2004. 32p. bds. 11.00 (978-0-687-02654-8(7)) Abingdon Pr.

Willoughby, R. A. Guia de la Biblia para Ninos.Tr. of Children's Guide to the Bible. (SPA.). (J). 12.99 (978-0-7899-0418-8(7) , 498029) Editorial Unilit.

Willoughby, Robert. Children's Guide to the Bible. 2000. (Illus.). 128p. (J). pap. 14.99 (978-0-310-21847-0(0)) Zondervan.

Wingfield, Al. The Little Snail That Lives near a Pail. Ramey, Lisa L., illus. Ramey, Lisa L., photos by. 1999. 14p. (J). (ps-3). pap. 7.95 (978-1-930260-00-9(8)) CTS Family Pr.

Wisconsin Evangelical Lutheran Synod Staff. Christ-Light 2: Topical - T. G. - "What About . . . ?" 1998. (J). (gr. 7-8). 12.50 (978-0-8100-0745-1(2)) Northwestern Publishing Hse.

—Christ-Light 2 Bk. A: Student Lessons. 1998. (J). (gr. 5-6). 4.50 (978-0-8100-0635-5(9)) Northwestern Publishing Hse.

Woodruff, Lisa. The ABC's of the Bible: A Companion to My First Study Bible. 2006. 196p. (J). pap. 19.99 (978-1-4185-0626-1(5)) Nelson, Thomas Inc.

World Bible Publishing Staff. God's Child New Testament. 1999. 256p. (J). lthr. 5.99 (978-0-529-11081-7(4)) World Bible Pubs.

World Famous Bible Trivia. (Illus.). 16p. (J). pap. 1.50 (978-0-87162-837-4(6) , E4510) Warner Pr. Pubs.

Wright, Lani, ed. Beginnings. 2001. (Being There Ser.: Bk. 1). 40p. (YA). (gr. 9-12). pap. 15.95 (978-0-8361-9159-2(5)) Herald Pr.

Wright, Scott. The Philippians Check. 1999. (Illus.). 98p. (YA). pap. 8.95 (978-0-7392-0102-2(6) , PO2993) Morris Publishing.

Yancey, Philip & Stafford, Tim, eds. NIV Student Bible. rev. ltd. ed. 2004. 1472p. (YA). lthr. 34.99 (978-0-310-92963-5(6)) Zondervan.

Youth Specialties Staff. Biblia G3 de Crecimiento Juvenil Dos Tonos Negro/Verde. 2005. (Especialidades Juveniles Ser.). 1596p. lthr. 34.99 (978-0-8297-4481-1(9)) Vida Pubs.

—Biblia G3 de Crecimiento Juvenil Dos Tonos Rosa/Verde. 2005. (Especialidades Juveniles Ser.). 1596p. lthr. 34.99 (978-0-8297-4480-4(0)) Vida Pubs.

Zobel-Nolan. Sp Babys Bedtime Bible. 2002. (Baby's First Ser.). bds. 10.99 (978-0-7899-0295-5(8)) Editorial Unilit.

Zobel-Nolan, Allia. Bible Friend Adventures. Chambliss, Maxie & Hunter, Linda, illus. 1999. 10p. (J). (ps-1). 8.99 (978-0-8054-1962-7(4)) B&H Publishing Grp.

Zondervan. Beginner's Bible', the - Noah's Busy Ark Scholastic. 2006. 14p. (J). bds. 14.99 (978-0-310-60444-0(3)) Zonderkidz.

—Her First Bible & Cross Boxed Gift Set. 2003. 23.97 (978-0-310-60073-2(1)) Zondervan.

—His First Bible & Cross Boxed Gift Set. 2003. 23.97 (978-0-310-60072-5(3)) Zondervan.

—Holy Bible. Pulley, Kelly, illus. 2005. (Beginner's Bible' Ser.). 1024p. (J). 22.99 (978-0-310-71106-3(1)) Zonderkidz.

—Jesus & the Children. DeVries, Catherine, ed. Pulley, Kelly, illus. 2005. (Beginner's Bible Ser.). 22p. (J). (ps). 5.99 (978-0-310-71104-9(5)) Zonderkidz.

—Kids' Quest Study Bible-NIRV: Real Questions, Real Answers. rev. ed. 2005. (Illus.). 1696p. (J). (ps-7). 27.99 (978-0-310-70878-0(8)); pap. 22.99 (978-0-310-70879-7(6)) Zondervan.

—KJV Kids' Study Bible. 2002. (Illus.). 1600p. (J). 29.99 (978-0-310-70488-1(X)) Zonderkidz.

—NIRV Kids Devotional Bible. 2006. 1664p. (J). 27.99 (978-0-310-71243-5(2)); pap. 21.99 (978-0-310-71244-2(0)) Zondervan.

—The NIV Adventure Bible Bungee Toggle SEA. 2005. (Illus.). 1472p. (J). (gr. 3-7). 34.99 (978-0-310-71170-4(3)); lthr. 34.99 (978-0-310-71169-8(X)) Zondervan.

—NIV Backpack Bible. LeBarre, Matt, illus. 2004. 992p. (J). (gr. 3-6). 19.99 (978-0-310-93095-2(2)) Zonderkidz.

—NIV Backpack Bible: 52 Backpack Bible. 2005. 992p. (J). pap. 19.99 (978-0-310-71013-4(8)) Zondervan.

—NIV Backpack Bible/NIV Faithgirlz! Bible. 2005. (Faithgirlz!#8482; Ser.). 992p. (J). pap. 19.99 (978-0-310-71012-7(X)) Zondervan.

—Niv Kids Red Duo-Tone. 2003. (J). lthr. 12.99 (978-0-310-62813-2(X)) Zondervan.

—NIV Student Bible. Yancey, Philip & Stafford, Tim, eds. rev. ltd. ed. 2004. 1472p. (YA). 34.99 (978-0-310-92964-2(4)) Zondervan.

—Niv teen study bib red/blk Duo. 2006. 1664p. 44.99 (978-0-310-93530-8(X)) Zondervan.

—Niv teen study bib silver Duo. 2006. 1664p. 44.99 (978-0-310-93519-3(9)) Zondervan.

—NIV Teen Study Bible. rev. ed. 2004. 1664p. (J). pap. 21.99 (978-0-310-92837-9(0)) Zondervan.

—Noah & the Ark. DeVries, Catherine, ed. Pulley, Kelly, illus. 2005. (Beginner's Bible' Ser.). 22p. (J). (ps). 5.99 (978-0-310-71103-2(7)) Zonderkidz.

—Noah's Busy Ark. Zonderkidz Staff, ed. Pulley, Kelly, illus. 2006. (Beginners Bible Ser.). 12p. (J). bds. 14.99 (978-0-310-71139-1(8)) Zonderkidz.

—NVI Biblia Palabritas. 2003. (SPA.). 1208p. 20.99 (978-0-8297-3620-5(4)) Vida Pubs.

—Promesas Eternas para Niños. 2001. Tr. of Bible Promises for Kids. (SPA.). 160p. pap. 3.99 (978-0-8297-3349-5(3)) Vida Pubs.

—Teen Devotional Bible. Barnhill, Carla & Oestreicher, Mark, eds. 1999. 1600p. (YA). pap. 21.99 (978-0-310-91654-3(2)) Zondervan.

—Teen Devotional Bible: Devotions for Teens, Written by Teens. Barnhill, Carla & Oestreicher, Mark, eds. 1999. (Illus.). 1600p. (J). 27.99 (978-0-310-91653-6(4)) Zondervan.

—Teen Study Bible. rev. ed. 2004. 1664p. (J). 26.99 (978-0-310-92836-2(2)) Zondervan.

—True Images: Devotions & Scriptures for Teen Girls from the NIV Bible. 2004. (Illus.). 160p. 9.99 (978-0-310-80622-6(4)) Inspirio.

Zondervan, contrib. by. NIRV Kids' Quest Study Bible. 1998. (Illus.). 1696p. (J). (gr. 1-5). pap. 21.99 (978-0-310-92559-0(2)) Zondervan.

Zondervan & Inspirio Staff. True Images for Teen Girls: A Guided Journal. 2004. 128p. pap. 9.99 (978-0-310-80547-2(3)) Inspirio.

10 Commandments Gift & Award Bible. 2000. (Illus.). 768p. (J). (gr. 4-7). lthr. 8.99 (978-0-7852-5531-4(1)) Nelson, Thomas Inc.

The 10 Commandments Gift & Award Bible. 2000. (Illus.). (J). (gr. 4-7). 864p. im. lthr. 8.99 (978-0-7852-5528-4(1)); 864p. lthr. 8.99 (978-0-7852-5530-7(3)); 768p. lthr. 8.99 (978-0-7852-5533-8(8)) Nelson, Thomas Inc.

BIBLE—ANIMALS

see Bible—Natural History

BIBLE—ANTIQUITIES

Dowley, Tim. La Guia Portavoz de la Vida en Tiempos Biblicos. 1999. (Guias de Estudio Portavoz; Student Bible Guides). (SPA.). 32p. 8.99 (978-0-8254-1171-7(8), Editorial Portavoz) Kregel Pubns.

Osborne, Rick. Bible Fortresses, Temples & Tombs. 2003. (gr. 3-6). lib. bdg. 16.45 (978-0-613-71764-9(3)) Tandem Library Bks.

Osborne, Rick & Wooding, Marnie. Bible Fortresses, Temples & Tombs. 2003. (2:52 Soul Gear Ser.). (Illus.). 128p. (J). pap. 7.99 (978-0-310-70483-6(9)) Zonderkidz.

BIBLE—ASTRONOMY

James, Diane. Birds. 2004. (My First Look at Animals Ser.). (SPA., Illus.). 24p. (ps-2). 9.95 (978-1-58728-858-6(3), Two Can Publishing) T&N Children's Publishing.

BIBLE—BIOGRAPHY

see also Apostles; Christian Biography; Prophets; Women in the Bible

Beck, Susan Elizabeth. God Loves Me Bible. Oostema, Gloria, illus. rev. ed. 2004. (Bible Storybooks Ser.). 128p. (J). 7.99 (978-0-310-70779-0(X)) Zonderkidz.

Bible Games Co. Staff. Bible Characters Card Game. 2004. 9.99 (978-0-8280-1320-8(9)) Review & Herald Publishing Assn.

Bible Guess Who? A Slide & See Book. 2003. (Illus.). 14p. (J). bds. 10.99 (978-0-8254-5508-7(1)) Kregel Pubns.

Brighter Vision Publishing Staff. Bible Heroes. pap. 2.25 (978-1-55254-026-8(X)) Brighter Vision Pubns.

Bringing Bible Characters to Life. (Illus.). 48p. (J). (gr. 1-7). pap. 5.95 (978-0-87162-634-9(9), E4604) Warner Pr. Pubs.

Christian Focus Staff. Men of Courage: Elijah & Elisha. 2004. (Geared for Growth Bible Studies). 40-56p. pap. (978-1-85792-913-3(6), Christian Focus) Christian Focus Pubns.

De Graaf, Anne. Joseph. Montero, Jose Perez, illus. 2000. (Little Children's Bible Bks.). 38p. (J). (ps-1). 5.99 (978-0-8054-2175-0(0)) B&H Publishing Grp.

—Joshua. Montero, Jose Perez, illus. 2000. (Little Children's Bible Bks.). 38p. (J). (ps-1). 5.99 (978-0-8054-2176-7(9)) B&H Publishing Grp.

—Paul. Montero, Jose Perez, illus. 2001. (Little Children's Bible Bks.: No. 24). 38p. (J). (ps-1). 5.99 (978-0-8054-2194-1(7)) B&H Publishing Grp.

—Ruth. Montero, Jose Perez, illus. 2001. (Little Children's Bible Bks.). 38p. (J). (ps-1). 5.99 (978-0-8054-2190-3(4)) B&H Publishing Grp.

Dorn, Owen A. Ruth: A Love Story. 2003. (God's People Ser.). (Illus.). pap. 6.99 (978-0-8100-1348-3(7)) Northwestern Publishing Hse.

Elkins, Stephen. Children in the Bible, Vol. 9. O'Connor, Tim, illus. 2002. (Word & Song Ser.: Vol. 9). 32p. (J). (ps-5). 9.99 (978-0-8054-2474-4(1)) B&H Publishing Grp.

Favourite Bible Characters. 2000. (Illus.). 516p. 29.95 (978-87-7247-151-8(4)) Scandinavia Publishing Hse. DNK. *Dist:* National Bk. Network.

Frank, Penny. Adam & Eve. (Illus.). 24p. 2.99 (978-0-7459-4102-8(8), Lion) Lion Hudson plc GBR. *Dist:* Trafalgar Square Publishing.

Fun-Faith Builders: Name That Bible Character! 2004. 32p. (J). pap. 3.99 (978-0-88724-223-6(5), CD-2044) Carson-Dellosa Publishing Co., Inc.

Fun Faith Builders: Name That Bible Character! 2004. 32p. (J). pap. 3.99 (978-0-88724-224-3(3), CD-2045); pap. 3.99 (978-0-88724-225-0(1), CD-2046) Carson-Dellosa Publishing Co., Inc.

Gallery, Philip D. Can You Find Bible Heroes? Introducing Your Child to the Old Testament. 1998. (Search & Learn Bks.). (Illus.). 48p. (J). (ps-3). 15.95 (978-0-86716-335-3(6)) St. Anthony Messenger Pr. & Franciscan Communications.

Gemmen, Heather & McNeil, Mary. Walk This Way, Pre-Level 1. Ochoa, Ana, tr. Ochoa, Ana, illus. 2003. (Rocket Readers Ser.). 40p. (J). (ps-1). pap. 8.99 (978-0-7814-3983-1(3), 0781439833) Cook, David C. Publishing Co.

—What Will You Be?, Level 4. Mones, Isidre, tr. Mones, Isidre, illus. 1999. (Rocket Readers Ser.). 32p. (J). (gr. 4 up). pap., pap. 4.99 (978-0-7814-3977-0(9), 0781439779) Cook, David C. Publishing Co.

—What Will You Do?, Level 4. Burris, Priscilla, tr. Burris, Priscilla, illus. 1999. (Rocket Readers Ser.). 32p. (J). (gr. 4 up). pap., pap. 4.99 (978-0-7814-3979-4(5), 0781439795) Cook, David C. Publishing Co.

Henley, Karyn. Bible Heroes & Helpers. 2000. (Tails Activity Bks.). (Illus.). (J). pap. 7.99 (978-0-8054-2287-0(0)) B&H Publishing Grp.

Heroes en la Biblia: Quarter 3, Level 2. (Caminando con Jesus (Walking with Jesus) Series A).Tr. of Heroes in the Bible. (SPA.). (J). (gr. 1-2). stu. ed. 3.50 (978-0-570-05134-3(7), 16-2813) Concordia Publishing Hse.

Hodges, George. Saints & Heroes to the End of the Middle Ages (Yesterday's Classics) 2006. (Illus.). 188p. (J). per. 9.95 (978-1-59915-093-2(X)) Yesterday's Classics.

Hoffman, Mary & Dorling Kindersley Publishing Staff. A First Book of Jewish Bible Stories. Downing, Julie, illus. 2002. 48p. (J). 14.99 (978-0-7894-8504-5(4)) Dorling Kindersley Publishing, Inc.

Jander, Martha Streufert. Philip & the Ethiopian: Acts 8:26-40 for Children. Mitter, Kathy, illus. 2005. (ENG.). 16p. (J). (ps-ps). 1.99 (978-0-7586-0619-8(2)) Concordia Publishing Hse.

Jeffs, Stephanie. A Giant, a Crown & an Open Air Bus. 2003. (SnapShots Ser.). (Illus.). 128p. 5.99 (978-1-85999-452-8(0)) Scripture Union GBR. *Dist:* Gabriel Resources.

—People Jesus Met. Tulip, Jenny, illus. 2004. (My First Find Out about Book Ser.). 24p. (ps up). pap. 3.95 (978-0-8294-1731-9(1)) Loyola Pr.

Koralek, Jenny. The Moses Basket. Baynes, Pauline, illus. 2004. 32p. (J). 16.00 (978-0-8028-5251-9(3)) Eerdmans, William B. Publishing Co.

Loesch, Joe. Joshua - Victory Through God: As Told by God's Animals. Cox, Brian T., illus. 2006. 56p. (J). 13.50 incl. audio compact disk (978-1-932332-62-9(6)) Toy Box Productions.

Lowry, Mark. Ol' Jonah's Tossed into the Ocean. 2001. (Illus.). 24p. (J). 12.99 (978-0-310-70188-0(0)) Zondervan.

Lundy, Charlotte. Thank You, Noah. Waldrep, Evelyn L., ed. Claremont, Heather, illus. 1999. 32p. (ps-3). 15.95 (978-0-9670280-2-6(7)) Bay Light Publishing.

Matimore, P. Henry. Heroes of God's Church. Boog, Michel, illus. Date not set. 286p. (YA). (gr. 5-8). reprint ed. 21.00 (978-0-911845-44-0(5)) Neumann Pr., The.

McKinney, Donna & Herrmann, Angela. Undercover Heroes of the Bible: Ages 2 & 3. 2004. 96p. (J). pap. 11.95 (978-1-58411-009-5(0)) Rainbow Pubs. & Legacy Pr.

—Undercover Heroes of the Bible: Ages 4 & 5. 2004. 96p. (J). pap. 11.95 (978-1-58411-010-1(4)) Rainbow Pubs. & Legacy Pr.

—Undercover Heroes of the Bible: Grades 1 & 2. 2004. 96p. (J). (gr. 1-2). pap. 11.95 (978-1-58411-011-8(2)) Rainbow Pubs. & Legacy Pr.

—Undercover Heroes of the Bible: Grades 3 & 4. 2004. 96p. (J). (gr. 3-4). pap. 11.95 (978-1-58411-012-5(0)) Rainbow Pubs. & Legacy Pr.

—Undercover Heroes of the Bible: Grades 5 & 6. 2004. 96p. (J). (gr. 5-6). pap. 11.95 (978-1-58411-013-2(9)) Rainbow Pubs. & Legacy Pr.

Meaker, Dennis. Extraordinary New Testament People. 2005. (Illus.). 96p. pap. 8.00 (978-0-687-06558-5(5)) Abingdon Pr.

Miller, Stephen. Who's Who & Where's Where in the Bible for Kids. 2006. 160p. (J). pap. 12.97 (978-1-59789-227-8(0), Barbour Bks.) Barbour Publishing, Inc.

My Very Own Bulletin. (Bulletin Bks.). (Illus.). (J). (gr. k-3). pap. 14.95 (978-0-87162-857-2(0), U8607) Warner Pr. Pubs.

New Kids Media Staff. Nueva Biblia Ilustrada (Heroes of the Bible) 1999. (SPA., Illus.). 398p. (J). (ps-3). pap. 12.99 (978-0-7899-0653-3(8), 495094) Editorial Unilit.

Noah. 1998. (Bible Stories for the Very Young Ser.). (J). (978-2-7289-0893-6(1)) Editions Fleurus.

Philip & the Ethiopian. (Illus.). (gr. 1-4). 3.00 (978-0-570-05526-6(1), 54-1036) Concordia Publishing Hse.

Ross, Lillian Hammer. Daughters of Eve: Strong Women of the Bible. Teis, Kyra, illus. 2000. 96p. (J). (gr. 3-7). 19.99 (978-1-902283-82-1(1)) Barefoot Bks., Inc.

Rottmann, Erik. Timothy Joins Paul. Snyder, Joel, illus. 2005. (ENG.). 16p. (J). 1.99 (978-0-7586-0506-1(4)) Concordia Publishing Hse.

Sampson Activity Book. Date not set. stu. ed. 1.49 (978-0-88271-234-5(9), 1750) Regina Pr., Malhame & Co.

Sanders, Karen Nordberg. Ruth & Naomi. Rooney, Ronnie, illus. 2007. 16p. (J). (gr. k-4). 1.99 (***978-0-7586-1283-0(4)***) Concordia Publishing Hse.

Sanderson, Ruth. Tapestries: Stories of Women in the Bible. Sanderson, Ruth, illus. 1998. (Illus.). 32p. (J). (gr. 3-7). 15.95 (978-0-316-77093-4(0)) Little Brown & Co.

Sasso, Sandy Eisenberg. Adam & Eve's First Sunset: God's New Day. Rothenberg, Joani Keller, illus. 2003. 32p. (J). 17.95 (978-1-58023-177-0(2)) Jewish Lights Publishing.

—Cain & Abel: Finding the Fruits of Peace. Rothenberg, Joani Keller, illus. 2001. 32p. (J). (gr. k-3). 16.95 (978-1-58023-123-7(3)) Jewish Lights Publishing.

Schlegl, William. Bible Character Codes. 1998. (Illus.). 64p. (gr. 3-6). 9.99 (978-0-570-05325-5(0)) Concordia Publishing Hse.

School Specialty Publishing. Biblical Women. 2004. (Flip-Flashtm Ser.). 160p. (J). (gr. k up). 7.99 (978-0-7424-2865-2(6)) School Specialty Publishing.

Scovil, Elisabeth R. Wee Folks ABC's of the Bible. 2004. (Wee Books for Wee Folks). (Illus.). 64p. (J). (gr. 4-7). reprint ed. 6.95 (978-1-55709-413-1(6)) Applewood Bks.

Spanish House Inc. Staff. Biblia Dios Me Ama. 2000. (SPA., Illus.). (J). (ps-3). 8.99 (978-0-7899-0689-2(9), 494618); 8.99 (978-0-7899-0690-8(2), 494619) Editorial Unilit.

Taylor, Damon. The Ark & the Park: The Story of Noah. 2002. (Child Sockology Ser.). 32p. 10.99 (978-0-8254-3857-8(8)) Kregel Pubns.

—Beauty & the Booster: The Story of Esther. 2002. (Child Sockology Ser.). (Illus.). 32p. (J). 10.99 (978-0-8254-3858-5(6)) Kregel Pubns.

—Forgive & Forget: The Story of Joseph. 2002. (Child Sockology Ser.). (Illus.). 32p. (J). 10.99 (978-0-8254-3856-1(X)) Kregel Pubns.

—Hide & Sink: The Story of Jonah. 2002. (Child Sockology Ser.). 32p. (J). 10.99 (978-0-8254-3855-4(1)) Kregel Pubns.

Turnbull, Helen & Kershner, Jan, eds. Bible-Times Crafts Your Kids Will Love. 1998. (Illus.). 112p. (J). (ps-6). pap. 16.99 (978-0-7644-2067-2(4), Flagship Church Resources) Group Publishing, Inc.

Zobel-Nolan, Allia. Bible Hero Adventures. Chambliss, Maxie & Hunter, Linda, illus. 1999. 10p. (J). (gr. k-1). 8.99 (978-0-8054-1961-0(6)) B&H Publishing Grp.

BIBLE—BIRDS

see Bible—Natural History

BIBLE—BOTANY

see Bible—Natural History

BIBLE—COMMENTARIES

Acts: The Church Alive! 1998. (Club 56 Ser.). (J). (gr. 5-6). tchr. ed., spiral bd. 29.99 (978-1-57405-361-6(2)); 28p. pap., wbk. ed. 2.79 (978-1-57405-362-3(0)) CharismaLife Pubs.

Acts: The Holy Spirit at Work in Believers. 2005. (C). stu. ed. (978-0-7617-0894-0(4), BBIB115E-90) Global Univ.

Africa/French/Benin Book of Hope: Revised Childrren's Edition. 2003. (J). 1.00 net. (978-1-931940-49-8(5)) Book of Hope International.

Africa/Portuguese/Portugal Book of Hope. rev. ed. 2003. (J). 1.00 net. (978-1-931940-48-1(7)) Book of Hope International.

Africa/Portuguese/Portugal Book of Hope: International Pictorial Edition. 2003. (J). 1.00 net. (978-1-931940-47-4(9)) Book of Hope International.

Allen, Joey. The Gospel: Big Thoughts for Little Thinkers. 2005. (Illus.). 32p. (J). 5.99 (978-0-89221-617-8(4)) New Leaf Pr., Inc.

—The Mission: Big Thoughts for Little Thinkers. 2005. (Illus.). 32p. (J). 5.99 (978-0-89221-616-1(6)) New Leaf Pr., Inc.

—The Trinity: Big Thoughts for Little Thinkers. 2005. (Illus.). 32p. (J). 5.99 (978-0-89221-614-7(X)) New Leaf Pr., Inc.

Ana Bok Mormon (in Kiribati/Gilbertese) Kakoauan taekan jesu Kristo. 2001. (Illus.). 632p. pap. 2.00 (978-1-59297-511-2(9)) Church of Jesus Christ of Latter Day Saints, Historical Dept.

Anderson, Paul N. Wading with Children & Swimming with Elephants: Navigating the Living Waters. 2000. (Pendle Hill Pamphlet Ser.). 32p. pap. 4.00 (978-0-87574-352-3(8)) Pendle Hill Pubns.

Arabic Book of Hope. 2003. (J). tchr. ed 1.00 net. (978-1-931940-92-4(4)) Book of Hope International.

Arabic Book of Hope: Early Elementary Edition. 2003. (J). 1.00 net. (978-1-931940-93-1(2)) Book of Hope International.

Arabic Book of Hope: Revised International Pictorial Edition. 2003. (J). 1.00 net. (978-1-931940-91-7(6)) Book of Hope International.

Barnett, Paul. 1 Corinthians: Holiness & Hope of a Rescued People. 2000. (Focus on the Bible Ser.). (Illus.). 320p. pap. (978-1-85792-598-2(X), Mentor) Christian Focus Pubns.

Barron's Educational Editorial Staff. Romans: History Society Religion. 1999. (Bravo Ser.). (Illus.). 124p. (J). (gr. 6 up). pap. 8.95 (978-0-7641-0949-2(9)) Barron's Educational Series, Inc.

Bauman, Lester. Exploring the Epistles of John. 2004. (Exploring the Bible Ser.). 77p. 4.80 (978-0-7399-2307-8(2), 2219) Rod & Staff Pubs., Inc.

Beerman, Merlin, creator. El Camino a Cristo Guia de Estudios Biblicos. 2001. (SPA.). per. 6.95 (978-0-9668482-3-6(3)) Revelation Pubns.

Beginnings II - Jesus, My Shepherd - Answer Key: New Testament Lessons for Young Readers. 2004. (Beginnings II Ser.). 28p. (J). 6.99 (978-1-889015-90-3(3)) Explorer's Bible Study.

Bible Visual International, compiled by. The Crucifixion Pt. I, Vol. 11: New Testament. 2006. (Illus.). (J). pap. (978-1-932381-41-2(4), 1011) Bible Visuals International, Inc.

Bible Visuals International, comment. Conduct of the Church Vol. 24: New Testament. 2006. (Illus.). (J). pap. (978-1-932381-53-5(8), 1024) Bible Visuals International, Inc.

—Joseph, a Picture of the Lord Jesus Pt. 2, Vol. 5: Old Testament. 2006. (Illus.). (J). pap. (978-1-932381-70-2(8), 2005) Bible Visuals International, Inc.

—A Kingdom Forever Vol. 23: Old Testament. 2006. (Illus.). (J). pap. (978-1-932381-83-2(X), 2023) Bible Visuals International, Inc.

—Law & Grace Volume 27: New Testament. 2006. (Illus.). (J). pap. (978-1-932381-55-9(4), 1027) Bible Visuals International, Inc.

—The Word of God Vol. 16: Old Testament. 2006. (Illus.). (J). pap. (978-1-932381-76-4(7), 2016) Bible Visuals International, Inc.

Bible Visuals International, compiled by. Believers in Christ Volume 29: New Testament. 2006: (Illus.). (J). pap. (978-1-932381-26-9(0), 1029) Bible Visuals International, Inc.

—Christ Is God the Son Vol. 34: New Testament. 2006. (Illus.). (J). pap. (978-1-932381-59-7(7), 1034) Bible Visuals International, Inc.

—Christ, the Head of the Church Vol. 31: New Testament. 2006. (Illus.). (J). pap. (978-1-932381-57-3(0), 1031) Bible Visuals International, Inc.

—Christian Growth Vol. 40: New Testament. 2006. (Illus.). (J). pap. (978-1-932381-64-1(3), 1040) Bible Visuals International, Inc.

—Christian Joy: New Testament Volume 30. 2006. (Illus.). (J). pap. (978-1-932381-27-6(9), 1030) Bible Visuals International, Inc.

—Condemnation Vol. 19: New Testament. 2006. (Illus.). (J). pap. (978-1-932381-49-8(X), 1019) Bible Visuals International, Inc.

—Conversion Volume 17: New Testament. 2006. (Illus.). (J). pap. (978-1-932381-47-4(3), 1017) Bible Visuals International, Inc.

—The Crucifixion Pt. 2, Vol. 12: New Testament. 2006. (Illus.). (J). pap. (978-1-932381-42-9(2), 1012) Bible Visuals International, Inc.

—Disobedience Vol.20: Old Testament. 2006. (Illus.). (J). pap. (978-1-932381-80-1(5), 2020) Bible Visuals International, Inc.

—Election Vol. 06: Old Testament. 2006. (Illus.). (J). pap. (978-1-932381-32-0(5), 2006) Bible Visuals International, Inc.

—Eternal Salvation: New Testament Volume 35. 2006. (Illus.). (J). pap. (978-1-932381-60-3(0), 1035) Bible Visuals International, Inc.

—Forgiveness: New Testament Volume 10. 2006. (Illus.). (J). pap. (978-1-932381-40-5(6), 1010) Bible Visuals International, Inc.

—Great Is Thy Faithfulness. 2006. (Illus.). (J). pap. (978-1-932381-94-8(5), 6180) Bible Visuals International, Inc.

—The Holy Spirit Vol. 14: New Testament. 2006. (J). pap. (978-1-932381-44-3(9), 1014) Bible Visuals International, Inc.

—Human Suffering (Job) Vol. 29: Old Testament. 2006. (Illus.). (J). pap. (978-1-932381-88-7(0), 2029) Bible Visuals International, Inc.

—In the Beginning Volume 01: Old Testament. 2006. (Illus.). (J). pap. (978-1-932381-66-5(X), 2001) Bible Visuals International, Inc.

—Israel Vol. 22: New Testament. 2006. (Illus.). (J). pap. (978-1-932381-51-1(1), 1022) Bible Visuals International, Inc.

—Jehovah Vol. 30: Old Testament. 2006. (Illus.). (J). pap. (978-1-932381-89-4(9), 2030) Bible Visuals International, Inc.

—Justification. 2006. (Illus.). (J). pap. (978-1-932381-24-5(4)) Bible Visuals International, Inc.

—Law & Faith Volume 26: New Testament. 2006. (Illus.). (J). pap. (978-1-932381-54-2(6), 1026) Bible Visuals International, Inc.

—Law & Liberty Volume 28: New Testament. 2006. (Illus.). (J). pap. (978-1-932381-56-6(2), 1028) Bible Visuals International, Inc.

—The Lord-He Is God Vol. 25: Old Testament. 2006. (Illus.). (J). pap. (978-1-932381-85-6(6), 2025) Bible Visuals International, Inc.

—The Lordship of Christ Volume 07: New Testament. 2006. (Illus.). (J). pap. (978-1-932381-37-5(6), 1007) Bible Visuals International, Inc.

—Nature of Man: Old Testament Volume 03. 2006. (Illus.). (J). pap. (978-1-932381-68-9(6), 2003) Bible Visuals International, Inc.

—The New Covenant Vol. 37: New Testament. 2006. (Illus.). (J). pap. (978-1-932381-62-7(7), 1037) Bible Visuals International, Inc.

—The Providence of God Vol. 8: Old Testament. 2006. (Illus.). (J). pap. (978-1-932381-71-9(6), 2008) Bible Visuals International, Inc.

—Rebellion Vol. 18: Old Testament. 2006. (Illus.). (J). pap. (978-1-932381-78-8(3), 2018) Bible Visuals International, Inc.

—Redemption Vol. 07: Old Testament. 2006. (Illus.). (J). pap. (978-1-932381-33-7(3), 2007) Bible Visuals International, Inc.

—The Resurrection Vol. 14: New Testament. 2006. (Illus.). (J). pap. (978-1-932381-43-6(0), 1013) Bible Visuals International, Inc.

—Sanctification Vol. 21: New Testament. 2006. (Illus.). (J). pap. (978-1-932381-50-4(3), 1021) Bible Visuals International, Inc.

—Servants of God Vol. 25: New Testament. 2006. (Illus.). (J). pap. (978-1-932381-25-2(2), 1025) Bible Visuals International, Inc.

—Service Vol. 18: New Testament. 2006. (Illus.). (J). pap. (978-1-932381-48-1(1), 1018) Bible Visuals International, Inc.

—Suffering Vol. 16: New Testament. 2006. (Illus.). (J). pap. (978-1-932381-46-7(5), 1016) Bible Visuals International, Inc.

—The Tabernacle Vol. 09, Pt. 1: Old Testament. 2006. (Illus.). (J). pap. (978-1-932381-72-6(4), 2009) Bible Visuals International, Inc.

—The Tabernacle Vol. 10, Pt. 2: Old Testament. 2006. (Illus.). (J). pap. (978-1-932381-73-3(2), 2010) Bible Visuals International, Inc.

—Tests of True Faith Vol.39: New Testament. 2006. (Illus.). (J). pap. (978-1-932381-63-4(5), 1039) Bible Visuals International, Inc.

—Wisdom Vol. 31: Old Testament. 2006. (Illus.). (J). pap. (978-1-932381-90-0(2), 2031) Bible Visuals International, Inc.

Blitz, Shmuel. Megilat Ester: The ArtScroll Children's Megillah. Katz, Tova, illus. 2003. (ArtScroll Ser.). (ENG & HEB.). 79p. (J). 16.99 (978-1-57819-708-8(2), MCHH); pap. 10.99 (978-1-57819-709-5(0), MCHP) Mesorah Pubns., Ltd.

Blumenthal, Scott. The Explorer's Bible/By Scott Blumenthal. 2006. (Illus.). (978-0-87441-792-0(9)) Behrman Hse., Inc.

BOK in MORMON (Marshallese) Bar juon kalimmur kon jisos Kraist. 2003. (Illus.). 591p. per. 2.00 (978-1-59297-513-6(5)) Church of Jesus Christ of Latter Day Saints, Historical Dept.

The Book of Acts. ldr.'s ed. 1998. (Cross Training Ser.: Vol. 4). 72p. (YA). (gr. 10-12). pap. 15.00 incl. VHS (978-1-57405-032-5(X)) CharismaLife Pubs.

Book of Mormon - Afrikaans: Another Testament of Jesus Christ. 2003. Tr. of Die boek van Mormon. (AFR., Illus.). 251p. pap. 2.00 (978-1-59297-510-5(0) , 34407 501) Church of Jesus Christ of Latter Day Saints, Historical Dept.

Brazil/Portuguese Book of Hope: International Graphic Edition. 2003. (J). 1.00 net. (978-1-931940-68-9(1)) Book of Hope International.

Brazil/Portuguese Book of Hope: Revised International Pictorial Edition. 2003. (J). 1.00 net. (978-1-931940-67-2(3)) Book of Hope International.

Bridges, Nancy S. Discovery - Words of Wisdom: Job, Psalms, & Proverbs. Clark, Virginia A. & Constance, Tom M., Jr., eds. 1998. (Discovery Ser.). 288p. (J). (gr. 3-6). stu. ed., per., wbk. ed. 21.99 (978-1-889015-25-5(3)) Explorer's Bible Study.

Brost, Corey. Gospel Connections for Teens: Reflections for Sunday Mass, Cycle B. 2005. 129p. (J). (gr. 8-12). pap. 4.95 (978-0-88489-848-1(2)) St. Mary's Pr.

Buevara, Isaias, illus. Revelation: A Visual Journey. 2005. 96p. per. 41.99 (978-0-9763800-3-0(X) , 10) Orison Pubs.

Carlsen, Derek. Faith & Courage Commentary on Acts. 2004. 544p. per. 12.95 (978-1-930367-98-2(8) , CLP80091) Christian Liberty Pr.

Children's Bible Class Staff. Tesoros para Ninos. 1999. Tr. of Keys for Kids. (SPA.). 368p. pap. 11.99 (978-0-8254-1123-6(8) , 196-169, Editorial Portavoz) Kregel Pubns.

Chinese Book of Hope: Early Elementary Edition (Simplified Characters) 2003. (J). 1.00 net. (978-1-931940-87-0(8)) Book of Hope International.

Chinese Book of Hope: Early Elementary Edition (Traditional Characters) 2003. (J). 1.00 net. (978-1-931940-86-3(X)) Book of Hope International.

Chinese Book of Hope: Revised International Pictorial Edition -d (Simplified) 2003. (J). 1.00 net. (978-1-931940-82-5(7)) Book of Hope International.

Chinese Book of Hope: Revised International Pictorial Edition -d (Traditional) 2003. (J). 1.00 net. (978-1-931940-84-9(3)) Book of Hope International.

Cohen, Ron. Bible Survey for High School — Student Workbook, 2 vols. 2005. 149p. (YA). spiral bd., wbk. ed. (978-0-9767618-1-5(5)) Jew-El Pr. Co.

—Bible Survey for High School — Study Guide, 2 vols. 2005. (Illus.). 187p. (YA). stu. ed., spiral bd. (978-0-9767618-0-8(7)) Jew-El Pr. Co.

Connect Booklet. 2003. 47p. (YA). pap. 1.49 (978-1-59312-053-5(2)) North American Mission Board, SBC.

Courtney, Claudia. Modest King: Palm Sunday. 2000. (ps-2). lib. bdg. 10.65 (978-0-613-72824-9(6)) Tandem Library Bks.

Cromer, J. T. Survey of the Scripture: Seeing the Big Picture in the Old Testament. 2002. 142p. per. 12.95 (978-0-9724895-0-8(9)) Cromer, J.T.

Cuba/Spanish Book of Hope: (Spanish) Revised International Graphic Edition. 2003. (J). 1.00 net. (978-1-931940-98-6(3)) Book of Hope International.

Davis, Mary. Five-Minute Sunday School Activities: Jesus' Miracles & Messages. 2004. (Illus.). 96p. (J). pap. 11.95 (978-1-58411-049-1(X)) Rainbow Pubs. & Legacy Pr.

De Graaf, A. M. La Torre de Babel. (Divertidas Historias Biblicas para Ninos Ser.).Tr. of Tower of Babel. (SPA.). (J). 3.49 (978-0-7899-0525-3(6) , 496642) Editorial Unilit.

De Heer, Jolene & Grussing, Robert. Jonah. 2001. (Devotions to Go Ser.). 80p. (gr. 7-12). 3.95 (978-1-56212-539-4(7) , 160465, Faith Alive Christian Resources) CRC Pubns.

Discovery - in the Beginning - Answer Key: Genesis. 2003. (Bible Discovery Ser.). 43p. (J). 6.99 (978-1-889015-32-3(6)) Explorer's Bible Study.

Dowley, Tim. Guia Portavoz de la Historia de la Biblia. 2005. (Guias de Estudio Portavoz; Student Bible Guides). (SPA., Illus.). 32p. 8.99 (978-0-8254-1167-0(X) , Editorial Portavoz) Kregel Pubns.

English Book of Hope: Affect Destiny Book. 2003. (YA). 1.00 net. (978-1-931940-75-7(4)) Book of Hope International.

English Book of Hope: HopeXtreme. 2003. 48p. (J). 1.00 net. (978-1-931940-71-9(1)) Book of Hope International.

English Book of Hope: Resource Guide. 2003. (YA). 1.00 net. (978-1-931940-74-0(6)) Book of Hope International.

English Book of Hope: Revised International Graphic Edition. 2003. (J). 1.00 net. (978-1-931940-76-4(2)) Book of Hope International.

English Book of Hope: The Life & Teachings of Jesus of Nazareth. 2003. per. 1.00 net. (978-1-931940-77-1(0)) Book of Hope International.

English/Botswana Book of Hope: Revised International Pictorial Edition. 2003. (J). 1.00 net. (978-1-931940-44-3(4)) Book of Hope International.

English/Oceania Book of Hope. rev. ed. 2003. (J). 1.00 net. (978-1-931940-58-0(4)) Book of Hope International.

English/Oceania Book of Hope: Revised International Pictorial Edition. 2003. (J). 1.00 net. (978-1-931940-52-8(5)) Book of Hope International.

English/Philippines Book of Hope: Revised International Pictorial Edition. 2003. (J). 1.00 net. (978-1-931940-51-1(7)) Book of Hope International.

France Book of Hope: All They Want Is the Truth. 2003. (J). 1.00 net. (978-1-931940-41-2(X)) Book of Hope International.

France Book of Hope: Graphic Edition. 2003. (J). 1.00 net. (978-1-931940-42-9(8)) Book of Hope International.

France/French Book of Hope. 2003. (J). tchr. ed. 1.00 net. (978-1-931940-50-4(9)) Book of Hope International.

France/French Book of Hope: Early Elementary Edition. 2003. (J). 1.00 net. (978-1-931940-45-0(2)) Book of Hope International.

France/French Book of Hope: Then Seeds of Spiritual Lineage. 2003. (J). 1.00 net. (978-1-931940-62-7(2)) Book of Hope International.

Ganz, Nancy. Herein Is Love: Numbers. 2005. (YA). pap. 13.00 (***978-0-9767582-2-8(9)***) Shepherd Pr. Inc.

—Herein Is Love Vol. 1: Genesis. 2nd rev. ed. 2002. 576p. (J). pap., tchr. ed. 20.00 (978-0-9723046-0-3(6)) Shepherd Pr. Inc.

—Herein Is Love Vol. 2: Exodus. 2nd rev. ed. 2002. 296p. (J). pap., tchr. ed. 15.00 (978-0-9723046-1-0(4)) Shepherd Pr. Inc.

—Herein Is Love Vol. 3: Leviticus. 2nd rev. ed. 2002. 160p. (J). pap., tchr. ed. 12.00 (978-0-9723046-2-7(2)) Shepherd Pr. Inc.

Gordon Brown, Doris. Jesus Brought Lazarus Back to Life. 2003. 5.95 (978-1-59427-023-9(6)) Aglob Publishing.

Greenwald, Zev. Stories My Grandfather Told Me Volume 1 — Bereishis: Memorable tales based on the weekly Sidrah. 2000. 245p. pap. 13.99 (978-1-57819-526-8(8) , SG1P) Mesorah Pubns., Ltd.

Grinovald, Ze'ev. Stories My Grandfather Told Me: Memorable Tales Arranged According to the Weekly Sidrah. Katz, Tova, illus. (ArtScroll Youth Ser.). (J). 2001. 247p. pap. 13.99 (978-1-57819-534-3(9) , SG5P); 2000. 245p. 16.99 (978-1-57819-525-1(X) , SG1H) Mesorah Pubns., Ltd.

Halper, Sharon. To Learn Is to Do: A Tikkun Olam Road Map. Koffsky, Ann D., illus. 2004. vi, 56p. (gr. 4-6). pap. 8.95 (978-0-8074-0729-5(1) , 123935) URJ Pr.

Harvey, Edwin, et al. Asking Father. 2001. (RUM & RUS., Illus.). 120p. (J). 6.00 (978-0-932774-16-0(5)) Christian, Harvey Pubs. Inc.

Hash, John A. The Best of Bible Pathway 2004. exp. ed. 2003. (Illus.). pap. 14.95 (978-1-879595-37-8(0)) Bible Pathway Ministries.

Hausa New Testament. 2004. Tr. of Sabon Alkawali. (HAU.). (YA). pap. 1.50 (978-1-882536-67-2(3)) Bible League.

Hibsman, Tim. Christian Comparisons: Christians Today & in Biblical Times: Comparisons for Children. Hibsman, Tim, illus. 2001. 100p. (J). cd-rom (978-1-889858-03-6(X)) True Arts Graphics & Printing.

La Historicas de Exodo (The Story of Exodus) (SPA.). (J). 1.59 (978-0-7899-0549-9(3) , 490535) Editorial Unilit.

Howick, E. Keith. The Miracles of Jesus the Messiah. 2003. 237p. 18.95 (978-1-886249-00-4(8)) WindRiver Publishing.

—The Parables of Jesus the Messiah. 2003. 197p. 18.95 (978-1-886249-01-1(6)) WindRiver Publishing.

India/English Book of Hope. 2003. 1.00 net. (978-1-931940-38-2(X)); 2002. (J). 1.00 net. (978-1-890525-48-4(0)) Book of Hope International.

India/English Book of Hope: Revised Children's Edition. rev. ed. 2003. (J). 1.00 net. (978-1-931940-36-8(3)) Book of Hope International.

India/English Book of Hope: Revised International Pictorial Edition. rev. ed. 2003. (Illus.). (J). 1.00 net. (978-1-931940-37-5(1)) Book of Hope International.

India/Gujarathi Book of Hope. 2003. 1.00 net. (978-1-931940-32-0(0)); (J). 1.00 net. (978-1-931940-30-6(4)); (Illus.). 1.00 net. (978-1-931940-31-3(2)) Book of Hope International.

India/Kannada Book of Hope. 2003. 1.00 net. (978-1-931940-25-2(8)); (J). 1.00 net. (978-1-931940-23-8(1)) Book of Hope International.

India/Khasi Book of Hope. rev. ed. 2003. (J). 1.00 net. (978-1-931940-27-6(4)) Book of Hope International.

India/Malayalam Book of Hope. 2003. 1.00 net. (978-1-931940-22-1(3)); (J). 1.00 net. (978-1-931940-20-7(7)); (Illus.). 1.00 net. (978-1-931940-21-4(5)) Book of Hope International.

India/Marathi Book of Hope. 2003. 1.00 net. (978-1-931940-16-0(9)); 2002. (J). 1.00 net. (978-1-931940-14-6(2)) Book of Hope International.

India/Punjabi Book of Hope. rev. ed. 2003. (J). 1.00 net. (978-1-931940-33-7(9)) Book of Hope International.

India/Tamil Book of Hope. 2003. 1.00 net. (978-1-931940-19-1(3)); (J). 1.00 net. (978-1-931940-17-7(7)); (Illus.). 1.00 net. (978-1-931940-18-4(5)) Book of Hope International.

Indonesia/Bahasa Book of Hope. ed. (J). 2003. 1.00 net. (978-1-931940-53-5(3)); 2002. 1.00 net. (978-1-890525-55-2(3)) Book of Hope International.

Indonesia/Bahasa Book of Hope: Early Elementary Edition. 2003. (J). 1.00 net. (978-1-931940-60-3(6)) Book of Hope International.

Indonesian Book of Hope. 2003. (J). tchr. ed. 1.00 net. (978-1-931940-80-1(0)) Book of Hope International.

The International Student Bible for Catholics. 2001. 1664p. (YA). stu. ed. 21.99 (978-0-7180-0063-9(3)) Nelson, Thomas Inc.

Japanese/Japan Book of Hope: Early Elementary Edition. 2003. (J). 1.00 net. (978-1-931940-69-6(X)) Book of Hope International.

Japan/Japanese Book of Hope. 2003. (J). tchr. ed. 1.00 net. (978-1-931940-73-3(8)) Book of Hope International.

Jeffery, Peter. Opening up Ephesians: For Young People. 2002. 100p. (YA). per. 8.95 (978-0-9710169-7-2(6)) Solid Ground Christian Bks.

Jesus Company: Bible Time. 30p. (gr. 4 up). stu. ed. 9.00 (978-0-570-00672-5(4) , 22-2775) Concordia Publishing Hse.

Jesus Company: Bible Time, Grade 5. 30p. (gr. 5 up). stu. ed. 9.00 (978-0-570-00678-7(3) , 7.99) Concordia Publishing Hse.

Johnson, John L. The Original Names & Descriptions of God & Jesus. 2002. (YA). spiral bd. 4.95 (978-0-9709715-7-9(5)) Johnson Bks., Inc.

Kanzlemar, Joseph. Biblical Creation Authenticated. 2006. (Illus.). 159p. (***978-0-9797786-1-2(1)***) Bible Based Studies.

—Biblical Creation Authenticated - Youth Edition. abr. ed. 2007. 18p. (YA). (***978-0-9797786-4-3(6)***) Bible Based Studies.

Keene, Michael. St. Mark's Gospel & the Christian Faith. 2nd ed. 2002. (Illus.). 112p. pap., stu. ed. (978-0-7487-6775-5(4)) Nelson Thornes Ltd.

Kimbrough, Lawrence. Bible Promises for Kids. 2003. 128p. pap. 3.99 (978-0-8054-2740-0(6)) B&H Publishing Grp.

Kizer, Andy. To the Overcomers. 2003. (YA). per. 10.00 (978-0-9725894-0-6(6)) Riddle Creek Publishing.

Kuhn, Pamela J. More Instant Bible Lessons: Jesus' Disciples. 2004. 96p. (J). pap. 11.95 (978-1-58411-017-0(1)) Rainbow Pubs. & Legacy Pr.

—More Instant Bible Lessons: Walking with Jesus. 2004. 96p. (J). pap. 11.95 (978-1-58411-016-3(3)) Rainbow Pubs. & Legacy Pr.

—More Instant Bible Lessons: Wisdom from God's Word. 2004. 96p. (J). pap. 11.95 (978-1-58411-018-7(X)) Rainbow Pubs. & Legacy Pr.

Lee, Witness. Estudio-Vida de 1 y 2 Samuel. 2001. (SPA.). 276p. (J). (gr. 6). per. 12.50 (978-0-7363-1280-6(3) , 10-112-002) Living Stream Ministry.

—The Holy Word for Morning Revival: Crystallization-Study of Revelation. 2000. (J). (gr. 6). Vol. 3. 136p. 7.00 (978-0-7363-0816-8(4) , 13-099-011); Vol. 4. 109p. 7.00 (978-0-7363-0817-5(2) , 13-100-001) Living Stream Ministry.

—The Holy Word for Morning Revival: Crystallization-Study of the Gospel of Matthew. 2001. 109p. (J). (gr. 6). Vol. 3. per. 7.00 (978-0-7363-1380-3(X) , 13-141-001); Vol. 4. per. 7.00 (978-0-7363-1383-4(4) , 13-142-001) Living Stream Ministry.

—The Holy Word for Morning Revival: Matthew 1:1-7:29, Vol. 1. 2000. 71p. (J). (gr. 6). 6.00 (978-0-7363-1108-3(4) , 13-133-001) Living Stream Ministry.

—La Palabra Santa para el Avivamiento Matutino: Estudio de Crystalizacion del Evangelio de Mateo, Vol. 2. 2001. Tr. of Holy Word for Morning Revival: Crystallization Study of the Gospel of Matthew. (SPA.). 107p. (J). (gr. 6). per. 7.00 (978-0-7363-1185-4(8) , 13-140-002) Living Stream Ministry.

—La Palabra Santa para el Avivamiento Matutino: Mateo 1:1-7:29, Vol. 1. 2001. Tr. of Holy Word for Morning Revival: Matthew 1:1-7:29. (SPA.). 71p. (J). (gr. 6). per. 6.00 (978-0-7363-1139-7(4) , 13-133-002) Living Stream Ministry.

—La Palabra Santa para el Avivamiento Matutino: Mateo 8:1-13:52, Vol. 2. 2001. Tr. of Holy Word for Morning Revival: Matthew 8:1-13:52. (SPA.). 90p. (J). (gr. 6). per. 6.00 (978-0-7363-1140-3(8) , 13-134-002) Living Stream Ministry.

—The Spirit in the Epistles. 2001. 215p. (J). (gr. 6). per. 9.50 (978-0-7363-1189-2(0) , 07-951-001) Living Stream Ministry.

—The Subjective Truths in the Holy Scriptures. 2000. 108p. (J). (gr. 6). per. 6.75 (978-0-7363-0995-0(0) , 10-912-001) Living Stream Ministry.

Lucy Show Bible Study Guide, Vol. 2. 2005. (Illus.). 48p. pap., stu. ed. 7.99 (978-0-9765142-1-3(4)) Entertainment Ministry, The.

The MacArthur Daily Bible: Read Through the Bible in One Year, with Notes from John Macarthur. 2003. 1376p. pap. 19.99 (978-0-7180-0639-6(9)) Nelson, Thomas Inc.

Mackall, Dandi Daley. The Golden Rule. Dippold, Jane, illus. 2006. 36p. (J). 9.99 (978-0-7847-1822-3(9)) Standard Publishing.

Mackenzie, Carine. The Bible Explorer. (Illus.). 168p. (J). 15.99 (978-1-85792-533-3(5) , Christian Focus) Christian Focus Pubns. GBR. *Dist:* Riverside.

Madagascar/Malagasy Book of Hope. rev. ed. 2003. (J). 1.00 net. (978-1-931940-43-6(6)) Book of Hope International.

Madagascar/Malagasy Book of Hope: International Pictorial Edition. 2003. (J). 1.00 net. (978-1-931940-70-2(3)) Book of Hope International.

Marchon, Benoit & Rosa, Jean-Pierre. Descubrir la Biblia. Truong, Marcelino, illus. (SPA.). 50p. (J). (gr. 3-5). 7.96 (978-84-263-3188-5(2)) Vives, Luis Editorial (Edelvives) ESP. *Dist:* Lectorum Pubns., Inc.

Martin, Harold S. Brethren New Testament Commentary: 1 & 2 Timothy & Titus. 2004. 15.00 (978-0-9745027-3-1(1)) Brethren Revival Fellowship.

—Brethren New Testament Commentary: 2 Corinthians. 2006. 224p. 12.00 (978-0-9745027-8-6(2)) Brethren Revival Fellowship.

McKenzie, Marni Shideler. Quest - Words of Wisdom: Job, Psalms, & Proverbs. Constance, Nellie E. & Eades, Lois, eds. 1998. (Quest Ser.). 265p. (YA). (gr. 3-6). stu. ed., per., wbk. ed. 21.99 (978-1-889015-26-2(1)) Explorer's Bible Study.

McKenzie, Marni Shideler & Bridges, Nancy S. Quest - Faith at Work: Romans, Galatians, & James. Murtha, Dee, ed. 2004. (Bible Quest Ser.). 231p. (YA). stu. ed., per., wbk. ed. 21.99 (978-1-889015-91-0(1)) Explorer's Bible Study.

McLean, Max E., narrated by. The Listener's Bible. 2001. 66p. im. lthr. 199.95 incl. audio compact disk (978-1-931047-17-3(0)) Fellowship for the Performing Arts.

—The Listener's New Testament. 2001. 16p. im. lthr. 69.95 incl. audio compact disk (978-1-931047-19-7(7)) Fellowship for the Performing Arts.

Miller, Mark A. & Zelman, Laurie. Bethlehem's Best: A Children's Musical Based on the Story from Luke 2:1-20; Matthew 2:1-2, 8-11. 2004. pap. 4.00 (978-0-687-06320-8(5)) Abingdon Pr.

Nystrom, Carolyn. Children's Bible Basics: Questions Kids Ask about Belief. 2000. (Illus.). 128p. (J). (ps-3). 6.99 (978-0-8024-7914-3(6)) Moody Pubs.

Palmer, Edward G. Book of Edward Christian Mythology, 4 vols., Set. l.t. ed. 2005. (Illus.). 1306p. per. 123.80 (978-0-9768833-4-0(1) , 0976883341) JVED Publishing.

—Book of Edward Christian Mythology: Itching Christian Ears, 4 vols., Vol. 3. l.t. ed. 2005. (Illus.). 616p. per. 39.95 (978-0-9768833-2-6(5) , 0976883325) JVED Publishing.

—Book of Edward Christian Mythology Vol. II: God Does Not Change, 4 vols. l.t. ed. 2005. (Illus.). 356p. per. 27.95 (978-0-9768833-1-9(7) , 0976883317) JVED Publishing.

—Book of Edward Christian Mythology Vol. IV: Appendixes Reference, 4 vols. l.t. ed. 2005. (Illus.). 208p. per. 27.95 (978-0-9768833-3-3(3) , 0976883333) JVED Publishing.

Pattyn, Denny & Flecker, Katie. SRT 434 for Small Groups. 2005. (YA). ldr.'s hndbk. ed. 59.95 (978-0-9771248-0-0(0)) SRT Publishing.

—SRT 434 Leaders Guide. 2005. (YA). 9.95 (978-0-9771248-3-1(5)) SRT Publishing.

Philippines/Cebuano Book of Hope: Early Elementary Edition. 2003. (J). 1.00 net. (978-1-931940-55-9(X)) Book of Hope International.

Philippines/Ilocano Book of Hope: Early Elementary Edition. 2003. (J). 1.00 net. (978-1-931940-56-6(8)) Book of Hope International.

Philippines/Tagalog Book of Hope: Early Elementary Edition. 2003. (J). 1.00 net. (978-1-931940-54-2(1)) Book of Hope International.

Poland/Polish Book of Hope: Early Elementary Edition. 2003. (J). 1.00 net. (978-1-931940-59-7(2)) Book of Hope International.

Por Que Estaba agradecida Maria ? Serie para ninos Historias maravillosas. 2000. pap. (978-1-57697-807-8(9)) United Bible Societies/Americas Service Ctr.

Por Que Estaba confuso el Faraon? Serie para ninos Historias maravillosas. 2000. pap. (978-1-57697-797-2(8)) United Bible Societies/Americas Service Ctr.

Por Que Estaba contento el pastor ? Serie para ninos Historias maravillosas. 2000. pap. (978-1-57697-805-4(2)) United Bible Societies/Americas Service Ctr.

Por Que Estaba preocupado Gedeon ? Serie para ninos Historias maravillosas. 2000. pap. (978-1-57697-799-6(4)) United Bible Societies/Americas Service Ctr.

Por Que Estaba sorprendido Andres ? Serie para ninos Historias maravillosas. 2000. pap. (978-1-57697-806-1(0)) United Bible Societies/Americas Service Ctr.

Por Que Estaba triste Jeremias ? Serie para ninos Historias maravillosas. 2000. pap. (978-1-57697-802-3(8)) United Bible Societies/Americas Service Ctr.

Por que no tuvo miedo Daniel ? Serie para ninos Historias maravillosas. 2000. pap. (978-1-57697-803-0(6)) United Bible Societies/Americas Service Ctr.

Por que se enfado Debora? Serie para ninos Historias maravillosas. 2000. pap. (978-1-57697-798-9(6)) United Bible Societies/Americas Service Ctr.

Por que se escondio Elias ? Serie para ninos Historias maravillosas. 2000. pap. (978-1-57697-801-6(X)) United Bible Societies/Americas Service Ctr.

Por que se rio Sara? Serie para ninos Historias maravillosas. 2000. pap. (978-1-57697-796-5(X)) United Bible Societies/Americas Service Ctr.

Por que trabajo tan duro Nehemias ? Serie para ninos Historias maravillosas. 2000. pap. (978-1-57697-804-7(4)) United Bible Societies/Americas Service Ctr.

Portuguese Book of Hope: Then Seeds of Spiritual Lineage. 2003. (J). 1.00 net. (978-1-931940-63-4(0)) Book of Hope International.

Portuguese/Portugal Book of Hope. (J). 2003. tchr. ed. 1.00 net. (978-1-931940-46-7(0)); 2002. 1.00 net. (978-1-890525-36-1(7)) Book of Hope International.

Postulation For Judgement Day. 2001. 52p. 5.95 (978-0-9707469-2-4(X) , DLS Bks.) Denney Literary Services.

PowerXpress Building the Tabernacle Unit. 2007. 115.00 (978-0-687-04060-5(4)) Abingdon Pr.

PowerXpress Burning Bush & Other Images of God Unit. 2007. 115.00 (978-0-687-04080-3(9)) Abingdon Pr.

Providing Hope Latin America: Providing Hope Latin America Child Care Life Stories (Donor Book) 2003. (J). 1.00 net. (978-1-931940-90-0(8)) Book of Hope International.

Quest - Faith at Work - Answer Key: Romans, Galatians, & James. 2004. (Quest Ser.). 25p. (YA). 6.99 (978-1-889015-92-7(X)) Explorer's Bible Study.

Ramirez, Frank. Apocalypse When? Daniel & Revelation. 1998. (Generation Why Ser.: No. 4, Pt. 1). 40p. (YA). (gr. 9-12). pap. 12.95 (978-0-87303-281-0(0)) Faith & Life Pr.

Revelation Vol. 7: Cross Training. 1998. 64p. (YA). (gr. 10-12). pap., tchr. ed. 15.00 incl. VHS (978-1-57405-250-3(0)) CharismaLife Pubs.

Rich, J. Milton. Heavenly Fathers Plan of Salvation Coloring Book. Knaupp, Andrew & Koford, Adam, illus. 2003. 108p. (J). per. 7.95 (978-0-9726670-2-9(4)) Rich Publishing.

Romania Book of Hope. 2003. (J). tchr. ed. 1.00 net. (978-1-931940-95-5(9)) Book of Hope International.

Romania Book of Hope: Early Elementary Edition. 2003. (J). 1.00 net. (978-1-931940-94-8(0)) Book of Hope International.

Romania Book of Hope: Revised Children's Edition. 2003. (J). 1.00 net. (978-1-931940-96-2(7)) Book of Hope International.

Romania Book of Hope: Revised International Pictorial Edition. 2003. (J). 1.00 net. (978-1-931940-99-3(1)) Book of Hope International.

Romania/Romanian Book of Hope: International Pictorial Edition. 2003. (J). 1.00 net. (978-1-931940-57-3(6)) Book of Hope International.

Romans: On Assignment for God. 1999. (Club 56 Ser.). (J). (gr. 5-6). 160p. tchr. ed., spiral bd. 29.99 (978-1-57405-243-5(8)); pap., wbk. ed. 2.79 (978-1-57405-244-2(6)) CharismaLife Pubs.

Ross, Allen P. Holiness to the Lord: A Guide to the Exposition of the Book of Leviticus. 2002. 496p. (C). (gr. 13 up). 42.99 (978-0-8010-2285-2(1)) Baker Academic.

Russell, Patricia Constance. Beginnings II - Jesus, My Shepherd: New Testament Lessons for Young Readers. Murtha, Dee M., ed. 2004. (Beginnings II Ser.). 301p. (J). stu. ed., spiral bd., wbk. ed. 23.99 (978-1-889015-89-7(X)) Explorer's Bible Study.

Russia Book of Hope: HopeXtreme. 2003. 48p. (J). 1.00 net. (978-1-931940-79-5(7)) Book of Hope International.

Russia/Russia Book of Hope: Teen Challenge. 2003. (J). 1.00 net. (978-1-931940-88-7(6)) Book of Hope International.

Russia/Russian Book of Hope. 2003. (J). 1.00 net. (978-1-931940-89-4(4)) Book of Hope International.

Russia/Russian Book of Hope: Revised International Pictorial Edition. 2003. (J). 1.00 net. (978-1-931940-85-6(1)) Book of Hope International.

Rut: Serie para ninos Amigos de la Biblia. 2000. pap. (978-1-57697-792-7(7)) United Bible Societies/Americas Service Ctr.

The Sanctified Life Bible Study Guide. 2002. per. 6.95 (978-0-9668482-4-3(1)) Revelation Pubns.

Saul y David: Serie para ninos Amigos de la Biblia. 2000. pap. (978-1-57697-790-3(0)) United Bible Societies/Americas Service Ctr.

Slattery, Kathryn, et al, illus. Gospel for Kids. 2003. 13p. 5.99 (978-0-7814-3208-5(1) , 0781432081) Cook, David C. Publishing Co.

South Africa/ English Book of Hope: Revised International Pictorial Edition. 2003. (J). 1.00 net. (978-1-931940-83-2(5)) Book of Hope International.

Spanish Book of Hope: (Cuba/Spanish) Revised International Pictorial Editiion. 2003. (J). 1.00 net. (978-1-931940-97-9(5)) Book of Hope International.

Spanish Book of Hope: Teen Challenge. 2003. (J). 1.00 net. (978-1-931940-64-1(9)) Book of Hope International.

Spanish Book of Hope: Then Seeds of Spiritual Lineage. 2003. (J). 1.00 net. (978-1-931940-61-0(4)) Book of Hope International.

Spanish (New Lenguaje Sencillo) Book of Hope. rev. ed. 2003. (J). 1.00 net. (978-1-931940-72-6(X)) Book of Hope International.

St. John, Patricia. Missing the Way: How Israel Missed God's Rest. 2004. (RUM.). 42p. 3.50 (978-1-932774-60-3(2)) Christian, Harvey Pubs. Inc.

Strauss, Ed. Big Bad Bible Giants. Carpenter, Anthony, illus. 2005. (2:52 Ser.). 112p. (J). pap. 7.99 (978-0-310-70869-8(9)) Zonderkidz.

Suriname/Dutch Book of Hope. 2003. 1.00 net. (978-1-931940-39-9(8)); (Illus.). 1.00 net. (978-1-931940-40-5(1)) Book of Hope International.

Tabb, Mark A. Song of the Shepherd: Psalm 23. 1999. (Foundations of the Faith Ser.). 176p. pap. 8.99 (978-0-8024-6190-2(5)) Moody Pubs.

Tesoros Escondidos No. 7: Libros para ninos. 2001. (978-1-57697-838-2(9)) United Bible Societies/Americas Service Ctr.

Tesoros Escondidos No. 8: Libro para ninos. 2001. pap. (978-1-57697-836-8(2)) United Bible Societies/ Americas Service Ctr.

Tesoros Escondidos No. 9: Libros para ninos. 2001. pap. (978-1-57697-837-5(0)) United Bible Societies/ Americas Service Ctr.

Tesoros Escondidos Vol. 1: Libro para ninos. 2000. (SPA.). pap. (978-1-57697-932-7(6)) United Bible Societies/ Americas Service Ctr.

Trummel, D. Pauline. Old Testament Survey, Year 2, Semester 1, 1 Kings 1 Through Esther 10. Nichols, Gregory G., ed. 2000. (Reformed Baptist Sunday School Curriculum: Vol. 3). (Illus.). 160p. (J). tchr. ed., ring bd. 25.00 (978-1-889520-14-8(4)) Truth For Eternity Ministries.

—Old Testament Survey, Year 2, Semester 2, Job 1 Through Malachi. Nichols, Gregory G., ed. 2000. (Reformed Baptist Sunday School Curriculum: Vol. 4). (Illus.). 160p. (J). (gr. 3-6). ring bd. 25.00 (978-1-889520-15-5(2)) Truth For Eternity Ministries.

Wegener, Bill, illus. & des. The Bible Game - Old Testament: The Bible Game - Old Testament. Wegener, Bill, des. 2004. (YA). bds. 34.95 (978-0-9753620-0-6(3) , Bible Game) IMAGINEX, LLC.

Where Did Cain Get His Wife? 2003. (BUL.). (YA). 0.75 (978-1-893345-12-6(2)) Answers in Genesis Ministries.

White, Joseph A. Introduction to the New Testament: Bible 101 Series. Chism, Jerry, ed. 2001. (Introduction to the New Testament). 180p. per. 16.95 (978-0-9636278-8-9(0)) White DEI.

—Introduction to the Old Testament: Bible 101 Series. White, Joseph A. & Chism, Jerry, eds. 2001. (Introduction to the Old Testament). 218p. per. 16.95 (978-0-9636278-1-0(3)) White DEI.

100 Prophecies (Unlaminated) 2003. (YA). pap. 9.99 (978-0-9744451-2-0(6)) Ascension Pr.

2003 Devotional Book of Hope: Devotional. 2003. (YA). per. 1.00 net. (978-1-931940-66-5(5)) Book of Hope International.

BIBLE—DICTIONARIES

Augustine, Peg, ed. Young Reader's Bible Dictionary. 2004. (Illus.). 288p. (gr. 6 up). 20.00 (978-0-687-09211-6(6)) Abingdon Pr.

Big Idea, Inc. Staff. Veggie Bible Atlapedia: A Bible Atlas & Encyclopedia in One. 2006. (Illus.). 160p. (gr. 4-7). 14.99 (978-1-59145-447-2(6)) Nelson, Thomas Inc.

Fisk, Sally. A Christian Child's Guide to Grammar: Grade 2. Fisk, Sally, illus. 2000. (Illus.). 28p. (J). (gr. 2-3). pap. 6.95 (978-1-930338-04-3(X) , G1002) Praise Pubns.

—A Christian Child's Guide to Grammar: Grade 4, 3 vols., Vol. 3. Fisk, Sally, illus. 2000. (Illus.). 28p. (J). (gr. 4-6). pap. 6.95 (978-1-930338-06-7(6) , G1004) Praise Pubns.

—A Christian Child's Guide to Grammar Vol. 2: Grade 3. Fisk, Sally, illus. 2000. (Illus.). 28p. (J). (gr. 3-5). pap. 6.95 (978-1-930338-05-0(8) , G1003) Praise Pubns.

Kenney, Cindy, et al. VeggieTales Bible Dictionary. 2005. (Illus.). 158p. (ps-5). 14.99 (978-1-59145-252-2(X)) Nelson, Thomas Inc.

Lucas, Daryl J. Baker Bible Dictionary for Kids. abr. ed. 2002. 288p. 12.99 (978-0-8010-4506-6(1)) Baker Bks.

Osborne, Rick & Miller, Kevin. Kidictionary. 2002. (NIrV Kid Reference Library). (Illus.). 128p. (J). 14.99 (978-0-310-70077-7(9)) Zonderkidz.

Van Dyken, Harry. Covenantal Catechism Bk. 4: The Gospels. 2000. 152p. (J). (gr. 8-10). pap. 7.95 (978-0-9705251-4-7(1)) Line of Promise Pr.

Van Dyken, Harry & Van Dyken, Donald. Covenantal Catechism Bk. 1: For Beginners. 2000. 128p. (J). (gr. 6-8). pap. 7.95 (978-0-9705251-1-6(7)) Line of Promise Pr.

—Covenantal Catechism Bk. 3: I Kings to Malachi. 2000. 158p. (J). (gr. 7-9). pap. 7.95 (978-0-9705251-3-0(3)) Line of Promise Pr.

White, Tracye Wilson. The Holman Bible Concordance for Kids: A Personal Guide Through the Word for Kids Who Want Answers. 2004. (Illus.). 350p. 14.99 (978-0-8054-9373-3(5)) B&H Publishing Grp.

Youngblood, Ronald F., et al. International Children's Bible Dictionary: A Fun & Easy-to-Use Guide to the Words, People, & Places in the Bible. 2006. (Illus.). 224p. (J). pap. 12.99 (978-1-4003-0809-5(7)) Nelson, Thomas Inc.

Zondervan. The Bible. 2005. (Illus.). 10p. bds. 9.98 (978-0-7853-6777-2(2) , 7166700) Publications International, Ltd.

BIBLE—DRAMA

see Bible As Literature; Mysteries and Miracle Plays

BIBLE—FESTIVALS

see Fasts and Feasts

BIBLE—FICTION

see Bible—History of Biblical Events—Fiction

BIBLE—FLOWERS

see Bible—Natural History

BIBLE—GARDENS

see Bible—Natural History

BIBLE—GEOGRAPHY

Bible Maps & Charts for Kids. (Illus.). (gr. 1-6). 16.99 (978-0-7847-1023-4(6)) Standard Publishing.

Bible Maps for Children: Effectives & Missions Programs. (J). pap. 10.00 (978-0-8307-1502-2(9)) Gospel Light Pubns.

Big Idea, Inc. Staff. Veggie Bible Atlapedia: A Bible Atlas & Encyclopedia in One. 2006. (Illus.). 160p. (gr. 4-7). 14.99 (978-1-59145-447-2(6)) Nelson, Thomas Inc.

Dowley, Tim. The Student Bible Atlas. Scott, Richard, illus. 2004. 32p. (gr. 4-7). 7.99 (978-0-8066-2038-1(2) , 9-2038, Augsburg Bks.) Augsburg Fortress, Pubs.

Feiler, Bruce S. Walking the Bible: A Journey by Land Through the Five Books of Moses. 2002. (gr. 7-12). lib. bdg. 24.55 (978-0-613-62166-3(2)) Tandem Library Bks.

—Walking the Bible: An Illustrated Journey for Kids Through the Greatest Stories Ever Told. Meret, Sasha, tr. Meret, Sasha, illus. ed. 2004. 112p. (J). (gr. 2 up). 16.99 (978-0-06-051117-3(6)) HarperCollins Pubs.

Rowley, H. H., ed. Student's Bible Atlas. 2004. (Illus.). 40p. reprint ed. pap. 12.00 (978-0-7188-0896-9(7)) Lutherworth Pr., The GBR. *Dist:* Parkwest Pubns., Inc.

Standard Publishing Staff. Maps & Charts. 2006. cd-rom 14.99 (978-0-7847-1875-9(X)) Standard Publishing.

—Standard Bible Atlas. 2006. 48p. pap. 12.99 (978-0-7847-1872-8(3)) Standard Publishing.

Tubb, Jonathan N. Bible Lands. 2000. (Eyewitness Bks.). (Illus.). 64p. (J). (gr. 5-9). 15.99 (978-0-7894-5770-7(9)) Dorling Kindersley Publishing, Inc.

BIBLE—HISTORY

Here are entered works on the origin, authorship and composition of the Bible as a book. Works dealing with historical events as described in the Bible are entered under Bible—History of Biblical Events.

Chaikin, Miriam. Angels Sweep the Desert Floor: Bible Legends about Moses in the Wilderness. Koshkin, Alexander, illus. 2002. 112p. (J). (gr. 3-5). 19.00 (978-0-395-97825-2(4) , Clarion Bks.) Houghton Mifflin Co. Trade & Reference Div.

Doney, Meryl. How the Bible Came to Us: The Story of the Book That Changed the World. 2003. (Illus.). 48p. (J). (gr. 3-7). pap., pap. 10.99 (978-0-7459-2098-6(5) , 0745920985) Cook, David C. Publishing Co.

FBS Historias Biblicas Para Preescolares Alumnos. 1.40 (978-0-7673-4674-0(2)) LifeWay Christian Resources.

Hannah, John. Guia Portavoz de Historia de la Iglesia. 2001. (Guias de Estudio Portavoz; Student Bible Guides).Tr. of Student Church History Timeline. (SPA.). 24p. 9.99 (978-0-8254-1053-6(3) , Editorial Portavoz) Kregel Pubns.

Herzog, Joyce. History in His Hands, Volume 1: Study Guide. 2004. (YA). 10.00 (***978-1-887225-14-4(5)***) JoyceHerzog.com, Inc.

Lowry-Manning, Lillie. Color God Love. 2006. (J). per. 11.95 (978-1-56167-951-5(8)) American Literary Pr.

Miller, Robin Spanier. A Biblical Journey of ABC's. 2006. 32p. (J). per. 13.99 (***978-1-59886-760-2(1)***) Tate Publishing & Enterprises, L.L.C.

Miller, Stephen. Who's Who & Where's Where in the Bible for Kids. 2006. 160p. (J). pap. 12.97 (978-1-59789-227-8(0) , Barbour Bks.) Barbour Publishing, Inc.

Perry, Cheryl. The Story of the Bible: How the World's Bestselling Book Came to Be. 1998. (J). 59.95 (978-1-55145-298-2(7)) Wood Lake Bks., Inc. CAN. *Dist:* Logos Productions, Inc.

Saint Mary'S Press Staff. The Bible in History Timeline: Expanded from the Catholic Youth Bible. 2003. 4p. (YA). 24.95 (978-0-88489-713-2(3)) St. Mary's Pr.

Taylor, Kenneth N. La Nueva Biblia en Cuadros para Ninos. 2003. Tr. of New Bible in Pictures for Little Eyes. (SPA.). 384p. 14.99 (978-0-8254-1709-2(0) , Editorial Portavoz) Kregel Pubns.

BIBLE—HISTORY OF BIBLICAL EVENTS

Due, Andrea. The Atlas of the Bible Lands. Ravalgia, Paola & Chesi, Matteo, illus. 2001. (Atlas Ser.). 64p. (J). (gr. 5 up). 19.95 (978-0-87226-559-2(5) , 65595B, Bedrick, Peter Bks.) School Specialty Publishing.

Evenson, Wallace. Bible Dates - From Adam to Christ. 2003. 121p. (Orig.). (YA). pap. 7.95 (978-0-9666834-1-7(2)) Evenson, Laurel.

Foce, Natalia, tr. from ENG. Daniel, el Príncipe que Oraba, Apps, Fred, illus. l.t. ed. 2004. (SPA.). 36p. (J). 2.99 (978-1-932789-19-5(7)) Editorial Sendas Antiguas, LLC.

—David, el Luchador Valiente, Apps, Fred, illus. l.t. ed. 2004. (SPA.). 36p. (J). 2.99 (978-1-932789-18-8(9)) Editorial Sendas Antiguas, LLC.

—La Historia de Pablo — Viajes de Aventura, 1. Apps, Fred, illus. l.t. ed. 2004. Orig. Title: Journeys of Adventure — the Story of Paul. (SPA.). 36p. (J). 2.99 (978-1-932789-23-2(5)) Editorial Sendas Antiguas, LLC.

—Jesus Narrador. Anderson, Jeff, illus. l.t. ed. 2004. Orig. Title: Jesus the Storyteller. (SPA.). 24p. (J). 2.99 (978-1-932789-25-6(1)) Editorial Sendas Antiguas, LLC.

—Jesus Salvador. Anderson, Jeff, illus. l.t. ed. 2004. Orig. Title: Jesus the Saviour. (SPA.). 24p. (J). 2.99 (978-1-932789-29-4(4)) Editorial Sendas Antiguas, LLC.

—Jesus Sanador. Anderson, Jeff, illus. l.t. ed. 2004. Orig. Title: Jesus the Healer. (SPA.). 24p. (J). 2.99 (978-1-932789-27-0(8)) Editorial Sendas Antiguas, LLC.

—El Nacimiento de Jesus: El Niño Prometido, 1. Apps, Fred, illus. l.t. ed. 2004. Orig. Title: The Birth of Jesus — the Promised Child. (SPA.). 36p. (J). 2.99 (978-1-932789-20-1(0)) Editorial Sendas Antiguas, LLC.

—La Resurreccion: Jesus Esta Vivo, 1. Apps, Fred, illus. l.t. ed. 2004. Orig. Title: The Resurrection — Jesus Is Alive. (SPA.). 36p. (J). 2.99 (978-1-932789-21-8(9)) Editorial Sendas Antiguas, LLC.

—Samuel, el Niño que Escuchaba. Apps, Fred, illus. l.t. ed. 2004. (SPA.). 36p. (J). 2.99 (978-1-932789-17-1(0)) Editorial Sendas Antiguas, LLC.

—Saul — el Milagro en el Camino, 1. Apps, Fred, illus. l.t. ed. 2004. Orig. Title: Saul — the Miracle on the Road. (SPA.). 36p. (J). 2.99 (978-1-932789-22-5(7)) Editorial Sendas Antiguas, LLC.

Friendship, Rites of Passage for Males & Females: Strange Stuff in the Bible. 2000. (Connect Ser.: Vol. 8). (YA). 20.00 (978-0-687-72149-8(0)) Abingdon Pr.

Glen, Jo. 30 Days with Mary & Joseph. 2004. (Illus.). 30p. (ps-3). 11.95 (978-0-8294-1475-2(4)) Loyola Pr.

Mackenzie, Carine. The Jesus Files. 2005. (Illus.). 119p. (J). (ps-ps). per. (978-1-84550-040-5(7) , Christian Focus) Christian Focus Pubns.

Osborne, Rick. Bible Fortresses, Temples & Tombs. 2003. (gr. 3-6). lib. bdg. 16.45 (978-0-613-71764-9(3)) Tandem Library Bks.

Osborne, Rick & Wooding, Marnie. Bible Fortresses, Temples & Tombs. 2003. (2:52 Soul Gear Ser.). (Illus.). 128p. (J). pap. 7.99 (978-0-310-70483-6(9)) Zonderkidz.

Robb, Andy. Hodgepodge Hebrews. 2004. (Holy Happenings Ser.). (Illus.). 128p. pap. 6.50 (978-0-687-02326-4(2)) Abingdon Pr.

Vamosh, Miriam F. Daily Life at the Time of Jesus. 2004. (Illus.). 104p. 18.00 (978-0-687-04891-5(5)) Abingdon Pr.

—Daily Life at the Time of Jesus. 2001. (Illus.). 104p. (J). (gr. 3 up). pap. 16.99 (978-0-570-05292-0(0)) Concordia Publishing Hse.

Waldman, Neil. The Promised Land: The Birth of the Jewish People. Waldman, Neil, illus. 2003. (Illus.). 40p. (YA). (gr. 6-9). 21.95 (978-1-56397-332-1(4)) Boyds Mills Pr.

Ward, Elaine M. Old Testament Women. 2003. (Art Revelations Ser.). (Illus.). 32p. (J). (gr. 6-9). 18.95 (978-1-59270-011-0(X)) Enchanted Lion Bks., LLC.

Waring, Diana. Ancient Civilizations & the Bible Elementary Activity Book Bk. A: A Digging Deeper Study Guide Activity Book. Waring, Isaac, photos by. 1999. (Illus.). 91p. (J). pap., stu. ed. 11.95 (978-1-930514-13-3(1)) Diana Waring Presents.

Yonge, Charlotte Mary. The Chosen People: A Compendium of Sacred & Church History for School-Children. 2006. 202p. pap. 12.99 (978-1-4264-2274-4(1)) ; 214p. pap. 15.99 (978-1-4264-2309-3(8)) BiblioBazaar.

BIBLE—HISTORY OF BIBLICAL EVENTS—FICTION

Banks, Lynne Reid. Moses in Egypt: A Novel Inspired by The Prince of Egypt & The Book of Exodus. 1998. (Prince of Egypt Ser.). (Illus.). 128p. (J). (gr. 5-9). pap. 4.99 (978-0-8499-5898-4(9)) Nelson, Thomas Inc.

Big Idea Productions Staff. Jonah: A Worm's Eye View. 2003. (Illus.). 40p. (J). 12.99 (978-0-310-70469-0(3)) Zonderkidz.

Black, Chuck. Kingdom's Reign, 4 bks. Black, Andrea & Black, Brittney, eds. Johnson, Marcella, illus. 2004. 160p. (YA). per. 9.95 (978-0-9679240-3-8(0)) Perfect Praise Publishing.

Booth, Bradley. Shepherd Warrior. 2007. 127p. (J). (***978-0-8163-2161-2(2)***) Pacific Pr. Pubns.

Borchard, Therese Johnson. Whitney Rides the Whale with Jonah: And Learns She Can't Run Away. 1999. (Emerald Bible Collection). (Illus.). 80p. (gr. 3-7). 5.95 (978-0-8091-6663-3(1) , 6663-1) Paulist Pr.

—Whitney Sews Joseph's Many-Colored Coat: And Learns a Lesson about Jealousy. 1999. (Emerald Bible Collection). (Illus.). 80p. (gr. 3-7). 5.95 (978-0-8091-6664-0(X) , 6664-x) Paulist Pr.

—Whitney Stows Away on Noah's Ark: And Learns How to Deal with Peer Pressure. VanNest, Wendy, illus. 2000. (Emerald Bible Collection). 80p. (gr. 3-7). 5.95 (978-0-8091-6674-9(7) , 6674-7) Paulist Pr.

Burns, Joanne. Ollie Oyster's Ouch. 2005. 21p. 8.99 (978-1-4116-5337-5(8)) Lulu.com.

Card, Orson Scott. Stone Tables. 1998. 432p. 19.95 (978-1-57345-115-4(0)) Deseret Bk. Co.

Cohen, Deborah Bodin. Papa Jethro: A Story of Moses' Interfaith Family. Dippold, Jane, illus. 2007. (Jewish Identity Ser.). (J). (gr. k-3). pap. 7.95 (***978-1-58013-252-7(9)***) Kar-Ben Publishing.

Davis, Buddy. When Dragons' Hearts Were Good. 1999. (Illus.). 40p. (J). (ps-3). 12.99 (978-0-89051-259-3(0) , 303-087) Master Bks.

De Graaf, Anne. Jonah. Perez-Montero, Jose, illus. 1999. (Little Children's Bible Bks.). 38p. (J). (ps-1). 5.99 (978-0-8054-2070-8(3)) B&H Publishing Grp.

Dennis, Jeanne Gowen & Seifert, Sheila. Deadly Expedition! Hohn, David, tr. Hohn, David, illus. 2003. (Survivor Ser.). 96p. (J). pap., pap. 5.99 (978-0-7814-3897-1(7) , 0781438977) Cook, David C. Publishing Co.

Garrelts, Christopher. Squarey Head Tells a Lie. Mayabb, Darrell, ed. 2003. (Adventures of Squarey Head Ser.: Bk. 1). (Illus.). 30p. (J). (gr. k-6). 4.95 (978-0-9742003-0-9(1)) Squarey Head, Inc.

Gormley, Beatrice. Adara. 2004. 160p. (J). (gr. 4 up). pap. 7.00 (978-0-8028-5216-8(5)) Eerdmans, William B. Publishing Co.

—Salome. 2007. 288p. (gr. 6-8). (J). 15.99 (978-0-375-83908-5(9)); (YA). lib. bdg. 18.99 (978-0-375-93908-2(3)) Random Hse. Children's Bks. (Knopf Bks. for Young Readers).

Grimes, Nikki. Dark Sons. 2005. 224p. (gr. 7-17). 15.99 (978-0-7868-1888-4(3)) Hyperion Bks. for Children.

Guess, Catherine Ritch. Kipper Finds a Home: A White Squirrel Parable Volume 1. Pace, Christine, illus. 2005. 32p. (J). (ps-7). 13.95 (978-1-933341-00-2(9)) CRM.

Halverson, Mathew. Concord Cunningham Returns: The Scripture Sleuth 2. pap. 8.95 (978-1-885904-25-6(8)) Focus Publishing.

Hartman, Bob. More Bible Bad Guys...& Gals. Anderson, Jeff, illus. 2001. 94p. (gr. 3-7). 13.99 (978-0-8066-4099-0(5) , Augsburg Bks.) Augsburg Fortress, Pubs.

Hoffman, Mary. Parables & Miracles of Jesus. Morris, Jackie, illus. 2007. 64p. (J). 19.95 (***978-1-84507-786-0(5)***) Lincoln, Frances Ltd. GBR. *Dist:* Perseus Distribution.

Howard, Elizabeth Fitzgerald. What's in Aunt Mary's Room? Lucas, Cedric, illus. 2002. 32p. (J). (gr. k-3). pap. 5.95 (978-0-618-24621-2(5) , Clarion Bks.) Houghton Mifflin Co. Trade & Reference Div.

—What's in Aunt Mary's Room? 2002. (gr. k-3). lib. bdg. 14.10 (978-0-613-72911-6(0)) Tandem Library Bks.

Hyman, Frieda Clark. Victory on the Walls: A Story of Nehemiah. 2005. 182p. (J). pap. (***978-1-883937-96-6(5)***) Bethlehem Bks.

Kelly, Clint & Ware, Jim. Escape Underground & the Prophet's Kid. 2001. (KidWitness Tales Ser.). 128p. (J). (gr. 3-8). pap. 5.99 (978-1-56179-965-7(3)) Bethany Hse. Pubs.

Lester, Julius. Pharaoh's Daughter: A Novel of Ancient Egypt. 2002. 192p. (J). (gr. 5 up). pap. 5.99 (978-0-06-440969-8(4) , Harper Trophy) HarperCollins Pubs.

—Pharaoh's Daughter: A Novel of Ancient Egypt. 2002. (gr. 5-8). lib. bdg. 14.15 (978-0-613-87835-7(3)) Tandem Library Bks.

Lewis, C. S. El Principe Caspian. 2003. (SPA.). pap. (978-956-13-1670-6(6) , AB7202) Bello, Andres CHL. *Dist:* Lectorum Pubns., Inc.

—El Principe Caspian. 2001. (978-0-606-22693-6(1)) Tandem Library Bks.

Little Hamster & the Great Flood. 2001. (Illus.). 10p. (J). (ps-k). 10.99 (978-0-8254-7228-2(8)) Kregel Pubns.

Loesch, Joe. David Faces Goliath: Showdown in the Desert. Hutchinson, Cheryl, ed. Denney, Ott, illus. unabr. ed. 1999. (Bible Stories for Kids Ser.). 48p. (gr. k-5). reprint ed. 16.95 incl. audio compact disk (978-1-932332-15-5(4)) Toy Box Productions.

—David Faces Goliath: Showdown in the Desert. Hutchinson, Cheryl J., ed. Cox, Brian T., illus. unabr. ed. 1999. (Bible Stories for Kids Ser.). (J). (ps-3). pap. 16.95 incl. audio compact disk (978-1-887729-22-2(4)); pap. 14.95 incl. audio (978-1-887729-21-5(6)) Toy Box Productions.

Lundy, Charlotte. Thank You, God. Waldrep, Evelyn L., ed. James, Margaret Ray, illus. 2004. 32p. (J). (gr. k-3). 15.95 (978-0-9670280-9-5(4)) Bay Light Publishing.

McCaughrean, Geraldine. Not the End of the World. 256p. (J). 2005. 16.99 (978-0-06-076030-4(3)); 2005. lib. bdg. 17.89 (978-0-06-076031-1(1)); 2006. reprint ed. pap. 6.99 (978-0-06-076032-8(X)) HarperCollins Pubs. (HarperTeen).

—Not the End of the World. l.t. ed. 2006. 285p. 22.95 (978-0-7862-8642-3(3)) Thorndike Pr.

Meek, Carol. Believer Boy's Power. 2007. 32p. (J). pap. 9.00 (***978-0-8059-7249-8(8)***) Dorrance Publishing Co., Inc.

Miklowitz, Gloria D. Masada: The Last Fortress. 2004. 198p. (YA). (gr. 4-7). 16.00 (978-0-8028-5165-9(7)) Eerdmans, William B. Publishing Co.

Napoli, Donna Jo. Song of the Magdalene: A Novel. 1998. (Illus.). 256p. (YA). (gr. 7-12). pap. 4.99 (978-0-590-93706-1(5) , Scholastic Paperbacks) Scholastic, Inc.

—Song of the Magdalene: A Novel. 2004. (Illus.). 256p. (YA). pap. 6.99 (978-0-689-87396-6(4) , Simon Pulse) Simon & Schuster Children's Publishing.

—Song of the Magdalene: A Novel. 1998. (J). (978-0-606-13789-8(0)) Tandem Library Bks.

Nicole, Karen. Bible Tells Me About. 1998. (Illus.). 32p. (J). (ps-3). pap. 1.11 (978-0-8280-0913-3(9)) Review & Herald Publishing Assn.

Paterson, Katherine. The Angel & the Donkey. Koshkin, Alexander, illus. 2003. 40p. (J). (gr. k-3). pap. 5.95 (978-0-618-37840-1(5) , Clarion Bks.) Houghton Mifflin Co. Trade & Reference Div.

Pearson, Mary Rose. Bible Town Detectives. 2003. 96p. (J). pap. 9.99 (978-0-8054-3923-6(4)) B&H Publishing Grp.

Reed, Gary & Shelley, Mary Wollstonecraft. Frankenstein: The Graphic Novel. Irving, Frazer, illus. 2005. (Puffin Graphics Ser.). 176p. (J). (gr. 4). pap. 10.99 (978-0-14-240407-2(1) , Puffin) Penguin Group (USA) Inc.

Reynolds, Aaron. Breaking Out of the Bungle Bird: Based on Proverbs 13:10. Whitehead, Peter, illus. 2005. (Insect-Inside Ser.). 40p. (J). 9.99 (978-0-310-70956-5(3)) Zonderkidz.

Sasso, Sandy Eisenberg. Noah's Wife: The Story of Naamah. Andersen, Bethanne, illus. 2002. 32p. (J). 16.95 (978-1-58023-134-3(9)) Jewish Lights Publishing.

Schall, Jane. Jump at the Sun Bible Classics David & Goliath. Roos, Maryn, illus. 2007. (J). (ps-2). pap. 3.50 (***978-0-7868-5517-9(7)*** , Jump at the Sun) Hyperion Bks. for Children.

—Jump at the Sun Bible Classics Jonah & the Whale. Roos, Maryn, illus. 2007. (J). (ps-2). pap. 3.50 (***978-0-7868-5518-6(5)*** , Jump at the Sun) Hyperion Bks. for Children.

Scripture Teachers: Solomon & Friends Learn about Being Wonderfully Made. 2003. pap. (***978-0-9712894-3-7(3)***) Lighthouse Christian Products Co.

Scripture Teachers: Solomon & Friends Learn about Forgiveness. 2003. pap. (***978-0-9712894-1-3(7)***) Lighthouse Christian Products Co.

Scripture Teachers: Solomon & Friends Learn about Prayer. 2003. pap. (***978-0-9712894-0-6(9)***) Lighthouse Christian Products Co.

Scripture Teachers: Solomon & Friends Learn about Trusting God. 2003. pap. (***978-0-9712894-2-0(5)***) Lighthouse Christian Products Co.

Seay, LaNell. The Great Parting. Seay, LaNell, illus. 1998. (Illus.). 32p. (J). (gr. k-4). pap. (978-1-891797-11-8(5)) Silver Fox Marketing.

Shilson, Anabel T. First Puffin Picture Book of Bible Stories. (Illus.). 48p. (J). pap. 13.95 (978-0-14-054897-6(1)) Penguin Bks., Ltd. GBR. *Dist:* Trafalgar Square Publishing.

Spoor, Trudy. Women of the Bible: Stories for 4 & 5 year Children. 2006. (ENG.). 68p. (J). per. 31.99 (***978-1-4141-0637-3(8)***) Pleasant Word.

Tenney, Tommy. Hadassah: The Girl Who Became Queen Esther. 2005. (Illus.). 168p. (J). 9.99 (978-0-7642-2738-7(6)) Bethany Hse. Pubs.

Vogelaar, Alie. A Shot Through the Window. Bazen, Edith, tr. from DUT. Visser, Rino, illus. 2000. Orig. Title: Een Schot Door Het Raam. 107p. lib. bdg. 8.95 (978-0-9670728-1-4(6)) Early Foundations Pubs.

Wallace, Lew. Ben-Hur. (SPA., Illus.). (YA). 11.95 (978-84-7281-099-0(2) , AF1099) Auriga, Ediciones S.A. ESP. *Dist:* Continental Bk. Co., Inc.

Ware, Jim. Dangerous Dreams. 2001. (Kidwitness Tales Ser.). (Illus.). 128p. (J). (gr. 4-7). mass mkt. (978-1-56179-956-5(4)) Focus on the Family Publishing.

Youd, Pauline. I Wonder . . . Books: Pack 1, 6 bks. Garvin, Elaine, illus. Incl. Why Did Sarah Laugh? pap. 1.50 (978-0-8198-8275-2(5)); Why Was Daniel Scared? pap. 1.50 (978-0-8198-8282-0(8)); Why Was David Brave? pap. 1.50 (978-0-8198-8280-6(1)); Why Was Pharoah Puzzled? pap. 1.50 (978-0-8198-8278-3(X)); Why Was the Shepherd Glad? pap. 1.50 (978-0-8198-8276-9(3)); Pack 1. Why Did Nehemiah Work So Hard? pap. 1.50 (978-0-8198-8279-0(8)); (Illus.). 16p. (J). (gr. 2-4). 1996. 7.95 (978-0-8198-3675-5(3)) Pauline Bks. & Media.

—I Wonder . . . Books: Pack 2, 6 bks. Garvin, Elaine, illus. Incl. Why Was Andrew Surprised? pap. 1.50 (978-0-8198-8285-1(2)); Why Was Deborah Mad? pap. 1.50 (978-0-8198-8286-8(0)); Why Was Gideon Worried? pap. 2.95 (978-0-8198-8283-7(6)); Why Was Jeremiah Sad? pap. 2.95 (978-0-8198-8277-6(1)); Why Was Mary Embarrassed? pap. 1.50 (978-0-8198-8284-4(4)); Pack 2. Why Did Elijah Hide? pap. 1.50 (978-0-8198-8287-5(9)); (Illus.). 16p. (J). (gr. 2-4). 1996. 7.95 (978-0-8198-3676-2(1)) Pauline Bks. & Media.

BIBLE—HISTORY OF CONTEMPORARY EVENTS

Exploring God's Word: Grade 8 - Contemporary Issues. (Voyages Ser.). stu. ed. 8.95 (978-0-570-00304-5(0) , 57-0821) Concordia Publishing Hse.

Sanders, Nancy I. Old Testament Days: An Activity Guide. 1999. (Illus.). 144p. (J). (gr. k-7). pap. 16.95 (978-1-55652-354-0(8)) Chicago Review Pr., Inc.

BIBLE—INTERPRETATION

see Bible—Commentaries

BIBLE—INTRODUCTIONS

see Bible—Study

BIBLE—LANGUAGE, STYLE

see Bible As Literature

BIBLE—LITERARY CHARACTER

see Bible As Literature

BIBLE—MAPS

see Bible—Geography

BIBLE—NATURAL HISTORY

ABC Animales de le Biblia: Interactivo para Ninos. 2001. cd-rom (978-1-57697-999-0(7)) United Bible Societies/ Americas Service Ctr.

Animals of the Bible. (Illus.). 16p. (J). pap. 1.50 (978-0-87162-874-9(0) , E6035) Warner Pr. Pubs.

Coburn, Claudia. Did the Aardvarks Say "No Ark"? Hoard, Angela, illus. 2004. 32p. (J). (978-0-9759343-1-9(7)) Purfect Promises.

Currie, Robin. Baby Bible Animals. 2003. (Baby Bible Ser.). (Illus.). 48p. (J). bds. 12.99 (978-0-7814-3865-0(9) , 0781438659) Cook, David C. Publishing Co.

Dorling Kindersley Publishing Staff, ed. Bible Animals. 2005. (My Little Church Book Ser.). (Illus.). 24p. (J). pap. 5.99 (978-0-7566-1468-3(6)) Dorling Kindersley Publishing, Inc.

Hahn, Samuel J. Stories Told under the Sycamore Tree: Bible Plant Object Lessons. Patton, Scott, tr. Patton, Scott, illus. 2003. 191p. (J). pap. (978-0-7880-1972-2(4)) CSS Publishing Co.

Ham, Ken & Snelling. Dinosaurs of Eden: A Biblical Journey through Time. 2000. (Illus.). 64p. (J). (gr. 4-7). 13.99 (978-0-89051-340-8(6)) Master Bks.

Zobel-Nolan, Allia. Touch & Feel Bible Animal Friends. 2004. 12p. (J). bds. 10.99 (978-0-8254-5512-4(X)) Kregel Pubns.

BIBLE—NEW TESTAMENT

Arthur, Kay & Arndt, Janna. Bible Prophecy for Kids: Revelation 1-7. 2006. 160p. (YA). pap. 9.99 (978-0-7369-1527-4(3)) Harvest Hse. Pubs.

Baker Book House Staff. Seeking Sammy in the New Testament. 1999. (Bible Fun Series for Kids Ser.). (Illus.). (J). (ps-3). pap. 9.99 (978-0-8010-0280-9(X) , New Kids Media) Baker Bks.

Bible Visuals International, compiled by. Christ & the Church Vol. 42: New Testament. 2005. (Illus.). (J). pap. (978-1-932381-29-0(5) , 1042) Bible Visuals International, Inc.

—Priesthood of Christ Vol. 36: New Testament. 2005. (Illus.). (J). pap. (978-1-932381-61-0(9) , 1036) Bible Visuals International, Inc.

Broadman and Holman Publishers Staff. KJV Read to Me Bible for Kids. 2004. (Illus.). 1560p. 19.99 (978-1-55819-845-6(8)) B&H Publishing Grp.

Calaway, Bernie L. & Ledford, Jan Roadarmel. Operation Revelation: A Teen's Script to Earth's Final Curtain. 2006. 195p. pap. 19.95 (978-1-4241-1657-7(0)) PublishAmerica, Inc.

Cook Communication Ministry Staff. Nuevo Testamento Ilustrado. 1999. Tr. of Illustrated New Testament. (SPA., Illus.). 256p. (J). pap. 8.99 (978-0-311-38642-0(3) , Editorial Mundo Hispano) Casa Bautista de Publicaciones.

Courtney, Claudia. Modest King: Palm Sunday. 2000. (ps-2). lib. bdg. 10.65 (978-0-613-72824-9(6)) Tandem Library Bks.

De Heer, Jolene & Grussing, Robert. James. 2000. (Devotions to Go Ser.). 104p. (J). (gr. 7-12). 3.95 (978-1-56212-540-0(0) , 160470, Faith Alive Christian Resources) CRC Pubns.

Diesslin, Richard L., illus. The Cartoon Gospels: Cartoons & Meditations on Selected Scriptures from the Gospels of Matthew, Mark, Luke & John. 2002. Orig. Title: The Cartoon Gospel of Matthew, the Cartoon Gospel of Mark, the Cartoon Gospel of Luke. 380p. (YA). cd-rom 24.95 (978-0-9702244-5-3(1)) Diesslin, Richard L.

Fenton, Amy. Fundamentals: Get the Picture: a Study of 1 Corinthians Childs Bk. 2002. (J). (gr. 1-6). 5.95 (978-0-633-01968-6(2)) LifeWay Christian Resources.

Good Apple Staff. Bible Word Search New Testament. Date not set. 48p. (J). pap. 6.95 (978-0-86653-765-0(1) , SS2880, In Celebration) Schaffer, Frank Pubns.

Greiner, Ruth B. Faith Volume 5: New Testament. Hertzler, Frances H.. et al, illus. 2004. 36p. (J). pap. (978-1-932381-36-8(8)) Bible Visuals International, Inc.

—Repentance Vol. 6: New Testament Volume 6, Life of Christ, Part 6. 2006. (Illus.). 40p. (J). pap. (978-1-932381-04-7(X) , 1006) Bible Visuals International, Inc.

—The Saviour Vol. 3: New Testament : The Life of Christ. Hertzler, Frances H.. et al, illus. 2004. 36p. (J). pap. (978-1-932381-02-3(3) , 1003) Bible Visuals International, Inc.

Greiner, Ruth B., et al. Eternity Vol. 45: New Testament , Revelation Part 4: the Lord Reigns Forever. Henkel, Vernon et al, illus. 2005. 36p. (J). pap. (978-1-932381-31-3(7) , 1045) Bible Visuals International, Inc.

—GOD His Son, His Book, His Home: New Testament Introductory Volume. Hertzler, Frances H.. & Olson, Ed, illus. 2004. 32p. (J). pap. (978-1-932381-35-1(X) , 1000) Bible Visuals International, Inc.

—Sin Vol. 4: New Testament Volume 4, Life of Christ, Part 4. Hertzler, Frances H.. et al, illus. 2005. 36p. (J). pap. (978-1-932381-23-8(6) , 1004) Bible Visuals International, Inc.

Group Publishing Staff. Holyword, Elementary Student Books. 2000. (J). pap., stu. ed. 2.99 (978-0-7644-2183-9(2)) Group Publishing, Inc.

Hardy, Janet Norris. The Four in One: The Four Gospels from the King James Version Merged into a Single Narrative. 2003. 235p. (gr. 1-12). pap. 16.95 (978-0-9743567-0-9(0)) CSE Publishing.

Harman, Debbie G. Jesus Said- 2004. (Illus.). 17.95 (978-1-59156-091-3(8)) Covenant Communications, Inc.

Hertzler, Frances B. & Ober, Jonathan, illus. The Eternal God Vol. 1: New Testament. 2004. 36p. (J). pap. (978-1-932381-03-0(1) , 1001) Bible Visuals International, Inc.

Holman Csb Student New Testament. 2003. (J). (gr. 7-12). 1.50 (978-0-633-09343-3(2)) LifeWay Christian Resources.

Jackson, Cindy. New Testament Fun Activities - First & Second Grade. 1998. (Illus.). 16p. (J). (gr. 1-2). wbk. ed. 3.95 (978-1-878669-80-3(X) , CRE 3544) Creative Teaching Assocs.

—New Testament Fun Activities - Pre-School & Kindergarten. 1998. (Illus.). 16p. (J). (ps-k). 3.95 (978-1-878669-79-7(6) , CRE 3543) Creative Teaching Assocs.

—New Testament Fun Activities - Third & Fourth Grade. 1998. (Illus.). 16p. (J). (gr. 3-4). wbk. ed. 3.95 (978-1-878669-81-0(8) , CRE 3545) Creative Teaching Assocs.

Keene, Michael. St. Mark's Gospel & the Christian Faith. 2nd ed. 2002. (Illus.). 112p. pap., stu. ed. (978-0-7487-6775-5(4)) Nelson Thornes Ltd.

Kiefer, Velma, et al. Fellowship, Enjoying God Vol. 41: New Testament. Henkel, Vernon et al, illus. 2004. 36p. (J). pap. (978-1-932381-00-9(7) , 1041) Bible Visuals International, Inc.

King, Wanda Fulbright. Fundamentals: Live it Out!, Study of Book of James, Yngr Child Bk. 2000. (J). (gr. 1-6). 4.95 (978-0-633-00435-4(9)) LifeWay Christian Resources.

—Fundamentals: Living it Out Study of Book of James, Oldr Child Bk. (J). (gr. 1-6). (978-0-633-05792-3(4)) LifeWay Christian Resources.

—Fundamentals: Living it Out Study of Book of James, Yngr Child Bk. (J). (gr. 1-6). (978-0-633-05793-0(2)) LifeWay Christian Resources.

Kuyper, Vicki J. Jesus Speaks to Teens: Not Your Ordinary Meditations on the Word of Jesus. 2004. (Jesus Speaks Ser.). (Illus.). 192p. (J). 14.99 (978-0-7642-2866-7(8)) Bethany Hse. Pubs.

Lee, Witness. The Conclusion of the New Testament: Messages 265-275. 2000. 98p. (J). (gr. 6). per. 6.00 (978-0-7363-0152-7(6) , 10-046-001) Living Stream Ministry.

—Estudio-Vida de Filipenses Vol. 2: Mensajes 24-42. 2001. Tr. of Life-Study of Philippians: Messages 24-42. (SPA.). 177p. (J). (gr. 6). per. 10.25 (978-0-7363-0340-8(5) , 10-192-002) Living Stream Ministry.

—The Holy Word for Morning Revival: Crystallization-Study of the Gospel of Matthew. 2001. (J). (gr. 6). Vol. 1. 109p. per. 7.00 (978-0-7363-1182-3(3) , 13-139-001); Vol. 2. 108p. per. 7.00 (978-0-7363-1183-0(1) , 13-140-001); Vol. 3. 109p. per. 7.00 (978-0-7363-1380-3(X) , 13-141-001); Vol. 4. 109p. per. 7.00 (978-0-7363-1383-4(4) , 13-142-001) Living Stream Ministry.

—La Palabra Santa para el Avivamiento Matutino: Estudio de Cristalizacion del Evangelio de Mateo. 2001. Tr. of Holy Word for Morning Revival: Crystallization-Study of the Gospel of Matthew. (SPA.). 109p. (J). (gr. 6). Vol. 3. per. 7.00 (978-0-7363-1381-0(8) , 13-141-002); Vol. 4. per. 7.00 (978-0-7363-1384-1(2) , 13-142-002) Living Stream Ministry.

—La Palabra Santa para el Avivamiento Matutino: Estudio de Crystalizacion del Evangelio de Mateo. 2001. Tr. of Holy Word for Morning Revival: Crystallization Study of the Gospel of Matthew. (SPA.). (J). (gr. 6). Vol. 1 109p. per. 7.00 (978-0-7363-1184-7(X) , 13-139-002); Vol. 2. 107p. per. 7.00 (978-0-7363-1185-4(8) , 13-140-002) Living Stream Ministry.

—La Palabra Santa para el Avivamiento Matutino: Mateo 1:1-7:29, Vol. 1. 2001. Tr. of Holy Word for Morning Revival: Matthew 1:1-7:29. (SPA.). 71p. (J). (gr. 6). per. 6.00 (978-0-7363-1139-7(4) , 13-133-002) Living Stream Ministry.

—La Palabra Santa para el Avivamiento Matutino: Mateo 13:53-21:22, Vol. 3. 2001. Tr. of Holy Word for Morning Revival: Matthew 13:53-21:22. (SPA.). 83p. (J). (gr. 6). per. 6.00 (978-0-7363-1141-0(6) , 13-135-002) Living Stream Ministry.

—La Palabra Santa para el Avivamiento Matutino: Mateo 21:23-28:20, Vol. 4. 2001. Tr. of Holy Word for Morning Revival: Matthew 21:23-28:20. (SPA.). 83p. (J). (gr. 6). per. 6.00 (978-0-7363-1142-7(4) , 13-136-002) Living Stream Ministry.

Lingo, Susan L. Who's Who Object Talks That Teach about the New Testament. 2006. 48p. (YA). pap. 6.99 (978-0-7847-1312-9(X) , 42010) Standard Publishing.

Lucado, Max. 3:16 - the Code for Your Life: Elementary Edition. 2007. 48p. (J). pap. 2.99 (***978-1-4003-1107-1(1)***) Nelson, Thomas Inc.

Lyster, R. Iona, et al. The Inspiration of the Scriptures: New Testament Volume 33: 1 & 2 Timothy, Titus, Philemon. Hertzler, Frances & Olson, Ed, illus. 2004. 34p. (J). pap. (978-1-932381-05-4(8) , 1033) Bible Visuals International, Inc.

MacKall, Dandi Daley. We All Need Faith & Hope but the Best Thing Is Love. Gevry, Claudine, illus. 2006. 36p. (J). 9.99 (978-0-7847-1532-1(7) , 04157) Standard Publishing.

Martin, Harold S., comment. Brethren New Testament Commentary: Colossians & Philemon. 2003. 10.00 (978-0-9745027-0-0(7)) Brethren Revival Fellowship.

—Brethren New Testament Commentary: James & Jude. 2003. 10.00 (978-0-9745027-1-7(5)) Brethren Revival Fellowship.

Mooney, Belinda. Itty-Bitty Book: New Testament. 2006. (J). pap. 1.49 (***978-1-59317-167-4(6)***) Warner Pr. Pubs.

Nelson Bibles Staff, ed. Revolve: The Complete New Testament. 2003. (gr. 7-12). lib. bdg. 24.60 (978-0-613-73232-1(4)) Tandem Library Bks.

New, David W. The New Testament for Beginners. 2002. 52p. (J). (978-0-9721333-0-2(5)) Pocket Publication, A.

Perrotta, Kevin & Darring, Gerald. John 11-21: My Peace I Give You. 2004. (Six Weeks with the Bible for Catholic Teens Ser.). 96p. (YA). pap. 6.95 (978-0-8294-2084-5(3)) Loyola Pr.

—Six Weeks with the Bible for Catholic Teens Luke: The Good News of God's Mercy. 2004. (Six Week for Catholic Teens Ser.). 96p. 6.95 (978-0-8294-2052-4(5)) Loyola Pr.

—Six Weeks with the Bible for Catholic Teens Revelation: God's Gift of Hope. 2004. (Six Week for Catholic Teens Ser.). 96p. 6.95 (978-0-8294-2049-4(5)) Loyola Pr.

Pfeifer, Alice Ann. Jesus & the Gospels, 6 booklets. 1998. (Illus.). (YA). (gr. 9-13). pap., stu. ed. 7.45 (978-0-89837-157-4(0)) Pflaum Publishing Group.

Polich, Laurie. Dive into Living Water. 2004. (Illus.). 112p. 8.00 (978-0-687-05223-3(8)) Abingdon Pr.

Reagan, Dawn. New Testament Bible Adventure Kit: Bible Storyboard Adventures for Kids. Takes, Toon, ed. Reagan, Dawn, illus. 1999. (Illus.). 16p. (ps-5). pap. 29.95 (978-1-929456-01-7(8)) Myrtle-Seal Publishing.

Reymond, Robert L. Paul Missionary Theologian: A Survey of His Missionary Labours & Theology. 2000. (Illus.). 640p. (978-1-85792-497-8(5) , Mentor) Christian Focus Pubns.

Rock, Lois. The Time of Jesus: Crafts that Recreate Every-day Life. 2003. (Illus.). 64p. (J). pap. 19.99 (978-0-7459-3881-3(7) , Lion) Lion Hudson plc GBR. *Dist:* Independent Pubs. Group.

Ross & Guymon-King. Primary Partners: New Testament. 2004. cd-rom 12.95 (978-1-59156-165-1(5)) Covenant Communications, Inc.

Route 52 Staff. Follow Jesus. 2006. 320p. (J). 29.99 (978-0-7847-1328-0(6) , 42077) Standard Publishing.

—Grow up in Christ. 2004. pap. 29.99 (978-0-7847-1628-1(5)) Standard Publishing.

Starburst Publishers. Revelation for Teens. 2002. (Learn the Word Ser.: Vol. 2). 272p. pap. 14.99 (978-1-892016-55-3(9)) Starburst Pubs.

Steen & Front. A Child's Bible in Colour: The New Testament. 2000. (Illus.). 288p. (J). (ps-3). pap. (978-0-330-23690-4(3) , Macmillan Children's Bks.) Pan Macmillan.

Strawn, Kathy. Bible Buddies Activity Book for New Testament Grade 1. 2000. (J). (gr. 1-3). 5.25 (978-0-633-00464-4(2)) LifeWay Christian Resources.

Taylor, Damon J. Aprende de las Emociones con la Biblia. 2004. (Mis Calcetines Ser.). (SPA., Illus.). 24p. 5.99 (978-0-8254-0775-8(3) , Editorial Portavoz) Kregel Pubns.

Thomas Nelson Publishing Staff. Bibleman: the Complete New Testament: Biblezine. 2006. (Bibleman Power-Source Ser.). 400p. (J). pap. 16.99 (978-1-4003-0876-7(3)) Nelson, Thomas Inc.

—My Big Bible Sticker Book: New Testament. 2007. 84p. (J). pap. 12.99 (978-1-4003-0826-2(7)) Nelson, Thomas Inc.

Thomas Nelson Publishing Staff, ed. Magnify: NT Biblezine for Kids. 2005. 400p. (J). pap. 16.99 (978-1-4003-0528-5(4)) Nelson, Thomas Inc.

TNT Ministries. Game Is Up Vol. 3,Bk. 3: New Testament. 96p. (J). pap. 11.99 (978-1-85792-820-4(2) , Christian Focus) Christian Focus Pubns. GBR. *Dist:* Riverside.

—Game Is Up Vol. 4,Bk. 4: New Testament. 96p. (J). pap. 11.99 (978-1-85792-821-1(0) , Christian Focus) Christian Focus Pubns. GBR. *Dist:* Riverside.

Weckbaugh, Ernest. Bible Fun: From the New Testament. Weckbaugh, Patricia G., ed. 1999. (Illus.). 80p. (YA). (gr. 3-12). pap. 5.99 (978-1-881474-27-2(5)) Casa Graphics, Inc.

—The Bible's ABCs (Matthew - Revelation & Fun Book) Series of 7 Summaries Plus Bible Story/Puzzles, 8 bks. Weckbaugh, Patricia G., ed. 1999. (Illus.). 296p. (J). pap. 26.99 (978-1-881474-28-9(3)) Casa Graphics, Inc.

World Bible Publishing Staff. God's Child New Testament. 1999. 256p. (J). 5.99 (978-0-529-11083-1(0)); lthr. 5.99 (978-0-529-11082-4(2)) World Bible Pubs.

Yaconelli, Mike. Devotion: A Raw Truth Journal for Following Jesus. 2004. (Invert Ser.). (Illus.). 80p. (YA). pap. 10.99 (978-0-310-25559-8(7)) Zondervan.

BIBLE—OLD TESTAMENT

Beck, William F. Bible Stories in Pictures. Rogers, Ruth W. et al, illus. 2nd ed. 2003. (ALB, SPA & SWE.). 376p. pap. 6.50 (978-1-931891-08-0(7)) Multi-Language Pubns.

Beginnings II - God's Promises - Answer Key: Old Testament Lessons for Young Readers. 2005. (Beginnings II Ser.). 32p. (J). spiral bd. 6.99 (978-1-889015-03-3(2)) Explorer's Bible Study.

Bible Visuals International, compiled by. Death, the Wages of Sin Vol. 14: Old Testament. 2005. (Illus.). (J). pap. (978-1-932381-07-8(4) , 2014) Bible Visuals International, Inc.

—Discovering God's Ways Vol. 17: Old Testament. 2005. (Illus.). (J). pap. (978-1-932381-77-1(5) , 2017) Bible Visuals International, Inc.

—God Is Sovereign Vol. 27: Old Testament. 2006. (Illus.). (J). pap. (978-1-932381-87-0(2) , 2027) Bible Visuals International, Inc.

—Godliness Vol. 23: Old Testament. 2006. (Illus.). (J). pap. (978-1-932381-81-8(3) , 2021) Bible Visuals International, Inc.

—Godly/Ungodly Living Vol. 26: Old Testament. 2006. (Illus.). (J). pap. (978-1-932381-86-3(4) , 2026) Bible Visuals International, Inc.

—God's Chosen People: Old Testament Volume 12. 2005. (Illus.). (J). pap. (978-1-932381-74-0(0) , 2012) Bible Visuals International, Inc.

—God's Faithfulness Vol. 15: Old Testament. 2005. (Illus.). (J). pap. (978-1-932381-34-4(1) , 2015) Bible Visuals International, Inc.

—God's King Vol. 22: Old Testament. 2006. (Illus.). (J). pap. (978-1-932381-82-5(1) , 2022) Bible Visuals International, Inc.

—The Grace of God Volume 19: Old Testament. 2005. (Illus.). (J). pap. (978-1-932381-79-5(1) , 2019) Bible Visuals International, Inc.

—Joseph, a Picture of the Lord Jesus Pt. 1, Vol. 4: Old Testament. 2005. (Illus.). (J). pap. (978-1-932381-69-6(4) , 2004) Bible Visuals International, Inc.

—Sacrifice Vol. 11: Old Testament. 2005. (Illus.). (J). pap. (978-1-932381-06-1(6) , 2011) Bible Visuals International, Inc.

Blundell, Trevor & Thalia. Game Is Up: Old Testament. (Illus.). 96p. (J). Bk. 1. pap. 11.99 (978-1-85792-550-0(5)); Vol. 2. pap. 11.99 (978-1-85792-760-3(5)) Christian Focus Pubns. GBR. (Christian Focus). *Dist:* Riverside.

Broadman and Holman Publishers Staff. KJV Read to Me Bible for Kids. 2004. (Illus.). 1560p. 19.99 (978-1-55819-845-6(8)) B&H Publishing Grp.

Busch, Melinda Kay. The Fiery Furnace. Koehler, Ed, illus. 2004. (Arch Bks.). 16p. (J). (gr. k-4). 1.99 (978-0-7586-0479-8(3)) Concordia Publishing Hse.

Daly, Jude, illus. To Everything There Is a Season. 2006. 32p. (Orig.). (J). 16.00 (978-0-8028-5286-1(6) , Eerdmans Bks For Young Readers) Eerdmans, William B. Publishing Co.

Dillon, Leo. Jazz on a Saturday Night. Dillon, Diane, illus. 2007. 40p. (J). (ps-3). pap. 16.99 (978-0-590-47893-9(1)) Scholastic, Inc.

Dillon, Leo & Dillon, Diane. To Every Thing There Is a Season. Dillon, Leo & Dillon, Diane, illus. 2002. (Illus.). (J). 25.06 (978-0-7587-3819-6(6)) Book Wholesalers, Inc.

—To Every Thing There Is a Season. 1998. (Illus.). 40p. (J). (ps-3). pap. 16.95 (978-0-590-47887-8(7) , Blue Sky Pr., The) Scholastic, Inc.

Donaher, D. F. & Bibleco. Biblemania: The Old Testament Magazine. 2003. (Illus.). (YA). pap. 8.95 (978-0-9746058-0-7(8)) Bibleco, Inc.

Eisenberg, Ann & Schanzer, Rosalyn. Bible Heroes I Can Be. 2004. (Illus.). 20p. (J). (ps up). 6.95 (978-1-58013-124-7(7)) Kar-Ben Publishing.

Feiler, Bruce S. Walking the Bible: An Illustrated Journey for Kids Through the Greatest Stories Ever Told. Meret, Sasha, tr. Meret, Sasha, illus. ed. 2004. 112p. (J). (gr. 2 up). 16.99 (978-0-06-051117-3(6)) HarperCollins Pubs.

French, Fiona. Paradise: With Words from the King James Bible. 2004. (Illus.). 32p. (J). 15.95 (978-1-84507-007-6(0)) Lincoln, Frances Ltd. GBR. *Dist:* Perseus Distribution.

Ganz, Nancy. Herein Is Love Vol. 1: Genesis. 2nd rev. ed. 2002. 576p. (J). pap., tchr. ed. 20.00 (978-0-9723046-0-3(6)) Shepherd Pr. Inc.

—Herein Is Love Vol. 2: Exodus. 2nd rev. ed. 2002. 296p. (J). pap., tchr. ed. 15.00 (978-0-9723046-1-0(4)) Shepherd Pr. Inc.

—Herein Is Love Vol. 3: Leviticus. 2nd rev. ed. 2002. 160p. (J). pap., tchr. ed. 12.00 (978-0-9723046-2-7(2)) Shepherd Pr. Inc.

Hernandez, Emilia. El Arca de Noe. 2002. (Historias de la Biblia Ser.). (SPA & ENG., Illus.). 24p. 9.95 (978-84-7864-585-5(3)) Combel Editorial, S.A. ESP. *Dist:* Independent Pubs. Group.

Jackson, Cindy. Old Testament Fun Activities - First & Second Grade. 1998. (Illus.). 16p. (J). (gr. 1-2). 3.95 (978-1-878669-69-8(9) , CRE 3541) Creative Teaching Assocs.

—Old Testament Fun Activities - Pre-School & Kindergarten. 1998. (Illus.). 16p. (J). (ps-k). 3.95 (978-1-878669-68-1(0) , CRE 3540) Creative Teaching Assocs.

—Old Testament Fun Activities - Third & Fourth Grade. 1998. (Illus.). 16p. (J). (gr. 3-4). 3.95 (978-1-878669-70-4(2) , CRE 3542) Creative Teaching Assocs.

JBible Visuals International, compiled by. God's Discipline Vol. 13: Old Testament. 2005. (Illus.). (J). pap. (978-1-932381-75-7(9) , 2013) Bible Visuals International, Inc.

Johnson, John L. 500 Questions & Answers on the Black Presenc in the Bible. 2002. (YA). per. 10.95 (978-0-9709715-6-2(7)) Johnson Bks., Inc.

Kendall, R. T. Between the Times: Malachi: God's Last Prophet of the Old Testament. 2004. 208p. pap. (978-1-85792-792-4(3) , Christian Focus) Christian Focus Pubns.

Lee, Witness. Life-Study of Pentateuch: (Genesis-Deuteronomy), 22 vols., Set. 2000. (J). (gr. 6). per. 184.50 (978-0-7363-1423-7(7) , 10-081-001) Living Stream Ministry.

Lersch, Jean. Scrapbook: Faith for Life2 Course Three. Janssen, Patricia E., ed. 2nd ed. 2003. (J). stu. ed., spiral bd. 14.99 (978-0-9727146-4-8(2)) LOGOS System Assocs.

Lindbergh, Reeve. On Morning Wings. Meade, Holly, illus. 2002. 32p. (J). (ps-1). 15.99 (978-0-7636-1106-4(9)) Candlewick Pr.

Lingo, Susan L. Who's Who Object Talks That Teach about the Old Testament. 2006. 48p. (YA). pap. 6.99 (978-0-7847-1311-2(1) , 42009) Standard Publishing.

Lottridge, Celia Barker. Stories from Adam & Eve to Ezekiel: Retold from the Bible. Clement, Gary, illus. 2004. 144p. (J). 24.95 (978-0-88899-490-5(7)) Groundwood Bks. CAN. *Dist:* Perseus Distribution.

Mooney, Belinda. Itty-Bitty Book: Old Testament. 2006. (J). pap. 1.49 (***978-1-59317-166-7(8)***) Warner Pr. Pubs.

Paluch, Beily. I am a Torah: A Playful Action Rhyme. Argoff, Patti, illus. 2004. 12p. (J). bds. 5.95 (978-1-929628-18-6(8)) Hachai Publishing.

Perrotta, Kevin & Darring, Gerald. Six Weeks with the Bible for Catholic Teens Exodus: God to the Rescue. 2004. (Six Week for Catholic Teens Ser.). 96p. 6.95 (978-0-8294-2051-7(7)) Loyola Pr.

—Six Weeks with the Bible for Catholic Teens Genesis 1-11: God Makes a Start. 2004. (Six Week for Catholic Teens Ser.). 96p. 6.95 (978-0-8294-2050-0(9)) Loyola Pr.

Perry, Marilyn. The Adventures of David: The Story of a Shepherd Who Became King, 4 bklts., Set. 2003. (Illus.). 208p. (J). 69.95 (978-1-55145-483-2(1)) Northstone Publishing, Inc. CAN. *Dist:* Pilgrim Pr., The/ United Church Pr.

Regina Press Staff. Old Testament for Children. (J). (ps-3). 1.95 (978-0-88271-044-0(3)) Regina Pr., Malhame & Co.

Ross & King. Primary Partners: Old Testament. 2004. cd-rom 11.95 (978-1-57734-966-2(0)) Covenant Communications, Inc.

Russell, Patricia C. Beginnings I - & It Was Good! Old Testament Lessons for Little Listeners. Clark, Virginia A., ed. 1999. (Beginnings I Ser.). 301p. (J). (ps-k). spiral bd. 23.99 (978-1-889015-27-9(X)) Explorer's Bible Study.

Russell, Patricia Constance. Beginnings II - God's Promises: Old Testament Lessons for Young Readers. Murtha, Dee M., ed. 2005. (Beginnings II Ser.). 301p. (J). stu. ed., spiral bd., wbk. ed. 23.99 (978-1-889015-01-9(6)) Explorer's Bible Study.

Sanders, Nancy I. The Fall into Sin: Genesis 2-3 for Children. Van Severen, Joe, illus. 2004. (Arch Books). (ENG.). 16p. (J). 1.99 (978-0-7586-0618-1(4)) Concordia Publishing Hse.

Sasso, Sandy Eisenberg. Cain & Abel: Finding the Fruits of Peace. Rothenberg, Joani Keller, illus. 2001. 32p. (J). (gr. k-3). 16.95 (978-1-58023-123-7(3)) Jewish Lights Publishing.

Smith-Christopher, Daniel. The Old Testament: Our Call to Faith & Justice - Student Text. (Illus.). 288p. stu. ed. 22.95 (978-0-87793-721-0(4)) Ave Maria Pr.

Steen & Front. A Child's Bible in Colour: The Old Testament. 2000. (Illus.). 384p. (J). (ps-3). pap. (978-0-330-23688-1(1) , Macmillan Children's Bks.) Pan Macmillan.

Strawn, Kathy. Bible Buddies Activity Book for Old Testament Grade 1. 2000. (J). (gr. 1-3). 5.25 (978-0-633-00462-0(6)) LifeWay Christian Resources.

Whited, Linda Robinson. The Promised Land: An Old Testament Activity Book. 1999. 48p. (J). (gr. 4-7). act. bk. ed. 4.00 (978-0-687-08191-2(2)) Abingdon Pr.

Youngblood, Ronald. The Heart of the Old Testament: A Survey of Key Theological Themes. 2nd ed. 1998. 128p. (C). pap. 13.99 (978-0-8010-2172-5(3)) Baker Academic.

BIBLE—OLD TESTAMENT—BIOGRAPHY

Frank, Penny. La Nueva Familia de Rut.Tr. of Ruth's New Family. (SPA.). (J). 1.99 (978-1-56063-785-1(4) , 490315) Editorial Unilit.

Morris, Neil & Foglia, Enrico. The Life of Moses. 2003. (Art Revelations Ser.). (Illus.). 32p. (J). (gr. 6-9). 18.95 (978-1-59270-001-1(2)) Enchanted Lion Bks., LLC.

Nederveld, Patricia L. A Girl Named Rebekah: The Story of God's Answer to Abraham. 1998. (God Loves Me Ser.). (Illus.). 24p. (J). (ps-3). pap. 2.95 (978-1-56212-277-5(0) , 001208, Faith Alive Christian Resources) CRC Pubns.

—Plenty to Eat: The Story of Joseph & His Brothers. 1998. (God Loves Me Ser.). (Illus.). 24p. (J). (ps-3). pap. 2.95 (978-1-56212-279-9(7) , 001210, Faith Alive Christian Resources) CRC Pubns.

—Safe in a Basket: The Story of Baby Moses. 1998. (God Loves Me Ser.). (Illus.). 24p. (J). (ps-3). pap. 2.95 (978-1-56212-280-5(0) , 001211, Faith Alive Christian Resources) CRC Pubns.

Pennington, Jack & Tank, Darrel, illus. Joseph. 2004. 87p. (J). pap. (978-0-8280-1855-5(3)) Review & Herald Publishing Assn.

Pingry, Patricia A. The Story of Jonah. Venturi-Pickett, Stacy, illus. 1998. 26p. (J). (ps-k). bds. 6.95 (978-0-8249-4094-2(6) , Ideals Children's Bks.) Ideals Pubns.

Pulley, Kelly, illus. Esther & the King. 2007. (I Can Read!). 32p. (J). pap. 3.99 (***978-0-310-71460-6(5)***) Zonderkidz.

van Rijswijk, Cor. Abraham's Sacrifice. Visser, Rino, illus. 2001. 43p. (J). pap. (978-1-894666-21-3(6)) Inheritance Pubns.

White, John & Tank, Darrel, illus. Abraham. 2004. (Family Bible Story Ser.). 109p. (J). pap. (978-0-8280-1857-9(X)) Review & Herald Publishing Assn.

Yolen, Jane. The Prince of Egypt: Classic Edition. 1998. (Prince of Egypt Ser.). (Illus.). 80p. (J). (ps-4). 8.99 (978-0-8499-5894-6(6)) Nelson, Thomas Inc.

BIBLE—OLD TESTAMENT—PSALMS

Bluedorn, Johannah, illus. The Lord Builds the House: The 127th Psalm. 2004. 32p. (J). 10.00 (978-0-9743616-1-1(5)) Trivium Pursuit.

Chocheli, Niko, illus. The Praises: Psalm 148 : A Psalm of David. 2000. 32p. (J). 17.00 (978-0-88141-206-2(6)) St. Vladimir's Seminary Pr.

Delval, Marie-Hélène. Psalms for Young Children. Arno, illus. 2007. (J). (***978-0-8028-5322-6(6)*** , Eerdmans Bks For Young Readers) Eerdmans, William B. Publishing Co.

Haas, David. Children's Psalms to Pray, Sing & Do. 2004. (Illus.). 80p. (J). pap. 9.95 (978-0-86716-453-4(0)) St. Anthony Messenger Pr. & Franciscan Communications.

Haidle, Helen. Comfort for a Child's Heart. 2001. 90p. 9.99 (978-0-310-70126-2(0)) Zondervan.

—Comfort for a Child's Heart: The 23rd Psalm & Bible Promises. Haidle, David, illus. 1999. 96p. (ps-1). 9.99 (978-1-57673-569-5(9) , Multnomah) WaterBrook Pr.

Hernandez, Emilia. Daniel y los Leones. 2002. (Historias de la Biblia Ser.). (SPA & ENG., Illus.). 24p. 9.95 (978-84-7864-588-6(8)) Combel Editorial, S.A. ESP. *Dist:* Independent Pubs. Group.

—David y Goliat. 2002. (Historias de la Biblia Series Ser.). (SPA & ENG., Illus.). 24p. 9.95 (978-84-7864-586-2(1)) Combel Editorial, S.A. ESP. *Dist:* Independent Pubs. Group, Libros Sin Fronteras.

—Moises en Egipto. 2002. (Historias de la Biblia Ser.). (SPA & ENG., Illus.). 24p. 9.95 (978-84-7864-587-9(X)) Combel Editorial, S.A. ESP. *Dist:* Independent Pubs. Group, Libros Sin Fronteras.

Kitch, Anne. Bless This Way. Conahan, Carolyn Digby, illus. 2003. 20p. 9.95 (978-0-8192-1917-6(7)) Morehouse Publishing.

Legacy Press Staff & Davis, Mary J. My Praise Journal: A Celebration of Psalms for Kids. 2004. (Journals Just for Kids Ser.). (Illus.). 144p. (J). (gr. 4-7). pap. 9.99 (978-1-885358-71-4(7) , Legacy Pr.) Rainbow Pubs. & Legacy Pr.

MacKall, Dandi Daley. God Is My Shepherd & I'm His Lamb. Dippold, Jane, illus. 2006. 36p. (J). 9.99 (978-0-7847-1533-8(5) , 04158) Standard Publishing.

Maselli, Christopher P. N. Invasion of the Psalm Psnatchers Ages 8-12: 12 Mystery Stories to Solve Using the Book of Psalms. 2006. 48p. pap. (978-1-59441-382-7(7)) Carson-Dellosa Publishing Co., Inc.

McDaniels, Preston, illus. The Lord Is My Shepherd: Psalm 23 for Children. 2004. (Psalms for Children Ser.). 24p. 9.95 (978-0-8192-1986-2(X)) Morehouse Publishing.

Miller, James E. My Shepherd Is the Lord: The Timeless Message of the 23rd Psalm. 2002. 32p. 3.95 (978-1-885933-33-1(9) , K823) Willowgreen Publishing.

Moreland, Melanie, illus. Psalm 23 for Kidz: The Lord Is my Shepherd. I am His Lamb. 2007. 32p. (J). 10.00 (***978-0-9779194-1-3(2)***) Little Sprout Publishing Hse.

Moser, Barry, illus. Barry Moser's Psalm 23. 2008. 32p. (J). (***978-0-310-71085-1(5)***) Zonderkidz.

Moss, Donna. How I Praise You! 150 Little Psalms in Song. Moss, Rebecca, illus. 1998. 240p. (J). (ps-8). pap. (978-0-9663809-2-7(4)) Apex Publishing Services.

Papademetriou, Dorrie. Celebrate the Earth: Psalm 104. 2000. (Illus.). 32p. (J). 15.00 (978-0-88141-204-8(X)) St. Vladimir's Seminary Pr.

Psalm 148: Let all Heaven & Earth Praise the Lord! 2006. (J). (***978-0-9779194-0-6(4)***) Little Sprout Publishing Hse.

Los Salmos y los Profetas (The Psalms & the Prophets) Quarter 1, Level 4. 2000. (Caminando con Jesus (Walking with Jesus) Series A). (SPA.). (J). (gr. 5-6). stu. ed. 3.50 (978-0-570-05161-9(4) , 16-4811) Concordia Publishing Hse.

Spirin, Gennady, illus. The Lord Is My Shepherd. 2008. 32p. (J). (ps). 17.99 (***978-0-399-24527-5(8)*** , Philomel) Penguin Group (USA) Inc.

Tamberino, Tony. Pray Your Heart Resource Manual: Music-Based Sessions & Prayer Experiences for Teens. 2003. 32p. (YA). pap. 12.95 (978-0-88489-562-6(9)) St. Mary's Pr.

Thompson, Patricia. Psalms 23: A Child's Story. 2005. (J). 12.95 (978-0-9776780-0-6(8)) G Publishing LLC.

Webber, Christopher L. Praise the Lord, My Soul: Psalm 104 for Children. McDaniels, Preston, illus. 2002. 32p. (ps-1). 14.95 (978-0-8192-1889-6(8)) Morehouse Publishing.

—Shout for Joy & Sing! Psalm 65 for Children. McDaniels, Preston, illus. 2003. (Psalms for Children Ser.). 32p. 14.95 (978-0-8192-1934-3(7)) Morehouse Publishing.

Wilson, Anne. The Lord Is My Shepherd. Wilson, Anne, illus. 2004. (Illus.). 32p. 16.00 (978-0-8028-5250-2(5)) Eerdmans, William B. Publishing Co.

Wilson, Karma. I Will Rejoice: Celebrating Psalm 118. Bates, Amy June, illus. 2007. 32p. (J). 14.99 (978-0-310-71117-9(7)) Zonderkidz.

Wilson, Karma & Bates, Amy June. Let's Make a Joyful Noise! A Celebration of Psalm 100. 2008. 32p. (J). (978-0-310-71119-3(3)) Zonderkidz.

BIBLE—PARABLES

see Jesus Christ—Parables

BIBLE—PICTORIAL WORKS

Beck, William F. Bible Stories in Pictures: Creation to the Early Church. Essmann, Harold, ed. Rogers, Ruth W et al, illus. 2000. (SPA, SWE & ALB.). 220p. reprint ed. pap. (978-0-9703210-0-8(7) , 38-7321) Multi-Language Pubns.

Daly, Jude, illus. To Everything There Is a Season. 2006. 32p. (Orig.). (J). 16.00 (978-0-8028-5286-1(6) , Eerdmans Bks For Young Readers) Eerdmans, William B. Publishing Co.

Illustrated Living Bible, Youth. 1999. (Illus.). (J). pap. 12.95 (978-1-55513-397-9(5)) Cook, David C. Publishing Co.

Lindvall, Ella K. The Bible in Pictures for Toddlers. Langton, Roger, illus. 2003. (Leading Young Hearts & Minds to God Ser.). 144p. (J). 9.99 (978-0-8024-3058-8(9)) Moody Pubs.

—La Biblia en Cuadros para Nino Pequenos. 2004. (SPA.). 144p. 9.99 (978-0-8254-1710-8(4) , Editorial Portavoz) Kregel Pubns.

Mark. First Step Bible. 2001. (Illus.). (J). (ps-3). 15.99 (978-0-310-70136-1(8)) Zondervan.

Neely, Keith, illus. The Illustrated Bible: Complete New Testament. 2007. 640p. (J). 19.99 (978-1-4003-0831-6(3)) Nelson, Thomas Inc.

New Picture Bible. 1998. 760p. (J). (978-0-7814-0307-8(3)) Cook, David C. Publishing Co.

Sattgast, Linda J. My Little Promise Bible. Brooks, Nan, illus. 2001. (Bible Storybooks Ser.). 96p. (J). 6.99 (978-0-310-70132-3(5)) Zonderkidz.

Taylor, Kenneth N. My First Picture Bible Stories, Catholic Edition. 2000. (Illus.). (J). (ps-3). 262p. 12.95 (978-0-87973-108-3(7)) ; 256p. 16.95 (978-0-87973-109-0(5)) Our Sunday Visitor, Publishing Div.

—The New Bible in Pictures for Little Eyes. Spenceley, Annabel, illus. 2002. (Leading Young Hearts & Minds to God Ser.). 384p. (J). 15.99 (978-0-8024-3057-1(0)) Moody Pubs.

Thomas Nelson Publishing Staff. Really Woolly Little Lambs Bible: Baby New Testament - Gift Edition. 2007. 384p. (J). im. lthr. 16.99 (978-1-4003-0976-4(X)) Nelson, Thomas Inc.

Widmer, Becky. Bible Awareness Series, 6 vols. Christian, Heather, illus. Date not set. (J). (ps up). 9.95 (978-1-888537-00-0(0)) Publisher Plus.

Woychuk, N. A. Bible Forget-Me-Nots No. 1: Memory Book. Jones, Mary E., illus. 1998. 48p. (J). (ps). spiral bd. 12.95 (978-1-880960-31-8(1)) Scripture Memory Fellowship International.

BIBLE—PLANTS

see Bible—Natural History

BIBLE—STUDY

Acts 2. (LifeLight Bible Studies: Course 14). stu. ed. 5.50 (978-0-570-09287-2(6) , 20-2312) Concordia Publishing Hse.

Adelman, Penina V. The Bible from Alef to Tav. Jacobs, Michael, photos by. 1998. (Illus.). 185p. (J). (gr. 1-4). pap. 14.95 (978-0-933873-22-3(0)) Torah Aura Productions.

Armor of God: With Sticker. 2006. (Illus.). 28p. (J). (ps-2). pap. 3.49 (978-0-7847-1251-1(4) , 22084) Standard Publishing.

Arthur, Kay & Arndt, Janna. Boy, Have I Got Problems! James. 2000. (Discover 4 Yourself Inductive Bible Studies for Kids Ser.). (Illus.). 144p. (gr. 3-7). pap. 9.99 (978-0-7369-0148-2(5)) Harvest Hse. Pubs.

—Digging up the Past Chapters 3-11: Genesis. 2001. (Discover 4 Yourself Inductive Bible Studies for Kids Ser.). (Illus.). 224p. pap. 10.99 (978-0-7369-0374-5(7)) Harvest Hse. Pubs.

—God, What's Your Name? 2003. (Discover 4 Yourself Inductive Bible Studies for Kids Ser.). 192p. pap., wbk. ed. 10.99 (978-0-7369-1161-0(8)) Harvest Hse. Pubs.

—God's Amazing Creation Pt. 1, Chpts. 1 & 2: Genesis. 2001. (Discover 4 Yourself Inductive Bible Studies for Kids Ser.). 160p. pap. 9.99 (978-0-7369-0143-7(4)) Harvest Hse. Pubs.

—How to Study Your Bible for Kids. 2002. (Discover 4 Yourself Inductive Bible Studies for Kids Ser.). (Illus.). 192p. (gr. 4-7). pap. 10.99 (978-0-7369-0362-2(3)) Harvest Hse. Pubs.

—How to Study Your Bible for Kids. (Discover-4-Yourself for Kids Ser.). 185p. (J). 2006. pap. 9.99 (978-1-888655-29-2(1)); 2005. pap. 9.99 (978-1-888655-77-3(1)) Precept Ministries.

—Joseph - God's Superhero: Genesis 37-50. 2002. (Discover 4 Yourself Inductive Bible Studies for Kids Ser.). 160p. (gr. 4-7). pap. 9.99 (978-0-7369-0739-2(4)) Harvest Hse. Pubs.

Arthur, Kay & Shearer, Cyndy. Jesus in the Spotlight Pt. 1: John 1-10. 1999. (Discover 4 Yourself Inductive Bible Studies for Kids Ser.). (Illus.). 128p. (gr. 4-7). pap. 8.99 (978-0-7369-0119-2(1)) Harvest Hse. Pubs.

Arthur, Kay, et al. How to Study Your Bible for Teens. 2004. 176p. (YA). pap. 9.99 (978-0-7369-0965-5(6)) Harvest Hse. Pubs.

Association of Christian Schools International Staff. Doing What's Right: First Grade. 2000. (Character Foundation Curriculum Ser.). (Illus.). 96p. (gr. 1-2). pap., stu. ed. 12.75 (978-1-58331-142-4(4) , 7027) Assn. of Christian Schls. International.

Augustine, Peg. Meeting Bible Characters. 2002. 16p. 5.00 (978-0-687-09394-6(5)) Abingdon Pr.

Augustine, Peg & Flegal, Daphna. Alphabet Rhymes for Bible Times. Easter, Paige, illus. 2004. 9.00 (978-0-687-03021-7(8)) Abingdon Pr.

—Bible Verse Board Books, Set. Easter, Paige, illus. 2002. 24.00 (978-0-687-03044-6(7)) Abingdon Pr.

Ausenhus, Pam. Running the Race of Faith. 2001. 176p. (YA). (gr. 9-13). 7.99 (978-0-570-05221-0(1)) Concordia Publishing Hse.

Babb, Katherine Bailey. What Do You Mean, "Study the Bible"? A Survey of the Old Testament for High School Groups. 2001. (J). (gr. 8-12). pap. 11.50 (978-0-7880-1802-7(7)) CSS Publishing Co.

Bacchiocchi, Samuele. Hal Lindsey's Prophetic Jigsaw Puzzle: Five Predictions That Failed! 6th deluxe ed. 1998. (Biblical Perspectives Ser.: Vol. 3). 150p. (YA). pap. 20.00 (978-1-930987-02-9(1)) Biblical Perspectives.

Bagley, Val Chadwick. Follow the Prophet. 2001. (J). (ps-3). bds. 13.95 (978-1-57734-851-1(6)) Covenant Communications, Inc.

Baker Book House Staff. Seeking Sammy in the New Testament. 1999. (Bible Fun Series for Kids Ser.). (Illus.). (J). (ps-3). pap. 9.99 (978-0-8010-0280-9(X) , New Kids Media) Baker Bks.

Baker, Mary. Bible Study Guide for All Ages: Beginner Level Activity Pages - Lessons 1-26. Needels, Greg, illus. 2nd rev. ed. 2000. 26p. (J). pap., wbk. ed. 4.95 (978-1-879614-59-8(6)) Bible Study Guide For All Ages.

—Bible Study Guide for All Ages: Beginner Level Activity Pages - Lessons 209-234. Needels, Greg, illus. 2001. 26p. (J). (ps-2). pap., wbk. ed. 4.95 (978-1-879614-75-8(8)) Bible Study Guide For All Ages.

—Bible Study Guide for All Ages: Beginner Level Activity Pages - Lessons 235-260. Needels, Greg, illus. 2001. 26p. (J). (ps-2). pap., wbk. ed. 4.95 (978-1-879614-76-5(6)) Bible Study Guide For All Ages.

—Bible Study Guide for All Ages: Beginner Level Activity Pages - Lessons 261-286. Needels, Greg, illus. 2001. 26p. (J). (ps-2). pap., wbk. ed. 4.95 (978-1-879614-77-2(4)) Bible Study Guide For All Ages.

—Bible Study Guide for All Ages: Beginner Level Activity Pages - Lessons 27-52. Needels, Greg, illus. 2nd rev. ed. 2000. 26p. (J). (ps-2). pap., wbk. ed. 4.95 (978-1-879614-60-4(X)) Bible Study Guide For All Ages.

A B

—Bible Study Guide for All Ages: Beginner Level Activity Pages - Lessons 287-312. Needels, Greg, illus. 2001. 26p. (J). (ps-2). pap., wbk. ed. 4.95 (978-1-879614-78-9(2)) Bible Study Guide For All Ages.

—Bible Study Guide for All Ages: Beginner Level Activity Pages - Lessons 53-78. Needels, Greg, illus. 2nd rev. ed. 2000. 26p. (J). (ps-2). pap., wbk. ed. 4.95 (978-1-879614-61-1(8)) Bible Study Guide For All Ages.

—Bible Study Guide for All Ages: Beginner Level Activity Pages - Lessons 79-104. Needels, Greg, illus. 2nd rev. ed. 2000. 26p. (J). (ps-2). pap., wbk. ed. 4.95 (978-1-879614-62-8(6)) Bible Study Guide For All Ages.

—Bible Study Guide for All Ages: Beginner Level Activity Pages—Lessons 105-130. Baker, Mary, ed. Needels, Greg, illus. 2000. 26p. (J). (ps-2). pap., wbk. ed. 4.95 (978-1-879614-63-5(4)) Bible Study Guide For All Ages.

—Bible Study Guide for All Ages: Beginner Level Activity Pages—Lessons 131-156. Needels, Greg, illus. 2000. 26p. (J). pap., wbk. ed. 4.95 (978-1-879614-64-2(2)) Bible Study Guide For All Ages.

—Bible Study Guide for All Ages: Beginner Level Activity Pages—Lessons 157-182. Needels, Greg, illus. 2000. 26p. (J). pap., wbk. ed. 4.95 (978-1-879614-65-9(0)) Bible Study Guide For All Ages.

—Bible Study Guide for All Ages: Beginner Level Activity Pages—Lessons 183-208. Needels, Greg, illus. 2000. 26p. (J). pap., wbk. ed. 4.95 (978-1-879614-66-6(9)) Bible Study Guide For All Ages.

—Bible Study Guide for All Ages: Intermediate Level Activity Pages - Lessons 209-234. Needels, Greg, illus. 2001. 26p. (J). (gr. 3-7). pap., wbk. ed. 4.95 (978-1-879614-79-6(0)) Bible Study Guide For All Ages.

—Bible Study Guide for All Ages: Intermediate Level Activity Pages - Lessons 235-260. Needels, Greg, illus. 2001. 26p. (J). (gr. 3-7). pap., wbk. ed. 4.95 (978-1-879614-80-2(4)) Bible Study Guide For All Ages.

—Bible Study Guide for All Ages: Intermediate Level Activity Pages - Lessons 261-286. Needels, Greg, illus. 2001. 26p. (J). (gr. 3-7). pap., wbk. ed. 4.95 (978-1-879614-81-9(2)) Bible Study Guide For All Ages.

—Bible Study Guide for All Ages: Intermediate Level Activity Pages - Lessons 27-52. Needels, Greg, illus. 2nd ed. 2000. 26p. (J). (gr. 3-7). pap., wbk. ed. 4.95 (978-1-879614-55-0(3)) Bible Study Guide For All Ages.

—Bible Study Guide for All Ages: Intermediate Level Activity Pages - Lessons 287-312. Needels, Greg, illus. 2001. 26p. (J). (gr. 3-7). pap., wbk. ed. 4.95 (978-1-879614-82-6(0)) Bible Study Guide For All Ages.

—Bible Study Guide for All Ages: Intermediate Level Activity Pages - Lessons 79-104. Needels, Greg, illus. 2nd rev. ed. 2000. 26p. (J). (gr. 3-7). pap., wbk. ed. 4.95 (978-1-879614-58-1(8)) Bible Study Guide For All Ages.

—Bible Study Guide for All Ages: Intermediate Level Activity Pages—Lesson 131-156. Needels, Greg, illus. 2000. 26p. (J). (gr. 3-7). pap., wbk. ed. 4.95 (978-1-879614-68-0(5)) Bible Study Guide For All Ages.

—Bible Study Guide for All Ages: Intermediate Level Activity Pages—Lessons 105-130. Needels, Greg, illus. 2000. 26p. (J). (gr. 3-7). pap., wbk. ed. 4.95 (978-1-879614-67-3(7)) Bible Study Guide For All Ages.

—Bible Study Guide for All Ages: Intermediate Level Activity Pages—Lessons 157-182. Needels, Greg, illus. 2000. 26p. (J). pap., wbk. ed. 4.95 (978-1-879614-69-7(3)) Bible Study Guide For All Ages.

—Bible Study Guide for All Ages: Intermediate Level Activity Pages—Lessons 183-208. Needels, Greg, illus. 2000. 26p. (J). (gr. 3-7). pap., wbk. ed. 4.95 (978-1-879614-70-3(7)) Bible Study Guide For All Ages.

—Bible Study Guide for All Ages: Multi-Level Worksheets - First Year - Third Quarter. 1999. (Illus.). (J). (gr. 5-7). wbk. ed. 4.95 (978-1-879614-45-1(6)) Bible Study Guide For All Ages.

Baker, Mary & Needels, Greg. Bible Study Guide: Intermediate Level Activity Pages - Lessons 53-78. 2nd rev. ed. 2000. (Illus.). 26p. (J). (gr. 3-7). pap., wbk. ed. 4.95 (978-1-879614-57-4(X)) Bible Study Guide For All Ages.

—Bible Study Guide for All Ages: Intermediate Level Activity Pages - Lessons 1-26. 2nd rev. ed. 2000. (Illus.). 26p. (J). (gr. 3-7). pap., wbk. ed. 4.95 (978-1-879614-56-7(1)) Bible Study Guide For All Ages.

Balzora, Renaud & Balzora, Lulrick. Fondation: Doctrines Bibliques en 52 Leçons. 2004. (FRE.). 198p. (YA). per. 15.00 (978-1-58432-189-7(X)) Educa Vision.

Barton, David Charles, creator. Decision for Christ Study of the Bible. 2004. 154p. pap. 3.95 (978-0-9759426-3-5(8)) Barton, D.C. Publishing.

Beck, Susan Elizabeth. God Loves Me Bible (Girls) 1999. (Illus.). 160p. (J). 12.99 (978-0-310-95846-8(6)) Zondervan.

Betz, Eva K. The Man Who Fought the Devil: The Curi of Ars. 2001. (Illus.). 144p. (J). reprint ed. 17.00 (978-1-930873-25-4(5)) Neumann Pr., The.

Bible. 2004. (Illus.). (gr. 1). tchr. ed., stu. ed. 67.95 (978-0-86717-671-1(7) , BIB0115, Lifepac) Alpha Omega Pubns., Inc.

Bible: Student Testing Kit. 2004. (Illus.). (YA). (gr. 7-12). pap., stu. ed. 5.00 (978-0-7403-0042-4(3) , BD002) Alpha Omega Pubns., Inc.

The Bible & Me. 2003. (Faith 4 Life Ser.). 48p. 14.99 (978-0-7644-2480-9(7) , Flagship Church Resources) Group Publishing, Inc.

Bible Buzz: Spring 2001. 2001. (Faith Weaver Ser.). (J). (gr. 5-6). pap., stu. ed. 3.99 (978-0-7644-1066-6(0)) Group Publishing, Inc.

Bible Buzz: Summer 2001. 2001. (Faith Weaver Ser.). (J). (gr. 5-6). pap., stu. ed. 3.99 (978-0-7644-1086-4(5)) Group Publishing, Inc.

Bible Characters & Bulletin Boards. (Illus.). 48p. (J). (gr. 1-7). pap. 5.95 (978-0-87162-632-5(2) , E4605) Warner Pr. Pubs.

Bible, Debbie. One Year Book of Devotions for Boys. 2000. (gr. 3-6). lib. bdg. 22.25 (978-0-613-76797-2(7)) Tandem Library Bks.

—One Year Book of Devotions for Girls. 2000. (gr. 3-6). lib. bdg. 22.25 (978-0-613-76795-8(0)) Tandem Library Bks.

Bible KJV Childrens. 2004. (Illus.). 826p. (J). pap. 16.99 (978-1-55819-757-2(5)) B&H Publishing Grp.

Bible Learning Is Fun. 1998. (Illus.). (J). pap. 1.50 (978-0-87162-975-3(5)) Warner Pr. Pubs.

The Bible Question Book for Children. 2000. per. 17.95 (978-1-890436-19-3(4)) MEGA Corp.

Bible Skills, Drills, & Thrills Activity Bk Gr 1,3 Green Cycle. 2004. (J). 5.95 (978-0-633-19425-3(5)) LifeWay Christian Resources.

Bible Truth Sleuth: Fall 2001. 2001. (Faith Weaver Ser.). (J). (gr. 3-4). pap., stu. ed. 3.99 (978-0-7644-1188-5(8)) Group Publishing, Inc.

Bible Truth Sleuth: Spring 2001. 2001. (Faith Weaver Ser.). (J). (gr. 3-4). pap., stu. ed. 3.99 (978-0-7644-1065-9(2)) Group Publishing, Inc.

Bible Truth Sleuth: Summer 2001. 2001. (Faith Weaver Ser.). (J). (gr. 3-4). pap., stu. ed. 3.99 (978-0-7644-1085-7(7)) Group Publishing, Inc.

Bible Verse Coloring Pages, Vol. 2. 216p. (gr. 1-6). 17.99 (978-0-8307-2585-4(7) , Gospel Light) Gospel Light Pubns.

The Big Book of Bible Games, Vol. 2. (Big Book Ser.). 176p. (gr. 1-6). 17.99 (978-0-8307-3053-7(2) , Gospel Light) Gospel Light Pubns.

Bingham, Anne. My Help along the Way: The Seven Sacraments. Larkin, Jean, ed. Thompson, Larissa, illus. 2000. (Active Learning for Catholic Kids Ser.). 28p. (YA). (gr. 7-9). pap. 7.95 (978-0-937997-91-8(9)) Pflaum Publishing Group.

—Understanding & Using the Bible: Hands-On Scripture Stury. Larkin, Jean, ed. Lynch, Patricia, illus. 2000. (Active Learning for Catholic Kids Ser.). 28p. (J). (gr. 4-6). pap. 7.95 (978-0-937997-87-1(0)) Pflaum Publishing Group.

BJU Staff. Bible Truths Stu Materials Gk5. 2004. pap. 13.50 (978-1-59166-238-9(9)) Jones, Bob Univ. Pr.

Blackwell, Jodi. Fundamentals: Secret Mission 001 Child's Pack. 2000. (J). (gr. 1-6). 5.95 (978-0-633-00476-7(6)) LifeWay Christian Resources.

Blauser, Tami S. The Basket of Flowers: A Tale for the Young an Exhaustive Study Guide. 1998. 133p. (YA). 7.00 (978-0-9717917-1-8(6)) SAT Pubs.

Blundell, Thalia & Blundell, Trevor. On the Way For 11 - 14's. 96p. (J). pap. 11.99 (978-1-85792-704-7(4) , Christian Focus) Christian Focus Pubns. GBR. *Dist:* Riverside.

Blundell, Trevor & Blundell, Thalia. Beginning with the Bible: First Class. (Illus.). 68-84p. (J). pap. 11.99 (978-1-85792-224-0(7) , Christian Focus) Christian Focus Pubns. GBR. *Dist:* Riverside.

Blundell, Trevor & Thalia. On the Way for 11 - 14's. 96p. (J). Vol. 2. pap. 11.99 (978-1-85792-705-4(2)); Vol. 3. pap. 11.99 (978-1-85792-706-1(0)) Christian Focus Pubns. GBR. (Christian Focus). *Dist:* Riverside.

Broadman and Holman Publishers Staff. Kindergarten. 2004. (Learning Activities from the Bible Ser.). (Illus.). (ps-2). act. bk. ed. 15.99 incl. cd-rom (978-0-8054-0983-3(1)) B&H Publishing Grp.

—Learning Activities from the Bible Series. 2004. (Learning Activities from the Bible Ser.). (Illus.). (ps-2). act. bk. ed. 15.99 incl. cd-rom (978-0-8054-0984-0(X)); act. bk. ed. 15.99 incl. cd-rom (978-0-8054-0985-7(8)) B&H Publishing Grp.

—Preschool. 2004. (Learning Activities from the Bible Ser.). (Illus.). (ps-2). act. bk. ed. 15.99 incl. cd-rom (978-0-8054-0982-6(3)) B&H Publishing Grp.

—Read to Me Bible for Kids. 2004. (Illus.). 1864p. 19.99 (978-1-55819-844-9(X)) B&H Publishing Grp.

Brown, Terry. Bible Stories for Bedtime. 2004. (Illus.). 240p. (J). pap. 5.97 (978-1-59310-359-0(X)) Barbour Publishing, Inc.

Brunson, Dorothy & DaHarb, Peggy. God's Promises for Me. Levering, Marcy, ed. McCallum, Jodie, illus. 2000. (Easy-to-Teach Bible Picture Lessons Ser.). 40p. (J). (ps-k). 10.99 (978-0-7847-1195-8(X) , 42119) Standard Publishing.

Bunyan, John. The Pilgrim's Progress. Dowley, Tim, ed. Smallman, Steve, illus. 2004. 160p. (gr. k-2). 12.99 (978-0-8254-7274-9(1)) Kregel Pubns.

—El Sacrificio Aceptable. Greendyk, William, tr. from ENG. 2003. Orig. Title: The Acceptable Sacrifice. (SPA.). 102p. (J). pap. (978-1-932789-05-8(7)) Editorial Sendas Antiguas, LLC.

Burns, Jim & Devries, Mike. Instant Bible Studies. 176p. 17.99 (978-0-8307-2919-7(4) , Gospel Light) Gospel Light Pubns.

Los Cambios Que Dios Produce (The Changes That God Produces) Quarter 3, Level 4. 2000. (Caminando con Jesus (Walking with Jesus) Series A). (SPA.). stu. ed. 3.50 (978-0-570-05157-2(6) , 16-4803); (J). (gr. 5-6). stu. ed. 3.50 (978-0-570-05163-3(0)) Concordia Publishing Hse.

Canaday, Matt & Canaday, Cindi. Book of Mormon Circle a Word, Bk. 2. Griffin, Grace, ed. 51p. (Orig.). (YA). pap., stu. ed. 2.95 (978-1-56998-000-2(4)) Gospel Puzzles.

Caribe Betania Staff & Grupo Nelson Staff. Biblioteca Electronica Caribe Edicion Profesional. 2004. (SPA.). cd-rom 99.99 (978-0-89922-656-9(6)) Grupo Nelson.

Caughey, Ellen. Zacchaeus Meets Jesus. 2000. (Little Bible Bks.). (Illus.). 24p. (J). (ps-3). 1.99 (978-1-57748-683-1(8)) Barbour Publishing, Inc.

The Champion: Batting a Thousand, Sacrifice Fly, The Comeback Kid, The Rookies, Spring 2001. ldr.'s ed. 2001. (Faithweaver Youth Bible Studies). (YA). (gr. 8-12). 19.99 (978-0-7644-1060-4(1)) Group Publishing, Inc.

Chance, Brenda K. Being a Christian Soldier: The Armor of God. 2001. (Illus.). 61p. (J). (gr. k-7). ring bd. 65.00 (978-0-9700603-1-0(9)) End Times Children's Curriculm, The.

Child Bible Activity Sheets, Vol. 2. (J). 4.95 (978-0-687-06494-6(5)) Abingdon Pr.

Choosing Kindness. 2003. (Illus.). 94p. (J). (gr. k-5). pap. 7.99 (978-0-9703069-3-7(8)) Train-Up A Child, LLC.

Choosing Self-Control. 2004. (Illus.). 94p. (J). (gr. k-5). pap. 7.99 (978-0-9703069-4-4(6)) Train-Up A Child, LLC.

Christian, Judith A. Hallelujah! Hurray! 2000. (Illus.). 64p. (J). (gr. 2-5). 8.99 (978-0-570-05596-9(2)) Concordia Publishing Hse.

Christian Reformed Church Staff, contrib. by. What We Believe Pt. 1: Sessions 1-12. 2nd ed. 2000. (Reformed Faith Ser.). 32p. (gr. 8-12). stu. ed. 4.50 (978-1-56212-529-5(X) , 135700, Faith Alive Christian Resources) CRC Pubns.

Cobb, Deborah B., illus. Bible Verse ABC's with the Cobblekids. 2001. vii, 64p. (J). (ps-1). 18.95 (978-0-9709793-0-8(4)) Lollipop Publishing, LLC.

Concordia Publishing Staff. Favorite Bible People, 1. 1999. (Surprise Bible Painting Bks.). (Illus.). 12p. (J). (gr. 1-4). pap. 4.00 (978-0-570-05598-3(9)) Concordia Publishing Hse.

—Jesus & His Friends. 1999. (Surprise Bible Painting Bks.). (Illus.). 12p. (J). (gr. 1-4). pap. 4.00 (978-0-570-05597-6(0)) Concordia Publishing Hse.

Constance, Tom M., Jr. Quest -in the Beginning: Genesis. Constance, Nellie E. & Eades, Lois, eds. 2000. (Quest Ser.). 221p. (YA). (gr. 7-12). stu. ed., per., wbk. ed. 21.99 (978-1-889015-06-4(7)) Explorer's Bible Study.

Cook, David C. Publishing Staff & Harmon, Jeannie. Elisha, God's Helper. 2003. (Pencil Fun Bks.: Vol. 10). 16p. (J). (ps-3). pap. 9.90 (978-1-55513-269-9(3) , 1555132693) Cook, David C. Publishing Co.

—God's Promise to Abraham. 2003. (Pencil Fun Bks.: Vol. 10). 16p. (J). (ps-3). pap. 9.90 (978-1-55513-126-5(3) , 1555131263) Cook, David C. Publishing Co.

Cook, David C. Publishing Staff & Veranos, Sandi. Joseph's Carpenter Shop. 2003. (Pencil Fun Bks.: Vol. 10). 16p. (J). (ps-3). pap. 9.90 (978-1-55513-152-4(2) , 1555131522) Cook, David C. Publishing Co.

Cooper, Emmett. HoneyWord Bible. 2004. 1464p. (J). pap. 24.99 (978-0-8423-3835-6(7)) Tyndale Hse. Pubs.

Cripe, Daniel Earl. The Other Side of Jordan: A Study in the Book of Hebrews. (New Testament Ser.). (Illus.). (J). 36.00 (978-1-890875-13-8(9)) ; pap. 42.00 (978-1-890875-14-5(7)) Jordan Publishing Hse.

Custom Spanish Curriculum January Year 3 - Elementary. 2005. 96p. pap. 14.95 (978-0-7814-4047-9(5) , 0781440475) Cook, David C. Publishing Co.

Custom Spanish Curriculum January Year 3 - Middle School. 2005. 96p. pap. 14.95 (978-0-7814-4053-0(X) , 078144053X) Cook, David C. Publishing Co.

Custom Spanish Curriculum January Year 3 - Preschool. 2005. 96p. pap. 14.95 (978-0-7814-4041-7(6) , 0781440416) Cook, David C. Publishing Co.

Custom Spanish Curriculum July Year 3 - Elementary. 2005. 96p. pap. 14.95 (978-0-7814-4048-6(3) , 0781440483) Cook, David C. Publishing Co.

Custom Spanish Curriculum July Year 3 - Middle School. 2005. 96p. pap. 14.95 (978-0-7814-4054-7(8) , 0781440548) Cook, David C. Publishing Co.

Custom Spanish Curriculum July Year 3 - Preschool. 2005. 96p. pap. 14.95 (978-0-7814-4042-4(4) , 0781440424) Cook, David C. Publishing Co.

Dalmatian Press Staff. The Ultimate Bible Fun Book. 1998. (Ultimate Fun Bks.). (Illus.). 512p. (J). pap. 5.99 (978-1-57759-016-3(3)) Dalmatian Pr.

—Ultimate Fun Book: The Greatest Collection of Fun & Learning Ever Assembled. 1998. (Ultimate Fun Bks.). (Illus.). 512p. (J). (ps-3). pap. 5.99 (978-1-57759-015-6(5)) Dalmatian Pr.

DeVries, Catherine. My Very First Devotional Bible: Selections from the New International Reader's Version. Luetkemeyer, Leanne Mebust, illus. 2000. (Bible Storybooks Ser.). 320p. (J). 14.99 (978-0-310-93251-2(3)) Zonderkidz.

Discover God's Love: 52 Bible Lessons. 2006. 320p. (J). 29.99 (978-0-7847-1322-8(7) , 42071) Standard Publishing.

Discovering Acts: A Bible Study for Teens. 1998. 72p. pap. 9.99 (978-0-8341-1715-0(0)) Beacon Hill Pr. of Kansas City.

Discovery - God's Perfect Plan - Answer Key: Exploring Bible Prophecy from Genesis to Revelation. 2000. (Bible Discovery Ser.). 48p. (J). (gr. 3-6). 6.99 (978-1-889015-77-4(6)) Explorer's Bible Study.

Donahoe, Sydney. Christian Virtues Made Fun & Easy!, Grades 1 - 2. 1999. (Bible Lessons to Grow By Ser.). 64p. pap. 6.99 (978-1-56822-815-0(5) , In Celebration) Schaffer, Frank Pubns.

—Christian Virtues Made Fun & Easy!, Grades 3 - 4. 1999. (Bible Lessons to Grow By Ser.). 64p. pap. 6.99 (978-1-56822-816-7(3) , In Celebration) Schaffer, Frank Pubns.

Dowley, Tim. Pop-up Bible Adventures. 2005. (Illus.). 12p. (J). (gr. k-2). 11.99 (978-0-8254-7298-5(9)) Kregel Pubns.

Early Childhood. (ps-k). 2004. 24.99 (978-0-7644-1614-9(6)); 2004. 4.29 (978-0-7644-1608-8(1)); 2004. tchr. ed. 7.99 (978-0-7644-1600-2(6)); 2004. 24.99 (978-0-7644-1613-2(8)); 2004. 4.29 (978-0-7644-1607-1(3)); 2004. tchr. ed. 7.99 (978-0-7644-1599-9(9)); 2004. 24.99 (978-0-7644-1705-4(3)); 2004. 4.29 (978-0-7644-1699-6(5)); 2004. tchr. ed. 7.99 (978-0-7644-1692-7(8)); 2004. 24.99 (978-0-7644-1704-7(5)); 2004. 4.29 (978-0-7644-1698-9(7)); 2004. tchr. ed. 7.99 (978-0-7644-1691-0(X)); 2004. 4.29 (978-0-7644-1679-8(0)); 2004. 24.99 (978-0-7644-1685-9(5)); 2004. tchr. ed. 7.99 (978-0-7644-1672-9(3)); 2004. 4.29 (978-0-7644-1678-1(2)); 2004. 24.99 (978-0-7644-1684-2(7)); 2004. tchr. ed. 7.99 (978-0-7644-1671-2(5)); 2003. 24.99 (978-0-7644-1591-3(3)); 2003. 4.29 (978-0-7644-1585-2(9)); 2003. tchr. ed. 7.99 (978-0-7644-1575-3(1)); 2003. 24.99 (978-0-7644-1590-6(5)); 2003. tchr. ed. 7.99 (978-0-7644-1574-6(3)) Group Publishing, Inc. (Flagship Church Resources).

Editorial Vida Staff. Ambassador-Student (Russian) Vol. 6, Bk. 2: Russian Sunday School. Life Publishers International Staff, tr. from SPA. 2000. Orig. Title: El Embajador. Alumno. (RUS.). 61p. (YA). stu. ed. (978-0-7361-0203-2(5)) Life Pubs. International.

Egbert, Rebecca A. Bible & Me. 1999. (Illus.). 48p. (J). (gr. k-3). 10.00 (978-0-570-05552-5(0)) Concordia Publishing Hse.

Elementary. 2004. (gr. 1-2). 19.99 (978-0-7644-1615-6(4)); 2004. (gr. 1-2). 4.29 (978-0-7644-1609-5(X)); 2004. (gr. 1-2). tchr. ed. 7.99 (978-0-7644-1601-9(4)); 2004. (gr. 3-4). 4.29 (978-0-7644-1610-1(3)); 2004. (gr. 3-4). 19.99 (978-0-7644-1616-3(2)); 2004. (gr. 3-4). tchr. ed. 7.99 (978-0-7644-1602-6(2)); 2004. (gr. 5-6). 4.29 (978-0-7644-1611-8(1)); 2004. (gr. 5-6). 19.99 (978-0-7644-1617-0(0)); 2004. (gr. 5-6). tchr. ed. 7.99 (978-0-7644-1603-3(0)); 2004. (gr. 1-2). 44.99 (978-0-7644-0387-3(7)); 2004. (gr. 1-2). 44.99 (978-0-7644-0399-6(0)); 2004. (gr. 1-2). tchr. ed. 19.99 (978-0-7644-0393-4(1)); 2004. (gr. 1-2). tchr. ed. 19.99 (978-0-7644-0379-8(6)); 2004. (gr. 3-4). 44.99 (978-0-7644-0386-6(9)); 2004. (gr. 3-4). 44.99 (978-0-7644-0398-9(2)); 2004. (gr. 3-4). tchr. ed. 19.99 (978-0-7644-0392-7(3)); 2004. (gr. 3-4). tchr. ed. 19.99 (978-0-7644-0378-1(8)); 2004. (gr. 5-6). 44.99 (978-0-7644-0383-5(4)); 2004. (gr. 5-6). 44.99 (978-0-7644-0397-2(4)); 2004. (gr. 5-6). tchr. ed. 19.99 (978-0-7644-0391-0(5)); 2004. (gr. 5-6). tchr. ed. 19.99 (978-0-7644-0377-4(X)); 2004. (gr. 1-2). 4.29 (978-0-7644-1700-9(2)); 2004. (gr. 1-2). 44.99 (978-0-7644-0373-6(7)); 2004. (gr. 1-2). 19.99 (978-0-7644-1706-1(1)); 2004. (gr. 1-2). tchr. ed. 19.99 (978-0-7644-0367-5(2)); 2004. (gr. 1-2). tchr. ed. 7.99 (978-0-7644-1693-4(6)); 2004. (gr. 3-4). 4.29 (978-0-7644-1701-6(0)); 2004. (gr. 3-4). 44.99 (978-0-7644-0372-9(9)); 2004. (gr. 3-4). 19.99 (978-0-7644-1707-8(X)); 2004. (gr. 3-4). tchr. ed. 19.99 (978-0-7644-0366-8(4)); 2004. (gr. 3-4). tchr. ed. 7.99 (978-0-7644-1694-1(4)); 2004. (gr. 5-6). 44.99 (978-0-7644-0371-2(0)); 2004. (gr. 5-6). 19.99 (978-0-7644-1708-5(8)); 2004. (gr. 5-6). 4.29 (978-0-7644-1702-3(9)); 2004. (gr. 5-6). tchr. ed. 7.99 (978-0-7644-1695-8(2)); 2004. (gr. 5-6). tchr. ed. 19.99 (978-0-7644-0365-1(6)); 2004. (gr. 1-2). 4.29 (978-0-7644-1680-4(4)); 2004. (gr. 1-2). 19.99 (978-0-7644-1686-6(3)); 2004. (gr. 1-2). tchr. ed. 7.99 (978-0-7644-1673-6(1)); 2004. (gr. 3-4). 19.99 (978-0-7644-1687-3(1)); 2004. (gr. 3-4). 4.29 (978-0-7644-1681-1(2)); 2004. (gr. 3-4). tchr. ed. 7.99 (978-0-7644-1674-3(X)); 2004. (gr. 5-6). 4.29 (978-0-7644-1682-8(0)); 2004. (gr. 5-6). 19.99 (978-0-7644-1688-0(X)); 2004. (gr. 5-6). tchr. ed. 7.99 (978-0-7644-1675-0(8)); 2003. (gr. 1-2). 44.99 (978-0-7644-0361-3(3)); 2003. (gr. 1-2). 4.29 (978-0-7644-1586-9(7)); 2003. (gr. 1-2). 19.99 (978-0-7644-1592-0(1)); 2003. (gr. 1-2). tchr. ed. 7.99 (978-0-7644-1576-0(X)); 2003. (gr. 1-2). tchr. ed. 19.99 (978-0-7644-0355-2(9)); 2003. (gr. 3-4). 44.99 (978-0-7644-0360-6(5)); 2003. (gr. 3-4). 4.29 (978-0-7644-1587-6(5)); 2003. (gr. 3-4). 19.99 (978-0-7644-1593-7(X)); 2003. (gr. 3-4). tchr. ed. 19.99 (978-0-7644-0354-5(0)); 2003. (gr. 3-4). tchr. ed. 7.99 (978-0-7644-1577-7(8)); 2003. (gr. 5-6). 19.99 (978-0-7644-1594-4(8)); 2003. (gr. 5-6). 4.29 (978-0-7644-1588-3(3)); 2003. (gr. 5-6). 44.99 (978-0-7644-0359-0(1)); 2003. (gr. 5-6). tchr. ed. 7.99 (978-0-7644-1578-4(6)); 2003. (gr. 5-6). tchr. ed. 19.99 (978-0-7644-0353-8(2)) Group Publishing, Inc. (Flagship Church Resources).

Elementary Leaders Kit: Spring 2001. ldr.'s ed. 2001. (FW Friends Ser.). (J). (ps-6). 129.99 (978-0-7644-1172-4(1)) Group Publishing, Inc.

Elementary Leaders Kit: Summer 2001. ldr.'s ed. 2001. (FW Friends Ser.). (J). (ps-6). 129.99 (978-0-7644-1253-0(1)) Group Publishing, Inc.

Elkins, Stephen. Baby's First Book of Psalms. Colton, Ellie, illus. 2002. (Lulla-Bible Ser.). 14p. (J). (ps). 6.99 (978-0-8054-2582-6(9)) B&H Publishing Grp.

Elliott, Sharon Norris. What? Teenagers in the Bible? The Bible's Teens Speak to Teens Today. 2003. 132p. pap. 12.99 (978-1-57921-654-2(4)) Pleasant Word.

Encuentra a Jesucristo Hoy. 2002. (SPA.). 248p. (J). 18.99 (978-1-58516-470-7(4) , 106860) American Bible Society.

Ethridge, Shannon & Arterburn, Stephen. Every Young Woman's Battle: Guarding Your Mind, Heart, & Body in a Sex-Saturated World. 2004. (Illus.). 240p. pap. 13.99 (978-1-57856-856-7(0) , WaterBrook Pr.) WaterBrook Pr.

Los Evangelios (The Gospel) Quarter 2, Level 4. 2000. (Caminando con Jesus (Walking with Jesus) Series A). (SPA.). (J). (gr. 5-6). stu. ed. 3.50 (978-0-570-05162-6(2) , 16-4812) Concordia Publishing Hse.

Explore Bible People: 52 Bible Lessons. 2006. 320p. (J). 29.99 (978-0-7847-1323-5(5) , 42072) Standard Publishing.

Exploring God's Word: Grade 4 - Student Materials. (Voyages Ser.). (Illus.). 10.95 (978-0-570-00274-1(5) , 57-0411) Concordia Publishing Hse.

Exploring God's Word: Grade 5 - Student Materials. (Voyages Ser.). (Illus.). 12.95 (978-0-570-00279-6(6) , 57-0511) Concordia Publishing Hse.

Exploring God's Word: Grade 6 - Student Materials. (Voyages Ser.). (Illus.). 12.95 (978-0-570-00286-4(9) , 57-0611) Concordia Publishing Hse.

Exploring God's Word: Grade 7 - Old Testament Student Materials. (Voyages Ser.). (Illus.). 10.95 (978-0-570-00292-5(3) , 57-0711) Concordia Publishing Hse.

FaithWeaver Children's Curriculum: Grades 1 & 2 Summer 2000 Student Book My Bible Fun. 2000. (FaithWeaver Bible Curriculum Ser.). (J). (gr. 1-2). pap., stu. ed. 3.99 (978-0-7644-0988-2(3)) Group Publishing, Inc.

FaithWeaver Children's Curriculum: Grades 5 & 6 Spring 2000 Student Book Bible Buzz. 2000. (FaithWeaver Bible Curriculum Ser.). (J). (gr. 5-6). pap., stu. ed. 3.99 (978-0-7644-0963-9(8)) Group Publishing, Inc.

Farah, Gregg. Risk It! Daring to Act on the Truth of God (A Creative Study of the Book of Esther) Reeves, Dale, ed. Angle, Scott, illus. 1999. 64p. (YA). pap., wbk. ed. 8.99 (978-0-7847-0951-1(3) , 23317) Standard Publishing.

Fill-in-the-Blank Bible Fun 1-3. 2004. 32p. (J). pap. 3.99 (978-0-88724-221-2(9) , CD-2042) Carson-Dellosa Publishing Co., Inc.

First Reconciliation Certificate (Spanish) 2004. (Together in Jesus Ser.). (Illus.). 1p. (J). pap. 9.95 (978-0-89837-244-1(5) , 952110) Pflaum Publishing Group.

Fischer, Carl. First Reconciliation Certificate. 2004. (Together in Jesus Ser.). (Illus.). (J). pap. 9.95 (978-0-937997-75-8(7) , 912110) Pflaum Publishing Group.

Flegal, Daphna. Sing & Say: Bibles Verses for Children. 2004. 48p. (ps-2). 13.00 (978-0-687-05373-5(0)) Abingdon Pr.

Flegal, Daphna & Augustine, Peg. Jesus Says. Easter, Paige, illus. 2002. 16p. (J). (ps-k). 8.00 (978-0-687-09374-8(0)) Abingdon Pr.

Follow the Bible: 52 Bible Lessons for Beginning Readers. 2006. 320p. (J). 29.99 (978-0-7847-1324-2(3) , 42073) Standard Publishing.

Frantz, Rosemary. Bible Men & Women from A to Z: Rhymes, Questions & Activities. 2004. (Illus.). 80p. pap. 8.00 (978-0-687-08344-2(3)) Abingdon Pr.

Freed, Shirley Ann & Moon, Louise. Daniel Prayed. Morelan, Bill, ed. Butler, Steven, illus. l.t. ed. 2002. 8p. (J). (gr. 6). pap. 3.99 (978-1-58938-012-7(6)) Concerned Communications.

—The Jailer's Surprise. Morelan, Bill, ed. Butler, Steven, illus. l.t. ed. 2002. 24p. (J). (gr. 2). pap. 3.99 (978-1-58938-047-9(9)) Concerned Communications.

—Rahab's Red Rope. Morelan, Bill, ed. Butler, Steven, illus. l.t. ed. 2002. 16p. (J). (gr. 2). pap. 3.99 (978-1-58938-045-5(2)) Concerned Communications.

—Who Will Be in Heaven? Morelan, Bill, ed. Butler, Steven, illus. l.t. ed. 2002. 8p. (J). (gr. 5). pap. 3.99 (978-1-58938-009-7(6)) Concerned Communications.

Freedman, Claire. The Bible Book of How, Which, What & Why. 2001. (Illus.). 14p. (J). (gr. 1-3). 8.99 (978-0-570-07162-4(3)) Concordia Publishing Hse.

Frost, Marie. Jesus Feeds the 5000. 2003. (Pencil Fun Bks.: Vol. 50). 16p. (J). (gr. 7-4). pap., pap. 9.90 (978-1-55513-158-6(1) , 1555131581) Cook, David C. Publishing Co.

Galindo, Israel. The Bible, Live! Experience-Centered Activities for Children. 1999. 208p. (gr. 1-7). 7.00 (978-0-8170-1315-8(6)) Judson Pr.

God at Work: God Delivers, God Provides, God Commands, God Wins. ldr.'s ed. (Faithweaver Youth Bible Studies). (YA). (gr. 8-12). 19.99 (978-0-7644-1004-8(0)) Group Publishing, Inc.

God Comes to Us: Bible Learning Tool. 2004. (ps-1). 1.99 (978-0-8066-6432-3(0)) Augsburg Fortress, Pubs.

God Feeds Us: Bible Learning Tool. 2004. (gr. 2-3). 1.99 (978-0-8066-6414-9(2)); (gr. 3-4). 1.99 (978-0-8066-6415-6(0)) Augsburg Fortress, Pubs.

Goeser, Christi & Powell, Kara Eckmann, eds. Reaching Your World: Reproducible Manual. 2001. (Pulse Ser.: Vol. 14). (Illus.). 96p. (gr. 6-9). 14.99 (978-0-8307-2550-2(4) , Gospel Light) Gospel Light Pubns.

Gospel Light Staff. Planet 56 Power Source: Take-Home Papers. 2001. (Planet 56 Ser.). (J). (gr. 5-7). pap. 3.00 (978-0-8307-2307-2(2)) Gospel Light Pubns.

—Surprises! Take-Home Papers. 2001. (Movers & Shakers Ser.). (J). (ps). pap. (978-0-8307-2291-4(2)) Gospel Light Pubns.

—Walk with Jesus. 2001. (Network 34 Ser.). (J). (gr. 3-5). pap. (978-0-8307-2109-2(6)) Gospel Light Pubns.

—Walk with Jesus: Home Pages. 2001. (Network 34 Ser.). (J). (gr. 3-5). pap. (978-0-8307-2111-5(8)) Gospel Light Pubns.

Got Jesus? Get Ready, Get Born, Get Called, Get Surprised. 1999. (Faithweaver Youth Bible Studies). (YA). (gr. 8-12). 19.99 (978-0-7644-0938-7(7)) Group Publishing, Inc.

Grades 3-4 Activity Fall 2002. 2002. pap. 3.29 (978-1-59185-025-0(8)) CharismaLife Pubs.

Grades 3-4 Activity Winter 2002-03. 2002. pap. 3.29 (978-1-59185-112-7(2)) CharismaLife Pubs.

Grades 3-4 Resource Fall 2002. 2002. pap. 12.99 (978-1-59185-026-7(6)) CharismaLife Pubs.

Grades 3-4 Resource Winter 2002-03. 2002. pap. 12.99 (978-1-59185-113-4(0)) CharismaLife Pubs.

Grassimid, Donna M. Bread of Life for Kids. 1998. (J). (gr. k-7). (978-1-57838-124-1(X)) CrossLife Expressions.

Grinovald, Ze'ev. Stories My Grandfather Told Me: Memorable Tales Arranged According to the Weekly Sidrah. Katz, Tova, illus. 2001. (ArtScroll Youth Ser.). (J). 202p. 16.99 (978-1-57819-531-2(4) , SG4H); 202p. 16.99 (978-1-57819-529-9(2) , SG3H); 215p. 16.99 (978-1-57819-527-5(6) , SG2H) Mesorah Pubns., Ltd.

Group Publishing Staff. FaithWeaver Children's Messages 2, Vol. 2. 2004. (Illus.). 99p. 15.99 (978-0-7644-2222-5(7) , Flagship Church Resources) Group Publishing, Inc.

Group Publishing Staff, contrib. by. Pure Power: Youth Bible Studies. 2000. (Faithweaver Youth Bible Studies). (Illus.). 128p. (YA). (gr. 8-12). pap. 19.99 (978-0-7644-0957-8(3)) Group Publishing, Inc.

Grow Through the Bible: 52 Bible Lessons from Genesis to Revelation. 2006. 320p. (YA). 29.99 (978-0-7847-1325-9(1) , 42074) Standard Publishing.

Gurvis, Laura K. Learn & Do Bible Book. Ben-Moshe, Jana, illus. 64p. (J). (gr. k-2). pap. 4.95 (978-0-87441-530-8(6)) Behrman Hse., Inc.

Hall, Simon & Banks, Duncan. Breakfast with God, Vol. 1. 2000. (Illus.). 128p. (J). pap., pupil's gde. ed. 9.99 (978-0-551-03250-7(2) , Collins) HarperCollins Pubs. Ltd. GBR. *Dist:* Trafalgar Square Publishing.

Hamrick, Frank. The Christian Adventure. 2001. (J). stu. ed., per. 11.95 (978-1-929784-75-2(9)) Positive Action For Christ.

Hands-On Bible Curriculum Learning Lab, Spring 2001: Toddlers & 2s. 2001. (Hands-On Bible Curriculum Ser.). (J). pap. 54.99 incl. audio compact disk (978-0-7644-0238-8(2)) Group Publishing, Inc.

Harder Tangvald, Christine. God Loves Me. Stewart, Jennifer, ed. Garris, Norma, illus. 1999. (Patty Cake Devotions Ser.). 14p. (J). (ps). bds. 3.99 (978-0-7847-0987-0(4) , 04295, Bean Sprouts) Standard Publishing.

Harpine, Elaine Clanton. Come, Follow Me! Vol. 1: Sessions 1-26, 2 vols. 2004. (Illus.). 256p. spiral bd. 35.00 (978-0-687-09207-9(8)) Abingdon Pr.

—Come, Follow Me! Vol. 2: Sessions 27-59, Vol. 2. 2004. (Illus.). 256p. (ps-7). spiral bd. 35.00 (978-0-687-09212-3(4)) Abingdon Pr.

Henley, Karyn. Studying the Bible: The Foundation for Knowing God. Eichenberger, Jim, ed. Koehler, Ed, illus. 2000. (Foundations Curriculum). 96p. (YA). (gr. 3-6). 12.99 (978-0-7847-1214-6(X) , 42063) Standard Publishing.

Hewitt Staff, contrib. by. Devotional Bible Study: Syllabus. 1998. 20p. (YA). (gr. 10-12). pap. 3.50 (978-1-57896-030-9(4) , 2531, Hewitt Homeschooling Resources) Hewitt Research Foundation, Inc.

—Masterworks Bible Study Syllabus. 1998. 20p. (YA). pap. 3.50 (978-1-57896-031-6(2) , 2532) Hewitt Research Foundation, Inc.

Hindson, Edward E. & Dobson, Edward G., eds. The Knowing Jesus Study Bible: A One-Year Study of Jesus in Every Book of the Bible: New International Version. 1999. (Illus.). 1856p. (J). 34.99 (978-0-310-92125-7(2)) Zondervan.

Holmes, Andy. Bible for Me, Quiet Time. 2004. (Illus.). 48p. (J). 9.99 (978-1-4003-0515-5(2)) Nelson, Thomas Inc.

Hood, Karen Jean Matsko. Replace. Scripture-Smith, Mary, illus. 2005. 160p. (J). pap. 19.95 (978-0-9679368-7-1(X)) Whispering Pine Pr., Inc.

Horman, John D., et al. Something Old, Something New Vol. 2: Hymns to Explore, Things to Do. Keithahn, Mary Nelson, ed. 2004. 96p. (gr. 2-5). pap. 17.00 (978-0-687-09101-0(2)) Abingdon Pr.

Horton, T. C. & Hurlburt, C. E. Los Nombres de Cristo. 2nd ed. 1999. (SPA.). 176p. pap. 6.99 (978-0-8254-1333-9(8) , Editorial Portavoz) Kregel Pubns.

Hudson Sue & Kennedy Graham. 40 Days with Esther. 2006. 80p. pap. 7.99 (978-1-86024-550-3(1)) Authentic Media.

Hummel, Rand & Diedrich, Jeff. In Their Sandals. 2000. (J). stu. ed., per. 5.50 (978-1-929784-58-5(9)) Positive Action For Christ.

I Wonder What Jesus Would Do: Fun to Color & Do. 2001. (978-0-7424-0020-7(4) , Instructional Fair) Schaffer, Frank Pubns.

International Inductive Study Bible. 2006. (YA). pap. (978-1-888655-67-4(4)) Precept Ministries.

The International Student Bible for Catholics. 1999. 1664p. (YA). (gr. 8-12). pap. 16.99 (978-0-7852-0977-5(8)) Nelson, Thomas Inc.

Jesus Live! Coming Soon, A Star Is Born, The Main Event, The Road Show. ldr.'s ed. (Faithweaver Youth Bible Studies). (YA). (gr. 8-12). 19.99 (978-0-7644-1026-0(1)) Group Publishing, Inc.

Johns, Helen. Say What? The Power of the Tongue. 1999. (Fast Lane Bible Studies Ser.). 45p. (YA). (gr. 7-9). pap. 9.95 (978-0-87303-337-4(X)) Faith & Life Pr.

Johnson, Kevin W. Stick Tight: Glue Yourself to Godly Friends. 2001. (Early Teen Discipleship Ser.). 128p. (J). pap. 7.99 (978-0-7642-2434-8(4)) Bethany Hse. Pubs.

Jones, Dennis. Read with Me Bible. deluxe ed. 2000. (Illus.). 444p. (J). 19.99 (978-0-310-92009-0(4)) Zondervan.

Keels, Steve, ed. TruthQuest Inductive Student Bible. 2004. (TruthQuest Family Ser.). (Illus.). 1506p. lthr. 44.99 (978-1-55819-849-4(0)) B&H Publishing Grp.

Kennedy, Andy & Kennedy, Catherine. Big Cell 1: Children in the Bible. 2005. 48p. pap. 12.99 (978-1-85078-513-2(9)) Authentic Media.

—Big Cell 2: History Makers - Your Mission from God. 2005. 48p. pap. 12.99 (978-1-85078-514-9(7)) Authentic Media.

KidsTime: Big Book of Bible Skits. (Big Book Ser.). 176p. (gr. 1-6). 19.99 (978-0-8307-2346-1(3) , Gospel Light) Gospel Light Pubns.

King, Wanda. Fundamentals: Secret Mission 002 Child's Pack. 2001. (J). (gr. 1-6). 5.95 (978-0-633-00374-6(3)) LifeWay Christian Resources.

KJV Drill Bible. 2004. (Illus.). 1084p. 12.99 (978-0-87981-600-1(7)) B&H Publishing Grp.

Klotz, Emily, ed. Little Ones to Him Belong: Celebrating Your Precious Gift from God. Clark, Karen, illus. gif. ed. 2001. 96p. (J). 9.99 (978-0-310-97974-6(9)) Zondervan.

Kohlenberger, John, et al. Truth Quest Inductive Student Bible. 2004. (TruthQuest Family Ser.). (Illus.). 1506p. lthr. 44.99 (978-1-55819-843-2(1)) B&H Publishing Grp.

Kollin, Bob. Revelation Unlocked: Keys to Understanding End-time Events. 2003. (ENG.). per. 15.99 (978-0-9728899-1-9(4)) 21st Century Pr.

Krahenbuhl, Lee. Bad News, Good News: The Prophets Speak Truth to Power. 1998. (Generation Why Ser.: Vol. 4, Pt. 4). 28p. (YA). (gr. 9-12). pap. 12.95 (978-0-87303-283-4(7)) Faith & Life Pr.

Kuhn, Pamela J. Instant Bible Lessons for Preschoolers: God's Servants Teach Me. 1998. (Illus.). 96p. (J). 11.95 (978-1-885358-56-1(3) , RB36852) Rainbow Pubs. & Legacy Pr.

—Instant Bible Lessons for Preschoolers: I Am God's Child. 1998. (Illus.). 96p. (J). pap. 11.95 (978-1-885358-58-5(X) , RB36854) Rainbow Pubs. & Legacy Pr.

—Instant Bible Lessons for Preschoolers: I Belong to Jesus. 1998. (Illus.). 96p. (J). pap. 11.95 (978-1-885358-55-4(5) , RB36851) Rainbow Pubs. & Legacy Pr.

—Instant Bible Lessons for Preschoolers: I Learn Respect. 1998. (Illus.). 96p. (J). pap. 11.95 (978-1-885358-57-8(1) , RB36853) Rainbow Pubs. & Legacy Pr.

Lane, Leena. The Kids Bible. Chapman, Gillian, illus. 2003. (ENG.). 64p. (J). 9.99 (978-0-7586-0561-0(7)) Concordia Publishing Hse.

Lane, Leena & Boshof, Penny. My Little Yellow Book: First Steps in Bible Reading. 2004. 64p. 4.99 (978-1-85999-693-5(0)) Scripture Union GBR. *Dist:* Gabriel Resources.

Larchar, Martha. Bible Discovery Devotions. 2000. (Illus.). 128p. (J). (ps-3). 10.99 (978-0-570-05225-8(4)) Concordia Publishing Hse.

Larsen, Carolyn. Little Boys Bible Library. 2002. (Illus.). 80p. (J). (ps-3). 9.99 (978-0-8010-4498-4(7) , New Kids Media) Baker Bks.

—Little Girls Bible Library. 2002. (Illus.). 80p. (J). (ps-3). 9.99 (978-0-8010-4499-1(5) , New Kids Media) Baker Bks.

—Little Girls Bible Storybook for Mothers & Daughters. Turk, Caron, illus. 1998. 360p. (gr. 1-4). 16.99 (978-0-8010-4407-6(3) , New Kids Media) Baker Bks.

Last Trump Gathering Bible Studies, Vol. 1. 2004. (YA). per. 10.95 (978-0-9760159-0-1(0)) Rogers, Al M. Jr.

Lea, Thomas. A Student's Guide to Studying the Bible. 2000. (J). (gr. 7-12). 7.95 (978-0-633-00454-5(5)) LifeWay Christian Resources.

Leader Guide: Summer 2001. ldr.'s ed. 2001. (KidsOwn Worship Ser.). (J). (ps-6). pap. 29.99 (978-0-7644-1094-9(6)) Group Publishing, Inc.

The Learning Bible. 2001. (J). (978-0-8066-3993-2(8)) Augsburg Fortress, Pubs.

Learning Lab: Fall 2001. (Hands-On Bible Curriculum Ser.). (J). (ps). 54.99 incl. audio compact disk (978-0-7644-0260-9(9)) Group Publishing, Inc.

Learning Lab: Spring 2001. (Hands-On Bible Curriculum Ser.). (J). (ps). 54.99 incl. audio compact disk (978-0-7644-0236-4(6)); 2001. (gr. 1-2). 44.99 incl. audio compact disk (978-0-7644-0235-7(8)); 2001. (gr. 3-4). 44.99 incl. audio compact disk (978-0-7644-0234-0(X)); 2001. (gr. 5-6). 44.99 incl. audio compact disk (978-0-7644-0233-3(1)); 2001. (ps-k). 54.99 incl. audio compact disk (978-0-7644-0237-1(4)) Group Publishing, Inc.

Learning Lab: Summer 2001. (Hands-On Bible Curriculum Ser.). (J). (ps). 54.99 incl. audio compact disk (978-0-7644-0248-7(X)); 2001. (gr. k-1). 54.99 incl. audio compact disk (978-0-7644-0249-4(8)); 2001. (gr. 1-2). 44.99 incl. audio compact disk (978-0-7644-0247-0(1)); 2001. (gr. 3-4). 44.99 incl. audio compact disk (978-0-7644-0246-3(3)); 2001. (gr. 5-6). 44.99 incl. audio compact disk (978-0-7644-0245-6(5)); 2001. (ps). 54.99 incl. audio compact disk (978-0-7644-0250-0(1)) Group Publishing, Inc.

Lee, Witness. Los Aspectos Cruciales de las Prioridades en el Recobro del Senor Hoy. 2001. Tr. of Crucial Points of the Major Items of the Lord's Recovery Today. (SPA.). 22p. (J). (gr. 6). 3.00 (978-0-7363-1276-9(5) , 04-021-002) Living Stream Ministry.

—Cinco Priordades en el Recobro del Senor. 2001. Tr. of Five Emphases in the Lord's Recovery. (SPA.). 72p. (J). (gr. 6). per. 5.75 (978-0-7363-1240-0(4) , 08-021-002) Living Stream Ministry.

Estudio-Vida de Lucas, 3 vols., Set. 2001. Tr. of Life-Study of Luke. (SPA.). 672p. (J). (gr. 6). per. 29.00 (978-0-7363-1203-5(X) , 10-265-002) Living Stream Ministry.

—Estudio-Vida de Lucas Vol. 1: Mensajes 1-25. 2001. Tr. of Life-Study of Luke: Messages 1-25. (SPA.). 218p. (J). (gr. 6). per. 11.25 (978-0-7363-0086-5(4) , 10-185-002) Living Stream Ministry.

—Estudio-Vida de Lucas Vol. 2: Mensajes 26-50. 2001. Tr. of Life-Study of Luke: Messages 26-50. (SPA.). 216p. (J). (gr. 6). per. 11.25 (978-0-7363-0724-6(9) , 10-186-002) Living Stream Ministry.

—Estudio-Vida de Lucas Vol. 3: Mensajes 51-79. 2001. Tr. of Life-Study of Luke: Messages 51-79. (SPA.). 238p. (J). (gr. 6). per. 12.00 (978-0-7363-0725-3(7) , 10-187-002) Living Stream Ministry.

—The Holy Word for Morning Revival: Crystallization-Study of Ephesians. Vol. 1. 2002. 109p. (J). (gr. 6). per. 7.00 (978-0-7363-1549-4(7) , 13-146-001) Living Stream Ministry.

—The Holy Word for Morning Revival: Matthew 21:23-28:20, Vol. 4. 2001. 83p. (J). (gr. 6). 6.00 (978-0-7363-1111-3(4) , 13-136-001) Living Stream Ministry.

—Life-Study of Luke Vol. 1: Messages 1-25. 2001. 220p. (J). (gr. 6). per. 11.25 (978-0-7363-1199-1(8) , 10-185-001) Living Stream Ministry.

—Life-Study of Luke Vol. 2: Messages 26-50. 2001. 218p. (J). (gr. 6). per. 11.25 (978-0-7363-1200-4(5) , 10-186-001) Living Stream Ministry.

—Life-Study of Luke Vol. 3: Messages 51-79. 2001. 234p. (J). (gr. 6). per. 12.00 (978-0-7363-1201-1(3) , 10-187-001) Living Stream Ministry.

—Life-Study of Pentateuch: (Genesis-Deuteronomy), 22 vols., Set. 2000. (J). (gr. 6). per. 184.50 (978-0-7363-1423-7(7) , 10-081-001) Living Stream Ministry.

—Life-Study of Philippians, 3 vols., Set. 2000. 547p. (J). per. 25.75 (978-0-7363-0912-7(8) , 10-275-001) Living Stream Ministry.

—Life-Study of Philippians Vol. 3: Messages 43-62. 2000. 172p. (J). (gr. 6). per. 10.25 (978-0-7363-0911-0(X) , 10-193-001) Living Stream Ministry.

—La Palabra Santa para el Avivamiento Matutino: Estudio de Cristalizacion de Efesions, Vol. 1. 2002. Tr. of Holy Word for Morning Revival: Crystallization-Study of Ephesians. 109p. (J). (gr. 6). per. 7.00 (978-0-7363-1551-7(9) , 13-146-002) Living Stream Ministry.

Lepley, Lynne. Scrumptious Scriptures. 96p. (J). 2004. (gr. 1-5). pap. 11.95 (978-1-885358-47-9(4) , RB36822); 1998. (Illus.). (ps-k). pap. 11.95 (978-1-885358-46-2(6) , RB36821) Rainbow Pubs. & Legacy Pr.

Leuthauser, Karl, ed. Student-Led Discussions: How Can I Know God Exists? 1998. (Illus.). 96p. (YA). (gr. 8-12). pap., ldr.'s assessmt. gde. ed. 16.99 (978-0-7644-2071-9(2) , Flagship Church Resources) Group Publishing, Inc.

Lewis, Carole. Begin Again. 2004. (First Place Bible Studies). 240p. pap. 19.99 (978-0-8307-3233-3(0) , Gospel Light) Gospel Light Pubns.

—Everyday Victory for Everyday People. 2004. (First Place Bible Studies). 232p. pap. 19.99 (978-0-8307-2865-7(1) , Gospel Light) Gospel Light Pubns.

—Pressing on to the Prize. 2004. (First Place Bible Studies). 224p. pap. 19.99 (978-0-8307-2926-5(7) , Gospel Light) Gospel Light Pubns.

Lewolt, Bruce. Bible by Heart: The Ultimate Bible Study & Memorization System. 2004. (Illus.). 39p. cd-rom 69.95 (978-0-9741604-6-7(6)) BrainX, Inc.

Lietha, Dan. Beginnings: Helping Kids Build a Firm Foundation to Their Faith. 2005. pap. (978-1-893345-53-9(X)) Answers in Genesis Ministries.

Life Publishers International Staff. El Companero Alumno Vol. 10, Tome 3: March 2001-May 2001. 2001. (Vida Nueva Ser.). (SPA., Illus.). 48p. (J). (gr. 4-6). pap., stu. ed. (978-0-7361-0183-7(7)) Life Pubs. International.

—El Companero Ayudas Visuales Vol. Com-2: March 2001-August 2001. 2001. (Vida Nueva Ser.). (SPA., Illus.). 26p. (J). (gr. 4-6). pap. (978-0-7361-0182-0(9)) Life Pubs. International.

—El Embajador Alumno Vol. 10, No. 3: March 2001-May 2001. 2001. (Vida Nueva Ser.). (SPA., Illus.). 48p. (YA). (gr. 10 up). pap., stu. ed. (978-0-7361-0189-9(6)) Life Pubs. International.

—El Embajador Alumno Vol. 10, No. 4: June 2001-August 2001. 2001. (Vida Nueva Ser.). (SPA., Illus.). 48p. (YA). (gr. 10-12). pap., stu. ed. (978-0-7361-0190-5(X)) Life Pubs. International.

—El Explorado Alumno Vol. 10, Tomo 4: Jun. 2001-Aug. 2001. 2001. (Vida Nueva Ser.). (SPA., Illus.). 48p. (YA). (gr. 7-9). pap., stu. ed. (978-0-7361-0187-5(X)) Life Pubs. International.

—El Explorador Alumno Vol. 10, No. 3: Mar. 2001-May 2001. 2001. (Vida Nueva Ser.). (SPA., Illus.). 48p. (YA). (gr. 7-9). pap., stu. ed. (978-0-7361-0186-8(1)) Life Pubs. International.

—El Explorador Maestro Vol. 10, Tomos 3y4: Mar 2001-Aug. 2001. 2001. (Vida Nueva Ser.). (SPA., Illus.). 112p. (YA). (gr. 7-9). pap. (978-0-7361-0185-1(3)) Life Pubs. International.

—Mis Amigos Alumno Vol. 10, No. 3: Mar. 2001-May 2001. Life Publishers International Staff, tr. 2001. (Vida Nueva Ser.). (SPA., Illus.). 32p. (J). (gr. 1-3). pap., stu. ed. (978-0-7361-0179-0(9)) Life Pubs. International.

—Mis Amigos Alumno Vol. 10, No. 4: Jun. 2001-Aug. 2001. Life Publishers International Staff, tr. 2001. (Vida Nueva Ser.). (SPA., Illus.). 26p. (J). (gr. 1-3). pap., stu. ed. (978-0-7361-0180-6(2)) Life Pubs. International.

—Mis Amigos Ayudas Visuales Vol. AMI-04: Mar. 2001-Aug. 2001. Life Publishers International Staff, tr. 2001. (Vida Nueva Ser.). (SPA., Illus.). 26p. (J). (gr. 1-3). pap. (978-0-7361-0178-3(0)) Life Pubs. International.

—Primeros Pasos Manual: June 2001-August 2001. Life Publishers International Staff, tr. 2001. (Vida Nueva Ser.). (SPA., Illus.). 16p. (J). (ps). pap., stu. ed. (978-0-7361-0172-1(1)) Life Pubs. International.

—Primeros Pasos Trabajo Manual: March 2001-May 2001. Life Publishers International Staff, tr. 2001. (Vida Nueva Ser.). (SPA., Illus.). 16p. (J). (ps). pap., stu. ed. (978-0-7361-0171-4(3)) Life Pubs. International.

—Tesoros del Rey Ayudas Visuales Vol. TES-02: March 2001-August 2001. Life Publishers International Staff, tr. 2001. (Vida Nueva Ser.). (SPA., Illus.). 28p. (J). (ps-k). pap. (978-0-7361-0174-5(8)) Life Pubs. International.

—Tesoros del Rey Trabajo Manual Vol. 10: Mar. 2001-May 2001. Life Publishers International Staff, tr. 2001. (Vida Nueva Ser.). (SPA., Illus.). 16p. (J). pap., stu. ed. (978-0-7361-0175-2(6)) Life Pubs. International.

—Tesoros del Rey Trabajo Manual 2 Vol. 10: Jun. 2001-Aug. 2001. Life Publishers International Staff, tr. 2001. (Vida Nueva Ser.). (SPA., Illus.). 16p. (J). (ps-k). pap., stu. ed. (978-0-7361-0176-9(4)) Life Pubs. International.

Life Publishers International Staff, prod. El Companero Alumno Vol. 10, Tome 4: June 2001-August 2001. 2001. (Vida Nueva Ser.). (SPA., Illus.). 48p. (J). (gr. 4-6). pap., stu. ed. (978-0-7361-0184-4(5)) Life Pubs. International.

Lingo, Susan L. Collect-N-Do Object Talks for Kids: 34 Awesome Object Talks with Powerful Points All from a Few Simple Supplies! Barr, Marilynn G. & Becker, Paula, illus. 2006. 112p. (YA). 15.99 (978-0-7847-1417-1(7) , 02455) Standard Publishing.

Lloyd, Janet E. Joy & Wonder in All God's Works: Year B. Date not set. 132p. (Orig.). (J). pap. 14.95 (978-0-9646362-6-2(3)) Via Media, Pr.

A B

Lundy, Charlotte. Gracias Noe. Waldrep, Evelyn L., ed. Henry, Margie, tr. from ENG. Claremont, Heather, illus. 2002. Tr. of Thank You, Noah. (SPA.). 32p. (gr. k-3). pap. 9.95 (978-0-9670280-5-7(1)) Bay Light Publishing.

Lutz, Norma Jean. Mandy the Outsider: Prelude to the Second World War. 2004. 144p. (J). pap. 4.97 (978-1-59310-353-8(0)) Barbour Publishing, Inc.

MacArthur, John. The Gospel According to the Apostles. Butcher, Sam, illus. 2005. 272p. pap. 14.99 (978-0-7852-7180-2(5)) Nelson, Thomas Inc.

Los Mandamientos (The Commandments) Quarter 1, Level 4. 2000. (Caminando con Jesus (Walking with Jesus) Series B). (SPA.). (J). (gr. 5-6). stu. ed. 3.50 (978-0-570-05164-0(9) , 16-4911) Concordia Publishing Hse.

Marguerite, Mary. Their Hearts Are His Garden. (Illus.). 100p. (J). 2001. (gr. 1-4). 20.00 (978-1-930873-27-8(1)); 2002. reprint ed. 15.00 (978-1-930873-52-0(2)) Neumann Pr., The.

Marshall, Mark. God Knows What It's Like to Be a Teenager: Teen Life & the Psalms. 2002. (gr. 7-12). lib. bdg. 24.55 (978-0-613-77808-4(1)) Tandem Library Bks.

Mas Que Vencedores. 2002. (Sabio y Prudente Ser.: No. 5). Tr. of More Than Conquerors #5. (SPA., Illus.). 95p. (YA). (gr. 8-12). pap. 7.99 (978-0-8254-0893-9(8) , Editorial Portavoz) Kregel Pubns.

McCallum, Jodi. Fun with Bible Friends. 1999. (Illus.). 48p. (J). (ps-2). 2.99 (978-0-7847-0760-9(X) , Bean Sprouts) Standard Publishing.

McIntruff, Stephen. Look What God Made! 1999. (Illus.). 48p. (J). (ps-2). pap. 2.49 (978-0-7847-0887-3(8) , 22059, Bean Sprouts) Standard Publishing.

McKinney, Karl & McKinney, Kellie. Relatively Loving: Family Dynamics in the Bible. 1999. (Generation Why Ser.: Vol. 4.8). 42p. (YA). (gr. 9-12). pap. 14.95 (978-0-87303-288-9(8)) Faith & Life Pr.

Meaker, Dennis. Jesus, the Christ. 2003. (Bible Studies for Senior High). 96p. pap. 7.00 (978-0-687-06538-7(0)) Abingdon Pr.

—Radical Jesus. 2003. (Bible Studies for Senior High). 96p. pap. 7.00 (978-0-687-06528-8(3)) Abingdon Pr.

Miller, Kathy Collard. The un-Devotional for Teens. 164p. pap. 10.99 (978-0-8307-3510-5(0) , Gospel Light) Gospel Light Pubns.

Minnis, Angela G. Wisdom: From the Book of Proverbs, 2 vols. 2002. xi, 130p. (J). (gr. k-5). ring bd. 49.99 (978-0-9717174-9-7(4)) Wisdom Co., The.

Misal 2005 Para Ninos: Tengo una Cita. 2005. (SPA.). 272p. pap. 6.50 (978-0-8146-4137-8(7)) Liturgical Pr.

My Bible. 2004. (Exploring Luther's Small Catechism Ser.). (gr. 3-4). 2.99 (978-0-8066-6752-2(4)) Augsburg Fortress, Pubs.

My Bible. 2006. 16p. (J). pap. 1.99 (978-0-7847-1454-6(1) , 22133) Standard Publishing.

My Bible Fun: Fall 2001. 2001. (Faith Weaver Ser.). (J). (gr. 1-2). pap., stu. ed. 3.99 (978-0-7644-1187-8(X)) Group Publishing, Inc.

My Bible Fun: Spring 2001. 2001. (Faith Weaver Ser.). (J). (gr. 1-2). pap., stu. ed. 3.99 (978-0-7644-1064-2(4)) Group Publishing, Inc.

My Bible Fun: Summer 2001. 2001. (Faith Weaver Ser.). (J). (gr. 1-2). pap., stu. ed. 3.99 (978-0-7644-1084-0(9)) Group Publishing, Inc.

My Bible Hugs: Spring 2001. 2001. (Faith Weaver Ser.). (J). (ps). pap., stu. ed. 3.99 (978-0-7644-1124-3(1)) Group Publishing, Inc.

My Bible Hugs: Summer 2001. 2001. (Faith Weaver Ser.). (J). (ps). stu. ed. 3.99 (978-0-7644-1127-4(6)) Group Publishing, Inc.

My Bible Playground - Pre-K & K: Summer 2001. 2001. (Faith Weaver Ser.). (J). (gr. k-1). pap., stu. ed. 3.99 (978-0-7644-1083-3(0)) Group Publishing, Inc.

My Bible Playground: Fall 2001. 2001. (Faith Weaver Ser.). (J). (gr. k-1). pap., stu. ed. 3.99 (978-0-7644-1186-1(1)) Group Publishing, Inc.

My Bible Teaches Me about God's Good News: Leader's Manual. 1999. (Junior Kids Church Ser.: Vol. 7). 160p. tchr. ed. 15.00 (978-1-57405-464-4(3)) CharismaLife Pubs.

Neely, J. Crucifixion - Countdown to a Promise. 2004. (Daily Bible Study Ser.). 500p. per. 39.95 (978-1-893968-40-0(5)) Neely, Judy.

—Daily Bible Study Charts & Graphs. 2004. (Daily Bible Study Ser.). 40p. per. 9.95 (978-1-893968-34-9(0)) Neely, Judy.

—Daniel: Chapter 1-4. 2000. (Daily Bible Study Ser.). 163p. per. 21.95 (978-1-893968-31-8(6)) Neely, Judy.

—Daniel: Chapter 5-8. 2002. (Daily Bible Study Ser.). 164p. pap. 21.95 (978-1-893968-32-5(4)) Neely, Judy.

—Daniel: Chapter 9-12. 2002. (Daily Bible Study Ser.). 151p. pap. 21.95 (978-1-893968-33-2(2)) Neely, Judy.

—Genesis: Chapter 1-4. 2000. (Daily Bible Study Ser.). 153p. per. 21.95 (978-1-893968-36-3(7)) Neely, Judy.

—Genesis: Chapter 11-15. 2001. (Daily Bible Study Ser.). 160p. per. 21.95 (978-1-893968-38-7(3)) Neely, Judy.

—Genesis: Chapter 16-20. 2001. (Daily Bible Study Ser.). 160p. per. 21.95 (978-1-893968-39-4(1)) Neely, Judy.

—Genesis: Chapter 5-10. 2000. (Daily Bible Study Ser.). 160p. pap. 21.95 (978-1-893968-37-0(5)) Neely, Judy.

—Levitians: Chapter 1-7. 2001. (Daily Bible Study Ser.). 156p. per. 21.95 (978-1-893968-35-6(9)) Neely, Judy.

—Philippians. 2000. (Daily Bible Study Ser.). 138p. per. 21.95 (978-1-893968-26-4(X)) Neely, Judy.

—Revelation: Chapter 1-3. 2000. (Daily Bible Study Ser.). 119p. per. 21.95 (978-1-893968-27-1(8)) Neely, Judy.

—Revelation: Chapter 4-7. 2000. (Daily Bible Study Ser.). 121p. per. 21.95 (978-1-893968-28-8(6)) Neely, Judy.

—Ruth. 2002. (Daily Bible Study Ser.). 77p. pap. 19.95 (978-1-893968-25-7(1)) Neely, Judy.

New International Reader's Version Staff. The NIRV Kid's Study Bible. Tanis, Joel, illus. rev. ed. 1998. 1824p. (J). pap. 21.99 (978-0-310-92654-2(8)); 26.99 (978-0-310-92655-9(6)) Zondervan.

New Kids Media Staff. My Bible Coloring Book. 1998. (Bible Fun Ser.). (Illus.). (J). (gr. 1-4). pap. 9.99 (978-0-8010-0247-2(8) , New Kids Media) Baker Bks.

New Testament Mazes: Bible Story Puzzle. 1998. (Illus.). (J). pap. 5.95 (978-0-7647-0432-1(X) , Schaffer, Frank) Schaffer, Frank Pubns.

Newberger, Anne E. St. Therese in Jesus' Garden. 2002. (Saints for Childrens Ser.). (Illus.). 32p. (J). (ps-12). pap. 7.95 (978-1-931709-08-8(4)) Our Sunday Visitor, Publishing Div.

Newman-St. John, Judy. In the Beginning. 2002. 16p. (J). 5.00 (978-0-687-09404-2(6)) Abingdon Pr.

No-Miss Lessons for Preteen Kids, Vol. 2. 2004. pap. 16.99 (978-0-7644-2290-4(1) , Flagship Church Resources) Group Publishing, Inc.

Noonan, Robert, et al. Three Weavers Plus Companion: A Father's Guide to Guarding His Daughter's Purity. 2004. 120p. pap. 13.95 (978-0-9700273-5-1(4)) Pumpkin Seed Pr.

Northwestern Publishing House Staff. Good News Daily Student Lesson Level 1. 2001. (Vacation Bible Study Ser.). pap. (978-0-8100-1307-0(X)) Northwestern Publishing Hse.

—Good News Daily Student Lesson Level 2. 2001. (Vacation Bible Study Ser.). pap. (978-0-8100-1308-7(8)) Northwestern Publishing Hse.

—Good News Daily Student Lesson Level 3. 2001. (Vacation Bible Study Ser.). pap. (978-0-8100-1309-4(6)) Northwestern Publishing Hse.

—Good News Daily Student Lesson Level 4. 2001. (Vacation Bible Study Ser.). pap. (978-0-8100-1310-0(X)) Northwestern Publishing Hse.

—Good News Daily Student Lesson Level 5. 2001. (Vacation Bible Study Ser.). pap. (978-0-8100-1311-7(8)) Northwestern Publishing Hse.

Older Elementary KidKit. 2003. (Godprints Curriculum Ser.). (Illus.). 8.99 (978-0-7814-3680-9(X) , 2043) Cook, David C. Publishing Co.

One Room Sunday School Fall: Resource Kit. (Illus.). 52.00 (978-0-687-03622-6(4)) Abingdon Pr.

One Room Sunday School Spring: Resource Kit. (Illus.). 52.00 (978-0-687-03629-5(1)) Abingdon Pr.

One Room Sunday School Winter: Resource Kit. (Illus.). 52.00 (978-0-687-03619-6(4)) Abingdon Pr.

One to One April-May-June, 1998, Vol. 10. 1998. 82p. (YA). (gr. 8-10). 20.00 (978-0-913585-42-9(4)) Scripture Union, USA.

Osborne, Rick, et al. Kidatlas. Vezina, Lori, illus. 2002. 64p. (J). 14.99 (978-0-310-70059-3(0)) Zonderkidz.

Outcalt, Todd. Show Me the Way: 50 Bible Study Methods for Youth. 2004. (Illus.). 112p. (gr. 7-12). pap. 14.00 (978-0-687-09562-9(X)) Abingdon Pr.

Outrageous Obedience: Gideon, Samson, Hannah, David. ldr.'s ed. 2001. (Faithweaver Youth Bible Studies). (YA). (gr. 8-12). 19.99 (978-0-7644-1080-2(6)) Group Publishing, Inc.

Page, Don, illus. How Big Was Noah's Ark? And Other Questions Kids Ask about the Bible. 1998. 48p. (J). (gr. 4-7). pap. 7.99 (978-0-88486-221-5(6) , Arrowood Pr.) BBS Publishing Corp.

Paisley, Rhonda. My Power Diary. 1998. (Illus.). 200p. (J). (gr. 4-7). pap. (978-1-84030-028-4(0)) Ambassador Productions, Ltd.

Partner, Daniel. Bible Devotions for Bedtime. 2004. 256p. (J). pap. 5.97 (978-1-59310-358-3(1)) Barbour Publishing, Inc.

Pearson, Mary Rose. When You Run Out of Soap. 2001. (J). (ps-1). pap. 15.95 (978-0-7880-1808-4(6)) CSS Publishing Co.

Perrotta, Kevin & Darring, Gerald. John 1-10: I Am the Bread of Life. 2004. (Six Weeks with the Bible for Catholic Teens Ser.). 96p. (YA). pap. 6.95 (978-0-8294-2083-8(5)) Loyola Pr.

—John 11-21: My Peace I Give You. 2004. (Six Weeks with the Bible for Catholic Teens Ser.). 96p. (YA). pap. 6.95 (978-0-8294-2084-5(3)) Loyola Pr.

—Six Weeks with the Bible for Catholic Teens Exodus: God to the Rescue. 2004. (Six Week for Catholic Teens Ser.). 96p. 6.95 (978-0-8294-2051-7(7)) Loyola Pr.

—Six Weeks with the Bible for Catholic Teens Genesis 1-11: God Makes a Start. 2004. (Six Week for Catholic Teens Ser.). 96p. 6.95 (978-0-8294-2050-0(9)) Loyola Pr.

—Six Weeks with the Bible for Catholic Teens Luke: The Good News of God's Mercy. 2004. (Six Week for Catholic Teens Ser.). 96p. 6.95 (978-0-8294-2052-4(5)) Loyola Pr.

—Six Weeks with the Bible for Catholic Teens Revelation: God's Gift of Hope. 2004. (Six Week for Catholic Teens Ser.). 96p. 6.95 (978-0-8294-2049-4(5)) Loyola Pr.

Petrusic, Anthony A. My First Communion - Boy Image. Parker, Sue H., ed. Shanahan, Sue & Fincher, Kathryn Andrews, illus. 2nd rev. ed. 1999. 128p. (J). (gr. 1-3). 6.00 (978-0-937739-35-8(9) , 10248) Roman, Inc.

—My First Communion - Boy Image, Padded Cover. Parker, Sue H., ed. Shanahan, Sue & Fincher, Kathryn Andrews, illus. 2nd rev. ed. 1999. 128p. (J). (gr. 1-3). 10.00 (978-0-937739-37-2(5) , 10288) Roman, Inc.

—My First Communion - Faux Mother of Pearl, Grey. Parker, Sue H., ed. Shanahan, Sue & Meyer, Anita, illus. 2nd rev. ed. 1999. 128p. (J). (gr. 1-3). 15.00 (978-0-937739-41-9(3) , 10278) Roman, Inc.

—My First Communion - Faux Mother of Pearl, White. Parker, Sue H., ed. Shanahan, Sue & Meyer, Anita, illus. 2nd rev. ed. 1999. 128p. (J). (gr. 1-3). 15.00 (978-0-937739-42-6(1) , 10279) Roman, Inc.

—My First Communion - Girl Image. Parker, Sue H., ed. Shanahan, Sue & Fincher, Kathryn Andrews, illus. 2nd rev. ed. 1999. 128p. (J). (gr. 1-3). 6.00 (978-0-937739-36-5(7) , 10249) Roman, Inc.

—My First Communion - Girl Image, Padded Cover. Parker, Sue H., ed. Shanahan, Sue & Fincher, Kathryn Andrews, illus. 2nd rev. ed. 1999. 128p. (J). (gr. 1-3). 10.00 (978-0-937739-38-9(3) , 10289) Roman, Inc.

—My First Communion - Symbol Design, Black. Parker, Sue H., ed. Shanahan, Sue & Meyer, Anita, illus. 2nd rev. ed. 1999. 128p. (J). (gr. 1-3). 4.50 (978-0-937739-39-6(1) , 10268) Roman, Inc.

—My First Communion - Symbol Design, White. Parker, Sue H., ed. Shanahan, Sue & Meyer, Anita, illus. 2nd rev. ed. 1999. 128p. (J). (gr. 1-3). 4.50 (978-0-937739-40-2(5) , 10269) Roman, Inc.

Pingry, Patricia A. The Story of Samson & His Great Strength. Sheets, Leslie, illus. 2001. (J). (ps-3). pap. 3.95 (978-0-8249-5413-0(0) , Ideals Children's Bks.) Ideals Pubns.

—The Story of the Garden of Eden. Ragland, Teresa B., illus. 2001. 24p. (J). (ps). pap. 3.95 (978-0-8249-5407-9(6) , Ideals Children's Bks.) Ideals Pubns.

Polich, Laurie. I Am Not Ashamed: Devotions on Romans for Teens. 2003. 112p. 8.00 (978-0-687-08118-9(1)) Abingdon Pr.

PowerPak of Scripture Memory Fun. 1999. 112p. (J). 12.99 (978-1-57405-448-4(1)) CharismaLife Pubs.

Pre-K & K. (ps-k). 2004. 54.99 (978-0-7644-0388-0(5)); 2004. 54.99 (978-0-7644-0400-9(8)); 2004. tchr. ed. 19.99 (978-0-7644-0380-4(X)); 2004. tchr. ed. 19.99 (978-0-7644-0394-1(X)); 2004. 54.99 (978-0-7644-0375-0(3)); 2004. tchr. ed. 19.99 (978-0-7644-0369-9(9)); 2003. tchr. ed. 54.99 (978-0-7644-0363-7(X)); 2003. tchr. ed. 19.99 (978-0-7644-0357-6(5)) Group Publishing, Inc. (Flagship Church Resources).

Preschool Leaders Kit: Spring 2001. ldr.'s ed. 2001. (FW Friends Ser.). (J). (ps-6). 79.99 (978-0-7644-1173-1(X)) Group Publishing, Inc.

Preschool Leaders Kit: Summer 2001. ldr.'s ed. 2001. (FW Friends Ser.). (J). (ps-6). 79.99 (978-0-7644-1254-7(X)) Group Publishing, Inc.

Quest - God's Perfect Plan - Answer Key: Exploring Bible Prophecy from Genesis to Revelation. 2000. (Bible Quest Ser.). 44p. (YA). (gr. 7-12). 6.99 (978-1-889015-82-8(2)) Explorer's Bible Study.

Quest - in the Beginning - Answer Key: Genesis. 2000. (Bible Quest Ser.). 32p. (YA). (gr. 7-12). 6.99 (978-1-889015-78-1(4)) Explorer's Bible Study.

Real Heroes for Teens: Patriarchs, Prophets & Kings, 8 vols. 2000. 32p. (J). pap. 15.75 (978-1-58516-422-6(4)) American Bible Society.

Real Life: Creation, the Fall, Noah, Abraham. 1999. (Faithweaver Youth Bible Studies). Orig. Title: Bible Beginnings. (YA). (gr. 8-12). pap. 19.99 (978-0-7644-0911-0(5) , Group's Active Bible Curriculum) Group Publishing, Inc.

Reece, Colleen L. Rebekah in Danger: Peril at Plymouth Colony. 2004. (Sisters in Time Ser.). 144p. (J). pap. 4.97 (978-1-59310-352-1(2)) Barbour Publishing, Inc.

Regensburger, Nancy. From Advent to Christ the King: Following the Liturgical Calendar. Larkin, Jean, ed. Becker, Linda, illus. 2000. (Active Learning for Catholic Kids Ser.). 28p. (YA). (gr. 7-9). pap. 7.95 (978-0-937997-90-1(0)) Pflaum Publishing Group.

Rhodes, David & Norris, Chad. Broken: When Life Falls Apart. 2005. (Following God Ser.). 168p. pap. (978-0-89957-738-8(5)) AMG Pubs.

Richards, Lawrence O. The KJV Kids' Study Bible. 2001. 1600p. (J). 22.99 (978-0-310-91909-4(6)) Zonderkidz.

Richards, Lawrence O. & Richards, Sue W. Teen Study Bible. rev. ed. 2001. 1664p. 49.99 (978-0-310-92711-2(0)) Zondervan.

Rikkers, Doris & Syswerda, Jean E., eds. Read with Me Bible: An NIrV Story Bible for Children. Jones, Dennis, illus. rev. ed. 2000. (Bible Storybooks Ser.). 448p. (J). 16.99 (978-0-310-92008-3(6)) Zonderkidz.

Robb, Andy. Hyper Holy Happenings. 2004. (Holy Happenings Ser.). (Illus.). 128p. pap. 6.50 (978-0-687-02286-1(X)) Abingdon Pr.

Rodgers, Barbara. Bible Activities in a Snap: Bible Stories Come to Life. 1998. 96p. (J). (ps-3). pap. 9.95 (978-1-885358-42-4(3) , RB36811) Rainbow Pubs. & Legacy Pr.

—Bible Activities in a Snap: Holidays. 2004. 96p. (J). (ps-3). pap. 9.95 (978-1-885358-44-8(X) , RB36813) Rainbow Pubs. & Legacy Pr.

—Bible Activities in a Snap: Living by God's Word. 1998. (Illus.). 96p. (J). (ps-3). pap. 9.95 (978-1-885358-43-1(1)) Rainbow Pubs. & Legacy Pr.

—Bible Activities in a Snap: Sharing God's Love. 1998. (Illus.). 96p. (J). (gr. 3-8). pap. 9.95 (978-1-885358-45-5(8) , RB36814) Rainbow Pubs. & Legacy Pr.

Rose, Shirley. Let's Discover the Bible, Vol. 1. Yerkes, Lane, illus. 64p. (J). (gr. k-2). pap. 4.75 (978-0-87441-538-4(1)) Behrman Hse., Inc.

Ross, Kathy. Crafts to Celebrate God's Creation. Holm, Sharon Lane, illus. 2001. (Crafts from Kathy Ross Ser.: 3). 64p. (J). (gr. k-3). pap. 7.95 (978-0-7613-1330-4(3) , First Avenue Editions) Lerner Publishing Group.

Ross, Suzanne. Bible Activity Book. 2003. (Dover Little Activity Bks.). (Illus.). 64p. (J). (ps-3). pap. 1.50 (978-0-486-42335-7(2)) Dover Pubns., Inc.

Russell, Patricia C. Beginnings I - Precious in His Sight: New Testament Lessons for Little Listeners. Clark, Virginia A., ed. 2001. (Beginnings I Ser.). 301p. (J). (ps-k). spiral bd. 23.99 (978-1-889015-30-9(X)) Explorer's Bible Study.

—Discovery - in the Beginning: Genesis. 2003. (Bible Discovery Ser.). 220p. (J). stu. ed., per., wbk. ed. 21.99 (978-1-889015-31-6(8)) Explorer's Bible Study.

Sabio & Prudente. Numeros, Conceptos y Figuras Geometricas. 2004. (Sabio Y Prudente Ser.). (SPA.). 64p. (J). No. 1. 4.99 (978-0-8254-0997-4(7)); Vol. 3. (Illus.). 4.99 (978-0-8254-0999-8(3)) Kregel Pubns. (Editorial Portavoz).

Sabio, et al. Numeros, Conceptos y Figuras Geometricas, Vol. 2. 2nd ed. 2000. (Sabio Y Prudente Ser.). (SPA.). 64p. (J). 4.99 (978-0-8254-0998-1(5) ; 196-133, Editorial Portavoz) Kregel Pubns.

Sanford, Gene. Discovering Acts: A Bible Study for Teens. 1998. 84p. pap., tchr. ed. 9.99 (978-0-8341-1714-3(2)) Beacon Hill Pr. of Kansas City.

Save, Vickie. Kids' Bible Activities. 2005. (Illus.). 224p. (J). (ps-7). pap. 3.97 (978-1-59310-694-2(7)) Barbour Publishing, Inc.

—Kids' Bible Crosswords. 2005. (Illus.). 224p. (J). (ps-7). pap. 3.97 (978-1-59310-693-5(9)) Barbour Publishing, Inc.

—Kids' Bible Picture Fun. 2005. (Illus.). 224p. (J). (ps-ps). pap. 3.97 (978-1-59310-696-6(3)) Barbour Publishing, Inc.

—Kids' Bible Q & A. 2005. (Illus.). 224p. (J). (ps-7). pap. 3.97 (978-1-59310-695-9(5)) Barbour Publishing, Inc.

Scharlemann, John. Acts: An Introductory Course. (Journeys Through God's Word Ser.). pap., stu. ed. 6.50 (978-0-570-07821-0(0) , 20-2822); pap. 6.50 (978-0-570-07822-7(9) , 20-2823) Concordia Publishing Hse.

School of the Bible for Kids: The Blood of Jesus. 2005. ring bd. 74.95 (978-0-9767647-4-8(1)) Kids in Ministry International.

Schurb, Ken. Advent 3. (Advent Bible Study Series A). pap., stu. ed. 4.99 (978-0-570-07827-2(X) , 20-2862) Concordia Publishing Hse.

Schurb, Ken & Shuta, Richard. Advent 1. (Advent Bible Study Series B). pap., stu. ed. 4.99 (978-0-570-06949-2(1) , 20-2854) Concordia Publishing Hse.

—Advent 2. (Advent Bible Study Series C). stu. ed. 5.99 (978-0-570-07823-4(7) , 20-2858) Concordia Publishing Hse.

Scripture on the Go Staff. Scripture on the Go: Kids 4-7. 1999. (J). 9.95 (978-1-930350-08-3(2)) Scripture On The Go.

—Scripture on the Go: Kids 7-10. 1999. (J). 9.95 (978-1-930350-09-0(0)) Scripture On The Go.

Senior High Bible Studies. 2004. 19.99 (978-0-7644-1696-5(0)); 2004. 19.99 (978-0-7644-1676-7(6)); 2003. 19.99 (978-0-7644-1604-0(9)); 2003. 19.99 (978-0-7644-1579-1(4)) Group Publishing, Inc. (Flagship Church Resources).

Share Your Faith Bible Study: Six Lessons of Bible Study, Fellowship, & Growth. 2000. 28p. (YA). pap. 2.00 (978-1-888568-58-5(5)) Doughten, Russ Films, Inc.

Sheffield, Bill. The Beginnings under Attack. 2003. 192p. per. 10.99 (978-0-9728899-3-3(0)) 21st Century Pr.

Shellenberger, Susie. Young Women of Faith Bible. 2001. 1664p. (J). 26.99 (978-0-310-91394-8(2)); (Illus.). pap. 21.99 (978-0-310-70278-8(X)) Zonderkidz.

Singer-Towns, Brian & Calderone-Stewart, Lisa-Marie. Bringing Catholic Youth & the Bible Together: Strategies & Activities for Parishes & Schools. 2003. (Illus.). 96p. (YA). (gr. 8-12). pap. 14.95 (978-0-88489-692-0(7)) St. Mary's Pr.

Sorvillo, Carmen R. Bible Wheels to Make & Enjoy. 2000. (Illus.). 64p. (ps-2). 9.99 (978-0-570-05382-8(X)) Concordia Publishing Hse.

Spence, Christine, ed. The Bible Tells Me So, Grades Preschool-1. 1998. (Children's Bible Study Ser.). (Illus.). 320p. pap., tchr. ed. 26.99 (978-0-7847-0817-0(7) , 42037) Standard Publishing.

Spiritual Disciplines. 2003. (Learn It, Live It Bible Studiestm Ser.). 80-112p. pap. 7.99 (978-0-7644-2670-4(2) , Flagship Church Resources) Group Publishing, Inc.

Spiritual Gifts. 2002. 7.99 (978-1-56390-046-4(7)); 3rd ed. per. 12.99 (978-1-56390-024-2(6)) Global Univ.

Spiritual Gifts. 2003. (Learn It, Live It Bible Studiestm Ser.). 80-112p. pap. 39.99 (978-0-7644-2559-2(5) , Flagship Church Resources) Group Publishing, Inc.

Spiritual Gifts Student Book. 2003. (Learn It, Live It Bible Studiestm Ser.). 80-112p. pap. 7.99 (978-0-7644-2671-1(0) , Flagship Church Resources) Group Publishing, Inc.

Starburst Publishers Staff. Bible Bytes for Teens: A Study-Devotional for Logging In to God's Word. 2001. (Illus.). 284p. (gr. 8 up). pap. 13.99 (978-1-892016-49-2(4)) Starburst Pubs.

Steinbock, Steven E. The Gift of Wisdom: The Books of Prophets & Writings. Mantell, Ahuva & Sperling, S. David, illus. 2004. (J). (gr. 4-6). pap. 13.95 (978-0-8074-0752-3(6) , 123944) URJ Pr.

Stickler, LeeDell. Bible Brain Teasers: Fun Little Activities That Teach Big Bible Messages. 2004. 64p. (gr. 1-3). pap. 12.00 (978-0-687-09324-3(4)) Abingdon Pr.

Stickler, LeeDell & Newman, Judy. From Bags to Bushes. 2004. (Just Add Kids Ser.). (Illus.). 112p. (gr. 1-6). 14.00 (978-0-687-04900-4(8)) Abingdon Pr.

Stickler, LeeDell, et al. Ring 'Round Jericho. 2004. (Just Add Kids Ser.). (Illus.). 112p. (ps up). 14.00 (978-0-687-04820-5(6)) Abingdon Pr.

Stohs, Anita R. I Believe! 2000. (Illus.). 48p. (ps-1). 4.99 (978-0-570-07123-5(2)) Concordia Publishing Hse.

Strang Communications Company Staff, ed. Ages 1-2 Activities: Winter 2001/2002. 2002. (J). pap., act. bk. ed. 6.49 (978-1-57405-885-7(1)) CharismaLife Pubs.

—Ages 1-2 Teachers Manual: Winter 2001/2002. 2002. (J). pap., tchr. ed. 4.99 (978-1-57405-886-4(X)) CharismaLife Pubs.

—Ages 1-2 Teaching Pictures: Winter 2001/2002. 2002. (J). pap. 10.99 (978-1-57405-887-1(8)) CharismaLife Pubs.

—Ages 2-3 Resources: Winter 2001/2002. 2002. (J). pap. 10.99 (978-1-57405-890-1(8)) CharismaLife Pubs.

—Ages 2-3 Take-Home Papers: Discovering Together. 2001. (J). pap. 13.49 (978-1-57405-777-5(4) , TTTH) CharismaLife Pubs.

—Ages 2-3 Take-Home Papers Winter 2001/2002: Discovering Together. 2002. (J). pap. 13.49 (978-1-57405-891-8(6)) CharismaLife Pubs.

—Ages 2-3 Teaching Pictures: Winter 2001/2002. 2002. (J). pap. 10.99 (978-1-57405-893-2(2)) CharismaLife Pubs.

—Ages 4-5 Activities: Spring 2000. 2001. (J). pap. 2.99 (978-1-57405-781-2(2) , FFAC) CharismaLife Pubs.

—Ages 4-5 Activities: Summer 2001. 2001. (J). (ps-k). pap., act. bk. ed. 2.99 (978-1-57405-821-5(5)) CharismaLife Pubs.

—Ages 4-5 Resources: Summer 2001. 2001. (J). (ps-k). pap. 10.99 (978-1-57405-820-8(7)) CharismaLife Pubs.

—Ages 4-5 Take-Home Papers: Summer 2001. 2001. (J). (ps-k). pap. 13.49 (978-1-57405-822-2(3)) CharismaLife Pubs.

—Ages 4-5 Teaching Pictures: Summer 2001. 2001. (J). (ps-k). pap. 10.99 (978-1-57405-819-2(3)) CharismaLife Pubs.

—Grades 1-2 Activities: Summer 2001. 2001. (J). (gr. 1-2). pap., act. bk. ed. 4.99 (978-1-57405-827-7(4)) CharismaLife Pubs.

—Grades 1-2 Picture Lesson Cards: Spring 2001. 2001. (J). (gr. 1-2). pap. 0.99 (978-1-57405-789-8(8) , PLCO) CharismaLife Pubs.

—Grades 1-2 Resources: Summer 2001. 2001. (J). (gr. 1-2). pap. 10.99 (978-1-57405-826-0(6)) CharismaLife Pubs.

—Grades 1-2 Teaching Pictures: Summer 2001. 2001. (J). (gr. 1-2). pap. 10.99 (978-1-57405-825-3(8)) CharismaLife Pubs.

—Grades 1-2 Weekly Bible Reader: Spring 2001. 2001. (J). (gr. 1-2). pap. 13.49 (978-1-57405-788-1(X) , PRTH) CharismaLife Pubs.

—Grades 1-2 Weekly Bible Reader: Summer 2001. 2001. (J). (gr. 1-2). pap. 13.49 (978-1-57405-828-4(2)) CharismaLife Pubs.

—Grades 1-2 Weekly Bible Reader: Summer 2002. 2002. (J). (gr. 1-2). pap. 14.99 (978-1-57405-974-8(2)) CharismaLife Pubs.

—Grades 3-4 Activities: Spring 2001. 2001. (J). (gr. 3-4). pap. 2.99 (978-1-57405-793-5(6) , MIAC) CharismaLife Pubs.

—Grades 3-4 Activities: Summer 2001. 2001. (J). (gr. 3-4). pap., act. bk. ed. 2.99 (978-1-57405-833-8(9)) CharismaLife Pubs.

—Grades 3-4 Activities: Summer 2002. 2002. (J). (gr. 3-4). pap., act. bk. ed. 3.29 (978-1-57405-977-9(7)) CharismaLife Pubs.

—Grades 3-4 Activities: Winter 2001/2002. 2002. (J). (gr. 3-4). pap., act. bk. ed. 2.99 (978-1-57405-910-6(6)) CharismaLife Pubs.

—Grades 3-4 Kidz Chat: Spring 2001. 2001. (J). (gr. 3-4). pap. 13.49 (978-1-57405-794-2(4) , JRTM) CharismaLife Pubs.

—Grades 3-4 Kidz Chat: Summer 2001. 2001. (J). (gr. 3-4). pap. 13.49 (978-1-57405-834-5(7)) CharismaLife Pubs.

—Grades 3-4 Resources: Spring 2001. 2001. (J). (gr. 3-4). pap. 10.99 (978-1-57405-792-8(8) , MILR) CharismaLife Pubs.

—Grades 3-4 Resources: Spring 2002. 2002. (J). pap. 12.99 (978-1-57405-940-3(8)); (gr. 3-4). pap. 3.29 (978-1-57405-939-7(4)) CharismaLife Pubs.

—Grades 3-4 Resources: Summer 2001. 2001. (J). (gr. 3-4). pap. 10.99 (978-1-57405-832-1(0)) CharismaLife Pubs.

—Grades 3-4 Resources: Summer 2002. 2002. (J). (gr. 3-4). pap. 12.99 (978-1-57405-978-6(5)) CharismaLife Pubs.

—Grades 3-4 Resources: Winter 2001/2002. 2002. (J). (gr. 3-4). pap. 10.99 (978-1-57405-911-3(4)) CharismaLife Pubs.

—Grades 5-6 Activities: Spring 2001. 2001. (J). (gr. 5-6). pap. 2.99 (978-1-57405-797-3(9) , JRAC) CharismaLife Pubs.

—Grades 5-6 Activities: Summer 2001. 2001. (J). (gr. 5-6). pap., act. bk. ed. 2.99 (978-1-57405-837-6(1)) CharismaLife Pubs.

—Grades 5-6 Activities: Summer 2002. 2002. (J). (gr. 5-6). pap. 3.29 (978-1-57405-963-2(7)) CharismaLife Pubs.

—Grades 5-6 Activities: Winter 2001/2002. 2002. (J). (gr. 5-6). pap., act. bk. ed. 2.99 (978-1-57405-896-3(7)) CharismaLife Pubs.

—Grades 5-6 Live Wire: Spring 2001. 2001. (J). (gr. 5-6). pap. 13.49 (978-1-57405-798-0(7) , JRTH) CharismaLife Pubs.

—Grades 5-6 Live Wire: Summer 2001. 2001. (J). (gr. 5-6). pap. 13.49 (978-1-57405-838-3(X)) CharismaLife Pubs.

—Grades 5-6 Live Wire: Winter 2001/2002. 2002. (J). (gr. 5-6). pap. 13.49 (978-1-57405-898-7(3)) CharismaLife Pubs.

—Grades 5-6 Resources: Spring 2001. 2001. (J). (gr. 5-6). pap. 10.99 (978-1-57405-796-6(0) , JRLR) CharismaLife Pubs.

—Grades 5-6 Resources: Spring 2002. 2002. (J). (gr. 5-6). pap. 12.99 (978-1-57405-926-7(2)) CharismaLife Pubs.

—Grades 5-6 Resources: Summer 2001. 2001. (J). (gr. 10-11). pap. 10.99 (978-1-57405-836-9(3)) CharismaLife Pubs.

—Grades 5-6 Resources: Summer 2002. 2002. (J). (gr. 5-6). pap. 12.99 (978-1-57405-964-9(5)) CharismaLife Pubs.

—Grades 5-6 Resources: Winter 2001/2002. 2002. (J). (gr. 5-6). pap. 10.99 (978-1-57405-897-0(5)) CharismaLife Pubs.

—Grades 5-6 Teachers Manual: Winter 2001/2002. 2002. (J). (gr. 5-6). pap., tchr. ed. 4.99 (978-1-57405-899-4(1)) CharismaLife Pubs.

—Kids in Missions. 1999. (J). pap., ldr.'s hndbk. ed. 10.00 (978-1-57405-870-3(3) , MISLDR) CharismaLife Pubs.

—Kids in Victory Manual. 2000. (J). pap., tchr. ed. 10.00 (978-1-57405-875-8(4) , VICMAN) CharismaLife Pubs.

—Kids in Worship Extra Leader Manual. 1999. (J). pap., tchr. ed. 10.00 (978-1-57405-876-5(2) , WORLDR) CharismaLife Pubs.

—Picture Lesson Cards: Summer 2001. 2001. (J). pap. 0.99 (978-1-57405-829-1(0)) CharismaLife Pubs.

—Picture Lesson Cards: Winter 2001/2002. 2002. (J). pap. 0.99 (978-1-57405-895-6(9)) CharismaLife Pubs.

—Picture Lesson Cards & Albums: Spring 2001. 2001. (J). pap. 1.99 (978-1-57405-790-4(1)) CharismaLife Pubs.

—Picture Lesson Cards & Albums: Summer 2001. 2001. (J). pap. 1.99 (978-1-57405-830-7(4)) CharismaLife Pubs.

—Picture Lesson Cards & Albums: Winter 2001/2002. 2002. (J). pap. 1.99 (978-1-57405-894-9(0)) CharismaLife Pubs.

—Weekly Bible Reader: Spring 2002. 2002. (J). pap. 14.99 (978-1-57405-936-6(X)) CharismaLife Pubs.

—Weekly Bible Reader: Winter 2001/2002. 2002. (J). pap. 13.49 (978-1-57405-907-6(6)) CharismaLife Pubs.

Stulp, Keith. 29 More Great Bible Studies for Youth. 1999. (Great Bible Studies for Youth! Ser.). 75p. 20.50 (978-1-56212-412-0(9) , 130610, Faith Alive Christian Resources) CRC Pubns.

—31 More Great Bible Studies for Youth. 2001. (Prime-Time Ser.). 20.50 (978-1-56212-526-4(5) , 130620, Faith Alive Christian Resources) CRC Pubns.

Sume, Lori. Jesus Wants Me for a Sunbeam. 2004. (ps-3). bds. 9.95 (978-1-57734-857-3(5)) Covenant Communications, Inc.

Swan, Susan Reith. LifeSavers: 20 Quick & Easy-to-Use Bible Lessons for Kids. O'Neill, Susan, illus. 1999. 144p. (gr. 1-7). 15.00 (978-0-8170-1301-1(6)) Judson Pr.

Tallarico, Tony. I Can Draw the Bible: The Old Testament. 1998. (I Can Draw Ser.). (978-0-606-13501-6(4)) Tandem Library Bks.

Thomas Nelson. My Time with God: 15 Minute Devotions for the Entire Year. 2003. 656p. 14.99 (978-0-7180-0646-4(1)) Nelson, Thomas Inc.

Thomas, Publishers Nelson. International Student Bible for Catholics. 1999. (gr. 7-12). lib. bdg. 26.90 (978-0-613-74992-3(8)) Tandem Library Bks.

Tnt Ministries Staff. On the Way 11 - 14's, Vol. 4. 96p. (J). pap. 11.99 (978-1-85792-707-8(9) , Christian Focus) Christian Focus Pubns. GBR. *Dist:* Riverside.

TNT Resource Material Staff. On the Way For 11 - 14's, Vol. 6. 2004. 96p. (J). pap. 12.99 (978-1-85792-709-2(5) , Christian Focus) Christian Focus Pubns. GBR. *Dist:* Riverside.

—On the Way for 11-14's, Vol. 5. 2004. 96p. (J). pap. 12.99 (978-1-85792-708-5(7) , Christian Focus) Christian Focus Pubns. GBR. *Dist:* Riverside.

Toddlers & 2s. 2004. tchr. ed. 19.99 (978-0-7644-0382-8(6)); 2004. tchr. ed. 19.99 (978-0-7644-0396-5(6)); 2004. 54.99 (978-0-7644-0376-7(1)); 2004. tchr. ed. 19.99 (978-0-7644-0370-5(2)); 2003. 54.99 (978-0-7644-0364-4(8)); 2003. tchr. ed. 19.99 (978-0-7644-0358-3(3)) Group Publishing, Inc. (Flagship Church Resources).

Toddlers And 2s. 2004. 54.99 (978-0-7644-0390-3(7)); 54.99 (978-0-7644-0402-3(4)) Group Publishing, Inc. (Flagship Church Resources).

Tudor, Tasha. And It Was So: Words from the Scripture. 2nd rev. ed. 1999. (Illus.). 48p. (J). (gr. 1-4). pap. 16.95 (978-0-664-25716-3(X)) Westminster John Knox Pr.

Twork, Carol Camp, des. Scripture Notebook. 2003. 48p. (YA). 3.99 (978-0-9707979-4-0(X)) Contemplation Corner Pr.

Vander Meer, Lew. What We Believe Pt. 1: Sessions 1-12. 2nd ed. 2000. (Reformed Faith Ser.). 80p. (gr. 8-12). tchr. ed. 14.25 (978-1-56212-527-1(3) , 135705, Faith Alive Christian Resources) CRC Pubns.

—What We Believe Pt. 2: Sessions 13-24. 2nd ed. 2000. (Reformed Faith Ser.). 88p. (gr. 8-12). tchr. ed. 14.25 (978-1-56212-528-8(1) , 135805, Faith Alive Christian Resources) CRC Pubns.

Vanus, Lori G. Latter-Day Letters: The New Testament. Vanus, Lori G., illus. 1998. (Illus.). 56p. (J). (gr. k-6). pap. 9.95 (978-1-892318-00-8(8)) White Stone Publishing Co.

VBS Ready, Set, Gold! 2003. (J). (978-0-8100-1537-1(4)); (J). stu. ed. (978-0-8100-1518-0(8)); (J). cd-rom (978-0-8100-1534-0(X)); Level 1. (J). tchr. ed. (978-0-8100-1522-7(6)); Level 1. (J). stu. ed. (978-0-8100-1517-3(X)); Level 2. (J). tchr. ed. (978-0-8100-1523-4(4)); Level 3. (YA). tchr. ed. (978-0-8100-1524-1(2)) Northwestern Publishing Hse.

Vbs Ready, Set, Gold!, Level 3. 2003. (J). stu. ed. (978-0-8100-1519-7(6)) Northwestern Publishing Hse.

VBS Ready, Set, Gold! 2003. (J). Level 4. tchr. ed. (978-0-8100-1525-8(0)); Level 4. stu. ed. (978-0-8100-1520-3(X)); Level 5. tchr. ed. (978-0-8100-1526-5(9)); Level 5. stu. ed. (978-0-8100-1521-0(8)) Northwestern Publishing Hse.

VBS Ready, Set, Gold! Craft Book. 2003. (J). (978-0-8100-1527-2(7)) Northwestern Publishing Hse.

VBS Ready, Set, Gold! Planning Guide. 2003. (J). (978-0-8100-1535-7(8)) Northwestern Publishing Hse.

Veerman, David R., et al. 103 Preguntas Que los Ninos Hacen Acerca de lo Quees Bueno O Es Malo, Vol. 3. 2nd ed. 1998. (Right from Wrong Ser.).Tr. of 103 Questions Children Ask about Right & Wrong. (SPA., Illus.). 256p. (J). (gr. 1 up). pap. 9.99 (978-0-311-38652-9(0) , Editorial Mundo Hispano) Casa Bautista de Publicaciones.

Visual Resources for Bible Teaching: Ages 9-12. 1999. pap. 11.00 (978-0-8307-2308-9(0)) Gospel Light Pubns.

Vivir la Fe (Living Our Faith) Quarter 3, Level 4. 2000. (Caminando con Jesus (Walking with Jesus) Series B). (SPA.). (J). (gr. 5-6). stu. ed. 3.50 (978-0-570-05166-4(5) , 16-4913) Concordia Publishing Hse.

Walters, David. The Gifts of the Spirit, 6 vols. Ellis, Jessica, illus. 2005. 64p. (J). pap. 8.95 (978-1-888081-68-8(6)) Good News Fellowship Ministries.

Warden, Michael D. What's Your Point? Making Sense Out of Life (A Creative Study of the Book of Colossians) Reeves, Dale, ed. Angle, Scott, illus. 1999. 64p. (YA). pap., wbk. ed. 8.99 (978-0-7847-0952-8(1) , 23318) Standard Publishing.

Washington, Linda. Home & Back. 2004. (Illus.). 96p. (J). (gr. 1-2). pap. 11.95 (978-1-885358-50-9(4) , RB36842); (gr. 3-4). pap. 11.95 (978-1-885358-51-6(2) , RB36843); (gr. 5-6). pap. 11.95 (978-1-885358-52-3(0) , RB36844) Rainbow Pubs. & Legacy Pr.

Washington, Linda & Dall, Jeanette. Home & Back: Bible Activities. 2004. 96p. (J). (ps-k). pap. 11.95 (978-1-885358-63-9(6) , RB36841) Rainbow Pubs. & Legacy Pr.

The Way of the Cross, the Way to Life: Answer Guide. 2002. (Little Rock Scripture Study Ser.). (YA). 1.00 (978-0-8146-1699-4(2)) Liturgical Pr.

The Way of the Cross, the Way to Life: Participant's Book. 2002. (Little Rock Scripture Study Ser.). (YA). 4.95 (978-0-8146-1698-7(4)) Liturgical Pr.

Wells, Jan. Philemon - an Inductive Bible Study. 2004. 49p. per. (978-1-932934-13-7(8)) Sunergos Bible Studies.

Wilde, Gary. Maxed Out! How Old Testament Personalities Handled the Stress. 1999. (Generation Why Ser.: Vol. 5.1). 46p. (gr. 9-12). pap. 14.95 (978-0-87303-384-8(1)) Faith & Life Pr.

Wilkes, C. Gene. Jesus on Leadership: The Man with the Miracle Touch. 1998. (Illus.). 272p. pap. 12.99 (978-0-8423-1863-1(1)) Tyndale Hse. Pubs.

Willoughby, Robert. Children's Guide to the Bible. Morris, Tony, illus. 2003. 128p. 9.99 (978-1-85999-072-8(X)) Scripture Union GBR. *Dist:* Gabriel Resources.

Wisconsin Evangelical Lutheran Synod Staff. Christ-Light: Cradle Roll - God Shows Us His Love. 1999. (J). 5.99 (978-0-8100-1003-1(8)) Northwestern Publishing Hse.

—Christ-Light: Cradle Roll - God Teaches Us to Love. 1999. (J). 5.99 (978-0-8100-1004-8(6)) Northwestern Publishing Hse.

—Christ-Light: Cradle Roll - Help Me Learn about God. 1999. (J). 2.99 (978-0-8100-1089-5(5)) Northwestern Publishing Hse.

—Christ-Light: Cradle Roll - Jesus Loves All People. 1999. (J). 2.99 (978-0-8100-1090-1(9)) Northwestern Publishing Hse.

—Christ-Light: Cradle Roll - Jesus Loves Me (Kindura) 1999. (J). 3.99 (978-0-8100-1136-6(0)) Northwestern Publishing Hse.

—Christ-Light: Cradle Roll - Special Baby Jesus (Kindura) 1999. (J). 2.49 (978-0-8100-1137-3(9)) Northwestern Publishing Hse.

—Christ-Light: Cradle Roll - Tips & Truths. 1999. (J). 20.00 (978-0-8100-1022-2(4)); 20.00 (978-0-8100-1023-9(2)); 20.00 (978-0-8100-1024-6(0)); 20.00 (978-0-8100-1025-3(9)); 20.00 (978-0-8100-1026-0(7)); 20.00 (978-0-8100-1027-7(5)); 20.00 (978-0-8100-1028-4(3)); 20.00 (978-0-8100-1029-1(1)); 20.00 (978-0-8100-1030-7(5)) Northwestern Publishing Hse.

—Christ-Light: Cradle Roll - Ups, Downs, Grins, Frowns. 1999. (J). 3.99 (978-0-8100-1033-8(X)) Northwestern Publishing Hse.

Woychuk, N. A. God Loves Us: Scripture Memory Book 1. Terpstra, Jeffery Scott, illus. 2000. 36p. (J). (gr. 1). pap. 4.00 (978-1-880960-38-7(9)) Scripture Memory Fellowship International.

—God Made All Things: Scripture Memory Book 2. Terpstra, Jeffery Scott, illus. 2000. 40p. (J). (gr. 2). pap. 4.00 (978-1-880960-39-4(7)) Scripture Memory Fellowship International.

Wright, Christine. My Little Green Book: First Steps in Bible Reading. 2004. 64p. 4.99 (978-1-85999-696-6(5)) Scripture Union GBR. *Dist:* Gabriel Resources.

Younger, Barbara & Flinn, Lisa. Flood Punch, Bowl Bread, & Group Soup: 60 Multi-Age Activities for Christian Kids. 2004. 112p. pap. 16.00 (978-0-687-09334-2(1)) Abingdon Pr.

—Good News Travels Fast! 2004. (ps-3). 5.00 (978-0-687-09656-5(1)) Abingdon Pr.

Younger Elementary KidKit. 2003. (Godprints Curriculum Ser.). 8.99 (978-0-7814-3672-4(9) , 2023) Cook, David C. Publishing Co.

Youth Bible Studies. ldr.'s ed. 2001. (Faithweaver Youth Bible Studies). (YA). (gr. 8-12). 19.99 (978-0-7644-1180-9(2)) Group Publishing, Inc.

Zondervan. First Communion Bible: GNT New Testament. 2004. 416p. (J). 12.99 (978-0-310-70831-5(1)); pap. 12.99 (978-0-310-70832-2(X)) Zonderkidz.

—KJV Kids' Study Bible. 2002. (Illus.). 1600p. (J). 29.99 (978-0-310-70487-4(1)) Zonderkidz.

—Nirv Kid's Study Bible. Tanis, Joel, illus. rev. ed. 2004. 1824p. (J). 27.99 (978-0-310-70801-8(X)) Zonderkidz.

—Nirv Kid's Study Bible. Tanis, Joel, illus. rev. ed. 2004. 1824p. (J). pap. 22.99 (978-0-310-70802-5(8)) Zondervan.

—NIV Teen Study Bible: Orange. Richards, Lawrence O. & Richards, Sue W., eds. rev. ed. 2004. 1664p. (J). 44.99 (978-0-310-92097-7(3)) Zondervan.

—NIV Teen Study Bible: Red. Richards, Lawrence O. & Richards, Sue W., eds. rev. ed. 2004. 1664p. (J). 44.99 (978-0-310-92098-4(1)) Zondervan.

—Revolution: The Bible for Teen Guys. Livingstone Corporation Staff, ed. 2004. 1664p. (YA). 44.99 (978-0-310-92094-6(9)) Zondervan.

—True Images: The Bible for Teen Girls. Livingstone Corporation Staff, ed. 2004. 1696p. (YA). 44.99 (978-0-310-92096-0(5)) Zondervan.

Zondervan & Nikiel, Laura Gibbons. Sing along Bible Songs. 2000. (Illus.). 24p. (J). 12.99 (978-0-310-97998-2(6)) Zonderkidz.

Zoom Zone Passport: Learner Resource. 2004. (J). (ps-1). 2.99 (978-0-8066-4976-4(3) , Augsburg Bks.) Augsburg Fortress, Pubs.

BIBLE—THEOLOGY

see Theology

BIBLE—USE

Center for Learning Network Staff. Faith: Minicourse. 2005. (Religion Ser.). 81p. (YA). spiral bd. 12.95 (978-1-56077-796-0(6)) Ctr. for Learning, The.

Maves, Paul B. & Maves, Carolyn. Finding Your Way Through the Bible. 2004. 176p. (gr. 3-6). pap. 5.50 (978-0-687-04544-0(4)) Abingdon Pr.

BIBLE—ZOOLOGY

see Bible—Natural History

BIBLE AS LITERATURE

see also Religious Literature

Zondervan, contrib. by. Mom, You're Berry Sweet. 2004. (Illus.). 48p. (J). 7.99 (978-0-310-80512-0(0)) Zondervan.

BIBLE CLASSES

see Bible—Study

BIBLE GAMES AND PUZZLES

ABC Poster Book. 2004. (J). pap. 12.99 (***978-1-59317-080-6(7)***) Warner Pr. Pubs.

Abingdon. More Tween Bible Puzzles Another Year's Worth of Fun. 2006. (Illus.). 144p. pap. 18.00 (978-0-687-33321-9(0)) Abingdon Pr.

Berthel, Alice H. Power Puzzles: John. 2007. (J). per. 12.95 (978-1-59352-193-6(6)) Christian Services Publishing.

—Power Puzzles: Luke. 2007. (J). per. 12.95 (978-1-59352-192-9(8)) Christian Services Publishing.

—Power Puzzles: Mark. 2007. (J). per. 12.95 (978-1-59352-191-2(X)) Christian Services Publishing.

—Power Puzzles: Matthew. 2006. (J). per. 12.95 (978-1-59352-174-5(X)) Christian Services Publishing.

Bible Fun Puzzle Series: The Miracles of Jesus. 2005. 48p. (J). (ps-2). pap. 7.99 (978-0-7647-0527-4(X)) School Specialty Publishing.

Bible Fun Puzzle Series: The Stories of Noah & Joseph. 2005. (J). (ps-2). pap. 7.99 (978-0-7647-0526-7(1)) School Specialty Publishing.

Campbell, Julie. Itty-bitty Bible Activity Book Vol 6, Vol. 6. 2006. (Illus.). 48p. (J). pap. 1.49 (***978-1-59317-165-0(X)***) Warner Pr. Pubs.

Clayton, Meloda & Bennett, Daina. Books of the Holy Bible Learning Activity: Support Activities for Group Play. 2006. (J). spiral bd. 15.00 (***978-0-9777756-1-3(5)***) Educational Materials, Distributors.

Concordia Publishing House, compiled by. Wiggles & Squiggles: 60 Bible Based Classroom Games & Activities. 2007. (ENG.). 64p. (J). 10.99 (***978-0-7586-1347-9(4)***) Concordia Publishing Hse.

Created By the Master Bible Puzzles Ages 8 & Up. 2006. (YA). per. (978-1-59872-337-3(5)) Instantpublisher.com.

Fogle, Robin. Bible Story Hidden Pictures. 2006. (J). pap. 1.79 (***978-1-59317-160-5(9)***) Warner Pr. Pubs.

—Bible Story Hidden Pictures: Intermediate. 2006. (J). pap. 1.79 (***978-1-59317-161-2(7)***) Warner Pr. Pubs.

—Itty-bitty Bible Activity Book, Love. 2007. (Illus.). 48p. (J). pap. 1.49 (***978-1-59317-213-8(3)***) Warner Pr. Pubs.

—Itty-bitty Bible Activity Book, the Legend of the Candy Cane. 2007. (Illus.). 48p. (J). pap. 1.49 (***978-1-59317-212-1(5)***) Warner Pr. Pubs.

Fogle, Robin & Campbell, Julie. Itty-bitty Bible Verse Crossword Puzzles. 2007. (Illus.). 48p. (J). pap. 1.49 (***978-1-59317-197-1(8)***) Warner Pr. Pubs.

Golden Books Staff. The Little Golden Bible Puzzle Book. Williams, Susan, illus. 2006. 10p. (J). (ps-1). 9.99 (978-0-375-83863-7(5) , Golden Inspirational) Random Hse. Children's Bks.

Gospel, Light. Really Big BK of Bible Games. 2006. 304p. pap. 29.99 (978-0-8307-4272-1(7) , Gospel Light) Gospel Light Pubns.

I Wonder What Jesus Would Do: Fun to Color & Do. 2001. (978-0-7424-0020-7(4) , Instructional Fair) Schaffer, Frank Pubns.

Itt-bitty Bible, No. 5. 2005. (J). pap. 1.49 (***978-1-59317-068-4(8)***) Warner Pr. Pubs.

Itty-Bitty Bible Activity Book. 2005. (J). pap. 2.50 (978-1-59317-013-4(0)) Warner Pr. Pubs.

Itty-Bitty Bible Activity Book: Christmas Edition. 2005. (J). pap. (978-1-59317-015-8(7)) Warner Pr. Pubs.

Itty-Bitty Bible No. 4: Jesus/Child. 2005. (J). pap. 2.10 (978-1-59317-014-1(9)) Warner Pr. Pubs.

Itty-Bitty Book: Jesus. 2006. (J). pap. 1.49 (***978-1-59317-164-3(1)***) Warner Pr. Pubs.

Itty-Bitty Trivia Activity Books, pkg. of 6. 2005. (J). pap. 5.99 (978-1-59317-069-1(6)) Warner Pr. Pubs.

Itty-Bitty/Crossword Puzzles. 2006. 11.99 (978-1-59317-151-3(X)) Warner Pr. Pubs.

Maschke, Ruby A. Bible Puzzles for Children Vol. 3: The Words of Jesus, Vol. 3. 1998. 64p. (gr. 3-7). 7.00 (978-0-8170-1295-3(8)) Judson Pr.

Molski, Carol. Bible Puzzlers: 51 Mind Stretchers. 2007. (ENG.). 64p. (J). 10.99 (***978-0-7586-1332-5(6)***) Concordia Publishing Hse.

Mooney, Belinda. Itty-Bitty Book: New Testament. 2006. (J). pap. 1.49 (***978-1-59317-167-4(6)***) Warner Pr. Pubs.

—Itty-Bitty Book: Old Testament. 2006. (J). pap. 1.49 (***978-1-59317-166-7(8)***) Warner Pr. Pubs.

Moses: God's Man of the Hour—Activity Book. 2005. pap. 1.69 (978-1-59317-109-4(9)) Warner Pr. Pubs.

New Kids Media Staff. Bible Activities: Games, Puzzles & More! 1998. (Bible Fun Ser.). (J). (gr. 1-4). pap. 9.99 (978-0-8010-0248-9(6) , New Kids Media) Baker Bks.

Noah's Big Animal Adventure Game. 2006. 12p. (J). spiral bd. 15.99 (978-0-89051-485-6(2)) Master Bks.

Rhodes, Karen, ed. Super Size itty-bitty Bible Activity Book. 2006. (ENG., Illus.). 192p. (J). pap. 4.99 (978-1-59317-114-8(5)) Warner Pr. Pubs.

School Specialty Publishing. Battle of Jericho. 2004. (Bible Card Games Ser.). nap. (J). (gr. k-8). 0.99 (978-0-7647-1004-9(4) , In Celebration) Schaffer, Frank Pubns.

—Bible Crazy Eights. 2004. (Bible Card Games Ser.). nap. (J). (gr. k-8). 0.99 (978-0-7647-1005-6(2) , In Celebration) Schaffer, Frank Pubns.

—Bible Puzzle Book: Fun for the Whole Family. 2004. (Bible Puzzle Bks.). 128p. (J). pap. 2.99 (978-0-7647-1028-5(1)); pap. 2.99 (978-0-7647-1029-2(X)); pap. 2.99 (978-0-7647-1030-8(3)) Schaffer, Frank Pubns. (In Celebration).

—Bible Puzzle Book Vol. 8: Fun for the Whole Family. 2004. (Bible Puzzle Bks.). 128p. (J). pap. 2.99 (978-0-7647-1031-5(1) , In Celebration) Schaffer, Frank Pubns.

School Specialty Publishing Staff. Hidden Pictures: Old Testament Heroes: Fun to Color & Do Activity Books. 2003. 32p. pap. (978-0-7424-0279-9(7)) School Specialty Publishing.

Spear, Kevin. Itty-bitty Bible Activity Book, Easter. 2007. (Illus.). 48p. (J). pap. 1.49 (***978-1-59317-196-4(X)***) Warner Pr. Pubs.

Spiering, Richard & Spiering, Ruth. Bible Memory Word Searches for Kids. 2006. 176p. (YA). pap. 8.99 (978-0-7369-1900-5(7)) Harvest Hse. Pubs.

Standke, Linda. Bible-Based Word Games, Intermediate. 1999. 32p. (J). (gr. 3-6). pap. 4.99 (978-1-56822-320-9(X) , In Celebration) Schaffer, Frank Pubns.

—Bible-Based Word Games, Primary. 1999. 32p. (J). (gr. 1-3). pap. 4.99 (978-1-56822-319-3(6) , In Celebration) Schaffer, Frank Pubns.

Star Chasers. 2006. (J). pap. 1.79 (***978-1-59317-170-4(6)***) Warner Pr. Pubs.

Strickler, LeeDell. Books of the Bible Games. 2006. 64p. pap. 10.00 (978-0-687-49480-4(X)) Abingdon Pr.

Thomas Nelson Publishing Staff. My First Puzzle Bible. 2007. 12p. (J). bds. 12.99 (***978-1-4003-0975-7(1)***) Nelson, Thomas Inc.

Van Leeuwen, Wendy. Itty-bitty Bible Activity Book, God's Big Christmas Plan. 2007. (Illus.). 48p. (J). pap. 1.49 (***978-1-59317-211-4(7)***) Warner Pr. Pubs.

VBS-Fiesta-Games: Preschool Leader Manual (Silly Chilies Preschool) 2006. (J). pap. 6.99 (978-0-7644-3123-4(4)); 56p. pap. 6.99 (978-0-7644-3124-1(2)) Group Publishing, Inc.

VBS-Fiesta-Grande Games: Leader Manual (Group's Fiesta! Where Kids Are Fired Up about Jesus) 2006. 59p. pap. 9.99 (978-0-7644-2955-2(8)) Group Publishing, Inc.

VN Industries, Inc. Editorial Staff, ed. 5 Angels - A Jigsaw Puzzle Book: With Inspirational Messages from the Bible. 2005. (Illus.). 12p. bds. 19.95 (978-1-882330-71-3(4)) Magni.

Wallis, MaryAlice Lloyd & Lindstrom, C. G. LDS Puzzle Pals. 2007. (J). (***978-1-55517-994-6(0)***) Cedar Fort, Inc./CFI Distribution.

BIBLE PLAYS

see Mysteries and Miracle Plays

BIBLE PUZZLES

see Bible Games and Puzzles

BIBLE STORIES

ABC Personas de la Biblia: Libro para ninos. 2000. pap. (978-1-57697-834-4(6)) United Bible Societies/ Americas Service Ctr.

ABC's of the Bible. 2004. 32p. (J). pap. 3.99 (978-0-88724-214-4(6) , CD-2028) Carson-Dellosa Publishing Co., Inc.

ABCs of the Bible Coloring Book. (Illus.). 16p. (J). pap. 1.50 (978-0-87162-873-2(2) , E6036) Warner Pr. Pubs.

Abingdon. PowerXpress David the Boy Disciple. 2.95 incl. cd-rom (978-0-687-00191-0(9)) Abingdon Pr.

—PowerXpress David the King Disciple. 2.95 incl. cd-rom (978-0-687-00211-5(7)) Abingdon Pr.

—PowerXpress Psalms & Songs. 9.95 incl. audio compact disk (978-0-687-07972-8(1)) Abingdon Pr.

—PowerXpress Samuel Disciple. 2.95 incl. cd-rom (978-0-687-00201-6(X)) Abingdon Pr.

—PowerXpress Three Women of Faith. 9.95 incl. audio compact disk (978-0-687-07962-9(4)) Abingdon Pr.

Abraham, Ken. Jesus Loves Me Bible Storybook. 2002. (Illus.). 448p. (J). 14.99 (978-1-4003-0183-6(1)) Nelson, Thomas Inc.

—Jesus Loves Me Bible Storybook & Devotional Combo. 2003. (Illus.). 672p. (J). 24.99 (978-1-4003-0185-0(8)) Nelson, Thomas Inc.

Adams, Georgia & Utton, Peter. Cuentame la Biblia.Tr. of Bible Storybook. (SPA.). 96p. (J). (gr. k-3). 17.56 (978-84-480-1120-8(1)) Timun Mas, Editorial S.A. ESP. *Dist:* Lectorum Pubns., Inc.

The Adventures of David. 2003. (Rub & See Activity Bks.). (Illus.). 24p. (J). 2.99 (978-0-8254-7261-9(X)) Kregel Pubns.

The Adventures of Moses. 2003. (Rub & See Activity Bks.). (Illus.). 24p. (J). 2.99 (978-0-8254-7260-2(1)) Kregel Pubns.

Ages 4-5 Take Home Winter 2002-2003. 2002. pap. 14.99 (978-1-59185-104-2(1)) CharismaLife Pubs.

Ahora Puedo Leer Mi Biblia. 1998. (Biblias para Ninos Ser.).Tr. of Eager Reader Bible. (SPA., Illus.). 432p. (J). (ps-3). 14.99 (978-0-7899-0521-5(3) , 497780) Editorial Unilit.

Alexander, Pat. The Children's Story Bible. Cox, Carolyn, illus. 2001. 256p. (J). (gr. 4-7). 19.95 (978-0-664-22389-2(3)) Westminster John Knox Pr.

—My First Bible. Baxter, Leon, illus. 2002. (Bestselling Children's Books - Religious Ser.). 480p. (J). (gr. k-4). 14.99 (978-1-56148-360-0(5)) Good Bks.

All about Me: Bible Story: God Made People. (Scripture Bites Ser.). (Illus.). (J). 7.99 (978-0-7847-9018-2(3) , 00711) Standard Publishing.

Allen, Jan. Now I Know the Story of Samson. l.t. ed. 2006. (Illus.). 40p. (J). (978-0-9765514-1-6(1)) Light Bugs Publishing.

Alsbrooks, Stephanie. Cow Moooves Through the Books of the Bible: Genesis. Burg, Donna, illus. 2004. (J). bds. 9.99 (978-1-4183-0002-9(0)) Christ Inspired, Inc.

—Cow Moooves Through the Books of the Bible: Job. Burg, Donna, illus. 2004. (J). bds. 9.99 (978-1-4183-0006-7(3)) Christ Inspired, Inc.

—Cow Moooves Through the Books of the Bible - Exodus. Burg, Donna, illus. 2004. (J). bds. 9.99 (978-1-4183-0007-4(1)) Christ Inspired, Inc.

—Cow Moooves Through the Books of the Bible - Joshua. Burg, Donna, illus. 2004. (J). bds. 9.99 (978-1-4183-0017-3(9)) Christ Inspired, Inc.

The Amazing Escape: A Bible Story Maze Book. 2002. 14p. (J). (gr. k-3). 12.99 (978-0-8254-7255-8(5)) Kregel Pubns.

American Bible Society Staff, ed. My First Read & Learn Bible. 2006. (Illus.). 37p. (J). bds. 9.99 (978-0-439-65128-8(X)) Scholastic, Inc.

Amery, H. Bible Stories Jigsaw Book. 2004. 20p. (J). 14.95 (978-0-7945-0558-5(9)) EDC Publishing.

—Joseph & the Amazing Coat. 2004. (Bible Tales Readers Ser.). (SPA., Illus.). 16p. (J). lib. bdg. 12.95 (978-1-58086-540-1(2)) EDC Publishing.

—Moses in the Bulrushes. 2004. (Bible Tales Readers Ser.). (SPA., Illus.). 16p. (J). lib. bdg. 12.95 (978-1-58086-541-8(0)) EDC Publishing.

Amery, Heather. Bible Stories. Young, Norman, illus. gif. ed. 2004. (Bible Tales Readers Ser.). 200p. (J). (ps-3). 24.95 (978-0-7460-4145-1(4)) EDC Publishing.

—First Stories From the Bible. Doherty, Gillian, ed. 2007. (Bible Tales Readers Ser.). 144p. (J). 17.99 (***978-0-7945-1668-0(8)*** , Usborne) EDC Publishing.

—Story of Baby Jesus Board Bk. rev. ed. 2006. 10p. (J). bds. 7.99 (978-0-7945-1187-6(2) , Usborne) EDC Publishing.

—Story of Jesus. 2005. (Illus.). 100p. (J). 14.99 incl. audio compact disk (978-0-7945-0831-9(6) , Usborne) EDC Publishing.

Amery, Heather & Temporin, Elena. Family Bible. 2004. (Illus.). 192p. (J). 19.95 (978-0-7945-0333-8(0) , Usborne) EDC Publishing.

Andersen, Hans Christian. Hans Christian Andersen: Illustrated Fairy Tales, Vol. 2. 2001. (Illus.). 416p. 29.95 (978-87-7247-271-3(5)) Scandinavia Publishing Hse. DNK. *Dist:* National Bk. Network.

Anderson, J. & Maddox, Mike. The Lion Graphic Bible: The Whole Story from Genesis to Revelation. 2004. (Illus.). 256p. pap. 12.95 (978-0-7459-4923-9(1)) Lion Hudson plc GBR. *Dist:* Independent Pubs. Group.

Andrews, Jackie, retold by. 100 Bible Stories for Children. 2005. (Illus.). 208p. (J). 7.99 (978-0-517-22586-8(7) , Testament) Random Hse. Value Publishing.

Animals Big & Small: Bible Story: Noah's Big Boat. (Scripture Bites Ser.). (Illus.). (J). 7.99 (978-0-7847-9006-9(X) , 00703) Standard Publishing.

Anonymous. Wee Ones' Bible Stories. 2004. reprint ed. pap. 15.95 (978-1-4191-9335-4(X)); pap. 1.99 (978-1-4192-9335-1(4)) Kessinger Publishing, LLC.

Arch Books Set. 2004. pap. 99.00 (978-0-570-09025-0(3)) Concordia Publishing Hse.

Arch Books Staff. Noahs 2 by 2 Adventures Spanis. 2004. (SPA.). 24p. (J). 2.49 (978-0-570-08320-7(6)) Concordia Publishing Hse.

—Spanish David & Goliat. 2004. (SPA.). 24p. (J). 2.49 (978-0-570-08322-1(2)) Concordia Publishing Hse.

—Spanish down Thru the Roof. 2004. (SPA.). 24p. (J). 2.49 (978-0-570-08323-8(0)) Concordia Publishing Hse.

—Spanish Moses Dry Feet. 2004. (SPA.). 24p. (J). 2.49 (978-0-570-08321-4(4)) Concordia Publishing Hse.

Arthur, Kay & Arndt, Janna. You're a Brave Man, Daniel! Daniel 1-6. 2000. (Discover 4 Yourself Inductive Bible Studies for Kids Ser.). 160p. (gr. 4-7). pap. 9.99 (978-0-7369-0147-5(7)) Harvest Hse. Pubs.

Aston, Al. Gifts for a King. Hutchinson, Joy, illus. 2005. 16p. pap. 2.00 (978-1-84427-179-5(X)) Scripture Union GBR. *Dist:* STL Distribution North America.

Atchison, Beth. The Story of Creation: Genesis 1-2 for Children. Koehler, Ed, illus. 2005. (ENG.). 16p. (J). (ps-ps). 1.99 (978-0-7586-0406-4(8)) Concordia Publishing Hse.

Augustine, Peg. Family Time with God: Bible Story Activities for Every Day. 2004. 128p. pap. 12.00 (978-0-687-04823-6(0)) Abingdon Pr.

Augustine, Peg, ed. Read to Me: Bible Stories for Preschoolers. 2004. 160p. (ps). 18.00 (978-0-687-09208-6(6)) Abingdon Pr.

—Read with Me: Bible Stories for First Readers. 2004. 160p. (ps-3). 18.00 (978-0-687-09209-3(4)) Abingdon Pr.

Aydin, Robert, tr. Syriac Bible for Children. 2007. (SYR.). (J). 48.00 (***978-1-59333-749-0(3)***) Gorgias Pr., LLC.

Baby Blessings Staff. Bathtime Bible Stories. 2006. 8p. 10.99 (978-0-7847-1502-4(5) , 04153) Standard Publishing.

Babyfaith. God Made Christmas: The Story of Baby Jesus. 2006. (Illus.). 12p. (J). (ps-k). bds. 6.99 (978-1-59145-295-9(3)) Nelson, Thomas Inc.

Baby's Bedtime Bible Stories. 2006. (First Bible Collection(R) Ser.). 20p. (J). 12.99 (978-0-7847-1207-8(7) , 03993) Standard Publishing.

Baby's First Bible. 2002. (J). spiral bd. (978-0-9720158-0-6(9)) Story Reader, Inc.

Baden, Robert. Jesus Returns to Heaven. Hackett, Michael, illus. rev. ed. 2004. (ENG.). 16p. (J). 1.99 (978-0-7586-0407-1(6)) Concordia Publishing Hse.

Bader, Joanne. God Provides Victory Through Gideon. Giliewe, Unada, illus. 2004. (Arch Books). 16p. (J). 1.99 (978-0-7586-0673-0(7)) Concordia Publishing Hse.

Bagley, Val. Hidden Treasures of the Book of Mormon. 2004. 13.95 (978-1-57734-759-0(5)) Covenant Communications, Inc.

Bagley, Val Chadwick & Mullins, Amy. My Favorite Stories from the Bible. 2006. (Illus.). 28p. (J). (***978-1-59811-173-6(6)***) Covenant Communications.

Baker, Marvin G. Matthew's Story: Based on the Gospel of Matthew. 2004. 160p. pap. 9.95 (978-0-9729256-2-4(7) , Tweener Pr.) Baker Trittin Pr.

Ball, Ann & Will, Julianne. Catholic Bible Stories for Children. 2006. per. 19.95 (978-1-59276-243-9(3)) Our Sunday Visitor, Publishing Div.

Ball, Liz, illus. Bible Stories: Find-the-Picture Puzzles. 2004. (Find-the-Picture Puzzle Ser.: 1). 24p. (J). pap. 2.95 (978-0-8198-1163-9(7) , 332-026) Pauline Bks. & Media.

Banks, Celia. Jacob's Promise. 2006. pap. 13.99 (978-0-9764460-6-4(5)) HonorNet.

Barfield, Maggie. Welcome the Baby Jesus. 2004. 32p. (J). 6.99 (978-0-7586-0249-7(9)) Concordia Publishing Hse.

Barnes, Trevor. The Kingfisher Children's Bible. 2001. (Bibles & Bible References Ser.). (Illus.). 256p. (J). (gr. k-3). tchr. ed. 24.95 (978-0-7534-5364-3(9) , Kingfisher) Houghton Mifflin Co. Trade & Reference Div.

Baro, Joan. The Bible: A People Listen to God. Aquinaco, Carmen, tr. from CAT. Rius, Marla, illus. 1998. 352p. (gr. 5-9). 24.95 (978-0-8146-2509-5(6)) Liturgical Pr.

Batchelor, Mary & Boshoff, Penny. My First Bedtime Bible. 2005. (Illus.). 256p. (J). (ps-2). 9.95 (978-1-84610-026-0(7)) Make Believe Ideas GBR. *Dist:* Ingram Pub. Services.

Bauman, Amy. Jonah & the Whale: Deluxe Sound Storybook. Forlini, Victoria, ed. Mada Design Staff, illus. 2005. 22p. (J). (ps-ps). 14.95 (978-0-696-22819-3(X)) Meredith Bks.

—Joseph & His Coat of Many Colors: Deluxe Sound Storybook. Forlini, Victoria, ed. Mada Design Staff, illus. 2005. 22p. (J). (ps-ps). 14.95 (978-0-696-22818-6(1)) Meredith Bks.

Beachy, Mary Ellen. Light on Your Path: True Stories & Scriptures. 1999. 237p. (YA). (gr. 2-12). pap. 10.95 (978-1-890050-35-1(0)) Carlisle Pr.- Walnut Creek.

Bean Sprouts Editors. Favorite Bible Stories. Pepper, Bob, illus. 2000. (Place-a-Piece Bks.). 10p. (J). (ps-k). bds. 14.99 (978-0-7847-1212-2(3) , 04394, Bean Sprouts) Standard Publishing.

Beck, Susan Elizabeth. God Loves Me Bible. Oostema, Gloria, illus. rev. ed. 2004. (Bible Storybooks Ser.). 128p. (J). 7.99 (978-0-310-70779-0(X)) Zonderkidz.

Beck, William F. Bible Stories in Pictures. Rogers, Ruth W. et al, illus. 2nd ed. 2003. (ALB, SPA & SWE.). 376p. pap. 6.50 (978-1-931891-08-0(7)) Multi-Language Pubns.

—Histori Biblike Me Llustrime: Nga Krijimi Ne Kishen e Hershme. Rogers, Ruth W. et al, illus. 2003. (ALB, SPA & SWE.). 374p. (J). pap. 6.50 (978-1-931891-07-3(9) , 38-7378) Multi-Language Pubns.

—Historias Biblicas Ilustradas: De la Creacion a la Iglesia Primitiva. Rogers, Ruth W. et al, illus. 2002. Orig. Title: Bible Story in Pictures. (ALB, SPA & SWE.). 376p. (YA). pap. 6.50 (978-1-931891-05-9(2) , 38-7374) Multi-Language Pubns.

Beers, Gilbert. The One Year Bible for Children. 2001. (Tyndale Kids Ser.). (Illus.). 432p. 14.99 (978-0-8423-7355-5(1)) Tyndale Hse. Pubs.

Bek, et al. Rahab Saves Spies & Esther Rescues Her People. Bek et al, illus. 2006. (Upside down Bible Stories Ser.). 62p. (J). pap. 7.99 (978-0-7814-4392-0(X)) Cook, David C. Publishing Co.

Belec, Glynis. Jesus Washes Peter's Feet. 2001. (gr. k-3). lib. bdg. 9.85 (978-0-613-71025-1(8)) Tandem Library Bks.

Bell, Bill. Noah: The Incredible Voyager. Bell, Bill, illus. 2004. (Illus.). 48p. (J). (ps-3). pap. 14.99 (978-0-88092-801-4(8)) Royal Fireworks Publishing Co.

Benjamin-Farren, Joan. Shuli & Me: From Slavery to Freedom A Storybook Omer Calendar. Benjamin-Farren, Joan, illus. 2006. (J). 19.95 (***978-0-9788802-0-0(X)***) Black Jasmine.

Benjamin's House. (Gospel Road Story Bks.). (Illus.). 12p. (J). (ps-k). 0.99 (978-0-8254-7224-4(5)) Kregel Pubns.

Bennett, William J. El libro de la familia y el hogar para Ninos. Alonso Blanco, Maria Victoria, tr. 2005. (SPA., Illus.). 112p. 18.95 (978-84-666-1662-1(4)) Ediciones B ESP. *Dist:* Independent Pubs. Group.

Benton, James. The Case Files of Herman Ootix, B. I. Faith for Life2 Course Five Student Book. Janssen, Patricia E., ed. 2nd ed. 2003. (J). stu. ed., spiral bd. 14.99 (978-0-9727146-6-2(9)) LOGOS System Assocs.

Betzer, Dan. Dan & Louie Vol. 2: The Greatest Stories Ever Told. enl. ed. 2005. (J). 89.00 incl. audio compact disk (978-1-933497-01-3(7)) Robison Gamble Creative.

Bible Adventure Stories. 2002. (J). spiral bd. (978-0-9720158-2-4(9)) Story Reader, Inc.

Bible Heroes. 2004. 32p. (J). 0.99 (978-0-7647-1032-2(X)); 0.99 (978-0-7647-1033-9(8)); 0.99 (978-0-7647-1034-6(6)); 0.99 (978-0-7647-1035-3(4)) Schaffer, Frank Pubns. (In Celebration).

Bible Lessons for Juniors, Book 3: The Life of Christ. 2007. (J). (***978-1-60178-014-0(1)***) Reformation Heritage Bks.

Bible Stories. 2003. (Illus.). 256p. (J). 11.95 (978-0-7525-8974-9(1)) Parragon, Inc.

Bible Stories from A to Z. 2002. (Christian Bks.). 144p. (J). (gr. k-4). 14.99 (978-0-7439-7102-7(7) , 7102) Teacher Created Materials, Inc.

Bible Story Coloring Pages, Vol. 2. 2004. 248p. 17.99 (978-0-8307-3095-7(8) , Gospel Light) Gospel Light Pubns.

Bible Story Fun: My Wipe-off Book. 2003. spiral bd. (978-0-7853-8573-8(8)) Publications International, Ltd.

Bible Story Puzzles Grade 1-3. 2002. (Christian Product Ser.). (J). per. 3.99 (978-0-88724-866-5(7) , CD-2023) Carson-Dellosa Publishing Co., Inc.

Bible Story Puzzles Grade 4-6. 2002. (Christian Product Ser.). (J). per. 3.99 (978-0-88724-867-2(5) , CD-2024) Carson-Dellosa Publishing Co., Inc.

Bible Time Line. 11.99 (978-0-7847-1004-3(X)) Standard Publishing.

Bible Visuals International, compiled by. Doming the Popsicle Boy. 2005. (Illus.). (J). pap. (978-1-932381-11-5(2) , 5100) Bible Visuals International, Inc.

—John & Betty Stam. 2005. (Illus.). (J). pap. (978-1-932381-12-2(0) , 5190) Bible Visuals International, Inc.

—Rainbow Garden. 2005. (Illus.). (J). pap. (978-1-932381-15-3(5) , 5500) Bible Visuals International, Inc.

—Until the Letter Came. 2004. (Illus.). (J). cd-rom (978-1-933206-45-5(4)) Bible Visuals International, Inc.

La Biblia Leemela. rev. ed. 2004. (SPA., Illus.). 992p. 15.99 (978-1-55819-286-7(7)) B&H Publishing Grp.

The Big Book of Bible Story Art Activities: Involve Children As They Hear & Talk about Bible Stories Reproducible Manual. 2004. (Big Book Ser.). 216p. pap. 19.99 (978-0-8307-3308-8(6) , Gospel Light) Gospel Light Pubns.

Big Fishs Supper. 2004. bds. 5.99 (978-0-8254-7287-9(3)) Kregel Pubns.

Big Idea Productions Staff & Kenney, Cindy. Veggie Bible Mania: Amazing Facts, Wonders & Mysteries. 2006. (Illus.). 176p. (J). (gr. 4-7). 14.99 (978-1-59145-434-2(4)) Nelson, Thomas Inc.

Biggs-Scribner, Stephanie, comment. Children of the Bible. 2005. (KOR.). 184p. (YA). pap. (978-1-890569-91-4(7) , WD/GBGM Bks.) General Board of Global Ministries, The United Methodist Church.

The Birth of a Savior. 2002. (Illus.). 24p. (J). (gr. k-4). 5.99 (978-1-57759-512-0(2)) Dalmatian Pr.

The birth of Samson. 2007. (J). mass mkt. (***978-0-9769722-0-4(4)***) Leslie, Beverly J.

Blakeney, Anita. Little Golden Nuggets for Children. 2001. (J). 7.99 (978-0-9719241-7-8(1)) Chosen Word Publishing.

The Blue Jackal. 2004. bds. 7.99 (978-0-8254-7283-1(0)) Kregel Pubns.

Bluedorn, Johannah, illus. Bless the Lord: The 103rd Psalm. 2005. 32p. (J). 13.00 (978-1-933228-02-0(4) , 3000) Trivium Pursuit.

Blundell, T. On the Way for 9 - 11's. 80p. (J). Vol. 2. (Illus.). pap. 11.99 (978-1-85792-552-4(1)); Vol. 3. pap. 11.99 (978-1-85792-553-1(X)) Christian Focus Pubns. GBR. (Christian Focus). *Dist:* Riverside.

Blundell, Thalia & Blundell, Trevor. On the Way for 9 - 11's. 80p. (J). Vol. 4. pap. 11.99 (978-1-85792-554-8(8)); Vol. 5. pap. 11.99 (978-1-85792-555-5(6)) Christian Focus Pubns. GBR. (Christian Focus). *Dist:* Riverside.

Blundell, Trevor. On the Way for 9 - 11's, Bk. 1. 80p. (J). pap. 11.99 (978-1-85792-551-7(3) , Christian Focus) Christian Focus Pubns. GBR. *Dist:* Riverside.

Blundell, Trevor & Biblewise Staff. On the Way for 3 - 9's: Christmas & Jesus' Miracles, Vol. 2. 88-104p. (J). pap. 11.99 (978-1-85792-319-3(7) , Christian Focus) Christian Focus Pubns. GBR. *Dist:* Riverside.

Blundell, Trevor & Blundell, Thalia. On the Way for 3 - 9's: Creation, Abraham & Jacob. (Illus.). 88-104p. (J). pap. 11.99 (978-1-85792-301-8(4) , Christian Focus) Christian Focus Pubns. GBR. *Dist:* Riverside.

—On the Way for 3 - 9's Vol. 3: Prayer, Easter & Peter. 88-104p. (J). pap. 11.99 (978-1-85792-320-9(0) , Christian Focus) Christian Focus Pubns. GBR. *Dist:* Riverside.

—On the Way for 3 - 9's Vol. 4: Joseph, Job & Moses. (Illus.). 88-104p. (J). pap. 11.99 (978-1-85792-324-7(3) , Christian Focus) Christian Focus Pubns. GBR. *Dist:* Riverside.

—On the Way for 3 - 9's Vol. 5: The Exodus, Joshua & Gideon. (Illus.). 88-104p. (J). pap. 11.99 (978-1-85792-325-4(1) , Christian Focus) Christian Focus Pubns. GBR. *Dist:* Riverside.

—On the Way for 3 - 9's Vol. 9: David & Solomon. 88-104p. (J). pap. 11.99 (978-1-85792-404-6(5) , Christian Focus) Christian Focus Pubns. GBR. *Dist:* Riverside.

—On the Way for 3 - 9's Vol. 10: Elijah, Elisha & Jonah. 88-104p. (J). pap. 11.99 (978-1-85792-405-3(3) , Christian Focus) Christian Focus Pubns. GBR. *Dist:* Riverside.

Blyton, Enid. El Nino en el Templo. 2nd ed. 1999. (Historias Biblicas Ilustradas; Illustrated Bible Stories Ser.). (SPA., Illus.). 32p. (ps-3). pap. 4.99 (978-0-8254-1066-6(5) , Editorial Portavoz) Kregel Pubns.

—La Pequena Hija de Jairo. 1999. (Historias Biblicas Ilustradas; Illustrated Bible Stories Ser.). (SPA., Illus.). 32p. (ps-3). pap. 4.99 (978-0-8254-1068-0(1) , Editorial Portavoz) Kregel Pubns.

Las Bodas de Cana Vol. 18: Serie Minilibritos Aventuras de la Biblia. 2001. pap. (978-1-930564-88-6(0)) United Bible Societies/Americas Service Ctr.

Bollen, Christine. Frogs by the Dozen. Matyschenko, Tanya, illus. l.t. ed. 2006. 24p. (J). per. 9.99 (978-1-59879-115-0(X)) Lifevest Publishing, Inc.

Bone, David L. PowerXpress How the Bible Came to Be Unit. 2004. 144p. 115.00 (978-0-687-00648-9(1)) Abingdon Pr.

Boyd, Charles F. What God has Always Wanted. 2006. (***978-1-57229-725-8(5)***) FamilyLife.

Brand, Ruth. Joseph. Pennington, Jack & Tank, Darrel, illus. 2004. 87p. (J). 19.99 (978-0-8280-1854-8(5) , 104-522) Review & Herald Publishing Assn.

Brand, Ruth R. Adam & Eve. Vitale, Raoul & Tank, Darrel, illus. 2005. (Family Bible Story Ser.). 95p. (J). (ps-7). per. 19.99 (978-0-8280-1850-0(2)) Review & Herald Publishing Assn.

Brand, Ruth Redding. Jacob, Vol. 101-180. 2005. (Family Bible Story Ser.). (Illus.). 127p. (J). 19.99 (978-0-8280-1852-4(9)) Review & Herald Publishing Assn.

Bratton, Heidi, photos by. The Little Shepherd. 2000. (Walking with God Board Bks.). (Illus.). 16p. (ps-k). bds. 5.95 (978-0-8091-6660-2(7) , 6660-7) Paulist Pr.

Breems, Beau. The Promise. Breems, Beau, illus. 2006. (YA). 10.00 (978-0-9768680-9-5(1)); 20.00 (978-0-9768680-8-8(3)) Burning Bush Creation.

Breems, Beau A. La Gran Historia: The Illustrated Gospel from Creation to Resurrection. Breems, Beau A., illus. 2005. Tr. of His Story. (SPA.). (J). 10.99 (978-0-9768680-5-7(9)); (Illus.). 50p. 19.95 (978-0-9768680-1-9(6) , 1000); (Illus.). 50p. per. 14.95 (978-0-9768680-3-3(2) , 3000) Burning Bush Creation.

—His Story: The Illustrated Gospel from Creation to Resurrection. Breems, Beau A., illus. l.t. ed. 2005. Tr. of Gran Historia. (Illus.). 50p. (J). 19.95 (978-0-9768680-0-2(8) , 0-976868O-0-8) Burning Bush Creation.

Breems, Beau Alan. His Story: The Illustrated Gospel from Creation to Resurrection. Breems, Beau Alan, illus. 2005. (J). per. 14.95 (978-0-9768680-2-6(4)) Burning Bush Creation.

Britt, Stephanie M., illus. My Little Bible: YMLBR. 2005. 96p. (J). 5.99 (978-1-4003-0647-3(7)) Nelson, Thomas Inc.

Broadman, Holman. First Christmas. 1999. 19.95 (978-0-88271-676-3(X)) Regina Pr., Malhame & Co.

Brolsma, Jody, ed. Pray & Play Bible for Young Children. 2004. (Illus.). 176p. (Orig.). (ps). pap. 19.99 (978-0-7644-2024-5(0) , Flagship Church Resources) Group Publishing, Inc.

Brooks, F. & Litchfield, J. Nativity Lift-the-Flap. 2004. (First Stories Ser.). 24p. (J). 10.95 (978-0-7945-0529-5(5)) EDC Publishing.

Brown, Brian & Melrose. The Complete Storykeepers Collection. Meiro, Andrew, illus. 1998. 302p. (J). (ps-5). reprint ed. 17.99 (978-1-85608-395-9(0)) Hunt, John Publishing Ltd. GBR. *Dist:* O. M. Literature.

Brown, Janet Allison, et al. David & Goliath. Durantz, Summer, illus. 2003. (Inspirational Collection). 24p. (J). pap. 3.99 (978-0-7696-3127-1(4) , Brighter Child) School Specialty Publishing.

—Noah's Ark. Durantz, Summer, illus. 2003. (Inspirational Collection). 24p. (J). pap. 3.99 (978-0-7696-3125-7(8) , Brighter Child) School Specialty Publishing.

Brown, Toni Sorenson, photos by. Heroes of the Bible. 2004. (Illus.). 32p. (J). 17.95 (978-1-59156-097-5(7)) Covenant Communications, Inc.

Bruno, Bonnie & Reinsma, Carol. Read Together Bible. Schneider, Jennifer & Lemelman, Martin, illus. 2006. (Read Together Ser.). 312p. (J). 14.99 (978-0-7847-1741-7(9) , 04367) Standard Publishing.

—Young Readers Bible. 2006. (Illus.). 448p. pap. 9.99 (978-0-7847-1908-4(X)) Standard Publishing.

Budensiek, Joy. Jesus My Very Best Friend: Chinese/English. 2005. (CHI.). (J). 2.95 (978-0-9749168-7-3(0)) FEA Ministries.

—Jesus My Very Best Friend: Russian/English. 2005. (RUS.). (J). per. 2.95 (978-0-9749168-5-9(4)) FEA Ministries.

Buell, Jean. Sacred Stories: A Beginner's Bible Book. Larkin, Jean K., ed. 2005. (Illus.). 32p. (J). 3.95 (978-1-933178-21-9(3) , 3510) Pflaum Publishing Group.

Burkart, Jeffrey E. A Surprise in Disguise. Dorenkamp, Michelle, illus. 2000. (Arch Bks.). (ENG.). 16p. (J). (gr. k-4). 1.99 (978-0-570-07564-6(5)) Concordia Publishing Hse.

Burroughs, Chrysti & Burroughs, Scott. The Super Short, Amazing Story of David & Goliath. Burroughs, Scott, illus. 2005. (Illus.). 30p. (J). (ps-ps). 10.99 (978-0-8254-2412-0(7)) Kregel Pubns.

Burroughs, Scott & Burroughs, Chrysti. The Super Short Amazing Story of Daniel in the Lions' Den. 2005. (J). 10.99 (978-0-8254-2299-7(X)) Kregel Pubns.

Butcher, Sam. My First Book of Catholic Bible Stories. 1999. (Illus.). 96p. (J). (ps-3). 9.95 (978-0-88271-752-4(9)) Regina Pr., Malhame & Co.

Butcher, Sam, illus. Precious Moments: Storybook Bible & Girl Prayer Pal Set. 2003. 14.60 (978-0-7180-0569-6(4)) Nelson, Thomas Inc.

Butler, Heather. Stories to Make You Think. Smith, Simon, illus. 1999. 128p. (J). pap. (978-1-84101-034-2(0) , Barnabas) Bible Reading Fellowship.

La Calda de Jerico. 2004. 15.95 (978-1-56814-617-1(5)) CCC of America.

Caldwell, Lise. Christmas: A Classic Bible Story. 2001. 20p. 9.99 (978-0-7847-1160-6(7) , Bean Sprouts) Standard Publishing.

—Jesus: A Classic Bible Story. Stanley, Robin, ed. 2006. (Classic Bible Stories). 20p. (YA). 9.99 (978-0-7847-1276-4(X) , 04009) Standard Publishing.

Camel's Hair & Honey. 2000. (Arch Bks.). (Illus.). 16p. (J). (gr. k-4). 1.99 (978-0-570-07567-7(X)) Concordia Publishing Hse.

Campbell, Julie. Get A Clue: Bible Mysteries. 2006. (J). pap. 4.50 (***978-1-59317-157-5(9)***) Warner Pr. Pubs.

Campdepadros, Jorgelina & Campdepadros, Eduardo. Los Dos Cimientos. 2004. (Parabolas Para Ninos; Parables for Kids Ser.).Tr. of Two Foundations. (SPA.). 32p. 3.99 (978-0-8254-0884-7(9) , Editorial Portavoz) Kregel Pubns.

—La Ovejita Perdida. 2002. (Parabolas Para Ninos; Parables for Kids Ser.).Tr. of Lost Sheep. (SPA.). 32p. pap. 3.99 (978-0-8254-0886-1(5) , Editorial Portavoz) Kregel Pubns.

—Yaco el Sembrador. 2004. (Bible Stories Ser.).Tr. of Yaco, the Seedsower. (SPA.). 32p. 3.99 (978-0-8254-1146-5(7) , Editorial Portavoz) Kregel Pubns.

Carlson, Melody. A Treasure Beyond Measure. Bjorkman, Steve, illus. 2005. 32p. 9.99 (978-1-58134-343-4(4) , Crossway Bibles) Crossway Bks.

Carr, Jon & Carr, Debra. Jeremy the Giraffe. 2004. 6.00 (978-1-59089-723-2(4)) Creflo Dollar Ministries Pubns.

Carvin, Rose-Mae. Ly Huy's Escape: A Story of Vietnam. Neal, Sharon & Mayer, Kristin, eds. Olson, Ed & Willoughby, Yuko, illus. 2007. (ENG.). 40p. (J). pap. (978-1-932381-13-9(9) , 5275) Bible Visuals International, Inc.

Cedarmont, Ninos. Cantos Biblicos: 16 Cantos Biblicos Clasicos Para Ninos. 1999. 7.99 (978-0-7601-2850-3(2)) Brentwood Music, Inc.

—Cantos de Escuela Dominical. 1999. (SPA.). 7.99 (978-0-7601-2852-7(9)) Brentwood Productions.

Chariot Victor Publishing Staff. Daniel & the Lion's Den Puzzle Book. 2000. (Illus.). 5p. (J). (ps-3). 9.99 (978-0-7814-3411-9(4)) Cook, David C. Publishing Co.

—Four in One Toddler Book. 2000. 12.99 (978-0-7814-3423-2(8)) Cook, David C. Publishing Co.

Charlie Church Mouse Bible Adventures! Early Elementary. 2003. (J). cd-rom 19.98 (978-0-9714753-1-1(8)) Life-Line Studios, Inc.

Charman, Andy. The Story of Christmas. Banazi, Pauline, illus. 2000. 16p. (ps-k). pap. 5.00 (978-0-7548-0236-5(1)) Anness Publishing, Inc.

A Child's First Bible. 2002. (J). spiral bd. (978-0-9720158-5-1(X)) Story Reader, Inc.

Choi, Young-Jin. Jesus Feeds Everybody! Kim, Jung-cho, illus. 2007. Tr. of Jesus' Breadbasket. (J). bds. 5.95 (***978-0-8198-3987-9(6)***) Pauline Bks. & Media.

—Mary's Big Surprise. Kim, Jung-cho, illus. 2007. Tr. of Mary, Crying & Laughing. (J). bds. 5.95 (***978-0-8198-4853-6(0)***) Pauline Bks. & Media.

—Where Are You, Little Lamb? Kim, Jung-cho, illus. 2007. (J). bds. 5.95 (***978-0-8198-8316-2(6)***) Pauline Bks. & Media.

Christian Focus Publishing Staff. Joseph: God's Dreamer. 2000. (Bible Wise Ser.). (Illus.). 32p. (J). (gr. k-3). pap. (978-1-85792-343-8(X) , Christian Focus) Christian Focus Pubns.

—The Little Rich Man. 2000. (Illus.). 10p. (J). (ps-k). (978-1-85792-345-2(6) , Christian Focus) Christian Focus Pubns.

—Safe at Sea. 2000. (Illus.). 10p. (J). (ps-k). (978-1-85792-346-9(4) , Christian Focus) Christian Focus Pubns.

—The Singing Shepherd - David. 1999. (Illus.). 10p. (J). (ps-k). (978-1-85792-463-3(0) , Christian Focus) Christian Focus Pubns.

Christian, Kristy L. & Merrill, Kathryn L. In Jesus' Time: Teaching Bible History to Children of All Ages. 2nd ed. 2002. (Illus.). 278p. (YA). (gr. 6-12). reprint ed. pap. 16.95 (978-0-9626535-3-7(5)) Infinite Discovery.

Cjs Closet. 2004. cd-rom, audio compact disk 24.95 (978-0-9707201-0-8(6)) Kay Productions LLC.

Classic Bible Stories: A Reproducible Coloring Book. (Illus.). 80p. 6.99 (978-0-7847-0606-0(9) , 02255) Standard Publishing.

Clayden, Julie. Daniel. Joliffe, Angela, illus. 2005. 14p. (J). (gr. 3-5). bds. 5.95 (978-1-904637-10-3(8)) Pupfish Ltd. GBR. *Dist:* Penton Overseas, Inc.

—David. Joliffe, Angella, illus. 2005. Tr. of David. 14p. (J). (gr. 3-5). bds. 5.95 (978-1-904637-09-7(4) , Penton Kids) Penton Overseas, Inc.

—Jonah. Joliffe, Angella, illus. 2005. Tr. of Jona. 14p. (J). (gr. 3-5). bds. 5.95 (978-1-904637-12-7(4)) Pupfish Ltd. GBR. *Dist:* Penton Overseas, Inc.

—Noah. Joliffe, Angella, illus. 2005. 14p. (J). (gr. 3-5). bds. 5.95 (978-1-904637-11-0(6)) Pupfish Ltd. GBR. *Dist:* Penton Overseas, Inc.

Cleveland, Viney. David & Goliath. 2002. 32p. (J). pap. 12.00 (978-0-8059-5439-5(2)) Dorrance Publishing Co., Inc.

Coleman, Michael. Bible Stories. 1999. (Top Ten Ser.). (Illus.). 192p. (gr. 6-12). pap. 4.50 (978-0-439-07801-6(6)) Scholastic, Inc.

Colson, Charles. Fundamentals: Creation vs. Evolution, Real Story Teach Pack. (J). (gr. 4-6). (978-0-633-05790-9(8)) LifeWay Christian Resources.

Come to God's Party: Bible Story Album. 2004. (Firelight Ser.). (ps-k). 4.99 (978-0-8066-6483-5(5)) Augsburg Fortress, Pubs.

Come to God's Party: Bible Story Flipbook. 2004. (Firelight Ser.). (gr. 3-4). 4.99 (978-0-8066-6487-3(8)) Augsburg Fortress, Pubs.

Come to God's Party: Bible Story Foldout. 2004. (Firelight Ser.). (ps). 4.99 (978-0-8066-6481-1(9)) Augsburg Fortress, Pubs.

Come to God's Party: Bible Story Magazine. 2004. (Firelight Ser.). (gr. 5-6). 4.99 (978-0-8066-6489-7(4)) Augsburg Fortress, Pubs.

Come to God's Party: Bible Storybook. 2004. (Firelight Ser.). (gr. 1-2). 4.99 (978-0-8066-6485-9(1)) Augsburg Fortress, Pubs.

Comley, Kathryn. Follow God. Lane, Ranae, illus. 2004. (J). bds. 9.99 (978-1-4183-0009-8(8)) Christ Inspired, Inc.

—God Made My Hands. Wacker, Ranae, illus. 2004. (J). bds. 9.99 (978-1-4183-0005-0(5)) Christ Inspired, Inc.

—Know & Remember all These Things. Lane, Ranae, illus. 2004. (J). bds. (978-1-4183-0011-1(X)) Christ Inspired, Inc.

Concordia Publishing Staff, ed. One Hundred Bible Stories. 2005. (ENG., Illus.). 208p. (J). 12.99 (978-0-7586-0857-4(8)) Concordia Publishing Hse.

Concordia Publishing House Staff. One Hundred Bible Stories. 1998. (gr. 3-6). lib. bdg. 18.80 (978-0-613-72653-5(7)) Tandem Library Bks.

Concordia Publishing Staff. Bing! Bing! Bing! 2000. (Hear Me Read Bible Stories Ser.). (SPA., Illus.). 32p. (J). (ps-3). 2.75 (978-0-570-09914-7(5)) Concordia Publishing Hse.

—Date Prisa! 2000. (Hear Me Read Bible Stories Ser.). (SPA., Illus.). 32p. (J). (ps-3). 2.75 (978-0-570-09911-6(0)) Concordia Publishing Hse.

—Muy Alto Muy Bajito. 2000. (Hear Me Read Bible Stories Ser.). (SPA., Illus.). 32p. (J). (ps-3). 2.75 (978-0-570-09917-8(X)) Concordia Publishing Hse.

—My Bible Story Coloring Book. 1998. (ps-2). Vol. 6. (Illus.). 32p. pap. 2.95 (978-0-570-05073-5(1)); Vol. 8. (J). pap. 1.99 (978-0-570-05085-8(5)) Concordia Publishing Hse.

—One Hundred Bible Stories. 1998. (Illus.). 224p. (J). (gr. 4-7). 9.99 (978-0-570-05465-8(6) , 56-1928) Concordia Publishing Hse.

—Que Sucedera Despues. 2000. (Hear Me Read Bible Stories Ser.). (SPA., Illus.). 32p. (J). (ps-3). 2.75 (978-0-570-09909-3(9)) Concordia Publishing Hse.

—Quien Ayudara? 2000. (Hear Me Read Bible Stories Ser.). (SPA., Illus.). 32p. (J). (ps-3). 2.75 (978-0-570-09913-0(7)) Concordia Publishing Hse.

—Remen la Barca. 2000. (Hear Me Read Bible Stories Ser.). (SPA., Illus.). 32p. (J). (ps-3). 2.75 (978-0-570-09918-5(8)) Concordia Publishing Hse.

—Ron, Ron. 2000. (Hear Me Read Bible Stories Ser.). (SPA., Illus.). 32p. (J). (ps-3). 2.75 (978-0-570-09912-3(9)) Concordia Publishing Hse.

—The Shepherd & the Lost Sheep. 2000. (Bible Soft Pockets Ser.). (Illus.). 10p. (J). (ps). 6.99 (978-0-570-07065-8(1)) Concordia Publishing Hse.

—Sigue Esa Estrella. 2000. (Hear Me Read Bible Stories Ser.). (SPA., Illus.). 32p. (J). (ps-3). 2.75 (978-0-570-09915-4(3)) Concordia Publishing Hse.

—Tarara! Tarara! 2000. (Hear Me Read Bible Stories Ser.). (SPA., Illus.). 32p. (J). (ps-3). 2.75 (978-0-570-09916-1(1)) Concordia Publishing Hse.

—Ten Steps to Z-Z-Zing Development or Decline? 1999. (Arch Bks.). (Illus.). 16p. (J). (gr. k-4). 1.99 (978-0-570-07557-8(2)) Concordia Publishing Hse.

Cook, David C. Children's Bible Story Book. 2006. (Illus.). 416p. (J). 14.99 (978-0-7814-4386-9(5)) Cook, David C. Publishing Co.

Cooley, Dan. Bizarre Bible Stories: Flying Pigs, Walking Bones, & 24 Other Things That Really Happened. 2004. (Illus.). 160p. (J). 10.99 (978-0-8010-4520-2(7)) Baker Bks.

Courtney, Claudia. Barns of Barley: The Parable of the Rich Fool, Luke 12. 1998. (ps-2). lib. bdg. 10.65 (978-0-613-72817-1(3)) Tandem Library Bks.

—Blessings: Jesus & the Children. Dorenkamp, Michelle, illus. 2000. (Phonetic Bible Stories Ser.). (ENG.). 16p. (J). (ps-1). 2.99 (978-0-570-07090-0(2)) Concordia Publishing Hse.

—Modest King: Palm Sunday. 2000. (ps-2). lib. bdg. 10.65 (978-0-613-72824-9(6)) Tandem Library Bks.

—Rise & Shine: The Story of Easter. Clark, Bill, illus. 2000. (Phonetic Bible Stories Ser.). (ENG.). 16p. (J). (ps-1). 2.99 (978-0-570-07002-3(3)) Concordia Publishing Hse.

Cox, Joe & Butler-Moore, Nylea L., contrib. by. The Grumpy Shepherd. (gr. 2-6). 40.00 incl. audio (978-0-687-05037-6(5)) Abingdon Pr.

Craig, J. Ann, intro. Children of the Bible: Twelve Stories of Children. 2005. 72p. (YA). pap. (978-1-890569-89-1(5) , WD/GBGM Bks.) General Board of Global Ministries, The United Methodist Church.

Crandall, Janet. In a Manger. 2006. per. (978-1-59872-604-6(8)) Instantpublisher.com.

Crazy & Creative Bible Stories for Preteens. 2006. 112p. (YA). pap. 15.99 (978-0-7847-1631-1(5) , 42015) Standard Publishing.

La Creacion y el Diluvio: Serie para Ninos Amigos de la Biblia. 2000. (SPA.). pap. (978-1-57697-786-6(2)) United Bible Societies/Americas Service Ctr.

Creation: A Bible Storybook in Color. (Illus.). 16p. (J). pap. 1.50 (978-0-87162-962-3(3) , E4911) Warner Pr. Pubs.

La Crucifixion Vol. 23: Serie Minilibritos Aventuras de la Biblia. 2001. pap. (978-1-930564-93-0(7)) United Bible Societies/Americas Service Ctr.

Crump, Fred, Jr. Favorite Bible Stories: Retold & Illustrated by Fred Crump, Jr. Crump, Fred, Jr., illus. adapted l.t. ed. 2002. (Illus.). 50p. 16.95 (978-0-940955-75-2(X) , 0-69719, UMI) UMI (Urban Ministries, Inc.).

—Three Kings & a Star. 2005. 40p. (J). (ps-3). 12.95 (978-1-932715-52-1(5)) UMI (Urban Ministries, Inc.).

Curren, Joan E. Jericho's Tumbling Walls. 2001. (gr. k-3). lib. bdg. 9.85 (978-0-613-71023-7(1)) Tandem Library Bks.

Currie, Robin. Baby Bible 123. 2005. (Baby Bible Ser.). (Illus.). 48p. (J). bds. 12.99 (978-0-7814-3906-0(X) , 078143906X) Cook, David C. Publishing Co.

—Baby Bible ABC. 2004. (Baby Bible Ser.). (Illus.). 48p. (J). bds. 12.99 (978-0-7814-3907-7(8) , 0781439078) Cook, David C. Publishing Co.

—La Biblia Para los Bebes. 2003. (Baby Bible Ser.). (SPA., Illus.). 48p. bds. 10.99 (978-0-7814-3613-7(3) , 0781436133) Cook, David C. Publishing Co.

—La Biblia Para los Bebes Mas Historias. 2003. (Baby Bible Ser.). (SPA., Illus.). 48p. bds. 10.99 (978-0-7814-3614-4(1) , 0781436141) Cook, David C. Publishing Co.

Dalmatian Press Staff. Adam & Eve. 2004. (Illus.). 24p. (J). 2.99 (978-1-4037-0967-7(X) , Spirit Pr.) Dalmatian Pr.

—Beautiful Bible Stories for Children. 1998. (Illus.). 92p. (J). (ps-3). pap. 5.99 (978-1-57759-120-7(8)) Dalmatian Pr.

—Bible Songs Book. 2005. (Illus.). 24p. (J). pap. 10.99 (978-1-4037-1603-3(X)) Dalmatian Pr.

—Bible Stories Activity Pad. 2004. 32p. pap. 49.00 (978-1-57759-889-3(X)) Dalmatian Pr.

—The Birth of a Savior. 2004. (Illus.). 24p. (J). 2.99 (978-1-4037-0970-7(X) , Spirit Pr.) Dalmatian Pr.

—David & Goliath. 2000. (Illus.). (J). (ps-3). pap. 4.97 incl. audio (978-1-888567-35-9(X)) Dalmatian Pr.

—God's Creation. 2004. (Illus.). 24p. (J). 2.99 (978-1-4037-0962-2(9) , Spirit Pr.) Dalmatian Pr.

—Jonah & the Big Fish: Bright Idea Book to Color. 2003. (Bright Idea Book to Color Ser.). (Illus.). 32p. (J). pap. 3.99 (978-1-57759-894-7(6)) Dalmatian Pr.

—My Coloring Book God Loves Me. 2004. 32p. pap. 99.00 (978-1-4037-0305-7(1)) Dalmatian Pr.

—My Coloring Book Two by Two. 2004. 32p. pap. 99.00 (978-1-4037-0304-0(3)) Dalmatian Pr.

—My Favorite Bible Storybook for Early Readers. 2003. (Illus.). 528p. (J). 14.99 (978-1-4037-0286-9(1) , Spirit Pr.) Dalmatian Pr.

—My Favorite Bible Storybook for Little Ones. 2002. (Illus.). 20p. (J). bds. 8.99 (978-1-57759-811-4(3)) Dalmatian Pr.

—My Favorite Bible Storybook for Toddlers. 2002. (Illus.). 40p. (J). bds. 8.99 (978-1-4037-0093-3(1) , Spirit Pr.) Dalmatian Pr.

—Noah's Ark. 2004. (Illus.). 24p. (J). 2.99 (978-1-4037-0968-4(8) , Spirit Pr.) Dalmatian Pr.

—VeggieTale Champs of the Bible. 2005. (Big Idea's Veggie Tales Ser.). (Illus.). 80p. (J). pap. 2.99 (978-1-4037-1177-9(1) , Spirit Pr.) Dalmatian Pr.

—3-Minute Bible Stories. 2004. (3-D Vinyl Cover Book Ser.). (Illus.). 10p. (J). bds. 10.99 (978-1-4037-0738-3(3)) Dalmatian Pr.

Dalmatian Press Staff, ed. The Children's Illustrated Bible. rev. ed. 2005. (Illus.). 512p. (J). 17.99 (978-1-4037-1610-1(2)) Dalmatian Pr.

Daniel & the Lions. 2006. 16p. (J). pap. 1.99 (978-0-7847-1711-0(7) , 04172) Standard Publishing.

Daniel & the Lions' Den. (Bible Friends plus Book Ser.). (Illus.). 10p. (J). (ps-k). 6.99 (978-0-8254-7210-7(5)) Kregel Pubns.

Daniel & the Lion's Den: A Bible Story to Color. (Illus.). 16p. (J). pap. 1.50 (978-0-87162-831-2(7) , E6020) Warner Pr. Pubs.

Daniel en el Foso de los Leones, 6 vols. 2000. (Arch Bks.). (SPA.). 24p. (J). (ps-3). 2.49 (978-0-570-05172-5(X)) Concordia Publishing Hse.

Daniewicz, Mark. When Jesus Was A Kid. 2004. 14.95 (978-0-9709575-2-8(1)) Singing River Pubns.

David C. Cook. Jonah & the Big Fish. 2003. (My Jesus Pocket Bks.). (Illus.). 32p. (J). (gr. 5-3). pap. 8.90 (978-1-55513-015-2(1) , 1555130151) Cook, David C. Publishing Co.

Davidson, Alice Joyce. Baby Blessings Bible: With Removable Cover. Smath, Jerry, illus. 2000. (Baby Blessings Ser.). 20p. (ps-k). bds. 15.99 (978-0-7847-1189-7(5) , 04329) Standard Publishing.

—David y el Gran Gigante. 1998. (My Bible Friends Ser.).Tr. of David & the Big Giant. (SPA.). 7p. (J). (ps-3). 3.99 (978-0-8297-2485-1(0)) Vida Pubs.

—Joseph & the Splendid Coat. 2003. 12p. (J). 6.99 (978-0-310-70855-1(9)) Zondervan.

—María y el Niño Jesus. 1999. (My Bible Friends Ser.).Tr. of Mary & the Baby Jesus. (SPA.). 12p. (J). 3.99 (978-0-8297-2486-8(9)) Vida Pubs.

—María y la Tumba Vacía. 1998. (My Bible Friends Ser.).Tr. of Mary & the Empty Tomb. (SPA.). 12p. (J). (ps-3). 3.99 (978-0-8297-2488-2(5)) Vida Pubs.

—Mis Amigos de la Biblia Jonas y el Gran Pez. 2003. (SPA.). 12p. 6.99 (978-0-8297-3957-2(2)) Zondervan.

—My Take-Along Bible. Mazille, Capucine, illus. 2004. 20p. (J). bds. 9.99 (978-0-89221-577-5(1)) New Leaf Pr., Inc.

—Noah & the Big Boat. 2003. (My Bible Friends Ser.). 12p. (J). bds. 6.99 (978-0-310-70853-7(2)) Zondervan.

—Noé y el Gran Barco. 1998. (My Bible Friends Ser.).Tr. of Noah & the Big Boat. (SPA.). 12p. (J). (ps-3). 3.99 (978-0-8297-2487-5(7)) Vida Pubs.

Davies, Rhona. The One Year Children's Bible. Piwowarski, Marcln, illus. 2007. (One Year Bks.). 345p. (J). (gr. 1-5). 19.99 (***978-1-4143-1499-0(X)*** , Tyndale Kids) Tyndale Hse. Pubs.

Davis, B. Jacob's Dream. 2001. (gr. k-3). lib. bdg. 9.85 (978-0-613-71022-0(3)) Tandem Library Bks.

Davis, Mary J. Five-Minute Sunday School Activities for Preschoolers: Bible Adventures. Galey, Chuck, illus. 2005. 96p. (J). pap. 11.95 (978-1-58411-046-0(5)) Rainbow Pubs. & Legacy Pr.

De Graaf, Anne. Childrens Bible Stories. Montero, Jose Perez, illus. 1998. (J). (ps-3). 16.97 (978-0-7852-6261-9(X)) Nelson, Thomas Inc.

—God Makes the World. Perez-Montero, Jose, illus. 1998. (Little Children's Bible Bks.). 38p. (J). 5.99 (978-0-8054-1782-1(6)) B&H Publishing Grp.

—Historias de la Biblia. l.t. ed. 2002. (SPA., Illus.). (J). 17.95 (978-87-7247-309-3(6) , 107211) Scandinavia Publishing Hse. DNK. *Dist:* American Bible Society.

—Jesus' Stories. Perez-Montero, Jose, illus. 1999. (Little Children's Bible Bks.). 38p. (J). (ps-1). 5.99 (978-0-8054-2071-5(1)) B&H Publishing Grp.

—John. Montero, Jose Perez, illus. 2001. (Little Children's Bible Bks.: No. 23). 38p. (J). (ps-1). 5.99 (978-0-8054-2195-8(5)) B&H Publishing Grp.

—The Little Children's Bible Storybook. Montero, Jose Perez, illus. 2003. 448p. 16.95 (978-87-7247-132-7(8)) Scandinavia Publishing Hse. DNK. *Dist:* National Bk. Network.

—Sam's Son. Perez-Montero, Jose, illus. 1999. (Little Children's Bible Bks.). 38p. (J). (ps-1). 5.99 (978-0-8054-2069-2(X)) B&H Publishing Grp.

De Graaf, Anne, ed. My Favorite Bible Storybook for Children. Montero, Jose Perez, illus. 2002. 448p. (J). (ps-4). 10.99 (978-1-57759-908-1(X)) Dalmatian Pr.

De Maleissye Melun, Judith. God is Good: Bedtime Morals for Children. 1999. 64p. (J). Vol. 2. pap. 8.95 (978-1-893551-02-2(4)); Vol. 3. pap. 8.95 (978-1-893551-03-9(2)); Vol. 4. pap. 8.95 (978-1-893551-04-6(0)) Seabird Publishing International, LLC.

A B

de Paola, Tomie. Tomie de Paola's Book of Bible Stories. 2002. 128p. (J). pap. 12.99 (978-0-698-11923-9(1) , Putnam Juvenile) Penguin Group (USA) Inc.

—Tomie de Paola's Book of Bible Stories. 2002. (gr. k-3). lib. bdg. 19.95 (978-0-613-50545-1(X)) Tandem Library Bks.

De Sturtz, Mari. Living for Jesus. 2004. (ENG & SPA.). 32p. 1.99 (978-0-7586-0295-4(2)) Concordia Publishing Hse.

De Villiers Family. Peekaboo, I Love You. De Villiers Family, illus. 2005. (Seedling Ser.). (Illus.). 40p. (J). (ps-k). 9.99 (978-1-4000-7122-7(4) , WaterBrook Pr.) WaterBrook Pr.

—Seedling Bible: Sixteen Favorite Bible Stories for Toddlers. 2005. (Seedling Ser.). (Illus.). 96p. (J). 12.99 (978-1-4000-7121-0(6) , WaterBrook Pr.) WaterBrook Pr.

—Sprout Bible: Thirty-Four Favorite Bible Stories for Kids. 2006. (Learn & Grow with Sprout Ser.). (Illus.). 208p. (J). 12.99 (978-1-4000-7194-4(1) , WaterBrook Pr.) WaterBrook Pr.

—Super Duper Sundae Sleepover. De Villiers Family, illus. 2005. (Seedling Ser.). (Illus.). 40p. (J). (ps-k). 9.99 (978-1-4000-7123-4(2) , WaterBrook Pr.) WaterBrook Pr.

DeBoer, Rondi & Rondi, Christine. A Boy & His Lunch. Conger, Holli, illus. 2007. (J). 5.99 (*978-0-7847-1949-7(7)) Standard Publishing.

DeBoer, Rondi & Tangvald, Christine. Daniel & the Lions. Conger, Holli, illus. 2007. (J). 5.99 (*978-0-7847-1948-0(9)) Standard Publishing.

Decker, Marjorie Ainsborough. Rock-a-Bye Bible. Endersby, Frank et al, illus. 2002. (Christian Mother Goose Ser.). 96p. (J). 9.99 (978-0-448-42868-0(7) , Grosset & Dunlap) Penguin Group (USA) Inc.

Dennis, Trevor. The Book of Books. 2003. (Illus.). 468p. pap. 17.99 (978-0-7459-3625-3(3) , Lion) Lion Hudson plc GBR. *Dist:* Independent Pubs. Group.

Derico, Laura. Bible for Babies. Gohman, Vera & Karch, P., illus. 2006. (Read Together Ser.). 40p. (J). bds. 7.99 (978-0-7847-1742-4(7) , 04368) Standard Publishing.

—Bible for Toddlers. Ebert, Len, illus. 2006. (Read Together Ser.). 92p. (J). 9.99 (978-0-7847-1743-1(5) , 04369) Standard Publishing.

—Noah & God's Promise. Beylon, Cathy, illus. 2000. (Snow Globe Book Ser.). 10p. (J). (ps up). bds. 9.99 (978-0-7847-1059-3(7) , 03535, Bean Sprouts) Standard Publishing.

Diedrich, Jeff. Tried By Fire: The Story of Ruth. 2000. (Hotshots Ser.: Vol. 19). 44p. (J). pap. 10.25 (978-1-929784-32-5(5)) Positive Action For Christ.

Ditchfield, Christin. Bible Heroes. Cook, Ande, illus. 2004. (Little Golden Book Ser.). 24p. (J). (gr. k-k). 2.99 (978-0-375-82816-4(8) , Golden Bks.) Random Hse. Children's Bks.

The DK Best of Everything. 1998. 192p. (J). pap. 14.95 (978-0-7894-3427-2(X)) Dorling Kindersley Publishing, Inc.

Domingo, Roger. Eye Openers & Show Stoppers in the Bible. 2003. 128p. (YA). pap. 9.95 (978-0-9668541-2-1(8)) Turnstyle.

Donaldson, Bryna. Bible Stories. 1999. (J). lib. bdg. (978-0-394-93761-8(9) , Random Hse. Bks. for Young Readers) Random Hse. Children's Bks.

Dorling Kindersley Publishing Staff. Bible Stories. 2005. (My Little Church Book Ser.). (Illus.). 24p. (J). pap. 5.99 (978-0-7566-1469-0(4)) Dorling Kindersley Publishing, Inc.

Dorling Kindersley Publishing Staff, et al. Children's Everyday Bible. 2002. (Illus.). 384p. (J). 19.99 (978-0-7894-8858-9(2)) Dorling Kindersley Publishing, Inc.

Douglas, Vincent & School Specialty Publishing Staff. Bible Stories. 2003. (Rhythm & Rhyme Ser.). (Illus.). 53p. (J). (ps up). bds. 19.95 (978-1-58845-526-0(2)) School Specialty Publishing.

—My Little Library of Bible Stories, 12 bks. 2001. (My Little Library). (Illus.). 120p. (J). (ps-k). bds. 12.95 (978-1-58845-232-0(8)) School Specialty Publishing.

Dowley, T. Encuentra la Solucion (Favorite Bible Stories), No. 2. 1998. (SPA.). (J). pap. 1.99 (978-0-7899-0436-2(5) , 497767) Editorial Unilit.

Dowley, Tim. Bedtime Book of Bible Stories. 2003. (Illus.). 256p. (J). 10.99 (978-0-8254-7272-5(5)) Kregel Pubns.

—Changing Picture Bible Stories. 2004. (Illus.). 14p. 10.99 (978-0-8254-7279-4(2)) Kregel Pubns.

—Donkey to the Rescue: Bible Animal. Smallman, Steve, illus. 2005. 14p. (J). bds. 5.99 (978-0-8254-7300-5(4)) Kregel Pubns.

—Duck's Loud Quak: Bible Animal. Smallman, Steve, illus. 2005. 14p. (J). bds. 5.99 (978-0-8254-7299-2(7)) Kregel Pubns.

—My First Story of Christmas. Langton, Roger, illus. 2004. (First Christmas Reader Ser.). 24p. (J). 7.99 (978-0-8024-1758-9(2)) Moody Pubs.

—The Pig Who Shared: Bible Animal. Smallman, Steve, illus. 2005. (J). bds. 5.99 (978-0-8254-7302-9(0)) Kregel Pubns.

—Raven Delivers Food: Bible Animal. Smallman, Steve, illus. 2005. 14p. (J). bds. 5.99 (978-0-8254-7301-2(2)) Kregel Pubns.

Downing, Julie, illus. A First Bible Story Book. 1998. 80p. (J). (ps-3). 12.99 (978-1-57727-119-2(X)) Jubilee Publishing Group.

Doyle, Christopher. Best Bible Stories. Fereday, Roger, illus. 64p. (J). 9.99 (978-0-7586-0719-5(9)) Concordia Publishing Hse.

Duerksen, Carol. God's Gift of Sex. 2000. (Fast Lane Bible Studies Ser.). 52p. (YA). pap. 9.95 (978-0-87303-400-5(7)) Faith & Life Pr.

Dunn, Connie. Under the Wisdom Tree: A Storytelling Curriculum about Values for Unitarian Universalists. 2001. 225p. (YA). pap. 125.00 (978-1-890641-05-4(7)) No Stress Pr.

Dyson, Janet. Calming the Storm & Other Stories. 2002. (First Bible Stories Ser.). (Illus.). 16p. (ps-k). pap. 4.95 (978-0-7548-0794-0(0) , Lorenz Bks.) Anness Publishing, Inc.

—The First Christmas & Other Stories. 2002. (First Bible Stories Ser.). (Illus.). 16p. (ps-k). pap. 4.95 (978-0-7548-0883-1(1) , Lorenz Bks.) Anness Publishing, Inc.

Ebert, Len, illus. Bible Stories to Color & Tell: Ages 6-8. 2005. 240p. (J). per. 15.99 (978-0-7847-1348-8(0) , 02492) Standard Publishing.

Editorial Vida Staff. My Friends-Student (Ukrainian) Vol. 1 Bk. 2: Ukrainian Sunday School, Life Publishers International Staff, tr. from SPA. 2002. Orig. Title: Mis Amigos. Alumno. (UKR.). 32p. (J). pupil's gde. ed. (978-0-7361-0318-3(X)) Life Pubs. International.

—My Friends-Student (Ukrainian) Vol. 2 Bk. 1: Ukrainian Sunday School. Life Publishers International Staff, tr. from SPA. 2002. Orig. Title: Mis Amigos. Alumno. (UKR.). 32p. (J). pupil's gde. ed. (978-0-7361-0319-0(8)) Life Pubs. International.

—My Friends-Student (Ukrainian) Vol. 2, Bk. 2: Ukrainian Sunday School, Life Publishers International Staff, tr. from SPA. 2002. Orig. Title: Mis Amigos. Alumno. (UKR.). 32p. (J). pupil's gde. ed. (978-0-7361-0320-6(1)) Life Pubs. International.

Edlund, Anita. From Zero to Hero. 2007. 72p. pap. 15.00 (*978-0-687-64294-6(9)) Abingdon Pr.

Egermeier, Elsie. Egermeier's ABC Bible Storybook w/Audio CD. 2007. (Illus.). 56p. (J). 14.99 (*978-1-59317-198-8(6)) Warner Pr. Pubs.

Egermeier, Elsie E. Egermeier's ABC Bible Storybook: Favorite Stories Adapted for Young Children. 2006. 12.99 (978-1-59317-156-8(0)) Warner Pr. Pubs.

—Stories from the Bible Book & Charm. Ivanov, Aleksey, illus. 2006. (Gifts of Grace Ser.). 272p. (J). pap. 6.99 (978-0-06-076134-9(2) , Harper Festival) HarperCollins Pubs.

Elephant Keeps Safe. 2004. bds. 5.99 (978-0-8254-7285-5(7)) Kregel Pubns.

Eliakopoulos, Angeline. O God of Demetrios: The Story of Saint Demetrios of Thessaloniki. Linden, Tom, illus. 2002. 50p. (YA). (gr. 4-12). pap. 15.95 (978-0-9670030-2-3(4)) Destro Pubs., LLC.

Elias y Jonas: Serie para Ninos Amigos de la Biblia. 2000. pap. (978-1-57697-791-0(9)) United Bible Societies/ Americas Service Ctr.

Elijah & the Big Black Birds. 2005. 16p. (J). per. 4.99 (978-1-59441-087-1(9) , CD-204014) Carson-Dellosa Publishing Co., Inc.

Elkins, Stephen. Amazing Miracles, Vol. 6. O'Connor, Tim, illus. 2002. (Word & Song Ser.: Vol. 6). 32p. (J). (ps-5). 9.99 (978-0-8054-2471-3(7)) B&H Publishing Grp.

—Baby's First Book of Bible Stories. 2002. (Lulla-Bible Ser.). (Illus.). 14p. (J). (ps). 6.99 (978-0-8054-2583-3(7)) B&H Publishing Grp.

—Courage & Strength, Vol. 3. O'Connor, Tim, illus. 2002. (Word & Song Ser.: Vol. 3). 32p. (J). (ps-5). 9.99 (978-0-8054-2468-3(7)) B&H Publishing Grp.

—The Good Shepherd, Vol. 10. O'Connor, Tim, illus. 2002. (Word & Song Ser.: Vol. 10). 32p. (J). (ps-5). 9.99 (978-0-8054-2475-1(X)) B&H Publishing Grp.

—The Memory Bible: The Sure-Fire, Fun Way to Learn 52 Bible Verses. Semple, David, illus. 2003. 224p. (J). (ps-3). 25.99 incl. audio compact disk (978-1-59145-063-4(2)) Nelson, Thomas Inc.

—Prayer & Promise, Vol. 7. O'Connor, Tim, illus. 2002. (Word & Song Ser.: Vol. 7). 32p. (J). (ps-5). 9.99 (978-0-8054-2472-0(5)) B&H Publishing Grp.

—Special Families, Vol. 2. O'Connor, Tim, illus. 2002. (Word & Song Ser.: Vol. 2). 32p. (J). (ps-5). 9.99 (978-0-8054-2467-6(9)) B&H Publishing Grp.

—Stories of Faith, Vol. 5. O'Connor, Tim, illus. 2002. (Word & Song Ser.: Vol. 5). 32p. (J). (ps-5). 9.99 (978-0-8054-2470-6(9)) B&H Publishing Grp.

—Stories That Build Character, Vol. 4. O'Connor, Tim, illus. 2002. (Word & Song Ser.: Vol. 4). 32p. (J). (ps-5). 9.99 (978-0-8054-2469-0(5)) B&H Publishing Grp.

—Word & Song Christmas Storybook. 2000. (Illus.). 32p. (J). (gr. k-5). 14.99 incl. audio compact disk (978-0-8054-2196-5(3)) B&H Publishing Grp.

—100 Bible Heroes, 100 Bible Songs. 2007. 208p. (J). 19.99 (*978-1-4003-1078-4(4)) Nelson, Thomas Inc.

Elkins, Stephen. 100 Favorite Bible Stories. 2005. (Illus.). 205p. (J). (ps-3). 19.99 incl. audio compact disk (978-1-59145-239-3(2)) Nelson, Thomas Inc.

Elkins, Stephen, creator. Read & See Bible. 2006. (Illus.). 176p. (ps-3). bds. 19.99 (978-1-59145-486-1(7)) Nelson, Thomas Inc.

Ellis, Gwen. Bible Adventures. Cox, Steve, illus. 2006. (ENG.). 20p. (J). 8.99 (978-0-7586-1130-7(7)) Concordia Publishing Hse.

Ellis, Gwen. I Can Learn Bible Stories. Regan, Dana, illus. 2006. 10.99 (*978-0-8254-5530-8(8)) Kregel Pubns.

Ellis, Gwen, creator. Read & Share Bible: Over 120 Best Loved Bible Stories. 2007. (Illus.). 440p. (J). 14.99 (978-1-4003-0853-8(4)) Nelson, Thomas Inc.

Erickson, Jenny. My Favorite Bible. 2003. 112p. (J). pap., act. bk. ed. 14.95 (978-1-58595-268-7(0)) Twenty-Third Pubns./Bayard.

Erickson, Mary E. Picture Word Prayers & Bible Stories. 1999. 48p. 7.99 (978-0-88486-260-4(7) , Galahad Bks.) BBS Publishing Corp.

A Family Christmas: Advent Calendar & Storybook. 2000. 32p. (J). 10.99 (978-0-570-07122-8(4)) Concordia Publishing Hse.

Family Time Bible Stories: Devotions & Interactive Bible Stories for Preschoolers. 2004. (Here's What's Inside the Bright Beginnings Kit Ser.). (Illus.). 224p. 14.99 (978-0-8307-3247-0(0) , Regal Bks.) Gospel Light Pubns.

Favorite Bible Stories for Children. 2002. (Illus.). 96p. (J). (gr. k-7). 9.99 (978-1-57759-420-8(7)) Dalmatian Pr.

Ferris, Audrey. Bible Story Skits Kids Can Do: Quick & Easy Scripts for Ages 8-12. Caldwell, Lise & Frederick, Ruth, eds. 1999. (Illus.). 64p. (J). (gr. 3-7). 8.99 (978-0-7847-1074-6(0) , 03395) Standard Publishing.

A Few Who Dared to Trust God: With Imprimatur. 2000. (Illus.). 234p. (J). pap. 17.62 (978-1-58516-295-6(7)) American Bible Society.

First Bible Stories. 2002. (J). 384p. 29.95 (978-0-7525-6443-2(9)); bds. 9.98 (978-0-7525-4200-3(1)) Parragon, Inc.

Fisher, Adam. God's Garden: Children's Stories Grown from the Bible. 1999. 176p. (J). (gr. k-6). pap. 12.95 (978-0-87441-696-1(5)) Behrman Hse., Inc.

Fisher, Martha. ABC Book of Bible People. 2004. (Bible Stories for Young Readers Ser.). (Illus.). 88p. (ps-5). 3.85 (978-0-7399-2331-3(5) , 2717) Rod & Staff Pubs., Inc.

—Bible Time. 2005. (Bible Stories for Young Readers Ser.). (Illus.). 40p. (ps-5). 3.05 (978-0-7399-2332-0(3) , 2719) Rod & Staff Pubs., Inc.

—Dictionary of Bible Animals. 2004. (Bible Stories for Young Readers Ser.). (Illus.). 45p. (ps-5). 3.05 (978-0-7399-2330-6(7) , 2716) Rod & Staff Pubs., Inc.

Fletcher, Sarah. La Historia de Jesus (My Stories about Jesus) Historias del Nuevo Testamento. (SPA., Illus.). 32p. (ps-3). 1.95 (978-0-570-09970-3(6) , 16-6013) Concordia Publishing Hse.

—My Stories about Jesus: New Testament Stories for Small Children. (CHI.). 32p. (J). (ps-3). 1.95 (978-0-570-09971-0(4) , 16-6014) Concordia Publishing Hse.

—My Turn Bible Stories about ABCs. 1999. (My Turn Bible Stories Ser.). (Illus.). 32p. (J). (ps-1). 7.00 (978-0-570-05493-1(1) , 56-1956GJ) Concordia Publishing Hse.

—My Turn Bible Stories about Numbers. 1998. (My Turn Bible Stories Ser.). (Illus.). 32p. (J). (ps-1). 6.99 (978-0-570-05060-5(X)) Concordia Publishing Hse.

—My Turn Bible Stories about Opposites. 1999. (My Turn Bible Stories Ser.). (Illus.). 32p. (J). (ps-1). 7.00 (978-0-570-05492-4(3) , 56-1955GJ) Concordia Publishing Hse.

Flinn. The Symbols Speak. 3.00 (978-0-687-07575-1(0)) Abingdon Pr.

Fogle, Robin. David & Golaith Coloring Book. 2007. (Illus.). 16p. (J). pap. 1.89 (*978-1-59317-205-3(2)) Warner Pr. Pubs.

—The Legend of the Candy Cane. 2006. (J). pap. 1.79 (*978-1-59317-158-2(7)) Warner Pr. Pubs.

—My Favorite Bible Stories Color-by-number. 2007. (Illus.). 16p. (J). pap. 1.89 (*978-1-59317-208-4(7)) Warner Pr. Pubs.

—The Shepherd Boy's Christmas. 2005. (J). pap. 1.79 (*978-1-59317-105-6(6)) Warner Pr. Pubs.

Forlini, Victoria, ed. The Birth of Jesus. Mada Design Staff, illus. 2005. 22p. (J). (ps-ps). 9.99 (978-0-696-22827-8(0)) Meredith Bks.

—Noah's Ark. Mada Design Staff, illus. 2005. 22p. (J). (ps-ps). 9.99 (978-0-696-22826-1(2)) Meredith Bks.

Forlini, Victoria & Sidey, Ken, eds. Jonah & the Whale. 2005. (I See, You See Ser.). (Illus.). 22p. (J). 6.99 (978-0-696-22821-6(1)) Meredith Bks.

Four Faithful Friends. 2006. 16p. (J). pap. 1.99 (978-0-7847-1716-5(8) , 04177) Standard Publishing.

Frank, Penny. Jesus the Teacher. (Illus.). 24p. 2.99 (978-0-7459-4117-2(6) , Lion) Lion Hudson plc GBR. *Dist:* Trafalgar Square Publishing.

—King David. 1999. (Lion Story Bible Ser.). (Illus.). 24p. pap. 2.99 (978-0-7459-4112-7(5) , Lion) Lion Hudson plc GBR. *Dist:* Independent Pubs. Group.

—When Zacchaeus Met Jesus. Morris, Tony, illus. 2004. 24p. (J). pap. 30.00 (978-0-7459-4925-3(8) , Lion) Lion Hudson plc GBR. *Dist:* Independent Pubs. Group.

Freed, Shirley Ann & Moon, Louise. A Dark Dark Night. Morelan, Bill, ed. Butler, Steven, illus. l.t. ed. 2002. 8p. (J). (gr. 1-2). pap. 3.99 (978-1-58938-015-8(0)) Concerned Communications.

—How Far Is It? Morelan, Bill, ed. Butler, Steven, illus. l.t. ed. 2002. 16p. (J). (gr. 6). pap. 3.99 (978-1-58938-032-5(0)) Concerned Communications.

French, Vivian. Story of Christmas. Chapman, Jane, illus. 2003. 22p. (J). (gr. k-k). bds. 5.99 (978-0-7636-2202-2(8)) Candlewick Pr.

Frothingham, Octavius Brook. Stories of the Patriarchs. 2006. pap. 26.95 (*978-1-4286-0972-3(5)) Kessinger Publishing, LLC.

Fun with Colors: Bible Story: Joseph's Colorful Coat. (Scripture Bites Ser.). (Illus.). (J). 7.99 (978-0-7847-9014-4(0) , 00707) Standard Publishing.

Fun with Foster Kids Story Book - English / Spanish Bilingual Translation. 2005. (J). 19.95 (978-1-59649-500-5(6)); spiral bd. 19.95 (978-1-59649-501-2(4)); per. 19.95 (978-1-59649-499-2(9)); cd-rom 19.95 (978-1-59649-502-9(2)) Whispering Pine Pr., Inc.

Ganeri, Anita. Christian Stories. Phillips, Rachael, illus. 2006. 32p. (J). (gr. 4-6). 23.95 (978-1-4048-1312-0(8)) Picture Window Bks.

Garwin, Elaine & Youd, Pauline. The Wonder Bible Storybook: 12 Little Stories for Little People. 2003. (Illus.). 192p. 9.95 (978-87-7247-280-5(4)) Scandinavia Publishing Hse. DNK. *Dist:* National Bk. Network.

Gemmen, Heather. Learn-to-Read Bible. Wilber, Peggy M., ed. 1999. (Rocket Readers Ser.). (Illus.). 448p. (J). (gr. 1-2). 16.99 (978-0-7814-3975-6(2) , 0781439752) Cook, David C. Publishing Co.

Gevry, Claudine. The Big Book of Bible Fish Tales. 2004. (Illus.). 10p. bds. 8.99 (978-0-8254-5514-8(6)) Kregel Pubns.

Giampa, Linda. Journey Through the Bible. 2004. 64p. (ps-3). 9.99 (978-0-7586-0248-0(0)) Concordia Publishing Hse.

Gilles, Sebaoun. A Young Child's Bible. Robins, Joan, tr. from FRE. Roederer, Charlotte, illus. 2001. 96p. (J). (ps-3). 12.95 (978-0-06-029464-9(7)) HarperCollins Pubs.

Gladden, Washington. Catholic Child's Baptismal Bible. 2000. (J). (ps-3). 12.95 (978-0-88271-008-2(7)) Regina Pr., Malhame & Co.

Glavich, Mary Kathleen. Student Pack of Bible Stories. 2004. (978-0-8294-1040-2(6)) Loyola Pr.

Gnt Bible for Children. 2004. pap. 29.93 (978-1-58516-526-1(3)) American Bible Society.

God Comes to Us: Bible Story Album. 2004. (Firelight Ser.). (ps-k). 4.99 (978-0-8066-6436-1(3)) Augsburg Fortress, Pubs.

God Comes to Us: Bible Story Flipbook. 2004. (Firelight Ser.). (gr. 3-4). 4.99 (978-0-8066-6440-8(1)) Augsburg Fortress, Pubs.

God Comes to Us: Bible Story Foldout. 2004. (ps). 4.99 (978-0-8066-6434-7(7)) Augsburg Fortress, Pubs.

God Comes to Us: Bible Story Magazine "Blaze" 2004. (Firelight Ser.). (gr. 5-6). 4.99 (978-0-8066-6442-2(8)) Augsburg Fortress, Pubs.

God Comes to Us: Bible Storybook. 2004. (gr. 1-2). 4.99 (978-0-8066-6438-5(X)) Augsburg Fortress, Pubs.

God Feeds Us: Bible Story Album. 2004. (Firelight Ser.). (ps-k). 4.99 (978-0-8066-6418-7(5)) Augsburg Fortress, Pubs.

God Feeds Us: Bible Story Flipbook. 2004. (Firelight Ser.). (gr. 3-4). 4.99 (978-0-8066-6422-4(3)) Augsburg Fortress, Pubs.

God Feeds Us: Bible Story Foldout. 2004. (Firelight Ser.). (ps). 4.99 (978-0-8066-6416-3(9)) Augsburg Fortress, Pubs.

God Feeds Us: Bible Story Magazine "Blaze" 2004. (Firelight Ser.). (gr. 5-6). 4.99 (978-0-8066-6424-8(X)) Augsburg Fortress, Pubs.

God Feeds Us: Bible Storybook. 2004. (Firelight Ser.). (gr. 1-2). 4.99 (978-0-8066-6420-0(7)) Augsburg Fortress, Pubs.

Godfrey, Jan. The Hidden Treasure. Saunderson, Chris, illus. 2001. (J). (ps-k). 5.00 (978-0-687-04950-9(4)) Abingdon Pr.

—The Two Houses. Saunderson, Chris, illus. 2001. (J). (ps-k). 5.00 (978-0-687-05000-0(6)) Abingdon Pr.

God's Creation. 2002. (Illus.). 24p. (J). 5.99 (978-1-57759-514-4(9)) Dalmatian Pr.

God's Wonderful World, 3 vols. 2003. 20p. (J). bds. 6.99 (978-0-8254-7269-5(5)) Kregel Pubns.

Golden Books Staff. David & Other Bible Heroes. 2005. (Jumbo Coloring Book Ser.). (Illus.). 128p. (J). (ps-2). pap. 2.99 (978-0-375-83544-5(X) , Golden Inspirational) Random Hse. Children's Bks.

—Jonah & Other Bible Stories. 2005. (Illus.). 128p. (J). (ps-2). pap. 2.99 (978-0-375-83545-2(8) , Golden Inspirational) Random Hse. Children's Bks.

—A Treasury of Bible Stories. 1999. (Illus.). 204p. (J). (ps-3). (978-0-307-10382-6(X)) Golden Bks. Publishing (Canada), Inc.

Golden Books Staff, et al. Little Golden Book Collection: Inspirational Tales. Williams, Garth & Edge, Liz, illus. 2006. (Little Golden Book Ser.). 224p. (J). (gr. k-1). 10.95 (978-0-375-83233-8(5) , Golden Inspirational) Random Hse. Children's Bks.

Goldin, Barbara Diamond, et al. The 40 Greatest Jewish Stories Ever Told, 4 vols., Set. Allon, Jeffrey, illus. 2005. 192p. (J). (gr. 1-4). 49.95 (978-0-943706-89-4(0) , Devora Publishing) Pitspopany Pr.

Gordh, Bill. Building a Children's Chapel: One Story at a Time. 2007. 200p. pap. 25.00 (*978-0-89869-564-9(3)) Church Publishing, Inc.

Gordon Brown, Doris. Lazarus; the Talk of the Town. 2003. 9.99 (978-0-9708560-0-5(8)) Aglob Publishing.

The Gospel for Kids a Character Book: God's Good News of Eternal Life. 2004. (Illus.). 115p. (J). per. 7.00 (978-0-9778494-1-3(4)) Huseby, Kirby.

Gospel Road Story, Books, ed. Antony's House. (Gospel Road Story Bks.). (Illus.). 12p. (J). (ps-k). 0.99 (978-0-8254-7225-1(3)) Kregel Pubns.

Graham, Michelle. Where's the Fire? 1999. 88p. (J). (gr. 4-8). pap. 5.00 (978-0-9658766-3-6(2)) Rays of Hope.

Gran, Mary Alice. A Child Is Born. 2008. 15.00 (*978-0-687-49168-1(1)) Abingdon Pr.

Grant, Myrna. Ivan & the American Journey. 140p. (YA). mass mkt. 5.99 (978-1-85792-621-7(8) , Christian Focus) Christian Focus Pubns. GBR. *Dist:* Riverside.

—Ivan & the Hidden Bible. 122p. (YA). mass mkt. 5.99 (978-1-85792-623-1(4) , Christian Focus) Christian Focus Pubns. GBR. *Dist:* Riverside.

—Ivan & the Secret in the Suitcase. (Illus.). 154p. (YA). mass mkt. 5.99 (978-1-85792-622-4(6) , Christian Focus) Christian Focus Pubns. GBR. *Dist:* Riverside.

Gray, Charlotte. Bible Folks Shape Books. Henderson, Liz, illus. 2003. (J). spiral bd. 14.99 (978-0-89098-267-9(8)) Twentieth Century Christian Bks.

—My Bible Box in Color. Henderson, Liz, illus. 2003. (J). spiral bd. 24.99 (978-0-89098-266-2(X)) Twentieth Century Christian Bks.

Grier, Gene & Everson, Lowell. Midnight Miracle Singer's Edition: A Musical Christmas Story: Singer's Edition. 2004. 24p. (gr. 2-6). 4.00 (978-0-687-01515-3(4)) Abingdon Pr.

Grindley, Sally. Bible Stories for the Young. Barger, Jan, illus. 1998. 96p. (J). (gr. k-4). 16.95 (978-1-888444-42-1(8)) Little Tiger Pr.

Groenboom, Roger, et al. King Jesus. (Walk with Me Ser.). (gr. k-8). 12.95 (978-1-59255-174-3(2) , 017110, Faith Alive Christian Resources) CRC Pubns.

—Rough Waves? Jesus Saves!, Vol. 2. (Walk with Me Ser.). (gr. k-8). 24.95 (978-1-59255-177-4(7) , 017220, Faith Alive Christian Resources) CRC Pubns.

—Sharable Parables. (Walk with Me Ser.). (gr. k-8). 24.95 (978-1-59255-176-7(9) , 017210, Faith Alive Christian Resources) CRC Pubns.

Gross, Arthur. A Child's Garden of Bible Stories. Barr, Marilyn, illus. 2005. (ENG.). 144p. (J). 9.99 (978-0-7586-0858-1(6)) Concordia Publishing Hse.

Grossmann, Dan, illus. Bible Stories to Color & Tell: Ages 3-6. 2005. 240p. (J). (ps-3). pap. 15.99 (978-0-7847-1779-0(6) , 02493) Standard Publishing.

Grunke, Leal V., prod. The Bible in Lvng Sound, 8 vols. 2004. (gr. 1-12). (978-1-57764-080-6(2)) Bible in Living Sound, The.

Hagan, Scott. Big Bad Bible Bullies. Horne, Doug, illus. 2005. 24p. (J). (ps-3). 9.99 (978-1-59185-604-7(3)) Strang Communications Co.

—Los Buscapleitos de la Biblia. Horne, Doug, illus. 2005. 22p. (J). (gr. 1-3). 8.99 (978-1-59185-482-1(2) , Charisma Kids) Strang Communications Co.

Halliday, M. A Ladder, a BBQ & a Pillar of Salt. 2003. (Bible Bites Ser.). (Illus.). 128p. 5.99 (978-1-85999-367-5(2)) Scripture Union GBR. *Dist:* Gabriel Resources.

Halliday, Marc & Potter, Ian. A Giant, a Crown & an Open Air Bath. 2001. (Bible Bites Ser.). (Illus.). 128p. (J). pap. 5.99 (978-1-85999-368-2(0)) Scripture Union GBR. *Dist:* Gabriel Resources.

—A Red Sea, a Burning Bush & a Plague of Frogs. 2003. (Bible Bites Ser.). (Illus.). 128p. 5.99 (978-1-85999-365-1(6)) Scripture Union GBR. *Dist:* Gabriel Resources.

—A Tent Peg, a Jawbone & a Sheepskin Rug. 2003. (Bible Bites Ser.). (Illus.). 128p. 5.99 (978-1-85999-294-4(3)) Scripture Union GBR. *Dist:* Gabriel Resources.

Halter, Pam. Beatrice Loses Her Doll. Sponaugle, Kim, tr. Sponaugle, Kim, illus. 2001. 32p. (J). 6.99 (978-0-570-07117-4(8)) Concordia Publishing Hse.

Ham, Ken. All God's Children: Why We Look Different. 2005. (Illus.). 12p. (J). 9.99 (978-0-89051-439-9(9) , 303-211) Master Bks.

Hanft, Joshua E. Miracles of the Bible. Chwast, Seymour, illus. 2007. 32p. (J). (ps-3). 16.95 ***(978-1-59354-617-5(3))*** Blue Apple Bks.

Hannula, Richard. Trial & Triumph: Stories from Church History. 8th ed. 1999. 304p. (J). (gr. 7-11). per. 21.00 (978-1-885767-54-7(4)) Canon Pr.

Happy Birthday, Jesus!, 6 vols. 2001. (Let the Children Come Ser.: Vol. 2). 80p. tchr. ed., per. 24.95 (978-1-889108-81-0(2)); 32p. (J). pap. 2.95 (978-1-889108-84-1(7)) Living the Good News.

Harrast, Tracy. Cuéntame, Mama Bilingue/Tell Me the Story, Mom. 1999. (SPA & ENG.). 168p. (J). (ps-3). pap. 9.99 (978-0-8297-1978-9(4)) Vida Pubs.

—Little David & Big Goliath. 1999. (Peek-A-Boo Ser.). 6.99 (978-0-310-97586-1(7)) Zondervan.

—La Oveja Perdida. 2000. (SPA., Illus.). 18p. (J). (ps-k). 6.99 (978-0-8297-2220-8(3)) Vida Pubs.

—Picture That! Bible Storybook. Colby, Garry, illus. 1998. (Bible Storybooks Ser.). 160p. (J). 12.99 (978-0-310-92600-9(9)) Zonderkidz.

—Viaje en el Gran Barco. 2000. (SPA., Illus.). 18p. (J). (ps-k). 6.99 (978-0-8297-2223-9(8)) Vida Pubs.

Harrast, Tracy & Carlson, Melody. Baby's First Bible. 2002. (Bible Storybooks Ser.). (Illus.). 96p. (J). 6.99 (978-0-310-70448-5(0)) Zonderkidz.

Harrast, Tracy L., et al. Guess What? Story Bible. Sharp, Paul & Sharp, Alice, illus. 2004. (Bible Storybooks Ser.). 192p. (J). 16.99 (978-0-310-70701-1(3)) Zonderkidz.

Harston, Jerry, illus. Bible Treasury for LDS Children. 1999. viii, 134p. (J). (978-1-57345-162-8(2)) Deseret Bk. Co.

Hartin, Dennis. The Surprising Christmas Pageant: The Story of the Birth of Christ Told with Humor, Mystery & Awe! 2004. 64p. (gr. k-6). spiral bd. 29.00 (978-0-687-05146-5(0)) Abingdon Pr.

Hartman, Bob. Easter Stories. 2005. (Illus.). 96p. (J). pap. 18.00 (978-0-7459-4873-7(1) , Lion) Lion Hudson plc GBR. *Dist:* Independent Pubs. Group.

Hatfield, Tyrel & Hatfield, Justin. Fix Your Eyes on Jesus. Hatfield, Lisa & Hatfield, Kari, eds. Hatfield, Tyrel, illus. 2006. (J). cd-rom 99.00 (978-0-9766703-1-5(3)) Little Acorn LLC.

—The Mystery of Christ. Hatfield, Lisa & Hatfield, Kari, eds. Hatfield, Tyrel, illus. 2006. (J). cd-rom 99.00 (978-0-9766703-2-2(1)) Little Acorn LLC.

Hawksley, Gerald. Amazing Journey of Noah & His Incredible Ark. 2004. 20p. pap. 11.99 (978-0-8254-7275-6(X)) Kregel Pubns.

—Lift & Look Creation. Stanley, Mandy, illus. 2006. 8p. (J). bds. 7.99 (978-0-7847-1458-4(4) , 04085) Standard Publishing.

Hayford, Jack. The Acts Bible Story Book: What Kids Want to Know about the Holy Spirit. 2005. (Illus.). 60p. (J). 11.99 (978-1-59185-211-7(0) , Charisma Kids) Strang Communications Co.

Hayford, Jack W. Jack Hayford Presenta Hechos una Historia de la Biblia. Foote, Dan, illus. 2005. 60p. (J). (ps-5). 9.99 (978-1-59185-487-6(3) , Charisma Kids) Strang Communications Co.

Heart Of Dakota. Little Hands to Heaven. 2004. pap. 29.99 (978-0-9747695-4-7(1)) Ebed Pr.

Heley, Veronica. Stories of Everyday Saints: 40 Stories with Bible Links & Related Activities. 2005. (Illus.). 96p. (J). pap. (978-1-84101-224-7(6) , Barnabas) Bible Reading Fellowship.

Helm, David R. The Big Picture Story Bible. Schoonmaker, Gail, illus. 2005. 456p. 22.99 (978-1-58134-277-2(2) , Crossway Bibles) Crossway Bks.

Helms, Selah & Thompson, Susan. Small Talks on Big Questions Vol. 2: A Historical Companion to the Children's Catechism, 2 vols. Whitney, Caffy, illus. 2003. 192p. 26.99 (978-1-894400-05-3(4)) Joshua Pr., Inc. CAN. *Dist:* Gabriel Resources.

Henderson, Felicity. The Adventure Story Picture Bible. 2001. 126p. (J). lib. bdg. 16.95 (978-1-59325-024-9(X)) Word Among Us Pr.

Heness, Clay, illus. Noah's Ark, 8 vols., Vol. 1. 1999. 10p. (J). 6.00 (978-0-9668763-0-7(X)) LightHouse Ministries.

Henley, K. P. La Historia de Dios (God's Story) (SPA.). (J). (978-0-7899-0628-1(7) , 497542) Editorial Unilit.

Henley, Karyn. Day by Day Kid's Bible: The Bible for Young Readers. 2002. (Tyndale Kids Ser.). (Illus.). 876p. (J). 19.99 (978-0-8423-5536-0(7)) Tyndale Hse. Pubs.

—Exploring God's World Through Simple Science: Bible Story Activities for Ages 2 To 5. 2006. (J). tchr. ed., per. 19.99 (978-1-933803-03-6(7) , EG1) Child Sensitive Communication, LLC.

—God Made Land, Sea, & Sky. (Children's Ministry Folders). (Illus.). 8p. (ps-k). 2.99 (978-0-7847-0652-7(2) , 42202) Standard Publishing.

—Jesus Is My Friend. (Children's Ministry Folders). (Illus.). 8p. (ps-k). 2.99 (978-0-7847-0672-5(7) , 42222) Standard Publishing.

—Jesus Made People Well. (Children's Ministry Folders). (Illus.). 8p. (ps-k). 2.99 (978-0-7847-0671-8(9) , 42221) Standard Publishing.

—My Learn-to-Pray Bible. Dippold, Jane, illus. 2004. 66p. (J). bds. 12.99 (978-0-8423-8733-0(1)) Tyndale Hse. Pubs.

—Story Telling: Bible Class Activities for Ages 2 To5. 2006. 186p. (J). tchr. ed., per. 19.99 (978-1-933803-05-0(3) , STRY1) Child Sensitive Communication, LLC.

Henley, Karyn & Morley, Taia. Before I Dream Bedtime: Bedtime Bible Storybook. 2005. (Karyn Henley Playsongs Ser.). (Illus.). 148p. (J). 14.99 incl. audio compact disk (978-1-4143-0092-4(1)) Tyndale Hse. Pubs.

Henley, Karyn & Sapulich, Joseph. Day by Day Begin-to-Read Bible. 2007. (Tyndale Kids Ser.). (Illus.). 448p. (J). 14.99 (978-1-4143-0934-7(1) , Tyndale Kids) Tyndale Hse. Pubs.

Higuchi, Masakazu. Manga Bible Story-Japanese. 2006. 880p. pap. 38.00 (978-4-264-01798-1(X)) STL Distribution North America.

El Hijo Prodigo, 6 vols. 2000. (Arch Bks.). (SPA.). 24p. (J). (ps-3). 2.49 (978-0-570-05169-5(X)) Concordia Publishing Hse.

El Hijo Prodigo. (SPA.). (J). (978-0-89265-493-2(7)) Randall Hse. Pubns.

La Historia de la Creacion, 6 vols. 2000. (Arch Bks.). (SPA.). 24p. (J). (ps-3). 2.49 (978-0-570-05170-1(3)) Concordia Publishing Hse.

La Historia de Navidad de Maria, 6 vols. 2000. (Arch Bks.). (SPA.). 24p. (J). (ps). 2.49 (978-0-570-05173-2(8)) Concordia Publishing Hse.

Historias Acerca de Jesus para Pequenitos. 1999. Tr. of Stories about Jesus for Little Ones. (SPA.). (J). bds. 8.99 (978-0-7899-0614-4(7) , 494616) Editorial Unilit.

Hoffman, Mary. A First Bible Story Book. Downing, Julie, illus. 1998. 80p. (J). (gr. 5-2). 12.99 (978-0-7894-1555-4(0)) Dorling Kindersley Publishing, Inc.

—Un Primer Libro de Cuentas Biblicos. Downing, Julie, illus. 2005. 80p. (J). 12.99 (978-0-7566-1507-9(0)) Dorling Kindersley Publishing, Inc.

Hoffman, Mary & Dorling Kindersley Publishing Staff. A First Bible Story Book. 2000. (Read & Listen Ser.). (Illus.). 80p. (J). (ps-3). pap. 9.99 (978-0-7894-5464-5(5)); pap. 9.99 incl. audio compact disk (978-0-7894-6098-1(X)) Dorling Kindersley Publishing, Inc.

Hollingsworth, Mary. Mi Biblia y Yo. 2002. (SPA.). 384p. pap. 10.99 (978-0-8297-3579-6(8)) Vida Pubs.

—My Bible Journey. 2004. 360p. (J). 15.99 (978-0-529-11580-5(8)) Nelson, Thomas Inc.

—My Bible Journey Supersaver. 2004. 360p. 11.88 (978-0-529-11810-3(6)) Nelson, Thomas Inc.

Holman and Broadman Staff. The Greatest Stories Ever Told. 1999. (Illus.). 128p. (J). (gr. k-1). 14.99 (978-0-8054-9344-3(1)) B&H Publishing Grp.

Holmes, Andy. Bible for Me: 12 Favorite Stories. Voltz, Ralph, illus. 2003. 48p. (J). 9.99 (978-1-4003-0234-5(X)) Nelson, Thomas Inc.

—Bible for Me: Easter. Voltz, Ralph, illus. 2006. 48p. (J). 9.99 (978-1-4003-0698-5(1)) Nelson, Thomas Inc.

—Biblia para Mi. Voltz, Ralph, illus. 2004. Tr. of Bible for Me. (SPA.). 24p. 9.99 (978-0-88113-785-9(5)) Grupo Nelson.

—My First Devotional Bible. 2007. 128p. (J). 9.99 ***(978-1-4003-0908-5(5))*** Nelson, Thomas Inc.

Holmes, Andy. My Great Big God. Turk, Caron, illus. 2006. 44p. (J). (ps-k). 9.99 (978-1-59145-497-7(2)) Nelson, Thomas Inc.

Hoop, Cathy C. PowerXpress Easter: Peter's Story Unit. 2004. 115.00 (978-0-687-07336-8(7)) Abingdon Pr.

HOP, LLC. Hooked on Bible Stories. deluxe ed. 2006. 99.99 (978-1-933863-00-9(5)) HOP, LLC.

—Hooked on Bible Stories NT Stories. 2006. 24.99 (978-1-931020-98-5(1)) HOP, LLC.

—Hooked on Bible Stories Old Testament Stories. 2006. 24.99 (978-1-931020-97-8(3)) HOP, LLC.

—Hooked on Bible Stories Premium Edition. 2006. 64.99 (978-1-931020-99-2(X)) HOP, LLC.

—Hooked on Phonics Beginning Reading with Bible Stories. 2006. 29.99 (978-1-931020-80-0(9)) HOP, LLC.

Howe, Michele. Bible Stories, Food & Fun: Worship Activities for Children. 1999. 48p. pap. 6.25 (978-0-7880-1523-6(0)) CSS Publishing Co.

Howie, Vicki. Easy to Say, Easy to Play: Three Popular Bible Stories & Sixteen Easy Songs to Sing & Play. 2005. (Illus.). 96p. (J). pap. (978-1-84101-221-6(1) , Barnabas) Bible Reading Fellowship.

—Easy Ways to Bible Fun for the Very Young: Twelve Bible-Based Activities For 3-5s. Taylor, Jane, illus. 2005. 96p. (J). pap. (978-1-84101-135-6(5) , Barnabas) Bible Reading Fellowship.

Howie, Vicky, et al. Cnoc, Cnoc! Pwy Sy 'na? Llyfr Fflapiau Stori'r Nadolig. 2005. (WEL., Illus.). 20p. (978-1-85994-498-1(1)) Cyhoeddiadau'r Gair.

Hudson, Angus. Historias Favoritas de la Biblia (Favorite Bible Stories) (Serie Uniendo los Puntos - Dot to Dot Ser.). (SPA.). (J). Bk. 1. 1.89 (978-1-56063-966-4(0) , 497757); Bk. 2. 1.89 (978-1-56063-967-1(9) , 497758) Editorial Unilit.

Hudson, Sue. 70 Days with Mark. 2006. 80p. pap. 7.99 (978-1-86024-536-7(6)) Authentic Media.

Hughes, Greg. The Shapes & Colors Bible. Hughes, Greg, illus. 2004. (Illus.). 80p. (J). 7.99 (978-0-9741091-3-8(4) , 7002) smart Life Ministries, Inc., The.

Hummell, Victoria R. A. Friends of Jesus: Stories & Activities for Chrldren, Parents, & Teachers. 2003. (J). pap. 9.95 net. (978-0-7648-1101-2(0)) Liguori Pubns.

Hupp, S. Mi librito de historias Biblicas. 2002. (God's Little Book Ser.).Tr. of God's Little Story Book. 7.99 (978-0-7899-0904-6(9)) Editorial Unilit.

—Mi librito de historias biblicas acerca de Jesus. 2002. (God's Little Book Ser.).Tr. of God's Little Story Book About Jesus. 7.99 (978-0-7899-0903-9(0)) Editorial Unilit.

Hurry up, Noah. 2006. 16p. (J). pap. 1.99 (978-0-7847-1714-1(1) , 04175) Standard Publishing.

Hurst, Diane. Calming the Storm. Overstreet, Laura, illus. 2006. (Sing A Story Ser.). 20p. (J). bds. 4.99 (978-0-7847-1814-8(8) , 04136) Standard Publishing.

—Creation. Overstreet, Laura, illus. 2006. (Sing A Story Ser.). 20p. (J). bds. 4.99 (978-0-7847-1811-7(3) , 04133) Standard Publishing.

I May Be Little. 2004. bds. 7.99 (978-0-8254-7284-8(9)) Kregel Pubns.

Icb Translation Staff & Nelson, Tommy. Magnify - Psalms & Proverbs Big Book of Bible Games: Biblezine for Kids. 2006. 240p. (J). pap. 14.99 (978-1-4003-0600-8(0)) Nelson, Thomas Inc.

Illustrated Bible Storybook. 2000. (Illus.). 304p. (J). (gr. 4-7). 29.98 (978-1-58516-050-1(4)) American Bible Society.

IMB. My Life His Mission. 2006. 166p. (YA). (gr. 8-12). pap. 9.99 (978-1-59145-488-5(3)) Nelson, Thomas Inc.

Isherwood, Shirley. Miracles, Whales, & Wonderful Tales. 2002. (Illus.). 128p. 22.99 (978-0-09-176869-0(1) , Hutchinson) Random Hse. GBR. *Dist:* Independent Pubs. Group.

Jackson, Dave & Jackson, Neta. Hero Tales. 2005. (Illus.). 192p. (J). (ps-7). pap. 12.99 (978-0-7642-0078-6(X)) Bethany Hse. Pubs.

Jairus's House. (Gospel Road Story Bks.). (Illus.). 12p. (J). (ps-k). 0.99 (978-0-8254-7223-7(7)) Kregel Pubns.

James, Kari. My Big Book of Bible Stories. Miralles, Jose, illus. 1999. (At Your Fingertips Ser.). 5p. (J). (ps-3). mass mkt. 6.95 (978-0-7681-0103-4(4) , McClanahan Bk.) Learning Horizons, Inc.

Jander, Martha S. The Visit of the Wise Men. Wang, Lin, illus. 2007. 32p. (J). (gr. k up). 14.99 ***(978-0-7586-1345-5(8))*** Concordia Publishing Hse.

Jander, Martha Streufert. Philip & the Ethiopian: Acts 8:26-40 for Children. Mitter, Kathy, illus. 2005. (ENG.). 16p. (J). (ps-ps). 1.99 (978-0-7586-0619-8(2)) Concordia Publishing Hse.

Jeffs, Stephanie. The Bedtime Bible. 1999. (Illus.). 96p. 12.99 (978-0-551-03218-7(9)) Zondervan.

—If You'd Been There in Bible Times. Thomas, Jacqui, illus. 2004. 64p. 14.00 (978-0-687-01507-8(3)) Abingdon Pr.

—Jacob: Wrestler with God. 2003. (SnapShots Ser.). (Illus.). 96p. 5.99 (978-1-85999-444-3(X)) Scripture Union GBR. *Dist:* Gabriel Resources.

—Joshua: Warrior for God. 2003. (SnapShots Ser.). (Illus.). 96p. 5.99 (978-1-85999-451-1(2)) Scripture Union GBR. *Dist:* Gabriel Resources.

—Peter: Fisherman for God. 2003. (SnapShots Ser.). (Illus.). 96p. 5.99 (978-1-85999-453-5(9)) Scripture Union GBR. *Dist:* Gabriel Resources.

—The Story of Christmas. 2005. 32p. 15.00 (978-0-687-05501-2(6)) Abingdon Pr.

Jeffs, Stephanie & Williams, Derek. Children's Bible Stories & Fascinating Facts. Knight, Jane, ed. 2000. (Illus.). 189p. (J). (gr. 1-6). 15.00 (978-0-8358-0924-5(2)) Upper Room Bks.

Jeffs, Stephanie, et al. Bywyd Iesu. 2005. (WEL., Illus.). 92p. (978-1-85994-496-7(5)) Cyhoeddiadau'r Gair.

The Jesus & the Children, Beginner's Biblereg; 2007. (Biblia para Principiantes Ser.). 24p. (J). 5.99 (978-0-8297-5011-9(8)) Vida Pubs.

Jesus Calma la Tempestad Vol. 22: Serie Minilibritos Aventuras de la Biblia. 2001. pap. (978-1-930564-92-3(9)) United Bible Societies/Americas Service Ctr.

Jesus Feeds 5,000 People. 2001. (Favorite Stories about Jesus Bks.). (Illus.). 12p. (J). 0.99 (978-0-8254-7230-5(X)) Kregel Pubns.

Jesus Heals Ten Lepers. (Illus.). (J). (gr. 1-4). 3.00 (978-0-570-05523-5(7) , 54-1033) Concordia Publishing Hse.

Jesus Is a Friend of Mine, 3 vols. 2001. (Let the Children Come Ser.: Vol. 3). (J). 32p. pap. 2.95 (978-1-889108-85-8(5)); 80p. pap., tchr. ed. 24.95 (978-1-889108-82-7(0)) Living the Good News.

Jesus Is a Friend to Zacchaeus. (Illus.). (gr. 1-4). 3.00 (978-0-570-05522-8(9) , 54-1032) Concordia Publishing Hse.

The Jesus Is Risen!, Beginner's Biblereg; 2007. (Biblia para Principiantes Ser.). 24p. (J). 5.99 (978-0-8297-5012-6(6)) Vida Pubs.

Jesus' Life Hidden Pictures. 1998. 48p. (J). (gr. 4-6). pap. 5.95 (978-0-7647-0428-4(1) , SS4863, In Celebration) Schaffer, Frank Pubns.

Jesus Miracles. 2004. (gr. 3-4). pap. 6.95 (978-0-382-30784-3(4)) Cobblestone Publishing Co.

Johnson, Linda & Hodges, Quae. 21st Century Parables: A Child's Book. 2006. 48p. pap. 14.95 ***(978-1-60145-071-5(0))*** Booklocker.com, Inc.

Jonah & the Big Fish. 2002. (Illus.). 24p. (J). 5.99 (978-1-57759-522-9(X)) Dalmatian Pr.

Jonah & the Big Fish. 2003. (J). per. (978-1-57657-981-7(6)) Paradise Pr., Inc.

Jones, Mary A. Bible Stories: God at Work with Man. Armstrong, Tom, illus. 1999. 80p. (J). (gr. 1-4). 1.00 (978-0-687-03384-3(5)) Abingdon Pr.

Jones, S. Historias para el Bebe: Dios hizo el Mundo. 2001. (Baby's First Ser.).Tr. of Baby's Bible Stories: God made the world. bds. 7.99 (978-0-7899-0960-2(X)) Editorial Unilit.

Jones, Sally Lloyd. The Little Bear Story Bible. Oleynikov, Igor, illus. 2007. 22p. (J). 12.99 (978-0-310-71082-0(0)) Zonderkidz.

Jose: Serie para ninos Amigos de la Biblia. 2000. pap. (978-1-57697-788-0(9)) United Bible Societies/Americas Service Ctr.

Joseph Bible Sticker Book. 2003. (Illus.). 16p. (J). 2.98 (978-1-4054-1556-9(8)) Parragon, Inc.

Kasen, Marty, ed. Favorite Bible Stories. 1998. (Illus.). 24p. (J). (gr. 1-3). 3.98 (978-1-890095-10-9(9)); Vol. 2. 3.98 (978-1-890095-11-6(7)) Nesak International.

Keck, Kraig. Word Perfect: Timeless Truths of the Bible. 2000. (Hotshots Ser.: Vol. 12). 48p. (J). pap. 10.25 (978-1-929784-25-7(2)) Positive Action For Christ.

Kenney, Cindy. VeggieTales Bible Storybook: With Scripture from the NIrV. Big Idea Design Staff, illus. 2006. (Big Idea Books' Ser.). 256p. (J). 16.99 (978-0-310-71008-0(1)) Zonderkidz.

Kieda, Alyson. Bible Story Mini Books. 1999. 64p. pap. 6.99 (978-1-56822-698-9(5) , In Celebration) Schaffer, Frank Pubns.

Kile, Joan. God's Fig Tree. Ragland, Teresa, illus. 2005. 32p. (J). pap. 7.95 (978-1-57736-345-3(0) , Providence Hse. Pubs.) Providence Hse Pubs.

—God's Fruit Tree. Ragland, Teresa, illus. 2005. 28p. (J). (ps-ps). pap. 7.95 (978-1-57736-344-6(2) , Providence Hse. Pubs.) Providence Hse Pubs.

—God's Mustard Seed, Vol. 1. Ragland, Teresa, illus. 2005. 32p. (J). (ps-17). per. 11.95 (978-1-57736-342-2(6) , Providence Hse. Pubs.) Providence Hse Pubs.

—God's Protecting Angels. Ragland, Teresa, illus. 2005. 28p. (J). (ps-ps). pap. 7.95 (978-1-57736-346-0(9) , Providence Hse. Pubs.) Providence Hse Pubs.

—God's Rugged Cross. Ragland, Teresa, illus. 2005. 32p. (Orig.). (J). (ps-ps). pap. 4.95 (978-1-57736-343-9(4) , Providence Hse. Pubs.) Providence Hse Pubs.

Kimmel, Eric A. The Brass Serpent. Miller, Joanna, illus. 2005. 32p. (J). 14.95 (978-1-930143-41-8(9) , 3419); pap. 9.95 (978-1-930143-42-5(7) , 3427) Pitspopany Pr. (Devora Publishing).

Kingfisher Editors, ed. The Kingfisher Book of Bible Stories. Denton, Kady MacDonald, illus. 2003. (Bibles & Bible References Ser.). 160p. (J). (gr. k-3). tchr. ed. 18.95 (978-0-7534-5626-2(5) , Kingfisher) Houghton Mifflin Co. Trade & Reference Div.

Kleyn, Diana. Taking Root: Conversion Stories for Children. 2006. (J). per. 8.00 ***(978-1-60178-001-0(X))*** Reformation Heritage Bks.

Knowlton, Laurie Lazzaro. God's Blessings Story Bible. Ettlinger, Doris, illus. 2004. (Bible Storybooks Ser.). 224p. (J). 19.99 (978-0-310-70932-9(6)) Zonderkidz.

Knowlton, Laurie Lazzaro, et al. Catholic Book of Bible Stories. Ettlinger, Doris, illus. 2004. (Bible Storybooks Ser.). 224p. (J). 16.99 (978-0-310-70505-5(3)) Zonderkidz.

Kolbrek, Loyal A. Zacchaeus. Needham, James, illus. 2005. (ENG.). 16p. (J). 1.99 (978-0-7586-0866-6(7)) Concordia Publishing Hse.

Kondeatis, Christos. Scenes from the Life of Jesus Christ: A Three-Dimensional Bible Storybook. Kondeatis, Christos, illus. 2006. (Illus.). 10p. (J). (gr. k-4). reprint ed. 20.00 (978-0-7567-9826-0(4)) DIANE Publishing Co.

Konzen, Lisa M. Good News for Naaman. Snyder, Joel, illus. 2004. (ENG.). 16p. (J). 1.99 (978-0-570-07573-8(4)) Concordia Publishing Hse.

Krause, Bill & Waner. From Abe to Zach. 3.99 (978-0-87162-636-3(5)) Warner Pr. Pubs.

Kregel Publications Staff, contrib. by. La Aventura Biblica: Un Fabuloso y Espectacular Viaje Electronico a Traves de la Biblia. 2nd ed. 2000. (SPA.). 258p. (gr. 3-7). pap. 22.99 (978-0-8254-1972-0(7) , Editorial Portavoz) Kregel Pubns.

Kucharik, E. NT y Salmos Pequenas Bendiciones. 2003. (Little Hearts Ser.).Tr. of Little Blessings NT & Psalms. 16.99 (978-0-7899-1118-6(3)) Editorial Unilit.

Kuskin, Karla & Grejniec, Michael. Animals & the Ark. 2002. (Illus.). 44p. (J). (gr. k-3). 16.95 (978-0-689-83095-2(5) , Atheneum) Simon & Schuster Children's Publishing.

Lane, Leena. Christmas Fun: My First Bible Activity BK. Bishop, Roma, illus. 2004. 32p. pap. 6.95 (978-1-59325-043-0(6)) Word Among Us Pr.

—Friends of God: My First Bible Activity BK. Bishop, Roma, illus. 2004. 32p. pap. 6.95 (978-1-59325-042-3(8)) Word Among Us Pr.

—My First Bible. Chapman, Gillian, illus. 2005. (ENG.). 256p. (J). 12.99 (978-0-7586-0910-6(8)) Concordia Publishing Hse.

Larcombe, Jennifer Rees. Lost in Jerusalem! Bjorkman, Steve, illus. 2004. (Best Bible Stories Ser.). 24p. (ps-3). pap. 2.99 (978-1-58134-150-8(4)) Crossway Bks.

—The Walls That Fell down Flat. Bjorkman, Steve, illus. 2004. (Best Bible Stories Ser.). 24p. (ps-3). pap. 2.99 (978-1-58134-151-5(2)) Crossway Bks.

Larrison, Joanne. Week That Led to Easter. 2001. (gr. k-3). lib. bdg. 9.85 (978-0-613-71027-5(4)) Tandem Library Bks.

Larsen, Carolyn. Little Boys Bible Storybook: For Fathers & Sons. Turk, Caron, illus. 2001. 360p. (J). (ps-2). 16.99 (978-0-8010-4459-5(6) , New Kids Media) Baker Bks.

—Little Boys Bible Storybook for Mothers & Sons. Turk, Caron, illus. 1999. 360p. (J). (gr. 1-4). 16.99 (978-0-8010-4433-5(2) , New Kids Media) Baker Bks.

—Little Boys Tiny Bible Storybook. Turk, Caron, illus. 2001. 96p. (J). (gr. 1-4). 6.99 (978-0-8010-4472-4(3) , New Kids Media) Baker Bks.

—Little Girls Tiny Bible Storybook. Turk, Caron, illus. 2001. 96p. (J). (gr. 1-4). 6.99 (978-0-8010-4467-0(7) , New Kids Media) Baker Bks.

Larsen, Carolyn & Turk, Caron. The Toddler's 1-2-3 Bible Storybook. 2008. (J). (*978-1-4335-0107-4(4)) Crossway Bks.

Larsen, Carolyn & Turk, Caron. The Toddler's ABC Bible Storybook. 2007. (Illus.). 52p. (J). (978-1-58134-802-6(9)) Crossway Bks.

Larson, Beverly. El Cuento de la Ballena (The Whale's Tale) 2000. (Play along Ser.). (SPA.). (J). (ps-k). bds. 4.99 (978-0-7899-0820-9(4) , 493788) Editorial Unilit.

—Toca y Siente las Historias de la Biblia. Pineda, Nancy, tr. Dillard, Sarah, illus. 2003. (Touch & Feel Ser.). (SPA.). (J). (ps-k). bds. 8.99 (978-0-7899-1088-2(8)) Editorial Unilit.

Lashbrook, Marilyn. Alguien a Quien Amar: La Historia de la Creacion. Britt, Stephanie McFetridge, illus. 2000. (Libros Yo Tambien! Ser.).Tr. of Someone to Love. (SPA.). 32p. (J). (ps-2). 5.95 (978-1-58170-039-8(3)) Standard Publishing.

—Aunque Soy Pequeno: La Historia Del Crecimiento de David. Britt, Stephanie McFetridge, illus. 2000. (Libros Yo Tambien! Ser.).Tr. of I May Be Little. (SPA.). 32p. (J). (ps-2). 5.95 (978-1-58170-044-2(X)) Standard Publishing.

—De Dos En Dos: La Historia de la de Nos. Britt, Stephanie McFetridge, illus. 2000. (Libros Yo Tambien! Ser.).Tr. of Two by Two. (SPA.). 32p. (J). (ps-2). 5.95 (978-1-58170-043-5(1)) Standard Publishing.

—Desaparecete, Hermanito: La Historia de Jose. Britt, Stephanie McFetridge, illus. 2000. (Libros Yo Tambien! Ser.).Tr. of Get Lost, Little Brother. (SPA.). 32p. (J). (ps-2). 5.95 (978-1-58170-040-4(7)) Standard Publishing.

—Me Too! Chunky Book of Bible Stories. Britt, Stephanie McFetridge, illus. 2000. (Me Too! Bks.). (J). bds. 9.95 (978-1-58170-050-3(4)) Standard Publishing.

—No Quiero: La Historia de Jonas. Britt, Stephanie McFetridge, illus. 2000. (Libros Yo Tambien! Ser.).Tr. of I Don't Want To. (SPA.). 32p. (J). (ps-2). 5.95 (978-1-58170-041-1(5)) Standard Publishing.

—Puedo Ver: La Historia Del Hombre Que Nacio Ciego. Britt, Stephanie McFetridge, illus. 2000. (Libros Yo Tambien! Ser.).Tr. of Now I See. (SPA.). 32p. (J). (ps-2). 5.95 (978-1-58170-038-1(5)) Standard Publishing.

—Quien Necesita un Barco? La Historia de Moises. Britt, Stephanie McFetridge, illus. 2000. (Libros Yo Tambien! Ser.).Tr. of Who Needs a Boat?. (SPA.). 32p. (J). (ps-2). 5.95 (978-1-58170-037-4(7)) Standard Publishing.

Lava Lava Bible Book. 2003. (J). (ps). pap. 17.71 (*978-0-7644-2637-7(0)) Group Publishing, Inc.

Lava Lava Bible Book: Elementary. 2003. pap. 1.00 (*978-0-7644-2636-0(2)) Group Publishing, Inc.

Learner Resources: Blue Semester. 2004. (978-0-8066-4752-4(3)); (gr. 1-2). (978-0-8066-4758-6(2)); (gr. 3-4). (978-0-8066-4761-6(2)); (gr. 5-6). (978-0-8066-4765-4(5)); (gr. 7-8). (978-0-8066-4768-5(X)); (ps-k). (978-0-8066-4755-5(8)); Vol. 2. (978-0-8066-4773-9(6)); Vol. 2. (gr. 1-2). (978-0-8066-4779-1(5)); Vol. 2. (gr. 3-4). (978-0-8066-4782-1(5)); Vol. 2. (gr. 5-6). (978-0-8066-4786-9(8)); Vol. 2. (gr. 7-8). (978-0-8066-4789-0(2)); Vol. 2. (ps-k). (978-0-8066-4776-0(0)) Augsburg Fortress, Pubs.

Lee, Helen, compiled by. Guide's Greatest Prayer Stories. 2002. 142p. (YA). pap. 10.99 (978-0-8280-1647-6(X) , 079-975) Review & Herald Publishing Assn.

Lee, Helen, ed. Guide's Greatest Miracle Stories. 2001. 144p. (YA). pap. 9.99 (978-0-8280-1575-2(9)) Review & Herald Publishing Assn.

Lee, Hye-Seong, illus. The Call of Samuel: From 1 Samuel 3:1-10. 2003. 29p. (J). 13.50 (978-0-9659164-9-3(9)) Fountain Publishing.

Lee, Quinlan B. Bible Tales. Harpster, Steve, illus. 2006. (Scribble & Sing Ser.). 80p. (J). 4.99 (978-1-4169-2730-3(1) , Simon Scribbles) Simon & Schuster Children's Publishing.

Lessa, Charlotte F. My Bible Storybook. 2003. 455p. (J). 18.99 (978-0-8280-1792-3(1)) Review & Herald Publishing Assn.

Let's Practice Faith: Bible Story Flipbook. 2004. (Firelight Ser.). (gr. 3-4). 4.99 (978-0-8066-6512-2(2)) Augsburg Fortress, Pubs.

Let's Practice Faith: Bible Story Foldout. 2004. (Firelight Ser.). (ps). 4.99 (978-0-8066-6506-1(8)) Augsburg Fortress, Pubs.

Let's Practice Faith: Bible Storybook. 2004. (Firelight Ser.). (gr. 1-2). 4.99 (978-0-8066-6510-8(6)) Augsburg Fortress, Pubs.

Let's Practice Faith, Ages 2-3: Bible Story Album. 2004. (Firelight Ser.). (ps-k). 4.99 (978-0-8066-6508-5(4)) Augsburg Fortress, Pubs.

Life Publishers. My Friends-Student (Russian) Vol. 4, Bk. 1: Russian Sunday School, 2000. Orig. Title: Mis Amigos. Alumno. (RUS.). 32p. (J). pupil's gde. ed. (978-0-7361-0212-4(4)) Life Pubs. International.

Lillis, Sonya. God's Kids: Being a Light in a Dark World. l.t. ed. 2006. 36p. (J). per. 9.95 (*978-0-9786580-6-9(X)) Christian Voice Publishing, A.

—God's Kids: Great Bit Thoughts for Young Minds. l.t. ed. 2006. 36p. (J). per. 9.95 (*978-0-9786580-7-6(8)) Christian Voice Publishing, A.

—God's Kids: Growing up Holy in an Unholy World, book 1. l.t. ed. 2006. (Illus.). (J). per. 9.95 (*978-0-9786580-5-2(1)) Christian Voice Publishing, A.

Lindvall, Ella K. La Biblia en Cuadros para Nino Pequenos. 2004. (SPA.). 144p. 9.99 (978-0-8254-1710-8(4) , Editorial Portavoz) Kregel Pubns.

Lingo, Susan L. Collect-n-Tell Bible Stories for Kids: 34 Awesome Bible Stories with Powerful Points from a Few Simple Supplies! Barr, Marilynn G., illus. 2006. 112p. (YA). 15.99 (978-0-7847-1418-8(5) , 02456) Standard Publishing.

—Hope Finders. Barr, Marilynn G. & Jeffery, Megan E., illus. 2006. (Power Builders Curriculum Ser.). 128p. (J). (gr. 1-5). 15.99 (978-0-7847-1235-1(2) , 42118) Standard Publishing.

—Joy Builders. Barr, Marilynn G. & Jeffery, Megan E., illus. 2006. (Power Builders Curriculum Ser.). 128p. (J). (gr. 1-5). 15.99 (978-0-7847-1234-4(4) , 42117) Standard Publishing.

—Peace Makers. Barr, Marilynn G. & Jeffery, Megan E., illus. 2006. (Power Builders Curriculum Ser.). 128p. (J). (gr. 1-5). 15.99 (978-0-7847-1233-7(6) , 42116) Standard Publishing.

—Power Boosters. Barr, Marilynn G. & Jeffery, Megan E., illus. 2006. (Power Builders Curriculum Ser.). 128p. (J). (gr. 1-5). 15.99 (978-0-7847-1232-0(8) , 42115) Standard Publishing.

—Sleepy Animals: My Good Night(r) Bible Doorknob Book. Ring, Laura, ed. Parks, Kathy, illus. 2000. (My Good Night Bible Doorknob Bks.). 10p. (J). (ps up). 5.99 (978-0-7847-1056-2(2) , 03549, Bean Sprouts) Standard Publishing.

Lion Misses Breakfast. 2004. bds. 5.99 (978-0-8254-7288-6(1)) Kregel Pubns.

Lion Puppet, Vol. 2. 2003. 19.00 (978-0-687-05612-5(8)) Abingdon Pr.

The Lions that didn't Roar. 2005. 16p. (J). per. 4.99 (978-1-59441-088-8(7) , CD-204015) Carson-Dellosa Publishing Co., Inc.

Lipara, Laura. Gramma Shares Her Faith: Cain & Abel. 2006. per. 7.95 (*978-0-9791757-1-8(2)) Oak Manor Publishing, Inc.

Lipari, Laura. Gramma Shares Her Faith: Adam & Eve. 2006. 64p. (J). per. 6.95 (978-0-9747361-4-3(7)) Oak Manor Publishing, Inc.

Little Books of the Bible Stories of Jesus. (J). 14.95 (978-0-8249-5464-2(5)) Ideals Pubns.

Little Girls Bible Storybook. 32p. (J). 2.69 (978-0-7847-1460-7(6)) Standard Publishing.

Lloyd-Jones, Sally. A Child's First Bible. 2nd ed. 2000. (Illus.). 24p. (J). (ps up). 12.99 (978-0-7847-1173-6(9) , 03980, Bean Sprouts) Standard Publishing.

—The Jesus Bible Storybook: From Creation to Happily Ever After. Nguyen, Vincent & Jago, illus. 2007. 352p. (J). 16.99 (978-0-310-70825-4(7)) Zonderkidz.

—Levanta la Tapita la Biblia (Life the Flap Bible) 2000. (Lift the Flap Ser.). (SPA., Illus.). (J). (ps). 10.99 (978-0-7899-0821-6(2) , 493789) Editorial Unilit.

—My Promise Rainbow: And the Story of Noah's Ark. 2006. (Illus.). 14p. (YA). bds. 10.99 (978-0-7847-1357-0(X) , 04018) Standard Publishing.

Locusts for Lunch Intermediate: And Other Gross Dinners, Breakfasts, Suppers, & Snacks in the Bible. 2005. 16p. (J). pap. 10.99 (978-1-59317-110-0(2)) Warner Pr. Pubs.

Look & Find Activity Books. 2004. (Illus.). 24p. (J). 2.99 (978-0-8254-7262-6(8)); Vol. 2. 2.99 (978-0-8254-7263-3(6)) Kregel Pubns.

Lord, Jill Roman. Bible Story Favorites: A Fun Googly Eyes Book. McGee, Warner, illus. 2006. bds. 7.99 (978-1-59052-713-9(5) , Multnomah) WaterBrook Pr.

Lord, Jill Roman. Busy Bible Storybook. Moroney, Trace, illus. 2006. 12.99 (*978-0-8254-5529-2(4)) Kregel Pubns.

The Lost Son. 2003. (Illus.). 12p. (J). bds. 6.99 (978-0-8254-5506-3(5)) Kregel Pubns.

Lottridge, Celia Barker. Stories from the Bible. Clement, Gary & Wolfsgruber, Linda, illus. 2005. 332p. (J). 45.00 (978-0-88899-661-9(6)) Groundwood Bks. CAN. *Dist:* Transition Vendor.

Lucado, Max. All You Ever Need. Klauba, Douglas, illus. 2000. 32p. (ps-3). 15.99 (978-1-58134-134-8(2) , Crossway Bibles) Crossway Bks.

Lucas, Daryl J., ed. The Eager Reader Bible: Bible Stories to Grow On. Hochstatter, Daniel J., illus. 1999. 432p. (J). (ps-3). 14.99 (978-0-8423-1338-4(9)) Tyndale Hse. Pubs.

Lundy, Charlotte. Thank You, Esther. Waldrep, Evelyn L., ed. James, Margaret Ray, illus. 2001. 32p. (ps-3). 15.95 (978-0-9670280-4-0(3)) Bay Light Publishing.

—Thank You, Solomon. Waldrep, Evelyn L., ed. Sagasti, Miriam, illus. 2001. 32p. (ps-3). 15.95 (978-0-9670280-0-2(0)) Bay Light Publishing.

Lyons, P. J. The Wonderful World That God Made. Esposito, Lori, illus. 2004. 13.99 (978-0-8254-3166-1(2)) Kregel Pubns.

Maas, Alice E. Baby Jesus Visits the Temple. Miyake, Yoshi, illus. 2004. (ENG.). 16p. (J). 1.99 (978-0-570-07575-2(0)) Concordia Publishing Hse.

Mackall, Dandi Daley. In the Beginning. Kandt, James, illus. 2005. 32p. (J). 17.99 (978-1-4003-0525-4(X)) Nelson, Thomas Inc.

MacKenzie, Carine. The Beautiful Garden Dot to Dot. 16p. (J). pap., act. bk. ed. 1.50 (978-1-85792-829-7(6) , Christian Focus) Christian Focus Pubns. GBR. *Dist:* Riverside.

Mackenzie, Carine. Bible Alive: Jesus the Child. (Illus.). 24p. (J). pap. 2.99 (978-1-85792-749-8(4) , Christian Focus) Christian Focus Pubns. GBR. *Dist:* Riverside.

—Bible Alive: Jesus the Healer. (Illus.). 24p. (J). pap. 2.99 (978-1-85792-751-1(6) , Christian Focus) Christian Focus Pubns. GBR. *Dist:* Riverside.

—Bible Alive: Jesus the Miracle Worker. (Illus.). 24p. (J). pap. 2.99 (978-1-85792-752-8(4) , Christian Focus) Christian Focus Pubns. GBR. *Dist:* Riverside.

—Bible Alive: Jesus the Saviour. (Illus.). 24p. (J). pap. 2.99 (978-1-85792-754-2(0) , Christian Focus) Christian Focus Pubns. GBR. *Dist:* Riverside.

—Bible Alive: Jesus the Storyteller. (Illus.). 24p. (J). pap. 2.99 (978-1-85792-750-4(8) , Christian Focus) Christian Focus Pubns. GBR. *Dist:* Riverside.

—Bible Alive: Jesus the Teacher. (Illus.). 24p. (J). pap. 2.99 (978-1-85792-753-5(2) , Christian Focus) Christian Focus Pubns. GBR. *Dist:* Riverside.

MacKenzie, Carine. Bible Stories for Bedtime. 2000. (Illus.). 40p. (J). (ps-2). (978-1-85792-467-1(3) , Christian Focus) Christian Focus Pubns.

Mackenzie, Carine. How to Handle Your Life. (Illus.). 192p. (J). pap. 8.99 (978-1-85792-520-3(3) , Christian Focus) Christian Focus Pubns. GBR. *Dist:* Riverside.

—Jonah & the Big Fish. Apps, Fred, illus. 2005. 12p. (J). (ps-k). per. (978-1-84550-087-0(3) , Christian Focus) Christian Focus Pubns.

MacKenzie, Carine. Little Hands Story Bible. 1999. (Illus.). 144p. (J). (ps). (978-1-85792-342-1(1) , Christian Focus) Christian Focus Pubns.

—The Long Journey Dot to Dot. 16p. (J). pap., act. bk. ed. 1.50 (978-1-85792-832-7(6) , Christian Focus) Christian Focus Pubns. GBR. *Dist:* Riverside.

—Long, Long Ago in Bethlehem: The Birth of Jesus. 1999. (Illus.). 48p. (J). (ps-3). (978-1-85792-386-5(3) , Christian Focus) Christian Focus Pubns.

Mackenzie, Carine. Long, Long Ago in Jerusalem. (Illus.). 48p. (J). 10.99 (978-1-85792-390-2(1) , Christian Focus) Christian Focus Pubns. GBR. *Dist:* Riverside.

MacKenzie, Carine. Mary Colouring Book. 16p. (J). pap., act. bk. ed. 1.50 (978-1-85792-828-0(8) , Christian Focus) Christian Focus Pubns. GBR. *Dist:* Riverside.

—Noah Colouring Book. 16p. (J). pap., act. bk. ed. 1.50 (978-1-85792-823-5(7) , Christian Focus) Christian Focus Pubns. GBR. *Dist:* Riverside.

—Paul: Journeys of Adventure. 1999. (Illus.). 32p. (J). (gr. 1-5). pap. (978-1-85792-465-7(7) , Christian Focus) Christian Focus Pubns.

—Peter Colouring Book. 16p. (J). pap., act. bk. ed. 1.50 (978-1-85792-826-6(1) , Christian Focus) Christian Focus Pubns. GBR. *Dist:* Riverside.

Mackenzie, Carine. Samuel's Surprise. Apps, Fred, illus. 2005. 12p. (J). (ps-k). per. (978-1-84550-088-7(1) , Christian Focus) Christian Focus Pubns.

MacKenzie, Carine. The Very Busy Week Dot to Dot. 16p. (J). pap., act. bk. ed. 1.50 (978-1-85792-831-0(8) , Christian Focus) Christian Focus Pubns. GBR. *Dist:* Riverside.

—The Wonderful Boat Dot to Dot. 16p. (J). pap., act. bk. ed. 1.50 (978-1-85792-830-3(X) , Christian Focus) Christian Focus Pubns. GBR. *Dist:* Riverside.

Mackenzie, Carine & Gair, Cyhoeddiadau'r. 3 Hosea - Malachi. 2005. (978-1-85994-272-7(5)) Cyhoeddiadau'r Gair.

—4 Mathew - Actau. 2005. (978-1-85994-271-0(7)) Cyhoeddiadau'r Gair.

—6 1 Timotheus - Datguddiad. 2005. (978-1-85994-269-7(5)) Cyhoeddiadau'r Gair.

Mackenzie, Carine, et al. Beibl y Bobl Bach: 69 o Storïau. 2005. (WEL., Illus.). 144p. (978-1-85049-183-5(6) , Gwasg y Bwthyn) Gwasg Pantycelyn.

MacKenzie, Catherine. The Hall of Fame - New Testament. 2000. (Newsbox Ser.). (Illus.). 48p. (J). (ps-3). pap. (978-1-85792-546-3(7) , Christian Focus) Christian Focus Pubns.

—The Hall of Fame - Old Testament. 2000. (Newsbox Ser.). (Illus.). 48p. (J). (ps-3). pap. (978-1-85792-545-6(9) , Christian Focus) Christian Focus Pubns.

Mackenzie, Catherine. My Bible ABC. 64p. (J). pap. 7.99 (978-1-85792-605-7(6) , Christian Focus) Christian Focus Pubns. GBR. *Dist:* Riverside.

MacLean, G. Helen of the Glen. Date not set. (Flamingo Ser.). 3.99 (978-0-906731-80-2(1)) Christian Focus Pubns. GBR. *Dist:* Spring Arbor Distributors, Inc.

MacLean, Moira. Follow the Star Pushalong Book. (Illus.). 12p. (J). (ps-k). 6.99 (978-0-8254-7242-8(3)) Kregel Pubns.

MacLean, Mrs. Alistair, pseud. David & Bathsheba. Milton, illus. l.t. ed. 1998. (Yesterday & Tomorrow Bible Cartoon Ser.). 75p. (YA). spiral bd. 10.00 (978-0-940178-77-9(X)) Sitare, Ltd.

MacMaster, Eve. Children's Illustrated Bible. 2006. (Illus.). xiii, 498p. (*978-0-8361-9344-2(X)) Herald Pr.

Maddox, Mike. The Lion Graphic Bible. Anderson, Jeff, illus. 2001. 256p. (J). pap. 16.99 (978-0-7459-4598-9(8) , Lion) Lion Hudson plc GBR. *Dist:* Independent Pubs. Group.

Magarino, Aurel. La Evangelizando Por Medio De. 2004. (SPA.). 91p. 4.95 (978-0-570-05185-5(1)) Concordia Publishing Hse.

Make Believe Ideas. Jonah the Moaner. 2006. (Illus.). 32p. (J). (ps-3). 8.97 (978-1-59145-527-1(8)) Nelson, Thomas Inc.

—My First Bedtime Bible. 2006. (Illus.). 256p. (J). (ps-3). 9.95 (978-1-59145-525-7(1)) Nelson, Thomas Inc.

Make Believe Ideas, Ltd. Shiny, Touchy, Smelly Creation. 2007. (Illus.). 12p. (J). (ps). 9.97 (978-1-59145-553-0(7)) Nelson, Thomas Inc.

Mandhardt, Laurie. Life of Jesus. 2005. (J). pap. 10.00 (978-1-931018-28-9(6)) Emmaus Road Publishing.

Marmol, Pablo, illus. La Biblia de los Jovenes: Antiguo y Nuevo Testamento, 2 vols. 2001. (SPA.). 127p. (J). (gr. 4-7). 27.95 (978-84-670-0001-6(5)) Espasa Calpe, S.A. ESP. *Dist:* Planeta Publishing Corp.

Martin, Oscar, Jr., creator. David & Goliath, l.t. ed. 2003. (Illus.). 25p. (J). E-Book 19.95 incl. cd-rom (978-0-9748416-3-2(3)) Build Your Story.

The Mary & Little Jesus, Beginner's Biblereg; 2007. 24p. (J). 5.99 (978-0-8297-5010-2(X)) Vida Pubs.

Matuszak, Pat. Spiders! 2002. (Illus.). 40p. 9.99 (978-0-310-70481-2(2)) Zondervan.

McAlister, Sharon. That First Christmas. 2005. 48p. pap. 19.95 (978-1-4137-6966-1(7)) PublishAmerica, Inc.

McBryde, Tom. PowerXpress Zacchaeus Unit. 2006. 115.00 (978-0-687-03950-0(9)) Abingdon Pr.

McCardell, Kenneth/W. Bible Rhymes' Creation. Chirco, Antonella, illus. 2007. 32p. (J). 17.95 (*978-0-9790605-0-2(8) , BibleRhymes) BibleRhymes Publishing, L.L.C.

—Bible Rhymes' Noah & the Ark. Chirco, Antonella, illus. 2007. 32p. (J). 17.95 (*978-0-9790605-1-9(6) , BibleRhymes) BibleRhymes Publishing, L.L.C.

McClanahan. First Mazes: Bible Stories. 1999. (High Q Books Ser.). (Illus.). 48p. (J). (ps-3). pap. 3.99 (978-0-7681-0113-3(1) , McClanahan Bk.) Learning Horizons, Inc.

McGraw-Hill Staff. David & Goliath. 2003. (gr. k-3). lib. bdg. 11.80 (978-0-613-88031-2(5)) Tandem Library Bks.

McKinney, Nancy Kruschke, compiled by. A Bible Story Collection: For Kids, by Kids. 2006. (J). 12.95 (978-0-9721961-1-3(2)) Action Organizing.

Meade, Starr. Grandpa's Box: Retelling the Biblical Story of Redemption. Van Patter, Bruce, illus. 2005. 286p. (J). (gr. 3-7). per. 13.99 (978-0-87552-866-3(X)) P & R Publishing.

Meet God's First Friends, 3 vols. 2001. (Let the Children Come Ser.: Vol. 1). 80p. pap. 24.95 (978-1-889108-80-3(4)); 32p. (J). pap. 2.95 (978-1-889108-83-4(9)) Living the Good News.

Mendenhall, Cheryl, illus. Beautiful Bible Stories: A Bible Story Collection. 2004. (Keepsake Quality Ser.). 224p. (J). 10.99 (978-1-4037-0627-0(1)) Dalmatian Pr.

—Moses Baby in the Bulrushes. 2004. 24p. (J). 2.99 (978-1-4037-0963-9(7) , Spirit Pr.) Dalmatian Pr.

—Moses Parting the Red Sea. 2004. 24p. (J). 2.99 (978-1-4037-0964-6(5) , Spirit Pr.) Dalmatian Pr.

Metaxas, Eric. Even Fish Slappers Need a Second Chance. 2002. (Illus.). 32p. (J). 6.99 (978-0-310-70461-4(8)) Zonderkidz.

Metts, Wallis C., et al. Children's Book of the Bible. 2005. (Illus.). 320p. (J). 15.98 (978-0-7853-7808-2(1) , 3922102) Publications International, Ltd.

Mi Libro de Pascua, 6 vols. 2000. (Arch Bks.). (SPA.). 24p. (J). (ps-3). 2.49 (978-0-570-05167-1(3)) Concordia Publishing Hse.

Mi Primera Pascua (My Happy Easter) (Arch Bks.). (SPA.). (J). (gr. k-4). 2.75 (978-0-570-05175-6(4) , 16-6051) Concordia Publishing Hse.

Miller, Christopher & Miller, Allan. The Legend of Gid the Kid & the Black Bean Bandits: Doing the Right Thing Ain't Always Easy. 2007. (Illus.). 32p. (J). (gr. 1-5). 12.99 (*978-1-59317-202-2(8)) Warner Pr. Pubs.

Miller, Claire. The Ten Commandments. Miyake, Yoshi, illus. 2004. (Arch Books). 16p. (J). 1.99 (978-0-7586-0672-3(9)) Concordia Publishing Hse.

Mills, Peter. Fire! Fire! Window Book. 1999. (Illus.). 16p. (J). pap. (978-1-85608-199-3(0)) Hunt, John Publishing Ltd.

—Jailbreak: Window Book. 1999. (Illus.). 16p. (J). pap. (978-1-85608-189-4(3)) Hunt, John Publishing Ltd.

—Rain! Rain! Window Book. 1999. (Illus.). 16p. (J). (978-1-85608-194-8(X)) Hunt, John Publishing Ltd.

—Star of Bethlehem. 1999. (Illus.). 16p. (J). pap. (978-1-85608-184-9(2)) Hunt, John Publishing Ltd.

Ministries, Tnt. On the Way For 9 - 11's, Vol. 6. 80p. (J). pap. 11.99 (978-1-85792-556-2(4) , Christian Focus) Christian Focus Pubns. GBR. *Dist:* Riverside.

Mission City Press Staff. The Beginners Bible for Toddlers. Pulley, Kelly, illus. 2007. (Beginner's Bible' Ser.). 160p. (J). 9.99 (978-0-310-71408-8(7)) Zonderkidz.

Mitchell, Kathy. Bible Stories from the Old Testament. 2001. (gr. k-3). lib. bdg. 10.95 (978-0-613-32325-3(4)) Tandem Library Bks.

Mitchell, Kathy, illus. Bible Stories from the Old Testament. 1999. (Easter Mini Storybooks Ser.: Vol. 3). (J). (gr. k-3). 3.25 (978-0-7666-0249-6(4) , Honey Bear Bks.) Modern Publishing.

Mitzo Thompson, Kim & Mitzo Hilderbrand, Karen. Two by Two. Kauffman, Ron, illus. 2005. (Read & Sing along Board Books with CDs Ser.). 18p. (J). (ps-k). bds., bds. 7.49 incl. audio compact disk (978-0-7696-4458-5(9)) School Specialty Publishing.

Molski, Carol. A Little Taste of God's Love: Bible Story Recipes & Activities. 2001. (Illus.). 64p. (ps-2). 9.99 (978-0-570-05281-4(5) , 12-4094) Concordia Publishing Hse.

Monroe, Colleen. A Is for Ark: Noah's Journey. Monroe, Michael Glenn, illus. 2004. 38p. (ps-1). pap. 17.95 (978-0-9754942-0-2(1)) Storytime Pr., Inc.

Montero, Jose Perez, illus. The Little Children's Bible Storybook. 2005. 448p. (J). 14.99 (978-1-59052-606-4(6) , Multnomah) WaterBrook Pr.

—Seek & Find in the Bible. 2003. 64p. 18.95 incl. cd-rom (978-87-7247-305-5(3)) Scandinavia Publishing Hse. DNK. *Dist:* National Bk. Network.

Moody, Dwight Lyman. Children's Stories. 160p. (J). mass mkt. 5.99 (978-1-85792-640-8(4) , Christian Heritage) Christian Focus Pubns. GBR. *Dist:* Riverside.

Moore, Beth. A Parable About the King. Warren, Beverly, illus. 2003. 24p. (J). 12.99 (978-0-8054-2679-3(5)) B&H Publishing Grp.

Moore, Eva. Jesus in Jerusalem. 2007. 32p. (J). pap. 3.99 (978-0-439-89038-0(1)) Scholastic, Inc.

—Time of Miracles. 2006. 32p. (J). pap. 3.99 (978-0-439-85879-3(8)) Scholastic, Inc.

—Year of Favorite Stories. 2006. (Illus.). 160p. (J). pap. 14.99 (978-0-439-87201-0(4)) Scholastic, Inc.

Moroney, T. Levanta la Tapita: Aventuras Biblicas. 2002. (Lift the Flap Ser.).Tr. of Lift the Flap: Bible Adventures. bds. 10.99 (978-0-7899-0787-5(9)) Editorial Unilit.

Moroney, Tracey, illus. The First Christmas. 1999. (Christmas Bible Play Bks.). 18p. (ps-k). 5.99 (978-0-7847-1051-7(1) , 03999, Bean Sprouts) Standard Publishing.

Moses & the Princess. 14p. (J). bds. 7.99 (978-0-7847-1403-4(7)) Standard Publishing.

Moses in the Bulrushes. (Bible Friends plus Book Ser.). (Illus.). 10p. (J). (ps-k). 6.99 (978-0-8254-7237-4(7)) Kregel Pubns.

Mueller, Arthur W. Stories of God & His People. 2005. 226p. (J). (gr. 3-6). 12.99 (978-0-570-05510-5(5)) Concordia Publishing Hse.

Mummery, Sue. Why 2000. Mummery, Sue, illus. 1999. (Illus.). 32p. (J). (ps-3). pap. (978-1-85792-483-1(5)) Christian Focus Pubns.

My Bible Book. 2006. pap. 9.99 (978-0-8341-2267-3(7)) Nazarene Publishing Hse.

My Bible Story Coloring Book. 1998. (My Bible Story Coloring Bks.). (Illus.). 32p. (J). (ps-3). pap. 1.99 (978-0-570-05072-8(3)) Concordia Publishing Hse.

My Bible Teaches Me about God. 1998. (Junior Kids Church Ser.: Vol. 5). 160p. (J). (ps). 134.99 incl. audio (978-1-57405-436-1(8)) CharismaLife Pubs.

My Little Book of Bible Storie. 2004. 6.99 (978-0-8254-7278-7(4)) Kregel Pubns.

My TakeAlong Li, ed. Bible Stories. 2007. (My Take-along Library). 120p. (J). (ps-k). bds. 14.95 (*978-0-7696-5529-1(7)) School Specialty Publishing.

My Very Own Activity Pages: Summer 2004. 2004. (J). pap. 1.79 (*978-1-59317-067-7(X)) Warner Pr. Pubs.

Nelson, Dorothy N. God Spoke to a Girl. Gorunoff, Oleg, illus. 1998. 32p. (J). (ps-2). pap. 1.97 (978-0-8163-1655-7(4)) Pacific Pr. Publishing Assn.

Nelson, Tommy. My Shining Bible: A First Bible for Children. Clearwater, Linda, illus. 2005. 20p. (J). (ps-ps). bds. 12.99 (978-1-4003-0590-2(X)) Nelson, Thomas Inc.

New Kids Media Staff. Nueva Biblia Ilustrada (Heroes of the Bible) 1999. (SPA., Illus.). 398p. (J). (ps-3). pap. 12.99 (978-0-7899-0653-3(8) , 495094) Editorial Unilit.

New Leaf Press Staff & Ham, Ken. The Promised Land: From Joshua to the First Leaders of Israel. 2000. (Awsome Adventure Bible Stories Ser.). (Illus.). 33p. (J). (gr. 2-7). pap. 5.99 (978-0-89051-327-9(9)) Master Bks.

Un Nino Dios. 2002. Tr. of One Baby Jesus. (SPA.). 24p. (J). 6.95 (978-0-8249-4234-2(5)) Ideals Pubns.

The Noah & the Ark, Beginner's Biblereg; 2007. (Biblia para Principiantes Ser.). 24p. (J). 5.99 (978-0-8297-4940-3(3)) Vida Pubs.

Noah's Ark Fun Book. (Illus.). 16p. (J). pap. 1.50 (978-0-87162-977-7(1) , E4982) Warner Pr. Pubs.

Noahs Biblical Flood & Dinos. 2004. pap. 14.95 (978-1-931602-64-8(6)) Grizzly Adams Productions, Inc.

Noah's Big Boat: A Bible Book. 2003. (Illus.). 12p. (J). bds. 10.99 (978-0-8254-5503-2(0)) Kregel Pubns.

Noahs Incredible Voyage. 2004. pap. 13.99 (978-1-929296-91-0(6)) Grizzly Adams Productions, Inc.

Nolan, Allia. My Giant Fold-Out Book of Bible Stories. 2006. 10p. (J). bds. 12.99 (978-0-7944-1015-5(4)) Reader's Digest Assn., Inc., The.

Nolan, Allia Zobel & Mitter, Matt. Bible Animal Friends: A Fun Goggly Eyes Book. McGee, Warner, illus. 2007. 12p. bds. 7.99 (978-1-59052-964-5(2) , Multnomah) WaterBrook Pr.

Numbers/Counting: Bible Story: God's Ten Special Rules. (Scripture Bites Ser.). (Illus.). (J). (ps). 7.99 (978-0-7847-9004-5(3) , 00701) Standard Publishing.

Nystrom, Carolyn. Fish, Peter! 2004. (Follow Me Bks.). 10.99 (978-0-8254-3332-0(0)) Kregel Pubns.

O'Brien, Kathryn. I'd Be Your Princess. 2006. (Illus.). 32p. (J). 15.99 (978-0-7847-1350-1(2) , 04034) Standard Publishing.

Olesen, Cecilie. My First Handy Bible. Mazali, Gustavo, illus. 2006. 64p. (J). bds. 12.99 (978-1-59052-608-8(2) , Multnomah) WaterBrook Pr.

Olshine, David. The Revelation Epic Vol. 2: Preparing Youth Groups for the Earth's Final Days. 2006. (Empowered(R) Bible Studies). 64p. ldr.'s training gde. ed. 12.99 (978-0-7847-1301-3(4) , 23334) Standard Publishing.

On the Way for 3 - 9's: Parables, Easter & 2nd Coming. 88-104p. (J). pap. 11.99 (978-1-85792-403-9(7) , Christian Focus) Christian Focus Pubns. GBR. *Dist:* Riverside.

One Hundred Bible Stories. rev. ed. 2004. 128p. (gr. 3-6). per., act. bk. ed. 7.95 (978-0-7586-0691-4(5)) Concordia Publishing Hse.

O'Neal, Debbie & Satchell, Jonathan. The Big Bedtime Book of Bible Stories & Prayers. 1999. 64p. (J). pap. 22.00 (978-1-85608-356-0(X)) Hunt, John Publishing Ltd. GBR. *Dist:* State Mutual Bk. & Periodical Service, Ltd.

Open Your Eyes Complete Set. 2004. pap. 64.99 (978-1-58516-554-4(9)) American Bible Society.

Osborne, Rick. Bible Wars & Weapons. Moore, Michael, illus. 2002. (2:52 Ser.). 128p. (J). pap. 7.99 (978-0-310-70323-5(9)) Zonderkidz.

Osborne, Rick & Bowler, K. Christie. I Want to Know - Heritage Edition: Bible Stories, Articles, Facts, & Fun about God, Jesus, the Bible, & Prayer. 2001. 168p. (J). pap. 24.99 (978-0-310-70058-6(2)) Zonderkidz.

Osborne, Rick & Strauss, Ed. Bible Angels & Demons. 2004. (2:52 Ser.). (Illus.). 112p. (J). pap. 7.99 (978-0-310-70775-2(7)) Zonderkidz.

Osborne, Rick & Zondervan. The Boys Bible: Your Ultimate Manual. 2002. (Illus.). 1696p. (J). pap. 21.99 (978-0-310-70552-9(5)) Zonderkidz.

Osborne, Rick, et al. Bible Heroes & Bad Guys. Snider, Jack, illus. 2002. (2:52 Ser.). 128p. (J). pap. 7.99 (978-0-310-70322-8(0)) Zonderkidz.

Otto-Hinds, Maureen. Short Bible Stories for Children: The Life of Jesus Christ. Hinds, George, illus. 2003. 112p. (J). pap. 11.95 (978-1-58736-194-4(9)) Wheatmark.

Paddock, Susan Star. I Want to Be a Christian: The Story of Blessed Kateri Tekakwitha. Jaurequi, Leticia & Gomez, Elisa, trs. Matheny, Jean Sherlock, illus. 2004. (J). (978-0-9747571-8-6(7)) Catholic World Mission.

Page, Nick & Claire. The Good Samaritan. 2006. (Read with Me (Make Believe Ideas) Ser.). (Illus.). 31p. (J). (gr. k-2). 3.95 (978-1-84610-174-8(3)) Make Believe Ideas GBR. *Dist:* Ingram Pub. Services.

—Noah & the Ark. 2006. (Read with Me (Make Believe Ideas) Ser.). (Illus.). 32p. (J). (gr. k-2). 3.95 (978-1-84610-168-7(9)) Make Believe Ideas GBR. *Dist:* Ingram Pub. Services.

—The Runaway Son. 2006. (Read with Me Ser.). (Illus.). 31p. (J). (gr. k-2). 3.95 (978-1-84610-176-2(X)) Make Believe Ideas GBR. *Dist:* Ingram Pub. Services.

Page, Nick And Claire. Giant Sticker Activity Bible Stories. 2006. (Giant Sticker Bks.). (Illus.). 144p. (J). (ps-3). pap. 12.95 (978-1-84610-304-9(5)) Make Believe Ideas GBR. *Dist:* Ingram Pub. Services.

Palmer, Glenda. My Bible Story Book of ABCs, Colors, Numbers & Opposites. 1999. (Illus.). 128p. (J). (ps-1). 9.99 (978-0-88486-258-1(5) , Galahad Bks.) BBS Publishing Corp.

Palmer, Peter. The Children's Bible Story Book. Green, Jay P., Sr., ed. 2000. (Illus.). 336p. (J). (ps-3). pap. 19.99 (978-1-878442-89-5(9)) Sovereign Grace Pubs., Inc.

Parable Venture Partners Staff. Ethan's Parables: Ethan & Goliath & Ethan & His Jacket of Many Colors. 2003. 32p. cd-rom 19.95 (978-0-9728501-0-0(4)) Parable Venture Partners, LLC.

Parker, Victoria. Children's Illustrated Bible: Classic Stories Set in Religious & Historical Context. 2001. (Illus.). 512p. (gr. 3 up). 40.00 (978-0-7548-0648-6(0)) Anness Publishing, Inc.

—Children's Illustrated Bible: The Best-Loved Stories of the Old & New Testaments. Dyson, Janet, ed. 2003. (Illus.). 512p. pap. 19.99 (978-0-7548-1096-4(8) , Lorenz Bks.) Anness Publishing GBR. *Dist:* National Bk. Network.

—Jesus in Galilee: And Other New Testament Stories. 2000. (Discovering the Bible Ser.). (Illus.). 64p. (gr. 3-7). 12.95 (978-0-7548-0477-2(1) , Lorenz Bks.) Anness Publishing GBR. *Dist:* National Bk. Network.

—Noah's Ark & Other First Bible Stories. 1999. (Discovering the Bible Ser.). (Illus.). 64p. (gr. 3-7). 12.95 (978-0-7548-0205-1(1) , Lorenz Bks.) Anness Publishing GBR. *Dist:* National Bk. Network.

Parker, Victoria & Dyson, Janet. Bible Stories for Children. 2007. (Illus.). 512p. 24.99 (978-0-7548-1674-4(5) , Lorenz Bks.) Anness Publishing GBR. *Dist:* National Bk. Network.

—Saint Paul & the Disciples. 2003. (Bible Discoverers Ser.). (Illus.). 64p. (gr. 3-7). pap. 7.99 (978-1-84215-740-4(X) , Southwater) Anness Publishing GBR. *Dist:* National Bk. Network.

Parry, et al. Primera Biblia del Osito. 2002. (Bears Ser.).Tr. of Bears First Bible. bds. 7.99 (978-0-7899-1029-5(2)) Editorial Unilit.

Parry, Alan. The Bible Made Easy: A Pop-Up, Pull-Out, Interactive Bible Adventure. Parry, Linda, illus. (J). 14.99 (978-1-85608-399-7(3)) Hunt, John Publishing Ltd. GBR. *Dist:* O. M. Literature.

Parry, Alan & Parry, Linda. The Herald Angels. 2003. (Illus.). 16p. 9.99 (978-1-85608-253-2(9)) Hunt, John Publishing Ltd. GBR. *Dist:* STL Distribution North America.

Parry, Linda. Bible Story Time with Mr. Bear, 5 vols. 2006. (Illus.). 12p. (J). bds. 11.99 (978-0-7847-1467-6(3) , 04387) Standard Publishing.

—Prayer Time with Mr. Bear, 5 vols. 2006. (Illus.). 12p. (J). bds. 11.99 (978-0-7847-1468-3(1) , 04388) Standard Publishing.

Parry, Linda & Parry, Alan. Baby Jesus: A Touch & Feel Book. 2003. (Illus.). 14p. 6.99 (978-1-85608-220-4(2)) Hunt, John Publishing Ltd. GBR. *Dist:* STL Distribution North America.

—Bear's First Bible. 2003. (Illus.). 16p. 9.99 (978-1-903019-85-6(0)) Hunt, John Publishing Ltd. GBR. *Dist:* STL Distribution North America.

—Follow the Star. 2003. (Illus.). 16p. 12.99 (978-1-85608-147-4(8)) Hunt, John Publishing Ltd. GBR. *Dist:* STL Distribution North America.

Paydos, Michael. The Everything' Bible Stories Book: Timeless Favorites from the Old & New Testaments. 2003. (Everything Ser.). (Illus.). 304p. (J). 14.95 (978-1-58062-547-0(9)) Adams Media Corp.

Peace Be with You: Bible Story Album. 2004. (Firelight Ser.). (ps-k). 4.99 (978-0-8066-6533-7(5)) Augsburg Fortress, Pubs.

Peace Be with You: Bible Story Flipbook. 2004. (Firelight Ser.). (gr. 3-4). 4.99 (978-0-8066-6537-5(8)) Augsburg Fortress, Pubs.

Peace Be with You: Bible Story Foldout. 2004. (Firelight Ser.). (ps). 4.99 (978-0-8066-6531-3(9)) Augsburg Fortress, Pubs.

Peace Be with You: Bible Story Magazine. 2004. (Firelight Ser.). (gr. 5-6). 4.99 (978-0-8066-6539-9(4)) Augsburg Fortress, Pubs.

Peace Be with You: Bible Storybook. 2004. (Firelight Ser.). (gr. 1-2). 4.99 (978-0-8066-6535-1(1)) Augsburg Fortress, Pubs.

Peter's House. (Gospel Road Story Bks.). (Illus.). 12p. (J). (ps-k). 0.99 (978-0-8254-7227-5(X)) Kregel Pubns.

Philip & the Ethiopian. (Illus.). (gr. 1-4). 3.00 (978-0-570-05526-6(1) , 54-1036) Concordia Publishing Hse.

Pilling, Ann. A Kingfisher Treasury of Bible Stories, Poems, & Prayers for Bedtime. Denton, Kady MacDonald, illus. 2000. (Bibles & Bible References Ser.). 92p. (J). (gr. k-3). tchr. ed. 18.95 (978-0-7534-5329-2(0) , Kingfisher) Houghton Mifflin Co. Trade & Reference Div.

Pinchbeck, Neil, illus. Crash, Bang, Yell! 16p. (J). (978-1-85792-366-7(9)) Christian Focus Pubns. GBR. *Dist:* Riverside.

—The Praying Man. 16p. (J). (978-1-85792-363-6(4)) Christian Focus Pubns. GBR. *Dist:* Riverside.

—Rescue on the Road. 16p. (J). (978-1-85792-365-0(0)) Christian Focus Pubns. GBR. *Dist:* Riverside.

—There's a Hole in My Roof! 16p. (J). (978-1-85792-361-2(8)) Christian Focus Pubns. GBR. *Dist:* Riverside.

Pingry, Patricia A. La Historia de Noe. Venturi-Pickett, Stacy, illus. 2000. (SPA.). 24p. (J). (ps-k). 6.95 (978-0-8249-4190-1(X)) Ideals Pubns.

—The Story of the Ten Commandments. 2006. (Illus.). 26p. (J). bds. 10.95 (978-0-8249-6656-0(2) , Candy Cane Pr.) Ideals Pubns.

Piper, Sophie & Archbold, Tim. The Good Bad Guy & Other Peculiar Parables. 2004. (Illus.). 64p. (J). pap. 6.99 (978-0-7459-4695-5(X) , Lion) Lion Hudson plc GBR. *Dist:* Independent Pubs. Group.

Plante, Patty. Early Bird Baby Bible Curriculum. 2nd ed. 2003. 59p. ring bd. (978-1-889723-06-8(1)) Family Harvest Church.

Plenty to Spare. (Illus.). 16p. (J). (978-1-85792-362-9(6)) Christian Focus Pubns. GBR. *Dist:* Riverside.

Pliskin, Jacqueline J. The Bible Story Activity Book. wbk. ed. 5.95 (978-0-944007-01-3(5)) SPI Bks.

Pomeroy, John. A Little Child Shall Lead Them. Pomeroy, John, illus. 2005. (Illus.). 24p. (J). 9.99 (978-1-59185-632-0(9) , Charisma Kids) Strang Communications Co.

Pope, Amy. Moving Day. George, John, 3rd, illus. 2004. (J). bds. 9.99 (978-1-4183-0010-4(1)) Christ Inspired, Inc.

PowerXpress 1 Corinthians 13 Unit. 2008. 115.00 (978-0-687-04130-5(9)) Abingdon Pr.

PowerXpress 3,000 More Unit. 99.00 (978-0-687-00659-5(7)) Abingdon Pr.

PowerXpress Abraham & Sarah. 9.95 incl. audio compact disk (978-0-687-09589-6(1)) Abingdon Pr.

PowerXpress Adam & Eve Unit. 2004. 115.00 (978-0-687-00588-8(4)) Abingdon Pr.

PowerXpress Barnabas. 9.95 incl. audio compact disk (978-0-687-03944-9(4)) Abingdon Pr.

PowerXpress Barnabas Unit. 99.00 (978-0-687-04071-1(X)) Abingdon Pr.

PowerXpress Beatitude Attitude Unit. 2008. 115.00 (978-0-687-04110-7(4)) Abingdon Pr.

PowerXpress Creation. 9.95 incl. audio compact disk (978-0-687-09418-9(6)) Abingdon Pr.

PowerXpress Easter: Go & Tell. 9.95 incl. audio compact disk (978-0-687-09268-0(X)) Abingdon Pr.

PowerXpress Easter: Mary's Story Unit. 2006. 115.00 (978-0-687-03980-7(0)) Abingdon Pr.

PowerXpress Easter: People. 9.95 incl. audio compact disk (978-0-687-09482-0(8)) Abingdon Pr.

PowerXpress Easter: People Unit. 99.00 (978-0-687-09494-3(1)) Abingdon Pr.

PowerXpress Easter: Peter's Story Disciple Disc. 2.95 incl. cd-rom (978-0-687-00219-1(2)) Abingdon Pr.

PowerXpress Follow the Star Unit. 2006. 115.00 (978-0-687-04090-2(6)) Abingdon Pr.

PowerXpress Fruits of the Spirit. 9.95 incl. audio compact disk (978-0-687-04033-9(7)) Abingdon Pr.

PowerXpress Fruits of the Spirit Unit. 99.00 (978-0-687-04160-2(0)) Abingdon Pr.

PowerXpress Good Samaritan Disciple. 2.95 incl. cd-rom (978-0-687-00179-8(X)) Abingdon Pr.

PowerXpress Here Comes the Judges. 9.95 incl. audio compact disk (978-0-687-04043-8(4)) Abingdon Pr.

PowerXpress Here Comes the Judges Unit. 2007. 110.00 (978-0-687-04180-0(5)) Abingdon Pr.

PowerXpress in the Stable Unit. 2005. 115.00 (978-0-687-03940-1(1)) Abingdon Pr.

PowerXpress into the Bible 3,000 More. 9.95 incl. audio compact disk (978-0-687-03942-5(8)) Abingdon Pr.

PowerXpress into the Bible Jesus at the Synagogue. 9.95 incl. audio compact disk (978-0-687-04181-7(3)) Abingdon Pr.

PowerXpress into the Bible Jesus at the Synagogue Unit. 2005. 115.00 (978-0-687-00709-7(7)) Abingdon Pr.

PowerXpress into the Bible Living as Caretakers Unit. 2004. 115.00 (978-0-687-00638-0(4)) Abingdon Pr.

PowerXpress into the Bible Love Your Enemies Unit. 2005. 115.00 (978-0-687-00619-9(8)) Abingdon Pr.

PowerXpress into the Bible Seven Helpers Unit. 2006. 115.00 (978-0-687-00609-0(0)) Abingdon Pr.

PowerXpress into the Bible Who Is Jesus. 9.95 incl. audio compact disk (978-0-687-04191-6(0)) Abingdon Pr.

PowerXpress into the Promised Land. 9.95 incl. audio compact disk (978-0-687-02039-3(5)) Abingdon Pr.

PowerXpress Jericho Unit. 2007. 115.00 (978-0-687-04030-8(2)) Abingdon Pr.

PowerXpress Jesus & the Children. 2.95 incl. cd-rom (978-0-687-05371-1(4)) Abingdon Pr.

PowerXpress Jesus & the Children Unit. 2005. 115.00 (978-0-687-00649-6(X)) Abingdon Pr.

PowerXpress Living God's Word - Honesty. 99.00 (978-0-687-00099-9(8)) Abingdon Pr.

PowerXpress Living God's Word Acceptance. 2005. 115.00 (978-0-687-06271-3(3)) Abingdon Pr.

PowerXpress Living God's Word Honesty. 9.95 incl. audio compact disk (978-0-687-05661-3(6)) Abingdon Pr.

PowerXpress Living God's Word Making Choices. 2005. 115.00 (978-0-687-06311-6(6)) Abingdon Pr.

PowerXpress Living God's Word Peer Pressure. 2004. 115.00 (978-0-687-00109-5(9)) Abingdon Pr.

PowerXpress Living God's Word Respect. 2005. 115.00 (978-0-687-06351-2(5)) Abingdon Pr.

PowerXpress Living God's Word Self-Esteem. 2005. 115.00 (978-0-687-00119-4(6)) Abingdon Pr.

PowerXpress LIving God's Word Sharing & Kindness. 2005. 115.00 (978-0-687-06321-5(3)) Abingdon Pr.

PowerXpress Living God's Word Time & Money. 2005. 115.00 (978-0-687-00730-1(5)) Abingdon Pr.

PowerXpress Lost & Found Unit. 2007. 115.00 (978-0-687-07393-1(6)) Abingdon Pr.

PowerXpress Man Beside the Pool Unit. 2006. 115.00 (978-0-687-03960-9(6)) Abingdon Pr.

PowerXpress Mary Anoints Jesus Unit. 2006. 115.00 (978-0-687-03970-8(3)) Abingdon Pr.

PowerXpress Messengers Unit. 2007. 115.00 (978-0-687-03991-3(6)) Abingdon Pr.

PowerXpress Namaan & the Servant Girl. 9.95 incl. audio compact disk (978-0-687-04073-5(6)) Abingdon Pr.

PowerXpress Namaan & the Servant Girl Unit. 99.00 (978-0-687-03941-8(X)) Abingdon Pr.

PowerXpress Noah's Ark. 9.95 incl. audio compact disk (978-0-687-09398-4(8)) Abingdon Pr.

PowerXpress Noah's Ark Music Pak. 15.00 (978-0-687-03054-5(4)) Abingdon Pr.

PowerXpress Noah's Ark Sampler. (978-0-687-04673-7(4)) Abingdon Pr.

PowerXpress Occupations in Bible Times. 9.95 incl. audio compact disk (978-0-687-09504-9(2)) Abingdon Pr.

PowerXpress Out of Egypt. 9.95 incl. audio compact disk (978-0-687-02069-0(7)) Abingdon Pr.

PowerXpress Paul Disciple. 2.95 incl. cd-rom (978-0-687-00229-0(X)) Abingdon Pr.

PowerXpress Paul Unit. 2004. 115.00 (978-0-687-07356-6(1)) Abingdon Pr.

PowerXpress Paul's Journey. 9.95 incl. audio compact disk (978-0-687-03954-8(1)) Abingdon Pr.

PowerXpress Paul's Journey Unit. 99.00 (978-0-687-04061-2(2)) Abingdon Pr.

PowerXpress Peacemakers. 9.95 incl. audio compact disk (978-0-687-09492-9(5)) Abingdon Pr.

PowerXpress Pentecost. 9.95 incl. audio compact disk (978-0-687-09487-5(9)) Abingdon Pr.

PowerXpress Peter in Prison Unit. 2006. 115.00 (978-0-687-04010-0(8)) Abingdon Pr.

PowerXpress Philip & the Ethiopian. 9.95 incl. audio compact disk (978-0-687-04133-6(3)) Abingdon Pr.

PowerXpress Philip & the Ethiopian Unit. 99.00 (978-0-687-03971-5(1)) Abingdon Pr.

PowerXpress Pilate's Plight. 9.95 incl. audio compact disk (978-0-687-04183-1(X)) Abingdon Pr.

PowerXpress Pilate's Plight Unit. 99.00 (978-0-687-04041-4(8)) Abingdon Pr.

PowerXpress Proverbs. 9.95 incl. audio compact disk (978-0-687-04063-6(9)) Abingdon Pr.

PowerXpress Psalm 23 Unit. 99.00 (978-0-687-03921-0(5)) Abingdon Pr.

PowerXpress Rebekah Unit. 2006. 115.00 (978-0-687-04020-9(5)) Abingdon Pr.

PowerXpress Resurrection & Road to Emmaus. 9.95 incl. audio compact disk (978-0-687-07842-4(3)) Abingdon Pr.

PowerXpress Road to Emmaus Unit. 99.00 (978-0-687-02883-2(3)) Abingdon Pr.

PowerXpress Ruth Disciple. 2.95 incl. cd-rom (978-0-687-00239-9(7)) Abingdon Pr.

PowerXpress Ruth Unit. 2004. 115.00 (978-0-687-07386-3(3)) Abingdon Pr.

PowerXpress Signs of Faith. 9.95 incl. audio compact disk (978-0-687-07446-4(0)) Abingdon Pr.

PowerXpress Signs of Faith Disciple Disc. 2.95 incl. cd-rom (978-0-687-00570-3(1)) Abingdon Pr.

PowerXpress Signs of Faith Unit. 99.00 (978-0-687-07426-6(6)) Abingdon Pr.

PowerXpress Symbols of Holy Week Unit. 2007. 115.00 (978-0-687-04140-4(6)) Abingdon Pr.

PowerXpress the Easter Message. 9.95 incl. audio compact disk (978-0-687-04193-0(7)) Abingdon Pr.

PowerXpress the Easter Message Unit. 99.00 (978-0-687-04051-3(5)) Abingdon Pr.

PowerXpress the Empty Tomb Unit. 2007. 115.00 (978-0-687-04150-3(3)) Abingdon Pr.

PowerXpress the Four Friends. 9.95 incl. audio compact disk (978-0-687-09798-2(3)) Abingdon Pr.

PowerXpress the Garden of Gethsemane Unit. 2005. 115.00 (978-0-687-00679-3(1)) Abingdon Pr.

PowerXpress the Gift of Jesus. 9.95 incl. audio compact disk (978-0-687-09368-7(6)) Abingdon Pr.

PowerXpress the Golden Rule. 9.95 incl. audio compact disk (978-0-687-03934-0(7)) Abingdon Pr.

PowerXpress the Golden Rule Unit. 2009. 115.00 (978-0-687-04081-0(7)) Abingdon Pr.

PowerXpress the Lord's Supper. 9.95 incl. audio compact disk (978-0-687-08111-0(4)) Abingdon Pr.

PowerXpress the Sower. 9.95 incl. audio compact disk (978-0-687-04163-3(5)) Abingdon Pr.

PowerXpress the Sower Unit. 99.00 (978-0-687-04031-5(0)) Abingdon Pr.

A
B

PowerXpress the Ten Commandments. 9.95 incl. audio compact disk (978-0-687-04192-3(9)) Abingdon Pr.

PowerXpress the Ten Commandments Unit. 2006. 115.00 (978-0-687-04050-6(7)) Abingdon Pr.

PowerXpress Timothy, Eunice, & Lois Unit. 2006. 115.00 (978-0-687-04040-7(X)) Abingdon Pr.

PowerXpress Triumphal Entry. 9.95 incl. audio compact disk (978-0-687-09474-5(7)) Abingdon Pr.

PowerXpress Triumphal Entry Unit. 99.00 (978-0-687-09464-6(X)) Abingdon Pr.

PowerXpress Two by Two. 9.95 incl. audio compact disk (978-0-687-04083-4(3)) Abingdon Pr.

PowerXpress Two by Two Unit. 99.00 (978-0-687-03961-6(4)) Abingdon Pr.

PowerXpress upon this Rock. 9.95 incl. audio compact disk (978-0-687-03924-1(X)) Abingdon Pr.

PowerXpress upon this Rock Unit. 99.00 (978-0-687-04091-9(4)) Abingdon Pr.

PowerXpress Washing Feet. 9.95 incl. audio compact disk (978-0-687-07326-9(X)) Abingdon Pr.

PowerXpress Washing Feet Disciple. 2.95 incl. cd-rom (978-0-687-00189-7(7)) Abingdon Pr.

PowerXpress Washing Feet Unit. 99.00 (978-0-687-07343-6(X)) Abingdon Pr.

Preschool KidKit. 2003. (Godprints Curriculum Ser.). (Illus.). 8.99 (978-0-7814-3664-9(8) , 2013) Cook, David C. Publishing Co.

Primetime Starter Pack. 2004. pap. 44.99 (978-0-8307-3025-4(7)) Gospel Light Pubns.

Prodigal Son. 2004. pap. 5.95 (978-1-58516-149-2(7)) American Bible Society.

Przybille, Crystal, illus. Bible Stories with Songs & Fingerplays: Stories Come Alive for Young Children. 1998. (Whole People of God Library). 64p. (J). pap. 9.95 (978-1-55145-297-5(9)) Wood Lake Bks., Inc. CAN. *Dist:* Logos Productions, Inc.

Publications International, Ltd Staff, contrib. by. My First Library: 12 Bible Stories, 12 vols. 2003. (Illus.). (J). (978-0-7853-8156-3(2)); (978-0-7853-8158-7(9)); (978-0-7853-8166-2(X)); (978-0-7853-8155-6(4)); (978-0-7853-8161-7(9)); (978-0-7853-8162-4(7)); (978-0-7853-8165-5(1)); (978-0-7853-8159-4(7)); (978-0-7853-8164-8(3)); (978-0-7853-8163-1(5)); (978-0-7853-8160-0(0)); (978-0-7853-8157-0(0)) Publications International, Ltd.

—Read-Together Treasury Bible Stories. 2003. (Illus.). 96p. (J). per. 12.98 (978-0-7853-7251-6(2)) Publications International, Ltd.

Pulley, Kelly. Little Lamb Scare. 2007. (Beginner's Bible' Ser.). 20p. (J). 6.99 (978-0-310-71401-9(X)) Zonderkidz.

The Quest for Seven Castles. 2006. (J). per. 7.99 (978-0-9785523-1-2(8)) Dunlop, Edward.

Rachel's House. (Gospel Road Story Bks.). (Illus.). 12p. (J). (ps-k). 0.99 (978-0-8254-7226-8(1)) Kregel Pubns.

Racklin-Siegel, Carol, illus. Noah's Ark. 2003. 32p. (J). per. 9.95 (978-0-939144-42-6(5)) EKS Publishing Co.

Rainbolt, Kelly A. The Savior That God Sent. 2000. (Illus.). 32p. (J). (ps-k). 9.99 (978-0-570-07095-5(3)) Concordia Publishing Hse.

Reader's Digest Editors. Noah's Ark. Moroney, Tracey, illus. 1998. (Little Bible Playbks.: Vol. 1). 18p. (J). (ps-3). bds. 5.99 (978-1-57584-260-8(2) , Reader's Digest Children's Bks.) Reader's Digest Children's Publishing, Inc.

Redding, David Asbury. He Never Spoke Without a Parable: Your Father. l.t. ed. 2001. 64p. per. 6.00 (978-0-9671701-2-1(5)) Starborne Hse.

—He Never Spoke Without a Parable: Your Neighbor. rev. l.t. ed. 2000. 65p. pap. 10.00 (978-0-9671701-1-4(7) , 0-9671701-1-7) Starborne Hse.

Reeves, Eira. My Very First Bible. 2003. (Illus.). 128p. (J). 10.99 (978-0-8254-7271-8(7)) Kregel Pubns.

Regina Press Staff. Christmas Story. 1999. (J). (ps-3). 6.95 (978-0-88271-713-5(8)) Regina Pr., Malhame & Co.

—First Christmas. 1999. (Illus.). 32p. (ps-3). 19.95 (978-0-88271-463-9(5)) Regina Pr., Malhame & Co.

—Noah & the Ark. 1999. 5.99 (978-0-88271-681-7(6)); (J). 6.95 (978-0-88271-645-9(X)) Regina Pr., Malhame & Co.

—Noah's Ark. 1999. (ps-3). 4.95 (978-0-88271-671-8(9)); (J). 6.95 (978-0-88271-712-8(X)) Regina Pr., Malhame & Co.

—Who's Coming to Stay? 1999. 3.95 (978-0-88271-680-0(8)) Regina Pr., Malhame & Co.

Reinhart, Matthew, illus. & adapted by. The Ark. Reinhart, Matthew, adapted by. 2005. 12p. (J). 16.95 (978-0-689-85909-0(0) , Little Simon) Simon & Schuster Children's Publishing.

La Resurreccion Vol. 24: Serie Minilibritos Aventuras de la Biblia. 2001. pap. (978-1-930564-94-7(5)) United Bible Societies/Americas Service Ctr.

Revolve Devos. 2005. 320p. (YA). pap. 9.99 (978-0-7180-0903-8(7)) Nelson, Thomas Inc.

Reynolds, Annette. First COLL of Bible Stories & Stickers: Daniel, Jonah, Jesus & Other Stories. MacLean, Moira, illus. 2004. 16p. pap. 8.95 (978-1-59325-045-4(2)) Word Among Us Pr.

—First COLL of Bible Stories & Stickers: Noahn, Samson, Jesus & Other Stories. MacLean, Moira, illus. 2004. 16p. pap. 8.95 (978-1-59325-044-7(4)) Word Among Us Pr.

Rhodes, Karen. God's Word Then & Now Activity Book. 2007. (Illus.). 16p. (J). pap. 1.89 (***978-1-59317-207-7(9)***) Warner Pr. Pubs.

—7 Sensational Stories. 2005. (J). pap. 1.79 (***978-1-59317-084-4(X)***) Warner Pr. Pubs.

Rice, John R. John R. Rice Bible Stories. 2000. 445p. (J). pap. 11.95 (978-0-87398-722-6(5)) Sword of the Lord Pubs.

Richards, Lawrence O. & Zondervan. Adventure Bible, NIV. rev. ed. 2000. 1472p. (J). 26.99 (978-0-310-91144-9(3)) Zonderkidz.

Richards, Virginia Helen & Halpin, D. Thomas, illus. My Christmas Picture Book. 2005. 14p. (J). 4.95 (978-0-8198-4829-1(8) , 332-220) Pauline Bks. & Media.

Ring, Laura. The First Christmas: An ABC Book. Caldwell, Lise, ed. Cottrell, Kelly, illus. 1999. (Happy Day Bks.). 24p. (J). (ps-2). pap. 2.49 (978-0-7847-1087-6(2) , 04283, Bean Sprouts) Standard Publishing.

Robb, Andy. Ballistic Beginnings. 2004. (Holy Happenings Ser.). (Illus.). 128p. pap. 6.50 (978-0-687-02336-3(X)) Abingdon Pr.

—Bigger & Bigger Book of Bible Stories, 1. 1999. (Illus.). 30p. (J). (ps-2). 9.99 (978-0-570-05589-1(X)) Conceivable Concepts, Inc.

—Super Son. 2004. (Holy Happenings Ser.). (Illus.). 128p. pap. 6.50 (978-0-687-02296-0(7)) Abingdon Pr.

Robison Gamble Creative, photos by & des. Dan & Louie Vol. 1: The Greatest Stories Ever Told, Robison Gamble Creative, des. deluxe ed. 2005. (J). 89.95 incl. audio compact disk (978-1-933497-00-6(9)) Robison Gamble Creative.

Rock, Lois. Baby Jesus. Ayliffe, Alex, illus. 2005. (Board Books). 16p. (J). (ps-ps). per. 5.99 (978-1-56148-497-3(0)) Good Bks.

—Five-Minute Bible Stories. 2005. (Illus.). 96p. 17.99 (978-0-8066-5125-5(3) , Augsburg Bks.) Augsburg Fortress, Pubs.

—The Lion Bible: Everlasting Stories. Balit, Christina, illus. 2006. 223p. (J). 24.95 (***978-0-7459-3954-4(6)***) Lion Hudson plc GBR. *Dist:* Independent Pubs. Group.

—Lion Illustrated Bible for Children. Balit, Christina, illus. 2007. 224p. (J). 17.99 (***978-0-7459-4936-9(3)*** , Lion) Lion Hudson plc GBR. *Dist:* Independent Pubs. Group.

—The Lost Sheep. Ayliffe, Alex, illus. 2005. 16p. (J). (ps-ps). per. 5.99 (978-1-56148-498-0(9)) Good Bks.

—My Very First Bible. Ayliffe, Alex, illus. 2003. (Bestselling Children's Books - Religious Ser.). 256p. (J). 18.99 (978-1-56148-370-9(2)) Good Bks.

—My Very First Christmas. Ayliffe, Alex, illus. 2006. 128p. (J). 14.99 (978-1-56148-531-4(4)) Good Bks.

—Noah & the Ark. Ayliffe, Alex, illus. 2005. 16p. (J). (ps-ps). bds. 5.99 (978-1-56148-496-6(2)) Good Bks.

—Our Father. Ayliffe, Alex, illus. 2005. 16p. (J). (ps-ps). bds. 5.99 (978-1-56148-499-7(7)) Good Bks.

—Words of Gold: A Treasury of the Bible's Poetry & Wisdom. Young, Sarah, illus. 2000. 48p. (J). (gr. 3-11). 18.00 (978-0-8028-5199-4(1) , Eerdmans Bks For Young Readers) Eerdmans, William B. Publishing Co.

Rock, Lois, et al. Beibl y Plant Lleiaf. 2005. (WEL., Illus.). 256p. (978-1-85994-514-8(7)) Cyhoeddiadau'r Gair.

Rock Steady. 2001. (J). 101.70 incl. cd-rom (978-0-06-623706-0(8)) HarperCollins Pubs.

Rockenstein, James. Scripture Stories with Micah. 2003. (Illus.). 91p. (J). per. (978-1-932077-21-6(9)) Athena Pr.

Roos, Maryn, illus. God Made the World. 2006. (Bible Classics Ser.). 24p. (ps-2). pap. 3.50 (978-0-7868-5516-2(9) , Jump at the Sun) Hyperion Bks. for Children.

—Noah Builds an Ark - Bible Classics. 2006. (Jump at the Sun Ser.). 24p. (J). (ps-2). pap. 3.50 (978-0-7868-5519-3(3) , Jump at the Sun) Hyperion Bks. for Children.

Root, Phyllis. Big Momma Makes the World. Oxenbury, Helen, illus. 2002. 48p. (J). (ps-3). 16.99 (978-0-7636-1132-3(8)) Candlewick Pr.

Ropp, Steve. Some Body! 1998. (Fast Lane Bible Studies Ser.). 44p. (YA). (gr. 7-9). pap. 9.95 (978-0-87303-333-6(7)) Faith & Life Pr.

Rose, Drew, illus. God's Heroes. 2005. (Bible Activity Bks.). 96p. (J). (ps-3). 2.99 (978-0-7814-4313-5(X) , 078144313X) Cook, David C. Publishing Co.

—God's Son, Jesus. 2005. (Bible Activity Bks.). 96p. (J). (ps-3). 2.99 (978-0-7814-4314-2(8) , 0781443148) Cook, David C. Publishing Co.

—God's World. 2005. (Bible Activity Bks.). 96p. (J). (ps-3). 2.99 (978-0-7814-4312-8(1) , 0781443121) Cook, David C. Publishing Co.

Rostrom, Laura Lee. My Bible Storybook. Rostrom, Laura Lee, illus. 2000. (Illus.). 282p. (J). 19.95 (978-1-55517-496-5(5)) Cedar Fort, Inc./CFI Distribution.

Round, Graham. Bible Masks Storybook. 2001. (Illus.). 12p. (J). (ps-5). pap. 7.99 (978-0-8254-7232-9(6)) Kregel Pubns.

—Historia de David (The Story of David) 1999. (SPA.). (J). (ps-3). pap. (978-0-7899-0721-9(6) , 498777) Editorial Unilit.

—Historia de Moises (The Story of Moses) 1999. (SPA.). (J). (ps-3). pap. (978-0-7899-0722-6(4) , 498776) Editorial Unilit.

Rowlands, Avril. The Rainbow's End & Other Tales from the Ark. Moran, Rosslyn, illus. 128p. (J). pap. 6.95 (978-0-7459-4073-1(0) , Lion) Lion Hudson plc GBR. *Dist:* Trafalgar Square Publishing.

Running Press Staff. The Story of Christmas. 2006. (Illus.). 128p. 4.95 (978-0-7624-2816-8(3) , Running Pr.) Running Pr. Bk. Pubs.

RV 1960 Staff. La Biblia de Promesas. 1998. (Biblias para Ninos Ser.). (SPA., Illus.). (J). (ps-3). 14.99 (978-0-7899-0570-3(1) , 490870) Editorial Unilit.

Ryle, J. C. Children's Stories. 144p. (J). mass mkt. 5.99 (978-1-85792-639-2(0) , Christian Heritage) Christian Focus Pubns. GBR. *Dist:* Riverside.

Los Sabios de Oriente Vol. 17: Serie Minilibritos Aventuras de la Biblia. 2001. pap. (978-1-930564-87-9(2)) United Bible Societies/Americas Service Ctr.

Samson meets Delilah. 2007. (J). mass mkt. (***978-0-9769722-3-5(9)***) Leslie, Beverly J.

Samson meets his Wife. 2007. (J). mass mkt. (***978-0-9769722-1-1(2)***) Leslie, Beverly J.

Samson's destruction of the Philistines. 2007. (J). mass mkt. (***978-0-9769722-2-8(0)***) Leslie, Beverly J.

Samsons Super Strength. 2004. pap. 13.99 (978-1-929296-96-5(7)) Grizzly Adams Productions, Inc.

Sandenbergh, Kobus. Bible Stories for Tiny Tots. 2001. 36p. (J). 8.99 (978-0-8254-7212-1(1)) Kregel Pubns.

Sanders, Nancy I. The Fall into Sin: Genesis 2-3 for Children. Van Severen, Joe, illus. 2004. (Arch Books). (ENG.). 16p. (J). 1.99 (978-0-7586-0618-1(4)) Concordia Publishing Hse.

Sanderson, Ruth. Tapestries: Stories of Women in the Bible. Sanderson, Ruth, illus. 1998. (Illus.). 32p. (J). (gr. 3-7). 15.95 (978-0-316-77093-4(0)) Little Brown & Co.

Santamaria, Leslie. Mother Who Prayed. 2000. (gr. k-3). lib. bdg. 9.85 (978-0-613-71026-8(6)) Tandem Library Bks.

Sasso, Sandy Eisenberg. Naamah, Noah's Wife. Andersen, Bethanne, illus. 2002. (SkyLight Lives Ser.). 24p. (J). (ps-k). bds. 7.95 (978-1-893361-56-0(X)) SkyLight Paths Publishing.

Sattgast, L. J. The Rhyme Bible Storybook for Toddlers. Goffe, Toni, illus. 2000. (Bible Storybooks Ser.). 256p. (J). 12.99 (978-0-310-70078-4(7)) Zonderkidz.

Schmitt, Betsy & Sokolava, Valerie. The Promise of Abraham. 2006. (Illus.). 36p. 15.99 (978-0-7847-1823-0(7)) Standard Publishing.

Scholastic, Inc. Staff. Read & Learn Bible (Leer Y Aprender) 2007. 544p. (J). 14.99 (***978-0-545-00339-1(3)*** , Scholastic en Espanol) Scholastic, Inc.

School Specialty Publishing. Bible Heroes. 2004. 10p. (J). 1.99 (978-0-7647-1044-5(3) , In Celebration) Schaffer, Frank Pubns.

School Specialty Publishing Staff. All about God's Love. 2001. (All about Coloring Book Ser.). 32p. (J). (gr. k-3). pap. 3.99 (978-0-7647-0583-0(0) , In Celebration) Schaffer, Frank Pubns.

Schwartz, Stephen. Through Heaven's Eyes: Prince of Egypt. 1998. (Illus.). 32p. (J). (gr. k-3). 14.99 (978-0-8499-5897-7(0)) Nelson, Thomas Inc.

Schwirzer, Jennifer. I Want It All. 2002. (Illus.). 144p. (YA). pap. 10.99 (978-0-8280-1628-5(3) , 090-570) Review & Herald Publishing Assn.

Scrimshire, Hazel. Food to Share. (Illus.). 16p. (J). (978-1-85792-364-3(2)) Christian Focus Pubns. GBR. *Dist:* Riverside.

El Sembrador Vol. 19: Serie Minilibritos Aventuras de la Biblia. 2001. pap. (978-1-930564-89-3(9)) United Bible Societies/Americas Service Ctr.

Send a Baby. (Hear Me Read Classroom Sets Ser.). 32.00 (978-0-570-07170-9(4)) Concordia Publishing Hse.

The Servant Who Would Not Forgive: A Bible Story in Color. (Illus.). 16p. (J). pap. 1.50 (978-0-87162-845-9(7) , E4316) Warner Pr. Pubs.

Sewell, Christina. Legends of the Christ Child. Boatfield, Jonny, illus. 2004. 80p. pap. 12.00 (978-0-7188-3026-7(1)) Lutherworth Pr., The GBR. *Dist:* Parkwest Pubns., Inc.

Shea, George Beverly. Grandpa's Sleepy-Time Bible Stories with George Beverly Shea. 2004. (J). (978-0-8423-8137-6(6)) Tyndale Hse. Pubs.

Sheep Gets Lost. 2004. bds. 5.99 (978-0-8254-7286-2(5)) Kregel Pubns.

Shirley Dobson Bible Story Coloring Book Sampler Merchandiser. 129.00 (978-0-8307-2753-7(1) , Gospel Light) Gospel Light Pubns.

Shirley Dobson Bible Story Coloring Book Sampler Merchandiser: 55 Unit Mini-Merch. 70.95 (978-0-8307-3024-7(9) , Gospel Light) Gospel Light Pubns.

Shouting in the Hush Arbor Older Elementary Bible Story Leader. 7.00 (978-0-687-32662-4(1)) Abingdon Pr.

Shouting in the Hush Arbor Student Handbook Older Elementary. 2.50 (978-0-687-32592-4(7)) Abingdon Pr.

Shouting in the Hush Arbor Younger Elementary Bible Story Leader. 7.00 (978-0-687-32672-3(9)) Abingdon Pr.

Simeon, Sexton & Golden Books Staff. The Little Golden Bible Storybook. Sexton, Brenton, illus. 2005. 36p. (J). (ps-2). 6.99 (978-0-375-83549-0(0) , Golden Inspirational) Random Hse. Children's Bks.

Simon, Mary. Ay Que Lio. 2004. (SPA.). 32p. (J). 2.75 (978-0-570-05187-9(8)) Concordia Publishing Hse.

—Oh Oh. 2004. (SPA.). 32p. (J). 2.75 (978-0-570-05186-2(X)) Concordia Publishing Hse.

Simon, Mary Mans. Fishes & Loaves: Read & Learn the Bible. 2005. (Illus.). 24p. (J). pap. 2.99 (978-1-4037-1162-5(3) , Spirit Pr.) Dalmatian Pr.

—The Good Samaritan: Read & Learn the Bible. 2005. (Illus.). 24p. (J). pap. 2.99 (978-1-4037-1159-5(3) , Spirit Pr.) Dalmatian Pr.

—Jesus Blesses the Children: Read & Learn the Bible. 2005. (Illus.). 24p. (J). pap. 2.99 (978-1-4037-1155-7(0) , Spirit Pr.) Dalmatian Pr.

—Jesus Fills the Nets: Read & Learn the Bible. 2005. (Illus.). 24p. (J). pap. 2.99 (978-1-4037-1163-2(1) , Spirit Pr.) Dalmatian Pr.

—Noah's Ark: Read & Learn the Bible. 2005. (Illus.). 24p. (J). pap. 2.99 (978-1-4037-1157-1(7) , Spirit Pr.) Dalmatian Pr.

—See What God Made! Read & Learn the Bible. 2005. (Illus.). 24p. (J). pap. 2.99 (978-1-4037-1160-1(7) , Spirit Pr.) Dalmatian Pr.

—Too Tall, Too Small: Read & Learn the Bible. 2005. (Illus.). 24p. (J). pap. 2.99 (978-1-4037-1156-4(9) , Spirit Pr.) Dalmatian Pr.

Simon, Mary Manz. The Big Boat. 2004. 16p. (J). pap. 4.99 (978-0-88724-762-0(8) , CD-2061) Carson-Dellosa Publishing Co., Inc.

—The Bright Star. 2004. 16p. (J). pap. 4.99 (978-0-88724-869-6(1) , CD-2062) Carson-Dellosa Publishing Co., Inc.

—Build A Tower. 2004. 16p. (J). pap. 4.99 (978-0-88724-755-2(5) , CD-2059) Carson-Dellosa Publishing Co., Inc.

—A Busy Day. 2004. 16p. (J). pap. 4.99 (978-0-88724-523-7(4) , CD-2058) Carson-Dellosa Publishing Co., Inc.

—Compendio de la Doctrina Cristiana: Una Presentacion Popular de las Ensenanzas de la Biblia. 2nd ed. 1999. (Hear Me Read Bible Stories Ser.). (SPA., Illus.). 384p. (ps-k). 11.95 (978-0-570-09935-2(8)) Concordia Publishing Hse.

—Connections Bible. 2006. (New Living Translation Bible Story Ser.). 384p. pap. 14.99 (978-0-7847-1500-0(9) , 04147) Standard Publishing.

—Flap-and-Tab Bible. 2006. (New Living Translation Bible Story Ser.). (Illus.). 20p. (J). bds. 12.99 (978-0-7847-1596-3(3) , 04143) Standard Publishing.

—Koala Does His Best. Harris, Phyllis & Clearwater, Linda, illus. 2006. (First Virtuestm for Toddlers Ser.). 20p. (J). 5.99 (978-0-7847-1578-9(5) , 04072) Standard Publishing.

—Let's Catch Fish. 2004. 16p. (J). pap. 4.99 (978-0-88724-756-9(3) , CD-2060) Carson-Dellosa Publishing Co., Inc.

—On-My-Own Reader Bible. 2006. (New Living Translation Bible Story Ser.). 312p. 15.99 (978-0-7847-1598-7(X) , 04145) Standard Publishing.

—One Way Bible. 2006. (New Living Translation Bible Story Ser.). 208p. 14.99 (978-0-7847-1599-4(8) , 04146) Standard Publishing.

—Play-and-Learn Bible. 2006. (New Living Translation Bible Story Ser.). (Illus.). 208p. (J). 15.99 (978-0-7847-1597-0(1) , 04144) Standard Publishing.

—Set of eight Books. (Hear Me Read Level 2 Ser.). (J). 34.99 (978-0-570-05096-4(0)) Concordia Publishing Hse.

—Sit Down. (Hear Me Read Classroom Sets Ser.). 32.00 (978-0-570-05098-8(7)) Concordia Publishing Hse.

—Trouble at the Well. 2004. 16p. (J). pap. 4.99 (978-0-88724-981-5(7) , CD-2063) Carson-Dellosa Publishing Co., Inc.

—Where Is Jesus? (Hear Me Read Classroom Sets Ser.). 32.00 (978-0-570-05460-3(5)) Concordia Publishing Hse.

—The Young Learner's Bible Storybook: 52 Stories with Activities for Family Fun & Learning. Harper, Piers, illus. 2006. (First Virtues for Toddlers Ser.). 336p. (J). (ps-2). 17.99 (978-0-7847-1277-1(8) , 04010) Standard Publishing.

Sing & Learn, ed. Stories. 2007. (Sing & Learn Padded Board Bks.). 53p. (J). bds. 16.95 (***978-0-7696-5449-2(5)***) School Specialty Publishing.

Sing, Wee. Wee Sing Musical Bible. 2001. (Wee Sing Ser.). (Illus.). 160p. (J). (ps-3). 12.99 (978-0-8423-3514-0(5)) Tyndale Hse. Pubs.

Slater, Teddy. Jonah & the Big Fish. 2006. 32p. (J). pap. 3.99 (978-0-439-85878-6(X)) Scholastic, Inc.

—Joseph's Amazing Coat. 2006. (Illus.). 32p. (J). pap. 3.99 (978-0-439-81509-3(6)) Scholastic, Inc.

Smart Kids Publishing Staff. Jonah & the Whale: All about Responsibility. 2006. 12p. (ps). bds. 14.95 (978-0-8249-6661-4(9) , Candy Cane Pr.) Ideals Pubns.

Smith, Betty. Friends of Jesus. Steed, Cicely, illus. 2nd ed. 2004. (Stories of Jesus Ser.). 32p. (J). (ps-3). pap. 6.00 (978-0-7188-1670-4(6)) Lutherworth Pr., The GBR. *Dist:* Parkwest Pubns., Inc.

Smoot, Donna. Bible Stories for Children. 1999. 88p. (J). reprint ed. pap. 6.00 (978-0-934666-50-3(4)) Artisan Pubs.

Snyder, Jennifer. Grandad's Book. Bruner, Tammy, illus. 2004. (J). bds. 9.99 (978-1-4183-0015-9(2)) Christ Inspired, Inc.

Sorvillo, Carmen R. & Moore, Helen H. Pop-Up Parables & Other Bible Stories. 1999. 48p. (gr. 1-3). tchr. ed. 9.99 (978-0-570-05353-8(6) , 12-3404GJ) Concordia Publishing Hse.

Spanish House Inc. Staff. Biblia Dios Me Ama. 2000. (SPA., Illus.). (J). (ps-3). 8.99 (978-0-7899-0689-2(9) , 494618); 8.99 (978-0-7899-0690-8(2) , 494619) Editorial Unilit.

—Mi Hermosa Biblia. 1999. Tr. of Baby's First Bible. (SPA., Illus.). 20p. (J). (ps-k). bds. 10.99 (978-0-7899-0703-5(8) , 493778) Editorial Unilit.

Spanish Kingsley's Meadow: Escoge Bien (Wise Guy) (SPA.). 32p. pap., act. bk. ed. 2.95 (978-1-58516-564-3(6)) American Bible Society.

Spear, Kevin. David & the Giant. 2005. (J). pap. 1.79 (***978-1-59317-087-5(4)***) Warner Pr. Pubs.

—My Very Own Activity Pages: Spring 2004. 2004. (J). pap. 1.79 (***978-1-59317-077-6(7)***) Warner Pr. Pubs.

Squeak along Bible, 3 vols. 2000. (Illus.). (J). (ps-k). bds. 14.95 (978-0-88271-693-0(X)) Regina Pr., Malhame & Co.

St. John, Patricia. Until the Letter Came. Brownlie, Ian D., illus. 2004. 44p. (J). pap. (978-1-932381-14-6(7) , 5580) Bible Visuals International, Inc.

Standard Publishing Staff. Bible Adventures. Caldwell, Lise, ed. McCallum, Jodie, illus. 1998. (Happy Day Bks.). 24p. (J). (ps-2). pap. 2.49 (978-0-7847-0829-3(0) , 04259, Bean Sprouts) Standard Publishing.

Standard Publishing Staff, contrib. by. Favorite Bible Stories to Color: For Ages 6 - 10, Old & New Testament Stories. 2006. (Heartshaper Ser.). 192p. (J). pap. 15.99 (978-0-7847-1797-4(4) , 02447) Standard Publishing.

Standke, Linda. Hidden Pictures: Explore Hidden Treasures in God's Word. 2003. (Christian Product Ser.). 32p. (J). 3.99 (978-0-88724-910-5(8)); 3.99 (978-0-88724-911-2(6)); 3.99 (978-0-88724-912-9(4)) Carson-Dellosa Publishing Co., Inc.

Stanley, Mandy, illus. Baby Blessings Baby's Bible. 2005. 6p. (YA). (ps-ps). 15.99 (978-0-7847-1739-4(7) , 04382) Standard Publishing.

Stephenson, Kristina, illus. Baby Bible. 2007. 160p. (J). 14.99 (***978-1-56148-571-0(3)***) Good Bks.

—Baby Boy Bible. 2007. 160p. (J). 16.99 (***978-1-56148-570-3(5)***) Good Bks.

—Baby Girl Bible. 2007. 160p. (J). 16.99 (***978-1-56148-569-7(1)***) Good Bks.

Stepping Stones for Youth. 2002. (J). pap. (978-1-932744-08-8(8)) Revival Fires Publishing.

Stewart, Jennifer. My Good Night Bible: Sticker & Activity Book. Parks, Kathy, illus. 2000. (My Good Night Bible Collection). 28p. (J). (ps-2). pap. 3.49 (978-0-7847-1129-3(1) , 22081) Standard Publishing.

—Noah! Noah! Bettoli, Delana, illus. 2000. (Place-a-Piece Bks.). 10p. (J). (ps-k). bds. 14.99 (978-0-7847-1213-9(1) , 04395, Bean Sprouts) Standard Publishing.

Stewart, Jennifer, ed. Jesus Is Born! Ebert, Len, illus. 1999. 48p. (J). (ps-2). pap. 2.49 (978-0-7847-0995-5(5) , 20065, Bean Sprouts) Standard Publishing.

—Little Girl's Bible Storybook. Turk, Caron, illus. 1999. 48p. (J). (ps-2). pap. 2.49 (978-0-7847-0986-3(6) , 22056, Bean Sprouts) Standard Publishing.

—Little Girls Bible Storybook. Turk, Caron, illus. 1999. 28p. (J). (ps-2). 3.29 (978-0-7847-1094-4(5) , 20078, Bean Sprouts) Standard Publishing.

—Merry Christmas, Jesus! Coloring Book. McCallum, Jodie, illus. 1999. 48p. (J). (ps-2). 2.99 (978-0-7847-0996-2(3) , 22066, Bean Sprouts) Standard Publishing.

Stiegemeyer, Julie. Stephen Stands Strong. Myers, Glenn, illus. 2004. (ENG.). 16p. (J). 1.99 (978-0-570-07576-9(9)) Concordia Publishing Hse.

Stiles, Andy. Fun Bible Tales: About Learning to Trust God. 1999. (Happy Bks.). (Illus.). 104p. (J). (ps-3). 7.99 (978-0-88486-231-4(3) , Galahad Bks.) BBS Publishing Corp.

Stockstill. Jesus Nacio en Belen. 2004. (SPA.). 20p. bds. 4.99 (978-0-7586-0261-9(8)) Concordia Publishing Hse.

Stockstill, Gloria McQueen. Basket in the River. Girouard, Patrick, illus. 2004. (ENG.). 20p. (J). bds. 4.99 (978-0-7586-0052-3(6)) Concordia Publishing Hse.

Stoddard, Jeffery. Pete & Pillar - The Big Rain: A Story of Friendship Based on John 15:13. 2007. (Illus.). 32p. (J). (ps-2). 12.99 (***978-1-59317-203-9(6)***) Warner Pr. Pubs.

Stoddard, Sandol. A Child's First Bible Storybook. 1998. (Illus.). 96p. (J). (gr. k-1). 9.99 (978-0-88486-215-4(1) , Arrowood Pr.) BBS Publishing Corp.

Stohs, Anita Reith. Praise God with Paper Cups: 45 Easy Bible Crafts. 2005. (ENG., Illus.). 64p. (J). 9.99 (978-0-7586-0842-0(X)) Concordia Publishing Hse.

Stone, Elaine Murphy & Rayburn, Cathy. Angels in the Bible. Sabatte, Frank, illus. 2006. 88p. (J). pap. 7.95 (978-0-8091-6729-6(8) , 6729-8) Paulist Pr.

Stories about David. (Pict-O-Graph Ser.). (Illus.). (J). 10.99 (978-0-7847-1038-8(4) , 02238) Standard Publishing.

Stories from the Bible: A Look Inside Flapbook. 2003. 18p. (J). bds. 10.99 (978-0-8254-7270-1(9)) Kregel Pubns.

Stowell, Charlotte, illus. Favorite Bible Stories. 2001. 24p. (J). 2.99 (978-0-8254-7204-6(0)) Kregel Pubns.

Stowell, Gordon. Libro de Actividades Biblicas (Bible Story Activities) (SPA.). (J). No. 1. 1.89 (978-1-56063-761-5(7) , 497741); No. 2. 1.89 (978-1-56063-791-2(9) , 497742); No. 3. 1.89 (978-1-56063-792-9(7) , 497743); No. 4. 1.89 (978-1-56063-793-6(5) , 497744) Editorial Unilit.

Stowell, Gordon, et al. Y Ddihangfa Anhygoel! Llyfr Drysfa Beiblaidd. 2005. (WEL., Illus.). 12p. (978-1-85994-469-1(8)) Cyhoeddiadau'r Gair.

Strang Communications Company Staff, ed. Kidz Chat: Summer 2002. 2002. (J). pap. 14.99 (978-1-57405-979-3(3)) CharismaLife Pubs.

—Live Wire: Spring 2002. 2002. (J). pap. 14.99 (978-1-57405-927-4(0)) CharismaLife Pubs.

—Live Wire: Summer 2002. 2002. (J). pap. 14.99 (978-1-57405-965-6(3)) CharismaLife Pubs.

Streit, Jakob. We Will Build A Temple: The Path of Israel from King Solomon to John the Baptist. Mitchell, David, ed. Samson, Donald, tr. 2004. Orig. Title: Lasst uns den Tempel Bauen. (J). per. 15.00 (978-1-888365-55-9(2)) Assn. of Waldorf Schls. of North America Pubns. (AWSNA).

Summer, Joan R. A Gift for Jesus. 2002. (Illus.). 24p. (J). 8.95 (978-1-57921-421-0(5)) WinePress Publishing.

Surprised by God's Grace: Bible Story Album. 2004. (Firelight Ser.). (ps-k). 4.99 (978-0-8066-6456-9(8)) Augsburg Fortress, Pubs.

Surprised by God's Grace: Bible Story Flipbook. 2004. (Firelight Ser.). (gr. 3-4). 4.99 (978-0-8066-6460-6(6)) Augsburg Fortress, Pubs.

Surprised by God's Grace: Bible Story Foldout. 2004. (Firelight Ser.). (ps). 4.99 (978-0-8066-6454-5(1)) Augsburg Fortress, Pubs.

Surprised by God's Grace: Bible Story Magazine. 2004. (Firelight Ser.). (gr. 5-6). 4.99 (978-0-8066-6462-0(2)) Augsburg Fortress, Pubs.

Surprised by God's Grace: Bible Storybook. 2004. (Firelight Ser.). (gr. 1-2). 4.99 (978-0-8066-6458-3(4)) Augsburg Fortress, Pubs.

Swartz, Nancy Sohn. In Our Image: God's First Creatures. Hall, Melanie, illus. 1998. 32p. (ps-3). 16.95 (978-1-879045-99-6(0)) Jewish Lights Publishing.

Swift, Jane, illus. First Bible Stories. 2002. (J). bds. 4.98 (978-0-7525-6590-3(7)) Parragon, Inc.

The Sword, the Ring, & the Parchment. 2006. (J). per. 7.99 (978-0-9785523-0-5(X)) Dunlop, Edward.

Syswerda, Jean E. My Sleep-Tight Bible Stories: Bedtime Bible Stories. Wheeler, Jody, illus. 2002. (Bible Storybooks Ser.). 64p. (J). 7.99 (978-0-310-70174-3(0)) Zonderkidz.

Take-Home Papers. 2004. 19.99 (978-0-7644-1606-4(5)); 2004. 19.99 (978-0-7644-1709-2(6)); 2004. 19.99 (978-0-7644-1689-7(8)); 2003. 19.99 (978-0-7644-1583-8(2)) Group Publishing, Inc. (Flagship Church Resources).

Tangvald, Christine Harder & DeBoer, Rondi. Listen, Live & Laugh Bible Stories. Neubecker, Robert, illus. 2006. 14p. (J). 9.99 (978-0-310-70892-6(3)) Zonderkidz.

Taylor, Damon. Touch & Feel Bible Stories. 12p. (J). (ps-k). 10.99 (978-0-8254-5501-8(4)) Kregel Pubns.

Taylor, Damon J. Aprende los Opuestos con la Biblia. 2004. (Mis Calcetines Ser.). (SPA., Illus.). 24p. 5.99 (978-0-8254-0776-5(1) , Editorial Portavoz) Kregel Pubns.

—Bible Babies. 2003. (Child Sockology Ser.). 10p. (J). bds. 6.99 (978-0-8254-3863-9(2)) Kregel Pubns.

Taylor, Kenneth N. Family-Time Bible in Pictures. 2007. 320p. (J). 12.99 (***978-1-4143-1577-5(5)*** , Tyndale Kids) Tyndale Hse. Pubs.

—I Can Learn about God: In Easy Words & Pictures. 2006. 208p. (J). 9.99 (978-1-4143-0768-8(3)) Tyndale Hse. Pubs.

—Jesus in Pictures for Little Eyes. Spenceley, Annabel, illus. 2003. (Leading Young Hearts & Minds to God Ser.). 112p. (J). (gr. k-3). 9.99 (978-0-8024-3059-5(7)) Moody Pubs.

—My First Bible in Pictures. 15th l.t. anniv. ed. 2004. (Illus.). 256p. (J). (ps-1). 13.99 (978-0-8423-4630-6(9)) Tyndale Hse. Pubs.

—My First Bible in Pictures. Hook, Richard & Hook, Francis, illus. 15th l.t. anniv. ed. 2004. 250p. (J). (ps-1). 9.99 (978-0-8423-4633-7(3) , 01-4633-3) Tyndale Hse. Pubs.

—My First Picture Bible Stories, Catholic Edition. 2000. (Illus.). (J). (ps-3). 262p. 12.95 (978-0-87973-108-3(7)); 256p. 16.95 (978-0-87973-109-0(5)) Our Sunday Visitor, Publishing Div.

—The New Bible in Pictures for Little Eyes. Spenceley, Annabel, illus. gif. ed. 2004. (Leading Young Hearts & Minds to God Ser.). 384p. (J). 24.99 (978-0-8024-3078-6(3)) Moody Pubs.

Thaler, Mike. God's Anchorman. 2001. (gr. 5-8). lib. bdg. 11.80 (978-0-613-74917-6(0)) Tandem Library Bks.

—God's Fair Ladies. 2001. (gr. 5-8). lib. bdg. 11.80 (978-0-613-74916-9(2)) Tandem Library Bks.

Thank You Jesus. 2002. (Illus.). 8p. (J). bds. 7.99 (978-0-7853-6377-4(7)) Publications International, Ltd.

Thomas, Jerry D. Shoebox Kids Bible Stories, Vol. 3. Sox, Aileen Andres, ed. 2002. (Illus.). 128p. (J). pap. 7.99 (978-0-8163-1911-4(1)) Pacific Pr. Publishing Assn.

Thompson, Sharon. Bible Story Puppets & Poems. 2004. (J). per. 11.99 (978-1-59441-007-9(0) , CD-204001) Carson-Dellosa Publishing Co., Inc.

Tiner, John Hudson. Bible Story Word Searches. 2001. 64p. (gr. 3-6). 9.99 (978-0-570-05284-5(X)) Concordia Publishing Hse.

Too Tall, Too Small. (Hear Me Read Classroom Sets Ser.). 32.00 (978-0-570-07171-6(2)) Concordia Publishing Hse.

Touched by Him: Bible Story Coloring Book. ed. 2006. (ENG, CHI & RUS.). (J). 1.99 (978-0-9777446-0-2(4)) Childrens Bible Society.

Treasures of the Bible. 1998. (Illus.). 580p. (J). (gr. 4-7). 24.95 (978-2-215-04276-1(1)) Continental Enterprises Group, Inc. (CEG).

Treasury of Bible Stories. 2000. (Illus.). (J). (ps-3). 19.95 (978-0-88271-012-9(5)) Regina Pr., Malhame & Co.

A Treasury of Bible Stories. 1999. (Religious Ser.). (J). pap. 4.99 (978-0-307-29509-5(5) , Golden Bks.) Random Hse. Children's Bks.

Tres Regalos Para el Nino Jesus, 6 vols. 2000. (Arch Bks.). (SPA.). 24p. (J). (ps-3). 2.49 (978-0-570-05171-8(1)) Concordia Publishing Hse.

Truitt, Gloria A. My Happy Birthday Book: Exodus 2:1-10; 1 Samuel 1, Luke 2:1-20, Mark 10:13-16 for Children. Sharp, Chris, illus. rev. ed. 2005. (ENG.). 16p. (J). (ps-ps). 1.99 (978-0-7586-0408-8(4)) Concordia Publishing Hse.

Trujillo, Kelli & Trujillo, David. Student Book. 2005. (Illus.). 123p. pap. 5.99 (978-0-7644-2932-3(9)) Group Publishing, Inc.

The Truth about Evil. 1998. (Core Belief Bible Study Ser.). (YA). (gr. 7-9). pap. 11.99 (978-0-7644-0854-0(2)) Group Publishing, Inc.

The Truth about Humanity. 1998. (Core Belief Bible Study Ser.). (Illus.). 60p. (YA). (gr. 7-9). pap. 11.99 (978-0-7644-0853-3(4)) Group Publishing, Inc.

Tuck, Mildred. A Child's Book of Miracles & Wonders. Moroney, Tracey, illus. 2006. 28p. (J). (ps-3). 15.99 (978-0-7847-1437-9(1) , 04076) Standard Publishing.

Tucker, Mary. Stories & Activities David. 2007. 48p. pap. 7.99 (***978-1-4206-7067-7(0)***) Teacher Created Resources, Inc.

—Stories & Activities Paul. 2007. 48p. pap. 7.99 (***978-1-4206-7069-1(7)***) Teacher Created Resources, Inc.

—Stories & Activities Ruth. 2007. 48p. pap. 7.99 (***978-1-4206-7068-4(9)***) Teacher Created Resources, Inc.

Tuttle, Emily. Baby's First Easter. 2006. (First Bible Collection). (Illus.). 10p. (J). (ps-k). 9.99 (978-0-7847-1206-1(9) , 04393) Standard Publishing.

Twin Sisters Productions Staff, prod. Bible Stories: Songs That Teach. 2005. (J). per. 12.99 (978-1-57583-822-9(2)) Twin Sisters Productions, LLC.

Two by Two a Puzzle Book. 2004. bds. 10.99 (978-0-8254-5510-0(3)) Kregel Pubns.

Ulmer, Louise. The Bible That Wouldn't Burn: William Tyndale's New Testament. Ulmer, Louise, illus. 3rd ed. 2005. Orig. Title: The Bible That Wouldn't Burn: How the Tyndale English Version of the New Testament Came About. (Illus.). 34p. (YA). per., act. bk. ed. 8.95 (978-0-941367-24-0(X)) Peach Blossom Pubns.

Under the Baobab Tree: Keep the Faith, Raise up Hope, Tell of God's Love: Student Handbook. (gr. 1-3). pap., stu. ed. 2.50 (978-0-687-05799-3(X)); Vol. 2. (ps-k). pap., stu. ed. 2.50 (978-0-687-00670-0(8)) Abingdon Pr.

The Untearable Bible...for the Terrible Twos. 2001. 34p. (J). 6.99 (978-0-88270-884-3(8)) Bridge-Logos Pubs.

Van Der Veer, Andrew. Bible Lessons for Juniors, Book 1: Creation through Moses. 2007. (J). (***978-1-60178-012-6(5)***) Reformation Heritage Bks.

—Bible Lessons for Juniors, Book 2: Kings & Prophets. 2007. (J). (***978-1-60178-013-3(3)***) Reformation Heritage Bks.

—Bible Lessons for Juniors, Book 4: The Early Church. 2007. (J). (***978-1-60178-015-7(X)***) Reformation Heritage Bks.

Van Gool, A, illus. A Child's Treasury of Bible Stories. 2002. 125p. (J). per. 16.95 (978-1-58087-072-6(4)) Stampley, C.D. Enterprises, Inc.

Van Stockum, Hilda. Andries. Van Stockum, Hilda, illus. 1998. (Hilda van Stockum Family Collection). (Illus.). 200p. (YA). (gr. 4 up). reprint ed. pap. 11.95 (978-1-883937-36-2(1) , 36-1) Bethlehem Bks.

VanBibber, Jodi. CD: An Early Childhood Learning Program designed especially for One-Year-Olds. 2005. cd-rom 34.95 (978-0-9755818-3-4(X)) Sunny Hollow Pr.

—CD: An Early Childhood Learning Program designed especially for two & three year olds. It's educational & easy to do. but best of all, it's fun!: Bible Story Concepts for 2s And 3s. 2005. cd-rom 34.95 (978-0-9755818-2-7(1)) Sunny Hollow Pr.

—CD-Bible Story Concepts for 4s And 5s: An Early Childhood Learning Program designed especially for four & five year olds. It's educational & easy to do. but best of all, it's Fun! 2005. cd-rom 34.95 (978-0-9755818-4-1(8)) Sunny Hollow Pr.

VBS-Fiesta-Bible Adventures & Missions: Preschool Leader Manual (Silly Chilies Preschool) 2006. pap. 6.99 (978-0-7644-3125-8(0)) Group Publishing, Inc.

VBS-Fiesta-Hot Bible Adventures: Leader Manual (Group's Fiesta! Where Kids Are Fired Up about Jesus) 2006. pap. 9.99 (978-0-7644-2956-9(6)) Group Publishing, Inc.

Veggie Tales Cast. Esther, the Girl Who Became Queen. 2004. 24p. pap. 1.99 (978-1-4037-0491-7(0)) Dalmatian Pr.

—King George & the Ducky. rev. ed. 2004. 24p. pap. 1.99 (978-1-4037-0490-0(2)) Dalmatian Pr.

—Veggietales Lots of Fun Color. rev. ed. 2004. (Illus.). 400p. (J). pap. 5.99 (978-1-4037-0538-9(0) , Spirit Pr.) Dalmatian Pr.

Vivas, Julie, illus. The Nativity. 2006. 36p. (J). pap. 7.00 (978-0-15-206085-5(5) , Voyager Bks./Libros Viajeros) Harcourt Children's Bks.

Wade, Connie. Battle of Jerico. Overstreet, Laura, illus. 2006. (Sing A Story Ser.). 20p. (J). bds. 4.99 (978-0-7847-1813-1(X) , 04135) Standard Publishing.

—Noah's Ark. Overstreet, Laura, illus. 2006. (Sing A Story Ser.). 20p. (J). bds. 4.99 (978-0-7847-1812-4(1) , 04134) Standard Publishing.

Walker, Joni. Jesus Rose on Easter Morn Span. 2004. (SPA.). 20p. bds. 4.99 (978-0-7586-0322-7(3)) Concordia Publishing Hse.

Walls, Steven. The Ark Endeavor. 2005. 55p. pap. 12.95 (978-1-4137-9566-0(8)) PublishAmerica, Inc.

Walsh, Sheila, contrib. by. God's Little Princess Devotional Bible: Bible Storybook. 2006. 352p. (J). 15.99 (978-1-4003-0879-8(8) , 04396) Nelson, Thomas Inc.

Walsh, Sheila, contrib. by. God's Mighty Warrior Devotional Bible. 2007. 352p. (J). 15.99 (***978-1-4003-1006-7(7)***) Nelson, Thomas Inc.

Warner Press Staff. Courage. 2000. (Lion Cub Upside-Down Books Ser.). (J). (ps-3). pap. 5.95 (978-0-87162-822-0(8)) Warner Pr. Pubs.

—Love. 2000. (Lion Cub Upside-Down Books Ser.). (Illus.). (J). (ps-3). pap. 5.95 (978-0-87162-826-8(0)) Warner Pr. Pubs.

—Obedience. 2000. (Lion Cub Upside-Down Books Ser.). (Illus.). (J). (ps-3). pap. 5.95 (978-0-87162-820-6(1)) Warner Pr. Pubs.

—Patience. 2000. (Lion Cub Upside-Down Books Ser.). (Illus.). (J). (ps-3). pap. 5.95 (978-0-87162-830-5(9)) Warner Pr. Pubs.

—Preschool: Bible Coloring & Crafts Pages. 1999. (Illus.). (J). pap. 3.95 (978-0-87162-863-3(5)) Warner Pr. Pubs.

Warner Press Staff, ed. Giving: Jesus & Jennifer. 2000. (Lion Cub Upside-Down Bks.). (Illus.). 24p. (J). (ps-3). pap. 5.95 (978-0-87162-846-6(5)) Warner Pr. Pubs.

Water, Mark. The Pilgrim Book of Bible Stories. Shimon, Diana, illus. 2003. 320p. (J). 22.50 (978-0-8298-1487-3(6)) Pilgrim Pr., The/United Church Pr.

Watson-Brugess, Linda. Readers Theatre. 3.25 (978-0-687-35550-1(8)) Abingdon Pr.

Watts, Murray. The Bible for Children. Cann, Helen, illus. 2002. (Bestselling Children's Books - Religious Ser.). 352p. (J). (gr. 3-7). 23.99 (978-1-56148-362-4(1)) Good Bks.

Weber, Lou, ed. Bible Stories Read a Long Treasury. 2005. (Illus.). 40p. (J). bds. 12.98 (978-1-4127-3502-5(5) , 7248100) Publications International, Ltd.

—Mi Premera Biblioteca Cuentos. 2004. (ESP.). 72p. 10.98 (978-0-7853-9727-4(2)) Publications International, Ltd.

Wee Witness. Baby's First Little Bible. gif. ed. 2003. 32p. 7.99 (978-0-7369-1184-9(7)) Harvest Hse. Pubs.

Weiss, Sam. Jesus Plays the Catskills. 2004. 96p. per. 11.95 (978-0-9754699-0-3(8)) Gross, H. H.

Wells, Catherine. Parable Time: Juan Cepana's Stories for the Church Year. 2004. (J). pap. 11.99 (978-0-8066-4948-1(8)) Augsburg Fortress, Pubs.

What Next? (Hear Me Read Classroom Sets Ser.). 32.00 (978-0-570-07173-0(9)) Concordia Publishing Hse.

Widenhouse, Kathy. The Un-Bunny Book. 2004. (Illus.). 168p. (J). pap. 14.99 (978-1-58411-028-6(7) , Legacy Pr.) Rainbow Pubs. & Legacy Pr.

Wilhelm, Hans. Jesus Wants Me for a Sunbeam. 2007. 24p. (J). pap. 3.99 (978-0-439-80923-8(1)) Scholastic, Inc.

—The Lord Is My Shepherd. 24p. (J). 2007. pap. 3.99 (978-0-439-80922-1(3)); 2006. (Illus.). 5.99 (978-0-439-80002-0(1)) Scholastic, Inc.

Wilkeshuis, Cornelis. The Gift for the Child: A Story. Verstegen, Jeska, illus. 28p. (J). 16.95 (978-0-86315-349-5(6)) Floris Bks. GBR. *Dist:* SteinerBooks, Inc.

Wilkinson, Bruce. My 100 Best-Loved Bible Stories. 2005. (Illus.). (J). 12.99 (978-1-59185-866-9(6)) Strang Communications Co.

Will, Julianne & Ball, Ann. Catholic bible stories for Children: First communion Edition. 2006. per. 19.95 (978-1-59276-221-7(2)) Our Sunday Visitor, Publishing Div.

Wills, Sally W. PowerXpress into the Bible Breakfast on the Beach Unit. 2005. 115.00 (978-0-687-00669-4(4)) Abingdon Pr.

—PowerXpress the Good Samaritan Unit. 2004. 115.00 (978-0-687-07363-4(4)) Abingdon Pr.

Wilson, N. D. In the Time of Noah. Bentley, Peter V., illus. 2007. (J). per. (***978-1-59128-045-3(1)***) Canon Pr.

Wolf, Kathryn. Make a Joyful Noise: Bible Poems, Songs & Fingerplays. 2007. (J). per. 21.99 (978-0-9789056-8-2(7)) New Day Publishing, Inc.

Wooding, Marnie & Kielesinski, Chris. The Kid Who Would Be King: One-Minute Bible Stories about Kids. 2000. (Illus.). 432p. (J). 12.99 (978-0-8054-9399-3(9)) B&H Publishing Grp.

Woodman, Ros. Bible Detectives: Luke. 64p. (YA). pap., act. bk. ed. 7.99 (978-1-85792-758-0(3) , Christian Focus) Christian Focus Pubns. GBR. *Dist:* Riverside.

Wright, Melissa & Curelli, Augusta. My Bible: The Story of God's Love. Curreli, Augusta, illus. 2004. 236p. (J). 24.95 (978-0-8198-4834-5(4) , 332-223) Pauline Bks. & Media.

Wright, Sally Ann. Bible Turn & Learn. McLean, Moira, illus. 2007. 12p. (J). (ps-3). 13.00 (***978-0-687-49176-6(2)***) Abingdon Pr.

—Look & See Bible. 2006. (Children's Bibles & Bible Story Collections). (Illus.). 96p. (J). 12.95 (978-0-8091-6735-7(2) , 6735-2) Paulist Pr.

—What Did the Fishermen Catch? 2006. 28p. (J). 10.95 (978-0-8091-6732-6(8) , 6732-8) Paulist Pr.

—Who Built the Ark? 2006. 28p. (J). 10.95 (978-0-8091-6730-2(1) , 6730-1) Paulist Pr.

Wright, Sally Ann & Ayres, Honor. A Child's Bible. 2005. (Illus.). 140p. (J). (ps-1). 18.99 (978-0-7847-1776-9(1)) Standard Publishing.

Yorke, Jane. Big Book of Bible Animals: American Edition. 2001. (Illus.). (J). (978-0-7566-0003-7(0)) Dorling Kindersley Publishing, Inc.

Ziegler, Sonja, et al. Bible Story Puppet Skits Kids Can Do. Hayes, Theresa, ed. 2000. (Illus.). 64p. (J). (gr. 3-7). pap. 8.99 (978-0-7847-1153-8(4) , 03398) Standard Publishing.

Zobel-Nolan, Allia. The Big Book of Bible Fiery Tales. Gevry, Claudine, illus. 2004. 12p. (J). bds. 8.99 (978-0-8254-5516-2(2)) Kregel Pubns.

—The Creation. MacLean, Moira, illus. 2000. (Mini Handle Bks.). 5p. (J). (ps). bds. 7.99 (978-1-57584-672-9(1)) Reader's Digest Children's Publishing, Inc.

—God Made the World. MacLean, Moira, illus. 2000. (Baby's First Bible Stories Ser.). 10p. (J). (ps). 9.99 (978-0-7847-1208-5(5) , 04396) Standard Publishing.

—Historias para el Bebe: Ha nacido el bebe Jesus. 2001. (Baby's First Ser.).Tr. of Baby's Bible Stories: Baby Jesus is Born. bds. 7.99 (978-0-7899-0957-2(X)) Editorial Unilit.

—Historias para el Bebe: Jesus y los Ninos. 2001. (Baby's First Ser.).Tr. of Baby's Bible Stories: Jesus & the children. bds. 7.99 (978-0-7899-0958-9(8)) Editorial Unilit.

—Historias para el Bebe: Noe y el Arca. 2001. (Baby's First Ser.).Tr. of Baby's Bible Stories: Noah & the Ark. bds. 7.99 (978-0-7899-0959-6(6)) Editorial Unilit.

—Jesus & the Children. MacLean, Moira, illus. 2000. (Mini Handle Bks.:). 5p. (J). (ps). bds. 7.99 (978-1-57584-669-9(1)) Reader's Digest Children's Publishing, Inc.

—Levanta la Tapita: Natividad. 2002. (Lift the Flap Ser.).Tr. of Lift the Flap: Nativity. bds. 10.99 (978-0-7899-0731-8(3)) Editorial Unilit.

—Levanta la Tapita: Quien esta Escondido? 2002. (Lift the Flap Ser.).Tr. of Lift the Flap: Who's Hiding. bds. 5.99 (978-0-7899-1020-2(9)) Editorial Unilit.

—Levanta la Tapita: Quien Quien lo Dice? 2002. (Lift the Flap Ser.).Tr. of Lift the Flap: Who Say's That. bds. 5.99 (978-0-7899-1019-6(5)) Editorial Unilit.

—Librito para Jugar: Historia de la Creacion. 2002. (Play along Ser.).Tr. of Play along book: Story of Creation. bds. 4.99 (978-0-7899-1004-2(7)) Editorial Unilit.

—Librito para Jugar: Historia del bebe Moises. 2002. (Play along Ser.).Tr. of Play along book: Story of Baby Moses. bds. 4.99 (978-0-7899-1003-5(9)) Editorial Unilit.

—My Bible Story Collection. 2004. 14.99 (978-0-8254-5515-5(4)) Kregel Pubns.

—Ninos en la Biblia. 2003. Tr. of Children of the Bible. bds. 8.99 (978-0-7899-1089-9(6)) Editorial Unilit.

—La Primera Biblia del Bebe. 2003. (First Bible Collection). (ENG & SPA., Illus.). 20p. (J). bds. 12.99 (978-0-7944-0139-9(2) , Reader's Digest Children's Bks.) Reader's Digest Children's Publishing, Inc.

—Touch & Feel Bible Animal Friends. 2004. 12p. (J). bds. 10.99 (978-0-8254-5512-4(X)) Kregel Pubns.

Zona Biblica en la Casa de Dios Preschool Leader's Guide. 2007. 29.99 (***978-0-687-64660-9(X)***) Abingdon Pr.

Zona Biblica en la Casa de Dios Younger Elementary Leader's Guide. 2007. 29.99 (***978-0-687-64670-8(7)***) Abingdon Pr.

Zonderkidz Staff, contrib. by. GNT Children's Bible, Catholic Edition. 2002. (Illus.). 1664p. (J). 20.99 (978-0-310-70489-8(8)) Zonderkidz.

Zondervan. Beginner's Bible Activity Pack GM. 2006. (J). bds. 20.98 (978-0-310-60524-9(5)) Zonderkidz.

—La Biblia de Mi Primer Paso. Vida Publishers Staff, ed. 2000. (SPA., Illus.). 448p. (ps). 14.99 (978-0-8297-2344-1(7)) Vida Pubs.

A B

—Daniel & the Lions. Zonderkidz Staff, ed. Pulley, Kelly, illus. 2006. (Beginners Bible Ser.). 22p. (J). 5.99 (978-0-310-71114-8(2)) Zonderkidz.

—David & Goliath. Zonderkidz Staff, ed. Pulley, Kelly, illus. 2006. (Beginners Bible Ser.). 22p. (J). 5.99 (978-0-310-71113-1(4)) Zonderkidz.

—Fish's Big Catch & Jonah's Big Journey. Pulley, Kelly, illus. 2006. (Beginner's Bible' Ser.). 20p. (J). 6.99 (978-0-310-71339-5(0)) Zonderkidz.

—Jesus Is Risen! Zonderkidz Staff, ed. Pulley, Kelly, illus. 2006. (Beginners Bible Ser.). 22p. (J). 5.99 (978-0-310-71115-5(0)) Zonderkidz.

—Jesus, Mary, & Martha. Zonderkidz Staff, ed. Pulley, Kelly, illus. 2006. (Beginners Bible Ser.). 22p. (J). 5.99 (978-0-310-71116-2(9)) Zonderkidz.

—NIRV Discoverer's Bible for Young Readers. rev. ed. 2002. (Illus.). 2048p. (J). (gr. 5-7). 32.99 (978-0-310-70383-9(2)); pap. 32.99 (978-0-310-70491-1(X)) Zondervan Bibles.

—NIRV Discoverer's Bible for Young Readers. O'Malley, Kathleen, illus. rev. ed. 2002. 2048p. (J). (gr. 5-7). 22.99 (978-0-310-70382-2(4)) Zonderkidz.

—See with Me Bible: The Bible Told in Pictures. Jones, Dennis G., illus. 2005. 352p. (J). (ps-1). 16.99 (978-0-310-70926-8(1)) Zonderkidz.

Zondervan & Richards, Lawrence O. Little Kids Adventure Bible. 2000. (Bible Storybooks Ser.). (Illus.). 448p. (J). pap. 17.99 (978-0-310-92142-4(2)) Zonderkidz.

Zwerger, Lisbeth. Stories from the Bible. 2002. (Illus.). 160p. (J). (gr. k-5). 19.95 (978-0-7358-1413-4(9)) North-South Bks., Inc.

Zyromski, Page McKean. Jesus & Mary in the Rosary: Echo Stories for Children. 2001. 128p. pap. 19.95 (978-1-58595-140-6(4)) Twenty-Third Pubns./Bayard.

365 Bible Activities for Kids: A Bible Story & Actitivity for Each Day of the Year. 2003. (Illus.). 366p. (J). 7.99 (978-0-8254-7273-2(3)) Kregel Pubns.

BIBLE STORIES—N.T.

Amery, H. New Testament. 2004. (Children's Bibles Ser.). 72p. (J). 15.95 (978-0-7945-0048-1(X) , Usborne) EDC Publishing.

Amery, Heather. El Buen Samaritano. 2001. (Coleccion Cuentos de la Biblia).Tr. of Good Samaritan. (SPA., Illus.). 16p. (J). (gr. k-3). 6.95 (978-0-7460-3875-8(5)) EDC Publishing.

—Prodigal Son. 1999. (gr. k-3). lib. bdg. 12.40 (978-0-613-74479-9(9)) Tandem Library Bks.

Amoss, Berthe. Draw Yourself into a Starlit Journey. 2003. 32p. (J). spiral bd. 12.95 (978-1-59325-004-1(5)) Word Among Us Pr.

Andrews, Jackie, retold by. 100 New Testament Bible Stories for Children. 2005. (Illus.). 208p. (J). 7.99 (978-0-517-22587-5(5) , Testament) Random Hse. Value Publishing.

Anonymous. Mother Stories from the New Testament (a. 2006. pap. 87.99 (*978-1-4219-7133-9(X)) IndyPublish-.com.

Aquilina, Michael, III. St. Jude: A Friend in Hard Times. Neely, Keith, illus. 2004. 76p. (J). 14.95 (978-0-8198-7075-9(7) , 332-371) Pauline Bks. & Media.

Baker, Marvin G. Luke's Story: Based on the Gospel of Luke. 2005. 160p. pap. 9.95 (978-0-9752880-8-5(3)) Baker Trittin Pr.

Ballman, Swanee. Mary & Martha's Dinner Guest. Boddy, Joe, illus. 1998. (Arch Bks.). (ENG.). 16p. (J). (gr. k-4). 1.99 (978-0-570-07548-6(3)) Concordia Publishing Hse.

Beers, Gilbert. Tell Me the Story of Jesus. 2001. (Illus.). 128p. (J). (gr. k-3). 14.99 (978-0-8423-3868-4(3)) Tyndale Hse. Pubs.

Belec, Glynis. Jesus Washes Peter's Feet: The Story of Jesus Washing the Disciple's Feet. Gliewe, Unada G., illus. 2001. (Arch Bks.). (ENG.). 16p. (J). (gr. k-4). 1.99 (978-0-570-07571-4(8)) Concordia Publishing Hse.

Bergt, Carolyn. A Child's Garden of Bible Stories Workbooks: New Testament Workbook. 80p. (gr. 1-3). wbk. ed. 9.95 (978-0-7586-0474-3(2)) Concordia Publishing Hse.

Bergt, Carolyn S. Who's the Greatest? Jesus Talks about Greatness: Mattew 18:1-9: 19:13-15; 20:17-28: John 13:12-17 for Children. Blanchette, Dave, illus. 2005. (J). (978-0-7586-0931-1(0)) Concordia Publishing Hse.

Bible Stories Crafts & More NT. 2004. 7.99 (978-0-7647-0501-4(6)) School Specialty Publishing.

Bishop, Jennie. The Garden Wall. 2006. (J). 12.99 (*978-1-59317-168-1(4)) Warner Pr. Pubs.

Blyton, Enid. El Ninito Jesus. 2nd ed. 1999. (Historias de la Biblia Ser.). (SPA., Illus.). 32p. (ps-3). pap. 4.99 (978-0-8254-1067-3(3) , Editorial Portavoz) Kregel Pubns.

—El Nino con los Panes y los Peces. 2nd ed. 1999. (Historias Biblicas Ilustradas; Illustrated Bible Stories Ser.). (SPA., Illus.). 32p. (ps-3). pap. 4.99 (978-0-8254-1065-9(7) , Editorial Portavoz) Kregel Pubns.

Bohnet, Eric C. Mary's Easter Story: The Story of Easter: Matthew 21:1-11 & John 18:1-20:31 for Children. Swisher, Elizabeth & Swisher, Elizabeth, illus. 2002. (ENG.). 16p. (J). 1.99 (978-0-570-07579-0(3)) Concordia Publishing Hse.

—Saul's Conversion: Acts 9:1-22: 21:1-22:21 for Children. Ramsey, Marcy Dunn, illus. 2006. (Arch Books). (ENG.). 16p. (J). 1.99 (978-0-7586-0868-0(3)) Concordia Publishing Hse.

Brighter Child Publishing Staff. The Beginners Bible: New Testament Favorites: Birth of Jesus & Story of Easter. 1999. (Beginner's Bible Ser.). (J). (ps-3). cd-rom 19.95 (978-1-57791-003-9(6)) Brighter Minds Children's Publishing.

Bryce, Ellen. Once upon a Holy Night: Value Pak. 2004. (gr. 2-5). 25.00 (978-0-687-09900-9(5)) Abingdon Pr.

Busch, Melinda Kay. Jesus & the Woman at the Well. Clark, Bill, illus. 2005. (Arch Books). (ENG.). 16p. (J). 1.99 (978-0-7586-0675-4(3)) Concordia Publishing Hse.

Butcher, Sam. Precious Moments Bible Stories. 2000. (Illus.). (J). (978-0-8010-4447-2(2)) Baker Bks.

Caldwell, Lise. The Life of Christ: Classic Bible Stories. 1998. (Happy Day Bks.). (Illus.). 24p. (J). (ps-2). pap. 2.49 (978-0-7847-0828-6(2) , 04258, Bean Sprouts) Standard Publishing.

Campdepadros, Jorgelina & Campdepadros, Eduardo. El Viaje de Pablo. 2004. (Bible Stories Ser.).Tr. of Paul's Journey. (SPA.). 32p. 3.99 (978-0-8254-1147-2(5) , Editorial Portavoz) Kregel Pubns.

Champions of the King: The Story of the Apostles. 2004. (Illus.). 231p. (J). pap. 10.99 (978-0-8280-1704-6(2) , 030-970) Review & Herald Publishing Assn.

Christian Focus Publishing Staff. The Special Baby - The Birth of Jesus. 1999. (Illus.). 10p. (J). (ps-k). bds. (978-1-85792-464-0(9) , Christian Focus) Christian Focus Pubns.

Concordia Publishing Staff. Bethlehem Stable. 1999. (Illus.). (J). (ps-k). 7.99 (978-0-570-07047-4(3)) Cajun Prairie Habitat Preservation Society.

—Herod's Palace. 1999. (J). (ps-3). 8.00 (978-0-570-07051-1(1)) Concordia Publishing Hse.

—The Man Who Couldn't Speak. 1999. (Arch Bks.). (Illus.). 16p. (J). (gr. k-4). 1.99 (978-0-570-07560-8(2)) Concordia Publishing Hse.

—Mary's House. 1999. (J). (ps-3). 8.00 (978-0-570-07049-8(X)) Concordia Publishing Hse.

—Shepherds' Fields. 1999. (J). (ps-3). 8.00 (978-0-570-07048-1(1)) Concordia Publishing Hse.

—Where Is Jesus? 1999. (Illus.). 12p. (J). (ps-k). 7.00 (978-0-570-05583-9(0)) Concordia Publishing Hse.

—Wise Men's Palace. 1999. (J). (ps-3). 8.00 (978-0-570-07050-4(3)) Concordia Publishing Hse.

Concordia Publishing Staff, ed. Stories about Jesus for Little Ones. 1998. (Illus.). 35p. (J). (ps-1). 8.99 (978-0-570-05476-4(1)) Concordia Publishing Hse.

Courtney, Claudia. Barns of Barley: The Parable of the Rich Fool. Mitter, Kathy, illus. 1998. (Phonetic Bible Stories Ser.). (ENG.). 16p. (J). (ps-1). 2.99 (978-0-570-05095-7(2)) Concordia Publishing Hse.

—Bleat! The Parable of the Lost Sheep. Mitter, Kathy, illus. 1998. (Phonetic Bible Stories Ser.). (ENG.). 16p. (J). (ps-1). 2.99 (978-0-570-05092-6(8)) Concordia Publishing Hse.

—Blow! Jesus Calms the Storm. Sandland, Reg, illus. 1998. (Phonetic Bible Stories Ser.). (ENG.). 16p. (J). (ps-1). 2.99 (978-0-570-05093-3(6)) Concordia Publishing Hse.

—Blow: Jesus Calms the Storm, Matthew 8. 1998. (ps-2). lib. bdg. 10.65 (978-0-613-72812-6(2)) Tandem Library Bks.

—Jesus Is Born! The Story of Christmas. Sharp, Chris, illus. 1998. (Phonetic Bible Stories Ser.). (ENG.). 16p. (J). (ps-1). 2.99 (978-0-570-05462-7(1) , 56-1925GJ) Concordia Publishing Hse.

—Little Is Big: Jesus Feeds The 5,000. Sandland, Reg, illus. 1998. (Phonetic Bible Stories Ser.). (ENG.). 16p. (J). (ps-1). 2.99 (978-0-570-05094-0(4)) Concordia Publishing Hse.

—Tan Man: The Parable of the Good Samaritan. 1999. (ps-2). lib. bdg. 10.65 (978-0-613-72902-4(1)) Tandem Library Bks.

—The Tan Man: The Parable of the Good Samaritan, Vol. 1. Nolte, Larry, illus. 1999. (Phonetic Bible Stories Ser.). (ENG.). 16p. (J). (ps-1). 2.99 (978-0-570-05559-4(8)) Concordia Publishing Hse.

Cynthia. The Night There Was Thunder & Stuff. Date not set. (Illus.). 32p. (J). pap. 4.95 (978-1-895562-67-5(8)) Wood Lake Bks., Inc. CAN. *Dist:* Logos Productions, Inc.

Davidson, Alice Joyce. Mary & the Baby Jesus. 2003. (Illus.). 12p. (J). (ps). bds. 6.99 (978-0-310-70851-3(6)) Zonderkidz.

Davis, Joy M. On a Silent Night. Billin-Frye, Paige, illus. 2000. (Arch Bks.). (ENG.). 16p. (J). (gr. k-4). 1.99 (978-0-570-07568-4(8)) Concordia Publishing Hse.

Daybell, Chad G. Through the Eyes of John. Murray, Rhett E., illus. 2004. 29p. (J). 19.95 (978-1-932898-16-3(6) , 98166) Spring Creek Bk. Co.

Dede, Vivian Hughes. Jesus' First Miracle. Dyrud, Chris Wold, illus. 2005. (ENG.). 16p. (J). 1.99 (978-0-7586-0865-9(9)) Concordia Publishing Hse.

dePaola, Tomie. The Miracles of Jesus. 2008. 32p. (J). (ps). pap. 6.99 (*978-0-14-241068-4(3) , Puffin) Penguin Group (USA) Inc.

Derico, Laura. Jesus, God's Precious Gift. Beylon, Cathy, illus. 2000. (Snow Globe Book Ser.). 10p. (J). (ps up). bds. 9.99 (978-0-7847-1058-6(9) , 03536, Bean Sprouts) Standard Publishing.

Dowley, Tim. Changing Picture Bible Stories: Jesus & His Friends. Martin, Stuart, illus. 2005. 14p. (J). (ps). bds. 11.99 (978-0-8254-7293-0(8)) Kregel Pubns.

Doyle, Christopher. The Story of Jesus. Chapman, Gillian, illus. 2005. (ENG.). 64p. (J). 9.99 (978-0-7586-0986-1(8)) Concordia Publishing Hse.

Dreyer, Nicole E. Peter's Easter Story. Motoyama, Keiko, illus. 2004. (ENG.). 16p. (J). 1.99 (978-0-7586-0477-4(7)) Concordia Publishing Hse.

Dudley-Smith, Timothy, retold by. Stories of Jesus. (Illus.). 160p. (J). (gr. 2-5). pap. 8.95 (978-0-7459-4292-6(X) , Lion) Lion Hudson plc GBR. *Dist:* Trafalgar Square Publishing.

Dyson, Janet. The Last Supper & Other Stories. 2002. (First Bible Stories Ser.). (Illus.). 16p. pap. 4.95 (978-0-7548-0884-8(X) , Lorenz Bks.) Anness Publishing, Inc.

Elliot, Julie. Easter Stories. Kyle, Margaret, illus. 2001. 32p. (J). (ps-5). incl. VHS (978-1-55145-434-4(3)) Wood Lake Bks., Inc.

Erickson, Dorie A. Revelation for Children. 2001. (Illus.). 100p. (gr. 6). per. 29.95 (978-0-937242-08-7(X)) Scandia Pubs.

Ewald, Thomas. New Testament Take-Home Bible Stories: Easy-to-Make, Reproducible Mini-Books That Children Can Make & Keep. 2002. 128p. pap. (978-0-88724-872-6(1)) Carson-Dellosa Publishing Co., Inc.

Fisher, Aileen. The Story of Easter. 1998. (Trophy Picture Bks.). (978-0-606-13043-1(8)) Tandem Library Bks.

Five Small Loaves & Two Small Fish. 2006. 16p. (J). pap. 1.99 (978-0-7847-1713-4(3) , 04174) Standard Publishing.

Fletcher, Sarah. Jesus & the Family Trip. Jones, Doug, illus. 1998. (Arch Bks.). (ENG.). 16p. (J). (gr. k-4). 1.99 (978-0-570-07547-9(5)) Concordia Publishing Hse.

Follow That Star. (Hear Me Read Classroom Sets Ser.). 32.00 (978-0-570-07172-3(0)) Concordia Publishing Hse.

Foster, Charles. Story of the Gospel. 2004. reprint ed. pap. 33.95 (978-1-4191-1372-7(0)) Kessinger Publishing, LLC.

Frank, Penny. The First Christmas. (Illus.). 24p. 2.99 (978-0-7459-4115-8(X) , Lion) Lion Hudson plc GBR. *Dist:* Trafalgar Square Publishing.

—The First Easter. (Illus.). 24p. pap. 2.99 (978-0-7459-4123-3(0) , Lion) Lion Hudson plc GBR. *Dist:* Trafalgar Square Publishing.

—The Story of the Good Samaritan. (Illus.). 24p. 2.99 (978-0-7459-4119-6(2) , Lion) Lion Hudson plc GBR. *Dist:* Trafalgar Square Publishing.

Freed, Shirley & Moon, Louise. Tabitha. Morelan, Bill, ed. Butler, Steven, illus. 2003. 16p. (J). (gr. 2 up). pap. 3.99 (978-1-58938-117-9(3)) Concerned Communications.

Freed, Shirley Ann. Come to Me. Butler, Steven, illus. l.t. ed. 2002. 8p. (J). (gr. 1-6). pap. 3.99 (978-1-58938-001-1(0)) Concerned Communications.

Freed, Shirley Ann & Moon, Louise. Baby Lamb. Morelan, Bill, ed. Butler, Steven, illus. l.t. ed. 2002. 8p. (J). (gr. 5). pap. 3.99 (978-1-58938-010-3(X)) Concerned Communications.

—Fishers of Men. Morelan, Bill, ed. Butler, Steven, illus. l.t. ed. 2002. 16p. (J). (gr. 6). pap. 3.99 (978-1-58938-029-5(0)) Concerned Communications.

—Jesus Helps His Dad. Morelan, Bill, ed. Butler, Steven, illus. l.t. ed. 2002. 16p. (J). (gr. 6). pap. 3.99 (978-1-58938-022-6(3)) Concerned Communications.

—The Lame Man. Morelan, Bill, ed. Butler, Steven, illus. l.t. ed. 2002. 16p. (J). (gr. 2). pap. 3.99 (978-1-58938-044-8(4)) Concerned Communications.

—The Mysterious Star. Morelan, Bill, ed. Butler, Steven, illus. l.t. ed. 2002. 24p. (J). (gr. 3-4). pap. 3.99 (978-1-58938-037-0(1)) Concerned Communications.

—See Baby Jesus. Morelan, Bill, ed. Butler, Steven, illus. l.t. ed. 2002. 8p. (J). (gr. 5). pap. 3.99 (978-1-58938-004-2(5)) Concerned Communications.

—The Ten Lepers. Morelan, Bill, ed. Butler, Steven, illus. l.t. ed. 2002. 24p. (J). (gr. 7). pap. 3.99 (978-1-58938-038-7(X)) Concerned Communications.

French, Fiona. Bethlehem: With Words from the King James Bible. 2001. (Illus.). 32p. (J). (gr. k-3). 15.95 (978-0-06-029623-0(2)) HarperCollins Pubs.

Fryar, Jane L. Jesus Enters Jerusalem. Dorenkamp, Michelle, illus. 2004. (ENG.). 16p. (J). 1.99 (978-0-7586-0641-9(9)) Concordia Publishing Hse.

Gemmen, Heather & McNeil, Mary. Faithful Friends, Level 1. Swisher, Elizabeth, tr. Swisher, Elizabeth, illus. 2004. (Rocket ReaderT2 Ser.). 40p. (J). (gr. 1 up). pap., pap. 8.99 (978-0-7814-4010-3(6) , 0781440106) Cook, David C. Publishing Co.

—Jesus Loves Me: Level 2. Clar, David Austin, tr. Clar, David Austin, illus. 2004. (Rocket ReaderT2 Ser.). 40p. (J). (gr. 2 up). pap., pap. 8.99 (978-0-7814-4013-4(0) , 0781440130) Cook, David C. Publishing Co.

—Something New, Level 3. Johnson, Meredith, ed. Johnson, Meredith, tr. 1999. (Rocket Readers Ser.). 24p. (J). (gr. 3 up). pap., pap. 8.99 (978-0-7814-3986-2(8) , 0781439868) Cook, David C. Publishing Co.

Glen, Jo. Thirty Activity Days, Story of Mary & Joseph: The Story of Mary & Joseph. 1998. (Illus.). 24p. 9.99 (978-1-85608-367-6(5)) Hunt, John Publishing Ltd. GBR. *Dist:* APG Sales and Fulfillment.

Godfrey, Jan. The Camel & the Needle. Saunderson, Chris, illus. 2001. (J). (ps-k). 5.00 (978-0-687-05010-9(3)) Abingdon Pr.

Goodings, Christina. Looking High & Low for One Lost Sheep. Ayliffe, Alex, illus. 2003. 32p. (J). pap. 9.99 (978-0-7459-4524-8(4) , Lion) Lion Hudson plc GBR. *Dist:* Trafalgar Square Publishing.

—Looking High & Low for One Lost Sheep. 2000. (ChrInsight ProductsIm Not Afraid Goodings Ser.). (Illus.). 32p. (J). (gr. k-2). pap. 19.99 (978-0-7459-4504-0(X) , 074594504X, Lion) Lion Hudson plc GBR. *Dist:* Independent Pubs. Group.

Gore, Leonid & Bunting, Eve. Who Was Born This Special Day? 2003. (Illus.). 32p. (J). pap. 6.99 (978-0-689-85955-7(4) , Aladdin) Simon & Schuster Children's Publishing.

Greene, Carol. My Turn Bible Stories about Colors. 1998. (My Turn Bible Stories Ser.). (Illus.). 32p. (J). (ps-1). 6.99 (978-0-570-05061-2(8)) Penguin Group (USA) Inc.

Greene, Rhonda Gowler. The Stable Where Jesus Was Born. Gaber, Susan, illus. 2002. 40p. (J). 6.99 (978-0-689-85350-0(5) , Aladdin) Simon & Schuster Children's Publishing.

Gross, Arthur William. A Child's Garden of Bible Stories: The Classic Edition. 2004. (Illus.). 144p. (J). (gr. k-3). 8.99 (978-0-570-07163-1(1)) Concordia Publishing Hse.

Haines, Geri Berger. The Little Lost Lamb. rev. ed. 2001. (Illus.). 40p. (J). pap. 5.50 (978-0-8198-4489-7(6) , 332-170) Pauline Bks. & Media.

Halperin, Wendy Anderson & King James Bible Staff. Love Is... 2001. (Illus.). 32p. (J). (gr. k-3). pap. 16.00 (978-0-689-82980-2(9)) Simon & Schuster Children's Publishing.

Harrast, Tracy. The Lost & Found Lamb. Moore, Carl, illus. 1998. (Peek-a-Bible Ser.). 18p. (J). 6.99 (978-0-310-97459-8(3)) Zondervan.

Harston, Jerry, tr. & illus. My First New Testament Stories. Harston, Jerry, illus. 2002. (J). 12.95 (978-1-57008-867-4(5)) Scribbulations LLC.

Hartman, Bob. Bob Hartmans Easter Stories. 2008. (Illus.). 96p. (J). pap. 8.95 (*978-0-7459-4793-8(X)) Lion Hudson plc GBR. *Dist:* Independent Pubs. Group.

—Parables to Learn By: Based on Stories Told by Jesus. Julien, Terry, illus. 2001. 160p. (J). pap. 14.95 (978-0-8198-5933-4(8) , 332-280) Pauline Bks. & Media.

—Who Frightened the Fishermen. (Illus.). 48p. pap. 6.99 (978-0-7459-4987-1(8)) Lion Hudson plc GBR. *Dist:* Trafalgar Square Publishing.

Hartman, Sara. Mary Magdalene's Easter Story. Koehler, Ed, illus. 2005. (ENG.). 16p. (J). 1.99 (978-0-7586-0722-5(9)) Concordia Publishing Hse.

Heffernan, Eileen & Jablonski, Patricia E., eds. Jesus Is Good! Five Gospel-Based Stories for Little People. 2001. (J). pap. (978-0-8198-3973-2(6)) Daughters of St. Paul.

Henley, Karyn. Jesus Is Alive! Easter. (Children's Ministry Folders). (Illus.). 8p. (ps-k). 2.99 (978-0-7847-0669-5(7) , 42219) Standard Publishing.

Hickman, Martha Whitmore. A Baby Born in Bethlehem. Ferri, Giuliano, illus. 1999. 32p. (J). (gr. k-4). 15.95 (978-0-8075-5522-4(3)) Whitman, Albert & Co.

Hinkle, Cynthia. Star of Wonder. van der Sterre, Johanna, illus. 2005. (Arch Books). (ENG.). 16p. (J). 1.99 (978-0-7586-0724-9(5)) Concordia Publishing Hse.

Hoffman, Patricia A. In Bethlehem Town, 1. 1999. (Undercover Bible Story Ser.). (Illus.). 24p. (J). (ps-2). 8.99 (978-0-570-05564-8(4)) Cajun Prairie Habitat Preservation Society.

—Miraculous Catch of Fish, 1. 1999. (Undercover Bible Story Ser.). (Illus.). 24p. (J). (ps-2). 8.99 (978-0-570-05565-5(2)) Cajun Prairie Habitat Preservation Society.

Hook, Richard & Hook, Frances, illus. Jesus, the Friend of Children. 6th ed. 2006. 112p. (J). 14.99 (978-0-7814-4390-6(3)) Cook, David C. Publishing Co.

HOP, LLC. Hooked on Bible Stories NT Stories. 2006. 24.99 (978-1-931020-98-5(1)) HOP, LLC.

Hudson, Sue. Miracles of Jesus. Graham, Kennedy, illus. 2005. 20p. pap. 7.99 (978-1-86024-504-6(8)) Authentic Media.

—Parables of Jesus. Graham, Kennedy, illus. 2005. 20p. pap. 7.99 (978-1-86024-505-3(6)) Authentic Media.

Humble-Jackson, Sally. The Miracle Maker: The Greatest Story Ever Told. (Illus.). 48p. (J). pap. (978-0-340-74958-6(X) , Hodder & Stoughton) Hodder General Publishing Division.

Intermediate/Bible Fun New Testament: Coloring Book. 2006. (J). 14.99 (978-1-59317-147-6(1)) Warner Pr. Pubs.

Jackson, Cindy. New Testament Fun Activities - First & Second Grade. 1998. (Illus.). 16p. (J). (gr. 1-2). wbk. ed. 3.95 (978-1-878669-80-3(X) , CRE 3544) Creative Teaching Assocs.

—New Testament Fun Activities - Pre-School & Kindergarten. 1998. (Illus.). 16p. (J). (ps-k). 3.95 (978-1-878669-79-7(6) , CRE 3543) Creative Teaching Assocs.

—New Testament Fun Activities - Third & Fourth Grade. 1998. (Illus.). 16p. (J). (gr. 3-4). wbk. ed. 3.95 (978-1-878669-81-0(8) , CRE 3545) Creative Teaching Assocs.

James, Ben, illus. Los Tres Reyes Magos, the Three Wise Men. 2006. (J). bds. (978-0-9786863-2-1(2)) ITRON Publishing.

James, Steven. JawDroppers: 36 Shocking Stories for Students Based on the Sayings of Jesus. Reeves, Dale, ed. 2001. 160p. (gr. 7 up). 10.99 (978-0-7847-1264-1(6)) Standard Publishing.

James, Steven. 30 New Testament Interactive Stories for Young Children. 2007. (J). per. 15.99 (*978-0-7847-1940-4(3)) Standard Publishing.

Jeffs, Stephanie. Feed a Crowd with Jesus. 2004. (Action Rhyme Bks.). (Illus.). (ps-3). pap. 5.00 (978-0-687-04821-2(4)) Abingdon Pr.

—Follow the Star with the Wise Men. 2001. (Action Rhyme Bks.). (Illus.). (J). (ps-3). 5.00 (978-0-687-04811-3(7)) Abingdon Pr.

Jesus & the Man in a Tree. 2001. (Favorite Stories about Jesus Bks.). (Illus.). 12p. (J). 0.99 (978-0-8254-7240-4(7)) Kregel Pubns.

Jesus Heals a Blind Man. 2001. (Favorite Stories about Jesus Bks.). (Illus.). 12p. (J). 0.99 (978-0-8254-7239-8(3)) Kregel Pubns.

Jesus Is Baptized. 2001. (Favorite Stories about Jesus Bks.). (Illus.). 12p. (J). 0.99 (978-0-8254-7241-1(5)) Kregel Pubns.

Jesus Lava los Pies a Sus Discipulos. 2001. (Libros Arco Ser.). (SPA.). 24p. (J). (gr. k-4). 2.49 (978-0-570-05181-7(9)) Concordia Publishing Hse.

Jesus Stops a Storm. 2001. (Favorite Stories about Jesus Bks.). (Illus.). 12p. (J). 0.99 (978-0-8254-7231-2(8)) Kregel Pubns.

Johnson, Cathy Ann, illus. The Christmas Story. 2005. 24p. (J). (ps-k). bds. 6.99 (978-1-4003-0633-6(7)) Nelson, Thomas Inc.

Konzen, Lisa. The Great Catch of Fish: Luke 5:1-11 for Children. Rooney, Ronnie, illus. 2006. (Arch Books). (ENG.). (J). 1.99 (978-0-7586-0871-0(3)) Concordia Publishing Hse.

Kunkel, Jeff. Jesus, This Is Your Life: Stories & Pictures by Kids. 2001. (Illus.). 48p. (gr. k-7). 12.99 (978-0-8066-4165-2(7) , Augsburg Bks.) Augsburg Fortress, Pubs.

Lane, Leena. Stories of Jesus. Bishop, Roma, illus. 2003. 32p. 8.00 (978-0-687-06537-0(2)) Abingdon Pr.

Larcombe & Rees. Surprise for Peter. 2000. (Illus.). 24p. pap. 6.99 (978-0-551-03246-0(4)) Zondervan.

Larrison, Joanne. The Week That Led to Easter. Williams, Jenny, illus. 2004. (Arch Bks.). (ENG.). 16p. (J). (gr. k-4). 1.99 (978-0-570-07572-1(6)) Concordia Publishing Hse.

Lashbrook, Marilyn. Sowing & Growing: The Parable of the Sower & the Soils. 1998. (Me Too! Bks.). (J). (ps-2). 5.95 (978-0-933657-74-8(9) , 3000893) Standard Publishing.

Le Joly, Edward & Chaliha, Jaya. Stories Told by Mother Teresa. Drummond, Allan, illus. 2000. 32p. (J). (ps up). 15.95 (978-1-902618-65-4(3)) Element Children's Bks.

Lindecker, Leslie. The First Christmas. Calvert-Weyant, Lynda, tr. Calvert-Weyant, Lynda, illus. 2002. (My First Treasury Ser.). 40p. (J). (978-0-7853-6878-6(7) , 7167800) Publications International, Ltd.

Lingo, Susan L. A to Z Object Talks That Teach about the New Testament: 26 Memorable Messages Your Kids Will Love. Stoker, Bruce, ed. Lynch, Jason, illus. 2006. 48p. (YA). (gr. 1-7). pap. 6.99 (978-0-7847-1237-5(9) , 02854) Standard Publishing.

The Little Lost Sheep. 2006. 16p. (J). pap. 1.99 (978-0-7847-1718-9(4) , 04179) Standard Publishing.

Littleton, Mark. Stories Jesus Told: Lift-the-Flap. Moroney, Trace, illus. 2004. 20p. (J). bds. 10.99 (978-0-8254-5519-3(7)) Kregel Pubns.

Lloyd-Jones, Sally. My Thankful Heart. 2004. (Sweet Hearts Ser.). (Illus.). 12p. (J). bds. 8.99 (978-1-4143-0064-1(6)) Tyndale Hse. Pubs.

Lois, Rock. Jesus & His Friends. Alex, Ayliffe, illus. 2007. 16p. pap. 5.99 (***978-1-56148-560-4(8)***) Good Bks.

—Jonah & Whale. Alex, Ayliffe, illus. 2007. 0016p. pap. 5.99 (***978-1-56148-558-1(6)***) Good Bks.

Lottridge, Celia B. Stories from the Life of Jesus. Wolfsgruber, Linda, tr. Wolfsgruber, Linda, illus. 2004. 128p. (J). 24.95 (978-0-88899-497-4(4)) Groundwood Bks. CAN. *Dist:* Perseus Distribution.

Lottridge, Celia B. Stories from the Life of Jesus. Wolfsgruber, Linda, illus. 2007. 168p. (J). 10.00 (***978-0-88899-840-8(6)***) Groundwood Bks. CAN. *Dist:* Perseus Distribution.

Maier, Paul L. The Very First Christmas. 32p. (J). 9.99 (978-0-570-07186-0(0)) Concordia Publishing Hse.

—The Very First Christmas. Ordaz, Francisco, illus. 2004. 20p. (J). (ps-k). bds. 6.99 (978-0-7586-0689-1(3)) Concordia Publishing Hse.

—The Very First Christmas. 1998. (Illus.). 32p. (J). (gr. k-5). 12.99 (978-0-570-05064-3(2)) Concordia Publishing Hse.

Mayfield, Al A. The Word for Children: An Illustrated Beginner's Bible about Jesus Christ, the Son of God. 1998. (Illus.). 16p. (J). (gr. k-3). pap. 7.00 (978-0-8059-4390-0(0)) Dorrance Publishing Co., Inc.

McCarthy, Zoe. Pearls in the Muddle: Twelve Christian Stories. Lahti, Greg, illus. 1998. 128p. pap. 9.95 (978-0-9662499-0-3(9)) Holy Ghost Writers Publishing.

Miller, Claire. Shipwrecked Paul: The Story of Paul's Journey to Rome: Acts 27:1-44 for Children. Gleiwe, Unada, tr. Gleiwe, Unada, illus. 2002. (ENG.). 16p. (J). 1.99 (978-0-570-07580-6(7)) Concordia Publishing Hse.

Mitchell, Kathy. Bible Stories from the New Testament. 2001. (gr. k-3). lib. bdg. 10.95 (978-0-613-32324-6(6)) Tandem Library Bks.

Mitchell, Kathy, illus. Bible Stories from the New Testament. 1999. (Easter Mini Storybooks Ser.: Vol. 4). 32p. (J). (gr. k-3). 3.25 (978-0-7666-0250-2(8) , Honey Bear Bks.) Modern Publishing.

Moseley, Stuart. The First Christmas. Smith, Sarah, illus. 1999. (J). 14.99 (978-0-8054-2034-0(7)) B&H Publishing Grp.

Nederveld, Patricia L. An Amazing Star! The Story of the Wise Men. 1998. (God Loves Me Ser.). (Illus.). 24p. (J). (ps-3). pap. 2.95 (978-1-56212-295-9(9) , 001226, Faith Alive Christian Resources) CRC Pubns.

—The Best Day Ever! The Story of Easter. 1998. (God Loves Me Ser.). (Illus.). 24p. (J). (ps-3). pap. 2.95 (978-1-56212-313-0(0) , 001244, Faith Alive Christian Resources) CRC Pubns.

—A Better Thing to Do: The Story of Jesus & Two Sisters. 1998. (God Loves Me Ser.). (Illus.). 24p. (J). (ps-3). pap. 2.95 (978-1-56212-307-9(6) , 001238, Faith Alive Christian Resources) CRC Pubns.

—Come to Me! The Story of Jesus & the Children. 1998. (God Loves Me Ser.). (Illus.). 24p. (J). (ps-3). pap. 2.95 (978-1-56212-309-3(2) , 001240, Faith Alive Christian Resources) CRC Pubns.

—A Father's Wish: The Story of Jesus & a Little Boy. 1998. (God Loves Me Ser.). (Illus.). 24p. (J). (ps-3). pap. 2.95 (978-1-56212-300-0(9) , 001231, Faith Alive Christian Resources) CRC Pubns.

—Follow Me! The Story of Twelve Helpers for Jesus. 1998. (God Loves Me Ser.). (Illus.). 24p. (J). (ps-3). pap. 2.95 (978-1-56212-298-0(3) , 001229, Faith Alive Christian Resources) CRC Pubns.

—Get up & Walk! The Story of Jesus & a Man Who Couldn't Walk. 1998. (God Loves Me Ser.). (Illus.). 24p. (J). (ps-3). pap. 2.95 (978-1-56212-302-4(5) , 001233, Faith Alive Christian Resources) CRC Pubns.

—Good News! The Story of the Shepherds. 1998. (God Loves Me Ser.). (Illus.). 24p. (J). (ps-3). pap. 2.95 (978-1-56212-294-2(0) , 001225, Faith Alive Christian Resources) CRC Pubns.

—Goodbye for Now! The Story of Jesus' Return to Heaven. 1998. (God Loves Me Ser.). (Illus.). 24p. (J). (ps-3). pap. 2.95 (978-1-56212-314-7(9) , 001245, Faith Alive Christian Resources) CRC Pubns.

—The Greatest Gift: The Story of Jesus & the Woman at the Well. 1998. (God Loves Me Ser.). (Illus.). 24p. (J). (ps-3). pap. 2.95 (978-1-56212-299-7(1) , 001230, Faith Alive Christian Resources) CRC Pubns.

—Have a Great Day! The Story of Jesus & Zacchaeus. 1998. (God Loves Me Ser.). (Illus.). 24p. (J). (ps-3). pap. 2.95 (978-1-56212-310-9(6) , 001241, Faith Alive Christian Resources) CRC Pubns.

—Hosannah! The Story of Palm Sunday. 1998. (God Loves Me Ser.). (Illus.). 24p. (J). (ps-3). pap. 2.95 (978-1-56212-312-3(2) , 001243, Faith Alive Christian Resources) CRC Pubns.

—I Love You, Jesus! The Story of Mary's Gift to Jesus. 1998. (God Loves Me Ser.). (Illus.). 24p. (J). (ps-3). pap. 2.95 (978-1-56212-311-6(4) , 001242, Faith Alive Christian Resources) CRC Pubns.

—Just Believe! The Story of Jesus & a Little Girl. 1998. (God Loves Me Ser.). (Illus.). 24p. (J). (ps-3). pap. 2.95 (978-1-56212-301-7(7) , 001232, Faith Alive Christian Resources) CRC Pubns.

—A Little Lunch: The Story of Jesus & the Hungry Crowd. 1998. (God Loves Me Ser.). (Illus.). 24p. (J). (ps-3). pap. 2.95 (978-1-56212-303-1(3) , 001234, Faith Alive Christian Resources) CRC Pubns.

—A Lost Lamb: The Story of the Good Shepherd. 1998. (God Loves Me Ser.). (Illus.). 24p. (J). (ps-3). pap. 2.95 (978-1-56212-308-6(4) , 001239, Faith Alive Christian Resources) CRC Pubns.

—A New Friend: The Story of Paul's Conversion. Stoub, Paul, illus. 1998. (God Loves Me Ser.). 24p. (J). (ps-3). pap. 2.95 (978-1-56212-317-8(3) , 001248, Faith Alive Christian Resources) CRC Pubns.

—Over the Wall: The Story of Paul's Escape in a Basket. 1998. (God Loves Me Ser.). (Illus.). 24p. (J). (ps-4). pap. 2.95 (978-1-56212-318-5(1) , 001249, Faith Alive Christian Resources) CRC Pubns.

—A Prayer for Peter: The Story of Peter in Prison. 1998. (God Loves Me Ser.). (Illus.). 24p. (J). (ps-3). pap. 2.95 (978-1-56212-315-4(7) , 001246, Faith Alive Christian Resources) CRC Pubns.

—A Ride in the Night: The Story of Paul's Escape on Horseback. 1998. (God Loves Me Ser.). (Illus.). 24p. (J). (ps-4). pap. 2.95 (978-1-56212-320-8(3) , 001242, Faith Alive Christian Resources) CRC Pubns.

—Sad Day, Happy Day! The Story of Peter & Dorcas. 1998. (God Loves Me Ser.). (Illus.). 24p. (J). (ps-3). pap. 2.95 (978-1-56212-316-1(5) , 001247, Faith Alive Christian Resources) CRC Pubns.

—A Scary Storm: The Story of Jesus & a Storm. 1998. (God Loves Me Ser.). (Illus.). 24p. (J). (ps-3). pap. 2.95 (978-1-56212-304-8(1) , 001235, Faith Alive Christian Resources) CRC Pubns.

—The Shipwreck: The Story of Paul's Rescue at Sea. 1998. (God Loves Me Ser.). (Illus.). 24p. (J). (ps-4). pap. 2.95 (978-1-56212-321-5(1) , 001252, Faith Alive Christian Resources) CRC Pubns.

—A Song in the Night: The Story of Paul & Silas in Prison. 1998. (God Loves Me Ser.). (Illus.). 24p. (J). (ps-4). pap. 2.95 (978-1-56212-319-2(X) , 001250, Faith Alive Christian Resources) CRC Pubns.

—Thank You, Jesus! The Story of Jesus & One Thankful Man. 1998. (God Loves Me Ser.). (Illus.). 24p. (J). (ps-3). pap. 2.95 (978-1-56212-305-5(X) , 001236, Faith Alive Christian Resources) CRC Pubns.

—Waiting, Waiting, Waiting! The Story of Simeon & Anna. 1998. (God Loves Me Ser.). (Illus.). 24p. (J). (ps-3). pap. 2.95 (978-1-56212-296-7(6) , 001227, Faith Alive Christian Resources) CRC Pubns.

—Who Is This Child? The Story of Jesus in the Temple. 1998. (God Loves Me Ser.). (Illus.). 24p. (J). (ps-3). pap. 2.95 (978-1-56212-297-3(5) , 001228, Faith Alive Christian Resources) CRC Pubns.

—A Wonderful Sight! The Story of Jesus & a Man Who Couldn't See. 1998. (God Loves Me Ser.). (Illus.). 24p. (J). (ps-3). pap. 2.95 (978-1-56212-306-2(8) , 001237, Faith Alive Christian Resources) CRC Pubns.

Neff, LaVonne. The Jesus Book: 40 Bible Stories. Goffe, Toni, illus. 2004. (Life of Christ for Children Ser.). 84p. (ps-k). 9.95 (978-0-8294-1373-1(1)) Loyola Pr.

New Testament Hidden Pictures. 1998. (Illus.). 48p. (J). (gr. 1-3). pap. 5.95 (978-0-7647-0436-9(2) , SS4871, In Celebration) Schaffer, Frank Pubns.

Newberger, Anne C. Jesus' Journey. 2002. (J). (ps-2). 19.95 (978-0-9707756-8-9(7)) Our Sunday Visitor, Publishing Div.

Niemann, Sibyl. The Centurion & the Songbird: Stories about the Gospels. 2003. (J). 32p. 5.00 (978-0-88489-629-6(3)) ; 128p. per. 6.95 (978-0-88489-628-9(5)) St. Mary's Pr.

Northwestern Publishing House Staff. Back to Jerusalem Sample Kit. 2002. (Vacation Bible Study Ser.). (978-0-8100-1393-3(2)) Northwestern Publishing Hse.

—Back to Jerusalem Student Lesson Level 1. 2002. (Vacation Bible Study Ser.). pap. (978-0-8100-1374-2(6)) Northwestern Publishing Hse.

—Back to Jerusalem Student Lesson Level 2. 2002. (Vacation Bible Study Ser.). pap. (978-0-8100-1375-9(4)) Northwestern Publishing Hse.

—Back to Jerusalem Student Lesson Level 3. 2002. (Vacation Bible Study Ser.). pap. (978-0-8100-1376-6(2)) Northwestern Publishing Hse.

—Back to Jerusalem Student Lesson Level 5. 2002. (Vacation Bible Study Ser.). pap. (978-0-8100-1378-0(9)) Northwestern Publishing Hse.

O'Connor, Francine M. A Journey with Jesus: Stories from the Bible. Larkin, Jean, ed. Lynch, Patricia, illus. 2000. (Active Learning for Catholic Kids Ser.). 28p. (J). (gr. 1-3). pap. 7.95 (978-0-937997-84-0(6)) Pflaum Publishing Group.

Parker, Victoria. The Nativity. 2004. (Bible Discoverers Ser.). (Illus.). 64p. pap. 7.99 (978-1-84215-925-5(9) , Southwater) Anness Publishing GBR. *Dist:* National Bk. Network.

—The Resurrection of Jesus: And Other New Testament Stories. 2000. (Discovering the Bible Ser.). (Illus.). 64p. (gr. 3-7). 15.00 (978-0-7548-0534-2(4) , Lorenz Bks.) Anness Publishing GBR. *Dist:* National Bk. Network.

—The Road to Damascus: And Other New Testament Stories. 2000. (Discovering the Bible Ser.). (Illus.). 64p. (gr. 3-7). 15.00 (978-0-7548-0533-5(6) , Lorenz Bks.) Anness Publishing GBR. *Dist:* National Bk. Network.

Pingry, Patricia. Treasury of New Testament Heroes. 2005. (Illus.). 192p. (J). 8.97 (978-0-8249-5494-9(7)) Ideals Pubns.

Pingry, Patricia A. The Story of Loaves & Fishes. Venturi-Pickett, Stacy, illus. 2003. 26p. (J). bds. 6.95 (978-0-8249-6518-1(3)) Ideals Pubns.

—The Story of the Good Samaritan. Venturi-Pickett, Stacy, illus. 2001. 26p. (J). (ps-3). bds. 6.95 (978-0-8249-4109-3(8)) Ideals Pubns.

—The Story of Zacchaeus. Britt, Stephanie M., illus. 2001. 26p. (J). bds. 6.95 (978-0-8249-4130-7(6)) Ideals Pubns.

Pingry, Patricia A. & Venturi-Pickett, Stacy. The Story of Mary. 2000. (Illus.). 26p. (J). (ps-3). bds. 6.95 (978-0-8249-4183-3(7) , Ideals Children's Bks.) Ideals Pubns.

Pinkney, Debbie, illus. The First Christmas. 2004. (J). (***978-0-7853-1894-1(1)***) Publications International, Ltd.

Poole, Susie, illus. New Testament Tales: From the Lion Storyteller Bible. 2000. 32p. (J). pap. 6.99 (978-0-7459-4405-0(1) , Lion) Lion Hudson plc GBR. *Dist:* Independent Pubs. Group.

Puppet Prod. Puppet Production Vol. 1 & 2: New Testament Programs 1 & 2. Life Publishers International Staff, tr. from ENG. 2000. Orig. Title: The Children's Programming Collection. (RUS.). 79p. (J). (978-0-7361-0199-8(3)) Life Pubs. International.

Rabbit. Parables That Jesus Told. (J). pap. 19.95 (978-0-689-80229-4(3) , Simon & Schuster Children's Publishing) Simon & Schuster Children's Publishing.

Reeves, Eira & Sanders, Nancy I. Martha & Mary: With Envelope Surprises. 2001. (Kingdom Kidz Bible Ser.). (Illus.). 12p. (J). (ps-3). 5.99 (978-1-58660-308-3(6)) Barbour Publishing, Inc.

Robb, Andy. Jesus Makes a Difference. 2001. (Illus.). 10p. (J). (ps-3). 5.99 (978-0-570-07145-7(3)) Concordia Publishing Hse.

—Lost Sheep, 1. 1999. (Illus.). 12p. (J). (ps-1). 6.00 (978-0-570-05586-0(5)) Concordia Publishing Hse.

Rock, Lois. The Easter Story. Mayo, Diana, illus. 2002. 32p. (J). (gr. 1-6). pap. 5.95 (978-0-7459-4741-9(7) , Lion Children's) Lion Hudson plc GBR. *Dist:* Independent Pubs. Group.

Rottmann, Erik. The Easter Victory: The Story of Easter: Matthew 26-28 for Children. Billin-Frye, Paige, illus. 2006. (ENG.). (J). 1.99 (978-0-7586-0869-7(1)) Concordia Publishing Hse.

—Jesus, My Good Shepherd. Miyake, Yoski, illus. 2005. (ENG.). 16p. (J). 1.99 (978-0-7586-0725-6(3)) Concordia Publishing Hse.

—Timothy Joins Paul. Snyder, Joel, illus. 2005. (ENG.). 16p. (J). 1.99 (978-0-7586-0506-1(4)) Concordia Publishing Hse.

Round, Graham. Stories Jesus Told. 2001. (Bible Story Sticker Book Ser.). (Illus.). 16p. (J). (ps-5). pap. 4.99 (978-0-8254-7244-2(X)) Kregel Pubns.

Sanders, Nancy I. Zacchaeus: Zacchaeus, Luke 19:1-9 (With Envelope Surprises!) Reeves, Eira, illus. 2001. (Kingdom Kidz Bible Ser.). 12p. (J). (ps-3). 5.99 (978-1-58660-304-5(3)) Barbour Publishing, Inc.

Schkade, Jonathan. Get up, Lazarus! Dorenkamp, Michelle, illus. 2004. (ENG.). 16p. (J). 1.99 (978-0-7586-0480-4(7)) Concordia Publishing Hse.

School Specialty Publishing Staff & Mears, Henrietta C. All about the New Testament. 2001. (All about Coloring Book Ser.). 32p. (J). (gr. k-3). pap. 3.99 (978-0-7647-0581-6(4) , In Celebration) Schaffer, Frank Pubns.

Simon, Mary Manz. Plip, Plop: Drip Drop - The Flood. 2000. (Hear Me Read Bible Stories Ser.). (SPA., Illus.). 32p. (J). (ps-1). 2.75 (978-0-570-09910-9(7) , 16-2002) Concordia Publishing Hse.

—What Did Jesus Do? Kennedy, Anne, illus. 1998. (What Did Jesus Do? Ser.: Vol. 1). 40p. (J). (ps-3). 7.99 (978-0-8499-5856-4(3)) Nelson, Thomas Inc.

Simon, Mary Manz & Preston, Jeff. Hidden Treasures: Amazing Stories from the New Testament. 2000. (Illus.). 40p. (J). (ps-3). 9.99 (978-0-8054-2329-7(X)) B&H Publishing Grp.

Skevington, Andrea. The Story of Jesus. 2008. (Illus.). 128p. (J). 16.95 (***978-0-7459-4982-6(7)***) Lion Hudson plc GBR. *Dist:* Independent Pubs. Group.

Smith, Cyncie. The Joyful Shepherd. 2004. (Illus.). 32p. (J). 9.99 (978-1-56309-484-2(3)) New Hope Pubs.

Southwater Staff. Children's Illustrated Bible Stories from the New Testament. 2001. (Illus.). 256p. pap. 19.95 (978-1-84215-524-0(5) , Southwater) Anness Publishing GBR. *Dist:* National Bk. Network.

Standard Publishing Staff. Jesus & His Friends. Caldwell, Lise, ed. McCallum, Jodie, illus. 1998. (Happy Day Bks.). 24p. (J). (ps-2). 2.49 (978-0-7847-0830-9(4) , 04260, Bean Sprouts) Standard Publishing.

Stiegemeyer, Julie. Bethlehem Night. Capaldi, Gina, illus. 2005. 32p. (J). (ps-ps). 12.99 (978-0-7586-0907-6(8)) Concordia Publishing Hse.

Stowell, Charlotte, illus. Favorite Stories about Jesus. 2001. 24p. (J). (gr. k up). pap. 2.99 (978-0-8254-7205-3(9)) Kregel Pubns.

Tangvald, Christine H. Just Look in the Stable. Williams, Jerry, illus. 1999. (Arch Bks.). (ENG.). 16p. (J). (gr. k-4). 1.99 (978-0-570-07559-2(9)) Concordia Publishing Hse.

Taylor, Damon. Bible Feelings: The New Testament. 2002. (Child Sockology Ser.). 24p. (J). 6.99 (978-0-8254-3854-7(3)) Kregel Pubns.

—Francis Takes a Tumble: The Story of the Good Samaritan. 2003. (Child Sockology Ser.). (Illus.). 32p. (J). 10.99 (978-0-8254-3867-7(5)) Kregel Pubns.

Taylor, Damon J. Lunchtime Life Change: The Story of Zacchaeus. 2003. (Child Sockology Ser.). (Illus.). 36p. (J). 10.99 (978-0-8254-3862-2(4)) Kregel Pubns.

A Walk on the Waves. 2007. (Illus.). (J). bds. 5.95 (***978-0-8198-8315-5(8)***) Pauline Bks. & Media.

Warner Press Staff. New Testament. 1999. (Illus.). (J). pap. 3.95 (978-0-87162-862-6(7)) Warner Pr. Pubs.

Weckbaugh, Ernest. The Bible's ABCs (Matthew - Revelation & Fun Book) Series of 7 Summaries Plus Bible Story/Puzzles, 8 bks. Weckbaugh, Patricia G., ed. 1999. (Illus.). 296p. (J). pap. 26.99 (978-1-881474-28-9(3)) Casa Graphics, Inc.

Widmer, Becky. Bible Awareness Series, 6 vols. Christian, Heather, illus. Date not set. (J). (ps up). 9.95 (978-1-888537-00-0(0)) Publisher Plus.

Wilber, Peggy M. Why Did Jesus Do That?, Level 4. Foote, Dan, tr. Foote, Dan, illus. 1999. (Rocket Readers Ser.). 32p. (J). (gr. 4 up). pap., pap. 4.99 (978-0-7814-3994-7(9) , 0781439949) Cook, David C. Publishing Co.

Wilber, Peggy M., et al. God Can Help!, Level 3. Graham, Alastair, tr. Graham, Alastair, illus. 1999. (Rocket Readers Ser.). 48p. (J). (gr. 3 up). pap., pap. 8.99 (978-0-7814-3998-5(1) , 0781439981) Cook, David C. Publishing Co.

—Great Acts of God!, Level 3. Mahan, Ben, tr. Mahan, Ben, illus. 1999. (Rocket Readers Ser.). 48p. (gr. 3 up). pap. 8.99 (978-0-7814-3999-2(X) , 078143999X) Cook, David C. Publishing Co.

Wildsmith, Brian. The Easter Story. Wildsmith, Brian, illus. 2004. (Illus.). 24p. (ps-7). 18.00 (978-0-8028-5189-5(4)) Eerdmans, William B. Publishing Co.

Wilson, Etta. A Child's Story of Easter. Utt, Mary Ann, illus. 2001. 32p. (J). 7.95 (978-0-8249-5365-2(7)) Ideals Pubns.

Wood-Bryce, Ellen, ed. Once upon a Holy Night. 2004. (gr. 2-5). 12.00 incl. audio (978-0-687-09870-5(X)) Abingdon Pr.

Wooding, Marnie. The Guy Who Lost His Beach House: One-Minute Bible Parables for Kids. Kielesinski, Chris, illus. 2000. 432p. (J). 12.99 (978-0-8054-9398-6(0)) B&H Publishing Grp.

Word Search: New Testament. (Illus.). 32p. (YA). (gr. 5 up). pap. 2.25 (978-0-87162-497-0(4) , E4801) Warner Pr. Pubs.

Zacchaeus: Physically Small but Spiritually Tall! (Illus.). 16p. (J). pap. 1.50 (978-0-87162-871-8(6) , E6038) Warner Pr. Pubs.

Zobel-Nolan, Allia. Baby Jesus Is Born. MacLean, Moira, illus. 2000. (Baby's First Bible Stories Ser.). 10p. (ps). 9.99 (978-0-7847-1211-5(5) , 04399, Bean Sprouts) Standard Publishing.

—Mary & Martha's House. 2000. (My Bible Village Ser.). (Illus.). 12p. (J). 5.99 (978-0-310-98254-8(5)) Zonderkidz.

—Zacchaeus' House. 2000. (My Bible Village Ser.). (Illus.). 12p. (J). 5.99 (978-0-310-98253-1(7)) Zonderkidz.

BIBLE STORIES—O.T.

Abbey, Rita Deanin. Isaiah Stained-Glass Windows. Sanders, Laura, ed. Preston, Gregory, photos by. 2002. (ENG & HEB., Illus.). 40p. (J). pap. (978-0-9652870-1-2(7)) Gan Or.

Abingdon. Samuel, Paul & David, Unit 5. 1998. (Children's Teaching Pictures Ser.). (Illus.). 22p. (J). 16.00 (978-0-687-09537-7(9)) Abingdon Pr.

Abraham. (Divertidas Historias Biblicas para Ninos Ser.). (SPA.). (J). 3.49 (978-0-7899-0600-7(7) , 496647) Editorial Unilit.

Adam & Eve. 2002. (Illus.). (J). (gr. k-4). 24p. 5.99 (978-1-57759-515-1(7)); 14p. bds. 5.97 (978-1-57759-452-9(5)) Dalmatian Pr.

Adam & Eve. (Bible Friends plus Book Ser.). (Illus.). 10p. (J). (ps-k). 6.99 (978-0-8254-7236-7(9)) Kregel Pubns.

Adam & Eve, 6 vols., Set. 1999. (Illus.). (J). pap. 1.50 (978-0-87162-843-5(0)) Warner Pr. Pubs.

Adams, Georgie. Noah's Ark. Leplar, Anna C., illus. 1999. 24p. (J). (ps-2). 12.99 (978-0-8054-2037-1(1)) B&H Publishing Grp.

Amazing Bible Trips - Old Testament. 2005. 48p. (J). (gr. 1-4). pap. 7.99 (978-0-7647-0600-4(4)) School Specialty Publishing.

Amery, H. Daniel & the Lions. rev. ed. 2004. (Bible Tales Readers Ser.). (Illus.). 16p. (J). pap. 4.95 (978-0-7945-0626-1(7)) EDC Publishing.

—Jonah & the Whale. 2004. (Bible Tales Readers Ser.). 16p. (J). lib. bdg. 12.95 (978-1-58086-632-3(8) , Usborne); (Illus.). pap. 4.95 (978-0-7945-0414-4(0)) EDC Publishing.

—Joseph & the Amazing Coat. 2004. (Bible Tales Readers Ser.). (SPA., Illus.). 16p. (J). pap. 4.95 (978-0-7945-0417-5(5)) EDC Publishing.

—Moses in the Bulrushes. 2004. (Bible Tales Readers Ser.). (SPA., Illus.). 16p. (J). pap. 4.95 (978-0-7945-0415-1(9)) EDC Publishing.

—Noah's Ark. rev. ed. 2004. (Bible Tales Readers Ser.). (Illus.). 16p. (J). lib. bdg. 12.95 (978-1-58086-542-5(9)) EDC Publishing.

Amery, Heather. The Old Testament: A Collection of Bible Stories. 2004. (Children's Bible Ser.). (Illus.). 72p. (J). (ps-3). 15.95 (978-0-7460-3457-6(1)) EDC Publishing.

Ammerman, Mark. Jonah & the Big Fish. 2000. (Little Bible Bks.). (Illus.). 24p. (J). (ps-3). 1.99 (978-1-57748-684-8(6)) Barbour Publishing, Inc.

Ammerman, Mark & Wheeler, Ron. Daniel & the Lion's Den. 1999. (Little Bible Bks.). (Illus.). 24p. (J). 1.99 (978-1-57748-660-2(9)) Barbour Publishing, Inc.

Arch Books Staff. Bright Light, Saul's Sight. 1998. (Arch Bks.). (Illus.). 16p. (J). (gr. k-4). 1.99 (978-0-570-07552-3(1) , 59-1525GJ) Concordia Publishing Hse.

A B

Arthur, Kay & Arndt, Janna. Abraham - God's Brave Explorer: Genesis 11-25. 2003. (Discover 4 Yourself Inductive Bible Studies for Kids Ser.). 208p. pap., wbk. ed. 10.99 (978-0-7369-0936-5(2) , 6909362) Harvest Hse. Pubs.

Audia, John P. The Creation Story: In Words & Sign Language. Spohn, David, illus. 2007. (J). (***978-0-8146-3174-4(6)**) Liturgical Pr.

Auld, Mary. Daniel in the Lions' Den. 2000. (Bible Stories Ser.). (Illus.). 32p. (J). (gr. 2-4). pap. 7.95 (978-0-531-15385-7(1) , Watts, Franklin) Scholastic Library Publishing.

—Daniel in the Lion's Den. 1999. (gr. 3-6). lib. bdg. 16.40 (978-0-613-36294-8(2)) Tandem Library Bks.

—David & Goliath. Mayo, Diana, illus. 2000. (Bible Stories Ser.). 32p. (J). (gr. 2-4). pap. 7.95 (978-0-531-15393-2(2) , Watts, Franklin) Scholastic Library Publishing.

—Exodus from Egypt. 2000. (Bible Stories Ser.). (Illus.). 32p. (J). pap. 7.95 (978-0-531-15437-3(8) , Watts, Franklin) Scholastic Library Publishing.

—Exodus from Egypt. Mayo, Diana, illus. 2000. 31p. (J). (ps-3). lib. bdg. 16.40 (978-0-613-62460-2(2)) Tandem Library Bks.

—Jacob & Esau. Mayo, Diana, illus. 2000. (Bible Stories Ser.). 32p. (J). (gr. 2-4). pap. 7.95 (978-0-531-15436-6(X) , Watts, Franklin) Scholastic Library Publishing.

—Jacob & Esau. 2000. (gr. 3-6). lib. bdg. 16.40 (978-0-613-62466-4(1)) Tandem Library Bks.

—Noah's Ark. Mayo, Diana, illus. 2000. (Bible Stories Ser.). 32p. (gr. 2-4). pap. 7.95 (978-0-531-15394-9(0) , Watts, Franklin) Scholastic Library Publishing.

—Story of Jonah. 1999. (gr. 3-6). lib. bdg. 16.40 (978-0-613-62489-3(0)) Tandem Library Bks.

Auld, Mary & Mayo, Diana. Moses in the Bulrushes. 2000. (Bible Stories Ser.). (Illus.). 32p. (J). (gr. 2-4). pap. 7.95 (978-0-531-15387-1(8) , Watts, Franklin) Scholastic Library Publishing.

Baez, Kjersti H. Ruth. 1998. (Young Reader's Christian Library). (Illus.). 224p. (J). (gr. 7 up). per. 1.39 (978-1-55748-173-3(3)) Barbour Publishing, Inc.

Balsley, Tilda. Let My People Go. Kahn, Katherine, illus. 2008. (J). pap. (***978-0-8225-7241-1(9)**) Kar-Ben Publishing.

Banks, Lynne Reid. Moses in Egypt: A Novel Inspired by The Prince of Egypt & The Book of Exodus. 1998. (Prince of Egypt Ser.). (Illus.). 128p. (J). (gr. 5-9). pap. 4.99 (978-0-8499-5898-4(9)) Nelson, Thomas Inc.

Bear. Stories from the Old Testament, Vol 1. 1998. (J). 16.00 (978-0-671-88661-5(4) , Simon & Schuster Children's Publishing) Simon & Schuster Children's Publishing.

The Beginners Bible Favorite Carry-Along Stories: Noah & the Ark; David & Goliath; Daniel & the Lions' Den; Jonah & the Big Fish, 4 bks. 1998. (J). (ps). 9.99 (978-0-310-97421-5(6)) Zondervan.

Behnken, Patricia A. Bayless. A Story of David Set, 3 vols., Set. 2002. (Story of David Ser.). (J). (gr. 1-8). 15.95 (978-0-9637811-6-1(2)) Morning Joy Publishing.

Belec, Glynis. Jailhouse Rock. Koehler, Ed, illus. 2000. (Arch Bks.). (ENG.). 16p. (J). (gr. k-4). 1.99 (978-0-570-07563-9(7)) Concordia Publishing Hse.

Beneduce, Ann. Moses: The Long Road to Freedom. Spirin, Gennady, illus. 2004. 32p. (J). pap. 16.95 (978-0-439-35225-3(8)) Scholastic, Inc.

Bergt, Carolyn. A Child's Garden of Bible Stories Workbooks: Old Testament Workbook. 80p. (gr. 1-3). wbk. ed. 9.95 (978-0-7586-0473-6(4)) Concordia Publishing Hse.

Blyton, Enid. El Bebe Entre los Juncos. 1999. (Historias Biblicas Ilustradas; Illustrated Bible Stories Ser.). (SPA., Illus.). 32p. (ps-3). pap. 4.99 (978-0-8254-1063-5(0) , Editorial Portavoz) Kregel Pubns.

—El Bebe Entre los Juncos. 1999. (SPA.). (gr. k-3). lib. bdg. 13.00 (978-0-613-76710-1(1)) Tandem Library Bks.

—David, el Nino Pastor. 2nd ed. 1999. (Historias Biblicas Ilustradas; Illustrated Bible Stories Ser.). (SPA., Illus.). 32p. (ps-3). pap. 4.99 (978-0-8254-1064-2(9) , Editorial Portavoz) Kregel Pubns.

—David, el Nino Pastor. 1999. (SPA.). (gr. k-3). lib. bdg. 13.00 (978-0-613-76711-8(X)) Tandem Library Bks.

Bohnet, Eric C. Faithful Hezekiah Prays: The Story of Hezekiah & the Assyrian Battle: 2 Kings 18:1-19:37 for Children. Snyder, Joel, tr. Snyder, Joel, illus. 2002. (ENG.). 16p. (J). 1.99 (978-0-570-07578-3(5)) Concordia Publishing Hse.

Bostrom, Kathleen Long. Green Plagues & Lamb: The Story of Moses & Pharaoh. McKinsey, Dennis, illus. 2003. 48p. 12.95 (978-0-664-22635-0(3)) Westminster John Knox Pr.

—The Snake in the Grass: The Story of Adam & Eve. McKinsey, Dennis, illus. 2003. 48p. (J). 12.95 (978-0-664-22592-6(6)) Westminster John Knox Pr.

Brighter Child Publishing Staff. The Beginners Bible: Old Testament Favorites: Noah's Ark, Moses Activity Center, David Activity Center. 1999. (Beginner's Bible Ser.). (J). (ps-3). cd-rom 19.95 (978-1-57791-002-2(8)) Brighter Minds Children's Publishing.

Brown, Janet Allison, et al. Jonah & the Whale. Durantz, Summer, illus. 2003. (Inspirational Collection). 24p. (J). pap. 3.99 (978-0-7696-3126-4(6) , Brighter Child) School Specialty Publishing.

Brown, Laaren. Children's Illustrated Jewish Bible. 2007. 102p. (J). 19.99 (978-0-7566-2665-5(X)) Dorling Kindersley Publishing, Inc.

Buck, Deanna Draper. My First Old Testament Stories. 2001. (Illus.). 36p. (J). 12.95 (978-1-57345-960-0(7) , Bookcraft, Inc.) Deseret Bk. Co.

Burkart, Jeffrey E. Down Through the Roof, 6 vols. Billin-Grye, Paige, illus. 2000. (Arch Bks.). (ENG.). 16p. (J). (gr. k-4). 1.99 (978-0-570-07562-2(9)) Concordia Publishing Hse.

Burstein, Chaya M. The Kids' Cartoon Bible. 2002. (Illus.). 132p. pap. 17.95 (978-0-8276-0729-3(6)) Jewish Pubn. Society.

—The Kids' Catalog of Bible Treasures. Burstein, Chaya M., illus. 1999. (Jps Kids' Catalog Ser.). (Illus.). 284p. (gr. 3-7). pap. 15.95 (978-0-8276-0667-8(2)) Jewish Pubn. Society.

Caduto, Michael J. In the Beginning: The Story of Genesis & Earth Activities for Children. 2004. 48p. 16.95 (978-0-8091-6717-3(4) , 6717-4) Paulist Pr.

Caring for My Books: Bible Story: My Bible, God's Special Book. (Scripture Bites Ser.). (Illus.). (J). 7.99 (978-0-7847-9025-0(6) , 00715) Standard Publishing.

Carlson, Melody. Noah & the Incredible Flood, 5 vols. Francisco, Wendy, illus. 2003. (Bible Adventure Club). 36p. wbk. ed. 19.99 incl. audio, cd-rom (978-1-58134-336-6(1)) Crossway Bks.

—Piercing Proverbs: Wise Words for Today's Generation. 2002. 96p. pap. 7.99 (978-1-57673-895-5(7) , Multnomah) WaterBrook Pr.

Chancellor, Debra. Come Aboard Noah's Ark. Downing, Julie, illus. 2004. (ps). bds. 6.95 (978-0-8294-1379-3(0)) Loyola Pr.

Cohen, Barbara. David: A Biography. 2000. 108p. (J). (gr. 4-6). reprint ed. 16.00 (978-0-7881-9501-3(8)) DIANE Publishing Co.

Cohen, Daphne M. In Search of the Seven Wonders of Noah. Jarcik, Katerina, illus. 1998. 64p. (J). (gr. 1-6). pap. 9.95 (978-0-9668892-0-8(7)) Treasure Garden Productions.

Coloring Book/Intermediate/Bible Fun Old Testament. 2006. (J). 14.99 (978-1-59317-146-9(3)) Warner Pr. Pubs.

Concordia Publishing Staff. All about the Ark Giant Pop-Up Book. 1999. (Illus.). (J). (ps-2). 9.99 (978-0-570-05588-4(1)) Concordia Publishing Hse.

—Where Is Moses? 1999. (Illus.). 12p. (J). (ps-k). 7.00 (978-0-570-05584-6(9)) Concordia Publishing Hse.

—2000 Years Since Then, 1. 1999. (J). 6.99 (978-0-570-05566-2(0)) Concordia Publishing Hse.

Connelly, Gwen, illus. The Story of Ruth. 2005. 32p. (J). (gr. 2-4). pap. 6.95 (978-1-58013-130-8(1)) Kar-Ben Publishing.

La Conquista de Jerico. 2001. (SPA.). 24p. (J). (gr. k-4). 2.49 (978-0-570-05184-8(3)) Concordia Publishing Hse.

Courtney, Claudia. Choose! Nolte, Larry, illus. 2000. (Phonetic Bible Stories Ser.). (ENG.). 16p. (J). (ps-1). 2.99 (978-0-570-07003-0(1)) Concordia Publishing Hse.

—Choose! The Story of Ruth. 2000. (ps-2). lib. bdg. 10.65 (978-0-613-72826-3(2)) Tandem Library Bks.

—Daniel Blessed Vol. 1: Daniel & the Lion's Den. Clark, Bill, illus. 1999. (Phonetic Bible Stories Ser.). (ENG.). 16p. (J). (ps-1). 2.99 (978-0-570-05560-0(1)) Concordia Publishing Hse.

—Defiant Giant: David & Goliath. Nolte, Larry, illus. 1999. (Phonetic Bible Stories Ser.). (ENG.). 16p. (J). (ps-1). 2.99 (978-0-570-05561-7(X)) Concordia Publishing Hse.

—Defiant Giant: The Story of David & Goliath. 1999. (ps-2). lib. bdg. 10.65 (978-0-613-72900-0(5)) Tandem Library Bks.

—The Grand Plan: The Creation Story. Morris, Susan, illus. 2000. (Phonetic Bible Stories Ser.). (ENG.). 16p. (J). (ps-1). 2.99 (978-0-570-07088-7(0)) Concordia Publishing Hse.

—The Modest King: Pa;m Sunday. Clark, Bill, illus. 2000. (Phonetic Bible Stories Ser.). (ENG.). 16p. (J). (ps-1). 2.99 (978-0-570-07001-6(5)) Concordia Publishing Hse.

Cousins, Lucy. Noah's Ark. Cousins, Lucy, illus. 2002. (Illus.). (J). 13.83 (978-0-7587-5895-8(2)) Book Wholesalers, Inc.

—Noah's Ark. braille ed. 2000. (J). (gr. 1). bds. (978-0-616-01862-0(2)) Canadian National Institute for the Blind/Institut National Canadien pour les Aveugles.

—Noah's Ark. Cousins, Lucy, illus. 2004. (Illus.). 22p. (J). (gr. k-k). bds. 6.99 (978-0-7636-2446-0(2)) Candlewick Pr.

Cousins, Lucy, retold by. Noah's Ark. 1999. (Illus.). 24p. (J). (ps). bds. 6.99 (978-0-8499-5972-1(1)) Nelson, Thomas Inc.

Curren, Joan E. First Brothers. 2000. (gr. k-3). lib. bdg. 9.85 (978-0-613-71020-6(7)) Tandem Library Bks.

—The First Brothers: Genesis 4. Eitzen, Allan, illus. 2000. (Arch Bks.). (ENG.). 16p. (J). (gr. k-4). 1.99 (978-0-570-07565-3(3)) Concordia Publishing Hse.

—Jericho's Tumbling Walls: The Story of Joshua & the Battle of Jericho. Edwards, Steve, illus. 2001. (Arch Bks.). (ENG.). 16p. (J). (gr. k-4). 1.99 (978-0-570-07570-7(X)) Concordia Publishing Hse.

Dalmatian Press Staff. Daniel & the Lions Den. 2000. (Illus.). (J). pap. 4.97 (978-1-888567-34-2(1)) Dalmatian Pr.

—David & Goliath. 2004. (Illus.). 24p. (J). 2.99 (978-1-4037-0971-4(8) , Spirit Pr.) Dalmatian Pr.

—David & Goliath. 2002. (Illus.). 24p. (J). (gr. k-5). pap. 2.99 (978-1-57759-474-1(6)) Dalmatian Pr.

—Jonah & the Big Fish. 2004. 24p. (J). 2.99 (978-1-4037-0969-1(6) , Spirit Pr.) Dalmatian Pr.

—The Lord Told Noah. 2002. (Paint Box Bks.). (Illus.). 32p. (J). (ps-4). pap. 2.99 (978-1-57759-601-1(3)) Dalmatian Pr.

—Noah's Ark. 2002. (Illus.). 24p. (J). (gr. k-5). pap. 2.99 (978-1-57759-478-9(9)) Dalmatian Pr.

Dalmatian Press Staff, ed. Daniel in the Lion's Den. 2004. (Illus.). 24p. (J). 2.99 (978-1-4037-0965-3(3) , Spirit Pr.) Dalmatian Pr.

—Old Testament Bible Stories: Paint Box Book. 2002. (Paint Box Bks.). (Illus.). 32p. (J). pap. 2.99 (978-1-57759-602-8(1)) Dalmatian Pr.

The Daniel & the Lions- Beginner's Biblereg; 2007. 24p. (J). 5.99 (978-0-8297-4938-0(1)) Vida Pubs.

Daniel & the Lion's Den. 2002. (Illus.). 24p. (J). pap. 2.29 (978-1-57759-170-2(4)) Dalmatian Pr.

Daniel in the Lion's Den. 2002. (Illus.). 24p. (J). 5.99 (978-1-57759-521-2(1)) Dalmatian Pr.

David & Goliath. 2002. (Illus.). 24p. (J). 5.99 (978-1-57759-520-5(3)); pap. 2.29 (978-1-57759-171-9(2)) Dalmatian Pr.

David & Goliath. 2003. (J). per. (978-1-57657-980-0(8)) Paradise Pr., Inc.

David & Goliath. 2006. 16p. (J). pap. 1.99 (978-0-7847-1712-7(5) , 04173) Standard Publishing.

David & Goliath: A Bible Story to Color. (Illus.). 16p. (J). pap. 1.50 (978-0-87162-825-1(2) , E6018) Warner Pr. Pubs.

The David & Goliath, Beginner's Biblereg; 2007. 24p. (J). 5.99 (978-0-8297-4937-3(3)) Vida Pubs.

David & Goliath Bible Sticker Book. 2003. (Illus.). 16p. (J). 2.98 (978-1-4054-1554-5(1)) Parragon, Inc.

David & Goliath Read Along. 1999. (Sunday Morning Ser.). (J). (ps-3). pap. 6.98 incl. audio (978-0-7634-0577-9(9)) Walt Disney Records.

David C. Cook. Daniel in the Lion's Den. 2003. (My Jesus Pocket Bks.). (Illus.). 32p. (J). (gr. 5-3). pap., pap. 8.90 (978-1-55513-136-4(0) , 1555131360) Cook, David C. Publishing Co.

—Noah & the Floating Zoo. 2003. (My Jesus Pocket Bks.). (Illus.). 32p. (J). (gr. 5-3). pap., pap. 8.90 (978-1-55513-130-2(1) , 1555131301) Cook, David C. Publishing Co.

Davidson, Alice Joyce. Esther & the Mighty King. Lyon, Tammie Speer, illus. 1998. (Bible Friends Ser.). 12p. (J). (ps). 3.99 (978-0-310-97600-4(6)) Zondervan.

—Jonah & the Big Fish. 2003. 12p. (J). bds. 6.99 (978-0-310-70852-0(4)) Zonderkidz.

—Jonas y el Gran Pez. 1998. (My Bible Friends Ser.).Tr. of Jonah & the Big Fish. (SPA.). 12p. (J). 3.99 (978-0-8297-2484-4(2)) Vida Pubs.

—Joseph & the Splendid Coat. Lyon, Tammie Speer, illus. 1998. (My Bible Friends Board Bks.). 12p. (J). 3.99 (978-0-310-97325-6(2)) Zondervan.

—Samson & His Strength. Lyon, Tammie Speer, illus. 1998. (My Bible Friends Board Bks.). 12p. (J). 3.99 (978-0-310-97324-9(4)) Zonderkidz.

Davis, Bryan. Jacob's Dream: The Story of Jacob's Ladder. Garrett, Caroline, illus. 2001. (Arch Bks.). (ENG.). 16p. (J). (gr. k-4). 1.99 (978-0-570-07569-1(6)) Concordia Publishing Hse.

De Graaf, A. M. Dios Crea al Mundo. (Divertidas Historias Biblicas para Ninos Ser.).Tr. of God Makes the World. (SPA.). (J). 3.49 (978-0-7899-0523-9(X) , 496640) Editorial Unilit.

De Graaf, Anne. Esther. Montero, Jose Perez, illus. 2001. (Little Children's Bible Bks.: No. 22). 38p. (J). (ps-1). 5.99 (978-0-8054-2193-4(9)) B&H Publishing Grp.

—Noah & the Ark. Perez-Montero, Jose, illus. 1998. (Little Children's Bible Bks.). 38p. (J). 5.99 (978-0-8054-1781-4(8)) B&H Publishing Grp.

—The Tower of Babel. Perez-Montero, Jose, illus. 1998. (Little Children's Bible Bks.). 38p. (J). 5.99 (978-0-8054-1783-8(4)) B&H Publishing Grp.

DeBoer, Rondi & Tangvald, Christine. Brave Queen Esther. Conger, Holli, illus. 2007. (J). 5.99 (***978-0-7847-1947-3(0)**) Standard Publishing.

—David & Goliath. Conger, Holli, illus. 2007. (J). 5.99 (***978-0-7847-1950-3(0)**) Standard Publishing.

DeVries, Mike & Murphy, Troy. Exodus: The Sacred Journey. 2003. (No Limits Ser.). 112p. (YA). pap. 12.99 (978-0-8341-5005-8(0)) Beacon Hill Pr. of Kansas City.

Dillon, Sally Pierson. Survivors of the Dark Rebellion: God's Heroes from Adam to David. 2002. 176p. (YA). pap. 10.99 (978-0-8280-1686-5(0) , 197-880) Review & Herald Publishing Assn.

Doing What I'm Asked: Bible Story: When a Woman Obeyed Elijah. (Scripture Bites Ser.). (Illus.). (J). 7.99 (978-0-7847-9017-5(5) , 00710) Standard Publishing.

Donaher, D F. & Bibleco. Daniel & the Lions. 2004. (Illus.). (J). bds. (978-0-9746058-2-1(4) , Biblemania) Bibleco, Inc.

Dorn, Owen A. Ruth: A Love Story. 2003. (God's People Ser.). (Illus.). pap. 6.99 (978-0-8100-1348-3(7)) Northwestern Publishing Hse.

Dyson, Janet. Daniel & the Lions: Classic Stories from the Old Testament. 2002. (Bible Discoverers Ser.). (Illus.). 64p. pap. 7.99 (978-1-84215-672-8(1) , Southwater) Anness Publishing GBR. *Dist:* National Bk. Network.

—David & the Giant: Classic Stories from the Old Testament. 2003. (Bible Discoverers Ser.). (Illus.). 64p. pap. 7.99 (978-1-84215-732-9(9) , Southwater) Anness Publishing GBR. *Dist:* National Bk. Network.

—Jesus Goes to Heaven & Other Stories. 2001. (First Bible Stories Ser.). (Illus.). (ps-k). pap. 4.95 (978-0-7548-0885-5(8) , Lorenz Bks.) Anness Publishing, Inc.

Eder, Enelle. Create & Take Bible Crafts: Old Testament Heroes. 2004. 96p. (J). (gr. k-6). pap. 11.95 (978-1-58411-006-4(6)) Rainbow Pubs. & Legacy Pr.

Ewald, Thomas. Old Testament Take-Home Bible Stories: Easy-to-Make, Reproducible Mini-Books That Children Can Make & Keep. 2002. 128p. pap. (978-0-88724-871-9(3)) Carson-Dellosa Publishing Co., Inc.

Fair, Virginia S. Through the Eyes of Gabriel. 1999. (Illus.). 94p. (YA). pap. 12.95 (978-0-9655035-8-7(5)) Threesie Pubns.

Farah, Gregg. Risk It! Daring to Act on the Truth of God (A Creative Study of the Book of Esther) Reeves, Dale, ed. Angle, Scott, illus. 1999. 64p. (YA). pap., wbk. ed. 8.99 (978-0-7847-0951-1(3) , 23317) Standard Publishing.

Ferri, Giuliano, illus. The Story of Noah & the Ark. 2001. 32p. (J). (ps-2). 16.99 (978-1-84148-361-0(3)) Barefoot Bks., Inc.

Fish-Ocean Life: Bible Story: Jonah & the Big Fish. (Scripture Bites Ser.). (Illus.). (J). 7.99 (978-0-7847-9009-0(4) , 00706) Standard Publishing.

Frank, Penny. Abraham, Friend of God. 1999. (Lion Story Bible Ser.). (Illus.). 24p. pap. 2.99 (978-0-7459-4104-2(4) , Lion) Lion Hudson plc GBR. *Dist:* Independent Pubs. Group.

—Daniel in the Lions' Den. (Illus.). 24p. 2.99 (978-0-7459-4113-4(3) , Lion) Lion Hudson plc GBR. *Dist:* Trafalgar Square Publishing.

—David & Goliath. (Illus.). 24p. 2.99 (978-0-7459-4111-0(7) , Lion) Lion Hudson plc GBR. *Dist:* Trafalgar Square Publishing.

—God Speaks to Samuel. 1999. (Lion Story Bible Ser.). (Illus.). 24p. pap. 2.99 (978-0-7459-4110-3(9) , Lion) Lion Hudson plc GBR. *Dist:* Independent Pubs. Group.

—Jonah Runs Away. 1999. (Lion Story Bible Ser.). (Illus.). 24p. pap. 2.99 (978-0-7459-4114-1(1) , Lion) Lion Hudson plc GBR. *Dist:* Independent Pubs. Group.

—Joseph & the King of Egypt. 1999. (Lion Story Bible Ser.). (Illus.). 24p. pap. 2.99 (978-0-7459-4106-6(0) , Lion) Lion Hudson plc GBR. *Dist:* Independent Pubs. Group.

—Joseph the Dreamer. 1999. (Lion Story Bible Ser.). (Illus.). 24p. pap. 2.99 (978-0-7459-4105-9(2) , Lion) Lion Hudson plc GBR. *Dist:* Independent Pubs. Group.

—Let My People Go! (Illus.). 24p. 2.99 (978-0-7459-4108-0(7) , Lion) Lion Hudson plc GBR. *Dist:* Trafalgar Square Publishing.

—Noah & the Great Flood. 1999. (Lion Story Bible Ser.). (Illus.). 24p. pap. 2.99 (978-0-7459-4103-5(6) , Lion) Lion Hudson plc GBR. *Dist:* Independent Pubs. Group.

—La Nueva Familia de Rut.Tr. of Ruth's New Family. (SPA.). (J). 1.99 (978-1-56063-785-1(4) , 490315) Editorial Unilit.

—The Princess & the Baby. (Illus.). 24p. 2.99 (978-0-7459-4107-3(9) , Lion) Lion Hudson plc GBR. *Dist:* Trafalgar Square Publishing.

Freed, Shirley & Moon, Louise. The Day God Rested. Morelan, Bill, ed. Butler, Steven, illus. 2003. 16p. (J). (gr. 1 up). pap. 3.99 (978-1-58938-102-5(5)) Concerned Communications.

—Esther Becomes Queen. Morelan, Bill, ed. Butler, Steven, illus. 2002. 24p. (J). (gr. 2 up). pap. 3.99 (978-1-58938-048-6(7)) Concerned Communications.

—God Made Animals. Morelan, Bill, ed. Butler, Steven, illus. 2003. 16p. (J). (gr. 1 up). pap. 3.99 (978-1-58938-114-8(9)) Concerned Communications.

—God Made Birds. Morelan, Bill, ed. Butler, Steven, illus. 2003. 8p. (J). (gr. 1 up). pap. 3.99 (978-1-58938-111-7(4)) Concerned Communications.

—God Made Light. Morelan, Bill, ed. Butler, Steven, illus. 2003. 8p. (J). (gr. 1 up). pap. 3.99 (978-1-58938-109-4(2)) Concerned Communications.

—God Made Sea Creatures. Morelan, Bill, ed. Butler, Steven, illus. 2003. 16p. (J). (gr. 2 up). pap. 3.99 (978-1-58938-118-6(1)) Concerned Communications.

—God Made the Sun. Morelan, Bill, ed. Butler, Steven, illus. 2003. 8p. (J). (gr. 1 up). pap. 3.99 (978-1-58938-115-5(7)) Concerned Communications.

Freed, Shirley Ann & Moon, Louise. Daniel & the Lions. Morelan, Bill, ed. Butler, Steven, illus. l.t. ed. 2002. 8p. (J). (gr. 5). pap. 3.99 (978-1-58938-011-0(8)) Concerned Communications.

—God Calls Samuel. Morelan, Bill, ed. Butler, Steven, illus. l.t. ed. 2002. 24p. (J). (gr. 6). pap. 3.99 Concerned Communications.

—Joseph's New Coat. Morelan, Bill, ed. Butler, Steven, illus. l.t. ed. 2002. 8p. (J). (ps-k). pap. 3.99 (978-1-58938-008-0(8)) Concerned Communications.

—Levi's Lunch. Morelan, Bill, ed. Butler, Steven, illus. l.t. ed. 2002. 16p. (J). (gr. 6). pap. 3.99 (978-1-58938-040-0(1)) Concerned Communications.

—Naaman. Morelan, Bill, ed. Butler, Steven, illus. l.t. ed. 2002. 16p. (J). (gr. 1-2). pap. 3.99 (978-1-58938-027-1(4)) Concerned Communications.

—Noah's Ark. Morelan, Bill, ed. Butler, Steven, illus. l.t. ed. 2002. 16p. (J). (gr. 6). pap. 3.99 (978-1-58938-018-9(5)) Concerned Communications.

Freedom/Flag/God/Country: Bible Story: God Frees His People. (Scripture Bites Ser.). (Illus.). (J). 7.99 (978-0-7847-9015-1(9) , 00708) Standard Publishing.

Fry & Hooper. Little Books of the Bible Stories from the Old Testament. 2004. (J). 14.95 (978-0-8249-5445-1(9)) Ideals Pubns.

Gardens/Plants: Bible Story: God Made a Beautiful Garden. (Scripture Bites Ser.). (Illus.). (J). 7.99 (978-0-7847-9007-6(8) , 00704) Standard Publishing.

Gemmen, Heather & McNeil, Mary. Escape, Level 3. Argoff, Patti, tr. Argoff, Patti, illus. 1999. (Rocket Readers Ser.). 24p. (J). (gr. 3 up). pap., pap. 8.99 (978-0-7814-3987-9(6) , 0781439876) Cook, David C. Publishing Co.

—God & You, Level 2. Ulrich, George, tr. Ulrich, George, illus. abr. ed. 2004. (Rocket ReaderT2 Ser.). 40p. (J). (gr. 2 up). pap., pap. 8.99 (978-0-7814-4014-1(9) , 0781440149) Cook, David C. Publishing Co.

—Walk This Way, Pre-Level 1. Ochoa, Ana, tr. Ochoa, Ana, illus. 2003. (Rocket Readers Ser.). 40p. (J). (ps-1). pap. 8.99 (978-0-7814-3983-1(3) , 0781439833) Cook, David C. Publishing Co.

Goldsack, Gaby. Little Camel & Joseph: A Finger Puppet Play & Read Story. 2003. (Snuffleheads Ser.). (Illus.). 14p. (J). 7.99 (978-0-8254-7267-1(9)) Kregel Pubns.

—Little Lion & Daniel: A Finger Puppet Play & Read Story. 2003. (Snuffleheads Ser.). (Illus.). 14p. (J). 7.99 (978-0-8254-7268-8(7)) Kregel Pubns.

Goldsack, Gaby & Dawson, Peter. Noah's Ark: My Little Bible Book. 2003. (Illus.). 12p. (J). bds. 10.99 (978-0-8254-7266-4(0)) Kregel Pubns.

Graham, Lorenz. How God Fix Jonah. Bryan, Ashley, illus. 2003. 160p. (YA). (gr. 6-9). 17.95 (978-1-56397-698-8(6)) Boyds Mills Pr.

Groffman, Simcha. Simcha's Kinder Torah: Torah Stories & Thoughts on the Weekly Parasha. 2003. (Illus.). 320p. 19.95 (978-1-58330-658-1(7)) Feldheim Pubs.

Haas, David. Children's Psalms to Pray, Sing & Do. 2004. (Illus.). 80p. (J). pap. 9.95 (978-0-86716-453-4(0)) St. Anthony Messenger Pr. & Franciscan Communications.

Haidle, Helen. Creation. Haidle, David, illus. 2000. 40p. (J). 12.99 (978-0-310-70018-0(3)) Zonderkidz.

Hansen, Janis. Creation: God's Wonderful Gift, 5 vols. Francisco, Wendy, illus. 2003. (Bible Adventure Club). 36p. wbk. ed. 19.99 incl. audio, cd-rom (978-1-58134-292-5(6)) Crossway Bks.

—Creation: God's Wonderful Gift. Francisco, Wendy, illus. 2001. (J). (978-1-58134-295-6(0)) Crossway Bks.

—David & His Giant Battle, 5 vols. Francisco, Wendy, illus. (Bible Adventure Club). 2003. 36p. wbk. ed. 19.99 incl. audio, cd-rom (978-1-58134-321-2(3)); 2001. (J). (978-1-58134-324-3(8)) Crossway Bks.

—Jonah & His Amazing Voyage, 5 vols. Wendy, Francisco, illus. 2003. (Bible Adventure Club). 36p. wbk. ed. 19.99 incl. audio, cd-rom (978-1-58134-326-7(4)) Crossway Bks.

—Jonah & His Amazing Voyage. Francisco, Wendy, illus. 2001. (J). (978-1-58134-329-8(9)) Crossway Bks.

—Noah & the Incredible Flood. Francisco, Wendy, illus. 2001. (J). (978-1-58134-339-7(6)) Crossway Bks.

Harrast, Tracy. The Big Boat Ride. Moore, Carl, illus. 1998. (Peek-a-Bible Ser.). 18p. (J). 6.99 (978-0-310-97460-4(7)) Zondervan.

—Jonas Huye Dentro de un Pez. 2002. (SPA.). 18p. (J). pap. 6.99 (978-0-8297-3590-1(9)) Vida Pubs.

—Pequeño David y el Grandullon Goliat. 2002. (SPA.). 12p. (J). pap. 6.99 (978-0-8297-3591-8(7)) Vida Pubs.

Hartman, Bob. Dinner in the Lions' Den. Raglin, Tim, illus. 2007. 32p. (J). (ps-2). 16.99 (978-0-399-24674-6(6), Putnam Juvenile) Penguin Group (USA) Inc.

Hartman, Bob & Samuel, Janet. Noahs Big Boat. 2007. (Illus.). 32p. (J). pap. 9.95 (***978-0-7459-4995-6(9)***) Lion Hudson plc GBR. *Dist:* Independent Pubs. Group.

Heaps, Kelly S. & Dunn, Susan. Promise: The Story of Noah's Ark. Lindgren, Renae, illus. 1999. (Holy Bear's Travel Ser.). 32p. (J). (gr. k-5). pap. 7.95 (978-1-885628-30-5(7)) Buckaroo Bks.

Heck, Cathy. Noah'sArk. 2007. 10p. bds. 5.99 (***978-1-4037-3302-3(3)***) Dalmatian Pr.

Hodges, George. Castle of Zion. 2006. pap. 26.95 (***978-1-4286-3420-6(7)***) Kessinger Publishing, LLC.

—The Garden of Eden: Stories from the Fir. 2006. (Illus.). pap. 26.95 (***978-1-4254-9577-0(X)***) Kessinger Publishing, LLC.

Hodges, Margaret. Moses. Wimmer, Mike & Moser, Barry, illus. 2006. 32p. (J). (gr. 3-5). 16.00 (978-0-15-200946-5(9)) Harcourt Children's Bks.

Hoffman, Mary & Dorling Kindersley Publishing Staff. A First Book of Jewish Bible Stories. Downing, Julie, illus. 2002. 48p. (J). 14.99 (978-0-7894-8504-5(4)) Dorling Kindersley Publishing, Inc.

Hoffman, Patricia A. Crossing the Red Sea, 1. 1999. (Undercover Bible Story Ser.). (Illus.). 24p. (J). (ps-2). 8.99 (978-0-570-05562-4(8)) Cajun Prairie Habitat Preservation Society.

—Tumbling Walls of Jerico, 1. 1999. (Undercover Bible Story Ser.). (Illus.). 21p. (J). (ps-2). 8.99 (978-0-570-05563-1(6)) Cajun Prairie Habitat Preservation Society.

Holder, Greg. Noah's Ark. McCallum, Jodie, illus. 1999. (Record Your Own Voice Ser.). 10p. (J). (ps-k). 14.99 (978-0-7847-1112-5(7), 03538, Bean Sprouts) Standard Publishing.

—Noah's Ark. Shuttleworth, Cathie, illus. 1999. (Felt Board Bks.). 10p. (J). (ps-k). bds. 14.99 (978-0-7847-1117-0(8), 03526) Standard Publishing.

HOP, LLC. Hooked on Bible Stories Old Testament Stories. 2006. 24.99 (978-1-931020-97-8(3)) HOP, LLC.

Hudson, Sue. David & Goliath. Graham, Kennedy, illus. 2005. 20p. pap. 7.99 (978-1-86024-507-7(2)) Authentic Media.

—Jonah & the Big Fish. Graham, Kennedy, illus. 2005. 20p. pap. 7.99 (978-1-86024-506-0(4)) Authentic Media.

Huisjen, Donna. My Tall Book of Proverbs. 2000. (My Tall Bks.). (Illus.). (J). 6.99 (978-0-310-91862-2(6)) Zondervan.

—My Tall Book of Psalms. 2000. (My Tall Bks.). (J). 6.99 (978-0-310-91861-5(8)) Zondervan.

Insects/Bugs/Small Creatures: Bible Story: God Made All Creatures - Great & Small. (Scripture Bites Ser.). (Illus.). (J). (ps). 7.99 (978-0-7847-9005-2(1), 00702) Standard Publishing.

Jablonski, Patricia Edward, ed. The Wonderful Story of Creation. Kim, Magdalena, illus. 2001. 32p. (J). pap. 6.95 (978-0-8198-8300-1(X), 332-409) Pauline Bks. & Media.

Jackson, Cindy. Old Testament Fun Activities - First & Second Grade. 1998. (Illus.). 16p. (J). (gr. 1-2). 3.95 (978-1-878669-69-8(9), CRE 3541) Creative Teaching Assocs.

—Old Testament Fun Activities - Pre-School & Kindergarten. 1998. (Illus.). 16p. (J). (ps-k). 3.95 (978-1-878669-68-1(0), CRE 3540) Creative Teaching Assocs.

—Old Testament Fun Activities - Third & Fourth Grade. 1998. (Illus.). 16p. (J). (gr. 3-4). 3.95 (978-1-878669-70-4(2), CRE 3542) Creative Teaching Assocs.

James, Steven. 30 Old Testament Interactive Stories for Young Children. 2007. (J). per. 15.99 (***978-0-7847-1939-8(X)***) Standard Publishing.

Jeffs, Stephanie. Come into the Ark with Noah. 2001. (Action Rhyme Bks.). (Illus.). (J). (ps-3). pap. 5.00 (978-0-687-04791-8(9)) Abingdon Pr.

—March 'Round the Walls with Joshua. 2004. (Action Rhyme Bks.). (Illus.). (ps-3). 5.00 (978-0-687-04801-4(X)) Abingdon Pr.

Jensen, Rebecca Ridges & Jensen, Daniel Loran. The Creation-From the Book of Moses. 2007. 32p. (J). 15.99 (978-1-55517-894-9(4)) Cedar Fort, Inc./CFI Distribution.

Jonah. (J). bds. 5.95 (978-0-87162-984-5(4)) Warner Pr. Pubs.

The Jonah & the Big Fish, Beginner's Biblereg; 2007. (Biblia para Principiantes Ser.). 24p. (J). 5.99 (978-0-8297-5009-6(6)) Vida Pubs.

Jonah & the Great Fish. 2002. (Illus.). 14p. (J). (ps). bds. 5.97 (978-1-57759-454-3(1)) Dalmatian Pr.

Jonah & the Great Fish. 2004. 24.95 incl. audio (978-1-56008-042-8(6)) Weston Woods Studios, Inc.

Jonah Bible Sticker Book. 2003. (Illus.). 16p. (J). 2.98 (978-1-4054-1555-2(X)) Parragon, Inc.

Jose Perdona a Sus Hermanos, 6 vols. 2000. (Arch Bks.). (SPA.). 24p. (J). (ps-3). 2.49 (978-0-570-05168-8(1)) Concordia Publishing Hse.

Joseph & His Coat of Many Colors. 2002. (Illus.). 24p. (J). 5.99 (978-1-57759-517-5(3)) Dalmatian Pr.

Joseph & His Coat of Many Colors. 2003. (J). per. (978-1-57657-982-4(4)) Paradise Pr., Inc.

Jules, Jacqueline. Sarah Laughs. Ugliano, Natascia, illus. 2008. (Bible Ser.). 24p. (J). lib. bdg. 17.95 (***978-0-8225-7216-9(8)***) Kar-Ben Publishing.

Juravel, Rabbi. Parsha with Rabbi Juravel: Bereishis. Toron, Eli, illus. 2005. (J). 26.95 (***978-1-931681-83-4(X)***) Israel Bk. Shop.

Kenney, Cindy. Special Collector's Edition of Big Idea's Jonah—a VeggieTales Movie. collector's ed. 2002. (Big Idea Books). (Illus.). 96p. (J). 19.99 (978-0-310-70462-1(6)) Zondervan.

Kenny, Cindy. Draw with Jonah & Friends. 2002. (Big Idea Books Ser.). (Illus.). 18p. (J). 6.99 (978-0-310-70463-8(4)) Zonderkidz.

Kershner, Jan, ed. Elijah & the Big Showdown. 2003. (Bible Big Bks.). (Illus.). 8p. (ps-k). pap. 15.99 (978-1-55945-432-2(6), Flagship Church Resources) Group Publishing, Inc.

—Noah. 2003. (Bible Big Bks.). (Illus.). 8p. (ps-k). pap. 15.99 (978-1-55945-433-9(4), Flagship Church Resources) Group Publishing, Inc.

—Peter Tells the Easter Story. 2004. (Bible Big Bks.). (Illus.). 8p. (ps-k). pap. 15.99 (978-1-55945-426-1(1), Flagship Church Resources) Group Publishing, Inc.

—Ruth. 2004. (Bible Big Bks.). (Illus.). 8p. (ps-k). pap. 15.99 (978-1-55945-431-5(8), Flagship Church Resources) Group Publishing, Inc.

Koralek, Jenny. The Moses Basket. Baynes, Pauline, illus. 2004. 32p. (J). 16.00 (978-0-8028-5251-9(3)) Eerdmans, William B. Publishing Co.

Kunkel, Jeff, ed. Noah, Build Your Boat: Old Testament Stories & Pictures by Kids. 2002. (Illus.). 48p. (ps-4). 12.99 (978-0-8066-4402-8(8), Augsburg Bks.) Augsburg Fortress, Pubs.

Lane, Leena. Old Testament Stories. Bishop, Roma, illus. 2003. 32p. 8.00 (978-0-687-06527-1(5)) Abingdon Pr.

Larcombe & Rees. Inside a Fish. 2000. (Illus.). 24p. pap. 6.99 (978-0-551-03247-7(2)) Zondervan.

Larcombe, Jennifer Rees. The Terrible Giant. Bjorkman, Steve, illus. 2004. (Best Bible Stories Ser.). 24p. (ps-3). 2.99 (978-1-58134-054-9(0)) Crossway Bks.

Lashbrook, Marilyn. Two by Two: The Story of Noah's Faith. 1998. (J). (ps-2). 5.95 (978-0-933657-66-3(8), 3000850) Standard Publishing.

—The Weak Strongman: Samson. 1998. (J). (gr. 3-5). pap. 5.95 (978-0-933657-81-6(1)) Standard Publishing.

LeapFrog Staff, compiled by. Bible Stories: Seven Tales from the Old Testament. 2002. (J). (ps-1). spiral bd. 14.99 (978-1-58605-937-8(8)) LeapFrog Enterprises, Inc.

Lehman-Wilzig, Tami. Tasty Bible Stories: A Menu of Tales & Matching Recipes. Kahn, Katherine Janus, illus. 2003. 64p. (J). (gr. 2 up). pap. 10.95 (978-1-58013-080-6(1)) Kar-Ben Publishing.

Lepon, Shoshana. The Ten Tests of Avraham. Friedman, Aaron, illus. 2000. (J). (ps-3). 12.95 (978-1-880582-61-9(9)) Judaica Pr., Inc., The.

—The Ten Tests of Avraham. 2000. (J). (ps-3). pap. 9.95 (978-1-880582-70-1(8)) Judaica Pr., Inc., The.

Lingo, Susan L. A to Z Object Talks That Teach about the Old Testament: 26 Memorable Messages Your Kids Will Love. Stoker, Bruce, ed. Lynch, Jason, illus. 2006. 48p. (YA). (gr. 1-7). pap. 6.99 (978-0-7847-1236-8(0), 02853) Standard Publishing.

Lloyd-Jones, Sally. El Arca de Noe (Noah's Ark) 2000. (Play along Ser.). (SPA.). (J). (ps-k). bds. 4.99 (978-0-7899-0819-3(0), 493787) Editorial Unilit.

Lorenz Editors. The Burning Bush & Other Stories. 2001. (First Bible Stories Boardbks.). (Illus.). 16p. (ps-3). 4.95 (978-0-7548-0880-0(7)) Anness Publishing GBR. *Dist:* National Bk. Network.

—David Fights the Giant: And Other Stories. 2001. (First Bible Stories Boardbks.). (Illus.). 16p. (ps). 4.95 (978-0-7548-0881-7(5)) Anness Publishing GBR. *Dist:* National Bk. Network.

—How the World Began & Other Stories. 2001. (First Bible Stories Boardbks.). (Illus.). 16p. (ps). 4.95 (978-0-7548-0792-6(4)) Anness Publishing GBR. *Dist:* National Bk. Network.

—Jonah & the Whale: And Other Stories. 2001. (First Bible Stories Boardbks.). (Illus.). 16p. (ps). 4.95 (978-0-7548-0882-4(3)) Anness Publishing GBR. *Dist:* National Bk. Network.

Lottridge, Celia Barker. Stories from Adam & Eve to Ezekiel: Retold from the Bible. Clement, Gary, illus. 2004. 144p. (J). 24.95 (978-0-88899-490-5(7)) Groundwood Bks. CAN. *Dist:* Perseus Distribution.

Loveland, Seymour. The Illustrated Bible Story Book Old Tes. 2005. reprint ed. pap. 20.95 (978-1-4179-0226-2(4)) Kessinger Publishing, LLC.

Lowry, Mark. Ol' Jonah's Tossed into the Ocean. 2001. (Illus.). 24p. (J). 12.99 (978-0-310-70188-0(0)) Zondervan.

Luci, Shaw & Lane, Mary. The Genesis of It All. Miao, Huai-Kuang, Sr., illus. 2006. 32p. (J). 17.95 (978-1-55725-480-1(X)) Paraclete Pr., Inc.

Mackenzie, Carine. Naaman: The Soldier. Apps, Fred, illus. 2005. 12p. (J). (ps-k). per. (978-1-84550-085-6(7), Christian Focus) Christian Focus Pubns.

—Ruth's Journey. Apps, Fred, illus. 2005. 12p. (J). (ps-k). per. (978-1-84550-086-3(5), Christian Focus) Christian Focus Pubns.

MacLean, Moira, illus. Noah & the Ark Pushalong. 2001. 10p. (J). (ps-k). 6.99 (978-0-8254-7215-2(6)) Kregel Pubns.

Mayo, Margaret. First Bible Stories. Smee, Nicola, illus. 1998. 96p. (J). (gr. k-3). 14.95 (978-0-7641-5082-1(0)) Barron's Educational Series, Inc.

McDermott, Gerald. Creation. McDermott, Gerald, illus. 2003. (Illus.). 32p. (J). (gr. k). 16.99 (978-0-525-46905-6(2), Dutton Juvenile) Penguin Group (USA) Inc.

McKissack, Patricia C. & McKissack, Fredrick L., Jr. Let My People Go: Bible Stories Told by a Freeman of Color. Ransome, James E., illus. 1998. 144p. (YA). (gr. 4-7). 21.99 (978-0-689-80856-2(9), Atheneum/Anne Schwartz Bks.) Simon & Schuster Children's Publishing.

Mendenhall, Cheryl, illus. Joseph & His Coat of Many Colors. 2004. 24p. (J). 2.99 (978-1-4037-0966-0(1), Spirit Pr.) Dalmatian Pr.

Miyoshi, Sekiya. David & Goliath. 2002. (Illus.). 28p. (J). (ps-3). 14.00 (978-0-8298-1453-8(1)) Pilgrim Pr., The/ United Church Pr.

Miyoshi, Sekiya, as told by. Jacob's Ladder. 2002. (Illus.). 28p. (J). (ps-3). 14.00 (978-0-8298-1454-5(X)) Pilgrim Pr., The/United Church Pr.

Mortimer, F. L. Precept upon Precept. 192p. (J). pap. 7.99 (978-1-85792-587-6(4)) Christian Focus Pubns. GBR. *Dist:* Riverside.

Moser. Stories from the Old Testament. 1998. (J). Vol 2. 16.00 (978-0-671-88662-2(2)); Vol 3. 16.00 (978-0-671-88663-9(0)); Vol 4. 16.00 (978-0-671-88664-6(9)) Simon & Schuster Children's Publishing. (Simon & Schuster Children's Publishing).

Moses - Baby in the Bulrushes. 2002. (Illus.). 24p. (J). 5.99 (978-1-57759-518-2(1)); pap. 2.29 (978-1-57759-172-6(0)) Dalmatian Pr.

Moses - Parting in the Red Sea. 2002. (Illus.). 24p. (J). 5.99 (978-1-57759-519-9(X)) Dalmatian Pr.

My Five Senses: Bible Story: Young Samuel Listens to God's Voice. (Scripture Bites Ser.). (Illus.). (J). 7.99 (978-0-7847-9022-9(1), 00713) Standard Publishing.

Nederveld, Patricia L. A Baby for Hannah: The Story of an Answered Prayer. 1998. (God Loves Me Ser.). (Illus.). 24p. (J). (ps-3). pap. 2.95 (978-1-56212-285-0(1), 001216, Faith Alive Christian Resources) CRC Pubns.

—A Big Fish Story: The Story of Jonah. 1998. (God Loves Me Ser.). (Illus.). 24p. (J). (ps-3). pap. 2.95 (978-1-56212-291-1(6), 001222, Faith Alive Christian Resources) CRC Pubns.

—Blue & Green & Purple Too! The Story of God's Colorful World. 1998. (God Loves Me Ser.). (Illus.). 24p. (J). (ps-3). pap. 2.95 (978-1-56212-270-6(3), 001201, Faith Alive Christian Resources) CRC Pubns.

—Count the Stars! The Story of God's Promise to Abraham & Sarah. 1998. (God Loves Me Ser.). (Illus.). 24p. (J). (ps-3). pap. 2.95 (978-1-56212-276-8(2), 001207, Faith Alive Christian Resources) CRC Pubns.

—David & the Giant: The Story of David & Goliath. 1998. (God Loves Me Ser.). (Illus.). 24p. (J). (ps-3). pap. 2.95 (978-1-56212-288-1(6), 001219, Faith Alive Christian Resources) CRC Pubns.

—A Girl Named Rebekah: The Story of God's Answer to Abraham. 1998. (God Loves Me Ser.). (Illus.). 24p. (J). (ps-3). pap. 2.95 (978-1-56212-277-5(0), 001208, Faith Alive Christian Resources) CRC Pubns.

—I'll Do It! The Story of Moses & the Burning Bush. 1998. (God Loves Me Ser.). (Illus.). 24p. (J). (ps-3). pap. 2.95 (978-1-56212-281-2(9), 001212, Faith Alive Christian Resources) CRC Pubns.

—It's a Noisy Place! The Story of the First Creatures. 1998. (God Loves Me Ser.). (Illus.). 24p. (J). (ps-3). pap. 2.95 (978-1-56212-271-3(1), 001202, Faith Alive Christian Resources) CRC Pubns.

—Lions & Bears! The Story of David the Shepherd Boy. 1998. (God Loves Me Ser.). (Illus.). 24p. (J). (ps-3). pap. 2.95 (978-1-56212-287-4(8), 001218, Faith Alive Christian Resources) CRC Pubns.

—Lions, Lions! The Story of Daniel. 1998. (God Loves Me Ser.: Vol. 23). (Illus.). 24p. (J). (ps-3). pap. 2.95 (978-1-56212-292-8(4), 001223, Faith Alive Christian Resources) CRC Pubns.

—A Little Jar of Oil: The Story of Elisha & the Widow. 1998. (God Loves Me Ser.). (Illus.). 24p. (J). (ps-3). pap. 2.95 (978-1-56212-289-8(4), 001220, Faith Alive Christian Resources) CRC Pubns.

—One, Two, Three, Four, Five, Six, Seven! The Story of Elisha & Naaman. 1998. (God Loves Me Ser.). (Illus.). 24p. (J). (ps-3). pap. 2.95 (978-1-56212-290-4(8), 001221, Faith Alive Christian Resources) CRC Pubns.

—Plenty to Eat: The Story of Joseph & His Brothers. 1998. (God Loves Me Ser.). (Illus.). 24p. (J). (ps-3). pap. 2.95 (978-1-56212-279-9(7), 001210, Faith Alive Christian Resources) CRC Pubns.

—A Rainy, Rainy Day: The Story of Noah. 1998. (God Loves Me Ser.). (Illus.). 24p. (J). (ps-3). pap. 2.95 (978-1-56212-275-1(4), 001206) CRC Pubns.

—Safe at Last! The Story of Moses & the Red Sea. 1998. (God Loves Me Ser.). (Illus.). 24p. (J). (ps-3). pap. 2.95 (978-1-56212-282-9(7), 001213, Faith Alive Christian Resources) CRC Pubns.

—Samuel, Samuel! The Story of God's Call to Samuel. 1998. (God Loves Me Ser.). (Illus.). 24p. (J). (ps-3). pap. 2.95 (978-1-56212-286-7(X), 001217, Faith Alive Christian Resources) CRC Pubns.

—Take Good Care of My World! The Story of Adam & Eve in the Garden. 1998. (God Loves Me Ser.). (Illus.). 24p. (J). (ps-3). pap. 2.95 (978-1-56212-273-7(8), 001204, Faith Alive Christian Resources) CRC Pubns.

—A Tall Wall: The Story of Jericho. 1998. (God Loves Me Ser.). (Illus.). 24p. (J). (ps-3). pap. 2.95 (978-1-56212-284-3(3), 001215, Faith Alive Christian Resources) CRC Pubns.

—Two Coats for Joseph: The Story of Young Joseph. 1998. (God Loves Me Ser.). (Illus.). 24p. (J). (ps-3). pap. 2.95 (978-1-56212-278-2(9), 001209, Faith Alive Christian Resources) CRC Pubns.

—A Very Sad Day: The Story of Adam & Eve's Disobedience. 1998. (God Loves Me Ser.). (Illus.). 24p. (J). (ps-3). pap. 2.95 (978-1-56212-274-4(6), 001205, Faith Alive Christian Resources) CRC Pubns.

—What Is It? The Story of Manna in the Desert. 1998. (God Loves Me Ser.). (Illus.). 24p. (J). (ps-3). pap. 2.95 (978-1-56212-283-6(5), 001214, Faith Alive Christian Resources) CRC Pubns.

Noah & the Ark. (Bible Friends plus Book Ser.). (Illus.). 10p. (J). (ps-k). 6.99 (978-0-8254-7211-4(3)) Kregel Pubns.

Noah & the Ark. 2004. 5.95 (978-1-57264-240-9(8)) Parsons Technology.

Noah & the Ark. Date not set. (J). 8.95 (978-0-88271-533-9(X), 10521) Regina Pr., Malhame & Co.

Noah's Ark. 2002. (Illus.). 24p. (J). 5.99 (978-1-57759-516-8(5)); pap. 2.29 (978-1-57759-052-1(X)); 1.49 (978-1-57759-272-3(7)) Dalmatian Pr.

Noah's Ark. 2000. (Illus.). (J). (ps-k). bds. 4.95 (978-0-88271-687-9(5)) Regina Pr., Malhame & Co.

Noah's Ark. 2002. (J). spiral bd. (978-0-9720158-9-9(2)) Story Reader, Inc.

Noah's Ark: A Bible Story to Color. (Illus.). 16p. (J). pap. 1.50 (978-0-87162-823-7(6), E6017) Warner Pr. Pubs.

Noah's Ark: Sunday School Songs. 2001. (Illus.). (J). 7.98 (978-0-7853-4851-1(4), 0785348514) Cook, David C. Publishing Co.

Noah's Ark Read Along. 1999. (Sunday Morning Ser.). (J). (ps-3). pap. 6.98 incl. audio compact disk (978-0-7634-0576-2(0)) Walt Disney Records.

Noble, Marty. Stories from the Old Testament. 2001. (Dover Coloring Bks.). (Illus.). 64p. (J). pap. 3.50 (978-0-486-41323-5(3)) Dover Pubns., Inc.

Nystrom, Carolyn. Courage, Esther! Dahl, Sharon, illus. 1998. (Follow the Leader Stories Ser.). 32p. (J). (ps-3). 7.99 (978-0-8024-2206-4(3)) Moody Pubs.

Okrant, Mark. Judson's Island. 2006. per. 10.95 (***978-0-9791757-2-5(0)***) Oak Manor Publishing, Inc.

Old Testament Carry Home Stori. 2004. pap. 10.95 (978-0-7647-0498-7(2)) School Specialty Publishing.

Old Testament Stories. 2004. (In Celebration Coloring & Activity Book Ser.). (Illus.). 32p. (J). (gr. k-2). pap. 1.99 (978-0-7647-1015-5(X), In Celebration) Schaffer, Frank Pubns.

Pagnucci, Franco & Pagnucci, Susan. Jonah & the Whale & Other Old Testament Stories. Pagnucci, Susan, illus. 2000. (Illus.). 64p. (J). (ps-3). pap. 8.99 (978-0-929326-15-3(6)) Bur Oak Pr., Inc.

Parker, Victoria. Adam & Eve & Other Stories. 2002. (Bible Discoverers Ser.). (Illus.). 64p. (gr. 3-7). pap. 7.95 (978-1-84215-630-8(6), Southwater) Anness Publishing GBR. *Dist:* National Bk. Network.

—David & Goliath: And Other Old Testament Stories. 2000. (Discovering the Bible Ser.). (Illus.). 64p. (gr. 3-7). 12.95 (978-0-7548-0458-1(5), Lorenz Bks.) Anness Publishing GBR. *Dist:* National Bk. Network.

—Jonah & the Whale: Discovering the Bible & Other Old Testament Stories. 2000. (Discovering the Bible Ser.). (Illus.). 64p. (gr. 3-7). 12.95 (978-0-7548-0456-7(9), Lorenz Bks.) Anness Publishing GBR. *Dist:* National Bk. Network.

—Samson, Delilah & Other Old Testament Stories. 2000. (Discovering the Bible Ser.). (Illus.). 64p. (gr. 3-7). 12.95 (978-0-7548-0206-8(X), Lorenz Bks.) Anness Publishing GBR. *Dist:* National Bk. Network.

Parker, Victoria, ed. Children's Illustrated Bible Old Testament: Retold for the Young Reader with Context Facts, Notes, & Features. 2000. (Illus.). 256p. (J). (gr. 4-7). (978-1-84215-187-7(8), Southwater) Anness Publishing.

Parker, Victoria, retold by. Children's Illustrated Bible Stories from the Old Testament. 2001. (Illus.). 256p. pap. 19.95 (978-1-84215-523-3(7), Southwater) Anness Publishing GBR. *Dist:* National Bk. Network.

Parry, Alan. Noah's Ark: A Touch & Feel Book. Parry, Linda, illus. 2000. (J). (ps). 9.00 (978-0-687-03530-4(9)) Abingdon Pr.

Parry, Alan & Parry, Linda. Look for the Rainbow: Look Through the Telescope, Lift the Flaps, Work the Puzzles, See the Pop-Ups, & Enjoy Hours of Fun with Noah. 2003. (Illus.). 14p. 12.99 (978-1-85608-212-9(1)) Hunt, John Publishing Ltd. GBR. *Dist:* STL Distribution North America.

Pennington, Jack & Tank, Darrel, illus. Joseph. 2004. 87p. (J). pap. (978-0-8280-1855-5(3)) Review & Herald Publishing Assn.

Pierce, David, et al. Tales from the Ark. LeBarre, Matt, illus. 2001. 128p. (J). 12.99 (978-0-310-23218-6(X)) Zonderkidz.

Pingry, Patricia. Treasury of Old Testament Heroes. 2005. (Illus.). 192p. (J). 8.97 (978-0-8249-4258-8(2)) Ideals Pubns.

Pingry, Patricia A. Bible Story Cards: The Story of Noah. 2006. (Illus.). 10p. 7.95 (978-0-8249-1703-6(0)) Ideals Pubns.

A B

—David & Goliath: A Story about Trusting in God: Based on 1 Samuel 17:1/50. Munger, Nancy, illus. 2005. (Children of the Bible Ser.). 23p. (J). bds. 6.95 (978-0-8249-6570-9(1)) Ideals Pubns.

—La Historia de los Diez Mandamientos. Venturi-Pickett, Stacy, illus. 2000. Tr. of Story of the Ten Commandments. (SPA.). 26p. (J). (ps-k). 6.95 (978-0-8249-4191-8(8)) Ideals Pubns.

—Jonah & the Fish: Based on Jonah 1-3:3. 2005. (Stories from the Bible Ser.). (Illus.). 26p. (J). bds. 6.95 (978-0-8249-6626-3(0)) Ideals Pubns.

—Joseph & the Dream: Based on Genesis 37/46:7. 2005. (Stories from the Bible Ser.). (Illus.). 26p. (J). bds. 6.95 (978-0-8249-6625-6(2)) Ideals Pubns.

—The Story of Adam & Eve. Thornburgh, Rebecca McKillip, illus. 2002. 26p. (J). bds. 6.95 (978-0-8249-6280-7(X) , Candy Cane Pr.) Ideals Pubns.

—The Story of Jonah. Venturi-Pickett, Stacy, illus. 1998. 26p. (J). (ps-k). bds. 6.95 (978-0-8249-4094-2(6) , Ideals Children's Bks.) Ideals Pubns.

—The Story of Joseph. Spence, Jim, illus. 1999. 26p. (J). (ps-k). bds. 6.95 (978-0-8249-4152-9(7) , Ideals Children's Bks.) Ideals Pubns.

—The Story of Joshua. Spence, Jim, illus. 1999. 26p. (J). (ps-3). bds. 6.95 (978-0-8249-4153-6(5) , Ideals Children's Bks.) Ideals Pubns.

—The Story of Miriam & Baby Moses. Venturi-Pickett, Stacy, illus. 2000. 26p. (J). (ps-3). bds. 6.95 (978-0-8249-4180-2(2) , Candy Cane Pr.) Ideals Pubns.

Pingry, Patricia A. The Story of Noah. Venturi-Pickett, Stacy, illus. 2007. 32p. pap. 3.99 (***978-0-8249-5569-4(2)*** , Ideals Children's Bks.) Ideals Pubns.

Pingry, Patricia A. & Venturi-Pickett, Stacy, trs. The Story of Creation. Venturi-Pickett, Stacy, illus. 2003. (Illus.). 26p. (J). bds. 7.95 (978-0-8249-6504-4(3)) Ideals Pubns.

Pinkney, Jerry. Noah's Ark. 2002. (Illus.). 40p. (J). (gr. k-4). 16.95 (978-1-58717-201-4(1) , SeaStar Bks.) Chronicle Bks. LLC.

—Noah's Ark. 2004. (J). (gr. k-3). 24.95 incl. audio (978-1-55592-530-7(8)); 29.95 incl. cd-rom (978-1-55592-533-8(2)) Weston Woods Studios, Inc.

Pinsker, Marlee. In the Days of Sand & Stars. Thisdale, Francois, illus. 2006. 88p. (J). (gr. 4-8). 22.95 (978-0-88776-724-1(9)) Tundra Bks., Inc./Livres Toundra, Inc. CAN. *Dist:* Random Hse., Inc.

Poole, Susie, illus. Old Testament Tales: From the Lion Storyteller Bible. 2000. 32p. (J). pap. 6.99 (978-0-7459-4407-4(8) , Lion) Lion Hudson plc GBR. *Dist:* Independent Pubs. Group.

Precious Moments Bible: Small Hands Edition. 1999. (Illus.). 1088p. (J). (ps-3). im. lthr. 24.99 (978-0-7852-0043-7(6)) Nelson, Thomas Inc.

Pulley, Kelly, illus. Adam & Eve in the Garden: My First I Can Read! 2008. 32p. (J). pap. (***978-0-310-71552-8(0)***) Zonderkidz.

—Daniel & the Lions: My First I Can Read! 2008. 32p. (J). pap. (***978-0-310-71551-1(2)***) Zonderkidz.

—Esther & the King. 2007. (I Can Read!). 32p. (J). pap. 3.99 (***978-0-310-71460-6(5)***) Zonderkidz.

—Jonah & the Big Fish. 2007. (I Can Read!). 32p. (J). pap. 3.99 (***978-0-310-71459-0(1)***) Zonderkidz.

Puppet Prod. Puppet Production - Old Testament Programs (Russian) Life Publishers International Staff, tr. from ENG. 2003. Orig. Title: The Children's Programming Collection. (RUS.). 88p. (J). (978-0-7361-0332-9(5)) Life Pubs. International.

Quere, France. Sarah, Who Loved Laughter. Marsh, Gwen, tr. from FRE. Duntze, Dorothee, illus. 1998. (Tales of Heaven & Earth Ser.).Tr. of Celle Qui Riait Quand Dieu Parlait. 32p. (YA). (gr. 3-7). pap. 19.95 (978-0-88682-826-4(0) , Creative Education) Creative Co., The.

Rabbit. Ruth in Canaan. 2005. (J). 10.95 (978-0-689-80232-4(3) , Simon & Schuster Children's Publishing) Simon & Schuster Children's Publishing.

Racklin-Siegel, Alison, illus. Jacob's Travels. 2005. (ENG & HEB.). (J). per. 9.95 (978-0-939144-53-2(0)) EKS Publishing Co.

Racklin-Siegel, Carol, illus. Lech Lecha: The Story of Abraham & Rebecca. 2004. (HEB & ENG.). (J). per. 8.50 (978-0-939144-49-5(2)) EKS Publishing Co.

Ray, Jane. Adam & Eve & the Garden of Eden. Ray, Jane, illus. 2005. (Illus.). 32p. (J). 17.00 (978-0-8028-5278-6(5)) Eerdmans, William B. Publishing Co.

—Adam & Eve & the Garden of Eden. 2006. (Illus.). 32p. (J). pap. (978-1-903919-07-1(X) , Eden Project Books) Transworld Publishers Ltd.

The Roach Approach, Noah's Journey of Faith: Read along. 2003. (J). audio compact disk 12.99 (978-0-9742997-1-6(5)) Wacky World Studios LLC.

Robb, Andy. The Adventures of Moses. 2001. (Illus.). 10p. (J). (ps-3). 5.99 (978-0-570-07146-4(1)) Concordia Publishing Hse.

—Lost Son, 1. 1999. (Illus.). 10p. (J). (ps). 6.00 (978-0-570-05587-7(3)) Concordia Publishing Hse.

—Magnificent Moses. 2004. (Holy Happenings Ser.). (Illus.). 128p. pap. 6.50 (978-0-687-02316-5(5)) Abingdon Pr.

Rodriguez, Orlando & Sabio Y Prudente Ministries Staff. Libro a Color Abel y Cain. 2002. (Sabio Y Prudente Ser.).Tr. of Cain & Abel Story Book. (SPA.). 32p. (J). pap. 4.99 (978-0-8254-0985-1(3) , Editorial Portavoz) Kregel Pubns.

Russell, Patricia C. Beginnings I - & It Was Good! Old Testament Lessons for Little Listeners. Clark, Virginia A., ed. 1999. (Beginnings I Ser.). 301p. (J). (ps-k). spiral bd. 23.99 (978-1-889015-27-9(X)) Explorer's Bible Study.

Ruth. 14p. (J). bds. 7.99 (978-0-7847-1404-1(5)) Standard Publishing.

Ryan, John. The Very Hungry Lions. 1998. (Illus.). 28p. (J). pap. 9.99 (978-0-7459-3919-3(8) , Lion) Lion Hudson plc GBR. *Dist:* Independent Pubs. Group.

Santamaria, Leslie. A Mother Who Prayed: 1 Samuel 1. Grant-Barr, Marilynn, illus. 2000. (Arch Bks.). (ENG.). 16p. (J). (gr. k-4). 1.99 (978-0-570-07566-0(1)) Concordia Publishing Hse.

Sasso, Sandy Eisenberg. Adam & Eve's First Sunset: God's New Day. Rothenberg, Joani Keller, illus. 2003. 32p. (J). 17.95 (978-1-58023-177-0(2)) Jewish Lights Publishing.

School Specialty Publishing. David & Goliath. 2004. 10p. (J). 1.99 (978-0-7647-1045-2(1) , In Celebration) Schaffer, Frank Pubns.

—Joseph & His Coat of Many Colors. 2004. (Bible Card Games Ser.). nap. (J). (gr. k-8). 0.99 (978-0-7647-1006-3(0) , In Celebration) Schaffer, Frank Pubns.

Schur, Maxine Rose. The Story of Ruth. Connelly, Gwen, illus. 2005. 32p. (J). (gr. 2-4). lib. bdg. 16.95 (978-1-58013-114-8(X)) Kar-Ben Publishing.

Seis Lindos Dias. 2003. (SPA.). 6.99 (978-0-7814-3598-7(6) , 0781435986) Cook, David C. Publishing Co.

Shapes & Sizes: Bible Story: Solomon Builds God's House. (Scripture Bites Ser.). (Illus.). (J). 7.99 (978-0-7847-9024-3(8) , 00714) Standard Publishing.

Shoemaker, Tim. Tried & True Job, 6 vols. Hohnstadt, Cedric, illus. 2000. (Arch Bks.). (ENG.). 16p. (J). (gr. k-4). 1.99 (978-0-570-07561-5(0)) Concordia Publishing Hse.

Simon, Mary Mans. David & Goliath: Read & Learn the Bible. 2005. (Illus.). 24p. (J). pap. 2.99 (978-1-4037-1161-8(5) , Spirit Pr.) Dalmatian Pr.

—Jonah & the Big Fish: Read & Learn the Bible. 2005. (Illus.). 24p. (J). pap. 2.99 (978-1-4037-1158-8(5) , Spirit Pr.) Dalmatian Pr.

Simon, Mary Manz. Touch-and-See Bible. 2006. (New Living Translation Bible Story Ser.). 14p. bds. 9.99 (978-0-7847-1595-6(5) , 04142) Standard Publishing.

—Word-and-Picture Bible. 2006. (New Living Translation Bible Story Ser.). 14p. bds. 6.99 (978-0-7847-1594-9(7) , 04141) Standard Publishing.

Simon, Norma. The Story of Passover. 1998. (Trophy Picture Bks.). (978-0-606-13044-8(6)) Tandem Library Bks.

Smart Kids Publishing Staff. Adam & Eve: All about Doing What's Right. 2006. 12p. (ps). bds. 14.95 (978-0-8249-6660-7(0) , Candy Cane Pr.) Ideals Pubns.

—David & Goliath: All about Courage. 2006. (Illus.). 12p. (ps). bds. 14.95 (978-0-8249-6659-1(7) , Candy Cane Pr.) Ideals Pubns.

—Noah & the Ark: All about Being Thankful. 2006. 12p. (ps). bds. 19.95 (978-0-8249-6658-4(9) , Candy Cane Pr.) Ideals Pubns.

Smart Kids Publishing Staff. Noah's Ark Story of Being Thankful. 2007. 16p. (J). 19.99 (***978-0-8249-6703-1(8)***) Ideals Pubns.

Stewart, Jennifer, ed. Noah's Ark. Marlin, Kathy, illus. 1999. 28p. (J). (ps-2). pap. 3.49 (978-0-7847-1096-8(1) , 22080) Standard Publishing.

Stories about Daniel. (Old Testament Pict-O-Graph Ser.). (J). 10.99 (978-0-7847-1040-1(6)) Standard Publishing.

The Story of Adam & Eve. 2003. (Illus.). 24p. (J). bds. 6.95 (978-0-8249-4229-8(9)) Ideals Pubns.

The Story of Baby Moses. 2002. (Illus.). 14p. (J). (ps). bds. 5.97 (978-1-57759-453-6(3)) Dalmatian Pr.

The Story of Creation. 2000. (Illus.). (J). (ps-k). bds. 4.95 (978-0-88271-688-6(3)) Regina Pr., Malhame & Co.

The Story of Creation. 2002. (J). spiral bd. (978-0-9720158-7-5(6)) Story Reader, Inc.

The Story of David. 2000. (Illus.). 24p. (J). (ps-k). bds. 6.95 (978-0-8249-4171-0(3)) Ideals Pubns.

The Story of Noah: La Historia de Noe. 2001. (ENG & SPA.). 28p. (J). pap. 3.95 (978-0-8249-4135-2(7)) Ideals Pubns.

The Story of Samson. 2002. (Illus.). 24p. (J). bds. 6.95 (978-0-8249-4226-7(4)) Ideals Pubns.

The Story of the Ten Commandments. 1999. (Illus.). 24p. (J). (ps-k). bds. 6.95 (978-0-8249-4165-9(9)) Ideals Pubns.

The Story of the Ten Commandments/la Historia de Los Diez Mandamientos. 2002. (SPA & ENG., Illus.). 28p. (J). pap. 3.95 (978-0-8249-4205-2(1)) Ideals Pubns.

El Sueno de Jacob. 2001. (Libros Arco Ser.). (SPA.). 24p. (J). (gr. k-4). 2.49 (978-0-570-05183-1(5)) Concordia Publishing Hse.

Sun/Moon/Stars/Planets: Bible Story: God Made Our World. (Scripture Bites Ser.). (Illus.). (J). 7.99 (978-0-7847-9016-8(7) , 00709) Standard Publishing.

Taylor, Damon. To Cheese or Not to Cheese: The Story of Ruth. 2003. (Child Sockology Ser.). (Illus.). 32p. (J). 10.99 (978-0-8254-3866-0(7)) Kregel Pubns.

Taylor, Damon J. Bible Feelings: Old Testament. 2003. (Child Sockology Ser.). 10p. (J). bds. 6.99 (978-0-8254-3860-8(8)) Kregel Pubns.

—Escondido y Hundido: La Historia de Jonas. 2003. (Mis Calcetines Ser.).Tr. of Hide & Sink the Story of Jonah. (SPA., Illus.).-32p. (YA). 6.99 (978-0-8254-0751-2(6) , Editorial Portavoz) Kregel Pubns.

—A Little Man with a Big Plan: The Story of Young David. 2003. (Child Sockology Ser.). (Illus.). 36p. (J). 10.99 (978-0-8254-3861-5(6)) Kregel Pubns.

Thaler, Mike. Sermonators. 2001. (gr. 5-8). lib. bdg. 11.80 (978-0-613-74915-2(4)) Tandem Library Bks.

Thanksgiving: Bible Story: Give Thanks to the Lord. (Scripture Bites Ser.). (Illus.). (J). 7.99 (978-0-7847-9019-9(1) , 00712) Standard Publishing.

Thomas, Jerry D. Shoebox Kids' Bible Stories. 2001. (Illus.). (J). 126p. (978-0-8163-1823-0(9)); Vol. 2. 128p. 7.99 (978-0-8163-1877-3(8)) Pacific Pr. Publishing Assn.

Thomas Nelson Publishing Staff. My Big Bible Sticker Book: Old Testament. 2006. 84p. (J). pap. 12.99 (978-1-4003-0825-5(9)) Nelson, Thomas Inc.

Thomas Nelson Publishing Staff, creator. Magnify Old Testament Stories-ICB. 2005. (Illus.). 400p. (J). (gr. 2-6). pap. 16.99 (978-1-4003-0641-1(8)) Nelson, Thomas Inc.

Tucker, Jennifer Herrick. Two by Two: A Noah's Ark Adventure. Ward, Jordan, illus. 2002. 80p. (J). per. 11.95 (978-0-9715198-2-4(X)) PJN & Assocs.

Turner, Steve. In the Beginning. Newton, Jill, illus. 2002. 32p. (ps-3). 10.99 (978-0-8066-4363-2(3) , Augsburg Bks.) Augsburg Fortress, Pubs.

van Rijswijk, Cor. Abraham's Sacrifice. Visser, Rino, illus. 2001. 43p. (J). pap. (978-1-894666-21-3(6)) Inheritance Pubns.

—David & Goliath. Visser, Rino, illus. 2003. 43p. (J). (978-1-894666-23-7(2)) Inheritance Pubns.

—Gideon Blows the Trumpet. Visser, Rino, illus. 2003. 43p. (J). (978-1-894666-22-0(4)) Inheritance Pubns.

Veranos, Sandi. David, the Giant Fighter. 2003. (Pencil Fun Bks.: Vol. 10). 16p. (J). (gr. 7-4). pap., pap. 9.90 (978-1-55513-026-8(7) , 1555130267) Cook, David C. Publishing Co.

Ward, Brenda. Noah & the Big Boat. Fuller, Dollar, photos by. 1998. (Bible Babies Ser.). (Illus.). 16p. (J). 7.95 (978-0-8054-1779-1(6)) B&H Publishing Grp.

Warner Press Staff. Old Testament. 1999. (Illus.). (J). pap. 3.95 (978-0-87162-861-9(9)) Warner Pr. Pubs.

—Think Again: Old Testament Bible Activities. 1999. (Illus.). (J). pap. 3.95 (978-0-87162-865-7(1)) Warner Pr. Pubs.

Wedeven, Carol. Just in Time Esther, 6 vols. Giliewe, Unada, illus. 1999. (Arch Bks.). (ENG.). 16p. (J). (gr. k-4). 1.99 (978-0-570-07558-5(0)) Concordia Publishing Hse.

Whalin, Terry. Joshua & the Jericho Project. Bergin, Mark, illus. 1998. (Sticker Story Adventures Ser.). 16p. (J). (gr. 2 up). pap. 5.99 (978-0-8054-1669-5(2)) B&H Publishing Grp.

—Moses & the Great Escape. Bergin, Mark, illus. 1998. (Sticker Story Adventures Ser.). 16p. (J). (gr. 2 up). pap. 5.99 (978-0-8054-1670-1(6)) B&H Publishing Grp.

White, John & Tank, Darrel, illus. Abraham. 2004. (Family Bible Story Ser.). 109p. (J). pap. (978-0-8280-1857-9(X)) Review & Herald Publishing Assn.

Wiesel, Elie. King Solomon & His Magic Ring. Podwal, Mark H., illus. 1999. 51p. (J). (978-0-688-16960-2(0)) HarperCollins Pubs.

Wildsmith, Brian. Exodus. Wildsmith, Brian, illus. 1998. (Illus.). 24p. (gr. k-4). 20.00 (978-0-8028-5175-8(4)) Eerdmans, William B. Publishing Co.

Wilger, Jennifer R., ed. Abraham. 2004. (Bible Big Bks.). (Illus.). 8p. (ps up). pap. 15.99 (978-1-55945-437-7(7) , Flagship Church Resources) Group Publishing, Inc.

—God Made Our World. 2003. (Bible Big Bks.). (Illus.). 8p. (ps up). pap. 15.99 (978-1-55945-436-0(9) , Flagship Church Resources) Group Publishing, Inc.

—Jonah. 2003. (Bible Big Bks.). (Illus.). 8p. (ps up). pap. 15.99 (978-1-55945-435-3(0) , Flagship Church Resources) Group Publishing, Inc.

—Samuel. 2003. (Bible Big Bks.). (Illus.). 8p. (ps up). pap. 15.99 (978-1-55945-434-6(2) , Flagship Church Resources) Group Publishing, Inc.

Williams, Marcia. God & His Creations: Stories from the Old Testament. Williams, Marcia, illus. 2004. (Illus.). 40p. (J). (gr. 3-7). 15.99 (978-0-7636-2211-4(7)) Candlewick Pr.

Wilson, N. D. The Dragon & the Garden. 2007. (J). per. 12.00 (***978-1-59128-044-6(3)***) Canon Pr.

Winch, John. Two by Two. 2004. (Illus.). 32p. (J). (gr. k-3). tchr. ed. 16.95 (978-0-8234-1840-4(5)) Holiday Hse., Inc.

Wood, Nancy. Mr. & Mrs. God in the Creation Kitchen. Ering, Timothy Basil, illus. 2006. 32p. (J). (gr. k). 16.99 (978-0-7636-1258-0(8)) Candlewick Pr.

Word Search: Old Testament. (Illus.). 32p. (YA). (gr. 5 up). pap. 2.25 (978-0-87162-496-3(6) , E4800) Warner Pr. Pubs.

Yolen, Jane. The Prince of Egypt: Classic Edition. 1998. (Prince of Egypt Ser.). (Illus.). 80p. (J). (ps-4). 8.99 (978-0-8499-5894-6(6)) Nelson, Thomas Inc.

Zimmer, Giles. God's Fire for Elijah. Eitzen, Allan, illus. 1998. (Arch Bks.). (ENG.). 16p. (J). (gr. k-4). 1.99 (978-0-570-07550-9(5) , 59-1523GJ) Concordia Publishing Hse.

Zobel-Nolan, Allia. Noah & the Ark. MacLean, Moira, illus. 2000. (Baby's First Bible Stories Ser.). 10p. (J). (ps). 9.99 (978-0-7847-1210-8(7) , 04398) Standard Publishing.

Zobel Nolan, Allia & Davis, Caroline. Day the Rain Came. 2006. (Illus.). 8p. (J). bds. 12.99 (978-0-7847-1857-5(1)) Standard Publishing.

Zondervan. The Beginner's Bible' Noah's Ark Backpack. 2007. (J). 14.99 (***978-0-310-81170-1(8)***) Zondervan.

BIBLE STUDY

see Bible—Study

BIBLICAL ARCHEOLOGY

see Bible—Antiquities

BIBLICAL CHARACTERS

see Bible—Biography

BIBLIOGRAPHY—BEST BOOKS

see Best Books

BIBLIOGRAPHY—REFERENCE BOOKS

see Reference Books

BICYCLE RACING—FICTION

The Bike Race: First Wave Satellite Individual Title Six-Packs. (Sails Literacy Ser.). 16p. (gr. k up). 27.00 (978-0-7578-6859-7(2)) Rigby Education.

Hamilton, Virginia. Dustland. 1998. (Justice Cycle Ser.: Bk. 2). 214p. (YA). (gr. 6-12). pap. 4.50 (978-0-590-36217-7(8)) Scholastic, Inc.

—Dustland. 1998. (Justice Cycle Ser.). (978-0-606-12927-5(8)) Tandem Library Bks.

Harcourt School Publishers Staff. Go! Take-Home Book. 1999. (Signatures Ser.). (Illus.). (J). pap. 1.70 (978-0-15-314554-4(4)) Harcourt Schl. Pubs.

Keene, Carolyn. A Race Against Time. 2004. (Nancy Drew Ser.: No. 2). 160p. (J). (gr. 3-7). pap. 4.99 (978-0-689-86567-1(8) , Aladdin) Simon & Schuster Children's Publishing.

Lawrie, Robin & Lawrie, Christine, illus. Cheat Challenge. 2007. 32p. (J). pap. (***978-1-59889-442-4(0)***) Stone Arch Bks.

—Fear 3.1. 2007. 32p. (J). pap. (***978-1-59889-443-1(9)***) Stone Arch Bks.

—Snow Bored. 2007. (J). 32p. pap. (***978-1-59889-444-8(7)***); 40p. (gr. 2-6). lib. bdg. 21.26 (***978-1-59889-349-6(1)***) Stone Arch Bks.

—White Lightning. 2007. (J). 32p. pap. (***978-1-59889-445-5(5)***); 40p. (gr. 2-6). lib. bdg. 21.26 (***978-1-59889-350-2(5)***) Stone Arch Bks.

Marvin Redpost: Super Fast, Out of Control! 2002. (Marvin Redpost Ser.). (Illus.). (J). 11.91 (978-0-7587-6199-6(6)) Book Wholesalers, Inc.

Stinson, Kathy. The Great Bike Race. 2005. (Streetlights Ser.). 104p. (J). (gr. 2-5). 7.95 (978-1-55028-890-2(3)) Lorimer, James & Co., Ltd., Pubs. CAN. *Dist:* Casemate Pubs. & Bk. Distributors, LLC.

Stone Arch Books (Firm : Afton, Minn.) Staff. Cheat Challenge. Lawrie, Robin & Lawrie, Christine, illus. 2007. (Ridge Riders Ser.). 40p. (J). (gr. 2-6). lib. bdg. 21.26 (***978-1-59889-347-2(5)***) Stone Arch Bks.

—Fear 3.1. Lawrie, Robin & Lawrie, Christine, illus. 2007. (Ridge Riders Ser.). 40p. (J). (gr. 2-6). lib. bdg. 21.26 (***978-1-59889-348-9(3)***) Stone Arch Bks.

Wax, Wendy. Watch Out, Otto! Pilar-Newton, Michelle, illus. 2002. (Rocket Power Ready-to-Read Ser.: Vol. 1). 32p. (J). pap. 3.99 (978-0-689-85008-0(5) , Simon Spotlight/ Nickelodeon) Simon & Schuster Children's Publishing.

—Watch Out, Otto! 2002. lib. bdg. 11.80 (978-0-613-57588-1(1)) Tandem Library Bks.

BICYCLES AND BICYCLING

see also Motorcycles

Bach, Julie S. Bicycling. 2000. (World of Sports Ser.). (Illus.). 32p. (J). (gr. 4 up). lib. bdg. 16.95 (978-1-887068-53-6(8)) Smart Apple Media.

Bales, Donnie & Milan, Garth. Freestyle Motocross: Jump Tricks from the Pros. rev. ed. 2000. (Cycle Pro Ser.). (Illus.). 128p. pap. 19.95 (978-0-7603-0926-1(4) , 130526AP) MBI Publishing Co. LLC.

Barraclough, Sue. Bicycle Safety. 2007. (J). (***978-1-4034-9857-1(1)***); pap. (***978-1-4034-9864-9(4)***) Heinemann Library.

Behind the Moves: Extreme Bicycle Stunt Riding Moves; Extreme In-Line Skating Moves; Extreme Skateboarding Moves; Extreme Snowboarding Moves, 4 bks. 2000. (Illus.). (J). (gr. 3-4). lib. bdg. 85.04 (978-0-7368-0874-3(4) , Capstone High-Interest Bks.) Capstone Pr., Inc.

Behr, Steve. Mountain Biking. 1998. (Extreme Sports Ser.). (Illus.). 32p. (J). (gr. 5-9). pap. 6.95 (978-0-7641-0796-2(8)) Barron's Educational Series, Inc.

Beyer, Mark. Bicicletas Del Pasado. 2004. (Transporte Ayer y Hoy Ser.). (SPA & ENG., Illus.). 24p. (J). (gr. 3-6). lib. bdg. 17.25 (978-0-8239-6853-4(7) , Buenas Letra) Rosen Publishing Group, Inc., The.

—Bicycles of the Past. 2002. (Reading Power Ser.). (Illus.). 24p. (J). (gr. 1). lib. bdg. 17.25 (978-0-8239-5985-3(6) , PowerKids Pr.) Rosen Publishing Group, Inc., The.

Bicicletas del Pasado: Individual Title Six-Packs. (On Deck en Espanol Ser.).Tr. of Bicycles of the Past. (SPA.). 24p. (gr. 4-5). 35.00 (978-0-7578-6425-4(2)) Rigby Education.

The Bicycle Book: Individual Nonfiction Title Six-Packs. 24p. (gr. 3-4). 44.00 (978-0-7635-4485-0(X)) Rigby Education.

Bicycles of the Past: Individual Title Six-Packs. (On Deck Ser.). 24p. (gr. 4-5). 35.00 (978-0-7578-1050-3(0)) Rigby Education.

Bicycling Adventures, 6 vols. (gr. 4 up). 39.95 (978-0-7368-9283-4(4)) Red Brick Learning.

Bidder, Jane. Inventions We Use to Go Places. 2006. (Illus.). 32p. lib. bdg. (978-0-8368-6901-9(X)) Stevens, Gareth Inc.

Biking to the Arctic Circle: Adventures with Grandchildren. 2000. 239p. 15.00 (978-1-880675-03-8(X)) Creative Enterprises.

Bledsoe, Karen & Bledsoe, Glen. Bicycling Adventures. 2001. (Dangerous Adventures Ser.). (Illus.). 48p. (J). (gr. 3-4). lib. bdg. 21.26 (978-0-7368-0904-7(X) , Capstone High-Interest Bks.) Capstone Pr., Inc.

Bloomquist, Christopher. BMX in the X Games. 2003. (Kids Guide to the X Games Ser.). (Illus.). 24p. (J). lib. bdg. 19.95 (978-0-8239-6298-3(9) , PowerKids Pr.) Rosen Publishing Group, Inc., The.

BMX Freestyle. (To the Extreme Ser.). 32p. (YA). 7.95 (978-0-7368-5224-1(7)) Capstone Pr., Inc.

Bodden, Valerie. Bicycling. 2007. (J). (978-1-58341-467-5(3) , Creative Education) Creative Co., The.

Brill, Marlene Targ. Marshall Major Taylor: Bicycle Superstar. 2007. (Trailblazer Biographies Ser.). 112p. (YA). (gr. 5-9). lib. bdg. 31.93 (978-0-8225-6610-6(9) , Twenty-First Century Bks.) Lerner Publishing Group.

Brouwer, Sigmund. Mountain Biking—to the Extreme: Cliff Dive. 2002. (Illus.). 60p. (YA). (gr. 3). pap. 3.99 (978-1-55305-012-4(6)) Cygnet Publishing Group, Inc./ Coolreading.com CAN. *Dist:* Orca Bk. Pubs. USA.

Buckley, Annie. Be a Better Biker. 2006. (Girls Rock! Ser.). (Illus.). 32p. (J). (gr. 1-5). 24.21 (978-1-59296-741-4(8)) Child's World, Inc.

Cline-Ransome, Lesa. Major Taylor, Champion Cyclist. Ransome, James E., illus. 2003. 40p. (J). 16.95 (978-0-689-83159-1(5) , Atheneum/Anne Schwartz Bks.) Simon & Schuster Children's Publishing.

Cole, Steve. Kids' Easy Bike Care: Tune-Ups, Tools & Quick Fixes. 2004. (Williamson's Quick Starts for Kids!(R) Ser.). (Illus.). 64p. (J). pap. 8.95 (978-1-885593-86-3(4) , Williamson Bks.) Ideals Pubns.

Cook, J. Mountain Bikes. 1999. (Superskills Ser.). (Illus.). 48p. (YA). (gr. 6-10). lib. bdg. 13.95 (978-0-88110-426-4(4)) EDC Publishing.

Cotter, Alison. Cycling. 2002. (History of Sports Ser.). (Illus.). 104p. (YA). (gr. 6-9). 29.95 (978-1-59018-071-6(2) , Lucent Bks.) Thomson Gale.

Craats, Rennay. Biking. 2001. (For the Love of Sports Ser.). (Illus.). 24p. (J). lib. bdg. 15.95 (978-1-930954-12-0(3)) Weigl Pubs., Inc.

Crossingham, John. Extreme BMX. 2003. (Extreme Sports - No Limits Ser.). (Illus.). 32p. (J). (gr. 3). (978-0-7787-1666-2(X)) Crabtree Publishing Co.

Crowther, Nicky. Ultimate Mountain Bike Book. 2002. (gr. 7-12). lib. bdg. 36.15 (978-0-613-56665-0(3)) Tandem Library Bks.

David, Jack. BMX Racing. 2007. (Illus.). 24p. (J). lib. bdg. 19.95 (978-1-60014-122-5(6)) Bellwether Media.

—BMX Racing. 2007. (Torque: Action Sports Ser.). (Illus.). 24p. (J). (gr. 3-7). lib. bdg. 20.00 (***978-0-531-18490-5(0)*** , Children's Pr.) Scholastic Library Publishing.

De Medeiros, Michael. Mountain Biking. 2007. (J). (***978-1-59036-665-3(4) ; (978-1-59036-666-0(2))*** Weigl Pubs., Inc.

Deady, Kathleen W. BMX Bikes. 2001. (Wild Rides! Ser.). (Illus.). 32p. (J). (gr. 3-4). lib. bdg. 21.26 (978-0-7368-0925-2(2) , Capstone High-Interest Bks.) Capstone Pr., Inc.

—BMX Bikes. (Wild Rides! Ser.). 32p. (YA). pap. 7.95 (978-0-7368-9190-5(0)) Capstone Pr., Inc.

—Extreme Mountain Biking Moves. 2003. (Behind the Moves Ser.). (Illus.). 32p. (J). (gr. 3-4). lib. bdg. 21.26 (978-0-7368-1513-0(9) , Capstone High-Interest Bks.) Capstone Pr., Inc.

DeGraaf, Rob L. Fat Tire Favorites: South Florida off-Road Bicycling. DeGraaf, Rob L. & DeGraaf, Rebecca L., eds. DeGraaf, Rebecca L., photos by. 2003. Orig. Title: Guide to South Florida off-Road Bicycling. (Illus.). 111p. per. 12.95 (978-0-9678385-2-6(5)) DeGraaf Publishing.

Dick, Scott. BMX. 2002. (Radical Sports Ser.). (Illus.). 32p. (J). (gr. 5-7). pap. 7.50 (978-1-4034-0103-8(9) , 91651); lib. bdg. 25.64 (978-1-58810-623-0(3)) Heinemann Library.

Ditchfield, Christin. Cycling. 2000. (gr. 3-6). lib. bdg. 15.25 (978-0-613-51631-0(1)) Tandem Library Bks.

Doeden, Matt. BMX Freestyle. 2004. (To the Extreme Ser.). (Illus.). 149p. (J). 19.93 (978-0-7368-2728-7(5)) Capstone Pr., Inc.

Donaldson, Tony. Bmx Trix & Techniques for the Park & Street. rev. ed. 2004. (Illus.). 128p. pap. 19.95 (978-0-7603-1963-5(4) , Motorbooks) MBI Publishing Co. LLC.

Downhill BMX. (To the Extreme Ser.). 32p. (YA). 7.95 (978-0-7368-5220-3(4)) Capstone Pr., Inc.

Eck, Kristin. Bicycle Stunt Riding: Check It Out. 2001. (Reading Power Ser.). (Illus.). 24p. (J). (gr. 1). lib. bdg. 17.25 (978-0-8239-5697-5(0) , PowerKids Pr.) Rosen Publishing Group, Inc., The.

—Mountain Biking: Check It Out. 2001. (Reading Power Ser.). (Illus.). 24p. (J). (gr. 2-4). lib. bdg. 17.25 (978-0-8239-5698-2(9) , PKMOBI, PowerKids Pr.) Rosen Publishing Group, Inc., The.

Eckart, Edana. I Can Ride a Bike. 2002. (Wel-Sports Ser.). (Illus.). 24p. (J). (ps-2). 18.00 (978-0-516-23967-5(8)); pap. 4.95 (978-0-516-24032-9(3)) Scholastic Library Publishing. (Children's Pr.).

—I Can Ride a Bike. 2002. (gr. k-3). lib. bdg. 12.95 (978-0-613-58843-0(6)) Tandem Library Bks.

Endres, Hollie. Mountain Biking. 2007. (Illus.). 24p. (J). lib. bdg. 19.95 (978-1-60014-126-3(9)) Bellwether Media.

Firestone, Mary. Extreme Downhill BMX Racing Moves. 2003. (Behind the Moves Ser.). (Illus.). 32p. (J). lib. bdg. 22.60 (978-0-7368-2152-0(X) , Capstone High/Low Bks.) Capstone Pr., Inc.

Franks, Katie. Tricks with Bikes. 2007. (Motorcycles Ser.). (Illus.). 24p. (J). (gr. k-5). lib. bdg. 21.25 (978-1-4042-3657-8(0)) Rosen Publishing Group, Inc., The.

Friddle-Ponder, Alma. Bicycle Unit Study Part 1. 2007. (Illus.). spiral bd. 14.95 (***978-1-934627-08-2(9))*** Fish Head Pubns., LLC.

—Bicycle Unit Study Part 1 Reading Enhanced Edition. 2007. (Illus.). spiral bd. 14.95 (***978-1-934627-13-6(5))*** Fish Head Pubns., LLC.

—Bicycle Unit Study Parts 1 & 2 Comprehensive Edition. 2007. (Illus.). 86p. spiral bd. 19.95 (***978-1-934627-07-5(0))*** Fish Head Pubns., LLC.

Friddle=Ponder, Alma. Bicycle Unit Study Part 2. 2007. (Illus.). spiral bd. 14.95 (***978-1-934627-09-9(7))*** Fish Head Pubns., LLC.

Gardner, Robert. Bicycle Science Projects: Physics on Wheels. 2004. (Science Fair Success Ser.). (Illus.). 112p. (J). lib. bdg. 26.60 (978-0-7660-1630-9(7)) Enslow Pubs., Inc.

Gedatus, Gus. Bicycling for Fitness. 2000. (Nutrition & Fitness Ser.). (Illus.). 64p. (J). (gr. 4-6). lib. bdg. 23.93 (978-0-7368-0705-0(5) , LifeMatters Bks.) Capstone Pr., Inc.

Gifford, Clive. Mountain Biking. 2005. (Adrenalin! Ser.). (Illus.). 32p. (J). (gr. 4 up). lib. bdg. 27.10 (978-1-59389-237-1(3)) Chrysalis Education.

Gilbert, Grant. Tour de France. 2007. (J). (***978-1-59036-693-6(X) ; (978-1-59036-694-3(8))*** Weigl Pubs., Inc.

Glaser, Jason. Bicycle Stunt Riding. 1999. (Extreme Sports Ser.). (Illus.). 48p. (J). (gr. 3-4). lib. bdg. 21.26 (978-0-7368-0167-6(7) , Capstone High-Interest Bks.) Capstone Pr., Inc.

Graham, Ian. Cars & Bikes: Machines at Work. 2007. (J). lib. bdg. 19.95 (978-1-59566-317-7(7)) QEB Publishing Inc.

Green, Robert. Bicycles. 2008. (J). lib. bdg. 25.26 (***978-1-60279-024-7(8))*** Cherry Lake Publishing.

Gutman, Bill. Greg LeMond. 1998. (Overcoming the Odds Ser.). (Illus.). 48p. (J). (gr. 3-8). (978-0-8172-4130-8(2)) Raintree.

Hayhurst, Chris. Bicycle Stunt Riding! Catch Air. 2000. (Extreme Sports Collection). (Illus.). 64p. (YA). (gr. 5-8). lib. bdg. 26.50 (978-0-8239-3011-1(4) , EXBIST, Rosen Central) Rosen Publishing Group, Inc., The.

—Bicycle Stunt Riding! Catch Air. 2000. (Illus.). 64p. (YA). per. 9.95 (978-1-56254-300-6(8) , SP 3008) Saddleback Educational Publishing.

—Bike Trekking: Have Fun, Be Smart. 2005. (Explore the Outdoors Ser.). (Illus.). 64p. (J). (gr. 7-12). lib. bdg. 26.50 (978-0-8239-3172-9(2) , EOBITR) Rosen Publishing Group, Inc., The.

—Mountain Biking! Get on the Trail. 2000. (Extreme Sports Collection). (Illus.). 64p. (YA). (gr. 5-8). lib. bdg. 26.50 (978-0-8239-3013-5(0) , EXMOBI, Rosen Central) Rosen Publishing Group, Inc., The.

—Mountain Biking! Get on the Trail. 2000. (Illus.). 64p. (YA). per. 9.95 (978-1-56254-303-7(2) , SP 3032) Saddleback Educational Publishing.

Heller, D. M. Let's Make a Bike with Everyday Materials. 2006. (Illus.). 24p. (J). lib. bdg. (978-1-4042-3064-4(5)) Rosen Publishing Group, Inc., The.

Herran, Joe & Thomas, Ron. BMX Riding. 2002. (Action Sports Ser.). (Illus.). 32p. (gr. 4-8). 28.00 (978-0-7910-7002-4(6) , Chelsea Hse.) Facts On File, Inc.

Hills, Larry. The Bicycle. 2004. (Fact Finders Ser.). (Illus.). 32p. (J). (gr. 3-5). lib. bdg. 22.60 (978-0-7368-2668-6(8) , Fact Finders) Capstone Pr., Inc.

Housel, Debra J. & Migiliaccio, Eric. Cycling: Easy Olympic Sports Reader. 2004. (U. S. Olympic Committee Easy Olympic Sports Readers Ser.). (Illus.). 16p. (J). pap. 2.99 (978-1-58000-111-3(4)) Griffin Publishing Group.

How Bicycles Work: Second Grade Big Books. (On Our Way to English Ser.). (gr. 2 up). 29.95 (978-0-7578-1425-9(5)) Rigby Education.

How Bicycles Work: Small Versions of Big Books. (On Our Way to English Ser.). (gr. 2 up). 29.00 (978-0-7578-7236-5(0)) Rigby Education.

Hughes, Morgan. Bicycles. 2003. (Wheels in Motion Ser.). (Illus.). 24p. (J). 20.64 (978-1-58952-665-5(1)) Rourke Publishing, LLC.

Jefferis, David. All-Terrain Biking. 2001. (Young Library - Super Sports). (Illus.). 32p. (J). lib. bdg. 25.69 (978-0-7398-4345-1(1)) Raintree.

Job, Chris. BMX. 2004. (Extreme Sports Ser.). (Illus.). 32p. (J). (gr. 3-6). lib. bdg. 22.60 (978-0-8225-1243-1(2)) Lerner Publishing Group.

Kaelberer, Angie Peterson. BMX Racing. 2006. (Blazers—To the Extreme Ser.). (Illus.). 32p. (J). (978-0-7368-4397-3(3)) Capstone Pr., Inc.

Kalman, Bobbie. Extreme BMX. 2003. (gr. 3-6). lib. bdg. 15.25 (978-0-613-82412-5(1)) Tandem Library Bks.

Kalman, Bobbie & Crossingham, John. Cycling in Action. 2002. (Sports in Action Ser.). (Illus.). 32p. (J). (gr. 3-4). (978-0-7787-0118-7(2)); pap. (978-0-7787-0124-8(7)) Crabtree Publishing Co.

Kelley, K. C. Mountain Biking. 2003. (Extreme Sports Ser.). (Illus.). 24p. (J). (gr. 2 up). lib. bdg. 22.00 (978-0-8368-3723-0(1)) Stevens, Gareth Inc.

—Stunt Bicycle Riding. 2003. (Extreme Sports Ser.). (Illus.). 24p. (J). (gr. 2 up). lib. bdg. 22.00 (978-0-8368-3726-1(6)) Stevens, Gareth Inc.

King, Andy. Mountain Biking. rev. ed. 2005. (Play-by-Play Ser.). (Illus.). 80p. (gr. 4-8). pap., lib. bdg. 23.93 (978-0-8225-9879-4(5)) Lerner Publishing Group.

—Play-by-Play Mountain Biking. King, Andy, photos by. 2001. (Illus.). 63p. (J). (gr. 4-7). lib. bdg. 16.40 (978-0-613-32955-2(4)) Tandem Library Bks.

Leaney, Cindy. Look Out! Safety on Bicycles. Wilks, Peter, tr. Wilks, Peter, illus. 2003. 32p. (J). 28.50 (978-1-58952-744-7(5)) Rourke Publishing, LLC.

Lindeen, Carol K. Let's Ride Bikes. 2006. (Pebble Plus Ser.). (Illus.). 24p. (J). (978-0-7368-5364-4(2)) Capstone Pr., Inc.

Loves, June. Bicycles & Motorcycles. 2001. (Database Transportation Ser.). (Illus.). 32p. (J). (gr. 4 up). 22.95 (978-0-7910-6591-4(X) , 010502, Chelsea Hse.) Facts On File, Inc.

MacAulay, Kelley & Kalman, Bobbie. Extreme Mountain Biking. 2006. (Extreme Sports No Limits! Ser.). (Illus.). 32p. (J). (gr. 3-9). (978-0-7787-1678-5(3)) Crabtree Publishing Co.

MacEachern, Ashley. Lance in France. Barbera, Michelle, illus. 2008. 32p. (J). 16.99 (***978-0-06-113192-9(X) ;*** lib. bdg. 17.89 (***978-0-06-113193-6(8))*** HarperCollins Pubs. (Collins).

Mahaney, Ian F. Dave Mirra: Bicycle Stunt Champ. 2005. (Extreme Sports Biographies Ser.). (Illus.). 24p. (J). 19.95 (978-1-4042-2744-6(X) , PowerKids Pr.) Rosen Publishing Group, Inc., The.

Mason, Paul. Biking. 2007. (J). (***978-1-59920-130-6(5))*** Smart Apple Media.

—Mountain Biking. 2001. (To the Limit Ser.). (Illus.). 32p. (J). (gr. 4-7). lib. bdg. 25.69 (978-0-7398-3274-5(3)) Raintree.

—A World-Class Mountain Biker. 2004. (Making of a Champion Ser.). (J). pap. 8.50 (978-1-4034-5536-9(8)); lib. bdg. 27.07 (978-1-4034-4674-9(1)) Heinemann Library.

Mattern, Joanne. Safety on Your Bicycle. 1999. (Safety First Ser.). (Illus.). 24p. (J). (gr. k-6). lib. bdg. 21.35 (978-1-57765-073-7(5) , Checkerboard Library) ABDO Publishing Co.

Maurer, Tracy. BMX Freestyle. 2001. (Radsports Guides). (Illus.). 48p. (J). (gr. 4-8). lib. bdg. 29.93 (978-1-58952-102-5(1)) Rourke Publishing, LLC.

Mayer, Cassie. By Bicycle. 2006. (Illus.). 24p. (J). (978-1-4034-8391-1(4)); pap. (978-1-4034-8398-0(1)) Heinemann Library.

—En Bicicletaleta. 2006. (Illus.). 24p. (J). (978-1-4034-8632-5(8)); pap. (978-1-4034-8639-4(5)) Heinemann Library.

McClellan, Ray. BMX Freestyle. 2008. (Illus.). 24p. (J). lib. bdg. 19.95 (***978-1-60014-138-6(2))*** Bellwether Media.

—Downhill BMX. 2008. (Illus.). 24p. (J). lib. bdg. 19.95 (***978-1-60014-139-3(0))*** Bellwether Media.

Miller, Connie Colwell. BMX Park. 2008. (J). (***978-1-4296-0105-4(1))*** Capstone Pr., Inc.

—Moto X Freestyle. 2008. (J). (***978-1-4296-0107-8(8))*** Capstone Pr., Inc.

Mirabella, Erin. Gracie Goat's Big Bike Race. Horstman, Lisa, illus. 2007. (Barnyard Sports Squad Ser.). 32p. 15.95 (978-1-931382-88-5(3)) VeloPress.

Molzahn, Arlene Bourgeois. Extreme Mountain Biking. 2000. (Extreme Sports Ser.). (Illus.). 48p. (J). (gr. 3-4). lib. bdg. 21.26 (978-0-7368-0483-7(8) , Capstone High-Interest Bks.) Capstone Pr., Inc.

Morgan, Jed. Mountain Biking. 2006. (J). (978-1-58340-958-9(0)) Smart Apple Media.

Mugford, Simon. Essential BMX. 2004. (Twenty4Sevens Ser.). (Illus.). 48p. (J). pap. (978-0-439-68104-9(9)) Scholastic, Inc.

Nelson, Julie. BMX Racing & Freestyle. 2001. (Extreme Sports Ser.). (Illus.). 48p. (J). (gr. 3-6). lib. bdg. 24.26 (978-0-7398-4687-2(6)) Raintree.

Oregon Center for Applied Science, creator. Bike Smart. 2006. (J). cd-rom 19.95 (***978-1-933898-09-4(7))*** Oregon Ctr. for Applied Science, Inc.

Osborne, Ian. Mountain Biking. 2004. (Extreme Sports Ser.). (Illus.). 32p. (J). (gr. 3-6). lib. bdg. 22.60 (978-0-8225-1245-5(9)) Lerner Publishing Group.

—Mountain Biking. 2004. (gr. 3-6). lib. bdg. 15.25 (978-0-613-81323-5(5)) Tandem Library Bks.

Oxlade, Chris. Bicycles. 2000. (Transportation Around the World Ser.). (Illus.). 32p. (J). (gr. k-2). lib. bdg. 21.36 (978-1-57572-300-6(X)) Heinemann Library.

Pancella, Peggy. Bicycle Safety. 2004. (Heinemann First Library). (Illus.). 32p. (J). pap. 6.95 (978-1-4034-4939-9(2)); lib. bdg. 22.79 (978-1-4034-4930-6(9)) Heinemann Library.

Parr, Danny. Dirt Bikes. 2001. (Wild Rides! Ser.). (Illus.). 32p. (J). (gr. 3-4). lib. bdg. 21.26 (978-0-7368-0927-6(9) , Capstone High-Interest Bks.) Capstone Pr., Inc.

—Extreme Bicycle Stunt Riding Moves. 2001. (Behind the Moves Ser.). (Illus.). 32p. (J). (gr. 3-4). lib. bdg. 21.26 (978-0-7368-0781-4(0) , Capstone High-Interest Bks.) Capstone Pr., Inc.

Peterson, Monique. Bike! 2002. (gr. 3-6). lib. bdg. 17.60 (978-0-613-81331-0(6)) Tandem Library Bks.

Peterson, Monique & Zimmerman, Zachary. Bike! Extreme Sports. 2002. (Illus.). 64p. (J). (gr. 4-9). pap. 8.95 (978-0-7922-6742-3(7) , National Geographic Children's Bks.) National Geographic Society.

Petty, Kate. Bicycles, 4 vols. 2006. (Illus.). 32p. 14.95 (978-1-58728-529-5(0) , Two Can Publishing) T&N Children's Publishing.

Petty Kate. Bicycles (World Show-and-Tell) 2006. (Illus.). 32p. (J). 8.95 (978-1-58728-530-1(4) , Two Can Publishing) T&N Children's Publishing.

Pinchuk, Amy Ruth. The Best Book of Bikes. Holdcroft, Tina & Moon, Alan, illus. 2003. (Popular Mechanics for Kids Ser.). 64p. (J). (gr. 4-8). pap. 12.95 (978-1-894379-44-1(6)) Maple Tree Pr. CAN. *Dist:* Firefly Bks., Ltd.

Pohl, Kathleen. What Happens at a Bike Shop? 2006. (Illus.). 24p. (J). pap. (978-0-8368-6892-0(7)); lib. bdg. (978-0-8368-6885-2(4)) Stevens, Gareth Inc.

—What Happens at a Bike Shop? ¿Qué Pasa en una Tienda de Bicicletas? 2006. (ENG & SPA., Illus.). 24p. (J). pap. (978-0-8368-7393-1(9)); lib. bdg. (978-0-8368-7386-3(6)) Stevens, Gareth Inc. (Weekly Reader Early Learning Library).

Raatma, Lucia. Bike Safety. 2003. (Living Well). (Illus.). 32p. (J). (gr. 2-6). 27.07 (978-1-59296-085-9(5)) Child's World, Inc.

Rafael, Janis. Playing It Safe with Mr. See-More Safety Vol. 2: Let's Learn about Bicycle Safety. Walsh, Jennifer, illus. Date not set. 24p. (J). (ps-8). (978-0-9655604-1-2(4)) Safeworld Publishing Co.

Red Bird Press, creator. 3D Cyclo Mania. 2005. (Mission Xtreme 3D Ser.). (Illus.). 18p. (J). pap. 4.95 (978-1-902626-82-6(6)) Red Bird Publishing GBR. *Dist:* Perseus Distribution.

Rigby Education Staff. Learning to Ride a Bicycle. (Illus.). 8p. (J). bds. 3.95 (978-0-7635-6496-4(6) , 764966C99) Rigby Education.

Rosenberg, Aaron. Dave Mirra. 2005. (Illus.). 64p. (J). (gr. 5-8). lib. bdg. 26.50 (978-1-4042-0067-8(3)) Rosen Publishing Group, Inc., The.

—Mountain Biking. 2005. (Rad Sports Techniques & Tricks Ser.). (Illus.). 48p. (YA). (gr. 5-8). lib. bdg. 26.50 (978-0-8239-3845-2(X)) Rosen Publishing Group, Inc., The.

Royston, Angela. How Is a Bicycle Made? 2005. (How Are Things Made? Ser.). (Illus.). 32p. (J). (ps-ps). lib. bdg. 25.36 (978-1-4034-6637-2(8)); pap. (978-1-4034-6644-0(0)) Heinemann Library.

Savage, Jeff. Dave Mirra. 2007. (Amazing Athletes Ser.). (J). 23.93 (978-0-8225-6593-2(5) , Lerner Pubns.) Lerner Publishing Group.

—Mountain Bikes. 2003. (Wild Rides! Ser.). (Illus.). 32p. (J). (gr. 3-4). lib. bdg. 21.26 (978-0-7368-1518-5(X) , Capstone High-Interest Bks.) Capstone Pr., Inc.

Saviola, Joseph A. The Tour de France: Solving Addition Problems Involving Renaming. 2004. (PowerMath Ser.). (Illus.). 24p. (J). lib. bdg. (978-0-8239-8851-8(1) , PowerKids Pr.) Rosen Publishing Group, Inc., The.

—The Tour de France: Solving Addition Problems Using Regrouping. 2004. (PowerMath Ser.). (Illus.). 24p. (J). lib. bdg. 21.25 (978-0-8239-8963-8(1) , PowerKids Pr.) Rosen Publishing Group, Inc., The.

Schaefer, A. R. Motocross Cycles. 2001. (Wild Rides! Ser.). (Illus.). 32p. (J). (gr. 3-4). lib. bdg. 21.26 (978-0-7368-0930-6(9) , Capstone High-Interest Bks.) Capstone Pr., Inc.

Schaefer, Lola M. Bicicletas. 2003. (Ruedas, Alas y Agua Ser.).Tr. of Bicycles. (SPA., 24p. (J). (gr. k-1). Illus.). lib. bdg. 18.50 (978-1-4034-0915-7(3)); pap. 5.25 (978-1-4034-3530-9(8)) Heinemann Library.

—Bicycles. 2003. (Illus.). 24p. pap. 5.25 (978-1-4034-3617-7(7)); (J). lib. bdg. 18.50 (978-1-4034-0878-5(5)) Heinemann Library.

—Bicycles. 1999. (Illus.). pap. 14.60 (978-0-516-21870-0(0) , Children's Pr.) Scholastic Library Publishing.

Schoenherr, Alicia. Mountain Biking. 2005. (Kids' Guides Ser.). (Illus.). 32p. (J). (gr. 1-5). 25.64 (978-1-59296-209-9(2)) Child's World, Inc.

Schuette, Sarah L. Downhill BMX. 2005. (Blazers—To the Extreme Ser.). (Illus.). 149p. (J). 19.93 (978-0-7368-3785-9(X)) Capstone Pr., Inc.

—Mountain Biking. 2005. (Blazers—To the Extreme Ser.). (Illus.). 32p. (J). 19.93 (978-0-7368-3787-3(6)) Capstone Pr., Inc.

Shuter. Cycle Power. 2004. (Technology Through Time Ser.). (Illus.). pap. 7.50 (978-1-4109-0979-4(4)) Raintree.

Shuter, Jane. Cycle Power: Two-Wheeled Travel. 2004. (Technology Through Time Ser.). (Illus.). 32p. (J). lib. bdg. 25.70 (978-1-4109-0580-2(2)) Raintree.

Smalley, Carol. Extreme Cycling with Dale Holmes. 2006. (Extreme Sports Ser.). (Illus.). 32p. (J). (gr. 1-4). lib. bdg. (978-1-58415-487-7(X)) Mitchell Lane Pubs., Inc.

Spencer, Russ. Bicycle Stunt Riding. 2005. (Kids' Guides Ser.). (Illus.). 32p. (J). (gr. 1-5). 25.64 (978-1-59296-207-5(6)) Child's World, Inc.

Stevens, Beth Dvergsten. Bicycles. Sharp, Amy et al, illus. 1999. (Cover-to-Cover Bks.). 56p. (J). pap. (978-0-7891-2873-7(X)); (gr. 1-4). lib. bdg. 16.95 (978-0-7807-7833-7(2)) Perfection Learning Corp.

Stewart, Mark. Sweet Victory: Lance Armstrong's Incredible Journey. 2000. 64p. (gr. 4-7). (Single Titles Ser.: up). pap. (978-0-7613-1387-8(7) , Millbrook Pr.); (Inspiring People Ser.). (Illus.). lib. bdg. 24.90 (978-0-7613-1861-3(5) , Twenty-First Century Bks.) Lerner Publishing Group.

—Sweet Victory: Lance Armstrong's Incredible Journey. 2000. (J). (978-0-606-19176-0(3)); (gr. 3-6). lib. bdg. 16.40 (978-0-613-27144-8(0)) Tandem Library Bks.

Streissguth, Thomas. Trials Bikes. 2008. (Illus.). 24p. (J). lib. bdg. 19.95 (***978-1-60014-160-7(9))*** Bellwether Media.

Teitelbaum, Michael. Mountain Biking. 2008. (J). pap. 7.95 (***978-1-60279-087-2(6) ;*** lib. bdg. 25.26 (***978-1-60279-016-2(7))*** Cherry Lake Publishing.

Travis, Tim & Travis, Cindie. The Road That Has No End: How We Traded in Our Ordinary Lives for an Around the World Bicycle Adventure. 2004. (Illus.). 313p. pap. 21.95 (978-0-9754427-0-8(8)) Down The Road Publishing.

Turner, Cherie. Marathon Cycling. 2002. (Ultra Sports Ser.). (Illus.). 64p. (YA). (gr. 5-8). lib. bdg. 26.50 (978-0-8239-3553-6(1) , Rosen Central) Rosen Publishing Group, Inc., The.

U. S. Olympic Committee. A Basic Guide to Cycling. 2001. (Olympic Guides). (Illus.). 160p. (J). (gr. 6 up). lib. bdg. 23.33 (978-0-8368-2795-8(3)) Stevens, Gareth Inc.

Vieregger, K. E. BMX Biking. 2003. (X-Treme Sports Ser.). (Illus.). 32p. (J). (gr. k-6). lib. bdg. 22.78 (978-1-57765-926-6(0)) ABDO Publishing Co.

Ward, Nathan. Salida Singletrack: Mountain Biking in Colorado's Upper Arkansas Valley. 1972nd ed. 2004. (Illus.). 110p. per. 14.95 (978-0-9748814-0-9(6)) Ice Mountain Publishing.

Weintraub, Aileen. Mountain Biking. 2003. (X-Treme Outdoors Ser.). (Illus.). 48p. (YA). 24.00 (978-0-516-24321-4(7) , Children's Pr.); (gr. 7-12). pap. 6.95 (978-0-516-24384-9(5) , Watts, Franklin) Scholastic Library Publishing.

—Mountain Biking. 2003. (gr. 7-12). lib. bdg. 15.25 (978-0-613-59690-9(0)) Tandem Library Bks.

Wilds, Mary. A Forgotten Champion: The Story of Major Taylor, Fastest Bicycle Racer in the World. 2002. (Illus.). 100p. (J). (gr. 6-12). 19.95 (978-1-888105-52-0(6)) Avisson Pr., Inc.

Wingate, Brian. BMX Bicycle Racing. 2005. (Rad Sports Ser.). (Illus.). 48p. (YA). (gr. 5-8). lib. bdg. 26.50 (978-0-8239-3843-8(3)) Rosen Publishing Group, Inc., The.

Woods, Bob. Mat Hoffman. 2006. (World's Greatest Athletes Ser.). (Illus.). 32p. (J). (gr. 1-5). 27.07 (978-1-59296-755-1(8)) Child's World, Inc.

Wurdinger, Scott D. & Rapparlie, Leslie. Mountain Biking. 2006. (Adventure Sports Ser.). (Illus.). 48p. 21.95 (978-1-58341-396-8(0) , Creative Education) Creative Co., The.

BICYCLES AND BICYCLING—FICTION

Ander, illus. Me & My Bike. 2008. 68p. (J). 16.95 (***978-0-9787550-2-7(2))*** Heryin Publishing Corp.

Arena, Felice & Kettle, Phil. Bike Daredevils. Cox, David, illus. 2004. (J). pap. (978-1-59336-371-0(0)) Mondo Publishing.

Barbot, Daniel. Rosaura en Bicicleta. Fuenmayor, Morella, illus. 2005. (SPA.). 23p. (J). (ps-2). reprint ed. pap. 14.00 (978-0-7567-8947-3(8)) DIANE Publishing Co.

Berenstain, Stan & Berenstain, Jan. The Bike Lesson. Berenstain, Stan & Berenstain, Jan, illus. 2002. (Berenstain Bears Beginner Bks.). (Illus.). (J). (gr. k-3). 15.74 (978-0-7587-0998-1(6)) Book Wholesalers, Inc.

Best, Cari & Davenier, Christine. Sally Jean, the Bicycle Queen. 2006. (Illus.). 32p. (J). (gr. k-2). 16.00 (978-0-374-36386-4(2) , Nelanie Kroupa Bks.) Farrar, Straus & Giroux.

A Bike for Brad: Individual Title Six-Packs. 16p. (gr. 2 up). 35.00 (978-0-7635-9236-3(6)) Rigby Education.

The Bike Parade: Individual Title Six-Packs. (Literatura 2000 Ser.). (gr. k-1). 28.00 (978-0-7635-0024-5(0)) Rigby Education.

Blackaby, Susan. Allie's Bike. Tenney, Shawna, illus. 2006. (Read-It! Readers Ser.). (J). 19.93 (978-1-4048-2403-4(0)) Picture Window Bks.

Blackstone, Stella. Oso en bicicleta (Bear on a Bike) Sarfatti, Esther, tr. Harter, Debbie, illus. 2003. (Bear Ser.). (SPA.). 32p. (J). 5.99 (978-1-84148-775-5(9)) Barefoot Bks., Inc.

Bourgeois, Paulette. Franklin Rides A Bike. Clark, Brenda & Southern, Shelley, illus. ed. 2005. (Franklin Picture Books II). 30p. (J). lib. bdg. 15.00 (978-1-59054-712-0(8)) Fitzgerald Bks.

Bourgeois, Paulette & Clark, Brenda. Franklin's Bicycle Helmet. 2000. (Franklin TV StoryBks.). (Illus.). 32p. (J). (gr. k-3). (978-1-55074-730-0(4)); (978-1-55074-728-7(2)) Kids Can Pr., Ltd.

Braver, Vanita. Madison's Patriotic Project. DiRocco, Carl, illus. 2007. 32p. (J). 14.95 (***978-1-59572-110-5(X)**) Star Bright Bks., Inc.

Bray, Chirs. The Christmas Bike. Hefner, Seyan, illus. 2001. 28p. (J). (gr. k-12). pap. 10.00 (978-0-9712484-0-3(0)) Dunlap, J.A. & Sons Pubs.

Brown, Marc. D. W. Rides Again! Brown, Marc, illus. 2002. (D. W. Ser.). (Illus.). (J). 13.15 (978-0-7587-2327-7(X)) Book Wholesalers, Inc.

—D. W. Rides Again! 1998. (D. W. Ser.). (Illus.). 24p. (J). (ps-k). bds. 5.95 (978-0-316-11128-7(7)) Little, Brown Bks. for Young Readers.

Cameron, Ann. Julian's Glorious Summer. 2002. (Illus.). (J). 12.87 (978-0-7587-1354-4(1)) Book Wholesalers, Inc.

Chenn, Eric. Willie the Wheel. 2006. (Illus.). 40p. (J). 16.95 (978-0-9762056-7-8(X)) Heryin Publishing Corp.

Christopher, Matt & #1 Sports Writer for Kids Staff. Mountain Bike Mania. 1998. 160p. (J). (gr. 3-7). pap. 4.99 (978-0-316-14292-2(1)) Little Brown & Co.

—Mountain Bike Mania: Is Will Pedaling Out of Control? 1998. 160p. (J). (gr. 3-7). 15.95 (978-0-316-14355-4(3)) Little Brown & Co.

Clark, Brenda, illus. Franklin Rides a Bike. 2002. (Franklin Ser.). 12.40 (978-1-4046-0318-9(2)) Book Wholesalers, Inc.

—Franklin's Bicycle Helmet. 2002. (Franklin Ser.). (J). 12.40 (978-1-4046-0322-6(0)) Book Wholesalers, Inc.

Cockerill, Pamela. Finders Keepers. 2000. 137p. pap. 12.95 (978-1-85902-816-2(0)) Beekman Bks., Inc.

Coulman, Valerie. Rafi et les Cochons Volants. Duchesne, Christiane, tr. from ENG. Girard, Roge, illus. (FRE.). 32p. (J). pap. 6.95 (***978-2-922435-02-3(4)**) Editions Homard CAN. *Dist:* Univ. of Toronto Pr.

Cristaldi, Kathryn. No More Training Wheels. 2000. (gr. k-3). lib. bdg. 11.80 (978-0-613-65051-9(4)) Tandem Library Bks.

Dadey, Debbie & Jones, Marcia Thornton. Genies Don't Ride Bicycles. (Adventures of the Bailey School Kids Ser.: No. 8). (FRE., Illus.). (J). (gr. 2-4). pap. 5.99 (978-0-590-24377-3(2)) Scholastic, Inc.

Delton, Judy. Pedal Power. Tiegreen, Alan, illus. 1998. (Pee Wee Scouts Ser.: No. 35). (J). (gr. 2-5). (978-0-606-13700-3(9)) Tandem Library Bks.

El desfile de Bicicletas, 6 Pack. (Literatura 2000 Ser.). (SPA.). (gr. k-1). 28.00 (978-0-7635-1016-9(5)) Rigby Education.

Dorfman, Ariel & Dorfman, Joaquin. The Burning City. 2005. 272p. (J). (gr. 5-9). lib. bdg. 17.95 (978-0-375-93203-8(8) , Random Hse. Bks. for Young Readers) Random Hse. Children's Bks.

—Burning City. (YA). mass mkt. (978-0-375-83205-5(X)); 2006. 288p. (J). (gr. 5-9). reprint ed. pap. 7.95 (978-0-375-83204-8(1) , Random Hse. Bks. for Young Readers) Random Hse. Children's Bks.

Eriksson, Eva. A Crash Course for Molly. Dyssegaard, Elisabeth Kallick, tr. from SWE. 2005. (Illus.). 32p. (J). 16.00 (978-91-29-66156-9(0)) R & S Bks. SWE. *Dist:* Macmillan.

Gordon, Wendy. I'm Safe! on My Bike. 1999. 24p. (J). (ps-3). pap., act. bk. ed. 2.49 (978-1-891596-11-7(X)) Backyard Pub. Co., Inc.

Harcourt School Publishers Staff. The Case of the Red Bicycle. 3rd ed. 2002. (Trophies English Language Learners Ser.). (Illus.). pap. 5.10 (978-0-15-327766-5(1)) Harcourt Schl. Pubs.

—The Swap Meet Advanced Level. 3rd ed. 2002. (Trophies Reading Program Ser.). (Illus.). pap. 5.10 (978-0-15-323215-2(3)) Harcourt Schl. Pubs.

Harley, Bill. The Amazing Flight of Darius Frobisher. 2006. (Illus.). 160p. (J). 14.95 (978-1-56145-381-8(1) , Peachtree Junior) Peachtree Pubs., Ltd.

Hill, William. The Magic Bicycle. 1998. 322p. (YA). (gr. 3-10). 22.95 (978-1-890611-07-1(7) , 07-7) Otter Creek Pr., Inc.

Jakob, Donna. My Bike. Davis, Nelle, illus. 2000. 32p. (J). (ps-2). reprint ed. 14.00 (978-0-7881-6941-0(6)) DIANE Publishing Co.

Johnston, Annie Fell. The Quilt That Jack Built; and, How He W. 2006. (Illus.). pap. (***978-1-4065-1126-0(9)**) Dodo Pr.

Kerr, Bob. Mechanical Harry & the Flying Bicycle. Kerr, Bob, illus. 1999. (Illus.). 27p. (J). (gr. 2 up). lib. bdg. 23.33 (978-0-8368-2444-5(X)) Stevens, Gareth Inc.

Klein, Abby. Yikes! Bikes! McKinley, John, illus. 2006. (Ready, Freddy! Ser.: No. 7). 96p. (J). pap. 3.99 (978-0-439-78456-6(5) , Blue Sky Pr., The) Scholastic, Inc.

Kurtz, Jane. Bicycle Madness. Peck, Beth, illus. rev. ed. 2003. 128p. (J). 15.95 (978-0-8050-6981-5(X) , Holt, Henry & Co. Bks. For Young Readers) Holt, Henry & Co.

Langton, Jane. The Time Bike. (Hall Family Chronicles). 192p. (J). 2002. (gr. 5 up). pap. 5.99 (978-0-06-440792-2(6) , Harper Trophy); 2000. (gr. 4 up). 15.99 (978-0-06-028437-4(4)) HarperCollins Pubs.

—The Time Bike. 2002. (gr. 5-8). lib. bdg. 14.10 (978-0-613-86713-9(0)) Tandem Library Bks.

Larsen, Ramonita. Yes, I Can Do It: Si, lo Puedo Hacer. Larsen, Ramonita, illus. l.t. ed. 2006. (Illus.). 25p. (J). per. 10.99 (***978-1-59879-292-8(X)**) Lifevest Publishing, Inc.

Lawrie, Robin. Ballerina Biker. 2003. (Chain Gang Ser.). (Illus.). 32p. (YA). pap. 9.99 (978-0-237-52561-3(5) , Evans Brothers, Limited) Evans Publishing Group GBR. *Dist:* Independent Pubs. Group.

—First among Losers. 2003. (Chain Gang Ser.). (Illus.). 32p. (YA). pap. 9.99 (978-0-237-52562-0(3) , Evans Brothers, Limited) Evans Publishing Group GBR. *Dist:* Independent Pubs. Group.

—Gone Green. 2003. (Chain Gang Ser.). (Illus.). 32p. (YA). pap. 9.99 (978-0-237-52563-7(1) , Evans Brothers, Limited) Evans Publishing Group GBR. *Dist:* Independent Pubs. Group.

—Paintball Panic. 2003. (Chain Gang Ser.). (Illus.). 32p. (YA). pap. 11.00 (978-0-237-52559-0(3) , Evans Brothers, Limited) Evans Publishing Group GBR. *Dist:* Independent Pubs. Group.

—Radar Riders. 2003. (Chain Gang Ser.). (Illus.). 32p. (YA). pap. 9.99 (978-0-237-52560-6(7) , Evans Brothers, Limited) Evans Publishing Group GBR. *Dist:* Independent Pubs. Group.

Lawrie, Robin & Lawrie, Chris, illus. Chain Reaction. 32p. pap. (978-0-237-52110-3(5) , Evans Brothers, Limited) Evans Publishing Group.

—Fear 3.1. 32p. (J). pap. (978-0-237-52107-3(5) , Evans Brothers, Limited) Evans Publishing Group.

—Muddy Mayhem. 32p. (J). pap. (978-0-237-52105-9(9) , Evans Brothers, Limited) Evans Publishing Group.

Lawrie, Robin & Lawrie, Christine. Paintball Panic. Lawrie, Robin, illus. 2007. (Illus.). 32p. (J). (gr. 3-8). lib. bdg. 19.93 (978-1-59889-126-3(X)) Stone Arch Bks.

Lawrie, Robin & Lawrie, Christine, illus. Block Busters. 2001. (Chain Gang Ser.). 32p. pap. 7.99 (978-0-237-52263-6(2) , Evans Brothers, Limited) Evans Publishing Group GBR. *Dist:* Independent Pubs. Group.

—Cheat Challenge. 2001. (Chain Gang Ser.). 30p. pap. 7.99 (978-0-237-52259-9(4) , Evans Brothers, Limited) Evans Publishing Group GBR. *Dist:* Independent Pubs. Group.

Lewis, Beverly. Big Bad Beans. 2000. (Cul-de-Sac Kids Ser.: Vol. 22). (Illus.). 80p. (J). (gr. 2-5). pap. 3.99 (978-0-7642-2127-9(2)) Bethany Hse. Pubs.

Lewman, David. The Magic Spell Book Club. Ross, illus. 2002. 64p. mass mkt. 3.99 (978-0-689-85621-1(0) , Simon Spotlight/Nickelodeon) Simon & Schuster Children's Publishing.

London, Jonathan. Froggy Rides a Bike. Remkiewicz, Frank, illus. (Froggy Ser.). 32p. (J). (ps). 2008. pap. 5.99 (***978-0-14-241067-7(5)** , Puffin); 2006. 15.99 (978-0-670-06099-3(2) , Viking Adult) Penguin Group (USA) Inc.

Lujan, Jorge Elias. Sky Blue Accident/Accidente Celeste. Amado, Elisa, tr. Grobler, Piet, illus. 2007. (ENG & SPA.). 32p. (J). (gr. k-2). 17.95 (978-0-88899-805-7(8)) Groundwood Bks. CAN. *Dist:* Perseus Distribution.

Mantell, Paul. Mountain Bike Mania. 2007. 148p. (J). lib. bdg. (***978-1-59953-108-3(9)**) Norwood Hse. Pr.

McClear, Preston. Old Man Brown & His Magic Bike. Dollak, Nicholas, illus. 1999. 30p. (J). (gr. k-5). 16.95 (978-1-929084-06-7(4)); pap. 12.95 (978-1-929084-07-4(2)) Malibu Bks. for Children.

McIntosh, C. Ruth Bay & the Minotaur. 2004. 91p. pap. 14.95 (978-1-4137-4811-6(2)) PublishAmerica, Inc.

McMahon, P. J. Mystery of the Swimming Gorilla. Manders, John, illus. 2004. 106p. (J). lib. bdg. 15.38 (***978-1-4242-0401-4(1)**) Fitzgerald Bks.

McOmber, Rachel B., ed. McOmber Phonics Storybooks: Pete's Bike Ride. rev. ed. (Illus.). (J). (978-0-944991-40-4(8)) Swift Learning Resources.

Mike's Bike: Set D Individual Title Six-Packs. (gr. k-3). 29.00 (978-0-7635-0549-3(8)) Rigby Education.

Miles, Betty. I Would If I Could. 2000. 128p. (gr. 4-7). pap. 9.95 (978-0-595-00490-4(3) , Backinprint.com) iUniverse, Inc.

Mills, Claudia. Gus & Grandpa & the Two-Wheeled Bike. Stock, Catherine, illus. Stock, Catherine, photos by. 1999. (Gus & Grandpa Ser.). 48p. (J). (gr. 1-3). 15.00 (978-0-374-32821-4(8) , Farrar, Straus & Giroux (BYR)) Farrar, Straus & Giroux.

—The Two Wheeled Bike. Stock, Catherine, illus. 2001. (Gus & Grandpa Ser.). 48p. (J). pap. 4.95 (978-0-374-42816-7(6) , Sunburst) Farrar, Straus & Giroux.

Mollel, Tololwa M. My Rows & Piles of Coins. Lewis, Earl, illus. 2002. (J). 22.45 (978-0-7587-0385-9(6)) Book Wholesalers, Inc.

—My Rows & Piles of Coins. Lewis, E. B., illus. 1999. 32p. (J). (gr. k-3). tchr. ed. 16.00 (978-0-395-75186-2(1) , Clarion Bks.) Houghton Mifflin Co. Trade & Reference Div.

Morris, Gilbert. Too Smart Jones & the Stolen Bicycle: A Gilbert Morris Mystery. 2000. (Gilbert Morris Mysteries Ser.: Vol. 9). (Illus.). 133p. (J). (gr. 4-7). pap. 5.99 (978-0-8024-4031-0(2)) Moody Pubs.

Nolan, Allia Zobel. Let's Ride Bikes. Terry, Michael, illus. 2005. 10p. (J). bds. 10.99 (978-0-7944-0610-3(6)) Reader's Digest Assn., Inc., The.

Norman, Tony. Sky Bikers. Savage, Paul, illus. 2008. (J). pap. (***978-1-59889-903-0(1)**); 33p. (YA). (gr. 5-9). lib. bdg. 21.26 (***978-1-59889-851-4(5)**) Stone Arch Bks.

Olaleye, Isaac. Bikes for Rent! Demarest, Chris L., illus. 2000. (J). (gr. k-4). lib. bdg. 16.95 (978-0-531-33290-0(X) , Orchard Bks.) Scholastic, Inc.

Powers, Nacole. Push Daddy Push. 2006. (ENG.). 36p. per. 15.95 (***978-1-4259-6963-9(1)**) AuthorHouse.

Preller, James. The Case of the Bicycle Bandit. 2001. (Jigsaw Jones Mystery Ser.: No. 14). (Illus.). 80p. (J). (gr. 1-4). pap. 3.99 (978-0-439-18477-9(0)) Scholastic, Inc.

—The Case of the Bicycle Bandit. 2001. (Jigsaw Jones Mystery Ser.). (Illus.). (J). 10.79 (978-0-606-21268-7(X)) Tandem Library Bks.

—Case of the Bicycle Bandit. 2001. (gr. 3-6). lib. bdg. 11.80 (978-0-613-35680-0(2)) Tandem Library Bks.

Rand, Johnathan. Freddie Fernortner: Fearless First Grader. 2005. 89p. (J). pap. 4.99 (978-1-893699-78-6(1)) AudioCraft Publishing, Inc.

Ready to Ride: Individual Title, 6 packs. (ps-2). 27.00 (978-0-7635-9470-1(9)) Rigby Education.

Rey, H. A. Jorge el Curioso Monta en Bicicleta. Canetti, Yanitzia, tr. 2002. Tr. of Curious George Rides a Bike. (SPA., Illus.). 48p. (J). (gr. k-3). pap. 6.95 (978-0-618-19677-7(3)); tchr. ed. 14.95 (978-0-618-21615-4(4)) Houghton Mifflin Co. Trade & Reference Div.

—Jorge el Curioso Monta en Bicicleta. 2002. Tr. of Curious George Rides a Bike. (SPA.). (gr. k-3). lib. bdg. 14.10 (978-0-613-60749-0(X)) Tandem Library Bks.

Robinson, Amy. Bobby's Biking Lesson. Carrozza, Kyle A., illus. 2001. 36p. (J). 9.95 (978-1-58284-005-5(9) , BBL001, Thoughtful Education Pr., The) Silver Strong & Assocs.

Rosenberry, Vera. Vera Rides a Bike. rev. ed. 2004. (Illus.). 32p. (J). 16.95 (978-0-8050-7125-2(3) , Holt, Henry & Co. Bks. For Young Readers) Holt, Henry & Co.

Rylant, Cynthia. Poppleton in Spring. Teague, Mark, illus. 2002. (Poppleton Ser.). (J). 11.91 (978-0-7587-1589-0(7)) Book Wholesalers, Inc.

—Poppleton in Spring. Teague, Mark, illus. 1999. (Poppleton Ser.). 48p. (J). (ps-2). pap. 15.95 (978-0-590-84818-3(6) , Blue Sky Pr., The) Scholastic, Inc.

—Poppleton in Spring. 1999. (Poppleton Ser.). (J). (gr. k-3). (978-0-606-16594-5(0)) Tandem Library Bks.

Sachar, Louis. Super Fast, Out of Control! Wummer, Amy, illus. 2000. (Marvin Redpost Ser.: No. 7). 96p. (J). (gr. 1-4). lib. bdg. 11.99 (978-0-679-99001-7(1)); 7th ed. pap. 3.99 (978-0-679-89001-0(7)) Random Hse. Children's Bks. (Random Hse. Bks. for Young Readers).

—Super Fast, Out of Control! 2000. (Marvin Redpost Ser.: Bk. 7). (978-0-606-18502-8(X)); (gr. 3-6). lib. bdg. 11.80 (978-0-613-26149-4(6)) Tandem Library Bks.

Santillo, LuAnn. Rose. Santillo, LuAnn, ed. 2003. (Half-Pint Kids Readers Ser.). (Illus.). 7p. (J). (ps-1). pap. (978-1-59256-101-8(2)) Half-Pint Kids, Inc.

Sarmonpol, Paulette. Where Are My Onions? Vignale, Silvia, illus. 2000. 32p. (J). (ps-3). pap. (978-1-896580-32-6(7)) Tradewind Bks.

Say, Allen. The Bicycle Man. Say, Allen, illus. 2002. (Illus.). (J). 13.79 (978-0-7587-2086-3(6)) Book Wholesalers, Inc.

Seuling, Barbara. Robert & the Happy Endings. Brewer, Paul, illus. 2007. (Robert Bks.). 160p. (J). (gr. 2-4). 16.95 (978-0-8126-2748-0(2)) Cricket Bks.

Shannon, David. Duck on a Bike. Shannon, David, illus. 2002. (Illus.). 40p. (J). (ps up). pap. 15.95 (978-0-439-05023-4(5) , Blue Sky Pr., The) Scholastic, Inc.

—Pato Va en Bici. 2005. (SPA.). 40p. (J). (gr. k-2). 17.99 (978-84-261-3270-3(7)) Juventud, Editorial ESP. *Dist:* Lectorum Pubns., Inc., Iaconi, Mariuccia Bk. Imports.

Stanley, George. The Case of the Dirty Clue: Third-Grade Detectives. Murdocca, Salvatore, illus. 2005. (Ready-for-Chapters Ser.). (J). lib. bdg. 15.00 (978-1-59054-898-1(1)) Fitzgerald Bks.

Stock, Catherine, illus. Gus & Grandpa & the Two-Wheeled Bike. 2002. (Gus & Grandpa Ser.). (J). 24.36 (978-0-7587-1235-6(9)) Book Wholesalers, Inc.

Tabatha-Jean. A Trophy with Wheels. DeLuz, Tony, illus. 2000. (J). cd-rom 9.95 (978-1-58338-467-1(7)) CrossroadsPub.com.

T'choupi Fait du Velo. 2000. (FRE.). (J). (978-2-09-202022-7(6)) Nathan, Fernand FRA. *Dist:* Distribooks, Inc.

Von Ahnen, Katherine & Young Bear, Joan A. Charlie Young Bear. Lambert, Paulette L., illus. 2000. (Council for Indian Education Ser.). 48p. (gr. 2-4). pap. 4.95 (978-1-57098-001-5(2)) Rinehart, Roberts Pubs.

Warner, Gertrude Chandler. The Great Bicycle Race Mystery. 2000. (Boxcar Children Ser.: No. 76). (Illus.). (J). (gr. 2-5). 10.60 (978-0-606-18907-1(6)) Tandem Library Bks.

—Great Bicycle Race Mystery. 2000. (gr. 3-6). lib. bdg. 11.80 (978-0-613-27863-8(1)) Tandem Library Bks.

Warner, Gertrude Chandler, creator. The Great Bicycle Race Mystery, Vol. 76. 2004. (Boxcar Children Ser.: No. 76). (Illus.). 115p. (J). (gr. 2-5). pap. 4.50 (978-0-8075-3049-8(2)) Whitman, Albert & Co.

West, Colin. Grandpa's Boneshaker Bicycle. 2006. (Read-It! Chapter Books). (J). 21.26 (978-1-4048-2732-5(3)) Picture Window Bks.

Wood, Audrey. The Red Racer. Wood, Audrey, illus. 2002. (Illus.). (J). 14.47 (978-0-7587-3506-5(5)) Book Wholesalers, Inc.

—The Red Racer. 1999. (978-0-606-16308-8(5)) Tandem Library Bks.

Zullo, Germano. Marta & the Bicycle. Albertine, illus. 2002. 28p. (J). (gr. k-3). 14.95 (978-1-929132-35-5(2)) Kane/Miller Bk. Pubs., Inc.

BIGOTRY

see Toleration

BILINGUAL BOOKS

Alexie, Oscar & Berlin, James, Sr., trs. Maniar Angun. Sloat, Teri, illus. l.t. ed. 2000. 12p. (J). pap. 17.00 (978-1-58084-186-3(4)) Lower Kuskokwim Schl. District.

Azean, Evon, Sr. Pissuryugtua. Mute, Frank, Jr., illus. l.t. ed. 2000. 8p. (J). pap. 14.50 (978-1-58084-189-4(9)) Lower Kuskokwim Schl. District.

Benton, Imogene. Boxes. Berlin, James, tr. Strum, Beth & Brunk, Cara, illus. l.t. ed. 2001. 8p. (J). pap. 17.00 (978-1-58084-178-8(3)) Lower Kuskokwim Schl. District.

Bolchazy, Marie Carducci. How Many Animals? Quot Animalia? Stock, Kristie, illus. 2002. (I Am Reading Latin Ser.). (LAT & ENG.). 64p. (J). 12.00 (978-0-86516-540-3(8)) Bolchazy-Carducci Pubs.

—What Will I Eat? Quid Edam? Fraczak, Michelle Kathryn, illus. 2002. (I Am Reading Latin Ser.). (LAT & ENG.). 64p. (J). 12.00 (978-0-86516-542-7(4)) Bolchazy-Carducci Pubs.

Buddhist Text Translation Society Staff, contrib. by. Standards for Students: Instructions in Virtue from the Chinese Heritage = [Di Zi Gui]. 2003. (ENG & CHI., Illus.). 41p. (J). (978-0-88139-489-4(0)) Buddhist Text Translation Society.

Carle, Eric & Iwamura, Kazuo. Where Are You Going? To See My Friend! Carle, Eric, illus. 2003. (JPN & ENG., Illus.). 40p. (J). pap. 19.95 (978-0-439-41659-7(0) , Orchard Bks.) Scholastic, Inc.

Derby, Sally. Mi Escalera. de la Vega, Eida, tr. Burrowes, Adjoa J., illus. 1998. (SPA & ENG.). 32p. (J). (ps-3). pap. 6.95 (978-1-880000-75-5(X) , LW7771) Lee & Low Bks., Inc.

Dumont, Deborah, intro. Hippocrene Children's Illustrated Dutch Dictionary: English-Dutch/Dutch-English. 2002. (Children's Illustrated Foreign Language Dictionaries Ser.). (ENG & DUT., Illus.). 94p. (gr. k-5). pap. 11.95 (978-0-7818-0888-0(X)) Hippocrene Bks., Inc.

Girl Who Didn't Mind. 2002. Tr. of Caileag a Bha Coma. 64p. (J). lib. bdg. 17.95 (978-0-9703632-6-8(5)) Wakefield Connection, The.

Karapetian, Marjam. Bilingual Content Dictionary: English to Armenian. 2004. (ARM & ENG.). 4.95 (978-0-9767958-2-7(5)); 9.95 (978-0-9767958-4-1(1)); 4.95 (978-0-9767958-3-4(3)); 13.95 (978-0-9767958-6-5(8)); 15.95 (978-0-9767958-7-2(6)) WizdomInc.

—Bilingual Content Dictionary: English to Armenian: Social Studies - American History Through 1776. 2004. (ARM & ENG.). 14.95 (978-0-9767958-5-8(X)) WizdomInc.

—Bilingual Content Dictionary: English to Korean. 2004. (KOR & ENG.). 4.95 (978-0-9764829-7-0(5)); 4.95 (978-0-9764829-6-3(7)); 13.95 (978-0-9767958-0-3(9)); 9.95 (978-0-9764829-8-7(3)); 15.95 (978-0-9767958-1-0(7)) WizdomInc.

—Bilingual Content Dictionary: English to Korean: Social Studies - American History Through 1776. 2004. (KOR & ENG.). 14.95 (978-0-9764829-9-4(1)) WizdomInc.

—Bilingual Content Dictionary: English to Mandarin Chinese. 2004. (CHI & ENG.). 4.95 (978-0-9768053-0-4(8)); 4.95 (978-0-9768053-1-1(6)); 9.95 (978-0-9768053-2-8(4)); 13.95 (978-0-9768053-4-2(0)); 15.95 (978-0-9768053-5-9(9)) WizdomInc.

—Bilingual Content Dictionary: English to Mandarin Chinese: Social Studies - American History Through 1776. 2004. (CHI & ENG.). 14.95 (978-0-9768053-3-5(2)) WizdomInc.

Kita, Suzanne. Three Whales Who Won the Heart of the World. Sundram, Steve, illus. 2000. (ENG & JPN.). (J). 12.99 (978-0-89610-336-8(6)) Island Heritage Publishing.

McDalton, Magdalena. Carar Kuimarayarturtur (Cupik) Kiokun, Dorothy, tr. McDalton, Magdalena, illus. l.t. ed. 2000. 8p. (J). pap. 14.50 (978-1-58084-188-7(0)) Lower Kuskokwim Schl. District.

Priddy, Roger. Bilingual Sticker Flash Cards Animals. 2006. 30p. (J). 5.95 (978-0-312-49793-4(8) , Priddy Bks.) St. Martin's Pr.

Sarda, Rosa & Curto, Rosa Maria. I Like Acting Grown-Up (Me Gusta Hacer Como Mayores) 2002. (SPA & ENG., Illus.). 22p. (J). pap. 4.95 (978-1-930332-33-1(5)) Lectorum Pubns., Inc.

—I Like Getting Dirty (Me Gusta Ensuciarme) 2002. (ENG & SPA., Illus.). 22p. (J). 4.95 (978-1-930332-32-4(7)) Lectorum Pubns., Inc.

—I Like Growing Up (Me Gusta Ser Mayor) 2002. (ENG & SPA., Illus.). 22p. (J). 4.95 (978-1-930332-31-7(9)) Lectorum Pubns., Inc.

Shepard, Aaron. Lady White Snake: A Tale from Chinese Opera. Chen, Isabella, tr. Zhang, Song Nan, illus. 2001. (ENG & CHI.). 32p. (J). 16.95 (978-1-57227-074-9(8)) Pan Asia Pubns. (USA), Inc.

—Lady White Snake: A Tale from Chinese Opera. Vu, Khanh Yen, tr. Zhang, Song Nan, illus. 2001. (ENG & VIE.). 32p. (J). 16.95 (978-1-57227-075-6(6)) Pan Asia Pubns. (USA), Inc.

Shin, Sun Yung. Cooper's Lesson. Cogan, Kim & Paek, Min, trs. from ENG. Cogan, Kim, illus. 2004. (ENG & KOR.). 32p. (J). 16.95 (978-0-89239-193-6(6)) Children's Bk. Pr.

A to EZ Handbook for Bilingual Teachers: Staff Development Guide: Bilingual. (Staff Development Ser.). (gr. 1-5). (978-0-02-178068-6(4)) Macmillan/McGraw-Hill Schl. Div.

Tran, Truong. Going Home, Coming Home / Ve Nha Tham Que Hu'O'Ng. Phong, Ann, illus. 2003. Tr. of Ve Nha Tham Que Hu'O'Ng. (ENG & VIE.). 32p. (J). 16.95 (978-0-89239-179-0(0)) Children's Bk. Pr.

Van Dien, Tran. A Magic Crossbow: Beginning Through Intermediate. 1998. (Bilingual Readers in Vietnamese & English Ser.). (ENG & VIE., Illus.). (gr. 1-4). pap. 8.40 (978-0-8442-6111-9(4) , E6111-4) McGraw-Hill/Contemporary.

Van Dien, Tran & Tran, Canh Xuan. A Shadow on the Wall. 1998. (Bilingual Readers in Vietnamese & English Ser.). (ENG & VIE., Illus.). (gr. 1-4). pap. 8.40 (978-0-8442-6113-3(0) , E6113-0) McGraw-Hill/Contemporary.

Van Dien, Tran, et al. The Bridge of Reunion. 1998. (Bilingual Readers in Vietnamese & English Ser.). (ENG & VIE., Illus.). (gr. 1-4). pap. 8.40 (978-0-8442-6112-6(2) , E6112-2) McGraw-Hill/Contemporary.

Waite, Elsie, et al. Maligtaqucaraq. Sparck, Carole C., illus. l.t. ed. 2001. 8p. (J). pap. 6.00 (978-1-58084-170-2(8)) Lower Kuskokwim Schl. District.

—Malirqelluki Aarrutet. Kiokun, Dorothy, tr. Sparck, Carole C., illus. 2001. 8p. (J). pap. 6.00 (978-1-58084-171-9(6)) Lower Kuskokwim Schl. District.

Wood, Audrey. Quick As a Cricket: Nrawm Npaum Le Ih Tug Kaab Roj/Nrawm Npaum Li Ib Tug Kab Npis. Vang, Mao J., tr. Wood, Don, illus. 2000. 32p. (J). (ps-3). pap. 6.95 (978-0-9629298-3-0(2) , MHC-3-2) Minnesota Humanities Commission.

BILINGUAL BOOKS—FRENCH-ENGLISH

Beaton, Clare, illus. Transportation: English-French. 2002. (Bilingual First Bks.).Tr. of Transporte. (ENG & FRE.). 24p. (J). pap. 5.99 (978-0-7641-2212-5(6)) Barron's Educational Series, Inc.

Irwin-Ayotte, Tracy. Bilingual Songs: English-French. 2003. 48p. (J). pap. 14.95 incl. audio (978-1-894262-77-4(8) , JMP F24K) Jordan Music Productions, Inc.

—Bilingual Songs Vol. 1: English-French. 2003. 48p. (J). pap. 14.95 incl. audio (978-1-894262-72-9(7) , JMP F23K) Jordan Music Productions, Inc.

Morton, Lone & Dillinger, Christophe. Get Dressed, Robbie. Leplar, Anna C., illus. 2000. (Language Learning Story Bks.).Tr. of Habille-Toi, Robbie. (ENG & FRE.). (J). (978-0-7641-1389-5(5)) Barron's Educational Series, Inc.

Morton, Lone & Risk, Mary. Bon Anniversaire. 1998. (I Can Read Bks.).Tr. of Happ Birthday. (ENG & FRE.). (J). (ps up). 9.95 incl. audio (978-0-7641-7187-1(9)) Barron's Educational Series, Inc.

—I'm Too Big. 1998. (I Can Read Bks.).Tr. of Je Suis Mucho Grande. (ENG & FRE., Illus.). 28p. (J). (ps up). pap. 9.95 incl. audio (978-0-7641-7189-5(5)) Barron's Educational Series, Inc.

Risk, Mary & Dillinger, Christophe. Qu'est-ce Qu'on Mange ce Soir? Thompson, Carol, illus. 2000. (Language Learning Story Bks.). (ENG & FRE.). (J). (978-0-7641-1388-8(7)) Barron's Educational Series, Inc.

Risk, Mary & Jansen, Jacqueline. I Want My Banana: English-French Version: Je Veux Ma Banane. De Wolf, Alex, illus. 1998. (I Can Read Bks.). (ENG & FRE.). (J). (ps up). pap. 9.95 incl. audio (978-0-7641-7190-1(9)) Barron's Educational Series, Inc.

Shaw, Mary. Pierre & Sophia: A True Tale. Agin, Sue, illus. 2000. (ENG & FRE.). 44p. (J). (ps-4). 18.50 (978-0-9705404-0-9(X)) Criqueville Pr.

Wildsmith, Brian. L' Abecedaire. Wildsmith, Brian, illus. 2001. (FRE., Illus.). 32p. (J). pap. 6.95 (978-1-887734-83-7(X)) Star Bright Bks., Inc.

BILINGUAL BOOKS—SPANISH-ENGLISH

Ada, Alma Flor. Gathering the Sun: An Alphabet in Spanish & English. (ENG & SPA.). (J). (gr. k-2). 12.95 net. (978-1-58186-202-7(4) , DSP8805) Del Sol Publishing.

—Gathering the Sun: An Alphabet in Spanish & English. Silva, Simon, illus. 2001. (ENG & SPA.). 40p. (J). pap. 6.99 (978-0-688-17067-7(6) , Harper Trophy) HarperCollins Pubs.

—Gathering the Sun: An Alphabet in Spanish & English. 2001. (SPA.). (gr. k-3). lib. bdg. 15.30 (978-0-613-44389-0(6)) Tandem Library Bks.

—Me Encantan los Saturdays y los Domingos. Savadier, Elivia, illus. 2006. Tr. of I Love Saturdays y Domingos. (SPA.). (J). (gr. 1-2). 11.95 (978-1-59437-576-7(3) , AF33204) Santillana USA Publishing Co., Inc.

Ada, Alma Flor & Savadier, Elivia. I Love Saturdays y Domingos. 2002. (Illus.). 32p. (J). (gr. k-3). 17.99 (978-0-689-31819-1(7) , Atheneum) Simon & Schuster Children's Publishing.

Alarcon, Francisco X. Angels Ride Bikes & Other Fall Poems (Los Angeles Andan en Bicicleta y Otros Poemas de Otono) Gonzalez, Maya Christina, illus. 1999. (ENG & SPA.). 32p. (J). (gr. 1 up). 16.95 (978-0-89239-160-8(X)) Children's Bk. Pr.

Alarcon, Pedro Antonio de. The Three-Cornered Hat & Captain Poison: A Dual Language Book. Appelbaum, Stanley, ed. 2002. (Dual-Language Bks.). (SPA & ENG.). 271p. pap. 11.95 (978-0-486-41943-5(6)) Dover Pubns., Inc.

Alexander Greene, Alesia. A Mural for Mamita. Lara, Susana, tr. Teis, Kyra, illus. 2001. Tr. of Mural Para Mamita. (ENG & SPA.). (J). 8.95 (978-1-56123-154-6(1) , MFMC) Centering Corp.

Alexander, Linda. Collection 1 Bilingual. 2003. (SPA.). (J). cd-rom (978-0-9714299-4-9(4)) I Save A Tree.

Allen, Nancy Kelly. On the Banks of the Amazon/en las orillas del Amazonas. de la Vega, Eida, tr. Driessen, Elizabeth, illus. 2004. Tr. of En las orillas del Amazonas. (SPA & ENG.). 32p. (J). (gr. 4-6). 16.95 (978-0-9720192-7-9(8) , 626999) Raven Tree Pr.

Allison, Alida. Toddler's Potty Book. Parmentier, Henry, illus. 2003. Tr. of Libro de Basinica del Pequenito. (SPA.). 16p. (J). (ps-1). bds. 5.99 (978-0-8431-0502-5(X) , Price Stern Sloan) Penguin Group (USA) Inc.

American Heritage Dictionary Editors. How Can I Get There? (Como Puedo Llegar Alla?) Cote, Pamela & Zagarenski, Pamela, illus. 2001. (Good Beginnings/Un Buen Comienzo Ser.). (SPA & ENG.). 4p. (J). (gr. k-ps). bds. 3.95 (978-0-618-16934-4(2)) Houghton Mifflin Co. Trade & Reference Div.

—How Do I Feel? (Como Me Siento?) Cote, Pamela & Zagarenski, Pamela, illus. 2001. (Good Beginnings/Un Buen Comienzo Ser.). (SPA & ENG.). 4p. (J). (gr. k-ps). bds. 3.95 (978-0-618-16931-3(8)) Houghton Mifflin Co. Trade & Reference Div.

—What Color Is It? Cote, Pamela & Zagarenski, Pamela, illus. 2001. (Good Beginnings/Un Buen Comienzo Ser.). Orig. Title: Que Color Es Este?. (SPA & ENG.). 4p. (J). (gr. k-ps). bds. 3.95 (978-0-618-16932-0(6)) Houghton Mifflin Co. Trade & Reference Div.

—Where Can I Go? Cote, Pamela & Zagarenski, Pamela, illus. 2001. (Good Beginnings/Un Buen Comienzo Ser.). Orig. Title: Adonde Puedo Ir?. (SPA & ENG.). 4p. (J). (gr. k-ps). bds. 3.95 (978-0-618-16933-7(4)) Houghton Mifflin Co. Trade & Reference Div.

American Heritage Dictionary Editors, ed. What Am I Playing? Zagarenski, Pamela, illus. 2004. (Good Beginnings Ser.). 4p. (J). (ps-k). bds. 3.95 (978-0-618-43169-4(1)) Houghton Mifflin Co. Trade & Reference Div.

Ancona, George. Mi Musica. 2006. Tr. of My Music. (SPA.). 32p. (J). (gr. 1-3). pap. 8.95 (978-0-516-25494-4(4) , Children's Pr.) Scholastic Library Publishing.

—Mi Musica/My Music. 2005. (Somos Latinos (We Are Latinos) Ser.). (ENG & SPA.). 32p. (J). 21.00 (978-0-516-25295-7(X) , Children's Pr.) Scholastic Library Publishing.

—Mis Comidas. 2006. Tr. of My Food. (SPA.). 32p. (J). (gr. 1-3). pap. 8.95 (978-0-516-25496-8(0) , Children's Pr.) Scholastic Library Publishing.

—Mis Comidas/My Foods. 2005. (Somos Latinos (We Are Latinos) Ser.). (ENG & SPA., Illus.). 32p. (J). 21.00 (978-0-516-25292-6(5) , Children's Pr.) Scholastic Library Publishing.

—Mis Juegos. 32p. (J). 2006. (SPA.). (gr. 1-3). pap. 8.95 (978-0-516-25498-2(7)); 2005. (ENG & SPA.). 21.00 (978-0-516-25293-3(3)) Scholastic Library Publishing. (Children's Pr.).

—Mis Quehaceres. 2006. (SPA.). 32p. (J). (gr. 1-3). pap. 8.95 (978-0-516-25499-9(5) , Children's Pr.) Scholastic Library Publishing.

Andersen, Hans Christian & Capdevila. The Little Mermaid. Max, illus. 2003. Tr. of La Sirenita. (ENG & SPA.). 32p. (J). pap. 6.95 (978-0-8118-3911-2(7)) Chronicle Bks. LLC.

Andersen, Hans Christian & Capdevila, Bas. Ugly Duckling (El Patito Feo) A Bilingual Book. Capdevila, Francesc, illus. 2004. (ENG & SPA.). 32p. (J). 14.95 (978-0-8118-4454-3(4)) Chronicle Bks. LLC.

Arengo, Sue. Classic Tales: Classic Tales Beginner 1: The Magic Cooking Pot Activity Book. Taylor, Jane, ed. 2003. (Illus.). 2.95 (978-0-19-422080-4(X)) Oxford Univ. Pr., Inc.

Argueta, Jorge. Xochitl & the Flowers / Xochitl, la Nina de Las Flores. Angel, Carl, illus. 2003. Tr. of Xochitl, la Nina de Las Flores. (ENG & SPA.). 32p. (J). 16.95 (978-0-89239-181-3(2)) Children's Bk. Pr.

Armas, Teresa. Remembering Grandma / Recordando a Abuela. Baeza Ventura, Gabriela, tr. from ENG. Rodriguez Howard, Pauline, illus. 2003. (ENG & SPA.). 32p. (J). 14.95 (978-1-55885-344-7(8) , Piñata Books) Arte Publico Pr.

Las Aventuras Internas de Paco Flaco. 2002. Tr. of Internal Adventures of Marcus Snarkis. (SPA.). lib. bdg. (978-1-59168-020-8(4)) Flying Rhinoceros, Inc.

Awdry, Wilbert V. Para, Trencito, Para! Un Cuento de Thomas the Tank Engine. Marquez, Desiree, tr. 2001. (SPA., Illus.). 24p. (J). (gr. k-ps). bds. 4.99 (978-0-375-81502-7(3) , RH Para Ninos) Random Hse. Children's Bks.

Baca, Ana. Benito's Bizcochitos. Castilla, Julia Mercedes, tr. Accardo, Anthony, illus. 1999. Tr. of Bizcochitos de Benito. (ENG & SPA.). 32p. (J). (ps-3). 14.95 (978-1-55885-264-8(6) , Piñata Books) Arte Publico Pr.

Barret & Allen. El Coyote. 2002. (Perros Salvajes Serie).Tr. of Wild Dogs: The Coyote. (SPA.). 24p. (J). (gr. 3-5). 22.45 (978-1-4103-0013-7(3) , Blackbirch Pr., Inc.) Thomson Gale.

—El Lince. 2002. (Gatos Salvajes Serie).Tr. of Wild Cats: The Bobcat. (SPA.). 24p. (J). (gr. 3-5). 22.45 (978-1-4103-0010-2(2) , Blackbirch Pr., Inc.) Thomson Gale.

—El Lobo. 2002. (Perros Salvajes Serie).Tr. of Wild Dogs: The Wolf. (SPA.). 24p. (J). (gr. 3-5). 22.45 (978-1-4103-0014-0(5) , Blackbirch Pr., Inc.) Thomson Gale.

—El Puma. 2002. (Gatos Salvajes Serie).Tr. of Wild Cats: The Cougar. (SPA.). 24p. (J). (gr. 3-5). 22.45 (978-1-4103-0012-6(9) , Blackbirch Pr., Inc.) Thomson Gale.

—El Zorro. 2002. (Perros Salvajes Serie).Tr. of Wild Dogs: The Fox. (SPA.). 24p. (J). (gr. 3-5). 22.45 (978-1-4103-0015-7(3) , Blackbirch Pr., Inc.) Thomson Gale.

Beaton, Clare, illus. At Home: A la Casa. 2001. (Bilingual First Bks.). (SPA & ENG.). 24p. (J). (ps-k). pap. 4.99 (978-0-7641-1692-6(4)) Barron's Educational Series, Inc.

—Family: La Familia. l.t. ed. 1998. (English-Spanish Bilingual First Bks.). (ENG & SPA.). 24p. (J). (ps up). lib. bdg. 14.45 (978-1-56674-250-4(1)) Forest Hse. Publishing Co., Inc.

—Opposites: Los Contrarios. l.t. ed. 1998. (English-Spanish Bilingual First Bks.). (ENG & SPA.). 24p. (J). (ps up). lib. bdg. 14.45 (978-1-56674-252-8(8)) Forest Hse. Publishing Co., Inc.

—Toys: Los Juguetes. 2003. (Bilingual First Bks.). (ENG & SPA.). 24p. (J). pap. 4.95 (978-0-7641-2611-6(3)) Barron's Educational Series, Inc.

—Transportation: English-Spanish. 2002. (Bilingual First Books/English-Spanish Ser.).Tr. of Transporte. (ENG & SPA.). 24p. (J). pap. 4.95 (978-0-7641-2211-8(8)) Barron's Educational Series, Inc.

—Weather (El Tiempo) 2001. (Bilingual First Bks.). (SPA & ENG.). 24p. (J). (ps up). pap. 4.99 (978-0-7641-1690-2(8)) Barron's Educational Series, Inc.

—Wild Animals: English-Spanish. 2002. (Bilingual First Bks.). (ENG & SPA.). 24p. (J). pap. 4.95 (978-0-7641-2213-2(4)) Barron's Educational Series, Inc.

Beinstein, Phoebe. Dora. Mangano, Tom, illus. 2003. (Dora the Explorer Ser.). (ENG & SPA.). 12p. (J). bds. 7.99 (978-0-689-85484-2(6) , Simon Spotlight/Nickelodeon) Simon & Schuster Children's Publishing.

—Dora's Opposites/Opuestos de Dora. Roper, Robert, illus. 2002. (Dora the Explorer Ser.). 14p. (J). bds. 4.99 (978-0-689-84819-3(6) , Simon Spotlight/Nickelodeon) Simon & Schuster Children's Publishing.

Benatar, Raquel. Isabel Allende: Memories for a Story: Recuerdos para un Cuento / Isabel Allende. Petersen, Patricia, tr. Molinari, Fernando, illus. (SPA & ENG.). 32p. 15.95 (978-1-55885-379-9(0) , Piñata Books) Arte Publico Pr.

Benatar, Raquel & Torrecilla, Pablo. Isabel Allende: Recuerdos para un Cuento. Petersen, Patricia, tr. Benatar, Raquel & Torrecilla, Pablo, illus. 2004. (ENG & SPA.). (J). 14.95 (978-1-56492-341-7(X) , Piñata Books) Arte Publico Pr.

Bertrand, Diane Gonzales. The Last Doll/la ultima Muñeca. Balestra, Alejandra, tr. Accardo, Anthony, illus. 2001. Tr. of Ultima Muneca. (ENG & SPA.). 32p. (J). (ps-2). 14.95 (978-1-55885-290-7(5) , Piñata Books) Arte Publico Pr.

—My Pal, Victor/Mi amigo, Víctor. Raven Tree Press Staff, ed. de la Vega, Eida, tr. Sweetland, Robert, illus. 2004. Tr. of Mi amigo, Víctor. (SPA & ENG.). 32p. (J). 16.95 (978-0-9720192-9-3(4) , 626999) Raven Tree Pr.

—Uncle Chente's Picnic/el picnic de Tío Chente. Castilla, Julia Mercedes, tr. Howard, Pauline Rodriguez, illus. Tr. of Picnic de Tio Chente. (ENG & SPA.). 32p. (J). (ps-3). 15.95 (978-1-55885-337-9(5) , Piñata Books) Arte Publico Pr.

Bishop, Dorothy S., et al. Leonardo el Leon y Ramon el Raton. 2001. Tr. of Lion & the Mouse. (SPA & ENG., Illus.). 64p. (J). 6.95 (978-0-8442-7445-4(3) , NT268) McGraw-Hill/Contemporary.

Blanco, Julia. Agualinda Aguaclara. Mondeja, Omar, illus. 2000. (SPA.). 32p. (J). lib. bdg. (978-1-894628-00-6(4)) RosaBlanca.

Boada, Francesc & Andersen, Hans Christian. The Princess & the Pea (La Princesa y el Guisante) A Bilingual Book. Estrada, Pau, illus. 2004. (ENG & SPA.). 32p. (J). 14.95 (978-0-8118-4451-2(X)) Chronicle Bks. LLC.

Bock, Lee. Oh, Crumps!/¡Ay, Caramba! de la Vega, Eida, tr. Midgett, Morgan, illus. 2003. Tr. of ¡Ay, Caramba!. (SPA & ENG.). 32p. (J). (gr. k-3). 16.95 (978-0-9720192-4-8(3) , 626999) Raven Tree Pr.

Bowdish, Lynea. Preguntas Tontitas. Doty, Eldon C., illus. 2002. (Rookie Reader Espanol Ser.). (SPA.). (J). (gr. k-2). pap. 4.95 (978-0-516-26319-9(6) , Children's Pr.) Scholastic Library Publishing.

—Los Truenos No Me Asustan! Wallace, John, illus. 2001. (Rookie Espanol Ser.). (SPA.). 32p. (J). (gr. k-2). 19.50 (978-0-516-22354-4(2) , Children's Pr.) Scholastic Library Publishing.

Brammer, Ethriam Cash. My Tata's Guitar / la guitarra de mi Tata. Lechon, Daniel, illus. (ENG & SPA.). 32p. (J). 15.95 (978-1-55885-369-0(3) , Piñata Books) Arte Publico Pr.

Brennan, Kevin. Jimmy Jammers/Jaimito Pijama. Raven Tree Press, L. L. C., ed. de la Vega, Eida, tr. Driessen, Elizabeth, illus. 2002. Tr. of Jaimito Pijama. (SPA & ENG.). 32p. (J). (gr. k-3). 16.95 (978-0-9701107-9-4(0) , 626999) Raven Tree Pr.

Bridwell, Norman. Clifford y el Dia de Pascua. 2003. (Clifford, the Big Red Dog Ser.). (SPA., Illus.). 32p. (J). (ps-k). pap. 3.50 (978-0-590-11740-1(8) , SO7533, Scholastic en Espanol) Scholastic, Inc.

Brown, Margaret Wise. My World. Mlawer, Teresa, tr. Hurd, Clement, illus. 2001. (SPA.). 32p. (J). (ps up). 16.99 (978-0-06-623841-8(2) , HC30646, Rayo) HarperCollins Pubs.

Byrd, Lee Merrill. Treasure on Gold Street: A Neighborhood Story in Spanish & English. Castro, Antonio, tr. Castro, Antonio, illus. 2003. Tr. of Tesoro de la Calle Oro. (ENG & SPA.). 40p. (J). 16.95 (978-0-938317-75-3(X)) Cinco Puntos Pr.

Campos, Tito. Muffler Man/el hombre Mofle. Vigil-Pion, Evangelina, tr. Alvarez, Lamberto & Alvarez, Beto, illus. 2001. Tr. of Hombre Mofle. (ENG & SPA.). 32p. (J). (ps-3). 14.95 (978-1-55885-318-8(9) , Piñata Books) Arte Publico Pr.

Canetti, Yanitzia, tr. from ENG. Jorge el Curioso y el Conejito. Rey, H. A., illus. 2002. (SPA.). 26p. (J). (gr. k-ps). bds. 5.95 (978-0-618-20316-1(8)) Houghton Mifflin Co. Trade & Reference Div.

Cano, Robin B. Lucita Regresa a Oaxaca (Lucita Comes Home to Oaxaca) Ricardez, Rafael E., tr. Smith, Kerry, illus. 1998. (ENG & SPA.). 32p. (J). (gr. 3-6). 16.95 (978-1-56492-111-6(5)) Laredo Publishing Co., Inc.

Cano, Robin B., et al. Ramona Viaja Al Norte (North with Ramona) 1998. (Tales in Two Languages, LS Ser.). (ENG & SPA.). (J). (gr. 3-6). 16.95 (978-1-56492-254-0(5)) Laredo Publishing Co., Inc.

Caraballo, Samuel. Estrellita se despide de su isla/Estrellita Says Good-bye to Her Island. Caraballo, Samuel, tr. Torrecilla, Pablo, illus. Tr. of Estrellita Says Good-Bye to Her Island. (ENG & SPA.). 32p. (J). stu. ed. 15.95 (978-1-55885-338-6(3) , Piñata Books) Arte Publico Pr.

Carlson, Lori M. Bilingual Plays Anthology. 1999. (J). lib. bdg. (978-0-688-16238-2(X)) HarperCollins Pubs.

Cazenave, Florencia. Nos Mudamos. 2001. (Que Pasa Coleccion). (SPA., Illus.). (J). pap. 6.36 (978-950-24-0682-4(6)) Albatros ARG. *Dist:* Lectorum Pubns., Inc.

—Nos Mudamos. 2000. (SPA., Illus.). (J). (ps-k). pap. 7.95 (978-950-24-0732-6(6)) Lectorum Pubns., Inc.

Cenicienta. 2001. (First Class Ser.). (SPA.). 20p. (J). (ps-3). pap. (978-968-5308-29-8(2) , Silver Dolphin en Español) Advanced Marketing, S. de R. L. de C. V.

Cenicienta. 4th ed. 2002. (Troquelados Clasicos Ser.). (SPA & ENG., Illus.). 16p. pap. 2.95 (978-84-7864-216-8(1)) Combel Editorial, S.A. ESP. *Dist:* Independent Pubs. Group.

Chanko, Pamela. Sea Creatures: Criaturas Marinas. 2002. (Science Emergent Readers Ser.). (ENG & SPA., Illus.). (J). pap. (978-0-439-41161-5(0)) Scholastic, Inc.

Charlesworth, Liza. My First Bilingual Little Readers. 2007. 64p. Level C. pap. 11.99 ***(978-0-439-02425-9(0));*** Level B. pap. 11.99 ***(978-0-439-02424-2(2))*** Scholastic, Inc.

Cobb, Annie & Jones, Davy. Ruedas! Jones, Davy, illus. 2003. (Road to Reading Ser.). (J). lib. bdg. 11.99 (978-0-375-91500-0(1) , Golden Bks.) Random Hse. Children's Bks.

Codina, Josep. Hola, Maria! Rius, Roser, illus. 2002. (Praying with Little Ones Ser.: 4). Tr. of I Meet Mary!. (SPA.). 20p. (J). 5.95 (978-0-8198-3683-0(4) , 332-136) Pauline Bks. & Media.

—Prego Com Jesus! Rius, Roser, illus. 2002. (Praying with Little Ones Ser.: 3). Tr. of I Pray Like Jesus!. (SPA.). 20p. (J). 5.95 (978-0-8198-3684-7(2) , 332-137) Pauline Bks. & Media.

—Que N'Ets de Bo! Rius, Roser, illus. 2002. (Praying with Little Ones Ser.: 1). Tr. of I Can Pray!. (SPA.). 20p. 5.95 (978-0-8198-3682-3(6) , 332-135) Pauline Bks. & Media.

Colato Lainez, Rene. Waiting for Papa/Esperando a Papa. Accardo, Anthony, illus. Tr. of Esperando a Papa. (ENG & SPA.). 32p. (gr. 1-3). 15.95 (978-1-55885-403-1(7) , Piñata Books) Arte Publico Pr.

Cole. El Ballena. 2002. (Animales Marinos Salvajes Serie).Tr. of Wild Marine Animals: The Whale. (SPA.). 24p. (J). (gr. 3-5). 24.94 (978-1-4103-0007-2(2) , Blackbirch Pr., Inc.) Thomson Gale.

—El Delfin. 2002. Tr. of Wild Marine Animals: The Dolphin. (SPA.). 24p. (J). (gr. 3-5). 24.94 (978-1-4103-0006-5(4) , Blackbirch Pr., Inc.) Thomson Gale.

Cole & Leeson. El Jaguar y el Leopardo. 2002. (Gatos Salvajes del Mundo Serie).Tr. of Wild Cats Of The World: The Jaguar And The Leopard. (SPA.). 24p. (J). (gr. 3-5). 24.94 (978-1-4103-0005-8(6) , Blackbirch Pr., Inc.) Thomson Gale.

—El Oso Panda. 2002. (Osos Salvajes Serie).Tr. of Wild Bears: The Panda Bear. (SPA.). 24p. (J). (gr. 3-5). 24.94 (978-1-4103-0001-0(3) , Blackbirch Pr., Inc.) Thomson Gale.

—El Oso Pardo. 2002. (Osos Salvajes Serie).Tr. of Wild Bears: The Grizzly Bear. (SPA.). 24p. (J). (gr. 3-5). 24.94 (978-1-4103-0000-3(5) , Blackbirch Pr., Inc.) Thomson Gale.

—El Tiburon. 2002. (Animales Marinos Salvajes Serie).Tr. of Wild Marine Animals: The Shark. (SPA.). 24p. (J). (gr. 3-5). 24.94 (978-1-4103-0008-9(0) , Blackbirch Pr., Inc.) Thomson Gale.

—El Tigre. 2002. (Gatos Salvajes del Mundo Serie).Tr. of Wild Cats Of The World: The Tiger. (SPA.). 24p. (J). (gr. 3-5). 24.94 (978-1-4103-0002-7(1) , Blackbirch Pr., Inc.) Thomson Gale.

Como Dibujar Caricaturas. 2002. Tr. of How to Draw Cartoons. (SPA.). lib. bdg. (978-1-59168-017-8(4)) Flying Rhinoceros, Inc.

Corpi, Lucha. Where Fireflies Dance (Ahi, Donde Bailan las Luciernagas) Reisberg, Mira, illus. 2002. 32p. (J). (gr. 1 up). pap. 7.95 (978-0-89239-177-6(4)) Children's Bk. Pr.

Crane Johnson, Amy. Cinnamon & the April Shower/Canela y el aguacero de Abril: A Solomon Raven Story/un cuento del cuervo Salomon, 4 vols. de la Vega, Eida, tr. Mommaerts, Robb, illus. 2003. (Solomon Raven Ser. : 3). Tr. of Canela y el aguacero de abril:un cuento del cuervo Salomon. (SPA & ENG.). 32p. (J). (gr. k-3). 16.95 (978-0-9720192-2-4(7) , 626999) Raven Tree Pr.

—A Home for Pearl Squirrel/una casa para la ardilla Perla: A Solomon Raven Story/ un cuento del cuervo Salomon, 4 vols. de la Vega, Eida, tr. Mommaerts, Robb, illus. rev. ed. 2004. (Solomon Raven Ser. : 1). Tr. of casa para la ardilla Perla. (SPA & ENG.). 32p. (J). 16.95 (978-0-9724973-4-3(X) , 626999) Raven Tree Pr.

—Lewis Cardinal's First Winter/el primer invierno de Luis, el Cardenal: A Solomon Raven Story/un cuento del cuervo Salomon, 4 vols. de la Vega, Eida, tr. Mommaerts, Robb, illus. rev. ed. 2002. (Solomon Raven Ser. : 2). Tr. of primer invierno de Luis, el cardenal: un cuento del cuervo Salomon. (SPA & ENG.). 32p. (J). 16.95 (978-0-9724973-5-0(8) , 626999) Raven Tree Pr.

Danziger, Paula. Ambar en Cuarto y Sin Su Amigo, Level 3.7. Ross, Tony, illus. 2003. (SPA.). 136p. (J). (gr. 3-5). pap. 10.95 (978-84-204-4412-3(X) , SAN412X) Alfaguara, Ediciones, S.A.- Grupo Santillana ESP. *Dist:* Santillana USA Publishing Co., Inc.

—Ambar en Cuarto y Sin Su Amigo. Ross, Tony, illus. (SPA.). 136p. (J). (gr. 3-5). pap. 10.95 (978-968-19-1021-1(4)) Santillana USA Publishing Co., Inc.

de Beer, Hans. Llevame a Casa, Osito Polar! Gambolini, Gerardo, tr. from GER. 2001. (SPA & ENG., Illus.). 32p. (J). (gr. k-3). pap. 6.95 (978-0-7358-1500-1(3) , NS30711) North-South Bks., Inc.

—Llevame a Casa, Osito Polar! 2001. (978-0-606-22735-3(0)) Tandem Library Bks.

De Capua, Sarah. Como Nos Orientamos? 2006. (SPA.). 32p. (J), (gr. k-2). pap. 5.95 (978-0-516-24691-8(7) , Children's Pr.) Scholastic Library Publishing.

De Capua, Sarah E. Como Nos Orientamos? 2005. (Rookie Reader Espaanol Ser.). (SPA., Illus.). 32p. (J). (gr. k-2). 19.50 (978-0-516-24442-6(6) , Children's Pr.) Scholastic Library Publishing.

del Castillo, Richard Griswold. César Chavez: La lucha por la Justicia. Colin, Jose Juan, tr. from ENG. Accardo, Anthony, illus. 2001. (Hispanic Civil Rights Ser.). (ENG & SPA.). 32p. (J). (ps-3). 15.95 (978-1-55885-324-9(3) , Piñata Books) Arte Publico Pr.

Delacre, Lulu, illus. & compiled by. Arrorro Mi Nino: Latino Lullabies & Gentle Games. Delacre, Lulu, compiled by. 2004. (ENG & SPA.). 32p. (J). 16.95 (978-1-58430-159-2(7)) Lee & Low Bks., Inc.

Derby, Sally. Mi Escalera. de la Vega, Eida, tr. Burrowes, Adjoa J., illus. 1998. (SPA & ENG.). 32p. (J). (ps-3). 15.95 (978-1-880000-74-8(1) , LW7547) Lee & Low Bks., Inc.

Desclot, Miquel. Sleeping Beauty. Abbrederis, Christoph, illus. 2003. Tr. of Bella Durmiente. (ENG & SPA.). 32p. (J). pap. 6.95 (978-0-8118-3913-6(3)) Chronicle Bks. LLC.

Desclot, Miquel & DC Comics Staff. The Sleeping Beauty. Abbrederis, Christoph, illus. 2003. Tr. of La Bella Durmiente. (ENG & SPA.). 32p. (J). 14.95 (978-0-8118-3912-9(5)) Chronicle Bks. LLC.

Dientes de Madera y Caramelos de Goma. 2002. Tr. of Wooden Teeth & Jelly Beans. (SPA.). lib. bdg. (978-1-59168-018-5(2)) Flying Rhinoceros, Inc.

Un Dinosaurio Se Comio Me Tarea. 2002. Tr. of Dinosaur Ate My Homework. (SPA.). lib. bdg. (978-1-59168-015-4(8)) Flying Rhinoceros, Inc.

Dole, Mayra L. Drum, Chavi, Drum ! / Toca, Chavi, Toca! Tonel, illus. 2003. Tr. of Toca, Chavi, Toca!. (ENG & SPA.). 32p. (J). 16.95 (978-0-89239-186-8(3)) Children's Bk. Pr.

Dorling Kindersley Publishing Staff. My First Spanish Animal Book. 2002. (Illus.). 36p. (J). (ps-1). bds. 6.99 (978-0-7894-8590-8(7)) Dorling Kindersley Publishing, Inc.

—My First Spanish Number Book. 2002. (Illus.). 36p. (J). (ps-1). bds. 6.99 (978-0-7894-8591-5(5)) Dorling Kindersley Publishing, Inc.

—My First Spanish Truck Board Book / Mi Primer Libro de Camoines en Espanol. 2002. (ENG & SPA., Illus.). 36p. (J). (ps-1). bds. 6.99 (978-0-7894-8592-2(3)) Dorling Kindersley Publishing, Inc.

Dr. Hope. El Dia Para Reir. Conrique, Ruth, tr. Hamilton, Dan, illus. 2001. (Life Lessons Ser.). (SPA.). (J). (ps-3). 16.95 (978-1-885624-60-4(3)) Alpine Publishing.

Drew, Alejandrina. Abra Cadabra, Patas De Cabra: A Spanish, English Story for Young Readers. Satcher, David & Ford, Richard, trs. Mora, Mauricio, illus. 41p. (J). pap. 15.95 (978-1-57168-505-6(7)); 2001. (ENG & SPA.). 46p. (gr. 2-4). 18.95 (978-1-57168-506-3(5)) Eakin Pr.

Eastman, P. D. ¿Eres Mi Mama? Eastman, P. D., illus. 2001. (Bright & Early Board Bks.). (SPA., Illus.). 24p. (J). (gr. k-ps). bds. 4.99 (978-0-375-81505-8(8) , Random Hse. Bks. for Young Readers) Random Hse. Children's Bks.

Emberley, Rebecca. Let's Go (Vamos) A Book in Two Languages. 2000. (Illus.). (J). (978-0-606-18259-1(4)) Tandem Library Bks.

—My Animals/Mis Animales. Emberley, Rebecca, illus. 2002. (SPA & ENG., Illus.). 10p. (J). (ps-ps). bds. 6.99 (978-0-316-17343-8(6)) Little, Brown Bks. for Young Readers.

—My Clothes/Mi Ropa. Emberley, Rebecca, illus. 2002. (SPA & ENG., Illus.). 10p. (J). (ps-ps). bds. 6.99 (978-0-316-17454-1(8)) Little, Brown Bks. for Young Readers.

—My Day/Mi Día: A Book in Two Languages/Un Libro en Dos Lenguas. Emberley, Rebecca, illus. 2000. (ENG & SPA., Illus.). 28p. (J). (ps-3). pap. 6.99 (978-0-316-22983-8(0)) Little Brown & Co.

—My Food/Mi Comida. Emberley, Rebecca, illus. 2002. (SPA & ENG., Illus.). 10p. (J). (ps-ps). bds. 6.99 (978-0-316-17718-4(0)) Little, Brown Bks. for Young Readers.

—My Numbers/ Mis Numeros. Emberley, Rebecca, illus. 2000. (ENG & SPA., Illus.). 10p. (J). (ps-ps). bds. 6.99 (978-0-316-23350-7(1)) Little Brown & Co.

—My Opposites/Mis Opuestos. Emberley, Rebecca, illus. 2000. (ENG & SPA., Illus.). 10p. (J). (ps-ps). bds. 6.99 (978-0-316-23345-3(5)) Little Brown & Co.

—My Shapes/ Mis Formas. Emberley, Rebecca, illus. 2000. (ENG & SPA., Illus.). 10p. (J). (ps-ps). bds. 6.99 (978-0-316-23355-2(2)) Little Brown & Co.

—My Toys/Mis Juguetes. Emberley, Rebecca, illus. 2002. (SPA & ENG., Illus.). 10p. (J). (ps-ps). bds. 6.99 (978-0-316-17494-7(7)) Little, Brown Bks. for Young Readers.

Espinosa, Resurreccion. Don Quijote in America: Plays in English & Spanish, Grades 1-6. 2002. (ENG & SPA., Illus.). 221p. (J). (gr. 1-6). pap. 38.00 (978-1-56308-927-5(0) , LU9270) Libraries Unlimited, Inc.

Facklam, Margery. Insectos para el Almuerzo (Bugs for Lunch) Valenzuela, Liliana, tr. from SPA. Long, Sylvia, illus. 2004. 32p. (J). (ps-3). pap. 7.95 (978-1-57091-506-2(7)) Charlesbridge Publishing, Inc.

Ferré, Rosario. El Medio Pollito. 2003. (SPA., Illus.). 32p. (J). (gr. 3-5). pap. 7.95 (978-968-19-0299-5(8)) Aguilar, Altea, Taurus, Alfaguara, S.A. de C.V MEX. *Dist:* Lectorum Pubns., Inc., Santillana USA Publishing Co., Inc.

Franco, Betsy. Mi Dedo Menique. Lucas, Margeaux, illus. (Rookie Reader Espanol Ser.). (SPA.). (J). (gr. k-2). 2002. 24p. pap. 4.95 (978-0-516-26318-2(8)); 2001. 32p. 19.50 (978-0-516-22359-9(3)) Scholastic Library Publishing. (Children's Pr.).

Frankel, Alona. Mi Bacinica y Yo: Para El. Frankel, Alona, illus. 2002. (Once upon a Potty Ser.). (SPA., Illus.). 48p. (J). (ps up). 6.95 (978-0-694-01649-5(7)) HarperCollins Pubs.

—Mi Bacinica y Yo (Para Ella) Frankel, Alona, illus. 2002. (Once upon a Potty Ser.). (SPA., Illus.). 48p. (J). (ps up). 6.95 (978-0-694-01648-8(9)) HarperCollins Pubs.

Galindo, Mary Sue & Howard, Pauline Rodriguez. Icy Watermelon. 2000. Tr. of Sandia Fria. (SPA & ENG., Illus.). 32p. (J). (ps-2). 14.95 (978-1-55885-306-5(5) , Piñata Books) Arte Publico Pr.

Garcia, Geronimo, illus. Tell Me a Cuento (Cuenta Me un Story) No Way Jose; Mariposa Mariposa; Monday, Tuesday, Wednesday, O!; the Terrible Tragadabas. 2004. (ENG & SPA.). 64p. (ps-3). pap. 11.95 (978-0-938317-43-2(1) , CPP7431) Cinco Puntos Pr.

Gelsey, James. Scooby-Doo & the Haunted Castle: Scooby-Doo Y el Castillo Hechizado. 2002. (Scooby-Doo Mysteries Ser.: No. 1). (SPA., Illus.). 64p. (J). (gr. 2-4). mass mkt. 3.99 (978-0-439-40984-1(5) , Scholastic en Espanol) Scholastic, Inc.

—Scooby-Doo y el Castillo Hechizado. 2002. Tr. of Scooby-Doo & the Haunted Castle. (SPA.). (gr. k-3). lib. bdg. 13.00 (978-0-613-82494-1(6)) Tandem Library Bks.

Gershator, David. Bread Is for Eating. 1998. Tr. of Spanish). 13.75 (978-0-606-13225-1(2)) Tandem Library Bks.

Gershator, David & Gershator, Phillis. Bread Is for Eating. Shaw-Smith, Emma, illus. 2003. Tr. of Spanish). (ENG & SPA.). 25p. (J). (gr. k-4). reprint ed. 16.00 (978-0-7567-9033-2(6)) DIANE Publishing Co.

—Bread Is for Eating. Shaw-Smith, Emma, illus. rev. ed. 1998. Tr. of Spanish). 32p. (J). pap. 7.95 (978-0-8050-5798-0(6) , Holt, Henry & Co. Bks. For Young Readers) Holt, Henry & Co.

Gillis, Jennifer Blizin & Jordan, Denise M. Feliz Cumpleanos! 2002. (Fiestas Con Velas (Candle Time) Ser.). (SPA.). 24p. (J). (ps-1). lib. bdg. 18.50 (978-1-58810-870-8(8)); (Illus.). pap. 5.25 (978-1-58810-871-5(6) , 91594) Heinemann Library.

Glass, Sue. Remember Me?/¿Te acuerdas de Mí? Alzheimer's Through the Eyes of a Child/la enfermedad de Alzheimer a través de los ojos de un Niño. de la Vega, Eida, tr. Yunker, W., illus. 2003. Tr. of ¿Te acuerdas de mí? la enfermedad de Alzheimer a través de los ojos de un Niño. (SPA & ENG.). 32p. (J). (gr. 4-6). 16.95 (978-0-9720192-5-5(1) , 626999) Raven Tree Pr.

Gomi, Taro. My Friends. 2006. (ENG & SPA., Illus.). 40p. (J). pap. 6.95 (978-0-8118-5204-3(0)) Chronicle Bks. LLC.

Gonzales Bertrand, Diane. Family, Familia. Castilla, Julia Mercedes, tr. Howard, Pauline Rodriguez, illus. 1999. (SPA & ENG.). 32p. (J). (ps-3). 14.95 (978-1-55885-269-3(7) , Piñata Books) Arte Publico Pr.

Gorman, Jacqueline Laks. Bus Driver/El Conductor del Autobus. Acosta, Tatiana & Gutiérrez, Guillermo, trs. Andersen, Gregg, photos by. 2002. (Weekly Reader Early Learning Library). (SPA & ENG., Illus.). 24p. (J). (ps up). lib. bdg. 19.33 (978-0-8368-3306-5(6) , Weekly Reader Early Learning Library) Stevens, Gareth Inc.

—Dentist/El Dentista. Acosta, Tatiana & Gutiérrez, Guillermo, trs. 2002. (Weekly Reader Early Learning Library). (SPA & ENG., Illus.). 24p. (J). (ps up). lib. bdg. 19.33 (978-0-8368-3307-2(4) , Weekly Reader Early Learning Library) Stevens, Gareth Inc.

—Firefighter/El Bombero. Acosta, Tatiana & Gutiérrez, Guillermo, trs. 2002. (Weekly Reader Early Learning Library). (SPA & ENG., Illus.). 24p. (J). (ps up). lib. bdg. 19.33 (978-0-8368-3309-6(0) , Weekly Reader Early Learning Library) Stevens, Gareth Inc.

—Police Officer/El Policia. Acosta, Tatiana & Gutiérrez, Guillermo, trs. 2002. (Weekly Reader Early Learning Library). (SPA & ENG., Illus.). 24p. (J). (ps up). lib. bdg. 19.33 (978-0-8368-3311-9(2) , Weekly Reader Early Learning Library) Stevens, Gareth Inc.

Gorman, Jacqueline Laks & Macken, JoAnn Early. Bus Driver/El Conductor del Autobus. Coffey, Colleen & Carrillo, Consuelo, trs. Andersen, Gregg, photos by. 2002. (Weekly Reader Early Learning Library). (ENG & SPA., Illus.). 24p. (J). (ps up). pap. 7.93 (978-0-8368-3340-9(6) , Weekly Reader Early Learning Library) Stevens, Gareth Inc.

—Dentist/El Dentista. Coffey, Colleen & Carrillo, Consuelo, trs. Andersen, Gregg, photos by. 2002. (Weekly Reader Early Learning Library). (ENG & SPA., Illus.). 24p. (J). (ps up). pap. 5.95 (978-0-8368-3341-6(4) , Weekly Reader Early Learning Library) Stevens, Gareth Inc.

—Firefighter/El Bombero. Coffey, Colleen & Carrillo, Consuelo, trs. from ENG. Andersen, Gregg, photos by. 2002. (Weekly Reader Early Learning Library). (ENG & SPA., Illus.). 24p. (J). (ps up). pap. 7.93 (978-0-8368-3343-0(0) , Weekly Reader Early Learning Library) Stevens, Gareth Inc.

—Police Officer/El Policia. Coffey, Colleen & Carrillo, Consuelo, trs. Andersen, Gregg, photos by. 2002. (Weekly Reader Early Learning Library). (ENG & SPA., Illus.). 24p. (J). (ps up). pap. 7.93 (978-0-8368-3345-4(7) , Weekly Reader Early Learning Library) Stevens, Gareth Inc.

El Gran Despegue de Maria y Sofia. 2001. (SPA.). (J). per. (978-1-883772-65-9(6)) Flying Rhinoceros, Inc.

Granjero Bob Hace Surf. 2002. Tr. of Farmer Bob Goes Surfing. (SPA.). lib. bdg. (978-1-59168-013-0(1)) Flying Rhinoceros, Inc.

Grimm, Jacob W., et al. Little Red Riding Hood/Capercuita Roja: A Bilingual Book. Surges, James, tr. from CAT. Estrada, Pau, illus. 1999. (ENG & SPA.). 32p. (J). (ps-3). pap. 6.95 (978-0-8118-2562-7(0)) Chronicle Bks. LLC.

Hallinan, P. K. How Do I Love You/Como Te Amo. 2003. (SPA & ENG., Illus.). 32p. (J). 3.95 (978-0-8249-5471-0(8)) Ideals Pubns.

Harris, Zoe & Williams, Suzanne. Pinatas & Smiling Skeletons: Celebrating Mexican Festivals. Woo, Yolanda G., illus. 1998. 48p. (YA). (gr. 2-8). lib. bdg. 19.95 (978-1-881896-19-7(6) , Dragon Bks.) Pacific View Pr.

Hayes, Joe. Pajaro Verde. Castro, Antonio, illus. 2002. (SPA & ENG.). 40p. (J). (gr. 1-3). 16.95 (978-0-938317-65-4(2)) Cinco Puntos Pr.

Heling, Kathryn & Hembrook, Deborah. I Wish I Had Freckles Like Abby/Quisiera tener pecas como Abby. de la Vega, Eida, tr. Adamson, Bonnie, illus. 2006. Tr. of Quisiera tener pecas como Abby. (SPA.). (J). 4.99 (978-0-9770906-6-2(3)) Raven Tree Pr.

—I Wish I Had Freckles Like Abby/Quisiera tener pecas como Abby. de la Vega, Eida, tr. Parins, Kris, illus. 2005. Tr. of Quisiera tener pecas como Abby. (SPA & ENG.). 32p. (J). 16.95 (978-0-9724973-8-1(2) , 626999) Raven Tree Pr.

—I Wish I Had Glasses Like Rosa/Quisiera tener lentes como Rosa. de la Vega, Eida, tr. Adamson, Bonnie, illus. Tr. of Quisiera tener lentes como Rosa. (SPA.). (J). 2006. 4.99 (978-0-9770906-5-5(5)); 2005. 32p. 16.95 (978-0-9724973-7-4(4) , 626999) Raven Tree Pr.

Herrera, Juan Felipe. Grandma & Me at the Flea / Los Meros Meros Remateros. Rohmer, Harriet & Cumpiano, Ina, eds. Lucio-Brock, Anita de, illus. 2002. Tr. of Los Meros Meros Remateros. (ENG & SPA.). 32p. (J). (gr. 1 up). 16.95 (978-0-89239-171-4(5)) Children's Bk. Pr.

—Laughing Out Loud, I Fly: Poems in English & Spanish. Barbour, Karen, illus. 1998. (ENG & SPA.). 48p. (J). (gr. 7-12). 15.99 (978-0-06-027604-1(5) , Cotler, Joanna Books) HarperCollins Pubs.

—Super Cilantro Girl / La Supernina del Cilantro. Robledo Tapia, Honorio, illus. 2003. (ENG & SPA.). 32p. (J). 16.95 (978-0-89239-187-5(1)) Children's Bk. Pr.

Hoffman, Eric. Best Colors (Los Mejores Colores) de la Vega, Eida, tr. Henriquez, Celeste, illus. 2004. (Anti-Bias Books for Kids). (ENG & SPA.). 32p. (J). (ps-3). pap. 11.95 (978-1-884834-69-1(8) , 709201) Redleaf Pr.

—Play Lady - La Senora Juguentona. 2004. (Anti-Bias Books for Kids). (ENG & SPA., Illus.). 32p. (J). (ps-3). pap. 11.95 (978-1-884834-61-5(2)) Redleaf Pr.

Holland, Gini. I Live in a Town/Vivo en un Pueblo. Coffey, Colleen & Carrillo, Consuelo, trs. 2004. (Weekly Reader Early Learning Library). (SPA & ENG., Illus.). 24p. (J). (gr. k up). pap. 5.95 (978-0-8368-4138-1(7)); lib. bdg. 19.33 (978-0-8368-4131-2(X)) Stevens, Gareth Inc. (Weekly Reader Early Learning Library).

—I Live in the City/Vivo en la Ciudad. Coffey, Colleen & Carrillo, Consuelo, trs. 2004. (Weekly Reader Early Learning Library). (SPA & ENG., Illus.). 24p. (J). (gr. k up). pap. 5.95 (978-0-8368-4133-6(6)); lib. bdg. 19.33 (978-0-8368-4126-8(3)) Stevens, Gareth Inc. (Weekly Reader Early Learning Library).

—I Live in the Country/Vivo en el Campo. Coffey, Colleen & Carrillo, Consuelo, trs. 2004. (Weekly Reader Early Learning Library). (Illus.). 24p. (J). (gr. k up). (ENG & SPA.). pap. 5.95 (978-0-8368-4134-3(4)); (SPA & ENG., lib. bdg. 19.33 (978-0-8368-4127-5(1)) Stevens, Gareth Inc. (Weekly Reader Early Learning Library).

—I Live in the Desert/Vivo en el Desierto. Coffey, Colleen & Carrillo, Consuelo, trs. 2004. (Weekly Reader Early Learning Library). (ENG & SPA., Illus.). 24p. (J). (gr. k up). pap. 5.95 (978-0-8368-4135-0(2)); lib. bdg. 19.33 (978-0-8368-4128-2(X)) Stevens, Gareth Inc. (Weekly Reader Early Learning Library).

—I Live in the Mountains/Vivo en las Montañas. Coffey, Colleen & Carrillo, Consuelo, trs. 2004. (Weekly Reader Early Learning Library). (ENG & SPA., Illus.). 24p. (J). (gr. k up). pap. 5.95 (978-0-8368-4136-7(0)); lib. bdg. 19.33 (978-0-8368-4129-9(8)) Stevens, Gareth Inc. (Weekly Reader Early Learning Library).

—I Live near the Ocean/Vivo cerca del Mar. Coffey, Colleen & Carrillo, Consuelo, trs. 2004. (Weekly Reader Early Learning Library). (SPA & ENG., Illus.). 24p. (J). (gr. k up). pap. 5.95 (978-0-8368-4137-4(9)); lib. bdg. 19.33 (978-0-8368-4130-5(1)) Stevens, Gareth Inc. (Weekly Reader Early Learning Library).

—Where I Live/Donde Vivo, 6 bks. Coffey, Colleen & Carrillo, Consuelo, trs. Incl. I Live in a Town/Vivo en un Pueblo. pap. 5.95 (978-0-8368-4138-1(7)); I Live in the City/Vivo en la Ciudad. pap. 5.95 (978-0-8368-4133-6(6)); I Live in the Country/Vivo en el Campo. pap. 5.95 (978-0-8368-4134-3(4)); I Live in the Desert/Vivo en el Desierto. pap. 5.95 (978-0-8368-4135-0(2)); I Live in the Mountains/Vivo en las Montañas. pap. 5.95 (978-0-8368-4136-7(0)); I Live near the Ocean/Vivo cerca del Mar. pap. 5.95 (978-0-8368-4137-4(9)); 24p. (J). (gr. k up). (SPA & ENG., Illus.). 2004. Set pap. 35.70 (978-0-8368-4132-9(8)); Set lib. bdg. 115.98 (978-0-8368-4125-1(5)) Stevens, Gareth Inc. (Weekly Reader Early Learning Library).

Holmes, Melody Moore. Buenos Dias, Carlitos! Garvin, Elaine, illus. 1999. Tr. of Good Day, Carlitos. (SPA.). 32p. (J). (ps-1). pap. 6.49 (978-1-57924-230-5(8) , 115022) Jones, Bob Univ. Pr.

Homero Va a la Playa. l.t. ed. 2002. Tr. of Sam Goes to the Beach. (SPA.). 32p. lib. bdg. (978-1-59168-065-9(4)) Flying Rhinoceros, Inc.

Hoppey, Tim. Tito, the Firefighter/Tito, el Bombero. de la Vega, Eida, tr. Hoffman, Kimberly, illus. 2005. Tr. of Tito, el Bombero. (SPA & ENG.). 32p. (J). (gr. 1-3). 16.95 (978-0-9724973-3-6(1) , 626999) Raven Tree Pr.

—Tito, the Firefighter/Tito, el Bombero. Hoffman, Kimberly, illus. 2005. Tr. of Tito, el Bombero. (SPA & ENG.). 32p. (J). pap. 4.99 (978-0-9741992-6-9(5) , 626999) Raven Tree Pr.

Howell, Theresa. A Is for Airplane, A es para Avion. Brooks, David, illus. 2003. (SPA & ENG.). 28p. (J). bds. 6.95 (978-0-87358-831-7(2) , Rising Moon Bks. for Young Readers) Northland Publishing.

Hoy Voy a Mugir. 2000. (SPA.). (J). per. 9.00 (978-1-883772-81-9(8)) Flying Rhinoceros, Inc.

Huggins-Cooper, Lynn. Alien Invaders/Invasores Extraterrestres. de la Vega, Eida, tr. Leick, Bonnie, illus. 2005. Tr. of Invasores Extraterrestres. (SPA & ENG.). 32p. (J). (gr. 1-3). 16.95 (978-0-9724973-9-8(0) , 626999) Raven Tree Pr.

—Alien Invaders/Invasores Extraterrestres. Leick, Bonnie, illus. 2005. Tr. of Invasores Extraterrestres. (SPA & ENG.). 32p. (J). pap. 4.99 (978-0-9741992-7-6(3) , 626999) Raven Tree Pr.

Izquierdo, Oriol, et al. Little Mermaid. Max, illus. 2003. Tr. of Sirenita. (ENG & SPA.). 32p. (J). 13.95 (978-0-8118-3910-5(9)) Chronicle Bks. LLC.

Jackson, Marjorie. La Sorpresa de Mai-Li. Romo, Alberto, tr. Noll, Cheryl Kirk, illus. 1999. (Books for Young Learners).Tr. of Mai-Li's Surprise. (SPA.). 16p. (J). (gr. k-2). pap. 5.00 (978-1-57274-288-8(7)) Owen, Richard C. Pubs., Inc.

Jeffers, Dawn. Vegetable Dreams/Huerto Soñado. Schneider, Claude, illus. 2006. Tr. of Huerto Soñado. (SPA & ENG.). 32p. (J). lib. bdg. 16.95 (978-0-9741992-9-0(X) , 626999) Raven Tree Pr.

Jimenez, Francisco. Cajas de Carton: The Circuit Spanish Edition. 2002. (SPA., Illus.). 144p. (J). (gr. 5 up). pap. 6.95 (978-0-618-22616-0(8)) Houghton Mifflin Co. Trade & Reference Div.

Jiménez, Francisco. Cajas de Carton: The Circuit Spanish Edition. 2002. (SPA., Illus.). 144p. (J). (gr. 5). tchr. ed. 16.00 (978-0-618-22615-3(X)) Houghton Mifflin Co. Trade & Reference Div.

Jimenez, Francisco. Senderos Fronterizos: Breaking Through Spanish Edition. 2002. (SPA., Illus.). 240p. (J). tchr. ed. 16.00 (978-0-618-22617-7(6)) Houghton Mifflin Co. Trade & Reference Div.

Jiménez, Francisco. Senderos Fronterizos: Breaking Through Spanish Edition. 2002. (SPA., Illus.). 240p. (J). (gr. 5 up). pap. 6.95 (978-0-618-22618-4(4)) Houghton Mifflin Co. Trade & Reference Div.

Jimenez, Juan Ramon. Platero & I/Platero y Yo: A Dual Language Book. Appelbaum, Stanley, ed. Appelbaum, Stanley, tr. from SPA. 2004. (Dual-Language Bks.). (ENG & SPA.). 192p. pap. 9.95 (978-0-486-43565-7(2)) Dover Pubns., Inc.

Johnson, Amy Crane. Mason Moves Away/Mason se Muda: A Solomon Raven Story: un cuento del cuervo Salomon, 4 vols. de la Vega, Eida, tr. Mommaerts, Robb, illus. 2004. (Solomon Raven Ser. : 4). Tr. of Mason se Muda. (SPA & ENG.). 32p. (J). (gr. k-3). 16.95 (978-0-9720192-3-1(5) , 626999) Raven Tree Pr.

Juana Va a Nadar. l.t. ed. 2002. (Farmer Bob Ser.).Tr. of Jenny Goes Swimming. (SPA.). 32p. lib. bdg. (978-1-59168-061-1(1)) Flying Rhinoceros, Inc.

Keister, Douglas. Fernando's Gift/el Regalo de Fernando. Keister, Douglas, photos by. 2001. (SPA., Illus.). 32p. (J). (ps-3). pap. 7.95 (978-0-87156-927-1(2)) Sierra Club Bks. for Children.

—El Regalo de Fernando. 1998. (Sierra Club Bks.).Tr. of Fernando's Gift. (J). 13.75 (978-0-606-13382-1(8)) Tandem Library Bks.

Klingel, Cynthia Fitterer & Noyed, Robert B. Ears/Orejas. Acosta, Tatiana & Gutiérrez, Guillermo, trs. Andersen, Gregg, photos by. 2002. (Weekly Reader Early Learning Library). (Illus.). 24p. (J). (ps up). (SPA & ENG.). pap. (978-0-8368-3320-1(1)); (ENG & SPA., lib. bdg. 19.33 (978-0-8368-3071-2(7)) Stevens, Gareth Inc. (Weekly Reader Early Learning Library).

—Eyes/Ojos. Acosta, Tatiana & Gutiérrez, Guillermo, trs. Andersen, Gregg, photos by. 2002. (Weekly Reader Early Learning Library). (ENG & SPA., Illus.). 24p. (J). (ps up). pap. (978-0-8368-3321-8(X)); lib. bdg. 19.33 (978-0-8368-3072-9(5)) Stevens, Gareth Inc. (Weekly Reader Early Learning Library).

—Feet/Pies. Acosta, Tatiana & Gutiérrez, Guillermo, trs. Andersen, Gregg, photos by. 2002. (Weekly Reader Early Learning Library). (Illus.). 24p. (J). (ps up). (SPA & ENG.). pap. (978-0-8368-3322-5(8)); (ENG & SPA., lib. bdg. 19.33 (978-0-8368-3073-6(3)) Stevens, Gareth Inc. (Weekly Reader Early Learning Library).

—Hair/Pelo. Acosta, Tatiana & Gutiérrez, Guillermo, trs. Andersen, Gregg, photos by. 2002. (Weekly Reader Early Learning Library). (Illus.). 24p. (J). (ps up). pap. (978-0-8368-3323-2(6)); (ENG & SPA., lib. bdg. 19.33 (978-0-8368-3074-3(1)) Stevens, Gareth Inc. (Weekly Reader Early Learning Library).

—Mouth/Boca. Acosta, Tatiana & Gutiérrez, Guillermo, trs. Andersen, Gregg, photos by. 2002. (Weekly Reader Early Learning Library). (Illus.). 24p. (J). (ps up). pap. (978-0-8368-3325-6(2)); (ENG & SPA., lib. bdg. 19.33 (978-0-8368-3076-7(8)) Stevens, Gareth Inc. (Weekly Reader Early Learning Library).

—Nose/Nariz. Acosta, Tatiana & Gutiérrez, Guillermo, trs. Andersen, Gregg, photos by. 2002. (Weekly Reader Early Learning Library). (Illus.). 24p. (J). (ps up). (SPA & ENG.). pap. (978-0-8368-3326-3(0)); (ENG & SPA., lib. bdg. 19.33 (978-0-8368-3077-4(6)) Stevens, Gareth Inc. (Weekly Reader Early Learning Library).

—Skin/Piel. Acosta, Tatiana & Gutiérrez, Guillermo, trs. Andersen, Gregg, photos by. 2002. (Weekly Reader Early Learning Library). (Illus.). 24p. (J). (ps up). (SPA & ENG.). pap. (978-0-8368-3327-0(9)); (ENG & SPA., lib. bdg. 19.33 (978-0-8368-3078-1(4)) Stevens, Gareth Inc. (Weekly Reader Early Learning Library).

Lee, Betsy B. 10,000 White Horses 10,000 Caballos Blancos. Cruz-Torres, Natty, tr. Varnedoe, Catharine E., illus. l.t. ed. 2002. (SPA & ENG.). 24p. (J). pap. 5.95 (978-0-9720267-2-7(X)) Learning Abilities Bks.

Leeson, Cole. El Oso Negro. 2002. (Osos Salvajes Serie).Tr. of Wild Bears: The Black Bear. (SPA.). 24p. (J). (gr. 3-5). 24.94 (978-1-56711-959-6(X) , Blackbirch Pr., Inc.) Thomson Gale.

—El Oso Polar. 2002. (Osos Salvajes Serie).Tr. of Wild Bears: The Polar Bear. (SPA.). 24p. (J). (gr. 3-5). 24.94 (978-1-56711-963-3(8) , Blackbirch Pr., Inc.) Thomson Gale.

El Libro de Chancho Sancho en el Verano. 2000. (SPA.). (J). per. (978-1-883772-30-7(3)) Flying Rhinoceros, Inc.

El Libro de Hercules en el Primavera. 2000. (SPA.). (J). per. (978-1-883772-29-1(X)) Flying Rhinoceros, Inc.

Lomas Garza, Carmen. Magic Windows (Ventanas Magicas) Lomas Garza, Carmen, illus. 1999. (ENG & SPA., Illus.). 32p. (J). (gr. 1-4). 15.95 (978-0-89239-157-8(X)) Children's Bk. Pr.

Lowell, Susan. The Tortoise & the Jackrabbit. Harris, Jim, illus. 2004. (New Bilingual Picture Book Ser.). (ENG & SPA.). 32p. (J). 7.95 incl. 5.25 hd (978-0-87358-869-0(X) , Rising Moon Bks. for Young Readers) Northland Publishing.

Luenn, Nancy. A Gift for Abuelita: Celebrating the Day of the Dead. Chapman, Robert, illus. 1998. Tr. of Un Regalo para Abuelita: En Celebration del Dia de los Muertos. (ENG & SPA.). 32p. (gr. k-3). 15.95 (978-0-87358-688-7(3) , Rising Moon Bks. for Young Readers) Northland Publishing.

Lujan, Jorge & Monroy, Manuel. Rooster Gallo. Monroy, Manuel & Amado, Elisa, trs. Lujan, Jorge, illus. 2004. (ENG & SPA., Illus.). 24p. (J). 14.95 (978-0-88899-558-2(X)) Groundwood Bks. CAN. *Dist:* Perseus Distribution.

Lundell, Margo. A Girl Named Helen Keller: Una Nina Llamada Helen Keller. Trivas, Irene, illus. 2003. (SPA.). 48p. (J). (ps-3). pap. 3.99 (978-0-439-46786-5(1) , Scholastic en Espanol) Scholastic, Inc.

Macken, JoAnn Early. Bears/Los Osos. Coffey, Colleen & Carrillo, Consuelo, trs. from ENG. 2003. (Weekly Reader Early Learning Library). (ENG & SPA., Illus.). 24p. (J). (ps up). lib. bdg. 19.33 (978-0-8368-3998-2(6) , Weekly Reader Early Learning Library) Stevens, Gareth Inc.

—Giraffes/Las Jirafas. Coffey, Colleen & Carrillo, Consuelo, trs. from SPA. 2003. (Weekly Reader Early Learning Library). (ENG & SPA., Illus.). 24p. (J). (ps up). lib. bdg. 19.33 (978-0-8368-4000-1(3) , Weekly Reader Early Learning Library) Stevens, Gareth Inc.

Marcos, Subcomandante. The Story of Colors (La Historia de los Colores) A Bilingual Folktale from the Jungles of Chiapas. 2003. (ENG & SPA., Illus.). 40p. (J). pap. 8.95 (978-0-938317-71-5(7)) Cinco Puntos Pr.

Martin, Bill. Oso Pardo, Oso Pardo, ¿Qué Ves Ahí? Mlawer, Teresa, tr. Carle, Eric, illus. rev. ed. 2002. (SPA.). 28p. (J). (ps-k). bds. 7.95 (978-0-8050-6901-3(1) , Holt, Henry & Co. Bks. For Young Readers) Holt, Henry & Co.

—Oso Polar, Oso Polar, Que es Ese Ruido? Mlawer, Teresa, tr. Carle, Eric, illus. rev. ed. 2002. (SPA.). 28p. (J). (ps-k). bds. 7.95 (978-0-8050-6902-0(X) , Holt, Henry & Co. Bks. For Young Readers) Holt, Henry & Co.

Masurel, Claire. No, Tito, No! No, No, Titus! Lasconi, Diego, tr. Halpern, Shari, illus. 1999. (SPA.). 32p. (J). (ps-1). 15.95 (978-0-7358-1208-6(X) , NS3699); pap. 6.95 (978-0-7358-1209-3(8) , NS3707) North-South Bks., Inc.

Matt Otra Vez en Problemas! Podra Ayudarlo la Consejera de la Escuela? 2001. 22p. (J). pap. 8.95 (978-0-9713839-2-0(8)) MarLin Bks.

McDermott, Gerald. Zomo el Conejo: Un Cuento de Africa Occidental. Ada, Alma Flor & Campoy, F. Isabel, trs. 2002. Tr. of Zomo the Rabbit. (SPA., Illus.). 32p. (J). (gr. k-3). pap. 7.00 (978-0-15-216777-6(3) , Voyager Bks./Libros Viajeros) Harcourt Children's Bks.

—Zomo el Conejo: Un Cuento de Africa Occidental. 2002. Tr. of Zomo the Rabbit. (SPA.). (gr. k-3). lib. bdg. 15.30 (978-0-613-82221-3(8)) Tandem Library Bks.

McGrath, Liz & Quick, Barbara. Even More/Todavía Mas. de la Vega, Eida, tr. McGrath, Liz, illus. 2004. Tr. of Todavía Mas. (SPA & ENG., Illus.). 34p. (J). (gr. k-3). 16.95 (978-0-9720192-8-6(6) , 626999) Raven Tree Pr.

McKee, David. Elmer's Friends. Pullin, Beatriz, tr. 2004. (Elmer Ser.).Tr. of Amigos de Elmer. (SPA, ENG, URD, TUR & VIE., Illus.). 16p. (J). (ps-k). bds. 6.95 (978-1-84059-072-2(6)) Milet Publishing.

Me Llamo Hercules. 2000. (J). per. 9.00 (978-1-883772-92-5(3)) Flying Rhinoceros, Inc.

Me Llamo Homero. 2000. (SPA.). (J). per. 9.00 (978-1-883772-80-2(X)) Flying Rhinoceros, Inc.

Me Llamo Juana. 2000. (J). per. 9.00 (978-1-883772-95-6(8)) Flying Rhinoceros, Inc.

Me Llamo Sancho Chancho. 2000. (SPA.). (J). per. 9.00 (978-1-883772-94-9(X)) Flying Rhinoceros, Inc.

Meister, Cari. Me Fascinan las Piedras. Sirrell, Terry, illus. (Rookie Reader Espanol Ser.). (J). (gr. k-2). 2002. pap. 4.95 (978-0-516-26212-3(2)); 2001. (SPA.). 32p. 19.50 (978-0-516-22356 8(9)) Scholastic Library Publishing. (Children's Pr.).

Mi Abuelita. 2001. (SPA.). (J). pap. 14.95 (978-0-9630310-5-1(8)) Will Hall Bks.

Mi Cara Curiosa. 2002. (Wild Imagination Ser.).Tr. of My Fantastic Face. (SPA.). 24p. (J). lib. bdg. 19.95 (978-1-59168-062-8(X)) Flying Rhinoceros, Inc.

Mi Cola Cautividora Adventure Pack. 2002. Tr. of My Fantastic Face Adventure Pack. (SPA.). (978-1-59168-000-0(X)) Flying Rhinoceros, Inc.

Miller, Elizabeth I. Just Like Home: Como en Mi Tierra. Reisberg, Mira, illus. 2004. 32p. (J). (gr. 1-3). pap. 6.95 (978-0-8075-4069-5(2)) Whitman, Albert & Co.

Miller, Sara Swan. La Gatita en la Maleta. Mahan, Benton, illus. 2001. (Rookie Espanol Ser.). (SPA.). 32p. (J). (gr. k-2). 19.50 (978-0-516-22355-1(0) , Children's Pr.) Scholastic Library Publishing.

Montalvo, Margarita. Zoolygico de Poemas / Poetry Zoo. Montalvo, Margarita, illus. 2006. (SPA., Illus.). 48p. (J). (gr. 2-5). pap. 4.99 (978-0-439-70681-0(5) , Scholastic en Espanol) Scholastic, Inc.

Mora, Pat. The Bakery Lady/la señora de la Panadería. Mora, Pat & Ventura, Gabriela Baeza, trs. Torrecilla, Pablo, illus. Tr. of Señora de la Panaderia. (ENG & SPA.). 32p. (J). (ps-3). 15.95 (978-1-55885-343-0(X) , Piñata Books) Arte Publico Pr.

—A Birthday Basket for Tia. 1998. (J). pap. 4.99 (978-0-87628-395-0(4)) Ctr. for Applied Research in Education, The.

Morales, Maximino. Juan & the Three Wise Men (Juan y los Tres Reyes Mogos) 2002. (ENG & SPA., Illus.). 28p. (J). (gr. k-3). pap. 6.95 (978-0-9740308-1-4(3)) Maximum Publishing Co.

—Lucky Me! (Que Suerte!) 2002. (ENG & SPA., Illus.). 32p. (J). (gr. k-3). pap. 6.95 (978-0-9740308-2-1(1)) Maximum Publishing Co.

—The Wooden Go-Cart (El Carrito de Madera) 2002. (ENG & SPA., Illus.). 24p. (J). (gr. k-3). pap. 6.95 (978-0-9740308-0-7(5)) Maximum Publishing Co.

Morton, Lone & Risk, Mary. Feliz Cumpleanos. 1998. (I Can Read Bks.).Tr. of Happy Birthday. (ENG & SPA., Illus.). 28p. (J). (ps up). audio 9.95 (978-0-7641-7192-5(5)) Barron's Educational Series, Inc.

—Get Dressed, Roberto. 1998. (Language Learning Story Bks.).Tr. of Vistete, Roberto. (ENG & SPA., Illus.). 28p. (J). (ps-3). 7.99 (978-0-7641-5129-3(0) , BA290) Barron's Educational Series, Inc.

—I'm Too Big. 1998. (I Can Read Bks.).Tr. of Je Suis Mucho Grande. (ENG & SPA., Illus.). 28p. (J). (ps up). audio 9.95 (978-0-7641-7193-2(3)) Barron's Educational Series, Inc.

Moses, Brian. Me Siento Preocupada. Gordon, Mike, illus. 2001. (Mis Sentimientos Coleccion). (SPA.). (J). pap. 6.36 (978-950-24-0843-9(8)) Albatros ARG. *Dist:* Lectorum Pubns., Inc.

—Me Siento Solo. Gordon, Mike, illus. 2001. (Mis Sentimientos Coleccion). (SPA.). (J). pap. 6.36 (978-950-24-0842-2(X)) Albatros ARG. *Dist:* Lectorum Pubns., Inc.

—No Es Justo. Gordon, Mike, illus. 2001. (Mis Sentimientos Coleccion). (SPA.). (J). pap. 6.36 (978-950-24-0844-6(6)) Albatros ARG. *Dist:* Lectorum Pubns., Inc.

Musara'as No Pueden Jugar Al Basquet Adventure Pack. 2002. Tr. of Shrews Can't Hoop Adventure Pack. (SPA.). (978-1-59168-008-6(5)); lib. bdg. (978-1-59168-019-2(0)) Flying Rhinoceros, Inc.

One Baby Jesus/Un Nino Dios. 2003. (ENG & SPA., Illus.). 30p. (J). 3.95 (978-0-8249-5472-7(6)) Ideals Pubns.

Oral Language Flip Chart. 2000. (SPA.). (gr. k up). suppl. ed. 116.50 (978-0-673-60755-3(0)) Addison-Wesley Educational Pubs., Inc.

Perez, Amada Irma. My Diary from Here to There / Mi Diario de Aqui Hasta Alla. Gonzalez, Maya Christina, illus. 2002. Tr. of Mi Diario de Aqui Hasta Alla. (ENG & SPA.). 32p. (J). (gr. 2-5). 16.95 (978-0-89239-175-2(8)) Children's Bk. Pr.

—My Very Own Room (Mi Propio Cuartito) Gonzalez, Maya Christina, illus. 2000. (ENG & SPA.). 32p. (J). (gr. 1 up). 16.95 (978-0-89239-164-6(2)) Children's Bk. Pr.

—Nana's Big Surprise/¡Nana, Que Sorpresa! Gonzalez, Maya Christina, tr. Gonzalez, Maya Christina, illus. 2007. (ENG & SPA.). 32p. (J). (gr. 1-2). 16.95 (978-0-89239-190-5(1)) Children's Bk. Pr.

Petersen, Patricia. Magali/Magali: An Aztec Legend about Good Fortune (Una Ieyenja Azteca Sobre La Buena Fortuna) Petersen, Sheli, illus. 1998. (Cuentos en Dos Idiomas Ser.). 32p. (J). (gr. 3-6). 16.95 (978-1-56492-250-2(2)) Laredo Publishing Co., Inc.

Pietrapiana. Tomasa the Cow. Pietrapiana, illus. 1999. Tr. of Vaca Tomasa. (SPA & ENG., Illus.). 32p. (J). (ps-3). 14.95 (978-1-55885-284-6(0) , Piñata Books) Arte Publico Pr.

Pilkey, Dav. El Capitan Calzoncillos y el Perverso Plan del Profesor Pipicaca. 2002. (Captain Underpants Ser.: No. 4). (SPA.). 160p. (J). (gr. 1-5). pap. 4.99 (978-0-439-41037-3(1) , Scholastic en Espanol) Scholastic, Inc.

Polette, Keith. Isabel & the Hungry Coyote/Isabel y el Coyote Hambriento. Raven Tree Press Staff, ed. Szegedy, Esther, illus. 2004. Tr. of Isabel y el coyote Hambriento. (SPA.). 32p. (J). 16.95 (978-0-9724973-0-5(7) , 626999) Raven Tree Pr.

Rau, Dana Meachen. Carlitos Friolento. Lemelman, Martin, illus. (Rookie Reader Espanol Ser.). (SPA.). 24p. (J). (gr. k-2). 2002. pap. 4.95 (978-0-516-26208-6(4)); 2001. 19.50 (978-0-516-22352-0(6) , CP1128) Scholastic Library Publishing. (Children's Pr.).

Read & Color Book Series. Date not set. (Illus.). (J). (ps-5). pap. (978-0-86545-223-7(7)) Spizzirri Pr., Inc.

Read & Understand. 2005. (SPA.). 304p. (gr. 1 up). 29.99 (978-1-55799-999-3(6) , EMC 5307); (gr. 2 up). 29.99 (978-1-55799-000-7(5) , EMC 5308); (gr. 3 up). 29.99 (978-1-59673-001-4(3) , EMC 5309) Evan-Moor Educational Pubs.

Rey, H. A. Jorge el Curioso Monta en Bicicleta. Canetti, Yanitzia, tr. 2002. Tr. of Curious George Rides a Bike. (SPA., Illus.). 48p. (J). (gr. k-3). pap. 6.95 (978-0-618-19677-7(3)); tchr. ed. 14.95 (978-0-618-21615-4(4)) Houghton Mifflin Co. Trade & Reference Div.

—Jorge el Curioso Monta en Bicicleta. 2002. Tr. of Curious George Rides a Bike. (SPA.). (gr. k-3). lib. bdg. 14.10 (978-0-613-60749-0(X)) Tandem Library Bks.

Rey, H. A. & Rey, Margret, creators. Opuestos con Jorge el Curioso. 2002. (SPA., Illus.). 8p. (J). (gr. k-ps). bds. 5.95 (978-0-618-20317-8(6)) Houghton Mifflin Co. Trade & Reference Div.

Rice, Judith Anne. Those Icky Sticky Smelly Cavity-Causing but—Invisible Germs/Esos Sucios Pegajosos Olorosos Causantes de Caries Pero... Invisibles Germenes. Stricklin, Julie A., illus. 2004. (SPA & ENG.). 32p. (J). (gr. k-3). pap. 14.95 (978-1-884834-30-1(2)) Redleaf Pr.

—Those Itsy-Bitsy Teeny-Tiny Not-So-Nice Head Lice/Esos Pequenines Chiquitines para Nada Simpaticos Piojos. Stricklin, Julie A. & Ytsma, Petronella J., illus. 2004. (SPA & ENG.). 32p. (J). (gr. k-3). pap. 12.95 (978-1-884834-54-7(X)) Redleaf Pr.

Risk, Mary & Morton, Lone. What's for Supper? Que Hay Para Cenar? 1998. (Language Learning Story Bks.). (ENG & SPA., Illus.). 28p. (J). (ps up). 8.99 (978-0-7641-5127-9(4) , BA274) Barron's Educational Series, Inc.

Rivera-Ashford, Roni Capin. My Nana's Remedies: Los Remedios de Mi Nana. 2002. (SPA.). 32p. (J). (ps-4). 15.95 (978-1-886679-19-1(3)) Arizona Sonora Desert Museum Pr.

Robinson, Fay. Un Dinosaurio Llamado Sue: El Hallzgo del Siglo. 2002. (SPA., Illus.). 48p. (J). (gr. k-2). pap. 3.99 (978-0-439-42110-2(1) , Scholastic en Espanol) Scholastic, Inc.

Rockhill, Dennis. Ocean Whisper/Susurro del Océano. de la Vega, Eida, tr. Rockhill, Dennis, illus. 2005. Tr. of Susurro del Océano. (SPA & ENG., Illus.). 32p. (J). 16.95 (978-0-9741992-4-5(9) , 626999) Raven Tree Pr.

—Polar Slumber/Sueño Polar. Raven Tree Press Staff, ed. de la Vega, Eida, tr. Rockhill, Dennis, illus. 2004. Tr. of Sueño Polar. (SPA & ENG., Illus.). 32p. (J). (ps-3). 16.95 (978-0-9724973-1-2(5) , 1234791) Raven Tree Pr.

Rodriguez, Luis J. La Llaman America. Villanueva, Tino, tr. Vazquez, Carlos, illus. 2004. (SPA.). 32p. (gr. 4-7). reprint ed. 16.95 (978-1-880684-41-2(1)) Curbstone Pr.

Ros, Roser. The Musicians of Bremen/Los Musicos de Bremen. Montserrat, Pep, illus. 2005. (ENG & SPA.). 32p. (J). (ps-ps). 14.95 (978-0-8118-4795-7(0)) Chronicle Bks. LLC.

Rosa-Mendoza, Gladys. My Family & I. Cifuentes, Carolina, ed. Snider, Jackie, illus. 2004. (English-Spanish Foundations Ser.: Vol. 4). Tr. of Mi Familia y Yo. (ENG & SPA.). 20p. (J). (ps-4). bds. 6.95 (978-0-9679748-4-2(4)) Me+Mi Publishing.

—Opposites. Cifuentes, Carolina, ed. McGeehan, Dan, illus. 2004. (English-Spanish Foundations Ser.: Vol. 5). Tr. of Opuestos. (ENG & SPA.). 20p. (J). (ps-4). bds. 6.95 (978-0-9679748-6-6(0)) Me+Mi Publishing.

—The Weather. Cifuentes, Carolina, ed. Hullinger, C. D., illus. 2004. (English-Spanish Foundations Ser.: Vol. 6). Orig. Title: El Tiempo. (ENG & SPA.). 20p. (J). (ps-4). bds. 6.95 (978-0-9679748-5-9(2)) Me+Mi Publishing.

—What Time Is It? Cifuentes, Carolina, ed. 2004. (English-Spanish Foundations Ser.: Vol. 7). Tr. of ¿Que Hora Es?. (ENG & SPA., Illus.). 20p. (J). (ps-4). bds. 6.95 (978-0-9679748-9-7(5)) Me+Mi Publishing.

Saenz, Benjamin Alire. A Gift from Papa Diego (Un Regalo de Papa Diego) Garcia, Geronimo, illus. 2004. (ENG & SPA.). 40p. (gr. k-7). pap. 10.95 (978-0-938317-33-3(4)) Cinco Puntos Pr.

Sagel, Jim. Always the Heart. 1998. (Red Crane Literature Ser.).Tr. of Siempre el Corazon. (ENG & SPA., Illus.). 168p. (gr. 8-12). pap. 12.95 (978-1-878610-68-3(6)) Red Crane Bks., Inc.

—Always the Heart. 1998. Tr. of Siempre el Corazon. (gr. 7-12). lib. bdg. 22.20 (978-0-613-80111-9(3)) Tandem Library Bks.

Saludos Desde Los Estados Unidos. 2002. Tr. of Greetings from America. (SPA.). lib. bdg. (978-1-59168-014-7(X)) Flying Rhinoceros, Inc.

San Vicente, Luis. The Festival of Bones, el Festival de las Calaveras: The Little-Bitty Book for the Day of the Dead. Byrd, John Williams & Byrd, Bobby, trs. San Vicente, Luis, illus. 2002. (SPA & ENG., Illus.). 32p. (J). (gr. k-5). 14.95 (978-0-938317-67-8(9)) Cinco Puntos Pr.

Sandhaus, Ellen. 26 of the Most Interesting Letters in the Alphabet: 26 de las letras mas intersantes del alfabeto. Blanco, Osvaldo J., tr. Sandhaus, Ellen, illus. unabr. ed. 1999. (SPA & ENG., Illus.). 28p. (J). (gr. k-4). pap. 4.95 (978-1-893266-02-5(8)) Sandhaus, Paul Assocs., Inc.

Saunders-Smith, Gail & Guzman Ferrer, Martin Luis. La Luz Del Sol. 2004. (Pebble Bilingual Books). (ENG & SPA., Illus.). 24p. (J). 15.93 (978-0-7368-2310-4(7)) Capstone Pr., Inc.

Schaefer, Lola M. Animales Acorazados 123. 2002. (Animales Acorazados (Musty-Crusty Animals) Ser.). (SPA.). 24p. (J). (ps-1). lib. bdg. 18.50 (978-1-58810-859-3(7)); (Illus.). pap. 5.25 (978-1-58810-821-0(X) , 91556) Heinemann Library.

—La Babosa. 2002. (Animales Resbalosos (Ooey-Gooey Animals) Ser.). (SPA.). 24p. (J). (ps-1). lib. bdg. 18.50 (978-1-58810-768-8(X)); (Illus.). pap. 5.25 (978-1-58810-812-8(0) , 91517) Heinemann Library.

—La Bellota de Mar. 2002. (Animales Acorazados (Musty-Crusty Animals) Ser.). (SPA.). 24p. (J). (ps-1). lib. bdg. 18.50 (978-1-58810-771-8(X)); (Illus.). pap. 5.25 (978-1-58810-815-9(5) , 91561) Heinemann Library.

—El Cangrejo Bayoneta. 2002. (Animales Acorazados (Musty-Crusty Animals) Ser.). (SPA.). 24p. (J). (ps-1). lib. bdg. 18.50 (978-1-58810-774-9(4)); (Illus.). pap. 5.25 (978-1-58810-818-0(X) , 91558) Heinemann Library.

—El Cangrejo de Rio. 2002. (Animales Acorazados (Musty-Crusty Animals) Ser.). (SPA.). 24p. (J). (ps-1). lib. bdg. 18.50 (978-1-58810-772-5(8)); (Illus.). pap. 5.25 (978-1-58810-816-6(3) , 91559) Heinemann Library.

—El Cangrejo Ermitano. 2002. (Animales Acorazados (Musty-Crusty Animals) Ser.). (SPA.). 24p. (J). (ps-1). lib. bdg. 18.50 (978-1-58810-773-2(6)); (Illus.). pap. 5.25 (978-1-58810-817-3(1) , 91560) Heinemann Library.

—La Medusa. 2002. (Animales Resbalosos (Ooey-Gooey Animals) Ser.). (SPA.). 24p. (J). (ps-1). lib. bdg. 18.50 (978-1-58810-765-7(5)); (Illus.). pap. 5.25 (978-1-58810-809-8(0) , 91519) Heinemann Library.

—La Sanguijuela. 2002. (Animales Resbalosos (Ooey-Gooey Animals) Ser.). (SPA.). 24p. (J). (ps-1). lib. bdg. 18.50 (978-1-58810-766-4(3)); (Illus.). pap. 5.25 (978-1-58810-810-4(4) , 91515) Heinemann Library.

Scholastic, Inc. Staff & Salas, Macarena, eds. Dive Right In!/-LyNzate Al Agua! 2004. (Rubbadubbers Ser.). (ENG & SPA.). 80p. (J). 2.99 (978-0-439-63204-1(8) , Scholastic en Espanol) Scholastic, Inc.

School Zone Publishing Company Staff. ABC Dot-to-Dot Bilingual: Get Ready! 2004. 64p. (J). pap. 3.79 (978-1-58947-972-2(6)) School Zone Publishing Co.

—Beginning Sounds Bilingual: Get Ready! 2004. 64p. (J). pap. 3.79 (978-1-58947-974-6(2)) School Zone Publishing Co.

—Lowercase Alphabet Bilingual: Get Ready! 2004. 64p. (J). pap. 3.79 (978-1-58947-970-8(X)) School Zone Publishing Co.

—Manuscript Writing K-2 Bilingual: I Know It! 2004. 64p. (J). (gr. k-1). pap. 3.79 (978-1-58947-961-6(0)) School Zone Publishing Co.

Shah, Idries. The Farmer's Wife/la Esposa Del Granjero. Santiago, Rose Mary, illus. 2003. (SPA & ENG.). (J). 18.00 (978-1-883536-33-6(2) , FAWI2, Hoopoe Bks.) ISHK.

—The Lion Who Saw Himself in the Water/el Leon Que Se Vio en el Aqua. Rodriguez, Ingrid, illus. 2003. (SPA & ENG.). (J). 18.00 (978-1-883536-31-2(6) , LIWS3); 6.95 (978-1-883536-32-9(4) , LIWS4) ISHK. (Hoopoe Bks.).

Shannon, David. Un Caso Grave de Rayas. 2002. (SPA., Illus.). 32p. (J). (gr. k-4). pap. 3.99 (978-0-439-40986-5(1) , Scholastic en Espanol) Scholastic, Inc.

Shepard, Aaron. Lady White Snake: A Tale from Chinese Opera. de la Vega, Eida, tr. Zhang, Song Nan, illus. 2001. (ENG & SPA.). 32p. (J). 16.95 (978-1-57227-073-2(X)) Pan Asia Pubns. (USA), Inc.

Silvano, Wendi. Counting Coconuts/Contando Cocos: A Counting Story in English & Spanish. Raven Tree Press Staff, ed. Granius, Marty, illus. 2004. Tr. of Contando Cocos. (SPA & ENG.). 32p. (J). (ps-3). 16.95 (978-0-9720192-6-2(X) , 626999) Raven Tree Pr.

Snicket, Lemony, pseud. La Habitacion de los Reptiles. Helquist, Brett, illus. 2002. (Series of Unfortunate Events Ser.). (SPA.). 208p. (J). (gr. 4-6). 10.95 (978-84-264-3741-9(9) , LM31164) Editorial Lumen ESP. *Dist:* Lectorum Pubns., Inc.

—Un Mal Principio. Helquist, Brett, illus. 2002. (Series of Unfortunate Events Ser.). (SPA.). 224p. (J). (gr. 4-6). 10.95 (978-84-264-3740-2(0) , LM31162) Editorial Lumen ESP. *Dist:* Lectorum Pubns., Inc.

Stanford, Candice & Wroth, William. The Man Who Set the Town Dancing. Dougherty, Flo Hosa, illus. 2002. (ENG & SPA.). 40p. (J). (gr. 2-4). 16.95 (978-1-57416-050-5(8)) Clear Light Pubs.

Stewart, Mark & Kennedy, Mike. Latino Baseball's Finest Fielders/Las Mas Destacados Guantes del Beisbol Latino. Kalmanovitz, Manuel, tr. 2003. (En Fuego Ser.). (ENG & SPA., Illus.). 48p. (J). (gr. 5 up). pap. 9.95 (978-0-7613-1749-4(X) , Twenty-First Century Bks.) Lerner Publishing Group.

Suarez, Ana, tr. from ENG. Le Semana Atareada de Clifford'. Bridwell, Norman, illus. 2002. (Clifford, the Big Red Dog Ser.). (SPA.). 32p. (J). (ps-1). pap. 3.50 (978-0-439-41833-1(X) , Scholastic en Espanol) Scholastic, Inc.

Suen, Anastasia. Toddler Two: Dos Anos. Cheon, Winnie, illus. 2002. (ENG & SPA.). (J). bds. 5.95 (978-1-58430-054-0(X)) Lee & Low Bks., Inc.

Sweetland, Nancy Rose. Yelly Kelly/Kelly, el Griton. de la Vega, Eida, tr. Sweetland, Robert, illus. rev. ed. 2004. Tr. of Kelly, el Griton. (SPA & ENG.). 32p. (J). (gr. k-3). 16.95 (978-0-9720192-0-0(0) , 626999) Raven Tree Pr.

Thompson, Kim Mitzo. Hello, How Are You? 2006. (Dual Language Readers Ser.). (ENG & SPA.). 32p. (J). pap., pap. 4.99 (978-0-7696-4615-2(8)) School Specialty Publishing.

Tocalli-Beller, Agustina. Bilingual Songs Vol. 1: English-Spanish. Ramirez, Gloria & Howard, Joan, eds. Brough-Jordan, Jessica & El-Shinnawy, Ihab, illus. 2002. (SPA & ENG.). 48p. (J). pap. 14.95 incl. audio (978-1-894262-66-8(2) , JMP S23K) Jordan Music Productions, Inc.

—Bilingual Songs Vol. 2: English-Spanish. Ranirez, Gloria & Howard, Joan, eds. El-Shinnawy, Ihab, illus. 2002. (ENG & SPA.). 48p. (J). pap. 14.95 incl. audio (978-1-894262-71-2(9) , JMP S24K) Jordan Music Productions, Inc.

Tolstoy, Alexei. El Nabo Gigante (The Gigantic Turnip) Sarfatti, Esther, tr. Sharkey, Niamh, illus. 2001. Tr. of Gigantic Turnip. (SPA.). 40p. (J). (ps-1). reprint ed. pap. 6.99 (978-1-84148-396-2(6) , BFP0577) Barefoot Bks., Inc.

Tolstoy, Alexei, ed. El Nabo Gigante. 2000. Tr. of Gigantic Turnip. (J). (978-0-606-19703-8(6)) Tandem Library Bks.

Tripp, Valerie. Josefina Entra en Accion: Un Cuento de Verano. Tibbles, Jean-Paul, illus. 1998. (American Girls Collection: Bk. 5). Tr. of Josefina Saves the Day. (SPA.). (YA). (gr. 2 up). 12.75 (978-0-606-13540-5(5)) Tandem Library Bks.

Villarreal Elizondo, Cesar. La Tierra de las Adivinanzas. Garcia, Nasario, tr. from SPA. Accardo, Anthony, illus. 2002. Tr. of Land of the Riddles. (ENG & SPA.). 32p. (J). (gr. 2-3). 14.95 (978-1-55885-352-2(9) , Piñata Books) Arte Publico Pr.

Vogel, Elizabeth. El Cuidado de Tu Cabello. 2004. (Limpieza y Salud Todo el Dia Ser.). (SPA & ENG., Illus.). 24p. (J). lib. bdg. 16.00 (978-0-8239-6611-0(9) , Buenas Letra) Rosen Publishing Group, Inc., The.

Wagener, Gerda. Hay un Raton en Casa! 2002. Tr. of There's a Mouse in the House!. (SPA.). (gr. k-3). lib. bdg. 14.10 (978-0-613-73551-3(X)) Tandem Library Bks.

Walsh, Melanie. Trinan los Monos? Walsh, Melanie, illus. 2002. Tr. of Do Monkeys Tweet?. (SPA., Illus.). 14p. (J). (gr. k-ps). bds. 5.95 (978-0-618-20318-5(4)) Houghton Mifflin Co. Trade & Reference Div.

Weber, Jane. The Riches of Rangoberra/Las riquezas de Rangoberra. de la Vega, Eida, tr. Saari, Rijalynne, illus. 2002. Tr. of Las riquezas de Rangoberra. (SPA & ENG.). 32p. (J). (gr. 4-6). 16.95 (978-0-9720192-1-7(9) , 626999) Raven Tree Pr.

West, Tracey. Liz Busca un Hogar. 1999. (Coleccion Liz). (SPA., Illus.). 24p. (J). (gr. k-3). pap. 3.50 (978-0-590-68935-9(5) , SO6032, Scholastic en Espanol) Scholastic, Inc.

Whitehouse, Patricia. Las Estaciones, 5 vols., Set. 2003. (SPA.). (J). (ps-1). lib. bdg. 92.50 (978-1-4034-0338-4(4)) Heinemann Library.

—Las Hojas. (Plantas (Plants) Ser.). (SPA.). 24p. (J). (ps-1). 2003. lib. bdg. 17.08 (978-1-58810-777-0(9)); 2002. (Illus.). pap. 5.25 (978-1-58810-824-1(4) , 91647) Heinemann Library.

—Matematicas con Plantas. (Plantas (Plants) Ser.). (SPA.). 24p. (J). (ps-1). 2003. lib. bdg. 17.08 (978-1-58810-780-0(9)); 2002. (Illus.). pap. 5.25 (978-1-58810-827-2(9) , 91648) Heinemann Library.

—Que Esta Despierto? 1 2 3. 2002. (Que Esta Despierto? (What's Awake?) Ser.).Tr. of What's Awake? 1 2 3. (SPA.). 24p. (J). (ps-1). pap. 5.25 (978-1-4034-0640-8(5)) Heinemann Library.

—Las Raices. (Plantas (Plants) Ser.). (SPA.). 24p. (J). (ps-1). 2003. lib. bdg. 17.08 (978-1-58810-778-7(7)); 2002. (Illus.). pap. 5.25 (978-1-58810-825-8(2) , 91649) Heinemann Library.

—Las Semillas. 2002. (Plantas (Plants) Ser.). (SPA.). 24p. (J). (ps-1). lib. bdg. 17.08 (978-1-58810-779-4(5)); (Illus.). pap. 5.25 (978-1-58810-826-5(0) , 91650) Heinemann Library.

Wilkes, Angela. My First Spanish Word Board Book. 2002. (SPA., Illus.). 36p. (J). (ps-1). bds. 6.99 (978-0-7894-8593-9(1)) Dorling Kindersley Publishing, Inc.

Zapata, Elizabeth. You Say Hola, I Say Hello. Johnson, Cathy Ann, illus. 2006. (SPA.). 24p. (J). (gr. k-2). pap. 4.95 (978-0-516-25018-2(3) , Children's Pr.) Scholastic Library Publishing.

—You Say Hola, I Say Hello. Johnson, Cathy Ann, illus. 2005. (Rookie Reader Ser.). 24p. (J). 19.50 (978-0-516-24859-2(6) , Children's Pr.) Scholastic Library Publishing.

BILL OF RIGHTS (UNITED STATES)

see Constitutional Amendments—United States

BILLBOARDS

see Signs and Signboards

BILLIARDS

Givens, R. The Eight Ball Bible: A Guide to Bar Table Play. Givens, R, illus. 2004. (Illus.). 288p. (YA). per. 29.95 (978-0-9747273-7-0(7) , 415-776-1596) 8-Ball Express, Inc.

BILLS OF CREDIT

see Credit; Paper Money

BILLS OF FARE

see Menus

BILLY, THE KID

Bruns, Roger A. Billy the Kid: Outlaw of the Wild West. 2000. (Historical American Biographies Ser.). (Illus.). 128p. (YA). (gr. 6-12). lib. bdg. 26.60 (978-0-7660-1091-8(0)) Enslow Pubs., Inc.

Harmon, Daniel E. Billy the Kid. 2001. (Famous Figures of the American Frontier Ser.). (Illus.). 64p. (J). pap. 25.00 (978-0-7910-6484-9(0)); 25.00 (978-0-7910-6483-2(2)) Facts On File, Inc. (Chelsea Hse.).

—Billy the Kid. 2002. (gr. 5-8). lib. bdg. 17.60 (978-0-613-50869-8(6)) Tandem Library Bks.

Healy, Nick. Billy the Kid. 2005. (Illus.). 48p. (gr. 5-9). 21.95 (978-1-58341-335-7(9) , Creative Education) Creative Co., The.

Hefner, Bobby E. The Trial of Billy the Kid. (Illus.). 95p. (YA). (978-1-886709-08-9(4)) Outlaw Pubns.

Landau, Elaine. Billy the Kid: Wild West Outlaw. 2004. (Best of the West Biographies Ser.). (Illus.). 48p. (J). lib. bdg. 23.93 (978-0-7660-2207-2(2)) Enslow Pubs., Inc.

BIMETALLISM

see Gold; Silver

BINARY SYSTEM (MATHEMATICS)

Schaefer, Ted. ¿Cuanto Es un Par? 2007. (J). (***978-1-60044-284-1(6)***) Rourke Publishing, LLC.

Schaefer, Ted. How Many Is a Pair? 2007. (Illus.). 24p. (J). (978-1-59515-976-2(2)); pap. (***978-1-59515-947-2(9)***) Rourke Publishing, LLC.

BINDERGARTEN, MISS (FICTITIOUS CHARACTER)—FICTION

Slate, Joseph. Miss Bindergarten Celebrates the 100th Day of Kindergarten. 2002. (Miss Bindergarten Ser.). (Illus.). (YA). 15.53 (978-1-4046-2578-5(X)) Book Wholesalers, Inc.

—Miss Bindergarten Celebrates the 100th Day of Kindergarten. Wolff, Ashley, illus. (J). (gr. k-1). 2002. 40p. pap. 6.99 (978-0-14-250005-7(4) , Puffin); 1998. 32p. 16.99 (978-0-525-46000-8(4) , Dutton Juvenile) Penguin Group (USA) Inc.

—Miss Bindergarten Celebrates the 100th Day of Kindergarten. 2003. (gr. k-3). lib. bdg. 15.30 (978-0-613-58122-6(9)) Tandem Library Bks.

—Miss Bindergarten Gets Ready for Kindergarten. Wolff, Ashley, illus. 2001. 40p. (J). pap. 6.99 (978-0-14-056273-6(7) , Puffin) Penguin Group (USA) Inc.

—Miss Bindergarten Gets Ready for Kindergarten. 2001. (gr. k-3). lib. bdg. 15.30 (978-0-613-35982-5(8)); (Illus.). (J). (978-0-606-21333-2(3)) Tandem Library Bks.

—Miss Bindergarten Plans a Circus with Kindergarten. Wolff, Ashley, illus. 2005. 40p. (J). (gr. k-1). pap. 6.99 (978-0-14-240273-3(7) , Puffin) Penguin Group (USA) Inc.

—Miss Bindergarten Stays Home from Kindergarten. Wolff, Ashley, illus. (J). (ps-2). 2000. 1p. 16.99 (978-0-525-46396-2(8) , Dutton Juvenile); 2004. 48p. reprint ed. pap. 6.99 (978-0-14-230127-2(2) , Puffin) Penguin Group (USA) Inc.

—Miss Bindergarten Takes a Field Trip with Kindergarten. Wolff, Ashley, illus. (J). (ps up). 2004. 40p. pap. 6.99 (978-0-14-240139-2(0) , Puffin); 2001. 32p. 16.99 (978-0-525-46710-6(6) , Dutton Juvenile) Penguin Group (USA) Inc.

—Miss Bindergarten's Wild Day. Wolff, Ashley, illus. 2005. 40p. (J). (ps). 16.99 (978-0-525-47084-7(0) , Dutton Juvenile) Penguin Group (USA) Inc.

Wolff, Ashley. Miss Bindergarten Plans a Circus with Kindergarten. Slate, Joseph & Wolff, Ashley, illus. 2002. 40p. (J). 16.99 (978-0-525-46884-4(6) , Dutton Juvenile) Penguin Group (USA) Inc.

Wolff, Ashley, illus. Miss Bindergarten Stays Home from Kindergarten. 2002. (Miss Bindergarten Ser.). (J). 25.45 (978-0-7587-3144-9(2)) Book Wholesalers, Inc.

BINDING OF BOOKS

see Bookbinding

BIOCHEMISTRY

see also Metabolism; Molecular Biology

Holt, Rinehart and Winston Staff. Holt Chemistry Chptr.20: Biological Chemistry. 4th ed. Date not set. pap. 11.20 (978-0-03-068146-2(4)) Holt, Rinehart & Winston.

Levete, Sarah. Rot & Decay: Decomposing & Recycling. 2008. (J). (***978-1-60044-602-3(7)***) Rourke Publishing, LLC.

BIODIVERSITY

Here are entered works on the totality of the variety of living organisms, the genetic differences among them, and the communities and ecosystems in which they occur.

see also Species Diversity

Gallant, Roy A. The Wonders of Biodiversity. 2002. (Story of Science Ser.). (Illus.). 80p. (J). 29.93 (978-0-7614-1427-8(4) , Benchmark Bks.) Cavendish, Marshall Corp.

Holt, Rinehart and Winston Staff. Environmental Science Chptr. 10: Biodiversity. 4th ed. Date not set. pap. 11.20 (978-0-03-068069-4(7)) Holt, Rinehart & Winston.

Jakab, Cheryl. Biodiversity. 2007. (J). (***978-1-59920-124-5(0)***) Smart Apple Media.

Modules: Life Science; Diversity of Living Things PE. 2005. (gr. 6-12). (978-0-618-33434-6(3) , 2-01021) McDougal Littell Inc.

Snedden, Robert. The Diversity of Life: From Single Cells to Multicellular Organisms. 2003. (Cell & Life Ser.). (Illus.). 48p. (J). (gr. 6-8). lib. bdg. 27.86 (978-1-58810-673-5(X)) Heinemann Library.

Strauss, Rochelle. Tree of Life: The Incredible Biodiversity of Life on Earth. Thompson, Margot, illus. 2005. 40p. (YA). (gr. 3 up). 17.95 (978-1-55337-669-9(2)) Kids Can Pr., Ltd.

BIOGRAPHY

see also Autobiographies; Christian Biography; Heraldry; Naval Biography; Portraits

also names of classes of persons (e.g. Artists; Authors; Musicians; etc.); names of countries, cities, etc. and special subjects with the subdivision Biography (e.g. United States—Biography; African Americans—Biography; Religions—Biography; Women—Biography; etc.) and names of persons for biographies of individuals

Abbey, Cherie D., ed. Biography Today: Profiles of People of Interest to Young Readers. 2002. (Sports Ser.: Vol. 8). (YA). lib. bdg. (978-0-7808-0637-5(9)) Omnigraphics, Inc.

—Biography Today 2005 Annual Cumulation: Profiles of People of Interest to Young Readers. 2005. (Biography Today Ser.). 550p. (YA). lib. bdg. 69.00 (978-0-7808-0692-4(1)) Omnigraphics, Inc.

—Biography Today, Annual Cumulation 2001: Profiles of People of Interest to Young Readers. 2001. (Biography Today General Series: Annual Cumulation Ser.). 400p. (J). lib. bdg. 69.00 (978-0-7808-0456-2(2)) Omnigraphics, Inc.

—Biography Today Annual Cumulation 2002: Profiles of People of Interest to Young Readers. 2002. (Biography Today General Series: Annual Cumulation Ser.). 450p. (YA). lib. bdg. (978-0-7808-0510-1(0)) Omnigraphics, Inc.

—Biography Today, Annual Cumulation 2003: Profiles of People of Interest to Young Readers. 2003. (YA). lib. bdg. 62.00 (978-0-7808-0642-9(5)) Omnigraphics, Inc.

—Biography Today Annual Cumulation 2004: Profiles of People of Interest to Young Readers. 2004. (Biography Today General Series: Annual Cumulation Ser.). (YA). lib. bdg. (978-0-7808-0686-3(7)) Omnigraphics, Inc.

—Biography Today Annual Cumulation 2006: Profiles of People of Interest to Young Readers. 2006. (Biography Today General Series: Annual Cumulation Ser.). 524p. (YA). (gr. 14 up). lib. bdg. 69.00 (978-0-7808-0815-7(0)) Omnigraphics, Inc.

Ada, Alma Flor. Caminos. 2004. (Puertas al Sol Ser.: Bk. D). (SPA., Illus.). 40p. (YA). (gr. 3-4). 14.95 (978-1-58105-415-6(7)) Santillana USA Publishing Co., Inc.

—Pasos. 2004. (Puertas al Sol Ser.). (SPA., Illus.). 32p. (YA). (gr. 1-2). 11.95 (978-1-58105-411-8(4)) Santillana USA Publishing Co., Inc.

—Sonrisas. 1999. (Puertas al Sol Ser.). (SPA., Illus.). (J). (ps-1). pap. 10.95 (978-1-58105-409-5(2)) Santillana USA Publishing Co., Inc.

—Voces. 2004. (Puertas al Sol Ser.). (SPA., Illus.). 32p. (YA). (gr. 2-3). 11.95 (978-1-58105-413-2(0)) Santillana USA Publishing Co., Inc.

Ada, Alma Flor & Campoy, F. Isabel, contrib. by. Caminos. (Literature Collection of Puertas Al Sol Ser.). (SPA.). 48p. (J). (gr. k-6). pap. 16.95 (978-1-59437-710-5(3)) Santillana USA Publishing Co., Inc.

Adams, Emanuel F., Sr. Poor Butterfly: Untitled Memories. l.t. ed. 2002. 240p. (YA). bds. 16.00 (978-0-9644282-1-8(0)) Stick to The Word Publishing.

Ahlers, Lena C. Sons Known to Fame. 2005. pap. 28.95 (978-1-4191-1208-9(2)) Kessinger Publishing, LLC.

Anderson, William T. Prairie Girl: The Life of Laura Ingalls Wilder. Graef, Renee, illus. 2008. (Little House Ser.). 80p. (J). (gr. 2-5). pap. 5.99 (978-0-06-442133-1(3)) HarperCollins Pubs.

Another Great Achiever Biographies Read-along Series, 4 vols. 2003. (Another Great Achiever Ser.). (Illus.). (J). lib. bdg. 95.80 incl. audio compact disk (978-1-57537-744-5(6)); lib. bdg. 95.80 incl. audio (978-1-57537-794-0(2)) Advance Publishing, Inc.

Another Great Achiever Series, Set, 4 bks. 2000. (Another Great Achiever Ser.). 48 p. 39.80 (978-1-57537-148-1(0)); lib. bdg. 59.80 (978-1-57537-149-8(9)) Advance Publishing, Inc.

Autobiography & Biography (Gr. PreK-5) 2003. (J). (978-1-58232-017-5(9)) Bryan Hse. Pubs., Inc.

Baker, Frances Shands. From Mountain Man to Millionaire: The Story of Colonel Robert Campbell, 1804-1879 & Other Heroes in St. Louis, Missouri. Kunstmann, Sue, ed. Baker, Frances Shands & Fifth Grade Students, illus. l.t. ed. 2001. 64p. (J). (gr. 8 up). pap. 16.99 (978-0-9674867-7-2(7)) Campbell Hse. Museum.

Barancik, Sue. Guide to Collective Biographies for Children & Young Adults. 2004. 456p. pap. 49.95 (978-0-8108-5033-0(8)) Scarecrow Pr., Inc.

Barnes, Dana R. & DeRemer, Leigh Ann. Contemporary Heroes & Heroines. 2000. (Illus.). 628p. (J). 110.00 (978-0-7876-3262-5(7) , GML12001-112883) Thomson Gale.

Benchmark Education Staff, compiled by. Biography Strands Set. 2005. spiral bd. 350.00 (***978-1-4108-5563-3(5)***) Benchmark Education Co.

—Career/Biography Strands Set. 2005. spiral bd. 720.00 (***978-1-4108-5460-5(4)***) Benchmark Education Co.

—People Who Changed Our World. 2006. spiral bd. 159.00 (***978-1-4108-7116-9(9)***) Benchmark Education Co.

Biographical Connections, 8 vols. 2006. 896p. (gr. 8-12). 299.00 (978-0-7166-1821-8(4) , 20188) World Bk., Inc.

Biographies of Note. (Biographies Ser.). (Illus.). (978-0-7613-3306-7(1) , Twenty-First Century Bks.) Lerner Publishing Group.

A Blue Banner Biography Series, 15 bks. 2004. (YA). 254.25 (978-1-58415-236-1(2)) Mitchell Lane Pubs., Inc.

Bluedorn, Ava. Lives in Print: Good Biographies & Autobiographies. 2000. (Illus.). 29p. 6.00 (978-0-9743616-7-3(4)) Trivium Pursuit.

Bontrager, Ernest. Ernie: An Autobiography of Ernest Bontrager. 2001. 70p. (YA). (gr. 5 up). pap. 7.95 (978-0-9716810-0-2(7)) Ernie Publications.

Breakthrough Biographies, 6 vols. 2005. (Breakthrough Biographies Ser.). (Illus.). 32p. (gr. 3-5). pap. 138.00 (978-0-7910-7310-0(6) , Chelsea Hse.) Facts On File, Inc.

Brimner, Larry Dane. Aggie & Will. Thornburgh, Rebecca McKillip, illus. 1998. (Rookie Readers Ser.). 32p. (J). (gr. 1-2). 19.50 (978-0-516-20754-4(7) , Children's Pr.) Scholastic Library Publishing.

Brooks, E. S. Historic Boys: Their Endeavors, Their Achievements & Their Times. (YA). 2003. (Illus.). 259p. 26.95 (978-0-918736-55-0(2)); 2000. 260p. pap. 13.95 (978-0-918736-24-6(2)) Rock, James A. & Co. Pubs. (Castle Keep Pr.).

Carriere, Ed. Puget Sound Clam Basket: Autobiography of Ed Eugene Carriere. Carriere, Fanie Ann, ed. 2001. 200p. per. 29.95 (978-0-937242-25-4(X)) Scandia Pubs.

Casad, Dede Weldon. Intriguing Texans of the 20th Century. 2002. (Illus.). 178p. (J). 18.95 (978-1-57168-603-9(7)) Eakin Pr.

Cayleff, Susan E. Babe Didrikson: The Greatest All-Sport Athlete of All Time. 2000. (Barnard Biography Ser.: Vol. 4). (Illus.). 168p. (YA). (gr. 7-12). pap. 8.95 (978-1-57324-194-6(6) , Red Wheel) Red Wheel/Weiser.

Cherry Lake Publishing, compiled by. LIfe Skills Biographics. 2008. lib. bdg. (***978-1-60279-110-7(4)***) Cherry Lake Publishing.

Chin-Lee, Cynthia. Akira to Zoltan: Twenty-Six Men Who Changed the World. Halsey, Megan & Addy, Sean, illus. 2006. 32p. (J). 15.95 (978-1-57091-579-6(2)) Charlesbridge Publishing, Inc.

Collective Biographies, 43 bks., Set. (Illus.). (YA). (gr. 6-12). lib. bdg. 838.00 (978-0-89490-570-4(8)) Enslow Pubs., Inc.

Contemporary Biographies, 16 bks., Set. Incl. Barbara Jordan. Patrick-Wexler, Diane. 1996. lib. bdg. 17.98 (978-0-8172-3976-3(6)); Colin Powell. Patrick-Wexler, Diane. 1996. lib. bdg. (978-0-8172-3977-0(4)); Dolores Huerta. Perez, Frank. 1995. lib. bdg. (978-0-8172-3981-7(2)); Edward James Olmos. Carrillo, Louis. 1997. lib. bdg. 17.98 (978-0-8172-3989-3(8)); John Lucas. Simmons, Alex. 1996. lib. bdg. 17.98 (978-0-8172-3978-7(2)); Jose Canseco. Ling, Bettina. 1996. lib. bdg. (978-0-8172-3983-1(9)); Ladonna Harris. Schwartz, Michael. 1997. lib. bdg. 17.98 (978-0-8172-3995-4(2)); Luis Rodriguez. Schwartz, Michael. 1997. lib. bdg. 17.98 (978-0-8172-3990-9(1)); Maya Lin. Ling, Bettina. 1997. lib. bdg. 17.98 (978-0-8172-3992-3(8)); Michael Dorris. Weil, Ann. 1997. lib. bdg. 17.98 (978-0-8172-3994-7(4)); Nely Galan. Rodriguez, Janel. 1997. lib. bdg. 17.98 (978-0-8172-3991-6(X)); Oscar de la Renta. Carrillo, Louis. 1995. lib. bdg. (978-0-8172-3980-0(4)); Raul Julia. Perez, Frank & Weil, Ann. 1995. lib. bdg. (978-0-8172-3984-8(7)); Seiji Ozawa. Tan, Sheri. 1997. lib. bdg. 17.98 (978-0-8172-3993-0(6)); Toni Morrison. Patrick-Wexler, Diane. 1997. lib. bdg. 17.98 (978-0-8172-3987-9(1)); Wynton Marsalis. Ellis, Veronica Freeman. 1997. lib. bdg. 17.98 (978-0-8172-3988-6(X)); 48p. (J). (gr. 3-8). (Illus.). Set lib. bdg. 287.68 (978-0-7398-4110-5(6)) Raintree.

Crompton, Samuel Willard. 100 Military Leaders Who Shaped World History. 1999. (gr. 7-12). lib. bdg. 16.40 (978-0-613-67577-2(0)) Tandem Library Bks.

Cross, Brenda. Chester Holden Worthington II. Eldridge, Christina, illus. 2002. 80p. (J). pap. (978-1-57579-257-6(5)) Pine Hill Pr., Inc.

Cruz, Barbara C. Jose Clemente Orozco: Mexican Artist. 1998. (Hispanic Biographies Ser.). (Illus.). 128p. (YA). (gr. 6-12). lib. bdg. 26.60 (978-0-7660-1041-3(4)) Enslow Pubs., Inc.

Davidson, Margaret. Louis Braille. (FRE.). (J). pap. 5.99 (978-0-590-71110-4(5)) Scholastic, Inc.

Davis, Kenneth C. Don't Know Much about George Washington. Shepperson, Rob, illus. 2003. (Don't Know Much About Ser.). 128p. (J). (gr. 3). pap. 4.99 (978-0-06-442124-9(4)) HarperCollins Pubs.

—Don't Know Much about Martin Luther King Jr., Vol. 6. Kodaira, Machiyo, illus. 2006. (Don't Know Much About Ser.). 144p. (J). (gr. 2-5). pap. 4.99 (978-0-06-442129-4(5)) HarperCollins Pubs.

—Don't Know Much about Rosa Parks. Martinez, Sergio, illus. 2005. (Don't Know Much About Ser.). 128p. (J). (gr. 2-5). pap. 4.99 (978-0-06-442126-3(0)); Vol. 3. lib. bdg. 15.89 (978-0-06-028819-8(1)) HarperCollins Pubs.

—Don't Know Much about Thomas Jefferson. Shepperson, Rob, illus. 2005. (Don't Know Much About Ser.). 128p. (J). (gr. 2-5). pap. 4.99 (978-0-06-442128-7(7)) HarperCollins Pubs.

Devillier, Christy. First Biographies, 6 vols., Set I. Incl. Abraham Lincoln. lib. bdg. 22.78 (978-1-57765-591-6(5)); Amelia Earhart. lib. bdg. 22.78 (978-1-57765-596-1(6)); Christopher Columbus. lib. bdg. 22.78 (978-1-57765-594-7(X)); George Washington. lib. bdg. 22.78 (978-1-57765-593-0(1)); Lewis & Clark. lib. bdg. 22.78 (978-1-57765-595-4(8)); Martin Luther King, Jr. lib. bdg. 22.78 (978-1-57765-592-3(3)); 32p. (J). (gr. k-4). 2001. (Illus.). 2001. Set lib. bdg. 136.68 (978-1-57765-508-4(7) , Buddy Bks.) ABDO Publishing Co.

DeWitt, Lisa F. Nobel Prize Winners Text/3 CD's Package: Biographical Sketches for Listening & Reading. 2005. pap. 27.00 incl. audio compact disk (978-0-86647-203-6(7)) Pro Lingua Assocs., Inc.

Douglas, Bettye. Portrait of a People: The Bettye Douglas Forum, Inc. Multicultural Resource Book. Douglas, Bettye, ed. Douglas, Ana & Douglas, Garbrielle, illus. 222p. (YA). (gr. 5-13). 100.00 (978-0-9703183-1-2(6)) Douglas, Bettye Forum, Inc., The.

Edgar, Kathleen J., et al. Compassion. 2003. (J). (978-1-59203-055-2(6)) Learning Challenge, Inc.

—Courage. 2003. (J). (978-1-59203-056-9(4)) Learning Challenge, Inc.

—Determination. 2003. (J). (978-1-59203-057-6(2)) Learning Challenge, Inc.

—Imagination. 2003. (J). (978-1-59203-058-3(0)) Learning Challenge, Inc.

—Responsibility. 2003. (J). (978-1-59203-059-0(9)) Learning Challenge, Inc.

—Vision. 2003. (J). (978-1-59203-060-6(2)) Learning Challenge, Inc.

Egan, Terry. The Good Guys of Baseball: Seventeen True Sports Stories. 2000. (Illus.). (J). (978-0-606-17920-1(8)) Tandem Library Bks.

Famous Lives, 6 vols. 2004. (Illus.). 171.36 (978-0-7398-6632-0(X)); 456.96 (978-0-7398-6633-7(8)) Raintree.

Famous Lives, 6 bks., Set. Incl. Anne Frank : Voice of Hope. Senker, Cath. 2001. lib. bdg. 27.12 (978-0-8172-5719-4(5)); Fidel Castro : Leader of Cuba's Revolution. Gibb, Tom. 2001. lib. bdg. 27.12 (978-0-8172-5718-7(7)); Muhammad Ali : The Greatest. Hook, Jason. 2001. lib. bdg. 27.12 (978-0-8172-5717-0(9)); Nelson Mandela : Father of Freedom. Adi, Hakim. 2001. lib. bdg. 27.12 (978-0-8172-5716-3(0)); Pope John Paul II : Pope for the People. Burns, Peggy. 2000. lib. bdg. 27.12 (978-0-8172-5714-9(4)); Queen Mother : Grandmother of a Nation. Wood, Richard & Barton-Wood, Sara. 2000. lib. bdg. 27.12 (978-0-8172-5715-6(2)); (Illus.). 48p. (J). (gr. 3-7). 2001. Set lib. bdg. 162.72 (978-0-8172-5720-0(9)) Raintree.

Famous Lives, 10 bks. l.t. ed. Incl. Story of Abraham Lincoln : President for the People. Weinberg, Larry. LaPadula, Tom, illus. 1997. lib. bdg. 22.60 (978-0-8368-1484-2(3)); Story of Alexander Graham Bell : Inventor of the Telephone. Davidson, Margaret. Marchesi, Stephen, illus. 1997. lib. bdg. 22.60 (978-0-8368-1483-5(5)); Story of Babe Ruth : Baseball's Greatest Legend. Eisenberg, Lisa. 1997. lib. bdg. 22.60 (978-0-8368-1486-6(X)); Story of Benjamin Franklin : Amazing American. Davidson, Margaret. Speirs, John, illus. 1997. lib. bdg. 22.60 (978-0-8368-1475-0(4)); Story of Christopher Columbus. Osborne, Mary Pope. Marchesi, Stephen, illus. 1997. lib. bdg. 22.60 (978-0-8368-1482-8(7)); Story of Davy Crockett : Frontier Hero. Retan, Walter. Petruccio, Steven James, illus. 1997. lib. bdg. 22.60 (978-0-8368-1485-9(1)); Story of George Bush : The Forty-First President of the United States. Sufrin, Mark. 1997. lib. bdg. 22.60 (978-0-8368-1478-1(9)); Story of Shirley Temple Black : Hollywood's Youngest Star. Fiori, Carlo. 1997. lib. bdg. 22.60 (978-0-8368-1481-1(9)); Story of Sitting Bull : Great Sioux Chief. Eisenberg, Lisa. Rickman, David, illus. 1996. lib. bdg. 22.60 (978-0-8368-1465-1(7)); Story of Walt Disney : Maker of Magical Worlds. Selden, Bernice. 1996. lib. bdg. 22.60 (978-0-8368-1468-2(1)); 100p. (J). (gr. 3 up). (Illus.). Set lib. bdg. 226.00 (978-0-8368-1998-4(5)) Stevens, Gareth Inc.

Ferguson. Ferguson Career Biographies Set. 2005. (Ferguson Career Biographies Ser.). (gr. 9-12). 128p. 1275.00 (978-0-8160-6532-5(2)); 128-160p. 1025.00 (978-0-8160-6327-7(3)) Facts On File, Inc. (Ferguson Publishing Co.).

Finn, Francis J. Fr. Finn's Famous 3: Tom Playfair, Percy Wynn, Harry Dee. 2000. (YA). (gr. 5-8). reprint ed. pap. 21.00 (978-0-89555-687-5(1) , 1758) TAN Bks. and Pubs., Inc.

First Biographies, Set. 2005. (First Biographies Ser.). (YA). (gr. k-3). 267.30 (978-0-7368-4195-5(4)); Vol. 2. 267.30 (978-0-7368-4196-2(2)) Capstone Pr., Inc. (Pebble Bks.).

First Biographies, 9 bks., Set. Incl. Bill Clinton. Holland, Gini. Rees, Gary, illus. 1997. lib. bdg. 25.69 (978-0-8172-4450-7(6)); Booker T. Washington. Gleiter, Jan & Thompson, Kathleen. 1995. lib. bdg. 25.69 (978-0-8114-8454-1(8)); Diego Rivera. Holland, Gini. Rees, Gary, illus. 1997. lib. bdg. 25.69 (978-0-8172-4453-8(0)); Johnny Appleseed. Holland, Gini. 1997. lib. bdg. 25.69 (978-0-8172-4452-1(2)); Nelson Mandela. Holland, Gini. White, Mike, illus. 1997. lib. bdg. 25.69 (978-0-8172-4454-5(9)); P. T. Barnum. Wright, David K. White, Mike, illus. 1997. lib. bdg. 25.69 (978-0-8172-4456-9(5)); Rosa Parks. Holland, Gini. Price, David, illus. 1997. lib. bdg. 25.69 (978-0-8172-4451-4(4)); Sandra Day O'Connor. Holland, Gini. Roberts, Mark, illus. 1997. lib. bdg. 25.69 (978-0-8172-4455-2(7)); Wilma Mankiller. Holland, Gini. Crompton, Paul H., illus. 1997. lib. bdg. 25.69 (978-0-8172-4457-6(3)); 32p. (J). (gr. 1-4). Set lib. bdg. 231.21 (978-0-7398-4111-2(4)) Raintree.

Frank, Anne. Anne Frank: The Diary of a Young Girl. 241p. (J). (gr. 4-6). pap. 4.99 (978-0-8072-1363-6(2) , Listening Library) Random Hse. Audio Publishing Group.

—Anne Frank: The Diary of a Young Girl. 1999. (Literature Guides). (Illus.). 16p. (J). pap. 3.95 (978-0-590-51377-7(X)) Scholastic, Inc.

Frost, Helen. First Biographies. 2005. (Pebble Ser.). (Illus.). (J). (gr. k-1). lib. bdg. 653.13 (978-0-7368-4400-0(7)) Capstone Pr., Inc.

Gale Research Staff. Contemporary Heroes & Heroines, Bk. III. 1998. (Illus.). 699p. (J). 110.00 (978-0-7876-2215-2(X) , GML14099-111730) Thomson Gale.

Galens, Judy, et al. UXL Newsmakers, 4 vols. 2004. (J). 800p. 235.00 (978-0-7876-9189-9(5)); (978-0-7876-9190-5(9)); (978-0-7876-9191-2(7)); (978-0-7876-9194-3(1)); (978-0-7876-9195-0(X)) Thomson Gale. (UXL).

Georgiady, Nicholas P., et al. Michigan Men, Vol. 2. Schimmels, John H., illus. 2nd ed. 1998. 32p. (J). (gr. 4-8). reprint ed. pap. 4.50 (978-0-917961-07-6(2)) Argee Pubs.

Gifford, Clive. Ten 20th Century Leaders Who Changed the World. 2007. 64p. (J). (gr. 5). 14.95 (978-0-7534-6104-4(8) , Kingfisher) Houghton Mifflin Co. Trade & Reference Div.

Gillis, Jennifer Blitzin & Hall, M.C. Lives & Times, 6 bks., Set 6. 2004. (J). (gr. k-2). lib. bdg. 145.29 (978-1-4034-5330-3(6)) Heinemann Library.

Ginyard, Caleb N., III. My Name Is Caleb N. Ginyard, Jr. 2002. (Illus.). 180p. (YA). pap. (978-0-913911-15-0(1)) Akashic Pr., Inc., The.

Gomez, Rebecca. First Biographies, 6 vols., Set III. 2003. (Illus.). (J). (gr. k-4). lib. bdg. 136.68 (978-1-57765-943-3(0) , Buddy Bks.) ABDO Publishing Co.

Gonzales, Raymond Bences. A Boy on the Hill. Gursky, Judy, ed. Jandacek, Petr, illus. 2001. 70p. (J). pap. 10.95 (978-0-941232-29-6(8)) Los Alamos Historical Society.

Gosda, Randy T. First Biographies, 6 vols., Set II. Incl. Ben Franklin. lib. bdg. 22.78 (978-1-57765-733-0(0)); Booker T. Washington. lib. bdg. 22.78 (978-1-57765-734-7(9)); Daniel Boone. lib. bdg. 22.78 (978-1-57765-735-4(7)); Harriet Tubman. lib. bdg. 22.78 (978-1-57765-736-1(5)); Pocahontas. lib. bdg. 22.78 (978-1-57765-732-3(2)); Sitting Bull. lib. bdg. 22.78 (978-1-57765-737-8(3)); 32p. (J). (gr. k-4). (Illus.). 2002. Set lib. bdg. 136.68 (978-1-57765-511-1(7) , Buddy Bks.) ABDO Publishing Co.

Graphic Biographies. 2005. (Graphic Library). (Illus.). (J). (gr. 3-4). lib. bdg. 303.12 (978-0-7368-4342-3(6)) Capstone Pr., Inc.

Graphic Biographies, 6 bks., Set. Incl. Bob Marley : The Life of a Reggae Superstar. Jeffrey, Gary. Riley, Terry, illus. lib. bdg. 29.95 (978-1-4042-0854-4(2)); Martin Luther King, Jr : The Life of a Civil Rights Leader. Jeffrey, Gary. Riley, Terry, illus. lib. bdg. 29.95 (978-1-4042-0858-2(5)); Muhammed Ali : The Life of a Boxing Hero. Shone, Rob. Spender, Nick, illus. (gr. 3-8). lib. bdg. 29.95 (978-1-4042-0856-8(9)); Nelson Mandela : The Life of an African Statesman. Shone, Rob. (Illus.). lib. bdg. 29.95 (978-1-4042-0860-5(7)); Oprah Winfrey : The Life of a Media Superstar. Jeffrey, Gary. lib. bdg. 29.95 (978-1-4042-0862-9(3)); Rosa Parks : The Life of a Civil Rights Heroine. Shone, Rob. Spender, Nik, illus. (gr. 3-8). lib. bdg. 29.95 (978-1-4042-0864-3(X)); 48p. (J). 2006. 2006. 179.70 (978-1-4042-1009-7(1)) Rosen Publishing Group, Inc., The.

Great Life Stories, 6 bks. 2004. (Illus.). 112-128p. (YA). (gr. 6-8). 177.00 (978-0-531-16710-6(0)); 295.00 (978-0-531-19327-3(6)) Scholastic Library Publishing.

Hacker, Carlotta. Humanitarians. 1998. (Women in Profile Ser.). (Illus.). 48p. (J). (gr. 4). lib. bdg. (978-0-7787-0011-1(9)) Crabtree Publishing Co.

Harris, Laurie Lanzen, ed. Biography for Beginners Fall 1998. 1998. 102p. (J). lib. bdg. 20.00 (978-1-931360-07-4(3)) Favorable Impressions.

—Biography for Beginners Fall 1998 Vol. 4: Sketches for Early Readers. 1998. (Illus.). 100p. (J). (gr. 1-3). lib. bdg. 20.00 (978-0-7808-0368-8(X) , B909) Favorable Impressions.

—Biography for Beginners Fall 1999: Sketches for Early Readers. 1999. 102p. (J). lib. bdg. 20.00 (978-1-931360-09-8(X)) Favorable Impressions.

—Biography for Beginners Fall 1999 Vol. 5: Sketches for Early Readers. 1999. (Illus.). 100p. (J). (gr. 1-4). lib. bdg. 20.00 (978-0-7808-0401-2(5)) Favorable Impressions.

—Biography for Beginners Fall 2000: Sketches for Early Readers. 2000. 102p. (J). lib. bdg. 20.00 (978-1-931360-11-1(1)) Favorable Impressions.

—Biography for Beginners Fall 2000 Vol. 6: Sketches for Early Readers. 2000. (Illus.). 100p. (J). (gr. 1-3). lib. bdg. 20.00 (978-0-7808-0412-8(0)) Favorable Impressions.

—Biography for Beginners Fall 2001: Sketches for Early Readers. 2001. 120p. (J). lib. bdg. 20.00 (978-1-931360-17-3(0)) Favorable Impressions.

—Biography for Beginners Spring 1998: Sketches for Early Readers. 1998. 102p. (J). lib. bdg. 20.00 (978-1-931360-06-7(5)) Favorable Impressions.

—Biography for Beginners Spring 1998 Vol. 4: Sketches for Early Readers. 1998. (Illus.). 100p. (J). (gr. 1-3). lib. bdg. 20.00 (978-0-7808-0367-1(1) , B908) Favorable Impressions.

—Biography for Beginners Spring 1999: Sketches for Early Readers. 1999. 102p. (J). lib. bdg. 20.00 (978-1-931360-08-1(1)) Favorable Impressions.

—Biography for Beginners Spring 1999 Vol. 5: Sketches for Early Readers. 1999. (Illus.). 100p. (J). (gr. 1-4). lib. bdg. 20.00 (978-0-7808-0400-5(7)) Favorable Impressions.

—Biography for Beginners Spring 2000: Sketches for Early Readers. 2000. 102p. (J). lib. bdg. 20.00 (978-1-931360-10-4(3)) Favorable Impressions.

—Biography for Beginners Spring 2000 Vol. 6: Sketches for Early Readers. 2000. (Illus.). 100p. (J). (gr. 1-3). lib. bdg. 20.00 (978-0-7808-0411-1(2)) Favorable Impressions.

—Biography for Beginners Spring 2001: Sketches for Early Readers. 2001. 120p. (J). lib. bdg. 20.00 (978-1-931360-16-6(2)) Favorable Impressions.

—Biography for You, Fall 2000. 2000. (Illus.). 100p. (YA). (gr. 4 up). pap. 21.00 (978-0-7808-0437-1(6)) Favorable Impressions.

—Biography for You, Spring 2000. 2000. (Illus.). 100p. (YA). (gr. 4 up). pap. 21.00 (978-0-7808-0436-4(8)) Favorable Impressions.

—Biography Today: Profiles of People of Interest to Young Readers. (Illus.). (YA). 2000. (Sports Ser.: Vol. 5). 200p. (gr. 5 up). lib. bdg. (978-0-7808-0417-3(1)); 2000. (Scientists & Inventors Ser.: Vol. 4). 200p. (gr. 5 up). lib. bdg. (978-0-7808-0415-9(5)); 2000. (Author Ser.: Vol. 8). 200p. (gr. 5 up). lib. bdg. 44.00 (978-0-7808-0414-2(7)); 2000. (Sports Ser.: Vol. 4). 219p. (gr. 5 up). lib. bdg. (978-0-7808-0416-6(3)); 2000. (Author Ser.: Vol. 7). 211p. (gr. 5 up). lib. bdg. 44.00 (978-0-7808-0413-5(9)); 1999. (Author Ser.: Vol. 6). 200p. (gr. 4-12). lib. bdg. 44.00 (978-0-7808-0402-9(3)) Omnigraphics, Inc.

—Biography Today, Annual Cumulation 2000: Profiles of People of Interest to Young Readers. annual 2000. (Biography Today General Series: Annual Cumulation Ser.). (Illus.). 350p. (J). (gr. 3-12). lib. bdg. (978-0-7808-0410-4(4)) Omnigraphics, Inc.

Hazell, Rebecca. The Barefoot Book of Heroic Children. Cann, Helen, illus. 2000. 96p. (J). (gr. 4-7). 19.95 (978-1-902283-23-4(6)) Barefoot Bks., Inc.

Heinemann Profiles, 20 bks. (Illus.). (J). (gr. 4-6). Set 1-3. lib. bdg. 484.40 (978-1-58810-184-6(3)); Set 2. lib. bdg. 145.32 (978-1-57572-295-5(X)) Heinemann Library.

Horn, Maurice, ed. World Encyclopedia of Cartoons. 1999. 35.00 (978-0-7910-5184-9(6) , Chelsea Hse.) Facts On File, Inc.

Ishii, Takayuki. One Thousand Paper Cranes: The Story of Sadako & the Children's Peace Statue. 2002. (J). (gr. 6 up). 20.25 (978-0-8446-7219-9(X)) Smith, Peter Pub., Inc.

—One Thousand Paper Cranes: The Story of Sadako & the Children's Peace Statue. 2001. (gr. 5-8). lib. bdg. 13.00 (978-0-613-32918-7(X)); (Illus.). (J). (978-0-606-20832-1(1)) Tandem Library Bks.

January, Brendan. De Witt & Lila Wallace: Charity for All. De Capua, Sarah, ed. 1998. (Community Builders Ser.). (Illus.). 48p. (J). (gr. 3-5). pap. 6.95 (978-0-516-26329-8(3) , Children's Pr.) Scholastic Library Publishing.

Jones, Lynda. Great Black Heroes: Five Brilliant Scientists. 2000. (gr. 3-6). lib. bdg. 11.80 (978-0-613-21631-9(8)); (Hello Reader! Ser.: Level 4). (Illus.). (J). 10.79 (978-0-606-18544-8(5)) Tandem Library Bks.

Kimball, Violet T. Stories of Young Pioneers: In Their Own Words. rev. ed. 2000. (Illus.). 225p. (J). (gr. 4-11). pap. 14.00 (978-0-87842-423-8(7) , 655) Mountain Pr. Publishing Co., Inc.

—Stories of Young Pioneers: In Their Own Words. 2000. (gr. 5-8). lib. bdg. 23.45 (978-0-613-84455-0(6)) Tandem Library Bks.

Kostyal, K. M. Trial by Ice: A Photobiography of Sir Ernest Shackleton. 1999. (Illus.). 64p. (J). (gr. 3-7). 17.95 (978-0-7922-7393-6(1) , National Geographic Children's Bks.) National Geographic Society.

Lesinski, Jeanne M. Bill Gates. (Biography Ser.). (Illus.). 112p. (gr. 6-12). 2005. lib. bdg. 27.93 (978-0-8225-4949-9(2)); 2003. (J). pap. 7.95 (978-0-8225-9689-9(X)) Lerner Publishing Group.

—Bill Gates. 2000. (Illus.). (J). 15.50 (978-0-606-18814-2(2)) Tandem Library Bks.

Let Freedom Ring: Exploring the West Biographies, 6 bks. Incl. Brigham Young : Pioneer & Prophet. Gunderson, Cory Gideon. lib. bdg. 22.60 (978-0-7368-1346-4(2)); Daniel Boone : Frontier Scout. Boraas, Tracey. lib. bdg. 22.60 (978-0-7368-1347-1(0)); John Charles Fremont : Western Pathfinder. Witteman, Barbara. lib. bdg. 22.60 (978-0-7368-1348-8(9)); Kit Carson : Mountain Man. Boraas, Tracey. lib. bdg. 22.60 (978-0-7368-1349-5(7)); Sam Houston : Soldier & Statesman. Boraas, Tracey. lib. bdg. 22.60 (978-0-7368-1350-1(0)); Zebulon Pike : Soldier & Explorer. Witteman, Barbara. lib. bdg. 22.60 (978-0-7368-1351-8(9)); 48p. (J). (gr. 3-4). 2002. (Illus.). 2002. Set lib. bdg. 135.60 (978-0-7368-1352-5(7) , Bridgestone Bks.) Capstone Pr., Inc.

The Library of American Lives & Times, 12 vols., Set 3. 2005. (Illus.). (gr. 4-8). lib. bdg. 383.40 (978-0-8239-6657-8(7)) Rosen Publishing Group, Inc., The.

The Library of Author Biographies, 6 Bks, Set 4. 2004. (J). 159.00 (978-1-4042-0368-6(0)) Rosen Publishing, Inc.

Lucke, Deb. The Book of Time Outs. Lucke, Deb, illus. 2008. 32p. (J). 15.99 (978-1-4169-2829-4(4) , Simon & Schuster Children's Publishing) Simon & Schuster Children's Publishing.

Mabie, Hamilton Wright. Heroes Every Child Should Know. 2005. 31.95 (978-1-4218-0941-0(9) , 1st World Library - Literary Society) 1st World Publishing, Inc.

Mahmout, Ulfet & Thompson, Alan. My Life Story. 2004. (CZE, SPA, SER, URD & SOM., Illus.). 34p. (J). (978-1-85269-885-0(3)) Mantra Publishing, Ltd.

Matthews, Rupert, et al. Heinemann Profiles, 7 bks., Set 3. 2001. (Illus.). (J). (gr. 4-6). lib. bdg. 169.54 (978-1-58810-011-5(1)) Heinemann Library.

McGraw-Hill - Jamestown Education Staff. In the Spotlight. 2005. pap. 15.96 (978-0-07-874318-4(4) , 9780078743184) Glencoe/McGraw-Hill.

McLeese, Don. Equal Rights Leaders Discovery Library. 2003. (Discover the Life of an Equal Rights Leader Discovery Library Ser.). (gr. 2-5). 59.80 (978-1-58952-283-1(4)) Rourke Publishing, LLC.

Meyer, Jone, ed. Vocational Biographies, 7. 2001. (YA). lib. bdg. 265.00 (978-0-87063-807-7(6) , E-01) Vocational Biographies.

Mitchell Lane Publishers. Biography from Ancient Civilizations. 2007. (Biography from Ancient Civilizations Ser.). (J). lib. bdg. 838.60 (***978-1-58415-546-1(9)***) Mitchell Lane Pubs., Inc.

—Blue Banner Biographies, 67 vols. 2007. (Blue Banner Biography Ser.). (J). lib. bdg. 1747.60 (***978-1-58415-621-5(X)***) Mitchell Lane Pubs., Inc.

—A Robbie Reader-Contemporary Biographies, 25 vols., Set. 2007. (Robbie Reader Ser.). (J). (gr. 1-4). lib. bdg. 642.50 (***978-1-58415-597-3(3)***) Mitchell Lane Pubs., Inc.

Morina, Barbara. Memories of Our Family Journal: Journals Unlimited Inc., 27 vols., Vol. 26. Morina, Barbara, ed. 2001. (Write It down Ser.: Vol. 1). (Illus.). 202p. (YA). (gr. 2 up). 19.95 (978-1-892033-24-6(0)) Journals Unlimited, Inc.

Multicultural Junior Biographies, 5 bks., Set. (Illus.). (YA). (gr. 4-10). lib. bdg. 104.75 (978-0-89490-661-9(5)) Enslow Pubs., Inc.

My First Biographies, 6 bks., Set. 2006. (J). (gr. 1-3). 34.95 (***978-0-8225-5694-7(4)***) Lerner Publishing Group.

Nathan, M. M. MTV Photobooth: An MTV Overground Book. 2002. (gr. 7-12). lib. bdg. 28.00 (978-0-613-60582-3(9)) Tandem Library Bks.

O'Hern, Kerri. Graphic Biographies. 2005. 156.00 (978-0-8368-6193-8(0)) Stevens, Gareth Inc.

On My Own Biographies Set, Vol. 2. 2004. (Illus.). lib. bdg. 7.95 (978-0-8225-3385-6(5)) Lerner Publishing Group.

Overcoming Adversity. 2005. pap. 720.00 (978-0-7910-9159-3(7) , Chelsea Hse.) Facts On File, Inc.

Overcoming Adversity, 6 bks., Set. Incl. Abraham Lincoln : U. S. President. Bracken, Thomas. 112p. (YA). (gr. 5 up). 1997. 30.00 (978-0-7910-4704-0(0)); Bill Clinton : U. S. President. Kelly, Michael. 112p. (YA). (gr. 5 up). 1997. 30.00 (978-0-7910-4700-2(8)); James Earl Jones : Actor. Hasday, Judy L. 128p. (YA). (gr. 5 up). 1999. 32.00 (978-0-7910-4702-6(4)); Roseanne : Entertainer. Gaines, Ann Graham. 128p. (YA). (gr. 5 up). 1999. lib. bdg. 21.95 (978-0-7910-4706-4(7)); Tim Allen. Wukovits, John F. 112p. (gr. 3 up). 1997. 30.00 (978-0-7910-4696-8(6)); William Penn : Pennsylvania's Founder. Stefoff, Rebecca. 128p. (YA). (gr. 5 up). 1999. lib. bdg. 21.95 (978-0-7910-4873-3(X)); (Illus.). 1999. 139.65 o.p. (978-0-7910-4694-4(X) , Chelsea Hse.) Facts On File, Inc.

Owen, Annie. From Snowflakes to Sandcastles: A Child's Year in Words & Pictures. (Illus.). 24p. (J). pap. 16.99 (978-0-590-24749-8(2)) Scholastic, Inc.

Paparchontis, Kathy. 100 World Leaders Who Shaped World History. 2001. (gr. 7-12). lib. bdg. 16.40 (978-0-613-67513-0(4)) Tandem Library Bks.

Parham, Jerrill, Boundary Breakers: Remarkable People. 2007. (Shockwave: History & Politics Ser.). (Illus.). 36p. (J). (gr. 4-6). 25.00 (***978-0-531-17752-5(1)*** , Children's Pr.) Scholastic Library Publishing.

Pebble Books: First Biographies. 2005. (YA). (gr. k-3). 653.40 (978-0-7368-4218-1(7) , Pebble Bks.) Capstone Pr., Inc.

People Who Changed the World, 4 bks. Incl. 100 Artists Who Changed the World. Krystal, Barbara. lib. bdg. 30.00 (978-0-8368-5469-5(1)); 100 Leaders Who Changed the World. Paparchontis, Kathleen. lib. bdg. 30.00 (978-0-8368-5472-5(1)); 100 Military Leaders Who Changed the World. Crompton, Samuel Willard. lib. bdg. 30.00 (978-0-8368-5470-1(5)); 100 Scientists Who Changed the World. Tiner, John Hudson. lib. bdg. 30.00 (978-0-8368-5471-8(3)); 112p. (J). (gr. 5 up). 2003. (Illus.). 2002. Set lib. bdg. 120.00 (978-0-8368-5468-8(3) , World Almanac Library) Stevens, Gareth Inc.

People Who Made History, 4 bks., Set. Incl. Ancient Egypt. Shuter, Jane. Hook, Christa, illus. 2000. lib. bdg. 27.12 (978-0-7398-2748-2(0)); Ancient Greece. Morgan, Nicola. 2000. lib. bdg. 27.12 (978-0-7398-2747-5(2)); Ancient Rome. Levy, Patricia. 2001. lib. bdg. 27.12 (978-0-7398-2749-9(9)); Native Americans. Hook, Jason. 2001. lib. bdg. 27.12 (978-0-7398-2750-5(2)); 48p. (J). (gr. 4-7). (Illus.). 1999. Set lib. bdg. 108.48 (978-0-7398-2751-2(0)) Raintree.

Pesek, Betty, et al, eds. The Circle of Life: Stories of Ordinary People & the Gift of Spirit. Magyar, Steve, illus. 2000. 172p. (Orig.). (YA). (gr. 7-12). pap. 29.95 (978-1-930913-00-4(1)) Institute of Cultural Affairs, (USA).

Peterson, Susan Lynn. Legends of the Martial Arts Masters. 2003. (Illus.). 120p. pap. 7.95 (978-0-8048-3518-3(7)) Tuttle Publishing.

Pfleger, Susanne. Henri Rousseau: A Jungle Expedition. 1998. (Adventures in Art Ser.). (Illus.). 30p. (J). (ps-7). 14.95 (978-3-7913-1987-2(6)) Prestel Publishing.

Powell, Phelan. Jeff Gordon. 1999. (Real-Life Reader Biography Ser.). (Illus.). 32p. (J). (gr. 3-7). lib. bdg. 15.95 (978-1-58415-005-3(X)) Mitchell Lane Pubs., Inc.

Raintree Biographies, 16 bks. 2003. 411.20 (978-1-4109-0153-8(X)) Raintree.

Raintree Biographies 6 Pack, 3 bks., Set. 2004. pap. 243.00 (978-1-4109-1272-5(8)) Raintree.

Raintree Biographies Series, 10 bks., Set. 2003. (Illus.). (YA). lib. bdg. (978-0-7398-5682-6(0)) Raintree.

Raintree Steck-Vaughn Staff. Biographies: Level G. 2000. (J). pap. 3.75 (978-1-56260-342-7(6)) Educational Developmental Laboratories, Inc.

—Biography: Arkansas Edition, 42 bks., Set. 2003. (Illus.). 1147.20 (978-1-4109-0157-6(2)) Raintree.

—Lives of The...., 5 bks. 1999. (gr. 3-8). 104.90 (978-0-7398-0666-1(1)) Raintree.

Raphael, Morris. My Natchez Years. 1998. (Illus.). 160p. (YA). (gr. 5 up). 19.95 (978-0-8187-0312-6(1)) Raphael, Morris Bks.

Real-Life Reader Biographies Set 2: Oscar De La Hoya, Jimmy Smits, Cristina Saralegui, Andres Galarraga, Gloria Estefan, Mary Joe Fernandez, 6 bks. 1998. (Illus.). (J). (gr. 3-7). lib. bdg. 95.70 (978-1-883845-64-3(5)) Mitchell Lane Pubs., Inc.

Real-Life Reader Biographies Set 3: Celine Dion, Sinbad, Vanessa Williams, Chuck Norris, Cesar Chavez, Paula Abdul, 6 vols. 1998. (Illus.). (J). (gr. 3-8). lib. bdg. 95.70 (978-1-883845-77-3(7)) Mitchell Lane Pubs., Inc.

Reisfeld, Randi & Morreale, Marie. Got Issues Much? Celebrities Share Their Traumas & Triumphs. 1999. (Illus.). 144p. (gr. 3-9). pap. 5.99 (978-0-590-63274-4(4)) Scholastic, Inc.

Rice, Dorothy M. & Payne, Lucille M. The Seventeenth Child. 1998. (Illus.). 101p. (YA). (gr. 4-7). 18.50 (978-0-208-02414-5(X) , Linnet Bks.) Shoe String Pr., Inc.

A Robbie Reader: Contemporary Biographies, 18 bks., Set. Incl. Alex Rodriquez : Professional Baseball Player. Kjelle, Marylou Morano. 2005. lib. bdg. (978-1-58415-394-8(6)); Brittany Murphy. Kjelle, Marylou Morano. 2006. lib. bdg. (978-1-58415-520-1(5)); Charles Schulz. Marvis, Barbara J. 2004. lib. bdg. 25.70 (978-1-58415-289-7(3)); Dakota Fanning. Mattern, Joanne. 2006. lib. bdg. (978-1-58415-519-5(1)); Dale Earnhardt, Jr. Sherman, Josepha. 2005. lib. bdg. (978-1-58415-360-3(1)); Donovan Mcnabb. Mattern, Joanne. 2004. lib. bdg. 25.70 (978-1-58415-294-1(X)); Dr. Seuss. Adil, Janeen R. 2004. lib. bdg. 25.70 (978-1-58415-288-0(5)); Hilary Duff. Kjelle, Marylou Morano. 2004. lib. bdg. 25.70 (978-1-58415-295-8(8)); Jamie Lynn Spears. Adams, Michelle Medlock. 2005. lib. bdg. (978-1-58415-395-5(4)); Jessie Mccartney. Kjelle, Marylou Morano. 2006. lib. bdg. 25.70 (978-1-58415-500-3(0)); Johnny Gruelle : And the Story of Raggedy Ann & Andy. Sherman, Josepha. 2005. lib. bdg. (978-1-58415-359-7(8)); LeBron James. Mattern, Joanne. 2004. lib. bdg. 25.70 (978-1-58415-293-4(1)); Mia Hamm. Zarzycki, Daryl. 2004. lib. bdg. 25.70 (978-1-58415-286-6(9)); Shaquille O'Neal. Sherman, Josepha. 2005. lib. bdg. (978-1-58415-361-0(X)); Story of Harley-Davidson. Sherman, Josepha. 2005. lib. bdg. (978-1-58415-358-0(X) , 1244893); Syd Hoff. Sherman, Josepha. 2005. lib. bdg. (978-1-58415-357-3(1)); Tiki Barber. Mattern, Joanne. 2006. lib. bdg. (978-1-58415-522-5(1)); Tony Hawk. Kjelle, Marylou Morano. 2004. lib. bdg. 25.70 (978-1-58415-285-9(0)); (Illus.). 32p. (J). (gr. 1-4). 2007. 305.10 (***978-1-58415-299-6(0)***) Mitchell Lane Pubs., Inc.

Roets, Lois F. Famous People. 3rd rev. ed. 1999. 48p. (YA). (gr. 3-8). pap. 11.00 (978-0-911943-66-5(8)) Leadership Pub., Inc.

Rookie Biographies, 4 Bks. 2004. 76.00 (978-0-516-23718-3(7) , Children's Pr.) Scholastic Library Publishing.

Rookie Biographies, 4 bks., Set. Incl. John F. Kennedy. Jones, Veda Boyd. 20.50 (978-0-516-25038-0(8)); Lewis & Clark. McCormick, Lisa Wade. 20.50 (978-0-516-25039-7(6)); Marie Curie. McCormick, Lisa Wade. 20.50 (978-0-516-25040-3(X)); Thurgood Marshall. Taylor-Butler, Christine. 20.50 (978-0-516-25015-1(9)); 32p. (J). (gr. 1-2). 2006. (Illus.). 2006. 78.00 (978-0-516-25413-5(8) , Children's Pr.) Scholastic Library Publishing.

Ross, Inez A. The Bear & the Castle: The James Oliver Curwood Story. Conger, Ivan, illus. 1998. 48p. (J). (ps-6). pap. 6.98 (978-0-9664337-0-8(X)) Ashley Hse.

Rovin-Murphy, Deborah. 30 Biography Book Reports. 2001. 48p. pap. 9.95 (978-0-439-21570-1(6)) Scholastic, Inc.

Schlesinger, Arthur M., Jr., ed. Major World Leaders. (Illus.). (gr. 6-12). lib. bdg. (978-0-7910-8055-9(2) , Chelsea Hse.) Facts On File, Inc.

Schlesinger, Arthur M., Jr. & Schweitzer, Albert, intros. Ancient World Leaders. 2005. (Illus.). 112p. (gr. 6-12). pap. 180.00 (978-0-7910-7218-9(5) , Chelsea Hse.) Facts On File, Inc.

Schoell, William. Heartbreaker: The Dorothy Dandridge Story. 2002. (Illus.). 127p. (Orig.). (J). (gr. 6-12). pap. 19.95 (978-1-888105-51-3(8)) Avisson Pr., Inc.

Shaw, Maura D. Ten Amazing People: And How They Changed the World. Marchesi, Stephen, illus. 2002. (SkyLight Lives Ser.). 48p. (J). (gr. 1-5). 17.95 (978-1-893361-47-8(0)) SkyLight Paths Publishing.

Signature Lives, 16 vols. (YA). (gr. 5-7). 2006. 112p. 489.60 (978-0-7565-1893-6(8)); Complete Set. 2005. lib. bdg. 1346.40 (978-0-7565-1575-1(0)) Compass Point Bks.

Simon, Charnan. Brigham Young: Mormon & Pioneer. 1998. (Community Builders Ser.). (Illus.). 48p. (J). (gr. 3-5). 25.00 (978-0-516-20392-8(4) , Children's Pr.) Scholastic Library Publishing.

Spirn, Michele Sobel. Mysterious People: A Chapter Book. 2005. (True Tales Ser.). (Illus.). 48p. (J). (ps-ps). 22.50 (978-0-516-25181-3(3) , Children's Pr.) Scholastic Library Publishing.

Star Files, 6 bks., Set 1. 2004. 179.57 (978-1-4109-1091-2(1)) Harcourt Schl. Pubs.

Strangis, Joel. Lewis Hayden & the War Against Slavery. 1999. (Illus.). xiv, 167p. (YA). (gr. 9 up). 25.00 (978-0-208-02430-5(1) , Linnet Bks.) Shoe String Pr., Inc.

Techies, 9 vols. 2004. (Illus.). (YA). (gr. 5 up). (978-0-7613-3145-2(X) , Twenty-First Century Bks.) Lerner Publishing Group.

Thatcher, Rebecca. Ronaldinho. 2007. (No Hands Allowed Ser.). (Illus.). 32p. (J). lib. bdg. 25.70 (***978-1-58415-600-0(7)***) Mitchell Lane Pubs., Inc.

Thomas, Paul. Revolutionaries. (History Makers Ser.). (Illus.). 48p. lib. bdg. 28.50 (978-1-931983-41-9(0)) Chrysalis Education.

Time-Life Books Editors. Famous Faces of the 20th Century: What Makes a Leader? (Illus.). (J). pap. 17.95 (978-0-7835-5079-4(0)) Time-Life Education, Inc.

Toole, Darlene. Living Legends II: Six Stories about Incredible Deaf People. 1998. 64p. (YA). (gr. 7-12). pap., stu. ed. 7.95 (978-1-884362-32-3(X)) Butte Pubns., Inc.

Torres, John Albert. Mia Hamm. 1999. (Real-Life Reader Biography Ser.). (Illus.). 32p. (J). (gr. 3-8). lib. bdg. 15.95 (978-1-883845-94-0(7)) Mitchell Lane Pubs., Inc.

Trailblazers Biographies. 2004. (Illus.). lib. bdg. 7.95 (978-0-8225-3361-0(8)); lib. bdg. 7.95 (978-0-8225-5224-6(8)); Vol. 1. lib. bdg. 7.95 (978-0-8225-4402-9(4)) Lerner Publishing Group.

Trailblazers of the Modern World New Releases: Muhammad Ali; Cesar Chavez; Thurgood Marshall; Margaret Mead; Jonas Salk; Frank Lloyd Wright, 6 bks. 2004. (Illus.). (J). (gr. 5 up). pap. 71.70 (978-0-8368-5255-4(9)); lib. bdg. 175.60 (978-0-8368-5108-3(0)) Stevens, Gareth Inc. (World Almanac Library).

Uhlig, Elizabeth. Memoir Writing & Illustrating for Children. 2003. 58p. (J). per. 15.95 (978-0-9677047-2-2(3)) Marble House Editions.

Van Steenwyk, Elizabeth. Seneca Chief, Army General: A Story about Ely Parker. Ritz, Karen, illus. 2000. (Creative Minds Biographies Ser.). 64p. (J). (gr. 3-6). lib. bdg. 22.60 (978-1-57505-431-5(0) , Carolrhoda Bks.) Lerner Publishing Group.

Venezia, Mike. Alexander Calder. Venezia, Mike, illus. 1998. (Getting to Know the World's Greatest Artists Ser.). (Illus.). 32p. (J). (gr. 3-4). 23.00 (978-0-516-20966-1(3) , Children's Pr.) Scholastic Library Publishing.

Wade, Mary H. The Light-Bringers. 2006. (ENG.). 264p. per. 27.95 (***978-1-4286-2450-4(3)***) Kessinger Publishing, LLC.

Walker, Rebecca, frwd. It's up to Me: Stories of Choices, Predicaments & Decisions by San Francisco Youth. 2003. (Illus.). 232p. (J). per. 15.00 (978-0-9710606-2-3(2)) Streetside Stories, Inc.

Wallace, Archer. Men Who Played the Game. 2003. 127p. 89.00 (978-0-7950-5139-5(5)) New Library Press.Net.

Weber, Terri Smith. Bios for Kids: Library Set, Series 1. 2003. (J). lib. bdg. (978-1-932724-17-2(6) , Bios for Kids) Panda Publishing, L.L.C.

—Bios for Kids: Series Set 1. 2003. (J). pap. (978-1-932724-15-8(X) , Bios for Kids) Panda Publishing, L.L.C.

—Bios for Kids: Series Set, Series 1. 2003. (J). lib. bdg. (978-1-932724-16-5(8) , Bios for Kids) Panda Publishing, L.L.C.

Weber, Valerie & Mcnamara, Valerie J. Fun in Grandma's Day. 1999. (In Grandma's Day Ser.). (Illus.). 32p. (J). (gr. 2-4). lib. bdg. 21.27 (978-1-57505-325-7(X) , Carolrhoda Bks.) Lerner Publishing Group.

Whalin, W. Terry. Samuel Morris: Missionary to America. 1999. (Heroes of the Faith Ser.). 208p. (YA). (gr. 4-7). lib. bdg. 17.95 (978-0-7910-5039-2(4) , Chelsea Hse.) Facts On File, Inc.

Wheeler, Jill C. Breaking Barriers, Set. Incl. Amelia Earhart. lib. bdg. 25.65 (978-1-57765-318-9(1)); Clara Barton. lib. bdg. 25.65 (978-1-57765-317-2(3)); Colin Powell. lib. bdg. 25.65 (978-1-57765-638-8(5)); Mother Teresa. lib. bdg. 25.65 (978-1-57765-315-8(7)); Nelson Mandela. lib. bdg. 25.65 (978-1-57765-639-5(3)); Oprah Winfrey. lib. bdg. 25.65 (978-1-57765-319-6(X)); 64p. (J). (gr. 3-8). (Illus.). 2002. Set lib. bdg. 153.90 (978-1-57765-528-2(1) , ABDO & Daughters) ABDO Publishing Co.

Zalben, Jane. Paths to Peace: People Who Changed the World. 2006. (Illus.). 48p. (J). (gr. 3). 18.99 (978-0-525-47734-1(9) , Dutton Juvenile) Penguin Group (USA) Inc.

BIOGRAPHY—DICTIONARIES

Biographies, 6 bks., Set. 2003. (Illus.). (J). (978-0-7398-6867-6(5)) Raintree.

Biographies. rev. ed. 2004. (High Interest/Low Readability Ser.). 80p. (J). (gr. 5-8). pap. 10.99 (978-0-7696-3394-7(3) , MH1018) School Specialty Publishing.

Biographies, 6 bks., Set. Incl. Christopher Columbus. McCormick, Lisa Wade. 19.00 (978-0-516-24938-4(X)); George Washington Carver. Kittinger, Jo S. 19.00 (978-0-516-24939-1(8)); Jane Goodall. Kittinger, Jo S. 19.00 (978-0-516-24940-7(1)); Madame C. J. Walker. Nichols, Catherine. 19.00 (978-0-516-24941-4(X)); Sally Ride. Nichols, Catherine. 19.00 (978-0-516-24942-1(8)); Wright Brothers. McCormick, Lisa Wade. 19.00 (978-0-516-24937-7(1)); (Illus.). 24p. (J). (gr. 1-2). 2005. (Scholastic News Nonfiction Readers Ser.). 2005. 108.00 (978-0-516-25392-3(1) , Children's Pr.) Scholastic Library Publishing.

Carnibucci, Patricia. Biographies: Over 15 Complete Printable Unit Studies with Interactive Links. 2002. 160p. (gr. k-12). cd-rom 15.95 (978-1-891400-69-8(X)) Champion Pr., Ltd.

Dungworth, Richard, et al. The Usborne Book of Famous Lives. 2004. (Famous Lives Ser.). (Illus.). 245p. (J). (gr. 5 up). lib. bdg. 32.95 (978-0-88110-998-6(3)) EDC Publishing.

Gale Research Staff. U-X-L Encyclopedia of World Biography, 10 vols., Set. 2002. (Illus.). 2080p. (J). 520.00 (978-0-7876-6465-7(0) , GML00402-182070, UXL) Thomson Gale.

Ganeri, Anita. What Would You Ask?, 8 vols., Set. Incl. Alexander Graham Bell. 2000. lib. bdg. 16.95 (978-1-929298-76-1(5)); Amelia Earhart. 1999. lib. bdg. 16.95 (978-1-929298-01-3(3)); Ferdinand Magellan. 1999. lib. bdg. 16.95 (978-1-929298-02-0(1)); Marco Polo. 1999. lib. bdg. 16.95 (978-1-929298-00-6(5)); Marie Curie. 2000. lib. bdg. 16.95 (978-1-929298-09-9(9)); Michael Faraday. 2000. lib. bdg. 16.95 (978-1-929298-77-8(3)); Neil Armstrong. 1999. lib. bdg. 16.95 (978-1-929298-03-7(X)); Thomas Edison. 2000. pap. 16.95 (978-1-929298-10-5(2)); 32p. (J). (gr. 2-6). (Illus.). 2000. Set lib. bdg. 180.80 (978-1-929298-16-7(1)) Chrysalis Education.

Hatt, Christine. Judge for Yourself, 4 bks. Incl. Catherine the Great. 2003. lib. bdg. 30.00 (978-0-8368-5535-7(3)); Mahatma Ghandhi. 2004. lib. bdg. 30.00 (978-0-8368-5561-6(2)); Mao Zedong. 2003. lib. bdg. 30.00 (978-0-8368-5536-4(1)); Martin Luther King, Jr. 2004. lib. bdg. 30.00 (978-0-8368-5562-3(0)); 64p. (J). (gr. 5 up). (Illus.). 2003. Set lib. bdg. 120.00 (978-0-8368-5619-4(8) , World Almanac Library) Stevens, Gareth Inc.

Henderson, Andrea, ed. Abridged Encyclopedia of World Biography, 6 vols., Set. 2nd abr. ed. 1999. (Illus.). 4650p. (YA). (gr. 9 up). 680.00 (978-0-7876-3904-4(4) , GML00502-113701, Gale Research International, Ltd.) Thomson Gale.

History Makers. 2003. 320p. 5.98 (978-1-4054-0325-2(X)) Parragon, Inc.

Mishler, Donna. Historical People for Young Learners. Melvin, James, illus. l.t. ed. 1999. 32p. (J). (gr. k-5). pap., stu. ed. 5.95 (978-1-893709-03-4(5)) Suthernsky.

Nettleton, Pamela Hill. Biographies, 6 bks. Yesh, Jeff, illus. Incl. Abraham Lincoln. 22.60 (978-1-4048-0185-1(5)); Benjamin Franklin. 22.60 (978-1-4048-0186-8(3)); George Washington. 22.60 (978-1-4048-0184-4(7)); Martin Luther King, Jr. 22.60 (978-1-4048-0188-2(X)); Pocahontas. 22.60 (978-1-4048-0187-5(1)); Sally Ride. 22.60 (978-1-4048-0189-9(8)); 24p. (C). (gr. k-3). 2004. (Illus.). 2003. 127.56 (978-1-4048-0183-7(9)) Picture Window Bks.

People Who Made History. 2000. (Illus.). (J). (978-0-7398-4235-5(8)) Raintree.

Price, Sean. The Kids' Fun-Filled Biographies: More Than 500 People. Tallarico, Tony, illus. 2001. 189p. (J). (978-1-56156-917-5(8)) Kidsbooks, Inc.

Reid, Struan, et al. Historical Biographies. 2002. (J). (gr. 2-4). lib. bdg. 136.74 (978-1-58810-427-4(3)) Heinemann Library.

Short Biographies, 28 bks. Incl. African-American Astronauts. Jones, Stanley P. & Tripp, L. Octavia. 1998. lib. bdg. 22.60 (978-1-56065-695-1(6)); African-American Aviators. Jones, Stanley P. & Tripp, L. Octavia. 1998. lib. bdg. 22.60 (978-1-56065-696-8(4)); African-American Inventors. St. John, Jetty. 1996. lib. bdg. 22.60 (978-1-56065-361-5(2)); African-American Inventors II. Henderson, Susan K. 1998. lib. bdg. 22.60 (978-1-56065-697-5(2)); African-American Inventors III. Henderson, Susan K. 1998. lib. bdg. 22.60 (978-1-56065-698-2(0)); African-American Scientists. St. John, Jetty. 1996. lib. bdg. 22.60 (978-1-56065-358-5(2)); Hispanic Scientists. St. John, Jetty. 1996. lib. bdg. 22.60 (978-1-56065-360-8(4)); Native American Scientists. Kahn, Jetty. 1996. lib. bdg. 22.60 (978-1-56065-359-2(0)); Women Explorers in Africa. McLoone, Margo. 1997. lib. bdg. 22.60 (978-1-56065-505-3(4)); Women Explorers in Asia. McLoone, Margo. 1997. lib. bdg. 22.60 (978-1-56065-506-0(2)); Women Explorers in North & South America. McLoone, Margo. 1997. lib. bdg. 22.60 (978-1-56065-507-7(0)); Women Explorers in Polar Regions. McLoone, Margo. 1997. lib. bdg. 22.60 (978-1-56065-508-4(9)); Women Explorers of the Air. McLoone, Margo. 1999. lib. bdg. 22.60 (978-0-7368-0310-6(6)); Women Explorers of the Mountains. McLoone, Margo. 1999. lib. bdg. 22.60 (978-0-7368-0311-3(4)); Women Explorers of the Oceans. McLoone, Margo. 1999. lib. bdg. 22.60 (978-0-7368-0312-0(2)); Women Explorers of the World. McLoone, Margo. 1999. lib. bdg. 22.60 (978-0-7368-0313-7(0)); Women in Agricultural Science Careers. Kahn, Jetty. 1999. lib. bdg. 22.60 (978-0-7368-0314-4(9)); Women in Chemistry Careers. Kahn, Jetty. 1999. lib. bdg. 22.60 (978-0-7368-0315-1(7)); Women in Computer Science Careers. Kahn, Jetty. 1999. lib. bdg. 22.60 (978-0-7368-0316-8(5)); Women in Earth Science Careers. Kahn, Jetty. 1998. lib. bdg. 22.60 (978-0-7368-0012-9(3)); Women in Engineering Careers. Kahn, Jetty. 1998. lib. bdg. 22.60 (978-0-7368-0013-6(1)); Women in Life Science Careers. Kahn, Jetty. 1998. lib. bdg. 22.60 (978-0-7368-0014-3(X)); Women in Medical Science Careers. Kahn, Jetty. 1999. lib. bdg. 22.60 (978-0-7368-0317-5(3)); Women in Physical Science Careers. Kahn, Jetty. 1998. lib. bdg. 22.60 (978-0-7368-0015-0(8)); Women Inventors 1. Blashfield, Jean F. 1995. lib. bdg. 22.60 (978-1-56065-274-8(8)); Women Inventors 2. Blashfield, Jean F. 1995. lib. bdg. 22.60 (978-1-56065-275-5(6)); Women Inventors 3. Blashfield, Jean F. 1995. lib. bdg. 22.60 (978-1-56065-276-2(4)); Women Inventors 4. Blashfield, Jean F. 1995. lib. bdg. 22.60 (978-1-56065-277-9(2)); 48p. (J). (gr. 3-4). (Illus.). Set lib. bdg. 632.80 (978-0-7368-0441-7(2) , Bridgestone Bks.) Capstone Pr., Inc.

UXL Newsmakers. 2005. Vol. 5. 67.00 (978-1-4144-0156-0(6)); Vol. 6. 67.00 (978-1-4144-0157-7(4)); Vol. 56. 400p. 120.00 (978-1-4144-0155-3(8)) Thomson Gale. (UXL).

BIOGRAPHY (AS A LITERARY FORM)

Rosinsky, Natalie M. Write Your Own Biography. 2007. (J). lib. bdg. (***978-0-7565-3366-3(X)***) Compass Point Bks.

BIOLOGICAL CHEMISTRY

see Biochemistry

BIOLOGICAL DIVERSITY

see Biodiversity

BIOLOGY

see also Adaptation (Biology); Anatomy; Biodiversity; Cells; Embryology; Evolution; Fresh-Water Biology; Genetics; Life (Biology); Marine Biology; Microbiology; Natural History; Physiology; Reproduction; Sex; Zoology

Ace Academics, ed. Biology: A Whole Course in a Box! 2007. (Exambusters Ser.). 384p. (J). (gr. 7 up). 12.95 (978-1-881374-94-7(7) , Exambusters) Ace Academics, Inc.

Adds, John, et al. Tools, Techniques & Assessment in Biology: A Course Guide for Students & Teachers. 1999. (Illus.). 160p. (C). pap. 47.50 (978-0-17-448273-4(6)) Nelson Thornes Ltd. GBR. *Dist:* Trans-Atlantic Pubns., Inc.

Applin, David. Biology. 2nd ed. 2002. (Key Science Ser.). (Illus.). 464p. pap., stu. ed. 39.50 (978-0-7487-6241-5(8)) Nelson Thornes Ltd. GBR. *Dist:* Trans-Atlantic Pubns., Inc.

Baldwin, Carol. Living Habitats, 4 bks., Set. 2003. (Illus.). (J). (gr. 3-5). lib. bdg. 96.88 (978-1-58810-762-6(0)) Heinemann Library.

Ballard, Carol. Soil. 2004. (Using Materials Ser.). (Illus.). 32p. (J). pap. 7.50 (978-1-4109-0897-1(6)) Harcourt Schl. Pubs.

Barton, Di & Cambridge International Examinations Staff. IGCSE Biology Module 4. 2nd rev. ed. 2001. (Cambridge Open Learning Project in South Africa Ser.). (Illus.). 136p. pap. 8.25 (978-0-521-89202-5(3)) Cambridge Univ. Pr.

Batten, Mary. Aliens from Earth: When Animals & Plants Invade Other Ecosystems. Doyle, Beverly, illus. 2003. 32p. (J). 15.95 (978-1-56145-236-1(X)) Peachtree Pubs., Ltd.

Bellamy, Rufus. Protecting Habitats. 2005. (Action for the Environment Ser.). (Illus.). 32p. (J). (gr. 4-7). lib. bdg. 27.10 (978-1-58340-600-7(X)) Smart Apple Media.

Benchmark Education Staff, compiled by. Biology. 2006. spiral bd. 209.00 (***978-1-4108-7148-0(7)***) Benchmark Education Co.

—Science Theme: Life Science. 2005. spiral bd. 220.00 (***978-1-4108-5318-9(7)***) Benchmark Education Co.

—Structures of Life. 2006. spiral bd. 1060.00 (***978-1-4108-6790-2(0)***) Benchmark Education Co.

Berger, Melvin & Berger, Gilda. Seres Vivos: Living Things. 2006. (ENG & SPA., Illus.). (***978-0-439-82867-3(8)***) Scholastic, Inc.

Biologie. 4th ed. (Duden-Schuelerduden Ser.). (GER.). 540p. (YA). (978-3-411-05424-4(7)) Bibliographisches Institut & F. A. Brockhaus AG DEU. *Dist:* International Bk. Import Service, Inc.

Biology Laboratory Handbook. 2002. (YA). spiral bd. (978-0-9752935-0-8(8)) Townsley, William W. Pubns.

Biology Syllabus & Tests. 1999. 24p. (J). ring bd. 3.00 (978-1-57896-060-6(6) , 2437, Hewitt Homeschooling Resources) Hewitt Research Foundation, Inc.

Blackbirch Press Staff, creator. Cheats. 2005. (Planet's Most Extreme Ser.). (Illus.). 48p. (J). (ps-7). lib. bdg. 24.95 (978-1-4103-0381-3(0) , Blackbirch Pr., Inc.) Thomson Gale.

Blashfield, Jean F. Sparks of Life, 6 bks., Set. 1998. (Illus.). (YA). (gr. 6-12). 162.72 (978-0-8172-5043-0(3)) Raintree.

Bruno, Leonard C. UXL Complete Life Science Resource, Vol. 3. Carnagie, Julie L., ed. 2001. (Illus.). xxxvii, 608p. (J). (978-0-7876-4854-1(X) , UXL) Thomson Gale.

BSC 1005. 5th ed. 1999. 124p. (C). 18.20 (978-0-8087-6540-0(X)) Pearson Custom Publishing.

Burgraff, Frederick. Thinking Connections Book A1: Concept Maps for Life Science. 2001. (J). pap. 23.99 (978-0-89455-702-6(5)) Critical Thinking Bks. & Software.

Cambridge International Examinations Staff. IGCSE Biology Module 1. 2nd rev. ed. 2001. (Cambridge Open Learning Project in South Africa Ser.). (Illus.). 108p. pap. 8.25 (978-0-521-89203-2(1)) Cambridge Univ. Pr.

—IGCSE Biology Module 2. 2nd rev. ed. 2001. (Cambridge Open Learning Project in South Africa Ser.). (Illus.). 168p. pap. 8.25 (978-0-521-89205-6(8)) Cambridge Univ. Pr.

Campbell, Neil C., et al. Biology: Exploring Life, 3 vols. 2004. 922p. (YA). (gr. 9-12). 461.00 (978-0-13-062592-2(2)) Prentice Hall Pr.

Carnibucci, Patricia. Our Living World: Over 15 Complete Printable Unit Studies with Interactive Links. 2002. 160p. (gr. k-12). cd-rom 15.95 (978-1-891400-71-1(1)) Champion Pr., Ltd.

Chancellor, Deborah & Murrell, Deborah. Everything You Need to Know: An Encyclopedia for Inquiring Young Minds. 2007. (Illus.). 320p. (J). (ps-3). 24.95 (***978-0-7534-6089-4(0)*** , Kingfisher) Houghton Mifflin Co. Trade & Reference Div.

Christian Kids Explore Biology. 2004. pap. 29.95 (978-1-892427-05-2(2)) Bright Ideas! Educational Resources.

Cientificos! 7: Ciencias Biologicas. (SPA.). (J). 55.00 (978-958-04-6346-7(8)) Norma S.A. COL. *Dist:* Distribuidora Norma, Inc.

Classification, 2 bks. Incl. Animal Kingdom : A Guide to Vertebrate Classification & Biodiversity. Whyman, Kathryn. (J). lib. bdg. 27.12 (978-0-8172-5885-6(X)); Plant Kingdom : A Guide to Plant Classification & Biodiversity. Greenaway, Theresa. (YA). lib. bdg. 27.12 (978-0-8172-5886-3(8)); 48p. (gr. 6-8). 1999. (Illus.). 1999. Set lib. bdg. 54.24 (978-0-7398-1381-2(1)) Raintree.

Coldiron, Deborah. Coral. 2007. (Underwater World Ser.). (Illus.). 32p. (J). (gr. k-4). lib. bdg. 24.21 (***978-1-59928-811-6(7)*** , Buddy Bks.) ABDO Publishing Co.

Colvin, Leslie & Speare, Emma, eds. Living World Encyclopedia. 1999. (Usborne Encyclopedia Ser.). (Illus.). 128p. (J). (gr. 3-7). pap. 14.99 (978-0-7460-3051-6(7)) EDC Publishing.

Contemporary Discourse in the Field of Biology, 6 bks., Set. 2006. (YA). lib. bdg. 183.60 (978-1-4042-0629-8(9)) Rosen Publishing Group, Inc., The.

Cooke, Andy & Martin, Jean, eds. Spectrum Biology Class. 2004. (Spectrum Key Stage 3 Science Ser.). (Illus.). 176p. pap. 15.00 (978-0-521-54921-9(3)) Cambridge Univ. Pr.

Cooper, Jason. Camuflaje y Disfraz. 2007. (ENG & SPA., Illus.). 24p. (J). (978-1-60044-268-1(4)) Rourke Publishing, LLC.

Crewe, Sabrina. Life Cycles Complete Classroom: Library/Trade Edition. 1998. (Illus.). (J). pap. (978-0-7398-1216-7(5)) Steck-Vaughn.

Cullen, Katherine. Biology: The People Behind the Science. 2005. (Pioneers in Science Ser.). (Illus.). 192p. (J). (gr. 6-12). 29.95 (978-0-8160-5461-9(4)) Facts On File, Inc.

Davidson, Avelyn. Beach Biology. 2007. (Shockwave: Life Science & Medicine Ser.). (Illus.). 36p. (J). (gr. 4-6). lib. bdg. 25.00 (***978-0-531-17764-8(5)*** , Children's Pr.) Scholastic Library Publishing.

Davies, Valerie. Animals in Disguise. 2004. (J). 23.70 (978-1-4103-0458-2(2) , Greenhaven Pr., Inc.) Thomson Gale.

Dell, Pamela. Why Do Tigers Have Stripes? A Book about Camouflage. 2007. (First Facts Ser.). (Illus.). 24p. (J). 21.26 (978-0-7368-6381-0(8)) Capstone Pr., Inc.

Diagram Group. Biology. 2006. (Science Visual Resources Ser.). 208p. (J). (gr. 6-12). 49.50 (978-0-8160-6162-4(9)) Facts On File, Inc.

—The Facts on File Biology Handbook. 2nd rev. ed. 2006. (Science Handbook Ser.). 272p. (gr. 6-12). 35.00 (978-0-8160-5877-8(6)) Facts On File, Inc.

Diagram Group, contrib. by. First Life. 2004. (Life on Earth Ser.). (Illus.). 112p. (J). (gr. 4-9). 35.00 (978-0-8160-5046-8(5)) Facts On File, Inc.

Ebersole, Rene. Gorilla Mountain: The Story of Wildlife Biologist Amy Vedder. 2006. (Women's Adventures in Science Ser.). (Illus.). 128p. pap. 9.95 (978-0-309-09551-8(4) , Joseph Henry Pr.) National Academies Pr.

Eck, Kristin. Hide-and-Seek Animals. 2004. (Hide-And-Seek Books). (Illus.). (J). lib. bdg. 7.95 (978-1-4042-2702-6(4) , PowerKids Pr.) Rosen Publishing Group, Inc., The.

The Encyclopedia of Life Sciences, 11 vols. rev. ed. 2000. (Illus.). 1584p. (YA). lib. bdg. 657.07 (978-0-7614-0254-1(3) , Cavendish, Marshall Reference Bks.) Cavendish, Marshall Corp.

Enderle, Dotti. Storytime Discoveries: Biological Science. 2003. (Illus.). 64p. (J). pap. 9.95 (978-1-57310-411-1(6)) Teaching & Learning Co.

Evolution Series, 7 cass.; set. 2004. (gr. 7 up). 99.95 incl. VHS (978-1-57807-641-3(2) , WG1158) WGBH Boston Video.

Exploring Life on Earth. 2003. 128p. (gr. 5-8). 12.99 (978-1-56822-902-7(X) , IF87014) School Specialty Publishing.

Farndon, John. Living Things. 2004. (J). 23.70 (978-1-4103-0122-2(2) , Blackbirch Pr., Inc.) Thomson Gale.

Favor, Lesli J. Eukaryotic & Prokaryotic Cell Structures: Understanding Cells with & Without a Nucleus. 2004. (Library of Cells). (Illus.). 48p. (YA). lib. bdg. 25.25 (978-1-4042-0323-5(0)) Rosen Publishing Group, Inc., The.

Ferguson, creator. Biology. 2nd rev. ed. 2005. (Careers in Focus Ser.). (Illus.). 204p. (J). (gr. 6-12). 22.95 (978-0-8160-5867-9(9) , Ferguson Publishing Co.) Facts On File, Inc.

Frank, Marjorie Slavick, et al. Science Instant Readers: Life Science Collection. 1999. (Harcourt Science Ser.). (gr. 1 up). pap. 12.40 (978-0-15-316228-7(7)); (gr. 2 up). pap. 12.40 (978-0-15-316231-2(7)) Harcourt Schl. Pubs.

—Science Instant Readers Bk. 1: Living or Nonliving? 1999. (Harcourt Science Ser.). (gr. 1 up). pap. 15.50 (978-0-15-316199-5(X)) Harcourt Schl. Pubs.

—Science Instant Readers Bk. 3: What Is a Food Chain? 1999. (Harcourt Science Ser.). (gr. 2 up). pap. 15.50 (978-0-15-316213-8(9)) Harcourt Schl. Pubs.

Friedman, Michael & Friedman, Brett. Cell Communication: Understanding How Information Is Stored & Used in Cells. 2004. (Library of Cells). (Illus.). 48p. (YA). lib. bdg. 25.25 (978-1-4042-0319-8(2)) Rosen Publishing Group, Inc., The.

Fullick, Ann. The Living World. 2003. (Science Topics Ser.). (Illus.). 32p. (YA). (gr. 6-8). lib. bdg. 24.22 (978-1-57572-768-4(4)) Heinemann Library.

—Variation & Classification. 2005. (Life Science In-Depth Ser.). (Illus.). 64p. (J). (978-1-4034-7524-4(5)); pap. (978-1-4034-7532-9(6)) Heinemann Library.

Gaff, Jackie. Looking at Growing Up: How Do People Change? 2008. (Looking at Science: How Things Change Ser.). 32p. (J). (gr. 1-3). lib. bdg. 22.60 (***978-0-7660-3090-9(3)***) Enslow Pubs., Inc.

Garnsey, Wayne H. Biology: Living Environment STARe-view. Fairbanks, Eugene B., illus. 2000. (ENG.). 336p. (YA). (gr. 7-12). per. 15.95 (978-0-935487-73-2(5) , STAReviews) N&N Publishing Co., Inc.

Garvin, J. W. & Boyd, J. D. Skills in Advanced Biology Vol. 3: Investigating Students Text. 1998. (Illus.). 141p. (YA). (gr. 11 up). spiral bd. 43.50 (978-0-7487-2048-4(0)) State Mutual Bk. & Periodical Service, Ltd.

Gifford, Clive & Cadle, Jerry. The Kingfisher Young People's Book of Living Worlds. 2002. (Kingfisher Book of Ser.). (Illus.). 80p. (J). (gr. 4-8). tchr. ed. 21.95 (978-0-7534-5390-2(8) , Kingfisher) Houghton Mifflin Co. Trade & Reference Div.

Gore, Bryson. Biology: Spider Silk Is Stronger Than Steel. 2005. (Illus.). 32p. (J). (gr. 3-7). lib. bdg. 27.10 (978-1-59604-069-4(6)) Stargazer Bks.

Green, Jen. A Dead Log. 1999. (Small Worlds Ser.). (Illus.). 32p. (J). (gr. 3-4). pap. (978-0-7787-0150-7(6)) Crabtree Publishing Co.

Griffith, Dave. Biology Student Workbook. 1999. (Illus.). (J). pap. 12.00 (978-1-886998-05-6(1)) Pasco Scientific.

Grolier Educational Staff, contrib. by. Biology Matters!, 10 vols. 2004. (Illus.). (J). 389.00 (978-0-7172-5979-3(X)); (978-0-7172-5980-9(3)); (978-0-7172-5981-6(1)); (978-0-7172-5982-3(X)); (978-0-7172-5983-0(8)); (978-0-7172-5984-7(6)); (978-0-7172-5985-4(4)); (978-0-7172-5986-1(2)); (978-0-7172-5987-8(0)); (978-0-7172-5988-5(9)); (978-0-7172-5989-2(7)) Scholastic Library Publishing. (Grolier).

Hanauer, Ethel. Biology Experiments for Children. unabr. ed. 1998. (Dover Science Bks.). (Illus.). 96p. (J). (gr. 5-8). pap. 4.95 (978-0-486-22032-1(X) , 22032-X) Dover Pubns., Inc.

Handwerker, Mark J. Ready-to-Use Human Biology & Health Activities for Grades 5-12. 2000. (Secondary Science Curriculum Activities Library: Vol. 5). (Illus.). 256p. (J). pap. 27.50 (978-0-13-029112-7(9) , Addison Wesley) Benjamin-Cummings Publishing Co.

Hantula, Richard. Plants & Animals. 2006. (Real World Science Ser.). (Illus.). 32p. (J). lib. bdg. 24.67 (978-0-8368-6308-6(9)) Stevens, Gareth Inc.

Harcourt School Publishers Staff. Harcourt Ciencias: Take-Home Book. 1999. (Harcourt Ciencias Ser.). (SPA., Illus.). (gr. 5 up). pap. 34.30 (978-0-15-316175-9(2)) Harcourt Schl. Pubs.

—Harcourt Ciencias Unit A: Las Plantas y los Animales a Nuestro Big Book. 1999. (Harcourt Ciencias Ser.). (SPA., Illus.). (gr. 1 up). pap., pupil's gde. ed. 130.60 (978-0-15-316829-1(3)) Harcourt Schl. Pubs.

—Harcourt Science, Grade 1 Vol. 1: Life Science: Louisiana Edition. 2nd ed. 2002. tchr. ed. 100.70 (978-0-15-328352-9(1)) Harcourt Schl. Pubs.

—Harcourt Science, Grade 1 Vol. 1: Life Science: Tennessee Edition. 2nd ed. 2002. tchr. ed. 106.70 (978-0-15-328334-5(3)) Harcourt Schl. Pubs.

—Harcourt Science, Grade 1 Vol. 2: Earth Scinece: Louisiana Edition. 2nd ed. 2002. tchr. ed. 100.70 (978-0-15-328353-6(X)) Harcourt Schl. Pubs.

—Harcourt Science, Grade 2 Vol. 1: Life Science: Louisiana Edition. 2nd ed. 2002. tchr. ed. 100.70 (978-0-15-328356-7(4)) Harcourt Schl. Pubs.

—Harcourt Science, Grade 2 Vol. 1: Life Science: Tennessee Edition. 2nd ed. 2002. tchr. ed. 106.70 (978-0-15-328337-6(8)) Harcourt Schl. Pubs.

—Harcourt Science, Grade 6 Vol. 1: Life Science: Louisiana Edition. 2nd ed. 2002. tchr. ed. 113.50 (978-0-15-328368-0(8)) Harcourt Schl. Pubs.

—Harcourt Science, Grade 6 Vol. 1: Life Science: Tennessee Edition. 2nd ed. 2002. tchr. ed. 120.30 (978-0-15-328349-9(1)) Harcourt Schl. Pubs.

—Life Science: Instant Reader Standard Package. 2000. (Harcourt Ciencias Ser.). (SPA., Illus.). (gr. 1 up). pap. 17.70 (978-0-15-316952-6(4)); (gr. 2 up). pap. 17.70 (978-0-15-316955-7(9)) Harcourt Schl. Pubs.

Helman, Andrea. Hide & Seek: Nature's Best Vanishing Acts. Jecan, Gavriel, illus. 2008. 40p. (J). 17.85 ***(978-0-8027-9691-2(5));*** 16.95 ***(978-0-8027-9690-5(7))*** Walker & Co.

Hibbert, Clare. Life Cycles, 6 vols., Set 1. 2004. (Illus.). 154.20 (978 1 4109-0540-6(3)) Raintree.

Hickman, Pamela. A New Frog: The Life Cycle of an Amphibian. Collins, Heather, illus. unabr. ed. 1999. (My First Look at Nature Ser.). 20p. (J). (gr. k-3). (978-1-55074-615-0(4)) Kids Can Pr., Ltd.

Hickman, Pamela & Collins, Heather. A New Duck: My First Look at the Life Cycle of a Bird. 1999. (My First Look at Nature Ser.). (Illus.). 20p. (J). (gr. k-3). (978-1-55074-613-6(8)) Kids Can Pr., Ltd.

Hil, Mcgraw. Sciasmtbk Cells Growth & 2000. (McGraw-Hill Science Ser.). (gr. 6 up). (978-0-02-277772-2(5)) Macmillan/McGraw-Hill Schl. Div.

—Sciasmtbk Classfyng Lvng. 2000. (McGraw-Hill Science Ser.). (gr. 4 up). (978-0-02-277755-5(5)) Macmillan/McGraw-Hill Schl. Div.

Hoff, Mary. Mimicry & Camouflage. 2002. (World of Wonder Ser.). (Illus.). 32p. (J). lib. bdg. (978-1-58341-237-4(9) , Creative Education) Creative Co., The.

Holly Wallace. Life Cycles. 2nd ed. 2006. (Life Processes Ser.). (Illus.). 32p. (J). pap. ***(978-1-4034-8854-1(1))*** Heinemann Library.

Holt, Rinehart and Winston Staff. Basic Units of Life: Chapter Resources: Tennessee Edition. 3rd ed. 2003. (Holt Science & Technology Ser.). pap. 11.40 (978-0-03-069132-4(X)) Holt, Rinehart & Winston.

—Biology. 4th ed. 2003. trans. 301.81 (978-0-03-069919-1(3)); (SPA., Illus.). pap., stu. ed. 15.46 (978-0-03-069987-0(8)) Holt, Rinehart & Winston.

—Biology: Chapter Resource Package. 6th ed. 2006. pap. 415.60 (978-0-03-041317-9(6)) Harcourt Schl. Pubs.

—Biology: Chromosomes & Reproduction: Resources for Chapter 6. 4th ed. 2004. (Illus.). pap. 9.20 (978-0-03-069934-4(7)) Holt, Rinehart & Winston.

—Biology: New York Test Preparation for the Regents Exam. 5th ed. 2005. pap. 17.20 (978-0-03-070816-9(8)) Holt, Rinehart & Winston.

—Biology: Principles & Explorations: Strategies & Practice for Reading - Tennessee Edition. 2001. pap. 12.20 (978-0-03-068487-6(0)) Holt, Rinehart & Winston.

—Biology: Strategies & Practices Answer Key. 4th ed. 2004. (Illus.). pap. 6.00 (978-0-03-020438-8(0)) Holt, Rinehart & Winston.

—Holt Biology 2004: Texas Edition. 2004. (J). stu. ed. 83.93 (978-0-03-068264-3(9)) Holt, Rinehart & Winston.

—Holt Modern Biology 2002: South Carolina Strategies & Practice for Reading. 2nd ed. 2002. pap. 13.86 (978-0-03-068982-6(1)) Holt, Rinehart & Winston.

—Holt Science & Technology: Life Science. 5th ed. 2004. tchr. ed. 128.80 (978-0-03-066477-9(2)) Holt, Rinehart & Winston.

—Holt Science & Technology: Life Science: Enhanced Online Edition. 4th ed. 2004. 17.26 (978-0-03-037149-3(X)) Holt, Rinehart & Winston.

—Holt Science & Technology: Life Science: Reading & Comprehension Guide. 5th ed. 2004. (Illus.). pap. 17.13 (978-0-03-036061-9(7)) Holt, Rinehart & Winston.

—Holt Science & Technology: Life Science: Special Needs Workbook. 5th ed. 2004. pap., wbk. ed. 17.13 (978-0-03-036053-4(6)) Holt, Rinehart & Winston.

—Holt Science & Technology: Life Science Study Guide. 5th ed. 2004. (Illus.). pap., stu. ed. 17.13 (978-0-03-030158-2(0)) Holt, Rinehart & Winston.

—Holt Science & Technology: Life Science: Tutorial Site License. 2nd ed. 2002. 861.84 (978-0-03-070397-3(2)) Holt, Rinehart & Winston.

—Holt Science & Technology: Life Sciences: Study Guide & Answer Key. 2000. pap., stu. ed. 12.20 (978-0-03-050594-2(1)) Holt, Rinehart & Winston.

—Holt Science & Technology Chapter 1: Life Science: The World of Life Science. 5th ed. 2004. (Illus.). pap. 12.86 (978-0-03-030163-6(7)) Holt, Rinehart & Winston.

—Holt Science & Technology Chapter 2: Life Science: It's Alive!! or Is It? 5th ed. 2004. (Illus.). pap. 12.86 (978-0-03-030166-7(1)) Holt, Rinehart & Winston.

—Holt Science & Technology Chapter 7: Life Science: Evolution & Living. 5th ed. 2004. (Illus.). pap. 12.86 (978-0-03-030191-9(2)) Holt, Rinehart & Winston.

—Holt Science & Technology Chapter 9: Life Science: Classification. 5th ed. 2004. (Illus.). pap. 12.86 (978-0-03-030201-5(3)) Holt, Rinehart & Winston.

—Holt Science & Technology Chptr. 2: It's Alive!: Chapter Resources - Tennessee Edition. 3rd ed. 2003. (YA). (gr. 7). pap. 11.40 (978-0-03-069131-7(1)) Holt, Rinehart & Winston.

—Holt Science & Technology Chptr. 2: Living Things: Chapter Resources - Tennessee Edition. 3rd ed. 2003. (J). pap. 11.40 (978-0-03-069107-2(9)) Holt, Rinehart & Winston.

—Modern Biology. 6th ed. 2006. tchr. ed. 114.60 (978-0-03-073542-4(4)); pap., stu. ed. 21.80 (978-0-03-036718-2(2)) Harcourt Schl. Pubs.

—Modern Biology. 2nd ed. 2002. 79.33 (978-0-03-056541-0(3)); 2nd ed. 2002. pap., stu. ed. 21.40 (978-0-03-064276-0(0)); 2nd annot. ed. 2002. tchr. ed. 108.86 (978-0-03-056542-7(1)); 6th ed. Date not set. 83.93 (978-0-03-065178-6(6)); 6th ed. Date not set. cd-rom 83.93 (978-0-03-036746-5(8)) Holt, Rinehart & Winston.

—Modern Biology: Active Reading Guide with Answer Key. 2nd ed. 2002. 23.33 (978-0-03-064272-2(8)) Holt, Rinehart & Winston.

—Modern Biology: Alabama Edition. 2nd annot. ed. 2002. tchr. ed. 108.86 (978-0-03-067793-9(9)) Holt, Rinehart & Winston.

—Modern Biology: Chapter Tests with Answer Key. 1999. pap. 36.93 (978-0-03-051762-4(1)); 2nd ed. 2002. pap. 36.93 (978-0-03-064273-9(6)) Holt, Rinehart & Winston.

—Modern Biology: Georgia Edition. 2nd annot. ed. 2002. tchr. ed. 108.86 (978-0-03-066902-6(2)) Holt, Rinehart & Winston.

—Modern Biology: Strategies & Practice for Reading - Tennessee Edition. 2nd ed. 2002. pap. 13.86 (978-0-03-068493-7(5)) Holt, Rinehart & Winston.

—Modern Biology: With Answer Key. 2nd ed. 2002. pap., stu. ed. 13.00 (978-0-03-064274-6(4)) Holt, Rinehart & Winston.

—Modern Biology 2002: Louisiana Edition. 2nd annot. ed. 2002. tchr. ed. 104.53 (978-0-03-071222-7(X)) Holt, Rinehart & Winston.

—Modern Biology 2002: Middle School. 2nd annot. ed. 2002. tchr. ed. 108.86 (978-0-03-067899-8(4)) Holt, Rinehart & Winston.

—Modern Biology 2002: Strategies & Practice for Reading in Science - Louisiana Edition. 2nd ed. 2002. pap. 13.86 (978-0-03-071231-9(9)) Holt, Rinehart & Winston.

—Principles & Exploration 2001: Louisiana. 2nd annot. ed. 2002. tchr. ed. 105.60 (978-0-03-071208-1(4)) Holt, Rinehart & Winston.

—Standard Test Preparation Workbook: South Carolina Edition - Biology. 2nd ed. 2002. (J). pap. 11.00 (978-0-03-069039-6(0)) Holt, Rinehart & Winston.

—Taks Practice Exams Biology. 4th ed. 2003. (YA). (gr. 10-11). pap. 14.00 (978-0-03-074082-4(7)) Holt, Rinehart & Winston.

Imlay-Gillespie, Iain & Hwang, Eun-Soo. Cambridge HSC Biology Study Guide. 2004. (Cambridge HSC Study Guides). 256p. pap. 16.95 (978-0-521-54433-7(5)) Cambridge Univ. Pr.

It's Alive. 2000. (J). stu. ed. (978-0-13-019756-6(4)) Prentice Hall PTR.

Jackson, Ellen B. The Tree of Life: The Wonders of Evolution. Winter, Judeanne, illus. 2004. 41p. pap. 12.00 (978-1-59102-240-4(1) , Pyr Bks.) Prometheus Bks., Pubs.

Jennings, Terry. Camouflage. 2004. (QEB Start Talking Ser.). (Illus.). 24p. (J). lib. bdg. 15.95 (978-1-59566-001-5(1)) QEB Publishing Inc.

Jepson, Maud. Illustrated Biology, 2 pts., Pt. 2: Animals. (Illus.). (YA). (gr. 8-12). 6.95 (978-0-7195-0734-2(0)) Transatlantic Arts, Inc.

Johnson. Biology: Online Edition Upgrade. 4th ed. 2004. 31.93 (978-0-03-037173-8(2)) Holt, Rinehart & Winston.

—Holt Biology: Enhanced Online Edition. 4th ed. 2004. 17.26 (978-0-03-037153-0(8)); 6th ed. Date not set. stu. ed. 83.93 (978-0-03-074066-4(5)) Holt, Rinehart & Winston.

—Holt Biology: Online Edition Upgrade. 4th ed. 2004. 7.93 (978-0-03-037216-2(X)) Holt, Rinehart & Winston.

Jones, Mary & Gregory, Jennifer. Biology 2. 2001. (Cambridge Advanced Sciences Ser.). (Illus.). 152p. (YA). pap. 24.00 (978-0-521-79714-6(4)) Cambridge Univ. Pr.

Jones, Mary & Jones, Geoff. CSEC Biology: A Foundation Course. 2008. pap. ***(978-0-521-70114-3(7))*** Cambridge Univ. Pr.

Jones, Mary, et al. CIE Biology AS Level & A Level. 2003. (Cambridge Advanced Sciences Ser.). (Illus.). 352p. pap. 37.00 (978-0-521-53674-5(X)) Cambridge Univ. Pr.

Kalman, Bobbie. Camouflage: Changing to Hide. 2005. (Nature's Changes Ser.). (Illus.). 32p. (J). (978-0-7787-2272-4(4)) Crabtree Publishing Co.

—Camouflage Changing to Hide. 2005. (Nature's Changes Ser.). (Illus.). 32p. (J). (ps-k). pap. (978-0-7787-2306-6(2)) Crabtree Publishing Co.

—Le Camouflage et le Mimetisme. 2001. (FRE., Illus.). 32p. pap. (978-2-920660-74-8(8)) Crabtree Publishing Co.

—Qué Es el Ciclo de Vida? 2005. (Ciencia de los Seres Vivos Ser.). (SPA., Illus.). 32p. (J). (978-0-7787-8754-9(0)) Crabtree Publishing Co.

—Qué Son los Seres Vivos? 2005. (SPA., Illus.). 32p. (J). (978-0-7787-8760-0(5)) Crabtree Publishing Co.

—Qué son los seres Vivos? 2005. (Ciencia de los Seres Vivos Ser.). (SPA., Illus.). 32p. (J). (gr. 3-4). pap. (978-0-7787-8806-5(7)) Crabtree Publishing Co.

—What Is a Living Thing? 1999. (Science of Living Things Ser.). (Illus.). 32p. (J). (gr. 2-3). pap. (978-0-86505-891-0(1)) Crabtree Publishing Co.

Kelley, Robin B. Fuzzy Freddy Fungus. 2004. 27p. pap. 14.95 (978-1-4137-0987-2(7)) PublishAmerica, Inc.

Kloepfer, Deanne & Abarca, Patricia. Francisco Dallmeier. (Biografías Hispanoamericanas Ser.). 64p. (J). 2006. (SPA.). lib. bdg. 32.86 ***(978-1-4109-2130-7(1));*** 2005. (Illus.). pap. 9.50 (978-1-4109-1308-1(2)) Raintree.

Kottke, Jan. How Things Grow, 6 bks., Set. 2004. (Welcome Books Ser.). (J). (ps-2). 87.00 (978-0-516-23376-5(9) , Children's Pr.) Scholastic Library Publishing.

Kummer, Patricia K. The Great Barrier Reef. 2008. (J). ***(978-0-7614-2852-7(6))*** Cavendish, Marshall Bks., Ltd.

Lanier, Wendy. Life Cycles. 2006. (KidHaven Science Library). (Illus.). 48p. (J). (gr. 4-8). 26.20 (978-0-7377-2073-0(5) , Greenhaven Pr., Inc.) Thomson Gale.

Laskey, Elizabeth. Gross & Gory. 2004. (Heinemann Infosearch Ser.). (Illus.). 32p. (J). pap. 7.50 (978-1-4034-4964-1(3)) Heinemann Library.

Leather, Harry & Leather, Jan. Cambridge Checkpoints VCE Biology Unit 3 2005. 2004. (Cambridge Checkpoints Ser.). 184p. pap., stu. ed. 11.35 (978-0-521-60835-0(X)) Cambridge Univ. Pr.

Life, Module A. 2003. (gr. 3 up). suppl. ed. 15.50 (978-0-328-03435-2(5)); (gr. 4 up). suppl. ed. 15.50 (978-0-328-03439-0(8)); (gr. 5 up). suppl. ed. 16.00 (978-0-328-03443-7(6)); (gr. 6 up). suppl. ed. 16.00 (978-0-328-03447-5(9)) Addison-Wesley Educational Pubs., Inc.

Life Cycles Series Package, 6, Pack. 2004. pap. 486.00 (978-1-4109-1261-9(2)) Raintree.

Life Science Student Text: Grade 7. 2004. 32.00 (978-0-89084-884-5(X)) Jones, Bob Univ. Pr.

Lindeen, Carol. Life in a Desert. 2003. (Pebble Plus: Living in a Biome Ser.). (Illus.). 24p. (J). lib. bdg. 17.26 (978-0-7368-2097-4(3)) Capstone Pr., Inc.

The Living Earth Series, 8 vols., Set. 2002. (YA). (gr. 7-12). 440.00 (978-0-8160-5017-8(1)) Facts On File, Inc.

Living in a Biome. 2005. (Earth & Outer Space Ser.). (YA). (gr. k-3). 237.60 (978-0-7368-4213-6(6) , Pebble Bks.) Capstone Pr., Inc.

Madgwick, Wendy. Living Things. 1999. (Science Starters Ser.). (Illus.). 32p. (J). (gr. k-4). lib. bdg. 25.70 (978-0-8172-5332-5(7)) Raintree.

Marshall Cavendish Corporation Staff, contrib. by. Exploring Life Science, 11 vols., Set. 2000. (Illus.). 800p. (gr. 4-6). 471.36 (978-0-7614-7135-6(9) , Cavendish, Marshall Reference Bks.) Cavendish, Marshall Corp.

Marsico, Katie. Scholastic News Nonfiction Readers: Life Cycles, 6 bks., Set. Incl. Baby Lobster Grows Up. (Illus.). 19.00 (978-0-531-17475-3(1)); Kangaroo Joey Grows Up. (Illus.). 19.00 (978-0-531-17476-0(X)); Komodo Dragon Hatchling Grows Up. (Illus.). 19.00 (978-0-531-17477-7(8)); Ladybug Larva Grows Up. (Illus.). 19.00 (978-0-531-17478-4(6)); Manatee Calf Grows Up. 19.00 (978-0-531-17479-1(4)); Peachick Grows Up. (Illus.). 19.00 (978-0-531-17480-7(8)); 24p. (J). (gr. 1-2). 2007. 2007. 114.00 ***(978-0-531-12606-6(4)*** , Children's Pr.) Scholastic Library Publishing.

Martin, Jean. Science Foundation Presents Biology 1. 2004. (Illus.). (YA). cd-rom 120.00 (978-1-84565-015-5(8)) Cambridge Univ. Pr.

Mason, Adrienne. Living Things. Boudreau, Ray, illus. 2000. (Starting with Science Ser.). 32p. (J). (gr. k-3). (978-1-55074-393-7(7)) Kids Can Pr., Ltd.

Mason, Paul. Creature Camouflage. 2007. (J). ***(978-1-4109-2960-0(4));*** pap. ***(978-1-4109-2981-5(7))*** Steck-Vaughn.

Mauk, Susan & Stettler, Linda. Taxonomy Trail. 2004. (Illus.). (J). (gr. 2-5). 42.00 (978-1-57336-396-9(0) , 11125) Interaction Pubs., Inc.

McGraw-Hill Staff. Biology: A Community Context. 2002. stu. ed. 82.00 (978-0-07-830694-5(9) , 9780078306945) Glencoe/McGraw-Hill.

—Biology: An Everyday Experience. 2002. stu. ed. 91.32 (978-0-07-829749-6(4) , 9780078297496) Glencoe/McGraw-Hill.

—Biology: The Dynamics of Life. 2003. (C). (gr. 6-12). pap., stu. ed., lab manual ed. 19.00 (978-0-07-860228-3(9) , 9780078602283); 2003. (gr. 6-12). pap., stu. ed., lab manual ed. 17.32 (978-0-07-860226-9(2) , 9780078602269); 2001. stu. ed. 92.64 (978-0-07-825925-8(8) , 9780078259258); 2nd ed. 2003. (gr. 6-12). pap., stu. ed. 18.00 (978-0-07-860232-0(7) , 9780078602320) Glencoe/McGraw-Hill.

—Biology: The Dynamics of Life Online: MHLN Stand Alone Version. 2003. (C). (gr. 6-12). stu. ed. 91.96 (978-0-07-861529-0(1) , 9780078615290) Glencoe/McGraw-Hill.

—Glencoe Life Science: Reinforcement. 2004. pap., stu. ed. 11.96 (978-0-07-867127-2(2) , 9780078671272) Glencoe/McGraw-Hill.

—Glencoe Science: Life Science Modules. 2004. pap., stu. ed. 8.64 (978-0-07-867136-4(1) , 9780078671364) Glencoe/McGraw-Hill.

—Life's Structure & Function. 2nd ed. 2004. (Glencoe Science Ser.). stu. ed. 20.64 (978-0-07-861734-8(0) , 9780078617348) Glencoe/McGraw-Hill.

Meacham, Nancy. Plantas: Libro de Actividades de Descubrimiento Cientifico. Zuman, John & Barra, Nancy, eds. Deming, Linda, illus. 2nd ed. 2002. (Sunflower/Girasol Ser.). (SPA.). 20p. (J). 5.00 (978-1-58332-002-0(4)) Intercultural Center for Research in Education (I N C R E).

Meredith, Sue. El GRAN LIBRO DELAWARE LOS GENES y el ADN - INTERNET LINKED. 2005. (SPA.). 64p. (J). pap. 11.95 (978-0-7460-6748-2(8) , Usborne) EDC Publishing.

Metamorphosis Curriculum Kit. 2003. 249.99 (978-0-7441-3947-1(3)) Willow Creek Assn.

Milner, Bryan, et al, eds. Core Science 1: Key Concepts. 1998. (Core Science Ser.). (Illus.). 302p. pap. 30.00 (978-0-521-58850-8(2)) Cambridge Univ. Pr.

—Core Science 2: Consolidation. 1998. (Core Science Ser.). (Illus.). 244p. pap. 24.00 (978-0-521-58849-2(9)) Cambridge Univ. Pr.

Modules: Life Science; Human Biology PE. 2005. (gr. 6-12). (978-0-618-33431-5(9) , 2-01019) McDougal Littell Inc.

Modules: Life Science; Life over Time PE. 2005. (gr. 6-12). (978-0-618-33436-0(X) , 2-01023) McDougal Littell Inc.

Modules: Physical Science. 2005. (gr. 6-12). lab manual ed. (978-0-618-43730-6(4) , 2-01223) McDougal Littell Inc.

Modules: Physical Science; Content Review CD-ROM: Life Science. 2005. (gr. 6-12). cd-rom (978-0-618-42025-4(8) , 2-01139) McDougal Littell Inc.

Morgan, Jennifer. Mammals Who Morph: The Universe Tells Our Evolution Story. Andersen, Dana Lynne, illus. 2006. (Sharing Nature with Children Book Ser.). 48p. (J). (gr. 2-5). 19.95 (978-1-58469-084-9(4)); pap. 9.95 (978-1-58469-085-6(2)) Dawn Pubns.

Morgan, Sally. Life In..., 4 vols., Set. Incl. Clearing in the Forest. lib. bdg. 16.95 (978-1-929298-84-6(6)); Giant Tree in the Rainforest. lib. bdg. 16.95 (978-1-929298-85-3(4)); Pond in the Meadow. lib. bdg. 16.95 (978-1-929298-86-0(2)); Tide on the Seashore. lib. bdg. 16.95 (978-1-929298-87-7(0)); 32p. (J). (gr. 2-6). (Illus.). 2000. Set lib. bdg. 67.80 (978-1-929298-88-4(9)) Chrysalis Education.

Munro, Margaret. The Story of Life on Earth. Reczuch, Karen, illus. 2000. 64p. (J). (ps-3). pap. (978-0-88899-401-1(X)) Groundwood Bks.

Oceanor Staff. Biologia - Atlas Visuales. 1999. (SPA.). (gr. 3-6). lib. bdg. 20.00 (978-0-613-80879-8(7)) Tandem Library Bks.

O'Daly, Anne. Encyclopedia of Life Sciences, 13 vols. 2nd ed. 2004. (Illus.). ***(978-0-7614-7443-2(9)); (978-0-7614-7444-9(7)); (978-0-7614-7445-6(5)); (978-0-7614-7446-3(3)); (978-0-7614-7447-0(1)); (978-0-7614-7448-7(X)); (978-0-7614-7449-4(8)); (978-0-7614-7450-0(1)); (978-0-7614-7451-7(X)); (978-0-7614-7452-4(8)); (978-0-7614-7453-1(6)); (978-0-7614-7454-8(4)); (978-0-7614-7455-5(2))*** Cavendish, Marshall Corp.

O'Daly, Anne, ed. Encyclopedia of Life Sciences, 13 vols. 2nd ed. 2003. (Illus.). 1,800p. 657.07 (978-0-7614-7442-5(0) , Cavendish, Marshall Reference Bks.) Cavendish, Marshall Corp.

Oliver, Narelle. Twilight Hunt. Oliver, Narelle, illus. 2007. (Illus.). 40p. (J). 16.95 ***(978-1-59572-107-5(X))*** Star Bright Bks., Inc.

Oram & McGraw-Hill Staff. Biology: Living Systems. 4th ed. 2002. stu. ed. 91.32 (978-0-07-829731-1(1) , 9780078297311) Glencoe/McGraw-Hill.

Oxlade, C. Illustrated Dictionary of Biology. 2007. 128p. (J). pap. 12.99 (978-0-7945-1559-1(2) , Usborne) EDC Publishing.

Panno, Joseph. The New Biology Set. 2004. (New Biology Ser.). 176-208p. (gr. 6-12). 210.00 (978-0-8160-4945-5(9)) Facts On File, Inc.

Parker, Steve. In Vitro Fertilization. 2006. (Illus.). 64p. (J). lib. bdg. ***(978-0-8368-7866-0(3)*** , World Almanac Library) Stevens, Gareth Inc.

A B

Parker, Victoria. Light. 2006. (Illus.). 24p. (J). (978-1-4034-7886-3(4)); pap. (978-1-4034-7892-4(9)) Steck-Vaughn.

Parks, Deborah. Nature's Machines: The Story of Biomechanist Mimi Koehl. 2006. (Women's Adventures in Science Ser.). (Illus.). 128p. pap. 9.95 (978-0-309-09559-4(X) , Joseph Henry Pr.) National Academies Pr.

Parratore, Phil. Hands-On Life Science. 2001. (Cool, Awesome, Simple Science Ser.). (Illus.). 64p. (J). pap. 9.99 (978-0-88724-650-0(8) , CD-7321) Carson-Dellosa Publishing Co., Inc.

Pascoe, Elaine. Animals Grow New Parts. Kuhn, Dwight, photos by. 2002. (Springboards into Science Ser.). (Illus.). 24p. (J). (gr. 1 up). lib. bdg. 20.67 (978-0-8368-3003-3(2)) Stevens, Gareth Inc.

—Ants. Kuhn, Dwight, photos by. 1998. (Nature Close-Up Ser.). (Illus.). 48p. (J). (gr. 4-8). 23.70 (978-1-56711-183-5(1) , Blackbirch Pr., Inc.) Thomson Gale.

Patent, Dorothy Hinshaw. Biodiversity. Munoz, William, illus. 2003. 112p. (J). (gr. 5). pap. 7.95 (978-0-618-31514-7(4) , Clarion Bks.) Houghton Mifflin Co. Trade & Reference Div.

Petty, Kate. Animal Camouflage & Defense. 2004. (Nature Files Ser.). (Illus.). 32p. (J). (gr. 4-8). 28.00 (978-0-7910-8213-3(X) , Chelsea Hse.) Facts On File, Inc.

Pipe, Jim. Ecosystems. 2004. (Earthwise Ser.). (J). lib. bdg. 27.10 (978-1-932799-50-7(8)) Stargazer Bks.

—Growth & Life Cycles: Tadpole to Frog. 2005. (Illus.). 32p. (J). (gr. 1-4). lib. bdg. 27.10 (978-1-59604-024-3(6)) Stargazer Bks.

Pitts, Kieren. Hitchers & Thieves. 2003. (Parasites & Partners Ser.). (Illus.). 32p. (J). pap. 7.50 (978-1-4109-0356-3(7)); lib. bdg. (978-0-7398-6989-5(2)) Raintree.

—Hitchers & Thieves. 2003. (gr. 5-8). lib. bdg. 15.90 (978-0-613-78249-4(6)) Tandem Library Bks.

Pope, Colleen & Thompson, Simon. Biology VCE, Units 3 & 4. 2002. (Cambridge Wizard Subject Guides). (Illus.). 128p. pap., stu. ed. 8.00 (978-1-876973-10-0(2)) Cambridge Univ. Pr.

¿Por Que la Gente Es Diferente? (Coleccion Primeros Pasos en la Ciencia). (SPA., Illus.). (J). (gr. 1-3). pap. (978-950-724-396-7(8) , LMA8225) Lumen ARG. *Dist:* Lectorum Pubns., Inc.

QEB Start Reading & Talking National Book Stores Edition: Camouflage. 2006. (J). per. (978-1-59566-251-4(0)) QEB Publishing Inc.

Raab & Kiefe, Raab. Exploring Living Systems: Life Science. (YA). (gr. 6-12). 38.95 (978-1-55675-802-7(2)) Globe Fearon Educational Publishing.

Reis, Ronald A. Eugenie Clark: Marine Biologist. 2005. (Ferguson Career Biographies Ser.). (Illus.). 128p. (J). (gr. 6-12). 25.00 (978-0-8160-5883-9(0) , Ferguson Publishing Co.) Facts On File, Inc.

Riley, Peter D. Life on Earth. 2005. (Illus.). 32p. (J). (gr. 4-7). lib. bdg. 27.10 (978-1-58340-714-1(6)) Smart Apple Media.

Ring, Susan. The Sun. 2003. (Yellow Umbrella Books). (Illus.). 16p. (J). (gr. 1). lib. bdg. 14.60 (978-0-7368-2022-6(1) , Pebble Bks.) Capstone Pr., Inc.

—The Sun. 2003. (J). (978-0-7368-1714-1(X)) Yellow Umbrella Pr.

Rittner, Don & McCabe, Timothy Lee. Encyclopedia of Biology. 2004. (Facts on File Science Library). (Illus.). 416p. (gr. 9). 75.00 (978-0-8160-4859-5(2)) Facts On File, Inc.

Roberts, M. B. V. & Ingram, Neil. Biology. 2nd rev. ed. 2001. (Nelson Science Ser.). (Illus.). 344p. (YA). pap., stu. ed. 36.50 (978-0-7487-6238-5(8)) Nelson Thornes Ltd. GBR. *Dist:* Trans-Atlantic Pubns., Inc.

Robinson, Richard, ed. Biology for Students, 4 vols. 2000. (Science Library for Students). (Illus.). 192p. (J). 85.00 (978-0-02-865552-9(4) , Macmillan Reference USA) Thomson Gale.

Rose, Elizabeth. Classification. 2006. (Life Science Library). (Illus.). 24p. (J). 21.25 (978-1-4042-2818-4(7) , PowerKids Pr.) Rosen Publishing Group, Inc., The.

Ross, Michael Elsohn. Re-Cycles. Mooore, Gustav, illus. 2003. 32p. (J). (gr. 2-5). pap. 7.95 (978-0-7613-1949-8(2) , First Avenue Editions) Lerner Publishing Group.

Rouan, Chris. Basic Biology Questions for GCSE. 1998. (Illus.). 278p. (YA). (gr. 9-11). pap. 23.00 (978-0-7487-1726-2(9)) State Mutual Bk. & Periodical Service, Ltd.

Royston, Angela. Looking at Life Cycles: How Do Plants & Animals Change? 2008. (Looking at Science: How Things Change Ser.). 32p. (J). (gr. 1-3). lib. bdg. 22.60 ***(978-0-7660-3091-6(1))*** Enslow Pubs., Inc.

Ryan, Lawrie, et al. Biology. 2003. (Illus.). 80p. pap. (978-0-7487-6799-1(1)) Nelson Thornes Ltd.

Salzmann, Mary Elizabeth. What Has Spots? 2007. (Creature Features Ser.). (ENG., Illus.). 24p. (J). (ps-3). lib. bdg. 24.21 ***(978-1-59928-872-7(9)*** , Super SandCastle) ABDO Publishing Co.

—What Has Stripes? 2007. (Creature Features Ser.). (ENG., Illus.). 24p. (J). (ps-3). lib. bdg. 24.21 ***(978-1-59928-873-4(7)*** , Super SandCastle) ABDO Publishing Co.

Schaffer, Donna. Life Cycles, 6 bks. Incl. Mealworms. lib. bdg. 18.60 (978-0-7368-0209-3(6)); Milkweed Bugs. lib. bdg. 18.60 (978-0-7368-0208-6(8)); Millipedes. lib. bdg. 18.60 (978-0-7368-0210-9(X)); Painted Lady Butterflies. lib. bdg. 18.60 (978-0-7368-0211-6(8)); Pillbugs. lib. bdg. 18.60 (978-0-7368-0212-3(6)); Silkworms. lib. bdg. 18.60 (978-0-7368-0213-0(4)); 24p. (J). (gr. 2-3). 1999. (Illus.). Set lib. bdg. 111.60 (978-0-7368-0298-7(3) , Bridgestone Bks.) Capstone Pr., Inc.

Schulte, Mary Knudson. Classification, 6 bks., Set. Incl. Ants & Other Insects. 19.00 (978-0-516-24935-3(5)); Monkeys & Other Mammals. 19.00 (978-0-516-24933-9(9)); Newts & Other Amphibians. 19.00 (978-0-516-24934-6(7)); Parrots & Other Birds. 19.00 (978-0-516-24931-5(2)); Piranhas & Other Fish. 19.00 (978-0-516-24932-2(0)); Snakes & Other Reptiles. 19.00 (978-0-516-24936-0(3)); (Illus.). 24p. (J). (gr. 1-2). 2005. (Scholastic News Nonfiction Readers Ser.). 2005. 108.00 (978-0-516-25391-6(3) , Children's Pr.) Scholastic Library Publishing.

Schwartz, David M. El Ejote. Kuhn, Dwight, photos by. 2001. (Springboards into Science Ser.). (SPA., Illus.). 24p. (J). (gr. 1 up). lib. bdg. 20.67 (978-0-8368-2995-2(6) , GHS31414) Stevens, Gareth Inc.

Seeger, Laura Vaccaro. First the Egg. 2007. (Illus.). 32p. (J). (ps-1). 14.95 ***(978-1-59643-272-7(1))*** Roaring Brook Pr.

Seidensticker, John & Lumpkin, Susan. Predators/John Saeidensticker & Susan Lumpkin. 2008. (Insiders Ser.). 64p. (J). 16.99 ***(978-1-4169-3863-7(X)*** , Simon & Schuster Children's Publishing) Simon & Schuster Children's Publishing.

Los Seres Vivos. (SPA.). 96p. (YA). (gr. 5-8). 18.36 (978-84-241-1995-9(9)) Everest de Ediciones y Distribucion, S.L. ESP. *Dist:* Lectorum Pubns., Inc.

Shaw, Victoria. Body Talk: A Girl's Guide to What's Happening to Your Body. 1999. (Girls' Guides). (Illus.). 48p. (YA). (gr. 5-8). lib. bdg. 23.95 (978-0-8239-2977-1(9) , GGBOTA) Rosen Publishing Group, Inc., The.

Silverstein, Alvin. Life in a Bucket of Soil. 2000. (gr. 3-6). lib. bdg. 12.95 (978-0-613-88897-4(9)) Tandem Library Bks.

Silverstein, Alvin & Silverstein, Virginia. Life in a Bucket of Soil. 2000. (Illus.). 96p. (J). (gr. 5-8). pap. 5.95 (978-0-486-41057-9(9)) Dover Pubns., Inc.

Silverstein, Alvin & Silverstein, Virginia B. A World in a Drop of Water: Exploring with a Microscope. 1998. (Illus.). 64p. (J). (gr. 5-8). pap. 4.95 (978-0-486-40381-6(5) , 40381-5) Dover Pubns., Inc.

Silverstein, Alvin, et al. Growth & Development. 2007. (Science Concepts, Second Ser.). (Illus.). 112p. (YA). (gr. 6-8). lib. bdg. 31.93 ***(978-0-8225-6057-9(7)*** , Twenty-First Century Bks.) Lerner Publishing Group.

Silverstein, Alvin, et al. Symbiosis. 1998. (Science Concepts Ser.). (Illus.). 64p. (gr. 5-8). lib. bdg. 26.90 (978-0-7613-3001-1(1) , Twenty-First Century Bks.) Lerner Publishing Group.

Sklavos, Shirley J. Biology Topics. 2000. 132p. (YA). per. 29.95 (978-0-9718117-0-6(9)) Science Topics LLC.

Slade, Suzanne. The Elements Common to Most Living Organisms. 2007. (Library of Physical Sciences). (J). (978-1-4042-2361-5(4)); (Illus.). 24p. pap. (978-1-4042-2171-0(9)); (Illus.). 24p. lib. bdg. (978-1-4042-3424-6(1)) Rosen Publishing Group, Inc., The. (PowerKids Pr.).

Snedden, Robert. Who Eats Who in City Habitats? 2006. (Food Chains in Action Ser.). (Illus.). 32p. (J). (978-1-58340-965-7(3) , 1262626) Smart Apple Media.

Spilsbury, Louise & Spilsbury, Richard. Classification: From Mammals to Fungi. 2004. (Science Answers Ser.). (Illus.). 32p. (J). pap. 7.50 (978-1-4034-5509-3(0)); lib. bdg. 24.22 (978-1-4034-4763-0(2)) Heinemann Library.

Spilsbury, Louise, et al. Classifying Living Things, 6 bks., Set. 2003. (Illus.). (J). (gr. 3-5). lib. bdg. 145.32 (978-1-4034-0850-1(5)) Heinemann Library.

Sponges & Other Minor Phyla. 2004. pap. 51.30 (978-1-4109-1357-9(0)) Harcourt Schl. Pubs.

Spyglass Books-Life Science Complete Set. (Spyglass Books-Life Science Ser.). (gr. 1-2). 458.39 (978-0-7565-0800-5(2)) Compass Point Bks.

Squishy, Squashy Sponges: Early Childhood Guide for Teachers. 2003. (J). 16.95 (978-1-883822-36-1(X)) Terrific Science Pr.

Steck-Vaughn Staff. Science: Life Science. 2002. (Illus.). (J). pap. (978-0-7398-5424-2(0)) Steck-Vaughn.

Stephens, Catherine. Classification Clues. 2004. (National Geographic Reading Expeditions Ser.). (Illus.). 32p. (J). pap. (978-0-7922-4576-6(8)) National Geographic Society.

—Life Cycles. 2004. (National Geographic Reading Expeditions Ser.). (Illus.). 32p. (J). pap. (978-0-7922-4579-7(2)) National Geographic Society.

Stewart, Melissa. Classification of Life. 2007. (J). lib. bdg. ***(978-0-8225-6604-5(4))*** Twenty First Century Bks.

Stockland, Patricia M. Stripes, Spots or Diamonds: A Book about Animal Patterns. Ouren, Todd, illus. 2005. (Animal Wise Ser.). 24p. (C). (gr. k-2). 22.60 (978-1-4048-0934-5(1)) Picture Window Bks.

Stockley, Corinne. Dictionary of Biology. 1999. (Usborne Illustrated Dictionaries Ser.). (Illus.). 128p. (J). (gr. 7-11). lib. bdg. 18.95 (978-0-88110-229-1(6)) EDC Publishing.

Stone, Lynn M. Camouflage & Disguise. 2007. (Illus.). 24p. (J). (978-1-60044-170-7(X)) Rourke Publishing, LLC.

Stonehouse, Bernard. Camouflage. Francis, John, illus. 1999. (J). (978-0-439-09591-4(3)) Scholastic, Inc.

Strauss, Eric & Lisowski, Marylin. Biology: The Web of Life. 1999. (YA). (gr. 6-9). tchr. ed. (978-0-201-33441-8(0)) Addison-Wesley Longman, Inc.

Strauss, Rochelle. Tree of Life: The Incredible Biodiversity of Life on Earth. Thompson, Margot, illus. 2005. 40p. (YA). (gr. 3 up). (978-1-55337-669-9(2)) Kids Can Pr., Ltd.

Thain, Michael. The Penguin Dictionary of Biology. 2001. (Illus.). (J). (978-0-606-20848-2(8)) Tandem Library Bks.

Tildes, Phyllis L. Animals in Camouflage. 2000. (gr. k-3). lib. bdg. 15.25 (978-0-613-28275-8(2)) Tandem Library Bks.

Tocci, Salvatore. High-Tech Ids: From Finger Scans to Voice Patterns. 2000. (978-0-606-19784-7(2)) Tandem Library Bks.

Toole, Glenn & Toole, Susan. New Understanding Biology for Advanced Level. 4th ed. 1999. (Illus.). 704p. (YA). (gr. 11). pap. 79.50 (978-0-7487-3957-8(2)) Nelson Thornes Ltd. GBR. *Dist:* Trans-Atlantic Pubns., Inc.

Towle. Modern Biology: Enhanced Online Edition. 2nd ed. 2002. 76.66 (978-0-03-072487-9(2)) Holt, Rinehart & Winston.

Townsend, John. Bizarre Biology. 2006. (Illus.). 56p. (J). (978-1-4109-2376-9(2)); pap. (978-1-4109-2381-3(9)) Steck-Vaughn.

University Of Leeds, prod. Life Cycles. (Life Cycles Ser.). (YA). cd-rom 99.95 (978-0-7365-0887-2(2)) Films Media Group.

VanCleave, Janice Pratt. Janice VanCleave's Science Around the World: Activities on Biomes from Pole to Pole. 2004. (Illus.). 128p. pap. 14.95 (978-0-471-20547-0(8) , Wiley) Wiley, John & Sons, Inc.

Vriesenga, Daryl. Life Sciences. 1999. (100+ Seriestm Ser.). 128p. (J). (gr. 5-8). pap. 12.99 (978-0-88012-828-5(3) , IF8756) School Specialty Publishing.

The Wacky Words of Biology. 2002. 49p. (YA). 7.95 (978-0-9703694-5-1(X)) Awesome Guides, Inc.

Wadsworth, Pamela. Pethau Byw Ar Waith. 2005. (WEL., Illus.). 24p. pap. (978-1-85596-233-0(0)) Dref Wen.

Wallace, Holly. Classification. (Life Processes Ser.). 32p. pap. 7.50 (978-1-4034-4073-0(5)); 2006. (Illus.). (J). (gr. 4-7). lib. bdg. 20.50 ***(978-1-4034-8845-9(2));*** 2000. (Illus.). (J). (gr. 4-6). lib. bdg. 21.36 (978-1-57572-337-2(9)) Heinemann Library.

Wallace, Holly. Life Cycles. (Life Processes Ser.). 32p. pap. 7.50 (978-1-4034-4075-4(1)); 2006. (Illus.). (J). ***(978-1-4034-8847-3(9));*** 2000. (Illus.). (J). (gr. 4-6). lib. bdg. 21.36 (978-1-57572-339-6(5)) Heinemann Library.

Weber, Belinda. I Wonder Why Caterpillars Eat So Much & Other Questions about Life Cycles. 2006. (I Wonder Why Ser.). (Illus.). 32p. (J). (gr. k-3). 12.95 (978-0-7534-6030-6(0) , Kingfisher) Houghton Mifflin Co. Trade & Reference Div.

Weigel, Marlene. UXL Encyclopedia of Biomes, 3 vols. Carnagie, Julie L., ed. 1999. (Illus.). (J). (978-0-7876-3734-7(3)) Thomson Gale.

Whitehouse, Patricia. Hiding in a Coral Reef. 2003. (Illus.). 32p. pap. 6.50 (978-1-4034-3185-1(X)); (J). lib. bdg. 22.79 (978-1-4034-0795-9(5)) Heinemann Library.

—Hiding in a Desert. 2003. (Animal Camouflage Ser.). (Illus.). 32p. (J). lib. bdg. 22.79 (978-1-4034-0796-2(7)) Heinemann Library.

—Hiding in a Forest. 2003. (Illus.). 32p. pap. 6.50 (978-1-4034-3187-5(6)); (J). lib. bdg. 22.79 (978-1-4034-0797-9(5)) Heinemann Library.

—Hiding in a Rain Forest. 2003. (Illus.). 32p. pap. 6.50 (978-1-4034-3188-2(4)); (J). lib. bdg. 22.79 (978-1-4034-0799-3(1)) Heinemann Library.

—Hiding in the Ocean. 2003. (Illus.). 32p. pap. 6.50 (978-1-4034-3189-9(2)); (J). lib. bdg. 22.79 (978-1-4034-0798-6(3)) Heinemann Library.

Wile, Jay L. & Durnell, Marilyn F. Exploring Creation with Biology, 2 Bks., Set. 2nd ed. 2005. 85.00 (978-1-932012-57-6(5)) Apologia Educational Ministries, Inc.

Williams, Gareth. Advanced Biology for You. 2000. (Illus.). 464p. (YA). (gr. 11 up). pap. 62.50 (978-0-7487-5298-0(6)) Nelson Thornes Ltd. GBR. *Dist:* Trans-Atlantic Pubns., Inc.

—Biology for You. 1998. (Illus.). 352p. pap., stu. ed. 40.50 (978-0-7487-2366-9(8)) State Mutual Bk. & Periodical Service, Ltd.

Williams, Gareth & Paul, Nick. Biology for You. 2nd rev. ed. 2002. (Illus.). 400p. pap., pupil's gde. ed. 36.50 (978-0-7487-6232-3(9)) Nelson Thornes Ltd. GBR. *Dist:* Trans-Atlantic Pubns., Inc.

Winner, Cherie. Cryobiology. 2006. (Cool Science Ser.). (Illus.). 48p. (J). (gr. 4-8). lib. bdg. 26.60 (978-0-8225-2907-1(6) , Lerner Pubns.) Lerner Publishing Group.

Wohlrabe, Sarah C. Whose Spots Are These? A Look at Animal Markings - Round, Bright, & Big. Alderman, Derrick & Shea, Denise, illus. 2004. (Whose Is It? Ser.). 24p. (C). (gr. k-2). 22.60 (978-1-4048-0611-5(3)) Picture Window Bks.

Woodward, John. Clever Camouflage. (Amazing Nature Ser.). (Illus.). 32p. (J). (ps-7). 2005. pap. 7.50 (978-1-4034-5399-0(3)); 2003. lib. bdg. (978-1-4034-4703-6(9)) Heinemann Library.

—Disguises. 2005. (Planet's Most Extreme Ser.). (Illus.). 48p. (J). (gr. 3-7). 24.95 (978-1-4103-0393-6(4) , Blackbirch Pr., Inc.) Thomson Gale.

BIOLOGY—ECOLOGY

see Ecology

BIOLOGY, ECONOMIC

see Botany, Economic; Zoology, Economic

BIOLOGY—EXPERIMENTS

Bottone, Frank G., Jr. The Science of Life: Projects & Principles for Beginning Biologists. 2001. (Illus.). 144p. (J). (gr. 4 up). pap. 14.95 (978-1-55652-382-3(3)) Chicago Review Pr., Inc.

Branzei, Sylvia. Hands on Grossology: Really Gross Science Experiments. Keely, Jack, illus. 2003. (Grossology Ser.). 80p. (J). (gr. 3-8). mass mkt. 6.99 (978-0-8431-0305-2(1) , Price Stern Sloan) Penguin Group (USA) Inc.

Gardner, Robert. Genetics & Evolution Science Fair Projects: Using Skeletons, Cereal, Earthworms, & More. 2005. (Biology! Best Science Projects Ser.). (Illus.). 128p. (J). (gr. 6-13). lib. bdg. 26.60 (978-0-7660-1175-5(5)) Enslow Pubs., Inc.

—Health Science Projects about Anatomy & Physiology. 2001. (Science Projects Ser.). (Illus.). 128p. (YA). (gr. 6-12). lib. bdg. 26.60 (978-0-7660-1440-4(1)) Enslow Pubs., Inc.

—Health Science Projects about Heredity. 2001. (Science Projects Ser.). (Illus.). 128p. (YA). (gr. 6-12). lib. bdg. 26.60 (978-0-7660-1438-1(X)) Enslow Pubs., Inc.

—Health Science Projects about Your Senses. 2001. (Science Projects Ser.). (Illus.). 112p. (YA). (gr. 6-12). lib. bdg. 26.60 (978-0-7660-1437-4(1)) Enslow Pubs., Inc.

Griffith, Dave. Biology. 1999. pap., tchr. ed. 40.00 (978-1-886998-04-9(3)) Pasco Scientific.

Holt, Rinehart and Winston Staff. Biology: Practice & Experimental Labs. 4th ed. 2003. (Illus.). pap., lab manual ed. 17.20 (978-0-03-074078-7(X)) Holt, Rinehart & Winston.

—Biology: Quick Data & Math. 4th ed. 2003. (Illus.). pap., lab manual ed. 17.20 (978-0-03-074079-4(7)) Holt, Rinehart & Winston.

Loeschnig, L. V. Experimentos Sencillos de Geologia y Biologia. 2004. (Juego de la Ciencia Ser.). (SPA.). 128p. (gr. 5-8). 9.99 (978-84-95456-60-1(5) , 87804) Ediciones Oniro S.A. ESP. *Dist:* Bilingual Pubns. Co., The, Lectorum Pubns., Inc., Libros Sin Fronteras.

McGraw-Hill Staff. Glencoe Science: Human Body Systems. 2004. pap., stu. ed., lab manual ed. 8.64 (978-0-07-866997-2(9) , 9780078669972) Glencoe/McGraw-Hill.

Pascoe, Elaine. Ants. Kuhn, Dwight, photos by. 1998. (Nature Close-Up Ser.). (Illus.). 48p. (J). (gr. 4-8). 23.70 (978-1-56711-183-5(1) , Blackbirch Pr., Inc.) Thomson Gale.

Scientific American Editors. Scientific American the Amateur Biologist. Carlson, Shawn, ed. 2002. (Illus.). 240p. pap. 16.95 (978-0-471-38281-2(7) , Wiley) Wiley, John & Sons, Inc.

Stein, Sara. The Evolution Book. Stein, Sara, illus. 1999. (Illus.). 400p. (YA). (gr. 7-12). pap. 12.95 (978-0-89480-927-9(X) , 927) Workman Publishing Co., Inc.

Tocci, Salvatore. Biology Projects for Young Scientists. 2nd rev. ed. 2000. (Projects for Young Scientists Ser.). (Illus.). 143p. (YA). (gr. 9-12). pap. 6.95 (978-0-531-16460-0(8) , Watts, Franklin) Scholastic Library Publishing.

—Biology Projects for Young Scientists. 1999. (J). (978-0-606-19402-0(9)) Tandem Library Bks.

VanCleave, Janice Pratt. Janice VanCleave's Microscopes & Magnifying Lenses: Mind-Boggling Chemistry & Biology Experiments You Can Turn into Science Fair Projects. 2002. (Janice Vancleave Ser.). (Illus.). (J). 19.72 (978-0-7587-4631-3(8)) Book Wholesalers, Inc.

BIOLOGY—HISTORY

Haugen & Peter. Biology. 2007. (Twentieth-Century Science Ser.). 368p. (J). (gr. 6-12). 49.50 (978-0-8160-5530-2(0)) Facts On File, Inc.

Yount, Lisa. Antoni van Leeuwenhoek: First to See Microscopic Life. 2001. (Great Minds of Science Ser.). (Illus.). 128p. (YA). (gr. 4-10). pap. 13.26 (978-0-7660-1866-2(0)) Enslow Pubs., Inc.

BIOLOGY, MARINE

see Marine Biology

BIOLOGY, MOLECULAR

see Molecular Biology

BIOLOGY—PERIODICITY

Thornhill, Jan. I Found a Dead Bird: The Kids' Guide to the Cycle of Life & Death. 2006. (Illus.). 64p. 21.95 (978-1-897066-70-6(8)) Maple Tree Pr. CAN. *Dist:* Perseus Distribution.

BIOLOGY—STUDY AND TEACHING

Holt, Rinehart and Winston Staff. Biology Study Guide. 4th ed. 2004. (Illus.). pap., stu. ed. 19.80 (978-0-03-069982-5(7)) Holt, Rinehart & Winston.

King, Tim & Reiss, Michael. Practical Advanced Biology. 2nd ed. 2001. (Illus.). 336p. (YA). pap. 43.50 (978-0-17-448308-3(2)) Nelson Thornes Ltd. GBR. *Dist:* Trans-Atlantic Pubns., Inc.

Roza, Greg. Looking at the Differences Between Living & Nonliving Things with Graphic Organizers. 2005. (Using Graphic Organizers to Study the Living Environment Ser.). (Illus.). 48p. (J). (978-1-4042-0611-3(6)) Rosen Publishing Group, Inc., The.

BIOLOGY—VOCATIONAL GUIDANCE

McAlary, Florence & Cohen, Judith Love. You Can Be a Woman Marine Biologist. Wheeler, Janice, ed. Katz, David Arthur, illus. 2001. 40p. (J). 13.95 (978-1-880599-54-9(6)) Cascade Pass, Inc.

—You Can Be a Woman Marine Biologist. Katz, David Arthur, illus. 2001. 40p. (J). pap. 7.00 (978-1-880599-53-2(8)) Cascade Pass, Inc.

BIOLUMINESCENCE

Batten, Mary. Winking, Blinking Sea. 2000. (gr. 3-6). lib. bdg. 16.40 (978-0-613-44373-9(X)) Tandem Library Bks.

Collard, Sneed B., III. In the Deep Sea. 2005. (Science Adventures Ser.). (Illus.). 44p. (J). (gr. 3-7). lib. bdg. 25.64 (978-0-7614-1952-5(7) , Benchmark Bks.) Cavendish, Marshall Corp.

Hirschmann, Kris. Creatures That Glow. 2005. (Creatures of the Sea Ser.). (Illus.). 48p. (J). (gr. 4-8). 26.20 (978-0-7377-2340-3(8) , Greenhaven Pr., Inc.) Thomson Gale.

Widder, Edith. The Bioluminescence Coloring Book. Baker, Charissa, illus. 2nd rev. l.t. ed. 2002. 25p. (J). 19.95 (978-0-9659686-6-9(9)) Harbor Branch Oceanographic Institution, Inc.

BIONICS

see also Artificial Intelligence

Cobb, Allan B. The Bionic Human. 2005. (Library of Future Medicine). (Illus.). 64p. (YA). (gr. 7-12). lib. bdg. 26.50 (978-0-8239-3670-0(8)) Rosen Publishing Group, Inc., The.

Jango-Cohen, Judith. Bionics. 2007. (Cool Science Ser.). (Illus.). 48p. (J). (gr. 4-8). lib. bdg. 26.60 (978-0-8225-5937-5(4) , Lerner Pubns.) Lerner Publishing Group.

Kroll, Mary, et al. Fields of Genes: Making Sense of Biotechnology in Agriculture. Hoff, Mary, ed. Morales, Elizabeth, illus. 1999. 96p. (YA). pap. 30.00 (978-0-7881-7569-5(6)) DIANE Publishing Co.

Rainis, Kenneth G. & Nassis, George. Biotechnology Projects for Young Scientists. 1998. (Projects for Young Scientists Ser.). (Illus.). 160p. (J). (gr. 9-12). 25.00 (978-0-531-11419-3(8) , Watts, Franklin) Scholastic Library Publishing.

Rosaler, Maxine. Bionics. 2003. (Science on the Edge Ser.). (Illus.). 48p. (J). 24.95 (978-1-56711-784-4(8) , Blackbirch Pr., Inc.) Thomson Gale.

Tant, Carl. Awesome Oceans: Advances in Marine Biotechnology. Crask, Tammy, illus. 1998. (Awesome Science of Biology Ser.). (Orig.). (YA). (gr. 9-12). pap. 18.95 (978-1-880319-15-4(2)) Biotech Publishing.

BIOTECHNOLOGY

see also Genetic Engineering

Bio Related Technology. 4th rev. ed. 2004. 48p. stu. ed., wbk. ed. (978-0-86657-509-6(X)) Lab-Volt Systems, Inc.

Bio Related Technology TCG. 5th rev. ed. 2004. 75p. pap. (978-0-86657-508-9(1)) Lab-Volt Systems, Inc.

Creative Media Applications Staff. A Student Guides to Biotechnology: Debatable Issues, 4 vols., Vol. IV. 2002. (Illus.). (J). (978-0-313-32260-0(0)) Greenwood Publishing Group, Inc.

—A Student Guides to Biotechnology: Important People in Biotechnology, 4 vols., Vol. 2. 2002. (Illus.). (J). (978-0-313-32258-7(9)) Greenwood Publishing Group, Inc.

—A Student Guides to Biotechnology: The History of Biotechnology, 4 vols., Vol. 3. 2002. (Illus.). (J). (978-0-313-32259-4(7)) Greenwood Publishing Group, Inc.

—A Student Guides to Biotechnology: Words & Terms, 4 vols., Vol. 1. 2002. (Illus.). (J). (978-0-313-32257-0(0)) Greenwood Publishing Group, Inc.

—A Student's Guide to Biotechnology: The History of Biotechnology, 4 vols. 2002. (Illus.). 576p. (gr. 6-8). 167.95 (978-0-313-32256-3(2) , MS2256, Middle School Reference) Greenwood Publishing Group, Inc.

Eskeland, N. Lucia & Bailey, N. Celeste. My Name Is Gene. 2nd l.t. ed. 2002. 110p. (J). per. 19.95 (978-0-9673811-5-2(0)) Science2Discover, Inc.

Fridell, Ron. Genetic Engineering. 2006. (Cool Science Ser.). (Illus.). 48p. (J). (gr. 4-8). lib. bdg. 26.60 (978-0-8225-2633-9(6) , Lerner Pubns.) Lerner Publishing Group.

Hall, Linley Erin. Careers in Biotechnology. 2006. (Cutting Edge Careers Ser.). (Illus.). 64p. (J). (gr. 7-12). lib. bdg. 27.95 (978-1-4042-0954-1(9) , 1267025) Rosen Publishing Group, Inc., The.

Hopkins, William G. Plant Biotechnology. 2006. (Green World Ser.). (Illus.). 152p. (J). (gr. 6-12). 37.50 (978-0-7910-8964-4(9) , Chelsea Hse.) Facts On File, Inc.

Jefferis, David. BioTech: Frontiers of Medicine. 2002. (Megatech Ser.). (Illus.). 32p. (J). (gr. 4-5). pap. (978-0-7787-0061-6(5)); lib. bdg. (978-0-7787-0051-7(8)) Crabtree Publishing Co.

—Biotech: Frontiers of Medicine. 2002. (gr. 3-6). lib. bdg. 17.60 (978-0-613-52937-2(5)) Tandem Library Bks.

Lerner, K. Lee & Lerner, Brenda Wilmoth. Biotechnology: Changing Life Through Science. 2007. (J). (**978-1-4144-0154-6(X)) Thomson Gale.

McGraw-Hill Staff. Bdol, Biotechnology & Forensic Lab Manual. 2003. (gr. 6-12). pap., stu. ed., lab manual ed. 17.32 (978-0-07-860224-5(6) , 9780078602245) Glencoe/McGraw-Hill.

Seiple, Todd & Seiple, Samantha. Mutants, Clones, & Killer Corn: Unlocking the Secrets of Biotechnology. 2005. (Discovery! Ser.). (Illus.). 112p. (J). (gr. 6-12). lib. bdg. 29.27 (978-0-8225-4860-7(7)) Lerner Publishing Group.

Ternay, Andrew. The Language of Nightmares. 2003. per. 15.95 (978-0-9619806-4-1(8)) Simpler Life Pr.

BIPLANES

see Airplanes

BIRD HOUSES

see Birdhouses

BIRD SONG

Berkes, Marianne. Marsh Morning. Noreika, Robert, illus. 2003. 32p. lib. bdg. 22.90 (978-0-7613-2568-0(9)); (J). 14.95 (978-0-7613-1936-8(0)) Lerner Publishing Group. (Millbrook Pr.).

de Guilbert, Francoise. Sing, Nightingale, Sing! A Book & CD for Discovering the Birds of the World. Miyamoto, Chiaki, illus. 2006. 48p. (J). pap. 13.95 incl. cd-rom (978-1-929132-98-0(0)) Kane/Miller Bk. Pubs., Inc.

Johnson, Sylvia A. Songbirds: The Language of Song. 2000. (Nature Watch Ser.). (Illus.). 48p. (J). (gr. 3-6). lib. bdg. 25.26 (978-1-57505-483-4(3) , Carolrhoda Bks.) Lerner Publishing Group.

BIRD WATCHING

see Birds

BIRDHOUSES

Haus, Robyn. Make Your Own Birdhouses & Feeders. Jaskiel, Stan, illus. 2001. (Quick Starts for Kids! Ser.). 64p. (J). (gr. 3 up). pap. 8.95 (978-1-885593-55-9(4) , Williamson Bks.) Ideals Pubns.

Schwarz, Renee. Birdhouses. 2005. (Kids Can Do It Ser.). (Illus.). 40p. (YA). (gr. 3 up). (978-1-55337-550-0(5)); (978-1-55337-549-4(1)) Kids Can Pr., Ltd.

Weinberger, Kimberly. Home Depot Build-Your-Own Birdhouse 1-2-3. Miller, Edward, illus. 2001. (Home Depot Ser.). 32p. (J). (ps-1). pap. 3.50 (978-0-439-29499-7(1) , Cartwheel Bks.) Scholastic, Inc.

BIRDHOUSES—FICTION

Cole, Joanna. Files from the Nest. Bracken, Carolyn, illus. 2005. 32p. (J). (ps-3). lib. bdg. 11.19 (978-0-606-33806-6(3)) Tandem Library Bks.

Sturges, Philemon. I Love Tools! Halpern, Shari, illus. 2006. 32p. (J). 12.99 (978-0-06-009287-0(4)); lib. bdg. 14.89 (978-0-06-009288-7(2)) HarperCollins Pubs.

BIRDS

see also Birds of Prey; State Birds; Water Birds

AA. Delux Garden Birds Kit. 2004. (Illus.). 64p. pap. 30.00 (978-0-7495-4179-8(2)) Automobile Assn. GBR. *Dist:* Independent Pubs. Group.

Aigner-Clark, Julie. Aves. 2004. (Baby Einstein Ser.).Tr. of Birds. (SPA., Illus.). 20p. (J). bds. 3.95 (978-970-718-154-0(0) , Silver Dolphin en Español) Advanced Marketing, S. de R. L. de C. V. MEX. *Dist:* Perseus Distribution.

Alden, Peter C. Birds. Sill, John, illus. 2003. (Peterson Field Guide Coloring Bks.). 64p. pap. 7.95 (978-0-618-30722-7(2)) Houghton Mifflin Co. Trade & Reference Div.

Alderton, David. Los Pajaros Domésticos: Preguntas y Respuestas. 2002. (SPA., Illus.). 216p. 19.95 (978-84-662-0361-6(3) , LA13803) Libsa, Editorial S.A. ESP. *Dist:* Lectorum Pubns., Inc.

—Spotting Birds in Britain & Europe. 2005. (Illus.). 96p. 10.99 (978-0-7548-1371-2(1) , Lorenz Bks.) Anness Publishing GBR. *Dist:* National Bk. Network.

Alexander, Florence & Alexander, Stanley. Come with Me & See... Birds of the World. l.t. ed. 2003. (Illus.). 32p. (J). 7.99 net. (978-0-915960-95-8(8)) Ebon Research Systems Publishing, LLC.

All about Birds, 6 vols., set. 2002. (Zoobooks). (Illus.). (J). (gr. k-7). pap. 14.85 (978-1-888153-69-9(5)) Wildlife Education, Ltd.

Allen, Francine. Caillou Goes Birdwatching. Lapierre, Claude, illus. rev. ed. 2007. (Lift-the-Flap Book Ser.). 20p. (J). pap. 5.95 (*978-2-89450-611-0(2)) Chouette Publishing CAN. *Dist:* Independent Pubs. Group.

American Education Publishing Staff & School Specialty Publishing Staff. Birds. 2001. (Brighter Child Fact Card Ser.). (Illus.). 54p. (J). (gr. 3-5). 2.99 (978-1-56189-688-2(8) , 31384, American Education Publishing) School Specialty Publishing.

Anderson, Ashley & Shriver, Chelsea. Flamingo Grows Up. 2005. (Let's Go to the Zoo! Ser.). (Illus.). 16p. (J). (ps). bds. 5.95 (978-1-56899-974-6(7) , B9009) Soundprints.

Anderson, Bendix. Birds of Prey Know It Alls. 2001. (Illus.). 24p. (J). pap. 2.79 (978-0-7681-0232-1(4) , 57093) Learning Horizons, Inc.

Arjas, Pirkko & Butcher, Sally K., illus. Friend Owl: A Children's Book. 1000th ed. 2005. 48p. (J). 18.00 (978-0-9762132-0-8(6)) Old Bess Publishing Co.

Armstrong, Jennifer. Audubon: Painter of Birds in the Wild Frontier. Smith, Joseph A., illus. 2003. 40p. (J). (gr. k-4). 17.95 (978-0-8109-4238-7(0)) Abrams, Harry N. , Inc.

Arnosky, Jim. Watching Water Birds. Arnosky, Jim, illus. 2002. (Illus.). 32p. (J). (gr. 4-7). pap. 7.95 (978-0-7922-6739-3(7) , National Geographic Children's Bks.) National Geographic Society.

Aubinais, Marie. Birds. Martin, Jean-Francois, illus. 1998. (Big, Bigger, Biggest Ser.). 32p. (J). 16.95 (978-0-7892-0387-8(1) , Abbeville Kids) Abbeville Pr., Inc.

Automobile Association (Great Britain) Staff. AA Garden Birds Guide. 2005. (Illus.). 60p. 11.00 (978-0-7495-4535-2(6)) Automobile Assn. GBR. *Dist:* Independent Pubs. Group.

—AA the Garden Bird Kit. 2005. (Illus.). n/ap. 25.00 (978-0-7495-4178-1(4)) Automobile Assn. GBR. *Dist:* Trafalgar Square Publishing.

Babcock, Charles A. Bird Day How to Prepare for It. 2004. reprint ed. pap. 15.95 (978-1-4179-1820-1(9)) Kessinger Publishing, LLC.

Baby Birds, Vol. 3. 2005. (Animals, Animals, Animals Ser.). (YA). (gr. k-3). (978-0-7368-8193-7(X) , Pebble Bks.) Capstone Pr., Inc.

Baby Birds, 6 vols. (gr. k-2). 28.95 (978-0-7368-8233-0(2)) Red Brick Learning.

Backyard Birds. 36p. (J). (gr. 1-5). pap. (978-1-882210-05-3(0)) Action Publishing, Inc.

Barlowe, Dot. Birds to Paint or Color. 2006. 48p. (J). pap. 4.95 (978-0-486-45171-8(2)) Dover Pubns., Inc.

—Seashore Birds. 2003. (Dover Little Activity Bks.). (Illus.). 4p. (J). (ps-5). pap. 1.50 (978-0-486-43005-8(7)) Dover Pubns., Inc.

Barlowe, Sy. Learning about Shore Birds. 2002. (Learning about Ser.). (Illus.). 16p. (J). (gr. 3-5). pap. 1.50 (978-0-486-42056-1(6)) Dover Pubns., Inc.

Barnard, Edward S. Birds. 2007. (J). (*978-1-59939-131-1(7) , Reader's Digest Young Families, Inc.) Reader's Digest Children's Publishing, Inc.

Bauld, Jane Scoggins & Waldrip, Gayle. Feathered Friends of Texas. 2003. (J). pap. 7.95 (978-1-57168-771-5(8) , Eakin Pr.) Eakin Pr.

Berger, Melvin & Berger, Gilda. Egg to Robin. 2004. (Illus.). (J). (978-0-439-57485-3(4)) Scholastic, Inc.

BHB International Staff. Birds. 1998. (Our Animal World in Pictures Ser.). (J). (978-2-215-06158-8(8)) Editions Fleurus.

A Bird Can Fly. (Lexile Levels Ser.). 7.98 (978-1-56334-685-9(0)) Hampton-Brown Bks.

Bird Families, 6 vols. (gr. k-2). 28.95 (978-0-7368-8235-4(9)) Red Brick Learning.

A Bird for You. (Pet Care Ser.). 24p. (J). 7.95 (978-1-4048-0390-9(4)) Picture Window Bks.

The Bird Lady, 6 Pack. (Story Steps Ser.). (gr. k-2). 32.00 (978-0-7635-9849-5(6)) Rigby Education.

Bird Talk. 2005. (Book Treks Ser.). (J). (gr. 3 up). stu. ed. 34.95 (978-0-673-62846-6(9)) Celebration Pr.

Bird-Watcher: Level O, 6 vols. (Wonder Worldtm Ser.). 48p. 39.95 (978-0-7802-2946-4(0)) Wright Group, The.

Bird Watchers: Level L, 6 vols. 128p. (gr. 2-3). 40.50 (978-0-7699-1031-4(9)) Shortland Pubns. (U. S. A.) Inc.

Birds. (All about Pets Ser.). 24p. (J). 5.95 (978-0-7368-8782-3(2)) Capstone Pr., Inc.

Birds. (Nature's Friends Ser.). 32p. (J). 7.95 (978-0-7565-1226-2(3)) Compass Point Bks.

Birds, 6 Pack. (Rigby Focus Ser.). 16p. (gr. k up). 28.00 (978-0-7578-5512-2(1)) Rigby Education.

Birds: Individual Title Six-Packs. (Rigby Focus Ser.). 16p. (gr. k up). 26.00 (978-0-7578-5278-7(5)) Rigby Education.

Birds & Fish. 2001. 63p. (YA). 8.65 (978-0-7525-4877-7(8)) Parragon, Inc.

Birds & Reptiles Action Sticker Book. 2002. 12p. (J). pap. 3.98 (978-0-7525-8034-0(5)) Parragon, Inc.

A Birds Eye View, 6 vols., Pack. (Sails Literacy Ser.). (gr. 1-2). 36.00 (978-0-7578-6774-3(X)) Rigby Education.

Birds of North America. 2003. (Smithsonian Kids Field Guides Ser.). 240p. (J). pap. 14.95 (978-0-7894-8852-7(3)) Dorling Kindersley Publishing, Inc.

Birds of Prey & Other Feathered Friends. 2002. (Wild, Wild World Ser.). 32p. (J). 9.95 (978-0-7525-4685-8(6)) Parragon, Inc.

Birds of the Great Lakes. 2001. (Smithsonian Handbooks Ser.). 368p. (YA). pap. 19.95 (978-0-7894-8401-7(3)) Dorling Kindersley Publishing, Inc.

Birds of the Great Plains. 2001. (Smithsonian Handbooks Ser.). 384p. (YA). pap. 19.95 (978-0-7894-8402-4(1)) Dorling Kindersley Publishing, Inc.

Birds of the Northwest & Alaska. 2001. (Smithsonian Handbooks Ser.). 464p. (YA). pap. 19.95 (978-0-7894-8403-1(X)) Dorling Kindersley Publishing, Inc.

Birds of the Rockies. 2002. (Smithsonian Handbooks Ser.). 384p. (YA). pap. 19.95 (978-0-7894-8429-1(3)) Dorling Kindersley Publishing, Inc.

Birds of the San Bernardino Mountains: A Walking & Watching Guide to 90 of the Mountain's Most Popular Birds. 2001. (Illus.). 110p. 14.95 (978-0-9748702-0-5(X)) AKB Design.

Birds Set. (gr. k-2). 114.95 (978-0-7368-9043-4(2)) Red Brick Learning.

Birkhozz, Sonia. How Do I Get My Feathers? 2004. pap. 16.95 (978-0-533-14681-9(X)) Vantage Pr., Inc.

Bishop, Nic. Digging for Bird Dinosaurs: An Expedition to Madagascar. 2000. (Scientists in the Field Ser.). (Illus.). 48p. (J). (gr. 4-6). tchr. ed. 16.00 (978-0-395-96056-1(8)) Houghton Mifflin Co. Trade & Reference Div.

Black, Ted, et al. Birds of Michigan. rev. ed. 2003. (Illus.). 360p. (J). (gr. 4). pap. 19.95 (978-1-55105-336-3(5)) Lone Pine Publishing USA.

Blackaby, Susan. A Bird for You: Caring for Your Bird. DeLage, Charlene, illus. 2004. (Pet Care Ser.). 24p. (C). (gr. k-3). 22.60 (978-1-4048-0117-2(0)) Picture Window Bks.

Blanchan, Neltje. Birds Every Child Should Know. Stetter, Christine, illus. 2000. 348p. (gr. 4-7). reprint ed. (J). 34.95 (978-0-87745-716-9(6)); pap. 16.95 (978-0-87745-705-3(0)) Univ. of Iowa Pr.

Blanchan, Neltje. Birds That Every Child Should Know. 2006. pap. 31.95 (*978-1-4286-2047-6(8)) Kessinger Publishing, LLC.

Bozzo, Linda. Amazing Beaks. 2008. (J). lib. bdg. (*978-1-4042-4169-5(8) , PowerKids Pr.) Rosen Publishing Group, Inc., The.

Bozzo, Linda. My First Bird. 2007. (My First Pet Library from the American Humane Association Ser.). (Illus.). 32p. (J). (gr. 1-3). lib. bdg. 22.60 (978-0-7660-2749-7(X) , Enslow Elementary) Enslow Pubs., Inc.

Brandt, Deanna. Bird Log Kids. 1998. (Illus.). 80p. (J). (gr. k-7). pap. 9.95 (978-1-885061-55-3(2)) Adventure Pubns., Inc.

Brian Wildsmith's Birds. 2004. (J). pap. 14.95 incl. audio (978-1-56008-164-7(3)) Weston Woods Studios, Inc.

Brighter Vision Publishing Staff. Birds. 1999. (Learning Adventures Kindergarten Ser.). (Illus.). (J). (gr. k-1). pap. 2.25 (978-1-55254-059-6(6) , BV12021); pap. 2.50 (978-1-55254-071-8(5)) Brighter Vision Pubns.

Brown. Birds in England. 2002. (Illus.). 350p. (978-0-85661-123-0(9) , Academic Pr.) Elsevier Science & Technology Bks.

Brown, Mary Barrett. Wings along the Waterway. Brown, Mary Barrett, illus. 1999. (Illus.). 80p. (J). (gr. 3-6). pap. 8.95 (978-0-531-07114-4(6) , Orchard Bks.) Scholastic, Inc.

—Wings along the Waterway. 1999. (978-0-606-16919-6(9)) Tandem Library Bks.

Buckley, Annie. The World's Most Beautiful Birds. 2007. (Girls Rock! Ser.). 32p. (J). (gr. 1-5). 24.21 (*978-1-59296-864-0(3)) Child's World, Inc.

Burch, Lynda S. I SEE Seaside Birds! Burch, Lynda S. & Roberts, MarySue, photos by. 2004. (Illus.). 52p. (J). E-Book 9.95 incl. cd-rom (978-1-933090-05-4(7)) Guardian Angel Publishing, Inc.

Burch, Lynda S. & Roberts, MarySue, photos by. I SEE Seaside Birds! 2006. (Illus.). 32p. (J). 16.99 (978-1-933090-16-0(2)) Guardian Angel Publishing, Inc.

Burgess, Thornton W. The Burgess Bird Book for Children. (J). 24.95 (978-0-8488-0404-6(X)) Amereon LTD.

—The Burgess Bird Book for Children. Fuertes, Louis Agassiz, illus. 2003. (General Juvenile Ser.). 272p. (J). (gr. 4-7). pap. 7.95 (978-0-486-42840-6(0)) Dover Pubns., Inc.

—The Burgess Bird Book for Children. 2004. reprint ed. pap. 22.95 (978-1-4191-5556-7(3)); pap. 1.99 (978-1-4192-5556-4(8)) Kessinger Publishing, LLC.

Burgess, Thornton W. The Burgess Bird Book for Children (Yesterday's Classics) Fuertes, Louis Agassiz, illus. 2006. (J). per. 13.95 (*978-1-59915-170-0(7)) Yesterday's Classics.

Burnie, David. Bird. 2008. (DK Eyewitness Bks.). 72p. (J). (gr. 3-8). 15.99 (*978-0-7566-3768-2(6)) Dorling Kindersley Publishing, Inc.

Burnie, David & Dorling Kindersley Publishing Staff. Bird. 2004. (Eyewitness Books). 72p. (J). lib. bdg. 19.99 (978-0-7566-0657-2(8)) Dorling Kindersley Publishing, Inc.

Burrows, Roger & Gilligan, Jeff. Birds of Oregon. Ross, Gary & Nordhagen, Ted, illus. rev. ed. 2003. 384p. (J). (gr. 4). pap. 19.95 (978-1-55105-374-5(8)) Lone Pine Publishing USA.

Canizares, Susan & Chessen, Betsey. From Egg to Robin. 1998. (Science Emergent Readers Ser.). 185p. (J). pap. 2.50 (978-0-590-76162-8(5)) Scholastic, Inc.

Carper, Virginia. Animal Teachings Volume Two: Birds, 3 vol. 2005. (Illus.). mass mkt. 20.00 (978-0-9788858-1-6(3)) Animal Teachers Enterprises.

Cartwright, Pauline. Birds. Smith, E. Silas, illus. 1999. 16p. (J). (978-0-7685-0401-9(5)) Dominie Pr., Inc.

—Every Bird Has a Beak. Smith, E. Silas, illus. 1999. 16p. (J). 5.50 (978-0-7685-0403-3(1)) Dominie Pr., Inc.

—Every Bird Has Feathers. Smith, David P., illus. 1999. 16p. (J). 5.50 (978-0-7685-0404-0(X)) Dominie Pr., Inc.

—Every Bird Has Two Feet. Smith, E. Silas, illus. 1999. 16p. (J). 5.50 (978-0-7685-0402-6(3)) Dominie Pr., Inc.

—Every Mother Bird Builds a Nest. Smith, David P., illus. 1999. 16p. (J). 5.50 (978-0-7685-0405-7(8)) Dominie Pr., Inc.

Chandler, David. Animal Fact Files Birds, Vol. 3. 2005. (Animals, Animals, Animals Ser.). (YA). (gr. k-3). 118.80 (978-0-7368-4209-9(8) , Pebble Bks.) Capstone Pr., Inc.

—Animal Fact Files Birds. 2004. (Collins Gem Ser.). (Illus.). 256p. pap. 7.95 (978-0-00-717860-5(3)) HarperCollins Pubs. Ltd. GBR. *Dist:* Trafalgar Square Publishing.

—Animal Fact Files Birds. 2000. 32p. (YA). 9.95 (978-0-7525-4315-4(6)) Parragon, Inc.

—Animal Fact Files Birds, 6 vols. (gr. k-2). 28.95 (978-0-7368-9234-6(6)) Red Brick Learning.

—Animal Fact Files Birds, 10 vols. 2003. (Illus.). (J). Vol. 1. (978-0-7172-5732-4(0)); Vol. 2. (978-0-7172-5733-1(9)); Vol. 3. (978-0-7172-5734-8(7)); Vol. 4. (978-0-7172-5735-5(5)); Vol. 5. (978-0-7172-5736-2(3)); Vol. 6. (978-0-7172-5737-9(1)); Vol. 7. (978-0-7172-5738-6(X)); Vol. 8. (978-0-7172-5739-3(8)); Vol. 9. (978-0-7172-5740-9(1)); Vol. 10. (978-0-7172-5741-6(X)) Scholastic Library Publishing. (Grolier).

Chanko, Pamela. The Beak Book. 1998. (Science Emergent Readers Ser.). (J). pap. 2.50 (978-0-590-76969-3(3)) Scholastic, Inc.

Choiniere, Joseph & Golding, Claire Mowbray. What's That Bird? Robins, James, illus. Vezo, Tom, photos by. 2005. 128p. (J). 24.95 (978-1-58017-555-5(4)) Storey Publishing, LLC.

Choiniere, Joseph, et al. What's That Bird? 2005. (Illus.). 128p. (J). pap. 14.95 (978-1-58017-554-8(6)) Storey Publishing, LLC.

Chrustowski, Rick. Blue Sky Bluebird. rev. ed. 2004. (Illus.). 32p. (J). 16.95 (978-0-8050-7104-7(0) , Holt, Henry & Co. Bks. For Young Readers) Holt, Henry & Co.

Coetzee, Philip. Birds for Beginners. Wolfaardt, Leigh-Anne, illus. 2002. 86p. (J). pap. (978-0-7981-4219-9(7)) Human & Rousseau.

Collard, Sneed B., III. Beaks. Brickman, Robin, illus. 2002. (J). 16.95 (978-1-57091-387-7(0)); 32p. pap. 6.95 (978-1-57091-388-4(9)) Charlesbridge Publishing, Inc.

—Beaks. 2002. (gr. k-3). lib. bdg. 15.25 (978-0-613-56725-1(0)) Tandem Library Bks.

Collins, Fergus & Garner, Braum A. Birds. 2001. (Questions & Answers about... Ser.). (Illus.). 40p. (J). (gr. 4-6). pap. 7.95 (978-0-7534-5370-4(3) , Kingfisher) Houghton Mifflin Co. Trade & Reference Div.

¿Como Vuela un Pajaro? (Coleccion Primeros Pasos en la Ciencia). (SPA., Illus.). (J). (gr. 1-3). pap. (978-950-724-219-9(8) , LMA8223) Lumen ARG. *Dist:* Lectorum Pubns., Inc.

Coulton, Mia. The Bird Feeder. 2004. 12p. (J). pap. 4.95 (978-1-57874-046-8(0)) Kaeden Corp.

Crawford, Tracey. Birds. 2006. 24p. (J). (978-1-4034-8456-7(2)); pap. (978-1-4034-8463-5(5)) Heinemann Library.

Cruce, Lana. Caring for Your Pet Bird. 2005. (Illus.). 20p. (J). (*978-0-328-13401-4(5) , Scott Foresman) Addison-Wesley Educational Pubs., Inc.

Cummins, Judi, creator. Flying Free Again. 2005. (Illus.). 34p. (J). per. (978-0-9760377-2-9(6)) Cummins, Judi.

Dalgleish, Sharon. Feathers & Flight. Cavaluzzo, Laura & McEwen, Rebecca, eds. 1999. (Explorers Ser.). (Illus.). 32p. (J). (978-0-7699-0474-0(2)) Shortland Pubns. (U. S. A.) Inc.

Daniel. Amazing Birds of the Rain Forest. 1999. pap. 5.60 (978-0-7398-2401-6(5)) Steck-Vaughn.

—Theme Pack: Birds. 2002. (Pair-It Bks.). (Illus.). (J). pap. (978-0-7398-6377-0(0)) Steck-Vaughn.

Davies, Nicola. Birds. (Science Kids Ser.). (Illus.). 48p. (J). (gr. k-3). 2007. pap. 6.95 (*978-0-7534-6124-2(2)); 2003. tchr. ed. 9.95 (978-0-7534-5617-0(6)) Houghton Mifflin Co. Trade & Reference Div. (Kingfisher).

Davies, Valerie. Beautiful Birds. Tomblin, Gill, illus. 2006. (Wildlife!). 28p. (J). (gr. 3-8). 17.95 (978-0-7696-4824-8(X)) School Specialty Publishing.

Davis Buddy & Davis Kay. Breathtaking Birds. 2006. (Illus.). 80p. (J). 12.99 (978-0-89051-457-3(7)) Master Bks.

Dawe, Neil & Dawe, Karen. The Bird Book: How to attract, identify, & cater to 24 feathered friends, with tips on observing the pecking order. 1999. (Illus.). 64p. (J). (gr. k-7). pap. 14.95 (978-0-89480-614-8(9) , 1614) Workman Publishing Co., Inc.

de Guilbert, Francoise. Sing, Nightingale, Sing! A Book & CD for Discovering the Birds of the World. Miyamoto, Chiaki, illus. 2006. 48p. (J). pap. 13.95 incl. cd-rom (978-1-929132-98-0(0)) Kane/Miller Bk. Pubs., Inc.

Deiters, Jim & Deiters, Erika. Macaws. 2001. (Animals of the Rain Forest Ser.). (Illus.). 32p. (YA). lib. bdg. 22.83 (978-0-7398-4682-7(5)) Raintree.

DePrisco, Dorothea. Bluebird's Nest. Parry, Jo, illus. 2005. 16p. (J). 9.95 (978-1-58117-390-1(3) , Intervisual/Piggy Toes) Dalmatian Pr.

Dittrich, Tina & Morrison, Kathryn. Stellaluna: An Study of Birds & Bats. 2005. pap. 10.95 (***978-1-931334-85-3(4)***) Pieces of Learning.

Dixon, Dougal. In the Sky. 2001. (Dinosaurs Ser.). (Illus.). 36p. (J). (gr. 4 up). lib. bdg. 24.67 (978-0-8368-2918-1(2)) Stevens, Gareth Inc.

Doherty, Gillian. Aves. 2004. Tr. of Birds. (SPA., Illus.). 64p. (J). pap. 8.95 (978-0-7460-4514-5(X)); lib. bdg. 16.95 (978-1-58086-347-6(7)) EDC Publishing.

—Birds. 2004. (Discovery Program Ser.). (SPA., Illus.). 64p. (J). (gr. 2 up). pap. 8.95 (978-0-7460-3738-6(4)); lib. bdg. 16.95 (978-1-58086-334-6(5)) EDC Publishing.

Domnauer, Teresa. Odd Birds, Level 1. 2007. (Extreme Readers Ser.). 32p. (J). pap. 3.95 (***978-0-7696-5259-7(X)***) School Specialty Publishing.

Donovan, Sandy. Quetzals. 2002. (Animals of the Rain Forest Ser.). (Illus.). 32p. (YA). (gr. 4 up). lib. bdg. 22.83 (978-0-7398-5530-0(1)) Raintree.

Dorenkamp, S. R. My Canary & Me. 2002. (For the Love of Animals Ser.). (Illus.). 64p. 6.95 (978-0-7641-1988-0(5)) Barron's Educational Series, Inc.

Dorling Kindersley Publishing Staff. Bird. 2006. (Eye Know Ser.). (Illus.). 24p. (J). 8.99 (978-0-7566-1774-5(X)) Dorling Kindersley Publishing, Inc.

—Birds. 2005. (Look Closer Ser.). (Illus.). 24p. (J). (ps-ps). 9.99 (978-0-7566-1433-1(3)) Dorling Kindersley Publishing, Inc.

—Pajaro. 2004. (Eyewitness Books).Tr. of Bird. 72p. (J). lib. bdg. 19.99 (978-0-7566-0798-2(1)) Dorling Kindersley Publishing, Inc.

—Smithsonian Bird Watcher. 2005. (Nature Activity Ser.). (Illus.). 72p. (J). (gr. 8). pap. 9.99 (978-0-7566-1029-6(X)) Dorling Kindersley Publishing, Inc.

Dudley Morrison, Susan. The Passenger Pigeon: Gone Forever. 1998. (Illus.). 48p. (J). (gr. 5-8). 12.00 (978-0-7881-5834-6(1)) DIANE Publishing Co.

Durand, Stephane & Poyet, Guillaume. Winged Migration: The Junior Edition. Wharry, David, tr. 2006. (Illus.). 46p. (J). (gr. k-4). reprint ed. 20.00 (978-0-7567-9996-0(1)) DIANE Publishing Co.

Eco-Force: Series One: Birds of North America. 2005. (J). 11.99 (978-1-933232-00-3(5)) Terra Denuo, Inc.

Eldin, Peter. Born Free Exotic Birds Sticker Facts. Q2A Solutions, illus. 2005. 18p. (J). (978-1-84510-753-6(5)) Top That! Publishing PLC.

Endangered Birds: Level P, 6 vols. (Wonder Worldtm Ser.). 48p. 39.95 (978-0-7802-7077-0(0)) Wright Group, The.

Exiting & Unusual Animals: Includes: Birds of Prey; Land Predators; Night Creatures; When Dinosaurs Ruled the Earth, 4 bks., Set. (Remarkable World Ser.). (Illus.). (J). (gr. 4-7). lib. bdg. 75.92 (978-0-8172-5153-6(7)) Raintree.

Feathered Friends. (My Animal Library). (Illus.). 10p. (J). (978-2-7643-0153-1(7)) Phidal Publishing, Inc./Editions Phidal, Inc.

Feathers: Level M, 6 vols. 128p. (gr. 2-3). 41.95 (978-0-7699-1021-5(1)) Shortland Pubns. (U. S. A.) Inc.

Feathers & Flight: 6 Each of 1 Student Book, 6 vols. (Sunshinetm Science Ser.). 24p. (gr. 1-2). 41.95 (978-0-7802-1395-1(5)) Wright Group, The.

Feathers & Flight: Big Book. (Sunshinetm Science Ser.). 24p. (gr. 1-2). 37.50 (978-0-7802-1396-8(3)) Wright Group, The.

Feathers & Flight: Level O, 6 vols. (Explorers Ser.). 32p. (gr. 3-6). 44.95 (978-0-7699-0597-6(8)) Shortland Pubns. (U. S. A.) Inc.

Formato, Vicki. Jayson: The True Story of a 20 Year Old Blue Jay. 2004. (Illus.). 264p. 24.95 (978-0-9760072-0-3(7)) CEM Ventures, Ltd.

Fowler, Allan. Seeing Seabirds. 1999. (gr. k-3). lib. bdg. 12.95 (978-0-613-54650-8(4)) Tandem Library Bks.

—These Birds Can't Fly. 1999. (Rookie Read-About Science Ser.). (Illus.). 32p. (YA). (gr. 1-2). pap. 4.95 (978-0-516-26420-2(6) , Children's Pr.) Scholastic Library Publishing.

—These Birds Can't Fly. 1999. (Illus.). 31p. (J). (gr. 1-2). lib. bdg. 12.95 (978-0-613-37558-0(0)) Tandem Library Bks.

Frost, Helen. Birds. 2000. (All about Pets Ser.). (Illus.). 24p. (J). (gr. k-1). lib. bdg. 15.93 (978-0-7368-0654-1(7) , Pebble Bks.) Capstone Pr., Inc.

—Birds, 4 bks. Saunders-Smith, Gail, ed. Incl. Baby Birds. lib. bdg. 14.60 (978-0-7368-0222-2(3)); Bird Eggs. lib. bdg. 14.60 (978-0-7368-0223-9(1)); Bird Families. lib. bdg. 14.60 (978-0-7368-0224-6(X)); Bird Nests. lib. bdg. 14.60 (978-0-7368-0225-3(8)); 24p. (J). (gr. k-1). 1999. (Illus.). Set lib. bdg. 58.40 (978-0-7368-0262-8(2) , Pebble Bks.) Capstone Pr., Inc.

Ganeri, Anita. All about Birds. 2005. (Illus.). 38p. (J). (ps-8). lib. bdg. 28.00 (978-0-7910-8688-9(7) , Chelsea Hse.) Facts On File, Inc.

Gareth Stevens Publishing Staff, contrib. by. Birds. 2002. (Discovery Channel School Science Ser.). (Illus.). 32p. (J). (gr. 5 up). lib. bdg. 24.67 (978-0-8368-3210-5(8)) Stevens, Gareth Inc.

George, Jean Craighead. Winter Moon. 2003. (J). (gr. 3-7). 20.75 (978-0-8446-7244-1(0)) Smith, Peter Pub., Inc.

—Winter Moon. 2001. (gr. 3-6). lib. bdg. 14.10 (978-0-613-50525-3(5)) Tandem Library Bks.

Gerlach, Barbara, et al, photos by. Baby Birds 2002. 2001. (Illus.). 28p. (J). (gr. 2-12). pap. 8.95 (978-1-890050-58-0(X)) Carlisle Pr.- Walnut Creek.

Gierecke, Ernestine. Birds. 1999. (Outside My Window Ser.). 24p. (J). (gr. 1-3). lib. bdg. 21.36 (978-1-57572-682-3(3)) Heinemann Library.

Gillis, Jennifer Blizin. Birds. 2004. (Heinemann Read & Learn Ser.). (Illus.). 24p. (J). 18.50 (978-1-4034-5055-5(2)); pap. 5.75 (978-1-4034-6018-9(3)) Heinemann Library.

Gingold, Janet. My Adventure as a Birder: Advanced My Adventure. 2007. 44p. (J). pap. 8.99 (978-1-59092-406-8(1) , Orchard Academy Pr.) Windstorm Creative.

Glover, David & Glover, Penny. Bird. 2006. (Owning a Pet Ser.). (J). (978-1-59771-058-9(X)) Sea-To-Sea Pubns.

Grack, David. Birds of the Northwoods Activity Book: A Coloring & Learning Guide. 2007. 64p. pap. 7.95 (***978-1-59193-166-9(5)***) Adventure Pubns., Inc.

Grambo, Rebecca L., et al. Animal Kingdom. 2000. (Eyes on Nature Ser.). (Illus.). 109p. (J). (978-1-56156-882-6(1)) Kidsbooks, Inc.

Gray, Samantha. Birds. Ling, Mary, ed. 2002. (Eye Wonder Ser.). (Illus.). 48p. (J). (gr. k-3). 9.99 (978-0-7894-8550-2(8)) Dorling Kindersley Publishing, Inc.

Green, Jen. Birds. Baker, Cy, illus. 1998. (Young Scientist Concepts & Projects Ser.). 68p. (J). (gr. 4 up). lib. bdg. 26.60 (978-0-8368-2161-1(0)) Stevens, Gareth Inc.

Grolier Educational Staff, contrib. by. Boobies. 2001. (Nature's Children Ser.). (Illus.). 47p. (J). (978-0-7172-5535-1(2) , Grolier) Scholastic Library Publishing.

Group/McGraw-Hill, Wright. Purl & the Bird: Decodable Books, 6 vols. (Fasttrack Reading Ser.). 24p. (gr. 4-8). 40.95 (978-0-322-05982-5(8)) Wright Group, The.

Grzimek, Bernhard & McDade, Melissa C. Birds, Grzimeks Student Animal, 5 vols. 2004. (Grzimek's Student Animal Life Resource Ser.). (Illus.). 1,000p. (J). 290.00 (978-0-7876-9235-3(2) , UXL) Thomson Gale.

—Grzimek's Student Animal Life Resource, 5 vols. 2004. (Illus.). (J). (978-0-7876-9236-0(0)); (978-0-7876-9237-7(9)); (978-0-7876-9238-4(7)); (978-0-7876-9239-1(5)); (978-0-7876-9240-7(9)) Thomson Gale. (UXL).

Guiberson, Brenda Z. Mud City: A Flamingo Story. rev. ed. 2005. (Illus.). 32p. (J). 16.95 (978-0-8050-7177-1(6) , Holt, Henry & Co. Bks. For Young Readers) Holt, Henry & Co.

Hall, Kirsten. Great Bustard: The World's Heaviest Flying Bird. 2007. (SuperSized! Ser.). (Illus.). 24p. (J). (gr. k-2). lib. bdg. 21.28 (978-1-59716-390-3(2) , 1265935) Bearport Publishing Co., Inc.

Hamilton, Lynn. Caring for Your Bird. 2003. (gr. 3-6). lib. bdg. 16.40 (978-0-613-79823-5(6)) Tandem Library Bks.

—Caring for Your Bird. 2002. (Caring for Your Pet Ser.). (Illus.). 32p. (J). lib. bdg. 16.95 (978-1-59036-037-8(0)) Weigl Pubs., Inc.

Hamilton, Lynn A. Caring for Your Bird. Marshall, Diana & Nault, Jennifer, eds. 2003. (Caring for Your Pet Ser.). (Illus.). 32p. (J). pap. 7.95 (978-1-59036-067-5(2)) Weigl Pubs., Inc.

Harcourt School Publishers Staff. All about Birds: Take-Home Book. 1999. (Collections Ser.). (Illus.). (J). pap. 1.90 (978-0-15-317239-7(8)) Harcourt Schl. Pubs.

—Beaks & Wings. 3rd ed. 2002. (Trophies English Language Learners Ser.). (Illus.). pap. 5.10 (978-0-15-327757-3(2)) Harcourt Schl. Pubs.

—Flying High 5-Pack, Below Level. 3rd ed. 2002. (Trophies Reading Program Ser.). (Illus.). (gr. 1). pap. 20.10 (978-0-15-326815-1(8)) Harcourt Schl. Pubs.

—Trofeos Advanced Level: Pajaros y Picos. 3rd ed. 2002. (SPA., Illus.). pap. 6.80 (978-0-15-323935-9(2)) Harcourt Schl. Pubs.

—What Has a Beak? 3rd ed. 2002. (Illus.). (J). pap. 3.20 (978-0-15-327579-1(0)) Harcourt Schl. Pubs.

Harvey, Bev. Birds. 2002. (Chelsea Clubhouse Science Exploration Ser.). (Illus.). 32p. (gr. k-2). 23.00 (978-0-7910-6985-1(0) , Chelsea Hse.) Facts On File, Inc.

Heinrichs, Ann. Birds. 2003. (Nature's Friends Ser.). (Illus.). 32p. (J). (gr. 2 up). lib. bdg. 21.26 (978-0-7565-0433-5(3)) Compass Point Bks.

Heller, Ruth. How to Hide a Parakeet: And Other Birds. unabr. ed. 2001. (How to Hide Ser.). (Illus.). (J). (gr. k-3). pap. 14.45 incl. audio (978-0-8045-6570-7(8) , 6570) Spoken Arts, Inc.

Hemingway, Carol. Oswald, an American Osprey. Gilleon, R. Tom, illus. 2001. 39p. (J). (gr. 4-7). pap. 15.95 (978-0-9708007-0-1(3)) Kilimanjaro Co.

Herkert, Barbara. Birds in Your Backyard. Herkert, Barbara, illus. 2001. (Illus.). 35p. (J). (ps-5). lib. bdg. 17.60 (978-0-613-49717-6(1)) Tandem Library Bks.

Herkert, Barbara, illus. Birds in Your Backyard. 2004. (Sharing Nature with Children Book Ser.). 36p. (J). pap. 8.95 (978-1-58469-025-2(9)); 17.95 (978-1-58469-026-9(7)) Dawn Pubns.

Hewett, Joan. A Flamingo Chick Grows Up. Hewett, Richard, photos by. (Baby Animals Ser.). (Illus.). 32p. (gr. k-3). 2005. lib. bdg. 21.27 (978-1-57505-164-2(8)); 2003. (J). pap. 6.95 (978-0-8225-0090-2(6) , Lerner Pubns.) Lerner Publishing Group.

—Flamingo Chick Grows Up. 2002. (gr. k-3). lib. bdg. 15.25 (978-0-613-56374-1(3)) Tandem Library Bks.

Hickman, Pamela. Bird Book. Collins, Heather, illus. unabr. ed. 2000. (Starting with Nature Ser.). 32p. (J). (gr. 4-6). (978-1-55074-810-9(6)) Kids Can Pr., Ltd.

—Bird Book. 2000. (Starting with Nature). (978-0-606-18230-0(6)) Tandem Library Bks.

—Starting with Nature Bird Book. Collins, Heather, illus. 2000. 32p. (J). (ps-ps). lib. bdg. 14.10 (978-0-613-24365-0(X)) Tandem Library Bks.

Hoglund, Rudy. Roger Tory Peterson's Colors: A Book for Beginner Bird Watchers & Crayon Users. Peterson, Roger Tory, illus. 2002. 48p. (J). 14.95 (978-0-7893-0805-4(3)) Universe Publishing.

Holt, Rinehart and Winston Staff. Birds & Mammals: Chapter Resources: Tennessee Edition. 3rd ed. 2003. (Holt Science & Technology Ser.). pap. 11.40 (978-0-03-069141-6(9)) Holt, Rinehart & Winston.

—Holt Science & Technology Chapter 17: Life Science: Birds & Mammals. 5th ed. 2004. (Illus.). pap. 12.86 (978-0-03-030226-8(9)) Holt, Rinehart & Winston.

Holub, Joan. Why Do Birds Sing? Divito, Anna, illus. 2004. (Easy-to-Read, Puffin Ser.). 48p. (J). (gr. k-2). pap. 3.99 (978-0-14-240106-4(4) , Puffin) Penguin Group (USA) Inc.

How Birds Live: 6 Each of 1 Student Book, 6 vols. (Sunshinetm Science Ser.). 24p. (gr. 1-2). 41.95 (978-0-7802-1398-2(X)) Wright Group, The.

How Birds Live: Big Book. (Sunshinetm Science Ser.). 24p. (gr. 1-2). 37.50 (978-0-7802-1399-9(8)) Wright Group, The.

Howell, Catherine. My First Pocket Guide to Backyard Wilderness. Emmett, Jennifer, ed. 2003. 80p. (J). (gr. 1-4). pap. 5.95 (978-0-7922-6927-4(6) , National Geographic Children's Bks.) National Geographic Society.

Hudak, Heather C. Birds. 2004. (Animal Facts Ser.). (Illus.). 24p. (J). lib. bdg. 24.45 (978-1-59036-203-7(9)) Weigl Pubs., Inc.

Hughes, Monica. Flying Giants. 2008. (J). lib. bdg. (***978-1-59716-541-9(7)***) Bearport Publishing Co., Inc.

Imbriaco, Alison. The California Condor: Help Save This Endangered Species! 2007. (Saving Endangered Species Ser.). (Illus.). 128p. (J). (gr. 5). lib. bdg. 33.27 (978-1-59845-043-9(3) , MyReportLinks.com Bks.) Enslow Pubs., Inc.

Jackson, Tom. Nature Watch: Parrots, Tropical & Rainforest Birds. 2005. (Illus.). 64p. 15.99 (978-0-7548-1450-4(5) , Lorenz Bks.) Anness Publishing GBR. *Dist:* National Bk. Network.

Jacobs, Liza. Flamingos. 2003. (Wild Wild World Ser.). (Illus.). 24p. (J). 22.45 (978-1-4103-0035-5(8) , Blackbirch Pr., Inc.) Thomson Gale.

James, Diane. Birds. 2004. (My First Look at Animals Ser.). (SPA., Illus.). 24p. (ps-2). 9.95 (978-1-58728-858-6(3) , Two Can Publishing) T&N Children's Publishing.

—Birds. Lynn, Sara, illus. rev. ed. 2004. (My First Look at Animals Ser.). (SPA.). 24p. (J). (ps-2). pap. 5.95 (978-1-58728-865-4(6) , Two Can Publishing) T&N Children's Publishing.

—Pajaros. 2001. Tr. of Birds. (978-0-606-22732-2(6)) Tandem Library Bks.

James, Diane & Lynn, Sara. Pajaros. 2004. (Descubre los Animales Ser.).Tr. of Birds. (SPA., Illus.). (ps-2). 24p. (J). pap. 5.95 (978-1-58728-391-8(3) , TWO31334); 20p. 9.95 (978-1-58728-387-1(5)) T&N Children's Publishing. (Two Can Publishing).

Janssen, Robert B. & Tessen, Daryl D. Birds of Minnesota & Wisconsin. rev. ed. 2003. (Illus.). 376p. (J). (gr. 4). pap. 19.95 (978-1-55105-324-0(1)) Lone Pine Publishing USA.

Jay, Michael. Flying Creatures. 2003. (Illus.). 32p. (J). lib. bdg. 25.70 (978-1-4109-0007-4(X)) Raintree.

Jeffrey, Laura S. Birds: How to Choose & Care for a Bird. 2004. (American Humane Pet Care Library). (Illus.). 48p. (J). (gr. 3-4). lib. bdg. 23.93 (978-0-7660-2515-8(2)) Enslow Pubs., Inc.

Johnson, Jinny. Birds. 2003. (Illus.). 48p. (J). (gr. 3 up). lib. bdg. (978-1-59084-447-2(5)) Mason Crest Pubs.

Johnston, Marianne. From the Dinosaurs of the Past to the Birds of the Present. 2000. (Prehistoric Animals & Their Modern-Day Relatives Ser.). 24p. (J). (gr. k-4). lib. bdg. 18.75 (978-0-8239-5204-5(5) , PowerKids Pr.) Rosen Publishing Group, Inc., The.

Julivert, Maria Angeles. Birds. Blasco, Amadeu & Martin, Gabi, illus. 2006. (Field Guides). 32p. (gr. 4-8). 16.95 (978-1-59270-058-5(6)) Enchanted Lion Bks., LLC.

Kalas, Sybille. The Goose Family Book. 2000. (Illus.). (J). (978-0-606-18320-8(5)) Tandem Library Bks.

Kalman, Bobbie. Life Cycle of a Bird. 2002. (gr. 3-6). lib. bdg. 14.10 (978-0-613-52969-3(3)) Tandem Library Bks.

—Les Oiseaux. 2004. (FRE., Illus.). 32p. pap. (978-2-89579-013-6(2)) Crabtree Publishing Co.

—Rainforest Birds. 1998. (Birds Up Close Ser.). (Illus.). 32p. (J). (gr. 3-4). pap. (978-0-86505-767-8(2)); lib. bdg. (978-0-86505-753-1(2)) Crabtree Publishing Co.

—What Is a Bird? 1999. (Science of Living Things Ser.). (Illus.). 32p. (J). (gr. 2-3). pap. (978-0-86505-892-7(X)) Crabtree Publishing Co.

Kalman, Bobbie & Smithyman, Kathryn. The Life Cycle of a Bird. 2001. (Life Cycle Ser.). (Illus.). 32p. (J). (gr. 2-3). (978-0-7787-0654-0(0)); pap. (978-0-7787-0684-7(2)) Crabtree Publishing Co.

Kalman, Bobbie, et al. Les Oiseaux: Life Cycle of a Bird. 2006. (FRE., Illus.). 32p. pap. (978-2-89579-078-5(7)) Crabtree Publishing Co.

Kavanagh, James. African Birds: An Introduction to Familiar Species. Leung, Raymond, illus. 2001. (Pocket Traveller Ser.). 12p. pap. 5.95 (978-1-58355-033-5(X)) Waterford Pr., Ltd.

—Australian Birds: An Introduction to Familiar Species. Leung, Raymond, illus. 2001. (Pocket Traveller Ser.). 12p. pap. 5.95 (978-1-58355-036-6(4)) Waterford Pr., Ltd.

—Colorado Birds. rev. ed. 2001. (Pocket Naturalist Ser.). (Illus.). 12p. (gr. 8). pap. 5.95 (978-1-58355-068-7(2)) Waterford Pr., Ltd.

—Kansas Birds. Leung, Raymond, illus. 2001. (Pocket Naturalist Ser.). 12p. pap. 5.95 (978-1-58355-047-2(X)) Waterford Pr., Ltd.

—Manitoba & Saskatchewan Birds. Leung, Raymond, illus. 1999. (Pocket Naturalist Ser.). (J). 5.95 (978-1-58355-038-0(0)) Waterford Pr., Ltd.

—Nebraska Birds. Leung, Raymond, illus. 1999. (Pocket Naturalist Ser.). (YA). 5.95 (978-1-58355-002-1(X)) Waterford Pr., Ltd.

—New York City Birds. Leung, Raymond, illus. 2001. (Pocket Naturalist Ser.). 12p. pap. 5.95 (978-1-58355-012-0(7)) Waterford Pr., Ltd.

—Oklahoma Birds. Leung, Raymond, illus. 2001. (Pocket Naturalist Ser.). 12p. (gr. 9). pap. 5.95 (978-1-58355-008-3(9)) Waterford Pr., Ltd.

—Pennsylvania Birds. Leung, Raymond, illus. 2001. (Pocket Naturalist Ser.). 12p. (gr. 9). pap. 5.95 (978-1-58355-009-0(7)) Waterford Pr., Ltd.

—Philadelphia Birds: An Introduction to Familiar Species in the Metropolitan Area. Leung, Raymond, illus. 2001. (Pocket Naturalist Ser.). 12p. pap. 5.95 (978-1-58355-013-7(5)) Waterford Pr., Ltd.

Kenyon, Linda J. Rainforest Bird Rescue: Changing the Future for Endangered Wildlife. 2006. (Firefly Animal Rescue Ser.). (Illus.). 64p. (J). (gr. 5-12). pap. 9.95 (978-1-55407-152-4(6)); lib. bdg. 19.95 (978-1-55407-153-1(4)) Firefly Bks., Ltd.

Khan, Sarah. Birds Lift-the-Flap. Scott, Peter, illus. 2004. (Luxury Lift-the-Flap Ser.). 16p. (J). (gr. 1 up). 11.95 (978-0-7945-0714-5(X) , Usborne) EDC Publishing.

Kirkland, Jane. Take a Backyard Bird Walk. Easter, Dennis, illus. 2005. (Take a Walk Ser.). 32p. (J). pap. 9.95 (978-0-9709754-0-9(6) , Take a Walk Bk.) Stillwater Publishing.

Knoebel, Suzanne. Something to Crow About: A Bird's Tale. 1998. (Illus.). 75p. (J). (gr. k-6). 15.95 (978-1-57860-059-5(6)) Emmis Bks.

Kops, Deborah. Vultures. 2000. (Wild Birds of Prey! Ser.). (Illus.). 24p. (J). (gr. 3-6). 24.94 (978-1-56711-273-3(0) , Blackbirch Pr., Inc.) Thomson Gale.

Lappi, Megan. Birds. 2004. (Prehistoric Life Ser.). (J). pap. 7.95 (978-1-59036-170-2(9)); (Illus.). 32p. lib. bdg. 15.95 (978-1-59036-111-5(3)) Weigl Pubs., Inc.

Larson, Helen C. Bird's Life. Larson, Helen C. & Shantz, Joy, illus. l.t. ed. 1999. 8p. (J). (gr. k-3). pap. 14.50 (978-1-58084-086-6(8)) Lower Kuskokwim Schl. District.

—Tengmiam Cullra. Larson, Helen C. & Shantz, Joy, illus. l.t. ed. 1999. Tr. of Bird's Life. (ESK.). 8p. (J). (gr. k-3). pap. 14.50 (978-1-58084-147-4(3)) Lower Kuskokwim Schl. District.

—Yaqulgem Angliurallra (Bird's Life) Larson, Helen C. & Shantz, Joy, illus. l.t. ed. 1999. (ESK.). 8p. (J). (gr. k-3). pap. 14.95 (978-1-58084-087-3(6)) Lower Kuskokwim Schl. District.

Latimer, Jonathan P. Backyard Birds. 1999. (gr. 3-6). lib. bdg. 14.10 (978-0-613-14553-4(4)) Tandem Library Bks.

—Shorebirds. 1999. (gr. 3-6). lib. bdg. 14.10 (978-0-613-15153-5(4)) Tandem Library Bks.

—Songbirds. 2000. (gr. 3-6). lib. bdg. 14.10 (978-0-613-28079-2(2)) Tandem Library Bks.

Latimer, Jonathan P. & Nolting, Karen Stray. Shorebirds. Peterson, Roger Tory, illus. 1999. (Peterson Field Guides for Young Naturalists). 48p. (J). (gr. 4-6). pap. 5.95 (978-0-395-92278-1(X)) Houghton Mifflin Co. Trade & Reference Div.

—Songbirds. Wright, Amy Bartlett & Peterson, Roger Tory, illus. 2000. (Peterson Field Guides for Young Naturalists). 48p. (J). (gr. 4-6). tchr. ed. 15.00 (978-0-395-97941-9(2)) Houghton Mifflin Co. Trade & Reference Div.

Latimer, Jonathan P., et al. Backyard Birds. Peterson, Roger Tory, illus. 1999. (Peterson Field Guides for Young Naturalists). 48p. (J). (gr. 4-6). pap. 5.95 (978-0-395-92276-7(3)) Houghton Mifflin Co. Trade & Reference Div.

—Bizarre Birds. Peterson, Roger Tory, illus. 1999. (Peterson Field Guides for Young Naturalists). 48p. (J). (gr. 4-6). tchr. ed. 15.00 (978-0-395-95213-9(1)); pap. 5.95 (978-0-395-92279-8(8)) Houghton Mifflin Co. Trade & Reference Div.

—Shorebirds. Peterson, Roger Tory, illus. 1999. (Peterson Field Guides for Young Naturalists). 48p. (J). (gr. 4-6). tchr. ed. 15.00 (978-0-395-95212-2(3)) Houghton Mifflin Co. Trade & Reference Div.

Laws, John Muir. Sierra Birds: A Hiker's Guide. 2004. (Illus.). 64p. pap. 9.95 (978-1-890771-78-2(3)) Heyday Bks.

Lee, Fran. Backyard Birding for Kids: A Field Guide & Activities. Lee, Fran, illus. 2005. (Illus.). 64p. (J). pap. 9.95 (978-1-58685-411-9(9)) Gibbs Smith, Publisher.

Legg, Gerald. Birds of Prey. Hersey, Bob, illus. 2004. (Scary Creatures Ser.). 32p. (J). (gr. 2-4). pap. 6.95 (978-0-531-16747-2(X) , Watts, Franklin) Scholastic Library Publishing.

Leon, Vicki, contrib. by. A Rainbow of Songbirds. 1999. (J). (978-0-382-39720-2(7)) Cobblestone Publishing Co.

Lessem, Dino Don. Flying Giants of Dinosaur Time. Bindon, John, illus. 2005. 32p. (J). (ps-k). pap. 6.95 (978-0-8225-2622-3(0)) Lerner Publishing Group.

Lessem, Don. Flying Giants of Dinosaur Time. Bindon, John, illus. 2005. (Meet the Dinosaurs Ser.). 32p. (J). (gr. 2-4). 23.93 (978-0-8225-1424-4(9)) Lerner Publishing Group.

Listen-Read-Think Science: Bird Watch. 2006. pap. 4.49 (978-1-4206-8151-2(6)) Teacher Created Materials, Inc.

Lockwood, Mark W. Learn about ... Texas Birds. Ivy, Elena T., illus. 2007. 52p. pap. 10.95 (***978-0-292-71685-8(0)***) Univ. of Texas Pr.

London, Jonathan. Flamingo Sunset. Rodanas, Kristina, illus. 2008. (J). (***978-0-7614-5384-0(9)***) Cavendish, Marshall Corp.

London, Jonathan. Gone Again Ptarmigan. Van Zyle, Jon, illus. 2001. 32p. (J). (ps-3). 16.95 (978-0-7922-7561-9(6) , National Geographic Children's Bks.) National Geographic Society.

Love, Donna. Awesome Ospreys: Fishing Birds of the World. Turley, Joyce Mihran, illus. rev. ed. 64p. (J). (gr. 3 up). pap. 12.00 (978-0-87842-512-9(8) , 341) Mountain Pr. Publishing Co., Inc.

Loves, June. Birds. 2003. (Pets Ser.). (Illus.). 32p. (gr. 2-4). 23.00 (978-0-7910-7547-0(8) , Chelsea Hse.) Facts On File, Inc.

Macken, JoAnn Early. The Life Cycle of a Flamingo. 2006. (Illus.). 24p. (J). pap. (978-0-8368-6389-5(5)); lib. bdg. 19.33 (978-0-8368-6382-6(8)) Stevens, Gareth Inc.

Marsico, Katie. A Peachick Grows Up. 2007. (Scholastic News Nonfiction Readers Ser.). (Illus.). 24p. (J). (gr. 1-2). 19.00 (978-0-531-17480-7(8) , Children's Pr.) Scholastic Library Publishing.

Mayer, Cassie. Feathers. 2006. (Illus.). 24p. (J). (978-1-4034-8372-0(8)); pap. (978-1-4034-8378-2(7)) Heinemann Library.

McCarthy, Meghan. City Hawk: The Story of Pale Male. McCarthy, Meghan, illus. 2007. 40p. (J). (ps-3). 15.99 (*978-1-4169-3359-5(X)) Simon & Schuster Children's Publishing.

McEvoy, Paul. Birds. 2003. (Animal Facts Ser.). (Illus.). 24p. (gr. 2-4). 23.00 (978-0-7910-7280-6(0) , Chelsea Hse.) Facts On File, Inc.

McNeil, Niki, et al. HOCPP 1129 Birds. 2006. spiral bd. 15.50 (*978-1-60308-129-0(1)) In the Hands of a Child.

Mertz, Leslie A., et al. Grzimeks Student Animal Life Resource:, 20 vols. 2004. (Grzimek's Student Animal Life Resource Ser.). (Illus.). 5000p. (J). 1050.00 (978-0-7876-9402-9(9) , UXL) Thomson Gale.

Mettler, Ren'e. El Pajaro. (Coleccion Mundo Maravilloso). (SPA., Illus.). 40p. (J). (gr. 2-4). (978-84-348-3726-3(9) , SM5470) SM Ediciones ESP. *Dist:* Lectorum Pubns., Inc.

Meyer, Therese. The Little Ballerina & Her Friends the Swans. 2004. (Illus.). 52p. 16.95 (978-0-9750325-0-3(X)) Baby Swan AUS. *Dist:* Biblio Distribution.

Meyer, Velma. Robby: The True Story of an Incredible Friendship Between a Robin & his Human Family. 1998. 96p. (Orig.). (J). (ps up). pap. 7.99 (978-0-8280-1291-1(1)) Review & Herald Publishing Assn.

Milbourne, Anna. In the Nest. 2005. (First Discovery Ser.). 24p. (J). 9.95 (978-0-7945-0735-0(2) , Usborne) EDC Publishing.

Miller, Sara Swan. Bizarre Birds. 2001. (Animals Ser.). (Illus.). 64p. (J). (gr. 5-7). 25.50 (978-0-531-11796-5(0) , Watts, Franklin) Scholastic Library Publishing.

—Bizarre Birds. 2001. (gr. 3-6). lib. bdg. 17.60 (978-0-613-37291-6(3)) Tandem Library Bks.

—Perching Birds of North America. 1999. (Animals in Order Ser.). (Illus.). 48p. (J). (gr. 4-6). 26.50 (978-0-531-11520-6(8) , Watts, Franklin) Scholastic Library Publishing.

—Perching Birds of North America. 1999. (gr. 3-6). lib. bdg. 15.25 (978-0-613-36589-5(5)) Tandem Library Bks.

—Shorebirds: From Stilts to Sanderlings. 2001. (Animals in Order Ser.). (Illus.). 48p. (J). (gr. 4-6). pap. 6.95 (978-0-531-16498-3(5) , Watts, Franklin) Scholastic Library Publishing.

—Shorebirds: From Stilts to Sanderlings. 2000. (gr. 3-6). lib. bdg. 15.25 (978-0-613-34466-1(9)) Tandem Library Bks.

—Wading Birds: From Herons to Hammerheads. 2001. (Animals in Order Ser.). (Illus.). 48p. (J). (gr. 4-6). 26.50 (978-0-531-11630-2(1) , Watts, Franklin) Scholastic Library Publishing.

—Wading Birds: From Herons to Hammerkops. 2001. (Animals in Order Ser.). (Illus.). 48p. (J). (gr. 4-6). pap. 6.95 (978-0-531-13959-2(X) , Watts, Franklin) Scholastic Library Publishing.

—Woodpeckers, Toucans, & Their Kin. 2003. (gr. 3-6). lib. bdg. 15.25 (978-0-613-67946-6(6)) Tandem Library Bks.

Miller, Sara Swan & Savage, Stephen. Shorebirds: From Stilts to Sanderlings. Gonzales, Jose, illus. 2000. (Animals in Order Ser.). 48p. (J). (gr. 4-6). 26.50 (978-0-531-11596-1(8) , Watts, Franklin) Scholastic Library Publishing.

Monroe, Guy. A Bird's Day at Yaquina Head. Monroe, Karol, ed. Golding, J. C., illus. 2003. 52p. 7.95 (978-0-9742443-0-3(9)) Monroe, Guy.

Morgan, Ben. Birds. 2006. (DK Guides Ser.). 64p. (J). pap. 7.99 (978-0-7566-1790-5(1)) Dorling Kindersley Publishing, Inc.

Morgan, Sally. Birds. 2004. (Illus.). 64p. (J). 32.79 (978-1-4109-1047-9(1)); pap. 9.50 (978-1-4109-1344-9(9)) Harcourt Schl. Pubs.

—Ducks & Other Birds. 2001. (Illus.). 32p. (J). lib. bdg. 24.25 (978-1-930643-44-4(6)) Chrysalis Education.

Morina, Barbara. Bird Watching My Bird Journal. Morina, Barbara, ed. 2002. (Write It down Ser.). (Illus.). 202p. 19.95 (978-1-892033-33-8(X)) Journals Unlimited, Inc.

Murray, Peter. Birds. 2004. (Science Around Us Ser.). 32p. (J). (gr. 2-6). 27.07 (978-1-59296-213-6(0)) Child's World, Inc.

National Wildlife Federation Staff. Birds, Birds, Birds. 1999. (Ranger Rick's Naturescope Ser.). (Illus.). 96p. (J). (gr. 1-7). 27.95 (978-0-7910-4830-6(6) , Chelsea Hse.) Facts On File, Inc.

Northey, Neil W. The Bluebirds & Their Neighbors. 1998. (Illus.). 160p. (J). (gr. 4-7). pap. 6.95 (978-1-881545-80-4(6)) A B Publishing.

—The Mallords & Their Neighbors. 1998. (Illus.). 181p. (J). (gr. 4-7). pap. 6.95 (978-1-881545-82-8(2)) A B Publishing.

Oberle, Mark William. Las Aves de Puerto Rico en Fotografias. Placer, José, tr. 2nd ed. 2006. (SPA., Illus.). 136p. per. 17.95 (978-0-9650104-2-9(2)) Editorial Humanitas.

O'Donnell, Kerri. Birds: Modern-Day Dinosaurs. 2002. (Reading Room Collection). (Illus.). 24p. (J). pap. 4.40 (978-0-8239-8170-0(3)); lib. bdg. 18.75 (978-0-8239-3733-2(X)) Rosen Publishing Group, Inc., The.

Ohare, Ted. Aves. 2005. (Que Es un Animal? Biblioteca del Descubrimiento Ser.).Tr. of Birds. (SPA.). 24p. pap. 5.45 (978-1-59515-686-0(0)) Rourke Publishing, LLC.

O'Hare, Ted. Birds. 2006. (What Is an Animal Ser.). (Illus.). 24p. (gr. 1-4). 14.95 (978-1-59515-416-3(7)) Rourke Publishing, LLC.

Ohare, Ted. Birds. 2005. 24p. pap. 5.45 (978-1-59515-730-0(1)) Rourke Publishing, LLC.

One Bird Sat on the Fence: Level B, 6 vols. (Wonder Worldtm Ser.). 16p. 24.95 (978-0-7802-1044-8(1)) Wright Group, The.

O'Neil, Sarah. Beaks & Feet. 1999. (gr. k-3). lib. bdg. 11.80 (978-0-613-19336-8(9)) Tandem Library Bks.

Otten, Jack. Watch Me Make a Bird Feeder. 2002. (Welcome Bks.). (Illus.). 24p. (J). (ps-2). pap. 4.95 (978-0-516-23497-7(8) , Children's Pr.) Scholastic Library Publishing.

—Watch Me Make a Bird Feeder. 2002. (gr. k-3). lib. bdg. 12.95 (978-0-613-58810-2(X)) Tandem Library Bks.

Ouilette, K. T. Two Birds in a Box. 2006. 64p. pap. 6.95 (978-1-882190-55-3(6)) Polar Bear & Co.

Palika, Liz. What Your Bird Needs. 2000. (gr. 7-12). lib. bdg. 12.95 (978-0-613-33226-2(1)) Tandem Library Bks.

Palin, Steve, illus. The Songs of Birds: Stories & Poems from Many Cultures. 2000. 80p. (YA). (gr. 3-7). 19.95 (978-1-84148-045-9(2)) Barefoot Bks., Inc.

Parker, Edward, photos by. Birds. 2002. (Rain Forest Pilot Ser.). (Illus.). 48p. (J). lib. bdg. 27.12 (978-0-7398-5239-2(6)) Raintree.

Parker, Janice. Birds. 2007. (J). (*978-1-59036-703-2(0)); (*978-1-59036-704-9(9)) Weigl Pubs., Inc.

Parker, Janice. The Science of Birds. 1999. (Living Science Ser.). (Illus.). 32p. (J). (gr. 2 up). lib. bdg. 24.67 (978-0-8368-2465-0(2)) Stevens, Gareth Inc.

Parker, Steve. Peacocks, Penguins & Other Birds. 2005. (Animal Kingdom Classification Ser.). (Illus.). 48p. (J). (gr. 4-6). (978-0-7565-1251-4(4)) Compass Point Bks.

Parks, Tim & Calasso, Roberto. Ka, the Story of Garuda: Based on the English Translation by Tim Parks of the Italian Original by Roberto Calasso. Basu, Suddhasattwa, illus. 2004. (J). (978-81-89020-04-0(8)) Katha.

Pascoe, Elaine. Birds Use Their Beaks. Kuhn, Dwight, photos by. 2002. (Springboards into Science Ser.). (Illus.). 24p. (J). (gr. 1 up). lib. bdg. 20.67 (978-0-8368-3008-8(3)) Stevens, Gareth Inc.

—How & Why Birds Use Their Bills. Kupperstein, Joel, ed. Kuhn, Dwight, photos by. 2000. (How & Why Ser.). (Illus.). 16p. (J). (gr. 1-3). pap. 2.99 (978-1-57471-659-7(X) , 2966) Creative Teaching Pr., Inc.

Patent, Dorothy Hinshaw. Brown Pelicans. 2005. (Early Bird Nature Bks.). (Illus.). (gr. 2-4). lib. bdg. 25.26 (978-0-8225-2417-5(1)) Lerner Publishing Group.

Paulsen, Gary. The Amazing Life of Birds: The Twenty-Day Puberty Journal of Duane Homer Leech. 2006. (Illus.). 96p. (J). lib. bdg. 15.99 (978-0-385-90897-9(0) , Lamb, Wendy) Random Hse. Children's Bks.

Pearce, Q. L. James Quadrino: Wildlife Protector. 2006. (Young Heroes Ser.). 64p. (J). (gr. 4-8). lib. bdg. 27.45 (978-0-7377-3612-0(7) , Kidhaven) Thomson Gale.

Peck, George K. Birdbooks, 7 bks., Set. Incl. Blackbirds. (Illus.). 1996. lib. bdg. 16.95 (978-1-887068-14-7(7)); Doves. (Illus.). 1996. lib. bdg. 16.95 (978-1-887068-16-1(3)); Gulls. (Illus.). 1997. lib. bdg. 16.95 (978-1-887068-13-0(9)); Hawks & Eagles. (Illus.). 1997. lib. bdg. 16.95 (978-1-887068-15-4(5)); Hummingbirds. 1997. lib. bdg. 16.95 (978-1-887068-09-3(0)); Robins. (Illus.). 1996. lib. bdg. 16.95 (978-1-887068-11-6(2)); Woodpeckers. (Illus.). 1996. lib. bdg. 16.95 (978-1-887068-12-3(0)); 32p. (YA). (gr. 3-12). 1999. 118.65 (978-1-887068-17-8(1)) Smart Apple Media.

Peterson, Roger Tory. Peterson First Guide to Birds of North America. 2nd ed. 1998. (First Guides). (Illus.). 128p. pap. 5.95 (978-0-395-90666-8(0)) Houghton Mifflin Co. Trade & Reference Div.

Phillips, Meredith. Bird World. 2004. (Pet's Point of View Ser.). (Illus.). 32p. (J). (gr. 4 up). lib. bdg. 22.60 (978-0-7565-0700-8(6)) Compass Point Bks.

Pingry, Patricia A. Baby Flamingo. Sharp, Chris, illus. 2004. (San Diego Zoo Animal Library: Vol. 8). 26p. (J). bds. 6.95 (978-0-8249-6557-0(4)) Ideals Pubns.

Points, Larry & Jauck, Andrea. Barrier Islands Are for the Birds. 2000. 32p. 7.95 (978-1-58071-023-7(9)) Sierra Pr.

Preszler, June. Caring for Your Bird. 2008. (J). (*978-1-4296-1252-4(5)) Capstone Pr., Inc.

Pyers, Greg. Why Am I a Bird? 2005. (Raintree Perspectives Ser.). (Illus.). 32p. (J). (978-1-4109-2014-0(3)); (gr. 5-8). pap. 7.85 (978-1-4109-2021-8(6)) Steck-Vaughn.

Quinlan, Susan E. Puffins. Lehnhausen, Bud, photos by. 1998. (Nature Watch Ser.). (Illus.). 48p. (J). (gr. 3-6). lib. bdg. 25.26 (978-1-57505-090-4(0) , Carolrhoda Bks.) Lerner Publishing Group.

Radley, Gail. Skies. 1998. (Vanishing from Ser.). (J). lib. bdg. (978-0-8225-1938-6(0)) Lerner Publishing Group.

Raintree Steck-Vaughn Staff. Encyclopedia of Birds. 2nd ed. 1999. (Encyclopedias of Animals Ser.). (Illus.). 240p. (J). (gr. 4-7). pap. 68.50 (978-0-7398-0684-5(X)) Raintree.

Raptors: Talons & Talents, 6 vols. (Book2WebTM Ser.). (gr. 4-8). 36.50 (978-0-322-02974-3(0)) Wright Group, The.

Reed, Janet. Muestranos tus Alas. 2005. Tr. of Show Us Your Wings. (SPA., Illus.). 16p. (J). (gr. 1 up). lib. bdg. 15.93 (978-0-7368-4165-8(2)) Capstone Pr., Inc.

Reed, Sharon R. The Bird Book. 1999. (Illus.). 24p. (J). (gr. k-6). spiral bd. 7.00 (978-0-8059-4583-6(0)) Dorrance Publishing Co., Inc.

Reilly, Pauline & Rolland, Will. Lyrebird. (Picture Roo Bks.). (Illus.). 32p. (J). pap. (978-0-86417-615-8(5) , Kangaroo Pr.) Simon & Schuster Australia.

Richardson, Adele D. Birds. 2004. (Exploring the Animal Kingdom Ser.). (Illus.). 24p. (J). lib. bdg. 21.26 (978-0-7368-2621-1(1) , First Facts) Capstone Pr., Inc.

Richardson, Joy. Birds. 2005. (Illus.). 32p. (J). lib. bdg. 23.33 (978-0-8368-4502-0(1)) Stevens, Gareth Inc.

Rigby Education Staff. Hold on Tight. (Sails Literacy Ser.). (Illus.). 16p. (gr. k-1). 27.00 (978-0-7635-9861-7(5)) Rigby Education.

—Using a Beak. (Sails Literacy Ser.). (Illus.). 16p. (gr. 2-3). 27.00 (978-0-7635-9959-1(X) , 699599C99) Rigby Education.

Ring, Susan. Show Us Your Wings. 2003. (Illus.). 17p. (J). 15.93 (978-0-7368-2922-9(9)); pap. (978-0-7368-2881-9(8)) Yellow Umbrella Pr.

Robertson, Matthew. Aves. 2002. (SPA.). 64p. (978-970-651-634-3(4) , 1610) Editorial Oceano De Mexico, S.A. DE C.V.

Robinson, W. Wright. How Birds Build Their Amazing Homes. Calvert, Trudy L., illus. 1999. (Animal Architects Ser.). 64p. (J). (gr. 5-9). 24.95 (978-1-56711-376-1(1) , Blackbirch Pr., Inc.) Thomson Gale.

Rohrer, Martha. Birds, Birds, Birds. 2004. (Illus.). 32p. (ps-5). 1.70 (978-0-7399-2349-8(8) , 2951) Rod & Staff Pubs., Inc.

Romeu, Emma. The Flamingo's Legs. Vigil, Luis Gerardo Sanchez & Broeck, Fabricio Vanden, illus. (SPA.). 48p. (J). (gr. 3-5). pap. 7.95 (978-1-59437-846-1(0)) Santillana USA Publishing Co., Inc.

—Las Patas del Flamenco. Sanchez Vigil, Luis Gerardo & Vanden Broeck, Fabricio, illus. 2004. (Coleccion Animales de America). (SPA.). 32p. (J). (gr. 5-8). pap. 7.95 (978-970-29-0514-1(1)) Santillana USA Publishing Co., Inc.

Royston, Angela. Birds. (Illus.). 32p. (YA). (gr. 2 up). lib. bdg. 27.10 (978-1-932333-34-3(7)) Chrysalis Education.

Royston, Angela, ed. Birds of North America. 1998. (Science Nature Guides). (Illus.). 16p. (J). (ps-3). 12.95 (978-1-85028-261-7(7) , Thunder Bay Pr.) Advantage Pubs. Group.

Rupp, Rebecca. Everything You Never Learned about Birds. Domm, Jeffrey C., illus. 2003. 144p. (gr. 4-7). pap. 14.95 (978-0-88266-345-6(3) , 66345) Storey Publishing, LLC.

Ryder, Joanne. Wild Birds. Kwas, Susan Estelle, illus. 2003. 40p. (J). (ps-2). 16.99 (978-0-06-027738-3(6)) HarperCollins Pubs.

Salmansohn, Pete & Kress, Stephen W. Saving Birds: Heroes Around the World. 2005. (Illus.). 40p. (gr. 3-6). pap. 7.95 (978-0-88448-276-5(6)) Tilbury Hse. Pubs.

Salzmann, Mary Elizabeth. Brilliant Birds. Nobens, C. A., illus. 2007. (Perfect Pets Ser.). 24p. (J). (gr. k-3). lib. bdg. 19.93 (*978-1-59928-744-7(7) , SandCastle) ABDO Publishing Co.

—What Has Wings? 2007. (Creature Features Ser.). (ENG., Illus.). 24p. (J). (ps-3). lib. bdg. 24.21 (*978-1-59928-876-5(1) , Super SandCastle) ABDO Publishing Co.

Sanchez, Claudia. Cuidador de Pajaros (Bird Trainer & Other Legends) (SPA.). (J). 14.95 (978-950-02-8449-3(9)) El Ateneo ARG. *Dist:* AIMS International Bks., Inc.

Savage, Stephen. Birds. 1999. (What's the Difference? Ser.). (Illus.). 32p. (J). (gr. 2-4). lib. bdg. 25.69 (978-0-7398-1356-0(0)) Raintree.

—Birds. 2000. (What's the Difference? Ser.). (Illus.). 32p. (J). (ps-3). pap. 9.95 (978-0-7398-1820-6(1)) Steck-Vaughn.

—Blackbird. 2005. (Illus.). (J). (978-0-7502-4662-0(6) , Hodder Wayland) Hodder Children's Division.

Save the Birds: Third Grade Guided Reading Level N. (On Our Way to English Ser.). (gr. 3 up). 34.50 (978-0-7578-7137-5(2)) Rigby Education.

Sayre, April Pulley. Bird, Bird, Bird: A Chirping Chant. Locke, Gary, illus. 2007. 32p. (*978-1-55971-978-0(8) , NorthWord Bks. for Young Readers) T&N Children's Publishing.

Schaefer, Lola M. What Is a Bird? Saunders-Smith, Gail, ed. 2001. (Animal Kingdom Ser.). (Illus.). 24p. (J). (gr. k-1). lib. bdg. 14.60 (978-0-7368-0864-4(7) , Pebble Bks.) Capstone Pr., Inc.

—What Is a Bird? 2005. (Animals, Animals, Animals Ser.). 24p. (YA). (gr. k-3). pap. (978-0-7368-9093-9(9) , Pebble Bks.) Capstone Pr., Inc.

School Specialty Publishing. Birds. 2004. (On-File Ser.). 4p. (J). (gr. 3-5). ring bd. 4.99 (978-0-7424-2887-4(7)) Schaffer, Frank Pubns.

Schulte, Mary Knudson. Parrots & Other Birds. 2005. (Scholastic News Nonfiction Readers Ser.). (Illus.). 24p. (J). (gr. 1-2). 19.00 (978-0-516-24931-5(2) , Children's Pr.) Scholastic Library Publishing.

Schwarz, Renee. Birdfeeders. 2005. (Kids Can Do It Ser.). (Illus.). 40p. (J). (gr. 4-7). (978-1-55337-699-6(4)); (978-1-55337-700-9(1)) Kids Can Pr., Ltd.

Sharp, Lore Dallas. Roof & Meadow. 2006. 32.99 (*978-1-4280-2973-6(7)) IndyPublish.com.

Shaw, Frank. Birds of the United States & Canada. 2004. (World Book's Science & Nature Guides Ser.). (Illus.). 80p. (J). (978-0-7166-4210-7(7)) World Bk., Inc.

Sheen, Martin, contrib. by. Bird. 2007. 16p. (J). (gr. 3-8). pap. 29.99 (*978-0-7566-3133-8(5)) Dorling Kindersley Publishing, Inc.

Silverman, Buffy. Birds. (Illus.). (J). (gr. 2-4). pap., wbk. ed. 4.99 (978-0-88743-965-0(9)) School Zone Publishing Co.

Silverstein, Alvin, et al. Beautiful Birds. 2003. (What a Pet! Ser.). (Illus.). 48p. (gr. 5-8). lib. bdg. 23.90 (978-0-7613-2513-0(1) , Millbrook Pr.) Lerner Publishing Group.

Sjonger, Rebecca & Kalman, Bobbie. Aves de Todo Tipo. 2005. (SPA., Illus.). 32p. (J). (978-0-7787-8834-8(2)) Crabtree Publishing Co.

—Aves de Topo Tipo: Birds of All Kinds. 2006. (SPA., Illus.). 32p. pap. (978-0-7787-8870-6(9)) Crabtree Publishing Co.

—Birds of All Kinds. 2005. (What Kind of Animal Is It? Ser.). (Illus.). 32p. (J). (978-0-7787-2160-4(4)); pap. (978-0-7787-2218-2(X)) Crabtree Publishing Co.

Slater, Patrick. Australian Birdlife. 2002. (Nature Kids Ser.). (Illus.). 52p. (J). (gr. 3 up). lib. bdg. 24.22 (978-1-59084-214-0(6)) Mason Crest Pubs.

Snake & the Birds: Individual Title Six-Packs. (Sails Literacy Ser.). (gr. 1-2). 36.00 (978-0-7578-4012-8(4)) Rigby Education.

Snedden, Robert. Birds. 2007. (J). (*978-1-59920-076-7(7)) Smart Apple Media.

Soffer, Ruth. Amazing Birds. 2006. 32p. (J). pap. 3.95 (978-0-486-44796-4(0)) Dover Pubns., Inc.

—Birds Alphabet: Coloring Book. 2005. (Illus.). 32p. (J). (ps-ps). pap. 3.95 (978-0-486-44035-4(4)) Dover Pubns., Inc.

Solway, Andrew. Classifying Birds. 2003. (Classifying Living Things Ser.). (Illus.). 32p. (J). lib. bdg. 24.22 (978-1-4034-0844-0(0)); pap. (978-1-4034-3344-2(5)) Heinemann Library.

—Eagles & Other Birds. 2006. (Illus.). 48p. (J). (978-1-4034-8222-8(5)); pap. (978-1-4034-8229-7(2)) Heinemann Library.

Spizzirri, Linda, ed. Prehistoric Birds. Spizzirri, Peter M., illus. 32p. (J). (gr. 1-8). pap. 4.98 incl. audio (978-0-86545-023-3(4)) Spizzirri Pr., Inc.

Stefoff, Rebecca. The Bird Class. 2007. (Family Trees Ser.). 96p. (J). lib. bdg. 32.79 (*978-0-7614-2693-6(0) , Benchmark Bks.) Cavendish, Marshall Corp.

Stemple, David. High Ridge Gobbler. 2001. (gr. 3-6). lib. bdg. 19.90 (978-0-613-51839-0(X)) Tandem Library Bks.

Sterling Publishing Company Staff & Ward, Adam, contrib. by. Birds. 2004. (Pocket Factfiles Ser.). (Illus.). 256p. (J). 4.98 (978-1-4027-1848-9(9)) Sterling Publishing Co., Inc.

Stewart, Melissa. Birds. 2001. (True Bks.). (Illus.). 48p. (J). (gr. 3-5). pap. 6.95 (978-0-516-25954-3(7) , Children's Pr.) Scholastic Library Publishing.

—Birds. 2001. (Illus.). 47p. (J). (ps-3). lib. bdg. 15.25 (978-0-613-53968-5(0)) Tandem Library Bks.

—Small Birds. 2002. (Perfect Pets Ser.). (Illus.). 32p. (J). 25.64 (978-0-7614-1397-4(9) , Benchmark Bks.) Cavendish, Marshall Corp.

Stone, Tanya Lee. Peacocks. 2003. (Wild Wild World Ser.). 24p. (YA). 24.94 (978-1-56711-818-6(6) , Blackbirch Pr., Inc.) Thomson Gale.

Swain, Cynthia, told to. They Have No Cares. 2003. (BuildUp Ser.). (J). pap. 22.00 (978-1-4108-0768-7(1)) Benchmark Education Co.

Swinburne, Stephen R. In Good Hands: Behind the Scenes at a Center for Orphaned & Injured Birds. 1998. (Illus.). 32p. (J). (gr. 2-6). 16.95 (978-0-87156-397-2(5)) Sierra Club Bks. for Children.

Taylor. Atlas Visual de las Aves. (Coleccion Atlas Visual). (SPA., Illus.). 324p. (YA). (gr. 5-8). (978-84-216-2575-0(6) , BU1497) Bruño, Editorial ESP. *Dist:* Lectorum Pubns., Inc.

Taylor, Barbara. Birds & Other Flying Animals. 2002. (J). 24.95 (978-1-57768-965-2(8) , Bedrick, Peter Bks.) School Specialty Publishing.

Taylor, Barbara & Dorling Kindersley Publishing Staff. Birds. 2nd ed. 2004. (Pocket Guides Ser.). (Illus.). 160p. (J). pap. 6.99 (978-0-7566-0203-1(3)) Dorling Kindersley Publishing, Inc.

Theodorou, Rod. Birds. (Illus.). 32p. (J). 2007. (*978-1-4034-9249-4(2)); 2007. (*978-1-4034-9242-5(5)); 2002. (gr. 1-4). pap. 6.95 (978-1-57572-541-3(X) , 90483) Heinemann Library.

Theodorou, Rod. Whooping Crane. 2002. (Animals in Danger Ser.). (Illus.). 32p. (J). (gr. k-2). pap. 6.95 (978-1-58810-448-9(6) , 91156) Heinemann Library.

Thompson, Desmond. Shorebirds. 2001. (WorldLife Library). (Illus.). 72p. pap. 17.95 (978-0-89658-561-4(1)) Voyageur Pr., Inc.

Those Birds! Level M, 6 vols. 128p. (gr. 2-3). 49.95 (978-0-7699-1020-8(3)) Shortland Pubns. (U. S. A.) Inc.

Top That Publishing Staff, ed. Birds of Paradise. 2005. (Illus.). 24p. (978-1-84510-534-1(6)) Top That! Publishing PLC.

—Birds of World. 2004. (Know How Know Why Ser.). (Illus.). 48p. (J). pap. (978-1-84510-075-9(1)) Top That! Publishing PLC.

—Wacky Hen. 2004. (Wacky Animals Ser.). (Illus.). 10p. (J). pap. (978-1-84510-091-9(3)) Top That! Publishing PLC.

Torrey, Bradford. Everyday Birds. reprint ed. pap. 125.00 (978-1-4047-9776-5(9)) Classic Textbooks.

—Everyday Birds. 1999. (Notable American Authors). reprint ed. lib. bdg. 125.00 (978-0-7812-9776-9(1)) Reprint Services Co.

Townsend. Incredible Birds. 2004. (Illus.). (J). pap. 9.50 (978-1-4109-0851-3(8)); Pack. pap. 51.30 (978-1-4109-0860-5(7)) Harcourt Schl. Pubs.

Townsend, John. Incredible Birds. 2004. (Illus.). 56p. (J). (ps-6). lib. bdg. 31.36 (978-1-4109-0527-7(6)) Harcourt Schl. Pubs.

—Incredible Birds. 2005. (Illus.). 56p. (J). (978-1-4109-1720-1(7)); (978-1-4109-1711-9(8)) Steck-Vaughn.

Twist, Clint. Feathery Creatures. 2005. (Animal Touch Ser.). (Illus.). 32p. (J). (ps-ps). 12.95 (978-0-7696-4152-2(0) , Waterbird Bks.) School Specialty Publishing.

—Furry Creatures. 2005. (Animal Touch Ser.). (Illus.). 32p. (J). (ps-ps). 12.95 (978-0-7696-4153-9(9) , Waterbird Bks.) School Specialty Publishing.

Underwood, Deborah. Colorful Peacocks. 2006. (Pull Ahead Books). (Illus.). 32p. (J). pap. 5.95 (978-0-8225-6507-9(2) , First Avenue Editions) Lerner Publishing Group.

Unwin, Mike. The Life Cycle of Birds. 2003. (From Egg to Adult Ser.). 32p. (ps-k). (Illus.). (J). lib. bdg. 24.22 (978-1-4034-0784-9(3)); pap. 7.50 (978-1-4034-3404-3(2)) Heinemann Library.

Wallace. The British Birdwatcher. 2002. (Illus.). 250p. (978-0-85661-138-4(7) , Academic Pr.) Elsevier Science & Technology Bks.

Warren, Jean. Birds. Cubley, Kathleen, ed. 1998. (Sticker Book Ser.). (Illus.). 32p. (J). (ps). pap. 3.95 (978-1-57029-212-5(4) , WPH 3702, Totline Pubns.) Schaffer, Frank Pubns.

Waters, Jo. The Wild Side of Birds. 2004. (Raintree Perspectives Ser.). (Illus.). 32p. (J). (978-1-4109-1405-7(4)); pap. (978-1-4109-1411-8(9)) Harcourt Schl. Pubs.

Webb, Sophie. Looking for Seabirds: Journal from an Alaskan Voyage. 2004. (Illus.). 48p. (J). (gr. 5 up). tchr. ed. 16.00 (978-0-618-21235-4(3)) Houghton Mifflin Co. Trade & Reference Div.

Wechsler, Doug. Bizarre Birds. (Illus.). 48p. 2004. (YA). (gr. 4-6). pap. 9.95 (978-1-59078-277-4(1)); 2003. (J). (gr. 3-7). 17.95 (978-1-56397-760-2(5)) Boyds Mills Pr.

—Ospreys. 2001. (Really Wild Life of Birds of Prey Ser.). (Illus.). 24p. (J). lib. bdg. 18.75 (978-0-8239-5597-8(4) , PowerKids Pr.) Rosen Publishing Group, Inc., The.

—Really Wild Life of Birds of Prey, 2 vols., set. (Illus.). 80.70 (978-0-8239-7077-3(9)) Rosen Publishing Group, Inc., The.

—Vultures. 2001. (Really Wild Life of Birds of Prey Ser.). (Illus.). 24p. (J). lib. bdg. 18.75 (978-0-8239-5594-7(X) , PowerKids Pr.) Rosen Publishing Group, Inc., The.

Weidensaul, Scott. Birds. 1998. (Illus.). 160p. lib. bdg. 16.50 (978-0-606-18582-0(8)) Tandem Library Bks.

Welsbacher, Anne. Wading Birds. Netherton, John, photos by. (Pull Ahead Bks.). (Illus.). 32p. (J). (gr. k-2). 1999. lib. bdg. 22.60 (978-0-8225-3614-7(5) , Lerner Pubns.); 1998. pap. 5.95 (978-0-8225-3620-8(X) , Carolrhoda Bks.) Lerner Publishing Group.

West, Keith R. & West, Jonathan. Birds. 2007. (J). (***978-1-60044-258-2(7)***) Rourke Publishing, LLC.

What Is a Bird?, 6 vols. (gr. k-2). 28.95 (978-0-7368-9114-1(5)) Red Brick Learning.

Where the Birds Are. 2001. 352p. (YA). pap. 29.95 (978-0-7894-8598-4(2)) Dorling Kindersley Publishing, Inc.

Whitehouse, Patricia. El Flamenco. 2003. (Animales del Zoologico (Zoo Animals) Ser.). (SPA., Illus.). 24p. (ps-1). (J). lib. bdg. 17.08 (978-1-4034-0404-6(6)); pap. 5.25 (978-1-4034-0652-1(9)) Heinemann Library.

—Qué Puede Volar? 2003. (SPA., Illus.). 24p. pap. 5.25 (978-1-4034-4392-2(0)) Heinemann Library.

Wicker, Jan Lee. Those Funny Flamingos. (J). 2006. 14.95 (978-1-56164-357-8(2)); 2004. (Illus.). 56p. 8.95 (978-1-56164-295-3(9)) Pineapple Pr., Inc.

Wilkes, Angela. Birds. 2002. (Question Time Ser.). (Illus.). 32p. (J). (gr. k-3). tchr. ed. 11.95 (978-0-7534-5450-3(5)); pap. 6.95 (978-0-7534-5462-6(9)) Houghton Mifflin Co. Trade & Reference Div. (Kingfisher).

—Question Time: Birds. 2002. (gr. k-3). lib. bdg. 15.25 (978-0-613-88141-8(9)) Tandem Library Bks.

Wilkes, Sarah. Birds. 2006. (Illus.). 48p. (J). pap. (978-0-8368-6228-7(7)); lib. bdg. 30.00 (978-0-8368-6209-6(0)) Stevens, Gareth Inc. (World Almanac Library).

Willis, Nancy Carol. The Robins in Your Backyard. Willis, Nancy Carol, illus. 2001. (Accelerated Reader Program Ser.). (Illus.). 32p. (J). (gr. k-3). pap. 6.99 (978-0-9662761-1-4(6)); (gr. 4-7). reprint ed. 15.95 (978-0-9662761-0-7(8)) Birdsong Bks.

Windsor, Jo. Birds' Feet: Early Level Satellite Individual Title Six-Packs. (Sails Literacy Ser.). 16p. (gr. 1-2). 27.00 (978-0-7578-6498-8(8)) Rigby Education.

—Some Birds Can Fly: Emergent Level Satellite Individual Title Six-Packs. (Sails Literacy Ser.). (gr. k-1). 27.00 (978-0-7578-7938-8(1)) Rigby Education.

—Some Birds Cannot Fly: Emergent Level Satellite Individual Title Six-Packs. (Sails Literacy Ser.). (gr. k-1). 27.00 (978-0-7578-7946-3(2)) Rigby Education.

Wingerter, Linda S., illus. Bird Tales from Near & Far. 1999. (Tales Alive Bks.: Vol. 3). 96p. (J). (ps up). pap. 12.95 (978-1-885593-18-4(X) , Williamson Bks.) Ideals Pubns.

Winner, Cherie. Everything Bird: What Kids Really Want to Know about Birds. 2007. (Kids' FAQs Ser.). (Illus.). 64p. (J). (gr. 3-6). 10.95 (978-1-55971-962-9(1) , 1267598); pap. 9.95 (978-1-55971-963-6(X) , 1267598) T&N Children's Publishing. (NorthWord Bks. for Young Readers).

Words about Birds. 12p. (J). (978-2-7643-0192-0(8)) Phidal Publishing, Inc./Editions Phidal, Inc.

World Book, Inc. Staff, contrib. by. All about Birds: A Supplement to Childcraft—The How & Why Library. 2005. (Illus.). 208p. (gr. 2-6). 24.95 (978-0-7166-0613-0(5)) World Bk., Inc.

—Storks & Other Large Wading Birds. 2005. (World Book's Animals of the World Ser.). (Illus.). 64p. (J). (978-0-7166-1267-4(4)) World Bk., Inc.

Zim, Herbert S. & Gabrielson, Ira N. Birds: A Golden Guide from St. Martin's Press. Irving, James Gordon, illus. rev. ed. 2001. (Golden Guides Ser.). 160p. pap. 6.95 (978-1-58238-128-2(3) , Golden Guides from Saint Martin's Pr.) St. Martin's Pr.

1000 Things You Should Know about Birds. (Illus.). 64p. (YA). (gr. 5 up). lib. bdg. (978-1-59084-462-5(9)) Mason Crest Pubs.

BIRDS, AQUATIC

see Water Birds

BIRDS—EGGS AND NESTS

Bird Eggs, Vol. 3. 2005. (Animals, Animals, Animals Ser.). (YA). (gr. k-3). (978-0-7368-8194-4(8) , Pebble Bks.) Capstone Pr., Inc.

Bird Eggs, 6 vols. (gr. k-2). 28.95 (978-0-7368-8234-7(0)) Red Brick Learning.

Bird Families, Vol. 3. 2005. (Animals, Animals, Animals Ser.). (YA). (gr. k-3). (978-0-7368-8195-1(6) , Pebble Bks.) Capstone Pr., Inc.

Bird Nests, Vol. 3. 2005. (Animals, Animals, Animals Ser.). (YA). (gr. k-3). (978-0-7368-8196-8(4) , Pebble Bks.) Capstone Pr., Inc.

Bird Nests, 6 vols. (gr. k-2). 28.95 (978-0-7368-8236-1(7)) Red Brick Learning.

Birds & Eggs Sets: 1 Each of 3 Big Books. (Sunshinetm Science Ser.). (gr. 1-2). 111.50 (978-0-7802-1393-7(9)) Wright Group, The.

Birds & Eggs Sets: 1 Each of 3 Student Books. (Sunshinetm Science Ser.). (gr. 1-2). 20.95 (978-0-7802-1746-1(2)) Wright Group, The.

Birds & Their Nests. (Animal Homes Ser.). 24p. (J). 6.95 (978-0-7368-5123-7(2)) Capstone Pr., Inc.

Boring, Mel. Birds, Nests & Eggs. Garrow, Linda, illus. 2004. (Take-Along Guide Ser.). 48p. (J). (gr. 2-5). pap. 7.95 (978-1-55971-624-6(X) , NorthWord Bks. for Young Readers) T&N Children's Publishing.

Cole, Joanna. Flies from the Nest. Bracken, Carolyn, illus. 2005. (Msb Science Reader Ser.). 32p. (J). pap. 3.99 (978-0-439-56991-0(5) , Cartwheel Bks.) Scholastic, Inc.

Eggs & Baby Birds, 6 vols. (Sunshinetm Science Ser.). 24p. (gr. 1-2). 37.50 (978-0-7802-1392-0(0)); 41.95 (978-0-7802-1391-3(2)) Wright Group, The.

The Missing Osprey Nest, 6 vols. (Ragged Island Mysteriestm Ser.). 161p. (gr. 5-7). 42.50 (978-0-322-01646-0(0)) Wright Group, The.

The Nest: KinderConcepts Individual Title, 6 packs. (Kinderstarters Ser.). 8p. (ps-1). 21.00 (978-0-7635-8727-7(3)) Rigby Education.

Pascoe, Elaine. Birds Build Nests. Kuhn, Dwight, photos by. 2002. (Springboards into Science Ser.). (Illus.). 24p. (J). (gr. 1 up). lib. bdg. 20.67 (978-0-8368-3007-1(5)) Stevens, Gareth Inc.

—How & Why Birds Build Nests. Kupperstein, Joel, ed. Kuhn, Dwight, photos by. 2000. (How & Why Ser.). (Illus.). 16p. (J). (gr. 1-3). pap. 2.99 (978-1-57471-656-6(5) , 2963) Creative Teaching Pr., Inc.

Stevens, Ann Shepard. Strange Nests. Dewey, Jennifer Owings, illus. 1998. (All about Animals Ser.). 32p. (J). (gr. 2-5). lib. bdg. 21.90 (978-0-7613-0413-5(4) , Millbrook Pr.) Lerner Publishing Group.

Stradling, Jan. Nests & Shelters: Level H, 6 vols. (First Explorers Ser.). 24p. (gr. 1-2). 29.95 (978-0-7699-1448-0(9)) Shortland Pubns. (U. S. A.) Inc.

Tagliaferro, Linda. Birds & Their Nests. 2004. (Pebble Plus, Animal Homes Ser.). (Illus.). 24p. (J). 13.95 (978-0-7368-2383-8(2)) Capstone Pr., Inc.

Whitehouse, Patricia. What Can Build? 2003. (Illus.). 24p. (J). lib. bdg. 18.50 (978-1-4034-4370-0(X)) Heinemann Library.

—What Can Build? 2003. (ps-2). lib. bdg. 28.65 (978-0-613-87966-8(X)) Tandem Library Bks.

Windsor, Jo. Inside Nests: Early Level Satellite Individual Title Six-Packs. (Sails Literacy Ser.). 16p. (gr. 1-2). 27.00 (978-0-7578-6500-8(3)) Rigby Education.

—Nests: Emergent Level Satellite Individual Title Six-Packs. (Sails Literacy Ser.). (gr. k-1). 27.00 (978-0-7578-7931-9(4)) Rigby Education.

Winer, Yvonne. Birds Build Nests. Oliver, Tony, illus. 2002. (J). (gr. k-3). 16.95 (978-1-57091-500-0(8)); pap. 6.95 (978-1-57091-501-7(6)) Charlesbridge Publishing, Inc.

—Birds Build Nests. Oliver, Tony, illus. 2002. (J). (ps-ps). lib. bdg. 15.25 (978-0-613-56728-2(5)) Tandem Library Bks.

BIRDS—FICTION

Abarca, Jesse, Jr. Las Adventuras de Dodie el Pajaro Dodo y sus amigos: En el Vidrio Magico. Abarca, Jesse, Jr., ed. Gutierrez, Ericka, tr. 2001. (Las Aventuras de Dodie el Pajaro Dodo y sus amigos). (SPA., Illus.). 48p. (Orig.). (J). (gr. 1-6). pap. 12.95 (978-0-9704850-2-1(6)) Dodo Bks.

—The Adventures of Dodi the Dodo Bird & His Friends: In the Magic Glass. Abarca, Jesse, Jr., ed. 2001. (Illus.). 48p. (J). (gr. 1-10). pap. 12.95 (978-0-9704850-1-4(8)) Dodo Bks.

—Who's Dodie. Abarca, Jesse, Jr., ed. 2001. (Las Aventuras de Dodie el Pajaro Dodo y sus amigos). (Illus.). 8p. (Orig.). (J). pap. 4.95 (978-0-9704850-0-7(X)) Dodo Bks.

Ada, Alma Flor. The Golden Cage. 2000. (gr. k-3). lib. bdg. 17.60 (978-0-613-79387-2(0)) Tandem Library Bks.

Ada, Alma Flor & Campoy, F. Isabel. On the Wings of the Condor. Davalos, Felipe et al, illus. (Gateways to the Sun). 48p. (J). (gr. k-6). pap. 13.95 (978-1-58105-964-9(7)) Santillana USA Publishing Co., Inc.

Aigner-Clark, Julie. Birds. 2002. (Baby Einstein Ser.). (Illus.). 20p. (ps-17). 3.99 (978-0-7868-0837-3(3)) Hyperion Bks. for Children.

—What Does Violet See? Birds & Nests. Zaidi, Nadeem, illus. 2002. (Baby Einstein Ser.). 16p. (ps-ps). 5.99 (978-0-7868-0874-8(8)) Disney Pr.

Aiken, Joan. Nightbirds on Nantucket. 1999. 224p. (J). (gr. 5-9). 15.00 (978-0-395-97124-6(1)); pap. 5.95 (978-0-395-97185-7(3)) Houghton Mifflin Co. Trade & Reference Div.

Aiken, Joan & Aiken, Joan. Nightbirds on Nantucket. 1999. 218p. (J). (gr. k-9). per. 14.10 (978-0-613-22098-9(6)) Tandem Library Bks.

Albee, Sarah. Sesame Street Follow Elmo. Leigh, Tom, illus. 2005. (Flocked Googly Eyes Book Ser.). 10p. (J). (ps-ps). bds. 10.99 (978-0-7944-0669-1(6)) Reader's Digest Assn., Inc., The.

Alcantara, Ricardo. El Viaje de los Pajaros. Esteban, Asun, illus. 2001. Tr. of Bird's Flight. (SPA.). 32p. (J). (gr. 3). 9.20 (978-84-261-2356-5(2)) Juventud, Editorial ESP. *Dist:* Lectorum Pubns., Inc.

Alexie, Oscar & Berlin, James, Sr., trs. Maniar Angun. Sloat, Teri, illus. l.t. ed. 2000. 12p. (J). pap. 17.00 (978-1-58084-186-3(4)) Lower Kuskokwim Schl. District.

Allen, Casey Lynn. And Then There Were Birds. Newson, Gregory G., illus. 2000. (Books for Young Learners). 12p. (J). pap. 5.00 (978-1-57274-284-0(4)) Owen, Richard C. Pubs., Inc.

Almond, David. My Dad's A Birdman. Dunbar, Polly, illus. 2008. (J). 15.99 (***978-0-7636-3667-8(3)***) Candlewick Pr.

Alonso, Fernando. El Mandarin y los Pajaros (The Mandarin's Birds) (Superbks./Superlibros). (Illus.). 16p. (J). (gr. k-3). pap. 6.95 (978-0-88272-505-5(X)) Santillana USA Publishing Co., Inc.

Anaya, Rudolfo. The First Tortilla: A Bilingual Story. Lamadrid, Enrique R., tr. Cordova, Amy, illus. 2007. (SPA & ENG.). 32p. (J). (gr. 2-4). 16.95 (***978-0-8263-4214-0(0)***) Univ. of New Mexico Pr.

Andersen, Hans Christian. The Nightingale. Oleynikov, Igor, illus. 2007. Tr. of Nattergalen. 40p. (J). 16.50 (978-1-933327-31-0(6)); 15.95 (978-1-933327-30-3(8)) Purple Bear Bks., Inc.

—The Nightingale. Ibatoulline, Bagram, illus. 48p. (J). (gr. 1-5). 2006. pap. 6.99 (978-0-7636-2406-4(3)); 2002. 17.99 (978-0-7636-1521-5(8)) Candlewick Pr.

—The Nightingale. Pinkney, Jerry, illus. 2002. Tr. of Nattergalen. 40p. (J). 16.99 (978-0-8037-2464-8(0) , Dial) Penguin Group (USA) Inc.

—El Ruisenor. Mitchell, Stephen, ed. Fischer, Maite Rodriguez, tr. Ibattouline, Bagram, illus. 2004. (SPA.). 48p. 15.95 (978-84-95939-25-8(8)) Blume ESP. *Dist:* Independent Pubs. Group.

—El Ruisenor. (SPA.). 32p. (J). (gr. 2-3). 12.95 (978-84-233-1567-3(3)) Ediciones Destino ESP. *Dist:* Lectorum Pubns., Inc., Planeta Publishing Corp.

Anderson, Derek. Blue Burt & Wiggles. Anderson, Derek, illus. 2006. (Illus.). 32p. (J). (ps-3). 14.95 (978-1-4169-0593-6(6) , Simon & Schuster Children's Publishing) Simon & Schuster Children's Publishing.

Anholt, Laurence. Billy & the Big New School. 1999. (gr. k-3). lib. bdg. 16.40 (978-0-613-62597-5(8)) Tandem Library Bks.

—Billy & the Big New School. Anholt, Catherine, illus. 2004. (Concept Book Ser.). 32p. (J). (ps-1). pap. 7.95 (978-0-8075-0744-5(X)) Whitman, Albert & Co.

Appelt, Kathi. Siempre Pienso en Ti. Dyer, Jane, illus. 2002. (SPA.). 40p. (J). (gr. k-2). 19.99 (978-84-261-3173-7(5) , JV30139) Juventud, Editorial ESP. *Dist:* Lectorum Pubns., Inc.

Apperley, Dawn. Good Night, Sleep Tight, Little Bunnies. Apperley, Dawn, illus. 2002. (Illus.). 32p. (J). (ps-k). pap. 9.95 (978-0-439-22525-0(6) , Cartwheel Bks.) Scholastic, Inc.

—Princess Rosebud: Perfectly Perfect Princess. 2007. 32p. (J). (gr. k-1). 14.99 (978-0-7641-6033-2(8)) Barron's Educational Series, Inc.

Araten, Michel. Honey the Hummingbird. 2004. 57p. per. 13.08 (978-1-4116-1805-3(X)) Lulu.com.

El Arco Iris y Los Pajaros (The Rainbow & the Birds), Big Book. (Superbks./Superlibros). (J). (gr. k-1). 21.95 (978-0-88272-456-0(8)) Santillana USA Publishing Co., Inc.

Aryal, Aimee. Hello Cocky! Graybill, Joni, illus. 2004. (J). 19.95 (978-1-932888-07-2(1)) Mascot Bks., Inc.

Asare, Meshack. Chipo & the Bird on the Hill: A Tale of Ancient Zimbabwe. 2002. (Illus.). 35p. (J). (ps-7). pap. (978-9988-550-44-8(8)) Sub-Saharan Pubs. & Traders.

Asch, Frank. Baby Bird's First Nest. 1999. (Illus.). 32p. (J). (ps-1). 16.00 (978-0-15-201726-2(7) , Gulliver Bks.) Harcourt Children's Bks.

—Moonbear's Dream. Asch, Frank, illus. 2002. (Illus.). 32p. (J). (ps-1). pap. 6.99 (978-0-689-85310-4(6) , Aladdin) Simon & Schuster Children's Publishing.

—Moonbear's Pet. Asch, Frank, illus. 2002. (Moonbear Ser.). (Illus.). (J). 14.47 (978-1-4046-0167-3(8)) Book Wholesalers, Inc.

Aston, Dianna Hutts. Mama Outside, Mama Inside. Gaber, Susan, illus. rev. ed. 2006. 32p. (J). 15.95 (978-0-8050-7716-2(2)) Holt, Henry & Co.

Atwater-Rhodes, Amelia. Falcondance. 2005. 192p. (YA). (gr. 7-12). lib. bdg. 16.99 (978-0-385-90334-9(0) , Delacorte Bks. for Young Readers) Random Hse. Children's Bks.

—Falcondance Vol. III: The Kiesha'ra. 2007. 208p. (YA). (gr. 7). pap. 7.99 (978-0-440-23885-0(4) , Delacorte Bks. for Young Readers) Random Hse. Children's Bks.

—Falcondance Vol. 3: The Kiesha'ra. 2005. 192p. (YA). (gr. 7-12). 14.95 (978-0-385-73194-2(9) , Delacorte Bks. for Young Readers) Random Hse. Children's Bks.

—Wolfcry. 2008. 208p. (YA). (gr. 9). pap. 7.99 (***978-0-440-23886-7(2)*** , Delacorte Bks. for Young Readers) Random Hse. Children's Bks.

Atwater-Rhodes, Amelia. Wolfcry Vol. 4: The Kiesha'ra. 2006. (Illus.). 208p. (YA). (gr. 7). 14.95 (978-0-385-73195-9(7)); lib. bdg. 16.99 (978-0-385-90354-7(5)) Random Hse. Children's Bks. (Delacorte Bks. for Young Readers).

Baby Lauren & Theodore, Paperback. 2007. (J). pap. 9.95 (***978-0-9779643-0-7(2)***) Healing Tree Arts.

Baglio, Ben M. Owl in the Office. 1999. (Animal Ark Ser.: No. 11). (J). (gr. 3-5). (978-0-606-19934-6(9)) Tandem Library Bks.

Baker, Austin. Eddy the Eagle & the Diamond. 1998. (J). (978-1-56763-431-0(1)); pap. (978-1-56763-432-7(X)) Ozark Publishing.

Baker, Keith. Little Green. (Illus.). (J). (ps-k). 2001. 32p. 16.00 (978-0-15-292859-9(6)); 2005. 30p. bds. 6.95 (978-0-15-205308-6(5) , Red Wagon Bks.) Harcourt Children's Bks.

Bang, Molly Garrett. The Paper Crane. Bang, Molly Garrett, illus. 2002. (Illus.). (J). 14.43 (978-0-7587-3372-6(0)) Book Wholesalers, Inc.

—The Paper Crane: Tus Noog Qej Qawg. Vang, Mao J., tr. 2000. (Illus.). 32p. (J). (ps-3). pap. 6.95 (978-0-9629298-1-6(6)) Minnesota Humanities Commission.

Barsy, Kalman. The Three Castaways. Perez-Moliere, Marnie, illus. 2004. (Orange Ser.). (SPA.). 40p. (J). (gr. 3-5). pap. 5.95 (978-1-57581-469-8(2)) Santillana USA Publishing Co., Inc.

Bauer, Joan. Backwater. 2005. 185p. (YA). (gr. 7-12). pap. 7.99 (978-0-14-240434-8(9) , Puffin) Penguin Group (USA) Inc.

—Backwater. 2000. (978-0-606-20077-6(0)) Tandem Library Bks.

Baumgart, Klaus. Lenny & Tweek. 2002. (Illus.). (J). 31p. pap. (978-1-59034-387-6(5)); 32p. 15.95 (978-1-59034-197-1(X)) Mondo Publishing.

Beck, Scott. Pepito the Brave. Van Metre, Susan, ed. 2001. (Illus.). 32p. (J). (ps). 12.99 (978-0-525-46524-9(3) , Dutton Juvenile) Penguin Group (USA) Inc.

Benjamin, A. H. & Holstien, Elisabeth. A Duck So Small. 1998. (Illus.). 32p. (J). (ps-3). 14.95 (978-1-888444-30-8(4) , 21028) Little Tiger Pr.

Bentley, Dawn. Welcome Back, Puffin! Stover, Beth, illus. 2005. (Read-and-Discover Atlantic Wilderness Adventures Ser.). 32p. (J). (ps-1). pap. 3.95 (978-1-59249-009-7(3) , S2014) Soundprints.

Berends, Polly Berrien. I Heard, Said the Bird. Sneed, Brad, illus. 1998. (Picture Puffin Ser.). 32p. (J). (ps-1). pap. 6.99 (978-0-14-056426-6(8) , Puffin) Penguin Group (USA) Inc.

Big Bird's Best Friends. 2001. (J). (978-1-931312-02-8(8)) SoftPlay, Inc.

The Bird: Individual Title Six-Packs. (Sails Literacy Ser.). 16p. (gr. k up). 27.00 (978-0-7635-4431-7(0)) Rigby Education.

Bird Song: The Little Stories of Manoosh & Baloosh. 2003. (J). mass mkt. (978-1-932233-02-5(4)) Aurora Libris Corp.

Blake, Quentin. Loveykins. Blake, Quentin, illus. 2003. (Illus.). 32p. (J). 15.95 (978-1-56145-282-8(3)) Peachtree Pubs., Ltd.

Bloom, Deborah R. The Bird Who Could Fly. 2006. pap. 7.50 (978-1-59971-075-4(7)) Aardvark Global Publishing.

Bluege, Wilor. The Golden Bough: A Fairytale Ballet for Children. 2000. (Illus.). 28p. (J). (ps-12). pap. 25.00 (978-1-883477-39-4(5)) Lone Oak Pr., Ltd.

Blunt, Patricia. George the Jackdaw. 2005. (Illus.). 52p. pap. (***978-1-84401-540-5(8)***) Athena Pr.

Bogacki, Tomek. The Story of a Blue Bird. Bogacki, Tomek, illus. 1998. (Illus.). 32p. (J). (ps-k). 16.00 (978-0-374-37197-5(0) , Farrar, Straus & Giroux (BYR)) Farrar, Straus & Giroux.

Bonnell, Kris. Feathers. 2005. (J). 3.75 (978-1-933727-06-6(3)) Reading Reading Bks., LLC.

Borra, Julian. The Man Who Put Words on Birds. Borra, Julian, illus. 2007. (Illus.). 32p. (J). 16.95 (***978-1-905636-00-6(8)***) Beautiful Bks. GBR. *Dist:* International Publishers Marketing.

Bradman, Tony. Elvis the Squirrel. Finlay, Lizzie, illus. 2006. (Read-It! Chapter Books). 48p. (J). (***978-1-4048-3119-3(3)*** , 1265806) Picture Window Bks.

Branch, Beverly, illus. The Nightingale. 2006. (J). 6.99 (978-1-59939-020-8(5) , Reader's Digest Young Families, Inc.) Reader's Digest Children's Publishing, Inc.

Brandon, Taylor. The Bird Who Didn't Want to Fly South for the Winter! Sandow, Paris, illus. 1999. (World's Greatest Children's Bks.). 48p. (J). (gr. k-5). 14.99 (978-1-889945-55-2(2)) Imperius.

—The Bird Who Was Afraid to Clean the Crocodile's Teeth! Sandow, Paris, illus. 1999. (World's Greatest Children's Bks.). 48p. (J). (gr. k-5). 14.99 (978-1-889945-56-9(0)) Imperius.

Branson, Terri. Pete, the Peacock, Goes to Town. 2007. (Illus.). 22p. (J). 7.98 (***978-0-9794660-8-3(3)***) Dragonfly Publishing, Inc.

—Pete, the Peacock, Goes to Town. Taylor, Chet, illus. l.t. ed. 2005. 22p. (J). lib. bdg. 24.95 (978-0-9765786-1-1(1)) Dragonfly Publishing, Inc.

Brian, Janeen. Where Does Thursday Go? King, Stephen Michael, illus. 2002. 32p. (J). (gr. k-3). 14.00 (978-0-618-21264-4(7) , Clarion Bks.) Houghton Mifflin Co. Trade & Reference Div.

Bridwell, Norman. The Cat & the Bird in the Hat. Bridwell, Norman, illus. 2000. (Hello Reader! Ser.). (Illus.). 32p. (J). (ps-3). pap. 3.99 (978-0-439-15433-8(2)) Scholastic, Inc.

—The Cat & the Bird in the Hat. 2000. (Hello Reader! Ser.). (Illus.). (J). (978-0-606-18531-8(3)) Tandem Library Bks.

Brinkley, Edward. Birds. 2003. (gr. 3-6). lib. bdg. 16.45 (978-0-613-87225-6(8)) Tandem Library Bks.

Brown, Janet Allison. Hello, Mr. Snowman. Chaffey, Samantha, illus. 2005. (Holidays In 3D Ser.). 8p. (J). bds. 4.95 (978-0-7641-5832-2(5)) Barron's Educational Series, Inc.

Brown, Margaret Wise. The Dead Bird. Date not set. 32p. (J). 15.99 (978-0-06-028931-7(7)); pap. 5.99 (978-0-06-443668-7(3)); lib. bdg. 16.89 (978-0-06-028932-4(5)) HarperCollins Pubs.

Brown, Peter. The Flight of the Dodo. 2005. (Illus.). 32p. (J). (ps-1). 15.99 (978-0-316-11038-9(8)) Little Brown & Co.

Brown, Ruth. The Old Tree: An Environmental Fable. Brown, Ruth, illus. 2007. (Illus.). 32p. (J). (ps-3). 16.99 (***978-0-7636-3461-2(1)***) Candlewick Pr.

Browne, A. SunBirds: #3 Great Lengths. 2003. 112p. pap. 9.95 (978-0-595-26709-5(2) , Writers Club Pr.) iUniverse, Inc.

Browne, Andrew. SunBirds. 2001. 112p. (J). pap. 10.95 (978-0-595-19378-3(1)) iUniverse, Inc.

Browne, N. M. Silverboy. 2007. (Illus.). 240p. (YA). 16.95 (978-1-58234-780-6(8) , Bloomsbury Children) Bloomsbury Publishing.

Bruel, Nick. Little Red Bird. 2008. 32p. (J). 16.95 (***978-1-59643-339-7(6)***) Roaring Brook Pr.

Bryant, Megan E. Strawberry Shortcake's Show-and-Tell Surprise: All Aboard Reading Station Stop 1. Neely, Scott, illus. 2005. (All Aboard Reading Ser.). 32p. (J). (ps-2). pap. 3.99 (978-0-448-43848-1(8) , Grosset & Dunlap) Penguin Group (USA) Inc.

Buggs, Michael A. Tabard. Buggs, Michael A., illus. (Illus.). 64p. (Orig.). (J). (gr. 2-6). pap. 15.00 (978-0-9657723-0-3(6)) Mogul Comics.

Bunting, Eve. Rudi's Pond. Himler, Ronald, illus. 2004. 32p. (J). (gr. k-3). pap. 5.95 (978-0-618-48604-5(6) , Clarion Bks.) Houghton Mifflin Co. Trade & Reference Div.

Burgess, Thornton W. The Adventures of Sammy Jay. (J). 15.95 (978-0-8488-0381-0(7)) Amereon LTD.

Burke, Tina. Fly Little Bird. Burke, Tina, illus. 2006. (Illus.). 32p. (J). 14.95 (978-1-933605-02-9(2)) Kane/Miller Bk. Pubs., Inc.

Buss, Fran Leeper. Journey of the Sparrows. 2002. 160p. (J). pap. 6.99 (978-0-14-230209-5(0) , Puffin) Penguin Group (USA) Inc.

Butterfield, Moira. Do Frogs Fly? Canals, Sonia, illus. 2007. (Animal Flappers Bks.). 16p. (J). (gr. k-k). 7.99 (978-0-7641-6027-1(3)) Barron's Educational Series, Inc.

Byars, Betsy. The Blossoms Meet the Vulture Lady. unabr. ed. 2000. (J). (gr. 4-6). pap. 23.00 incl. audio (978-0-8072-7323-4(6) , YA824SP, Listening Library) Random Hse. Audio Publishing Group.

Byers, Letha. Tesa, the Adopted Cow-bird. 2007. pap. 9.00 (***978-0-8059-8438-5(0)***) Dorrance Publishing Co., Inc.

Calvert, Deanna. Feeding the Gulls. Ulrich, George, illus. 2004. (Rookie Reader Skill Set Ser.). 32p. (J). (gr. k-2). pap. 4.95 (978-0-516-24622-2(4) , Children's Pr.) Scholastic Library Publishing.

Campbell, Rod. Little Bird. 2000. (Illus.). (J). 17p. pap. (978-0-333-63340-3(7) , Macmillan Children's Bks.); 20p. pap. (978-1-85292-234-4(6) , Campbell Bks.) Pan Macmillan.

Cannon, Janell. Stellaluna. Cannon, Janell, illus. 2002. (Illus.). (J). 23.40 (978-0-7587-3703-8(3)) Book Wholesalers, Inc.

Cannon, Janell. Stellaluna. 2007. (Illus.). 42p. (J). (ps). bds. 7.95 (***978-0-15-206287-3(4)*** , Red Wagon Bks.) Harcourt Children's Bks.

Captain Quake & Boss Bird: 3-in-1 Package. (Sails Literacy Ser.). 24p. (gr. 2 up). 57.00 (978-0-7578-6834-4(7)) Rigby Education.

Captain Quake & Boss Bird: 6 Small Books. (Sails Literacy Ser.). 24p. (gr. 2 up). 25.00 (978-0-7578-6830-6(4)) Rigby Education.

Captain Quake & Boss Bird: Big Book Only. (Sails Literacy Ser.). 24p. (gr. 2 up). 27.00 (978-0-7578-6822-1(3)) Rigby Education.

Carr, Roger. Bird Watching. 2001. (gr. k-3). lib. bdg. 11.65 (978-0-613-33338-2(1)) Tandem Library Bks.

Carruth, George. The Boy Who Loved Birds. Carruth Krock, Libby, illus. 2007. (ENG.). 32p. (J). 15.95 (***978-0-9773167-1-7(8)***) Too Much Fun, LLC.

Casey & the Nest. 2005. (J). (978-1-932570-47-2(0)) Literacy Footprints Inc.

Caso, George R. The Mission. Caso, George R., illus. 2003. (Illus.). 16p. (J). (ps-6). pap. 4.95 (978-0-9719290-1-2(7)) Caso, George R.

Cat in the Hen House: KinderConcepts Individual Title Six-Packs. (Kinderstarters Ser.). 8p. (ps-1). 21.00 (978-0-7635-8728-4(1)) Rigby Education.

Cazet, Denys. Elvis the Rooster & the Magic Words. 2004. (Illus.). 48p. (J). lib. bdg. 13.85 (***978-1-4242-0562-2(X)***) Fitzgerald Bks.

—Elvis the Rooster & the Magic Words. Cazet, Denys, illus. 2005. (I Can Read Bks.). 48p. (J). pap. 3.99 (978-0-06-000511-5(4) , Harper Trophy) HarperCollins Pubs.

—Elvis the Rooster & the Magic Words. unabr. ed. 2006. (Readalongs for Beginning Readers Ser.). (J). 29.95 incl. audio (978-1-59519-694-1(3)); 28.95 incl. audio compact disk (978-1-59519-695-8(1)); pap. 16.95 incl. audio (978-1-59519-690-3(0)); pap. 18.95 incl. audio compact disk (978-1-59519-691-0(9)); Set. pap. 29.95 incl. audio (978-1-59519-692-7(7)); Set. pap. 31.95 incl. audio compact disk (978-1-59519-693-4(5)) Live Oak Media.

Chambers, Melinda. We Are Whoooo We Are. Spiker, Sue Ann, illus. 2006. 32p. (J). 16.95 (978-0-929915-46-3(1)) Headline Bks., Inc.

Charlotte Latin School Staff. Ann & the Starling. Sher, illus. 2001. 32p. (J). per. 4.95 (978-0-9707920-8-2(5)) Charlotte's Storybooks.

—Ann & the Swallows. Sher, illus. 2001. 32p. (J). per. 4.95 (978-0-9707920-9-9(3)) Charlotte's Storybooks.

Cherrington, Janelle. There's No Nest Like Home. 2000. (gr. k-3). lib. bdg. 11.25 (978-0-613-31798-6(X)) Tandem Library Bks.

Chrismer, Melanie. Phoebe Clappsaddle for Sheriff. Roeder, Virginia M., illus. 2003. 32p. (J). pap. 14.95 (978-1-58980-127-1(X)) Pelican Publishing Co., Inc.

Clifton, Dorinda. Ginger Bird & the Big Bad Bug with the Hard, Hard Heart. 2006. (J). 6.95 (978-0-9771973-1-6(X)) Bedbug Pr., Inc.

Cofer, Judith Ortiz. The Hunger of Birds. 2005. (978-0-374-33517-5(6) , Farrar, Straus & Giroux (BYR)) Farrar, Straus & Giroux.

Cohn, Arlen. Friends of a Feather. Sullivan, Don, illus. (ps up). 1998. (Eyeball Animation Ser.: Vol. 5). 32p. 15.99 (978-0-939251-96-4(5)); 2001. (Eyeball Animation! Ser.). 28p. (J). bds. 9.99 (978-1-57939-097-6(8)) Accord Publishing, Ltd.

Cole, Joanna. Files from the Nest. Bracken, Carolyn, illus. 2005. 32p. (J). (ps-3). lib. bdg. 11.19 (978-0-606-33806-6(3)) Tandem Library Bks.

Conkling, Neil & Philip, Hilda. A Bird's Way of Singing. Date not set. (J). 12.95 (978-0-8050-4795-0(6) , Holt, Henry & Co. Bks. For Young Readers) Holt, Henry & Co.

Cook, Sherry & Johnson, Martin. Underwater Utley, 26. Kuhn, Jesse, illus. l.t. ed. 2006. (Quirkles—Exploring Phonics through Science Ser.: 21). 32p. (J). 7.99 (978-1-933815-20-6(5) , Quirkles, The) Creative 3, LLC.

Copeland, Cynthia L. Funny Faces, Wacky Wings, & Other Silly Big Bird Things. 2002. (gr. k-3). lib. bdg. 13.00 (978-0-613-55834-1(0)) Tandem Library Bks.

Copeland, Cynthia L. & Lewis, Alexandra P. Funny Faces, Wacky Wings, & Other Silly Big Bird Things. 2002. (Silly Millies Ser.). (Illus.). 32p. (gr. k-2). lib. bdg. 17.90 (978-0-7613-2863-6(7) , Millbrook Pr.) Lerner Publishing Group.

Corning, Spring Mary. Miss Elliot's Girls (Stories of Beasts. 2006. 32.99 (***978-1-4280-2822-7(6)***) IndyPublish.com.

Cosby, Bill. Friends of a Feather: One of Life's Little Fables. Cosby, Erika, illus. 2003. 64p. (gr. k-3). 16.95 (978-0-06-009147-7(9) , Harper Entertainment) HarperCollins Pubs.

Cosgrove, Stephen. Frazzle. James, Robin, illus. ed. 2003. (Serendipity Bks.). 32p. (Orig.). (J). (gr. k-5). pap. 4.99 (978-0-8431-0247-5(0) , Price Stern Sloan) Penguin Group (USA) Inc.

—Frazzle. 2003. (Orig.). (gr. k-3). lib. bdg. 13.00 (978-0-613-81300-6(6)) Tandem Library Bks.

Costanza, Stephen. Mozart Finds a Melody. rev. ed. 2004. (Illus.). 40p. (J). 17.95 (978-0-8050-6627-2(6) , Holt, Henry & Co. Bks. For Young Readers) Holt, Henry & Co.

Coyle, Kathleen. The Magical Realm: An Irish Childhood. 1998. (Illus.). 272p. (J). (gr. 4-7). pap. 14.95 (978-0-86327-548-7(6)) Wolfhound Pr. IRL. *Dist:* Irish American Bk. Co.

Creech, Sharon. Chasing Redbird. Burckhardt, Marc, illus. 1998. 272p. (J). (gr. 3 up). pap. 5.99 (978-0-06-440696-3(2) , Harper Trophy) HarperCollins Pubs.

—Chasing Redbird. 1998. (J). 12.64 (978-0-606-13265-7(1)) Tandem Library Bks.

Creevy, Anne. Lets Go Birding, You & Me. ed. 2006. (J). pap. (978-0-9785108-0-0(1)) ABC Bks.

Cromwell, Timothy. Little Bird Cal. 2004. 67p. pap. 14.95 (978-1-4137-0983-4(4)) PublishAmerica, Inc.

—Little Bird Cal 2: Mack Attack. 2005. 83p. pap. 14.95 (978-1-4137-6735-3(4)) PublishAmerica, Inc.

Crowther, Kitty. Jack & Jim: Picture Book. Date not set. (Illus.). 32p. (J). pap. 5.99 (978-0-7868-1439-8(X)); 15.99 (978-0-7868-0614-0(1)); 16.49 (978-0-7868-2527-1(8)) Hyperion Bks. for Children.

Cruickshank, Margrit. We're Going to Feed the Ducks. Reeve, Rosie, illus. 2004. 24p. (J). (gr. 1 up). lib. bdg. 23.33 (978-0-8368-4027-8(5)) Stevens, Gareth Inc.

Cuckoo Clock of Doom. 2003. (J). 84.00 (978-0-590-22756-8(4)) Scholastic, Inc.

Cuffe-Perez, Mary. Skylar. Liwska, Renata, illus. 2008. 144p. (J). (gr. 3). 14.99 (***978-0-399-24543-5(X)*** , Philomel) Penguin Group (USA) Inc.

Cutler, Jane. Common Sense & Fowls. Barasch, Lynne, illus. 2005. 144p. (J). 16.00 (978-0-374-32262-5(7) , Farrar, Straus & Giroux (BYR)) Farrar, Straus & Giroux.

Dalmatian Press Staff, ed. Sesame Street: Sleep Tight. 2006. (Illus.). 24p. pap. 3.50 (978-1-4037-2738-1(4)) Dalmatian Pr.

—Sesame Street: Spooky Sleep-Out. 2006. 24p. pap. 3.50 (978-1-4037-2432-8(6)) Dalmatian Pr.

Damjan, Mischa. The False Flamingoes. Steadman, Ralph, illus. 32p. (J). (ps-3). 13.95 (978-0-87592-016-0(0)) Scroll Pr., Inc.

Dans, Peter E. Perry's Baltimore Adventure: A Bird's-Eye View of Charm City. Harrell, Kim, illus. 2003. 30p. (J). 11.95 (978-0-87033-540-2(5) , Tidewater Pubs.) Cornell Maritime Pr., Inc.

Day, Alexandra. The Flight of a Dove. 2004. (Illus.). 32p. (J). 16.00 (978-0-374-39952-8(2) , Farrar, Straus & Giroux (BYR)) Farrar, Straus & Giroux.

de Brunhoff, Laurent. Babar & the Succotash Bird. 2000. (Babar Ser.). (Illus.). 38p. (J). (ps-3). 16.95 (978-0-8109-5700-8(0)) Abrams, Harry N. , Inc.

—Babar dans l'Ile aux Oiseaux.Tr. of Babar in the Jungle. (FRE., Illus.). (J). pap. 16.95 (***978-2-211-09806-9(1)***) Archimede Editions FRA. *Dist:* Distribooks, Inc.

—Babar dans l'Ile aux Oiseaux. (Babar Ser.).Tr. of Babar in the Jungle. (FRE., Illus.). 29p. (J). (ps-3). 15.95 (978-0-7859-0681-0(9) , F2002) French & European Pubns., Inc.

—Babar dans l'Ile aux Oiseaux. 1999. (Babar Ser.).Tr. of Babar in the Jungle. (FRE., Illus.). (J). (ps-3). (978-2-01-002547-1(4)) Istra.

de Mariscal, Blanca Lopez. The Harvest Birds (Los Pajaros de la Cosecha) Flores, Enrique, illus. 2001. (ENG & SPA.). 32p. (J). (gr. 1 up). pap. 7.95 (978-0-89239-169-1(3)) Children's Bk. Pr.

de Paola, Tomie. Bill & Pete to the Rescue. 2001. (Illus.). 48p. (J). (ps-3). pap. 5.99 (978-0-698-11884-3(7) , Putnam Juvenile) Penguin Group (USA) Inc.

—Bill & Pete to the Rescue. 2001. (Illus.). (J). 12.79 (978-0-606-21067-6(9)) Tandem Library Bks.

DeArmond, Dale. The Raven Charm. 1998. (Illus.). 51p. (J). (gr. k-4). 12.95 (978-0-9641998-6-6(6)) Lapcat Pubns.

Decary, Marie. Adam et le Raton Dessinateur. Beshwathy, Steve, illus. 2004. (Premier Roman Ser.). (FRE.). 64p. (J). (gr. 1-4). pap. (978-2-89021-643-3(8)) Diffusion du livre Mirabel.

Decary, Marie. Adam's Tropical Adventure. Beshwaty, Steve, illus. 2005. 54p. (J). lib. bdg. 12.00 (***978-1-4242-1202-6(2)***) Fitzgerald Bks.

Del Amo, Montserrat. Montes, Pajaros y Amigos. (SPA.). 104p. (YA). (gr. 5-8). (978-84-207-2788-2(1) , GS6293) Grupo Anaya, S.A. ESP. *Dist:* Lectorum Pubns., Inc.

Delval, Marie-Helene. Lolo y Lorito son muy Educados. Courtin, Thierry, illus. 2004. (Palabras menudas Ser.). (SPA.). 14p. 5.95 (978-84-7864-708-8(2)) Combel Editorial, S.A. ESP. *Dist:* Independent Pubs. Group.

Demi. The Firebird. 2005. (Illus.). 32p. (J). reprint ed. pap. 7.95 (978-0-8050-7811-4(8) , Owlet Paperbacks for Young Readers) Holt, Henry & Co.

Dent, Jenny. Peter Parrot & His Magic Star. 2001. (Peter Parrot Ser.). (Illus.). 32p. (gr. k-3). 12.95 (978-0-85487-119-3(5)) White Eagle Publishing Trust GBR. *Dist:* DeVorss & Co.

DePalma, Mary Newell. The Strange Egg. 2001. (Illus.). 32p. (J). (gr. k-3). tchr. ed. 15.00 (978-0-618-09507-0(1)) Houghton Mifflin Co. Trade & Reference Div.

DePaola, Tomie. Tomie's Mother Goose Flies Again. DePaola, Tomie, illus. 2005. (Illus.). 30p. (J). (ps-k). pap. 7.99 (978-0-399-24466-7(2) , Putnam Juvenile) Penguin Group (USA) Inc.

DePrisco, Dorothea. Mini Bluebirds Nest. 2006. 14p. 5.95 (978-1-58117-504-2(3) , Intervisual/Piggy Toes) Dalmatian Pr.

DeVos, Janie. How High Can You Fly? Rejent, Renee, illus. l.t. ed. 2005. 32p. 16.95 (978-0-9663276-2-5(4)) Red Engine Pr.

Dickins, Rosie. Emperor & the Nightingale. Philpot, Graham, illus. 2007. (First Reading Level 4 Ser.). 48p. (J). 8.99 (***978-0-7945-1614-7(9)*** , Usborne) EDC Publishing.

Dipucchio, Kelly. What's the Magic Word? Winborn, Marsha, illus. 2005. 32p. (J). (ps-1). 15.99 (978-0-06-000578-8(5)) HarperCollins Pubs.

Dodd, Lynley. Slinky Malinki, Open the Door. Dodd, Lynley, illus. 2001. (Gold Star First Readers Ser.). (Illus.). 32p. (J). (gr. 1 up). lib. bdg. 22.00 (978-0-8368-2785-9(6)) Stevens, Gareth Inc.

—Slinky Malinki, Open the Door. 2006. (Illus.). 0032p. (J). pap. 5.95 (978-1-58246-176-2(7) , Tricycle Pr.) Ten Speed Pr.

Domm, Kristin & Domm, Jeff. Ahmed & the Nest of Sand. Domm, Jeffrey, illus. 2000. 32p. (ps-3). pap. 8.95 (978-1-55109-338-3(3)) Nimbus Publishing, Ltd. CAN. *Dist:* National Bk. Network.

Domm, Kristin Bieber & Domm, Jeffrey. Atlantic Puffin: Little Brother of the North. 2005. (Illus.). pap. 8.95 (978-1-55109-518-9(1)) Down East Bks.

Donaldson, Julia. Follow the Swallow. Ursell, Martin, illus. 2001. (Blue Bananas Ser.). 48p. (J). (gr. 1-2). (978-0-7787-0842-1(X)); pap. (978-0-7787-0888-9(8)) Crabtree Publishing Co.

—Follow the Swallow. 2002. (gr. k-3). lib. bdg. 12.95 (978-0-613-52844-3(1)) Tandem Library Bks.

Dorling Kindersley Publishing Staff & Junor, Amy. Happy Feet. 2006. (Ultimate Sticker Books Ser.). 16p. (J). pap. 6.99 (978-0-7566-2241-1(7)) Dorling Kindersley Publishing, Inc.

Driscoll, Laura. Beck & the Great Berry Battle. Clarke, Judith, illus. 2006. (Stepping Stone Bks.). 128p. (J). (gr. 2-4). 5.99 (978-0-7364-2373-1(7) , RH/Disney) Random Hse. Children's Bks.

Dubarle-Bossy, Philippe. Flutter the Bird. Rinaldo, Luana, illus. 2005. (Playful Puppet Bks.). 10p. (J). 6.95 (978-0-7641-3045-8(5)) Barron's Educational Series, Inc.

Dubowski, Mark. Crane Crossing. 2002. (gr. 3-6). lib. bdg. 11.80 (978-0-613-51298-5(7)) Tandem Library Bks.

Due, Becky. Blue the Bird: On Flying. 2006. (Illus.). 38p. 6.95 (978-0-9746212-1-0(8)) Due Pubns.

Dunn, Matthew. Day One. 2007. 192p. (YA). per. 15.00 (***978-0-9794908-0-4(4)***) Onondaga Hill Publishing.

Dunn, Paul. The Why Bird. 2004. (Illus.). 42p. per. 11.95 (978-1-59405-056-5(2) , N2Print) New Age World Publishing.

Dunphy, Madeleine. The Peregrine's Journey: A Story of Migration. Kest, Kristin, illus. 2008. 32p. (J). pap. 9.95 (***978-0-9777539-2-5(1)***) Web of Life Children's Bks.

Durant, Alan. Bird Flies South, Level 2. Lucas, Kath, illus. 2005. (Lightning Readers Ser.). 32p. (J). (gr. k-1). pap., pap. 3.95 (978-0-7696-4210-9(1) , Gingham Dog Pr.) School Specialty Publishing.

Durant/Lucas, Alan/Kath. Bird Flies South. 2005. (Illus.). 32p. (J). lib. bdg. 9.00 (***978-1-4242-0888-3(2)***) Fitzgerald Bks.

Dureke, Jottn O. Z - the Goodluck Bird. Dureke, Jottn O., tr. 2004. (Illus.). 44p. (YA). pap. 6.95 (978-0-9701144-1-9(9)) Jahs Publishing Group.

Duvall, Deborah L. Rabbit Goes to Kansas. 2007. (Illus.). 32p. (J). (gr. 1 up). 16.95 (***978-0-8263-4181-5(0)***) Univ. of New Mexico Pr.

Eastman, P. D. Flap Your Wings. 2000. (Beginner Books(R) Ser.). (Illus.). 48p. (J). (gr. k-3). 8.99 (978-0-375-80243-0(6) , Random Hse. Bks. for Young Readers) Random Hse. Children's Bks.

Edwards, Pamela Duncan. Honk! The Story of a Prima Swanerina. 2000. (gr. k-3). lib. bdg. 14.15 (978-0-613-29978-7(7)) Tandem Library Bks.

Eggleton, Jill. My Life with Birds, 6 Packs. Webb, Philip, illus. (Sails Literacy Ser.). 20p. (gr. 2-3). 27.00 (978-0-7578-0721-3(6)) Rigby Education.

—Yellow Bird: Early Level Satellite Individual Title Six-Packs. (Sails Literacy Ser.). 16p. (gr. 1-2). 27.00 (978-0-7578-2936-9(8)) Rigby Education.

Ehlert, Lois. Cuckoo/Cucu: A Mexican Folktale/Un Cuento Folklorico Mexicano. Andujar, Gloria de Aragon, illus. 2000. (SPA & ENG.). 36p. (J). (ps-3). pap. 7.00 (978-0-15-202428-4(X) , Voyager Bks./Libros Viajeros) Harcourt Children's Bks.

Ehrlich, Fred. You Can't See a Dodo at the Zoo. Haley, Amanda, illus. 2005. 40p. (ps-ps). 15.95 (978-1-59354-072-8(X)) Blue Apple Bks.

Eischen, Michael. The Clever Pheasant. Peterson, Mark, ed. 2005. (Illus.). (J). 16.95 (978-0-9765621-0-8(3)) Small Waters Publishing.

Elliott, David. And Here's to You! Cecil, Randy, illus. 2004. 32p. (J). (ps-2). 15.99 (978-0-7636-1427-0(0)) Candlewick Pr.

Ende, Michael. Norberto Nucagorda, Level 5.5. Wittenberg, Stella, illus. 2003. (SPA.). 32p. (J). (gr. 3-5). pap. 8.95 (978-84-204-3719-4(0) , AF1328) Santillana USA Publishing Co., Inc.

Engelbreit, Mary. Queen of Easter. Engelbreit, Mary, illus. 2006. (Ann Estelle Stories Ser.). (Illus.). 32p. (J). 15.99 (978-0-06-008184-3(8)); lib. bdg. 16.89 (978-0-06-008185-0(6)) HarperCollins Pubs.

Erdman & Perez. Mitos y Leyendas Indigenas. 2005. (SPA.). 72p. 13.99 (978-84-241-8013-3(5)) Everest de Ediciones y Distribucion, S.L. ESP. *Dist:* Lectorum Pubns., Inc.

Erickson, Betty. Use Your Beak! Srba, Lynne, illus. 1998. 8p. (J). (gr. k-2). pap. 3.75 (978-1-880612-76-7(3) , Seedling Pubns.) Continental Pr., Inc.

Eudes-Pascal, Elisabeth, illus. Raffi's Animal Rescue. 2007. (First Novel Ser.). 64p. (J). (gr. 2). 4.95 (***978-0-88780-740-4(2)***) Formac Publishing Co., Ltd. CAN. *Dist:* Casemate Pubs. & Bk. Distributors, LLC.

Eure, Wesley. A Fish Out of Water. Meredith College Art Department Staff, illus. 2000. 32p. (J). (ps-3). 15.95 (978-1-56554-850-3(7)) Pelican Publishing Co., Inc.

Fan, Nancy Yi. Sword Quest. Rioux, Jo-Anne, illus. 2008. 288p. (J). 15.99 (***978-0-06-124335-6(3)***); lib. bdg. 16.89 (***978-0-06-124336-3(1)***) HarperCollins Pubs.

—Swordbird. Zug, Mark, illus. 2008. 256p. (J). pap. 6.99 (***978-0-06-113101-1(6)*** , Harper Trophy) HarperCollins Pubs.

Farber, Erica. The Swamp Thing. Mayer, Mercer, illus. 2006. (Critter Kids Adventure Ser.). 32p. (J). (gr. 2-5). pap. 4.95 (978-0-7696-4762-3(6) , Gingham Dog Pr.) School Specialty Publishing.

Faye, Charlet. The Chilling Adventures of Marshall McCaw. 2004. (Illus.). 60p. (J). 18.95 (978-0-9655222-1-2(0)) FayeHouse. Pr. International.

Featherbocker Chirpslee Bird Takes His Heart to School. 2000. 36p. (J). (978-0-9704781-0-8(0)) Featherbocker Enterprises.

Feathers at Las Flores - Teaching Guide. 2000. 17.95 (978-1-55942-172-0(X)) Marsh Media.

Fernandez, Laura. Pajaros en la Cabeza. 2001. (SPA., Illus.). (J). (gr. k-2). pap. (978-968-24-1554-8(3) , TR7471) Trillas Editorial, S. A. MEX. *Dist:* Lectorum Pubns., Inc.

Figiel, Lisa. Another Bird in Our Nest. 2007. (J). per. 6.99 (***978-1-60247-356-0(0)***) Tate Publishing & Enterprises, L.L.C.

Fish, Mister, illus. Snerfy Cat Meets Prancy Finch. Fish, Mister, . 2007. 80p. (J). 14.99 (***978-0-9794753-0-6(9)***) Children's Classic Book Pubs.

Fitzwater, Ivan W. Cappy the Christmas Woodpecker. Paul Hudgins, illus. 2002. pap. 8.95 (978-0-934955-51-5(4)) Watercress Pr.

Fleming, Candace. When Agnes Caws. Potter, Giselle, illus. 1999. 40p. (J). (ps-3). 16.00 (978-0-689-81471-6(2) , Atheneum/Anne Schwartz Bks.) Simon & Schuster Children's Publishing.

Flock Watch: Individual Title Six-Packs. (Story Steps Ser.). (gr. k-2). 32.00 (978-0-7635-9799-3(6)) Rigby Education.

Foote, Catherine. A Goose, a Moose, & a Caboose. 1999. (J). (gr. k-2). pap. 6.95 (978-0-533-12985-0(0)) Vantage Pr., Inc.

Fowler, Zinita. Bubba Bailey & the Farkleberry Bush. 1998. 64p. (gr. 3-4). 14.95 (978-1-57168-187-4(6)) Eakin Pr.

The Fox & the Thrush. l.t. ed. 1999. (J). (gr. k-6). reprint ed. pap. 2.50 (978-1-893688-03-2(8)) Carroll Schl., The.

Fox, Mem. Feathers & Fools. Wilton, Nicholas, illus. 2000. 36p. (J). (gr. k-3). pap. 7.00 (978-0-15-202365-2(8) , Harcourt Paperbacks) Harcourt Children's Bks.

—Feathers & Fools. 2000. (Illus.). (J). (978-0-606-18740-4(5)) Tandem Library Bks.

Franco, Betsy. Birdsongs: A Backwards Counting Book. Jenkins, Steve, illus. 2007. 40p. (J). (ps 2). 16.99 (978-0-689-87777-3(3) , McElderry, Margaret K.) Simon & Schuster Children's Publishing.

French & Currey. Squeaky Cleaners: In a Muddle. (Illus.). 63p. pap. 7.99 (978-0-340-72665-5(2) , Hodder & Stoughton) Hodder General Publishing Division GBR. *Dist:* Trafalgar Square Publishing.

Friends, Paz. Dos Amigos. 2001. Tr. of Two Friends. (SPA.). (J). (gr. 2-4). 16.76 (978-84-88342-17-1(9)) S.A. Kokinos ESP. *Dist:* Lectorum Pubns., Inc.

Fuertes, Gloria. Cuentos de Animales: La Pata Mete la Pata. 2003. (SPA.). 246p. (978-84-305-7806-1(4) , SU5196) Susaeta Ediciones, S.A. ESP. *Dist:* Lectorum Pubns., Inc.

Fuller, Sandy Ferguson. Moon Loon. 2004. (Illus.). 32p. 15.95 (978-0-89272-614-1(8)) Down East Bks.

Gable, Paul. Love Flute. 2001. (J). (gr. k-3). pap. 16.95 incl. audio. pap. 16.95 incl. audio (978-0-8045-6843-2(X) , 6843) Spoken Arts, Inc.

Gallico, Paul & Swan. The Snow Goose & Other Stories, Level 3. 2001. (Illus.). vi, 52p. (C). pap. 9.00 (978-0-582-42695-5(2)) Longman Publishing Group.

Gates, Larry Kenneth. The Sad, Glad Story of Johnny B. Gull. Rubinstein, Abby, illus. 2000. Tr. of Las Tristezas y Alegrias de Juancho C. Gaviota. (ENG & SPA.). 44p. (J). 9.00 (978-0-9705154-0-7(5)) Wildfire Starts.

Gavril, David. Penelope Nuthatch & the Big Surprise. 2006. (Illus.). 32p. (J). (ps-2). 14.95 (978-0-8109-5762-6(0)) Abrams, Harry N. , Inc.

George, Jean Craighead. Charlie's Raven. 2004. (Illus.). 208p. (J). (gr. 4). 15.99 (978-0-525-47219-3(3) , Dutton Juvenile) Penguin Group (USA) Inc.

—Luck. Minor, Wendell, illus. 2006. (Outdoor Adventures Ser.). 32p. (J). lib. bdg. 17.89 (978-0-06-008202-4(X) , Geringer, Laura Book) HarperCollins Pubs.

—Luck: The Story of a Sandhill Crane. Minor, Wendell, illus. 2006. (Outdoor Adventures Ser.). 32p. (J). 16.99 (978-0-06-008201-7(1) , Geringer, Laura Book) HarperCollins Pubs.

George, Kristine O'Connell. Hummingbird Nest: A Journal of Poems. Moser, Barry, illus. 2004. 48p. (J). 16.00 (978-0-15-202325-6(9)) Harcourt Children's Bks.

Geringswald, Rita T. Benny: The bird who was too lazy to Fly. 2004. (Illus.). 12p. (J). 5.95 (***978-0-9797566-0-3(X)***) R & D Publishing of Lakeland, Florida.

Geshell, Carmen. Mele da Mynah's Noisy 'Ohana. Pagay, Jeff, illus. 2004. 24p. 10.95 (978-1-57306-225-1(1)) Bess Pr., Inc.

Gingold, Janet. Finch Goes Wild. 2007. 280p. (YA). pap. 14.99 (978-1-59092-385-6(5) , Blue Works) Windstorm Creative.

The Golden Bird. rev. ed. 2006. 152p. 26.95 (***978-1-4218-2343-0(8)***); pap. 11.95 (***978-1-4218-2443-7(4)***) 1st World Publishing, Inc. (1st World Library - Literary Society).

Goldsmith, Howard. Lost Little Robin. Bond, Denny, illus. 2003. 30p. (J). (ps-3). pap. 12.95 (978-0-07-024800-7(1)) McGraw-Hill Trade.

Goodall, Jane. Eagle & the Wren. 2002. (gr. k-3). lib. bdg. 15.25 (978-0-613-66075-4(7)) Tandem Library Bks.

Goulet, Charles O. Little Snowbird. 2002. (gr. 7-12). lib. bdg. 18.75 (978-0-613-87273-7(8)) Tandem Library Bks.

—Little Snowbird. 2002. 108p. (YA). (gr. 7-12). pap. 9.95 (978-0-595-21430-3(4) , Writers Club Pr.) iUniverse, Inc.

The Great Bird Adventure. 2003. (J). lib. bdg. 18.95 (978-0-9725485-1-9(3)) Waterfall Ridge.

Greenslade, David & Rushton, Rhian Wyn. Gloria A'r Berllan Bupur. 2005. (WEL., Illus.). 36p. pap. (978-0-86243-415-1(7)) Y Lolfa.

Griffin, Andrew. Bird Bonkers Stanley. 2001. (Illus.). 32p. (ps-2). 13.99 incl. cd-rom (978-0-7868-0683-6(4)) Hyperion Bks. for Children.

Griffiths, Marlene. Crafty Crane of Potpourri Pond. 2004. 40p. pap. 17.00 (978-0-8059-5928-4(9)) Dorrance Publishing Co., Inc.

Grobler, Piet. Little Bird's ABC. Grobler, Piet, illus. 2005. (Illus.). 52p. (J). (ps-3). 8.95 (978-1-932425-52-9(7) , Lemniscaat) Boyds Mills Pr.

Haas, Irene. Bess & Bella. Haas, Irene, illus. 2005. (Illus.). 32p. (J). 14.95 (978-1-4169-0013-9(6) , McElderry, Margaret K.) Simon & Schuster Children's Publishing.

Hall, Amanda. Prince of the Birds. 2005. (Illus.). 32p. (J). 15.95 (978-1-84507-102-8(6)) Lincoln, Frances Ltd. GBR. *Dist:* Perseus Distribution.

Hall, Matthew Henry. Phoebe & Chub. Aldridge, Sheila, illus. 2005. 32p. (gr. 1-4). 15.95 (978-0-87358-879-9(7) , Rising Moon Bks. for Young Readers) Northland Publishing.

Hamilton, Matthew. Bobby's Dove. Sosebee, Cheryl, illus. 2005. (J). bds. 9.99 (978-1-4183-0061-6(6)) Christ Inspired, Inc.

Handelsman, Valerie. Birdies' Seaside Gym. 2005. (Illus.). 32p. (J). 7.95 (978-0-9748884-2-2(7)) Little Thoughts For Little Ones Publishing, Inc.

Harcourt School Publishers Staff. Bird on the Beach: Take-Home Book. 2001. (Collections Ser.). (Illus.). (J). pap. 1.90 (978-0-15-319490-0(1)) Harcourt Schl. Pubs.

—The Bird on the Beach Below Level. 3rd ed. 2002. (Trophies Reading Program Ser.). (Illus.). pap. 5.10 (978-0-15-323228-2(5)) Harcourt Schl. Pubs.

—Dear Friend On Level. 3rd ed. 2002. (Trophies Reading Program Ser.). (Illus.). pap. 5.10 (978-0-15-323092-9(4)) Harcourt Schl. Pubs.

—The Flute's Journey: Reader's Choice Book. 2001. (Collections Ser.). (Illus.). (J). (gr. 4). 5.90 (978-0-15-314369-4(X)) Harcourt Schl. Pubs.

—Flying High: Below Level. 3rd ed. 2002. (Trophies Reading Program Ser.). (Illus.). (J). pap. 4.10 (978-0-15-322965-7(9)) Harcourt Schl. Pubs.

—Go Away: Take-Home Book. rev. ed. 2001. (Collections Ser.: Bk. 15). (Illus.). (J). pap. 1.90 (978-0-15-319073-5(6)) Harcourt Schl. Pubs.

—Little Red Hen Bakes a Cake: Independent Reader. 3rd ed. 2002. (Trophies Reading Program Ser.). (Illus.). (J). pap. 2.90 (978-0-15-325490-1(4)) Harcourt Schl. Pubs.

—Minnie, the Talking Bird Below Level. 3rd ed. 2002. (Trophies Reading Program Ser.). (Illus.). pap. 5.10 (978-0-15-323061-5(4)) Harcourt Schl. Pubs.

—Pop the Corn: On Level. 3rd ed. 2002. (Trophies Reading Program Ser.). (Illus.). (J). pap. 3.20 (978-0-15-322978-7(0)) Harcourt Schl. Pubs.

—Soon I Will: Below Level. 3rd ed. 2002. (Trophies Reading Program Ser.). (Illus.). (J). pap. 3.20 (978-0-15-322951-0(9)) Harcourt Schl. Pubs.

—A Story by Dorie: Take-Home Book. 2001. (Collections Ser.). (Illus.). (J). pap. 1.90 (978-0-15-319530-3(4)) Harcourt Schl. Pubs.

—A Story by Dorie Below Level. 3rd ed. 2002. (Trophies Reading Program Ser.). (Illus.). pap. 5.10 (978-0-15-323328-9(1)) Harcourt Schl. Pubs.

—Town Bird & Country Bird 5-Pack, On Level. 3rd ed. 2002. (Trophies Reading Program Ser.). (Illus.). (gr. 1). pap. 20.10 (978-0-15-326842-7(5)) Harcourt Schl. Pubs.

—The Town Bird & the Country Bird: On Level. 3rd ed. 2002. (Trophies Reading Program Ser.). (Illus.). (J). (gr. 1). pap. 4.10 (978-0-15-322992-3(6)) Harcourt Schl. Pubs.

—Trofeos Below Level: Vuela Muy Alto. 3rd ed. 2002. (SPA., Illus.). pap. 5.50 (978-0-15-323876-5(3)) Harcourt Schl. Pubs.

—Trofeos Below Level: Ya Pronto. 3rd ed. 2002. (SPA., Illus.). (J). pap. 3.50 (978-0-15-323862-8(3)) Harcourt Schl. Pubs.

Hardway, Margaret. Adventures of Lady Peacock. Smith, Eloise, ed. 1998. (Illus.). 20p. (J). (ps-6). 7.00 (978-0-9664035-2-7(5)) Mask Flight Pr.

Harms, John, II. The Saving of Valiant Blue Heron. Belizar, Denise H., ed. Makowski, Robin Lee, illus. 2001. 32p. (J). (gr. 2-7). pap. 6.95 (978-0-9653871-8-7(6)) Frederick Pr.

Harris, Rae Ann & Weintraub, David. Sereena's Secret. Craft, Danna, illus. 2005. (ENG & YID.). 40p. (J). 16.95 (978-1-932687-41-5(6)); pap. 9.95 (978-1-932687-42-2(4)) Pitspopany Pr. (Devora Publishing).

Harris, Robin. Marmalade & the Magic Birds. 2001. (Illus.). 32p. (J). (ps-1). 15.99 (978-1-84148-316-0(8)) Barefoot Bks., Inc.

Harrison, Troon. Courage to Fly. Huang, Zhong-Yang, illus. 2004. 32p. (J). (ps-2). 17.95 (978-0-88995-273-7(6)) Red Deer Pr. CAN. *Dist:* Fitzhenry & Whiteside, Ltd.

Hayes, Joe & Castro Leal, Antonio. Pajaro Verde. 2005. (SPA.). 40p. pap. 8.95 (978-0-938317-90-6(3)) Cinco Puntos Pr.

Hébert, Marie-Francine. Bird Brain. 1999. (Illus.). 48p. (YA). (gr. 3-6). pap. 4.95 (978-1-896764-17-7(7)) Second Story Pr. CAN. *Dist:* Orca Bk. Pubs. USA.

—Un Oiseau dans la Tete. Germaine, Philippe, illus. 2002. (Premier Roman Ser.). (FRE.). 64p. (J). (gr. 2-5). pap. (978-2-89021-278-7(5)) Diffusion du livre Mirabel.

Heine, Helme. Ricardo. Heine, Helme, illus. 2003. (la Orilla Del Viento Ser.). (SPA., Illus.). 28p. (J). (ps-7). pap. 3.99 (978-968-16-6422-0(1) , 152) Fondo de Cultura Economica USA.

Heller, Sarah E. & Cristaldi, Kathryn. Around the World in Tweety Time: Tattoo Storybook. Batcheller, Keith, illus. 2000. 24p. (J). (ps-3). pap. 5.99 (978-0-439-20282-4(5)) Scholastic, Inc.

—Tweety's High Flying Adventures. Summers, Ethan, illus. 2000. 32p. (J). (ps-3). pap. 3.50 (978-0-439-20281-7(7)) Scholastic, Inc.

Hepworth, David G. The Picture Stone. 2006. (Illus.). 76p. pap. (***978-1-4120-9053-7(9)***) Trafford Publishing.

Herman Horatio Hornblower III. 2005. (YA). per. 5.00 (978-1-59872-239-0(5)) Instantpublisher.com.

Herrera, Juan Felipe. Calling the Doves / el Canto de Las Palomas. Simmons, Elly, illus. 2001. Tr. of Canto de Las Palomas. (ENG & SPA.). 32p. (J). (gr. 1 up). pap. 7.95 (978-0-89239-166-0(9)) Children's Bk. Pr.

Herring, Patricia R. Paloma the Dove. 1998. 25p. (J). (gr. 2-5). pap. 12.95 (978-0-9616484-1-1(4)) Santos-Santos Pubns.

Heurtelou, Maude. Istwa Ti Zwazo Ble a. Louissaint, Louis, illus. 1999. Tr. of Blue Bird. (CRP.). 24p. (J). (gr. 3-5). pap. 19.00 incl. audio (978-1-881839-91-0(5)) Educa Vision.

Heusler, Marianna. Night the Penningtons Vanished. 2002. (gr. 7-12). lib. bdg. 24.60 (978-0-613-88682-6(8)) Tandem Library Bks.

Hill, Karen. I Am Good at Being Me. Graef, Renee, illus. 2005. 24p. (J). 3.99 (978-1-4169-0319-2(4)); 9.99 (978-1-4169-0512-7(X)) Simon & Schuster Children's Publishing. (Little Simon).

—One Bird. Hill, Karen, illus. l.t. ed. 2001. 28p. 8.00 (978-0-9714042-0-5(8)) Hill Publishing.

Hindley, Judy. Ten Bright Eyes. Bartlett, Alison, illus. 1998. 32p. (J). (ps-3). 14.95 (978-1-56145-173-9(8)) Peachtree Pubs., Ltd.

Hoffman, Basia. The Bird & the Tadpole, Vol. 1. l.t. ed. 1998. (Tadpole Ser.: Series 1). (Illus.). 32p. (J). (gr. k-2). 15.95 (978-1-890582-03-6(4)) Creations by Basia.

Hohl, Richard. The Prairie: A Novelette. 2006. (Illus.). 67p. pap. (***978-1-4120-9073-5(3)***) Trafford Publishing.

Hoover, Marie, et al. Mikelngur Tenqmiar (Little Bird) (Cupig) Isaac, Cheri & Brunk, Cara, illus. l.t. ed. 1999. (ESK.). 8p. (J). (gr. k-3). pap. 6.00 (978-1-58084-165-8(1)) Lower Kuskokwim Schl. District.

—Yaquliyagaq. Isaac, Cheri & Brunk, Cara, illus. l.t. ed. 1999. (ESK.). 8p. (J). (gr. k-3). pap. 6.00 (978-1-58084-164-1(3)) Lower Kuskokwim Schl. District.

Hopkinson, Deborah. Bluebird Summer. Andersen, Bethanne, illus. 2001. 32p. (J). (gr. 1 up). 15.95 (978-0-688-17398-2(5)) HarperCollins Pubs.

Horacek, Pete. Bird Fly High. Horacek, Pete, illus. 2005. (Illus.). 16p. (J). (gr. k-ps). bds. 5.99 (978-0-7636-2823-9(9)) Candlewick Pr.

Horowitz, Dave. Beware of Tigers. Horowitz, Dave, illus. 2006. (Illus.). 40p. (J). (ps-3). 12.99 (978-0-399-24508-4(1)) Penguin Group (USA) Inc.

I Can Fly: Individual Title Six-Pack Pouch - Level C. (Lighthouse Ser.). (gr. k-1). 24.00 (978-0-7578-0821-0(2)) Rigby Education.

I Love Birds. 2004. (Illus.). 26p. (J). lib. bdg. 12.95 (978-0-9748165-0-0(7)) Jaylil Publishing Co.

Inches, Alison. Dizzy's Bird Watch. 2001. 10.79 (978-0-606-22130-6(1)); lib. bdg. 11.80 (978-0-613-51300-5(2)) Tandem Library Bks.

Ishii, Momoko. El Gorrion de la Lengua Cortada. Akaba, Suekichi, illus. Tr. of Tongue-Cut Sparrow. (SPA.). 40p. (J). (gr. 3 up). 14.95 (978-980-257-073-7(7)) Ekare, Ediciones VEN. *Dist:* Kane/Miller Bk. Pubs., Inc.

Italia, John. The Birds of the Harbor. 2007. 32p. 15.95 (***978-0-9726614-7-8(6)***) Shenanigan Bks.

Ives, Bob. The Three Ants & Mother Bird. Deskov, Vladimir, ed. Fairy, Meg, illus. 2004. 40p. (J). (978-1-920832-06-3(8)) Four Heads Publishing Group Pty, Ltd.

Jackson, Sarah. Preep of Old Washington Square: A Collection of East Texas Tales. Jenkins, Delores, illus. l.t. ed. 2005. 48p. (J). 16.95 (978-1-931823-25-8(1)) Halcyon Pr., Ltd.

Jacques, Brian. Loamhedge. Elliot, David, illus. 2005. (Redwall Ser.). 464p. (J). (gr. 5). pap. 8.99 (978-0-14-240377-8(6) , Puffin) Penguin Group (USA) Inc.

Jane, Pamela. Take a Bow, Winky Blue! Tilley, Debbie, illus. 1998. (Mondo Ser.). 56p. (J). (gr. 2-6). pap. 3.95 (978-1-57255-550-1(5)) Mondo Publishing.

—Way to Go, Winky Blue! Tilley, Debbie, illus. 2002. 64p. (J). pap. (978-1-59034-389-0(1)); (gr. 2-5). 13.95 (978-1-59034-388-3(3)) Mondo Publishing.

Jarrett, Clare. Jamie & the Lost Bird. 2002. (Illus.). 32p. pap. 8.99 (978-0-00-664768-3(5)) HarperCollins Pubs. Ltd. GBR. *Dist:* Trafalgar Square Publishing.

—Jamie Picture Book. (Illus.). 25p. 13.95 (978-0-00-198414-1(4) , HarperSport) HarperCollins Pubs. Ltd. GBR. *Dist:* Trafalgar Square Publishing.

Jenkins, Amanda. How the Turtle Cracked its Shell: A Tale from Guatemala. 2006. 23.00 (***978-1-4108-6171-9(6)***) Benchmark Education Co.

Jenkins, Jane J. The Little Fir Tree. 2005. (Illus.). 32p. (J). per. 7.95 (978-1-59453-184-2(6) , Airleaf Publishing) Airleaf Publishing & Bookselling.

Jensen, Kerry L. Goshawk & the Legend of Ooozi. 1998. 135p. (YA). (gr. 4-9). pap. 14.95 (978-0-9667043-0-3(4)) Hoot Owl Bks.

Jessop, Sherry. The Great BooDinie Bird: Faith, 5 vols., Vol. 1. Staples, Deb, ed. Sketchit, Elly, illus. 2000. cd-rom 6.50 (978-1-931540-25-4(X)) SynergEbks.

Jewell, Sandra. Paula Peacock Discovers She Is Unique. 2005. per. (978-0-8059-9613-5(3)) Dorrance Publishing Co., Inc.

Jeyaveeran, Ruth. The Spectacular Adventures of Sophie & Sebastian. Jeyaveeran, Ruth, illus. 2005. (Illus.). 32p. (J). (gr. k-3). 16.00 (978-0-618-50756-6(6)) Houghton Mifflin Co. Trade & Reference Div.

Jonas, Ann. Bird Talk. 1999. (Illus.). 32p. (J). (ps-3). 14.89 (978-0-688-14173-8(0)) HarperCollins Pubs.

Kaczman, James. A Bird & His Worm. Kaczman, James, illus. 2002. (Illus.). 32p. (J). (gr. k-3). tchr. ed. 15.00 (978-0-618-09460-8(1)) Houghton Mifflin Co. Trade & Reference Div.

Kasischke, Laura. White Bird in a Blizzard. 1999. 249p. 22.95 (978-0-7868-6366-2(8)) Hyperion Pr.

Kasza, Keiko. A Mother for Choco. 2003. 32p. (J). (ps-1). bds. 6.99 (978-0-399-24191-8(4) , Putnam Juvenile) Penguin Group (USA) Inc.

Kaths, Kathy. The Soaring Feather. 1999. (Illus.). 80p. (J). pap. 8.95 (978-0-9672533-0-5(6)) Kichita Productions.

Keats, Ezra Jack. Jennie's Hat. Keats, Ezra Jack, illus. 2003. (Illus.). 40p. (J). pap. 6.99 (978-0-14-250035-4(6) , Puffin) Penguin Group (USA) Inc.

—Jennie's Hat. 2003. (Illus.). 40p. (J). (gr. k-3). 15.99 (978-0-670-03625-7(0) , Viking Juvenile) Penguin Group (USA) Inc.

—Jennie's Hat. 2003. (gr. k-3). lib. bdg. 15.30 (978-0-613-61710-9(X)) Tandem Library Bks.

Keller, Holly. Sophie's Window. Keller, Holly, illus. 2005. (Illus.). 32p. (J). 15.99 (978-0-06-056282-3(X)); 16.89 (978-0-06-056283-0(8)) HarperCollins Pubs.

Kerns, Thelma. A Ducky Wedding. Owens, Bryant, illus. 1999. 32p. (J). (ps-k). 9.95 (978-1-57072-101-4(7)) Overmountain Pr.

Kiki & the Cuckoo: Evaluation Guide. 2006. (J). (978-1-55942-412-7(5)) Marsh Media.

Kimble, Maggie T. Peep Learns to Sing. 2004. 21p. pap. 14.95 (978-1-4137-2005-1(6)) PublishAmerica, Inc.

King-Smith, Dick. Billy the Bird. Jenkin-Pearce, Susie, illus. 2001. 80p. (gr. 2-5). 14.99 (978-0-7868-0586-0(2)) Hyperion Bks. for Children.

The King's Ring: KinderReaders Individual Title Six-Packs. (Kinderstarters Ser.). 8p. (ps-1). 21.00 (978-0-7635-8656-0(0)) Rigby Education.

Kitamura, Satoshi. Igor, the Bird Who Couldn't Sing. Kitamura, Satoshi, illus. 2005. (Illus.). 40p. (J). (ps-ps). 16.00 (978-0-374-33558-8(3) , Farrar, Straus & Giroux (BYR)) Farrar, Straus & Giroux.

Klein, Abby. King of Show-and-Tell. McKinley, John, illus. 2004. (Ready, Freddy! Ser.). 96p. (J). pap. 3.99 (978-0-439-55598-2(1) , Blue Sky Pr., The) Scholastic, Inc.

Knight, Betty. Sailwind the Seabird. Aton, Barbara, illus. 2005. (J). per. 19.95 (978-1-59858-017-4(5)) Dog Ear Publishing, LLC.

Knowles, Sheena. Edward the Emu. Clement, Rod, illus. 1998. 32p. (J). (ps-1). pap. 6.99 (978-0-06-443499-7(0)) HarperCollins Pubs.

—Edward the Emu. Clement, Rod, illus. 1998. 13.75 (978-0-606-11288-8(X)) Tandem Library Bks.

Kret, Itzah C. The Man with the Sneezes. 2003. per. 16.99 (978-1-4134-2895-7(9)) Xlibris Corp.

Krohn, Kathryn T. Sarah's Most Perfect Day. 2007. 24p. (J). 13.99 (***978-1-59879-325-3(X)*** , Lifevest) Lifevest Publishing, Inc.

Langley, Charles P. North, East, South, West: Catherine, Anna & Geku Take a Long Trip. Holbrook, Kathryn, illus. 2001. (J). (gr. 1-5). per. 9.95 (978-0-9674510-0-8(0)) Anacat Pubns.

Langton, Jane. The Fledgling. unabr. ed. 2004. 192p. (J). (gr. 4-7). pap. 36.00 incl. audio (978-0-8072-8779-8(2) , YA265SP, Listening Library) Random Hse. Audio Publishing Group.

Larsen, Alison. Birds Don't Say 'Bow ¿ Wow!' 2006. (Illus.). 28p. (J). per. 12.95 (978-1-59453-937-4(5) , Airleaf Publishing) Airleaf Publishing & Bookselling.

Lasky, Kathryn. She's Wearing a Dead Bird on Her Head! Catrow, David, illus. 1999. 40p. pap. 6.99 (978-0-7868-1164-9(1)) Disney Pr.

—To Be a King. 2006. (Guardians of Ga'Hoole Ser.: Bk. 11). 224p. (J). (gr. 4-7). pap. 4.99 (978-0-439-79570-8(2) , Scholastic Paperbacks) Scholastic, Inc.

Law, Felicia. The Bookseller Bird. Evans, Nicola, illus. 2005. (Bamboo & Friends Ser.). 24p. (J). (ps-7). lib. bdg. 22.60 (978-1-4048-1283-0(0)) Picture Window Bks.

—The Creeping Vine. Evans, Nicola, illus. 2005. (Bamboo & Friends Ser.). 24p. (J). (ps-3). lib. bdg. 22.60 (978-1-4048-1284-0(9)) Picture Window Bks.

—The Dragonfly. Philpott, Claire, illus. 2005. (Bamboo & Friends Ser.). 24p. (J). (ps-3). lib. bdg. 22.60 (978-1-4048-1302-1(0)) Picture Window Bks.

—The Flower's Busy Day. Evans, Nicola, illus. 2005. (Bamboo & Friends Ser.). 24p. (J). (ps-3). lib. bdg. 22.60 (978-1-4048-1281-9(4)) Picture Window Bks.

—Marvelous Meals. Evans, Nicola, illus. 2005. (Bamboo & Friends Ser.). 24p. (J). (ps-3). lib. bdg. 22.60 (978-1-4048-1285-7(7)) Picture Window Bks.

—The Snowflakes. Philpott, Claire & Radford, Karen, illus. 2007. (J). (978-1-4048-2597-0(5)) Picture Window Bks.

—The Tree. Philpott, Claire, illus. 2005. (Bamboo & Friends Ser.). 24p. (J). (ps-3). lib. bdg. 22.60 (978-1-4048-1301-4(2)) Picture Window Bks.

Lawrence, Michael. The Poltergoose. l.t. ed. 2005. (Illus.). 168p. (J). pap. (978-0-7540-7836-4(1) , CLP 427) BBC Audio.

Lawston, Lisa. Can You Sing? Vere, Ed, illus. 1999. 10p. (J). (ps). pap. 5.95 (978-0-531-30132-6(X) , Orchard Bks.) Scholastic, Inc.

Leatham, Alan D. Four Cats, Five Monkeys, Absurd Birds & Other Fanciful Stuff. 2006. 108p. pap. 16.95 (***978-1-4241-0692-9(3)***) PublishAmerica, Inc.

Lerner, Harriet & Goldhor, Susan. Franny B. Kranny, There's a Bird in Your Hair! Oxenbury, Helen, illus. 2001. 40p. (J). (ps-3). 15.89 (978-0-06-029503-5(1)) HarperCollins Pubs.

Lillegard, Dee. Who Will Sing a Lullaby? Yaccarino, Dan, illus. 2007. 32p. (J). (ps-1). 15.99 (***978-0-375-81573-7(2)***); lib. bdg. 18.99 (***978-0-375-91573-4(7)***) Random Hse. Children's Bks. (Knopf Bks. for Young Readers).

Lingard, Joan. Egg Thieves. (Illus.). 96p. pap. 7.99 (978-0-340-73264-9(4) , Hodder & Stoughton) Hodder General Publishing Division GBR. *Dist:* Trafalgar Square Publishing.

Lionni, Leo. Inch by Inch. Lionni, Leo, illus. 2002. (Illus.). (J). 14.47 (978-0-7587-0120-6(9)) Book Wholesalers, Inc.

—Inch by Inch. Lionni, Leo, illus. unabr. ed. 2006. (J). (ps-1). pap. 14.95 incl. audio (***978-0-439-90584-8(2)*** , WPRA699); pap. 18.95 incl. audio compact disk (***978-0-439-90585-5(0)*** , WPCD699) Weston Woods Studios, Inc.

—Nicolas, Where Have You Been? 2007. 32p. (J). (ps-3). 16.99 (978-0-375-84450-8(3)); lib. bdg. 19.99 (978-0-375-94450-5(8)) Random Hse. Children's Bks. (Knopf Bks. for Young Readers).

Lionni, Leo. Tico & the Golden Wings. 2007. 32p. (J). (ps-3). 16.99 (***978-0-394-81749-1(4)*** , Knopf Bks. for Young Readers) Random Hse. Children's Bks.

List, Gloria A. The Journey: A Young Swallows Flight to the Mission of San Juan Capistrano. Ramirez, Ivan D., ed. Wasif, Sohail & Han, Ben, illus. 1999. 32p. (J). (gr. 2-4). 14.95 (978-1-57159-006-0(4)) Los Andes Publishing Co.

The Little Bluebird. 2001. (Illus.). (J). 20.00 (978-0-9715494-0-1(0)) Weintraub, Melody.

Little Red Hen. 2005. (J). bds. 39.99 (978-1-933200-14-9(6)) Family Bks. at Home.

Lohr, Nancy. Songbird. Berg, Johanna, illus. 1999. (Light Line Ser.). 67p. (J). (gr. 4-7). pap. 7.49 (978-1-57924-297-8(9) , 117382) Jones, Bob Univ. Pr.

London, Jonathan. Condor's Egg. Chaffee, James, illus. 1999. (Endangered Species Ser.). 32p. (J). (ps-3). pap. 7.95 (978-0-8118-2312-8(1)) Chronicle Bks. LLC.

Louie, Therese On. Raymond's Perfect Present. Wang, Suling, illus. 2002. (J). (gr. 2-4). 16.95 (978-1-58430-055-7(8)) Lee & Low Bks., Inc.

Lowe, Anne. Raven's Flight. Clover, Gordon, illus. 1999. 76p. (J). (gr. 3-9). pap. 8.95 (978-0-89716-932-5(8)) Peanut Butter Publishing.

Lubbert, Constance. Killdeer. 2004. 81p. pap. 14.95 (978-1-4137-1138-7(3)) PublishAmerica, Inc.

Luneau, Terri Roberts. Big Woods Bird: An Ivory-bill Story. Trevor, Bennett, illus. 2005. 36p. (J). per. 8.95 (978-0-9768839-0-6(2)) Kury Lane Inc.

Lunianski, Stephanie. Luke's Perfect Day. 2003. 48p. (J). pap. 8.95 (978-0-595-28286-9(5)) iUniverse, Inc.

Luz Uribe, Maria. El Primer Pajaro de Piko-Niko. (SPA.). 32p. (J). 12.95 (978-84-261-2307-7(4) , JV0593) Juventud, Editorial ESP. *Dist:* AIMS International Bks., Inc., Lectorum Pubns., Inc.

Macaulay, David. Angelo. 2006. (Illus.). 48p. (J). reprint ed. pap. 6.95 (978-0-618-69336-8(X)) Houghton Mifflin Co.

MacHado, Ana Maria. Pimienta en la Cebecita. (Torre de Papel Ser.). (SPA., Illus.). (J). 7.95 (978-958-04-5049-8(8) , NR3067) Norma S.A. COL. *Dist:* Distribuidora Norma, Inc., Lectorum Pubns., Inc.

Mackall, Debbie. Be Still! The Story of Little Bird & How He Found His Purpose. l.t. ed. 2005. (Illus.). 32p. (J). lib. bdg. 19.95 (978-0-9762273-0-4(4)) Dimensions in Media, Inc.

Manuli'i & the Colorful Cape. 2001. (J). 8.99 (978-0-89610-423-5(0)) Island Heritage Publishing.

Marcus, John V. Birdy Bird & the Plane. 2007. 9.00 (***978-0-8059-7312-9(5)***) Dorrance Publishing Co., Inc.

Markarian, Marianne. The Pesky Bird, Wasielewski, Margaret M., illus. l.t. ed. 2005. 32p. (J). 16.00 (978-0-9767377-0-4(1)) Pomegranate Publishing.

Marvin's Egg: Early Level Satellite Individual Title Six-Packs. (Sails Literacy Ser.). 16p. (gr. 1-2). 27.00 (978-0-7578-3155-3(9)) Rigby Education.

Mason, Patricia. Return of the Osprey. Bateman, Christopher, illus. unabr. ed. 1999. 22p. (J). (gr. 1-3). pap. (978-1-55017-203-4(4)) Harbour Publishing Co., Ltd.

Massie, Diane Redfield. The Baby Beebee Bird. Kellogg, Steven, illus. 32p. (J). (ps-1). 2003. pap. 6.99 (978-0-06-051784-7(0)); 2000. 16.99 (978-0-06-028083-3(2)) HarperCollins Pubs.

—The Baby Beebee Bird. 2003. (gr. k-3). lib. bdg. 14.15 (978-0-613-65762-4(4)) Tandem Library Bks.

Mathers, Petra. Lottie's New Friend. Mathers, Petra, illus. (Illus.). 32p. (J). (ps-3). 2002. pap. 5.99 (978-0-689-84896-4(X) , Aladdin); 1999. 15.00 (978-0-689-82014-4(3) , Atheneum/Anne Schwartz Bks.) Simon & Schuster Children's Publishing.

—Lottie's New Friend. 2002. (gr. k-3). lib. bdg. 14.15 (978-0-613-73374-8(6)) Tandem Library Bks.

McCallum, C. Dawn. The Caretaker of Tree Palace. Doxey, Morgan, illus. l.t. ed. 2006. 120p. (J). lib. bdg. 16.95 (978-0-9764026-3-3(7) , 3300) Longhorn Creek Pr.

McCann, Jesse Leon. Tweety. 2001. (Looney Tunes Teacher's Pets Ser.). (Illus.). 32p. (J). (gr. 1-5). 4.95 (978-0-439-28659-6(X) , Tangerine Pr.) Scholastic, Inc.

McCloskey, Robert. A Robert McCloskey Collection. 2003. 198p. (J). 19.99 (978-0-670-05901-0(3) , Viking Juvenile) Penguin Group (USA) Inc.

McLerran, Alice. Mountain That Loved a Bird. 2000. (978-0-606-17930-0(5)) Tandem Library Bks.

Meadows, Melissa. What's the Word, Thunderbird? 2007. (Illus.). 80p. (J). pap. 4.99 (*978-1-934517-00-0(3)) Firelight Press, Inc.

Middleton-Blake, Lou. Daydreams, Moonbeams & Wings over the. 2005. 491p. pap. 29.95 (978-1-4137-4982-3(8)) PublishAmerica, Inc.

Milano, Jacque. Stay-at-Home Hank: The Little Hummingbird That Couldn't Fly. Milano, Jacque, illus. l.t. ed. 2003. (Illus.). 30p. (J). 9.95 (978-0-9728432-0-1(5)) Milano, Jacque & Assocs.

Miller, Lynda. Bird & His Ring. Miller, Lynda, illus. 1999. (Illus.). 20p. (J). (gr. k-7). 10.00 (978-0-9636140-4-9(5) , Neon Rose Productions) Smart Alternatives, Inc.

Mitchell, Marianne. Currucucu. de la Vega, Eida, tr. Henry, Marilyn, illus. 2001. (Books for Young Learners).Tr. of Coo Coo Caroo. (SPA.). 12p. (J). (gr. k-2). pap. 5.00 (978-1-57274-441-7(3) , 2845) Owen, Richard C. Pubs., Inc.

Moeller, Kathleen H. The Birds at My Barn. Lusardi, Rosi, illus. 2000. (Books for Young Learners). 16p. (J). pap. 5.00 (978-1-57274-249-9(6)) Owen, Richard C. Pubs., Inc.

Moncure, Jane Belk. Watch Out! Word Bird. 2002. (New Word Bird Library). (Illus.). 32p. (J). (ps-3). 22.79 (978-1-56766-992-3(1)) Child's World, Inc.

—Word Bird Asks What? What? What? 2002. (New Word Bird Library). (Illus.). 32p. (J). (ps-3). 22.79 (978-1-56766-994-7(8)) Child's World, Inc.

—Word Bird Builds a City. 2002. (New Word Bird Library). (Illus.). 32p. (J). (ps-3). 22.79 (978-1-56766-995-4(6)) Child's World, Inc.

—Word Bird's Dinosaur Days. 2002. (New Word Bird Library). (Illus.). 32p. (J). (ps-3). 22.79 (978-1-56766-999-2(9)) Child's World, Inc.

—Word Bird's Hats. 2002. (New Word Bird Library). (Illus.). 32p. (J). (ps-3). 22.79 (978-1-56766-997-8(2)) Child's World, Inc.

—Word Bird's Magic Wand. 2002. (New Word Bird Library). (Illus.). 32p. (J). (ps-3). 22.79 (978-1-56766-630-4(2)) Child's World, Inc.

—Word Bird's New Friend. 2002. (New Word Bird Library). (Illus.). 32p. (J). (ps-3). 22.79 (978-1-56766-844-5(5)) Child's World, Inc.

—Word Bird's Rainy-Day Dance. 2002. (New Word Bird Library). (Illus.). 32p. (J). (ps-3). 22.79 (978-1-56766-893-3(3)) Child's World, Inc.

—Word Bird's Shapes. 2002. (New Word Bird Library). (Illus.). 32p. (J). (ps-3). 22.79 (978-1-56766-998-5(0)) Child's World, Inc.

Montenegro, Laura Nyman. A Poet's Bird Garden. 2007. (Illus.). 32p. (J). (ps-3). 16.00 (978-0-374-36038-2(3)) Farrar, Straus & Giroux.

Morgan, Ruth. Sglod & the Sand Dragon. Carpenter, Suzanne, illus. 2000. 32p. pap. 12.95 (978-1-85902-831-5(4)) Beekman Bks., Inc.

Morison, Toby. Little Louie Takes Off. Morison, Toby, illus. 2007. (Illus.). 32p. (J). (ps-2). 16.95 (*978-0-8027-9645-5(1)) Walker & Co.

Morpurgo, Michael. Colly's Barn. Andrew, Ian P., illus. 2002. (Yellow Bananas Ser.). 48p. (J). (gr. 3-4). pap. (978-0-7787-0978-7(7)); lib. bdg. (978-0-7787-0932-9(9)) Crabtree Publishing Co.

—Colly's Barn. 2002. (gr. 3-6). lib. bdg. 12.95 (978-0-613-52822-1(0)) Tandem Library Bks.

—Little Albatross. Foreman, Michael, illus. 2006. 32p. (J). (gr. 1-2). pap. 8.99 (978-0-552-54698-0(4) , Corgi) Transworld Publishers Ltd. GBR. *Dist:* Independent Pubs. Group.

Morrow, Bradford. Didn't Didn't Do It. Wilson, Gahan, illus. 2007. 32p. (J). (gr. k-2). 16.99 (978-0-399-24480-3(8) , Putnam Juvenile) Penguin Group (USA) Inc.

Morrow, John. Happy Birthday Oklahoma! collector's ed. 2007. (Illus.). (J). lib. bdg. 17.95 (*978-0-9790832-2-8(2)) Three Ring Circus Publishing Company.

Mother Goose: My First Library. pap. 12.98 (978-0-7853-7395-7(0)) Publications International, Ltd.

Mother Goose & the Children: Take-Home Book. 2005. (Lee Bennett Hopkins Mother Goose Ser.). (YA). (ps-1). 13.50 (978-0-8215-0561-8(0)) Sadlier, William H. Inc.

Mother Goose Around the World: Take-Home Book. 2005. (Lee Bennett Hopkins Mother Goose Ser.). (YA). (ps-1). 13.50 (978-0-8215-0564-9(5)) Sadlier, William H. Inc.

Mother Goose Collection. 2001. (Take-Home Bks.). (YA). (ps-k). 54.00 (978-0-8215-6988-7(0)) Sadlier, William H. Inc.

Mother Goose Through the Seasons: Take-Home Book. 2005. (Lee Bennett Hopkins Mother Goose Ser.). (YA). (ps-1). 13.50 (978-0-8215-0563-2(7)) Sadlier, William H. Inc.

Mubiru, Betha. Muzinge the Bird. 2004. (Illus.). 16p. pap. 9.95 (978-9970-02-447-6(7)) Fountain Pubs. Ltd. UGA. *Dist:* Michigan State Univ. Pr.

Myers, Christopher A. Fly! Myers, Christopher A., illus. 2001. (Illus.). 32p. (ps-17). 16.49 (978-0-7868-2373-4(9) , Jump at the Sun) Hyperion Bks. for Children.

Naidu, Vayu. Eyes on the Peacock's Tail. 1998. (Under the Banyan Ser.). (Illus.). 22p. (YA). (gr. 2 up). 11.99 incl. audio (978-81-86838-27-3(9)) APG Sales and Fulfillment.

Napoli, Donna Jo. Albert. LaMarche, Jim, illus. 32p. (J). (gr. k-3). 2001. 17.00 (978-0-15-201572-5(8)); 2005. reprint ed. pap. 7.00 (978-0-15-205249-2(6) , Voyager Bks./Libros Viajeros) Harcourt Children's Bks.

Newman, Marjorie. Mole & the Baby Bird. Benson, Patrick, illus. 32p. (J). 2004. bds. 6.95 (978-1-58234-914-5(2)); 2002. 16.95 (978-1-58234-784-4(0)) Bloomsbury Publishing. (Bloomsbury Children).

Norman, Howard. Between Heaven & Earth: Bird Tales from Around the World. Dillon, Leo & Dillon, Diane, illus. 2004. 88p. (YA). 22.00 (978-0-15-201982-2(0)) Harcourt Children's Bks.

O'Brien, May. How Crows Became Black. Leaney, Angela, illus. 2001. 40p. (J). pap. 9.95 (978-1-86368-027-1(6)) Fremantle Pr. AUS. *Dist:* International Specialized Bk. Services.

Oliver, Narelle. The Best Beak in Boonaroo Bay. Oliver, Narelle, illus. (Illus.). 48p. (YA). pap. (978-0-85091-671-3(2) , Lothian Bks.) Hachette Livre Australia.

Osborne, M. D. The Rescue of Mr. Goldsmith. l.t. ed. 2005. (Illus.). 40p. (J). 12.95 (978-0-9762852-1-2(5)) Wooden Shoe Pr.

Palatini, Margie. Gorgonzola. Bowers, Tim, illus. 2008. 32p. (J). 16.99 (978-0-06-073897-6(9)); lib. bdg. 17.89 (978-0-06-073898-3(7)) HarperCollins Pubs.

Paloma y la Hormiga. (SPA.). pap. 7.95 (978-88-8148-801-8(9)) European Language Institute ITA. *Dist:* Distribooks, Inc.

Pantelides, Sherry. It's Blue Like You! A Story about Loyalty. Perez, Debi, illus. 2007. 32p. (J). 12.99 (*978-0-9771076-1-2(2)) Lacey Productions.

Paterson, Katherine. Marvin's Best Christmas Present Ever. Brown, Jane Clark, illus. 2002. (J). 11.91 (978-0-7587-6200-9(3)) Book Wholesalers, Inc.

—Marvin's Best Christmas Present Ever. 1999. (I Can Read Bks.). (J). (978-0-606-17299-8(8)); lib. bdg. 11.80 (978-0-613-22890-9(1)) Tandem Library Bks.

Patterson, Stacey. Fidget's Freedom. Gorbatov, Vadim, illus. 2006. (EST.). 32p. 17.95 (978-0-9723422-6-1(5)) Moonlight Publishing.

Paulsen, Gary. The Amazing Life of Birds: The Nineteen Day Puberty Journal of Duane Homer Leech. 2008. 96p. (YA). (gr. 5-9). 6.50 (*978-0-553-49428-0(7) , Yearling) Random Hse. Children's Bks.

Peep and Big Wide World & Galvin, Laura. When Will I Fly. 2006. 28p. pap. 2.99 (978-1-59249-551-1(6)) Soundprints.

Peirce, Ken. Flying Lessons. 2001. 40p. (J). pap. 17.95 (978-1-58597-071-1(9)) Leathers Publishing.

Pérez Sabbi, Mercedes & Barreiro, S. Carmela y Valentín. 2004. (SPA.). 32p. 6.95 (978-1-4000-9293-2(0)) Random House Mondadori ESP. *Dist:* Random Hse., Inc,

Perrine, David L. Birdie School Days: The First Day of School. Perry, Margie, illus. 2005. (J). pap. 15.00 (978-0-8059-6699-2(4)) Dorrance Publishing Co., Inc.

Peterson, Bruce & Peterson, Marilyn. The Adventures of Bo the Cloud: The Rainbow Bird. Horton, Pamela, ed. Panasiti, Peg, illus. 2001. 28p. (J). mass mkt. 9.95 incl. audio (978-0-9708417-0-4(1)) High Hopes Publishing.

Peterson, Elizabeth J. Christina & the Little Red Bird. Mcknight, C. D., illus. 1999. 23p. (J). (ps-5). reprint ed. spiral bd. 5.95 (978-0-938911-02-9(3)) Individualized Education Systems/Poppy Lane Publishing.

Peyton, K. M. Swallow Tale. 2000. (Illus.). 188p. (J). pap 6.95 (978-0-552-52807-8(2)) Transworld Publishers Ltd. GBR. *Dist:* Trafalgar Square Publishing.

Pierre, Stephanie. What the Sea Saw. Doyle, Beverly, illus. 2006. 48p. (J). 16.95 (978-1-56145-359-7(5)) Peachtree Pubs., Ltd.

Piggy Toes Press Staff. Baby Tweety's Bedtime. 2000. (Lovable Huggable Baby Looney Tunes Cloth Bks.). (Illus.). 6p. (J). (ps up). 14.95 (978-1-58117-077-1(7) , Intervisual/Piggy Toes) Dalmatian Pr.

Pixton, Amy, creator. Things with Wings. 2006. (J). (978-0-9779631-2-6(8)) TyBook.

Podoshen, Lois. The Birthday Bird. Schaedler, Sally, illus. 1998. (Books for Young Learners). 8p. (J). (gr. k-2). pap. 5.00 (978-1-57274-154-6(6) , A2430) Owen, Richard C. Pubs., Inc.

Polacco, Patricia. Mr. Lincoln's Way. Polacco, Patricia, illus. 2001. (Illus.). 40p. (J). (gr. 1-4). 16.99 (978-0-399-23754-6(2) , Philomel) Penguin Group (USA) Inc.

Polak, Monique. Finding Elmo. 2007. (Orca Currents Ser.). 112p. (YA). (gr. 5 up). pap. (*978-1-55143-686-9(8)); lib. bdg. (*978-1-55143-688-3(4)) Orca Bk. Pubs.

Polette, Nancy. Flying with Mother Goose. 2003. pap. 7.95 (978-1-931334-19-8(6) , CLC0285) Pieces of Learning.

Powell, Kristen. Flappy & the Big Red Sky. 2006. 17p. (J). 12.00 (978-1-4116-7756-2(0)) Lulu.com.

Prince, Sarah. Benny & the Birds. 2001. (gr. k-3). lib. bdg. 11.80 (978-0-613-33334-4(9)) Tandem Library Bks.

—Butterfly, the Bird, the Beetle, & Me. 2000. (gr. k-3). lib. bdg. 11.80 (978-0-613-29568-0(4)) Tandem Library Bks.

Pugliano-Martin, Carol. Ready for Fall! 2006. (Early Explorers Ser.). (J). 34.00 (*978-1-4108-6103-0(1)) Benchmark Education Co.

—See You in Spring! 2006. (Early Explorers Ser.). (J). 34.00 (*978-1-4108-6105-4(8)) Benchmark Education Co.

Radunsky, Vladimir. The Mighty Asparagus. 2004. (Illus.). 34p. (J). 16.00 (978-0-15-216743-1(9) , Silver Whistle) Harcourt Trade Pubs.

Raintree Steck-Vaughn Staff, contrib. by. Stellaluna. 1999. (J). (ps-3). 16.00 (978-0-8172-9782-4(0)); pap. 22.00 (978-0-8172-9784-8(7)) Steck-Vaughn.

Ramakar, Ram. Little Crow Feather. 2006. (ENG.). 48p. per. 12.95 (*978-1-4241-5134-9(1)) PublishAmerica, Inc.

Ramirez, Michael Rose. Legend of the Hummingbird: A Tale from Puerto Rico. 1998. (gr. k-3). lib. bdg. 12.95 (978-0-613-87443-4(9)) Tandem Library Bks.

Random House Staff. Super Friends: Flying High. 2008. (Step into Reading Ser.). 32p. (J). (ps-1). lib. bdg. 11.99 (*978-0-375-95208-1(X) , Random Hse. Bks. for Young Readers) Random Hse. Children's Bks.

Ray, Mary Lyn. Welcome, Brown Bird. Sylvada, Peter, illus. 2004. 32p. (J). 16.00 (978-0-15-292863-6(4)) Harcourt Children's Bks.

Reece, Robert. Freeman A. Freelander. Gallina, Todd, illus. 2002. 40p. (J). 11.95 (978-0-9702308-1-2(8)) Dark Horse Pr.

Richards, Kitty. Bird Who Cried Wolf. 2000. (gr. k-3). lib. bdg. 11.80 (978-0-613-24367-4(6)) Tandem Library Bks.

Richardson, Kara, illus. Simon & Barklee in Mexico. 2002. (Simon & Barklee in Mexico). 64p. (J). per. 15.00 (978-0-9714502-0-2(X) , Explorer Media) Simon & Barklee, Inc./ExplorerMedia.

Riddell, Chris. The Emperor of Absurdia. 2006. (Illus.). 32p. (J). (*978-1-4050-5061-6(6) , Macmillan Children's Bks.) Pan Macmillan.

Rigby Education Staff. Animals of the Rainforest. (Sails Literacy Ser.). (Illus.). 16p. (gr. k-1). 27.00 (978-0-7635-9867-9(4) , 698674C99) Rigby Education.

—Animals Say... (Sails Literacy Ser.). (Illus.). 16p. (gr. 2-3). 27.00 (978-0-7635-9943-0(3) , 699433C99) Rigby Education.

—Bird Hotel. (Sails Literacy Ser.). (Illus.). 16p. (gr. 1-2). 27.00 (978-0-7635-9924-9(7) , 699247C99) Rigby Education.

—Clean My Teeth. (Sails Literacy Ser.). (Illus.). 16p. (gr. k-1). 27.00 (978-0-7635-9882-2(8) , 698828C99) Rigby Education.

—Feathered Friends. (Sails Literacy Ser.). (Illus.). 16p. (gr. 1-2). 27.00 (978-0-7635-9905-8(0) , 699050C99) Rigby Education.

—Five Little Chickadees. (Illus.). 8p. (J). bds. 3.95 (978-0-7635-6460-5(5) , 764605C99) Rigby Education.

—The Happy House. (Sails Literacy Ser.). (Illus.). 16p. (gr. 1-2). 27.00 (978-0-7635-9908-9(5) , 699085C99) Rigby Education.

—Watch Out for Trash Cans! (Sails Literacy Ser.). (Illus.). 16p. (gr. 1-2). 27.00 (978-0-7635-9910-2(7) , 699107C99) Rigby Education.

Robinson, Tim. Tobias, the Quig & the Rumplenut Tree. Robinson, Tim, illus. 2000. (Illus.). 40p. (J). (ps-3). 16.95 (978-1-890817-20-6(1)) Winslow Pr.

Rosasco, Jose Luis. La Mariposa Negra y Otros Cuentos. 2003. (SPA.). pap. (978-956-13-1661-4(7) , AB12831) Bello, Andres CHL. *Dist:* Lectorum Pubns., Inc.

Roth, Susan L. Happy Birthday Mr. Kang. 2001. (Illus.). 32p. (J). (ps-3). 16.95 (978-0-7922-7723-1(6) , National Geographic Children's Bks.) National Geographic Society.

Ryan, Pam Muñoz. Nacho & Lolita. Rueda, Claudia, illus. 2005. 40p. (J). (ps-3). pap. 16.99 (978-0-439-26968-1(7) , Scholastic Pr.) Scholastic, Inc.

—Nacho y Lolita. Rueda, Claudia, illus. 2005. (SPA.). 40p. (J). (ps-3). pap. 5.99 (978-0-439-76418-6(1) , Scholastic en Espanol) Scholastic, Inc.

Rylant, Cynthia. The Bird House. Moser, Barry, illus. 1998. 32p. (J). (gr. 1-4). pap. 16.95 (978-0-590-47345-3(X) , Blue Sky Pr., The) Scholastic, Inc.

Salzmann, Mary Elizabeth. Hummingbird Hummer. Nobens, C. A., illus. (Fact & Fiction Ser.). 24p. (J). 2007. 21.35 (978-1-59928-442-2(1)); 2006. (978-1-59928-443-9(X)) ABDO Publishing Co.

Sand, George. The Wings of Courage. Bloom, Margaret, tr. from FRE. Frasconi, Antonio, illus. 1998. 70p. (gr. 4-7). 12.95 (978-0-8076-1434-1(3)) Braziller, George Inc.

Sanner, Jennifer Jackson, ed. The Three Little Jayhawks. Pearson, Larry Leroy, illus. 2006. 40p. (J). per. 20.00 (*978-0-9742918-1-9(1)) Kansas Alumni Assoc.

Santillo, LuAnn. Bluejay. Santillo, LuAnn, ed. 2003. (Half-Pint Kids Readers Ser.). (Illus.). 7p. (J). (ps-1). pap. (978-1-59256-110-0(1)) Half-Pint Kids, Inc.

—Flap. Santillo, LuAnn, ed. 2003. (Half-Pint Kids Readers Ser.). (Illus.). 7p. (J). (ps-1). pap. (978-1-59256-096-7(2)) Half-Pint Kids, Inc.

Santucci, Barbara. Loon Summer. Shine, Andrea, illus. 2004. 32p. (J). (gr. k-3). 16.00 (978-0-8028-5182-6(7)) Eerdmans, William B. Publishing Co.

Sargent, Dave. Bogart Blue Jay: Be Thoughtful, 19, vol. 4. Lenoir, Jane, illus. 2003. (Feather Tales Ser.: 4). 42p. (J). pap. (978-1-56763-726-7(4)) Ozark Publishing.

Sargent, Dave & Sargent, David, Jr. Hummer Hummingbird: Being Small Is Okay, 19, 10. Lenoir, Jane, illus. 2003. (Feather Tales Ser.: 10). (J). 42p. pap. 6.95 (978-1-56763-738-0(8)); 2nd ed. 24p. lib. bdg. 19.95 (978-1-56763-737-3(X)) Ozark Publishing.

—Kitty Hawk: Stealing, 20, 11. Lenoir, Jane, illus. 2nd ed. 2003. (Feather Tales Ser.: 11). 42p. (J). lib. bdg. 19.95 (978-1-56763-739-7(6)) Ozark Publishing.

—Pinkie Flamingo: Leaving Home, 20, 15. Lenoir, Jane, illus. 2nd ed. 2003. (Feather Tales Ser.: 15). 42p. (J). lib. bdg. 19.95 (978-1-56763-747-2(7)) Ozark Publishing.

—Storky Stork: Be Trustworthy, 20, 18. Lenoir, Jane, illus. 2nd ed. 2003. (Feather Tales Ser.: 18). 42p. (J). lib. bdg. 19.95 (978-1-56763-753-3(1)) Ozark Publishing.

—Tin Wren: Be Nice, 20, 19. Lenoir, Jane, illus. 2nd ed. 2003. (Feather Tales Ser.: No. 19). 42p. (J). lib. bdg. 19.95 (978-1-56763-755-7(8)) Ozark Publishing.

—Tom Turkey: Don't Bully, 20, 20. Lenoir, Jane, illus. 2nd ed. 2003. (Feather Tales Ser.: 20). 42p. (J). lib. bdg. 19.95 (978-1-56763-757-1(4)) Ozark Publishing.

Sargent, Dave & Sargent, David M. Bogart Blue Jay: Be Thoughtful, 20, 4. Lenoir, Jane, illus. 2nd ed. 2003. (Feather Tales Ser.: 3). 42p. (J). lib. bdg. 19.95 (978-1-56763-725-0(6)) Ozark Publishing.

—Buzz Buzzard: Obey the Rules, 19, 5. Lenoir, Jane, illus. 2003. (Feather Tales Ser.: 5). 42p. (J). pap. 6.95 (978-1-56763-728-1(0)); 2nd ed. lib. bdg. 19.95 (978-1-56763-727-4(2)) Ozark Publishing.

Sargent, Dave & Sargent, David M., Jr. Speedy Roadrunner: Helping Others, 20 bks., 17. Lenoir, Jane, illus. 2nd ed. 2003. (Feather Tales Ser.: 17). 42p. (J). lib. bdg. 19.95 (978-1-56763-751-9(5)) Ozark Publishing.

Savage, Deborah. Summer Hawk. 1999. 304p. (YA). (gr. 7-12). tchr. ed. 16.00 (978-0-395-91163-1(X)) Houghton Mifflin Co. Trade & Reference Div.

Scarry, Richard. The Early Bird. 2003. (Step into Reading Step 1 Bks. Ser.). (Illus.). 32p. (J). (gr. k-3). 11.99 (978-0-679-98920-2(X) , Random Hse. Bks. for Young Readers) Random Hse. Children's Bks.

—The Early Bird. 1999. (J). 10.79 (978-0-606-16890-8(7)) Tandem Library Bks.

Schabacker, Betsy & Schabacker, Susan. Huckleberry Robin: A Story for Children. Schabacker, Betty B., illus. 1998. 24p. (J). (gr. 1-6). pap. 7.95 (978-0-86534-285-9(7)) Sunstone Pr.

Schatzer, Jeffrey L. The Bird in Santa's Beard: How a Christmas Legend Was Forever Changed. 2004. (Illus.). 34p. (J). (978-0-9749554-0-7(X)) Big Belly Bks.

Scheunemann, Pam. Peacock Fan. Chawla, Neena, illus. (Fact & Fiction Ser.). 24p. (J). 2007. 21.35 (978-1-59928-460-6(X)); 2006. (978-1-59928-461-3(8)) ABDO Publishing Co.

Schmid, Robert. War Birds-Justice Friends: What Are We Fighting For? 2004. 95p. pap. 14.95 (978-1-4137-5955-6(6)) PublishAmerica, Inc.

Scholastic, Inc. Staff. Nightingale/Ruisenor. 2007. (Bilingual Tales Ser.). (ENG & SPA.). 24p. (J). pap. 3.99 (*978-0-439-87970-5(1)) Scholastic, Inc.

Schoolland, Marian M. Mrs. Monty & the Birds. Hershberger, Paul, illus. 3rd ed. 1999. 128p. (J). (gr. 4-6). reprint ed. pap. (978-0-9673806-0-5(X)) King's Bookshelf Pubns.

Schreiber, Anne. The Bug & the Bird. Thornburgh, Rebecca McKillip, illus. 1999. (Scholastic At-Home Phonics Reading Program Ser.: Vol. 36). 24p. (J). (978-0-590-68791-1(3)) Scholastic, Inc.

Schwartz, Ellen. Abby's Birds. Shefrin, Sima Elizabeth, illus. 2007. 32p. (J). (gr. k-3). 16.95 (*978-1-896580-86-9(6)) Tradewind Bks. CAN. *Dist:* Orca Bk. Pubs. USA.

Scott, Rose Marie, illus. A Nest of Bluebirds. 2001. 64p. (J). (ps-3). 22.95 (978-1-888683-41-7(4)) Wooster Bk. Co., The.

The Seagull, 6 Packs. (Story Steps Ser.). (gr. k-2). 20.00 (978-0-7635-9584-5(5)) Rigby Education.

Segal, John. The Lonely Moose. rev. ed. 2007. 40p. (ps-2). 15.99 (*978-1-4231-0173-4(1)) Hyperion Pr.

Seidler, Tor. The Silent Spillbills. 1998. 224p. (J). (gr. 3-7). 14.95 (978-0-06-205180-6(6)); 14.89 (978-0-06-205181-3(4)) HarperCollins Pubs.

—Silent Spillbills. 2003. 224p. (J). pap. 5.99 (978-0-06-052106-6(6)) HarperCollins Pubs.

—Silent Spillbills. 2003. (gr. 3-6). lib. bdg. 14.15 (978-0-613-65711-2(X)) Tandem Library Bks.

Sepulveda, Luis. Gaviota y del Gato. 9th ed. 2003. (SPA.). 144p. (978-968-7723-11-2(4) , 6020) Tusquests Editores Mexico, S.A. de C.V.

Shah, Indries. The Farmer's Wife/la Esposa Del Granjero. Santiago, Rose Mary, illus. 2003. (SPA & ENG.). (J). 6.95 (978-1-883536-34-3(0) , FAWI3, Hoopoe Bks.) ISHK.

Sheffield, Marilyn. Fizza the Flamingo. Al-Fakhri, Patricia, illus. 2003. 3p. pap. 7.95 (978-1-900988-63-6(1)) Interlink Publishing Group, Inc.

Shepperson, Jacqueline. Martins of the Everglades. 2007. (ENG.). 152p. per. 19.95 (*978-1-4241-5446-3(4)) PublishAmerica, Inc.

Sherrell, Deborah. Baby Lauren & Theodore,hardcover. 2007. (J). bds. 17.95 (*978-0-9779643-5-2(3)) Healing Tree Arts.

Silkman, Anne. Country Songbird. Doghouse Press Inc. Staff, ed. (Togetherness Ser.). (Illus.). 200p. (YA). pap. (978-1-885531-34-6(6)) Mess Hall Writers.

Silly Seagull. 2004. (J). per. (978-1-57657-372-3(9)) Paradise Pr., Inc.

Simmons, Jane. Que Valiente Eres, Daisy! (SPA.). 216p. (J). (978-84-488-0950-8(5)) Beascoa, Ediciones S.A. ESP. *Dist:* Lectorum Pubns., Inc.

Simon & Barklee in Mexico. 2002. 70p. tchr. ed. 20.00 (978-0-9714502-2-6(6) , Explorer Media) Simon & Barklee, Inc./ExplorerMedia.

Simon, Annette. Mocking Birdies. 2005. (Illus.). 32p. (J). 16.95 (978-1-894965-29-3(9)) Simply Read Bks. CAN. *Dist:* Perseus Distribution.

Sly Fox & the Little Red Hen. 2005. (J). bds. 3.99 (978-1-933200-11-8(1)) Family Bks. at Home.

Smith, Bruce L. Song of Life. l.t. ed. 2006. (Illus.). 32p. (J). lib. bdg. (*978-1-934190-08-1(X)) Ocean Front Bk. Publishing, Inc.

Smith, Duane. Heritage Revealed Series, 3. (J). (gr. 2-9). pap. 13.95 (978-1-886218-00-0(5)) Azimuth Pr.

Smucker, Anna. Outside the Window. Schuett, Stacey, illus. 2005. 32p. (J). reprint ed. per. 7.95 (978-1-891852-40-4(X)) Quarrier Pr.

Snyder, Zilpha Keatley. The Unseen. 2005. 208p. 5.99 (978-0-440-41930-3(1) , Yearling) Random Hse. Children's Bks.

Sommers, Joan. Rainbow Bird Tunnel Book: El Pajaro Del Arco Iris: un Libro Tunel. Shull, Valerie, tr. Spiess-Ferris, Eleanor, illus. 2007. (Take a Peek Ser.). 16p. (J). 14.95 (***978-0-9754150-5-4(0)***) Tunnel Vision.

Spain, Frederick. Maynerd the Australian Cockatiel. Garlets, Peggy L., illus. 1999. i, 36p. (J). (ps-6). 13.95 (978-1-929792-01-6(8)) Roehm Pubs.

Spira, Harriett & Spira, Robert. The First Peep. 2000. (Illus.). vi, 40p. (J). (gr. 1-3). 9.95 (978-0-911455-11-3(6)) Quartz Pr.

Spyri, Johanna. What Sami Sings with the Birds. 2006. pap. 87.99 (***978-1-4280-4365-7(9)***) IndyPublish.com.

Staton, Debbie. Twiggle. Patzelt, Kasie, illus. l.t. ed. 2006. 26p. (J). per. 12.99 (***978-1-59879-199-0(0)***) Lifevest Publishing, Inc.

Stellaluna. (Literature Notes Ser.). (gr. k-6). 2.99 (978-0-7682-0745-3(2) , FS128207) Schaffer, Frank Pubns.

Stellaluna. 1998. (J). 3.95 (978-0-439-04432-5(4)) Scholastic, Inc.

Stewart, Maddie. Peg. Willey, Bee, illus. 2001. (Blue Bananas Ser.). 48p. (J). (gr. 1-2). (978-0-7787-0841-4(1)); pap. (978-0-7787-0887-2(X)) Crabtree Publishing Co.

—Peg. 2002. (gr. k-3). lib. bdg. 12.95 (978-0-613-52895-5(6)) Tandem Library Bks.

Stiegemeyer, Julie. Cheep! Cheep! Baicker-McKee, Carol, illus. 2006. 24p. (J). 9.95 (978-1-58234-682-3(8)) Bloomsbury Publishing.

Stine, R.L. Calling All Birdbrains. Park, Trip, illus. 2007. (Rotten School Ser.: No. 15). 128p. (J). lib. bdg. 14.89 (***978-0-06-123276-3(9)***); (gr. 3-7). 6.99 (***978-0-06-123275-6(0)***) HarperCollins Pubs.

Storad, Conrad J. Lizards for Lunch: A Roadrunner's Tale. 1999. 32p. (J). (ps-3). 15.95 (978-1-891795-02-2(3)) RGU Group, The.

—Lizards for Lunch: A Roadrunner's Tale. 1999. (gr. k-3). lib. bdg. 15.25 (978-0-613-61916-5(1)) Tandem Library Bks.

Strasser, Todd. Buzzards' Feast. 1999. (Against the Odds Ser.). (J). 10.64 (978-0-606-17253-0(X)) Tandem Library Bks.

—Buzzard's Feast. 1999. (Against the Odds Ser.). 160p. (J). (gr. 4-7). pap. 3.99 (978-0-671-02311-9(X) , Aladdin) Simon & Schuster Children's Publishing.

Stratton-Porter, Gene. Birds of the Limberlost. (J). 35.95 (978-0-8488-1526-4(2)) Amereon LTD.

Suplicki, Mark J. Mirthburdz: The Discovery. 2004. (Illus.). 51p. (J). 19.95 (978-0-9764385-0-2(X) , 00B1) Jon'taar Graphxs.

Swager, Christine R. Black Crows & White Cockades. 1999. 208p. (YA). (gr. 6-9). pap. 12.95 (978-0-941072-31-1(2)) Southern Heritage Pr., Inc.

Swinburne, Stephen R. Swallows in the Birdhouse. Brickman, Robin, illus. 2004. 32p. (J). pap. 9.95 (978-1-59078-329-0(8)) Boyds Mills Pr.

Tafuri, Nancy. Where Did Bunny Go? A Bunny & Bird Story. 2001. (Illus.). (J). pap. (978-0-439-16960-8(7)) Scholastic, Inc.

—Where Did Bunny Go? A Bunny & Bird Story. Tafuri, Nancy, illus. 2001. (Illus.). 32p. (J). (ps-2). pap. 15.95 (978-0-439-16959-2(3) , Levine, Arthur A. Bks.) Scholastic, Inc.

—Whose Chick Are You? Tafuri, Nancy, illus. 2007. (Illus.). 40p. (J). (ps-k). 16.99 (978-0-06-082514-0(6)); lib. bdg. 17.89 (978-0-06-082515-7(4)) HarperCollins Pubs.

—Will You Be My Friend? A Bunny & Bird Story. 2000. (Illus.). (J). (978-0-439-05943-5(7)); 32p. pap. 16.95 (978-0-590-63782-4(7) , Scholastic Reference) Scholastic, Inc.

Tankard, Jeremy. Grumpy Bird. 2007. (Illus.). 32p. (J). (ps-k). pap. 12.99 (978-0-439-85147-3(5) , Scholastic Pr.) Scholastic, Inc.

Taravant, Jacques. The Little Wing Giver. Ignatowicz, Nina, tr. from FRE. Sis, Peter, illus. 2004. 30p. (J). (gr. k-4). reprint ed. 15.00 (978-0-7567-7970-2(7)) DIANE Publishing Co.

Tate, Suzanne. Johnny Longlegs: A Tale of Big Birds. Melvin, James, illus. 2005. (Suzanne Tate's Nature Ser.: 28). 28p. (J). pap. 4.95 (978-1-878405-50-0(0)) Nags Head Art, Inc.

Teevin, Toni. What to Do? What to Do? Pedersen, Janet, illus. 2006. 32p. (J). (gr. k-3). 16.00 (978-0-618-44632-2(X) , Clarion Bks.) Houghton Mifflin Co. Trade & Reference Div.

Temple, Philip & Gaskin, Chris. The Legend of the Kea. rev. ed. 2000. (Illus.). 32p. (J). (gr. 1-5). pap. 9.95 (978-1-877135-33-0(X)) Longacre Pr. NZL. *Dist:* Pacific Island Bks.

Tentas, Jane Grant. Alice & the Bird Lady. Tentas, Jane Grant, illus. l.t. ed. 2002. 36p. per. 13.95 (978-0-9658983-6-2(9)) Book Nook Pr.

Tezuka, Osamu. Phoenix. 2006. (Phoenix Ser.). 208p. (YA). Vol. 7. pap. 15.99 (978-1-4215-0517-6(7)); Vol. 8. pap. 15.99 (978-1-4215-0518-3(5)) Viz Media.

Thurston, Dorie. Thank-You for the Thistle. Hawkins, Mecca, illus. 2001. 36p. (J). (ps-3). pap. 9.95 (978-0-9703326-0-8(2)) Dorie Bks.

Tito Vuela al Sur. 2002. (Let's Start Teacher's Pets Ser.).Tr. of Timothy Flies South. (SPA., Illus.). 32p. (J). (ps-3). (978-968-5308-17-5(9) , Silver Dolphin en Español) Advanced Marketing, S. de R. L. de C. V.

Torres, David M. A Whooper Named Frank. 1999. (Illus.). 96p. 14.95 (978-1-57168-329-8(1)) Eakin Pr.

Two Little Birds & Other Stories: Individual Title Six-Pack. (Story Steps Ser.). (gr. k-2). 42.00 (978-0-7635-9568-5(3)) Rigby Education.

Umbrellabird's Umbrella. 2001. (ps-2). lib. bdg. 9.80 (978-0-613-33177-7(X)) Tandem Library Bks.

Useman, Sharon & Useman, Ernie. Tibby Tried It. Pillo, Cary, illus. 1999. 44p. (J). (ps-3). (978-1-55798-558-3(8) , 441-5588, Magination Pr.) American Psychological Assn.

Uslan, Michael E. Chatterbox: The Bird Who Wore Glasses. Gurney, John Steven, illus. 2006. 34p. (J). 17.99 (978-0-9753843-2-9(5)) ee publishing & productions, inc.

van Kampen, Vlasta. A Drop of Gold. van Kampen, Vlasta, illus. 2001. (Illus.). 32p. (J). (ps-k). pap. 7.95 (978-1-55037-676-0(4)); lib. bdg. 18.95 (978-1-55037-677-7(2)) Annick Pr., Ltd. CAN. *Dist:* Firefly Bks., Ltd.

—Drop of Gold. 2001. (ps-2). lib. bdg. 15.25 (978-0-613-53179-5(5)) Tandem Library Bks.

Velma the Vomiting Vulture. 2001. (Illus.). 32p. (J). pap. (978-0-9703754-0-7(9)) Blue Fish.

Ventura, Antonio. Lucas y el Ruisenor. Angela-Lago, illus. 2005. (SPA.). 24p. (J). (ps-ps). pap. 6.99 (978-980-257-285-4(3)) Ekare, Ediciones VEN. *Dist:* Lectorum Pubns., Inc., Iaconi, Mariuccia Bk. Imports.

Voigt, Cynthia. The Wings of a Falcon. 1999. (Kingdom Ser.). 467p. (J). (gr. 10-12). reprint ed. 16.00 (978-0-7881-6604-4(2)) DIANE Publishing Co.

Wall, Suzy. The Dodo's Last Stand. 2005. 40.00 (***978-1-4108-4221-3(5)***) Benchmark Education Co.

Wallace, Bill. The Legend of Thunderfoot. 2006. 160p. (J). 15.95 (978-1-4169-0691-9(6)) Simon & Schuster Children's Publishing.

Wallace, Carol. Flying Flea, Callie & Me. 1999. (gr. 3-6). lib. bdg. 13.00 (978-0-613-84533-5(1)) Tandem Library Bks.

Wallace, Carol & Wallace, Bill. The Flying Flea, Callie & Me. 1999. (Gray Cat Ser.: Vol. 1). 96p. (J). (gr. 3-6). pap. 4.99 (978-0-671-03968-4(7) , Aladdin) Simon & Schuster Children's Publishing.

—The Flying Flea, Callie & Me. 1999. (Illus.). (J). 11.79 (978-0-606-18368-0(X)) Tandem Library Bks.

Walters, Jack C. Bird Stories & Sightings in Nevada Vol. 1: Loons to Nighthawks, 2004. (Illus.). 436p. pap. 38.50 (978-0-9754658-0-6(5)) Walters, Jack C.

Warren, Celia. Bouncing with the Birdie, 8 vols. 2005. (QEB Readers). (Illus.). 24p. (J). (ps-3). lib. bdg. 15.95 (978-1-59566-064-0(X)) QEB Publishing Inc.

Watkins, Greg. A Big Beaked, Big Bellied Bird Named Bill. Watkins, Greg, illus. 2005. (Illus.). 30p. 13.95 (978-0-9761318-1-6(1) , 1239651) Cute & Cuddly Productions, Inc.

—A Big Beaked, Big Bellied Bird Named Bill. 2006. 32p. 15.99 (978-1-58980-441-8(4)) Pelican Publishing Co., Inc.

—Brendon Mouse's Big Idea to Save the Bad Bird Bunch. 2007. 32p. (J). 15.95 (978-1-58980-449-4(X)) Pelican Publishing Co., Inc.

Watt, Fiona & Wells, Rachel. Hen. 2004. (Illus.). 10p. (J). 10.95 (978-0-7945-0384-0(5) , Usborne) EDC Publishing.

Wax, Wendy. Follow That Bird! A Book & Bird Feeder Set. 2005. (Dora the Explorer Ser.). 14p. (J). bds. 4.99 (978-1-4169-0022-1(5) , Simon Spotlight/Nickelodeon) Simon & Schuster Children's Publishing.

Weaver, Anna E. Birds at My Window. 2004. (Illus.). 231p. 9.35 (978-0-7399-2301-6(3) , 2138) Rod & Staff Pubs., Inc.

Webster, Christy. Lots of Opposites: All about Opposites. Moroney, Christopher, illus. 2007. 22p. (J). (gr. k-ps). bds. 7.99 (978-0-375-83778-4(7) , Random Hse. Bks. for Young Readers) Random Hse. Children's Bks.

Wiggin, Kate Douglas. The Birds' Christmas Carol. reprint ed. (J). lib. bdg. 48.00 (978-0-7426-1056-9(X)); 2001. (Illus.). pap. 28.00 (978-0-7426-6056-4(7)) Classic Bks.

—The Birds' Christmas Carol. Gillespie, Jessie, illus. 1999. 80p. (J). (gr. 4-6). pap. 4.95 (978-0-395-89110-0(8)) Houghton Mifflin Co. Trade & Reference Div.

—The Birds' Christmas Carol. 1999. (gr. 3-6). lib. bdg. 12.95 (978-0-613-22824-4(3)) Tandem Library Bks.

—The Birds' Christmas Carol. 1999. (Illus.). 96p. 16.95 (978-0-941807-52-4(5) , Welcome Bks.) Welcome Enterprises, Inc.

Wildsmith, Brian. The Owl & the Woodpecker. Wildsmith, Brian, illus. 2006. (Illus.). 32p. (J). 16.95 (978-1-59572-043-6(X)) Star Bright Bks., Inc.

Willems, Mo. Don't Let the Pigeon Drive the Bus! 2003. (Illus.). 36p. (J). (ps-1). 12.99 (978-0-7868-1988-1(X)) Hyperion Bks. for Children.

Willems, Mo. There Is a Bird on Your Head! An Elephant & Piggie Book. Willems, Mo, illus. rev. ed. 2007. 64p. (J). (ps-3). 8.99 (***978-1-4231-0686-9(5)***) Hyperion Pr.

Willems, Mo, illus. Don't Let the Pigeon Drive the Bus! 2005. 40p. (J). (978-1-84428-013-1(6)) Walker Bks. Australia Pty, Ltd.

Williamson, Barbara. Sparino de Birdarack. 2006. (Illus.). 24p. (J). per. 12.95 (978-1-59453-774-5(7) , Airleaf Publishing) Airleaf Publishing & Bookselling.

Winstead, Rosie. Ruby & Bubbles. 2006. (Illus.). 32p. (J). (ps). 15.99 (978-0-8037-3024-3(1) , Dial) Penguin Group (USA) Inc.

Winston, Pat. Earl the EMU: God Has a Purpose for Those Who Are Different. Allen, Cathy H., photos by. 2000. (Illus.). 24p. (J). (ps-5). 12.95 (978-0-9702821-0-1(9)) Light Way Pubns., The.

Wolverton, Ray & Livingston, Wayne. The Stories of Zapy Yapy. 1999. (Illus.). 96p. (J). (978-0-9674101-1-1(8)) Wolverton.

Wood, Audrey. Birdsong. 2001. (J). 12.80 (978-0-606-21069-0(5)) Tandem Library Bks.

Yi Fan, Nancy. Swordbird. Zug, Mark, illus. 2007. 240p. (J). (gr. k-7). 15.99 (978-0-06-113099-1(0) , HarperCollins); lib. bdg. 16.89 (978-0-06-113100-4(8)) HarperCollins Pubs.

Yorinks, Arthur. Hey, Al. Egielski, Richard, illus. 2002. (J). 14.43 (978-0-7587-0051-3(2)) Book Wholesalers, Inc.

—Hey, Al. Egielski, Richard, illus. 2001. (J). (gr. k-3). pap. 15.90 incl. audio (978-0-8045-6872-2(3)) Spoken Arts, Inc.

Ziefert, Harriet. Birdhouse for Rent. Dreifuss, Donald, illus. 2001. 32p. (J). (gr. k-3). tchr. ed. 16.00 (978-0-618-04881-6(2) , Walter Lorraine) Houghton Mifflin Co. Trade & Reference Div.

Zubizarreta, Patxi. Paloma, Llegaste Por el Aire. Balzola, Asun, illus. 2003. (SPA.). 24p. (978-84-246-5913-4(9) , GL3212) La Galera, S.A. Editorial ESP. *Dist:* Lectorum Pubns., Inc.

Zuk-Lloyd, Lynn. Christmas in North Woods: 10 Animated Stories for Children. Zuk-Lloyd, Lynn, illus. l.t. ed. 2002. (Illus.). (J). cd-rom 24.95 (978-0-9723773-0-0(1)) PromiseGarden.com.

BIRDS—FLIGHT

Arnold, Caroline. Birds: Nature's Magnificent Flying Machines. Wynne, Patricia J., illus. 2004. 32p. (J). (ps-3). 16.95 (978-1-57091-516-1(4)); pap. 6.95 (978-1-57091-572-7(5)) Charlesbridge Publishing, Inc.

—Birds: Nature's Magnificent Flying Machines. 2003. (gr. 3-6). lib. bdg. 15.25 (978-0-613-67319-8(0)) Tandem Library Bks.

Cartwright, Pauline. What Helps a Bird to Fly? Smith, David P., illus. 1999. 16p. (J). 5.50 (978-0-7685-0406-4(6)) Dominie Pr., Inc.

Leake, Diyan. Wings. 2007. (J). (***978-1-4329-0003-8(X)***); pap. (***978-1-4329-0008-3(0)***) Heinemann Library.

Stewart, Melissa. How Do Birds Fly? 2006. (Tell Me Why, Tell Me How Ser.). (Illus.). 32p. (J). lib. bdg. 28.50 (978-0-7614-2110-8(6) , Benchmark Bks.) Cavendish, Marshall Corp.

BIRDS—HABITS AND BEHAVIOR

Chessen, Betsey & Moreton, Daniel. Where Do Birds Live? 1998. (Science Emergent Readers Ser.). (J). pap. 2.50 (978-0-590-76967-9(7)) Scholastic, Inc.

Foley, Cate. Find the Bird. 2000. (Welcome Bks.). (Illus.). 24p. (J). (ps-2). 17.00 (978-0-516-23094-8(8) , Children's Pr.) Scholastic Library Publishing.

—Find the Bird. 2000. (gr. k-3). lib. bdg. 12.95 (978-0-613-52043-0(2)) Tandem Library Bks.

Green, Jen. Birds: Fantastic Facts. 2000. (Fantastic Facts Ser.). (Illus.). 64p. (gr. 2-7). pap. 6.95 (978-1-84215-086-3(3) , Southwater) Anness Publishing GBR. *Dist:* National Bk. Network.

Harcourt School Publishers Staff. Bird's Beaks & Bills Advanced Level. 3rd ed. 2002. (Trophies Reading Program Ser.). (Illus.). pap. 5.10 (978-0-15-323024-0(X)) Harcourt Schl. Pubs.

Hickman, Pamela. Starting with Nature Bird Book. Collins, Heather, illus. unabr. ed. 2000. (Starting with Nature Ser.). 32p. (J). (gr. 4-6). (978-1-55074-471-2(2)) Kids Can Pr., Ltd.

Kirkland, Jane. Take a Backyard Bird Walk. Easter, Dennis, illus. 2005. (Take a Walk Ser.). 32p. (J). pap. 9.95 (978-0-9709754-0-9(6) , Take a Walk Bk.) Stillwater Publishing.

Kress, Stephen W. Bird Life: A Golden Guide from St. Martin's Press. Dawson, John D., illus. rev. ed. 2001. (Golden Guides Ser.). 160p. pap. 6.95 (978-1-58238-135-0(6) , Golden Guides from Saint Martin's Pr.) St. Martin's Pr.

Lamstein, Sarah. Sleepy Birds. Alter, Anna, illus. 2006. (J). (978-1-58089-305-3(8)) Charlesbridge Publishing, Inc.

Roxbee-Cox, Phil. Find the Bird. Cartwright, Stephen, illus. 2004. (Treasury of Farmyard Tales Ser.). 10p. (J). stu. ed., bds. 3.95 (978-0-7460-3820-8(8)) EDC Publishing.

Sayre, April Pulley. The Hungry Hummingbird. Holland, Gay W., illus. 2001. (All about Animals Ser.). 32p. (ps-2). lib. bdg. 22.90 (978-0-7613-1951-1(4) , Millbrook Pr.) Lerner Publishing Group.

Tagliaferro, Linda. Birds & Their Nests. 2004. (Pebble Plus, Animal Homes Ser.). (Illus.). 24p. (J). 13.95 (978-0-7368-2383-8(2)) Capstone Pr., Inc.

BIRDS—MIGRATION

Ball, Jacqueline A. Migrating Animals of the Air. 2007. (J). pap. (***978-0-8368-8422-7(1)***); 24p. (gr. 2-4). lib. bdg. 19.93 (***978-0-8368-8417-3(5)***) Stevens, Gareth Inc. (Weekly Reader Early Learning Library).

Benchmark Education Staff, compiled by. Bringing Back the Whooping Crane & ¡Vamos a rescatar a la grulla Blanca! 2005. 52.00 (***978-1-4108-4494-1(3)***) Benchmark Education Co.

Bronson, Franklin. Why Don't Birds get Lost? Differentiated Studies in Bird Migration: Upper Elementary through Secondary Levels. 2005. (Illus.). 70p. (978-0-910609-49-4(7)) Gifted Education Pr.

The Migration: Level D, 6 vols. (Wonder Worldtm Ser.). 16p. 24.95 (978-0-7802-4585-3(7)) Wright Group, The.

Salariya, David. The Journey of a Swallow. Sorace, Carolyn, photos by. 2000. (Lifecycles Ser.). (Illus.). 32p. (J). (gr. k-2). 25.50 (978-0-531-14519-7(0) , Watts, Franklin) Scholastic Library Publishing.

Willis, Nancy Carol. Red Knot: A Shorebird's Incredible Journey. 2006. (Illus.). 32p. (J). 15.95 (978-0-9662761-4-5(0)); pap. 6.95 (978-0-9662761-5-2(9)) Birdsong Bks.

BIRDS—PICTORIAL WORKS

Barlowe, Sy. Beginning Birdwatcher's Book: With 48 Stickers. 2000. (Illus.). 32p. (J). (gr. 4-7). pap. 5.95 (978-0-486-41059-3(5)) Dover Pubns., Inc.

—Learning about Birds of Prey. 1998. (Learning about Ser.). 16p. (J). pap. 1.50 (978-0-486-40332-8(7) , 40332-7) Dover Pubns., Inc.

Beylon, Cathy. Birds Sticker. 1999. (Dover Little Activity Bks.). (Illus.). 4p. (J). pap., act. bk. ed. 1.50 (978-0-486-40744-9(6)) Dover Pubns., Inc.

Bown, Deni & Dorling Kindersley Publishing Staff. Birds. 1998. (Ultimate Sticker Bks.). (Illus.). 16p. (J). (ps-3). pap. 6.99 (978-0-7894-2973-5(X)) Dorling Kindersley Publishing, Inc.

Burnie, David & Dorling Kindersley Publishing Staff. Bird. 2004. (Dk Eyewitness Books Ser.). 72p. (J). 15.99 (978-0-7566-0658-9(6)) Dorling Kindersley Publishing, Inc.

DK Publishing Staff. My First Learning Library: My First Word Board Book; My First ABC Board Book; My First Numbers Board Book. 2004. (My 1ST Board Books Ser.). (Illus.). 108p. (J). bds. 16.99 (978-0-7566-0822-4(8)) Dorling Kindersley Publishing, Inc.

Dorling Kindersley Publishing Staff. Pajaro. 2004. (Dk Eyewitness Books Ser.).Tr. of Bird. (SPA.). 72p. (J). 15.99 (978-0-7566-0634-3(9)) Dorling Kindersley Publishing, Inc.

Harvey, Bev. Birds. 2002. (Questions & Answers Ser.). 32p. (J). 3.98 (978-0-7525-7246-8(6)) Parragon, Inc.

Kress, Stephen W. Bird Life: A Golden Guide from St. Martin's Press. Dawson, John D., illus. rev. ed. 2001. (Golden Guides Ser.). 160p. pap. 6.95 (978-1-58238-135-0(6) , Golden Guides from Saint Martin's Pr.) St. Martin's Pr.

Magner Publishing Staff. Color the Hummingbirds. Magner Publishing Staff, illus. 1999. (Illus.). 20p. (J). (ps-7). pap. 4.95 (978-1-929416-05-9(9)) Magner Publishing & American Binding & Publishing.

—Color the Owl Family. Magner Publishing Staff, illus. 1999. (Illus.). 20p. (J). (ps-7). pap. 4.95 (978-1-929416-02-8(4)) Magner Publishing & American Binding & Publishing.

Oppenheim, Joanne. Has Visto Estas Aves? Reid, Barbara, illus. (SPA.). 32p. (J). 4.99 (978-0-590-46321-8(7)) Scholastic, Inc.

Zim, Herbert S. Birds. 2001. (Golden Guides Ser.). (J). mass mkt. 6.95 net. (978-0-307-64053-6(1)) St. Martin's Pr.

BIRDS—POETRY

Delessert, Etienne, illus. Who Killed Cock Robin? 2004. 32p. (gr. k-4). 17.95 (978-1-56846-191-5(7) , Creative Editions) Creative Co., The.

Florian, Douglas. On the Wing. 2000. (Illus.). 48p. (J). (ps-3). pap. 7.00 (978-0-15-202366-9(6) , Harcourt Paperbacks) Harcourt Children's Bks.

—On the Wing. 2000. (978-0-606-18185-3(7)); lib. bdg. 14.15 (978-0-613-28594-0(8)) Tandem Library Bks.

Nash, Myrna Lee. Spinman, Katydid & Bump: A Spider Vane Collection. Johnson, Sharon, illus. 2003. 48p. (YA). (gr. 4-10). 11.95 (978-0-9724549-0-2(X)) Chapter & Verse Pr.

Ruddell, Deborah. Today at the Bluebird Café: A Branchful of Birds. Rankin, Joan, illus. 2007. 40p. (J). (ps-5). 15.99 (978-0-689-87153-5(8) , McElderry, Margaret K.) Simon & Schuster Children's Publishing.

Sierra, Judy. Antarctic Antics. 2003. (gr. k-3). lib. bdg. 14.15 (978-0-613-59876-7(8)) Tandem Library Bks.

—Antarctic Antics: A Book of Penguin Poems. Aruego, Jose & Dewey, Ariane, illus. 2003. 32p. (J). pap. 6.00 (978-0-15-204602-6(X) , Voyager Bks./Libros Viajeros) Harcourt Children's Bks.

Spinelli, Eileen. Feathers: Poems about Birds. McCue, Lisa, illus. rev. ed. 2004. 40p. (J). 16.95 (978-0-8050-6713-2(2) , Holt, Henry & Co. Bks. For Young Readers) Holt, Henry & Co.

—Song for the Whooping Crane. Warnick, Elsa, illus. 2004. 32p. (J). (gr. 3-6). 16.00 (978-0-8028-5172-7(X)) Eerdmans, William B. Publishing Co.

Van Wassenhove, Sue. The Seldom-Ever-Shady Glades: Poems & Quilts. 2008. (J). (***978-1-59078-352-8(2)***, Wordsong) Boyds Mills Pr.

Yolen, Jane. Fine Feathered Friends: Poems for Young People to Perform. Stemple, Jason, illus. Stemple, Jason, photos by. 2004. 32p. (J). (gr. 4-6). 17.95 (978-1-59078-193-7(7)) Boyds Mills Pr.

BIRDS—PROTECTION

Patent, Dorothy Hinshaw. The Bald Eagle Returns. Munoz, William, illus. 2000. 80p. (J). (gr. 4-6). tchr. ed. 16.00 (978-0-395-91416-8(7) , Clarion Bks.) Houghton Mifflin Co. Trade & Reference Div.

Priebe, Mac. The Peregrine Falcon: Endangered No More. Priebe, Jennifer, illus. 1999. (Wildlife Winners). 30p. (J). (gr. 2-5). 15.95 (978-0-9669551-9-4(6)) Mindfull Publishing.

Salmansohn, Pete & Kress, Stephen. Saving Birds: Heroes Around the World. 2005. (Illus.). 40p. (gr. 3-6). 16.95 (978-0-88448-237-6(5)) Tilbury Hse. Pubs.

BIRDS—SONG

see Bird Song

BIRDS' EGGS

see Birds—Eggs and Nests

BIRDS IN ART

Baumbusch, Brigitte. Birds in Art. 2005. (Illus.). 32p. (J). lib. bdg. 22.00 (978-0-8368-4443-6(2)) Stevens, Gareth Inc.

Heller, D. M. Let's Make an Owl with Everyday Materials. 2006. (Illus.). 24p. (J). lib. bdg. (978-1-4042-3063-7(7)) Rosen Publishing Group, Inc., The.

LaFosse, Michael. Making Origami Birds Step by Step. 2004. (Kid's Guide to Origami Ser.). (Illus.). 24p. (J). lib. bdg. 21.25 (978-0-8239-6702-5(6) , PowerKids Pr.) Rosen Publishing Group, Inc., The.

Nguyen, Duy. Origami Birds. 2006. (Illus.). 96p. 19.95 (978-1-4027-1932-5(9)) Sterling Publishing Co., Inc.

Randolph, Joanne. Drawing Birds. 2005. (Let's Draw with Shapes Ser.). (Illus.). 24p. (J). 17.25 (978-1-4042-2792-7(X) , PowerKids Pr.) Rosen Publishing Group, Inc., The.

—Let's Draw a Bird with Shapes: Vamos a Dibujar un Ave Usando Figuras. Muschinske, Emily, illus. 2005. (Let's Draw with Shapes/ Vamos a dibujar con Figuras Ser.). (J). 17.25 (978-1-4042-7555-3(X) , PowerKids Pr.) Rosen Publishing Group, Inc., The.

Visca, Kelley & Visca, Curt. How to Draw Cartoon Birds. 2003. (Kid's Guide to Drawing Ser.). (Illus.). 24p. (J). lib. bdg. 21.25 (978-0-8239-6156-6(7) , PowerKids Pr.) Rosen Publishing Group, Inc., The.

BIRDS' NESTS

see Birds—Eggs and Nests

BIRDS OF PREY

see also names of birds of prey, e.g. Eagles, etc.

Barlowe, Sy. Learning about Birds of Prey. 1998. (Learning about Ser.). 16p. (J). pap. 1.50 (978-0-486-40332-8(7) , 40332-7) Dover Pubns., Inc.

Birds of Prey: Level M, 6 vols. 128p. (gr. 2-3). 40.50 (978-0-7699-1030-7(0)) Shortland Pubns. (U. S. A.) Inc.

Chevat, Richie. Ripley's Birds of Prey. 2004. (Illus.). 59p. (J). (978-0-439-63360-4(5)) Scholastic, Inc.

Collard, Sneed B., III. Birds of Prey: A Look at Daytime Raptors. 1999. (Watts Library). (Illus.). 64p. (J). (gr. 5-7). 25.50 (978-0-531-20363-7(8) , Watts, Franklin) Scholastic Library Publishing.

—Birds of Prey: A Look at Daytime Raptors. 1999. (gr. 3-6). lib. bdg. 17.60 (978-0-613-29406-5(8)) Tandem Library Bks.

Donovan, Amy & Shafran, Michael. Birds of Prey. Emmett, Jennifer, ed. 2003. (My First Pocket Guide Ser.). 80p. (J). (gr. 1-4). 5.95 (978-0-7922-6929-8(2) , National Geographic Children's Bks.) National Geographic Society.

Hickman, Pamela. Birds of Prey Rescue: Changing the Future for Endangered Wildlife. 2006. (Firefly Animal Rescue Ser.). (Illus.). 64p. (J). (gr. 5-12). pap. 9.95 (978-1-55407-144-9(5)); lib. bdg. 19.95 (978-1-55407-145-6(3)) Firefly Bks., Ltd.

Kerrod, Robin. Birds of Prey. Anness Publishing Staff, ed. 1999. (Nature Watch Ser.). (Illus.). 64p. (ps-2). 12.95 (978-1-85967-641-7(3)) Anness Publishing GBR. *Dist:* National Bk. Network.

—Birds of Prey. 2002. (Nature Fact File Ser.). (Illus.). 64p. (gr. 3-7). pap. 7.95 (978-1-84215-627-8(6) , Southwater) Anness Publishing GBR. *Dist:* National Bk. Network.

Kops, Deborah. Hawks. 2000. (Wild Birds of Prey! Ser.). (Illus.). 24p. (J). (gr. 3-6). 22.45 (978-1-56711-271-9(4) , Blackbirch Pr., Inc.) Thomson Gale.

Latimer, Jonathan P. & Nolting, Karen Stray. Birds of Prey. Peterson, Roger Tory, illus. 1999. 48p. (J). (ps-7). lib. bdg. 14.10 (978-0-613-14578-7(X)) Tandem Library Bks.

Latimer, Jonathan P., et al. Birds of Prey. Peterson, Roger Tory, illus. 1999. (Peterson Field Guides for Young Naturalists). 48p. (J). (gr. 4-6). tchr. ed. 15.00 (978-0-395-95211-5(5)); pap. 5.95 (978-0-395-92277-4(1)) Houghton Mifflin Co. Trade & Reference Div.

Laubach, Christyna M. Raptor! A Kid's Guide to Birds of Prey. 2002. (gr. k-3). lib. bdg. 24.55 (978-0-613-63747-3(X)) Tandem Library Bks.

Laubach, Christyna M., et al. Raptor! A Kid's Guide to Birds of Prey. 2002. (Illus.). 128p. (J). (gr. 4-8). pap. 14.95 (978-1-58017-445-9(0) , 67445, Storey Kids) Storey Publishing, LLC.

Legg, Gerald. Birds of Prey. Hersey, Bob, illus. 2004. (Scary Creatures Ser.). (J). 22.50 (978-0-531-12376-8(6) , Watts, Franklin) Scholastic Library Publishing.

Lynch, Wayne & Evert, Laura. Birds of Prey. Neidigh, Sherry & McGee, John F., illus. 2005. 192p. 16.95 (978-1-55971-925-4(7) , NorthWord Bks. for Young Readers) T&N Children's Publishing.

Miller, Sara Swan. Owls: The Silent Hunters. 2000. (gr. 3-6). lib. bdg. 15.25 (978-0-613-34397-8(2)) Tandem Library Bks.

Miller, Sara Swan & Savage, Stephen. Owls: The Silent Hunters. 2001. (Animals in Order Ser.). (Illus.). 48p. (gr. 4-6). pap. 6.95 (978-0-531-16496-9(9) , Watts, Franklin) Scholastic Library Publishing.

Parry-Jones, Jemima. Eagle & Birds of Prey. 2000. (Eyewitness Bks.). (Illus.). 64p. (J). (gr. 4-7). 15.99 (978-0-7894-5860-5(8)) Dorling Kindersley Publishing, Inc.

Parry-Jones, Jemima & Dorling Kindersley Publishing Staff. Eagle & Birds of Prey. 2000. (Eyewitness Bks.). (Illus.). 64p. (J). (gr. 4-7). lib. bdg. 19.99 (978-0-7894-6618-1(X)) Dorling Kindersley Publishing, Inc.

Raptors - Birds of Prey Coloring Book. 2005. (Illus.). 24p. (J). pap. 4.95 (978-0-88839-600-6(7)) Hancock Hse. Pubs., Ltd. CAN. *Dist:* Hancock Hse. Pubs.

Reid, Mary Ebeltoft. Owls & Other Birds of Prey, Vol. 8. World Book, Inc. Staff, ed. 2002. (World Book's Animals of the World Ser.: Set 1). 64p. (J). (978-0-7166-1245-2(3)) World Bk., Inc.

Soffer, Ruth. Birds of Prey Stained Glass Coloring Book. 2001. (Dover Little Activity Bks.). (Illus.). 8p. (J). (ps up). pap. 1.50 (978-0-486-41616-8(X)) Dover Pubns., Inc.

Solway, Andrew. Birds of Prey. 2004. (J). 29.93 (978-1-4034-5765-3(4)); pap. 8.50 (978-1-4034-5771-4(9)) Heinemann Library.

Wechsler, Doug. Vultures. 2001. (Really Wild Life of Birds of Prey Ser.). (Illus.). 24p. (J). lib. bdg. 18.75 (978-0-8239-5594-7(X) , PowerKids Pr.) Rosen Publishing Group, Inc., The.

Wildlife Education, Ltd. Staff. Birds of Prey. Goldman, Kenneth et al, illus. 2001. (Zoobooks Ser.). 18p. (Orig.). (YA). (gr. 5 up). pap. 2.95 (978-0-937934-01-2(1)) Wildlife Education, Ltd.

BIRMINGHAM (ALA.)

Morris, Ann. Grandma Lois Remembers: An African-American Family Story. Linenthal, Peter, illus. 2002. (What Was It Like, Grandma? Ser.). 32p. (gr. k-3). lib. bdg. 22.90 (978-0-7613-2316-7(3) , Millbrook Pr.) Lerner Publishing Group.

BIRTH

see Childbirth

BIRTH CONTROL

see also Abortion

Birth Control Choices for Teens. 2004. (YA). 4.00 net. (978-1-930996-62-5(4)) Planned Parenthood Federation of America, Inc.

Cox, Vicki. Margaret Sanger. 2004. (Women in Medicine Ser.). (Illus.). 112p. (gr. 6-12). 30.00 (978-0-7910-8030-6(7) , Chelsea Hse.) Facts On File, Inc.

Fisher, Nick. Living with a Willy. Venning, Harry, illus. 2003. 117p. (J). pap. 9.99 (978-0-330-33248-4(1) , Macmillan Children's Bks.) Pan Macmillan GBR. *Dist:* Trafalgar Square Publishing.

Harris, H. Robie. Its Perfectly Normal: Changing Bodies, Growing up, Sex, & Sexual Health. Emberley, Michael, illus. 10th anniv. ed. 2004. 96p. (J). (gr. 5 up). 22.99 (978-0-7636-2610-5(4)) Candlewick Pr.

Harris, Robie H. Its Perfectly Normal: A Book about Changing Bodies, Growing Up, Sex, & Sexual Health. Emberley, Michael, illus. 10th anniv. ed. 2004. 96p. (gr. 5 up). pap. 10.99 (978-0-7636-2433-0(0)) Candlewick Pr.

Lange, Donna. Taking Responsibility: A Teen's Guide to Contraception & Pregnancy. 2004. (Science of Health Ser.). (Illus.). 128p. (J). (978-1-59084-841-8(1)) Mason Crest Pubs.

Mucciolo, Gary. Everything You Need to Know about Birth Control. rev. ed. 2000. (Need to Know Library). (Illus.). 64p. (YA). (gr. 4-6). lib. bdg. 25.25 (978-0-8239-3301-3(6)) Rosen Publishing Group, Inc., The.

Peacock, Judith. Birth Control & Protection: Options for Teens. 2000. (Perspectives on Healthy Sexuality Ser.). (Illus.). 64p. (J). (gr. 4-6). lib. bdg. 23.93 (978-0-7368-0715-9(2) , LifeMatters Bks.) Capstone Pr., Inc.

Planned Parenthood Federation of America, Inc. Staff. The Condom. 2003. (YA). pap. 3.00 net. (978-0-934586-80-1(2)) Planned Parenthood Federation of America, Inc.

Waters, Sophie. The Female Reproductive System. 2007. (J). (***978-1-4042-1950-2(1)***) Rosen Publishing Group, Inc., The.

BIRTH CONTROL—FICTION

Allan, Nicholas. More & More Rabbits. 2007. (Illus.). 32p. (J). pap. 9.95 (***978-0-09-947758-7(0)*** , Red Fox) Random Hse. Children's Bks. GBR. *Dist:* Independent Pubs. Group.

—More & More Rabbits. 2006. (Illus.). 32p. (J). 17.95 (978-0-09-189373-6(9) , Hutchinson) Random Hse. GBR. *Dist:* Independent Pubs. Group.

BIRTHDAYS

Advantage Publishers Group. Paula's Happy Birthday. 2002. (Let's Start! Play Alongs Ser.). 32p. (J). (ps-1). 15.95 (978-1-57145-694-6(5) , Silver Dolphin Bks.) Advantage Pubs. Group.

Asquith, Ros. Pass the Parcel. 2005. (Illus.). 32p. (J). pap. 11.95 (978-0-00-711269-2(6)); 19.99 (978-0-00-711268-5(8)) HarperCollins Pubs. Ltd. GBR. *Dist:* Trafalgar Square Publishing, Independent Pubs. Group.

Baby's Birthday: Individual Title Six-Packs. (Literatura 2000 Ser.). (gr. k-1). 28.00 (978-0-7635-0021-4(6)) Rigby Education.

Bemelmans, Ludwig & Wheeler, Jody. Madeline's Birthday. 1999. (Madeline Ser.). (Illus.). 16p. (J). (ps-3). act. bk. ed. 7.99 (978-0-670-88767-5(6) , Viking Juvenile) Penguin Group (USA) Inc.

Bickico Enterprises, concept. BabyKids: Birthday Book. 2005. 16p. (J). pap. 2.95 (978-0-9746508-9-0(7)) Bickico Enterprises, Inc.

The Birthday Cake, 6 Pack. (Rigby Focus Ser.). 16p. (gr. k up). 28.00 (978-0-7578-5534-4(2)) Rigby Education.

The Birthday Cake: Individual Title Six-Packs. (Rigby Focus Ser.). 16p. (gr. k up). 26.00 (978-0-7578-5300-5(5)) Rigby Education.

Birthday Cupcakes. (J). 26.20 (978-0-8136-8432-1(3)); 26.20 (978-0-8136-8431-4(5)); 59.50 (978-0-8136-7984-6(2)); 1998. pap. (978-0-8136-8303-4(3)) Modern Curriculum Pr.

Birthday in a Bathtub. (J). pap. 13.75 (978-0-8136-3401-2(6)) Modern Curriculum Pr.

Birthday Party Songs. (Early Learning Ser.). (J). incl. audio. 7.98 incl. audio NewSound, LLC.

Birthday Puzzles & Games. 2002. (Home Workbooks Ser.). 64p. pap. 2.49 (978-0-88724-698-2(2) , CD-4500) Carson-Dellosa Publishing Co., Inc.

Blocher, Wendy. Happy Birthday, Grades K-3. Yuh, Catherine, illus. 1999. (Primary Theme Ser.). 32p. pap., tchr. ed. 7.99 (978-1-57471-629-0(8) , 2457) Creative Teaching Pr., Inc.

Bruce, Lisa. Counting at a Birthday Party. 2003. (Illus.). 24p. (J). pap. 5.50 (978-1-4109-0658-8(2)); lib. bdg. 18.56 (978-1-4109-0632-8(9)) Raintree.

—Counting at a Birthday Party. 2003. (ps-2). lib. bdg. 13.55 (978-0-613-78199-2(6)) Tandem Library Bks.

Burton, Margie, et al. Birthday Celebrations. Evento, Susan, ed. 1998. (Early Connections Ser.). 16p. (J). (gr. k-2). pap. 4.25 (978-1-892393-73-9(5)) Benchmark Education Co.

Chariot Family Staff. A Very Special Birthday. 2003. (My Jesus Pocket Bks.). 32p. (J). (gr. 5-3). pap. 8.90 (978-1-55513-131-9(X) , 155513131X) Cook, David C. Publishing Co.

DK Publishing. Happy Birthday 1. 2008. 12p. (J). (ps-ps). bds. 4.99 (***978-0-7566-3794-1(5)***) Dorling Kindersley Publishing, Inc.

—Happy Birthday 2. 2008. 12p. (J). (ps-ps). bds. 4.99 (***978-0-7566-3795-8(3)***) Dorling Kindersley Publishing, Inc.

—Happy Birthday 3. 2008. 12p. (J). (ps-ps). bds. 4.99 (***978-0-7566-3796-5(1)***) Dorling Kindersley Publishing, Inc.

Dorling Kindersley Publishing Staff & Millard, Anne. Birthday. 2002. (Touch & Feel Ser.). (Illus.). 12p. (J). (ps-3). bds. 6.99 (978-0-7894-8536-6(2)) Dorling Kindersley Publishing, Inc.

Dover Staff. Birthday Bash: Silly Sticker Story. 2004. 4p. (J). pap. 1.50 (978-0-486-43950-1(X)) Dover Pubns., Inc.

Enderlein, Cheryl L. Birthdays Around the World. 1998. (Illus.). (J). (ps-3). (978-0-531-19414-0(0) , Watts, Franklin) Scholastic Library Publishing.

—Birthdays Around the World, 4 bks. Incl. Celebrating Birthdays in Australia. lib. bdg. 18.60 (978-1-56065-759-0(6)); Celebrating Birthdays in Brazil. lib. bdg. 18.60 (978-1-56065-760-6(X)); Celebrating Birthdays in China. lib. bdg. 18.60 (978-1-56065-761-3(8)); Celebrating Birthdays in Russia. lib. bdg. 18.60 (978-1-56065-762-0(6)); 24p. (J). (gr. 2-3). 1998. (Illus.). Set lib. bdg. 74.40 (978-0-7368-0457-8(9) , Bridgestone Bks.) Capstone Pr., Inc.

—Celebrating Birthdays in Australia. 1998. (Birthdays Around the World Ser.). (Illus.). 24p. (J). (gr. k-3). lib. bdg. 14.00 (978-0-531-11544-2(5) , Watts, Franklin) Scholastic Library Publishing.

—Celebrating Birthdays in Brazil. 1998. (Birthdays Around the World Ser.). (Illus.). 24p. (J). (gr. k-3). lib. bdg. 14.00 (978-0-531-11545-9(3) , Watts, Franklin) Scholastic Library Publishing.

—Celebrating Birthdays in China. 1998. (Birthdays Around the World Ser.). (Illus.). 24p. (J). (gr. k-3). lib. bdg. 14.00 (978-0-531-11546-6(1) , Watts, Franklin) Scholastic Library Publishing.

—Celebrating Birthdays in Russia. 1998. (Birthdays Around the World Ser.). (Illus.). 24p. (J). (gr. k-3). lib. bdg. 14.00 (978-0-531-11547-3(X) , Watts, Franklin) Scholastic Library Publishing.

Erlbach, Arlene. Happy Birthday, Everywhere! Holm, Sharon Lane, illus. 1998. 48p. (gr. 2-5). pap. 8.95 (978-0-7613-0346-6(4) , Millbrook Pr.) Lerner Publishing Group.

Forrester, Tina & Shapiro, Sheryl. The Birthday Book. Langlois, Suzane, illus. 2003. 24p. (J). (gr. 1-4). lib. bdg. 18.95 (978-1-55037-829-0(5)) Annick Pr., Ltd. CAN. *Dist:* Firefly Bks., Ltd.

Gamblin, Rose Tooley. The Birthday Party. 2007. (J). (***978-0-8127-0464-8(9)***) Autumn Hse. Publishing Co.

Gillis, Jennifer Blizin & Jordan, Denise M. Feliz Cumpleanos! 2002. (Fiestas Con Velas (Candle Time) Ser.). (SPA.). 24p. (J). (ps-1). lib. bdg. 18.50 (978-1-58810-870-8(8)); (Illus.). pap. 5.25 (978-1-58810-871-5(6) , 91594) Heinemann Library.

Golden Books Staff. Baby's First Year. 2004. (Pat the Bunny Ser.). (Illus.). 48p. (J). (gr. k-ps). bds. 9.99 (978-0-375-82867-6(2) , Golden Bks.) Random Hse. Children's Bks.

Harcourt School Publishers Staff. Happy Birthday: Independent Reader. 3rd ed. 2002. (Trophies Reading Program Ser.). (Illus.). (J). pap. 2.90 (978-0-15-325475-8(0)) Harcourt Schl. Pubs.

—Party - Grade 4. 3rd ed. 2002. (Trophies English Language Learners Ser.). pap. 5.10 (978-0-15-327774-0(2)) Harcourt Schl. Pubs.

Haugen, Brenda. Birthdays. Ouren, Todd, illus. 2004. (Holidays & Celebrations Ser.). 24p. (C). (gr. k-3). 22.60 (978-1-4048-0198-1(7)) Picture Window Bks.

Haworth, Margaret. It's My Birthday. Edwards, Paul, illus. 2003. 31p. (J). (ps-3). pap. 10.00 (978-0-9740313-0-9(5)) Haworth, Margaret.

Hewitt, Sally. Happy Birthday. Cameron, Craig, illus. 2003. 14p. (J). pap. 10.95 (978-1-57145-735-6(6) , Silver Dolphin Bks.) Advantage Pubs. Group.

Hogenkamp, Susan. My Birthday: Learning the IR Sound. (PowerPhonics Ser.). (Illus.). (J). 2002. 24p. (gr. 1). lib. bdg. 18.50 (978-0-8239-5948-8(1)); 2001. 23p. pap. 26.40 (978-0-8239-8293-6(9)) Rosen Publishing Group, Inc., The. (PowerKids Pr.).

Hoyt-Goldsmith, Diane. Celebrating a Quinceanera: A Latina's Fifteenth Birthday Celebration. Migdale, Lawrence, illus. Migdale, Lawrence, photos by. 2002. 32p. (J). (gr. 4-6). tchr. ed. 16.95 (978-0-8234-1693-6(3)) Holiday Hse., Inc.

It's Your Birthday... 2002. (Little Gift Books Ser.). 64p. (J). 2.98 (978-1-84273-526-8(8) , Exclusive Editions) Parragon, Inc.

Jordan, Denise M. Happy Birthday! 2002. (Candle Time Ser.). (Illus.). 24p. (J). (ps-1). lib. bdg. 18.50 (978-1-58810-526-4(1)) Heinemann Library.

Jordan, Denise M. & Gillis, Jennifer Blizin. Happy Birthday! 2002. (Candle Time Ser.). (Illus.). 24p. (J). (ps-1). pap. 5.25 (978-1-58810-735-0(3) , 91387) Heinemann Library.

Lankford, Mary D. Birthdays Around the World. Dugan, Karen M., illus. 2002. 32p. (J). (gr. k-3). 15.99 (978-0-688-15431-8(X)) HarperCollins Pubs.

MacKall, Dandi Daley & Kucharik, Elena. Birthday Blessings. 2001. (Little Blessings Ser.). (Illus.). 32p. (J). (ps-k). bds. 6.99 (978-0-8423-3957-5(4)) Tyndale Hse. Pubs.

Mayer, Becker. Happy Birthday: Mini Gift Books for Your Class. 2000. (Illus.). pap. 11.95 (978-0-439-20012-7(1)) Scholastic, Inc.

—The Happy Birthday Game: Make Each Child's Birthday Extra Special While Building Important Math Skills. 2001. -p. (ps-3). pap. 12.95 (978-0-439-22253-2(2)) Scholastic, Inc.

McGrath, Barbara Barbieri. The M & M's' Brand Birthday Book. Tagel, Peggy, illus. 2004. 12p. (J). (ps-3). bds. 6.95 (978-1-57091-480-5(X)) Charlesbridge Publishing, Inc.

Newman-D'Amico, Fran. Birthday. 2006. 64p. (J). (ps-2). pap., act. bk. ed. 1.50 (978-0-486-44441-3(4)) Dover Pubns., Inc.

Otten, Jack. Watch Me Make a Birthday Card. 2002. (Welcome Books). (Illus.). 24p. (J). (ps-2). 18.00 (978-0-516-23948-4(1)); pap. 4.95 (978-0-516-23498-4(6)) Scholastic Library Publishing. (Children's Pr.).

Powell, Jillian. A Birthday. 2006. (Illus.). 30p. (J). (978-1-58340-947-3(5)) Smart Apple Media.

Richmond, Marianne. Congrats on Another Year of You! 2004. (Illus.). 40p. (YA). 7.95 (978-0-9741465-7-7(9)) Marianne Richmond Studios, Inc.

Ross, Kathy. The Best Birthday Parties Ever! A Kid's Do-It-Yourself Guide. 1999. (Illus.). 80p. (J). (gr. 3-6). pap. 9.95 (978-0-7613-0989-5(6) , Millbrook Pr.) Lerner Publishing Group.

—The Best Birthday Parties Ever! A Kid's Do-it-Yourself Guide. Holm, Sharon Lane, illus. 1999. (Crafts from Kathy Ross Ser.). 80p. (gr. 3-6). lib. bdg. 24.90 (978-0-7613-1410-3(5) , Millbrook Pr.) Lerner Publishing Group.

—Best Birthday Parties Ever! A Kid's Do-It-Yourself Guide. Holm, Sharon Lane, illus. 1999. 78p. (J). (ps-7). lib. bdg. 18.75 (978-0-613-16597-6(7)) Tandem Library Bks.

Schaefer, Ted. When Is Your Birthday? 2007. (J). (978-1-59515-945-8(2)) Rourke Publishing, LLC.

Scholastic, Inc. Staff. Birthdays: The Hands-On Way to Build Reading Skills! 1999. 6p. (J). pap. 7.95 (978-0-439-04307-6(7)) Scholastic, Inc.

—Happy Birthday, 30 vols. 1999. (J). pap. 3.95 (978-0-439-07231-1(X)) Scholastic, Inc.

Shapiro, Sheryl & Forrester, Tina. The Birthday Book. Langlois, Suzane, illus. 2003. 24p. (J). (gr. 1-4). pap. 6.95 (978-1-55037-767-5(1)) Annick Pr., Ltd. CAN. *Dist:* Firefly Bks., Ltd.

Small, B. Crafty Birthday Balloons. 1999. (Illus.). 16p. (978-1-874735-57-1(3)) B Small Publishing.

St-Onge, Claire, adapted by. Caillou Birthday Party. 2001. (Scooter Ser.). (Illus.). 24p. (J). pap. 4.95 (978-2-89450-264-8(8)) Chouette Publishing CAN. *Dist:* Independent Pubs. Group.

Steckel, Richard & Steckel, Michele, photos by. Happy Birthday. 2007. (Illus.). 20p. (J). bds. 6.95 (***978-1-58246-210-3(0)*** , Tricycle Pr.) Ten Speed Pr.

The Surprise Dinner: Individual Title Six-Packs. 16p. (gr. 2 up). 35.00 (978-0-7635-9379-7(6)) Rigby Education.

Vallejo-Nagera, Alejandra. Cuando Llegara Mi Cumpleanos? Guerrero, Andrés, illus. (SPA.). 29p. (J). (gr. k-1). 8.95 (978-1-58986-548-8(0)) Santillana USA Publishing Co., Inc.

Wallace, Paula S. The World of Birthdays. 2003. (Life Around the World Ser.). (Illus.). 48p. (J). (gr. 2 up), lib. bdg. 24.67 (978-0-8368-3659-2(6)) Stevens, Gareth Inc.

Williams, Colleen Madonna Flood. My Adventure on My Birthday. 2007. 44p. (J). 8.99 (978-1-59092-553-9(X) , Orchard Academy Pr.) Windstorm Creative.

Woodworth, Viki. Birthday Party Sticker. 2004. (Illus.). 4p. (J). pap., act. bk. ed. 1.50 (978-0-486-43309-7(9)) Dover Pubns., Inc.

BIRTHDAYS—FICTION

Abbott, Jax. Super 16. 2005. (YA). mass mkt. 5.99 (978-0-8439-5407-4(8)) Dorchester Publishing Co., Inc.

Ada, Alma Flor & Campoy, F. Isabel. Feliz Cumpleanos, Caperucita Roja! Escriva, Ana Lopez, illus. (Gateway to the Sun Ser.). (SPA.). 32p. (J). (gr. k-6). pap. 13.95 (978-1-58105-756-0(3)) Santillana USA Publishing Co., Inc.

—Happy Birthday, Little Red Riding Hood! (Gateways to the Sun). 32p. (J). (gr. k-6). pap. 13.95 (978-1-58105-961-8(2)) Santillana USA Publishing Co., Inc.

Adler, David A. Bones & the Birthday Mystery. Newman, Barbara Johansen, illus. 2007. (Jeffrey Bones Mystery Ser.: No. 5). 32p. (J). (gr. k). 13.99 (978-0-670-06164-8(6) , Viking Adult) Penguin Group (USA) Inc.

—Cam Jansen & the Birthday Mystery. Natti, Susanna, illus. (Cam Jansen Ser.: No. 20). 64p. (J). 2005. (gr. 2-4). pap. 3.99 (978-0-14-240354-9(7) , Puffin); 2000. (gr. 3-7). 13.99 (978-0-670-88877-1(X) , Viking Juvenile) Penguin Group (USA) Inc.

Advantage Publishers Group. Desmond's Birthday Party. 2000. (Let's Start! Teacher's Pets Ser.). (Illus.). 32p. (J). (ps-1). 6.95 (978-1-57145-440-9(3) , Silver Dolphin Bks.) Advantage Pubs. Group.

Advantage Publishers Group & Saidens, Amy. Glamour Girl Sticker Book. 2007. (Illus.). 24p. (J). pap. 14.95 (***978-1-59223-631-2(6)*** , Silver Dolphin Bks.) Advantage Pubs. Group.

Aikins, Dave, illus. The Birthday Dance Party: Daisy's Fiesta de Quinceañera. 2006. (Dora the Explorer Ser.). 24p. (J). pap. 3.99 (978-1-4169-1303-0(3) , Simon Spotlight/Nickelodeon) Simon & Schuster Children's Publishing.

Allen, Francesca & Brooks, Felicity. Busy Truck. Crisp, Dan, illus. 2007. 10p. (J). bds. 10.99 (978-0-7945-1453-2(7) , Usborne) EDC Publishing.

Anderson, Airlie, illus. A Very Patchy Flap Book. 2004. 10p. (J). bds. 5.95 (978-1-58925-702-3(2) , tiger tales) ME Media LLC.

Anfousse, Ginette. Polo et L'anniversaire. Sarrazin, Marisol, tr. 2003. (Polo Baby Board Bks.). (FRE., Illus.). 16p. (J). (-ps). bds. (978-2-89021-656-3(X)) Diffusion du livre Mirabel.

Angeles, Maria. Tortilla for Emilia. 2001. (J). (978-0-7608-2264-7(6)); pap. (978-0-88741-929-4(1)) Sundance/ Newbridge Educational Publishing.

A B

Anholt, Catherine & Anholt, Laurence. Happy Birthday Chimp & Zee. 2006. (Chimp & Zee Ser.). (Illus.). 32p. (J). 15.95 (978-1-84507-507-1(2)) Lincoln, Frances Ltd. GBR. *Dist:* Perseus Distribution.

Arena, Felice & Kettle, Phil. Halloween Gotcha! Gordon, Gus, illus. 2004. (J). pap. (978-1-59336-373-4(7)) Mondo Publishing.

Arnold, Tedd. Huggly & the Toy Monster. Arnold, Tedd, illus. 1999. (Monster under the Bed Ser.). (Illus.). 32p. (J). (ps-3). pap. 3.25 (978-0-590-91821-3(4) , Cartwheel Bks.) Scholastic, Inc.

—Huggly & the Toy Monster. 1998. (Monster under the Bed Ser.). (J). pap. 3.50 (978-0-590-11761-6(0)) Scholastic, Inc.

Asch, Frank. Happy Birthday, Moon. Asch, Frank, illus. 2002. (Moonbear Ser.). (Illus.). (J). 15.53 (978-0-7587-2686-5(4)) Book Wholesalers, Inc.

—Happy Birthday, Moon. Asch, Frank, illus. (Stories to Go! Ser.). (Illus.). 32p. (J). 2005. 4.99 (978-1-4169-0307-9(0)); 2000. pap. 6.99 (978-0-689-83544-5(2)) Simon & Schuster Children's Publishing. (Aladdin).

Asch, Frank. Happy Birthday, Moon. 2005. (Stories to Go! Ser.). (Illus.). (J). (*978-1-4156-0411-3(8)* , Aladdin) Simon & Schuster Children's Publishing.

Asch, Frank & Asch, Frank. Happy Birthday, Moon. 1999. (Illus.). 28p. (J). (ps-3). lib. bdg. 15.30 (978-0-613-63293-5(1)) Tandem Library Bks.

Asher, Sandy. What a Party! Graves, Keith, illus. 2007. 32p. (J). (ps-1). 15.99 (978-0-399-24496-4(4) , Philomel) Penguin Group (USA) Inc.

Ashman, Linda. Maxwell's Magic Mix-up. Dunnick, Regan, illus. 2004. 30p. (J). (gr. k-3). reprint ed. 16.00 (978-0-7567-7156-0(0)) DIANE Publishing Co.

Aunt Nina & Her Nephews & Nieces. 2004. (J). 24.95 incl. audio (978-1-56008-160-9(0)) Weston Woods Studios, Inc.

Averill, Esther Holden. Jenny's Birthday Book. Averill, Esther Holden, illus. 2005. (New York Review Children's Collection). (Illus.). 44p. (J). (ps-ps). reprint ed. pap. 15.95 (978-1-59017-154-7(3) , NYR Children's Collection) New York Review of Bks., Inc., The.

Avi. Ereth's Birthday. Floca, Brian, illus. (Tales from Dimwood Forest Ser.). 192p. 2001. (gr. 3-7). pap. 5.99 (978-0-380-80490-0(5) , Harper Trophy); 2000. (J). (gr. 4-7). 17.99 (978-0-380-97734-5(6)) HarperCollins Pubs.

—Ereth's Birthday. 2001. (Illus.). viii, 180p. (gr. 3-6). lib. bdg. 14.15 (978-0-613-44206-0(7)) Tandem Library Bks.

Awdry, Wilbert V. Happy Birthday, Thomas. Bell, Owain, illus. 2003. (Step into Reading Ser.). 32p. (J). (ps-2). 11.99 (978-0-679-90809-8(9) , Random Hse. Bks. for Young Readers) Random Hse. Children's Bks.

Bailey, Debbie. Feliz Cumpleanos! Huszar, Susan, photos by. 1999. (Hablemos Ser.). (SPA., Illus.). 14p. (J). (gr. k-ps). bds. 5.95 (978-1-55037-575-6(X)) Annick Pr., Ltd. CAN. *Dist:* Firefly Bks., Ltd.

—Happy Birthday. Huszar, Susan, photos by. 1999. (Talk-about-Bks.: Vol. 14). (Illus.). 14p. (J). (gr. k-ps). bds. 5.95 (978-1-55037-559-6(8)) Annick Pr., Ltd. CAN. *Dist:* Firefly Bks., Ltd.

Bailey's Birthday - Evaluation Guide: Evaluation Guide. 2006. (J). (978-1-55942-399-1(4)) Marsh Media.

Balaban, Mariah, ed. Scooby-doo Pirates Ahoy. 2006. (Scooby-doo 8x8 Video Tie-in Ser.). (J). 24p. pap. 3.99 (978-0-439-83993-8(9)); 64p. pap. 3.99 (978-0-439-83992-1(0)) Scholastic, Inc.

Barn Party: Level M, 6 vols. 128p. (gr. 2-3). 49.95 (978-0-7699-0983-7(3)) Shortland Pubns. (U. S. A.) Inc.

Barrett, Anna Pearl. Neecie & the Freedom Celebration, 4 vols., Vol. 3. Edwards, Lana C. & Waters, Linda, eds. Pequero, Phillip, illus. 1999. (Neecie Bks.). 73p. (J). (gr. 2-5). pap. 10.95 (978-0-9661330-2-8(1)) Over the Rainbow Productions.

Baumgart, Klaus. No Tengas Miedo, Tom. 2001. (SPA., Illus.). 32p. (J). (gr. k-2). (978-84-480-1608-1(4) , TM6277) Timun Mas, Editorial S.A. ESP. *Dist:* Lectorum Pubns., Inc.

Beardshaw, Rosalind. I am a Spaceman! 2008. (Illus.). 12p. (J). bds. 12.95 (*978-1-4052-2759-9(1)*) Egmont Bks., Ltd. GBR. *Dist:* Independent Pubs. Group.

Beardshaw, Rosalind, illus. I am a Princess! 2008. 12p. (J). bds. 12.95 (*978-1-4052-2758-2(3)*) Egmont Bks., Ltd. GBR. *Dist:* Independent Pubs. Group.

Beck, Andrea. Elliot Bakes a Cake. Beck, Andrea, illus. 2004. (Elliot Moose Ser.). (Illus.). 32p. (J). (gr. k-3). (978-1-55074-696-9(0)) Kids Can Pr., Ltd.

—Elliot Bakes a Cake. 2004. (Elliot Moose Ser.). (Illus.). 32p. (J). (gr. k-3). (978-1-55074-443-9(7)) Kids Can Pr., Ltd.

—Elliot Bakes a Cake. 2000. (J). (978-0-606-19014-5(7)) Tandem Library Bks.

Beck, Scott. Happy Birthday, Monster! 2007. (Illus.). 32p. (J). (ps-2). 14.95 (*978-0-8109-9363-1(5)* , Abrams Bks. for Young Readers) Abrams, Harry N. , Inc.

Behr, Ashley F. Nailah's Surprise. O'Neill, Terry, ed. Karn, George, illus. 1998. 32p. (J). (ps-3). per. 5.95 (978-0-9660533-1-9(1)) Behr, D. J. Co.

Bella's Birthday. 2003. (J). (978-1-932570-09-0(8)) Literacy Footprints Inc.

Benchmark Education Staff, compiled by. Celebrations. 2006. spiral bd. 139.00 (*978-1-4108-7039-1(1)*) Benchmark Education Co.

Bennett, David. The Big Surprise. 2004. (Ben & Friends Ser.). (Illus.). 24p. (J). pap. 4.99 (978-1-85854-692-6(3)) Brimax Books Ltd. GBR. *Dist:* Byeway Bks.

Berenstain, Stan & Berenstain, Jan. The Berenstain Bears & the Green-Eyed Monster. Berenstain, Stan & Berenstain, Jan, illus. 2002. (Berenstain Bears First Time Bks.). (Illus.). (J). 11.19 (978-0-7587-0946-2(3)) Book Wholesalers, Inc.

—Los Osos Berenstain y Demasiada Fiesta. ed. 2004. Tr. of Berenstain Bears & Too Much Birthday. (SPA., Illus.). (J). (gr. k-3). spiral bd. (978-0-616-14610-1(8)) Canadian National Institute for the Blind/Institut National Canadien pour les Aveugles.

Berry, Bob, illus. Surprise Party. 2006. (Holly Hobbie & Friends Ser.). 16p. (J). pap. 5.99 (978-1-4169-2798-3(0) , Little Simon) Simon & Schuster Children's Publishing.

Bertrand, Diane Gonzales. The Last Doll/la ultima Muñeca. Balestra, Alejandra, tr. Accardo, Anthony, illus. 2001. Tr. of Ultima Muneca. (ENG & SPA.). 32p. (J). (ps-2). 14.95 (978-1-55885-290-7(5) , Piñata Books) Arte Publico Pr.

The Best Birthday Present: Individual Title Six-Packs. (Literatura 2000 Ser.). (gr. 2-3). 33.00 (978-0-7635-0216-4(2)) Rigby Education.

Best, Cari. Three Cheers for Catherine the Great! 2003. (gr. k-3). lib. bdg. 15.25 (978-0-613-71883-7(6)) Tandem Library Bks.

Best, Cari & Potter, Giselle. Three Cheers for Catherine the Great! 2003. (Illus.). 32p. (J). pap. 6.95 (978-0-374-47551-2(2) , Sunburst) Farrar, Straus & Giroux.

Bickel, Karla. Surprise Christmas Birthday Party. Bickel, Karla, illus. l.t. ed. 2004. (Illus.). 16p. (J). (ps-6). pap. 5.00 (978-1-891452-12-3(6) , 3) Heart Arbor Bks.

Birchall, Mark. Rabbit's Birthday Surprise. Birchall, Mark, illus. 2003. (Illus.). 32p. (J). (ps-3). 15.95 (978-0-87614-910-2(7) , Carolrhoda Bks.) Lerner Publishing Group.

Birthday Girl. (978-0-671-88670-7(3) , Atria) Simon & Schuster.

The Birthday Party. (Early Intervention Levels Ser.). 23.10 (978-0-7362-0002-8(9)) Hampton-Brown Bks.

A Birthday Present for Spaceboy. 2003. (J). (978-1-932570-03-8(9)) Literacy Footprints Inc.

A Birthday Surprise. 2000. (J). (978-1-58453-130-2(4)) Pioneer Valley Educational Pr., Inc.

Blackaby, Susan. Groceries for Grandpa. Lee, Ji Sun, illus. 2007. (J). lib. bdg. (*978-1-4048-2334-1(4)*) Picture Window Bks.

Blagden, Julia W., et al. Sapphire Blue Birthday Album. Brock, Laura, illus. 2000. (J). 14.00 incl. audio compact disk (978-0-9659511-3-5(8)) Multifaceted Productions.

Blyton, Enid. Birthday Kitten. (Illus.). (J). 95p. pap. 4.95 (978-0-09-924100-3(5)); 190p. pap. 5.95 (978-0-09-977930-8(7)) Random Hse. GBR. *Dist:* Trafalgar Square Publishing.

Bonnell, Kris. Presents for Mom. 2007. (J). 3.95 (*978-1-933727-61-5(6)*) Reading Reading Bks., LLC.

Book Company Staff. Gilbert's Birthday Surprise. 2002. (Magical World of Teddies Ser.). 14p. (J). 12.95 (978-1-74047-161-9(X)) Book Co. Publishing Pty, Ltd., The AUS. *Dist:* Penton Overseas, Inc.

Bottner, Barbara. You Have to be Nice to Someone on Their Birthday. Mai-Wyss, Tatjana, illus. 2007. 32p. (J). 15.99 (978-0-399-24295-3(3) , Putnam Juvenile) Penguin Group (USA) Inc.

Bourgeois, Paulette. Franklin Says I Love You. Clark, Brenda, illus. 2004. (Franklin the Turtle Ser.). 32p. (J). (gr. k-3). (978-1-55337-035-2(X)) Kids Can Pr., Ltd.

—Franklin's Birthday Party. 2001. (Franklin TV Storybook Ser.). (Illus.). (J). 11.30 (978-0-606-21198-7(5)) Tandem Library Bks.

Brandreth, Gyles. Amanda Mouse & the Birthday Cake. 2000. (Illus.). 32p. (J). 9.99 (978-0-233-99574-8(9)) Andre Deutsch GBR. *Dist:* Independent Pubs. Group.

Brian, Janeen. Party Time! Join Mia in the Mystery & Magic of the Fairy Shop! Norling, Beth, illus. 2006. (Nibbles Ser.). 72p. (J). (gr. 1-4). pap. 3.95 (978-0-7624-2627-0(6) , Running Pr. Kids) Running Pr. Bk. Pubs.

Brian, Kate. Sweet 16. 2007. 288p. (YA). pap. 8.99 (*978-1-4169-0033-7(0)* , Simon Pulse) Simon & Schuster Children's Publishing.

Brimner, Larry Dane. Country Bear's Surprise. Cooncell, Ruth T., illus. 2003. 32p. (J). (ps up). pap. 7.95 (978-1-56397-674-2(9)) Boyds Mills Pr.

Brisson, Pat. Mama Loves Me From Away. Caple, Laurie, illus. 2004. 32p. (YA). (gr. 2-4). 15.95 (978-1-56397-966-8(7)) Boyds Mills Pr.

Brooks, Felicity. The Birthday Surprise. 2000. (gr. k-3). lib. bdg. 14.10 (978-0-613-67530-7(4)) Tandem Library Bks.

Brooks, Jillian. Birthday Blues. 2003. 141p. (J). (978-0-439-45141-3(8)) Scholastic, Inc.

Brouwer, Sigmund. Fly Trap. 2003. (Watch Out for Joel Ser.). (Illus.). 32p. (J). (gr. 1-3). pap. 3.99 (978-0-7642-2583-3(9)) Bethany Hse. Pubs.

—Fly Trap. 2003. (gr. k-3). lib. bdg. 11.80 (978-0-613-87753-4(5)) Tandem Library Bks.

Brown, Beverly Swerdlow. Panda's Birthday Surprise. Christian, Sara, illus. 1998. 8p. (J). (gr. k-2). pap. 3.75 (978-1-880612-80-4(1) , Seedling Pubns.) Continental Pr., Inc.

Brown, Marc. Arthur's Birthday. Brown, Marc, illus. 2005. (Arthur Adventure Ser.). (Illus.). 32p. (J). (ps-3). pap., pap. 10.99 incl. audio compact disk (978-0-316-05957-2(9)) Little Brown & Co.

—Arthur's Birthday. ed. 1998. (Arthur Adventure Ser.). (J). pap. 5.95 (978-0-316-10573-6(2)) Little Brown & Co.

—Arthur's Birthday. 1998. (Arthur Adventure Ser.). (Illus.). 30p. (J). (ps-3). bds. 5.95 (978-0-316-11857-6(5)) Little, Brown Bks. for Young Readers.

—Arthur's First Kiss with Sticker. 2001. (Arthur Ser.). (gr. k-3). lib. bdg. 11.80 (978-0-613-84580-9(3)) Tandem Library Bks.

—El Cumpleanos de Arturo. 2000. (J). 13.75 (978-0-606-20187-2(4)) Tandem Library Bks.

—Cumpleanos de Arturo. 2000. (SPA.). (gr. k-3). lib. bdg. 15.25 (978-0-613-28287-1(6)) Tandem Library Bks.

—El Cumpleaños de Arturo. Sarfatti, Esther, tr. from ENG. 2000. (Arthur Adventure Ser.). (SPA., Illus.). (J). (ps-3). pap. 6.95 (978-1-880507-78-0(1) , LC7609) Lectorum Pubns., Inc.

Bruno's Birthday: Individual Title Six-Packs. (Literatura 2000 Ser.). (gr. 1-2). 28.00 (978-0-7635-0086-3(0)) Rigby Education.

Brust, Beth Wagner. The Great Tulip Trade. Mattheson, Jenny, illus. 2005. (Step into Reading Ser.: Vol. 3). 48p. (J). (gr. 1-3). pap. 3.99 (978-0-375-82573-6(8) , Random Hse. Bks. for Young Readers) Random Hse. Children's Bks.

Bryant, Ann. Jack's Party. Henley, Claire, illus. 2004. (Read-It! Readers Ser.). 32p. (C). (gr. k-3). 18.60 (978-1-4048-0060-1(3)) Picture Window Bks.

Bryant, Bonnie. Dude Ranch. 2007. (Saddle Club Ser.: No. 6). 144p. (J). (gr. 4-6). lib. bdg. 11.99 (978-0-385-90422-3(3) , Yearling) Random Hse. Children's Bks.

Bunting, Eve. The Baby Shower. Love, Judy, illus. 2007. 28p. (J). (ps-1). 15.95 (978-1-58089-139-4(X)) Charlesbridge Publishing, Inc.

—Flower Garden. 2002. (Illus.). (J). 13.19 (978-0-7587-2519-6(1)) Book Wholesalers, Inc.

—Flower Garden. Hewitt, Kathryn, illus. 2000. 32p. (J). (ps-3). pap. 7.00 (978-0-15-202372-0(0)) Harcourt Children's Bks.

—Flower Garden. Hewitt, Kathryn, illus. 1999. 32p. (J). (ps-3). 25.95 (978-0-15-201968-6(5)) Harcourt Trade Pubs.

—Flower Garden. Hewitt, Kathryn, illus. 2000. (J). (ps-ps). lib. bdg. 14.15 (978-0-613-28490-5(9)) Tandem Library Bks.

—Flower Garden. 2000. 12.80 (978-0-606-17842-6(2)) Tandem Library Bks.

Bunting, Eve. Flower Garden: Lap-Sized Board Book. Hewitt, Kathryn, illus. 2008. 30p. (J). bds. 10.95 (*978-0-15-206516-4(4)* , Red Wagon Bks.) Harcourt Children's Bks.

Butcher, Sam. Blessings for Your Birthday. 2005. 48p. (J). 10.99 (978-1-4003-0564-3(0)) Nelson, Thomas Inc.

Butler, Dorothy. My Brown Bear Barney at the Party. Fuller, Elizabeth, illus. 2001. 24p. (J). (ps). 15.89 (978-0-688-17549-8(X)); 15.95 (978-0-688-17548-1(1)) HarperCollins Pubs.

Butler, Kristi T. A Big Surprise. Paparone, Pamela, illus. 2005. (Green Light Readers Level 1 Ser.). 24p. (J). (ps-ps). 12.95 (978-0-15-205142-6(2)); pap. 3.95 (978-0-15-205141-9(4)) Harcourt Trade Pubs.

Butler, Kristi T. Big Surprise. Paparone, Pamela, illus. 2005. 24p. (J). lib. bdg. 10.00 (*978-1-4242-0175-4(6)*) Fitzgerald Bks.

Calmenson, Stephanie. Birthday at the Panda Palace. Cushman, Doug, illus. 2007. 32p. (J). (ps-1). 15.99 (978-0-06-052663-4(7)); lib. bdg. 16.89 (978-0-06-052664-1(5)) HarperCollins Pubs.

Cameron, Ann. Julian, Dream Doctor. 2002. (J). 12.32 (978-0-7587-6155-2(4)) Book Wholesalers, Inc.

Camila y Su Fiesta de Cumpleanos. 2003. (SPA.). 62p. (J). (ps-1). (978-968-5308-79-3(9) , Silver Dolphin en Español) Advanced Marketing, S. de R. L. de C. V.

Campoy, F. Isabel, et al. Celebrate a Powwow with Sandy Starbright. Alvarez, María Jesus, illus. 2006. 31p. (J). (*978-1-59820-127-7(1)*) Santillana USA Publishing Co., Inc.

Canal, Jade. Flame. 2004. 71p. pap. 14.95 (978-1-4137-4705-8(1)) PublishAmerica, Inc.

Cannon, A. E. Way Out West with Pirate Pete & Pirate Joe. Smith, Elwood H., illus. 2006. (Viking Easy-To-Read Ser.). 32p. (J). (ps). 13.99 (978-0-670-06080-1(1) , Viking Juvenile) Penguin Group (USA) Inc.

Capucilli, Alyssa Satin. Biscuit's Birthday. Schories, Pat, illus. 2005. (Biscuit Ser.). 24p. (J). (ps-1). 3.99 (978-0-06-057845-9(9) , Harper Festival) HarperCollins Pubs.

—Happy Birthday, Biscuit! Schories, Pat, illus. 1999. (Biscuit Ser.). 24p. (J). (ps-1). lib. bdg. 15.89 (978-0-06-028361-2(0)); 14.99 (978-0-06-028355-1(6)) HarperCollins Pubs.

Carle, Eric. Hello Red Fox. Carle, Eric & Beneduce, Ann, illus. 1998. 32p. (J). (ps-3). 19.95 (978-0-689-81775-5(4)) Simon & Schuster Children's Publishing.

—Hello Red Fox. 2001. (ps-2). lib. bdg. 16.45 (978-0-613-87058-0(1)); (Illus.). (J). 14.79 (978-0-606-21231-1(0)) Tandem Library Bks.

—The Secret Birthday Message. Carle, Eric, illus. 1998. (Illus.). 11p. (J). (ps up). 7.99 (978-0-694-01148-3(7) , Harper Festival) HarperCollins Pubs.

Carlstrom, Nancy White. Happy Birthday, Jesse Bear! 2000. (Illus.). (J). 13.79 (978-0-606-17922-5(4)) Tandem Library Bks.

Carney, Mary Lou. Tyler Timothy Bradford & the Birthday Surprise. Warren, Shari, illus. 2004. 32p. (J). 14.95 (978-0-7696-3168-4(1)) School Specialty Publishing.

Carter, Noelle. Birthday Fun 1, 2, 3! A Counting Flap Book. Carter, Noelle, illus. 2005. (Illus.). 14p. (J). bds. 6.99 (978-0-689-86027-0(7) , Little Simon) Simon & Schuster Children's Publishing.

Cazet, Denys. Minnie & Moo & the Haunted Sweater. Cazet, Denys, illus. 2007. (I Can Read Bks.). 48p. (J). (ps-3). 15.99 (*978-0-06-073016-1(1)*); lib. bdg. 16.89 (*978-0-06-073017-8(X)*) HarperCollins Pubs.

Celebrate Elmo's Birthday. (J). (978-0-375-88597-6(8) , Golden Bks.) Random Hse. Children's Bks.

Chanda, J-P. Happy Birthday, SpongeBob! Martinez, Heather, illus. 2005. (Ready-To-Read Ser.). 24p. (J). pap. 3.99 (978-0-689-87674-5(2) , Simon Spotlight/ Nickelodeon) Simon & Schuster Children's Publishing.

—Happy Birthday Spongebob! Martinez, Heather, illus. ed. 2005. 22p. (J). lib. bdg. 15.00 (978-1-59054-965-0(1)) Fitzgerald Bks.

Chato & the Party Animals. 2004. 29.95 incl. audio compact disk (978-1-55592-703-5(3)); 24.95 incl. audio (978-1-55592-693-9(2)); pap. 14.95 incl. audio (978-1-55592-687-8(8)) Weston Woods Studios, Inc.

Chavarria-Chairez, Becky. Magda's Pinata Magic. Ventura, Gabriela Baeza, tr. Vega, Anne, illus. 2001. Tr. of Magda y la Pi?Ata Magica. (ENG & SPA.). 32p. (J). (ps-3). 14.95 (978-1-55885-320-1(0) , Piñata Books) Arte Publico Pr.

Cheng, Andrea. The Lemon Sisters. Mai-Wyss, Tatjana, illus. 2006. 32p. (J). (ps). 16.99 (978-0-399-24023-2(3) , Putnam Juvenile) Penguin Group (USA) Inc.

Chichester-Clark, Emma. Happy Birthday to You, Blue Kangaroo. 2007. (Illus.). 32p. (J). (ps-k). 16.95 (*978-1-84270-518-6(0)*) Transworld Publishers Ltd. GBR. *Dist:* Independent Pubs. Group.

Child, Lauren. This is Actually My Party. 2007. (Charlie & Lola Ser.). 32p. (J). (ps-2). pap. 6.99 (*978-0-448-44694-3(4)* , Grosset & Dunlap) Penguin Group (USA) Inc.

Chima, Ahiru & Misu, Max. Ellena_- Ellen meets Frog King - 2005. 32p. pap. 14.99 (978-1-4116-4050-4(0)) Lulu.com.

Christelow, Eileen. Five Little Monkeys Bake a Birthday Cake. 2005. (Five Little Monkeys Ser.). (Illus.). (J). (gr. k-ps). 32p. 15.00 (978-0-618-49647-1(5)); 28p. pap. 5.95 (978-0-618-49648-8(3)) Houghton Mifflin Co. Trade & Reference Div. (Clarion Bks.).

—Five Little Monkeys Bake a Birthday Cake. Christelow, Eileen, illus. 2004. (Illus.). 28p. (J). (gr. k-ps). bds. 5.95 (978-0-618-46264-3(3) , Clarion Bks.) Houghton Mifflin Co. Trade & Reference Div.

Civardi, Anne. Going to a Party. 2007. 16p. (J). pap. 4.99 (978-0-7945-1011-4(6) , Usborne) EDC Publishing.

Clark, Brenda, illus. Franklin's Birthday Party. 2002. (Franklin Ser.). 12.40 (978-1-4046-0323-3(9)) Book Wholesalers, Inc.

Clark, Sherryl. Whose Birthday Is It? Smith, Jan, illus. 2004. (Read-It! Readers Ser.). 32p. (C). (gr. k-3). 18.60 (978-1-4048-0554-5(0)) Picture Window Bks.

Clarke, Jane. Prince Albert's Birthday. Chatterton, Martin, illus. 2005. 24p. (J). lib. bdg. 22.65 (*978-1-59646-748-4(7)*) Dingles & Co.

Claus, Nancy. Santa's Prize. Ferchaud, Steve, illus. 2006. (J). (*978-0-9746747-5-9(3)*) Cypress Bay Publishing.

Coats, Lucy. Neil's Numberless World. 2000. (J). (978-0-606-20123-0(8)) Tandem Library Bks.

Cocks, Nancy & Marton, Jirina. Fergie Has a Birthday Party. 2003. (Illus.). 16p. pap. (978-2-89507-301-7(5)) Novalis Publishing.

Cole, Stephen. The Adventures of Mr. Bean. 2002. (Illus.). 64p. (J). pap. 6.99 (978-1-84222-658-2(4)) Carlton Bks., Ltd. GBR. *Dist:* Independent Pubs. Group.

Connie & Bonnie's Birthday Blastoff Adventure Pack. 2001. (978-1-883772-26-0(5)) Flying Rhinoceros, Inc.

Conrad, Pam. Staying Nine. 1999. (Illus.). (J). (gr. 3-6). lib. bdg. 13.00 (978-0-8335-6162-6(6)) Tandem Library Bks.

Constantin, Pascale, illus. I'm Going to Read (Level 1): Little Monster. 2007. (I'm Going to Read Ser.). 80p. (J). pap. 3.95 (*978-1-4027-2078-9(5)*) Sterling Publishing Co., Inc.

Coppola, Denise. Sammy Beagle's Birthday Party. 2005. 15p. (J). 8.03 (978-1-4116-3367-4(9)) Lulu.com.

Cornish, Linda Sowa Young. Pong's Birthday Journey. 2006. (J). pap. 15.00 (978-0-8059-6993-1(4)) Dorrance Publishing Co., Inc.

Cousins, Lucy. Happy Birthday, Maisy: Mini Edition. 2004. (Maisy Ser.). (Illus.). 14p. (J). (gr. k-k). 4.99 (978-0-7636-2454-5(3)) Candlewick Pr.

Crystal, Billy. Grandpa's Little One. 2008. 40p. (J). (ps-k). pap. 6.99 (978-0-06-078175-0(0) , Harper Trophy) HarperCollins Pubs.

—Grandpa's Little One. Porfirio, Guy, illus. 2006. 40p. (J). (ps-k). lib. bdg. 17.89 (978-0-06-078174-3(2)) HarperCollins Pubs.

Cumpleanos de Paco. 2001. (Let's Start Teacher's Pets Ser.).Tr. of Desmond's Birthday Party. (SPA., Illus.). 32p. (J). (ps-3). (978-968-5308-19-9(5) , Silver Dolphin en Español) Advanced Marketing, S. de R. L. de C. V.

Cutler, Jane. The Birthday Doll. Nakata, Hiroe, illus. 2004. 32p. (J). 16.00 (978-0-374-30719-6(9) , Farrar, Straus & Giroux (BYR)) Farrar, Straus & Giroux.

Dadey, Debbie & Jones, Marcia Thornton. Happy Boo-Day to You! Francis, Guy & Tugeau, Jeremy, illus. 2004. (Ghostville Elementary Ser.). 96p. (J). (gr. 2-5). pap. 3.99 (978-0-439-56002-3(0) , Scholastic Paperbacks) Scholastic, Inc.

Dalton, Annie. Flying High, No. 3. 2003. (Angels Unlimited Ser.). (Illus.). 144p. (J). pap. 4.99 (978-0-06-008817-0(6)) HarperCollins Pubs.

Daly, Niki. Happy Birthday, Jamela! Daly, Niki, illus. 2006. (Jamela Ser.). (Illus.). 32p. (J). (gr. k-2). 16.00 (978-0-374-32842-9(0) , Farrar, Straus & Giroux (BYR)) Farrar, Straus & Giroux.

D'Andrea, Deborah, concept. Picture Me Baby's Birthday. 2001. (Picture Me Ser.). (Illus.). 10p. (J). (ps up). bds. 4.99 (978-1-57151-591-9(7)) Playhouse Publishing.

Danziger, Paula. It's Justin Time, Amber Brown. Ross, Tony, illus. 9.95 (978-1-59112-294-4(5)) Live Oak Media.

—It's Justin Time, Amber Brown. 2002. (Illus.). (J). pap., tchr.'s planning gde. ed. 29.95 incl. audio (978-0-87499-908-2(1)) Live Oak Media.

—It's Justin Time, Amber Brown. Ross, Tony, illus. 2002. 28.95 incl. audio compact disk (978-1-59112-567-9(7)); pap. 31.95 incl. audio compact disk (978-1-59112-566-2(9)) Live Oak Media.

—It's Justin Time, Amber Brown. abr. ed. 2002. (Illus.). (J). (ps-2). 25.95 incl. audio (978-0-87499-907-5(3)); pap. 16.95 incl. audio (978-0-87499-906-8(5)) Live Oak Media.

—It's Justin Time, Amber Brown. Ross, Tony, illus. 2001. (Amber Brown Ser.: No. 10). 1p. (J). (gr. 3-6). 13.99 (978-0-399-23470-5(5) , Putnam Juvenile) Penguin Group (USA) Inc.

—It's Justin Time, Amber Brown. 2001. 10.79 (978-0-606-22522-9(6)); lib. bdg. 11.80 (978-0-613-44396-8(9)) Tandem Library Bks.

Davis, Brian. Matt's Birthday Blessing. Wheeler, Ron, illus. 2003. (Book of Matt Ser.: Vol. 1). 80p. (J). pap. 4.99 (978-1-59269-056-5(4)) Mcruffy Pr.

Davis, Holly & Anderson, Nancy Munger. My Birthday, Jesus' Birthday. 1998. 32p. (J). 12.99 (978-0-310-21968-2(X)) Zondervan.

Davis, Holly & Tada, Eareckson J. My Birthday, Jesus' Birthday. Anderson, Nancy Munger, illus. 1998. (J). 5.99 (978-0-310-97420-8(8)) Zonderkidz.

Dawe, Bruce. Luke & Lulu: Lulu Likes to Always Do Things Luke Doesn't Want Her To! 2006. (Bites Ser.). (Illus.). 86p. (J). (gr. 2-5). pap. 3.95 (978-0-7624-2623-2(3) , Running Pr. Kids) Running Pr. Bk. Pubs.

Day, Alexandra. Carl's Birthday. Day, Alexandra, illus. 2002. (Illus.). (J). 22.13 (978-0-7587-2194-5(3)) Book Wholesalers, Inc.

de Brunhoff, Laurent. L' Anniversaire de Babar. (Babar Ser.). (FRE., Illus.). (J). (ps-3). pap. (978-2-01-002551-8(2)) Hachette Groupe Livre.

de Estevez, Flor Roffe. El Cumpleanos de la Gallinita. (SPA.). (J). pap. 6.00 (978-980-01-0556-6(5)) Monte Avila Editores Latinoamericana CA VEN. *Dist:* Lectorum Pubns., Inc.

de Tena, Torcuato Luca. El Fabricante de Suenos. (SPA.). 112p. (J). (978-84-348-4787-3(6)) SM Ediciones ESP. *Dist:* Lectorum Pubns., Inc.

Degen, Bruce, illus. Happy Birthday, Jesse Bear! 2002. (J). 14.47 (978-0-7587-2685-8(6)) Book Wholesalers, Inc.

DeGrazia, John. The Three Little Tigers & Their Birthday Party. Spirin, Ilya, illus. 1999. (Three Little Tigers Ser.: Vol. 1). 20p. (J). (gr. 1-8). pap. 6.00 (978-0-9670522-0-5(3)) Big Cats Publishing.

deGroat, Diane. Happy Birthday to You, You Belong in a Zoo. deGroat, Diane, illus. 2007. 32p. (J). pap. 6.99 (978-0-06-001029-4(0) , Harper Trophy) HarperCollins Pubs.

—Happy Birthday to You, You Belong in a Zoo. 1999. (Illus.). 32p. (J). (ps-3). 15.00 (978-0-688-16544-4(3)) HarperCollins Pubs.

—Happy Birthday to You, You Belong in a Zoo. deGroat, Diane, illus. 1999. (Illus.). 32p. (J). (ps-3). lib. bdg. 16.89 (978-0-688-16545-1(1)) HarperCollins Pubs.

Del Moral, Susana, tr. Sr. Cuadrado. 2005. (Mis figuras Geometricas Ser.). (SPA., Illus.). 6p. (J). (ps-7). 9.95 (978-970-718-294-3(6) , Silver Dolphin en Español) Advanced Marketing, S. de R. L. de C. V. MEX. *Dist:* Perseus Distribution.

Demas, Corinne. The Boy Who Was Generous with Salt. Hays, Michael, illus. 2002. 32p. (J). (gr. k-3). 15.95 (978-0-7614-5099-3(8) , Cavendish Children's Bks.) Cavendish, Marshall Corp.

deRubertis, Barbara. Deena's Lucky Penny. 1999. (Math Matters Ser.). (Illus.). (J). 11.75 (978-0-606-18218-8(7)) Tandem Library Bks.

—Deena's Lucky Penny: Math Concept: Money. Holub, Joan & Fisher, Cynthia, illus. 1999. (Math Matters Ser.). 32p. (J). (ps-1). pap. 4.95 (978-1-57565-091-3(6)) Kane Pr., The.

Desmazières, Sandra. Emma & Her Friends: A Book about Colors. 2006. (Illus.). 28p. (J). lib. bdg. (978-0-8368-6997-2(4)) Stevens, Gareth Inc.

Detective Dog & the Disappearing Donuts. 2001. (ps-2). lib. bdg. 9.80 (978-0-613-32460-1(9)) Tandem Library Bks.

Dickinson, Rebecca. Monster Cake. Dickinson, Rebecca, illus. 2000. (Illus.). 32p. (J). (ps-2). pap. 4.99 (978-0-439-06752-2(9)) Scholastic, Inc.

—Monster Cake. 2000. (J). (978-0-606-19579-9(3)) Tandem Library Bks.

Dillard, Mary Gregory. Finding Betsyanna. 2006. (ENG.). 48p. per. 12.95 (***978-1-4241-5492-0(8)***) PublishAmerica, Inc.

Dingles, Molly. Little Lee Lee's Birthday Band. Bingler, Aimee, illus. 2000. (Little Lee Lee Ser.). 32p. (J). (ps-1). 9.99 (978-1-891997-12-9(2)) Dingles & Co.

—Little Lee Lee's Birthday Bang. Bingler, Aimee, illus. 2001. 26p. (J). lib. bdg. 19.00 (978-1-891997-18-1(1)) Dingles & Co.

Doherty, Paula. Going Places-Car. Doherty, Paula, illus. 2005. (Going Places Board Bks.). (Illus.). 10p. (J). bds. 4.99 (978-0-7641-5885-8(6)) Barron's Educational Series, Inc.

Dominguez, Kelli Kyle. The Perfect Pinata: La Pinata Perfecta. Mlawer, Teresa, tr. Paterson, Diane, illus. 2002. (ENG & SPA.). 32p. (J). (gr. k-3). 15.95 (978-0-8075-6495-0(8)) Whitman, Albert & Co.

Donahue, Jill L. Benny & the Birthday Gift. 2007. (Illus.). 24p. (J). (***978-1-4048-0590-3(7)***) Picture Window Bks.

—Benny & the Birthday Gift. Senturk, Burak, illus. 2006. (Read It! Readers Ser.). 24p. (J). (gr. 1-2). 19.93 (***978-1-4048-3164-3(9)***) Picture Window Bks.

Donahue, Jill L. Urban. Danny's Birthday. Rooney, Ronnie, illus. 2007. (Read-It! Readers Ser.). (J). 19.93 (978-1-4048-2408-9(1)) Picture Window Bks.

Dorling Kindersley Publishing Staff. Party Fun. 2003. (Dk Readers Ser.). (Illus.). 32p. (J). pap. 3.99 (978-0-7894-9992-9(4)) Dorling Kindersley Publishing, Inc.

—Party Fun. 2003. (ps-2). lib. bdg. 11.80 (978-0-613-75244-2(9)) Tandem Library Bks.

Dower, Laura. Red to the Rescue. 2007. (Firehouse Tales Ser.). (J). bds. 5.99 (978-0-439-89462-3(X)) Scholastic, Inc.

Down, Reg. The Magic Knot: And other Tangles. 2007. (Illus.). 100p. (J). per. 14.95 (***978-0-9794452-0-0(5)***) Lightly Pr.

Downey, Lynn. Papa's Birthday Gift. Schuett, Stacey, tr. Schuett, Stacey, illus. 2004. 32p. 16.99 (978-0-8066-4557-5(1) , Augsburg Bks.) Augsburg Fortress, Pubs.

Driehaus, Cyndy Ann. The Royal Adventures of Princess Daisy & Princess Darcy. Huser, Jessie Ann, illus. 2007. (J). (***978-1-933197-31-9(5)***) Orange Frazer Pr.

Duncan, Lois. The Longest Hair in the World. unabr. ed. 1999. (J). (gr. 1 up). pap., stu. ed. 35.95 incl. audio (978-0-7887-2661-3(7) , 40821X4) Recorded Bks., LLC.

Dwyer, Cynthia. Can You See Me Now? Schuepbach, Lynnette, illus. 2006. 24p. (J). 12.95 (***978-0-9677685-8-8(6)*** , Thumbprint Pr.) McIntyre, Connie.

Eagle, Michele, illus. My Birthday! (Boy) 1998. 15p. (J). (ps-4). pap. 12.00 (978-1-890703-10-3(9) , Bookmates) Penny Laine Papers, Inc.

—My Birthday (Girl) 1998. 15p. (J). (ps-4). pap. 12.00 (978-1-890703-11-0(7) , Bookmates) Penny Laine Papers, Inc.

Elya, Susan Middleton. F Is for Fiesta. Karas, G. Brian, illus. 2006. 32p. (J). (ps-2). 12.99 (978-0-399-24225-0(2) , Putnam Juvenile) Penguin Group (USA) Inc.

Epstein, Robin. Sleepover Surprise: A Twin-Sational Birthday. 2004. 60p. (J). (978-0-439-65791-4(1)) Scholastic, Inc.

—Sleepover Surprise: A Twin-sational Birthday. 2005. (Groovy Girls Ser.). (Illus.). 80p. (J). pap. 3.99 (978-0-439-81433-1(2)) Scholastic, Inc.

Eric's Birthday, 6 Pks. (ps-2). 27.00 (978-0-7635-9447-3(4)) Rigby Education.

Eurpsville U. S. A. Inc. Staff, ed. The Alphabet Eurps & the Birthday Surprise. 1999. (Illus.). (J). 19.95 (978-1-892522-13-9(6)) Eurpsville USA, Inc.

Evans, Cambria. Martha Moth Makes Socks. 2006. (Illus.). 40p. (J). (gr. k-3). 16.00 (978-0-618-55745-5(8)) Houghton Mifflin Co.

Evans, Pamela. Tina Queen of the Dragons. 2006. 101p. pap. 14.95 (978-1-4241-3356-7(4)) PublishAmerica, Inc.

Evelyn. Lucy the Elephant & Sami the Mouse: The Birthday Party. Conforti, John W., illus. 2004. (J). (978-0-9740115-1-6(7)) WeBeANS Corp.

Evlin, Frances. Ginger Gold. 2004. (J). pap. 12.95 (978-1-59374-119-8(7)) Whiskey Creek Pr., LLC.

Faglia, Matteo. Happy Birthday - I'm 1! Rinaldo, Luana, illus. 2001. (Happy Birthday Ser.).Tr. of Buon Compleanno Ho 1 Anno!. 16p. (J). (ps). bds. 6.95 (978-1-929132-07-2(7)) Kane/Miller Bk. Pubs., Inc.

—Happy Birthday - I'm 2!, Vol. 2. Vignale, Silvia, illus. 2001. (Happy Birthday Ser.).Tr. of Buon Compleanno Ho 2 Anni!. 16p. (J). (ps). bds. 6.95 (978-1-929132-08-9(5)) Kane/Miller Bk. Pubs., Inc.

—Happy Birthday - I'm 4!, Vol. 4. Abbatiello, Antonella, illus. 2001. (Happy Birthday Ser.).Tr. of Buon Compleanno Ho 4 Anni!. 48p. (J). (ps). 7.95 (978-1-929132-10-2(7)) Kane/Miller Bk. Pubs., Inc.

Faundez, Anne. Teddy's Birthday. 2004. (QEB Start Talking Ser.). (Illus.). 24p. (J). lib. bdg. 15.95 (978-1-59566-004-6(6)) QEB Publishing Inc.

Fearnley, Jan. Mr. Wolf & the Three Bears. 2002. (Illus.). 32p. (J). (ps-2). 16.00 (978-0-15-216423-2(5)) Harcourt Children's Bks.

Feely, Jenny. Birthday Cakes. 1999. (ps-2). lib. bdg. 11.80 (978-0-613-30278-4(8)) Tandem Library Bks.

Fernandez, Giselle. Gigi & the Birthday Ring. Petersen, Sheli, illus. 2005. (J). (978-1-56492-358-5(4)) Laredo Publishing Co., Inc.

Fisher, Doris. Happy Birthday to Whooo? Downey, Lisa, illus. (J). 2007. 1p. 8.95 (***978-1-934359-06-8(8));*** 2006. 32p. 15.95 (978-0-9768823-1-2(0)) Sylvan Dell Pubng.

Fisscher, Tiny. RUBY & the LION. 2008. 48p. 11.95 (***978-1-60136-014-4(2)***) Mars Media Pubs.

Flack, Marjorie. Ask Mr. Bear. Flack, Marjorie, illus. 2002. (Illus.). (J). 14.47 (978-0-7587-1995-9(7)) Book Wholesalers, Inc.

Flam, Chanie. Happy Birthday, Vol. 1. (Goldie Gold Board Book Ser.: Vol. 1). (Illus.). (J). (ps-1). bds. 4.95 (978-1-58330-025-1(2)) Feldheim Pubs.

Fleming, Sean & Ewald, Jenny, eds. To Catch a Mall Thief. 2004. 85p. (YA). pap. 9.95 (978-0-7414-2196-8(8)) Infinity Publishing.

Foreman, George & Manushkin, Fran. Let George Do It! Martin, Whitney, illus. 2005. 32p. (J). 15.95 (978-0-689-87807-7(9) , Simon & Schuster Children's Publishing) Simon & Schuster Children's Publishing.

Foreman, Michael. Surprise! Surprise! 2004. (Illus.). 32p. (J). pap. (978-1-84270-379-3(X)) Andersen.

Foster, Kinsley. Kitty in the City. McGaren, Kari, illus. 1999. 28p. (J). (gr. k-4). 15.95 (978-0-9667634-0-9(8)) What's Inside Pr.

Franklin's Birthday Party. 2004. (Franklin Tv Storybooks Ser.). (Illus.). 32p. (J). (ps-ps). (978-1-55074-882-6(3)) Kids Can Pr., Ltd.

Frasier, Debra. A Birthday Cake Is No Ordinary Cake. 2006. (Illus.). 40p. (J). 16.00 (978-0-15-205742-8(0)) Harcourt Trade Pubs.

Freeman, Don & Inches, Alison. Corduroy Makes a Cake. Eitzen, Allan, illus. 2003. 32p. (J). (gr. k-3). pap. 3.99 (978-0-14-250163-4(8) , Puffin) Penguin Group (USA) Inc.

Freeman, Martha. The Trouble with Twins. Smith, Cat Bowman, illus. 2007. 112p. (J). (gr. 2-6). 16.95 (978-0-8234-2025-4(6)) Holiday Hse., Inc.

Freeman, Tor. Hooray, I'm Five Today! Freeman, Tor, illus. 2004. (Illus.). 32p. (J). (gr. k-k). 16.99 (978-0-7636-2452-1(7)) Candlewick Pr.

French, Jackie. Alicia's Happy Day (English/Spanish Bilingual) Van Wright, Cornelius & Hu, Ying-Hwa, illus. 2007. 36p. (J). pap. 5.95 (***978-1-59572-116-7(9)***) Star Bright Bks., Inc.

Friedman, Laurie. Happy Birthday, Mallory! Schmitz, Tamara, illus. 2006. 160p. (J). (gr. 2-5). pap. 5.95 (978-0-8225-6502-4(1) , First Avenue Editions) Lerner Publishing Group.

Friedman, Laurie B. Happy Birthday, Mallory! Schmitz, Tamara, illus. 2005. 159p. (J). (ps-k). per. 15.95 (978-1-57505-823-8(5) , Carolrhoda Bks.) Lerner Publishing Group.

Friend, Ronda. R. Friend Swallows Her Pride. 2005. (Down on Friendly Acres Ser.: 1). (J). lib. bdg. (978-0-9743627-3-1(5)) Sunflower Seeds Pr.

Fuchs, Menucha. The Best Gift of All. 2004. (Illus.). 20p. (J). 6.95 (978-1-932443-15-8(0) , BGAH) Judaica Pr., Inc., The.

—The Flying Invitation. 2004. (Illus.). 20p. (J). 6.95 (978-1-932443-07-3(X) , FLIH) Judaica Pr., Inc., The.

Gago, Jenny. Perfect Gift. 2001. (gr. k-3). lib. bdg. 11.80 (978-0-613-82082-0(7)) Tandem Library Bks.

Gambrell, Linda B. & Dorling Kindersley Publishing Staff. Party Fun. 2003. (Readers Ser.). (Illus.). 32p. (J). 12.99 (978-0-7894-9994-3(0)) Dorling Kindersley Publishing, Inc.

Garfield, Valerie. Harold & the Purple Crayon: The Birthday Present. 2002. (ps-2). lib. bdg. 11.80 (978-0-613-50411-9(9)) Tandem Library Bks.

George, Olivia. My Birthday Cake. Aviles, Martha, illus. 2005. (My First Reader Ser.). 31p. (J). (gr. k-1). pap. 3.95 (978-0-516-25276-6(3) , Children's Pr.) Scholastic Library Publishing.

—My Birthday Cake. Aviles Junco, Martha, illus. 2005. (My First Reader Ser.). 32p. (J). (gr. k-1). 18.50 (978-0-516-25178-3(3) , Children's Pr.) Scholastic Library Publishing.

Gill, Janie S. Bob's Springtime Birthday. Reese, Robert, illus. 1999. 23p. (J). 5.95 (978-0-89868-480-3(3)); pap. 3.95 (978-0-89868-479-7(X)); lib. bdg. 10.95 (978-0-89868-478-0(1)) ARO Publishing Co.

Gilman, Phoebe. Jillian Jiggs & the Secret Surprise. ed. 2004. (J). (ps-2). spiral bd. (978-0-616-01655-8(7)) Canadian National Institute for the Blind/Institut National Canadien pour les Aveugles.

Glass, Julie. A Dollar for Penny. Allen, Joy, illus. 2000. (Step into Reading Ser.: No. 3). 32p. (J). (gr. k-3). pap. 3.99 (978-0-679-88973-1(6) , Random Hse. Bks. for Young Readers) Random Hse. Children's Bks.

—A Dollar for Penny. Allen, Joy, illus. 2000. 32p. (J). (ps-ps). lib. bdg. 11.80 (978-0-613-07631-9(1)) Tandem Library Bks.

—A Dollar for Penny. 2000. (Illus.). (J). 10.79 (978-0-606-18492-2(9)) Tandem Library Bks.

Glassman, Jackie. Happy Birthday, Princess Lolly! 2000. (ps-2). lib. bdg. 11.80 (978-0-613-32630-8(X)) Tandem Library Bks.

Golden Books Staff. Move to the Beat! 2006. (Illus.). 32p. (J). (ps-2). pap. 3.99 (978-0-375-83623-7(3) , Golden Bks.) Random Hse. Children's Bks.

Golden, Kathleen M. Cleopatra's Big Birthday BBQ. Golden, Kathleen M., illus. 2003. (Illus.). 18p. (J). (ps-k). mass mkt. 14.95 (978-0-9726418-0-7(7)) Happyland Media.

Gomes, Barbara K. Esau at the Big House. 2006. 76p. pap. 14.95 (978-1-4241-2288-2(0)) PublishAmerica, Inc.

Gomez de Salazar, Carmen & Martilotti, Carla. Pinky's Birthday. 2007. (ENG.). 28p. per. 12.95 (***978-1-59800-732-9(7)***) Outskirts Press, Inc.

Gonzalez Bertrand, Diane. The Ruiz Street Kids (Los Muchachos de la Calle Ruiz) Baeza Ventura, Gabriela, tr. (ENG & SPA., Illus.). (J). pap. 9.95 (978-1-55885-321-8(9) , Piñata Books) Arte Publico Pr.

Goode, Teresa. Jayhawk Adventures, Jed's Birthday Surprise. Kotrous, Chad, illus. 2006. 27p. (J). (gr. 1-3). pap. 5.95 (978-0-9646898-6-2(3)) Leathers Publishing.

Goodhart, Pippa. Hoppy Birthday, Jo-Jo! Birkett, Georgie, illus. 2005. (Green Bananas Ser.). 48p. (J). (978-0-7787-1025-7(4)) Crabtree Publishing Co.

—Hoppy Birthday, Jo-Jo! 2005. (Green Bananas Ser.). (Illus.). 48p. (J). (ps). pap. (978-0-7787-1041-7(6)) Crabtree Publishing Co.

Graham, Bob. Oscar's Half Birthday. Graham, Bob, illus. 2005. (Illus.). 32p. (J). (gr. k-1). 16.99 (978-0-7636-2699-0(6)) Candlewick Pr.

Grandpa's Birthday: Individual Title Six-Packs. (Literatura 2000 Ser.). (gr. 2-3). 33.00 (978-0-7635-0199-0(9)) Rigby Education.

Granowsky, Alvin. My Family. 2001. (978-0-606-22434-5(3)) Tandem Library Bks.

Gray, Kes & Parsons, Garry. Billy's Bucket. 2003. (Illus.). 32p. (J). 24.95 (978-0-370-32596-5(6)) Random Hse. GBR. *Dist:* Random Hse. of Canada, Ltd.

Green, John F. Alice & the Birthday Giant. Kovalski, Maryann, illus. 2000. (First Flight Ser.). 32p. (J). pap. (978-1-55041-540-7(9)); (gr. 1-3). lib. bdg. (978-1-55041-538-4(7)) Fitzhenry & Whiteside, Ltd.

Greig, Allison. Stacey's Adventures. 2006. (Illus.). 64p. pap. (***978-1-84401-035-6(X)***) Athena Pr.

Griffith, Helen V. How Many Candles? Lamut, Sonja, illus. 1999. 24p. (J). (gr. k-3). 16.00 (978-0-688-16258-0(4)); (gr. 7 up). 15.89 (978-0-688-16259-7(2)) HarperCollins Pubs.

Guest, Elissa Haden. Iris & Walter & the Birthday Party. Davenier, Christine, illus. 2008. (Iris & Walter Ser.). 44p. (J). pap. 5.95 (***978-0-15-205388-8(3)*** , Harcourt Paperbacks) Harcourt Children's Bks.

—Iris & Walter & the Birthday Party. Davenier, Christine, illus. 2006. (Iris & Walter Ser.). 44p. (J). 15.00 (978-0-15-205015-3(9)) Harcourt Trade Pubs.

Hagemann, Bernhard. Charlie Gallina Ciega. (Torre de Papel Ser.). (SPA., Illus.). (J). 7.95 (978-958-04-5032-0(3)) Norma S.A. COL. *Dist:* Distribuidora Norma, Inc.

Hall, Kirsten. Birthday Beastie: All about Counting. 2004. (Beastieville Ser.). (J). (gr. k-1). pap. 3.95 (978-0-516-24651-2(8) , Children's Pr.) Scholastic Library Publishing.

—Birthday Beastie: All about Counting. Luedecke, Bev, illus. 2003. (Beastieville Ser.). 32p. (J). 19.50 (978-0-516-22891-4(9) , Children's Pr.) Scholastic Library Publishing.

Hallinan, P. K. Happy Birthday! 2003. (J). (Illus.). 26p. bds. 7.95 (978-0-8249-5453-6(X)); (978-0-8249-6507-5(8) , Candy Cane Pr.) Ideals Pubns.

—Today Is Your Birthday! 2001. (Illus.). 24p. (J). (ps-3). pap. 5.95 (978-0-8249-5383-6(5) , Ideals) Ideals Pubns.

Hallwood, Cheri L. The Curious Polka-Dot Present. 2007. (J). 16.99 (***978-0-9774422-1-8(7)***) Forever Young Pubs.

Hamilton, Elizabeth L. Jeremy Rabbit's Honesty Pie. 2003. (Character Critters Ser.: No. 2). (Illus.). 32p. (J). (ps-3). per. 5.95 (978-0-9713749-5-9(3) , Character-in-Action) Quiet Impact, Inc.

Handler, Daniel & Dudley, Dick, illus. The Alphabet Eurps & the Birthday Surprise. 1999. 10p. (J). 7.95 (978-1-892522-02-3(0)) Eurpsville USA, Inc.

Happy Birthday, Moon. 2004. (J). 24.95 incl. audio (978-1-56008-031-2(0)) Weston Woods Studios, Inc.

Happy Birthday Moon. 2004. 29.95 incl. cd-rom (978-1-55592-842-1(0)); pap. 32.75 incl. audio (978-1-55592-236-8(8)); (J). pap. 18.95 incl. audio compact disk (978-1-55592-805-6(6)); (J). pap. 18.95 incl. audio compact disk (978-1-55592-773-8(4)); (J). pap. 38.75 incl. audio compact disk (978-1-55592-822-3(6)); (J). pap. 38.75 incl. audio compact disk (978-1-55592-788-2(2)); (J). pap. 32.75 incl. audio (978-1-55592-237-5(6)); (J). pap. 14.95 incl. audio (978-1-55592-657-1(6)) Weston Woods Studios, Inc.

Happy Birthday, Thomas. 2002. (Thomas the Tank Engine Ser.). (Illus.). (J). 11.91 (978-0-7587-1242-4(1)) Book Wholesalers, Inc.

Harcourt School Publishers Staff. A Birthday Basket: Library Book. 1999. (Collections Ser.). (Illus.). pap. 14.90 (978-0-15-313402-9(X)) Harcourt Schl. Pubs.

—Birthday Cookies: Take-Home Book. 1999. (Collections Ser.). (Illus.). (J). pap. 1.90 (978-0-15-317226-7(6)) Harcourt Schl. Pubs.

—Birthday Cookies Below Level. 3rd ed. 2002. (Trophies Reading Program Ser.). (Illus.). pap. 5.10 (978-0-15-323049-3(5)) Harcourt Schl. Pubs.

—Happy Birthday, Grandma. 3rd ed. 2002. (Trophies English Language Learners Ser.). (Illus.). pap. 5.10 (978-0-15-327651-4(7)) Harcourt Schl. Pubs.

—The Ice Storm Birthday Advanced Level. 3rd ed. 2002. (Trophies Reading Program Ser.). (Illus.). pap. 5.10 (978-0-15-323386-9(9)) Harcourt Schl. Pubs.

—Ingredientes Secretos On Level. 3rd ed. 2002. (Trofeos Ser.).Tr. of Secret Ingredients. (SPA., Illus.). pap. 6.80 (978-0-15-324176-5(4)) Harcourt Schl. Pubs.

—Sam's Chase On Level. 3rd ed. 2002. (Trophies Reading Program Ser.). (Illus.). pap. 5.10 (978-0-15-323091-2(6)) Harcourt Schl. Pubs.

—That's My Shot: Take-Home Book. 1999. (Collections Ser.). (Illus.). (J). pap. 1.90 (978-0-15-317294-6(0)) Harcourt Schl. Pubs.

Hargreaves, Roger. Little Miss Birthday. 2007. 32p. (J). pap. 3.99 (978-0-8431-2131-5(9) , Price Stern Sloan) Penguin Group (USA) Inc.

—Mr. Birthday. 2007. 32p. (J). pap. 3.99 (978-0-8431-2130-8(0) , Price Stern Sloan) Penguin Group (USA) Inc.

Harper, Charise Mericle. When Randolph Turned Rotten. 2007. 40p. (J). (gr. k-3). 16.99 (***978-0-375-84071-5(0)***); lib. bdg. 19.99 (***978-0-375-94071-2(5)***) Random Hse. Children's Bks. (Knopf Bks. for Young Readers).

Hartfield, Claire. Me & Uncle Romie: A Story Inspired by the Life & Art of Romare Beardon. Lagarrigue, Jerome, illus. 2002. 40p. (J). 16.99 (978-0-8037-2520-1(5) , Dial) Penguin Group (USA) Inc.

Harvey, Damian. A Gift for the King. Remphry, Martin, illus. 2005. (Reading Corner Ser.). 24p. (J). (gr. k-3). lib. bdg. 22.80 (978-1-59771-013-8(X)) Sea-To-Sea Pubns.

Hawkins, Colin. Mr Wolf's Birthday Surprise. 2004. (Illus.). 32p. (J). pap. 9.99 (978-1-4052-0685-3(3)) Egmont Bks., Ltd. GBR. *Dist:* Trafalgar Square Publishing.

Head, Honor. Direction. Stower, Adam, illus. 1998. (Ed Mouse Finds Out about Ser.). 32p. (J). (ps-2). 19.98 (978-0-8172-5200-7(2)) Raintree.

—Direction. Stower, Adam, illus. 1998. (Ed Mouse Finds Out about Ser.). 32p. (J). (ps-2). pap. 5.95 (978-0-8172-8100-7(2)) Steck-Vaughn.

Hedderwick, Mairi. Katie Morag & the Birthdays. 2006. (Illus.). 48p. (J). pap. 9.99 (978-0-09-946426-6(8) , Red Fox) Random Hse. Children's Bks. GBR. *Dist:* Trafalgar Square Publishing.

—Katie Morag & the Birthdays: A Story, Activity & Birthday Book. 2006. (Illus.). 48p. (J). 20.00 (978-0-370-32850-8(7)) Random Hse. GBR. *Dist:* Independent Pubs. Group.

Henkes, Kevin. The Birthday Room. Henkes, Kevin, illus. 2001. (Illus.). 160p. (J). (gr. 3 up). pap. 6.99 (978-0-06-443828-5(7)) HarperCollins Pubs.

Herfurtner, Rudolf. Cumpleanos con Animales. 2002. Tr. of Birthday with Animals. (SPA.). 118p. (gr. 3-4). 3.99 (978-968-16-4266-2(X)) Fondo de Cultura Economica USA.

Herman, Gail & Bratun, Katy. Hay una Cuidad. Bratun, Katy, illus. 2003. (SPA.). (J). lib. bdg. (978-0-375-91499-7(4)) Random House Publishing Group.

Hest, Amy. Jamaica Louise James. (gr. k-3). lib. bdg. 14.15 (978-0-613-70961-3(6)) Tandem Library Bks.

Higginson, Hadley. Keeker & the Crazy Upside-Down Day. Perrett, Lisa, illus. 2008. (J). (***978-0-8118-6255-4(0)***); pap. (***978-0-8118-6256-1(9)***) Chronicle Bks. LLC.

Higginson, Sheila. Happy Birthday! A Lift-the-Flap Surprise Story. Disney Storybook Artists Staff, illus. 2007. 16p. (J). (ps-k). pap. 5.99 (***978-1-4231-0652-4(0)***) Disney Pr.

Hill, Eric. Spot Bakes a Cake. Hill, Eric, illus. 2005. 20p. (J). pap. 6.99 (978-0-14-240329-7(6) , Puffin) Penguin Group (USA) Inc.

—Spot's Birthday Party. Hill, Eric, illus. 2003. (Illus.). 24p. (J). pap. 6.99 (978-0-14-250125-2(5) , Puffin) Penguin Group (USA) Inc.

—Spot's Birthday Party. 2003. (gr. k-3). lib. bdg. 15.30 (978-0-613-87829-6(9)) Tandem Library Bks.

—Spot's First Words. Hill, Eric, illus. 2006. 12p. (J). (ps-k). bds. 12.99 (978-0-399-24616-6(9) , Putnam Juvenile) Penguin Group (USA) Inc.

Hillert, Margaret. The Birthday Car. 2002. (Illus.). (J). 15.00 (978-1-4046-0064-5(7)) Book Wholesalers, Inc.

—The Birthday Car. Oechsli, Kelly, illus. rev. exp. ed. 2007. (Beginning to Read Ser.). 32p. (J). lib. bdg. (978-1-59953-043-7(0)) Norwood Hse. Pr.

—Happy Birthday, Dear Dragon. Kock, Carl, illus. rev. exp. ed. 2007. (Beginning to Read Ser.). 32p. (J). lib. bdg. (978-1-59953-037-6(6)) Norwood Hse. Pr.

Hoban, Lillian. Arthur's Birthday Party. Hoban, Lillian, illus. 2002. (Arthur the Chimpanzee Ser.). (Illus.). (J). 12.34 (978-0-7587-4386-2(6)) Book Wholesalers, Inc.

—Arthur's Birthday Party. Hoban, Lillian, illus. (I Can Read Bks.). (Illus.). 64p. (J). (ps-3). 2000. pap. 3.99 (978-0-06-444280-0(2) , Harper Trophy); 1999. 14.89 (978-0-06-027799-4(8)); 1999. 14.95 (978-0-06-027798-7(X)) HarperCollins Pubs.

—Arthur's Birthday Party. 2000. (Illus.). (J). (ps-ps). 64p. lib. bdg. 11.80 (978-0-613-24246-2(7)); (978-0-606-18674-2(3)) Tandem Library Bks.

Hoban, Lillian, illus. Arthur's Birthday Party. 2000. 64p. (J). lib. bdg. 13.85 (***978-1-4242-0535-6(2)***) Fitzgerald Bks.

Hoban, Lillian, illus. A Birthday for Frances. 2002. (Frances Ser.). (J). 12.30 (978-0-7587-2113-6(7)) Book Wholesalers, Inc.

Hoban, Russell. A Birthday for Frances. 2000. (J). pap. 3.95 (978-0-590-04360-1(9)) Scholastic, Inc.

Hobbie, Holly. A Present for Toot. Hobbie, Holly, illus. 1998. (Toot & Puddle Ser.). (Illus.). 32p. (J). (ps-3). 15.99 (978-0-316-36556-7(4)) Little Brown & Co.

Hobson, Sally, illus. All Aboard! 2000. 24p. (J). (978-1-86233-079-5(4) , Gullane Children's Bks.) Pinwheel.

Hock, Dan. The Birthday Bash 2 vols. An Iggy & Igor Mystery (#2) Hock, Dan, illus. l.t. ed. 2004. (Illus.). 51p. (J). per. 4.99 (978-0-9754046-1-4(X)) Anticipation Pr.

Holabird, Katharine. Angelina's Birthday. Craig, Helen, illus. 2006. 32p. (J). (ps). 12.99 (978-0-670-06057-3(7) , Viking Juvenile) Penguin Group (USA) Inc.

The Hole: Individual Title Six-Packs. (Sails Literacy Ser.). 16p. (gr. k up). 27.00 (978-0-7635-4418-8(3)) Rigby Education.

Horse, Harry. Little Rabbit Lost. 2005. (Illus.). 32p. (J). (ps). per. 9.95 (978-1-56145-345-0(5) , Peachtree Junior) Peachtree Pubs., Ltd.

Houghton Mifflin Company Staff. Birthday Fun with Curious George. 2005. (J). (ps-k). pap. (978-0-618-69654-3(7)) Houghton Mifflin Co. Trade & Reference Div.

Howe, James. Creepy-Crawly Birthday. Morrill, Leslie H., illus. 1999. (Bunnicula & Friends Ser.). 48p. (J). (gr. k-3). pap. 5.95 (978-0-688-16700-4(4)) HarperCollins Pubs.

—Creepy-Crawly Birthday. Mack, Jeff, illus. 2007. (Bunnicula & Friends Ser.). 48p. (J). 16.99 (978-0-689-85728-7(4) , Atheneum) Simon & Schuster Children's Publishing.

—Houndsley & Catina & the Birthday Surprise. Gay, Marie-Louise, illus. 2006. 48p. (J). (gr. k-3). 14.99 (978-0-7636-2405-7(5)) Candlewick Pr.

Howe, James. Houndsley & Catina & the Birthday Surprise. Gay, Marie-Louise, illus. 2007. 48p. (J). (gr. k-3). pap. 4.99 (***978-0-7636-3640-1(1)***) Candlewick Pr.

Hudson, Angus. Nacimiento Especial (Special Birthday) (SPA.). (J). 1.69 (978-0-7899-0535-2(3) , 498798) Editorial Unilit.

Huens, Sara, illus. The Cranberry Kids: And the Birthday Surprise. 2001. 16p. (J). (gr. k-3). pap. 7.95 (978-0-9702818-0-7(3)) C & R Enterprises.

Hughes, Shirley. Alfie & the Birthday Surprise. 1998. (Illus.). 32p. (J). (ps-1). 16.00 (978-0-688-15187-4(6)) HarperCollins Pubs.

—Alfie & the Birthday Surprise. 2007. (Illus.). 32p. (J). pap. 8.95 (***978-0-09-920862-4(8)*** , Red Fox) Random Hse. Children's Bks. GBR. *Dist:* Independent Pubs. Group.

—Alfie & the Birthday Surprise. Hughes, Shirley, illus. 1999. (Illus.). 30p. (J). 9.99 (978-1-58048-086-4(1)) Sandvik Publishing.

Hundal, Nancy. Twilight Fairies. Kilby, Don, illus. 2002. 32p. (J). (gr. k-3). (978-1-55041-645-9(6)) Fitzhenry & Whiteside, Ltd.

—Twilight Fairies. Kilby, Don, illus. 2006. 32p. pap. 7.95 (978-1-55041-961-0(7)) Fitzhenry & Whiteside, Ltd. CAN. *Dist:* F & W Pubns., Inc.

Hutchins, Pat. Favorite Author Collection: Pat Hutchins, 3 bks., Set. unabr. ed. 1999. (Illus.). (J). (ps-3). pap. 42.95 incl. audio (978-0-87499-485-8(3)) Live Oak Media.

—Happy Birthday, Sam. Hutchins, Pat, illus. 2005. (Illus.). (J). (gr. k-3). pap. 16.95 incl. audio (978-0-87499-287-8(7)) BBC Audiobooks America.

—There's Only One of Me! Hutchins, Pat, illus. 2003. (Illus.). 24p. (J). 16.99 (978-0-06-029819-7(7)) HarperCollins Pubs.

—There's Only One of Me! Hutchins, Pat, illus. 2006. (J). (ps-2). 25.95 incl. audio (978-1-59519-490-9(8)); (Illus.). 28.95 incl. audio compact disk (978-1-59519-494-7(0)) Live Oak Media.

Inches, Alison. Corduroy Makes a Cake. Eitzen, Allan, illus. 2004. 32p. lib. bdg. 10.79 (978-0-606-30118-3(6)) Tandem Library Bks.

—Corduroy Makes a Cake. 2003. (gr. k-3). lib. bdg. 11.80 (978-0-613-87824-1(8)) Tandem Library Bks.

Inkpen, Mick. Kipper's Birthday. 2000. (Illus.). (J). (978-0-606-18181-5(4)) Tandem Library Bks.

Jennings, Sharon. The Happily Ever Afternoon. Lightburn, Ron, illus. 2006. 24p. (J). (ps-k). pap. 7.95 (978-1-55037-944-0(5)); lib. bdg. 19.95 (978-1-55037-945-7(3)) Annick Pr., Ltd. CAN. *Dist:* Firefly Bks., Ltd.

Jennings, Sharon, et al. Franklin Snoops. Jeffrey, Sean, illus. 2003. (Franklin TV Storybook Ser.). 32p. (J). (ps-3). (978-1-55337-364-3(2)) Kids Can Pr., Ltd.

Jensen, Roberta Joan. The Marriage of Princess Winter Bk. 1: Princess Winter. 2005. 64p. pap. 12.95 (978-1-4137-7769-7(4)) PublishAmerica, Inc.

Jocelyn, Marthe. Hannah & the Seven Dresses. 2006. (Illus.). 23p. (J). (gr. k-4). reprint ed. 15.00 (978-1-4223-5552-7(7)) DIANE Publishing Co.

Jones, Christianne C. Nate the Dinosaur. Epstein, Len, illus. 2006. (Read-It! Readers Ser.). 24p. (J). (ps-3). 18.60 (978-1-4048-1728-9(X)) Picture Window Bks.

Kalz, Jill. Pony Party. Schultz, Sara, illus. 2006. (Read-It! Readers Ser.). 24p. (J). (ps-3). 18.60 (978-1-4048-1612-1(7)) Picture Window Bks.

Karasyov, Carrie & Kargman, Jill. Bittersweet Sixteen. 2007. 240p. (J). pap. 7.99 (***978-0-06-077846-0(6)*** , HarperTeen) HarperCollins Pubs.

Kargman, Jill & Karasyov, Carrie. Bittersweet Sixteen. 2006. 240p. (J). 15.99 (978-0-06-077844-6(X)); lib. bdg. 16.89 (978-0-06-077845-3(8)) HarperCollins Pubs.

Kay's Birthday: KinderReaders Individual Title Six-Packs. (Kinderstarters Ser.). 8p. (ps-1). 21.00 (978-0-7635-8651-5(X)) Rigby Education.

Keats, Ezra Jack. A Letter to Amy. Keats, Ezra Jack, illus. 2002. (Illus.). (J). 14.04 (978-0-7587-2977-4(4)) Book Wholesalers, Inc.

—A Letter to Amy. Keats, Ezra Jack, illus. 1998. (Picture Puffin Ser.). (Illus.). 40p. (J). (ps-3). 16.99 (978-0-670-88063-8(9) , Viking Juvenile); pap. 6.99 (978-0-14-056442-6(X) , Puffin) Penguin Group (USA) Inc.

Keffer, Lois & Haidle, Helen. Ripples Raccoon Shares His Balloon. Spengler, Ken, illus. 1999. (Read-To-Me Puppet Buddies Ser.: Vol. 9). 24p. (J). (ps-1). 9.99 (978-1-57673-438-4(2) , Multnomah) WaterBrook Pr.

Kelley, Gloria. Beverly Babes & Guys: Alicia's Thirtee. 2006. 64p. pap. 12.95 (978-1-4241-2610-1(X)) PublishAmerica, Inc.

Kellogg, Steven, illus. Jimmy's Boa & the Big Splash Birthday Bash. 2002. (Jimmy's Boa Constrictor Ser.). (J). 25.45 (978-0-7587-2902-6(2)) Book Wholesalers, Inc.

Kempf, Molly. Happy Birthday. Huxtable, Tonja & Huxtable, John, illus. 2008. (Strawberry Shortcake Ser.). 24p. (J). (ps-2). 4.99 (***978-0-448-44714-8(2)*** , Grosset & Dunlap) Penguin Group (USA) Inc.

Kennemore, Tim. Alice's Birthday Pig. 2005. (Illus.). 64p. (J). pap. (978-1-84270-240-6(8)) Andersen.

Kerr, Judith. Mog's Amazing Birthday Caper. 2005. (Illus.). 48p. (J). pap. 8.99 (978-0-00-717131-6(5)) HarperCollins Pubs. Ltd. GBR. *Dist:* Independent Pubs. Group.

King-Smith, Dick. The Stray. unabr. ed. 2002. (J). pap. 24.95 incl. audio (978-0-7540-6201-1(5)) BBC Audiobooks America.

Kirk, David. Miss Spider's Abc. Kirk, David, illus. 2002. (Little Miss Spider Ser.). (Illus.). (J). 26.11 (978-0-7587-3149-4(3)) Book Wholesalers, Inc.

Kleven, Elisa. Hooray, a Pinata! 2000. (J). 13.79 (978-0-606-19775-5(3)) Tandem Library Bks.

—The Paper Princess Flies Again: With Her Dog! 2005. (Illus.). 32p. (J). (gr. k-2). 15.95 (978-1-58246-146-5(5) , Tricycle Pr.) Ten Speed Pr.

Kline, Suzy. Horrible Harry & the Triple Revenge. Remkiewicz, Frank, illus. 2008. (Horrible Harry Ser.). 64p. (J). (gr. 2). 3.99 (***978-0-14-241081-3(0)*** , Puffin) Penguin Group (USA) Inc.

Klinting, Lars. Harvey the Baker. 2005. (Handy Harvey Ser.). (Illus.). 40p. (J). (ps-k). pap., pap. 4.95 (978-0-7534-5913-3(2) , Kingfisher) Houghton Mifflin Co. Trade & Reference Div.

Koeppel, Ruth. Goddard, Come Home! 2003. (gr. k-3). lib. bdg. 11.80 (978-0-613-66357-1(8)) Tandem Library Bks.

Krensky, Stephen. Eeyore Has a Birthday. 2001. 10.79 (978-0-606-22514-4(5)) Tandem Library Bks.

—Lionel's Birthday. Natti, Susanna, illus. 2003. (Easy-to-Read Ser.). 48p. (J). (gr. k-3). 13.99 (978-0-8037-2752-6(6) , Dial) Penguin Group (USA) Inc.

Kromhout, Rindert. Little Donkey & the Birthday Present. Martens, Marianne, tr. from DUT. Van Haeringen, Annemarie, illus. 2007. 32p. (J). (ps-2). 15.95 (***978-0-7358-2132-3(1)***) North-South Bks., Inc.

Kropf, Latifa Berry. Happy Birthday, World: A Rosh Hashanah Celebration. Carlson, Lisa, illus. 2005. 12p. (J). (gr. 1 up). per. 5.95 (978-0-929371-32-0(1)) Kar-Ben Publishing.

Krosoczka, Jarrett J. Annie Was Warned. 2003. (Illus.). 30p. (J). (ps-3). 15.95 (978-0-375-81567-6(8)); lib. bdg. 17.99 (978-0-375-91567-3(2)) Random Hse. Children's Bks. (Knopf Bks. for Young Readers).

Kuchman, D. S. Krystal Steps: The Journey Begins. 2006. 57p. pap. 12.95 (***978-1-4241-5135-6(X)***) PublishAmerica, Inc.

LaLumiere, Michael & Messinger, Kim. Birthday Snow. 2006. (Illus.). 32p. (J). 14.95 (***978-0-9791006-1-1(5)***) Stagger Lee Bks.

Le Masne, Christophe. El Cumpleanos de Tom. 2002. (Tom Series Ser.). (ENG & SPA., Illus.). 24p. 9.95 (978-84-7864-344-8(3)) Combel Editorial, S.A. ESP. *Dist:* Independent Pubs. Group.

LeapFrog Staff, compiled by. The Birthday Hunt. 2001. (J). (ps-2). spiral bd. 14.99 (978-1-58605-029-0(X)) LeapFrog Enterprises, Inc.

Lepp, Royden. Happy Birthday Barnabas. 2008. 32p. (J). pap. 3.99 (***978-0-310-71586-3(5)***) Zondervan.

Lester, Helen. Princess Penelope's Parrot. Munsinger, Lynn M., illus. 2001. 32p. (J). (gr. k-3). reprint ed. pap. 6.95 (978-0-618-13845-6(5) , Walter Lorraine) Houghton Mifflin Co. Trade & Reference Div.

A Letter to Amy. 2004. (J). 24.95 incl. audio (978-0-89719-887-5(5)); pap. 14.95 incl. audio (978-1-56008-060-2(4)) Weston Woods Studios, Inc.

Lieberman, Channah. Happy Birthday to Me! - Boys' Edition. Argoff, Patti, illus. 2006. 32p. (J). 12.95 (978-1-929628-27-8(7)) Hachai Publishing.

—Happy Birthday to Me! Girls' Edition. Argoff, Patti, illus. 2006. 32p. (J). 12.95 (978-1-929628-31-5(5)) Hachai Publishing.

Lilienstein, Jennel. Birthday! 2003. 36p. (J). 8.99 (978-0-9741215-0-5(9)) Stories of My Life, The.

Ling, Bettina. Lemonade for Sale. Handelman, Dorothy, photos by. 1998. (Real Kids Readers Ser.). (Illus.). 48p. (gr. 1-3). lib. bdg. 18.90 (978-0-7613-2010-4(5)); 32p. (J). (gr. 2-4). pap. 4.99 (978-0-7613-2035-7(0)) Lerner Publishing Group. (Millbrook Pr.).

Lipe, Riki. Hanging with Yum-Yum & Yuck. 2007. (J). 10.00 (***978-0-9659381-6-7(6)***) Hoot N' Cackle Pr.

Little, Jean. The Birthday Girl. Lawrason, June, illus. 2004. 64p. (J). lib. bdg. 20.00 (***978-1-4242-1256-9(1)***) Fitzgerald Bks.

—The Birthday Girl. Lawrason, June, illus. 2004. (Orca Echoes Ser.). 64p. (J). (gr. 2-3). pap. 4.99 (978-1-55143-292-2(7) , 1234535) Orca Bk. Pubs. USA.

Lively, Penelope. Dragon Trouble. 2002. (gr. 3-6). lib. bdg. 12.95 (978-0-613-52832-0(8)) Tandem Library Bks.

LoGuidice, Mike. Open up & Say Aggh! 2005. (J). pap. 16.00 (978-0-8059-7037-1(1)) Dorrance Publishing Co., Inc.

London, Jonathan. Froggy Bakes a Cake. Remkiewicz, Frank, illus. 2000. (Reading Railroad Bks.). 32p. (J). (ps-3). pap. 3.99 (978-0-448-42153-7(4) , Grosset & Dunlap) Penguin Group (USA) Inc.

—Froggy Bakes a Cake. 2000. (ps-2). lib. bdg. 11.25 (978-0-613-25269-0(1)); (Illus.). (J). 10.29 (978-0-606-21801-6(7)) Tandem Library Bks.

—Shawn & Keeper & the Birthday Party. 1999. (Easy-to-Read Ser.). (J). (978-0-606-19507-2(6)); lib. bdg. 11.80 (978-0-613-22368-3(3)) Tandem Library Bks.

Long, Loretta. Courtney's Birthday Party. 1998. (Illus.). 32p. (J). (ps-3). pap. 6.95 (978-0-940975-83-5(1) , Sankofa Bks.) Just Us Bks., Inc.

Look, Lenore. Henry's First-Moon Birthday. ed. 2004. (Illus.). (J). (gr. k-3). spiral bd. (978-0-616-07256-1(2)) Canadian National Institute for the Blind/Institut National Canadien pour les Aveugles.

Lopez, Loretta. The Birthday Swap. Lopez, Loretta, illus. 1999. (Illus.). 32p. (J). (gr. k-3). pap. 6.95 (978-1-880000-89-2(X)) Lee & Low Bks., Inc.

—Que Suppresa de Cumpleanos! ed. 2004. (SPA.). (J). (gr. k-3). spiral bd. (978-0-616-07277-6(5)) Canadian National Institute for the Blind/Institut National Canadien pour les Aveugles.

Lorenzen, Margaret Brownell. Petunia Patch Pockets & the Golden Locket. Jocelyn, Sawyer & Liza, Behles, illus. 2005. 76p. (J). per. 12.50 (978-0-9724922-7-0(5)) Authors & Artists Publishers of New York, Inc.

Lorimer, Janet. The Mystery Quilt: Set 1. 2002. 32p. (YA). 2.95 (978-1-56254-410-2(1) , SP 4101) Saddleback Educational Publishing.

Lynn, Tammy. Happy Birthday Puppy: An I See Puppy Book. Stewart, Elaine, ed. Lynn, Tammy, illus. 2006. (Illus.). 12p. (J). bds. 6.99 (978-0-9774277-0-3(6) , 0-9774277-0-6) I See Puppy, LLP.

Mackall, Dandi Daley. My Big Birthday. O'Neill, Rachael, illus. 2005. (Carry Me Along Ser.). 24p. (J). (ps). 6.99 (978-0-310-70939-8(3)) Zonderkidz.

Madrigal, Antonio Hernandez. Erandi's Braids. 2001. (gr. k-3). lib. bdg. 15.30 (978-0-613-35941-2(0)) Tandem Library Bks.

Marlow, Herb. The Lost Kitten. Head, Pat, illus. 2003. 16p. (J). 19.95 (978-1-893595-34-7(X)) Four Seasons Bks., Inc.

Marsoli, Lisa Ann. Harold's Birthday Surprise: Harold & the Purple Crayon. Murawski, Kevin, illus. 2005. 10p. (J). 6.95 (978-1-58117-261-4(3) , Intervisual/Piggy Toes) Dalmatian Pr.

Martin, Ann M. Best Friends. 2008. (Main Street Ser.). 208p. (J). 6.99 (***978-0-439-86882-2(3)*** , Scholastic Paperbacks) Scholastic, Inc.

Martín, JoElle. A Bridge in the Forest, Pt. 1. 2007. 280p. (YA). pap. 14.99 (978-1-59092-372-6(3) , Blue Works) Windstorm Creative.

—A Promise in the Forest, Vol. 2. 2008. 280p. (YA). pap. 16.99 (978-1-59092-541-6(6) , Blue Works) Windstorm Creative.

Mass, Wendy. Leap Day. 2006. 224p. (J). (gr. 5-8). pap. 7.99 (978-0-316-05828-5(9)) Little Brown & Co.

Matsuura, Richard & Matsuura, Ruth. Birthday Wish. Chao, Linus, illus. (J). 8.95 (978-1-887916-04-2(0)) Orchid Isle Publishing Co.

Maurer, Amy J. A Purple Hippopotamus Pillow & Pink Penguin Sheets. Smith, Rachael, illus. 2006. 56p. (J). per. 19.99 (***978-1-59879-239-3(3)***); per. 15.99 (***978-1-59879-167-9(2)***) Lifevest Publishing, Inc.

Mayer, Mercer. Little Critter's the Best Present. 2000. (Little Critter Ser.). (J). (ps-3). (978-0-606-18923-1(8)) Tandem Library Bks.

—Surprise. 2001. (gr. k-3). lib. bdg. 11.80 (978-0-613-90238-0(6)) Tandem Library Bks.

—Surprise!, Vol. 3. 2002. (Little Critter First Readers Ser.). (Illus.). 24p. (J). (gr. 1-2). pap. 3.95 (978-1-57768-814-3(7)) School Specialty Publishing.

—Tiger's Birthday. Mayer, Mercer, illus. 2003. (Little Critter Ser.). (Illus.). 24p. (J). (ps-2). 10.95 (978-1-57768-645-3(4)) School Specialty Publishing.

—Tiger's Birthday. 2002. (Little Critter First Readers Ser.). (Illus.). 24p. (J). (gr. k-1). pap. 3.95 (978-1-57768-828-0(7)) School Specialty Publishing.

—Tiger's Birthday. 2001. (gr. k-3). lib. bdg. 11.80 (978-0-613-67675-5(0)) Tandem Library Bks.

McAllister, Margaret. Tromso the Troll. Cox, Steve, illus. 2006. 24p. (J). lib. bdg. (***978-1-4048-3144-5(4)***) Picture Window Bks.

McDonald, Erin Melodie. My Birthday Party. Hanrahan, Denise, illus. 2002. 24p. (J). per. 9.95 (978-0-9721427-1-7(1)) Talking Hands, Inc.

McElligott, Matthew. Backbeard & the Birthday Suit. 2006. (Illus.). 32p. (J). 17.85 (978-0-8027-8066-9(0)); 16.95 (978-0-8027-8065-2(2)) Walker & Co.

McElroy, Laurie. Drake & Josh: Chapter Book. 2007. (Teenick Ser.: No. 6). 112p. (J). pap. 4.99 (***978-0-439-91645-5(3)***) Scholastic, Inc.

McGeorge, Constance W. Chestnut. Whyte, Mary, illus. 2004. 32p. (J). 16.95 (978-1-56145-321-4(8)) Peachtree Pubs., Ltd.

McKay, Hilary. Birthday Wish. 1998. (Pudding Bag School Sr.: Bk 1). (Illus.). 171p. (J). pap. 8.99 (978-0-340-69833-4(0) , Hodder & Stoughton) Hodder General Publishing Division GBR. *Dist:* Trafalgar Square Publishing.

McKissack, Patricia C. & McKissack, Fredrick. Bessey la Desordenada Pasa una Noche de Cumpleanos. 2004. (Rookie Reader Espanol Ser.). (SPA.). (J). (gr. k-2). pap. 4.95 (978-0-516-24620-8(8) , Children's Pr.) Scholastic Library Publishing.

—Bessey la Desordenada Pasa una Noche de Cumpleanos. Regan, Dana, illus. 2003. (Rookie Reader Espanol Ser.). (SPA.). (J). 19.50 (978-0-516-25893-5(1) , Children's Pr.) Scholastic Library Publishing.

McKissack, Patricia C. & McKissack, Fredrick L. Messy Bessey & the Birthday Overnight. Regan, Dana, illus. (Rookie Reader Espanol Ser.). 32p. (J). 1999. (gr. k-2). pap. 4.95 (978-0-516-26411-0(7)); 1998. (gr. 1-2). 19.50 (978-0-516-20828-2(4)) Scholastic Library Publishing. (Children's Pr.).

McMullan, Kate. Pearl & Wagner: Three Secrets. Alley, R. W., illus. 2004. (Easy-to-Read, Dial Ser.). 48p. (J). (gr. 2). 14.99 (978-0-8037-2574-4(4) , Dial) Penguin Group (USA) Inc.

McPhail, David. Big Brown Bear's Birthday Surprise. O'Connor, John, illus. 2007. (Big Brown Bear Ser.). 32p. (J). (ps-2). 16.00 (978-0-15-206098-5(7)) Harcourt Trade Pubs.

Merer, Laura, illus. Fuzzy Ducky's Birthday: A Touch-and-Feel Pop-up Book. 2005. 10p. (J). 8.95 (978-1-58117-324-6(5) , Intervisual/Piggy Toes) Dalmatian Pr.

Metzger, Steve. Ladybug's Birthday. Williamson, James, illus. 2000. (Side-by-Side Ser.). (J). pap. 3.50 (978-0-590-02599-7(6)) Scholastic, Inc.

Millender, Gwyn. Essie's Birthday Surprise. 2004. (J). 8.95 (978-0-9727142-0-4(0)) F.R.O.G. the Rock Pubns.

Milne, A. A. Disney's Pooh's Treasury of Special Days. Case, Cassandra, ed. 2000. (Illus.). 85p. (J). (978-0-7172-6413-1(0) , Grolier) Scholastic Library Publishing.

—In Which Everyone Has a Birthday & Gets Two Presents. Shepard, Ernest H., illus. unabr. ed. (Winnie-the-Pooh Ser.). (J). incl. audio (978-1-57375-015-8(8) , 70134) Audioscope.

Minarik, Else Holmelund. Present for Mother Bear. 2002. (gr. k-3). lib. bdg. 11.80 (978-0-613-62535-7(8)) Tandem Library Bks.

Miranda, Anne. Alphabet Fiesta. 2001. (ENG & SPA., Illus.). 56p. (J). (ps-3). 12.95 (978-1-890515-30-0(2)) Turtle Bks.

—Alphabet Fiesta: An English/Spanish Alphabet Story. 2001. (ENG & SPA., Illus.). 56p. (J). (ps-3). 18.95 (978-1-890515-29-4(9)) Turtle Bks.

—Monster Math. Powell, Polly, illus. 2002. 32p. (J). (ps-2). pap. 7.00 (978-0-15-216530-7(4) , Voyager Bks./Libros Viajeros) Harcourt Children's Bks.

—Monster Math. 2002. (ps-2). lib. bdg. 14.15 (978-0-613-53840-4(4)) Tandem Library Bks.

Mitton, Tony. Spooky Hour. Parker-Rees, Guy, illus. 2004. 32p. (J). pap. 16.95 (978-0-439-60373-7(0) , Orchard Bks.) Scholastic, Inc.

Montgomery, R. A. Your Purrr-fect Birthday. 2007. (Dragonlarks Ser.). (Illus.). 64p. (J). (gr. k-3). pap. 6.99 (***978-1-933390-55-0(7)***) Chooseco LLC.

Moodie, Fiona. Noko's Suprise Party. 2008. (Illus.). 32p. (J). 16.95 (***978-1-84507-587-3(0)***) Lincoln, Frances Ltd. GBR. *Dist:* Perseus Distribution.

Moon, Nicola. Happy Birthday, Amelia. Jones, Jenny, illus. 1999. 32p. (J). reprint ed. 17.99 (978-1-86205-208-6(5) , Pavilion Bks., Ltd.) Anova Bks. GBR. *Dist:* Trafalgar Square Publishing.

Mora, Pat. A Birthday Basket for Tia. 1998. (J). pap. 4.99 (978-0-87628-395-0(4)) Ctr. for Applied Research in Education, The.

—Una Cesta de Cumpleanos para Tia Abuela. Lang, Cecily, illus. (SPA.). (J). (gr. k-2). pap. 3.16 net. (978-0-395-78817-2(X) , HMS088) Houghton Mifflin Co.

— Uno, Dos, Tres. Lavallee, Barbara, illus. 2002. Tr. of One, Two, Three. (SPA.). (J). 14.74 (978-0-7587-3892-9(7)) Book Wholesalers, Inc.

—Uno, Dos, Tres. Lavallee, Barbara, illus. 2000. Tr. of One, Two, Three. (SPA & ENG.). 48p. (J). (gr. k-3). pap. 6.95 (978-0-618-05468-8(5) , Clarion Bks.) Houghton Mifflin Co. Trade & Reference Div.

—Uno, Dos, Tres: One, Two, Three. Lavallee, Barbara, illus. 2000. (SPA.). 43p. (ps-ps). lib. bdg. 15.25 (978-0-613-28687-9(1)) Tandem Library Bks.

Moran, Alex. What Day Is It?/Que dia es Hoy? Moreton, Daniel, illus. 2008. (Green Light Readers Level 1 Ser.). 28p. (J). pap. 3.95 (*978-0-15-206281-1(5), Green Light Readers) Harcourt Children's Bks.

—What Day Is It?/Que dia es Hoy? Campoy, F. Isabel & Ada, Alma Flor, trs. Moreton, Daniel, illus. 2008. (Green Light Readers Level 1 Ser.). 28p. (J). 12.95 (*978-0-15-206275-0(0), Green Light Readers) Harcourt Children's Bks.

Morgan, Richard & Rose, Maddy. Dance Fever. 2007. (Illus.). 24p. (J). pap. 9.95 (*978-1-86230-161-0(1)) Transworld Publishers Ltd. GBR. *Dist:* Independent Pubs. Group.

Munoz-Furlong, Anne. Alexander Goes to a Birthday Party. Furlong, Mariel Christine, illus. 1999. 24p. (J). (gr. k-6). pap. 5.00 (978-1-882541-11-9(1)) Food Allergy & Anaphylaxis Network.

Munsch, Robert. Moira's Birthday. Martchenko, Michael, illus. 2003. (Annikins Ser.: Vol. 14). 32p. (J). (ps-2). pap. 1.25 (978-1-55037-389-9(7)) Annick Pr., Ltd. CAN. *Dist:* Firefly Bks., Ltd.

My Day! 2005. (J). bds. (978-0-9769910-0-7(4)) Terrific Twins LLC.

Namm, Diane. Pick a Pet. Suarez, Maribel, tr. Suarez, Maribel, illus. 2004. (My First Reader Ser.). 31p. (J). 18.50 (978-0-516-24417-4(5), Children's Pr.) Scholastic Library Publishing.

Naylor, Phyllis Reynolds. The Great Chicken Debacle. 96p. 2005. (YA). (gr. 4-8). pap. 5.95 (978-0-7614-5148-8(X)); 2001. (Illus.). (J). (gr. 3-7). 14.95 (978-0-7614-5095-5(5), Cavendish Children's Bks.) Cavendish, Marshall Corp.

The Night Walk: Individual Title, 6 packs. 16p. (gr. 2 up). 35.00 (978-0-7635-9387-2(7)) Rigby Education.

O'Brien, Robert C. The Silver Crown. 2001. (gr. 5-8). lib. bdg. 13.00 (978-0-613-37168-1(2)) Tandem Library Bks.

O'Connor, Jane. Fancy Nancy: Bonjour, Butterfly. Glasser, Robin Preiss, illus. 2008. (Fancy Nancy Ser.). 32p. (J). 16.99 (*978-0-06-123588-7(1)); lib. bdg. 17.89 (*978-0-06-123589-4(X)) HarperCollins Pubs.

Older, Effin. Birthday Party. 1998. (You're Invited to Mary-Kate & Ashley's Ser.). (Illus.). 48p. (J). (gr. 2-4). pap. 12.95 (978-0-590-22593-9(6)) Scholastic, Inc.

OLIVER, Jane, Jane. Nick's Birthday Surprise, Level P. RAGA, Silvia, illus. 2006. (Lightning Readers Ser.). 32p. (J). pap. 3.95 (978-0-7696-4188-1(1), Gingham Dog Pr.) School Specialty Publishing.

—La sorpresa del cumpleanos de Nico, Level P. RAGA, Silvia, illus. 2006. (Lightning Readers Ser.). 32p. (J). pap. 3.95 (978-0-7696-4218-5(7), Gingham Dog Pr.) School Specialty Publishing.

Oliver/Raga, Jane/Silvia. Nick's Birthday Surprise. 2006. (Illus.). 32p. (J). lib. bdg. 9.00 (*978-1-4242-0882-1(3)) Fitzgerald Bks.

O'Neil, Amy. I'm Glad I Asked. Silver, Pattie, illus. 2002. (Read-to-Me Ser.). 24p. (J). (978-0-7665-1217-7(7)) Letter People, The.

oneones. Happy Birthday Coco. oneones, illus. 2006. (Illus.). 56p. (J). 12.95 (978-1-933605-13-5(8)) Kane/Miller Bk. Pubs., Inc.

Oram, Hiawyn & Su, Lucy. The Best Party of All. 2004. (Illus.). 32p. (J). (978-0-7112-2062-1(X)) Lincoln, Frances Ltd. GBR. *Dist:* Transition Vendor.

Oxenbury, Helen. La Fiesta de Cumpleanos.Tr. of Birthday Party. (SPA.). 16p. (J). 7.50 (978-84-261-1943-8(3)) Juventud, Editorial ESP. *Dist:* AIMS International Bks., Inc.

—It's My Birthday. Oxenbury, Helen, illus. 2002. (Illus.). (J). 11.91 (978-0-7587-5178-2(8)) Book Wholesalers, Inc.

Pachela, Czes, illus. The Birthday Present. 2001. 24p. (J). pap. 3.50 (978-1-58925-363-6(9), tiger tales) ME Media LLC.

Packard, Mary. The Grand & Wonderful Day. Baker, Darrell, illus. 2000. (Little Golden Bks.). 24p. (J). (ps-2). bds. 2.99 (978-0-307-30263-2(6), 98737, Golden Bks.) Random Hse. Children's Bks.

Paratore, Coleen. Catching the Sun. Catalanotto, Peter, illus. 2008. (J). (*978-1-57091-720-2(5)) Charlesbridge Publishing, Inc.

—Catching the Sun. 2010. (J). (978-0-618-45780-9(1)) Houghton Mifflin Co.

Parish, Peggy. Be Ready at Eight. Fisher, Cynthia, illus. 2000. pap. 18.95 incl. audio compact disk (978-1-59112-654-6(1)); pap. 31.95 incl. audio compact disk (978-1-59112-655-3(X)) Live Oak Media.

Park, Barbara. Junie B. Jones & That Meanie Jim's Birthday, Vol. 6. unabr. ed. 2004. (Junie B. Jones Ser.: No. 6). 85p. (J). (gr. k-3). pap. 17.00 incl. audio (978-0-8072-0642-3(3), Listening Library) Random Hse. Audio Publishing Group.

—Junie B. Jones y el Cumpleanos del Malo de Jim. Brunkus, Denise, illus. 2005. (SPA.). 96p. (J). (ps-ps). pap. 3.99 (978-0-439-56028-3(4), Scholastic en Espanol) Scholastic, Inc.

Parr, Todd. Otto Has a Birthday Party. 2004. (Illus.). 24p. (J). (ps-3). 9.95 (978-0-316-73907-8(3)) Little Brown & Co.

The Party, 6 Packs. (Sails Literacy Ser.). 16p. (gr. k up). 27.00 (978-0-7635-4414-0(0)) Rigby Education.

The Party Game: Individual Title Six-Packs. (gr. k-1). 23.00 (978-0-7635-8825-0(3)) Rigby Education.

The Party Game: KinderConcepts Individual Title Six-Packs. (Kinderstarters Ser.). 8p. (ps-1). 21.00 (978-0-7635-8723-9(0)) Rigby Education.

Pastor, Melanie Joy. Wishes for One More Day. Grantford, Jacqui, illus. 2006. 32p. (J). 15.95 (978-0-9729225-7-9(1)) Flashlight Pr.

Patricelli, Leslie. The Birthday Box. Patricelli, Leslie, illus. 2007. (Illus.). 32p. (J). (gr. k-k). 15.99 (978-0-7636-2825-3(5)) Candlewick Pr.

Peters, Stephanie True. Raggedy Ann & the Birthday Surprise. 2000. (gr. k-3). lib. bdg. 15.30 (978-0-613-67663-2(7)) Tandem Library Bks.

Peters, Stephanie True & Mitter, Kathryn. Raggedy Ann & the Birthday Surprise. 2003. (My First Raggedy Ann Ser.). (Illus.). 32p. (J). pap. 6.99 (978-0-689-86013-3(7), Aladdin) Simon & Schuster Children's Publishing.

Peterson, John. The Littles & the Secret Letter. 2001. (978-0-606-22186-3(7)) Tandem Library Bks.

Pilgrim, Elza. The China Doll. Segovia, Carmen, illus. 2005. 32p. (J). (gr. k-2). 14.95 (978-1-4027-2223-3(0)) Sterling Publishing Co., Inc.

Piper, Sophie. Little Teddy's Birthday Book. Massey, Jane, illus. 2002. 64p. (J). 6.99 (978-0-7459-4709-9(3), Lion) Lion Hudson plc GBR. *Dist:* Independent Pubs. Group.

Pockets Learning Staff. Birthday Cake. 1998. (Illus.). (J). (ps-1). 30.00 (978-1-888074-93-2(0)) Pockets of Learning.

Podoshen, Lois. The Birthday Bird. Schaedler, Sally, illus. 1998. (Books for Young Learners). 8p. (J). (gr. k-2). pap. 5.00 (978-1-57274-154-6(6), A2430) Owen, Richard C. Pubs., Inc.

Pomerantz, Charlotte. The Birthday Letters. Adinolfi, JoAnn, illus. 2000. 32p. (J). (gr. k-3). 15.95 (978-0-688-16335-8(1)); 15.89 (978-0-688-16336-5(X)) HarperCollins Pubs.

Porte, Barbara Ann. Harry's Birthday. Abolafia, Yossi, illus. 2003. (I Can Read Bks.). 48p. (J). 15.99 (978-0-06-050355-0(6)); 16.89 (978-0-06-050356-7(4)) HarperCollins Pubs.

—Harry's Birthday. 2003. (gr. k-3). lib. bdg. 11.80 (978-0-613-68428-6(1)) Tandem Library Bks.

Pow, Tom. Callum's Big Day. Hedderick, Mairi, illus. 2002. 32p. (J). 12.95 (978-0-9535413-4-8(7)) iynx publishing GBR. *Dist:* Dufour Editions, Inc.

Prince, Sarah. Sebastian's Special Present. 2000. (gr. k-3). lib. bdg. 11.80 (978-0-613-29742-4(3)) Tandem Library Bks.

Quattlebaum, Mary. Aunt Ceecee, Aunt Belle & Mama's Surprise. 2000. (J). (978-0-606-20016-5(9)) Tandem Library Bks.

Ramsey, Dave. The Big Birthday Surprise: Junior Discovers Giving. Ramsey, Marshall, illus. 2003. 26p. (J). 9.99 (978-0-9726323-2-4(8)) Lampo Group Inc., The.

Random House Staff. Elmo's Birthday Party. Swanson, Maggie, illus. 2002. (Touch-and-Feel Ser.). 12p. (J). (gr. k-k). bds. 7.99 (978-0-375-82190-5(2), Random Hse. Bks. for Young Readers) Random Hse. Children's Bks.

—Feliz Cumpleanos, Tomas! Marquez, Desiree, tr. Bell, Owain, illus. 2002. (SPA.). 32p. (J). (ps-1). pap. 3.99 (978-0-375-82339-8(5)); lib. bdg. 11.99 (978-0-375-92339-5(X)) Random Hse. Children's Bks. (RH Para Ninos).

Rau, Dana Meachen. Hands. Stromoski, Rick, illus. 2000. (Rookie Reader Espanol Ser.). 24p. (J). (gr. k-2). pap. 4.95 (978-0-516-27043-2(5)); 19.50 (978-0-516-22009-3(8)) Scholastic Library Publishing. (Children's Pr.).

—Hands. 2000. (gr. k-3). lib. bdg. 12.95 (978-0-613-54531-0(1)) Tandem Library Bks.

—Manos. 2000. (SPA.). (gr. k-3). lib. bdg. 12.95 (978-0-613-54422-1(6)) Tandem Library Bks.

Redmond, Diane. Bob's Birthday. 2001. (gr. k-3). lib. bdg. 11.25 (978-0-613-51294-7(4)) Tandem Library Bks.

Regan, Dana, illus. Messy Bessey & the Birthday Overnight. 2002. (Messy Bessey Ser.). (J). 12.83 (978-0-7587-7185-8(1)) Book Wholesalers, Inc.

Remkiewicz, Frank, illus. Froggy Bakes a Cake. 2002. (Froggy Ser.). (J). 11.06 (978-0-7587-5541-4(4)) Book Wholesalers, Inc.

Rey, H. A. Curious George & the Birthday Suprise. 2003. (gr. k-3). lib. bdg. 11.80 (978-0-613-90050-8(2)) Tandem Library Bks.

Rey, H. A. & Rey, Margret. Curious George & the Birthday Surprise. Weston, Martha, illus. 2003. 24p. (J). (gr. k-3). 12.95 (978-0-618-34688-2(0)); pap. 3.95 (978-0-618-34687-5(2)) Houghton Mifflin Co. Trade & Reference Div.

Reynolds, Marilynn. A Present for Mrs. Kazinski. Smith-Ary, Lynn, illus. 2001. 32p. (J). (ps-2). 7.95 (978-1-55143-198-7(X)); 15.95 (978-1-55143-196-3(3)) Orca Bk. Pubs. USA.

Riddell, Chris. Platypus & the Birthday Party. 2003. (Platypus Ser.). (Illus.). 32p. (J). 16.00 (978-0-15-204753-5(0)) Harcourt Children's Bks.

Riddle, Peter. Twelfth Birthday. 2001. 223p. pap. 21.95 (978-1-58851-777-7(2)) PublishAmerica, Inc.

Roberts, Bethany. Birthday Mice! Cushman, Doug, illus. 2002. 32p. (J). (gr. k-ps). tchr. ed. 13.00 (978-0-618-07772-4(3), Clarion Bks.) Houghton Mifflin Co. Trade & Reference Div.

Robinson, Ella M. Happy Home Stories. 2005. 137p. per. 10.95 (978-1-57258-313-9(4)) TEACH Services, Inc.

Rock, Lois & Buckingham, Gabriella. Now You Are. 2002. (Illus.). 28p. 4.99 (978-1-56148-394-5(X)); 2nd ed. 4.99 (978-1-56148-395-2(8)); 3rd ed. 4.99 (978-1-56148-396-9(6)) Good Bks.

—Now You Are 4. 2002. (Illus.). 28p. 4.99 (978-1-56148-397-6(4)) Good Bks.

Rodda, Emily. The Magic Key. Vitale, Raoul, illus. 2004. (Fairy Realm Ser.: No. 5). 128p. (J). lib. bdg. 15.89 (978-0-06-009596-3(2)); Book 5. 8.99 (978-0-06-009595-6(4)) HarperCollins Pubs.

—The Magic Key. Vitale, Raoul, illus. 2007. (Fairy Realm Ser.). 128p. (J). (gr. 3-6). 25.65 (978-1-59961-327-7(1)) Spotlight.

Rolston, Steve. One Bad Day. 2003. (Illus.). 120p. pap. 9.95 (978-1-929998-50-0(3)) Oni Pr., Inc.

Rose, Deborah Lee. Birthday Zoo. Munsinger, Lynne, illus. 2006. 24p. (J). pap. 6.95 (978-0-8075-0777-3(6)) Whitman, Albert & Co.

—Birthday Zoo. Munsinger, Lynn, illus. 2002. 24p. (J). (ps-1). 15.95 (978-0-8075-0776-6(8)) Whitman, Albert & Co.

Rouss, Sylvia A. Tali's Jerusalem Scrapbook. Oppenheimer, Nancy, illus. 2003. 32p. (gr. 1-4). 14.95 (978-1-930143-68-5(0)); pap. 9.95 (978-1-930143-69-2(9)) Pitspopany Pr.

—Tali's Jerusalem Scrapbook. 2003. (gr. k-3). lib. bdg. 18.75 (978-0-613-81198-9(4)) Tandem Library Bks.

Ruckdeschel, Liz & James, Sara. What If... You Broke All the Rules. 2007. (What If... Ser.). 304p. (YA). (gr. 7). 11.99 (*978-0-385-90495-7(9)); (Illus.). pap. 8.99 (*978-0-385-73501-8(4)) Random Hse. Children's Bks. (Delacorte Bks. for Young Readers).

Ryan, Pam Muñoz. Mice & Beans. Cepeda, Joe, illus. 2001. 32p. (J). (ps-2). pap. 16.95 (978-0-439-18303-1(0), Levine, Arthur A. Bks.) Scholastic, Inc.

Rylant, Cynthia. Annie & Snowball & the Dress-Up Birthday. Stevenson, Sucie, illus. 2007. (Annie & Snowball Ser.). 40p. (J). (gr. k-3). 14.99 (978-1-4169-0938-5(9), Simon & Schuster Children's Publishing) Simon & Schuster Children's Publishing.

—Henry & Mudge & the Best Day of All. Stevenson, Sucie, illus. 2002. (Henry & Mudge Ser.). (J). 11.91 (978-0-7587-1268-4(5)) Book Wholesalers, Inc.

—Mr. Putter & Tabby Make a Wish. 2005. (Illus.). 38p. (J). lib. bdg. 20.00 (*978-1-4242-1954-4(X)) Fitzgerald Bks.

—Mr. Putter & Tabby Make a Wish. Howard, Arthur, illus. 2006. (Mr. Putter & Tabby Ser.). 44p. (J). pap. 5.95 (978-0-15-205443-4(X), Harcourt Paperbacks) Harcourt Children's Bks.

—Mr. Putter & Tabby Make a Wish. Howard, Arthur, illus. 2005. (Mr. Putter & Tabby Ser.). 44p. (J). (ps-2). 14.00 (978-0-15-202426-0(3)) Harcourt Trade Pubs.

—Poppleton in Winter. Teague, Mark, illus. 2002. (Poppleton Ser.). (J). 11.91 (978-0-7587-6873-5(7)) Book Wholesalers, Inc.

—Poppleton in Winter. Teague, Mark, illus. 2001. (Poppleton Ser.). 58p. (J). (ps-2). pap. 15.95 (978-0-590-84837-4(2), Blue Sky Pr., The) Scholastic, Inc.

Saenz, Benjamin Alire. Gift from Papa Diego.Tr. of Regalo De Papa Diego. (gr. k-3). lib. bdg. 19.90 (978-0-613-06587-0(5)) Tandem Library Bks.

—A Gift from Papa Diego (Un Regalo de Papa Diego) Garcia, Geronimo, illus. 2004. (ENG & SPA.). 40p. (gr. k-7). pap. 10.95 (978-0-938317-33-3(4)) Cinco Puntos Pr.

—Grandma Fina & Her Wonderful Umbrellas. 2001. (gr. k-3). lib. bdg. 16.40 (978-0-613-77727-8(1)) Tandem Library Bks.

Sage, Angie. Molly & the Birthday Party. 2001. (Illus.). 12p. (J). (ps-1). 9.95 (978-1-56145-248-4(3)) Peachtree Pubs., Ltd.

Sager, Elizabeth R. Clif & Simmons Vol. 2: A Tale of Two Birthdays. 2000. (Illus.). 20p. (J). (gr. k-5). pap. 6.95 (978-0-9678386-2-5(2)) C.S. Publishing.

Salley, Coleen. Epossumondas Saves the Day. Stevens, Janet, illus. 2006. 48p. (J). 16.00 (978-0-15-205701-5(3)) Harcourt Trade Pubs.

Saltzberg, Barney. The Flying Garbanzos. 2000. (Illus.). (J). (978-0-606-18089-4(3)) Tandem Library Bks.

Salzmann, Mary Elizabeth. Leaping Lizards. Chawla, Neena, illus. (Fact & Fiction Ser.). 24p. (J). 2007. 21.35 (978-1-59928-450-7(2)); 2006. (978-1-59928-451-4(0)) ABDO Publishing Co.

Sample, Stephanie & Sample, Scott. Audreena the Birthday Fairy. 2001. (Illus.). 32p. (J). (ps-3). 15.95 (978-0-86573-485-2(2), Creative Publishing International) Quayside.

Sanders, Nancy I. & Osborne, Susan Titus. Cooks, Cakes & Chocolate Shakes. 2000. (Parables in Action Ser.: Vol. 5). (Illus.). 48p. (J). (ps-2). 4.99 (978-0-570-07112-9(7)) Concordia Publishing Hse.

Santa's Birthday. 2005. (J). 5.95 (978-0-9769321-1-6(3)) Steingart, Nathan Publishing.

Santillo, LuAnn. Jake's Big Day. Santillo, LuAnn, ed. 2003. (Half-Pint Kids Readers Ser.). (Illus.). 7p. (J). (ps-1). pap. (978-1-59256-104-9(7)) Half-Pint Kids, Inc.

Santomero, Angela C. Blue's Big Birthday. Johnson, Traci Paige & Kim, Soo Kyung, illus. 1998. (Blue's Clues Ser.). 24p. (J). (ps-k). 9.99 (978-0-689-82151-6(4), Simon Spotlight/Nickelodeon) Simon & Schuster Children's Publishing.

—Blue's Big Birthday. 2002. (gr. k-3). lib. bdg. 11.25 (978-0-613-51292-3(8)) Tandem Library Bks.

Sato, Wakiko. Grandma Baba's Birthday Party, Vol. 4. 2004. (Grandma Baba Ser.). (Illus.). 32p. 10.95 (978-0-8048-3562-6(4)) Tuttle Publishing.

Scamell, Ragnhild. Toby's Doll's House. Reynolds, Adrian, illus. 1999. 32p. (J). (ps-3). 14.95 (978-1-86233-026-9(3)) Sterling Publishing Co., Inc.

Scamell, Ragnhild & Reynolds, Adrian. Toby's Doll's House. 2000. (Illus.). 32p. (J). (ps-1). pap. 6.95 (978-1-86233-067-2(0)) Sterling Publishing Co., Inc.

Schecter, Ellen. Murky Monster's Birthday Bash. Ulrich, George, illus. 1999. (Bank Street Ready-to-Read Ser.). (J). trans. 20.01 (978-0-553-37588-6(1)) Bantam Bks.

Schneider, Antonie. The Birthday Bear. 2000. (J). 12.75 (978-0-606-19469-3(X)) Tandem Library Bks.

Schoenherr, Ian. Pip & Squeak. Schoenherr, Ian, illus. 2007. (Illus.). 32p. (J). (ps-1). 16.99 (978-0-06-087253-5(5)); lib. bdg. 17.89 (978-0-06-087254-2(3)) HarperCollins Pubs.

Scholastic, Inc. Staff & Muntz, Percival. Batman Reader No. 4: The Birthday Bash. Burchett, Rick, illus. 2004. (Batman Ser.: No. 5). 40p. (J). (ps-3). pap. 3.99 (978-0-439-47099-5(4), Cartwheel Bks.) Scholastic, Inc.

Schotter, Roni. Mama, I'll Give You the World. Gallagher, Susan Saelig, illus. 2006. 40p. (J). (ps-3). lib. bdg. 18.99 (978-0-375-93612-8(2)); 16.95 (978-0-375-83612-1(8)) Random Hse. Children's Bks. (Schwartz & Wade Bks.).

—The World. Gallagher, Susan Saelig, illus. 2003. (J). 16.95 (978-0-689-84485-0(9), Atheneum/Anne Schwartz Bks.) Simon & Schuster Children's Publishing.

Scraper, Katherine. The Gift-Guessing Kid. 2005. 22.00 (*978-1-4108-4211-4(8)) Benchmark Education Co.

Scrimger, Richard. Bun Bun's Birthday. Johnson, Gillian, illus. 2003. 24p. (J). (ps-1). pap. 6.95 (978-0-88776-637-4(4)) Tundra Bks., Inc./Livres Toundra, Inc. CAN. *Dist:* Random Hse., Inc.

Segal, Lore. Morris the Artist. Kulikov, Boris, illus. 2003. 32p. (J). (gr. k-4). 16.00 (978-0-374-35063-5(9), Farrar, Straus & Giroux (BYR)) Farrar, Straus & Giroux.

Seibold, J. Otto. The Fuchsia Is Now. 2006. (Illus.). 40p. (J). (ps-k). pap. 16.99 (978-0-439-63559-2(4), Orchard Bks.) Scholastic, Inc.

Sendak, Maurice. We Love You, Mama! 2003. (gr. k-3). lib. bdg. 11.80 (978-0-613-68299-2(8)) Tandem Library Bks.

Seuss, Dr. Happy Birthday to You! 2003. (Illus.). 12p. (J). (gr. k-12). 6.99 (978-0-375-82311-4(5), Random Hse. Bks. for Young Readers) Random Hse. Children's Bks.

Shaskan, Trisha. The Treasure Map. Muehlenhardt, Amy Bailey, illus. 2006. (Read-It! Readers Ser.). (J). 19.93 (978-1-4048-2416-4(2)) Picture Window Bks.

Shaskan, Trisha Speed. Princess Bella's Birthday Cake. Eroglu, Aysin D., illus. 2006. 24p. (J). (*978-1-4048-3166-7(5)) Picture Window Bks.

—Princess Bella_s Birthday Cake. 2007. (Illus.). 24p. (J). (*978-1-4048-1240-6(7)) Picture Window Bks.

Shoemaker, Carolyn. Cute As a Button. Babb, Sandra, illus. 2002. (J). (gr. k-4). 14.99 (978-0-9720150-0-4(0)) Shoemaker Bks.

Simon, Charnan. Surprise! Handelman, Dorothy, illus. 1999. (Real Kids Readers Ser.). 32p. (J). (gr. k-2). pap. 4.99 (978-0-7613-2093-7(8), Millbrook Pr.) Lerner Publishing Group.

—Surprise! Handelman, Dorothy, photos by. 1999. (Real Kids Readers Ser.). (Illus.). 32p. (gr. k-2). lib. bdg. 18.90 (978-0-7613-2068-5(7), Millbrook Pr.) Lerner Publishing Group.

—Surprise! 1999. (J). (978-0-606-19175-3(5)); lib. bdg. 11.80 (978-0-613-18164-8(6)) Tandem Library Bks.

Simpson, Lesley. The Purim Surprise. Church, Peter, illus. 2004. (Purim Ser.). 32p. (J). (ps-3). pap. 6.95 (978-1-58013-090-5(9)) Kar-Ben Publishing.

Sims, Janet. Mark's Big Surprise. 2007. (J). pap. 8.00 (*978-0-8059-7355-6(9)) Dorrance Publishing Co., Inc.

Smith, Dianne M. Happy Birthday to You! l.t. ed. 2004. 24p. per. (978-1-59196-679-1(5)) Instantpublisher.com.

Soto, Gary. Chato & the Party Animals. Guevara, Susan, illus. 25.95 incl. audio (978-1-59112-460-3(3)); 28.95 incl. audio compact disk (978-1-59112-920-2(6)); pap. 37.95 incl. audio (978-1-59112-461-0(1)); pap. 39.95 incl. audio compact disk (978-1-59112-921-9(4)) Live Oak Media.

—Chato & the Party Animals. Guevara, Susan, illus. 2000. (SPA.). 32p. (J). (ps-3). 16.99 (978-0-399-23159-9(5), Putnam Juvenile) Penguin Group (USA) Inc.

—Chato & the Party Animals. 2004. (gr. k-3). lib. bdg. 15.30 (978-0-613-89799-0(4)) Tandem Library Bks.

—Chato & the Party Animals. Guevara, Susan, illus. 2004. (J). (ps-ps). lib. bdg. 13.79 (978-0-606-29661-8(1)) Tandem Library Bks.

—Chato & the Party Animals. Guevara, Susan, illus. 2004. 32p. (J). (gr. k-3). reprint ed. pap. 6.99 (978-0-14-240032-6(7), Puffin) Penguin Group (USA) Inc.

—Chato y los Amigos Pachangueros. Guevara, Susan, illus. 2004. Tr. of Chato & the Party Animals. (SPA.). 32p. (J). (gr. k-3). reprint ed. pap. 7.99 (978-0-14-240033-3(5), Puffin) Penguin Group (USA) Inc.

Space Monster's Birthday Party. 2005. (J). (978-1-932570-30-4(6)) Literacy Footprints Inc.

Sperring, Mark. The Fairytale Cake. Langley, Jonathan, illus. 2005. 32p. (J). (ps-ps). pap. 15.95 (978-0-439-68329-6(7), Chicken Hse., The) Scholastic, Inc.

Springer, Pat. A Mirror Image. 2005. 57p. pap. 12.95 (978-1-4137-7939-4(5)) PublishAmerica, Inc.

St-Onge, Claire. Caillou: L'anniversaire. (FRE., Illus.). 32p. pap. 11.95 (978-2-89450-263-1(X)) Chouette Publishing CAN. *Dist:* Distribooks, Inc.

Stanton, Karen. Papi's Gift. Moreno, Rene King, illus. 2007. 32p. (J). (gr. k-3). 16.95 (978-1-59078-422-8(7)) Boyds Mills Pr.

Starr, Meg. Alicia's Happy Day. Van Wright, Cornelius & Hu, Ying-Hwa, illus. 2003. 36p. (J). pap. 5.95 (978-1-932065-06-0(7)) Star Bright Bks., Inc.

—Alicia's Happy Day. Hu, Ying-Hwa & Van Wright, Cornelius, illus. 2003. 36p. (J). (ps-3). 15.95 (978-1-887734-85-1(6)) Star Bright Bks., Inc.

—Alicia's Happy Day (English/Spanish Bilingual) Van Wright, Cornelius & Hu, Ying-Hwa, illus. 2007. 36p. (J). 15.95 (*978-1-59572-115-0(0)) Star Bright Bks., Inc.

—El Día Mas Feliz de Alicia. Van Wright, Cornelius & Hu, Ying-Hwa, illus. 2002. (SPA & ENG.). 36p. (J). 15.95 (978-1-932065-01-5(6)) Star Bright Bks., Inc.

—El Dia Mas Feliz de Alicia. Van Wright, Cornelius & Hu, Ying-Hwa, illus. 2003. (SPA.). 36p. (J). pap. 5.95 (978-1-932065-03-9(2)) Star Bright Bks., Inc.

Staunton, Ted. Morgan's Birthday. Slavin, Bill, illus. 2002. 64p. (gr. 1-5). (First Novel Ser.). (J). (*978-0-88780-561-5(2)); (First Novels Ser.: Vol. 21). 4.95 (978-0-88780-560-8(4)) Formac Publishing Co., Ltd. CAN. *Dist:* Casemate Pubs. & Bk. Distributors, LLC.

Stephens, Ann Marie. A Surprise for Ray. Bolan, Michael P., illus. 2003. 47p. (J). per. 11.95 (978-0-9729285-1-9(0) , 0-9729285-1-0) Kinkachoo Pr., The.

—Surprise for Ray. 2005. (Illus.). 44p. (J). pap. 16.99 (***978-1-59092-115-9(1)*** , Little Blue Works) Windstorm Creative.

Stephens, Ann Marie. Surprise for Ray: Complete Story Experience (TM) Edition. Bolan, Michael, illus. 2nd exp. ed. 2006. 44p. (J). pap. 9.99 (978-1-59092-175-3(5) , Little Blue Works) Windstorm Creative.

Stewart, Amber. Birthday Countdown. Marlow, Layn, illus. 2007. 20p. (J). (ps-k). bds. 12.95 (***978-0-7696-5352-5(9)*** , Gingham Dog Pr.) School Specialty Publishing.

Stewart, Paul. Un Regalo de Cumpleanos. Riddell, Chris, illus. (SPA.). 30p. (J). (gr. k-2). (978-84-348-6840-3(7) , SM30935) SM Ediciones ESP. *Dist:* Lectorum Pubns., Inc.

Stine, R. L. Scary Birthday to You! 1999. (Give Yourself Goosebumps Ser.: No. 39). 144p. (gr. 3-7). pap. 3.99 (978-0-590-99390-6(9)) Scholastic, Inc.

Straczynski, J. Michael. Happy Birthday. Romita, John, Jr., illus. 2004. 100p. lib. bdg. 24.35 (978-1-4176-6025-4(2)) Tandem Library Bks.

Stuart-Russell, C. Playtime with the Animals. 2007. 61p. pap. 12.95 (***978-1-4241-5473-9(1)***) PublishAmerica, Inc.

Stubbs, Lisa. Sonny's Birthday Prize. 1998. (978-0-606-13790-4(4)) Tandem Library Bks.

Su Chen Fang & Gui Fong Chang. Happy Birthday to You! l.t. ed. 1999. (Children's Stories Published in Other Lands Ser.). (Illus.). 32p. (J). (ps up). lib. bdg. 15.95 (978-1-56674-241-2(2)) Forest Hse. Publishing Co., Inc.

Suen, Anastasia & Keats, Ezra Jack. Willie's Birthday. Eitzen, Allan, illus. 2001. (Easy-to-Read Ser.). 32p. (J). (gr. k-3). 13.99 (978-0-670-88943-3(1) , Viking Juvenile) Penguin Group (USA) Inc.

Summers, Kim. Senor Mundo & Me: A Happy Birthday Story. Mariscal, Javier, illus. 2004. 31p. (J). (gr. k-4). 20.00 (978-0-7567-7759-3(3)) DIANE Publishing Co.

Swain, Cynthia. The Birthday Flowers. 2006. (Early Explorers Ser.). (J). 30.00 (***978-1-4108-6025-5(6)***) Benchmark Education Co.

Tang, Charles, illus. The Mystery of the Empty Safe. 2000. (Boxcar Children Ser.: No. 75). (J). (gr. 2-5). (978-0-606-18768-8(5)) Tandem Library Bks.

—The Mystery of the Empty Safe, Vol. 75. 2004. (Boxcar Children Ser.: No. 75). 120p. (J). (gr. 2-5). pap. 4.50 (978-0-8075-5463-0(4)) Whitman, Albert & Co.

Tatcheva, Eva. Witch Zelda's Birthday Cake: A Wild & Wicked Pop-up, Pull-the-Tab Book. Tatcheva, Eva, illus. 2004. (Illus.). 12p. (J). (gr. k-3). reprint ed. 18.00 (978-0-7567-7225-3(7)) DIANE Publishing Co.

Taylor-Butler, Christine. Who Needs Friends? Havice, Susan, illus. 2006. (Rookie Reader Skill Set Ser.). 32p. (J). (gr. k-2). 19.50 (978-0-516-24979-7(7) , Children's Pr.) Scholastic Library Publishing.

Taylor-Butler, Christine & Havice, Susan. Who Needs Friends? 2006. (Rookie Reader Ser.). (Illus.). 32p. (J). pap. 4.95 (978-0-516-24997-1(5) , Children's Pr.) Scholastic Library Publishing.

Tessie & Devore, David. Happy Birthday to Me. 2005. (Charisma Kids Ser.). (Illus.). 24p. (J). (gr. k-3). 9.99 (978-1-59185-207-0(2)) Strang Communications Co.

Thomas, Frances. Polly's Absolutely Worst Birthday Ever. Gardner, Sally, illus. 2003. 96p. (gr. 1-4). lib. bdg. 16.99 (978-0-385-90122-2(4) , Delacorte Bks. for Young Readers) Random Hse. Children's Bks.

Thomas, Jan. A Birthday for Cow! 2008. 40p. (J). 12.95 (***978-0-15-206072-5(3)***) Harcourt Trade Pubs.

Thorup, Bryce. Two Birthdays. Muller, Daniel, illus. 2005. (J). 18.95 (978-0-9765964-0-0(7)) Round Tower Pr.

Torkellson, Debie. New Witches Club (Book No. 1) Bk. 1: The Sleepover Curse. ed. 2005. (Illus.). 80p. (J). per. 6.99 (978-1-59772-010-6(0) , Your Own World Bks.) Your Own World, Inc.

—New Witches Club (Book No. 2) Bk. 2: Witch Hanne Returns. 2005. (Illus.). 88p. (J). per. 6.99 (978-1-59772-015-1(1) , Your Own World Bks.) Your Own World, Inc.

Trimble, Marcia. Liberty Cafe Is Open. Hayden, Jennifer, illus. ed. 2006. (J). pap. 895.00 (978-1-891577-91-8(3)); 32p. lib. bdg. 15.95 (978-1-891577-90-1(5)) Images Pr.

Trimble, Patti. What Day Is It? (gr. k-3). 2003. lib. bdg. 11.80 (978-0-613-66388-5(8)); 2000. (978-0-606-18195-2(4)) Tandem Library Bks.

Trimble, Patti & Moran, Alex. What Day Is It? Moreton, Daniel, illus. 2003. (Green Light Readers Level 1 Ser.). 24p. (J). 11.95 (978-0-15-204806-8(5)); pap. 3.95 (978-0-15-204846-4(4)) Harcourt Children's Bks. (Green Light Readers).

Tripp, Valerie. Happy Birthday, Kit! A Springtime Story, Bk. 4. 2000. (American Girls Collection: Bk. 4). (Illus.). 80p. (J). (gr. 2 up). 12.95 (978-1-58485-023-6(X)) American Girl Publishing, Inc.

—Happy Birthday, Kit! A Springtime Story, Bk. 4. Rane, Walter, illus. 2000. (American Girls Collection: Bk. 4). 80p. (YA). (gr. 2 up). pap. 6.95 (978-1-58485-022-9(1)) American Girl Publishing, Inc.

—Happy Birthday, Kit! A Springtime Story. (American Girls Collection). (J). 2001. (Illus.). 12.75 (978-0-606-21225-0(6)); 2000. (978-0-606-22805-3(5)) Tandem Library Bks.

Tryon, Leslie. Albert's Birthday. Tryon, Leslie, illus. 2002. (Illus.). 48p. (J). pap. 6.99 (978-0-689-85251-0(7) , Aladdin) Simon & Schuster Children's Publishing.

—Albert's Birthday. 2002. (gr. k-3). lib. bdg. 15.30 (978-0-613-88158-6(3)) Tandem Library Bks.

Uff, Caroline. Happy Birthday, Lulu! Uff, Caroline, illus. 2000. (Illus.). 24p. (J). (ps-k). 14.95 (978-0-8027-8751-4(7)) Walker & Co.

Uff, Caroline, reader. Feliz Cumpleanos, Lulu. 2003. (Lovable Lulu Ser.). (SPA.). (J). pap. (978-970-690-566-6(9)) Planeta Mexicana Editorial S. A. de C. V.

Upton, Deborah. Barbie: My First Telephone. Wolfson, Tom, illus. Wolfson, Tom, photos by. 2001. (Play-a-Sound Ser.). (J). 16.98 (978-0-7853-4800-9(X)) Publications International, Ltd.

Van Allsburg, Chris. Probuditi! 2006. (Illus.). 32p. (J). (gr. 3-5). 18.95 (978-0-618-75502-8(0)) Houghton Mifflin Co. Trade & Reference Div.

Van Draanen, Wendelin. Sammy Keyes & the Psycho Kitty Queen. 2004. (Sammy Keyes Ser.: Bk. 9). (Illus.). 304p. (J). (gr. 5-8). 15.95 (978-0-375-82349-7(2)); lib. bdg. 17.99 (978-0-375-92349-4(7)) Random Hse. Children's Bks. (Knopf Bks. for Young Readers).

Van Lieshout, Elle & Van Os, Erik. Nice Party. 1998. (Illus.). 32p. (J). 15.95 (978-1-886910-89-8(8) , Lemniscaat) Boyds Mills Pr.

Veggietales. Veggie Birthday to You. 2007. (VeggieTales Ser.). (Illus.). 32p. (J). 7.99 (978-1-4165-4049-6(0) , Howard Bks.) Simon & Schuster.

Viorst, Judith. Just in Case. Bluthenthal, Diana Cain, illus. 2006. 40p. (J). (ps-2). 15.95 (978-0-689-87164-1(3) , Atheneum) Simon & Schuster Children's Publishing.

Volker, Kerstin. Lilly's Birthday Party. 2003. (Funny Friends Lift-and-Learn Bks.). (Illus.). 14p. (J). 5.99 (978-1-59384-022-8(5)) Parklane Publishing.

Wade, Barrie. My Birthday Party. Fairclough, Chris, photos by. 2005. (Reading Corner Ser.). (Illus.). 24p. (J). (gr. k-3). lib. bdg. 22.80 (978-1-59771-016-9(4) , 1247649) Sea-To-Sea Pubns.

Wagele, Elizabeth. Finding the Birthday Cake: Helping Children Raise Their Self-Esteem. Wagele, Elizabeth, illus. 2007. (Let's Talk Ser.). (Illus.). 48p. (J). pap. 8.95 (978-0-88282-277-8(2)) New Horizon Pr. Pubs., Inc.

Wales, Dirk. Penny House. Kenna, Diane, illus. 2005. 32p. (J). 16.95 (978-0-9632459-1-5(0)) Great Plains Pr.

Wallace, John. Tiny Rabbit Goes to a Birthday Party. Wallace, John, illus. 2000. (Illus.). 32p. (J). (gr. k-3). 16.95 (978-0-8234-1489-5(2)) Holiday Hse., Inc.

Wallace, Nancy Elizabeth. Tell-a-Bunny. 2007. 32p. (J). pap. 5.99 (***978-0-7614-5369-7(5)***) Cavendish, Marshall Corp.

—Tell-a-Bunny. Wallace, Nancy Elizabeth, illus. 2000. (Illus.). 40p. (J). (ps-2). 15.95 (978-1-890817-29-9(5)) Winslow Pr.

Wang, Margaret. Teddy Bear's Picnic. 2008. 12p. (J). (ps-2). 16.99 (***978-0-7641-6069-1(9)***) Barron's Educational Series, Inc.

Wardlaw, Lee. Bow-Wow Birthday. Johnson-Petrov, Arden, illus. 1998. 32p. (J). (gr. k-3). 14.95 (978-1-56397-489-2(4)) Boyds Mills Pr.

Warner, Gertrude Chandler. The Mystery of the Empty Safe. Tang, Charles, illus. 2000. 120p. (J). (gr. 2-7). lib. bdg. 11.80 (978-0-613-27992-5(1)) Tandem Library Bks.

Warner, Gertrude Chandler, creator. The Mystery of the Empty Safe, Vol. 75. 2004. (Boxcar Children Ser.: No. 75). (Illus.). 120p. (J). (gr. 2-5). 14.95 (978-0-8075-5462-3(6)) Whitman, Albert & Co.

Warnes, Tim. Happy Birthday, Dotty. Warnes, Tim, illus. 2003. (Illus.). 32p. (J). tchr. ed. 15.95 (978-1-58925-026-0(5) , tiger tales) ME Media LLC.

Watanabe, Etsuko. Oscar's Party. 2006. (Illus.). 12p. (J). 14.95 (978-1-58234-697-7(6) , Bloomsbury Children) Bloomsbury Publishing.

Waters, Aubrey. Thirteen & Surviving. 2006. pap. 14.49 (***978-1-4259-4644-9(5)***) AuthorHouse.

Watts, Jeri Hanel. Keepers. Marshall, Felicia, illus. 2000. 32p. (gr. k up). (YA). 15.95 (978-1-880000-58-8(X)); (J). 6.95 (978-1-58430-013-7(2)) Lee & Low Bks., Inc.

—Keepers. 2000. (J). (978-0-606-19832-5(6)) Tandem Library Bks.

Wayans, Kim & Knotts, Kevin. Happy Birthday to Me. 2008. 112p. (J). (gr. 2-4). 4.99 (***978-0-448-44855-8(6)*** , Grosset & Dunlap) Penguin Group (USA) Inc.

Weber, Lenora Mattingly. Happy Birthday, Dear Beany. 1999. (Beany Malone Ser.). 299p. (J). reprint ed. pap. 12.95 (978-0-9639607-9-5(2)) Image Cascade Publishing.

Wegman, William. Surprise Party. Wegman, William, photos by. 2000. (Illus.). 32p. (ps-17). 16.99 (978-0-7868-0585-3(4)) Hyperion Bks. for Children.

Weinberg, Jennifer. Surprise for a Princess. Emslie, Peter & Marrucchi, Elisa, illus. 2003. (Disney Princess Ser.). 32p. (J). (ps-1). pap. 3.99 (978-0-7364-2132-4(7) , RH/Disney) Random Hse. Children's Bks.

—Surprise for a Princess. 2003. (Disney Princess Ser.). (ps-2). lib. bdg. 11.80 (978-0-613-73686-2(9)) Tandem Library Bks.

Wells, Rosemary. Max's Birthday. 2004. 12p. (J). pap. 5.99 (978-0-670-88711-8(0) , Viking Juvenile) Penguin Group (USA) Inc.

—McDuff's Birthday. 2005. 12p. (J). 6.99 (978-0-7868-0513-6(7)) Hyperion Bks. for Children.

—The Secret Birthday. Nez, John & Wheeler, Jody, illus. 2002. (Yoko & Friends School Days Ser.: No. 7). 32p. (gr. k-2). 9.99 (978-0-7868-0729-1(6)) Hyperion Bks. for Children.

—Yoko's Paper Cranes. Wells, Rosemary, illus. 2001. (Illus.). 32p. (ps-2). 15.99 (978-0-7868-0737-6(7)) Hyperion Bks. for Children.

When I'm Older, 6 Packs. (Literatura 2000 Ser.). (gr. 1-2). 28.00 (978-0-7635-0154-9(9)) Rigby Education.

White, Tim. A Single Heart. 2006. 193p. pap. 19.95 (978-1-4137-9418-2(1)) PublishAmerica, Inc.

Whittington, Mary K. The Patchwork Lady. Dyer, Jane, illus. 1999. pap. 5.00 (978-0-15-201489-6(6)) Harcourt Trade Pubs.

Wilder, Laura Ingalls. A Farmer Boy Birthday. 1999. (My First Little House Bks.). (Illus.). 32p. (J). (ps-3). pap. 5.95 (978-0-06-443570-3(9)) HarperCollins Pubs.

—A Farmer Boy Birthday. Wheeler, Jody, illus. 1998. (My First Little House Bks.). 40p. (J). (ps-3). lib. bdg. 16.89 (978-0-06-027477-1(8)) HarperCollins Pubs.

Williams, Barbara. Albert's Gift for Grandmother. Cushman, Doug, illus. 2006. 32p. (J). (ps-1). 16.99 (978-0-7636-2097-4(1)) Candlewick Pr.

Williams, Jacklyn. Happy Birthday, Gus! Cushman, Doug, illus. 2005. (Read-It! Readers Ser.). 32p. (J). (gr. k-3). 18.60 (978-1-4048-0957-4(0)) Picture Window Bks.

Wilson, Mary. Mark & the Mega Buffet. 2005. 37p. (J). pap. 15.58 (978-1-4116-4172-3(8)) Lulu.com.

Winfrey, Michelle Whitaker. It's My Birthday. . . Finally! A Leap Year Story. Turley, Joyce M., illus. 2003. 88p. (J). (gr. 3-7). per. 11.95 (978-0-9727179-0-8(0)) Hobby Hse. Publishing Group.

Winkler, Henry & Oliver, Lin. Day of the Iguana. 2006. (Hank Zipzer Ser.: No. 3). (J). (gr. 3-8). 24.21 (978-1-59961-102-0(3)) Spotlight.

Wojtowycz, David. Dudley's Birthday Party. 2000. (Illus.). 14p. (J). (ps-3). pap. 7.95 (978-1-888444-72-8(X)) Little Tiger Pr.

Woolson, Constance Fenimore. The Old Stone House. 2006. 196p. pap. 11.99 (***978-1-4264-4971-0(2)***) BiblioBazaar.

Wooters, Duane. The Unnamed Manuscript. 2003. 70p. (YA). pap. 8.95 (978-0-595-29612-5(2)) iUniverse, Inc.

Wright, Betty Ren. The Blizzard. Himler, Ronald, illus. 32p. (J). 2005. pap. 6.95 (978-0-8234-1981-4(9)); 2003. 16.95 (978-0-8234-1656-1(9)) Holiday Hse., Inc.

Yaccarino, Dan. The Birthday Fish. rev. ed. 2005. (Illus.). 40p. (J). 16.95 (978-0-8050-7493-2(7) , Holt, Henry & Co. Bks. For Young Readers) Holt, Henry & Co.

Yoon, Salina. Birthday Boy! Yoon, Salina, illus. 2006. (Illus.). 10p. (J). (ps-1). bds. 5.99 (978-0-8431-1791-2(5) , Price Stern Sloan) Penguin Group (USA) Inc.

—Birthday Girl! 2006. (Illus.). 10p. (J). (ps-1). bds. 5.99 (978-0-8431-1790-5(7) , Price Stern Sloan) Penguin Group (USA) Inc.

Ziefert, Harriet. Buzzy's Birthday. Bolam, Emily, illus. 2004. 24p. 9.95 (978-1-59354-062-3(0)) Blue Apple Bks.

Zoehfeld, Kathleen Weidner. Pooh's Birthday Surprise: Learn & Grow. 2000. (Lift the Flaps Bks.). 14p. (J). (ps-3). 5.99 (978-0-7364-1007-6(4)) Mouse Works.

Zolotow, Charlotte. El Senor Conejo y el Hermoso Regalo. Sendak, Maurice, illus. 2006. (SPA.). 40p. (J). pap. 6.99 (978-0-06-088704-9(4) , Rayo) HarperCollins Pubs.

BIRTHDAYS—POETRY

Kulka, Joe. Wolf's Coming! Kulka, Joe, illus. 2007. (Illus.). 32p. (J). (ps-4). spiral bd. 15.95 (978-1-57505-930-3(4) , Carolrhoda Bks.) Lerner Publishing Group.

Lansky, Bruce. Happy Birthday to Me! Lindstrom, Jack, illus. 1998. 27p. (J). 8.95 (978-0-88166-305-1(0)) Meadowbrook Pr.

Sandburg, Carl. Not Everyday an Aurora Borealis for Your Birthday: A Love Poem. 1998. pap. 13.00 (978-0-679-88169-8(7) , Random Hse. Bks. for Young Readers) Random Hse. Children's Bks.

BISCUIT (FICTITIOUS CHARACTER : CAPUCILLI)—FICTION

Capucilli, Alyssa Satin. Bathtime for Biscuit. Schories, Pat, illus. (My First I Can Read Bks.). 32p. (J). (ps up). 1999. pap. 3.99 (978-0-06-444264-0(0) , Harper Trophy); 1998. lib. bdg. 16.89 (978-0-06-027938-7(9)) HarperCollins Pubs.

—Biscuit & the Baby. Schories, Pat, illus. 2005. 24p. (J). lib. bdg. 13.85 (***978-1-4242-0702-2(9)***) Fitzgerald Bks.

—Biscuit Finds a Friend. Schories, Pat, illus. 1998. (My First I Can Read Bks.). 32p. (J). (ps up). pap. 3.99 (978-0-06-444243-5(8) , Harper Trophy) HarperCollins Pubs.

—Biscuit Finds a Friend. Schories, Pat, illus. 1998. (My First I Can Read Bks.). (J). (ps-k). 10.79 (978-0-606-13203-9(1)) Tandem Library Bks.

—Biscuit Gives a Gift. Schories, Pat, illus. 2004. 16p. (J). (ps-1). 4.99 (978-0-06-009467-6(2) , Harper Festival) HarperCollins Pubs.

—Biscuit Goes to School. Schories, Pat, illus. (Biscuit Ser.). 32p. (J). (ps up). 2003. pap. 3.99 (978-0-06-443616-8(0)); 2002. 15.99 (978-0-06-028682-8(2)); 2002. lib. bdg. 16.89 (978-0-06-028683-5(0)) HarperCollins Pubs.

—Biscuit Goes to School. Schories, Pat, illus. 2003. 21p. (J). (ps-ps). lib. bdg. 11.80 (978-0-613-66941-2(X)) Tandem Library Bks.

—Biscuit Mini Book & Puppy. Schories, Pat, illus. 1999. (Biscuit Ser.). (J). (ps-1). 14.95 (978-0-694-01444-6(3)) HarperCollins Pubs.

—Biscuit Storybook Collection. Schories, Pat, illus. 2005. (Biscuit Ser.). 192p. (J). (ps-1). 10.99 (978-0-06-075904-9(6) , Harper Festival) HarperCollins Pubs.

—Biscuit Treasury. Schories, Pat, illus. 2000. (Biscuit Ser.). (J). (ps-1). (978-0-06-029128-0(1)) HarperCollins Pubs.

—Biscuit Visits the Big City. Schories, Pat, illus. 2006. (My First I Can Read Bks.). 32p. (J). 15.99 (978-0-06-074164-8(3)); lib. bdg. 15.89 (978-0-06-074165-5(1)) HarperCollins Pubs.

—Biscuit Visits the Pumpkin Patch. Schories, Pat, illus. 2004. 16p. (J). (ps-1). 4.99 (978-0-06-009466-9(4) , Harper Festival) HarperCollins Pubs.

—Biscuit Wants to Play. Schories, Pat, illus. (My First I Can Read Bks.). 32p. (J). (ps-k). 2002. pap. 3.99 (978-0-06-444315-9(9) , Harper Trophy); 2001. 15.99 (978-0-06-028069-7(7)); 2001. lib. bdg. 15.89 (978-0-06-028070-3(0)) HarperCollins Pubs.

—Biscuit Wins a Prize. Schories, Pat, illus. 2004. 24p. (J). lib. bdg. 13.85 (***978-1-4242-0807-4(6)***) Fitzgerald Bks.

—Biscuit's Christmas. Schories, Pat, illus. 2000. (Biscuit Ser.). 16p. (J). (ps-1). pap. 6.99 (978-0-694-01516-0(4) , Harper Festival) HarperCollins Pubs.

—Biscuit's Christmas. 2003. (gr. k-3). lib. bdg. 15.25 (978-0-613-70855-5(5)) Tandem Library Bks.

—Biscuit's Day at the Farm. Schories, Pat, illus. 2008. (My First I Can Read Bks.). 32p. (J). pap. 3.99 (***978-0-06-074169-3(4)*** , Harper Trophy) HarperCollins Pubs.

—Biscuit's Hanukkah. Schories, Pat, illus. 2005. (Biscuit Ser.). 16p. (J). 4.99 (978-0-06-009469-0(9) , Harper Festival) HarperCollins Pubs.

—Biscuit's New Trick. Schories, Pat, illus. 2000. (My First I Can Read Bks.). 32p. (J). (ps-k). 16.99 (978-0-06-028067-3(0)); lib. bdg. 15.89 (978-0-06-028068-0(9)) HarperCollins Pubs.

—Biscuit's Pet & Play Easter. Berlin, Rose Mary, illus. 2008. (Biscuit Ser.). 12p. (J). 6.99 (***978-0-06-112839-4(2)*** , Harper Festival) HarperCollins Pubs.

—Biscuit's Picnic. Schories, Pat, illus. 1998. (Biscuit Ser.). 24p. (J). (ps-1). 12.95 (978-0-06-028072-7(7)) HarperCollins Pubs.

—Biscuit's Snowy Day. Schories, Pat, illus. 2005. (Biscuit Ser.). 16p. (J). 4.99 (978-0-06-009468-3(0) , Harper Festival) HarperCollins Pubs.

—Biscuit's Vacation. Schories, Pat, illus. 2002. (Biscuit Ser.). 24p. (J). (ps-1). lib. bdg. 12.89 (978-0-06-028681-1(4)) HarperCollins Pubs.

—Bizcocho. Mlawer, Teresa, tr. Schories, Pat, illus. 2nd ed. 2001. (Coleccion Ya Se Leer). (SPA.). 32p. (J). (ps up). pap. 4.99 (978-0-06-444310-4(8) , HC30732) HarperCollins Pubs.

—Meet Biscuit! Schories, Pat, illus. 2005. (Biscuit Ser.). 24p. (J). (ps-1). 3.99 (978-0-06-057846-6(7) , Harper Festival) HarperCollins Pubs.

Schories, Pat, illus. Biscuit's Fourth of July. 2005. (J). (***978-1-4156-0311-6(1)*** , Harper Festival) HarperCollins Pubs.

—Biscuit's Graduation Day. 2005. (J). (***978-1-4155-9660-9(3)*** , Harper Festival) HarperCollins Pubs.

BISHOP, ELVIN (FICTITIOUS CHARACTER)—FICTION

Lynch, Chris. Extreme Elvin. 1999. 240p. (YA). (gr. 7 up). 15.95 (978-0-06-028040-6(9)) HarperCollins Pubs.

BISMARCK (BATTLESHIP)

Crompton, Samuel Willard. Sinking of the Bismarck. (Great Battles Through the Ages Ser.). (Illus.). 112p. (gr. 6-12). 2004. pap. 13.25 (978-0-7910-7793-1(4)); 2003. 30.00 (978-0-7910-7438-1(2)) Facts On File, Inc. (Chelsea Hse.).

—Sinking of the Bismarck. 2004. (gr. 5-8). lib. bdg. 18.75 (978-0-613-81337-2(5)) Tandem Library Bks.

BISON

see also American Bison

The American Bison, 6 vols. (gr. 4 up). 39.95 (978-0-7368-8493-8(9)) Red Brick Learning.

Brodsky, Beverly, contrib. by. Buffalo: With Selections from Native American Song-Poems. 2003. (Illus.). 40p. (YA). 18.95 (978-0-7614-5133-4(1)) Cavendish, Marshall Corp.

Brodsky, Beverly, illus. Buffalo. 2002. (J). (978-1-890817-65-7(1)) Winslow Hse. Bks.

Caper, William. American Bison: A Scary Prediction. 2008. (America's Animal Comebacks Ser.). (J). lib. bdg. 25.27 (***978-1-59716-504-4(2)***) Bearport Publishing Co., Inc.

Costain, Meredith. American Buffalo. 2000. (gr. k-3). lib. bdg. 11.80 (978-0-613-30217-3(6)) Tandem Library Bks.

Crewe, Sabrina. Life Cycle of the Buffalo. 1999. (Life Cycles Ser.). (Illus.). 32p. (gr. 2-5). pap. 6.95 (978-0-8172-6238-9(5)) Steck-Vaughn.

Harcourt School Publishers Staff. The Bison, People & the Plains Advanced Level. 3rd ed. 2002. (Trophies Reading Program Ser.). (Illus.). pap. 5.10 (978-0-15-323399-9(0)) Harcourt Schl. Pubs.

Larson, Jenny. Mighty Bison. 2006. (Pull Ahead Books). (Illus.). 32p. (J). 22.60 (978-0-8225-3485-3(1) , Lerner Pubns.) Lerner Publishing Group.

Lee, Evelyn. Bluestem Horizon: A Story of a Tallgrass Prairie. Braukmann-Towns, Krista, illus. 1998. (Habitat Ser.: Vol. 10). 36p. (J). (gr. 1-4). 15.95 (978-1-56899-595-3(4)) Soundprints.

—Bluestem Horizon: A Story of a Tallgrass Prairie. Braukmann-Towns, Krista, illus. 1998. (Habitat Ser.: Vol. 10). 36p. (J). (gr. 1-4). 19.95 incl. reel tape (978-1-56899-597-7(0) , BC7010) Soundprints.

—Bluestem Horizon: A Story of a Tallgrass Prairie. Braukmann-Towns, Krista, illus. 1998. (Habitat Ser.: Vol. 10). (J). (gr. 1-4). 32p. pap. 6.95 (978-1-56899-596-0(2)); 36p. pap. 10.95 incl. audio (978-1-56899-598-4(9)); Incl. toy. 36p. 26.95 (978-1-56899-599-1(7)); Incl. toy. 36p. 31.95 incl. audio (978-1-56899-601-1(2)); Incl. toy. 36p. pap. 19.95 incl. audio (978-1-56899-602-8(0)) Soundprints.

Patent, Dorothy Hinshaw. Mystery of the Lascaux Cave. 1998. (Frozen in Time Ser.). (Illus.). 64p. (J). (gr. 5-9). lib. bdg. 28.50 (978-0-7614-0784-3(7)) Cavendish, Marshall Corp.

Waldman, Neil. They Came from the Bronx: How the Buffalo Were Saved from Extinction. Waldman, Neil, illus. 2003. (Illus.). 32p. (J). (gr. 2-4). 16.95 (978-1-56397-891-3(1)) Boyds Mills Pr.

Webber, Desiree. Buffalo Train Ride. 1999. (Illus.). 104p. 14.95 (978-1-57168-275-8(9)) Eakin Pr.

Winner, Cherie. Bison. McGee, John F., illus. 2004. (Our Wild World Ser.). 48p. (J). (gr. 2-5). pap. 7.95 (978-1-55971-775-5(0) , NorthWord Bks. for Young Readers) T&N Children's Publishing.

—Bison. 2001. (gr. 3-6). lib. bdg. 16.40 (978-0-613-55794-8(8)) Tandem Library Bks.

BISON—FICTION

Arnosky, Jim. Grandfather Buffalo. Arnosky, Jim, illus. 2006. (Illus.). 32p. (J). (ps). 16.99 (978-0-399-24169-7(8) , Putnam Juvenile) Penguin Group (USA) Inc.

Brauckmann-Towns, Krista, illus. Buffalo Prairie. 2005. (Amazing Animal Adventures Ser.). (J). (ps-2). 36p. 15.95 (978-1-59249-432-3(3) , B7110); 32p. 2.95 incl. cd-rom (978-1-59249-434-7(X) , S7160); 32p. pap. 6.95 (978-1-59249-433-0(1) , S7110) Soundprints.

Brown, Marc. Buster Hits the Trail. 2005. (Postcards from Buster Ser.). (Illus.). 48p. (J). (gr. 1-4). 14.99 (978-0-316-15900-5(X)) Little, Brown Bks. for Young Readers.

Doner, Kim. Buffalo Dreams. 1999. (Illus.). 40p. (YA). (gr. 2-7). 16.95 (978-1-55868-475-1(1)); pap. 9.95 (978-1-55868-476-8(X)) Graphic Arts Ctr. Publishing Co. (West Winds Pr.).

Fern, Tracey E. Buffalo Music. Castillo, Lauren, illus. 2008. 32p. (J). 16.00 (***978-0-618-72341-6(2)*** , Clarion Bks.) Houghton Mifflin Co. Trade & Reference Div.

Griffis, Molly. The Buffalo in the Mall. Doner, Kim, illus. 32p. 8.95 (978-1-57168-635-0(5)) Eakin Pr.

Lee, Evelyn. Bluestem Horizon: A Story of a Tallgrass Prairie. Braukmann-Towns, Krista, illus. 1998. (Habitat Ser.: Vol. 10). (J). (gr. 1-4). 36p. 15.95 (978-1-56899-595-3(4)); 32p. pap. 6.95 (978-1-56899-596-0(2)) Soundprints.

—Bluestem Horizon: A Story of a Tallgrass Prairie. Brauckmann-Towns, Krista, illus. 2005. (Soundprints' Wild Habitats Ser.). 32p. (J). (gr. 1-4). pap. 8.95 incl. reel tape (978-1-59249-098-1(0)) Soundprints.

Lewis, Preston. Blanca Is My Name: Or, How I Saved the Buffalo on the Texas Plains. Eckhardt, Jason C., illus. 2002. (Animal Legends Ser.: Vol. 2). 188p. 15.95 (978-1-57168-699-2(1)); 9.95 (978-1-57168-700-5(9)) Eakin Pr.

McKay, Erin & Huynh, Quang Nhuong. Water Buffalo Days: Growing up in Vietnam. Tseng, Jean & Tseng, Mou-Sien, illus. 1999. 128p. (J). (gr. 2-5). pap. 5.99 (978-0-06-446211-2(0) , Harper Trophy) HarperCollins Pubs.

Meyer, Kay L. The Adventures of Billie & Annie—Baby Bison. Kirchoff, Arthur, illus. l.t. ed. 2004. 32p. (J). 6.00 (978-0-9744536-0-6(9) , 9780974453606) Meyer, Tjaden.

Savage, Nancy. Nickel, the Baby Buffalo Who Thought He Was a Dog. Parks, Kathy, illus. 1999. 31p. (J). pap. (978-0-9669130-0-2(0)) Savage Parks Pr.

Schnell, Robert W. Bonko. Wilkon, Jozef, illus. 28p. (J). (ps-3). 12.95 (978-0-87592-008-5(X)) Scroll Pr., Inc.

Thomas, Rosie. Cowgirl Rosie & Her Five Baby Bison. 2001. (Illus.). 24p. (J). (ps-3). 12.95 (978-0-316-64712-0(8)) Little Brown & Co.

BLACK AMERICANS

see African Americans

BLACK DEATH

Here are entered works on the outbreak of the plague that swept parts of Asia and Europe in the fourteenth century.

see also Plague

Coping with Catastrophe: The Black Death of the 14th Century. (YA). (gr. 6-9). spiral bd., tchr.'s planning gde. ed. 12.00 (978-0-382-44466-1(3)) Cobblestone Publishing Co.

Coping with Catastrophe: The Black Death of the 14th Century. (YA). (gr. 6 up). 16.50 (978-0-8126-7557-3(6)) Cricket Bks.

De Hahn, Tracee. The Black Death. 2001. (Great Disasters, Reforms & Ramifications Ser.). (Illus.). 112p. (J). 30.00 (978-0-7910-6326-2(7) , Chelsea Hse.) Facts On File, Inc.

Dunn, John M. Life During the Black Death. 1999. (Way People Live Ser.). (Illus.). 96p. (J). (gr. 7-10). 28.70 (978-1-56006-542-5(7) , LML00902-177899, Lucent Bks.) Thomson Gale.

Elliott, Lynne. Medieval Medicine & the Plague. 2005. (Medieval World Ser.). (Illus.). 32p. (J). (gr. 4-9). (978-0-7787-1358-6(X)) Crabtree Publishing Co.

Narayan, Natasha. Black Death & Other Putrid Plagues of London. 2004. (... . of London Ser.). (Illus.). 96p. 8.99 (978-1-904153-01-6(1)) Watling St., Ltd. GBR. *Dist:* Trafalgar Square Publishing.

Peters, Stephanie True. The Black Death. 2003. (Epidemics Ser.). (J). 29.93 (978-0-7614-1633-3(1) , Benchmark Bks.) Cavendish, Marshall Corp.

Senker, Cath. The Black Death 1347-1350: The Plague Spreads Across Europe. 2006. (When Disaster Struck Ser.). (Illus.). 56p. (J). (gr. 4-7). lib. bdg. 32.86 (978-1-4109-2278-6(2)) Raintree.

BLACK HAWK, SAUK CHIEF, 1767-1838

Marsh, Carole. Black Hawk. 2002. (One Thousand Readers Ser.). (Illus.). 12p. (J). (gr. k-4). 2.95 (978-0-635-01486-3(6) , 14866) Gallopade International.

Poulakidas, Georgene. Black Hawk's War. 2004. (Primary Sources of American Wars Ser.). (Illus.). 24p. (J). lib. bdg. (978-1-4042-2682-1(6)) Rosen Publishing Group, Inc., The.

BLACK LITERATURE (AMERICAN)

see American Literature—African American Authors

BLACK MUSLIMS

Benson, Michael. Malcolm X. 2001. (Biography Ser.). (Illus.). 112p. (YA). (gr. 6-12). 27.93 (978-0-8225-5025-9(3) , Lerner Pubns.) Lerner Publishing Group.

DeAngelis, Therese. Louis Farrakhan: Political Activist. 1999. (Black Americans of Achievement Ser.). (Illus.). 144p. (YA). (gr. 5 up). pap. 9.95 (978-0-7910-4689-0(3)); 32.00 (978-0-7910-4688-3(5)) Facts On File, Inc. (Chelsea Hse.).

Downing, David. Malcolm X. 2003. (Leading Lives Ser.). (Illus.). 64p. (J). lib. bdg. 28.50 (978-1-58810-579-0(2)) Heinemann Library.

—Malcolm X. 2003. (gr. 5-8). lib. bdg. 17.60 (978-0-613-60899-2(2)) Tandem Library Bks.

Gormley, Beatrice. Malcolm X: A Revolutionary Voice. 2008. (Sterling Biographies Ser.). (Illus.). 128p. (J). pap. 5.95 (***978-1-4027-4589-8(3)***) Sterling Publishing Co., Inc.

Graves, Renee. Malcolm X. 2007. (Cornerstones of Freedomtrade;, Second Ser.). 48p. (J). 5.95 (***978-0-531-18691-6(1)*** , Children's Pr.) Scholastic Library Publishing.

Jeffrey, Laura S. Betty Shabazz: Sharing the Vision of Malcolm X. 2000. (African-American Biographies Ser.). (Illus.). 128p. (YA). (gr. 6-12). lib. bdg. 26.60 (978-0-7660-1210-3(7)) Enslow Pubs., Inc.

Thoennes Keller, Kristin. Malcolm X. 2005. (Fact Finders Ser.). (Illus.). 32p. (J). (978-0-7368-4347-8(7)) Capstone Pr., Inc.

BLACK POETRY (AMERICAN)

see American Poetry—African American Authors

BLACK STALLION (FICTITIOUS CHARACTER)—FICTION

Farley, Steven. The Black Stallion's Shadow. 2000. (Black Stallion Ser.). (Illus.). 192p. (J). (gr. 5-8). pap. 5.99 (978-0-679-89046-1(7) , Random Hse. Bks. for Young Readers) Random Hse. Children's Bks.

—Hard Lessons. Schwartz, Joanie, illus. 1999. (Young Black Stallion Ser.: No. 6). 144p. (J). (gr. 4-6). lib. bdg. 11.99 (978-0-375-90092-1(6) , Random Hse. Bks. for Young Readers) Random Hse. Children's Bks.

—Hard Lessons. 1999. (Young Black Stallion Ser.: No. 6). (J). (gr. 4-6). (978-0-606-16965-3(2)) Tandem Library Bks.

—The Homecoming. 1999. (Young Black Stallion Ser.: No. 3). (J). (gr. 4-6). (978-0-606-16962-2(8)) Tandem Library Bks.

—South Wind Spring. 2000. (Young Black Stallion Ser.: No. 7). (Illus.). 144p. (J). (gr. 4-6). pap. 3.99 (978-0-375-80139-6(1) , Random Hse. Bks. for Young Readers) Random Hse. Children's Bks.

Farley, Walter. The Black Stallion. l.t. ed. 2005. 290p. (J). pap. (978-0-7540-6198-4(1) , CLP 390) BBC Audio.

—The Black Stallion & Satan. 2002. (Black Stallion Ser.). 224p. (J). (gr. 5-8). pap. 5.99 (978-0-679-81346-0(2) , Yearling) Random Hse. Children's Bks.

—The Black Stallion Challenged. 2003. (Black Stallion Ser.). (Illus.). 240p. (J). (gr. 5-8). pap. 5.99 (978-0-394-84371-1(1) , Random Hse. Bks. for Young Readers) Random Hse. Children's Bks.

—The Black Stallion Challenged. 2003. (gr. 5-8). lib. bdg. 14.15 (978-0-613-81950-3(0)) Tandem Library Bks.

—The Black Stallion Mystery. 2004. (Black Stallion Ser.). 224p. (J). (gr. 5-8). reprint ed. pap. 5.99 (978-0-679-82700-9(5) , Yearling) Random Hse. Children's Bks.

—The Black Stallion Revolts. Rowe, John, illus. 2002. (Black Stallion Ser.). 288p. (J). (gr. 5-8). pap. 5.99 (978-0-394-83613-3(8) , Yearling) Random Hse. Children's Bks.

—The Black Stallion's Courage. 2004. (Black Stallion Ser.). (Illus.). 240p. (J). (gr. 5-8). pap. 5.99 (978-0-394-83918-9(8) , Yearling) Random Hse. Children's Bks.

—The Black Stallion's Filly. Rowe, John, illus. 2002. (Black Stallion Ser.). 288p. (J). (gr. 5-8). pap. 5.99 (978-0-394-83916-5(1) , Yearling) Random Hse. Children's Bks.

—The Island Stallion. 2003. (Black Stallion Ser.). (Illus.). 240p. (J). (gr. 5-8). pap. 5.99 (978-0-394-84376-6(2) , Yearling) Random Hse. Children's Bks.

—The Island Stallion Races. 2003. (Black Stallion Ser.). (Illus.). 256p. (J). (gr. 5-8). pap. 5.99 (978-0-394-84375-9(4) , Yearling) Random Hse. Children's Bks.

—The Island Stallion's Fury. 2003. (Black Stallion Ser.). (Illus.). 224p. (J). (gr. 5-8). pap. 5.99 (978-0-394-84373-5(8) , Yearling) Random Hse. Children's Bks.

BLACKBOARD DRAWING

see Crayon Drawing

BLACKS

Here are entered works on blacks as an element in the population. Works on black people in countries whose racial composition is predominantly black are assigned headings appropriate for the country as a whole without the use of the heading Blacks. The heading Blacks is assigned to works on such countries only if the work discusses blacks apart from other groups in the country.

Dingles, Molly. Black as a Bat/Negro como un Murcielago. Velez, Walter, illus. 2003. (Community of Color Ser.). (SPA.). 32p. (J). lib. bdg. 20.65 (978-1-891997-33-4(5)) Dingles & Co.

The Little Black Book: Why Blacks Don't Support One Another, a Black Psychotherapist's Perspective. 2002. (YA). per. 9.95 (978-1-931413-68-8(1)) Fundcraft Publishing.

Toussaint, Pamela. Great Books for African Americans. 1999. (J). (978-0-606-17070-3(7)) Tandem Library Bks.

BLACKS—BIOGRAPHY

Aaseng, Nathan. Sports Great David Robinson. rev. ed. 1998. (Sports Great Bks.). (Illus.). 64p. (YA). (gr. 4-10). lib. bdg. 22.60 (978-0-7660-1077-2(5)) Enslow Pubs., Inc.

Adler, David A. A Picture Book of George Washington Carver. Brown, Dan, illus. 1999. 32p. (J). (gr. k-3). tchr. ed. 16.95 (978-0-8234-1429-1(9)) Holiday Hse., Inc.

African-American Chemical Engineers. 2000. (My Ancestors—My Heroes Ser.: Vol. 42). (J). (gr. 3-4). (978-1-893091-41-2(4)) Parker Publishing Co.

Beecroft, Simon. The Release of Nelson Mandela. 2004. (Days That Changed the World Ser.). (Illus.). 48p. (J). (gr. 5 up). pap. 11.95 (978-0-8368-5578-4(7)); lib. bdg. 30.00 (978-0-8368-5571-5(X)) Stevens, Gareth Inc. (World Almanac Library).

Bolden, Tonya. And Not Afraid to Dare: The Stories of Ten African-American Women. 1998. 244p. (J). (gr. 4-9). pap. 16.95 (978-0-590-48080-2(4)) Scholastic, Inc.

Cameron, Ann. The Kidnapped Prince: The Life of Olaudah Equiano. 2000. (Illus.). 160p. (YA). (gr. 5-8). 5.50 (978-0-375-80346-8(7) , Yearling) Random Hse. Children's Bks.

Caper, William. Whoopi Goldberg: Comedian & Movie Star. 1999. (African-American Biographies Ser.). (Illus.). 128p. (YA). (gr. 6-12). lib. bdg. 26.60 (978-0-7660-1205-9(0)) Enslow Pubs., Inc.

Chapman, Ferguson. Spike Lee. 1998. (Ovations Ser.). (Illus.). 32p. (YA). (gr. 4-7). lib. bdg. (978-0-88682-697-0(7) , Creative Education) Creative Co., The.

Christopher, Matt. On the Court with... Lisa Leslie. 1998. (Matt Christopher Sports Biographies Ser.). 128p. (J). (gr. 3-7). pap. 4.99 (978-0-316-14216-8(6)) Little, Brown Bks. for Young Readers.

Collins, David R. Servant to the Slaves: The Story of Henriette Delille. 2000. (Weaver Bks.). 68p. (J). (gr. 7-9). pap. 3.95 (978-0-8198-7039-1(0)) Pauline Bks. & Media.

Connolly, Sean. Nelson Mandela: An Unauthorized Biography. 2000. (Profiles Ser.). (Illus.). 56p. (J). (gr. 4-6). lib. bdg. 24.22 (978-1-57572-225-2(9)) Heinemann Library.

Cooper, Floyd. Coming Home: From the Life of Langston Hughes. 1998. (Illus.). 32p. (J). (gr. k-3). pap. 6.99 (978-0-698-11612-2(7) , Putnam Juvenile) Penguin Group (USA) Inc.

Cooper, John. Rapid Ray: The Story of Ray Lewis. 2002. (Illus.). 160p. (J). (gr. 5-9). pap. 8.95 (978-0-88776-612-1(9)) Tundra Bks., Inc./Livres Toundra, Inc. CAN. *Dist:* Random Hse., Inc.

Dougherty, Terri. Barry Sanders. 1999. (Jam Session Ser.). (Illus.). 32p. (J). (gr. 3-8). lib. bdg. 24.21 (978-1-57765-037-9(9) , ABDO & Daughters) ABDO Publishing Co.

—Kevin Garnett. 1999. (Jam Session Ser.). (Illus.). 32p. (J). (gr. 3-8). lib. bdg. 24.21 (978-1-57765-039-3(5) , ABDO & Daughters) ABDO Publishing Co.

Durden, Robert F. Carter G. Woodson: Father of African-American History. 1998. (African-American Biographies Ser.). (Illus.). 128p. (YA). (gr. 6-12). lib. bdg. 26.60 (978-0-89490-946-7(0)) Enslow Pubs., Inc.

Equiano, Olaudiah. Kidnapped Prince: The Life of Olaudah Equiano. 2000. (Illus.). (J). (978-0-606-18237-9(3)) Tandem Library Bks.

Ferris, Jeri Chase. With Open Hands: A Story about Biddy Mason. 2003. (Creative Minds Biographies Ser.). (Illus.). 64p. (J). (gr. 3-6). pap. 6.95 (978-0-87614-845-7(3) , Carolrhoda Bks.) Lerner Publishing Group.

—With Open Hands: A Story about Biddy Mason. Ramstad, Ralph L., illus. 1999. (Creative Minds Biographies Ser.). 64p. (J). (gr. 3-6). lib. bdg. 22.60 (978-1-57505-330-1(6) , Carolrhoda Bks.) Lerner Publishing Group.

—With Open Hands: A Story about Biddy Mason. 1999. (gr. 3-6). lib. bdg. 15.25 (978-0-613-68482-8(6)) Tandem Library Bks.

Folsom, Franklin. Black Cowboy: The Life & Legend of George McJunkin. 3rd rev. ed. 1999. (Forgotten Pioneers Ser.). (Illus.). 162p. (gr. 2 up). pap. 7.95 (978-1-879373-14-3(9)) Rinehart, Roberts Pubs.

Gogerly, Liz. The Freeing of Nelson Mandela. 2004. (Days That Shook the World Ser.). (Illus.). 47p. (J). lib. bdg. 28.56 (978-0-7398-6648-1(6)) Raintree.

—Nelson Mandela. 2003. (Leading Lives Ser.). (Illus.). 64p. (J). lib. bdg. 28.50 (978-1-4034-0834-1(3)) Heinemann Library.

Green, Robert. Nelson Mandela: Activist for Equality. 2002. (Journey to Freedom Ser.). (Illus.). 40p. (J). (gr. 3-7). 28.50 (978-1-56766-648-9(5)) Child's World, Inc.

Grimes, Nikki. Talkin' 'Bout Bess: The Story of Aviator Bessie Coleman. Lewis, Ted G., illus. 1998. (J). lib. bdg. (978-0-531-33069-2(9) , Orchard Bks.) Scholastic, Inc.

Grody, Carl W. Sports Great Mitch Richmond. 1999. (Sports Great Bks.). (Illus.). 64p. (YA). (gr. 4-10). lib. bdg. 17.95 (978-0-7660-1070-3(8)) Enslow Pubs., Inc.

Gutman, Bill. Gail Devers. 1998. (Overcoming the Odds Ser.). (Illus.). 48p. (J). (gr. 4-7). pap. 7.95 (978-0-8172-8003-1(0)) Steck-Vaughn.

Hasday, Judy L. James Earl Jones: Actor. 1999. (Overcoming Adversity Ser.). (Illus.). 128p. (YA). (gr. 5 up). 32.00 (978-0-7910-4702-6(4)); pap. 6.65 (978-0-7910-4703-3(2)) Facts On File, Inc. (Chelsea Hse.).

Haskins, Jim. African American Entrepreneurs. 1998. (Black Stars Ser.). (Illus.). 192p. (gr. 5-9). 24.95 (978-0-471-14576-9(9) , Wiley) Wiley, John & Sons, Inc.

—African American Military Heroes. 1998. (Black Stars Ser.). (Illus.). 192p. (gr. 5-9). 24.95 (978-0-471-14577-6(7) , Wiley) Wiley, John & Sons, Inc.

—Carter G. Woodson: The Man Who Put "Black" in American History. Reim, Melanie K., illus. 2000. (Inspiring People Ser.). 48p. (gr. 4-6). lib. bdg. (978-0-7613-1264-2(1) , Twenty-First Century Bks.) Lerner Publishing Group.

Holland, Gini. Nelson Mandela. 2002. (Trailblazers of the Modern World Ser.). (Illus.). 48p. (J). (gr. 5 up). pap. 14.95 (978-0-8368-5238-7(9)); lib. bdg. 30.00 (978-0-8368-5078-9(5)) Stevens, Gareth Inc. (World Almanac Library).

Joseph, Paul. Will Smith. 1999. (Young Profiles Ser.). (Illus.). 32p. (J). (gr. k-6). lib. bdg. 22.78 (978-1-57765-320-2(3) , Checkerboard Library) ABDO Publishing Co.

Katz, William Loren. Black Pioneers: An Untold Story. 1999. (Illus.). 208p. (YA). (gr. 7 up). 21.99 (978-0-689-81410-5(0) , Atheneum) Simon & Schuster Children's Publishing.

Kavanaugh, Lee Hill. Quincy Jones: Musician, Composer, Producer. 1998. (African-American Biographies Ser.). (Illus.). 128p. (YA). (gr. 6-12). lib. bdg. 20.95 (978-0-89490-814-9(6)) Enslow Pubs., Inc.

Kite, L. Patricia. Maya Angelou. 1999. (Biography Ser.). (Illus.). 112p. (YA). (gr. 6-12). lib. bdg. 27.93 (978-0-8225-4944-4(1) , Lerner Pubns.) Lerner Publishing Group.

Knapp, Ron. Sports Great Barry Sanders. rev. ed. 1999. (Sports Great Bks.). (Illus.). 64p. (YA). (gr. 4-10). lib. bdg. 22.60 (978-0-7660-1067-3(8)) Enslow Pubs., Inc.

Lazo, Caroline Evensen. Arthur Ashe. 1998. (Biography Ser.). (Illus.). 128p. (YA). (gr. 6-12). lib. bdg. 25.26 (978-0-8225-4932-1(8) , Lerner Pubns.) Lerner Publishing Group.

Lisandrelli, Elaine Slivinski. Ida B. Wells-Barnett: Crusader Against Lynching. 1998. (African-American Biographies Ser.). (Illus.). 128p. (YA). (gr. 6-12). lib. bdg. 26.60 (978-0-89490-947-4(9)) Enslow Pubs., Inc.

Loeper, John J. Meet the Webbers of Philadelphia. 1998. (Early American Family Ser.). (Illus.). 64p. (J). (gr. 3 up). lib. bdg. 25.64 (978-0-7614-0843-7(6) , Benchmark Bks.) Cavendish, Marshall Corp.

Lowery, Linda. Aunt Clara Brown: Official Pioneer. Porter, Janice Lee, illus. 1999. (On My Own Biographies Ser.). 48p. (J). (gr. 2-5). lib. bdg. 23.93 (978-1-57505-045-4(5)) Lerner Publishing Group.

Lyons, Mary E. Stitching Stars: The Story Quilts of Harriet Powers. 1998. (J). pap. 6.99 (978-0-87628-344-8(X)) Ctr. for Applied Research in Education, The.

Macnow, Glen. Sports Great Chris Webber. 1999. (Sports Great Bks.). (Illus.). 64p. (YA). (gr. 4-10). lib. bdg. 17.95 (978-0-7660-1069-7(4)) Enslow Pubs., Inc.

—Sports Great Deion Sanders. 1999. (Sports Great Bks.). (Illus.). 64p. (YA). (gr. 4-10). lib. bdg. 22.60 (978-0-7660-1068-0(6)) Enslow Pubs., Inc.

Malam, John. The Release of Nelson Mandela. 2002. (Dates with History Ser.). (Illus.). 31p. (J). lib. bdg. 24.25 (978-1-58340-216-0(0)) Smart Apple Media.

Marlowe, Sam. Learning about Dedication from the Life of Frederick Douglass. 2004. (Character Building Book Ser.). (Illus.). 24p. (J). lib. bdg. 18.75 (978-0-8239-6928-9(2) , PowerKids Pr.) Rosen Publishing Group, Inc., The.

Marsh, Carole. Best Book of Black Biographies. 2003. (gr. 5-8). lib. bdg. 22.20 (978-0-613-73032-7(1)) Tandem Library Bks.

Martin, Marvin. Arthur Ashe: Of Tennis & the Human Spirit. 1999. (Impact Biographies Ser.). (Illus.). 176p. (J). (gr. 8-12). 18.95 (978-0-531-11432-2(5) , Watts, Franklin) Scholastic Library Publishing.

McDonough, Yona Zeldis & Zeldis, Malcah. Peaceful Protest. 2006. (Illus.). 40p. (J). pap. 8.95 (978-0-8027-8948-8(X)) Walker & Co.

Molzahn, Arlene Bourgeois. Top 10 American Women Sprinters. 1998. (Sports Top 10 Ser.). (Illus.). 48p. (YA). (gr. 4-10). lib. bdg. 23.93 (978-0-7660-1011-6(2)) Enslow Pubs., Inc.

Murdico, Suzanne J. Hakeem Olajuwon. 1998. (Overcoming the Odds Ser.). (Illus.). 48p. (J). (gr. 3-8). lib. bdg. (978-0-8172-4131-5(0)) Raintree.

—Hakeem Olajuwon. 1998. (Overcoming the Odds Ser.). (Illus.). 48p. (J). (gr. 4-7). pap. 7.95 (978-0-8172-8002-4(2)) Steck-Vaughn.

Old, Wendie C. Louis Armstrong: King of Jazz. 1998. (African-American Biographies Ser.). (Illus.). 128p. (YA). (gr. 6-12). lib. bdg. 26.60 (978-0-89490-997-9(5)) Enslow Pubs., Inc.

Orgill, Roxane. If I Only Had a Horn: Young Louis Armstrong. Jenkins, Leonard, illus. 2002. 32p. (J). (gr. 4-6). pap. 5.95 (978-0-618-25076-9(X)) Houghton Mifflin Co. Trade & Reference Div.

—If I Only Had a Horn: Young Louis Armstrong. 2002. (gr. k-3). lib. bdg. 14.10 (978-0-613-70726-8(5)) Tandem Library Bks.

Pogrund, Benjamin. Nelson Mandela. (Pacificadores Mundiales Ser.). 64p. (gr. 5-8). 28.70 (978-1-4103-0543-5(0) , Blackbirch Pr., Inc.) Thomson Gale.

Rambeck, Richard & Klingel, Cynthia Fitterer. Hockey. 2003. (Wonder Books Level 2: Sports Ser.). (Illus.). 24p. (J). (ps-2). 22.79 (978-1-56766-460-7(1)) Child's World, Inc.

Rappoport, Ken. Scottie Pippen: Star Forward. 1999. (Sports Reports). (Illus.). 104p. (YA). (gr. 4-10). lib. bdg. 20.95 (978-0-7660-1080-2(5)) Enslow Pubs., Inc.

Rekela, George R. Karl Malone: Star Forward. 1998. (Sports Reports). (Illus.). 104p. (YA). (gr. 4-10). lib. bdg. 26.60 (978-0-89490-931-3(2)) Enslow Pubs., Inc.

Roop, Peter & Roop, Connie. Martin Luther King, Jr., Set 1. 2002. (Lives & Times Ser.). (Illus.). 24p. (J). (gr. k-3). pap. 6.50 (978-1-58810-346-8(3) , 91106) Heinemann Library.

Ross, H. K. Black American Women, No. 3. Date not set. (Illus.). 160p. (YA). (gr. 6-12). 11.95 (978-0-87460-365-1(X)) Lion Bks.

Ross, Harriet. Great Black Americans in Science. 2000. (Illus.). 160p. (J). (gr. 3-9). lib. bdg. 14.95 (978-0-87460-392-7(7)) Lion Bks.

Savage, Jeff. Sports Great Juwan Howard. 1999. (Sports Great Bks.). (Illus.). 64p. (YA). (gr. 4-10). lib. bdg. 22.60 (978-0-7660-1065-9(1)) Enslow Pubs., Inc.

Scheader, Catherine. Lorraine Hansberry: Playwright & Voice of Justice. 1998. (African-American Biographies Ser.). (Illus.). 128p. (YA). (gr. 6-12). lib. bdg. 26.60 (978-0-89490-945-0(2)) Enslow Pubs., Inc.

Schnakenberg, Robert E. Derek Jeter: Surefire Shortstop. (Sports Achievers Biographies Ser.). (Illus.). 1999. 80p. (gr. 7-12). lib. bdg. 22.60 (978-0-8225-3671-0(4)); 1998. 64p. (YA). (gr. 4-9). pap. (978-0-8225-9838-1(8) , LernerSports) Lerner Publishing Group.

Schraff, Anne. Ralph Bunche: Winner of the Nobel Peace Prize. 1999. (African-American Biographies Ser.). (Illus.). 128p. (J). (gr. 6-12). lib. bdg. 26.60 (978-0-7660-1203-5(4)) Enslow Pubs., Inc.

Schwartz, Michael. Luis Rodriguez. 1998. (Contemporary African Americans Ser.). (Illus.). 48p. (J). (gr. 3-7). pap. 7.95 (978-0-8172-6879-4(0)) Steck-Vaughn.

Schwartzman, Myron. Romare Bearden: Celebrating the Victory. 2000. (Illus.). 143p. (YA). (gr. 8-12). lib. bdg. 22.20 (978-0-613-29504-8(8)) Tandem Library Bks.

Sullivan, Michael J. Sports Great Shaquille O'Neal. rev. ed. 1998. (Sports Great Bks.). (Illus.). 64p. (YA). (gr. 4-10). lib. bdg. 22.60 (978-0-7660-1003-1(1)) Enslow Pubs., Inc.

Sullivan, Otha Richard. African American Inventors. Haskins, Jim, ed. 1998. (Black Stars Ser.). (Illus.). 176p. (gr. 5-9). 24.95 (978-0-471-14804-3(0) , Jossey-Bass) Wiley, John & Sons, Inc.

Thoennes Keller, Kristin. Malcolm X. 2005. (Fact Finders Ser.). (Illus.). 32p. (J). (978-0-7368-4347-8(7)) Capstone Pr., Inc.

Townsend, Brad. Shaquille O'Neal: Center of Attention. 3rd rev. ed. 1998. (Sports Achievers Biographies Ser.). (Illus.). 64p. (YA). (gr. 4-9). pap. (978-0-8225-9818-3(3) , LernerSports) Lerner Publishing Group.

—Shaquille O'Neal, Center of Attention. 1998. (Achievers Ser.). (J). lib. bdg. 19.93 (978-0-8225-3665-9(X)) Lerner Publishing Group.

Weber, Valerie & Lewis, Geneva. Home Life in Grandma's Day. 1999. (In Grandma's Day Ser.). (Illus.). 32p. (J). (gr. 2-4). lib. bdg. 21.27 (978-1-57505-329-5(2) , Carolrhoda Bks.) Lerner Publishing Group.

Whalin, W. Terry. Samuel Morris: Missionary to America. 1999. (Heroes of the Faith Ser.). 208p. (YA). (gr. 4-7). lib. bdg. 17.95 (978-0-7910-5039-2(4) , Chelsea Hse.) Facts On File, Inc.

Wright, David K. Paul Robeson: Actor, Singer, Political Activist. 1998. (African-American Biographies Ser.). (Illus.). 128p. (YA). (gr. 6-12). lib. bdg. 26.60 (978-0-89490-944-3(4)) Enslow Pubs., Inc.

Yannuzzi, Della A. Mae Jemison: A Space Biography. 1998. (Countdown to Space Ser.). (Illus.). 48p. (YA). (gr. 4-10). lib. bdg. 23.93 (978-0-89490-813-2(8)) Enslow Pubs., Inc.

BLACKS—FICTION

Adebayo, Yinka. Big Diss. 1999. (Drummond Hill Crew Ser.). 187p. (978-1-874509-68-4(9)) X Pr., The.

—Glamma Kids. 1999. (Drummond Hill Crew Ser.). 185p. (978-1-874509-67-7(0)) X Pr., The.

—Ragga to Riches. 1999. 187p. (J). (978-1-874509-69-1(7)) X Pr., The.

Ashley, Bernard. Little Soldier: A Novel. 2002. (Illus.). 240p. (J). (gr. 9 up). pap. 16.95 (978-0-439-22424-6(1) , Scholastic Pr.) Scholastic, Inc.

Bell, William. Zack. l.t. ed. 2000. (LRS Large Print Cornerstone Ser.). 256p. (YA). (gr. 5-12). lib. bdg. 28.95 (978-1-58118-072-5(1) , 23656) LRS.

—Zack. 2000. (J). (978-0-606-20095-0(9)) Tandem Library Bks.

Cobb, Nyelah. True Identity. 2003. 104p. pap. 9.95 (978-0-595-28227-2(X)) iUniverse, Inc.

Curtis, Christopher Paul. Elijah of Buxton. 2007. (J). (*978-0-439-02345-0(9)); 352p. (gr. 4-7). 16.99 (*978-0-439-02344-3(0) , Scholastic Pr.) Scholastic, Inc.

Daly, Niki. Happy Birthday, Jamela! Daly, Niki, illus. 2006. (Jamela Ser.). (Illus.). 32p. (J). (gr. k-2). 16.00 (978-0-374-32842-9(0) , Farrar, Straus & Giroux (BYR)) Farrar, Straus & Giroux.

—Jamela's Dress. Daly, Niki, illus. 2004. (Jamela Ser.). (Illus.). 32p. (J). reprint ed. pap. 6.95 (978-0-374-43720-6(3) , Sunburst) Farrar, Straus & Giroux.

—Jamela's Dress. 2001. (J). (ps-2). 26.95 incl. audio (978-0-8045-6878-4(2) , 6878) Spoken Arts, Inc.

—Not So Fast, Songololo. 1998. (J). pap. 4.95 (978-0-87628-975-4(8)) Ctr. for Applied Research in Education, The.

—Once upon a Time. Daly, Niki, illus. 2003. (Illus.). 32p. (J). (gr. k-3). 16.00 (978-0-374-35633-0(5) , Farrar, Straus & Giroux (BYR)) Farrar, Straus & Giroux.

—What's Cooking, Jamela? Daly, Niki, illus. 2001. (Jamela Ser.). (Illus.). 32p. (J). (ps-2). 16.95 (978-0-374-35602-6(5) , Farrar, Straus & Giroux (BYR)) Farrar, Straus & Giroux.

—Where's Jamela? 2004. (Jamela Ser.). (Illus.). 36p. (J). 16.00 (978-0-374-38324-4(3) , Farrar, Straus & Giroux (BYR)) Farrar, Straus & Giroux.

Dunagan, Ted. A Yellow Watermelon. 2007. 256p. (J). 23.95 (*978-1-58838-197-2(8) , Junebug Bks.) NewSouth, Inc.

Foggo, Cheryl. One Thing That's True. unabr. ed. 128p. (YA). (gr. 13 up). 2002. (Illus.). (978-1-55074-377-7(5)); 1998. (978-1-55074-411-8(9)) Kids Can Pr., Ltd.

—Sam Finds a Monster. Sarrazin, Marisol, illus. 2004. (Kids Can Read! Ser.). 32p. (J). (gr. k-3). (978-1-55337-351-3(0)) Kids Can Pr., Ltd.

Gates, Susan. Bill's Baggy Pants. Axworthy, Anni, illus. 2004. (Read-It! Readers Ser.). 32p. (C). (gr. k-3). 18.60 (978-1-4048-0050-2(6)) Picture Window Bks.

Gillard, Denise. Music from the Sky. Taylor, Stephen, illus. 2001. 32p. (J). (gr. k-2). 15.95 (978-0-88899-311-3(0)) Groundwood Bks. CAN. *Dist:* Perseus Distribution.

Glasser, Margaret D. Kofi's Story. 1999. (Illus.). 28p. (J). (gr. k-3). pap. 8.95 (978-1-58521-003-9(X)) Books for Black Children, Inc.

Grifalconi, Ann. The Village That Vanished. Nelson, Kadir A., illus. 2002. 40p. (J). (gr. k up). 16.99 (978-0-8037-2623-9(6) , Dial) Penguin Group (USA) Inc.

—The Village That Vanished. Nelson, Kadir A., illus. 2004. 40p. (J). reprint ed. pap. 6.99 (978-0-14-240190-3(0) , Puffin) Penguin Group (USA) Inc.

Hanson, Regina. A Season for Mangoes. Velasquez, Eric, illus. 2005. 40p. (J). (gr. k-3). 15.00 (978-0-618-15972-7(X) , Clarion Bks.) Houghton Mifflin Co. Trade & Reference Div.

Harp, O. J. Across Time: Love Eternal. 2002. pap. 19.95 (978-1-885778-97-0(X)) Seaburn Pubs.

Hodge, Merle. For the Life of Laetitia. 2003. 21.25 (978-0-8446-7246-5(7)) Smith, Peter Pub., Inc.

Isadora, Rachel. Caribbean Dream. Isadora, Rachel, illus. 2002. (Illus.). 32p. (J). pap. 6.99 (978-0-698-11944-4(4) , Putnam Juvenile) Penguin Group (USA) Inc.

—Caribbean Dream. 2002. (ps-2). lib. bdg. 15.30 (978-0-613-51441-5(6)) Tandem Library Bks.

Literature Connections English: I, Juan de Pareja. 2004. (gr. 6-12). (978-0-395-77531-8(0) , 2-80100) McDougal Littell Inc.

MacHado, Ana Maria. Nina Bonita. Iribarren, Elena, tr. Faria, Rosana, illus. 2001. 24p. (J). (gr. k-4). reprint ed. 7.95 (978-1-929132-11-9(5)) Kane/Miller Bk. Pubs., Inc.

—Nina Bonita. 2001. (J). (978-0-606-20824-6(0)) Tandem Library Bks.

McBrier, Page. Beatrice's Goat. Lohstoeter, Lori, illus. 2004. 34p. (J). (ps-ps). lib. bdg. 15.60 (978-1-4176-3045-5(0)) Tandem Library Bks.

Medearis, Angela Shelf. Seven Spools of Thread: A Kwanzaa Story. Minter, Daniel, illus. 2000. 40p. (J). (gr. 2-5). 15.95 (978-0-8075-7315-0(9)); pap. 6.95 (978-0-8075-7316-7(7)) Whitman, Albert & Co.

Mitchell, Rita Phillips. Hue Boy. Binch, Caroline, illus. 1999. 32p. (J). (gr. k-3). pap. 11.95 (978-0-14-056354-2(7)) Penguin Bks., Ltd. GBR. *Dist:* Trafalgar Square Publishing.

Mussi, Sarah. The Door of No Return. 2008. (YA). (*978-1-4169-1550-8(8) , McElderry, Margaret K.) Simon & Schuster Children's Publishing.

Naidoo, Beverley. No Turning Back: A Novel of South Africa. 1999. 208p. (J). (gr. 3-7). pap. 5.99 (978-0-06-440749-6(7) , Harper Trophy) HarperCollins Pubs.

—No Turning Back: A Novel of South Africa. 1999. 189p. lib. bdg. 12.64 (978-0-606-15856-5(1)); (J). per. 14.10 (978-0-613-11922-1(3)) Tandem Library Bks.

The Other Side of the Invisible Fence. 2006. (YA). per. 9.95 (*978-0-9787783-8-5(3)) Trevor Romain Co., The.

Owens, Ora L. Victory over My Master. 2002. 158p. (YA). pap. 12.00 (978-0-9717698-0-9(X)) Celestial Commotion.

Perera, Hilda. Cuentos de Apolo. 3rd ed. 2001. (Coleccion Caniqui Ser.). (SPA., Illus.). 103p. (gr. 6 up). 5.00 (978-0-89729-438-6(6)) Ediciones Universal.

Perkyns, Dorothy. Last Days in Africville. 2005. (Illus.). 144p. (YA). pap., tchr. ed. (978-0-88878-446-9(5) , Sandcastle Bks.) Dundurn Group, The.

—Last Days in Africville. 2006. 120p. (J). pap. 10.99 (*978-1-55002-630-6(5) , Dundurn Pr.) Dundurn Group, The CAN. *Dist:* Univ. of Toronto Pr.

Prescott, Yolanda. Mama's Pickaninny. 2004. 7.00 (978-0-9719241-3-0(9)) Chosen Word Publishing.

Pullman, Philip. The Broken Bridge. 2002. 20.50 (978-0-8446-7229-8(7)) Smith, Peter Pub., Inc.

Sisulu, Eleanor Batezat. The Day Gogo Went to Vote. Wilson, Sharon, illus. 1999. 32p. (J). (ps-3). pap. 6.99 (978-0-316-70271-3(4)) Little, Brown Bks. for Young Readers.

Sisulu, Elinor Batezat. The Day Gogo Went to Vote. Wilson, Sharon, illus. 1999. (J). (ps-ps). lib. bdg. 14.10 (978-0-613-22837-4(5)) Tandem Library Bks.

Soriano, Osvaldo. El Negro de Paris. (Torre de Papel Ser.). (SPA.). (J). (gr. 4 up). 8.95 (978-958-04-3450-4(6)) Norma S.A. COL. *Dist:* Distribuidora Norma, Inc.

Southgate, Martha. Fall of Rome. 2003. (gr. 7-12). lib. bdg. 21.10 (978-0-613-62902-7(7)) Tandem Library Bks.

Stewart, Dianne. El Regalo del Sol. Daly, Jude, illus. 2000. (SPA.). 28p. (J). (ps-3). pap. 6.99 (978-980-257-258-8(6) , EK(1977)) Ekare, Ediciones VEN. *Dist:* Kane/Miller Bk. Pubs., Inc., Lectorum Pubns., Inc.

Stokes, Jeremiah & Jones, Denise G. Thunder Cave: The Thrilling Adventures of Jasper & Zebbie & the Good Giant Wigwah. Sears, Jack, illus. 2001. (YA). (gr. 4-12). 44.95 (978-0-9718474-0-8(1)) Kitkooh Pubns.

Stratton, Allan. Chanda's Wars. 2008. 400p. (J). 17.99 (*978-0-06-087262-5(4)); lib. bdg. 18.89 (*978-0-06-087264-9(0)) HarperCollins Pubs.

Taylor, Theodore. The Cay. 2000. 171p. (J). 15.60 (978-0-03-054604-4(4)) Holt, Rinehart & Winston.

—The Cay. 144p. 2003. (J). (gr. 5). mass mkt. 5.99 (978-0-440-22912-4(X) , Laurel Leaf); 2002. (gr. 4-7). 5.99 (978-0-440-41663-0(9) , Yearling) Random Hse. Children's Bks.

—Cay. 2003. (gr. 5-8). lib. bdg. 13.55 (978-0-613-72282-7(5)); 2002. (gr. 3-6). lib. bdg. 13.55 (978-0-613-33748-9(4)) Tandem Library Bks.

—Timothy of the Cay. 2007. (Illus.). 176p. (YA). pap. 5.95 (978-0-15-206320-7(X) , Harcourt Paperbacks) Harcourt Children's Bks.

Zephaniah, Benjamin. Gangsta Rap. 2004. 200p. (J). (gr. 9 up). pap. 7.95 (978-1-58234-886-5(3) , Bloomsbury Children) Bloomsbury Publishing.

BLACKS—HISTORY

Barnette, Donald. Is My Skin My Only Sin? Breaking the Color Barrier. 2004. (Illus.). 95p. (YA). pap. 14.95 (978-0-9747816-0-0(6)) Barnette, Donald.

Good, Janet. History Must Be Truthfully Re-Written to Include Afrikans. 1998. (Illus.). 32p. (J). (gr. k-12). pap. 7.95 (978-0-9661602-7-7(4)) Hadassah Investments, Inc.

Hansen, Joyce, et al. Breaking Ground, Breaking Silence: The Story of New York's African Burial Ground. McGowan, Gary, illus. rev. ed. 1998. (Illus.). 144p. (J). (gr. 5-9). 19.95 (978-0-8050-5012-7(4) , Holt, Henry & Co. Bks. For Young Readers) Holt, Henry & Co.

Lester, Julius. To Be a Slave. Feelings, Tom, illus. 30th anniv. ed. 1998. 168p. (J). (gr. 7-12). 20.00 (978-0-8037-2347-4(4) , Dial) Penguin Group (USA) Inc.

—To Be a Slave. 2000. (J). (978-0-606-20261-9(7)) Tandem Library Bks.

Lester, Julius & Feelings, Tom. To Be a Slave. 2005. 176p. (J). (gr. 5). pap. 5.99 (978-0-14-240386-0(5) , Puffin) Penguin Group (USA) Inc.

Lewis, J. Patrick. Freedom Like Sunlight: Praisesongs for Black Americans. Thompson, John, illus. 2000. 40p. (gr. 4 up). 17.95 (978-1-56846-163-2(1) , Creative Editions) Creative Co., The.

—Freedom Like Sunlight: Praisesongs for Black Americans. 2003. (gr. 3-6). lib. bdg. 16.40 (978-0-613-77490-1(6)) Tandem Library Bks.

Mack-Williams, Kibibi. Food & Our History. Date not set. (African American Life Ser.). 48p. (J). (gr. 4-8). lib. bdg. 17.95 (978-0-86625-033-7(6)) Rourke Publishing, LLC.

Saunders, Lesley. When We Were the Toast of Black Kansas City. Pulliam, Henry, ed. Blair, Leola, illus. Clark, Ken, photos by. 1999. 175p. (YA). (gr. 6-12). pap. 15.95 (978-0-9676736-0-8(7)) Les-Man Pubns.

Shaheed, Omar. Hip Hop Land. 2003. (Illus.). 24p. (J). (gr. 2-8). pap. 7.95 (978-0-913543-46-7(2)) African American Images.

Stimpson, Bea. Black People of the Americas. 2001. (Illus.). 48p. (J). pap. 19.95 (978-0-7487-6013-8(X)) Nelson Thornes Ltd. GBR. *Dist:* Trans-Atlantic Pubns., Inc.

BLACKS—SOCIAL LIFE AND CUSTOMS

Papi, Liza. Carnavalia! African-Brazilian Folklore & Crafts. Papi, Liza, illus. 2004. (Illus.). 48p. (J). (gr. k-4). reprint ed. 20.00 (978-0-7567-7760-9(7)) DIANE Publishing Co.

BLACKWELL, ELIZABETH, 1821-1910

Auster, Michael A. They Led the Way. 2005. (Yellow Umbrella Ser.). (J). (978-0-7368-5315-6(4)); (Illus.). 16p. (978-0-7368-5279-1(4)) Capstone Pr., Inc.

Bank Street Staff & Glimm, Adele. Elizabeth Blackwell: First Woman Doctor to Modern Times. 2000. (Ideas on Trial Ser.). (Illus.). 124p. (C). (gr. 5-10). pap. 8.95 (978-0-07-134335-0(0)) McGraw-Hill Cos., The.

Binns, Tristan Boyer. Elizabeth Blackwell: First Woman Physician. 2005. (Great Life Stories Ser.). (Illus.). 111p. (J). (gr. 6-8). 30.50 (978-0-531-12402-4(9) , Watts, Franklin) Scholastic Library Publishing.

Kent, Deborah. Elizabeth Blackwell: Physician & Health Educator. 2003. (Spirit of America). (Illus.). 32p. (J). (gr. 2-6). 27.07 (978-1-59296-002-6(2)) Child's World, Inc.

Kishel, Ann-Marie. Elizabeth Blackwell: A Life of Diligence. 2007. (Pull Ahead Books-Biographies Ser.). (J). 22.60 (978-0-8225-6459-1(9) , Lerner Pubns.) Lerner Publishing Group.

Klobuchar, Lisa. Elizabeth Blackwell: With Profiles of Elizabeth Garrett Anderson & Susan la Flesche Picotte. 2006. (Biographical Connections Ser.). (Illus.). 112p. (978-0-7166-1826-3(5)) World Bk., Inc.

Leavitt, Amie. Elizabeth Blackwell. 2007. (What's So Great About... ? Ser.). (J). lib. bdg. 25.70 (*978-1-58415-579-9(5)) Mitchell Lane Pubs., Inc.

Mader, Jan. Elizabeth Blackwell. 2007. (J). (978-0-7368-6704-7(X) , Pebble Bks.) Capstone Pr., Inc.

Robbins, Trina. Elizabeth Blackwell: America's First Woman Doctor. Martin, Cynthia & Timmons, Anne, illus. 2007. (Graphic Library). 32p. (J). 25.26 (978-0-7368-6497-8(0)); (*978-0-7368-9660-3(0)) Capstone Pr., Inc.

BLAKE, JENNA (FICTITIOUS CHARACTER)—FICTION

Golden, Christopher. Meets the Eye. 2000. (Body of Evidence Ser.: No. 4). 256p. (YA). (gr. 7 up). pap. 4.99 (978-0-671-03495-5(2) , Simon Pulse) Simon & Schuster Children's Publishing.

—Thief of Hearts. 1999. 245p. (YA). (gr. 8-12). per. 13.00 (978-0-613-73104-1(2)) Tandem Library Bks.

BLAKE, WILLIAM, 1757-1827

Bedard, Michael. William Blake: The Gates of Paradise. 2006. (Illus.). 200p. (J). (gr. 9). 19.95 (978-0-88776-763-0(X)) Tundra Bks., Inc./Livres Toundra, Inc. CAN. *Dist:* Random Hse., Inc.

BLIND

Brocker, Susan. Vision Without Sight: Human Capabilities. 2007. (Shockwave: Life Science & Medicine Ser.). (Illus.). 36p. (J). (gr. 4-6). lib. bdg. 25.00 (*978-0-531-17769-3(6) , Children's Pr.) Scholastic Library Publishing.

Clements, Andrew. Brave Norman: A True Story. 2002. (ps-2). lib. bdg. 11.80 (978-0-613-57568-3(7)) Tandem Library Bks.

Devillier, Christy. Helen Keller. 2004. (First Biographies Set Iv Ser.). (Illus.). 32p. (J). (gr. k-4). lib. bdg. 22.78 (978-1-59197-514-4(X)) ABDO Publishing Co.

Fetty, Margaret. Helen Keller: Break down the Walls! 2007. (Defining Moments Ser.). (Illus.). 32p. (J). lib. bdg. 25.27 (978-1-59716-271-5(X)) Bearport Publishing Co., Inc.

Jeffrey, Laura S. All about Braille: Reading by Touch. 2004. (Transportation & Communication Ser.). (Illus.). 48p. (J). lib. bdg. 23.93 (978-0-7660-2184-6(X)) Enslow Pubs., Inc.

Koestler-Grack, Rachel A. The Story of Helen Keller. 2003. (Breakthrough Biographies Ser.). (Illus.). 32p. (J). (gr. 3-5). 23.00 (978-0-7910-7315-5(7) , Chelsea Hse.) Facts On File, Inc.

Lakin, Patricia. Helen Keller & the Big Storm. Magnuson, Diana, illus. 2002. (Ready-to-Read Ser.: Level 2). 32p. (J). pap. 3.99 (978-0-689-84104-0(3) , Aladdin) Simon & Schuster Children's Publishing.

McLeese, Don. Helen Keller. 2002. (J). lib. bdg. 20.64 (978-1-58952-302-9(4)) Rourke Publishing, LLC.

Sabin, Francene. Helen Keller: Una Chica Valiente. abr. ed. 2007. 64p. (J). pap. 3.99 (*978-0-439-87999-6(X) , Scholastic en Espanol) Scholastic, Inc.

Schaefer, Lola M. Some Kids Are Blind. 2008. (J). (*978-1-4296-0810-7(2)) Capstone Pr., Inc.

—Some Kids Are Blind. Saunders-Smith, Gail, ed. 2001. (Understanding Differences Ser.). (Illus.). 24p. (J). (gr. k-1). lib. bdg. 15.93 (978-0-7368-0664-0(4) , Pebble Bks.) Capstone Pr., Inc.

Seeing Color It's My Rainbow Too: An Introduction to Color Vision Deficiency. 2003. (J). per. 11.95 (978-0-9743520-0-8(4)) CVD Publishing.

Some Kids Are Blind, 6 vols. (gr. k-2). 28.95 (978-0-7368-8816-5(0)) Red Brick Learning.

Souder, Patti. A Different Way of Seeing: Youth with Blindness & Vision Impairment. 2004. (Youth with Special Needs Ser.). (Illus.). 128p. (J). (978-1-59084-733-6(4)) Mason Crest Pubs.

Sutcliffe, Jane. Helen Keller. Verstraete, Elaine, illus. 2002. (On My Own Biographies Ser.). 48p. (J). lib. bdg. 23.93 (978-0-87614-600-2(0) , Carolrhoda Bks.) Lerner Publishing Group.

—Helen Keller. 2002. (gr. 3-6). lib. bdg. 14.10 (978-0-613-52398-1(9)) Tandem Library Bks.

Westcott, Patsy. Living with Blindness. 1999. (Living with... Ser.). (Illus.). 32p. (J). (gr. 1-5). lib. bdg. 25.69 (978-0-8172-5741-5(1)) Raintree.

White, Peter. Being Blind. 1999. (Think about Ser.). (Illus.). 32p. (J). (gr. 2-5). lib. bdg. 16.95 (978-1-887068-84-0(8)) Smart Apple Media.

Woodhouse, Jayne. Helen Keller. 2002. (Lives & Times Ser.). (Illus.). 24p. (J). (gr. k-3). pap. 6.50 (978-1-4034-0030-7(X) , 91474) Heinemann Library.

—Helen Keller. 2002. (gr. k-3). lib. bdg. 12.95 (978-0-613-88095-4(1)) Tandem Library Bks.

BLIND—BIOGRAPHY

Adler, David A. Helen Keller. Wallner, John, illus. 32p. (J). 4.95 (978-0-8234-2042-1(6)) Holiday Hse., Inc.

Beyer, Mark. Ray Charles. 2006. (Rock & Roll Hall of Famers Ser.). (Illus.). 112p. (YA). (gr. 5-8). lib. bdg. 29.25 (978-0-8239-3642-7(2)) Rosen Publishing Group, Inc., The.

—Stevie Wonder. 2006. (Rock & Roll Hall of Famers Ser.). (Illus.). 112p. (YA). (gr. 5-8). lib. bdg. 29.25 (978-0-8239-3525-3(6)) Rosen Publishing Group, Inc., The.

Davidson, Margaret. Louis Braille. (FRE.). (J). pap. 5.99 (978-0-590-71110-4(5)) Scholastic, Inc.

Hall, Becky. Morris & Buddy: The Story of the First Seeing Eye Dog. Doris, Ettlinger, illus. 2007. 40p. (J). 15.95 (*978-0-8075-5284-1(4)) Whitman, Albert & Co.

Harrah, Madge. Blind Boone: Piano Prodigy. 2004. (Trailblazers Biographies Ser.). (Illus.). 112p. (J). (gr. 5-9). lib. bdg. 30.60 (978-1-57505-057-7(9)) Lerner Publishing Group.

Lawlor, Laurie. Helen Keller, Rebellious Spirit: The Life & Times of Helen Keller. 2001. (Illus.). 176p. (J). (gr. 4-6). tchr. ed. 22.95 (978-0-8234-1588-5(0)) Holiday Hse., Inc.

Lynch, Emma. Helen Keller. 2005. (Lives & Times Ser.). 32p. (J). (Illus.). (gr. 2-4). lib. bdg. 24.21 (978-1-4034-6350-0(6)); pap. (978-1-4034-6364-7(6)) Heinemann Library.

Malokas, Ann. Zak & Lizzie. Nicholas, Corasue, illus. 2001. 32p. (J). (gr. k-8). 7.99 (978-0-9708415-1-3(5)) Guilty Mom Pr.

Marsh, Carole. Helen Keller. 2002. (One Thousand Readers Ser.). (Illus.). 12p. (J). (gr. k-4). 2.95 (978-0-635-01478-8(5) , 14785) Gallopade International.

Sloate, Susan. Ray Charles: Young Musician. Henderson, Meryl, illus. 2007. (Childhood of Famous Americans Ser.). 176p. (J). pap. 5.99 (978-1-4169-1437-2(4) , Aladdin) Simon & Schuster Children's Publishing.

BLIND, DOGS FOR THE

see Guide Dogs

BLIND—EDUCATION

Cunningham, Ann Elizabeth. Sadie Can Count: A Multi-sensory Book. Cunningham, Ann Elizabeth, illus. l.t. ed. 2006. (Illus.). 16p. (J). bds. 29.95 (978-0-9770054-8-2(8)) Sensational Bks.

Souder, Patti. A Different Way of Seeing: Youth with Blindness & Vision Impairment. 2004. (Youth with Special Needs Ser.). (Illus.). 128p. (J). (978-1-59084-733-6(4)) Mason Crest Pubs.

BLIND—FICTION

Anderson, Laurie Halse. Teacher's Pet. 2003. (Wild at Heart Ser.). (Illus.). 132p. (J). (gr. 4 up). lib. bdg. 23.33 (978-0-8368-3261-7(2)) Stevens, Gareth Inc.

—Teacher's Pet. 2001. (American Girl Wild at Heart Ser.: Bk. 7). (Illus.). (YA). (978-0-606-21529-9(8)) Tandem Library Bks.

Arterburn, Stephen & Hunt, Angela Elwell. Paige. 2004. (Young Believer on Tour Ser.). (J). pap. 3.99 (978-0-8423-8338-7(7)) Tyndale Hse. Pubs.

Bauer, Marion Dane. The Double-Digit Club. 2004. 126p. (J). (gr. 4-6). tchr. ed. 15.95 (978-0-8234-1805-3(7)) Holiday Hse., Inc.

Bellingham, Brenda. Lilly Makes a Friend. MacDonald, Clarke, illus. 2004. 62p. (J). lib. bdg. 12.00 (*978-1-4242-1221-7(9)) Fitzgerald Bks.

Bevins, Rose. Coming to Terms. 2004. (Cover-To-Cover Books). (Illus.). (J). 64p. pap. (978-0-7891-6018-8(8)); 56p. (gr. 1-4). lib. bdg. 16.95 (978-0-7569-1371-7(3)) Perfection Learning Corp.

The Blind Alley. 2001. 32p. (YA). (gr. 6-12). pap. (978-0-8224-1453-7(8)) Globe Fearon Educational Publishing.

Bolme, Edward Sarah. Jesus Helps a Blind Man. Gillette, Tim, illus. l.t. ed. 2003. 20p. (J). bds. 6.99 (978-0-9725546-2-6(9)) CREST Pubns.

Clements, Andrew. Things Not Seen. (J). 2002. 176p. (gr. 6-9). 15.99 (978-0-399-23626-6(0) , Philomel); 2004. 251p. reprint ed. pap. 6.99 (978-0-14-240076-0(9) , Puffin) Penguin Group (USA) Inc.

—Things Not Seen. 2004. 256p. (J). (gr. 4-7). pap. 38.00 incl. audio (978-1-4000-9014-3(8) , Listening Library) Random Hse. Audio Publishing Group.

Coates, Jan. Rainbows in the Dark. Priestly, Alice, illus. 2005. 24p. (J). 11.95 (978-1-896764-95-5(9)) Second Story Pr. CAN. *Dist:* Orca Bk. Pubs. USA.

Cole, Barbara. Anna & Natalie. Himler, Ronald, illus. 2007. 32p. (J). 16.95 (*978-1-59572-105-1(3)) Star Bright Bks., Inc.

Condra, Estelle. See the Ocean. Crockett-Blassingame, Linda, illus. 2002. 32p. (gr. k-3). 9.95 (978-1-59093-067-0(3)) Warehousing & Fulfillment Specialists, LLC (WFS, LLC).

Creech, Sharon. Granny Torrelli Makes Soup. Raschka, Chris, illus. 160p. (J). 2003. (gr. 3-6). 15.99 (978-0-06-029290-4(3) , HarperChildren's Audio); 2003. (gr. 4-7). lib. bdg. 16.89 (978-0-06-029291-1(1) , Cotler, Joanna Books); 2005. reprint ed. pap. 5.99 (978-0-06-440960-5(0) , Harper Trophy) HarperCollins Pubs.

Creel, Ann Howard. Water at the Blue Earth. 1998. (Illus.). 148p. (gr. 5-9). pap. 8.95 (978-1-57098-224-8(4)) Rinehart, Roberts Pubs.

Crew, Gary. The Kraken. McBride, Marc, illus. 2002. 32p. (YA). (978-0-7344-0182-3(5) , Lothian Bks.) Hachette Livre Australia.

Crockett-Blassingame, Linda, illus. See the Ocean. 2006. 32p. (J). 14.95 (978-0-9778143-0-5(0)) Inclusive Books LLC.

Crosiar, Sally J. My Uncle Dave. Williams, Ted, illus. 2002. 27p. 9.35 (978-1-930289-01-7(4)) Healthy People Pr.

Denenberg, Barry. Mirror Mirror on the Wall: The Diary of Bess Brennan. 2002. (Dear America Ser.). (Illus.). 144p. (J). (gr. 4-9). pap. 10.95 (978-0-439-19446-4(6)) Scholastic, Inc.

Dorris, Michael. Sees Behind Trees. rev. ed. 1999. 128p. (gr. 4-17). pap. 4.99 (978-0-7868-1357-5(1)) Disney Pr.

—Sees Behind Trees. 104p. (J). (gr. 4-6). pap. 4.95 (978-0-8072-1516-6(3)); 1998. pap. 28.00 incl. audio (978-0-8072-7957-1(9) , YA949SP) Random Hse. Audio Publishing Group. (Listening Library).

Eyerly, Jeannette. The Seeing Summer. Ishiwata, Make, illus. 1999. 153p. (YA). (gr. 3 up). pap. 10.00 (978-1-885218-15-5(X)) National Federation of the Blind.

Fraustino, Lisa Rowe & Andrews, Benny, illus. Blind Sight. 2000. (J). 10.01 (978-0-590-52252-6(3)) Scholastic, Inc.

Freed, Shirley Ann & Moon, Louise. Blind, Blind Bart. Morelan, Bill, ed. Butler, Steven, illus. l.t. ed. 2002. 8p. (J). (gr. 3-4). pap. 3.99 (978-1-58938-020-2(7)) Concerned Communications.

Gantos, Jack. What Would Joey Do? 2002. (Joey Pigza Ser.). 240p. (J). (gr. 5-9). 16.00 (978-0-374-39986-3(7) , Farrar, Straus & Giroux (BYR)) Farrar, Straus & Giroux.

—What Would Joey Do? 2004. 240p. (J). (gr. 5 up). reprint ed. pap. 5.99 (978-0-06-054403-4(1) , Harper Trophy) HarperCollins Pubs.

—What Would Joey Do? l.t. ed. 2003. (Juvenile Ser.). 264p. (J). 22.95 (978-0-7862-5468-2(8)) Thorndike Pr.

—What Would Joey Do? A Dazzling Conclusion to the Joey Pigza Trilogy! 2004. 240p. (J). (gr. 5-9). pap. 36.00 incl. audio (978-1-4000-9020-4(2) , Listening Library) Random Hse. Audio Publishing Group.

Gutman, Dan. The Million Dollar Putt. 2006. 176p. (gr. 3-7). 15.99 (978-0-7868-3641-3(5)) Hyperion Bks. for Children.

Gutman, Dan. Million Dollar Putt. 2007. 176p. (gr. 3-7). pap. 5.99 (*978-0-7868-3642-0(3)) Hyperion Pr.

Hubler, Marsha. The Winning Summer. 2005. (Keystone Stables Ser.: Bk. 5). (Illus.). 144p. (J). pap. 4.99 (978-0-310-70798-1(6)) Zonderkidz.

Ingold, Jeanette. Window. 2003. (gr. 7-12). lib. bdg. 8.10 (978-0-613-70529-5(7)) Tandem Library Bks.

Karim, Roberta. Mandy Sue Day. Ritz, Karen, illus. 2003. 32p. (J). 5.95 (978-0-618-31675-5(2) , Clarion Bks.) Houghton Mifflin Co. Trade & Reference Div.

Keats, Ezra Jack. Apt. 3. Keats, Ezra Jack, illus. 1999. (Illus.). 32p. (J). (ps-3). 15.99 (978-0-670-88342-4(5) , Viking Juvenile) Penguin Group (USA) Inc.

—Apt. 3. 1999. (J). 13.79 (978-0-606-16772-7(2)) Tandem Library Bks.

Kent, Deborah. Belonging. 2000. (gr. 7-12). lib. bdg. 24.55 (978-0-613-84549-6(8)) Tandem Library Bks.

Kent, Deoborah. Belonging. 2001. 210p. (YA). pap. 14.95 (978-0-595-19395-0(1) , People with Disabilities Pr.) iUniverse, Inc.

Kimmel, Elizabeth Cody. Mary Leaves Little House. 2008. (Little House Ser.). 192p. (J). lib. bdg. 16.89 (*978-0-06-000906-9(3)); (gr. 3-7). 15.99 (*978-0-06-000905-2(5)) HarperCollins Pubs.

Kinsey-Warnock, Natalie. Lumber Camp Library. Bernardin, James, illus. 2003. 96p. (J). pap. 4.99 (978-0-06-444292-3(6)) HarperCollins Pubs.

—Lumber Camp Library. 2002. (gr. 3-6). lib. bdg. 13.00 (978-0-613-68447-7(8)) Tandem Library Bks.

Lang, Glenna. Looking Out for Sarah. 2003. 32p. (J). (gr. 4-7). pap. 6.95 (978-1-57091-607-6(1)) Charlesbridge Publishing, Inc.

—Looking Out for Sarah. Lang, Glenna, illus. 2001. (Illus.). 32p. (J). (ps-3). 15.95 (978-0-88106-647-0(8)) Charlesbridge Publishing, Inc.

—Looking Out for Sarah. 2003. (gr. k-3). lib. bdg. 15.25 (978-0-613-88753-3(0)) Tandem Library Bks.

Lawton, Wendy. The Tinker's Daughter: A Story Based on the Life of Mary Bunyan. 2002. (Daughters of the Faith Ser.). 144p. (YA). pap. 6.99 (978-0-8024-4099-0(1)) Moody Pubs.

Liao, Jimmy. The Sound of Colors: A Journey of the Imagination. 2006. (Illus.). 80p. (J). (ps-17). 16.99 (978-0-316-93992-8(7)) Little Brown & Co.

Madden, Kerry. Gentle's Holler. 2007. 272p. (YA). (gr. 4 up). 6.99 (978-0-14-240751-6(8) , Puffin) Penguin Group (USA) Inc.

Marshall, Catherine. Midnight Rescue/the Proposal/Christy's Choice. 2005. (Christy Juvenile Ser.). 384p. (J). pap. 9.99 (978-1-4003-0773-9(2)) Nelson, Thomas Inc.

McElfresh, Lynn E. Can You Feel the Thunder? 1999. (YA). pap., stu. ed. 52.00 incl. audio (978-0-7887-3837-1(2) , 41031) Recorded Bks., LLC.

McMurtry, Robby, tr. Song of Moon Pony. 2003. (Illus.). 17.95 (978-1-57168-740-1(8)) Eakin Pr.

McNicoll, Sylvia. Beauty Returns. 2006. 208p. (J). 17.95 (978-1-55005-149-0(0)) Fitzhenry & Whiteside, Ltd. CAN. *Dist:* F & W Pubns., Inc.

Miller, Sarah Elizabeth. Miss Spitfire: Reaching Helen Keller. 2007. 240p. (J). (gr. 5-9). 16.99 (978-1-4169-2542-2(2)) Simon & Schuster Children's Publishing.

O'Donnell, Liam. Ginger Leads Way. Diefendorf, Cathy, illus. 2005. (Pet Tales Ser.). 32p. (J). (ps-2). 9.95 (978-1-59249-360-9(2) , 1B025); 2.95 (978-1-59249-359-3(9) , 1B024); 4.95 incl. cd-rom (978-1-59249-358-6(0) , 1B023) Soundprints.

Petrillo, Genevieve & Lyon, Lea. Keep Your Ear on the Ball. 2007. (Illus.). 32p. (J). (gr. 3-7). 16.95 (*978-0-88448-296-3(0)) Tilbury Hse. Pubs.

Pitts, Constance. Chulita the Blind Cat. 2007. (Illus.). 48p. (J). (*978-0-9652902-2-7(0)) Beevinwood, Inc.

Purkapile, Sue. Otto the Blind Otter. Ducommun, Barbara, illus. 2004. (J). 13.95 (978-1-930596-27-6(8)) Amherst Pr.

Rodanas, Kristina. The Blind Hunter. 2003. (Illus.). 32p. (J). 16.95 (978-0-7614-5132-7(3)) Cavendish, Marshall Corp.

Rosensweig, Jay B. & Repka, Janice. The Stupendous Dodgeball Fiasco. Dibley, Glin, illus. 2004. 192p. (J). (gr. 3). 16.99 (978-0-525-47346-6(7) , Dutton Juvenile) Penguin Group (USA) Inc.

Sappey, Maureen S. Dreams of Ships, Dreams of Julia: At Sea with the Monitor & the Merrimack-Virginia, 1862. 1998. (Young American Ser.: Vol. 2). (Illus.). 140p. (YA). (gr. 4-7). 5.99 (978-1-57249-134-2(5)) White Mane Publishing Co., Inc.

Scrimger, Richard. From Charlie's Point of View. 2007. 288p. (YA). (gr. 3). pap. 6.99 (978-0-14-240818-6(2) , Puffin) Penguin Group (USA) Inc.

Siete Ratones Ciegos. 1999. (SPA.). (J). mass mkt. 4.95 (978-0-590-48525-8(3) , SO5874) Scholastic, Inc.

St. John, Patricia. Star of Light. 2002. (Illus.). 160p. (YA). pap. 6.99 (978-0-8024-6577-1(3)) Moody Pubs.

Stahler, David, Jr. Truesight. (Illus.). (J). (gr. 7 up). 2005. 256p. pap. 6.99 (978-0-06-052287-2(9)); Vol. 1. 2004. 192p. 16.99 (978-0-06-052285-8(2)); Vol. 1. 2004. 192p. lib. bdg. 16.89 (978-0-06-052286-5(0)) HarperCollins Pubs.

Stockstill, Gloria McQueen. The Blind Man by the Road. Girouard, Patricia L., illus. 2003. (ENG.). 20p. (J). bds. 4.99 (978-0-7586-0144-5(1)) Concordia Publishing Hse.

Taylor, Theodore. Timothy of the Cay. 2007. (Illus.). 176p. (YA). pap. 5.95 (978-0-15-206320-7(X) , Harcourt Paperbacks) Harcourt Children's Bks.

Townley, Roderick. Sky. 2004. (Illus.). 272p. (J). 16.95 (978-0-689-85712-6(8) , Atheneum/Richard Jackson Bks.) Simon & Schuster Children's Publishing.

White, Lee A. What Is Pretty? 1998. 20p. (J). pap. 7.95 (978-1-889745-02-2(2)) Triangle Pubns.

BLIND—REHABILITATION

see Blind—Education

BLOOD

Ganeri, Anita. Your Blood. Shott, Steve, photos by. 2003. (How Your Body Works). (Illus.). 32p. (J). (gr. 2 up). lib. bdg. 23.33 (978-0-8368-3631-8(6)) Stevens, Gareth Inc.

Green, Jen. Blood & Heart. 2005. (Illus.). 32p. (J). (gr. 3-7). lib. bdg. 27.10 (978-1-59604-051-9(3)) Stargazer Bks.

Jakab, Cheryl. The Circulatory System. 2006. (Illus.). 32p. (J). (978-1-58340-733-2(2)) Smart Apple Media.

Johnson, Rebecca L. Respiration & Circulation. 2004. (National Geographic Reading Expeditions Ser.). (Illus.). 32p. (J). pap. (978-0-7922-4586-5(5)) National Geographic Society.

Llamas, Andreu. Respiration & Circulation. Rizo, Luis, illus. 1998. (Human Body Ser.). 32p. (J). (gr. 5 up). lib. bdg. 24.67 (978-0-8368-2110-9(6)) Stevens, Gareth Inc.

Ring, Susan. Blood. 2003. (Science Links Ser.). (Illus.). 32p. (gr. 3-5). 23.00 (978-0-7910-7418-3(8) , Chelsea Hse.) Facts On File, Inc.

Rollins, Barbara B. & Dahl, Michael. A Bloody Trail: Analyzing Blood. 2004. (Forensic Crime Solvers Ser.). (Illus.). 32p. (J). 22.60 (978-0-7368-2418-7(9)) Capstone Pr., Inc.

Romanek, Trudee. Squirt! The Most Interesting Book You'll Ever Read about Blood & the Heart. Cowles, Rose, illus. 2006. 40p. 7.95 (978-1-55337-777-1(X)) Kids Can Pr., Ltd. CAN. *Dist:* Wybel Marketing Group.

Royston, Angela. Why Do Bruises Change Color? And Other Questions about Blood. 2003. (Body Matters Ser.). (Illus.). 32p. (J). (gr. 3-5). lib. bdg. 24.22 (978-1-4034-0202-8(7)); pap. 7.50 (978-1-4034-0457-2(7)) Heinemann Library.

Showers, Paul. A Drop of Blood. Miller, Edward, illus. 2004. (Let's-Read-and-Find-Out Science Ser.). 32p. (J). (gr. k-4). 15.99 (978-0-06-009108-8(8)); pap. 5.99 (978-0-06-009110-1(X) , Harper Trophy); lib. bdg. 16.89 (978-0-06-009109-5(6)) HarperCollins Pubs.

Winner, Cherie. Circulating Life: Blood Transfusion from Ancient Superstition to Modern Medicine. 2007. (Discovery! Ser.). (Illus.). 112p. (J). (gr. 6-12). 29.27 (*978-0-8225-6606-9(0) , Twenty-First Century Bks.) Lerner Publishing Group.

BLOOD—CIRCULATION

Angliss, Sarah. The Power Pack: Cardiovascular System. 1999. 32p. (J). lib. bdg. 16.95 (978-1-929298-19-8(6)) Chrysalis Education.

Ballard, Carol. The Heart & Blood. 2002. (Body Focus Ser.). (Illus.). 48p. (J). pap. (978-1-4034-0452-7(6)) Heinemann Library.

The Circulatory System. (Human Body Systems Ser.). 24p. (J). 5.95 (978-0-7368-8776-2(8)) Capstone Pr., Inc.

Donavan, Barbar A. Body Systems: Respiratory & Circulatory. 2005. (Navigators Ser.). (J). pap. 42.00 (*978-1-4108-5084-3(6)) Benchmark Education Co.

Elford, Jole Shack. William Harvey & the Mechanics of the Heart. 2005. (Illus.). 141p. (YA). (gr. 6-10). reprint ed. 28.00 (978-0-7567-9712-6(8)) DIANE Publishing Co.

Frost, Helen. The Circulatory System. Saunders-Smith, Gail, ed. 2000. (Human Body Systems Ser.). (Illus.). 24p. (J). (gr. k-1). lib. bdg. 15.93 (978-0-7368-0648-0(2) , Pebble Bks.) Capstone Pr., Inc.

Gold, John C. The Circulatory & Lymphatic Systems. 2004. (Human Body Library Ser.). (Illus.). 48p. (J). lib. bdg. 23.93 (978-0-7660-2019-1(3)) Enslow Pubs., Inc.

Gray, Susan Heinrichs. The Circulatory System. 2003. (Body Systems Ser.). (Illus.). 32p. (J). (gr. 2-6). 27.07 (978-1-59296-036-1(7)) Child's World, Inc.

Green, Jen. Blood & Heart. 2005. (Illus.). 32p. (J). (gr. 3-7). lib. bdg. 27.10 (978-1-59604-051-9(3)) Stargazer Bks.

Holt, Rinehart and Winston Staff. Holt Science & Technology Chapter 23: Life Science: Circulation & Respiration. 5th ed. 2004. (Illus.). pap. 12.86 (978-0-03-030239-8(0)) Holt, Rinehart & Winston.

Libra, Anna. How Do My Cuts Heal? An Inside Look at the Circulatory System. 2003. (J). (978-1-58417-003-7(4)); pap. (978-1-58417-066-2(2)) Lake Street Pubs.

Llamas, Andreu. Respiration & Circulation. Rizo, Luis, illus. 1998. (Human Body Ser.). 32p. (J). (gr. 5 up). lib. bdg. 24.67 (978-0-8368-2110-9(6)) Stevens, Gareth Inc.

Oleksy, Walter. The Circulatory System. 2001. (Insider's Guide to the Body Ser.). (Illus.). 48p. (YA). (gr. 5-8). lib. bdg. 23.95 (978-0-8239-3336-5(9) , Rosen Central) Rosen Publishing Group, Inc., The.

Parker, Steve. Heart, Lungs, & Blood. 2004. (Our Bodies Ser.). (Illus.). 48p. (J). lib. bdg. 28.56 (978-0-7398-6621-4(4)) Raintree.

—Pump It Up! Respiration & Circulation. 2006. (Illus.). 48p. (J). (978-1-4109-1878-9(5)); pap. (978-1-4109-1885-7(8)) Steck-Vaughn.

Royston, Angela. Why Do Bruises Change Color? And Other Questions about Blood. 2003. (Body Matters Ser.). (Illus.). 32p. (J). pap. 7.50 (978-1-4034-0457-2(7)) Heinemann Library.

Simon, Seymour. The Heart: Our Circulatory System. 1999. (Illus.). (J). (ps-3). pap. 6.99 (978-0-688-17059-2(5) , Harper Trophy) HarperCollins Pubs.

Stille, Darlene R. The Circulatory System. 1998. (True Bks.). (Illus.). 48p. (J). (gr. 3-5). pap. 6.95 (978-0-516-26261-1(0) , Children's Pr.) Scholastic Library Publishing.

Storad, Conrad J. Circulatory System. 2005. (Illus.). 48p. (YA). pap. (978-0-8225-2518-9(6) , Lerner Pubns.) Lerner Publishing Group.

Viegas, Jennifer. The Heart: Learning How Our Blood Circulates. 2002. (3-D Library of the Human Body). (Illus.). 48p. (YA). (gr. 5-8). lib. bdg. 26.50 (978-0-8239-3532-1(9) , Rosen Central) Rosen Publishing Group, Inc., The.

Vv. Como Circula la Sangre. (SPA.). 76p. (J). 10.00 (978-84-342-1467-5(9)) Parramon Ediciones S.A. ESP. *Dist:* Distribuidora Norma, Inc.

Walker, Richard. The Heart in Action. 2004. (Body Science Ser.). (J). lib. bdg. 27.10 (978-1-58340-457-7(0)) Smart Apple Media.

Whittemore, Susan. The Circulatory System. 2003. (Your Body, How It Works). (Illus.). 112p. (gr. 9-13). 31.95 (978-0-7910-7626-2(1) , Chelsea Hse.) Facts On File, Inc.

Yount, Lisa. William Harvey: Discoverer of How Blood Circulates. 2008. (Great Minds of Science Ser.). 128p. (J). (gr. 5 up). lib. bdg. 31.93 (*978-0-7660-3010-7(5)) Enslow Pubs., Inc.

BLOOD—CIRCULATION—FICTION

Ashworth, Caspian. The Odyssey: The Pulsating Voyage & Adventures of a White Blood Cell. Ashworth, Neil, illus. 2001. 120p. (YA). (gr. 2 up). 23.50 (978-1-85776-670-7(9)) Book Guild, Ltd. GBR. *Dist:* Trans-Atlantic Pubns., Inc.

BLOOD—DISEASES

Ross, Allison J. Everything You Need to Know about Anemia. 2005. (Need to Know Library). (Illus.). 64p. (YA). (gr. 7-12). 25.25 (978-0-8239-3218-4(4) , NTANEM) Rosen Publishing Group, Inc., The.

Silverstein, Alvin, et al. The Sickle Cell Anemia Update. 2006. (Disease Update Ser.). (Illus.). 112p. (J). (gr. 5 up). lib. bdg. 31.93 (978-0-7660-2479-3(2)) Enslow Pubs., Inc.

BLUE (FICTITIOUS CHARACTER)—FICTION

Albee, Sarah. Blue's Checkup. Chernichaw, Ian, illus. 2003. (Blue's Clues Ser.). 24p. (J). pap. 3.99 (978-0-689-85449-1(8) , Simon Spotlight/Nickelodeon) Simon & Schuster Children's Publishing.

—One for Me, One for You: A Book about Sharing. Craig, Karen, illus. 2006. (Blue's Clues Ser.). 24p. (J). pap. 3.99 (978-1-4169-1300-9(9) , Simon Spotlight/Nickelodeon) Simon & Schuster Children's Publishing.

Blue's Clues Box Set. 1999. (Blue's Clues Ser.). (J). (ps-k). 19.96 (978-0-689-83312-0(1) , Simon Spotlight) Simon & Schuster Children's Publishing.

Blue's Treasury of Stories. 2003. (Illus.). (J). 15.25 (978-0-689-85883-3(3) , Simon Spotlight/Nickelodeon) Simon & Schuster Children's Publishing.

Bumpy Slide Books Staff. Blue Makes Breakfast. Nickelodeon/Viacom International Staff, ed. 2000. (Blue's Clues: No. 4). (Illus.). 32p. (J). (ps-1). 3.49 (978-1-57973-070-3(1)) Advance Pubs. LLC.

—Blue's Art Day. Nickelodeon/Viacom International Staff, ed. 2000. (Blue's Clues: No. 13). (Illus.). 32p. (J). (ps-1). 3.49 (978-1-57973-079-6(5)) Advance Pubs. LLC.

—Blue's Bedtime. Nickelodeon/Viacom International Staff, ed. 2000. (Blue's Clues: No. 10). (Illus.). 32p. (J). (ps-1). 3.49 (978-1-57973-076-5(0)) Advance Pubs. LLC.

—Blue's Cool Idea. Nickelodeon/Viacom International Staff, ed. 2000. (Blue's Clues: No. 1). (Illus.). 32p. (J). (ps-1). 3.49 (978-1-57973-067-3(1)) Advance Pubs. LLC.

—Blue's Garden. Nickelodeon/Viacom International Staff, ed. 2000. (Blue's Clues: No. 6). (Illus.). 32p. (J). (ps-1). 3.49 (978-1-57973-072-7(8)) Advance Pubs. LLC.

—Blue's Rainy Day Music. Nickelodeon/Viacom International Staff, ed. 2000. (Blue's Clues: No. 2). (Illus.). 32p. (J). (ps-1). 3.49 (978-1-57973-068-0(X)) Advance Pubs. LLC.

—Blue's Windy Day. Nickelodeon/Viacom International Staff, ed. 2000. (Blue's Clues: No. 9). (Illus.). 32p. (J). (ps-1). 3.49 (978-1-57973-075-8(2)) Advance Pubs. LLC.

—Something to Say. Nickelodeon/Viacom International Staff, ed. 2000. (Blue's Clues: No. 8). (Illus.). 32p. (J). (ps-1). 3.49 (978-1-57973-074-1(4)) Advance Pubs. LLC.

—Things That Fly. Nickelodeon/Viacom International Staff, ed. 2000. (Blue's Clues: No. 7). (Illus.). 32p. (J). (ps-1). 3.49 (978-1-57973-073-4(6)) Advance Pubs. LLC.

Fry, Sonali. Blue Makes a Kite! Miller, Victoria A., illus. 2005. (Blue's Clues Ser.). 14p. (J). 5.99 (978-0-689-87168-9(6) , Simon Spotlight/Nickelodeon) Simon & Schuster Children's Publishing.

—Blue's Colors: A Book & Blocks Play Set. Style Guide Staff, illus. 2003. (Baby Blue's Clues Ser.). 14p. (J). bds. 7.99 (978-0-689-85502-3(8) , Simon Spotlight/Nickelodeon) Simon & Schuster Children's Publishing.

Golden Books Staff & Newton, Astora. Blue's Friendship Day/What's Blue Building? Levy, David, illus. 2003. 64p. (J). (ps-2). pap. 2.99 (978-0-307-10122-8(3) , Golden Bks.) Random Hse. Children's Bks.

Inches, Alison. Blue Talks! Style Guide Staff, illus. 2004. (Blue's Clues Ser.). 12p. (J). bds. 8.99 (978-0-689-86459-9(0) , Simon Spotlight/Nickelodeon) Simon & Schuster Children's Publishing.

—Hooray for Polka Dots! Chernichaw, Ian, illus. ed. 2005. 22p. (J). lib. bdg. 15.00 (978-1-59054-972-8(4)) Fitzgerald Bks.

—Spring Is Here! Chernichaw, Ian, illus. 2006. (Blue's Clues Ser.). 16p. (J). pap. 5.99 (978-1-4169-0920-0(6) , Simon Spotlight/Nickelodeon) Simon & Schuster Children's Publishing.

Landy, Sarah. Blue's Snack Party. Cardinali, Kevin, illus. 2000. (Blue's Clues Ser.). 16p. (J). (ps-k). 5.99 (978-0-689-83432-5(2) , Simon Spotlight/Nickelodeon) Simon & Schuster Children's Publishing.

Lissy, Jessica. A Blue's Clues Chanukah. Kanemoto, Dan & Oxley, Jennifer, illus. 2003. (Blue's Clues Ser.). 24p. (J). (ps-2). pap. 3.99 (978-0-689-85840-6(X) , Simon Spotlight/Nickelodeon) Simon & Schuster Children's Publishing.

Miglis, Jenny. Blue's Baby Animals. Style Guide Staff, illus. 2003. (Blue's Clues Ser.). 14p. (J). bds. 4.99 (978-0-689-85231-2(2) , Simon Spotlight/Nickelodeon) Simon & Schuster Children's Publishing.

—Faces. Pontillo, Jenine, illus. Barrett, John E., photos by. 2002. (Blue's Clues Ser.). 12p. (J). bds. 5.99 (978-0-689-84842-1(0) , Simon Spotlight/Nickelodeon) Simon & Schuster Children's Publishing.

—Feelings: A Baby & Blue Book. Pontillo, Jenine, illus. Barrett, John E., photos by. 2002. (Blue's Clues Ser.). 12p. (J). bds. 5.99 (978-0-689-84843-8(9) , Simon Spotlight/Nickelodeon) Simon & Schuster Children's Publishing.

Reber, Deborah. Blue's Egg Hunt. Norden, Carolyn, illus. 2001. (Blue's Clues Ser.). 24p. (J). (ps-k). pap. 3.50 (978-0-689-83873-6(5) , Simon Spotlight/Nickelodeon) Simon & Schuster Children's Publishing.

—Blue's Egg Hunt. 2001. (gr. k-3). lib. bdg. 11.25 (978-0-613-31009-3(8)) Tandem Library Bks.

—Blue's Valentines Day. Pontillo, Jenine, illus. 2000. (Blue's Clues Ser.). 16p. (J). (ps-k). pap. 3.99 (978-0-689-83062-4(9) , Simon Spotlight/Nickelodeon) Simon & Schuster Children's Publishing.

—Guess Who Loves Blue! 2002. (Blue's Clues Ser.). (Illus.). 14p. (J). bds. 4.99 (978-0-689-84870-4(6) , Simon Spotlight/Nickelodeon) Simon & Schuster Children's Publishing.

—Magenta & Me. Bishop, Don, illus. 2000. (Blues Clue's Ready to Read Ser.: No. 2). 24p. (J). (ps-1). pap. 3.99 (978-0-689-83123-2(4) , Simon Spotlight/Nickelodeon) Simon & Schuster Children's Publishing.

—Magenta & Me. 2000. (gr. k-3). lib. bdg. 11.80 (978-0-613-26094-7(5)) Tandem Library Bks.

—Magenta Gets Glasses! Dugas, Troy, illus. 2002. (Blue's Clues Ser.: Vol. 10). 24p. (J). pap. 3.50 (978-0-689-84745-5(9) , Simon Spotlight/Nickelodeon) Simon & Schuster Children's Publishing.

—Magenta Gets Glasses! 2002. (gr. k-3). lib. bdg. 11.25 (978-0-613-51314-2(2)) Tandem Library Bks.

Santomero, Angela C. Blue Is My Name! My First Preschool Ready to Read, Level 1. Craig, Karen, illus. 2000. (Blues Clue's Ready to Read Ser.: No. 1). 24p. (J). (ps-1). pap. 3.99 (978-0-689-83122-5(6) , Simon Spotlight/Nickelodeon) Simon & Schuster Children's Publishing.

—Blue Skidoos to the Farm A Storybook with 63 Stickers. Speer-Lyon, Tammie, illus. 1998. (Blue's Clues Ser.). 24p. (J). (ps-k). pap. 3.99 (978-0-689-81698-7(7) , Simon Spotlight/Nickelodeon) Simon & Schuster Children's Publishing.

—Blue y tu, Detective de Formas! Craig, Karen, illus. 2004. (Blue's Clues Ser.). (SPA.). 14p. (J). bds. 5.99 (978-0-689-87323-2(9) , Libros Para Ninos) Simon & Schuster Children's Publishing.

—Blue's Big Birthday. Johnson, Traci Paige & Kim, Soo Kyung, illus. (Blue's Clues Ser.). 24p. (J). (ps-1). 2002. pap. 3.50 (978-0-689-85103-2(0)); 1998. 9.99 (978-0-689-82151-6(4)) Simon & Schuster Children's Publishing. (Simon Spotlight/Nickelodeon).

—Blue's Big Treasure Hunt. Johnson, Traci Paige & Kim, Soo Kyung, illus. 1999. (Blue's Clues Ser.). 24p. (J). (ps-k). 5.99 (978-0-689-82540-8(4) , Simon Spotlight/ Nickelodeon) Simon & Schuster Children's Publishing.

—Blue's Big Treasure Hunt. 1999. (gr. k-3). lib. bdg. 14.15 (978-0-613-63255-3(9)) Tandem Library Bks.

—A Blue's Clues Holiday. 2004. (Blue's Clues Ser.). 24p. (J). pap. 3.99 (978-0-689-86797-2(2) , Simon Spotlight/ Nickelodeon) Simon & Schuster Children's Publishing.

—Crayon World. Johnson, Traci Paige & Kim, Soo Kyung, illus. 1999. (Blue's Clues Ser.). 6p. (J). (ps-k). bds. 4.99 (978-0-689-82448-7(3) , Simon Spotlight/Nickelodeon) Simon & Schuster Children's Publishing.

—Good Night Blue. Pontillo, Jenine, illus. 1999. (Blue's Clues Ser.). 10p. (J). (ps-k). bds. 4.99 (978-0-689-82950-5(7) , Simon Spotlight/Nickelodeon) Simon & Schuster Children's Publishing.

—Lights On! Lights Off! 1999. (Blue's Clues Ser.). (Illus.). 140p. (J). (ps-k). pap. 9.00 (978-0-7416-1009-6(4)) Havoc Publishing.

—Super Chubby 2 Blues Felt Friends. Johnson, Traci Paige, illus. 1998. (Blue's Clues Ser.). 20p. (J). (ps-k). bds. 4.99 (978-0-689-81910-0(2) , Simon Spotlight/ Nickelodeon) Simon & Schuster Children's Publishing.

—Welcome to Blue's Clues! Kim, Soo Kyung, illus. 1999. (Blue's Clues Ser.). 12p. (J). (ps-k). bds. 10.95 (978-0-689-82952-9(3) , Simon Spotlight/Nickelodeon) Simon & Schuster Children's Publishing.

—What to Do, Blue? Johnson, Traci Paige & Craig, Karen, illus. 1999. (Blue's Clues Ser.: Vol. 2). 24p. (J). (ps-k). pap. 3.50 (978-0-689-82444-9(0) , 076714003507, Simon Spotlight/Nickelodeon) Simon & Schuster Children's Publishing.

—What to Do, Blue? 1999. (gr. k-3). lib. bdg. 11.25 (978-0-613-16035-3(5)) Tandem Library Bks.

Santomero, Angela C., et al. Lights On! Lights Off! Rillo, Cary, illus. 1998. (Blue's Clues Ser.). 20p. (J). (ps-k). bds. 4.99 (978-0-689-81909-4(9) , Simon Spotlight/ Nickelodeon) Simon & Schuster Children's Publishing.

—What to Do, Blue? 1999. (Blue's Clues Ser.). (Illus.). 24p. (J). (gr. k-3). pap. 3.50 (978-0-689-83214-7(1) , Simon Spotlight/Nickelodeon) Simon & Schuster Children's Publishing.

Silverhardt, Lauryn. Blue's Friends. 2001. (Blue's Clues Ser.). (Illus.). 14p. (J). 4.99 (978-0-689-84544-4(8) , Simon Spotlight/Nickelodeon) Simon & Schuster Children's Publishing.

—A contar con Blue (Counting with Blue) Style Guide Staff, illus. 2005. (Blue's Clues Ser.). (SPA.). 14p. (J). bds. 4.99 (978-0-689-87748-3(X) , Libros Para Ninos) Simon & Schuster Children's Publishing.

—Counting with Blue. 2001. (Blue's Clues Ser.). (Illus.). 14p. (J). bds. 4.99 (978-0-689-84543-7(X) , Simon Spotlight/Nickelodeon) Simon & Schuster Children's Publishing.

—I Can Get Dressed! 2003. (Baby Blue's Clues Ser.). (Illus.). 8p. (J). 17.95 (978-0-689-85977-9(5) , Simon Spotlight/Nickelodeon) Simon & Schuster Children's Publishing.

Smith, Michael T. Blue's Halloween Hide-and-Seek: A Lift-the-Flap Story. Cardinali, Kevin, illus. 2000. (Blue's Clues Ser.). 16p. (J). (ps-k). 5.99 (978-0-689-83433-2(0) , Simon Spotlight/Nickelodeon) Simon & Schuster Children's Publishing.

Style Guide Staff, illus. Blue's Bedtime: A Cloth Book to Touch & Feel. 2001. (Blue's Clues Ser.). 8p. (J). 12.95 (978-0-689-84041-8(1) , Simon Spotlight/Nickelodeon) Simon & Schuster Children's Publishing.

Wilder, Alice. It's Present Day. Levy, David B., illus. 1999. (Blue's Clues Ser.). 16p. (J). (ps-k). pap. 5.99 (978-0-689-82898-0(5) , Simon Spotlight/Nickelodeon) Simon & Schuster Children's Publishing.

Wilder, Alice & Smith, Michael T. Blue's Lost Backpack. Johnson, Traci Paige & Pontillo, Jenine, illus. 1999. (Blue's Clues Ser.: Bk. 2). 16p. (J). (ps-k). 3.99 (978-0-689-82442-5(4) , Simon Spotlight/Nickelodeon) Simon & Schuster Children's Publishing.

Willson, Sarah. Blue's Big Beach Party. Oxley, Jennifer, illus. 2004. 8p. (J). mass mkt. (978-0-689-85162-9(6) , Simon Spotlight/Nickelodeon) Simon & Schuster Children's Publishing.

BLY, NELLIE, 1867-1922

Butcher, Nancy. It Can't Be Done, Nellie Bly! A Reporter's Race Around the World. 2003. (Illus.). 144p. (J). (gr. 1-5). 12.95 (978-1-56145-289-7(0)) Peachtree Pubs., Ltd.

Christensen, Bonnie. The Daring Nellie Bly: America's Star Reporter. Christensen, Bonnie, illus. 2003. (Illus.). 32p. (J). (gr. 1-7). 16.95 (978-0-375-81568-3(6) , Knopf Bks. for Young Readers) Random Hse. Children's Bks.

—The Daring Nellie Bly: America's Star Reporter. 2003. (Illus.). 32p. (J). (gr. 1-7). lib. bdg. 18.99 (978-0-375-91568-0(0) , Knopf Bks. for Young Readers) Random Hse. Children's Bks.

Fredeen, Charles. Nellie Bly: Daredevil Reporter. 1999. (Lerner Biographies Ser.). (Illus.). 112p. (YA). (gr. 6-12). lib. bdg. 25.26 (978-0-8225-4956-7(5) , Lerner Pubns.) Lerner Publishing Group.

Knudsen, Shannon. Nellie Bly. 2006. (History Maker Bios Ser.). (Illus.). 48p. (J). (gr. 4-7). 26.60 (978-0-8225-2943-9(2) , Lerner Pubns.) Lerner Publishing Group.

Peck, Ira & Bly, Nellie. Nellie Bly's Book: Around the World in 72 Days. abr. ed. 1998. (Single Titles Ser.). (Illus.). 128p. (gr. 5-9). lib. bdg. 27.90 (978-0-7613-0971-0(3) , Millbrook Pr.) Lerner Publishing Group.

BOADICEA, QUEEN, D. 62

Ross, Stewart. Down with the Romans. 2007. (Flashbacks Ser.). (Illus.). 64p. (J). (gr. 4-7). pap. 8.95 (***978-0-237-53150-8(X)*** , Evans Brothers, Limited) Evans Publishing Group GBR. *Dist:* Independent Pubs. Group.

BOARDING HOUSES

see Hotels, Motels, etc.

BOARDING SCHOOLS

Littlefield, Holly. Children of the Indian Boarding Schools. 2005. (Picture the American Past Ser.). (Illus.). 48p. (J). (gr. 2-5). lib. bdg. 22.60 (978-1-57505-467-4(1)) Lerner Publishing Group.

BOARDING SCHOOLS—FICTION

Alcott, Louisa May. Jo's Boys. 2002. (Dover Juvenile Classics Ser.). 288p. (J). (gr. 4-7). pap. 3.00 (978-0-486-42226-8(7)) Dover Pubns., Inc.

—Jo's Boys. l.t. ed. 2005. 424p. pap. (978-1-84637-067-0(1)) Echo Library.

—Little Men: Life at Plumfield with Jo's Boys. 2001. (Dover Juvenile Classics Ser.). 304p. (J). (gr. 4-7). pap. 3.00 (978-0-486-41808-7(1)) Dover Pubns., Inc.

Alger, Horatio. Hector's Inheritance: Or, The Boys of Smith Institute. 2006. pap. (***978-1-4065-0708-9(3)***) Dodo Pr.

—Hector's Inheritance: Or, The Boys of Smith Institute. unabr. ed. 2002. (Polyglot Press Alger Ser.). (Illus.). (J). pap. 17.95 (978-1-4115-0004-4(0)) Polyglot Pr., Inc.

Alger Jr. Horatio Staff. Hector's Inheritance. rev. ed. 2006. 276p. 28.95 (978-1-4218-1758-3(6)); pap. 13.95 (978-1-4218-1858-0(2)) 1st World Publishing, Inc. (1st World Library - Literary Society).

Allen, C. William. The African Interior Mission. Lee, Xiongpao, illus. 2006. 232p. (J). pap. 20.00 (978-0-9653308-5-5(0)) Africana Homestead Legacy Pubs.

Alphin, Elaine Marie. Simon Says. (YA). (gr. 9-12). 2005. 264p. pap. 6.95 (978-0-15-204678-1(X) , Harcourt Paperbacks); 2002. (Illus.). 272p. 17.00 (978-0-15-216355-6(7)) Harcourt Children's Bks.

Bray, Libba. A Great & Terrible Beauty. (YA). (gr. 7). 2003. 416p. 16.95 (978-0-385-73028-0(4)); 2005. 432p. reprint ed. pap. 8.95 (978-0-385-73231-4(7)) Random Hse. Children's Bks. (Delacorte Bks. for Young Readers).

—A Great & Terrible Beauty. 2005. 403p. (YA). (gr. 8-12). per. 15.60 (978-0-606-33978-0(7)) Tandem Library Bks.

—A Great & Terrible Beauty. l.t. ed. 2005. 512p. (YA). (gr. 8-12). pap. 10.95 (978-0-7862-8082-7(4)); 2004. 507p. 23.95 (978-0-7862-6504-6(3) , Large Print Pr.) Thorndike Pr.

—Rebel Angels. (gr. 7). 2006. 592p. (YA). pap. 9.99 (978-0-385-73341-0(0)); 2005. 560p. (J). lib. bdg. 18.99 (978-0-385-90257-1(3)); 2005. 560p. (YA). 16.95 (978-0-385-73029-7(2)) Random Hse. Children's Bks. (Delacorte Bks. for Young Readers).

—Rebel Angels. l.t. ed. 2006. (Thorndike Press Large Print the Literacy Bridge Ser.). 655p. (J). 23.95 (978-0-7862-8087-2(5)) Thorndike Pr.

Bray, Libba. The Sweet Far Thing. 2007. 448p. (YA). (gr. 7). 17.99 (***978-0-385-73030-3(6)***); lib. bdg. 20.99 (***978-0-385-90295-3(6)***) Random Hse. Children's Bks. (Delacorte Bks. for Young Readers).

Brazil, Angela. Monitress Merle. 2004. reprint ed. pap. 19.95 (978-1-4191-3491-3(4)) Kessinger Publishing, LLC.

Brooke, Lauren. All or Nothing. 2007. (Chestnut Hill Ser.: No. 6). 184p. (J). lib. bdg. 15.38 (***978-1-4242-1719-9(9)***) Fitzgerald Bks.

Brooke, Lauren. Chestnut Hill. 2006. 208p. (J). pap. 4.99 (978-0-439-73857-6(1) , Scholastic Paperbacks) Scholastic, Inc.

Bruchac, Joseph. The Dark Pond. Comport, Sally Wern, illus. 160p. (J). (gr. 5 up). 2005. pap. 5.99 (978-0-06-052998-7(9) , Harper Trophy); 2004. lib. bdg. 16.89 (978-0-06-052997-0(0)) HarperCollins Pubs.

Bunting, Eve. Cheyenne Again. Toddy, Irving, illus. 2002. 32p. (J). (gr. k-3). pap. 5.95 (978-0-618-19465-0(7) , Clarion Bks.) Houghton Mifflin Co. Trade & Reference Div.

Burnett, Frances Hodgson. A Little Princess. Corvino, Lucy, illus. 2005. (Classic Starts Ser.). 160p. 4.95 (978-1-4027-1275-3(8)) Sterling Publishing Co., Inc.

—A Little Princess. Marcos, Pablo, illus. 2005. (Great Illustrated Classics Ser.). 239p. (J). (gr. 3-8). 21.35 (978-1-59679-246-3(9) , ABDO & Daughters) ABDO Publishing Co.

—A Little Princess: The Story of Sara Crewe. (J). 16.95 (978-0-8488-1253-9(0)) Amereon LTD.

—A Little Princess: The Story of Sara Crewe. Warren, Eliza, ed. Marcos, Pablo, illus. 2006. 239p. (YA). reprint ed. 10.00 (978-0-7567-9835-2(3)) DIANE Publishing Co.

—A Little Princess: The Story of Sara Crewe. 2005. 112p. per. 4.95 (978-1-4209-2529-6(6)) Digireads.com.

—A Little Princess: The Story of Sara Crewe. unabr. ed. 2000. (Dover Juvenile Classics Ser.). (Illus.). 240p. (J). (gr. 4-7). pap. 2.00 (978-0-486-41446-1(9)) Dover Pubns., Inc.

—A Little Princess: The Story of Sara Crewe. Rust, Graham, illus. 2000. 192p. (YA). (gr. 4-7). reprint ed. 18.95 (978-0-87923-784-4(8)) Godine, David R. Pub.

—A Little Princess: The Story of Sara Crewe. Collier, Mary & McClintock, Barbara, illus. 2000. 32p. (J). (ps-3). 18.99 (978-0-06-027891-5(9)) HarperCollins Pubs.

—A Little Princess: The Story of Sara Crewe. 2000. (Illus.). 32p. (J). (ps-3). 16.89 (978-0-06-029010-8(2)) HarperCollins Pubs.

—A Little Princess: The Story of Sara Crewe. Tudor, Tasha, illus. 1999. 336p. (J). (gr. 4 up). 17.99 (978-0-397-30693-0(8)) HarperCollins Pubs.

—A Little Princess: The Story of Sara Crewe. 2004. reprint ed. pap. 1.99 (978-1-4192-0213-1(8)); pap. 22.95 (978-1-4191-0213-4(3)) Kessinger Publishing, LLC.

—A Little Princess: The Story of Sara Crewe. 2006. 204p. (YA). 19.95 (***978-1-934169-20-9(X)***); pap. 7.95 (***978-1-934169-21-6(8)***) Norilana Bks.

—A Little Princess: The Story of Sara Crewe. 2005. (Twelve-Point Ser.). lib. bdg. 25.00 (978-1-58287-320-6(8)); lib. bdg. 26.00 (978-1-58287-814-0(5)) North Bks.

—A Little Princess: The Story of Sara Crewe. Lindskoog, Kathryn, ed. Chitouras, Barbara, illus. 2002. (Classics for Young Readers Ser.). 208p. (J). pap. 7.99 (978-0-87552-727-7(2)) P & R Publishing.

—A Little Princess: The Story of Sara Crewe. (Puffin Classics Ser.). 2008. 320p. (J). (gr. 3). pap. 4.99 (***978-0-14-132112-7(1)*** , Puffin); 2002. (Illus.). 272p. pap. 10.00 (978-0-14-243701-8(8) , Penguin Classics) Penguin Group (USA) Inc.

—A Little Princess: The Story of Sara Crewe. 2006. (Scholastic Classics Ser.). v, 178p. (J). (gr. 9-12). 25.00 (978-0-531-16991-9(X) , Watts, Franklin) Scholastic Library Publishing.

—A Little Princess: The Story of Sara Crewe. Rust, Graham, illus. (J). pap. 22.95 (978-0-590-24079-6(X)) Scholastic, Inc.

—A Little Princess: The Story of Sara Crewe. 2001. (gr. 3-6). lib. bdg. 11.80 (978-0-613-63210-2(9)) Tandem Library Bks.

—A Little Princess: The Story of Sara Crewe. l.t. ed. 2003. 342p. pap. 10.95 (978-0-7862-6247-2(8)); (J). 29.95 (978-0-7862-5842-0(X)) Thorndike Pr.

—A Little Princess: With a Discussion of Generosity. Gribbon, Sean & Jael, illus. Gribbon, Sean & Jael, trs. 2003. (Values in Action Illustrated Classics Ser.). (J). (978-1-59203-050-7(5)) Learning Challenge, Inc.

—A Little Princess Book & Charm. Tudor, Tasha, illus. 1999. (Charming Classics). 336p. (J). (gr. 4 up). pap. 6.99 (978-0-694-01236-7(X) , Harper Festival) HarperCollins Pubs.

—Sara Crewe or What Happened at Miss Minchin's. 2006. (ENG.). 88p. per. 9.45 (978-1-59462-359-2(7) , 395, Book Jungle) Standard Pubns., Inc.

—Sara Crewe or What Happened at Miss Minchin's - 1903. 2006. (ENG.). 88p. per. 9.45 (978-1-59462-360-8(0) , 396, Book Jungle) Standard Pubns., Inc.

Burton, Jennifer. Princess's Journey. 2003. (Topeka Heights Ser.). (YA). (gr. 9-12). pap. 10.99 (978-0-9724733-0-9(0)) Allen Publishing, USA.

Canales, Viola. The Tequila Worm. 208p. (YA). (gr. 7-11). 2007. pap. 7.99 (978-0-375-84089-0(3)); 2005. 15.95 (978-0-385-74674-8(1)); 2005. 17.99 (978-0-385-90905-1(5)) Random Hse. Children's Bks. (Lamb, Wendy).

Carney, Jeffrey K. The Adventures of Michael MacInnes. 2006. 256p. (YA). 17.00 (978-0-374-30146-0(8)) Farrar, Straus & Giroux.

Carrier, Roch. The Basketball Player. Fischman, Sheila, tr. from FRE. Cohen, Sheldon, illus. 2001. 24p. (J). (gr. 3). pap. 7.95 (978-0-88776-553-7(X)) Tundra Bks., Inc./ Livres Toundra, Inc. CAN. *Dist:* Random Hse., Inc.

Carter, Ally. Cross My Heart & Hope to Spy. rev. ed. 2007. (Gallagher Girls Ser.). 240p. (J). (gr. 6 up). 16.99 (***978-1-4231-0005-8(0)***) Hyperion Pr.

Carter, Ally. I'd Tell You I Love You, but Then I'd Have to Kill You. (Gallagher Girls Ser.). 288p. (gr. 7 up). 2007. pap. 8.99 (***978-1-4231-0004-1(2)***); 2006. (978-1-4231-0003-4(4)) Hyperion Pr.

Carvell, Marlene. Sweetgrass Basket. 2005. 256p. (J). (gr. 3-6). 16.99 (978-0-525-47547-7(8) , Dutton Juvenile) Penguin Group (USA) Inc.

Caulfield, Annie. Katie Milk Solves Crimes & So On. 2006. 208p. (J). pap. 9.95 (***978-0-440-86686-2(3)***) Transworld Publishers Ltd. GBR. *Dist:* Independent Pubs. Group.

—Katie Milk Solves Reality TV Crimes. 2007. (Illus.). 208p. (J). pap. 9.95 (***978-0-440-86687-9(1)***) Transworld Publishers Ltd. GBR. *Dist:* Independent Pubs. Group.

Chapman, Allen. Tom Fairfield's Pluck & Luck. rev. ed. 2006. (ENG.). 184p. 26.95 (978-1-4218-2018-7(8)); per. 11.95 (978-1-4218-2118-4(4)) 1st World Publishing, Inc. (1st World Library - Literary Society).

—Tom Fairfield's Pluck & Luck. 2007. 138p. pap. 10.99 (***978-1-4264-7576-4(4)***); 152p. pap. 14.99 (***978-1-4264-7627-3(2)***) BiblioBazaar.

—Tom Fairfield's Pluck & Luck or Workin. 2006. 77.99 (***978-1-4280-1991-1(X)***) IndyPublish.com.

—Tom Fairfields Pluck & Luck or Working. 2007. pap. (***978-1-4065-1433-9(0)***) Dodo Pr.

Coolidge, Susan. What Katy Did at School. 2004. reprint ed. pap. 20.95 (978-1-4191-9354-5(6)); pap. 1.99 (978-1-4192-9354-2(0)) Kessinger Publishing, LLC.

—What Katy Did at School. 2006. (ENG.). 180p. per. 12.45 (***978-1-59462-472-8(0)*** , 508, Book Jungle) Standard Pubns., Inc.

Cormier, Robert. The Chocolate War. 2003. 253p. reprint ed. 25.00 (978-0-7567-6585-9(4)) DIANE Publishing Co.

Creech, Sharon. Bloomability. 288p. (J). (gr. 3-7). 1999. (Illus.). pap. 6.99 (978-0-06-440823-3(X) , Harper Trophy); 1998. 17.99 (978-0-06-026993-7(6) , Cotler, Joanna Books) HarperCollins Pubs.

de Witt, Peter. Toaster Pond. 2006. 248p. (YA). pap. 14.95 (978-1-933255-21-7(8)) DNA Pr.

D'Lacey, Chris. Fire Star. 2008. 560p. (J). pap. 7.99 (978-0-439-80185-7(5) , Orchard Bks.) Scholastic, Inc.

Doyle, Bill. Silenced! The 1969 Journal of Malcolm. Kelleher, Kathie, illus. 2006. 141p. (J). lib. bdg. 18.46 (***978-1-4242-1736-6(9)***) Fitzgerald Bks.

Doyle, Malachy. Georgie. 2002. 150p. (YA). 13.95 (978-1-58234-753-0(0) , Bloomsbury Children) Bloomsbury Publishing.

Dubowski, Cathy East. Wild Thornberrys Movie. 2002. (gr. 3-6). lib. bdg. 13.00 (978-0-613-58171-4(7)) Tandem Library Bks.

Ehrenhaft, Daniel. Drawing a Blank: Or How I Tried to Solve a Mystery, End a Feud, & Land the Girl of My Dreams. Ristow, Trevor, illus. 2006. 336p. (J). 16.99 (978-0-06-075252-1(1)); lib. bdg. 16.89 (978-0-06-075253-8(X)) HarperCollins Pubs.

Emerson, Alice. Betty Gordon at Boarding School. 2004. reprint ed. pap. 20.95 (978-1-4191-0976-8(6)); pap. 1.99 (978-1-4192-0976-5(0)) Kessinger Publishing, LLC.

Emerson, Alice B. Betty Gordon at Boarding School: The Treasure of Indian Chasm. l.t. ed. 2006. 156p. pap. 14.99 (***978-1-4264-4097-7(9)***) BiblioBazaar.

Emerson, B. Alice. Betty Gordon at Boarding School or the T. 2006. 95.99 (***978-1-4219-7400-2(2)***); pap. 88.99 (***978-1-4219-7411-8(8)***) IndyPublish.com.

Franklin, Emily. All You Need Is Love: The Principles of Love. 2006. 256p. (gr. 12). pap. 9.99 (978-0-451-21961-9(9) , N A L Trade) Penguin Group (USA) Inc.

—The Principles of Love. 2005. 256p. (gr. 12-12). pap. 9.99 (978-0-451-21517-8(6) , N A L Trade) Penguin Group (USA) Inc.

—Summer of Love: The Principles of Love. 2007. 256p. (YA). pap. 9.99 (978-0-451-22040-0(4) , N A L Trade) Penguin Group (USA) Inc.

Gratz, Alan. Samurai Shortstop. 2006. 288p. (J). (gr. 6 up). 17.99 (978-0-8037-3075-5(6) , Dial) Penguin Group (USA) Inc.

Gratz, Alan M. Samurai Shortstop. 2008. 288p. (YA). (gr. 6). pap. 7.99 (***978-0-14-241099-8(3)*** , Puffin) Penguin Group (USA) Inc.

Green, John. Looking for Alaska. 2005. 160p. (YA). (gr. 8-12). 15.99 (978-0-525-47506-4(0) , Dutton Juvenile) Penguin Group (USA) Inc.

Hamilton, Morse. Yellow Blue Bus Means I Love You. 2000. 192p. (YA). (gr. 7 up). pap. 6.99 (978-0-380-73301-9(3)) HarperCollins Pubs.

Harlen, Jonathan. Brain Scam. 2004. (Illus.). 204p. (Orig.). (J). pap. 7.95 (978-1-86508-687-3(8)) Allen & Unwin AUS. *Dist:* Independent Pubs. Group.

Harold, Gwyneth. Bad Girls in School. 2006. 148p. (YA). pap. (978-0-435-21517-0(5)) Heinemann.

Higson, Charlie. Blood Fever. 2nd rev. ed. 2007. (Young Bond Ser.). 368p. (gr. 7 up). pap. 7.99 (***978-1-4231-0029-4(8)***) Miramax Bks.

Hopkins, Cathy. From Geek to Goddess. 2007. (Zodiac Girls Ser.). 200p. (J). (gr. 4-6). pap. 5.95 (978-0-7534-5895-2(0) , Kingfisher) Houghton Mifflin Co. Trade & Reference Div.

Horowitz, Anthony. Groosham Grange. 2008. 192p. (YA). (gr. 5-8). 15.99 (***978-0-399-25061-3(1)*** , Philomel) Penguin Group (USA) Inc.

Houston, Julian. New Boy. 288p. (J). (gr. 7). 2008. pap. 7.99 (***978-0-618-88405-6(X)***); 2005. 16.00 (978-0-618-43253-0(1)) Houghton Mifflin Co. Trade & Reference Div.

Klein, Rachel. The Moth Diaries. 2002. 256p. (YA). (978-1-58243-205-2(8)) Counterpoint.

Koponen, Libby. Blow Out the Moon. 2006. 224p. (gr. 8-17). pap. 15.99 (978-0-316-01480-9(X) , Tingley, Megan Bks.) Little, Brown Bks. for Young Readers.

Korman, Gordon. Something Fishy at MacDonald Hall. 2000. (Illus.). 208p. (J). (gr. 4-7). pap. 4.99 (978-0-590-25522-6(3) , Scholastic Paperbacks) Scholastic, Inc.

Lambert, Janet. A Dream for Susan. 2001. (Jordon Ser.: Vol. 4). (YA). pap. 12.95 (978-1-930009-35-6(6)) Image Cascade Publishing.

Lawrence, Sara. Those Girls. 2007. 320p. (YA). (gr. 9). pap. 9.99 (***978-1-59514-169-9(3)*** , Razorbill) Penguin Group (USA) Inc.

Lebert, Benjamin. Crazy. 2000. (gr. 7-12). lib. bdg. 19.95 (978-0-613-33881-3(2)) Tandem Library Bks.

Lockwood, Cara. Wuthering High. 2006. (Bard Academy Ser.: No. 1). 272p. pap. 9.95 (978-1-4165-2475-5(4) , MTV) Simon & Schuster.

Mason, Jane. Zoey 101: Chapter Book. 2006. (Zoey 101 Ser.). 112p. (J). pap. 4.99 (978-0-439-84872-5(5)) Scholastic, Inc.

McCutchan, Betty. First Things First. 2001. 96p. (J). pap. 9.95 (978-1-57736-247-0(0)) Providence Hse Pubs.

Moss, Alexandra. Boys or Ballet? 2006. 142p. (J). (***978-1-4156-8361-3(1)*** , Grosset & Dunlap) Penguin Group (USA) Inc.

Moss, Alexandra. Sophie's Flight of Fancy, No. 4. 2005. (Royal Ballet School Diaries: No. 4). 144p. (gr. 3-5). mass mkt. 4.99 (978-0-448-43770-5(8) , Grosset & Dunlap) Penguin Group (USA) Inc.

Nascimbene, Yan. Ocean Deep. 1999. 40p. 18.00 (978-1-56846-161-8(5) , Creative Editions) Creative Co., The.

Nimmo, Jenny. Charlie Bone & the Hidden King. 2006. (Children of the Red King Ser.: Bk. 5). xx, 441p. (J). (***978-1-4156-7832-9(4)*** , Orchard Bks.) Scholastic, Inc.

O'Connell, Tyne. Dumping Princes. (YA). 2007. 256p. pap. 7.95 (***978-1-59990-150-3(1)*** , Bloomsbury Children); 2006. (Calypso Chronicles Ser.: Bk. 4). (Illus.). 304p. (gr. 7-10). 16.95 (978-1-58234-852-0(9)) Bloomsbury Publishing.

O'Connell, Tyne. Stealing Princes. 2006. (Calypso Chronicles Ser.: Bk. 2). 304p. (YA). reprint ed. pap. 7.95 (978-1-58234-905-3(3) , Bloomsbury Children) Bloomsbury Publishing.

Orenstein, Denise Gosliner. Unseen Companion. 368p. (J). 2003. 15.99 (978-0-06-052056-4(6)); 2003. lib. bdg. 16.89 (978-0-06-052057-1(4)); 2005. reprint ed. pap. 7.99 (978-0-06-052058-8(2) , HarperTeen) HarperCollins Pubs.

Palmer, Pamela. Horse of the Dawn. 2005. 89p. pap. 14.95 (978-1-4137-9545-5(5)) PublishAmerica, Inc.

Shulman, Polly. Enthusiasm. (YA). 2007. 208p. (gr. 7 up). 7.99 (***978-0-14-240935-0(9)*** , Puffin); 2006. 212p. (gr. 6). 15.99 (978-0-399-24389-9(5) , Putnam Juvenile) Penguin Group (USA) Inc.

Snicket, Lemony, pseud. The Austere Academy. Helquist, Brett, illus. 2008. (Series of Unfortunate Events Ser.: Bk. 5). 240p. (J). (gr. 5 up). pap. 6.99 (***978-0-06-114634-3(X)***, Harper Trophy) HarperCollins Pubs.

—The Austere Academy. 2000. (Series of Unfortunate Events Ser.: Bk. 5). (J). (gr. 4-7). pupil's gde. ed. (978-0-06-029312-3(8)) HarperCollins Pubs.

—The Austere Academy. Helquist, Brett, illus. 2000. (Series of Unfortunate Events Ser.: Bk. 5). 240p. (J). (gr. 5 up). 12.99 (978-0-06-440863-9(9)); lib. bdg. 15.89 (978-0-06-028888-4(4)) HarperCollins Pubs.

Sorrells, Walter. Silent Room. 2006. 240p. (YA). (gr. 7). 16.99 (978-0-525-47697-9(0) , Dutton Juvenile) Penguin Group (USA) Inc.

Spradlin, Michael P. Live & Let Shop. 2006. (Spy Goddess Ser.). (Illus.). 288p. (J). pap. 5.99 (978-0-06-059409-1(8)) HarperCollins Pubs.

—To Hawaii, with Love. 2006. (Spy Goddess Ser.). (Illus.). 208p. (J). lib. bdg. 16.89 (978-0-06-059411-4(X)); (YA). 15.99 (978-0-06-059410-7(1)) HarperCollins Pubs.

Spradlin, Michael P., illus. & reader. Live & Let Shop. Spradlin, Michael P., reader. 2005. (Spy Goddess Ser.: Bk. 1). 224p. (gr. 7 up). 15.99 (978-0-06-059407-7(1)) HarperCollins Pubs.

Stanley, Diane. The Mysterious Case of the Allbright Academy. 2008. 272p. (J). lib. bdg. 17.89 (***978-0-06-085818-6(4));*** (gr. 3-7). 16.99 (***978-0-06-085817-9(6))*** HarperCollins Pubs.

Stine, R. L. The Great Smelling Bee. Park, Trip, illus. 2005. (Rotten School Ser.). 128p. (J). lib. bdg. 14.89 (978-0-06-078590-1(X)); 6.99 (978-0-06-078589-5(6)) HarperCollins Pubs.

—Party Poopers. Park, Trip, illus. 2006. (Rotten School Ser.: No. 9). 128p. (J). 6.99 (978-0-06-078824-7(0)); lib. bdg. 14.89 (978-0-06-078825-4(9)) HarperCollins Pubs.

—The Teacher from Heck. Park, Trip, illus. 2006. (Rotten School Ser.: No. 8). 128p. (J). 6.99 (978-0-06-078821-6(6)); lib. bdg. 14.89 (978-0-06-078822-3(4)) HarperCollins Pubs.

Stine, R.L. Calling All Birdbrains. Park, Trip, illus. 2007. (Rotten School Ser.: No. 15). 128p. (J). lib. bdg. 14.89 (***978-0-06-123276-3(9));*** (gr. 3-7). 6.99 (***978-0-06-123275-6(0))*** HarperCollins Pubs.

—Night of the Creepy Things. Park, Trip, illus. 2007. (Rotten School Ser.: No. 14). 128p. (J). lib. bdg. 14.89 (***978-0-06-123273-2(4));*** (gr. 3-7). 6.99 (***978-0-06-123272-5(6))*** HarperCollins Pubs.

—Punk'd & Skunked. Park, Trip, illus. 2007. 108p. (J). pap. (***978-0-06-078832-2(1))*** HarperCollins Pubs.

—Rotten School #1: the Big Blueberry Barf-off! Park, Trip, illus. 2008. (Rotten School Ser.). 128p. (J). pap. 4.99 (***978-0-06-078588-8(8)***, Harper Trophy) HarperCollins Pubs.

—Rotten School #16: Dumb Clucks. Park, Trip, illus. 2008. (Rotten School Ser.). 128p. (J). 6.99 (***978-0-06-123278-7(5));*** lib. bdg. 14.89 (***978-0-06-123279-4(3))*** HarperCollins Pubs.

van de Ruit, John. Spud. 2007. 352p. (YA). (gr. 7 up). 16.99 (***978-1-59514-170-5(7)***, Razorbill) Penguin Group (USA) Inc.

Vogiel, Eva. Invisible Chains. 2000. 288p. (YA). (gr. 8-12). 19.95 (978-1-880582-57-2(0)) Judaica Pr., Inc., The.

von Ziegesar, Cecily. Lucky. 2007. (It Girl Ser.: No. 5). 256p. (YA). (gr. 10-17). pap. 9.99 (***978-0-316-11347-2(6)***, Poppy) Little, Brown Bks. for Young Readers.

—Notorious. 2nd ed. 2006. (It Girl Ser.: No. 2). 288p. (J). (gr. 7-17). pap. 9.99 (978-0-316-01186-0(X) , Poppy) Little, Brown Bks. for Young Readers.

—Reckless. 2006. (It Girl Ser.: No. 3). 288p. (J). (gr. 7-17). pap. 9.99 (978-0-316-01187-7(8) , Poppy) Little, Brown Bks. for Young Readers.

Wallace, Barbara Brooks. The Perils of Peppermints. (Illus.). 272p. (J). 2005. pap. 4.99 (978-0-689-85045-5(X) , Aladdin); 2003. 16.95 (978-0-689-85043-1(3) , Atheneum) Simon & Schuster Children's Publishing.

Webster, V. Frank. The Boys of Bellwood School or Frank Jor. 2006. 62.99 (***978-1-4219-9655-4(3));*** pap. 56.99 (***978-1-4219-9645-5(6))*** IndyPublish.com.

Wells, Helen. Cherry Ames, Boarding School Nurse. 2007. (YA). (***978-0-8261-0413-7(4))*** Springer.

Werlin, Nancy. Black Mirror. 2003. 256p. (YA). (gr. 7-12). pap. 6.99 (978-0-14-250028-6(3) , Puffin) Penguin Group (USA) Inc.

—Black Mirror. Nielsen, Cliff, illus. 2001. 244p. (YA). (gr. 7 up). 16.99 (978-0-8037-2605-5(8) , Dial) Penguin Group (USA) Inc.

—Black Mirror. 2003. (gr. 7-12). lib. bdg. 15.30 (978-0-613-61606-5(5)) Tandem Library Bks.

Winfield, Arthur M. Rover Boys in the Land of Luck or Stirri. 2006. pap. 30.95 (***978-1-4286-4101-3(7))*** Kessinger Publishing, LLC.

Wodehouse, P. G. Mike at Wrykyn. reprint ed. (J). lib. bdg. 98.00 (978-0-7426-3265-3(2)); 2001. pap. 28.00 (978-0-7426-8265-8(X)) Classic Bks.

Wollman, Jessica. Switched. 2007. 256p. (gr. 7). (J). lib. bdg. 18.99 (978-0-385-90410-0(X)); (YA). 15.99 (978-0-385-73396-0(8)) Random Hse. Children's Bks. (Delacorte Bks. for Young Readers).

BOAT RACING—FICTION

Bracken, Carolyn, illus. The Great Boat Race. 1999. (Stuart-Little Ser.). 24p. (J). (ps-2). pap. 2.99 (978-0-06-444268-8(3)) HarperCollins Pubs.

BOATBUILDING

see also Shipbuilding

Ansel, Will. A Kid's Book on Boatbuilding. 2001. 32p. pap. 10.95 (978-0-937822-66-1(3)) WoodenBoat Pubns.

Frederick, Dawn. How It Happens at the Boat Factory. Wolfe, Bob & Wolfe, Diane, photos by. 2002. (How It Happens Ser.). (Illus.). 32p. (J). (gr. 2-5). lib. bdg. 19.95 (978-1-881508-90-8(0)) Oliver Pr., Inc.

Icanberry, Mark. Picnic on a Cloud. Mount, Arthur, illus. 2000. (Look, Learn & Do Ser.). 48p. (J). (ps-3). pap. 7.95 (978-1-893327-02-3(7)) Look, Learn & Do Pubns.

Whynott, Douglas. Unit of Water, a Unit of Time: Joel White's Last Boat. 2000. (gr. 7-12). lib. bdg. 23.40 (978-0-613-29123-1(9)) Tandem Library Bks.

BOATBUILDING—FICTION

Collins, Pat L. Schooner. Collins, Pat L., illus. 2002. (Illus.). 32p. (J). (gr. 2-5). 14.95 (978-1-889833-35-4(5)) Commonwealth Editions.

BOATING

see Boats and Boating

BOATS AND BOATING

see also Boatbuilding; Canoes and Canoeing; Houseboats; Motorboats; Sailing; Ships; Steamboats; Submarines (Ships)

Ardagh, Philip. A Hole in the Road. (Illus.). 32p. (J). lib. bdg. 24.25 (978-1-931983-02-0(X)) Chrysalis Education.

Armentrout, David. Boating. 1998. (Outdoor Adventures Ser.). (Illus.). 24p. (J). (gr. 2-6). lib. bdg. 23.93 (978-1-57103-201-0(0)) Rourke Publishing, LLC.

Arnosky, Jim. Hook, Line & Seeker: A Beginner's Guide to Fishing, Boating & Watching Water Wildlife. Arnosky, Jim, illus. 2005. (Hook, Line & Seeker Ser.). (Illus.). 192p. (J). pap. 12.95 (978-0-439-45584-8(7) , Scholastic Reference) Scholastic, Inc.

Barcos del Pasado, 6, Pack. (On Deck en Espanol Ser.).Tr. of Boats of the Past. (SPA.). 24p. (gr. 4-5). 35.00 (978-0-7578-6428-5(7)) Rigby Education.

Barton, Byron. Boats. Barton, Byron, illus. 1998. (Illus.). 16p. (J). (ps up). bds. 6.99 (978-0-694-01165-0(7) , Harper Festival) HarperCollins Pubs.

—Boats Lap Edition. Barton, Byron, illus. 2006. 34p. (J). 12.99 (978-0-06-115017-3(7) , Harper Festival) HarperCollins Pubs.

Beech, Sandy. Worst Class Trip Ever. 2005. 173p. (J). (***978-1-4156-0619-3(6)***, Aladdin) Simon & Schuster Children's Publishing.

Bender, Lionel. Ships & Boats. 2006. (J). (978-1-59389-268-5(3)) Chrysalis Education.

Berger, Samantha. The Boat Book. 1999. (Science Emergent Readers Ser.). (Illus.). (J). pap. 2.50 (978-0-439-08125-2(4)) Scholastic, Inc.

Boating Safety for Kids. (USPS Learning Guides Ser.). (Illus.). 159p. (J). pap. (978-1-891148-25-5(7)) United States Power Squadrons.

Boating Safety Sidekicks: US Power Squadron Version. 2004. (J). (978-0-9718864-3-8(1)) Within Reach, Inc.

Boats. 2005. (Transportation Ser.). (YA). (gr. k-3). (978-1-56065-968-6(8) , Pebble Bks.) Capstone Pr., Inc.

Boats, 6 Pack. (Sails Literacy Ser.). (gr. 1-2). 36.00 (978-0-7578-6729-3(4)) Rigby Education.

Boats of the Past: Individual Title Six-Packs. (On Deck Ser.). 24p. (gr. 4-5). 35.00 (978-0-7578-1053-4(5)) Rigby Education.

Bornhoft, Simon. High-Speed Boats. (Need for Speed Ser.). (Illus.). 32p. (gr. 3-6). 2003. (J). pap. 7.95 (978-0-8225-9856-5(6)); 1999. lib. bdg. 23.93 (978-0-8225-2488-5(0)) Lerner Publishing Group.

Broutin, Christian. El Barco. (Coleccion Mundo Maravilloso). (SPA., Illus.). 40p. (J). (gr. 2-4). (978-84-348-3810-9(9) , BA9293) SM Ediciones ESP. *Dist:* Lectorum Pubns., Inc.

Bryant, Raymond. On the Water. 2003. (Funtime Rhymes Ser.). (Illus.). 10p. (J). bds. 4.95 (978-0-7641-2656-7(3)) Barron's Educational Series, Inc.

Built for Speed: World's Fastest Boats; Cars; Helicopters; Military Airplanes; Superbikes; Trains; Trucks; Wildest Roller Coasters, 8 bks. (Illus.). (J). (gr. 3-4). lib. bdg. 170.08 (978-0-7368-1081-4(1) , Capstone High-Interest Bks.) Capstone Pr., Inc.

Burch, Lynda S. Wicky wacky Things that Go! Boats 1. Burch, Lynda S., photos by. 2004. (Illus.). 28p. (J). E-Book 9.95 incl. cd-rom (978-1-933090-03-0(0)) Guardian Angel Publishing, Inc.

The Catboat & How to Sail Her. 5th ed. 2000. 36p. 10.00 (978-0-9715041-0-3(5)) Catboat Assn., Inc.

Chan, Arlene. Awakening the Dragon: The Dragon Boat Festival. Zhang, Song Nan, illus. 2007. 24p. (J). (gr. 1-4). pap. 10.95 (978-0-88776-805-7(9)) Tundra Bks., Inc./Livres Toundra, Inc. CAN. *Dist:* Random Hse., Inc.

Cook, Nick. The World's Fastest Boats. 2000. (Built for Speed Ser.). (Illus.). 48p. (J). (gr. 3-4). lib. bdg. 21.26 (978-0-7368-0569-8(9) , Capstone High-Interest Bks.) Capstone Pr., Inc.

—The World's Fastest Boats, 6 vols. (gr. 4 up). 39.95 (978-0-7368-8946-9(9)) Red Brick Learning.

Cooper, Jason. Fishing Boats. 1999. (Boats & Ships Discovery Library). (Illus.). 24p. (J). (gr. 1-4). lib. bdg. 19.27 (978-0-86593-562-4(9)) Rourke Publishing, LLC.

Court, Rob. How to Draw Watercraft. 2008. (Doodle Bks.). 32p. (J). 21.36 (***978-1-59296-958-6(5))*** Child's World, Inc.

Davies, Gill. Trains, Boats & Planes. Guile, Gill, illus. 2005. 20p. (J). (gr. k-4). reprint ed. 20.00 (978-0-7567-8703-5(3)) DIANE Publishing Co.

Dieker, Wendy Strobel. Hydroplanes. 2007. (Blazers—Horsepower Ser.). (Illus.). 32p. (J). 19.93 (978-0-7368-6450-3(4)) Capstone Pr., Inc.

Ditchfield, Christin. Kayaking, Canoeing, Rowing & Yachting. 2000. (True Bks.). (Illus.). 48p. (J). (gr. 3-5). 25.00 (978-0-516-21610-2(4) , Children's Pr.) Scholastic Library Publishing.

—Kayaking, Canoeing, Rowing & Yachting. 2000. (gr. 3-6). lib. bdg. 15.25 (978-0-613-51656-3(7)) Tandem Library Bks.

Dodds, James. Alphabet of Boats. 2002. (Illus.). 32p. 9.95 (978-0-939510-72-6(3) , 1017229) Mystic Seaport Museum Stores, Inc.

Dorling Kindersley Publishing Staff. Boat. 2005. 8p. (J). 5.99 (978-0-7566-1713-4(8)) Dorling Kindersley Publishing, Inc.

Dubowski, Mark. Superfast Boats. 2005. (Ultimate Speed Ser.). (Illus.). 32p. (J). lib. bdg. 25.27 (978-1-59716-079-7(2)) Bearport Publishing Co., Inc.

Ethan, Eric. Rescue Boats. Ethan, Eric, photos by. 2002. (Emergency Vehicles Ser.). (Illus.). 24p. (YA). (gr. 1 up). lib. bdg. 20.67 (978-0-8368-3048-4(2)) Stevens, Gareth Inc.

Feely, Jenny. Under Sail. 2001. (gr. k-3). lib. bdg. 11.65 (978-0-613-33448-8(5)) Tandem Library Bks.

Fire Boats, 6 vols. (gr. k-2). 28.95 (978-0-7368-8126-5(3)) Red Brick Learning.

Graham, Ian. Boats. 1999. (Built for Speed Ser.). (Illus.). 32p. (J). (gr. 3-7). lib. bdg. 25.69 (978-0-8172-4221-3(X)) Raintree.

—Boats. Connell, Tom, illus. 1998. (Built for Speed Ser.). 32p. (J). (gr. 3-7). pap. 7.95 (978-0-8172-8071-0(5)) Steck-Vaughn.

Green, Michael. PT Boats. 1998. (J). 19.93 (978-0-516-21454-2(3) , Children's Pr.) Scholastic Library Publishing.

—River Patrol Boats. 1998. (J). lib. bdg. 19.93 (978-0-516-21455-9(1) , Children's Pr.) Scholastic Library Publishing.

Hanson, Anders. Let's Go by Boat. 2007. (Let's Go! Ser.). (Illus.). 24p. (J). (ps-3). lib. bdg. 19.93 (***978-1-59928-894-9(X)***, SandCastle) ABDO Publishing Co.

Hart, Simon. Vamos, Vamos, Aviones! 2006. 10p. (J). (ps-ps). bds. 4.99 (978-0-8431-2107-0(6) , Price Stern Sloan) Penguin Group (USA) Inc.

Heat-Moon, William Least. River-Horse: The Logbook of a Boat Across America. 2001. (gr. 7-12). lib. bdg. 23.45 (978-0-613-36633-5(6)) Tandem Library Bks.

Hill, Lee Sullivan. Get Around on Water. 1999. (Get Around Bks.). (Illus.). 32p. (J). (gr. k-3). lib. bdg. 14.60 (978-1-57505-309-7(8) , Carolrhoda Bks.) Lerner Publishing Group.

The History of Water Travel. 2005. (Moving People, Things, & Ideas Ser.). (Illus.). 48p. (J). (ps-7). lib. bdg. 24.95 (978-1-4103-0662-3(3) , Blackbirch Pr., Inc.) Thomson Gale.

HOP, LLC. Hooked on Boats Super Activity Kit. 2006. (J). (ps). 9.99 (978-1-60143-002-1(7)) HOP, LLC.

Kalman, Maira. Fireboat: The Heroic Adventure of the John J. Harvey. Kalman, Maira, illus. (Illus.). pap. 16.95 incl. audio (978-1-59112-983-7(4)); pap. incl. audio (978-1-59112-985-1(0)); pap. 18.95 incl. audio compact disk (978-1-59112-987-5(7)); pap. incl. audio compact disk (978-1-59112-989-9(3)) Live Oak Media.

—Fireboat: The Heroic Adventures of the John J. Harvey. Kalman, Maira, illus. (Illus.). 48p. (J). 2002. (gr. 2-6). 16.99 (978-0-399-23953-3(7) , Putnam Juvenile); 2005. (ps). reprint ed. pap. 6.99 (978-0-14-240362-4(8) , Puffin) Penguin Group (USA) Inc.

Kentley, Eric. Boat. 2000. (Eyewitness Bks.). (Illus.). 64p. (J). (gr. 4-7). 15.99 (978-0-7894-5758-5(X)) Dorling Kindersley Publishing, Inc.

Kentley, Eric & Dorling Kindersley Publishing Staff. Boat. 2000. (Eyewitness Bks.). (Illus.). 64p. (J). (gr. 4-7). lib. bdg. 19.99 (978-0-7894-6585-6(X)) Dorling Kindersley Publishing, Inc.

Keoke, Emory Dean & Porterfield, Kay Marie. American Indian Contributions to the World. 2005. (American Indian Contributions to the World Ser.). (Illus.). 160p. (gr. 4-9). (J). 35.00 (978-0-8160-5395-7(2)); (YA). 35.00 (978-0-8160-5397-1(9)) Facts On File, Inc.

Kihm, Steve. The Lost Candy Bar. 2004. (J). mass mkt. 6.95 (978-0-9786794-0-8(7)) Lost Candy Bar Pr., LLC.

Koroknay, Tom. Lyman Boats: America's Lapstake Classic Legend of the Lakes. 2004. (Illus.). 156p. 3.95 (978-0-9749705-0-9(6)) Koroknay, Thomas.

Kreisler, Ken. Daddy & I Go Boating. O'Connor, John P., ed. Kaufman, John P., illus. 1999. 32p. (J). (ps-3). spiral bd. 9.95 (978-1-892216-14-4(0)) Bristol Fashion Publishing Co.

LeapFrog Staff, compiled by. Boats Afloat. 2001. (J). (ps-2). spiral bd. 14.95 (978-1-58605-061-0(3)) LeapFrog Enterprises, Inc.

Lindeen, Carol K. Barcos de Rescate. 2006. (ENG & SPA.). (J). (978-0-7368-5876-2(8)) Capstone Pr., Inc.

—Rescue Boats. 2005. (Pebble Plus: Mighty Machines Ser.). (Illus.). 24p. (J). 19.93 (978-0-7368-3655-5(1) , Pebble Bks.) Capstone Pr., Inc.

Loves, June. Ships. 2001. (Database Transportation Ser.). (Illus.). 32p. (J). (gr. 4 up). 22.95 (978-0-7910-6590-7(1) , 010504, Chelsea Hse.) Facts On File, Inc.

Maurer, Tracy. Watercross. 2003. (Radsports Guides Ser.). (Illus.). 48p. (gr. 4-8). 20.95 (978-1-58952-278-7(8)) Rourke Publishing, LLC.

Mayer, Cassie. By Boat. 2006. (Illus.). 24p. (J). (978-1-4034-8389-8(2)); pap. (978-1-4034-8396-6(5)) Heinemann Library.

—En Barco. 2006. (ENG & SPA., Illus.). 24p. (J). (978-1-4034-8630-1(1)); pap. (978-1-4034-8637-0(9)) Heinemann Library.

McNeil, Florence. Sail Away. McPhail, David M., illus. 2001. 32p. (J). (ps-2). 7.95 (978-1-55143-202-1(1)) Orca Bk. Pubs. USA.

Mitton, Tony. Busy Boats. Parker, Ant, illus. (Amazing Machines Ser.). 24p. (J). (ps-k). 2005. pap., pap. 3.95 (978-0-7534-5916-4(7)); 2002. tchr. ed. 9.95 (978-0-7534-5404-6(1)) Houghton Mifflin Co. Trade & Reference Div. (Kingfisher).

Molzahn, Arlene Bourgeois. Ships & Boats. 2003. (Transportation & Communication Ser.). (Illus.). 48p. (J). (gr. 1-4). lib. bdg. 23.93 (978-0-7660-2025-2(8)) Enslow Pubs., Inc.

Morse, Jenifer Corr. Boats. 2001. (Speed! Ser.). (Illus.). 24p. (J). (gr. 3-6). 22.45 (978-1-56711-468-3(7) , Blackbirch Pr., Inc.) Thomson Gale.

Oxlade, Chris. Boats & Ships. 2000. (Transportation Around the World Ser.). (Illus.). 32p. (J). (gr. k-2). lib. bdg. 21.36 (978-1-57572-301-3(8)) Heinemann Library.

Page, Jason. On the Water: Rowing, Yachting, Canoeing & Lots, Lots More. Alston, John, illus. 2000. (Zeke's Olympic Pocket Guide Ser.). 32p. (J). (gr. 4-7). pap. 3.95 (978-0-8225-5051-8(2)) Lerner Publishing Group.

Pallotta, Jerry. The Boat Alphabet Book. Biedrzycki, David, illus. 1998. 32p. (J). (ps-3). 16.95 (978-0-88106-910-5(8)) Charlesbridge Publishing, Inc.

Parker, Steve. Boat-Mania! 2003. (Vehicle-Mania! Ser.). (Illus.). 32p. (J). (gr. 2 up). lib. bdg. 23.33 (978-0-8368-3782-7(7)) Stevens, Gareth Inc.

Pastel, JoAnne & Fitzsimmons, Kakie. Bur Bur's TM Boating ABC's: Learn the Most Amazing Things with the ABC's of Boating! 2007. (J). (***978-0-9777121-2-0(5))*** Interface Publishing.

Paulsen, Gary. Caught by the Sea. l.t. ed. 2002. 104p. (J). 22.95 (978-0-7862-4160-6(8)) Thomson Gale.

—Caught by the Sea: My Life on Boats. (Illus.). 112p. (YA). 2003. (gr. 7). mass mkt. 5.50 (978-0-440-40716-4(8) , Laurel Leaf); 2001. (gr. 5 up). 15.95 (978-0-385-32645-2(9) , Delacorte Bks. for Young Readers) Random Hse. Children's Bks.

—Caught by the Sea: My Life on Boats. 2003. (gr. 7-12). lib. bdg. 13.55 (978-0-613-72185-1(3)) Tandem Library Bks.

Peterson, Tiffany. Watercraft. Westerfield, David, illus. 2003. (Draw It! Ser.). 32p. (J). (gr. 3-5). lib. bdg. 24.22 (978-1-4034-0214-1(0)); pap. 7.50 (978-1-4034-4033-4(6)) Heinemann Library.

—Watercraft. 2003. (gr. 3-6). lib. bdg. 15.25 (978-0-613-61000-1(8)) Tandem Library Bks.

Pike, Dag. Practical Motor Cruising. 2003. (Illus.). 192p. 22.95 (978-0-229-11827-4(5)) A & C Black GBR. *Dist:* MBI Distribution Services.

Purcell, Cindy. From Glass to Boat. 1998. (Changes Ser.). (Illus.). 32p. (J). (gr. 2-3). pap. 6.95 (978-0-516-20367-6(3) , Children's Pr.) Scholastic Library Publishing.

Randolph, Joanne. Coast Guard Boats. 2008. (J). lib. bdg. (***978-1-4042-4152-7(3)***, PowerKids Pr.) Rosen Publishing Group, Inc., The.

Richter, Abigail. Boats That Float: Learning the OA Sound. (PowerPhonics Ser.). (Illus.). (J). 2002. 24p. (gr. 1). lib. bdg. 18.50 (978-0-8239-5935-8(X)); 2001. 23p. pap. 26.40 (978-0-8239-8280-6(7)) Rosen Publishing Group, Inc., The. (PowerKids Pr.).

Ring, Susan. Boats, Boats, Boats. 2005. (Yellow Umbrella Ser.). (Illus.). 17p. (J). (978-0-7368-5273-9(5)); (978-0-7368-5309-5(X)) Capstone Pr., Inc.

Rogers, Alan. Ronda Redonda. 2004. (Pequenos Gigantes Ser.). (SPA., Illus.). 16p. (ps-k). (J). pap. 3.95 (978-1-58728-962-0(8)); 5.95 (978-1-58728-297-3(6)) T&N Children's Publishing. (Two Can Publishing).

Rotner, Shelley. Boats Afloat. 1998. (Illus.). 32p. (J). (ps-k). 16.99 (978-0-531-33112-5(1)); pap. 15.95 (978-0-531-30112-8(5)) Scholastic, Inc. (Orchard Bks.).

Ruane, Joanna. Boats, Boats, Boats. Boyd, Patti, illus. 2003. (My First Reader Ser.). 32p. (J). 18.50 (978-0-516-22922-5(2) , Children's Pr.) Scholastic Library Publishing.

Saunders-Smith, Gail. Boats. 1998. (J). pap. 13.25 (978-0-516-21228-9(1) , Children's Pr.) Scholastic Library Publishing.

Schaefer, Lola M. Barcos. 2003. (Ruedas, Alas y Agua Ser.).Tr. of Boats. (SPA., Illus.). 24p. (J). lib. bdg. 18.50 (978-1-4034-0916-4(1)) Heinemann Library.

—Boats. 2003. (Wheels, Wings, & Water Ser.). (Illus.). 24p. (J). lib. bdg. 18.50 (978-1-4034-0879-2(3)); pap. (978-1-4034-3618-4(5)) Heinemann Library.

Schaefer, Lola M. & Cano, Patricia. Barcos. 2003. (Ruedas, Alas y Agua Ser.).Tr. of Boats. (SPA.). 24p. (J). pap. 5.25 (978-1-4034-3529-3(4)) Heinemann Library.

Scraper, Katherine. You Can Sort Boats. 2006. (Early Explorers Ser.). (J). 30.00 (***978-1-4108-6038-5(8))*** Benchmark Education Co.

Shuter. Making Waves. 2004. (Technology Through Time Ser.). (Illus.). pap. 7.50 (978-1-4109-0980-0(8)) Raintree.

Sipos, Miklos. Surviving the Deep Blue Sea: Your Guide to Safe Boating. rev. ed. 2001. (Illus.). 14p. spiral bd. 24.95 (978-0-9705290-0-8(7) , 686943767011) Sentinel Pr. L.L.C.

Sloan, Peter. My Boat. 1999. (gr. k-3). lib. bdg. 11.80 (978-0-613-30618-8(X)) Tandem Library Bks.

—Ships & Boats. 1999. (gr. k-3). lib. bdg. 11.80 (978-0-613-30726-0(7)) Tandem Library Bks.

Smith, A. G. Boats Stained Glass Coloring Book. 1999. 8p. (J). pap. 1.50 (978-0-486-40737-1(3)) Dover Pubns., Inc.

—Traditional Boats from Around the World. 2001. (Illus.). 48p. (J). pap. 3.95 (978-0-486-41866-7(9)) Dover Pubns., Inc.

Stickland, Paul. Boats. 2004. (By Air, Sea, & Land Ser.). (Illus.). 24p. (J). pap. 3.99 (978-0-7696-3372-5(2) , Waterbird Bks.) School Specialty Publishing.

—Boats. Stickland, Paul, illus. 1998. (On the Move Ser.). (Illus.). 16p. (J). (ps up). lib. bdg. 19.93 (978-0-8368-2151-2(3)) Stevens, Gareth Inc.

Stille, Darlene R. Boats. 2002. (Illus.). 32p. (J). (gr. 1 up). lib. bdg. 19.93 (978-0-7565-0289-8(6)) Compass Point Bks.

Strickland, Paul. On the Move: Boats; Cars; Planes; Trains, 4 bks. Strickland, Paul, illus. 2002. (Illus.). (J). (ps up). pap. (978-0-8368-3333-1(3) , Weekly Reader Early Learning Library) Stevens, Gareth Inc.

Sunfish Sailboats Owner's Manual: AMF, Alcort, Pearson, & Vanguard Sailboats. 2004. (Illus.). 37p. (YA). 30.00 (978-0-9760569-0-4(9)) Wilson, Rebecca.

Tatge, Cathy. Boats. 2007. (J). (***978-1-58341-526-9(2)** , Creative Education) Creative Co., The.

Thompson, Luke. Essential Boating for Teens. 2000. (High Interest Bks.). (Illus.). 48p. (J). (gr. 7-12). 24.00 (978-0-516-23352-9(1) , Children's Pr.) Scholastic Library Publishing.

—Essential Boating for Teens. 2000. (Illus.). 48p. (YA). (gr. 8-12). lib. bdg. 15.25 (978-0-613-52029-4(7)) Tandem Library Bks.

Tiner, John Hudson. Ships & Boats. (Illus.). 32p. 2004. pap. 8.95 (978-0-89812-390-6(9) , Creative Paperbacks); 2003. (J). lib. bdg. 18.95 (978-1-58341-257-2(3) , Creative Education) Creative Co., The.

Trapani, Iza. Row Row Row Your Boat. Trapani, Iza, illus. 2000. (Extended Nursery Rhymes Ser.). (Illus.). 32p. (J). (ps up). lib. bdg. 23.33 (978-0-8368-2668-5(X)) Stevens, Gareth Inc.

—Sing along with Iza & Friends: Row Row Row Your Boat. Trapani, Iza, illus. 2004. (Illus.). 32p. (J). pap. 9.95 incl. audio compact disk (978-1-58089-102-8(0)) Charlesbridge Publishing, Inc.

Travis-Bildahl, Sandra. The Boat Book of Fun Vol. 1: An Activity Book for Nautical Kids. 2000. (Illus.). 100p. (J). pap. (978-1-878797-16-2(6)) Weems & Plath, Inc.

Tripp, Will. Water Adventures. 2005. (Real Deal Ser.). (Illus.). 32p. (J). pap. (978-0-7608-9636-5(4)) Sundance/Newbridge Educational Publishing.

Troughton, Lester & Everett, Lee, illus. Brilliant Boats. 2001. 24p. (J). (gr. 1-3). pap. 7.99 (978-1-903276-60-0(8)) Lego Media International, Inc.

Volke, Gordon. Louis the Lifeboat Activity Sticker Book. Bowler, Colin, illus. 2004. 16p. pap. 6.00 (978-1-84161-120-4(4)) Ravette Publishing, Ltd. GBR. *Dist:* Parkwest Pubns., Inc.

Walker, Pam. Boat Rides. 2000. (Welcome Bks.). (Illus.). 24p. (J). (ps-2). pap. 4.95 (978-0-516-23024-5(7)); 17.00 (978-0-516-23099-3(9)) Scholastic Library Publishing. (Children's Pr.).

Wurdinger, Scott D. & Rapparlie, Leslie. Kayaking. 2006. (Adventure Sports Ser.). (Illus.). 48p. 21.95 (978-1-58341-397-5(9) , 1262845, Creative Education) Creative Co., The.

Zuehlke, Jeffrey. Tugboats. 2007. (J). (Illus.). 32p. pap. 5.95 (***978-0-8225-6422-5(X)** , First Avenue Editions); 22.60 (978-0-8225-6417-1(3) , Lerner Pubns.) Lerner Publishing Group.

BOATS AND BOATING—FICTION

Alvord, Douglas. Sarah's Boat. Alvord, Douglas, illus. 2005. (Illus.). 48p. (J). (gr. 3-6). pap. 7.95 (978-0-88448-118-8(2)) Tilbury Hse. Pubs.

Appleton, Victor. Tom Swift & His Motor Boat. 2004. (Tom Swift Original Ser.: No. 2). 212p. (J). (ps-3). 14.95 (978-1-55709-176-5(5)) Applewood Bks.

—Tom Swift & His Motor Boat. 2000. (Tom Swift Original Ser.: Vol. No. 2). 112p. (gr. 3-7). 19.95 (978-1-57646-356-7(7)); 112p. (gr. 3-7). pap. 7.95 (978-1-57646-202-7(1)); 182p. pap. 12.99 (978-1-57646-357-4(5)) Quiet Vision Publishing.

—Tom Swift & His MotorBoat or the Rival. 2006. pap. (***978-1-4065-0904-5(3))** Dodo Pr.

Appleton, Victor. Tom Swift & His Submarine Boat. 2004. reprint ed. pap. 20.95 (978-1-4191-8462-8(8)); pap. 1.99 (978-1-4192-8462-5(2)) Kessinger Publishing, LLC.

Ardagh, Philip. Terrible Times. Roberts, David, illus. 2004. (Eddie Dickens Trilogy: Bk. 3). 160p. (J). (gr. 4-7). mass mkt. 5.99 (978-0-439-53761-2(4) , Scholastic Paperbacks) Scholastic, Inc.

Arena, Felice & Kettle, Phil. Pirate Ship: By Felice Arena & Phil Kettle: Illustrated by Susy Boyer. Boyer, Susy, illus. 2004. (J). pap. (978-1-59336-362-8(1)) Mondo Publishing.

Ballantyne, R. M. Saved by the Lifeboat. 2004. reprint ed. pap. 15.95 (978-1-4191-4624-4(6)); pap. 1.99 (978-1-4192-4624-1(0)) Kessinger Publishing, LLC.

Banks, Steven. Wild River Adventure. 2002. (gr. k-3). lib. bdg. 11.80 (978-0-613-57590-4(3)) Tandem Library Bks.

El Barco Sin Capitan. (SPA.). pap. (978-958-30-0722-4(6)) Panamericana Editorial COL. *Dist:* Lectorum Pubns., Inc.

Bardhan-Quallen, Sudipta. Meet Rainbow Sherbet. Yee, Josie, illus. 2005. (Strawberry Shortcake Ser.). 32p. (J). (ps-2). 3.99 (978-0-448-43826-9(7) , Grosset & Dunlap) Penguin Group (USA) Inc.

Barton, Janet. Boathouse. 2001. (gr. 7-12). lib. bdg. 24.55 (978-0-613-82472-9(5)) Tandem Library Bks.

Baumhofer, J. A. Where the Boats Are. 2002. (Illus.). 96p. (J). pap. 12.95 (978-0-9703086-2-7(0)) Simpson, J.R. & Assocs., Inc.

Beresford, Elisabeth. Beautiful Boating Weather. (Illus.). 15p. (J). (gr. k-6). pap. 6.99 (978-0-340-73583-1(X) , Hodder & Stoughton) Hodder General Publishing Division GBR. *Dist:* Trafalgar Square Publishing.

Beskow, Elsa. Uncle Blue's New Boat. 2002. (Illus.). 32p. (J). 17.95 (978-0-86315-364-8(X)) Floris Bks. GBR. *Dist:* SteinerBooks, Inc.

Bick, Janice. Belinda Lee. 2006. 17.00 (***978-0-8059-8850-5(5))** Dorrance Publishing Co., Inc.

Blackstone, Stella. Ship Shapes. Bell, Siobhan, illus. 2006. (J). 0024p. 15.99 (978-1-905236-34-3(4)); (***978-1-4156-6474-2(9))** Barefoot Bks., Inc.

The Boat, 6 pack. (Sails Literacy Ser.). 16p. (gr. k up). 27.00 (978-0-7635-4424-9(8)) Rigby Education.

Boat. 2004. (J). per. (978-1-57657-353-2(2)) Paradise Pr., Inc.

Bodett, Tom. Williwaw! 2000. 208p. (YA). (gr. 5-8). pap. 5.99 (978-0-375-80687-2(3) , Yearling) Random Hse. Children's Bks.

—Williwaw! 2000. (J). (978-0-606-19440-2(1)) Tandem Library Bks.

Bolognese, Don, illus. Abigail Takes the Wheel. 2002. (Avi Ser.). (J). 12.30 (978-0-7587-5967-2(3)) Book Wholesalers, Inc.

Bonnell, Kris. The Little Boat. 2006. (J). 3.95 (***978-1-933727-34-9(9))** Reading Reading Bks., LLC.

Book Company Staff. Mighty Tugboats. 2003. (Button Bks.). (Illus.). (J). bds. 12.95 (978-1-74047-312-5(4)) Book Co. Publishing Pty, Ltd., The AUS. *Dist:* Penton Overseas, Inc.

Brown, Richard & Ruttle, Kate. Afloat in a Boat. Beardshaw, Rosalind, illus. 1999. (Cambridge Reading Ser.). 10p. pap., pap. 19.00 (978-0-521-66703-6(8)) Cambridge Univ. Pr.

—Afloat in a Boat (ELT Edition) Beardshaw, Rosalind, illus. 2001. (Cambridge Storybooks Ser.). 8p. pap. 3.00 (978-0-521-00697-2(X)) Cambridge Univ. Pr.

Buell, Janet. Sail Away, Little Boat. Ishida, Jui, illus. 2006. 32p. (J). 15.95 (978-1-57505-821-4(9) , Carolrhoda Bks.) Lerner Publishing Group.

Bulion, Leslie. Uncharted Waters. 2006. 155p. (J). 14.95 (978-1-56145-365-8(X) , Peachtree Junior) Peachtree Pubs., Ltd.

Bunting, Eve. Little Bear's Little Boat. Carpenter, Nancy, illus. 2003. 32p. (J). (gr. k-ps). tchr. ed. 12.00 (978-0-395-97462-9(3) , Clarion Bks.) Houghton Mifflin Co. Trade & Reference Div.

Burchett, Loni. Bear & Katie in A Riverboat Ride, 4 vols., Vol. 4. 2006. (Illus.). 104p. (J). per. 12.95 (978-0-9742815-3-7(0)) Black Lab Publishing LLC.

Burleigh, Cyril. The Hilltop Boys on the River. 2005. 172p. pap. 11.95 (978-1-4218-0427-9(1) , 1st World Library - Literary Society) 1st World Publishing, Inc.

Burningham, John. Mr. Gumpy's Outing. Burningham, John, illus. 2002. (Illus.). (J). 15.49 (978-0-7587-3187-6(6)) Book Wholesalers, Inc.

—Mr. Gumpy's Outing. (Illus.). (J). Date not set. bds. 6.95 (978-0-8050-7373-7(6)); 2001. 34p. bds. 6.95 (978-0-8050-6629-6(2)) Holt, Henry & Co. (Holt, Henry & Co. Bks. For Young Readers).

Burtinshaw, Julie. Adrift. 2002. (Illus.). 140p. (J). (gr. 6-9). pap. 7.95 (978-1-55192-469-4(2)) Raincoast Bk. Distribution CAN. *Dist:* Perseus Distribution.

—Adrift. 2002. (gr. 3-6). lib. bdg. 16.40 (978-0-613-78645-4(9)) Tandem Library Bks.

—Dead Reckoning. 2002. 128p. (J). (gr. 8-12). pap. 6.95 (978-1-55192-342-0(4)) Raincoast Bk. Distribution CAN. *Dist:* Perseus Distribution.

Cargile, Michael E. Spike's Erie Adventure: On the Steamship William G. Mather. Campbell, Jenny, illus. 2000. 32p. (J). (ps-6). pap. 9.95 (978-0-9665995-1-0(9)) Spike Enterprises.

Carter, Joey. The Great Airboat Ride! A Cantor Kids! Book. 2006. 72p. pap. 9.95 (978-1-59800-523-3(5)) Outskirts Press, Inc.

Charlie Canoe & Other Boats, Too. 2006. (J). (978-0-9755348-2-3(3)) Kids Life Pr.

Coffey, Maria. Cat Adrift. 2002. (gr. k-3). lib. bdg. 15.25 (978-0-613-63025-2(4)) Tandem Library Bks.

Cooke, James. Pink Pig in a Boat. 2004. 59p. pap. 12.95 (978-1-4137-4338-8(2)) PublishAmerica, Inc.

Corey, Shana. Boats. Reed, Mike, illus. 2001. (Early Step into Reading Ser.). 32p. (J). (ps-1). pap. 3.99 (978-0-375-80221-8(5) , Random Hse. Bks. for Young Readers) Random Hse. Children's Bks.

—Boats. 2001. (ps-2). lib. bdg. 11.80 (978-0-613-33792-2(1)); (Illus.). (J). 10.79 (978-0-606-21076-8(8)) Tandem Library Bks.

Crampton, Gertrude. Scuffy the Tugboat. Gergely, Tibor, illus. deluxe ed. Date not set. (J). (ps-2). reprint ed. (978-1-929566-59-4(X)) Cronies.

—Scuffy the Tugboat: Classic Edition. Gergely, Tibor, illus. Date not set. (J). reprint ed. (978-1-929566-52-5(2)) Cronies.

Creech, Sharon. The Wanderer. l.t. ed. 2003. 263p. pap. 10.95 (978-0-7862-6186-4(2)) Thorndike Pr.

Crew, Gary & Rogers, Gregory. The Rainbow. 2002. (Illus.). 32p. (YA). (978-0-7344-0175-5(2) , Lothian Bks.) Hachette Livre Australia.

Cummings, Priscilla. Red Kayak. (gr. 5). 2006. 224p. (YA). pap. 6.99 (978-0-14-240573-4(6) , Puffin); 2004. 192p. (J). 15.99 (978-0-525-47317-6(3) , Dutton Juvenile) Penguin Group (USA) Inc.

de la Cruz, Melissa. Fresh off the Boat. 2006. 256p. (J). pap. 7.99 (978-0-06-054542-0(9) , Harper Trophy) HarperCollins Pubs.

de Seve, Randall. Toy Boat. Long, Loren, illus. 2007. 40p. (J). (ps-3). 16.99 (***978-0-399-24374-5(7)** , Philomel) Penguin Group (USA) Inc.

DeFelice, Cynthia. The Missing Manatee. 2008. 192p. (J). pap. 6.95 (***978-0-374-40020-0(2)** , Farrar, Straus & Giroux (BYR)) Farrar, Straus & Giroux.

DeFelice, Cynthia C. The Missing Manatee. 2005. 192p. (J). 16.00 (978-0-374-31257-2(5) , Farrar, Straus & Giroux (BYR)) Farrar, Straus & Giroux.

—The Missing Manatee. l.t. ed. 2005. 183p. (J). 20.95 (978-0-7862-8178-7(2)) Thorndike Pr.

Demarest, Chris L. My Blue Boat. 1998. (978-0-606-13629-7(0)) Tandem Library Bks.

D'Lacey, Chris. Dexter's Journey. Roberts, David, illus. 2001. (Blue Bananas Ser.). 48p. (J). (gr. 1-2). (978-0-7787-0846-9(2)); pap. (978-0-7787-0892-6(6)) Crabtree Publishing Co.

—Dexter's Journey. 2002. (gr. k-3). lib. bdg. 12.95 (978-0-613-52829-0(8)) Tandem Library Bks.

Dream Boat: Individual Title Six-Packs. (Action Packs Ser.). 120p. (gr. 3-5). 44.00 (978-0-7635-8429-0(0)) Rigby Education.

Dussling, Jennifer. The 100-Pound Problem. Thornburgh, Rebecca McKillip, illus. 2005. (Math Matters Ser.). 32p. (gr. k-2). pap. 4.95 (978-1-57565-095-1(9)) Kane Pr., The.

—The 100-Pound Problem. 2000. (Math Matters Ser.). (J). (978-0-606-20180-3(7)) Tandem Library Bks.

—100-Pound Problem. 2000. (gr. k-3). lib. bdg. 12.95 (978-0-613-39348-5(1)) Tandem Library Bks.

Ennis, Judith. Kalakala Comes Home: No Dream Is Too Big! McCoy, Lisa et al, eds. Ingram, Dean, tr. Wilburn, Kathy, photos by. l.t. ed. 2000. (Illus.). 50p. (J). 18.95 (978-0-9660092-7-9(4)) Puget Sound Pr.

Esbaum, Jill. Ste-e-e-e-eamboat A-Comin'! Rex, Adam, illus. 2005. 40p. (J). 16.00 (978-0-374-37236-1(5) , Farrar, Straus & Giroux (BYR)) Farrar, Straus & Giroux.

Feldman, Thea. Things That Go. 2006. 3p. 5.99 (978-1-932915-31-0(1)) Sandvik Publishing.

Ferguson, Sarah. Little Red's Summer Adventure. Williams, Sam, illus. 2006. 40p. (J). (ps-2). 15.95 (978-0-689-85562-7(1)) Simon & Schuster Children's Publishing.

Finley, Martha. Elsie Yachting with the Raymonds, Bk. 16. 2001. mass mkt. 5.99 (978-1-931343-25-1(X)) Hibbard Pubns., Inc.

Fletcher, Ralph. The One O'Clock Chop. 2007. 192p. (J). (gr. 5-11). 16.95 (***978-0-8050-8143-5(7)** , Holt, Henry & Co. Bks. For Young Readers) Holt, Henry & Co.

Fredrick, J. L. Cursed by the Wind. 2004. 120p. (YA). pap. 9.95 (978-0-9749058-0-8(1)) Lovstad, Joel Publishing.

Fuller, Harvey. Tommy & the Island. Fuller, Harvey, illus. 2007. (J). pap. 18.95 (***978-0-9773725-7-7(X))** Flat Hammock Pr.

Furbush, Helen. Lying Awake. McCroskey, Christine, illus. l.t. ed. 2004. 32p. (J). (gr. 1-6). 15.95 (978-0-9741787-0-7(5) , 1239134) Harbor Island Bks.

Gaetz, Dayle. Sea Dog. Meissner, Amy, illus. 2006. 64p. (gr. 2-3). pap. 4.99 (978-1-55143-406-3(7)) Orca Bk. Pubs. USA.

Gaetz, Dayle Campbell. Sea Dog. Meissner, Amy, illus. 2006. 62p. (J). lib. bdg. 20.00 (***978-1-4242-1249-1(9))** Fitzgerald Bks.

Gershator, Phillis. Someday Cyril. Lucas, Cedric, illus. 2000. (MONDO Chapter Books). 46p. (J). (978-1-57255-748-2(6)) Mondo Publishing.

Gill, Janie S. The Tub That Became a Boat. 1998. (ps-3). pap. 4.95 (978-0-89868-403-2(X)) ARO Publishing Co.

—The Tub That Became a Boat. Resse, Bob, illus. 1998. 24p. (ps-3). 5.95 (978-0-89868-323-3(8)) ARO Publishing Co.

Graham, Ian. Botes, Buques, Submarinos. 1999. (SPA.). lib. bdg. 11.65 (978-0-613-89814-0(1)) Tandem Library Bks.

Gramatky, Hardie. Tub Time with Little Toot. Long, Laurie Struck, illus. 1999. 8p. (J). (ps). 4.99 (978-0-448-41550-5(X) , Grosset & Dunlap) Penguin Group (USA) Inc.

Grandpa's Boat. 2001. (J). (978-1-58453-168-5(1)) Pioneer Valley Educational Pr., Inc.

Graves, Kassie. Brave Little Sailboat. Graves, Kassie, illus. 2003. (Illus.). 20p. (J). 14.95 (978-0-9728019-0-4(1)) Bright Eyes Pr.

Gray, Dianne E. Tomorrow, the River. Cooper, Stephanie, illus. 2006. 240p. (J). (gr. 5-9). 16.00 (978-0-618-56329-6(6)) Houghton Mifflin Co.

Gutman, Anne & Hallensleben, Georg. Gaspard on Vacation. 2001. (Illus.). 32p. (J). (ps-1). 9.95 (978-0-375-81115-9(X) , Knopf Bks. for Young Readers) Random Hse. Children's Bks.

Hammond, Jo. Home Before Dark. 2005. 144p. (YA). (gr. 7-12). pap. 7.95 (978-1-55143-340-0(0)) Orca Bk. Pubs. USA.

Harcourt School Publishers Staff. Fire Boats On Level. 3rd ed. 2002. (Trophies Reading Program Ser.). (Illus.). pap. 5.10 (978-0-15-323271-8(4)) Harcourt Schl. Pubs.

—Thunder Lake Advanced Level. 3rd ed. 2002. (Trophies Reading Program Ser.). (Illus.). pap. 5.10 (978-0-15-323469-9(5)) Harcourt Schl. Pubs.

—Togetherness: A Modern Fable: Take-Home Book. 2001. (Collections Ser.). (Illus.). (J). pap. 1.90 (978-0-15-319488-7(X)) Harcourt Schl. Pubs.

Harrah, Madge. Honey Girl. 2001. (Illus.). 120p. (J). (gr. 3-6). reprint ed. pap. 7.95 (978-0-9709152-1-4(7)) Trailway Bks.

Henderson, Kathy. The Little Boat. 1998. (J). (978-0-606-13573-3(1)) Tandem Library Bks.

Hiaasen, Carl. Flush. 2007. 272p. (J). (gr. 5). pap. 8.99 (***978-0-375-84185-9(7)** , Knopf Bks. for Young Readers) Random Hse. Children's Bks.

Hicks, Greg & Foster, Rick Foster. The Martha Is Mine: An Almost True Story. Sheldon, Kristin, illus. 2007. (J). per. 16.95 (***978-0-9790709-0-7(2))** Foster, Hicks & Assocs.

Hill, Susan. Stuart Sets Sail. Halverson, Lydia, illus. 2001. (I Can Read Bks.). 32p. (J). (ps-3). pap. 3.99 (978-0-06-444302-9(7) , Harper Trophy); Bk. 1. 14.95 (978-0-06-029537-0(6)) HarperCollins Pubs.

—Stuart Sets Sail. 2001. (gr. k-3). lib. bdg. 11.80 (978-0-613-35578-0(4)) Tandem Library Bks.

Holabird, Katharine. Two Mice in a Boat. Craig, Helen, illus. 2006. (Angelina Ballerina Ser.). 24p. (J). 3.99 (978-0-448-44450-5(X) , Grosset & Dunlap) Penguin Group (USA) Inc.

—Two Mice in a Boat. 2002. (gr. k-3). lib. bdg. 11.25 (978-0-613-88472-3(8)) Tandem Library Bks.

Hoogstad, Alice. BOLDER & BOAT. 2008. 32p. 13.95 (***978-1-60136-015-1(0))** Mars Media Pubs.

Hutchens, Paul. The White Boat Rescue. rev. ed. 1998. (Sugar Creek Gang Ser.: No. 26). 128p. (J). (gr. 4-7). 4.99 (978-0-8024-7030-0(0)) Moody Pubs.

Inkpen, Mick. The Thing. 2001. (978-0-606-22350-8(9)) Tandem Library Bks.

Jacques, Brian. Castaways of the Flying Dutchman. (Castaways of the Flying Dutchman Ser.: No. 1). 2002. (gr. 3-6). lib. bdg. 15.30 (978-0-613-72303-9(1)); 2001. (gr. 5-8). lib. bdg. 16.45 (978-0-613-62934-8(5)) Tandem Library Bks.

Jerome, Jerome K. Three Men in a Boat, Level 4. 2nd abr. ed. 2000. (Bookworms Ser.). (Illus.). 112p. 6.50 (978-0-19-423049-0(X)) Oxford Univ. Pr., Inc.

The Journey of the Little Red Boat: A Story from the Coast of Maine, 1. 2003. (Illus.). 29p. (J). bds. 16.95 (978-0-9740434-0-1(0) , 255-3716) Smith, George Publishing.

Kimmel, Eric A. The Erie Canal Pirates. Glass, Andrew, illus. 2002. 32p. (J). (gr. k-3). tchr. ed. 16.95 (978-0-8234-1657-8(7)) Holiday Hse., Inc.

Kline, Suzy. Horrible Harry Goes to Sea: Puffine Chapters. Remkiewicz, Frank, illus. (Horrible Harry Ser.). 64p. (J). (gr. 2-5). 2003. pap. 3.99 (978-0-14-250002-6(X) , Puffin); 2001. 13.99 (978-0-670-03516-8(5) , Viking Juvenile) Penguin Group (USA) Inc.

—Horrible Harry Goes to Sea: Puffine Chapters. 2003. (gr. 3-6). lib. bdg. 11.80 (978-0-613-61629-4(4)) Tandem Library Bks.

Lenski, Lois. The Little Sailboat. Lenski, Lois, illus. 2003. (Illus.). 56p. (J). (ps-1). reprint ed. 11.95 (978-0-375-81078-7(1) , Random Hse. Bks. for Young Readers) Random Hse. Children's Bks.

Lewis, Anthony, illus. Little Ocean Explorers. 2007. 14p. bds. 7.99 (***978-1-84643-039-8(9))** Child's Play International Ltd. GBR. *Dist:* Child's Play-International.

Lewis, Kevin. Tugga Tugga Tug Boat. Kirk, Daniel, illus. 2006. 32p. (ps-k). 15.99 (978-0-7868-5615-2(7)) Hyperion Pr.

Light, John. Making a Splash! 2005. (Illus.). 24p. (978-1-897968-20-8(5)) Photon Pr.

Lloyd-Jones, Sally. Old MacNoah Had an Ark. 2008. (HarperBlessings Ser.). (Illus.). 32p. (J). 17.89 (978-0-06-055718-8(4)) HarperCollins Pubs.

—Old MacNoah Had an Ark. Newton, Jill, illus. 2008. (HarperBlessings Ser.). 32p. (J). 16.99 (978-0-06-055717-1(6)) HarperCollins Pubs.

Mabee, Andrea. Dory Glory: Building A Boat from Stem to Stern. Mabee, Andrea, photos by. 2005. (Illus.). 67p. (YA). per. 15.95 (978-0-9630074-1-4(6)) Bass Cove Bks.

Maddox, Tony & Wen, Dref. Ffred ar y Dwr. 2005. (WEL., Illus.). 28p. (978-1-85596-666-6(2)) Dref Wen.

Marshall, James. Speedboat. 1999. (978-0-606-16540-2(1)) Tandem Library Bks.

Martin, Jacqueline Briggs. On Sand Island. Johnson, David A., illus. 2003. 32p. (J). (gr. k-3). tchr. ed. 16.00 (978-0-618-23151-5(X)) Houghton Mifflin Co. Trade & Reference Div.

Maybank, Roger. The Sun Boat: A Fairytale. 2005. 324p. pap. (***978-1-4120-6452-1(X))** Trafford Publishing.

Mayfield, Sue. The Four Franks. Parsons, Garry, illus. 2005. (Blue Go Bananas Ser.). 38p. (J). (978-0-7787-2629-6(0)) Crabtree Publishing Co.

McMenemy, Sarah. Jack's New Boat. McMenemy, Sarah, illus. 2005. (Illus.). 32p. (J). (ps-k). 15.99 (978-0-7636-2477-4(2)) Candlewick Pr.

McNeil, Florence. Sail Away. 2001. (gr. k-3). lib. bdg. 16.40 (978-0-613-88506-5(6)); (Illus.). (J). (978-0-606-21408-7(9)) Tandem Library Bks.

Morgan, Allen. Nicole's Boat. Marton, Jirina, illus. rev. ed. 2000. 24p. (J). (gr. k-ps). pap. 5.95 (978-1-55037-630-2(6)); lib. bdg. 15.95 (978-1-55037-631-9(4)) Annick Pr., Ltd. CAN. *Dist:* Firefly Bks., Ltd.

Murphy, Jim. Desperate Journey. 2006. (Illus.). 288p. (J). pap. 16.99 (978-0-439-07806-1(7) , Scholastic Pr.) Scholastic, Inc.

O'Donnell, Liam. Lucy & the Busy Boat. Hynes, Robert, illus. 2005. (Pet Tales Ser.). 32p. (J). (ps-2). 2.95 (978-1-59249-296-1(7) , 1B021) Soundprints.

Optic, Oliver. Little by Little or the Cruise of the Fl. 2005. pap. 27.95 (978-1-4179-9436-6(3)) Kessinger Publishing, LLC.

—Stand by the Union. 2006. 96.99 (***978-1-4280-4413-5(2)**); pap. 90.99 (***978-1-4280-4406-7(X))** IndyPublish.com.

—Taken by the Enemy. 2006. 96.99 (***978-1-4280-3960-5(0)**); pap. 89.99 (***978-1-4280-3988-9(0))** IndyPublish.com.

Orr, Wendy. Mokie & Bik. Bean, Jonathan, illus. 2007. 80p. (J). (gr. 2-5). 15.95 (978-0-8050-7979-1(3)) Holt, Henry & Co.

Pallotta, Jerry. Dory Story. Biedrzycki, David, illus. 32p. (J). (gr. k-2). 2004. pap. 7.95 (978-0-88106-076-8(3)); 2000. 15.95 (978-0-88106-075-1(5)) Charlesbridge Publishing, Inc.

—Dory Story. Biedrzycki, David, illus. 2004. (J). (ps-ps). lib. bdg. 14.50 (978-0-606-30230-2(1)) Tandem Library Bks.

Pearl, Jason E. Charlie-the Sailboat. 2005. pap. 7.95 (978-0-533-15019-9(1)) Vantage Pr., Inc.

Perry, Robert. The Ferry Boat Ride Colouring Book. Guzek, Greta, illus. unabr. ed. 32p. (Orig.). (J). (978-0-88971-159-4(3)) Harbour Publishing Co., Ltd.

Preiss, Thomas. The Boat under the Boat. 2004. pap. 7.95 (978-0-533-14799-1(9)) Vantage Pr., Inc.

Ransome, Arthur. The Big Six. 1999. (Swallows & Amazons Ser.). (Illus.). 367p. (J). (gr. 5 up). reprint ed. pap. 14.95 (978-1-56792-119-9(1)) Godine, David R. Pub.

—Great Northern? 2003. (Swallows & Amazons Ser.). (Illus.). 352p. (J). pap. 14.95 (978-1-56792-259-2(7)) Godine, David R. Pub.

—The Picts & the Martyrs: or Not Welcome at All. 2002. (Swallows & Amazons Ser.). (Illus.). 320p. (J). pap. 14.95 (978-1-56792-228-8(7)) Godine, David R. Pub.

—Swallows & Amazons. 1998. (Swallows & Amazons Ser.). (gr. 3-6). lib. bdg. 24.55 (978-0-613-77196-2(6)) Tandem Library Bks.

Rau, Dana Meachen. My Red Rowboat, Level A. Sagasti, Miriam, illus. 2002. (Compass Point Early Reader Ser.). 24p. (J). (gr. k up). lib. bdg. 18.60 (978-0-7565-0174-7(1)) Compass Point Bks.

Raven, Margot Theis. Night Boat to Freedom. Lewis, E. B., illus. 2006. 40p. (J). (gr. 2-6). 16.00 (978-0-374-31266-4(4) , Farrar, Straus & Giroux (BYR)) Farrar, Straus & Giroux.

Rigby Education Staff. Row, Row, Row Your Boat. (Illus.). (J). suppl. ed. 20.00 (978-0-7635-6457-5(5) , 764575C99) Rigby Education.

Riggs, Sandy. Joe Boat. 2006. (Reader's Clubhouse Set B Ser.). (Illus.). 24p. (J). pap. 3.99 (978-0-7641-3296-4(2)) Barron's Educational Series, Inc.

Robb, R. E. I Learned about Boating from This... 2004. per. 11.99 (978-0-9716681-5-7(9)) Magic Valley Pubs.

Rockity Rock: KinderReaders Individual Title Six-Packs. (Kinderstarters Ser.). 8p. (ps-1). 21.00 (978-0-7635-8643-0(9)) Rigby Education.

Rogers, Scott. The Little Red Boat. 2001. (Illus.). 78p. (J). (gr. k-3). pap. 9.95 (978-0-9705237-2-3(6)) 1stCoBooks.

Rohmann, Eric. Cinder-Eyed Cat. 2001. (gr. k-3). lib. bdg. 15.30 (978-0-613-36797-4(9)) Tandem Library Bks.

Roitman, Tanya, illus. I'm Going to Boston to Visit the Ducks. 2006. (I'm Going to Read Ser.). 24p. (J). pap. 3.95 (978-1-4027-3092-4(6)) Sterling Publishing Co., Inc.

Ruane, Joanna. Boats, Boats, Boats. 2004. (My First Reader Ser.). (Illus.). 29p. (J). (gr. k-1). pap. 3.95 (978-0-516-24624-6(0) , Children's Pr.) Scholastic Library Publishing.

Rylant, Cynthia. Mr. Putter & Tabby Row the Boat. Howard, Arthur, illus. 2002. (Mr. Putter & Tabby Ser.). (J). 13.15 (978-0-7587-0685-0(5)) Book Wholesalers, Inc.

Saar, David. The Yellow Boat: Touring Version. 1999. 64p. (YA). pap. 7.00 (978-0-87602-366-2(9)) Anchorage Pr.

Sailor Sam up the Mast: Early Level Satellite Individual Title Six-Packs. (Sails Literacy Ser.). 16p. (gr. 1-2). 27.00 (978-0-7578-3154-6(0)) Rigby Education.

Santillo, LuAnn. Toad. Santillo, LuAnn, ed. 2003. (Half-Pint Kids Readers Ser.). (Illus.). 7p. (ps-1). pap. (978-1-59256-107-0(1)) Half-Pint Kids, Inc.

Schwegler, Tomas. Cuentos de Barcos Fantasma para Ninos. 1999. (Stories for Children Ser.).Tr. of Stories of Haunted Boats for Kids. (SPA.). 125p. (J). 7.95 (978-970-643-156-1(X)) Selector, S.A. de C.V. MEX. *Dist:* Libros Sin Fronteras.

Sea Wind: Individual Chapter Book Title, 6 Packs. Vol. 30. 32p. (gr. 5 up). 44.00 (978-0-7578-0982-8(0)) Rigby Education.

Segal, John. Alistair & Kip's Great Adventure. Segal, John, illus. 2008. 32p. (J). 15.99 (978-1-4169-0280-5(5) , McElderry, Margaret K.) Simon & Schuster Children's Publishing.

Shahan, Sherry. In Eisiger Kalte. 2002. (GER.). 160p. pap. 15.00 (978-1-4000-3957-9(6) , New Media German Language) Random House Foreign Language Publishing.

Sims, Matt. Deep Sea. 1999. (gr. 3-6). lib. bdg. 10.85 (978-0-613-30351-4(2)) Tandem Library Bks.

Singleton, Glynn. Buddy Boy Brooks Takes the Wheel: A Mile Wide Tale from the Mighty Mississippi. 2007. 32p. (J). 12.95 (***978-1-57072-320-9(6)***) Overmountain Pr.

Smith, George. The Journey of the Little Red Boat: A Story from the Coast of Maine. 2nd ed. 2004. (Illus.). 50p. (J). per. 7.99 (978-0-9740434-1-8(9) , 255-3716) Smith, George Publishing.

Soap Boat. 2004. (Illus.). (J). (978-1-59577-011-0(9)) Starfall Education.

Splash! 2001. (SPA.). 24p. (J). 15.95 (978-980-6437-19-7(5)) Playco Editores, C.A.

Stuck in the MUD. l.t. ed. 2004. (Illus.). 20p. (J). cd-rom 19.95 (978-0-9759370-0-6(6)) Brown&Matthews.

Thomson, John. A Small Boat at the Bottom of the Sea. 2005. (Illus.). (J). (ps-7). 152p. 16.95 (978-1-57131-657-8(4)); 156p. pap. 6.95 (978-1-57131-656-1(6)) Milkweed Editions.

Tiller, Steve. Boat & Wind. Tecosky, Kathryn, ed. Cremeans, Robert, illus. 2002. 28p. (J). (ps-3). 15.95 (978-0-9704597-8-7(5)) MichaelsMind LLC.

Vischer, Phil. How Many Veggies? A Veggiecational Book about Numbers! 1999. (Veggiecational Ser.: Vol. 1). (Illus.). 12p. (J). (ps). 8.99 (978-0-8499-5985-1(3)) Nelson, Thomas Inc.

White, Carolyn. The Adventure of Louey & Frank. Dronzek, Laura, illus. 2001. 24p. (J). (ps). 14.95 (978-0-688-16503-1(6)) HarperCollins Pubs.

Winkler, Henry & Oliver, Lin. The Night I Flunked My Field Trip. 2006. (Hank Zipzer Ser.: No. 5). (J). (gr. 3-8). 24.21 (978-1-59961-104-4(X)) Spotlight.

Wood, Robert E. Candle & the Magic Boat. Femrite, Gina, illus. l.t. ed. 1999. (Oozooland Adventures Ser.: Vol. 1). 52p. (J). (ps-7). 18.95 (978-1-892458-00-1(4)) Life's Footprints, Inc.

Wynne-Jones, Tim. The Boat in the Tree. Shelley, John, illus. 2007. 40p. (J). (ps-2). 17.95 (978-1-932425-49-9(7) , Front Street) Boyds Mills Pr.

Yakowicz, Susie. Saving the Schooner. Fisher, Dolly & Yakowicz, Pete, illus. 2001. 125p. (J). (gr. 2-6). pap. 12.95 (978-0-9652546-2-5(3)) JESSPress.

Young, Selina. Big Dog & Little Dog Go Sailing. Young, Selina, illus. 2001. (Blue Bananas Ser.). (Illus.). 48p. (J). (gr. 1-2). (978-0-7787-0845-2(4)); pap. (978-0-7787-0891-9(8)) Crabtree Publishing Co.

—Big Dog & Little Dog Go Sailing. 2002. (gr. k-3). lib. bdg. 12.95 (978-0-613-52810-8(7)) Tandem Library Bks.

Zagwyn, Deborah Turney. The Sea House. Zagwyn, Deborah Turney, illus. 2004. (Illus.). 32p. (J). (gr. k-3). 15.95 (978-1-58246-030-7(2) , Tricycle Pr.) Ten Speed Pr.

BOATS AND BOATING—HISTORY

Beyer, Mark. Barcos Del Pasado. 2004. (Transporte Ayer y Hoy Ser.). (SPA & ENG., Illus.). 24p. (J). (gr. 3-6). lib. bdg. 17.25 (978-0-8239-6855-8(3) , Buenas Letra) Rosen Publishing Group, Inc., The.

—Boats of the Past. 2002. (Reading Power Ser.). (Illus.). 24p. (J). (gr. 1). lib. bdg. 17.25 (978-0-8239-5988-4(0) , PowerKids Pr.) Rosen Publishing Group, Inc., The.

Delgado, James P. Native American Shipwrecks. 2000. (Watts Library). (Illus.). 64p. (J). (gr. 5-7). 25.50 (978-0-531-20379-8(4) , Watts, Franklin) Scholastic Library Publishing.

—Native American Shipwrecks. 2000. (Illus.). 63p. (J). (gr. 4-7). lib. bdg. 17.60 (978-0-613-54041-4(7)) Tandem Library Bks.

Nicholson, John. Fishing for Islands: Traditional Boats & Seafarers of the Pacific. Nicholson, John, illus. 2002. (Illus.). 40p. (J). (gr. 3-8). pap. 7.95 (978-1-86448-587-5(6)) Allen & Unwin AUS. *Dist:* Independent Pubs. Group.

Shuter, Jane. Making Waves: Travel by Sea. 2004. (Technology Through Time Ser.). (Illus.). 32p. (J). lib. bdg. 25.70 (978-1-4109-0581-9(0)) Raintree.

BOB THE BUILDER (FICTITIOUS CHARACTER)—FICTION

Auerbach, Annie. A Day at the Barn. Giarrano, Vincent, illus. 2001. (Bob the Builder Ser.). 12p. (J). 5.99 (978-0-689-84380-8(1) , Simon Spotlight) Simon & Schuster Children's Publishing.

—Dizzy & Muck Work It Out. 2002. (gr. k-3). lib. bdg. 11.25 (978-0-613-51299-2(5)) Tandem Library Bks.

—Lego's a Day at the Barn. Giarrano, Vincent, illus. 2001. (Bob the Builder Ser.). 12p. (J). bds. 7.99 (978-0-689-84929-9(X) , Simon Spotlight) Simon & Schuster Children's Publishing.

Bob the Builder. 2002. mass mkt. 187.68 (978-0-689-02429-0(0) , Simon Spotlight) Simon & Schuster Children's Publishing.

Bob the Builder: Camera Book. 2003. bds. 15.98 (978-0-7853-7979-9(7)) Publications International, Ltd.

Capozzi, Suzy. Fix that Fence! 2006. (Illus.). 14p. (J). (ps-1). bds. 9.99 (978-0-375-83238-3(6) , Golden Bks.) Random Hse. Children's Bks.

Farrell, Melissa. Roley & the Rock Star. Hot Animation Staff, Animation, illus. 2003. (Bob the Builder Ser.: No. 7). 24p. (J). pap. 3.50 (978-0-689-85461-3(7) , Simon Spotlight) Simon & Schuster Children's Publishing.

—Roley & the Rock Star. 2003. (gr. k-3). lib. bdg. 11.25 (978-0-613-63227-0(3)) Tandem Library Bks.

Fry, Sonali. Best in Show! 2003. (Illus.). 32p. (gr. k-3). lib. bdg. 11.25 (978-0-613-64461-7(1)) Tandem Library Bks.

Golden Books Staff. Bob's Handy Hammer. 2003. (Fix It with Bob Ser.). (Illus.). 14p. (J). (ps-1). bds. 9.99 (978-0-375-82645-0(9) , Golden Bks.) Random Hse. Children's Bks.

—The House That Bob Built. 2004. (Bob the Builder Ser.). (Illus.). 8p. (J). (ps-1). bds. 10.99 (978-0-375-82732-7(3) , Golden Bks.) Random Hse. Children's Bks.

—Paint It. 2002. (Bob the Builder Ser.). (Illus.). 32p. (J). (ps-2). pap. 4.99 (978-0-307-29961-1(9) , Golden Bks.) Random Hse. Children's Bks.

Inches, Alison. Dizzy's Bird Watch. 2001. 10.79 (978-0-606-22130-6(1)); lib. bdg. 11.80 (978-0-613-51300-5(2)) Tandem Library Bks.

—Run-Away Roley. Ellis, Art, illus. 2002. (Bob the Builder Ready-to-Read Ser.: Bk. 3). 32p. (J). (ps-1). pap. 3.99 (978-0-689-84753-0(X) , Simon Spotlight) Simon & Schuster Children's Publishing.

—Run-Away Roley. 2002. (gr. k-3). lib. bdg. 11.80 (978-0-613-51322-7(3)) Tandem Library Bks.

—A Surprise for Wendy. Dubreuil, Diane, illus. 2002. (Bob the Builder Ready-to-Read Ser.: Vol. 4). 24p. (J). pap. 3.99 (978-0-689-84754-7(8) , Simon Spotlight) Simon & Schuster Children's Publishing.

—Wendy Helps Out. 2001. (978-0-606-22131-3(X)); lib. bdg. 11.80 (978-0-613-51329-6(0)) Tandem Library Bks.

Maslen, Bobby Lynn & Maslen, John R. Long Vowels! 2006. (Bob Books Ser.: No. 5). 16p. (J). pap. 16.99 (978-0-439-86541-8(7) , Scholastic Paperbacks) Scholastic, Inc.

Maslen, John R. & Maslen, Bobby Lynn. Advancing Beginners. 2006. (Bob Books Set 2 Ser.). (Illus.). 16p. (J). pap. 16.99 (978-0-439-84502-1(5) , Scholastic Paperbacks) Scholastic, Inc.

—Compound Words. 2006. (Bob Books Set 4 Ser.). (Illus.). 16p. (J). pap. 16.99 (978-0-439-84506-9(8) , Scholastic Paperbacks) Scholastic, Inc.

Mayer, Mercer & Capozzi, Suzy. Bob Paints the Town. Mayer, Mercer, illus. 2003. (Little Critter Ser.). (Illus.). 10p. (J). (gr. k-1). 7.99 (978-0-307-10603-2(9) , 10603, Golden Bks.) Random Hse. Children's Bks.

McCune, Krisha. Meet Lofty. Hot Animation Staff, Animation, illus. 2003. (Bob the Builder Ser.). 12p. (J). bds. 5.99 (978-0-689-85777-5(2) , Simon Spotlight) Simon & Schuster Children's Publishing.

—Meet Scoop. Hot Animation Staff, Animation, illus. 2003. (Bob the Builder Ser.). 12p. (J). bds. 5.99 (978-0-689-85776-8(4) , Simon Spotlight) Simon & Schuster Children's Publishing.

Ostrow, Kim. Muck's Map. Giles, Mike Lee, illus. 2002. (Bob the Builder Ser.). 14p. (J). bds. 5.99 (978-0-689-85010-3(7) , Simon Spotlight) Simon & Schuster Children's Publishing.

—Rock-and-Roll Bob. Hot Animation Staff, Animation, illus. 2003. (Bob the Builder Ser.: Vol. 6). 24p. (J). pap. 3.99 (978-0-689-85832-1(9) , Simon Spotlight) Simon & Schuster Children's Publishing.

Redmond, Diane. Bob's Birthday. 2001. (gr. k-3). lib. bdg. 11.25 (978-0-613-51294-7(4)) Tandem Library Bks.

—Scoop Saves the Day. 2001. (ps-2). lib. bdg. 11.25 (978-0-613-51323-4(1)) Tandem Library Bks.

—Wendy's Big Game. 2003. (Illus.). 32p. (gr. k-3). lib. bdg. 11.25 (978-0-613-58170-7(9)) Tandem Library Bks.

Redmond, Diane & HIT Entertainment Staff. Bob the Builder: Storybook: Spud the Dragon, Bob's Boots, Bob's Big Surprise, & Pilchard Goes Fishing. rev. ed. 2004. (Bob the Builder Ser.). 104p. (J). (gr. 4-7). 14.95 incl. cd-rom (978-1-74121-082-8(8)) Hinkler Bks. Pty, Ltd. AUS. *Dist:* Penton Overseas, Inc.

Running Press Staff. Opposites. 2004. (Sticker Math Ser.). 24p. (J). pap., act. bk. ed. 4.95 (978-0-7945-0042-9(0) , Usborne) EDC Publishing.

—Opposites. 2001. (Early Learning Ser.). (J). (gr. k-12). vinyl bd. 4.95 (978-1-58845-055-5(4)) School Specialty Publishing.

—Opposites. Pinwheel, ed. 2001. (Bounce-Along Bks.). (Illus.). 12p. (J). bds. 4.95 (978-0-8069-8091-1(5)) Sterling Publishing Co., Inc.

Running Press Staff & Lorenz Editors. Opposites, 4 vols., Set 2. 2001. (Mini Board Bks.). (Illus.). 10p. bds. 12.95 (978-0-7548-0826-8(2)) Anness Publishing GBR. *Dist:* National Bk. Network.

Shealy, Dennis. Bob & the Hungry Bunnies. Goldberg, Barry, illus. 2004. 24p. (J). (gr. k-3). 2.99 (978-0-375-82714-3(5) , Golden Bks.) Random Hse. Children's Bks.

Silverhardt. Bob the Builder. 2002. mass mkt. 95.88 (978-0-689-02506-8(8) , Simon Spotlight) Simon & Schuster Children's Publishing.

Silverhardt, Lauryn. Playtime with Bob. 2004. (Bob the Builder Ser.). (Illus.). 10p. (J). bds. 8.99 (978-0-689-86530-5(9) , Simon Spotlight) Simon & Schuster Children's Publishing.

Sing-along Bob the Builder: Story Reader. 2004. 26p. (J). spiral bd. (978-1-4127-3238-3(7) , 7236900) Publications International, Ltd.

Thorpe, Kiki. El atareado martillo de Bob (Bob's Busy Hammer) Goldberg, Barry, illus. 2005. (Bob the Builder Ser.). (SPA.). 12p. (J). bds. 5.99 (978-0-689-87750-6(1) , Libros Para Ninos) Simon & Schuster Children's Publishing.

Weber, Lou. Bob the Builder Active Point. 2006. 24p. (J). 19.98 (978-1-4127-3767-8(2) , 7257100) Publications International, Ltd.

Willson, Sarah. Travis & Scoop's Big Race. Castellano, Giuseppe, illus. 2003. (Bob the Builder Ser.). 16p. (J). pap. 5.99 (978-0-689-85302-9(5) , Simon Spotlight) Simon & Schuster Children's Publishing.

Willson, Sarah & Hot Animation Staff, Animation. Bob's Spring Parade. Giles, Mike, illus. 2005. (Bob the Builder Ser.). 16p. (J). pap. 5.99 (978-0-689-87475-8(8) , Simon Spotlight) Simon & Schuster Children's Publishing.

BOBBSEY TWINS (FICTITIOUS CHARACTERS)—FICTION

Hope, Laura. Bobbsey Twins or Merry Days Indoors and. 2006. 18.99 (***978-1-4219-7001-1(5)***); pap. 12.99 (***978-1-4219-7002-8(3)***) IndyPublish.com.

Hope, Laura Lee. The Bobbsey Twins' Adventure in the Country, Vol. 2. 2004. (Bobbsey Twins Ser.: Vol. 2). (Illus.). 196p. (J). (gr. 3-8). 5.99 (978-0-448-43753-8(8) , Grosset & Dunlap) Penguin Group (USA) Inc.

—The Bobbsey Twins' Adventure in Washington, Vol. 12. 2004. (Bobbsey Twins Ser.: Vol. 12). (Illus.). 182p. (J). (gr. 3-8). 5.99 (978-0-448-43763-7(5) , Grosset & Dunlap) Penguin Group (USA) Inc.

—The Bobbsey Twins & the Mystery at Snow Lodge, Vol. 5. 2004. (Bobbsey Twins Ser.: Vol. 5). (Illus.). 196p. (J). (gr. 3-8). 5.99 (978-0-448-43756-9(2) , Grosset & Dunlap) Penguin Group (USA) Inc.

—Bobbsey Twins at Home. 2006. 95.99 (***978-1-4280-2894-4(3)***) IndyPublish.com.

—The Bobbsey Twins' Big Adventure at Home, Vol. 8. 2004. (Bobbsey Twins Ser.: Vol. 8). (Illus.). 196p. (J). (gr. 3-8). 5.99 (978-0-448-43759-0(7) , Grosset & Dunlap) Penguin Group (USA) Inc.

—Bobbsey Twins in A Great City. 2006. 77.99 (***978-1-4280-3757-1(8)***); pap. 71.99 (***978-1-4280-3715-1(2)***) IndyPublish.com.

—Bobbsey Twins in the Great West. 2006. 62.99 (***978-1-4280-2320-8(8)***) IndyPublish.com.

—Bobbsey Twins in Washington. 2006. 62.99 (***978-1-4280-2468-7(9)***) IndyPublish.com.

—The Bobbsey Twins' Mystery at Meadowbrook, Vol. 7. 2004. (Bobbsey Twins Ser.: Vol. 7). (Illus.). 196p. (J). (gr. 3-8). 5.99 (978-0-448-43758-3(9) , Grosset & Dunlap) Penguin Group (USA) Inc.

—The Bobbsey Twins' Mystery at School. 2004. (Bobbsey Twins Ser.: Vol. 4). (Illus.). 196p. (J). (gr. 3-8). 5.99 (978-0-448-43755-2(4) , Grosset & Dunlap) Penguin Group (USA) Inc.

—The Bobbsey Twins of Lakeport: The Bobbsey Twins, 1. 2004. (Bobbsey Twins Ser.: Vol. 1). (Illus.). 196p. (J). (gr. 3-8). 5.99 (978-0-448-43752-1(X) , Grosset & Dunlap) Penguin Group (USA) Inc.

—Bobbsey Twins on A Houseboat. 2006. 62.99 (***978-1-4280-2339-0(9)***) IndyPublish.com.

—The Bobbsey Twins on a Houseboat, Vol. 6. 2004. (Bobbsey Twins Ser.: Vol. 6). (Illus.). 196p. (J). (gr. 3-8). 5.99 (978-0-448-43757-6(0) , Grosset & Dunlap) Penguin Group (USA) Inc.

—The Bobbsey Twins on Blueberry Island, Vol. 10. 2004. (Bobbsey Twins Ser.: Vol. 10). (Illus.). 196p. (J). (gr. 3-8). 5.99 (978-0-448-43761-3(9) , Grosset & Dunlap) Penguin Group (USA) Inc.

—The Bobbsey Twins' Search in the Great City: The Bobbsey Twins, Vol. 9. 2004. (Bobbsey Twins Ser.: Vol. 9). (Illus.). 192p. (J). 5.99 (978-0-448-43760-6(0) , Grosset & Dunlap) Penguin Group (USA) Inc.

—Freddie & Flossie. Pyle, Chuck, illus. ed. 2005. 32p. (J). lib. bdg. 15.00 (978-1-59054-999-5(6)) Fitzgerald Bks.

—Mystery on the Deep Blue Sea, Vol. 11. 2004. (Bobbsey Twins Ser.: Vol. 11). (Illus.). 196p. (J). (gr. 3-8). 5.99 (978-0-448-43762-0(7) , Grosset & Dunlap) Penguin Group (USA) Inc.

—The Secret at the Seashore. 2004. (Bobbsey Twins Ser.: Vol. 3). (Illus.). 182p. (J). (gr. 3-8). 5.99 (978-0-448-43754-5(6) , Grosset & Dunlap) Penguin Group (USA) Inc.

BODY, HUMAN

see also Anatomy; Physiology

Aigner-Clark, Julie. Baby da Vinci: My Body. Zaidi, Nadeem, illus. 2005. (Baby Einstein Ser.). 12p. (J). (ps-ps). bds. 7.99 (978-0-7868-5477-6(4)) Hyperion Bks. for Children.

Alton, Steve. Chewy, Gooey, Rumble, Plop! Sharratt, Nick, illus. 2007. 10p. (J). (gr. 2). 17.99 (***978-0-8037-3226-1(0)*** , Dial) Penguin Group (USA) Inc.

The Amazing Body: The Five Senses. 2005. (Illus.). (C). (gr. k-3). 113.00 (978-1-4048-1000-6(5)) Picture Window Bks.

Andrews, Barbara. The Circulatory System. 2006. pap. 39.00 (***978-1-4108-6510-6(X)***) Benchmark Education Co.

—Discover the Circulatory System. 2006. pap. 39.00 (***978-1-4108-6513-7(4)***) Benchmark Education Co.

Angliss, Sarah. The Human Machine, 6 vols. 1999. 32p. (J). lib. bdg. 101.70 (978-1-929298-23-5(4)) Chrysalis Education.

El Aparato Digestivo (the Digestive System) 2007. (J). pap. 7.95 (978-0-8225-6649-6(4) , Ediciones Lerner) Lerner Publishing Group.

El Aparato Respiratorio (the Respiratory System) 2007. (J). pap. 7.95 (978-0-8225-6652-6(4) , Ediciones Lerner) Lerner Publishing Group.

Arnold, Nick. Huesos, Sangre y Otros Pedazos del Cuerpo. De Saulles, Tony, illus. 2003. (Coleccion Esa Horrible Cienca). (SPA.). 156p. (YA). (gr. 5-8). (978-84-272-2051-5(0) , ML8311) Molino, Editorial ESP. *Dist:* Lectorum Pubns., Inc.

Atlas de Anatomia. (Conoce y Cuida Tu Cuerpo Ser.). (SPA., Illus.). 32p. (YA). 32.00 (978-84-342-1963-2(8)) Parramon Ediciones S.A. ESP. *Dist:* Distribuidora Norma, Inc.

Baggaley, Ann & Page, Martyn, eds. Human Body. 2001. (Illus.). 448p. (gr. 12). pap. 18.00 (978-0-7894-7988-4(5)) Dorling Kindersley Publishing, Inc.

Bailey, Jill. Life in the Human Body. 2003. (Illus.). (J). pap. 7.50 (978-1-4109-0351-8(6)); 32p. lib. bdg. 24.28 (978-0-7398-6803-4(9)) Raintree.

Baillie, Marilyn. Nose to Toes. Sarrazin, Marisol, illus. 2003. 32p. (J). (gr. k-2). 15.95 (978-1-56397-319-2(7)) Boyds Mills Pr.

—Nose to Toes. Sarrazin, Marisol, illus. 2001. 32p. (J). (gr. k-3). pap. (978-1-894379-06-9(3)) Maple Tree Pr. CAN. *Dist:* Firefly Bks., Ltd.

Ballard, Carol. Digestive System. 2003. (gr. 5-8). lib. bdg. 17.05 (978-0-613-60867-1(4)) Tandem Library Bks.

Ballard, Carol & Parker, Steve. Body Focus, 12 bks., Set. 2003. (Illus.). (YA). (gr. 6-8). lib. bdg. 324.84 (978-1-4034-0755-9(X)) Heinemann Library.

Baquedano, Elizabeth & Parker, Steve. Cuerpo Humano. 2004. (Dk Eyewitness Books Ser.). (SPA.). 64p. (J). 15.99 (978-0-7566-0420-2(6)) Dorling Kindersley Publishing, Inc.

Beare, Emma. Tell Me about the Human Body. 2006. (Tell Me About Ser.). 224p. (J). (gr. 3-6). 18.95 (978-0-7696-4288-8(8)) School Specialty Publishing.

Beck, Paul. Disney Light up: el cuerpo Humano: Disney Light up: Human Body, Spanish-Language Edition. 2007. (Illus.). 48p. (J). 15.99 (***978-970-718-436-7(1)*** , Silver Dolphin en Español) Advanced Marketing, S. de R. L. de C. V. MEX. *Dist:* Perseus Distribution.

Beck, Paul. The Human Body. Fairman, Jennifer, illus. 2006. (Disney Learning Ser.). 48p. (gr. 1-4). 15.99 (978-0-7868-4751-8(4)) Disney Pr.

Benchmark Education Staff, compiled by. Health & Human Body. 2006. spiral bd. 179.00 (***978-1-4108-7108-4(8)***) Benchmark Education Co.

—Human Body. 2006. spiral bd. 640.00 (***978-1-4108-6789-6(7)***); spiral bd. 135.00 (***978-1-4108-7079-7(0)***) Benchmark Education Co.

—The Human Body. 2006. spiral bd. 330.00 (***978-1-4108-7020-9(0)***); 2006. spiral bd. 199.00 (***978-1-4108-7133-6(9)***); 2005. (J). spiral bd. 265.00 (***978-1-4108-5763-7(8)***) Benchmark Education Co.

Bendell, Norm, illus. The Care & Keeping of Me: The Body Book Journal. 2001. (American Girl Library). 96p. (J). (gr. 3 up). spiral bd. 7.95 (978-1-58485-460-9(X)) American Girl Publishing, Inc.

Berendes, Mary. Body. 2007. (WordBooks/Libros de Palabras Ser.). (SPA & ENG.). 24p. (J). 19.93 (***978-1-59296-796-4(5)***) Child's World, Inc.

Beres, Samantha. The Human Body: Absolutely Everything You Need to Know about Your Body! Bryson, Mary, illus. 2001. (Kidsource Ser.). 128p. (J). (gr. 3-7). pap. 9.95 (978-0-7373-0580-7(0)) Lowell Hse.

Berger, Gilda & Berger, Melvin. Why Don't Haircuts Hurt? Questions & Answers about the Human Body. Barnes, Karen, illus. 1999. (Scholastic Question & Answer Ser.). 48p. (J). (gr. 2-4). pap. 6.99 (978-0-439-08569-4(1) , Scholastic Reference) Scholastic, Inc.

Berger, Melvin. Why Don't Haircuts Hurt? Questions & Answers about Your Body. 1999. (Question & Answer Ser.). (J). (978-0-606-20067-7(3)) Tandem Library Bks.

—Why I Cough, Sneeze, Shiver, Hiccup, & Yawn. Meisel, Paul, illus. 2000. (Let's-Read-and-Find-Out Science Ser.). 40p. (J). (gr. k-4). 15.95 (978-0-06-028144-1(8)) HarperCollins Pubs.

—Why I Sneeze, Shiver, Hiccup, & Yawn. Meisel, Paul, illus. 2000. (Let's-Read-and-Find-Out Science Ser.). 40p. (J). (gr. k-4). pap. 5.99 (978-0-06-445193-2(3), Harper Trophy) HarperCollins Pubs.

—Why I Sneeze, Shiver, Hiccup, & Yawn. 2000. (gr. k-3). lib. bdg. 13.00 (978-0-613-22633-2(X)) Tandem Library Bks.

Berger, Melvin & Berger, Gilda. Why Don't Haircuts Hurt? Questions & Answers about Your Body. Barnes, Karen, illus. 1999. (Scholastic Question & Answer Ser.). 48p. (J). (gr. 2-4). pap. 12.95 (978-0-590-13079-0(X), Scholastic Reference) Scholastic, Inc.

—Why I Cough, Sneeze, Shiver, Hiccup, & Yawn. 2000. (978-0-606-18730-5(8)) Tandem Library Bks.

—Your Body. 2005. (Illus.). pap. (978-0-439-77363-8(6)) Scholastic, Inc.

—You're Tall in the Morning, but Shorter at Night. 2004. (Speedy Facts Ser.). (Illus.). 48p. (J). pap. 7.99 (978-0-439-62536-4(X), Scholastic Reference) Scholastic, Inc.

Beshkin, Gina. The Tour of the Human Body. 2004. (Illus.). 61p. (J). pap. 12.95 (978-1-932373-57-8(8), Cedar Hill Pr.) Cedar Hill Publishing.

Biesty, Stephen & Platt, Richard. The Coolest Cross-Sections Ever. 2001. (Illus.). 128p. (J). 24.99 (978-0-7894-7964-8(8)) Dorling Kindersley Publishing, Inc.

Bingham, Caroline. Human Body. 2003. (Eye Wonder Ser.). (Illus.). 48p. (J). (gr. k). 9.99 (978-0-7894-9044-5(7)) Dorling Kindersley Publishing, Inc.

Bingham, Jane. The Human Body: From Head to Toe. 2004. (Science Answers Ser.). (Illus.). 32p. (J). 22.95 (978-1-4034-5512-3(0)); lib. bdg. 24.22 (978-1-4034-4766-1(7)) Heinemann Library.

Body Focus, 6 vols. 2003. (Illus.). (YA). Set 1. (gr. 6-8). lib. bdg. 162.42 (978-1-4034-0200-4(0)); Set 2. lib. bdg. 162.42 (978-1-4034-0754-2(1)) Heinemann Library.

Book Studio Staff. My First Big Book of the Human Body. 2006. 12p. (J). 14.99 (978-0-7566-2434-7(7)) Dorling Kindersley Publishing, Inc.

Branzei, Sylvia. Grossology & You. Keely, Jack, illus. 2002. 80p. (J). pap. 9.99 (978-0-8431-7736-7(5), Price Stern Sloan) Penguin Group (USA) Inc.

—Grossology & You. 2002. (gr. 3-6). lib. bdg. 18.80 (978-0-613-58573-6(9)) Tandem Library Bks.

The Bridgestone Science Library: Your Body, 6 bks. Incl. Your Bones. DeGezelle, Terri. lib. bdg. 18.60 (978-0-7368-1146-0(X)); Your Brain. DeGezelle, Terri. lib. bdg. 18.60 (978-0-7368-1147-7(8)); Your Heart. DeGezelle, Terri. lib. bdg. 18.60 (978-0-7368-1148-4(6)); Your Lungs. Ylvisaker, Anne. lib. bdg. 18.60 (978-0-7368-1149-1(4)); Your Muscles. Ylvisaker, Anne. lib. bdg. 18.60 (978-0-7368-1150-7(8)); Your Stomach. Ylvisaker, Anne. lib. bdg. 18.60 (978-0-7368-1151-4(6)); 24p. (J). (gr. 1-2). 2002. (Illus.). 2001. Set lib. bdg. 111.60 (978-0-7368-1164-4(8), Bridgestone Bks.) Capstone Pr., Inc.

Brown Bear Books (Firm) Staff, contrib. by. Our Bodies. 2007. (J). (***978-1-933834-17-7(X)***) Brown Bear Books.

Brown, Jonatha A. Animal Heads & Necks. 2006. (Illus.). 24p. (J). pap. (978-0-8368-6866-1(8)); lib. bdg. (978-0-8368-6861-6(7)) Stevens, Gareth Inc.

Brown, Mark. The Human Body. 2005. (J). per. 14.99 (978-1-59441-701-6(6), K04029) Carson-Dellosa Publishing Co., Inc.

Bruno, Stephen. The Human Body. 2002. (Nature's Record-Breakers Ser.). (Illus.). 32p. (J). (gr. 3 up). lib. bdg. 23.33 (978-0-8368-2905-1(0)) Stevens, Gareth Inc.

Bryan, Jenny. El Milagro del Nacimiento: Una Ventana Transparente. (Coleccion Ventana Transparente). (SPA., Illus.). 18p. (J). (gr. 3-5). 29.95 (978-950-11-1027-2(3), SGM273) Sigmar ARG. *Dist:* AIMS International Bks., Inc., Continental Bk. Co., Inc., Lectorum Pubns., Inc.

Building Blocks of Science: Human Bodyworks Teacher's Guide (Firsthand Learning) 2007. ring bd. (***978-0-89278-337-3(0)***) Carolina Biological Supply Co.

Building Blocks of Science: Human Bodyworks Unit Kit (Firsthand Learning) 2007. ring bd. (***978-0-89278-332-8(X)***) Carolina Biological Supply Co.

Bullard, Lisa. Big & Small: An Animal Opposites Book. Saunders-Smith, Gail, ed. 2005. (A+ Books). (Illus.). 32p. (J). (ps-7). lib. bdg. 22.60 (978-0-7368-4273-0(X)) Capstone Pr., Inc.

Bulletpoints Human Body. 2005. (Illus.). (J). per. 4.99 (978-1-933581-03-3(4)) Byeway Bks.

Burton, Margie & French, Tammy, Cathy - Jones. Tu cuerpo & Your Body. 2005. spiral bd. 66.00 (***978-1-4108-5634-0(8)***) Benchmark Education Co.

Butler, Brian, et al. Theology of the Body for Teens: Student Workbook. 2006. per. 14.95 (***978-1-932927-86-3(7)***) Ascension Pr.

Cagliano, Stefano. El Cuerpo Humano. (Coleccion Hiperlibros de la Ciencia). (SPA.). 196p. (YA). (gr. 5-8). (978-84-7131-938-8(1), EDI30282) Editex, Editorial S.A. ESP. *Dist:* Lectorum Pubns., Inc.

Calabresi, Linda. Human Body. 2008. (Insiders Ser.). 64p. (J). 16.99 (***978-1-4169-3861-3(3)***, Simon & Schuster Children's Publishing) Simon & Schuster Children's Publishing.

Carey, Joely. Body Changes. 2002. (gr. 7-12). lib. bdg. 15.25 (978-0-613-84513-7(7)) Tandem Library Bks.

Cassan, Adolfo. The Heart & Lungs. 2005. (Inside the Human Body Ser.). (Illus.). 32p. (gr. 4-8). 28.00 (978-0-7910-9012-1(4), Chelsea Clubhouse) Facts On File, Inc.

Caviezel, Giovanni. Mi Propio Cuerpo: Spanish Edition of My Own Human Body. Mesturini, Cristina, illus. 2004. (SPA.). 10p. (J). bds. 10.95 (978-0-7641-5773-8(6)) Barron's Educational Series, Inc.

—My Own Human Body. Mesturini, Cristina, illus. 2003. 10p. (J). (ps-2). bds. 10.99 (978-0-7641-5630-4(6)) Barron's Educational Series, Inc.

Chandler, Fiona. First Encyclopedia of the Human Body - Internet Linked. Hancock, David, illus. 2004. (First Encyclopedias Ser.). 64p. (J). (gr. 3 up). pap. 9.99 (978-0-7945-0695-7(X), Usborne) EDC Publishing.

—Little Encyclopedia of the Human Body - Internet Linked. 2005. 64p. (J). 6.99 (978-0-7945-1094-7(9), Usborne) EDC Publishing.

Cho, Shinta. Gas We Pass: The Story of Farts. 2001. (gr. k-3). lib. bdg. 15.25 (978-0-613-68588-7(1)) Tandem Library Bks.

Claybourne, A. Complete Book of the Human Body. 2004. 96p. (J). lib. bdg. 22.95 (978-1-58086-617-0(4), Usborne); (Illus.). pap. 14.95 (978-0-7945-0628-5(3)) EDC Publishing.

Claybourne, Anna. Compl Bk of the Human Body - Internet Linked. rev. ed. 2006. 112p. (J). pap. 14.99 (978-0-7945-1557-7(6), Usborne) EDC Publishing.

—The Human Body. 2006. (Science in Focus Ser.). (Illus.). 48p. (J). 27.00 (978-0-7910-8858-6(8), Chelsea Hse.) Facts On File, Inc.

Coder, Kelly, ed. Investigating Science - Taking Care of Me. 2003. 48p. 9.95 (978-1-56234-570-9(2), Mailbox Bks., The) Education Ctr., Inc.

Columbo, Luann & Fairman, Jennifer. Uncover the Human Body: Take a Three-Dimensional Look Inside the Human Body. Zukerman, Craig, illus. 2003. (Uncover Ser.). 16p. (J). 18.95 (978-1-57145-789-9(5)) Advantage Pubs. Group.

Conrad, David. Burps, Boogers, & Bad Breath. 2002. (Spyglass Books). (Illus.). 24p. (J). (gr. 1 up). lib. bdg. 18.60 (978-0-7565-0228-7(4)) Compass Point Bks.

Cooley, Denton A., intro. Your Body: How it Works. 2005. (Illus.). 112p. (gr. 9-13). pap. 287.55 (978-0-7910-7742-9(X), Chelsea Hse.) Facts On File, Inc.

Cooper, Sharon Katz. Major Organs: Sustaining Life. 2006. (Illus.). 48p. (J). (978-0-7565-1959-9(4), 1265926) Compass Point Bks.

Coster-Longman, Christina. The Human Body. Stalio, Ivan, illus. 2001. (Blow Up! Junior Science Ser.). 48p. (J). (gr. 2-5). pap. (978-0-439-98702-8(4)) Scholastic, Inc.

Coupe, Robert. The Human Body. 1999. (Explorers Ser.). (Illus.). 32p. (J). (978-0-7699-0476-4(9)) Shortland Pubns. (U. S. A.) Inc.

Creative Media Applications Staff. The Human Body & Environment: Skeletal & Muscular Systems, 4 vols., Vol. 1. 2003. (Middle School Reference Ser.). (Illus.). (J). (gr. 4-8). 160.00 (978-0-313-32559-5(6)) Greenwood Publishing Group, Inc.

Croker, Mark. Atlas del Cuerpo Humano. (SPA., Illus.). 64p. (YA). 19.95 (978-950-11-0888-0(0), SGM8880) Sigmar ARG. *Dist:* Continental Bk. Co., Inc.

El Cuerpo. 2003. (Megabites Ser.). (SPA., Illus.). (J). pap. 8.95 (978-0-9715256-7-2(6)) Planeta Publishing Corp.

El Cuerpo Humano: Una Ventana Transparente. (Coleccion Ventana Transparente). (SPA., Illus.). 17p. (J). (gr. 3-5). 27.95 (978-950-11-0926-9(7), SGM9267) Sigmar ARG. *Dist:* Continental Bk. Co., Inc., Lectorum Pubns., Inc.

Cuida Tu Cuerpo. (Conoce y Cuida Tu Cuerpo Ser.). (SPA.). 32p. (YA). 32.00 (978-84-342-1880-2(1)) Parramon Ediciones S.A. ESP. *Dist:* Distribuidora Norma, Inc.

Curry, Don L. How Do Your Lungs Work? 2004. (Rookie Read-About Health Ser.). 31p. (J). (gr. k-2). pap. 5.95 (978-0-516-27856-8(8), Children's Pr.) Scholastic Library Publishing.

Dawson, Paul. Explora el Cuerpo Humano. 2002. (SPA., Illus.). 96p. (J). (gr. 1-3). (978-84-272-4880-9(6)) Molino, Editorial ESP. *Dist:* Lectorum Pubns., Inc.

Daynes, Katie. See Inside: Your Body. 2006. 16p. (J). bds. 12.99 (978-0-7945-1233-0(X), Usborne) EDC Publishing.

—Your Body (Level 2) - Internet Referenced. 2006. 32p. (J). 4.99 (978-0-7945-1402-0(2), Usborne) EDC Publishing.

del Moral, Susana. Baby Einstein: Baby da Vinci, mi Cuerpo: Baby Einstein: Baby da Vinci, My Body, Spanish-Language Edition. Zaidi, Nadeem, illus. 2006. 6p. (J). bds. 7.95 (***978-970-718-455-8(8)***, Silver Dolphin en Español) Advanced Marketing, S. de R. L. de C. V. MEX. *Dist:* Perseus Distribution.

del Moral, Susana & Zaidi, Nadeem. Baby Einstein: el Concurso: Baby Einstein: Mirror Me, Spanish-Lanuage Edition. 2006. (Illus.). 5p. (J). bds. 6.95 (***978-970-718-458-9(2)***, Silver Dolphin en Español) Advanced Marketing, S. de R. L. de C. V. MEX. *Dist:* Perseus Distribution.

Delafosse, Claude, et al. Human Body. 2000. (Hidden World Ser.). (Illus.). 24p. (J). (ps-3). 12.95 (978-0-439-10681-8(8), Scholastic Reference) Scholastic, Inc.

DePalma, Vanessa. This Is My Body: A Safety for Little Girls. Depalma, Victoria, illus. 2003. 15p. (J). (ps-4). (978-0-9728135-0-1(0)) DePalma, Vanessa.

Derkins, Susie. The Immune System. 2001. (Insider's Guide to the Body Ser.). (Illus.). 48p. (YA). (gr. 5-8). lib. bdg. 23.95 (978-0-8239-3339-6(3), Rosen Central) Rosen Publishing Group, Inc., The.

Diagram Group. Skeletal & Muscular System. 2005. (Illus.). 112p. (J). (978-0-8160-5981-2(0)) Facts On File, Inc.

Dicks, Ian & Watton, Nick, illus. The Human Body God Made. 1999. (Zoomers Ser.). 4p. (J). (gr. 3-7). 2.99 (978-0-7847-1122-4(4), 03532, Bean Sprouts) Standard Publishing.

DK Publishing. Body. 2008. (Eye Know Ser.). 24p. (J). 8.99 (***978-0-7566-3440-7(7)***) Dorling Kindersley Publishing, Inc.

—Eyes, Nose, Toes. 2008. 12p. (J). (ps-ps). bds. 6.99 (***978-0-7566-3759-0(7)***) Dorling Kindersley Publishing, Inc.

DK Publishing Staff. Alive! 2007. 18p. (J). (gr. 3-5). 24.99 (***978-0-7566-3211-3(0)***) Dorling Kindersley Publishing, Inc.

Dolphin, Colleen. Armpits to Zits: The Body from A to Z. Craig, Diane, ed. 2007. (Let's See A to Z Ser.). (ENG., Illus.). 32p. (J). (ps-3). lib. bdg. 25.65 (***978-1-59928-884-0(2)***, Super SandCastle) ABDO Publishing Co.

Dorling Kindersley Publishing Staff. All about Me. 2003. (Lift-the-Flap Books Ser.). (Illus.). 1p. (J). bds. 6.99 (978-0-7894-9236-4(9)) Dorling Kindersley Publishing, Inc.

—Big Book of the Human Body. 2006. (Illus.). 12p. (J). pap. (***978-1-4053-1745-0(0)***) Dorling Kindersley Publishing, Inc.

—The Concise Encyclopedia of the Human Body. 2000. (978-0-606-17802-0(3)) Tandem Library Bks.

—First Human Body Encyclopedia. 2005. (DK First Reference Ser.). (Illus.). 128p. (J). (gr. 5). 15.99 (978-0-7566-0997-9(6)) Dorling Kindersley Publishing, Inc.

—Human Body. 2002. (Eye Wonder Ser.). (Illus.). 48p. (J). (gr. k-3). lib. bdg. 17.99 (978-0-7894-9045-2(5)) Dorling Kindersley Publishing, Inc.

—What's Inside My Body? 1999. (978-0-606-17818-1(X)) Tandem Library Bks.

—1001 Facts about the Human Body. 2002. (gr. 3-6). lib. bdg. 17.60 (978-0-613-75145-2(0)) Tandem Library Bks.

Dorling Kindersley Publishing Staff, ed. Human Body. 2004. (Dk Eyewitness Books Ser.). (Illus.). 72p. (J). 15.99 (978-0-7566-0688-6(8)) Dorling Kindersley Publishing, Inc.

Doudna, Kelly. Stand Up! 2007. 24p. (J). 19.93 (***978-1-59928-742-3(0)***) ABDO Publishing Co.

Douglas, Lloyd G. My Mouth. 2004. (Welcome Bks.). 24p. (J). (ps-2). pap. 4.95 (978-0-516-22131-1(0), Children's Pr.) Scholastic Library Publishing.

—My Nose. 2004. (Welcome Bks.). 24p. (J). (ps-2). pap. 4.95 (978-0-516-22132-8(9), Children's Pr.) Scholastic Library Publishing.

Eldan, Dorry. Lyrical Life Science: The Human Body, Vol. 3. Altenderf, Eric & Raskauskas, Sally, illus. 1998. 92p. (YA). (gr. 5-10). pap. 29.50 incl. audio compact disk (978-0-9646367-6-7(X)) Lyrical Learning.

Ewald, Wendy. The Best Part of Me: Children Talk about Their Bodies in Pictures & Words. Ewald, Wendy, illus. 2002. (Illus.). 32p. (ps-3). 16.99 (978-0-316-70306-2(0), Tingley, Megan Bks.) Little, Brown Bks. for Young Readers.

Faces. 2003. 8p. pap. 1.95 (978-0-7624-1946-3(6)) Running Pr. Bk. Pubs.

The Facts on File Illustrated Guide to the Human Body, 8 vols.; set. Incl. Brain & Nervous System. Diagram Group. (J). (978-0-8160-5986-7(1)); Cells & Genetics. Diagram Group. (J). (978-0-8160-5980-5(2)); Digestive System. Diagram Group. (J). (978-0-8160-5984-3(5)); Heart & Circulatory System. Diagram Group, contrib. by. (J). (978-0-8160-5982-9(9)); Reproductive System. Diagram Group. (***978-0-8160-5985-0(3)***); Senses. Diagram Group. (J). (978-0-8160-5987-4(X)); Skeletal & Muscular System. Diagram Group. (J). (978-0-8160-5981-2(0)); 112p. 2005. (Illustrated Guide to the Human Body Ser.). (Illus.). 896p. 2005. 280.00 (978-0-8160-5979-9(8)) Facts On File, Inc.

Farndon, John. The Human Body. 2001. (Science Experiments Ser.). (Illus.). 32p. (J). (gr. 3-5). lib. bdg. 25.64 (978-0-7614-1339-4(1), Benchmark Bks.) Cavendish, Marshall Corp.

—The Human Body. 2001. (Science Fact Files Ser.). (Illus.). 48p. (J). (gr. 4-7). lib. bdg. 27.12 (978-0-7398-1013-2(8)) Raintree.

Federer, Jessica Joy. Bobby Bacteria & Friends: Inside UR Body Books Presents. l.t. ed. 2005. (Illus.). 80p. (J). bds. 9.99 (978-0-9753455-3-5(2)) Amerisearch, Inc.

Fernandez, A. & Fernandez, Q. Hooray for My Nose. (Hooray for My Senses Ser.). (Illus.). (J). 19.27 (978-1-58952-375-3(X)) Rourke Publishing, LLC.

Fitzhugh, Karla. Body Image. 2004. (Health Issues Ser.). (Illus.). 64p. (J). 32.79 (978-0-7398-6891-1(8)) Harcourt Schl. Pubs.

Forte, Imogene & Frank, Marjorie. Human Body & Health. 2002. (Basic Not Boring Ser.). tchr. ed., per. 7.95 (978-0-86530-552-6(8)) Incentive Pubns., Inc.

Frank, Marjorie Slavick, et al. Science Instant Readers Bk. 2: Body Parts Work Together. 1999. (Harcourt Science Ser.). (gr. 2 up). pap. 15.50 (978-0-15-316212-1(0)) Harcourt Schl. Pubs.

Fredericks, Anthony D. Your Amazing, Fantastic, Incredible Body. 2002. (J). (978-0-531-11699-9(9), Watts, Franklin) Scholastic Library Publishing.

French, Cathy. Las células & Cells. 2005. spiral bd. 88.00 (***978-1-4108-5726-2(3)***) Benchmark Education Co.

Frost, Helen. Human Body Systems, 6 bks. Saunders-Smith, Gail, ed. Incl. Circulatory System. lib. bdg. 15.93 (978-0-7368-0648-0(2)); Digestive System. lib. bdg. 15.93 (978-0-7368-0649-7(0)); Muscular System. lib. bdg. 15.93 (978-0-7368-0650-3(4)); Nervous System. lib. bdg. 15.93 (978-0-7368-0651-0(2)); Respiratory System. lib. bdg. 15.93 (978-0-7368-0652-7(0)); Skeletal System. lib. bdg. 15.93 (978-0-7368-0653-4(9)); 24p. (J). (gr. k-1). 2000. (Illus.). 2000. Set lib. bdg. 95.58 (978-0-7368-0688-6(1), Pebble Bks.) Capstone Pr., Inc.

—The Muscular System, 6 vols. Saunders-Smith, Gail, ed. (gr. k-2). 28.95 (978-0-7368-8802-8(0)) Red Brick Learning.

Gallavotti, Barbara. El Cuerpo Humano en Accion. (Coleccion Bravo). (SPA., Illus.). 76p. (978-84-7131-904-3(7), EDI30261) Editex, Editorial S.A. ESP. *Dist:* Lectorum Pubns., Inc.

—The Human Body in Action. Shapiro, Brett, tr. from ITA. Inklink, Studio, illus. 2004. 123p. (J). (gr. 4-8). reprint ed. pap. 9.00 (978-0-7567-8334-1(8)) DIANE Publishing Co.

Ganeri, Anita. How Your Body Works, 6 bks. Shott, Steve, photos by. Incl. Your Blood. lib. bdg. 23.33 (978-0-8368-3631-8(6)); Your Brain. lib. bdg. 23.33 (978-0-8368-3632-5(4)); Your Digestive System. lib. bdg. 23.33 (978-0-8368-3633-2(2)); Your Lungs. lib. bdg. 23.33 (978-0-8368-3634-9(0)); Your Muscles & Bones. lib. bdg. 23.33 (978-0-8368-3635-6(9)); Your Senses. lib. bdg. 23.33 (978-0-8368-3636-3(7)); 32p. (J). (gr. 2 up). 2003. (Illus.). 2002. Set lib. bdg. 139.98 (978-0-8368-3630-1(8)) Stevens, Gareth Inc.

—Your Lungs. Shott, Steve, photos by. 2003. (How Your Body Works). (Illus.). 32p. (J). (gr. 2 up). lib. bdg. 23.33 (978-0-8368-3634-9(0)) Stevens, Gareth Inc.

Gardner, Robert. Health Science Projects about Anatomy & Physiology. 2001. (Science Projects Ser.). (Illus.). 128p. (YA). (gr. 6-12). lib. bdg. 26.60 (978-0-7660-1440-4(1)) Enslow Pubs., Inc.

Gareth Stevens Publishing Staff, contrib. by. Human Biology. 2002. (Discovery Channel School Science Ser.). (Illus.). 32p. (J). (gr. 5 up). lib. bdg. 24.67 (978-0-8368-3214-3(0)) Stevens, Gareth Inc.

—The Structure of the Body. 2002. (Twenty-First Century Science Ser.). (Illus.). 64p. (J). (gr. 5 up). lib. bdg. 32.67 (978-0-8368-5008-6(4), World Almanac Library) Stevens, Gareth Inc.

Gave, Marc. Human Body/el cuerpo Humano: English/Spanish Pair, 12 texts, 2 titles, Vol. 2. ed. 2004. (Navigators Ser.). (J). pap., instr.'s gde. ed. 84.00 (978-1-4108-1775-4(X), 1775X) Benchmark Education Co.

Gay, Kathlyn & Whittington, Christine. Body Marks: Tattooing, Piercing, & Scarification. 2002. (Single Titles Ser.). (Illus.). 112p. (gr. 10-12). pap. 14.95 (978-0-7613-1742-5(2)); (gr. 7 up). lib. bdg. 29.90 (978-0-7613-2352-5(X)) Lerner Publishing Group. (Twenty-First Century Bks.).

Glover, David. My Body. 2001. (Experiments in Science Ser.). (Illus.). (J). (978-0-7894-7469-8(7)) Dorling Kindersley Publishing, Inc.

God Made Our Bodies. 2006. 16p. (J). pap. 1.99 (978-0-7847-1701-1(X), 04162) Standard Publishing.

Gordon, Sharon. My Stomach. 2004. (Bookworms Ser.). (ENG & SPA., Illus.). 31p. (J). 21.36 (978-0-7614-1782-8(6)) Cavendish, Marshall Corp.

Gordon, Sharon. What's Inside? (¿Qué Hay Dentro?), 6 bks., Set. Incl. Whats Inside a Fire Truck? (¿Qué Hay Dentro de un Camion de Bomberos?) lib. bdg. 22.79 (978-0-7614-2472-7(5)); What's Inside a Firehouse? (¿Qué Hay Dentro de un Cuartel de Bomberos?) lib. bdg. 22.79 (978-0-7614-2473-4(3)); What's Inside a Hospital? (¿Qué Hay Dentro de un Hospital?) lib. bdg. 22.79 (978-0-7614-2474-1(1)); What's Inside a Police Car? (¿Qué Hay Dentro de un Carro de Policía?) lib. bdg. 22.79 (978-0-7614-2475-8(X)); What's Inside a Police Station? (¿Qué Hay Dentro de una Estacion de Policía?) lib. bdg. 22.79 (978-0-7614-2476-5(8)); What's Inside an Ambulance? (Qué Hay Dentro de una Ambulancia?) lib. bdg. 22.79 (978-0-7614-2471-0(7)); (Illus.). 32p. (J). 2006. (ENG & SPA.). 2007. Set lib. bdg. 136.71 (***978-0-7614-2469-7(5)***) Cavendish, Marshall Corp.

Gottlieb. The Human Body. 2004. pap., tchr. ed. 17.60 incl. cd-rom (978-0-7398-9182-7(0)); (Illus.). pap. 15.60 incl. cd-rom (978-0-7398-9176-6(5)) Steck-Vaughn.

Gr 4 Human Body: A Body Sci Pe. 2000. (McGraw-Hill Science Ser.). (gr. 4 up). (978-0-02-278222-1(2)) Macmillan/McGraw-Hill Schl. Div.

Gr 6 Human Body: Resp & Chg Sc. 2000. (McGraw-Hill Science Ser.). (gr. 6 up). (978-0-02-278237-5(0)) Macmillan/McGraw-Hill Schl. Div.

Graves, Bonnie. Tattooing & Body Piercing. 2000. (Perspectives on Physical Health Ser.). (Illus.). 64p. (J). (gr. 4-6). lib. bdg. 23.93 (978-0-7368-0417-2(X), LifeMatters Bks.) Capstone Pr., Inc.

Gray, Susan Heinrichs. The Digestive System. 2003. (Body Systems Ser.). (Illus.). 32p. (J). (gr. 2-6). 27.07 (978-1-59296-037-8(5)) Child's World, Inc.

—The Lungs. 2005. (Human Body Ser.). (Illus.). 32p. (J). (gr. 2-6). 27.07 (978-1-59296-428-4(1)) Child's World, Inc.

Grossblatt, Ben, ed. SmartLab: Human Body Challenge. Bradrick, Jim, illus. 2007. 144p. 19.99 (***978-1-932855-71-5(8)***) becker&mayer! books.

Guillen, Michael. Dr. Universe Tells U about Ur Body. 2000. (J). 64p. pap. 10.00 (978-0-517-88559-8(X)); lib. bdg. 16.99 (978-0-517-88560-4(3)) Random Hse. Children's Bks. (Random Hse. Bks. for Young Readers).

Gurgles & Growls. (Amazing Body Ser.). 24p. (J). 7.95 (978-1-4048-0504-0(4)) Picture Window Bks.

Han, Kakao. A Journey into the Human Body, Vol. 2. Yoon, Seok, illus. 2005. (Everyday Science Ser.). 160p. (J). pap. 12.95 (978-981-05-2767-9(5)) Youngjin (Singapore) Pte Ltd. SGP. *Dist:* Independent Pubs. Group.

Hands-On Crafts for Kids. How Do You Move? 2002. (Balloon Ser.). (Illus.). 12p. (J). bds. 3.95 (978-1-4027-0176-4(4), Balloon Bks.) Sterling Publishing Co., Inc.

Harcourt School Publishers Staff. The Body Book: Library Book. 3rd ed. 2002. (Trophies Reading Program Ser.). (Illus.). pap. 13.50 (978-0-15-326525-9(6)) Harcourt Schl. Pubs.

—Harcourt Science: Body Parts Work Together Reader. 1999. (Illus.). pap. 3.10 (978-0-15-314864-4(0)) Harcourt Schl. Pubs.

—How Body Parts Work: Science Reader. 1999. (SPA., Illus.). (J). pap. 3.70 (978-0-15-316117-9(5)) Harcourt Schl. Pubs.

—Kid Care - Grade 4. 3rd ed. 2002. (Trophies English Language Learners Ser.). pap. 5.10 (978-0-15-327759-7(9)) Harcourt Schl. Pubs.

—Touch Your Nose, Wiggle Your Toes. 3rd ed. 2002. (Trophies English Language Learners Ser.). (Illus.). (J). pap. 4.10 (978-0-15-327594-4(4)) Harcourt Schl. Pubs.

—Touch Your Nose, Wiggles Your Toes - 5 Pack - Grade 1. 3rd ed. 2002. (Trophies English Language Learners Ser.). 20.10 (978-0-15-327628-6(2)) Harcourt Schl. Pubs.

Harper, P. Thandi Hicks. Hip-Hop Development. 2005. (978-1-887191-02-9(X)) Youth Popular Culture Institute, Inc.

Harris, David & Van Til, Meaghan. Eye See. 2005. (X-Zone Ser.). (Illus.). 30p. (gr. 4-8). 23.00 (978-0-7910-8975-0(4)) Facts On File, Inc.

Harris, Robie H. Sexo... Que Es? 2003. (SPA., Illus.). (YA). (gr. 7-8). pap. (978-84-95040-35-0(2) , RR7144) Serres, Ediciones, S. L. ESP. *Dist:* Lectorum Pubns., Inc.

—Sexo... Que Es? Emberley, Michael, illus. 2000. (YA). (gr. 5-8). (SPA.). 90p. 17.95 (978-84-88061-90-4(0)); 2nd ed. (CAT.). 96p. pap. 17.95 (978-84-95040-28-2(X)) Serres, Ediciones, S. L. ESP. *Dist:* Lectorum Pubns., Inc.

Hawkes, Chris. The Human Body: Uncovering Science. 2006. (Uncovering Ser.). (Illus.). 52p. (J). (gr. 3-12). 16.95 (978-1-55407-135-7(6)) Firefly Bks., Ltd.

Health & the Human Body Classroom Library. (gr. k-2). lib. bdg. 81.95 (978-0-7368-7134-1(9)) Red Brick Learning.

Health & the Human Body Complete Unit. (gr. k-2). 468.95 (978-0-7368-7144-0(6)) Red Brick Learning.

Health & the Human Body II Classroom Library. (gr. k-2). lib. bdg. 63.95 (978-0-7368-8825-7(X)) Red Brick Learning.

Health & the Human Body II Complete Unit. (gr. k-2). 363.95 (978-0-7368-9068-7(8)) Red Brick Learning.

Henderson, Kathy. Look at You! A Baby Body Book. Howard, Paul, illus. 2007. 40p. (J). (ps). 15.99 (978-0-7636-2745-4(3)) Candlewick Pr.

Hewitt, Sally. Human Body. 2005. (Science Starters Ser.). (Illus.). 32p. (J). (978-1-59604-007-6(6)) Stargazer Bks.

Hil, Mcgraw. Gr 5 Human Body: Pthwy S. 2000. (McGraw-Hill Science Ser.). (gr. 5 up). (978-0-02-278229-0(X)) Macmillan/McGraw-Hill Schl. Div.

—Gr3 Human Body Kp Hlthy. 2000. (McGraw-Hill Science Ser.). (gr. 3 up). (978-0-02-278214-6(1)) Macmillan/ McGraw-Hill Schl. Div.

—Sciasmtbk Human Body: Kpng. 2000. (McGraw-Hill Science Ser.). (gr. 3 up). (978-0-02-277754-8(7)) Macmillan/McGraw-Hill Schl. Div.

—Sciasmtbk Human Body: Pat. 2000. (McGraw-Hill Science Ser.). (gr. 5 up). (978-0-02-277769-2(5)) Macmillan/McGraw-Hill Schl. Div.

—Trfpaswak Human Body: Kpng. 2000. (McGraw-Hill Science Ser.). (gr. 3 up). (978-0-02-277635-0(4)) Macmillan/McGraw-Hill Schl. Div.

Hindley, Judy. Eyes, Nose, Fingers & Toes: A First Book All about You. Granstrom, Brita, illus. 2002. 32p. (J). (gr. k-k). pap. 5.99 (978-0-7636-1708-0(3)) Candlewick Pr.

—Eyes, Nose, Fingers, & Toes: A First Book All about You. Granstrom, Brita, illus. 2002. (J). 23.40 (978-0-7587-2471-7(3)) Book Wholesalers, Inc.

—Eyes, Nose, Fingers, & Toes: A First Book All about You. Granstrom, Brita, illus. 2004. 24p. (J). (gr. k-k). bds. 6.99 (978-0-7636-2383-8(0)) Candlewick Pr.

—Eyes, Nose, Fingers, & Toes: A First Book All about You. 2002. (ps-2). lib. bdg. 14.15 (978-0-613-74778-3(X)) Tandem Library Bks.

Holden, Arianne. Body. 2003. (Playschool Ser.). (Illus.). 32p. pap. 5.99 (978-1-84215-774-9(4) , Southwater) Anness Publishing GBR. *Dist:* National Bk. Network.

Holt, Rinehart and Winston Staff. Decisions for Health Red Chptr. 16: Your Changing Body. 4th ed. 2004. pap. 11.20 (978-0-03-068043-4(3)) Holt, Rinehart & Winston.

—Holt Science & Technology Chapter 22: Life Science: Body Organization. 5th ed. 2004. (Illus.). pap. 12.86 (978-0-03-030238-1(2)) Holt, Rinehart & Winston.

—Holt Science & Technology Chapter 24: Life Science: Digestive & Urinary Systems. 5th ed. 2004. (Illus.). pap. 12.86 (978-0-03-030241-1(2)) Holt, Rinehart & Winston.

—Holt Science & Technology Chptr. 11: The Human Body's Organisms: Chapter Resources - Tennessee Edition. 3rd ed. 2003. (YA). pap. 11.40 (978-0-03-069142-3(7)) Holt, Rinehart & Winston.

—The Human Body & Health, Vol. D. 3rd ed. 2003. (Holt Science & Technology Ser.). (SPA.). 18.60 (978-0-03-069243-7(1)) Holt, Rinehart & Winston.

Hook, Sue & Jackson, Carolyn, eds. All about People: How We Grow, How Our Bodies Work, & How We Feel. 2005. (Illus.). 93p. (J). (gr. k-4). reprint ed. 20.00 (978-0-7567-8683-0(5)) DIANE Publishing Co.

Horner, Susan. What Is God's Design for My Body? 2004. (Miracle of Creation Ser.). (Illus.). 64p. (J). pap. 5.99 (978-0-8024-0923-2(7)) Moody Pubs.

Houghton, Gillian. Bones: The Skeletal System. 2007. (Body Works). (Illus.). 24p. (J). (gr. 2-4). lib. bdg. 21.25 (978-1-4042-3473-4(X) , PowerKids Pr.) Rosen Publishing Group, Inc., The.

—The Skeletal System. 2007. (How Your Body Works). (Illus.). 24p. (J). (978-1-4042-2372-1(X)); pap. (978-1-4042-2182-6(4)) Rosen Publishing Group, Inc., The. (PowerKids Pr.).

How the Body Works, 10 bks., Big Bk. Set. (J). 230.00 (978-0-8136-2946-9(2)) Modern Curriculum Pr.

The Human Body. 2007. (First Discovery Book Ser.). 24p. (J). pap. 5.99 (***978-0-439-91088-0(9)***) Scholastic, Inc.

The Human Body: Level O, 6 vols. (Explorers Ser.). 32p. (gr. 3-6). 44.95 (978-0-7699-0599-0(4)) Shortland Pubns. (U. S. A.) Inc.

Human Body 2-3. 2003. 128p. (J). per. 10.99 (978-0-88724-953-2(1) , CD-4328) Carson-Dellosa Publishing Co., Inc.

Human Body Systems Set. (gr. k-2). 172.95 (978-0-7368-9032-8(7)) Red Brick Learning.

Indside the Human Body: Using Exonential & Scientific Notation. (Math Big Bookstm Ser.). 32p. (YA). (gr. 6-7). 53.25 (978-1-4042-6366-6(7)) Rosen Publishing Group, Inc., The.

Inside Our Bodies: Fifth Grade Newcomer Books. (On Our Way to English Ser.). (gr. 5 up). 34.50 (978-0-7578-7280-8(8)) Rigby Education.

Inside Our Bodies: Fourth Grade Class Collection Books. (On Our Way to English Ser.). (gr. 4 up). 29.95 (978-0-7578-4344-0(1)) Rigby Education.

Inside Our Bodies: Small Versions of Class Collection Books. (On Our Way to English Ser.). (gr. 4 up). 34.50 (978-0-7578-7267-9(0)) Rigby Education.

Inside the Human Body. 2005. (Illus.). 32p. (gr. 4-8). pap. 112.00 (978-0-7910-9086-2(8) , Chelsea Clubhouse) Facts On File, Inc.

Inside the Human Body, 6 vols. (Book2WebTM Ser.). (gr. 4-8). 36.50 (978-0-322-02979-8(1)) Wright Group, The.

Insider's Guide to the Body, 8 bks. Incl. Circulatory System. Oleksy, Walter. lib. bdg. 23.95 (978-0-8239-3336-5(9)); Digestive System. Morrison, Ben. lib. bdg. 23.95 (978-0-8239-3337-2(7)); Immune System. Derkins, Susie. lib. bdg. 23.95 (978-0-8239-3339-6(3)); Muscular System. Taylor, Barbara. lib. bdg. 23.95 (978-0-8239-3340-2(7)); Nervous System. Oleksy, Walter. lib. bdg. 23.95 (978-0-8239-3341-9(5)); Reproductive System. O'Donnell, Kerri. lib. bdg. 23.95 (978-0-8239-3334-1(2)); Respiratory System. Lee, Justin. lib. bdg. 23.95 (978-0-8239-3335-8(0)); Skeletal System. Gilbert, Laura. lib. bdg. 23.95 (978-0-8239-3338-9(5)); 48p. (YA). (gr. 5-8). 2001. (Illus.). 2000. Set lib. bdg. 191.60 (978-0-8239-9210-2(1) , Rosen Central) Rosen Publishing Group, Inc., The.

Intrater, Roberta Grobel. Two Eyes, a Nose, & a Mouth. 2000. (978-0-606-18610-0(7)) Tandem Library Bks.

It's Amazing: It's Amazing Package. 2003. 125.95 (978-0-673-61613-5(4)) Celebration Pr.

Jackson, Donna. In Your Face. 2004. (Illus.). 48p. (J). (gr. 3-7). 17.99 (978-0-670-03657-8(9) , Viking Juvenile) Penguin Group (USA) Inc.

Jerome, Kate Boehm. More Science of You. 2004. (National Geographic Reading Expeditions Ser.). (Illus.). 24p. (J). pap. (978-0-7922-4566-7(0)) National Geographic Society.

Johnson, Rebecca L. El Aparato Digestivo. 2006. (Libros Sobre el Cuerpo Humano para Madrugadores Ser.). (ENG & SPA.). 48p. (J). 25.26 (978-0-8225-6253-5(7)) Lerner Publishing Group.

—The Digestive System. 2005. (Early Bird Body Systems Ser.). (Illus.). 48p. (J). (gr. 2-4). lib. bdg. 25.26 (978-0-8225-1247-9(5)) Lerner Publishing Group.

K/H (Kyb). Grade 1 Know Your Body Student Workbook. 3rd rev. ed. 2006. 70p. 8.95 (978-0-7575-2852-1(X)) Kendall/Hunt Publishing Co.

—Grade 2 Know Your Body Student Workbook. 3rd rev. ed. 2006. 76p. 8.95 (978-0-7575-2871-2(6)) Kendall/Hunt Publishing Co.

—Grade 3 Know Your Body Student Workbook. 3rd rev. ed. 2006. 76p. 8.95 (978-0-7575-2877-4(5)) Kendall/Hunt Publishing Co.

—Grade 5 Know Your Body Student Textbook. 3rd rev. ed. 2007. 294p. pap. 19.95 (***978-0-7575-2951-1(8)***) Kendall/Hunt Publishing Co.

—Grade 6 Know Your Body Student Textbook. 3rd rev. ed. 2007. 314p. pap. 19.95 (***978-0-7575-2950-4(X)***) Kendall/Hunt Publishing Co.

—Grade K Know Your Body Student Workbook. 3rd rev. ed. 2006. 66p. 8.95 (978-0-7575-2760-9(4)) Kendall/Hunt Publishing Co.

—Know Your Body Grade K Kit. 3rd rev. ed. 2006. pap. 249.95 (978-0-7575-2566-7(0)) Kendall/Hunt Publishing Co.

Katz Cooper, Sharon. Major Organs: Sustaining Life. 2007. (Illus.). 48p. (J). pap. (***978-0-7565-1965-0(9)*** , 1265926) Compass Point Bks.

Katz, Karen & Bauer, Marion Dane. Baby's Box of Fun Set: Where Is Baby's Belly Button; Where Is Baby's Mommy?; Toes, Ears, & Nose. Katz, Karen, illus. gif. ed. 2004. (Illus.). 44p. (J). 15.99 (978-0-689-03862-4(3) , Little Simon) Simon & Schuster Children's Publishing.

Ke Kino - The Body. 2005. Orig. Title: Ke Kino. (HAW.). (J). (978-1-933835-02-0(8)) Partners in Development.

Kenah, Katharine. The Bizarre Body. 2004. (Extreme Readers Ser.). (Illus.). 32p. (J). (gr. 1-2). pap. 3.95 (978-0-7696-3180-6(0)) School Specialty Publishing.

Kim, Jeannie. Body & Mind. 2003. (Whole You Ser.). 160p. (J). pap. 4.50 (978-0-439-40464-8(9) , Scholastic Paperbacks) Scholastic, Inc.

Kittredge, Mary. Human Body: An Overview. 2000. (Twenty-First Century Health & Wellness Ser.). (Illus.). 144p. (J). (gr. 7-12). 36.00 (978-0-7910-5980-7(4) , Chelsea Hse.) Facts On File, Inc.

Klingel, Cynthia Fitterer & Noyed, Robert B. Conozcamos Nuestro Cuerpo/Let's Read about Our Bodies, 8 bks. Acosta, Tatiana & Gutiérrez, Guillermo, trs. Andersen, Gregg, photos by. Incl. Ears/Orejas. pap. (978-0-8368-3320-1(1)); Eyes/Ojos. pap. (978-0-8368-3321-8(X)); Feet/Pies. pap. (978-0-8368-3322-5(8)); Hair/Pelo. pap. (978-0-8368-3323-2(6)); Hands/Manos. pap. (978-0-8368-3324-9(4)); Mouth/Boca. pap. (978-0-8368-3325-6(2)); Nose/Nariz. pap. (978-0-8368-3326-3(0)); Skin/Piel. pap. (978-0-8368-3327-0(9)); 24p. (J). (ps up). (SPA & ENG., Illus.). 2002. pap. (978-0-8368-3319-5(8)); Set lib. bdg. 154.64 (978-0-8368-3070-5(9)) Stevens, Gareth Inc. (Weekly Reader Early Learning Library).

—Let's Read about Our Bodies, 8 bks. Andersen, Gregg, photos by. Incl. Ears. pap. 5.95 (978-0-8368-3151-1(9)); Eyes. pap. 5.95 (978-0-8368-3152-8(7)); Feet. pap. 5.95 (978-0-8368-3153-5(5)); Hair. pap. 5.95 (978-0-8368-3154-2(3)); Hands. pap. 5.95 (978-0-8368-3155-9(1)); Mouth. pap. 5.95 (978-0-8368-3156-6(X)); Nose. pap. 5.95 (978-0-8368-3157-3(8)); Skin. pap. 5.95 (978-0-8368-3158-0(6)); 24p. (J). (ps up). (Illus.). 2002. pap. (978-0-8368-3150-4(0) , Weekly Reader Early Learning Library) Stevens, Gareth Inc.

Koerper und Ihre Berechnung I. (Duden-Schuelerhilfen Ser.). (GER.). 96p. (YA). (gr. 5-8). (978-3-411-04291-3(5)) Bibliographisches Institut & F. A. Brockhaus AG DEU. *Dist:* International Bk. Import Service, Inc.

Koerper und Ihre Berechnung II. (Duden-Schuelerhilfen Ser.). (GER.). 96p. (YA). (gr. 9-10). (978-3-411-05161-8(2)) Bibliographisches Institut & F. A. Brockhaus AG DEU. *Dist:* International Bk. Import Service, Inc.

Larousse Mexico Staff, ed. El Cuerpo Humano. 2005. (Mi Pequena Enciclopedia Ser.). (SPA.). 38p. (ps-k). pap. 3.95 (978-970-22-0860-0(2)) Larousse, Ediciones, S. A. de C. V. MEX. *Dist:* Houghton Mifflin Co. Trade & Reference Div.

Lauw, Darlene. Human Body. 2003. (gr. 3-6). lib. bdg. 16.40 (978-0-613-52858-0(1)) Tandem Library Bks.

Lauw, Darlene & Puay, Lim Cheng. The Human Body. 2002. (Science Alive! Ser.). (Illus.). 32p. (J). (gr. 4-5). pap. (978-0-7787-0614-4(1)); lib. bdg. (978-0-7787-0568-0(4)) Crabtree Publishing Co.

LeapFrog Staff, compiled by. Leap into Science: The Human Body. 2001. (J). (ps-1). spiral bd. 19.99 (978-1-58605-076-4(1)) LeapFrog Enterprises, Inc.

Lectorum Publications Staff. Huesos, Sangre y Otros Pedazos del Cuerpo. 1999. Tr. of Blood, Bones & Body Bits. (SPA.). (gr. k-3). lib. bdg. 16.45 (978-0-613-83084-3(9)) Tandem Library Bks.

Lee, Frances. Can You See Me? 1999. (ps-2). lib. bdg. 11.10 (978-0-613-30301-9(6)) Tandem Library Bks.

Lerner Publishing Group Staff. Body Systems: Classroom Set. 2005. (Illus.). (J). (gr. 2-4). 46.95 (978-0-8225-2347-5(7)) Lerner Publishing Group.

LeVert, Suzanne. Human Body - Group 1, 4 bks., Set. Incl. Bones & Muscles. lib. bdg. 25.64 (978-0-7614-1309-7(X)); Brain. lib. bdg. 25.64 (978-0-7614-1308-0(1)); Heart. lib. bdg. 25.64 (978-0-7614-1306-6(5)); Lungs. lib. bdg. 25.64 (978-0-7614-1307-3(3)); 48p. (J). (gr. 3 up). , Benchmark Bks. (Illus.). 2001. Set lib. bdg. 102.57 (978-0-7614-1305-9(7)) Cavendish, Marshall Corp.

Levine, Shar & Johnstone, Leslie. The Amazing Human Body. Harpster, Steve, illus. 2006. (First Science Experiments Ser.). 48p. (J). 14.95 (978-1-4027-2437-4(3)) Sterling Publishing Co., Inc.

Lewellen, Judie. The Teen Body Book: A Guide to Your Changing Body. 1999. (Your Body, Your Self Bks.). (Illus.). 144p. (YA). (gr. 4-9). pap. 11.95 (978-0-7373-0165-6(1) , 01651W) McGraw-Hill/Contemporary.

Lewis Tilden, Thomasine E. Belly-Busting Worm Invasions! Parasites That Love Your Insides! 2007. (24/7: Science Behind the Scenes: Medical Files Ser.). 64p. (YA). (gr. 5 up). pap. 7.95 (***978-0-531-18736-4(5)*** , Watts, Franklin) Scholastic Library Publishing.

Lewis Tilden, Thomasine E. Belly-Busting Worm Invasions! Parasites That Love Your Insides. 2007. (24/7 - Science Behind the Scenes Ser.). 64p. (YA). (gr. 8-12). 26.00 (978-0-531-12068-2(6) , Watts, Franklin) Scholastic Library Publishing.

Lindsay, Elizabeth, ed. Investigating Science - the Human Body. 2000. 48p. 9.95 (978-1-56234-372-9(6) , Mailbox Bks., The) Education Ctr., Inc.

Llewellyn, Claire. How Bodies Work. 2006. (Illus.). 24p. (J). (978-1-59771-023-7(7)) Sea-To-Sea Pubns.

Llewellyn, Claire. Your Body. 2007. (J). (***978-1-59771-096-1(2)***) Sea-To-Sea Pubns.

Lorenz Books Staff. My Body. 2000. (Sticker Fun Ser.). (Illus.). 16p. (ps-k). pap. 4.95 (978-0-7548-0435-2(6)) Anness Publishing GBR. *Dist:* National Bk. Network.

Lowe, Rosalind. Amazing Body Science. 2000. (Info Adventure Ser.). (J). (978-0-606-20543-6(8)) Tandem Library Bks.

Macnair, Patricia Ann. Movers & Shapers. 2004. (Bodyscope Ser.). (Illus.). 40p. (J). (gr. 3-5). 9.95 (978-0-7534-5791-7(1) , Kingfisher) Houghton Mifflin Co. Trade & Reference Div.

Madaras, Lynda & Madaras, Area. My Body, My Self for Girls: The "What's Happening to My Body" 2nd ed. 2000. (Illus.). 128p. (YA). (gr. 4-7). reprint ed. pap., wbk. ed. 12.95 (978-1-55704-441-9(4) , Newmarket Shooting Scripts) Newmarket Pr.

Margulies, Sheldon. The Fascinating Body: How It Works. 2004. (Illus.). 424p. pap. 34.95 (978-1-57886-076-0(8)) Scarecrow Pr., Inc.

Markle, Sandra. Amazing Human Body. Bosson, Jo-Ellen C., illus. 2002. 48p. (J). (978-0-439-35613-8(X)) Scholastic, Inc.

Martin, Michael. Bodyworx Vacation Bible School. 2003. cd-rom (978-0-9709763-5-2(6)) Return To The Word.

Mason, Paul. Are You Tough Enough? 2005. (Illus.). 32p. (J). (gr. 6-9). lib. bdg. 28.21 (978-1-4109-1932-8(3)) Steck-Vaughn.

—Are You Tough Enough? Body Systems. 2005. (Illus.). 32p. (J). (gr. 3-5). 7.85 (978-1-4109-1963-2(3)) Steck-Vaughn.

Maurer, Tracy. A to Z of All of Me. 2002. (A to Z Ser.). (Illus.). 48p. (gr. k-2). 20.95 (978-1-58952-059-2(9)) Rourke Publishing, LLC.

Maynard, Christopher, et al. How Your Body Works. 2004. (Knowledge Masters Plus Ser.). (Illus.). 32p. (YA). pap. incl. cd-rom (978-1-903954-44-7(4)) Chrysalis Children's Bks.

McCave, Marta. Puberty's Wild Ride, Latest & Greatest: The Ups & Downs, Ins & Downs, Zigs & Zags of Growing Up. Landry, Kim, ed. Man, Joe Rade, illus. rev. ed. 2001. (Puberty's Wild Ride Ser.). 133p. (YA). (gr. 4-10). reprint ed. pap. 5.00 (978-0-9727746-0-4(2)) Family Planning Counsel.

McCormick, Rosie. Our Bodies & Art Activities. 2002. (Arty Facts Ser.). (Illus.). 48p. (J). (gr. 3-4). pap. (978-0-7787-1145-2(5)); lib. bdg. (978-0-7787-1117-9(X)) Crabtree Publishing Co.

—Our Bodies & Art Activities. 2002. (gr. 3-6). lib. bdg. 17.60 (978-0-613-52891-7(3)) Tandem Library Bks.

Mcgraw-Hill Science Staff. Trfpaswak Human Body: Pathways. 2000. (McGraw-Hill Science Ser.). (gr. 5 up). (978-0-02-277627-5(3)) Macmillan/McGraw-Hill Schl. Div.

McGraw-Hill Staff. Glencoe Science: Human Body Systems. 2nd ed. 2004. stu. ed. 20.64 (978-0-07-861743-0(X) , 9780078617430) Glencoe/McGraw-Hill.

McNeil, Niki, et al. HOCPP 1066 Human Body. 2006. spiral bd. 22.00 (***978-1-60308-066-8(X)***) In the Hands of a Child.

—HOCPP 1122 Healthy Bodies. 2006. spiral bd. 12.50 (***978-1-60308-122-1(4)***) In the Hands of a Child.

Meacham, Nancy. Human Body: Science Discovery Activity Book, Zuman, John & Barra, Nancy, eds. Deming, Linda, illus. 2002. (Sunflower/Girasol Ser.). 24p. (J). 5.00 (978-1-58332-008-2(3)) Intercultural Center for Research in Education (I N C R E).

Meecham, Nancy. Cuerpo Humano: Libro de Actividades de Descubrubrimiento Cientifico. Zuman, John & Barra, Nancy, eds. Deming, Linda, illus. 2002. (Sunflower/ Girasol Ser.). (SPA.). 24p. (J). 5.00 (978-1-58332-010-5(5)) Intercultural Center for Research in Education (I N C R E).

Menendez-Ponte, Maria. Que Magico Es Mi Cuerpo. 2001. (Barco de Vapor). (SPA.). 94p. (978-84-348-7162-5(9)) SM Ediciones ESP. *Dist:* AIMS International Bks., Inc.

Meredith, Susan. What's Inside You? rev. ed. 2007. 24p. (J). pap. 4.99 (978-0-7945-1625-3(4) , Usborne) EDC Publishing.

Miller, Sara Swan. All Kinds of Mouths. 2007. (All Kinds Of Ser.). (Illus.). 48p. (J). (ps-3). lib. bdg. 28.50 (978-0-7614-2521-2(7)) Cavendish, Marshall Corp.

—All Kinds of Noses. 2007. (All Kinds Of Ser.). (Illus.). 48p. (J). (ps-3). lib. bdg. 28.50 (978-0-7614-2522-9(5)) Cavendish, Marshall Corp.

Molino. Mi Primer Libro Del Cuerpo Humano. (SPA., Illus.). pap. 12.95 (978-84-272-1734-8(X)) Molino, Editorial ESP. *Dist:* Distribooks, Inc.

Morgan, Sally. Inside Your Mouth & Other Body Parts. 2006. (Hidden Habitats Ser.). (J). (978-1-59389-282-1(9)) Chrysalis Education.

Moses, Brian. Munching, Crunching, Sniffing, & Snooping. 1999. (gr. k-3). lib. bdg. 11.80 (978-0-613-22043-9(9)) Tandem Library Bks.

Mullins, Patty Rutland. All about You. Holub, Joan, illus. 2004. (Treasure Tree Ser.). 32p. (J). (978-0-7166-1646-7(7)) World Bk., Inc.

My Body. (All about Me Ser.). 24p. (J). 6.95 (978-1-4048-0158-5(8)) Picture Window Bks.

My Body: Individual Title Six-Packs. (Discovery World Ser.). 12p. (gr. k-1). 28.00 (978-0-7635-8450-4(9)) Rigby Education.

My Body: Kindergarten Newcomer Books. (On Our Way to English Ser.). (gr. k up). 23.50 (978-0-7578-7193-1(3)) Rigby Education.

My Body & Me Complete Materials Package. 2001. (Illus.). (YA). ring bd. (978-1-887725-31-6(8)) Lab-Aids, Inc.

My Body & Me Complete Materials Package W/Teacher's Guide & Student Books. 2001. (Illus.). (YA). ring bd. (978-1-887725-54-5(7)) Lab-Aids, Inc.

My Pats Equal Me! 2005. (J). bds. 5.95 (***978-0-9752860-2-9(1)***) OurRainbow Pr., LLC.

Myers, Jack. On Top of Mount Everest: And Other Explorations of Science in Action. Rice, John, illus. 2005. 64p. (J). (ps 7). 17.95 (978-1-59078-252-1(6)) Boyds Mills Pr.

Nervensystem und Sinnesorgane: Fachliche Inhalte und Uebungsaufgaben. 2nd ed. (Duden Abiturhilfen Ser.). (GER.). 112p. (YA). (gr. 12-13). (978-3-411-04152-7(8)) Bibliographisches Institut & F. A. Brockhaus AG DEU. *Dist:* International Bk. Import Service, Inc.

Nettleton, Pamela Hill. The Amazing Body, 6 bks. Incl. Bend & Stretch : Learning about Your Bones & Muscles. Shipe, Becky, illus. 22.60 (978-1-4048-0256-8(8)); Breathe In, Breathe Out : Learning about Your Lungs. Shipe, Becky, illus. 22.60 (978-1-4048-0254-4(1)); Gurgles & Growls : Learning about Your Stomach. Shipe, Becky. 22.60 (978-1-4048-0253-7(3)); Look, Listen, Taste, Touch & Smell : Learning about Your Five Senses. Shipe, Becky, illus. 22.60 (978-1-4048-0257-5(6)); Think, Think, Think : Learning about Your Brain. Shipe, Becky, illus. 22.60 (978-1-4048-0252-0(5)); Thump-Thump : Learning about Your Heart. Shipe, Becky, illus. 22.60 (978-1-4048-0255-1(X)); 24p. (C). (gr. k-3). 2004. 2004. 135.60 (978-1-4048-0251-3(7)) Picture Window Bks.

—Breathe In, Breathe Out: Learning about Your Lungs. Shipe, Becky, illus. 2004. (Amazing Body Ser.). 24p. (C). (gr. k-3). 22.60 (978-1-4048-0254-4(1)) Picture Window Bks.

Nettleton, Pamela Hill & Shipe, Becky. Inhala y Exhala: Conoce Tus Pulmones. Shipe, Becky, illus. 2007. (SPA & ENG.). (J). lib. bdg. (***978-1-4048-3812-3(0)***) Picture Window Bks.

Newson, Lesley. Scholastic First Encyclopedia: All about People. 2000. (978-0-606-18597-4(6)) Tandem Library Bks.

Noyed, Robert B. Let's Read about Our Bodies, 8 bks. Andersen, Gregg, photos by. Incl. Ears. Klingel, Cynthia Fitterer. lib. bdg. 19.33 (978-0-8368-3062-0(8));

Eyes. Klingel, Cynthia Fitterer. lib. bdg. 19.33 (978-0-8368-3063-7(6)); Feet. Klingel, Cynthia Fitterer. lib. bdg. 19.33 (978-0-8368-3064-4(4)); Hair. Klingel, Cynthia Fitterer, photos by. lib. bdg. 19.33 (978-0-8368-3065-1(2)); Hands. Klingel, Cynthia Fitterer. lib. bdg. 19.33 (978-0-8368-3066-8(0)); Mouth. Klingel, Cynthia Fitterer. lib. bdg. 19.33 (978-0-8368-3067-5(9)); Nose. Klingel, Cynthia Fitterer. lib. bdg. 19.33 (978-0-8368-3068-2(7)); Skin. Klingel, Cynthia Fitterer. lib. bdg. 19.33 (978-0-8368-3069-9(5)); 24p. (J). (ps up). (Weekly Reader Early Learning Library). (Illus.). 2002. Set lib. bdg. 154.64 (978-0-8368-3061-3(X) , Weekly Reader Early Learning Library) Stevens, Gareth Inc.

Nuestro Cuerpo Habla, 6 vols., Vol. 3. (Explorers. Explorадores Nonfiction Sets Ser.). (SPA.). (gr. 3-6). (978-0-7699-0657-7(5)) Shortland Pubns. (U. S. A.) Inc.

Nunn, Daniel. Mouths. 2006. (Illus.). 24p. (J). (978-1-4034-8475-8(9)); pap. (978-1-4034-8480-2(5)) Heinemann Library.

Olien, Rebecca. The Digestive System. 2006. (J). (978-0-7368-5409-2(6)) Capstone Pr., Inc.

—The Endocrine System. 2006. (J). (978-0-7368-5410-8(X)) Capstone Pr., Inc.

—The Muscular System. 2006. (J). (978-0-7368-5411-5(8)) Capstone Pr., Inc.

—The Respiratory System. 2006. (J). (978-0-7368-5413-9(4)) Capstone Pr., Inc.

O'Sullivan, Robyn. Your 206 Bones: And Other Body Math. 2006. (National Geographic Science Chapters Ser.). 48p. (gr. 1-4). 17.90 (978-0-7922-5955-8(6) , National Geographic Children's Bks.) National Geographic Society.

Our Busy Bodies, 6, Pack. (gr. k-1). 23.00 (978-0-7635-9049-9(5)) Rigby Education.

Parker, Stephen. The Body: Fantastic Facts. 2000. (Fantastic Facts Ser.). (Illus.). 64p. (gr. 2-7). pap. 6.95 (978-1-84215-084-9(7) , Southwater) Anness Publishing GBR. *Dist:* National Bk. Network.

Parker, Steve. Cuerpo Humano. 2004. (DK Guides Ser.). 64p. (J). lib. bdg. 19.99 (978-0-7566-0421-9(4)) Dorling Kindersley Publishing, Inc.

—Digestion & Reproduction. 2004. (Understanding the Human Body Ser.). (Illus.). 32p. (J). lib. bdg. 24.67 (978-0-8368-4205-0(7)) Stevens, Gareth Inc.

—Understanding the Human Body, 4 Vols. 98.68 (978-0-8368-4203-6(0)) Stevens, Gareth Inc.

—Your Body. 2006. (Inside & Out Guides Ser.). (Illus.). 32p. (J). pap. (978-1-4034-9093-3(7)); lib. bdg. (978-1-4034-9086-5(4)) Heinemann Library.

Parker, Steve & Dorling Kindersley Publishing Staff. Human Body. 2004. (Eyewitness Books). (Illus.). 72p. (J). lib. bdg. 19.99 (978-0-7566-0687-9(X)) Dorling Kindersley Publishing, Inc.

Parrott, Leslie & Zondervan. God Made You Nose to Toes. Petrone, Valeria, illus. 2002. 18p. (J). bds. 6.99 (978-0-310-70216-0(X)) Zonderkidz.

Pascoe, Elaine, ed. Crash: The Body in Crisis. 2003. (Body Story Ser.). (Illus.). 48p. (J). 24.95 (978-1-4103-0062-1(5)); 11.20 (978-1-4103-0183-3(4)) Thomson Gale. (Blackbirch Pr., Inc.).

Paul, Karen. Kegginaqa. Cleary, Janice A., illus. l.t. ed. 2000. Tr. of My Face. (ESK.). 8p. (J). (gr. k-3). pap. 6.00 (978-1-58084-198-6(8)) Lower Kuskokwim Schl. District.

—My Face. Cleary, Janice A., illus. l.t. ed. 2000. 8p. (J). (gr. k-3). pap. 6.00 (978-1-58084-197-9(X)) Lower Kuskokwim Schl. District.

—My Face (Cup'ik) Cleary, Janice A., illus. l.t. ed. 2000. 8p. (J). (gr. k-3). pap. 6.00 (978-1-58084-199-3(6)) Lower Kuskokwim Schl. District.

Perkins, Wendy. Let's Look at Animal Noses. 2007. (Pebble Plus Ser.). (Illus.). 24p. (J). 19.93 (978-0-7368-6351-3(0)) Capstone Pr., Inc.

Perols, Sylvaine. El Cuerpo. (Coleccion Mundo Maravilloso). (SPA., Illus.). 24p. (J). (gr. 2-4). (978-84-348-6321-7(9) , SM30013) SM Ediciones ESP. *Dist:* Lectorum Pubns., Inc.

Petreycik, Rick. Headaches. 2006. (Health Alert Ser.). (Illus.). 64p. (J). lib. bdg. 31.36 (978-0-7614-2210-5(2) , Benchmark Bks.) Cavendish, Marshall Corp.

Pilobolus. The Human Alphabet: Pilobolus. Kane, John, photos by. 2005. (Illus.). 32p. (J). (gr. k-4). 16.95 (978-1-59643-066-2(4)) Roaring Brook Pr.

Playdays Staff. All about Me. Date not set. (Illus.). 32p. (J). pap. (978-0-563-36703-1(2)) BBC Worldwide.

Powell, Jillian. Sore Throat. 2007. (J). (*978-1-84234-473-6(0)) Cherrytree Pubns., Inc.

Priddy, Roger. Body IQ. 2006. (Smart Kids Ser.). 18p. (J). bds. 14.95 (978-0-312-49701-9(6) , Priddy Bks.) St. Martin's Pr.

Publishing Staff, Carson Dellosa. Human Body 4-6. 2002. 128p. pap. (978-0-88724-954-9(X) , CD-4329) Carson-Dellosa Publishing Co., Inc.

¿Que Hay Dentro de Mi? (Coleccion Primeros Pasos en la Ciencia). (SPA.). (J). (gr. 1-3). pap. (978-950-724-156-7(6) , LMA8219) Lumen ARG. *Dist:* Lectorum Pubns., Inc.

¿Que Te Hace Enferma? (Coleccion Primeros Pasos en la Ciencia). (SPA., Illus.). (J). (gr. 1-3). (978-950-724-495-7(6) , LMA8227) Lumen ARG. *Dist:* Lectorum Pubns., Inc.

Rabe, Tish. Inside Your Outside! All about the Human Body. Ruiz, Aristides, illus. 2003. (Cat in the Hat's Learning Library). 48p. (J). (gr. k-3). 8.99 (978-0-375-81100-5(1) , Random Hse. Bks. for Young Readers) Random Hse. Children's Bks.

—Inside Your Outsides. Ruiz, Aristides, illus. 2003. (Cat in the Hat's Learning Library). 48p. (J). (gr. k-3). lib. bdg. 11.99 (978-0-375-91100-2(6) , Random Hse. Bks. for Young Readers) Random Hse. Children's Bks.

Rau, Dana Meachen. El Corazon y la Sangre. 2006. (Bookworms Ser.). (SPA & ENG., Illus.). 32p. (J). lib. bdg. 22.79 (978-0-7614-2404-8(0)) Cavendish, Marshall Corp.

—My Heart & Blood (El Corazon y la Sangre) 2006. (Bookworms Ser.). (ENG & SPA., Illus.). 32p. (J). lib. bdg. 22.79 (978-0-7614-2482-6(2)) Cavendish, Marshall Corp.

—My Lungs (Los Pulmones) 2006. (Bookworms Ser.). (ENG & SPA., Illus.). 32p. (J). lib. bdg. 22.79 (978-0-7614-2483-3(0)) Cavendish, Marshall Corp.

—Pies. 2000. (SPA.). (gr. k-3). lib. bdg. 12.95 (978-0-613-54427-6(7)) Tandem Library Bks.

—Los Pulmones. 2006. (Bookworms Ser.). (SPA & ENG., Illus.). 32p. (J). lib. bdg. 22.79 (978-0-7614-2405-5(9)) Cavendish, Marshall Corp.

Rau, Dana Meachen. What's Inside Me? (¿Qué Hay Dentro de Mi?), 6 bks., Set. Incl. My Bones & Muscles (Huesos y Musculos) lib. bdg. 22.79 (978-0-7614-2479-6(2)); My Brain (El Cerebro) lib. bdg. 22.79 (978-0-7614-2480-2(6)); My Heart & Blood (El Corazon y la Sangre) lib. bdg. 22.79 (978-0-7614-2482-6(2)); My Lungs (Los Pulmones) lib. bdg. 22.79 (978-0-7614-2483-3(0)); My Skin (La Piel) lib. bdg. 22.79 (978-0-7614-2484-0(9)); My Stomach (El Estomago) lib. bdg. 22.79 (978-0-7614-2485-7(7)); (Illus.). 32p. (J). 2006. (ENG & SPA.). 2007. Set lib. bdg. 136.71 (*978-0-7614-2477-2(6)) Cavendish, Marshall Corp.

Reader's Digest Editors. God Made You. 2004. (Small Miracles Ser.: No. 1). 12p. (J). 5.99 (978-1-4003-0314-4(1)) Nelson, Thomas Inc.

Rigby Education Staff. Discovery World: My Body. (Discovery World Ser.). (Illus.). 12p. (gr. k-1). 23.00 (978-0-7635-2697-9(5)) Rigby Education.

—Head, Shoulders, Knees & Toes. (Illus.). (J). suppl. ed. 20.00 (978-0-7635-6429-2(X) , 764299C99) Rigby Education.

Riley, Peter D. The Human Body. 2005. (Illus.). 32p. (J). (gr. 4-7). lib. bdg. 27.10 (978-1-58340-717-2(0)) Smart Apple Media.

Rockwell, Lizzy. The Busy Body Book. Rockwell, Lizzy, illus. 2004. (Illus.). 40p. (J). (gr. k-4). lib. bdg. 17.99 (978-0-375-92203-9(2) , Crown Books For Young Readers) Random Hse. Children's Bks.

—The Busy Body Book: A Kid's Guide to Fitness. Rockwell, Lizzy, illus. 2004. (Illus.). 40p. (J). (gr. k-4). 15.95 (978-0-375-82203-2(8) , Crown Books For Young Readers) Random Hse. Children's Bks.

Rosa-Mendoza, Gladys, creator. My Body. 2004. (English-Spanish Foundations Ser.: 8). Tr. of Mi Cuerpo. (SPA & ENG., Illus.). 20p. (J). bds. 6.95 (978-1-931398-08-4(9)) Me+Mi Publishing.

Rosoff, Iris, ed. My First Body Book. 2004. (Illus.). 36p. (J). bds. 5.99 (978-0-7566-0279-6(3)) Dorling Kindersley Publishing, Inc.

Ross, Michael. Body Cycles. 2003. (Illus.). 32p. (J). (gr. 2-5). pap. 7.95 (978-0-7613-1976-4(X) , First Avenue Editions) Lerner Publishing Group.

Rotner, Shelley & Calcagnino, Stephen. The Body Book. 2000. (Illus.). 32p. (J). (ps-1). 16.99 (978-0-531-33256-6(X) , Orchard Bks.) Scholastic, Inc.

Royston. Moving. 2004. (My Amazing Body Ser.). (Illus.). pap. 7.50 (978-1-4109-0951-0(4)) Raintree.

—Moving 6-Pack. 2004. (My Amazing Body Ser.). (Illus.). pap. 40.50 (978-1-4109-0958-9(1)) Raintree.

—My Amazing Body, 6 vols., Set 1. 2004. (Illus.). 154.20 (978-1-4109-0485-0(7)); pap. 40.50 (978-1-4109-0954-1(9)) Raintree.

Royston, Angela. Body Matters Series. 2003. (J). (gr. 3-5). lib. bdg. 193.76 (978-1-4034-0209-7(4)) Heinemann Library.

—Moving. 2004. (My Amazing Body Ser.). (Illus.). 32p. 25.70 (978-1-4109-0482-9(2)) Raintree.

—Why Does My Body Smell? 2003. (Body Matters Ser.). (Illus.). 32p. pap. 7.50 (978-1-4034-0463-3(1)) Heinemann Library.

Roza, Greg. Inside the Human Body: Using Scientific & Exponential Notation. 2006. (Math for the Real World Ser.). (Illus.). 32p. (J). pap. (978-1-4042-6077-1(3)); lib. bdg. (978-1-4042-3362-1(8)) Rosen Publishing Group, Inc., The.

Rue, Nancy N. The Body Book: It's a God Thing. Mach, Steven, illus. 2000. (Young Women of Faith Library Ser.). 104p. (J). pap. 7.99 (978-0-310-70015-9(9)) Zonderkidz.

Sacks, Janet. The Human Body. Smith, Jan, illus. 2004. (Magic Color Bks.). 12p. (J). 9.95 (978-1-4027-1214-2(6)) Sterling Publishing Co., Inc.

Saltz, Gail. Amazing You! Getting Smart about Your Private Parts. Cravath, Lynne, illus. 2005. 32p. (J). (ps). 15.99 (978-0-525-47389-3(0) , Dutton Juvenile) Penguin Group (USA) Inc.

Schaefer, Lola M. Body Pairs. 2003. (It's My Body Ser.). (Illus.). 24p. (J). (ps-1). lib. bdg. 18.50 (978-1-4034-0895-2(5)); pap. (978-1-4034-3479-1(4)) Heinemann Library.

—Brazos, Codos, Manos y Dedos. 2003. (Es Mi Cuerpo (It's My Body) Ser.).Tr. of Arms, Elbows, Hands & Fingers. (SPA & ENG., Illus.). 24p. (J). lib. bdg. 18.50 (978-1-4034-0925-6(0)) Heinemann Library.

—La Cabeza. (Es Mi Cuerpo (It's My Body) Ser.). 24p. pap. 5.25 (978-1-4034-3383-1(6)); 2003. (SPA & ENG., Illus.). (J). lib. bdg. 18.50 (978-1-4034-0927-0(7)) Heinemann Library.

—El Cuello y Los Hombros. 2003. (Es Mi Cuerpo (It's My Body) Ser.).Tr. of My Neck & Shoulders. (SPA & ENG., Illus.). 24p. (J). lib. bdg. 18.50 (978-1-4034-0928-7(5)) Heinemann Library.

—Es Mi Cuerpo, 6 bks., Set. 2003. Tr. of It's My Body. (SPA & ENG., Illus.). (J). lib. bdg. 111.00 (978-1-4034-0931-7(5)) Heinemann Library.

—It's My Body, 7 bks., Set. 2003. (It's My Body Ser.). (Illus.). (J). (ps-1). lib. bdg. 129.50 (978-1-4034-0896-9(3)) Heinemann Library.

—It's My Body ABC. 2003. (It's My Body Ser.). (Illus.). 24p. (J). (ps-1). lib. bdg. 18.50 (978-1-4034-0894-5(7)); pap. 5.25 (978-1-4034-3481-4(6)) Heinemann Library.

—Pares del Cuerpo. (Es Mi Cuerpo (It's My Body) Ser.).Tr. of Body Pairs. 24p. pap. 5.25 (978-1-4034-3384-8(4)); 2003. (SPA & ENG., Illus.). (J). lib. bdg. 18.50 (978-1-4034-0930-0(7)) Heinemann Library.

—Piernas, Rodillas, Pies y Dedos. (Es Mi Cuerpo (It's My Body) Ser.).Tr. of Legs, Knees, Feet, & Toes. 24p. pap. 5.25 (978-1-4034-3385-5(2)); 2003. (SPA & ENG., Illus.). (J). lib. bdg. 18.50 (978-1-4034-0926-3(9)) Heinemann Library.

School Specialty Publishing. The Human Body. 2005. (Science Search Lab Ser.). (J). (gr. 3-5). pap. 24.95 (978-0-7682-2846-5(8) , Ideal School Supply) Schaffer, Frank Pubns.

Schumacher, Bev. Body Parts: Partes Del Cuerpo. St. John-Lagenaur, Elaine, tr. 2005. Tr. of Las Partes Del Cuerpo. (SPA., Illus.). 20p. (J). lib. bdg. 9.95 net. (978-0-9741549-4-7(6)) Learning Props.

Schumacher, Bev, creator. Body Parts. 2005. (J). (*978-0-9768706-0-9(6)) Learning Props.

Seidlitz, Lauri. Human Body. 2007. (J). (*978-1-59036-705-6(7)); (*978-1-59036-706-3(5)) Weigl Pubs., Inc.

Seuling, Barbara. From Head to Toe: The Amazing Human Body & How It Works. Miller, Edward, illus. 2002. 32p. (J). (gr. k-3). tchr. ed. 16.95 (978-0-8234-1699-8(2)) Holiday Hse., Inc.

Seuling, Barbara. Your Skin Weighs More Than Your Brain: And Other Freaky Facts about Your Skin, Skeleton, & Other Body Parts. Skeens, Matthew, illus. 2007. (J). lib. bdg. (*978-1-4048-3751-5(5)) Picture Window Bks.

Shorten, Chris, photos by. Eyes Are for Seeing: My Book about Body Parts. 1999. (Illus.). 16p. (J). reprint ed. 5.95 (978-1-892374-21-9(8)) Weldon Owen, Inc.

Shufen, Li. Questions about the Human Body. 2003. 62p. pap. (978-7-80051-850-8(7)) Dolphin Books, China.

Sian Revision Body Basics. 2004. (Science in A Nutshell(R) Ser.). (J). (978-1-59242-004-9(4)) Delta Education, LLC.

Sian Revision Human Machine. 2004. (J). (978-1-59242-077-3(X)) Delta Education, LLC.

Sian revision peek inside You. 2004. (Science in A Nutshell(R) Ser.). (Illus.). (J). (978-1-59242-000-1(1)) Delta Education, LLC.

Sideri, Simona. Let's Look at Mouths. Noble, Sheilagh, illus. 2003. (Let's Look at Ser.). 24p. (J). (978-1-84089-147-8(5) , Zero to Ten, Limited) Evans Publishing Group.

Silver Dolphin en Español Editors. Qué? Como? Por Qué? Esa Eres Tu Y Este Soy Yo: What? How? Why? You Are That & I Am This. 2006. (SPA., Illus.). 16p. (J). 9.95 (978-970-718-346-9(2)) Advantage Pubs. Group.

Simon, Seymour & Carle, Eric. From Head to Toe: De la Cabeza a los Pies. Carle, Eric, illus. 2003. (SPA., Illus.). 32p. (J). (gr. k-3). 16.99 (978-0-06-051302-3(0)) HarperCollins Pubs.

Smith, A. & Tatchell, J. How are Babies Made? How do Your Senses Work? What Happens to Your Food? rev. ed. 2004. (Flip Flaps Ser.). 48p. (J). (gr. 2 up). 14.95 (978-0-7945-0618-6(6) , Usborne) EDC Publishing.

Snedden, Robert. The Diversity of Life: From Single Cells to Multicellular Organizations. 2003. (Cells & Life Ser.). (Illus.). 48p. (YA). (gr. 6-8). pap. 8.50 (978-1-58810-935-4(6)) Heinemann Library.

Solway, Andrew. What's Living Inside Your Body? 2004. (Hidden Life Ser.). (Illus.). 32p. (J). pap. 7.50 (978-1-4034-5486-7(8)); lib. bdg. (978-1-4034-4847-7(7)) Heinemann Library.

—What's Living on Your Body? 2004. (Hidden Life Ser.). (Illus.). 32p. (J). pap. 7.50 (978-1-4034-5487-4(6)); lib. bdg. (978-1-4034-4848-4(5)) Heinemann Library.

Southwater Books Staff. Let's Stick & Learn. 2000. (Illus.). 64p. pap. 7.95 (978-1-84215-124-2(X) , Southwater) Anness Publishing GBR. *Dist:* National Bk. Network.

Southwater Staff. Look & Learn: My Body. 2000. (Look & Learn Ser.). (Illus.). 32p. (ps). 7.95 (978-1-84215-048-1(0) , Southwater) Anness Publishing GBR. *Dist:* National Bk. Network.

Souza, D.M. Look What Mouths Can Do. 2007. (Look What Animals Can Do Ser.). (Illus.). 48p. (J). 22.60 (978-0-7613-9462-4(1) , Lerner Pubns.) Lerner Publishing Group.

Spitters, Christopher. What's Inside You. 2002. 32p. pap. 13.00 (978-0-8059-5625-2(5)) Dorrance Publishing Co., Inc.

Stangl, Jean. Cough, Sneeze, Burp, Hiccup, Blink, Yawn, Sweat & Shiver. 2000. (My Health Ser.). (Illus.). (J). (978-0-606-20616-7(7)) Tandem Library Bks.

—What Makes You Cough, Sneeze, Burp, Hiccup, Blink, Yawn, Sweat & Shiver? 2001. (My Health Ser.). (Illus.). 48p. (J). (gr. 3-5). pap. 6.95 (978-0-531-16510-2(8) , Watts, Franklin) Scholastic Library Publishing.

Stark, Fred. Gray's Anatomy: A Fact-Filled Coloring Book. rev. ed. 2000. (Start Exploring Ser.). (Illus.). 128p. (J). (gr. 2 up). pap. 9.95 (978-0-7624-0944-0(4) , Running Pr. Kids) Running Pr. Bk. Pubs.

Steck-Vaughn Staff. Bones! The Frame Inside Us. 2003. pap. 4.10 (978-0-7398-7630-5(9)) Steck-Vaughn.

—Early Reader Program Level C: Your Body up Close, 6 Pack. 2004. (Illus.). pap. 33.00 (978-0-7398-8310-5(0)) Steck-Vaughn.

—From Head to Toe. 2000. pap. (978-0-7398-4476-2(8)) Steck-Vaughn.

Stewart, David. How Your Body Works. (Amaze Ser.). 32p. (J). 2008. pap. 8.95 (*978-0-531-20455-9(3)); 2007. spiral bd. 26.00 (*978-0-531-20444-3(8)) Scholastic Library Publishing. (Children's Pr.).

Stinson, Kathy. The Bare Naked Book. Collins, Heather, illus. 2006. 32p. (J). (ps-1). 12th anniv. ed. pap. 5.95 (978-1-55451-049-8(X)); 20th ed. lib. bdg. 19.95 (978-1-55451-050-4(3)) Annick Pr., Ltd. CAN. *Dist:* Firefly Bks., Ltd.

Stone, Lynn M. How Do Animals Use Their Mouths? 2008. (J). (*978-1-60044-506-4(3)) Rourke Publishing, LLC.

Sullivan, Erin Ash. Matematicas del cuerpo humano & Human Body Math. 2005. spiral bd. 77.00 (*978-1-4108-5682-1(8)) Benchmark Education Co.

Superlibro de el cuerpo humano: como Eres? Unit 6: el cuerpo humano: como eres? (Human Body: Being You) 2000. (McGraw-Hill Ciencias Ser.). (ENG & SPA.). (gr. 1 up). (978-0-02-277169-0(7)) Macmillan/McGraw-Hill Schl. Div.

Superlibro de el cuerpo humano: corazon y Pulmones: Unit 6: el cuerpo humano: corazon y pulmones (Human Body: Heart & Lungs) 2000. (McGraw-Hill Ciencias Ser.). (ENG & SPA.). (gr. 2 up). (978-0-02-277176-8(X)) Macmillan/McGraw-Hill Schl. Div.

Sweeney, Alyse. Nonfiction Read & Write Booklets: Human Body: 10 Interactive Reproducible Booklets That Help Students Build Content Knowledge & Reading Comprehension Skills. 2007. 48p. pap. 10.99 (978-0-439-56759-6(9) , Teaching Resources) Scholastic, Inc.

Sweeney, Joan. Me & My Amazing Body. 2000. (978-0-606-18090-0(7)); lib. bdg. 15.30 (978-0-613-26170-8(4)) Tandem Library Bks.

Szpirglas, Jeff. Gross Universe: Your Guide to All Disgusting Things under the Sun. Cho, Michael, illus. 2005. 64p. (J). 19.95 (978-1-897066-63-8(5)) Maple Tree Pr. CAN. *Dist:* Perseus Distribution.

Tanaka, Shelley. Mummies: The Newest, Coolest & Creepiest from Around the World. 2005. (Illus.). 48p. (J). (gr. k-4). 16.95 (978-0-8109-5797-8(3) , Abrams Bks. for Young Readers) Abrams, Harry N. , Inc.

Taylor, Barbara. The Best Book of the Human Body. 2006. (J). (*978-0-7534-6031-3(9) , Kingfisher) Houghton Mifflin Co. Trade & Reference Div.

Taylor-Butler, Christine. The Digestive System. 2007. (True Booktrade;: Health & the Human Body Ser.). 48p. (J). spiral bd. 26.00 (*978-0-531-16857-8(3) , Children's Pr.) Scholastic Library Publishing.

—The Respiratory System. 2007. (True Booktrade;: Health & the Human Body Ser.). 48p. (J). spiral bd. 26.00 (*978-0-531-16862-2(X) , Children's Pr.) Scholastic Library Publishing.

Taylor-Butler, Christine. Tiny Life on Your Body. (J). 2006. 32p. (gr. 1-2). pap. 4.95 (978-0-516-25480-7(4)); 2005. (Illus.). 31p. (ps-ps). 20.50 (978-0-516-25299-5(2)) Scholastic Library Publishing. (Children's Pr.).

Tether, Graham. The Knee Book. Wickstrom, Sylvie Kantorovitz, illus. 2005. (Bright & Early Bks.). 36p. (J). (gr. k-1). 8.99 (978-0-375-83116-4(9)); lib. bdg. 12.99 (978-0-375-93116-1(3)) Random Hse. Children's Bks. (Random Hse. Bks. for Young Readers).

Theisen, Patricia. The Enchanting Song of the Human: Composed of Thoughts Generated by Ancient Eastern Tradition & Modern Western Science. 2005. (Illus.). 500p. (*978-0-9793076-0-7(0)) Theisen, Patricia.

—A Magical Mystery Tour of hte Senses: What Does it Mean to be a Human? All about Your Body & You, 1 CD. Theisen, Patricia, illus. l.t. ed. 2007. (Illus.). 160p. (YA). (*978-0-9793076-1-4(9)) Theisen, Patricia.

Thomson, Ruth. Eat Just Sweets? And Other Questions about My Body. 2001. (Why Can't I Ser.). (Illus.). 30p. (J). lib. bdg. 24.25 (978-1-930643-01-7(2)) Chrysalis Education.

Top That Publishing Staff, ed. Human Body. 2004. (Know How Know Why Ser.). (Illus.). (J). 48p. pap. (978-1-84510-027-8(1)); 48p. pap. (978-1-84510-046-9(8)); 24p. pap. (978-1-84510-115-2(4)) Top That! Publishing PLC.

Traditional. Head, Shoulders, Knees & Toes. Winston, Jeannie, illus. 2003. (Ready-to-Read Ser.). 24p. (J). pap. 3.99 (978-0-689-85813-0(2) , Aladdin) Simon & Schuster Children's Publishing.

Treays, Rebecca & Fox, Christyan. Understanding Your Muscles & Bones. 2004. (Illus.). 32p. (J). pap. (*978-0-439-78505-1(7)) Scholastic, Inc.

Trumbauer, Lisa. The Body in Motion. 2003. (Science Links Ser.). (Illus.). 32p. (gr. 3-5). 23.00 (978-0-7910-7419-0(6) , Chelsea Hse.) Facts On File, Inc.

—Body Warriors. 2006. 32p. (J). (978-1-4109-2581-7(1)); (Illus.). pap. (978-1-4109-2610-4(9)) Steck-Vaughn.

Tuxworth, Nicola. Bodies. 2005. (Illus.). 12p. (gr. 2-13). bds. 6.99 (978-0-7548-1415-3(7) , Lorenz Bks.) Anness Publishing GBR. *Dist:* National Bk. Network.

Van der Meer, Ron & Van der Meer, Atie. Your Amazing Senses. Motoyama, Keiko, illus. 2001. 12p. (J). (gr. k-3). 12.95 (978-1-58117-088-7(2) , Intervisual/Piggy Toes) Dalmatian Pr.

Vargas Ocampo, Francisco. Educacion para la Salud. 1999. (SPA., Illus.). 188p. (C). (978-968-18-5849-0(2) , Limusa) Noriega Editores.

Verplancke, Klass & Sanctobin, Veroniek. Que Hace el Bebe? 2002. (Que Hace? Ser.). (SPA & ENG., Illus.). 16p. 4.95 (978-84-7864-388-2(5)) Combel Editorial, S.A. ESP. *Dist:* Independent Pubs. Group.

—Que Hace la Gallina? 2002. (Que Hace? Ser.). (SPA & ENG., Illus.). 16p. 4.95 (978-84-7864-389-9(3)) Combel Editorial, S.A. ESP. *Dist:* Independent Pubs. Group.

—Que Me Pongo? 2002. (Que Hace? Ser.). (SPA & ENG., Illus.). 16p. 4.95 (978-84-7864-386-8(9)) Combel Editorial, S.A. ESP. *Dist:* Independent Pubs. Group.

—Que Veo? 2002. (Que Hace? Ser.). (SPA & ENG., Illus.). 16p. 4.95 (978-84-7864-387-5(7)) Combel Editorial, S.A. ESP. *Dist:* Independent Pubs. Group.

Walker, Richard. Body. 2005. (Illus.). 96p. (J). (gr. 4-7). ring bd. 19.99 (978-0-7566-1371-6(X)) Dorling Kindersley Publishing, Inc.

—Digesting Food. 2004. (Body Science Ser.). (Illus.). 32p. (J). lib. bdg. 27.10 (978-1-58340-461-4(9)) Smart Apple Media.

—How the Incredible Human Body Works by the Brainwaves. Lazar, Ralph & Swerling, Lisa, illus. 2007. 64p. (J). (gr. 3-8). 19.99 (***978-0-7566-3145-1(9))*** Dorling Kindersley Publishing, Inc.

—Human Body. 2006. (Dk Online Ser.). (J). (Illus.). 96p. pap. 9.99 (978-0-7566-2293-0(X)); 64p. pap. 7.99 (978-0-7566-2232-9(8)) Dorling Kindersley Publishing, Inc.

—Human Body. 2006. (Kingfisher Knowledge Ser.). (Illus.). 64p. (J). (gr. 5-9). 12.95 (978-0-7534-5972-0(8)); (***978-0-7534-1317-3(5))*** Houghton Mifflin Co. Trade & Reference Div. (Kingfisher).

—Ouch! How Your Body Makes It Through a Very Bad Day. 2007. 72p. (J). (gr. 3-8). 16.99 (978-0-7566-2536-8(X)) Dorling Kindersley Publishing, Inc.

—Under the Microscope: The Human Body, 8 vols., Set. 1998. (Illus.). (YA). (gr. 2 up). lib. bdg. 235.00 (978-0-7172-9265-3(7) , Grolier) Scholastic Library Publishing.

Walker, Richard & Dorling Kindersley Publishing Staff. Human Body. 2005. (Google E Guides Ser.). (Illus.). 96p. (J). 17.99 (978-0-7566-1009-8(5)) Dorling Kindersley Publishing, Inc.

Walsh, Kieran. Medical Math. 2003. (Illus.). 48p. (J). 29.93 (978-1-58952-380-7(6)) Rourke Publishing, LLC.

Walt, Larimore, et al. Lintball Leo's Not-So-Stupid Questions about Your Body. Phillips, Mike, illus. 2003. 128p. (J). pap. 7.99 (978-0-310-70545-1(2)) Zonderkidz.

Ward, Brian R. Microscopic Life in Your Body. 2004. (J). lib. bdg. (978-1-58340-470-6(8)) Smart Apple Media.

Watts, Claire & Nicholson, Robert. Amazing Body Science. 2000. (Info Adventure Ser.). (Illus.). 32p. (J). (gr. 3-6). pap. 3.95 (978-1-58728-101-3(5) , Two Can Publishing) T&N Children's Publishing.

Webb, Spider. The Big Book of Tattoo. 2002. (Illus.). 512p. (gr. 10-13). pap. 24.95 (978-0-7643-1560-2(9)) Schiffer Publishing, Ltd.

—Pushing Ink: The Fine Art of Tattooing. 2001. (Illus.). 192p. (gr. 10-13). pap. 19.95 (978-0-7643-1539-8(0)) Schiffer Publishing, Ltd.

Weber, Rebecca. The Body's Business. 2004. (Spyglass Books). (Illus.). 24p. (J). (gr. k-1). lib. bdg. 18.60 (978-0-7565-0622-3(0)) Compass Point Bks.

Weschler, Toni. Cycle Savvy: The Smart Teen's Guide to the Mysteries of Her Body. 2006. (Illus.). 224p. pap. 14.95 (978-0-06-082964-3(8)) HarperCollins Pubs.

Weston, Steve, illus. Inside the Human Body. 2001. (Inside Look Ser.). 48p. (J). (gr. 4 up). lib. bdg. 26.00 (978-0-8368-2901-3(8)) Stevens, Gareth Inc.

What's Inside Me?, 5 Bks, Set. 2004. (J). 128.14 (978-0-7614-1776-7(1)) Cavendish, Marshall Corp.

Wiese, Jim. Head to Toe Science: Over 40 Eye-Popping, Spine-Tingling, Heart-Pounding Activit. 2000. (gr. 3-6). lib. bdg. 22.20 (978-0-613-25472-4(4)) Tandem Library Bks.

—Head to Toe Science: Over 40 Eye-Popping, Spine-Tingling, Heart-Pounding Activities That Teach Kids about the Human Body. Cash-Walsh, Tina, illus. 2000. 128p. (gr. 3-7). pap. 12.95 (978-0-471-33203-9(8) , Wiley-IEEE Pr.) Wiley, John & Sons, Inc.

Wile, Jay L. & Shannon, Marilyn. Companion CD-ROM for the Human Body: Fearfully & Wonderfully Made! on CD-ROM. 2004. cd-rom 15.00 (***978-1-932012-53-8(2))*** Apologia Educational Ministries, Inc.

Wilkes, Angela. The Human Body. 2001. (Question Time Ser.). (Illus.). 32p. (J). (gr. k-3). tchr. ed. 11.95 (978-0-7534-5341-4(X)); pap. 6.95 (978-0-7534-5412-1(2)) Houghton Mifflin Co. Trade & Reference Div. (Kingfisher).

—Me & My Body. rev. ed. 2004. (Ladders Ser.). (Illus.). 32p. (J). (ps-3). pap. 6.95 (978-1-58728-614-8(9) , Two Can Publishing) T&N Children's Publishing.

—Me & My Body. James, Rhian Nest, illus. rev. ed. 2004. (Ladders Ser.). 32p. (ps-3). 12.95 (978-1-58728-603-2(3) , Two Can Publishing) T&N Children's Publishing.

—Me & My Body. 2000. (ps-2). lib. bdg. 15.25 (978-0-613-43472-0(2)) Tandem Library Bks.

Wilkes, Angela, contrib. by. Mi Cuerpo y Yo: Me & My Body. 2004. (Ladders—Spanish Ser.). (SPA., Illus.). 32p. 12.95 (978-1-58728-443-4(X) , Two Can Publishing) T&N Children's Publishing.

Windsor, Jo. Fingers & Thumbs: Early Level Satellite Individual Title Six-Packs. (Sails Literacy Ser.). 16p. (gr. 1-2). 27.00 (978-0-7578-6503-9(8)) Rigby Education.

Winston, Jeannie. Head, Shoulders, Knees, & Toes. 2003. (gr. k-3). lib. bdg. 11.80 (978-0-613-66510-0(4)) Tandem Library Bks.

Winston, Jeannie, illus. Head, Shoulders, Knees, & Toes. ed. 2005. (Ready-to-Read Ser. PreLevel 1). 24p. (J). lib. bdg. 15.00 (978-1-59054-962-9(7)) Fitzgerald Bks.

Winston, Robert M. L. What Makes Me, Me? 2004. 96p. (J). 15.99 (978-0-7566-0325-0(0)) Dorling Kindersley Publishing, Inc.

Woodward, John. What Lives on Your Body? 2006. (Illus.). 48p. (J). lib. bdg. (***978-0-8368-7861-5(2))*** Stevens, Gareth Inc.

World Book, Inc Staff, contrib. by. The Digestive System/ The Urinary System. 2006. (World Book's Human Body Works). (Illus.). 48p. (J). (978-0-7166-4429-3(0)) World Bk., Inc.

—My Body. 2007. (J). (***978-0-7166-7727-7(X))*** World Bk., Inc.

World Book, Inc Staff, contrib. by. The Respiratory System. 2006. (World Book's Human Body Works). (Illus.). 48p. (J). (978-0-7166-4428-6(2)) World Bk., Inc.

Wright, Rachel. My Amazing Body. 2004. (Discovery Guides Ser.). (SPA., Illus.). 32p. (gr. 2-5). (J). pap. 6.95 (978-1-58728-212-6(7)); 11.95 (978-1-58728-218-6(8)) T&N Children's Publishing. (Two Can Publishing).

Your Heart & Blood, 6 Pack. (Rigby Focus Ser.). 24p. (gr. 2 up). 28.00 (978-0-7578-5358-6(7)) Rigby Education.

Your Heart & Blood: Individual Title Six-Packs. (Rigby Focus Ser.). 24p. (gr. 2 up). 30.00 (978-0-7578-5588-7(1)) Rigby Education.

Your Lungs. (Your Body Ser.). 24p. (J). 6.95 (978-0-7368-3353-0(6)) Capstone Pr., Inc.

Your Stomach. (Your Body Ser.). 24p. (J). 6.95 (978-0-7368-3355-4(2)) Capstone Pr., Inc.

Zimmermann, Dottie, creator. Interactive Sing-along Big Books Funny Face. 2007. (J). spiral bd. 12.95 (***978-1-58650-715-2(X))*** Super Duper Pubns.

Zoehfeld, Kathleen Weidner. Human Body. 2001. (Illus.). 32p. (J). (ps-3). lib. bdg. 11.80 (978-0-613-66639-8(9)) Tandem Library Bks.

—The Human Body. 2000. (Scholastic Science Readers Ser.). (Illus.). 32p. (J). (978-0-439-16296-8(3)) Scholastic, Inc.

—The Human Body. 2001. (Scholastic Science Ser.). (Illus.). (J). 10.79 (978-0-606-21417-9(8)) Tandem Library Bks.

Zoehfeld, Kathleen Weidner & Nye, Bill. Bill Nye the Science Guy's Great Big Book of Tiny Germs. Barnard, Bryn, illus. 2005. 48p. (J). (gr. 1-4). 16.99 (978-0-7868-0543-3(9)) Hyperion Bks. for Children.

The 3-D Library of the Human Body, 10 bks. Incl. Brain & Spinal Cord : Learning How We Think, Feel & Move. Hayhurst, Chris. lib. bdg. 26.50 (978-0-8239-3528-4(0)); Ear : Learning How We Hear. Sherman, Josepha. lib. bdg. 26.50 (978-0-8239-3529-1(9)); Eye : Learning How We See. Viegas, Jennifer. lib. bdg. 26.50 (978-0-8239-3530-7(2)); Head & Neck : Learning How We Use Our Muscles. Oleksy, Walter. lib. bdg. 26.50 (978-0-8239-3531-4(0)); Heart : Learning How Our Blood Circulates. Viegas, Jennifer. lib. bdg. 26.50 (978-0-8239-3532-1(9)); Lower Limbs : Learning How We Use Our Thighs, Knees, Legs, & Feet. Viegas, Jennifer. lib. bdg. 26.50 (978-0-8239-3533-8(7)); Lungs : Learning How We Breathe. Hayhurst, Chris. lib. bdg. 26.50 (978-0-8239-3534-5(5)); Mouth & Nose : Learning How We Taste & Smell. Viegas, Jennifer. lib. bdg. 26.50 (978-0-8239-3535-2(3)); Stomach : Learning How We Digest. Toriello, James. lib. bdg. 26.50 (978-0-8239-3536-9(1)); Upper Limbs : Learning about How We Use Our Arms, Elbows, Forearms, & Hands. Sherman, Josepha. lib. bdg. 26.50 (978-0-8239-3537-6(X)); 48p. (YA). (gr. 5-8). 2002. (Illus.). 2001. Set lib. bdg. 265.00 (978-0-8239-9695-7(6) , Rosen Central) Rosen Publishing Group, Inc., The.

BODY AND MIND

see Mind and Body

BODY FLUIDS

Branzei, Sylvia. Hands on Grossology: Really Gross Science Experiments. Keely, Jack, illus. 2003. (Grossology Ser.). 80p. (J). (gr. 3-8). mass mkt. 6.99 (978-0-8431-0305-2(1) , Price Stern Sloan) Penguin Group (USA) Inc.

Conrad, David. Burps, Boogers, & Bad Breath. 2002. (Spyglass Books). (Illus.). 24p. (J). (gr. 1 up). lib. bdg. 18.60 (978-0-7565-0228-7(4)) Compass Point Bks.

Goodman, Susan. Gee Whiz! It's All about Pee. Smith, Elwood, illus. 2006. 44p. (J). (gr. 2). 15.99 (978-0-670-06064-1(X) , Viking Juvenile) Penguin Group (USA) Inc.

Rosenberg, Pam. Body. 2007. (Icky, Sticky, Gross-Out Bks.). 24p. (J). (gr. 2-6). 22.79 (***978-1-59296-894-7(5))*** Child's World, Inc.

BODY WEIGHT CONTROL

see Weight Control

BOGS

see Marshes

BOHR, NEILS HENRIK DAVID, 1885-1962

Pasachoff, Naomi E. Niels Bohr: Physicist & Humanitarian. 2003. (Great Minds of Science Ser.). (Illus.). 128p. (J). (gr. 4-10). lib. bdg. 26.60 (978-0-7660-1997-3(7)) Enslow Pubs., Inc.

Spangenburg, Ray & Moser, Diane Kit. Niels Bohr: Atomic Physicist & Moral Mediator. 2nd rev. ed. 2008. (Makers of Modern Science Ser.). 160p. (gr. 6-12). 29.95 (***978-0-8160-6178-5(5)*** , Chelsea Hse.) Facts On File, Inc.

BOLEYN, ANNE, 1507-1536

see Anne Boleyn, Queen, Consort of Henry VIII, King of England, 1507-1536

BOLIVAR, SIMON, 1783-1830

Goodnough, David. Simon Bolivar: South American Liberator. 1998. (Hispanic Biographies Ser.). (Illus.). 112p. (YA). (gr. 6-12). lib. bdg. 26.60 (978-0-7660-1044-4(9)) Enslow Pubs., Inc.

Harcourt School Publishers Staff. Simon Bolivar. 3rd ed. 2002. (Horizons Ser.). (Illus.). (J). pap. 7.30 (978-0-15-333612-6(9)) Harcourt Schl. Pubs.

BOLIVIA

Augustin, Byron & Morrison, Marion. Bolivia. 2nd ed. 2001. (Enchantment of the World, Second Ser.). (Illus.). 144p. (J). (gr. 5-9). 36.00 (978-0-516-21050-6(5) , Children's Pr.) Scholastic Library Publishing.

Bolivia. (First Reports). 48p. (J). 7.95 (978-0-7565-1200-2(X)) Compass Point Bks.

DiPiazza, Francesca. Bolivia in Pictures. 2008. (J). lib. bdg. (***978-0-8225-8568-8(5))*** Twenty First Century Bks.

Gelletly, LeeAnne. Bolivia. 2003. (Discovering South America Ser.). (Illus.). 64p. (YA). (gr. 5 up). lib. bdg. (978-1-59084-291-1(X)) Mason Crest Pubs.

Gomez, Leticia. Bolivia. 2004. (Countries of the World Ser.). (Illus.). 96p. (J). (gr. 6 up). lib. bdg. 30.00 (978-0-8368-3108-5(X)) Stevens, Gareth Inc.

Kistler, Marguerite A. Bolivia. 2004. (Modern Nations of the World Ser.). (Illus.). 112p. (J). 29.95 (978-1-59018-531-5(5) , Lucent Bks.) Thomson Gale.

Klingel, Cynthia Fitterer & Noyed, Robert B. Bolivia. 2002. (First Reports). (Illus.). 48p. (J). (gr. 3 up). lib. bdg. 22.60 (978-0-7565-0182-2(2)) Compass Point Bks.

Lineback, Mandy & Gritzner, Jason. Bolivia. 2003. (Modern World Nations Ser.). (Illus.). 150p. (gr. 6-12). 30.00 (978-0-7910-7481-7(1) , Chelsea Hse.) Facts On File, Inc.

Ng, Li-San. Welcome to Bolivia. 2005. (Welcome to My Country Ser.). (Illus.). 48p. (J). lib. bdg. 26.00 (978-0-8368-3126-9(8)) Stevens, Gareth Inc.

Pateman, Robert & Cramer, Marcus. Bolivia. 2nd ed. 2006. (Cultures of the World Ser.). 144p. (J). lib. bdg. 39.93 (978-0-7614-2066-8(5) , Benchmark Bks.) Cavendish, Marshall Corp.

BOLIVIA—FICTION

Ellis, Deborah. I Am a Taxi. 2008. 208p. (J). (gr. 5-8). pap. 8.95 (***978-0-88899-736-4(1));*** 2006. 176p. 16.95 (978-0-88899-735-7(3)) Groundwood Bks. CAN. *Dist:* Perseus Distribution.

—Sacred Leaf. 2007. 208p. (J). (gr. 5-9). 16.95 (***978-0-88899-751-7(5))*** Groundwood Bks. CAN. *Dist:* Perseus Distribution.

Pinilla, Luis Dario Bernal. El Amanecer de las Kantutas. 2002. (SPA., Illus.). 86p. (J). (gr. 3-5). pap. 9.95 (978-84-89765-01-6(4)) Santillana USA Publishing Co., Inc.

Windle, Jeanette. Jungle Hideout. 2001. (Parker Twins Ser.: No. 2). 160p. pap. 5.99 (978-0-8254-4146-2(3)) Kregel Pubns.

BOLL-WEEVIL

Kravetz, Jonathan. Boll Weevils. 2006. (Gross Bugs Ser.). (Illus.). 24p. (J). lib. bdg. (978-1-4042-3041-5(6) , PowerKids Pr.) Rosen Publishing Group, Inc., The.

BOLSHEVISM

see Communism

BOMBERS

Baker, David. Suicide Bombers. 2006. (Fighting Terrorism Ser.). (Illus.). 48p. (gr. 4-8). 20.95 (978-1-59515-487-3(6)) Rourke Publishing, LLC.

Berliner, Don. Stealth Fighters & Bombers. 2001. (Aircraft Ser.). (Illus.). 48p. (YA). (gr. 4-10). lib. bdg. 23.93 (978-0-7660-1567-8(X)) Enslow Pubs., Inc.

Braulick, Carrie A. U.S. Air Force Bombers. 2006. (Blazers—Military Vehicles Ser.). (Illus.). 32p. (J). (978-0-7368-5466-5(5)) Capstone Pr., Inc.

Carey, Alan C. Leatherneck Bombers: Marine Corps B-25/ PBJ Mitchell Squadrons in WWII. 2002. (Illus.). 112p. (gr. 10-13). pap. 24.95 (978-0-7643-1501-5(3)) Schiffer Publishing, Ltd.

Casil, Amy Sterling. The B-1 Lancer. 2005. (U. S. Warplanes Ser.). (Illus.). 48p. (YA). (gr. 5-8). lib. bdg. 26.50 (978-0-8239-3871-1(9)) Rosen Publishing Group, Inc., The.

Chant, Christopher. Role of the Fighters & Bombers. 1999. (World's Greatest Aircraft Ser.). (Illus.). 60p. (J). (gr. 5 up). 24.15 (978-0-7910-5419-2(5) , Chelsea Hse.) Facts On File, Inc.

Dartford, Mark. Bombers. 2004. (Military Hardware in Action Ser.). (Illus.). 48p. (J). (gr. 4-9). lib. bdg. 25.26 (978-0-8225-4705-1(8)) Lerner Publishing Group.

David, Jack. B-2 Stealth Bombers. 2007. (Illus.). 24p. (J). lib. bdg. 19.95 (978-1-60014-103-4(X)) Bellwether Media.

—B-2 Stealth Bombers. 2007. (Torque: Military Machines Ser.). (Illus.). 24p. (J). (gr. 3-7). lib. bdg. 20.00 (***978-0-531-18450-9(1)*** , Children's Pr.) Scholastic Library Publishing.

Green, Michael & Green, Gladys. Heavy Bombers: The B-52 Stratofortresses. 2003. (War Planes Ser.). (Illus.). 32p. (J). lib. bdg. 22.60 (978-0-7368-2151-3(1) , Capstone High/Low Bks.) Capstone Pr., Inc.

—Long-Range Bombers: The B-1B Lancers. 2003. (War Planes Ser.). (Illus.). 32p. (J). (gr. 3-4). lib. bdg. 21.26 (978-0-7368-1508-6(2) , Capstone High-Interest Bks.) Capstone Pr., Inc.

Greene, Meg. The B-52 Stratofortress. 2005. (U. S. Warplanes Ser.). (Illus.). 48p. (YA). (gr. 5-8). lib. bdg. 26.50 (978-0-8239-3872-8(7)) Rosen Publishing Group, Inc., The.

Hansen, Ole Steen. The B-2 Spirit Stealth Bomber. 2006. (Illus.). 32p. (YA). (978-0-7368-5255-5(7) , 1244017) Capstone Pr., Inc.

Landau, Elaine. Suicide Bombers: Foot Soldiers of the Terrorist Movement. 2006. (Exceptional Social Studies Titles for Upper Grades). (Illus.). 160p. (J). lib. bdg. 31.93 (978-0-7613-3470-5(X) , Millbrook Pr.) Lerner Publishing Group.

Myhra, David. Sanger: Germany's Orbital Rocket Bomber in WWII. 2002. (Schiffer Military History Book Ser.). (Illus.). 176p. (gr. 10-13). 39.95 (978-0-7643-1549-7(8)) Schiffer Publishing, Ltd.

Perkins, Brent William. Memphis Belle: Biography of a B-17 Flying Fortress. 2002. (Illus.). 224p. (gr. 10-13). 45.00 (978-0-7643-1499-5(8)) Schiffer Publishing, Ltd.

Reed, Jennifer. Bombers. 2007. (J). (***978-1-4296-0028-6(4))*** Capstone Pr., Inc.

Thiel, Troy D. The M26 Pershing & Variants T26E3/M26, M26a1, M45, M46/M46A1. 2002. (Illus.). 88p. (gr. 10-13). pap. 14.95 (978-0-7643-1544-2(7)) Schiffer Publishing, Ltd.

Vasco, John. Messerschmitt BF 110: Bombsights over England. 2002. (Illus.). 192p. (gr. 10-13). 49.95 (978-0-7643-1445-2(9)) Schiffer Publishing, Ltd.

BOMBS, FLYING

see Guided Missiles

BOMBINGS

Here are entered works on the use of explosive devices for the purposes of political terrorism, protest, etc. .

Baker, David. Suicide Bombers. 2006. (Fighting Terrorism Ser.). (Illus.). 48p. (gr. 4-8). 20.95 (978-1-59515-487-3(6)) Rourke Publishing, LLC.

Brownell, Richard. The Oklahoma City Bombing. 2007. (Crime Scene Investigations Ser.). 128p. (J). (gr. 7-10). 32.45 (***978-1-59018-843-9(8)*** , Lucent Bks.) Thomson Gale.

Burnett, Betty. The Attack on the U. S. S. Cole in Yemen on October 12, 2000. 2005. (Terrorist Attacks Ser.). (Illus.). 64p. (YA). (gr. 7-12). lib. bdg. 26.50 (978-0-8239-3860-5(3)) Rosen Publishing Group, Inc., The.

Fine, Jil. Bomb Squad Specialist: Danger Is My Business. 2003. (gr. 7-12). lib. bdg. 15.25 (978-0-613-67876-6(1)) Tandem Library Bks.

—Bomb Squad Specialists. 2003. (High Interest Bks.). 48p. (J). 24.00 (978-0-516-24340-5(3) , Children's Pr.) Scholastic Library Publishing.

Giordano, Geraldine. The Oklahoma City Bombing. 2005. (Terrorist Attacks Ser.). (Illus.). 64p. (YA). (gr. 7-12). lib. bdg. 26.50 (978-0-8239-3655-7(4)) Rosen Publishing Group, Inc., The.

Howard, Amanda. Terroist Bombing File: The Lockerbie Investigation. 2008. (J). lib. bdg. (***978-1-59716-552-5(2))*** Bearport Publishing Co., Inc.

Parsons, Martin. Air Raids. (Illus.). 32p. pap. 12.99 (978-0-7502-2843-5(1) , Hodder & Stoughton) Hodder General Publishing Division GBR. *Dist:* Trafalgar Square Publishing.

Sherrow, Victoria. The Oklahoma City Bombing: Terror in the Heartland. 1998. (American Disasters Ser.). (Illus.). 48p. (YA). (gr. 4-10). lib. bdg. 23.93 (978-0-7660-1061-1(9)) Enslow Pubs., Inc.

—The World Trade Center Bombing: Terror in the Towers. 1998. (American Disasters Ser.). (Illus.). 48p. (YA). (gr. 4-10). lib. bdg. 23.93 (978-0-7660-1056-7(2)) Enslow Pubs., Inc.

Shields, Charles J. The World Trade Center Bombing. 2001. (Great Disasters, Reforms & Ramifications Ser.). (J). pap. 13.25 (978-0-7910-6915-8(X) , Chelsea Hse.) Facts On File, Inc.

—The 1993 World Trade Center Bombing. 2001. (Great Disasters, Reforms & Ramifications Ser.). (Illus.). 112p. (YA). (gr. 6-9). 30.00 (978-0-7910-5789-6(5) , Chelsea Hse.) Facts On File, Inc.

Stein, R. Conrad. The Oklahoma City National Memorial. 2003. (Cornerstones of Freedom). (Illus.). 48p. (J). (gr. 4-6). 26.00 (978-0-516-24205-7(9) , Children's Pr.) Scholastic Library Publishing.

Stewart, Gail. Bombings. 2006. (Crime Scene Investigations Ser.). (Illus.). 112p. (J). (gr. 7-10). 32.45 (978-1-59018-620-6(6) , Lucent Bks.) Thomson Gale.

BOMBINGS—FICTION

Hayes, Rosemary. Mixing It. 2007. 192p. (YA). (gr. 5 up). pap. 7.95 (***978-1-84507-495-1(5))*** Lincoln, Frances Ltd. GBR. *Dist:* Perseus Distribution.

Heidell, Valerie. Mirika's Story. 2006. (YA). per. 10.95 (978-0-9774822-4-5(3)) Crosam Pr.

LeFaucheur, Sandi. The Secret Shelter. 2005. (Illus.). 144p. (J). pap. 12.95 (978-0-9746481-4-9(0)) Brown Barn Bks.

Ross, Stewart. What If the Bomb Goes Off? Clark, Linda, illus. 2001. (Coming Alive Ser.). 54p. 15.99 (978-0-237-52320-6(5) , Evans Brothers, Limited) Evans Publishing Group GBR. *Dist:* Independent Pubs. Group.

Stein, Tammar. Light Years. 2008. 272p. (YA). (gr. 9). mass mkt. 6.99 (***978-0-440-23902-4(8)*** , Laurel Leaf) Random Hse. Children's Bks.

BONAPARTE, NAPOLEON, 1769-1821

see Napoleon I, Emperor of The French, 1769-1821

BOND, JAMES (FICTITIOUS CHARACTER)—FICTION

Higson, Charlie. Blood Fever. 2nd rev. ed. 2007. (Young Bond Ser.). 368p. (gr. 7 up). pap. 7.99 (***978-1-4231-0029-4(8))*** Miramax Bks.

Higson, Charlie. Silverfin: A James Bond Adventure. 2005. (J). pap. 7.99 (978-0-7868-3814-1(0)) Miramax Bks.

—Silverfin: A James Bond Adventure. Lt. ed. 2005. 514p. (YA). 22.95 (978-0-7862-7910-4(9)) Thorndike Pr.

BONDS, BARRY, 1964-

Bernstein, Ross. Barry Bonds. 2004. (Sports Heroes & Legends Ser.). (Illus.). 112p. (J). (gr. 6-12). lib. bdg. 27.93 (978-0-8225-1791-7(4)) Lerner Publishing Group.

Dougherty, Terri. Barry Bonds. 2002. (Jam Session Ser.). (Illus.). 32p. (J). (gr. 3-8). lib. bdg. 24.21 (978-1-57765-675-3(X) , ABDO & Daughters) ABDO Publishing Co.

Goodman, Michael E. Barry Bonds. 1998. (Ovations Ser.). (Illus.). 32p. (YA). (gr. 4-7). lib. bdg. 21.30 (978-0-88682-694-9(2) , Creative Education) Creative Co., The.

Miller, Raymond H. Barry Bonds. 2002. (Stars of Sports Ser.). (Illus.). 48p. (J). 26.20 (978-0-7377-1393-0(3) , Greenhaven Pr., Inc.) Thomson Gale.

Savage, Jeff. Barry Bonds. 2004. (Amazing Athletes Ser.). (Illus.). 32p. (J). (gr. 3-4). lib. bdg. 23.93 (978-0-8225-3688-8(9)) Lerner Publishing Group.

—Barry Bonds: Record Breaker. 2nd rev. ed. 2003. (Sports Achievers Biographies Ser.). (Illus.). 64p. (J). (gr. 4-9). 5.95 (978-0-8225-0472-6(3) , Carolrhoda Bks.) Lerner Publishing Group.

BONDS

see also Investments; Securities; Stocks

Condon, Daniel. Playing the Market: Stocks & Bonds. (Everyday Economics Ser.). (Illus.). 48p. (J). 2003. (gr. 3-5). lib. bdg. (978-1-58810-495-3(8)); 2002. pap. 8.50 (978-1-58810-958-3(5)) Heinemann Library.

Giesecke, Ernestine. Playing the Market: Stocks & Bonds. 2003. (gr. 3-6). lib. bdg. 16.40 (978-0-613-45812-2(5)) Tandem Library Bks.

BONES

Angliss, Sarah. Movers & Shapers: Muscle & Bones. 1999. (Human Machine Ser.). (Illus.). 32p. (J). lib. bdg. 16.95 (978-1-929298-18-1(8)) Chrysalis Education.

Arnold, Caroline. The Skeletal System. 2005. (Early Bird Body Systems Ser.). (Illus.). 48p. (J). (gr. 2-4). lib. bdg. 25.26 (978-0-8225-5140-9(3)) Lerner Publishing Group.

Ballard, Carol. Bones. 2002. (Body Focus Ser.). (Illus.). 48p. (J). pap. (978-1-4034-0450-3(X)) Heinemann Library.

Berger, Melvin & Berger, Gilda. Your Bones. 2005. (Illus.). pap. (978-0-439-77373-7(3)) Scholastic, Inc.

Bones, 6 pack. (Rigby Focus Ser.). 24p. (gr. 2 up). 30.00 (978-0-7578-5563-4(6)) Rigby Education.

Bones: Individual Title Six-Packs. (Rigby Focus Ser.). 24p. (gr. 2 up). 28.00 (978-0-7578-5333-3(1)) Rigby Education.

Burles, Kenneth T. Broken Bones. 1998. (Learning about Your Health Ser.). (J). lib. bdg. 26.60 (978-0-86625-652-0(0)) Rourke Publishing, LLC.

Crowe, Karen. Me & My Marrow: A Kid's Guide to Bone Marrow Transplants. Bendell, Norm, illus. 2000. 48p. (J). (gr. 3-8). pap. 5.95 (978-0-9702446-0-4(6)) Astellas Pharma US, Inc.

—Mi Medula y Yo: Guia de Trasplantes de Medula para Ninos. Levy, Dana, tr. Bendell, Norm, illus. 2000. (SPA.). 48p. (J). (gr. 3-8). pap. 5.95 (978-0-9702446-1-1(4)) Astellas Pharma US, Inc.

DeGezelle, Terri. Your Bones. 2002. (Bridgestone Science Library). (Illus.). 24p. (J). (gr. 1-2). lib. bdg. 18.60 (978-0-7368-1146-0(X) , Bridgestone Bks.) Capstone Pr., Inc.

Derkazarian, Susan. You Have Healthy Bones! 2005. (Rookie Read-about Health Ser.). (Illus.). (J). (gr. k-2). 31p. pap. 5.95 (978-0-516-27919-0(X)); 32p. 20.50 (978-0-516-25878-2(8)) Scholastic Library Publishing. (Children's Pr.).

Domnauer, Teresa. The Skeletal System. 2003. (Illus.). 24p. (J). lib. bdg. 21.35 (978-1-58340-311-2(6)) Smart Apple Media.

Ehrlich, Fred. You Can't See Your Bones W/ Bi. 2006. (Illus.). 40p. pap. 6.95 (978-1-59354-173-6(2)) Blue Apple Bks.

Ganeri, Anita. Your Muscles & Bones. Shott, Steve, photos by. 2003. (How Your Body Works). (Illus.). 32p. (J). (gr. 2 up). lib. bdg. 23.33 (978-0-8368-3635-6(9)) Stevens, Gareth Inc.

Gilbert, Laura. The Skeletal System. 2001. (Insider's Guide to the Body Ser.). (Illus.). 48p. (YA). (gr. 5-8). lib. bdg. 23.95 (978-0-8239-3338-9(5) , Rosen Central) Rosen Publishing Group, Inc., The.

Glaser, Jason. Broken Bones. 2007. (First Facts Ser.). (Illus.). 24p. (J). 21.26 (978-0-7368-6330-8(3)) Capstone Pr., Inc.

Gold, Susan Dudley. The Musculoskeletal System & the Skin. 2003. (Human Body Library Ser.). (Illus.). 48p. (YA). (gr. 4-10). lib. bdg. 23.93 (978-0-7660-2023-8(1)) Enslow Pubs., Inc.

Gray, Susan Heinrichs. The Skeletal System. 2003. (Body Systems Ser.). (Illus.). 32p. (J). (gr. 2-6). 27.07 (978-1-59296-041-5(3)) Child's World, Inc.

Hansen, Rosanna. Bones! All Kinds of Hands, All Kinds of Feet. 2001. (Hello Reader! Science Ser.). (Illus.). (J). (978-0-439-31707-8(X)) Scholastic, Inc.

Harcourt School Publishers Staff. Mr. Peale's Bones Level D: Library Edition. 2001. (Collections Ser.). (Illus.). (J). 5.90 (978-0-15-314432-5(7)) Harcourt Schl. Pubs.

Johansen, K. V. Pippin & the Bones. Lum, Bernice, illus. unabr. ed. 2002. (Pippin & Mabel Ser.). 32p. (J). (gr. k-3). (978-1-55074-629-7(4)) Kids Can Pr., Ltd.

Krensky, Stephen. Bones. Jones, Davy, illus. 1999. (Step into Reading Step 1 Bks.). 32p. (J). (ps-2). pap. 3.99 (978-0-679-89036-2(X) , Random Hse. Bks. for Young Readers) Random Hse. Children's Bks.

—Bones. 1999. (Step into Reading Ser.). (J). 10.79 (978-0-606-16976-9(8)) Tandem Library Bks.

Landau, Elaine. Broken Bones. 2008. (J). ***(978-0-7614-2847-3(X))*** Cavendish, Marshall Bks., Ltd.

Lennard, Kate. Bones. Gulliksen, Eivind, illus. 2007. (Young Genius Bks.). 32p. (J). (gr. k-3). pap. 6.99 (978-0-7641-3669-6(0)) Barron's Educational Series, Inc.

LeVert, Suzanne. Bones & Muscles. 2001. (Kaleidoscope Ser.). (Illus.). 48p. (J). (gr. 3 up). lib. bdg. 25.64 (978-0-7614-1309-7(X) , Benchmark Bks.) Cavendish, Marshall Corp.

Lindeen, Carol. Bones Inside & Out. 2007. 24p. (J). (978-0-7368-6696-5(5) , Pebble Bks.) Capstone Pr., Inc.

Llamas, Andreu. Muscles & Bones. Rizo, Luis, illus. 1998. (Human Body Ser.). 32p. (J). (gr. 5 up). lib. bdg. 24.67 (978-0-8368-2112-3(2)) Stevens, Gareth Inc.

Llewellyn, Claire. Bones. 2004. (Starters Ser.). (J). lib. bdg. (978-1-58340-562-8(3)) Smart Apple Media.

Lum, Bernice, illus. Pippin & the Bones. 2002. (Pippin Ser.). 32p. (J). (gr. k-3). (978-1-55337-419-0(3)) Kids Can Pr., Ltd.

Macnair, Patricia Ann. Movers & Shapers. 2004. (Bodyscope Ser.). (Illus.). 40p. (J). (gr. 3-5). 9.95 (978-0-7534-5791-7(1) , Kingfisher) Houghton Mifflin Co. Trade & Reference Div.

Maestro, Betsy. What Is a Skeleton. Date not set. 40p. (J). (ps-1). 15.99 (978-0-06-029006-1(4)); lib. bdg. 16.89 (978-0-06-029007-8(2)) HarperCollins Pubs.

—What Is a Skeleton? Date not set. 40p. (J). (ps-1). pap. 4.99 (978-0-06-445215-1(8)) HarperCollins Pubs.

Moore, Eva. Search for the Missing Bones. 1999. (gr. 3-6). lib. bdg. 11.80 (978-0-613-22347-8(0)) Tandem Library Bks.

Olien, Rebecca. The Skeletal System. 2006. 24p. (J). (978-0-7368-5414-6(2)) Capstone Pr., Inc.

Orr, Tamra. Frequently Asked Questions about Bone Cancer. 2007. (J). ***(978-1-4042-1934-2(X))*** Rosen Publishing Group, Inc., The.

Parker, Steve. Move Your Body! Bones & Muscles. 2006. (Illus.). 48p. (J). pap. (978-1-4109-1884-0(X)); lib. bdg. (978-1-4109-1877-2(7)) Steck-Vaughn.

Ratway, Michael J. & Ratway, Virginia K. Fractured Femur Fable. l.t. ed. 2003. (Illus.). 24p. (J). spiral bd. 10.00 (978-0-9724698-1-4(8)) Ratway, Michael.

Rau, Dana Meachen. Huesos y Musculos. 2006. (Bookworms Ser.). (SPA & ENG., Illus.). 32p. (J). lib. bdg. 22.79 (978-0-7614-2401-7(6)) Cavendish, Marshall Corp.

—My Bones & Muscles. 2004. (Bookworms Ser.). (ENG & SPA., Illus.). 31p. (J). 21.36 (978-0-7614-1777-4(X) , Benchmark Bks.) Cavendish, Marshall Corp.

—My Bones & Muscles (Huesos y Musculos) 2006. (Bookworms Ser.). (ENG & SPA., Illus.). 32p. (J). lib. bdg. 22.79 (978-0-7614-2479-6(2)) Cavendish, Marshall Corp.

Royston, Angela. Broken Bones. 2004. (Illus.). 32p. (J). lib. bdg. (978-1-4034-4822-4(1)) Heinemann Library.

Silverstein, Alvin. Scoliosis. (gr. 3-6). 2003. lib. bdg. 15.25 (978-0-613-72731-0(2)); 2002. lib. bdg. 15.25 (978-0-613-59546-9(7)) Tandem Library Bks.

Silverstein, Alvin, et al. Broken Bones. 2001. (My Health Ser.). (Illus.). 48p. (J). (gr. 3-5). pap. 6.95 (978-0-531-13968-4(9)); 25.50 (978-0-531-11781-1(2)) Scholastic Library Publishing. (Watts, Franklin).

—Scoliosis. (My Health Ser.). 48p. (J). (gr. 3-5). 2003. pap. 6.95 (978-0-531-16639-0(2)); 2002. (Illus.). pap. 25.50 (978-0-531-12046-0(5)) Scholastic Library Publishing. (Watts, Franklin).

Simon, Seymour. Bones: Our Skeletal System. (Illus.). 32p. (J). (ps-3). 2000. pap. 6.99 (978-0-688-17721-8(2) , Harper Trophy); 1998. lib. bdg. 17.89 (978-0-688-14645-0(7)) HarperCollins Pubs.

Thames, Susan. Our Skeleton. 2008. (J). ***(978-1-60044-514-9(4))*** Rourke Publishing, LLC.

Treays, Rebecca. Understanding Your Muscles & Bone - Internet Link. rev. ed. 2004. 32p. (J). pap. 7.99 (978-0-7945-0813-5(8) , Usborne) EDC Publishing.

Walker, Sally M. Written in Bone. 2008. (J). lib. bdg. ***(978-0-8225-7135-3(8)*** , Carolrhoda Bks.) Lerner Publishing Group.

Wood, Lily. Skeletons. 2001. (Scholastic Science Readers Ser.). (Illus.). 48p. (J). (gr. 2-3). pap. 3.99 (978-0-439-29586-4(6) , Scholastic Reference); 3.99 (978-0-439-20547-4(6)) Scholastic, Inc.

Your Bones. (Your Body Ser.). 24p. (J). 6.95 (978-0-7368-3350-9(1)) Capstone Pr., Inc.

Ziefert, Harriet. You Can't See Your Bones with Binoculars: A Guide to Your 206 Bones. Haley, Amanda, illus. 2003. 32p. 15.95 (978-1-59354-015-9(9)) Blue Apple Bks.

BOOK ILLUSTRATION

see Illustration of Books

BOOK INDUSTRIES AND TRADE

see also Bookbinding; Paper Making and Trade; Printing; Publishers and Publishing

Christelow, Eileen. What Do Illustrators Do? Christelow, Eileen, illus. (Illus.). 40p. (J). (ps-3). 2007. pap. 6.95 ***(978-0-618-87423-1(2));*** 1999. tchr. ed. 15.00 (978-0-395-90230-1(4)) Houghton Mifflin Co. Trade & Reference Div. (Clarion Bks.).

De la idea al libro (from Idea to Book) 2007. (J). pap. 4.95 (978-0-8225-6632-8(X) , Ediciones Lerner) Lerner Publishing Group.

Facts on File, Inc. Staff, contrib. by. Discovering Careers for Your Future. 2005. (Discovering Careers for Your Future Ser.). (Illus.). 96p. (J). (gr. 4-9). 21.95 (978-0-8160-5845-7(8) , Ferguson Publishing Co.) Facts On File, Inc.

Ferguson. Careers in Focus: Publishing. 3rd rev. ed. 2007. (Careers in Focus Ser.). 192p. (YA). (gr. 6-12). 29.95 ***(978-0-8160-6572-1(1)*** , Ferguson Publishing Co.) Facts On File, Inc.

Hayward, Linda. I Am a Book. Nicklaus, Carol, illus. (Silly Millies Ser.). 32p. (J). (gr. k-2). 2005. pap. 4.99 (978-0-7613-1826-2(7) , First Avenue Editions); 2004. lib. bdg. 17.90 (978-0-7613-2905-3(6) , Millbrook Pr.) Lerner Publishing Group.

—I Am a Book. 2004. (gr. k-3). lib. bdg. 13.00 (978-0-613-86946-1(X)) Tandem Library Bks.

J. G. Ferguson Publishing Company Staff, contrib. by. Careers in Focus: Publishing. 2nd ed. 2002. (Careers in Focus Ser.). 192p. (YA). (gr. 6-12). 22.95 (978-0-89434-436-7(6) , F515, Ferguson Publishing Co.) Facts On File, Inc.

Marshall, Pam. De la Idea al Libro (From Idea to Book) 2006. (De Principio a Fin Ser.). (ENG & SPA.). 24p. (J). 18.60 (978-0-8225-6495-9(5) , Ediciones Lerner) Lerner Publishing Group.

—From Idea to Book. 2004. (Start to Finish Ser.). (Illus.). 24p. (J). pap. 4.95 (978-0-8225-2143-3(1)); 18.60 (978-0-8225-1385-8(4) , Lerner Pubns.) Lerner Publishing Group.

Reeves, Diane Lindsey. Career Ideas for Kids Who Like Writing. 2nd rev. ed. (Career Ideas for Kids Ser.). 200p. (J). (gr. 4-9). pap. 16.95 ***(978-0-8160-6556-1(X)*** , Checkmark Bks.); 2007. 32.95 ***(978-0-8160-6555-4(1)*** , Ferguson Publishing Co.) Facts On File, Inc.

Reeves, Diane Lindsey, ed. Career Ideas for Kids Who Like Writing. Bond, Nancy, illus. 1998. (Career Ideas for Kids Ser.). 166p. (J). (gr. 4-8). pap. 12.95 (978-0-8160-3691-2(8)) Facts On File, Inc.

Royston, Angela. Book. 2005. (How Are Things Made? Ser.). (Illus.). 32p. (J). pap. (978-0-431-05051-5(1)); tchr. ed. (978-0-431-05044-7(9)) Heinemann Library.

—How Is a Book Made? 2005. (Illus.). 32p. (J). (gr. k-2). lib. bdg. 24.21 (978-1-4034-6639-6(4)); pap. (978-0-431-46646-0(7)); lib. bdg. (978-0-431-46639-2(4)); pap. 7.60 (978-1-4034-6646-4(7)) Heinemann Library.

Ventresca, Yvonne. Publishing. 2005. (Careers for the Twenty-First Century Ser.). (Illus.). 112p. (J). (gr. k-8). per. 29.95 (978-1-59018-298-7(7) , Lucent Bks.) Thomson Gale.

BOOK LISTS

see Best Books

BOOK REVIEWS

Eggleton, Jill. Have You Read It? Individual Title Six-Packs. Hawley, Kelvin, illus. (Sails Literacy Ser.). 20p. (gr. 2-3). 27.00 (978-0-7578-0726-8(7)) Rigby Education.

Rovin-Murphy, Deborah. 30 Biography Book Reports. 2001. 48p. pap. 9.95 (978-0-439-21570-1(6)) Scholastic, Inc.

BOOK TRADE

see Book Industries and Trade; Publishers and Publishing

BOOKBINDING

Aliki. How a Book Is Made. 1999. (Illus.). (J). (gr. 3-6). lib. bdg. 15.30 (978-0-8335-2008-1(3)) Tandem Library Bks.

Bergeron, Caroline & Berger, D. Bind Your Own Book (Children's) 2000. 25p. (J). (978-0-9679662-0-5(5)) HardBound, Inc.

Hufford, Deborah. Book Making & Paper Making: Be Your Own Publisher. 2005. (Snap Books Craft Ser.). (Illus.). 32p. (J). (gr. 3-5). lib. bdg. 22.60 (978-0-7368-4382-9(5)) Capstone Pr., Inc.

Smith, Keith A. Quick Leather Bindings: Non-Adhesive Binding Volume V. 2003. (Illus.). 320p. (C). pap. 30.00 (978-0-9637682-9-2(8)) Smith, Keith Bks.

BOOKMOBILES—FICTION

Houston, Gloria M. Miss Dorothy's Bookmobile. 32p. (J). (ps-3). Date not set. pap. 5.99 (978-0-06-443726-4(4)); 2007. 16.89 (978-0-06-029156-3(7)); 2007. 15.99 (978-0-06-029155-6(9)) HarperCollins Pubs.

—Miss Dorothy's Bookmobile. 2000. (ps-2). lib. bdg. 14.10 (978-0-613-58522-4(4)) Tandem Library Bks.

Sierra, Judy. Wild about Books. Brown, Marc, tr. Brown, Marc, illus. 2004. 40p. (J). (ps-3). 16.95 (978-0-375-82538-5(X)); lib. bdg. 18.99 (978-0-375-92538-2(4)) Random Hse. Children's Bks. (Knopf Bks. for Young Readers).

Sorensen. Curious Missie C. 2003. (J). (978-0-15-204717-7(4)) Harcourt Trade Pubs.

—Curious Missie P. 2003. (J). pap. (978-0-15-204716-0(6)) Harcourt Trade Pubs.

BOOKS

see also Authors; Best Books; Bilingual Books; Illustration of Books; Libraries; Printing; Publishers and Publishing

also headings beginning with the word Book

Aboff, Marcie. Mike's Mystery. Muehlenhardt, Amy Bailey, illus. 2007. (J). lib. bdg. ***(978-1-4048-3667-9(5))*** Picture Window Bks.

Benini Pietromarchi, Sophie. The Book Book. Benini Pietromarchi, Sophie, illus. 2007. (Illus.). 128p. (J). 19.95 ***(978-81-86211-24-3(1))*** Tara Publishing IND. *Dist:* Consortium Bk. Sales & Distribution.

Canizares, Susan. All Kinds of Books. 1999. (J). pap. 2.50 (978-0-439-04607-7(6)) Scholastic, Inc.

De la idea al libro (from Idea to Book) 2007. (J). pap. 4.95 (978-0-8225-6632-8(X) , Ediciones Lerner) Lerner Publishing Group.

Gaylord, Susan Kapuscinski & Jabbour, Joyce. Make, Draw, & Design Your Own Book. Labat, Yancey C., illus. 2006. 48p. (J). ***(978-0-439-81339-6(5))*** Scholastic, Inc.

Hamilton, John. Books. 2005. (Straight to the Source Ser.). (J). (gr. k-6). lib. bdg. 22.78 (978-1-59197-543-4(3)) ABDO Publishing Co.

Hayward, Linda. I Am a Book. Nicklaus, Carol, illus. (Silly Millies Ser.). 32p. (J). (gr. k-2). 2005. pap. 4.99 (978-0-7613-1826-2(7) , First Avenue Editions); 2004. lib. bdg. 17.90 (978-0-7613-2905-3(6) , Millbrook Pr.) Lerner Publishing Group.

—I Am a Book. 2004. (gr. k-3). lib. bdg. 13.00 (978-0-613-86946-1(X)) Tandem Library Bks.

Libros, 6, Pack. (Chiquilibros Ser.). (SPA.). (gr. k-1). 23.00 (978-0-7635-8599-0(8)) Rigby Education.

Marshall, Pam. De la Idea al Libro (From Idea to Book) 2006. (De Principio a Fin Ser.). (ENG & SPA.). 24p. (J). 18.60 (978-0-8225-6495-9(5) , Ediciones Lerner) Lerner Publishing Group.

—From Idea to Book. 2004. (Start to Finish Ser.). (Illus.). 24p. (J). pap. 4.95 (978-0-8225-2143-3(1)); 18.60 (978-0-8225-1385-8(4) , Lerner Pubns.) Lerner Publishing Group.

Pensiero, Janet. Totally Cool Journals, Notebooks & Diaries. 2005. (Illus.). 96p. (J). pap. 9.95 (978-1-4027-2241-7(9)) Sterling Publishing Co., Inc.

Pike, Kathy. Books Don't Have to Be Flat! 1998. 96p. (J). pap. 12.95 (978-0-590-12049-4(2)) Scholastic, Inc.

Prieto, Anita C. B Is for Bookworm: A Library Alphabet. Graef, Renee, illus. 2005. (National Alphabet Bks.). 40p. (J). (gr. k-5). 16.95 (978-1-58536-145-8(3)) Sleeping Bear Pr.

Realtime Associates and Mazer Corporation Staff & LeapFrog Staff, compiled by. Recognize Parts of a Book. 2002. (J). (gr. 2). 66.75 (978-1-58605-315-4(9) , LeapFrog Schl. Hse.) LeapFrog Enterprises, Inc.

Royston, Angela. Book. 2005. (How Are Things Made? Ser.). (Illus.). 32p. (J). pap. (978-0-431-05051-5(1)); tchr. ed. (978-0-431-05044-7(9)) Heinemann Library.

—How Is a Book Made? 2005. (Illus.). 32p. (J). (gr. k-2). lib. bdg. 24.21 (978-1-4034-6639-6(4)); pap. (978-0-431-46646-0(7)); lib. bdg. (978-0-431-46639-2(4)); pap. 7.60 (978-1-4034-6646-4(7)) Heinemann Library.

Starring Me Diary. 2000. 64p. (J). (gr. 4-7). pap. 9.95 (978-0-439-23312-5(7)) Scholastic, Inc.

BOOKS—BILINGUAL EDITIONS

see Bilingual Books

BOOKS—FICTION

Adams, Mark Wayne. Miss Mary's Missing Book Bag. Adams, Mark Wayne, illus. l.t. ed. 2004. (Illus.). (J). (gr. k-6). pap. 8.95 (978-1-59616-000-2(4)) Caballo Bks.

Alter, Stephen. The Phantom Isles. 2007. (Illus.). 244p. (J). (gr. 4-6). 16.95 (978-1-58234-738-7(7) , Bloomsbury Children) Bloomsbury Publishing.

Beich, Everett. My Dirty Book. Beich, Carol, ed. DeAsis, Papo & Leech, Patrice, illus. 2002. 26p. (J). (gr. 1-3). 8.95 (978-0-9631098-3-5(9)) Beich Publishing Co.

Berg, Brook. What Happened to Marion's Book? Alberg, Nathan, illus. 2003. 48p. (J). (ps-2). per. 16.95 (978-1-932146-05-9(9) , Upstart Bks.) Highsmith Inc.

Bumpy Slide Books Staff. Blue Looks for Books. Nickelodeon/Viacom International Staff, ed. 2000. (Blue's Clues: No. 16). (Illus.). 32p. (J). (ps-1). 3.49 (978-1-57973-082-6(5)) Advance Pubs. LLC.

Comer, James E. The Rare Editions. 1998. 134p. (YA). (gr. 5-12). pap. 11.00 (978-0-9650690-4-5(4)) Lyndel Pubns.

Cowley, Joy. Mrs. Goodstory. Dornbusch, Erica, illus. 2003. 32p. (J). (gr. k-2). 15.95 (978-1-56397-774-9(5)) Boyds Mills Pr.

Donaldson, Julia. Charlie Cook's Favorite Book. Scheffler, Axel, illus. 2008. 32p. (J). (ps-k). pap. 6.99 ***(978-0-14-241138-4(8)*** , Puffin) Penguin Group (USA) Inc.

Dougherty, John. Niteracy Hour. 2005. (Young Corgi Ser.). (Illus.). 96p. pap. 6.99 (978-0-552-55082-6(5) , Corgi) Transworld Publishers Ltd. GBR. *Dist:* Independent Pubs. Group.

Emigh, Karen. Bookworm. 2007. (Illus.). 21p. (J). (ps-3). pap. 9.95 ***(978-1-932565-42-3(6))*** Future Horizons, Inc.

Ernst, Lisa Campbell. Donde Esta el Libro de Clara? 2001. (SPA., Illus.). 40p. (J). (gr. k-2). 14.00 (978-84-261-3118-8(2) , JV7258) Juventud, Editorial ESP. *Dist:* Lectorum Pubns., Inc.

Gorewitz, Rubin. A New Look at an Old Book. 1998. (Illus.). 16p. (J). (gr. 1-4). pap. 6.00 (978-0-8059-4424-2(9)) Dorrance Publishing Co., Inc.

Harcourt School Publishers Staff. A Circle Story On Level. 3rd ed. 2002. (Trophies Reading Program Ser.). (Illus.). pap. 5.10 (978-0-15-323187-2(4)) Harcourt Schl. Pubs.

—My Life in a Picture Book On Level. 3rd ed. 2002. (Trophies Reading Program Ser.). pap. 5.10 (978-0-15-323358-6(3)) Harcourt Schl. Pubs.

Hopkins, Lee Bennett. Good Books, Good Times! Stevenson, Harvey, illus. 2000. (Trophy Picture Bk.). 32p. (J). (ps-3). pap. 6.99 (978-0-06-446222-8(6) , Harper Trophy) HarperCollins Pubs.

Jeffers, Oliver. The Incredible Book Eating Boy. Jeffers, Oliver, illus. 2007. 32p. (J). (ps-3). 16.99 (978-0-399-24749-1(1) , Philomel) Penguin Group (USA) Inc.

Jennings, Sharon. Franklin's Library Books. Gagnon, Celeste et al, illus. 2005. 32p. (J). lib. bdg. 15.38 ***(978-1-4242-1172-2(7))*** Fitzgerald Bks.

Lacy, Kendra. The Stone Garden. 2004. 72p. (YA). pap. 8.95 (978-0-595-30719-7(1)) iUniverse, Inc.

Maitland, Barbara. The Bookstore Burglar Level 2. Westcott, Nadine Bernard, illus. 2001. (Easy-to-Read, Puffin Ser.). 32p. (J). pap. 3.99 (978-0-14-131033-6(2) , Puffin) Penguin Group (USA) Inc.

Power, Suzanne. Love & the Monroes. 2006. 466p. pap. 11.95 ***(978-0-340-75203-6(3)*** , Hodder & Stoughton) Hodder General Publishing Division GBR. *Dist:* Independent Pubs. Group.

Ray, Price V. The Somebody Book. 2004. (Illus.). 32p. (J). per. 9.99 (978-0-9761844-2-3(7)) South Hadley Publishing.

Robertson, Elysia Hill. Tool of Life My Pink School Books. Robertson, Elysia Hill, illus. 2005. (Illus.). 112p. (J). per. 12.95 (978-0-9764444-3-5(7) , EJWV-004) E. J. Publishing.

Rocheleau, Nicole. Ryan, Me, & the Mysterious Book. 2006. (ENG.). 204p. per. 19.95 ***(978-1-4241-3422-9(6))*** PublishAmerica, Inc.

Skelton, Matthew. Endymion Spring. 2006. (Illus.). 400p. (J). (gr. 7). 17.95 (978-0-385-73380-9(1)); lib. bdg. 19.99 (978-0-385-90397-4(9)) Random Hse. Children's Bks. (Delacorte Bks. for Young Readers).

Slangerup, Erik Jon. Santa & Me. Janes, Joshua, illus. 2003. 32p. (J). (gr. k-2). 14.95 (978-1-57768-411-4(7) , Gingham Dog Pr.) School Specialty Publishing.

Sturtevant, Katherine. At the Sign of the Star. 2000. 144p. (YA). (gr. 5 up). 16.00 (978-0-374-30449-2(1) , Farrar, Straus & Giroux (BYR)) Farrar, Straus & Giroux.

Tamaro, Susanna. Leopoldo und der Buecherberg: Mit Bildern von Ute Krause. Stemmermann, Christine, tr. from ITA. Krause, Ute, illus. 1999. (GER.). 40p. (J). pap. (978-3-257-00856-2(2)) Diogenes Verlag AG CHE. *Dist:* International Bk. Import Service, Inc.

Tasker, Rod. Jack's Book. 2003. 60p. pap. 9.95 (978-1-59286-966-4(1)) PublishAmerica, Inc.

Taylor, Lori. Lissy-Lost! 2003. 113p. pap. 13.95 (978-1-59286-964-0(5)) PublishAmerica, Inc.

BOOKS—HISTORY

Aber, Linda Williams. World History. Tiritilli, Jerry, illus. 2005. (Look, Find & Learn Ser.). 32p. (J). per. (978-1-4127-1048-0(0) , 7234800) Publications International, Ltd.

Brookfield, Karen & Dorling Kindersley Publishing Staff. Book. 2000. (Eyewitness Bks.). (Illus.). 64p. (J). (gr. 4-7). lib. bdg. 19.99 (978-0-7894-6597-9(3)) Dorling Kindersley Publishing, Inc.

Krensky, Stephen. Breaking into Print: Before & after the Invention of the Printing Press. Christensen, Bonnie, illus. 2003. 30p. (J). (gr. 3-8). reprint ed. 18.00 (978-0-7567-6843-0(8)) DIANE Publishing Co.

Olson, Kay. Johann Gutenberg & the Printing Press. 2007. (Graphic Library). (Illus.). 32p. (J). ***(978-0-7368-9644-3(9))*** Capstone Pr., Inc.

Olson, Kay Melchisedech. Johann Gutenberg & the Printing Press. Smith, Tod, illus. 2007. (Graphic Library). 32p. (J). 25.26 (978-0-7368-6482-4(2)) Capstone Pr., Inc.

World History. (YA). 2003. 320p. (978-0-7525-8227-6(5)); 2000. 40p. 8.34 (978-0-7525-4526-4(4)) Parragon, Inc.

BOOKS—REVIEWS

see Book Reviews

BOOKS AND READING

see also Book Reviews; Children's Literature; Libraries; Reference Books

Adams, Carol J., et al. Journey to Gameland: How to Make a Board Game from Your Favorite Children's Book. 2001. (Illus.). 112p. 12.95 (978-1-930051-51-5(4)) Lantern Bks.

Allen, Susan & Lindaman, Jane. Read Anything Good Lately? Enright, Vicky, illus. 32p. (gr. k-2). 2006. (J). pap. 6.95 (978-0-8225-6470-6(X) , First Avenue Editions); 2003. 22.90 (978-0-7613-2322-8(8) , Millbrook Pr.); 2003. (J). 14.95 (978-0-7613-1889-7(5) , Millbrook Pr.) Lerner Publishing Group.

Beylon, Cathy. Twelve Mother Goose Bookmarks. 2003. (Dover Little Activity Bks.). (Illus.). 6p. (J). (gr. k). pap. 1.50 (978-0-486-43020-1(0)) Dover Pubns., Inc.

Black, Iris. I Can Read 200 Words, 2 vols. Black, Iris, ed. Black, Iris, illus. 2000. (Illus.). 85p. (J). (gr. k-2). pap. 25.95 (978-0-9742214-0-3(6)) Black, Iris Pubns.

Brookfield, Karen & Dorling Kindersley Publishing Staff. Book. 2000. (Eyewitness Bks.). (Illus.). 64p. (J). (gr. 4-7). 15.99 (978-0-7894-5892-6(6)) Dorling Kindersley Publishing, Inc.

Brown, Don. Across a Dark & Wild Sea. ed. 2004. (Illus.). (J). (gr. k-3). spiral bd. (978-0-616-14616-3(7)) Canadian National Institute for the Blind/Institut National Canadien pour les Aveugles.

—Across a Dark & Wild Sea. Brown, Don, illus. rev. ed. 2002. (Illus.). 32p. (J). (gr. 1-4). 22.90 (978-0-7613-2415-7(1)); 15.95 (978-0-7613-1534-6(9)) Roaring Brook Pr.

Coleman, Omer, Jr. ABC Land: Learning Is Great Fun. Coleman, Omer, Jr., ed. 2002. (Illus.). 32p. (J). (ps-1). pap. 10.00 (978-0-9720341-0-4(2)) Coleman, Omer.

Fiorello, Frank. When I Read. Fiorello, Frank, illus. 2000. (Illus.). 32p. (J). (ps-6). lib. bdg. 12.95 (978-0-9646300-7-9(9)) Pumpkin Patch Publishing.

Genres of Literature: An Elementary Exploration of the World of Books. 80p. (gr. k-5). 9.99 (978-0-7424-0181-5(2) , IF19213) School Specialty Publishing.

Harcourt School Publishers Staff. Just for You Level 2-1. 3rd ed. 2003. (Trophies Reading Program Ser.). (Illus.). (gr. 2 up). pupil's gde. ed. 42.70 (978-0-15-322474-4(6)) Harcourt Schl. Pubs.

—Lead the Way. 3rd ed. (Trophies Reading Program Ser.). (Illus.). 2003. (gr. 4 up). pupil's gde. ed. 64.60 (978-0-15-322478-2(9)); 2002. (gr. 6). pap. 5.10 (978-0-15-327892-1(7)) Harcourt Schl. Pubs.

—On Your Mark Level 3-2. 3rd ed. 2003. (Trophies Reading Program Ser.). (Illus.). (gr. 3 up). pupil's gde. ed. 46.70 (978-0-15-322477-5(0)) Harcourt Schl. Pubs.

—Time/Kids. (Horizontes (Social Studies) Ser.). Bk. 1. 3rd ed. 2002. (SPA.). (J). (gr. 1). pap. 4.50 (978-0-15-333708-6(7)); Bk. 1. 3rd ed. 2002. (SPA.). (J). (gr. 2). pap. 4.00 (978-0-15-333745-1(1)); Bk. 2. 2002. (SPA., Illus.). (J). (gr. 2). pap. 4.00 (978-0-15-333747-5(8)); Bk. 3. 2002. (SPA., Illus.). (J). pap. 4.00 (978-0-15-333749-9(4)); Bk. 4. 2002. (SPA., Illus.). (J). (gr. 2). pap. 4.00 (978-0-15-333751-2(6)); Bk. 5. 2002. (SPA., Illus.). (J). (gr. 2). pap. 4.00 (978-0-15-333753-6(2)); Bk. 6. 2002. (SPA., Illus.). (J). pap. 4.00 (978-0-15-333755-0(9)); Bk. 7. 2002. (SPA., Illus.). (J). pap. 4.00 (978-0-15-333757-4(5)); Bk. 8. 2002. (SPA., Illus.). (J). pap. 4.00 (978-0-15-333759-8(1)); Bk. 9. 2002. (SPA., Illus.). (J). pap. 4.00 (978-0-15-333761-1(3)); Bk. 10. 2002. (SPA., Illus.). (J). (gr. 2). pap. 4.00 (978-0-15-333763-5(X)); Bk. 10. 3rd ed. 2002. (SPA., Illus.). (gr. 3). pap. 7.00 (978-0-15-333800-7(8)); Bk. 11. 2002. (SPA., Illus.). (J). (gr. 2). pap. 4.00 (978-0-15-333765-9(6)); Bk. 11. 3rd ed. 2003. (SPA., Illus.). pap. 7.00 (978-0-15-333802-1(4)); Bk. 12. 2002. (SPA., Illus.). (J). pap. 4.00 (978-0-15-333767-3(2)); Bk. 12. 3rd ed. 2002. (Illus.). pap. 7.00 (978-0-15-333804-5(0)); Bk. 13. 2002. (SPA., Illus.). (J). pap. 4.00 (978-0-15-333769-7(9)); Bk. 14. 2002. (SPA., Illus.). (J). pap. 4.00 (978-0-15-333771-0(0)); Bk. 15. 2002. (SPA., Illus.). (J). (gr. 2). pap. 4.00 (978-0-15-333773-4(7)); Bk. 16. 2002. (SPA., Illus.). (J). pap. 4.00 (978-0-15-333775-8(3)); Bk. 17. 2002. (SPA., Illus.). (J). pap. 4.00 (978-0-15-333777-2(X)); Bk. 18. 2002. (SPA., Illus.). (J). pap. 4.00 (978-0-15-333779-6(6)) Harcourt Schl. Pubs.

—Vamos de Fiesta: Benchmark Books Manual. 2000. (SPA., Illus.). (gr. 4). pap. 10.70 (978-0-15-319385-9(9)); (gr. 5). pap. 10.70 (978-0-15-319386-6(7)); (gr. 1). pap. 10.70 (978-0-15-319382-8(4)); (gr. 2). pap. 10.70 (978-0-15-319383-5(2)); (gr. 3). pap. 10.70 (978-0-15-319384-2(0)) Harcourt Schl. Pubs.

Here's My Book Please Read to Me. 1999. (Illus.). 69p. (J). (ps-3). pap. 10.00 (978-0-9665911-1-8(9)) Lewis, C. Deanna.

Lock, Deborah & Dorling Kindersley Publishing Staff. A Trip to the Doctor. 2004. (Dk Readers Ser.). (Illus.). 32p. (J). 12.99 (978-0-7566-0278-9(5)) Dorling Kindersley Publishing, Inc.

Odean, Kathleen. Great Books about Things That Kids Love. 2001. (Illus.). (J). 20.65 (978-0-606-21218-2(3)) Tandem Library Bks.

Pearl, Sydelle & Iantorno, Danlyn. Books for Children of the World: The Story of Jella Lepman. 2007. 32p. (J). 15.95 (978-1-58980-438-8(4)) Pelican Publishing Co., Inc.

Ross, Val. You Can't Read This: Forbidden Books, Lost Writing, Mistranslations, & Codes. 2006. (Illus.). 152p. (J). (gr. 6). 19.95 (978-0-88776-732-6(X)) Tundra Bks., Inc./Livres Toundra, Inc. CAN. *Dist:* Random Hse., Inc.

Scholastic, Inc. Staff. Scholastic Explains Reading Homework: Everything Children (And Parents) Need to Survive 2nd & 3rd Grades. 1998. (Scholastic Explains Ser.). (Illus.). 64p. (J). (gr. 2-4). pap. 14.95 (978-0-590-39755-1(9)); pap. 6.95 (978-0-590-39758-2(3)) Scholastic, Inc.

Thorne, Randy. Quick & Short Book Reports. (FRE.). (YA). pap. 8.99 (978-0-590-74468-3(2)) Scholastic, Inc.

Trisler, Alana & Cardiel, Patrice Howe. Writing about Reading: A Reading Response Journal for Grades 3-4. 2001. (Illus.). 72p. (J). (gr. 4-5). wbk. ed. 2.75 (978-1-56762-165-5(1)) Modern Learning Pr.

Uncle Wiggily: A Child's First Reading Game. 2000. (Illus.). 16p. (J). 14.95 (978-1-891056-01-7(8)) Winning Moves.

Wallace, Karen & Dorling Kindersley Publishing Staff. A Trip to the Library. 2004. (Dk Readers Ser.). (Illus.). 32p. (J). pap. 3.99 (978-0-7566-0277-2(7)) Dorling Kindersley Publishing, Inc.

BOOKS AND READING—FICTION

Abraham, Susan Gonzales. Cecilia's Year. 2004. (Latino Fiction for Young Adults Ser.). (Illus.). 160p. (J). (gr. 5 up). 16.95 (978-0-938317-87-6(3)) Cinco Puntos Pr.

Abraham, Susan Gonzales & Abraham, Denise Gonzales. Cecilia's Year. 2007. (Latino Fiction for Young Adults Ser.). 210p. (J). pap. 11.95 (978-1-933693-02-6(9)) Cinco Puntos Pr.

Avi. Prairie School. Farnsworth, Bill, illus. 2003. (I Can Read Bks.). 48p. (J). (gr. 3 up). pap. 3.99 (978-0-06-051318-4(7)) HarperCollins Pubs.

—Prairie School. 2001. (gr. 3-6). lib. bdg. 11.80 (978-0-613-66991-7(6)) Tandem Library Bks.

Baker, Barbara. Anna's Book. O'Neil, Catherine, illus. 2004. 24p. (J). (ps). 8.99 (978-0-525-47231-5(2) , Dutton Juvenile) Penguin Group (USA) Inc.

Bauer, A. C. E. No Castles Here. 2007. 288p. (J). (gr. 4-8). 15.99 (978-0-375-83921-4(6)); lib. bdg. 18.99 (978-0-375-93921-1(0)) Random Hse. Children's Bks. (Random Hse. Bks. for Young Readers).

Berg, Brook. What Happened to Marion's Book? Alberg, Nathan, illus. 2003. 48p. (J). (ps-2). per. 16.95 (978-1-932146-05-9(9) , Upstart Bks.) Highsmith Inc.

Bernstein, Nina. Magic by the Book. Kulikov, Boris, illus. 2005. 240p. (J). 17.00 (978-0-374-34718-5(2) , Farrar, Straus & Giroux (BYR)) Farrar, Straus & Giroux.

—Magic by the Book. unabr. ed. 2005. (J). 63.75 incl. audio (978-1-4193-3607-2(X) , 42048) Recorded Bks., LLC.

—Magic by the Book. l.t. ed. 2006. 248p. (J). 22.95 (978-0-7862-8382-8(3)) Thorndike Pr.

Bloom, Becky. Wolf. Biet, Pascal, illus. 1999. 32p. (J). (ps-3). pap. 16.95 (978-0-531-30155-5(9) , Orchard Bks.) Scholastic, Inc.

Bloor, Edward. Story Time. 2002. (J). 17.95 (978-0-439-26686-4(6)) Scholastic, Inc.

Bode, N. E. Nobodies. Ferguson, Peter, illus. 2005. 304p. (J). 16.99 (978-0-06-055738-6(9)); lib. bdg. 17.89 (978-0-06-055739-3(7)) HarperCollins Pubs.

—The Somebodies. 2006. (Illus.). 288p. (J). lib. bdg. 17.89 (978-0-06-079112-4(8)) HarperCollins Pubs.

—The Somebodies. Ferguson, Peter, illus. 2006. 288p. (J). 16.99 (978-0-06-079111-7(X) , HarperCollins) HarperCollins Pubs.

Borden, Louise & Gustavson, Adam. The Day Eddie Met the Author. 2004. (Illus.). 44p. (J). pap. 6.99 (978-0-689-86720-0(4) , Aladdin) Simon & Schuster Children's Publishing.

Brown, Marc. D. W.'s Library Card. Brown, Marc, illus. 2002. (D. W. Ser.). (Illus.). (YA). 20.60 (978-0-7587-9783-4(4)) Book Wholesalers, Inc.

—D. W.'s Library Card. Brown, Marc, illus. (D. W. Ser.). (Illus.). 24p. (J). (ps-1). 2003. pap. 5.99 (978-0-316-73820-0(4)); 2001. 14.95 (978-0-316-11013-6(2)) Little, Brown Bks. for Young Readers.

Brown, Marc & Sarfatti, Esther. D. W. y el Carne de Biblioteca. 2004. Tr. of D.W.'s Library Card. (ENG & SPA., Illus.). (J). pap. 6.95 (978-1-930332-47-8(5)) Lectorum Pubns., Inc.

Bruss, Deborah. Book! Book! Book! Beeke, Tiphanie, illus. 2001. (J). (ps-1). 40p. pap. 16.95 (978-0-439-13525-2(7)); pap. (978-0-439-13526-9(5)) Scholastic, Inc.

Bulla, Lynda. The Old Clock on the Wall. Hergenroeder, Ernie, illus. 2002. 20p. (J). lib. bdg. 17.95 (978-0-9724272-0-3(1) , 3000) Katydid Publishing LLC.

Burleigh, Robert. I Love Going Through This Book. Yaccarino, Dan, illus. 40p. (J). (ps-3). Date not set. pap. 5.99 (978-0-06-443647-2(0)); 2001. 15.99 (978-0-06-028805-1(1) , Cotler, Joanna Books); 2001. 15.89 (978-0-06-028806-8(X) , Cotler, Joanna Books) HarperCollins Pubs.

Carlson, Nancy. I Don't Like to Read! Carlson, Nancy, illus. 2007. (Illus.). 32p. (J). (gr. k-2). 15.99 (978-0-670-06191-4(3) , Viking Juvenile) Penguin Group (USA) Inc.

Catalanotto, Peter. Ivan the Terrier. Catalanotto, Peter, illus. 2007. 32p. (J). (ps-k). 16.99 (978-1-4169-1247-7(9)) Simon & Schuster Children's Publishing.

Cazet, Denys. Will You Read to Me? Cazet, Denys, illus. 2007. 32p. (J). (ps-1). 16.99 (978-1-4169-0935-4(4)) Simon & Schuster Children's Publishing.

Charlip, Remy. Why I Will Never Ever Ever Ever Have Enough Time to Read This Book. Muth, Jon J., illus. 2004. 38p. (gr. 1 up). 14.95 (978-1-58246-018-5(3) , Tricycle Pr.) Ten Speed Pr.

Child, Lauren. Beware of the Storybook Wolves. ed. 2004. (Illus.). (J). (gr. k-3). spiral bd. (978-0-616-14568-5(3)) Canadian National Institute for the Blind/Institut National Canadien pour les Aveugles.

—But, Excuse Me, That Is My Book. 2006. (Illus.). 32p. (J). (ps). 16.99 (978-0-8037-3096-0(9) , Dial) Penguin Group (USA) Inc.

—Who's Afraid of the Big Bad Book? Child, Lauren, illus. 2003. (Illus.). 36p. (ps-2). 16.99 (978-0-7868-0926-4(4)) Hyperion Bks. for Children.

Christian, Peggy. The Bookstore Mouse. Lippincott, Gary A., illus. 2002. 144p. (YA). (gr. 3-7). pap. 6.95 (978-0-15-204564-7(3) , Harcourt Paperbacks) Harcourt Children's Bks.

—Bookstore Mouse. 2002. (gr. 3-6). lib. bdg. 14.10 (978-0-613-56250-8(X)) Tandem Library Bks.

Colfer, Eoin. The Legend of Spud Murphy. McCoy, Glenn, illus. 112p. (gr. 2-6). 2005. reprint ed. pap. 4.99 (978-0-7868-5504-9(5)); Bk. 1. 2004. (J). 12.95 (978-0-7868-5501-8(0)) Miramax Bks.

—The Legend of the Worst Boy in the World, Bk. 3. McCoy, Glenn, illus. 3rd rev. ed. 2007. 112p. (J). (gr. 2-6). 12.95 (978-0-7868-5503-2(7)) Hyperion Pr.

Conover, Chris. The Lion's Share. Conover, Chris, illus. 2003. (Illus.). 40p. (J). pap. 6.95 (978-0-374-44481-5(1) , Sunburst) Farrar, Straus & Giroux.

Cowell, Cressida. Little Bo Peep's Library Book. Cowell, Cressida, illus. 1999. (Illus.). 32p. (J). (ps-2). pap. 14.95 (978-0-531-30179-1(6) , Orchard Bks.) Scholastic, Inc.

Craig, Paula M. Mr. Wiggle's Book. Sharp, Dan, illus. 2000. 20p. (J). 3.99 (978-1-56822-975-1(5) , IF22085) School Specialty Publishing.

Craig, Paula M. & Thompson, Carol L. Mr. Wiggle's Book. rev. ed. 2003. (Mr. Wiggle Ser.). (Illus.). 32p. (J). 9.95 (978-1-57768-616-3(0) , Waterbird Bks.) School Specialty Publishing.

Crimi, Carolyn. Henry & the Buccaneer Bunnies. Manders, John, illus. 2005. 40p. (J). (ps-3). 15.99 (978-0-7636-2449-1(7)) Candlewick Pr.

Dahl, Michael. Attack of the Paperbats. Garvey, Brann, illus. 2007. (J). 40p. (***978-1-59889-325-0(4)***); 33p. pap. (***978-1-59889-420-2(X)***) Stone Arch Bks.

—The Beast Beneath the Stairs. Garvey, Brann, illus. 2007. (J). 40p. (***978-1-59889-323-6(8)***); 33p. pap. (***978-1-59889-418-9(8)***) Stone Arch Bks.

—The Book That Dripped Blood. Kendall, Bradford, illus. 2007. (J). 40p. (***978-1-59889-324-3(6)***); 33p. pap. (***978-1-59889-419-6(6)***) Stone Arch Bks.

—The Eye in the Graveyard. Garvey, Brann, illus. 2007. (J). 40p. (***978-1-59889-328-1(9)***); 33p. pap. (***978-1-59889-423-3(4)***) Stone Arch Bks.

—Poison Pages. Garvey, Brann, illus. 2007. (J). 40p. (***978-1-59889-327-4(0)***); 33p. pap. (***978-1-59889-422-6(6)***) Stone Arch Bks.

—The Smashing Scroll. Kendall, Bradford, illus. 2007. (J). 40p. (***978-1-59889-326-7(2)***); 33p. pap. (***978-1-59889-421-9(8)***) Stone Arch Bks.

Dakos, Kalli & Desmarteau, Alicia. Our Principal Promised to Kiss a Pig. DiRocco, Carl, illus. 2004. 32p. (J). (gr. 2-5). 15.95 (978-0-8075-6629-9(2)) Whitman, Albert & Co.

De Smet, Marian. Anna's Tight Squeeze. Meijer, Marja, illus. 2003. Orig. Title: Op Slot. 32p. (J). pap. 5.95 (978-1-58925-378-0(7) , tiger tales) ME Media LLC.

—Anna's Tight Squeeze. 2003. Orig. Title: Op Slot. (gr. k-3). lib. bdg. 14.10 (978-0-613-84707-0(5)) Tandem Library Bks.

DeFelice, Cynthia C. The Real, True Dulcie Campbell. Alley, R. W., illus. 2002. 32p. (J). (gr. k-3). 16.00 (978-0-374-36220-1(3) , Farrar, Straus & Giroux (BYR)) Farrar, Straus & Giroux.

deRubertis, Barbara. Rooney 'Roo. Cockrille, Eva V., illus. 1998. (Let's Read Together Ser.). 32p. (J). (ps-3). pap. 4.95 (978-1-57565-044-9(4)); pap. 8.95 incl. audio (978-1-57565-049-4(5)) Kane Pr., The.

Donaldson, Julia. Charlie Cook's Favourite Book. Scheffler, Axel, illus. 2006. 32p. (J). (ps). 16.99 (978-0-8037-3142-4(6) , Dial) Penguin Group (USA) Inc.

Donaldson, Julia & Richards, Lucy. The Quick Brown Fox Club. 2006. (Red Bananas Ser.). (Illus.). 48p. (J). (978-0-7787-1080-6(7)) Crabtree Publishing Co.

Ernst, Lisa Campbell. Stella Louella's Runaway Book. Ernst, Lisa Campbell, illus. (Illus.). 40p. (J). 2001. pap. 7.99 (978-0-689-84460-7(3) , Aladdin); 1998. 16.95 (978-0-689-81883-7(1)) Simon & Schuster Children's Publishing.

—Stella Louella's Runaway Book. 2001. (ps-2). lib. bdg. 15.30 (978-0-613-52296-0(6)) Tandem Library Bks.

Faulkner, Keith. The Monster Who Loved Books. Lambert, Jonathan, illus. 2002. 16p. (J). (ps-k). pap. 10.95 (978-0-439-34099-1(3) , Orchard Bks.) Scholastic, Inc.

Fernandez, Giselle. Gigi & the Birthday Ring. Petersen, Sheli, illus. 2005. (J). (978-1-56492-358-5(4)) Laredo Publishing Co., Inc.

Finchler, Judy & O'Malley, Kevin. Miss Malarkey Leaves No Reader Behind. O'Malley, Kevin, illus. 2006. (Illus.). 32p. (J). 17.85 (978-0-8027-8085-0(7)); 16.95 (978-0-8027-8084-3(9)) Walker & Co.

Frederick, Heather Vogel. The Mother-Daughter Book Club. 2007. 256p. (J). (gr. 4-7). 15.99 (978-0-689-86412-4(4)) Simon & Schuster Children's Publishing.

Funke, Cornelia. Inkheart. 2008. (Inkheart Movie Ser.). 576p. (J). 9.99 (***978-0-545-04626-8(2)*** , Scholastic) Scholastic, Inc.

—Inkheart. Bell, Anthea, tr. 2005. (Illus.). 560p. (ps-7). pap. 8.99 (978-0-439-70910-1(5)) Scholastic, Inc.

—Inkheart. 2003. 544p. (J). 60.00 (978-0-439-61671-3(9) , Chicken Hse., The) Scholastic, Inc.

—Inkheart. Bell, Anthea, tr. from GER. 2003. (Illus.). 544p. (J). (gr. 3-6). pap. 19.95 (978-0-439-53164-1(0) , Chicken Hse., The) Scholastic, Inc.

—Inkheart. Bell, Anthea, tr. 2005. 550p. (J). (ps-7). lib. bdg. 15.04 (978-0-606-33803-5(9)) Tandem Library Bks.

—Inkheart. l.t. ed. 2006. 709p. (YA). pap. 10.95 (978-0-7862-8363-7(7)) Thorndike Pr.

—Inkheart. Bell, Anthea, tr. l.t. ed. 2005. (Illus.). 709p. (J). (gr. 3-7). 23.95 (978-0-7862-8041-4(7) , Large Print Pr.) Thorndike Pr.

—Inkspell. 2007. 656p. (J). (gr. 4-7). pap. 9.99 (978-0-439-55401-5(2) , Chicken Hse., The) Scholastic, Inc.

—Inkspell. l.t. ed. 2006. 779p. (YA). 23.95 (978-0-7862-8040-7(9)) Thorndike Pr.

Garland, Michael. Miss Smith Reads Again! Garland, Michael, illus. 2006. (Illus.). 32p. (J). (ps). 15.99 (978-0-525-47722-8(5) , Dutton Juvenile) Penguin Group (USA) Inc.

—Miss Smith Reads Again! 2006. (Illus.). (J). (***978-1-4156-8098-8(1)*** , Dutton Juvenile) Penguin Group (USA) Inc.

Garland, Michael. Miss Smith's Incredible Storybook. Garland, Michael, illus. 32p. (J). 2005. pap. 6.99 (978-0-14-240282-5(6) , Puffin); 2003. (Illus.). 16.99 (978-0-525-47133-2(2) , Dutton Juvenile) Penguin Group (USA) Inc.

—Miss Smith's Incredible Storybook. 2007. 27.95 incl. audio (***978-0-8045-6945-3(2)***); 29.95 incl. audio compact disk (***978-0-8045-4159-6(0)***) Spoken Arts, Inc.

Gifford, Peggy. Moxy Maxwell Does Not Love Stuart Little. Fisher, Valorie, photos by. 2007. (Illus.). 104p. (J). (gr. 2-6). 12.99 (978-0-375-83915-3(1)); lib. bdg. 15.99 (978-0-375-93915-0(6)) Random Hse. Children's Bks. (Schwartz & Wade Bks.).

Gifford, Peggy. Moxy Maxwell Does Not Love Stuart Little. Fisher, Valorie, photos by. 2008. (Illus.). 112p. (J). (gr. 2-6). 5.50 (***978-0-440-42230-3(2)*** , Yearling) Random Hse. Children's Bks.

Gravett, Emily. Wolves. Gravett, Emily, illus. 2006. (Illus.). 40p. (J). (gr. k-3). 16.99 (978-1-4169-1491-4(9) , Simon & Schuster Children's Publishing) Simon & Schuster Children's Publishing.

Hahn, Mary Downing. Janey & the Famous Author. Bush, Timothy, illus. 2005. 48p. (J). (gr. k-3). 15.00 (978-0-618-35408-5(5) , Clarion Bks.) Houghton Mifflin Co. Trade & Reference Div.

Hallinan, P. K. Just Open a Book. (J). 24p. 7.95 (978-0-8249-5353-9(3) , Ideals); 22p. pap. 5.95 (978-0-8249-5354-6(1)); 24p. lib. bdg. 11.00 (978-0-8249-5355-3(X) , Ideals); 2004. (Illus.). 48p. pap. 9.95 (978-0-8249-5490-1(4)) Ideals Pubns.

Harcourt School Publishers Staff. Working Hard 5-Pack, On Level. 3rd ed. 2002. (Trophies Reading Program Ser.). (Illus.). (gr. 1). pap. 20.10 (978-0-15-326837-3(9)) Harcourt Schl. Pubs.

Hardinge, Frances. Fly by Night. 2008. 512p. (J). pap. 7.99 (***978-0-06-087630-2(1)*** , Harper Trophy) HarperCollins Pubs.

Harris, Robie H. Maybe a Bear Ate It! Emberley, Michael, illus. 2008. (Jewel Fairies Ser.). 40p. (J). pap. 15.99 (***978-0-439-92961-5(X)*** , Orchard Bks.) Scholastic, Inc.

Haseley, Dennis. A Story for Bear. LaMarche, Jim, illus. 2002. 32p. (J). (gr. k-3). 16.00 (978-0-15-200239-8(1) , Silver Whistle) Harcourt Trade Pubs.

Haselhurst, Maureen. The Tickety Tale Teller. 2007. (J). lib. bdg. 16.95 (***978-1-59566-335-1(5)***) QEB Publishing Inc.

Hautzig, Deborah. Little Witch Learns to Read. Wickstrom, Sylvie K., illus. 2003. (Step into Reading Ser.). 48p. (J). (gr. 1-3). pap. 3.99 (978-0-375-82179-0(1) , Random Hse. Bks. for Young Readers) Random Hse. Children's Bks.

—Little Witch Learns to Read. 2003. (gr. k-3). lib. bdg. 11.80 (978-0-613-89789-1(7)) Tandem Library Bks.

Heap, Sue. Four Friends Together. Heap, Sue, illus. 2003. (Illus.). 32p. (J). (ps). 15.99 (978-0-7636-2111-7(0)) Candlewick Pr.

Hennessy, B. G. Claire & the Unicorn Happy Ever After. Mitchell, Susan, illus. 2005. 32p. (J). 12.95 (978-1-4169-0815-9(3)) Simon & Schuster Children's Publishing.

Henson, Heather. That Bookwoman. Small, David, illus. 2008. (J). (***978-1-4169-0812-8(9)***) Simon & Schuster Children's Publishing.

Herman, Gail. Sam's First Library Card. 2003. (gr. k-3). lib. bdg. 11.25 (978-0-613-67583-3(5)) Tandem Library Bks.

Hill, Susan. Stuart at the Library. Halverson, Lydia, illus. 2001. (I Can Read Bks.). 32p. (J). (ps-1). pap. 3.99 (978-0-06-444303-6(5) , Harper Trophy); Bk. 1. 15.99 (978-0-06-029538-7(4)); Bk. 1. 15.89 (978-0-06-029632-2(1)) HarperCollins Pubs.

Hillenbrand, Will. My Book Box. 2006. (Illus.). 32p. (J). 16.00 (978-0-15-202029-3(2)) Harcourt Trade Pubs.

Holstead, Christy. Benjamin Saves the Books: An Adventure in Words & Wisdom. 2001. 40p. (J). pap. (978-0-88362-354-1(4)); 60p. pap., tchr. ed. (978-0-88362-355-8(2)) GATFPress.

Hurd, Clement, illus. Johnny Lion's Book. 2002. (Johnny Lion Ser.). (J). 12.34 (978-0-7587-4936-9(8)) Book Wholesalers, Inc.

Hurd, Edith Thacher. Johnny Lion's Book. Hurd, Clement, illus. (I Can Read Bks.). 64p. (J). (gr. k-3). 2001. pap. 3.99 (978-0-06-444297-8(7) , Harper Trophy); 2000. 14.95 (978-0-06-029333-8(0)) HarperCollins Pubs.

—Johnny Lion's Book. 2001. (I Can Read Bks.). (Illus.). (J). 10.79 (978-0-606-20745-4(7)) Tandem Library Bks.

—Johnny Lion's Book. Hurd, Clement, illus. 2001. 63p. (J). (ps-ps). lib. bdg. 11.80 (978-0-613-33707-6(7)) Tandem Library Bks.

Ivey, Randall. Jay & the Bounty of Books. Galey, Chuck, illus. 2007. 32p. (J). (gr. k-3). 15.95 (978-1-58980-372-5(8)) Pelican Publishing Co., Inc.

Jenkins, Jerry B. & Fabry, Chris. The Book of the King. 2007. (Wormling Ser.). 288p. (J). (gr. 5-9). pap. 7.99 (***978-1-4143-0155-6(3)***) Tyndale Hse. Pubs.

Jennings, Sharon, et al. Franklin's Reading Club. Jeffrey, Sean & Koren, Mark, illus. 2004. (Kids Can Read Ser.). 32p. (J). (gr. k-3). (978-1-55337-370-4(7)); (978-1-55337-369-8(3)) Kids Can Pr., Ltd.

A B

Jeram, Anita. I Love My Little Storybook. Jeram, Anita, illus. 2002. (Illus.). 32p. (J). (gr. k-k). 12.99 (978-0-7636-1698-4(2)) Candlewick Pr.

Jorgensen, Richard. Reading with Dad. Hanson, Warren, illus. 2000. 40p. (J). (ps-k). 15.95 (978-0-931674-41-9(7)) Waldman Hse. Pr., Inc.

Kinsey-Warnock, Natalie. Lumber Camp Library. Bernardin, James, illus. 2003. 96p. (J). pap. 4.99 (978-0-06-444292-3(6)) HarperCollins Pubs.

—Lumber Camp Library. 2002. (gr. 3-6). lib. bdg. 13.00 (978-0-613-68447-7(8)) Tandem Library Bks.

Klein, Adria F. Max Goes to the Library. Gallagher-Cole, Mernie, illus. 2005. (Read-It! Readers Ser.). 24p. (J). (ps). lib. bdg. 18.60 (978-1-4048-1182-9(6)) Picture Window Bks.

Krensky, Stephen. Arthur & the Scare-Your-Pants-off Club. 1998. (Arthur Chapter Bks. : Bk. 2). (J). (gr. 3-6). pap. 3.95 (978-0-316-10496-8(5)); (Illus.). 64p. (gr. 2-4). pap. 4.25 (978-0-316-11549-0(5)) Little, Brown Bks. for Young Readers.

—Arthur & the Scare-Your-Pants-off Club. 1998. (Arthur Chapter Bks.: Bk. 2). (J). (gr. 3-6). 11.05 (978-0-606-13151-3(5)) Tandem Library Bks.

Ladd, Debbie. Ethan the Ending Eater. Nakasone, Shaun, illus. 2007. 64p. (J). 16.95 (978-0-9727615-2-9(7)) Deb on Air Bks.

Lakin, Patricia. Rainy Day! Nash, Scott, illus. 2007. 40p. (J). (ps-1). 16.99 (978-0-8037-3092-2(6) , Dial) Penguin Group (USA) Inc.

Lamm, Drew. Pirates. Schuett, Stacey, illus. 2001. 40p. (gr. 4-7). 15.99 (978-0-7868-0392-7(4)) Hyperion Bks. for Children.

Langlois, Florence. The Extraordinary Gift. Goodman, John, tr. from FRE. Langlois, Florence, illus. 2005. (Illus.). 48p. (J). (ps-2). reprint ed. 15.00 (978-0-7567-8942-8(7)) DIANE Publishing Co.

Lavette, Lavaille. That's Not Punny. Kuon, Vuthy, illus. 2007. (Steve Harvey Presents the Adventures of Roopster Roux Ser.: Vol. 5). 32p. (J). 16.95 ***(978-1-58980-483-8(X))*** Pelican Publishing Co., Inc.

Lock, Deborah. A Trip to the Library. 2004. (Illus.). 32p. (J). (ps-ps). lib. bdg. 10.79 (978-0-606-30871-7(7)) Tandem Library Bks.

Maitland, Barbara. The Bookstore Valentine. LaRochelle, David, illus. 2002. (Easy-to-Read Ser.). 48p. (J). pap. 3.99 (978-0-14-230187-6(6) , Puffin) Penguin Group (USA) Inc.

Marshall, Rita. I Still Hate to Read! Delessert, Etienne, illus. 2007. (J). (gr. 3 up). ***(978-1-56846-174-8(7)*** , Creative Editions) Creative Co., The.

McDonald, Megan. Lucky Star. 2000. (J). (978-0-606-18924-8(6)) Tandem Library Bks.

McGee, Marni. Winston the Book Wolf. Beck, Ian, illus. 2006. 32p. (J). 16.95 (978-0-8027-9569-4(2)) Walker & Co.

McNaughton, Janet. The Secret under My Skin. (J). 2006. 368p. pap. 6.99 (978-0-06-008991-7(1)); 2005. 272p. (gr. 7 up). 15.99 (978-0-06-008989-4(X)); 2005. 272p. (gr. 7 up). lib. bdg. 16.89 (978-0-06-008990-0(3)) HarperCollins Pubs.

McPhail, David M. Fix It. McPhail, David M., illus. 2002. (Illus.). (J). 12.34 (978-0-7587-2515-8(9)) Book Wholesalers, Inc.

McQuinn, Anna. Lola at the Library. Beardshaw, Rosalind, illus. 2006. 32p. (J). 15.95 (978-1-58089-113-4(6)); pap. 6.95 (978-1-58089-142-4(X)) Charlesbridge Publishing, Inc.

Medearis, Angela Shelf. Lucy's Quiet Book. Ernst, Lisa Campbell, illus. 2004. (Green Light Readers Level 2 Ser.). 24p. (J). 12.95 (978-0-15-205144-0(9)); pap. 3.95 (978-0-15-205143-3(0)) Harcourt Children's Bks. (Green Light Readers).

Meister, Cari. Tiny Goes to the Library. Davis, Rich, illus. 2000. (Easy-to-Read Ser.). 32p. (J). (ps-2). pap. 3.99 (978-0-14-130488-5(X) , Puffin); 13.89 (978-0-670-88556-5(8) , Viking Juvenile) Penguin Group (USA) Inc.

—Tiny Goes to the Library. 2000. (Puffin Easy-to-Read Ser.). (978-0-606-18458-8(9)) Tandem Library Bks.

Michaels, Jamie. Kiss My Book. 2007. 288p. (YA). (gr. 7). pap. 7.99 ***(978-0-385-73499-8(9));*** lib. bdg. 10.99 ***(978-0-385-90493-3(2))*** Random Hse. Children's Bks. (Delacorte Bks. for Young Readers).

Miller, William. Richard Wright & the Library Card. Christie, Gregory R., illus. 1999. 32p. (J). (gr. k up). 6.95 (978-1-880000-88-5(1)) Lee & Low Bks., Inc.

—Richard Wright y el Carne de Biblioteca. Christie, Gregory R., illus. 2003. (SPA.). (J). 32p. 16.95 (978-1-58430-180-6(5)); pap. 6.95 (978-1-58430-181-3(3)) Lee & Low Bks., Inc.

Montanari, Eva. My First... 2007. (Illus.). 32p. (J). (ps-k). 17.00 ***(978-0-618-64644-9(2))*** Houghton Mifflin Co.

Mora, Pat. Una Biblioteca para Juana. Vidal, Beatriz, illus. 2002. (SPA.). 40p. (J). (gr. k-3). pap. 6.99 (978-0-440-41765-1(1)); lib. bdg. 17.99 (978-0-385-90863-4(6)) Random Hse. Children's Bks. (Dragonfly Bks.).

—Tomas & the Library Lady. Colon, Raul, illus. 2000. 40p. (J). (gr. k-3). pap. 6.99 (978-0-375-80349-9(1) , Dragonfly Bks.) Random Hse. Children's Bks.

—Tomas & the Library Lady. 2000. (978-0-606-18093-1(1)); lib. bdg. 15.30 (978-0-613-28362-5(7)) Tandem Library Bks.

—Tomas y la Senora de la Biblioteca. ed. 2004. (SPA., Illus.). (J). (gr. k-3). spiral bd. (978-0-616-03092-9(4)) Canadian National Institute for the Blind/Institut National Canadien pour les Aveugles.

Moreillon, Judi. Read to Me. Teis, Kyra, illus. 24p. (J). (ps-ps). 2004. per. 6.95 (978-1-59572-014-6(6)); 2003. 6.95 (978-1-932065-49-7(0) , 1-718-784-9112) Star Bright Bks., Inc.

Moriarty, Jaclyn. The Spell Book of Listen Taylor. 2007. (YA). ***(978-0-439-84679-0(X));*** 496p. (J). (gr. 9 up). 16.99 ***(978-0-439-84678-3(1))*** Scholastic, Inc. (Levine, Arthur A. Bks.).

Moulton, Mark Kimball. Scarecrow Pete & His Suitcase of Dreams. Crouch, Karen Hillard, illus. 2005. 36p. (J). (ps-3). 14.95 (978-0-8249-5151-1(4)) Ideals Pubns.

Muntean, Michaela. Do Not Open This Book! Lemaitre, Pascal, illus. 2006. 40p. (J). (ps-3). pap. 16.99 (978-0-439-69839-9(1) , Scholastic Pr.) Scholastic, Inc.

Nesbit, E. Lionel & the Book of Beasts. Hague, Michael, illus. 2006. 48p. (J). (gr. 2-4). lib. bdg. 17.89 (978-0-06-084272-7(5)); 16.99 (978-0-688-14006-9(8)) HarperCollins Pubs.

Newman, Nanette. Ben's Book. Birkett, Georgie, illus. 2007. 24p. (J). pap. 8.99 ***(978-1-84458-125-2(X))*** Anova Bks. GBR. *Dist:* Independent Pubs. Group.

Oppenheim, Joanne. The Prince's Bedtime. Latimer, Miriam, illus. 2005. 32p. (J). 16.99 (978-1-84148-597-3(7)) Barefoot Bks., Inc.

Parlato, Stephen. The World That Loved Books. Parlato, Stephen, illus. 2004. (Illus.). 36p. (gr. 1-6). 16.95 (978-1-894965-04-0(3)) Simply Read Bks. CAN. *Dist:* Perseus Distribution.

Parr, Todd. Reading Makes You Feel Good. 2005. (Illus.). 32p. (J). (ps-3). 15.99 (978-0-316-16004-9(0)) Little Brown & Co.

Patschke, Steve. The Spooky Book. McElligott, Matthew, illus. 32p. (J). (gr. k-3). 1999. lib. bdg. 16.85 (978-0-8027-8693-7(6)); 2006. reprint ed. pap. 6.95 (978-0-8027-8870-2(X)) Walker & Co.

Paulsen, Gary, ed. Shelf Life: Stories by the Book. 2003. (Illus.). 192p. (J). (gr. 5-9). 17.99 (978-0-689-84180-4(9)) Simon & Schuster Children's Publishing.

Pawagi, Manjusha. The Girl Who Hated Books. Franson, Leanne, illus. 2005. 24p. (J). 12.95 (978-1-896764-11-5(8)) Second Story Pr. CAN. *Dist:* Orca Bk. Pubs. USA.

Pawagi, Manjusha & Franson, Leanne. The Girl Who Hated Books. 2005. (Illus.). 24p. (J). pap. 5.95 (978-1-896764-09-2(6)) Second Story Pr. CAN. *Dist:* Orca Bk. Pubs. USA.

Pearson, Debora. When I Went to the Library. 2002. 120p. (J). pap. 9.95 (978-0-88899-513-1(X)) Groundwood Bks. CAN. *Dist:* Perseus Distribution.

Pearson, Mary E. I Can Do It All: Level B. Shelly, Jeff, illus. 2002. (Rookie Readers Ser.). 32p. (J). (gr. 1-2). 19.50 (978-0-516-22240-0(6) , Children's Pr.) Scholastic Library Publishing.

Pinczes, Elinor J. My Full Moon Is Square. Enos, Randall, illus. 2002. 32p. (J). (gr. k-3). tchr. ed. 15.00 (978-0-618-15489-0(2)) Houghton Mifflin Co. Trade & Reference Div.

Plourde, Lynn. Book Fair Day. Wickstrom, Thor, illus. (J). 2008. 40p. (gr. 1-3). pap. 6.99 ***(978-0-14-241139-1(6)*** , Puffin); 2006. 34p. (gr. k-3). 16.99 (978-0-525-47696-2(2) , Dutton Juvenile); 2006. ***(978-1-4156-8095-7(7)*** , Dutton Juvenile) Penguin Group (USA) Inc.

Polacco, Patricia. Aunt Chip & the Great Triple Creek Dam Affair. Polacco, Patricia, illus. 2002. (Illus.). (J). 23.64 (978-0-7587-1998-0(1)) Book Wholesalers, Inc.

—The Bee Tree. Polacco, Patricia, illus. 1998. (Illus.). 32p. (J). (ps-3). pap. 7.99 (978-0-698-11696-2(8) , Putnam Juvenile) Penguin Group (USA) Inc.

—The Bee Tree. 1998. (J). 13.79 (978-0-606-13187-2(6)) Tandem Library Bks.

Pulver, Robin. Author Day for Room 3T. Richards, Chuck, illus. 2005. 32p. (J). (gr. 3-5). 16.00 (978-0-618-35406-1(9) , Clarion Bks.) Houghton Mifflin Co. Trade & Reference Div.

Rau, Dana Meachen. My Book by Me. Rau, Dana Meachen, tr. 2000. (Rookie Readers Ser.). (Illus.). 31p. (J). (gr. 1-2). 19.50 (978-0-516-22032-1(2) , Children's Pr.) Scholastic Library Publishing.

Rylant, Cynthia. Poppleton. Teague, Mark, illus. 2002. (Poppleton Ser.). (J). 11.91 (978-0-7587-1590-6(0)) Book Wholesalers, Inc.

Sanvoisin, Eric. Ink Drinker. 2002. (gr. 3-6). lib. bdg. 13.00 (978-0-613-59386-1(3)) Tandem Library Bks.

Scieszka, Jon. Summer Reading Is Killing Me! Smith, Lane, illus. 2004. (Time Warp Trio Ser.: No. 7). 80p. (J). (gr. 2-6). pap. 4.99 (978-0-14-240115-6(3) , Puffin) Penguin Group (USA) Inc.

—Summer Reading Is Killing Me! Smith, Lane & McCauley, Adam, illus. 1998. (Time Warp Trio Ser.: No. 7). 64p. (J). (gr. 3-7). 14.99 (978-0-670-88041-6(8) , Viking Juvenile) Penguin Group (USA) Inc.

Scruffy Teddy & His Box of Books, 4 vols. 2002. 64p. (J). bds. 15.95 (978-0-7525-5491-4(3)) Parragon, Inc.

Shelton, Jayne C. In Grandmother's Arms. Katz, Karen, illus. 2001. 32p. (J). pap. 3.25 (978-0-439-21314-1(2)) Scholastic, Inc.

Shore, Diane Z. A Rosa le Gusta Leer. Day, Larry, illus. 2005. (Rookie Reader Espanol Ser.). (SPA & ESP.). 31p. (J). (gr. k-2). pap. 4.95 (978-0-516-24698-7(4) , Children's Pr.) Scholastic Library Publishing.

Shore, Diane ZuHone. Rosa Loves to Read. Day, Larry, tr. Day, Larry, illus. 2004. (Rookie Reader Ser.). 31p. (J). 19.50 (978-0-516-21723-9(2) , Children's Pr.) Scholastic Library Publishing.

Sierra, Judy. Born to Read. Brown, Marc, illus. 2008. (J). ***(978-0-375-84687-8(5));*** lib. bdg. ***(978-0-375-94687-5(X))*** Knopf, Alfred A. Inc.

Sierra, Judy. Wild about Books. Brown, Marc, tr. Brown, Marc, illus. 2004. 40p. (J). (ps-3). 16.95 (978-0-375-82538-5(X)); lib. bdg. 18.99 (978-0-375-92538-2(4)) Random Hse. Children's Bks. (Knopf Bks. for Young Readers).

Smothers, Ethel Footman. The Hard-Times Jar. Holyfield, John, illus. 2003. 32p. (J). 16.00 (978-0-374-32852-8(8) , Farrar, Straus & Giroux (BYR)) Farrar, Straus & Giroux.

Sortland, Bjorn. The Story of the Search for the Story. Elling, Lars, illus. 2003. (Picture Bks.). 40p. (J). (ps-3). 15.95 (978-1-57505-375-2(6) , Carolrhoda Bks.) Lerner Publishing Group.

Spanyol, Jessica. Carlo Likes Reading. Spanyol, Jessica, illus. 2005. (Illus.). 24p. (J). (ps-2). reprint ed. 15.00 (978-0-7567-8660-1(6)) DIANE Publishing Co.

Spinelli, Jerry. The Library Card. 1998. (Apple Signature Edition Ser.). 160p. (J). (gr. 3-9). mass mkt. 4.99 (978-0-590-38633-3(6) , Scholastic Paperbacks) Scholastic, Inc.

—The Library Card. 1998. (YA). (978-0-606-13568-9(5)) Tandem Library Bks.

Stadler, Alexander. Beverly Billingsly Borrows a Book. 2002. (Illus.). 32p. (J). (ps-2). 16.00 (978-0-15-202510-6(3) , Silver Whistle) Harcourt Trade Pubs.

Stadler, John. What's So Scary? (Illus.). (J). (gr. k-4). 2001. 32p. pap. 16.95 (978-0-531-30301-6(2)); 2000. lib. bdg. 16.95 (978-0-531-33301-3(9)) Scholastic, Inc. (Orchard Bks.).

Stanley, Diane. The Mysterious Matter of I. M. Fine. 208p. (J). (gr. 4 up). 2002. pap. 5.99 (978-0-380-73327-9(7)); 2001. (Illus.). 15.99 (978-0-688-17546-7(5)); 2001. (Illus.). lib. bdg. 16.89 (978-0-06-029619-3(4)) HarperCollins Pubs.

—The Mysterious Matter of I. M. Fine. 2002. (gr. 3-6). lib. bdg. 14.15 (978-0-613-60392-8(3)) Tandem Library Bks.

Stewart, Sarah. The Library. Small, David, illus. 2002. (J). 14.43 (978-0-7587-2983-5(9)) Book Wholesalers, Inc.

—The Library. Small, David, illus. 2000. (J). pap. 19.97 incl. audio (978-0-7366-9189-5(8)) Books on Tape, Inc.

—The Library. Small, David, illus. 1999. (Sunburst Bks.). 40p. (J). (ps-3). pap. 6.95 (978-0-374-44394-8(7) , Sunburst) Farrar, Straus & Giroux.

—The Library. Small, David, illus. 28.95 incl. audio compact disk (978-1-59519-011-6(2)); pap. 35.95 incl. audio compact disk (978-1-59519-010-9(4)); 2004. (J). 18.95 (978-1-59519-009-3(0)) Live Oak Media.

—The Library. Small, David, illus. 1999. (J). (ps-ps). lib. bdg. 14.10 (978-0-613-22882-4(0)) Tandem Library Bks.

Stinson, Kathy. King of the Castle. Charko, Kasia, illus. 2005. (Early Chapter Bks.). 64p. (YA). (gr. 2-5). pap. 5.95 (978-1-896764-35-1(5)) Second Story Pr. CAN. *Dist:* Orca Bk. Pubs. USA.

Thompson, Carol L. Mr. Wiggle Loves to Read. 2003. (Mr. Wiggle Ser.). (Illus.). 32p. (J). 9.95 (978-1-57768-614-9(4) , Waterbird Bks.) School Specialty Publishing.

Townley, Roderick. The Constellation of Sylvie. 2006. (Illus.). 208p. (J). (gr. 5 up). 16.95 (978-0-689-85713-3(6) , Atheneum) Simon & Schuster Children's Publishing.

—The Great Good Thing. unabr. ed. 2004. (Middle Grade Cassette Librariestm Ser.). 176p. (J). (gr. 4-6). pap. 29.00 incl. audio (978-0-8072-1001-7(3) , S YA 302 SP, Listening Library) Random Hse. Audio Publishing Group.

—The Great Good Thing. Anderson, Stephanie, illus. 2002. 240p. (J). (gr. 5-9). pap. 4.99 (978-0-689-85328-9(9) , Aladdin) Simon & Schuster Children's Publishing.

—The Great Good Thing. 2001. (Illus.). 232p. (J). (gr. 5-9). 17.00 (978-0-689-84324-2(0) , Atheneum/Richard Jackson Bks.) Simon & Schuster Children's Publishing.

—Into the Labyrinth. (Illus.). 272p. (gr. 5-9). 2006. (YA). pap. 5.99 (978-1-4169-1392-4(0) , Aladdin); 2002. (J). 16.95 (978-0-689-84615-1(0) , Atheneum/Richard Jackson Bks.) Simon & Schuster Children's Publishing.

Van Leeuwen, Jean. Amanda Pig, First Grader. Schweninger, Ann, illus. 2007. 40p. (J). (ps-1). 14.99 (978-0-8037-3181-3(7) , Dial) Penguin Group (USA) Inc.

Warner, Mike. The Titanic Game. Ordaz, Frank, illus. 2007. 201p. (J). pap. 9.95 (978-0-9744446-2-8(6)) All About Kids Publishing.

Wells, Rosemary. Read to Your Bunny. Wells, Rosemary, illus. (Illus.). (J). 2003. 12p. bds. 7.99 (978-0-439-54337-8(1) , Cartwheel Bks.); 1999. 32p. pap. 3.99 (978-0-439-08717-9(1)) Scholastic, Inc.

—Read to Your Bunny. 1998. (Bruno & Boots Book Ser.). (Illus.). 32p. (J). (ps). bds. 7.95 (978-0-590-30284-5(1)) Scholastic, Inc.

—Read to Your Bunny. 1999. (978-0-606-17056-7(1)); lib. bdg. 10.65 (978-0-613-16996-7(4)) Tandem Library Bks.

—Read to Your Bunny Very First Library Gift Set. 2006. 64p. (J). pap. 19.99 (978-0-439-87190-7(5) , Scholastic Pr.) Scholastic, Inc.

Wersba, Barbara. Walter: The Story of a Rat. Diamond, Donna, illus. 2005. 64p. (J). (gr. 4-8). 16.95 (978-1-932425-41-3(1) , Lemniscaat) Boyds Mills Pr.

Willson, Sarah. La Mochila de Dora. Roper, Robert, illus. 2003. (Dora the Explorer Ser.).Tr. of Dora's Backpack. (SPA.). 24p. (J). pap. 3.99 (978-0-689-86306-6(3) , Libros Para Ninos) Simon & Schuster Children's Publishing.

Windham, Kathryn. Ernest's Gift. Hardy, Frank, illus. 2004. 20p. 15.95 (978-1-58838-149-1(8)) NewSouth, Inc.

Yolen, Jane. Baby Bear's Books. Sweet, Melissa, illus. 2006. 40p. (J). 16.00 (978-0-15-205290-4(9)) Harcourt Trade Pubs.

Zusak, Markus. The Book Thief. (YA). (gr. 7 up). 2007. 576p. pap. 11.99 ***(978-0-375-84220-7(9));*** 2006. 560p. 16.95 (978-0-375-83100-3(2)); 2006. 560p. lib. bdg. 18.99 (978-0-375-93100-0(7)) Random Hse. Children's Bks. (Knopf Bks. for Young Readers).

BOOKS AND READING FOR CHILDREN

see Children—Books and Reading

BOOKS FOR CHILDREN

see Children's Literature

BOONE, DANIEL, 1734-1820

Alter, Judy. Daniel Boone: Frontiersman. 2002. (Spirit of America: Our People Ser.). (Illus.). 32p. (J). (gr. 2-6). 27.07 (978-1-56766-162-0(9)) Child's World, Inc.

Armentrout, David & Armentrout, Patricia. Daniel Boone. 2002. (People Who Made a Difference Ser.). (Illus.). 24p. (gr. 2-5). 14.95 (978-1-58952-052-3(1)) Rourke Publishing, LLC.

—Daniel Boone. Sarfatti, Esther & de la Vega, Eida, trs. (Personas que Cambiaron la Historia (People Who Made a Difference) Ser.). (SPA., Illus.). 24p. 2002. mass mkt. 5.95 (978-1-58952-247-3(8) , RK31463); 2001. (J). (gr. 1-4). lib. bdg. 19.27 (978-1-58952-166-7(8) , RK7295) Rourke Publishing, LLC.

Benge, Janet & Benge, Geoff. Daniel Boone: Frontiersman. 2004. pap. 8.99 (978-1-932096-09-5(4)) Emerald Bks.

Blair, Eric. The Legend of Daniel Boone: A Retelling of the Classic Traditional Tale. Chambers-Goldbert, Micah, illus. 2005. (Read-It! Readers Ser.). 32p. (J). (gr. k-3). 18.60 (978-1-4048-0974-1(0)) Picture Window Bks.

—La Leyenda de Daniel Boone. Chambers-Goldberg, Micah, illus. 2006. (Read-It! Readers en Espanol Ser.).Tr. of Legend of Daniel Boone. (SPA.). 32p. (J). (ps-3). 19.95 (978-1-4048-1656-5(9)) Picture Window Bks.

Boone, Daniel & Hawks, Francis L. Daniel Boone: His Own Story & the Adventures of Daniel Boone. 2004. 128p. (YA). (gr. 10 up). per. 14.95 (978-1-55709-426-1(8)) Applewood Bks.

Boraas, Tracey. Daniel Boone: Frontier Scout. 2002. (Let Freedom Ring Ser.). (Illus.). 48p. (J). (gr. 3-4). lib. bdg. 22.60 (978-0-7368-1347-1(0) , Bridgestone Bks.) Capstone Pr., Inc.

Brown, John Mason. Sterling Point Books: Daniel Boone: the Opening of the Wilderness. 2007. (Sterling Point Bks.). 176p. (J). pap. 6.95 ***(978-1-4027-5119-6(2))*** Sterling Publishing Co., Inc.

Burke, Rick. Daniel Boone. 2003. (American Lives Ser.). (Illus.). 32p. (J). pap. 6.95 (978-1-4034-4197-3(9)); lib. bdg. 24.22 (978-1-4034-4189-8(8)) Heinemann Library.

Calvert, Patricia, et al. Daniel Boone: Beyond the Mountains. 2001. (Great Explorations Ser.). (Illus.). 80p. (J). (gr. 4 up). lib. bdg. 29.93 (978-0-7614-1243-4(3) , Benchmark Bks.) Cavendish, Marshall Corp.

Capstone Press, contrib. by. Daniel Boone. (Exploring the West Biographies Ser.). 48p. (YA). pap. 7.95 (978-0-7368-4509-0(7)) Capstone Pr., Inc.

Copeland, Peter F. Daniel Boone Coloring Book. 2006. 32p. (J). pap. 3.95 (978-0-486-44738-4(3)) Dover Pubns., Inc.

De Capua, Sarah. The Wilderness Road. 2006. (We the People Ser.). (Illus.). 48p. (J). (gr. 4-6). 23.93 (978-0-7565-1637-6(4)) Compass Point Bks.

Dean, Arlan. The Wilderness Road: From the Shenandoah Valley to the Ohio River. 2003. (Reading Power Ser.). (Illus.). 24p. (J). lib. bdg. 17.25 (978-0-8239-6477-2(9) , PowerKids Pr.) Rosen Publishing Group, Inc., The.

Gosda, Randy T. Daniel Boone. 2002. (First Biographies Ser.). (Illus.). 32p. (J). (gr. k-4). lib. bdg. 22.78 (978-1-57765-735-4(7) , Buddy Bks.) ABDO Publishing Co.

Green, Carl R. Blazing the Wilderness Road with Daniel Boone in American History. 2000. (In American History Ser.). (Illus.). 128p. (YA). (gr. 5-12). lib. bdg. 26.60 (978-0-7660-1346-9(4)) Enslow Pubs., Inc.

Harcourt School Publishers Staff. Daniel Boone Advanced Level. 3rd ed. 2002. (Trophies Reading Program Ser.). (Illus.). pap. 5.10 (978-0-15-323111-7(4)) Harcourt Schl. Pubs.

Harness, Cheryl. The Trailblazing Life of Daniel Boone & How Early Americans Took to the Road. 2007. (Cheryl Harness Histories Ser.). (Illus.). 144p. (J). (gr. 5-9). 16.95 ***(978-1-4263-0145-2(6));*** lib. bdg. 25.90 ***(978-1-4263-0146-9(4))*** National Geographic Society. (National Geographic Children's Bks.).

Johnston, Marianne. Daniel Boone. 2001. (American Legends Ser.). (Illus.). 24p. (J). (gr. 3). lib. bdg. 18.75 (978-0-8239-5579-4(6) , PowerKids Pr.) Rosen Publishing Group, Inc., The.

Kelly Allen, Nancy. Daniel Boone: Trailblazer. Waites, Joan C., illus. 2005. 32p. (J). (gr. 2-4). 15.95 (978-1-58980-212-4(8)) Pelican Publishing Co., Inc.

Kozar, Richard. Daniel Boone & the Exploration of the Frontier. 2000. (Explorers of the New World Ser.). (Illus.). 64p. (YA). (gr. 4 up). 25.00 (978-0-7910-5510-6(8) , Chelsea Hse.) Facts On File, Inc.

Kramer, Sydelle. Who Was Daniel Boone? Ulrich, George, illus. 2006. (Who Was... ? Ser.). 112p. (J). (gr. 2-5). pap. 4.99 (978-0-448-43902-0(6) , Grosset & Dunlap) Penguin Group (USA) Inc.

Lawlor, Laurie. Daniel Boone. Dodson, Bert, illus. 2004. 160p. (YA). reprint ed. (978-0-7567-7793-7(3)) DIANE Publishing Co.

McCarthy, Pat. Daniel Boone: Frontier Legend. 2000. (Historical American Biographies Ser.). (Illus.). 128p. (YA). (gr. 6-12). lib. bdg. 26.60 (978-0-7660-1256-1(5)) Enslow Pubs., Inc.

Nemerson, Roy. Daniel Boone. 2005. (Heroes of America Ser.). (Illus.). 240p. (J). (gr. 3-8). lib. bdg. 21.35 (978-1-59679-256-2(6)) ABDO Publishing Co.

Petrie, Kristin. Daniel Boone. 2004. (Explorers Set I Ser.). (J). (gr. k-6). lib. bdg. 22.78 (978-1-59197-592-2(1)) ABDO Publishing Co.

Ransom, Candice. Daniel Boone. 2006. (History Maker Bios Ser.). (Illus.). 48p. (J). (gr. 3-7). 26.60 (978-0-8225-2941-5(6) , Lerner Pubns.) Lerner Publishing Group.

Riehecky, Janet. Daniel Boone. 2002. (Rookie Biographies Ser.). (Illus.). 32p. (J). lib. bdg. 25.69 (978-0-7398-5672-7(3)) Raintree.

Roberts, Russell. Daniel Boone. 2006. (What's So Great About... ? Ser.). (Illus.). 32p. (J). (gr. 1-4). lib. bdg. (978-1-58415-475-4(6)) Mitchell Lane Pubs., Inc.

Salas, Laura Purdie. The Wilderness Road 1775. 2003. (Let Freedom Ring Ser.). (Illus.). 48p. (J). (gr. 3-4). lib. bdg. 22.60 (978-0-7368-1561-1(9) , Bridgestone Bks.) Capstone Pr., Inc.

Santella, Andrew. Daniel Boone & the Cumberland Gap. (Cornerstones of Freedomtrade;, Second Ser.). 48p. (J). 2007. 5.95 (*978-0-531-18687-9(3));* 2002. (Illus.). (gr. 4-6). 26.00 (978-0-516-22526-5(X)) Scholastic Library Publishing. (Children's Pr.).

Streissguth, Thomas. Daniel Boone. Chantland, Loren, illus. (On My Own Biographies Ser.). 48p. (J). 2005. (gr. 2-5). lib. bdg. 23.93 (978-1-57505-520-6(1)); 2003. (gr. 1-3). pap. 5.95 (978-1-57505-532-9(5)) Lerner Publishing Group.

Zronik, John Paul. Daniel Boone: Woodsman of Kentucky. 2006. (In the Footsteps of Explorers Ser.). (Illus.). 32p. (J). (gr. 3-9). pap. (978-0-7787-2464-3(6) , 1253442); (978-0-7787-2428-5(X) , 1253442) Crabtree Publishing Co.

BOONE, DANIEL, 1734-1820—FICTION

Glass, Andrew. Bewildered for Three Days: As to Why Daniel Boone Never Wore His Coonskin Cap. Glass, Andrew, illus. 2000. (Illus.). 32p. (J). (gr. k-3). tchr. ed. 16.95 (978-0-8234-1446-8(9)) Holiday Hse., Inc.

Harcourt School Publishers Staff. Daniel Boone Advanced Level. 3rd ed. 2002. (Trofeos Ser.). (SPA., Illus.). pap. 6.80 (978-0-15-324022-5(9)) Harcourt Schl. Pubs.

Winston, Annie. Admiral Wright's Heroical Strroicals: Daniel Boone & the Battle of Boonesborough. 2002. 120p. per. 9.95 (978-0-9717009-6-3(6) , Sonship Pr.) 21st Century Pr.

BOOTH, WILLIAM, 1829-1912

Benge, Janet & Benge, Geoff. William Booth: Soup, Soap, & Salvation. 2002. 208p. pap. 8.99 (978-1-57658-258-9(2)) YWAM Publishing.

BOOTS

see Shoes

BORDEN, LIZZIE, 1860-1927

Axelrod-Contrada, Joan. The Lizzie Borden "Axe Murder" Trial: A Headline Court Case. 2000. (Headline Court Cases Ser.). (Illus.). 128p. (J). (gr. 6-12). lib. bdg. 26.60 (978-0-7660-1422-0(3)) Enslow Pubs., Inc.

BORDER LIFE

see Frontier and Pioneer Life

BORGLUM, JOHN GUTZON DE LA MOTHE, 1867-1941

Curlee, Lynn. Rushmore. (J). (gr. 3-5). (978-0-439-06013-4(3)) Scholastic, Inc.

—Rushmore: Monument for the Ages. 1998. 48p. (J). pap. 16.95 (978-0-590-22201-3(5)) Scholastic, Inc.

Patrick, Jean L. S. Who Carved the Mountain? The Story of Mount Rushmore. Graef, Renee, illus. 2005. 37p. (J). 16.99 (978-0-9752617-4-3(6)) Mount Rushmore History Assn.

BORNEO

Pascoe, Elaine & Corwin, Jeff. Into Wild Borneo. 2003. (Jeff Corwin Experience Ser.). (Illus.). 48p. (J). 11.20 (978-1-4103-0170-3(2) , Blackbirch Pr., Inc.) Thomson Gale.

BORNEO—FICTION

Cushman, Doug. The Mystery of the Monkey's Maze. Cushman, Doug, illus. 1999. (From the Casebook of Seymour Sleuth Ser.). (Illus.). 32p. (J). (gr. k-3). 15.95 (978-0-06-027719-2(X)); 15.89 (978-0-06-027720-8(3)) HarperCollins Pubs.

Lumry, Amanda & Hurwitz, Laura. Operation Orangutan. 2007. 36p. 15.95 (978-0-9748411-4-4(5)) Eaglemont Pr.

Smith, Dale. What the Orangutan Told Alice: A Rain Forest Adventure. Smith, Dale & Russon, Anne E., photos by. 2003. (Illus.). 192p. (gr. 6-12). pap. 15.95 (978-0-9651452-8-2(X)) Deer Creek Publishing.

Youngberg, Norma R. Jungle Thorn. 2000. (Illus.). 112p. (J). reprint ed. per. 8.95 (978-1-57258-157-9(3) , 945-6024) TEACH Services, Inc.

BORROWERS (FICTITIOUS CHARACTERS)—FICTION

Norton, Mary. The Borrowers. Krush, Beth & Krush, Joe, illus. 2003. (Borrowers Ser.). 192p. (J). pap. 5.95 (978-0-15-204737-5(9) , Odyssey Classics) Harcourt Children's Bks.

—The Borrowers. Stanley, Diana, illus. 50th anniv. gif. ed. 2003. (Borrowers Ser.). 176p. (J). 19.95 (978-0-15-204928-7(2)) Harcourt Children's Bks.

—The Borrowers Afield. Krush, Beth & Krush, Joe, illus. 50th anniv. ed. 2003. (Borrowers Ser.). 224p. (J). pap. 5.95 (978-0-15-204732-0(8) , Odyssey Classics) Harcourt Children's Bks.

—The Borrowers Afloat. Krush, Beth & Krush, Joe, illus. 2003. (Borrowers Ser.). 192p. (J). pap. 5.95 (978-0-15-204733-7(6) , Odyssey Classics) Harcourt Children's Bks.

—The Borrowers Aloft: Plus the Short Tale Poor Stainless. Krush, Beth & Krush, Joe, illus. 50th anniv. ed. 2003. (Borrowers Ser.). 224p. (J). (gr. 3-7). pap. 5.95 (978-0-15-204734-4(4) , Odyssey Classics) Harcourt Children's Bks.

—The Borrowers Avenged. Krush, Joe & Krush, Beth, illus. 50th anniv. ed. 2003. (Borrowers Ser.). 304p. (J). pap. 5.95 (978-0-15-204731-3(X) , Odyssey Classics) Harcourt Children's Bks.

BOSNIA AND HERCEGOVINA

Englar, Mary. Bosnia-Herzegovina in Pictures. 2007. (Visual Geography Ser.). (Illus.). 80p. (J). 27.93 (978-0-8225-2393-2(0) , Twenty-First Century Bks.) Lerner Publishing Group.

Gabrielpillai, Matilda. Bosnia & Herzegovina. 2001. (Countries of the World Ser.). (Illus.). 96p. (J). (gr. 6 up). lib. bdg. 30.00 (978-0-8368-2329-5(X)) Stevens, Gareth Inc.

Halilbegovich, Nadja. My Childhood under Fire: A Sarajevo Diary. 2006. (Illus.). 120p. (YA). 14.95 (978-1-55337-797-9(4)) Kids Can Pr., Ltd. CAN. *Dist:* Wybel Marketing Group.

King, David C. Bosnia & Herzegovina. 2005. (Cultures of the World Ser.). (Illus.). 144p. (J). 37.07 (978-0-7614-1853-5(9)) Benchmark Investigative Group.

Milivojevic, JoAnn. Bosnia & Herzegovina. 2004. (Enchantment of the World, Second Ser.). (Illus.). 144p. (YA). (gr. 5-9). 36.00 (978-0-516-24247-7(4) , Children's Pr.) Scholastic Library Publishing.

Mulla-Feroze, Umaima & Gabrielpillai, Matilda. Welcome to Bosnia & Herzegovina. 2002. (Welcome to My Country Ser.). (Illus.). 48p. (J). (gr. 2 up). lib. bdg. 26.00 (978-0-8368-2529-9(2)) Stevens, Gareth Inc.

Phillips, Douglas A. Bosnia & Herzegovina. 2004. (Modern World Nations Ser.). (Illus.). 120p. (gr. 6-12). 30.00 (978-0-7910-7911-9(2) , Chelsea Hse.) Facts On File, Inc.

Sacco, Joe. Safe Area Gorazde: The War in Eastern Bosnia, 1992-1995. 2001. (gr. 7-12). lib. bdg. 30.35 (978-0-613-50994-7(3)) Tandem Library Bks.

Woolf, Alex. Assassination in Sarajevo. 2003. (Days That Shook the World Ser.). (Illus.). 47p. (J). lib. bdg. 28.56 (978-0-7398-6048-9(8)) Raintree.

BOSNIA AND HERCEGOVINA—FICTION

Dorros, Arthur. Under the Sun. (YA). (gr. 5-11). 2006. 240p. pap. 5.95 (978-0-8109-9250-4(7)); 2004. (Illus.). 224p. 16.95 (978-0-8109-4933-1(4)) Abrams, Harry N. , Inc.

Kubert, Joe. Fax from Sarajevo: A Story of Survival. Kubert, Joe, illus. 1998. (Illus.). 224p. (YA). (gr. 9 up). pap. 16.95 (978-1-56971-346-4(4)) Dark Horse Comics.

Linden, Dianne. Peacekeepers. (J). 82p. stu. ed. 9.95 (978-1-55050-297-8(2)); 2004. (Illus.). 220p. (gr. 4-7). pap. 7.95 (978-1-55050-271-8(9)) Coteau Bks. CAN. *Dist:* Fitzhenry & Whiteside, Ltd.

BOSTON (MASS.)

Adventures in Suburbia Boston 2003. 2003. 365p. (J). per. 19.95 (978-0-9743319-0-4(2)) Kiwi Media Group, Inc.

Burgan, Michael. The Boston Massacre. 2004. (We the People Ser.). (Illus.). 48p. (J). 22.60 (978-0-7565-0832-6(0)) Compass Point Bks.

Byers, Helen. Boston: What to Do, Where to Go & How to Have Fun in Boston. 2nd ed. 2000. (Kidding Around! Ser.). (Illus.). 144p. pap. 8.95 (978-1-56261-586-4(6)) Avalon Travel Publishing.

Draper, Allison Stark. The Boston Massacre: Five Colonists Killed by British Soldiers. 2001. (Headlines from History Ser.). (Illus.). 24p. (J). (gr. 3). lib. bdg. 19.95 (978-0-8239-5670-8(9) , PKBOMA, PowerKids Pr.) Rosen Publishing Group, Inc., The.

Furstinger, Nancy. Boston. 2005. (Cities Ser.). (Illus.). 32p. (J). (gr. k-6). lib. bdg. 22.78 (978-1-59197-854-1(8)) ABDO Publishing Co.

Kent, Deborah. Boston. Downing, Joan, ed. 1998. (Cities of the World Ser.). (Illus.). 64p. (J). (gr. 4-9). pap. 9.95 (978-0-516-26325-0(0) , Children's Pr.) Scholastic Library Publishing.

Lodge, Henry Cabot. Boston. 2004. (Illus.). vii, 241p. (978-1-929154-16-6(X)) Levenger Pr.

Weintraub, Aileen. Boston Light: The First Lighthouse in North America. 2003. (Great Lighthouses of North America Ser.). (Illus.). 24p. (J). pap. 18.75 (978-0-8239-6170-2(2) , PowerKids Pr.) Rosen Publishing Group, Inc., The.

Wilson, Deirdre. The Lobster Kids' Guide to Exploring Boston. 2001. (Lobster Kids' City Explorers Ser.). (Illus.). 235p. (J). (ps-3). pap. 12.95 (978-1-894222-41-9(5)) Lobster Pr. CAN. *Dist:* Univ. of Toronto Pr.

Zschock, Martha Day. Journey Around Boston from A to Z. Zschock, Martha Day, illus. 2001. (Journey Around Ser.). 32p. (J). 17.95 (978-1-889833-19-4(3)) Commonwealth Editions.

BOSTON (MASS.)—FICTION

Alger, Horatio. Do & Dare. 2006. pap. (*978-1-4250-1766-8(5));* pap. (*978-1-4250-2027-9(5));* pap. (*978-1-4250-2300-3(2));* pap. (*978-1-4250-2118-4(2))* Assistedreadingbooks.com Inc.

—Do & Dare: Or, A Brave Boy's Fight for Fortune. 2006. 182p. pap. 11.99 (978-1-4264-0880-9(3)); 170p. pap. 14.99 (978-1-4264-0861-8(7)) BiblioBazaar.

—Do & Dare: Or, A Brave Boy's Fight for Fortune. 2006. pap. (*978-1-4065-0701-0(6))* Dodo Pr.

—Do & Dare: Or, A Brave Boy's Fight for Fortune. unabr. ed. 2002. (Illus.). (J). pap. 17.95 (978-1-931927-90-1(1)) Polyglot Pr., Inc.

Ayres, Katherine. Under Copp's Hill. 2000. (American Girl Collection). (Illus.). (J). (978-0-606-20963-2(8)) Tandem Library Bks.

Borden, Louise. Sleds on Boston Common: A Story from the American Revolution. Parker, Robert A., illus. 2000. 40p. (J). (gr. 3-7). 17.99 (978-0-689-82812-6(8) , McElderry, Margaret K.) Simon & Schuster Children's Publishing.

Brodeur, Tom. Regina Silsby's Phantom Militia. 2005. (Illus.). 267p. (J). (ps-7). 7.49 (978-1-59166-385-0(7)) Jones, Bob Univ. Pr.

—Regina Silsby's Secret War. 2004. 248p. (J). 7.49 (978-1-59166-235-8(4)) Jones, Bob Univ. Pr.

Cocca-Leffler, Maryann. Bus Route to Boston. Cocca-Leffler, Maryann, illus. 2003. (Illus.). 32p. (J). (gr. k-2). 15.95 (978-1-56397-723-7(0)) Boyds Mills Pr.

Duey, Kathleen. Silence & Lily: 1773. 2007. 176p. (J). (gr. 5). pap. 5.99 (*978-0-14-240909-1(X)* , Puffin) Penguin Group (USA) Inc.

Dwyer, Kerry, illus. Rhett's Colorful Campus Tour- Boston University A-Z. 2004. (J). 9.99 (978-1-933069-03-6(1)) Odd Duck Ink, Inc.

Emily Breaks Free - Evaluation Guide. 2006. (J). (978-1-55942-404-2(4)) Marsh Media.

Emily Breaks Free - Teaching Guide. 2000. 17.95 (978-1-55942-157-7(6)) Marsh Media.

Forbes, Esther. Johnny Tremain. Ward, Lynd, illus. 2002. (J). 15.00 (978-0-7587-0196-1(9)) Book Wholesalers, Inc.

—Johnny Tremain. 2002. (EMC Masterpiece Series Access Editions). (Illus.). xvi, 308p. (J). 10.95 (978-0-8219-2408-2(7)) EMC/Paradigm Publishing.

—Johnny Tremain. McCurdy, Michael, illus. l.t. ed. 412p. 2005. (YA). pap. 10.95 (978-0-7862-7178-8(7)); 2004. (J). 22.95 (978-0-7862-7066-8(7)) Thorndike Pr.

Gamble, Adam. Good Night Boston. Veno, Joe, illus. 2005. (J). bds. 9.95 (978-0-9758502-4-4(5)) On Cape Pubns.

—Good Night Boston. Veno, Joe, illus. 2007. (Good Night Our World Ser.). 18p. (J). bds. 9.95 (*978-1-60219-003-0(8))* Our World of Books.

Gerritsen, Tess. The Apprentice. 2003. (gr. 7-12). lib. bdg. 16.45 (978-0-613-65524-8(9)) Tandem Library Bks.

Gerwitz, Christina & Gerwitz, Felice. The Missing Link: Found. 2000. (Truth Seeker's Mystery Ser.: Vol. 1). 192p. (YA). (gr. 7-12). pap. 7.99 (978-0-9700385-9-3(3)) Media Angels, Inc.

Golden, Christopher. Meets the Eye. 2000. (Body of Evidence Ser.: No. 4). 256p. (YA). (gr. 7 up). pap. 4.99 (978-0-671-03495-5(2) , Simon Pulse) Simon & Schuster Children's Publishing.

—Thief of Hearts. 1999. 245p. (YA). (gr. 8-12). per. 13.00 (978-0-613-73104-1(2)) Tandem Library Bks.

Grote, JoAnn A. The American Revolution. Wallenta, Adam, illus. 1999. (American Adventure Ser.: No. 11). (J). (gr. 3-7). (978-0-7910-5591-5(4) , Chelsea Hse.) Facts On File, Inc.

—Danger in the Harbor: Grain Riots Threaten Boston. 1999. (American Adventure Ser.: No. 6). (Illus.). 144p. (J). (gr. 3-7). lib. bdg. 15.95 (978-0-7910-5046-0(7) , Chelsea Hse.) Facts On File, Inc.

—Queen Anne's War. 1999. (American Adventure Ser.: No. 5). 144p. (J). (gr. 3-7). lib. bdg. 15.95 (978-0-7910-5045-3(9) , Chelsea Hse.) Facts On File, Inc.

Halpin, Brendan. How Ya Like Me Now. 2007. 208p. (YA). (gr. 7 up). 16.00 (978-0-374-33495-6(1)) Farrar, Straus & Giroux.

Harlow, Joan Hiatt. Joshua's Song. (Illus.). (J). 2003. 160p. pap. 4.99 (978-0-689-85542-9(7) , Aladdin); 2001. 192p. (gr. 3-7). 16.95 (978-0-689-84119-4(1) , McElderry, Margaret K.) Simon & Schuster Children's Publishing.

—Joshua's Song. 2003. (gr. 3-6). lib. bdg. 13.00 (978-0-613-61785-7(1)) Tandem Library Bks.

Hawthorne, Nathaniel. The Scarlet Letter. adapted ed. (YA). (gr. 5-12). pap. 8.50 (978-0-8359-0262-5(5)) Globe Fearon Educational Publishing.

—The Scarlet Letter. l.t. ed. 2000. (LRS Large Print Heritage Ser.). 379p. (YA). (gr. 7-12). lib. bdg. 34.95 (978-1-58118-065-7(9) , 23660) LRS.

—The Scarlet Letter. 1998. (YA). 40p. 11.95 (978-1-56137-339-0(7) , NU3397SP); 32p. 9.95 (978-1-56137-338-3(9) , NU3389) Novel Units, Inc.

—The Scarlet Letter - Spotlight Edition. Grudzina, Douglas, ed. 2004. (Illus.). 150p. (YA). per. 5.95 (978-1-58049-550-9(8) , PWH5508) Prestwick Hse., Inc.

Hemphill, Kris. A Secret Party in Boston Harbor. Martin, John F. & Van Pelt, Dan, illus. 1998. (Mysteries in Time Ser.: Vol. 6). 96p. (J). (gr. 4-7). 14.95 (978-1-881889-88-5(2)) Silver Moon Pr.

Holm, Jennifer L. Claim No. 3. 2004. (Boston Jane Ser.). 240p. (J). (gr. 5 up). lib. bdg. 16.89 (978-0-06-029046-7(3)); 15.99 (978-0-06-029045-0(5)) HarperCollins Pubs.

Johnson, Nancy. A Sweet-Sounding Place: A Civil War Story. 2007. 160p. (gr. 5-9). 14.95 (*978-0-89272-757-5(8))* Down East Bks.

Kelley, Nancy J. The Whispering Rod: A Tale of Old Massachusetts. 2002. 160p. (J). lib. bdg. 17.95 (978-1-57249-248-6(1) , White Mane Kids) White Mane Publishing Co., Inc.

King, M. C. Room of Doom, Bk. 3. 3rd rev. ed. 2006. (Suite Life of Zack & Cody Ser.: Vol. 3). (Illus.) 80p. (gr. 2-5). pap. 3.99 (978-0-7868-4937-6(1)) Disney Pr.

Lasky, Kathryn. Home at Last: Sofia's Immigrant Diary. 2003. (My America Ser.). (Illus.). 112p. (J). pap. 12.95 (978-0-439-44963-2(4)); (gr. 3-4). pap. 4.99 (978-0-439-20644-0(8)) Scholastic, Inc.

Lawlor, Laurie. Horseback on the Boston Post Road, Seventeen Hundred & Four. 2002. (gr. 3-6). lib. bdg. 13.00 (978-0-613-50323-5(6)) Tandem Library Bks.

Lough, Loree. Fire by Night: The Great Fire Devastates Boston. 1999. (American Adventure Ser.: No. 4). 144p. (J). (gr. 3-7). lib. bdg. 15.95 (978-0-7910-5044-6(0) , Chelsea Hse.) Facts On File, Inc.

Lowry, Lois. Anastasia Elige Profesion. 2003. Tr. of Anastasia's Chosen Career. (SPA.). 188p. (J). 9.95 (978-84-239-9066-5(4)) Espasa Calpe, S.A. ESP. *Dist:* Planeta Publishing Corp.

Lupica, Mike. Miracle on 49th Street. 256p. (gr. 5). 2007. (J). pap. 7.99 (*978-0-14-240942-8(1)* , Puffin); 2006. (YA). 17.99 (978-0-399-24488-9(3) , Philomel) Penguin Group (USA) Inc.

Lutz, Norma Jean. Maggie's Choice: Jonathan Edwards & the Great Awakening. 1999. (American Adventure Ser.: No. 8). (Illus.). 144p. (J). (gr. 3-7). lib. bdg. 15.95 (978-0-7910-5048-4(3) , Chelsea Hse.) Facts On File, Inc.

—Smallpox Strikes! Cotton Mather's Bold Experiment. 1999. (American Adventure Ser.: No. 7). (Illus.). 144p. (J). (gr. 3-7). lib. bdg. 15.95 (978-0-7910-5047-7(5) , Chelsea Hse.) Facts On File, Inc.

Lynch, Chris. Gold Dust. 2002. 208p. (J). (gr. 5 up). pap. 7.99 (978-0-06-447201-2(9)) HarperCollins Pubs.

—Gold Dust. 2002. (gr. 5-8). lib. bdg. 14.10 (978-0-613-67089-0(2)) Tandem Library Bks.

—Sins of the Fathers. 2006. 240p. (J). lib. bdg. 17.89 (978-0-06-074038-2(8) , HarperTeen) HarperCollins Pubs.

Make Way for Ducklings. 2004. 24.95 incl. audio (978-0-89719-892-9(1)); pap. 32.75 incl. audio (978-1-55592-262-7(7)); pap. 32.75 incl. audio (978-1-55592-263-4(5)); pap. 14.95 incl. audio (978-1-56008-065-7(5)); pap. 14.95 incl. audio (978-0-7882-0507-1(2)) Weston Woods Studios, Inc.

Marino, Jan. The Mona Lisa of Salem Street. 1999. 155p. (J). (gr. 3-6). reprint ed. 15.00 (978-0-7881-6635-8(2)) DIANE Publishing Co.

Marsh, Carole. The Mystery at the Boston Marathon. 2003. 160p. (gr. 2-8). 14.95 (978-0-635-01642-3(7) , Marsh, Carole Bks.); pap. 5.95 (978-0-635-01640-9(0)) Gallopade International.

—Mystery at the Boston Marathon. 2003. (gr. 3-6). lib. bdg. 14.10 (978-0-613-73036-5(4)) Tandem Library Bks.

McCloskey, Robert. Abran Paso a los Patitos. 2000. (SPA., Illus.). (J). (gr. k-3). 25.95 incl. audio (978-0-87499-660-9(0)) Live Oak Media.

—Abran Paso a los Patitos. McCloskey, Robert, illus. 2000. (Illus.). 28.95 incl. audio compact disk (978-1-59519-122-9(4)); pap. 39.95 incl. audio compact disk (978-1-59519-121-2(6)); (SPA., (J). pap. 18.95 incl. audio compact disk (978-1-59519-120-5(8)) Live Oak Media.

—Abran Paso a los Patitos. Blanco, Osvaldo, tr. from ENG. 2005. (SPA., Illus.). 62p. (J). (gr. k-4). reprint ed. 15.00 (978-0-7567-8841-4(2)) DIANE Publishing Co.

—Make Way for Ducklings. McCloskey, Robert, illus. 2002. (Illus.). (J). 13.60 (978-0-7587-0056-8(3)) Book Wholesalers, Inc.

—Make Way for Ducklings. 2000. (J). pap. 19.97 incl. audio (978-0-7366-9196-3(0)) Books on Tape, Inc.

—Make Way for Ducklings. 1999. (Illus.). 76p. (J). (ps-3). pap. 7.99 (978-0-14-056434-1(9) , Puffin) Penguin Group (USA) Inc.

—Make Way for Ducklings. 2000. (J). (ps-k). pap. 12.95 incl. audio Weston Woods Studios, Inc.

—Make Way for Ducklings. McCloskey, Robert, illus. 2005. (Illus.). (J). pap. 18.95 incl. audio compact disk (978-1-59112-731-4(9)) Live Oak Media.

McDonald, Megan. Judy Moody Declares Independence. Reynolds, Peter H., illus. (Judy Moody Ser.: No. 6). 160p. (J). (gr. 1-4). 2007. pap. 5.99 (978-0-7636-2800-0(X)); 2005. 15.99 (978-0-7636-2361-6(X)) Candlewick Pr.

Meyer, Louis A. Curse of the Blue Tattoo: Being an Account of the Misadventures of Jacky Faber, Midshipman & Fine Lady. 2004. (Bloody Jack Adventures Ser.). (Illus.). 496p. (YA). 17.00 (978-0-15-205115-0(5)) Harcourt Children's Bks.

Miller, Susan Martins. Lydia the Patriot: The Boston Massacre. 2004. (Sisters in Time Ser.). 144p. (J). pap. 4.97 (978-1-59310-204-3(6)) Barbour Publishing, Inc.

Moss, Marissa. Emma's Journal: The Story of a Colonial Girl. Moss, Marissa, illus. 2001. (Young American Voices Ser.: Bk. 2). (Illus.). 56p. (YA). (gr. 3-7). pap. 7.00 (978-0-15-216325-9(5) , Silver Whistle) Harcourt Trade Pubs.

—Emma's Journal: The Story of a Colonial Girl. 2001. (gr. 3-6). lib. bdg. 15.30 (978-0-613-35506-3(7)); (Illus.). (J). 13.80 (978-0-606-21179-6(9)) Tandem Library Bks.

Remy, Jerry. Hello, Wally! Moore, Danny, illus. 2006. (J). 17.95 (*978-1-932888-80-5(2))* Mascot Bks., Inc.

Rinaldi, Ann. The Fifth of March: A Story of the Boston Massacre. 2004. (Great Episodes Ser.). 352p. (YA). pap. 6.95 (978-0-15-205078-8(7) , Gulliver Bks.) Harcourt Children's Bks.

—The Fifth of March: A Story of the Boston Massacre. 2nd ed. 2002. (J). 4.80 (978-0-03-073524-0(6)) Holt, Rinehart & Winston.

Roitman, Tanya, illus. I'm Going to Boston to Visit the Ducks. 2006. (I'm Going to Read Ser.). 24p. (J). pap. 3.95 (978-1-4027-3092-4(6)) Sterling Publishing Co., Inc.

Schneider, Richard H. The Christmas Pea Coat. Bond, Higgins, illus. 2004. 32p. (J). 14.95 (978-0-8249-5474-1(2)) Ideals Pubns.

Speck, Nancy. The Freedom Trail Mystery. Barstow, Susannah Driver, ed. Farnsworth, Bill, illus. 2001. (Going to Ser.). 173p. (gr. 4-8). pap. 6.95 (978-1-893577-07-7(4)) Four Corners Publishing Co., Inc.

Staffier, Jane Sarah. Casey & the Boston Freedom Trail. Staffier, Jane Sarah, illus. l.t. ed. 1999. (Beacon Hill Ser.: No. 2). (Illus.). 28p. (J). (gr. k-7). spiral bd. 9.95 (978-1-928895-01-5(8)) B.A.B., Ltd.

—Casey the Beacon Hill Cat Coloring Book Adventures, 4 vols., Set. Staffier, Jane Sarah, illus. l.t. ed. 2001. 130p. (J). (ps-7). pap. 32.95 (978-1-928895-04-6(2)) B.A.B., Ltd.

Story, George. Vanessa's Valley. 2005. 74p. pap. 14.95 (978-1-4137-8913-3(7)) PublishAmerica, Inc.

Thomas, Carroll. Ring Out Wild Bells: A Matty Trescott Novel. 2001. (Illus.). viii, 169p. (J). 9.95 (978-1-57525-291-9(0)) Smith and Kraus Publishers, Incorporated.

Tirabassi, Maren. Footlights & Fairy Dust: Matt & Maria Go to the Theatre. Miller, Brandie, illus. 2007. (J). pap. 14.95 (978-1-933002-26-2(3)) PublishingWorks.

Voelkel, J&P. Middleworld. 2007. (Jaguar Stones Trilogy Ser.: Bk. 1). (Illus.). 400p. (J). (gr. 6-9). 17.95 (*978-1-57525-561-3(8))* Smith and Kraus Publishers, Incorporated.

Weitzman, Jacqueline Preiss. You Can't Take a Balloon into the Museum of Fine Arts. Glasser, Robin Preiss, illus. 2002. 40p. (J). (gr. k-4). 18.99 (978-0-8037-2570-6(1) , Dial) Penguin Group (USA) Inc.

Wiley, Melissa. Across the Puddingstone Dam. Andreasen, Dan, illus. 2004. (Little House Ser.). 224p. (J). pap. 6.99 (978-0-06-440740-3(3)) HarperCollins Pubs.

Wiley, Melissa. Road from Roxbury. 2008. (Little House Ser.). 176p. (J). pap. 5.99 (*978-0-06-114830-9(X)* , Harper Trophy) HarperCollins Pubs.

A B

Wilson, Diane Lee. Firehorse. 2006. 336p. (J). (gr. 7 up). 16.95 (978-1-4169-1551-5(6) , McElderry, Margaret K.) Simon & Schuster Children's Publishing.

BOSTON (MASS.)—HISTORY

Barter, James. Colonial Boston. 2003. (Illus.). 112p. (J). 29.95 (978-1-59018-357-1(6) , Lucent Bks.) Thomson Gale.

Belovitch, Jeanne. Boston Firsts: A Coloring Book about Boston's History & America's. Parker, Edward, illus. 2002. 28p. (J). (ps-7). pap. 2.50 (978-0-9722969-0-8(5)) CMB Publishing Co.

Boston: The Way It Was. 2004. (Wgbh Specials Ser.). (gr. 7 up). 120p. 39.95 incl. VHS (978-1-57807-239-2(5) , WG114); Pt. 1. 19.95 incl. VHS (978-1-884738-58-6(3) , WG158) WGBH Boston Video.

The Boston Massacre, 6 vols. (gr. 2-5). 39.95 (978-0-7368-4578-6(X)) Red Brick Learning.

Burgan, Michael. The Battle of Bunker Hill: An Interactive History. 2008. (You Choose Bks.). 112p. (J). (gr. 3-7). lib. bdg. 27.23 (***978-1-4296-0159-7(0)***) Capstone Pr., Inc.

—The Boston Massacre. Wiacek, Bob et al, illus. 2005. (Graphic Library). 32p. (J). (gr. 4-7). lib. bdg. 25.26 (978-0-7368-4368-3(X)) Capstone Pr., Inc.

—The Boston Tea Party. 2000. (We the People Ser.). (Illus.). 48p. (J). (gr. 4 up). lib. bdg. 22.60 (978-0-7565-0040-5(0)) Compass Point Bks.

Burt, Barbara. Colonial Life: The Adventures of Benjamin Wilcox. 2002. (Reading Expeditions Ser.). (Illus.). 40p. (J). (978-0-7922-8678-3(2)) National Geographic Society.

—The Eve of Revolution: The Colonial Adventures of Benjamin Wilcox. 2004. (Illus.). 40p. (J). (gr. 4-8). pap. 7.00 (978-0-7567-8215-3(5)) DIANE Publishing Co.

Clinton, Catherine. Underground Railroad. 2007. 32p. (J). lib. bdg. 17.89 (978-0-06-050426-7(9)) HarperCollins Pubs.

—When Harriet Met Sojourner. Evans, Shane, illus. 2007. 32p. (J). (gr. k-2). 16.99 (978-0-06-050425-0(0)) HarperCollins Pubs.

Gillis, Jennifer Blizin. Life in Colonial Boston. 2003. (Picture the Past Ser.). (J). 532.84 (978-1-4034-4282-6(7)); (Illus.). 32p. pap. 6.95 (978-1-4034-4284-0(3)); (Illus.). 32p. lib. bdg. 24.22 (978-1-4034-3795-2(5)) Heinemann Library.

Heims, Neil. Reading Johnny Tremain. 2005. (Engaged Reader Ser.). (Illus.). 82p. (J). (ps-8). lib. bdg. 25.00 (978-0-7910-8831-9(6) , Chelsea Hse.) Facts On File, Inc.

Hull, Mary E. The Boston Tea Party in American History. 1999. (In American History Ser.). (Illus.). 128p. (YA). (gr. 5-12). lib. bdg. 26.60 (978-0-7660-1139-7(9)) Enslow Pubs., Inc.

Ready, Dee. The Boston Massacre. 2002. (Let Freedom Ring Ser.). (Illus.). 48p. (J). (gr. 3-4). lib. bdg. 22.60 (978-0-7368-1092-0(7) , Bridgestone Bks.) Capstone Pr., Inc.

Richards, Laura E. Jiggle Joggle Jee! 2001. (Illus.). 32p. (J). (ps-3). 15.89 (978-0-688-17833-8(2)) HarperCollins Pubs.

Santella, Andrew. The Boston Massacre. 2004. (Cornerstones of Freedom Ser.). (Illus.). 48p. (J). 26.00 (978-0-516-24226-2(1) , Children's Pr.) Scholastic Library Publishing.

Trumbauer, Lisa. Hopes Fulfilled: The Irish Immigrants in Boston. 2005. (Illus.). 32p. (J). pap. (***978-0-7367-2881-2(3)***) Zaner-Bloser, Inc.

BOSTON MASSACRE, 1770

Boston Massacre. (American Revolution Ser.). 32p. (YA). 7.95 (978-0-7368-4492-5(9)) Capstone Pr., Inc.

BOSTON RED SOX (BASEBALL TEAM)

Campbell, Peter A. Old Time Baseball & the First. 2002. (Illus.). 48p. (gr. 3-6). lib. bdg. 24.90 (978-0-7613-2466-9(6) , Millbrook Pr.) Lerner Publishing Group.

Epstein, Brad M. Boston Red Sox 101: My first Team-board-book. l.t. ed. 2007. (101—My First Text-Board Books). (Illus.). 22p. (J). bds. 10.95 (***978-1-932530-92-6(4)*** , 101 Bk.) Michaelson Entertainment.

Frisch, Aaron. Boston Red Sox. 2002. (Baseball Ser.). (Illus.). 32p. (J). (978-1-58341-202-2(6) , Creative Education) Creative Co., The.

Grabowski, John F. The Boston Red Sox Baseball Team. 2001. (Great Sports Teams Ser.). (Illus.). 48p. (YA). (gr. 4-10). lib. bdg. 23.93 (978-0-7660-1488-6(6)) Enslow Pubs., Inc.

Rambeck, Richard. The History of the Boston Red Sox. 1998. (Baseball, the Great American Game Ser.). (Illus.). 32p. (YA). (gr. 3-12). pap. 21.30 (978-0-88682-900-1(3) , Creative Education) Creative Co., The.

Sandler, Michael. Baseball: The 2004 Boston Red Sox. 2006. (Upsets & Comebacks Ser.). (Illus.). 32p. (J). lib. bdg. 25.27 (978-1-59716-165-7(9)) Bearport Publishing Co., Inc.

Shaughnessy, Dan. The Legend of the Curse of the Bambino. Payne, C. F., illus. 2005. 32p. (J). 16.95 (978-0-689-87235-8(6) , Simon & Schuster Children's Publishing) Simon & Schuster Children's Publishing.

Stewart, Mark. Boston Red Sox. 48p. 2008. pap. 9.95 (***978-1-60357-007-7(1)***); 2006. (Illus.). (J). lib. bdg. (978-1-59953-059-8(7)) Norwood Hse. Pr.

BOSTON TEA PARTY, 1773

Benchmark Education Staff. The Boston Tea Party. 2005. 2.00 (***978-1-4108-4674-7(1)***) Benchmark Education Co.

Boston Tea Party. (American Revolution Ser.). 32p. (YA). 7.95 (978-0-7368-4493-2(7)) Capstone Pr., Inc.

Brannon, Barbara. Discover the Boston Tea Party. 2005. 39.00 (***978-1-4108-5157-4(5)***) Benchmark Education Co.

Burgan, Michael. The Boston Tea Party. 2000. (We the People Ser.). (Illus.). 48p. (J). (gr. 4 up). lib. bdg. 22.60 (978-0-7565-0040-5(0)) Compass Point Bks.

Cook, Peter. You Wouldn't Want to Be at the Boston Tea Party. Antram, David, illus. 2006. 32p. (J). (gr. 2-5). pap. 9.95 (978-0-531-12447-5(9) , Watts, Franklin) Scholastic Library Publishing.

—You Wouldn't Want to Be at the Boston Tea Party: Wharf Water Tea, You'D Rather Not Drink. Antram, David, illus. 2006. (You Wouldn't Want To Ser.). 32p. (J). (gr. 2-5). 28.50 (978-0-531-12422-2(3) , Watts, Franklin) Scholastic Library Publishing.

Cooper, Terry, ed. Boston Tea Party: Scholastic Technology Activity Folder. 2001. 6p. 3.95 (978-0-439-30951-6(4)) Scholastic, Inc.

Dahl, Michael. Trouble Brewing! A Fun Song about the Boston Tea Party. D'Antonio, Sandra, illus. 2004. (Fun Songs Ser.). 24p. (gr. k-3). 22.60 (978-1-4048-0131-8(6)) Picture Window Bks.

Doeden, Matt. The Boston Tea Party. (Graphic History Ser.). 32p. (YA). pap. 7.95 (978-0-7368-5243-2(3)) Capstone Pr., Inc.

—The Boston Tea Party. 2005. (Graphic Library). (Illus.). 32p. (J). 22.60 (978-0-7368-3846-7(5)) Capstone Pr., Inc.

Dolan, Edward F., Jr. The Boston Tea Party. 2001. (Kaleidoscope Ser.). (Illus.). 48p. (J). (gr. 3). lib. bdg. 25.64 (978-0-7614-1303-5(0) , Benchmark Bks.) Cavendish, Marshall Corp.

Draper, Allison Stark. The Boston Tea Party: Angry Colonists Dump British Tea. 2001. (Headlines from History Ser.). (Illus.). 24p. (J). (gr. 3). lib. bdg. 19.95 (978-0-8239-5671-5(7) , PKBOTE, PowerKids Pr.) Rosen Publishing Group, Inc., The.

Edwards, Pamela Duncan. Boston Tea Party. Cole, Henry, illus. 2001. 1p. (J). (gr. 1-3). 16.99 (978-0-399-23357-9(1) , Putnam Juvenile) Penguin Group (USA) Inc.

Espinosa, Rod. The Boston Tea Party. 2007. (Graphic History Ser.). (Illus.). 32p. (J). (gr. 3-6). lib. bdg. 27.07 (***978-1-60270-075-8(3)*** , Graphic Planet) Magic Wagon.

Fradin, Dennis B. The Boston Tea Party. 2007. (Turning Points in U. S. History Ser.). (J). lib. bdg. (978-0-7614-2035-4(5) , Benchmark Bks.) Cavendish, Marshall Corp.

Furstinger, Nancy. The Boston Tea Party. 2002. (Let Freedom Ring Ser.). (Illus.). 48p. (J). (gr. 3-4). lib. bdg. 22.60 (978-0-7368-1093-7(5) , Bridgestone Bks.) Capstone Pr., Inc.

Gunderson, Cory. Boston Tea Party. 2005. (American Moments Ser.). (Illus.). 48p. (J). (gr. 4-8). lib. bdg. 25.65 (978-1-59197-280-8(9) , ABDO & Daughters) ABDO Publishing Co.

Hossell, Karen Price. Boston Tea Party: Rebellion in the Colonies. 2003. (gr. 5-8). lib. bdg. 15.25 (978-0-613-58195-0(4)) Tandem Library Bks.

Hull, Mary E. The Boston Tea Party in American History. 1999. (In American History Ser.). (Illus.). 128p. (YA). (gr. 5-12). lib. bdg. 26.60 (978-0-7660-1139-7(9)) Enslow Pubs., Inc.

Klingel, Cynthia Fitterer & Noyed, Robert B. The Boston Tea Party. 2001. (Wonder Books Level 3: U. S. History Ser.). (Illus.). 32p. (J). (ps-3). 22.79 (978-1-56766-958-9(1)) Child's World, Inc.

Kroll, Steven. The Boston Tea Party. Fiore, Peter, illus. 2000. 32p. (J). (ps-7). pap. 6.95 (978-0-8234-1557-1(0)) Holiday Hse., Inc.

Landau, Elaine. Witness the Boston Tea Party with Elaine Landau. 2006. (Explore Colonial America with Elaine Landau Ser.). (Illus.). 48p. (J). lib. bdg. 23.93 (978-0-7660-2553-0(5) , Enslow Elementary) Enslow Pubs., Inc.

Lilly, Melinda. The Boston Tea Party. 2003. (Rourke Discovery Library). (Illus.). 24p. (gr. 1-4). 14.95 (978-1-58952-357-9(1)) Rourke Publishing, LLC.

Price Hossell, Karen. The Boston Tea Party: Rebellion in the Colonies. 2003. (Point of Impact Ser.). (Illus.). 32p. (J). (gr. 5-7). lib. bdg. 25.64 (978-1-58810-906-4(2)); pap. (978-1-4034-0534-0(4)) Heinemann Library.

Roza, Greg. Analyzing the Boston Tea Party: Establishing Cause & Effect Relationships. 2005. (Critical Thinking in American History Ser.). (Illus.). 48p. (J). (gr. 5-8). lib. bdg. 25.25 (978-1-4042-0411-9(3)) Rosen Publishing Group, Inc., The.

Sutton, Adam J. What Happened at the Boston Tea Party? 2006. (Rosen Publishing Group's Reading Room Collection). (Illus.). 16p. (J). lib. bdg. (978-1-4042-3350-8(4) , PowerKids Pr.) Rosen Publishing Group, Inc., The.

Trueit, Trudi Strain. The Boston Tea Party. 2005. (Cornerstones of Freedom Ser.). 48p. (J). 26.00 (978-0-516-23636-0(9) , Children's Pr.) Scholastic Library Publishing.

Wachter, Joanne. The Boston Tea Party. 2005. 39.00 (***978-1-4108-4626-6(1)***) Benchmark Education Co.

Walker, Ida. The Boston Tea Party. 2007. (Essential Events Ser.). (ENG., Illus.). 112p. (YA). (gr. 8-12). lib. bdg. 32.79 (***978-1-59928-849-9(4)*** , Essential Library) ABDO Publishing Co.

BOSTON TEA PARTY, 1773—FICTION

Brodeur, Tom. Regina Silsby's Secret War. 2004. 248p. (J). 7.49 (978-1-59166-235-8(4)) Jones, Bob Univ. Pr.

Duey, Kathleen. Silence & Lily: 1773. 2007. 176p. (J). (gr. 5). pap. 5.99 (***978-0-14-240909-1(X)*** , Puffin) Penguin Group (USA) Inc.

Grote, JoAnn A. The American Revolution. Wallenta, Adam, illus. 1999. (American Adventure Ser.: No. 11). (J). (gr. 3-7). (978-0-7910-5591-5(4) , Chelsea Hse.) Facts On File, Inc.

Hemphill, Kris. A Secret Party in Boston Harbor. Martin, John F. & Van Pelt, Dan, illus. 1998. (Mysteries in Time Ser.: Vol. 6). 96p. (J). (gr. 4-7). 14.95 (978-1-881889-88-5(2)) Silver Moon Pr.

Holben, Jennifer. The Brothers of Liberty. 2006. 48p. (J). per. 7.95 (978-1-59886-359-8(2)) Tate Publishing & Enterprises, L.L.C.

Rocca, Al. Patriot Courage: The Boston Tea Party 1773. l.t. ed. 2006. (Illus.). 56p. (J). per. 4.95 (***978-0-9643378-2-4(7)***) Renown Publishing Co.

Stein, R. Conrad. The Boston Tea Party. 1998. (Cornerstones of Freedom Ser.). (Illus.). 32p. (J). (gr. 4-6). pap. 5.95 (978-0-516-26285-7(8) , Children's Pr.) Scholastic Library Publishing.

BOTANY

see also Flower Gardening; Flowers; Fruit; Leaves; Plant Anatomy; Plant Ecology; Plant Physiology; Plants; Plants, Fossil; Seeds; Shrubs; Trees; Vegetables

Arbel, Ilil. Amazing Plants. 2004. (Dover Coloring Bks.). (Illus.). 32p. (J). pap. 3.95 (978-0-486-43336-3(6)) Dover Pubns., Inc.

Barbour, Michael, et al. Sg/Wb-Plant Biology. 2nd ed. 2005. (C). pap. 34.95 (978-0-534-49592-3(3)) Brooks/Cole.

Bodach, Vijaya. Roots. 2007. (Illus.). 24p. (J). 19.93 (978-0-7368-6345-2(1) , Pebble Bks.) Capstone Pr., Inc.

Bozak, Kristin & Cohen, Judith Love. You Can Be a Woman Botanist. Katz, David Arthur, illus. Date not set. 40p. (J). (gr. 3-6). 13.95 (978-1-880599-41-9(4)) Cascade Pass, Inc.

Branigan, Carrie & Dunne, Richard. All Kinds of Plants. 2005. (World of Plants Ser.). (Illus.). 31p. (J). (gr. 2-5). lib. bdg. 27.10 (978-1-58340-610-6(7)) Smart Apple Media.

—Fruits & Vegetables. 2005. (World of Plants Ser.). (Illus.). 31p. (J). (gr. 2-5). lib. bdg. 27.10 (978-1-58340-613-7(1)) Smart Apple Media.

Chinery, Michael. Plants & Planteaters. 2000. (Secrets of the Rainforest Ser.). (Illus.). 32p. (J). (gr. 3-4). pap. (978-0-7787-0228-3(6)) Crabtree Publishing Co.

Corbett, Pie. Plants. 2005. (Illus.). 24p. (YA). (gr. 1 up). lib. bdg. 22.80 (978-1-59389-207-4(1)) Chrysalis Education.

Dixon, Malcolm & Smith, Karen. Plants Around Us. 1998. (Young Scientists Ser.). (Illus.). 32p. (J). (ps-3). lib. bdg. 16.95 (978-1-887068-71-0(6)) Smart Apple Media.

Elpel, Thomas J. Shanleya's Quest: A Botany Adventure for Kids Ages 9 - 99, 1 vol. Brown, Gloria Dean, illus. 32p. 12.50 (978-1-892784-16-2(5) , 1511) HOPS Pr., LLC.

Farndon, John. Stems. 2005. (Illus.). 24p. (J). (gr. 2-4). 23.70 (978-1-4103-0420-9(5) , Blackbirch Pr., Inc.) Thomson Gale.

Freeman, Marcia S. What Plant Is This? 2005. (Everything Science Ser.). (Illus.). 24p. (gr. 1-4). 14.95 (978-1-59515-124-7(9)) Rourke Publishing, LLC.

Fulbright, Jeannie. Exploring Creation with Botany. Wile, Jay L., ed. 2004. 35.00 (978-1-932012-49-1(4)) Apologia Educational Ministries, Inc.

Gardner, Robert. Science Projects about Plants. 1999. (Science Projects Ser.). (Illus.). 112p. (YA). (gr. 6-12). lib. bdg. 26.60 (978-0-89490-952-8(5)) Enslow Pubs., Inc.

Germination. 2001. (Botany Ser.). (J). (gr. k-12). vinyl bd. 4.95 (978-1-58845-141-5(0)) School Specialty Publishing.

Gottlieb. Plant Life. 2004. pap., tchr. ed. 17.60 incl. cd-rom (978-0-7398-9186-5(3)); (Illus.). pap. 15.60 incl. cd-rom (978-0-7398-9180-3(4)) Steck-Vaughn.

Grieveson, Margaret. Plants. 2005. (Illus.). 32p. (J). (gr. 3-7). lib. bdg. 27.10 (978-1-59604-037-3(8)) Stargazer Bks.

Grolier Educational Staff, contrib. by. Plants, 10 vols. 2000. (Illus.). (J). (978-0-7172-9511-1(7) , Grolier) Scholastic Library Publishing.

Gumm, Amy L. Let It Grow, Let It Grow, Let It Grow: Hands-on Activities to Explore the Plant Kingdom. 2005. (Illus.). 104p. spiral bd. 14.95 (978-0-9761724-6-8(1)) NSR Pubns.

Hewitt, Sally. Amazing Plants. 2007. 32p. pap. (***978-0-7787-3628-8(8)***) Crabtree Publishing Co.

Hixson, Bryce. Plant Stigmas & Other Botanical Concerns. Hixson, Bryce, illus. 2003. (Illus.). (J). per. 12.95 (978-1-931801-09-6(5)) Loose In The Lab.

Holmes, Anita. Flowers & Friends. 2000. (We Can Read about Nature! Ser.). (Illus.). 32p. (J). (gr. 1-2). lib. bdg. 21.36 (978-0-7614-1113-0(5) , Benchmark Bks.) Cavendish, Marshall Corp.

Howell, Laura & Rogers, Kirsteen. World of Plants. 2004. (Internet-Linked Library of Science). 64p. (J). pap. 9.95 (978-0-7945-0086-3(2) , Usborne); lib. bdg. 17.95 (978-1-58086-379-7(5)) EDC Publishing.

Jakab, Cheryl. The Plant Life Cycle. 2007. (J). (***978-1-59920-147-4(X)***) Smart Apple Media.

Kalman, Bobbie. Que son las Plantas? 2005. (Ciencia de los Seres Vivos Ser.).Tr. of What are Plants?. (SPA., Illus.). 32p. (YA). (gr. 7-12). pap. (978-0-7787-8805-8(9)) Crabtree Publishing Co.

—Qué Son las Plantas? 2005. (SPA., Illus.). 32p. (J). (978-0-7787-8759-4(1)) Crabtree Publishing Co.

—What Is a Plant? 2000. (gr. 3-6). lib. bdg. 14.10 (978-0-613-28132-4(2)) Tandem Library Bks.

Kalman, Bobbie & Walker, Niki. What Is a Plant? 2000. (Science of Living Things Ser.). (Illus.). 32p. (J). (gr. 2-3). pap. (978-0-86505-959-7(4)); (978-0-86505-982-5(9)) Crabtree Publishing Co.

Knotts, Bob. Florida Plants & Animals. 2002. (State Studies). (Illus.). 48p. (J). pap. 8.50 (978-1-4034-0566-1(2)); lib. bdg. (978-1-4034-0350-6(3)) Heinemann Library.

Legg, Gerald. The World of Plant Life. 2002. (Inside Look Ser.). (Illus.). 48p. (J). (gr. 4 up). lib. bdg. 26.00 (978-0-8368-3180-1(2)) Stevens, Gareth Inc.

Markle, Sandra. Grow a Giant Beanstalk & 15 More Amazing Plant Projects. Brace, Eric, illus. 2003. (Science Dares You! Ser.). 64p. (J). (978-0-439-44434-7(9)) Scholastic, Inc.

Mason, Adrienne & Hodge, Deborah. Plants. Boudreau, Ray, illus. 1998. (Starting with Science Ser.). 32p. (J). (gr. k-3). (978-1-55074-193-3(4)) Kids Can Pr., Ltd.

McNeil, Niki, et al. HOCPP 1116 Botany. 2006. spiral bd. 20.00 (***978-1-60308-116-0(X)***) In the Hands of a Child.

Mi manzano Science, 6 vols.Tr. of My Apple Tree Science. (SPA.). (gr. k-2). 28.95 (978-0-7368-3125-3(8) , Yellow Umbrella Bks.) Capstone Pr., Inc.

Microscopic Investigations: Plant Biology. 2001. (J). pap. 5.95 (978-1-56911-745-3(4)) Learning Resources, Inc.

Mitchell, Melanie S. Stems. 2003. (First Step Nonfiction Ser.). (Illus.). 8p. (J). pap. 3.95 (978-0-8225-3921-6(7) , Lerner Pubns.) Lerner Publishing Group.

Morgan, Sally. Flowers, Trees, & Fruits. 2002. (Young Discoverers Ser.). (Illus.). 32p. (J). (gr. k-3). pap. 7.95 (978-0-7534-5500-5(5) , Kingfisher) Houghton Mifflin Co. Trade & Reference Div.

Morris, Neil. Living & Growing. (Our World Ser.). (Illus.). 32p. (J). lib. bdg. 24.25 (978-1-930643-80-2(2)) Chrysalis Education.

Murphy, Patricia J. Peeking at Plants with a Scientist. 2004. (I Like Science! Ser.). (Illus.). 24p. (J). lib. bdg. 21.26 (978-0-7660-2266-9(8)) Enslow Pubs., Inc.

My Apple Tree Science, 6 vols. (gr. k-2). 28.95 (978-0-7368-1743-1(3) , Yellow Umbrella Bks.) Capstone Pr., Inc.

Pascoe, Elaine. Slime, Molds & Fungi. Kuhn, Dwight, photos by. 1998. (Nature Close-Up Ser.). (Illus.). 48p. (J). (gr. 4-8). 23.70 (978-1-56711-182-8(3) , Blackbirch Pr., Inc.) Thomson Gale.

Patent, Dorothy Hinshaw. Plants on the Trail with Lewis & Clark. Munoz, William, photos by. 2003. (Illus.). 112p. (J). (gr. 4-6). tchr. ed. 18.00 (978-0-618-06776-3(0) , Clarion Bks.) Houghton Mifflin Co. Trade & Reference Div.

Paul, Heather. Discovering Scottish Plants. Galloway, Fhiona, illus. 1999. (Scottie Bks.). 40p. (J). (gr. 3-7). pap. 6.95 (978-0-11-495760-5(6)) Stationery Office, The GBR. *Dist:* Balogh International, Inc.

Perry, Phyllis J. Science Fair Success with Plants. 1999. (Science Fair Success Ser.). (Illus.). 104p. (YA). (gr. 6-12). lib. bdg. 26.60 (978-0-7660-1170-0(4)) Enslow Pubs., Inc.

El planeta Preguntón 14: Leveled Books. 2001. (McGraw-Hill. Lectura Ser.). (ENG & SPA.). (gr. 2 up). (978-0-02-188015-7(8)) Macmillan/McGraw-Hill Schl. Div.

Plantemos Semillas. 2000. (McGraw-Hill Ciencias Ser.). (ENG & SPA.). (gr. 1 up). (978-0-02-279562-7(6)) Macmillan/McGraw-Hill Schl. Div.

Plants. 2005. (Illus.). 32p. (gr. 2-4). pap. 138.00 (978-0-7910-8464-9(7) , Chelsea Hse.) Facts On File, Inc.

Rao, Sirish. Leaf Life. 2006. (Illus.). 32p. 12.95 (978-81-86211-93-9(4)) Consortium Bk. Sales & Distribution.

Robinson, Richard, ed. Plant Sciences, 4 vols., Set. 2000. (Macmillan Science Library). 800p. (J). 460.00 (978-0-02-865434-8(X) , GML00502-170601, Macmillan Reference USA) Thomson Gale.

Santella, Andrew. Illinois Plants & Animals. 2002. (Heinemann State Studies). (Illus.). 48p. (J). (gr. 3-5). lib. bdg. 27.07 (978-1-4034-0011-6(3)) Heinemann Library.

Saunders-Smith, Gail. Plants Science. (gr. k-2). 19.95 (978-0-7368-9215-5(X)) Red Brick Learning.

Schonberg, Marcia. Ohio Plants & Animals. 2003. (Heinemann State Studies). (Illus.). 48p. (J). pap. 8.50 (978-1-4034-2691-8(0)); lib. bdg. 27.07 (978-1-4034-0669-9(3)) Heinemann Library.

Seeds & Weeds & Plants Galore. 2002. (Illus.). 48p. (J). 2.99 (978-0-88724-805-4(5) , WG 3034) Carson-Dellosa Publishing Co., Inc.

Silverstein, Alvin & Silverstein, Virginia B. Nature's Champions: The Biggest, the Fastest, the Best. Zallinger, Jean, tr. Zallinger, Jean, illus. 2003. 64p. (gr. 5-8). pap. 5.95 (978-0-486-42888-8(5)) Dover Pubns., Inc.

Silverstein, Alvin, et al. Photosynthesis. 1998. (Science Concepts Ser.: 8). (Illus.). 64p. (gr. 5-8). lib. bdg. 26.90 (978-0-7613-3000-4(3) , Twenty-First Century Bks.) Lerner Publishing Group.

Smith, Karla. Virginia Plants & Animals. 2003. (Heinemann State Studies). (Illus.). 48p. (J). pap. 8.50 (978-1-4034-0582-1(4)); (gr. 3-5). lib. bdg. (978-1-4034-0360-5(0)) Heinemann Library.

—Virginia Plants & Animals. 2003. (gr. 3-6). lib. bdg. 17.05 (978-0-613-60996-8(4)) Tandem Library Bks.

Spilsbury, Louise & Spilsbury, Richard. Green Plants: From Roots to Leaves. 2004. (Science Answers Ser.). (Illus.). 32p. (J). (ps-k). pap. 7.50 (978-1-4034-5511-6(2)); lib. bdg. 24.22 (978-1-4034-4765-4(9)) Heinemann Library.

Spilsbury, Richard & Spilsbury, Louise. Plant Classification. 2003. (Life of Plants Ser.). (Illus.). 48p. (J). (gr. 3-5). lib. bdg. 25.64 (978-1-4034-0293-6(0)) Heinemann Library.

Stewart, Mark. New Jersey Plants & Animals. 2003. (State Studies). (Illus.). 48p. (J). pap. 8.50 (978-1-4034-2685-7(6)); lib. bdg. 27.07 (978-1-4034-0676-7(6)) Heinemann Library.

Stewart, Melissa. Plants. 2003. (Simply Science Ser.). (Illus.). 32p. (J). (gr. 3 up). lib. bdg. 19.93 (978-0-7565-0444-1(9)) Compass Point Bks.

Stone, Lynn M. Stems. 2008. (J). (***978-1-60044-556-9(X)***) Rourke Publishing, LLC.

Talmadge, Ellen. Unearthing Garden Mysteries Vol. 1: Experiments for Kids. Curtis, Bruce, photos by. 2004. (Illus.). 96p. (gr. 4-7). 17.95 (978-1-55591-993-1(6)) Fulcrum Publishing.

Thomas, Lyndall. Plants. 1999. (Interfact Reference Ser.). (Illus.). 48p. (J). (gr. 2-8). 15.00 (978-0-7166-7239-5(1) , 1544) World Bk., Inc.

Tocci, Salvatore. Experiments with Plants. (True Books Ser.). (Illus.). 48p. (J). (gr. 3-5). 2002. pap. 6.95 (978-0-516-27351-8(5)); Set. 2001. 25.00 (978-0-516-22252-3(X)) Scholastic Library Publishing. (Children's Pr.).

—Plant Projects for Young Scientists. 2000. (Projects for Young Scientists Ser.). (Illus.). 144p. (YA). (gr. 9-12). 23.50 (978-0-531-11704-0(9) , Watts, Franklin) Scholastic Library Publishing.

VanCleave, Janice Pratt. Janice VanCleave's Plants: Mind-Boggling Experiments You Can Turn into Science Fair Projects. 2002. (Janice Vancleave Ser.). (Illus.). (J). 19.72 (978-0-7587-4632-0(6)) Book Wholesalers, Inc.

Wadsworth, Pamela. Golwg Gyntaf Ar Bethau Byw. 2005. (WEL., Illus.). 24p. pap. (978-1-85596-250-7(0)) Dref Wen.

What a Weird Plant!, 6 vols. (Book2WebTM Ser.). (gr. 4-8). 36.50 (978-0-322-02980-4(5)) Wright Group, The.

What Grows. 2002. (J). pap. 3.74 (978-0-7398-5832-5(7)) Steck-Vaughn.

Whitehouse, Patricia. Plants. 2007. (J). ***978-1-4034-7918-1(6))** Heinemann Library.

Woodward, John. What Lives in the Garden? 2002. (gr. 3-6). lib. bdg. 16.40 (978-0-613-85657-7(0)) Tandem Library Bks.

BOTANY, AGRICULTURAL

see Botany, Economic

BOTANY—ANATOMY

see Plant Anatomy

BOTANY—ECOLOGY

see Plant Ecology

BOTANY, ECONOMIC

see also Cotton; Grasses; Plant Introduction; Plants, Edible; Weeds

Llewellyn, Claire. Plants & Humans. 2007. (J). ***978-1-59920-031-6(7))** Smart Apple Media.

Morgan, Sally. Plants & Life. 2002. (Looking at Plants Ser.). (Illus.). 32p. (J). lib. bdg. 24.25 (978-1-931983-12-9(7)) Chrysalis Education.

BOTANY, FOSSIL

see Plants, Fossil

BOTANY—GEOGRAPHICAL DISTRIBUTION

see Geographical Distribution of Animals and Plants

BOTANY, MEDICAL

Ballard, Carol. The Search for Cures from the Rainforest. 2005. (Science Quest Ser.). (Illus.). 32p. (J). lib. bdg. 24.67 (978-0-8368-4554-9(4)) Stevens, Gareth Inc.

Guttmacher, Joyce. Harvesting Medicine on the Hill. 2005. (Illus.). 24p. (J). ***978-0-328-13510-3(0)** , Scott Foresman) Addison-Wesley Educational Pubs., Inc.

BOTANY—PHYSIOLOGY

see Plant Physiology

BOTANY—VOCATIONAL GUIDANCE

Bozak, Kristin & Cohen, Judith Love. You Can Be a Woman Botanist. Katz, David Arthur, illus. Date not set. 40p. (J). (gr. 3-6). pap. 12.95 (978-1-880599-42-6(2)) Cascade Pass, Inc.

BOTANY OF THE BIBLE

see Bible—Natural History

BOTSWANA

Brimson, Samuel. Afghanistan-Botswana, 8 vols. 2003. (Nations of the World Ser.: Vol. 1). (Illus.). 64p. (J). (gr. 5 up). lib. bdg. 30.00 (978-0-8368-5485-5(3) , World Almanac Library) Stevens, Gareth Inc.

Kras, Sara Louise. Botswana. 2007. 144p. (J). 37.00 (***978-0-516-24874-5(X)** , Children's Pr.) Scholastic Library Publishing.

LeVert, Suzanne. Botswana. 2007. (Cultures of the World Ser.). (Illus.). 128p. (J). lib. bdg. 39.93 (978-0-7614-2330-0(3) , Benchmark Bks.) Cavendish, Marshall Corp.

Wittman, Kelly. Botswana. 2007. (J). (978-1-4222-0087-?(6)) Mason Crest Pubs.

BOTSWANA—FICTION

Dow, Unity. Far & Beyon' 2002. 208p. (YA). (gr. 7 up). pap. 11.95 (978-1-879960-64-0(8)) Aunt Lute Bks.

Dyer, Olive & Scurlock, Val. Kabo's Diary. 2002. (Illus.). 36p. pap. 12.95 (978-1-84323-017-5(8)); 32p. pap. 29.95 (978-1-84323-018-2(6)) Beekman Bks., Inc.

Smith, Alexander McCall. Tears of the Giraffe. 2002. (No. 1 Ladies' Detective Agency Ser.: Bk. 2). (gr. 7-12). lib. bdg. 21.05 (978-0-613-64790-8(4)) Tandem Library Bks.

BOTTICELLI, SANDRO, 1447?-1510

Connolly, Sean. Botticelli. 2004. (Lives of the Artists Ser.). (Illus.). 48p. (J). pap. 11.95 (978-0-8368-5653-8(8)); lib. bdg. 30.00 (978-0-8368-5648-4(1)) Stevens, Gareth Inc. (World Almanac Library).

Mattern, Joanne. Sandro Botticelli. 2005. (Checkerboard Biography Library). (Illus.). 32p. (J). (gr. k-6). lib. bdg. 22.78 (978-1-59197-839-8(4)) ABDO Publishing Co.

BOULDER DAM (ARIZ. AND NEV.)

see Hoover Dam (Ariz. and Nev.)

BOUNTY (SHIP)

Bligh, William. The Mutiny on Board HMS Bounty. Lynch, Brendan, illus. 2002. (Great Illustrated Classics Ser.). 240p. (J). (gr. 3-8). 21.35 (978-1-57765-696-8(2) , ABDO & Daughters) ABDO Publishing Co.

O'Brien, Patrick. The Mutiny on the Bounty. O'Brien, Patrick, illus. 2007. (Illus.). 40p. (J). (gr. 3-6). 17.95 (978-0-8027-9587-8(0)); 18.85 (978-0-8027-9588-5(9)) Walker & Co.

BOURKE-WHITE, MARGARET, 1906-1971

Wooten, Sara McIntosh. Margaret Bourke-White: Daring Photographer. 2002. (People to Know Ser.). (Illus.). 112p. (YA). (gr. 6-12). lib. bdg. 26.60 (978-0-7660-1534-0(3)) Enslow Pubs., Inc.

BOWDITCH, NATHANIEL, 1773-1838

Latham, Jean Lee. Carry on, Mr. Bowditch. 2003. (Illus.). (YA). (gr. 7). 256p. pap. 6.95 (978-0-618-25074-5(3)); 258p. tchr. ed. 17.00 (978-0-618-25081-3(6)) Houghton Mifflin Co. Trade & Reference Div.

BOWED INSTRUMENTS

see Stringed Instruments

BOWIE, JAMES, 1805-1836

Edmondson, J. R. Jim Bowie: Frontier Legend, Alamo Hero. 2005. (Library of American Lives & Times). (Illus.). 112p. (YA). (gr. 4-8). lib. bdg. 31.95 (978-0-8239-5734-7(9)) Rosen Publishing Group, Inc., The.

Gaines, Ann Graham. Jim Bowie: Hero of the Alamo. 2000. (Historical American Biographies Ser.). (Illus.). 128p. (YA). (gr. 6-12). lib. bdg. 26.60 (978-0-7660-1253-0(0)) Enslow Pubs., Inc.

Johnston, Marianne. Jim Bowie. 2001. (American Legends Ser.). (Illus.). 24p. (J). (gr. 3). lib. bdg. 18.75 (978-0-8239-5578-7(8) , PowerKids Pr.) Rosen Publishing Group, Inc., The.

BOWLING

Cruikshank, Don. For the Love of Bowling. 2006. (For the Love of Sports Ser.). (J). (978-1-59036-384-3(1)); (978-1-59036-385-0(X)) Weigl Pubs., Inc.

Eckart, Edana. I Can Bowl. 2002. (Welcome Bks.). (Illus.). 24p. (J). (ps-2). pap. 4.95 (978-0-516-24028-2(5) , Children's Pr.) Scholastic Library Publishing.

—I Can Bowl. 2002. (gr. k-3). lib. bdg. 12.95 (978-0-613-58839-3(8)) Tandem Library Bks.

Kalman, Bobbie. Bowling in Action. 2003. (gr. 3-6). lib. bdg. 15.25 (978-0-613-59055-6(4)) Tandem Library Bks.

Walker, Niki & Dann, Sarah. Bowling in Action. 2003. (Sports in Action Ser.). (Illus.). 32p. (J). (gr. 1-4). (978-0-7787-0335-8(5)); (gr. 3-4). pap. (978-0-7787-0355-6(X)) Crabtree Publishing Co.

BOXCAR CHILDREN (FICTITIOUS CHARACTERS)—FICTION

Duffy, Daniel M., illus. Benny Goes into Business, Vol. 5. 1999. (Adventures of Benny & Watch: Vol. 5). 32p. (J). (ps-2). pap. 3.95 (978-0-8075-0637-0(0)) Whitman, Albert & Co.

—Benny's New Friend, Vol. 3. 1998. (Adventures of Benny & Watch: Vol. No. 3). 32p. (J). (ps-2). pap. 3.95 (978-0-8075-0649-3(4)) Whitman, Albert & Co.

—The Magic Show Mystery, Vol. 4. 1998. (Adventures of Benny & Watch: Vol. No. 4). 32p. (J). (ps-2). pap. 3.95 (978-0-8075-4939-1(8)) Whitman, Albert & Co.

—Meet the Boxcar Children. 1998. (Adventures of Benny & Watch: Vol. No. 1). 48p. (J). (ps-2). pap. 3.95 (978-0-8075-5034-2(5)) Whitman, Albert & Co.

—A Present for Grandfather, Vol. 2. 1998. (Adventures of Benny & Watch: Vol. No. 2). 32p. (J). (ps-2). pap. 3.95 (978-0-8075-6625-1(X)) Whitman, Albert & Co.

—Watch Runs Away, Vol. 6. 1999. (Adventures of Benny & Watch: Vol. No. 6). 32p. (J). (ps-2). pap. 3.95 (978-0-8075-8681-5(1)) Whitman, Albert & Co.

Duffy, Daniel Mark, illus. Benny's New Friend. 1998. (J). (ps-ps). lib. bdg. 11.80 (978-0-613-07332-5(0)) Tandem Library Bks.

Long, Donna Lee. A Guide for Using Boxcar Children: Surprise Island in the Classroom. 2000. (Literature Units Ser.). (Illus.). 48p. (J). pap., tchr. ed. 7.99 (978-1-57690-338-4(9) , TCM 2338) Teacher Created Materials, Inc.

Soileau, Hodges, illus. The Great Shark Mystery, Vol. 20. 2004. (Boxcar Children Mysteries Ser.: Vol. 20). 128p. pap. 4.50 (978-0-8075-5532-3(0)) Whitman, Albert & Co.

Tang, Charles, illus. The Basketball Mystery, Vol. 68. 1999. (Boxcar Children Ser.: No. 68). 128p. (J). (gr. 2-5). pap. 3.95 (978-0-8075-0576-2(5)) Whitman, Albert & Co.

—The Black Pearl Mystery, Vol. 64. 1998. (Boxcar Children Ser.: No. 64). 128p. (J). (gr. 2-7). pap. 4.50 (978-0-8075-0784-1(9)) Whitman, Albert & Co.

—The Cereal Box Mystery. 1998. (Boxcar Children Ser.: No. 65). (J). (gr. 2-5). 10.60 (978-0-606-13214-5(7)) Tandem Library Bks.

—The Cereal Box Mystery, Vol. 65. 1998. (Boxcar Children Ser.: No. 65). (J). (gr. 2-5). 128p. 14.95 (978-0-8075-1114-5(5)); 111p. pap. 4.50 (978-0-8075-1115-2(3)) Whitman, Albert & Co.

—The Gymnastics Mystery, Vol. 73. 2004. (Boxcar Children Ser.: No. 73). 128p. (gr. 2-5). mass mkt. 4.50 (978-0-8075-3101-3(4)) Whitman, Albert & Co.

—The Mystery in New York, Vol. 13. 2004. (Boxcar Children Special Ser.: No. 13). 121p. (J). (gr. 2-5). 14.95 (978-0-8075-5459-3(6)); pap. 4.50 (978-0-8075-5460-9(X)) Whitman, Albert & Co.

—The Mystery of the Empty Safe. 2000. (Boxcar Children Ser.: No. 75). (J). (gr. 2-5). (978-0-606-18768-8(5)) Tandem Library Bks.

—The Mystery of the Empty Safe, Vol. 75. 2004. (Boxcar Children Ser.: No. 75). 120p. (J). (gr. 2-5). pap. 4.50 (978-0-8075-5463-0(4)) Whitman, Albert & Co.

—The Mystery of the Stolen Sword. 1998. (Boxcar Children Ser.: No. 67). 121p. (J). (gr. 2-5). mass mkt. 4.50 (978-0-8075-7623-6(9)) Whitman, Albert & Co.

Warner, Gertrude Chandler. Benny Goes into Business. 1999. (gr. k-3). lib. bdg. 11.80 (978-0-613-11318-2(7)); (Adventures of Benny & Watch: No.5). (J). (gr. 1-3). 10.75 (978-0-606-16916-5(4)) Tandem Library Bks.

—Blue Bay Mystery, Vol. 6. Gringhuis, Dirk, illus. 2004. (Boxcar Children Ser.: No. 6). 128p. (gr. 2-7). reprint ed. mass mkt. 4.50 (978-0-8075-0794-0(6)) Whitman, Albert & Co.

—The Box That Watch Found, Vol. 113. 2007. (Boxcar Children Mysteries Ser.). 128p. (J). (gr. 2-7). 14.95 (***978-0-8075-5568-2(1)**); pap. 4.50 (***978-0-8075-5569-9(X))** Whitman, Albert & Co.

—The Boxcar Children. Date not set. (Boxcar Children Ser.: No. 1). (J). (gr. 2-5). lib. bdg. 18.95 (978-0-8488-1712-1(5)) Amereon LTD.

—The Boxcar Children. (Boxcar Children Ser.: No. 1). 154p. (J). (gr. 2-5). pap. 3.95 (978-0-8072-1447-3(7) , Listening Library) Random Hse. Audio Publishing Group.

—The Boxcar Children. Deal, L. Kate, illus. 2004. (Boxcar Children Ser.: No. 1). 128p. (gr. 2-7). reprint ed. mass mkt. 4.50 (978-0-8075-0852-7(7)) Whitman, Albert & Co.

—The Caboose Mystery. Cunningham, David, illus. 1999. (Boxcar Children Ser.: No. 11). 128p. (J). (gr. 2-5). pap. (978-0-590-42681-7(8)) Scholastic, Inc.

—The Cereal Box Mystery. Tang, Charles, illus. 1998. 111p. (J). (ps-7). per. 11.80 (978-0-613-07455-1(6)) Tandem Library Bks.

—The Ghost in the First Row, Vol. 112. Papp, Robert, illus. 2007. (Boxcar Children Mysteries Ser.). 109p. (J). (gr. 2-7). per. 4.50 (***978-0-8075-5567-5(3))** Whitman, Albert & Co.

—The Ghost Town Mystery. 1999. (Boxcar Children Ser.: No. 71). (J). (gr. 2-5). 10.75 (978-0-606-18764-0(2)) Tandem Library Bks.

—The Great Bicycle Race Mystery. 2000. (Boxcar Children Ser.: No. 76). (Illus.). (J). (gr. 2-5). 10.60 (978-0-606-18907-1(6)) Tandem Library Bks.

—The Gymnastics Mystery. 1999. (Boxcar Children Ser.: No. 73). (J). (gr. 2-5). 10.60 (978-0-606-18766-4(9)) Tandem Library Bks.

—Haunted Clock Tower Mystery. 2001. (gr. 3-6). lib. bdg. 11.80 (978-0-613-49434-2(2)) Tandem Library Bks.

—The Hockey Mystery. 2001. (Boxcar Children Ser.: No. 80). 10.60 (978-0-606-20318-0(4)) Tandem Library Bks.

—The Hockey Mystery, Vol. 80. 2004. (Boxcar Children Ser.: No. 80). (Illus.). 135p. (J). (gr. 2-5). pap. 4.50 (978-0-8075-3343-7(2)); 14.95 (978-0-8075-3342-0(4)) Whitman, Albert & Co.

—The Homerun Mystery. 2000. (Boxcar Children Special Ser.: No. 14). (J). (gr. 2-5). 10.60 (978-0-606-18772-5(3)) Tandem Library Bks.

—The Honeybee Mystery. 2000. (Boxcar Children Special Ser.: No. 15). (J). (gr. 2-5). (978-0-606-20301-2(X)); 10.60 (978-0-606-20319-7(2)) Tandem Library Bks.

—The Honeybee Mystery, Vol. 15. 2004. (Boxcar Children Special Ser.: No. 15). (Illus.). 135p. (J). (gr. 2-5). 14.95 (978-0-8075-3373-4(4)); pap. 4.50 (978-0-8075-3374-1(2)) Whitman, Albert & Co.

—The Lighthouse Mystery. (Boxcar Children Ser.: No. 8). 147p. (J). (gr. 2-5). pap. 3.95 (978-0-8072-1474-9(4) , Listening Library) Random Hse. Audio Publishing Group.

—The Lighthouse Mystery, Vol. 8. Cunningham, David, illus. 2004. (Boxcar Children Ser.: No. 8). 128p. (J). (gr. 2-7). reprint ed. pap. 4.50 (978-0-8075-4546-1(5)) Whitman, Albert & Co.

—Meet the Boxcar Children. Duffy, Daniel Mark, illus. 1998. (J). (ps-ps). lib. bdg. 11.80 (978-0-613-08335-5(0)) Tandem Library Bks.

—Mike's Mystery. (Boxcar Children Ser.: No. 5). 128p. (J). (gr. 2-5). pap. 3.95 (978-0-8072-1462-6(0) , Listening Library) Random Hse. Audio Publishing Group.

—Mike's Mystery, Vol. 5. Gringhuis, Dirk, illus. 2004. (Boxcar Children Ser.: No. 5). 128p. (J). (gr. 2-7). reprint ed. pap. 4.50 (978-0-8075-5141-7(4)) Whitman, Albert & Co.

—The Movie Star Mystery. 1999. (Boxcar Children Ser.: No. 69). (J). (gr. 2-5). (978-0-606-18762-6(6)) Tandem Library Bks.

—The Mystery at Skeleton Point, Vol. 91. 2004. (Boxcar Children Mystery Ser.: No. 91). (Illus.). 128p. (J). (gr. 4-7). pap. 3.95 (978-0-8075-5520-0(7)) Whitman, Albert & Co.

—The Mystery in New York. 1999. (Boxcar Children Special Ser.: No.13). (Illus.). (J). (gr. 2-5). (978-0-606-18771-8(5)) Tandem Library Bks.

—The Mystery in the Computer Game. 2000. (Boxcar Children Ser.: No. 78). (J). (gr. 2-5). (978-0-606-20298-5(6)) Tandem Library Bks.

—The Mystery in the Mall. 1999. (Boxcar Children Ser.: No. 72). (J). (gr. 2-5). (978-0-606-18765-7(0)) Tandem Library Bks.

—The Mystery of Alligator Swamp, Vol. 19. 2004. (Boxcar Children Special Ser.: No. 19). (Illus.) 144p. (J). 14.95 (978-0-8075-5516-3(9)); (gr. 4-7). pap. 4.50 (978-0-8075-5517-0(7)) Whitman, Albert & Co.

—The Mystery of the Black Raven. 1999. (Boxcar Children Special Ser.: No. 12). (Illus.). (J). (gr. 2-5). (978-0-606-18770-1(7)) Tandem Library Bks.

—The Mystery of the Crooked House. 2000. (Boxcar Children Ser.: No. 79). (J). (gr. 2-5). (978-0-606-20299-2(4)) Tandem Library Bks.

—The Mystery of the Midnight Dog. 2001. (Boxcar Children Ser.). (Illus.). (J). (978-0-606-21080-5(6)) Tandem Library Bks.

—The Mystery of the Mummy's Curse, Vol. 88. 2004. (Boxcar Children Ser.: Vol. 88). 128p. (J). pap. 4.50 (978-0-8075-5504-0(5)) Whitman, Albert & Co.

—The Mystery of the Pirate's Map. 1999. (Boxcar Children Ser.: No. 70). (J). (gr. 2-5). (978-0-606-18763-3(4)) Tandem Library Bks.

—The Mystery of the Screech Owl. 2001. (Boxcar Children Special Ser.). (Illus.). (J). (978-0-606-21085-0(7)) Tandem Library Bks.

—The Mystery of the Star Ruby. 2002. (Boxcar Children Ser.: Vol. 89). (Illus.). (J). lib. bdg. 13.95 (978-0-8075-5509-5(6)) Whitman, Albert & Co.

—The Mystery of the Star Ruby, Vol. 89. 2004. (Boxcar Children Mystery Ser.: Vol. 89). (Illus.). 128p. (J). pap. 3.95 (978-0-8075-5510-1(X)) Whitman, Albert & Co.

—The Mystery of the Wild Ponies. 2000. (Boxcar Children Ser.: Vol. 77). (Illus.). (J). (gr. 2-5). (978-0-606-18908-8(4)) Tandem Library Bks.

—Mystery Ranch. (Boxcar Children Ser.: No. 4). 128p. (J). (gr. 2-5). pap. 3.95 (978-0-8072-1450-3(7) , Listening Library) Random Hse. Audio Publishing Group.

—Mystery Ranch, Vol. 4. Gringhuis, Dirk, illus. 2004. (Boxcar Children Ser.: No. 4). 128p. (gr. 2-7). reprint ed. mass mkt. 4.50 (978-0-8075-5391-6(3)) Whitman, Albert & Co.

—The Poison Frog Mystery. 2000. (Boxcar Children Ser.: No. 74). (J). (gr. 2-5). (978-0-606-18767-1(7)) Tandem Library Bks.

—The Seattle Puzzle. 2007. (Boxcar Children Mysteries Ser.: No. 111). 128p. (J). (gr. 2-7). pap. 4.50 (***978-0-8075-5561-3(4)**); lib. bdg. 14.95 (***978-0-8075-5560-6(6))** Whitman, Albert & Co.

—The Secret of the Mask. 2007. (Boxcar Children Mysteries Ser.: No. 110). 128p. (J). (gr. 2-7). pap. 4.50 (***978-0-8075-5565-1(7)**); lib. bdg. 14.95 (***978-0-8075-5564-4(9))** Whitman, Albert & Co.

—The Secret under the Tree. 2001. (Boxcar Children Early Reader Ser.). (Illus.). (J). (978-0-606-21083-6(0)) Tandem Library Bks.

—The Stuffed Bear Mystery, Vol. 90. 2004. (Boxcar Children Mystery Ser.: No. 90). (Illus.). 128p. (J). (gr. 4-7). pap. 4.50 (978-0-8075-5513-2(4)) Whitman, Albert & Co.

—The Summer Camp Mystery. 2001. (Boxcar Children Ser.). (Illus.). (J). (978-0-606-21081-2(4)) Tandem Library Bks.

—Surprise Island, Vol. 2. Gehr, Mary, illus. 2004. (Boxcar Children Ser.: No. 2). 128p. (YA). (gr. 2-7). reprint ed. mass mkt. 4.50 (978-0-8075-7674-8(3)) Whitman, Albert & Co.

—The Tattletale Mystery, Vol. 92. 2004. (Boxcar Children Ser.: No. 92). (Illus.). 128p. (J). pap. 3.95 (978-0-8075-5526-2(6)) Whitman, Albert & Co.

—Watch Runs Away. 1999. (Adventures of Benny & Watch: No. 6). (J). (gr. 1-3). (978-0-606-16915-8(6)) Tandem Library Bks.

—The Woodshed Mystery, Vol. 7. 2004. (Boxcar Children Ser.: No. 7). (Illus.). 128p. (J). (gr. 2-7). reprint ed. pap. 4.50 (978-0-8075-9207-6(2)) Whitman, Albert & Co.

—The Yellow House Mystery. (Boxcar Children Ser.: No. 3). 191p. (J). (gr. 2-5). pap. 3.95 (978-0-8072-1449-7(3) , Listening Library) Random Hse. Audio Publishing Group.

—The Yellow House Mystery, Vol. 3. Gehr, Mary, illus. 2004. (Boxcar Children Ser.: No. 3). 128p. (YA). (gr. 2-7). reprint ed. mass mkt. 4.50 (978-0-8075-9366-0(4)) Whitman, Albert & Co.

Warner, Gertrude Chandler, creator. The Basketball Mystery. 1999. (Boxcar Children Ser.: No. 68). (J). (gr. 2-5). 10.60 (978-0-606-17179-3(7)) Tandem Library Bks.

—The Basketball Mystery. 1999. (Boxcar Children Ser.: No. 68). (Illus.). 128p. (J). (gr. 2-5). lib. bdg. 13.95 (978-0-8075-0575-5(7)) Whitman, Albert & Co.

—Benny's New Friend. 1998. (Adventures of Benny & Watch: No. 3). (J). (gr. 1-3). 10.75 (978-0-606-13217-6(1)) Tandem Library Bks.

—The Black Pearl Mystery. 1998. (Boxcar Children Ser.: No. 64). (J). (gr. 2-5). 10.60 (978-0-606-13213-8(9)) Tandem Library Bks.

—The Black Pearl Mystery, Vol. 64. 1998. (Boxcar Children Ser.: No. 64). (Illus.). 128p. (J). (gr. 2-5). 14.95 (978-0-8075-0783-4(0)) Whitman, Albert & Co.

—The Ghost Town Mystery, Vol. 71. 1999. (Boxcar Children Ser.: No. 71). (Illus.). 128p. (J). (gr. 2-5). 14.95 (978-0-8075-2858-7(7)); pap. 3.95 (978-0-8075-2859-4(5)) Whitman, Albert & Co.

—The Great Bicycle Race Mystery, Vol. 76. 2004. (Boxcar Children Ser.: No. 76). (Illus.). 115p. (J). (gr. 2-5). pap. 4.50 (978-0-8075-3049-8(2)) Whitman, Albert & Co.

—The Homerun Mystery. (Boxcar Children Special Ser.: No. 14). (Illus.). 120p. (J). (gr. 2-5). 2000. lib. bdg. 13.95 (978-0-8075-3368-0(8)); Vol. 14. 2004. pap. 4.50 (978-0-8075-3369-7(6)) Whitman, Albert & Co.

—Meet the Boxcar Children. 1998. (Adventures of Benny & Watch: No. 1). (J). (gr. 1-3). (978-0-606-13215-2(5)) Tandem Library Bks.

—The Movie Star Mystery, Vol. 69. 1999. (Boxcar Children Ser.: No. 69). (Illus.). 128p. (J). (gr. 2-5). 14.95 (978-0-8075-5303-9(4)); pap. 4.50 (978-0-8075-5304-6(2)) Whitman, Albert & Co.

—The Mystery at Peacock Hall. 1998. (Boxcar Children Ser.: No. 63). (J). (gr. 2-5). (978-0-606-13212-1(0)) Tandem Library Bks.

—The Mystery at Peacock Hall, Vol. 63. 1998. (Boxcar Children Ser.: No. 63). (Illus.). 128p. (J). (gr. 2-5). pap. 4.50 (978-0-8075-5445-6(6)) Whitman, Albert & Co.

—The Mystery in the Computer Game. (Boxcar Children Ser.: No. 78). (Illus.). 115p. (J). (gr. 2-5). 2000. lib. bdg. 13.95 (978-0-8075-5468-5(5)); Vol. 78. 2004. pap. 4.50 (978-0-8075-5469-2(3)) Whitman, Albert & Co.

—The Mystery in the Mall, Vol. 72. 2004. (Boxcar Children Ser.: No. 72). (Illus.). 128p. (J). (gr. 2-5). 14.95 (978-0-8075-5456-2(1)); pap. 4.50 (978-0-8075-5457-9(X)) Whitman, Albert & Co.

—The Mystery of the Black Raven, Vol. 12. 1999. (Boxcar Children Special Ser.: No. 12). (Illus.). 144p. (J). (gr. 2-5). 14.95 (978-0-8075-2988-1(5)); pap. 3.95 (978-0-8075-2989-8(3)) Whitman, Albert & Co.

—The Mystery of the Crooked House. (Boxcar Children Ser.: No. 79). (Illus.). 112p. (J). (gr. 2-5). 2000. lib. bdg. 13.95 (978-0-8075-5471-5(5)); Vol. 79. 2004. pap. 4.50 (978-0-8075-5472-2(3)) Whitman, Albert & Co.

—The Mystery of the Empty Safe, Vol. 75. 2004. (Boxcar Children Ser.: No. 75). (Illus.). 120p. (J). (gr. 2-5). 14.95 (978-0-8075-5462-3(6)) Whitman, Albert & Co.

—The Mystery of the Pirate's Map, Vol. 70. (Boxcar Children Ser.: No.70). (Illus.). (J). (gr. 2-5). 2004. 14.95 (978-0-8075-5453-1(7)); 1999. 128p. pap. 4.50 (978-0-8075-5454-8(5)) Whitman, Albert & Co.

—The Mystery of the Queen's Jewels, Vol. 11. 1998. (Boxcar Children Special Ser.: No. 11). (Illus.). 144p. (J). (gr. 2-5). 14.95 (978-0-8075-5450-0(2)); pap. 4.50 (978-0-8075-5451-7(0)) Whitman, Albert & Co.

—The Mystery of the Stolen Sword, Vol. 67. 1998. (Boxcar Children Ser.: No. 67). (Illus.). 128p. (J). (gr. 2-5). 14.95 (978-0-8075-7622-9(0)) Whitman, Albert & Co.

—The Mystery of the Wild Ponies, Vol. 77. 2004. (Boxcar Children Ser.: No. 77). (Illus.). 135p. (J). (gr. 2-5). pap. 3.95 (978-0-8075-5466-1(9)) Whitman, Albert & Co.

—The Panther Mystery, Vol. 66. 1998. (Boxcar Children Ser.: No. 66). (Illus.). 128p. (J). (gr. 2-5). pap. 4.50 (978-0-8075-6328-1(5)) Whitman, Albert & Co.

—The Poison Frog Mystery, Vol. 74. 2004. (Boxcar Children Ser.: No. 74). (Illus.). 128p. (J). (gr. 2-5). pap. 3.95 (978-0-8075-6587-2(3)) Whitman, Albert & Co.

—A Present for Grandfather. 1998. (Adventures of Benny & Watch: No. 2). (J). (gr. 1-3). (978-0-606-13216-9(3)) Tandem Library Bks.

—The Windy City Mystery. 1998. (Boxcar Children Special Ser.: No. 10). (J). (gr. 2-5). (978-0-606-13219-0(8)) Tandem Library Bks.

—The Windy City Mystery, Vol. 10. 1998. (Boxcar Children Special Ser.: No. 10). (Illus.). 144p. (J). (gr. 2-5). 14.95 (978-0-8075-5447-0(2)); pap. 4.50 (978-0-8075-5448-7(0)) Whitman, Albert & Co.

BOXERS (SPORTS)

Adler, David A. & Berkower, Amy. Joe Louis: America's Fighter. Widener, Terry, illus. 2005. 32p. (J). (gr. 2-6). 16.00 (978-0-15-216480-5(4)) Harcourt Children's Bks.

Ali, Maryum. I Shook up the World: The Incredible Life of Muhammad Ali. Johnson, Patrick, illus. 2004. 32p. (J). 16.95 (978-1-58270-090-8(7)) Beyond Words Publishing, Inc.

—I Shook up the World: The Incredible Life of Muhammad Ali. Johnson, Patrick, illus. 2004. 32p. (J). (gr. 3 up). lib. bdg. 24.67 (978-0-8368-4098-8(4)) Stevens, Gareth Inc.

Bolden, Tonya. The Champ. Christie, R. Gregory, illus. 2004. 40p. (J). (gr. k-3). 17.95 (978-0-375-82401-2(4) , Knopf Bks. for Young Readers) Random Hse. Children's Bks.

—The Champ: The Story of Muhamad Ali. Gregory Christie, R. Gregory, illus. 2007. 40p. (J). (gr. k-3). pap. 6.99 (***978-0-440-41782-8(1)*** , Dragonfly Bks.) Random Hse. Children's Bks.

Bolden, Tonya. The Champ: The Story of Muhammad Ali. Christie, R. Gregory, illus. 2004. 40p. (J). (gr. k-3). 19.99 (978-0-375-92401-9(9) , Knopf Bks. for Young Readers) Random Hse. Children's Bks.

Brown, Jonatha A. Muhammad Ali. 2005. (Illus.). 24p. (J). pap. (978-0-8368-4750-5(4)); lib. bdg. 19.33 (978-0-8368-4743-7(1)) Stevens, Gareth Inc.

Buckley, James. Muhammad Ali. 2004. (Trailblazers of the Modern World Ser.). (Illus.). 48p. (J). (gr. 5 up). pap. 11.95 (978-0-8368-5256-1(7)); lib. bdg. 30.00 (978-0-8368-5096-3(3)) Stevens, Gareth Inc. (World Almanac Library).

De La Hoya, Oscar. Super Oscar. Montejo, Andrea, tr. Kopelke, Lisa, illus. 2006. (ENG & SPA.). 32p. (J). (ps-3). 15.95 (978-1-4169-0611-7(8)) Simon & Schuster Children's Publishing.

Dyson, Cindy. Laila Ali. 2001. (Women Who Win Ser.). (J). pap. (978-0-7910-6538-9(3)); (Illus.). 64p. (gr. 3 up). 25.00 (978-0-7910-6537-2(5)) Facts On File, Inc. (Chelsea Hse.).

Feinstein, Stephen. Muhammad Ali. 2007. (African-American Heroes Ser.). (Illus.). 24p. (J). (gr. 1-3). lib. bdg. 21.26 (978-0-7660-2763-3(5) , Enslow Elementary) Enslow Pubs., Inc.

Garrett, Leslie & Dorling Kindersley Publishing Staff. The Story of Muhammad Ali. 2002. (Readers Ser.). (Illus.). 48p. (J). (gr. 1-4). 12.99 (978-0-7894-8516-8(5)); Vol. 4. pap. 3.99 (978-0-7894-8517-5(6)) Dorling Kindersley Publishing, Inc.

Golus, Carrie. Muhammad Ali. 2006. (Sports Heroes & Legends Ser.). (Illus.). 110p. (J). 27.93 (978-0-8225-5960-3(9) , Lerner Pubns.) Lerner Publishing Group.

Haskins, James. Champion: The Story of Muhammad Ali. Velasquez, Eric, illus. 2001. (J). (gr. 1-5). 18.85 (978-0-8027-8785-9(1)) Walker & Co.

Healy, Nick. Jack Johnson. 2003. (African-American Biographies Ser.). (Illus.). 64p. pap. 8.95 (978-1-4109-0036-4(3)); (J). lib. bdg. 28.56 (978-0-7398-6873-7(X)) Raintree.

—Muhammad Ali. 2005. (Genius Ser.). (Illus.). 48p. (gr. 5-9). 21.95 (978-1-58341-333-3(2) , Creative Education) Creative Co., The.

Hook, Jason. Muhammad Ali: The Greatest. 2001. (Famous Lives Ser.). (Illus.). 48p. (J). (gr. 3-7). lib. bdg. 27.12 (978-0-8172-5717-0(9)) Raintree.

Horn, Geoffrey M. Laila Ali. 2006. (Today's Superstars). (Illus.). 32p. (YA). (gr. 5 up). lib. bdg. 23.93 (978-0-8368-6181-5(7)) Stevens, Gareth Inc.

Jordan, Denise M. Muhammad Ali: Meet the Champion. 2003. (Meeting Famous People Ser.). (Illus.). 32p. (J). lib. bdg. 22.60 (978-0-7660-2272-0(2)) Enslow Pubs., Inc.

Kent, Daniel T. Muhammad Ali & Laila Ali. 2004. (Famous Families Ser.). (Illus.). 48p. (J). lib. bdg. 25.25 (978-1-4042-0261-0(7)) Rosen Publishing Group, Inc., The.

Kirkpatrick, Rob. Evander Holyfield: Heavyweight Champion. 2000. (Reading Power Ser.). (Illus.). 24p. (J). (gr. 1). lib. bdg. 17.25 (978-0-8239-5542-8(7) , PowerKids Pr.) Rosen Publishing Group, Inc., The.

—Evander Holyfield, Campeon de los Pesos Pesados. 2002. (Coleccion Power Kids). (SPA & ENG., Illus.). 24p. (J). (gr. k-2). lib. bdg. 17.25 (978-0-8239-6148-1(6) , RN31316, Buenas Letra) Rosen Publishing Group, Inc., The.

—Oscar de la Hoya: Boxeador de Medalla de Oro. 2002. (Grandes Idoles Ser.).Tr. of Oscar de la Hoya: Gold Medal Boxer. (SPA.). 24p. (J). lib. bdg. 17.25 (978-0-8239-6131-3(1) , Buenas Letra) Rosen Publishing Group, Inc., The.

—Oscar de la Hoya: Gold-Medal Boxer. 2000. (Reading Power Ser.). (Illus.). 24p. (J). (gr. 1). lib. bdg. 17.25 (978-0-8239-5543-5(5) , PowerKids Pr.) Rosen Publishing Group, Inc., The.

—Oscar de la Hoya, Boxeador de Medalla de Oro. 2002. (Coleccion Power Kids). (SPA & ENG., Illus.). 24p. (J). (gr. k-2). lib. bdg. 17.25 (978-0-8239-6149-8(4) , RN31302, Buenas Letra) Rosen Publishing Group, Inc., The.

Myers, Walter Dean. The Greatest: Muhammad Ali. 2001. 11.64 (978-0-606-22250-1(2)) Tandem Library Bks.

—Muhammad Ali Biography. Date not set. 40p. (J). (gr. k-3). 15.99 (978-0-06-029131-0(1)); 16.89 (978-0-06-029132-7(X)); pap. 5.99 (978-0-06-443718-9(3)) HarperCollins Pubs.

Probert, Ian. A World-Class Boxer. 2004. (Making of a Champion Ser.). (J). 27.07 (978-1-4034-5366-2(7)); pap. 8.50 (978-1-4034-5550-5(3)) Heinemann Library.

Quinn, Rob. Oscar de la Hoya. (Latinos in the Limelight Ser.). (Illus.). 64p. (J). 2001. (gr. 3 up). 27.50 (978-0-7910-6098-8(5)); 2000. pap. (978-0-7910-6099-5(3)) Facts On File, Inc. (Chelsea Hse.).

Rummel, Jack. Muhammad Ali. (Black Americans of Achievement Ser.). (Illus.). 112p. (J). (gr. 6-12). 2005. pap. 13.25 (978-0-7910-8330-7(6)); 2004. 30.00 (978-0-7910-8156-3(7)) Facts On File, Inc. (Chelsea Hse.).

Savage, Jeff. Muhammad Ali: The Greatest. 2006. (Fact Finders Ser.). (Illus.). 32p. (J). 22.60 (978-0-7368-6422-0(9)) Capstone Pr., Inc.

—Oscar de la Hoya: Golden Boy. 2006. (Fact Finders Ser.). (Illus.). 32p. (J). 22.60 (978-0-7368-6418-3(0)) Capstone Pr., Inc.

Schulman, Arlene. Muhammad Ali. (Just the Facts Biographies Ser.). (Illus.). (J). (gr. 6-12). 2005. 112p. 27.93 (978-0-8225-2448-9(1)); 2003. 128p. pap. 7.95 (978-0-8225-9693-6(8) , Lerner Pubns.) Lerner Publishing Group.

Shone, Rob. Muhammad Ali: The Life of a Boxing Hero. Spender, Nik, illus. 2006. 48p. (J). (978-1-4042-0918-3(2)); pap. (978-1-4042-0919-0(0)) Rosen Publishing Group, Inc., The.

—Muhammed Ali: The Life of a Boxing Hero. Spender, Nick, illus. 2006. (Graphic Biographies Ser.). 48p. (J). (gr. 3-8). lib. bdg. 29.95 (978-1-4042-0856-8(9)) Rosen Publishing Group, Inc., The.

Stout, Glenn & Christopher, Matt. Muhammad Ali: Legends in Sports. 2005. (Matt Christopher Legends of Sports Ser.). (Illus.). 128p. (J). (gr. 5-8). pap. 4.99 (978-0-316-10843-0(X)) Little Brown & Co.

Torres, John Albert. Sports Great Oscar de la Hoya. 1999. (Sports Great Bks.). (Illus.). 64p. (YA). (gr. 4-10). lib. bdg. 22.60 (978-0-7660-1066-6(X)) Enslow Pubs., Inc.

Velazquez, Mauricio, tr. Evander Holyfield, Campeon de los Pesos Pesados. 2002. (Power Kids Coleccion). (SPA.). 24p. (J). (gr. 2-3). lib. bdg. 17.25 (978-0-8239-6130-6(3) , RN30778, Buenas Letra) Rosen Publishing Group, Inc., The.

Wilmore, Kathy. Muhammad Ali: With a Discussion of Honesty. 2003. (Values in Action Ser.). (J). (978-1-59203-065-1(3)) Learning Challenge, Inc.

Wilson, Hoyt R. Joe Louis: The Brown Bomber. 2005. (Alabama Roots Biography Ser.). (Illus.). 100p. (J). (978-1-59421-013-6(6)) Seacoast Publishing, Inc.

Wilson, Mike. Lennox Lewis. 2001. (Livewire Ser.). (Illus.). 28p. pap. (978-0-340-80087-4(9) , Hodder Arnold) Hodder Education.

Winter, Jonah. Muhammad Ali: Champion of the World. Roca, Francois, illus. 2008. 40p. (J). (ps-3). 16.99 (978-0-375-83622-0(5)) Random Hse. Children's Bks.

—Muhammad Ali: Champion of the World. Roca, Francois, illus. 2006. (J). (978-0-375-83787-6(6) , Schwartz & Wade Bks.) Random Hse. Children's Bks.

Winter, Jonah. Muhammad Ali: Champion of the World. Roca, Francois, illus. 2008. 40p. (J). (ps-3). lib. bdg. 19.99 (***978-0-375-93787-3(0)*** , Schwartz & Wade Bks.) Random Hse. Children's Bks.

BOXING

Ford, Carin T. Muhammad Ali: I Am the Greatest. 2006. (African-American Biography Library). (Illus.). 128p. (J). lib. bdg. 31.93 (978-0-7660-2460-1(1)) Enslow Pubs., Inc.

Grabowski, John F. Boxing. 2003. (History of Sports Ser.). (J). 29.95 (978-1-59018-353-3(3) , Lucent Bks.) Thomson Gale.

Hannibal, Sharon. Living with a Boxer. 2002. (Living with a Pet Ser.). (Illus.). 128p. 16.99 (978-0-7641-5430-0(3)) Barron's Educational Series, Inc.

Kaelberer, Angie Peterson. Kickboxing. 2006. (Blazers—To the Extreme Ser.). (Illus.). 32p. (J). (978-0-7368-4399-7(X)) Capstone Pr., Inc.

Lewin, Ted. At Gleason's Gym. 2007. (Illus.). 40p. (J). (gr. k-4). 17.95 (***978-1-59643-231-4(4)***) Roaring Brook Pr.

Myler, Patrick. A Century of Boxing Greats: Inside the Ring with the Hundred Best Boxers. 1998. (Illus.). 394p. (YA). pap. (978-1-86105-258-2(8) , Robson Bks. Ltd.) Anova Bks.

Nonnemacher, Klaus. Kick-Boxing. 2004. (J). lib. bdg. 24.67 (978-0-8368-4194-7(8)) Stevens, Gareth Inc.

Page, Jason. Combat: Fencing, Judo, Wrestling, Boxing, Taekwondo & Lots, Lots More. 2000. (Zeke's Olympic Pocket Guide Ser.). (Illus.). 32p. (J). pap. 3.95 (978-0-8225-5055-6(5) , LernerSports) Lerner Publishing Group.

Powell, Phelan. Fitness Stars of Boxing. 2000. (Legends of Health & Fitness Ser.). (Illus.). 96p. (gr. 6-10). lib. bdg. 25.70 (978-1-58415-013-8(0)) Mitchell Lane Pubs., Inc.

Probert, Ian. A World-Class Boxer. 2004. (Making of a Champion Ser.). (J). 27.07 (978-1-4034-5366-2(7)); pap. 8.50 (978-1-4034-5550-5(3)) Heinemann Library.

Weber, Terri. Oscar de la Hoya. 2004. (J). pap. (978-1-932724-31-8(1)); lib. bdg. (978-1-932724-30-1(3)) Panda Publishing, L.L.C. (Bios for Kids).

BOXING—FICTION

Charlton-Trujillo, E. E. Prizefighter en Mi Casa. (J). (gr. 5-7). 2007. 192p. 5.99 (***978-0-440-42117-7(9)*** , Yearling); 2006. 224p. 15.95 (978-0-385-73325-0(9) , Delacorte Bks. for Young Readers); 2006. 224p. lib. bdg. 17.99 (978-0-385-90344-8(8) , Delacorte Bks. for Young Readers) Random Hse. Children's Bks.

Courtenay, Bryce. The Power of One. 2005. 304p. (J). (gr. 5-12). lib. bdg. 17.99 (978-0-385-90274-8(3) , Delacorte Bks. for Young Readers) Random Hse. Children's Bks.

Disney Press Staff. Fight for Your Right. 2001. (gr. 3-6). lib. bdg. 13.00 (978-0-613-75081-3(0)) Tandem Library Bks.

Disney Staff. Fight for Your Right. 2001. (Jersey Ser.). (Illus.). (J). 11.64 (978-0-606-21265-6(5)) Tandem Library Bks.

Karr, Kathleen. The Boxer. 144p. (YA). 2000. (Illus.). (gr. 7 up). 17.00 (978-0-374-30921-3(3) , Farrar, Straus & Giroux (BYR)); 2004. reprint ed. pap. 6.95 (978-0-374-40886-2(6) , Sunburst) Farrar, Straus & Giroux.

Klingel, Cynthia Fitterer & Noyed, Robert B. Xavier & the Letter X. 2003. (Alphaphonics Ser.). (Illus.). 24p. (J). (ps-2). 21.36 (978-1-59296-114-6(2)) Child's World, Inc.

Kroeger, Mary Kay. Paperboy. 2001. (gr. k-3). lib. bdg. 15.25 (978-0-613-34023-6(X)) Tandem Library Bks.

Lipsyte, Robert. Warrior Angel. 2004. 192p. (J). (gr. 7 up). pap. 5.99 (978-0-06-000498-9(3) , Harper Trophy) HarperCollins Pubs.

Mantell, Paul. Fight for Your Right. 2001. (Jersey Ser.: No. 7). (Illus.). 128p. (J). (gr. 3-7). reprint ed. pap. 4.99 (978-0-7868-4466-1(3)) Disney Pr.

Parker, Robert B. The Boxer & the Spy. 2008. 224p. (YA). (gr. 7). 17.99 (***978-0-399-24775-0(0)*** , Philomel) Penguin Group (USA) Inc.

Zusak, Markus. Fighting Ruben Wolfe. 2001. (Illus.). 208p. (YA). (gr. 5-10). pap. 15.95 (978-0-439-24188-5(X) , Levine, Arthur A. Bks.) Scholastic, Inc.

BOXING—HISTORY

History of Boxing: The Joe Louis Story. (Sports Legacy Ser.). (J). (gr. 6-10). 26.60 (978-0-8225-3330-6(8)) Lerner Publishing Group.

BOY SCOUTS

Baden-Powell, Robert. Young Knights of the Empire. 2006. pap. (***978-1-4065-0430-9(0)***) Dodo Pr.

BOY SCOUTS—FICTION

Blaine, John. The Boy Scouts on a Submarine. 2006. 62.99 (***978-1-4280-0926-4(4)***); pap. 55.99 (***978-1-4280-0929-5(9)***) IndyPublish.com.

Carter, Herbert. The Boy Scouts on Sturgeon Island. 2007. pap. (***978-1-4065-1300-4(8)***) Dodo Pr.

—The Boy Scouts on Sturgeon Island. 2004. reprint ed. pap. 21.95 (978-1-4191-5507-9(5)); pap. 1.99 (978-1-4192-5507-6(X)) Kessinger Publishing, LLC.

Drake, Robert L. The Boy Scouts of the Eagle Patrol. 2007. 150p. pap. 11.99 (***978-1-4264-5808-8(8)***); 164p. pap. 14.99 (***978-1-4264-5868-2(1)***) BiblioBazaar.

—The Boy Scouts of the Eagle Patrol. 2004. reprint ed. pap. 21.95 (978-1-4191-5506-2(7)); pap. 1.99 (978-1-4192-5506-9(1)) Kessinger Publishing, LLC.

Durston, George. Boy Scout Aviators. 2006. 62.99 (***978-1-4280-2433-5(6)***) IndyPublish.com.

Eaton, Walter Prichard. Boy Scouts in the White Mountains: the Story of a Long Hike. Merrill, Frank T., illus. 2006. (ENG.). 316p. per. 30.95 (***978-1-4286-4117-4(3)***) Kessinger Publishing, LLC.

Fitzhugh, K. Percy. Tom Slade at Temple Camp. 2007. (ENG.). 136p. 95.99 (***978-1-4280-7410-1(4)***); per. 88.99 (***978-1-4280-7390-6(6)***) IndyPublish.com.

Fitzhugh, Keese Perc. Roy Blakeley (His Story) 2006. 95.99 (***978-1-4280-0398-9(3)***); pap. 88.99 (***978-1-4280-0390-3(8)***) IndyPublish.com.

Fitzhugh, Percy. Tom Slade on Mystery Trail. 2006. pap. 12.95 (***978-1-55742-910-0(3)***) Wildside Pr.

Fletcher, Archibald Lee. Boy Scouts in Northern Wilds. 2007. 124p. pap. 10.99 (***978-1-4264-6161-3(5)***); 134p. pap. 13.99 (***978-1-4264-6216-0(6)***) BiblioBazaar.

Fletcher, Lee Archib. Boy Scouts in the Coal Caverns or the Li. 2006. 25.99 (***978-1-4280-0741-3(5)***); pap. 18.99 (***978-1-4280-0750-5(4)***) IndyPublish.com.

Fletcher, Lee Archibald. Boy Scouts on A Long Hike or to the Resc. 2006. 94.99 (***978-1-4280-5014-3(0)***); pap. 88.99 (***978-1-4280-5033-4(7)***) IndyPublish.com.

Nuttbucket, Oliver S., III. A Boy Scout's Handbook of Madcap Tales. Glover, Robert, illus. 2003. 48p. (YA). per. 7.95 (978-0-9741310-0-9(8) , 0-9741310-0-8) Lost Scout Pr.

Ralphson, George Harvey. Boy Scouts in Southern Waters. 2007. 158p. pap. 11.99 (***978-1-4264-7439-2(3)***); 182p. pap. 14.99 (***978-1-4264-7516-0(0)***) BiblioBazaar.

Ralphson, Harvey G. Boy Scouts in Southern Waters or Spaniar. 2006. 78.99 (***978-1-4280-1931-7(6)***) IndyPublish.com.

Salisbury, Graham. Night of the Howling Dogs. 2007. 208p. (J). (gr. 3-7). 16.99 (***978-0-385-73122-5(1)***); lib. bdg. 19.99 (***978-0-385-90146-8(1)***) Random Hse. Children's Bks. (Lamb, Wendy).

Shaler, Robert. Boy Scouts of the Flying Squadron. 2006. pap. (***978-1-4068-0464-5(9)***) Echo Library.

—The Boy Scouts of the Geological Survey. 2006. 94.99 (***978-1-4280-0690-4(7)***); pap. 88.99 (***978-1-4280-0700-0(8)***) IndyPublish.com.

—Boy Scouts of the Geological Survey. 2006. pap. (***978-1-4068-0465-2(7)***) Echo Library.

—The Boy Scouts on Picket Duty. 2006. pap. 33.99 (***978-1-4219-7290-9(5)***) IndyPublish.com.

—Boy Scouts on Picket Duty. 2006. pap. (***978-1-4068-0466-9(5)***) Echo Library.

—Boy Scouts with the Motion Picture Playe. 2006. pap. (***978-1-4068-0463-8(0)***) Echo Library.

Van Valkenburgh, Norman J. Cub Scouts Climb the Tower: Hunter Mountain, 1963. Van Valkenburgh, Russell V., illus. 2000. 46p. (J). pap. 6.00 (978-1-930098-06-0(5)) Purple Mountain Pr., Ltd.

Victor, Ralph. Boy Scouts Patrol. 2006. 62.99 (***978-1-4280-2470-0(0)***) IndyPublish.com.

Victor, Ralph. The Boy Scouts Patrol. rev. ed. 2006. 160p. 26.95 (978-1-4218-1806-1(X)); pap. 11.95 (978-1-4218-1906-8(6)) 1st World Publishing, Inc. (1st World Library - Literary Society).

Warren George A. Staff. The Banner Boy Scouts. rev. ed. 2006. 248p. 27.95 (978-1-4218-1729-3(2)); pap. 12.95 (978-1-4218-1829-0(9)) 1st World Publishing, Inc. (1st World Library - Literary Society).

BOY SCOUTS—HANDBOOKS, MANUALS, ETC.

Boy Scouts of America Staff. Project COPE. 1999. (Illus.). 152p. (J). pap. 25.95 (978-0-8395-4371-8(9)) Boy Scouts of America.

—Ranger Guidebook. 1998. (Illus.). 84p. (YA). (gr. 8 up). pap. 5.95 (978-0-8395-3128-9(1)) Boy Scouts of America.

—Venturer Handbook. 1999. (Illus.). 88p. (YA). (gr. 8 up). pap. 5.95 (978-0-8395-3493-8(0)) Boy Scouts of America.

Delman, Steven & Delman, Elisa. The Boy Scout Council Shoulder Patch Guide: 1997 National Jamboree Edition. 1999. (Illus.). 112p. pap. 20.00 (978-0-9657239-3-0(3)) S&E Publishing Co.

DK Publishing Staff. Aloha Cub Scouting: Cub Scout Activity Series. 2006. 16p. (J). (gr. k-5). pap. 2.49 (***978-0-7566-3054-6(1)***) Dorling Kindersley Publishing, Inc.

BOYLE, ROBERT, 1627-1691

Allen, John. Robert Boyle: Father of Chemistry. 2005. (Giants of Science Ser.). (Illus.). 64p. (J). (ps-7). lib. bdg. 26.20 (978-1-56711-887-2(9) , Blackbirch Pr., Inc.) Thomson Gale.

Baxter, Roberta. Skeptical Chemist: The Story of Robert Boyle. 2006. (Profiles in Science Ser.). (Illus.). 128p. (YA). (gr. 6-12). lib. bdg. 27.95 (978-1-59935-025-7(4)) Reynolds, Morgan Inc.

Gow, Mary. Robert Boyle: Pioneer of Experimental Chemistry. 2005. (Great Minds of Science Ser.). (Illus.). 128p. (J). lib. bdg. 26.60 (978-0-7660-2501-1(2)) Enslow Pubs., Inc.

John Allen. Robert Boyle. 2005. (Giants of Science Ser.). (gr. 5-7). 24.95 (978-1-4103-0354-7(3) , Blackbirch Pr., Inc.) Thomson Gale.

BOYS

see also Boy Scouts; Newsboys; Youth

Aronson, Marc & Newquist, H. P. For Boys Only: The Biggest, Baddest, Best Book Ever! 2007. (Illus.). 160p. (J). 14.95 (***978-0-312-37706-9(1)***) Feiwel & Friends.

Beard, Daniel Carter. The American Boy's Handy Book: Turn-of-the-Century Classic of Crafts & Activities. 2003. (Dover Value Editions Ser.). (Illus.). 464p. (J). pap. 9.95 (978-0-486-43138-3(X)) Dover Pubns., Inc.

Bishop, Jennie & Henson, Susan. Life Lessons from the Squire & the Scroll (Squire & the Scroll) 2005. 65p. (J). pap. 9.99 (***978-0-940110-67-0(9)***) Life Action Publishing.

A Boy's Guide to Growing up. 2005. (Illus.). tchr. ed. 22.95 (978-1-55942-210-9(6)) Marsh Media.

A Boy's Guide to Growing up - Booklet, 10 per packet. 2005. (Illus.). (J). 63.95 (978-1-55942-211-6(4)) Marsh Media.

Boys to Men: A Christian Teen Survival Guide by Young Men Who Are Survivors. 2007. 165p. (J). (***978-0-929540-59-7(X)***) Publishing Designs, Inc.

Brown, Tricia. Salaam: A Muslim American Boy's Story. Cardwell, Kenneth, photos by. 2006. (Illus.). 40p. (J). (ps-3). 17.95 (978-0-8050-6538-1(5) , Holt, Henry & Co. Bks. For Young Readers) Holt, Henry & Co.

Clark, Travis & Ziff, Jane. A Guys' Guide to Stress; A Girls' Guide to Stress. 2008. (Flip-It-over Guides to Teen Emotions Ser.). (Illus.). 128p. (J). (gr. 5 up). lib. bdg. 31.93 (***978-0-7660-2857-9(7)***) Enslow Pubs., Inc.

Cole, Sheila. To Be Young in America: Growing up with the Country, 1776-1940. 2005. (Illus.). 160p. (J). (gr. 8-17). 19.99 (978-0-316-15196-2(3)) Little Brown & Co.

CosmoGIRL! Editors. All about Guys. Cosmopolitan Editors, ed. 2004. (CosmoGIRL Quiz Book Ser.). (Illus.). 128p. pap. 5.95 (978-1-58816-382-0(2)) Hearst Bks.

Desouza, Lar, illus. Boys Who Rocked the World: From King Tut to Tiger Woods. 2001. 64p. (gr. 3-7). pap. (978-1-58270-045-8(1)) Beyond Words Publishing, Inc.

DiMarco, Michael. The Man Manual: Mastering the Moves, Power-Ups, & Pitfalls to Becoming a Real Man. 2007. 192p. pap. 12.99 (978-0-8007-3150-2(6)) Revell.

Doudna, Kelly. Boys & Girls Around the World. 2004. (Around the World Ser.). (Illus.). 23p. (J). (ps-3). lib. bdg. 19.93 (978-1-59197-564-9(6)) ABDO Publishing Co.

Dunham, Kelli S. The Boy's Body Book: Everything You Need to Know for Growing up You. Bjorkman, Steven, illus. 2007. 112p. (YA). (gr. 5 up). pap. 9.95 (*978-1-933662-74-9(3)) Cider Mill Pr. Bk. Pubs. LLC.

Enright, Dominique & MacDonald, Guy. The Boys' Book: How to Be the Best at Everything. Catlow, Niki, illus. 2007. (Boys' Book Ser.). 128p. (J). (gr. 4-7). 9.99 (*978-0-545-01628-5(2) , Scholastic Pr.) Scholastic, Inc.

Finnis, Anne & Bond, Denis. It's A Boy/Girl Thing. 2003. (Illus.). 144p. (J). pap. 10.95 (978-0-09-943212-8(9) , Red Fox) Random Hse. Children's Bks. GBR. *Dist:* Random Hse. of Canada, Ltd.

Gallagher, Jim & Cavenaugh, Dorothy. A Guys' Guide to Conflict; A Girls' Guide to Conflict. 2008. (Flip-It-over Guides to Teen Emotions Ser.). (Illus.). 128p. (J). (gr. 5 up). lib. bdg. 31.93 (*978-0-7660-2852-4(6)) Enslow Pubs., Inc.

Gravelle, Karen. What's Going on down There? Answers to Questions Boys Find Hard to Ask. 1998. (gr. 5-8). lib. bdg. 17.60 (978-0-613-75331-9(3)) Tandem Library Bks.

Gravelle, Karen, et al. What's Going on down There? Answers to Questions Boys Find Hard to Ask. Leighton, Robert, illus. 1998. (gr. 5-9). 128p. (J). 15.95 (978-0-8027-8671-5(5)); 160p. (YA). pap. 8.95 (978-0-8027-7540-5(3)) Walker & Co.

Howat, Irene. Ten Boys Who Changed the World. 160p. (J). pap. 5.99 (978-1-85792-579-1(3) , Christian Focus) Christian Focus Pubns. GBR. *Dist:* Riverside.

—Ten Boys Who Made a Difference. 160p. (J). pap. 5.99 (978-1-85792-775-7(3) , Christian Focus) Christian Focus Pubns. GBR. *Dist:* Riverside.

Jukes, Mavis. The Guy Book: An Owner's Manual: Maintenance, Safety, & Operating Instructions for Boys. 2002. (Illus.). 160p. (YA). (gr. 7 up). 12.95 (978-0-679-89028-7(9) , Crown Books For Young Readers) Random Hse. Children's Bks.

Kelly, Bill. You Ought to Know: A Guy's Guide to Sex. 2005. (Guys' Guides Ser.). (Illus.). 48p. (J). (gr. 5-8). lib. bdg. 23.95 (978-0-8239-3084-5(X) , GUYOSH) Rosen Publishing Group, Inc., The.

King, Bart. The Big Book of Boy Stuff. Cressy, Mike, illus. 2004. 312p. (J). (gr. 3-9). reprint ed. 19.95 (978-1-58685-333-4(3)) Gibbs Smith, Publisher.

LaVoice, Patricia. Helmets & Hoses, Toes & Noses. 2006. 44p. (J). 10.99 (978-1-59092-233-0(6) , Orchard Academy Pr.) Windstorm Creative.

Lessons in Responsibility for Boys: Level One. 2007. (YA). per. 18.95 (*978-0-9792446-0-5(9)) Messiah Publishing - Pearables.

Lessons in Responsibility for boys Level Two. 2007. (YA). per. 18.95 (*978-0-9792446-1-2(7)) Messiah Publishing - Pearables.

Madaras, Lynda & Madaras, Area. My Body, My Self for Boys. (Illus.). 112p. 2nd ed. 2000. (gr. 4-7). reprint ed. 12.95 (978-1-55704-440-2(6) , Newmarket Shooting Scripts); 3rd rev. ed. 2007. (YA). pap. 12.95 (*978-1-55704-767-0(7)) Newmarket Pr.

Madaras, Lynda & Madaras, Area. The What's Happening to My Body Book for Boys. 3rd ed. 2007. (Illus.). 272p. (YA). 24.95 (*978-1-55704-769-4(3)); pap. 12.95 (*978-1-55704-765-6(0)) Newmarket Pr.

Marcovitz, Hal & Snyder, Gail. A Guys' Guide to Anger; A Girls' Guide to Anger. 2008. (Flip-It-over Guides to Teen Emotions Ser.). (Illus.). 128p. (J). (gr. 5 up). lib. bdg. 31.93 (*978-0-7660-2853-1(4)) Enslow Pubs., Inc.

Martin, Sam. The Curious Boy's Book of Adventure: 100 Hijinks & Escapades. 2007. 160p. (J). (gr. 5). pap. 15.00 (*978-1-59514-206-1(1)) Penguin Group (USA) Inc.

—The Curious Boy's Book of Exploration. 2008. 160p. pap. 15.00 (*978-1-59514-207-8(X) , Razorbill) Penguin Group (USA) Inc.

Pfeffer, Wendy. Many Ways to Be a Soldier. 2008. (On My Own History Ser.). (J). lib. bdg. 25.26 (*978-0-8225-7279-4(6) , Millbrook Pr.) Lerner Publishing Group.

Pitt, Steve. Guyness: Deal with it body & Soul. Murray, Steven, illus. 2005. (Deal with It Ser.). 32p. (J). (gr. 4-8). pap. 12.95 (978-1-55028-892-6(X)) Lorimer, James & Co., Ltd., Pubs. CAN. *Dist:* Casemate Pubs. & Bk. Distributors, LLC.

Roehm, Michelle, compiled by. Boys Know It All: Wise Thoughts & Wacky Ideas from Guys Like You. l.t. ed. 1999. (Girls Know Best Ser.). (Illus.). 167p. (J). (gr. 3 up). lib. bdg. 23.33 (978-0-8368-2455-1(5)) Stevens, Gareth Inc.

Sateren, Shelley Swanson. A Civil War Drummer Boy: The Diary of William Bircher, 1861-1865. 1999. (Diaries, Letters & Memoirs Ser.). (Illus.). 32p. (J). (gr. 2-7). pap. 21.00 (978-0-516-21850-2(6) , Children's Pr.) Scholastic Library Publishing.

Scholastic, Inc. Staff. Boys We Love. 1998. (Illus.). 48p. (J). (gr. 2-5). pap. 5.99 (978-0-590-63483-0(6)) Scholastic, Inc.

Secret Life of Guys. 2001. (gr. 3-6). lib. bdg. 13.00 (978-0-613-54649-2(0)) Tandem Library Bks.

Shoemaker, Tim. Reboot Your Brain: Byte-Sized Devotions for Boys. Baumann, Marty, illus. 2004. 160p. (J). (gr. 3-6). pap. 7.99 (978-0-310-70719-6(6)) Zonderkidz.

Strauss, Ed. Bible Freaks & Geeks. Haya, Erwin, illus. 2007. (2: 52 Ser.). 117p. (J). (gr. 3-7). per. (*978-0-310-71309-8(9)) Zonderkidz.

Wesemann, Tim. The Book of Cool: Cool Questions, Cooler Answers. 2004. (2:52 / Soul Gear#8482; Ser.). (Illus.). 112p. (J). (gr. 3-6). 7.99 (978-0-310-70696-0(3)) Zonderkidz.

Wiggin, Kate Douglas. The Story of Patsy. 2004. reprint ed. pap. 15.95 (978-1-4179-2620-6(1)) Kessinger Publishing, LLC.

Wilkinson, Bruce & Thomas, Mack. A Life God Rewards: Guys Only. ltd. ed. 2006. 96p. bds. 9.99 (978-1-60142-002-2(1) , Multnomah Kidz) WaterBrook Pr.

Wong, Alice & Tabori, Lena. The Little Big Book for Boys. (Illus.). 352p. 24.95 (978-0-941807-70-8(3) , Welcome Bks.) Welcome Enterprises, Inc.

Zimmerman, Bill. 100 Things Guys Need to Know. 2005. (Illus.). 128p. (J). (gr. 4-8). pap. 13.95 (978-1-57542-167-4(4)) Free Spirit Publishing, Inc.

BOYS—EMPLOYMENT

see Children—Employment

BOYS—FICTION

A. B. Publishing Staff. Tom's Revenge. 1998. (J). (gr. 4-7). pap. 6.95 (978-1-881545-91-0(1)) A B Publishing.

Abbott, Hailey. Next Summer: A Summer Boys Novel. 2005. (Summer Boys Ser.). 224p. (YA). (gr. 10 up). 8.99 (978-0-439-75540-5(9)) Scholastic, Inc.

—Summer Boys. 2004. 224p. (J). 8.99 (978-0-439-54020-9(8)) Scholastic, Inc.

Abbott, Hailey. Waking up to Boys. 2007. 256p. (J). pap. 8.99 (*978-0-06-082435-8(2) , HarperTeen) HarperCollins Pubs.

Aboff, Marcie. Open Your Eyes, Sidney Miffet! Seaman, Chris, illus. 1999. 12p. (J). (gr. k-2). pap. 3.75 (978-1-880612-92-7(5) , Seedling Pubns.) Continental Pr., Inc.

Abril, Paco. Resdan. Amargo, Pablo, illus. 2000. (Coleccion Rascacielos Ser.). (SPA.). 31p. (J). (gr. k-2). 12.95 (978-84-241-7979-3(X) , EV30303) Everest de Ediciones y Distribucion, S.L. ESP. *Dist:* Continental Bk. Co., Inc., Lectorum Pubns., Inc.

Abshire, Lisa D. Sam's Magical Day. 2006. 48p. pap. 12.95 (978-1-4241-1484-9(5)) PublishAmerica, Inc.

Adkinson, Clarissa W. Bubba's Last Farewell. (J). (gr. 1-8). pap. (978-1-885005-07-6(5)) LynHawk Publishing Co., Inc.

Alcott, Louisa May. Hombrecitos.Tr. of Little Men. (SPA., Illus.). 160p. (YA). 11.95 (978-84-7281-168-3(9) , AF1168) Auriga, Ediciones S.A. ESP. *Dist:* Continental Bk. Co., Inc.

—Little Men: Life at Plumfield with Jo's Boys. l.t. ed. 2005. 496p. 20.95 (978-0-7862-7928-9(1) , Large Print Pr.) Thorndike Pr.

—Los Muchachos de Jo. (SPA., Illus.). 160p. (YA). 11.95 (978-84-7281-055-6(0) , AF1055) Auriga, Ediciones S.A. ESP. *Dist:* Continental Bk. Co., Inc.

Alegria, Ciro. Sacha en el Reino de los Arboles. (SPA.). 96p. (YA). (gr. 5-8). (978-84-204-3693-7(3) , AF1748) Alfaguara, Ediciones, S.A.- Grupo Santillana ESP. *Dist:* Lectorum Pubns., Inc.

—Sacha en el Reino de los Arboles. (SPA.). (YA). (gr. 5-8). (978-956-11-0965-0(4) , UV6346) Universitaria, Editorial S.A.

Alexander, Cecil Frances. All Things Bright & Beautiful. Whatley, Bruce, illus. 2001. 32p. (J). 16.99 (978-0-06-026617-2(1)) HarperCollins Pubs.

Alexander, Liza. Remember When. 1999. (Elmo's World Ser.: No. 5). pap. 3.25 (978-0-679-89424-7(1) , Random Hse. Bks. for Young Readers) Random Hse. Children's Bks.

—Snuggle Up. 1999. (Elmo's World Ser.: No. 6). pap. 3.25 (978-0-679-89425-4(X)); lib. bdg. 8.99 (978-0-679-99425-1(4)) Random Hse. Children's Bks. (Random Hse. Bks. for Young Readers).

Alexander, Martha. You're a Genius, Blackboard Bear. Alexander, Martha, illus. 2002. (Blackboard Bear Ser.). (Illus.). (J). 11.91 (978-0-7587-4064-9(6)) Book Wholesalers, Inc.

Alger, Horatio. Do & Dare: Or, A Brave Boy's Fight for Fortune. reprint ed. pap. 79.00 (978-1-4047-3563-7(1)) Classic Textbooks.

—The Errand Boy. 2005. 296p. pap. 13.95 (978-1-4218-0455-2(7) , 1st World Library - Literary Society) 1st World Publishing, Inc.

—Frank Fowler, the Cash Boy. reprint ed. pap. 79.00 (978-1-4047-3558-3(5)) Classic Textbooks.

—Joe the Hotel Boy: Or, Winning Out by Pluck. 363p. reprint ed. pap. 79.00 (978-1-4047-3578-1(X)) Classic Textbooks.

—Making His Way: Or, Frank Courtneys Struggle. 2006. 96.99 (*978-1-4280-2109-9(4)); pap. 89.99 (*978-1-4280-2133-4(7)) IndyPublish.com.

Alger, Horatio. Paul Prescott's Charge. rev. ed. 2006. (ENG.). 308p. 29.95 (978-1-4218-2089-7(7) , 1st World Library - Literary Society) 1st World Publishing, Inc.

Alger Jr. Horatio Staff. Struggling Upward. rev. ed. 2006. 284p. 28.95 (978-1-4218-1760-6(8)); pap. 13.95 (978-1-4218-1860-3(4)) 1st World Publishing, Inc. (1st World Library - Literary Society).

Allan, Nicholas. Demon Teddy. 2000. (Illus.). 32p. (J). pap. 9.99 (978-0-09-940761-4(2)) Random Hse. GBR. *Dist:* Independent Pubs. Group.

Almond, David. The Fire-Eaters. 2005. 224p. (gr. 4-7). reprint ed. 5.99 (978-0-440-42012-5(1) , Yearling) Random Hse. Children's Bks.

Alphin, Elaine Marie. Counterfeit Son. 2000. (Illus.). 192p. (YA). (gr. 9 up). 17.00 (978-0-15-202645-5(2)) Harcourt Children's Bks.

Anaya, Hector. Cuenta, Cuenta. Moreno, Sergio, illus. 2nd rev. ed. 2004. (Castillo de la Lectura Verde Ser.). (SPA.). 184p. (J). pap. 7.95 (978-970-20-0135-5(8)) Castillo, Ediciones, S. A. de C. V. MEX. *Dist:* Macmillan.

Anderson, Ebony. If I Were Just a Little Taller. Barrett, Noah, illus. 2005. 48p. (J). (ps-3). per. 9.99 (978-0-9760901-8-2(X)) Morgan James Publishing, LLC.

Anderson, Pamela. My New School: Blonde Boy. Lee, Han & Wu, Stacie, illus. 2004. (J). 12.95 (978-1-932555-05-9(6)) Watch Me Grow Kids.

—My New School: Brunette Boy. Lee, Han & Wu, Stacie, illus. 2004. (J). 12.95 (978-1-932555-07-3(2)) Watch Me Grow Kids.

Anderson, William. River Boy. Date not set. 32p. (J). (gr. 2-5). pap. 5.99 (978-0-06-443573-4(3)) HarperCollins Pubs.

—River Boy: The Story of Mark Twain. Andreasen, Dan, illus. 2003. 40p. (J). (ps-2). 16.99 (978-0-06-028400-8(5)) HarperCollins Pubs.

Animal Rage. 2003. (gr. 7-12). lib. bdg. 14.15 (978-0-613-50635-9(9)) Tandem Library Bks.

Anna, Jennifer. Maxwell Dreams of Trains. Blue, Buster, illus. 2007. 88p. (J). 10.99 (978-1-883573-05-8(X) , Little Blue Works) Windstorm Creative.

Anza, Ana Luisa. El Misterio de la Casa Chueca (y el Bulto Color Mugre) Escobar, Antonio Rocha, illus. rev. ed. 2006. (Castillo de la Lectura Naranja Ser.). (SPA.). 120p. (J). pap. 7.95 (978-970-20-0200-0(1)) Castillo, Ediciones, S. A. de C. V. MEX. *Dist:* Macmillan.

Appleton, Victor. The Alien Probe. (Tom Swift Ser.). (J). (gr. 3-7). 20.95 (978-0-88411-464-2(3)) Amereon LTD.

—The City in the Stars. (Tom Swift Ser.). (J). (gr. 3-7). 20.95 (978-0-88411-463-5(5)) Amereon LTD.

—The Moving Picture Boys at Panama. 2005. 27.95 (978-1-4218-1499-5(4)); 208p. pap. 12.95 (978-1-4218-1599-2(0)) 1st World Publishing, Inc. (1st World Library - Literary Society).

—The Moving Picture Boys at Panama. 2004. reprint ed. pap. 20.95 (978-1-4191-7472-8(X)); pap. 1.99 (978-1-4192-7472-5(4)) Kessinger Publishing, LLC.

—The Rescue Mission. (Tom Swift Ser.). (J). (gr. 3-7). 20.95 (978-0-88411-458-1(9)) Amereon LTD.

—Terror on the Moons of Jupiter. (Tom Swift Ser.). (J). (gr. 3-7). 20.95 (978-0-88411-460-4(0)) Amereon LTD.

—Tom Swift & His Electric Rifle. 1998. (Tom Swift Original Ser.: No. 10). (J). (gr. 3-7). lib. bdg. 18.95 (978-1-56723-020-8(2)) Yestermorrow, Inc.

—Tom Swift & His Electronic Electroscope. (J). (gr. 5-6). 20.95 (978-0-88411-462-8(7)) Amereon LTD.

—Tom Swift & His Space Solatron. (Tom Swift Ser.). (J). (gr. 5-6). 20.95 (978-0-88411-457-4(0)) Amereon LTD.

—Tom Swift & His Triphibian Atomicar. (Tom Swift Ser.). (J). (gr. 5-6). 20.95 (978-0-88411-459-8(7)) Amereon LTD.

Arai, Kiyoko. Beauty Pop, Vol. 1. 2006. (Beauty Pop Ser.). (Illus.). 200p. (YA). pap. 8.99 (978-1-4215-0575-6(4)) Viz Media.

Armstrong, Nancy. Navajo Long Walk. Livers-Lambert, Paulette, illus. 2nd ed. 2001. (Council for Indian Education Ser.). 128p. (gr. 4-7). pap. 10.95 (978-1-879373-56-3(4)) Rinehart, Roberts Pubs.

Armstrong, Robb. Got Game? Smith, Bruce, illus. 1998. (Patrick's Pals Ser.: No. 3). 96p. (J). (gr. 2-7). mass mkt. 3.99 (978-0-06-107069-3(6) , Harper Entertainment) HarperCollins Pubs.

Arnold, Adam. Aoi House, Vol. 1. 2006. (Illus.). 192p. (YA). pap. 10.99 (978-1-933164-12-0(3)) Seven Seas Entertainment, LLC.

Arnold, Adolf W. A Boy Without Toys. 2004. (Illus.). 240p. 24.95 (978-1-57197-157-9(2)) Pentland Pr., Inc.

Arnold, Tedd. Even More Parts. Arnold, Tedd, illus. 2007. 40p. (J). pap. 6.99 (978-0-14-240714-1(3) , Puffin) Penguin Group (USA) Inc.

—Even More Parts: Idioms from Head to Toe. Arnold, Tedd, illus. 2004. (Illus.). 40p. (J). (ps-3). 16.99 (978-0-8037-2938-4(3) , Dial) Penguin Group (USA) Inc.

Arthur M. Winfield (Staff. The Rover Boys at School or the Cadets O. 2006. pap. 27.99 (*978-1-4219-7693-8(5)) IndyPublish.com.

Arthur's Teacher Moves In. 2001. (Arthur Adventure Ser.). (Illus.). (J). pap. 5.95 (978-0-316-12206-1(8)) Little Brown & Co.

Asch, Frank. The Earth & I. 2008. (Illus.). 32p. (J). pap. 7.00 (*978-0-15-206395-5(1) , Voyager Bks./Libros Viajeros) Harcourt Children's Bks.

Asher, Sandy & Harrison, David. Dude! Stories & Stuff for Boys. 2006. (Illus.). 272p. (J). (gr. 3-7). 17.99 (978-0-525-47684-9(9) , Dutton Juvenile) Penguin Group (USA) Inc.

Asher, Sandy & Harrison, David L. Dude! Stories & Stuff for Boys. 2006. (Illus.). xi, 258p. (J). (*978-1-4156-8094-0(9) , Dutton Juvenile) Penguin Group (USA) Inc.

Ashley, Bernard. Johnnie's Blitz. 2005. 218p. (J). (gr. k-17). pap. 6.95 (978-1-903015-28-5(6)) Barn Owl Bks, London GBR. *Dist:* Independent Pubs. Group.

Asner, Anne-Marie. Klutzy Boy. Asner, Anne-Marie, illus. l.t. ed. 2007. (Illus.). 32p. (J). per. 6.95 (978-0-9753629-4-5(1)) Matzah Ball Bks.

—Kvetchy Boy. Asner, Anne-Marie, illus. l.t. ed. 2006. (Illus.). 32p. (J). per. 6.95 (978-0-9753629-3-8(3)) Matzah Ball Bks.

Atwood, Debbie A. Jasper's Magic Blanket. Gordon, Danny, illus. l.t. ed. 2001. 36p. (J). (ps-4). 16.95 (978-0-9701013-0-3(9)) Novel Approach Pubns., LLC.

Avery, Pat McGrath. Tommy's War: A Parent Goes to War, 1. Ray, Eric, illus. 2003. 36p. (J). per. 5.95 (978-0-9663276-8-7(3)) Red Engine Pr.

Awdry, Wilbert V. Thomas & the Rumors Book & CD. 2005. (Illus.). 24p. (J). (ps-2). 9.95 (978-0-375-83505-6(9) , Random Hse. Bks. for Young Readers) Random Hse. Children's Bks.

—Thomas's ABC Book. McArthur, Kenny et al, photos by. 1998. (Please Read to Me Ser.). (Illus.). 24p. (J). (gr. k-3). pap. 3.25 (978-0-679-89357-8(1) , Random Hse. Bks. for Young Readers) Random Hse. Children's Bks.

—Trouble for Thomas Book & CD. 2005. (Book & CD Ser.). (Illus.). 24p. (J). (ps-2). 9.95 (978-0-375-83502-5(4) , Random Hse. Bks. for Young Readers) Random Hse. Children's Bks.

Baggette, Susan K. Jonathan Goes to the Airport. Moriarty, William J., photos by. 1998. (Jonathan Adventures Ser.). (Illus.). 16p. (J). (ps-k). bds. 5.95 (978-0-9660172-6-7(9)) Brookfield Reader, Inc., The.

—Jonathan Goes to the Doctor. Moriarty, William J., photos by. 1998. (Jonathan Adventures Ser.). (Illus.). 16p. (J). (ps-k). bds. 5.95 (978-0-9660172-1-2(8)) Brookfield Reader, Inc., The.

—Jonathan Goes to the Grocery Store. Moriarty, William J., photos by. 1998. (Jonathan Adventures Ser.). (Illus.). 16p. (J). (ps-k). bds. 5.95 (978-0-9660172-2-9(6)) Brookfield Reader, Inc., The.

—Jonathan Goes to the Library. Moriarty, William J., photos by. 1998. (Jonathan Adventures Ser.). (Illus.). 16p. (J). (ps-k). bds. 5.95 (978-0-9660172-3-6(4)) Brookfield Reader, Inc., The.

—Jonathan Goes to the Post Office. Moriarty, William J., photos by. 1998. (Jonathan Adventures Ser.). (Illus.). 16p. (J). (ps-k). bds. 5.95 (978-0-9660172-5-0(0)) Brookfield Reader, Inc., The.

Bailey, Elinor Peace. Daniel & Dinner. Bailey, Elinor Peace, illus. 2002. (J). 9.50 (978-0-9716586-4-6(1)) Fairfield Processing Corp.

Baldwin, James. Fifty Famous People. l.t. ed. 2006. 126p. pap. 13.99 (978-1-4264-1427-5(7)) BiblioBazaar.

Balian, Lorna. Where in the World Is Henry? Balian, Lorna & Balian, Lecia, illus. 2005. 40p. (J). (978-1-59572-035-1(9)) Star Bright Bks., Inc.

Bancroft, Myles. The Trouble with Adam's Heart. Brouillette, Peter, ed. Smith, Richard, illus. 2004. (YA). per. 19.99 (978-0-9760419-4-8(4)) ThatsMyLife Co.

Barklem, Jill. Cuento de Otono.Tr. of Autumn Story. (SPA.). 32p. (J). 8.95 (978-84-233-2620-4(9)) Ediciones Destino ESP. *Dist:* Planeta Publishing Corp.

Barlow, Steve L. & Skidmore, Steve. Vernon Bright & the Magnetic Banana. l.t. ed. 2001. (Illus.). 178p. (J). 16.95 (978-0-7540-6178-6(7) , Gunsmoke) BBC Audiobooks America.

Baumgartner, Mary A. Buzzy Newton's Terrible Discovery. Baumgartner, Mary A., illus. 1999. (Illus.). 40p. (J). (ps-5). pap. (978-0-944576-10-6(9)) Rocky River Pubs., LLC.

Beaman, Cliff. The Boy Who Grew Too Small. 2006. 51p. (J). pap. 12.95 (978-0-9777290-4-3(4) , 349-021) High-Pitched Hum Inc.

Beckwith, Agnes. Zar Meets Rahbue: From the Land of Senga. 1998. (Illus.). 16p. (J). (gr. 3-6). pap. 6.00 (978-0-8059-4263-7(7)) Dorrance Publishing Co., Inc.

Bee, Clair. Championship Ball, Vol. 2. Farley, Cynthia B. & Farley, Randall, eds. rev. ed. 1998. (Chip Hilton Ser.: Vol. 2). (Illus.). 194p. (J). pap. 5.99 (978-0-8054-1815-6(6)) B&H Publishing Grp.

—Championship Ball. 1998. (gr. 5-8). lib. bdg. 14.15 (978-0-613-90137-6(1)) Tandem Library Bks.

—Clutch Hitter. (J). 17.95 (978-0-8488-1246-1(8)) Amereon LTD.

—Clutch Hitter, Vol. 4. Farley, Cynthia B. & Farley, Randall K., eds. rev. ed. 1998. (Chip Hilton Ser.: Vol. 4). 195p. (J). pap. 5.99 (978-0-8054-1817-0(2)) B&H Publishing Grp.

—No-Hitter, Vol. 17. 2001. (Chip Hilton Sports Ser.). x, 197p. (J). pap. 5.99 (978-0-8054-2096-8(7)) B&H Publishing Grp.

—Strike Three, Vol. 3. Farley, Cynthia B. & Farley, Randall K., eds. rev. ed. 1998. (Chip Hilton Ser.: Vol. 3). 211p. (J). pap. 5.99 (978-0-8054-1816-3(4)) B&H Publishing Grp.

—Touchdown Pass. Farley, Cynthia B. & Farley, Randall, eds. rev. ed. 1998. (Chip Hilton Ser.: Vol. 1). 198p. (J). 5.99 (978-0-8054-1686-2(2)) B&H Publishing Grp.

Benjamin, Ruth. Yesterday's Child. Cohen, Deene, illus. (YA). 16.95 (978-1-56062-176-8(1) , CFR122H); pap. 13.95 (978-1-56062-177-5(X) , CFR122S) CIS Communications, Inc.

Bergeron, Lowell. The New Kid. 2002. 125p. pap. 17.95 (978-1-59286-121-7(0)) PublishAmerica, Inc.

Beveridge, Donna. Henry. Romo, Alberto, tr. Nicol, Brock, illus. 1999. (Books for Young Learners).Tr. of Henry. (SPA.). 12p. (J). (gr. k-2). pap. 5.00 (978-1-57274-342-7(5) , A2866) Owen, Richard C. Pubs., Inc.

Bezek, Lyn. Daisy: The Cripple Creek Donkey. 2004. (J). pap. 7.95 (978-1-932738-09-4(6)) Western Reflections Publishing Co.

Biemiller, Carl L. The Magic Ball from Mars & Starboy. Voute, Kathleen, illus. 2003. 302p. (J). pap. 19.95 (978-0-918736-09-3(9) , Sense of Wonder Pr.) Rock, James A. & Co. Pubs.

Biggs, Pauline. A Wild Ride. Mayne, Michael, illus. 2004. 20p. (J). per. 12.95 (978-0-9760129-0-0(1)) Avant Garde Publishing.

Billy Ray Pyle's Style. Date not set. 5.95 (978-0-89868-363-9(7)) ARO Publishing Co.

Bischoff, Linda L. Ben & the Big Black Dog. 2000. (Illus.). 24p. (J). (gr. 2-4). pap. 9.95 (978-1-892614-32-2(4)) Briarwood Pubns.

A Bit Haywire. 2006. (YA). per. 11.95 (978-0-9777883-5-4(0)) Viper Comics.

Blacker, Terence. Hotshots: Shooting Star, Bk. 2. 2003. (Illus.). 167p. (J). pap. 6.99 (978-0-330-32913-2(8) , Pan) Pan Macmillan GBR. *Dist:* Trafalgar Square Publishing.

Blackman, Malorie. Pig-Heart Boy. (Illus.). 2001. 208p. pap. 9.99 (978-0-552-54684-3(4)); 2000. 207p. (J). pap. 6.95 (978-0-552-52841-2(2)) Transworld Publishers Ltd. GBR. *Dist:* Trafalgar Square Publishing.

Blatchford, Claire H. Nick's Secret. Harden, Laurie, illus. 2003. (Lerner Mysteries Ser.). 168p. (J). (gr. 4-7). 14.95 (978-0-8225-0743-7(9), Lerner Pubns.) Lerner Publishing Group.

Blythe, Enid. Three Boys & a Circus. (Illus.). 80p. (J). (gr. k-6). pap. 5.95 (978-0-09-987870-4(4)) Random Hse. GBR. *Dist:* Trafalgar Square Publishing.

Boeve, Eunice. The Summer of the Crow. 2000. 224p. (J). pap. 12.95 (978-1-58597-059-9(X)) Leathers Publishing.

Bond, Michael. A Bear Called Paddington. Fortnum, Peggy, illus. rev. ed. 2001. (Paddington Ser.). 144p. (J). (gr. 4-6). pap. 5.95 (978-0-618-15071-7(4)) Houghton Mifflin Co. Trade & Reference Div.

Bone, Ian. Fat Boy Saves World. 2001. 240p. (YA). pap. 5.99 (978-0-7434-2245-1(7), Simon Pulse) Simon & Schuster Children's Publishing.

—Fat Boy Saves World. 2001. (gr. 7-12). lib. bdg. 14.15 (978-0-613-74240-5(0)) Tandem Library Bks.

Boone, Connie. The Lost Zoo. 2004. 24p. (J). 12.95 (978-1-56167-768-9(X)) American Literary Pr.

Borden, Louise. Albie the Lifeguard. 1999. (Illus.). 32p. (J). (ps-3). pap. 5.99 (978-0-590-44586-3(3)) Scholastic, Inc.

Bornemann, Elsa. Nada de Tucanes! Rojas, María P, illus. 2003. (SPA.). 80p. (J). (gr. 5-8). pap. 10.95 (978-950-511-637-9(3)) Santillana USA Publishing Co., Inc.

Bosch, Pseudonymous. The Name of This Book Is Secret. Ford, Gilbert, illus. rev. ed. 2007. 384p. (J). (gr. 3-7). 16.99 (***978-0-316-11366-3(2)***) Little, Brown Bks. for Young Readers.

Boulden, Jim & Boulden, Joan. Tall Paul. Tate, Susan, ed. Drengenberg, Heiko, illus. 1999. 24p. (YA). (gr. 6-9). pap. 5.95 (978-1-892421-12-8(7), 12-7ab) Boulden Publishing.

Bourgeois, Paulette. Franklin Goes to the Hospital. ed. 2004. (Illus.). (J). (ps-2). spiral bd. (978-0-616-03024-0(X)); spiral bd. (978-0-616-04547-3(6)) Canadian National Institute for the Blind/Institut National Canadien pour les Aveugles.

—Franklin Goes to the Hospital. Clark, Brenda, illus. 2000. (J). (ps-ps). lib. bdg. 12.40 (978-0-613-25254-6(3)) Tandem Library Bks.

Bowen, Fred. Off the Rim. Barrow, Ann, illus. 1998. (All-Star Sport Story Ser.). 112p. (J). (gr. 3-7). pap. 4.95 (978-1-56145-161-6(4)) Peachtree Pubs., Ltd.

The Boy Who Cried Wolf: Individual Title Six-Packs. 32p. (gr. 2 up). 37.00 (978-0-7635-9218-9(8)) Rigby Education.

The Boy Who Went to the North Wind: Individual Title Six-Packs. (Literatura 2000 Ser.). (gr. 2-3). 33.00 (978-0-7635-0217-1(0)) Rigby Education.

Boza, Eduardo Robles. Mi Amiga Quiere - Grande (My Friend Wants to Be Big) (SPA.). (J). 4.95 (978-968-419-981-1(3)) Grijalbo, Editorial MEX. *Dist:* AIMS International Bks., Inc.

Bradman, Tony. Has Anyone Seen Jack? Chamberlain, Margaret, illus. 1999. 24p. (J). (ps-1). pap. 7.99 (978-0-7112-0728-8(3)) Lincoln, Frances Ltd. GBR. *Dist:* Transition Vendor.

Bradman, Tony & Ross, Tony. Michael. 1998. (Illus.). 32p. (J). (ps-1). pap. 9.95 (978-0-86264-759-9(2)) Andersen GBR. *Dist:* Trafalgar Square Publishing.

Braffet, Mary. No Slippers! 2005. (Illus.). 32p. (J). 10.95 (978-1-56647-730-7(1)) Mutual Publishing LLC.

Brandon's Really Bad, Really Good Day. 2007. (J). 3.99 (***978-0-9726075-1-3(X)***) Executive Pubs. International.

Branson, Terri. Brother Dragon. Taylor, Chet, illus. 2004. (J). 18.99 (978-0-9755888-5-7(0)) Dragonfly Publishing, Inc.

Breckenridge, Gerald. Radio Boys on the Mexican Border. 2006. 78.99 (***978-1-4280-2532-5(4)***) IndyPublish.com.

Breitschwerdt, Rose. Hey Tommy Hey Figure. 2000. (Illus.). 16p. (J). (ps-2). 7.95 (978-1-56167-557-9(1), Shooting Star Edition) American Literary Pr.

Breslin, Theresa. Simon's Challenge. 2nd ed. 2002. (Kelpies Ser.). (Illus.). 112p. pap. 10.00 (978-0-86315-408-9(5)) Floris Bks. GBR. *Dist:* SteinerBooks, Inc.

Brignole, Giancarla, tr. El Globo de Pablito. Casagrande, Donata Dal Molin, illus. (Fabulas De Familia Ser.). (SPA.). 32p. (978-970-20-0269-7(9)) Castillo, Ediciones, S. A. de C. V.

Brimner, Larry Dane. Elliot Fry's Good-Bye. Fernandes, Eugenie, illus. 2003. 32p. (J). (gr. k-2). 8.95 (978-1-56397-715-2(X)) Boyds Mills Pr.

Brisson, Pat. The Summer My Father Was Ten. 2003. (Illus.). 32p. (J). (gr. k-2). 15.95 (978-1-56397-435-9(5)) Boyds Mills Pr.

—The Summer My Father Was Ten. Shine, Andrea, illus. 2003. 32p. (J). (gr. k-2). pap. 9.95 (978-1-56397-829-6(6)) Boyds Mills Pr.

—The Summer My Father Was Ten. 1999. (978-0-606-18015-3(X)) Tandem Library Bks.

Brookes, Diane. David's Day. Shank, Jacob, illus. 1998. (J). (ps-3). pap. (978-0-9683640-6-2(3)) Raven Rock Publishing.

Brown, Don. Kid Blink Beats the World. Brown, Don, illus. rev. ed. 2004. (Illus.). 32p. (J). 16.95 (978-1-59643-003-7(6)) Roaring Brook Pr.

Brown, Jeff. Flat Stanley. Bjorkman, Steve, illus. 2002. (J). 12.62 (978-0-7587-0553-2(0)) Book Wholesalers, Inc.

—Flat Stanley. Nash, Scott, illus. 40th anniv. ed. 2003. (Stanley Lambchop Adventure Ser.). 80p. (J). (gr. 1-5). pap. 4.99 (978-0-06-009791-2(4), Harper Trophy) HarperCollins Pubs.

—Flat Stanley. 2003. (gr. k-3). lib. bdg. 13.00 (978-0-613-65076-2(X)) Tandem Library Bks.

Brown, Marc. Arthur & the Lost Diary. 9th ed. 1998. (Arthur Chapter Bks. : Bk. 9). (Illus.). 64p. (J). (gr. 2-4). pap. 4.25 (978-0-316-11537-7(1)) Little, Brown Bks. for Young Readers.

—Arthur & the True Francine. 1998. (Arthur Adventure Ser.). (Illus.). 32p. (J). (ps-3). 9.95 (978-0-316-11946-7(6)) Little, Brown Bks. for Young Readers.

—Arthur Goes to Camp. Brown, Marc, illus. 1998. (Arthur Adventure Ser.). (Illus.). 32p. (J). (gr. k-3). pap. 5.95 (978-0-316-11529-2(0)) Little, Brown Bks. for Young Readers.

—Arthur in a Pickle. 1999. (Arthur Ser.). (Illus.). 24p. (J). (gr. k-3). lib. bdg. 11.99 (978-0-679-98469-6(0), Random Hse. Bks. for Young Readers) Random Hse. Children's Bks.

—Arthur in a Pickle. 1999. (Arthur Ser.). lib. bdg. 11.80 (978-0-613-65119-6(7)) Tandem Library Bks.

—Arthur, It's Only Rock 'n' Roll. Brown, Marc, illus. 2002. (Illus.). 32p. (J). (ps-3). 15.95 (978-0-316-11854-5(0)) Little, Brown Bks. for Young Readers.

—Arthur Writes a Story. Brown, Marc, illus. (Arthur Adventure Ser.). (Illus.). 32p. (J). (ps-3). 1999. 9.95 (978-0-316-11976-4(8)); 1998. pap. 6.99 (978-0-316-11164-5(3)) Little, Brown Bks. for Young Readers.

—Arthur's Family Vacation. Brown, Marc, illus. 1998. (Arthur Adventure Ser.). (Illus.). (J). (gr. k-3). pap. 5.95 (978-0-316-11528-5(2)) Little, Brown Bks. for Young Readers.

—Arthur's New Puppy. 1998. (Arthur Adventure Ser.). (Illus.). 32p. (J). (ps-3). 9.95 (978-0-316-11949-8(0)) Little, Brown Bks. for Young Readers.

—Arthur's Teacher Moves In. 2000. (Arthur Adventure Ser.). (Illus.). (J). 15.95 (978-0-316-11809-5(5)) Little Brown & Co.

—Binky Rules. Brown, Marc, illus. 24th ed. 2000. (Arthur Chapter Bks.: Bk. 24). (Illus.). 64p. (J). (gr. 2-4). pap. 3.95 (978-0-316-12333-4(1)) Little Brown & Co.

—Binky Rules. Brown, Marc, illus. 24th ed. 2000. (Arthur Chapter Bks. : Bk. 24). (Illus.). 64p. (J). (gr. 2-4). 13.95 (978-0-316-12193-4(2)) Little, Brown Bks. for Young Readers.

—Binky Rules. 2000. (Arthur Chapter Bks.: Bk. 24). (gr. k-3). lib. bdg. 11.80 (978-0-613-30275-3(3)); (J). (gr. 3-6). 10.75 (978-0-606-19447-1(9)) Tandem Library Bks.

—Buster's New Friend. Brown, Marc, illus. 23rd ed. 2000. (Arthur Chapter Bks.: Bk. 23). (Illus.). 64p. (J). (gr. 2-4). pap. 4.25 (978-0-316-12307-5(2)) Little Brown & Co.

—Buster's New Friend. Brown, Marc, illus. 23rd ed. 2000. (Arthur Chapter Bks. : Bk. 23). (Illus.). 64p. (J). (gr. 2-4). 13.95 (978-0-316-12212-2(2)) Little, Brown Bks. for Young Readers.

—Buster's New Friend. 2000. (Arthur Chapter Bks.: Bk. 23). (gr. k-3). lib. bdg. 12.10 (978-0-613-30292-0(3)); (J). (gr. 3-6). 10.75 (978-0-606-19446-4(0)) Tandem Library Bks.

Buchanan, Steve. More True Tales of Shorty Stevens the le. 2006. pap. 15.50 (***978-1-4259-8161-7(5)***) AuthorHouse.

Buckeridge, Anthony. Jennings Goes to School. 2002. 240p. pap. (978-0-7551-1368-2(3)) House of Stratus, Inc.

Buff, Conrad & Buff, Mary. The Apple & the Arrow. Buff, Conrad & Buff, Mary, illus. 2001. (Illus.). 80p. (J). (gr. 4-6). tchr. ed. 16.00 (978-0-618-12807-5(7)); pap. 8.95 (978-0-618-12809-9(3)) Houghton Mifflin Co. Trade & Reference Div.

Bunting, Eve. Rudi's Pond. Himler, Ronald, illus. 1999. 32p. (J). (gr. k-3). tchr. ed. 16.00 (978-0-395-89067-7(5), Clarion Bks.) Houghton Mifflin Co. Trade & Reference Div.

Burd, Allan. The Adventures of Little Al: The Lie. Linbrunner, Lisa, illus. 2001. 37p. (J). (ps-5). per. 16.95 (978-0-9705588-6-0(0)) Bed Bug Publishing, Inc.

Burgess, Melvin. Billy Elliot. 2001. 224p. (J). (gr. 5-12). pap. 4.50 (978-0-439-31228-8(0)) Scholastic, Inc.

Burks, Catherine. Hi! Let's Meet Billy, Vol. 1. Lee, Rudolph, illus. 1998. (J). (gr. 1-5). pap. 6.95 (978-1-892750-00-6(7)) Different Friends.

—Hi! Let's Meet Pete, Vol. 2. Lee, Rudolph, illus. 1998. (J). (gr. 1-5). pap. 6.95 (978-1-892750-01-3(5)) Different Friends.

—Hi! Let's Meet Sam, Vol. 3. Lee, Rudolph, illus. 1998. (J). (gr. 1-5). pap. 6.95 (978-1-892750-02-0(3)) Different Friends.

Burleigh, Cyril. The Hilltop Boys on the River. 2007. 118p. pap. 10.99 (***978-1-4264-6538-3(6)***) BiblioBazaar.

Burton, Martin Nelson. Dear Mr. Leprechaun: Letters from My First Friendship. Hansen, Clint, illus. Tanner, Dean, photos by. 2003. 32p. 17.00 (978-0-9666490-0-0(1)) London Town Pr.

Bush, Max. The Boy Who Left Home to Find Out about the Shivers. 1999. (J). pap. 7.00 (978-0-87602-372-3(3)) Anchorage Pr.

Butler, Geoff. The Killick: A Newfoundland Story. Butler, Geoff, illus. 1998. (Illus.). 32p. (J). (gr. k-9). lib. bdg. 15.25 (978-0-613-09458-0(1)) Tandem Library Bks.

Butterworth, W. E., pseud. Leroy & the Old Man. 1999. 176p. (J). (gr. 7-9). pap. 5.99 (978-0-590-42711-1(3)) Scholastic, Inc.

Byars, Betsy. La Casa de las Alas. (SPA., Illus.). (YA). (gr. 5-8). pap. (978-84-406-0861-1(6), EB3416) Ediciones B ESP. *Dist:* Lectorum Pubns., Inc.

Campagna, Phil. The Liberty Circle. 2004. 243p. (YA). (gr. 8-12). pap. 7.95 (978-0-929141-69-5(5)) Napoleon Publishing/Rendezvous Pr. CAN. *Dist:* AtlasBooks Distribution.

Campbell, Joanna. Dylan's Choice. 1998. (Thoroughbred Ser.: No. 30). 176p. (gr. 4-7). mass mkt. 4.99 (978-0-06-106539-2(0), Harper Entertainment) HarperCollins Pubs.

Campbell, Rod. Buster's Bedtime. (Illus.). 12p. (J). (ps-k). bds. (978-1-56021-376-5(0), #223) W.J. Fantasy, Inc.

Cann, Kate. Hard Cash. 2003. (Illus.). 336p. (YA). mass mkt. 5.99 (978-0-689-85905-2(8), Simon Pulse) Simon & Schuster Children's Publishing.

—Hard Cash. 2003. (gr. 7-12). lib. bdg. 14.15 (978-0-613-73411-0(4)) Tandem Library Bks.

—Speeding. 2004. (Illus.). 384p. (YA). mass mkt. 5.99 (978-0-689-85907-6(4), Simon Pulse) Simon & Schuster Children's Publishing.

Cantrell, Pam Bullman. The Three Little Boys & the Big Bad Devil. 2004. pap. 6.95 (978-0-533-14193-7(1)) Vantage Pr., Inc.

Capdevila, Juan. Teo en la Escuela (Teo at School) (SPA.). 32p. (J). 12.95 (978-84-7176-311-2(7)) Timun Mas, Editorial S.A. ESP. *Dist:* AIMS International Bks., Inc.

Capote, Truman. A Christmas Memory. Peck, Beth, illus. 2006. 48p. (J). (gr. 7). 17.95 incl. audio compact disk (978-0-375-83789-0(2), Knopf Bks. for Young Readers) Random Hse. Children's Bks.

Capriola, Arlene & Swenson, Rigmor. The Boy Who Cried Wolf. Mastry, Cherisse, ed. Burns, Kathy, illus. 1998. (Once upon a Time Ser.). (J). (gr. k-2). pap., wbk. ed. incl. audio (978-1-57022-170-5(7)) ECS Learning Systems, Inc.

Carlson, Nancy. Loudmouth George & the New Neighbors. 2003. (gr. k-3). lib. bdg. 15.25 (978-0-613-58926-0(2)) Tandem Library Bks.

Carlson, Nancy, illus. Loudmouth George & the New Neighbors. 20th anniv. ed. 2003. (Nancy Carlson's Neighborhood Ser.). 32p. (J). (gr. k-2). pap. 6.95 (978-1-57505-614-2(3)) Lerner Publishing Group.

Carrera, Jaume. Santi No Quiere Levantarse. Vila, Jordi, illus. 2002. (Santi No Quiere... Ser.).Tr. of Santi Doesn't Want to Get Up. (SPA & ENG.). 12p. (gr. k-2). pap. 2.95 (978-84-7864-577-0(2)) Combel Editorial, S.A. ESP. *Dist:* Independent Pubs. Group.

—Santi no quiere Obedecer. Vila, Jordi, illus. 2002. (Santi No Quiere... Ser.).Tr. of Santi Doesn't Want to Obey His Parents. (SPA & ENG.). 12p. (gr. k-2). pap. 2.95 (978-84-7864-580-0(2)) Combel Editorial, S.A. ESP. *Dist:* Independent Pubs. Group.

Carrick, Carol. What Happened to Patrick's Dinosaurs? Carrick, Donald, illus. 2002. (J). 13.79 (978-0-7587-3960-5(5)) Book Wholesalers, Inc.

Carse, Jodi & Gallagher, Maria. Catch That Kid! Spangler, Brie, illus. 2006. (Stinky Boys Club Ser.: Vol. 4). 64p. (J). pap. 4.99 (978-0-448-43355-4(9), Grosset & Dunlap) Penguin Group (USA) Inc.

Carter, Herbert. The Boy Scouts on Sturgeon Island. rev. ed. 2006. (ENG.). 212p. 27.95 (978-1-4218-2084-2(6), 1st World Library - Literary Society) 1st World Publishing, Inc.

Castlemon, Harry. The Sportsman's Club among the Trappers. 2005. pap. 28.95 (978-1-4179-5498-8(1)) Kessinger Publishing, LLC.

Castlemon, Harry. Sportsmans Club in the Saddle. 2006. pap. 30.95 (***978-1-4286-5231-6(0)***) Kessinger Publishing, LLC.

Cat Concert: Individual Title Six-Packs. (Literatura 2000 Ser.). (gr. 2-3). 33.00 (978-0-7635-0163-1(8)) Rigby Education.

Center for Learning Network Staff. Belle Prater's Boy/ My Louisiana Sky: Curriculum Unit — Novel Series. 2001. (Novel Ser.). 77p. (YA). tchr. ed., spiral bd. 19.95 (978-1-56077-662-8(5)) Ctr. for Learning, The.

Charley Skedaddle. 2000. (J). 9.95 (978-1-56137-588-2(8)) Novel Units, Inc.

Chikere, Chidi. The Adventures of Alfalfa. 1999. (Illus.). 100p. pap. 10.95 (978-1-58521-000-8(5)) Books for Black Children, Inc.

Ciavonne, Jean. Carlos, Light the Farolito. Clair, Donna, illus. 2001. 32p. (J). (gr. k-3). pap. 5.95 (978-0-618-13052-8(7), Clarion Bks.) Houghton Mifflin Co. Trade & Reference Div.

—Carlos, Light the Farolito. 2001. (gr. k-3). lib. bdg. 14.10 (978-0-613-44192-6(3)) Tandem Library Bks.

Ciocca, Donna. Harley & Homer for Hire. 2006. (YA). per. 11.95 (***978-0-9747361-9-8(8)***) Oak Manor Publishing, Inc.

Cioffi, Dom, illus. Digby & the Lake Monster. l.t. ed. 2003. 36p. (J). per. (978-0-9745931-0-4(9)) Vermont Bookworks.

Clague, Mary H. Fort Brooke Drummer Boy: A Story of Old Florida. 1998. 93p. (J). pap. 6.99 (978-1-57502-747-0(X), PO2075) Morris Publishing.

Claire, Elizabeth. The New Boy Is Lost! Reader/Teacher's Guide/CD Package: An ESL Picture Novel. 2005. pap. 39.00 incl. audio compact disk (978-0-86647-194-7(4)) Pro Lingua Assocs., Inc.

Clark, Sheryl. Asking for Trouble: Prove It!, Take a Hike!, Knock It Off! 2005. (Triple Play-Yellow Ser.). (Illus.). 48p. (gr. 4-8). 41.85 (978-0-7910-9079-4(5)) Facts On File, Inc.

Cleary, Beverly. Henry & Beezus. 2002. (Illus.). (J). 13.83 (978-0-7587-0018-6(0)) Book Wholesalers, Inc.

—Henry Huggins. Darling, Louis, illus. 2004. (SPA.). 160p. (J). pap. 6.99 (978-0-06-073600-2(3), Rayo) HarperCollins Pubs.

Clements, Andrew. The Janitor's Boy. 2004. 144p. (J). (gr. 3-7). pap. 29.00 incl. audio (978-0-8072-8360-8(6), Listening Library) Random Hse. Audio Publishing Group.

—The Janitor's Boy. Selznick, Brian, illus. 2001. 144p. mass mkt. 4.99 (978-0-689-84916-9(8), Aladdin) Simon & Schuster Children's Publishing.

Clinton, Cathryn. Simeon's Fire. 2005. 128p. (J). (gr. 5-9). 15.99 (978-0-7636-2707-2(0)) Candlewick Pr.

Coakley, Lena & Watts, Leslie Elizabeth. On the Night of the Comet. 2004. (Illus.). 32p. (J). (ps-2). 16.95 (978-1-55143-287-8(0), 1234126) Orca Bk. Pubs. USA.

Cogar, Tubal U., et al. The Journeys of Wobblefoot the Beginning. Cogar, Karen S., ed. O'Connor, Tim, illus. 2003. (J). pap. 17.50 (978-0-9747149-0-5(9)) Wobblefoot Ltd.

Collier, Kevin Scott. Diligence the Dragon Vol. 1: A Prebiblical Fable. l.t. ed. 2005. (Illus.). 22p. (J). E-Book 9.95 incl. cd-rom (978-1-933090-25-2(1)) Guardian Angel Publishing, Inc.

Collins, Billy. Daddy's Little Boy. Date not set. 32p. (J). (ps-3). pap. 5.99 (978-0-06-443687-8(X)) HarperCollins Pubs.

Conkin, Barbara. Ramzy's Story. Steinrock, Larry, illus. 2001. 16p. (J). (gr. 1-5). pap. 4.75 (978-0-9674662-3-1(7)) Hycliffe Publishing.

Connor, Joynce. Micheal & Mr. B. 2006. 48p. (J). (gr. k-3). 19.95 (978-0-9765469-1-7(4)) Diamond Cutter Pr., LLC.

Corbett, Terry. Nicholas & the Elves. Corbett, Mary Lark, illus. 1999. 20p. (Orig.). (J). pap. 5.99 (978-1-929731-03-9(5)) Rowfant Pr.

Coren, Alan. Arthur & the Purple Panic. 2004. (Illus.). 64p. (978-0-86051-141-0(3), Robson Bks. Ltd.) Anova Bks.

—Arthur's Last Stand. 2004. (Illus.). 64p. (978-0-903895-94-1(3), Robson Bks. Ltd.) Anova Bks.

Corey, Shana. Where Is Elmo's Blanket. Stevenson, Nancy, illus. 1999. (Nifty Lift-and-Look Book Ser.). 12p. (J). (gr. k-ps). bds. 5.99 (978-0-375-80138-9(3), Random Hse. Bks. for Young Readers) Random Hse. Children's Bks.

Cory, Kim Delmar. Charlie Boy. Kemnitz, Milt & Lewis, Jason, illus. State Archives of Michigan Staff, photos by. 1999. 124p. (J). (gr. 3-7). pap. 9.99 (978-0-88092-496-2(9), 4969) Royal Fireworks Publishing Co.

Cosby, Bill. Little Bill's Punch-Out Valentines. Honeywood, Varnette P., illus. 1999. (Little Bill Books for Beginning Readers Ser.). 16p. (J). (gr. k-3). pap. 2.99 (978-0-439-05204-7(1)) Scholastic, Inc.

Counsel, June. But Martin! 2000. (Illus.). 32p. (J). pap. 6.95 (978-0-552-52312-7(7)) Transworld Publishers Ltd. GBR. *Dist:* Trafalgar Square Publishing.

Cox, Stephen Angus. The Dare Boys of 1776. 2004. reprint ed. pap. 15.95 (978-1-4191-5856-8(2)); pap. 1.99 (978-1-4192-5856-5(7)) Kessinger Publishing, LLC.

Craig, Janet. Good Luck Clover. 1999. (gr. k-3). lib. bdg. 10.10 (978-0-613-76296-0(7)) Tandem Library Bks.

Crawford, Teresa. I'm Not Stupid! I'm ADHD! 2004. 23p. pap. 14.95 (978-1-4137-3249-8(6)) PublishAmerica, Inc.

Crompton, Richmal. Just William As Seen on TV. 2003. (Illus.). 176p. (J). pap. 6.95 (978-0-333-62802-7(0)) Macmillan Publishers Ltd. GBR. *Dist:* Trafalgar Square Publishing.

—William at War. 2nd rev. ed. (Illus.). 239p. (J). mass mkt. (978-0-333-63793-7(3), Macmillan Children's Bks.) Pan Macmillan.

Curry, Jane Louise. Poor Tom's Ghost. 2001. 188p. (YA). (gr. 4-7). pap. 11.95 (978-0-595-15090-8(X)) iUniverse, Inc.

Curry, Kenneth. Chuka & the Drum. 2007. (Illus.). 22p. (J). 10.95 (***978-0-9798364-4-2(1)***) Curry Brothers Publishing.

Curtis. Tell Me a Boy Story. 2000. (J). 304p. (gr. 5 up). 16.89 (978-0-06-029021-4(8)); 40p. (ps-1). 16.95 (978-0-06-029020-7(X)); (Illus.). 40p. (ps-1). pap. 6.95 (978-0-06-443698-4(5)) HarperCollins Pubs.

Curtis, Gavin. The Bat Boy & His Violin. ed. 2004. (Illus.). (J). (gr. k-3). spiral bd. (978-0-616-07254-7(6)) Canadian National Institute for the Blind/Institut National Canadien pour les Aveugles.

Czernecki, Stefan. Beastly Boys & Ghastly Girls. 2000. (Illus.). 48p. (J). (gr. 2-5). 14.95 (978-0-06-024952-6(8)) HarperCollins Pubs.

Dahl, Michael. Worm Tunnel. 1999. (Illus.). (J). (978-0-606-21798-9(3)) Tandem Library Bks.

Dahl, Roald. Boy: Relatos de la Infancia. 22nd ed. 2000. (SPA., Illus.). 192p. (YA). (gr. 9-12). 13.95 (978-84-204-4547-2(9)) Alfaguara, Ediciones, S.A.- Grupo Santillana ESP. *Dist:* Santillana USA Publishing Co., Inc.

—Charlie y el Gran Ascensor de Cristal. Jacques, Faith, illus. 2003. (SPA.). 164p. (J). (gr. 5-8). pap. 12.95 (978-968-19-0988-8(7)) Santillana USA Publishing Co., Inc.

—Charlie y el Gran Ascensor de Cristal. 1998. (SPA.). 168p. (J). (gr. 4-7). 8.95 (978-84-204-3214-4(8), AF0152) Santillana USA Publishing Co., Inc.

—Charlie y la Fabrica de Chocolate. Jacques, Faith, illus. 2003. (SPA.). 176p. (J). (gr. 4-7). (978-84-204-4771-1(4), AF0153) Alfaguara, Ediciones, S.A.- Grupo Santillana.

—Charlie y la Fabrica de Chocolate. (SPA.). (J). 8.95 (978-968-6026-71-9(1)) Santillana USA Publishing Co., Inc.

—Danny el Campeon del Mundo. Blake, Quentin, illus. 2003. (SPA.). 200p. (YA). (gr. 5-8). 9.95 (978-84-204-4431-4(6)) Alfaguara, Ediciones, S.A.- Grupo Santillana ESP. *Dist:* Santillana USA Publishing Co., Inc.

—James & the Giant Peach. 1999. (J). 11.95 (978-1-56137-487-8(3)) Novel Units, Inc.

—A Novel Study for Grades Two & Three Based on James & the Giant Peach. Brookes, Diane, ed. 1998. (J). pap., tchr. ed. (978-0-9683234-9-6(9)) Raven Rock Publishing.

Dale, Jenny. Big Ben. 2000. (Puppy Patrol Ser.: Vol. 2). (Illus.). 112p. (J). (gr. 3-6). pap. 3.99 (978-0-439-11324-3(5)) Scholastic, Inc.

—Big Ben. 1999. (gr. 3-6). lib. bdg. 11.80 (978-0-613-24353-7(6)) Tandem Library Bks.

Daly, Maureen. The Small War of Sergeant Donkey. Dennis, Wesley, illus. 2000. (Living History Library). 104p. (J). (gr. 5-9). reprint ed. pap. 11.95 (978-1-883937-47-8(7)) Bethlehem Bks.

Damon, Sidney. Harold the Orange Juice Boy. 40p. (Orig.). (J). (gr. k-4). pap. (978-0-937148-14-3(8)) Wild Horses Publishing Co.

Danziger, Paula. Earth to Matthew. 1998. (Matthew Martin Ser.: No. 3). 154p. (J). (gr. 3-7). pap. 5.99 (978-0-698-11692-4(5) , Putnam Juvenile) Penguin Group (USA) Inc.

Darden, Hunter D. Pete's Angel - A Story of Self-Love. Vacca, Sally, illus. 1998. 40p. (J). (gr. k-7). 19.95 (978-0-9653729-1-6(X)) Sunfleur Pubns., Inc.

Davis, Brian. Matthew & Goliath. Wheeler, Ron, illus. 2003. (Book of Matt Ser.: 3). 80p. (J). pap. 4.99 (978-1-59269-058-9(0)) Mcruffy Pr.

de las Casas, Diane. Cajun Cornbread Boy. de las Casas, Diane, illus. 2005. (Illus.). 32p. (J). 15.95 (978-1-58980-224-7(1)) Pelican Publishing Co., Inc.

de Paola, Tomie. Andy: That's My Name. 1999. (Illus.). 32p. (J). (ps-3). pap. 6.99 (978-0-689-82697-9(4) , 076714005990, Aladdin) Simon & Schuster Children's Publishing.

—Andy That's My Name. 1999. (J). 12.79 (978-0-606-16323-1(9)); lib. bdg. 14.15 (978-0-613-15712-4(5)) Tandem Library Bks.

—Tom. de Paola, Tomie, illus. 2002. (Illus.). (J). 13.19 (978-0-7587-3827-1(7)) Book Wholesalers, Inc.

De Velasco, Miguel Martin Fernandez. Pabluras. (SPA.). 120p. (YA). (gr. 5-8). (978-84-279-3146-6(8) , NG3678) Noguer y Caralt Editores, S. A. ESP. *Dist:* Lectorum Pubns., Inc.

Dean, Lani. One Misty Morning. Cassidy, Al, illus. 2004. 36p. (J). 14.95 (978-0-9645844-9-5(2)) Manor Hse. Publishing Co., Inc.

Deford, Ted. Po & the Gang: In Two Big Adventures. 2005. 49p. pap. 12.95 (978-1-4137-9068-9(2)) PublishAmerica, Inc.

Defraites, Henry. Little Henry & the Phantom Dream. Clement, Dane, photos by. 1999. (Illus.). 32p. (J). (gr. 1-7). 7.95 (978-0-9676825-0-1(9)) Abound Inc. Publishing.

DeLoach, Kathleen. Le Monde de Daniel: Un livre sur les enfants Handicapés. Best, Cathy, illus. 2005. (FRE.). (J). pap. 15.95 (978-1-933514-01-7(9)) Three Moons Media.

—El Mundo de Daniel: Un libro sobre niños Minusvalidos. Best, Cathy, illus. 2005. (SPA.). 20p. (J). pap. 15.95 (978-1-933514-00-0(0)) Three Moons Media.

Derwent, Lavinia. The Boy from Sula. 2002. (Kelpies Ser.). (Illus.). 160p. pap. 10.00 (978-0-86315-400-3(X)) Floris Bks. GBR. *Dist:* SteinerBooks, Inc.

Desrosiers, Sylvie & Franson, Leanne. Je Suis Thomas. 2003. (Premier Roman Ser.). (FRE., Illus.). 64p. (J). (gr. 1-4). pap. (978-2-89021-617-4(9)) Diffusion du livre Mirabel.

Dickens, Frank. Albert Herbert Hawkins: The Naughtiest Boy in the World. Dickens, Frank, illus. (Illus.). 32p. (J). (ps-3). 12.95 (978-0-87592-000-9(4)) Scroll Pr., Inc.

Diehl, Jean Heilprin. Loon Chase. Freeman, Kathryn, illus. 2006. 32p. (J). 15.95 (978-0-9764943-8-6(8)) Sylvan Dell Pubng.

Dike, Tina. His Greatest Challenge. Schulman, Cory & Johnstone, Sandy, eds. 2000. 125p. (YA). (gr. 7-9). pap. 9.95 (978-0-9642997-1-9(2)) Best Seller Pubns., Inc.

Dixon, Franklin W. Feeding Frenzy. 2008. (Hardy Boys (All New) Undercover Brothers Ser.). 160p. (J). pap. 4.99 (***978-1-4169-5499-6(6)*** , Aladdin) Simon & Schuster Children's Publishing.

—A Game Called Chaos. 2000. (Hardy Boys Ser.: No. 160). 160p. (J). (gr. 3-6). pap. 9.95 (978-0-671-03870-0(2) , Aladdin) Simon & Schuster Children's Publishing.

—A Game Called Chaos. 2000. (gr. 5-8). lib. bdg. 13.00 (978-0-613-27846-1(1)) Tandem Library Bks.

—Secret Warning, No. 17. 2006. (Hardy Boys (Hardcover) Ser.). 228p. (J). (gr. 4-7). per. 17.95 (978-1-55709-285-4(0)) Applewood Bks.

—Spy Set: Extreme Danger; Running on Fumes; Boardwalk Bust; Thrill Ride. 2005. (Hardy Boys Ser.). 672p. (J). pap. 17.95 (978-1-4169-1324-5(6) , Aladdin) Simon & Schuster Children's Publishing.

DNA Productions Staff, ed. Jimmy Neutron, 2 vols., Vol. 1. 2003. (Illus.). 96p. pap. 7.99 (978-1-59182-401-5(X)) TOKYOPOP, Inc.

The Doctor, 2 Pack. (Chiquilibros Ser.). (ps-1). 12.00 (978-0-7635-8544-0(0)) Rigby Education.

Dodge, Wayne. The Bongo Boys: An Almost True Story. 2004. 172p. 25.95 (978-1-932852-63-9(8)) Wasteland Pr.

Doyle, Brian. Pure Spring. 2007. 174p. (J). (gr. 6-9). 16.95 (***978-0-88899-774-6(4)***) Groundwood Bks. CAN. *Dist:* Perseus Distribution.

Doyle, Brian. Spud Sweetgrass. 2006. 140p. (J). pap. 5.95 (978-0-88899-756-2(6)) Groundwood Bks. CAN. *Dist:* Perseus Distribution.

Dr MacTavish's Creature: Individual Chapter Book Title Six-Packs. Vol. 25. 32p. (gr. 3-4). 44.00 (978-0-7635-4472-0(8)) Rigby Education.

Dragland. Simon Jesse's Journey. (J). pap. 2.95 (978-0-88899-025-9(1) , Libros Tigrillo) Groundwood Bks. CAN. *Dist:* Transition Vendor.

Dresser, Delvin. A Better Way. 2000. 56p. (J). pap. 8.00 (978-0-8059-4869-1(4)) Dorrance Publishing Co., Inc.

Driscoll, James R. The Brighton Boys with the Flying Corps. 2005. 152p. pap. 11.95 (978-1-59540-820-4(7) , 1st World Library - Literary Society) 1st World Publishing, Inc.

Du Jardin, Rosamond. Marcy Catches Up. 2003. (YA). pap. 12.95 (978-1-930009-75-2(5) , 800-691-7779) Image Cascade Publishing.

Duchesne, Christiane, et al. A Kiss for Peter. 2000. (Illus.). 32p. (J). (ps-3). pap. (978-1-894363-40-2(X)) Dominique & Friends.

Duffield, W. J. The Radio Boys in the Thousand Islands O. 2006. pap. 71.99 (***978-1-4219-9966-1(8)***) IndyPublish.com.

—Radio Boys in the Thousand Islands or Th. 2006. 78.99 (***978-1-4219-9957-9(9)***) IndyPublish.com.

Durant, Alan. Burger Boy. 2006. (Illus.). 32p. (J). (ps-4). pap. (978-1-84270-537-7(7)) Andersen.

Dyan, Penelope, creator. For Love of Pete! The Story of the Boy Who Played the Taps on Iwo Jima. 2005. 292p. (YA). per. 15.95 (978-0-9768417-9-1(7)) Bellissima Publishing, LLC.

Dyer, Jill. The Plant of the Zorks. 2005. 11p. 6.65 (978-1-4116-6641-2(0)) Lulu.com.

Eagle Feathers, 6 vols. (Multicultural Programs Ser.). 16p. (gr. 1-6). 31.95 (978-0-7802-8327-5(9)) Wright Group, The.

Echerique, Alfredo Bryce & Duenas, Ana Maria. Goig. Roederer, Charlotte, illus. (Literary Encounters Ser.). (SPA.). (J). (gr. 3-5). pap. (978-968-494-065-9(3) , CI7706) Centro de Informacion y Desarrollo de la Comunicacion y la Literatura MEX. *Dist:* Lectorum Pubns., Inc.

Echols, Jennifer. The Boys Next Door. 2007. (Romantic Comedies Ser.). 336p. (YA). mass mkt. 6.99 (***978-1-4169-1831-8(0)*** , Simon Pulse) Simon & Schuster Children's Publishing.

Eckert, Allan W. The Dreaming Tree. 2000. 304p. (YA). (gr. 7-12). pap. 18.95 (978-0-595-08989-5(5) , Backinprint.com) iUniverse, Inc.

Elgar, Edward & Briggs, Raymond. The Puddleman. (Illus.). 32p. pap. 7.99 (***978-0-09-945642-1(7)*** , Red Fox) Random Hse. Children's Bks. GBR. *Dist:* Trafalgar Square Publishing.

Elliott, George. The Boy Who Loved Bananas. Krystoforski, Andrei, illus. 2006. 32p. (978-1-55453-119-6(5)) Kids Can Pr., Ltd.

—The Boy Who Loved Bananas. Krystoforski, Andrej, illus. 2005. 32p. (J). (ps-2). (978-1-55337-744-3(3)) Kids Can Pr., Ltd.

Ely, Lesley. Cuidando a Louis. 2004. (SPA., Illus.). 25p. (J). 18.99 (978-84-8488-115-5(6)) Serres, Ediciones, S. L. ESP. *Dist:* Lectorum Pubns., Inc.

Erickson, Betty. Sherman. Dillard, Kristine, illus. 1999. 8p. (J). (gr. k-2). pap. (978-1-880612-99-6(2) , Seedling Pubns.) Continental Pr., Inc.

Erickson, Timothy Ronald. Death's Whisper Recoil, 2. Erickson, Timothy Ronald, illus. 2003. (YA). pap. 14.95 (978-1-59492-001-1(X)) Erickson, Tim.

Erlings, Fridrik. Benjamin Dove. 2007. 224p. (YA). (gr. 5-9). pap. 7.95 (***978-0-7358-2149-1(6)***) North-South Bks., Inc.

Ewing, Lynne. Drive-By. 1998. 96p. (J). (gr. 5 up). pap. 4.99 (978-0-06-440649-9(0) , Harper Trophy) HarperCollins Pubs.

Exelby, Kathy. My Dog Harpo: The Biggest Kid I Know. Wall Darby, Colleen, illus. 2007. (J). per. 20.00 (***978-1-932583-39-7(4)***) digital@batesjackson llc.

Fabra, Jordi Sierra. El Nino Que Vivia en las Estrellas. (SPA.). 120p. (YA). (gr. 5-8). 8.95 (978-84-204-4429-1(4)) Alfaguara, Ediciones, S.A.- Grupo Santillana ESP. *Dist:* Santillana USA Publishing Co., Inc.

Fallon, Joan & Feltenstein, Arlene. Will the New Baby Be Bigger Than Me? Escriva, Vivi, illus. 1998. (J). (ps-3). 9.95 (978-1-56492-252-6(9)) Laredo Publishing Co., Inc.

Farley, Colby King. A Warm Familiar Feeling. 2nd ed. 2003. (YA). per. 13.50 (978-0-943864-48-8(8)) Davenport, May Pubs.

Fedrau, Noel. An Autumn Leaf. Houston, Barbara, illus. 2007. (ENG.). 40p. (J). per. 21.99 (***978-1-4141-0828-5(1)***) Pleasant Word.

Fenner, Carol. Randall's Wall. 2000. (Illus.). 96p. (J). (gr. 4-7). pap. 7.95 (978-0-689-83558-2(2) , Aladdin) Simon & Schuster Children's Publishing.

—Randall's Wall. 2000. (978-0-606-17935-5(6)); (gr. 3-6). lib. bdg. 13.00 (978-0-8335-9175-3(4)) Tandem Library Bks.

Fernandes, Eugenie. Little Toby & the Big Hair. Fernandes, Kim, illus. 1998. 32p. (J). (gr. k-2). 14.95 (978-1-55209-273-6(9)) Firefly Bks., Ltd.

Fernandes, Kim & Fernandes, Eugenie. Little Toby & the Big Hair. Fernandes, Kim & Fernandes, Eugenie, illus. 1998. (Illus.). 32p. (J). (gr. k-2). pap. 5.95 (978-1-55209-257-6(7)) Firefly Bks., Ltd.

Fienberg, Anna. The Hottest Boy Who Ever Lived. Gamble, Kim, illus. 2000. 32p. (J). pap. 7.95 (978-1-86508-093-2(4)) Allen & Unwin AUS. *Dist:* Independent Pubs. Group.

Fienberg, Anna. Number 8. 2007. 288p. (YA). 16.95 (***978-0-8027-9660-8(5)***) Walker & Co.

Findlay, Andrew. Roddy & the Magic Mattress. 2005. 54p. pap. 5.61 (978-1-4116-3612-5(0)) Lulu.com.

Findon, Joanne. The Dream of Aengus. Nasmith, Ted, illus. unabr. ed. 1998. 32p. (gr. 1-4). 6.95 (978-0-7737-5930-5(1)) Stoddart Kids CAN. *Dist:* Fitzhenry & Whiteside, Ltd.

Finkelstein, Chaim. The Burksfield Bike Club, Book 2: Lost & Found. Jennings, R. W., illus. 2007. 224p. (J). 15.95 (978-1-932443-69-1(X) , BBC1H) Judaica Pr., Inc., The.

Finley, Martha. Mildred's Boys & Girls. 1999. (Mildred Keith Collection Ser.: vol. 6). (J). reprint ed. 14.00 (978-1-889128-36-8(8)) Mantle Ministries.

Finn, Francis J. Tom Playfair. 2001. (gr. 5-8). lib. bdg. 17.65 (978-0-613-90090-4(1)) Tandem Library Bks.

Fishman, Cathy Goldberg. Car Wash Kid. Gott, Barry, illus. 2003. (Rookie Reader Skill Set Ser.). (J). (gr. k-2). pap. 4.95 (978-0-516-27811-7(8) , Children's Pr.) Scholastic Library Publishing.

—Car Wash Kid. 2003. (gr. k-3). lib. bdg. 12.95 (978-0-613-67601-4(7)) Tandem Library Bks.

Fleming, Denise. Buster. rev. ed. 2003. (Illus.). 40p. (J). 15.95 (978-0-8050-6279-3(3) , Holt, Henry & Co. Bks. For Young Readers) Holt, Henry & Co.

Flesh, Chris P. Been There, Crossed Over #4. 2008. 176p. (J). (gr. 3). pap. 4.99 (***978-0-448-44812-1(2)*** , Grosset & Dunlap) Penguin Group (USA) Inc.

Fletcher, Ralph J. Spider Boy. 1998. 192p. (J). (gr. 4-7). 5.99 (978-0-440-41483-4(0) , Yearling) Random Hse. Children's Bks.

—Spider Boy. 1998. (978-0-606-13794-2(7)) Tandem Library Bks.

Flint, Timothy. Little Henry: The Stolen Child. (J). reprint ed. lib. bdg. 40.00 (978-0-8398-0558-8(6)) Irvington Pubs.

Flores, Sergio. Good Morning Alberto. Ramirez, Ivan D., ed. Cossio, Edgar, illus. 1999. 121p. (YA). (gr. 6 up). pap. (978-1-57159-004-6(8)) Los Andes Publishing Co.

Flynn, Arthur. Luke on Alcatraz. 2001. 128p. (YA). (gr. 5-9). per. (978-1-84210-021-9(1)) Mentor Bks.

Foley, Sue. Tyrone: A Turtle Tale. Kobak, Carrie, illus. 2001. 32p. (J). (ps-5). 14.95 (978-1-885003-88-1(9)) Reed, Robert D. Pubs.

Fontenay, Charles L. Kipton & the Matter Transmitter, 18 vols. 1999. (Kipton Chronicles Ser.: Vol. 15). 190p. (YA). (gr. 6). 9.99 (978-0-88092-455-9(1)) Royal Fireworks Publishing Co.

Forde, Catherine. Firestarter. 2006. 160p. (J). pap. 8.99 (***978-1-4052-1056-0(7)***) Egmont Bks., Ltd. GBR. *Dist:* Independent Pubs. Group.

Foreman, Michael. Jack's Big Race. 1998. (Illus.). 29p. (J). 19.99 (978-0-86264-808-4(4)) Andersen GBR. *Dist:* Independent Pubs. Group.

—Norman's Ark. Foreman, Michael, illus. 2006. (Illus.). 32p. (J). pap. 6.95 (978-1-58925-401-5(5) , tiger tales) ME Media LLC.

Forgey, Winchester. Chronicle of the Bent Nail. 2004. (J). per. (978-0-9666572-7-2(6)) Acacia Publishing, Inc.

Foster, Bill. The Boy Who Wouldn't Comb His Hair. Kilgore, Jeannette Vrlin, illus. 2002. 32p. (J). (gr. k-6). 14.95 (978-1-931650-15-1(2)) Coastal Publishing Carolina, Inc.

Fox, Mem. Tough Boris. 2002. (Illus.). (J). 13.19 (978-0-7587-3850-9(1)) Book Wholesalers, Inc.

—Tough Boris. 1998. (J). (978-0-606-13859-8(5)) Tandem Library Bks.

Francomano, Alfred. Dilemma: Story of a Father & Two Sons. 1998. 64p. pap. 8.00 (978-0-8059-4431-0(1)) Dorrance Publishing Co., Inc.

French & Currey. In a Hole. (Illus.). 64p. pap. 7.99 (978-0-340-72667-9(9) , Hodder & Stoughton) Hodder General Publishing Division GBR. *Dist:* Trafalgar Square Publishing.

Fridman, Sashi. When I Fell into My Kiddush Cup. Kranz, Sarah, illus. 1999. 32p. (J). (ps-1). 12.95 (978-0-8266-0026-4(3)) Merkos L'Inyonei Chinuch.

Friedrich. 1999. (J). 9.95 (978-1-56137-658-2(2)) Novel Units, Inc.

Friel, Maeve. Charlie's Story. 2004. 112p. (YA). (gr. 7-9). pap. 5.95 (978-1-56145-315-3(3)) Peachtree Pubs., Ltd.

Friesen, Gayle. Men of stone. unabr. ed. 2002. (Gayle Friesen Ser.). (Illus.). 216p. (YA). (gr. 13 up). (978-1-55074-782-9(7)) Kids Can Pr., Ltd.

From Here to There: A Boy's Tale. 2000. 192p. (J). pap. 12.95 (978-0-9663666-4-8(6)) AAcorn Bks.

Fuqua, Jonathon Scott. King of the Pygmies. 2005. 256p. (YA). (gr. 7 up). 16.99 (978-0-7636-1418-8(1)) Candlewick Pr.

Furgang, Kathy. A Happy Summer Day. ed. 2003. (Early Connections Ser.). (J). pap. 33.00 (978-1-4108-1371-8(1)) Benchmark Education Co.

Gamble, Eugenia. Bennet. 1998. 80p. (J). (gr. 4-8). 10.95 (978-1-57895-065-2(1)) Bridge Resources.

Gangopadhyay, Narayan. 4 Heroes & the Haunted House. 1998. 114p. (J). pap. (978-81-86211-34-2(9)) Tara Publishing.

Gardner, Sally. Magical Kids: The Strongest Girl in the World & the Invisible Boy. 2007. (Illus.). 224p. (J). (gr. 2-5). 15.99 (978-0-8037-3158-5(2) , Dial) Penguin Group (USA) Inc.

Garis, Howard Roger. Buddy & His Winter Fun or a Boy in a Snow Camp. 2005. reprint ed. pap. 24.95 (978-1-4179-0679-6(0)) Kessinger Publishing, LLC.

Gauthier, Gilles. Edgar le Bizarre. 2001. (Roman Jeunesse Ser.). (FRE.). 96p. (YA). (gr. 4-7). pap. (978-2-89021-159-9(2)) Diffusion du livre Mirabel.

Geis, Patricia. Pequeno Bouyei. 2005. (Ninos y ninas del mundo Ser.). (SPA., Illus.). 32p. (J). 5.95 (978-84-7864-881-8(X)) Combel Editorial, S.A. ESP. *Dist:* Independent Pubs. Group.

Geissen, Steve. Willie & the World Wide Web. Kuon, Vuthy, illus. 1998. 40p. (J). (gr. 1-7). lib. bdg. 15.95 (978-0-9661974-0-2(2)) Three Leaves Publishing.

Geldart, Thomas. Emilie the Peacemaker. 2004. reprint ed. pap. 1.99 (978-1-4192-1769-2(0)) Kessinger Publishing, LLC.

Geller, Mark. Raymond. (SPA.). 94p. (YA). (gr. 5-8). (978-84-279-3215-9(4) , NG0896) Noguer y Caralt Editores, S. A. ESP. *Dist:* Lectorum Pubns., Inc.

Getting Rid of Harold. 80p. (YA). (gr. 6-12). pap. 10.95 (978-0-8224-3944-8(1)) Globe Fearon Educational Publishing.

Gibbons, Alan. Ganging Up. 2nd ed. 2006. (Illus.). 96p. (J). pap. 11.99 (***978-1-85881-194-9(5)***) Orion Publishing Group, Ltd. GBR. *Dist:* Independent Pubs. Group.

—Julie & Me: Treble Trouble. 2006. 176p. (J). pap. 11.99 (***978-1-84255-077-9(2)***) Orion Publishing Group, Ltd. GBR. *Dist:* Independent Pubs. Group.

—Julie & Me & Michael Owen Makes Three. 2006. 208p. (J). pap. 11.99 (***978-1-84255-048-9(9)***) Orion Publishing Group, Ltd. GBR. *Dist:* Independent Pubs. Group.

Gibbons, Gail. The Seasons of Arnold's Apple Tree. Gibbons, Gail, illus. 2002. (Illus.). (J). 13.83 (978-0-7587-3590-4(1)) Book Wholesalers, Inc.

Gilge-Barnes, Jeanette. City-Kid Farmer. 2000. 128p. (J). (gr. 5-7). pap. 4.95 (978-0-9679371-6-8(7)) WinePress Publishing.

Gill, Janie S. Billy's Biscuits. Wing, Lori, illus. 1999. (J). 5.95 (978-0-89868-486-5(2)); pap. 3.95 (978-0-89868-485-8(4)); lib. bdg. 10.95 (978-0-89868-484-1(6)) ARO Publishing Co.

—The Crooked Boy. 1999. 23p. (J). 5.95 (978-0-89868-495-7(1)); pap. 3.95 (978-0-89868-494-0(3)); lib. bdg. 10.95 (978-0-89868-493-3(5)) ARO Publishing Co.

—Jimmy McRay Was Different. Rogers, Gerald, illus. 1999. 23p. (J). 5.95 (978-0-89868-483-4(8)); pap. 3.95 (978-0-89868-482-7(X)); lib. bdg. 10.95 (978-0-89868-481-0(1)) ARO Publishing Co.

Gilliland, Hap. Flint's Rock. Livers-Lambert, Paulette, illus. 2001. (Council for Indian Education Ser.). 144p. (gr. 4 up). pap. 8.95 (978-1-879373-82-2(3)) Rinehart, Roberts Pubs.

Gillmor, Don. The Christmas Orange. ed. 2004. (Illus.). (J). (gr. k-3). spiral bd. (978-0-616-03035-6(5)) Canadian National Institute for the Blind/Institut National Canadien pour les Aveugles.

—The Christmas Orange. Gay, Marie-Louise, illus. 1999. 15p. (J). (gr. k-4). 16.95 (978-0-7737-3100-4(8)) Stoddart Kids CAN. *Dist:* Fitzhenry & Whiteside, Ltd.

Gillmor, Don & Gay, Marie-Louise. The Christmas Orange. 2003. (Illus.). 32p. pap. (978-1-55005-075-2(3)) Fitzhenry & Whiteside, Ltd.

The Gingerbread Boy. 2005. (J). (978-1-58453-306-1(4)) Pioneer Valley Educational Pr., Inc.

Gipson, Fred. Old Yeller. Date not set. 192p. (J). 20.95 (978-0-8488-2273-6(0)) Amereon LTD.

—Old Yeller. 2001. 132p. (J). (ps-7). lib. bdg. 16.45 (978-0-613-85744-4(5)) Tandem Library Bks.

—Old Yeller. 1999. (J). lib. bdg. 21.95 (978-1-56723-204-2(3)) Yestermorrow, Inc.

Gipson, Fred & Polson, Steven. Old Yeller. 2001. (Perennial Classics Ser.). (Illus.). 144p. (gr. 4-7). pap. 8.00 (978-0-06-093547-4(2)) HarperCollins Pubs.

Gipson, Frederick. Old Yeller. Burger, Carl, illus. 2002. 14.47 (978-0-7587-0299-9(X)) Book Wholesalers, Inc.

Gloliorte, John I. An Inuk Boy Becomes a Hunter. Gloliorte, John I., illus. 1999. (Illus.). 104p. (YA). (gr. 5-8). reprint ed. pap. 15.00 (978-0-7881-6562-7(3)) DIANE Publishing Co.

Golden Books Staff. Battle of the Benders. 2008. 24p. (J). (gr. k-5). pap. 5.99 (***978-0-375-84331-0(0)*** , Golden Bks.) Random Hse., Inc.

—Little Boy with a Big Horn. Yaccarino, Dan, illus. 2008. (Golden Classic Ser.). 48p. (J). (gr. k-k). lib. bdg. 17.99 (***978-0-375-93903-7(2)*** , Golden Bks.) Random Hse., Inc.

Golding, William. El Senor de las Moscas. (SPA.). 240p. (J). 10.95 (978-84-206-1381-9(9) , AZ9078); 2001. (Illus.). 249p. 11.95 (978-84-206-3411-1(5)) Alianza Editorial, S. A. ESP. *Dist:* AIMS International Bks., Inc., Lectorum Pubns., Inc., AIMS International Bks., Inc., Distribooks, Inc.

Goldman, Lisa Bear. Amadito & Spider Woman. Pena, Amado M., Jr., illus. 2003. 32p. (J). 15.95 (978-1-885772-30-5(0)) Kiva Publishing, Inc.

Goodridge, Jim. A Sterling Plan: The Yankees, the Durang. 2005. 156p. pap. 19.95 (978-1-4137-4088-2(X)) PublishAmerica, Inc.

Goscinny, René. Nicholas. Bell, Anthea, tr. from FRE. Sempé, Jean-Jacques, illus. 2005. 160p. 19.95 (978-0-7148-4482-4(9)) Phaidon Pr. GBR. *Dist:* Hachette Bk. Group.

—Petit Nicolas. Date not set. (FRE., Illus.). 80p. (J). pap. 46.50 (978-0-582-36071-6(4)) Addison-Wesley Longman, Ltd. GBR. *Dist:* Trans-Atlantic Pubns., Inc.

Gould, Marilyn. Xavier's Promise. 1998. 188p. (Orig.). (YA). (gr. 7-12). pap. 12.95 (978-0-9632305-6-0(5)) Allied Crafts Pr.

Gower, Catherine. Long-Long's New Year: A Story about the Chinese Spring Festival. Zhihong, He, illus. 2004. 32p. 16.95 (978-0-8048-3666-1(3)) Tuttle Publishing.

Grace, Roz. Why Is John Special? Srba, Lynne, illus. 1998. 22p. (J). (ps-6). pap. 6.95 (978-0-9659181-0-7(6)) BMF Pr.

Graham, William W., Jr. Breakfast with Sammy. VanLaar, Susan & Morris, MacKenzie, illus. 1998. 52p. (J). (gr. 1-3). 12.95 (978-1-892217-00-4(7)) Elert Pubns.

Gray, Libba Moore. Dear Willie Rudd. Fiore, Peter M., illus. 2000. 40p. (J). (gr. k-3). pap. 6.99 (978-0-689-83105-8(6) , Aladdin) Simon & Schuster Children's Publishing.

Greenburg, Dan. The Day Everything Tasted Like Broccoli. Swearingen, Greg, tr. Swearingen, Greg, illus. 2001. 86p. (J). pap. (978-0-439-33105-0(6)) Scholastic, Inc.

—Me & My Mummy. Davis, Jack E., illus. 2002. (Zack Files Ser.: No. 26). 64p. (J). pap. 4.99 (978-0-448-42633-4(1) , Grosset & Dunlap) Penguin Group (USA) Inc.

—Me & My Mummy. 2002. (gr. 3-6). lib. bdg. 13.00 (978-0-613-50079-1(2)) Tandem Library Bks.

—The Shluffmuffin Boy Is History. Fischer, Scott M., illus. 2006. (Secrets of Dripping Fang Ser.: Bk. 5). 176p. (J). 9.95 (978-0-15-206035-0(9)) Harcourt Children's Bks.

—Superhero... Or Super Thief? 2001. (Maximum Boy Ser.: No. 3). (Illus.). 96p. (J). (gr. 2-4). pap. 3.99 (978-0-439-21946-4(9) , Scholastic Paperbacks) Scholastic, Inc.

Greene, Stephanie. Owen Foote, Second Grade Strongman. DeRosa, Dee, illus. 2001. 96p. (J). (gr. 4-6). pap. 4.95 (978-0-618-13054-2(3) , Clarion Bks.) Houghton Mifflin Co. Trade & Reference Div.

Griek, Susan Vande & Gerber, Mary J. A Gift for Ampato. 1999. (Illus.). (J). (gr. 3-7). pap. (978-0-88899-359-5(5)) Groundwood Bks.

AB

Gutsche, Brigitte. To Be a Friend, Vol. 2. Dodge, Chris, illus. 2000. (Holt's Friends Ser.: No. 2). 116p. (J). (gr. 4-6). 9.99 (978-0-88092-515-0(9) , 5159) Royal Fireworks Publishing Co.

Hall, John. Where the Boys Are. 1998. (978-0-606-13911-3(7)) Tandem Library Bks.

Hall, Traci. Diary of a Bad Boy. 2007. (YA). 9.99 (978-1-932815-79-5(1) , Bronze Medallion) Medallion Pr., Inc.

Hall, Wesley. Cain McGee, Junior G-man: A Boy's Life in the River Bend. 2001. 287p. (J). pap. 15.95 (978-0-595-21275-0(1) , Writers Club Pr.) iUniverse, Inc.

Halpert, David. The Nexus Chronicles: In Search of Swallowtails. 2004. 330p. pap. 24.95 (978-1-4137-1605-4(9)) PublishAmerica, Inc.

Hamanaka, Sheila. Boys Will Be Boys. 2000. (J). (978-0-688-16548-2(6)); (978-0-688-16549-9(4)) HarperCollins Pubs.

Hamilton, Patricia Birdsong & Scripts Publishing Staff. What's Up: William Explains Ataxia to His New Friends. l.t. ed. 2005. (Ataxia: A Lifestyle Change). 44p. 18.95 (978-1-889826-90-5(1)) Scripts Publishing.

Hancock, H. Irving. The High School Boys' Canoe Club. rev. ed. 2006. 220p. 27.95 (978-1-4218-1753-8(5)); pap. 12.95 (978-1-4218-1853-5(1)) 1st World Publishing, Inc. (1st World Library - Literary Society).

—The High School Pitcher. rev. ed. 2006. 212p. 27.95 (978-1-4218-1743-9(8)); pap. 12.95 (978-1-4218-1843-6(4)) 1st World Publishing, Inc. (1st World Library - Literary Society).

Hannigan, Lynne. Sam's Passover. 2004. (Illus.). 32p. pap. 5.95 (978-0-7136-4084-7(7) , 93342) A & C Black GBR. *Dist:* Consortium Bk. Sales & Distribution.

Harcourt School Publishers Staff. El Camino a Casa On Level. 3rd ed. 2002. (Trofeos Ser.).Tr. of Road Home. (SPA.). pap. 6.80 (978-0-15-324082-9(2)) Harcourt Schl. Pubs.

—The Emperor & the Peasant Boy Below Level. 3rd ed. 2002. (Trophies Reading Program Ser.). (Illus.). pap. 5.10 (978-0-15-323238-1(2)) Harcourt Schl. Pubs.

—Food for Fun. 3rd ed. 2002. (Trophies English Language Learners Ser.). (Illus.). pap. 5.10 (978-0-15-327835-8(8)) Harcourt Schl. Pubs.

—He Sees Behind Trees Level D: Library Edition. 2001. (Collections Ser.). (Illus.). pap. 12.10 (978-0-15-314404-2(1)) Harcourt Schl. Pubs.

—The King of the Pumpkin Fair On Level. 3rd ed. 2002. (Trophies Reading Program Ser.). (Illus.). pap. 5.10 (978-0-15-323085-1(1)) Harcourt Schl. Pubs.

—The Legend of the Arctic Ice Advanced Level. 3rd ed. 2002. (Trophies Reading Program Ser.). (Illus.). pap. 5.10 (978-0-15-323378-4(8)) Harcourt Schl. Pubs.

—The Little School in the Valley: Take-Home Book. 2001. (Collections Ser.). (Illus.). (J). pap. 1.90 (978-0-15-319506-8(1)) Harcourt Schl. Pubs.

—The Little School in the Valley Below Level. 3rd ed. 2002. (Trophies Reading Program Ser.). (Illus.). pap. 5.10 (978-0-15-323244-2(7)) Harcourt Schl. Pubs.

—Look at Me: Take-Home Book. 1999. (Collections Ser.). (Illus.). (J). pap. 1.90 (978-0-15-317133-8(2)) Harcourt Schl. Pubs.

—Lost in a Sea of Grass Below Level. 3rd ed. 2002. (Trophies Reading Program Ser.). (Illus.). pap. 5.10 (978-0-15-323231-2(5)) Harcourt Schl. Pubs.

—A Mess in My Room: Take-Home Book. 1999. (Signatures Ser.). (Illus.). (J). pap. 1.70 (978-0-15-314558-2(7)) Harcourt Schl. Pubs.

—Mi Mayor Deseo: Take-Home Book. 2001. (Vamos Ser.). (SPA., Illus.). (J). pap. 2.80 (978-0-15-319928-8(8)) Harcourt Schl. Pubs.

—Sam. 1999. (Collections Ser.). (Illus.). (gr. 1). 6.40 (978-0-15-314981-8(7)) Harcourt Schl. Pubs.

—Sam: Take-Home Book. 1999. (Signatures Ser.). (Illus.). (J). pap. 1.70 (978-0-15-314555-1(2)) Harcourt Schl. Pubs.

Harms, John, II. The Saving of Sly Manatee. Belizar, Denise H., ed. Makowski, Robin Lee, illus. 2001. (J). 32p. lib. bdg. 18.95 (978-1-931329-02-6(8)); (gr. 2-7). pap. 6.95 (978-0-9653871-9-4(4)) Frederick Pr.

—The Saving of Valiant Blue Heron. Belizar, Denise H., ed. Makowski, Robin Lee, illus. 2001. 32p. (J). (gr. 2-7). pap. 6.95 (978-0-9653871-8-7(6)) Frederick Pr.

Harms, John, II & Nelson, Brian. The Saving of Arma Armadillo. 2001. (Illus.). (J). (gr. 2-7). pap. 6.95 (978-0-9653871-2-5(7)) Frederick Pr.

Hastings, Eileen. Rufus & Christopher Series, 3 vols., Set. (Illus.). (J). (gr. 2-4). pap. 23.82 incl. audio (978-0-87783-234-8(X)); lib. bdg. 29.95 (978-0-87783-168-6(8)); pap. 11.82 (978-0-87783-169-3(6)) Oddo Publishing, Inc.

Havill, Juanita. Eyes Like Willy's. Johnson, David, illus. 2004. 144p. (J). (gr. 3 up). lib. bdg. 16.89 (978-0-688-13673-4(7)) HarperCollins Pubs.

Hawes, Louise. Nelson Malone Meets the Man from Mush-Nut. 2001. (Illus.). 132p. (gr. 4-7). pap. 9.95 (978-0-595-15936-9(2) , Backinprint.com) iUniverse, Inc.

Hawkins, Colin. Max & the School Dinners. (Illus.). 28p. (J). pap. 9.95 (978-0-14-055591-2(9)) Penguin Bks., Ltd. GBR. *Dist:* Trafalgar Square Publishing.

Hecker, Howard. Mike McGill, Pirate. Falkey, Mark, illus. 2000. 240p. (YA). (gr. 6-11). pap. 5.99 (978-0-9676870-3-2(9)) Chesire Pr.

—Mike McGill, Wizard. Falkey, Mark, illus. 2000. 240p. (YA). (gr. 6-11). pap. 5.99 (978-0-9676870-2-5(0)) Chesire Pr.

Hedderwick, Mairi. Katie Morag & the Tiresome Ted. 1999. (Illus.). 32p. (J). (gr. 1-4). pap. 9.99 (978-0-09-911881-7(5)) Random Hse. GBR. *Dist:* Independent Pubs. Group.

Heide, Florence Parry. A Promise Is a Promise. Auth, Tony, illus. 2007. 40p. (J). (gr. k-4). 15.99 (978-0-7636-2285-5(0)) Candlewick Pr.

Heller, Andrew. Turn Your Heart On. Burgos, Javier Gonzalez, illus. 2005. (ENG.). 40p. (J). (ps-3). per. 23.00 (978-1-4208-1866-6(X)) AuthorHouse.

Henderson, Aileen Kilgore. Hard Times for Jake Smith. 2004. (Historical Fiction for Young Readers Ser.). 232p. pap. 6.95 (978-1-57131-649-3(3)) Milkweed Editions.

Hendry, Diana. Harvey Angell & the Ghost Child. 2002. (gr. 3-6). lib. bdg. 13.00 (978-0-613-57904-9(6)) Tandem Library Bks.

Hennessy, B. G. The Boy Who Cried Wolf. Kulikov, Boris, illus. 2006. 40p. (J). (ps-2). 15.95 (978-0-689-87433-8(2)) Simon & Schuster Children's Publishing.

Henry Huggins. 1999. (J). 9.95 (978-1-56137-601-8(9)) Novel Units, Inc.

Henry, Joanne L. Log Cabin in the Woods: A True Story about a Pioneer Boy. 2002. (Illus.). 60p. (J). 15.95 (978-1-57860-107-3(X)) Emmis Bks.

Henty, G. A. A Knight of the White Cross: A Tale of the Siege of Rhodes. Peacock, Ralph & Fitterling, Michael A., illus. 1999. 487p. (J). (gr. 4-7). reprint ed. per. 16.95 (978-1-890623-06-7(7)) Lost Classics Bk. Co.

—A Knight of the White Cross: A Tale of the Siege of Rhodes. Preston Speed Publications Staff, ed. Peacock, Ralph, illus. 1999. 336p. (YA). 21.99 (978-1-887159-24-1(X)) Preston-Speed Pubns.

Henty, G. A. & Fitterling, Michael A. For the Temple: A Tale of the Fall of Jerusalem. Fitterling, Michael A. & Solomon, Solomon J., illus. 1999. 403p. (J). (gr. 4-7). reprint ed. per. 16.95 (978-1-890623-07-4(5)) Lost Classics Bk. Co.

Hest, Amy. Cuando Jessie Cruzo el Oceano. Mlawer, Teresa, tr. from ENG. Lynch, P. J., illus. 1998. Tr. of When Jessie Came Across the Sea. (SPA.). 40p. (J). (gr. 3-5). lib. bdg. 16.95 (978-1-880507-46-9(3) , LC7834) Lectorum Pubns., Inc.

High, Linda Oatman. Barn Savers. Lewin, Ted, illus. 2003. 32p. (J). (gr. 2-4). 15.95 (978-1-56397-403-8(7)) Boyds Mills Pr.

Hill, Elizabeth Starr. Bird Boy. Liu, Lesley, illus. 2003. 64p. (J). pap. 5.95 (978-0-374-40659-2(6) , Sunburst) Farrar, Straus & Giroux.

Hilton, James. Goodbye, Mr. Chips. 2004. 144p. (J). (gr. 7-17). mass mkt. 5.99 (978-0-316-01013-9(8)) Little Brown & Co.

Hinton, S. E. The Outsiders 40th Anniversary Edition. 2007. 192p. (YA). (gr. 7 up). 17.99 (***978-0-670-06251-5(0)*** , Viking Juvenile) Penguin Group (USA) Inc.

Hitchcock, Alfred. Misterio de la Calavera Parlante. (Alfred Hitchcock y los Tres Investigadores Ser.). (SPA.). (YA). 8.95 (978-84-272-4911-0(X) , MO63) Molino, Editorial ESP. *Dist:* Continental Bk. Co., Inc.

—Misterio de la Cueva de los Lamentos. (Alfred Hitchcock y los Tres Investigadores Ser.). (SPA.). 160p. (YA). 8.95 (978-84-272-4910-3(1) , MO62) Molino, Editorial ESP. *Dist:* Continental Bk. Co., Inc.

—Misterio de la Montana del Monstruo. (Alfred Hitchcock y los Tres Investigadores Ser.). (SPA.). (YA). 8.95 (978-84-272-4920-2(9) , MO72) Molino, Editorial ESP. *Dist:* Continental Bk. Co., Inc.

—Misterio de Leon Mervioso. (Alfred Hitchcock y los Tres Investigadores Ser.). (SPA.). 192p. (YA). 8.95 (978-84-272-4916-5(0) , MO68) Molino, Editorial ESP. *Dist:* Continental Bk. Co., Inc.

—Misterio del Dragon. (Alfred Hitchcock y los Tres Investigadores Ser.). (SPA.). 176p. (YA). 8.95 (978-84-272-4914-1(4) , MO66) Molino, Editorial ESP. *Dist:* Continental Bk. Co., Inc.

—Misterio del Gato de Trapo. (Alfred Hitchcock y los Tres Investigadores Ser.). (SPA.). 152p. (YA). 8.95 (978-84-272-4913-4(6) , MO65) Molino, Editorial ESP. *Dist:* Continental Bk. Co., Inc.

—Misterio del Lago Fantasma. (Alfred Hitchcock y los Tres Investigadores Ser.). (SPA.). 173p. (YA). 8.95 (978-84-272-4919-6(5) , MO71) Molino, Editorial ESP. *Dist:* Continental Bk. Co., Inc.

—Misterio del Testamento Sorprendiente. (Alfred Hitchcock y los Tres Investigadores Ser.). (SPA.). (YA). 8.95 (978-84-272-4922-6(5) , MO74) Molino, Editorial ESP. *Dist:* Continental Bk. Co., Inc.

Hobbs, William. Down the Yukon. unabr. ed. 2004. (Middle Grade Cassette Librariestm Ser.). 208p. (J). (gr. 5-9). pap. 36.00 incl. audio (978-0-8072-0786-4(1) , S YA 310 SP, Listening Library) Random Hse. Audio Publishing Group.

Hockenberger, Henry. The Gold Case. 2006. (YA). pap. 15.95 (978-1-58736-584-3(7)) Wheatmark.

Hodge, Marie. Are You Sleepy yet, Petey? Graef, Renee, illus. 2005. 24p. (J). 12.95 (978-1-4027-1265-4(0) , 1241713) Sterling Publishing Co., Inc.

Hodson, Christopher. Lizo's Song: Chilomwe Version. Nkhoma, Wilson, tr. 1999. (Cambridge Reading Routes Ser.). (Illus.). 16p. pap. 3.70 (978-0-521-66854-5(9)) Cambridge Univ. Pr.

—Lizo's Song: Chitumbuka Version. Chirambo, Reuben, tr. 1999. (Cambridge Reading Routes Ser.). (Illus.). 16p. pap. 3.70 (978-0-521-66872-9(7)) Cambridge Univ. Pr.

—Lizo's Song: Chiyao Version. Mjaya, Ahmmardouh, tr. 1999. (Cambridge Reading Routes Ser.). (Illus.). 16p. pap. 3.70 (978-0-521-66865-1(4)) Cambridge Univ. Pr.

—Lizo's Song: Kiswahili Version. Kitunga, Demere, tr. 1999. (Cambridge Reading Routes Ser.). (Illus.). 16p. pap. 3.70 (978-0-521-66894-1(8)) Cambridge Univ. Pr.

Hofmeister, Alan, et al. I See Sam. (Reading for All Learners Ser.). (Illus.). (J). pap. (978-1-56861-073-3(4)) Swift Learning Resources.

—Sam. (Reading for All Learners Ser.). (Illus.). (J). pap. (978-1-56861-074-0(2)) Swift Learning Resources.

—Sam Sat. (Reading for All Learners Ser.). (Illus.). (J). pap. (978-1-56861-083-2(1)) Swift Learning Resources.

—See Sam. (Reading for All Learners Ser.). (Illus.). (J). pap. (978-1-56861-075-7(0)) Swift Learning Resources.

—Sis. (Reading for All Learners Ser.). (Illus.). (J). pap. (978-1-56861-082-5(3)) Swift Learning Resources.

Holland, Robert. Harry the Hook. 2001. (Books for boys & young men). 240p. (YA). pap. (978-0-9658523-7-1(7)) Frost Hollow Pubs., LLC.

—Mad Max Murphy. 2001. (Books for boys & Young men). 188p. (YA). pap. 10.95 (978-0-9658523-8-8(5)) Frost Hollow Pubs., LLC.

Holm, Anne S. I Am David. l.t. ed. 2000. 208p. (J). pap. (978-0-7540-6121-2(3) , CLP 316) BBC Audio.

Hood, Susan. Pup & Hound Stay up Late. Hendry, Linda, illus. 2005. 32p. (J). (ps-ps). lib. bdg. 11.15 (978-0-606-33687-1(7)) Tandem Library Bks.

Hopkinson, Deborah. Adventure in Gold Town. Farnsworth, Bill, illus. ed. 2005. 84p. (J). lib. bdg. 15.00 (978-1-59054-895-0(7)) Fitzgerald Bks.

Horgan, Dorothy. Charlie's Eye Pops Out All over the Place. (Illus.). 128p. (J). pap. 7.95 (978-0-14-038237-2(2)) Penguin Group (USA) Inc.

Hudson, Wade. Anthony's Big Surprise Vol. 3: Neate. 1998. (Illus.). 90p. (J). (gr. 3-7). pap. 3.95 (978-0-940975-73-6(4) , Sankofa Bks.) Just Us Bks., Inc.

Hughes, Shirley. Alfie & the Big Boys. 2008. (Illus.). 32p. (J). 17.95 (***978-0-370-32884-3(1)***) Transworld Publishers Ltd. GBR. *Dist:* Independent Pubs. Group.

—Alfie Gets in First. 2007. (Illus.). 32p. (J). pap. 8.95 (***978-0-09-925605-2(3)*** , Red Fox) Random Hse. Children's Bks. GBR. *Dist:* Independent Pubs. Group.

—Alfie Gives a Hand. 2007. (Illus.). 32p. (J). pap. 8.95 (***978-0-09-925607-6(X)*** , Red Fox) Random Hse. Children's Bks. GBR. *Dist:* Independent Pubs. Group.

—Alfie's Feet. 2007. (Illus.). 32p. (J). pap. 8.95 (***978-0-09-925606-9(1)*** , Red Fox) Random Hse. Children's Bks. GBR. *Dist:* Independent Pubs. Group.

Hulme, Lucy V. Passages, 1 bk. Redpath, Dale, illus. 2005. 40p. (J). 7.95 (978-0-9769854-0-2(3) , 001) Combs-Hulme Publishing.

Hurwitz, Johanna. Even Stephen. 1998. (Illus.). 128p. (YA). (gr. 5-9). reprint ed. pap. 4.95 (978-0-688-16362-4(9)) HarperCollins Pubs.

—Russell Rides Again. 1999. (Beech Tree Chapter Bks.). (Illus.). (J). (978-0-606-21760-6(6)) Tandem Library Bks.

—Russell Sprouts. Tilley, Debbie, illus. 2001. (Riverside Kids Ser.). 96p. (J). pap. 4.99 (978-0-06-442144-7(9) , Harper Trophy) HarperCollins Pubs.

—Russell Sprouts. 1999. (Beech Tree Chapter Bks.). (Illus.). 80p. (gr. k-4). mass mkt. 4.95 (978-0-688-16667-0(9)) HarperCollins Pubs.

—Russell Sprouts. 2001. (gr. 3-6). lib. bdg. 12.10 (978-0-613-43875-9(2)); (Illus.). (J). (978-0-606-22037-8(2)) Tandem Library Bks.

Hutchens, Paul. The Bull Fighter. 1998. (gr. 3-6). lib. bdg. 13.00 (978-0-613-90324-0(2)) Tandem Library Bks.

Hutchins, Hazel J. The Three & Many Wishes of Jason Reid. Richmond, John & Dannenberg, Thomas, illus. rev. ed. 2000. 80p. (J). (gr. 3-7). 18.95 (978-1-55037-653-1(5)); pap. 6.95 (978-1-55037-652-4(7)) Annick Pr., Ltd. CAN. *Dist:* Firefly Bks., Ltd.

Hutchins, Pat. Happy Birthday, Sam. Hutchins, Pat, illus. 2005. (Illus.). (J). (gr. k-3). pap. 16.95 incl. audio (978-0-87499-287-8(7)) BBC Audiobooks America.

Hyde, Catherine Ryan. Pay It Forward. 2000. (gr. 7-12). lib. bdg. 16.45 (978-0-613-33844-8(8)) Tandem Library Bks.

I Don't Believe It!, 6 Packs. (gr. k-1). 23.00 (978-0-7635-9056-7(8)) Rigby Education.

I Never Want to go There Again. 2007. per. (***978-1-59916-217-1(2)***) Printing Systems.

Ilka, Benjamin Alexander. A Boy & His Shadow. Ilka, Benjamin Alexander, illus. (YA). Pt. 1. 2005. per. 4.95 net. (978-0-9779504-0-9(9)); Pt. 2. 2006. 3.95 net. (978-0-9779504-1-6(7)) Hogan Publishing LLC.

I'll Run Away: Individual Title Six-Packs. (ps-2). 23.00 (978-0-7635-8793-2(1)) Rigby Education.

Ingelow, Jean. Mopsa the Fairy. 2004. reprint ed. pap. 19.95 (978-1-4191-3510-1(4)); pap. 1.99 (978-1-4192-3510-8(9)) Kessinger Publishing, LLC.

Inkpen, Mick & Butterworth, Nick. Just Like Jasper. (Illus.). 32p. (J). pap. 11.95 (978-0-340-52582-1(7) , Hodder & Stoughton) Hodder General Publishing Division GBR. *Dist:* Trafalgar Square Publishing.

Irwin, Esther. White Cloud: A Little Boy's Dream. Puett, Gayle, ed. Roberson, Ron, illus. 2006. 61p. (J). spiral bd. 10.00 (978-0-9778462-0-7(X)) Irwin, Esther L.

Itabashi, Masahiro. Boys Be..., 20 vols., Vol. 1. Tamakoshi, Hiroyuki, illus. 2004. (Graphic Novel-Manga Ser.). 216p. (gr. 7 up). pap. 9.99 (978-1-59532-099-5(7) , Tokyopop Adult) TOKYOPOP, Inc.

Italia, John. The Birds of the Harbor. 2007. 32p. 15.95 (***978-0-9726614-7-8(6)***) Shenanigan Bks.

Jacques, Brian. Castaways of the Flying Dutchman. (Castaways of the Flying Dutchman Ser.: No. 1). 2002. (gr. 3-6). lib. bdg. 15.30 (978-0-613-72303-9(1)); 2001. (gr. 5-8). lib. bdg. 16.45 (978-0-613-62934-8(5)) Tandem Library Bks.

James, Leah. Always after It Rains. 2002. 170p. (YA). pap. 12.95 (978-0-595-23611-4(1) , Writer's Showcase Pr.) iUniverse, Inc.

James, Simon. Leon & Bob. James, Simon, illus. 2006. 32p. (J). (ps-3). pap. 6.99 (978-0-7636-2686-0(4)) Candlewick Pr.

Jantti, Mariana. Christopher Has a Dream. 2006. (Illus.). 28p. (J). 12.95 (978-9974-7960-0-3(8)) Hardenville SA URY. *Dist:* Independent Pubs. Group.

Jarrell, Pamela R. Jennifer & Danny. Linke, Don, Jr., illus. l.t. ed. 1999. (Cuddle Bks.). 7p. (J). (ps-k). pap. 10.95 (978-1-57332-124-2(9)) HighReach Learning, Inc.

Jarvis, Martin & Crompton, Richmal. William's Birthday & Other Stories. Ross, Tony, illus. 2003. 82p. (J). pap. 8.99 (978-0-330-39097-2(X) , Pan) Pan Macmillan GBR. *Dist:* Trafalgar Square Publishing.

—William's Haunted House & Other Stories, Vol. 5. Ross, Tony, illus. 2003. (Meet Just William Ser.). 76p. (J). pap. 8.99 (978-0-330-39101-6(1) , Pan) Pan Macmillan GBR. *Dist:* Trafalgar Square Publishing.

Jarvis, Robin & Jarvis, Robert M. The Alchemist's Cat. 2004. 320p. (YA). 17.95 (978-1-58717-257-1(7) , Sea-Star Bks.) Chronicle Bks. LLC.

Jeans, Peter. Stoker's Bay. 2003. (Illus.). 240p. (YA). pap. 13.50 (978-1-876268-97-8(2)) Univ. of Western Australia Pr. AUS. *Dist:* International Specialized Bk. Services.

Jeffers, Stewart. The Collapse of the Crew. 2005. 111p. pap. 16.95 (978-1-4137-8714-6(2)) PublishAmerica, Inc.

Jennings, Linda. Tom's Tail. Warnes, Tim, tr. Warnes, Tim, illus. 2003. 32p. (J). pap. 6.95 (978-1-58925-383-4(3) , tiger tales) ME Media LLC.

—Tom's Tail. 2003. (ps-2). lib. bdg. 15.25 (978-0-613-82625-9(6)) Tandem Library Bks.

Jennings, Sharon. Sleep Tight, Mrs. Ming. ed. 2004. (Illus.). (J). (ps-3). spiral bd. (978-0-616-01683-1(2)) Canadian National Institute for the Blind/Institut National Canadien pour les Aveugles.

Johnson, Angela. Bird. 2006. 144p. (YA). (gr. 5). reprint ed. pap. 5.99 (978-0-14-240544-4(2) , Puffin) Penguin Group (USA) Inc.

Johnson, Barbara. The Tasty Taffy Tale & Super-Stretching the Truth: A Book about Honesty. Frazier, Victoria Ponikvar, illus. 1999. (Geranium Lady Ser.: Vol. 4). 32p. (J). (ps-2). 4.97 (978-0-8499-5951-6(9)) Nelson, Thomas Inc.

Johnston, William. Limpy. 2003. 356p. pap. 34.95 (978-1-932080-47-6(3)) Ross & Perry, Inc.

Jones, Shelley Lynn. The Story of Corey & Alice. 2005. (J). pap. 8.00 (978-0-8059-6846-0(6)) Dorrance Publishing Co., Inc.

Joseph: Velvet Pack. 2000. (J). pap. 9.49 (978-0-06-449201-0(X) , Harper Trophy) HarperCollins Pubs.

Joyce, William. Billy's Booger. Date not set. 32p. (J). (ps-3). pap. 14.99 (978-0-06-027111-4(6)); lib. bdg. 15.89 (978-0-06-027112-1(4)) HarperCollins Pubs.

—Life with Bob. 1998. (Illus.). 24p. (J). (ps-k). 6.95 (978-0-694-01181-0(9)) HarperCollins Pubs.

Kaczmarczyk, Kyle J. The Misadventures of Silent Boy - Volume II: the Stupid Strikes Back. 2005. 52p. (YA). pap. 17.99 (978-1-4116-5231-6(2)) Lulu.com.

Kamens, Gerald. Leopold & Clinton. 2007. 44p. (J). pap. 8.99 (978-1-59092-395-5(2) , Little Blue Works) Windstorm Creative.

Karen & Kary. Little Wizard. 2004. 21p. pap. 14.95 (978-1-4137-2956-6(8)) PublishAmerica, Inc.

Katula, Bob. Larryboy y el Atroz Ataque de los Tapones de Cerilla Afonica. 2003. Tr. of Larryboy & the Awful Earwax Attacks. (SPA.). 94p. (J). pap. 4.99 (978-0-8297-3749-3(9)) Vida Pubs.

Katz, T. Miss L'eau. 2007. 44p. (YA). pap. 14.99 (978-1-59092-404-4(5) , Blue Works) Windstorm Creative.

Katz, Welwyn W. Time Ghost. 2002. (Illus.). (J). (gr. 4-7). pap. (978-0-88899-275-8(0)) Groundwood Bks.

—Time Ghost. 2002. 172p. (J). (gr. 4-7). 16.95 (978-0-88899-216-1(5) , Libros Tigrillo) Groundwood Bks. CAN. *Dist:* Perseus Distribution.

—Time Ghost. 2002. (gr. 3-6). lib. bdg. 15.25 (978-0-613-88591-1(0)) Tandem Library Bks.

—Witchery Hill. 2003. (J). pap. 6.95 (978-0-88899-245-1(9)) Groundwood Bks. CAN. *Dist:* Transition Vendor.

Keats, Ezra Jack. Pet Show! 2001. (978-0-606-22504-5(8)) Tandem Library Bks.

—La Silla de Pedro. Keats, Ezra Jack, illus. 1999. (Penguin Ediciones Ser.). (SPA., Illus.). 40p. (J). (ps-3). pap. 6.99 (978-0-14-056654-3(6) , Puffin) Penguin Group (USA) Inc.

Keen, Karl D. They Call Me Chief. 2004. (YA). per. 10.95 (978-0-9742791-3-8(7)) Litho Tech, LLC.

Kelly, Jack. Keoni's Dream. 1999. (J). 17.95 (978-0-9662777-1-5(6)) Pleiades Publishing.

Kenny A Portrait of a Prodigy. 2004. per. (978-1-59581-010-6(2)) Brentwood Communications Group.

Kerrin, Jessica Scott. Martin Bridge: On the Lookout! Kelly, Joseph, illus. 2005. 144p. (J). (978-1-55337-689-7(7)) Kids Can Pr., Ltd.

Keselman, Porter Gabr. Ponete Los Zapatos. (SPA.). pap. 7.95 (978-950-07-2021-2(3)) Editorial Sudamericana S.A. ARG. *Dist:* Distribooks, Inc.

King-Smith, Dick. Mixed-Up Max. 1998. (978-0-606-13613-6(4)) Tandem Library Bks.

Kingsley, Kaza. Erec Rex: The Dragon's Eye. Payne, John, ed. Grant, Melvyn, illus. 2006. 360p. (J). 17.99 (978-0-9786555-6-3(7)) Firelight Press, Inc.

Kirk, Daniel. Moondogs. 1999. (Illus.). 1p. (J). (ps-3). 16.99 (978-0-399-23128-5(5) , Putnam Juvenile) Penguin Group (USA) Inc.

Kirkpatrick, Taylor. Worthwhile. Lynch, Jason, illus. 2003. 32p. (J). 15.95 (978-0-9725420-5-0(0)) Chapman Pr., LLC.

Kishimoto, Seishi. O-Parts Hunter. 2007. (O-Parts Hunter Ser.). 200p. (YA). Vol. 2. pap. 9.99 (978-1-4215-0856-6(7)); Vol. 3. pap. 9.99 (978-1-4215-0857-3(5)) Viz Media.

Klein-Higger, Joni. Ten Tzedakah Pennies. Leff, Tova, illus. 2005. 30p. (J). 10.95 (978-1-929628-19-3(6)) Hachai Publishing.

Kline, Suzy. Herbie Jones. 2002. (Herbie Jones Ser.). (Illus.). 96p. (J). pap. 4.99 (978-0-698-11939-0(8) , Putnam Juvenile) Penguin Group (USA) Inc.

—Herbie Jones. 96p. (J). (gr. 3-4). pap. 3.99 (978-0-8072-1269-1(5) , Listening Library) Random Hse. Audio Publishing Group.

—Herbie Jones. 2002. (gr. 3-6). lib. bdg. 13.00 (978-0-613-73419-6(X)) Tandem Library Bks.

—Herbie Jones & Hamburger Head. Williams, Richard, illus. 2002. (Herbie Jones Ser.). 112p. (J). pap. 4.99 (978-0-698-11940-6(1) , Putnam Juvenile) Penguin Group (USA) Inc.

—Herbie Jones & Hamburger Head. 2002. (gr. 3-6). lib. bdg. 13.00 (978-0-613-73470-7(X)) Tandem Library Bks.

—Herbie Jones & the Class Gift. Williams, Richard, illus. 2002. (Herbie Jones Ser.). 96p. (J). pap. 4.99 (978-0-698-11941-3(X) , Putnam Juvenile) Penguin Group (USA) Inc.

—Horrible Harry & the Green Slime. Remkiewicz, Frank, illus. 1998. (Horrible Harry Ser.: No. 3). 64p. (gr. 2-4). pap. 3.99 (978-0-14-038970-8(9) , Puffin) Penguin Group (USA) Inc.

—What's the Matter with Herbie Jones? Williams, Richard, illus. 2002. (Herbie Jones Ser.). 112p. (J). pap. 4.99 (978-0-698-11942-0(8) , Putnam Juvenile) Penguin Group (USA) Inc.

—What's the Matter with Herbie Jones? 2002. (gr. 3-6). lib. bdg. 13.00 (978-0-613-73476-9(9)) Tandem Library Bks.

Kline, Suzy & Kline, Suzy. Herbie Jones & the Class Gift. 2002. (Illus.). 95p. (J). (gr. 4-7). lib. bdg. 13.00 (978-0-613-62518-0(8)) Tandem Library Bks.

Korman, Gordon. Maxx Comedy: The Funniest Kid in America. 2003. (Illus.). 160p. (gr. 3-7). 15.99 (978-0-7868-0746-8(6)) Hyperion Bks. for Children.

Krasilovsky, Phyllis. Benny's Flag. Fowler, Jim, illus. 2002. 32p. (gr. k-3). 15.95 (978-1-57098-289-7(9)) ; pap. 8.95 (978-1-57098-320-7(8)) Rinehart, Roberts Pubs.

Krauss, Ruth. The Growing Story. Oxenbury, Helen, illus. 2000. 40p. (J). (ps-3). 16.99 (978-0-06-024716-4(9)); lib. bdg. 17.89 (978-0-06-024717-1(7)) HarperCollins Pubs.

Kravetz, Nathan. Moscow, Farewell! A Russian Boy's Adventure in Times Past. 2000. (gr. 7-12). lib. bdg. 31.55 (978-0-613-73907-8(8)) Tandem Library Bks.

Krensky, Stephen. Locked in the Library! Krensky, Stephen, illus. 1998. (Arthur Chapter Bks.: Bk. 6). (Illus.). 64p. (J). (gr. 2-4). pap. 4.25 (978-0-316-11558-2(4)) Little, Brown Bks. for Young Readers.

—Locked in the Library! unabr. ed. 1998. (Arthur Chapter Bks.: Bk. 6). 58p. (J). (gr. 2-4). pap. 17.00 incl. audio (978-0-8072-0388-0(2) , FTR192SP, Listening Library) Random Hse. Audio Publishing Group.

Kroeger, Mary Kay & Borden, Louise W. Paperboy. Lewin, Ted, illus. 2001. 40p. (J). (gr. k-3). pap. 6.95 (978-0-618-11142-8(5) , Clarion Bks.) Houghton Mifflin Co. Trade & Reference Div.

Kropf, Latifa Berry. Happy Birthday, World: A Rosh Hashanah Celebration. Carlson, Lisa, illus. 2005. 12p. (J). (gr. 1 up). per. 5.95 (978-0-929371-32-0(1)) Kar-Ben Publishing.

Krulik, Nancy E. Doug Makes the Team. 1999. (Doug Ser.). (Illus.). 32p. (J). (gr. k-4). 8.99 (978-0-7868-3193-7(6)) Disney Pr.

Kytle, Calvin. Like a Tree. 2007. 430p. 28.95 ***(978-1-58838-220-7(6)*** , NewSouth Bks.) NewSouth, Inc.

Lagerlof, Selma. The Wonderful Adventures of Nils: And, the Further Adventures of Nils, 2 bks. in 1. 2000. 420p. (YA). (gr. 5 up). reprint ed. pap. 16.95 (978-1-57216-036-1(5)) Penfield Pr.

Laminack, Lester L. Trevor's Wiggly-Wobbly Tooth. McCord, Kathi Garry, illus. 2002. 32p. (J). pap. 7.95 (978-1-56145-279-8(3)) Peachtree Pubs., Ltd.

—Trevor's Wiggly-Wobbly Tooth. McCord, Kathi G., illus. 1998. 32p. (J). (ps-2). 15.95 (978-1-56145-175-3(4)) Peachtree Pubs., Ltd.

Landowne, Youme. Selavi, That Is Life: A Haitian Story of Hope. 2005. (Illus.). 40p. (ps-7). pap. 8.95 (978-0-938317-95-1(4)) Cinco Puntos Pr.

Lang, George. Pixy's Holiday Journey. 2006. 33.99 ***(*978-1-4280-4243-8(1)***); pap. 26.99 ***(*978-1-4280-4261-2(X))*** IndyPublish.com.

Langworthy, John Luther. The Aeroplane Boys Flight. 2004. reprint ed. pap. 1.99 (978-1-4192-5169-6(4)) Kessinger Publishing, LLC.

Larichev, Andrei Borisovich. The Boy Who was President. Moresco, Jamie, ed. Roberts, Marilyn, illus. 2004. 24p. (J). 9.95 (978-0-9724386-0-5(2) , 2002096236) BlueSky Publishing.

Lawhead, Stephen R. The Tale of Jeremy Vole. 2003. (Riverbank Stories Ser.: Bk. 1). (Illus.). 112p. pap. 7.50 (978-0-7459-4675-7(5) , Lion) Lion Hudson plc GBR. *Dist:* Trafalgar Square Publishing.

—The Tale of Timothy Mallard. l.t. ed. 2005. (J). pap. (978-0-7540-7932-3(5) , CLP 486) BBC Audio.

—The Tale of Timothy Mallard. 2003. (Illus.). 112p. pap. 7.50 (978-0-7459-4676-4(3) , Lion) Lion Hudson plc GBR. *Dist:* Trafalgar Square Publishing.

Lawston, Lisa & Sams, B. B. A Pair of Red Sneakers. 1998. (Illus.). 32p. (J). (ps-3). 16.99 (978-0-531-33104-0(0) , Orchard Bks.) Scholastic, Inc.

Le Fanu, J. Sheridan. Madam Crowl's Ghost & the Dead Sexton. 2004. reprint ed. pap. 15.95 (978-1-4191-3188-2(5)); pap. 1.99 (978-1-4192-3188-9(X)) Kessinger Publishing, LLC.

Le Moult, Dolph. Running Horsemen. 2004. 272p. (YA). pap. (978-0-9746481-0-1(8)) Brown Barn Bks.

Lee, Marie G. Necessary Roughness. 1998. 240p. (J). (gr. 7 up). pap. 6.50 (978-0-06-447169-5(1) , Harper Trophy) HarperCollins Pubs.

—Necessary Roughness. 1998. (J). (978-0-606-13000-4(4)) Tandem Library Bks.

Leeson, Robert. Tom's Private War. (Illus.). 96p. (J). 7.95 (978-0-14-038427-7(8)) Penguin Bks., Ltd. GBR. *Dist:* Trafalgar Square Publishing.

Lenam, Salva. Buenas Noches, Kiko! Roman, Santi, illus. 2005. (Kiko Ser.). (SPA.). 10p. (J). 3.95 (978-84-95761-74-3(2)) Ediciones Norte, Inc.

—Hoy Empieza la Escuela, Kiko! Roman, Santi, illus. 2005. (Kiko Ser.). (SPA.). 10p. (J). 3.95 (978-84-95761-76-7(9)) Ediciones Norte, Inc.

—Kiko Dibuja y Pinta. Roman, Santi, illus. 2005. (Kiko Ser.). (SPA.). 10p. (J). 3.95 (978-84-95761-78-1(5)) Ediciones Norte, Inc.

—Kiko en Casa de los Abuelos. Roman, Santi, illus. 2005. (Kiko Ser.). (SPA.). 10p. (J). 3.95 (978-84-95761-81-1(5)) Ediciones Norte, Inc.

—Kiko Juega con Sus Amigos. Roman, Santi, illus. 2005. (Kiko Ser.). (SPA.). 10p. (J). 3.95 (978-84-95761-79-8(3)) Ediciones Norte, Inc.

—A Kiko le Gusta la Playa. Roman, Santi, illus. 2005. (Kiko Ser.). (SPA.). 10p. (J). 3.95 (978-84-95761-75-0(0)) Ediciones Norte, Inc.

—Kiko No Quiere Comer. Roman, Santi, illus. 2005. (Kiko Ser.). (SPA.). 10p. (J). 3.95 (978-84-95761-77-4(7)) Ediciones Norte, Inc.

—Kiko Ya Se Viste Solo. Roman, Santi, illus. 2005. (Kiko Ser.). (SPA.). 10p. (J). 3.95 (978-84-95761-80-4(7)) Ediciones Norte, Inc.

Let's Pretend: Individual Title Six-Packs. (ps-2). 23.00 (978-0-7635-9001-7(0)) Rigby Education.

Levithan, David. 101 Ways to Get Away with Anything! 2002. (Malcolm in the Middle Ser.). (Illus.). 96p. (J). (gr. 3-7). pap. 4.50 (978-0-439-35132-4(4)) Scholastic, Inc.

Lewandowski, Frrich. Babci's Angel. Delisle, Kathryn H., illus. 1998. 20p. (J). (gr. 2-3). 9.50 (978-0-9646439-5-6(2)) Ambassador Bks., Inc.

—Shooting Stardust. Delisle, Kathryn H., illus. 1998. 20p. (J). (gr. 2-3). 9.50 (978-0-9646439-4-9(4)) Ambassador Bks., Inc.

Lewis, C. S. The Horse & His Boy. Baynes, Pauline, illus. 2006. (Narnia Ser.). 240p. (J). 11.99 (978-0-06-112524-9(5)) HarperCollins Pubs.

Lewis, Robert. Try Again, Trevor. 1998. (Illus.). 30p. (J). pap. 9.99 (978-0-09-946171-5(4)) Random Hse. GBR. *Dist:* Trafalgar Square Publishing.

Linz, Kathryn. Jim Brandon's Adventures. 2006. (ENG.). 100p. per. 14.95 ***(*978-1-4241-3160-0(X))*** PublishAmerica, Inc.

The Little Dutch Boy: 6 Small Books. (gr. k-2). 23.00 (978-0-7635-8509-9(2)) Rigby Education.

The Little Dutch Boy: Big Book. (gr. k-2). 26.00 (978-0-7635-2427-2(1)) Rigby Education.

The Little House. 2004. pap. 14.95 incl. audio (978-1-56008-061-9(2)) Weston Woods Studios, Inc.

Little, Jean. Emma's Yucky Brother. Plecas, Jennifer, illus. 2002. (I Can Read Bks.). 64p. (J). pap. 3.99 (978-0-06-444258-9(6)) HarperCollins Pubs.

Living Books, Inc. Staff. Arthur Adventures Library. 1998. (J). cd-rom 119.95 net. (978-1-57404-434-8(6)) Broderbund Software, Inc.

LoGuidice, Mike. Open up & Say Aggh! 2005. (J). pap. 16.00 (978-0-8059-7037-1(1)) Dorrance Publishing Co., Inc.

Lord of the Flies. 1998. 40p. (YA). 11.95 (978-1-56137-384-0(2) , NU3842SP) Novel Units, Inc.

Los zapatos de Mari: Individual Title Six-Packs. (Coleccion Pm Ser.: Vol. 2). Tr. of Sally's new shoes. (SPA.). 16p. (gr. k-1). 26.00 (978-0-7578-0682-7(1)) Rigby Education.

Lujan, Jorge Elias. Sky Blue Accident/Accidente Celeste. Amado, Elisa, tr. Grobler, Piet, illus. 2007. (ENG & SPA.). 32p. (J). (gr. k-2). 17.95 (978-0-88899-805-7(8)) Groundwood Bks. CAN. *Dist:* Perseus Distribution.

Lynch, Chris. Wolf Gang, 5. 1998. (He-Man Women Haters Club Ser.). (J). (978-0-606-12964-0(2)) Tandem Library Bks.

Lyon, Steve. The Gift Moves. 2006. 240p. (YA). (gr. 7). mass mkt. 6.50 (978-0-553-49494-5(5) , Laurel Leaf) Random Hse. Children's Bks.

Mabee, Andrea. Dory Glory: Building A Boat from Stem to Stern. Mabee, Andrea, photos by. 2005. (Illus.). 67p. (YA). per. 15.95 (978-0-9630074-1-4(6)) Bass Cove Bks.

MacDonald, George. At the Back of the North Wind. 1998. (Twelve-Point Ser.). 280p. reprint ed. lib. bdg. 25.00 (978-1-58287-015-1(2)) North Bks.

MacDonald, George. The Golden Key. 2006. pap. ***(*978-1-4250-0937-3(9))*** Assistedreadingbooks.com Inc.

Machover, Alexandra. The Little Brave Son. 2001. (Illus.). (J). (gr. k-2). 10.95 (978-0-533-13474-8(9)) Vantage Pr., Inc.

Mackinnon, Bernard. The Boy Who Turned Green. 2005. 119p. pap. 16.95 (978-1-4137-7262-3(5)) PublishAmerica, Inc.

MacLachlan, Patricia. Caleb's Story. (Sarah, Plain & Tall Ser.). 128p. (J). 2002. (gr. 5 up). pap. 5.99 (978-0-06-440590-4(7)); 2001. (gr. 3-5). 16.99 (978-0-06-023605-2(1) , Cotler, Joanna Books) HarperCollins Pubs.

—Caleb's Story. 2002. (gr. k-3). lib. bdg. 13.00 (978-0-613-53342-3(9)) Tandem Library Bks.

MacMullen, Grace Rice. A Reward for Jerry. 2000. 96p. (J). (gr. 3-7). pap. 2.95 (978-0-87398-707-3(1)) Sword of the Lord Pubs.

Madison, Ron. Ned & the Gift of Life: A Lesson about Blood. Cololo, David, illus. l.t. ed. 2000. (Health & Safety Ser.). 20p. (ps-4). 4.95 (978-1-887206-22-8(1)) Ned's Head Productions.

Mahy, Margaret. El Muchacho Que Inventaba Historias y Otro Cuentos. (Torre de Papel Ser.). (SPA.). (YA). (gr. 6 up). 8.95 (978-958-04-4521-0(4)) Norma S.A. COL. *Dist:* Distribuidora Norma, Inc.

Makinson, Robert. Horace Morris II. Makinson, Robert, ed. Paduano, Joseph, illus. 2000. 17p. (J). (ps-5). spiral bd. 6.00 (978-0-9654228-7-1(9)) Makinson, R. B.

Manning, Brennan. The Boy Who Cried Abba: A Parable of Trust & Acceptance. 2001. 85p. (J). pap. 13.95 (978-1-879290-19-8(7) , PageMill Pr.) Council Oak Bks.

Mariconda, Barbara. Sleepy Ted. 2001. 32p. (J). 14.99 (978-0-7868-0496-2(3)) Hyperion Bks. for Children.

Marks, Graham. How It Works: Everyone Gets the Angel They Deserve. 224p. (J). pap. 12.99 (978-0-7475-7015-8(9)) Bloomsbury Publishing Plc GBR. *Dist:* Trafalgar Square Publishing.

Marrell, Mar'ce. Ben & the Carrot Predicament. (Illus.). 48p. (J). pap. 4.95 (978-1-895836-54-7(9)) River Bks. CAN. *Dist:* Coteau Bks.

Marsh, Carole. The Case of the Crybaby Cowboy. 2006. 64p. (gr. 1-3). 14.95 ***(*978-0-635-06199-7(6))*** Gallopade International.

—Mystery of Blackbeard the Pirate. 2003. (gr. 5-8). lib. bdg. 14.10 (978-0-613-73037-2(2)) Tandem Library Bks.

—Mystery of the Alamo Ghost. 2003. (gr. 3-6). lib. bdg. 14.10 (978-0-613-73038-9(0)) Tandem Library Bks.

Martinez, Victor. Parrot in the Oven: Mi Vida. Scott, Steve, illus. rev. ed. 1998. 240p. (J). (gr. 7 up). pap. 5.99 (978-0-06-447186-2(1) , Harper Trophy) HarperCollins Pubs.

Mason, Tom & Danko, Dan. Malcolm for President!, No. 5. 2001. 112p. (J). (gr. 3-7). pap. 4.99 (978-0-439-23080-3(2)) Scholastic, Inc.

Massie, Elizabeth. Son of Liberty: 1776. 2000. (gr. 5-8). lib. bdg. 13.00 (978-0-613-28077-8(6)) Tandem Library Bks.

—1609: Winter of the Dead: A Novel of the Founding of Jamestown. 2007. (Young Founders Ser.). 192p. (YA). 5.99 (978-0-7653-5604-8(X) , Tor Kids) Doherty, Tom Assocs., LLC.

—1776: Son of Liberty: A Novel of the American Revolution. 2007. (Young Founders Ser.). 192p. (YA). 5.99 (978-0-7653-5273-6(7) , Tor Bks.) Doherty, Tom Assocs., LLC.

Mast, Edward. Wolf Child: The Correction of Joseph. 1999. 54p. (J). pap. 7.00 (978-0-87602-368-6(5)) Anchorage Pr.

Masterson, Rebecca. Jesus & the Great Garbage War. 2008. 120p. (YA). pap. 14.99 (978-1-59092-393-1(6) , Blue Works) Windstorm Creative.

Mateos, Pilar. Historias de Ninguno. (Barco de Vapor). (SPA.). 120p. (J). (gr. 4-5). (978-84-348-0907-9(9)) SM Ediciones.

—Lucas y Lucas. (Barco de Vapor). (SPA.). 88p. (YA). (gr. 5-8). (978-84-348-1233-8(9)) SM Ediciones.

Matheson, Shirlee Smith. Fastback Beach. 2006. (Orca Soundings Ser.). 112p. (YA). lib. bdg. 14.95 (978-1-55143-580-0(2)) Orca Bk. Pubs. USA.

Matthews, Andrew & Birmingham, Christian. Tod & the Clock Angel. 1999. (Illus.). 32p. (J). (gr. k-4). pap. 8.99 (978-0-7112-1357-9(7)) Lincoln, Frances Ltd. GBR. *Dist:* Antique Collectors' Club.

Matthew's House. 2001. (Gospel Road Story Bks.). (Illus.). 12p. (J). (ps-k). 0.99 (978-0-8254-7222-0(9)) Kregel Pubns.

Mayer, Mercer. A Boy, a Dog & a Frog. Mayer, Mercer, illus. 2003. (Illus.). 32p. (J). (ps). 5.99 (978-0-8037-2880-6(8) , Dial) Penguin Group (USA) Inc.

Mayer, Mercer & Mayer, Marianna. A Boy, a Dog, a Frog & a Friend. Mayer, Mercer & Mayer, Marianna, illus. 2003. (Illus.). 32p. (J). (ps). 6.99 (978-0-8037-2882-0(4) , Dial) Penguin Group (USA) Inc.

Mayhew, James. Boy. 2004. (Illus.). 32p. (J). (gr. k). pap. 15.95 (978-0-439-65106-6(9) , Chicken Hse., The) Scholastic, Inc.

McBratney, Sam. Lo Siento. 2003. (SPA.). 32p. (J). 13.95 (978-84-241-8020-6(9)) Everest de Ediciones y Distribucion, S.L. ESP. *Dist:* Lectorum Pubns., Inc.

McCall, Edith. Abe & the Wild River. 1999. 184p. (J). (gr. 5-7). 9.99 (978-0-88092-439-9(X) , 439X) Royal Fireworks Publishing Co.

McCardie, Amanda. Davy & the Snake. 2000. (Illus.). 64p. (J). pap. 5.99 (978-0-09-940179-7(7)) Random Hse. GBR. *Dist:* Independent Pubs. Group.

McClear, Preston. Awful Roy. Dollak, Nicholas, illus. 1999. 50p. (J). (gr. k-5). 16.95 (978-1-929084-08-1(0)); pap. 12.95 (978-1-929084-09-8(9)) Malibu Bks. for Children.

—The Boy under the Bed. Dollak, Nicholas, illus. 1999. 50p. (J). (gr. k-5). 16.95 (978-1-929084-02-9(1)); pap. 12.95 (978-1-929084-03-6(X)) Malibu Bks. for Children.

McClure, Brian D. The Bubble. 2006. (Illus.). 64p. (J). 14.95 (978-1-933426-05-1(5)) Universal Flag Publishing.

—Who Am I? 2006. (Illus.). 52p. (J). 12.95 (978-1-933426-03-7(9)) Universal Flag Publishing.

McCusker, Paul. Glennall's Betrayal, Vol. 4. 1999. (Passages Ser.: Vol. 4). (Illus.). 208p. (J). (gr. 5-9). pap. 6.99 (978-1-56179-808-7(8)) Focus on the Family Publishing.

McDonald, Ann-Eve. The Bad Day. 2004. (J). (978-0-9770158-1-8(5)) BeachWalk Bks. Inc.

McElroy, Laurie. Go Hollywood. 2006. (Teenick Ser.: No. 3). 112p. (J). pap. 4.99 (978-0-439-89043-4(8)) Scholastic, Inc.

McElroy, Laurie. Josh Is Done. 2007. (Teenick Ser.: No. 7). 128p. (J). pap. 4.99 ***(*978-0-439-91647-9(X))*** Scholastic, Inc.

McKee, David. Not Now, Bernard. 2005. (Illus.). 32p. (J). 6.99 (978-1-84270-456-1(7)) Trafalgar Square Publishing.

McOmber, Rachel B., ed. McOmber Phonics Storybooks: Ben in Bed. rev. ed. (Illus.). (J). (978-0-944991-29-9(7)) Swift Learning Resources.

—McOmber Phonics Storybooks: Ben Will Get Well. rev. ed. (Illus.). (J). (978-0-944991-30-5(0)) Swift Learning Resources.

—McOmber Phonics Storybooks: Max. rev. ed. (Illus.). (J). (978-0-944991-01-5(7)) Swift Learning Resources.

—McOmber Phonics Storybooks: Max Is Six. rev. ed. (Illus.). (J). (978-0-944991-43-5(2)) Swift Learning Resources.

—McOmber Phonics Storybooks: Max Ran. rev. ed. (Illus.). (J). (978-0-944991-02-2(5)) Swift Learning Resources.

—McOmber Phonics Storybooks: Max the Grand. rev. ed. (Illus.). (J). (978-0-944991-57-2(2)) Swift Learning Resources.

McPhail, David M. A Bug, a Bear & a Boy. 1998. (Hello Reader! Ser.). (J). (ps-1). 10.79 (978-0-606-13231-2(7)) Tandem Library Bks.

—A Bug, a Bear & a Boy Go to School. 1999. (Illus.). (J). 10.79 (978-0-606-20469-9(5)) Tandem Library Bks.

—The Puddle. McPhail, David M., illus. 2002. (Illus.). (J). 13.36 (978-0-7587-3458-7(1)) Book Wholesalers, Inc.

—The Puddle. McPhail, David M., illus. 2000. (Illus.). 32p. (J). (ps-k). pap. 5.95 (978-0-374-46030-3(2) , Sunburst) Farrar, Straus & Giroux.

Mead, Alice. Adem's Cross. 1998. (978-0-606-13110-0(8)) Tandem Library Bks.

Meaders, Barton Scott. The Journey Thus Far. 2004. 152p. pap. 19.95 (978-1-4137-1968-0(6)) PublishAmerica, Inc.

Medina, Jane. My Name Is Jorge: On Both Sides of the River. Vanden Broeck, Fabricio, illus. 2003. (SPA & ENG.). 48p. (YA). (gr. 2-4). 15.95 (978-1-56397-811-1(3)) Boyds Mills Pr.

—My Name Is Jorge: On Both Sides of the River. Broeck, Fabricio Vanden, illus. 2003. (SPA & ENG.). 48p. (YA). (gr. 2-4). pap. 9.95 (978-1-56397-842-5(3)) Boyds Mills Pr.

—My Name Is Jorge: On Both Sides of the River. 1999. (978-0-606-18014-6(1)) Tandem Library Bks.

Mendes, Valerie. Girl in the Attic. 2002. 213p. (YA). pap. 8.99 (978-0-689-83680-0(5)) Simon & Schuster, Ltd. GBR. *Dist:* Independent Pubs. Group.

Mercado, Nancy. Every Man for Himself: Ten Short Stories about Being a Guy. 2007. 176p. (J). (gr. 4-7). pap. 6.99 (978-0-14-240813-1(1) , Puffin) Penguin Group (USA) Inc.

Mercer, Gary. Justin Flowers & the Orb of Time. 2003. 147p. pap. 16.95 (978-1-59286-530-7(5)) PublishAmerica, Inc.

Metzenthen, David. Boys of Blood & Bone. 2004. 276p. pap. 9.95 (978-0-14-300130-0(2) , Penguin Global) Penguin Group (USA) Inc.

Meyer, Brad. A Matchless Age. 2006. 302p. pap. 24.95 (978-1-4241-0523-6(4)) PublishAmerica, Inc.

Milbourne, Anna. In the Castle. Davies, Benji, illus. 2006. 24p. (J). 9.99 (978-0-7945-1243-9(7) , Usborne) EDC Publishing.

Miller, Jorg. El Libro en el Libro en el Libro. 2002. (SPA., Illus.). 32p. (978-84-8488-066-0(4)) Serres, Ediciones, S. L.

Miller, Tom. Full Court Press: Tom Miller. Hier, Marjorie A., illus. 2000. 70p. (J). pap. 7.50 (978-0-931209-91-8(9)) Mid-Prairie Bks.

Milligan, Bryce. With the Wind, Kevin Dolan. 2003. (Illus.). 200p. (J). pap. 13.00 (978-0-930324-96-4(X)) Wings Pr.

Millman, Selena. Our Dream Project. 2006. 99p. (YA). per. 11.51 ***(*978-1-4243-2352-4(5))*** Independent Publisher Services.

Miner, Larry. The Little Green Boy. Enders, Barb, illus. 2006. 80p. per. 16.95 ***(*978-1-59453-644-1(9)*** , 2842, Airleaf Publishing) Airleaf Publishing & Bookselling.

Mishica, Clare. Cody's New Friends. Ring, Laura, ed. Britt, Stephanie M., illus. 2000. (Happy Day Bks.). 24p. (J). (ps-2). 2.49 (978-0-7847-1103-3(8) , 04308, Bean Sprouts) Standard Publishing.

Mitchelhill, Barbara. Eric & the Pimple Potion. MacKeith, Bridget, illus. 2000. 80p. (J). (gr. 3 up). 13.99 (978-0-86264-963-0(3)) Andersen GBR. *Dist:* Independent Pubs. Group.

Mochizuki, Ken. El Beisbol Nos Salvo. ed. 2004. (SPA., Illus.). (J). (gr. k-4). spiral bd. (978-0-616-03090-5(8)) Canadian National Institute for the Blind/Institut National Canadien pour les Aveugles.

Modern Staff. Marcos is Magnificent Big Book, No. 1. (J). 22.95 (978-0-8136-4829-3(7)) Modern Curriculum Pr.

Montes, Juan Mari. Diario del Autobus a de la Linea 3. Fra, Irene, illus. 2006. (SPA.). 96p. (J). (978-84-667-5192-6(0)) Grupo Anaya, S.A.

Moore, Johnny Ray. Talking Tyrone Said It. 1999. (Illus.). 60p. pap. 6.95 (978-1-58521-007-7(2)) Books for Black Children, Inc.

Moore-Mallinos, Jennifer. It's OK to Be Me: Just Like You, I Can Do Almost Anything. Fabrega, Marta, illus. 2007. (Live & Learn Ser.). 36p. (J). (gr. k-2). pap. 6.99 (978-0-7641-3584-2(8)) Barron's Educational Series, Inc.

—Que bien es ser yo Mismo: Puedo hacer casi todo lo que me de la Gana! Fabrega, Marta, illus. 2007. (Live & Learn Ser.). 36p. (J). (gr. k-2). pap. 6.99 (978-0-7641-3585-9(6)) Barron's Educational Series, Inc.

Morgan, Allen. Mateo y la Grua de Medianoche. Langer, Shirley, tr. Martchenko, Michael, illus. 2003. (SPA.). 32p. (J). (gr. k). pap. 5.95 (978-1-55037-190-1(8)) Annick Pr., Ltd. CAN. *Dist:* Firefly Bks., Ltd.

—Mateo y los Pavos de Medianoche. Langer, Shirley, tr. Martchenko, Michael, illus. 2003. Tr. of Matthew & the Midnight Turkeys. (SPA.). 24p. (J). (gr. k). pap. 5.95 (978-1-55037-188-8(6)) Annick Pr., Ltd. CAN. *Dist:* Firefly Bks., Ltd.

—Matthew & the Midnight Money Van. Martchenko, Michael, illus. 2003. 24p. (J). (ps-2). lib. bdg. 14.95 (978-0-920303-75-7(7)) Annick Pr., Ltd. CAN. *Dist:* Firefly Bks., Ltd.

—Matthew & the Midnight Wrestlers. 2000. (gr. k-3). lib. bdg. 15.30 (978-0-613-84051-4(8)) Tandem Library Bks.

Morgan, Allen & Martchenko, Michael. Matthew & the Midnight Wrestlers. 2000. (Matthew's Midnight Adventures Ser.). (Illus.). 32p. (J). (ps-3). 6.99 (978-0-7737-6053-0(9)) Stoddart Kids CAN. *Dist:* Fitzhenry & Whiteside, Ltd.

Morgan, Ruth. Big Liam, Little Liam. Archbold, Tim, illus. 2005. 24p. (J). lib. bdg. 22.65 (*978-1-59646-728-6(2)) Dingles & Co.

Morinaga, Ai. Duck Prince: Transformation, 6 bks, Bk. 1. Pannone, Frank, ed. Jackson, Laura & Kobayashi, Yoko, trs. from JPN. Morinaga, Ai, illus. 2004. Orig. Title: Ahiruno Oujisama 1. (Illus.). 176p. pap. 9.99 (978-1-58664-931-9(0) , CMX 65201G, CPM Manga) Central Park Media Corp.

Morpurgo, Michael. The Kingfisher Book of Great Boy Stories: A Treasury of Classics from Children's Literature. 2000. (Kingfisher Treasury of Stories Ser.). (Illus.). 160p. (J). (gr. k-3). tchr. ed. 19.95 (978-0-7534-5320-9(7) , Kingfisher) Houghton Mifflin Co. Trade & Reference Div.

Morris, Willie. Good Old Boy & the Witch of Yazoo. 2nd ed. 1998. 164p. (J). (gr. 7-10). pap. 10.95 (978-0-916242-67-1(6)) Yoknapatawpha Pr.

Moser, Kay. David's Gift. 2000. 260p. (YA). pap. 11.99 (978-1-890236-16-8(0)) Seton St. Clare Bks.

Mostoller, Gordon. Randy Walter & Rex. 2006. pap. 12.95 (*978-1-4259-6498-6(2)) AuthorHouse.

Mowat, Farley. The Dog Who Wouldn't Be. 1999. mass mkt. (978-0-553-20951-8(5)) Random Hse., Inc.

Mowry, Jess. Tyger Tales. 2007. 280p. (YA). pap. 14.99 (978-1-59092-358-0(8) , Blue Works) Windstorm Creative.

Muchamore, Robert. Divine Madness. 2006. (Cherub Ser.). 400p. (YA). mass mkt. 5.99 (978-1-4169-2724-2(7) , Simon Pulse) Simon & Schuster Children's Publishing.

Mukerji, Dhan Gopal. Jungle Beasts & Men. Allen, J. E., illus. 2005. reprint ed. pap. 22.95 (978-0-7661-9403-8(5)) Kessinger Publishing, LLC.

Mullican, Judy. Kenny & the Poison. Carroll, Ken, Jr., illus. 1998. (Big Bks.). 8p. (Orig.). (J). (ps-k). pap. 10.95 (978-1-57332-089-4(7)); pap. 10.95 (978-1-57332-088-7(9)) HighReach Learning, Inc.

Munnik, Hema. Bhole: Adventures of a Young Yogi. 2006. 352p. pap. 18.95 (978-81-88157-37-2(6)) Lotus Pr.

Munsch, Robert. Mortimer. Martchenko, Michael, illus. 2003. (Annikins Ser.: Vol. 3). 24p. (J). (ps-2). pap. 1.25 (978-0-920236-68-0(5)) Annick Pr., Ltd. CAN. *Dist:* Firefly Bks., Ltd.

Mwangi, Meja. The Mzungu Boy. (J). 2006. 152p. pap. 6.95 (978-0-88899-664-0(0)); 2005. 160p. 15.95 (978-0-88899-653-4(5)) Groundwood Bks. CAN. *Dist:* Perseus Distribution.

Myers, Walter Dean. Every Man for Himself: 10 Short Stories about Being a Guy. Mercado, Nancy, ed. 2005. (Illus.). 176p. (YA). (gr. 9). 16.99 (978-0-8037-2896-7(4) , Dial) Penguin Group (USA) Inc.

Mysak, Mary. Little Train! Stickley, Kelly, illus. 2004. 16p. (J). 7.50 (978-0-9762274-0-3(1)) Helping Hands Children's Bks.

Najar, Qasim M. Ibrahim's Search. Meehan, Patricia, illus. 1998. 30p. (J). (gr. 1-4). pap. 5.95 (978-1-889720-20-3(8)) Amirah Publishing.

Nash, Naomi. Beaner O'Brian's Absolutely Ginormous Guidebook to Guys. 2004. (YA). mass mkt. 5.99 (978-0-8439-5403-6(5)) Dorchester Publishing Co., Inc.

Naylor, Phyllis Reynolds. The Boy with the Helium Head. 1998. 11.30 (978-0-606-13224-4(4)) Tandem Library Bks.

Nelson, Vaunda Micheaux. Ready? Set Raymond! 2002. (gr. k-3). lib. bdg. 11.80 (978-0-613-87307-9(6)) Tandem Library Bks.

Nemeth, Sally. The Heights, the Depths, & Everything in Between. 2006. 272p. (J). (gr. 5). 17.99 (978-0-375-93458-2(8)); 15.95 (978-0-375-83458-5(3)) Random Hse. Children's Bks. (Knopf Bks. for Young Readers).

The Nevergreen. 2003. (J). 15.99 (978-0-9744565-9-1(4)) Heart-to-Heart Pubns.

Newell, Carol Donsky. Blue Lewis & Sasha the Great. Grisham, Betty, illus. 2005. (J). per. 6.95 (978-0-9766199-0-1(3)) Cally Pr.

Nicholson, John & Nicholson, Ed. Shall We Gather. 2002. (Illus.). 123p. reprint ed. pap. (978-0-9720828-0-8(8)) Nicholson, Ed.

Niner, Holly L. I Can't Stop! A Story about Tourette Syndrome. Treatner, Meryl, illus. 2005. 32p. (J). (gr. 2-5). lib. bdg. 15.95 (978-0-8075-3620-9(2)) Whitman, Albert & Co.

Noble, Trinka Hakes. The Last Brother: A Civil War Tale. Papp, Robert, illus. 2006. 48p. (J). (gr. k-5). 17.95 (978-1-58536-253-0(0)) Sleeping Bear Pr.

Null, Lucinda K. Billy, the Bear Hugger. Cangelosi, Sam M., illus. 1999. 12p. (J). (ps-2). pap. 4.00 (978-0-9671500-0-0(0)) Heartfelt Pubns.

Nunes, Lygia Bojunga. Seis Veces Lucas. (SPA.). (YA). (gr. 5-8). 8.95 (978-958-04-5050-4(1) , NR3069) Norma S.A. COL. *Dist:* Distribuidora Norma, Inc., Lectorum Pubns., Inc.

O'Connor, Jane. Fancy Nancy & the Boy from Paris. Glasser, Robin Preiss & Enik, Ted, illus. 2008. (I Can Read Bks.). 32p. (J). 16.99 (*978-0-06-123610-5(1)) HarperCollins Pubs.

—Fancy Nancy & the Boy from Paris. Glasser, Robin Preiss, illus. 2008. (I Can Read Bks.). 32p. (J). pap. 3.99 (*978-0-06-123609-9(8) , Harper Trophy) HarperCollins Pubs.

Ocorr, Dave. Matt & Shawn: Backcourt Duo. 1998. (Coach's Choice Ser.). 155p. (J). (gr. 4-9). pap. 8.95 (978-0-9660758-2-3(X)) Perth Pubns., Ltd.

O'Hare, C. True Freshman. 2004. 257p. pap. 21.95 (978-1-4137-3859-9(1)) PublishAmerica, Inc.

Old Yeller. 1999. (J). 9.95 (978-1-56137-081-8(9)) Novel Units, Inc.

Oldfield, Jenny. Danny Boy. 2001. (Illus.). (J). mass mkt. 9.99 (978-0-340-75729-1(9) , Hodder & Stoughton) Hodder General Publishing Division GBR. *Dist:* Trafalgar Square Publishing.

On Thin Ice. 2005. per. (978-0-9772505-2-3(0)) Adibooks.com.

Opie, Iona. I Saw Esau: The Schoolchild's Pocket Book. Sendak, Maurice, illus. 2000. (J). (978-0-606-19758-8(3)) Tandem Library Bks.

Opie, Iona & Opie, Peter, eds. I Saw Esau: The Schoolchild's Pocket Book. Sendak, Maurice, illus. 2000. 160p. (J). (ps-3). pap. 9.99 (978-0-7636-1199-6(9)) Candlewick Pr.

Oppenheim, Shulamith Levey. What Is the Full Moon Full Of? Moore, Cyd, illus. 2003. 32p. (J). (ps up). 14.95 (978-1-56397-479-3(7)) Boyds Mills Pr.

—What Is the Moon Full Of? 2000. (978-0-606-18793-0(6)) Tandem Library Bks.

Optic, Oliver. Taken by the Enemy. Shute, A. B., illus. 1998. (Blue & the Gray Ser.). 351p. (J). (gr. 4-7). reprint ed. per. 14.95 (978-1-890623-03-6(2)) Lost Classics Bk. Co.

Oram, Hiawyn & Kitamura, Satoshi. A Boy Wants a Dinosaur. 2007. (Illus.). 32p. (J). pap. 8.95 (*978-1-84270-580-3(6)) Andersen GBR. *Dist:* Independent Pubs. Group.

Ord, Douglas. Tommy's Farm. 1998. 204p. (J). pap. (978-1-55128-061-5(2)) Mercury Pr., The.

Orlet-Schoen, Julie. Jackie Jack the Brave Little Boy. Comerford, Renee O., illus. 1998. 56p. 12.95 (978-0-9663076-0-3(7)); pap. 6.95 (978-0-9663076-1-0(5)) Woodland Studios, Inc.

Orlev, Uri. Hairy Tuesday. Gleich, Jacky, illus. 1999. 32p. (J). (gr. 1-5). 15.95 (978-1-57255-651-5(X)) Mondo Publishing.

Owens, Connie S. I know I am Special! 2003. pap. 5.99 (978-1-59317-010-3(6)) Warner Pr. Pubs.

Owens, Terrell & Parker, Courtney. Little T Learns to Share. Harris, Todd, illus. 2006. 24p. (J). 14.95 (978-1-933771-20-5(8)) BenBella Bks.

Ozlo's Beard: Individual Title Six-Pack Pouch - Level K. (Lighthouse Ser.). 16p. (gr. 2 up). 28.00 (978-0-7578-0875-3(1)) Rigby Education.

Pacheco, Miguel Angel. La Familia de Mic. Escriva, Ana Lopez, illus. 2003. (SPA.). (J). (978-970-690-761-5(0)) Planeta Mexicana Editorial S. A. de C. V.

Park, Barbara. Dear God, Help!!! Love, Earl. Lafreniere, Kenneth, ed. 2000. (Geek Chronicles Ser.: Vol. 3). (Illus.). 144p. (J). (gr. 3-7). pap. 5.50 (978-0-679-85395-4(2) , Yearling) Random Hse. Children's Bks.

—Dear God, Help!!! Love, Earl. 2000. (Geek Chronicles Ser.: Vol. 3). 125p. (J). (ps-7). lib. bdg. 11.15 (978-0-606-19897-4(0)) Tandem Library Bks.

—The Graduation of Jake Moon. unabr. ed. 2004. 115p. (J). (gr. 4-7). pap. 29.00 incl. audio (978-0-8072-8722-4(9) , Listening Library) Random Hse. Audio Publishing Group.

—The Graduation of Jake Moon. 2002. 128p. (J). (gr. 4-7). reprint ed. pap. 4.99 (978-0-689-83985-6(5) , Aladdin) Simon & Schuster Children's Publishing.

—Junie B. Jones Loves Handsome Warren. unabr. ed. 2004. (Junie B. Jones Ser.: No. 7). 71p. (J). (gr. k-3). pap. 17.00 incl. audio (978-0-8072-0643-0(1) , Listening Library) Random Hse. Audio Publishing Group.

Pasch, J. A. Arthur P. Snittles: The Magic Barrel. 2006. 116p. (YA). per. 10.95 (978-1-59886-199-0(9)) Tate Publishing & Enterprises, L.L.C.

Pass, Erica. Sleepover & Over. Lapadula, Tom, illus. ed. 2005. (Fairly Odd Parents Ser.: 5). 24p. (J). lib. bdg. 15.00 (978-1-59054-805-9(1)) Fitzgerald Bks.

Paterson, Katherine. Ame a Jacob. (SPA.). 222p. (J). (gr. 6-8). 9.20 (978-84-279-1501-5(2) , NG31211); 2003. (Illus.). (YA). (gr. 5-8). pap. (978-84-279-3251-7(0) , NG31211) Noguer y Caralt Editores, S. A. ESP. *Dist:* Lectorum Pubns., Inc.

Patrick Book. 2001. (J). 12.99 (978-1-58209-250-8(8)) Books Are Fun, Ltd.

Paulits, Philip & the Boy Who Said "Huh?" 2003. 60p. (J). pap. 12.95 (978-1-878044-72-3(9)) Mayhaven Publishing.

Paulsen, Gary. The Amazing Life of Birds: The Twenty-Day Puberty Journal of Duane Homer Leech. 2006. (Illus.). 96p. (J). (gr. 5-9). 13.95 (978-0-385-74660-1(1) , Lamb, Wendy) Random Hse. Children's Bks.

—Brian's Return. unabr. ed. 2004. (Middle Grade Cassette Librariestm Ser.). 115p. (J). (gr. 5-9). pap. 29.00 incl. audio (978-0-8072-0658-4(X) , S YA 292 SP, Listening Library) Random Hse. Audio Publishing Group.

—Brian's Return. 2004. (GLB Reprints Ser.). 128p. (YA). (gr. 5). lib. bdg. 17.99 (978-0-385-90223-6(9) , Delacorte Bks. for Young Readers) Random Hse. Children's Bks.

—Brian's Return. 2001. (gr. 7-12). lib. bdg. 13.55 (978-0-613-33796-0(4)) Tandem Library Bks.

—Dancing Carl. 2001. (YA). 21.25 (978-0-8446-7183-3(5)) Smith, Peter Pub., Inc.

—Harris & Me: A Summer Remembered. 2007. (Illus.). 168p. (J). (gr. 4-7). pap. 5.95 (978-0-15-205880-7(X) , Harcourt Paperbacks) Harcourt Children's Bks.

Payne, Raymond. Shelter from the Storm. rev. ed. 2004. 144p. (YA). pap. 9.95 (978-0-9740552-1-3(2)) Harbourside Pr.

Peake, M. Boy in Darkness. (Illus.). 144p. (J). pap. (978-0-340-67822-0(4) , Hodder & Stoughton) Hodder General Publishing Division.

Pean, Stanley & Poulin, Stephane. Un Petit Garcon Qui Avait Peur de Tout et de Rien. 1998. (Illus.). 24p. (J). pap. (978-2-89021-320-3(X)) Diffusion du livre Mirabel.

Pearson, Tracey Campbell. Where Does Joe Go? 2002. (ps-2). lib. bdg. 14.10 (978-0-613-71808-0(9)) Tandem Library Bks.

Peck, Robert Newton. Soup. 1998. (Illus.). 112p. (J). (gr. 5-8). pap. 5.50 (978-0-679-89261-8(3) , Yearling) Random Hse. Children's Bks.

Peek, Merle. Mary Wore Her Red Dress & Henry Wore His Green Sneakers. 1998. (Illus.). 11p. (J). (gr. k-ps). bds. 5.95 (978-0-395-90022-2(0) , Clarion Bks.) Houghton Mifflin Co. Trade & Reference Div.

Pennington, Beverly. Jonathan's Discovery. 2005. 32p. (J). per. 12.95 (978-1-56167-920-1(8)) American Literary Pr.

Perera, Hilda. Cuentos de Apolo. Moreiro, Enrique S., illus. 2000. (SPA.). 88p. (J). (gr. 5 up). pap. 7.95 (978-1-880507-68-1(4) , LC6354) Lectorum Pubns., Inc.

—Cuentos de Apolo. 2000. (SPA.). (gr. 3-6). lib. bdg. 16.40 (978-0-613-28286-4(8)) Tandem Library Bks.

Perrello, Yvonnie. Peace to the Ninja. Jones, Timothy Lee, illus. 2002. 49p. (J). (gr. 5-11). per. 8.95 (978-1-932301-01-4(1)) Airleaf Publishing & Bookselling.

Picard, Barbara Leonie. One Is One. 2006. 321p. pap. 9.95 (978-1-58988-027-6(7)) Consortium Bk. Sales & Distribution.

Picture Me Cute As Can Bee Mini. 2002. 10p. (J). (ps up). bds. 2.99 (978-1-57151-550-6(X)) Playhouse Publishing.

Pilkey, Dav. The Paperboy. Pilkey, Dav, illus. 1999. (Illus.). 32p. (J). (ps-5). pap. 5.95 (978-0-531-07139-7(1) , Orchard Bks.) Scholastic, Inc.

—The Paperboy. 1999. (Illus.). lib. bdg. 12.75 (978-0-606-17856-3(2)) Tandem Library Bks.

Pinkney, Brian. Max Found Two Sticks. Pinkney, Brian, illus. 2002. (Illus.). (J). 15.53 (978-0-7587-3106-7(X)) Book Wholesalers, Inc.

Pittar, Gill. Milly & Molly's Monday. Morrell, Cris, illus. 2nd rev. ed. 2003. 27p. (978-1-877297-06-9(2)) Milly Molly Bks.

Plunkett, N. Geraldine. Nathan's Secret. Gallo, Beth, illus. 2000. 87p. (J). pap. 7.95 (978-0-87178-029-4(1)) Brethren Pr.

Podoshen, Lois. El Huerto de Paco. Romo, Alberto, tr. Buket, illus. 1999. (Books for Young Learners).Tr. of Paco's Garden. (SPA.). 12p. (J). (gr. k-2). pap. 5.00 (978-1-57274-337-3(9) , A2869) Owen, Richard C. Pubs., Inc.

Polisar, Barry Louis. The Trouble with Ben. Clark, David, illus. 2003. (Rainbow Morning Music Picture Books Ser.). 34p. (J). (gr. k-5). 14.95 (978-0-938663-13-3(5)) Rainbow Morning Music Alternatives.

Potters, Harry P. Tory. 2006. 85p. 22.96 (978-1-4116-7958-0(X)) Lulu.com.

Poulsen, David A. Last Sam's Cage. rev. ed. 2004. 224p. pap. 9.95 (*978-1-55263-611-4(9)) Key Porter Bks. CAN. *Dist:* Perseus Distribution.

—Last Sam's Cage. 2001. 208p. (YA). pap. 8.95 (978-1-896184-78-4(2)) Roussan Pubs., Inc./Roussan Editeur, Inc. CAN. *Dist:* Orca Bk. Pubs. USA.

Prentice-Hall Staff. The Red Pony. 2nd ed. (J). stu. ed. (978-0-13-717133-0(1)) Prentice Hall (Schl. Div.).

Priddy, Roger. Baby Gund Baby Boy. 2006. 22p. (J). bds. 5.95 (978-0-312-49704-0(0) , Priddy Bks.) St. Martin's Pr.

Pringle, Nicholas. Silly Billy. 2005. 40p. (J). pap. 9.00 (978-1-4116-4981-1(8)) Lulu.com.

Project-00. 2003. (J). 15.95 (978-0-9743843-0-6(5)) Endeavor Publishing.

Prokofiev, Sergei & Malone, Peter. Sergei Prokofiev's Peter & the Wolf: With Fully-Orchestrated & Narrated CD. 2004. (Illus.). 40p. (J). 19.95 incl. audio compact disk (978-0-375-82430-2(8) , Knopf Bks. for Young Readers) Random Hse. Children's Bks.

Pryor, Bonnie. Seth of the Lion People. 2003. 116p. (J). pap. 5.95 (978-0-9729339-0-2(5)) Kid's Shelf.

Pulgarcito. 2001. Tr. of Tom Thumb. (SPA.). (978-968-6347-32-6(1)) Larousse, Ediciones, S. A. de C. V.

Purnell, Pamela. Denny & the Magic Pool. 2000. 133p. (J). pap. 11.95 (978-0-8464-4841-9(6)) Beekman Bks., Inc.

Pyle, Howard. The Garden Behind the Moon. 2002. (gr. 3-6). lib. bdg. 14.15 (978-0-613-57052-7(9)) Tandem Library Bks.

Pyle, Kevin C. Blindspot. 2007. (Illus.). (*978-1-4287-3845-4(2)) Holt, Henry & Co.

Queen, Erika V. Johnny Starlight. Wray, Jim, illus. 1999. 30p. (J). (gr. 1-6). 6.95 (978-0-9674878-0-9(3)) Goldwing Pubs.

Rabley, Stephen. Billy & the Queen. 2002. (Illus.). 16p. pap. (978-0-582-35288-9(6) , Putnam Juvenile) Penguin Group (USA) Inc.

Raintree Steck-Vaughn Staff. The Diary of a Pioneer Boy. 1999. (J). pap. 35.60 (978-0-7398-0913-6(X)) Steck-Vaughn.

Ralles, H. J. Keeper of the Kingdom. 2001. 200p. (gr. 3-11). pap. 9.95 (978-1-929976-03-4(8)) Top Pubns., Ltd.

Ramage, Jan. Eyes in the Night. Peterson, Laura, illus. 2006. 32p. pap. 15.25 (978-1-920694-67-8(6)) Univ. of Western Australia Pr. AUS. *Dist:* International Specialized Bk. Services.

The Rambunctious Tommy Turnpike. 2nd ed. 2005. (J). (978-0-9773760-0-1(1)) Johnson, Anthony.

Randall, MarilynMae. Wishes for Christmas. 2002. (Illus.). (J). 9.99 (978-0-9713589-5-9(8)) Ubavriel's Gifts.

Random House Staff, ed. Thomas Getting Ready for School. 1999. pap. 7.99 (978-0-375-80081-8(6) , Random Hse. Bks. for Young Readers) Random Hse. Children's Bks.

Raphael, Marie. A Boy from Ireland: A Novel. 2007. 224p. (YA). (gr. 7 up). 19.95 (978-0-89255-331-0(6)) Persea Bks., Inc.

Rate, Kristina. Potato Boy. Formosa, Natasha, illus. 2005. 32p. (ps). pap. 11.95 (978-0-9549372-0-1(5)) Fastback TV Ltd. GBR. *Dist:* Biblio Distribution.

Rawlings, Marjorie Kinnan. Yearling. 2001. (gr. 3-6). lib. bdg. 14.15 (978-0-613-90195-6(9)) Tandem Library Bks.

Rawls, Wilson. Where the Red Fern Grows. 1999. (Masterpiece Series Access Editions). (Illus.). xvii, 235p. (J). 10.95 (978-0-8219-1987-3(3) , 35337) Paradigm Publishing, Inc.

—Where the Red Fern Grows. 249p. (YA). (gr. 5 up). pap. 5.99 (978-0-8072-1467-1(1)); pap. 5.99 (978-0-8072-1358-2(6)) Random Hse. Audio Publishing Group. (Listening Library).

—Where the Red Fern Grows. l.t. ed. 2005. 376p. pap. 10.95 (978-0-7862-7312-6(7) , Large Print Pr.) Thorndike Pr.

Ray, Mary Lyn. The Basket Moon. Cooney, Barbara, illus. 1999. 32p. (J). (ps-3). 16.99 (978-0-316-73521-6(3)) Little Brown & Co.

Redmond, Patrick. Something Dangerous. l.t. ed. 2000. (J). 26.95 (978-1-56895-832-3(3) , Wheeler Publishing, Inc.) Thomson Gale.

Reed, Jennifer. Hadi's Journey. 2003. 110p. pap. 10.95 (978-0-595-29375-9(1)) iUniverse, Inc.

Reeder, Carolyn. Moonshiner's Son. 2003. (gr. 3-6). lib. bdg. 13.00 (978-0-613-61803-8(3)) Tandem Library Bks.

Reedy, Mokena Potae. Timo & the Kingfish. Gregory, Elton, illus. 2000. 32p. (J). pap. 12.95 (978-1-877266-26-3(4)) Huia Pubs. NZL. *Dist:* Pacific Island Bks.

Rees, Celia. The Soul Taker. 2nd ed. 2003. 160p. pap. (978-0-340-87817-0(7) , Hodder Children's Books) Hodder Children's Division.

Richards, Pat. Bardolph Bedivere Wolf Returns. Richards, Charles, illus. 2007. 42p. (J). (*978-0-9790796-4-1(0)) PJR Assocs., Ltd.

Richter, Conrad. The Light in the Forest. 2005. (Illus.). 176p. (*978-1-85715-515-0(7)) Knopf, Alfred A. Inc.

Riddell, Chris. Mr. Underbed. 1998. (Illus.). 32p. (J). (ps-1). pap. 9.99 (978-0-86264-786-5(X)) Andersen GBR. *Dist:* Trafalgar Square Publishing.

Ride Like the Wind. ed. 2005. (YA). per. (978-0-9744448-4-0(7)) McCourtie, Anne.

Ridgway, Dawn. The Clay Boy. 2002. (Illus.). pap. 0.40 (978-0-521-89013-7(6)) Cambridge Univ. Pr.

Ritsema van Eck, Patricia. The Dreaming of Paradise. 2005. 62p. (J). pap. 24.70 (978-1-4116-6097-7(8)) Lulu.com.

Ritter, John H. Choosing up Sides. 1998. 176p. (J). (gr. 4-9). 18.99 (978-0-399-23185-8(4) , Philomel) Penguin Group (USA) Inc.

Robertson, Elysia Hill. D. J. 's Sneakers. Robertson, Elysia Hill & Bruce, Cindy, illus. 2005. 104p. (J). per. 12.95 (978-0-9764444-2-8(9) , EJWV-003) E. J. Publishing.

Robertson, Keith. Henry Reed, Inc. abr. ed. (J). (gr. 4-7). pap. 15.95 incl. audio (978-0-670-36801-3(6)) Live Oak Media.

—Henry Reed, Inc., Set. McCloskey, Robert, illus. abr. ed. (J). (gr. 4-7). 24.95 incl. audio (978-0-670-36800-6(8)) Live Oak Media.

Robins, Eleanor. Boy of Their Dreams. 2003. (Illus.). 48p. (YA). per. 3.95 (978-1-56254-679-3(1) , SP6791) Saddleback Educational Publishing.

Robinson, Kim. Dale's Mango Tree. 2000. 28p. 3.99 (978-976-610-175-6(2)) Penguin Group (USA) Inc.

Robinson, Ronnie D. Yankee Doodle Boychik. 2002. (gr. 7-12). lib. bdg. 24.00 (978-0-613-74651-9(1)) Tandem Library Bks.

Robley Blake, Colleen. I Can't Wait till I'm Five. 2006. (J). 9.95 (978-0-9767342-0-8(6)) Imaajinn This.

Rock, Michelle L. Nighttime Adventures Counting Sheep. Longmore, Nickolai, illus. 2006. 32p. (J). 3.99 net. (978-0-9771700-1-2(2)) Mystic Arts, LLC.

Rockwell, Anne F. Disobedient Servant Boy. 2000. (J). lib. bdg. 15.89 (978-0-688-14882-9(4)) HarperCollins Pubs.

Rockwell, Thomas. How to Eat Fried Worms. (J). (gr. 3-5). 179p. pap. 4.99 (978-0-8072-1395-7(0)); 2004. 116p. pap. 29.00 incl. audio (978-0-8072-8797-2(0)) Random Hse. Audio Publishing Group. (Listening Library).

—How to Eat Fried Worms. 2006. 128p. (J). (gr. 2-5). 5.99 (978-0-440-42185-6(3) , Yearling) Random Hse. Children's Bks.

Rodowsky, Colby. Jason Rat-A-Tat. Peck, Beth, illus. 2002. 80p. (J). (gr. 2-4). 15.00 (978-0-374-33671-4(7) , Farrar, Straus & Giroux (BYR)) Farrar, Straus & Giroux.

Roeder, Mark. The Summer of My Discontent: A Better Place II. 2003. 294p. (YA). 28.95 (978-0-595-66057-5(6)); pap. 18.95 (978-0-595-29806-8(0)) iUniverse, Inc.

—This Time Around. 2003. 226p. (YA). pap. 15.95 (978-0-595-27361-4(0)) iUniverse, Inc.

Rogerson, George. Stillness of the Dawn - Book One - White Man Coming. 2007. 144p. (YA). pap. 12.95 (*978-1-60145-165-1(2)) Booklocker.com, Inc.

Roll, Claudia M. A Home for Nathan. Rizer, Finn, illus. 1999. 48p. (J). (ps-2). pap. 6.95 (978-0-9674058-0-3(7)) Snyder, William Foundation for Animals, The.

Romeu, Emma. Gregorio y el Mar. 2003. Tr. of Gregory & the Sea. (SPA., Illus.). 151p. (J). (gr. 5-8). pap. 15.95 (978-968-19-0316-9(1)) Santillana USA Publishing Co., Inc.

—Gregorio y el Mar. 1998. Tr. of Gregory & the Sea. (SPA.). (gr. 5-8). lib. bdg. 18.75 (978-0-613-82208-4(0)) Tandem Library Bks.

Rosenfeld, Dina. On the Ball. Nodel, Norman, illus. 1998. (Yossi & Laibel Ser.). (J). 9.95 (978-0-922613-83-0(4)) Hachai Publishing.

Ross, Michael & Koehler, Manfred. Tribe: A Warrior's Battles. 2006. 192p. (YA). per. 14.99 (978-1-58997-188-2(4)) Focus on the Family Publishing.

Rozen, Beti. Stolen Spirit. Lima, Graca, illus. 2nd ed. 2004. 32p. (gr. 3-7). pap. (978-0-9642333-1-7(2)) Sem Fronteiras Pr., Ltd.

Ryan, Kris. Spoon. 2005. 201p. pap. 19.95 (978-1-4137-7229-6(3)) PublishAmerica, Inc.

Rylant, Cynthia. Henry & Mudge & the Sneaky Crackers. Stevenson, Sucie, illus. 2002. (Henry & Mudge Ser.). (J). pap. 18.95 incl. audio compact disk (978-1-59112-638-6(X)); 25.95 incl. audio (978-0-87499-957-0(X)) Live Oak Media.

—Henry & Mudge in the Family Trees. Stevenson, Sucie, illus. 1998. (Henry & Mudge Ser.). 40p. (J). (gr. k-3). pap. 3.99 (978-0-689-82317-6(7) , Aladdin) Simon & Schuster Children's Publishing.

—Seasons with Henry & Mudge. Stevenson, Sucie, illus. 2000. (Henry & Mudge Ser.). pap. 68.95 incl. audio compact disk (978-1-59112-855-7(2)) Live Oak Media.

Sabattela, Liz. Children at Play: Tales of Gang Boys in Treatment. 1999. 90p. (J). pap. 9.95 (978-0-7392-0352-1(5) , PO3536) Morris Publishing.

Sachar, Louis. Johnny's in the Basement. 1998. 128p. (J). reprint ed. 17.00 (978-0-688-16085-2(9)) HarperCollins Pubs.

—There's a Boy in the Girls' Bathroom. 195p. (J). (gr. 4-6). pap. 4.99 (978-0-8072-1453-4(1) , Listening Library) Random Hse. Audio Publishing Group.

Sachi. 2006. 26p. 10.05 (978-1-4116-7248-2(8)) Lulu.com.

Sadu, Itah. Christopher Changes His Name. Condy, Roy, illus. 1998. 32p. (J). (gr. k-3). pap. 5.95 (978-1-55209-214-9(3)) Firefly Bks., Ltd.

Sadu, Itah & Condy, Roy. Christopher Changes His Name. (Illus.). 32p. (J). pap. 4.99 (978-0-590-24624-8(0)) Scholastic, Inc.

Sargent, Dave, et al. Summer Milky Way: (Blackfeet) Be Compassionate, 20, Vol. 16. Lenoir, Jane, illus. l.t. ed. 2004. (Story Keeper Ser.). 48p. (J). lib. bdg. 22.60 (978-1-56763-933-9(X)); pap. 6.95 (978-1-56763-934-6(8)) Ozark Publishing.

—Tattoos of Honor Vol. 17: (Osage) Be Gentle & Giving, 20 bks. Lenoir, Jane, illus. l.t. ed. 2004. (Story Keeper Ser.: Vol. 17). 42p. (J). pap. 6.95 (978-1-56763-936-0(4)); lib. bdg. 22.60 (978-1-56763-935-3(6)) Ozark Publishing.

—Truth, Power & Freedom Vol. 19: (Sioux) Show Respect, 20. Lenoir, Jane, illus. l.t. ed. 2004. (Story Keeper Ser.: 19). 42p. (J). 19. lib. bdg. 22.60 (978-1-56763-939-1(9)); Vol. 19. pap. 6.95 (978-1-56763-940-7(2)) Ozark Publishing.

Sasaki, Mutsumi. Happy Lesson, Vol.1. 2004. 170p. pap. (978-1-4139-0021-7(6)) ADV Manga.

Savoie, Jacques & Zekina, Daniela. Un Chapeau Qui Tournait Autour de la Terre. 2003. (Illus.). 24p. (J). pap. (978-2-89021-295-4(5)) Diffusion du livre Mirabel.

Schecter, Ellen. Sleep Tight, Pete. Weissman, Bari, illus. 1998. (Bank Street Reader Collection). 48p. (J). (ps-2). lib. bdg. 22.60 (978-0-8368-1766-9(4)) Stevens, Gareth Inc.

Schelly, Bill. Come with Me. 1999. 162p. (YA). per. (978-0-9645669-5-8(8) , 1) Hamster Pr.

Schindler, Nina. An Order of Amelie, Hold the Fries. Barrett, Robert, tr. from GER. 2004. (Illus.). 136p. (YA). (gr. 8). 18.95 (978-1-55037-861-0(9)); pap. 8.95 (978-1-55037-860-3(0)) Annick Pr., Ltd. CAN. *Dist:* Firefly Bks., Ltd.

Schmidt, Gary D. Anson's Way. 2001. (J). 12.64 (978-0-606-21039-3(3)) Tandem Library Bks.

Schmidt, Heidi. Martin's Last Chance. 1999. 176p. (YA). (gr. 4-8). mass mkt. 5.99 (978-1-85792-425-1(8) , Christian Focus) Christian Focus Pubns. GBR. *Dist:* Riverside.

Scholastic, Inc. Staff & Taylor-Butler, Christine. Just for You! No Boys Allowed! Page, Mark, illus. 2004. (Just for You! Ser.). 32p. pap. 3.99 (978-0-439-56856-2(0) , Teaching Resources) Scholastic, Inc.

Scholl, Charley. Dustin's Debut. 2001. (gr. 7-12). lib. bdg. 17.60 (978-0-613-79220-2(3)) Tandem Library Bks.

Schotter, Roni. The Boy Who Loved Words. Potter, Giselle, illus. 2006. 40p. (J). (ps-3). 16.95 (978-0-375-83601-5(2)); lib. bdg. 18.99 (978-0-375-93601-2(7)) Random Hse. Children's Bks. (Schwartz & Wade Bks.).

Schrecengost, Maity. Tasso of Tarpon Springs. Stock, Rose, illus. 1998. 118p. (J). (gr. 3-6). pap. 5.95 (978-0-929895-24-6(X) , Hoot Owl Bks.) Maupin Hse. Publishing.

Schroder, Jack. The Nasty Affair at the Lake, 1 bk. 2004. 152p. (J). per. 9.95 (978-0-9745665-8-0(6)) Catalpa Pr.

Schwed, Michael J. A Prayer for Jeremy. 2002. 108p. (J). pap. 9.95 (978-0-595-21863-9(6) , Writers Club Pr.) iUniverse, Inc.

Scieszka, Jon. The Not-So-Jolly Roger, Vol. 2. 2004. (Time Warp Trio Ser.: No. 2). (Illus.). 64p. (J). (gr. 2-6). pap. 4.99 (978-0-14-240045-6(9) , Puffin) Penguin Group (USA) Inc.

—The Not-So-Jolly Roger. unabr. ed. (Time Warp Trio Ser.: No. 2). (J). (gr. 2-4). 1999. pap. 29.98 incl. audio (978-0-8072-1302-5(0) , EFTR194MP); 1998. 57p. pap. 17.00 incl. audio (978-0-8072-0394-1(7) , EFTR194SP) Random Hse. Audio Publishing Group. (Listening Library).

Scott, Carlton T. Little Big Wolf. Scott, Carlton T., illus. 1999. (Illus.). 32p. (J). (gr. k-5). 9.95 (978-0-9636652-8-7(6)) Ends of the Earth Books.com.

Sculthorp, Jeffrey A. Will Walter Ever Win? Wingate, Lynae & Kober, John R., eds. Walter, Lorin, illus. 2000. (Wickleville Woods Ser.). 28p. (J). (ps-2). pap. 4.99 (978-1-889319-77-3(5) , Wickleville Woods) Trend Enterprises, Inc.

Seagrove, John K. Man, Oh, Man, You Have Fallen Too. 1998. 221p. (Orig.). (YA). per. 15.00 (978-0-9647633-1-9(1)) Kendall Publishing.

Selznick, Brian. The Boy of a Thousand Faces. Selznick, Brian, illus. 2001. (Illus.). 48p. (J). (gr. 3 up). pap. 6.99 (978-0-06-441080-9(3) , Harper Trophy) HarperCollins Pubs.

Sempé, Jean-Jacques & Goscinny, René. Nicholas. Bell, Anthea, tr. from FRE. rev. ed. 2005. (Illus.). 136p. (ps-7). 19.95 (978-0-7148-4529-6(9)) Phaidon Pr. GBR. *Dist:* Hachette Bk. Group.

Sendak, Maurice. La Cocina de Noche. Sendak, Maurice, illus. 2003. (Picture Books Collection). (SPA., Illus.). 40p. (J). (gr. k-3). 10.95 (978-84-204-4570-0(3)) Alfaguara, Ediciones, S.A.- Grupo Santillana ESP. *Dist:* Santillana USA Publishing Co., Inc.

Sennell, Joles. Yuyo, Nino No Podia... (Yuyo, Boy Who...) (SPA.). 24p. (J). 12.50 (978-84-7183-169-9(4)) El Hogar y La Moda, S.A. ESP. *Dist:* AIMS International Bks., Inc.

Serrano, Heather F. Always Alex. Mullinnix, Kathleen, illus. 1998. 32p. (J). (ps-3). 12.95 (978-1-56550-081-5(4)) Vision Bks. International.

Servi Machlin, Edda. My Puppy Marrano. 2007. (YA). 19.95 ***(978-1-878857-13-2(4))*** Giro Pr.

Shah, Idries & Caron, Mona. The Boy Without a Name. 2000. (Illus.). 32p. (J). (ps-3). 17.00 (978-1-883536-20-6(0) , BOWN1, Hoopoe Bks.) ISHK.

Shah, Idries & Santiago, Rose Mary. The Clever Boy & the Terrible, Dangerous Animal. 2000. (Illus.). 32p. (J). (gr. 1-4). 17.00 (978-1-883536-18-3(9) , CLBT1, Hoopoe Bks.) ISHK.

Shannon, David. David Goes to School. Shannon, David, illus. 2002. (Illus.). (J). 25.06 (978-0-7587-2350-5(4)) Book Wholesalers, Inc.

—David Goes to School. Shannon, David, illus. 1999. (Illus.). 32p. (J). (ps-3). pap. 15.95 (978-0-590-48087-1(1) , Blue Sky Pr., The) Scholastic, Inc.

Sharmat, Marjorie Weinman. Nate the Great & the Monster Mess. Weston, Martha, illus. 2001. (Nate the Great Ser.). 80p. (J). (gr. 1-4). pap. 4.50 (978-0-440-41662-3(0) , Yearling) Random Hse. Children's Bks.

—Nate the Great & the Monster Mess. 2001. (978-0-606-22399-7(1)); (gr. 3-6). lib. bdg. 12.40 (978-0-613-36847-6(9)) Tandem Library Bks.

Sharmat, Mitchell. Gregory, the Terrible Eater. Aruego, Jose, illus. 2002. (J). 12.87 (978-0-7587-2663-6(5)) Book Wholesalers, Inc.

Sharratt, Nick. Robopop. 2000. (Illus.). 121p. (J). pap. 7.99 (978-0-440-86352-6(X)) Transworld Publishers Ltd. GBR. *Dist:* Trafalgar Square Publishing.

Sharratt, Nick & Tucker, Stephen. El Tiempo Que Tardo Tomas. Davis, J., tr. from ENG. Sharratt, Nick, illus. 1998. (SPA., Illus.). 32p. (J). (gr. k-2). pap. 6.95 (978-1-880507-48-3(X) , LC8622) Lectorum Pubns., Inc.

Shelby, Patty. Trick or Treat at the House of the Man That Gave Away Fifty-Cent Pieces. l.t. ed. 2004. (Illus.). 16p. per. 19.95 (978-1-59453-496-6(9) , 2591) Airleaf Publishing & Bookselling.

Shepperson, Jacqueline Ruth. The Blue Jay Tales. 2005. 89p. pap. 14.95 (978-1-4137-3884-1(2)) PublishAmerica, Inc.

Shriver, Maria. Que le Pasa a Timmy? Speidel, Sandra, illus. 2001. (SPA.). 48p. (gr. 4-17). 14.95 (978-0-316-16794-9(0)) Little, Brown Bks. for Young Readers.

Shusterman, Neal. Bruiser. 2005. 160p. (J). pap. 6.99 (978-0-06-113410-4(4) , Harper Trophy) HarperCollins Pubs.

Shute, Henry A. The Real Diary of A Real Boy. 2004. reprint ed. pap. 1.99 (978-1-4192-7985-0(8)) Kessinger Publishing, LLC.

Simon, Charnan. A Busy Guy. Rau, Dana, ed. Holub, Joan, illus. 1998. (Rookie Reader Skill Set Ser.). 32p. (J). (gr. k-2). pap. 4.95 (978-0-516-26357-1(9) , Children's Pr.) Scholastic Library Publishing.

—Show & Tell Sam. Bialke, Gary, illus. 1999. (Rookie Reader Skill Set Ser.). 32p. (J). (gr. k-2). pap. 4.95 (978-0-516-26413-4(3) , Children's Pr.) Scholastic Library Publishing.

—Show-and-Tell Sam. Bialke, Gary, illus. 1998. (Rookie Readers Ser.). 32p. (J). (gr. 1-2). 19.50 (978-0-516-20945-6(0) , Children's Pr.) Scholastic Library Publishing.

—Show-and-Tell Sam. Bialke, Gary, illus. 1999. 31p. (J). (gr. k-3). lib. bdg. 12.95 (978-0-613-37537-5(8)) Tandem Library Bks.

Simon, Francesca. Horrid Henry & the Mummy's Curse. l.t. ed. 2001. (Illus.). 88p. (J). 16.95 (978-0-7540-6166-3(3) , Galaxy Children's Large Print) BBC Audiobooks America.

Simon, Les. The Secret of the Red Silk Pouch. 1998. 157p. (YA). (gr. 8-12). pap. 9.99 (978-0-88092-362-0(8) , 3628) Royal Fireworks Publishing Co.

Simpson, Fiona, ed. Novelization. 2006. 232p. (J). pap. 6.99 (978-0-439-74572-7(1)) Scholastic, Inc.

Singer, Marilyn. Fred's Bed. Adinolfi, JoAnn, illus. 2001. (Growing Tree Ser.). 24p. (J). (ps-1). 9.95 (978-0-694-01451-4(6) , Harper Festival) HarperCollins Pubs.

Singh, Pushpinder. The Boy with Long Hair. Singh, Pushpinder, illus. 1999. (Illus.). 24p. (J). (ps-3). pap. 4.95 (978-0-9700363-0-8(2)) Sikh Foundation.

Sitomer, Alan Lawrence. The Hoopster. 2006. 224p. (gr. 7-17). pap. 5.99 (978-0-7868-4910-9(X) , Jump at the Sun) Hyperion Bks. for Children.

Skrypuch, Marsha Forchuk. Aram's Choice. Wood, Muriel, illus. 2006. 72p. (J). (gr. 2-4). ***(978-1-55041-352-6(X))*** Fitzhenry & Whiteside, Ltd.

Slangerup, Erik Jon. Dirt Boy. Manders, John, illus. 2000. 32p. (J). (gr. 1-4). pap. 6.95 (978-0-8075-1617-1(1)) Whitman, Albert & Co.

Sleator, William. The Boy Who Couldn't Die. 2004. 174p. (J). (gr. 7-11). 16.95 (978-0-8109-4824-2(9)) Abrams, Harry N. , Inc.

—The Boy Who Reversed Himself. 1998. 176p. (J). (gr. 5-9). pap. 5.99 (978-0-14-038965-4(2) , Puffin) Penguin Group (USA) Inc.

—The Boy Who Reversed Himself. 2000. (J). (gr. 4-8). 21.75 (978-0-8446-7154-3(1)) Smith, Peter Pub., Inc.

—The Boy Who Reversed Himself. 1998. 12.64 (978-0-606-12896-4(4)) Tandem Library Bks.

Small, David. Paper John. Small, David, illus. 1998. (Illus.). pap., tchr. ed. 37.95 incl. audio (978-0-87499-452-0(7)); (J). 24.95 incl. audio (978-0-87499-451-3(9)); (J). pap. 16.95 incl. audio (978-0-87499-450-6(0)) Live Oak Media.

Smax, Willy & Ludlow, Keren. Benny Goes to the Seaside. 2000. (Illus.). 24p. (J). pap. 4.99 (978-1-85881-700-2(5)) Orion Children's Bks. GBR. *Dist:* Trafalgar Square Publishing.

Smith, Peggy. The Champ: The Adventures of a Boy & His New Puppy. Told in One-syllable Words for the Barton Reading & Spelling System. 2003. (J). pap. 7.95 (978-0-9744343-3-9(7) , SA-304) Bright Solutions for Dyslexia, LLC.

Smith, Rod. The Long Road. 2003. 16p. (C). pap. 9.00 (978-0-582-50494-3(5)) Pearson ESL.

Smith, Stu & Wolff, Julian. The Bubble Gum Kid. 2006. (Illus.). 32p. 15.95 (978-0-7624-2046-9(4)) Running Pr. Bk. Pubs.

Snell, Roy F. Wings for Victory. 2005. pap. 26.95 (978-1-4191-6999-1(8)) Kessinger Publishing, LLC.

A Soap Story: Individual Title, 6 packs. (ps-2). 27.00 (978-0-7635-9475-6(X)) Rigby Education.

Sokoloff, David, et al. Here I Am: For Boys. Sokoloff, David, illus. 1999. (Illus.). 10p. (J). (ps-3). 6.00 (978-1-889655-00-0(7)) Jewish Educational Toys.

Soloman, Ms Debra. Don't Look under the Bridge. 2006. 25p. 17.00 (978-1-4116-7114-0(7)) Lulu.com.

Sorel, Edward. Johnny on the Spot. 1998. (Illus.). 32p. (J). (gr. k-4). 16.00 (978-0-689-81293-4(0) , McElderry, Margaret K.) Simon & Schuster Children's Publishing.

Sparks, Evan. Freddy's Tale. 2006. 44p. pap. 14.88 (978-1-4116-7427-1(8)) Lulu.com.

Spinelli, Jerry. Milkweed. 2003. (Illus.). 224p. (J). (gr. 5). lib. bdg. 17.99 (978-0-375-91374-7(2) , Knopf Bks. for Young Readers) Random Hse. Children's Bks.

Stadler, John. One Seal. Stadler, John, illus. 1999. (Illus.). 32p. (J). (ps-2). 16.99 (978-0-531-33195-8(4) , Orchard Bks.) Scholastic, Inc.

Standish, Burt L. Frank Merriwell down South. Rudman, Jack, ed. (Frank Merriwell Ser.). (YA). (gr. 9 up). 29.95 (978-0-8373-9305-6(1)); 2003. pap. 9.95 (978-0-8373-9005-5(2) , FM-005) Merriwell, Frank Inc.

—Frank Merriwell in Europe. Rudman, Jack, ed. (Frank Merriwell Ser.). (YA). (gr. 9 up). 29.95 (978-0-8373-9308-7(6)); pap. 9.95 (978-0-8373-9008-6(7) , FM-008) Merriwell, Frank Inc.

—Frank Merriwell's Bravery. Rudman, Jack, ed. (Frank Merriwell Ser.). (YA). (gr. 9 up). 29.95 (978-0-8373-9306-3(X)); 2003. pap. 9.95 (978-0-8373-9006-2(0) , FM-006) Merriwell, Frank Inc.

—Frank Merriwell's Hunting Tour. Rudman, Jack, ed. (Frank Merriwell Ser.). (YA). (gr. 9 up). 29.95 (978-0-8373-9307-0(8)); 2003. pap. 9.95 (978-0-8373-9007-9(9) , FM-007) Merriwell, Frank Inc.

—Frank Merriwell's New Boy. Rudman, Jack, ed. 2003. (Frank Merriwell Ser.). pap. 9.95 (978-0-8373-9134-2(2)) Merriwell, Frank Inc.

—Frank Merriwell's Sports Afield. Rudman, Jack, ed. (Frank Merriwell Ser.). (YA). (gr. 9 up). 29.95 (978-0-8373-9310-0(8)); pap. 9.95 (978-0-8373-9010-9(9) , FM-010) Merriwell, Frank Inc.

—Frank Merriwell's Trip West. Rudman, Jack, ed. (Frank Merriwell Ser.). (YA). (gr. 9 up). 29.95 (978-0-8373-9304-9(3)); pap. 9.95 (978-0-8373-9004-8(4) , FM-004) Merriwell, Frank Inc.

Starlog Celebrity Series Presents No. 1: Justin vs. Nick. 1999. (Illus.). pap. 4.99 (978-0-934551-72-4(3)) Profile Entertainment, Inc.

Starlog Celebrity Series Presents No. 8: Kissable Pinups. 1998. pap. 4.99 (978-0-934551-56-4(1)) Profile Entertainment, Inc.

Stassen, Jean-Philippe. Deogratias. 2006. (Illus.). 96p. (J). pap. ***(978-0-330-44467-5(0)*** , First Second Bks.) Roaring Brook Pr.

Steck-Vaughn Staff. Mike Likes Stripes/Home By. 1999. (Take Me Home Ser.). (J). pap. (978-0-7398-2678-2(6)) Steck-Vaughn.

Steig, William. Toby, Where Are You? Euvremer, Teryl, illus. 1999. 32p. (J). (ps-1). pap. 4.95 (978-0-06-205929-1(7)) HarperCollins Pubs.

—Toby, Where Are You? 1999. 32p. (J). (ps-1). pap. 4.95 (978-0-06-205928-4(9)) HarperCollins Pubs.

Stenhouse, Ted. Murder on the ridge. 2006. 240p. 6.95 (978-1-55337-893-8(8)) Kids Can Pr., Ltd. CAN. *Dist:* Wybel Marketing Group.

Stern, Maggie. George. Sims, Blanche, illus. 1999. 47p. (J). (gr. 1-4). pap. 13.95 (978-0-531-30197-5(4) , Orchard Bks.) Scholastic, Inc.

—George. 1999. (George & Diggity Ser.). (Illus.). (J). (978-0-606-21774-3(6)) Tandem Library Bks.

Stevenson, Robert Louis, intro. Kidnapped: Catriona. 2007. 480p. pap. 15.00 ***(978-1-84697-033-7(4))*** BirlinnPolygon GBR. *Dist:* Interlink Publishing Group, Inc.

Stirnkorb, Patricia. All about Me! Regular Version. 2005. (Illus.). 12p. (J). bds. 12.99 (978-0-9758709-8-3(X) , A.W.A. Gang) Journey Stone Creations, LLC.

—Stranger Danger: The reluctantly written but absolutly necessary book for todays boys & Girls. 2005. (Illus.). 32p. (J). 12.99 (978-0-9758709-9-0(8)) Journey Stone Creations, LLC.

Stoddard, William O. Dab Kinzer: A Story of a Growing Boy. l.t. ed. 2006. 214p. pap. 12.99 ***(978-1-4264-4047-2(2))***; 232p. pap. 15.99 ***(978-1-4264-4106-6(1))*** BiblioBazaar.

Stoddard, William O. Dab Kinzer A Story of A Growing Boy. 2004. reprint ed. pap. 24.95 (978-1-4191-1488-5(3)); pap. 1.99 (978-1-4192-1488-2(8)) Kessinger Publishing, LLC.

Stodghill, Pat & Briley, Rita, illus. Jake's Snapping Catastrophe. 2000. 15.95 (978-1-57168-379-3(8)) Eakin Pr.

Stone Fox. 1998. (J). (gr. 5). pap. 3.95 (978-0-439-04473-8(1)) Scholastic, Inc.

Stouffer, N. K. Larry Potter & His Best Friend Lilly. Stouffer, N. K., illus. 2001. (Larry Potter Storybks.). (Illus.). 22p. (J). (ps-2). 7.95 (978-1-58989-300-9(X)) Thurman Hse., LLC.

—Lilly & Larry Potter: More Than Just Friends. Stouffer, N. K., illus. 2001. (Larry Potter Storybks.). (Illus.). 22p. (J). (ps-2). 7.95 (978-1-58989-302-3(6)) Thurman Hse., LLC.

—Lotty Potter: I Am Who I Am. Stouffer, N. K., illus. 2001. (Larry Potter Storybks.). (Illus.). 22p. (J). (ps-2). 7.95 (978-1-58989-303-0(4)) Thurman Hse., LLC.

Stratemeyer, Edward. The Minute Boys of Bunker Hill. Kennedy, J. W., illus. rev. ed. 1998. 316p. (J). (gr. 4-8). per. 14.95 (978-1-890623-05-0(9)) Lost Classics Bk. Co.

—The Rover Boys at School: Or the Cadets of Putnam Hall. 2006. 164p. pap. 11.99 (978-1-4264-2004-7(8)) BiblioBazaar.

—The Rover Boys on the Ocean: Or, a Chase for a Fortune. 2006. 158p. pap. 11.99 (978-1-4264-2766-4(2)); 170p. pap. 14.99 (978-1-4264-2804-3(9)) BiblioBazaar.

Strauss, Ed. Devotions to Make You Stronger: A 90- Day Devotional. 2007. (2:52 Ser.). 192p. (J). pap. 9.99 (978-0-310-71311-1(0)) Zonderkidz.

Stubbs, Lisa. Sonny's Treasure Hunt. 1999. (Illus.). 32p. (J). (ps-k). pap. 5.95 (978-0-7641-0902-7(2)) Barron's Educational Series, Inc.

Swaim, Jessica. Nate by Night. Carpenter, Christina, ed. O'Dea, Helen, illus. 2000. 32p. (J). (ps-3). 15.95 (978-1-886440-02-9(6)) Portunus Publishing Co.

Sweetser, Kate Dickinson. Boys & girls from Thackeray. l.t. ed. 2006. 264p. pap. 13.99 ***(978-1-4264-3943-8(1))*** BiblioBazaar.

Sydor, Colleen. Maxwell's Metamorphosis. Pavanel, Jane, ed. Vernex, Lenka, illus. 2000. (Generation Norah Ser.: Vol. 2). 112p. (J). (gr. 3-5). pap. 6.95 (978-1-894222-18-1(0)) Lobster Pr. CAN. *Dist:* Univ. of Toronto Pr.

—Maxwell's Metamorphosis. 2000. (gr. 3-6). lib. bdg. 15.25 (978-0-613-85218-0(4)) Tandem Library Bks.

Talbert, Marc. Toby. 2000. 180p. (gr. 4-7). pap. 12.95 (978-0-595-09772-2(3)) iUniverse, Inc.

Tan, Shaun. The Lost Thing. (Illus.). 32p. pap. (978-0-7344-0388-9(7)); 2002. (YA). (978-0-7344-0074-1(8)) Hachette Livre Australia. (Lothian Bks.).

—The Lost Thing. 2004. (Illus.). 32p. (J). 16.95 (978-1-894965-10-1(8)) Simply Read Bks. CAN. *Dist:* Perseus Distribution.

Tangman, Ann & Jungman, Ann. The Most Magnificant Mosque. Fowles, Shelley, illus. 2007. 32p. (J). pap. 7.95 ***(978-1-84507-085-4(2))*** Lincoln, Frances Ltd. GBR. *Dist:* Perseus Distribution.

Tarkington, Booth. Penrod & Sam. (J). reprint ed. lib. bdg. 22.95 (978-0-88411-702-5(2)) Amereon LTD.

Tate, Bill. Little Wyatt Tate. 12th ed. 2001. 123p. (YA). (gr. 10 up). pap. 12.95 (978-1-884242-74-8(X)); lib. bdg. 19.95 (978-1-884242-73-1(1)) Multicultural Pubns.

Tawhara, Merito & Robinson, Nikki Slade. Puriri. 2000. (MAO., Illus.). 37p. (J). pap. 12.95 (978-1-877266-17-1(5)) Huia Pubs. NZL. *Dist:* Pacific Island Bks.

—The Puriri Tree. 2000. (Illus.). 36p. (J). pap. 12.95 (978-1-877266-27-0(2)) Huia Pubs. NZL. *Dist:* Pacific Island Bks.

Taylor, Theodore. Timothy of the Cay. 2001. (J). (gr. 4-7). 21.00 (978-0-8446-7190-1(8)) Smith, Peter Pub., Inc.

Terrill, Mark. Kid with Gray Eyes. 2001. 76p. pap. 10.00 (978-1-891812-28-6(9)) Cedar Hill Bks.

Tetro, Marc. No Rest for Edwin. ed. 2004. (J). (gr. k-3). spiral bd. (978-0-616-01789-0(8)) Canadian National Institute for the Blind/Institut National Canadien pour les Aveugles.

Thiele, Colin. Storm Boy. Ingpen, Robert R., illus. 2004. 64p. (J). (gr. 4-6). pap. (978-1-74110-187-4(5)) New Holland Pubs. Pty, Ltd.

—Storm Boy. 40th ed. 2002. 60p. (J). (gr. 4-6). pap. (978-1-86436-804-8(7)) New Holland Pubs. Pty, Ltd.

Thompson, Jenean. All in a Day's Play. Thompson, Jenean, illus. l.t. ed. 2005. (Illus.). 40p. (J). 14.95 (978-1-59879-066-5(8)) Lifevest Publishing, Inc.

Thompson, Keith. Bells Lake Treasure. 2007. per. 14.99 ***(978-1-59886-565-3(X))*** Tate Publishing & Enterprises, L.L.C.

Tibo, Gilles. Alex & the New Equipment Level 3. Germain, Philippe, illus. 2000. 32p. (J). (gr. 1-4). pap. (978-1-894363-09-9(4)) Dominique & Friends.

—Simon et le Petit Cirque. ed. 2004. Tr. of Simon at the Circus. (FRE.). (J). (ps-2). spiral bd. (978-0-616-01846-0(0)) Canadian National Institute for the Blind/Institut National Canadien pour les Aveugles.

—Simon et les Deguisements. ed. 2004. Tr. of Simon's Disguise. (FRE.). (J). (ps-2). spiral bd. (978-0-616-01844-6(4)) Canadian National Institute for the Blind/Institut National Canadien pour les Aveugles.

—Simon Makes Music. ed. 2004. (J). (ps-2). spiral bd. (978-0-616-01792-0(8)); spiral bd. (978-0-616-01793-7(6)) Canadian National Institute for the Blind/Institut National Canadien pour les Aveugles.

—Simon Says: Seasons. 2006. (Illus.). 48p. (J). (ps-3). 17.95 (978-0-88776-793-7(1)) Tundra Bks., Inc./Livres Toundra, Inc. CAN. *Dist:* Random Hse., Inc.

Timothy, Ering. Frog Belly Rat F & G. 2003. (J). bds. 16.99 (978-0-7636-2248-0(6)) Candlewick Pr.

Timothy of the Cay. 1999. (J). 9.95 (978-1-56137-742-8(2)) Novel Units, Inc.

Titherington, Jeanne. Bonkers Fellini. Titherington, Jeanne, illus. 2001. (Illus.). 24p. (J). (gr. 3 up). 16.95 (978-0-688-15028-0(4)) HarperCollins Pubs.

—A Place for Ben. 1999. (Illus.). 24p. (J). (ps-3). pap. 4.95 (978-0-688-17064-6(1)) HarperCollins Pubs.

A B

Todd, John S. The Goodfellow Boys & the Talking Dinosaur. 2004. (Illus.). 32p. (gr. 3-5). 10.95 (978-1-57197-190-6(4)) Pentland Pr., Inc.

Torres, J. Teen Titans Chapter Book: Blinded by the Light. Mackenzie, Kevin, illus. 3rd ed. 2005. (Teen Titans Ser.). 64p. (J). 3.99 (978-0-439-69635-7(6)) Scholastic, Inc.

Torrey, Michele. Bottles of Eight & Pieces of Rum. 1998. 138p. (J). (ps-7). pap. 9.99 (978-0-88092-321-7(0), 3210) Royal Fireworks Publishing Co.

Tracey, Diane Eurich. Look Out for Virgil. Kuessner, Pat, ed. Golden, Debra Jean, illus. 2001. 24p. (J). (ps-7). pap. 12.00 (978-0-9701441-4-0(8), 628548) Bokmal Pr.

Trembath, Don. Big Show. 2003. (gr. 3-6). lib. bdg. 15.25 (978-0-613-83710-1(X)) Tandem Library Bks.

Tremblay, Marc. Le Petit Frere du Chaperon Rouge. Fil et al, illus. 2004. (était une Fois Ser.). (FRE.). 24p. (J). (ps). pap. (978-2-89021-698-3(5)) Diffusion du livre Mirabel.

Trottier, Maxine. Three Songs for Courage. 2006. 328p. (J). (gr. 9). 16.95 (978-0-88776-745-6(1)) Tundra Bks., Inc./ Livres Toundra, Inc. CAN. *Dist:* Random Hse., Inc.

Trudel, Sylvain. Le Garcon Qui Revait D'Etre un Heros. 2002. (Premier Roman Ser.). (FRE., Illus.). 64p. (J). (gr. 2-5). pap. (978-2-89021-245-9(9)) Diffusion du livre Mirabel.

Turner, Deborah & Mohler, Diana. How Willy Got His Wheels. Anderson, Mark, ed. McHugh, Rhonda, illus. 1999. 32p. (ps-3). 14.95 (978-0-944875-54-4(8)) Doral Publishing, Inc.

Tuthill, Louisa C. Hurrah for New England! or the Virginia Boy's Vacation. 2004. reprint ed. pap. 15.95 (978-1-4191-2504-1(4)); pap. 1.99 (978-1-4192-2504-8(9)) Kessinger Publishing, LLC.

Twachtman-Cullen, Diane. Trevor Trevor. Sassano, Deidre, illus. 1999. 44p. (J). (ps-5). pap. 15.00 (978-0-9666529-0-1(8), 860-345-2155) Starfish Specialty Pr., LLC.

Twain, Mark. The Adventures of Huckleberry Finn. 2007. (Children's Classics Ser.). (Illus.). 256p. (J). 6.99 (978-0-517-22999-6(4), Gramercy) Random Hse. Value Publishing.

—The Adventures of Huckleberry Finn. Hegarty, Carol, ed. 1998. (Classics Ser.: Set I). (Illus.). 77p. (YA). (gr. 5-12). pap. 6.95 (978-1-56254-250-4(8), SP2508) Saddleback Educational Publishing.

—The Adventures of Tom Sawyer. 2005. 264p. 28.95 (978-1-4218-0768-3(8), 1st World Library - Literary Society) 1st World Publishing, Inc.

—The Adventures of Tom Sawyer. (J). (978-0-448-41455-3(4), Putnam Juvenile); 2006. 272p. (gr. 12). pap. 7.00 (978-0-14-303956-3(3), Penguin Classics) Penguin Group (USA) Inc.

—The Adventures of Tom Sawyer. 2006. (Scholastic Classics Ser.). (Illus.). vi, 219p. (J). (gr. 9-12). 25.00 (978-0-531-16978-0(2), Watts, Franklin) Scholastic Library Publishing.

—The Adventures of Tom Sawyer. 2001. 184p. pap. 9.95 (978-1-57002-169-5(4)) University Publishing Hse., Inc.

—The Adventures of Tom Sawyer. Hegarty, Carol, ed. 1998. (Classics Ser.: Set II). (Illus.). 77p. (YA). (gr. 5-12). 6.95 (978-1-56254-252-8(4), SP2524) Saddleback Educational Publishing.

—The Adventures of Tom Sawyer. 2004. reprint ed. pap. 1.99 (978-1-4192-5166-5(X)) Kessinger Publishing, LLC.

—Tom Sawyer Abroad. 1999. 224p. (978-0-14-043383-8(X)) Penguin Group (USA) Inc.

Twain, Mark & Olmos. The Adventures of Huckleberry Finn. 2004. (SPA.). 360p. pap. 17.95 ***978-84-263-5252-1(9))** Vives, Luis Editorial (Edelvives) ESP. *Dist:* Lectorum Pubns., Inc.

Ungerer, Tomi. Rufus. Ungerer, Tomi, illus. 2003. (SPA., Illus.). 36p. (J). (gr. k-3). pap. 7.95 (978-968-19-0746-4(9)) Aguilar, Altea, Taurus, Alfaguara, S.A. de C.V MEX. *Dist:* Santillana USA Publishing Co., Inc.

The Unwelcome Visitors. 2004. (J). per. 11.00 (978-0-9746849-0-1(2)) Broader Horizon Bks.

Urmston, Kathleen & Urmston, Grant. A Rainy Day for Sammy. Gedeon, Gloria, illus. 2004. 22p. (J). (gr. k-3). pap. 4.95 (978-1-57874-078-9(9)) Kaeden Corp.

Vadeboncoeur, Isabelle & Savary, Fabien. Caillou - What Do You Like to Eat? Johanson, Sarah Margaret, tr. from FRE. Brignaud, Pierre, illus. rev. ed. 2005. (Butterfly Ser.).Tr. of Caillou Découvre les Aliments. 20p. (J). (ps-1). pap. 5.95 (978-2-89450-542-7(5)) Chouette Publishing CAN. *Dist:* Independent Pubs. Group.

Van Draanen, Wendelin. Swear to Howdy. 2005. 144p. (J). (gr. 5). reprint ed. pap. 5.99 (978-0-440-41943-3(3), Yearling) Random Hse. Children's Bks.

Varsell, Linda. A Journey for Rainbows. Curtis, E., illus. 2003. 166p. (YA). per. 6.00 (978-0-9725479-1-8(6)) Rainbow Communications.

Veremiah, Omari. Paper Boy Two: Over Whelming 0005. Rolling, Beanic, illus. 2004. 74p. (YA). (gr. 7-12). pap. 12.99 (978-1-929188-10-9(2)) Morton Bks.

Viorst, Judith. Alexander, Que Era Rico el Domingo Pasado. Cruz, Ray, illus. 1999. (Alexander Ser.). (SPA.). (J). (ps-2). lib. bdg. 14.15 (978-0-8335-4310-3(5)) Tandem Library Bks.

—Alexander, Who Used to Be Rich Last Sunday. 1999. (Alexander Ser.). (J). (gr. k-3). pap. 24.24 incl. audio (978-0-7887-3634-6(5), 40999) Recorded Bks., LLC.

—Alexander, Who Used to Be Rich Last Sunday. Cruz, Ray, illus. 1999. (Alexander Ser.). (J). (gr. k-3). lib. bdg. 14.15 (978-0-8085-2752-7(5)) Tandem Library Bks.

—Alexander y el Dia Terrible, Horrible, Espantoso, Horroroso. Cruz, Ray, illus. 1999. (Alexander Ser.). (SPA.). (J). (gr. k-3). lib. bdg. 14.15 (978-0-8335-4316-5(4)) Tandem Library Bks.

—Just in Case. Bluthenthal, Diana Cain, illus. 2006. 40p. (J). (ps-2). 15.95 (978-0-689-87164-1(3), Atheneum) Simon & Schuster Children's Publishing.

Vivelo, Jackie. Reading to Matthew. Saflund, Birgitta, illus. 1999. 40p. (gr. 4-9). 15.95 (978-1-879373-60-0(2)) Rinehart, Roberts Pubs.

Vulliamy, Clara. Tom & Small: A Big Moment in a Little Boy's Life. 2004. (Illus.). 32p. pap. 8.99 (978-0-00-713788-6(5)) HarperCollins Pubs. Ltd. GBR. *Dist:* Trafalgar Square Publishing.

Waber, Bernard. Ira Says Goodbye. Waber, Bernard, illus. unabr. ed. 2005. (Illus.). (J). (gr. k-3). pap. 16.95 incl. audio (978-0-87499-138-3(2)) BBC Audiobooks America.

—Ira Says Goodbye. 2000. (J). pap. 19.97 incl. audio (978-0-7366-9204-5(5)) Books on Tape, Inc.

Wakeman, Daniel & Van Stralen, Dirk. Ben's Big Dig. 2005. (Illus.). 32p. (J). (ps-2). 17.95 (978-1-55143-384-4(2)) Orca Bk. Pubs. USA.

Walker, Cheryl. The Little Black & White Pony. 2003. 28p. (J). pap. 2.50 (978-0-9726326-1-4(1)) TechArts International LLC.

Wallace, Ian. Boy of the Deeps. 2005. (Illus.). 32p. (J). pap. 6.95 (978-0-88899-660-2(8)) Groundwood Bks. CAN. *Dist:* Perseus Distribution.

—Duncan's Way. 2000. (Illus.). (J). (gr. k-3). (978-0-88899-388-5(9)) Groundwood Bks. CAN. *Dist:* Transition Vendor.

Wallace, Joseph. Big & Noisy Simon. Date not set. 32p. 5.99 (978-0-7868-1366-7(0)) Hyperion Paperbacks for Children.

Wallen, Virginia. Sonny & Sammy. 2006. 17.00 (978-0-8059-9809-2(8)) Dorrance Publishing Co., Inc.

Walsh, Ellen Stoll. For Pete's Sake. 1998. (Illus.). 40p. (J). (ps-3). 15.00 (978-0-15-200324-1(X)) Harcourt Children's Bks.

Walsh, Paton Jill. Pepi & the Secret Names. French, Fiona, illus. 2001. 32p. (J). (ps-3). pap. 8.99 (978-0-7112-1089-6(6)) Lincoln, Frances Ltd. GBR. *Dist:* Antique Collectors' Club.

Ward, Nick. I Wish. 2007. (Illus.). 24p. (J). pap. 8.99 ***(978-1-84458-126-9(8))** Anova Bks. GBR. *Dist:* Independent Pubs. Group.

Wardlaw, Lee. Hector's Hiccups. 1999. (Step into Reading Ser.). (J). (978-0-606-16892-2(3)) Tandem Library Bks.

Warner Bros Us Staff & Martin, Cory. OC: The Outsider. 2006. (Illus.). 320p. pap. 5.57 (978-0-14-131907-0(0)) Penguin Group (USA) Inc.

Warner, Charles Dudley. Being A Boy. 2005. 124p. pap. 10.95 (978-1-4218-0414-9(X), 1st World Library - Literary Society) 1st World Publishing, Inc.

—Being A Boy. 2004. reprint ed. pap. 15.95 (978-1-4191-0953-9(7)); pap. 1.99 (978-1-4192-0953-6(1)) Kessinger Publishing, LLC.

Waterton, Betty. Quincy Rumpel. 2000. (Quincy Rumpel Bks.). (Illus.). 144p. (J). (gr. 3-7). pap. 3.95 (978-0-88899-393-9(5), Libros Tigrillo) Groundwood Bks. CAN. *Dist:* Transition Vendor.

—A Salmon for Simon. rev. ed. 1998. (Illus.). 32p. (J). (ps-1). pap. 6.95 (978-0-88899-276-5(9)) Groundwood Bks. CAN. *Dist:* Perseus Distribution.

Watkins, Tracy D. Patrick the Pelaganty. Herbrechtsmeier, Keith, ed. Jones, Jerry D., illus. 1999. 40p. (J). (gr. k-6). 18.95 (978-1-883261-00-9(7)) Pelaganty Bks., Inc.

Wax, Wendy. Renoir & the Boy with the Long Hair. Lane, Nancy, illus. 2007. 32p. (J). (ps-3). 14.99 ***(978-0-7641-6041-7(9))** Barron's Educational Series, Inc.

Weeks, Sarah. Danger! Boys Dancing! 2006. (Boyds Will Be Boyds Ser.: No. 3). 160p. (J). pap. 4.99 (978-0-439-57471-6(4), Scholastic Paperbacks) Scholastic, Inc.

—Michael. Date not set. 32p. (J). (ps-2). 14.99 (978-0-06-028231-8(2)); pap. 4.99 (978-0-06-443541-3(5)) HarperCollins Pubs.

Weinberger, Kimberly. Erik. 2000. (Teacher's Pet Ser.: Vol. 2). (J). pap. 4.95 (978-0-439-13245-9(2)) Scholastic, Inc.

Weninger, Brigitte. What Have You Done, Davy? 1999. (gr. k-3). lib. bdg. 15.25 (978-0-613-37172-8(0)) Tandem Library Bks.

Westra, Elizabeth. Alexander & the Stallion. Ampel, Kenneth Robert, illus. 2003. (Books for Young Learners). 16p. (J). per. 5.00 net. (978-1-57274-534-6(7), 2721) Owen, Richard C. Pubs., Inc.

Weyn, Suzanne. The Grouchiest Wubby. Brannon, Tom, illus. 1999. (J). lib. bdg. 8.99 (978-0-375-90134-8(5), Random Hse. Bks. for Young Readers) Random Hse. Children's Bks.

Whalen, Erin T. Charlie's Head: A Series. l.t. ed. 1999. (Illus.). 32p. (J). (gr. 1-2). 16.95 (978-1-929265-00-8(X)); pap. 8.95 (978-1-929265-01-5(8)) Lily & Co. Publishing.

Whelan, Gloria. The Pathless Woods: Ernest Hemingway's Sixteenth Summer in Northern Michigan. Wolff, Glenn, illus. 2nd rev. ed. 1998. (J). (gr. 6-10). 16.95 (978-1-882376-63-6(3)); 176p. (gr. 7-12). pap. 11.95 (978-1-882376-44-5(7)) Thunder Bay Pr.

Whipple, Wayne. Radio Boys Cronies. 2004. reprint ed. pap. 15.95 (978-1-4191-4378-6(6)); pap. 1.99 (978-1-4192-4378-3(0)) Kessinger Publishing, LLC.

White, Allison Ramy. Sunny Boy & His Playmates. 2006. 94.99 ***(978-1-4280-1495-4(0));** pap. 88.99 ***(978-1-4280-1499-2(3))** IndyPublish.com.

White, Howard. Patrick & the Backhoe. Griffiths, Bus, illus. unabr. ed. 24p. (J). (978-0-88971-052-8(X)) Harbour Publishing Co., Ltd.

Wild, Margaret. Tom Goes to Kindergarten. Legge, David, illus. 2000. (Concept Book Ser.). 32p. (J). (ps-1). 15.95 (978-0-8075-8012-7(0)) Whitman, Albert & Co.

Wilford Gordon Mcdonald Partridge. 2004. (J). pap. 32.75 incl. audio (978-1-55592-337-2(2)) Weston Woods Studios, Inc.

Wilkins, Lisa. The Key Seekers. 2005. 68p. pap. 14.95 (978-1-4137-8681-1(2)) PublishAmerica, Inc.

Willett, Fangette H. The Boy Who Found Hashem. Jacobs, Jody, illus. 1998. ii, 14p. (J). (gr. 1-5). pap. 4.95 (978-0-9642613-1-0(6)) KinderWord.

Willever, Lisa Funari. Everybody Moos at Cows: Even Matthew McFarland. Poller, Elaine & Byrne, Glenn, illus. 2001. (Tales of Matthew McFarland Ser.). 32p. (ps-3). 11.95 (978-0-9679227-0-6(4), 329-004) Franklin Mason Pr.

William Bradford Pilgrim Boy. 2004. pap. 8.95 (978-0-01-210122-3(2)) Beautiful Feet Bks.

Williams, Garth. Benjamin's Treasure. Date not set. 32p. (J). (ps-2). pap. 5.99 (978-0-06-443636-6(5)) HarperCollins Pubs.

—Benjamin's Treasure. Wells, Rosemary, illus. 2001. 32p. (J). (ps-3). 15.89 (978-0-06-028741-2(1)); 15.95 (978-0-06-028740-5(3)) HarperCollins Pubs.

Williams, Joyce Hall & West, Nancy H. Ruffitt versus Do-Well: Let's Play Ball at the Taj Mahal. 2004. 112p. (YA). pap. 11.95 (978-0-7414-2095-4(3)) Infinity Publishing.

Williams, Vera B. Scooter. Williams, Vera B., illus. 2001. (Illus.). 160p. (J). (gr. 2 up). pap. 14.99 (978-0-06-440968-1(6), Harper Trophy) HarperCollins Pubs.

—Scooter. 2001. (gr. 3-6). lib. bdg. 19.90 (978-0-613-33726-7(3)); (Illus.). (J). (978-0-606-20898-7(4)) Tandem Library Bks.

Williamson, Peggy. Jake's American Story. 2003. 35 p. pap. 14.95 (978-1-4137-0428-0(X)) PublishAmerica, Inc.

Willis, Jeanne. El Nino Que Perdio el Ombligo. Ross, Tony, illus. (SPA.). (J). 8.95 (978-958-04-5632-2(1)) Norma S.A. COL. *Dist:* Distribuidora Norma, Inc., Lectorum Pubns., Inc.

Wilson, Kevin. Brown Spot. 2006. 60p. (J). pap. 12.00 (978-1-4116-8059-3(6)) Lulu.com.

Wilson, Nancy Hope. Becoming Felix. 1998. (J). (978-0-606-13185-8(X)) Tandem Library Bks.

Wilson, Ritchie. Kinji Goes to Kindergarten. 2006. (Illus.). 28p. pap. 11.95 (978-1-59800-516-5(2)) Outskirts Press, Inc.

Winfield (Edward Str Staff. The Rover Boys at School or the Cadets O. 2006. 26.99 ***(978-1-4280-1710-8(0))** IndyPublish.com.

Winfield, Arthur M. The Rover Boys at School. 2004. reprint ed. pap. 1.99 (978-1-4192-8115-0(1)) Kessinger Publishing, LLC.

Winfield, M. Arthur. The Rover Boys in the Mountains or a Hun. 2006. 78.99 ***(978-1-4280-1209-7(5));** pap. 72.99 ***(978-1-4280-1205-9(2))** IndyPublish.com.

Wiseman, David. Jeremy Visick. 2003. 176p. (YA). (gr. 5-9). pap. 5.95 (978-0-618-34514-4(0)) Houghton Mifflin Co. Trade & Reference Div.

—Jeremy Visick. 2003. (gr. 5-8). lib. bdg. 14.10 (978-0-613-60770-4(8)) Tandem Library Bks.

Wisler, G. Clifton. Caleb's Choice. 2002. 154p. (YA). (gr. 6-9). reprint ed. 15.00 (978-0-7567-5826-4(2)) DIANE Publishing Co.

—Caleb's Choice. 1998. (Puffin Novel Ser.). (J). 11.64 (978-0-606-13235-0(X)) Tandem Library Bks.

Witheridge, Fenwick. The Sword of Cedric & Jiff's Island. 2004. 81p. pap. 14.95 (978-1-4137-0904-9(4)) PublishAmerica, Inc.

Withers, Pam. Adrenalin Ride. 2004. (Take It to the Extreme Ser.). 176p. (YA). (gr. 7-11). pap. 6.95 (978-1-55285-604-8(6)) Whitecap Bks., Ltd. CAN. *Dist:* Firefly Bks., Ltd.

Wojtowycz, David. Dudley Helps Out! 2000. (Illus.). 14p. (J). (ps-3). pap. 7.95 (978-1-888444-71-1(1)) Little Tiger Pr.

Wolff, Virginia Euwer. Probably Still Nick Swansen. 2002. 160p. (YA). pap. 7.99 (978-0-689-85226-8(6), Simon Pulse) Simon & Schuster Children's Publishing.

Wood, Deanna Plummer. Whenever Monkeys Move Next Door, 1 volume. 2005. (Illus.). 24p. (J). pap. 8.50 (978-0-9762935-1-4(X)) Perkins Crawford.

Wood Jr., Richard L. Christopher & the Box in the Closet. 2004. (Illus.). 18p. 9.95 (978-1-59453-142-2(0), 2026) Airleaf Publishing & Bookselling.

Woodruff, Elvira. Dear Austin: Letters from the Underground Railroad. Carpenter, Nancy, illus. 2000. 144p. (YA). (gr. 5-8). 5.50 (978-0-375-80356-7(4), Yearling) Random Hse. Children's Bks.

—Dear Austin: Letters from the Underground Railroad. 2000. (Illus.). (J). 11.64 (978-0-606-18811-1(8)) Tandem Library Bks.

Woods, Shirley. The Magical Mystery. 2005. (Illus.). 102p. (J). per. 11.95 (978-1-59453-100-2(5), 3679) Airleaf Publishing & Bookselling.

Woodward/Amit, Kay/Ofra. Countdown! 2006. (Illus.). 32p. (J). lib. bdg. 9.00 ***(978-1-4242-0879-1(3))** Fitzgerald Bks.

Wright, K. Paige. Steven & Huggey: The story of a boy & his Blankey. 2004. (J). per. 5.95 (978-1-59196-705-7(8)) Instantpublisher.com.

Wright, Sue. Davey & Goliath Blind Mans Bluff. 2005. (Davey & Goliath Storybook #2 Ser.). (Illus.). 40p. (J). 3.99 (978-0-439-69832-0(4), Scholastic Paperbacks) Scholastic, Inc.

Wunderlich, Fran. How Does That Feel Stanley? l.t. ed. 1999. (Illus.). 25p. (J). (ps-4). pap. 10.95 (978-0-9649293-7-1(6)) Belle Terre Pr., Inc.

Yashima, Taro. Nino Cuervo. Fiol, María A., tr. 1999. (SPA.). (J). (gr. 2-4). pap. 6.95 (978-1-880507-61-2(7), LC0302) Lectorum Pubns., Inc.

Yoder, Karen L. Fire Kids! The Adventures of Hose Company No. 2. 2002. 124p. (J). 15.95 (978-0-9700487-4-5(2)) Stoney Creek Pr.

Yoon, Salina. Birthday Boy! Yoon, Salina, illus. 2006. (Illus.). 10p. (J). (ps-1). bds. 5.99 (978-0-8431-1791-2(5), Price Stern Sloan) Penguin Group (USA) Inc.

Young, D. Jean. Quicksilver Summer. 1998. 162p. (YA). (gr. 7-12). pap. 9.95 (978-1-896184-36-4(7)) Roussan Pubs., Inc./Roussan Editeur, Inc. CAN. *Dist:* Orca Bk. Pubs. USA.

Zalben, Jane Breskin. Earth to Andrew O. Blechman. 2000. (Illus.). 164p. (gr. 4-7). pap. 10.95 (978-0-595-12919-5(6), Backinprint.com) iUniverse, Inc.

Zamorano, Ana. A Comer! Vivas, Julie, illus. 1999. (SPA.). 32p. (J). (gr. k-1). pap. 5.99 (978-0-439-07191-8(7), SO3216, Scholastic en Espanol) Scholastic, Inc.

Zawadsky, Pat. The Boy Who Stole the Fourth of July: A Musical Comedy. 1998. (Illus.). 29p. (YA). (gr. 5-12). pap. 4.00 (978-0-88680-450-3(7), C4507) Clark, I. E. Pubns.

Zobel Nolan, Allia. My Messy Closet: A Totally Gross Flap Book. Roos, Maryn, illus. 2007. 16p. (J). 10.99 ***(978-0-7944-1308-8(0))** Reader's Digest Assn., Inc., The.

BOYS—POETRY

Keats, John. A Song about Myself. Prosek, James, illus. 2005. (J). 16.95 (978-0-689-86829-0(4), Simon & Schuster Children's Publishing) Simon & Schuster Children's Publishing.

Rockwell, Anne F. The Boy Who Wouldn't Obey: A Mayan Legend. Rockwell, Anne F., illus. 2000. (Illus.). 24p. (J). (gr. k up). 17.99 (978-0-688-14881-2(6)) HarperCollins Pubs.

—Disobedient Servant Boy. 2000. (J). lib. bdg. 15.89 (978-0-688-14882-9(4)) HarperCollins Pubs.

BOYS' CLUBS—FICTION

Gau, Barry. Brushy Cross: A Hill Away. 2002. 279p. pap. 17.95 (978-0-595-22706-8(6), Writers Club Pr.) iUniverse, Inc.

Howe, James. Horace & Morris but Mostly Delores. Walrod, Amy, illus. 2002. (J). 25.11 (978-0-7587-2749-7(6)) Book Wholesalers, Inc.

—Horace & Morris but Mostly Delores. Walrod, Amy, illus. 1999. 32p. (J). (ps-3). 16.00 (978-0-689-31874-0(X), Atheneum) Simon & Schuster Children's Publishing.

Rand, Edward A. The Knights of the White Shield: Up-the-Ladder Club Series Round One Play. 2007. 166p. pap. 11.99 ***(978-1-4264-8273-1(6));** 184p. pap. 14.99 ***(978-1-4264-8310-3(4))** BiblioBazaar.

Slammin' Ghost of the Boys Club. 2002. (Illus.). (J). (978-0-7868-2579-0(0)) Hyperion Pr.

Walker, E. G. Boys' Club. Graffam, Merle, illus. 2004. (J). (gr. 2-8). pap. 12.95 (978-0-9716071-5-6(X)) Walker, Esther.

BRADFORD, WILLIAM, 1588-1657

Doherty, Kieran. William Bradford: Rock of Plymouth. 1999. (Single Titles Ser.: up). (Illus.). 192p. (gr. 7 up). lib. bdg. 24.90 (978-0-7613-1304-5(4), Twenty-First Century Bks.) Lerner Publishing Group.

Hering, Marianne. William Bradford: Governor of Plymouth Colony. (Colonial Leaders Ser.). (Illus.). 80p. (gr. 3 up). 2000. (YA). 27.50 (978-0-7910-5341-6(5)); 1999. pap. 27.50 (978-0-7910-5684-4(8)) Facts On File, Inc. (Chelsea Hse.).

Philbrick, Nathaniel. The Mayflower & the Pilgrims' New World. 2008. 304p. (J). (gr. 4-6). 19.99 ***(978-0-399-24795-8(5)**, Putnam Juvenile) Penguin Group (USA) Inc.

Walsh, Kieran. William Bradford. 2004. (Illus.). 24p. (J). 20.64 (978-1-59515-136-0(2)) Rourke Publishing, LLC.

Whitehurst, Susan. William Bradford & Plymouth: A Colony Grows. 2002. (Library of the Pilgrims). (Illus.). 24p. (J). (gr. 3). lib. bdg. 19.95 (978-0-8239-5808-5(6), PowerKids Pr.) Rosen Publishing Group, Inc., The.

BRADLEY, BILL, 1943-

Andryszewski, Tricia. Bill Bradley: Scholar, Athlete, Statesman. 1999. (Gateway Biography Ser.). (Illus.). (J). (978-0-606-18278-2(0)) Tandem Library Bks.

Buckley, James, Jr. Bill Bradley. 2002. (Basketball Hall of Famers Ser.). (Illus.). 112p. (YA). (gr. 5-8). lib. bdg. 29.25 (978-0-8239-3479-9(9), Rosen Central) Rosen Publishing Group, Inc., The.

BRADY, MATHEW B., 1823-1896

Armstrong, Jennifer. Photo by Brady: A Picture of the Civil War. 2005. (Illus.). 160p. (J). (gr. 4-9). 18.95 (978-0-689-85785-0(3), Atheneum) Simon & Schuster Children's Publishing.

Donlan, Leni. Mathew Brady: Photographing the Civil War. 2007. (J). ***(978-1-4109-2699-9(0));** pap. ***(978-1-4109-2710-1(5))** Steck-Vaughn.

Pflueger, Lynda. Mathew Brady: Photographer of the Civil War. 2001. (Historical American Biographies Ser.). (Illus.). 128p. (J). (gr. 6-12). lib. bdg. 26.60 (978-0-7660-1444-2(4)) Enslow Pubs., Inc.

BRAHMS, JOHANNES, 1833-1897

Deiters, H. Life of Brahms. 2001. (YA). reprint ed. 150.00 (978-0-7222-5361-8(3)) Library Reprints, Inc.

Erb, John Lawrence. Brahms. 2001. 178p. (YA). reprint ed. 88.00 (978-0-7222-5363-2(X)) Library Reprints, Inc.

Getzinger, Donna & Felsenfeld, Daniel. Johannes Brahms & the Twilight of Romanticism. 2004. (Classical Composers Ser.). (Illus.). 144p. (YA). (gr. 6-12). 26.95 (978-1-931798-21-1(4)) Reynolds, Morgan Inc.

Henschel, George. Personal Recollections of Johannes Brahms. 2001. 95p. (YA). reprint ed. 88.00 (978-0-7222-5365-6(6)) Library Reprints, Inc.

Lee, Ernest M. Brahms the Man & His Music. 2001. 185p. (YA). reprint ed. 88.00 (978-0-7222-5367-0(2)) Library Reprints, Inc.

Rachlin, Ann. Brahms. 2002. (Ninos Famosos Ser.). (ENG & SPA.). 24p. 6.95 (978-85-7416-078-8(4)) Callis Editora Ltda BRA. *Dist:* Independent Pubs. Group.

Venezia, Mike. Johannes Brahms. 1999. (Getting to Know the World's Greatest Composers Ser.). (Illus.). 32p. (gr. 3-4). pap. 6.95 (978-0-516-26467-7(2)); (J). 27.00 (978-0-516-21056-8(4)) Scholastic Library Publishing. (Children's Pr.).

—Johannes Brahms. 1999. (gr. 3-6). lib. bdg. 15.25 (978-0-613-37418-7(5)) Tandem Library Bks.

BRAILLE, LOUIS, 1809-1852

Davidson, Margaret. Louis Braille. (FRE.). (J). pap. 5.99 (978-0-590-71110-4(5)) Scholastic, Inc.

Donaldson, Madeline. Louis Braille. 2007. (History Maker Biographies Ser.). (J). 26.60 ***978-0-8225-7608-2(2)** , Lerner Pubns.) Lerner Publishing Group.

Freedman, Russell. Out of Darkness: The Story of Louis Braille. Kiesler, Kate A., illus. 1999. 96p. (J). (gr. 5-9). pap. 7.95 (978-0-395-96888-8(7) , Clarion Bks.) Houghton Mifflin Co. Trade & Reference Div.

—Out of Darkness: The Story of Louis Braille. (gr. 5-8). lib. bdg. 9.25 (978-0-7857-1350-0(6)) Tandem Library Bks.

Jeffrey, Laura S. All about Braille: Reading by Touch. 2004. (Transportation & Communication Ser.). (Illus.). 48p. (J). lib. bdg. 23.93 (978-0-7660-2184-6(X)) Enslow Pubs., Inc.

Mellor, C. Michael. Louis Braille: A Touch of Genius. 2006. (Illus.). 144p. (J). 35.00 (978-0-939173-70-9(0)) National Braille Pr.

O'Connor, Barbara. The World at His Fingertips. 2003. (Creative Minds Biographies Ser.). (Illus.). 64p. (J). (ps-1). pap. 6.95 (978-1-57505-461-2(2)) Lerner Publishing Group.

BRAIN

see also Dreams; Mind and Body; Nervous System; Psychology; Sleep

Andrews, Linda Wasmer. Intelligence. 2004. (Life Balance Ser.). (YA). (gr. 5-8). pap. 6.95 (978-0-531-16608-6(2) , Watts, Franklin) Scholastic Library Publishing.

Angliss, Sarah. The Controls: Brain & Nervous System. 1999. (Human Machine Ser.). (Illus.). 32p. (J). lib. bdg. 16.95 (978-1-929298-22-8(6)) Chrysalis Education.

Ballard, Carol. The Brain & Nervous System. 2005. (Exploring the Human Body Ser.). (Illus.). 32p. (J). (gr. 4-7). lib. bdg. 24.95 (978-0-7377-3018-0(8) , Kidhaven) Thomson Gale.

Berger, Melvin & Berger, Gilda. Your Brain. 2005. (Illus.). pap. (978-0-439-77370-6(9)) Scholastic, Inc.

Brynie, Faith Hickman. The Physical Brain. 2001. (Amazing Brain Ser.). (Illus.). 64p. (J). (gr. 6-10). 26.20 (978-1-56711-424-9(5) , Blackbirch Pr., Inc.) Thomson Gale.

—101 Questions about Your Brain: With Answers That Really Make You Think. 2007. (J). lib. bdg. ***978-0-8225-6795-0(4)*** Twenty First Century Bks.

Brynie, Faith Hickman. 101 Questions Your Brain Has Asked about Itself but Couldn't Answer... until Now. Holm, Sharon Lane, illus. 1998. (One Hundred One Questions... Ser.). 176p. (gr. 7 up). lib. bdg. 27.90 (978-0-7613-0400-5(2) , Twenty-First Century Bks.) Lerner Publishing Group.

Bulging Brains. (YA). (gr. 5-8). pap. (978-0-439-14976-1(2)) Scholastic GBR. *Dist:* Lectorum Pubns., Inc.

Carlson, Dale. The Teen Brain Book: Who & What Are You? Teasdale, Nancy, ed. Nicklaus, Carol, illus. 2004. 230p. (gr. 7-12). pap. 14.95 (978-1-884158-29-2(3)) Bick Publishing Hse.

Cassan, Adolfo. The Brain. 2005. (Inside the Human Body Ser.). (Illus.). 32p. (J). (gr. 4-8). 28.00 (978-0-7910-9014-5(0) , Chelsea Clubhouse) Facts On File, Inc.

El Cerebro. 2003. (Megabites Ser.). (SPA., Illus.). (J). pap. (978-970-690-689-2(4)) Planeta Mexicana Editorial S. A. de C. V.

Chandler, Fiona, et al. Understanding Your Brain Kid Kit. 2001. (Titles in Spanish Ser.). (Illus.). 96p. (J). lib. bdg. 29.95 (978-1-58086-590-6(9)) EDC Publishing.

Chowdhury, Uttom & Robertson, Mary. Why Do You Do That? A Book about Tourette Syndrome for Children & Young People. Whallett, Liz, illus. 2006. 76p. (J). pap (978-1-84310-395-0(8)) Kingsley, Jessica Ltd.

Chudler, Eric H. Inside Your Brain. 2007. (Brain Works). (Illus.). 128p. (J). (gr. 5-8). 32.95 (978-0-7910-8944-6(4) , Chelsea Hse.) Facts On File, Inc.

Clark, Arda Darakjian. Brain Tumors. 2006. (Diseases & Disorders Ser.). (Illus.). 112p. (J). (gr. 7-10). 32.45 (978-1-59018-671-8(0) , Lucent Bks.) Thomson Gale.

Cleveland, Don. How Do We Know How the Brain Works. 2005. (Great Scientific Questions & the Scientists Who Answered Them Ser.). (Illus.). 112p. (J). (gr. 7-12). lib. bdg. 26.50 (978-1-4042-0078-4(9)) Rosen Publishing Group, Inc., The.

Como Funciona el Cerebro. 2003. (Essential Science Ser.). (SPA., Illus.). (J). pap. (978-970-690-601-4(0)) Planeta Mexicana Editorial S. A. de C. V.

Cross, Gillian. Mysterious Minds. (Illus.). 48p. (J). 7.95 (978-0-14-130140-2(6)) Penguin Bks., Ltd. GBR. *Dist:* Trafalgar Square Publishing.

Curry, Don L. How Does Your Brain Work? 2004. (Rookie Read-About Health Ser.). 31p. (J). (gr. k-2). pap. 5.95 (978-0-516-27853-7(3) , Children's Pr.) Scholastic Library Publishing.

DeGezelle, Terri. Your Brain. 2002. (Bridgestone Science Library). (Illus.). 24p. (J). (gr. 1-2). lib. bdg. 18.60 (978-0-7368-1147-7(8) , Bridgestone Bks.) Capstone Pr., Inc.

Diagram Group. Brain & Nervous System. 2005. (Illus.). 112p. (J). (978-0-8160-5986-7(1)) Facts On File, Inc.

—Digestive System. 2005. (Illus.). 112p. (J). (978-0-8160-5984-3(5)) Facts On File, Inc.

Diagram Group, contrib. by. Heart & Circulatory System. 2005. (Illus.). 112p. (J). (978-0-8160-5982-9(9)) Facts On File, Inc.

DiSpezio, Michael A. How Bright Is Your Brain? Amazing Games to Play with Your Mind. Leary, Catherine, illus. 2006. 80p. pap. 7.95 (978-1-4027-3463-2(8)) Sterling Publishing Co., Inc.

Ehrlich, Fred. You Can't Use Your Brain If You're a Jellyfish. 2007. (Illus.). 40p. pap. 6.95 ***978-1-59354-592-5(4)*** Blue Apple Bks.

Esherick, Joan. The Journey Toward Recovery: Youth with Brain Injury. 2004. (Youth with Special Needs Ser.). (Illus.). 128p. (J). (978-1-59084-734-3(2)) Mason Crest Pubs.

Farndon, John. Big Book of the Brain: All about the Body's Control Center. 2001. (Big Book of Ser.). (Illus.). 40p. (J). (gr. 3-7). 17.95 (978-0-658-01071-2(9) , Bedrick, Peter Bks.) School Specialty Publishing.

Fitzpatrick, Anne. The Brain. 2003. (Illus.). 24p. (J). lib. bdg. 21.35 (978-1-58340-310-5(8)) Smart Apple Media.

Funston, Sylvia & Ingram, Jay. It's All in Your Head: A Guide to Your Brilliant Brain. Clement, Gary, illus. 2nd ed. 2005. 64p. (J). (gr. 4-7). 16.95 (978-1-897066-43-0(0)); pap. 9.95 (978-1-897066-44-7(9)) Maple Tree Pr. CAN. *Dist:* Perseus Distribution.

Furgang, Kathy, et al, contrib. by. My Brain. 2001. (My Body Ser.). (Illus.). 24p. (J). lib. bdg. 19.95 (978-0-8239-5571-8(0) , PowerKids Pr.) Rosen Publishing Group, Inc., The.

Ganeri, Anita. Your Brain. Shott, Steve, photos by. 2003. (How Your Body Works). (Illus.). 32p. (J). (gr. 2 up). lib. bdg. 23.33 (978-0-8368-3632-5(4)) Stevens, Gareth Inc.

Gray Matter: Exploring the Brain. 2005. (Illus.). 128p. (gr. 6-12). pap. 329.50 (978-0-7910-9085-5(X) , Chelsea Hse.) Facts On File, Inc.

Gray, Susan Heinrichs. The Brain. 2005. (Human Body Ser.). (Illus.). 32p. (J). (gr. 2-6). 27.07 (978-1-59296-424-6(9)) Child's World, Inc.

Green, Jen. Brain & Senses. 2005. (Illus.). 32p. (J). (gr. 3-7). lib. bdg. 27.10 (978-1-59604-050-2(5)) Stargazer Bks.

Hayhurst, Chris. The Brain & Spinal Cord: Learning How We Think, Feel & Move. 2002. (3-D Library of the Human Body). (Illus.). 48p. (YA). (gr. 5-8). lib. bdg. 26.50 (978-0-8239-3528-4(0) , Rosen Central) Rosen Publishing Group, Inc., The.

Human Brain Power, 6 vols. (Book2WebTM Ser.). (gr. 4-8). 36.50 (978-0-322-02975-0(9)) Wright Group, The.

Hyde, Margaret O. & Setaro, John F. When the Brain Dies First. 2000. (Single Title - Science Ser.). (Illus.). 144p. (YA). (gr. 8-12). 24.00 (978-0-531-11543-5(7) , Watts, Franklin) Scholastic Library Publishing.

Jerome, Kate Boehm. Understanding the Brain. 2003. (Human Body Ser.). (Illus.). 32p. (J). pap. (978-0-7922-8859-6(9)) National Geographic Society.

Landau, Elaine. Head & Brain Injuries. 2002. (Diseases & People Ser.). (Illus.). 112p. (YA). (gr. 6-12). lib. bdg. 26.60 (978-0-7660-1473-2(8)) Enslow Pubs., Inc.

Lennard, Kate. Brains. Gulliksen, Eivind, illus. 2007. (Young Genius Bks.). 32p. (J). (gr. k-3). pap. 6.99 (978-0-7641-3670-2(4)) Barron's Educational Series, Inc.

LeVert, Suzanne. The Brain. 2001. (Kaleidoscope Ser.). (Illus.). 48p. (J). (gr. 3 up). lib. bdg. 25.64 (978-0-7614-1308-0(1) , Benchmark Bks.) Cavendish, Marshall Corp.

Libra, Anna. Why Does My Head Hurt? An Inside Look at the Nervous System. 2003. (J). pap. (978-1-58417-065-5(4)); lib. bdg. (978-1-58417-002-0(6)) Lake Street Pubs.

Lindeen, Carol. My Brain. 2007. 24p. (J). ***978-0-7368-6693-4(0)** , Pebble Bks.) Capstone Pr., Inc.

Macnair, Patricia Ann. Brain Power. 2005. (Bodyscope Ser.). (Illus.). 40p. (J). (gr. 3-5). 9.95 (978-0-7534-5793-1(8) , Kingfisher) Houghton Mifflin Co. Trade & Reference Div.

Miller, Steve & Papa, Susan. Addiction. 2001. (Amazing Brain Ser.). (Illus.). 64p. (J). (gr. 6-10). 24.95 (978-1-56711-421-8(0) , Blackbirch Pr., Inc.) Thomson Gale.

Nettleton, Pamela Hill. Think, Think, Think: Learning about Your Brain. Shipe, Becky, illus. 2004. (Amazing Body Ser.). 24p. (C). (gr. k-3). 22.60 (978-1-4048-0252-0(5)) Picture Window Bks.

Nettleton, Pamela Hill & Shipe, Becky. Piensa! Piensa! Conoce Tu Cerebro. Shipe, Becky, illus. 2007. (SPA & ENG.). (J). lib. bdg. ***978-1-4048-3815-4(5)*** Picture Window Bks.

Newquist, Harvey P. The Great Brain Book: An Inside Look at the Inside of Your Head. Kasnot, Keith, illus. 2005. 160p. (J). pap. 18.95 (978-0-439-45895-5(1)) Scholastic, Inc.

Parker, Steve. Brain. 2003. (Body Focus Ser.). 48p. (J). (Illus.). lib. bdg. 27.07 (978-1-4034-0748-1(7)); pap. (978-1-4034-3296-4(1)) Heinemann Library.

—The Brain & Nervous System. 2004. (Our Bodies Ser.). (Illus.). 48p. (J). lib. bdg. 28.56 (978-0-7398-6619-1(2)) Raintree.

Pascoe, Elaine, ed. Out of Control: Brain Function & Immune Reactions. 2003. (Body Story Ser.). (Illus.). 48p. (J). 24.95 (978-1-4103-0063-8(3)); pap. 11.20 (978-1-4103-0184-0(2)) Thomson Gale. (Blackbirch Pr., Inc.).

Phillips, Sherre Florence. The Teen Brain. 2007. (Gray Matter Ser.). 136p. (J). (gr. 9). 32.95 ***978-0-7910-9415-0(4)** , Chelsea Hse.) Facts On File, Inc.

Pierre, Yvette La. Neandertals: A Prehistoric Puzzle. 2008. (J). lib. bdg. ***978-0-8225-7524-5(8)*** Twenty First Century Bks.

Powell, Jillian. Thinking & Feeling. 2004. (J). pap. (978-1-58340-439-3(2)) Smart Apple Media.

Rau, Dana Meachen. El Cerebro. 2006. (Bookworms Ser.). (SPA & ENG., Illus.). 32p. (J). lib. bdg. 22.79 (978-0-7614-2402-4(4)) Cavendish, Marshall Corp.

—My Brain (El Cerebro) 2006. (Bookworms Ser.). (SPA & ENG., Illus.). 32p. (J). lib. bdg. 22.79 (978-0-7614-2480-2(6)) Cavendish, Marshall Corp.

Rodríguez, Ana María. A Day in the Life of the Brain. 2006. (Brain Works). (Illus.). 112p. (J). (gr. 5-8). 32.95 (978-0-7910-8947-7(9) , Chelsea Hse.) Facts On File, Inc.

Romanek, Trudee. Aha! The Most Interesting Book You'll Ever Read about Intelligence. Cowles, Rose, tr. Cowles, Rose, illus. 2004. (Mysterious You Ser.). 40p. (J). (gr. 4-6). (978-1-55337-569-2(6)); (978-1-55337-485-5(1)) Kids Can Pr., Ltd.

Rosen, Marvin. The Brain & Love. 2007. (Brain Works). 104p. (J). (gr. 5-8). 32.95 (978-0-7910-8950-7(9) , Chelsea Hse.) Facts On File, Inc.

Ross, Veronica. The Body: The Brain. 2004. (J). lib. bdg. (978-1-59389-163-3(6)) Chrysalis Education.

Silverman, Buffy. Who's in Control? 2006. (Illus.). 32p. (J). (978-1-4109-2583-1(8)); pap. (978-1-4109-2640-1(0)) Steck-Vaughn.

Simon, Seymour. The Brain: Our Nervous System. (J). 2006. 32p. 16.99 (978-0-06-087718-7(9)); 2006. (Illus.). 32p. pap. 6.99 (978-0-06-087719-4(7)); 1999. (Illus.). pap. 6.99 (978-0-688-17060-8(9)) HarperCollins Pubs.

El Sistema Nervioso, Nuestro Proceso de Datos. (Coleccion Mundo Invisible).Tr. of Nervous System & the Brain. (SPA.). (YA). (gr. 5-8). pap. 8.00 (978-958-04-3226-5(0)) Norma S.A. COL. *Dist:* Distribuidora Norma, Inc., Lectorum Pubns., Inc.

Spilsbury, Louise. Why Should I Go to Bed Now? And Other Questions about a Healthy Mind. 2003. (Body Matters Ser.). (Illus.). 32p. (J). lib. bdg. (978-1-4034-4682-4(2)) Heinemann Library.

Think, Think, Think. (Amazing Body Ser.). 24p. (J). 7.95 (978-1-4048-0503-3(6)) Picture Window Bks.

Viegas, Jennifer. The Revolution in Healing the Brain. 2005. (Library of Future Medicine). (Illus.). 64p. (YA). (gr. 7-12). lib. bdg. 26.50 (978-0-8239-3668-7(6)) Rosen Publishing Group, Inc., The.

Walker, Pam & Wood, Elaine. The Brain & Nervous System. 2002. (Understanding the Human Body Ser.). (Illus.). 112p. (J). 27.45 (978-1-59018-148-5(4) , Lucent Bks.) Thomson Gale.

Watt, Fiona. Understanding Your Brain Kid Kit. 2004. (Titles in Spanish Ser.). 96p. (J). lib. bdg. 26.95 (978-1-58086-594-4(1)) EDC Publishing.

Your Brain. (Your Body Ser.). 24p. (J). 6.95 (978-0-7368-3351-6(X)) Capstone Pr., Inc.

BRASS INSTRUMENTS

see Wind Instruments

BRAVERY

see Courage

BRAZIL

Auch, Alison. Welcome to Brazil. 2002. (Spyglass Books). (Illus.). 24p. (J). (gr. 1 up). lib. bdg. 18.60 (978-0-7565-0370-3(1)) Compass Point Bks.

Bauer, Brandy. Brazil: A Question & Answer Book. 2004. (Fact Finders Ser.). (Illus.). 32p. (J). lib. bdg. 22.60 (978-0-7368-2481-1(2)) Capstone Pr., Inc.

Boraas, Tracey. Brazil. 2001. (Countries & Cultures Ser.). (Illus.). 64p. (J). (gr. 3-4). lib. bdg. 23.93 (978-0-7368-0765-4(9) , Bridgestone Bks.) Capstone Pr., Inc.

Brimson, Samuel. Brazil-East Timor, 8 vols. 2003. (Nations of the World Ser.: Vol. 2). (Illus.). 64p. (J). (gr. 5 up). lib. bdg. 30.00 (978-0-8368-5486-2(1) , World Almanac Library) Stevens, Gareth Inc.

Campos, Maria de Fatima. A Child's Day in a Brazilian Village. 2001. (Child's Day Ser.). (Illus.). 32p. (J). (gr. k-2). lib. bdg. 25.64 (978-0-7614-1221-2(2) , Benchmark Bks.) Cavendish, Marshall Corp.

Corona, Laurel. Brazil. 1999. (Modern Nations of the World Ser.). (Illus.). 128p. (YA). (gr. 7-10). 27.45 (978-1-56006-621-7(0) , Lucent Bks.) Thomson Gale.

Corwin, Jeff. Into Wild Brazil. Pascoe, Elaine, ed. 2003. (Jeff Corwin Experience Ser.). (Illus.). 48p. (J). 24.95 (978-1-56711-853-7(4)); 11.20 (978-1-4103-0175-8(3)) Thomson Gale. (Blackbirch Pr., Inc.).

Costain, Meredith & Collins, Paul. Welcome to Brazil. 2001. (Countries of the World Ser.). (Illus.). 32p. (J). (gr. 4 up). 28.00 (978-0-7910-6547-1(2) , 010201, Chelsea Hse.) Facts On File, Inc.

Cunningham, Patrick. Brazil. Cunningham, Susan M., photos by. 2005. (Letters from Around the World Ser.). (Illus.). 32p. (J). (gr. 3-7). lib. bdg. (978-1-84234-253-4(3) , Cherrytree Books) Evans Publishing Group.

Dalal, Anita. Brazil. Kossmann, Walter, ed. 2001. (Nations of the World Ser.). (Illus.). 128p. (YA). (gr. 6-8). lib. bdg. 34.26 (978-0-7398-1284-6(X)) Raintree.

Dicks, Brian. Brazil. 2003. (Countries of the World Ser.). (Illus.). 64p. (gr. 6-12). 30.00 (978-0-8160-5382-7(0)) Facts On File, Inc.

Dominguez, Adriana. Brazil. 2002. (Steadwell Books World Tour). (Illus.). 48p. (J). lib. bdg. 24.26 (978-0-7398-4709-1(0)) Raintree.

Ferro, Jennifer. Brazilian Foods & Culture. 1999. (Festive Foods & Celebrations Ser.). (Illus.). 48p. (J). (gr. 3-6). lib. bdg. 27.93 (978-1-57103-301-7(7)) Rourke Publishing, LLC.

Fontes, Justine & Fontes, Ron. Brazil. (to Z Ser.). (Illus.). 40p. (J). 2004. (gr. 2-4). pap. 6.95 (978-0-516-26806-4(6)); 2003. 24.50 (978-0-516-24563-8(5)) Scholastic Library Publishing. (Children's Pr.).

Frank, Nicole & Jermyn, Leslie. Welcome to Brazil. 1999. (Welcome to My Country Ser.). (Illus.). 48p. (J). (gr. 2 up). lib. bdg. 26.00 (978-0-8368-2493-3(8)) Stevens, Gareth Inc.

Freland, Francois-Xavier. We Live in Brazil. Duffet, Sophie, illus. 2007. (Kids Around the World Ser.). 48p. (J). (gr. 3-7). 15.95 (978-0-8109-1221-2(X) , Abrams Bks. for Young Readers) Abrams, Harry N. , Inc.

Furlong, Kate A. Brazil. 2001. (Countries Ser.). (Illus.). 40p. (J). (gr. k-6). lib. bdg. 22.78 (978-1-57765-491-9(9) , Checkerboard Library) ABDO Publishing Co.

Gray, Shirley W. Brazil. 2000. (First Reports). (Illus.). 48p. (J). (gr. 3 up). lib. bdg. 22.60 (978-0-7565-0027-6(3)) Compass Point Bks.

Greenbaum, Harry. Brazil. 2003. (Modern World Nations Ser.). (Illus.). 150p. (gr. 6-12). 30.00 (978-0-7910-7240-0(1) , Chelsea Hse.) Facts On File, Inc.

—Iceland. 2003. (Modern World Nations Ser.). (Illus.). 150p. (gr. 6-12). 30.00 (978-0-7910-7232-5(0) , Chelsea Hse.) Facts On File, Inc.

Heinrichs, Ann. Brazil. 2007. 144p. (J). 37.00 ***978-0-516-25014-4(0)** , Children's Pr.) Scholastic Library Publishing.

Holiday, Jane. Exploring Brazil with the Five Themes of Geography. 2005. (Library of the Western Hemisphere). (Illus.). 24p. (J). 19.95 (978-1-4042-2679-1(6) , PowerKids Pr.); pap. (978-0-8239-4639-6(8)) Rosen Publishing Group, Inc., The.

Hollander, Malika. Brazil - The Culture. 2003. (Lands, Peoples & Cultures Ser.). (Illus.). 32p. (J). (gr. 2-9). (978-0-7787-9340-3(0)); pap. (978-0-7787-9708-1(2)) Crabtree Publishing Co.

—Brazil - The Culture. 2003. (gr. 3-6). lib. bdg. 16.40 (978-0-613-59056-3(2)) Tandem Library Bks.

—Brazil - The Land. 2003. (Lands, Peoples & Cultures Ser.). (Illus.). 32p. (J). (gr. 2-9). (978-0-7787-9338-0(9)); pap. (978-0-7787-9706-7(6)) Crabtree Publishing Co.

—Brazil - The Land. 2003. (gr. 3-6). lib. bdg. 16.40 (978-0-613-59057-0(0)) Tandem Library Bks.

—Brazil - The People. 2003. (gr. 3-6). lib. bdg. 16.40 (978-0-613-59058-7(9)) Tandem Library Bks.

Hynson, Colin. Living on the Street: Hamilton's Story. 2005. (Children in Crisis Ser.). (Illus.). 48p. (J). (gr. 6-9). lib. bdg. 30.00 (978-0-8368-5961-4(8) , World Almanac Library) Stevens, Gareth Inc.

Jermyn, Leslie. Brazil. 1999. (Countries of the World Ser.). (Illus.). 96p. (J). (gr. 6 up). lib. bdg. 30.00 (978-0-8368-2258-8(7)) Stevens, Gareth Inc.

Jones, Caryn Gracey & Compass Point Books Staff. Teens in Brazil. 2006. (Global Connections Ser.). (Illus.). 96p. (J). (gr. 5-7). 31.93 (978-0-7565-2442-5(3)) Compass Point Bks.

Lichtenberger, Andre. Brazil. 2000. (We Come from Ser.). (Illus.). 32p. (J). (gr. 1-4). lib. bdg. 25.69 (978-0-8172-5514-5(1)) Raintree.

Lynch, Emma. We're from Brazil. 2005. (We're from Ser.). (Illus.). 32p. (J). (978-1-4034-5802-5(2)) Heinemann Library.

Marshall, David. Brazil. 1998. (Worldfocus Ser.). (Illus.). 32p. (J). pap. (978-1-57572-029-6(9)) Heinemann Library.

—Brazil. (World Focus Ser.). (Illus.). 32p. (J). (gr. 3-7). pap. 3.99 (978-0-431-07256-2(6)) Oxfam Publishing GBR. *Dist:* Stylus Publishing, LLC.

McNamara, Margaret. Brazil. 2006. pap. 39.00 ***978-1-4108-6457-4(X)*** Benchmark Education Co.

Morrison, Marion. Brazil. 2003. (Country Files Ser.). 32p. (J). lib. bdg. 24.25 (978-1-58340-235-1(7)) Smart Apple Media.

Nations of the World: Includes: Brazil, Egypt, Germany, Israel, 4 bks., Set. 2001. (Illus.). (YA). (gr. 5-9). lib. bdg. 95.92 (978-0-7398-4289-8(7)) Raintree.

Papi, Liza. Carnavalia! African-Brazilian Folklore & Crafts. Papi, Liza, illus. 2004. (Illus.). 48p. (J). (gr. k-4). reprint ed. 20.00 (978-0-7567-7760-9(7)) DIANE Publishing Co.

Park, Ted. Brazil. 2000. (Taking Your Camera to Ser.). (Illus.). 32p. (J). (gr. 4-7). lib. bdg. 22.83 (978-0-7398-1802-2(3)) Raintree.

—Taking Your Camera To... Includes: Australia, Brazil, Canada, Egypt, France, Israel, Italy, Japan, Mexico, Panama, Russia, Spain, 12 bks., Set. 2000. (Taking Your Camera to Ser.). (Illus.). (J). (gr. 4-7). 273.96 (978-0-7398-3096-3(1)) Raintree.

—Taking Your Camera to Brazil. 1999. (Illus.). pap. (978-0-7398-2151-0(2)) Steck-Vaughn.

Parker, Edward. Brazil. 2002. (Changing Face Of... Ser.). (Illus.). 48p. (J). lib. bdg. 27.12 (978-0-7398-4965-1(4)) Raintree.

Reiser, Robert. Brazil. 2002. (Discovering Cultures Ser.). (Illus.). 48p. (J). 25.64 (978-0-7614-1180-2(1) , Benchmark Bks.) Cavendish, Marshall Corp.

Richard, Christopher & Jermyn, L. Brazil. 2nd ed. 2001. (Cultures of the World Ser.). (Illus.). 144p. (gr. 5 up). lib. bdg. 37.07 (978-0-7614-1359-2(6) , Cavendish, Marshall Reference Bks.) Cavendish, Marshall Corp.

Roop, Peter & Roop, Connie. A Visit to Brazil. (Visit to Ser.). 32p. pap. 6.50 (978-1-4034-4144-7(8)) Heinemann Library.

Schemenauer, Elma. Brazil. 1999. (Countries: Faces & Places Ser.). (Illus.). 32p. (J). (gr. 1-5). 25.64 (978-1-56766-597-0(7)) Child's World, Inc.

Scoones, Simon. Focus on Brazil. 2006. (Illus.). 64p. (J). pap. (978-0-8368-6727-5(0)); lib. bdg. (978-0-8368-6720-6(3)) Stevens, Gareth Inc. (World Almanac Library).

Seidman, David. Brazil ABCs: A Book about the People & Places of Brazil. Thompson, Jeffrey, illus. 2006. (Country ABCs Ser.). 32p. (J). (gr. k-5). lib. bdg. 25.26 ***978-1-4048-2248-1(8)*** Picture Window Bks.

Shields, Charles J. Brazil. 2003. (Discovering South America Ser.). (Illus.). 64p. (J). (gr. 5 up). lib. bdg. (978-1-59084-286-7(3)) Mason Crest Pubs.

Streissguth, Thomas & Streissguth, Tom. Brazil in Pictures. 2nd rev. ed. 2003. (Visual Geography Ser.). (Illus.). 80p. (J). (gr. 5-12). 27.93 (978-0-8225-1959-1(3)) Lerner Publishing Group.

Thomas, Mark. The Maracanaa: World's Largest Stadium. 2002. (Reading Power Ser.). (Illus.). 24p. (J). (gr. 1). lib. bdg. 17.25 (978-0-8239-5992-1(9) , PowerKids Pr.) Rosen Publishing Group, Inc., The.

A B

Walters, Tara. Brazil. 2007. (True Booktrade;: Geography: Countries Ser.). 48p. (J). spiral bd. 26.00 (***978-0-531-16851-6(4)***, Children's Pr.) Scholastic Library Publishing.

Weitzman, Elizabeth. Brazil. (Country Explorers Ser.). 48p. (J). 2007. (gr. 4-8). lib. bdg. 27.93 (***978-0-8225-7127-8(7)***, Lerner Pubns.); 1998. (Illus.). (gr. k-2). lib. bdg. 22.60 (978-1-57505-132-1(X), Carolrhoda Bks.); 1998. (Illus.). (gr. 3-5). lib. bdg. 22.60 (978-1-57505-107-9(9), Carolrhoda Bks.) Lerner Publishing Group.

BRAZIL—FICTION

Bell, Michele Ashman. Rescue: A Jungle Adventure. 2006. 246p. (J). pap. (978-1-59811-093-7(4)) Covenant Communications.

Connell, Richard. Most Dangerous Game. 2006. pap. 15.95 (***978-1-4304-5151-8(3)***) Kessinger Publishing, LLC.

Doder, Joshua. Grk & the Pelotti Gang. 2007. (Grk Bks.). 208p. (J). (gr. 4-7). 14.99 (***978-0-385-73360-1(7)***); lib. bdg. 17.99 (***978-0-385-90375-2(8)***) Random Hse. Children's Bks. (Delacorte Bks. for Young Readers).

Grisham, John. The Testament. 2000. (gr. 7-12). lib. bdg. 16.45 (978-0-613-23044-5(2)) Tandem Library Bks.

Hanson, Ed. Amazon Adventure. 2003. (Barclay Family Adventure Ser.: Bk. 1). 64p. (J). (gr. k-6). per. 3.95 (978-1-56254-550-5(7), SP 5507) Saddleback Educational Publishing.

Holtwijk, Inele. Asphalt Angels. Boeke, Wanda, tr. 2004. 184p. (YA). pap. 7.95 (978-1-886910-43-0(X), Lemniscaat) Boyds Mills Pr.

Ibbotson, Eva. Journey to the River Sea. Hawkes, Kevin, illus. 2002. 336p. (J). (gr. 4-8). 17.99 (978-0-525-46739-7(4), Dutton Juvenile) Penguin Group (USA) Inc.

—Journey to the River Sea. 2003. (gr. 3-6). lib. bdg. 14.15 (978-0-613-86704-7(1)) Tandem Library Bks.

Lumry, Amanda & Hurwitz, Laura. Amazon River Rescue. McIntyre, Sarah, illus. 2004. (Adventures of Riley Ser.). 36p. 15.95 (978-0-9662257-9-2(1)) Eaglemont Pr.

MacHado, Ana Maria. Del Otro Lado Hay Secretos. (SPA.). pap. 11.95 (978-950-07-2221-6(6)) Editorial Sudamericana S.A. ARG. *Dist:* Distribooks, Inc.

—Me in the Middle. Unger, David, tr. from POR. Merola, Caroline, illus. 2002. 96p. (J). (gr. 2-6). 14.95 (978-0-88899-463-9(X)) Groundwood Bks. CAN. *Dist:* Perseus Distribution.

—Nina Bonita. Iribarren, Elena, tr. Faria, Rosana, illus. 2001. 24p. (J). (gr. k-4). reprint ed. 7.95 (978-1-929132-11-9(5)) Kane/Miller Bk. Pubs., Inc.

—Nina Bonita. 2001. (J). (978-0-606-20824-6(0)) Tandem Library Bks.

MacHado, Ana Maria & Merola, Caroline. Me in the Middle. Unger, David, tr. from POR. 2003. (Illus.). 112p. (J). (gr. 3-6). pap. 4.95 (978-0-88899-467-7(2)) Groundwood Bks. CAN. *Dist:* Perseus Distribution.

Montgomery, R. A. Lost on the Amazon. 1999. (Illus.). 114p. mass mkt. (978-0-553-23733-7(0)) Random Hse., Inc.

Peet, Mal. Keeper. 2007. 240p. (J). (gr. 5). pap. 6.99 (978-0-7636-3286-1(4)) Candlewick Pr.

Smith, Roland. Jaguar. 1999. 256p. (gr. 4-7). pap. 5.95 (978-0-7868-1312-4(1)) Disney Pr.

Thomas, Rob. Green Thumb. unabr. ed. 2000. (YA). pap. 59.00 incl. audio (978-0-7887-3641-4(8), 41007) Recorded Bks., LLC.

—Green Thumb. 2000. (978-0-606-20048-6(7)) Tandem Library Bks.

Williams, Anita. The Captain's Hat. Banks, Timothy, illus. 2000. 104p. (J). (gr. 1-5). pap. 7.95 (978-1-57924-330-2(4), 119743) Jones, Bob Univ. Pr.

Zindel, Paul. Night of the Bat. 144p. (gr. 5-9). 2003. pap. 5.99 (978-0-7868-1226-4(5)); 2001. 15.99 (978-0-7868-0340-8(1)) Hyperion Bks. for Children.

Zoehfeld, Kathleen Weidner. Amazon Fever. Bogan, Paulette, illus. 2006. (Road to Reading Ser.). 48p. (J). (gr. 1-4). 11.99 (978-0-307-46407-1(5)); pap. 3.99 (978-0-307-26407-7(6)) Random Hse. Children's Bks. (Random Hse. Bks. for Young Readers).

BRAZIL—HISTORY

Brooks, Susie. Brazil. 2006. (Our Lives, Our World Ser.). (J). (978-1-59389-286-9(1)) Chrysalis Education.

Brownlie Bojang, Ali. Brazil. 2006. (Destination Detectives Ser.). (Illus.). 48p. (978-1-4109-2333-2(9)); pap. (978-1-4109-2344-8(4)) Steck-Vaughn.

Enderlein, Cheryl L. Celebrating Birthdays in Brazil. 1998. (Birthdays Around the World Ser.). (Illus.). 24p. (J). (gr. k-3). lib. bdg. 14.00 (978-0-531-11545-9(3), Watts, Franklin) Scholastic Library Publishing.

Ganeri, Anita. Living in the Amazon Rainforest. 2007. (J). pap. (***978-1-4109-2826-9(8)***); lib. bdg. (***978-1-4109-2817-7(9)***) Steck-Vaughn.

Hollander, Malika. Brazil - The People. 2003. (Lands, Peoples & Cultures Ser.). (Illus.). 32p. (J). (gr. 2-9). (978-0-7787-9339-7(7)); pap. (978-0-7787-9707-4(4)) Crabtree Publishing Co.

The Maracana: Individual Title Six-Packs. (On Deck Ser.). 24p. (gr. 4-5). 35.00 (978-0-7578-1075-6(6)) Rigby Education.

McNamara, Margaret. Discover Brazil. 2006. pap. 39.00 (***978-1-4108-6460-4(X)***) Benchmark Education Co.

Parker, Lewis K. Portuguese Colonies in the Americas. 2003. (Reading Power Ser.). (Illus.). 24p. (J). lib. bdg. 17.25 (978-0-8239-6474-1(4), PowerKids Pr.) Rosen Publishing Group, Inc., The.

Portuguese Colonies in the Americas: Individual Title Six-Packs. (On Deck Ser.: Vol. 2). 24p. (gr. 4-5). 35.00 (978-0-7578-6101-7(6)) Rigby Education.

Weitzman, Elizabeth. Brazil. 1998. (Globe-Trotters Club Ser.). (Illus.). 48p. (J). (gr. 3-5). lib. bdg. 22.60 (978-1-57505-107-9(9), Carolrhoda Bks.) Lerner Publishing Group.

BREAD

see also Baking

Anderson, Catherine. Bread Bakery. 2004. (Field Trip! Ser.). (Illus.). 24p. (J). pap. 5.75 (978-1-4034-6167-4(8)); lib. bdg. 20.64 (978-1-4034-6161-2(9)) Heinemann Library.

Bauer, David. Todos comen Pan! 2005. Tr. of Everyone Eats Bread. (SPA., Illus.). 16p. (J). (gr. 1 up). lib. bdg. 15.93 (978-0-7368-4174-0(1)) Capstone Pr., Inc.

Benduhn, Tea. Bread & Cereal. 2007. (J). pap. (***978-0-8368-8257-5(1)***); 24p. lib. bdg. 19.93 (***978-0-8368-8250-6(4)***) Stevens, Gareth Inc. (Weekly Reader Early Learning Library).

—Bread & Cereal: Pan y Cereales. 2007. (SPA & ENG.). (J). pap. (***978-0-8368-8461-6(2)***, Weekly Reader Early Learning Library) Stevens, Gareth Inc.

—Bread & Cereal/Pan y Cereales. 2007. (Find Out about Food/Conoce la Comida Ser.). (SPA & ENG.). 24p. (J). (gr. k-2). lib. bdg. 19.93 (***978-0-8368-8454-8(X)***, Weekly Reader Early Learning Library) Stevens, Gareth Inc.

Bentley, Joyce. Bread. 2005. (Illus.). 32p. (J). (gr. 2 up). lib. bdg. 27.10 (978-1-59389-218-0(7)) Chrysalis Education.

Harbison, Elizabeth M. Loaves of Fun: A History of Bread with Activities & Recipes from Around the World. Harbison, John, illus. 1999. 108p. (J). (gr. 1-7). pap. 14.95 (978-1-55652-311-3(4)) Chicago Review Pr., Inc.

Hill, Mary. Let's Make Bread. 2002. (Wel-in the Kitchen Ser.). (Illus.). 24p. (J). (ps-2). 18.00 (978-0-516-23955-2(4), Children's Pr.) Scholastic Library Publishing.

—Let's Make Bread. 2002. (gr. k-3). lib. bdg. 12.95 (978-0-613-58783-9(9)) Tandem Library Bks.

Innovative Cooking Enterprises Staff. Electric Bread for Kids: A Bread Machine Activity Book. McKay, D. John, ed. Tilly, Jim, illus. Parshin, Oleg, photos by. 1998. 176p. (J). (gr. 1-9). 29.95 (978-1-891705-00-7(8)) Innovative Cooking Enterprises - ICE, Inc.

Jones, Carol. Bread. 2002. (From Farm to You Ser.). (Illus.). 32p. (gr. 4-8). 28.00 (978-0-7910-7007-9(7), Chelsea Hse.) Facts On File, Inc.

Jones, Judith & Jones, Evan. Knead It, Punch It, Bake It! The Ultimate Breadmaking Book for Parents & Kids. 2nd ed. 1998. (Illus.). 144p. (gr. 4-7). pap. 17.00 (978-0-395-89256-5(2)) Houghton Mifflin Co. Trade & Reference Div.

Keller, Kristin Thoennes. Wheat to Bread. 2004. (First Facts Ser.). 24p. (J). lib. bdg. 21.26 (978-0-7368-2638-9(6)) Capstone Pr., Inc.

Klingel, Cynthia Fitterer & Noyed, Robert B. Bread & Cereal. Andersen, Gregg, photos by. 2002. (Weekly Reader Early Learning Library). (Illus.). 24p. (J). (ps up). pap. 5.95 (978-0-8368-3144-3(6)); lib. bdg. 19.33 (978-0-8368-3055-2(5)) Stevens, Gareth Inc. (Weekly Reader Early Learning Library).

Levenson, George. Bread Comes to Life: A Garden of Wheat & a Loaf to Eat. Thaler, Shmuel, photos by. 2004. (Illus.). 32p. (J). 15.95 (978-1-58246-114-4(7), Tricycle Pr.) Ten Speed Pr.

Llewellyn, Claire. Bread. 2005. (Illus.). 24p. (YA). (gr. 1 up). lib. bdg. 22.80 (978-1-932889-38-3(8)) Sea-To-Sea Pubns.

Martineau, Susan. Healthy Eating. 2006. (Illus.). 32p. (J). (978-1-58340-894-0(0), 1262655) Smart Apple Media.

Paulsen, Gary. La Tortilleria. Andujar, Gloria Dearagon, tr. from ENG. Paulsen, Ruth Wright, illus. 2006. 27p. (J). (gr. k-4). reprint ed. 16.00 (978-1-4223-5319-6(2)) DIANE Publishing Co.

Pickering, Robin. I Like Bagels. 2000. (Welcome Bks.). (Illus.). 24p. (J). (ps-2). pap. 4.95 (978-0-516-23006-1(9)); 17.00 (978-0-516-23081-8(6)) Scholastic Library Publishing. (Children's Pr.).

Rau, Dana Meachen. Bread. 2008. (J). (***978-0-7614-2892-3(5)***) Cavendish, Marshall Bks., Ltd.

Reed, Janet. Everyone Eats Bread! 2003. (Yellow Umbrella Books for Early Readers). (Illus.). 17p. (J). 15.93 (978-0-7368-2909-0(1)); pap. (978-0-7368-2868-0(0)) Yellow Umbrella Pr.

Rosenfeld, Dina. Where Does Bread Come From? A Brocho Discovery Book. Lyampe, Rina, illus. 2002. 32p. (J). (ps-k). (978-1-929628-06-3(4)) Hachai Publishing.

Snyder, Inez. Grains to Bread. 2005. (How Things Are Made Ser.). (Illus.). 24p. (J). (ps-2). pap. 4.95 (978-0-516-25527-9(4)); 18.00 (978-0-516-25197-4(X)) Scholastic Library Publishing. (Children's Pr.).

Spilsbury, Louise. Bread. 2001. (Food Ser.). (Illus.). 32p. (J). (gr. k-2). lib. bdg. 21.36 (978-1-58810-143-3(6)) Heinemann Library.

Taus-Bolstad, Stacy. From Wheat to Bread. (From Start to Finish Ser.). (J). 2003. (Illus.). 24p. 18.60 (978-0-8225-0715-4(3), Lerner Pubns.); 2002. pap. 4.95 (978-0-8225-0673-7(4)) Lerner Publishing Group.

BREATHING

see Respiration

BRECKINRIDGE, MARY, 1881-1965

Wells, Rosemary. Mary on Horseback: Three Mountain Stories. McCarty, Peter, illus. (J). 2000. 64p. (gr. 3-7). pap. 4.99 (978-0-14-130815-9(X), Puffin); 1999. 56p. (gr. 4-7). 16.99 (978-0-670-88923-5(7), Viking Juvenile) Penguin Group (USA) Inc.

—Mary on Horseback: Three Mountain Stories. 2000. (J). (978-0-606-20243-5(9)); (gr. 3-6). lib. bdg. 13.00 (978-0-613-33711-3(5)) Tandem Library Bks.

BRIDAL CUSTOMS

see Marriage Customs and Rites

BRIDGE (GAME)

Levin, David H. Bridge Puzzles for Children Vol. 1: Simple Card Play Problems to Introduce Them to This Wonderful Game. 2004. (Illus.). 128p. (J). pap. 14.95 (978-0-9638001-2-1(4)) Syllogism Pr.

BRIDGER, JAMES, 1804-1881

Maynard, Charles W. Jim Bridger: Frontiersman & Mountain Guide. 2003. (Famous Explorers of the American West Ser.). (Illus.). 24p. (J). lib. bdg. 18.75 (978-0-8239-6288-4(1), PowerKids Pr.) Rosen Publishing Group, Inc., The.

BRIDGES

see also names of cities with the subdivision Bridges (e.g. New York City—Bridges) also names of bridges, e.g. Brooklyn Bridge

Adkins, Jan E. Bridges: From My Side to Yours. Adkins, Jan E., illus. rev. ed. 2002. 8. (Illus.). 96p. (J). (gr. 4-9). 18.95 (978-0-7613-1542-1(X)) Roaring Brook Pr.

The Akashi Kaikyo Bridge, Pack 6. (On Deck Ser.). 24p. (gr. 4-5). 35.00 (978-0-7578-1071-8(3)) Rigby Education.

Baxter, Nicola. Bridges. 2001. (Topic Bks.). (Illus.). 32p. (J). (gr. 2-5). 23.50 (978-0-531-14549-4(2), Watts, Franklin) Scholastic Library Publishing.

—Bridges. 2000. (gr. 3-6). lib. bdg. 15.25 (978-0-613-34092-2(2)); (Illus.). (J). 13.75 (978-0-606-20581-8(0)) Tandem Library Bks.

Beers, Jack. Bridges - Blue. 2002. (Math Bridges Ser.). (gr. 8). (J). stu. ed., per. 13.95 (978-1-58830-339-4(X)); tchr. ed., per. 19.95 (978-1-58830-340-0(3)) Metropolitan Teaching & Learning Co.

—Bridges - Gold. 2002. (Metro Math Bridges Ser.). (J). (gr. 7). stu. ed., per. 13.95 (978-1-58830-329-5(2)) Metropolitan Teaching & Learning Co.

—Bridges - Green. 2002. (Math Bridges Ser.). (J). (gr. 5). stu. ed., per. 13.95 (978-1-58830-298-4(9)) Metropolitan Teaching & Learning Co.

Briscoe, Diana. Bridge Building: Bridge Designs & How They Work. 2005. (High Five Reading Ser.). (Illus.). 64p. (J). (ps-k). lib. bdg. 23.93 (978-0-7368-3881-8(3)) Capstone Pr., Inc.

Briscoe, Diana C. Bridge Building: Bridge Designs & How They Work. 2004. (High Five Reading Ser.). (J). (978-0-7368-3853-5(8)) Capstone Pr., Inc.

—Bridge Building: Bridge Designs & How They Work, 6 vols. (gr. 4 up). 49.95 (978-0-7368-3871-9(6), High Five) Red Brick Learning.

Carr, Roger. Roads & Bridges. 1999. (gr. k-3). lib. bdg. 11.80 (978-0-613-19436-5(5)) Tandem Library Bks.

Cortright, Robert S. Bridging the World. Cortright, Robert S., photos by. 2003. (Illus.). 208p. 35.00 (978-0-9641963-3-9(6)) Bridge Ink.

Del Cemento al Puente (From Cement to Bridge) 2006. (De Principio a Fin Ser.). (SPA.). 24p. (J). 18.60 (978-0-8225-6498-0(X), Ediciones Lerner) Lerner Publishing Group.

Engineering is Elementary Team. Javier Builds a Bridge: A Civil Engineering Story. 2005. (Illus.). 41p. (J). per. (***978-1-933758-01-5(5)***) Museum of Science.

Farbman, Melinda. Bridges. 2001. (Transportation & Communication Ser.). (Illus.). 48p. (J). (gr. 1-4). lib. bdg. 23.93 (978-0-7660-1647-7(1)) Enslow Pubs., Inc.

Franks, Gary L. Bridges at the Foot of the Rapids: An Illustrated History of Maumee-Perrysburg River Crossings & Construction of the 2002 Fort Meigs Memorial Bridge. 2003. 243p. per. (978-1-59196-333-2(8)) Instantpublisher.com.

Furgang, Kathy. Construccion de puentes & Building Bridges. 2005. spiral bd. 77.00 (***978-1-4108-5683-8(6)***) Benchmark Education Co.

Harper, Suzanne. The 10 Most Amazing Bridges. 2008. (Tentrade; Ser.). 48p. (J). pap. 14.99 (***978-1-55448-470-6(7)***, Watts, Franklin) Scholastic Library Publishing.

Johmann, Carol A. Bridges! Amazing Structures to Design, Build & Test. 1999. (gr. 3-6). lib. bdg. 19.90 (978-0-613-27751-8(1)) Tandem Library Bks.

Johmann, Carol A. & Rieth, Elizabeth J. Bridges! Amazing Structures to Design, Build & Test. 1999. (Kaleidoscope Kids Bks.). (Illus.). 96p. (J). (gr. 2-8). pap. 12.95 (978-1-885593-30-6(9), Williamson Bks.) Ideals Pubns.

Johnson, Darv. The Longest Bridge. 2002. (Extreme Places Ser.). (Illus.). 48p. (J). (gr. 3-5). 26.20 (978-0-7377-1416-6(6), Kidhaven) Thomson Gale.

Landau, Elaine. Bridges. 2001. (True Bks.). (Illus.). 48p. (J). (gr. 3-5). pap. 6.95 (978-0-516-27313-6(2)); 25.00 (978-0-516-22182-3(5)) Scholastic Library Publishing. (Children's Pr.).

—Bridges. 2001. (gr. 3-6). lib. bdg. 15.25 (978-0-613-53485-7(9)) Tandem Library Bks.

Mattern, Joanne. Bridges. 2002. (Illus.). 24p. (J). lib. bdg. 21.35 (978-1-58340-150-7(4)) Smart Apple Media.

Maxwell, Yolonda. Famous Bridges of the World: Measuring Length, Weight, & Volume. 2005. (PowerMath Ser.). (Illus.). 32p. (J). 22.50 (978-1-4042-2937-2(X)); pap. (978-1-4042-5137-3(5)); (***978-1-4042-5139-7(1)***) Rosen Publishing Group, Inc., The. (PowerKids Pr.).

Michelle Keller. The Akashi-Kaiko Bridge. 2004. (Building World Landmarks Ser.). (Illus.). 48p. (J). (gr. 4-7). 24.95 (978-1-4103-0140-6(0), Blackbirch Pr., Inc.) Thomson Gale.

Mitchell, Susan K. The Longest Bridges. 2007. (Megastructures Ser.). 32p. (J). (gr. 2-4). lib. bdg. 23.93 (***978-0-8368-8364-0(0)***) Stevens, Gareth Inc.

Murray, Julie. Golden Gate Bridge. 2005. (Buddy Book Ser.). (Illus.). 24p. (J). (gr. k-4). lib. bdg. 21.35 (978-1-57765-672-2(5)) ABDO Publishing Co.

Nardo, Don. Roman Roads & Aqueducts. 2000. (Building History Ser.). (Illus.). 96p. (J). (gr. 6-9). 28.70 (978-1-56006-721-4(7), Lucent Bks.) Thomson Gale.

Nelson, Sharlene. Golden Gate Bridge. 2001. (gr. 3-6). lib. bdg. 14.10 (978-0-613-51646-4(X)) Tandem Library Bks.

Nicholson, John. Building the Sydney Harbour Bridge. Nicholson, John, illus. 2000. (Illus.). 32p. (J). (978-1-86508-259-2(7)); mass mkt. (978-1-86508-258-5(9)) Allen & Unwin.

Oxlade, Chris. Bridges. (Building Amazing Structures Ser.). (Illus.). 32p. (J). 2000. (gr. 4-7). lib. bdg. 22.79 (978-1-57572-275-7(5)); 2nd ed. 2005. (978-1-4034-7901-3(1)) Heinemann Library.

Powell, Robert A. Kentucky's Covered Bridges. 2001. per. 7.90 (978-0-9651406-4-5(4)) Silverhawke Pubns.

Richards, Julie. Bridges. 2003. 32p. (J). lib. bdg. 24.25 (978-1-58340-344-0(2)) Smart Apple Media.

Richardson, Adele D. Covered Bridges. 2001. (J). lib. bdg. 19.95 (978-1-58341-004-2(X), Creative Education) Creative Co., The.

Spangenburg, Ray & Moser, Diane. The Story of America's Bridges. 1999. (Illus.). 96p. (J). lib. bdg. 23.95 (978-0-7351-0203-3(1)) Replica Bks.

Speaker-Yuan, Margaret. Royal Gorge Bridge. 2003. (Building World Landmarks Ser.). (Illus.). 48p. (J). 24.95 (978-1-56711-352-5(4), Blackbirch Pr., Inc.) Thomson Gale.

Stone, Lynn M. Bridges. 2001. (How are They Built? Ser.). (Illus.). 48p. (J). (gr. 4-8). lib. bdg. 29.93 (978-1-58952-135-3(8)) Rourke Publishing, LLC.

Sturges, Philemon. Bridges Are to Cross. Laroche, Giles, illus. 1998. 1p. (J). (ps-3). 15.99 (978-0-399-23174-2(9), Putnam Juvenile) Penguin Group (USA) Inc.

Thomas, Mark. The Akashi-Kaikyo Bridge: World's Longest Bridge. 2002. (Reading Power Ser.). (Illus.). 24p. (J). lib. bdg. 17.25 (978-0-8239-5990-7(2), PowerKids Pr.) Rosen Publishing Group, Inc., The.

—El Puente Akashi Kaikyo: El Puente Mas Largo Del Mundo. 2004. (Estructuras Extraordinarias Ser.). (SPA & ENG., Illus.). 24p. (J). (gr. 3-6). lib. bdg. 17.25 (978-0-8239-6866-4(9), Buenas Letra) Rosen Publishing Group, Inc., The.

Weg, Manya. Crossing Bridges. 2002. (Illus.). 16p. (J). (978-0-439-35111-9(1)) Scholastic, Inc.

White, Tekla N. The Flight of the Union. Ramstad, Ralph L., illus. 1998. (On My Own History Ser.). 48p. (J). (gr. 1-3). pap. 5.95 (978-1-57505-300-4(4)) Lerner Publishing Group.

Willard, Keith & Richardson, Adele D. Bridges. 1999. (Designing the Future Ser.). (Illus.). 32p. (J). (gr. 4-7). lib. bdg. (978-0-88682-718-2(3), Creative Education) Creative Co., The.

Zaunders, Bo. The Great Bridge-Building Contest. Munro, Roxie, illus. 2004. 32p. (J). (gr. k-4). 16.95 (978-0-8109-4929-4(6)) Abrams, Harry N., Inc.

—The Great Bridge-Building Contest. Munro, Roxie, illus. 2006. 30p. (J). (gr. 4-8). reprint ed. 17.00 (978-1-4223-5239-7(0)) DIANE Publishing Co.

BRIDGES—FICTION

Bell, Babs. The Bridge Is Up! Hefferan, Rob, illus. 2004. 32p. (J). (ps-k). 13.89 (978-0-06-053794-4(9)) HarperCollins Pubs.

Bunting, Eve. Pop's Bridge. Payne, C. F., illus. 2006. 32p. (J). 17.00 (978-0-15-204773-3(5)) Harcourt Trade Pubs.

Christen, Dennis H. Lundon's Bridge & the Three Keys. 2005. (YA). lib. bdg., act. bk. ed. 24.95 (978-0-9718151-3-1(5)); 2006. (ENG.). (J). per. 12.95 (978-0-9718151-2-4(7)) CG Star, L.L.C.

Edah, Omatseyin Mark. The Mystery Bridge. Eda, Martin M., ed. Edoja, Oke-Wiskee, illus. 2000. (J). (gr. 3 up). pap. (978-1-928903-04-8(5)) Edah Bks.

Grow, Kathy K. & Varvel, Lois H. The Day Bridger Got His Name. Clay, Nancy, illus. 2002. 40p. (J). pap. 10.95 (978-0-9704839-1-1(0)) Vintage Point Pr.

Hodo, Dennis. The Bamboo Bridge. Wingo, Lisa, ed. Rivera, Juan, illus. 1998. 100p. (J). (gr. 6-7). pap. 6.00 (978-0-9663901-0-0(5)) Gray Company Publishing.

Koury, Jen. Eddie Excavator Suspends a Bridge. Torgerson, Dell & Reyner, Mark, eds. Koury, Jen, illus. 1999. (John Deere Kids Toybook Ser.). (Illus.). 10p. (J). (ps up). mass mkt. 9.99 (978-1-887327-29-9(0)) Ertl Co., Inc.

Simon, Seymour. Bridges. 2005. (SeeMore Readers Ser.). (Illus.). 40p. (J). (gr. 1-3). 14.50 (978-1-58717-263-2(1)); pap. 3.95 (978-1-58717-264-9(X)) Chronicle Bks. LLC. (SeaStar Bks.).

Soloman, Ms Debra. Don't Look under the Bridge. 2006. 25p. 7.00 (978-1-4116-4608-7(8)) Lulu.com.

Whelan, Gloria. Mackinac Bridge: The Five-Mile Poem. van Frankenhuyzen, Gijsbert, illus. 2006. 40p. (J). 17.95 (978-1-58536-283-7(2)) Sleeping Bear Pr.

White, Tekla N. The Flight of the Union. Ramstad, Ralph L., illus. 1998. (On My Own History Ser.). 48p. (J). (gr. 1-3). lib. bdg. 23.93 (978-1-57505-093-5(5), Carolrhoda Bks.) Lerner Publishing Group.

Wolff, Patricia Rae. The Toll-Bridge Troll. Root, Kimberly B., illus. 2000. 24p. (J). (ps-2). pap. 7.00 (978-0-15-202105-4(1), Harcourt Paperbacks) Harcourt Children's Bks.

Wood, Audrey. The Rainbow Bridge. Florczak, Robert, illus. 2000. 32p. (J). (gr. k-5). pap. 7.00 (978-0-15-202106-1(X), Voyager Bks./Libros Viajeros) Harcourt Children's Bks.

BRIGANDS AND ROBBERS

see Robbers and Outlaws

BRITAIN, BATTLE OF, 1940

Chrisp, Peter. The Battle of Britain. 2003. (World Wars Ser.). (Illus.). 64p. (J). 28.56 (978-0-7398-6062-5(3)) Raintree.

BRITISH COLUMBIA

Bowers, Vivien. British Columbia. 1999. (Hello Canada Ser.). (J). pap. (978-1-55041-274-1(4)) Fitzhenry & Whiteside, Ltd.

Campbell, Marjorie Wilkins. The Savage River: Seventy-One Days with Simon Fraser. Delainey, James, illus. 2003. 149p. pap. 11.95 (978-1-894856-24-9(4)) Fifth Hse. Pubs. CAN. *Dist:* Fitzhenry & Whiteside, Ltd.

Francis, Daniel. Far West: A History of British Columbia for Young Readers. unabr. ed. 2006. (Illus.). 175p. (YA). 36.95 (***978-1-55017-410-6(X)*** Harbour Publishing Co., Ltd. CAN. *Dist:* Graphic Arts Ctr. Publishing Co.

Hancock, Lyn & Krueger, Guenther. Destination Vancouver. 1998. (Port Cities of North America Ser.). (Illus.). 80p. (J). (gr. 6-8). lib. bdg. 23.93 (978-0-8225-2787-9(1)) Lerner Publishing Group.

Hanna, Dawn. Best Hikes & Walks of Southwestern British Columbia, Vol. 1. 2nd rev. ed. 2006. (Illus.). 360p. (J). (gr. 4). pap. (978-1-55105-455-1(8)) Lone Pine Publishing.

Harcourt School Publishers Staff. Visit Vancouver. 3rd ed. 2002. (Horizons Ser.). (Illus.). (J). pap. 7.30 (978-0-15-333593-8(9)) Harcourt Schl. Pubs.

Kavanagh, James. British Columbia Trees & Wildflowers. Leung, Raymond, illus. 1999. (Pocket Naturalist Ser.). (J). 5.95 (978-1-58355-045-8(3)) Waterford Pr., Ltd.

—British Columbia Wildlife. Leung, Raymond, illus. 1999. (Pocket Naturalist Ser.). (J). 5.95 (978-1-58355-044-1(5)) Waterford Pr., Ltd.

LeVert, Suzanne. British Columbia. 2000. (Canada in the Twenty First Century Ser.). (Illus.). 64p. (J). (gr. 8-12). 18.95 (978-0-7910-6060-5(8) , Chelsea Hse.) Facts On File, Inc.

Palana, B. J. British Columbia. 2002. (Exploring Canada Ser.). (Illus.). 104p. (J). 29.95 (978-1-59018-046-4(1) , Lucent Bks.) Thomson Gale.

Percy, Robert. My Vancouver Sketchbook. Guzek, Greta, illus. 2002. 32p. (J). 12.95 (978-1-55192-436-6(6)) Raincoast Bk. Distribution CAN. *Dist:* Transition Vendor.

Roberts, G. Gregory. S Is for Spirit Bear: A British Columbia Alphabet. Doucet, Bob, illus. rev. ed. 2006. 40p. (J). 18.95 (978-1-58536-291-2(3)) Sleeping Bear Pr.

Rogers, Barbara Radcliffe. Vancouver. 2001. (gr. 5-8). lib. bdg. 18.75 (978-0-613-51520-7(X)) Tandem Library Bks.

Rogers, Barbara Radcliffe & Rogers, Stillman D. Vancouver. 2002. (Cities of the World Ser.). (Illus.). 64p. (J). (gr. 4-9). pap. 9.95 (978-0-516-25961-1(X) , Children's Pr.) Scholastic Library Publishing.

Tessier, Tess & Tess, Grandma. White Spirit Bear. Miller, Nancy, ed. 2nd ed. 2000. (Illus.). 48p. (J). (gr. k-7). 17.95 (978-0-88839-462-0(4)) Hancock Hse. Pubs.

Vancouver Sold C 2005. 2004. 388p. (YA). pap. 17.00 (978-1-58553-968-0(6) , 05GC0010) Entertainment Publications, Inc.

Wright, Jeni. The Lobster Kids' Guide to Exploring Vancouver: 12 Months of Fun. Kirner, Bob, ed. Battuz, Christine, illus. 2000. (Lobster Kids' City Explorers Ser.). 256p. (J). (ps-7). pap. 12.95 (978-1-894222-05-1(9)) Lobster Pr. CAN. *Dist:* Univ. of Toronto Pr.

BRITISH COLUMBIA—FICTION

Alma, Ann. Summer of Adventures. 2003. (Summer Ser.). 160p. (J). pap. 5.95 (978-1-55039-122-0(4)) Sono Nis Pr. CAN. *Dist:* Orca Bk. Pubs. USA.

Cameron, Anne. Dreamspeaker. unabr. ed. 2005. 128p. pap. 9.95 (978-1-55017-364-2(2)) Harbour Publishing Co., Ltd. CAN. *Dist:* Graphic Arts Ctr. Publishing Co.

—Dreamspeaker. 2000. 128p. (YA). (gr. 7-9). mass mkt. 5.95 (978-0-7736-7482-0(9)) Stoddart Kids CAN. *Dist:* Fitzhenry & Whiteside, Ltd.

Chamberlain, Penny. The Olden Days Locket. 2003. 200p. (J). pap. 6.95 (978-1-55039-128-2(3)) Sono Nis Pr. CAN. *Dist:* Orca Bk. Pubs. USA.

Charles, Norma. Boxcar Kid. 2007. 136p. (YA). pap. 9.99 (***978-1-55002-755-6(7)*** , Sandcastle Bks.) Dundurn Group, The CAN. *Dist:* Univ. of Toronto Pr.

De Vries, Maggie. Tale of a Great White Fish: A Sturgeon Story. Benoit, Renné, illus. 2006. 48p. 15.95 (978-1-55365-125-3(1) , Greystone Bks.) Douglas & McIntyre, Ltd. CAN. *Dist:* Transition Vendor.

Friesen, Gayle. Janey's Girl. (Gayle Friessen Ser.). 224p. (YA). (gr. 13 up). 2001. (978-1-55074-463-7(1)); 1998. (Illus.). (978-1-55074-461-3(5)) Kids Can Pr., Ltd.

Harris, Christie. Mouse Woman & the Vanished Princesses. Tait, Douglas, illus. 2005. 152p. (J). (gr. 3-17). pap. 7.95 (978-1-55192-811-1(6)) Raincoast Bk. Distribution CAN. *Dist:* Perseus Distribution.

Harris, Dorothy Joan. Ellen: Hobo Jungle. 2002. (Our Canadian Girl Ser.). (Illus.). 96p. (J). pap. (978-0-14-100270-5(0)) Penguin Group (USA) Inc.

Heneghan, James. Payback. 2007. 144p. (YA). (gr. 7 up). 17.95 (***978-0-88899-701-2(9)***) Groundwood Bks. CAN. *Dist:* Perseus Distribution.

Horne, Constance. The Tenth Pupil. 2005. 160p. (J). (gr. 3-9). pap., tchr. ed. 8.95 (978-0-921870-86-9(8)) Ronsdale Pr. CAN. *Dist:* Literary Pr. Group of Canada.

Horvath, Polly. The Corps of the Bare-Boned Plane. 2007. 272p. (J). (gr. 7 up). 17.00 (***978-0-374-31553-5(1)*** , Farrar, Straus & Giroux (BYR)) Farrar, Straus & Giroux.

Horvath, Polly. Everything on a Waffle. 2001. 160p. (J). (gr. 5 up). 16.00 (978-0-374-32236-6(8) , Farrar, Straus & Giroux (BYR)) Farrar, Straus & Giroux.

—Everything on a Waffle. 2008. 176p. (J). pap. 6.99 (***978-0-312-38004-5(6)***) Square Fish.

Johnson, E. Pauline. The Lost Island. Matsoureff, Atanas, illus. 2004. 40p. (J). 16.95 (978-1-894965-07-1(8)) Simply Read Bks. CAN. *Dist:* Perseus Distribution.

Juby, Susan. Alice, I Think. (J). 2003. (Illus.). 304p. lib. bdg. 16.89 (978-0-06-051544-7(9)); 2004. 320p. reprint ed. pap. 7.99 (978-0-06-051545-4(7)) HarperCollins Pubs. (HarperTeen).

—Alice, I Think. 2000. 224p. (YA). pap. (978-1-894345-12-5(6)) Thistledown Pr., Ltd.

—Alice MacLeod, Realist at Last. (J). 2006. 320p. pap. 8.99 (978-0-06-051552-2(X)); 2005. 15.99 (978-0-06-051549-2(X)); 2005. 320p. lib. bdg. 16.89 (978-0-06-051550-8(3)) HarperCollins Pubs. (HarperTeen).

—Another Kind of Cowboy. 2007. 352p. (J). lib. bdg. 17.89 (***978-0-06-076518-7(6)***); (YA). lib. bdg. (***978-0-06-076521-7(6)***); 352p. (YA). (gr. 9 up). 16.99 (***978-0-06-076517-0(8)***) HarperCollins Pubs. (HarperTeen).

Juby, Susan. Miss Smithers. 2004. (Illus.). 336p. (J). 15.99 (978-0-06-051546-1(5)); lib. bdg. 16.89 (978-0-06-051547-8(3)) HarperCollins Pubs. (HarperTeen).

Lawrence, Iain. The Lightkeeper's Daughter. (YA). (gr. 9). 2004. 272p. pap. 7.95 (978-0-385-73127-0(2)); 2002. 256p. lib. bdg. 18.99 (978-0-385-90062-1(7)) Random Hse. Children's Bks. (Delacorte Bks. for Young Readers).

Lawson, Julie. The Ghost of Avalanche Mountain. 2000. (Goldstone Trilogy Ser.). (Illus.). 232p. (YA). (gr. 5-9). pap. 7.95 (978-0-7737-6091-2(1)) Stoddart Kids CAN. *Dist:* Fitzhenry & Whiteside, Ltd.

—Goldstone. unabr. ed. 1998. 170p. (J). (gr. 5-9). pap. 7.95 (978-0-7737-5891-9(7)) Stoddart Kids CAN. *Dist:* Fitzhenry & Whiteside, Ltd.

Manuel, Lynn. Camels Always Do. Charko, Kasia, illus. 2004. 32p. (J). (ps-2). 7.95 (978-1-55143-470-4(9)) Orca Bk. Pubs. USA.

Maycock, Dianne. Lucky's Mountain. 2007. (Orca Young Readers Ser.). 112p. pap. (***978-1-55143-682-1(5)***) Orca Bk. Pubs.

McMurchy-Barber, Gina. Reading the Bones. 2008. 152p. (YA). pap. 9.99 (***978-1-55002-732-7(8)*** , Sandcastle Bks.) Dundurn Group, The CAN. *Dist:* Univ. of Toronto Pr.

McTighe, Carolyn. The Sakura Tree. Brownlee, Karen, illus. 2008. 32p. (J). (ps-3). 17.95 (***978-0-88995-354-3(6)***) Red Deer Pr. CAN. *Dist:* Fitzhenry & Whiteside, Ltd.

Olsen, Sylvia. No Time to Say Goodbye. 2002. (Illus.). 175p. (J). pap. 6.95 (978-1-55039-121-3(6)) Sono Nis Pr. CAN. *Dist:* Orca Bk. Pubs. USA.

Pearce, Jacqueline. Discovering Emily. 2004. (Orca Young Readers Ser.). (Illus.). 144p. (J). (gr. 3-6). pap. 4.99 (978-1-55143-295-3(1)) Orca Bk. Pubs. USA.

Reekie, Jocelyn. Tess. 2003. 296p. (YA). (gr. 5-8). pap. 7.95 (978-1-55192-471-7(4)) Raincoast Bk. Distribution CAN. *Dist:* Perseus Distribution.

—Tess. 2003. (gr. 7-12). lib. bdg. 16.40 (978-0-613-78646-1(7)) Tandem Library Bks.

Repp, Gloria. The Mystery of the Indian Carvings. Pelicano, Christopher J., illus. 2002. 118p. (J). (gr. 4-7). pap. 7.49 (978-1-57924-726-3(1)) Jones, Bob Univ. Pr.

Roberts, Ken. The Thumb in the Box. Franson, Leanne, illus. 2002. 96p. (J). (gr. 2-4). pap. 5.95 (978-0-88899-422-6(2)) Groundwood Bks. CAN. *Dist:* Perseus Distribution.

—Thumb on a Diamond. Franson, Leanne, illus. 128p. (J). 2007. (gr. 4-7). pap. 7.95 (978-0-88899-705-0(1)); 2006. 15.95 (978-0-88899-629-9(2)) Groundwood Bks. CAN. *Dist:* Perseus Distribution.

Spalding, Andrea. An Island of My Own. 2007. 112p. (YA). pap. 11.99 (***978-1-55002-635-1(6)*** , Sandcastle Bks.) Dundurn Group, The CAN. *Dist:* Univ. of Toronto Pr.

Walsh, Ann. By the Skin of His Teeth. 2006. 168p. (YA). pap. 10.99 (***978-1-55002-634-4(8)*** , Sandcastle Bks.) Dundurn Group, The CAN. *Dist:* Univ. of Toronto Pr.

—The Doctor's Apprentice. 2005. 160p. (YA). (gr. 3-8). pap., tchr. ed. 8.95 (978-0-88878-389-9(2)) Beach Holme Pubs., Ltd. CAN. *Dist:* Literary Pr. Group of Canada.

Walsh, Ann. The Doctors Apprentice. 2007. 160p. (J). pap. 9.99 (***978-1-55002-633-7(X)*** , Sandcastle Bks.) Dundurn Group, The CAN. *Dist:* Univ. of Toronto Pr.

Walters, Eric. War of the Eagles. 1998. 160p. (YA). (gr. 7-12). 14.00 (978-1-55143-118-5(1)) Orca Bk. Pubs. USA.

Wilson, John. Red Goodwin. 2006. (Illus.). 170p. (J). pap. (***978-1-55380-034-7(6)***) Ronsdale Pr.

Woodson, Marion. Charlotte's Vow. 2006. 144p. (J). pap., tchr. ed. 5.95 (978-0-88878-413-1(9) , Sandcastle Bks.) Dundurn Group, The CAN. *Dist:* Univ. of Toronto Pr.

Yee, Paul. The Bone Collector's Son. 2005. 144p. (YA). 15.95 (978-0-7614-5242-3(7)) Cavendish, Marshall Corp.

BRITISH GUIANA

see Guyana

BRITISH—UNITED STATES

Franchino, Vicky. English Americans. 2004. (Our Cultural Heritage Ser.). 32p. (J). (gr. 2-6). 27.07 (978-1-59296-179-5(7)) Child's World, Inc.

Morris, Ann. Grandma Susan Remembers: A British-American Family Story. Linenthal, Peter, illus. 2002. (What Was It Like, Grandma? Ser.). 32p. (gr. k-3). lib. bdg. 22.90 (978-0-7613-2319-8(8) , Millbrook Pr.) Lerner Publishing Group.

—Grandma Susan Remembers: A British-American Family Story. 2002. (gr. k-3). lib. bdg. 16.40 (978-0-613-56398-7(0)) Tandem Library Bks.

BROADCASTING

see also Radio Broadcasting; Television Broadcasting

Aaseng, Nathan. Business Builders in Broadcasting. 2005. (Business Builders Ser.: Vol. 8). (Illus.). 160p. (J). (gr. 5 up). lib. bdg. 24.95 (978-1-881508-83-0(8)) Oliver Pr., Inc.

Facts on File, Inc. Staff. Careers in Focus. 2nd ed. 2004. (Careers in Focus Ser.). (Illus.). 192p. (YA). (gr. 6-12). 22.95 (978-0-8160-5551-7(3) , Ferguson Publishing Co.) Facts On File, Inc.

Facts on File, Inc. Staff, ed. Aviation. 4th ed. 2004. (Careers in Focus Ser.). (Illus.). 192p. (J). (gr. 6-12). 22.95 (978-0-8160-5552-4(1) , Ferguson Publishing Co.) Facts On File, Inc.

Ferguson. Careers in Focus. 2nd ed. 2002. (Careers in Focus Ser.). 192p. (YA). (gr. 6-12). 22.95 (978-0-89434-440-4(4) , Ferguson Publishing Co.) Facts On File, Inc.

—Careers in Focus: Broadcasting. 3rd rev. ed. 2007. (Careers in Focus Ser.). 208p. (J). (gr. 6-12). 29.95 (***978-0-8160-6567-7(5)*** , Ferguson Publishing Co.) Facts On File, Inc.

—What Can I Do Now: Radio & Television. 2nd rev. ed. 2007. (What Can I Do Now Ser.). 176p. (gr. 6-12). 29.95 (***978-0-8160-6032-0(0)*** , Ferguson Publishing Co.) Facts On File, Inc.

J. G. Ferguson Publishing Company Staff. Careers in Focus: Broadcasting. 2001. (Careers in Focus Ser.). 188p. (J). (gr. 7 up). (978-0-89434-333-9(5) , F711, Ferguson Publishing Co.) Facts On File, Inc.

J. G. Ferguson Publishing Company Staff, contrib. by. Careers in Focus. 2nd ed. 2004. (Careers in Focus Ser.). (Illus.). 192p. (J). (gr. 6-12). 22.95 (978-0-8160-5549-4(1) , Ferguson Publishing Co.) Facts On File, Inc.

J. G. Ferguson Publishing Company Staff, ed. Careers in Focus, 12 vols., Set 3. 2001. 2304p. (YA). 186.00 (978-0-89434-423-7(4) , Ferguson Publishing Co.) Facts On File, Inc.

Sawyer, Sarah. Career Building Through Podcasting. 2007. (J). lib. bdg. (***978-1-4042-1944-1(7)***) Rosen Publishing Group, Inc., The.

Teitelbaum, Michael. Radio & Television. 2005. (Great Inventions Ser.). (Illus.). 48p. (YA). lib. bdg. 30.00 (978-0-8368-5802-0(6) , World Almanac Library) Stevens, Gareth Inc.

BROCK, ISAAC, SIR, 1769-1812

Fryer, Mary Beacock. Bold, Brave, & Born to Lead: Major General Isaac Brock & the Canadas. 2004. (Illus.). 200p. pap. 9.99 (978-1-55002-501-9(5)) Dundurn Group, The CAN. *Dist:* Univ. of Toronto Pr.

BRONTE, CHARLOTTE, 1816-1855

Bloom, Harold. Jane Eyre. 2007. (Bloom's Guides). 104p. (YA). (gr. 9 up). 30.00 (***978-0-7910-9362-7(X)*** , Chelsea Hse.) Facts On File, Inc.

Bloom, Harold, ed. Jane Eyre - Charlotte Bronte. 2006. (Bloom's Modern Critical Interpretations Ser.). 248p. (YA). (gr. 9 up). 45.00 (978-0-7910-9304-7(2) , Chelsea Hse.) Facts On File, Inc.

Brighton, Catherine. The Bronte's: Scenes from the Childhood of Charlotte, Branwell, Emily & Anne. 1999. (Illus.). (J). (gr. 1-5). pap. (978-0-7112-0882-7(4)) Lincoln, Frances Ltd.

Kenyon, Karen Smith. The Bronte Family: Passionate Literary Geniuses. 2005. (Lerner Biographies Ser.). (Illus.). 128p. (gr. 6-12). 27.93 (978-0-8225-0071-1(X)) Lerner Publishing Group.

Novel Units, Inc. Staff. Jane Eyre. (YA). 1999. 9.95 (978-1-56137-462-5(8)); 1998. 44p. 11.95 (978-1-56137-463-2(6) , NU4636SP) Novel Units, Inc.

Orme, David. The Brontes. 1999. (Writers in Britain Ser.). (Illus.). 32p. 24.99 (978-0-237-51744-1(2) , Evans Brothers, Limited) Evans Publishing Group GBR. *Dist:* Independent Pubs. Group.

Steinbauer, Janine. Bronte Sisters. 1999. (Profiles Ser.). (Illus.). 56p. (YA). (gr. 6 up). lib. bdg. 16.95 (978-0-88682-739-7(6) , Creative Education) Creative Co., The.

BRONTE, EMILY, 1818-1848

Bloom, Harold, ed. Emily Bronte's Wuthering Heights, Vol. 1. 1999. (Bloom's Reviews Comprehensive Research & Study Guides). 80p. (YA). (gr. 8-11). pap. 4.95 (978-0-7910-4170-3(0) , Chelsea Hse.) Facts On File, Inc.

Brighton, Catherine. The Bronte's: Scenes from the Childhood of Charlotte, Branwell, Emily & Anne. 1999. (Illus.). (J). (gr. 1-5). pap. (978-0-7112-0882-7(4)) Lincoln, Frances Ltd.

Kenyon, Karen Smith. The Bronte Family: Passionate Literary Geniuses. 2005. (Lerner Biographies Ser.). (Illus.). 128p. (gr. 6-12). 27.93 (978-0-8225-0071-1(X)) Lerner Publishing Group.

Mitchell, Hayley R. Readings on "Wuthering Heights" 1998. (Literary Companion to American Literature Ser.). (Illus.). 156p. (YA). (gr. 9 up). pap. 22.45 (978-1-56510-832-5(9) , Greenhaven Pr., Inc.) Thomson Gale.

BRONZE AGE

Nardo, Don. The Minoans. 2004. (Lost Civilizations Ser.). (Illus.). 112p. (J). (gr. 7-10). 29.95 (978-1-59018-565-0(X) , Lucent Bks.) Thomson Gale.

Williams, Brenda & Williams, Brian. Trading Up: Indus Valley Trade. 2007. (J). (***978-1-4109-2892-4(6)***); pap. (***978-1-4109-2899-3(3)***) Steck-Vaughn.

BRONZE AGE—FICTION

Dagg, Stephanie. Copper Lion. 2000. (Illus.). 160p. (J). (gr. 4-8). per. (978-1-84210-019-6(X)) Mentor Bks.

Mirarchi, Anthony J. The King's Challenge. 2007. (Illus.). 220p. (J). (gr. 5-7). per. 9.95 (***978-1-933255-32-3(3)***) DNA Pr.

BRONZES

Fritz, Jean. Leonardo's Horse. Talbott, Hudson, illus. 2001. 48p. (J). (gr. 1-6). 18.99 (978-0-399-23576-4(0) , Putnam Juvenile) Penguin Group (USA) Inc.

BROOKLYN (NEW YORK, N.Y.)

Brooklyn Public Library Staff. Brooklyn Pops Up: A Moveable Book of Brooklyn Landmarks. 2000. 16p. mass mkt. (978-1-891001-04-8(3) , Simon & Schuster) Simon & Schuster.

Brooklyn Public Library Staff, et al. Brooklyn Pops Up: A Moveable Book of Brooklyn Landmarks. 2000. (Illus.). 8p. (J). (gr. 4-7). 22.99 (978-0-689-84019-7(5) , Little Simon) Simon & Schuster Children's Publishing.

BROOKLYN (NEW YORK, N.Y.)—FICTION

Avi. Don't You Know There's a War On? 2001. 208p. (J). (gr. 4-6). 15.95 (978-0-380-97863-2(6)) HarperCollins Pubs.

—Don't You Know There's a War On? 2003. 200p. (J). (ps-7). lib. bdg. 14.15 (978-0-613-60338-6(9)) Tandem Library Bks.

Chaikin, Miriam. I Should Worry, I Should Care. 2000. (Illus.). 116p. (gr. 4-7). pap. 9.95 (978-0-595-09011-2(7) , Backinprint.com) iUniverse, Inc.

Chambers, Veronica. Quinceanera Means Sweet Fifteen. 2001. 192p. (Illus.). (J). (gr. 5-8). lib. bdg. 16.49 (978-0-7868-2426-7(3)); (gr. 3-7). 15.99 (978-0-7868-0497-9(1)) Hyperion Bks. for Children.

Christopher, Matt. Fairway Phenom. 2003. (gr. 3-6). lib. bdg. 12.40 (978-0-613-71602-4(7)) Tandem Library Bks.

Cohen, Miriam. Mimmy & Sophie All Around the Town. Yezerski, Thomas F., illus. 2004. 80p. (J). 16.00 (978-0-374-34989-9(4) , Farrar, Straus & Giroux (BYR)) Farrar, Straus & Giroux.

Crocitto, Frank. A Child's Christmas in Brooklyn. Horrigan, Jeremiah, ed. Horrigan, Grady Kane, illus. 2001. 96p. (YA). (gr. 4 up). 10.95 (978-0-9677558-2-3(4) , CHBO1) Candlepower, Inc.

Estes, Eleanor. The Alley. Ardizzone, Edward, illus. 2003. 288p. pap. 5.95 (978-0-15-204918-8(5) , Odyssey Classics) Harcourt Children's Bks.

—The Tunnel of Hugsy Goode. Ardizzone, Edward, illus. 2003. 256p. (J). 17.00 (978-0-15-204914-0(2) , Harcourt Young Classics); pap. 6.95 (978-0-15-204916-4(9) , Odyssey Classics) Harcourt Children's Bks.

—The Tunnel of Hugsy Goode. 2003. (gr. 3-6). lib. bdg. 14.10 (978-0-613-70526-4(2)) Tandem Library Bks.

Friedman, D. Dina. Playing Dad's Song. 2006. 144p. (YA). 16.00 (978-0-374-37173-9(3)) Farrar, Straus & Giroux.

Giff, Patricia Reilly. All the Way Home. 2003. (Illus.). 176p. (J). (gr. 3-7). pap. 5.99 (978-0-440-41182-6(3) , Yearling) Random Hse. Children's Bks.

—A House of Tailors. 2006. 160p. (YA). (gr. 4-7). 5.50 (978-0-440-23800-3(5) , Yearling) Random Hse. Children's Bks.

—Water Street. 2006. 176p. (J). (gr. 4-7). lib. bdg. 17.99 (978-0-385-90097-3(X) , Lamb, Wendy) Random Hse. Children's Bks.

Harris, Loretta. The Inside Struggle. 2006. (YA). (***978-0-9786681-3-6(8)***) Children's Heart Publishing Co.

Laskin, Pamela L. Getting to Know You. 2003. (YA). 16.95 (978-0-936389-92-9(3)) Tudor Pubs., Inc.

Lurie, April. Dancing in the Streets of Brooklyn. 2002. 208p. (gr. 3-7). lib. bdg. 17.99 (978-0-385-90066-9(X) , Delacorte Bks. for Young Readers) Random Hse. Children's Bks.

McCann, Thomas P. "Tom". The Tree Nobody Wanted: A Christmas Story. 2007. 14.95 (***978-0-9797407-0-1(3)***) Exeter Pr.

McDonald, Janet. Off-Color. 2007. 176p. (YA). (gr. 7 up). 16.00 (***978-0-374-37196-8(2)***) Farrar, Straus & Giroux.

McDonald, Janet. Twists & Turns. 144p. (YA). 2006. pap. 6.95 (978-0-374-40006-4(7)); 2003. 16.00 (978-0-374-39955-9(7)) Farrar, Straus & Giroux. (Farrar, Straus & Giroux (BYR)).

—Twists & Turns, Vol. 5. l.t. ed. 2004. 147p. 21.95 (978-0-7862-6664-7(3) , Large Print Pr.) Thorndike Pr.

Muldrow, Diane. Measure of Thanks. Pollack, Barbara, illus. 2007. (Dish Ser.: Vol. 10). 160p. (J). (gr. 4-7). pap. 4.99 (***978-0-448-44662-2(6)*** , Grosset & Dunlap) Penguin Group (USA) Inc.

Nelson, Carol Ann. Sammy Knows What to Do. Costain, illus. 2000. (J). (gr. 1-3). 11.95 (978-1-893886-02-5(6)) How I Learn & Grow.

Nemec, Thomas F., creator. Owenopolis: A New Childrens Book, Created by Thomas Nemec-N. Y. C. ed. 2007. (J). lib. bdg. 15.00 (***978-0-9791612-0-9(7)***) Goon Dog Publishing.

Rinaldi, Ann. Brooklyn Rose. 2005. 240p. (YA). 17.00 (978-0-15-205117-4(1)) Harcourt Children's Bks.

Schirripa, Steve & Fleming, Charles. Nicky Deuce: Welcome to the Family. 2006. 176p. (gr. 5-8). 5.99 (978-0-440-42053-8(9) , Yearling) Random Hse. Children's Bks.

Sheldon, Dyan. I Conquer Britain. 2007. (Illus.). 208p. (YA). (gr. 7). 15.99 (***978-0-7636-3300-4(3)***) Candlewick Pr.

—Sophie Pitt-Turnbull Discovers America. 2007. 192p. (YA). (gr. 7). pap. 7.99 (***978-0-7636-3295-3(3)***) Candlewick Pr.

Singer, Marilyn. Didi & Daddy on the Promenade. Gay, Marie-Louise, illus. 2001. 32p. (J). (gr. k-3). tchr. ed. 14.00 (978-0-618-04640-9(2) , Clarion Bks.) Houghton Mifflin Co. Trade & Reference Div.

Uhlberg, Myron. Flying over Brooklyn. Fitzgerald, Gerald, illus. 1999. 32p. (J). (ps-3). 15.95 (978-1-56145-194-4(0)) Peachtree Pubs., Ltd.

van Diepen, Allison. Snitch. 2007. 304p. (YA). pap. 6.99 (***978-1-4169-5030-1(3)*** , Simon Pulse) Simon & Schuster Children's Publishing.

Woodson, Jacqueline. Between Madison & Palmetto. 2002. 128p. (J). pap. 5.99 (978-0-698-11958-1(4)); (YA). 16.99 (978-0-399-23757-7(7)) Penguin Group (USA) Inc. (Putnam Juvenile).

—Between Madison & Palmetto. 2002. (gr. 5-8). lib. bdg. 14.15 (978-0-613-50092-0(X)) Tandem Library Bks.

—Last Summer with Maizon. 2002. 112p. (J). 17.99 (978-0-399-23755-3(0)); (Illus.). (gr. 3-7). pap. 5.99 (978-0-698-11929-1(0)) Penguin Group (USA) Inc. (Putnam Juvenile).

—Last Summer with Maizon. 2002. (gr. 3-6). lib. bdg. 13.00 (978-0-613-45286-1(0)) Tandem Library Bks.

BROOKLYN BRIDGE (NEW YORK, N.Y.)

Curlee, Lynn. Brooklyn Bridge. Curlee, Lynn, illus. 2001. (Illus.). 40p. (J). (gr. 3-7). 18.00 (978-0-689-83183-6(8) , Atheneum) Simon & Schuster Children's Publishing.

Mann, Elizabeth. The Brooklyn Bridge: The Story of the World's Most Famous Bridge & the Remarkable Family That Built It. Witschonke, Alan, illus. 2003. (Wonders of the World Ser.). 48p. (J). (ps up). 19.95 (978-0-9650493-0-6(2)) Mikaya Pr.

—The Brooklyn Bridge: The story of the world's most famous bridge & the remarkable family that built It. Witschonke, Alan, illus. 2006. (Wonders of the World Book Ser.). 48p. (J). (gr. 4-8). pap. 9.95 (978-1-931414-16-6(5)) Mikaya Pr.

Pascoe, Elaine. The Brooklyn Bridge. 1999. (Building America Ser.). (Illus.). 48p. (J). (gr. 5-8). 24.95 (978-1-56711-173-6(4) , Blackbirch Pr., Inc.) Thomson Gale.

Weiner, Vicki. The Brooklyn Bridge: New York City's Graceful Connection. 2004. (High Interest Bks.). (Illus.). 48p. (J). (gr. 7-12). pap. 6.95 (978-0-516-25905-5(9) , Children's Pr.) Scholastic Library Publishing.

BROOKLYN BRIDGE (NEW YORK, N.Y.)—FICTION

Bildner, Phil. Twenty-One Elephants. Pham, LeUyen, illus. 2004. 40p. (J). 16.95 (978-0-689-87011-8(6)) Simon & Schuster Children's Publishing.

Giff, Patricia Reilly. Water Street. (gr. 4-7). 2008. 144p. 6.50 ***(978-0-440-41921-1(2)*** , Yearling); 2006. 176p. (J). 15.95 (978-0-385-73068-6(3) , Lamb, Wendy) Random Hse. Children's Bks.

—Water Street. l.t. rev. ed. 2007. 193p. (YA). 23.95 ***(978-0-7862-9277-6(6))*** Thorndike Pr.

Lurie, April. Dancing in the Streets of Brooklyn. 2004. 208p. (gr. 3-7). pap. 5.99 (978-0-440-41825-2(9) , Yearling) Random Hse. Children's Bks.

Placide, Jaira. Fresh Girl. 2002. 224p. (YA). (gr. 7 up). 15.95 (978-0-385-32753-4(6) , Lamb, Wendy) Random Hse. Children's Bks.

Prince, April Jones. Twenty-One Elephants & Still Standing. Roca, Francois, illus. 2005. 32p. (J). (gr. k-3). 16.00 (978-0-618-44887-6(X)) Houghton Mifflin Co. Trade & Reference Div.

Sheldon, Dyan. Sophie Pitt-Turnbull Discovers America. 2005. 192p. (YA). (gr. 7 up). 15.99 (978-0-7636-2740-9(2)) Candlewick Pr.

Uhlberg, Myron. Flying over Brooklyn. 2003. (Illus.). 32p. (J). (gr. k-3). pap. 6.95 (978-1-56145-294-1(7)) Peachtree Pubs., Ltd.

—Flying over Brooklyn. Fitzgerald, Gerald, illus. 1999. 32p. (J). (ps-3). 15.95 (978-1-56145-194-4(0)) Peachtree Pubs., Ltd.

BROOKLYN DODGERS (BASEBALL TEAM)

Golenbock, Peter. Teammates. 1998. (Illus.). 32p. (ps-3). 16.98 (978-0-8172-4092-9(6)) Raintree.

BROTHERS AND SISTERS

Ashbe, Jeanne. And after That. Ashbe, Jeanne, illus. 2002. (Illus.). 12p. (J). 9.95 (978-1-929132-24-9(7)) Kane/Miller Bk. Pubs., Inc.

Auld, Mary. Mi Hermano. 2004. (Conoce la Familia Ser.). (SPA., Illus.). 24p. (J). (gr. 1 up). lib. bdg. 20.67 (978-0-8368-3931-9(5)) Stevens, Gareth Inc.

—My Brother. 2004. (Meet the Family Ser.). (Illus.). 24p. (J). (gr. 1 up). lib. bdg. 20.67 (978-0-8368-3924-1(2)) Stevens, Gareth Inc.

Bailey, Debbie. Hermanas. Huszar, Susan, photos by. 2003. (Hablemos Ser.). (SPA., Illus.). 14p. (J). (ps). bds. 5.95 (978-1-55037-307-3(2)) Annick Pr., Ltd. CAN. *Dist:* Firefly Bks., Ltd.

—Hermanos. Huszar, Susan, photos by. 2003. (Hablemos Ser.). (SPA., Illus.). 14p. (J). (ps). bds. 5.95 (978-1-55037-308-0(0)) Annick Pr., Ltd. CAN. *Dist:* Firefly Bks., Ltd.

Barber, Tiki & Barber, Ronde. By My Brother's Side. Root, Barry, illus. 2004. 32p. (J). (gr. 1-5). 16.95 (978-0-689-86559-6(7) , Simon & Schuster/Paula Wiseman Bks.) Simon & Schuster Children's Publishing.

—Game Day. Root, Barry, illus. 2005. 32p. (J). 16.95 (978-1-4169-0093-1(4) , Simon & Schuster Children's Publishing) Simon & Schuster Children's Publishing.

—Teammates. Root, Barry, illus. 2006. 32p. (J). (gr. 1-5). 16.95 (978-1-4169-2489-0(2) , Simon & Schuster Children's Publishing) Simon & Schuster Children's Publishing.

Brothers: The Hidden History of the Kennedy Years, 6 vols. (gr. k-2). 28.95 (978-0-7368-8264-4(2)) Red Brick Learning.

Cole, Joanna. The New Baby at Your House. Miller, Margaret, photos by. rev. ed. 1998. (Illus.). 48p. (J). (ps-3). 15.89 (978-0-688-13898-1(5)) HarperCollins Pubs.

Collman, Barbara J. Kid's Book to Welcome a New Baby: Fun for a Big Brother or Big Sister. 3rd rev. ed. 1999. (Illus.). 128p. (J). (ps-5). pap. 12.95 (978-1-892147-00-4(9)) Marlor Pr., Inc.

Dawson, Richard. My Baby Brother: A Fill-In & Keep Book. 2000. (Illus.). 30p. (J). (gr. k up). pap. (978-0-330-36970-1(9) , Macmillan Children's Bks.) Pan Macmillan.

—My Baby Sister: Fill-In & Keep Book. 2000. (Illus.). 32p. (YA). (gr. k up). pap. (978-0-330-36971-8(7) , Macmillan Children's Bks.) Pan Macmillan.

Edwards, Dianna. It's Not Easy Being Patou - Book One. 2004. (J). (978-0-9767756-1-4(1)) Patou Bks., LLC.

—Meet Patou. 2006. (J). pap. 29.95 (978-0-9767756-0-7(3)) Patou Bks., LLC.

—When Niki Got Sick, Bk. 2. 2004. (J). (978-0-9767756-2-1(X)) Patou Bks., LLC.

—Why Can't Everything Just Stay the Same? Book Three. 2004. (J). (978-0-9767756-3-8(8)) Patou Bks., LLC.

Giblin, James Cross. Good Brother, Bad Brother: The Story of Edwin Booth & John Wilkes Booth. 2005. (Illus.). 256p. (YA). (gr. 5-9). 22.00 (978-0-618-09642-8(6) , Clarion Bks.) Houghton Mifflin Co. Trade & Reference Div.

Godfrey, Jan. Sam's New Baby. Coulson, Jane, illus. 1998. 32p. (J). (ps-1). 2.99 (978-0-687-09570-4(0)) Abingdon Pr.

Hale, Natalie. Oh, Brother! Growing up with a Special Needs Sibling. Sternberg, Kate, tr. Sternberg, Kate, illus. 2004. 48p. (J). 14.95 (978-1-59147-060-1(9)); pap. 8.95 (978-1-59147-061-8(7)) American Psychological Assn. (Magination Pr.).

Helmer, Diana Star. Let's Talk about Having a New Brother or Sister. 1999. (Let's Talk Library). (Illus.). 24p. (J). (gr. 3). lib. bdg. 18.75 (978-0-8239-5191-8(X) , PowerKids Pr.) Rosen Publishing Group, Inc., The.

Hughes, Monica. My First Brother or Sister. 2003. (Illus.). 24p. (J). pap. 5.50 (978-1-4109-0670-0(1)); lib. bdg. 18.56 (978-1-4109-0644-1(2)) Raintree.

Jackson, Aariane R. Can You Hear Me Smiling? A Child Grieves a Sister. 2004. (New Child & Family Press Titles Ser.). (Illus.). 40p. (J). pap. 9.95 (978-0-87868-835-7(8) , 8358, Child & Family Pr.) Child Welfare League of America, Inc.

Kane, Darlene. Missing Hannah: Based on a True Story O. 2006. pap. 26.49 ***(978-1-4259-0136-3(0))*** AuthorHouse.

Kinkade, Thomas. A Sister Knows Your Heart. 2003. 80p. 5.99 (978-0-7407-3108-2(4)) Andrews McMeel Publishing.

Krohn, Katherine E. Everything You Need to Know about Birth Order. 2005. (Need to Know Library). (Illus.). 64p. (YA). (gr. 7-12). 25.25 (978-0-8239-3228-3(1) , NTBIOR) Rosen Publishing Group, Inc., The.

Lewis, Rob. Brothers & Sisters. (Illus.). (J). 2005. mass mkt. 8.99 (978-0-340-86601-6(2)); 2004. 20.00 (978-0-340-86600-9(4)) Hodder General Publishing Division GBR. (Hodder & Stoughton). *Dist:* Trafalgar Square Publishing.

Mally, Sarah, et al. Making Brothers & Sisters Best Friends: How to Fight the Good Fight at Home. Mally, Harold, illus. 2002. 272p. (YA). per. 12.00 (978-0-9719405-0-5(9)) Tomorrow's Forefathers, Inc.

Meyer, D J. Sibling Slam Book. 2005. (Illus.). 152p. pap. 15.95 (978-1-890627-52-2(6)) Woodbine Hse.

Meyer, Donald J. Living with a Brother or Sister with Special Needs: A Book for Sibs. 2nd exp. rev. ed. 2003. (Illus.). 144p. (ps up). pap. 18.95 (978-0-295-97547-4(4)) Univ. of Washington Pr.

Mi hermano Mayor: Individual Title Six-Packs. (Coleccion Pm Ser.).Tr. of My big brother. (SPA.). 16p. (gr. 1 up). 26.00 (978-0-7578-2997-0(X)) Rigby Education.

Newman, Gloria. My Mommy's Having a Baby. 2nd rev. ed. 2000. (Illus.). 20p. (J). (gr. k-3). pap. 12.95 (978-0-9659094-1-9(7)) Growing Up Great Productions.

Rock, Lois. Now We Have a Baby. Massey, Jane, illus. 2005. 32p. (J). (ps-3). 7.95 (978-1-56148-451-5(2)) Good Bks.

Rosenberg, Marsha Sarah. Coping When a Brother or Sister Is Autistic. 2005. (Coping Ser.). (Illus.). 192p. (YA). (gr. 7-12). lib. bdg. 26.50 (978-0-8239-3194-1(3)) Rosen Publishing Group, Inc., The.

—Everything You Need to Know When a Brother or Sister Is Autistic. 2005. (Need to Know Library). (Illus.). 64p. (YA). (gr. 7-12). lib. bdg. 25.25 (978-0-8239-3123-1(4) , NTAUTI) Rosen Publishing Group, Inc., The.

Schaefer, Lola M. Brothers. Saunders-Smith, Gail, ed. 1999. (Families Ser.). (Illus.). 24p. (J). (gr. k-1). lib. bdg. 15.93 (978-0-7368-0253-6(3) , Pebble Bks.) Capstone Pr., Inc.

Seidler, Tor. Hermanos Bajo Cero. 2005. Tr. of Brothers Below Zero. (SPA., Illus.). 118p. (J). (ps-7). pap. 11.99 (978-84-241-8076-8(3)) Everest de Ediciones y Distribucion, S.L. ESP. *Dist:* Lectorum Pubns., Inc.

Shanta, N. D. He's My Brother. 2006. 24p. (J). 19.95 ***(978-1-58909-380-5(1))*** Bookstand Publishing.

Sheldon, Annette. Big Sister Now: A Story about Me & Our New Baby. Maizel, Karen, illus. 2005. 32p. (J). (ps). 14.95 (978-1-59147-243-8(1)); pap. 8.95 (978-1-59147-244-5(X)) American Psychological Assn. (Magination Pr.).

Simon, Annette Dauphin. Libby Died: This Book Is for All Kids, but Especially My Sister, Libby. Simon, Annette Dauphin, illus. 2000. (Illus.). 32p. (J). (ps-6). 15.99 (978-0-9701853-0-3(8) , 00088AGPres) GSD&M.

Sisters, 6 vols. (gr. k-2). 28.95 (978-0-7368-8271-2(5)) Red Brick Learning.

Sullivan, Connor. I Love My Brother! A Preschooler's View of Living with a Brother Who Has Autism. Sullivan, Danielle, ed. Griffin, Christopher, illus. 2001. 28p. (J). (ps-1). 14.95 (978-0-9706581-1-1(7)) Phat Art 4.

Vogel, Elizabeth. Dealing with Being the Oldest Child in Your Family. 2000. (Conflict Resolution Library). (Illus.). 24p. (J). (gr. 3). lib. bdg. 18.75 (978-0-8239-5409-4(9) , PowerKids Pr.) Rosen Publishing Group, Inc., The.

—Dealing with Being the Youngest Child in Your Family. 2000. (Conflict Resolution Library). (Illus.). 24p. (J). (gr. 3). lib. bdg. 18.75 (978-0-8239-5407-0(2) , PowerKids Pr.) Rosen Publishing Group, Inc., The.

Wagner, Heather Lehr. Dealing with Terminal Illness in the Family. Rosen, Marvin, ed. 2002. (Focus on Family Matters Ser.). (Illus.). 64p. (YA). (gr. 5 up). 25.00 (978-0-7910-6692-8(4) , Chelsea Hse.) Facts On File, Inc.

Winchester, Elizabeth Siris. Sisters & Brothers: The ultimate guide to understanding your siblings & Yourself. 2007. (Scholastic Choices Ser.). 112p. (J). spiral bd. 27.00 ***(978-0-531-13870-0(4)*** , Children's Pr.) Scholastic Library Publishing.

Ziefert, Harriet. Brothers Are for Making Mud Pies. Demarest, Chris L., illus. 2001. (Lift-the-Flap Ser.). 16p. (J). (ps-1). pap. 6.99 (978-0-14-056849-3(2) , Puffin) Penguin Group (USA) Inc.

BROTHERS AND SISTERS—FICTION

Aarrestad, Thomas. The Potter Giselle. 2001. (Illus.). (J). (ps-3). 14.95 (978-0-8249-5403-1(3)) Ideals Pubns.

Abbott, Tony. Pirates of the Purple Dawn. 2007. (Secrets of Droon Ser.: No. 29). 128p. (J). pap. 3.99 (978-0-439-90250-2(9) , Scholastic Paperbacks) Scholastic, Inc.

Abrahams, Peter. Behind the Curtain: An Echo Falls Mystery. 2006. (Echo Falls Ser.). 352p. (J). 15.99 (978-0-06-073704-7(2) , Geringer, Laura Book) HarperCollins Pubs.

Acker, Rick. The Case of the Autumn Rose. 2003. (Davis Detective Mysteries Ser.). 192p. pap. 7.99 (978-0-8254-2004-7(0)) Kregel Pubns.

Ada, Alma Flor. Celebrate Hannukah with Bubbe's Tales. Epelbaum, Mariano, illus. 2006. 31p. (J). (978-1-59820-134-5(4)) Santillana USA Publishing Co., Inc.

Ada, Alma Flor & Campoy, F. Isabel. Celebrate Christmas & Three Kings' Day with Pablo & Carlitos. Torres, Walter, illus. 2006. (J). (978-1-59820-136-9(0)) Santillana USA Publishing Co., Inc.

Adamchuk, Rachelle G. Disappearance: The First Part of Trickery & Honest Deception. 2006. 169p. pap. ***(978-1-4120-8991-3(3))*** Trafford Publishing.

Adams, Michelle Medlock. Sister for Sale. Brooks, Karen Stormer, illus. 2004. 28p. (J). pap. 4.99 (978-0-310-70820-9(6)) Zonderkidz.

—Sister for Sale. 2002. (Illus.). 32p. 7.99 (978-0-310-70254-2(2)) Zondervan.

Adler, David A. Andy & Tamika. Hillenbrand, Will, illus. (Andy Russell Ser.). 144p. 2005. (J). pap. 4.95 (978-0-15-205446-5(4)); 1999. (YA). (gr. 2-5). 14.00 (978-0-15-201735-4(6)) Harcourt Children's Bks. (Gulliver Bks.).

Advantage Publishers Group & Rojany Buccieri, Lisa. Let's Make Noise Around the House. 2007. (Illus.). 10p. (J). 12.95 (978-1-59223-640-4(5) , Silver Dolphin Bks.) Advantage Pubs. Group.

Ahern, Dianne. Break-in at the Basilica: Adventures with Sister Philomena, Special Agent to the Pope. Larson, Katherine, illus. 2006. (J). (978-0-9679437-8-7(7)) Aunt Dee's Attic, Inc.

Ahlberg, Allan. My Brother's Ghost. l.t. ed. 2005. (Illus.). 64p. (J). pap. (978-0-7540-6181-6(7) , CLP 372) BBC Audio.

Aikins, Dave, illus. Big Sister Dora! 2005. (Dora the Explorer Ser.). 24p. (J). pap. 3.99 (978-0-689-87846-6(X) , Simon Spotlight/Nickelodeon) Simon & Schuster Children's Publishing.

Al Shaikh, Latifa. I'm Still Waiting for that Chocolate. 2007. 52p. (YA). per. 8.95 ***(978-0-595-42982-0(3))*** iUniverse, Inc.

Alarid, Carilyn & Markel, Marilyn. Talks All Day Has the Courage to Speak: Mimbres Children Learn Citizenship. Alarid, Carilyn & Markel, Marilyn, illus. 2006. (Illus.). 125p. (J). pap. 16.95 (978-0-86534-470-9(1)) Sunstone Pr.

Alcock, Deborah. The Spanish Brothers. 2001. (Reformation Trail Ser.). (Illus.). 326p. (YA). pap. (978-1-894666-02-2(X)) Inheritance Pubns.

Alfonsi, Alice. Freaked Out. 2004. 148p. (J). lib. bdg. 16.92 ***(978-1-4242-0687-2(1))*** Fitzgerald Bks.

Alley, R. W. Bratty Brothers & Selfish Sisters: All about Sibling Rivalry. Alley, R. W., illus. 2007. (J). per. 7.95 ***(978-0-87029-404-4(0))*** Abbey Pr.

Andersen, C. B. The Book of Mormon Sleuth Vol. 3: The Hidden Path. 2003. ix, 214p. (J). pap. (978-1-57008-988-6(4)) Deseret Bk. Co.

Anderson, Kevin J. & Moesta, Rebecca. Island Realm. 2007. (Crystal Door Ser.: No. 1). 304p. (J). (gr. 7-17). 7.99 ***(978-0-316-11295-6(X))*** Little, Brown Bks. for Young Readers.

—Ocean Realm. 2nd ed. 2007. (Crystal Doors Ser.: No. 2). 304p. (J). (gr. 5-8). 16.99 ***(978-0-316-01056-6(1))*** Little, Brown Bks. for Young Readers.

Andrews, Jerome. The Initiation. 2006. 40p. pap. 8.50 (978-1-4116-9167-4(9)) Lulu.com.

Andrews, Julie. The Little Grey Men: A Story for the Young in Heart. Watkins-Pitchford, Denys, illus. 2004. 304p. (J). 17.89 (978-0-06-055449-1(5) , Julie Andrews Collection) HarperCollins Pubs.

Andrews, Julie & "BB". The Little Grey Men: A Story for the Young in Heart. Watkins-Pitchford, Denys, illus. ed. 2004. 304p. (J). 17.99 (978-0-06-055448-4(7) , Julie Andrews Collection) HarperCollins Pubs.

Annie Auerbach & MikeNorton. The Good, the Bad & the Gassy. 2006. (Illus.). 96p. pap. 4.99 (978-1-59816-049-9(4) , Tokyopop Kids) TOKYOPOP, Inc.

Anno, Mitsumasa. All in a Day. 1999. (Illus.). 32p. (J). (ps-3). pap. 6.99 (978-0-698-11772-3(7) , Putnam Juvenile) Penguin Group (USA) Inc.

—All in a Day. 1999. (J). 13.79 (978-0-606-16797-0(8)); lib. bdg. 15.50 (978-0-613-14513-8(5)) Tandem Library Bks.

Ant Plays Bear. 9.95 (978-1-59112-166-4(3)) Live Oak Media.

Antieau, Kim. Broken Moon. 2007. 192p. (YA). (gr. 9 up). 15.99 (978-1-4169-1767-0(5) , McElderry, Margaret K.) Simon & Schuster Children's Publishing.

Arbuthnott, Gill. The Chaos Quest. 2004. (Kelpies Ser.). 192p. pap. 10.00 (978-0-86315-459-1(X)) Floris Bks. GBR. *Dist:* SteinerBooks, Inc.

Archer, Peggy. Turkey Surprise. Wickstrom, Thor, illus. 2005. 32p. (J). (ps-ps). 10.99 (978-0-8037-2969-8(3) , Dial) Penguin Group (USA) Inc.

Ardagh, Philip. The Fall of Fergal: The First Unlikely Exploit. Roberts, David, tr. Roberts, David, illus. 2004. (Unlikely Exploits Ser.). 144p. (J). 9.95 (978-0-8050-7476-5(7) , Holt, Henry & Co. Bks. For Young Readers) Holt, Henry & Co.

—Heir of Mystery: The Second Unlikely Exploit. Roberts, David, illus. 2004. (Unlikely Exploits Ser.). 144p. (J). 9.95 (978-0-8050-7477-2(5) , Holt, Henry & Co. Bks. For Young Readers) Holt, Henry & Co.

—The Rise of the House of McNally. Roberts, David, illus. 2005. (Unlikely Exploits Ser.: Vol. 3). 160p. (J). 9.95 (978-0-8050-7478-9(3) , Holt, Henry & Co. Bks. For Young Readers) Holt, Henry & Co.

Arnold, Tedd. More Parts. 2003. (Illus.). 32p. (J). pap. 5.99 (978-0-14-250149-8(2) , Puffin) Penguin Group (USA) Inc.

—More Parts. Arnold, Tedd, illus. 2001. (Illus.). 32p. (J). (ps-3). 16.99 (978-0-8037-1417-5(3) , Dial) Penguin Group (USA) Inc.

Arnosky, Jim. Little Champ. Arnosky, Jim, illus. 2001. (J). pap. 6.95 (978-0-9657144-5-7(4)) Onion River Pr.

Asch, Frank. Star Jumper: Journal of a Cardboard Genius. 2006. (Illus.). 128p. (J). (gr. 2-5). (978-1-55337-886-0(5)) Kids Can Pr., Ltd.

Asquith, Ros & Childs, Sam. Baby's Shoe. 2005. (Illus.). 32p. (J). (ps-7). pap., pap. 9.99 (978-0-09-945107-5(7) , Red Fox) Random Hse. Children's Bks. GBR. *Dist:* Trafalgar Square Publishing.

Atkinson, Elizabeth. Lisa's Totally Unforgettable Winter. 2006. (ENG.). 56p. per. 12.95 ***(978-1-4241-6249-9(1))*** PublishAmerica, Inc.

Auseon, Andrew. Funny Little Monkey. 2005. 304p. (YA). (gr. 9-12). 17.00 (978-0-15-205334-5(4)) Harcourt Children's Bks.

Aust, Patricia H. Hyper Harry. 2001. 92p. (J). pap. 5.99 (978-1-58608-501-8(8)) New Concepts Publishing.

Averbuch, Gloria. Turn for Lucas. Guterman, Yaacov, illus. 2006. 32p. (J). 17.95 (978-1-58726-291-3(6) , Mitten Pr.) Ann Arbor Media Group, LLC.

Avi. Keep Your Eye on Amanda! 1999. (J). (978-0-606-15600-4(3)) Tandem Library Bks.

—Never Mind! A Twin Novel. 2004. 208p. (J). (gr. 5 up). lib. bdg. 16.89 (978-0-06-054315-0(9)) HarperCollins Pubs.

Avi & Vail, Rachel. Never Mind! A Twin Novel. 2004. 208p. (J). (gr. 5 up). 15.99 (978-0-06-054314-3(0)) HarperCollins Pubs.

Ayers, Linda. The Time Bridge Travelers & the Time Travel Station, 3 bks., Bk. 3. Ayers, Ryan, illus. l.t. ed. 2007. (Time Bridge Travelers Ser.: 3). 140p. (J). lib. bdg. 16.95 ***(978-0-9786302-8-7(9))***; per. 7.95 ***(978-0-9786302-7-0(0))*** Blue Thistle Pr.

Babee says No. 2006. (YA). spiral bd. (978-1-59872-479-0(7)) Instantpublisher.com.

Baccalario, Pierdomenico. The Door to Time. Dunfey, Beth, ed. Janeczko, Leah, tr. from ITA. Bruno, Iacopo, illus. 2006. (Ulysses Moore Ser.: No. 1). 240p. (J). (gr. 4-7). pap. 12.99 (978-0-439-77438-3(1)) Scholastic, Inc.

Bahr, Mary. My Brother Loved Snowflakes: The Story of Wilson A. Bentley, the Snowflake Man. Jacobsen, Laura, illus. 2003. 32p. (J). (gr. k-2). 15.95 (978-1-56397-689-6(7)) Boyds Mills Pr.

Baicker, Karen. You Can Do It Too! Wilson-Max, Ken, illus. 2005. 24p. (J). (ps). 13.95 (978-1-59354-080-7(9)) Handprint Bks.

Bailer, Darice, adapted by. Lose the Blanket, Linus! ed. 2005. (Illus.). 32p. (J). lib. bdg. 15.00 (978-1-59054-949-0(X)) Fitzgerald Bks.

Bailey, J. L. Children's Gate. 2005. 292p. 21.95 (978-1-58939-814-6(9)) Virtualbookworm.com Publishing, Inc.

Bair, Sheila. Rock, Brock, & the Savings Shock. Gott, Barry, illus. 2006. (Way I ACT Ser.). 32p. (J). 15.95 (978-0-8075-7094-4(X)) Whitman, Albert & Co.

Ballantyne, R. M. Silver Lake. 2004. reprint ed. pap. 15.95 (978-1-4191-4729-6(3)); pap. 1.99 (978-1-4192-4729-3(8)) Kessinger Publishing, LLC.

Banks, Jacqueline Turner. Egg-Drop Blues. 2003. 128p. (J). (gr. 4-6). pap. 4.95 (978-0-618-25080-6(8)); 15.00 (978-0-618-34885-5(9)) Houghton Mifflin Co. Trade & Reference Div.

Banks, Kate. Monkeys & Dog Days. Bogacki, Tomasz, illus. 2008. (J). ***(978-0-374-35029-1(9))*** Farrar, Straus & Giroux.

Banks, Quentin. Ace of the Woods. 2005. 32p. (J). pap. 13.99 (978-1-4116-5211-8(8)) Lulu.com.

Banting, Celia. I only said I was telling the Truth. 2006. 240p. (YA). per. 14.99 ***(978-0-9786648-4-8(1))*** Wighita Pr.

Barclay, Jane. Going on a Journey to the Sea. Barrette, Doris, illus. 2001. 32p. (J). (ps-1). 16.95 (978-1-894222-34-1(2)) Lobster Pr. CAN. *Dist:* Univ. of Toronto Pr.

Basir, A. As Told By: Sofie. 2006. 51p. pap. 12.95 (978-1-4241-2030-7(6)) PublishAmerica, Inc.

Bass, L. G. The Outlaws of Moonshadow Marsh the Sign of Qin, Bk. 1. 2006. 400p. (gr. 5-17). reprint ed. pap. 7.99 (978-0-7868-5566-7(5)) Hyperion Pr.

—Sign of the Qin. l.t. ed. 2004. 513p. 23.95 (978-0-7862-6772-9(0) , Large Print Pr.) Thorndike Pr.

Bass, Ruth. Sarah's Daughter. 2007. pap. 14.95 ***(978-0-9774053-4-3(6))*** North River Pr. Publishing Corp., The.

Bassede, Francine. A Day with the Bellyflops. Bassede, Francine, illus. 2000. (Illus.). 32p. (J). (ps-2). 15.99 (978-0-531-33242-9(X) , Orchard Bks.) Scholastic, Inc.

Basye, Dale E. Heck: Where the Bad Kids Go. Dob, Bob, illus. 2008. (J). ***(978-0-375-84075-3(3))***; pap. ***(978-0-375-84076-0(1))***; lib. bdg. ***(978-0-375-94075-0(8))*** Random Hse., Inc.

Bateman, Anya. The Makeover of James Orville Wickenbee. 2007. 262p. (J). pap. ***(978-1-59038-707-8(4))*** Deseret Bk. Co.

Bauer, Marion Dane. The Secret of the Painted House. Gore, Leonid, illus. 2007. (Stepping Stone Bks.). 112p. (J). (gr. 1-4). 11.99 ***(978-0-375-84079-1(6))***; lib. bdg. 14.99 ***(978-0-375-94079-8(0))*** Random Hse. Children's Bks. (Random Hse. Bks. for Young Readers).

Baumgart, Klaus. Laura's Secret. Waite, Judy, tr. from GER. 2003. Orig. Title: German. (Illus.). 32p. (J). (ps-2). tchr. ed. 16.95 (978-1-58925-031-4(1) , tiger tales) ME Media LLC.

Beard, Darleen Bailey. Twister. Carpenter, Nancy, illus. 1999. 32p. (J). (ps-3). 16.00 (978-0-374-37977-3(7) , Farrar, Straus & Giroux (BYR)) Farrar, Straus & Giroux.

—Twister. 2003. (gr. k-3). lib. bdg. 14.10 (978-0-613-59749-4(4)) Tandem Library Bks.

Beasley, David R. Canoe Trip. Milner, Elizabeth B., illus. 2006. 129p. (YA). per. 15.00 (***978-0-915317-21-9(4)***) Davus Publishing.

Bedford, David. Big Bears Can! Hansen, Gaby, illus. 2001. 32p. (J). (ps-k). tchr. ed. 14.95 (978-1-58925-006-2(0)) ME Media LLC.

Bender, Esther. Search for a Fawn. Bender, Edna, illus. 1998. 32p. (J). (gr. k-5). pap. 8.99 (978-0-8361-9099-1(8)) Herald Pr.

—Virginia & the Tiny One. Keenan, Joy Dunn, illus. 1998. (Lemon Tree Ser.: Vol. 2). 104p. (J). (gr. 3-7). pap. 6.99 (978-0-8361-9090-8(4)) Herald Pr.

Benenfeld, Rikki. Let's Go Shopping. Benenfeld, Rikki, illus. 2005. (Illus.). 24p. (J). 10.95 (978-1-929628-20-9(X)) Hachai Publishing.

—Let's Go to Shul. Benenfeld, Rikki, illus. 2002. (Illus.). 24p. (J). (ps-1). 10.95 (978-1-929628-08-7(0)) Hachai Publishing.

Bennett, Holly. The Bonemender's Oath. 2006. 176p. (YA). (gr. 7 up). pap. 8.95 (978-1-55143-443-8(1)) Orca Bk. Pubs. USA.

Berenstain, Stan & Berenstain, Jan. The Berenstain Bears' Easter Surprise. l.t. ed. 1998. (Berenstain Bears Ser.). (Illus.). 48p. (J). (ps-3). pap. 10.95 (978-0-590-94730-5(3)) Scholastic, Inc.

—The Berenstain Bears Lend a Helping Hand. 1998. (Berenstain Bears First Time Bks.). (Illus.). 32p. (J). (gr. k-3). pap. 3.99 (978-0-679-88956-4(6) , Random Hse. Bks. for Young Readers) Random Hse. Children's Bks.

—The Berenstain Bears Play T-Ball. Berenstain, Stan & Berenstain, Jan, illus. Berenstain, Michael, illus. 2005. (Berenstain Bears Ser.). 32p. (J). (gr. k-3). 15.99 (978-0-06-058337-8(1)); pap. 3.99 (978-0-06-058338-5(X)) HarperCollins Pubs.

—The Berenstain Bears Play T-Ball. 2005. (Berenstain Bears Ser.). (Illus.). 32p. (J). (ps-3). lib. bdg. 11.19 (978-0-606-33323-8(1)) Tandem Library Bks.

Berenstain, Stan & Berenstain, Jan. Berenstain Bears Play T-Ball. Berenstain, Stan, illus. 2005. (Illus.). 32p. (J). lib. bdg. 9.00 (***978-1-4242-0818-0(1)***) Fitzgerald Bks.

Bergman, Mara. Snip Snap! What's That? Maland, Nick, illus. 2005. 32p. (J). (ps-17). 16.99 (978-0-06-077754-8(0)) HarperCollins Pubs.

Bergren, Lisa Tawn. God Gave Us Two. Bryant, Laura J., illus. 2001. 40p. (J). 9.99 (978-1-57856-507-8(3) , WaterBrook Pr.) WaterBrook Pr.

Berlin, Eric. The Puzzling World of Winston Breen. 2007. (Illus.). 215p. (YA). (gr. 8-12). 16.99 (978-0-399-24693-7(2)) Penguin Group (USA) Inc.

Bernstein, Nina. Magic by the Book. Kulikov, Boris, illus. 2005. 240p. (J). 17.00 (978-0-374-34718-5(2) , Farrar, Straus & Giroux (BYR)) Farrar, Straus & Giroux.

—Magic by the Book. unabr. ed. 2005. (J). 63.75 incl. audio (978-1-4193-3607-2(X) , 42048) Recorded Bks., LLC.

—Magic by the Book. l.t. ed. 2006. 248p. (J). 22.95 (978-0-7862-8382-8(3)) Thorndike Pr.

Berry, Janine Rachel. Nursing Baby. 2004. 29p. pap. 14.95 (978-1-4137-3079-1(5)) PublishAmerica, Inc.

Bildner, Phil & Long, Loren. Game 1. Long, Loren, illus. 2007. (Barnstormers Ser.). (Illus.). 144p. (J). (gr. 2-5). 9.99 (978-1-4169-1863-9(9)) Simon & Schuster Children's Publishing.

Birch, Beverley. Twelfth Night. 2007. (Illus.). 80p. 13.95 (***978-0-7502-4964-5(1)*** , Hodder Wayland) Hodder Children's Division GBR. *Dist:* Independent Pubs. Group.

Black, Holly & DiTerlizzi, Tony. The Chronicles of Spiderwick: A Grand Tour of the Enchanted World, Navigated by Thimbletack. 2007. (Spiderwick Chronicles). 32p. (J). 21.99 (***978-1-4169-5038-7(9)***) Simon & Schuster Children's Publishing.

—Deluxe Collector's Trunk: The Field Guide, the Seeing Stone, Lucinda's Secret, the Ironwood Tree, the Wrath of Mulgarath, Untitled, Set. DiTerlizzi, Tony, illus. 2007. (Spiderwick Chronicles). 672p. (J). 65.00 (***978-1-4169-5015-8(X)***) Simon & Schuster Children's Publishing.

—Spiderwick Chronicles Set: The Field Guide, the Seeing Stone, Lucinda's Secret, the Ironwood Tree, the Wrath of Mulgarath. DiTerlizzi, Tony, illus. movie tie-in ed. 2008. (Spiderwick Chronicles). 672p. (J). 49.99 (***978-1-4169-5016-5(8)***) Simon & Schuster Children's Publishing.

Blackaby, Susan. One up for Brad. Epstein, Len, illus. 2006. (Read-It! Readers Ser.). (J). 19.93 (978-1-4048-2418-8(9)) Picture Window Bks.

—Tricky Twins. Epstein, Len, illus. 2006. (Read-It! Readers Ser.). (J). 19.93 (978-1-4048-2419-5(7)) Picture Window Bks.

Blackford, Ami. Quest for the Dragon Stone: A Duncan Family Adventure. Blackford, Ami, illus. 2006. (Illus.). 48p. (J). (gr. 3-7). 16.95 (978-1-60108-008-0(5)) Red Cygnet Pr.

Blackford, Ami. Quest for the Elfin Elixir: A Duncan Family Adventure. Blackford, Ami, illus. 2007. 80p. (J). (gr. 3-7). 16.95 (***978-1-60108-021-9(2)***) Red Cygnet Pr.

Bledsoe, Lucy Jane. Hoop Girlz. 2002. (Illus.). 128p. (J). (gr. 4-6). tchr. ed. 16.95 (978-0-8234-1691-2(7)) Holiday Hse., Inc.

Block, Francesca Lia. Wasteland. 160p. (J). 2003. 15.99 (978-0-06-028644-6(X) , Cotler, Joanna Books); 2003. (Illus.). 16.89 (978-0-06-028645-3(8) , Cotler, Joanna Books); 2004. reprint ed. pap. 7.99 (978-0-06-440839-4(6)) HarperCollins Pubs.

Bloor, Edward. Tangerine. 1998. (Apple Signature Edition Ser.). 304p. (YA). (gr. 6 up). pap. 4.99 (978-0-590-43277-1(X) , Scholastic Paperbacks) Scholastic, Inc.

Blos. Brothers of the Heart. 1998. (J). pap. 3.95 (978-0-87628-338-7(5)) Ctr. for Applied Research in Education, The.

Blume, Judy. BFF: Two novels by Judy Blume—Just As Long As We're Together/Here's to You, Rachel Robinson (Best Friends Forever), 2 vols. 2007. (Illus.). 512p. (J). (gr. 4-7). lib. bdg. 22.99 (978-0-385-90416-2(9) , Delacorte Bks. for Young Readers) Random Hse. Children's Bks.

—BFF 2: Two Novels by Judy Blume—Just As Long As We're Together/Here's to You, Rachel Robinson (Best Friends Forever) 2007. (Illus.). 512p. (J). (gr. 4-7). 18.99 (978-0-385-73407-3(7) , Delacorte Bks. for Young Readers) Random Hse. Children's Bks.

—Cool Zone with the Pain & the Great One. Stevenson, James, illus. 2008. (J). 12.99 (***978-0-385-73306-9(2));*** 16.99 (***978-0-385-90325-7(1)***) Dell Publishing. (Delacorte Pr.).

—Double Fudge. (Fudge Ser.). 224p. 2007. (J). (gr. 2). 5.99 (***978-0-14-240878-0(6)*** , Puffin); 2002. (gr. 3-7). 15.99 (978-0-525-46926-1(5) , Dutton Juvenile) Penguin Group (USA) Inc.

—Double Fudge. 2004. (Fudge Ser.). 160p. (J). (gr. 3-7). pap. 36.00 incl. audio (978-0-8072-2036-8(1) , Listening Library) Random Hse. Audio Publishing Group.

—Fudge-a-Mania. 2002. (Fudge Ser.). (Illus.). (J). 13.40 (978-0-7587-0013-1(X)) Book Wholesalers, Inc.

—Fudge-a-Mania. 2007. (Fudge Ser.). 160p. (J). (gr. 2). pap. 5.99 (978-0-14-240877-3(8) , Puffin) Penguin Group (USA) Inc.

—Fudge-a-Mania. (Fudge Ser.). (gr. 3-6). 2004. lib. bdg. 14.15 (978-0-613-87580-6(X)); 2003. lib. bdg. 14.15 (978-0-613-63936-1(7)) Tandem Library Bks.

—Soupy Saturdays with the Pain & the Great One. Stevenson, James, illus. 2007. 128p. (J). (gr. k-4). lib. bdg. 16.99 (***978-0-385-90324-0(3));*** 12.99 (***978-0-385-73305-2(4)***) Random Hse. Children's Bks. (Delacorte Bks. for Young Readers).

Blume, Judy. Superfudge. 2002. (Fudge Ser.). (Illus.). (J). 13.40 (978-0-7587-6668-7(8)) Book Wholesalers, Inc.

—Superfudge. l.t. ed. 2000. (Fudge Ser.). 216p. (YA). (gr. 5-10). lib. bdg. 28.95 (978-1-58118-061-9(6) , 23475) LRS.

—Superfudge. 1999. (Fudge Ser.). (J). 9.95 (978-1-56137-175-4(0)) Novel Units, Inc.

—Superfudge. 2002. (Fudge Ser.). (Illus.). 176p. (J). 15.99 (978-0-525-46930-8(3) , Dutton Juvenile) Penguin Group (USA) Inc.

—Superfudge. (Fudge Ser.). 166p. (J). (gr. 2-4). pap. 4.99 (978-0-8072-1457-2(4) , Listening Library) Random Hse. Audio Publishing Group.

—Superfudge. (Fudge Ser.). (SPA.). 159p. (J). (gr. 5-8). pap. 9.95 (978-1-56014-665-0(6)) Santillana USA Publishing Co., Inc.

Blumenthal, Deborah. Don't Let the Peas Touch! Ering, Timothy B., illus. 2004. (J). (978-0-439-29733-2(8) , Levine, Arthur A. Bks.) Scholastic, Inc.

—Don't Let the Peas Touch: And Other Stories. Ering, Timothy B., illus. 2004. 48p. (J). (ps-3). pap. 15.95 (978-0-439-29732-5(X) , Levine, Arthur A. Bks.) Scholastic, Inc.

Blumer, J. Michael. The Book of Broken Promises, Bk. 2. 2007. 280p. (YA). pap. 14.99 (978-1-59092-540-9(8) , Blue Works) Windstorm Creative.

—The Book of Second Chances, Bk. 1. 2006. 380p. pap. 14.99 (978-1-59092-317-7(0) , Blue Works) Windstorm Creative.

Bo, Ben. Skullcrack. 2003. 168p. (J). pap. 6.95 (978-0-8225-3311-5(1)); (gr. 9-12). 14.95 (978-0-8225-3308-5(1)) Lerner Publishing Group.

—Skullcrack. 2000. (gr. 5-8). lib. bdg. 15.25 (978-0-613-58938-3(6)) Tandem Library Bks.

Bode, N. E. Nobodies. Ferguson, Peter, illus. 2005. 304p (J). 16.99 (978-0-06-055738-6(9)); lib. bdg. 17.89 (978-0-06-055739-3(7)) HarperCollins Pubs.

Bodett, Tom. Williwaw! 2000. 208p. (YA). (gr. 5-8). pap. 5.99 (978-0-375-80687-2(3) , Yearling) Random Hse. Children's Bks.

—Williwaw! 2000. (J). (978-0-606-19440-2(1)) Tandem Library Bks.

Boelts, Maribeth. Why Did You Bring Home a New Baby? A Book about Becoming a Sibling. Bladholm, Cheri, illus. 2006. 32p. (J). 9.99 (978-0-310-70901-5(6)) Zonderkidz.

Bogart, Jo Ellen. The Big Tree Gang. Griffiths, Dean, illus. 2005. 60p. (J). lib. bdg. 20.00 (***978-1-4242-1251-4(0)***) Fitzgerald Bks.

Boggs, Patdee. Island of Angels. 2006. 55p. pap. 12.95 (***978-1-4241-3758-9(6)***) PublishAmerica, Inc.

Bollback, Anthony G. Rescue at Cripple Creek, Vol. 4. 1999. (Jack & Jill Mysteries Ser.). 135p. (J). pap. 7.95 (978-1-885729-18-7(9)) Toccoa Falls College Pr.

Bolognese, Don. illus. Abigail Takes the Wheel. 2002. (Avi Ser.). (J). 12.30 (978-0-7587-5967-2(3)) Book Wholesalers, Inc.

Bond, Juliet C. Sam's Sister. Majewski, Dawn, illus. 2004. (J). 18.00 (978-0-944934-30-2(7)) Perspectives Pr., Inc.

Bonsall, Crosby N. The Day I Had to Play with My Sister. Bonsall, Crosby N., illus. 1999. (My First I Can Read Bks.). (Illus.). 32p. (J). (ps up). pap. 3.99 (978-0-06-444253-4(5) , Harper Trophy) HarperCollins Pubs.

—The Day I Had to Play with My Sister. 1999. (gr. k-3). lib. bdg. 11.80 (978-0-8335-1964-1(6)) Tandem Library Bks.

Booth, Martin. Doctor Illuminatus. 2006. (Alchemist's Son Ser.: Pt. 1). 192p. (J). (gr. 4-9). pap. 6.99 (978-0-316-01285-0(8)) Little Brown & Co.

—Soul Stealer. 2006. (Alchemist's Son Ser.: Pt. 2). 256p. (J). (gr. 5-9). pap. 6.99 (978-0-316-05993-0(5)) Little Brown & Co.

Bourgeois, Paulette. Franklin's Baby Sister. ed. 2004. (Illus.). (J). (gr. k-3). spiral bd. (978-0-616-07218-9(X)); spiral bd. (978-0-616-07219-6(8)) Canadian National Institute for the Blind/Institut National Canadien pour les Aveugles.

—Franklin's Baby Sister. Clark, Brenda, illus. (Franklin Ser.). (J). (ps-3). 96p. (978-1-55074-858-1(0)); 2000. 32p. (978-1-55074-794-2(0)) Kids Can Pr., Ltd.

Bourgeois, Paulette & Clark, Brenda, creators. Franklin & the Baby. 1999. (Illus.). (J). (978-0-439-12065-4(9)) Scholastic, Inc.

Bowen, Anne. When You Visit Grandma & Grandpa. Bogacki, Tomasz, tr. Bogacki, Tomasz, illus. 2004. (Carolrhoda Picture Books Ser.). 32p. (J). (ps-3). 15.95 (978-1-57505-610-4(0)) Lerner Publishing Group.

Bowman, Amy. Yes He Is My Brother. 2004. (Illus.). 18p. (J). pap. 12.95 (978-1-932373-41-7(1)) Cedar Hill Publishing.

Bowman, Andy. Pokey's Garden. Travis, Stephanie, illus. 26p. (J). (gr. k-5). pap. 6.95 (978-1-931650-08-3(X)); lib. bdg. 14.95 (978-1-931650-09-0(8)) Coastal Publishing Carolina, Inc.

Boyce, Frank Cottrell. Millions. 2004. (Illus.). 256p. (J). (gr. 3 up). 15.99 (978-0-06-073330-8(6)); lib. bdg. 16.89 (978-0-06-073331-5(4)) HarperCollins Pubs.

Bradman, Tony. Deadly Game. Chatterton, Martin, illus. 2004. (Tales of Terror Ser.). 105p. (J). (gr. 4-7). pap. 7.50 (978-1-4052-1127-7(X)) Egmont Bks., Ltd. GBR. *Dist:* Independent Pubs. Group.

Brandis, Marianne. Tinderbox. 2003. (gr. 5-8). lib. bdg. 18.75 (978-0-613-77303-4(9)) Tandem Library Bks.

Brandis, Marianne & Brender a Brandis, G. The Tinderbox. 2003. Orig. Title: Fyrtojet. (Illus.). 176p. (J). (gr. 6-9). pap. 9.95 (978-0-88776-626-8(9)) Tundra Bks., Inc./ Livres Toundra, Inc. CAN. *Dist:* Random Hse., Inc.

Branson, Terri. Brother Dragon. Taylor, Chet, illus. 2004. (J). 18.99 (978-0-9755888-5-7(0)) Dragonfly Publishing, Inc.

Break Away. 64p. (YA). (gr. 6-12). pap. (978-0-8224-2391-1(X)) Globe Fearon Educational Publishing.

Breathed, Berkeley. Edwurd Fudwupper Fibbed Big. 2000. (Illus.). 48p. (J). (ps-17). 15.99 (978-0-316-10675-7(5)) Little Brown & Co.

—Edwurd Fudwupper Fibbed Big. Breathed, Berkeley, illus. 2003. (Illus.). 40p. (J). (gr. 1-4). pap. 6.99 (978-0-316-14425-4(8)) Little, Brown Bks. for Young Readers.

—Edwurd Fudwupper Fibbed Big. 2003. (gr. k-3). lib. bdg. 15.30 (978-0-613-71786-1(4)) Tandem Library Bks.

Brenneman, Tim. Jimmie Boogie Learns about Smoking. Hedrick, Bonnie & Canning, Robert, eds. 3rd ed. 2002. (Illus.). 12p. (J). 5.99 (978-0-9700453-2-4(8)) Grand Unification Pr., Inc.

Brian, Kate. Megan Meade's Guide to the McGowan Boys. 2005. (Illus.). 272p. (YA). 15.99 (978-1-4169-0030-6(6)) Simon & Schuster Children's Publishing.

—Megan Meade's Guide to the Mcgowan Boys. 2006. 288p. (YA). pap. 8.99 (978-1-4169-0031-3(4) , Simon Pulse) Simon & Schuster Children's Publishing.

Bridwell, Norman. A Tiny Family. 1999. (Hello Reader! Ser.). 32p. (J). (ps-1). pap. 3.99 (978-0-439-04019-8(1)) Scholastic, Inc.

—Tiny Family. 1999. (Hello Reader! Ser.). (978-0-606-16632-4(7)) Tandem Library Bks.

Bright, Paul. I'm Not Going Out There! Cort, Ben, illus. 2006. 28p. (J). (ps-2). 16.00 (978-1-56148-535-2(7)) Good Bks.

Brightwood, Laura, illus. Ka-ulu the Strong. Brightwood, Laura, . 2006. (J). (***978-0-9789871-3-8(6)***) 3-C Institute for Social Development.

Brimner, Larry Dane. Bigger & Smaller. Girouard, Patrick, illus. 2005. (Magic Door to Learning Ser.). 24p. (J). (ps-3). 21.36 (978-1-59296-532-8(6)) Child's World, Inc.

Brink, Carol Ryrie. Caddie Woodlawn. Hyman, Trina Schart, illus. 2002. (J). 13.94 (978-0-7587-0174-9(8)) Book Wholesalers, Inc.

—Caddie Woodlawn. 288p. (J). 2007. pap. 2.99 (***978-1-4169-4818-6(X));*** 2006. pap. 6.99 (978-1-4169-4028-9(6)) Simon & Schuster Children's Publishing. (Aladdin).

—Caddie Woodlawn. l.t. ed. 2003. 260p. pap. 10.95 (978-0-7862-6182-6(X)) Thorndike Pr.

Brooke, Peggy. Jake's Orphan. 2001. 11.64 (978-0-606-22137-5(9)) Tandem Library Bks.

Brooks, Kevin. The Road of the Dead. 2006. 352p. (J). (gr. 7 up). pap. 16.99 (978-0-439-78623-2(1) , Chicken Hse., The) Scholastic, Inc.

Brooks, Kevin. Road of the Dead. rev. l.t. ed. 2007. 353p. (YA). 22.95 (***978-0-7862-9550-0(3)***) Thorndike Pr.

Brouwer, Sigmund. Bad Bug Blues. 2002. (Watch Out for Joel Ser.). (Illus.). 32p. (J). (gr. 1-3). reprint ed. pap. 3.99 (978-0-7642-2580-2(4)) Bethany Hse. Pubs.

—Bad Bug Blues. 2002. (gr. k-3). lib. bdg. 11.80 (978-0-613-84502-1(1)) Tandem Library Bks.

Brown, Alan. I Am a Dog. Allen, Jonathan, illus. 2002. 32p. (J). pap. 7.95 (978-1-929132-37-9(9)) Kane/Miller Bk. Pubs., Inc.

—I Am a Dog. 2002. (gr. k-3). lib. bdg. 16.40 (978-0-613-62780-1(6)) Tandem Library Bks.

Brown, Jeff. Invisible Stanley. Nash, Scott, illus. 2003. (Stanley Lambchop Adventure Ser.). 96p. (J). pap. 4.99 (978-0-06-009792-9(2)) HarperCollins Pubs.

—Invisible Stanley. 2003. (gr. k-3). lib. bdg. 13.00 (978-0-613-68434-7(6)) Tandem Library Bks.

Brown, Laurie Krasny. Rex & Lilly Schooltime: A Dino Easy Reader. Brown, Marc, illus. 2001. 32p. (J). (ps-1). pap. 4.95 (978-0-316-13535-1(6)) Little, Brown Bks. for Young Readers.

Brown, Marc. Arthur, Clean Your Room! 1999. (Arthur Ser.). (Illus.). 24p. (J). (gr. k-3). pap. 3.99 (978-0-679-88467-5(X) , Random Hse. Bks. for Young Readers) Random Hse. Children's Bks.

—Arthur in New York. 2008. (J). (***978-0-375-82976-5(8)); (978-0-375-92976-2(2))*** Random Hse., Inc.

—Arthur's Back-to-School Surprise. 2002. (Arthur Ser.). (Illus.). 24p. (J). (gr. k-3). pap. 3.99 (978-0-375-81000-8(5)); lib. bdg. 11.99 (978-0-375-91000-5(X)) Random Hse. Children's Bks. (Random Hse. Bks. for Young Readers).

—Arthur's Classroom Fib. 2007. (Illus.). 24p. (J). (gr. 1-3). pap. 3.99 (978-0-375-82975-8(X)); lib. bdg. 11.99 (978-0-375-92975-5(4)) Random Hse. Children's Bks. (Random Hse. Bks. for Young Readers).

—Arthur's First Kiss. Brown, Marc, illus. 2001. (Arthur Ser.). (Illus.). 24p. (J). (gr. k-3). pap. 3.99 (978-0-375-80602-5(4)); lib. bdg. 11.99 (978-0-375-90602-2(9)) Random Hse. Children's Bks. (Random Hse. Bks. for Young Readers).

—Arthur's TV Trouble. Brown, Marc, illus. 2002. (Arthur Adventure Ser.). (Illus.). (J). 13.15 (978-0-7587-1990-4(6)) Book Wholesalers, Inc.

—Arthur's TV Trouble. Brown, Marc, illus. 1999. (Arthur Adventure Ser.). 32p. (J). (ps-3). 9.95 (978-0-316-11594-0(0)) Little, Brown Bks. for Young Readers.

—D. W. Thinks Big. 1998. (D. W. Ser.). (Illus.). 24p. (J). (ps-k). bds. 5.95 (978-0-316-11112-6(0)) Little, Brown Bks. for Young Readers.

Brown, Marc & Sarfatti, Esther. D. W. y el Carne de Biblioteca. 2004. Tr. of D.W.'s Library Card. (ENG & SPA., Illus.). (J). pap. 6.95 (978-1-930332-47-8(5)) Lectorum Pubns., Inc.

Brown, Marc & Schulman, Lester. Arthur Breaks the Bank. 2004. (Arthur Ser.). (Illus.). 24p. (J). (gr. k-3). pap. 3.99 (978-0-375-81002-2(1)); lib. bdg. 11.99 (978-0-375-91002-9(6)) Random Hse. Children's Bks. (Random Hse. Bks. for Young Readers).

Brown, Richard. Snow in the Kitchen. 2005. (Cambridge Storybooks Ser.). 32p. pap. 7.00 (978-0-521-67480-5(8)) Cambridge Univ. Pr.

Brown, Ruth. Homey's Tales of Love & Adventure. 2005. 74p. pap. 14.95 (978-1-4137-7144-2(0)) PublishAmerica, Inc.

Bruce, Mary Grant. Back to Billabong. l.t. ed. 2006. 200p. pap. 15.99 (978-1-4264-2197-6(4)) BiblioBazaar.

Bryant, Jennifer. Into Enchanted Woods. Browne, James, illus. 2001. (Winterthur Book for Children Ser.). (J). (978-0-912724-59-1(5)) Winterthur, Henry Francis du-Pont Museum, Inc.

Buckless, Andrea. Too Many Cooks! 2000. (gr. k-3). lib. bdg. 11.80 (978-0-613-63571-4(X)) Tandem Library Bks.

Buckton, Chris. Survive. Savage, Paul, illus. 2008. (J). pap. (***978-1-59889-904-7(X));*** 33p. (YA). (gr. 5-9). lib. bdg. 21.26 (***978-1-59889-852-1(3)***) Stone Arch Bks.

Bucky Badger A Children's Story: Becky Gets a Brother, 4 vols. l.t. ed. 2005. (Illus.). (J). 9.99 (978-0-9765510-0-3(4)) Badgerland Bks. LLC.

Bulion, Leslie. Uncharted Waters. 2006. 155p. (J). 14.95 (978-1-56145-365-8(X) , Peachtree Junior) Peachtree Pubs., Ltd.

Bunting, Eve. A Sudden Silence. 2007. (Illus.). 144p. (YA). pap. 6.95 (978-0-15-205868-5(0) , Harcourt Paperbacks) Harcourt Children's Bks.

—Your Move. Ransome, James E., illus. 1998. 32p. (J). (gr. 1-5). 17.00 (978-0-15-200181-0(6)) Harcourt Children's Bks.

Burch, Christian. The Manny Files. 2006. (Illus.). 304p. (J). (gr. 4-7). 15.95 (978-1-4169-0039-9(X) , Atheneum) Simon & Schuster Children's Publishing.

Burns, Ian. Lissie Pendle. 2006. 196p. pap. 13.04 (978-1-4116-5491-4(9)) Lulu.com.

But I Knew Better: Individual Title, 6 pack. (gr. k-1). 23.00 (978-0-7635-9033-8(9)) Rigby Education.

Butler, Charles. Timon's Tide. Smith, George, illus. 2000. 192p. (YA). (gr. 7-12). 16.00 (978-0-689-82593-4(5) , McElderry, Margaret K.) Simon & Schuster Children's Publishing.

Byars, Betsy. Ant Plays Bear. Simont, Marc, illus. 2005. (Ant Ser.). (J). pap. 18.95 incl. audio compact disk (978-1-59112-630-0(4)) Live Oak Media.

—Ant Plays Bear. 1999. (gr. k-3). lib. bdg. 11.80 (978-0-613-19504-1(3)) Tandem Library Bks.

—Bingo Brown Amante Gitano. 2003. (gr. 3-6). lib. bdg. 19.90 (978-0-613-63015-3(7)) Tandem Library Bks.

—Boo's Dinosaur. Brooks, Erik, illus. 2006. 48p. (J). 15.95 (978-0-8050-7958-6(0) , Holt, Henry & Co. Bks. For Young Readers) Holt, Henry & Co.

—The Summer of the Swans. Coconis, Ted, illus. 2002. (J). 13.19 (978-0-7587-0217-3(5)) Book Wholesalers, Inc.

—The Summer of the Swans. 2001. (Reader's Choice Bks.). (Illus.). (gr. 6). pap. 13.20 (978-0-15-314422-6(X)) Harcourt Schl. Pubs.

—The Summer of the Swans. CoConis, Ted, illus. l.t. ed. 2000. (LRS Large Print Cornerstone Ser.). 176p. (YA). (gr. 5-12). lib. bdg. 27.95 (978-1-58118-060-2(8) , 23474) LRS.

—The Summer of the Swans. 2004. (Puffin Modern Classics Ser.). 144p. (gr. 3). pap. 5.99 (978-0-14-240114-9(5) , Puffin) Penguin Group (USA) Inc.

Cabot, Meg. Princess in Pink. 2004. (Princess Diaries: Vol. 5). (Illus.). 304p. (J). (gr. 7 up). pap. 6.99 (978-0-06-072601-0(6) , Harper Trophy) HarperCollins Pubs.

Cairo, Shelly, et al. Our Brother Has Down's Syndrome. McNeil, Irene, photos by. 2003. (Illus.). 24p. (J). (ps-3). pap. 5.95 (978-0-920303-31-3(5)); lib. bdg. 15.95 (978-0-920303-30-6(7)) Annick Pr., Ltd. CAN. *Dist:* Firefly Bks., Ltd.

A
B

Caldwell, V. M. Runt: Story of a Boy. 2006. 208p. (J). 16.95 (978-1-57131-662-2(0)) ; pap. 6.95 (978-1-57131-661-5(2)) Milkweed Editions.

Calkhoven, Laurie & McElroy, Laurie. Blues Brothers. 2006. (Teenick Ser.: No. 1). 113p. (J). pap. 4.99 (978-0-439-83162-8(8) , Scholastic) Scholastic, Inc.

Callahan, Thera S. All Wrapped Up. 2004. (Rookie Reader Espanol Ser.). (Illus.). 31p. (J). (gr. k-2). pap. 4.95 (978-0-516-21949-3(9) , Children's Pr.) Scholastic Library Publishing.

—All Wrapped Up. Gordon, Mike, illus. 2003. (Rookie Reader - Level C Ser.). 32p. (J). 19.50 (978-0-516-22844-0(7) , Children's Pr.) Scholastic Library Publishing.

Callaway, Phil. Jake & the Big Hairy Lie. 2002. (Jake Ser.). (Illus.). 36p. (J). pap. 3.99 (978-1-55305-030-8(4)) Cygnet Publishing Group, Inc./Coolreading.com CAN. *Dist:* Orca Bk. Pubs. USA.

—Jake & the Scrambled Snake. 2002. (Illus.). 36p. (J). pap. 3.99 (978-1-55305-029-2(0)) Cygnet Publishing Group, Inc./Coolreading.com CAN. *Dist:* Orca Bk. Pubs. USA.

Cameron, Ann. More Stories Huey Tells. Toft, Lis, illus. 1999. 128p. (J). (gr. k-4). pap. 4.99 (978-0-679-88363-0(0) , Random Hse. Bks. for Young Readers) Random Hse. Children's Bks.

—More Stories Huey Tells. 1998. (J). pap. 4.99 (978-0-679-88576-4(5) , Knopf Bks. for Young Readers) Random Hse. Children's Bks.

—More Stories Huey Tells. 1999. (J). (978-0-606-16567-9(3)) Tandem Library Bks.

—More Stories Huey Tells. Toft, Lis, illus. 1999. 117p. (J). (ps-ps). per. 13.00 (978-0-613-10978-9(3)) Tandem Library Bks.

Caple, Kathy. The Wimp. 2000. (Illus.). 32p. (J). (gr. k-3). pap. 5.95 (978-0-618-05577-7(0) , Walter Lorraine) Houghton Mifflin Co. Trade & Reference Div.

Carey, Janet Lee. Wenny Has Wings. 2004. 240p. (J). reprint ed. pap. 4.99 (978-0-689-86759-0(X) , Aladdin) Simon & Schuster Children's Publishing.

Carlson, Judy. Life with Max. 2000. (Metro Reading Program Ser.). (J). (gr. k). 7.98 (978-1-58120-973-0(8)); 45.95 (978-1-58830-031-7(5)) Metropolitan Teaching & Learning Co.

Carlson, Nancy. Harriet & Walt. rev. ed. (Carolrhoda Picture Books Ser.). (Illus.). 32p. (J). (gr. k-2). 2005. 15.95 (978-1-57505-672-2(0)); 2004. pap. (978-1-57505-723-1(9)) Lerner Publishing Group.

Carlson, Nancy, tr. & illus. Louanne Pig in the Perfect Family. Carlson, Nancy, illus. 2nd rev. ed. 2004. (Nancy Carlson's Neighborhood Ser.). 32p. (J). (gr. k-2). 15.95 (978-1-57505-611-1(9)); pap. (978-1-57505-616-6(X)) Lerner Publishing Group.

Carlson, Nancy L. Loudmouth George Earns His Allowance. 2007. (Illus.). 32p. (J). (gr. k-3). spiral bd. 15.95 (978-0-8225-6560-4(9) , Carolrhoda Bks.) Lerner Publishing Group.

Carmi, Daniella. Samir & Yonatan. Lotan, Yael, tr. from HEB. 2002. 192p. (J). (gr. 3-7). pap. 4.99 (978-0-439-13523-8(0) , Scholastic Paperbacks) Scholastic, Inc.

—Samir & Yonatan. 2000. (gr. 3-6). lib. bdg. 13.00 (978-0-613-45824-5(9)) Tandem Library Bks.

—Samir & Yonatan. 2000. (Illus.). 192p. (J). (gr. 3-7). pap. 15.95 (978-0-439-13504-7(4) , Levine, Arthur A. Bks.) Scholastic, Inc.

Carter, Dorothy. Grandma's General Store - The Ark. Allen, Thomas B., illus. 2005. 144p. (J). 16.00 (978-0-374-32766-8(1) , Farrar, Straus & Giroux (BYR)) Farrar, Straus & Giroux.

—Wilhe'mina Miles: After the Stork Night. Stevenson, Harvey, illus. 2005. 30p. (J). (gr. k-4). reprint ed. 16.00 (978-0-7567-9421-7(8)) DIANE Publishing Co.

Casanova, Mary. Curse of a Winter Moon. 2000. (gr. 5-8). lib. bdg. 14.15 (978-0-613-68226-8(2)) Tandem Library Bks.

—Curse of the Winter Moon. 2000. 144p. (gr. 3-7). 16.49 (978-0-7868-2475-5(1)) Hyperion Bks. for Children.

—Curse of the Winter Moon. 2002. (Illus.). 144p. (gr. 5-9). pap. 5.99 (978-0-7868-1602-6(3)) Hyperion Paperbacks for Children.

Cassell, Jody. Where's Leon? Storybook & Reader's Guide CD-ROM, 1. Kristof Pincheira, Kyra, illus. l.t. ed. 2006. 48p. (J). lib. bdg. 17.95 (***978-1-59494-013-2(4)***) CPCC Pr.

Cassidy, Anne. Naughty Nancy. Guicciardini, Desideria, illus. 2004. (Read-It! Readers Ser.). 32p. (J). (gr. k-3). 18.60 (978-1-4048-0558-3(3)) Picture Window Bks.

Castlemon, Harry. Sportsmans Club in the Saddle. 2006. pap. 30.95 (***978-1-4286-5231-6(0)***) Kessinger Publishing, LLC.

Catalano, Dominic. Mr. Basset Plays. 2004. (Illus.). 32p. (YA). (gr. k-2). pap. 7.95 (978-1-59078-314-6(X)) Boyds Mills Pr.

Celsi, Teresa. The Fourth Little Pig. (Metro Reading Program Ser.). (J). (gr. k). 2000. 45.95 (978-1-58830-030-0(7)); 1999. 29.95 (978-1-58120-118-5(4)) Metropolitan Teaching & Learning Co.

Chappas, Bess. Kiki & the Red Shoes. 2007. (J). 17.99 (***978-1-60131-012-5(9)***) Big Tent Bks.

Chardiet, Jon. Parker Penguin, Big Brother Blues. Micucci, Charles, illus. 1998. (Read with Me Paperback Ser.). (J). (978-0-590-14924-2(5)) Scholastic, Inc.

Charlton-Trujillo, E. E. Feels Like Home. 2007. 224p. (YA). (gr. 7 up). 15.99 (978-0-385-73332-8(1)); lib. bdg. 18.99 (978-0-385-90349-3(9)) Random Hse. Children's Bks. (Delacorte Bks. for Young Readers).

Chavarria-Chairez, Becky. Magda's Pinata Magic. Ventura, Gabriela Baeza, tr. Vega, Anne, illus. 2001. Tr. of Magda y la Pi?Ata Magica. (ENG & SPA.). 32p. (J). (ps-3). 14.95 (978-1-55885-320-1(0) , Piñata Books) Arte Publico Pr.

Cheaney, J. B. The Middle of Somewhere. 2007. (Illus.). 224p. (J). (gr. 4-6). 15.99 (978-0-375-83790-6(6)); lib. bdg. 18.99 (978-0-375-93790-3(0)) Random Hse. Children's Bks. (Knopf Bks. for Young Readers).

Chessa, Francesca. The Mysterious Package. Chessa, Francesca, illus. 2007. (Illus.). 32p. (J). (ps-2). 16.95 (***978-1-59990-028-5(9)***) Bloomsbury Publishing.

Child, Lauren. Boo! Made You Jump! 2007. (Charlie & Lola Ser.). 24p. (J). (ps-1). pap. 3.99 (***978-0-448-44696-7(0)*** , Grosset & Dunlap) Penguin Group (USA) Inc.

—But, Excuse Me, That Is My Book. 2006. (Illus.). 32p. (J). (ps). 16.99 (978-0-8037-3096-0(9) , Dial) Penguin Group (USA) Inc.

—But I Am an Alligator. 2008. (Charlie & Lola Ser.). 24p. (J). (ps-1). 3.99 (***978-0-448-44697-4(9)*** , Grosset & Dunlap) Penguin Group (USA) Inc.

—Can You Maybe Turn the Light On? 2007. 32p. (J). pap. 3.99 (978-0-448-44570-0(0) , Grosset & Dunlap) Penguin Group (USA) Inc.

—Charlie & Lola's Numbers. Child, Lauren, illus. 2007. (Charlie & Lola Ser.). (Illus.). 12p. (J). (ps). bds. 6.99 (***978-0-7636-3534-3(0)***) Candlewick Pr.

—Charlie & Lola's Opposites. Child, Lauren, illus. 2007. (Charlie & Lola Ser.). (Illus.). 12p. (J). (ps). bds. 6.99 (***978-0-7636-3535-0(9)***) Candlewick Pr.

—I Absolutely Must Do Coloring Now or Painting or Drawing. 2006. (Charlie & Lola Ser.). 24p. (J). (ps-1). 3.99 (978-0-448-44415-4(1) , Grosset & Dunlap) Penguin Group (USA) Inc.

—I Am Too Absolutely Small for School. Child, Lauren, illus. (Illus.). 32p. (J). (ps-1). 2004. 16.99 (978-0-7636-2403-3(9)); 2005. reprint ed. pap. 6.99 (978-0-7636-2887-1(5)) Candlewick Pr.

—I Completely Must Do Drawing Now & Painting & Coloring. 2007. (Charlie & Lola Ser.). 24p. (J). 3.99 (978-0-448-44560-1(3) , Grosset & Dunlap) Penguin Group (USA) Inc.

—I Will Never Not Ever Eat a Tomato. Child, Lauren, illus. 2000. (Illus.). 32p. (J). (ps-3). 16.99 (978-0-7636-1188-0(3)) Candlewick Pr.

—I Will Never Not Ever Eat a Tomato Pop-up. Child, Lauren, illus. 2007. (Charlie & Lola Ser.). (Illus.). 16p. (J). (ps). 18.99 (***978-0-7636-3708-8(4)***) Candlewick Pr.

—My Wobbly Tooth Must Not Ever Never Fall Out. Child, Lauren, illus. 2006. (Charlie & Lola Ser.). (Illus.). 32p. (J). (ps-2). pap. 6.99 (978-0-448-44255-6(8) , Grosset & Dunlap) Penguin Group (USA) Inc.

—Say Cheese! 2007. (Charlie & Lola (Hardcover) Ser.). (Illus.). 32p. (J). (ps-3). 16.99 (***978-0-8037-3095-3(0)*** , Dial) Penguin Group (USA) Inc.

—Sizzles Is Completely Not Here. 2007. (Charlie & Lola Ser.). 10p. (J). (ps-1). bds. 7.99 (978-0-448-44501-4(8) , Grosset & Dunlap) Penguin Group (USA) Inc.

—This is Actually My Party. 2007. (Charlie & Lola Ser.). 32p. (J). (ps-2). pap. 6.99 (***978-0-448-44694-3(4)***); pap. 6.99 (978-0-448-44569-4(7)) Penguin Group (USA) Inc. (Grosset & Dunlap).

—The Very Best Storytime Pack Ever! 2007. (Charlie & Lola Ser.). 96p. (J). pap. 15.99 (***978-0-448-44695-0(2)*** , Grosset & Dunlap) Penguin Group (USA) Inc.

—We Honestly Can Look after Your Dog. 2006. (Charlie & Lola Ser.). (Illus.). 32p. (J). (ps-2). pap. 5.99 (978-0-448-44414-7(3) , Grosset & Dunlap) Penguin Group (USA) Inc.

—Whoops! but It Wasn't Me. 2006. (Charlie & Lola Ser.). (Illus.). 32p. (J). (ps-2). pap. 5.99 (978-0-448-44413-0(5) , Grosset & Dunlap) Penguin Group (USA) Inc.

Child, Lauren, illus. I've Won, No I've Won, No I've Won. 2006. (Charlie & Lola Ser.). 32p. (J). (ps-2). pap. 5.99 (978-0-448-44350-8(3) , Grosset & Dunlap) Penguin Group (USA) Inc.

Child, Lauren, et al. Carys Blodyn, Dyma Fi. 2005. (WEL., Illus.). 30p. (978-1-85596-670-3(0)) Dref Wen.

—Fydda i Byth Bythoedd yn Bwyta Tomato. 2005. (WEL., Illus.). 32p. pap. (978-1-85596-668-0(9)) Dref Wen.

Chin, Oliver Clyde. Timmy & Tammy's Train of Thought. McPherson, Heath, illus. 2007. (ENG.). 36p. (J). 15.95 (978-1-59702-008-4(7)) Immedium.

Choldenko, Gennifer. Al Capone Does My Shirts. 240p. 2004. (Illus.). (YA). (gr. 4-6). 16.99 (978-0-399-23861-1(1) , Putnam Juvenile); 2006. (J). (gr. 5). reprint ed. pap. 6.99 (978-0-14-240370-9(9) , Puffin) Penguin Group (USA) Inc.

—Al Capone Does My Shirts. l.t. ed. 2005. 299p. (YA). 22.95 (978-0-7862-8043-8(3)) Thorndike Pr.

Christopher, Matt. Lacrosse Face-Off. 2006. 128p. (J). (gr. 3-7). pap. 4.99 (978-0-316-79641-5(7)) Little Brown & Co.

—Snowboard Showdown. ed. 2005. (Sports Classics IV Ser.). 167p. (J). lib. bdg. 15.00 (978-1-59054-770-0(5)) Fitzgerald Bks.

—Tennis Ace. 2000. (Illus.). 128p. (J). (gr. 3-6). 15.95 (978-0-316-13519-1(4)) Little Brown & Co.

—Tennis Ace. 2000. (978-0-606-18267-6(5)) Tandem Library Bks.

Cipriani, Nicholas J. A Brother's Love. 1998. 100p. (J). pap. 5.95 (978-0-9653570-5-0(8)) Cipriani, Nicholas J.

Clairmont, Patsy. Basil & Parsley. 2007. (Tails from the Pantry Ser.). 32p. (J). 9.99 (***978-1-4003-1039-5(3)***) Nelson, Thomas Inc.

Clairmont, Patsy. Spud. 2006. (Tails from the Pantry Ser.). (Illus.). 32p. (J). 9.99 (978-1-4003-0802-6(X)) Nelson, Thomas Inc.

Clammer, Virginia Grant. The Big Box. Handelman, Dorothy, photos by. 1999. (Real Kids Readers Ser.). (Illus.). 32p. (gr. k-1). (J). pap. 4.99 (978-0-7613-2049-4(0)); lib. bdg. 18.90 (978-0-7613-2024-1(5)) Lerner Publishing Group. (Millbrook Pr.).

—The Big Box. 1999. (J). 11.79 (978-0-606-19146-3(1)) Tandem Library Bks.

—Big Box. 1999. (ps-2). lib. bdg. 13.00 (978-0-613-16606-5(X)) Tandem Library Bks.

Clark, Brenda, illus. Franklin & Harriet. 2002. (Franklin Ser.). (J). 19.72 (978-0-7587-6483-6(9)) Book Wholesalers, Inc.

—Franklin & the Baby. 2002. (Franklin Ser.). (J). 12.40 (978-0-7587-0012-4(1)) Book Wholesalers, Inc.

—Franklin's Baby Sister. 2002. (Franklin Ser.). (J). 14.40 (978-0-7587-6436-2(7)) Book Wholesalers, Inc.

Clark, Catherine. Frozen Rodeo. 2003. 304p. (J). (gr. 8 up). 15.99 (978-0-06-009070-8(7)) HarperCollins Pubs.

—Frozen Rodeo. 2004. lib. bdg. 15.30 (978-0-613-71502-7(0)) Tandem Library Bks.

Clark, Eleanor. Mary Elizabeth: Welcome to America. 2007. (Eleanor Jo Ser.). (J). 14.99 (978-0-9753036-7-2(8)) HonorNet.

Clark, Emma Chichester. Mimi's Book of Opposites. Clark, Emma Chichester, illus. 2004. (Illus.). 24p. (J). 9.95 (978-1-57091-574-1(1)) Charlesbridge Publishing, Inc.

Clark, Gina Beth. The Peepes of Rock Garden Hill. 2004. 38p. per. 9.95 (978-1-59453-452-2(7) , 2545) Airleaf Publishing & Bookselling.

Clarke, Jane. G. E. M. 2008. (Illus.). 32p. (J). pap. 9.95 (***978-0-09-948012-9(3)***) Transworld Publishers Ltd. GBR. *Dist:* Independent Pubs. Group.

Clarke, Judith. One Whole & Perfect Day. 2007. 250p. (YA). (gr. 7 up). 16.95 (***978-1-932425-95-6(0)*** , Front Street) Boyds Mills Pr.

Clarke, Judith. Starry Nights. 2004. 148p. (YA). 15.95 (978-1-886910-82-9(0) , Lemniscaat) Boyds Mills Pr.

Clay, Margaret. Double Identity. 2007. 276p. (YA). pap. 12.95 (***978-0-9792328-6-2(4)***) Helm Publishing.

Cleary, Beverly. Beezus & Ramona. Dockray, Tracy, illus. 2006. 183p. (J). lib. bdg. 20.00 (***978-1-4242-0409-0(7)***) Fitzgerald Bks.

—Ramona the Pest. (Ramona Ser.). (J). (gr. 3-5). Dell Publishing.

—Two Times the Fun. Thompson, Carol, illus. 2005. 96p. (J). (ps-2). lib. bdg. 14.89 (978-0-06-057922-7(6)) HarperCollins Pubs.

—Two Times the Fun. Taylor, Thomas, illus. ed. 2005. 96p. (J). (ps-2). 13.99 (978-0-06-057921-0(8)) HarperCollins Pubs.

Cleaver, Vera & Cleaver, Bill. Donde Florecen los Lirios. (SPA.). 168p. (YA). (gr. 5-8). (978-84-204-3648-7(8) , AF0285) Alfaguara, Ediciones, S.A.- Grupo Santillana ESP. *Dist:* Lectorum Pubns., Inc.

Clement-Davies, David. Fell. 2007. 432p. (YA). pap. 19.95 (***978-0-8109-9470-6(4)***) Abrams, Harry N. , Inc.

Clements, Bruce. A Chapel of Thieves. 2002. 224p. (J). (gr. 6-9). 16.00 (978-0-374-37701-4(4) , Farrar, Straus & Giroux (BYR)) Farrar, Straus & Giroux.

Codell, Esmé Raji. Vive la Paris! 2006. 224p. (J). (gr. 3-7). 15.99 (978-0-7868-5124-9(4)) Hyperion Pr.

Cogan, Karen. My Little Brother Ben. Treatner, Meryl, illus. 1999. (Books for Young Learners). 12p. (J). (gr. k-2). pap. 5.00 (978-1-57274-142-3(2)) Owen, Richard C. Pubs., Inc.

Cole, Joanna. I'm a Big Brother. Stevens-Marzo, Bridget, illus. 2008. 32p. (J). 6.99 (***978-0-06-134906-5(2)***) HarperCollins Pubs.

—I'm a Big Brother Lap Edition. Chambliss, Maxie, illus. 2006. 28p. (J). 12.99 (978-0-06-085412-6(X) , Harper Festival) HarperCollins Pubs.

Cole, Joanna. I'm a Big Brother (Spanish Edition) Stevens-Marzo, Bridget, illus. 2008. (SPA.). 32p. (J). 6.99 (***978-0-06-134908-9(9)*** , Rayo) HarperCollins Pubs.

Colfer, Eoin. The Legend of Spud Murphy. McCoy, Glenn, illus. 112p. (gr. 2-6). 2005. reprint ed. pap. 4.99 (978-0-7868-5504-9(5)); Bk. 1. 2004. (J). 12.95 (978-0-7868-5501-8(0)) Miramax Bks.

—The Legend of the Worst Boy in the World, Bk. 3. McCoy, Glenn, illus. 3rd rev. ed. 2007. 112p. (J). (gr. 2-6). 12.95 (978-0-7868-5503-2(7)) Hyperion Pr.

Collier, James Lincoln. My Brother Sam Is Dead. 1999. (YA). 9.95 (978-1-56137-380-2(X)) Novel Units, Inc.

—My Brother Sam Is Dead. 2000. (Pathways to Critical Thinking Ser.). 32p. (J). pap., stu. ed., tchr.'s training gde. ed. 19.95 (978-1-58303-086-8(7)) Pathways Publishing.

Collier, James Lincoln & Collier, Christopher. My Brother Sam Is Dead. 1999. 11.95 (978-1-56137-823-4(2)) Novel Units, Inc.

Collins, Paul. Cyberkids: The Knockout, the Great Escape, the Final Countdown. 2005. (Triple Play-Yellow Ser.). (Illus.). 48p. (gr. 4-8). 41.85 (978-0-7910-9081-7(7)) Facts On File, Inc.

Collins, Suzanne. Gregor & the Code of Claw. 2007. (Underland Chronicles). 416p. (YA). (gr. 5-9). pap. 17.99 (***978-0-439-79143-4(X)*** , Scholastic Pr.) Scholastic, Inc.

—Gregor & the Curse of the Warmbloods. 368p. 2006. (J). pap. 6.99 (978-0-439-65624-5(9) , Scholastic Paperbacks); 2005. (Underland Chronicles: Bk. 3). pap. 16.95 (978-0-439-65623-8(0) , Scholastic Pr.) Scholastic, Inc.

—Gregor & the Curse of the Warmbloods. l.t. ed. 2006. 297p. (J). 23.95 (978-0-7862-8083-4(2)) Thorndike Pr.

—Gregor & the Prophecy of Bane. 2003. 320p. (J). (gr. 3-6). 16.95 (978-0-439-43536-9(6)) Scholastic, Inc.

—Gregor & the Prophecy of Bane. l.t. ed. 2006. 297p. 23.95 (978-0-7862-8084-1(0)) Thorndike Pr.

—When Charlie McButton Lost Power. Lester, Mike, illus. 2005. 32p. (J). (ps-3). 15.99 (978-0-399-24000-3(4) , Putnam Juvenile) Penguin Group (USA) Inc.

Collins, Suzanne. When Charlie Mcbutton Lost Power. Lester, Mike, illus. 2007. 32p. (J). (ps). pap. 5.99 (***978-0-14-240857-5(3)*** , Puffin) Penguin Group (USA) Inc.

Coman, Carolyn. Bee & Jacky. 2006. 104p. pap. 9.95 (978-1-932425-37-6(3) , Lemniscaat) Boyds Mills Pr.

—The Big House. Shepperson, Rob, illus. 2004. 224p. (J). 16.95 (978-1-932425-09-3(8) , Lemniscaat) Boyds Mills Pr.

—The Big House. Rob, Shepperson, illus. 2007. 224p. (J). (gr. 3 up). pap. 6.99 (978-0-14-240740-0(2) , Puffin) Penguin Group (USA) Inc.

Coman, Carolyn. Sneaking Suspicions. Shepperson, Rob, illus. 2007. 204p. (J). (gr. 3-7). 16.95 (***978-1-59078-491-4(X)*** , Front Street) Boyds Mills Pr.

Condon, Bill. A Waste of Space. Tulloch, Coral, illus. 1999. (Supa Doopers Ser.). 64p. (J). (978-0-7608-3294-3(3)) Sundance/Newbridge Educational Publishing.

—Waste of Space. 1999. (gr. 3-6). lib. bdg. 12.60 (978-0-613-30846-5(8)) Tandem Library Bks.

Conly, Jane Leslie. While No One Was Watching. 2000. (978-0-606-18728-2(6)) Tandem Library Bks.

Conrique, Samantha. The Pod-Poppers. 2007. (J). pap. 8.00 (***978-0-8059-7200-9(5)***) Dorrance Publishing Co., Inc.

Conway, David. The Most Important Gift of All. Littlewood, Karin, illus. 2006. 32p. (J). 15.95 (978-0-7696-4618-3(2) , Gingham Dog Pr.) School Specialty Publishing.

Cook, Vivian E. Alaska Adventure. Nelson, Grace I., illus. 1999. (Adventures of Spencer, Private Eye & His Psychic Sister, Tiffany Ser.: No. 6). 66p. (J). (gr. 3-5). pap. 8.95 (978-1-928659-05-1(5)) Two Sisters Publishing.

Coolidge, Susan. Clover. 2005. (Illus.). 133p. pap. (***978-1-59569-026-5(3)***) Mondial.

—What Katy Did. 2006. 62.99 (***978-1-4280-3108-1(1)***) IndyPublish.com.

Cooney, Caroline B. A Friend at Midnight. 2006. 192p. (YA). (gr. 7). 15.95 (978-0-385-73326-7(7) , Delacorte Bks. for Young Readers) Random Hse. Children's Bks.

—A Friend at Midnight. 2006. 192p. (YA). 15.95 (978-1-4000-7208-8(5) , WaterBrook Pr.) WaterBrook Pr.

—Prisoner of Time. 1999. (gr. 7-12). lib. bdg. 13.00 (978-0-613-19425-9(X)) Tandem Library Bks.

Cooper, Helen. Ha Sido el Pequeno Monstruo! 2000. (SPA., Illus.). 32p. (J). (ps-2). 12.76 net. (978-84-261-3109-6(3)) Lectorum Pubns., Inc.

Cooper, Patrick. I Is Someone Else. 2006. (Illus.). 304p. (YA). (gr. 9). 16.95 (978-0-385-73269-7(4)); lib. bdg. 18.99 (978-0-385-90286-1(7)) Random Hse. Children's Bks. (Delacorte Bks. for Young Readers).

Cooper, Susan. The Dark Is Rising. (Dark Is Rising Sequence Ser.). 244p. (YA). (gr. 5 up). pap. 4.99 (978-0-8072-1533-3(3) , Listening Library) Random Hse. Audio Publishing Group.

—The Dark Is Rising. (Dark Is Rising Sequence Ser.). 2007. 272p. (YA). pap. 8.99 (***978-1-4169-4965-7(8)*** , Simon Pulse); 2005. 232p. pap. 2.99 (978-1-4169-0528-8(6) , Aladdin); 1999. 232p. (J). (gr. 7 up). pap. 5.99 (978-0-689-82983-3(3) , Aladdin); 2007. 256p. (J). (gr. 4-8). pap. 6.99 (***978-1-4169-4995-4(X)*** , Aladdin); 2007. 272p. (YA). (gr. 7). pap. 8.99 (***978-1-4169-4969-5(0)*** , Simon Pulse) Simon & Schuster Children's Publishing.

—The Dark Is Rising. 1999. (Dark Is Rising Sequence Ser.). (gr. 5-8). lib. bdg. 13.00 (978-0-613-90606-7(3)) Tandem Library Bks.

—The Dark Is Rising. l.t. ed. 2001. (Dark Is Rising Sequence Ser.). 395p. (J). (gr. 4-7). 21.95 (978-0-7862-2920-8(9)) Thorndike Pr.

—The Dark Is Rising Boxed Set: The Dark Is Rising, Greenwitch, over Sea, under Stone, Silver on the Tree, the Grey King. 2007. (Dark Is Rising Sequence Ser.). 1088p. (J). pap., pap. 29.99 (***978-1-4169-4996-1(8)*** , Aladdin) Simon & Schuster Children's Publishing.

—Green Boy. (Illus.). 208p. (J). 2003. pap. 5.99 (978-0-689-84760-8(2) , Aladdin); 2002. (gr. 4-6). 16.00 (978-0-689-84751-6(3) , McElderry, Margaret K.) Simon & Schuster Children's Publishing.

—Greenwitch. (Dark Is Rising Sequence Ser.). 2007. 176p. (YA). pap. 8.99 (***978-1-4169-4966-4(6)*** , Simon Pulse); 2000. 144p. (J). (gr. 4-7). pap. 5.99 (978-0-689-84034-0(9) , Aladdin) Simon & Schuster Children's Publishing.

—Greenwitch. 2000. (Dark Is Rising Sequence Ser.). (J). 11.64 (978-0-606-19710-6(9)); (gr. 3-6). lib. bdg. 13.00 (978-0-613-29971-8(X)) Tandem Library Bks.

—Greenwitch. l.t. ed. 2001. (Dark Is Rising Sequence Ser.). 131p. (J). 21.95 (978-0-7862-2923-9(3)) Thorndike Pr.

Cooper, Susan. Over Sea, under Stone. 2002. (Dark Is Rising Sequence Ser.). (Illus.). (J). 13.40 (978-0-7587-5635-0(6)) Book Wholesalers, Inc.

—Over Sea, under Stone. 2007. (Dark Is Rising Sequence Ser.). 224p. (YA). pap. 8.99 (***978-1-4169-4964-0(X)*** , Simon Pulse) Simon & Schuster Children's Publishing.

—Over Sea, under Stone. Wiesner, David, illus. 2000. (Dark Is Rising Sequence Ser.). 208p. (J). (gr. 4-7). pap. 5.99 (978-0-689-84035-7(7) , Aladdin) Simon & Schuster Children's Publishing.

—Over Sea, under Stone. 2000. (Dark Is Rising Sequence Ser.). (gr. 7-12). lib. bdg. 13.00 (978-0-613-30082-7(3)) Tandem Library Bks.

—Over Sea, under Stone. l.t. ed. 2000. (Dark Is Rising Sequence Ser.). 332p. (J). (gr. 4-7). 22.95 (978-0-7862-2918-5(7)) Thorndike Pr.

Corbett, Sue. 12 Again. 2007. 240p. (J). (gr. 5 up). pap. 5.99 (978-0-14-240729-5(1) , Puffin) Penguin Group (USA) Inc.

Corlett, William. The Door in the Tree. 2000. 289p. (J). (gr. 5-8). per. 13.00 (978-0-613-74171-2(4)) Tandem Library Bks.

Corpi, Lucha. Where Fireflies Dance (Ahi, Donde Bailan las Luciernagas) Reisberg, Mira, illus. 2002. 32p. (J). (gr. 1 up). pap. 7.95 (978-0-89239-177-6(4)) Children's Bk. Pr.

Corso, Erika. The Day You Came. 2006. (ENG., Illus.). 28p. per. 12.95 (978-1-59800-242-3(2)) Outskirts Press, Inc.

Cory, Kim Delmar. Home to Mackinac: The Tale of Young Jack Murphy's Discovery of Loyalty, Family & Forgiveness. Evans, Laura, illus. 2007. 175p. (J). pap. 9.95 (978-0-911872-87-3(6)) Mackinac State Historic Parks.

Cosgrove, Stephen. Katy Didd Bigg: Standing up for Yourself. Arroyo, Fian, illus. 2004. (J). (978-1-58804-378-8(9)) PCI Educational Publishing.

Costain, Meredith, ed. My Brother, the Spy. Tulloch, Coral, illus. 1999. (Supa Doopers Ser.). 64p. (J). (978-0-7608-1930-2(0)) Sundance/Newbridge Educational Publishing.

Cousins, Lucy. Za-Za's Baby Brother. Cousins, Lucy, illus. 2002. (Illus.). (J). 15.74 (978-0-7587-4072-4(7)) Book Wholesalers, Inc.

Coville, Bruce & Dodge, Mary Mapes. Hans Brinker. Long, Laurel, illus. 2007. 40p. (J). (ps up). 16.99 (***978-0-8037-2868-4(9)***, Dial) Penguin Group (USA) Inc.

Cowen-Fletcher, Jane. It Takes a Village. Cowen-Fletcher, Jane, illus. 2002. (Illus.). (J). 25.06 (978-0-7587-2872-2(7)) Book Wholesalers, Inc.

—It Takes a Village. (J). (gr. 1-2). pap. (978-0-590-46598-4(8)) Scholastic, Inc.

Coyle, Carmela LaVigna. Do Princesses Scrape Their Knees? 2006. (Illus.). 32p. (J). 15.95 (978-0-87358-909-3(2)) Northland Publishing.

Crary, Elizabeth. Willy's Noisy Sister. Avishai, Susan, illus. 2000. (Kids Can Choose Book Ser.). 32p. (J). (gr. 1-5). lib. bdg. 17.95 (978-1-884734-58-8(8)); (ps-5). pap. 7.95 (978-1-884734-57-1(X)) Parenting Pr., Inc.

Creech, Sharon. The Castle Corona. Diaz, David, illus. 2007. 336p. (J). (gr. 3-7). lib. bdg. 19.89 (***978-0-06-084622-0(4)***); 18.99 (***978-0-06-084621-3(6)***) HarperCollins Pubs. (Cotler, Joanna Books).

Creech, Sharon. Ruby Holler. (J). 2004. 336p. pap. 6.99 (978-0-06-056015-7(0) , Harper Trophy); 2002. 320p. (gr. 3-7). lib. bdg. 17.89 (978-0-06-027733-8(5) , Cotler, Joanna Books); 2002. 320p. (gr. 4-7). 16.99 (978-0-06-027732-1(7) , Cotler, Joanna Books) HarperCollins Pubs.

—Ruby Holler. 2004. (gr. 3-6). lib. bdg. 14.15 (978-0-613-86272-1(4)) Tandem Library Bks.

—Ruby Holler. l.t. ed. 2003. (Juvenile Ser.). 250p. (J). 22.95 (978-0-7862-5429-3(7)) Thorndike Pr.

Crumbaugh, David. The Primrose Kids. 2006. 81p. pap. 14.95 (978-1-4241-3250-8(9)) PublishAmerica, Inc.

Crump, Fred, Jr. Brave Toy Soldier. 2006. (Illus.). 32p. (J). pap. 9.95 (978-1-932715-82-8(7)) UMI (Urban Ministries, Inc.).

Crump, Fred. Brave Toy Soldier. 2007. 32p. (J). 12.95 (***978-1-934056-20-2(0)***) UMI (Urban Ministries, Inc.).

Cullen, Lynn. Stink Bomb. 128p. (J). (gr. 3-7). 1999. pap. 3.99 (978-0-380-78507-0(2) , Harper Trophy); 1998. 14.00 (978-0-380-97647-8(1)) HarperCollins Pubs.

Cummings, Pat. Angel Baby. 2000. (Illus.). 24p. (J). (gr. k-2). 15.89 (978-0-688-14822-5(0)) HarperCollins Pubs.

Curtis, Christopher Paul. The Watsons Go to Birmingham - 1963. 2002. (Illus.). (J). 14.47 (978-0-7587-0328-6(7)) Book Wholesalers, Inc.

—The Watsons Go to Birmingham - 1963. 1998. 15p. pap., stu. ed., tchr.'s training gde. ed. 15.95 (978-1-58303-068-4(9)) Pathways Publishing.

—The Watsons Go to Birmingham - 1963. 210p. (YA). (gr. 5 up). pap. 5.50 (978-0-8072-8336-3(3)); 2004. (J). (gr. 4 up). pap. 38.00 incl. audio (978-0-8072-8335-6(5) , YA166SP) Random Hse. Audio Publishing Group. (Listening Library).

—The Watsons Go to Birmingham - 1963. 2000. 224p. (YA). (gr. 5-7). pap. 6.50 (978-0-440-22800-4(X) , Laurel Leaf) Random Hse. Children's Bks.

—The Watsons Go to Birmingham - 1963. 2000. (gr. 5-8). lib. bdg. 14.15 (978-0-613-85111-4(0)) Tandem Library Bks.

—The Watsons Go to Birmingham - 1963. l.t. ed. 2004. 254p. pap. 10.95 (978-0-7862-6406-3(3)) Thorndike Pr.

Curtis, Marci. Big Brother, Little Brother. 2004. (Illus.). 40p. (J). (gr. k). 12.99 (978-0-8037-2870-7(0) , Dial) Penguin Group (USA) Inc.

Cuscuna, Susan. Molly & Me & Manny Magee. 2007. (J). (***978-0-7666-2839-7(6)***) Modern Publishing.

Cussler, Clive. The Adventures of Vin Fiz. Farnsworth, William, illus. 2006. 144p. (J). (gr. 3). 15.99 (978-0-399-24474-2(3) , Philomel) Penguin Group (USA) Inc.

Cutler, Jane. Darcy & Gran Don't Like Babies. Ryan, Susannah, illus. rev. ed. 2002. 32p. (J). (ps-2). 16.50 (978-0-374-31696-9(1) , Farrar, Straus & Giroux (BYR)); pap. 6.95 (978-0-374-41686-7(9) , Sunburst) Farrar, Straus & Giroux.

Cyrkozuch, Alonda. Queenie's Pond: The Barker Brothers Arrive. Meurlot, Donny G., illus. 1999. 24p. (J). (ps-12). pap. 5.95 (978-1-929098-01-9(4) , 02) Story Teller, The.

Czuchna-Curl, Ardyce. Days of Gold. 2002. (Illus.). 128p. (J). pap. 12.95 (978-0-88196-012-9(8)) Oak Woods Media.

Daher, Anita. Two Foot Punch. 2007. (Orca Sports Ser.). 176p. pap. (***978-1-55143-876-4(3)***) Orca Bk. Pubs.

Dalmatian Press Staff. Sesame Street My Baby Brother Is a Little Monster. 2007. 24p. pap. 3.50 (***978-1-4037-3213-2(1)***) Dalmatian Pr.

Dana, Martha. No Talk! No Baby! Garamella, Joyce Orchard, illus. 2001. 48p. (J). (ps-3). pap. 11.95 (978-1-880158-31-9(0)) Townsend, J.N. Publishing.

Daniels, Teri. G-Rex. Pearson, Tracey Campbell, illus. 2000. 32p. (J). (gr. k-4). 17.99 (978-0-531-33243-6(8)); pap. 16.95 (978-0-531-30243-9(1)) Scholastic, Inc. (Orchard Bks.).

Dannhauss, Dianne. Big Brother, Big Sister, Big Deal. Bowen, Debbie, ed. Alexander, I. L., illus. 1998. 14p. (J). (gr. 1-4). lib. bdg. 19.95 (978-1-56763-151-7(7)) Ozark Publishing.

Danziger, Paula. Barfburger Baby, I Was Here First. Karas, G. Brian, tr. Karas, G. Brian, illus. 2004. 32p. (J). (ps-3). 16.99 (978-0-399-23204-6(4) , Putnam Juvenile) Penguin Group (USA) Inc.

—Barfburger Baby, I Was Here First. Karas, G. Brian, illus. 2007. 32p. (J). pap. 5.99 (978-0-14-240739-4(9) , Puffin) Penguin Group (USA) Inc.

Darrow, Sharon. Trash. 2006. 160p. (J). (gr. 7). 16.99 (978-0-7636-2624-2(4)) Candlewick Pr.

David, Lawrence. The Cupcaked Crusader. Gott, Barry, illus. 2002. (Horace Splattly Ser.: Vol. 1). 144p. (J). pap. 4.99 (978-0-14-230021-3(7) , Puffin) Penguin Group (USA) Inc.

—Horace Splattly: The Cupcaked Crusader. (gr. 3-6). 2003. lib. bdg. 13.00 (978-0-613-61708-6(8)); 2002. lib. bdg. 13.00 (978-0-613-45274-8(7)); 2002. lib. bdg. 13.00 (978-0-613-45275-5(5)) Tandem Library Bks.

—Terror of the Pink Dodo Balloons. Gott, Barry, illus. 3rd ed. 2003. (Horace Splattly Ser.: No. 3). 160p. (J). pap. 4.99 (978-0-14-250001-9(1) , Puffin) Penguin Group (USA) Inc.

—To Catch a Clownosaurus. Gott, Barry, tr. Gott, Barry, illus. 2003. (Horace Splattly Ser.). 160p. (J). pap. 4.99 (978-0-14-250135-1(2) , Puffin) Penguin Group (USA) Inc.

—When Second Graders Attack. Gott, Barry, illus. 2nd ed. 2002. (Horace Splattly Ser.). 160p. (J). pap. 4.99 (978-0-14-230118-0(3) , Puffin) Penguin Group (USA) Inc.

David, Luke. Oh, Brother! 1999. (gr. k-3). lib. bdg. 11.25 (978-0-613-15929-6(2)) Tandem Library Bks.

David, Luke. Tommy's New Playmate. 2007. 24p. (J). 21.35 (***978-1-59961-360-4(3)***) Spotlight.

Daviddi, Evelyn. My Sister Makes Me Happy! / My Sister Makes Me Mad! 2006. (Illus.). 32p. 10.95 (978-1-59687-170-0(9)) ibooks, Inc.

Davies, Jacqueline. The Lemonade War. 2007. 192p. (J). (gr. 3-5). 16.00 (***978-0-618-75043-6(6)***) Houghton Mifflin Co.

Davis, Catherine. Abby & Alex Feel Their Hearts' Little. 2006. 57p. pap. 12.95 (***978-1-4241-4586-7(4)***) PublishAmerica, Inc.

Davis, Jacky. Ladybug Girl. Soman, David, illus. 2008. 40p. (J). (ps). 16.99 (***978-0-8037-3195-0(7)***, Dial) Penguin Group (USA) Inc.

Davis, Rachel. My Life at Mapleleaf Cabin. 2nd ed. 2004. (YA). per. 10.00 (978-0-9741176-8-3(4)) Wu Li Turtle Corp.

De Groat, Diane. Mother, You're the Best! (but Sister, You're a Pest!) 2008. 32p. (J). 16.99 (***978-0-06-123899-4(6)***); lib. bdg. 17.89 (***978-0-06-123900-7(3)***) HarperCollins Pubs.

De Haven, Tom. The Orphan's Tent. 2005. (Illus.). 192p. mass mkt. 5.99 (978-0-7434-9772-5(4)) ibooks, Inc.

de la Vega, Eida, tr. from ENG. Estela en el Mercado de Pulgas. Sanchez, Enrique O., illus. 2005. (SPA.). 32p. (J). (ps-k). 16.95 (978-1-58430-245-2(3)) Lee & Low Bks., Inc.

de Mariscal, Blanca Lopez. The Harvest Birds. 2001. (gr. k-3). lib. bdg. 16.40 (978-0-613-90839-9(2)) Tandem Library Bks.

de Paola, Tomie. The Baby Sister. de Paola, Tomie, illus. 1999. (Illus.). 32p. (J). (ps-3). pap. 5.99 (978-0-698-11773-0(5) , Putnam Juvenile) Penguin Group (USA) Inc.

—The Baby Sister. 1999. (J). 12.79 (978-0-606-16794-9(3)); lib. bdg. 14.15 (978-0-8085-0222-7(0)) Tandem Library Bks.

—Meet the Barkers. 2003. (Barker Twins Ser.). (Illus.). 32p. (J). (gr. k-1). pap. 5.99 (978-0-14-250083-5(6) , Puffin) Penguin Group (USA) Inc.

—Meet the Barkers: Morgan & Moffat Go to School. de Paola, Tomie, illus. 2001. (Illus.). 1p. (J). (ps-1). 13.99 (978-0-399-23708-9(9) , Putnam Juvenile) Penguin Group (USA) Inc.

—Meet the Barkers: Morgan & Moffat Go to School. 2005. (J). (gr. k-3). pap. 17.95 incl. audio (978-0-8045-6934-7(7) , SAC6934); pap. 19.95 incl. audio compact disk (978-0-8045-4129-9(9) , SACD4129) Spoken Arts, Inc.

—Morgan & Moffat Go to School. 2003. (gr. k-3). lib. bdg. 14.15 (978-0-613-66367-0(5)) Tandem Library Bks.

—A New Barker in the House. (Illus.). 32p. (J). (ps up). 2004. pap. 5.99 (978-0-14-240141-5(2) , Puffin); 2002. (SPA., 13.99 (978-0-399-23865-9(4) , Putnam Juvenile) Penguin Group (USA) Inc.

De Rolf, Shane. The Cut-Up Sisters. 1998. (978-0-679-88451-4(3) , Random Hse. Bks. for Young Readers) Random Hse. Children's Bks.

Dealey, Erin. Goldie Locks Has Chicken Pox. ed. 2004. (Illus.). (J). (gr. k-3). spiral bd. (978-0-616-14572-2(1)); spiral bd. (978-0-616-14573-9(X)) Canadian National Institute for the Blind/Institut National Canadien pour les Aveugles.

—Goldie Locks Has Chicken Pox. Wakiyama, Hanako, illus. 40p. (J). 2002. 17.99 (978-0-689-82981-9(7) , Atheneum); 2005. reprint ed. 6.99 (978-0-689-87610-3(6) , Aladdin) Simon & Schuster Children's Publishing.

Deans, Sis Boulos. Every Day & All the Time, Vol. 5. l.t. ed. 2004. 304p. 21.95 (978-0-7862-6386-8(5)) Thorndike Pr.

—Racing the Past. 2005. 160p. (J). (gr. 3-9). reprint ed. pap. 5.99 (978-0-14-240308-2(3) , Puffin) Penguin Group (USA) Inc.

Dee, Barbara. Just Another Day in My Insanely Real Life. 2007. 256p. (J). pap. 5.99 (***978-1-4169-4739-4(6)***) Kaplan Bks.

—Just Another Day in My Insanely Real Life. 2006. (Illus.). 256p. (J). 15.95 (978-1-4169-0861-6(7) , McElderry, Margaret K.) Simon & Schuster Children's Publishing.

deGroat, Diane. Trick or Treat, Smell My Feet. deGroat, Diane, illus. 1999. (Illus.). 32p. (J). (ps-3). pap. 6.99 (978-0-688-17061-5(7) , Harper Trophy) HarperCollins Pubs.

deGroat, Diane & deGroat, Diane, illus. Trick or Treat, Smell My Feet. 1998. 32p. (J). (ps-3). 14.89 (978-0-688-15767-8(X)) HarperCollins Pubs.

—Trick or Treat, Smell My Feet. 1999. (978-0-606-17241-7(6)) Tandem Library Bks.

Deighton, Jo, adapted by. Codadad & His Brothers: Traditional Stories:The Grocer, the Student & the Elf: The Ugly Duckling. (Scheherezade Presents Ser.: No. 13). (Illus.). 48p. (J). pap. (978-1-85964-103-3(2) , Ithaca Pr.) Garnet Publishing, Ltd.

Delacre, Lulu. Rafi & Rosi. 2004. (Illus.). 64p. (J). lib. bdg. 13.85 (***978-1-4242-0596-7(4)***) Fitzgerald Bks.

—Rafi & Rosi. Delacre, Lulu, illus. (I Can Read Bks.). 64p. (J). (gr. k-3). 2005. pap. 3.99 (978-0-06-009897-1(X) , Rayo); 2004. (Illus.). lib. bdg. 16.89 (978-0-06-009896-4(1)) HarperCollins Pubs.

—Rafi & Rosi: Carnival! Delacre, Lulu, illus. 2008. (I Can Read Bks.). (J). 3.99 (***978-0-06-073599-9(6)***, Rayo) HarperCollins Pubs.

—Rafi y Rosi. Delacre, Lulu, illus. 2006. (I Can Read Bks.). (SPA.). 64p. (J). 15.99 (978-0-06-087277-9(2)); pap. 3.99 (978-0-06-087278-6(0)) HarperCollins Pubs. (Rayo).

—Rafi y Rosi: Carnival! Delacre, Lulu, illus. 2006. (I Can Read Bks.). 64p. (J). (SPA.). 15.99 (978-0-06-113134-9(2)); (SPA.). pap. 3.99 (978-0-06-113135-6(0)); (Illus.). 15.99 (978-0-06-073597-5(X)); (Illus.). lib. bdg. 16.89 (978-0-06-073598-2(8)) HarperCollins Pubs. (Rayo).

Delton, Judy. Angel in Charge. 1999. (Illus.). 160p. (J). (gr. 4-6). pap. 5.95 (978-0-395-96061-5(4)) Houghton Mifflin Co. Trade & Reference Div.

—Angel in Charge. 1999. (gr. 3-6). lib. bdg. 12.95 (978-0-613-18232-4(4)); (Illus.). (J). 11.60 (978-0-606-18206-5(3)) Tandem Library Bks.

Denslow, Sharon Phillips. All Their Names Were Courage. 2003. 144p. (J). (gr. 2 up). 15.99 (978-0-06-623810-4(2)) HarperCollins Pubs.

Devard, Nancy, et al, illus. I Told You I Can Play. 2006. (ENM.). 32p. (J). 16.95 (***978-1-933491-06-6(X)***) Just Us Bks., Inc.

Dewan, Ted. Crispin & the 3 Little Piglets. Dewan, Ted, illus. 2003. (Illus.). 32p. (J). (gr. k-3). 15.95 (978-0-385-74633-5(4) , Doubleday Bks. for Young Readers) Random Hse. Children's Bks.

DiCamillo, Jennifer. Big Boys Playing with Babies. 2007. 52p. (J). 10.00 (***978-0-615-14240-1(0)***) Tree Pr.

DiTerlizzi, Tony & Black, Holly. The Field Guide. DiTerlizzi, Tony, illus. (Spiderwick Chronicles: Bk. 1). 128p. (J). 2003. (Illus.). 10.99 (978-0-689-85936-6(8) , 53409542); 2008. 10.99 (***978-1-4169-5017-2(6)***) Simon & Schuster Children's Publishing.

—The Field Guide. l.t. ed. 2006. (Spiderwick Chronicles: Bk. 1). 120p. (J). 23.95 (978-0-7862-8284-5(3)) Thorndike Pr.

—The Ironwood Tree. (Spiderwick Chronicles: Bk. 4). 128p. (J). 2004. (Illus.). (gr. 1-5). 10.99 (978-0-689-85939-7(2)); 2008. 10.99 (***978-1-4169-5020-2(6)***) Simon & Schuster Children's Publishing.

—The Ironwood Tree. l.t. ed. 2006. (Spiderwick Chronicles: Bk. 4). 90p. (YA). (gr. 2 up). 23.95 (978-0-7862-8583-9(4)) Thorndike Pr.

—Lucinda's Secret. DiTerlizzi, Tony, illus. movie tie-in ed. (Spiderwick Chronicles: Bk. 3). 128p. 2008. (J). 10.99 (***978-1-4169-5019-6(2)***); BK. 3. 2003. (Illus.). (YA). 10.99 (978-0-689-85938-0(4)) Simon & Schuster Children's Publishing.

—Lucinda's Secret. l.t. ed. 2006. (Spiderwick Chronicles: Bk. 3). 93p. (YA). 23.95 (978-0-7862-8585-3(0)) Thorndike Pr.

—The Seeing Stone. DiTerlizzi, Tony, illus. movie tie-in ed. (Spiderwick Chronicles: Bk. 2). 128p. (J). 2008. 10.99 (***978-1-4169-5018-9(4)***); Bk. 2. 2003. (Illus.). 10.99 (978-0-689-85937-3(6) , 53409541) Simon & Schuster Children's Publishing.

—The Seeing Stone. l.t. ed. 2006. (Spiderwick Chronicles: No. 2). (YA). 23.95 (978-0-7862-8581-5(8)) Thorndike Pr.

—The Wrath of Mulgarath. DiTerlizzi, Tony, illus. movie tie-in ed. 2008. (Spiderwick Chronicles: Bk. 5). 160p. (J). (gr. 2 up). 10.99 (***978-1-4169-5021-9(4)***) Simon & Schuster Children's Publishing.

—The Wrath of Mulgarath. l.t. ed. 2006. (Spiderwick Chronicles: Bk. 5). 183p. (YA). 23.95 (978-0-7862-8579-2(6)) Thorndike Pr.

DiVito, Anna. Annie Oakley Saves the Day. DiVito, Anna, illus. ed. 2005. (Illus.). 32p. (J). lib. bdg. 15.00 (978-1-59054-939-1(2)) Fitzgerald Bks.

Dixon, Franklin W. Burned. 2005. (Hardy Boys Ser.: No. 6). (Illus.). 160p. (J). pap. 4.99 (978-1-4169-0008-5(X) , Aladdin) Simon & Schuster Children's Publishing.

Dixon, Franklin W. & Walker, Jeff. Typhoon Island, Vol. 180. 2003. (Hardy Boys Ser.). (Illus.). 160p. (J). pap. 4.99 (978-0-689-85884-0(1) , Aladdin) Simon & Schuster Children's Publishing.

Dodd, Quentin. The Princess of Neptune. 2004. 224p. (J). 17.00 (978-0-374-36119-8(3) , Farrar, Straus & Giroux (BYR)) Farrar, Straus & Giroux.

Dodds, Bill. My Sister Annie. Hunt, Judith, illus. 2003. 96p. (YA). (gr. 4-6). pap. 10.95 (978-1-56397-554-7(8)) Boyds Mills Pr.

Dodge, Mary. Hans Brinker, or the Silver Skates. 2005. (Illus.). 239p. (J). (***978-1-59605-666-4(5)***); pap. (***978-1-59605-415-8(8)***) Cosimo, Inc.

Dodge, Mary Mapes. Hans Brinker & the Silver Skates. Freshman, Floris, illus. 2002. (Great Illustrated Classics Ser.). 240p. (J). (gr. 3-8). 21.35 (978-1-57765-814-6(0) , ABDO & Daughters) ABDO Publishing Co.

—Hans Brinker or the Silver Skates. Lindskoog, Kathryn, ed. Wynne, Patrick, illus. 2001. (Classics for Young Readers Ser.). 224p. (J). (gr. 3-6). pap. 7.99 (978-0-87552-725-3(6)) P & R Publishing.

—Hans Brinker, or the Silver Skates. Kopito, Janet Baine, ed. 2003. (Dover Evergreen Classics Ser.). 288p. (J). (gr. 4-7). pap. 3.00 (978-0-486-42842-0(7)) Dover Pubns., Inc.

—Hans Brinker or the Silver Skates A Story of Life in Holland. Doggett, Allen B., illus. 2004. reprint ed. pap. 34.95 (978-1-4179-4127-8(8)) Kessinger Publishing, LLC.

Dodge, Mary Mapes. Hans Brinker; or, the Silver Skates (Dod. 2006. pap. (***978-1-4065-0961-8(2)***) Dodo Pr.

Donahue, Jill L. Benny & the Birthday Gift. 2007. (Illus.). 24p. (J). (***978-1-4048-0590-3(7)***) Picture Window Bks.

—Benny & the Birthday Gift. Senturk, Burak, illus. 2006. (Read It! Readers Ser.). 24p. (J). (gr. 1-2). 19.93 (***978-1-4048-3164-3(9)***) Picture Window Bks.

Donaldson, Julia. The Giants & the Joneses. Swearingen, Greg, illus. 2005. 224p. (J). (gr. 3-5). 14.95 (978-0-8050-7805-3(3)) Holt, Henry & Co.

—The Giants & the Joneses. Swearingen, Greg, illus. 2008. 240p. (J). pap. 6.99 (***978-0-312-37961-2(7)***) Square Fish.

Donlon, Diane Youngblood. Tippee Tippee Tiptoe. Suhr, James W., illus. 2003. (J). 16.95 (978-0-9720427-0-3(9)) OLLY Publishing Co.

Dorato, A. P. Arthur, Donna, & the Magic Crown of Tiabora. 2006. pap. 19.95 (978-1-4137-8898-3(X)) PublishAmerica, Inc.

Dorris, Michael. Morning Girl. 2005. 80p. (J). (gr. 3 up). 20.50 (978-0-8446-7272-4(6) , 3587) Smith, Peter Pub., Inc.

Dougherty, Terri. The Bath. Yi, Hye Won, illus. 2006. (Read-It! Readers Ser.). 32p. (J). (ps-3). 18.60 (978-1-4048-1576-6(7)) Picture Window Bks.

Dow, Unity. Far & Beyon' 2002. 208p. (YA). (gr. 7 up). pap. 11.95 (978-1-879960-64-0(8)) Aunt Lute Bks.

Dowd, Siobhan. The London Eye Mystery. 2008. 336p. (J). (***978-0-375-84976-3(9)***); lib. bdg. (***978-0-375-94976-0(3)***) Random Hse. Children's Bks. (Fickling, David Bks.).

Dowell, Frances O'Roark. Dovey Coe. 192p. (J). 2001. (Illus.). pap. 5.99 (978-0-689-84667-0(3) , Aladdin); 2000. (gr. 4-7). 16.99 (978-0-689-83174-4(9) , Atheneum) Simon & Schuster Children's Publishing.

—Dovey Coe. 2001. 11.64 (978-0-606-22127-6(1)) Tandem Library Bks.

—Dovey Coe. l.t. ed. 2001. 171p. (J). 22.95 (978-0-7862-3590-2(X)) Thorndike Pr.

Doyon, Stephanie. Buying Time. 1999. (On the Road Ser.: No. 2). (978-0-606-18898-2(3)) Tandem Library Bks.

Draper, Sharon M. Forged by Fire. 2002. (Illus.). (J). 13.40 (978-0-7587-0354-5(6)) Book Wholesalers, Inc.

—Forged by Fire. l.t. ed. 2006. 199p. pap. 10.95 (978-0-7862-8358-3(0)) Thorndike Pr.

—Forged by Fire No. 2: Hazelwood High Trilogy. l.t. ed. 2005. 199p. 21.95 (978-0-7862-7417-8(4)) Thorndike Pr.

Driscoll, Laura. My Brother, the Knight. Smath, Jerry, illus. 2004. 32p. (J). lib. bdg. 20.00 (***978-1-4242-1109-8(3)***) Fitzgerald Bks.

—My Brother, the Knight. Smath, Jerry, illus. 2004. (Social Studies Connects). 32p. (J). (gr. 1-3). pap. 4.99 (978-1-57565-140-8(8)) Kane Pr., The.

Driscoll, Laura. Super Specs. Gott, Barry, illus. 2005. 32p. (J). lib. bdg. 20.00 (***978-1-4242-1074-9(7)***) Fitzgerald Bks.

—Super Specs. Adams, Lynn, illus. 2005. (Math Matters Ser.). 32p. (J). pap. 4.95 (978-1-57565-145-3(9)) Kane Pr., The.

Dube, Jasmine. Gratelle au Bois Mordant. ed. 2004. (FRE., Illus.). (J). (ps-3). spiral bd. (978-0-616-01848-4(7)) Canadian National Institute for the Blind/Institut National Canadien pour les Aveugles.

Dubosarsky, Ursula. The Magic Wand: Poof! What Happened to Becky's Brother? Vane, Mitch, illus. 2006. (Nibbles Ser.). 72p. (J). pap. 3.95 (978-0-7624-2653-9(5) , Running Pr. Kids) Running Pr. Bk. Pubs.

Dubowski, Cathy East. Family Reunion. 2000. (gr. 3-6). lib. bdg. 13.00 (978-0-613-25123-5(7)) Tandem Library Bks.

—Family Reunion: Junior Novel. Richardson, Julia, ed. 2000. (So Weird Ser.: No. 1). (Illus.). 144p. (gr. 3-7). pap. 4.99 (978-0-7868-1397-1(0)) Disney Pr.

Duffy, Daniel M., illus. Meet the Boxcar Children. 1998. (Adventures of Benny & Watch: Vol. No. 1). 48p. (J). (ps-2). pap. 3.95 (978-0-8075-5034-2(5)) Whitman, Albert & Co.

Duggan, Matt. The Royal Woods. rev. ed. 2007. 244p. (gr. 7-12). 12.95 (***978-1-55263-826-2(X)***) Key Porter Bks. CAN. *Dist:* Perseus Distribution.

Duke, Kate. The Tale of Pip & Squeak. 2007. 32p. (J). (ps). 16.99 (978-0-525-47777-8(2) , Dutton Juvenile) Penguin Group (USA) Inc.

Dumas, Alexandre. The Man in the Iron Mask. Ho, Oliver & Howell, Troy, illus. 2008. (Classic Starts Ser.). 160p. (J). 5.95 (***978-1-4027-4579-9(6)***) Sterling Publishing Co., Inc.

Dumin, Jennifer. Wolfie & Freddie: the New Puppy. 2006. (ENG.). 44p. per. 22.65 (***978-1-4257-0680-7(0)***) Xlibris Corp.

Dunbar. Tell Me What Its Like to Be Big. 2001. (Illus.). (J). 16.00 (978-0-15-204741-2(7)) Harcourt Trade Pubs.

Dunbar, Joyce. Tell Me Something Happy Before I Go to Sleep. Gliori, Debi, illus. 1998. 32p. (J). (ps-3). 17.00 (978-0-15-201795-8(X)) Harcourt Children's Bks.

—Tell Me What It's Like to Be Big. Gliori, Debi, illus. 32p. (J). (ps-2). 2001. 16.00 (978-0-15-202564-9(2)); 2005. reprint ed. pap. 6.00 (978-0-15-205247-8(X) , Voyager Bks./Libros Viajeros) Harcourt Children's Bks.

Dunlop, Ed. Escape to Liechtenstein. 2003. 152p. (J). (gr. 4-7). 7.49 (978-1-59166-013-2(0)) Jones, Bob Univ. Pr.

—The Incredible Rescues. Halverson, Tom, illus. 2003. 166p. (J). (gr. 4-7). 7.49 (978-1-59166-012-5(2)) Jones, Bob Univ. Pr.

Dunmore, Helen. Brother Brother, Sister Sister. 2000. (Illus.). 116p. (J). (gr. 3-7). pap. 4.50 (978-0-439-11322-9(9)) Scholastic, Inc.

—Ingo. 336p. (J). 2008. pap. 6.99 (*978-0-06-081854-8(9)*, Harper Trophy); 2006. 16.99 (978-0-06-081852-4(2)); 2006. lib. bdg. 17.89 (978-0-06-081853-1(0)) HarperCollins Pubs.

—The Tide Knot. 2008. (J). (*978-0-06-081857-9(3)*); 336p. 16.99 (*978-0-06-081855-5(7)*); 336p. lib. bdg. 17.89 (*978-0-06-081856-2(5)*) HarperCollins Pubs.

Durant, Alan. Gamer: Next Level. Mason, Sue, illus. 2008. (J). pap. (*978-1-59889-909-2(0)*); lib. bdg. (*978-1-59889-873-6(6)*) Stone Arch Bks.

Dwyer, Cynthia. Can You See Me Now? Schuepbach, Lynnette, illus. 2006. 24p. (J). 12.95 (*978-0-9677685-8-8(6)*, Thumbprint Pr.) McIntyre, Connie.

Dyer, Heather. The GIRL with the BROKEN WIND. 2007. 160p. (J). pap. 4.99 (*978-0-439-74828-5(3)*, Scholastic Paperbacks) Scholastic, Inc.

Dyer, Sarah. Clementine & Mungo. 2004. (Illus.). 32p. (J). (ps-3). 16.95 (978-1-58234-883-4(9), Bloomsbury Children) Bloomsbury Publishing.

Easton, Kelly. The Life History of a Star. 2002. 208p. (YA). pap. 6.99 (978-0-689-85270-1(3), Simon Pulse) Simon & Schuster Children's Publishing.

—The Life History of a Star. 2002. (gr. 7-12). lib. bdg. 15.30 (978-0-613-60641-7(8)) Tandem Library Bks.

—The Life History of a Star. l.t. ed. 2002. 200p. 22.95 (978-0-7862-4786-8(X)) Thorndike Pr.

Eaton Deborah. Canciones de monstruos (Monster Songs) 2007. (Lecturas para niños de verdad - Nivel 2 (Real Kids Readers - Level 2) Ser.). (J). pap. 5.95 (*978-0-8225-7803-1(4)*, Ediciones Lerner) Lerner Publishing Group.

Eaton, Deborah. Monster Songs. Handelman, Dorothy, photos by. 1999. (Real Kids Readers Ser.). (Illus.). 32p. (gr. k-2). (J). pap. 4.99 (978-0-7613-2079-1(2)); lib. bdg. 18.90 (978-0-7613-2054-8(7)) Lerner Publishing Group. (Millbrook Pr.).

—Monster Songs. 1999. (J). (978-0-606-19162-3(3)); lib. bdg. 11.80 (978-0-613-16767-3(8)) Tandem Library Bks.

—The Rainy Day Grump. Handelman, Dorothy, photos by. 1998. (Real Kids Readers Ser.). (Illus.). 32p. (gr. k-2). (J). pap. 4.99 (978-0-7613-2043-2(1)); lib. bdg. 18.90 (978-0-7613-2018-0(0)) Lerner Publishing Group. (Millbrook Pr.).

Edgson, Alison, et al. Hansel & Gretel. 2006. (Illus.). 24p. pap. 5.99 (978-1-904550-73-0(8)); pap. 9.99 (978-1-904550-45-7(2)) Child's Play-International.

Edvall, Lilian. The Rabbit Who Couldn't Find His Daddy. Dyssegaard, Elisabeth Kallick, tr. from SWE. Gimbergsson, Sara, illus. 2006. 32p. (J). 15.00 (978-91-29-66429-4(2)) R & S Bks. SWE. *Dist:* Macmillan.

Edwards, Becky. My Brother Sammy. 2000. (Illus.). 25p. (J). 19.99 (978-0-7475-3996-4(0)) Bloomsbury Publishing Plc GBR. *Dist:* Independent Pubs. Group.

—My Brother Sammy. Newton, Jill, illus. 2000. 32p. pap. 9.99 (978-0-7475-4654-2(1)) Bloomsbury Publishing Plc GBR. *Dist:* Trafalgar Square Publishing.

—My Brother Sammy. Armitage, David, illus. 1999. 32p. (gr. k-3). lib. bdg. 23.90 (978-0-7613-1417-2(2), Millbrook Pr.) Lerner Publishing Group.

Edwards, Tanille & Edwards, Latoya. Jordan & Justine's Weekend Adventures Pts. 1-2: Plants. 2007. 32p. (J). (gr. k-3). 9.95 (*978-0-9787302-3-9(2)*) Fire Flies Entertainment, LLC.

Ehrmantraut, Brenda. I Want One Too! Short, Robbie, illus. 2003. (J). lib. bdg. 16.95 (978-0-9729833-1-0(7)); per. 9.95 (978-0-9729833-0-3(9)) Bubble Gum Pr.

Ellery, Amanda. If I Had a Dragon. Ellery, Tom, illus. 2006. 40p. (J). (ps-2). 14.95 (978-1-4169-0924-8(9), Simon & Schuster Children's Publishing) Simon & Schuster Children's Publishing.

Ellery, Tom, et al. If I Had a Dragon. Ellery, Tom & Ellery, Amanda, illus. 2006. (ENG & SPA.). (J). 12.99 (978-1-933032-16-0(2)); pap. 3.99 (978-1-933032-17-7(0)) Lectorum Pubns., Inc.

Elliott, Laura. Hunter's Annoying Big Sister. Munsinger, Lynn, illus. 2007. 32p. (J). (ps-2). 16.99 (978-0-06-000233-6(6)) HarperCollins Pubs.

Ellis, Sarah. Big Ben. LaFave, Kim, illus. ed. 2004. (J). (ps-1). spiral bd. (978-0-616-11108-6(8)); spiral bd. (978-0-616-11109-3(6)) Canadian National Institute for the Blind/Institut National Canadien pour les Aveugles.

—Big Ben. LaFave, Kim, illus. 2001. 32p. (J). (ps-1). (978-1-55041-679-4(0)) Fitzhenry & Whiteside, Ltd.

Emery, Joanna. Brothers of the Falls. Erickson, David, illus. 2004. (Adventures in America Ser.). (J). 14.95 (978-1-893110-37-3(0)) Silver Moon Pr.

Enderle, Dottie. Granny Gert & the Bunion Brothers. Kulka, Joe, illus. 2006. 32p. (J). (gr. k-3). 15.95 (978-1-58980-373-2(6)) Pelican Publishing Co., Inc.

Enderle, Judith Ross & Gordon, Stephanie Jacob. School Stinks! 2001. (Illus.). 148p. (J). pap. (978-0-439-32852-4(7)) Scholastic, Inc.

—Smile, Principessa! Litzinger, Rosanne & Curmi, Serena, illus. 2007. 40p. (J). (ps-3). 16.99 (978-1-4169-1004-6(2), McElderry, Margaret K.) Simon & Schuster Children's Publishing.

Enright, Elizabeth. The Four-Story Mistake. Enright, Elizabeth, illus. rev. ed. 2002. (Melendy Quartet Ser.: Bk. 2). (Illus.). 208p. (J). (gr. 3-7). 16.95 (978-0-8050-7061-3(3), Holt, Henry & Co. Bks. For Young Readers) Holt, Henry & Co.

—Gone-Away Lake. Krush, Beth & Krush, Joe, illus. 2006. 256p. (J). (gr. 4-8). reprint ed. pap. 6.00 (978-1-4223-5436-0(9)) DIANE Publishing Co.

—The Saturdays. Enright, Elizabeth, illus. rev. ed. 2002. (Melendy Quartet Ser.: Bk. 1). (Illus.). 176p. (J). (gr. 3-6). 17.95 (978-0-8050-7060-6(5), Holt, Henry & Co. Bks. For Young Readers) Holt, Henry & Co.

—The Saturdays. 2008. (Melendy Quartet Ser.). (Illus.). 208p. (J). pap. 6.99 (*978-0-312-37598-0(0)*) Square Fish.

—Then There Were Five. Enright, Elizabeth, illus. rev. ed. 2002. (Melendy Quartet Ser.: Bk. 3). (Illus.). 176p. (J). (gr. 3-7). 16.95 (978-0-8050-7062-0(1), Holt, Henry & Co. Bks. For Young Readers) Holt, Henry & Co.

—Then There Were Five. 2008. (Melendy Quartet Ser.). (Illus.). 288p. (J). pap. 6.99 (*978-0-312-37600-0(6)*) Square Fish.

Enright, Robert D. Rising above the Storm Clouds: What It's Like to Forgive. Finney, Kathryn Kunz, illus. 2004. 32p. (J). 14.95 (978-1-59147-075-5(7)); pap. 8.95 (978-1-59147-076-2(5)) American Psychological Assn. (Magination Pr.).

Erickson, R. C. The Mystery of Colborn's Treasure. 2007. 204p. pap. 13.95 (*978-0-615-15975-1(3)*) Quool Publishing.

Ernst, Kathleen. Hearts of Stone. 2006. 240p. (J). (gr. 7). 16.99 (978-0-525-47686-3(5), Dutton Juvenile) Penguin Group (USA) Inc.

Esbaum, Jill. Stink Soup. Roth, Roger, illus. 2004. 32p. (J). 16.00 (978-0-374-37252-1(7), Farrar, Straus & Giroux (BYR)) Farrar, Straus & Giroux.

Esckilsen, Erik E. Outside Groove. 2006. 272p. (J). (gr. 5). 16.00 (978-0-618-66854-0(3)) Houghton Mifflin Co.

Estep, Joanna, illus. Roadsong, Vol. 1. 2006. 200p. pap. 9.99 (978-1-59816-398-8(1), Tokyopop Adult) TOKYOPOP, Inc.

Estes, Eleanor. Ginger Pye. Estes, Eleanor, illus. 2000. (Illus.). 320p. (YA). (gr. 3 up). 17.00 (978-0-15-202499-4(9), Odyssey Classics); (gr. 4-7). pap. 6.00 (978-0-15-202505-2(7)) Harcourt Children's Bks.

—Ginger Pye. 2000. (Illus.). 306p. (J). (ps-7). lib. bdg. 14.15 (978-0-613-29963-3(9)) Tandem Library Bks.

—The Moffat Museum. 2001. (Odyssey Classics). (Illus.). 256p. (gr. 3 up). pap. 6.00 (978-0-15-202553-3(7), Odyssey Classics) Harcourt Children's Bks.

—The Moffat Museum. 2001. (J). (978-0-606-20805-5(4)); (gr. 3-6). lib. bdg. 14.15 (978-0-613-35463-9(X)) Tandem Library Bks.

—Rufus M. Slobodkin, Louis, illus. 2001. (Odyssey Classics). 256p. (YA). (gr. 3 up). pap. 6.00 (978-0-15-202577-9(4), Odyssey Classics) Harcourt Children's Bks.

Etchemendy, Nancy. Un Power Of. 2001. (gr. 3-6). lib. bdg. 12.40 (978-0-613-53445-1(X)) Tandem Library Bks.

—The Power of UN. 2000. 160p. (J). (gr. 3-7). 16.95 (978-0-8126-2850-0(0)) Cricket Bks.

Ewing, Lynne. Drive-By. 1998. 96p. (J). (gr. 5 up). pap. 4.99 (978-0-06-440649-9(0), Harper Trophy) HarperCollins Pubs.

Fallon, Joan & Feltenstein, Arlene. Will the New Baby Be Bigger Than Me? Escriva, Viví, illus. 1998. (J). (ps-3). 9.95 (978-1-56492-252-6(9)) Laredo Publishing Co., Inc.

Farmer, Nancy. The Sea of Trolls. 480p. (J). (gr. 5-8). 2004. (Illus.). 17.95 (978-0-689-86744-6(1), Atheneum); 2006. reprint ed. pap. 9.99 (978-0-689-86746-0(8), Simon Pulse) Simon & Schuster Children's Publishing.

—The Sea of Trolls. l.t. ed. 2005. 554p. 23.95 (978-0-7862-7151-1(5)) Thorndike Pr.

Faulkner, Matt. A Taste of Colored Water. Faulkner, Matt, illus. 2008. 48p. (J). 16.99 (*978-1-4169-1629-1(6)*) Simon & Schuster Children's Publishing.

Fearnley, Jan. Billy Tibble Moves Out! Fearnley, Jan, illus. 2006. (Illus.). 29p. (J). (gr. k-4). reprint ed. 16.00 (978-1-4223-5557-2(8)) DIANE Publishing Co.

Feeney, Josephine. Holy Terrors. 142p. 2001. pap. 7.99 (978-0-00-675533-3(X)); 2000. (Illus.). (YA). 19.99 (978-0-00-185745-2(2), HarperSport) HarperCollins Pubs. Ltd. GBR. *Dist:* Trafalgar Square Publishing.

Fellows-Johnsto, Annie. Big Brother. 2006. pap. 87.99 (*978-1-4280-4005-2(6)*) IndyPublish.com.

Fenner, Carol. Yolonda's Genius. Colon, Raul, illus. 2002. (J). 14.47 (978-0-7587-0333-0(3)) Book Wholesalers, Inc.

—Yolonda's Genius. unabr. ed. 2004. 211p. (J). (gr. 4-6). pap. 38.00 incl. audio (978-0-8072-0462-7(5), Listening Library) Random Hse. Audio Publishing Group.

Figler, Jeanie. Majestic Blue Horses. 1999. (Illus.). (J). 9.95 (978-1-56492-273-1(1)) Laredo Publishing Co., Inc.

Fine, Anne. Frozen Billy. McBain, Georgina, illus. 2006. 192p. (J). 16.00 (978-0-374-32481-0(6)) Farrar, Straus & Giroux.

Finkelstein, Ruth. Big Like Me. Touson, Esther, illus. 2001. 32p. (J). 9.95 (978-1-929628-04-9(8)) Hachai Publishing.

Finley, Mary Pearce. Meadow Lark. 2003. (Santa Fe Trail Triology Ser.). (Illus.). 199p. (J). 15.95 (978-0-86541-070-1(4)) Filter Pr., LLC.

Fishbone, Greg. The Penguins of Doom. 2007. (From the Desk of Septina Nash Ser.). (Illus.). 192p. (J). (gr. 3-9). 13.95 (*978-1-933831-03-9(0)*) Blooming Tree Pr.

Fisher, Catherine. Darkhenge. (J). 2007. 432p. pap. 7.99 (978-0-06-078584-0(5)); 2006. 352p. 15.99 (978-0-06-078582-6(9)) HarperCollins Pubs.

Fisher, Valorie. My Big Brother. Fisher, Valorie, photos by. 2002. (Illus.). 40p. (J). (ps-2). 15.95 (978-0-689-84327-3(5), Atheneum/Anne Schwartz Bks.) Simon & Schuster Children's Publishing.

Fitzgerald, John. Great Brain. 2006. 20.75 (978-0-8446-7293-9(9)) Smith, Peter Pub., Inc.

Fleischman, Sid. Disappearing Act. 2003. (Illus.). 144p. (J). (gr. 3 up). 15.99 (978-0-06-051962-9(2)); lib. bdg. 16.89 (978-0-06-051963-6(0)) HarperCollins Pubs.

Fleischman, Sid. The 13th Floor: A Ghost Story. Sis, Peter, illus. 2007. 240p. (J). pap. 5.99 (*978-0-06-134503-6(2)*, Harper Trophy) HarperCollins Pubs.

Fletcher, Ralph J. Tommy Trouble & the Magic Marble. Caldwell, Benjamin H., Jr., illus. rev. ed. 2000. 64p. (J). (gr. 2-5). 16.00 (978-0-8050-6387-5(0), Holt, Henry & Co. Bks. For Young Readers) Holt, Henry & Co.

—Tommy Trouble & the Magic Marble. Caldwell, Benjamin H., Jr., illus. 2002. 64p. pap. 3.99 (978-0-439-34048-9(9)) Scholastic, Inc.

Fletcher, Susan. Alphabet of Dreams. (YA). 2008. 432p. mass mkt. 6.99 (*978-0-689-85152-0(9)*, Simon Pulse); 2006. (Illus.). 304p. (gr. 7 up). 16.95 (978-0-689-85042-4(5), Atheneum) Simon & Schuster Children's Publishing.

Floyer, Edith S. The Young Huguenots. 1998. (Huguenots Inheritance Ser.). (J). (978-0-921100-65-2(5)) Inheritance Pubns.

Flynn, M. H. The Shadow City Ghost Hunters Vol. 1: The Mystery of Mapleshade Manor. 2006. 48p. pap. 12.95 (978-1-4241-2002-4(0)) PublishAmerica, Inc.

Forrester, Emma. Uncle Arthur's Art Studio. Nunn, Paul E., illus. 2008. (Spiderwick Chronicles). 48p. (J). 10.99 (*978-1-4169-4955-8(0)*, Simon Scribbles) Simon & Schuster Children's Publishing.

Forsberg, Crystal. Michael's Brothers. Hayes, John, illus. 1998. 16p. (J). (ps-k). pap. 5.95 (978-0-9655442-3-8(0)) Business Word, The.

Foster, Evelyn. The Mermaid of Cafur. Whelan, Olwyn, illus. 1999. 32p. (J). (gr. k-3). 15.95 (978-1-902283-40-1(6)) Barefoot Bks., Inc.

Fox, Paula. Gus Cara de Piedra. (SPA.). 128p. (J). (gr. 3-5). (978-84-279-3450-4(5), NG4694) Noguer y Caralt Editores, S. A. ESP. *Dist:* Lectorum Pubns., Inc.

—Radiance Descending. 1999. (978-0-606-17838-9(4)) Tandem Library Bks.

Franco, Betsy. Silly Sally Level 3. Lamb, Stacey, illus. 2002. (Rookie Readers Ser.). 24p. (J). (gr. k-1). 19.50 (978-0-516-22492-3(1), Children's Pr.) Scholastic Library Publishing.

Frank, E. R. Wrecked. 256p. (YA). (gr. 7 up). 2007. pap. 8.99 (978-0-689-87384-3(0), Simon Pulse); 2005. (Illus.). 16.99 (978-0-689-87383-6(2), Atheneum) Simon & Schuster Children's Publishing.

Franklin, Emily. The Other Half of Me. 2007. 256p. (YA). (gr. 9). 15.99 (*978-0-385-73445-5(X)*); lib. bdg. 18.99 (*978-0-385-90449-0(5)*) Random Hse. Children's Bks. (Delacorte Bks. for Young Readers).

Franklin, Kristine L. Dove Song. 2006. 192p. (J). (gr. 5-9). pap. 5.99 (978-0-7636-3219-9(8)) Candlewick Pr.

French, Jackie. Josephine Wants to Dance. Whatley, Bruce, illus. 2007. 32p. (J). (ps-1). 15.95 (*978-0-8109-9431-7(3)*, Abrams Bks. for Young Readers) Abrams, Harry N., Inc.

Freymann-Weyr, Garret. My Heartbeat. 2002. 160p. (YA). (gr. 7-12). 15.00 (978-0-618-14181-4(2)) Houghton Mifflin Co. Trade & Reference Div.

—When I Was Older. 2000. (Illus.). 176p. (YA). (gr. 5-9). tchr. ed. 15.00 (978-0-618-05545-6(2)) Houghton Mifflin Co. Trade & Reference Div.

—When I Was Older. l.t. ed. 2001. 159p. (J). 22.95 (978-0-7862-3546-9(2)) Thorndike Pr.

Friedrich, Joachim. 4 1/2 Friends & the Secret Cave, Bk. 1. Crawford, Elizabeth D., tr. from GER. 2001. (Illus.). 160p. (gr. 3-7). 14.99 (978-0-7868-0648-5(6)) Hyperion Bks. for Children.

Friend, Ronda. R. Friend Swallows Her Pride. 2005. (Down on Friendly Acres Ser.: 1). (J). lib. bdg. (978-0-9743627-3-1(5)) Sunflower Seeds Pr.

Friskey, Margaret. Surprise on Wheels. Patton, Lucia, illus. 2004. reprint ed. pap. 15.95 (978-1-4191-1496-0(4)) Kessinger Publishing, LLC.

Fromm, Pete. How All This Started: A Novel. 2001. (gr. 7-12). lib. bdg. 23.45 (978-0-613-45189-5(9)) Tandem Library Bks.

Funke, Cornelia. The Thief Lord. l.t. ed. 2005. 483p. (J). (gr. 4-7). pap. 10.95 (978-0-7862-8092-6(1)) Thorndike Pr.

—Thief Lord ('el Senor de Los Ladrones) 2007. 352p. (J). pap. 7.99 (*978-0-545-00517-3(5)*, Scholastic en Espanol) Scholastic, Inc.

Funke, Cornelia. The Wildest Brother. Latsch, Oliver, tr. from GER. Meyer, Kerstin, illus. 2006. 32p. (J). pap. 16.99 (978-0-439-82862-8(7), Chicken Hse., The) Scholastic, Inc.

Fuqua, Jonathon Scott. Willoughby Spit Wonder. 2004. (Illus.). 160p. (J). (gr. 5-8). 15.99 (978-0-7636-1776-9(8)) Candlewick Pr.

G de Guzman, Raquel. The Adventures of Eliseo & Stefano: My Daddy Can Fly! Guzman, Jacob, illus. 2006. 28p. (J). 16.95 (978-0-9788332-0-6(1)) Images and Pages.

Gaberman, Judith. A Home Is to Share...and Share...and Share... 2001. 164p. (J). (gr. 4-7). pap. 11.95 (978-0-595-15796-9(3), Backinprint.com) iUniverse, Inc.

Gabriel, Nat. Day with May. 2000. (ps-2). lib. bdg. 11.80 (978-0-613-24786-3(8)) Tandem Library Bks.

Gaiman, Neil. The Day I Swapped My Dad for Two Goldfish. McKean, Dave, illus. 2004. 64p. (J). 16.99 incl. audio compact disk (978-0-06-058701-7(6)) HarperCollins Pubs.

Gantos, Jack. Jack on the Tracks: Four Seasons of Fifth Grade. 1999. (Jack Henry Ser.). (Illus.). 192p. (J). (gr. 5-9). 16.00 (978-0-374-33665-3(2), Farrar, Straus & Giroux (BYR)) Farrar, Straus & Giroux.

—Jack on the Tracks: Four Seasons of Fifth Grade. 2001. (gr. 5-8). lib. bdg. 14.10 (978-0-613-85137-4(4)) Tandem Library Bks.

—Jack on the Tracks: Four Seasons of Fifth Grade. l.t. ed. 2002. 210p. (J). 22.95 (978-0-7862-4394-5(5)) Thorndike Pr.

Ganz, Yaffa. The Adventures of Jeremy & Heddy Levi. Katz, Avi, illus. 2005. 204p. (J). 16.95 (978-1-930143-50-0(8), 3508); pap. 12.95 (978-1-930143-51-7(6), 3516) Pitspopany Pr. (Devora Publishing).

Garcia, Maria. Las Aventuras de Connie y Diego. ed. 2004. (ENG & SPA., Illus.). (J). (gr. k-3). spiral bd. (978-0-616-14605-7(1)) Canadian National Institute for the Blind/Institut National Canadien pour les Aveugles.

Garfield, Henry. My Father the Werewolf. 2005. (Illus.). 240p. (J). (gr. 8-12). 17.95 (978-0-689-85180-3(4), Atheneum) Simon & Schuster Children's Publishing.

Garis, Howard Roger. The Curlytops on Star Island or Camping. 2006. 63.99 (*978-1-4280-0922-6(1)*); pap. 56.99 (*978-1-4280-0933-2(7)*) IndyPublish.com.

—Daddy Takes Us Skating. 2006. pap. 33.99 (*978-1-4219-7310-4(3)*) IndyPublish.com.

—Daddy Takes Us to the Garden. 2006. 77.99 (*978-1-4280-3218-7(5)*) IndyPublish.com.

Garner, Alan. The Weirdstone of Brisingamen: A Tale of Alderley. Call, Greg, illus. 2006. 288p. (J). pap. 6.95 (978-0-15-205636-0(X), Odyssey Classics) Harcourt Children's Bks.

Garren, Devorah-Leah. Shabbos Is Coming! We're Lost in the Zoo! Katz, Maya S., illus. 1999. 32p. (J). (ps-3). 12.95 (978-1-880582-32-9(5)) Judaica Pr., Inc., The.

Garrison, Terie. AutumnQuest. 2006. 192p. (YA). (gr. 7-9). pap. 8.95 (978-0-7387-0926-0(3), Flux) Llewellyn Pubns.

Garthwaite, Lynn D. Dirkle Smat Inside Mount Flatbottom. Howarth, Craig, illus. 2006. 48p. (J). pap. 9.95 (978-1-59663-512-8(6), Castle Keep Pr.) Rock, James A. & Co. Pubs.

Gauthier, Bertrand & Frischeteau, Gerard. De Tout Coeur, Ani Croche. 2000. (Roman Jeunesse Ser.). (FRE.). 96p. (J). (gr. 4-7). pap. (978-2-89021-427-9(3)) Diffusion du livre Mirabel.

Gay, Marie-Louise. Buenos Dias Samuel. 2004. (SPA.). (J). (gr. k up). pap. 7.99 (978-980-257-293-9(4)) Ekare, Ediciones VEN. *Dist:* Lectorum Pubns., Inc., Iaconi, Mariuccia Bk. Imports.

—Estela, Princesa de la Noche. 2006. Tr. of Stella Princess of the Sky. (SPA.). (J). (gr. 1-2). 10.99 (978-980-257-304-2(3), EK33231) Ekare, Ediciones VEN. *Dist:* Lectorum Pubns., Inc.

—Good Morning, Sam. Gay, Marie-Louise, illus. 2003. (Stella Ser.). (Illus.). 32p. (J). (ps-k). pap. 14.95 (978-0-88899-528-5(8)) Groundwood Bks. CAN. *Dist:* Perseus Distribution.

—Stella, Fairy of the Forest. ed. 2004. (Illus.). (J). (ps-2). spiral bd. (978-0-616-14580-7(2)); spiral bd. (978-0-616-14581-4(0)) Canadian National Institute for the Blind/Institut National Canadien pour les Aveugles.

—Stella, Fairy of the Forest. (Stella Ser.). (Illus.). 32p. (J). 2006. 7.95 (978-0-88899-710-4(8)); 2002. 15.95 (978-0-88899-448-6(6)) Groundwood Bks. CAN. *Dist:* Perseus Distribution.

—Stella, Princess of the Sky. 2007. (Stella Ser.). (Illus.). 32p. 7.95 (978-0-88899-749-4(3)) Groundwood Bks. CAN. *Dist:* Perseus Distribution.

—Stella, Queen of the Snow. ed. 2004. (J). (ps-1). spiral bd. (978-0-616-08493-9(5)) Canadian National Institute for the Blind/Institut National Canadien pour les Aveugles.

—Stella, Star of the Sea. 2004. (Illus.). (J). 7.95 (978-0-88899-572-8(5)) Groundwood Bks. CAN. *Dist:* Transition Vendor.

—Stella, Star of the Sea. Gay, Marie-Louise, illus. 1999. (Stella Ser.). (Illus.). 32p. (J). (ps-k). 15.95 (978-0-88899-337-3(4), Libros Tigrillo) Groundwood Bks. CAN. *Dist:* Perseus Distribution.

—What Are You Doing, Sam? 2006. (Illus.). 32p. 14.95 (978-0-88899-734-0(5)) Groundwood Bks. CAN. *Dist:* Perseus Distribution.

Geisert, Bonnie. Lessons. 2005. 192p. (J). (gr. 4-6). 15.00 (978-0-618-47899-6(X), Walter Lorraine) Houghton Mifflin Co. Trade & Reference Div.

George, Jean Craighead. Nutik, the Wolf Pup. Rand, Ted, illus. 2001. 40p. (J). (gr. k-3). 15.99 (978-0-06-028164-9(2)); lib. bdg. 17.89 (978-0-06-028165-6(0)) HarperCollins Pubs.

—Nutik, the Wolf Pup. 2000. 32p. (J). (gr. k-3). pap. 5.95 (978-0-06-443522-2(9)) HarperCollins Pubs.

—On the Far Side of the Mountain. 1999. (Illus.). 144p. (J). (gr. 4-7). 16.99 (978-0-525-46348-1(8), Dutton Juvenile) Penguin Group (USA) Inc.

—On the Far Side of the Mountain. 2001. (978-0-606-21366-0(X)) Tandem Library Bks.

Georgopolis, Annmarie H. An American flag for their Father. Spellman, Susan, illus. 2005. 80p. (J). per. 14.95 (978-1-933002-06-4(9)) PublishingWorks.

Getzinger, Donna. Special. 2004. 108p. (J). pap. 7.95 (978-0-87714-530-1(X)) Denlingers Pubs., Ltd.

Ghent, Natale. No Small Thing. 2005. 256p. (J). (gr. 5-9). 15.99 (978-0-7636-2422-4(5)) Candlewick Pr.

Gifaldi, David. Ben, King of the River. Johnson, Layne, illus. 2001. (Concept Book Ser.). 32p. (J). (gr. k-4). 15.95 (978-0-8075-0635-6(4)) Whitman, Albert & Co.

Giff, Patricia Reilly. Nory Ryan's Song. 2004. 160p. (J). (gr. 4-7). pap. 36.00 incl. audio (978-0-8072-2093-1(0), Listening Library) Random Hse. Audio Publishing Group.

—Nory Ryan's Song. 2002. 176p. (J). (gr. 3-7). pap. 5.99 (978-0-440-41829-0(1), Yearling) Random Hse. Children's Bks.

—Nory Ryan's Song. 2002. 148p. (J). (ps-7). per. 13.55 (978-0-613-57915-5(1)) Tandem Library Bks.

—Nory Ryan's Song. l.t. ed. 2001. 176p. (J). 23.95 (978-0-7862-3459-2(8)) Thorndike Pr.

Gifford, Peggy Elizabeth. Moxy Maxwell Does Not Love Writing Thank-You Notes. Fisher, Valorie, illus. Fisher, Valorie, photos by. 2008. (J). (*978-0-375-84270-2(5)); (*978-0-375-94552-6(0)) Random Hse. Children's Bks. (Schwartz & Wade Bks.).

Gingold, Katharine Kendzy. Ruth by Lake & Prairie: True Stories of Early Naperville, Illinois. 2006. (J). per. 12.95 (*978-0-9792419-0-1(1)) Gnu Ventures Co.

Giordano, Margaret A. The Bowditchers. 2006. 242p. per. 14.95 (*978-1-59824-406-9(X)) E-BookTime LLC.

Glass, Timothy. Sleepytown Beagles: Oh Brother! 2007. 24p. per. 13.95 (*978-1-59594-178-7(9) , Wingspan Pr.) WingSpan Publishing.

Gliori, Debi. Pure Dead Batty. 2007. (Illus.). 320p. (J). (gr. 4-7). 6.50 (*978-0-440-42074-3(1) , Yearling) Random Hse. Children's Bks.

Gliori, Debi. Where Did That Baby Come From? 2005. (Illus.). 32p. (J). 16.00 (978-0-15-205373-4(5)) Harcourt Children's Bks.

Gold, Becky. Phil & Lil Go to the Doctor. 2001. (gr. k-3). lib. bdg. 11.25 (978-0-613-43948-0(1)) Tandem Library Bks.

Goldsberry, Booty. Scaredy-Cat, I'm Not. 2007. (Illus.). 40p. pap. 9.95 (*978-0-9792875-0-3(2)) Goldsberry, Booty.

Gonzalez Bertrand, Diane. The Ruiz Street Kids (Los Muchachos de la Calle Ruiz) Baeza Ventura, Gabriela, tr. (ENG & SPA., Illus.). (J). pap. 9.95 (978-1-55885-321-8(9) , Piñata Books) Arte Publico Pr.

Good Night, Little Brother: Individual Title Six-Packs. (Literatura 2000 Ser.). (gr. 1-2). 28.00 (978-0-7635-0090-0(9)) Rigby Education.

Goodhart, Pippa. Ginny's Egg. Brouwer, Aafke, illus. 142p. (J). pap. 7.50 (978-0-7497-4557-8(6)) Egmont Bks., Ltd. GBR. *Dist:* Trafalgar Square Publishing.

Goodman, Joan. Bernard Wants a Baby. Catalano, Dominic, illus. 2004. 32p. (J). (ps up). 15.95 (978-1-59078-088-6(4)) Boyds Mills Pr.

Gordon, David. Hansel & Diesel. Gordon, David, illus. 2006. (Illus.). 32p. (J). 15.99 (978-0-06-058122-0(0) , Geringer, Laura Book); lib. bdg. 16.89 (978-0-06-058123-7(9)) HarperCollins Pubs.

—The Ugly Truckling. Gordon, David, illus. 2004. (Illus.). 32p. (J). (ps-2). lib. bdg. 16.89 (978-0-06-054601-4(8) , Geringer, Laura Book) HarperCollins Pubs.

Gorges, Julie A. Just Call Me Goody-Two-Shoes. 2006. 146p. (YA). per. 9.95 (978-0-9763274-1-7(4)) I.Form Ink, Pub.

Goudge, Elizabeth. Linnets & Valerians. 2001. 256p. (J). pap. 6.99 (978-0-14-230026-8(8) , Puffin) Penguin Group (USA) Inc.

Graham, Bob. Dimity Dumpty: The Story of Humpty's Little Sister. 2007. (Illus.). 40p. (J). (ps). 15.99 (978-0-7636-3078-2(0)) Candlewick Pr.

Graham, Richard. Jack y el Monstruo. Varley, Susan, illus. (Cotton Cloud Ser.). (SPA.). 32p. (J). (gr. 1-3). (978-84-7722-680-2(6)) Timun Mas, Editorial S.A. ESP. *Dist:* Lectorum Pubns., Inc.

Graham, Wendy. High Jinx: Sloanes Beach, Skateboard Hero, Rock on, Bearded Toad. 2005. (Triple Play Ser.). (Illus.). 48p. (gr. 4-8). 41.85 (978-0-7910-9074-9(4)) Facts On File, Inc.

Grahame, Kenneth. Dream Days. Shepard, Ernest H., illus. 2001. (Company of Books Ser.). 163p. (YA). 22.95 (978-1-58579-018-0(4) , Common Reader Editions) Akadine Pr., The.

Grahame, Kenneth. Golden Age. 2006. pap. (*978-1-4068-3332-4(0)) Echo Library.

Grant, K. M. Green Jasper. 2006. 256p. (J). 16.95 (978-0-8027-8073-7(3)) Walker & Co.

Gray, Luli. The Timespinners. 2003. 160p. (J). (gr. 5-9). tchr. ed. 15.00 (978-0-618-16412-7(X)) Houghton Mifflin Co. Trade & Reference Div.

Green, Lucyna A. M., illus. Love You Little Brother. 2006. (J). (*978-1-58669-186-8(4)); (*978-1-58669-185-1(6)) Childcraft Education Corp.

Greenburg, Dan. Attack of the Evil Elvises. Pamintuan, Macky, illus. 2007. (Weird Planet Ser.: No. 4). 96p. (J). (gr. 2-4). lib. bdg. 11.99 (978-0-375-93347-9(6)); 3.99 (978-0-375-83347-2(1)) Random Hse. Children's Bks. (Random Hse. Bks. for Young Readers).

—Attack of the Giant Octopus. Fischer, Scott M., illus. 2007. (Secrets of Dripping Fang Ser.: Bk. 6). 160p. (J). 9.95 (978-0-15-206041-1(3)) Harcourt Children's Bks.

—Chilling with the Great Ones. Pamintuan, Macky, illus. 2006. 96p. (J). (gr. 2-5). lib. bdg. 11.99 (978-0-375-93346-2(8)); (Weird Planet Ser.: No. 3). (gr. 1-4). pap. 3.99 (978-0-375-83346-5(3)) Random Hse. Children's Bks. (Random Hse. Bks. for Young Readers).

—Fall of the House of Mandible. Fischer, Scott M., illus. 2006. (Outrageously Funny Ser.: Bk. 4). 160p. (J). 9.95 (978-0-15-205475-5(8)) Harcourt Children's Bks.

—The Onts. Fischer, Scott M., illus. 2006. (Secrets of Dripping Fang Ser.: Bk. 1). 144p. (J). 2.99 (978-0-15-205995-8(4) , Harcourt Paperbacks) Harcourt Children's Bks.

—Please Don't Eat the Children. Fischer, Scott M., illus. 2007. (Secrets of Dripping Fang Ser.: Bk. 7). 160p. (J). 9.95 (978-0-15-206047-3(2)) Harcourt Children's Bks.

—Treachery & Betrayal at Jolly Days. Fischer, Scott M., illus. 2006. (Secrets of Dripping Fang Ser.: Bk. 2). 144p. (J). 9.95 (978-0-15-205463-2(4)) Harcourt Children's Bks.

—Weird Planet: Lights, Camera... Liftoff! Pamintuan, Macky, illus. 2007. (Weird Planet Ser.: No. 5). 96p. (J). (gr. 2-5). pap. 3.99 (*978-0-375-84336-5(1) , Random Hse. Bks. for Young Readers) Random Hse. Children's Bks.

—Weird Planet No. 5: Lights, Camera... Liftoff! Pamintuan, Macky, illus. 2007. (Stepping Stone Bks.). 96p. (J). (gr. 2-5). lib. bdg. 11.99 (*978-0-375-94336-2(6) , Random Hse. Bks. for Young Readers) Random Hse. Children's Bks.

Greenburg, Dan & Diterlizzi, Angela. The Vampire's Curse. Fischer, Scott M., illus. 2006. (Secrets of Dripping Fang Ser.: Bk. 3). 144p. (J). 9.95 (978-0-15-205469-4(3)) Harcourt Children's Bks.

Greenfield, Eloise. She Come Bringing Me That Little Baby Girl. Steptoe, John, illus. 1999. (J). (ps-ps). lib. bdg. 15.25 (978-0-7857-0466-9(3)) Tandem Library Bks.

Gregory, Kristiana. Cabin Creek Mysteries #1 Secret of Robber's Cave. 2008. (Cabin Creek Mysteries Ser.). 192p. (J). pap. 4.99 (*978-0-439-92950-9(4) , Scholastic Paperbacks) Scholastic, Inc.

—Cabin Creek Mysteries #2 Clue at the Bottom Lake. 2008. (Cabin Creek Mysteries Ser.). 176p. (J). pap. 4.99 (*978-0-439-92951-6(2) , Scholastic Paperbacks) Scholastic, Inc.

Gregory, Nan. I'll Sing You One-O. 2006. 224p. (J). (gr. 4-6). 16.00 (978-0-618-60708-2(0) , Clarion Bks.) Houghton Mifflin Co. Trade & Reference Div.

Gregory, Valiska. Shirley's Wonderful Baby. Degen, Bruce, illus. 32p. (ps-2). 2002. (J). 14.99 (978-0-06-028132-8(4)); 1999. pap. 5.95 (978-0-06-443513-0(X)) HarperCollins Pubs.

Griffin, Adele. Rainy Season. 1998. (978-0-606-13726-3(2)) Tandem Library Bks.

Griffin, Claire Janosik. Kidding Around. Wright, Jane Chambless, illus. 2000. (Rollicking Rhymes Ser.). 20p. (J). (gr. k-1). 3.99 (978-1-56822-978-2(X) , IF40212-E4, Instructional Fair) Schaffer, Frank Pubns.

Griffin, Peni R. The Ghost Sitter. (J). 2002. 144p. pap. 5.99 (978-0-14-230216-3(3) , Puffin); 2001. (Illus.). 128p. (gr. 4-6). 14.99 (978-0-525-46676-5(2) , Dutton Juvenile) Penguin Group (USA) Inc.

—The Ghost Sitter. 2002. (gr. 3-6). lib. bdg. 14.15 (978-0-613-53815-2(3)) Tandem Library Bks.

Griffith, Helen V. Dinosaur Habitat. 1999. (Avon Camelot Bks.). (Illus.). 112p. (J). (gr. 3-7). pap. 4.95 (978-0-380-73225-8(4)) HarperCollins Pubs.

—Dinosaur Habitat. 1999. (J). (978-0-606-17327-8(7)) Tandem Library Bks.

Grigsby, Cynthia. Hollow Creek: A Haunted Beginning, 01. 2006. 163p. (J). 14.95 (978-0-9786840-0-6(1)) Grigsby, Cynthia.

Grimes, Nikki. The Road to Paris. 2008. 160p. (J). (gr. 3). 6.99 (*978-0-14-241082-0(9) , Puffin) Penguin Group (USA) Inc.

Grindley, Sally. Hurricane Wills. 2008. 250p. (J). pap. 8.95 (*978-0-7475-9095-8(8)) Bloomsbury Publishing Plc GBR. *Dist:* Independent Pubs. Group.

Grindley, Sally. It's My School. Chamberlain, Margaret, illus. 2006. 32p. (J). 15.95 (978-0-8027-8086-7(5)) Walker & Co.

Gritton, Steve. ... & Then I... 2007. (J). 17.95 (*978-0-9795361-1-3(1)) Bad Frog Art/SMG Bks.

Grove, Vicki. Destiny. 2001. 12.64 (978-0-606-22525-0(0)) Tandem Library Bks.

Gruber, Wilhelm. Tomas Lee Al Reves. 2000. (SPA.). (gr. 3-6). lib. bdg. 14.10 (978-0-613-27279-7(X)) Tandem Library Bks.

—Upside-down Reader. 2000. (gr. 3-6). lib. bdg. 14.10 (978-0-613-28688-6(X)) Tandem Library Bks.

Gunn, Robin Jones. Without a Doubt. 1998. (Sierra Jensen Ser.: Bk. 5). 160p. (YA). (gr. 7-11). pap. (978-1-56179-519-2(4)) Focus on the Family Publishing.

Gutierrez, Akemi. The Mummy & Other Adventures of Sam & Alice. 2005. (Illus.). 64p. (J). (gr. k-3). 16.00 (978-0-618-50761-0(2)) Houghton Mifflin Co. Trade & Reference Div.

—The Pirate & Other Adventures of Sam & Alice. Gutierrez, Akemi, illus. 2007. (Illus.). 64p. (J). (gr. k-3). 17.00 (978-0-618-73737-6(5)) Houghton Mifflin Co.

Gutman, Dan. The Edison Mystery: Back in Time. 2002. (Illus.). 201p. lib. bdg. 13.00 (978-0-613-62098-7(4)) Tandem Library Bks.

—The Million Dollar Goal. 2nd ed. 2006. 176p. (J). (gr. 3-7). pap. 5.99 (978-1-4231-0083-6(2)) Hyperion Pr.

Guy, Ginger Foglesong. Siesta. Moreno, Rene King, illus. 2005. (ENG & SPA.). 32p. (J). lib. bdg. 16.89 (978-0-06-056063-8(0)); 15.99 (978-0-06-056061-4(4)) HarperCollins Pubs.

Haarsma, P. J. The Softwire: Virus on Orbis 1. 2008. (Illus.). 288p. (J). (gr. 5). 6.99 (*978-0-7636-3638-8(X)) Candlewick Pr.

Haas, Dan. You Can Call Me Worm. 1999. (978-0-606-16790-1(0)) Tandem Library Bks.

Haddix, Margaret Peterson. Among the Barons. (Shadow Children Ser.). (J). (gr. 3-7). 2003. 192p. 16.95 (978-0-689-83906-1(5)); 2004. 208p. reprint ed. pap. 5.99 (978-0-689-83910-8(3) , Aladdin) Simon & Schuster Children's Publishing.

Hahn, Mary Downing. As Ever, Gordy. 1998. 192p. (YA). (gr. 7-9). tchr. ed. 15.00 (978-0-395-83627-9(1) , Clarion Bks.) Houghton Mifflin Co. Trade & Reference Div.

—As Ever, Gordy. 2000. (gr. 5-8). lib. bdg. 14.15 (978-0-613-28405-9(4)) Tandem Library Bks.

—Deep & Dark & Dangerous: A Ghost Story. 2007. 192p. (J). (gr. 5-9). 16.00 (*978-0-618-66545-7(5) , Clarion Bks.) Houghton Mifflin Co. Trade & Reference Div.

—Hear the Wind Blow. 2003. (Illus.). 224p. (J). (gr. 5-9). tchr. ed. 16.00 (978-0-618-18190-2(3) , Clarion Bks.) Houghton Mifflin Co. Trade & Reference Div.

Hahn, Mary Downing. The Old Willis Place: A Ghost Story. 208p. (gr. 4-7). 2007. (J). pap. 5.95 (*978-0-618-89741-4(0)); 2004. (Illus.). (YA). 16.00 (978-0-618-43018-5(0)) Houghton Mifflin Co. Trade & Reference Div. (Clarion Bks.).

Haig, Matt. Samuel Blink & the Forbidden Forest. 2007. 352p. (J). 16.99 (978-0-399-24739-2(4) , Putnam Juvenile) Penguin Group (USA) Inc.

Haislip, Phyllis Hall. Lili's Gift: A Civil War Healer's Story. 2007. (Illus.). (J). pap. 8.95 (*978-1-57249-392-6(5) , White Mane Kids) White Mane Publishing Co., Inc.

Hale, Bruce. Pirates of Underwhere. Hillman, Shane, illus. 2008. (Underwhere Ser.). 160p. (J). 15.99 (*978-0-06-085127-9(9)); lib. bdg. 16.89 (*978-0-06-085128-6(7)) HarperCollins Pubs.

—Prince of Underwhere. Hillman, Shane, illus. 2008. (Underwhere Ser.). 176p. (J). lib. bdg. 16.89 (*978-0-06-085125-5(2)); (gr. 3-7). 15.99 (*978-0-06-085124-8(4)) HarperCollins Pubs.

Hall, Kirsten. My New School. Gott, Barry, tr. Gott, Barry, illus. 2004. (My First Reader Ser.). 31p. (J). 18.50 (978-0-516-24413-6(2) , Children's Pr.) Scholastic Library Publishing.

Hallinan, P. K. We're Very Good Friends, My Brother & I. 2001. (Illus.). 24p. (J). (ps-3). 5.95 (978-0-8249-5387-4(8)) Ideals Pubns.

Hank Zipzer: World's Best Underachiever. 2006. (J). (gr. 3-8). 217.89 (978-1-59961-101-3(5)) Spotlight.

Hansel et Gretel.Tr. of Hansel & Gretel. (FRE.). 48p. pap. 12.95 incl. audio compact disk (978-2-89558-055-3(3)) Coffragants CAN. *Dist:* Penton Overseas, Inc.

Hansen, Joyce. One True Friend. Giblin, James Cross, ed. 2001. 160p. (J). (gr. 5-9). tchr. ed. 14.00 (978-0-395-84983-5(7) , Clarion Bks.) Houghton Mifflin Co. Trade & Reference Div.

Hanson, Anders. Whale Tale. Nobens, C. A., illus. 2007. (Fact & Fiction Ser.). 24p. (J). pap. (978-1-59928-477-4(4)); 21.35 (978-1-59928-476-7(6)) ABDO Publishing Co.

Hapka, Cathy & Titlebaum, Ellen. How Not to Babysit Your Brother. Palen, Debbie, illus. 2005. (Step into Reading Ser.). 48p. (J). (gr. 2-4). pap. 3.99 (978-0-375-82856-0(7) , Random Hse. Bks. for Young Readers) Random Hse. Children's Bks.

Hapka, Cathy & Titlebaum, Ellen. How Not to Start Third Grade. Palen, Debbie, illus. 2007. (Step into Reading Ser.). 48p. (J). (gr. 2-4). 3.99 (*978-0-375-83904-7(6)); lib. bdg. 11.99 (*978-0-375-93904-4(0)) Random Hse. Children's Bks. (Random Hse. Bks. for Young Readers).

Harcourt School Publishers Staff. Are You There, Baby Bear: Library Book. 3rd ed. 2002. (Trophies Reading Program Ser.). (Illus.). pap. 13.50 (978-0-15-326529-7(9)) Harcourt Schl. Pubs.

—The Autumn of the Earthquake Below Level. 3rd ed. 2002. (Trophies Reading Program Ser.). (Illus.). pap. 5.10 (978-0-15-323407-1(5)) Harcourt Schl. Pubs.

—Basement Basketball On Level. 3rd ed. 2002. (Trophies Reading Program Ser.). (Illus.). pap. 5.10 (978-0-15-323164-3(5)) Harcourt Schl. Pubs.

—El Camino a Casa On Level. 3rd ed. 2002. (Trofeos Ser.).Tr. of Road Home. (SPA.). pap. 6.80 (978-0-15-324082-9(2)) Harcourt Schl. Pubs.

—I Swam with a Seal Little Book. 3rd ed. 2002. (Trophies Reading Program Ser.). (Illus.). (J). pap. 10.20 (978-0-15-329364-1(0)) Harcourt Schl. Pubs.

—Looking for Clues Advanced Level. 3rd ed. 2002. (Trophies Reading Program Ser.). (Illus.). pap. 5.10 (978-0-15-323036-3(3)) Harcourt Schl. Pubs.

—The Piano Piece On Level. 3rd ed. 2002. (Trophies Reading Program Ser.). (Illus.). pap. 5.10 (978-0-15-323172-8(6)) Harcourt Schl. Pubs.

—Shipwrecked! Take-Home Book. 2001. (Collections Ser.). (Illus.). (J). pap. 1.90 (978-0-15-319522-8(3)) Harcourt Schl. Pubs.

—Shipwrecked Below Level. 3rd ed. 2002. (Trophies Reading Program Ser.). (Illus.). pap. 5.10 (978-0-15-323320-3(6)) Harcourt Schl. Pubs.

—Silent Observer Level D: Reader. 2001. (Collections Ser.). (Illus.). (J). 5.90 (978-0-15-314376-2(2)) Harcourt Schl. Pubs.

—Trofeos Advanced Level: Aqui, Hay el Pista. 3rd ed. 2002. (SPA., Illus.). pap. 6.80 (978-0-15-323947-2(6)) Harcourt Schl. Pubs.

—Trofeos On Level: La Serie de los Subterraneos. 3rd ed. 2002. (SPA., Illus.). pap. 6.80 (978-0-15-324085-0(7)) Harcourt Schl. Pubs.

Harley, Bill. Dirty Joe, the Pirate: A True Story. Davis, Jack E., illus. 2008. 32p. (J). 16.99 (*978-0-06-623780-0(7)); lib. bdg. 17.89 (*978-0-06-623781-7(5)) HarperCollins Pubs.

Harmon, Michael. Skate. 2008. 256p. (J). (gr. 9). mass mkt. 6.50 (*978-0-553-49510-2(0) , Laurel Leaf) Random Hse. Children's Bks.

Harness, Cheryl. Just for You to Know. 2008. (J). pap. (*978-0-06-078315-0(X)) HarperCollins Pubs.

Harper, Anita. It's Not Fair! McQuillan, Mary, illus. 2007. 32p. (J). (ps-k). 16.95 (*978-0-8234-2094-0(9)) Holiday Hse., Inc.

Harper, Jamie. Night Night, Baby Bundt: A Recipe for Bedtime. Harper, Jamie, illus. 2007. (Illus.). 24p. (J). (gr. k-ps). bds. 6.99 (*978-0-7636-3239-7(2)) Candlewick Pr.

—Splish Splash, Baby Bundt: A Recipe for Bath Time. Harper, Jamie, illus. 2007. (Illus.). 24p. (J). (gr. k-ps). bds. 6.99 (*978-0-7636-3240-3(6)) Candlewick Pr.

Harper, Jessica. Jessie's Small Disaster. Berkeley, Jon, illus. 2008. 64p. (J). (gr. 1). 14.99 (*978-0-399-24671-5(1) , Putnam Juvenile) Penguin Group (USA) Inc.

Harper, Meg. My Mum & the Green Eyed Monster. 2006. (My Mum Ser.). 160p. (J). pap. 8.99 (*978-0-7459-4993-2(2)) Lion Hudson plc GBR. *Dist:* Independent Pubs. Group.

Harper, Meg. My Mum & the Gruesome Twosome. 160p. pap. 9.99 (978-0-7459-4829-4(4)); 2001. 144p. pap. 7.50 (978-0-7459-4567-5(8)) Lion Hudson plc GBR. (Lion). *Dist:* Trafalgar Square Publishing.

Harris, Diantha S. Sad Sandwiches. Carson, Sandy, illus. 2005. (ENG.). 28p. (J). per. (*978-1-4208-4694-2(9)) AuthorHouse.

Harris, Dorothy Joan. Cameron & Me. ed. 2004. (Illus.). (J). (gr. k-3). spiral bd. (978-0-616-01667-1(0)); spiral bd. (978-0-616-01668-8(9)) Canadian National Institute for the Blind/Institut National Canadien pour les Aveugles.

Hartnett, Sonya. Surrender. 2006. 256p. (YA). (gr. 9). 16.99 (978-0-7636-2768-3(2)) Candlewick Pr.

Harvey, Ken. Brothers of the Storm: A Tale of Boys Born to Fight. 2007. pr. per. 10.99 (*978-1-59886-676-6(1)) Tate Publishing & Enterprises, L.L.C.

Hasler, E. & Bhend, K. Tale of Two Brothers. 2006. (Illus.). 40p. (J). 16.95 (978-0-7358-2102-6(X)) North-South Bks., Inc.

Hathaway, Lucinda. Takashi's Voyage: The Wreck of the Sindia. DiPiazza, Ellen & Ganss, Leslee, illus. 2005. 107p. (gr. 4-7). (978-0-945582-24-3(2)) Down The Shore Publishing.

Hatton, Caroline K. Vero & Philippe. McDaniels, Preston, illus. 2001. 144p. (J). (gr. 3-7). 14.95 (978-0-8126-2940-8(X)) Cricket Bks.

Hauger, Torill Thorstad. Escape from the Vikings. Hamnes, Lisa, ed. Born, Anne, tr. from NOR. Hauger, Torill Thorstad, illus. 2000. Orig. Title: Flukten Fra Vikingene. (Illus.). 175p. (J). (gr. 4-12). pap. (978-1-57534-013-5(5)) Skandisk, Inc.

Hawkins-Walsh, Elizabeth & Pierson-Solís, Lennard. Katie's Premature Brother = el Hermano Prematuro de Katie. Blake, Anne Catharine, illus. 2006. (J). (978-1-56123-197-3(5)) Centering Corp.

Hawley, C. Mabel. Four Little Blossoms & Their Winter Fu. 2006. 77.99 (*978-1-4280-4760-0(3)); pap. 70.99 (*978-1-4280-4769-3(7)) IndyPublish.com.

—Four Little Blossoms on Apple Tree Islan. 2006. 24.99 (*978-1-4280-1723-8(2)) IndyPublish.com.

Hayes, Rosemary. Bright Horizon. 2004. (J). pap. 11.95 (978-0-340-85471-6(5) , Hodder & Stoughton) Hodder General Publishing Division GBR. *Dist:* Trafalgar Square Publishing.

—To the Edge of the Ocean. 2004. (J). pap. 9.95 (978-0-340-85470-9(7) , Hodder & Stoughton) Hodder General Publishing Division GBR. *Dist:* Trafalgar Square Publishing.

—Troubled Waters, 3 vols., Vol. 1. 2004. (J). mass mkt. 9.95 (978-0-340-85469-3(3) , Hodder & Stoughton) Hodder General Publishing Division GBR. *Dist:* Trafalgar Square Publishing.

Hayward, Linda. Monster Bug. Palmisciano, Diane, illus. 2004. 32p. (J). lib. bdg. 20.00 (*978-1-4242-1097-8(6)) Fitzgerald Bks.

Haywood, Carolyn. Here's a Penny. 2005. (Illus.). 160p. (J). pap. 5.95 (978-0-15-205225-6(9) , Odyssey Classics) Harcourt Children's Bks.

Hearne, Betsy. Wishes, Kisses, & Pigs. 2003. 144p. (J). pap. 4.99 (978-0-689-86347-9(0) , Aladdin) Simon & Schuster Children's Publishing.

—Wishes, Kisses, & Pigs. 2003. (gr. 3-6). lib. bdg. 13.00 (978-0-613-70812-8(1)) Tandem Library Bks.

Hegeman, Andrew. The Last Dinosaur Egg. Hegeman, Andrew, illus. 1998. (Illus.). 36p. (J). (ps-3). 15.95 (978-1-890817-04-6(X)) Winslow Pr.

Hegg, Tom & Hanson, Warren. Peef & the Baby Sister. Hegg, Tom & Hanson, Warren, illus. 2006. (J). (978-0-931674-67-9(0)) Waldman Hse. Pr., Inc.

Hendry, Frances. Quest for a Queen: The Jackdaw. 2006. pap. (*978-1-905665-05-1(9)) Pollinger In Print.

Henkes, Kevin. Sheila Rae's Peppermint Stick. Henkes, Kevin, illus. 2001. (Illus.). 24p. (J). (ps up). 6.99 (978-0-06-029451-9(5) , Harper Festival) HarperCollins Pubs.

—Sheila Rae's Peppermint Stick Book & Finger Puppet. Henkes, Kevin, illus. 2003. (Illus.). 24p. (J). 10.99 (978-0-06-054078-4(8) , Harper Festival) HarperCollins Pubs.

Hennessy, Claire. Afterwards. 2005. 188p. (YA). pap. (*978-1-84223-207-1(X)) Poolbeg Pr.

Henry, Marguerite. Misty de Chincoteague. 2001. (978-0-606-22665-3(6)) Tandem Library Bks.

—Misty of Chincoteague. 2002. (Illus.). (J). 13.40 (978-0-7587-0291-3(4)) Book Wholesalers, Inc.

—Misty of Chincoteague. Dennis, Wesley, illus. 2006. 176p. (J). pap. 5.99 (978-1-4169-2783-9(2) , Aladdin) Simon & Schuster Children's Publishing.

Henry, Panya A. Francis' Fear of Flying. 2006. (ENG.). 40p. per. 24.95 (*978-1-4259-3162-9(6)) AuthorHouse.

Henry, Steve. Nobody Asked Me! 2001. (Illus.). 32p. (J). (ps-k). 14.95 (978-0-688-17865-9(0)) HarperCollins Pubs.

Herman, Gail. Buried in the Back Yard. Smath, Jerry, illus. 2003. (Science Solves It! Ser.). 32p. (J). 4.99 (978-1-57565-126-2(2)) Kane Pr., The.

—Buried in the Back Yard. Smath, Jerry, illus. 2003. 32p. (J). (ps-3). lib. bdg. 13.00 (978-0-613-79274-5(2)) Tandem Library Bks.

—The Creeping Tide. Nez, John, illus. 2003. (Science Solves It! Ser.). 32p. (J). 4.99 (978-1-57565-128-6(9)) Kane Pr., The.

—Spike at Halloween. 2002. (ps-2). lib. bdg. 11.80 (978-0-613-64113-5(2)) Tandem Library Bks.

Hermes, Patricia. Emma Dilemma & the Two Nannies. 2007. (J). 112p. (gr. 2-4). 15.99 (*978-0-7614-5353-6(9)); 117p. (*978-1-4287-3961-1(0)) Cavendish, Marshall Corp.

Hermes, Patricia. Everything Stinks. MacDonald, Patricia, ed. 1999. (Cousins' Club Ser.). 176p. (J). 14.00 (978-0-671-89653-9(9) , Simon & Schuster Children's Publishing) Simon & Schuster Children's Publishing.

Hernandez, David. Suckerpunch. 2008. 224p. (J). 16.99 (*978-0-06-117330-1(4)); lib. bdg. 17.89 (*978-0-06-117331-8(2)) HarperCollins Pubs. (HarperTeen).

Herrick, Steven. By the River. 2006. 240p. (YA). 16.95 (978-1-932425-72-7(1) , Lemniscaat) Boyds Mills Pr.

Herron, Carolivia, photos by & adapted by. Little Georgia & the Apples: A Retelling of Aunt Georgia's First Catalpa Tale, Herron, Carolivia, adapted by. l.t. ed. 2004. (Illus.). 33p. (J). 10.00 (978-0-9760222-0-6(6) , Catalpa01) Epicenter Literary Software.

Hershenhorn, Esther. Fancy That. Lloyd, Megan, illus. 2003. 32p. (J). (gr. k-3). tchr. ed. 16.95 (978-0-8234-1605-9(4)) Holiday Hse., Inc.

Hicks, Betty. Out of Order. 2005. 176p. (J). (ps-7). 16.95 (978-1-59643-061-7(3)) Roaring Brook Pr.

—Out of Order. 2007. 176p. (J). pap. 6.99 (*978-0-312-37355-9(4)) Square Fish.

Hicks, John. Divided World. 2003. 192p. (YA). per. 6.50 (978-0-9742829-1-6(X)) Quiet Man Publishing.

Hill, Kirkpatrick. Toughboy & Sister. 2000. 128p. (J). (gr. 3-7). pap. 9.95 (978-0-689-83978-8(2) , Aladdin) Simon & Schuster Children's Publishing.

Hill, Laban Carrick. Casa Azul: An Encounter with Frida Kahlo. 2005. (Art Encounters Ser.). (Illus.). 160p. (YA). 15.95 (978-0-8230-0411-9(2)) Watson-Guptill Pubns., Inc.

Hines, Anna Grossnickle. Got You! 2001. (gr. k-3). lib. bdg. 12.95 (978-0-613-54521-1(4)) Tandem Library Bks.

Hinton, S. E. Rumble Fish. 2006. 21.50 (978-0-8446-7283-0(1)) Smith, Peter Pub., Inc.

Hoban, Lillian. Arthur's Birthday Party. Hoban, Lillian, illus. 1999. (I Can Read Bks.). (Illus.). 64p. (J). (ps-3). 14.95 (978-0-06-027798-7(X)) HarperCollins Pubs.

Hobbs, Valerie. Sonny's War. 2002. 224p. (YA). (gr. 7 up). 16.00 (978-0-374-37136-4(9) , Farrar, Straus & Giroux (BYR)) Farrar, Straus & Giroux.

—Sonny's War. 2006. 224p. (YA). pap. 7.95 (978-0-374-46970-2(9)) Macmillan.

Hobbs, William. Jackie's Wild Seattle. 208p. (J). (gr. 5 up). 2004. pap. 5.99 (978-0-380-73311-8(0) , Harper Trophy); 2003. 16.99 (978-0-688-17474-3(4)); 2003. lib. bdg. 16.89 (978-0-06-051631-4(3)) HarperCollins Pubs.

Hoberman, Mary Ann. The Seven Silly Eaters. Frazee, Marla, illus. 2000. 40p. (J). (ps-3). pap. 7.00 (978-0-15-202440-6(9) , Voyager Bks./Libros Viajeros) Harcourt Children's Bks.

—Seven Silly Eaters. 2000. (ps-2). lib. bdg. 14.15 (978-0-613-30122-0(6)) Tandem Library Bks.

—The Seven Silly Eaters. Frazee, Marla, illus. ed. 2004. (J). (gr. k-3). spiral bd. (978-0-616-14576-0(4)) Canadian National Institute for the Blind/Institut National Canadien pour les Aveugles.

Hoffman, Alice. Indigo. 2003. (gr. 5-8). lib. bdg. 13.00 (978-0-613-67496-6(0)) Tandem Library Bks.

Hoffmann, E. T. A. El Cascanueces. 2000. (SPA., Illus.). 32p. (J). (gr. k-2). 4.95 (978-84-392-8305-8(9)) Lectorum Pubns., Inc.

Holcomb, Jerry K. The Chinquapin Tree. 1998. (Accelerated Reader Bks.). 192p. (J). (gr. 3-7). 14.95 (978-0-7614-5028-3(9) , Cavendish Children's Bks.) Cavendish, Marshall Corp.

Holeman, Linda. Search of the Moon King's Daughter. 2003. (gr. 7-12). lib. bdg. 18.75 (978-0-613-77367-6(5)) Tandem Library Bks.

—Search of the Moon King's Daughter. 2003. 320p. (J). (gr. 6). pap. 9.95 (978-0-88776-609-1(9)) Tundra Bks., Inc./Livres Toundra, Inc. CAN. *Dist:* Random Hse., Inc.

Holm, Jennifer L. Our Only May Amelia. (Harper Trophy Bks.). (Illus.). (J). 2001. 272p. (gr. 4 up). pap. 5.99 (978-0-06-440856-1(6) , Harper Trophy); 1999. 253p. (gr. k-9). per. 15.89 (978-0-06-028354-4(8)); 1999. 272p. (gr. 4 up). 18.99 (978-0-06-027822-9(6)) HarperCollins Pubs.

—Our Only May Amelia. unabr. ed. 2004. 253p. (J). (gr. 5-9). pap. 36.00 incl. audio (978-0-8072-8366-0(5) , YA191SP, Listening Library) Random Hse. Audio Publishing Group.

—Our Only May Amelia. 2001. (Illus.). 251p. (J). (gr. k-9). lib. bdg. 14.15 (978-0-613-35995-5(X)) Tandem Library Bks.

—Our Only May Amelia. l.t. ed. 2000. (Illus.). 261p. (J). (ps up). 21.95 (978-0-7862-2742-6(7)) Thorndike Pr.

Holman, T. A. Stop It, Tyrone! (Illus.). 42p. (J). (gr. k-4). pap. 7.50 (978-0-9660617-1-0(3)) PLEO.

Hood, Karen Jean Matsko. Lost Medal. 2006. (J). spiral bd. 22.95 (978-1-59434-757-3(3)); cd-rom 24.95 (978-1-59434-760-3(3)); spiral bd. 22.95 (978-1-59434-756-6(5)) Whispering Pine Pr., Inc.

Hooks, William H. The Legend of the Christmas Rose. 1999. (Illus.). 32p. (J). (gr. k-4). 14.95 (978-0-06-027102-2(7)); 14.89 (978-0-06-027103-9(5)) HarperCollins Pubs.

—Mr. Big Brother. Duke, Kate, illus. 1999. (Bank Street Reader Collection). (J). (ps-2). lib. bdg. 22.60 (978-0-8368-2417-9(2)) Stevens, Gareth Inc.

—Mr. Monster. Meisel, Paul, illus. 1998. (Bank Street Reader Collection). 48p. (J). (gr. 2-4). lib. bdg. (978-0-8368-1774-4(5)) Stevens, Gareth Inc.

Hope, Laura. Bunny Brown & His Sister Sue Giving A. 2006. pap. 14.95 (*978-1-55742-655-0(4)) Wildside Pr.

Hope, Laura Lee. Bunny Brown & His Sister Sue. 2005. 188p. pap. 11.95 (978-1-4218-1165-9(0) , 1st World Library - Literary Society) 1st World Publishing, Inc.

—Bunny Brown & His Sister Sue. 2006. 63.99 (*978-1-4280-2447-2(6)) IndyPublish.com.

—Bunny Brown & his Sister Sue. 2006. 144p. pap. 10.99 (978-1-4264-1980-5(5)) BiblioBazaar.

—Bunny Brown & His Sister Sue. l.t. ed. 2006. 138p. pap. 13.99 (978-1-4264-2091-7(9)) BiblioBazaar.

—Bunny Brown & His Sister Sue Giving A. 2006. 41.99 (*978-1-4280-1491-6(8)); pap. 35.99 (*978-1-4280-1478-7(0)) IndyPublish.com.

—Bunny Brown & His Sister Sue Keeping S. 2006. 95.99 (*978-1-4280-2906-4(0)); pap. 89.99 (*978-1-4280-2908-8(7)) IndyPublish.com.

—Bunny Brown & His Sister Sue Keeping Store. 2006. 142p. pap. 10.99 (*978-1-4264-5200-0(4)); 160p. pap. 14.99 (*978-1-4264-5501-8(1)) BiblioBazaar.

—Freddie & Flossie. Pyle, Chuck, illus. 2005. (Bobbsey Twins Ser.). 32p. (J). (ps-ps). pap. 3.99 (978-1-4169-0270-6(8) , Aladdin) Simon & Schuster Children's Publishing.

—Freddie & Flossie. 2006. (Ready-To-Read Ser.). (J). (ps-2). 21.35 (978-1-59961-095-5(7)) Spotlight.

—Freddie & Flossie & Snap. Pyle, Chuck, illus. 2005. (Ready-To-Read Ser.). 32p. (J). pap. 3.99 (978-1-4169-0267-6(8) , Aladdin) Simon & Schuster Children's Publishing.

—Freddie & Flossie & Snap. 2006. (Ready-To-Read Ser.). (J). (ps-2). 21.35 (978-1-59961-096-2(5)) Spotlight.

—Freddie & Flossie & the Easter Egg Hunt. Downer, Maggie, illus. 2006. 32p. (J). lib. bdg. 15.00 (*978-1-4242-0966-8(8)) Fitzgerald Bks.

—Freddie & Flossie & the Easter Egg Hunt. Downer, Maggie, illus. 2006. (Bobbsey Twins Ser.). 32p. (J). pap. 3.99 (978-1-4169-1029-9(8) , Aladdin) Simon & Schuster Children's Publishing.

—Freddie & Flossie & the Easter Egg Hunt. 2006. (Ready-To-Read Ser.). (Illus.). 32p. (J). (ps-2). 21.35 (978-1-59961-100-6(7)) Spotlight.

—Freddie & Flossie & the Little Seed. Downer, Maggie, illus. 2006. (Bobbsey Twins Ser.). 32p. (J). (ps-k). pap. 3.99 (978-1-4169-1766-3(7) , Aladdin) Simon & Schuster Children's Publishing.

—Freddie & Flossie & the Train Ride. Pyle, Chuck, illus. 2005. (Ready-To-Read Ser.). 32p. (J). (ps-ps). pap. 3.99 (978-1-4169-0269-0(4) , Aladdin) Simon & Schuster Children's Publishing.

—Freddie & Flossie & the Train Ride. 2006. (Ready-To-Read Ser.). (J). (ps-2). 21.35 (978-1-59961-097-9(3)) Spotlight.

—Freddie & Flossie at the Beach. Pyle, Chuck, illus. 2005. (Ready-To-Read Ser.). 32p. (J). (ps-ps). pap. 3.99 (978-1-4169-0268-3(6) , Aladdin) Simon & Schuster Children's Publishing.

—Freddie & Flossie at the Beach. 2006. (Ready-To-Read Ser.). (J). (ps-2). 21.35 (978-1-59961-098-6(1)) Spotlight.

Hope, Laura Lee. Six Little Bunkers at Grandma Bell's. 2006. 33.99 (*978-1-4280-2818-0(8)) IndyPublish.com.

Horowitz, Anthony. Public Enemy Number Two. 2004. (Diamond Brothers Ser.). 208p. (J). (gr. 5). 16.99 (978-0-399-24154-3(X) , Philomel); pap. 6.99 (978-0-14-240218-4(4) , Puffin) Penguin Group (USA) Inc.

—South by Southeast. 2005. (Diamond Brothers Ser.). 160p. (J). (gr. 3-9). pap. 5.99 (978-0-14-240374-7(1) , Puffin); (YA). (gr. 5-9). 16.99 (978-0-399-24155-0(8) , Philomel) Penguin Group (USA) Inc.

—Three of Diamonds. 2005. (Diamond Brothers Ser.). 240p. (J). (gr. 5). pap. 6.99 (978-0-14-240298-6(2) , Puffin); (YA). (gr. 4). 16.99 (978-0-399-24157-4(4) , Philomel) Penguin Group (USA) Inc.

Horowitz, Ruth. Big Surprise in the Bug Tank. Holub, Joan, illus. 2005. (Easy-to-Read, Dial Ser.). 48p. (J). (gr. 1). 14.99 (978-0-8037-2874-5(3) , Dial) Penguin Group (USA) Inc.

Horrocks, Anita. Topher. 2000. 212p. (YA). (gr. 5-9). pap. 7.95 (978-0-7737-6092-9(X)) Stoddart Kids CAN. *Dist:* Fitzhenry & Whiteside, Ltd.

Horvath, Polly. The Trolls. 1999. 144p. (J). (gr. 3-7). 16.00 (978-0-374-37787-8(1) , Farrar, Straus & Giroux (BYR)) Farrar, Straus & Giroux.

—Trolls. 2001. (gr. 3-6). lib. bdg. 12.95 (978-0-613-82505-4(5)) Tandem Library Bks.

Howard, Elizabeth Fitzgerald. When Will Sarah Come. Crews, Nina, photos by. 1999. (Illus.). 24p. (J). (ps-3). 16.00 (978-0-688-16180-4(4)); 15.89 (978-0-688-16181-1(2)) HarperCollins Pubs.

Howe, James. Pinky & Rex & the New Baby. 1999. (gr. k-3). lib. bdg. 11.80 (978-0-7857-3870-1(3)) Tandem Library Bks.

—Pinky & Rex & the New Baby. 2006. (J). (gr. 1-4). 24.21 (978-1-59961-076-4(0)) Spotlight.

Hubery, Julia. A Christmas Wish. Williams, Sophy, illus. 2007. 28p. (J). (ps-2). 16.95 (*978-1-56148-589-5(6)) Good Bks.

Hudson, Cheryl Willis. What Do You Know? Snow! Walker, Sylvia, illus. 2004. 32p. (J). (ps-ps). lib. bdg. 10.79 (978-0-606-30031-5(7)) Tandem Library Bks.

Hudson, Cheryl Willis. What Do You Know? SNOW! Walker, Sylvia, illus. 2004. 32p. (J). lib. bdg. 15.00 (*978-1-4242-0233-1(7)) Fitzgerald Bks.

Hughes, Carol. Dirty Magic. 2006. (Illus.). 432p. (J). (gr. 4-9). 17.95 (978-0-375-83187-4(8)); (gr. 5-8). lib. bdg. 19.99 (978-0-375-93187-1(2)) Random Hse. Children's Bks. (Random Hse. Bks. for Young Readers).

—Dirty Magic. 2008. (Illus.). 432p. (J). (gr. 5-9). 5.99 (978-0-375-83188-1(6)) Random Hse., Inc.

Hughes, Pat. The Breaker Boys. 2004. (Illus.). 256p. (J). 18.00 (978-0-374-30956-5(6) , Farrar, Straus & Giroux (BYR)) Farrar, Straus & Giroux.

Hughes, Shirley. Alfie's ABC. Hughes, Shirley, illus. 1998. (Illus.). 32p. (J). (ps-k). 16.00 (978-0-688-16126-2(X)) HarperCollins Pubs.

—Annie Rose Is My Little Sister. Hughes, Shirley, illus. 2003. (Illus.). 32p. (J). (ps-2). 15.99 (978-0-7636-1959-6(0)) Candlewick Pr.

—The Big Alfie & Annie Rose Storybook. 2007. (Illus.). 64p. (J). pap. 12.95 (*978-0-09-975030-7(9) , Red Fox) Random Hse. Children's Bks. GBR. *Dist:* Independent Pubs. Group.

Hughes, Shirley. Olly & Me. Hughes, Shirley, illus. 2004. (Illus.). 32p. (J). (ps-2). 15.99 (978-0-7636-2374-6(1)) Candlewick Pr.

Hunt, L. J. The Abernathy Boys. 2004. (Abernathy Boys Ser.). 208p. (J). 15.99 (978-0-06-440953-7(8)); (Illus.). lib. bdg. 16.89 (978-0-06-029259-1(8)) HarperCollins Pubs.

Hunter, Erin. Dark River. 2008. (Warriors Ser.: Bk. 2). 352p. (J). (gr. 5 up). 16.99 (*978-0-06-089205-0(6)) HarperCollins Pubs.

Huntington, Amy, illus. Seagull Sam. 2007. 32p. (ps-2). 15.95 (*978-0-89272-715-5(2)) Down East Bks.

Hurst, Carol Otis. The Wrong One. 2003. 160p. (YA). (gr. 4-6). tchr. ed. 15.00 (978-0-618-27599-1(1) , Walter Lorraine) Houghton Mifflin Co. Trade & Reference Div.

Hurston, Zora Neale. The Three Witches. Tankersley, Ann & Ringgold, Faith, illus. 2006. 32p. (J). (gr. 1-5). 15.99 (978-0-06-000649-5(8)) HarperCollins Pubs.

Hurwitz, Johanna. Nora & Mrs. Mind-Your-Own-Business. 2001. (gr. 3-6). lib. bdg. 12.10 (978-0-613-35646-6(2)) Tandem Library Bks.

—Rip-Roaring Russell. Tilley, Debbie, illus. 2001. (Riverside Kids Ser.). 112p. (J). (gr. 1-4). pap. 4.99 (978-0-06-442155-3(4) , Harper Trophy) HarperCollins Pubs.

—Rip-Roaring Russell. 1999. (Beech Tree Chapter Bks.). (Illus.). 96p. (gr. k-4). mass mkt. 4.95 (978-0-688-16664-9(4)) HarperCollins Pubs.

—Rip-Roaring Russell. Tilley, Debbie, illus. 2001. 110p. (J). (ps-ps). per. 12.10 (978-0-613-34915-4(6)) Tandem Library Bks.

—Russell & Elisa. 1999. (Beech Tree Chapter Bks.). (Illus.). 96p. (J). (gr. k-4). mass mkt. 4.95 (978-0-688-16666-3(0)) HarperCollins Pubs.

—Russell & Elisa. Tilley, Debbie, illus. rev. ed. 2001. (Riverside Kids Ser.). 128p. (J). (ps-3). pap. 5.99 (978-0-06-442150-8(3) , Harper Trophy) HarperCollins Pubs.

—Russell & Elisa. 2001. (gr. 3-6). lib. bdg. 12.10 (978-0-613-35654-1(3)); 1999. (Illus.). (J). (978-0-606-21759-0(2)) Tandem Library Bks.

—Superduper Teddy. 2001. (Illus.). (J). (978-0-606-22039-2(9)) Tandem Library Bks.

Hutchins, Elizabeth. Personal Best: Snowbored, All That Jazz, Thief! 2005. (Triple Play Ser.). (Illus.). 48p. (gr. 4-8). 41.85 (978-0-7910-9075-6(2)) Facts On File, Inc.

Hutchins, Hazel J. Katie's Babbling Brother. Ohi, Ruth, illus. 2003. (Annikins Ser.: Vol. 15). 24p. (J). (ps-k). pap. 1.25 (978-1-55037-496-4(6)) Annick Pr., Ltd. CAN. *Dist:* Firefly Bks., Ltd.

Hutchins, Pat. Titch. Hutchins, Pat, illus. 2002. (Illus.). (J). 14.47 (978-0-7587-3818-9(8)) Book Wholesalers, Inc.

Hyde, Catherine Ryan. The Year of My Miraculous Reappearance. 2007. 240p. (gr. 7). (J). lib. bdg. 18.99 (978-0-375-93257-1(7)); (YA). 15.99 (978-0-375-83257-4(2)) Random Hse. Children's Bks. (Knopf Bks. for Young Readers).

Impey, Rose. Jumble Joan. Kemp, Moira, illus. 1998. (Creepies Ser.). 48p. (J). (gr. 1-3). lib. bdg. (978-1-57505-295-3(4) , Carolrhoda Bks.) Lerner Publishing Group.

—Scare Yourself to Sleep. Kemp, Moira, illus. 1998. (Creepies Ser.). 48p. (J). (gr. 1-3). pap. 6.95 (978-1-57505-316-5(0) , Carolrhoda Bks.) Lerner Publishing Group.

Inches, Alison. Big Sister Dora. 2006. (Illus.). (J). (ps-2). 21.35 (978-1-59961-067-2(1)) Spotlight.

—In the Mushroom Meadow. 2002. (gr. k-3). lib. bdg. 10.95 (978-0-613-86241-7(4)) Tandem Library Bks.

Interiano, Jeffrey. Critters of Forest City. 2006. pap. 10.00 (*978-1-4257-1721-6(7)) Xlibris Corp.

Jacobs, Deborah Lynn. Choices. 2007. 208p. (YA). (gr. 7 up). 16.95 (*978-1-59643-217-8(9)) Roaring Brook Pr.

James, B. J., et al. Supertwins Meet the Dangerous Dino-Robots, No. 3. Demarest, Chris L., illus. 2003. (Scholastic Reader Ser.). 32p. (J). pap. 3.99 (978-0-439-46625-7(3) , Cartwheel Bks.) Scholastic, Inc.

James, Betsy. Listening at the Gate. James, Betsy, illus. 2006. (Seeker Chronicles Ser.). (Illus.). 512p. (YA). (gr. 7 up). 16.95 (978-0-689-85068-4(9) , Atheneum) Simon & Schuster Children's Publishing.

James, Charlie. Billy the Fish. Jolliffe, Ned, illus. 2006. 176p. (J). 14.95 (978-1-58234-732-5(8)); pap. 5.95 (978-1-58234-733-2(6)) Bloomsbury Publishing. (Bloomsbury Children).

James, Richard E., III. Adventures of the Elements Vol. 3: Dangerous Games. Lyle, Maryann, ed. Welch, Chad, illus. 2004. 169p. (YA). (gr. 3-12). pap. 5.95 (978-0-9675901-2-7(4)) Three Rivers Council, BSA, Inc.

James, Will. In the Saddle with Uncle Bill. rev. ed. 2001. (Illus.). 208p. (J). (gr. 3-4). 26.00 (978-0-87842-427-6(X) , 808); pap. 14.00 (978-0-87842-428-3(8) , 807) Mountain Pr. Publishing Co., Inc.

Jane, Pamela. Milo & the Flapjack Fiasco! Johnson, Meredith, ed. Johnson, Meredith, tr. 2004. (Illus.). 32p. (J). 13.95 (978-1-59336-113-6(0)); pap. (978-1-59336-114-3(9)) Mondo Publishing.

Jaramillo, Ann. La Linea. 2006. (SPA.). 144p. (J). 16.95 (978-1-59643-154-6(7)) Roaring Brook Pr.

—La Linea. 2008. 160p. (YA). pap. 7.99 (*978-0-312-37354-2(6)) Square Fish.

Jaspersohn, William. The Two Brothers. Donato, Michael A., illus. 2005. (Family Heritage Ser.). 36p. (J). (gr. 1-5). 15.95 (978-0-916718-16-9(6)) Vermont Folklife Ctr.

Javier's Sister - A Family's Struggle with Drug Addiction: One Day the Sun Will Shine Again Series. 2005. (J). pap. 16.95 (978-0-9768827-8-7(7)) Prevention Through Puppetry, Inc.

Jaworski, Anna M. My Brother Needs an Operation. Ball, Linda, illus. 1998. 57p. (J). (ps-5). 20.00 (978-0-9652508-2-5(2)) Baby Hearts Pr.

Jeffers, Susan, illus. Hansel y Gretel. (SPA.). 32p. (J). (gr. 2-3). 10.36 (978-84-241-3339-9(0) , EV4674) Everest de Ediciones y Distribucion, S.L. ESP. *Dist:* Lectorum Pubns., Inc.

Jenck, Heidi Shelton. Gabe's Grocery List. Trover, Zachary, illus. 2006. 32p. (J). (*978-1-4048-3140-7(1)) Picture Window Bks.

Jenkins, Amanda. Mutant Bugs. 2005. 22.00 (*978-1-4108-4219-0(3)) Benchmark Education Co.

Jenkins, Jerry B. & Fabry, Chris. Wind Chill. 2006. (Tyndale Kids Ser.). 240p. (J). pap. 5.99 (978-1-4143-0153-2(7) , Tyndale Kids) Tyndale Hse. Pubs.

Jennings, Patrick. The Bird Shadow: An Ike & Mem Story. Alter, Anna, illus. 2001. 56p. (J). (gr. k-3). tchr. ed. 15.95 (978-0-8234-1670-7(4)) Holiday Hse., Inc.

—The Weeping Willow. Alter, Anna, illus. 2002. (Ike & Mem Story Ser.: No. 3). 56p. (J). (gr. k-3). tchr. ed. 15.95 (978-0-8234-1671-4(2)) Holiday Hse., Inc.

Jennings, Sharon. The Bye-Bye Pie. ed. 2004. (Illus.). (J). (gr. k-3). spiral bd. (978-0-616-01684-8(0)) Canadian National Institute for the Blind/Institut National Canadien pour les Aveugles.

—The Bye-Bye Pie. Ohi, Ruth, illus. (ps-k). 2001. 32p. (J). pap. (978-1-55041-664-0(2)); 1999. 31p. (J). (978-1-55041-405-9(4)); 2nd ed. 2002. 32p. pap. (978-1-55041-785-2(1)) Fitzhenry & Whiteside, Ltd.

Jinkins, Jim. Pinky Dinky Doo: Back to School Is Cool! 2005. (Step into Reading Ser.). (Illus.). 48p. (J). (gr. 1-3). pap. 3.99 (978-0-375-83237-6(8) , Random Hse. Bks. for Young Readers) Random Hse. Children's Bks.

—Pinky Dinky Doo: Polka Dot Pox. 2004. (Illus.). 48p. (J). (gr. 1-3). pap. 3.99 (978-0-375-82713-6(7) , Random Hse. Bks. for Young Readers) Random Hse. Children's Bks.

—Pinky Dinky Doo: Think Pink! 2006. (Step into Reading Ser.). (Illus.). 48p. (J). (gr. 1-3). pap. 3.99 (978-0-375-83573-5(3)); lib. bdg. 11.99 (978-0-375-93573-2(8)) Random Hse. Children's Bks. (Random Hse. Bks. for Young Readers).

—Pinky Dinky Doo: Where Are My Shoes? 2004. (Illus.). 48p. (J). (gr. 1-3). pap. 3.99 (978-0-375-82712-9(9) , Random Hse. Bks. for Young Readers) Random Hse. Children's Bks.

—Pinky Dinky Doo: Back to School Is Cool! 2005. (Step into Reading Ser.). (Illus.). 48p. (J). (gr. 1-3). lib. bdg. 11.99 (978-0-375-93237-3(2) , Random Hse. Bks. for Young Readers) Random Hse. Children's Bks.

—Pinky Dinky Doo: Shrinky Pinky! 2005. (Step into Reading Ser.). (Illus.). 48p. (J). (gr. 1-3). pap. 3.99 (978-0-375-83235-2(1) , Random Hse. Bks. for Young Readers) Random Hse. Children's Bks.

Johns, Michael-Anne. Zac Attack: Hanson's Little Brother. 1998. (J). (gr. 4-7). pap. 3.99 (978-0-590-03488-3(X)) Scholastic, Inc.

Johnson, Angela. Looking for Red. 128p. (YA). 2003. (Illus.). pap. 8.95 (978-0-689-86388-2(8) , Simon Pulse); 2002. (gr. 7 up). 15.95 (978-0-689-83253-6(2)) Simon & Schuster Children's Publishing.

—Looking for Red. 2003. (gr. 7-12). lib. bdg. 13.00 (978-0-613-73436-3(X)) Tandem Library Bks.

—Looking for Red. l.t. ed. 2003. 117p. (J). 24.95 (978-0-7862-5603-7(6)) Thorndike Pr.

Johnson, David. Trapped in Space. Liew, Sonny, illus. 2007. (J). 80p. (*978-1-59889-354-0(8)); 74p. pap. (*978-1-59889-449-3(8)) Stone Arch Bks.

Johnson, Kathleen Jeffrie. A Fast & Brutal Wing. 2007. 208p. (YA). pap. 6.99 (*978-0-312-37148-7(9)) Square Fish.

Johnson, Lissa Halls. The Worst Wish. 2000. (Kidwitness Tales Ser.). (Illus.). 128p. (J). (gr. 3-7). pap. 5.99 (978-1-56179-882-7(7)) Bethany Hse. Pubs.

Johnson, Marion. Caillou Watches Rosie. rev. ed. 2008. (Playtime Ser.). (Illus.). 20p. (J). pap. 4.95 (*978-2-89450-635-6(X)) Chouette Publishing CAN. *Dist:* Independent Pubs. Group.

Johnson, Sandi. White Wolf at Dawn. Johnson, Britt, ed. Sturgen, Bobbi, illus. 2002. 25p. (J). (gr. k-5). spiral bd. 5.99 (978-1-929063-72-7(5) , 171) Moons & Stars Publishing For Children.

Johnston, Julie. The Only Outcast. 1999. (J). (978-0-606-19122-7(4)) Tandem Library Bks.

—Only Outcast. 1999. (gr. 7-12). lib. bdg. 15.25 (978-0-613-28008-2(3)) Tandem Library Bks.

—The Only Outcast. 1999. 248p. (J). (gr. 6-9). reprint ed. pap. 6.95 (978-0-88776-488-2(6)) Tundra Bks., Inc./Livres Toundra, Inc. CAN. *Dist:* Random Hse., Inc.

Johnston, Tony. That Summer. Moser, Barry, illus. 2007. 32p. (J). (gr. 1-4). pap. 6.00 (978-0-15-205856-2(7) , Voyager Bks./Libros Viajeros) Harcourt Children's Bks.

Jonell, Lynne. It's My Birthday, Too! 2001. (Illus.). (J). (978-0-606-21256-4(6)) Tandem Library Bks.

Jones, Christianne C. Back to School. Haugen, Ryan, illus. 2005. (Read-It! Readers Ser.). 24p. (J). (ps-ps). lib. bdg. 18.60 (978-1-4048-1166-9(4)) Picture Window Bks.

Jones, Diana Wynn. The Game. 2007. (Firebird Ser.). 192p. (YA). (gr. 7 up). 11.99 (978-0-14-240718-9(6) , Puffin) Penguin Group (USA) Inc.

Jones, Kelly. Mama. Kewley, Ken, illus. 2004. 32p. (J). (978-0-9745930-0-5(1)) Stunt Publishing.

Jones, Lara. Fun at the Park. Jones, Lara, illus. 2003. (Lola & Binky Bks.). (Illus.). 8p. (J). bds. 5.95 (978-0-7641-5689-2(5)) Barron's Educational Series, Inc.

—Fun on the Farm. Jones, Lara, illus. 2003. (Lola & Binky Bks.). (Illus.). 8p. (J). bds. 5.95 (978-0-7641-5688-5(8)) Barron's Educational Series, Inc.

Jones, Michael. Finding Imagine Nation. 2007. (YA). per. 10.95 (*978-0-9789386-4-2(X)) Lucy Rose Publishing LLC.

Joosse, Barbara M. Hot City. Gauch, Patricia Lee, ed. Christie, Gregory R., illus. 2004. 32p. (J). (ps-3). 16.99 (978-0-399-23640-2(6) , Philomel) Penguin Group (USA) Inc.

Jordan, Mark. Courage the Monkey. 2006. (Illus.). 40p. (J). 13.95 (978-0-9717013-7-3(7)) Decere Publishing.

Joseph, Lynn. The Color of My Words. 2002. 144p. (J). (gr. 5 up). pap. 5.99 (978-0-06-447204-3(3) , Harper Trophy) HarperCollins Pubs.

—Color of My Words. 2002. (gr. 3-6). lib. bdg. 12.95 (978-0-613-44515-3(5)) Tandem Library Bks.

Jougla, Frederic. Tricked on Halloween: Rina & Jax's Stories. Jougla, Karina, illus. l.t. ed. 2004. 36p. (J). bds. 14.99 (978-0-9754287-0-2(5)) Imagery Pr.

Joyce, William. Rolie Polie Olie. 2001. (Rolie Polie Olie Ser.). (Illus.). (J). (ps). 5p. 3.99 (978-0-7364-0163-0(6)); Vol. 2. 10p. bds. 3.99 (978-0-7364-0164-7(4)) Mouse Works.

—Santa Calls. 1998. (Illus.). 36p. (J). (ps-k). bds. 6.95 (978-0-694-01212-1(2) , Harper Festival) HarperCollins Pubs.

Kaaberbol, Lene. Heartbreak Island. 2005. (W. I. T. C. H. Adventures Ser. : Bk. 3). (Illus.). 105p. (J). lib. bdg. 11.00 (***978-1-4242-0786-2(X))*** Fitzgerald Bks.

—The Serpent Gift. 3rd ed. 2007. (Shamer Chronicles Ser.). Orig. Title: Slangens Gave. 377p. (J). pap. 9.95 (***978-0-8050-8655-3(2)*** , Holt, Henry & Co. Bks. For Young Readers) Holt, Henry & Co.

—The Shamer's Signet. 2nd rev. ed. 2007. (Shamer Chronicles Ser.). 320p. (YA). pap. 8.95 (***978-0-8050-8217-3(4)*** , Holt, Henry & Co. Bks. For Young Readers) Holt, Henry & Co.

Kalz, Jill. I Hate to Read: Belle Pepper. 2004. (Illus.). 32p. (J). pap. 9.95 (978-0-89812-521-4(9) , Creative Paperbacks) Creative Co., The.

Kanter, Angela. My Ballerina Sister on Stage. 2002. (Illus.). 64p. (J). pap. 8.99 (978-0-09-941703-3(0)) Random Hse. GBR. *Dist:* Independent Pubs. Group.

Karas, G. Brian. Bebe's Bad Dream. 2000. (Illus.). 32p. (J). (gr. k up). 15.89 (978-0-688-16183-5(9)) HarperCollins Pubs.

Karr, Kathleen. The Seventh Knot. 2003. (Illus.). 192p. (J). 15.95 (978-0-7614-5135-8(8)) Cavendish, Marshall Corp.

Katz, Karen. Best-Ever Big Brother. 2006. (Illus.). 14p. (J). (ps-k). bds. 5.99 (978-0-448-43914-3(X) , Grosset & Dunlap) Penguin Group (USA) Inc.

Keats, Ezra Jack. Peter's Chair. (Illus.). 40p. (J). (gr. k-3). pap. 6.95 (978-1-931016-07-0(0) , MHC-07-0) Minnesota Humanities Commission.

—Peter's Chair. Keats, Ezra Jack, illus. 1998. (Illus.). 40p. (J). (ps-3). 15.99 (978-0-670-88064-5(7) , Viking Juvenile); pap. 6.99 (978-0-14-056441-9(1) , Puffin) Penguin Group (USA) Inc.

—Peter's Chair. Keats, Ezra Jack, illus. 1998. (Picture Puffin Ser.). (Illus.). (978-0-606-13701-0(7)) Tandem Library Bks.

—Peter's Chair. (J). (ps-3). pap. 12.95 incl. audio Weston Woods Studios, Inc.

—Peter's Chair. 2006. 32p. (J). (ps-ps). bds. 6.99 (978-0-670-06190-7(5) , Viking Juvenile) Penguin Group (USA) Inc.

—La Silla de Pedro. 1999. (978-0-606-17430-5(3)) Tandem Library Bks.

—Silla de Pedro. 1999. (SPA.). (gr. k-3). lib. bdg. 15.30 (978-0-613-22936-4(3)) Tandem Library Bks.

Keeling, Annie E. Andrew Golding A Tale of the Great Plague. 2004. reprint ed. pap. 15.95 (978-1-4191-0694-1(5)); pap. 1.99 (978-1-4192-0694-8(X)) Kessinger Publishing, LLC.

Keeling, E. Annie. Andrew Golding (a Tale of the Great Plag. 2006. 40.99 (***978-1-4280-0516-7(1)***); pap. 34.99 (***978-1-4280-0515-0(3))*** IndyPublish.com.

Kehret, Peg. Abduction! (J). 2006. 224p. (gr. 4). pap. 6.99 (978-0-14-240617-5(1) , Puffin); 2004. 192p. (gr. 5). reprint ed. 16.99 (978-0-525-47294-0(0) , Dutton Juvenile) Penguin Group (USA) Inc.

—Earthquake Terror. 1998. (Puffin Novel Ser.). 144p. (J). (gr. 3-7). pap. 5.99 (978-0-14-038343-0(3) , Puffin) Penguin Group (USA) Inc.

—Earthquake Terror. 1998. (Puffin Novel Ser.). (J). 11.64 (978-0-606-13073-8(X)) Tandem Library Bks.

—Escaping the Giant Wave. (Illus.). 160p. (J). 2004. pap. 5.99 (978-0-689-85273-2(8) , Aladdin); 2003. 16.99 (978-0-689-85272-5(X)) Simon & Schuster Children's Publishing.

—Escaping the Giant Wave. l.t. ed. 2003. 152p. (J). 21.95 (978-0-7862-5985-4(X)) Thorndike Pr.

—My Brother Made Me Do It: A Sister Remembers Growing up with the Rev. Dr. Martin Luther King Jr. 144p. (J). 2001. pap. 4.99 (978-0-671-03419-1(7) , Aladdin); 2000. (gr. 3-6). 16.00 (978-0-671-03418-4(9)) Simon & Schuster Children's Publishing.

—My Brother Made Me Do It: A Sister Remembers Growing up with the Rev. Dr. Martin Luther King Jr. 2001. (978-0-606-22136-8(0)) ; (gr. 3-6). lib. bdg. 13.00 (978-0-613-53443-7(3)) Tandem Library Bks.

Keller, Holly. Geraldine & Mrs. Duffy. 2000. (Illus.). (J). (gr. k-3). 24p. 15.95 (978-0-688-16887-2(6)) ; 32p. 15.89 (978-0-688-16888-9(4)) HarperCollins Pubs.

Kemler, Nancy. Dragon Box: The Key to Magic. 2005. 108p. pap. 16.95 (978-1-4137-8445-9(3)) PublishAmerica, Inc.

Kennedy, Pamela. A Sister for Matthew: A Story about Adoption. Wummer, Amy, illus. 2006. 32p. (J). 8.95 (978-0-8249-5527-4(7) , 1256104, Guideposts) Ideals Pubns.

Kennemore, Tim. Circle of Doom. 2003. 208p. (J). 16.00 (978-0-374-31284-8(2) , Farrar, Straus & Giroux (BYR)) Farrar, Straus & Giroux.

Kennemore, Tim & Archbold, Tim. Circle of Doom. 2006. (Illus.). 208p. (J). pap. 6.95 (978-0-374-41198-5(0)) Macmillan.

Kerr, P. B. The Akhenaten Adventure No. 1: Children of the Lamp. l.t. ed. 2005. 430p. 23.95 (978-0-7862-7299-0(6) , Large Print Pr.) Thorndike Pr.

—Cobra King of Kathmandu. 2007. (Children of the Lamp Ser.: No. 3). 400p. (J). pap. 6.99 (***978-0-439-67024-1(1)*** , Scholastic Paperbacks) Scholastic, Inc.

—The Cobra King of Kathmandu. 2007. (Children of the Lamp Ser.: No. 3). (Illus.). 384p. (J). (gr. 4-7). pap. 16.99 (978-0-439-67023-4(3) , Orchard Bks.) Scholastic, Inc.

Kerr, P. B. The Day of the Djinn Warriors. 2008. (Scholastic First Discovery Ser.). 400p. (J). pap. 17.99 (***978-0-439-93214-1(9)*** , Orchard Bks.) Scholastic, Inc.

Khalsa, Dayal Kaur. Green Cat. 2002. (Illus.). 24p. (J). (gr. k-3). 14.95 (978-0-88776-586-5(6)) Tundra Bks., Inc./ Livres Toundra, Inc. CAN. *Dist:* Random Hse., Inc.

Kibuishi, Kazu. Amulet: Book 1. 2008. 192p. (J). pap. 9.99 (***978-0-439-84681-3(1)*** , Graphix) Scholastic, Inc.

Kidd, Ronald. Undercover Kid: Comic Book King. Sklar, Andy, illus. 2007. (All Aboard Mystery Reader Ser.). 48p. (J). pap. 3.99 (***978-0-448-44438-3(0)*** , Grosset & Dunlap) Penguin Group (USA) Inc.

Kidder, Judy. The Special Brother. Field, Terri, illus. 1999. 16p. (J). pap. (978-0-9663764-1-8(2)) Reivers Pr.

Kimball, K. M. The Star-Spangled Secret. 2001. 234p. (J). (gr. 4-7). lib. bdg. 11.64 (978-0-606-22096-5(8)) Tandem Library Bks.

Kimble, Maggie T. Peep Learns to Sing. 2004. 21p. pap. 14.95 (978-1-4137-2005-1(6)) PublishAmerica, Inc.

King, Ron S. The Quantum July. 2007. 256p. (YA). (gr. 5). 15.99 (***978-0-385-73418-9(2)***); lib. bdg. 18.99 (***978-0-385-90432-2(0))*** Random Hse. Children's Bks. (Delacorte Bks. for Young Readers).

Kirkham, Teresa. Tattle Tom. 2003. 27p. pap. 9.95 (978-1-4137-0141-8(8)) PublishAmerica, Inc.

Klass, David. Dark Angel. 2005. 320p. (YA). (gr. 7). 17.00 (978-0-374-39950-4(6) , Farrar, Straus & Giroux (BYR)) Farrar, Straus & Giroux.

—Dark Angel. 2007. 320p. (J). (gr. 9 up). pap. 7.99 (***978-0-06-088700-1(1)*** , HarperTeen) HarperCollins Pubs.

Klein, Abby. Super-secret Valentine. 2007. (Ready, Freddy! Ser.: No. 10). 96p. (J). pap. 3.99 (978-0-439-78459-7(X) , Blue Sky Pr., The) Scholastic, Inc.

Kleven, Elisa. Ernst. 2002. (ps-2). lib. bdg. 15.25 (978-0-613-57830-1(9)) Tandem Library Bks.

—Ernst. 2004. (Illus.). 32p. (J). 6.95 (978-1-58246-053-6(1) , Tricycle Pr.) Ten Speed Pr.

Klingel, Cynthia Fitterer & Noyed, Robert B. Bernard, Me & the Letter B. 2003. (Alphaphonics Ser.). (Illus.). 24p. (J). (ps-2). 21.36 (978-1-59296-092-7(8)) Child's World, Inc.

Klise, Kate. Letters from Camp. Klise, M. Sarah, illus. 2000. 192p. (J). (gr. 4-7). pap. 5.99 (978-0-380-79348-8(2) , Harper Trophy) HarperCollins Pubs.

—Letters from Camp. 2000. (gr. 3-6). lib. bdg. 14.15 (978-0-613-28552-0(2)) Tandem Library Bks.

Knudsen, Michelle. A Moldy Mystery. Gott, Barry, illus. 2006. 32p. (J). lib. bdg. 20.00 (***978-1-4242-1096-1(8))*** Fitzgerald Bks.

Koch, Edward T. & Thaler, Pat Koch. Eddie's Little Sister Makes a Splash. Warhola, James, illus. 2007. 32p. (J). (gr. k). 16.99 (978-0-399-24310-3(0) , Putnam Juvenile) Penguin Group (USA) Inc.

Koger, Danny K. The Misadventures of Carson & C J Crenshaw: In Search of the Book of Life. 2007. 184p. per. 13.95 (***978-0-595-42365-1(5))*** iUniverse, Inc.

Kohlhepp, Michael. Within the Hearthstone: Book 1: the Trea. 2006. 127p. pap. 17.95 (978-1-4241-3744-2(6)) PublishAmerica, Inc.

Kohlhepp, Michael G. Within the Hearthstone Book 2: The Fountain of Balance. 2007. (ENG.). 184p. per. 19.95 (***978-1-4241-4446-4(9))*** PublishAmerica, Inc.

Koja, Kathe. Going Under. 2006. 128p. (YA). 16.00 (978-0-374-30393-8(2) , Frances Foster Bks.) Farrar, Straus & Giroux.

Koller, Jackie French. Baby for Sale. Pedersen, Janet, illus. 2002. 32p. (J). (ps-2). 16.95 (978-0-7614-5106-8(4)) Cavendish, Marshall Corp.

—The Promise. 2001. (gr. k-3). lib. bdg. 13.00 (978-0-613-37034-9(1)) Tandem Library Bks.

Komaiko, Leah. Annie Bananie & the Pain Sisters. 2000. (978-0-606-17890-7(2)) Tandem Library Bks.

Konigsburg, E. L. Father's Arcane Daughter. 1999. (J). (978-0-606-19131-9(3)) Tandem Library Bks.

—From the Mixed-Up Files of Mrs. Basil E. Frankweiler. 35th anniv. ed. 2002. 208p. (YA). mass mkt. 5.99 (978-0-689-85354-8(8) , Simon Pulse); 1998. (Illus.). 168p. (J). (gr. 3-7). pap. 6.99 (978-0-689-71181-7(6) , Aladdin) Simon & Schuster Children's Publishing.

—From the Mixed-Up Files of Mrs. Basil E. Frankweiler. 35th anniv. ed. 2002. (gr. 5-8). lib. bdg. 14.15 (978-0-613-73358-8(4)) Tandem Library Bks.

—From the Mixed-Up Files of Mrs. Basil E. Frankweiler. l.t. ed. 2005. (Illus.). 205p. (J). 22.95 (978-0-7862-7297-6(X) , Large Print Pr.) Thorndike Pr.

—Silent to the Bone. unabr. ed. 2004. (Middle Grade Cassette Librariestm Ser.). 272p. (J). (gr. 5-9). pap. 38.00 incl. audio (978-0-8072-8741-5(5) , S YA 253 SP, Listening Library) Random Hse. Audio Publishing Group.

—Silent to the Bone. 272p. 2004. (YA). mass mkt. 5.99 (978-0-689-86715-6(8) , Simon Pulse); 2002. pap. 5.99 (978-0-689-83602-2(3) , Aladdin) Simon & Schuster Children's Publishing.

—Silent to the Bone. Konigsburg, E. L., illus. 2000. (Jean Karl Bks.). (Illus.). 272p. (J). (gr. 5-9). 16.00 (978-0-689-83601-5(5) , Atheneum) Simon & Schuster Children's Publishing.

—Silent to the Bone. 2002. (gr. 5-8). lib. bdg. 14.15 (978-0-613-45102-4(3)) Tandem Library Bks.

—Silent to the Bone. l.t. ed. 2001. 271p. (J). (gr. 4-7). 23.95 (978-0-7862-3169-0(6)) Thorndike Pr.

Konigsburg, E. L. & Marcus, Barry David. From the Mixed-Up Files of Mrs. Basil E. Frankweiler. Konigsburg, E. L., illus. 35th anniv. ed. 2002. (Illus.). 176p. (J). (gr. 3-7). 17.99 (978-0-689-85322-7(X) , Atheneum) Simon & Schuster Children's Publishing.

Kono Juliet. Bravest Opihi. Fujitake Dennis, illus. 2005. 32p. 14.95 (978-1-933067-12-4(8)) Beachhouse Publishing, LLC.

Kopelke, Lisa. The Younger Brother's Survival Guide. Kopelke, Lisa, illus. 2006. (Illus.). 32p. (J). (ps-3). 15.95 (978-0-689-86249-6(0)) Simon & Schuster Children's Publishing.

Korman, Gordon. The Abduction. 2006. (Kidnapped Ser.). (J). 24.95 (978-0-439-89552-1(9)); 39.95 (978-0-439-89847-8(1)) Scholastic, Inc.

—Now You See Them, Now You Don't. 2005. (On the Run Ser.: No. 2). 146p. (J). (978-1-4156-1599-7(3)) Scholastic, Inc.

Kortepeter, Paul. Oliver's Red Toboggan. Wheeler, Susan, illus. 2006. 28p. (J). (ps). 15.99 (978-0-525-47752-5(7) , Dutton Juvenile) Penguin Group (USA) Inc.

Kraft, Erik P. Lenny & Mel's Summer Vacation. Kraft, Erik P., illus. 2004. (Ready-for-Chapters Ser.). (Illus.). 64p. (J). pap. 3.99 (978-0-689-86874-0(X) , Aladdin) Simon & Schuster Children's Publishing.

Krailing, Tessa. Disgusting Denzil. Phillips, Mike, illus. 2006. 48p. (J). lib. bdg. (***978-1-4048-3117-9(7))*** Picture Window Bks.

Kraus, Robert. Little Louie the Baby Bloomer. Aruego, Jose, illus. 1998. 32p. (J). (ps-3). 15.89 (978-0-06-026294-5(X)) HarperCollins Pubs.

—Little Louie the Baby Bloomer. 2000. (Illus.). (J). (978-0-606-18702-2(2)) Tandem Library Bks.

—Little Louie the Baby Bloomer. Aruego, Jose & Dewey, Ariane, illus. 2000. 32p. (J). (ps-3). pap. 5.95 (978-0-06-443656-4(X) , Harper Trophy) HarperCollins Pubs.

Krensky, Stephen. Lionel's Birthday. Natti, Susanna, illus. 2003. (Easy-to-Read Ser.). 48p. (J). (gr. k-3). 13.99 (978-0-8037-2752-6(6) , Dial) Penguin Group (USA) Inc.

Krishnaswami, Uma. Bringing Asha Home. Akib, Jamal, illus. 2006. 32p. (J). (978-1-58430-259-9(3)) Lee & Low Bks., Inc.

Krull, Kathleen. How to Trick or Treat in Outer Space. Brewer, Paul, illus. 2004. 32p. (J). (gr. k-3). tchr. ed. 16.95 (978-0-8234-1844-2(8)) Holiday Hse., Inc.

Krushner, Tony. Brundibar. 2002. 64p. (J). (978-0-7868-0905-9(1) , Di Capua, Michael) Scholastic, Inc.

Kubler, Annie, illus. Waiting for Baby. 2nd ed. 2000. 14p. (J). (ps-k). bds. 3.99 (978-0-85953-973-9(3)) Child's Play-International.

Kuchman, D. S. Krystal Steps: The Journey Begins. 2006. 57p. pap. 12.95 (***978-1-4241-5135-6(X))*** PublishAmerica, Inc.

Kurtz, Jane. In the Small, Small Night. Isadora, Rachel, illus. 2005. (Amistad Ser.). 32p. (J). 16.99 (978-0-06-623814-2(5)); lib. bdg. 17.89 (978-0-06-623813-5(7)) HarperCollins Pubs.

Laguna, Sofie. Surviving Aunt Marsha. 2005. 208p. (J). pap. 15.95 (978-0-439-64485-3(2)) Scholastic, Inc.

Lambert, Roy. Lamb, the Hip Cat Daddy. 2005. per. 13.95 (978-1-58909-253-2(8)) Bookstand Publishing.

Lamm, Drew. Pirates. Schuett, Stacey, illus. 2001. 40p. (gr. 4-7). 15.99 (978-0-7868-0392-7(4)) Hyperion Bks. for Children.

Lamstein, Sarah. Hunger Moon. 2004. (Illus.). 112p. (YA). 15.95 (978-1-932425-05-5(5) , Lemniscaat) Boyds Mills Pr.

Landa, Norbert. Little Bear & the Wishing Tree. Mendez, Simon, illus. 2007. 28p. (J). (ps-2). 16.95 (***978-1-56148-566-6(7))*** Good Bks.

Landolf, Diane Wright. What a Good Big Brother! Johnson, Steve & Fancher, Lou, illus. 2008. (J). (978-0-375-84258-0(6)); lib. bdg. (978-0-375-94258-7(0)) Random Hse. Children's Bks.

Landrey, Wanda A. The Ghost of Spindletop Hill. 2000. (Illus.). 144p. (J). 15.95 (978-1-57168-449-3(2)) Eakin Pr.

Lane, Leonie. Tom Turner & the Dream Box. 2006. 119p. pap. (***978-1-84685-460-6(1)*** , Exposure Publishing) Meadow Bks.

Lang, Greg. Costume Parade. 2000. (gr. k-3). lib. bdg. 11.80 (978-0-613-33352-8(7)) Tandem Library Bks.

—I'm on the Phone. 2000. (gr. k-3). lib. bdg. 11.80 (978-0-613-29649-6(4)) Tandem Library Bks.

Lansky, Bruce. When I'm a Big Brother. 2003. 22p. (J). bds. 9.95 (978-0-684-01868-3(3)) Meadowbrook Pr.

—When I'm a Big Sister. 2003. 22p. (J). bds. 9.95 (978-0-684-01865-2(9)) Meadowbrook Pr.

Lanthier, Jennifer. The Mystery of the Martello Tower. 2008. 272p. (J). 16.99 (***978-0-06-125712-4(5)***); lib. bdg. 17.89 (***978-0-06-125713-1(3))*** HarperCollins Pubs. (Geringer, Laura Book).

Lashbrook, Marilyn. Get Lost Little Brother. (J). (978-0-87973-863-1(4) , 863) Our Sunday Visitor, Publishing Div.

Laskin, Pamela L. Getting to Know You. 2003. (YA). 16.95 (978-0-936389-92-9(3)) Tudor Pubs., Inc.

Lasky, Kathryn. Broken Song. 160p. (J). 2007. pap. 6.99 (978-0-14-240741-7(0) , Puffin); 2005. (gr. 7). 15.99 (978-0-670-05931-7(5) , Viking Juvenile) Penguin Group (USA) Inc.

—Show & Tell Bunnies. Hafner, Marylin, illus. 2001. 32p. (J). (ps-3). pap. 5.99 (978-0-7636-1050-0(X)) Candlewick Pr.

—Show & Tell Bunnies. 2001. (ps-2). lib. bdg. 14.15 (978-0-613-44257-2(1)) Tandem Library Bks.

Latta, Sara L. Stella Brite & the Dark Matter Mystery. Johnson, Meredith, illus. 2006. 32p. (J). 16.95 (978-1-57091-883-4(X)); pap. 6.95 (978-1-57091-884-1(8)) Charlesbridge Publishing, Inc.

Lawlor, Laurie. The Biggest Pest on Eighth Avenue. Fisher, Cynthia, illus. (Holiday House Reader Ser.). 48p. (J). (gr. k-3). tchr. ed. 14.95 (978-0-8234-1321-8(7)) Holiday Hse., Inc.

Lawrence, Caroline. The Fugitive from Corinth. 2006. (Roman Mysteries Ser.). (Illus.). 208p. (J). 16.95 (978-1-59643-083-9(4)) Roaring Brook Pr.

Lawrence, Iain. Gemini Summer. 2006. 272p. (J). (gr. 3-7). 15.95 (978-0-385-73089-1(6) , Delacorte Bks. for Young Readers) Random Hse. Children's Bks.

—The Lightkeeper's Daughter. (YA). (gr. 9). 2004. 272p. pap. 7.95 (978-0-385-73127-0(2)); 2002. 256p. lib. bdg. 18.99 (978-0-385-90062-1(7)) Random Hse. Children's Bks. (Delacorte Bks. for Young Readers).

Lawrence, R. R. The Starsword. 2005. 416p. pap. 12.99 (978-0-9742549-0-6(8)) nightwares Bks.

Lears, Laurie. Ian's Walk: A Story about Autism. 2003. (gr. k-3). lib. bdg. 15.25 (978-0-613-75728-7(9)) Tandem Library Bks.

—Ian's Walk: A Story about Autism. Ritz, Karen, illus. 2004. 32p. (J). (gr. 1-4). pap. 6.95 (978-0-8075-3481-6(1)) Whitman, Albert & Co.

Leblanc, Louise. Maddie Stands Tall. Gay, Marie-Louise, illus. 2005. 61p. (J). lib. bdg. 12.00 (***978-1-4242-1200-2(6))*** Fitzgerald Bks.

Lees, Stewart. Runaway Jack. 2004. (Illus.). 32p. (J). 14.95 (978-0-7641-5712-7(4)) Barron's Educational Series, Inc.

Leitich Smith, Cynthia & Leitich Smith, Greg. Santa Knows. Bjorkman, Steve, illus. 2006. 32p. (J). (ps). 16.99 (978-0-525-47757-0(8) , Dutton Juvenile) Penguin Group (USA) Inc.

Lennon, Joan. Questors. 2007. 368p. (J). (gr. 5-9). 16.99 (***978-1-4169-3658-9(0)*** , McElderry, Margaret K.) Simon & Schuster Children's Publishing.

leo, domenic. The Messengers: The Secret of the Orbs. 2007. 324p. per. 19.95 (***978-0-595-42668-3(9))*** iUniverse, Inc.

Leonard, Marcia. Get the Ball, Slim. Handelman, Dorothy, photos by. 1998. (Real Kids Readers Ser.). (Illus.). 32p. (gr. k-1). (J). pap. 4.99 (978-0-7613-2025-8(3)); lib. bdg. 18.90 (978-0-7613-2000-5(8)) Lerner Publishing Group. (Millbrook Pr.).

—Trae la Pelota, Tito. Handelman, Dorothy, photos by. 2005. (Lecturas para Niños de Verdad (Real Kids Readers) Ser.). (Illus.). 32p. (J). (ps-1). (SPA.). pap. 4.99 (978-0-8225-3292-7(1) , Ediciones Lerner); (ENG & SPA., pap. 4.99 (978-0-8225-3293-4(X)) Lerner Publishing Group.

Lester, Julius. When Dad Killed Mom. 2003. (YA). 216p. pap. 6.95 (978-0-15-204698-9(4)) ; (gr. 7-12). mass mkt. 6.95 (978-0-15-524698-0(4)) Harcourt Trade Pubs. (Silver Whistle).

—When Dad Killed Mom. 2003. (gr. 7-12). lib. bdg. 15.25 (978-0-613-59932-0(2)) Tandem Library Bks.

Leuck, Laura. My Beastly Brother. Nash, Scott, illus. 2003. 32p. (J). (ps-1). 16.89 (978-0-06-029548-6(1)) HarperCollins Pubs.

Levin, Betty. Shoddy Cove. 2003. 208p. (J). (gr. 5 up). 15.99 (978-0-06-052271-1(2)) HarperCollins Pubs.

Levinson, Marilyn. And Don't Bring Jeremy. De Groat, Diane, illus. 2001. 132p. (gr. 4-7). pap. 9.95 (978-0-595-16919-1(8)) iUniverse, Inc.

Levithan, David. Are We There Yet? 224p. (gr. 7). 2007. (J). pap. 8.99 (978-0-375-83956-6(9)); 2005. (YA). 15.95 (978-0-375-82846-1(X)) Random Hse. Children's Bks. (Knopf Bks. for Young Readers).

Levitin, Sonia. Junkmans Girl. Porfirio, Guy, illus. rev. ed. 2007. (Tales of Young Americans Ser.). 40p. 17.95 (***978-1-58536-315-5(4))*** Sleeping Bear Pr.

Lewis, Beverly. The Granny Game. 1999. (Cul-de-Sac Kids Ser.: Vol. 20). (Illus.). 80p. (J). (gr. 2-5). pap. 3.99 (978-0-7642-2125-5(6)) Bethany Hse. Pubs.

—A Perfect Match. 1999. (Girls Only (Go!) Ser.: Vol. 3). (gr. 3-6). lib. bdg. 14.15 (978-0-613-23419-1(7)) Tandem Library Bks.

—Photo Perfect. 2001. (Girls Only (Go!) Ser.: Vol. 7). 128p. (J). (gr. 4-7). pap. 6.99 (978-1-55661-642-6(2)) Bethany Hse. Pubs.

Lewis, C. S. The Complete Chronicles of Narnia. 2002. (Chronicles of Narnia Ser.). pap. 29.99 (978-0-06-051758-8(1)) HarperCollins Pubs.

Lewis, Richard. The Killing Sea: A Novel of the Tsunami. 2006. 192p. (YA). (gr. 6-10). 15.95 (978-1-4169-1165-4(0)) Simon & Schuster Children's Publishing.

Lindenbaum, Pija. Bridget & the Moose Brothers. Board, Kjersti, tr. from SWE. 2004. (Illus.). 32p. (J). 16.00 (978-91-29-66046-3(7)) R & S Bks. SWE. *Dist:* Macmillan.

Lindgren, Astrid. The Red Bird. Crampton, Patricia, tr. from SWE. Tornqvist, Marit, illus. 2005. 48p. (J). reprint ed. pap. 16.95 (978-0-439-62796-2(6) , Levine, Arthur A. Bks.) Scholastic, Inc.

Lindgren, Astrid & Crampton, Patricia. The Red Bird. Tornqvist, Marit, illus. 2005. (J). 5.99 (978-0-439-62797-9(4) , Levine, Arthur A. Bks.) Scholastic, Inc.

Linko, G. J. Ben's Big Break. 2004. (Seekers Ser.: No. 4). 108p. 5.99 (978-0-8066-4185-0(1) , Augsburg Bks.) Augsburg Fortress, Pubs.

Linn, Margot. Sometimes I Share. Nicklaus, Carol, illus. 2005. (I'm Going to Read Ser.: Level 1). 28p. (J). 11.95 (978-1-4027-2068-0(8)) Sterling Publishing Co., Inc.

Lisle, Janet Taylor. How I Became a Writer & Oggie Learned to Drive. 2003. (Illus.). 160p. (YA). (ps-17). pap. 5.99 (978-0-14-250167-2(0) , Puffin) Penguin Group (USA) Inc.

Little, Jean. Emma's Strange Pet. Plecas, Jennifer, illus. (I Can Read Bks.). 64p. (J). (gr. k-3). 2004. pap. 3.99 (978-0-06-444259-6(4) , Harper Trophy); 2003. 15.99 (978-0-06-028350-6(5)) HarperCollins Pubs.

A B

—Emma's Yucky Brother. Plecas, Jennifer, illus. 2002. (I Can Read Bks.). 64p. (J). pap. 3.99 (978-0-06-444258-9(6)) HarperCollins Pubs.

Little, Jean & Little, Jean. Emma's Yucky Brother. Plecas, Jennifer, illus. 2002. 63p. (J). (ps-ps). lib. bdg. 11.80 (978-0-613-45486-5(3)) Tandem Library Bks.

Livingston, James E. The Wishing Well. 2002. 334p. (YA). pap. 16.95 (978-0-595-24957-2(4)); (ENG.). 336p. (gr. 2-13). 26.95 (*978-0-595-74674-3(8)) iUniverse, Inc. (Writers Advantage Pr.).

Loehr, Mallory. Earth Magic. 1999. (Magic Elements Quartet Ser.: Vol. 2). (Illus.). 112p. (J). (gr. 3-5). pap. 3.99 (978-0-679-89218-2(4) , Random Hse. Bks. for Young Readers) Random Hse. Children's Bks.

—Earth Magic. 1999. (J). 10.64 (978-0-606-19081-7(3)); (gr. 3-6). lib. bdg. 11.80 (978-0-613-21473-5(0)) Tandem Library Bks.

—Water Wishes. 1999. (Magic Elements Quartet Ser.: Vol. 1). 128p. (J). (gr. k-3). pap. 3.99 (978-0-679-89216-8(8) , Random Hse. Bks. for Young Readers) Random Hse. Children's Bks.

—Water Wishes. 1999. (J). (978-0-606-19085-5(6)); (gr. 3-6). lib. bdg. 11.80 (978-0-613-16234-0(X)) Tandem Library Bks.

Loehr, Patrick, illus. Mucumber McGee & the Lunch Lady's Liver. 2008. (J). (*978-0-06-082330-6(5)); lib. bdg. (*978-0-06-082331-3(3)) HarperCollins Pubs.

Loesch, Joe. The Abraham Lincoln Logues. Hutchinson, Cheryl, ed. Cox, Brian T., illus. unabr. ed. 2000. (Backyard Adventure Ser.). 60p. (J). (gr. k-5). reprint ed. 16.95 incl. audio compact disk (978-1-932332-03-2(0)) Toy Box Productions.

—The Abraham Lincoln Logues. Hutchinson, Cheryl J., ed. Cox, Brian T., illus. unabr. ed. (Backyard Adventure Ser.). (J). (gr. k-6). pap. 16.95 incl. audio compact disk (978-1-887729-77-2(1)); pap. 14.95 incl. audio (978-1-887729-76-5(3)) Toy Box Productions.

Lohans, Alison. Waiting for the Sun. Mets, Marilyn & Lawson, Peter, illus. 2007. 32p. pap. (*978-0-88995-358-1(9)) Fitzhenry & Whiteside, Ltd.

Lollino, Jessica. Lily's Little Brother Bother. Lollino, Jessica, ed. 2006. (Little Lily Mays Ser.: vol. 4). (Illus.). 32p. (J). pap. 20.00 (978-0-9712383-4-3(0)) Culture Connection, The.

London, Jonathan. Froggy's Baby Sister. Remkiewicz, Frank, illus. (Froggy Ser.). 32p. (J). 2005. pap. 5.99 (978-0-14-240342-6(3) , Puffin); 2003. 15.99 (978-0-670-03659-2(5) , Viking Juvenile) Penguin Group (USA) Inc.

—Moshi Moshi. Yoshi, Miyake, illus. 1998. (Around the World Ser.). 32p. (gr. k-4). lib. bdg. 23.90 (978-0-7613-0110-3(0) , Millbrook Pr.) Lerner Publishing Group.

Long, D. J. I Wish I Was the Baby. Johnson, Gary, illus. 2002. 32p. (J). 5.95 (978-0-8249-5441-3(6)) Ideals Pubns.

Look, Lenore. Henry's First-Moon Birthday. Heo, Yumi, illus. 2001. 40p. (J). (ps-2). 16.99 (978-0-689-82294-0(4) , Atheneum/Anne Schwartz Bks.) Simon & Schuster Children's Publishing.

Lord, Cynthia. Rules. 2006. 208p. (J). (gr. 4-7). pap. 15.99 (978-0-439-44382-1(2) , Scholastic Pr.) Scholastic, Inc.

—Rules. rev. l.t. ed. 2007. 200p. (YA). 23.95 (*978-0-7862-9559-3(7)) Thorndike Pr.

Lorimer, Janet. Ben Cody's Treasure: Set 2. 2002. 32p. (YA). 2.95 (978-1-56254-416-4(0) , SP 4160) Saddleback Educational Publishing.

Lotto, Anna. Heart So True. Dunfey, Beth, ed. 2005. (One Tree Hill Ser.: No. 2). 264p. (J). pap. 6.99 (978-0-439-71561-4(X)) Scholastic, Inc.

Love, D. Anne. Three Against the Tide. 2000. (978-0-606-18909-5(2)) Tandem Library Bks.

Low, Alice. The Witch Who Was Afraid of Witches. 1999. (I Can Read Chapter Bks.). (Illus.). 48p. (J). (gr. 3-4). 14.89 (978-0-06-028306-3(8)) HarperCollins Pubs.

—The Witch Who Was Afraid of Witches. Manning, Jane, illus. 1999. (I Can Read Bks.). 48p. (J). (gr. 3-4). 14.95 (978-0-06-028305-6(X)) HarperCollins Pubs.

—The Witch Who Was Afraid of Witches. Manning, Jane, illus. 2000. (J). (978-0-606-20009-7(6)) Tandem Library Bks.

—Witch Who Was Afraid of Witches. 2000. (978-0-606-20312-8(5)); (gr. 3-6). lib. bdg. 11.80 (978-0-613-29149-1(2)) Tandem Library Bks.

Lowden, Stephanie. Time of the Eagle: A Story of an Ojibwe Winter. 2004. 128p. (J). pap. 12.00 (978-1-883953-34-8(0)) Midwest Traditions, Inc.

Lowden, Stephanie Golightly. Time of the Eagle: A Story of an Ojibwe Winter. 2006. 128p. (J). 18.95 (978-1-883953-38-6(3) , Blue Horse Bks.) Midwest Traditions, Inc.

Lowry, Brigid. Follow the Blue. 2004. 205p. (J). (gr. 7 up). tchr. ed. 16.95 (978-0-8234-1827-5(8)) Holiday Hse., Inc.

—Follow the Blue. 2006. 208p. (YA). pap. 8.95 (978-0-312-34297-5(7) , St. Martin's Griffin) St. Martin's Pr.

Lowry, Lois. The Silent Boy. 2003. (Illus.). 192p. (YA). (gr. 5-12). tchr. ed. 15.00 (978-0-618-28231-9(9) , Walter Lorraine) Houghton Mifflin Co. Trade & Reference Div.

—A Summer to Die. 2007. 160p. (YA). (gr. 7). pap. 7.99 (978-0-385-73420-2(4) , Delacorte Bks. for Young Readers) Random Hse. Children's Bks.

—A Summer to Die. 1999. mass mkt. (978-0-553-14304-1(2)); mass mkt. (978-0-553-24389-5(6)); mass mkt. (978-0-553-25447-1(2)) Random Hse., Inc.

Lowry, Lois. The Willoughbys. 2008. (J). (*978-0-618-97974-5(3)) Houghton Mifflin Co.

Lubar, David. Sleeping Freshmen Never Lie. (YA). 2007. 288p. pap. 6.99 (978-0-14-240780-6(1) , Puffin); 2005. 160p. (gr. 6-10). 16.99 (978-0-525-47311-4(4) , Dutton Juvenile) Penguin Group (USA) Inc.

Lubbert, Constance. Killdeer. 2004. 81p. pap. 14.95 (978-1-4137-1138-7(3)) PublishAmerica, Inc.

Lucado, Max. Coming Home. 2007. (Illus.). 32p. (J). 15.99 (*978-1-58134-756-2(1)) Crossway Bks.

Luce, Philip. Gotno Tale. 2007. 24p. (J). per. 11.99 (*978-1-59886-754-1(7)) Tate Publishing & Enterprises, L.L.C.

Luchsinger, Dena. Playing by the Rules: A Story about Autism. Olson, Julie, illus. 2007. (Special Needs Collection). 36p. (J). (ps-3). 16.95 (*978-1-890627-83-6(6)) Woodbine Hse.

Lucke, Deb. The Boy Who Wouldn't Swim. 2008. (J). (*978-0-618-91484-5(6) , Clarion Bks.) Houghton Mifflin Co. Trade & Reference Div.

Lunney, Linda Hayward. Monster Bug. Palmisciano, Diane, tr. Palmisciano, Diane, illus. 2004. (Science Solves It! Ser.). (J). pap. 4.99 (978-1-57565-135-4(1)) Kane Pr., The.

Luongo, Jane. Jake's First Word. Kelley, Patrick, illus. 2003. (Books for Young Learners). 16p. (J). pap. 5.00 net. (978-1-57274-258-1(5) , 2456) Owen, Richard C. Pubs., Inc.

Lupica, Mike. Heat. 2007. 240p. (J). pap. 6.99 (978-0-14-240757-8(7) , Puffin); 2006. 220p. (YA). (gr. 5). 16.99 (978-0-399-24301-1(1) , Philomel) Penguin Group (USA) Inc.

Lupica, Mike. Hot Hand. 2007. (Mike Lupica's Comeback Kids Ser.). 165p. (J). (gr. 4-7). 9.99 (*978-0-399-24714-9(9) , Philomel) Penguin Group (USA) Inc.

Lurie, Alison. Baba Yaga & the Stolen Baby. Souhami, Jessica, illus. ed. 2008. 32p. (J). pap. 7.95 (*978-1-84507-753-2(9)) Lincoln, Frances Ltd. GBR. *Dist:* Perseus Distribution.

Lynch, Chris. The Gravedigger's Cottage. 2004. 208p. (J). (gr. 7 up). 15.99 (978-0-06-623940-8(0)) HarperCollins Pubs.

MacCullough, Carolyn. Stealing Henry. rev. ed. 2005. 208p. (YA). 16.95 (978-1-59643-045-7(1)) Roaring Brook Pr.

MacDonald, Alan. Contest Crazy. Brown, Judy, illus. 2006. (Read-It! Chapter Books). 48p. (J). lib. bdg. (*978-1-4048-3134-6(7) , 1265803) Picture Window Bks.

MacDonald, George. Ranald Bannerman's Boyhood. 2006. 63.99 (*978-1-4280-3039-8(5)) IndyPublish.com.

MacDonald, Ross. Bad Baby. MacDonald, Ross, illus. 2005. (Illus.). 32p. (J). 16.95 (978-1-59643-064-8(8)) Roaring Brook Pr.

Mack, Paulette. Cookout at Grandma's House: The Adventures of Mielle & Cheeky. 2006. (ENG., Illus.). 24p. per. 10.95 (*978-1-59800-998-9(2)) Outskirts Press, Inc.

Mack, Todd. Princess Penelope Takes Charge. Gran, Julia, illus. 2006. 32p. (J). pap. 16.99 (978-0-439-67380-8(1) , Scholastic Pr.) Scholastic, Inc.

MacKall, Dandi Daley. All the King's Horses. 2001. (gr. 7-12). lib. bdg. 14.15 (978-0-613-72846-1(7)) Tandem Library Bks.

—Horsefeathers Mystery, Vol. 7. 2001. (Horsefeathers Ser.: Vol. 7). (Illus.). 192p. (J). (gr. 7-12). 5.99 (978-0-570-07128-0(3)) Concordia Publishing Hse.

—Kyra's Story. 2003. (Degrees of Guilt Ser.). (YA). pap. 9.99 (978-0-8423-8284-7(4)) Tyndale Hse. Pubs.

Mackall, Dandi Daley. Upsetting Annie. 2007. (Faithgirlz!#8482; / Blog On! Ser.). 128p. (J). pap. 6.99 (978-0-310-71264-0(5)) Zonderkidz.

MacKenzie, Carine. El Secreto de la Hermana Mayor, el Maria.Tr. of Big Sister's Secret. (SPA.). (J). 1.99 (978-1-56063-700-4(5) , 497731) Editorial Unilit.

Maher, Mickle Brandt. Master Stitchum & the Moon. Dousias, Spiro, illus. 2003. (J). 19.99 (978-1-932188-01-1(0)) Bollix Bks.

Mahoney, Daniel J. A Really Good Snowman. 2005. (Illus.). 32p. (J). (gr. k-3). 15.00 (978-0-618-47554-4(0) , Clarion Bks.) Houghton Mifflin Co. Trade & Reference Div.

Mahy, Margaret. Al Borde del Acantilado. Abos, Elena, tr. 2002. (Gran Angular Ser.). (SPA.). 210p. (978-84-348-8566-0(2)) SM Ediciones ESP. *Dist:* Lectorum Pubns., Inc.

Maier, Inger M. When Lizzie Was Afraid: Of Trying New Things. Candon, Jennifer, illus. 2005. 32p. (J). 14.95 (978-1-59147-170-7(2)); pap. 8.95 (978-1-59147-171-4(0)) American Psychological Assn. (Magination Pr.).

Maisner, Heather. It's My Turn! Stephenson, Kristina, illus. 2005. (First Time Stories Ser.). 24p. (J). (gr. k-ps). pap. 3.95 (978-0-7534-5740-5(7) , Kingfisher) Houghton Mifflin Co. Trade & Reference Div.

—Our New Baby. Stephenson, Kristina, illus. 2005. (First Time Stories Ser.). 24p. (J). (gr. k-ps). pap. 3.95 (978-0-7534-5738-2(5) , Kingfisher) Houghton Mifflin Co. Trade & Reference Div.

Malea. Princess Melia. 2007. 145p. (J). pap. 15.95 (*978-1-58909-367-6(4)) Bookstand Publishing.

Malison, Anna. Through Thick & Thin. 2006. (ENG.). 136p. per. (978-1-897117-14-9(0)) Gospel Folio Pr.

Mallat, Kathy. Oh, Brother. Mallat, Kathy, illus. 2004. (Illus.). 32p. (J). 15.95 (978-0-8027-8875-7(0)) Walker & Co.

Mammay, Judith. Knowing Joseph. 2008. (Illus.). 256p. (YA). (gr. 2-7). 16.95 (*978-1-933831-05-3(7)) Blooming Tree Pr.

Mandarino, Gene. What's Autism? 2006. pap. 25.00 (978-0-9786795-0-7(4)) Charlie's Gift.

Manson, Ainslie. Ballerinas Don't Wear Glasses. Griffiths, Dean, illus. 2001. 32p. (J). (ps-2). 6.95 (978-1-55143-176-5(9)) Orca Bk. Pubs. USA.

—Ballerinas Don't Wear Glasses. 2000. (gr. 3-6). lib. bdg. 15.25 (978-0-613-53944-9(3)) Tandem Library Bks.

Mantell, Paul. Sacrifice. 2000. (gr. 3-6). lib. bdg. 13.00 (978-0-613-26807-3(5)) Tandem Library Bks.

Mantell, Paul. Snow Board Showdown. 2007. 143p. (J). lib. bdg. (*978-1-59953-109-0(7)) Norwood Hse. Pr.

Mariconda, Barbara. Turn the Cup Around. 1998. (978-0-606-13878-9(1)) Tandem Library Bks.

Mario, Heidi S. I'd Rather Have an Iguana. 1999. (Illus.). 32p. (J). (ps-3). 14.95 (978-0-88106-357-8(6)) Charlesbridge Publishing, Inc.

Marks, Graham. Missing in Tokyo. 2006. 256p. (YA). 16.95 (978-1-58234-907-7(X) , Bloomsbury Children) Bloomsbury Publishing.

Marquess, Dana. Night of the Lighted Freedom: A Firefly Fantasy. 2006. (Illus.). 32p. (J). 19.95 (978-1-932278-06-4(0)) Mayhaven Publishing.

Marr, Ella J. The Adventures of Curtis & Grammy. 2006. 57p. pap. 12.95 (*978-1-4241-4743-4(3)) PublishAmerica, Inc.

Marsh, Carole. The Earthshaking Earthquake MYST. 2007. 128p. pap. 5.99 (*978-0-635-06339-7(5)) Gallopade International.

—The Horrendous Hurricane MYST. 2007. 128p. pap. 5.99 (*978-0-635-06340-3(9)) Gallopade International.

—The Treacherous Tornado Mystery! 2007. 128p. pap. 5.99 (*978-0-635-06338-0(7)) Gallopade International.

Marshall, Catherine. Stage Fright/Goodbye, Sweet Prince/Brotherly Love. 2005. (Christy Juvenile Ser.). 368p. (J). (gr. 4-7). pap. 9.99 (978-1-4003-0775-3(9)) Nelson, Thomas Inc.

Martin, Ann M. Karen's Copycat. 1999. (Baby-Sitters Little Sister Ser.: No. 107). 112p. (J). (gr. 3-7). pap. 3.99 (978-0-590-50059-3(7)) Scholastic, Inc.

—Karen's Yo-Yo. 2000. (Baby-Sitters Little Sister Ser.: No. 119). (Illus.). 144p. (J). (gr. 3-7). pap. 3.99 (978-0-590-52511-4(5)) Scholastic, Inc.

Martin, Patricia. Lulu Atlantis & the Quest for True Blue Love. 2008. (J). (*978-0-375-84016-6(8)); 240p. (gr. 2-6). lib. bdg. 17.99 (*978-0-375-94016-3(2)) Random Hse. Children's Bks. (Schwartz & Wade Bks.).

Martin, Rafe. The Shark God. Shannon, David, illus. 2007. 32p. (J). (ps-3). pap. 5.99 (*978-0-590-39570-0(X)) Scholastic, Inc.

Marx, David F. Baby in the House. Fisher, Cynthia, illus. 2000. (Rookie Readers Ser.). 32p. (J). (gr. 1-2). 19.50 (978-0-516-21688-1(0) , Children's Pr.) Scholastic Library Publishing.

Marzollo, Jean. Baseball Brothers. Kelley, True, illus. 1999. (Hello Reader! Ser.). 32p. (J). pap. 3.99 (978-0-590-38398-1(1)) Scholastic, Inc.

—Baseball Brothers. 1999. (Hello Reader! Ser.). (J). 10.30 (978-0-606-16599-0(1)); lib. bdg. 11.25 (978-0-613-16897-7(6)) Tandem Library Bks.

Marzollo, Jean, et al. Baseball Brothers. Kelley, True, illus. 2004. 32p. (J). lib. bdg. 15.00 (978-1-59054-418-1(8)) Fitzgerald Bks.

Mason, Craig. Turtle Games. Mason, Bergetta, illus. 2003. 32p. (J). 4.99 (978-0-9729153-0-4(3)) 1 Sleeve Publishing.

Masters, Susan Rowan. Night Journey to Vicksburg. Killcoyne, Hope L., ed. Smith, Duane A., illus. 2003. (Adventures in America Ser.). 74p. (J). 14.95 (978-1-893110-30-4(3)) Silver Moon Pr.

Matheson, Shirlee Smith. Gambler's Daughter. 2008. 144p. (YA). pap. 11.99 (*978-1-55002-718-1(2) , Sandcastle Bks.) Dundurn Group, The CAN. *Dist:* Univ. of Toronto Pr.

Mathis, Sharon Bell. Teacup Full of Roses, Set. abr. ed. 1999. (J). (gr. 4-7). pap. 15.95 incl. audio (978-0-670-69438-9(X)) Live Oak Media.

Matthews, Kezi. Scorpio's Child. 2001. 160p. (YA). (gr. 6-8). 16.95 (978-0-8126-2890-6(X)) Cricket Bks.

May, Eleanor. The Great Shape-Up. Gott, Barry, illus. 2007. (Science Solves It! Ser.). 32p. (J). (gr. 1-3). 4.99 (*978-1-57565-248-1(X)) Kane Pr., The.

May, Sophie. Dotty Dimples Flyaway. 2007. 94.99 (*978-1-4280-5295-6(X)); pap. 88.99 (*978-1-4280-5304-5(2)) IndyPublish.com.

Mayer, Gina. Just a Bully. 1999. (ps-2). lib. bdg. 11.00 (978-0-613-27921-5(2)) Tandem Library Bks.

Mayer, Mercer. Goodnight, Little Critter, Vol. 3. 2002. (Little Critter First Readers Ser.). (Illus.). 24p. (J). (gr. 1-2). pap. 3.95 (978-1-57768-834-1(1)) School Specialty Publishing.

—Grandma's Garden. 2002. (Little Critter First Readers Ser.). (Illus.). 24p. (J). (gr. k-1). pap. 3.95 (978-1-57768-846-4(5)) School Specialty Publishing.

—Grandma's Garden. 2001. (gr. k-3). lib. bdg. 11.80 (978-0-613-67625-0(4)) Tandem Library Bks.

—It's Easter. Mayer, Mercer, illus. 2007. (Little Critter Ser.). 20p. (J). pap. 6.99 (978-0-06-053974-0(7) , Harper Festival) HarperCollins Pubs.

—Just Me & My Little Brother. Mayer, Mercer, illus. 1998. (Little Critter Ser.). (Illus.). 24p. (J). (gr. k-k). pap. 3.99 (978-0-307-12628-3(5) , 12628, Random Hse. Bks. for Young Readers) Random Hse. Children's Bks.

—Little Critter's the Best Present. 2000. (Little Critter Ser.). (J). (ps-3). (978-0-606-18923-1(8)) Tandem Library Bks.

—Me Too! Mayer, Mercer, illus. 2001. (Little Critter Ser.). (Illus.). 24p. (J). reprint ed. pap. 3.99 (978-0-307-11941-4(6) , 11941, Random Hse. Bks. for Young Readers) Random Hse. Children's Bks.

—Our Tree House, Vol. 3. 2002. (Little Critter First Readers Ser.). (Illus.). 24p. (J). (gr. 1-2). pap. 3.95 (978-1-57768-833-4(3)) School Specialty Publishing.

Mayer, Mercer & Mayer, Gina. Just a Bully. Mayer, Mercer, illus. 1999. (Little Critter Ser.). (J). (ps-3). 10.09 (978-0-606-19800-4(8)) Tandem Library Bks.

—The New Potty. 2003. (Illus.). 24p. (J). (gr. k-ps). pap. 3.25 (978-0-375-82631-3(9) , Random Hse. Bks. for Young Readers) Random Hse. Children's Bks.

Mayfield, Julie. The Magical First Day. Reis, Michael, illus. 1998. (J). pap. 5.95 (978-1-56763-337-5(4)); lib. bdg. 17.25 (978-1-56763-336-8(6)) Ozark Publishing.

Mayfield, Ruth. The Dooley Family. 2002. (Illus.). 16p. (J). (gr. 1-4). pap. 6.75 (978-0-9701193-1-5(3)) Mayfield, Ruth.

Mazer, Anne. Home Is Where the Heart Is. 2006. (Amazing Days of Abby Hayes Ser.: no. 17). 118p. (J). lib. bdg. 16.92 (*978-1-4242-1518-8(8)) Fitzgerald Bks.

Mbuthia, Waithira. My Sister's Wedding: A Story of Kenya. Karanja, Geoffrey Gacheru, illus. 2005. (Make Friends Around the World Ser.). 32p. (J). (gr. k-3). 15.95 (978-1-56899-896-1(1) , B8006); pap. 6.95 (978-1-56899-897-8(X) , S8006) Soundprints.

—My Sister's Wedding: A Story of Kenya. 2002. (gr. k-3). lib. bdg. 14.10 (978-0-613-70813-5(X)) Tandem Library Bks.

McClintock, Barbara. Adèle & Simon. McClintock, Barbara, illus. 2006. (Illus.). 40p. (J). 16.00 (978-0-374-38044-1(9) , Farrar, Straus & Giroux (BYR)) Farrar, Straus & Giroux.

McClintock, Barbara. Adèle & Simon in America. 2008. (J). (*978-0-374-39924-5(7)) Farrar, Straus & Giroux.

McCLure, Beverly Stowe. Listen to the Ghost. 2005. (J). per. 16.95 (978-1-933353-51-7(1) , Paladin Timeless) Twilight Times Bks.

McCormick, Patricia. My Brother's Keeper. 2005. 192p. (gr. 5-17). 15.99 (978-0-7868-5173-7(2)) Hyperion Bks. for Children.

—My Brother's Keeper. 2006. 192p. (gr. 5-17). reprint ed. pap. 5.99 (978-0-7868-5174-4(0)) Hyperion Pr.

McCormick, Wendy. The Night You Were Born. Williams, Sophy, illus. 2000. 32p. (J). (ps-2). 15.95 (978-1-56145-225-5(4)) Peachtree Pubs., Ltd.

McCullough, Sharon Pierce. Bunbun at the Fair. 2002. (Bunbun Ser.). (Illus.). 24p. (J). (gr. k-2). 14.99 (978-1-84148-900-1(X)) Barefoot Bks., Inc.

—Bunbun, the Middle One. McCullough, Sharon Pierce, illus. 2002. (Bunbun Ser.). (Illus.). 24p. (J). (gr. k-2). bds. 6.99 (978-1-84148-377-1(X)) Barefoot Bks., Inc.

McDaniel, Lurlene. Holly's Story. 2005. (Angels in Pink Ser.). 224p. (gr. 7). (YA). 10.95 (978-0-385-73158-4(2)); (J). lib. bdg. 12.99 (978-0-385-90195-6(X)) Random Hse. Children's Bks. (Delacorte Bks. for Young Readers).

—Raina's Story. 2006. (Angels in Pink Ser.). 208p. (YA). (gr. 7). pap. 6.50 (978-0-440-23866-9(8) , Laurel Leaf) Random Hse. Children's Bks.

McDonald, Megan. Doctor Is In! Reynolds, Peter H., illus. 2006. (Judy Moody Ser.: No. 5). 176p. (J). (gr. 1-5). pap. 5.99 (978-0-7636-2615-0(5)) Candlewick Pr.

—Doctor Is In! Reynolds, Peter H., tr. Reynolds, Peter H., illus. 2004. (Judy Moody Ser.: No. 5). 176p. (J). (gr. 1-5). 15.99 (978-0-7636-2024-0(6)) Candlewick Pr.

—Doctor Is In! Reynolds, Peter, illus. 2004. (Judy Moody Ser.: No. 5). 151p. (J). lib. bdg. 23.08 (*978-1-4242-1145-6(X)) Fitzgerald Bks.

—Judy Moody Gets Famous! Reynolds, Peter H., illus. (Judy Moody Ser.: No. 2). 144p. (J). (gr. 1-5). 2003. pap. 5.99 (978-0-7636-1931-2(0)); 2001. 15.99 (978-0-7636-0849-1(1)) Candlewick Pr.

—Judy Moody Gets Famous! 2003. (Judy Moody Ser.: No. 2). (gr. 3-6). lib. bdg. 14.15 (978-0-613-62107-6(7)) Tandem Library Bks.

—Judy Moody Saves the World! Reynolds, Peter H., illus. (Judy Moody Ser.: No. 3). 160p. (J). (gr. 1-5). 2004. pap. 5.99 (978-0-7636-2087-5(4)); 2002. 15.99 (978-0-7636-1446-1(7)) Candlewick Pr.

—Judy Moody se Vuelve Famosa! Mendoza Garcia, Isabel, tr. Reynolds, Peter H., illus. (SPA.). 144p. (J). (gr. 3-5). pap. 7.95 (978-1-59437-817-1(7)) Santillana USA Publishing Co., Inc.

—Stink: The Incredible Shrinking Kid. Reynolds, Peter H., illus. (J). (gr. k-3). 2006. 128p. pap. 4.99 (978-0-7636-2891-8(3)); 2005. 112p. 12.99 (978-0-7636-2025-7(4)) Candlewick Pr.

McDonald, Rae. A Fishing Surprise. Kemly, Kathleen Hadam, illus. 2007. 32p. (J). (*978-1-55971-977-3(X) , NorthWord Bks. for Young Readers) T&N Children's Publishing.

McElfresh, Lynn E. Can You Feel the Thunder? 1999. (YA). pap., stu. ed. 52.00 incl. audio (978-0-7887-3837-1(2) , 41031) Recorded Bks., LLC.

McElmurry, Jill. I'm Not a Baby. McElmurry, Jill, illus. 2006. (Illus.). 32p. (J). (ps-3). lib. bdg. 18.99 (978-0-375-93614-2(9) , Schwartz & Wade Bks.) Random Hse. Children's Bks.

McElroy, Laurie. Alien Invasion. 2007. (Teenick Ser.: No. 5). 112p. (J). pap. 4.99 (978-0-439-89044-1(6)) Scholastic, Inc.

—Go Hollywood. 2006. (Teenick Ser.: No. 3). 112p. (J). pap. 4.99 (978-0-439-89043-4(8)) Scholastic, Inc.

McElroy, Laurie. Josh Is Done. 2007. (Teenick Ser.: No. 7). 128p. (J). pap. 4.99 (*978-0-439-91647-9(X)) Scholastic, Inc.

McFarlane, Brian. The Season of Surprises. 9th ed. 2008. 184p. pap. 6.95 (*978-1-55168-300-3(8)) Key Porter Bks. CAN. *Dist:* Perseus Distribution.

McGugan, Jim. Bridge 6. ed. 2004. (Illus.). (J). (gr. k-3). spiral bd. (978-0-616-01721-0(9)) Canadian National Institute for the Blind/Institut National Canadien pour les Aveugles.

—Bridge 6. Mills, Judith Christine, illus. 1999. 15p. (J). (ps-3). 16.95 (978-0-7737-3137-0(7)) Stoddart Kids CAN. *Dist:* Fitzhenry & Whiteside, Ltd.

McKay, Hilary. Caddy Ever After. 224p. (J). 2007. pap. 5.99 (*978-1-4169-0931-6(1) , Aladdin); 2006. (gr. 5-9). 15.95 (978-1-4169-0930-9(3) , McElderry, Margaret K.) Simon & Schuster Children's Publishing.

—Dolphin Luck. l.t. ed. 2005. (Illus.). 272p. (J). pap. incl. audio (978-0-7540-7865-4(5) , CLP 449) BBC Audio.

—Dolphin Luck. 2004. (J). pap. 29.95 incl. audio (978-0-7540-6273-8(2) , Chivers Children's Audio Bks.) BBC Audiobooks America.

—Dolphin Luck. 2000. (J). (978-0-606-20086-8(X)) Tandem Library Bks.

—Dolphin Luck. l.t. ed. 2001. (Illus.). 198p. (J). (gr. 4-7). 21.95 (978-0-7862-2703-7(6)) Thorndike Pr.

—Indigo's Star. 272p. (J). (gr. 3-7). 2004. (Illus.). 16.95 (978-0-689-86563-3(5) , McElderry, Margaret K.); 2006. reprint ed. pap. 5.99 (978-1-4169-1403-7(X) , Aladdin) Simon & Schuster Children's Publishing.

—Permanent Rose. (J). (gr. 3-7). 2005. 240p. 16.99 (978-1-4169-0372-7(0) , McElderry, Margaret K.); 2006. 256p. reprint ed. pap. 5.99 (978-1-4169-2804-1(9) , Aladdin) Simon & Schuster Children's Publishing.

—Saffy's Angel. 2004. 160p. (J). (gr. 4-7). pap. 36.00 incl. audio (978-0-8072-2098-6(1) , Listening Library) Random Hse. Audio Publishing Group.

—Saffy's Angel. 160p. (J). (gr. 3-7). 2003. (Illus.). pap. 4.99 (978-0-689-84934-3(6) , Aladdin); 2002. 16.99 (978-0-689-84933-6(8) , McElderry, Margaret K.) Simon & Schuster Children's Publishing.

—Saffy's Angel. l.t. ed. 2003. (Juvenile Ser.). 227p. (J). 21.95 (978-0-7862-5500-9(5)) Thorndike Pr.

McKay, Sindy. We Both Read-Ben & Becky Get a Pet. Johnson, Meredith, illus. (We Both Read Ser.). 44p. (J). (gr. 2 up). 1999. pap. 3.99 (978-1-891327-10-0(0)); 1998. 7.99 (978-1-891327-06-3(2)) Treasure Bay, Inc.

McKinney, Linda. Tears in the Wind. 2002. 113p. pap. 16.95 (978-1-59286-103-3(2)) PublishAmerica, Inc.

McKy, Katie & Bernasconi, Pablo. Pumpkin Town! or, Nothing Is Better & Worse Than Pumpkins. McKy, Katie & Bernasconi, Pablo, illus. 2006. (Illus.). 32p. (J). (gr. k-3). 16.00 (978-0-618-60569-9(X)) Houghton Mifflin Co.

McMahan, Stephanie K. The Mystery of the Golden Rings. 2007. 140p. 21.95 ***(978-0-595-68451-9(3));*** per. 11.95 ***(978-0-595-43998-0(5))*** iUniverse, Inc.

McManis, Margaret Olivia. Ima & the Great Texas Ostrich Race. Dupree, Bruce, illus. 2002. (J). pap. (978-1-57168-671-8(1) , Eakin Pr.) Eakin Pr.

—Ima & the Great Texas Ostrich Race. 2002. (Illus.). 32p. 15.95 (978-1-57168-605-3(3)) Eakin Pr.

McMillan, Ernest. Psalms of Passion. 2006. 48p. pap. 8.95 (978-1-59800-224-9(4)) Outskirts Press, Inc.

McMillion, Gloria. Whirlwinds Whirl Around. 2007. 136p. per. 11.95 ***(978-0-595-42248-7(9))*** iUniverse, Inc.

McPhail, David M. My Little Brother. 2004. (Illus.). 32p. (J). 16.00 (978-0-15-204900-3(2)) Harcourt Children's Bks.

—Sisters. McPhail, David M., illus. 2003. (Illus.). 32p. (J). (ps-2). 9.95 (978-0-15-204659-0(3)) Harcourt Children's Bks.

McQuerry, Maureen Doyle. Wolfproof. Murphy, John, illus. 2006. (J). 183p. 24.95 (978-1-59597-006-0(1)); 176p. per. 14.95 (978-1-59597-009-1(6)) Idylls Pr.

Mead, Alice. Adem's Cross. 1998. (978-0-606-13110-0(8)) Tandem Library Bks.

—Girl of Kosovo. 2001. 128p. (J). (gr. 4-7). 16.00 (978-0-374-32620-3(7) , Farrar, Straus & Giroux (BYR)) Farrar, Straus & Giroux.

—Girl of Kosovo. 2003. (Illus.). 128p. (J). (gr. 5). pap. 5.50 (978-0-440-41853-5(4) , Yearling) Random Hse. Children's Bks.

—Girl of Kosovo. 2003. (gr. 3-6). lib. bdg. 13.00 (978-0-613-62205-9(7)) Tandem Library Bks.

Meade, Holly, illus. Inside, Inside, Inside. 2005. 32p. (J). 16.95 (978-0-7614-5125-9(0)) Cavendish, Marshall Corp.

Meddaugh, Susan. Cinderella's Rat. Meddaugh, Susan, illus. 2002. (Illus.). 32p. (J). (gr. k-3). pap. 5.95 (978-0-618-12540-1(X) , Walter Lorraine) Houghton Mifflin Co. Trade & Reference Div.

—Cinderella's Rat. 2002. (gr. k-3). lib. bdg. 14.10 (978-0-613-72920-8(X)) Tandem Library Bks.

Medearis, Angela Shelf. Lucy's Quick Book. Ernst, Lisa Campbell, illus. 2004. (Green Light Readers Level 2 Ser.). 24p. (J). 12.95 (978-0-15-205144-0(9)); pap. 3.95 (978-0-15-205143-3(0)) Harcourt Children's Bks. (Green Light Readers).

—Seven Spools of Thread: A Kwanzaa Story. Minter, Daniel, illus. 2000. 40p. (J). (gr. 2-5). 15.95 (978-0-8075-7315-0(9)); pap. 6.95 (978-0-8075-7316-7(7)) Whitman, Albert & Co.

—What Did I Do to Deserve a Sister Like You? Tate, Don, II & Galbreath, Mark, illus. 2002. (gr. 3-5). 123p. (J). pap. 7.95 (978-1-57168-642-8(8) , Eakin Pr.); 76p. 13.95 (978-1-57168-471-4(9)) Eakin Pr.

Mendes, Valerie. Look at Me, Grandma! Fletcher, Claire, illus. 2001. 32p. (J). (ps-1). pap. 15.95 (978-0-439-29654-0(4) , Chicken Hse., The) Scholastic, Inc.

Mercer, Sienna. Switched. 2007. (My Sister the Vampire Ser.). 208p. (J). 16.99 ***(978-0-06-087111-6(3));*** (gr. 3-7). pap. 5.99 ***(978-0-06-087113-0(X)*** , Harper Trophy) HarperCollins Pubs.

Merritt, Kate, illus. My Family: My Sister. 2003. 10p. (J). bds. 3.95 (978-0-8069-8581-7(X)) Sterling Publishing Co., Inc.

Metikosh, Anne. Terra Incognita. 2005. (Illus.). 142p. (J). (gr. 3-9). pap., tchr. ed. 8.95 (978-0-921870-76-0(0)) Ronsdale Pr. CAN. *Dist:* Literary Pr. Group of Canada.

Meunier, Sylvain & Lapierre, Steeve. Graindsel et Bretel. Fil et, Julie, illus. 2004. (était une Fois Ser.). (FRE.). 24p. (J). (ps). pap. (978-2-89021-699-0(3)) Diffusion du livre Mirabel.

Michael, Livi. The Whispering Road. 2006. 336p. (J). (gr. 5). pap. 6.99 (978-0-14-240724-0(0) , Puffin); 2005. 272p. (YA). (gr. 4). 17.99 (978-0-399-24357-8(7) , Putnam Juvenile) Penguin Group (USA) Inc.

Michels-Gualtieri, Akaela S. I Was Born to Be a Sister. Ramsey, Marcy Dunn, illus. 2001. 32p. (ps-7). 16.95 (978-1-930775-03-9(2)) Platypus Media, L.L.C.

Michels-Gualtieri, Zaydek G. I was Born to Be a Brother. Liegey, Daniel, illus. 2006. 32p. 18.95 (978-1-930775-10-7(5)) Platypus Media, L.L.C.

Michels-Gualtieri, Zaydek G. & Michels-Gualtieri, Akaela S. I Was Born to be a Brother/I Was Born to be a Sister. 2005. (Illus.). 32p. 34.95 (978-1-930775-21-3(0)) Platypus Media, L.L.C.

Michelson, Richard. Oh No, Not Ghosts! McCauley, Adam, illus. 2006. 44p. (J). 16.00 (978-0-15-205186-0(4)) Harcourt Trade Pubs.

Milgrim, David. Amelia Makes a Movie. Milgrim, David, illus. 2008. 32p. (J). (ps). 16.99 ***(978-0-399-24670-8(3)*** , Putnam Juvenile) Penguin Group (USA) Inc.

Miller, Victoria, illus. Meet Blue's Baby Brother! 2006. (Blue's Clues Ser.). 14p. (J). bds. 5.99 (978-1-4169-2748-8(4) , Simon Spotlight/Nickelodeon) Simon & Schuster Children's Publishing.

Minich, Eric. Digger & the Search for Home. 2006. 48p. pap. 12.95 (978-1-4241-0321-8(5)) PublishAmerica, Inc.

Mitchell, Todd. The Traitor King. 2007. 368p. (J). (gr. 4-7). pap. 16.99 (978-0-439-82788-1(4) , Scholastic Pr.) Scholastic, Inc.

Moerbeek, Kees. The Diary of Hansel & Gretel. Moerbeek, Kees, illus. 2002. (Illus.). 12p. (J). (gr. k-3). 12.95 (978-0-689-84602-1(9) , Little Simon) Simon & Schuster Children's Publishing.

Moeyaert, Bart. Brothers: The Oldest, the Quietest, the Realest, the Farthest, the Nicest, the Fastest, & I. Boeke, Wanda, tr. from DUT. 2005. (Illus.). 160p. (YA). (gr. 3-7). 16.95 (978-1-932425-18-5(7) , Lemniscaat) Boyds Mills Pr.

Mokosso, Henry Efesoa. One Child - One Wish: The Agony of a Single Child Family. 2006. 71p. per. 8.95 (978-1-59824-351-2(9)) E-BookTime LLC.

Molesworth. Rosy. 2006. 24.99 ***(978-1-4280-4161-5(3));*** pap. 18.99 ***(978-1-4280-4170-7(2))*** IndyPublish.com.

Montgomery, Bobbie. Donkey Cart Kids. 2000. (Pathfinder Junior Book Club Ser.). 110p. (J). pap. 6.99 (978-0-8280-1442-7(6)) Review & Herald Publishing Assn.

Moore, Eva. Good Children Get Rewards: A Story of Colonial Times. 2001. (Hello Reader! Ser.). (J). 10.79 (978-0-606-19563-8(7)) Tandem Library Bks.

Moore, Ulysses. The Long-Lost Map. Bruno, Iacopo, illus. 2006. (Ulysses Moore Ser.: No. 2). 272p. (J). pap. 12.99 (978-0-439-77439-0(X) , Scholastic) Scholastic, Inc.

Morck, Irene. Between Brothers. 2003. 160p. (J). (gr. 3-6). pap. 7.95 (978-0-7737-5530-7(6)) Stoddart Kids CAN. *Dist:* Fitzhenry & Whiteside, Ltd.

Morgan, Christopher. Pirates Eat Porridge. Curtis, Neil, illus. 2007. 80p. (J). (gr. 2-5). 14.95 ***(978-1-59643-304-5(3))*** Roaring Brook Pr.

Morgan, Melissa J. Fair to Remember, Vol. 13. 2007. (Camp Confidential Ser.). 160p. (J). pap. 4.99 (978-0-448-44451-2(8) , Grosset & Dunlap) Penguin Group (USA) Inc.

Morpurgo, Michael. Twist of Gold. 2004. 304p. (J). pap. 8.99 (978-0-7497-4687-2(4)) Egmont Bks., Ltd. GBR. *Dist:* Trafalgar Square Publishing.

Morrissey, Dean. The Crimson Comet. Morrissey, Dean, illus. 2006. (Illus.). 32p. (J). lib. bdg. 17.89 (978-0-06-008070-9(1)) HarperCollins Pubs.

Morrissey, Dean & Krensky, Stephen. The Crimson Comet. Morrissey, Dean, illus. 2006. (Illus.). 32p. (J). 16.99 (978-0-06-008068-6(X)) HarperCollins Pubs.

Mortenson, R. K. Landon Snow & the Igneus Forest. 2007. 224p. (J). 9.97 (978-1-59789-296-4(3) , Barbour Bks.) Barbour Publishing, Inc.

Moss, Miriam. One Day It Was Wet. 2000. (Cambridge Reading Ser.). (Illus.). 14p. pap. 5.00 (978-0-521-65950-5(7)) Cambridge Univ. Pr.

—One Day It Was Wet: American English Edition. 2000. (Cambridge Reading Ser.). (Illus.). 12p. pap. 5.00 (978-0-521-79529-6(X)) Cambridge Univ. Pr.

Mourlevat, Jean-Claude. The Pull of the Ocean. Maudet, Y., tr. from FRE. 2006. 208p. (gr. 7). (J). 13.95 (978-0-385-73348-9(8)); (YA). lib. bdg. 15.99 (978-0-385-90364-6(2)) Random Hse. Children's Bks. (Delacorte Bks. for Young Readers).

Mull, Brandon. Fablehaven. 2006. (Illus.). 368p. (J). 16.95 (978-1-59038-581-4(0) , Shadow Mountain) Deseret Bk. Co.

—Fablehaven. Dorman, Brandon, illus. 2007. (Fablehaven Ser.). 368p. (J). pap. 6.99 ***(978-1-4169-4720-2(5)*** , Aladdin) Simon & Schuster Children's Publishing.

—Fablehaven: Rise of the Evening Star. 2007. 456p. 17.95 ***(978-1-59038-742-9(2)*** , Shadow Mountain) Deseret Bk. Co.

Munoz, Isabel. Eric & Julieta: It's Mine/Es Mio. Mazali, Gustavo, illus. 2006. (ENG & SPA.). 24p. (J). pap. 3.99 (978-0-439-78370-5(4)) Scholastic, Inc.

—Eric & Julieta: Just Like Mom. Mazali, Gustavo, illus. 2006. (ENG & SPA.). 24p. (J). pap. 3.50 (978-0-439-78369-9(0)) Scholastic, Inc.

—Eric & Julieta: Now, What?/Ahora Que? Mazali, Gustavo, illus. 2006. (ENG & SPA.). 24p. (J). pap. 3.99 (978-0-439-78372-9(0)) Scholastic, Inc.

—Eric & Julieta: Where Is Eric?/Donde Esta Eric? Mazali, Gustavo, illus. 2006. (ENG & SPA.). 24p. (J). pap. 3.50 (978-0-439-78371-2(2)) Scholastic, Inc.

Murray, Jaye. Bottled Up. 2004. 220p. (J). (gr. 2-13). lib. bdg. 13.04 (978-0-606-32733-6(9)) Tandem Library Bks.

Muth, Jon J. Zen Shorts. Muth, Jon J., illus. 2005. (Illus.). 40p. (J). pap. 16.95 (978-0-439-33911-7(1)) Scholastic, Inc.

Muth, Jon J. Zen Ties. 2008. (J). pap. ***(978-0-439-63425-0(3)*** , Scholastic Pr.) Scholastic, Inc.

My Baby Sister, Annie: Big Book. (Pebble Soup Explorations Ser.). 16p. (ps up). 31.00 (978-0-7578-1654-3(1)) Rigby Education.

My Baby Sister, Annie: Small Book. (Pebble Soup Explorations Ser.). 16p. (ps up). 5.00 (978-0-7578-1694-9(0)) Rigby Education.

My Brother & I. 2003. (Illus.). 24p. (J). (ps-k). bds. 7.95 (978-0-8249-5455-0(6)) Ideals Pubns.

Myers, Anna. Hoggee. 2007. 192p. (J). pap. 6.95 ***(978-0-8027-9683-7(4))*** Walker & Co.

Myers, Bill. Phantom of the Haunted Church. 1998. (Bloodhounds, Inc. Ser.: Vol. 3). (Illus.). 128p. (J). (gr. 3-8). pap. 5.99 (978-1-55661-892-5(1)) Bethany Hse. Pubs.

Myers, Bill & Wimbish, David. Mystery of the Melodies from Mars. 2002. (Bloodhounds, Inc. Ser.: No. 11). 128p. (J). pap. 5.99 (978-0-7642-2623-6(1)) Bethany Hse. Pubs.

—Room with a Boo. 2002. (Bloodhounds Inc Ser.). 128p. (J). pap. 5.99 (978-0-7642-2624-3(X)) Bethany Hse. Pubs.

Myers, Laurie. Surviving Brick Johnson. Yaccarino, Dan, illus. 2000. 80p. (J). (gr. 4-6). tchr. ed. 15.00 (978-0-395-98031-6(3) , Clarion Bks.) Houghton Mifflin Co. Trade & Reference Div.

Myrddin ap Dafydd. Brwydr y Brodyr. 2005. (WEL.). 66p. (978-0-86381-906-3(0)) Gwasg Carreg Gwalch.

Na, An. Wait for Me. 2006. 240p. (YA). (gr. 4). 15.99 (978-0-399-24275-5(9) , Putnam Juvenile) Penguin Group (USA) Inc.

Naidoo, Beverley. The Other Side of Truth. 272p. (J). (gr. 5 up). 2003. pap. 6.99 (978-0-06-441002-1(1)); 2001. 17.99 (978-0-06-029628-5(3)) HarperCollins Pubs.

—The Other Side of Truth. 2000. 240p. (J). pap. (978-0-14-130476-2(6) , Putnam Juvenile) Penguin Group (USA) Inc.

—The Other Side of Truth. 2003. (gr. 5-8). lib. bdg. 14.15 (978-0-613-59158-4(5)) Tandem Library Bks.

Namioka, Lensey. Yang the Second & Her Secret Admirers. De Kiefte, Kees, illus. 1998. 144p. (J). (gr. 3-7). 15.95 (978-0-316-59731-9(7)) Little Brown & Co.

Napoli, Donna Jo. No Fair! Ben-Ami, Doren & Klementz-Harte, Lauren, illus. 2000. (Angelwings Ser.: No. 6). 96p. (J). (gr. 2-5). pap. 7.95 (978-0-689-83206-2(0) , Aladdin) Simon & Schuster Children's Publishing.

—No Fair! 2000. (Angelwings Ser.: No. 6). (Illus.). (J). (978-0-606-17909-6(7)) Tandem Library Bks.

—Pink Magic. Cameron, Chad, illus. 2005. 32p. (J). (gr. k-3). 15.00 (978-0-618-15985-7(1) , Clarion Bks.) Houghton Mifflin Co. Trade & Reference Div.

—Playing Games. Ben-Ami, Doren & Klementz-Harte, Lauren, illus. 2000. (Angelwings Ser.: No. 8). 80p. (J). (gr. 2-5). mass mkt. 7.95 (978-0-689-83208-6(7) , Aladdin) Simon & Schuster Children's Publishing.

—Playing Games. 2000. (Angelwings Ser.: No. 8). (Illus.). (J). (978-0-606-20386-9(9)) Tandem Library Bks.

Napoli, Donna Jo. The Wishing Club: A Story about Fractions. Currey, Anna, illus. rev. ed. 2007. 32p. (J). (gr. 1-4). 16.95 ***(978-0-8050-7665-3(4))*** Holt, Henry & Co.

Narsimhan, Mahtab. The Third Eye. 2007. 240p. (YA). pap. 11.99 ***(978-1-55002-750-1(6)*** , Boardwalk Bks.) Dundurn Group, The CAN. *Dist:* Univ. of Toronto Pr.

Nash, Mary. Lost Treasures Bk. 2: Mrs. Coverlet's Magician. 2001. 128p. (J). 13.49 (978-0-7868-2597-4(9)) Hyperion Pr.

Natti, Susanna, illus. Lionel & Louise. 2002. (Lionel Ser.). (J). 11.06 (978-0-7587-1388-9(6)) Book Wholesalers, Inc.

Naylor, Phyllis Reynolds. Alice in Blunderland. 2003. (Alice Ser.). (Illus.). 208p. (J). 15.95 (978-0-689-84397-6(6) , Atheneum) Simon & Schuster Children's Publishing.

—Bernie Magruder & the Parachute Peril. 2001. (Illus.). (J). 11.64 (978-0-606-21061-4(X)) Tandem Library Bks.

—Boys in Control. 2005. (Boy/Girl Battle Ser.). 160p. (J). (gr. 4-7). pap. 5.50 (978-0-440-41681-4(7) , Yearling) Random Hse. Children's Bks.

—The Boys Return. 2003. 144p. (gr. 4-7). pap. 5.50 (978-0-440-41675-3(2) , Yearling); 2001. (Illus.). 132p. (J). (978-0-385-32734-3(X) , Delacorte Bks. for Young Readers) Random Hse. Children's Bks.

—The Boys Return. l.t. ed. 2003. 170p. (J). 23.95 (978-0-7862-5822-2(5)) Thorndike Pr.

—Boys Rock! 144p. (gr. 4-7). 2007. 5.50 ***(978-0-440-41990-7(5)*** , Yearling); 2005. (J). 15.95 (978-0-385-73140-9(X) , Delacorte Bks. for Young Readers); 2005. (J). lib. bdg. 17.99 (978-0-385-90171-0(2) , Delacorte Bks. for Young Readers) Random Hse. Children's Bks.

—The Boys Start the War. l.t. ed. 2002. (Thorndike Press Large Print Juvenile Ser.). 144p. (J). 22.95 (978-0-7862-4651-9(0)) Thorndike Pr.

—The Girls' Revenge. 1999. (gr. 3-6). lib. bdg. 13.00 (978-0-613-22858-9(8)) Tandem Library Bks.

—The Girls' Revenge. l.t. ed. 2003. (Thorndike Press Large Print Juvenile Ser.). 172p. (J). 23.95 (978-0-7862-5180-3(8)) Thorndike Pr.

—Girls Rule! 2006. 160p. (gr. 4-7). 5.50 (978-0-440-41989-1(1) , Yearling) Random Hse. Children's Bks.

—The Girls Take Over. 2004. (gr. 3-6). lib. bdg. 13.00 (978-0-613-81402-7(9)) Tandem Library Bks.

—The Great Chicken Debacle. 96p. 2005. (YA). (gr. 4-8). pap. 5.95 (978-0-7614-5148-8(X)); 2001. (Illus.). (J). (gr. 3-7). 14.95 (978-0-7614-5095-5(5) , Cavendish Children's Bks.) Cavendish, Marshall Corp.

—Simply Alice. (Alice Ser.). 240p. (YA). 2003. (Illus.). mass mkt. 5.99 (978-0-689-85965-6(1) , Simon Pulse); 2002. (gr. 6-9). 16.00 (978-0-689-82635-1(4) , Atheneum) Simon & Schuster Children's Publishing.

—Simply Alice. 2003. (Alice Ser.). (gr. 7-12). lib. bdg. 13.00 (978-0-613-73415-8(7)) Tandem Library Bks.

—A Traitor among the Boys. 2001. (J). (978-0-606-20953-3(0)) Tandem Library Bks.

—Walker's Crossing. 2001. 240p. (J). (gr. 5-9). pap. 4.99 (978-0-689-84261-0(9) , Aladdin) Simon & Schuster Children's Publishing.

Naylor, Phyllis Reynolds & Vaccaro, Nick. Alice in Blunderland. 2005. (Alice Ser.). (Illus.). 208p. (J). reprint ed. pap. 4.99 (978-0-689-84398-3(4) , Aladdin) Simon & Schuster Children's Publishing.

Neale, Jonathan. Himalaya. 2004. 160p. (J). (gr. 5-9). tchr. ed. 16.00 (978-0-618-41200-6(X)) Houghton Mifflin Co. Trade & Reference Div.

—Lost at Sea. 112p. (J). (gr. 5-9). 2002. (Illus.). 15.00 (978-0-618-13920-0(6)); 2004. reprint ed. pap. 5.95 (978-0-618-43236-3(1)) Houghton Mifflin Co. Trade & Reference Div.

Neenan, Colin. Thick. 2006. 102p. (J). pap. 6.95 (978-0-9746481-9-4(1)) Brown Barn Bks.

Nelson, S. D. The Star People: A Lakota Story. 2003. (Illus.). 36p. (J). (ps-3). 14.95 (978-0-8109-4584-5(3)) Abrams, Harry N. , Inc.

Nelson, Theresa. Ruby Electric. 272p. (J). 2003. (Illus.). 16.95 (978-0-689-83852-1(2) , Atheneum/Richard Jackson Bks.); 2004. reprint ed. pap. 5.99 (978-0-689-87146-7(5) , Aladdin) Simon & Schuster Children's Publishing.

Nesbit, E. Five Children & IT. 207p. 20.95 (978-0-8488-2523-2(3)) Amereon LTD.

—Five Children & IT. 2002. (Dover Evergreen Classics Ser.). (Illus.). 160p. (J). (gr. 4-7). pap. 2.50 (978-0-486-42366-1(2)) Dover Pubns., Inc.

—Five Children & IT. Zelinsky, Paul O., illus. 1999. (Books of Wonder). 256p. (gr. 4-7). 22.95 (978-0-688-13545-4(5)) HarperCollins Pubs.

—Five Children & IT. Nesbit, E. & Millar, H. R., illus. 2004. 240p. (gr. 12). pap. 10.00 (978-0-14-303915-0(6) , Penguin Classics) Penguin Group (USA) Inc.

—Five Children & IT. 2002. 192p. pap. 14.95 (978-1-59224-938-1(8)); lib. bdg. 24.95 (978-1-59224-942-8(6)) Wildside Pr.

—Five Children & It. l.t. ed. 2005. 296p. pap. (978-1-84637-200-1(3)) Echo Library.

—The House of Arden. 2006. (New York Review Children's Collection). 248p. (J). (gr. 3). 17.95 (978-1-59017-202-5(7) , NYR Children's Collection) New York Review of Bks., Inc., The.

—The Railway Children. Dryhurst, Dinah, illus. 2000. 224p. (J). pap. 8.99 (978-1-86205-235-2(2) , Pavilion Bks., Ltd.) Anova Bks. GBR. *Dist:* Trafalgar Square Publishing.

—The Railway Children. Dryhurst, Dinah, tr. Dryhurst, Dinah, illus. 2004. 184p. 18.95 (978-1-56792-261-5(9)) Godine, David R. Pub.

—The Railway Children. 2002. (gr. 3-6). lib. bdg. 23.40 (978-0-613-86551-7(0)) Tandem Library Bks.

—The Railway Children. 1998. (Children's Classics). (ENG., Illus.). 208p. (J). (gr. 4-7). pap. (978-1-85326-107-7(6) , 1076WW) Wordsworth Editions, Ltd.

—Railway Children. Brock, C. E., illus. (YA). 14.95 (978-0-8118-4933-3(3)) Chronicle Bks. LLC.

—Railway Children. 2000. (Dover Juvenile Classics Ser.). (Illus.). 208p. (J). (gr. 4-7). pap. 2.50 (978-0-486-41022-7(6)) Dover Pubns., Inc.

—Railway Children. 2006. pap. ***(978-1-4068-3505-2(6))*** Echo Library.

—Railway Children. (J). (978-0-340-71497-3(2) , Hodder & Stoughton) Hodder General Publishing Division.

—Railway Children. 2004. (ENG.). 580p. ***(978-0-9548401-2-9(7))*** Shoes & Ships & Sealing Wax Ltd.

—The Railway Children. Brock, C. E., illus. l.t. ed. 100th ed. 2005. 240p. (J). (ps-7). 14.95 (978-1-58717-279-3(8)); pap. 9.95 (978-1-58717-280-9(1)) Chronicle Bks. LLC. (SeaStar Bks.).

—The Railway Children. unabr. ed. 2004. (Chrysalis Children's Classics Ser.). (Illus.). 190p. (YA). pap. (978-1-84365-050-8(9)) Chrysalis Children's Bks.

—The Railway Children. 2004. reprint ed. pap. 22.95 (978-1-4191-7972-3(1)); pap. 1.99 (978-1-4192-7972-0(6)) Kessinger Publishing, LLC.

—The Railway Children. l.t. ed. 2006. (Large Print Ser.). lib. bdg. 26.00 ***(978-1-58287-890-4(0))*** North Bks.

—The Railway Children, Level 3. 2nd ed. 2000. (Bookworms Ser.). (Illus.). 74p. 6.50 (978-0-19-423013-1(9)) Oxford Univ. Pr., Inc.

—The Railway Children, Level 2. 2000. (Illus.). 48p. (C). pap. 9.00 (978-0-582-41790-8(2)) Pearson ESL.

—The Story of the Amulet. 2006. pap. 46.99 ***(978-1-4280-0877-9(2))*** IndyPublish.com.

—Story of the Treasure Seekers. 2006. pap. ***(978-1-4068-3507-6(2))*** Echo Library.

Nesbit, E. The Story of the Treasure Seekers: Being the Adventures of the Bastable Children in Search of A Fortune. l.t. ed. 2005. 288p. pap. (978-1-84637-207-0(0)) Echo Library.

Nettrour, Nelani. Nunkey's Adventures Bk. 2: Birth of Reekey. 2006. (Illus.). 74p. (J). pap. 11.95 (978-1-932657-54-8(1)) Third Millennium Pubns.

Nicholson, William. Slaves of the Mastery. Sis, Peter, illus. 2001. (Wind on Fire Trilogy: Bk. 2). 448p. (gr. 5-9). 17.99 (978-0-7868-0570-9(6)) Hyperion Bks. for Children.

—The Wind Singer. 2000. (Wind on Fire Trilogy: Bk. 1). 368p. (gr. 5-9). 17.99 (978-0-7868-2494-6(8)) Hyperion Bks. for Children.

—The Wind Singer. 2004. (Wind on Fire Trilogy: Bk. 1). (YA). (gr. 5 up). lib. bdg. 16.45 (978-0-613-75034-9(9)) Tandem Library Bks.

Nielsen, Susin. Degrassi Junior High: Snake. 2006. (Degrassi Junior High Ser.). 184p. (YA). (gr. 5-10). 7.95 (978-1-55028-926-8(8)) Lorimer, James & Co., Ltd., Pubs. CAN. *Dist:* Casemate Pubs. & Bk. Distributors, LLC.

Nimmo, Jenny. The Box Boys & the Magic Shell. (Box Boys Ser.). (Illus.). 64p. (J). pap. (978-0-340-73290-8(3) , Hodder & Stoughton) Hodder General Publishing Division.

Nishimura, Kae, illus. Baby, I'm Bigger. 2007. (I'm Going to Read Ser.). 28p. (J). (gr. 1-2). pap. 3.95 ***(978-1-4027-4244-6(4))*** Sterling Publishing Co., Inc.

A B

Nitz, Kristin Wolden. Saving the Griffin. Jaeggi, Yoshiko, illus. 2007. 192p. (J). (gr. 3-6). 14.95 (978-1-56145-380-1(3) , Peachtree Junior) Peachtree Pubs., Ltd.

Nix, Garth. The Ragwitch. 2004. (Illus.). 400p. (gr. 7 up). pap. 6.99 (978-0-06-050807-4(8)) HarperCollins Pubs.

Noble, Trinka Hakes. The Last Brother: A Civil War Tale. Papp, Robert, illus. 2006. 48p. (J). (gr. k-5). 17.95 (978-1-58536-253-0(0)) Sleeping Bear Pr.

—The Scarlet Stockings Spy. Papp, Robert, illus. 2004. 48p. (J). (gr. 1-7). 16.95 (978-1-58536-230-1(1)) Sleeping Bear Pr.

Noland, Charles. The Adventures of Drew & Ellie: The Daring Rescue. Moyer, Tom, illus. 2nd ed. 2006. (J). per. 7.95 (***978-0-9789297-2-5(1)***) TMD Enterprises.

Norling, Beth. Little Brothers Are... Norling, Beth, illus. 2008. (Illus.). 24p. (J). pap. 4.99 (***978-1-933605-70-8(7)***) Kane/Miller Bk. Pubs., Inc.

—Little Sisters Are... Norling, Beth, illus. 2008. (Illus.). 24p. (J). pap. 4.99 (***978-1-933605-69-2(3)***) Kane/Miller Bk. Pubs., Inc.

Norton, Andre. Red Hart Magic. 2007. (Magic Bks.: Bk. 6). 224p. (J). 5.99 (978-0-7653-5302-3(4) , Starscape) Doherty, Tom Assocs., LLC.

Novak, Matt. The Pillow War. 1998. (Illus.). 32p. (J). (ps-1). 16.99 (978-0-531-33048-7(6)); pap. 15.95 (978-0-531-30048-0(X)) Scholastic, Inc. (Orchard Bks.).

Nugent, Matthew. Nightmares on Goose Rocks Beach in Kennebunkport, Maine: Book 4 of the Goose Rocks Tales. 2003. (Illus.). 204p. (J). per. 14.95 (978-0-9705812-3-5(8)) CBI Pr.

Numeroff, Laura Joffe. Beatrice Doesn't Want To. Munsinger, Lynn, illus. ed. 2004. 32p. (J). (ps-k). 15.99 (978-0-7636-1160-6(3)) Candlewick Pr.

—The Chicken Sisters. Collicott, Sharleen, illus. 1999. 32p. (J). (ps-2). pap. 6.99 (978-0-06-443520-8(2) , Harper Trophy) HarperCollins Pubs.

—The Chicken Sisters. 1999. (J). 13.79 (978-0-606-15843-5(X)) Tandem Library Bks.

Nyaradi, J. A. Catching Santa. 2006. 140p. pap. 11.95 (978-0-7414-3462-3(8)) Infinity Publishing.

O'Connell, Jenny. Plan B. 2006. 288p. pap. 9.95 (978-1-4165-2033-7(3) , MTV) Simon & Schuster.

O'Connor, Barbara. How to Steal a Dog. 2007. 176p. (J). (gr. 3-7). 16.00 (978-0-374-33497-0(8)) Farrar, Straus & Giroux.

O'Connor, Kerrie. Through the Tiger's Eye. Wagner, Erica, tr. 2005. (Telares Ser.: Bk. 1). (Illus.). 288p. (Orig.). (J). (ps-7). pap. 9.95 (978-1-86508-538-8(3)) Allen & Unwin AUS. *Dist:* Independent Pubs. Group.

O'Coyne, James. Gravelle's Land of Horror. Baer, Brian, illus. 2007. (J). per. 9.95 (***978-1-59649-604-0(5)***) Whispering Pine Pr., Inc.

Offen. Rita in Wonderland. (Illus.). 32p. (J). pap. 7.95 (978-0-14-038699-8(8)) Penguin Bks., Ltd. GBR. *Dist:* Trafalgar Square Publishing.

Ogden, Charles. Mischief Manual. Carton, Rick, illus. 2007. (Edgar & Ellen Ser.). 112p. (J). pap. 7.99 (978-1-4169-3935-1(0) , Aladdin) Simon & Schuster Children's Publishing.

—Nod's Limbs. Carton, Rick, illus. 2007. (Edgar & Ellen Ser.). (J). 224p. 9.99 (978-1-4169-1501-0(X)); 210p. (***978-1-4287-3214-8(4)***) Simon & Schuster Children's Publishing. (Aladdin).

—Triple Threat Vols. 1-3, Set: Their First Three Misadventures: Rare Beasts, Tourist Trap, under Town. Carton, Rick, illus. 2007. (Edgar & Ellen Ser.). 464p. (J). 29.99 (978-1-4169-3462-2(6) , Aladdin) Simon & Schuster Children's Publishing.

O'Hair, Margaret. Twin to Twin. Courtin, Thierry, illus. 2003. 32p. (J). 16.99 (978-0-689-84494-2(8) , McElderry, Margaret K.) Simon & Schuster Children's Publishing.

Ohi, Ruth. Me & My Brother. Ohi, Ruth, illus. 2007. (Ruth Ohi Picture Book Ser.). (Illus.). 24p. (J). (ps-k). pap. 5.95 (***978-1-55451-091-7(0)***); lib. bdg. 19.95 (***978-1-55451-092-4(9)***) Annick Pr., Ltd. CAN. *Dist:* Firefly Bks., Ltd.

Oldfield, J. Sunny the Hero. (Home Farm Twins Ser.: No. 7). (Illus.). 120p. (J). pap. 7.99 (978-0-340-68990-5(0) , Hodder & Stoughton) Hodder General Publishing Division GBR. *Dist:* Trafalgar Square Publishing.

Oldfield, Jenny. The Wilde Child. 2003. (Wilde Family Ser.: Vol. 4). (Illus.). pap. (978-0-340-87321-2(3) , Hodder Children's Books) Hodder Children's Division.

Oliver, Lin. Attack of the Growling Eyeballs. 2008. (Who Shrunk Daniel Funk? Ser.). 112p. (J). 14.99 (***978-1-4169-0951-4(6)*** , Simon & Schuster Children's Publishing) Simon & Schuster Children's Publishing.

Olson, Mary. An Alligator Ate My Brother. Lyon, Tammie Speer, illus. 2003. 32p. (J). (gr. k-2). 15.95 (978-1-56397-803-6(2)) Boyds Mills Pr.

One Tree Hill, No. 3. (YA). (978-0-439-71562-1(8)) Scholastic, Inc.

O'Neill, Alexis. Estela en el Mercado de Pulgas. de la Vega, Eida, tr. from ENG. Sanchez, Enrique O., illus. 2005. (SPA.). 32p. (J). (ps-k). pap. 7.95 (978-1-58430-246-9(1)) Lee & Low Bks., Inc.

O'Neill, Catharine. Annie & Simon. O'Neill, Catharine, illus. 2008. (Illus.). 64p. (J). (gr. k-2). 15.99 (978-0-7636-2688-4(0)) Candlewick Pr.

Oppel, Kenneth. Dead Water Zone. 2007. 208p. (J). (gr. 7 up). pap. 6.99 (***978-0-06-123442-2(7)*** , Eos) HarperCollins Pubs.

Optic, Oliver. Taken by the Enemy. 2006. 96.99 (***978-1-4280-3960-5(0)***); pap. 89.99 (***978-1-4280-3988-9(0)***) IndyPublish.com.

Oram, Hiawyn. The Best Party of Them All. Su, Lucy, illus. 2004. 32p. (J). pap. 7.95 (978-1-84507-157-8(3)) Lincoln, Frances Ltd. GBR. *Dist:* Perseus Distribution.

—Little Brother & the Cough. Rees, Mary, illus. 32p. (J). (ps-1). 10.99 (978-0-7112-0844-5(1)) Lincoln, Frances Ltd. GBR. *Dist:* Antique Collectors' Club.

Oram, Hiawyn & Rees, Mary. Little Brother & the Cough. (Illus.). 32p. (J). 2004. pap. 7.95 (978-1-84507-205-6(7)); 2000. pap. 10.99 (978-0-7112-0845-2(X)) Lincoln, Frances Ltd. GBR. *Dist:* Perseus Distribution, Transition Vendor.

Orgill, Roxane. Go-Go Baby! Salerno, Steven, tr. Salerno, Steven, illus. 2004. 32p. (J). 14.95 (978-0-7614-5157-0(9)) Cavendish, Marshall Corp.

Orme, Helen. Brother Bother. 2008. (Siti's Sisters Ser.). 36p. pap. 7.95 (***978-1-84167-684-5(5)***) Ransom Publishing Ltd. GBR. *Dist:* International Publishers Marketing.

Osborne, Mary Pope. Blizzard of the Blue Moon. Murdocca, Sal, illus. 2007. (Magic Tree House Ser.: No. 36). 144p. (J). (gr. 2-5). pap. 4.99 (978-0-375-83038-9(3) , Random Hse. Bks. for Young Readers) Random Hse. Children's Bks.

—Blizzard of the Blue Moon. 2006. (Magic Tree House Ser.: No. 36). (Illus.). 128p. (J). (gr. k-3). lib. bdg. 13.99 (978-0-375-93037-9(X)); (gr. 2-5). 11.95 (978-0-375-83037-2(5)) Random Hse. Children's Bks. (Random Hse. Bks. for Young Readers).

—Carnival at Candlelight. 2006. (Magic Tree House Ser.: No. 33). (Illus.). 144p. (J). (gr. 2-6). pap. 4.99 (978-0-375-83034-1(0) , Random Hse. Bks. for Young Readers) Random Hse. Children's Bks.

—Carnival at Candlelight. Murdocca, Sal, illus. 2005. (Magic Tree House Ser.: No. 33). 128p. (J). (gr. k-3). 11.95 (978-0-375-83033-4(2) , Random Hse. Bks. for Young Readers) Random Hse. Children's Bks.

—Christmas in Camelot. Murdocca, Sal, illus. 2001. (Magic Tree House Ser.: No. 29). 128p. (J). (gr. k-3). 11.95 (978-0-375-81373-3(X)); lib. bdg. 13.99 (978-0-375-91373-0(4)) Random Hse. Children's Bks. (Random Hse. Bks. for Young Readers).

—Dark Day in the Deep Sea. Murdocca, Sal, illus. 2008. (Stepping Stone Bks.). 128p. (J). (gr. 3-7). lib. bdg. 14.99 (***978-0-375-93731-6(5)*** , Random Hse. Bks. for Young Readers) Random Hse. Children's Bks.

—Dragon of the Red Dawn. Murdocca, Sal, illus. 2007. (Magic Tree House Ser.: No. 37). 128p. (J). (gr. k-3). 11.99 (978-0-375-83727-2(2) , Random Hse. Bks. for Young Readers) Random Hse. Children's Bks.

—Dragon of the Red Dawn. Murdocca, Sal, illus. 2007. (Magic Tree House Ser.: No. 37). 108p. (J). (gr. k-3). pap. (978-0-375-83728-9(0)) Random Hse., Inc.

—High Tide in Hawaii. Murdocca, Sal, illus. 2003. (Magic Tree House Ser.: No. 28). 96p. (J). (gr. k-3). lib. bdg. 11.99 (978-0-375-90616-9(9)); (gr. 1-4). pap. 3.99 (978-0-375-80616-2(4)) Random Hse. Children's Bks. (Random Hse. Bks. for Young Readers).

—High Tide in Hawaii. 2003. (Magic Tree House Ser. : No. 28). (J). (gr. k-3). lib. bdg. 11.80 (978-0-613-62386-5(X)) Tandem Library Bks.

—Monday with a Mad Genius. Murdocca, Sal, illus. 2007. (Stepping Stone Bks.). 128p. (J). (gr. 2-6). 11.99 (***978-0-375-83729-6(9)***); lib. bdg. 14.99 (***978-0-375-93729-3(3)***) Random Hse. Children's Bks. (Random Hse. Bks. for Young Readers).

—Monday with a Mad Genius. Murdocca, Sal, illus. 2007. (J). pap. (***978-0-375-83730-2(2)***) Random Hse., Inc.

—Night of the New Magicians. Murdocca, Sal, illus. (Magic Tree House Ser.: No. 35). (J). 2007. 144p. (gr. 2-5). pap. 4.99 (978-0-375-83036-5(7)); 2006. 128p. (gr. k-3). 11.95 (978-0-375-83035-8(9)); 2006. 128p. (gr. k-3). lib. bdg. 13.99 (978-0-375-93035-5(3)) Random Hse. Children's Bks. (Random Hse. Bks. for Young Readers).

—Season of the Sandstorms. 2006. (Magic Tree House Ser.: No. 34). 144p. (J). (gr. k-3). pap. 4.99 (978-0-375-83032-7(4) , Random Hse. Bks. for Young Readers) Random Hse. Children's Bks.

—Summer of the Sea Serpent. Murdocca, Sal, tr. Murdocca, Sal, illus. 2004. (Magic Tree House Ser.: No. 31). 128p. (J). (gr. k-3). lib. bdg. 13.99 (978-0-375-92735-5(2)); (gr. 2-5). 11.95 (978-0-375-82735-8(8)) Random Hse. Children's Bks. (Random Hse. Bks. for Young Readers).

Ostrow, Vivian. My Brother Is from Outer Space: The Book of Proof. Brace, Eric, illus. 1999. 32p. (J). (gr. k-4). pap. 6.95 (978-0-8075-5326-8(3)) Whitman, Albert & Co.

Oswald, Michael J. 3 Years Apart. 2006. 72p. pap. 11.95 (978-0-7414-3108-0(4)) Infinity Publishing.

Oyibo, Papa. Big Brother, Little Sister. Clementson, John, illus. 2000. 40p. (J). (ps-2). 15.95 (978-1-84148-117-3(3)) Barefoot Bks., Inc.

Packard, Mary. Don't Make a Sound. Yerkes, Lane, illus. 2004. 16p. (J). (gr. 1 up). lib. bdg. 19.33 (978-0-8368-4099-5(2)) Stevens, Gareth Inc.

Palatini, Margie. Goldie Is Mad. Palatini, Margie, illus. 2001. (Illus.). 32p. (ps-k). 15.49 (978-0-7868-2490-8(5)); 14.99 (978-0-7868-0565-5(X)) Hyperion Bks. for Children.

—Good As Goldie. Palatini, Margie, illus. 2000. (Illus.). 32p. (ps-k). 14.99 (978-0-7868-0502-0(1)) Hyperion Bks. for Children.

—Shelly. Francis, Guy, illus. 2006. 32p. (J). (ps). 15.99 (978-0-525-47565-1(6) , Dutton Juvenile) Penguin Group (USA) Inc.

Palmer, Pamela. Horse of the Dawn. 2005. 89p. pap. 14.95 (978-1-4137-9545-5(5)) PublishAmerica, Inc.

Papp, Robert, illus. The Ghost of the Chattering Bones, Vol. 102. 2005. (Boxcar Children Mysteries Ser.: 102). 128p. (J). pap. 4.50 (978-0-8075-0874-9(8)) Whitman, Albert & Co.

—The Giant Yo-Yo Mystery. 2006. 124p. (J). (***978-1-4156-6756-9(X)***) Whitman, Albert & Co.

Papp, Robert, illus. The Sword of the Silver Knight, Vol. 103. 2005. (Boxcar Children Mysteries Ser.: 103). 112p. (J). (ps-7). 14.95 (978-0-8075-0877-0(2)) Whitman, Albert & Co.

Park, Barbara. Junie B. Jones & a Little Monkey Business, Vol. 2. unabr. ed. 2004. (Junie B. Jones Ser.: Vol. 2). 68p. (J). (gr. k-3). pap. 17.00 incl. audio (978-0-8072-0779-6(9) , LFTR 238 SP, Listening Library) Random Hse. Audio Publishing Group.

—Junie B. Jones & a Little Monkey Business. Brunkus, Denise, illus. 2007. (Junie B. Jones Ser.: No. 2). 80p. (J). (gr. k-3). 9.99 (978-0-375-84157-6(1) , Random Hse. Bks. for Young Readers) Random Hse. Children's Bks.

—Junie B. Jones & the Stupid Smelly Bus. Brunkus, Denise, illus. 2007. (Junie B. Jones Ser.: No. 1). 80p. (J). (gr. k-3). 9.99 (978-0-375-84156-9(3) , Random Hse. Bks. for Young Readers) Random Hse. Children's Bks.

—Junie B. Jones y el Negocio del Mono. Brunkus, Denise, illus. 2005. (Junie B. Jones Ser.).Tr. of Junie B Jones Little Monkey Business. (SPA.). 80p. (J). pap. 3.99 (978-0-439-42514-8(X) , Scholastic en Espanol) Scholastic, Inc.

—Mick Harte Was Here. 88p. (J). (gr. 4-6). pap. 4.99 (978-0-8072-1502-9(3) , Listening Library) Random Hse. Audio Publishing Group.

Park, Barbara, ed. Mick Harte Was Here. unabr. ed. 2004. (Middle Grade Cassette Librariestm Ser.). 88p. (J). (gr. 3-7). pap. 29.00 incl. audio (978-0-8072-7797-3(5) , S YA 922 SP, Listening Library) Random Hse. Audio Publishing Group.

Parkinson, Siobhan. Sisters... No Way! 2002. 222p. (J). (gr. 5 up). pap. 7.95 (978-0-86278-495-9(6)) O'Brien Pr., Ltd., The IRL. *Dist:* Independent Pubs. Group, Irish American Bk. Co.

Parra, B. A. Tyler Trio Adventure on a Quest for Knighthood. 2007. 145p. pap. 10.50 (***978-0-615-15090-1(X)***) Parra, Beverly.

Partis, Joanne. Stripe's Naughty Sister. 2003. (Picture Bks.). (Illus.). 32p. (J). (ps-3). 15.95 (978-0-87614-466-4(0) , Carolrhoda Bks.) Lerner Publishing Group.

Paterson, Katherine. The Same Stuff as Stars. 2002. (Illus.). 256p. (J). (gr. 5-9). tchr. ed. 15.00 (978-0-618-24744-8(0) , Clarion Bks.) Houghton Mifflin Co. Trade & Reference Div.

Patneaude, David. Framed in Fire. 2001. (gr. 5-8). lib. bdg. 14.10 (978-0-613-35946-7(1)) Tandem Library Bks.

—Framed in Fire. 224p. (J). (gr. 6-9). 2004. pap. 5.95 (978-0-8075-9096-6(7)); 1999. (Illus.). 15.95 (978-0-8075-9098-0(3)) Whitman, Albert & Co.

Paulsen, Gary. Harris & Me: A Summer Remembered. 2007. (Illus.). 168p. (J). (gr. 4-7). pap. 5.95 (978-0-15-205880-7(X) , Harcourt Paperbacks) Harcourt Children's Bks.

Pausewang, Gudrun. Dark Hours. Brownjohn, John, tr. from GER. 2006. (Illus.). 212p. (YA). (gr. 7-12). 21.95 (978-1-55451-042-9(2)) Annick Pr., Ltd. CAN. *Dist:* Firefly Bks., Ltd.

PC Treasures, prod. Hansel & Gretel. 2007. (J). (***978-1-60072-030-7(7)***) PC Treasures, Inc.

Pearce, Jacqueline. The Truth about Rats (and Dogs) 2006. 176p. (J). pap. 7.95 (978-1-55143-473-5(3)) Orca Bk. Pubs. USA.

Pearce, Philippa. The Squirrel Wife. Anderson, Wayne, illus. 2007. 32p. (J). (gr. k-3). 16.99 (***978-0-7636-3551-0(0)***) Candlewick Pr.

Pearson, Tracey Campbell. Myrtle. Pearson, Tracey Campbell, illus. 2004. (Illus.). 32p. (J). 15.00 (978-0-374-35157-1(0) , Farrar, Straus & Giroux (BYR)) Farrar, Straus & Giroux.

Peck, Robert Newton. Bro. 2004. 160p. (J). (gr. 7 up). 16.99 (978-0-06-052974-1(1)); lib. bdg. 17.89 (978-0-06-052975-8(X)) HarperCollins Pubs.

—Cowboy Ghost. 1999. 208p. (YA). (gr. 7 up). 15.95 (978-0-06-028168-7(5) , Harper Trophy) HarperCollins Pubs.

—Cowboy Ghost. 1999. (YA). pap., stu. ed. 52.95 incl. audio (978-0-7887-3189-1(0) , 40924) Recorded Bks., LLC.

—Cowboy Ghost. 2000. (Illus.). (J). 11.60 (978-0-606-18684-1(0)) Tandem Library Bks.

Pegram, Laura. Daughter's Day Blues. 2002. (gr. k-3). lib. bdg. 15.30 (978-0-613-49468-7(7)) Tandem Library Bks.

Pemberton, Bonnie. The Cat Master. 2007. 259p. (YA). (gr. 5-9). 16.99 (***978-0-7614-5340-6(7)***) Cavendish, Marshall Corp.

Perdew, Suzanne, et al. The Mystery of the Abandoned Lighthouse. 2001. (Shoebox Kids Ser.: Bk. 12). (Illus.). 93p. (J). (978-0-8163-1819-3(0)) Pacific Pr. Publishing Assn.

Perfit, Dianne Beacher. The Bone on the Stone. Klocek, Michael, illus. 2002. 16p. (J). 5.95 (978-0-9710332-1-4(8)) Pelican Island Publishing.

Perry, Michael. Daniel's Ride. Ballard, Lee, illus. 2001. 32p. (J). (gr. 2-5). 16.00 (978-0-9701771-9-3(4)) Free Will Pr.

Peters, Julie Anne. Luna. 2006. 254p. (J). (gr. 9-17). reprint ed. pap. 7.99 (978-0-316-01127-3(4) , Tingley, Megan Bks.) Little, Brown Bks. for Young Readers.

Petersen, Alicia. A Sparrow Alone. 2004. 154p. (YA). (978-1-59166-204-4(4)) Jones, Bob Univ. Pr.

Petersen, P. J. Rising Water. 2003. (Illus.). 128p. (J). pap. 4.99 (978-0-689-86356-1(X) , Aladdin) Simon & Schuster Children's Publishing.

Peterson, John. The Littles & the Secret Letter. 2001. (978-0-606-22186-3(7)) Tandem Library Bks.

Petty, J. T. The Squampkin Patch: A Nasselrogt Adventure. Friend, David Michael, illus. 2006. 256p. (J). (gr. 4-9). 15.95 (978-1-4169-0274-4(0) , Simon & Schuster Children's Publishing) Simon & Schuster Children's Publishing.

Pevsner, Stella. Would My Fortune Cookie Lie? 1999. (978-0-606-14369-1(6)) Tandem Library Bks.

Pez, Alberto. Martes Peludo. Gleich, Jacky, illus. (SPA.). (J). 8.95 (978-958-04-5092-4(7)) Norma S.A. COL. *Dist:* Distribuidora Norma, Inc., Lectorum Pubns., Inc.

Pfister, Marcus. Holey Moley. James, J. Alison, tr. from GER. 2006. (Illus.). 32p. (J). (gr. k-3). 16.95 (978-0-7358-2064-7(3)) North-South Bks., Inc.

Phillips, Leigh Hope. Birthday Wishes. Fountain, John, illus. 2005. (J). pap. (978-1-933156-10-1(4)); per. 11.95 (978-1-933156-03-3(1)) GSVQ Publishing. (VisionQuest Kids).

Phoenix, Woodrow & Price, Robin. Count Milkula: A Tale of Milk & Monsters! 2007. 32p. (J). 19.95 (***978-0-9546576-5-9(9)***) Mogzilla GBR. *Dist:* Independent Pubs. Group.

Pinkwater, Daniel M. Go West. Rash, Andy, illus. 2002. (Fat Camp Commandos Ser.). 96p. (J). (gr. 3-8). pap. 14.95 (978-0-439-29772-1(9) , Scholastic Pr.) Scholastic, Inc.

—Go West. 2003. (gr. 3-6). lib. bdg. 12.40 (978-0-613-62511-1(0)) Tandem Library Bks.

Pisarik, Michael E. Loonhaunt. 2006. (J). per. 19.95 (978-1-59872-600-8(5)) Instantpublisher.com.

Place, Nick. The Kazillion Wish. Collins, Ross, illus. 2005. 208p. (Orig.). (J). pap. 15.95 (978-0-439-69215-1(6) , Chicken Hse., The) Scholastic, Inc.

Plum-Ucci, Carol. The She. 2003. (Illus.). 288p. (YA). 17.00 (978-0-15-216819-3(2)) Harcourt Children's Bks.

Polacco, Patricia. My Rotten, Redheaded Older Brother. Polacco, Patricia, illus. 2002. (Illus.). (J). 15.53 (978-0-7587-3229-3(5)) Book Wholesalers, Inc.

—My Rotten Redheaded Older Brother. Polacco, Patricia, illus. 1998. (Illus.). 32p. (J). (ps-3). pap. 7.99 (978-0-689-82036-6(4) , Aladdin) Simon & Schuster Children's Publishing.

—An Orange for Frankie. Polacco, Patricia, illus. 2004. (Illus.). 48p. (J). (gr. 1-5). 16.99 (978-0-399-24302-8(X) , Philomel) Penguin Group (USA) Inc.

—Rotten Richie & the Ultimate Dare. Polacco, Patricia, illus. 2006. (Illus.). 48p. (J). (gr. k). 16.99 (978-0-399-24531-2(6) , Philomel) Penguin Group (USA) Inc.

Poole, Richard. Jewel & Thorn. 2007. (Book of Lowmoor Ser.). (Illus.). 391p. (YA). (gr. 7 up). per. 11.95 (***978-0-689-87290-7(9)***) Simon & Schuster, Ltd. GBR. *Dist:* Independent Pubs. Group.

Poppenhager, N. & Gantschev. Snow Leopards. 2006. (Illus.). 32p. (J). 15.95 (978-0-7358-2087-6(2)) North-South Bks., Inc.

Portmann, Alan E. Jared & Joshua's Whopper. 2006. 32p. (J). per. 13.99 (***978-1-59886-665-0(6)***) Tate Publishing & Enterprises, L.L.C.

Powell. Tribute to Another Dead Rock Star. 2003. (gr. 7-12). lib. bdg. 14.10 (978-0-613-71884-4(4)) Tandem Library Bks.

Powell, Jillian. Izzy's Idea. Shearing, Leonie, illus. 2004. (Read-It! Readers Ser.). 32p. (C). (gr. k-3). 18.60 (978-1-4048-0644-3(X)) Picture Window Bks.

Powell, Randy. Tribute to Another Dead Rock Star. 1999. 224p. (YA). (gr. 7-12). 17.00 (978-0-374-37748-9(0) , Farrar, Straus & Giroux (BYR)) Farrar, Straus & Giroux.

—Tribute to Another Dead Rock Star. l.t. ed. 2000. 224p. (J). 21.95 (978-0-7862-2191-2(7)) Thorndike Pr.

Powling, Chris. On the Ghost Trail. Peterson, Shaunna, illus. 2006. (Read-It! Chapter Books). 48p. (J). (***978-1-4048-3125-4(8)*** , 1265811) Picture Window Bks.

Price, D. Michael. Across the River: Walter & Oliver's Amazing Adventure. Price, D. Michael, illus. 1998. (Illus.). 48p. (J). (ps-3). pap. 15.95 (978-0-86713-047-8(4)) Greenwich Workshop Pr.

Price, Olive. Three Golden Rivers. l.t. ed. 1999. (Golden Triangle Bks.). 272p. (YA). (gr. 4-7). pap. 9.95 (978-0-8229-5707-2(8)) Univ. of Pittsburgh Pr.

Prigger, Mary Skillings. Aunt Minnie McGranahan. Lewin, Betsy, illus. 1999. 40p. (J). (gr. k-3). tchr. ed. 15.00 (978-0-395-82270-8(X) , Clarion Bks.) Houghton Mifflin Co. Trade & Reference Div.

Prue, Sally. The Devil's Toenail. 2004. (Illus.). 208p. (J). 16.95 (978-0-439-48634-7(3)) Scholastic, Inc.

Pryor, Bonnie. The Porcupine Mouse. Begin, Mary Jane, illus. 2002. 32p. (J). (ps-4). 15.95 (978-1-58717-185-7(6) , SeaStar Bks.) Chronicle Bks. LLC.

Purkapile, Sue. Otto the Blind Otter. Ducommun, Barbara, illus. 2004. (J). 13.95 (978-1-930596-27-6(8)) Amherst Pr.

Pyle, Jack R. The Gold Bug of Farrow Point. 2003. 130p. (J). (978-1-887905-78-7(2)) Parkway Pubs., Inc.

Qualey, Marsha. Thin Ice. 2007. (YA). (***978-0-9793444-0-4(9)***) Quercus Pr.

—Thin Ice. 1999. (978-0-606-17348-3(X)) Tandem Library Bks.

Quarles, Heather. A Door Near Here. 2000. 11.64 (978-0-606-17796-2(5)) Tandem Library Bks.

—Door near Here. 2000. (gr. 7-12). lib. bdg. 13.00 (978-0-613-22981-4(9)) Tandem Library Bks.

—A Door near Here. 2000. (Illus.). 240p. (YA). (gr. 7 up). pap. 5.50 (978-0-440-22761-8(5) , Laurel Leaf) Random Hse. Children's Bks.

Quit Bugging Me. 2007. 150p. (YA). pap. 8.99 (***978-0-9776043-6-4(5)***) Aspirations Media, Inc.

Race to Moonrise Rev. 2006. 9.95 (978-1-932738-31-5(2)) Western Reflections Publishing Co.

Ragawa, Mirimo. Baby & Me, Vol. 5. Ragawa, Mirimo, illus. 2007. (Baby & Me Ser.). 192p. (YA). pap. 8.99 (***978-1-4215-1008-8(1)***) Viz Media.

Rallison, Janette. How to Take the Ex Out of Ex-Boyfriend. 2007. 272p. (YA). (gr. 7 up). 15.99 (978-0-399-24617-3(7) , Putnam Juvenile) Penguin Group (USA) Inc.

Rallison, Janette. Revenge of the Cheerleaders. 2007. (Illus.). 247p. (YA). (gr. 7 up). 16.95 (***978-0-8027-8999-0(4)***) Walker & Co.

Ramirez, Linda M. & Salcines, Maria Luisa. Playtime for Molly: A Story about Filial Therapy: How a Parent & Child Play to Improve Their Relationship. 2001. (Illus.). 24p. pap. 8.95 (978-0-9713839-0-6(1)) MarLin Bks.

Randall, MarilynMae. Wishes for Christmas. 2002. (Illus.). (J). 9.99 (978-0-9713589-5-9(8)) Ubaviel's Gifts.

Randall, Rod. Along Came a Spider. 2000. (Heebie Jeebies Ser.: Vol. 7). 138p. (J). (gr. 3-7). pap. 5.99 (978-0-8054-1981-8(0)) B&H Publishing Grp.

Random House Staff, ed. Mary's Story. 1999. (gr. 5-8). lib. bdg. 13.00 (978-0-613-21976-1(7)) Tandem Library Bks.

Ransom, Candice. Horses in the Wind: A Tale of Seabiscuit. 2007. 128p. (J). (gr. 1-5). pap. 4.99 (***978-0-7869-4355-5(6)*** , Mirrorstone) Wizards of the Coast.

—Rider in the Night: A Tale of Sleepy Hollow. 2007. 128p. (J). (gr. 1-5). pap. 4.99 (***978-0-7869-4354-8(8)*** , Mirrorstone) Wizards of the Coast.

Ransom, Candice. Signals in the Sky. 2007. 128p. (J). 4.99 (978-0-7869-4353-1(X) , Mirrorstone) Wizards of the Coast.

Recheis, Kathe. Little Raccoon Always Knows Best. Kunstreich, Pieter, illus. 2002. Tr. of Kleiner Waschbar Weiss Alles Besser. 24p. (J). 14.95 (978-0-7940-0009-7(6)); lib. bdg. 15.95 (978-0-7940-0010-3(X)) Munchweiler Pr.

Reece, Colleen L. Plymouth Pioneers. 1998. (American Adventure Ser.: No. 2). (Illus.). 142p. (J). (gr. 3-7). lib. bdg. 15.95 (978-0-7910-5042-2(4) , Chelsea Hse.) Facts On File, Inc.

Reeder, Carolyn. Captain Kate. 2002. 210p. (J). (gr. 4-7). reprint ed. pap. 6.50 (978-1-890920-14-2(2)) Children's Literature.

—Captain Kate. 224p. (J). 2000. (gr. 3-7). pap. 4.99 (978-0-380-79668-7(6)); 1999. (gr. 4-7). 15.00 (978-0-380-97628-7(5)) HarperCollins Pubs.

—Captain Kate. 1999. (Illus.). (J). (978-0-606-17963-8(1)) Tandem Library Bks.

Reeve, Philip. Larklight: A Rousing Tale of Dauntless Pluck in the Farthest Reaches of Space. Wyatt, David, illus. 2007. 416p. (J). (gr. 5 up). pap. 7.95 (***978-1-59990-145-9(5)*** , Bloomsbury Children) Bloomsbury Publishing.

—Starcross: An Intergalactic Adventure of Spies & Time Travel. Wyatt, David, illus. 2007. 320p. (J). (gr. 5 up). 16.95 (***978-1-59990-121-3(8)*** , Bloomsbury Children) Bloomsbury Publishing.

Reeve, Philip & Yancey, Rick. Larklight: A Rousing Tale of Dauntless Pluck in the Farthest Reaches of Space. Wyatt, David, illus. 2006. 250p. (YA). 16.95 (978-1-59990-020-9(3) , Bloomsbury Children) Bloomsbury Publishing.

Rehfuss, Mary E. The Pottsville Chronicles: A New Beginning. 2005. 102p. (YA). per. 9.95 (978-1-933290-49-2(8)) Tate Publishing & Enterprises, L.L.C.

Reiser, Lynn. My Baby & Me. Gentieu, Penny, illus. 2008. 32p. (J). (ps-1). 16.99 (***978-0-375-85205-3(0)*** , Knopf Bks. for Young Readers) Random Hse. Children's Bks.

Reynolds, Peter. The Best Kid in the World. 2006. (Illus.). (J). (***978-1-4156-9188-5(6)***) Simon & Schuster Children's Publishing.

Reynolds, Peter. Ish. Reynolds, Peter, illus. 2004. (Illus.). 32p. (J). (gr. k up). 14.00 (978-0-7636-2344-9(X)) Candlewick Pr.

Reynolds, Peter H. The Best Kid in the World: A SugarLoaf Book. Reynolds, Peter H., illus. 2006. (Illus.). 48p. (J). (ps-2). 15.95 (978-0-689-87624-0(6)) Simon & Schuster Children's Publishing.

Richardson, E. E. Devil's Footsteps. 2005. 192p. (gr. 7 up). (J). lib. bdg. 17.99 (978-0-385-90279-3(4)); (YA). 15.95 (978-0-385-73263-5(5)) Random Hse. Children's Bks. (Delacorte Bks. for Young Readers).

Ries, Lori. Super Sam! Rama, Sue, illus. (J). 2007. pap. 6.95 (***978-1-58089-171-4(3));*** 2004. 32p. 14.95 (978-1-58089-041-0(5)) Charlesbridge Publishing, Inc.

Robbins, Beth. Tom, Ally, & the New Baby. Stuart, Jon, illus. 2001. (It's OK! Ser.). 24p. (J). (ps-k). pap. 3.95 (978-0-7894-7430-8(1) , D K Ink) Dorling Kindersley Publishing, Inc.

Roberson, Karla. My Shoelaces Are Hard to Tie! Holley, Vanessa D., illus. 2004. 32p. (J). lib. bdg. 15.00 (***978-1-4242-0224-9(8)***) Fitzgerald Bks.

Robley Blake, Colleen. I Can't Wait till I'm Five. 2006. (J). 9.95 (978-0-9767342-0-8(6)) Imaajinn This.

Roche, Hannah. My Sister Is Super. 1998. (Science Made Simple Ser.). (Illus.). 24p. (J). (ps-k). pap. (978-1-84089-015-0(0) , 868238Q, Zero to Ten, Limited) Evans Publishing Group.

Rockwell, Anne F. Brendan & Belinda & the Slam Dunk. Meisel, Paul, illus. 2007. (Good Sports Ser.). 40p. (J). lib. bdg. 16.89 (978-0-06-028437-3(1)); 15.99 (978-0-06-028443-5(9)) HarperCollins Pubs.

Rockwell, Lizzy. Hello Baby! Rockwell, Lizzy, illus. 2002. (Illus.). (J). 14.79 (978-0-7587-4439-5(0)) Book Wholesalers, Inc.

—Hello Baby! Rockwell, Lizzy, illus. 2000. (Illus.). 32p. (J). (gr. k-k). pap. 6.99 (978-0-517-80074-4(8) , Dragonfly Bks.) Random Hse. Children's Bks.

—Hello Baby! 2000. (J). (978-0-606-18980-4(7)); lib. bdg. 15.30 (978-0-613-25484-7(8)) Tandem Library Bks.

Roddie, Shen. Baby Goes Too. Stojic, Manya, illus. 2003. 32p. (YA). (978-1-85602-460-0(1)) Chrysalis Children's Bks.

Rodman, Mary Ann. Jimmy's Stars. 2008. 272p. (J). 16.95 (***978-0-374-33703-2(9)***) Farrar, Straus & Giroux.

Rodowsky, Colby. Not Quite a Stranger. 2003. 192p. (J). (gr. 5 up). 16.00 (978-0-374-35548-7(7) , Farrar, Straus & Giroux (BYR)) Farrar, Straus & Giroux.

Roe. Con Me Hermano. 1998. Tr. of With My Brother. (J). pap. 5.99 (978-0-87628-126-0(9)) Ctr. for Applied Research in Education, The.

Roe, Eileen. Con Mi Hermano/with My Brother. 2000. (Metro Reading Program Ser.). (J). (gr. k). 7.98 (978-1-58120-965-5(7)); 45.95 (978-1-58830-025-6(0)) Metropolitan Teaching & Learning Co.

Romano, Christy. Grace's Turn. 2006. 272p. (gr. 4-7). 15.99 (978-0-7868-4884-3(7)) Hyperion Pr.

Romano, Ray. Raymie, Dickie, & the Bean: Why I Love & Hate My Brothers. Locke, Gary, illus. 2007. 30p. (J). 18.00 (***978-1-4223-6806-0(8)***) DIANE Publishing Co.

Roop, Peter. Eye for an Eye: A Story of the Revolutionary War. 2000. (gr. 5-8). lib. bdg. 15.70 (978-0-613-36805-6(3)) Tandem Library Bks.

Roop, Peter & Roop, Connie. An Eye for an Eye: A Story of the American Revolution. 2001. (Jamestown Classics Ser.). (Illus.). 168p. (J). (gr. 5-8). 15.32 (978-0-8092-0587-5(4) , 9780809205875) Jamestown.

—An Eye for an Eye: A Story of the Revolutionary War. 2004. (Jamestown's American Portraits Ser.). (Illus.). 176p. (J). (gr. 5-7). pap. 4.95 (978-0-7696-3422-7(2) , Waterbird Bks.) School Specialty Publishing.

Roop, Peter and Connie. An Eye for an Eye. 2004. 168p. (J). lib. bdg. 16.92 (***978-1-4242-0772-5(X)***) Fitzgerald Bks.

Root, Phyllis. What Baby Wants. Barton, Jill, illus. 2002. (J). 23.40 (978-0-7587-3955-1(9)) Book Wholesalers, Inc.

—What Baby Wants. Barton, Jill, illus. 1998. 18p. (J). (ps-3). pap. 12.98 (978-1-58048-027-7(6)) Sandvik Publishing.

—What Baby Wants. 2001. (J). (978-0-606-21514-5(X)) Tandem Library Bks.

Rose, Gill. William & the Guinea-Pig: A Book about Responsibility. Archbold, Tim, illus. 2004. (Making Good Choices Ser.). 24p. (C). (gr. k-3). 22.60 (978-1-4048-0664-1(4)) Picture Window Bks.

Roselle, Gayle. Moozelville Playground. 2007. (Illus.). 74p. (J). pap. 12.95 (***978-0-9788628-8-6(0)***) Just Write Bks.

Rosen, Wendy & End, Jackie. Chicken Fingers, Mac & Cheese... Why Do You Always Have to Say Please? Tuck-Bernstein, Cheryl, illus. 2005. 32p. (J). 14.99 (978-0-7666-1986-9(9)) Modern Publishing.

Rosoff, Meg. Just in Case. 2008. 256p. (gr. 12). 14.00 (***978-0-452-28937-6(8)*** , Plume) Penguin Group (USA) Inc.

—Just in Case. 2006. 256p. (YA). (gr. 9-11). 16.95 (978-0-385-74678-6(4) , Lamb, Wendy) Random Hse. Children's Bks.

Ross, Jil. The Real 'Nitty Gritty' 2006. (Illus.). 62p. (J). per. 6.95 (978-1-933324-40-1(6)) Cedar Hill Publishing.

Ross, Jil M. What's the Matter, Mr. Ticklebritches? Another installment in the Shenanigans Series. 2006. (Illus.). 62p. (J). per. 6.95 (978-1-933324-26-5(0)) Cedar Hill Publishing.

Ross, Sylvia. Lion Singer. 2005. (Illus.). 33p. (J). (gr. 1-4). 12.95 (978-1-59714-009-6(0) , Great Valley Bks.) Heyday Bks.

Ross, Tony. I Want a Sister. 2002. (Illus.). 22p. (J). 9.99 (978-1-84270-103-4(7)) Andersen GBR. *Dist:* Independent Pubs. Group.

Roter, Jordan. Girl of Development (Splashproof Ed) 2007. 1p. (YA). (gr. 7). pap. 7.99 (978-0-14-240838-4(7) , Puffin) Penguin Group (USA) Inc.

Rothstein, Evelyn. My Great Grandpa Dave. 2007. (J). per. 12.95 (***978-09786745-1-9(0)***) Marble House Editions.

Rottman, S. L. Head above Water. 2003. (gr. 7-12). lib. bdg. 15.25 (978-0-613-60386-7(9)) Tandem Library Bks.

—Rough Waters. 1998. (Illus.). 144p. (YA). (gr. 7-11). 14.95 (978-1-56145-172-2(X) , Q17398) Peachtree Pubs., Ltd.

—Rough Waters. 2000. (Illus.). 224p. (J). (gr. 7-12). pap. 6.99 (978-0-14-130703-9(X) , Puffin) Penguin Group (USA) Inc.

—Rough Waters. 2000. (978-0-606-17869-3(4)); (gr. 7-12). lib. bdg. 15.30 (978-0-613-28627-5(8)) Tandem Library Bks.

—Shadow of a Doubt. 2005. 224p. (YA). pap. 7.95 (978-1-56145-354-2(4)) Peachtree Pubs., Ltd.

—Stetson. 2002. 224p. (J). (gr. 9 up). 16.99 (978-0-670-03542-7(4) , Viking Juvenile) Penguin Group (USA) Inc.

Rouss, Sylvia A. Aaron's Bar Mitzvah. Dubois, Liz Goulet, tr. Dubois, Liz Goulet, illus. 2003. (J). 14.95 (978-0-8246-0447-9(4)) David, Jonathan Publishers, Inc.

—My Baby Brother: What a Miracle! Dubois, Liz Goulet, illus. 2002. (J). 14.95 (978-0-8246-0445-5(8)) David, Jonathan Publishers, Inc.

Rowinski, Kate. Cats in the Dark. Bishop, Bonnie, illus. 1998. 32p. (J). (ps-3). 14.95 (978-0-89272-427-7(7)) Down East Bks.

Rozanski, Bonnie. Borderline. 2007. 224p. (YA). pap. 22.95 (***978-0-88984-293-9(0)***) Porcupine's Quill, Inc. CAN. *Dist:* Univ. of Toronto Pr.

Rubel, Nicole. Ham & Pickles: First Day of School. 2006. (Illus.). 32p. (J). 16.00 (978-0-15-205039-9(6)) Harcourt Trade Pubs.

Ruby, Anne. Children of the Sea. Meier, Ty, illus. 2007. (YA). per. (978-0-9787881-0-0(9)) Seachild.

Rue, Nancy N. The Secret. 1998. (Christian Heritage Ser.). 192p. (Orig.). (J). (gr. 3-7). pap. (978-1-56179-443-0(0)) Focus on the Family Publishing.

—The Thief. 1998. (Christian Heritage Ser.). 192p. (J). (gr. 3-7). pap. (978-1-56179-479-9(1)) Focus on the Family Publishing.

Ruelle, Karen Gray. April Fool! (Illus.). 32p. (J). (gr. k-3). 4.95 (978-0-8234-1780-3(8)) Holiday Hse., Inc.

—April Fool! A Holiday House Reader. (Reader Level 2 Ser.). (Illus.). 32p. (J). (gr. k-3). tchr. ed. 14.95 (978-0-8234-1686-8(0)) Holiday Hse., Inc.

—Easter Egg Disaster: A Harry & Emily Adventure. (Illus.). 32p. (J). (gr. k-3). tchr. ed. 14.95 (978-0-8234-1806-0(5)) Holiday Hse., Inc.

—Just in Time for New Year'S! A Harry & Emily Adventure. (Illus.). 32p. (J). tchr. ed. 14.95 (978-0-8234-1841-1(3)) Holiday Hse., Inc.

—The Monster in Harry's Backyard. (Holiday House Readers Ser.). (Illus.). 32p. (J). (gr. k-3). 4.95 (978-0-8234-1783-4(2)) Holiday Hse., Inc.

—Mother's Day. (Illus.). 32p. (J). (gr. k-3). tchr. ed. 14.95 (978-0-8234-1773-5(5)) Holiday Hse., Inc.

—Mother's Day Mess. (Holiday House Readers Ser.). (Illus.). 32p. (J). (gr. k-3). 4.95 (978-0-8234-1781-0(6)) Holiday Hse., Inc.

—Spookier Than a Ghost. Ruelle, Karen Gray, illus. 2001. (Illus.). 32p. (J). (gr. k-3). tchr. ed. 14.95 (978-0-8234-1667-7(4)) Holiday Hse., Inc.

—Spookier Than a Ghost. (Holiday House Readers Ser.). (Illus.). 32p. (J). (gr. k-3). pap. 4.95 (978-0-8234-1801-5(4)) Holiday Hse., Inc.

—The Thanksgiving Beast Feast. (Holiday House Readers Ser.). (Illus.). 32p. (J). (gr. k-3). pap. 4.95 (978-0-8234-1802-2(2)) Holiday Hse., Inc.

—The Thanksgiving Beast Feast Level 2: A Holiday House Reader. Ruelle, Karen Gray, illus. (Illus.). 32p. (J). (gr. k-3). tchr. ed. 15.95 (978-0-8234-1511-3(2)) Holiday Hse., Inc.

Rumford, James. Dog-of-the-Sea-Waves. 2004. (ENG & HAW., Illus.). 48p. (J). (gr. k-3). tchr. ed. 16.00 (978-0-618-35611-9(8)) Houghton Mifflin Co. Trade & Reference Div.

Rupp, Rebecca. The Dragon of Lonely Island. 2004. 160p. (J). (gr. 4-8). reprint ed. (978-0-7567-7861-3(1)) DIANE Publishing Co.

—The Return of the Dragon. 2005. 160p. (J). (gr. 5-6). 15.99 (978-0-7636-2377-7(6)) Candlewick Pr.

Ruskin, John. The King of the Golden River. 2004. reprint ed. pap. 1.99 (978-1-4192-6821-2(X)) Kessinger Publishing, LLC.

—The King of the Golden River. Ghiuselev, Iassen, illus. 2005. 72p. (J). 19.95 (978-1-894965-15-6(9)) Simply Read Bks. CAN. *Dist:* Perseus Distribution.

Russo, Marisabina. The Trouble with Baby. Russo, Marisabina, illus. 2003. (Illus.). 32p. (J). (ps up). 16.89 (978-0-06-008925-2(3)) HarperCollins Pubs.

Ryan, Pam Muñoz. Becoming Naomi Leon. (J). (gr. 4-7). 2004. 240p. pap. 16.95 (978-0-439-26969-8(5) , Scholastic Pr.); 2005. 272p. reprint ed. pap. 5.99 (978-0-439-26997-1(0) , Scholastic Paperbacks) Scholastic, Inc.

—Yo, Naomi Leon. 2005. (SPA.). 272p. (J). (gr. 4-7). pap. 4.99 (978-0-439-75572-6(7) , Scholastic en Espanol) Scholastic, Inc.

Ryan, Sarah. The Rules for Hearts: A Family Drama. 2007. 224p. (YA). (gr. 9 up). 16.99 (978-0-670-05906-5(4) , Viking Juvenile) Penguin Group (USA) Inc.

Rynders, Dawn & Wallingford, Stephanie. A Day at the Lake. Villnave, Erica Pelton, illus. 2008. (J). (***978-1-55971-990-2(7)*** , NorthWord Bks. for Young Readers) T&N Children's Publishing.

Salisbury, Graham. Jungle Dogs. unabr. ed. 2000. (YA). (gr. 5 up). pap., stu. ed. 59.95 incl. audio (978-0-7887-4336-8(8) , 41131) Recorded Bks., LLC.

—Jungle Dogs. 1999. 11.64 (978-0-606-17837-2(6)) Tandem Library Bks.

Same Day, Different Way! 2005. (J). bds. (978-0-9769910-3-8(9)) Terrific Twins LLC.

Samuel, Lynette M. Mommy's Hat. Capps, Leigh, illus. 2005. (J). per. (978-0-9727703-3-0(X)) P.R.A. Publishing.

Sanschagrin, Joceline & Brignaud, Pierre. Caillou: Baby Sister. rev. ed. 2008. (Hand in Hand Ser.). (Illus.). 24p. (J). bds. 5.95 (***978-2-89450-642-4(2)***) Chouette Publishing CAN. *Dist:* Independent Pubs. Group.

Scampering Through Savannah. 2007. (YA). lib. bdg., act. bk. ed. (***978-0-9787589-2-9(7)***) ON Words Publishing, LLC.

Schaaf, Ron. Tiger's Quest: Rounding Cape Horn. 2007. (J). (***978-0-9787555-0-8(2)***) Hickory Tales Publishing.

Schietinger-Cachina, Daryl A. Hey New Baby in There. Schietinger-Cachina, Daryl A., illus. 1999. (Illus.). 8p. (J). (ps-5). pap. 5.00 (978-1-928641-02-5(4)) Daryl Ann Pubns.

Schneider, Josh. You'll Be Sorry. Schneider, Josh, illus. 2007. (Illus.). 32p. (J). (ps-1). 15.00 (***978-0-618-81932-4(0)*** , Clarion Bks.) Houghton Mifflin Co. Trade & Reference Div.

Schneider, Mical. Annie Quinn in America. (Adventures in Time Ser.). (J). 2003. (Illus.). 252p. (gr. 4-7). 15.95 (978-1-57505-510-7(4)); 2001. 6.95 (978-1-57505-535-0(X)) Lerner Publishing Group. (Carolrhoda Bks.).

Scholastic, Inc. Staff. Long-lost Map. 2007. (Ulysses Moore Ser.). 272p. (J). pap. 5.99 (***978-0-439-77673-8(2)***) Scholastic, Inc.

—Maya Soft Doll Maya & Miguel. 2005. (J). 16.99 (978-0-439-74087-6(8) , Sidekicks TM) Scholastic, Inc.

—Miguel Soft Doll. 2005. (J). 16.99 (978-0-439-74088-3(6) , Sidekicks TM) Scholastic, Inc.

Scholastic, Inc. Staff & Hooks, Gwendolyn. The Mystery of the Missing Dog. Devard, Nancy, illus. 2004. (Just for You! Ser.). 32p. (gr. k-3). pap. 3.99 (978-0-439-56864-7(1) , Teaching Resources) Scholastic, Inc.

Scholastic, Inc. Staff & Hudson, Cheryl. Just for You! What Do You Know? Snow! Walker, Sylvia, illus. 2004. (Just for You! Ser.). 32p. pap. 3.99 (978-0-439-56851-7(X) , Teaching Resources) Scholastic, Inc.

Scholastic, Inc. Staff & Roberson, Karla. My Shoelaces Are Hard to Tie. Holley, Vanessa, illus. 2004. (Just for You! Ser.). 32p. pap. 3.99 (978-0-439-56869-2(2) , Teaching Resources) Scholastic, Inc.

Schraff, Anne. Gingerbread Heart. 1999. 114p. (J). pap. (978-0-7891-4926-8(5)); (gr. 5-12). lib. bdg. 13.95 (978-0-7807-8005-7(1)) Perfection Learning Corp.

Schreiber, Ellen. Dance with a Vampire. 2007. (Vampire Kisses Ser.: Bk. 4). 192p. (J). lib. bdg. 16.89 (***978-0-06-113224-7(1));*** (gr. 7 up). 15.99 (***978-0-06-113223-0(3)***) HarperCollins Pubs. (HarperTeen).

Schulz, Charles M. Lose the Blanket, Linus! 2003. (gr. k-3). lib. bdg. 11.80 (978-0-613-61791-8(6)) Tandem Library Bks.

—Mischief on Daisy Hill. (Illus.). 32p. (J). (ps-3). 12.95 (978-0-915696-15-4(0)) Determined Productions, Inc.

Schwartz, Roslyn. The Mole Sisters & the Piece of Moss. Schwartz, Roslyn, illus. 2001. (Mole Sisters Ser.). (Illus.). 32p. (J). (ps-k). lib. bdg. 14.95 (978-1-55037-583-1(0)) Annick Pr., Ltd. CAN. *Dist:* Firefly Bks., Ltd.

—The Mole Sisters & the Rainy Day. Schwartz, Roslyn, illus. 2001. (Mole Sisters Ser.). (Illus.). 32p. (J). (ps-k). lib. bdg. 14.95 (978-1-55037-611-1(X)) Annick Pr., Ltd. CAN. *Dist:* Firefly Bks., Ltd.

Scott, Michael. The Alchemyst. 2007. (Secrets Imrtl Nicholas Flamel Ser.). (Illus.). 400p. (YA). (gr. 7 up). 16.99 (978-0-385-73357-1(7)); lib. bdg. 19.99 (978-0-385-90372-1(3)) Random Hse. Children's Bks. (Delacorte Bks. for Young Readers).

Sebag-Montefiore, Mary. Railway Children. Marks, Alan, illus. 2007. (Young Reading Series 2 Gift Bks). 64p. (J). 8.99 (***978-0-7945-1615-4(7)*** , Usborne) EDC Publishing.

Seidler, Tor. Brothers below Zero. McCarty, Peter, illus. 2003. 144p. (J). (gr. 5 up). pap. 5.99 (978-0-06-440936-0(8) , Harper Trophy) HarperCollins Pubs.

—Brothers below Zero. 2002. (Illus.). 144p. (J). (gr. 3 up). 14.95 (978-0-06-029179-2(6) , Geringer, Laura Book) HarperCollins Pubs.

—Brothers below Zero. McCarty, Peter, illus. 2002. 144p. (J). (gr. 5 up). lib. bdg. 15.89 (978-0-06-029180-8(X) , Geringer, Laura Book) HarperCollins Pubs.

—Brothers below Zero. 2003. (gr. 3-6). lib. bdg. 14.15 (978-0-613-57705-2(1)) Tandem Library Bks.

—The Dulcimer Boy. Selznick, Brian, illus. 160p. (J). reprint ed. 2004. pap. 6.99 (978-0-06-441048-9(X) , Harper Trophy); 2003. 15.99 (978-0-06-623609-4(6)) HarperCollins Pubs.

Seif, Adam, creator. Tacos, Beans & Rice... the Episodes: From the Beginning. l.t. ed. 2006. (Illus.). 32p. (J). (978-0-9719518-0-8(2)) Doodle Publishing.

Selfors, Suzanne. To Catch a Mermaid. Chien, Catia, illus. rev. ed. 2007. 254p. (J). (gr. 3-7). 14.99 (***978-0-316-01816-6(3)***) Little, Brown Bks. for Young Readers.

Seuss, Dr. ¡El Gato con Sombrero Viene de Nuevo! Canetti, Yanitzia, tr. from ENG. 2004. (SPA., Illus.). 63p. (ps-1). 8.99 (978-1-930332-43-0(2)) Lectorum Pubns., Inc.

Shahan, Sherry. Together for Kwanzaa. 2000. (Pictureback Ser.). (978-0-606-18504-2(6)) Tandem Library Bks.

Sharing: Individual Title Six-Packs. (Literatura 2000 Ser.). (gr. k-1). 28.00 (978-0-7635-0038-2(0)) Rigby Education.

Shaw, Dana Alton, III. My Friend Zundel. 2006. per. (***978-0-9791091-0-2(8)***) Shaw, Dana.

Shea, Pegi Deitz. New Moon. Falwell, Cathryn, illus. 2003. 32p. (J). (ps up). pap. 8.95 (978-1-56397-922-4(5)) Boyds Mills Pr.

—New Moon. 2000. (gr. k-3). lib. bdg. 17.60 (978-0-613-36929-9(7)) Tandem Library Bks.

Shearer, Alex. Sea Legs. 2005. 320p. (J). 16.95 (978-0-689-87143-6(0)) Simon & Schuster Children's Publishing.

—The Summer Sisters & the Dance Disaster. Kenyon, Tony, illus. 1998. 103p. (J). (gr. 3-7). pap. 14.95 (978-0-531-30080-0(3)); lib. bdg. 15.99 (978-0-531-33080-7(X)) Scholastic, Inc. (Orchard Bks.).

Sheldon, Dyan. My Brother Is a Superhero. 1998. (gr. 3-6). lib. bdg. 13.00 (978-0-613-74681-6(3)) Tandem Library Bks.

Sherrard, Valerie. Three Million Acres of Flame. 2007. 180p. (YA). pap. 10.99 (***978-1-55002-727-3(1)*** , Boardwalk Bks.) Dundurn Group, The CAN. *Dist:* Univ. of Toronto Pr.

Shi, Sharon. The Camera. Jones, David Phillip, illus. 2000. 24p. (J). (gr. k-3). mass mkt. 4.99 (978-0-9702195-0-3(4) , B011, Tattootles Bks.) Tattoo Manufacturing.

Shinohara, Chie. Red River, Volume 17. 2007. (Red River Ser.). 192p. (YA). pap. 9.99 (978-1-4215-0997-6(0)) Viz Media.

Shook, Karl. The Family Thing. 2004. 166p. (YA). pap. 12.95 (978-0-595-31121-7(0)) iUniverse, Inc.

Short, Robbie, illus. I Want One Too! 2003. 32p. (J). lib. bdg. 12.95 (978-0-9729833-2-7(5)) Bubble Gum Pr.

Shreve, Susan Richards. Ghost Cats. 1999. 162p. (J). (gr. 3-7). pap. 14.95 (978-0-590-37131-5(2) , Levine, Arthur A. Bks.) Scholastic, Inc.

Shusterman, Neal. Full Tilt. 208p. (YA). 2004. mass mkt. 5.99 (978-0-689-87325-6(5) , Simon Pulse); 2003. (Illus.). 16.95 (978-0-689-80374-1(5)) Simon & Schuster Children's Publishing.

—Full Tilt. l.t. ed. 2003. 243p. (J). 22.95 (978-0-7862-5886-4(1)) Thorndike Pr.

Shyer, Marlene Fanta. The Rainbow Kite. 2002. 208p. (YA). (gr. 7-10). 15.95 (978-0-7614-5122-8(6)) Cavendish, Marshall Corp.

The Siblings Four. 2006. (J). (978-0-9629124-6-7(8)) Floppinfish Publishing Co., Ltd.

Sidney, Margaret. Five Little Peppers & How They Grew. 2006. (Dover Value Editions Ser.). (Illus.). 224p. (J). pap. 5.95 (978-0-486-45267-8(0)) Dover Pubns., Inc.

Sidney, Margaret. Five Little Peppers & Their Friends. 2001. (YA). reprint ed. lib. bdg. 29.95 (978-0-89966-970-0(0)) Buccaneer Bks., Inc.

—Five Little Peppers & Their Friends. 2006. 65.99 (***978-1-4219-9625-7(1)***) IndyPublish.com.

Silberberg, Alan. Pond Scum. 2007. 288p. (gr. 3-7). pap. 5.99 (978-0-7868-5635-0(1)) Hyperion Pr.

Silberman, Shoshana. A Family Haggadah II, Vol. 2. Kahn, Katherine Janus, illus. l.t. ed. 2003. 64p. (J). pap. 6.95 (978-1-58013-014-1(3)) Kar-Ben Publishing.

Silent to the Bone. 2004. 261p. (J). (gr. 5-9). lib. bdg. 14.15 (978-0-613-73424-0(6)) Tandem Library Bks.

Silverman, Erica. Follow the Leader. Karas, G. Brian, illus. 2003. 32p. (J). pap. 6.95 (978-0-374-42403-9(9) , Sunburst) Farrar, Straus & Giroux.

Silverman, Manuel S. Rosie & the Mole: The Story of a Bris. 1999. (Illus.). 48p. (J). (gr. 1-4). 16.95 (978-0-943706-22-1(X) , Devora Publishing) Pitspopany Pr.

—Rosie & the Mole: The Story of a Bris. Kahn, Katherine Janus, illus. 1999. 48p. (J). (gr. 1-4). pap. 9.95 (978-0-943706-20-7(3) , Devora Publishing) Pitspopany Pr.

Simmons, Jane. Daisy & the Beastie. Simmons, Jane, illus. 2002. (Illus.). (J). 19.11 (978-0-7587-2334-5(2)) Book Wholesalers, Inc.

—Daisy & the Egg. Simmons, Jane, illus. 2002. (Illus.). (J). 19.96 (978-0-7587-2335-2(0)) Book Wholesalers, Inc.

—Daisy & the Egg. (Illus.). (ps-1). 2005. (ARA, ENG, VIE, CHI & BEN.). 32p. 11.95 (978-1-84059-216-0(8)); 2005. (VIE, ENG, CHI, ARA & BEN., 32p. pap. 11.95 (978-1-84059-176-7(5)); 2000. (CHI, ENG, VIE, ARA & BEN., 36p. (J). pap. 11.95 (978-1-84059-171-2(4)); 2000. (GUJ, ENG, VIE, CHI & ARA., 36p. (J). pap. 11.95 (978-1-84059-173-6(0)); 2000. (TUR, ENG, VIE, CHI & ARA., 36p. (J). pap. 11.95 (978-1-84059-174-3(9)); 2000. (ALB, ENG, VIE, CHI & ARA., 36p. (J). pap. 11.95 (978-1-84059-172-9(2)) Milet Publishing.

—Daisy & the Egg. Datta, Kanai, tr. 2000. (Daisy Ser.). (BEN, ENG, VIE, CHI & ARA., Illus.). 36p. (J). (ps-1). pap. 11.95 (978-1-84059-170-5(6)) Milet Publishing.

—Daisy & the Egg. Iqbal, Gulshan, tr. 2000. (Daisy Ser.). (ENG, URD, VIE, CHI & ARA., Illus.). 36p. (J). (ps-1). pap. 11.95 (978-1-84059-175-0(7)) Milet Publishing.

—Daisy & the Egg. 2003. (ps-2). lib. bdg. 15.30 (978-0-613-71811-0(9)) Tandem Library Bks.

Simmons, Michael. Vandal. 2006. 176p. (YA). 16.95 (978-1-59643-070-9(2)) Roaring Brook Pr.

—Vandal. 2007. 176p. (YA). pap. 6.99 (***978-0-312-37147-0(0)***) Square Fish.

Simoen, Jan. What about Anna? Nieuwenhuizen, John, tr. from DUT. 2002. (Illus.). 264p. (YA). (gr. 7 up). 16.95 (978-0-8027-8808-5(4)) Walker & Co.

Simon, Charnan. I Like to Win! Handelman, Dorothy, photos by. 1999. (Real Kids Readers Ser.). (Illus.). 32p. (J). (gr. k-1). pap. 4.99 (978-0-7613-2087-6(3) , Millbrook Pr.) Lerner Publishing Group.

—I Like to Win! 1999. (ps-2). lib. bdg. 13.00 (978-0-613-18157-0(3)) Tandem Library Bks.

—Tressa the Musical Princess. Allen, Joy, illus. 2005. 25p. (J). (978-1-58987-112-0(X)) Kindermusik International.

Simpson, Fiona, ed. Teenick Vol. 7: Zoey 101. 2006. (Zoey 101 Ser.). 112p. (J). pap. 4.99 (978-0-439-88259-0(1) , Scholastic) Scholastic, Inc.

Singleton, Clive. The City through the Clouds. 2006. 208p. pap. 13.99 (978-1-4116-5982-7(1)) Lulu.com.

Sion Charnan. ¡Me gusta ganar! (I Like to Win!) 2007. (Lecturas para niños de verdad - Nivel 1 (Real Kids Readers - Level 1) Ser.). (J). pap. 5.95 (***978-0-8225-7801-7(8)*** , Ediciones Lerner) Lerner Publishing Group.

Skinner, Daphne. Henry Keeps Score. O'Rourke, Page Eastburn, illus. 2001. (Math Matters Ser.). 32p. (J). (ps-2). pap. 4.95 (978-1-57565-102-6(5)) Kane Pr., The.

Skurzynski, Gloria. The Minstrel in the Tower. Heller, Julek, illus. 2004. (Stepping Stone Bks.). 64p. (J). (gr. 4-7). pap. 3.99 (978-0-394-89598-7(3) , Random Hse. Bks. for Young Readers) Random Hse. Children's Bks.

Slanina, Anne M. The Adventures of Annie Mouse: Baby Brother Goes to the Hospital. Agnew, Alicia, illus. 2007. 28p. (J). 16.99 (***978-0-9793379-1-8(7)***); per. 9.99 (***978-0-9793379-0-1(9)***) Annie Mouse Bks.

Slater, David Michael. Jacques & Spock. Tilley, Debbie, illus. 2004. 32p. (J). (gr. k-3). tchr. ed. 15.00 (978-0-618-15980-2(0) , Clarion Bks.) Houghton Mifflin Co. Trade & Reference Div.

Sleator, William. The Beasties, Vol. 1. 1999. (Illus.). 208p. (J). (gr. 3-7). pap. 6.99 (978-0-14-130639-1(4) , Puffin) Penguin Group (USA) Inc.

—The Beasties. 1999. (J). 12.64 (978-0-606-17410-7(9)); (gr. 5-8). lib. bdg. 14.15 (978-0-613-22820-6(0)) Tandem Library Bks.

—Fingers. ed. 2006. 208p. (YA). 6.99 (978-0-7653-5349-8(0) , Tor Teen) Doherty, Tom Assocs., LLC.

—The Last Universe. (J). (gr. 7-11). 2006. 240p. pap. 6.95 (978-0-8109-9213-9(2)); 2005. 224p. 16.95 (978-0-8109-5858-6(9) , Amulet Bks.) Abrams, Harry N. , Inc.

Smadja, Brigitte. Tarte aux Escargots. pap. 17.95 (978-2-211-03633-7(3)) Archimede Editions FRA. *Dist:* Distribooks, Inc.

Smith, Alexander McCall. The Five Lost Aunts of Harriet Bean. Rankin, Laura, illus. 2006. 96p. (J). 9.95 (978-1-58234-975-6(4) , Bloomsbury Children) Bloomsbury Publishing.

—Max & Maddy & the Bursting Balloons Mystery. Pamintuan, Macky, illus. 2007. 128p. (J). (gr. 2-4). 9.95 (978-1-59990-035-3(1) , Bloomsbury Children) Bloomsbury Publishing.

—Max & Maddy & the Chocolate Money Mystery. Pamintuan, Macky, illus. 2007. 128p. (J). (gr. 2-4). 9.95 (978-1-59990-036-0(X) , Bloomsbury Children) Bloomsbury Publishing.

Smith, Cheryl Jean. The Offering. 2006. 129p. pap. 11.95 (978-0-7414-3181-3(5)) Infinity Publishing.

Smith, Helene. Children of Morwena. 2002. 256p. (J). pap. 14.95 (978-1-86368-356-2(9)) Fremantle Pr. AUS. *Dist:* International Specialized Bk. Services.

Smith, M. J. Kevin Murphy Takes on the Father of Lies. 2005. (Illus.). 311p. (J). (gr. 4-8). pap. 10.95 (978-0-9765066-0-7(2)) B & S Publishing Corp.

Smith, Roland. Cryptid Hunters. 2005. 352p. (J). (gr. 5-17). 15.99 (978-0-7868-5161-4(9)) Hyperion Bks. for Children.

—Cryptid Hunters. 2006. 352p. (gr. 5-17). pap. 5.99 (978-0-7868-5162-1(7)) Hyperion Pr.

Smith, Sherwood. Trouble under Oz: Dreams of the Tin Man. Stout, William, illus. 2006. 256p. (J). 16.99 (978-0-06-029609-4(7)); lib. bdg. 17.89 (978-0-06-029610-0(0)) HarperCollins Pubs.

Smothers, Ethel Footman. Down in the Piney Woods. 2004. 128p. (J). pap. 7.00 (978-0-8028-5248-9(3)) Eerdmans, William B. Publishing Co.

—Down in the Piney Woods. 2003. (gr. 3-6). lib. bdg. 15.30 (978-0-613-75341-8(0)) Tandem Library Bks.

Snicket, Lemony, pseud. The Austere Academy. Helquist, Brett, illus. 2008. (Series of Unfortunate Events Ser.: Bk. 5). 240p. (J). (gr. 5 up). pap. 6.99 (***978-0-06-114634-3(X)*** , Harper Trophy) HarperCollins Pubs.

—The Austere Academy. 2000. (Series of Unfortunate Events Ser.: Bk. 5). (J). (gr. 4-7). pupil's gde. ed. (978-0-06-029312-3(8)) HarperCollins Pubs.

—The Austere Academy. Helquist, Brett, illus. 2000. (Series of Unfortunate Events Ser.: Bk. 5). 240p. (J). (gr. 5 up). 12.99 (978-0-06-440863-9(9)); lib. bdg. 15.89 (978-0-06-028888-4(4)) HarperCollins Pubs.

—The Bad Beginning. Helquist, Brett, illus. l.t. ed. 2002. (Series of Unfortunate Events Ser.: Bk. 1). 168p. (J). 16.95 (978-0-7540-7812-8(4) , Galaxy Children's Large Print) BBC Audiobooks America.

—The Bad Beginning. Helquist, Brett, illus. 1999. (Series of Unfortunate Events Ser.: Bk. 1). 176p. (J). (gr. 5 up). 12.99 (978-0-06-440766-3(7)); lib. bdg. 15.89 (978-0-06-028312-4(2)) HarperCollins Pubs.

—The Carnivorous Carnival. Helquist, Brett, illus. 2002. (Series of Unfortunate Events Ser.: Bk. 9). 304p. (J). (gr. 4-7). 12.99 (978-0-06-441012-0(9) , Harper Trophy); (ps-3). lib. bdg. 15.89 (978-0-06-029640-7(2)) HarperCollins Pubs.

—The Complete Wreck, Bks. 1-13. Helquist, Brett, illus. 2006. (Series of Unfortunate Events Ser.). (J). 150.00 (978-0-06-111906-4(7)) HarperCollins Pubs.

—The Ersatz Elevator. Helquist, Brett, illus. 2001. (Series of Unfortunate Events Ser.: Bk. 6). 272p. (J). (gr. 5 up). 12.99 (978-0-06-440864-6(7)); 6th ed. lib. bdg. 15.89 (978-0-06-028889-1(2)) HarperCollins Pubs.

—The Gloom Looms, Bks. 10-12. Helquist, Brett, illus. 2005. (Series of Unfortunate Events Ser.). (J). 38.99 (978-0-06-083909-3(0)) HarperCollins Pubs.

—The Grim Grotto. Helquist, Brett, illus. 2004. (Series of Unfortunate Events Ser.: Bk. 11). 352p. (YA). (gr. 3-6). 12.99 (978-0-06-441014-4(5) , HarperCollins) HarperCollins Pubs.

—La Habitacion de los Reptiles. Helquist, Brett, illus. 2002. (Series of Unfortunate Events Ser.). (SPA.). 208p. (J). (gr. 4-6). 10.95 (978-84-264-3741-9(9) , LM31164) Editorial Lumen ESP. *Dist:* Lectorum Pubns., Inc.

—The Hostile Hospital. Helquist, Brett, illus. 2001. (Series of Unfortunate Events Ser.: Bk. 8). (J). 272p. (gr. 5 up). 12.99 (978-0-06-440866-0(3)); 255p. (gr. 4-7). lib. bdg. (978-0-06-623919-4(2)); 8th ed. 272p. (gr. 5 up). lib. bdg. 15.89 (978-0-06-028891-4(4)) HarperCollins Pubs.

—The Loathsome Library, Bks. 1-6. Helquist, Brett, illus. 2005. (Series of Unfortunate Events Ser.: Vol. 1). (J). 65.00 (978-0-06-083353-4(X)) HarperCollins Pubs.

—Un Mal Principio. Helquist, Brett, illus. 2002. (Series of Unfortunate Events Ser.). (SPA.). 224p. (J). (gr. 4-6). 10.95 (978-84-264-3740-2(0) , LM31162) Editorial Lumen ESP. *Dist:* Lectorum Pubns., Inc.

—Un Mal Principio. Busquets, Nestor, tr. Helquist, Brett, illus. 2004. (Catastroficas Desdichas Ser.). (SPA.). 176p. (J). pap. 7.95 (978-0-307-20934-4(2) , Montena) Random House Mondadori ESP. *Dist:* Random Hse., Inc.

—The Miserable Mill. Helquist, Brett, illus. 2000. (Series of Unfortunate Events Ser.: Bk. 4). 208p. (J). (gr. 3-6). 12.99 (978-0-06-440769-4(1)); (ps-2). lib. bdg. 15.89 (978-0-06-028315-5(7)) HarperCollins Pubs.

—The Notorious Notations. Helquist, Brett, illus. 2006. (Series of Unfortunate Events Ser.). 176p. (J). pap. 9,99 (978-0-06-087235-9(7) , Harper Festival) HarperCollins Pubs.

—Omnibus. Helquist, Brett, illus. movie tie-in ed. 2004. (Series of Unfortunate Events Ser.). (J). 35.99 (978-0-06-075773-1(6)) HarperCollins Pubs.

—The Reptile Room. Helquist, Brett, illus. l.t. ed. 2002. (Series of Unfortunate Events Ser.: Bk. 2). 184p. (J). pap. 16.95 (978-0-7540-7823-4(X) , Galaxy Children's Large Print) BBC Audiobooks America.

—The Reptile Room. Helquist, Brett, illus. 1999. (Series of Unfortunate Events Ser.: Bk. 2). 208p. (J). (gr. 5 up). 12.99 (978-0-06-440767-0(5)); lib. bdg. 15.89 (978-0-06-028313-1(0)) HarperCollins Pubs.

—The Slippery Slope. Helquist, Brett, illus. 2003. (Series of Unfortunate Events Ser.: Bk. 10). (YA). (gr. 5 up). 197.82 (978-0-06-057743-8(6)); 352p. (J). (gr. 3-6). 12.99 (978-0-06-441013-7(7)); 352p. (J). (gr. 3-6). lib. bdg. 15.89 (978-0-06-029641-4(0)) HarperCollins Pubs.

—The Vile Village. Helquist, Brett, illus. 2001. (Series of Unfortunate Events Ser.: Bk. 7). 272p. (J). (gr. 5 up). 12.99 (978-0-06-440865-3(5)); 7th ed. lib. bdg. 15.89 (978-0-06-028890-7(6)) HarperCollins Pubs.

—The Wide Window. l.t. ed. 2003. (Series of Unfortunate Events Ser.: Bk. 3). (Illus.). 216p. (J). 16.95 (978-0-7540-7850-0(7) , Galaxy Children's Large Print) BBC Audiobooks America.

—The Wide Window. Helquist, Brett, illus. 2000. (Series of Unfortunate Events Ser.: Bk. 3). 224p. (J). (gr. 5 up). 12.99 (978-0-06-440768-7(3)) HarperCollins Pubs.

—The Wide Window. Helquist, Brett & Kupperman, Michael, illus. 2000. (Series of Unfortunate Events Ser.: Bk. 3). 224p. (J). (ps-2). lib. bdg. 15.89 (978-0-06-028314-8(9)) HarperCollins Pubs.

Snyder, Zilpha Keatley. The Unseen. l.t. ed. 2005. 276p. 22.95 (978-0-7862-7265-5(1) , Large Print Pr.) Thorndike Pr.

Soileau, Hodges, illus. The Haunted Clock Tower Mystery, Vol. 84. 2004. (Boxcar Children Ser.: No. 84). 128p. (J). (gr. 2-7). pap. 3.95 (978-0-8075-5485-2(5)) Whitman, Albert & Co.

Sonnenblick, Jordan. Drums, Girls & Dangerous Pie. (J). 2006. 29.95 (978-0-439-89550-7(2)); 2005. 288p. pap. 16.99 (978-0-439-75519-1(0) , Scholastic Pr.); 2004. 208p. 15.95 (978-0-9761030-1-1(X)) Scholastic, Inc.

Sorela, Pedro. Aire de Mar en Gador. 1998. (SPA.). (gr. 7-12). lib. bdg. 15.25 (978-0-613-80719-7(7)) Tandem Library Bks.

Sosna, Marvin. Brandon's Trail. 2006. 220p. per. 13.95 (978-1-58939-875-7(0)) Virtualbookworm.com Publishing, Inc.

Spalding, Andrea & Spalding, David A. E. The Klondike Ring. 2003. (Adventure Net Ser.). 128p. (J). (gr. 3-2). pap. 6.95 (978-1-55285-461-7(2)) Whitecap Bks., Ltd. CAN. *Dist:* Firefly Bks., Ltd.

Sperry, John Lamont. Where Is Home? 2006. 136p. pap. 19.95 (978-1-4241-1008-7(4)) PublishAmerica, Inc.

Spinelli, Eileen. Baby Loves You So Much! Wenzel, David, illus. 2007. 40p. (J). (ps-3). 16.99 (***978-0-8249-5550-2(1)*** , Ideals Children's Bks.) Ideals Pubns.

Spinelli, Jerry. Who Put That Hair in My Toothbrush? 2000. 225p. (J). (gr. 4-7). pap. 6.99 (978-0-316-80687-9(0)) Little Brown & Co.

Springham, James. Earth-n-Bones: Blue Things. 2006. 54p. pap. 12.95 (978-1-4137-9738-1(5)) PublishAmerica, Inc.

Stark, Ulf. Mi Hermano Mayor. 2002. Tr. of My Big Brother. (SPA.). 46p. (J). 8.95 (978-84-348-5123-8(7)) SM Ediciones ESP. *Dist:* AIMS International Bks., Inc.

Steele, Giselle. The off-Limits Watermelon Patch. 2006. (Illus.). 35p. (J). per. 12.95 (978-0-9769949-0-9(9)) Stuart & Weitz Publishing Group.

Stephen, Smith. Red Card. 2006. 128p. (J). pap. 5.99 (978-0-7847-1438-6(X) , 42143) Standard Publishing.

Stevenson, James. Peor Que Willy. (SPA., Illus.). (J). (gr. k-2). pap. (978-84-348-1895-8(7) , SM2858) SM Ediciones ESP. *Dist:* Lectorum Pubns., Inc.

Stoeke, Janet Morgan. Waiting for May. Stoeke, Janet Morgan, illus. 2007. 32p. (J). (gr. k). pap. 5.99 (978-0-14-240853-7(0) , Puffin) Penguin Group (USA) Inc.

Stokes, Phil. Phillip & Dickie. 2004. 384p. (YA). 28.95 (978-0-9744360-0-5(3)) Da Wong Bks.

Stone, Jeff. Crane. 2007. (Five Ancestors Ser.: Bk. 4). (J). (gr. 5-9). 256p. 15.99 (978-0-375-83077-8(4)); 224p. lib. bdg. 17.99 (978-0-375-93077-5(9)) Random Hse. Children's Bks. (Random Hse. Bks. for Young Readers).

—Crane. 2007. (Five Ancestors Ser.: Bk. 4). 248p. (J). pap. (***978-0-375-83078-5(2)***) Random Hse., Inc.

—Eagle. 2008. (Five Ancestors Ser.). 224p. (J). (gr. 5). 15.99 (***978-0-375-83083-9(9)***); lib. bdg. 18.99 (***978-0-375-93083-6(3)***) Random Hse. Children's Bks. (Random Hse. Bks. for Young Readers).

—The Five Ancestors Book #1: Tiger. (Five Ancestors Ser.: Bk. 1). 208p. (gr. 5). 2005. (J). lib. bdg. 17.99 (978-0-375-93071-3(X) , Random Hse. Bks. for Young Readers); 2005. (Illus.). (J). 15.95 (978-0-375-83071-6(5) , Random Hse. Bks. for Young Readers); 2006. reprint ed. 5.99 (978-0-375-83072-3(3) , Yearling) Random Hse. Children's Bks.

—Monkey. 2005. (Five Ancestors Ser.: Bk. 2). 208p. (J). (gr. 5-9). lib. bdg. 17.99 (978-0-375-93073-7(6)); 15.95 (978-0-375-83073-0(1)) Random Hse. Children's Bks. (Random Hse. Bks. for Young Readers).

Stonesifer, Gertrude. Sister & Me. 2003. (Illus.). 98p. pap. 7.95 (978-1-878044-62-4(1)) Mayhaven Publishing.

Strangway, Melissa. 56 Water Street. 2007. 104p. per. 9.95 (***978-0-595-42429-0(5)***) iUniverse, Inc.

Strasser, Todd. Battle Drift. Phillips, Craig, illus. 2006. (DriftX Ser.). 224p. (YA). pap. 6.99 (978-1-4169-0582-0(0) , Simon Pulse) Simon & Schuster Children's Publishing.

Streib, Sally. Octopus Encounter. 2007. (J). (***978-0-8163-2210-7(4)***) Pacific Pr. Publishing Assn.

Stretton, Hesba. Little Meg's Children. 2000. (Golden Inheritance Ser.: Vol. 5). (Illus.). 88p. (J). pap. (978-0-921100-92-8(2)) Inheritance Pubns.

—Little Meg's Children. (Early Children's Bks.). (J). reprint ed. 15.00 (978-0-384-56160-1(8)) Johnson Reprint Corp.

—Lost Gip. 2003. (Golden Inheritance Ser.: Vol. 7). (Illus.). 121p. (J). (978-0-921100-93-5(0)) Inheritance Pubns.

Strickland, Michael R. Haircuts at Sleepy Sam's. Holliday, Keaf, illus. 2003. 32p. (J). (gr. 2-4). 15.95 (978-1-56397-562-2(9)) Boyds Mills Pr.

Stroud, Jonathan. Buried Fire. 2004. 332p. (J). pap. (978-0-7818-5794-9(5)) Hippocrene Bks., Inc.

—Buried Fire. 2004. 336p. (gr. 5-17). pap. 6.95 (978-0-7868-5194-2(5)) Miramax Bks.

—The Leap. 2004. 240p. (gr. 5-17). pap. 6.95 (978-0-7868-5195-9(3)) Miramax Bks.

Sturges, Philemon. I Love School! Halpern, Shari, illus. 32p. (J). (ps-1). 2004. 12.99 (978-0-06-009284-9(X)); 2004. lib. bdg. 14.89 (978-0-06-009285-6(8)); 2006. reprint ed. pap. 5.99 (978-0-06-009286-3(6) , Harper Trophy) HarperCollins Pubs.

Stuve-Bodeen, Stephanie. Mama Elizabeti. Hale, Christy, illus. 2000. 32p. (J). (ps up). 12.76 (978-1-58430-002-1(7)) Lee & Low Bks., Inc.

—We'll Paint the Octopus Red. DeVito, Pamela, illus. 1998. 25p. (J). (ps-2). 15.95 (978-1-890627-06-5(2)) Woodbine Hse.

Summers, Sherri Pankratz. Humpty Dumpty, Back Together Again? Pankratz, Justin, illus. 2003. 32p. (J). 8.95 (978-0-9742637-1-7(0)) Pankratz Creations.

Summers, Tamara. He's with Me. 2007. (I Heart Bikinis Ser.: No. 1). 224p. (J). pap. 5.99 (***978-0-439-91850-3(2)*** , Scholastic Paperbacks) Scholastic, Inc.

Susi, Geraldine Lee. Looking for Pa: A Civil War Journey from Catlett to Manassas, 1861. French, Douglas P., illus. 2nd ed. 2001. 127p. (J). (gr. 4-7). pap. 10.95 (978-1-880664-33-9(X)) E. M. Productions.

Susie's Sister Has Food Allergy. 2004. (J). 5.00 (978-1-882541-36-2(7)) Food Allergy & Anaphylaxis Network.

Swan, S. Annie. Thankful Rest (a Tale) 2006. 77.99 (***978-1-4219-9988-3(9)***); pap. 70.99 (***978-1-4142-5872-0(0)***) IndyPublish.com.

Sweeney, Jacqueline. Lou Goes Too! Hart, G. K. & Empey, Mark, illus. 1999. (We Can Read! Ser.). 32p. (J). (gr. 1-2). lib. bdg. 21.36 (978-0-7614-0921-2(1) , Benchmark Bks.) Cavendish, Marshall Corp.

—What about Bettie? Hart, G. K. & Empey, Mark, illus. 2000. (We Can Read! Ser.). 32p. (J). (gr. 1-2). lib. bdg. 21.36 (978-0-7614-1118-5(6) , Benchmark Bks.) Cavendish, Marshall Corp.

Sykes, Julie. Wait for Me, Little Tiger! Warnes, Tim, illus. 2001. 28p. (J). (ps-k). tchr. ed. 14.95 (978-1-58925-009-3(5) , tiger tales) ME Media LLC.

Tabb, Robert C. The Rules: Trust No One. 2007. 156p. per. 11.95 (***978-0-595-44797-8(X)***) iUniverse, Inc.

Tamura, Yumi. Basara, Vol. 22. 2007. (Basara Ser.). 192p. (YA). pap. 9.99 (978-1-4215-0979-2(2)) Viz Media.

Tandori, Martha. Being Sam, No Matter What. 2005. 144p. pap. 19.95 (978-1-4137-6773-5(7)) PublishAmerica, Inc.

Tang, Charles, illus. The Basketball Mystery, Vol. 68. 1999. (Boxcar Children Ser.: No. 68). 128p. (J). (gr. 2-5). pap. 3.95 (978-0-8075-0576-2(5)) Whitman, Albert & Co.

—The Mystery in New York, Vol. 13. 2004. (Boxcar Children Special Ser.: No. 13). 121p. (J). (gr. 2-5). 14.95 (978-0-8075-5459-3(6)); pap. 4.50 (978-0-8075-5460-9(X)) Whitman, Albert & Co.

—The Mystery of the Empty Safe. 2000. (Boxcar Children Ser.: No. 75). (J). (gr. 2-5). (978-0-606-18768-8(5)) Tandem Library Bks.

—The Mystery of the Empty Safe, Vol. 75. 2004. (Boxcar Children Ser.: No. 75). 120p. (J). (gr. 2-5). pap. 4.50 (978-0-8075-5463-0(4)) Whitman, Albert & Co.

—The Mystery of the Pirate's Map. 1999. 121p. (J). (ps-7). per. 11.80 (978-0-613-16287-6(0)) Tandem Library Bks.

Tashjian, Janet. Tru Confessions. 1999. (Illus.). 176p. (J). pap. 4.99 (978-0-590-96047-2(4)) Scholastic, Inc.

—Tru Confessions. 2007. 176p. (J). pap. 6.99 (***978-0-312-37273-6(6)***) Square Fish.

—Tru Confessions. 1999. (978-0-606-16611-9(4)) Tandem Library Bks.

Taylor, Bonnie Highsmith. Simon Can't Say Hippopotamus. Hornung, Phyllis, tr. Hornung, Phyllis, illus. 2003. 24p. (J). 14.95 (978-1-59336-017-7(7)); pap. (978-1-59336-018-4(5)) Mondo Publishing.

Taylor, Donna. Dream Come True. 2000. (gr. k-3). lib. bdg. 11.25 (978-0-613-31140-3(X)) Tandem Library Bks.

Taylor, Theodore. Ice Drift. (Illus.). 240p. (J). 2006. pap. 5.95 (978-0-15-205550-9(9) , Harcourt Paperbacks); 2005. 16.00 (978-0-15-205081-8(7)) Harcourt Children's Bks.

Taylor, Vincent. Cornbread Has a Bad Habit. 2007. (Illus.). 96p. (J). pap. 4.99 (***978-0-9704512-5-5(3)***) TriEclipse, Inc.

Teal, Joyce Willard. The Point System. 1998. (Illus.). (J). pap. 8.80 (978-1-56763-399-3(4)); lib. bdg. 25.25 (978-1-56763-398-6(6)) Ozark Publishing.

Teenick: Drake And Josh: Ch Bk #2, et al. Sibling Revelry. 2006. (Teenick Ser.: Vol. 2). 113p. (J). pap. 4.99 (978-0-439-83163-5(6) , Scholastic) Scholastic, Inc.

Testa, Maria. Almost Forever. 2007. 80p. (J). (gr. 4-8). pap. 5.99 (978-0-7636-3366-0(6)) Candlewick Pr.

Tharp, Barbara, et al. Tillena Lou's Day in the Sun. Denk, James, ed. Lewis, T., illus. 2006. (My World & Me Ser.). 32p. (J). pap. (978-1-888997-44-6(3) , BioEd) Baylor College of Medicine.

Theriault, Francis. Just Another Ghost Story: A critical thinking Novel. 2007. 68p. (J). per. 8.95 (***978-0-595-45258-3(2)***) iUniverse, Inc.

Thiel, Annie. Chloe's New Baby Brother. 2006. (Playdate Kids Ser.). (Illus.). 32p. 14.95 (978-1-933721-01-9(4)) Playdate Kids Publishing.

Thomas, Becky. Hansel & Gretel. Zwerger, Lisbeth, illus. 2008. 32p. (J). (ps-3). 16.99 (***978-0-698-40078-8(X)*** , Minedition) Penguin Group (USA) Inc.

Thomas, Charlie. I Need Glasses. Goldfinger, Jennifer P., illus. (J). (gr. k-2). 2006. 32p. pap. 4.95 (978-0-516-25024-3(8)); 2005. 31p. 19.50 (978-0-516-24863-9(4)) Scholastic Library Publishing. (Children's Pr.).

Thorne, Donna Sloan & Felts, Marilyn Sloan. Buzz & Ollie's Steady Beat Adventure. Thorne, Donna Sloan & Felts, Marilyn Sloan, illus. 2002. (Illus.). 36p. (J). bds. 16.00 (978-0-9724147-2-2(X)) Sloan Publishing.

Tich, Jan & Jantti, Mariana. Paco Packs His Bag. 2006. (Magical Stories Ser.). (Illus.). 28p. (J). 16.95 (978-9974-7896-7-8(2)) Hardenville SA URY. *Dist:* Independent Pubs. Group.

Tilford, Michael. Reemie the Preemie. 2005. 22p. 8.72 (978-1-4116-1394-2(5)) Lulu.com.

Tilly, Meg. Porcupine. 2007. 192p. (J). (gr. 5-9). 15.95 (***978-0-88776-810-1(5)***) Tundra Bks., Inc./Livres Toundra, Inc. CAN. *Dist:* Random Hse., Inc.

Torrey, Michele. Voyage of Ice. 2004. 208p. (J). (gr. 5). 15.95 (978-0-375-82381-7(6)); lib. bdg. 17.99 (978-0-375-92381-4(0)) Random Hse. Children's Bks. (Knopf Bks. for Young Readers).

Treasure Quest Guide. 2004. pap. 5.99 (978-1-56309-913-7(6)) Woman's Missionary Union.

Trillo, Carlos. Bird. Bobillo, Juan, illus. 2003. 48p. (YA). (gr. 11 up). 12.95 (978-1-931724-22-7(9)) Diamond Select Toys & Collectibles.

Trottier, Maxine. Circle of Silver. 2000. (gr. 7-12). lib. bdg. 16.40 (978-0-613-81347-1(2)) Tandem Library Bks.

Trueman, Terry. Cruise Control. 2004. 160p. (J). 15.99 (978-0-06-623960-6(5)); lib. bdg. 16.89 (978-0-06-623961-3(3)) HarperCollins Pubs.

Tulloch, Richard. Freaky Stuff. Nagle, Shane, illus. 2007. 208p. (J). (gr. 3-7). 16.95 (978-0-8027-9623-3(0)) Walker & Co.

Tunis, John R. Keystone Kids. 2006. (Illus.). 252p. (J). pap. 5.95 (978-0-15-205634-6(3) , Odyssey Classics) Harcourt Children's Bks.

Turner, Ann. Maia of Thebes, 1463 B. C. 2005. (Life & Times Ser.). 176p. (J). pap. 10.95 (978-0-439-65223-0(5)) Scholastic, Inc.

Turner, Barbara. Treasure in Ghost Town. 2001. 126p. (J). pap. 11.95 (978-1-55517-540-5(6) , Bonneville Bks.) Cedar Fort, Inc./CFI Distribution.

Turner, Ethel. Seven Little Australians. 2006. (ENG.). 25.99 (***978-1-4280-4145-5(1)***) IndyPublish.com.

Twelfth Night Paperback Book. 2006. (YA). 7.95 (***978-1-56254-858-2(1)***) Saddleback Educational Publishing.

Twelfth Night Study Guide. 2006. (YA). per. 17.95 (***978-1-56254-859-9(X)***) Saddleback Educational Publishing.

Tyrrell, Melissa. Hansel & Gretel. McMullen, Nigel, illus. 2005. (Fairytale Friends Ser.). 12p. (J). bds. 5.95 (978-1-58117-152-5(8) , Intervisual/Piggy Toes) Dalmatian Pr.

Udry, Janice May. Thump & Plunk. (Illus.). 2001. (J). (978-0-606-20479-8(2)); 2000. lib. bdg. 11.80 (978-0-613-31814-3(5)) Tandem Library Bks.

Umansky, Kaye. Sophie in Charge. Currey, Anna, illus. 2005. 30p. (J). 3.95 (978-1-56148-480-5(6)); 9.95 (978-1-56148-478-2(4)) Good Bks.

Ungerer, Tomi. Christmas Eve at the Mellops' Ungerer, Tomi, illus. 1998. (Illus.). 32p. (J). (gr. k-4). pap. 5.95 (978-1-57098-227-9(9)) Rinehart, Roberts Pubs.

Vail, Rachel. Never Mind! A Twin Novel. 2005. 208p. (J). (gr. 5 up). reprint ed. pap. 5.99 (978-0-06-054316-7(7) , Harper Trophy) HarperCollins Pubs.

Van Allsburg, Chris. Probuditi! 2006. (Illus.). 32p. (J). (gr. 3-5). 18.95 (978-0-618-75502-8(0)) Houghton Mifflin Co. Trade & Reference Div.

Van Dyne, Edith. Aunt Jane's Nieces at Millville. 2004. reprint ed. pap. 21.95 (978-1-4191-0823-5(9)); pap. 1.99 (978-1-4192-0823-2(3)) Kessinger Publishing, LLC.

—Aunt Jane's Nieces in Society. 2004. reprint ed. pap. 20.95 (978-1-4191-0824-2(7)); pap. 1.99 (978-1-4192-0824-9(1)) Kessinger Publishing, LLC.

—Aunt Jane's Nieces on Vacation. 2004. reprint ed. pap. 21.95 (978-1-4191-0825-9(5)); pap. 1.99 (978-1-4192-0825-6(X)) Kessinger Publishing, LLC.

—Aunt Jane's Nieces Out West. 2004. reprint ed. pap. 21.95 (978-1-4191-0826-6(3)); pap. 1.99 (978-1-4192-0826-3(8)) Kessinger Publishing, LLC.

Van Leeuwen, Jean. Benny & Beautiful Baby Delilah. Pham, LeUyen, illus. 2006. 32p. (J). (ps). 16.99 (978-0-8037-2891-2(3) , Dial) Penguin Group (USA) Inc.

—Cabin on Trouble Creek. 2004. 224p. (J). (gr. 4). 16.99 (978-0-8037-2548-5(5) , Dial) Penguin Group (USA) Inc.

van Stockum, Hilda. A Day on Skates: 2007 Commemorative Edition. van Stockum, Hilda, illus. 2007. (Illus.). 44p. (J). 19.95 (***978-1-932350-18-0(7)***) Bethlehem Bks.

Vande Velde, Vivian. Tales from the Brothers Grimm & the Sisters Weird. Weinman, Brad, illus. 2005. 144p. (J). (ps-7). reprint ed. pap. 5.95 (978-0-15-205572-1(X) , Magic Carpet Bks.) Harcourt Children's Bks.

—There's a Dead Person Following My Sister Around. 2001. 160p. (J). pap. 5.99 (978-0-14-131281-1(5) , Puffin) Penguin Group (USA) Inc.

—There's a Dead Person Following My Sister Around. 2001. (gr. 5-8). lib. bdg. 13.00 (978-0-613-43899-5(X)) Tandem Library Bks.

Venable, Alan. Take Me with You When You Go. Marshall, Laurie, illus. 2008. 112p. (J). 12.95 (***978-0-9777082-7-7(6)***) One Monkey Books.

Vilcoq, Marianne. Espero un Hermanito. (SPA.). 24p. (J). (978-84-8470-013-5(5)) Corimbo, Editorial S.L. ESP. *Dist:* Lectorum Pubns., Inc.

Vogiel, Eva. Invisible Chains. 2000. 288p. (YA). (gr. 8-12). 19.95 (978-1-880582-57-2(0)) Judaica Pr., Inc., The.

Voigt, Cynthia. Dicey's Song. (Tillerman Cycle Ser.: Bk. 2). 368p. 2003. (Illus.). (J). pap. 5.99 (978-0-689-86362-2(4) , Aladdin); 2002. (YA). (gr. 7 up). mass mkt. 6.99 (978-0-689-85131-5(6) , Simon Pulse) Simon & Schuster Children's Publishing.

—Dicey's Song. (Tillerman Cycle Ser.: Bk. 2). 2003. (gr. 5-8). lib. bdg. 14.15 (978-0-613-73434-9(3)); 2002. (gr. 7-12). lib. bdg. 14.15 (978-0-613-45028-7(0)) Tandem Library Bks.

—Dicey's Song. l.t. ed. 2004. (Tillerman Cycle Ser.: Bk. 2). 355p. (J). 22.95 (978-0-7862-6288-5(5)); pap. 10.95 (978-0-7862-6352-3(0)) Thorndike Pr.

Vrettos, Adrienne Maria. Skin. 2007. 272p. (YA). pap. 6.99 (***978-1-4169-0656-8(8)*** , Simon Pulse); 2006. (Illus.). 240p. (J). (gr. 7 up). 16.95 (978-1-4169-0655-1(X) , McElderry, Margaret K.) Simon & Schuster Children's Publishing.

Waddell, Martin. Tiny's Big Adventure. Lawrence, John, illus. 2004. 32p. (J). (ps-1). 15.99 (978-0-7636-2170-4(6)) Candlewick Pr.

Wahl, Jan. Mabel Ran Away with the Toys. Woodruff, Liza, illus. 2000. 32p. (J). (ps-3). 16.95 (978-1-58089-059-5(8)); pap. 6.95 (978-1-58089-067-0(9)) Charlesbridge Publishing, Inc.

—Mabel Ran Away with the Toys. 2000. (gr. k-3). lib. bdg. 15.25 (978-0-613-35177-5(0)) Tandem Library Bks.

Wait, Lea. Stopping to Home. 2003. (gr. 3-6). lib. bdg. 13.00 (978-0-613-61659-1(6)) Tandem Library Bks.

—Wintering Well. (Illus.). 192p. (J). 2006. pap. 5.99 (978-0-689-85647-1(4) , Aladdin); 2004. 16.95 (978-0-689-85646-4(6) , McElderry, Margaret K.) Simon & Schuster Children's Publishing.

Wallace, Barbara Brooks. Secret in St. Something. 2003. (Illus.). 160p. (J). (ps-7). pap. 9.95 (978-0-689-85601-3(6) , Aladdin) Simon & Schuster Children's Publishing.

Wallace, Bill. Eye of the Great Bear. 1999. 176p. (J). (gr. 3-6). pap. 9.95 (978-0-671-02502-1(3) , Aladdin) Simon & Schuster Children's Publishing.

—Eye of the Great Bear. 1999. (J). 11.64 (978-0-606-19050-3(3)); (gr. 3-6). lib. bdg. 13.00 (978-0-613-21509-1(5)) Tandem Library Bks.

Wallace-Brodeur, Ruth. Blue Eyes Better. 2003. (Illus.). 112p. (J). (gr. 4-7). pap. 5.99 (978-0-14-250086-6(0) , Puffin) Penguin Group (USA) Inc.

—Blue Eyes Better. 2003. (gr. 5-8). lib. bdg. 14.15 (978-0-613-67139-2(2)) Tandem Library Bks.

Wallace, Karen. King Cudgel's Challenge. Flook, Helen, illus. 2007. (J). lib. bdg. (***978-1-4048-3706-5(X)***) Picture Window Bks.

Wallace, Karen. Wendy. 2003. 320p. (J). (978-0-689-83747-0(X) , Simon & Schuster Children's Publishing) Simon & Schuster Children's Publishing.

Wallace, Karen & Barrie, J. M. Wendy. 2005. 307p. (J). (***978-1-4156-1690-1(6)*** , Simon Pulse) Simon & Schuster Children's Publishing.

Wallace, Karen & Frost, Michael. Wendy. 2003. 320p. (J). 16.95 (978-0-689-86769-9(7)) Simon & Schuster Children's Publishing.

Ward, Nick. Don't Eat the Babysitter. 2006. 32p. (J). (gr. k-3). 9.95 (978-0-385-75062-2(5) , Fickling, David Bks.) Random Hse. Children's Bks.

Wargin, Kathy-Jo. Mitt & Minn's Illinois Adventure. Holman, Karen Busch, illus. 2007. 144p. (J). 14.95 (***978-1-58726-306-4(8)*** , Mitten Pr.) Ann Arbor Media Group, LLC.

Waring, Scott C. West's Time MacHine. 2007. 200p. 24.95 (***978-0-595-88775-0(9)***); per. 14.95 (***978-0-595-41887-9(2)***) iUniverse, Inc.

Warmuth, Donna Akers. Plumb Full of History: A Story of Abingdon, Virginia. Gobble, DeAnna Akers, illus. 2003. 64p. pap. 9.95 (978-1-932158-78-6(2)) Ingalls Publishing Group, Inc.

Warner, Gertrude Chandler. The Boxcar Children. 1998. (J). pap. 3.95 (978-0-439-04451-6(0)) Scholastic, Inc.

—The Boxcar Children. Deal, L. Kate, illus. 60th anniv. ed. 2002. 168p. (J). (gr. 2-7). 18.95 (978-0-8075-0848-0(9)) Whitman, Albert & Co.

—Candy Factory Mystery. 2002. (gr. 3-6). lib. bdg. 11.80 (978-0-613-58353-4(1)) Tandem Library Bks.

—The Candy Factory Mystery, Vol. 18. 2004. (Boxcar Children Special Ser.: Vol. 18). (Illus.). 128p. (J). pap. 4.50 (978-0-8075-5501-9(0)) Whitman, Albert & Co.

—The Copycat Mystery. Soileau, Hodges, illus. 2001. 137p. (J). (gr. 2-7). lib. bdg. 11.80 (978-0-613-35769-2(8)) Tandem Library Bks.

—The Copycat Mystery. 2001. (Boxcar Children Ser.). (Illus.). (J). 10.60 (978-0-606-21082-9(2)) Tandem Library Bks.

—The Copycat Mystery, Vol. 83. 2004. (Boxcar Children Ser.: No. 83). (Illus.). 128p. (J). (gr. 2-7). pap. 4.50 (978-0-8075-1297-5(4)) Whitman, Albert & Co.

—Disappearing Staircase Mystery. 2001. (gr. 3-6). lib. bdg. 11.80 (978-0-613-53176-4(0)) Tandem Library Bks.

—The Ghost Town Mystery. 1999. (Boxcar Children Ser.: No. 71). (J). (gr. 2-5). 10.75 (978-0-606-18764-0(2)) Tandem Library Bks.

—Ghost Town Mystery. 1999. (gr. 3-6). lib. bdg. 11.80 (978-0-613-16266-1(8)) Tandem Library Bks.

—The Giant Yo-Yo Mystery. 2006. (Boxcar Children Mysteries Ser.: 107). (Illus.). 128p. (J). 14.95 (978-0-8075-0878-7(0)); pap. 4.50 (978-0-8075-0879-4(9)) Whitman, Albert & Co.

—Great Bicycle Race Mystery. 2000. (gr. 3-6). lib. bdg. 11.80 (978-0-613-27863-8(1)) Tandem Library Bks.

—Haunted Clock Tower Mystery. 2001. (gr. 3-6). lib. bdg. 11.80 (978-0-613-49434-2(2)) Tandem Library Bks.

—Hockey Mystery. 2001. (gr. 3-6). lib. bdg. 11.80 (978-0-613-30474-0(8)) Tandem Library Bks.

—Honeybee Mystery. 2000. (gr. 3-6). lib. bdg. 11.80 (978-0-613-30471-1(2)) Tandem Library Bks.

—The Movie Star Mystery. 1999. (Boxcar Children Ser.: No. 69). (J). (gr. 2-5). (978-0-606-18762-6(6)) Tandem Library Bks.

—Movie Star Mystery. 1999. (gr. 3-6). lib. bdg. 11.80 (978-0-613-16285-2(4)) Tandem Library Bks.

—Mystery at Skeleton Point. 2002. (gr. 3-6). lib. bdg. 11.80 (978-0-613-65047-2(6)) Tandem Library Bks.

—Mystery at the Crooked House. 2000. (gr. 3-6). lib. bdg. 11.80 (978-0-613-31517-3(0)) Tandem Library Bks.

—The Mystery in New York. Tang, Charles, illus. 1999. 121p. (J). (ps-7). per. 11.80 (978-0-613-22056-9(0)) Tandem Library Bks.

—The Mystery in New York. 1999. (Boxcar Children Special Ser.: No.13). (Illus.). (J). (gr. 2-5). (978-0-606-18771-8(5)) Tandem Library Bks.

—The Mystery in the Computer Game. 2000. (Boxcar Children Ser.: No. 78). (J). (gr. 2-5). (978-0-606-20298-5(6)) Tandem Library Bks.

—The Mystery in the Mall. Tang, Charles, illus. 1999. 115p. (J). (ps-7). per. 11.80 (978-0-613-22057-6(9)) Tandem Library Bks.

—Mystery of Alligator Swamp. 2002. (gr. 3-6). lib. bdg. 11.80 (978-0-613-65048-9(4)) Tandem Library Bks.

—The Mystery of the Black Raven. 1999. (Boxcar Children Special Ser.: No. 12). (Illus.). (J). (gr. 2-5). (978-0-606-18770-1(7)) Tandem Library Bks.

—Mystery of the Black Raven. 1999. (gr. 3-6). lib. bdg. 11.80 (978-0-613-16286-9(2)) Tandem Library Bks.

—The Mystery of the Empty Safe. Tang, Charles, illus. 2000. 120p. (J). (gr. 2-7). lib. bdg. 11.80 (978-0-613-27992-5(1)) Tandem Library Bks.

—Mystery of the Midnight Dog. 2001. (gr. 3-6). lib. bdg. 11.80 (978-0-613-35789-0(2)) Tandem Library Bks.

—The Mystery of the Midnight Dog, Vol. 81. 2004. (Boxcar Children Ser.: No. 81). (Illus.). 122p. (J). (gr. 2-7). pap. 4.50 (978-0-8075-5476-0(6)) Whitman, Albert & Co.

—Mystery of the Mummy's Curse. 2002. (gr. 3-6). lib. bdg. 11.80 (978-0-613-58377-0(9)) Tandem Library Bks.

—The Mystery of the Pirate's Map. 1999. (Boxcar Children Ser.: No. 70). (J). (gr. 2-5). (978-0-606-18763-3(4)) Tandem Library Bks.

—The Mystery of the Screech Owl. Soileau, Hodges, illus. 2001. 117p. (J). (gr. 2-7). per. 11.80 (978-0-613-35790-6(6)) Tandem Library Bks.

—The Mystery of the Screech Owl, Vol. 16. 2004. (Boxcar Children Special Ser.: No. 16). (Illus.). 144p. (J). (gr. 2-5). 14.95 (978-0-8075-5481-4(2)); pap. 3.95 (978-0-8075-5482-1(0)) Whitman, Albert & Co.

—Mystery of the Spider's Clue. 2002. (gr. 3-6). lib. bdg. 11.80 (978-0-613-58378-7(7)) Tandem Library Bks.

—The Mystery of the Spider's Clue, Vol. 87. 2004. (Boxcar Children Ser.: Vol. 87). (Illus.). 128p. (J). pap. 3.95 (978-0-8075-5497-5(9)) Whitman, Albert & Co.

—Mystery of the Star Ruby. 2002. (gr. 3-6). lib. bdg. 11.80 (978-0-613-58379-4(5)) Tandem Library Bks.

—Mystery of the Tiger's Eye. 2001. (gr. 3-6). lib. bdg. 11.80 (978-0-613-49447-2(4)) Tandem Library Bks.

—The Mystery of the Wild Ponies. 2000. (Boxcar Children Ser.: Vol. 77). (Illus.). (J). (gr. 2-5). (978-0-606-18908-8(4)) Tandem Library Bks.

—Mystery of the Wild Ponies. 2000. (gr. 3-6). lib. bdg. 11.80 (978-0-613-27993-2(X)) Tandem Library Bks.

—Mystery on Blizzard Mountain. 2002. (gr. 3-6). lib. bdg. 11.80 (978-0-613-53287-7(2)) Tandem Library Bks.

—The Poison Frog Mystery. 2000. (Boxcar Children Ser.: No. 74). (J). (gr. 2-5). (978-0-606-18767-1(7)) Tandem Library Bks.

—Poison Frog Mystery. 2000. (gr. 3-6). lib. bdg. 11.80 (978-0-613-22192-4(3)) Tandem Library Bks.

—The Seattle Puzzle. 2007. (Boxcar Children Mysteries Ser.: No. 111). 128p. (J). (gr. 2-7). pap. 4.50 (***978-0-8075-5561-3(4)***); lib. bdg. 14.95 (***978-0-8075-5560-6(6)***) Whitman, Albert & Co.

—Stuffed Bear Mystery. 2002. (gr. 3-6). lib. bdg. 11.80 (978-0-613-62574-6(9)) Tandem Library Bks.

—The Vanishing Passenger. 2006. (Boxcar Children Mysteries Ser.: 106). (Illus.). 128p. (J). 14.95 (978-0-8075-1066-7(1)); pap. 4.50 (978-0-8075-1067-4(X)) Whitman, Albert & Co.

Warner, Gertrude Chandler, creator. The Basketball Mystery. 1999. (Boxcar Children Ser.: No. 68). (J). (gr. 2-5). 10.60 (978-0-606-17179-3(7)) Tandem Library Bks.

—The Basketball Mystery. 1999. (Boxcar Children Ser.: No. 68). (Illus.). 128p. (J). (gr. 2-5). lib. bdg. 13.95 (978-0-8075-0575-5(7)) Whitman, Albert & Co.

—The Boxcar Children Summer Special. 2007. (Boxcar Children Mysteries Ser.). 376p. (J). pap. 7.95 (***978-0-8075-0885-5(3)***) Whitman, Albert & Co.

—The Creature in Ogopogo Lake, Vol. 108. 2006. (Boxcar Children Mysteries Ser.: 108). (Illus.). 128p. (J). (gr. 2-7). 14.95 (978-0-8075-1336-1(9)); lib. bdg. 4.50 (978-0-8075-1337-8(7)) Whitman, Albert & Co.

—The Ghost Town Mystery, Vol. 71. 1999. (Boxcar Children Ser.: No. 71). (Illus.). 128p. (J). (gr. 2-5). 14.95 (978-0-8075-2858-7(7)); pap. 3.95 (978-0-8075-2859-4(5)) Whitman, Albert & Co.

—The Movie Star Mystery, Vol. 69. 1999. (Boxcar Children Ser.: No. 69). (Illus.). 128p. (J). (gr. 2-5). 14.95 (978-0-8075-5303-9(4)); pap. 4.50 (978-0-8075-5304-6(2)) Whitman, Albert & Co.

—The Mystery at Peacock Hall, Vol. 63. 1998. (Boxcar Children Ser.: No. 63). (Illus.). 128p. (J). (gr. 2-5). pap. 4.50 (978-0-8075-5445-6(6)) Whitman, Albert & Co.

—The Mystery in the Computer Game. (Boxcar Children Ser.: No. 78). (Illus.). 115p. (J). (gr. 2-5). 2000. lib. bdg. 13.95 (978-0-8075-5468-5(5)); Vol. 78. 2004. pap. 4.50 (978-0-8075-5469-2(3)) Whitman, Albert & Co.

—The Mystery in the Mall, Vol. 72. 2004. (Boxcar Children Ser.: No. 72). (Illus.). 128p. (J). (gr. 2-5). 14.95 (978-0-8075-5456-2(1)); pap. 4.50 (978-0-8075-5457-9(X)) Whitman, Albert & Co.

—The Mystery of the Black Raven, Vol. 12. 1999. (Boxcar Children Special Ser.: No. 12). (Illus.). 144p. (J). (gr. 2-5). 14.95 (978-0-8075-2988-1(5)); pap. 3.95 (978-0-8075-2989-8(3)) Whitman, Albert & Co.

—The Mystery of the Empty Safe, Vol. 75. 2004. (Boxcar Children Ser.: No. 75). (Illus.). 120p. (J). (gr. 2-5). 14.95 (978-0-8075-5462-3(6)) Whitman, Albert & Co.

—The Mystery of the Pirate's Map, Vol. 70. (Boxcar Children Ser.: No.70). (Illus.). (J). (gr. 2-5). 2004. 14.95 (978-0-8075-5453-1(7)); 1999. 128p. pap. 4.50 (978-0-8075-5454-8(5)) Whitman, Albert & Co.

—The Mystery of the Queen's Jewels, Vol. 11. 1998. (Boxcar Children Special Ser.: No. 11). (Illus.). 144p. (J). (gr. 2-5). 14.95 (978-0-8075-5450-0(2)); pap. 4.50 (978-0-8075-5451-7(0)) Whitman, Albert & Co.

—The Mystery of the Stolen Sword, Vol. 67. 1998. (Boxcar Children Ser.: No. 67). (Illus.). 128p. (J). (gr. 2-5). 14.95 (978-0-8075-7622-9(0)) Whitman, Albert & Co.

—The Mystery of the Tiger's Eye, Vol. 17. 2004. (Boxcar Children Special Ser.: No.17). (Illus.). 144p. (J). (gr. 2-5). pap. 4.50 (978-0-8075-5488-3(X)) Whitman, Albert & Co.

—The Mystery of the Wild Ponies, Vol. 77. 2004. (Boxcar Children Ser.: No. 77). (Illus.). 135p. (J). (gr. 2-5). pap. 3.95 (978-0-8075-5466-1(9)) Whitman, Albert & Co.

—The Mystery on Blizzard Mountain, Vol. 86. 2004. (Boxcar Children Ser.: No. 86). (Illus.). 122p. (J). (gr. 2-7). 14.95 (978-0-8075-5493-7(6)); pap. 4.50 (978-0-8075-5494-4(4)) Whitman, Albert & Co.

—The Panther Mystery, Vol. 66. 1998. (Boxcar Children Ser.: No. 66). (Illus.). 128p. (J). (gr. 2-5). pap. 4.50 (978-0-8075-6328-1(5)) Whitman, Albert & Co.

—The Poison Frog Mystery, Vol. 74. 2004. (Boxcar Children Ser.: No. 74). (Illus.). 128p. (J). (gr. 2-5). pap. 3.95 (978-0-8075-6587-2(3)) Whitman, Albert & Co.

—The Rock 'n' Roll Mystery, Vol. 109. 2006. (Boxcar Children Mysteries Ser.: 109). (Illus.). 128p. (J). (gr. 2-7). 14.95 (978-0-8075-7089-0(3)); lib. bdg. 4.50 (978-0-8075-7090-6(7)) Whitman, Albert & Co.

—The Sword of the Silver Knight, Vol. 103. 2005. (Boxcar Children Mysteries Ser.: 103). (Illus.). 128p. (J). pap. 4.50 (978-0-8075-0876-3(4)) Whitman, Albert & Co.

—The Windy City Mystery, Vol. 10. 1998. (Boxcar Children Special Ser.: No. 10). (Illus.). 144p. (J). (gr. 2-5). 14.95 (978-0-8075-5447-0(2)); pap. 4.50 (978-0-8075-5448-7(0)) Whitman, Albert & Co.

Warner, James. An Alien Adventure - The Magic Sled. Holder, Harry, illus. 1999. 107p. (YA). (gr. 5-8). pap. 14.95 (978-1-890549-08-4(8)) Alpha Publishing Group.

Warner, Mike. The Titanic Game. Ordaz, Frank, illus. 2007. 201p. (J). pap. 9.95 (978-0-9744446-2-8(6)) All About Kids Publishing.

Waters, Aubrey. Thirteen & Surviving. 2006. pap. 14.49 (***978-1-4259-4644-9(5)***) AuthorHouse.

Watson, T. E. The Monster in the Mailbox. Lancaster, Mari & Lancaster, Linus, illus. 2002. 32p. (J). (gr. 2-6). 16.95 (978-1-58478-011-3(8) , Paw Prints Pr.) Heather & Highlands Publishing.

Watts, Irene N. When the Bough Breaks. 2007. 152p. (J). (gr. 4-7). pap. 9.95 (***978-0-88776-821-7(0)***) Tundra Bks., Inc./Livres Toundra, Inc. CAN. *Dist:* Random Hse., Inc.

Watts, Leander. Wild Ride to Heaven. 2003. 176p. (YA). (gr. 5-9). tchr. ed. 16.00 (978-0-618-26805-4(7)) Houghton Mifflin Co. Trade & Reference Div.

Wax, Wendy. Reggie's Secret Admirer. 2004. (gr. k-3). lib. bdg. 11.80 (978-0-613-73384-7(3)) Tandem Library Bks.

—Too Many Turners. Moore, Harry, Jr., illus. 2004. (Ready-to-Read Ser.). 32p. (J). pap. 3.99 (978-0-689-86859-7(6) , Simon Spotlight/Nickelodeon) Simon & Schuster Children's Publishing.

Weber, Jen Funk. Thimbletack's Activity Book. 2008. (Spiderwick Chronicles). 64p. (J). pap. 4.99 (***978-1-4169-4954-1(2)*** , Simon Scribbles) Simon & Schuster Children's Publishing.

Weber, Lenora Mattingly. A Bright Star Falls. 1999. (Beany Malone Ser.). 278p. (J). reprint ed. pap. 12.95 (978-1-930009-01-1(1)) Image Cascade Publishing.

Weinstein, Natalie. Katrina's New Room. Pluum, Ave, illus. 2004. (J). pap. 19.95 (978-0-9749531-0-6(5)) Images For Presentation.

Welch, Leah. Pretty on the Inside. 2007. (J). per. 10.00 (***978-1-59872-779-1(6)***) Instantpublisher.com.

Wells, Carolyn. Marjorie's Maytime. 2007. (ENG.). 196p. per. 11.95 (***978-1-4218-3318-7(2)***) 1st World Publishing, Inc.

Wells, Rosemary. Bunny Cakes. Wells, Rosemary, illus. 2002. (Max the Bunny Ser.). (Illus.). (J). 13.19 (978-0-7587-5445-5(0)) Book Wholesalers, Inc.

—Bunny Cakes. 1999. (Max & Ruby Ser.). (Illus.). 32p. (J). (gr. k-2). 15.99 (978-0-670-88686-9(6) , Viking Juvenile) Penguin Group (USA) Inc.

—Bunny Money. 2000. (gr. k-3). lib. bdg. 14.15 (978-0-613-33681-9(X)) Tandem Library Bks.

—Bunny Party. 2003. (Max & Ruby Ser.). (Illus.). 24p. (J). (ps-k). pap. 5.99 (978-0-14-250162-7(X) , Puffin) Penguin Group (USA) Inc.

—Bunny Party. Wells, Rosemary, illus. 2001. (Max & Ruby Ser.). (Illus.). 32p. (J). (gr. k-2). 15.99 (978-0-670-03501-4(7) , Viking Juvenile) Penguin Group (USA) Inc.

—Max & Ruby Play School. 2003. (ps-2). lib. bdg. 11.80 (978-0-613-64064-0(0)) Tandem Library Bks.

—Max & Ruby's Christmas Tree. 2007. (Max & Ruby Ser.). 12p. (J). (ps-k). bds. 7.99 (***978-0-448-44685-1(5)*** , Grosset & Dunlap) Penguin Group (USA) Inc.

—Max & Ruby's Show-and-Tell. 2006. (All Aboard Bks.). 24p. (J). (ps-ps). pap. 3.99 (978-0-448-43952-5(2) , Grosset & Dunlap) Penguin Group (USA) Inc.

—Max & Ruby's Snowy Day. 2004. (Max & Ruby Ser.). 10p. (J). (ps). bds. 6.99 (978-0-448-43567-1(5) , Grosset & Dunlap) Penguin Group (USA) Inc.

—Max & Ruby's Winter Adventure. 2007. (Max & Ruby Ser.). 16p. (J). (ps-k). pap. 5.99 (***978-0-448-44684-4(7)*** , Grosset & Dunlap) Penguin Group (USA) Inc.

—Max Cleans Up. Wells, Rosemary, illus. 2002. (Max the Bunny Ser.). (Illus.). 13.19 (978-1-4046-0741-5(2)) Book Wholesalers, Inc.

—Max Cleans Up. (Max & Ruby Ser.). (Illus.). 32p. (J). 2002. pap. 5.99 (978-0-14-230133-3(7) , Puffin); 2000. 15.99 (978-0-670-89218-1(1) , Viking Juvenile) Penguin Group (USA) Inc.

—Max's ABC. 2006. (Illus.). 32p. (J). (ps). 15.99 (978-0-670-06074-0(7) , Viking Juvenile) Penguin Group (USA) Inc.

—Max's Breakfast. 2004. 12p. (J). 5.99 (978-0-670-88712-5(9) , Viking Juvenile) Penguin Group (USA) Inc.

—Max's Chocolate Chicken. Wells, Rosemary, illus. 2002. (Max the Bunny Ser.). (Illus.). (J). 13.19 (978-0-7587-3110-4(8)) Book Wholesalers, Inc.

—Max's Chocolate Chicken. Wells, Rosemary, illus. 2000. (Max & Ruby Ser.). (Illus.). 32p. (J). (gr. k-2). pap. 5.99 (978-0-14-056672-7(4) , Puffin) Penguin Group (USA) Inc.

—Max's Chocolate Chicken. 1999. (Max & Ruby Ser.). (Illus.). 32p. (J). (gr. k-2). 16.99 (978-0-670-88713-2(7) , Viking Juvenile) Penguin Group (USA) Inc.

—Max's Chocolate Chicken. Wells, Rosemary, illus. 2000. (Illus.). (J). (ps-ps). lib. bdg. 14.15 (978-0-613-28571-1(9)) Tandem Library Bks.

—Max's Chocolate Chicken. 2000. (Max & Ruby Ser.). (J). (gr. k-2). (978-0-606-18431-1(7)) Tandem Library Bks.

—Max's Christmas. 2000. (Max & Ruby Ser.). (J). (gr. k-2). (978-0-606-20244-2(7)) Tandem Library Bks.

—Play with Max & Ruby. 2002. (ps-2). lib. bdg. 11.80 (978-0-613-64094-7(2)) Tandem Library Bks.

—Ruby's Beauty Shop. Wells, Rosemary, illus. (Max & Ruby Ser.). 32p. (J). (gr. k-3). 2004. pap. 6.99 (978-0-14-240194-1(3) , Puffin); 2002. (Illus.). 15.99 (978-0-670-03553-3(X) , Viking Juvenile) Penguin Group (USA) Inc.

Wells, Rosemary. Ruby's Falling Leaves. 2007. (Max & Ruby Ser.). 24p. (J). (ps-k). 3.99 (*978-0-448-44686-8(3) , Grosset & Dunlap) Penguin Group (USA) Inc.

Welvaert, Scott R. The Curse of the Wendigo: An Agate & Buck Adventure. Garvey, Brann, illus. 2007. (Vortex Books). 105p. (J). (gr. 5 up). lib. bdg. 22.60 (978-1-59889-066-2(2)) Stone Arch Bks.

Welvaert, Scott R. The Mosquito King: An Agate & Buck Adventure. Garvey, Brann, illus. 2008. (J). pap. (*978-1-59889-923-8(6)); lib. bdg. (*978-1-59889-857-6(4)) Stone Arch Bks.

Wenzell, Tim. Absent Children. 2000. 316p. (YA). pap. 15.95 (978-0-595-12142-7(X)) iUniverse, Inc.

Werlin, Nancy. The Rules of Survival. 2008. 288p. (YA). (gr. 12). pap. 7.99 (*978-0-14-241071-4(3) , Puffin); 2006. 276p. (J). (gr. 7). 16.99 (978-0-8037-3001-4(2) , Dial) Penguin Group (USA) Inc.

West, Kipling. A Rattle of Bones: A Halloween Book of Collective Nouns. West, Kipling, illus. 1999. (Illus.). 32p. (J). (ps-1). pap. 15.95 (978-0-531-30196-8(6) , Orchard Bks.) Scholastic, Inc.

West, Tracey. The Movie Storybook. 2008. (Spiderwick Chronicles). 32p. (J). (gr. k-4). 8.99 (*978-1-4169-4947-3(X) , Simon Spotlight) Simon & Schuster Children's Publishing.

Weston, Anne. My Brother Needs a Boa. Nathan, Cheryl, illus. 2005. 32p. (J). (gr. 2-4). 15.95 (978-1-932065-96-1(2)) Star Bright Bks., Inc.

Weston, Carol. Melanie Martin Goes Dutch: The Private Diary of My Almost Bummer Summer with Cecily, Matt the Brat, & Vincent van Go Go Go. 2003. (Illus.). 240p. (J). (gr. 3-7). 5.99 (978-0-440-41899-3(2) , Yearling) Random Hse. Children's Bks.

—Melanie Martin Goes Dutch: The Private Diary of My Almost Bummer Summer with Cecily, Matt the Brat, & Vincent van Go Go Go. 2003. (gr. 3-6). lib. bdg. 25.70 (978-0-613-62527-2(7)) Tandem Library Bks.

Weston, Martha. Tuck's Haunted House. Weston, Martha, illus. 2002. (Illus.). 32p. (J). (gr. k-3). tchr. ed. 14.00 (978-0-618-15966-6(5) , Clarion Bks.) Houghton Mifflin Co. Trade & Reference Div.

Weyr, Garret. My Heartbeat. 2003. 176p. (YA). pap. 7.99 (978-0-14-240066-1(1) , Puffin) Penguin Group (USA) Inc.

—My Heartbeat. 2003. (gr. 7-12). lib. bdg. 16.45 (978-0-613-81700-4(1)) Tandem Library Bks.

Whatley, Tom. James & Jessie (This Is Not A Mushy Romantic Novel) 2005. 70p. pap. 9.67 (978-1-4116-4370-3(4)) Lulu.com.

Wheelus, Doris. The Plum Jelly Kids. 2005. 223p. pap. 19.95 (978-1-4137-5649-4(2)) PublishAmerica, Inc.

Whelan, Gloria. The Impossible Journey. 2004. 256p. (J). (gr. 5 up). reprint ed. pap. 5.99 (978-0-06-441083-0(8) , Harper Trophy) HarperCollins Pubs.

—The Impossible Journey. 2004. 248p. (J). (gr. k-9). per. 14.30 (978-0-613-99970-0(3)) Tandem Library Bks.

When Kids Dream & Trucks Fly. 2007. per. 14.99 (*978-0-9792258-6-4(8)) Bezalel Bks.

Whitaker, Marti. Sock-A-Nina. Kurtz Hubbard, Nancy, illus. 2005. (ENG.). 28p. (J). per. 18.00 (978-1-4208-4256-2(0)) AuthorHouse.

White, Amanda. Sand Sister. Morales, Yuyi, illus. 2004. 32p. (J). 16.99 (978-1-84148-617-8(5)) Barefoot Bks., Inc.

White, Ellen Emerson. The President's Daughter. 2008. (YA). pap. 8.99 (*978-0-312-37488-4(7)) Feiwel & Friends.

White, Tom. Lost in the Texas Desert. 2004. (Illus.). 132p. per. 7.95 (978-0-9753611-0-8(4)) Arlington Pubns.

Whitethorne, Baje, Sr. Father's Boots: Azhe'e bikenidoots'osii. Marvin, Yellowhair & Jerrold, Johnson, eds. Darlene, Redhair, tr. Whitethorne, Baje, Sr., illus. 2001. (ENG & NAV., Illus.). 32p. (gr. 1-6). 17.95 (978-1-893354-29-6(6)) Salina Bookshelf.

Whitmore, Benette. Shelter. 2006. 304p. (YA). 16.95 (978-0-8027-8884-9(X)) Walker & Co.

Whybrow, Ian. Badness for Beginners: A Little Wolf & Smellybreff Adventure. 2005. (Illus.). 32p. (J). (ps-ps). 16.95 (978-1-57505-861-0(8) , Carolrhoda Bks.) Lerner Publishing Group.

—Bella Gets Her Skates On. Reeve, Rosie, illus. 2007. 32p. (J). (ps-3). 15.95 (*978-0-8109-9416-4(X)) Abrams, Harry N. , Inc.

—Harry & the Snow King Book & Plush Set. Reynolds, Adrian, illus. 1999. 32p. (J). (ps-2). pap. 19.95 (978-1-86233-132-7(4)) Sterling Publishing Co., Inc.

—Little Wolf's Diary of Daring Deeds. Ross, Tony, illus. (Middle Grade Fiction Ser.). 132p. (gr. 3-6). 2005. 14.95 (978-1-57505-411-7(6)); 2003. (J). pap. 6.95 (978-0-87614-536-4(5) , Carolrhoda Bks.) Lerner Publishing Group.

—Little Wolf's Diary of Daring Deeds. 2000. (gr. 3-6). lib. bdg. 15.25 (978-0-613-68105-6(3)) Tandem Library Bks.

—Malicia para Principiantes: Una Aventura de Lobito y Apestosito. 2005. (Libros Ilustrados (Picture Bks.)). (SPA., Illus.). 32p. (gr. k-2). 16.95 (978-0-8225-3211-8(5) , Ediciones Lerner) Lerner Publishing Group.

Wigersma, Tanneke. Baby Brother. Talsma, Nynke Mare, illus. 2005. 32p. (J). (ps-ps). 16.95 (978-1-932425-55-0(1) , Lemniscaat) Boyds Mills Pr.

Wildman, Dale. Nicholas Knows: Big Brother Nicholas Knows It All! Sisung, Peter, illus. 2006. 24p. (J). per. 2.99 (978-1-59958-005-0(5)) Journey Stone Creations, LLC.

Wilkes, Maria D. Caroline & Her Sister. Ettlinger, Doris, illus. 2000. (Little House Chapter Bks.: No. 2). 80p. (J). (gr. 3-6). 14.89 (978-0-06-028155-7(3)) HarperCollins Pubs.

—Caroline & Her Sister. 2000. (Little House Chapter Bks.: No. 2). (J). (gr. 3-6). 11.05 (978-0-606-20285-5(4)) Tandem Library Bks.

Wilkins, Kim. Ghost Ship: Sunken Kingdom #1. Cornish, D. M., illus. 2008. 96p. (J). (gr. 4-7). pap. 5.99 (*978-0-375-84806-3(1) , Random Hse. Bks. for Young Readers) Random Hse. Children's Bks.

—Ghost Ship: Sunken Kingdom #1. Cornish, D. M., illus. 2008. 96p. (J). (gr. 4-7). lib. bdg. 11.99 (*978-0-375-94806-0(6) , Random Hse. Bks. for Young Readers) Random Hse. Children's Bks.

Williams, Annie Morris. Marianne's Secret Cousins. Oldham, Cindi, illus. 2005. (Family History Adventures for Young Readers Ser.: 2). 240p. (J). per. 10.00 (978-0-9645272-8-7(6)) Field Stone Pubs.

Williams, Carol Lynch. The True Colors of Caitlynne Jackson. 1998. (J). (978-0-606-13873-4(0)) Tandem Library Bks.

Williams, Jeanne. To Buy a Dream. 2001. 164p. (YA). pap. 11.95 (978-0-595-16527-8(3) , Backinprint.com) iUniverse, Inc.

Williams-Justesen, Kim. My Brother the Dog. 2006. (AKK.). 175p. (J). pap. 6.95 (978-0-9749303-5-0(0)) Tanglewood Pr.

Williams, Maiya. The Golden Hour. 2006. 288p. (J). (gr. 5-10). pap. 5.95 (978-0-8109-9216-0(7)) Abrams, Harry N. , Inc.

—The Hour of the Cobra. (YA). 2007. 320p. (gr. 2-7). pap. 5.95 (*978-0-8109-9362-4(7)); 2006. 312p. (gr. 4-9). 16.95 (978-0-8109-5970-5(4) , Amulet Bks.) Abrams, Harry N. , Inc.

—The Hour of the Outlaw. 2007. 360p. (YA). (gr. 4-9). 16.95 (*978-0-8109-9355-6(4)) Abrams, Harry N. , Inc.

Williams, Vera B. Amber Was Brave, Essie Was Smart. Williams, Vera B., illus. 2004. (Illus.). 72p. (J). (gr. 2 up). reprint ed. pap. 7.99 (978-0-06-057182-5(9) , Harper Trophy) HarperCollins Pubs.

Willner-Pardo, Gina. My Mom & Other Mysteries of the Universe. 2004. 176p. (YA). (gr. 4-6). tchr. ed. 15.00 (978-0-618-43020-8(2) , Clarion Bks.) Houghton Mifflin Co. Trade & Reference Div.

Willson, Sarah. Do Not Wake Jake. Johnson, Meredith, illus. 2006. (Step-By-Step Readers Ser.). (J). (978-1-59939-059-8(0) , Reader's Digest Young Families, Inc.) Reader's Digest Children's Publishing, Inc.

—Have No Fear, Chuckie's Here! 2001. (gr. k-3). lib. bdg. 11.25 (978-0-613-43969-5(4)) Tandem Library Bks.

—Pet Peeves! Nez, John A., illus. 2005. (Social Studies Connects). 32p. (J). pap. 4.99 (978-1-57565-149-1(1)) Kane Pr., The.

Willson, Sarah. Pet Peeves. Nez, John, illus. 2005. 32p. (J). lib. bdg. 20.00 (*978-1-4242-1114-2(X)) Fitzgerald Bks.

Wilson, Jacqueline. My Brother Bernadette. Roberts, David, illus. 2002. (Yellow Bananas Ser.). 48p. (J). (gr. 3-4). pap. (978-0-7787-0986-2(8)); lib. bdg. (978-0-7787-0940-4(X)) Crabtree Publishing Co.

—My Brother Bernadette. 2002. (gr. 3-6). lib. bdg. 12.95 (978-0-613-52884-9(0)) Tandem Library Bks.

Wilson, Jodi L. When I Grow Up. Anderson, Kari A., illus. 32p. (Orig.). (J). (gr. 1-3). pap. 4.95 (978-0-9628335-0-2(9)) Wilander Publishing Co.

Wilson, Linda Miller. A Few Days Journey. 1998. 124p. (YA). (gr. 4-8). 9.99 (978-0-88092-402-3(0) , 4020) Royal Fireworks Publishing Co.

Wilson, Sarah. Friends & Pals & Brothers, Too. Landry, Leo, illus. 2008. 32p. (J). 16.95 (*978-0-8050-7643-1(3)) Holt, Henry & Co.

Wilson, Shelliah. Samuel's Little Brother. 2005. 12p. 9.72 (978-1-4116-4789-3(0)) Lulu.com.

Winker, Michael & Ashley. One Good Quest Deserves Another: A Crown of Amaranth Story. 2007. 232p. 25.95 (*978-0-595-68779-4(2)); per. 15.95 (*978-0-595-43799-3(0)) iUniverse, Inc.

Winkler, Henry & Oliver, Lin. Day of the Iguana. Heyer, Carol, illus. 2003. (Hank Zipzer Ser.: No. 3). 160p. (J). 13.99 (978-0-448-43288-5(9)); (gr. 3-8). mass mkt. 4.99 (978-0-448-43212-0(9)) Penguin Group (USA) Inc. (Grosset & Dunlap).

—Day of the Iguana. 2004. (Hank Zipzer Ser.: No. 3). 160p. (J). (gr. 2-6). pap. 29.00 incl. audio (978-1-4000-9008-2(3) , Listening Library) Random Hse. Audio Publishing Group.

—Day of the Iguana. 2006. (Hank Zipzer Ser.: No. 3). (J). (gr. 3-8). 24.21 (978-1-59961-102-0(3)) Spotlight.

Winnick, Karen B. The Night of the Fireflies. Ito, Yoriko, illus. 2004. 32p. (J). (ps up). 15.95 (978-1-56397-725-1(7)) Boyds Mills Pr.

Winters, Susan. Yo Puedo. 1999. (Jardin de los Ninos Ser.). (SPA., Illus.). 24p. (J). (ps-1). pap. 6.99 (978-980-257-230-4(6)) Ekare, Ediciones VEN. Dist: Kane/Miller Bk. Pubs., Inc., Lectorum Pubns., Inc.

—Yo Tambien. 1999. (Jardin de los Ninos Ser.). (SPA., Illus.). 24p. (J). (ps-1). pap. 6.99 (978-980-257-231-1(4)) Ekare, Ediciones VEN. Dist: Kane/Miller Bk. Pubs., Inc., Lectorum Pubns., Inc.

Winthrop, Elizabeth. Red-Hot Rattoons. Lewin, Betsy, illus. 2006. 224p. (J). pap. 6.95 (978-0-8050-7986-9(6)) Holt, Henry & Co.

—The Red-Hot Rattoons. Lewin, Betsy, illus. rev. ed. 2003. 224p. (J). 15.95 (978-0-8050-7229-7(2) , Holt, Henry & Co. Bks. For Young Readers) Holt, Henry & Co.

Wishinsky, Frieda. Oonga Bonga. Thompson, Carol, illus. 2001. (SPA.). 32p. (J). (gr. k-2). (978-84-261-3113-3(1) , JV4392) Juventud, Editorial ESP. Dist: Lectorum Pubns., Inc.

Wishinsky, Frieda. Please, Louise! Gay, Marie-Louise, illus. 2007. 32p. (J). (ps-k). 17.95 (*978-0-88899-796-8(5)) Groundwood Bks. CAN. Dist: Perseus Distribution.

Wodehouse, P. G. Mike at Wrykyn. reprint ed. (J). lib. bdg. 98.00 (978-0-7426-3265-3(2)); 2001. pap. 28.00 (978-0-7426-8265-8(X)) Classic Bks.

Wojahn, Rebecca Hogue. Evan Early. Brian, Edward, illus. 2006. 32p. (J). 15.95 (978-1-890627-71-3(2)) Woodbine Hse.

Wolff, Virginia. Probably Still Nick Swansen. 2002. (gr. 5-8). lib. bdg. 16.45 (978-0-613-57323-8(4)) Tandem Library Bks.

Wollman, Jessica. Bunches of Fun. MacNeil, Chris, illus. 2006. 149p. (J). (*978-1-4156-5003-5(9) , Aladdin) Simon & Schuster Children's Publishing.

Wood, Brian. The Cramp Twins. 2001. (J). pap. 9.95 (978-0-385-32714-5(5) , Random Hse. Bks. for Young Readers) Random Hse. Children's Bks.

—Swamp Fever. 2001. (Cramp Twins Ser.). (J). pap. (978-0-385-32717-6(X) , Dell Books for Young Readers) Random Hse. Children's Bks.

Woodson, J. L. The Things I Could Tell You! Malone, Susan Mary et al, eds. collector's ed. 2003. 206p. pap. 14.95 (978-0-9702699-6-6(X)) Macro Publishing Group.

Woodson, Jacqueline. Miracle's Boys. 2006. 144p. (J). (gr. 5). pap. 5.99 (978-0-14-240602-1(3) , Puffin) Penguin Group (USA) Inc.

Woodward, J. Howland. A Moment in Time. 2006. 55p. pap. 12.95 (978-1-4241-1334-7(2)) PublishAmerica, Inc.

Woodworth, Chris. When Ratboy Lived Next Door. 2005. (Illus.). 192p. (J). 16.00 (978-0-374-34677-5(1) , Farrar, Straus & Giroux (BYR)) Farrar, Straus & Giroux.

Wright, Nancy Means. The Pea Soup Poisonings. 2006. 128p. (J). 26.95 (978-1-59133-161-2(7)); pap. 14.95 (978-1-59133-162-9(5)) Hilliard & Harris.

Wurst, Thomas. Pearl's Christmas Present. Wurst, Thomas, illus. 2004. 40p. 19.99 (*978-0-9790878-7-5(2)) Community Pr.

Wylie, Arlet & Wylie, Sam. Between Piety & Desire. 2005. (Neighborhood Story Project Ser.). (Illus.). 112p. (J). pap. (978-1-933368-29-0(2)) Counterpoint.

Wynne-Jones, Tim. The Boat in the Tree. Shelley, John, illus. 2007. 40p. (J). (ps-2). 17.95 (978-1-932425-49-9(7) , Front Street) Boyds Mills Pr.

Yaccarino, Dan. Where the Four Winds Blow. Yaccarino, Dan, illus. 2003. (Illus.). 104p. (J). 17.89 (978-0-06-623627-8(4) , Cotler, Joanna Books) HarperCollins Pubs.

Yamamoto, Lani. Albert III. 2006. (Illus.). 32p. (J). 10.95 (*978-1-84507-135-6(2)) Lincoln, Frances Ltd. GBR. Dist: Perseus Distribution.

Yang, Belle. Always Come Home to Me. Yang, Belle, illus. 2007. (Illus.). 32p. (J). (ps-3). 16.99 (*978-0-7636-2899-4(9)) Candlewick Pr.

Yang, Belle & Williams, Marcia. Archie's War. Williams, Marcia, illus. 2007. (Illus.). 48p. (J). (gr. 3-7). 17.99 (*978-0-7636-3532-9(4)) Candlewick Pr.

Yates, Dan. An Angel in the Family: A Novel. 1999. (Illus.). 188 p. pap. 12.95 (978-1-57734-282-3(8) , 01113461) Covenant Communications, Inc.

Yates, Elizabeth. American Haven. 2002. (Illus.). 112p. (J). (gr. 4-7). 7.49 (978-1-57924-896-3(9)) Jones, Bob Univ. Pr.

Yavin, T. S. All-Star Season. Orback, Craig, illus. 2007. 160p. (J). (gr. 4-6). spiral bd. 15.95 (978-1-58013-211-4(1)) Kar-Ben Publishing.

Yeomans, Ellen. Rubber Houses. 2007. 160p. (J). (gr. 7-17). 15.99 (978-0-316-10647-4(X)) Little Brown & Co.

Yin. Brothers. Soentpiet, Chris, illus. 2006. 32p. (J). (gr. k). 16.99 (978-0-399-23406-4(3) , Philomel) Penguin Group (USA) Inc.

Yolen, Jane. Soft House. Halperin, Wendy Anderson, illus. 2005. 32p. (J). (ps-2). 15.99 (978-0-7636-1697-7(4)) Candlewick Pr.

Youmans, Marly. Ingledove. 2005. (Illus.). 208p. (YA). 16.00 (978-0-374-33599-1(0) , Farrar, Straus & Giroux) Farrar, Straus & Giroux.

—Ingledove. 2006. 208p. (YA). (gr. 7). pap. 7.99 (978-0-14-240704-2(6) , Puffin) Penguin Group (USA) Inc.

Yourzek, Tammy. Dragons of the Soul. 2006. 192p. (YA). pap. 9.95 (978-1-56315-382-2(3)) SterlingHouse Pubs., Inc.

Yuki, Kaori. Angel Sanctuary, Volume 18. 2007. (Angel Sanctuary Ser.). 200p. (YA). pap. 9.99 (978-1-4215-0976-1(8)) Viz Media.

Yumoto, Kazumi. The Spring Tone. 2002. (YA). 20.25 (978-0-8446-7233-5(5)) Smith, Peter Pub., Inc.

—The Spring Tone. 2001. (J). (978-0-606-21453-7(4)) Tandem Library Bks.

Zalben, Jane Breskin. Baby Babka, the Gorgeous Genius. Chess, Victoria, illus. 2004. 40p. (J). (gr. k-3). tchr. ed. 15.00 (978-0-618-23489-9(6) , Clarion Bks.) Houghton Mifflin Co. Trade & Reference Div.

Zappa, Ahmet. The Monstrous Memoirs of a Mighty McFearless. 2006. (Illus.). 224p. (J). (gr. 3-7). 12.95 (978-0-375-83287-1(4) , Random Hse. Bks. for Young Readers) Random Hse. Children's Bks.

Zeinert, Karen. To Touch the Stars: A Story of World War II. 2004. (Jamestown's American Portraits Ser.). (Illus.). 136p. (J). (gr. 5-7). pap. 4.95 (978-0-7696-3442-5(7) , Waterbird Bks.) School Specialty Publishing.

—To Touch the Stars: A Story of World War II. 2000. (978-0-606-21878-8(5)) Tandem Library Bks.

Zeises, Lara M. Anyone but You. 256p. (YA). (gr. 9). 2007. mass mkt. 6.50 (*978-0-440-23858-4(7) , Laurel Leaf); 2005. 15.95 (978-0-385-73145-4(0) , Delacorte Bks. for Young Readers) Random Hse. Children's Bks.

Zeises, Lara M. Contents under Pressure. 256p. (YA). (gr. 7). 2004. 15.95 (978-0-385-73047-1(0) , Delacorte Bks. for Young Readers); 2005. reprint ed. pap. 5.99 (978-0-440-23787-7(4) , Laurel Leaf) Random Hse. Children's Bks.

Ziefert, Harriet. Sisters Are for Making Sand Castles. Demarest, Chris L., illus. 2001. 16p. (J). (ps-k). pap. 6.99 (978-0-14-056850-9(6) , Puffin) Penguin Group (USA) Inc.

Zimmerman, Andrea. Digger Man. Clemesha, David, illus. 2007. 32p. (J). (ps-k). pap. 6.95 (*978-0-8050-8203-6(4) , Holt, Henry & Co. Bks. For Young Readers) Holt, Henry & Co.

Zimmerman, Andrea Griffing & Clemesha, David. Digger Man. rev. ed. 2003. (Illus.). 32p. (J). 15.95 (978-0-8050-6628-9(4) , Holt, Henry & Co. Bks. For Young Readers) Holt, Henry & Co.

Zindel, Paul. Loch. 2005. 224p. (gr. 5-9). pap. 5.99 (978-0-7868-5150-8(3)) Hyperion Bks. for Children.

Zinnen, Linda. Holding at Third. 2006. 160p. (YA). (gr. 4). pap. 5.99 (978-0-14-240554-3(X) , Puffin) Penguin Group (USA) Inc.

Zitelman, Jem. Ventures Tested: One Teenager's Story . . . to Happiness. 2000. viii, 206p. (J). pap. 15.95 (978-1-891612-01-5(8) , 9701); lib. bdg. 24.95 (978-1-891612-02-2(6) , 9701) Celjon Bks.

Zollman, Pam. Don't Bug Me! 2001. (Illus.). 144p. (J). (gr. 4-6). tchr. ed. 15.95 (978-0-8234-1584-7(8)) Holiday Hse., Inc.

Zolotow, Charlotte. Do You Know What I'll Do? Steptoe, Javaka, illus. rev. ed. 2000. 32p. (J). (ps-2). 16.99 (978-0-06-027879-3(X)) HarperCollins Pubs.

Zusak, Markus. Fighting Ruben Wolfe. 2001. (Illus.). 208p. (YA). (gr. 5-10). pap. 15.95 (978-0-439-24188-5(X) , Levine, Arthur A. Bks.) Scholastic, Inc.

—Getting the Girl. 2004. 256p. (J). pap. 6.99 (978-0-439-38950-1(X) , Levine, Arthur A. Bks.) Scholastic, Inc.

BROWN, AMBER (FICTITIOUS CHARACTER)—FICTION

Danziger, Paula. Ambar en Cuarto y Sin Su Amigo, Level 3.7. Ross, Tony, illus. 2003. (SPA.). 136p. (J). (gr. 3-5). pap. 10.95 (978-84-204-4412-3(X) , SAN412X) Alfaguara, Ediciones, S.A.- Grupo Santillana ESP. Dist: Santillana USA Publishing Co., Inc.

—Ambar en Cuarto y Sin Su Amigo. Ross, Tony, illus. (SPA.). 136p. (J). (gr. 3-5). pap. 10.95 (978-968-19-1021-1(4)) Santillana USA Publishing Co., Inc.

—Amber Brown, Set 1. 2001. (Amber Brown Ser.). (Illus.). (J). (gr. 2-5). pap. 15.96 (978-0-439-26011-4(6)) Scholastic, Inc.

—Amber Brown Goes Fourth. Ross, Tony, illus. 2002. (Amber Brown Ser.: No. 3). (J). (gr. 3-6). 12.17 (978-0-7587-0417-7(8)) Book Wholesalers, Inc.

—Amber Brown Goes Fourth. (Amber Brown Ser.: No. 3). 112p. (J). (gr. 3-6). pap. 3.99 (978-0-8072-1291-2(1) , Listening Library) Random Hse. Audio Publishing Group.

—Amber Brown Is Feeling Blue. Ross, Tony, illus. 2002. (Amber Brown Ser.: No. 7). (J). (gr. 3-6). 12.17 (978-0-7587-0418-4(6)) Book Wholesalers, Inc.

—Amber Brown Is Feeling Blue. Ross, Tony, illus. 1998. (Amber Brown Ser.: No. 7). 128p. (J). (gr. 3-6). 14.99 (978-0-399-23179-7(X) , Putnam Juvenile) Penguin Group (USA) Inc.

—Amber Brown Is Feeling Blue. 2004. (Amber Brown Ser.: No. 7). 131p. (J). (gr. 2-4). pap. 17.00 incl. audio (978-0-8072-2063-4(9) , Listening Library) Random Hse. Audio Publishing Group.

—Amber Brown Is Feeling Blue. Ross, Tony & Rogers, Jacqueline, illus. 1999. (Amber Brown Ser.: No. 7). 144p. (J). (gr. 3-6). pap. 3.99 (978-0-439-07168-0(2)) Scholastic, Inc.

—Amber Brown Is Feeling Blue. 1999. (Amber Brown Ser.: No. 7). (J). (gr. 3-6). 10.64 (978-0-606-17275-2(0)); lib. bdg. 11.80 (978-0-613-20096-7(9)) Tandem Library Bks.

—Amber Brown Is Green with Envy. Ross, Tony, illus. 2003. (Amber Brown Ser.: No. 9). 160p. (J). (gr. 2-5). 15.99 (978-0-399-23181-0(1) , Putnam Juvenile) Penguin Group (USA) Inc.

—Amber Brown Is Green with Envy. Ross, Tony, illus. 2004. (Amber Brown Ser.: No. 9). 160p. (J). (gr. 3-6). pap. 4.99 (978-0-439-07171-0(2) , Scholastic Paperbacks) Scholastic, Inc.

—Amber Brown Is Not a Crayon. (Amber Brown Ser.: No. 1). 80p. (J). (gr. 3-6). pap. 3.50 (978-0-8072-1289-9(X) , Listening Library) Random Hse. Audio Publishing Group.

—Amber Brown Sees Red. Ross, Tony, illus. 2002. (Amber Brown Ser.: No. 6). (J). (gr. 3-6). 12.17 (978-0-7587-0420-7(8)) Book Wholesalers, Inc.

—Amber Brown Sees Red. (Amber Brown Ser.: No. 6). 116p. (J). (gr. 3-6). pap. 3.99 (978-0-8072-1294-3(6)); 1998. (gr. 2-4). pap. 17.00 incl. audio (978-0-8072-0369-9(6) , FTR186SP) Random Hse. Audio Publishing Group. (Listening Library).

—Amber Brown Sees Red. Ross, Tony, illus. 1998. (Amber Brown Ser.: No. 6). 130p. (J). (gr. 3-6). pap. 3.99 (978-0-590-94728-2(1)) Scholastic, Inc.

—Amber Brown Sees Red. 1998. (Amber Brown Ser.: No. 6). (J). (gr. 3-6). 10.64 (978-0-606-12874-2(3)) Tandem Library Bks.

—Amber Brown Series. Ross, Tony, illus. 2002. pap. 61.95 incl. audio (978-0-87499-998-3(7)); pap. 68.95 incl. audio compact disk (978-1-59112-856-4(0)) Live Oak Media.

—Amber Brown Wants Extra Credit. Ross, Tony, illus. 2002. (Amber Brown Ser.: No. 4). (J). (gr. 3-6). 12.17 (978-0-7587-0421-4(6)) Book Wholesalers, Inc.

—Amber Brown Wants Extra Credit. (Amber Brown Ser.: No. 4). 120p. (J). (gr. 3-6). pap. 3.99 (978-0-8072-1292-9(X) , Listening Library) Random Hse. Audio Publishing Group.

—Forever Amber Brown. (Amber Brown Ser.: No. 5). 101p. (J). (gr. 3-6). pap. 3.99 (978-0-8072-1293-6(8)); 1998. (gr. 2-4). pap. 17.00 incl. audio (978-0-8072-0366-8(1) , FTR185SP) Random Hse. Audio Publishing Group. (Listening Library).

—Get Ready for Second Grade, Amber Brown. 2003. (gr. k-3). lib. bdg. 11.80 (978-0-613-67547-5(9)) Tandem Library Bks.

—Get Ready for Second Grade, Amber Brown. Ross, Tony, illus. 2003. (J). (ps-2). audio compact disk 18.95 (978-1-59112-364-4(X)) Live Oak Media.

—I, Amber Brown. 2000. (Amber Brown Ser.: No. 8). (J). (gr. 3-6). (978-0-399-23242-8(7)) Penguin Group (USA) Inc.

—I, Amber Brown. Ross, Tony, illus. 1999. (Amber Brown Ser.: No. 8). 144p. (J). (gr. 3-6). 14.99 (978-0-399-23180-3(3) , Putnam Juvenile) Penguin Group (USA) Inc.

—I, Amber Brown. Ross, Tony, illus. 2000. (Amber Brown Ser.: No. 8). 144p. (J). (gr. 3-6). 3.99 (978-0-439-07169-7(0) , Scholastic Paperbacks) Scholastic, Inc.

—I, Amber Brown. 2000. (Amber Brown Ser.: No. 8). (Illus.). (J). (gr. 3-6). 10.64 (978-0-606-18877-7(0)) Tandem Library Bks.

—It's a Fair Day, Amber Brown. Ross, Tony, illus. 2003. 28.95 incl. audio compact disk (978-1-59112-565-5(0)); pap. 31.95 incl. audio compact disk (978-1-59112-564-8(2)) Live Oak Media.

—It's a Fair Day, Amber Brown. Ross, Tony, illus. 2002. 48p. (J). 12.99 (978-0-399-23606-8(6) , Putnam Juvenile) Penguin Group (USA) Inc.

—It's Justin Time, Amber Brown. Ross, Tony, illus. 9.95 (978-1-59112-294-4(5)) Live Oak Media.

—It's Justin Time, Amber Brown. 2002. (Illus.). (J). pap., tchr.'s planning gde. ed. 29.95 incl. audio (978-0-87499-908-2(1)) Live Oak Media.

—It's Justin Time, Amber Brown. Ross, Tony, illus. 2002. 28.95 incl. audio compact disk (978-1-59112-567-9(7)); pap. 31.95 incl. audio compact disk (978-1-59112-566-2(9)); (J). pap. 18.95 incl. audio compact disk (978-1-59112-366-8(6)) Live Oak Media.

—It's Justin Time, Amber Brown. abr. ed. 2002. (Illus.). (J). (ps-2). 25.95 incl. audio (978-0-87499-907-5(3)); pap. 16.95 incl. audio (978-0-87499-906-8(5)) Live Oak Media.

—It's Justin Time, Amber Brown. Ross, Tony, illus. 2001. (Amber Brown Ser.: No. 10). 1p. (J). (gr. 3-6). 13.99 (978-0-399-23470-5(5) , Putnam Juvenile) Penguin Group (USA) Inc.

—It's Justin Time, Amber Brown. 2001. 10.79 (978-0-606-22522-9(6)) Tandem Library Bks.

—What a Trip, Amber Brown. 2002. (Illus.). (J). pap. 16.95 incl. audio (978-0-87499-910-5(3)); pap. 18.95 incl. audio compact disk (978-1-59112-368-2(2)); pap., tchr.'s planning gde. ed. 29.95 incl. audio (978-0-87499-912-9(X)); 25.95 incl. audio (978-0-87499-911-2(1)) Live Oak Media.

—What a Trip, Amber Brown. Ross, Tony, illus. 2001. (J). 48p. pap. 3.99 (978-0-698-11908-6(8)); (Amber Brown Ser.: No. 9). 1p. (gr. 3-6). 13.99 (978-0-399-23469-9(1)) Penguin Group (USA) Inc. (Putnam Juvenile).

—What a Trip, Amber Brown. 2001. (978-0-606-22523-6(4)); lib. bdg. 11.80 (978-0-613-44429-3(9)) Tandem Library Bks.

—You Can't Eat Your Chicken Pox, Amber Brown. (Amber Brown Ser.: No. 2). 101p. (J). (gr. 3-6). pap. 3.50 (978-0-8072-1290-5(3) , Listening Library) Random Hse. Audio Publishing Group.

BROWN, CHARLIE (FICTITIOUS CHARACTER)—FICTION

Katschke, Judy, adapted by. It's a Home Run, Charlie Brown! ed. 2005. (Illus.). 32p. (J). lib. bdg. 15.00 (978-1-59054-947-6(3)) Fitzgerald Bks.

—It's Time for School, Charlie Brown. ed. 2005. (Illus.). 32p. (J). lib. bdg. 15.00 (978-1-59054-948-3(1)) Fitzgerald Bks.

Schultz, Charles M. Be My Valentine, Charlie Brown. 2007. (Illus.). 10p. (J). pap. 7.95 (***978-0-7624-3173-1(3)*** , Running Pr. Kids); 128p. 4.95 (***978-0-7624-2754-3(X)*** , Running Pr. Minature Editions) Running Pr. Bk. Pubs.

—A Charlie Brown Christmas. 2007. (Illus.). 10p. (J). bds. 7.95 (***978-0-7624-3172-4(5)***) Running Pr. Bk. Pubs.

—A Charlie Brown Christmas: A Book-and-Tree Kit. 2007. (Illus.). 128p. pap. 8.95 (***978-0-7624-3145-8(8)*** , Running Pr. Minature Editions) Running Pr. Bk. Pubs.

Schulz, Charles M. Alles Peanuts. Herbst, Gabriele & Rolle, Ekkehard, trs. from ENG. (Snoopy & die Peanuts Ser.: Vol. 26). (GER., Illus.). 96p. (J). pap. (978-3-8105-1871-2(9)) Kruger, Wolfgang Verlag, GmbH DEU. *Dist:* International Bk. Import Service, Inc.

—A Boy Named Charlie Brown. 2001. (Illus.). 144p. 9.98 (978-1-58663-188-8(8) , MetroBooks) Friedman, Michael Publishing Group, Inc.

—A Charlie Brown Christmas. 2003. (Miniature Editionstm Ser.). (Illus.). 128p. 4.95 (978-0-7624-1601-1(7) , Running Pr. Minature Editions) Running Pr. Bk. Pubs.

—Charlie Brown Christmas. 2001. (gr. k-3). lib. bdg. 14.15 (978-0-613-61753-6(3)) Tandem Library Bks.

—A Charlie Brown Christmas. Braddock, Paige, illus. 2004. 28p. (J). (ps-ps). lib. bdg. 12.79 (978-0-606-30053-7(8)) Tandem Library Bks.

—Charlie Brown Christmas, Spec Sales Ed. 2004. 128p. 4.95 (978-0-7624-2289-0(0)) Running Pr. Bk. Pubs.

—It's a Home Run, Charlie Brown! LoBianco, Peter & LoBianco, Nick, illus. 2002. (Ready-to-Read Ser.). 32p. (J). (gr. 1-4). pap. 3.99 (978-0-689-84939-8(7) , Little Simon) Simon & Schuster Children's Publishing.

—It's the Great Pumpkin, Charlie Brown. ed. 2004. (Illus.). 128p. 4.95 (978-0-7624-2033-9(2) , Running Pr. Minature Editions) Running Pr. Bk. Pubs.

—It's the Great Pumpkin, Charlie Brown. 2002. 24p. mass mkt. 5.99 (978-0-689-85946-5(5) , Little Simon) Simon & Schuster Children's Publishing.

—It's Time for School, Charlie Brown. 2002. (gr. k-3). lib. bdg. 11.80 (978-0-613-61782-6(7)) Tandem Library Bks.

—Kick the Football, Charlie Brown! 2001. (gr. k-3). lib. bdg. 11.80 (978-0-613-61786-4(X)) Tandem Library Bks.

—Lucy's Advice. 2003. (gr. k-3). lib. bdg. 11.80 (978-0-613-66460-8(4)) Tandem Library Bks.

Schulz, Charles M., illus. It's a Home Run, Charlie Brown! 2002. (gr. k-3). lib. bdg. 11.80 (978-0-613-61780-2(0)) Tandem Library Bks.

—Kick the Football, Charlie Brown! 2001. (Ready-to-Read Ser.). 32p. (J). pap. 3.99 (978-0-689-84594-9(4) , Little Simon) Simon & Schuster Children's Publishing.

BROWN, ENCYCLOPEDIA (FICTITIOUS CHARACTER)—FICTION

Encyclopedia Brown. 1999. (J). 9.95 (978-1-56137-282-9(X)) Novel Units, Inc.

Sobol, Donald J. Encyclopedia Brown & the Case of the Dead Eagles. 2008. (Encyclopedia Brown Ser.). 96p. (J). (gr. 1-3). pap. 4.99 (***978-0-14-241135-3(3)*** , Puffin) Penguin Group (USA) Inc.

—Encyclopedia Brown & the Case of the Jumping Frogs. 2003. (Encyclopedia Brown Ser.: No. 23). (Illus.). 80p. (gr. 3-7). 14.95 (978-0-385-72931-4(6)); lib. bdg. 16.99 (978-0-385-90148-2(8)) Random Hse. Children's Bks. (Delacorte Bks. for Young Readers).

—Encyclopedia Brown & the Case of the Midnight Visitor. 2008. (Encyclopedia Brown Ser.). 96p. (J). (gr. 1-3). pap. 4.99 (***978-0-14-241106-3(X)*** , Puffin) Penguin Group (USA) Inc.

—Encyclopedia Brown & the Case of the Secret Pitch. 2007. (Encyclopedia Brown Ser.: No. 2). 96p. (J). (gr. 2-6). 4.99 (***978-0-14-240889-6(1)*** , Puffin) Penguin Group (USA) Inc.

—Encyclopedia Brown & the Case of the Secret Pitch. 2004. (Encyclopedia Brown Ser.: No. 2). 112p. (J). (gr. 3-7). pap. 17.00 incl. audio (978-0-8072-1985-0(1) , Listening Library) Random Hse. Audio Publishing Group.

—Encyclopedia Brown & the Case of the Sleeping Dog. Chang, Warren, illus. 1999. (Encyclopedia Brown Ser.: No. 21). 80p. (J). (gr. 3-7). pap. 5.50 (978-0-553-48517-2(2) , Yearling) Random Hse. Children's Bks.

—Encyclopedia Brown & the Case of the Sleeping Dog. 1999. (Encyclopedia Brown Ser.: No. 21). (gr. 3-6). lib. bdg. 12.40 (978-0-613-22846-6(4)); (Illus.). (J). 11.30 (978-0-606-18628-5(X)) Tandem Library Bks.

—Encyclopedia Brown & the Case of the Slippery Salamander. Chang, Warren, illus. 2000. (Encyclopedia Brown Ser.: No. 22). 96p. (gr. 3-7). 5.50 (978-0-553-48521-9(0) , Yearling) Random Hse. Children's Bks.

—Encyclopedia Brown & the Case of the Slippery Salamander. 1999. (Encyclopedia Brown Ser.: No. 22). (Illus.). (J). 11.30 (978-0-606-18629-2(8)) Tandem Library Bks.

—Encyclopedia Brown, Boy Detective. 2007. (Encyclopedia Brown Ser.: No. 1). 96p. (J). (gr. 2). 4.99 (***978-0-14-240888-9(3)*** , Puffin) Penguin Group (USA) Inc.

—Encyclopedia Brown, Boy Detective. 2004. (Encyclopedia Brown Ser.: No. 1). 128p. (J). (gr. 3-7). pap. 17.00 incl. audio (978-0-8072-1984-3(3) , Listening Library) Random Hse. Audio Publishing Group.

—Encyclopedia Brown Finds the Clues. 2007. (Encyclopedia Brown Ser.: No. 3). 96p. (J). (gr. 2). 4.99 (***978-0-14-240890-2(5)*** , Puffin) Penguin Group (USA) Inc.

—Encyclopedia Brown Gets His Man. 2007. (Encyclopedia Brown Ser.: No. 4). 96p. (J). (gr. 2). pap. 4.99 (***978-0-14-240891-9(3)*** , Puffin) Penguin Group (USA) Inc.

—Encyclopedia Brown Lends a Hand. 2008. (Encyclopedia Brown Ser.). 96p. (J). (gr. 1-3). pap. 4.99 (***978-0-14-241105-6(1)*** , Puffin) Penguin Group (USA) Inc.

—Encyclopedia Brown Saves the Day. 2008. (Encyclopedia Brown Ser.: No. 7). 96p. (J). (gr. 2). 4.99 (***978-0-14-240921-3(9)*** , Puffin) Penguin Group (USA) Inc.

—Encyclopedia Brown Shows the Way. Shortall, Leonard, illus. 2008. (Encyclopedia Brown Ser.). 96p. (J). (gr. 2). 4.99 (***978-0-14-241086-8(1)*** , Puffin) Penguin Group (USA) Inc.

—Encyclopedia Brown Solves Them All. 2008. (Encyclopedia Brown Ser.: No. 5). 96p. (J). (gr. 2). 4.99 (***978-0-14-240920-6(0)*** , Puffin) Penguin Group (USA) Inc.

—Encyclopedia Brown Takes the Case. 2008. (Encyclopedia Brown Ser.: No. 10). 96p. (J). (gr. 2). 4.99 (***978-0-14-241085-1(3)*** , Puffin) Penguin Group (USA) Inc.

—Encyclopedia Brown Tracks Them Down. Shortall, Leonard, illus. 2008. (Encyclopedia Brown Ser.: No. 8). 96p. (J). (gr. 2). 4.99 (***978-0-14-240951-0(0)*** , Puffin) Penguin Group (USA) Inc.

BROWN, JOHN, 1800-1859

Brackett, Virginia. John Brown: Abolitionist. 2002. (gr. 5-8). lib. bdg. 17.60 (978-0-613-52693-7(7)) Tandem Library Bks.

Brackett, Virginia R. John Brown: Abolitionist. 2001. (Famous Figures of the Civil War Era Ser.). (Illus.). 80p. (J). (gr. 5 up). pap. 25.00 (978-0-7910-6409-2(3)); 25.00 (978-0-7910-6408-5(5)) Facts On File, Inc. (Chelsea Hse.).

DeVillers, David. The John Brown Slavery Revolt Trial: A Headline Court Case. 2000. (Headline Court Cases Ser.). (Illus.). 104p. (YA). (gr. 6-12). lib. bdg. 26.60 (978-0-7660-1385-8(5)) Enslow Pubs., Inc.

Glaser, Jason. John Brown's Raid on Harpers Ferry. Milgrom, Al et al, illus. 2005. (Graphic Library). 32p. (J). (gr. 3-7). lib. bdg. 25.26 (978-0-7368-4369-0(8)) Capstone Pr., Inc.

Lilley, Stephen R. Fighters Against American Slavery. 1998. (History Makers Ser.). (Illus.). 128p. (YA). (gr. 7-10). 27.45 (978-1-56006-036-9(0) , Lucent Bks.) Thomson Gale.

Marsh, Carole. John Brown. 2002. (One Thousand Readers Ser.). (Illus.). 12p. (J). (gr. k-4). 2.95 (978-0-635-01524-2(2) , 15242) Gallopade International.

Stein, R. Conrad. John Brown's Raid on Harpers Ferry in American History. 1999. (In American History Ser.). (Illus.). 128p. (YA). (gr. 5-12). lib. bdg. 26.60 (978-0-7660-1123-6(2)) Enslow Pubs., Inc.

Streissguth, Thomas. John Brown. Ramstad, Ralph L., illus. 1999. (On My Own Biographies Ser.). 48p. (J). (gr. 1-3). lib. bdg. 23.93 (978-1-57505-334-9(9) , Carolrhoda Bks.) Lerner Publishing Group.

BROWN, JOHN, 1800-1859—FICTION

Bryant, Louella. Father by Blood. 1999. (Illus.). 160p. (YA). (gr. 6-8). pap. 12.95 (978-1-881535-33-1(9)) New England Pr., Inc., The.

Kay, Alan N. On the Trail of John Brown's Body. 2001. (Young Heroes of History Ser.: Vol. 2). (Illus.). 175p. (J). (gr. 4-7). pap. 5.95 (978-1-57249-239-4(2) , 1572492406, Burd Street Pr.) White Mane Publishing Co., Inc.

Rees, Douglas. Lightning Time. 1999. (J). (978-0-606-19069-5(4)) Tandem Library Bks.

Rinaldi, Ann. Mine Eyes Have Seen. 2002. (978-0-606-22271-6(5)) Tandem Library Bks.

BROWN, MARGARET WISE, 1910-1952

Marcus, Leonard. Margaret Wise Brown: Awakened by the Moon. 1999. (gr. 7-12). lib. bdg. 24.55 (978-0-613-29289-4(8)) Tandem Library Bks.

Wheeler, Jill C. Margaret Wise Brown. 2007. (Children's Authors Ser.). (Illus.). 24p. (J). 21.35 (978-1-59679-762-8(2)) ABDO Publishing Co.

BROWNING, ROBERT, 1812-1889

Bloom, Harold. Robert Browning. 2000. (Major Poets Ser.). 120p. (YA). (gr. 10 up). 31.95 (978-0-7910-5931-9(6) , Chelsea Hse.) Facts On File, Inc.

BRUEGEL, PIETER, CA. 1525-1569

Malam, John. Pieter Bruegel. 1999. (Tell Me About Ser.). (Illus.). 24p. (J). (gr. 2-5). lib. bdg. 19.93 (978-1-57505-366-0(7)) Lerner Publishing Group.

Woodhouse, Jayne. Pieter Bruegel. 2001. (gr. k-3). lib. bdg. 14.75 (978-0-613-45811-5(7)) Tandem Library Bks.

BUCCANEERS

see also Pirates

Hamilton, Sue L. Henry Morgan. 2007. (Pirates! Ser.). (ENG., Illus.). 32p. (J). (gr. 3-6). 24.21 (***978-1-59928-760-7(9)*** , ABDO & Daughters) ABDO Publishing Co.

Jordan, Shirley. Pirates & Privateers in the New World: Moments in History. 2001. (Cover-to-Cover Bks.). (Illus.). 72p. (J). pap. 8.95 (978-0-7891-5396-8(3)); (gr. 4-7). lib. bdg. 17.95 (978-0-7807-9803-8(1)) Perfection Learning Corp.

Kozar, Richard. Infamous Pirates. 1998. (Costume, Tradition & Culture). (Illus.). 64p. (YA). 12.95 (978-0-7910-5165-8(X) , Chelsea Hse.) Facts On File, Inc.

Malam, John. You Wouldn't Want to Be a Pirate's Prisoner! Antram, David, illus. 2002. (You Wouldn't Want to Ser.). 32p. (J). (gr. 2-5). 28.50 (978-0-531-14607-1(3)); pap. 9.95 (978-0-531-16368-9(7)) Scholastic Library Publishing. (Watts, Franklin).

—You Wouldn't Want to Be a Pirate's Prisoner! 2002. (gr. 3-6). lib. bdg. 18.75 (978-0-613-53885-5(4)) Tandem Library Bks.

Smith, Helen. Pirates, Swashbucklers & Buccaneers of London. 2004. (... of London Ser.). (Illus.). 96p. 8.99 (978-1-904153-17-7(8)) Watling St., Ltd. GBR. *Dist:* Trafalgar Square Publishing.

Stockton, Frank Richard. Buccaneers & Pirates. 2007. (Illus.). 368p. pap. 12.95 (***978-0-486-45425-2(8)***) Dover Pubns., Inc.

—Buccaneers & Pirates of Our Coasts. 2006. pap. (***978-1-4068-3064-4(X)***) Echo Library.

—Buccaneers & Pirates of Our Coasts. 1999. (Notable American Authors Ser.). reprint ed. lib. bdg. 125.00 (978-0-7812-8936-8(X)) Reprint Services Co.

Teitelbaum, Michael. Pirate Life. 2007. (Boys Rock! Ser.). 32p. (J). (gr. 1-5). 24.21 (***978-1-59296-859-6(7)***) Child's World, Inc.

BUCCANEERS—FICTION

Lawrence, Iain. Buccaneers. 2003. (gr. 5-8). lib. bdg. 13.55 (978-0-613-64433-4(6)) Tandem Library Bks.

Pyle, Howard. Stolen Treasure. 2006. (ENG.). pap. (***978-1-4068-3429-1(7)***) Echo Library.

BUCHANAN, JAMES, 1791-1868

Donovan, Sandy. James Buchanan. 2005. (Presidential Leaders Ser.). (Illus.). 112p. (J). (gr. 6-12). 29.27 (978-0-8225-1399-5(4)) Lerner Publishing Group.

Joseph, Paul. James Buchanan. 2000. (United States Presidents Ser.). (Illus.). 32p. (J). (gr. k-6). lib. bdg. 22.78 (978-1-57765-241-0(X) , Checkerboard Library) ABDO Publishing Co.

Lassieur, Allison. James Buchanan. 2004. (Encyclopedia of Presidents Ser.). (Illus.). 110p. (J). 34.00 (978-0-516-22884-6(6) , Children's Pr.) Scholastic Library Publishing.

Mis, Melody S. How to Draw the Life & Times of James Buchanan. 2006. (Kid's Guide to Drawing the Presidents of the United States of America Ser.). (J). 25.25 (978-1-4042-2992-1(2) , PowerKids Pr.) Rosen Publishing Group, Inc., The.

Santella, Andrew. James Buchanan. 2003. (Profiles of the Presidents Ser.). (Illus.). 64p. (J). (gr. 4 up). lib. bdg. 23.93 (978-0-7565-0263-8(2)) Compass Point Bks.

Venezia, Mike. James Buchanan. Venezia, Mike, illus. 2006. (Illus.). 32p. (J). (gr. 3-4). pap. 7.95 (978-0-516-25486-9(3) , Children's Pr.) Scholastic Library Publishing.

Venezia, Mike, illus. James Buchanan. 2005. 32p. (J). 27.00 (978-0-516-22620-0(7) , Children's Pr.) Scholastic Library Publishing.

Young, Jeff C. James Buchanan: A MyReportLinks.com Book. 2003. (Presidents Ser.). (Illus.). 48p. (J). (gr. 4-10). lib. bdg. 25.26 (978-0-7660-5101-0(3) , MyReportLinks.com Bks.) Enslow Pubs., Inc.

BUDDHA

see Gautama Buddha

BUDDHISM

Adiccabandhu. My Buddhist Faith. 2006. (World Faiths Ser.). (Illus.). 31p. (J). (978-1-84234-388-3(2) , Cherrytree Books) Evans Publishing Group.

—My Buddhist Faith. 1999. (My Faith Ser.). (Illus.). 32p. 9.99 (978-0-237-51979-7(8) , Evans Brothers, Limited) Evans Publishing Group GBR. *Dist:* Independent Pubs. Group.

Adiccabandhu & Ganeri, Anita. Buddhist Prayer & Worship. 2007. (Illus.). (J). (***978-1-59771-095-4(4)***) Sea-To-Sea Pubns.

Aloka, illus. The Windhorse Colouring Book. 2004. 56p. pap. 17.95 (978-1-899579-42-6(7)) Windhorse Pubns. GBR. *Dist:* Consortium Bk. Sales & Distribution.

Beesley, Gary. Buddhism. Taylor, Ina, ed. 2006. (Illus.). 64p. (YA). pap., stu. ed. 21.00 (978-0-7487-9674-8(6)) Nelson Thornes Ltd. GBR. *Dist:* Trans-Atlantic Pubns., Inc.

Brown, Don. Far Beyond the Garden Gate: Alexandra David-Neel's Journey to Lhasa. Brown, Don, illus. 2002. (Illus.). 32p. (J). (gr. k-3). tchr. ed. 16.00 (978-0-618-08364-0(2)) Houghton Mifflin Co. Trade & Reference Div.

Buddhism. 2004. (Exploring World Beliefs Ser.). (Illus.). 48p. 7.99 (978-0-7439-3683-5(3)) Teacher Created Materials, Inc.

Buddhist Text Translation Society Staff & Dharma Realm Buddhist University Staff, trs. Human Roots for Young Readers, 2 vols. 2002. (Illus.). (J). 8.00 (978-0-88139-318-7(5)) Buddhist Text Translation Society.

Buddhist Text Translation Society Staff, et al. Spider Thread. 2000. (ENG & CHI., Illus.). 100p. (J). 8.00 (978-0-88139-856-4(X)) Buddhist Text Translation Society.

Carew-Miller, Anna. Buddha. 2002. (Great Names Ser.). (Illus.). 32p. (J). (gr. 3 up). lib. bdg. 19.95 (978-1-59084-137-2(9)) Mason Crest Pubs.

Chodzin, Sherab & Kohn, Alexandra. The Wisdom of the Crows & Other Buddhist Tales. Cameron, Marie, illus. 2004. 80p. (J). (gr. 2 up). pap. 17.95 (978-1-883672-68-3(6) , Tricycle Pr.) Ten Speed Pr.

Chopra, Swati. Buddhism - On the Path to Nirvana. 2005. (Illus.). 160p. 35.00 (978-1-904668-66-4(6)) Mercury Bks. Ltd. GBR. *Dist:* International Publishers Marketing.

Dharma Realm Buddhist University Staff, tr. Human Roots for Young Readers, 2 vols. 2002. (Illus.). (J). pap. 8.00 (978-0-88139-317-0(7)) Buddhist Text Translation Society.

Dorling Kindersley Publishing Staff & Wilkinson, Philip. Buddhism. 2003. (Eyewitness Books). 64p. (J). 15.99 (978-0-7894-9833-5(2)) Dorling Kindersley Publishing, Inc.

Foran, Jill. Buddha Day. 2003. (Celebrating Cultures Ser.). (Illus.). 24p. (J). lib. bdg. 15.95 (978-1-59036-090-3(7)) Weigl Pubs., Inc.

Fossey, Kevin & Fossey, Denise. Buddhism. 2006. (QEB World of Faiths Ser.). (Illus.). 32p. (J). (gr. 3-6). lib. bdg. 27.10 (978-1-59566-212-5(X)) QEB Publishing Inc.

Fu, Zhiying. Handing down the Light: The Biography of Venerable Master Hsing Yun. 2003. (Illus.). 335p. 14.00 (978-1-932293-00-5(0)) Buddha's Light Publishing.

Ganeri, Anita. Buddhism. 2005. (Illus.). 48p. (J). pap. (978-0-8368-5871-6(9)); lib. bdg. 30.00 (978-0-8368-5865-5(4)) Stevens, Gareth Inc. (World Almanac Library).

—Buddhism: Yuranan's Story. 2006. (This Is My Faith Bks.). (Illus.). 32p. (J). (gr. 1-4). 11.99 (978-0-7641-5962-6(3)); pap. 4.99 (978-0-7641-3472-2(8)) Barron's Educational Series, Inc.

—Buddhism Around the World. 2007. (J). (***978-1-59920-058-3(9)***) Smart Apple Media.

—Buddhist. (Illus.). 32p. (YA). (gr. 3 up). lib. bdg. 27.10 (978-1-932889-15-4(9)) Sea-To-Sea Pubns.

—Buddhist Festivals Through the Year. 2003. (Year of Festivals Ser.). (J). 30p. lib. bdg. 24.25 (978-1-58340-375-4(2)); (Illus.). 32p. (978-0-7496-4801-5(5)) Smart Apple Media.

—Buddhist Stories. Fennell, Tracy, illus. 2001. (Storyteller Ser.). 32p. (YA). 22.00 (978-0-237-52034-2(6) , Evans Brothers, Limited) Evans Publishing Group GBR. *Dist:* Independent Pubs. Group.

—Journey's End: Death & Mourning. 1999. (Life Times Ser.). (Illus.). 30p. (YA). (gr. 2 up). 15.95 (978-0-87226-289-8(8) , 62898B, Bedrick, Peter Bks.) School Specialty Publishing.

—Wedding Days: Celebrations of Marriage. 1999. (Life Times Ser.). (Illus.). 32p. (J). 15.95 (978-0-87226-288-1(X) , 6288XB, Bedrick, Peter Bks.) School Specialty Publishing.

Geldart, Anne. Buddhist Temples. 2005. (Let's Find Out about Ser.). (J). 25.36 (978-1-4034-7035-5(9)) Steck-Vaughn.

George, Charles. Buddhist. 2004. (What Makes Me A—? Ser.). (Illus.). 48p. (J). 26.20 (978-0-7377-2269-7(X) , Greenhaven Pr., Inc.) Thomson Gale.

Gibb, Christopher. The Dalai Lama: Peacemaker from Tibet. 2002. (Famous Lives Ser.). (Illus.). 48p. (J). lib. bdg. 27.12 (978-0-7398-5520-1(4)) Raintree.

Hanh, Thich Nhat. The Coconut Monk. Mai, Vo-Dinh, illus. 2006. 40p. (J). 14.95 (978-1-888375-53-4(1) , Plum Blossom Bks.) Parallax Pr.

—A Pebble for Your Pocket. Ames, Philippe & Dong, Nguyen, illus. 2001. 48p. (J). pap. 8.95 (978-1-888375-05-3(1)) Parallax Pr.

—Under the Rose-Apple Tree. 2002. 64p. (J). pap. 8.00 (978-1-888375-04-6(3)) Parallax Pr.

Hartney, Chris, et al. Livewire Investigates Buddhism. 2004. (Livewires Ser.). (Illus.). 32p. pap. 4.10 (978-0-521-60114-6(2)) Cambridge Univ. Pr.

Hsuan Hua. Dew Drops: Pearls of Wisdom by the Venerable Master Hua = [Zhao Lu: Xuanhuashangren Yi Li Ming Zhu]. 2003. (ENG & CHI., Illus.). 91p. (J). 5.00 (978-0-88139-862-5(4)) Buddhist Text Translation Society.

Lee, Jeanne M. I Once Was a Monkey: Stories Buddha Told. Lee, Jeanne M., illus. 1999. (Illus.). 40p. (J). (gr. k-3). 17.00 (978-0-374-33548-9(6) , Farrar, Straus & Giroux (BYR)) Farrar, Straus & Giroux.

The Lost Key of the Buddha: The Immortal Series, Book III. 2003. (Illus.). 350p. per. 19.95 (978-0-9665053-3-7(6) , 009) Great AD-Ventures.

Marchant, Kerena. Buddha & Buddhism. 2002. (Great Religious Leaders Ser.). (Illus.). 48p. (J). lib. bdg. 28.50 (978-1-58340-222-1(5)) Smart Apple Media.

Metcalf, Franz. Buddha in Your Backpack: Everyday Buddhism for Teens. 2002. (Illus.). 160p. (YA). (gr. 7-12). pap. 12.95 (978-1-56975-321-7(0)) Ulysses Pr.

Netzley, Patricia D. Buddhism. 2002. (Religions of the World Ser.). (Illus.). 112p. (YA). 29.95 (978-1-56006-983-6(X) , LML12001-179176, Lucent Bks.) Thomson Gale.

Penney, Sue. Buddhism. 2000. (World Beliefs & Cultures Ser.). (Illus.). 48p. (J). (gr. 5-7). lib. bdg. 25.64 (978-1-57572-354-9(9)) Heinemann Library.

Pritchard, Jean, photos by. I Like Meetings, 4 vols. 2000. 8p. (J). bds. 3.95 (978-0-915678-85-3(3)) World Tribune Pr.

—I Like My Book & Beads, 4 vols. 2000. 8p. (J). bds. 3.95 (978-0-915678-83-9(7)) World Tribune Pr.

—I Like the Altar, 4 vols. 2000. 8p. (J). bds. 3.95 (978-0-915678-84-6(5)) World Tribune Pr.

—I Like to Chant, 4 vols. 2000. (J). 8p. bds. 3.95 (978-0-915678-82-2(9)); 32p. bds. 13.95 (978-0-915678-86-0(1)) World Tribune Pr.

Quinn, Daniel P. I Am Buddhist. 2004. (Religions of the World Ser.). (Illus.). 24p. (J). lib. bdg. 18.75 (978-0-8239-6814-5(6) , PowerKids Pr.) Rosen Publishing Group, Inc., The.

Rivera, Sheila. The Dalai Lama: A Life of Compassion. 2007. (Pull Ahead Books). (Illus.). 32p. (J). 22.60 (978-0-8225-6386-0(X) , Lerner Pubns.) Lerner Publishing Group.

Ross. Bodh Gaya Holy Places, 6 bks. 2003. pap. 34.10 (978-1-4109-0239-9(0)) Raintree.

Ross, Mandy. Bodh Gaya. 2003. (Holy Places Ser.). (Illus.). 32p. (J). 24.28 (978-0-7398-6077-9(1)) Raintree.

Senker, Cath. My Buddhist Year. (Illus.). 2005. (J). pap. (978-0-7502-4059-8(8)); 2003. (978-0-7502-4058-1(X)) Hodder Children's Division. (Hodder Wayland).

—My Buddhist Year. 2007. (J). lib. bdg. (***978-1-4042-3730-8(5)*** , PowerKids Pr.) Rosen Publishing Group, Inc., The.

Shaw, Maura D. Thich Nhat Hanh: Buddhism in Action. Marchesi, Stephen, illus. 2003. (Spiritual Biographies for Young Readers Ser.). 32p. (J). (gr. 1-3). 12.95 (978-1-893361-87-4(X)) SkyLight Paths Publishing.

Stewart, Whitney. The 14th Dalai Lama: Spiritual Leader of Tibet. 2005. (Biography Ser.). (Illus.). 112p. (gr. 6-12). pap., lib. bdg. 27.93 (978-0-8225-9691-2(1)) Lerner Publishing Group.

Sullivan, Anne Marie. Dalai Lama: Spiritual Leader. 2002. (Great Names Ser.). (Illus.). 32p. (J). (gr. 3 up). lib. bdg. (978-1-59084-151-8(4)) Mason Crest Pubs.

Teece, Geoff. Buddhism. 2004. (Religion in Focus Ser.). (Illus.). 32p. (J). lib. bdg. (978-1-58340-464-5(3)) Smart Apple Media.

Walker, Peggy, illus. My First Book of Buddhist Treasures. 2003. 38p. (J). 8.95 (978-0-915678-81-5(0)) World Tribune Pr.

Wangu, Madhu Bazaz. Buddhism. (World Religions Ser.). 128p. (J). (gr. 6-12). 2nd rev. ed. 2002. (Illus.). 30.00 (978-0-8160-4728-4(6)); 3rd rev. ed. 2006. 30.00 (978-0-8160-6609-4(4)) Facts On File, Inc.

Welsh, Kenneth, narrated by. What, Where, When, How, Why & Who to Remember to Be Happy. 2001. 8p. (J). 14.95 (978-1-57097-115-0(3)) Dawn Horse Pr.

Wilkinson, Philip & Dorling Kindersley Publishing Staff. Buddhism. 2003. (Eyewitness Guides Ser.). (Illus.). 64p. (J). lib. bdg. 19.99 (978-0-7894-9834-2(0)) Dorling Kindersley Publishing, Inc.

Wood, Angela. Buddhist Temple. 1999. (Places of Worship Ser.). (Illus.). 32p. (J). (gr. 2 up). lib. bdg. 23.33 (978-0-8368-2605-0(1)) Stevens, Gareth Inc.

Wood, Cavan. Buddhism. 2003. (Living Religions Ser.). (Illus.). 62p. (J). 28.56 (978-0-7398-6382-4(7)) Raintree.

Worth, Richard. Dalai Lama (Tenzin Gyatso) 2004. (Spiritual Leaders & Thinkers Ser.). (Illus.). 120p. (gr. 9-13). 30.00 (978-0-7910-7868-6(X) , Chelsea Hse.) Facts On File, Inc.

Xingyun, et al. Prescription for the Heart: Between Ignorance & Enlightenment 2. 2003. (Between Ignorance & Enlightenment Ser.: Vol. 2). 131p. 13.00 (978-1-932293-02-9(7)) Buddha's Light Publishing.

BUDDHISM—FICTION

Bowser, Milton, illus. Cartoon Stories from the Teachings of Buddha. l.t. ed. 2003. (Cartoon Ser.). (JPN & SPA.). 72p. (YA). 10.00 (978-0-940178-34-2(6) , Buddha 1) Sitare, Ltd.

Gershator, Phillis. Sky Sweeper. Meade, Holly, illus. 2007. 40p. (J). (gr. k). 16.00 (978-0-374-37007-7(9)) Farrar, Straus & Giroux.

Hanh, Thich Nhat. The Hermit & the Well. Mai, Vo-Dinh, illus. 2004. 36p. (J). 15.00 (978-1-888375-31-2(0)) Parallax Pr.

Koja, Kathe. Buddha Boy. 2003. 128p. (YA). (gr. 7 up). 16.00 (978-0-374-30998-5(1) , Farrar, Straus & Giroux (BYR)) Farrar, Straus & Giroux.

—Buddha Boy. 2004. 128p. (YA). (gr. 6-11). reprint ed. pap. 5.99 (978-0-14-240209-2(5) , Puffin) Penguin Group (USA) Inc.

—Buddha Boy. l.t. ed. 2003. 113p. (J). 24.95 (978-0-7862-6012-6(2)) Thomson Gale.

Manos, Helen. Samsara Dog. Vivas, Julie, illus. 2007. 48p. (J). (gr. 3 up). 17.95 (***978-1-933605-51-7(0)*** Kane/Miller Bk. Pubs., Inc.

Millhouse, Jackie. The Tiger & the General. Girouard, Patrick, illus. 2007. (J). (***978-1-932911-32-9(4)*** World Tribune Pr.

Sonnenblick, Jordan. Zen & the Art of Faking It. 2007. 272p. (J). pap. 16.99 (***978-0-439-83707-1(3)*** , Scholastic Pr.) Scholastic, Inc.

Whitesel, Cheryl Aylward. Rebel: A Tibetan Odyssey. 2000. 208p. (J). (gr. 5 up). 16.99 (978-0-688-16735-6(7)) HarperCollins Pubs.

Whitfield, Peter. Bruno Dreams of Ice Cream. Bevington, Nancy, illus. 2005. (Zen Tails Ser.). 28p. (J). (gr. 1-17). 15.95 (978-1-894965-21-7(3)) Simply Read Bks. CAN. *Dist:* Perseus Distribution.

BUDGERIGARS

Barnes, Julia, et al. 101 Facts about Parakeets. 2002. (One Hundred One Facts about Pets Ser.). (Illus.). 32p. (J). (gr. 3 up). lib. bdg. 23.33 (978-0-8368-3020-0(2)) Stevens, Gareth Inc.

Birmelin, Immanuel. My Parakeet & Me. Holzner, Renate, illus. Wegler, Monika, photos by. 2001. (For the Love of Animals Ser.). 64p. (gr. 4-7). pap. 6.99 (978-0-7641-1807-4(2)) Barron's Educational Series, Inc.

Landau, Elaine. Parrots & Parakeets as Pets. 1998. (True Bks.). (Illus.). 48p. (J). (gr. 3-5). pap. 6.95 (978-0-516-26272-7(6) , Children's Pr.) Scholastic Library Publishing.

Lewis, David, contrib. by. Parakeets (Budgerigars) 1999. (Junior Pet Care Ser.). (Illus.). 48p. (gr. 4-7). 12.95 (978-0-7910-4909-9(4) , Chelsea Hse.) Facts On File, Inc.

MacAulay, Kelley & Kalman, Bobbie. Parakeets. 2004. (Pet Care Ser.). (Illus.). 32p. (J). (978-0-7787-1757-7(7)); pap. (978-0-7787-1789-8(5)) Crabtree Publishing Co.

Walker, Pam. My Parakeet. 2001. (My Pets Ser.). (Illus.). 24p. (J). (ps-2). 17.00 (978-0-516-23187-7(1) , Children's Pr.) Scholastic Library Publishing.

Walker, Pamela. My Parakeet. 2001. (gr. k-3). lib. bdg. 12.95 (978-0-613-58869-0(X)) Tandem Library Bks.

BUDGETS, PERSONAL

see Finance, Personal

BUFFALO, AMERICAN

see Bison

BUFFALO BILL, 1846-1917

Bair, Diane. Leyendas del Oeste & Western Legends. 2005. spiral bd. 88.00 (***978-1-4108-5735-4(2)*** Benchmark Education Co.

Goodman, Michael E. Buffalo Bill. 2005. (Illus.). 48p. (gr. 5-9). 21.95 (978-1-58341-336-4(7) , Creative Education) Creative Co., The.

Parim D'Aulaire, Ingri. Buffalo Bill. Parim D'Aulaire, Ingri & Parim D'Aulaire, Edgar, illus. 1998. 41p. (J). (gr. k-6). reprint ed. pap. 11.95 (978-0-9643803-7-0(4)) Beautiful Feet Bks.

Shields, Charles J. Buffalo Bill Cody. 2001. (Famous Figures of the American Frontier Ser.). (Illus.). 64p. (J). (gr. 3-6). pap. 8.95 (978-0-7910-6498-6(0)); 25.00 (978-0-7910-6497-9(2)) Facts On File, Inc. (Chelsea Hse.).

Spies, Karen Bornemann. Buffalo Bill Cody: Western Legend. 1998. (Historical American Biographies Ser.). (Illus.). 128p. (YA). (gr. 6-12). lib. bdg. 26.60 (978-0-7660-1015-4(5)) Enslow Pubs., Inc.

BUFFALOES

Here are entered works on buffaloes of the eastern hemisphere. Works on the American buffalo are entered under American bison.

Barnett, Tracy. The Buffalo Soldiers. 2002. (History of the Old West Ser.). (Illus.). 64p. (YA). (gr. 5 up). lib. bdg. (978-1-59084-072-6(0)) Mason Crest Pubs.

Group/McGraw-Hill, Wright. Spider & Buffalo: Level N, 6 vols. 128p. (gr. 3-6). 36.95 (978-0-322-05887-3(2)) Wright Group, The.

Huynh, Quang Nhuong. Water Buffalo Days: Growing up in Vietnam. 1999. (978-0-606-15859-6(6)) Tandem Library Bks.

Lawson, Cheri. Chip the Buffalo: Based on a True Story. Lawson, J., illus. Beerntsen, Tammy, photos by. 2006. 32p. (J). lib. bdg. 14.95 (978-1-930580-61-9(4) , Luminary Media Group) Pine Orchard, Inc.

BUFFALOES—FICTION

Aryal, Aimee. Hello, Wilbur! 2007. (J). 14.95 (***978-1-932888-40-9(3)*** Mascot Bks., Inc.

Brauckmann-Towns, Krista, illus. Buffalo Prairie. 2005. (Amazing Animal Adventures Ser.). (J). (ps-2). 36p. 15.95 (978-1-59249-432-3(3) , B7110); 32p. 2.95 incl. cd-rom (978-1-59249-434-7(X) , S7160); 32p. pap. 6.95 (978-1-59249-433-0(1) , S7110) Soundprints.

Buffalo Hunt. 1998. (J). (gr. 5). pap. 3.95 (978-0-439-04480-6(4)) Scholastic, Inc.

Job. Yakari & the White Buffalo. Jeffrey, Erica, tr. Derib, illus. 2007. 48p. pap. 9.99 (***978-1-905460-05-2(8)*** CineBook GBR. *Dist:* Biblio Distribution.

Merrell, Victoria Jane. The Buffalo & the Butterfly. Bilisoly, Harvey, illus. 2002. 12p. (J). (ps-4). 21.95 (978-0-9717556-0-4(4)) VJM Pubns.

Santillo, LuAnn. The Big Hunt. Santillo, LuAnn, ed. 2003. (Half-Pint Kids Readers Ser.). (Illus.). 7p. (J). (ps-1). pap. (978-1-59256-076-9(8)) Half-Pint Kids, Inc.

Sargent, Dave, et al. A Strand of Wampum Vol. 2: Be Honest, 20. Lenoir, Sue, illus. l.t. ed. 2003. (Story Keeper Ser.: 2). 42p. (J). pap. 6.95 (978-1-56763-906-3(2)) Ozark Publishing.

—A Strand of Wampum Vol. 2: Be Honest, 20. Lenoir, Jane, illus. l.t. ed. 2003. (Story Keeper Ser.: 2). 42p. (J). lib. bdg. 22.60 (978-1-56763-905-6(4)) Ozark Publishing.

Sharma, Yojana. Buffalo Thief. 1999. 480p. 29.99 (978-0-385-60013-2(5)) Transworld Publishers Ltd. GBR. *Dist:* Independent Pubs. Group.

Solomon, Selena. Dabu Grows Up. Nona, Dennis, illus. 2002. 28p. (J). pap. 13.60 (978-1-875641-58-1(0)) Magabala Bks. AUS. *Dist:* International Specialized Bk. Services.

Stapleton, E. J. The Calico Buffalo. 2001. 76p. (J). per. 15.95 (978-0-9710283-0-2(3)) BOSC Publishing Co., Inc.

BUFFY, THE VAMPIRE SLAYER (FICTITIOUS CHARACTER)—FICTION

Benson, Amber, et al. Willow & Tara. Watson, Andi, illus. 2003. 80p. (gr. 12 up). pap. 9.95 (978-1-56971-905-3(5)) Dark Horse Comics.

Beyer, Kirsten. One Thing or Your Mother. 2008. (Buffy the Vampire Slayer Ser.). 240p. (YA). mass mkt. 6.99 (***978-1-4169-3632-9(7)*** , Simon Spotlight Entertainment) Simon & Schuster.

Boal, Chris, et al. Autumnals. 2001. (Buffy the Vampire Slayer Ser.). (Illus.). 80p. (YA). pap. 9.95 (978-1-56971-554-3(8)) Dark Horse Comics.

Brereton, Dan. The Dust Waltz. 1998. (Buffy the Vampire Slayer Ser.). (Illus.). 80p. (YA). (gr. 7 up). pap. 9.95 (978-1-56971-342-6(1)) Dark Horse Comics.

Buffy the Vampire Slayer Vol. 1: Script Book, Season 1. 2000. (gr. 7-12). lib. bdg. 23.45 (978-0-613-63265-2(6)) Tandem Library Bks.

Buffy the Vampire Slayer Vol. 2: Script Book, Season 1. 2000. (gr. 7-12). lib. bdg. 23.45 (978-0-613-63261-4(3)) Tandem Library Bks.

Ciencin, Scott. Sweet Sixteen. 2002. (Buffy the Vampire Slayer Ser.: Bk. 24). (Illus.). 240p. (YA). pap. 5.99 (978-0-7434-2732-6(7)) Simon & Schuster.

—Sweet Sixteen. 2002. (gr. 7-12). lib. bdg. 14.15 (978-0-613-74182-8(X)) Tandem Library Bks.

Ciencin, Scott & Ciencin, Denise. Mortal Fear. 2003. (Buffy the Vampire Slayer Ser.). (Illus.). 496p. (YA). pap. 21.95 (978-0-7434-2771-5(8) , Simon Pulse) Simon & Schuster Children's Publishing.

Collins, Craig, et al. Visitors. 1999. (Buffy the Vampire Slayer Ser.: No. 9). 176p. (YA). (gr. 7 up). pap. 5.99 (978-0-671-02628-8(3) , Simon Pulse) Simon & Schuster Children's Publishing.

Fassbender, Tom, et al. Creatures of Habit. Allie, Scott, ed. Fassbender, Tom, tr. 2002. (Angel/Buffy the Vampire Slayer Ser.). (Illus.). 96p. (YA). pap. 17.95 (978-1-56971-563-5(7)) Dark Horse Comics.

Gallagher, Diana G. Bad Bargain. 2006. (Buffy the Vampire Slayer Ser.). 208p. (YA). pap. 6.99 (978-1-4169-1919-3(8) , Simon Spotlight Entertainment) Simon & Schuster.

—Doomsday Deck. 2000. (gr. 7-12). lib. bdg. 14.15 (978-0-613-63278-2(8)) Tandem Library Bks.

—Prime Evil. 2000. (Buffy the Vampire Slayer Ser.: No. 10). 272p. (YA). pap. 5.99 (978-0-671-03930-1(X) , Simon Pulse) Simon & Schuster Children's Publishing.

—Prime Evil. 2000. (gr. 7-12). lib. bdg. 14.15 (978-0-613-63335-2(0)) Tandem Library Bks.

Garton, Ray. Resurrecting Ravana. 2000. (gr. 7-12). lib. bdg. 14.15 (978-0-613-22261-7(X)); 1999. (Buffy the Vampire Slayer Ser.: No. 9). (Illus.). (J). (978-0-606-18366-6(3)) Tandem Library Bks.

Gilman, Laura Anne. Deep Water. 2000. (Buffy the Vampire Slayer Ser.: No. 14). (Illus.). (YA). (gr. 7 up). (978-0-606-18365-9(5)) Tandem Library Bks.

Gloden, et al. Tales of the Slayer, Vol. 3. Simon and Schuster Children's Staff, ed. 2003. (Buffy the Vampire Slayer Ser.). (Illus.). 336p. (YA). pap. 9.99 (978-0-689-86436-0(1) , Simon Pulse) Simon & Schuster Children's Publishing.

Golden, Christopher. Dark Congress. 2007. (Buffy the Vampire Slayer Ser.). 288p. (YA). pap. 9.99 (***978-1-4169-3631-2(9)*** , Simon Spotlight Entertainment) Simon & Schuster.

—Ghost Roads. 1999. (gr. 7-12). lib. bdg. 15.30 (978-0-613-73059-4(3)) Tandem Library Bks.

—Immortal. 2000. (gr. 7-12). lib. bdg. 14.15 (978-0-613-63302-4(4)) Tandem Library Bks.

—King of the Dead. 2001. (gr. 7-12). lib. bdg. 10.65 (978-0-613-63310-9(5)) Tandem Library Bks.

—The Lost Slayer Bind-up. 2003. (Buffy the Vampire Slayer Ser.). 592p. (YA). pap. 7.99 (978-0-7434-1226-1(5) , Simon Pulse) Simon & Schuster Children's Publishing.

—Oz: Into the Wild. 2002. (Buffy the Vampire Slayer Ser.). 288p. (YA). pap. 6.99 (978-0-7434-0038-1(0) , Simon Pulse) Simon & Schuster Children's Publishing.

—Oz: Into the Wild. 2002. (gr. 7-12). lib. bdg. 15.30 (978-0-613-63328-4(8)) Tandem Library Bks.

—The Wisdom of War. 2002. (Buffy the Vampire Slayer Ser.). 416p. (YA). pap. 6.99 (978-0-7434-2760-9(2) , Simon Pulse) Simon & Schuster Children's Publishing.

—Wisdom of War. 2002. (gr. 7-12). lib. bdg. 15.30 (978-0-613-63372-7(5)) Tandem Library Bks.

Golden, Christopher & Holder, Nancy. Ghost Roads, 3 vols. 1999. (Buffy the Vampire Slayer Ser.: No. 2). 384p. (YA). pap. 6.99 (978-0-671-02749-0(2) , Simon Pulse) Simon & Schuster Children's Publishing.

—The Watchers Guide Buffy the Vampire Slayer, Vol. 1. rev. ed. 1998. (Buffy the Vampire Slayer Ser.). (Illus.). 304p. (YA). pap. 17.95 (978-0-671-02433-8(7) , Simon Pulse) Simon & Schuster Children's Publishing.

Golden, Christopher, et al. The Blood of Carthage. 2001. (Buffy the Vampire Slayer Ser.). 128p. (YA). pap. 12.95 (978-1-56971-534-5(3)) Dark Horse Comics.

—The Origin. 1999. (Buffy the Vampire Slayer Ser.). 80p. (YA). (gr. 7 up). pap. 9.95 (978-1-56971-429-4(0)) Dark Horse Comics.

Holder, Nancy. The Angel Chronicles. (Buffy the Vampire Slayer Ser.: No. 6). (Illus.). (YA). (gr. 7 up). Vol. 1. 1998. 224p. pap. 5.99 (978-0-671-02133-7(8)); Vol. 3. 1999. 192p. pap. 5.99 (978-0-671-02631-8(3)) Simon & Schuster Children's Publishing. (Simon Pulse).

—Blood & Fog. 2003. (Buffy the Vampire Slayer Ser.: Vol. 16). 304p. (YA). mass mkt. 6.99 (978-0-7434-0039-8(9) , Simon Pulse) Simon & Schuster Children's Publishing.

—Book of Fours. 2002. (gr. 7-12). lib. bdg. 14.15 (978-0-613-63260-7(5)) Tandem Library Bks.

—Buffy the Vampire Slayer. 1999. (gr. 7-12). lib. bdg. 14.15 (978-0-613-73064-8(X)) Tandem Library Bks.

—Carnival of Souls. 2006. (Buffy the Vampire Slayer Ser.). 320p. (YA). pap. 15.95 (978-1-4169-1182-1(0) , Simon Spotlight Entertainment) Simon & Schuster.

—The Evil That Men Do. 2000. (Buffy the Vampire Slayer Ser.: No. 6). 352p. (YA). pap. 6.99 (978-0-671-02635-6(6) , Simon Pulse) Simon & Schuster Children's Publishing.

—Evil That Men Do. 2000. (gr. 7-12). lib. bdg. 15.30 (978-0-613-27810-2(0)) Tandem Library Bks.

—Heat. 2005. (Buffy/Angel Crossover Ser.). 464p. (YA). pap. 6.99 (978-0-689-86906-8(1) , Simon Spotlight Entertainment) Simon & Schuster.

—Journals of Rupert Giles. 2002. (gr. 7-12). lib. bdg. 14.15 (978-0-613-63306-2(7)) Tandem Library Bks.

—Unseen: The Burning. 2001. (gr. 7-12). lib. bdg. 15.30 (978-0-613-63361-1(X)) Tandem Library Bks.

Holder, Nancy & Matsuda, Jeff. Keep Me in Mind. 2005. (Buffy the Vampire Slayer Ser.). 256p. (YA). pap. 6.99 (978-0-689-86956-3(8) , Simon Spotlight Entertainment) Simon & Schuster.

Holder, Nancy, et al. Tales of the Slayer, Vol. 1. 2001. (Buffy the Vampire Slayer Ser.: Vol. 22). 288p. (YA). pap. 9.99 (978-0-7434-0045-9(3) , Simon Pulse) Simon & Schuster Children's Publishing.

Laurence, James. Faith Trials. 2001. (gr. 7-12). lib. bdg. 14.15 (978-0-613-63284-3(2)) Tandem Library Bks.

Lobdell, Scott. Note from the Underground. 2003. (Angel/Buffy the Vampire Slayer Ser.). (Illus.). 104p. (YA). (gr. 7 up). pap. 12.95 (978-1-56971-888-9(1)) Dark Horse Comics.

Marriotte, Jeff. Door to Alternity. 2001. (gr. 7-12). lib. bdg. 15.30 (978-0-613-63279-9(6)) Tandem Library Bks.

Moesta, Rebecca. Little Things. 2002. (Buffy the Vampire Slayer Ser.: Bk. 26). 208p. (YA). pap. 5.99 (978-0-7434-2736-4(X) , Simon Pulse) Simon & Schuster Children's Publishing.

—Little Things. 2002. (gr. 7-12). lib. bdg. 14.15 (978-0-613-63313-0(X)) Tandem Library Bks.

Navarro, Yvonne. Paleo. 2000. (Buffy the Vampire Slayer Ser.: No. 11). 272p. (YA). pap. 6.99 (978-0-7434-0034-3(8) , Simon Pulse) Simon & Schuster Children's Publishing.

—Paleo. 2000. (gr. 7-12). lib. bdg. 15.30 (978-0-613-63329-1(6)) Tandem Library Bks.

—Tempted Champions. 2001. (Buffy the Vampire Slayer Ser.: Vol. 13). (Illus.). 256p. (YA). pap. 6.99 (978-0-7434-0036-7(4) , Simon Pulse) Simon & Schuster Children's Publishing.

—Tempted Champions. 2002. (gr. 7-12). lib. bdg. 15.30 (978-0-613-63352-9(0)) Tandem Library Bks.

—The Willow Files, Vol. 1. 1999. (Buffy the Vampire Slayer Ser.: No. 13). (Illus.). (YA). (gr. 7 up). (978-0-606-18367-3(1)) Tandem Library Bks.

Odom, Mel. Buffy the Vampire Slayer: Unnatural Selection. 1999. (J). (978-0-606-17065-9(0)) Tandem Library Bks.

—Crossings. 2002. (Buffy the Vampire Slayer Ser.: Bk. 25). (Illus.). 256p. (YA). pap. 5.99 (978-0-7434-2734-0(3) , Simon Pulse) Simon & Schuster Children's Publishing.

—Cursed. 2003. (Buffy the Vampire Slayer & Angel Crossover Ser.). 448p. mass mkt. 7.99 (978-0-689-86437-7(X) , Simon Pulse) Simon & Schuster Children's Publishing.

—Redemption. 2000. (gr. 7-12). lib. bdg. 14.15 (978-0-613-28038-9(5)) Tandem Library Bks.

—Revenant. 2001. (Buffy the Vampire Slayer Ser.: No. 12). 400p. (YA). pap. 6.99 (978-0-7434-0035-0(6) , Simon Pulse) Simon & Schuster Children's Publishing.

—Revenant. 2001. (gr. 7-12). lib. bdg. 15.30 (978-0-613-63340-6(7)) Tandem Library Bks.

—Tales of the Slayer. 2001. (gr. 7-12). lib. bdg. 17.65 (978-0-613-63351-2(2)) Tandem Library Bks.

Petrie, Doug. Ring of Fire. 2000. (Buffy the Vampire Slayer Ser.). (Illus.). 80p. (YA). (gr. 7 up). pap. 9.95 (978-1-56971-482-9(7)) Dark Horse Comics.

—Ring of Fire. 2000. (gr. 7-12). lib. bdg. 18.75 (978-0-613-50992-3(7)) Tandem Library Bks.

Ruditis, Paul. The Watcher's Guide, Vol. 3. 2004. (Buffy the Vampire Slayer Ser.). (Illus.). 368p. (YA). pap. 17.95 (978-0-689-86984-6(3) , Simon Spotlight Entertainment) Simon & Schuster.

Scott, Stefanie. Meet the Stars of Buffy the Vampire Slayer. 1998. (Illus.). 128p. (J). (gr. 6-8). pap. 4.99 (978-0-590-51477-4(6)) Scholastic, Inc.

Simon and Schuster Children's Staff. Tales of the Slayer, Vol. 4. 2004. (Buffy the Vampire Slayer Ser.). 272p. (YA). pap. 14.95 (978-0-689-86955-6(X) , Simon Spotlight Entertainment) Simon & Schuster.

Stafford, Nikki. Bite Me! An Unofficial Guide to the World of Buffy the Vampire Slayer. 1998. (Illus.). 250p. pap. 19.95 (978-1-55022-361-3(5)) ECW Pr. CAN. *Dist:* Independent Pubs. Group.

Tales of the Slayer. 2003. (gr. 7-12). lib. bdg. 18.80 (978-0-613-61822-9(X)) Tandem Library Bks.

Vornholt, John. Seven Crows. 2003. (gr. 7-12). lib. bdg. 15.30 (978-0-613-66540-7(6)) Tandem Library Bks.

Watson, Andi, et al. Bad Blood. 2000. (Buffy the Vampire Slayer Ser.). (Illus.). 88p. (YA). (gr. 7 up). pap. 9.95 (978-1-56971-445-4(2)) Dark Horse Comics.

—Crash Test Demons. 2000. (Buffy the Vampire Slayer Ser.). (Illus.). 80p. (YA). (gr. 7 up). pap. 9.95 (978-1-56971-461-4(4)) Dark Horse Comics.

—The Remaining Sunlight. 1999. (Buffy the Vampire Slayer Ser.). (Illus.). 88p. (YA). (gr. 7 up). pap. 9.95 (978-1-56971-354-9(5)) Dark Horse Comics.

—Uninvited Guests. 1999. (Buffy the Vampire Slayer Ser.). (Illus.). 96p. (YA). (gr. 7 up). pap. 10.95 (978-1-56971-436-2(3)) Dark Horse Comics.

Whedon, Joss. Buffy the Vampire Slayer Vol. 2: Script Book, Season 2. 2001. lib. bdg. 23.45 (978-0-613-63266-9(4)) Tandem Library Bks.

—The Gift. 2005. (Illus.). 96p. (YA). (ps-7). pap. 7.99 (978-1-59816-029-1(X), Tokyopop Adult) TOKYOPOP, Inc.

Whedon, Joss & Others. Buffy the Vampire Slayer Omnibus Volume 1. 2007. (Illus.). 296p. (YA). pap. 24.95 (***978-1-59307-784-6(X)***) Dark Horse Comics.

BUGS

see Insects

BUGS BUNNY (FICTITIOUS CHARACTER)—FICTION

Carrotblanca. Date not set. (J). 7.98 incl. audio (978-1-57042-320-8(2)) Warner Brothers Records.

Glassman, Jackie. Looney Tunes Back in Action Reader. 2003. (gr. k-3). lib. bdg. 11.80 (978-0-613-72242-1(6)) Tandem Library Bks.

Markas, Jenny. Looney Tunes Back in Action Junior Novelization. 2003. (Looney Tunes Ser.). 80p. (J). pap. 4.99 (978-0-439-52136-9(X), Scholastic Paperbacks) Scholastic, Inc.

Mason, Jane. Looney Tunes Back in Action Movie Storybook. 2003. (gr. k-3). lib. bdg. 14.15 (978-0-613-72238-4(8)) Tandem Library Bks.

McCann, Jesse Leon. Bugs Bunny. 2001. (Looney Tunes Teacher's Pets Ser.). (Illus.). 32p. (J). (gr. 1-5). 4.95 (978-0-439-29624-3(2), Tangerine Pr.) Scholastic, Inc.

—Looney Tunes Back in Action. 2003. (gr. k-3). lib. bdg. 11.25 (978-0-613-72241-4(8)) Tandem Library Bks.

—Looney Tunes Back in Action Joke Book. 2003. (gr. 3-6). lib. bdg. 12.40 (978-0-613-72240-7(X)) Tandem Library Bks.

McCann, Jesse Leon & Mc Cann, Jesse Leon. Looney Tunes Back in Action Joke Book. 2003. (Looney Tunes Ser.). (Illus.). 64p. (J). pap. 4.50 (978-0-439-52138-3(6), Scholastic Paperbacks) Scholastic, Inc.

BUILDING

see also Architecture; Carpentry; Engineering

Aaseng, Nathan. Construction: Building the Impossible. 2000. (Innovators Ser.). (Illus.). 144p. (YA). (gr. 6-10). lib. bdg. 21.95 (978-1-881508-59-5(5)) Oliver Pr., Inc.

Adamson, Heather. A Day in the Life of a Construction Worker. 2003. (First Facts Ser.). (Illus.). 24p. (J). 15.95 (978-0-7368-2505-4(3)) Capstone Pr., Inc.

Anderson, Jenna. How It Happens at the Building Site. Wolfe, Bob & Wolfe, Diane, photos by. 2004. (How It Happens Ser.). (Illus.). 32p. (J). (gr. 2-5). lib. bdg. 19.95 (978-1-881508-95-3(1)) Oliver Pr., Inc.

Bergstrom, Joan M. Dynamite Dream Designs. 1999. (Illus.). (J). (gr. k-6). 29.95 (978-1-931042-02-4(0)) Activities Club, Inc., The.

Boekhoff, P. M. What Does a Construction Worker Do? 2006. (What Does a Community Helper Do? Ser.). (Illus.). 24p. (J). lib. bdg. 21.26 (978-0-7660-2326-0(5), Enslow Elementary) Enslow Pubs., Inc.

Building. (Make it Work Ser.). 42p. (J). (gr. 4-8). pap. (978-1-882210-45-9(X)) Action Publishing, Inc.

Caney, Steven. Steven Caney's Ultimate Building Book. House, Lauren, illus. 2006. 608p. (J). (gr. 4-8). 29.95 (978-0-7624-0409-4(4), Running Pr. Kids) Running Pr. Bk. Pubs.

Canizares, Susan & Moreton, Daniel. Construction Site. 2000. (Illus.). (J). pap. (978-0-439-15373-7(5)) Scholastic, Inc.

Clements, Gillian. A Picture History of Great Buildings. 2008. (Illus.). 64p. (J). 19.95 (***978-1-84507-488-3(2)***) Lincoln, Frances Ltd. GBR. *Dist:* Perseus Distribution.

Construction Workers. (Community Helpers Ser.). 24p. (J). 6.95 (978-0-7368-8030-5(5)) Capstone Pr., Inc.

Construir. (Coleccion Mundo Maravilloso). (SPA., Illus.). (J). (gr. 2-4). (978-84-348-5208-2(X), SM8405) SM Ediciones ESP. *Dist:* Lectorum Pubns., Inc.

Craats, Rennay. The Science of Construction: Style, Structures, & Building. 2003. (J). lib. bdg. 27.14 (978-0-7398-6993-2(0)) Raintree.

Dahl, Michael. One Big Building: A Counting Book about Construction. Ouren, Todd, illus. 2004. (Know Your Numbers Ser.). 24p. (C). (gr. k-3). 22.60 (978-1-4048-0580-4(X), 1229521) Picture Window Bks.

Day, Eileen. I'm Good at Building. 2003. (Heinemann Read & Learn Ser.). (Illus.). 24p. (J). pap. 5.25 (978-1-4034-3443-2(3)); lib. bdg. 18.50 (978-1-4034-0899-0(8)) Heinemann Library.

—I'm Good at Building. 2003. (gr. k-3). lib. bdg. 13.30 (978-0-613-70654-4(4)) Tandem Library Bks.

—Soy Bueno para Construir. 2003. (SPA.). 24p. pap. 5.25 (978-1-4034-3576-7(6)) Heinemann Library.

Deedrick, Tami. Construction Workers. l.t. ed. 1998. (Community Helpers Ser.). (Illus.). 24p. (J). (gr. k-3). pap. 14.00 (978-0-516-21258-6(3), Children's Pr.) Scholastic Library Publishing.

Del Cemento al Puente (From Cement to Bridge) 2006. (De Principio a Fin Ser.). (SPA.). 24p. (J). 18.60 (978-0-8225-6498-0(X), Ediciones Lerner) Lerner Publishing Group.

Drinkard, Lawson. Hiding in a Fort. 1999. (J). (978-0-606-17088-8(X)) Tandem Library Bks.

Edificios: Libros Aventuras (Adventure Books) 2000. (MacMillan/McGraw-Hill. Estudios Sociales Ser.). (ENG & SPA.). (gr. 1 up). (978-0-02-148665-6(4)) Macmillan/McGraw-Hill Schl. Div.

Elder, Jamie. Construction: Lift-A-Flap Fun. Wieland, Don, tr. Wieland, Don, illus. 2002. (Leap Frog Ser.). 12p. (J). bds. 12.98 (978-0-7853-6332-3(7), 7162100) Publications International, Ltd.

Evans, David & Williams, Claudette. Building Things. (Let's Explore Science Ser.). (Illus.). (J). 12.95 (978-0-590-74944-2(7)) Scholastic, Inc.

Flanagan, Alice K. Mr. Paul & Mr. Luecke Build Communities. 1999. (gr. k-3). lib. bdg. 15.25 (978-0-613-54032-2(8)) Tandem Library Bks.

Flanagan, Romie. Mr. Paul & Mr. Luecke Build Communities. Flanagan, Alice K., ed. 2000. (Our Neighborhood Ser.). (Illus.). 32p. (J). (gr. 1-2). pap. 6.95 (978-0-516-26540-7(7), Children's Pr.) Scholastic Library Publishing.

Ghione, Yvette. This Is Daniel Cook at the Construction Site. Gagnon, Céleste, illus. 2007. (This Is Daniel Cook Ser.). 24p. (J). (ps-1). (***978-1-55453-084-7(9)***); (***978-1-55453-083-0(0)***) Kids Can Pr., Ltd.

Good, Keith. Build It! Activities for Setting up Super Structures. 1999. (Design It! Ser.). (Illus.). 30p. (gr. 4-8). lib. bdg. 21.27 (978-0-8225-3567-6(X)) Lerner Publishing Group.

Goodhew, Jeanne, prod. Building Basics: An Interactive Guide to the Fundamentals of Construction. (YA). cd-rom 99.95 (978-0-7365-9980-1(0)) Films Media Group.

Grimshaw, Caroline. Buildings. 2000. (Connections Ser.). (Illus.). 32p. (J). (gr. 3-6). 9.95 (978-1-58728-314-7(X)); pap. 5.95 (978-1-58728-320-8(4)) T&N Children's Publishing. (Two Can Publishing).

Grossartige Bauwerke. (GER., Illus.). 40p. (978-3-411-08151-6(1)) Bibliographisches Institut & F. A. Brockhaus AG DEU. *Dist:* i.b.d., Ltd.

Hamilton, Sue L. Buildings: A Pictorial History of the Past One Thousand Years. 2000. (Millennium Ser.). (Illus.). 48p. (J). (gr. 3-8). lib. bdg. 25.65 (978-1-57765-363-9(7), ABDO & Daughters) ABDO Publishing Co.

Haslam, Andrew, et al. Building. (Make It Work! Ser.). (Illus.). 48p. (J). pap. 7.99 (978-0-590-24616-3(X)) Scholastic, Inc.

Hayward, Linda. Day in the Life of a Builder. 2001. (gr. k-3). lib. bdg. 11.80 (978-0-613-35096-9(0)) Tandem Library Bks.

Hayward, Linda & Dorling Kindersley Publishing Staff. Jobs People Do: A Day in the Life of a Builder. 2001. (Readers Ser.). (Illus.). 32p. (J). (gr. 5-3). pap. 3.99 (978-0-7894-7363-9(1)); (ps-3). 12.95 (978-0-7894-7364-6(X)) Dorling Kindersley Publishing, Inc.

Hickle, Victoria. Tonka Construction Time: Book & Magnet Fun. Klavins, Uldis, illus. 2002. (Tonka Ser.). 8p. (J). bds. 7.99 (978-0-439-33474-7(8)) Scholastic, Inc.

Hoban, Tana. Construction Zone. Hoban, Tana, illus. 1999. (Illus.). 15p. (J). (ps-2). 6.99 (978-0-688-16918-3(X)) HarperCollins Pubs.

Hofer, Charles. Construction Zone! Noisy Trucks at Work. Giraffe, Red, illus. 2005. (Tonka Ser.). 10p. bds. 15.99 (978-0-7944-0643-1(2)) Reader's Digest Assn., Inc., The.

Hudson, Cheryl Willis. Construction Zone. Sobol, Richard, photos by. 2006. (Illus.). 32p. (J). (ps-2). 15.99 (978-0-7636-2684-6(8)) Candlewick Pr.

Kalman, Bobbie. Everyday Structures from a to Z. 2000. (gr. 3-6). lib. bdg. 16.40 (978-0-613-21505-3(2)) Tandem Library Bks.

Klobuchar, Lisa. How Did They Do That? 2005. (Real Deal Ser.). (Illus.). 32p. (J). pap. (978-0-7608-9633-4(X)) Sundance/Newbridge Educational Publishing.

Klove, Lars. Trucks That Build. 1999. (Ready-to-Read Ser.). (J). (978-0-606-19731-1(1)) Tandem Library Bks.

Landau, Elaine. The Statue of Liberty. 2008. (True Book-trade;: American History Ser.). 48p. (J). pap. 6.95 (***978-0-531-14785-6(1)***, Children's Pr.) Scholastic Library Publishing.

Lee, Brian, illus. A Construction Site. 2005. (What's Inside Ser.). (J). (***978-0-7607-6570-8(7)***) backpackbook.

Litchfield, Jo & Brooks, Felicity. Building Site. 2004. (Chunky Board Bks.). (Illus.). 10p. (J). 4.95 (978-0-7945-0347-5(0), Usborne) EDC Publishing.

Llewellyn, Claire. Concrete. 2002. (Material World Ser.). (J). (gr. 2-4). pap. 6.95 (978-0-531-14833-4(5)); (Illus.). 32p. 24.00 (978-0-531-14634-7(0)) Scholastic Library Publishing. (Watts, Franklin).

—Concrete. 2002. (gr. 3-6). lib. bdg. 15.25 (978-0-613-53596-0(0)) Tandem Library Bks.

Lynette, Rachel. Ice Hotels. 2006. (J). (978-0-7377-3067-8(6), Greenhaven Pr., Inc.) Thomson Gale.

Macaulay, David. Building Big. 2004. (Illus.). 192p. (YA). (gr. 5 up). reprint ed. pap. 12.95 (978-0-618-46527-9(8), Walter Lorraine) Houghton Mifflin Co. Trade & Reference Div.

—Building Big, 5 cass.; set. 2004. (Building Big Ser.). (gr. 4 up). pap., act. bk. ed. 69.95 incl. VHS (978-1-57807-544-7(0), WG965) WGBH Boston Video.

Malam, John. Super Structures. 2000. (Fast Forward Ser.). (Illus.). 32p. (J). (gr. 4-8). 29.00 (978-0-531-11875-7(4), Watts, Franklin) Scholastic Library Publishing.

Mason, Adrienne. Build it Structures Systems. Davila, Claudia, illus. 2006. 32p. (978-1-55337-836-5(9)); (978-1-55337-835-8(0)) Kids Can Pr., Ltd.

Mason, Paul. The World's Most Amazing Buildings. 2006. (Illus.). 32p. (J). (978-1-4109-2522-0(6)); pap. (978-1-4109-2527-5(7)) Steck-Vaughn.

Mayell, Mark. Building Collapses. 2004. (Man-Made Disasters Ser.). (Illus.). 112p. (J). 29.95 (978-1-59018-055-6(0)) Thomson Gale.

McMillan, Dana. Construction Site: A Complete Theme Unit Including Learning Centers. Mitchell, Judy, ed. Rojas, Mary Galan, illus. 2000. 32p. (J). pap., tchr. ed. 5.95 (978-1-57310-238-4(5)) Teaching & Learning Co.

Miller, Heather. Construction Worker. 2003. (This Is What I Want to Be Ser.). (Illus.). 24p. (ps-1). (J). lib. bdg. 18.50 (978-1-4034-0365-0(1)); pap. 5.25 (978-1-4034-0587-6(5)) Heinemann Library.

—Obrero de Construccion. 2003. (Esto es lo Que Quiero Ser (This Is What I Want to Be) Ser.). (SPA., Illus.). 24p. (J). (ps-1). lib. bdg. 18.50 (978-1-4034-0375-9(9)) Heinemann Library.

Nelson, Robin. From Tree to House. 2004. (Start to Finish Ser.). (J). pap. 4.95 (978-0-8225-2147-1(4)); 18.60 (978-0-8225-1392-6(7), Lerner Pubns.) Lerner Publishing Group.

O'Connor, Rachel. Construction Worker. 2004. (Great Jobs Ser.). (Illus.). 48p. (J). 24.00 (978-0-516-24089-3(7), Children's Pr.) Scholastic Library Publishing.

One Big Building. (Know Your Numbers Ser.). 24p. (J). 7.95 (978-1-4048-1120-1(6)) Picture Window Bks.

O'Neil, Sarah. Making Concrete. 1999. (gr. k-3). lib. bdg. 11.80 (978-0-613-19391-7(1)) Tandem Library Bks.

Oxlade, Chris. Science Museum Book Construction. (Illus.). 128p. (J). pap. 8.99 (978-0-340-68994-3(3), Hodder & Stoughton) Hodder General Publishing Division GBR. *Dist:* Trafalgar Square Publishing.

Oxlade, Chris, contrib. by. Stadiums. 2000. (Building Amazing Structures Ser.). (Illus.). 32p. (J). (gr. 3-5). lib. bdg. 22.79 (978-1-57572-279-5(8)) Heinemann Library.

Pallotta, Jerry. The Construction Alphabet Book. Bolster, Rob, illus. 2006. (Jerry Pallotta's Alphabet Bks.). 32p. (J). (gr. 4). 16.95 (978-1-57091-437-9(0)); (ps-4). pap. 7.95 (978-1-57091-438-6(9)) Charlesbridge Publishing, Inc.

Parent, Nancy. Er. 2003. (ps-2). lib. bdg. 11.80 (978-0-613-85464-1(0)) Tandem Library Bks.

Parker, Janice. The Science of Structures. 2001. (Living Science Ser.). (Illus.). 32p. (J). (gr. 2 up). lib. bdg. 24.67 (978-0-8368-2792-7(9)) Stevens, Gareth Inc.

—The Science of Structures. 2003. (Living Science Ser.). (Illus.). 32p. (J). (gr. 1-3). pap. 7.95 (978-1-930954-26-7(3)) Weigl Pubs., Inc.

Pascoe, Elaine, ed. Thinking Big: America's Greatest Constructions. 2003. (Super Structures of the World Ser.). (Illus.). 48p. (J). 24.95 (978-1-56711-870-4(4)); 11.20 (978-1-4103-0193-2(1)) Thomson Gale. (Blackbirch Pr., Inc.).

Pattrick, Steve. Building: KinderFacts Individual Title Six-Packs. (Kinderstarters Ser.). 8p. (ps-1). 21.00 (978-0-7635-8742-0(7)) Rigby Education.

Petruccio, Steven James. At the Construction Site. 2004. 32p. (J). pap. 2.95 (978-0-486-43661-6(6)) Dover Pubns., Inc.

Phidal Publishing Staff, ed. Construction Crew, 3 vols. 2004. (Read & Roll Ser.). (Illus.). 10p. (J). bds. (978-2-7643-0208-8(8)) Phidal Publishing, Inc./Editions Phidal, Inc.

Rau, Dana Meachen. Builders. 2007. (Tools We Use Ser.). 32p. (J). lib. bdg. 22.79 (***978-0-7614-2656-1(6)***, Benchmark Bks.) Cavendish, Marshall Corp.

—Builders/Los Constructores. 2007. (Tools We Use/ Instrumentos de Trabajo Ser.). (SPA & ENG.). 32p. (J). lib. bdg. 22.79 (***978-0-7614-2821-3(6)***, Benchmark Bks.) Cavendish, Marshall Corp.

Richards, Julie. Stadiums & Domes. 2003. 32p. (J). lib. bdg. 24.25 (978-1-58340-349-5(3)) Smart Apple Media.

Ring, Susan. Quien Construye? 2005. Tr. of Who Builds?. (SPA., Illus.). 16p. (J). (gr. 2 up). lib. bdg. 15.93 (978-0-7368-4170-2(9)) Capstone Pr., Inc.

Sadler, Wendy. Construction Toys. 2005. (Heinemann First Library). (Illus.). 32p. (J). (ps). lib. bdg. 25.36 (978-1-4034-6826-0(5)); pap. (978-1-4034-6832-1(X)) Heinemann Library.

Schaefer, Lola M. Construction Site. 2000. (Who Works Here? Ser.). (Illus.). 32p. (J). (gr. 1-3). lib. bdg. 21.36 (978-1-57572-516-1(9)) Heinemann Library.

Sheehan, Thomas F. Bloques de Piedra. 2005. (Ciencia Citadina Ser.). (SPA.). (978-1-59515-663-1(1)) Rourke Publishing, LLC.

Shuter, Jane. Builders & Craftsmen. 1999. (Ancient Egypt Ser.). 32p. (J). (gr. 3-5). lib. bdg. 22.79 (978-1-57572-728-8(5)) Heinemann Library.

Smith, David R. & Interlocking Concrete Pavement Institute Staff. Patios, Driveways, & Plazas: The Pattern Language of Concrete Pavers. 2002. (Illus.). 192p. (gr. 10-13). pap. 29.95 (978-0-7643-1561-9(7)) Schiffer Publishing, Ltd.

Snyder, Margaret. Construction Site. deluxe ed. 1999. (Talking Pages Ser.). (Illus.). 12p. (J). (ps-3). 8.95 (978-1-58224-004-6(3)) Futech Interactive Products, Inc.

Sterling Publishing Company Staff. Make a Small Treehouse. 1999. (Balloon Ser.). (Illus.). 8p. (gr. k-2). pap. 2.95 (978-0-8069-1949-2(3)) Sterling Publishing Co., Inc.

Stone, Lynn M. Farm Buildings. 2002. (Life on the Farm Ser.). (Illus.). 24p. (J). (gr. 1-4). 14.95 (978-1-58952-091-2(2)) Rourke Publishing, LLC.

—Houses. 2001. (How are They Built? Ser.). (Illus.). 48p. (J). (gr. 4-8). lib. bdg. 29.93 (978-1-58952-137-7(4)) Rourke Publishing, LLC.

—Skyscrapers. 2001. (How are They Built? Ser.). (Illus.). 48p. (J). (gr. 4-8). lib. bdg. 29.93 (978-1-58952-139-1(0)) Rourke Publishing, LLC.

Stradling, Jan. Buildings for a Purpose: Level K, 6 vols., Vol. 2. (First Explorers Ser.). 24p. (gr. 1-2). 34.95 (978-0-7699-1456-5(X)) Shortland Pubns. (U. S. A.) Inc.

Tarsky, Sue. The Busy Building Book. 2000. (Illus.). (J). (978-0-606-18834-0(7)) Tandem Library Bks.

Thomas, Mark. A Day with a Brick Layer. 2001. (Welcome Bks.). (Illus.). 24p. (J). (ps-2). pap. 4.95 (978-0-516-23060-3(3), Children's Pr.) Scholastic Library Publishing.

—Day with a Bricklayer. 2001. (gr. k-3). lib. bdg. 12.95 (978-0-613-58757-0(X)) Tandem Library Bks.

—The Maracanaa: World's Largest Stadium. 2002. (Reading Power Ser.). (Illus.). 24p. (J). (gr. 1). lib. bdg. 17.25 (978-0-8239-5992-1(9), PowerKids Pr.) Rosen Publishing Group, Inc., The.

Las torres gemelas Petronas: Individual Title Six-Packs. (On Deck en Espanol Ser.).Tr. of Petronas Twin Towers. (SPA.). 24p. (gr. 4-5). 35.00 (978-0-7578-6441-4(4)) Rigby Education.

Trumbauer, Lisa. We Need Construction Workers. Saunders-Smith, Gail, ed. 2003. (Helpers in Our Community Ser.). (Illus.). 24p. (J). (gr. k-1). lib. bdg. 15.93 (978-0-7368-1649-6(6), Pebble Bks.) Capstone Pr., Inc.

VanVoorst, Jennifer. Who Builds? 2003. (Illus.). 17p. (J). 15.93 (978-0-7368-2924-3(5)) Yellow Umbrella Pr.

Whitehouse, Patricia. Que Puede Construir? Abello, Patricia, tr. 2004. 24p. (J). 12.95 (978-1-4034-4390-8(4)) Heinemann Library.

—What Can Build? 2003. (Illus.). 24p. (J). pap. 5.25 (978-1-4034-4377-9(7)); lib. bdg. 18.50 (978-1-4034-4370-0(X)) Heinemann Library.

—What Can Build? 2003. (ps-2). lib. bdg. 28.65 (978-0-613-87966-8(X)) Tandem Library Bks.

Who Builds? 2006. (Yellow Umbrella Science Ser.). 8,16p. (J). 6.50 (978-0-7368-2883-3(4)) Red Brick Learning.

Wilkinson, Philip. Building. 2000. (Eyewitness Bks.). (Illus.). 64p. (J). (gr. 4-7). 15.99 (978-0-7894-6026-4(2)) Dorling Kindersley Publishing, Inc.

Wilkinson, Philip & Donati, Paolo. Amazing Buildings. (Illus.). (J). pap. 21.95 (978-0-590-74608-3(1)) Scholastic, Inc.

Wilkinson, Philip & Dorling Kindersley Publishing Staff. Building. 2000. (Eyewitness Bks.). (Illus.). 64p. (J). (gr. 4-7). lib. bdg. 19.99 (978-0-7894-6607-5(4)) Dorling Kindersley Publishing, Inc.

Woods, Mary B. & Woods, Michael. Ancient Construction: From Tents to Towers. 2005. (Ancient Technology Ser.). (Illus.). 96p. (gr. 6-12). 25.26 (978-0-8225-2998-9(X)) Lerner Publishing Group.

BUILDING—FICTION

Beaty, Andrea. Iggy Peck, Architect. Roberts, David, illus. 2007. 32p. (J). (ps-3). 15.95 (978-0-8109-1106-2(X), Abrams Bks. for Young Readers) Abrams, Harry N., Inc.

Beil, Karen Magnuson. Jack's House. Wohnoutka, Mike, illus. 2008. (J). (***978-0-8234-1913-5(4)***) Holiday Hse., Inc.

Cabot, Meg. Project Princess. 2003. (Princess Diaries; Vol. 4 1/2). 64p. (J). (gr. 7 up). pap. 2.99 (978-0-06-057131-3(4)) HarperCollins Pubs.

—Project Princess. 2003. (Princess Diaries: Vol. 4 1/2). (gr. 7-12). lib. bdg. 10.65 (978-0-613-67515-4(0)) Tandem Library Bks.

Crum, Shutta. The House in the Meadow. Billin-Frye, Paige, illus. 2003. 32p. (J). (ps-2). 16.95 (978-0-8075-3393-2(9)) Whitman, Albert & Co.

Friskey, Margaret. Surprise on Wheels. Patton, Lucia, illus. 2004. reprint ed. pap. 15.95 (978-1-4191-1496-0(4)) Kessinger Publishing, LLC.

Fry, Sonali. Bang! Clang! 2005. (Ready-to-Read Ser.). (J). pap. 3.99 (978-0-689-87419-2(7), Simon Spotlight) Simon & Schuster Children's Publishing.

High, Linda Oatman. Barn Savers. Lewin, Ted, illus. 2003. 32p. (J). (gr. 2-4). 15.95 (978-1-56397-403-8(7)) Boyds Mills Pr.

Hofer, Charles. Construction Zone! Little People. Durk, Jim, illus. 10p. (J). bds. 7.98 (978-0-7853-4791-0(7)) Publications International, Ltd.

Hopkinson, Deborah. Sky Boys: Building the Empire State Building. Ransome, James E., illus. 2006. 48p. (J). (ps-4). lib. bdg. 18.99 (978-0-375-93610-4(6), Schwartz & Wade Bks.) Random Hse. Children's Bks.

—Sky Boys: How They Built the Empire State Building. Ransome, James E., illus. 2006. 48p. (J). (ps-4). 16.95 (978-0-375-83610-7(1), Schwartz & Wade Bks.) Random Hse. Children's Bks.

Johnson, Angela. Those Building Men. Moser, Barry, illus. 2001. 32p. (J). (ps-3). pap. 16.95 (978-0-590-66521-6(9), Blue Sky Pr., The) Scholastic, Inc.

Knopf, Susan. Barney Backhoe Love to Build. 2006. (John Deere Board Books Ser.). (Illus.). 8p. (J). pap. 5.95 (978-0-7624-2631-7(4), Running Pr. Kids) Running Pr. Bk. Pubs.

Lewis, Kevin. Lot at the End of My Block. Cartwright, Reg, illus. 2001. 32p. (ps-1). 15.49 (978-0-7868-2512-7(X)) Hyperion Bks. for Children.

Monroe, Chris. Monkey with a Tool Belt. 2008. (J). lib. bdg. (***978-0-8225-7631-0(7)***) Univ. of Minnesota Pr.

Nevius, Carol. Building with Dad. Thomson, Bill, illus. 2006. 32p. (J). (ps-3). 16.99 (978-0-7614-5312-3(1)) Cavendish, Marshall Corp.

Parish, Herman. Amelia Bedelia under Construction. Sweat, Lynn, illus. (I Can Read Bks.). 64p. (J). 2007. pap. 3.99 (***978-0-06-084346-5(2)***, Harper Trophy); 2006. 15.99 (978-0-06-084344-1(6)); 2006. lib. bdg. 16.89 (978-0-06-084345-8(4)) HarperCollins Pubs.

Reinhardt, Dana. How to Build a House. 2008. 240p. (YA). (gr. 7). lib. bdg. 18.99 (***978-0-375-94454-3(0)*** , Lamb, Wendy) Random Hse. Children's Bks.

Richards, Chuck. Jungle Gym Jitters. Richards, Chuck, illus. 2004. (Illus.). 32p. (J). 17.85 (978-0-8027-8932-7(3)); 16.95 (978-0-8027-8931-0(5)) Walker & Co.

Rockwell, Anne. Good Morning, Digger. Greenberg, Melanie Hope, illus. 2007. 32p. (J). (ps). pap. 5.99 (978-0-14-240823-0(9) , Puffin) Penguin Group (USA) Inc.

Rockwell, Anne F. Good Morning, Digger. Greenberg, Melanie Hope, illus. 2005. 32p. (J). (ps-1). 15.99 (978-0-670-05959-1(5) , Viking Juvenile) Penguin Group (USA) Inc.

Rogers, Karen M. Lo Mejor Que Hago. Alvarado, Ana María, tr. Taylor, Piper, illus. 2000. (Think-Kids Book Collection).Tr. of What I Do Best!. (SPA.). 16p. (J). pap. 2.95 (978-1-58237-052-1(4)) Creative Thinkers, Inc.

Roth, Susan L. Hard Hat Area. 2004. (Illus.). 40p. (J). (gr. k-4). 17.95 (978-1-58234-946-6(0) , Bloomsbury Children) Bloomsbury Publishing.

Schade, Susan. Dinosaur Ed, Level 2. Buller, Jon, illus. 2000. (All-Star Readers Ser.). 32p. (J). (gr. 1-2). pap. 3.99 (978-1-57584-385-8(4) , Reader's Digest Children's Bks.) Reader's Digest Children's Publishing, Inc.

—Dinosaur Ed. 2000. (gr. k-3). lib. bdg. 11.80 (978-0-613-24839-6(2)) Tandem Library Bks.

Shulman, Lisa. Old MacDonald Had a Woodshop. Wolff, Ashley, illus. 2002. 32p. (J). 16.99 (978-0-399-23596-2(5) , Putnam Juvenile) Penguin Group (USA) Inc.

Shulman, Lisa & Wolff, Ashley. Old MacDonald Had a Woodshop. 2004. (Illus.). 32p. (J). reprint ed. pap. 6.99 (978-0-14-240186-6(2) , Puffin) Penguin Group (USA) Inc.

Sobel, June. B Is for Bulldozer: A Construction ABC. Iwai, Melissa, illus. 2003. 32p. (J). 16.00 (978-0-15-202250-1(3)) Harcourt Children's Bks.

—B Is for Bulldozer: A Construction ABC. Iwai, Melissa, illus. 2006. 32p. (J). pap. 6.00 (978-0-15-205774-9(9) , Voyager Bks./Libros Viajeros) Harcourt Children's Bks.

Sorenson, Margo. Ambrose & the Cathedral Dream. Szegedi, Katalin, illus. 2006. 30p. (J). (978-0-8146-3004-4(9)) Liturgical Pr.

St-Aubin, Bruno, illus. Daddy's a Busy Beaver. 2005. (Read-It! Readers Ser.). 32p. (J). (gr. k-3). 18.60 (978-1-4048-1025-9(0)) Picture Window Bks.

Suen, Anastasia. Raise the Roof! Smith, Elwood H., illus. 2003. 32p. (J). (ps-1). 15.99 (978-0-670-89282-2(3) , Viking Juvenile) Penguin Group (USA) Inc.

Van Leeuwen, Jean. Oliver Pig & the Best Fort Ever. Schweninger, Ann, illus. 2006. 40p. (J). (ps). 15.99 (978-0-8037-2888-2(3) , Dial) Penguin Group (USA) Inc.

Vorst, Rochel Groner. The Sukkah That I Built. Victor-Elsby, Elizabeth, illus. 2002. 26p. (J). (ps-k). 9.95 (978-1-929628-07-0(2)) Hachai Publishing.

Warner, Gertrude Chandler. Disappearing Staircase Mystery. 2001. (gr. 3-6). lib. bdg. 11.80 (978-0-613-53176-4(0)) Tandem Library Bks.

Welsh, Irvine. You'll Have Had Your Hole. 2004. 76p. (J). pap. (978-0-413-72860-9(9)) Methuen Publishing Ltd.

Widmer, Kirsten & Buxton, Sarah. Workshops That Work! 2004. 160p. pap. 19.99 (978-0-439-44406-4(3) , Teaching Resources) Scholastic, Inc.

BUILDING—REPAIR AND RECONSTRUCTION

Cole, Doris. School Treasures: Architecture of Historic Boston Schools. Wheeler, Nick, photos by. 2002. (Illus.). 150p. (YA). pap. 24.95 incl. cd-rom (978-1-883280-14-7(1) , 1-800-647-9658) Font & Ctr. Pr.

Gish, Melissa. A Construction Site. 2003. 24p. (J). lib. bdg. 21.35 (978-1-58340-323-5(X)) Smart Apple Media.

Healy, Nick. The Statue of Liberty. 2003. (J). pap. (978-1-58417-117-1(0)) Lake Street Pubs.

Kane, Andy. Changing Rooms: Handy Andy's Homework. 2003. (Illus.). 192p. bds. 24.95 (978-0-563-55192-8(5)) BBC Worldwide Americas.

Skinner, Tina. Fire Spaces: Design Inspirations for Fireplaces & Stoves. 2002. (Illus.). 176p. (gr. 10-13). 34.95 (978-0-7643-1694-4(X)) Schiffer Publishing, Ltd.

BUILDING—VOCATIONAL GUIDANCE

Architecture & Construction Careers (AVA) 2001. (YA). pap. 6.00 (978-1-57078-016-5(1) , CEV00016) C E V Multimedia, Ltd.

Hayward, Linda. Jobs People: A Day in the Life of a Builder. 2001. (Jobs People Do Ser.). (Illus.). (J). 10.75 (978-0-606-21138-3(1)) Tandem Library Bks.

Howey, Paul M. Working in Construction. 1998. (Exploring Careers Ser.). (J). 17.95 (978-0-8225-1764-1(7)) Lerner Publishing Group.

Hyland, Tony. High-Rise Workers. 2006. (Extreme Jobs Ser.). 32p. (J). (gr. 4-6). lib. bdg. 27.10 (978-1-58340-742-4(1)) Smart Apple Media.

J. G. Ferguson Publishing Company Staff. Discovering Careers for Your Future/Construction. 2001. (Discovering Careers for Your Future Ser.). (Illus.). 96p. (J). (gr. 4-9). 21.95 (978-0-89434-390-2(4) , Ferguson Publishing Co.) Facts On File, Inc.

Liebman, Daniel. I Want to Be a Builder. 2003. (I Want to Be Ser.). (Illus.). 24p. (J). (ps-2). pap. 3.99 (978-1-55297-757-6(9)); lib. bdg. 14.95 (978-1-55297-758-3(7)) Firefly Bks., Ltd.

—Quiero Ser Constructor. 2003. (Quincy Rumpel Ser.). (SPA., Illus.). 24p. (J). (ps-2). pap. 5.99 (978-1-55297-762-0(5)) Firefly Bks., Ltd.

Miller, Heather. Construction Worker. 2003. (This Is What I Want to Be Ser.). (Illus.). 24p. (ps-1). (J). lib. bdg. 18.50 (978-1-4034-0365-0(1)); pap. 5.25 (978-1-4034-0587-6(5)) Heinemann Library.

—Obrero de Contruccion. 2002. (Esto es lo Que Quiero Ser (This Is What I Want to Be) Ser.). (SPA.). 24p. (J). pap. 5.25 (978-1-4034-0597-5(2)) Heinemann Library.

Mondschein, Ken. Construction & Trades. 2008. (Great Careers with a High School Diploma Ser.). 160p. (J). (gr. 9). 32.95 (***978-0-8160-7043-5(1)*** , Ferguson Publishing Co.) Facts On File, Inc.

O'Connor, Rachel. Construction Worker. 2004. (Great Jobs Ser.). (Illus.). 48p. (J). 24.00 (978-0-516-24089-3(7) , Children's Pr.) Scholastic Library Publishing.

Pasternak, Ceel & Thornburg, Linda. Cool Careers for Girls in Construction. 2000. (Illus.). 116p. (YA). (gr. 7 up). 19.95 (978-1-57023-135-3(4)) Impact Pubns.

BUILDING REPAIR

see Building—Repair and Reconstruction

BUILDINGS—MAINTENANCE AND REPAIR

see Building—Repair and Reconstruction

BUILDINGS—REMODELING

see Building—Repair and Reconstruction

BULGARIA

Goldstein, Margaret J. Bulgaria in Pictures. 2nd ed. 2005. (Visual Geography Series, Second Ser.). (Illus.). 80p. (J). (gr. 5-12). 27.93 (978-0-8225-3057-2(0)) Lerner Publishing Group.

Otfinoski, Steven. Bulgaria. 1998. (Nations in Transition Ser.). Orig. Title: Bulgaria. (Illus.). 128p. (J). (gr. 7-12). 35.00 (978-0-8160-3705-6(1)) Facts On File, Inc.

Stavreva, Kirilka & Quek, Lynette. Bulgaria. 2nd ed. 2007. (Cultures of the World Ser.). 144p. (J). lib. bdg. 39.93 (***978-0-7614-2078-1(9)*** , Benchmark Bks.) Cavendish, Marshall Corp.

Van Cleaf, Kristin. Bulgaria. 2007. (Countries Set VI Ser.). (Illus.). 40p. (J). (gr. k-6). lib. bdg. 24.21 (***978-1-59928-781-2(1)*** , Checkerboard Library) ABDO Publishing Co.

BULIMIA

see Eating Disorders

BULL RUN, 1ST BATTLE OF, VA., 1861

Hama, Larry. The Battle of First Bull Run: The Civil War Begins. 2007. (Graphic Battles of the Civil War Ser.). (Illus.). 48p. (J). lib. bdg. (978-1-4042-0776-9(7)) Rosen Publishing Group, Inc., The.

Vierow, Wendy. The Battle of Bull Run. 2004. (Headlines from History Ser.). (Illus.). 24p. (J). lib. bdg. 19.95 (978-0-8239-6221-1(0)) Rosen Publishing Group, Inc., The.

BULL RUN, 1ST BATTLE OF, VA., 1861—FICTION

Altsheler, Joseph A. The Guns of Bull Run: A Story of the Civ. 2006. pap. (***978-1-4065-0812-3(8)***) Dodo Pr.

Hansen, Lynne. Shades of Blue & Gray. 2007. (YA). pap. (***978-1-4114-9674-3(4)***) Spark Publishing Group.

Reisberg, Joanne A. Save the Colors: A Civil War Battle Cry. 2001. (Young Americans Ser.: Vol. 5). (Illus.). 92p. (J). 5.95 (978-1-57249-247-9(3) , White Mane Kids) White Mane Publishing Co., Inc.

Susi, Geraldine Lee. Looking for Pa: A Civil War Journey from Catlett to Manassas, 1861. French, Douglas P., illus. 2nd ed. 2001. 127p. (J). (gr. 4-7). pap. 10.95 (978-1-880664-33-9(X)) E. M. Productions.

BULLDOZERS

Alinas, Marv. Bulldozers. 2008. (Machines at Work Ser.). 24p. (J). 22.79 (***978-1-59296-947-0(X)***) Child's World, Inc.

Bailer, Darice. Dozer: (with Bulldozer) S. I. International Staff, illus. 2005. (Matchbox Ser.). 16p. (J). bds. 6.99 (978-0-689-87794-0(3) , Little Simon) Simon & Schuster Children's Publishing.

Bulldozers Mighty Machines. 2006. (Illus.). 24p. (J). (gr. k-2). 18.50 (***978-0-531-17895-9(1)***) Scholastic Library Publishing.

Butterfield, Moira. Bulldozers & Other Construction Machines. Lyon, Chris & Biggin, Gary, illus. (J). mass mkt. 8.99 (978-0-590-24556-2(2)) Scholastic, Inc.

Dorling Kindersley Publishing Staff. Bulldozer. 2003. (Wheelies Ser.). (Illus.). 12p. (J). bds. 6.99 (978-0-7894-9876-2(6)) Dorling Kindersley Publishing, Inc.

Glover, David & Glover, Penny. Bulldozers. 2005. (Big Machines Ser.). (Illus.). 30p. (J). (gr. 2-5). lib. bdg. 27.10 (978-1-58340-705-9(7)) Smart Apple Media.

Hoban, Tana. Construction Zone. Hoban, Tana, illus. 1999. (Illus.). 15p. (J). (ps-2). 6.99 (978-0-688-16918-3(X)) HarperCollins Pubs.

Martin, M. T. Bulldozers. 2006. (Blastoff! Readers Ser.). (Illus.). 24p. (J). lib. bdg. 16.95 (978-1-60014-043-3(2)) Bellwether Media.

Mezzanotte, Jim. Giant Bulldozers. 2005. (Illus.). 24p. (J). pap. (978-0-8368-4917-2(5)); lib. bdg. 22.00 (978-0-8368-4910-3(8)) Stevens, Gareth Inc.

—Niveladoras. 2006. (Vehiculos Gigantes (Giant Vehicles) Ser.). (SPA.). (Illus.). 24p. (J). pap. 5.95 (978-0-8368-5996-6(0)); lib. bdg. 22.00 (978-0-8368-5989-8(8)) Stevens, Gareth Inc.

Parent, Nancy. Bulldozer. 2003. (ps-2). lib. bdg. 11.80 (978-0-613-86022-2(5)) Tandem Library Bks.

Randolph, Joanne. Bulldozers. 2002. (PowerKids Readers Ser.). (Illus.). 24p. (J). (gr. 1). lib. bdg. 16.00 (978-0-8239-6025-5(0) , PowerKids Pr.) Rosen Publishing Group, Inc., The.

—Earth Movers, 6 bks. Incl. Backhoes. lib. bdg. 16.00 (978-0-8239-6029-3(3)); Bulldozers. lib. bdg. 16.00 (978-0-8239-6025-5(0)); Cranes. lib. bdg. 16.00 (978-0-8239-6030-9(7)); Tractors. lib. bdg. 16.00 (978-0-8239-6028-6(5)); Wheel Loaders. lib. bdg. 16.00 (978-0-8239-6026-2(9)); 24p. (J). (gr. 1). 2002. (Illus.). Set lib. bdg. 88.50 (978-0-8239-7113-8(9) , PowerKids Pr.) Rosen Publishing Group, Inc., The.

Stickland, Paul. Diggers. 2004. (By Air, Sea, & Land Ser.). (Illus.). 24p. (J). pap. 3.99 (978-0-7696-3374-9(9) , Waterbird Bks.) School Specialty Publishing.

Stille, Darlene R. Bulldozers. 2004. (Illus.). 32p. (J). (gr. 1 up). lib. bdg. 21.26 (978-0-7565-0605-6(0)) Compass Point Bks.

Wallace, Karen. Big Machines. 2000. (Readers Ser.). (Illus.). 32p. (J). (ps-1). pap. 3.99 (978-0-7894-5411-9(4)) Dorling Kindersley Publishing, Inc.

—Big Machines. 2000. (gr. k-3). lib. bdg. 11.80 (978-0-613-24358-2(7)); (Illus.). (J). 10.79 (978-0-606-18114-3(8)) Tandem Library Bks.

Wallace, Karen & Dorling Kindersley Publishing Staff. Big Machines. 2000. (Eyewitness Readers). (Illus.). 32p. (J). (ps-1). 12.99 (978-0-7894-5412-6(2)) Dorling Kindersley Publishing, Inc.

Williams, Linda D. Bulldozers. 2004. (Pebble Plus: Mighty Machines Ser.). (Illus.). 24p. (J). lib. bdg. 19.93 (978-0-7368-2593-1(2) , Pebble Bks.) Capstone Pr., Inc.

—Bulldozers. (Mighty MacHines Ser.). 24p. (J). pap. 6.95 (978-0-7368-5131-2(3)) Capstone Pr., Inc.

BULLDOZERS—FICTION

Biro, Val. Gumdrop & the Bulldozer. (Illus.). 32p. (J). (978-0-340-71444-7(1)); pap. (978-0-340-71445-4(X)) Hodder General Publishing Division. (Hodder & Stoughton).

McCune, Krisha. Meet Scoop. Hot Animation Staff, Animation, illus. 2003. (Bob the Builder Ser.). 12p. (J). bds. 5.99 (978-0-689-85776-8(4) , Simon Spotlight) Simon & Schuster Children's Publishing.

Stoddard, Jeffery. Pete & Pillar - The Big Rain: A Story of Friendship Based on John 15:13. 2007. (Illus.). 32p. (J). (ps-2). 12.99 (***978-1-59317-203-9(6)***) Warner Pr. Pubs.

Teitelbaum, Michael. If I Could Drive a Bulldozer. Klavins, Uldis & Walker, Jeff, illus. 2002. (Tonka Ser.). 24p. (J). (ps-2). pap. 3.50 (978-0-439-34175-2(2)) Scholastic, Inc.

BULLFIGHTS

Hollander, Jim, photos by & intro. Run to the Sun: Pamplona's Fiesta de San Fermín. Hollander, Jim, intro. 2nd unabr. ed. 2002. Tr. of Fiesta. 316p. (YA). 55.00 net. (978-0-9720778-0-4(4)) MasterArts Pr. LLC.

McLeese, Tex. Bull Riding & Bullfighting. 2000. (Illus.). 24p. (J). (gr. 1-4). lib. bdg. 19.27 (978-1-57103-345-1(9)) Rourke Publishing, LLC.

BULLFIGHTS—FICTION

Aryal, Aimee. Hello, Ralphie! 2007. (J). 14.95 (***978-1-932888-34-8(9)***) Mascot Bks., Inc.

Blasco Ibañez, Vicente. Sangre y Arena Level 4. 1998. (SPA.). (gr. 7-12). lib. bdg. 15.25 (978-0-613-80710-4(3)) Tandem Library Bks.

Leaf, Munro. The Story of Ferdinand. Lawson, Robert, illus. 2002. (J). 14.04 (978-0-7587-3711-3(4)) Book Wholesalers, Inc.

—The Story of Ferdinand. Lawson, Robert, illus. (Puffin Storytime Ser.). (J). (ps). 2007. 72p. 9.99 (***978-0-14-240952-7(9)*** , Puffin); 2000. 32p. 3.99 (978-0-448-42190-2(9) , Grosset & Dunlap) Penguin Group (USA) Inc.

—The Story of Ferdinand. 2000. (gr. k-3). lib. bdg. 11.25 (978-0-613-30144-2(7)) Tandem Library Bks.

Wojciechowska, Maia. Shadow of a Bull. Smith, Alvin, illus. 2007. 160p. (J). pap. 2.99 (***978-1-4169-4830-8(9)***); pap. 5.99 (978-1-4169-3395-3(6)) Simon & Schuster Children's Publishing. (Aladdin).

—Shadow of a Bull, Vol. 5. l.t. ed. 2004. 150p. 20.95 (978-0-7862-6900-6(6) , Large Print Pr.) Thorndike Pr.

BULLIES

Eniwaye, Olu O. Country Bully & the City Bully: A Children's Book. 2004. (J). per. 7.95 (978-1-59427-028-4(7)) Aglob Publishing.

Hibbert, Adam. Why Do People Bully? 2004. (Exploring Tough Issues Ser.). (Illus.). 48p. (J). 27.14 (978-0-7398-6681-8(8)) Raintree.

Johnston, Marianne. Dealing with Bullying. 1998. (Conflict Resolution Library). (Illus.). 24p. (J). (gr. k-4). pap. 6.95 (978-1-56838-266-1(9)) Hazelden Publishing & Educational Services.

Leaney, Cindy. Long Walk to School: Safety Outdoors. Wilks, Peter, illus. 2003. (Hero Club Safety Ser.). 32p. (J). 28.50 (978-1-58952-745-4(3)) Rourke Publishing, LLC.

Nass, Marcia Shoshana. No More Bullies! 1998. (Illus.). 92p. (J). (gr. k-7). pap. 17.95 (978-1-882732-75-3(8) , 61530) Childswork/Childsplay.

Simmons, Rachel. Odd Girl Speaks Out. 2004. (gr. 7-12). lib. bdg. 15.10 (978-0-613-70533-2(5)) Tandem Library Bks.

Slavens, Elaine. Bullying: Before Push Comes to Shove. Kerrigan, Brooke, illus. 2003. (Deal with It Ser.). 32p. (J). (gr. 4-8). 12.95 (978-1-55028-790-5(7)) Lorimer, James & Co., Ltd., Pubs. CAN. *Dist:* Casemate Pubs. & Bk. Distributors, LLC.

—Bullying: Resource Guide: Before Push Comes to Shove! 2003. (Deal with It Ser.). 30p. (978-1-55028-782-0(6)) Lorimer, James & Co., Ltd., Pubs. CAN. *Dist:* Casemate Pubs. & Bk. Distributors, LLC.

Toews, Rita Y. The Bully: A Discussion & Activity Story. Ljungberg, Jon, illus. l.t. ed. 2004. (ENG.). 40p. (J). (978-0-9736224-0-9(7)) Birds Hill Publishing.

BULLIES—FICTION

Abreu, Raquel, illus. Little Ruth Reddingford (and the Wolf) An Old Tale retold by Hank Wesselman, PH. D. 2004. 32p. (J). per. 15.95 (978-0-9740190-0-0(3)) Illumination Arts Publishing Co., Inc.

Albee, Sarah. Clever Trevor. Billin-Frye, Paige, illus. 2003. (Science Solves It! Ser.). 32p. (J). 4.99 (978-1-57565-123-1(8)) Kane Pr., The.

—Clever Trevor. 2003. (gr. k-3). lib. bdg. 13.00 (978-0-613-79229-5(7)) Tandem Library Bks.

Alger, Horatio. Finding a Fortune. unabr. ed. 2002. (Polyglot Press Alger Ser.). (Illus.). (J). pap. 17.95 (978-1-4115-0089-1(X)) Polyglot Pr., Inc.

Alpert, Sandra F. Horrible Howard: The Bully & Coward. Date not set. (Bully Busting Trilogy Ser.: Bk. 1). (Illus.). (Orig.). (J). (gr. k-5). pap. (978-1-884931-02-4(2)) Global Commitment Publishing.

Anderson, M. T. Burger Wuss. Butler, David, illus. 2001. 208p. (YA). (gr. 9 up). pap. 6.99 (978-0-7636-1567-3(6)) Candlewick Pr.

—Burger Wuss. 2001. 13.64 (978-0-606-22539-7(0)); (gr. 7-12). lib. bdg. 14.15 (978-0-613-44380-7(2)) Tandem Library Bks.

Arena, Felice & Kettle, Phil. Hit the Beach. Vane, Mitch, illus. 2004. (J). pap. (978-1-59336-361-1(3)) Mondo Publishing.

Arnold, Louise. Golden & Grey: An Unremarkable Boy & a Rather Remarkable Ghost. 2005. 272p. (J). 15.95 (978-0-689-87473-4(1) , McElderry, Margaret K.) Simon & Schuster Children's Publishing.

—Golden & Grey: (an Unremarkable Boy & a Rather Remarkable Ghost) l.t. ed. 2006. 317p. 22.95 (978-0-7862-8290-6(8)) Thorndike Pr.

—Golden & Grey: The Nightmares That Ghosts Have. 2006. 304p. (J). (gr. 3-7). 16.99 (978-0-689-87586-1(X) , McElderry, Margaret K.) Simon & Schuster Children's Publishing.

—Golden & Grey (an Unremarkable Boy & a Rather Remarkable Ghost) 2006. (Illus.). 272p. (J). reprint ed. pap. 5.99 (978-0-689-87585-4(1) , Aladdin) Simon & Schuster Children's Publishing.

Arnold, Louise. Golden & Grey: the Nightmares That Ghosts Have. 2007. 304p. (J). pap. 5.99 (***978-0-689-87587-8(8)*** , Aladdin) Simon & Schuster Children's Publishing.

Aston, Dianna Hutts. Not So Tall for Six. Dormer, Frank W., illus. 2008. (J). (***978-1-57091-705-9(1)***) Charlesbridge Publishing, Inc.

Barkow, Henriette. Don't Bully Me. Lamont, Priscilla, illus. 2004. (ENG, PAN & ALB.). (J). 31p. (978-1-84444-560-8(7)); (978-1-84444-561-5(5)); (978-1-84444-562-2(3)); 31p. (978-1-84444-563-9(1)); (978-1-84444-564-6(X)); (978-1-84444-565-3(8)); 31p. (978-1-84444-566-0(6)); 31p. (978-1-84444-567-7(4)); (978-1-84444-568-4(2)); (978-1-84444-569-1(0)); (978-1-84444-570-7(4)) Mantra Publishing, Ltd.

Bateman, Teresa. The Bully Blockers Club. Urbanovic, Jackie, illus. 32p. (J). (gr. 1-4). 2006. 6.95 (978-0-8075-0919-7(1)); 2004. 15.95 (978-0-8075-0918-0(3)) Whitman, Albert & Co.

Bauer, Michael Gerard. Don't Call Me Ishmael! 2007. 272p. (gr. 9 up). (J). 16.99 (***978-0-06-134834-1(1)***); (YA). lib. bdg. 17.89 (***978-0-06-134835-8(X)***) HarperCollins Pubs. (HarperTeen).

Baym, Nina. A N a Am Lit. 2002. (C). pap. (978-0-393-94312-2(7)) Norton, W. W. & Co., Inc.

Berenstain, Stan & Berenstain, Jan. The Berenstain Bears & the Bully. Berenstain, Stan & Berenstain, Jan, illus. 2002. (Berenstain Bears First Time Bks.). (Illus.). (J). 11.19 (978-0-7587-0947-9(1)) Book Wholesalers, Inc.

—The Wrong Crowd. 2001. (Berenstain Bears Ser.). (Illus.). (J). (gr. k-3). (978-0-606-21060-7(1)) Tandem Library Bks.

Big Bad Bully. 2005. 32p. (J). 12.99 (978-0-9758709-1-4(2) , A.W.A. Gang) Journey Stone Creations, LLC.

Binaohan, Simon & Tacang, Brian. The Misadventures of Millicent Madding No. 1: Bully-Be-Gone. 2006. (Illus.). 224p. (J). lib. bdg. 17.89 (978-0-06-073912-6(6)) HarperCollins Pubs.

—The Misadventures of Millicent Madding Vol. 1: Bully-Be-Gone. 2006. (Illus.). 224p. (J). 16.99 (978-0-06-073911-9(8)) HarperCollins Pubs.

Blackman, Malorie. Cloud Busting. 2004. (Illus.). 149p. (J). (978-0-385-60796-4(2)) Hudson Hills Pr. LLC.

Blake-Brekke, Carri. Billy Bully Bug: Learns a Lesson in Hawaii. Melton, Jodi, illus. 2003. (Mrs. B's Story Time... With a Twist! Ser.). 20p. (J). pap. 11.95 incl. audio compact disk (978-0-9720549-2-8(8)) Mom's Pride Enterprises.

Bradman, Tony. Deadly Game. Chatterton, Martin, illus. 2004. (Tales of Terror Ser.). 105p. (J). (gr. 4-7). pap. 7.50 (978-1-4052-1127-7(X)) Egmont Bks., Ltd. GBR. *Dist:* Independent Pubs. Group.

Bradman, Tony. Elvis the Squirrel. Finlay, Lizzie, illus. 2006. (Read-It! Chapter Books). 48p. (J). (***978-1-4048-3119-3(3)*** , 1265806) Picture Window Bks.

Brand, Hilary. Ossie the Ghostbuster. 2000. 192p. (J). pap. 8.99 (978-0-7459-4052-6(8) , Lion) Lion Hudson plc GBR. *Dist:* Independent Pubs. Group.

Brandenburg, Claire. Daniel & the Lion. 2002. (Illus.). 32p. pap. 8.95 (978-1-888212-35-8(7) , 005674) Conciliar Pr.

Brouwer, Sigmund. Camp Craziness. 2003. (Watch Out for Joel Ser.). (Illus.). 32p. (J). (gr. 1-3). reprint ed. pap. 3.99 (978-0-7642-2582-6(0)) Bethany Hse. Pubs.

—Camp Craziness. 2003. (gr. k-3). lib. bdg. 11.80 (978-0-613-87752-7(7)) Tandem Library Bks.

Butler, Dori Hillestad. Trading Places with Tank Talbott. 2003. 136p. (J). (gr. 3-6). 15.95 (978-0-8075-1708-6(9)) Whitman, Albert & Co.

Caple, Kathy. The Wimp. 2000. (Illus.). 32p. (J). (gr. k-3). pap. 5.95 (978-0-618-05577-7(0) , Walter Lorraine) Houghton Mifflin Co. Trade & Reference Div.

Carlson, Melody. Project, Girl Power. 2007. (Faith-girlz!#8482; / Girls of 622 Harbor View Ser.). 144p. (J). pap. 6.99 (978-0-310-71186-5(X)) Zonderkidz.

Carlson, Nancy. Loudmouth George & the Sixth Grade Bully. 20th anniv. ed. (Nancy Carlson's Neighborhood Ser.). (Illus.). 32p. (gr. k-2). 2005. 15.95 (978-1-57505-218-2(0)); 2003. (J). pap. 23.95 (978-1-57505-549-7(X)) Lerner Publishing Group.

—Loudmouth George & the Sixth Grade Bully. 2003. (gr. k-3). lib. bdg. 15.25 (978-0-613-58927-7(0)) Tandem Library Bks.

Christelow, Eileen. Jerome Camps Out. 2002. (Illus.). 32p. (J). (gr. k-3). 5.95 (978-0-618-19467-4(3) , Clarion Bks.) Houghton Mifflin Co. Trade & Reference Div.

—Jerome Camps Out. Christelow, Eileen, illus. 1998. (Illus.). 32p. (J). (gr. k-3). tchr. ed. 16.00 (978-0-395-75831-1(9) , Clarion Bks.) Houghton Mifflin Co. Trade & Reference Div.

—Jerome Camps Out. 2002. (gr. k-3). lib. bdg. 14.10 (978-0-613-72915-4(3)) Tandem Library Bks.

Christopher, Matt. Lacrosse Face-Off. 2006. 128p. (J). (gr. 3-7). pap. 4.99 (978-0-316-79641-5(7)) Little Brown & Co.

Clairmont, Patsy. Spud. 2006. (Tails from the Pantry Ser.). (Illus.). 32p. (J). 9.99 (978-1-4003-0802-6(X)) Nelson, Thomas Inc.

Clements, Andrew. Bully Buster. Harvey, Amanda, illus. 2001. (Jake Drake Ser.: Bk. 1). 80p. (J). (gr. 4-7). 15.95 (978-0-689-83917-7(0)) Simon & Schuster Children's Publishing.

—Bully Buster/Know-It-All. Harvey, Amanda & Avendano, Dolores, illus. 2004. (Jake Drake Ser.: Nos. 1 & 2). 192p. (J). pap. 3.99 (978-0-689-87104-7(X) , Aladdin) Simon & Schuster Children's Publishing.

—Jake Drake, Bully Buster. Pedersen, Janet, illus. 2007. (Jake Drake Ser.). 80p. (J). pap. 3.99 (*978-1-4169-3933-7(4) , Aladdin) Simon & Schuster Children's Publishing.

—Jake Drake, Bully Buster. 2001. (gr. 3-6). lib. bdg. 11.80 (978-0-613-31375-9(5)); (Illus.). (J). 10.79 (978-0-606-20733-1(3)) Tandem Library Bks.

Clevenger, Lee. IncrediBoy: Be Careful What You Wish. 2004. 267p. (J). pap. 12.95 (978-0-9764052-0-7(2)) Thomas Max Publishing.

Cocos, Deborah. Tale One of the Wignuts: The Golden Spriggot of Fritzwitz. 2007. (J). 19.99 (*978-1-60247-034-7(0)) Tate Publishing & Enterprises, L.L.C.

Codell, Esmé Raji. Vive la Paris! 2006. 224p. (J). (gr. 3-7). 15.99 (978-0-7868-5124-9(4)) Hyperion Pr.

Coleman, Evelyn. Freedom Train. Riley, David, illus. 2008. 160p. (J). 15.99 (*978-0-689-84716-5(5) , McElderry, Margaret K.) Simon & Schuster Children's Publishing.

Collard, Sneed B., III. Dog Sense. 2005. 192p. (J). 14.95 (978-1-56145-351-1(X)) Peachtree Pubs., Ltd.

Collins, Ross. Medusa Jones. 2008. (J). (*978-0-439-90101-7(4)); 144p. pap. 16.99 (*978-0-439-90100-0(6)) Scholastic, Inc. (Levine, Arthur A. Bks.).

Cooper, Ilene. The Annoying Team. Paine, Colin, illus. 2005. (Stepping Stones Ser.). 80p. (J). (gr. 2-5). pap. 3.99 (978-0-307-26512-8(9) , Random Hse. Bks. for Young Readers) Random Hse. Children's Bks.

Cooper, Ilene. Jake's Best Thumb. Muñoz, Claudio, illus. 2008. 32p. (J). (ps). 16.99 (*978-0-525-47788-4(8) , Dutton Juvenile) Penguin Group (USA) Inc.

Coulton, Mia. Danny & the Bully. Coulton, Mia, photos by. 2002. (J). 4.95 (978-0-9713518-7-5(2)) Maryruth Bks., Inc.

Coville, Bruce. The Monster's Ring. 2002. lib. bdg. 20.00 incl. audio (978-1-932076-10-3(7) , 02009) Full Cast Audio.

—The Monster's Ring. Coville, Katherine, illus. anniv. exp. ed. 2002. (Magic Shop Bks.). 128p. (YA). (gr. 3-7). 16.00 (978-0-15-204618-7(6)) Harcourt Children's Bks.

Cox, Judy. Mean, Mean Maureen Green. Fisher, Cynthia, illus. 1999. 80p. (J). (gr. 1-5). tchr. ed. 15.95 (978-0-8234-1502-1(3)) Holiday Hse., Inc.

—Mean, Mean Maureen Green. 2001. (Illus.). (J). (978-0-606-21322-6(8)) Tandem Library Bks.

Crocker, Nancy. Betty Lou Blue. Kulikov, Boris, illus. 2006. 32p. (J). (ps). 16.99 (978-0-8037-2937-7(5) , Dial) Penguin Group (USA) Inc.

Dail, Maggie. Getting to First Base - Chris Struggles to Read. 2006. 157p. pap. 13.95 (978-1-4116-8125-5(8)) Lulu.com.

Daly, Joseph M. Strange Town Volume One: The Woods Behind Trevor Malone's House. 2007. 265p. (YA). pap. (*978-0-9779921-0-2(1)) Wolfs Corner Publishing.

de Paola, Tomie. Trouble in the Barkers' Class. de Paola, Tomie, illus. 2003. (Barker Twins Ser.). (Illus.). 32p. (J). (ps-3). 14.99 (978-0-399-24164-2(7) , Putnam Juvenile) Penguin Group (USA) Inc.

DePaola, Tomie. Trouble in the Barkers' Class. DePaola, Tomie, illus. 2006. (Barker Twins Ser.). (Illus.). 32p. (J). (ps). reprint ed. pap. 5.99 (978-0-14-240585-7(X) , Puffin) Penguin Group (USA) Inc.

DePino, Catherine S. Blue Cheese Breath & Stinky Feet: How to Deal with Bullies. Matthews, Bonnie, illus. 2004. 48p. (J). 14.95 (978-1-59147-111-0(7)); pap. 8.95 (978-1-59147-112-7(5)) American Psychological Assn. (Magination Pr.).

Dewey, Ariane & Aruego, Jose. The Last Laugh. 2006. (Illus.). 32p. (J). (ps). 12.99 (978-0-8037-3093-9(4) , Dial) Penguin Group (USA) Inc.

Dodd, Lynley. Hairy Maclary from Donaldson's Dairy. Dodd, Lynley, illus. 2000. (Gold Star First Readers Ser.). (Illus.). 32p. (J). (gr. 1 up). lib. bdg. 21.26 (978-0-8368-2688-3(4)) Stevens, Gareth Inc.

—Hairy Maclary from Donaldson's Dairy. 2005. (Illus.). 36p. (J). 5.95 (978-1-58246-059-8(0) , Tricycle Pr.) Ten Speed Pr.

Donofrio, Beverly. Thank You, Lucky Stars. 2008. 240p. (J). 16.99 (*978-0-375-83964-1(X) , Schwartz & Wade Bks.) Random Hse. Children's Bks.

Don't Bully Me. 2004. (J). (CRO & ENG.). (978-1-84444-553-0(4)); (PER & ENG.). (978-1-84444-554-7(2)); (ENG & FRE.). (978-1-84444-555-4(0)); (ENG & GUJ.). (978-1-84444-556-1(9)); (ENG & HIN.). (978-1-84444-557-8(7)); (ARA, ENG & GAE., Illus.). (978-1-84444-549-3(6)); (BEN, ENG & GER., Illus.). (978-1-84444-550-9(X)); (CHI, ENG & ITA., Illus.). (978-1-84444-551-6(8)); (CHI, ENG & THA., Illus.). (978-1-84444-552-3(6)); (ALB, ENG & WEL., Illus.). (978-1-84444-548-6(8)) Mantra Publishing, Ltd.

Douglas, Marjory Stoneman. Alligator Crossing. Nicholson, Trudy, illus. 2003. 192p. (J). (gr. 3-8). pap. 6.95 (978-1-57131-644-8(2)) Milkweed Editions.

—Alligator Crossing. 2003. (gr. 3-6). lib. bdg. 15.25 (978-0-613-79196-0(7)) Tandem Library Bks.

Duane, Diane. So You Want to Be a Wizard. (Young Wizards Ser.). (YA). 2003. 408p. pap. 6.95 (978-0-15-204940-9(1) , Magic Carpet Bks.); 2001. 400p. (gr. 5 up). pap. 6.95 (978-0-15-216250-4(X) , Magic Carpet Bks.); 20th anniv. ed. 2003. (Illus.). 336p. 16.95 (978-0-15-204738-2(7)) Harcourt Children's Bks.

—So You Want to Be a Wizard. 2003. (gr. 3-6). lib. bdg. 15.25 (978-0-613-71630-7(2)); 2001. (gr. 5-8). lib. bdg. 15.25 (978-0-613-36077-7(X)) Tandem Library Bks.

Duffey, Betsy. Alien for Rent. 2000. (978-0-606-17889-1(9)) Tandem Library Bks.

—How to Be Cool in the Third Grade. Wilson, Janet, illus. 1999. (Chapters Ser.). 80p. (J). (gr. 2-5). pap. 4.99 (978-0-14-130466-3(9) , Puffin) Penguin Group (USA) Inc.

Dunlevy, Crystal. GOTHAM, Inc. 2005. 108p. pap. 11.95 (978-1-59113-702-3(0)) Booklocker.com, Inc.

Edwards, Michelle. Stinky Stern Forever: A Jackson Friends Book. 2007. (Jackson Friends Ser.). (Illus.). 56p. (J). pap. 5.95 (*978-0-15-206101-2(0) , Harcourt Paperbacks) Harcourt Children's Bks.

—Stinky Stern Forever: A Jackson Friends Book. 2005. (Jackson Friends Ser.). (Illus.). 56p. (J). (gr. 1-3). 14.00 (978-0-15-216389-1(1)) Harcourt Trade Pubs.

Emberley, Ed. Bye-Bye, Big Bad Bullybug. Emberley, Ed, illus. 2007. (Illus.). 32p. (J). (ps-1). 10.99 (978-0-316-01762-6(0)) Little Brown & Co.

Emily Breaks Free - Evaluation Guide. 2006. (J). (978-1-55942-404-2(4)) Marsh Media.

Emily Breaks Free - Teaching Guide. 2000. 17.95 (978-1-55942-157-7(6)) Marsh Media.

Epstein, Dwayne. Cooler King. 2001. (gr. 5-8). lib. bdg. 11.80 (978-0-613-63100-6(5)) Tandem Library Bks.

Erickson, John R. The Case of the Car-Barkaholic Dog. Holmes, Gerald L., illus. 1998. (Hank the Cowdog Ser.: No. 17). 144p. (J). (gr. 2-5). pap. 4.99 (978-0-14-130393-2(X) , Puffin) Penguin Group (USA) Inc.

The Fearsome Four: Individual Title Six-Packs. (Bookweb Ser.). 32p. (gr. 3 up). 34.00 (978-0-7635-3932-0(5)) Rigby Education.

Fontes, Justine. Henry's Turn. Hefferan, Rob, illus. 2004. (J). (978-1-59336-004-7(5)); pap. (978-1-59336-005-4(3)) Mondo Publishing.

Fox, Mem. A Cat Called Kite. Slack, Michael H., illus. 2008. (J). (*978-0-15-204909-6(6)) Harcourt Trade Pubs.

Garden, Nancy. Endgame. 2006. (Illus.). 304p. (YA). 17.00 (978-0-15-205416-8(2)) Harcourt Children's Bks.

Gardner, Graham. Inventing Elliot. 192p. (J). 2005. (gr. 7). pap. 5.99 (978-0-14-240344-0(X) , Puffin); 2004. (gr. 5). 16.99 (978-0-8037-2964-3(2) , Dial) Penguin Group (USA) Inc.

Gleitzman, Morris. Sticky Beak. l.t. ed. 2005. 200p. (J). pap. (978-0-7540-6180-9(9) , CLP 374) BBC Audio.

Goggles! 2004. (J). pap. 18.95 incl. audio compact disk (978-1-55592-417-1(4)); pap. 38.75 incl. audio compact disk (978-1-55592-418-8(2)); pap. 32.75 incl. audio (978-1-55592-232-0(5)); pap. 14.95 incl. audio (978-1-56008-084-8(1)) Weston Woods Studios, Inc.

Gorman, Carol. A Midsummer Night's Dork. 224p. (J). 2006. (Illus.). pap. 5.99 (978-0-06-050720-6(9) , Harper Trophy); 2004. 15.99 (978-0-06-050718-3(7)); 2004. lib. bdg. 16.89 (978-0-06-050719-0(5)) HarperCollins Pubs.

Greene, Janice. Fat Boy: Set 3. 2002. 32p. (YA). 2.95 (978-1-56254-428-7(4) , SP 4284) Saddleback Educational Publishing.

Greene, Stephanie. Owen Foote, Frontiersman. Weston, Martha, illus. 96p. (J). (gr. k-3). 2002. pap. 4.95 (978-0-618-24620-5(7)); 1999. tchr. ed. 14.00 (978-0-395-61578-2(X)) Houghton Mifflin Co. Trade & Reference Div. (Clarion Bks.).

—Owen Foote, Frontiersman. 2002. (gr. k-3). lib. bdg. 12.95 (978-0-613-72910-9(2)) Tandem Library Bks.

Grindley, Sally. Feather Wars. 2003. 224p. pap. 12.99 (978-0-7475-6338-9(1)) Bloomsbury Publishing Plc GBR. *Dist:* Independent Pubs. Group.

Halverson, Deborah. Big Mouth. 2008. 144p. (J). (gr. 5). 15.99 (*978-0-385-73394-6(1)); lib. bdg. 18.99 (*978-0-385-90408-7(8)) Random Hse. Children's Bks. (Delacorte Bks. for Young Readers).

Harper, Ben. Revenge of the Ants. Harris, Annmarie, ed. 2006. (Ant Bully Ser.). (Illus.). 24p. (J). pap. 3.50 (978-0-439-85679-9(5) , Scholastic) Scholastic, Inc.

Harpster, Steve, illus. Betty Stops the Bully: An Emotional Literacy Book. 2004. (Emotional Literacy Ser.). 44p. (J). (gr. 2 up). 14.95 (978-0-9747789-1-4(5) , 67313) CTC Publishing.

Harvey, Amanda. Dog Eared: Starring Otis. Harvey, Amanda, illus. 2004. (Illus.). 32p. (J). (ps-1). reprint ed. pap. 6.99 (978-0-440-41763-7(5) , Dragonfly Bks.) Random Hse. Children's Bks.

Hawley, Bobby. By Golly, Molly, You're Right. 2006. 48p. pap. 12.95 (978-1-4241-2085-7(3)) PublishAmerica, Inc.

Hayes, Geoffrey. Patrick & the Big Bully. 2001. (Illus.). (J). lib. bdg. 16.49 (978-0-7868-2594-3(4)) Hyperion Pr.

Heiner, Garth Farr. The Bully. Melander, Eric, illus. l.t. unabr. ed. 2001. (Fun-with-the-Law Ser.: No. 2). 32p. (J). (gr. k-7). pap. 5.95 (978-1-929905-02-7(5)) Fun With the Law, Inc.

Helgerson, Joseph. Horns & Wrinkles. Ceccoli, Nicoletta, illus. 2006. 368p. (J). (gr. 4-6). 16.00 (978-0-618-61679-4(9)) Houghton Mifflin Co.

Heneghan, James. Hit Squad. 2003. (Orca Soundings Ser.). 96p. (J). (gr. 7-12). pap. 7.95 (978-1-55143-269-4(2)) Orca Bk. Pubs. USA.

Hoffmire, A. B. The Ogre Bully. 2007. 32p. (J). pap. 3.95 (*978-0-87483-803-9(7)) August Hse. Pubs., Inc.

Hollstein, Stephanie. Connections. 2001. 192p. (YA). pap. 13.95 (978-0-595-17152-1(4) , Writers Club Pr.) iUniverse, Inc.

Holohan, Maureen. Ice Cold. 1999. (Broadway Ballplayers Ser.: No. 6). (Illus.). 164p. (J). (gr. 4-8). (978-0-9659091-5-0(8)) Broadway Ballplayers, Inc.

Howe, James. Pinky & Rex & the Bully. 2006. (J). (gr. 1-4). 24.21 (978-1-59961-074-0(4)) Spotlight.

Hudson, Marilyn A. Elephant Hips Are Expensive! A Tale of the Sooner State. Fulco, Haley, illus. 2007. 50p. (J). per. (*978-0-9778850-2-2(X)) Hudson House Publishing & Productions.

Hull, Donna L. Wally WaddleSnout & the Peppermint Race! Smith, Geoffrey P., illus. l.t. ed. 2001. 32p. (J). (ps-5). 13.95 (978-0-9710017-0-1(7)) TDH Bks.

Jackson, Teresa Jean. Huggable Harry. 2004. 21p. pap. 14.95 (978-1-4137-1102-8(2)) PublishAmerica, Inc.

Jackson, Vicky, illus. Poepal's Purpose. l.t. ed. 2005. 20p. (J). 7.95 (978-0-9718741-0-7(7)) Tawa Productions.

Jennings, Patrick. The Lightning Bugs. Alter, Anna, illus. 2003. 56p. (J). (gr. k-3). tchr. ed. 15.95 (978-0-8234-1673-8(9)) Holiday Hse., Inc.

Jennings, Paul. Undone! More Mad Endings. l.t. ed. 2005. (J). pap. (978-1-4056-6004-4(X)) BBC Audio.

Jeremiah, Omari. Paperboy 3: The School of Doom. Rollins, Bernie, illus. 2006. 75p. pap. 12.99 (978-1-929188-13-0(7)) Morton Bks.

Jinkins, Jim. Pinky Dinky Doo: Shrinky Pinky! 2005. (Step into Reading Ser.). (Illus.). 48p. (J). (gr. 1-3). pap. 3.99 (978-0-375-83235-2(1) , Random Hse. Bks. for Young Readers) Random Hse. Children's Bks.

Jones, H. Lena. Trapped on Planet Liska. 2006. 180p. pap. 19.95 (978-1-4241-0989-0(2)) PublishAmerica, Inc.

Jones, Jac. Alison & the Bully Monsters. 2000. (Illus.). 30p. (J). pap. 14.95 (978-1-85902-752-3(0)) Beekman Bks., Inc.

Joosse, Barbara M. Alien Brain Fryout. Truesdell, Sue, illus. 2000. (Wild Willie Mystery Ser.). 108p. (J). (gr. 4-6). tchr. ed. 15.00 (978-0-395-68964-6(3) , Clarion Bks.) Houghton Mifflin Co. Trade & Reference Div.

Karas, G. Brian, illus. Bootsie Barker Ballerina. 2002. (Bootsie Barker Ser.). (J). 11.91 (978-0-7587-6034-0(5)) Book Wholesalers, Inc.

—Bootsie Barker Bites. 2002. (J). 13.19 (978-0-7587-2135-8(8)) Book Wholesalers, Inc.

Keats, Ezra Jack. Goggles. Keats, Ezra Jack, illus. 1998. (Illus.). 40p. (J). 16.99 (978-0-670-88062-1(0) , Viking Juvenile); pap. 6.99 (978-0-14-056440-2(3) , Puffin) Penguin Group (USA) Inc.

—Goggles! Keats, Ezra Jack, illus. 2002. (Illus.). (J). 14.04 (978-0-7587-0111-4(X)) Book Wholesalers, Inc.

Keats, Ezra Jack & Keats, Ezra Jack. Goggles! 1998. (Illus.). (J). (ps-ps). lib. bdg. 15.30 (978-0-8085-2315-4(5)) Tandem Library Bks.

Kehret, Peg. Escaping the Giant Wave. 2003. (Illus.). 160p. (J). 16.99 (978-0-689-85272-5(X)) Simon & Schuster Children's Publishing.

Kessler, Liz. Emily Windsnap & the Monster from the Deep. Gibb, Sarah, illus. 2007. (Emily Windsnap Ser.). 240p. (J). (gr. 3-7). 5.99 (*978-0-7636-3301-1(1)) Candlewick Pr.

Key, Watt. Alabama Moon. 2006. 304p. (J). 16.00 (978-0-374-30184-2(0)) Farrar, Straus & Giroux.

Kimmel, Haven. Kaline Klattermaster's Tree House. Brown, Peter, illus. 2008. 160p. (J). 15.99 (*978-0-689-87402-4(2) , Atheneum) Simon & Schuster Children's Publishing.

Klein, Abby. Don't Sit on My Lunch! McKinley, John, illus. 2005. 96p. (J). (ps-3). lib. bdg. 11.19 (978-0-606-34119-6(6)) Tandem Library Bks.

—Don't Sit on My Lunch. Mckinley, John, illus. 2005. (Ready, Freddy! Ser.: No. 4). 96p. (J). pap. 15.95 (978-0-439-55601-9(5)); 4th ed. pap. 3.99 (978-0-439-55602-6(3)) Scholastic, Inc. (Blue Sky Pr., The).

—Super-secret Valentine. 2007. (Ready, Freddy! Ser.: No. 10). 96p. (J). pap. 3.99 (978-0-439-78459-7(X) , Blue Sky Pr., The) Scholastic, Inc.

—Talent Show Scaredy-Pants. McKinley, John, illus. 2005. (J). pap. (978-0-439-55603-3(1) , Blue Sky Pr., The); 5th ed. (Ready, Freddy! Ser.: No. 5). 96p. pap. 3.99 (978-0-439-55604-0(X)) Scholastic, Inc.

Krensky, Stephen. Louise Takes Charge. 2000. (gr. 3-6). lib. bdg. 11.80 (978-0-613-85723-9(2)); (Illus.). (J). (978-0-606-18423-6(6)) Tandem Library Bks.

Kristiansson, Leif. Not My Fault. Stenberg, Dick, illus. 2006. 32p. (J). 11.95 (978-0-9762056-6-1(1)) Heryin Publishing Corp.

Kroll, Steven. Jungle Bullies. Nguyen, Vincent, illus. 2006. 32p. (J). 16.99 (978-0-7614-5297-3(4)) Cavendish, Marshall Corp.

Kurzweil, Allen. Leon & the Champion Chip. Bertholf, Bret, illus. 2007. 352p. (J). pap. 6.99 (*978-0-06-053935-1(6) , Harper Trophy) HarperCollins Pubs.

Lee, Quinlan B. The Great Ant Adventure. Harris, Annmarie, ed. 2006. (Ant Bully Ser.). (Illus.). 32p. (J). pap. 3.99 (978-0-439-85680-5(9) , Scholastic) Scholastic, Inc.

Lenain, Thierry. Little Zizi. Zolinsky, Daniel, tr. from FRE. Poulin, Stephane, illus. 2008. 32p. (J). 16.95 (*978-1-933693-05-7(3)) Cinco Puntos Pr.

Linden, Dianne. Peacekeepers. (J). 82p. stu. ed. 9.95 (978-1-55050-297-8(2)); 2004. (Illus.). 220p. (gr. 4-7). pap. 7.95 (978-1-55050-271-8(9)) Coteau Bks. CAN. *Dist:* Fitzhenry & Whiteside, Ltd.

Lindquist, Susan Hart. Summer Soldiers. 2000. (J). (978-0-606-19132-6(1)) Tandem Library Bks.

Linko, G. J. Allie's Answers. 2004. (Seekers Ser.). 5.99 (978-0-8066-4179-9(7) , Augsburg Bks.) Augsburg Fortress, Pubs.

Lloyd, Ellen. Freckles. 2000. (Illus.). 36p. (J). (ps-2). 14.95 (978-0-9650449-0-5(4)) Butterfly Creations, Inc.

Lovell, Patty. Stand Tall, Molly Lou Melon. Catrow, David, illus. 2001. 32p. (J). (ps-3). 15.99 (978-0-399-23416-3(0) , Putnam Juvenile) Penguin Group (USA) Inc.

—Stand Tall, Molly Lou Melon. 2002. (J). (gr. k-3). 25.95 incl. audio (978-0-8045-6891-3(X)) Spoken Arts, Inc.

Ludwig, Trudy. Just Kidding. Gustavson, Adam, illus. 2006. 32p. (J). 15.95 (978-1-58246-163-2(5) , Tricycle Pr.) Ten Speed Pr.

—My Secret Bully. rev. ed. 2005. (Illus.). 32p. (J). (ps-6). 15.95 (978-1-58246-159-5(7) , Tricycle Pr.) Ten Speed Pr.

Ludwig Trudy. Solo Bromeando. Gustavson Adam, illus. 2006. (SPA.). 32p. 15.95 (978-1-58246-177-9(5) , Tricycle Pr.) Ten Speed Pr.

Lupica, Mike. Hot Hand. 2007. (Mike Lupica's Comeback Kids Ser.). 165p. (J). (gr. 4-7). 9.99 (*978-0-399-24714-9(9) , Philomel) Penguin Group (USA) Inc.

Lutz, Norma Jean. Grace & the Bully: Drought on the Frontier. 2006. 144p. (J). pap. 4.97 (978-1-59789-102-8(9)) Barbour Publishing, Inc.

—Trouble on the Ohio River: Drought Shuts Down a City, 1999. (American Adventure Ser.: No. 15). 144p. (J). (gr. 3-7). lib. bdg. 15.95 (978-0-7910-5588-5(4) , Chelsea Hse.) Facts On File, Inc.

Mackall, Dandi. Larger-Than-Life Lara. 2006. 195p. (J). (gr. 5). 16.99 (978-0-525-47726-6(8) , Dutton Juvenile) Penguin Group (USA) Inc.

Mackall, Dandi Daley. Don't Cry, Lion! 2007. 26p. (J). bds. 6.99 (*978-1-4003-1008-1(3)) Nelson, Thomas Inc.

Mackenzie, Catherine. The Dark Blue Bike at No 17: Tammy & Jake learn about Friendship & Bullying. (Illus.). 160p. (J). mass mkt. 5.99 (978-1-85792-732-0(X) , Christian Focus) Christian Focus Pubns. GBR. *Dist:* Riverside.

MacPhail, Catherine. Get That Ghost to Go! Donnelly, Karen, illus. 2006. (Pathway Books). 83p. (J). 21.26 (978-1-59889-004-4(2)) Stone Arch Bks.

Maddox, Jake. On the Line. Tiffany, Sean, illus. 2007. (Jake Maddox Sports Story Ser.). 65p. (J). (gr. 4-8). lib. bdg. 21.26 (978-1-59889-062-4(X)) Stone Arch Bks.

Maguire, Gregory. Three Rotten Eggs. Clayton, Elaine, illus. 2002. 192p. (J). (gr. 4-6). 16.00 (978-0-618-09655-8(8) , Clarion Bks.) Houghton Mifflin Co. Trade & Reference Div.

Malcolm, Jahnna N. Blubberina: Names Can Never Hurt Me! 2001. (Bad News Ballet Ser.: Vol. 5). 135p. (J). (gr. 3-7). pap. 3.95 (978-0-9700164-4-7(1)) Starcatcher Pr.

Mammay, Judith. Knowing Joseph. 2008. (Illus.). 256p. (YA). (gr. 2-7). 16.95 (*978-1-933831-05-3(7)) Blooming Tree Pr.

Marino, Peter. Dough Boy. 176p. (YA). (gr. 7-12). 16.95 (978-0-8234-1873-2(1)) Holiday Hse., Inc.

Mayer, Gina. Just a Bully. 1999. (ps-2). lib. bdg. 11.00 (978-0-613-27921-5(2)) Tandem Library Bks.

Mayer, Mercer & Mayer, Gina. Just a Bully. Mayer, Mercer, illus. 1999. (Little Critter Ser.). (J). (ps-3). 10.09 (978-0-606-19800-4(8)) Tandem Library Bks.

Mayfield, Sue. Drowning Anna. 2002. 320p. (gr. 5-9). 15.99 (978-0-7868-0870-0(5)) Disney Pr.

—Drowning Anna. 2004. 256p. (gr. 7-17). reprint ed. pap. 5.99 (978-0-7868-0957-8(4)) Hyperion Bks. for Children.

McCain, Becky Ray. Nobody Knew What to Do: A Story about Bullying. Leonardo, Todd, illus. 2001. (Concept Book Ser.). 32p. (J). (gr. 1-4). 15.95 (978-0-8075-5711-2(0)) Whitman, Albert & Co.

McCully, Emily Arnold. Grandmas Trick-or-Treat. McCully, Emily Arnold, illus. 2002. (Illus.). 12.34 (978-1-4046-1307-2(2)) Book Wholesalers, Inc.

—Grandmas Trick-or-Treat. McCully, Emily Arnold, illus. 2001. (I Can Read Bks.). (Illus.). 48p. (J). (gr. k-3). 14.95 (978-0-06-028730-6(6)) HarperCollins Pubs.

McKay, Hilary. Indigo's Star. 272p. (J). (gr. 3-7). 2004. (Illus.). 16.95 (978-0-689-86563-3(5) , McElderry, Margaret K.); 2006. reprint ed. pap. 5.99 (978-1-4169-1403-7(X) , Aladdin) Simon & Schuster Children's Publishing.

McKeon, Kathryn Cristaldi. Baseball Ballerina Strikes Out. 2000. (Illus.). (J). (978-0-606-18483-0(X)) Tandem Library Bks.

McLelland, Michael J. Beating the Bully. Kirk, Andrea Cope, illus. 2007. 16p. (J). 15.99 (*978-1-59955-006-0(7)) Cedar Fort, Inc./CFI Distribution.

McNish, Cliff. Angel. 2008. (Exceptional Reading & Language Arts Titles for Upper Grades Ser.). (J). 16.95 (*978-0-8225-8900-6(1) , Carolrhoda Bks.) Lerner Publishing Group.

Meacham, Margaret. Quiet! You're Invisible. 2001. 120p. (J). (gr. 4-6). tchr. ed. 15.95 (978-0-8234-1651-6(8)) Holiday Hse., Inc.

Mead, Alice. Junebug & the Reverend. 2002. (Illus.). (J). 13.40 (978-0-7587-6518-5(5)) Book Wholesalers, Inc.

—Junebug & the Reverend. 2000. (J). (ps-7). 186p. per. 13.00 (978-0-613-21831-3(0)); (Illus.). 11.64 (978-0-606-18785-5(5)) Tandem Library Bks.

Milky, Dj. Kung Fu Klutz & Karate Cool, Vol. 1. 2007. (Illus.). 192p. pap. 4.99 (*978-1-59816-052-9(4) , Tokyopop Kids) TOKYOPOP, Inc.

Montanari, Eva, illus. Carlo Castlecrusher. 2006. 40p. (J). 16.50 (978-1-933327-16-7(2)); 15.95 (978-1-933327-15-0(4)) Purple Bear Bks., Inc.

Montes, Marisa. A Crazy Mixed-Up Spanglish Day. Cepeda, Joe, illus. 2003. (Get Ready for Gabi Ser.). 128p. (J). pap. 12.95 (978-0-439-51710-2(9) , Scholastic Paperbacks) Scholastic, Inc.

—A Crazy Mixed-Up Spanglish Day. 2003. (gr. 3-6). lib. bdg. 11.80 (978-0-613-72003-8(2)) Tandem Library Bks.

Morpurgo, Michael. Snakes & Ladders. Wilson, Anne, illus. 2006. 46p. (J). (978-0-7787-0952-7(3)) Crabtree Publishing Co.

Morris, Rosalind. Drawkcab Brown Stops a Bully. 2004. 35p. pap. 17.95 (978-1-4137-1379-4(3)) PublishAmerica, Inc.

Moss, Marissa. Amelia Takes Command. 1999. (Amelia's Notebooks). (Illus.). 48p. (J). (ps-7). lib. bdg. 12.75 (978-0-606-19868-4(7)) Tandem Library Bks.

—Amelia's Bully Survival Guide. Moss, Marissa, illus. 2006. (Amelia's Notebooks). (Illus.). 40p. (J). 9.95 (978-1-4169-0907-1(9)) Simon & Schuster Children's Publishing.

Moss, Peggy. Say Something. Lyon, Lea, illus. 2005. 32p. (J). (gr. 2-6). 16.95 (978-0-88448-261-1(8)) Tilbury Hse. Pubs.

Muller, Mindy. Allie's Answers. ldr.'s ed. 2004. (Seekers Ser.). 3.99 (978-0-8066-4182-9(7)) Augsburg Fortress, Pubs.

Myers, Bill. My Life As a Smashed Burrito. 1999. (Incredible Worlds of Wally McDoogle Ser.: No. 1). 128p. (J). (gr. 3-7). pap. 1.99 (978-0-8499-7508-0(5)) Nelson, Thomas Inc.

—My Life As A Smashed Burrito. Mangiat, Jeff, illus. 2005. (Incredible Worlds of Wally McDoogle Ser.: Vol. 1). 128p. (J). 9.99 (978-1-4003-0571-1(3)) Nelson, Thomas Inc.

Myers, Walter Dean. Shooter. (J). 2004. 224p. 15.99 (978-0-06-029519-6(8) , HarperTeen); 2004. (Illus.). 240p. lib. bdg. 16.89 (978-0-06-029520-2(1) , HarperTeen); 2005. 256p. reprint ed. pap. 7.99 (978-0-06-447290-6(6) , Amistad) HarperCollins Pubs.

—Shooter. l.t. ed. 2004. 213p. 22.95 (978-0-7862-6969-3(3) , Large Print Pr.) Thorndike Pr.

Nagda, Ann Whitehead. Tarantula Power! Roth, Stéphanie, illus. 2007. 96p. (J). (gr. 2-5). 15.95 (978-0-8234-1991-3(6)) Holiday Hse., Inc.

Naylor, Phyllis Reynolds. Roxie & the Hooligans. Boiger, Alexandra, illus. 128p. (J). 2007. (gr. 3-5). pap. 4.99 (***978-1-4169-0244-7(9)*** , Aladdin); 2006. (gr. 2-5). 16.99 (978-1-4169-0243-0(0) , Atheneum) Simon & Schuster Children's Publishing.

Nickle, John. The Ant Bully. 2006. (Illus.). 32p. (J). pap. 5.99 (978-0-439-85116-9(5) , Scholastic); pap. 16.99 (978-0-590-39591-5(2)) Scholastic, Inc.

Nolen, Jerdine. Plantzilla Goes to Camp. Catrow, David, illus. 2006. 32p. (J). (gr. k-3). 16.95 (978-0-689-86803-0(0)) Simon & Schuster Children's Publishing.

Norman, Tony. Nervous. Savage, Paul, illus. 2006. 40p. (J). (gr. 2-3). lib. bdg. (978-1-59889-018-1(2)) Stone Arch Bks.

O'Dell, Kathleen. Agnes Parker... Girl in Progress. Harper, Charise Mericle. illus. 2003. 160p. (J). (gr. 5). 16.99 (978-0-8037-2648-2(1) , Dial) Penguin Group (USA) Inc.

—Agnes Parker... Girl in Progress. 2004. 176p. (J). (gr. 3-6). reprint ed. pap. 5.99 (978-0-14-240228-3(1) , Puffin) Penguin Group (USA) Inc.

O'Neill, Alexis. The Recess Queen. Huliska-Beith, Laura, illus. 2002. 32p. (J). (ps-2). pap. 16.95 (978-0-439-20637-2(5) , Scholastic Pr.) Scholastic, Inc.

Pascal, Francine. The Ruling Class. (YA). 2006. 208p. pap. 8.99 (978-0-689-87333-1(6) , Simon Pulse); 2004. 192p. 14.95 (978-0-689-87332-4(8) , Simon & Schuster/Paula Wiseman Bks.) Simon & Schuster Children's Publishing.

Paterson, Katherine. The Field of the Dogs. McCully, Emily Arnold, illus. (J). 2002. 112p. pap. 5.99 (978-0-06-442147-8(3)); 2001. 96p. (gr. 4-7). 14.89 (978-0-06-029475-5(2)) HarperCollins Pubs.

—The Field of the Dogs. 2002. (gr. 3-6). lib. bdg. 13.00 (978-0-613-62947-8(7)) Tandem Library Bks.

Patneaude, David. Colder Than Ice. 2003. (J). (gr. 4-7). 168p. 15.95 (978-0-8075-8135-3(6)); 167p. pap. 6.95 (978-0-8075-8136-0(4)) Whitman, Albert & Co.

Pearson, Tracey Campbell. Myrtle. Pearson, Tracey Campbell, illus. 2004. (Illus.). 32p. (J). 15.00 (978-0-374-35157-1(0) , Farrar, Straus & Giroux (BYR)) Farrar, Straus & Giroux.

Peretti, Frank. Hangman's Curse: The Veritas Project - Volume 1. 2008. 352p. (YA). mass mkt. 7.99 (***978-1-4003-1016-6(4)***) Nelson, Thomas Inc.

Pilkey, Dav. Ricky Ricotta's Giant Robot. Ontiveros, Martin, illus. 2000. (Ricky Ricotta Ser.: Bk. 1). (ps-3). 111p. (J). pap. 16.95 (978-0-590-30719-2(3)); 112p. mass mkt. 3.99 (978-0-590-30720-8(7)) Scholastic, Inc. (Blue Sky Pr., The).

Pinkwater, Daniel M. Yo-Yo Man. Davis, Jack E., illus. 2007. 32p. (J). (ps-3). 16.99 (978-0-06-055502-3(5)); lib. bdg. 17.89 (978-0-06-055503-0(3)) HarperCollins Pubs.

Pitts, Constance. Chulita the Blind Cat. 2007. (Illus.). 48p. (J). (***978-0-9652902-2-7(0)***) Beevinwood, Inc.

Polacco, Patricia. Mr. Lincoln's Way. Polacco, Patricia, illus. 2001. (Illus.). 40p. (J). (gr. 1-4). 16.99 (978-0-399-23754-6(2) , Philomel) Penguin Group (USA) Inc.

Proimos, James. Cowboy Boy. 2003. 96p. (J). 14.95 (978-0-439-41681-8(7) , Scholastic Pr.) Scholastic, Inc.

Prose, Francine. Bullyville. 2007. 272p. (J). (gr. 5-8). 16.99 (***978-0-06-057497-0(6)***; lib. bdg. 17.89 (***978-0-06-057498-7(4)***) HarperCollins Pubs. (HarperTeen).

Prue, Sally. The Devil's Toenail. 2004. (Illus.). 208p. (J). 16.95 (978-0-439-48634-7(3)) Scholastic, Inc.

Radford, Michelle. Almost Fabulous. 2008. 256p. (J). pap. 8.99 (***978-0-06-125235-8(2)*** , HarperTeen) HarperCollins Pubs.

Recorvits, Helen. Yoon & the Jade Bracelet. Swiatkowska, Gabriela, illus. 2008. (J). (978-0-374-38689-4(7)) Farrar, Straus & Giroux.

Robert, Na'íma bint. Don't Bully Me. Mistry, Nilesh, illus. 2004. (ENG, ITA & POL.). (J). (978-1-84444-558-5(5)) Mantra Publishing, Ltd.

Roberts, Willo Davis. The Kidnappers: A Mystery. 1999. (J). (978-0-606-16224-1(0)) Tandem Library Bks.

Robinson, Anne. Tom Turkey. 2001. (J). cd-rom 9.95 (978-1-58338-357-5(3)) CrossroadsPub.com.

Robinson, Catherine. Pigface. 2003. (Illus.). 129p. pap. 8.99 (978-0-552-54860-1(X) , Corgi) Transworld Publishers Ltd. GBR. *Dist:* Trafalgar Square Publishing.

Ross, Tony. Is it Because? 2005. (Illus.). 32p. (J). 9.95 (978-0-7641-5830-8(9)) Barron's Educational Series, Inc.

Rue, Nancy N. Sophie Breaks the Code, Vol. 7. 2005. (Faithgirlz Ser.). (Illus.). 144p. (J). pap. 6.99 (978-0-310-71022-6(7)) Zonderkidz.

Saksena, Kate. Hang on in There, Shelley. 2003. 219p. (J). 16.95 (978-1-58234-822-3(7) , Bloomsbury Children) Bloomsbury Publishing.

Schirripa, Steven R. & Fleming, Charles. Nicky Deuce: Home for the Holidays. 2006. 208p. (J). (gr. 4-7). 15.95 (978-0-385-73258-1(9)); lib. bdg. 17.99 (978-0-385-90276-2(X)) Random Hse. Children's Bks. (Delacorte Bks. for Young Readers).

Schneider, Richard H. The Christmas Pea Coat. Bond, Higgins, illus. 2004. 32p. (J). 14.95 (978-0-8249-5474-1(2)) Ideals Pubns.

Scholastic, Inc. Staff. The Ant Bully: Play-Along Sticker Storybook. Harris, Annmarie, ed. 2006. (Ant Bully Ser.). 16p. (J). pap. 4.99 (978-0-439-85682-9(5) , Scholastic) Scholastic, Inc.

Sfar, Joann. Little Vampire Does Kung Fu! Sfar, Joann, illus. 2003. (Illus.). 40p. (J). 12.95 (978-0-689-85769-0(1)) Simon & Schuster Children's Publishing.

Sheldon, Dyan. My Brother Is a Superhero. 1998. (gr. 3-6). lib. bdg. 13.00 (978-0-613-74681-6(3)) Tandem Library Bks.

Shepard, Aaron. Timothy Tolliver & the Bully Basher. 2005. 48p. (J). pap. 6.00 (978-0-938497-24-0(3)); lib. bdg. 15.00 (978-0-938497-23-3(5)) Shepard Pubns. (Skyhook Pr.).

Slater, David Michael. Comin' Through. Rooney, Ronnie, illus. 2007. (Missy Swiss & More Ser.). 32p. (J). (ps-4). lib. bdg. 27.07 (***978-1-60270-008-6(7)*** , Looking Glass Library) Magic Wagon.

Smallcomb, Pam. Camp Buccaneer. Lichtenheld, Tom, illus. 2002. (Ready-for-Chapters Ser.). 64p. (J). (gr. 1-3). lib. bdg. 11.89 (978-0-689-84383-9(6) , Aladdin Library) Simon & Schuster Children's Publishing.

Smith Dinbergs, Holly. Bowling Buddies. Foye, Lloyd, illus. 2005. (Girlz Rock! Ser.). (J). pap. (978-1-59336-699-5(X)) Mondo Publishing.

Sommer, Carl. Spike the Rebel. Vignolo, Enrique, illus. 2007. (J). (***978-1-57537-023-1(9)***); lib. bdg. (***978-1-57537-072-9(7)***) Advance Publishing, Inc.

Sonenklar, Carol. Mighty Boy. 1999. 128p. (J). (gr. 3-7). 16.99 (978-0-531-33203-0(9)); pap. 15.95 (978-0-531-30203-3(2)) Scholastic, Inc. (Orchard Bks.).

Stellinga, Mark. Buster Boogernose & the Bully. 2007. (J). per. 9.95 (***978-0-9796421-2-8(4)***) Stellinga, Mark.

Sweeney, Jacqueline. Freddy Bear. 2001. (We Can Read! Ser.). (Illus.). 32p. (J). (gr. 1-2). lib. bdg. 21.36 (978-0-7614-1121-5(6) , Benchmark Bks.) Cavendish, Marshall Corp.

Thesman, Jean. Other Ones. 2001. (gr. 5-8). lib. bdg. 14.15 (978-0-613-43861-2(2)) Tandem Library Bks.

Tipene, Tim. Taming the Taniwha. Campbell, Henry, illus. 2001. 32p. (J). pap. 12.95 (978-1-877266-52-2(3)) Huia Pubs. NZL. *Dist:* Pacific Island Bks.

Trouble in the Barkers' Class. 2005. (J). 27.95 incl. audio (978-0-8045-6935-4(5)); 29.95 incl. audio compact disk (978-0-8045-4134-3(5)) Spoken Arts, Inc.

Tullson, Diane. Edge. 2002. (Illus.). 212p. (YA). pap. 6.95 (978-0-7737-6230-5(2)) Stoddart Kids CAN. *Dist:* Fitzhenry & Whiteside, Ltd.

—Edge. 2003. (gr. 7-12). lib. bdg. 15.25 (978-0-613-81887-2(3)) Tandem Library Bks.

Van Draanen, Wendelin. Secret Identity. Biggs, Brian, illus. unabr. ed. 2006. (Shredderman Ser.: Bk. 1). (J). (gr. 2-4). pap. 24.95 incl. audio (***978-1-59519-762-7(1)***); pap. 28.95 incl. audio compact disk (***978-1-59519-763-4(X)***) Live Oak Media.

—Secret Identity. Biggs, Brian, illus. (Shredderman Ser.: Bk. 1). 144p. (J). (gr. 2-5). 2004. 12.95 (978-0-375-82351-0(4) , Knopf Bks. for Young Readers); 2004. lib. bdg. 14.99 (978-0-375-92351-7(9) , Knopf Bks. for Young Readers); 2006. reprint ed. 5.50 (978-0-440-41912-9(3) , Yearling) Random Hse. Children's Bks.

Voigt, Cynthia. Bad Girls, Bad Girls, Whatcha Gonna Do? 2006. (Bad Girls Ser.). 448p. (YA). (gr. 7 up). 17.95 (978-0-689-82474-6(2)) Simon & Schuster Children's Publishing.

Wallace, Carol & Wallace, Bob. Bub, Snow, & the Burly Bear Scare. 2003. (gr. 3-6). lib. bdg. 13.00 (978-0-613-70870-8(9)) Tandem Library Bks.

Warner, Sally. Super Emma. Harper, Jamie, illus. (J). 2008. 112p. (gr. 3). 5.99 (***978-0-14-241088-2(8)*** , Puffin); 2006. 96p. (gr. 2). 14.99 (978-0-670-06140-2(9) , Viking Juvenile) Penguin Group (USA) Inc.

Washakie, John. Yuse: The Bully & the Bear. Cox, Jon, illus. 2nd ed. 2004. 47p. (J). 14.95 (978-0-9759806-0-6(2)) Painted Pony, Inc.

Watkins, Greg. A Big Beaked, Big Bellied Bird Named Bill. 2006. 32p. 15.99 (978-1-58980-441-8(4)) Pelican Publishing Co., Inc.

Weeks, Jan. The Marathon Runner. Harrison, Paul, illus. 2006. (Read-It! Chapter Books). 64p. (J). (gr. 2-4). 19.95 (978-1-4048-1669-5(0)) Picture Window Bks.

Weeks, Sarah. Beware of Mad Dog! 2006. (Boyds Will Be Boyds Ser.: No. 1). 128p. (J). pap. 4.99 (978-0-439-57469-3(2)) Scholastic, Inc.

Wilhelm, Doug. The Revealers. 224p. (J). 2003. 16.00 (978-0-374-36255-3(6) , Farrar, Straus & Giroux (BYR)); 2005. reprint ed. pap. 6.95 (978-0-374-46243-7(7) , Sunburst) Farrar, Straus & Giroux.

Wilson, Jacqueline. Bad Girls. Sharratt, Nick, illus. 2000. (Yearling Book Ser.). 192p. pap. 9.99 (978-0-440-86356-4(2) , Corgi); 177p. (J). (gr. 3-7). 16.95 (978-0-385-40702-1(5)) Transworld Publishers Ltd. GBR. *Dist:* Trafalgar Square Publishing.

—My Brother Bernadette. Roberts, David, illus. 2002. (Yellow Bananas Ser.). 48p. (J). (gr. 3-4). pap. (978-0-7787-0986-2(8)); lib. bdg. (978-0-7787-0940-4(X)) Crabtree Publishing Co.

—My Brother Bernadette. 2002. (gr. 3-6). lib. bdg. 12.95 (978-0-613-52884-9(0)) Tandem Library Bks.

Winstead, Rosie. Ruby & Bubbles. 2006. (Illus.). 32p. (J). (ps). 15.99 (978-0-8037-3024-3(1) , Dial) Penguin Group (USA) Inc.

Wojciechowski, Susan. Beany & the Meany. Natti, Susanna, illus. 112p. (J). (gr. 1-4). 2006. pap. 4.99 (978-0-7636-2974-8(X)); 2005. 15.99 (978-0-7636-2630-3(9)) Candlewick Pr.

Yep, Laurence. Cockroach Cooties. 2001. 144p. (gr. 3-7). pap. 5.99 (978-0-7868-1338-4(5)) Hyperion Bks. for Children.

—Cockroach Cooties. 2001. (gr. 3-6). lib. bdg. 14.15 (978-0-613-45730-9(7)) Tandem Library Bks.

Young, Steve. Winchell Mink: The Misadventure Begins. 2004. 144p. (J). 16.89 (978-0-06-053500-1(8)) HarperCollins Pubs.

Zucker, Jonny. Skateboard Power. Savage, Paul, illus. 2006. 40p. (J). (gr. 2-3). lib. bdg. (978-1-59889-007-5(7)) Stone Arch Bks.

—Steel Eyes. Savage, Paul, illus. 2006. (Keystone Books (Stone Arch)). 33p. (J). (978-1-59889-019-8(0)) Stone Arch Bks.

BULLYING

Amos, Janine, et al. Why Tease? 2007. (Problem Solvers Ser.). (Illus.). 32p. (J). pap. 12.95 (***978-1-84234-196-4(0)*** , Evans Brothers, Limited) Evans Publishing Group GBR. *Dist:* Independent Pubs. Group.

Berry, Joy Wilt. A Book about Being Bullied. 2005. (Illus.). (J). (978-0-7172-8578-5(2)) Scholastic, Inc.

—A Book about Teasing. 2005. (Illus.). (J). (978-0-7172-8580-8(4)) Scholastic, Inc.

Birky, Joy. Bully Bill. Thompson, Chad, illus. 2007. (J). (ps-k). pap. 12.99 (***978-0-8361-9382-4(2)***) Herald Pr.

Boatwright, Becki H., et al. Getting Equipped to Stop Bullying: A Kid's Survival Kit for Understanding & Coping with Violence in the Schools. 1998. (Illus.). 254p. (YA). (gr. 5-8). pap. 12.95 (978-0-932796-84-4(2)) Educational Media Corp.

Cooper, Kathy. Ready Freddy: A Conflict-Resolution Program of Skits & Activities Dealing with Bullies. Lardner, Walter, illus. 2000. 104p. (J). (gr. 2-5). 15.95 (978-1-57543-105-5(X)) MAR*CO Products, Inc.

Dailey, D. C. Billy the Bully. l.t. ed. 2005. (Illus.). 32p. (J). 10.95 (978-1-929662-04-3(1)) Brighter Horizons Publishing.

—Billy the Bully Educators Edition. l.t. ed. 2005. (Illus.). 36p. (J). 15.95 (978-1-929662-05-0(X)) Brighter Horizons Publishing.

—Mindy the Meanie. l.t. ed. 2005. (Illus.). 34p. (J). 10.95 (978-1-929662-06-7(8)) Brighter Horizons Publishing.

—Mindy the Meanie Educators Edition. l.t. ed. 2005. (Illus.). 36p. (J). 15.95 (978-1-929662-07-4(6)) Brighter Horizons Publishing.

Elliott, Michelle. Bullying. 2nd ed. 2005. (Illus.). (YA). pap. 12.00 (978-0-340-88391-4(X) , Hodder & Stoughton) Hodder General Publishing Division GBR. *Dist:* Trafalgar Square Publishing.

Emzer, Counselor. Duane, You Must be Insane. 2005. 19p. 9.87 (978-1-4116-4461-8(1)) Lulu.com.

Everly, Nita. Early Social Behavior Books Can You Stand up for Yourself. 2007. (J). spiral bd. 11.95 (***978-0-7606-0740-4(0)***) LinguiSystems, Inc.

Fieldler, Julie & Kravetz, Jonathan. How to Deal with Teasing. 2007. (Let's Work It Out Ser.). (Illus.). 24p. (J). (gr. 2-5). lib. bdg. 21.25 (***978-1-4042-3675-2(9)*** , PowerKids Pr.) Rosen Publishing Group, Inc., The.

Finn, Carrie. Kids Talk about Bullying. Muehlenhardt, Amy Bailey, illus. 2006. (Kids Talk Junior Ser.). 32p. (J). (gr. k-2). lib. bdg. 23.93 (978-1-4048-2315-0(8)) Picture Window Bks.

Free Spirit Publishing. How to be Bully Free: Word Searches, Mazes, What-Ifs, & Other Fun Activities for Kids. 2006. (Illus.). 32p. (gr. 3-5). pap., wbk. ed. 5.95 (978-1-57542-215-2(8)) Free Spirit Publishing, Inc.

Harold, Elsie Louise. Stop Bullying: An ABC Guide for Children & the Adults Who Interact with Them. Harold, Elsie Louise, illus. 2004. (J). spiral bd. 14.99 (978-0-9764644-0-2(3)) Harold, Elsie L.

Heller Korin, Ellen S. Asperger Syndrome an Owner's Manual: What You, Your Parents & Your Teachers Need to Know. 2006. (YA). wbk. ed. 17.95 (978-1-931282-91-8(9)) Autism Asperger Publishing Co.

Johnson, Julie. Bullies & Gangs. 2007. (J). (***978-1-59604-150-9(1)***) Stargazer Bks.

Johnston, Marianne. Dealing with Bullying. 1998. (Conflict Resolution Library). (Illus.). 24p. (J). (gr. k-4). pap. 6.95 (978-1-56838-266-1(9)) Hazelden Publishing & Educational Services.

Kravetz, Jonathan. How to Deal with Bullies. 2007. (Let's Work It Out Ser.). (Illus.). 24p. (J). (gr. 2-5). lib. bdg. 21.25 (978-1-4042-3670-7(8)) Rosen Publishing Group, Inc., The.

Leaney, Cindy. Long Walk to School: Safety Outdoors. Wilks, Peter, illus. 2003. (Hello Club Safety Ser.). 32p. (J). 28.50 (978-1-58952-745-4(3)) Rourke Publishing, LLC.

Leigh, Susan K. God, I Need to Talk to You about Bullying. Clark, Bill, illus. 2005. (ENG.). 16p. (J). pap. 0.99 (978-0-7586-0796-6(2)) Concordia Publishing Hse.

Levete, Sarah. Keeping Safe. 2006. (Illus.). 32p. (J). (978-1-59604-088-5(2) , 1268913) Stargazer Bks.

Lovegrove, Emily. Help! I'm Being Bullied. 2007. (Illus.). 167p. pap. 16.95 (***978-1-905170-34-0(3)***) Accent Pr. GBR. *Dist:* Dufour Editions, Inc.

McIntosh, Kenneth & Walker, Ida. Youth with Aggression Issues: Bullying & Violence. 2008. (J). (***978-1-4222-0136-7(8)***) Mason Crest Pubs.

Noll, Kathy. Encounters with Every-Day Angels (Workbook) Can You See the Angels (A Workbook on Bullying & Character Development) 2004. (Illus.). 65p. (J). ring bd., wbk. ed. 12.95 (978-0-937004-03-6(0)) Unicorn Pr.

Pitt, Steve. Teasing: Deal with it before the joke's on You. Geoffroi, Remie, illus. 2006. (Deal with It Ser.). 32p. (J). (gr. 4-8). pap. 12.95 (***978-1-55028-946-6(2)***) Lorimer, James & Co., Ltd., Pubs. CAN. *Dist:* Casemate Pubs. & Bk. Distributors, LLC.

Powell, Jillian. Bullying. 1999. (Talking about Ser.). (Illus.). 32p. (J). (gr. k-4). lib. bdg. 25.70 (978-0-8172-5535-0(4)) Raintree.

Richards, Melissa. I Didn't Know I Was a Bully: A Meaningful & Memorable Reproducible Story Plus Six Literatur-Based Lessons on Bullying Behaviors. 2005. pap. 19.95 (***978-1-57543-138-3(6)***) MAR*CO Products, Inc.

Sanders, Pete. Dealing with Bullying. 2007. (Choices & Decisions Ser.). (Illus.). 32p. (J). (***978-1-59604-095-3(5)***) Stargazer Bks.

Slavens, Elaine. Fighting: Without Coming to Blows. Murray, Steven, illus. 2004. (Deal with It Ser.). 32p. (J). (gr. 4-8). 12.95 (978-1-55028-791-2(5)) Lorimer, James & Co., Ltd., Pubs. CAN. *Dist:* Casemate Pubs. & Bk. Distributors, LLC.

Steen, Joel. Home Room 7b. 2005. 64p. pap. 12.95 (978-1-4137-9822-7(5)) PublishAmerica, Inc.

Vandawalker, Marianne. Conquering Bullies: 27 Game-Oriented Guidance Lessons for Grades 2-5 & 12 Story-Based Guidance Lessons for Grades K-12. 2005. pap. 29.95 (***978-1-57543-136-9(X)***) MAR*CO Products, Inc.

Winkler, Kathleen. Bullying: How to Deal with Taunting, Teasing, & Tormenting. 2005. (Issues in Focus Today). (Illus.). 104p. (J). (gr. 6-10). lib. bdg. 31.93 (978-0-7660-2355-0(9)) Enslow Pubs., Inc.

BULLYING—FICTION

Abbott, Jan. Sundance & the Bully. 2002. pap. (978-0-9718565-7-8(5)) Playbooks, Inc.

Acquaire, M. T. Marty Boggs & the Curse of Kutkara's Tomb. 2006. 328p. (YA). 28.99 (978-1-59507-112-5(1) , ArcheBooks) ArcheBooks Publishing.

Aloha Potter! Evaluation Guide: Evaluation Guide. 2006. (J). (978-1-55942-397-7(8)) Marsh Media.

Amos, Janine. Bully. Green, Gwen, illus. 2007. (Good & Bad Ser.). 32p. (J). (ps-2). per. 9.95 (***978-1-84234-393-7(9)*** , Evans Brothers, Limited) Evans Publishing Group GBR. *Dist:* Independent Pubs. Group.

Angerman, Liane. Season of Haze. 2006. 13.00 (***978-0-8059-9197-0(2)***) Dorrance Publishing Co., Inc.

Ashley, Chris. Wasim the Wanderer. 2007. (Illus.). 80p. (J). 15.95 (***978-1-84507-776-1(8)***) Lincoln, Frances Ltd. GBR. *Dist:* Perseus Distribution.

—Wasim the Wanderer. Pankhurst, Kate, illus. 2007. 80p. (J). pap. 7.95 (***978-1-84507-745-7(8)***) Lincoln, Frances Ltd. GBR. *Dist:* Perseus Distribution.

Banting, Celia. I Only Said Yes So That They'd Like Me. 2006. 224p. (YA). per. 14.99 (***978-0-9786648-1-7(7)***) Wighita Pr.

Bates, Penny. A Murder of Crows. 2004. (Shades Ser.). 60p. (J). pap. 7.99 (978-0-237-52648-1(4) , Evans Brothers, Limited) Evans Publishing Group GBR. *Dist:* Independent Pubs. Group.

Beard, Candy J. Please Don't Do That: A Story about Bullying. 2006. (ENG., Illus.). 28p. per. 11.95 (978-1-59800-631-5(2)) Outskirts Press, Inc.

Blume, Judy. Blubber. l.t. ed. 2005. 166p. 23.95 (978-0-7862-7307-2(0) , Large Print Pr.) Thorndike Pr.

Brunstetter, Wanda E. Rachel Yoder: Back to School. 2007. (Rachel yoder Ser.). 160p. (J). pap. 4.97 (***978-1-59789-234-6(3)***) Barbour Publishing, Inc.

Bully Busters in the Adventures of Wooly Bully. 2003. (Illus.). 100p. (J). per. 8.95 (978-0-9770294-0-2(9)) Better Me Bks., Inc.

Carradice, Phil. Nat & the Havannah. 2000. 104p. pap. 12.95 (978-1-85902-719-6(9)) Beekman Bks., Inc.

Carradice, Phil & Thomas, Frances. Hannah Goes to War. 2005. 144p. pap. 12.95 (978-1-84323-461-6(0)) Beekman Bks., Inc.

Carson, Jana. We Both Read-Stop Teasing Taylor! Treatner, Meryl, illus. 2005. (We Both Read Ser.). 44p. (J). (gr. 1-2). 7.99 (978-1-891327-61-2(5)); pap. 3.99 (978-1-891327-62-9(3)) Treasure Bay, Inc.

CHaracter Ed & the Magical Lesson of the Bully. 2004. (J). pap. 15.95 (***978-1-59526-181-6(8)***) Media Creations, Inc.

Clark, Emma Chichester. No More Teasing! 2005. (Illus.). 32p. (J). pap. 8.99 (978-1-84270-470-7(2)) Trafalgar Square Publishing.

Clements, Andrew. Jake Drake, Bully Buster. Pedersen, Janet, illus. 2007. (Jake Drake Ser.). 80p. (J). pap. 3.99 (***978-1-4169-3933-7(4)*** , Aladdin) Simon & Schuster Children's Publishing.

Coughlin, Denise. Dragon in My Pocket. Kastan, Bill, illus. 2005. (J). (***978-0-9765905-0-7(6)***) Rose Valley Publishing.

Dadey, Debbie & Jones, Marcia Thornton. Ghosts Be Gone! Francis, Guy, illus. 2005. 79p. (J). (gr. 2-5). lib. bdg. 11.19 (978-0-606-33841-7(1)) Tandem Library Bks.

Dalton, Annie. Lilac Peabody, No. 4. 2005. (Illus.). 96p. (J). pap. 7.95 (*978-0-00-713774-9(5)) HarperCollins Pubs. Ltd. GBR. *Dist:* Independent Pubs. Group.

Davis, Heather J. The Friendship Hole. 2006. (ENG.). 28p. per. 13.99 (*978-1-4259-7184-7(9)) AuthorHouse.

Day-Bivins, Pat. Bullies Beware! 2006. (Illus.). (J). pap. 16.95 (978-0-9742806-5-3(8)) Heart to Heart Publishing.

Deekster, Deek. Ozzie Rozzie. 2005. 41p. (YA). pap. 7.85 (978-1-4116-6420-3(5)) Lulu.com.

Duracell and the National Center for Missing & Exploited Children (NCMEC), creator. The Great Tomato Adventure: A Story about Smart Safety Choices. 2007. 0.00 (*978-0-9795307-0-8(9)) Duracell & the National Ctr. for Missing & Exploited Children (NCMEC).

Dwyer, Cynthia. Four-Eyed Philip. Schuepbach, Lynnette, illus. 2007. (J). 14.95 (*978-0-9793296-0-9(4) , Thumbprint Pr.) McIntyre, Connie.

Ellis, Ann Dee. This Is What I Did. 2007. 176p. (YA). (gr. 7 up). 16.99 (978-0-316-01363-5(3)) Little Brown & Co.

Evangelista, Beth. Gifted. 2007. 192p. (J). pap. 6.95 (*978-0-8027-9644-8(3)) Walker & Co.

Forde, Catherine. The Drowning Pond. 2006. 256p. (J). pap. 8.99 (*978-1-4052-2176-4(3)) Egmont Bks., Ltd. GBR. *Dist:* Independent Pubs. Group.

Frizzell, Colin. Chill. 2006. 112p. (YA). lib. bdg. 14.95 (978-1-55143-670-8(1)); (gr. 7 up). pap. 8.95 (978-1-55143-507-7(1)) Orca Bk. Pubs. USA.

Gaffney, Linda. My Daddy Does GOOD Things, Too! Dabney, Undra & Goettling, Nickalas, illus. 2006. 55p. per. 10.99 (*978-0-9787501-0-7(1)) Gaffney, Linda.

Gormley, Greg. Rocky & the Lamb. Chapman, Lynne, illus. 2006. 32p. (J). 12.99 (978-0-7641-5939-8(9)) Barron's Educational Series, Inc.

Griffith, Amanda. Two Truths & a Lie. 2006. pap. 15.95 (*978-1-4259-4458-2(2)) AuthorHouse.

Hallam, Gwion. Creadyn: Neu, Huw Dafis A'r Draenog Wnaeth Gnoi at y Gwaed, A'r Corryn Sy'n Crwydro'i Hunllefau. 2005. (WEL.). 171p. 5.99 (978-1-84323-247-6(2)) Gomer Pr. GBR. *Dist:* Gomer Pr.

Hardin, Lori. Squiggly & the Bully. 2006. spiral bd. 9.95 (978-1-57166-407-5(6)) Quixote Pr.

Hayward, Linda. Monster Bug. Palmisciano, Diane, illus. 2004. 32p. (J). lib. bdg. 20.00 (*978-1-4242-1097-8(6)) Fitzgerald Bks.

Hileman, Linda L. Dawn's Secret. 2006. (J). per. 9.95 (978-1-59571-117-5(1)) Word Association Pubs.

Hopkins, Cathy. From Geek to Goddess. 2007. (Zodiac Girls Ser.). 200p. (J). (gr. 4-6). pap. 5.95 (978-0-7534-5895-2(0) , Kingfisher) Houghton Mifflin Co. Trade & Reference Div.

Hughes, Mair Wynn & West, Alex. Ragsi Ragsan. 2005. (WEL., Illus.). 13p. pap. (978-0-86243-455-7(6)) Y Lolfa.

Imes, Jarold. Worth Fighting 4. 2007. 168p. (YA). pap. 10.99 (978-1-934195-01-7(4)) Abednego's Free.

Imes, Jarold, adapted by. U Can't Break Me. 2007. 148p. (YA). pap. 10.99 (*978-1-934195-03-1(0)) Abednego's Free.

Inagaki, Riichiro. Eyeshield 21, Vol. 8. 2006. (Eyeshield 21 Ser.). 208p. (YA). pap. 7.99 (978-1-4215-0637-1(8)) Viz Media.

Jackson, A. Isaiah J. Jiffy: You, You, You. Bully! 2005. 50p. pap. 12.95 (978-1-4137-8524-1(7)) PublishAmerica, Inc.

Johnston, Tony. The Spoon in the Bathroom Wall. 2006. (Illus.). 144p. (J). pap. 5.95 (978-0-15-205625-4(4) , Harcourt Paperbacks) Harcourt Children's Bks.

Jones, Jac. Alison & the Bully Monsters. 2000. (Illus.). 30p. (J). pap. 14.95 (978-1-85902-752-3(0)) Beekman Bks., Inc.

Kita, Joy. Why Be Normal? 2005. 116p. pap. 16.95 (978-1-4137-8094-9(6)) PublishAmerica, Inc.

Knapp, J. Richard. Bobby's Story: An Amazing Story of Teen Courage. 2006. 234p. (YA). per. 12.95 (978-0-9774761-7-6(0) , Books To Believe In) Thornton Publishing.

Koss, Amy Goldman. Poison Ivy. 2006. 176p. (J). 16.95 (978-1-59643-118-8(0)) Macmillan.

Leblanc, Louise. Maddie Stands Tall. Gay, Marie-Louise, illus. 2005. 61p. (J). lib. bdg. 12.00 (*978-1-4242-1200-2(6)) Fitzgerald Bks.

—Maddie Stands Tall. Cummins, Sarah, tr. from FRE. Gay, Marie-Louise, illus. 2005. (First Novel Ser.). 64p. (J). (gr. 2-5). (*978-0-88780-683-4(X)); 4.95 (978-0-88780-682-7(1)) Formac Publishing Co., Ltd. CAN. *Dist:* Casemate Pubs. & Bk. Distributors, LLC.

Love, D. Anne. A Little Rebellion. 2008. 272p. (YA). 16.99 (*978-1-4169-3481-3(2) , McElderry, Margaret K.) Simon & Schuster Children's Publishing.

McAllister, Peter. Bites: Dracula Tooth: Beware Pains in the Neck! rev. ed. 2008. (Nibbles, Bites, & Chomps: Ser.). (Illus.). 112p. (J). pap. 3.95 (*978-0-7624-3055-0(9) , Running Pr. Kids) Running Pr. Bk. Pubs.

McEwan, Jamie. Rufus the Scrub Does Not Wear a Tutu! Margeson, John, illus. 2007. 64p. (J). (gr. 2-3). 14.95 (*978-1-58196-060-0(3)) Darby Creek Publishing.

McNamara, Margaret. Eloise Has a Lesson. Mitter, Kathryn, illus. 2005. (Eloise Ser.). 32p. (J). (ps-1). lib. bdg. 11.19 (978-0-606-33476-1(9)) Tandem Library Bks.

Moore, Monica A. Everyday Heroes. 2006. (ENG.). 52p. per. 12.95 (*978-1-59800-563-9(4)) Outskirts Press, Inc.

Morgan, Anna & Turkienicz, Rachel. My Worst/Best Sleepover Party. 2007. (Illus.). 96p. (J). (gr. 2-4). pap. 7.95 (*978-1-897187-20-3(3)) Second Story Pr. CAN. *Dist:* Orca Bk. Pubs. USA.

Muldrow, Diane. Deep Freeze. Pollack, Barbara, illus. 2007. (Dish Ser.: No. 12). 160p. (J). (gr. 4-7). pap. 4.99 (*978-0-448-44693-6(6) , Grosset & Dunlap) Penguin Group (USA) Inc.

Myers, Anna. Confessions from the Principal's Chair. 2006. 192p. 16.95 (978-0-8027-9560-1(9)) Walker & Co.

Myers, Bill. My Life as a Splatted Flat Quarterback. 2006. (Incredible Worlds of Wally McDoogle Ser.). pap. 6.99 (978-1-4003-0906-1(9)) Nelson, Thomas Inc.

Olsen, Sylvia. White Girl. 2005. (Illus.). 200p. (J). pap. 8.95 (978-1-55039-147-3(X)) Sono Nis Pr. CAN. *Dist:* Orca Bk. Pubs. USA.

Osborn, Kelly. The Green Knight. 2006. 64p. pap. 12.95 (978-1-4241-1741-3(0)) PublishAmerica, Inc.

Pasnak, William. The Ginger Princess. 2006. (Streetlights Ser.). 96p. (J). (gr. 2-5). 7.95 (*978-1-55028-952-7(7)) Lorimer, James & Co., Ltd., Pubs. CAN. *Dist:* Casemate Pubs. & Bk. Distributors, LLC.

Patricia, Murdoch. Exposure. 2006. 112p. (gr. 3-6). lib. bdg. 14.95 (978-1-55143-523-7(3)); (gr. 7-12). pap. 7.95 (978-1-55143-493-3(8)) Orca Bk. Pubs. USA.

Pearce, Jacqueline. Dog House Blues. 2005. 176p. (J). (gr. 3-7). pap. 6.95 (978-1-55143-360-8(5)) Orca Bk. Pubs. USA.

Pendziwol, Jean E. The Tale of Sir Dragon: Dealing with Bullies for Kids (And Dragons) Gourbault, Martine, illus. 2007. 32p. (J). (ps-2). (*978-1-55453-136-3(5)); (*978-1-55453-135-6(7)) Kids Can Pr., Ltd.

Peters, Andrew & Player, Stephen. Ed & the Witchblood. 2005. (Illus.). (J). 18.00 (978-0-340-86551-4(2) , Hodder & Stoughton) Hodder General Publishing Division GBR. *Dist:* Trafalgar Square Publishing.

Peters, Andrew Fusek. Ant & the Big Bad Bully Goat. Wadham, Anna, illus. 2007. 32p. pap. 7.99 (*978-1-84643-079-4(8)) Child's Play International Ltd. GBR. *Dist:* Child's Play-International.

Peters, Andrew Fusek & Player, Stephen. Ed & the Witchblood. 2005. (Illus.). (J). pap. 9.99 (978-0-340-86557-6(1) , Hodder & Stoughton) Hodder General Publishing Division GBR. *Dist:* Trafalgar Square Publishing.

Peterson, Matthew. Paraworld Zero, Pt. 1. 2007. 280p. (YA). pap. 14.99 (978-1-59092-491-4(6) , Blue Works) Windstorm Creative.

—The School of Magical Learning, Vol. 2. 2008. 280p. (YA). pap. 14.99 (978-1-59092-568-3(8) , Blue Works) Windstorm Creative.

Polanski, Sylvia. Pink Lemonade Sky: Five Girls Must Die. 2005. 111p. pap. 16.95 (978-1-4137-5563-3(1)) PublishAmerica, Inc.

Rateau, Loy. David's Prayers: A Boy's Perseverance of Conquering the Enemy. 2005. 17.00 (978-0-8059-9834-4(9)) Dorrance Publishing Co., Inc.

Reynolds, Wendy. Moby for Justice. 2006. 17.00 (*978-0-8059-8861-1(0)) Dorrance Publishing Co., Inc.

Richards, Kitty. Back off, Bully Boys. 2007. 24p. (J). 21.35 (*978-1-59961-355-0(7)) Spotlight.

Ruben, Pamela J. Don't Pick on Pepper! Take a Journey with Pepper as She Takes on a Schoolyard Bully with Brainpower, Humor, & a Dash of Spice! Ruben, Anthony R., ed. 2004. 31p. (J). 12.95 (978-0-9764813-1-7(6)) Peppery Pr.

Rue, Nancy. Sophie Loves Jimmy, Vol. 10. 2006. (Faithgirlz Ser.). 144p. (J). pap. 6.99 (978-0-310-71025-7(1)) Zonderkidz.

Ryan, Darlene. Responsible. 2007. (Orca Soundings Ser.). 112p. (YA). (gr. 7 up). pap. (*978-1-55143-685-2(X)); lib. bdg. (*978-1-55143-687-6(6)) Orca Bk. Pubs.

Said, S. F. The Outlaw Varjak Paw. McKean, Dave, illus. 2007. 272p. (J). (gr. 3-7). 6.50 (978-0-440-42172-6(1) , Yearling) Random Hse. Children's Bks.

Slater, Teddy & Springer, Sally. Trouble for Trudy. 2007. (No Bullies Allowed Ser.). (Illus.). (J). (*978-0-439-89709-9(2)) Scholastic, Inc.

Smith, James. The Wonderer of Time. 2006. 52p. pap. 12.95 (978-1-4241-3316-1(5)) PublishAmerica, Inc.

Soule, Jean Conder. Never Tease a Weasel. Booth, George, illus. 2007. (Picture Book Ser.). 40p. (J). (ps-2). 15.99 (978-0-375-83420-2(6)); lib. bdg. 18.99 (978-0-375-93420-9(0)) Random Hse. Children's Bks. (Random Hse. Bks. for Young Readers).

Sunderland, Margot. A Wibble Called Bipley (And a Few Honks) A Story for Children Who Have Hardened Their Hearts or Become Bullies, 2 vols. Armstrong, Nicky, tr. Armstrong, Nicky, illus. 40p. pap. (978-0-86388-494-8(6) , 002-5060) Speechmark Publishing Ltd.

Ure, Jean. Sugar & Spice. 2005. (Diary Ser.). (Illus.). 224p. (J). pap. 8.99 (*978-0-00-716137-9(9)) HarperCollins Pubs. Ltd. GBR. *Dist:* Independent Pubs. Group.

Walters, Eric & Williams, Jerome. Triple Threat. 2004. (Orca Young Readers Ser.). (Illus.). 144p. (J). (gr. 3-6). pap. 5.95 (978-1-55143-359-2(1)) Orca Bk. Pubs. USA.

Warner, Sally. Super Emma. Harper, Jamie, illus. 2008. 112p. (J). (gr. 3). 5.99 (*978-0-14-241088-2(8) , Puffin) Penguin Group (USA) Inc.

Washington, Kathleen. The School Bully. 2006. 9.00 (978-0-8059-8201-5(9)) Dorrance Publishing Co., Inc.

Watkins, Greg. A Big Beaked, Big Bellied Bird Named Bill. Watkins, Greg, illus. 2005. (Illus.). 30p. 13.95 (978-0-9761318-1-6(1) , 1239651) Cute & Cuddly Productions, Inc.

Watson, Carrie Gordon. Quad. 2007. 304p. (YA). (gr. 9 up). 16.99 (978-1-59514-138-5(3) , Razorbill) Penguin Group (USA) Inc.

Williams, Rachel. Alex & the Bully. 2006. (Illus.). 88p. pap. (*978-1-84401-651-8(X)) Athena Pr.

Wishinsky, Frieda. Dimples Delight. Laliberete, Louise-Andree, illus. 2005. (SPA.). 61p. (J). lib. bdg. 20.00 (*978-1-4242-1252-1(9)) Fitzgerald Bks.

—Dimples Delight. Laliberte, Louise-Andree, illus. 2005. (Orca Echoes Ser.). 64p. (J). (gr. 2-3). pap. 4.99 (978-1-55143-362-2(1)) Orca Bk. Pubs. USA.

BULLION

see Gold; Money; Silver

BUMPPO, NATTY (FICTITIOUS CHARACTER)—FICTION

Cooper, James Fenimore. The Last of the Mohicans. 2002. (Great Illustrated Classics Ser.). (Illus.). 240p. (J). (gr. 3-8). 21.35 (978-1-57765-692-0(X) , ABDO & Daughters) ABDO Publishing Co.

—The Last of the Mohicans. Carrillo, Fred, illus. 2nd ed. 1998. (Illustrated Classic Book Ser.). 61p. (J). (gr. 3 up). reprint ed. pap. 4.95 (978-1-56767-249-7(3)) Educational Insights, Inc.

—The Last of the Mohicans. 2001. (Saddleback Classics). (Illus.). (J). (978-0-606-21559-6(X)) Tandem Library Bks.

BUNCHE, RALPH J. (RALPH JOHNSON), 1904-1971

McKissack, Patricia C. & McKissack, Fredrick L. Ralph J. Bunche: Peacemaker. rev. ed. 2002. (Great African Americans Ser.). (Illus.). 32p. (J). (gr. 1-4). lib. bdg. 18.60 (978-0-7660-1701-6(X)) Enslow Pubs., Inc.

Schraff, Anne. Ralph Bunche: Winner of the Nobel Peace Prize. 1999. (African-American Biographies Ser.). (Illus.). 128p. (J). (gr. 6-12). lib. bdg. 26.60 (978-0-7660-1203-5(4)) Enslow Pubs., Inc.

BUNNICULA (FICTITIOUS CHARACTER)—FICTION

Howe, James. Bunnicula Strikes Again! Daniel, Alan, illus. 1999. (Bunnicula Ser.). 128p. (J). (gr. 3-5). 16.00 (978-0-689-81463-1(1) , Atheneum) Simon & Schuster Children's Publishing.

—Creepy-Crawly Birthday. Morrill, Leslie H., illus. 1999. (Bunnicula & Friends Ser.). 48p. (J). (gr. k-3). pap. 5.95 (978-0-688-16700-4(4)) HarperCollins Pubs.

—The Fright Before Christmas. 1999. (Bunnicula & Friends Ser.). (J). (gr. k-3). (978-0-606-17244-8(0)) Tandem Library Bks.

—Harold & Chester Stories. Date not set. (Bunnicula & Friends Ser.). (J). (gr. k-3). (978-0-688-10298-2(0)); lib. bdg. (978-0-688-10299-9(9)) HarperCollins Pubs.

—Hot Fudge. 1999. (Bunnicula & Friends Ser.). (J). (gr. k-3). (978-0-606-17394-0(3)) Tandem Library Bks.

—Howliday Inn. unabr. ed. 2004. (Bunnicula Ser.). 195p. (J). (gr. 3-7). pap. 29.00 incl. audio (978-0-8072-8382-0(7) , YA179SP, Listening Library) Random Hse. Audio Publishing Group.

—Nighty-Nightmare. unabr. ed. 2004. (Bunnicula Ser.). 128p. (J). (gr. 3-7). pap. 29.00 incl. audio (978-0-8072-8397-4(5) , YA201SP, Listening Library) Random Hse. Audio Publishing Group.

—Rabbit-Cadabra! Daniel, Alan, illus. 1999. (Bunnicula & Friends Ser.). 48p. (J). (gr. k-3). pap. 5.95 (978-0-688-16699-1(7)) HarperCollins Pubs.

—Scared Silly. Morrill, Leslie H., illus. 1998. (Bunnicula & Friends Ser.). 48p. (J). (gr. k-3). pap. 4.95 (978-0-688-16322-8(X)) HarperCollins Pubs.

Howe, James & Howe, Deborah. Bunnicula: A Rabbit-Tale of Mystery. Daniel, Alan, illus. 25th anniv. ed. 2004. 112p. (J). 16.95 (978-0-689-86775-0(1) , Atheneum) Simon & Schuster Children's Publishing.

BUNYAN, JOHN, 1628-1688

Deal, William. John Bunyan: The Tinker of Bedford. 2001. (Illus.). 221p. (YA). (gr. 6-12). pap. 7.00 (978-1-930367-59-3(7) , CLP29595) Christian Liberty Pr.

Wellman, Sam. John Bunyan: Author of The Pilgrim's Progress. 1999. (Heroes of the Faith Ser.). (Illus.). 208p. (YA). (gr. 4-7). 14.95 (978-0-7910-5035-4(1) , Chelsea Hse.) Facts On File, Inc.

BUNYAN, PAUL (LEGENDARY CHARACTER)

Blair, Eric. Paul Bunyan. Chambers-Goldberg, Micah, illus. 2006. (Read-It! Readers en Espanol Ser.).Tr. of Paul Bunyan. (SPA.). 32p. (J). (ps-3). 19.95 (978-1-4048-1657-2(7)) Picture Window Bks.

Furgang, Kathy. Paul Bunyan. 2005. 33.00 (*978-1-4108-4823-9(X)) Benchmark Education Co.

—Paul Bunyan (Spanish) & Paul Bunyan. 2005. spiral bd. 66.00 (*978-1-4108-5640-1(2)) Benchmark Education Co.

Gleeson, Brian. Paul Bunyan. Meyerowitz, Rick, illus. 2005. (Rabbit Ears-A Classic Tale Ser.). 40p. (J). (gr. k-5). 25.65 (978-1-59197-767-4(3)) Spotlight.

Harcourt School Publishers Staff. Paul Bunyan On Level. 3rd ed. 2002. (Trophies Reading Program Ser.). (Illus.). pap. 5.10 (978-0-15-323081-3(9)) Harcourt Schl. Pubs.

—Paul Bunyan Moves Out Below Level. 3rd ed. 2002. (Trophies Reading Program Ser.). (Illus.). pap. 5.10 (978-0-15-323150-6(5)) Harcourt Schl. Pubs.

Henry, Tom. Paul Bunyan on the West Coast. LaFave, Kim, illus. unabr. ed. 56p. (Orig.). (J). pap. (978-1-55017-109-9(7)) Harbour Publishing Co., Ltd.

Johnston, Marianne. Paul Bunyan. 2001. (American Legends Ser.). (Illus.). 24p. (J). (gr. 3). lib. bdg. 18.75 (978-0-8239-5580-0(X) , PowerKids Pr.) Rosen Publishing Group, Inc., The.

Kellogg, Steven. Paul Bunyan. Kellogg, Steven, illus. 2006. (SPA.). 48p. (J). pap. 6.99 (978-0-06-088705-6(2)) HarperCollins Pubs.

LaFontaine, Bruce. Paul Bunyan Coloring Book. 2003. (Dover Coloring Bks.). (Illus.). 32p. (J). pap. 3.95 (978-0-486-43043-0(X)) Dover Pubns., Inc.

Marsh, Carole. Paul Bunyan: An Ohio Experience Reader. 2001. (J). (gr. k-5). pap. 1.95 (978-0-635-00423-9(2)) Gallopade International.

Mason, Jane. Paul Bunyan & Other Tall Tales. 2002. (Junior Classics Ser.). (Illus.). 112p. (J). (gr. 4-6). pap. 3.99 (978-0-439-29154-5(2)) Scholastic, Inc.

McCaslin, Nellie. Paul Bunyan: Lumberjack. 2003. (Players Press Nellie McCaslin Ser.). 55p. (Orig.). (J). (gr. 1-6). pap. 5.00 (978-0-88734-477-0(1)) Players Pr., Inc.

Reason, Joyce. To Be a Pilgrim: The Story of John Bunyan. 2004. (Stories of Faith & Fame Ser.). 96p. (J). (gr. 4-7). pap. 6.00 (978-0-7188-2491-4(1)) Lutherworth Pr., The GBR. *Dist:* Parkwest Pubns., Inc.

BURBANK, LUTHER, 1849-1926

Quackenbush, Robert. Here a Plant, There a Plant, Everywhere a Plant, Plant! A Story of Luther Burbank. Quackenbush, Robert, illus. 1999. (Illus.). 36p. (J). (gr. 1-5). reprint ed. 10.00 (978-0-9637883-1-3(0)) Burbank, Luther Home & Gardens.

BURGLARS

see Robbers and Outlaws

BURGOYNE, JOHN, 1722-1792

Harmon, Daniel E. "Gentleman Johnny" Burgoyne. 2001. (Revolutionary War Leaders Ser.). (Illus.). 80p. (J). pap. 27.50 (978-0-7910-6391-0(7)); 27.50 (978-0-7910-6390-3(9)) Facts On File, Inc. (Chelsea Hse.).

—John Burgoyne: British General. 2002. (gr. 5-8). lib. bdg. 17.60 (978-0-613-50809-4(2)) Tandem Library Bks.

BURIAL

see Cemeteries; Funeral Rites and Ceremonies; Mounds and Mound Builders

BURIED CITIES

see Cities and Towns, Ruined, Extinct, Etc.

BURIED TREASURE

Addario, Yvonne. Treasure Diving with Captain Dom: Special Archival Section. 2007. (Illus.). 56p. (YA). per. 15.99 (*978-0-9743414-1-5(X)) Adventure in Discovery.

Claybourne, A. & Young, C. Treasure Hunting. 2004. (Illus.). 96p. (YA). (gr. 5 up). lib. bdg. 22.95 (978-1-58086-163-2(6)) EDC Publishing.

Claybourne, Anna & Young, Caroline, eds. Treasure Hunting. 1999. (Illus.). 96p. (YA). (gr. 5 up). pap. 14.95 (978-0-7460-3445-3(8)) EDC Publishing.

Clifford, Barry. Expedition Whydah: The Story of the World's First Excavation of a Pirate Treasure Ship & the Man Who Found Her. 1999. (gr. 7-12). lib. bdg. 24.60 (978-0-613-28837-8(8)) Tandem Library Bks.

Cousins, Lucy. Maisy's Pirate Treasure Hunt. Cousins, Lucy, illus. 2004. (Maisy Ser.). (Illus.). 12p. (J). (gr. k-k). bds. 10.99 (978-0-7636-2469-9(1)) Candlewick Pr.

Elton, Candice & Elton, Richard. Every Kid Needs a Treasure Hunt. 2006. (Illus.). 48p. (J). spiral bd. 19.95 (978-1-58685-710-3(X)) Gibbs Smith, Publisher.

Gallagher, Jim. The Search for Lost Treasure. 1999. (Costume, Tradition & Culture). (Illus.). 64p. (YA). (gr. 5 up). lib. bdg. 19.75 (978-0-7910-5167-2(6) , Chelsea Hse.) Facts On File, Inc.

Holdcroft, Tina. Hidden Treasures: Amazing Stories of Discovery. Holdcroft, Tina, illus. 2003. (Hidden! Ser.). (Illus.). 32p. (J). (gr. 2-5). pap. 6.95 (978-1-55037-802-3(3)); lib. bdg. 19.95 (978-1-55037-803-0(1)) Annick Pr., Ltd. CAN. *Dist:* Firefly Bks., Ltd.

Horner, William. Buried Treasure of Appleton, Wisconsin. Schneider, Claude, illus. 2001. 32p. (J). (gr. 2-4). lib. bdg. 24.95 (978-1-931765-00-8(6) , BHC502) Badger Hse., LLC.

Hort, Leonard C. Treasure Hunts! Treasure Hunts! Treasure & Scavenger Hunts to Play with Friends & Family. Pillo, Cary, illus. 2000. 80p. (J). (gr. 2-6). 15.95 (978-0-688-17245-9(8)) HarperCollins Pubs.

Jameson, W. C. Buried Treasures of New England. 1998. (gr. 3-6). lib. bdg. 21.05 (978-0-613-88810-3(3)) Tandem Library Bks.

—Buried Treasures of the Mid-Atlantic States: Legends of Island Treasure, Jewelry Caches & Secret Tunnels. 2001. (Buried Treasures Ser.). (Illus.). 192p. (J). (gr. 3-7). pap. 11.95 (978-0-87483-531-1(3)) August Hse. Pubs., Inc.

Leonard, Barry, ed. Treasure Trove of an Ancient Egyptian Child. 2005. (Illus.). 24p. (J). (gr. 4-8). 27.00 (978-0-7567-8939-8(7)) DIANE Publishing Co.

Levy, Debbie. Sunken Treasures. 2004. (Illus.). 48p. (J). (gr. 4-7). 26.20 (978 0 7377-2646-6(6) , Greenhaven Pr., Inc.) Thomson Gale.

Malam, John. Buried Treasure. 2007. (J). (*978-1-59920-107-8(0)) Smart Apple Media.

Mason, Paul. Lost Treasure. 2005. (Illus.). 32p. (J). (gr. 4-7). lib. bdg. 27.10 (978-1-58340-773-8(1)) Smart Apple Media.

Matsen, Bradford. The Incredible Search for the Treasure Ship Atocha. 2003. (Incredible Deep-Sea Adventures Ser.). (Illus.). 48p. (J). lib. bdg. 23.93 (978-0-7660-2193-8(9)) Enslow Pubs., Inc.

Nebold, Allyson Hicks. The Treasure of All Time. Nebold, Logan Amber, illus. 2000. 40p. (J). (gr. 1-3). 6.95 (978-1-880710-43-2(9)) Monterey Pacific Pubs.

O'Donnell, Liam. Pirate Treasure: Stolen Riches. 2007. (Edge Books, the Real World of Pirates). (Illus.). 32p. (J). 23.93 (978-0-7368-6428-2(8)) Capstone Pr., Inc.

Patent, Dorothy Hinshaw. Treasures of the Spanish Main. 2000. (Frozen in Time Ser.). (Illus.). (J). (gr. 5-9). lib. bdg. 28.50 (978-0-7614-0786-7(3) , Benchmark Bks.) Cavendish, Marshall Corp.

Pirotta, Saviour. Buried Treasure. 2001. (Young Library - Mysteries of the Past). (Illus.). 32p. (J). (gr. 3-5). lib. bdg. 25.69 (978-0-7398-4336-9(2)) Raintree.

—Buried Treasure. 2003. (gr. 3-6). lib. bdg. 16.40 (978-0-613-78226-5(7)) Tandem Library Bks.

Red Bird Press Staff. Secret Spex Treasure Hunt. 2004. (Secret Picture Search Ser.). 18p. (J). pap. 5.95 (978-1-902626-66-6(4)) Red Bird Publishing GBR. *Dist:* Weatherhill, Inc.

Scott, Caitlin. Treasure Hunting: Looking for Lost Riches. 2003. (High Five Reading (Red Level) Ser.). (Illus.). (J). 64p. lib. bdg. 22.60 (978-0-7368-2783-6(8)); 48p. pap. 23.93 (978-0-7368-2825-3(7)) Capstone Pr., Inc.

Silverberg, Robert. Treasures Beneath the Sea. 2003. 90p. pap. 29.00 (978-0-7581-0537-0(1)) Textbook Pubs.

Stilton, Geronimo. The Search for Sunken Treasure. 2006. (Geronimo Stilton Ser.: No. 25). 128p. (J). pap. 5.99 (978-0-439-84116-0(X) , Scholastic Paperbacks) Scholastic, Inc.

BURIED TREASURE—FICTION

Adventures at the Treasure House. 1998. (Captain Kangaroo Coloring Bks.: Vol. 2). (Illus.). 24p. (J). pap. (978-0-7666-0220-5(6) , Honey Bear Bks.) Modern Publishing.

Allende, Isabel. Kingdom of the Golden Dragon. Peden, Margaret Sayers, tr. from SPA. 2004. (Illus.). 448p. (J). (gr. 5 up). lib. bdg. 20.89 (978-0-06-058943-1(4)) HarperCollins Pubs.

Anderson, Janet. The Last Treasure. 2004. 272p. (J). (gr. 5). pap. 6.99 (978-0-14-240217-7(6) , Puffin) Penguin Group (USA) Inc.

Angstrom, Gwen R. The Eemlets & Grandma Eema Stories, Book 1: From Rainbow to Sunshine. 2006. 67p. pap. 14.95 (978-1-4241-1257-9(5)) PublishAmerica, Inc.

Archer, Chris. The Secret City. 2003. (Pyrates Ser.: No. 1). (Illus.). 192p. (J). (gr. 3-7). pap. 4.99 (978-0-439-36851-3(0)) Scholastic, Inc.

—Secret City. 2003. (gr. 3-6). lib. bdg. 12.40 (978-0-613-72030-4(X)) Tandem Library Bks.

Au, Steven T. Kid Posse & the Phantom Robber. 2003. (Illus.). pap. 24.95 (978-1-878044-89-1(3)) Mayhaven Publishing.

Barron, T. A. The Merlin Effect. 2004. 288p. (gr. 12). mass mkt. 6.99 (978-0-441-01222-0(1) , Ace Bks.) Penguin Group (USA) Inc.

Barry, Dave & Pearson, Ridley. Cave of the Dark Wind: A Never Land Adventure. Call, Greg, illus. 2007. 176p. (gr. 3 up). 9.99 (978-0-7868-3790-8(X)) Hyperion Bks. for Children.

Batson, Wayne Thomas. Isle of Swords. 2007. 352p. (J). 16.99 (*978-1-4003-1018-0(0)) Nelson, Thomas Inc.

Beck, Ana. Elliot Digs for Treasure. 2001. (ps-2). lib. bdg. 14.10 (978-0-613-53183-2(3)) Tandem Library Bks.

Beck, Andrea. Elliot Digs for Treasure. Beck, Andrea, illus. 2004. (Elliot Moose Ser.). (Illus.). 32p. (J). (gr. k-3). (978-1-55074-806-2(8)); (978-1-55074-808-6(4)) Kids Can Pr., Ltd.

Berenstain, Stan & Berenstain, Jan. The Berenstain Bears' Seashore Treasure. Berenstain, Stan, illus. 2005. (Illus.). 30p. (J). lib. bdg. 13.85 (*978-1-4242-0814-2(9)) Fitzgerald Bks.

—The Berenstain Bears' Seashore Treasure. Berenstain, Stan & Berenstain, Jan, illus. 2005. (Berenstain Bears Ser.). (Illus.). 32p. (J). (gr. k-3). 15.99 (978-0-06-058340-8(1) , Harper Festival) HarperCollins Pubs.

—The Berenstain Bears' Seashore Treasure. 2005. (Berenstain Bears Ser.). (Illus.). 32p. (J). (ps). pap. 3.99 (978-0-06-058341-5(X) , Harper Festival) HarperCollins Pubs.

Bessen, Luc. Arthur & the Minimoys. Sowchek, Ellen, tr. from FRE. 2005. 240p. (J). 15.99 (978-0-06-059623-1(6)) HarperCollins Pubs.

Besson, Luc. Arthur & the Forbidden City. (Illus.). 192p. (J). 2006. pap. 5.99 (978-0-06-059628-6(7) , Harper Trophy); 2005. 15.99 (978-0-06-059626-2(0)); 2005. lib. bdg. 16.89 (978-0-06-059627-9(9)) HarperCollins Pubs.

—Arthur & the Invisibles. movie tie-in ed. 2006. 416p. (J). pap. 7.99 (978-0-06-122726-4(9)) HarperCollins Pubs.

—Arthur & the Minimoys. (Illus.). (J). 2006. 256p. pap. 6.99 (978-0-06-059625-5(2) , Harper Trophy); 2005. 240p. lib. bdg. 16.89 (978-0-06-059624-8(4)) HarperCollins Pubs.

Bjerkvold, Belinda & Stevenson, Robert Louis. Treasure Island. Tod, Lluis M. & Andrada, Javier, illus. 2006. 36p. (J). lib. bdg. (*978-0-8368-7665-9(2)) Stevens, Gareth Inc.

Boey, Stephanie. Undersea Treasure Hunt: Find the Treasure with Little Fish & Friends. Boey, Stephanie, illus. 2005. (Illus.). 20p. (J). 15.95 (978-0-8118-4622-6(9)) Chronicle Bks. LLC.

Boniface, William. The Treasure Hunter. Harris, Jim, illus. 1998. 32p. (J). 15.99 (978-0-939251-97-1(3)) Accord Publishing, Ltd.

—The Treasure Hunter. Harris, Jim, illus. 2007. 28p. bds. 9.99 (*978-1-57939-354-0(3)) Andrews McMeel Publishing.

Boston, Lucy M. The Treasure of Green Knowe. Boston, Peter, illus. 2002. (Green Knowe Ser.). 224p. (YA). (gr. 4-7). reprint ed. pap. 7.00 (978-0-15-202601-1(0) , Odyssey Classics) Harcourt Children's Bks.

Brouwer, Sigmund, ed. Race for the Park Street Treasure. 2004. (Accidental Detectives Ser.). 144p. (J). pap. 5.99 (978-0-7642-2572-7(3)) Bethany Hse. Pubs.

Brown, Edi. A Pirate Treasure. 2000. ii, 232p. (YA). (gr. 5-10). 5.95 (978-0-9677953-0-0(3)) Red Fox Publishing Co.

Bucky Badger A Children's Story: Treasure. 2005. (J). 9.99 (978-0-9765510-2-7(0)) Badgerland Bks. LLC.

Burgess, Melvin. The Copper Treasure. Williams, Richard, illus. rev. ed. 2000. 112p. (YA). (gr. 4-7). 15.95 (978-0-8050-6381-3(1) , Holt, Henry & Co. Bks. For Young Readers) Holt, Henry & Co.

Butterworth, Nick. The Treasure Hunt. 2003. (Illus.). 32p. (J). pap. 11.00 (978-0-00-715517-0(4)) HarperCollins Pubs. Ltd. GBR. *Dist:* Independent Pubs. Group.

Campbell, Julie. The Secret of the Mansion. Stevens, Mary & Koelsch, Michael, illus. 2003. (Trixie Belden Ser.: Vol. 1). 272p. (gr. 3-7). lib. bdg. 9.99 (978-0-375-92412-5(4) , Random Hse. Bks. for Young Readers) Random Hse. Children's Bks.

—The Secret of the Mansion. Stevens, Mary, illus. 2003. (Trixie Belden Ser.: No. 1). 272p. (J). (gr. 3-7). 6.99 (978-0-375-82412-8(X) , Random Hse. Bks. for Young Readers) Random Hse. Children's Bks.

Carris, Joan D. A Ghost of a Chance. 2003. (Legends of the Carolinas Ser.). 155p. (J). 8.95 (978-1-928556-40-4(X)) Coastal Carolina Pr.

Chesworth, Michael. Alphaboat. Chesworth, Michael D., illus. 2002. 32p. (J). 16.00 (978-0-374-30244-3(8) , Farrar, Straus & Giroux (BYR)) Farrar, Straus & Giroux.

CJ & the Mysterious Map. 2000. (gr. k-3). lib. bdg. 11.80 (978-0-613-24597-5(0)) Tandem Library Bks.

Clover, Peter. Sheltie Saves the Day!, No. 2. 2001. (Sheltie Ser.). (Illus.). (J). (978-0-606-20913-7(1)) Tandem Library Bks.

Coerr, Eleanor. Mieko & the Fifth Treasure. 2003. (Illus.). 80p. (J). (gr. 4-7). pap. 5.99 (978-0-698-11990-1(8) , Puffin) Penguin Group (USA) Inc.

—Mieko & the Fifth Treasure. 2003. (gr. 3-6). lib. bdg. 14.15 (978-0-613-61642-3(1)) Tandem Library Bks.

Cole, Stephen. The Adventures of Mr. Bean. 2002. (Illus.). 64p. (J). pap. 6.99 (978-1-84222-657-5(6)) Carlton Bks., Ltd. GBR. *Dist:* Independent Pubs. Group.

Cosson, M. J. & MacPhail, C. The Pirate, Big Fist, & Me. Garvey, Brann, illus. 2007. 112p. (J). (*978-1-59889-279-6(7)) Stone Arch Bks.

Cowell, Cressida. How to Be a Pirate. 2005. (Illus.). 224p. (J). (gr. 3-7). 10.99 (978-0-316-15598-4(5)) Little Brown & Co.

Day, Jan. Pirate Pink & Treasures of the Reef. Mason, Janeen I., illus. 2003. 32p. (J). pap. 14.95 (978-1-58980-086-1(9)) Pelican Publishing Co., Inc.

Delessert, Etienne. Alert! 2007. (Illus.). 32p. (J). (gr. k-3). 17.00 (978-0-618-73474-0(0)) Houghton Mifflin Co.

DeMuth, Robert R. Grandpa's Treasures. 2006. (Illus.). 22p. (J). pap. 7.95 (978-1-933255-20-0(X)) DNA Pr.

Deshpande, Shashi. 3 Novels. 2006. 379p. (*978-0-14-333511-5(1) , Puffin) Penguin Group (USA) Inc.

Despain, Kellene. A Certain Kind of Treasure. 2000. (Illus.). 215p. (J). (gr. 5-9). per. 7.95 (978-0-9679046-0-3(9)) Gray Hse. Bks.

Desrosiers, Sylvie. Mais Qui Va Trouver le Tresor? 2003. (Roman Jeunesse Ser.). (FRE.). 96p. (YA). (gr. 4-7). pap. (978-2-89021-175-9(4)) Diffusion du livre Mirabel.

Dixon, Franklin W. Hunting for Hidden Gold. Rogers, Walter S., illus. 2004. (Hardy Boys Mystery Stories Ser.: No. 5). 210p. (J). (gr. 4-7). 17.95 (978-1-55709-148-2(X)) Applewood Bks.

Enderle, Dotti. Hidden. Gentry, T. Kyle, illus. 2007. 120p. (YA). (gr. 5-9). pap. 8.95 (*978-1-58980-481-4(3)) Pelican Publishing Co., Inc.

Erickson, R. C. The Mystery of Colborn's Treasure. 2007. 204p. pap. 13.95 (*978-0-615-15975-1(3)) Quool Publishing.

Ering, Timothy Basil. The Story of Frog Belly Rat Bone. Ering, Timothy Basil, illus. 2008. (Illus.). 48p. (J). (ps-2). pap. 6.99 (*978-0-7636-2611-2(2)) Candlewick Pr.

Farshtey, Greg. Prisoners of the Pit. 2007. (Bionicle Legends Ser.: No. 7). 144p. (J). pap. 4.99 (*978-0-439-89034-2(9)) Scholastic, Inc.

Ferrone, John M. Gus & the Pirate Treasure. Ferrone, John M., illus. Date not set. (Illus.). 36p. (J). (ps-5). pap. 16.95 (978-1-928811-01-5(9)) Story Stuff, Inc.

Ficklin, Jonene H. Orinoco Intrigue. 2005. (YA). 14.95 (978-0-9761188-1-7(5)) Victor's Crown Publishing.

Fleischman, Sid. The Ghost in the Noonday Sun. Sis, Peter, illus. 2007. 256p. (J). pap. 5.99 (*978-0-06-134502-9(4) , Harper Trophy) HarperCollins Pubs.

—The Ghost in the Noonday Sun. 1999. (J). (978-0-606-18960-6(2)) Tandem Library Bks.

Friedrich, Joachim. 4 1/2 Friends & the Secret Cave, Bk. 1. Crawford, Elizabeth D., tr. from GER. 2001. (Illus.). 160p. (gr. 3-7). 14.99 (978-0-7868-0648-5(6)) Hyperion Bks. for Children.

Funtime at the Treasure House. 1998. (Captain Kangaroo Coloring Bks.: Vol. 3). (Illus.). 24p. (J). pap. (978-0-7666-0221-2(4) , Honey Bear Bks.) Modern Publishing.

Gelsey, James. Scooby-Doo! & the Gruesome Goblin. 2004. (Illus.). 60p. (J). lib. bdg. 15.00 (*978-1-4242-0303-1(1)) Fitzgerald Bks.

—Sunken Ship: Scooby-Doo y el Barco Hundido. 2004. (Scooby-Doo Ser.). (ENG & SPA.). 64p. (J). mass mkt. 3.99 (978-0-439-55116-8(1) , Scholastic en Espanol) Scholastic, Inc.

—The Zombie's Treasure. 2000. (Scooby-Doo Mysteries Ser.: No. 9). (Illus.). 64p. (J). (ps-3). pap. 3.99 (978-0-439-11348-9(2)) Scholastic, Inc.

Gerwitz, Felice. Literature No. 1: The Missing Link Found. 2002. (Truth Seeker's Mystery Ser.: 1). (YA). stu. ed., per. 6.50 (978-1-931941-04-4(1)) Media Angels, Inc.

—Literature No. 3: Keys to the Past: Unlocked. 2003. (Truth Seeker's Mystery Ser.: 3). (YA). stu. ed., per. 6.50 (978-1-931941-06-8(8)) Media Angels, Inc.

Gerwitz, Felice & Gerwitz, Christina. Keys to the Past: Unlocked, Vol. 3. 2003. (Truth Seeker's Mystery Ser.). (YA). per. 8.99 (978-0-9700385-8-6(5)) Media Angels, Inc.

Goldstein, Alrica, ed. Pollytastic Adventure. 2007. 24p. (J). pap. 3.99 (*978-0-696-23647-1(8)) Meredith Bks.

—Whirlwind World Tour. 2007. 32p. (J). pap. 3.99 (*978-0-696-23646-4(X)) Meredith Bks.

Goodman, Julius. Treasure Diver. 1999. (Illus.). 114p. mass mkt. (978-0-553-24050-4(1)) Random Hse., Inc.

Griggs, Terry. Cat's Eye Corner. 2003. (Cat's Eye Corner Ser.). (Illus.). 168p. (J). pap. 7.95 (978-1-55192-350-5(5)) Raincoast Bk. Distribution CAN. *Dist:* Perseus Distribution.

—Cat's Eye Corner. 2003. (gr. 3-6). lib. bdg. 16.40 (978-0-613-78641-6(6)) Tandem Library Bks.

Haggard, H. Rider. King Solomon's Mines. Marcos, Pablo, illus. 2005. (Great Illustrated Classics Ser.). 239p. (J). (gr. 3-8). 21.35 (978-1-59679-244-9(2) , ABDO & Daughters) ABDO Publishing Co.

Hall, Kirsten. Buried Treasure: All about Using a Map. 2004. (Beastieville Ser.). (J). (gr. k-1). pap. 3.95 (978-0-516-24652-9(6) , Children's Pr.) Scholastic Library Publishing.

—Buried Treasure: All about Using a Map. Luedecke, Bev, illus. 2003. (Beastieville Ser.). 32p. (J). 19.50 (978-0-516-22894-5(3) , Children's Pr.) Scholastic Library Publishing.

Hanbury-Tenison, Robin. Jake's Treasure. 1998. 152p. (J). pap. 5.99 (978-0-09-925625-0(8)) Random Hse. GBR. *Dist:* Independent Pubs. Group.

Harcourt School Publishers Staff. Buried Treasure: Take-Home Book. 1999. (Signatures Ser.). (Illus.). (J). pap. 1.90 (978-0-15-313947-5(1)) Harcourt Schl. Pubs.

—The Treasure Map: Take-Home Book. 2001. (Collections Ser.). (Illus.). (J). pap. 1.90 (978-0-15-319505-1(3)) Harcourt Schl. Pubs.

Hawkins, Colin & Hawkins, Jacqui. Pirate Treasure Map: A Fairytale Adventure. Hawkins, Colin & Hawkins, Jacqui, illus. 2006. 40p. (J). (gr. k-3). 15.99 (978-0-7636-3205-2(8)) Candlewick Pr.

Heller, Ruth. A Cache of Jewels. 1998. (World of Language Ser.). (Illus.). 48p. (J). (ps-2). pap. 7.99 (978-0-698-11354-1(3) , Putnam Juvenile) Penguin Group (USA) Inc.

Hennessy, B. G. Once upon a Time Map Book. Joyce, Peter, illus. 2004. 16p. (J). (gr. 1-5). 11.99 (978-0-7636-2521-4(3)) Candlewick Pr.

Herman, Gail. Scooby Doo! & the Map in the Mystery Machine. 2000. (gr. k-3). lib. bdg. 11.80 (978-0-613-26117-3(8)) Tandem Library Bks.

Hobbs, Will. Leaving Protection. 192p. (J). (gr. 5 up). 2005. pap. 5.99 (978-0-380-73312-5(9) , Harper Trophy); 2004. 15.99 (978-0-688-17475-0(2)) HarperCollins Pubs.

Hobbs, William. Ghost Canoe. 1998. (Avon Camelot Bks.). 208p. (J). (gr. 5-9). pap. 5.99 (978-0-380-72537-3(1)) HarperCollins Pubs.

—Ghost Canoe. 1998. (J). 12.64 (978-0-606-13420-0(4)) Tandem Library Bks.

Hubbard, Coleen. Rush for Gold. Rabinowitz, Sandy & Keiffer, Christa, illus. l.t. ed. 1999. (Treasured Horses Collection). 128p. (J). (gr. 4 up). lib. bdg. 23.33 (978-0-8368-2405-6(9)) Stevens, Gareth Inc.

Hubley, Mary. Brad & Emily's Treasure Adventure. Hubley, Mary, illus. 2001. (Illus.). 32p. (J). (ps-2). 15.95 (978-0-9707267-0-4(8)) Bluefish Bay Publishing.

Hutchens, Paul. The Treasure Hunt. rev. ed. 1998. (Sugar Creek Gang Ser.: Vol. 14). 128p. (J). (gr. 4-7). 4.99 (978-0-8024-7018-8(1)) Moody Pubs.

—The Treasure Hunt. 1998. (gr. 3-6). lib. bdg. 13.00 (978-0-613-90127-7(4)) Tandem Library Bks.

Jewett, Eleanore M. The Hidden Treasure of Glaston. Chapman, Frederick T., illus. 2000. (Living History Library). 323p. (J). (gr. 8-12). reprint ed. pap. 14.95 (978-1-883937-48-5(5) , 48-5) Bethlehem Bks.

Katz, Welwyn W. Whalesinger. 2002. 212p. (YA). pap. 5.95 (978-0-88899-191-1(6)) Groundwood Bks. CAN. *Dist:* Perseus Distribution.

Kelman, Marcy. Disney's Little Einsteins: Pirate's Treasure. rev. ed. 2007. 16p. (ps-1). pap. 4.99 (*978-1-4231-0211-3(8)) Disney Pr.

Kendall, Cassie. Laurel & the Lost Treasure. Spector, Joel, illus. 2nd ed. 1998. (Stardust Classics). 117p. (J). (gr. 2-6). pap. 5.95 (978-1-889514-10-9(1)) Dolls Corp.

Kendrick, Robert. Treasure Quest: Journey to the Jungle. 2004. 46p. pap. 19.95 (978-1-4137-1467-8(6)) PublishAmerica, Inc.

Kennedy, Kim. Pirate Pete: "Where There's Gold I'm a Goin'" Kennedy, Doug, illus. 2002. 40p. (J). (ps-3). 15.95 (978-0-8109-4356-8(5)) Abrams, Harry N., Inc.

Kenny, Kathryn & Koelsch, Michael. The Mystery on Cobbett's Island. Frame, Paul, illus. 2005. (Trixie Belden Ser.: Vol. 13). 272p. (J). (gr. 3-7). 6.99 (978-0-375-83053-2(7)); lib. bdg. 9.99 (978-0-375-93053-9(1)) Random Hse. Children's Bks. (Random Hse. Bks. for Young Readers).

Kidd, Rob. Jack Sparrow: The Pirate Chase. Orpinas, Jean-Paul, illus. 2006. 119p. (J). lib. bdg. 16.00 (*978-1-4242-1570-6(6)) Fitzgerald Bks.

—Jack Sparrow: The Siren Song. Orpinas, Jean-Paul, illus. 2006. 122p. (J). lib. bdg. 16.00 (*978-1-4242-1571-3(4)) Fitzgerald Bks.

Kidd, Rob & Rudnick, Elizabeth M. Pirates of the Caribbean: the Curse of the Black Pearl. 2nd ed. 2006. (Illus.). 176p. (ps-3). pap. 4.99 (978-1-4231-0710-1(1)) Disney Pr.

Korman, Gordon. The Danger. 2003. (Dive Ser.: No. 3). 144p. (J). pap. 4.99 (978-0-439-50724-0(3)) Scholastic, Inc.

—The Deep. 2003. (Dive Ser.: No. 2). 144p. (J). (gr. 3-6). pap. 4.99 (978-0-439-50723-3(5) , Scholastic Paperbacks) Scholastic, Inc.

—The Deep. 2003. (Dive Ser.: No. 2). (gr. 3-6). lib. bdg. 12.40 (978-0-613-67483-6(9)) Tandem Library Bks.

—The Discovery. 2003. (Dive Ser.: No. 1). 144p. (J). (gr. 3-7). pap. 4.99 (978-0-439-50722-6(7) , Scholastic Paperbacks) Scholastic, Inc.

Lawrence, Carol & Lawrence, Caroline. The Dolphins of Laurentum. 2003. (Roman Mysteries Ser.: Bk. 5). 176p. (J). (gr. 6-9). 22.90 (978-0-7613-2606-9(5)) Roaring Brook Pr.

Lawrence, Caroline. The Dolphins of Laurentum. 2003. (Roman Mysteries Ser.: Bk. 5). 176p. (J). (gr. 6-9). 15.95 (978-0-7613-2349-5(X)) Roaring Brook Pr.

Lawson, Julie. Goldstone. unabr. ed. 1998. 170p. (J). (gr. 5-9). pap. 7.95 (978-0-7737-5891-9(7)) Stoddart Kids CAN. *Dist:* Fitzhenry & Whiteside, Ltd.

Lawton, Wilbur Capta. The Boy Aviators' Treasure Quest or the. 2006. 25.99 (*978-1-4280-0557-0(9)); pap. 19.99 (*978-1-4280-0560-0(9)) IndyPublish.com.

LeapFrog Staff, compiled by. Treasure Island. (J). 2002. (gr. 3-7). 14.95 (978-1-58605-920-0(3) , LeapFrog Schl. Hse.); 2001. spiral bd. 14.99 (978-1-58605-045-0(1)) LeapFrog Enterprises, Inc.

Learning Fun at the Treasure House. 1998. (Captain Kangaroo Coloring & Activity Bks.: Vol. 1). (Illus.). 32p. (J). pap. (978-0-7666-0223-6(0) , Honey Bear Bks.) Modern Publishing.

Leavey, Peggy Dymond. Treasure at Turtle Lake. 2007. 146p. (J). (gr. 4 up). pap. 7.95 (*978-1-894917-49-0(9)) Napoleon Publishing/Rendezvous Pr. CAN. *Dist:* Atlas-Books Distribution.

Let's Learn at the Treasure House. 1998. (Captain Kangaroo Coloring & Activity Bks.: Vol. 4). (Illus.). 32p. (J). pap. (978-0-7666-0226-7(5) , Honey Bear Bks.) Modern Publishing.

Life, Kay, illus. The Secret under the Tree, Vol. 7. 2004. (Adventures of Benny & Watch: Vol. No. 7). 32p. (J). (ps-2). pap. 3.95 (978-0-8075-0643-1(5)) Whitman, Albert & Co.

Looper, Grace W. Great-Grandpa's Hidden Treasure. 2006. (YA). pap. (*978-1-933523-18-7(2)) Bella Rosa Bks.

Lourie, Peter. The Lost Treasure of Captain Kidd. 2003. (Illus.). 96p. (YA). (gr. 4-6). pap. 9.95 (978-1-56397-851-7(2)) Boyds Mills Pr.

Mayer, Mercer. Surprise!, Vol. 3. 2002. (Little Critter First Readers Ser.). (Illus.). 24p. (J). (gr. 1-2). pap. 3.95 (978-1-57768-814-3(7)) School Specialty Publishing.

McCullagh, Sheila. Pirate Gold. 2007. (Three Pirates Ser.). (Illus.). 48p. 15.95 (*978-1-84560-042-6(8)) Mercury Bks. Ltd. GBR. *Dist:* International Publishers Marketing.

—Shipwrecked. 2007. (Three Pirates Ser.). (Illus.). 48p. 15.95 (*978-1-84560-043-3(6)) Mercury Bks. Ltd. GBR. *Dist:* International Publishers Marketing.

McMullan, Kate. Class Trip to the Cave of Doom. Basso, Bill, illus. 2003. (Dragon Slayers' Academy Ser.: No. 3). 112p. (J). (gr. 1-4). pap. 4.99 (978-0-448-43110-9(6) , Grosset & Dunlap) Penguin Group (USA) Inc.

—Class Trip to the Cave of Doom. 2006. (Dragon Slayers' Academy Ser.: No. 3). (J). (gr. 1-6). 24.21 (978-1-59961-123-5(6)) Spotlight.

—Class Trip to the Cave of Doom. 2003. (Dragon Slayers' Academy Ser.: No. 3). (gr. 3-6). lib. bdg. 13.00 (978-0-613-72615-3(4)) Tandem Library Bks.

McOmber, Rachel B., ed. McOmber Phonics Storybooks: The Confection Connection. rev. ed. (Illus.). (J). (978-0-944991-73-2(4)) Swift Learning Resources.

Messer, Celeste M. The Ghost of Piper's Landing. Hoeffner, Deb, illus. 2004. 82-92p. 4.95 (978-0-9702171-7-2(X)) AshleyAlan Enterprises.

Mitton, Tony. Once upon a Tide. Young, Selina, illus. 2006. 40p. (J). (gr. k-1). 16.95 (978-0-385-75100-1(1)); lib. bdg. 18.99 (978-0-385-75101-8(X)) Random Hse. Children's Bks. (Fickling, David Bks.).

Murphy, T. M. The Secrets of Cain's Castle. 2001. (Belltown Mystery Ser.). 144p. (J). (978-1-880158-38-8(8)) Townsend, J.N. Publishing.

Mussi, Sarah. The Door of No Return. 2008. (YA). (*978-1-4169-1550-8(8) , McElderry, Margaret K.) Simon & Schuster Children's Publishing.

Myers, Walter Dean. The Mouse Rap. 3rd ed. (J). pap. 3.95 (978-0-13-800087-5(5)) Prentice Hall (Schl. Div.).

—The Righteous Revenge of Artemis Bonner. 2003. (J). (gr. 5 up). 22.25 (978-0-8446-7250-2(5)) Smith, Peter Pub., Inc.

Naylor, Phyllis Reynolds. The Treasure of Bessledorf Hill. 1999. 144p. (J). (gr. 3-7). pap. 4.99 (978-0-689-81856-1(4) , Aladdin) Simon & Schuster Children's Publishing.

—The Treasure of Bessledorf Hill. 1999. (978-0-606-17322-3(6)) Tandem Library Bks.

Nesbit, E. The House of Arden. 2006. (New York Review Children's Collection). 248p. (J). (gr. 3). 17.95 (978-1-59017-202-5(7) , NYR Children's Collection) New York Review of Bks., Inc., The.

Oboh, Rolic. Treasure Hunt. 2006. pap. (*978-1-84426-318-9(5)) Upfront Publishing Ltd.

Ogden, Charles. Nod's Limbs. Carton, Rick, illus. 2007. (Edgar & Ellen Ser.). (J). 224p. 9.99 (978-1-4169-1501-0(X)); 210p. (*978-1-4287-3214-8(4)) Simon & Schuster Children's Publishing. (Aladdin).

Osborne, Mary Pope. Piratas Despues del Mediodia. 2003. (SPA.). (gr. 3-6). lib. bdg. 12.95 (978-0-613-64578-2(2)) Tandem Library Bks.

Owens, Greg. Rupert the Wrong-Word Pirate. Beaky, Suzanne, illus. 2006. (J). (978-1-58987-143-4(X)) Kindermusik International.

Parish, Peggy. Key to the Treasure. 154p. (J). pap. 4.50 (978-0-8072-1398-8(5) , Listening Library) Random Hse. Audio Publishing Group.

Paterson, Brian. Ziggy Hunts for Treasure. 2003. (Illus.). 32p. (J). (ps). pap. 8.99 (978-0-00-713181-5(X) , HarperCollins Children's Bks.) HarperCollins Pubs. Ltd. GBR. *Dist:* Independent Pubs. Group.

Penn, Audrey. Blackbeard & the Gift of Silence. 2007. 355p. (gr. 3-7). 15.95 (*978-1-933718-11-8(0)) Tanglewood Pr.

Penner, Lucille Recht. X Marks the Spot. Smath, Jerry, illus. 2002. (Math Matters Ser.). 32p. (J). pap. 4.95 (978-1-57565-111-8(4)) Kane Pr., The.

—X Marks the Spot! Smath, Jerry, illus. 2002. 32p. (J). (gr. 4-7). lib. bdg. 12.95 (978-0-613-53585-4(5)) Tandem Library Bks.

Perdew, Suzanne, et al. The Mystery of the Abandoned Lighthouse. 2001. (Shoebox Kids Ser.: Bk. 12). (Illus.). 93p. (J). (978-0-8163-1819-3(0)) Pacific Pr. Publishing Assn.

Peschke, M. Dead Man's Map. Smith, Tod, illus. 2008. (J). pap. (*978-1-59889-921-4(X)); (YA). (gr. 5-9). lib. bdg. 17.95 (*978-1-59889-855-2(8)) Stone Arch Bks.

Playtime with Captain Kangaroo & Friends. 1998. (Captain Kangaroo Coloring Bks.: Vol. 4). (Illus.). 24p. (J). pap. (978-0-7666-0222-9(2) , Honey Bear Bks.) Modern Publishing.

Prior, Natalie Jane. Lily Quench & the Treasure of Mote Ely, Vol. 3. 2004. (Illus.). 160p. (J). (gr. 3-7). pap. 4.99 (978-0-14-240022-7(X) , Puffin) Penguin Group (USA) Inc.

Reasoner, Charles. Inside Jolly Roger's Pirate Ship. Reasoner, Charles, illus. 2007. 12p. (J). (gr. k). bds. 9.99 (***978-1-84666-149-5(8)*** , Tide Mill Pr.) Top That! Publishing PLC GBR. *Dist:* Random Hse., Inc.

Redbank, Tennant. Captain Jack's Tale. 2007. (PiratesPirates of the Caribbean Ser.). (Illus.). 32p. (ps-3). pap. 3.99 (978-1-4231-0731-6(4)) Disney Pr.

—Curse of the Black Pearl - A Pirate's Life. 2007. (Pirates of the Caribbean Ser.). (Illus.). 32p. (ps-3). pap. 3.99 (978-1-4231-0732-3(2)) Disney Pr.

Rhyne, Nancy. The Crab Boys. 2007. (J). pap. (***978-0-87844-183-9(2)***) Sandlapper Publishing Co., Inc.

Roberts, Nora. The Reef. 1999. (gr. 7-12). lib. bdg. 16.45 (978-0-613-22257-0(1)) Tandem Library Bks.

Robertson, Barbara. Rosemary & the Island Treasure: Back to 1947. 2001. (Hourglass Adventures Ser.: Bk. 4). (Illus.). 128p. (J). (gr. 3-5). pap. 4.95 (978-1-890817-58-9(9)) Winslow Pr.

Robertson, Ivan T. Theodore & the Stormy Day. Edwards, Ken, illus. 1999. (Jellybean Bks.). 24p. (J). (ps-k). lib. bdg. 7.99 (978-0-375-90076-1(4) , Random Hse. Bks. for Young Readers) Random Hse. Children's Bks.

Roy, Ron. The Goose's Gold. Gurney, John Steven, illus. (A to Z Mysteries Ser.: No. 7). 96p. (gr. k-3). 1999. lib. bdg. 11.99 (978-0-679-99078-9(X)); 1998. (J). mass mkt. 3.99 (978-0-679-89078-2(5)) Random Hse. Children's Bks. (Random Hse. Bks. for Young Readers).

—The Goose's Gold. Gurney, John Steven, illus. 1999. (A to Z Mysteries Ser.: No. 7). (J). (gr. k-3). 10.79 (978-0-606-15977-7(0)); lib. bdg. 11.80 (978-0-613-11591-9(0)) Tandem Library Bks.

—Mayflower Treasure Hunt. Gurney, John Steven, illus. 2nd ed. 2007. (A to Z Mysteries Ser.: No. 28). 128p. (J). (gr. 1-4). pap. 4.99 (978-0-375-83937-5(2)); lib. bdg. 11.99 (978-0-375-93937-2(7)) Random Hse. Children's Bks. (Random Hse. Bks. for Young Readers).

Sachar, Louis. Buracos. pap. 29.95 (978-85-336-1280-8(X)) Livraria Martins Editora BRA. *Dist:* Distribooks, Inc.

—Holes. 1998. 240p. (J). (gr. 4-7). 17.00 (978-0-374-33265-5(7) , Farrar, Straus & Giroux (BYR)) Farrar, Straus & Giroux.

—Holes. 240p. (J). (gr. 4-6). pap. 5.99 (978-0-8072-8073-7(9) , Listening Library) Random Hse. Audio Publishing Group.

—Holes. 2000. (Newbery Ser.). (Illus.). 240p. (J). (gr. 5-6). reprint ed. pap. 6.50 (978-0-440-41480-3(6) , Yearling) Random Hse. Children's Bks.

—Holes. l.t. ed. 2003. 288p. pap. 10.95 (978-0-7862-6190-1(0)) Thorndike Pr.

Santillo, LuAnn. Stubs. Santillo, LuAnn, ed. 2003. (Half-Pint Kids Readers Ser.). (Illus.). 7p. (J). (ps-1). pap. (978-1-59256-097-4(0)) Half-Pint Kids, Inc.

Schaub, Michelle. The Lost Pirate. 2006. (Early Explorers Ser.). (J). 34.00 (***978-1-4108-6109-2(0)***) Benchmark Education Co.

Schiro, Michael. Treasure Hunt: Level R, 6 vols. 128p. (gr. 3-6). 36.95 (978-0-322-05897-2(X)) Wright Group, The.

Scotton, Rob. Russell & the Lost Treasure. Scotton, Rob, illus. 2006. (Illus.). 32p. (J). 15.99 (978-0-06-059851-8(4)); lib. bdg. 16.89 (978-0-06-059852-5(2)) HarperCollins Pubs.

Simner, Janni Lee. Secret of the Three Treasures. 2005. 160p. (J). 16.95 (978-0-8234-1914-2(2)) Holiday Hse., Inc.

Smallcomb, Pam. The Trimoni Twins & the Shrunken Treasure. 2005. 225p. (J). (gr. 3-6). 16.95 (978-1-58234-656-4(9) , Bloomsbury Children) Bloomsbury Publishing.

Soileau, Hodges, illus. The Haunted Clock Tower Mystery, Vol. 84. 2004. (Boxcar Children Ser.: No. 84). 128p. (J). (gr. 2-7). pap. 3.95 (978-0-8075-5485-2(5)) Whitman, Albert & Co.

Spangler, Brie. Peg Leg Peke. 2008. 40p. (J). (ps-1). lib. bdg. 18.99 (***978-0-375-94888-6(0)*** , Knopf Bks. for Young Readers) Random Hse. Children's Bks.

Stevenson, Robert Louis. Robert Louis Stevenson's Treasure Island: The Graphic Novel. 2005. (Puffin Graphics Ser.). (Illus.). 176p. (978-1-4156-2620-7(0) , Puffin) Penguin Group (USA) Inc.

—Robert Louis Stevenson/Treasure Island. Cruz, Nardo, illus. 2005. 48p. (J). (gr. 5-8). 25.50 (978-0-7910-9107-4(4)) Facts On File, Inc.

—Treasure Island. McAllister, A. J., illus. 2002. (Great Illustrated Classics Ser.). 240p. (J). (gr. 3-8). 21.35 (978-1-57765-805-4(1) , ABDO & Daughters) ABDO Publishing Co.

—Treasure Island. Todd, Justin, illus. 1999. (Abbeville Classics Ser.). 176p. (J). pap. 7.95 (978-0-7892-0551-3(3) , Abbeville Kids) Abbeville Pr., Inc.

—Treasure Island. 2002. (YA). 12.34 (978-0-7587-7947-2(X)) Book Wholesalers, Inc.

—Treasure Island. (Great Classics for Children Ser.). (Illus.). 192p. (J). (978-1-4037-0599-0(2)) Dalmatian Pr.

—Treasure Island. 2005. 116p. per. 5.95 (978-1-4209-2258-5(0)) Digireads.com.

—Treasure Island. 2001. (YA). (gr. 5-12). pap. 8.50 (978-0-8359-0234-2(X)) Globe Fearon Educational Publishing.

—Treasure Island. Lawrence, John, illus. 2001. (Kingfisher Classics Ser.). 352p. (J). (gr. 4-6). tchr. ed. 15.95 (978-0-7534-5380-3(0) , Kingfisher) Houghton Mifflin Co. Trade & Reference Div.

—Treasure Island. (Young Collector's Illustrated Classics Ser.). (Illus.). 192p. (J). (gr. 3-7). 9.95 (978-1-56156-456-9(7)) Kidsbooks, Inc.

—Treasure Island. Ingpen, Robert, illus. 2006. 192p. (J). 19.95 (978-0-9545103-6-7(4)) Palazzo Editions, Ltd. GBR. *Dist:* Trafalgar Square Publishing.

—Treasure Island. Seelye, John, ed. 1999. (Classics Ser.). (Illus.). 240p. (gr. 12). pap. 7.00 (978-0-14-043768-3(1) , Penguin Classics) Penguin Group (USA) Inc.

—Treasure Island. 1999. 1p. (J). (gr. 4-7). 2.99 (978-0-14-130545-5(2) , Puffin); 1998. 224p. mass mkt. 3.95 (978-0-451-52704-2(6) , Signet Classics) Penguin Group (USA) Inc.

—Treasure Island. Winter, Milo, illus. 2002. (Illustrated Library for Children). 272p. (J). 12.99 (978-0-517-22114-3(4) , Gramercy) Random Hse. Value Publishing.

—Treasure Island. 2006. (Scholastic Classics Ser.). (Illus.). x, 205p. (J). (gr. 9-12). 25.00 (978-0-531-16961-2(8) , Watts, Franklin) Scholastic Library Publishing.

—Treasure Island. Wyeth, N. C., illus. 2000. (Aladdin Classics Ser.). 368p. (gr. 3-7). mass mkt. 5.99 (978-0-689-83212-3(5) , Aladdin) Simon & Schuster Children's Publishing.

—Treasure Island. 2006. (J). (gr. 4-8). 24.21 (978-1-59961-119-8(8)) Spotlight.

—Treasure Island. 1999. (Saddleback Classics). (Illus.). (J). (978-0-606-21576-3(X)) Tandem Library Bks.

—Treasure Island. 1998. (Children's Classics). (ENG., Illus.). 224p. (J). (gr. 3-7). pap. (978-1-85326-103-9(3) , 1033WW) Wordsworth Editions, Ltd.

—Treasure Island. Corvino, Lucy, illus. 2005. (Classic Starts Ser.). 160p. 4.95 (978-1-4027-1318-7(5)) Sterling Publishing Co., Inc.

—Treasure Island. Cruz, Nardo, illus. 2nd ed. 1998. (Illustrated Classic Book Ser.). 61p. (J). (gr. 3 up). reprint ed. pap. 4.95 (978-1-56767-239-8(6)) Educational Insights, Inc.

—Treasure Island. unabr. ed. 1998. (Wordsworth Classics Ser.). (YA). (gr. 6-12). 5.27 (978-0-89061-103-6(3) , R1033WW) Jamestown.

—Treasure Island. 2004. reprint ed. pap. 1.99 (978-1-4192-9097-8(5)) Kessinger Publishing, LLC.

—Treasure Island. 1999. (Illus.). 240p. (YA). (gr. 3 up). reprint ed. 7.95 (978-1-56852-233-3(9) , Konecky & Konecky) Konecky, William S. Assocs., Inc.

—Treasure Island. 1998. (Twelve-Point Ser.). 204p. reprint ed. lib. bdg. 25.00 (978-1-58287-075-5(6)) North Bks.

—Treasure Island: With a Discussion of Courage. 2003. (Values in Action Illustrated Classics Ser.). (J). (978-1-59203-054-5(8)) Learning Challenge, Inc.

—Treasure Island: With Story of the Treasure of Normon Island. Date not set. (J). (gr. 5-6). reprint ed. lib. bdg. 22.95 (978-0-89190-236-2(8) , American Reprint Co.) Amereon LTD.

—Treasure Island #3: on the Island. Comport, Sally Wern, illus. 2007. (Easy Reader Classics Ser.). 32p. (J). pap. 3.95 (978-1-4027-4119-7(7)) Sterling Publishing Co., Inc.

—Treasure Island #4: Pirate Attack. Comport, Sally Wern, illus. 2007. (Easy Reader Classics Ser.). 32p. (J). pap. 3.95 (978-1-4027-4120-3(0)) Sterling Publishing Co., Inc.

Stevenson, Robert Louis. Treausre Island: #1 the Treasure Map. 2007. (Easy Reader Classics Ser.). 32p. (J). (ps-3). 21.35 (***978-1-59961-342-0(5)***) Spotlight.

Stevenson, Robert Louis & Brook, Henry. Treasure Island. 2006. 160p. (J). pap. 4.99 (978-0-7945-1230-9(5) , Usborne) EDC Publishing.

Stevenson, Robert Louis & Hitchner, Earle. Treasure Island. 1999. (Illus.). 245p. (J). (978-0-03-054463-7(7)) Holt, Rinehart & Winston.

Still, Wayne Anthony, illus. Desert Treasure. 1999. (J). 30.00 (978-0-8172-7296-8(8)) Steck-Vaughn.

Stilton, Geronimo. Lost Treasure of the Emerald Eye. Wolf, Matt, illus. 2004. (Geronimo Stilton Ser.: No. 1). 116p. (J). lib. bdg. 10.00 (***978-1-4242-0695-7(2)***) Fitzgerald Bks.

—Lost Treasure of the Emerald Eye. 2007. (Geronimo Stilton Ser.: No. 1). 128p. (J). pap. 2.99 (***978-0-545-01032-0(2)*** , Scholastic Paperbacks) Scholastic, Inc.

—Lost Treasure of the Emerald Eye. Wolf, Matt & Keys, Larry, illus. 2004. (Geronimo Stilton Ser.: No. 1). 128p. (J). (gr. 2-5). pap. 6.99 (978-0-439-55963-8(4) , Scholastic Paperbacks) Scholastic, Inc.

—The Temple of the Ruby of Fire. 2004. (Geronimo Stilton Ser.: No. 14). (Illus.). 128p. (J). (gr. 2-5). pap. 6.99 (978-0-439-66163-8(3) , Scholastic Paperbacks) Scholastic, Inc.

Stilton, Geronimo. Valley of the Giant Skeletons. 2008. (Geronimo Stilton Ser.: No. 32). 128p. (J). pap. 6.99 (***978-0-545-02132-6(4)*** , Scholastic Paperbacks) Scholastic, Inc.

Strickland, Brad & Fuller, Thomas E. The Treasure of Skeleton Reef. l.t. ed. 1999. (Wishbone Mysteries Ser.: No. 1). 144p. (J). (gr. 4 up). lib. bdg. 23.33 (978-0-8368-2382-0(6)) Stevens, Gareth Inc.

Strong, Jeremy. The Indoor Pirates on Treasure Island. (Illus.). 96p. (J). 7.95 (978-0-14-038637-0(8)) Penguin Bks., Ltd. GBR. *Dist:* Trafalgar Square Publishing.

Stubbs, Lisa. Sonny's Treasure Hunt. 1999. (Illus.). (J). 6.95 (978-0-7641-0903-4(0)) Barron's Educational Series, Inc.

Sturges, Philemon. This Little Pirate. Walrod, Amy, illus. 40p. (J). (ps). 2007. pap. 6.99 (978-0-14-240850-6(6) , Puffin); 2005. 16.99 (978-0-525-46440-2(9) , Dutton Juvenile) Penguin Group (USA) Inc.

Stutson, Caroline. Pirate Pup. Rayevsky, Robert, illus. 2005. 32p. (J). 15.95 (978-0-8118-4239-6(8)) Chronicle Bks. LLC.

Tang, Charles, illus. The Mystery of the Pirate's Map. 1999. 121p. (J). (ps-7). per. 11.80 (978-0-613-16287-6(0)) Tandem Library Bks.

Taylor, Theodore. Teetoncey & Ben O'Neal. 2004. (Illus.). 240p. (J). 17.00 (978-0-15-205296-6(8) , Harcourt Young Classics); (Cape Hatteras Trilogy: Bk. 2). pap. 5.95 (978-0-15-205297-3(6) , Odyssey Classics) Harcourt Children's Bks.

Teague, Bobbie T. Simon's Gold. Deppner, Charles, illus. 2001. 94p. (J). per. 13.00 (978-1-887774-09-3(2) , Wynden) Canmore Pr.

Thomas, Earl W. Mystery of the Pirates' Treasure. 1999. (Illus.). 44p. (J). (ps-7). lib. bdg. 11.60 (978-0-613-29174-3(3)) Tandem Library Bks.

Thomas, Jerry D. Detective Zack Secret of Blackloch Castle. 1998. (Detective Zack Ser.: Vol. 10). (Illus.). 126p. (J). (gr. 3-6). pap. 6.99 (978-0-8163-1399-0(7)) Pacific Pr. Publishing Assn.

Thompson, Lisa. Digging for Buried Treasure. Cantell, Brenda, illus. 2005. (Treasure Trackers Ser.). 80p. (gr. 5-9). 19.00 (978-0-7910-8872-2(3) , Chelsea Hse.) Facts On File, Inc.

Tichenor, Richard. Tales from the Woods of Wisdom, Bk. 1. (J). 2000. 185p. pap. 16.95 (978-1-888725-37-7(0) , BeachHouse Bks.); 2001. 275p. per. 24.95 (978-1-888725-50-6(8) , MacroPrintBooks) Science & Humanities Pr.

Treasure House Funtime Friends. 1998. (Captain Kangaroo Coloring & Activity Bks.: Vol. 2). (Illus.). 32p. (J). pap. (978-0-7666-0224-3(9) , Honey Bear Bks.) Modern Publishing.

A Treasure House Learning Adventure. 1998. (Captain Kangaroo Coloring & Activity Bks.: Vol. 3). (Illus.). 32p. (J). pap. (978-0-7666-0225-0(7) , Honey Bear Bks.) Modern Publishing.

The Treasure Hunt. 2008. (J). 19.95 (978-1-933872-25-4(X)) Lima Bear Pr LLC, The.

Treasure Hunt: Individual Title Six-Packs. (Chiquilibros Ser.). (gr. k-1). 23.00 (978-0-7635-0415-1(7)) Rigby Education.

Treasure Trackers. 2006. (Illus.). (gr. 5-9). 111.60 (978-0-7910-9082-4(5)) Facts On File, Inc.

Trout, Richard E. Cayman Gold: Lost Treasure of Devil's Grotto. 2005. (MacGregor Family Adventure Ser.). (Illus.). 224p. (YA). (gr. 14 up). 15.95 (978-1-58980-323-7(X)) Pelican Publishing Co., Inc.

Turner, Barbara. Treasure in Ghost Town. 2001. 126p. (J). pap. 11.95 (978-1-55517-540-5(6) , Bonneville Bks.) Cedar Fort, Inc./CFI Distribution.

Utton, Peter. Duncan & the Pirates. Utton, Peter, illus. 2005. (Read-It! Chapter Bks.). (Illus.). 52p. (J). (ps-k). lib. bdg. 19.95 (978-1-4048-1277-2(6)) Picture Window Bks.

Vaughan, Marcia. The Treasure of Ghostwood Gully: A Southwest Mystery. Terry, Will, illus. 2004. 32p. (gr. k-4). 15.95 (978-0-87358-858-4(4) , Rising Moon Bks. for Young Readers) Northland Publishing.

Walls, Pamela June. Quest for Treasure. Tribbles, Jean-Paul, illus. 2000. (Abby & the South Seas Adventures Ser.: No. 2). 224p. (J). (gr. 3-7). mass mkt. 5.99 (978-0-8423-3627-7(3)) Tyndale Hse. Pubs.

Warner, Gertrude Chandler. Mystery at the Crooked House. 2000. (gr. 3-6). lib. bdg. 11.80 (978-0-613-31517-3(0)) Tandem Library Bks.

—The Mystery of the Pirate's Map. 1999. (Boxcar Children Ser.: No. 70). (J). (gr. 2-5). (978-0-606-18763-3(4)) Tandem Library Bks.

—Mystery on Blizzard Mountain. 2002. (gr. 3-6). lib. bdg. 11.80 (978-0-613-53287-7(2)) Tandem Library Bks.

—Secret under the Tree. 2001. (gr. k-3). lib. bdg. 11.80 (978-0-613-35676-3(4)) Tandem Library Bks.

Warner, Gertrude Chandler, creator. The Creature in Ogopogo Lake, Vol. 108. 2006. (Boxcar Children Mysteries Ser.: 108). (Illus.). 128p. (J). (gr. 2-7). 14.95 (978-0-8075-1336-1(9)); lib. bdg. 4.50 (978-0-8075-1337-8(7)) Whitman, Albert & Co.

—The Mystery of the Pirate's Map, Vol. 70. (Boxcar Children Ser.: No.70). (Illus.). (J). (gr. 2-5). 2004. 14.95 (978-0-8075-5453-1(7)); 1999. 128p. pap. 4.50 (978-0-8075-5454-8(5)) Whitman, Albert & Co.

—The Mystery on Blizzard Mountain, Vol. 86. 2004. (Boxcar Children Ser.: No. 86). (Illus.). 122p. (J). (gr. 2-7). 14.95 (978-0-8075-5493-7(6)); pap. 4.50 (978-0-8075-5494-4(4)) Whitman, Albert & Co.

Warner, Penny. Mystery of the Haunted Cave. 2001. 102p. (J). (978-0-88166-390-7(5)) Meadowbrook Pr.

Wealth, Viktoria. Aadorn Kingdom of the Dragons' Light: Book-I. 2003. 214p. (YA). pap. 14.95 (978-0-595-28175-6(3)) iUniverse, Inc.

Weathers, Anah D. Secrets of the Cave. Weathers, Luther, illus. Weathers, Luther, photos by. unabr. ed. 2000. (Treasures from the Past Ser.). x, 104p. (J). (gr. 4-8). pap. 7.98 (978-0-9702584-0-3(2)) Creative Services.

Weinberger, Kimberly. C J & the Mysterious Map. del Sur, Duendes, illus. 2000. (Jumpstart Ser.). 32p. (J). (ps-3). pap. 3.99 (978-0-439-16448-1(6)) Scholastic, Inc.

Weise, Selene H. C. Gold for a Boat. 2001. (Illus.). 68p. (J). (gr. 1-6). 5.95 (978-1-57249-270-7(8) , Burd Street Pr.) White Mane Publishing Co., Inc.

Wilson, Eric G. The Lost Treasure of Casa Loma. 6th ed. 2001. (Tom & Liz Austen Mysteries Ser.). (Illus.). 103p. (J). (gr. 3-6). mass mkt. 5.95 (978-0-7736-7492-9(6)) Stoddart Kids CAN. *Dist:* Fitzhenry & Whiteside, Ltd.

Wilson, N. D. Leepike Ridge. 2007. (Illus.). 240p. (J). (gr. 3-7). 15.99 (978-0-375-83873-6(2)); lib. bdg. 18.99 (978-0-375-93873-3(7)) Random Hse. Children's Bks. (Random Hse. Bks. for Young Readers).

—Leepike Ridge. 2007. (Illus.). 224p. (J). pap. (978-0-375-83874-3(0)) Random Hse., Inc.

Winfield, Arthur M. Rover Boys on Treasure Isle or the Stran. 2006. pap. 30.95 (***978-1-4286-4112-9(2)***) Kessinger Publishing, LLC.

Young, Joseph R. Legend of the Lost Josephine Mine: A Fascinating Adventure. 2001. 221p. (J). pap. 13.95 (978-1-55517-550-4(3) , Bonneville Bks.) Cedar Fort, Inc./CFI Distribution.

Zindel, Paul. Reef of Death. 1998. (Illus.). 192p. (J). (gr. 3 up). 15.95 (978-0-06-024728-7(2)); (gr. 6-10). lib. bdg. 15.89 (978-0-06-024733-1(9)) HarperCollins Pubs.

—Reef of Death. 1999. (978-0-606-16669-0(6)) Tandem Library Bks.

BURMA

Hare, Eric B. Jungle Heroes & Other Stories. 2005. (Illus.). 106p. (J). (978-0-8163-2063-9(2)) Pacific Pr. Publishing Assn.

Khng, Pauline. Myanmar. 1999. (Countries of the World Ser.). (Illus.). 96p. (J). (gr. 6 up). lib. bdg. 30.00 (978-0-8368-2320-2(6)) Stevens, Gareth Inc.

Ling, Bettina. Aung San Suu Kyi: Standing up for Democracy in Burma. (Women Changing the World Ser.). (Illus.). 112p. (gr. 4-7). 2004. pap. 9.95 (978-1-55861-197-9(5)); 1998. 19.95 (978-1-55861-196-2(7)) Feminist Pr. at The City Univ. of New York.

Streissguth, Thomas. Myanmar in Pictures. 2007. (J). lib. bdg. (***978-0-8225-7146-9(3)***) Twenty First Century Bks.

Yin, Saw Myat. Myanmar. 2nd ed. 2001. (Cultures of the World Ser.). (Illus.). 144p. (gr. 5 up). lib. bdg. 37.07 (978-0-7614-1353-0(7) , Benchmark Bks.) Cavendish, Marshall Corp.

Yip, Dora & Khng, Pauline. Welcome to Myanmar. 2001. (Welcome to My Country Ser.). (Illus.). 48p. (J). (gr. 2 up). lib. bdg. 26.00 (978-0-8368-2520-6(9)) Stevens, Gareth Inc.

BURMA—FICTION

Hare, Eric B. Curse Proof. 2007. (Illus.). 95p. (J). (***978-0-8163-2208-4(2)***) Pacific Pr. Publishing Assn.

Howat, Irene. Adoniram Judson: Danger on the Streets of Gold. 160p. (J). mass mkt. 5.99 (978-1-85792-660-6(9) , Christian Focus) Christian Focus Pubns. GBR. *Dist:* Riverside.

Smith, Roland. Elephant Run. rev. ed. 2007. 336p. (gr. 3-7). 15.99 (***978-1-4231-0402-5(1)***) Hyperion Pr.

BURNETT, FRANCES HODGSON, 1849-1924

Collins, Carolyn Strom & Eriksson, Christina Wyss. Inside the Secret Garden: A Treasury of Crafts, Recipes, & Activities. Tudor, Tasha, illus. 2004. 130p. (J). (gr. 2-8). reprint ed. 25.00 (978-0-7567-7630-5(9)) DIANE Publishing Co.

Eriksson, Christina Wyss & Collins, Carolyn Strom. Inside the Secret Garden: A Treasury of Crafts, Recipes, & Activities. Collier, Mary & Tudor, Tasha, illus. 2002. 136p. (J). (gr. 3 up). 24.99 (978-0-06-027922-6(2)) HarperCollins Pubs.

BURR, AARON, 1756-1836

Ingram, Scott. Aaron Burr: And the Young Nation. 2002. (Notorious Americans & Their Times Ser.). (Illus.). 112p. (J). (gr. 5-9). 28.70 (978-1-56711-250-4(1) , Blackbirch Pr., Inc.) Thomson Gale.

Lucas, Eileen. The Aaron Burr Treason Trial. 2003. (Headline Court Cases Ser.). (Illus.). 128p. (J). (gr. 6-12). lib. bdg. 26.60 (978-0-7660-1765-8(6)) Enslow Pubs., Inc.

Melton, Buckner F. Aaron Burr: The Rise & Fall of an American Politician. 2005. (Library of American Lives & Times). (Illus.). 112p. (J). (gr. 4-8). lib. bdg. 31.95 (978-0-8239-6626-4(7)) Rosen Publishing Group, Inc., The.

Perrin, Pat. The Mystery of the Deadly Duel. 2004. (Illus.). 64p. (J). pap. (***978-0-7891-5996-0(1)***) Perfection Learning Corp.

Wise, William. Aaron Burr. 2001. 196p. (gr. 7-12). pap. 13.95 (978-0-595-19630-2(6)) iUniverse, Inc.

BURROUGHS, JOHN, 1837-1921

Bloodgood, Dorothy U. A Post Card Portrait with Memorabilia of John Burroughs Literary Naturalist. 2nd ed. 2004. (Illus.). 48p. per. 11.95 (978-0-910746-33-5(8)) Hope Farm Pr. & Bookshop.

BURTON, RICHARD FRANCIS, SIR, 1821-1890

Gilpin, Daniel. Burton & Speke's Source of the Nile Quest. 2007. (***978-1-4034-9752-9(4)***) Heinemann Library.

Young, Serenity. Richard Francis Burton: Explorer, Scholar, Spy. 2007. (Great Explorations Ser.). (Illus.). 80p. (YA). (gr. 5-9). lib. bdg. 32.79 (***978-0-7614-2222-8(6)*** , Benchmark Bks.) Cavendish, Marshall Corp.

BURYING GROUNDS

see Cemeteries

BUS DRIVERS

Frost, Helen. We Need School Bus Drivers. 2004. (Helpers in Our Community Ser.). (Illus.). 24p. (J). lib. bdg. 15.93 (978-0-7368-2577-1(0) , Pebble Bks.) Capstone Pr., Inc.

Gorman, Jacqueline Laks. Bus Driver. Andersen, Gregg, photos by. 2002. (People in My Community Ser.). (Illus.). 24p. (J). (ps up). lib. bdg. 19.33 (978-0-8368-3292-1(2) , Weekly Reader Early Learning Library) Stevens, Gareth Inc.

—Bus Driver/El Conductor del Autobus. Acosta, Tatiana & Gutiérrez, Guillermo, trs. Andersen, Gregg, photos by. 2002. (Weekly Reader Early Learning Library). (SPA & ENG., Illus.). 24p. (J). (ps up). lib. bdg. 19.33 (978-0-8368-3306-5(6) , Weekly Reader Early Learning Library) Stevens, Gareth Inc.

Gorman, Jacqueline Laks & Macken, JoAnn Early. Bus Driver. Andersen, Gregg, photos by. 2002. (Weekly Reader Early Learning Library). (Illus.). 24p. (J). (ps up). pap. 7.93 (978-0-8368-3299-0(X) , Weekly Reader Early Learning Library) Stevens, Gareth Inc.

—Bus Driver/El Conductor del Autobus. Coffey, Colleen & Carrillo, Consuelo, trs. Andersen, Gregg, photos by. 2002. (Weekly Reader Early Learning Library). (ENG & SPA., Illus.). 24p. (J). (ps up). pap. 7.93 (978-0-8368-3340-9(6) , Weekly Reader Early Learning Library) Stevens, Gareth Inc.

Klingel, Cynthia Fitterer & Noyed, Robert B. School Bus Drivers. 2001. (My School Helpers). (Illus.). 24p. (J). (gr. 1-4). lib. bdg. 19.27 (978-1-57103-329-1(7)) Rourke Publishing, LLC.

Krohn, Katherine E. Wild West Women. 2006. (First Step Nonfiction Ser.). (Illus.). 112p. (J). (gr. 3-7). 27.93 (978-0-8225-2646-9(8) , Lerner Pubns.) Lerner Publishing Group.

Mitchell, Melanie. School Bus Drivers. 2005. (Pull Ahead Bks.). 32p. (J). pap. 5.95 (978-0-8225-5472-1(0)); (Illus.). 22.60 (978-0-8225-1695-8(0)) Lerner Publishing Group.

Owen, Ann. Taking You Places: A Book about Bus Drivers. Thomas, Eric, illus. 2004. (Community Workers Ser.). 24p. (C). (gr. k-3). 22.60 (978-1-4048-0090-8(5)) Picture Window Bks.

Picture Window Books, contrib. by. Taking You Places. (Community Workers Ser.). 24p. (J). pap. 7.95 (978-1-4048-0484-5(6)) Picture Window Bks.

Ready, Dee. Choferes de Autobuses Escolares. Schon, Isabel, ed. Ferrer, Martín Luis Guzman, tr. 1998. (Servidores Comunitarios Ser.). (SPA., Illus.). 24p. (J). (gr. 1-2). lib. bdg. 18.60 (978-1-56065-803-0(7) , Bridgestone Bks.) Capstone Pr., Inc.

Rivera, Sheila. Bus Driver. 2004. (First Step Nonfiction Ser.). (J). pap. (978-0-8225-5362-5(7) , Lerner Pubns.) Lerner Publishing Group.

School Bus Drivers. (Community Helpers Ser.). 24p. (J). 6.95 (978-0-7368-8461-7(0)) Capstone Pr., Inc.

School Bus Drivers, 6 vols. (gr. 2-5). 36.95 (978-0-7368-8476-1(9)) Red Brick Learning.

BUS DRIVERS—FICTION

Cousins, Lucy. Maisy Drives the Bus. 2000. (ps-2). lib. bdg. 11.00 (978-0-613-27961-1(1)) Tandem Library Bks.

Helakoski, Leslie. The Smushy Bus. Murdocca, Sal, illus. 2002. 32p. (gr. k-3). (J). 15.95 (978-0-7613-1917-7(4)); lib. bdg. 22.90 (978-0-7613-1398-4(2)) Lerner Publishing Group. (Millbrook Pr.).

Moran, Lisa, et al. Big Cindy's School Bus. Mathieu, Joe, tr. Mathieu, Joe, illus. 2004. (Random House Pictureback Ser.). 24p. (J). (ps-2). pap. 3.99 (978-0-375-82817-1(6) , Random Hse. Bks. for Young Readers) Random Hse. Children's Bks.

Morris, Deborah. Runaway Bus & other True Stories: Real Kids Real Adventures. 2003. (Juvenile Ser.). (Illus.). (J). 21.95 (978-0-7862-5095-0(X)) Thorndike Pr.

Pulver, Robin. Axle Annie. Kane, Cindy, ed. 1999. (Illus.). 32p. (J). (ps-3). 15.99 (978-0-8037-2096-1(3) , Dial) Penguin Group (USA) Inc.

Thaler, Mike. School Bus Driver from the Black Lagoon. 1999. (gr. 3-6). lib. bdg. 10.95 (978-0-613-17939-3(0)) Tandem Library Bks.

Willems, Mo. Don't Let the Pigeon Stay up Late! 2006. (Illus.). 40p. (ps-1). 12.99 (978-0-7868-3746-5(2)) Hyperion Bks. for Children.

Willner-Pardo, Gina. Spider Storch's Fumbled Field Trip. Sharratt, Nick, illus. 1998. 68p. (J). (gr. 2-5). pap. 3.95 (978-0-8075-7582-6(8)) Whitman, Albert & Co.

BUSES

Amoroso, Gary M. & Klingel, Cynthia Fitterer. Buses. 2007. (Machines at Work Ser.). 24p. (J). 22.79 (978-1-59296-827-5(9)) Child's World, Inc.

Ashley, Susan. En Autobus. 2003. (Weekly Reader Early Learning Library). (SPA., Illus.). 24p. (J). (gr. 2 up). pap. 5.95 (978-0-8368-3839-8(4) , Weekly Reader Early Learning Library) Stevens, Gareth Inc.

—En Autobus. Coffey, Colleen & Carrillo, Consuelo, trs. 2003. (Weekly Reader Early Learning Library). (SPA., Illus.). 24p. (J). (gr. 2 up). lib. bdg. 19.33 (978-0-8368-3734-6(7) , Weekly Reader Early Learning Library) Stevens, Gareth Inc.

—Going by Bus. 2003. (Going Places Ser.). (Illus.). 24p. (gr. 2 up). (YA). lib. bdg. 19.33 (978-0-8368-3729-2(0)); (J). pap. 5.95 (978-0-8368-3834-3(3)) Stevens, Gareth Inc. (Weekly Reader Early Learning Library).

Beck, Isabel L., et al. Trophies Kindergarten: My Bus. 2003. (Trophies Ser.). (gr. k-6). 13.80 (978-0-15-329522-5(8)) Harcourt Schl. Pubs.

Burch, Lynda S. Wicky Wacky Things that Go! Busses. Burch, Lynda S., photos by. 2004. (Illus.). 28p. (J). E-Book 9.95 incl. cd-rom (978-1-933090-06-1(5)) Guardian Angel Publishing, Inc.

DK Publishing Staff. Wheels on the Bus Pop-up Sound Book. 2007. 12p. (J). bds. 14.99 (978-0-7566-2724-9(9)) Dorling Kindersley Publishing, Inc.

Dorling Kindersley Publishing Staff. The Bus. 1999. (Wheelies Ser.). (Illus.). 10p. (J). (gr. k-2). bds. 5.99 (978-0-7894-4731-9(2)) Dorling Kindersley Publishing, Inc.

Faircloth, Harry W. My First Bus Ride. Anderson, Billie Ann, illus. Date not set. 26p. (J). (ps-4). pap. 9.95 (978-0-9668650-1-1(4)) Maximilian Pr. Pubs.

Feldman, Heather. My School Bus: A Book about School Bus Safety. 2000. (PowerKids Readers Ser.). (Illus.). 24p. (J). (gr. 1). lib. bdg. 16.00 (978-0-8239-5523-7(0) , PKMYSC, PowerKids Pr.) Rosen Publishing Group, Inc., The.

Frost, Helen. We Need School Bus Drivers. 2004. (Helpers in Our Community Ser.). (Illus.). 24p. (J). lib. bdg. 15.93 (978-0-7368-2577-1(0) , Pebble Bks.) Capstone Pr., Inc.

Gorman, Jacqueline Laks. Bus Driver. Andersen, Gregg, photos by. 2002. (People in My Community Ser.). (Illus.). 24p. (J). (ps up). lib. bdg. 19.33 (978-0-8368-3292-1(2) , Weekly Reader Early Learning Library) Stevens, Gareth Inc.

—Bus Driver/El Conductor del Autobus. Acosta, Tatiana & Gutiérrez, Guillermo, trs. Andersen, Gregg, photos by. 2002. (Weekly Reader Early Learning Library). (SPA & ENG., Illus.). 24p. (J). (ps up). lib. bdg. 19.33 (978-0-8368-3306-5(6) , Weekly Reader Early Learning Library) Stevens, Gareth Inc.

Gorman, Jacqueline Laks & Macken, JoAnn Early. Bus Driver. Andersen, Gregg, photos by. 2002. (Weekly Reader Early Learning Library). (Illus.). 24p. (J). (ps up). pap. 7.93 (978-0-8368-3299-0(X) , Weekly Reader Early Learning Library) Stevens, Gareth Inc.

—Bus Driver/El Conductor del Autobus. Coffey, Colleen & Carrillo, Consuelo, trs. Andersen, Gregg, photos by. 2002. (Weekly Reader Early Learning Library). (ENG & SPA., Illus.). 24p. (J). (ps up). pap. 7.93 (978-0-8368-3340-9(6) , Weekly Reader Early Learning Library) Stevens, Gareth Inc.

Hanson, Anders. Let's Go by Bus. 2007. (Let's Go! Ser.). (ENG., Illus.). 24p. (J). (ps-3). lib. bdg. 19.93 ***978-1-59928-895-6(8)** , SandCastle) ABDO Publishing Co.

Hindley, Judy. Big Red Bus. Benedict, William, illus. 2000. 32p. (J). (ps-3). pap. 6.99 (978-0-7636-1250-4(2)) Candlewick Pr.

Hoberman, Mary Ann. The Wheels on the Bus. 2007. (J). bds. (978-0-316-93101-4(2)) Little Brown & Co.

Johnson, Marion. Caillou: The School Bus. 2003. (Clubhouse Ser.). (Illus.). 24p. (J). pap. 2.50 (978-2-89450-421-5(7)) Chouette Publishing CAN. *Dist:* Independent Pubs. Group.

Klingel, Cynthia Fitterer & Noyed, Robert B. School Buses. 2000. (Wonder Books Level 1: Transportation Ser.). (Illus.). 24p. (J). (ps-3). 22.79 (978-1-56766-807-0(0)) Child's World, Inc.

Lassieur, Allison. Buses. 2000. (Transportation Library). (Illus.). 24p. (J). (gr. 1-2). lib. bdg. 18.60 (978-0-7368-0360-1(2) , Bridgestone Bks.) Capstone Pr., Inc.

—Buses. 1999. (Illus.). 24p. pap. 14.60 (978-0-516-21871-7(9) , Children's Pr.) Scholastic Library Publishing.

Mattern, Joanne. Staying Safe on the School Bus. 2006. (Illus.). 24p. pap. ***978-0-8368-7802-8(7));** lib. bdg. ***978-0-8368-7795-3(0))** Stevens, Gareth Inc. (Weekly Reader Early Learning Library).

—Staying Safe on the School Bus: La Seguridad en el Autobus Escolar. 2006. (J). pap. ***978-0-8368-8067-0(6));** lib. bdg. ***978-0-8368-8060-1(9))** Stevens, Gareth Inc. (Weekly Reader Early Learning Library).

Mitchell, Melanie. School Bus Drivers. 2005. (Pull Ahead Bks.). 32p. (J). pap. 5.95 (978-0-8225-5472-1(0)); (Illus.). 22.60 (978-0-8225-1695-8(0)) Lerner Publishing Group.

Owen, Ann. Taking You Places: A Book about Bus Drivers. Thomas, Eric, illus. 2004. (Community Workers Ser.). 24p. (C). (gr. k-3). 22.60 (978-1-4048-0090-8(5)) Picture Window Bks.

Raatma, Lucia. Safety on the School Bus. 1998. (Safety First! Ser.). (Illus.). 24p. (J). (gr. 1-2). lib. bdg. 18.60 (978-0-7368-0063-1(8) , Bridgestone Bks.) Capstone Pr., Inc.

Randolph, Joanne. Drawing School Buses. 2005. (Let's Draw with Shapes Ser.). (Illus.). 24p. (J). 17.25 (978-1-4042-2791-0(1) , PowerKids Pr.) Rosen Publishing Group, Inc., The.

—Let's Draw a School Bus with Shapes: Vamos a Dibujar un Autobus Escolar Usando Figuras. Muschinske, Emily, illus. 2005. (Let's Draw with Shapes/ Vamos a dibujar con Figuras Ser.). (ENG & SPA.). (J). 17.25 (978-1-4042-7557-7(6) , PowerKids Pr.) Rosen Publishing Group, Inc., The.

Tlock, Andrew. Bus. 1999. (Illus.). (J). bds. 5.95 (978-1-57717-120-1(9)) New Line Bks.

Zuehlke, Jeffrey. Buses. 2005. (Pull Ahead Bks.). (Illus.). 32p. (J). (gr. k-2). lib. bdg. 22.60 (978-0-8225-1538-8(5)) Lerner Publishing Group.

BUSES—FICTION

Adler, David A. Bones & the Big Yellow Mystery. Newman, Barbara, illus. 2008. (Jeffrey Bones Mystery Ser.: No. 1). 32p. (J). (gr. k). pap. 3.99 ***978-0-14-241042-4(X)** , Puffin) Penguin Group (USA) Inc.

Allyson, Libby. Scottie Rides the Bus. 2004. 27p. pap. 14.95 (978-1-4137-3298-6(4)) PublishAmerica, Inc.

The Anywhere Everywhere Bus, 6 vols., Pack. (gr. k-1). 23.00 (978-0-7635-9065-9(7)) Rigby Education.

Applegate, Katherine. The Escape. 1998. (Animorphs Ser.: No. 15). 170p. (J). (gr. 3-7). pap. 4.99 (978-0-590-49424-3(4)) Scholastic, Inc.

Barlow, Andrew. Jellytoes Misses the Bus. Barlow, Andrew, illus. 2005. (Illus.). 32p. (J). pap. 8.95 (978-0-9764336-0-6(5)) MJS Publishing Group LLC.

Berenstain, Stan & Berenstain, Jan. The Berenstain Bears Catch the Bus. Berenstain, Stan & Berenstain, Jan, illus. 2002. (Berenstain Bears Ser.). (Illus.). (J). (gr. k-3). 11.91 (978-0-7587-0977-6(3)) Book Wholesalers, Inc.

—The Berenstain Bears Catch the Bus. 1999. (Berenstain Bears Ser.). (J). (ps-3). lib. bdg. 11.99 (978-0-679-99227-1(8)); pap. 3.99 (978-0-679-89227-4(3)) Random Hse. Children's Bks. (Random Hse. Bks. for Young Readers).

—The Berenstain Bears Catch the Bus. 1999. (Berenstain Bears Ser.). (J). (ps). (Illus.). 32p. lib. bdg. 11.80 (978-0-613-16056-8(8)); 10.79 (978-0-606-16944-8(X)) Tandem Library Bks.

Blance, Ellen & Cook. Monster on the Bus. Date not set. (Illus.). 24p. pap. 129.15 (978-0-582-18595-1(5)) Addison-Wesley Longman, Ltd. GBR. *Dist:* Trans-Atlantic Pubns., Inc.

Bloom, Suzanne. The Bus for Us. 2003. (Illus.). 32p. (J). (gr. k-2). 13.95 (978-1-56397-932-3(2)) Boyds Mills Pr.

Brillhart, Julie. Molly Rides the School Bus. 2002. (Illus.). 32p. (J). (ps-2). 15.95 (978-0-8075-5210-0(0)) Whitman, Albert & Co.

Brooks, Felicity. Busy Bus. 2007. (Play Bks). 10p. (J). bds. 10.99 ***978-0-7945-1701-4(3)** , Usborne) EDC Publishing.

Brown, Marc. Arthur Lost & Found. ed. 2004. (Arthur Adventure Ser.). (J). (gr. k-3). spiral bd. (978-0-616-11102-4(9)) Canadian National Institute for the Blind/Institut National Canadien pour les Aveugles.

—Arthur Lost & Found. Brown, Marc, illus. 1998. (Arthur Adventure Ser.). (Illus.). 32p. (J). (ps-3). 15.95 (978-0-316-10912-3(6)) Little, Brown Bks. for Young Readers.

—Arthur Lost & Found. 2000. (Arthur Adventure Ser.). (J). (gr. k-3). 12.75 (978-0-606-19835-6(0)) Tandem Library Bks.

Cazet, Denys. Minnie & Moo: Minnie & Moo Go to Paris. Cazet, Denys, illus. 2001. (Live Oak Readalong Ser.). (Illus.). (J). pap. 18.95 incl. audio compact disk (978-1-59112-394-1(1)) Live Oak Media.

—Minnie & Moo Go to Paris. Cazet, Denys, illus. 2001. (Illus.). 28.95 incl. audio compact disk (978-1-59112-595-2(2)); pap. 31.95 incl. audio compact disk (978-1-59112-594-5(4)); pap. 29.95 incl. audio (978-0-87499-768-2(2)) Live Oak Media.

Christian, Reinar Carl, Sr. Nate: The New Bus on the Block! l.t. ed. 2005. (Illus.), 41p. (J). 16.99 (978-0-9769866-0-7(4)) Meritage Publishing.

Cole, Joanna. El Autobus Magico Juega a la Pelota: Un Libro Sobre Fuerzas. 1998. (Magic School Bus Ser.). (SPA.). (J). (gr. 1-4). (978-0-606-13356-2(9)) Tandem Library Bks.

—The Magic School Bus & the Science Fair Expedition. Degen, Bruce, illus. 2006. (Magic School Bus Ser.). 56p. (J). pap. 15.99 (978-0-590-10824-9(7) , Scholastic) Scholastic, Inc.

—The Magic School Bus Explores the Senses. Degen, Bruce, illus. 1999. (Magic School Bus Ser.). (J). (gr. 1-4). 159.50 (978-0-439-05987-9(9)) Scholastic, Inc.

—The Magic School Bus Gets Programmed: A Book about Computers. 1999. (Magic School Bus Ser.). (J). (gr. 1-4). (978-0-606-17291-2(2)) Tandem Library Bks.

Cole, Joanna & White, Nancy. The Magic School Bus Gets a Bright Idea: A Book about Light. 1999. (Magic School Bus Ser.). (J). (gr. 1-4). (978-0-606-17292-9(0)) Tandem Library Bks.

—The Magic School Bus Kicks up a Storm: A Book about Weather. 2000. (Magic School Bus Ser.). (J). (gr. 1-4). (978-0-606-18577-6(1)) Tandem Library Bks.

Cooke, Andy. Wheels on the Bus. Cooke, Andy, illus. 1999. (Read & Share Ser.). (Illus.). 24p. (J). (ps). pap. 3.99 (978-0-7636-0877-4(7)) Candlewick Pr.

Cousins, Lucy. Maisy Drives the Bus. Cousins, Lucy, illus. 2000. (Maisy Bks.). (Illus.). 24p. (J). (gr. k-k). pap. 3.99 (978-0-7636-1085-2(2)) Candlewick Pr.

—Maisy Drives the Bus. 2000. (ps-2). lib. bdg. 11.00 (978-0-613-27961-1(1)) Tandem Library Bks.

Cowden, Christine Mullins. My Worst & Best Summer Ever. 2004. 48p. pap. 12.95 (978-1-4137-4188-9(6)) PublishAmerica, Inc.

Crews, Donald. School Bus Board Book. Crews, Donald, illus. 2002. (Illus.). 36p. (J). (ps up). 6.99 (978-0-694-01690-7(X)) HarperCollins Pubs.

Dann, Penny. The Wheels on the Bus. 1999. (Toddler Bks.). (Illus.). 20p. (J). pap. 4.95 (978-0-7641-0856-3(5)) Barron's Educational Series, Inc.

Derrick, Patricia. Mr Walrus & the Old School Bus. 2007. 32p. 18.95 (978-1-933818-13-9(1)) Animalations.

DK Publishing Staff. Let's Go Magic School Bus. 2007. 12p. (J). bds. 14.99 ***978-0-7566-3088-1(6))** Dorling Kindersley Publishing, Inc.

Gomi, Taro. Bus Stops. 1999. (JPN & ENG., Illus.). 34p. (J). (ps-k). bds. 6.95 (978-0-8118-2459-0(4)) Chronicle Bks. LLC.

Gulbis, Stephen, illus. The Wheels on the Bus. 2003. 22p. (YA). (978-1-85602-454-9(7)) Chrysalis Children's Bks.

Hay un esqueleto en el Autobus: Individual Title Six-Packs. (Literatura 2000 Ser.), (SPA.). (gr. 2-3). 33.00 (978-0-7635-1094-7(7)) Rigby Education.

Hedrick, Helen Groves. Baas on the Bus. 2000. (J). 12.00 (978-0-8059-5003-8(6)) Dorrance Publishing Co., Inc.

Hofmeister, Alan, et al. The Bus. (Reading for All Learners Ser.). (Illus.). (J). pap. (978-1-56861-122-8(6)) Swift Learning Resources.

Kalar, Bonnie. Gus on the Bus. Spreen, Kathe, illus. 1998. 8p. (J). (ps-2). pap. (978-1-891619-03-8(9)) Corona Pr.

Kubler, Annie, illus. Wheels on the Bus. 2005. (J). bds. 12.99 (978-0-85953-326-3(3)) Child's Play-International.

Lane, Jeanette. Magic School Bus & the Missing Tooth. 2007. (Magic School Bus Ser.). 32p. (J). pap. 3.99 (978-0-439-80107-2(9) , Cartwheel Bks.) Scholastic, Inc.

Linder, Cori. Bobby the Blue Bus. 2005. 21p. 10.75 (978-1-4116-3564-7(7)) Lulu.com.

Maggiore, Dominick. Dominick's School Bus. 2007. 34p. pap. 7.95 ***978-0-533-15671-9(8))** Vantage Pr., Inc.

Marin, Cheech. Cheech the School Bus Driver. Ramirez, Orlando L., illus. 2007. 32p. (J). (ps-3). lib. bdg. 17.89 ***978-0-06-113202-5(0));** 16.99 ***978-0-06-113201-8(2))** HarperCollins Pubs.

—Cheech the School Bus Driver (Spanish Edition) Cheech y su autobus Escolar. Ramirez, Orlando L., illus. 2007. (SPA.). 32p. (J). 16.99 ***978-0-06-113204-9(7)** , Rayo) HarperCollins Pubs.

McCarthy, Meghan. Adventures of Patty & the Big Red Bus. 2005. (Illus.). 40p. (J). (ps-1). 12.95 (978-0-375-82939-0(3)); lib. bdg. 14.99 (978-0-375-92939-7(8)) Random Hse. Children's Bks. (Knopf Bks. for Young Readers).

McDaid, Mark. Billy the Bus. 2006. (Illus.). 48p. pap. ***978-1-84401-714-0(1))** Athena Pr.

Mellentin, Kath. Wheels on the Bus. Tulip, Jenny, illus. 1998. 16p. (J). (ps). 13.99 (978-1-884628-37-5(0) , Flying Frog Publishing) Allied Publishing.

Milliron, Kerry. The Great Race. Kilgras, Heidi, ed. Binder, Eric & Lapadula, Thomas, illus. 2000. (Early Step into Reading Ser.). 32p. (J). (ps-k). lib. bdg. 11.99 (978-0-375-90284-0(8) , Random Hse. Bks. for Young Readers) Random Hse. Children's Bks.

—The Great Race. Kilgras, Heidi, ed. LaPadula, Tom et al, illus. 2000. (Early Step into Reading Ser.). 32p. (J). (ps-k). pap. 3.99 (978-0-375-80284-3(3) , Random Hse. Bks. for Young Readers) Random Hse. Children's Bks.

Montes, Juan Mari. Diario del Autobus a de la Linea 3. Fra, Irene, illus. 2006. (SPA.). 96p. (J). (978-84-667-5192-6(0)) Grupo Anaya, S.A.

Moran, Lisa, et al. Big Cindy's School Bus. Mathieu, Joe, tr. Mathieu, Joe, illus. 2004. (Random House Pictureback Ser.). 24p. (J). (ps-2). pap. 3.99 (978-0-375-82817-1(6) , Random Hse. Bks. for Young Readers) Random Hse. Children's Bks.

Neusner, Dena Wallenstein. Follow That School Bus. Yee, Josie, illus. 2003. (Clifford Ser.). 5p. (J). bds. 7.99 (978-0-439-44933-5(2)) Scholastic, Inc.

Newton, Jill & Roddie, Shen. Don't Chat to the Bus Driver. 2001. (Illus.). 32p. (J). (ps-k). pap. 10.95 (978-0-7475-5028-0(X)) Bloomsbury Publishing Plc GBR. *Dist:* Independent Pubs. Group.

Nothing Ever Happens 6 Packs. Individual Title. (ps-2). 27.00 (978-0-7635-9467-1(9)) Rigby Education.

O'Connor, Jane. Fancy Nancy at the Museum. Glasser, Robin Preiss & Enik, Ted, illus. 2008. (I Can Read Bks.). 32p. (J). 16.99 ***978-0-06-123608-2(X))** HarperCollins Pubs.

—Fancy Nancy at the Museum. Glasser, Robin Preiss, illus. 2008. (I Can Read Bks.). 32p. (J). pap. 3.99 ***978-0-06-123607-5(1)** , Harper Trophy) HarperCollins Pubs.

Parker, Marjorie Blain. Hello, School Bus! Kolar, Bob, tr. Kolar, Bob, illus. 2004. (Scholastic Reader Ser.). 32p. (J). pap. 3.99 (978-0-439-59889-7(3) , Cartwheel Bks.) Scholastic, Inc.

—Hello, School Bus! Kolar, Bob, illus. 2004. 28p. (ps-ps). lib. bdg. 11.19 (978-0-606-30604-1(8)) Tandem Library Bks.

Pulver, Robin. Axle Annie & the Speed Grump. Arnold, Tedd, illus. 2005. 36p. (J). (ps-3). 16.99 (978-0-8037-2787-8(9) , Dial) Penguin Group (USA) Inc.

Roth, Carol. The Little School Bus. 2004. (Illus.). 32p. (J). (gr. k-1). pap. 6.95 (978-0-7358-1905-4(X)) North-South Bks., Inc.

—The Little School Bus. Paparone, Pamela, illus. 2002. 32p. (J). (ps-1). 14.95 (978-0-7358-1646-6(8)) North-South Bks., Inc.

Ryan, Lisa & Scholastic, Inc. Staff. The Wheels on Barney's Bus. Winslow, Becky, illus. 2002. (Barney Ser.). 6p. (J). (ps-1). pap. 9.99 (978-1-58668-292-7(X)) Scholastic, Inc.

Scholastic, Inc. Staff. We're Gonna Take a Bus Ride. 2007. (Doodlebops Ser.). 10p. (J). bds. 5.99 ***978-0-545-00060-4(2))** Scholastic, Inc.

Schwabacher, Martin. The Magic School Bus Flies with the Dinosaurs. Bracken, Carolyn, illus. 2008. (Scholastic Reader Ser.). 32p. (J). pap. 3.99 ***978-0-439-80106-5(0))** Scholastic, Inc.

Shore, Diane Z. Bus-a-Saurus Bop. Clark, David, illus. 2003. 32p. (J). (gr. k-3). 16.95 (978-1-58234-850-6(2) , Bloomsbury Children) Bloomsbury Publishing.

Silvano, Wendi. Just One More. Gamboa, Ricardo, illus. 2007. 36p. (J). reprint ed. pap. 14.95 (978-0-9744446-5-9(0)) All About Kids Publishing.

The Skeleton on the Bus: Individual Title Six-Packs. (Literatura 2000 Ser.). (gr. 2-3). 33.00 (978-0-7635-0183-9(2)) Rigby Education.

Stanley, Mandy, illus. The Wheels on the Bus. 1998. (J). 11.98 (978-1-58048-007-9(1)) Sandvik Publishing.

Stoeke, Janet Morgan. The Bus Stop. Stoeke, Janet Morgan, illus. 2007. (Illus.). 24p. (J). (ps-k). 12.99 (978-0-525-47805-8(1) , Dutton Juvenile) Penguin Group (USA) Inc.

Stone, Tom B. El Autobus Siniestro. 2002. (Graveyard School Ser.). (SPA.). (J). pap. 5.95 (978-950-24-0873-6(X) , AL30667) Albatros ARG. *Dist:* Lectorum Pubns., Inc.

Strasser, Todd. Don't Get Caught Driving the School Bus. 2000. (Don't Get Caught Ser.). (J). 11.15 (978-0-606-19556-0(4)) Tandem Library Bks.

Stuart, Heather. Wheels on the Bus. 2007. (Illus.). 12p. (J). (ps-k). pap. 16.95 ***978-1-932403-23-7(X))** Handprint Bks.

Swindells, Robert. Last Bus. (Illus.). 95p. (J). 7.95 (978-0-14-037971-6(1)) Penguin Bks., Ltd. GBR. *Dist:* Trafalgar Square Publishing.

Tattum, Stephan. The Bus. 2005. (J). 4.95 (978-1-59792-004-9(5)) F.A.S.T. Learning LLLC.

Thaler, Mike. School Bus Driver from the Black Lagoon. 1999. (gr. 3-6). lib. bdg. 10.95 (978-0-613-17939-3(0)) Tandem Library Bks.

Thomas & the School Trip. 2002. (Thomas the Tank Engine Ser.). (Illus.). (J). 11.91 (978-0-7587-1737-5(7)) Book Wholesalers, Inc.

Wheels on the Bus. 2005. (J). bds. 6.99 (978-0-9753127-7-3(4)) Family Bks. at Home.

White, Nancy. The Magic School Bus Kicks up a Storm: A Book about Weather. Ruiz, Art, illus. 2000. (Magic School Bus Ser.). 32p. (J). (gr. 1-4). pap. 3.50 (978-0-439-10275-9(8)) Scholastic, Inc.

—The Magic School Bus Kicks up a Storm: A Book about Weather. 2000. (gr. k-3). lib. bdg. 11.25 (978-0-613-21949-5(X)) Tandem Library Bks.

Williams, Sam. School Bus, Bunny Bus. Trotter, Stuart, illus. 2006. 10p. (J). 12.95 (978-1-905417-17-9(9)) Boxer Bks., Ltd. GBR. *Dist:* Sterling Publishing Co., Inc.

Zindel, Paul. The Phantom of 86th Street. 2002. (gr. 3-6). lib. bdg. 13.00 (978-0-613-62914-0(0)) Tandem Library Bks.

BUSH, GEORGE, 1924-

Anderson, Ken. George Bush: A Lifetime of Service. 2002. (Illus.). v, 150p. (gr. 6-12). 16.95 (978-1-57168-663-3(0)); 12.95 (978-1-57168-600-8(2)) Eakin Pr.

Childress, Diana. George Herbert Walker Bush. 2007. (Presidential Leaders Ser.). 112p. (J). (gr. 6-12). 29.27 (978-0-8225-1510-4(5) , Lerner Pubns.) Lerner Publishing Group.

Davis, Marc. George H. W. Bush. 2002. (Profiles of the Presidents Ser.). (Illus.). 64p. (J). (gr. 4 up). lib. bdg. 23.93 (978-0-7565-0285-0(3)) Compass Point Bks.

Francis, Sandra. George Bush: Our Forty-First President. 2001. (Spirit of America: Our Presidents Ser.). (Illus.). 48p. (J). (gr. 2-6). 28.50 (978-1-56766-875-9(5)) Child's World, Inc.

Green, Robert. George Bush: Business Executive & U. S. President. 2000. (Career Biographies Ser.). (Illus.). 128p. (J). (gr. 6-12). 25.00 (978-0-89434-339-1(4) , F402, Ferguson Publishing Co.) Facts On File, Inc.

Joseph, Paul. George Bush. 1999. (United States Presidents Ser.). (Illus.). 32p. (J). (gr. k-6). lib. bdg. 22.78 (978-1-56239-816-3(4) , Checkerboard Library) ABDO Publishing Co.

Margaret, Amy. George Bush Presidential Library. 2004. (Presidential Libraries Ser.). (Illus.). 24p. (J). lib. bdg. 18.75 (978-0-8239-6273-0(3) , PowerKids Pr.) Rosen Publishing Group, Inc., The.

O'Shei, Tim & Marren, Joe. George H. W. Bush: A MyReportLinks. Com Book. 2003. (Presidents Ser.). (Illus.). 48p. (J). lib. bdg. 25.26 (978-0-7660-5132-4(3) , MyReportLinks.com Bks.) Enslow Pubs., Inc.

Parker, Lewis K. How to Draw the Life & Times of George H. W. Bush. 2007. (Kid's Guide to Drawing the Presidents of the United States of America Ser.). (Illus.). 32p. (J). 25.25 (978-1-4042-3017-0(3) , PowerKids Pr.) Rosen Publishing Group, Inc., The.

Schuman, Michael A. George H. W. Bush. 2002. (United States Presidents Ser.). (Illus.). 128p. (J). (gr. 5-12). lib. bdg. 26.60 (978-0-7660-1702-3(8)) Enslow Pubs., Inc.

Venezia, Mike. George Bush. 2008. (Getting to Know the U. S. Presidents Ser.). 32p. (J). pap. 7.95 ***(978-0-516-25536-1(3)*** , Children's Pr.) Scholastic Library Publishing.

Venezia, Mike, illus. George Bush. 2007. 32p. (J). 28.00 ***(978-0-516-22645-3(2)*** , Children's Pr.) Scholastic Library Publishing.

BUSH, GEORGE W. (GEORGE WALKER), 1946-

Ashby, Ruth. George W. & Laura Bush. 2004. (Illus.). 48p. (J). pap. (978-0-8368-5699-6(6)); lib. bdg. 30.00 (978-0-8368-5693-4(7)) Stevens, Gareth Inc. (World Almanac Library).

Blue, Rose & Naden, Corinne J. George W. Bush. 2004. (Importance of Ser.). (Illus.). 112p. (J). 32.45 (978-1-59018-282-6(0) , Lucent Bks.) Thomson Gale.

Bredeson, Carmen. George W. Bush: The 43rd President. 2002. (Heroes of American History Ser.). (Illus.). 32p. (J). (gr. 1-4). lib. bdg. 22.60 (978-0-7660-2100-6(9)) Enslow Pubs., Inc.

Burgan, Michael. George W. Bush. 2003. (Profiles of the Presidents Ser.). (Illus.). 64p. (J). (gr. 4 up). lib. bdg. 23.93 (978-0-7565-0338-3(8)) Compass Point Bks.

—George W Bush: Our Forty-third President. 2005. (Our Presidents Ser.). (Illus.). 48p. (J). (gr. 2-6). 28.50 (978-1-59296-494-9(X)) Child's World, Inc.

Burke, Rick. George W. Bush. (American Lives Ser.). (Illus.). 32p. (J). 2003. (gr. 2-4). lib. bdg. (978-1-4034-0157-1(8)); 2002. pap. 6.95 (978-1-4034-0413-8(5)) Heinemann Library.

Bush, George W. A Charge to Keep: My Journey to the White House. 2001. (Illus.). 253p. (gr. 7-12). per. 23.45 (978-0-613-45722-4(6)) Tandem Library Bks.

Cohen, Daniel. George W. Bush: The Family Business. 2000. 16.75 (978-0-606-22377-5(0)) Tandem Library Bks.

—George W Bush: The Family Business. 2000. (gr. 3-6). lib. bdg. 17.60 (978-0-613-45183-3(X)) Tandem Library Bks.

—George W. Bush: The Family Business. rev. ed. 2000. (Gateway Biography Ser.). (Illus.). 48p. (gr. 2-4). lib. bdg. 23.90 (978-0-7613-1851-4(8) , Millbrook Pr.) Lerner Publishing Group.

Donnelly, Matt. George W. Bush. 2005. (Encyc of Presidents, 2ND Ser.). (Illus.). 112p. (J). (gr. 6-8). 34.00 (978-0-516-22972-0(9) , Watts, Franklin) Scholastic Library Publishing.

Durrett, Deanne. George W. Bush. 2002. (Famous People Ser.). (Illus.). 48p. (J). (gr. 3-5). 26.20 (978-0-7377-1371-8(2) , Kidhaven) Thomson Gale.

Fry, Sonali. Let's Read About— George W. Bush. Heyer, Carol, illus. 2003. (Scholastic First Biographies Ser.). (J). pap. (978-0-439-45953-2(2)) Scholastic, Inc.

Gormley, Beatrice. President George W. Bush: A Biography of Our 43rd President. 2000. (J). (978-0-606-20090-5(8)) Tandem Library Bks.

—President George W. Bush: Our Forty-Third President. 2001. (Illus.). 176p. (J). (gr. 4-8). pap. 4.99 (978-0-689-84123-1(X) , Aladdin) Simon & Schuster Children's Publishing.

—President George W. Bush: Our Forty-Third President. 2001. (gr. 5-8). lib. bdg. 13.00 (978-0-613-70950-7(0)) Tandem Library Bks.

Hill, Mary. George W. Bush. 2003. (Welcome Bks.). (Illus.). 24p. (J). (ps-2). pap. 4.95 (978-0-516-27886-5(X) , Children's Pr.) Scholastic Library Publishing.

—George W. Bush. 2003. (gr. k-3). lib. bdg. 12.95 (978-0-613-67712-7(9)) Tandem Library Bks.

Hughes, Libby. George W. Bush: From Texas to the White House. 2003. (Great Life Stories Ser.). (Illus.). 128p. (J). 30.50 (978-0-531-12310-2(3) , Watts, Franklin) Scholastic Library Publishing.

Jones, Veda Boyd. George W. Bush. (Major World Leaders Ser.). (Illus.). (gr. 6-12). 2003. 144p. pap. 32.00 (978-0-7910-7184-7(7)); 2002. 112p. 30.00 (978-0-7910-6940-0(0)); 2nd rev. ed. 2006. 128p. (YA). 30.00 (978-0-7910-9217-0(8)) Facts On File, Inc. (Chelsea Hse.).

Kachurek, Sandra J. George W. Bush. 2004. (United States Presidents Ser.). (Illus.). 128p. (J). lib. bdg. 26.60 (978-0-7660-2040-5(1)) Enslow Pubs., Inc.

Mara, Wil. George W. Bush. 2003. (Rookie Biographies Ser.). (gr. 1-2). pap. 4.95 (978-0-516-27838-4(X) , Children's Pr.) Scholastic Library Publishing.

—George W. Bush. 2003. (gr. k-3). lib. bdg. 12.95 (978-0-613-67619-9(X)) Tandem Library Bks.

Marquez, Heron. George W. Bush. (Biography Ser.). (Illus.). 112p. (gr. 6-12). 2005. lib. bdg. 27.93 (978-0-8225-4995-6(6)); 2003. (YA). 7.95 (978-0-8225-5001-3(6) , Carolrhoda Bks.) Lerner Publishing Group.

—George W. Bush. 2002. (gr. 7-12). lib. bdg. 16.40 (978-0-613-81864-3(4)) Tandem Library Bks.

Marquez, Heron. George W. Bush. 2007. (Presidential Leaders Ser.). (Illus.). 112p. (J). 29.27 (978-0-8225-1507-4(5) , Lerner Pubns.) Lerner Publishing Group.

Marsh, Carole. George W. Bush: America's Newest President & His White House Family. 2001. (Here & Now Ser.). 48p. (J). (gr. 3-8). pap. 7.95 (978-0-635-01068-1(2)) Gallopade International.

Mattern, Joanne. Laura Bush. 2007. (First Ladies Ser.). (Illus.). 32p. (J). (gr. k-6). lib. bdg. 24.21 ***(978-1-59928-791-1(9)*** , Checkerboard Library) ABDO Publishing Co.

McNeese, Tim. George W. Bush: First President of the New Century. 2004. (Notable Americans Ser.). (Illus.). 112p. (YA). (gr. 6-12). 21.95 (978-1-883846-85-5(4) , First Biographies) Reynolds, Morgan Inc.

Ocherster, Betsy. George Bush. 2005. (Encyc of Presidents, 2ND Ser.). (Illus.). 112p. (J). (gr. 6-8). 34.00 (978-0-516-22971-3(0) , Watts, Franklin) Scholastic Library Publishing.

O'Shei, Tim & Marren, Joe. George W. Bush: A MyReportLinks. Com Book. 2003. (Presidents Ser.). (Illus.). 48p. (J). lib. bdg. 25.26 (978-0-7660-5133-1(1) , MyReportLinks.com Bks.) Enslow Pubs., Inc.

Ryan, Patrick. George W. Bush. 2001. (United States Presidents Ser.). (Illus.). 32p. (J). (gr. k-6). lib. bdg. 22.78 (978-1-57765-302-8(5) , Checkerboard Library) ABDO Publishing Co.

Schmidt, Roderic. How to Draw the Life & Times of George W. Bush. 2007. (Kid's Guide to Drawing the Presidents of the United States of America Ser.). (Illus.). 32p. (J). 25.25 (978-1-4042-3019-4(X) , PowerKids Pr.) Rosen Publishing Group, Inc., The.

Sergis, Diana K. Bush vs. Gore: Controversial Presidential Election Case. 2003. (Landmark Supreme Court Cases Ser.). (Illus.). 128p. (J). lib. bdg. 26.60 (978-0-7660-2095-5(9)) Enslow Pubs., Inc.

Thompson, William & Thompson, Dorcas. George W. Bush. 2003. (Childhoods of the Presidents Ser.). (Illus.). 48p. (J). (gr. 4 up). lib. bdg. (978-1-59084-281-2(2)) Mason Crest Pubs.

Venezia, Mike. George W. Bush. (Getting to Know the U. S. Presidents Ser.). 32p. (J). 2008. pap. 7.95 ***(978-0-516-25595-8(9))***; 2007. 28.00 ***(978-0-516-22649-1(5))*** Scholastic Library Publishing. (Children's Pr.).

Wade, Mary Dodson. George W. Bush: Governor of Texas. 1999. (Illus.). iv, 92p. (J). (gr. 4-8). 15.95 (978-0-87443-173-5(5) , 173-5); pap. 6.95 (978-0-87443-174-2(3) , 174-3) Benson, W. S. & Co., Inc.

—George W. Bush 43rd President of the United States: From Texas to Washington. 2002. 128p. (YA). (gr. 6-12). 16.95 (978-0-87443-128-5(X)) Benson, W. S. & Co., Inc.

Wheeler, Jill C. America's Leaders. 2002. (War on Terrorism Ser.). (Illus.). 64p. (J). (gr. 4-8). lib. bdg. 25.65 (978-1-57765-661-6(X) , ABDO & Daughters) ABDO Publishing Co.

—George W. Bush. 2002. (War on Terrorism Ser.). (Illus.). 64p. (J). (gr. 4-8). lib. bdg. 25.65 (978-1-57765-662-3(8) , ABDO & Daughters) ABDO Publishing Co.

Wukovits, John F. George W. Bush. 2000. (People in the News Ser.). (Illus.). 112p. (J). (gr. 6-9). 32.45 (978-1-56006-693-4(8) , Lucent Bks.) Thomson Gale.

—George W Bush: People in the News. 2004. (Illus.). 111p. (J). (gr. 4-8). reprint ed. 22.00 (978-0-7567-7902-3(2)) DIANE Publishing Co.

Zollman, Pam. George W. Bush: President in a Turbulent World. 2006. (People to Know Today Ser.). (Illus.). 128p. (J). lib. bdg. 31.93 (978-0-7660-2628-5(0)) Enslow Pubs., Inc.

BUSHMEN

Watson, Galadriel Findlay. Bushmen of South Africa. 2004. (Indigenous Peoples Ser.). (Illus.). 32p. (J). lib. bdg. 26.00 (978-1-59036-222-8(5)) Weigl Pubs., Inc.

BUSINESS

see also Advertising; Banks and Banking; Credit; Economic History; Industrial Management; Manufactures; Marketing; Markets; Merchants; Occupations; Real Estate Business; Sales Personnel; Small Business

Aaseng, Nathan. Business Builders in Fast Food. Sterling, Denise, ed. 2001. (Business Builders Ser.: Vol. 3). (Illus.). 160p. (gr. 5 up). lib. bdg. 22.95 (978-1-881508-58-8(7)) Oliver Pr., Inc.

Advanced Principles of Entrepreneurship, 2003. (YA). pap., stu. ed. 15.00 (978-1-890859-11-4(7)) National Foundation for Teaching Entrepreneurship, The.

Advanced Principles of Entrepreneurship, Student Text. 2003. (YA). pap. 35.00 (978-1-890859-10-7(9)) National Foundation for Teaching Entrepreneurship, The.

AIT/Kauffman Foundation Staff. The "E" & Me: The Entrepreneur in You. 1998. 96p. (YA). (gr. 11-12). pap., stu. ed. 65.50 (978-0-7842-0871-7(9)) Agency for Instructional Technology.

Barratt Brown, Michael. Young Person's Guide to the Global Crisis & the Alternative. 1999. (Illus.). 111p. (YA). pap. 26.50 (978-0-85124-620-8(6)) Spokesman Bks. GBR. *Dist:* Coronet Bks.

Bell, Lonnie. The Story of Coca-Cola. 2003. (Built for Success Ser.). (Illus.). 48p. (J). 28.50 (978-1-58340-292-4(6)) Smart Apple Media.

—The Story of the Ford Motor Company. 2003. (Built for Success Ser.). (Illus.). 48p. (J). 28.50 (978-1-58340-293-1(4)) Smart Apple Media.

Berg, Adriane G. Totally Awesome Business Book for Kids. 2001. (J). lib. bdg. 22.20 (978-0-613-45349-3(2)) Tandem Library Bks.

Bochner, Arthur Berg & Berg, Adriane G. The Totally Awesome Business Book for Kids. 2nd ed. 2002. (Childcare/Parenting Guides Ser.). 160p. 12.95 (978-1-55704-494-5(5)) Newmarket Pr.

Brashares, Ann & Gusti. Steve Jobs: Thinks Different. 2001. (Techies Ser.: up). 80p. pap. 6.95 (978-0-7613-1393-9(1) , Twenty-First Century Bks.) Lerner Publishing Group.

Brown, Jeff M. The Kids' Guide to Business: Preparing & Launching Kids into Business. 2004. 138p. pap. 17.95 (978-0-9733058-1-4(9)) TeachingKidsBusiness.com CAN. *Dist:* Biblio Distribution.

Bruce Woodcock's Business Network Writers Staff. The Great Universal Business Network: And How It Grew. Fisher, Suzanne, ed. Ritterbusch, Mark, illus. l.t. ed. 1999. (WeWrite Kids! Ser.: Vol. 43). 45p. (J). (gr. 3-8). pap. 3.95 (978-1-57635-051-5(7)) WeWrite LLC.

Cambridge International Examinations Staff. IGCSE Business Studies, Module 2. 2nd rev. ed. 2000. (Cambridge Open Learning Project in South Africa Ser.). (Illus.). 80p. pap. 9.20 (978-0-521-78703-1(3)) Cambridge Univ. Pr.

—IGCSE Business Studies Module 1, 2nd rev. ed. 2000. (Cambridge Open Learning Project in South Africa Ser.). (Illus.). 88p. pap. 9.20 (978-0-521-78702-4(5)) Cambridge Univ. Pr.

—IGCSE Business Studies Module 3, 2nd rev. ed. 2000. (Cambridge Open Learning Project in South Africa Ser.). (Illus.). 80p. pap. 9.20 (978-0-521-78704-8(1)) Cambridge Univ. Pr.

Chappell, Mike & Nuttall, Chris. Business & the European Union. 2003. (Illus.). 74p. pap. (978-0-7487-7112-7(3)) Nelson Thornes Ltd.

Downing, David. Global Business: Who Benefits? 2006. (Illus.). 56p. (J). lib. bdg. (978-1-4034-8831-2(2)) Heinemann Library.

Erickson, Christian. Biz4Kids Business Start-up Kit NEIGHBORHOOD BUSINESSES. 2005. (YA). 29.95 (978-0-9745218-2-4(5)) Round Cow Media Group.

Erickson, Christian, creator. Biz4KidsBusiness Start-up Guide - Lawn Care. 2004. (Illus.). (J). (978-0-9745218-0-0(9)) Round Cow Media Group.

Ferrell, Linda, et al. Business & Society: A Strategic Approach to Social Responsibility. 2nd ed. 2004. (Illus.). 555p. (YA). 120.36 (978-0-618-41596-0(3) , 355910) Houghton Mifflin College Div.

Ferry, Steven. The Story of Microsoft. 1999. (Illus.). 48p. (YA). (gr. 7-12). lib. bdg. 18.95 (978-1-58340-005-0(2)) Smart Apple Media.

Frisch, Aaron. The Story of Nike. 2003. (Built for Success Ser.). (Illus.). 48p. (J). lib. bdg. 19.95 (978-1-58340-295-5(0)) Smart Apple Media.

Goldish, Meish. Kids & Co. Pellaton, Karen E., illus. 2002. 16p. (J). (978-0-439-35179-9(0)) Scholastic, Inc.

Hall, Margaret. Ben Cohen & the Beginning of Ben & Jerry's Ice Cream. 2005. (Illus.). 32p. (J). pap. (978-1-4034-6363-0(8)) Heinemann Library.

Hall, Margaret & Hall, M. C. Ben Cohen: The Founder of Ben & Jerry's Ice Cream. 2005. (Lives & Times Ser.). (Illus.). 32p. (J). (gr. 1-2). lib. bdg. 24.21 (978-1-4034-6349-4(2)) Heinemann Library.

Halperin, Wendy Anderson. Once upon a Company. 1998. (Illus.). 40p. (J). (gr. k-4). 17.99 (978-0-531-33089-0(3)); pap. 16.95 (978-0-531-30089-3(7)) Scholastic, Inc. (Orchard Bks.).

Harcourt School Publishers Staff. Kid's Business Book Level D: Library Edition. 2001. (Collections Ser.). (Illus.). (J). 5.90 (978-0-15-314436-3(X)) Harcourt Schl. Pubs.

—Silly Business: Practice Book. 3rd ed. 2001. (Trophies Reading Program Ser.). (Illus.). (J). pap. 1.80 (978-0-15-325084-2(4)) Harcourt Schl. Pubs.

—Silly Business: Practice Book: Florida Edition. 3rd ed. 2002. (Trophies Reading Program Ser.). (Illus.). (J). pap. 2.00 (978-0-15-326599-0(X)) Harcourt Schl. Pubs.

Hays, Scott R. The Story of Sony. 1999. (Spirit of Success Ser.). (Illus.). 48p. (YA). (gr. 5-9). lib. bdg. 18.95 (978-1-58340-007-4(9)) Smart Apple Media.

Hibbert, Adam. Globalization. 2004. (Face the Facts Ser.). (Illus.). 56p. (J). 28.56 (978-1-4109-1071-4(7)) Harcourt Schl. Pubs.

Hill, Lee Sullivan. Get Around for Fun. 1999. (Get Around Bks.). (Illus.). 32p. (J). (gr. k-3). lib. bdg. 14.60 (978-1-57505-312-7(8) , Carolrhoda Bks.) Lerner Publishing Group.

Horsley, Lorraine. Getting down to Business. 2003. (First Guides). (Illus.). 32p. (J). (gr. 1-4). 14.95 (978-1-57768-558-6(X) , Waterbird Bks.) School Specialty Publishing.

Industrie und Dienstleistungen. (Duden Abiturhilfen Ser.). (GER.). 112p. (YA). (gr. 12-13). (978-3-411-06111-2(1)) Bibliographisches Institut & F. A. Brockhaus AG DEU. *Dist:* International Bk. Import Service, Inc.

Jenkins, Arthur. GCSE A-Z Business Studies Handbook. 2nd ed. 2002. (Illus.). 288p. pap. 24.50 ***(978-0-340-85042-8(6)*** , Hodder Arnold) Hodder Education GBR. *Dist:* Trans-Atlantic Pubns., Inc.

Jenkins, Arthur, et al. GCSE Business Studies A for AQA. 2001. (Illus.). 240p. pap. 47.50 ***(978-0-340-77268-3(9)*** , Hodder Arnold) Hodder Education GBR. *Dist:* Trans-Atlantic Pubns., Inc.

Kennerdell, Peter, et al. Business Studies for OCR GCSE. 2001. (Illus.). 288p. pap. 47.50 ***(978-0-340-79052-6(0)*** , Hodder Arnold) Hodder Education GBR. *Dist:* Trans-Atlantic Pubns., Inc.

Kiefer, Jeanne. Jobs for Kids: A Smart Kid's Q & A Guide. Green, Anne Canevari, illus. 2003. (Single Titles Ser.). 112p. (gr. 5-8). lib. bdg. 25.90 (978-0-7613-2611-3(1) , Millbrook Pr.) Lerner Publishing Group.

Linderman, Dianne. My Cookie Business. Johnson, Dolores, illus. 2005. 32p. (J). 8.95 (978-0-9704876-0-5(6)) First Mom's Club, The.

—My Fishing Business. Johnson, Dolores, illus. 2005. 32p. (J). 8.95 (978-0-9704876-2-9(2)) First Mom's Club, The.

—My Pony Ride Business. Johnson, Dolores, illus. 2005. 32p. (J). 8.95 (978-0-9704876-1-2(4)) First Mom's Club, The.

Loewen, Nancy. Lemons & Lemonade: A Book about Supply & Demand. Fitzpatrick, Brad, illus. 2004. (Money Matters Ser.). 24p. (J). 22.60 (978-1-4048-0956-7(2)) Picture Window Bks.

—Let's Trade: A Book about Bartering. Jensen, Brian, illus. 2005. (Money Matters Ser.). 24p. (J). (ps). lib. bdg. 22.60 (978-1-4048-1157-7(5)) Picture Window Bks.

MacGregor, Lucy. Choosing a Career as an Entrepreneur. 2005. (World of Work Ser.). (Illus.). 64p. (J). (gr. 7-12). lib. bdg. 25.25 (978-0-8239-3329-7(6)) Rosen Publishing Group, Inc., The.

Mackall, Joe. Research & Information Management. 2nd ed. 2004. (Career Skills Library). (Illus.). 128p. (YA). (gr. 6-12). 21.95 (978-0-8160-5518-0(1) , Ferguson Publishing Co.) Facts On File, Inc.

Marcom Group Ltd, prod. Business 101 Win Labpak. (YA). cd-rom 222.50 (978-0-7365-4346-0(5)) Films Media Group.

Maupin, Melissa. The Story of Coca-Cola. 1999. (Spirit of Success Ser.). (Illus.). 48p. (YA). (gr. 5-9). lib. bdg. 18.95 (978-1-58340-001-2(X)) Smart Apple Media.

McGraw-Hill Staff. Introduction to Business, Chapters 1-35. 5th ed. 2002. 384p. (gr. 6-12). pap., stu. ed., wbk. ed. 42.64 (978-0-07-827499-2(0) , 9780078274992) Glencoe/McGraw-Hill.

—Retailing. 2004. pap., stu. ed. 41.28 (978-0-07-861400-2(7) , 9780078614002) Glencoe/McGraw-Hill.

—Sports & Entertainment Marketing. 2004. (Glencoe Marketing Ser.). (C). pap., stu. ed. 41.28 (978-0-07-861401-9(5) , 9780078614019) Glencoe/McGraw-Hill.

—Synchronized Sounds: An Integrated Office Simulation, Student Edition. 1999. (gr. 6-12). pap. 17.32 (978-0-02-804183-4(6) , 9780028041834) Glencoe/McGraw-Hill.

McGraw-Hill Staff, et al. Introduction to Business, 2 vols. 5th ed. 2002. 676p. (gr. 9-12). stu. ed. 74.00 (978-0-07-825859-6(6) , 9780078258596) Glencoe/McGraw-Hill.

Miller, Heather. Cuidador del Zoologico. (Esto es lo Que Quiero Ser (This Is What I Want to Be) Ser.). 24p. pap. 5.25 (978-1-4034-0605-7(7)) Heinemann Library.

Moyer, Duane. Creating True Wealth: Christian Youth Entrepreneurship. 1999. (Other Helpful Resources Ser.). (Illus.). 144p. (gr. 7-12). 20.00 (978-0-9668337-1-3(6) , 139210) Youth Business Publishing.

Ostrovsky, Alexsandr. Birthday: Companies-Products-Services. Ostrovsky, Alexsandr, illus. (Childrens Ser.). (Illus.). (Orig.). (J). pap. 14.95 (978-0-934393-17-1(6)) Rector Pr., Ltd.

—Clouds: Companies-Products-Services. Ostrovsky, Alexsandr, illus. (Childrens Ser.). (Illus.). (Orig.). (J). pap. 14.95 (978-0-934393-20-1(6)) Rector Pr., Ltd.

Oxford Essential Business & Office Dictionary. 2002. (gr. 7-12). lib. bdg. 17.60 (978-0-613-64903-2(6)) Tandem Library Bks.

Passaro, John. The Story of Harley-Davidson. 1999. (Spirit of Success Ser.). (Illus.). 48p. (YA). (gr. 5-9). lib. bdg. 18.95 (978-1-58340-003-6(6)) Smart Apple Media.

Pile, Robert B. Top Entrepreneurs & Their Businesses. rev. ed. 1999. (Profiles Ser.). (Illus.). 160p. (gr. 5 up). lib. bdg. 19.95 (978-1-881508-04-5(8)) Oliver Pr., Inc.

Pratten, J. & Proctor, Nigel. Business, Government & Economics. 1999. (Illus.). 160p. (J). pap. 24.95 (978-1-872807-58-4(5)) Liverpool Academic Pr. GBR. *Dist:* International Specialized Bk. Services.

Schiffman, Stephan. The Young Entrepreneur's Guide to Business Terms. 2003. (Watts Reference Ser.). (Illus.). 128p. (YA). 39.00 (978-0-531-14665-1(0) , Watts, Franklin) Scholastic Library Publishing.

Sherman, Josepha. Jeff Bezos: King of Amazon. 2001. (Techies Ser.: up). (Illus.). 80p. (J). (gr. 5 up). lib. bdg. 23.90 (978-0-7613-1963-4(8) , Twenty-First Century Bks.) Lerner Publishing Group.

Sherman, Josepha & Pica, Steve. Jeff Bezos: King of Amazon. 2001. (Techies Ser.: up). 80p. (J). pap. 6.95 (978-0-7613-1394-6(X) , Twenty-First Century Bks.) Lerner Publishing Group.

Stimpson, Peter, et al. Business Studies for AS OCR. 2nd rev. ed. 2003. (Illus.). 295p. pap. 26.00 (978-0-521-54183-1(2)) Cambridge Univ. Pr.

Tangerine Press Staff & Scholastic, Inc. Staff, contrib. by. Kid Biz. 2004. (Illus.). 62p. (J). (978-0-439-69986-0(X)) Scholastic, Inc.

Vickers, Rebecca. J. L. Kraft: The Founder of Kraft Foods. 2005. (Illus.). 32p. (J). (ps-ps). lib. bdg. 25.36 (978-1-4034-6344-9(1)) Heinemann Library.

—J.L. Kraft. 2005. (Illus.). 32p. (J). pap. (978-1-4034-6358-6(1)) Heinemann Library.

Wiggins, Grant. Feedback. abr. ed. 1999. 36p. (J). pap. 295.00 (978-0-7879-5235-8(4) , G936-E2F, Jossey-Bass) Wiley, John & Sons, Inc.

Williams, Tim. Cambridge HSC Business Studies Study Guide. 2004. (Cambridge HSC Study Guides). 232p. pap., stu. ed. 11.95 (978-0-521-60322-5(6)) Cambridge Univ. Pr.

Working Partners Series 23. 2005. 256p. (J). 15.99 (978-0-06-087170-3(9)); 16.89 (978-0-06-087171-0(7)); pap. 5.99 (978-0-06-087172-7(5) , Harper Trophy) HarperCollins Pubs.

BUSINESS—BIOGRAPHY

Aaseng, Nathan. Business Builders in Broadcasting. 2005. (Business Builders Ser.: Vol. 8). (Illus.). 160p. (J). (gr. 5 up). lib. bdg. 24.95 (978-1-881508-83-0(8)) Oliver Pr., Inc.

—Business Builders in Real Estate. 2002. (Business Builders Ser.: Vol. 4). (Illus.). 160p. (gr. 5 up). lib. bdg. 22.95 (978-1-881508-79-3(X)) Oliver Pr., Inc.

—Business Builders in Sweets & Treats. 2005. (Business Builders Ser.: Vol. 9). (Illus.). 160p. (J). (gr. 5 up). lib. bdg. 24.95 (978-1-881508-84-7(6)) Oliver Pr., Inc.

African American Business Persons. 2000. (My Ancestors—My Heroes Ser.: Vol. 16). (J). (gr. 3-4). (978-1-893091-15-3(5)) Parker Publishing Co.

African-American International Business Leaders. 2000. (My Ancestors—My Heroes Ser.: Vol. 35). (J). (gr. 3-4). (978-1-893091-34-4(1)) Parker Publishing Co.

African-American Owners of International Companies. 2000. (My Ancestors—My Heroes Ser.: Vol. 45). (J). (gr. 3-4). (978-1-893091-44-3(9)) Parker Publishing Co.

Arrathoon, Leigh A. Men Who Changed the World Vol. I: The Henry Ford Story. Davio, John, ed. Hajdyla, Ken, illus. 56p. (J). (gr. 5-6). pap. 5.95 (978-0-9648564-5-5(X)) Paint Creek Pr., Ltd.

Bailey, Tom. A.G. Gaston: Visionary Businessman. 2003. (Alabama Roots Biography Ser.). (Illus.). 111p. (J). pap. (978-1-878561-99-2(5)) Seacoast Publishing, Inc.

Barton-Wood, Sara. Bill Gates: Computer Giant. 2001. (Famous Lives Ser.). (Illus.). 48p. (J). (gr. 4-6). lib. bdg. 27.12 (978-0-7398-4432-8(6)) Raintree.

Bill Gates. rev. ed. 2007. (Biography Ser.). 112p. (J). (gr. 6-12). 29.27 (***978-0-8225-7363-0(6)*** , Twenty-First Century Bks.) Lerner Publishing Group.

Boyd, Aaron. Smart Money: The Story of Bill Gates. rev. exp. ed. 2004. (American Business Leaders Ser.). (Illus.). 128p. (YA). (gr. 6-12). 23.95 (978-1-931798-32-7(X)) Reynolds, Morgan Inc.

Brackett, Virginia. Steve Jobs: Computer Genius of Apple. 2003. (Internet Biographies Ser.). (Illus.). 48p. (J). (gr. 4-10). lib. bdg. 23.93 (978-0-7660-1970-6(5)) Enslow Pubs., Inc.

Brackett, Virginia R. Jeff Bezos. (Latinos in the Limelight Ser.). (Illus.). 64p. (J). 2001. (gr. 3 up). 27.50 (978-0-7910-6104-6(3)); 2000. pap. (978-0-7910-6105-3(1)) Facts On File, Inc. (Chelsea Hse.).

Brashares, Ann. Steve Jobs: Thinks Different. 2001. (Techies Ser.: up). (Illus.). 80p. (gr. 5 up). lib. bdg. 23.90 (978-0-7613-1959-7(X) , Twenty-First Century Bks.) Lerner Publishing Group.

Brown, Jonatha A. Bill Gates. 2004. (Illus.). 24p. (J). pap. (978-0-8368-4317-0(7)); (YA). lib. bdg. 19.33 (978-0-8368-4310-1(X)) Stevens, Gareth Inc.

Burgan, Michael. The Story of Levi's. Himler, Ronald, illus. 2002. 16p. (J). (978-0-439-35181-2(2)) Scholastic, Inc.

Byers, Ann. Jeff Bezos: The Founder of Amazon.com. 2006. (Internet Career Biographies Ser.). (Illus.). 112p. (YA). (gr. 7-12). lib. bdg. 31.95 (978-1-4042-0717-2(1)) Rosen Publishing Group, Inc., The.

Byman, Jeremy. J. P. Morgan: Banker to a Growing Nation. 2004. (American Business Leaders Ser.). (Illus.). 112p. (YA). (gr. 6-12). 23.95 (978-1-883846-60-2(9) , First Biographies) Reynolds, Morgan Inc.

Compass Point Books, contrib. by. Levi Strauss. (Compass Point Early Biographies Ser.). 32p. (J). pap. 7.95 (978-0-7565-1175-3(5)) Compass Point Bks.

Copley, Robert E. The Tall Mexican: The Life of Hank Aguirre All-Star Pitcher, Businessman, Humanitarian. 2000. (J). (978-0-606-19189-0(5)); (gr. 7-12). lib. bdg. 18.75 (978-0-613-28666-4(9)) Tandem Library Bks.

Dougherty, Terri. Sam Walton: Department Store Giant. 2004. (Giants of American Industry Ser.). (Illus.). 64p. (J). 28.70 (978-1-4103-0258-8(X) , Blackbirch Pr., Inc.) Thomson Gale.

Fandel, Jennifer. George Eastman & the Kodak Camera. 2007. 32p. (J). (***978-0-7368-6848-8(8)***) Capstone Pr., Inc.

Ferry, Steven. The Story of Boeing. 1999. (Spirit of Success Ser.). (Illus.). 48p. (YA). (gr. 5-9). lib. bdg. 18.95 (978-1-58340-000-5(1)) Smart Apple Media.

French, Laura. Internet Pioneers: The Cyber-Elite. 2001. (Collective Biographies Ser.). (Illus.). 112p. (J). (gr. 6-12). lib. bdg. 26.60 (978-0-7660-1540-1(8)) Enslow Pubs., Inc.

Gaines, Ann Graham. Henry Ford. 2002. (SPA.). (gr. k-3). lib. bdg. 14.10 (978-0-613-79410-7(9)) Tandem Library Bks.

Ganeri, Anita, et al. Larry Ellison: Sheer Nerve. 2001. (Techies Ser.; up). (Illus.). 80p. (gr. 5 up). lib. bdg. 23.90 (978-0-7613-1962-7(X) , Twenty-First Century Bks.) Lerner Publishing Group.

Garty, Judy. Jeff Bezos: Business Genius of Amazon.com. 2003. (Internet Biographies Ser.). (Illus.). 48p. (J). (gr. 4-10). lib. bdg. 23.93 (978-0-7660-1972-0(1)) Enslow Pubs., Inc.

Hall, Margaret. H. J. Heinz. 2003. (Lives & Times Ser.). (Illus.). 24p. (J). pap. (978-1-4034-4640-4(7)) Heinemann Library.

—Madam C. J. Walker. 2003. (Lives & Times Ser.). (Illus.). 24p. (J). pap. (978-1-4034-4257-4(6)) Heinemann Library.

—William Wrigley, Jr. & the Beginning of Wrigley's Chewing Gum. 2005. (Illus.). 32p. (J). pap. (978-1-4034-6361-6(1)) Heinemann Library.

Hall, Margaret & Hall, M. C. William Wrigley JR: The Founder of Wrigley's Gum. 2005. (Illus.). 32p. (J). (gr. k-2). lib. bdg. 24.21 (978-1-4034-6347-0(6)) Heinemann Library.

Hayhurst, Chris. Jerry Yang & David Filo: The Founders of Yahoo! 2006. (Internet Career Biographies Ser.). (Illus.). 112p. (YA). (gr. 7-12). lib. bdg. 31.95 (978-1-4042-0718-9(X)) Rosen Publishing Group, Inc., The.

Hays, Scott R. The Story of Nike. 1999. (Spirit of Success Ser.). (Illus.). 48p. (YA). (gr. 5-9). lib. bdg. 18.95 (978-1-58340-006-7(0)) Smart Apple Media.

Jablonski, Carla. Esther Dyson: Web Guru. 2002. (Techies Ser.). (Illus.). 80p. (gr. 5 up). lib. bdg. 23.90 (978-0-7613-2657-1(X) , Twenty-First Century Bks.) Lerner Publishing Group.

Kent, Jacqueline C. Business Builders in Cosmetics. 2003. (Business Builders Ser.: Vol. 7). (Illus.). 160p. (gr. 5 up). lib. bdg. 22.95 (978-1-881508-82-3(X)) Oliver Pr., Inc.

Kerns, Anne. Martha Stewart. 2007. (Biography Ser.). (Illus.). 112p. (J). (gr. 6-12). 29.27 (978-0-8225-6613-7(3) , Twenty-First Century Bks.) Lerner Publishing Group.

Lasky, Kathryn. Vision of Beauty: The Story of Sarah Breedlove Walker. Bennett, Nneka, illus. 48p. (J). (gr. 3-7). 2003. pap. 6.99 (978-0-7636-1834-6(9)); 2000. 17.99 (978-0-7636-0253-6(1)) Candlewick Pr.

—Vision of Beauty: The Story of Sarah Breedlove Walker. 2003. (gr. 3-6). lib. bdg. 15.30 (978-0-613-74818-6(2)) Tandem Library Bks.

Lesinski, Jeanne M. Bill Gates. 2007. (J). pap. 7.95 (***978-0-8225-7027-1(0)*** , Lerner Pubns.) Lerner Publishing Group.

Llewellyn-Evans, Teresa. Livewire Real Lives Reverend John Flynn. 1999. (Livewires Ser.). 32p. (gr. 6-9). pap. 6.00 (978-0-521-77623-3(6)) Cambridge Univ. Pr.

Logan, Rochelle & Halverstadt, Julie. 100 Most Popular Business Leaders for Young Adults: Biographical Sketches & Professional Paths. 2002. (Profiles & Pathways Ser.). (Illus.). 419p. (gr. 6-12). 65.00 (978-1-56308-799-8(5) , LU7995) Libraries Unlimited, Inc.

Marsh, Carole. John Harold Johnson. 2002. (One Thousand Readers Ser.). (Illus.). 12p. (J). (gr. k-4). 2.95 (978-0-635-01545-7(5) , 15455) Gallopade International.

—William Wrigley, Jr. 2002. (One Thousand Readers Ser.). (Illus.). 12p. (J). (gr. k-4). 2.95 (978-0-635-01533-4(1) , 15331) Gallopade International.

McLuskey, Krista. Entrepreneurs. 1999. (Women in Profile Ser.). (J). (978-0-606-16434-4(0)); (Illus.). 48p. lib. bdg. 17.60 (978-0-613-11513-1(9)) Tandem Library Bks.

McPherson, Stephanie Sammartino. Levi Strauss. 2007. (History Maker Bios Ser.). (Illus.). 48p. (J). 26.60 (978-0-8225-6581-9(1) , Lerner Pubns.) Lerner Publishing Group.

Meachum, Virginia. Martha Stewart: Successful Businesswoman. 1998. (People to Know Ser.). (Illus.). 112p. (YA). (gr. 6-12). lib. bdg. 26.60 (978-0-89490-984-9(3)) Enslow Pubs., Inc.

Morales, Leslie. Esther Dyson: Internet Visionary. 2003. (Internet Biographies Ser.). (Illus.). 48p. (J). (gr. 4-10). lib. bdg. 23.93 (978-0-7660-1973-7(X)) Enslow Pubs., Inc.

Mortimer, Sean. Tony Hawk: Chairman of the Board. 2000. (J). (gr. 3-9). pap. 4.99 (978-1-930623-20-0(8)) Sports Illustrated For Kids.

Parker, Lewis K. Cornelius Vanderbilt & the Railroad Industry. 2003. (Reading Power Ser.). (Illus.). 24p. (J). lib. bdg. 17.25 (978-0-8239-6450-5(7) , PowerKids Pr.) Rosen Publishing Group, Inc., The.

—John Jacob Astor & the Fur Trade. 2003. (Reading Power Ser.). (Illus.). 24p. (J). lib. bdg. 17.25 (978-0-8239-6447-5(7) , PowerKids Pr.) Rosen Publishing Group, Inc., The.

Passaro, John. The Story of Disney. 1999. (Spirit of Success Ser.). (Illus.). 48p. (YA). (gr. 5-9). lib. bdg. 18.95 (978-1-58340-002-9(8)) Smart Apple Media.

Paxson, Jillip Naysinthe, told to. The First Thirty. 2005. 96p. (YA). 15.00 (978-0-9758794-1-2(3)) IdeaList Enterprises, Inc.

Paxson, Jillip Naysinthe & Siegman, Greg Forbes. The First Thirty. 2005. 96p. (YA). per. 10.00 (978-0-9758794-0-5(5)) IdeaList Enterprises, Inc.

Peters, Craig. Bill Gates: Software Genius of Microsoft. 2003. (Internet Biographies Ser.). (Illus.). 48p. (J). (gr. 4-10). lib. bdg. 23.93 (978-0-7660-1969-0(1)) Enslow Pubs., Inc.

—Larry Ellison: Database Genius of Oracle. 2003. (Internet Biographies Ser.). (Illus.). 48p. (J). (gr. 4-10). lib. bdg. 23.93 (978-0-7660-1974-4(8)) Enslow Pubs., Inc.

—Steve Case: Internet Genius of America Online. 2003. (Internet Biographies Ser.). (Illus.). 48p. (YA). (gr. 4-10). lib. bdg. 23.93 (978-0-7660-1971-3(3)) Enslow Pubs., Inc.

Peterson, Tiffany. Levi Strauss. 2003. (Lives & Times Ser.). (Illus.). (J). 24p. pap. (978-1-4034-4256-7(8)); 32p. lib. bdg. 22.79 (978-1-4034-3250-6(3)) Heinemann Library.

—Levi Strauss. 2003. (gr. k-3). lib. bdg. 14.75 (978-0-613-82820-8(8)) Tandem Library Bks.

—W. K. Kellogg. 2003. (Lives & Times Ser.). (Illus.). (J). 24p. pap. (978-1-4034-4259-8(2)); 32p. lib. bdg. 22.79 (978-1-4034-3249-0(X)) Heinemann Library.

Raatma, Lucia. Levi Strauss. 2004. (Compass Point Early Biographies Ser.). (Illus.). 32p. (J). (gr. 2 up). lib. bdg. 21.26 (978-0-7565-0568-4(2)) Compass Point Bks.

Richardson, Adele D. The Story of Microsoft. 2003. (Built for Success Ser.). (Illus.). 48p. (J). 28.50 (978-1-58340-294-8(2)) Smart Apple Media.

Rosen, Roslyn, intro. Business & Industry. 1999. (Female Firsts in Their Fields Ser.). (Illus.). 64p. (J). (gr. 4-7). 12.95 (978-0-7910-5142-9(0)) Facts On File, Inc.

Schuman, Michael. Bill Gates: Computer Mogul & Philanthropist. 2007. (People to Know Today Ser.). (Illus.). 128p. (J). (gr. 6). lib. bdg. 31.93 (***978-0-7660-2693-3(0)***) Enslow Pubs., Inc.

Sherman, Josepha. Jeff Bezos: King of Amazon. 2001. 13.75 (978-0-606-22375-1(4)); (gr. 5-8). lib. bdg. 15.25 (978-0-613-45195-6(3)) Tandem Library Bks.

—Jerry Yang & David Filo: Chief Yahoos of Yahoo! 2001. (Techies Ser.: up). (Illus.). 80p. (J). (gr. 5 up). lib. bdg. 23.90 (978-0-7613-1961-0(1) , Twenty-First Century Bks.) Lerner Publishing Group.

Simon, Charman. Bill Gates: Helping People Use Computers. 1998. (Community Builders Ser.). (Illus.). 48p. (J). (gr. 3-5). pap. 6.95 (978-0-516-26132-4(0) , Children's Pr.) Scholastic Library Publishing.

Simon, Charnan. Milton Hershey: Chocolate King, Town Builder. De Capua, Sarah, ed. 1998. (Community Builders Ser.). (Illus.). 48p. (J). (gr. 3-5). pap. 6.95 (978-0-516-26330-4(7) , Children's Pr.) Scholastic Library Publishing.

Spinale, Laura. The Story of Martha Stewart Living. 1999. (Spirit of Success Ser.). 48p. (J). (gr. 5-9). lib. bdg. 18.95 (978-1-58340-004-3(4)) Smart Apple Media.

Tracy, Kathleen. William Hewlett: Pioneer of the Computer Age. 2002. (Unlocking the Secrets of Science Ser.). (J). (978-1-58415-178-4(1)); (Illus.). 56p. (gr. 4-10). lib. bdg. 25.70 (978-1-58415-142-5(0)) Mitchell Lane Pubs., Inc.

Viegas, Jennifer. Pierre Omidyar: The Founder of eBay. 2006. (Internet Career Biographies Ser.). (Illus.). 112p. (YA). (gr. 7-12). lib. bdg. 31.95 (978-1-4042-0715-8(5)) Rosen Publishing Group, Inc., The.

Wilson, Suzan. Steve Jobs: Wizard of Apple Computer. 2001. (People to Know Ser.). (Illus.). 128p. (YA). (gr. 6-12). lib. bdg. 26.60 (978-0-7660-1536-4(X)) Enslow Pubs., Inc.

Woog, Adam. Bill Gates. (Famous People Ser.). (Illus.). 2002. 48p. (J). (gr. 3-5). 26.20 (978-0-7377-1400-5(X) , Kidhaven); 1998. 128p. (YA). (gr. 6-9). 28.70 (978-1-56006-256-1(8) , Lucent Bks.) Thomson Gale.

Wooten, Sara McIntosh. Donald Trump: From Real Estate to Reality TV. 2008. (J). (***978-0-7660-2890-6(9)***) Enslow Pubs., Inc.

Wyborny, Shelia. Frederick W. Smith: Founder of FedEx. 2007. (Innovators Ser.). (Illus.). 64p. (J). (gr. 4-8). 24.95 (***978-0-7377-3861-2(8)*** , Kidhaven) Thomson Gale.

BUSINESS, CHOICE OF

see Vocational Guidance

BUSINESS—FICTION

Bouani, Jennifer. Future Business Leaders' Series: Tyler & His Solve-a-matic Machine. Shelley, Jennifer, ed. Smalley, Guy, illus. 2006. 128p. (J). per. 6.99 (978-0-9779265-0-3(8)) Bouje Publishing, LLC.

Boyce, Frank Cottrell, ed. Framed. 2006. 320p. (J). 16.99 (978-0-06-073402-2(7)); lib. bdg. 17.89 (978-0-06-073403-9(5)) HarperCollins Pubs.

Brimner, Larry Dane. The Messy Lot. Tripp, Christine, illus. (Rookie Choices Ser.). 32p. (J). (gr. 1-2). 2002. pap. 5.95 (978-0-516-25975-8(X)); 2001. 19.50 (978-0-516-22156-4(6)) Scholastic Library Publishing. (Children's Pr.).

Brown, Harriet. Babysitter's Business Kit. 2007. 64p. (J). pap. 12.95 (***978-1-59369-186-8(6)*** , Pleasant Co.) American Girl Publishing, Inc.

Catran, Ken. Fries. 2002. (Takeaways Ser.). (Illus.). 160p. (YA). pap. (978-0-7344-0266-0(X) , Lothian Bks.) Hachette Livre Australia.

Chapman, Allen. Bart Sterlings Road to Success. rev. ed. 2006. (ENG.). 204p. 27.95 (978-1-4218-2015-6(3) , 1st World Library - Literary Society) 1st World Publishing, Inc.

Clyne, Margaret. Trash or Treasure. 2000. (gr. k-3). lib. bdg. 11.80 (978-0-613-29770-7(9)) Tandem Library Bks.

Cottrell Boyce, Frank. Framed. 2008. 320p. (J). pap. 6.99 (***978-0-06-073404-6(3)*** , Harper Trophy) HarperCollins Pubs.

Duffy, Daniel M., illus. Benny Goes into Business, Vol. 5. 1999. (Adventures of Benny & Watch: Vol. 5). 32p. (J). (ps-2). pap. 3.95 (978-0-8075-0637-0(0)) Whitman, Albert & Co.

Fisher, Anne. Look What Brains Can Do! 2005. reprint ed. pap. 20.95 (978-1-4179-9453-3(3)) Kessinger Publishing, LLC.

Froese, Dorothy Cheever. Captain Rhino's Progress: An Allegory of the Workplace. 2003. (Illus.). 32p. pap. 9.00 (978-1-890437-86-2(7)) Western Reflections Publishing Co.

Greene, Stephanie. Owen Foote, Money Man. Weston, Martha, illus. 96p. (J). 2003. (gr. k-3). pap. 4.95 (978-0-618-37837-1(5)); 2000. (gr. 5-9). tchr. ed. 15.00 (978-0-618-02369-1(0)) Houghton Mifflin Co. Trade & Reference Div. (Clarion Bks.).

Halperin, Wendy Anderson. Once upon a Company. 1998. (Illus.). 40p. (J). (gr. k-4). 17.99 (978-0-531-33089-0(3)); pap. 16.95 (978-0-531-30089-3(7)) Scholastic, Inc. (Orchard Bks.).

Hao, K. T. & Kim, Byung-Gyu. The 100th Customer. Ferri, Giuliano, illus. 2005. 32p. (J). (ps-17). 15.95 (978-1-933327-03-7(0)) Purple Bear Bks., Inc.

Harcourt School Publishers Staff. The Serai: Take-Home Book. 2001. (Collections Ser.). (Illus.). (J). pap. 1.90 (978-0-15-319554-9(1)) Harcourt Schl. Pubs.

Harper, Michael J. & Arrington, Jay. The Little Entrepreneur: Takes Flight. 2005. 66p. (J). per. 9.95 (978-0-9764161-3-5(1)) Harper-Arrington Publishing.

Haskins, Lori. No Money? No Problem! Nez, John, illus. 2004. 32p. (J). lib. bdg. 20.00 (***978-1-4242-1111-1(5)***) Fitzgerald Bks.

Hipscher, Jerome. White Slavery. 2004. 78p. (YA). pap. 8.95 (978-0-595-31441-6(4)) iUniverse, Inc.

Holding, James Malcolm, 3rd, et al. The Mullet Masters. 2007. pap. 8.00 (***978-0-8059-7147-7(5)***) Dorrance Publishing Co., Inc.

Hood, Sue. Monkey Business. Chapman, Susan, illus. 2005. (J). bds. (978-1-890647-17-9(9)) RC2 Corp.

Irwin, Inez. Maida's Little Shop. 2006. 41.99 (***978-1-4219-7069-1(4)***) IndyPublish.com.

Jamieson, Mark. Ico Island. 2007. (J). pap. 11.95 (***978-0-9792518-0-1(X)***) Gequalsa.

Kenrick, Angela Mastrodonato, creator. Flannery Fiddlesticks Goes into Business. 2002. (J). per. 12.99 (978-0-9707914-8-1(8)) Litterateur Pubns., Inc.

Lesczynski, Jim. The Walton Street Tycoons. 2007. 269p. (YA). pap. 9.95 (***978-0-9791283-0-1(7)***) East River Pr.

Levitin, Sonia. Boom Town. Smith, Cat Bowman, illus. 2004. 40p. (J). pap. 6.99 (978-0-439-64394-8(5)) Scholastic, Inc.

The Little Entrepreneurs. l.t. ed. 2001. 65p. (J). 14.95 (978-0-9709119-2-6(0)) Limpid Butterfly Productions, The.

Merrill, Jean. The Toothpaste Millionaire. 2006. (Illus.). 144p. (J). (gr. 4-6). 16.00 (978-0-618-75924-8(7)); pap. 5.95 (978-0-618-75925-5(5)) Houghton Mifflin Co. Trade & Reference Div.

Moonjar, ed. Noom & Raj Start Business. 2005. 36p. 19.95 (978-0-9724282-2-4(4)); 9.95 (978-0-9724282-5-5(9)) Moonjar, LLC.

Muldrow, Diane. Boiling Point, No. 3. Pollak, Barbara, illus. 2007. (Dish Ser.). 160p. (J). (gr. 4-7). pap. 4.99 (978-0-448-44528-1(X) , Grosset & Dunlap) Penguin Group (USA) Inc.

—Into the Mix. 2002. (gr. 3-6). lib. bdg. 13.00 (978-0-613-72425-8(9)) Tandem Library Bks.

My Busy Day. 2000. (J). (978-1-58453-098-5(7)) Pioneer Valley Educational Pr., Inc.

Norman, Kimberly E. Jack of All Tails. Clark, David H., illus. 2007. 32p. (J). 15.99 (978-0-525-47793-8(4) , Dutton Juvenile) Penguin Group (USA) Inc.

Nye, Naomi Shihab. Going Going. 2005. (Illus.). 240p. (J). 16.99 (978-0-688-16185-9(5)); 232p. (YA). (gr. 7 up). lib. bdg. 16.89 (978-0-06-029366-6(7)) HarperCollins Pubs.

Pants Builds a Business. 2004. (J). per. 7.99 (978-0-9755959-4-7(6)) Girl Named Pants, Inc., A.

Poyner, James R. Toy-Maker's Apprentice. 2006. 68p. (YA). per. 12.00 (***978-1-60002-282-1(0)*** , 4145, Airleaf Publishing) Airleaf Publishing & Bookselling.

Romer, Ruth. The Great Lemonade Stand-off. 2005. 22.00 (***978-1-4108-4200-8(2)***) Benchmark Education Co.

Rozen, Anna. The Merchant of Noises. Scarbrough, Carl W., tr. from FRE. Avril, Francois, illus. 2006. 28p. (J). (gr. k-5). 18.95 (***978-1-56792-321-6(6)***) Godine, David R. Pub.

Sensel, Joni. Reality Leak. Slade, Christian, illus. 2007. 218p. (J). (***978-1-4287-3983-3(1)***) Holt, Henry & Co.

Shoup, Andrew J. Andy & Elmer's Apple Dumpling Adventure. 2nd ed. 2007. (J). 16.95 (***978-0-9720436-3-2(2)***) TokoBooks.

—Andy & Elmer's Apple Dumpling Adventure Coloring & Activity Book. Shoup, Andrew J., illus. 2007. (Illus.). 36p. (J). 3.95 (***978-0-9720436-2-5(4)***) TokoBooks.

Stratemeyer, Edward. The Rover Boys in Business or the Search. 2004. reprint ed. pap. 22.95 (978-1-4191-8116-0(5)) Kessinger Publishing, LLC.

—The Rover Boys in Business or the Search for the Missing Bonds. 2004. reprint ed. pap. 1.99 (978-1-4192-8116-7(X)) Kessinger Publishing, LLC.

Warner, Gertrude Chandler. Benny Goes into Business. 1999. (gr. k-3). lib. bdg. 11.80 (978-0-613-11318-2(7)); (Adventures of Benny & Watch: No.5). (J). (gr. 1-3). 10.75 (978-0-606-16916-5(4)) Tandem Library Bks.

—Ice Cream Mystery. 2003. (gr. 3-6). lib. bdg. 11.80 (978-0-613-75719-5(X)) Tandem Library Bks.

Weaver, Richard G. & Farrell, John D. Crisis at Santa's Workshop: Using Facilitation to Get More Done in Less Time: Help Others Take Responsibility & Work Together Effectively. 2003. (Illus.). 150p. pap. 17.95 (978-1-57675-279-1(8)) Berrett-Koehler Pubs., Inc.

BUSINESS—HISTORY

Moriarty, J. T. The Birth of American Capitalism: The Rise of the American Bank. 2003. (America's Industrial Society in the 19th Century Ser.). (Illus.). 32p. (J). pap. (978-0-8239-4280-0(5)) Rosen Publishing Group, Inc., The.

BUSINESS, SMALL

see Small Business

BUSINESS—VOCATIONAL GUIDANCE

Giesecke, Ernestine. Be Your Own Boss: Small Businesses. 2002. (Everyday Economics Ser.). (Illus.). 48p. (J). pap. 8.50 (978-1-58810-956-9(9)) Heinemann Library.

Iannarelli, Cindy. ABC's of Business: Funfilled Activities from A to Z. 1998. (Illus.). 120p. (J). (gr. 2-5). pap. 16.95 (978-1-889107-02-8(6)) Business Cents Resources.

MacKall, Dandi Daley. Teamwork Skills. 2nd ed. 2004. (Career Skills Library). (Illus.). 144p. (YA). (gr. 6-12). 21.95 (978-0-8160-5524-1(6) , Ferguson Publishing Co.) Facts On File, Inc.

Pincus, Marilyn. Your Bright Future in Business Administration. 2002. (gr. 7-12). lib. bdg. 21.10 (978-0-613-56711-4(0)) Tandem Library Bks.

BUSINESS COLLEGES

see Business Education

BUSINESS CORRESPONDENCE

see Business Letters

BUSINESS DEPRESSIONS

see Depressions; Economic History

BUSINESS EDUCATION

see also Secretaries

McGraw-Hill Staff. Introduction to Business: Integrated Software Simulation. 5th ed. 2002. (gr. 6-12). stu. ed. 26.00 (978-0-07-827510-4(5) , 9780078275104) Glencoe/ McGraw-Hill.

BUSINESS ENGLISH

see English Language—Business English

BUSINESS ETHICS

see also Success

Ferguson. Mastering Career Skills: Professional Ethics & Etiquette. 2nd rev. ed. (Mastering Career Skills Ser.). (Illus.). 144p. pap. 12.95 (***978-0-8160-7117-3(9)***, Checkmark Bks.) Facts On File, Inc.

Harden, Michael P. Doing the Right Thing: A Guide to Business Ethics. 2004. 329p. per. 16.95 (978-1-59453-034-0(3) , 1665) Airleaf Publishing & Bookselling.

J. G. Ferguson Publishing Company Staff, contrib. by. Professional Ethics & Etiquette. 2nd ed. 2004. (Career Skills Library). (Illus.). 144p. (YA). (gr. 6-12). 21.95 (978-0-8160-5523-4(8) , Ferguson Publishing Co.) Facts On File, Inc.

BUSINESS LETTERS

see also English Language—Business English

Roy, Jennifer Rozines & Gordon, Sherri Mabry. You Can Write a Business Letter. 2003. (You Can Write Ser.). (Illus.). 64p. (J). (gr. 6-12). lib. bdg. 22.60 (978-0-7660-2088-7(6)) Enslow Pubs., Inc.

BUSINESS SCHOOLS

see Business Education

BUTT-UGLY MARTIANS (FICTITIOUS CHARACTERS)—FICTION

Scholastic, Inc. Staff. The Big Bang Theory. 2002. (Butt-Ugly Martians Chapter Bks.: No. 1). 80p. (J). (gr. k-7). pap. 4.99 (978-0-439-37023-3(X)) Scholastic, Inc.

BUTTERFLIES

see also Caterpillars; Moths

Allen, Judy. Are You a Butterfly? Humphries, Tudor, illus. (Backyard Bks.). 32p. (J). (ps-k). 2003. pap. 5.95 (978-0-7534-5608-8(7)); 2000. tchr. ed. 9.95 (978-0-7534-5240-0(5)) Houghton Mifflin Co. Trade & Reference Div. (Kingfisher).

—Are You a Butterfly? 2003. (ps-2). lib. bdg. 12.95 (978-0-613-90777-4(9)) Tandem Library Bks.

Animal Lives: Butterflies. 2006. pap. 4.99 (978-1-4206-8153-6(2)) Teacher Created Materials, Inc.

Ashepak, Agnes. Butterfly. Nevak, Caroline, illus. l.t. ed. 1999. 8p. (J). (gr. k-3). pap. 14.50 (978-1-58084-058-3(2)) Lower Kuskokwim Schl. District.

Ashley, Susan. Butterflies. 2004. (Weekly Reader Early Learning Library). (Illus.). 24p. (gr. 1 up). (J). pap. 5.95 (978-0-8368-4059-9(3)) ; (YA). lib. bdg. 19.33 (978-0-8368-4052-0(6)) Stevens, Gareth Inc. (Weekly Reader Early Learning Library).

Bailey, Jill. How Caterpillars Turn into Butterflies. 1998. (Nature's Mysteries Ser.). (Illus.). 32p. (J). (gr. 3-5). lib. bdg. 22.79 (978-0-7614-0857-4(6) , Benchmark Bks.) Cavendish, Marshall Corp.

Bair, Heather. Flying High with Butterflies: A Pre-K/ K Complete Supplemental Unit. Bruner, Garth, illus. 2004. per. 9.95 (978-1-891541-03-2(X)) Insect Lore.

—I Spy a Butterfly: A Second Grade Complete Supplemental Unit. Bruner, Garth, illus. 2005. per. 9.95 (978-1-891541-05-6(6)) Insect Lore.

—O'H Me O'H My A Butterfly: A First Grade Complete Supplemental Unit. Bruner, Garth, illus. 2005. per. 9.95 (978-1-891541-04-9(8)) Insect Lore.

Barnard, Edward S. Butterflies. 2006. (J). (978-1-59939-111-3(2) , Reader's Digest Young Families, Inc.) Reader's Digest Children's Publishing, Inc.

Bauman, Amy, et al. The Wonder of Butterflies. 2000. (Animal Wonders Ser.). (Illus.). 48p. (J). (gr. 1 up). lib. bdg. 26.00 (978-0-8368-2662-3(0)) Stevens, Gareth Inc.

Bentley, Dawn. Good Night, Sweet Butterflies: A Color Dreamland. Cahoon, Heather, illus. (J). 2003. 24p. 10.95 (978-0-689-85684-6(9)); 2007. 14p. 5.99 (978-1-4169-1296-5(7)) Simon & Schuster Children's Publishing. (Little Simon).

Berger, Melvin. Where Did the Butterfly Get Its Name? Questions & Answers about Butterflies A. 2002. (gr. 3-6). lib. bdg. 14.10 (978-0-613-66681-7(X)) Tandem Library Bks.

Berger, Melvin & Berger, Gilda. Butterflies. 2002. (Scholastic Readers Ser.). (Illus.). 14p. (J). pap. (978-0-439-44539-9(6)) Scholastic, Inc.

—Caterpillar to Butterfly. 2004. (Scholastic Readers Ser.). (Illus.). (J). (978-0-439-57483-9(8)) Scholastic, Inc.

Berger, Melvin & Berger, Gilda. Schol True of False #2 Butterflies & Caterpill. 2008. 48p. pap. 4.99 (***978-0-545-00392-6(X)***, Scholastic Reference) Scholastic, Inc.

Berkowitz, Henry. Butterflies & Moths: An Educational Coloring Book. Berkowitz, Henry, illus. 2001. (Illus.). 32p. (J). (ps-3). pap. 4.95 (978-0-932855-66-4(0)) Winner Enterprises.

Beylon, Cathy & Barbaresi, Nina. I Love Butterflies. 2007. 32p. (J). pap. 3.95 (***978-0-486-45659-1(5)***) Dover Pubns., Inc.

Bjerklie, David. Butterflies! 2006. 32p. (J). lib. bdg. 13.85 (***978-1-4242-0693-3(6)***) Fitzgerald Bks.

Braun, Eric & Donovan, Sandy. Butterflies. 2001. (Animals of the Rain Forest Ser.). (Illus.). 32p. (YA). lib. bdg. 22.83 (978-0-7398-4680-3(9)) Raintree.

Bredeson, Carmen. Monarch Butterflies up Close. 2006. (Zoom in on Animals! Ser.). (Illus.). 24p. (J). lib. bdg. 21.26 (978-0-7660-2494-6(6) , Enslow Elementary) Enslow Pubs., Inc.

Brimner, Larry Dane. Butterflies & Moths. 1999. (gr. 3-6). lib. bdg. 15.25 (978-0-613-37303-6(0)) Tandem Library Bks.

Bronson, Cary. I am Not a Flying Elephant Fish! A Children's Science Book on the Butterfly. Gomer, William, illus. l.t. ed. 2004. 32p. (J). lib. bdg. 14.95 (978-0-9746094-0-9(4)) Connect With Your Kid Bks.

Burke. A Butterflys Life. 1999. (Illus.). (J). pap. (978-0-7398-2397-2(3)) Steck-Vaughn.

Butterflies. (Color & Learn Ser.). 36p. (J). (gr. 1-5). pap. (978-1-882210-10-7(7)) Action Publishing, Inc.

Butterflies, Vol. 3. 2005. (Bugs, Bugs, Bugs Ser.). (YA). (gr. k-3). 118.80 (978-0-7368-4205-1(5) , Pebble Bks.) Capstone Pr., Inc.

Butterflies. 2007. (First Discovery Book Ser.). 24p. (J). pap. 5.99 (***978-0-439-91087-3(0)***) Scholastic, Inc.

Butterflies Set. (gr. k-2). 114.95 (978-0-7368-9038-0(6)) Red Brick Learning.

Butterfly Colors, Vol. 3. 2005. (Bugs, Bugs, Bugs Ser.). (YA). (gr. k-3). (978-0-7368-8197-5(2) , Pebble Bks.) Capstone Pr., Inc.

Butterfly Colors, 6 vols. (gr. k-2). 28.95 (978-0-7368-8237-8(5)) Red Brick Learning.

Butterfly Eggs, Vol. 3. 2005. (Bugs, Bugs, Bugs Ser.). (YA). (gr. k-3). (978-0-7368-8198-2(0) , Pebble Bks.) Capstone Pr., Inc.

Butterfly Eggs, 6 vols. (gr. k-2). 28.95 (978-0-7368-8238-5(3)) Red Brick Learning.

Butterfly Life Cycle. 2001. (Animal Kingdom Ser.). (J). vinyl bd. 4.95 (978-1-58845-102-6(X)) School Specialty Publishing.

Bygrave, Linda. Butterfly. (Illus.). 24p. (YA). (gr. 1 up). lib. bdg. 22.80 (978-1-931983-52-5(6)) Chrysalis Education.

Chang, Maria L. Early Themes: Life Cycles Butterflies, Chicks, Frogs & More!, 1. 1999. 48p. pap. 9.95 (978-0-590-68572-6(4)) Scholastic, Inc.

Chavez, R. J. Bob. Bye Bye Butterfly: A True-Life Children's Butterfly Adventure. 2006. (J). 3.99 (978-0-9778110-0-7(X)) R.J. Bob Chavez Images.

Cooper, Jason. Butterflies. (Insects Ser.). 24p. (gr. k-2). 2006. (Illus.). 14.95 (978-1-59515-425-5(6)); 2005. pap. 5.45 (978-1-59515-739-3(5)) Rourke Publishing, LLC.

—Monarch Butterfly. 2003. (Life Cycles Ser.). (Illus.). 24p. (gr. 1-4). 17.95 (978-1-58952-349-4(0)) Rourke Publishing, LLC.

Dalmatian Press Staff. Ponies & Butterflies: Velvet Bright Book to Color. rev. ed. 2003. (Fuzzy Book to Color Ser.). (Illus.). 4p. (J). pap. 4.49 (978-1-4037-0711-6(1)) Dalmatian Pr.

Del huevo a la mariposa (from Egg to Butterfly) 2007. (J). pap. 4.95 (978-0-8225-6631-1(1) , Ediciones Lerner) Lerner Publishing Group.

Del Huevo a la Mariposa (From Egg to Butterfly) 2006. (De Principio a Fin Ser.). (SPA.). 24p. (J). 18.60 (978-0-8225-6494-2(7) , Ediciones Lerner) Lerner Publishing Group.

Dingles, Molly. Blue as a Blueberry. Velez, Walter, illus. 2002. (Community of Color Ser.). 32p. (J). lib. bdg. 20.65 (978-1-891997-20-4(3)) Dingles & Co.

Dominquez, Amalia. Busy, Busy Butterfly. 2004. (Illus.). 24p. bds. 8.95 (978-1-932915-01-3(X)) Sandvik Publishing.

Dorling Kindersley Publishing Staff. Butterflies. 2006. (Ultimate Sticker Bks.). 16p. (J). (gr. 5). pap. 6.99 (978-0-7566-2096-7(1)) Dorling Kindersley Publishing, Inc.

—Butterfly. 2007. (See How They Grow Ser.). 24p. (J). (ps-1). pap. 3.99 (978-0-7566-3014-0(2)) Dorling Kindersley Publishing, Inc.

Echols, Jean C. Hide a Butterfly. Baker, Lisa H. & Klofkorn, Lisa, illus. Callaway, Jane et al, photos by. rev. ed. 2001. (Great Explorations in Math & Science Ser.). 44p. (Orig.). (J). reprint ed. pap., tchr. ed. 9.00 (978-0-924886-59-1(5) , GEMS) Univ. of California, Berkeley, Lawrence Hall of Science.

Eckart, Edana. Monarch Butterfly. 2005. (Welcome Bks.). (Illus.). 24p. (ps-2). (J). pap. 4.95 (978-0-516-25166-0(X)) ; 18.00 (978-0-516-25050-2(7)) Scholastic Library Publishing. (Children's Pr.).

Ehlert, Lois. Waiting for Wings. Ehlert, Lois, illus. 2001. (Illus.). 40p. (J). (ps-2). 17.00 (978-0-15-202608-0(8)) Harcourt Children's Bks.

Farndon, John. Butterflies & Moths. 2004. (Illus.). 32p. (J). 23.70 (978-1-4103-0123-9(0) , Blackbirch Pr., Inc.) Thomson Gale.

Feely, Jenny. Butterfly. 1999. (ps-2). lib. bdg. 11.55 (978-0-613 30294-4(X)) Tandem Library Bks.

Freeman, Darlene & Maydak, Mike. Butterflies! 2005. (Illus.). 24p. (J). (ps-ps). pap. 5.99 incl. audio compact disk (978-1-58610-931-8(6)) Learning Horizons, Inc.

Frost, Helen. Butterflies, 4 bks. Saunders-Smith, Gail, ed. Incl. Butterfly Colors. lib. bdg. 14.60 (978-0-7368-0226-0(6)); Butterfly Eggs. lib. bdg. 14.60 (978-0-7368-0227-7(4)); Caterpillars. lib. bdg. 14.60 (978-0-7368-0228-4(2)); Monarch Butterflies. lib. bdg. 14.60 (978-0-7368-0229-1(0)); 24p. (J). (gr. k-1). 1999. (Illus.). Set lib. bdg. 58.40 (978-0-7368-0263-5(0) , Pebble Bks.) Capstone Pr., Inc.

—Butterfly Eggs. Saunders-Smith, Gail, ed. 1999. (Butterflies Ser.). (Illus.). 24p. (J). (gr. k-1). lib. bdg. 14.60 (978-0-7368-0227-7(4) , Pebble Bks.) Capstone Pr., Inc.

—Monarch & Milkweed. Gore, Leonid, illus. 2008. 40p. (J). 17.99 (***978-1-4169-0085-6(3)***) Simon & Schuster Children's Publishing.

Frost, Helen. Monarch Butterflies. Saunders-Smith, Gail, ed. 1999. (Butterflies Ser.). (Illus.). 24p. (J). (gr. k-1). lib. bdg. 14.60 (978-0-7368-0229-1(0) , Pebble Bks.) Capstone Pr., Inc.

Ganeri, Anita. Butterflies & Caterpillars. 2007. (J). (***978-1-58340-808-7(8)***) Smart Apple Media.

Ganeri, Anita. From Caterpillar to Butterfly. 2006. (Illus.). 32p. (J). lib. bdg. 8.95 (978-1-4034-7855-9(4)); pap. (978-1-4034-7864-1(3)) Heinemann Library.

Gillis, Jennifer Blizin. Butterfly Gardens. 2008. (J). (***978-1-60044-560-6(8)***) Rourke Publishing, LLC.

Glaser, Linda. Magnificent Monarchs. Holland, Gay W., illus. 32p. (gr. k-3). 2002. (J). pap. 8.95 (978-0-7613-1636-7(1)); 2000. lib. bdg. 23.90 (978-0-7613-1700-5(7)) Lerner Publishing Group. (Millbrook Pr.).

—Magnificent Monarchs. 2000. (gr. k-3). lib. bdg. 16.40 (978-0-613-56502-8(9)) Tandem Library Bks.

Godwin, Sam. The Case of the Missing Caterpillar: A First Look at the Life Cycle of a Butterfly. Abel, Simone, illus. 2004. (First Look Science Ser.). 32p. (C). (gr. k-3). 22.60 (978-1-4048-0655-9(5)) Picture Window Bks.

Green, Jen. Butterflies. 1999. (Endangered! Ser.). (Illus.). 32p. (J). (gr. 3-5). lib. bdg. 25.64 (978-0-7614-0321-0(3) , Benchmark Bks.) Cavendish, Marshall Corp.

Grolier Educational Staff, contrib. by. Butterflies. 2001. (Nature's Children Ser.). (Illus.). 48p. (J). (978-0-7172-5536-8(0) , Grolier) Scholastic Library Publishing.

Grosset and Dunlap Staff. Butterflies & Moths. Conlon, Mara, ed. Collier-Morales, Roberta, illus. 2001. (Nature Sticker Stories Ser.). 1p. (J). (ps-3). pap. 4.99 (978-0-448-42193-3(3) , Grosset & Dunlap) Penguin Group (USA) Inc.

Halmes, Kevin J. Butterflies, 6 vols. (gr. 2-5). 36.95 (978-0-7368-8311-5(8)) Red Brick Learning.

Hamilton Waxman, Laura. Monarch Butterflies. 2003. (Pull Ahead Bks.). (Illus.). 32p. (J). 22.60 (978-0-8225-4669-6(8) , Lerner Pubns.) Lerner Publishing Group.

Harcourt School Publishers Staff. Butterfly: Library Book. 3rd ed. 2002. (Trophies Reading Program Ser.). (Illus.). (J). pap. 11.70 (978-0-15-326531-0(0)) Harcourt Schl. Pubs.

—Butterfly, Butterfly. 3rd ed. 2002. (Trophies English Language Learners Ser.). (Illus.). pap. 5.10 (978-0-15-327641-5(X)) Harcourt Schl. Pubs.

—The Journey of the Monarch Below Level. 3rd ed. 2002. (Trophies Reading Program Ser.). (Illus.). pap. 5.10 (978-0-15-323070-7(3)) Harcourt Schl. Pubs.

—Monarchs to Mexico: Take-Home Book. 1999. (Collections Ser.). (Illus.). (J). pap. 1.90 (978-0-15-317266-3(5)) Harcourt Schl. Pubs.

—The Very Hungry... 1999. (Collections Ser.). (Illus.). lib. bdg. 18.40 (978-0-15-313415-9(1)) Harcourt Schl. Pubs.

Heiligman, Deborah. From Caterpillar to Butterfly Big Book. Weissman, Bari, illus. 2008. (Let's-Read-and-Find-Out Science Ser.). 32p. (J). pap. 24.99 (***978-0-06-111975-0(X)***) HarperCollins Pubs.

Heinrichs, Ann. Butterflies. 2003. (Nature's Friends Ser.). (Illus.). 32p. (J). (gr. 2 up). lib. bdg. 21.26 (978-0-7565-0434-2(1)) Compass Point Bks.

Heller, Ruth. How to Hide a Butterfly: And Other Insects. unabr. ed. 2001. (How to Hide Ser.). (J). (gr. k-3). pap. 14.45 incl. audio (978-0-8045-6573-8(2) , 6573) Spoken Arts, Inc.

Hendrickson, Jean A. How Butterflies Get Their Wings. 2001. (Angell Ser.). (Illus.). 32p. (J). (gr. k up). pap. (978-1-929953-02-8(X)) Gates & Bridges Inc.

Hewitt, Sally. Life Cycles: From Caterpillar to Butterfly. 2004. (QEB Start Talking Ser.). (Illus.). 24p. (J). lib. bdg. 15.95 (978-1-59566-002-2(X)) QEB Publishing Inc.

Hibbert. Life of a Butterfly 6-Pack. 2004. (Life Cycles Ser.). pap. 40.50 (978-1-4109-0824-7(0)) Harcourt Schl. Pubs.

Hibbert, Clare. The Life of a Butterfly. 2004. (Raintree Perspectives Ser.). (Illus.). 32p. (J). pap. 7.50 (978-1-4109-0817-9(8)) Harcourt Schl. Pubs.

—The Life of a Butterfly. 2004. (Life Cycles (Perspectives) Ser.). (Illus.). 32p. (J). (gr. 3-5). lib. bdg. 19.25 (978-1-4109-0542-0(X)) Raintree.

Himmelman, John. A Monarch Butterfly's Life. 2000. (Nature Upclose Ser.). (Illus.). 32p. (J). (gr. k-2). pap. 6.95 (978-0-516-26537-7(7) , Children's Pr.) Scholastic Library Publishing.

—A Monarch Butterfly's Life. 1999. (gr. k-3). lib. bdg. 15.25 (978-0-613-37464-4(9)) Tandem Library Bks.

Hoffman, Don. Wanderer: The Monarch Butterfly. 2004. 7.95 (978-1-930401-21-1(3)) Central Coast Pr.

Hovanec, Erin M. I Wonder What It's Like to Be a Butterfly. 2000. (Life Science Wonder Bks.). (Illus.). 24p. (J). (gr. k-4). lib. bdg. 18.75 (978-0-8239-5451-3(X) , PowerKids Pr.) Rosen Publishing Group, Inc., The.

How Penguins & Butterflies Grow Set D, 6 vols. (Phonics Readers Ser.). (gr. k-2). 28.95 (978-0-7368-4053-8(2)) Red Brick Learning.

Howard, Fran. Butterflies. 2005. (Pebble Plus: Bugs, Bugs, Bugs! Ser.). (Illus.). 24p. (J). 19.93 (978-0-7368-3643-2(8)) Capstone Pr., Inc.

Hunt, Joni Phelps. A Shimmer of Butterflies: The Brief, Brilliant Life of a Magical Insect. Leon, Vicki, ed. 2nd ed. 2005. (Jean-Michel Cousteau Presents Ser.). Orig. Title: Butterflies. (Illus.). 48p. (J). pap. 7.95 (978-0-9666490-6-2(0)) London Town Pr.

Hurtig, Jennifer. Butterflies. 2007. (J). (***978-1-59036-683-7(2)); (*978-1-59036-684-4(0))*** Weigl Pubs., Inc.

The Incredible Pop-Out Butterfly Activity Kit & Calendar. 2001. (Illus.). 28p. (J). cd-rom 12.95 (978-1-57965-181-7(X)) Artisan.

Kalman, Bobbie. The Life Cycle of a Butterfly. Reiach, Margaret Amy, illus. 2001. (Life Cycle Ser.). 32p. (J). (gr. 2-3). pap. (978-0-7787-0680-9(X)); pap., lib. bdg. (978-0-7787-0650-2(8)) Crabtree Publishing Co.

—Life Cycle of a Butterfly. 2002. (gr. 3-6). lib. bdg. 14.10 (978-0-613-52970-9(7)) Tandem Library Bks.

Kalman, Bobbie & Johnson, Robin. Endangered Butterflies. 2006. (Illus.). 32p. (J). (gr. 2-8). pap. (978-0-7787-1916-8(2)); (978-0-7787-1870-3(0)) Crabtree Publishing Co.

Kalman, Bobbie & Mondor, Lyne. Les Papillons. 2005. (FRE., Illus.). 32p. pap. (978-2-89579-029-7(9)) Crabtree Publishing Co.

Kelly, Irene. It's a Butterfly's Life. 2007. (Illus.). 32p. (J). (ps-3). 16.95 (978-0-8234-1860-2(X)) Holiday Hse., Inc.

Lathan, Tamala. Black Butterflies. 2000. 250p. (J). 7.99 (978-0-9700599-0-1(6)) Sybrell Publishing.

Latimer, Jonathan P. Butterflies. 2000. (gr. 3-6). lib. bdg. 14.10 (978-0-613-27754-9(6)) Tandem Library Bks.

—Butterflies & Moths. 2000. (Peterson First Guides). (Illus.). (J). pap. (978-0-606-20586-3(1)) Tandem Library Bks.

Latimer, Jonathan P. & Nolting, Karen Stray. Butterflies. Wright, Amy Bartlett, illus. 2000. (Peterson Field Guides for Young Naturalists). 48p. (J). (gr. 4-6). pap. 5.95 (978-0-395-97944-0(7)); tchr. ed. 15.00 (978-0-395-97943-3(9)) Houghton Mifflin Co. Trade & Reference Div.

Legg, Gerald & Salariya, David. From Caterpillar to Butterfly. Scrace, Carolyn, illus. 1998. (Life Cycles Ser.). 32p. (J). (gr. k-2). 25.50 (978-0-531-14493-0(3) , Watts, Franklin) Scholastic Library Publishing.

Lerner, Carol. Butterflies in the Garden. Lerner, Carol, illus. 2002. (Illus.). 32p. (J). (gr. k-3). 16.99 (978-0-688-17478-1(7)) HarperCollins Pubs.

L'Hommedieu, Arthur John. Butterfly Play Pack. 2000. (Illus.). 12p. (J). (ps up). 7.99 (978-0-85953-003-3(5)) Child's Play-International.

The Life Cycle of a Butterfly, Vol. 2. 2005. (Animals, Animals, Animals Ser.). (YA). (gr. k-3). (978-0-7368-3390-5(0) , Pebble Bks.) Capstone Pr., Inc.

Life Cycles: From Caterpillar to Butterfly. 2005. (J). per. 8.95 (978-1-59566-129-6(8)) QEB Publishing Inc.

List, Ilka Katherine. Moths & Butterflies of North America. Gonzales, Jose & Savage, Steve, illus. 2002. (Animals in Order Ser.). 48p. (J). (gr. 4-6). 26.50 (978-0-531-11597-8(6) , Watts, Franklin) Scholastic Library Publishing.

Llewellyn, Claire. Asi Nace una Mariposa. Giraldo, Maria Cristina, tr. Mendez, Simon, illus. (Coleccion Asi Nace... Ser.). (SPA.). 24p. (J). (gr. k-6). pap. 8.95 (978-1-59437-788-4(X)) Santillana USA Publishing Co., Inc.

—Butterfly: Starting Life Butterly. Mendez, Simon, illus. 2003. (Starting Life Ser.). 24p. (ps-3). 16.95 (978-1-55971-868-4(4) , NorthWord Bks. for Young Readers) T&N Children's Publishing.

Lockwood, Sophie. Butterflies. 2007. (World of Insects Ser.). 40p. (J). (gr. 2-6). 29.93 (***978-1-59296-820-6(1)***) Child's World, Inc.

Loewen, Nancy. Flying Colors: Butterflies in Your Backyard. Peterson, Rick, illus. 2005. (Backyard Bugs Ser.). 24p. (J). (ps). lib. bdg. 22.60 (978-1-4048-1143-0(5)) Picture Window Bks.

Mariner Books Staff & Opler, Paul A. Peterson First Guide to Butterflies & Moths. Wright, Amy Bartlett, illus. 2nd ed. 1998. (First Guides). 128p. pap. 5.95 (978-0-395-90665-1(2)) Houghton Mifflin Co. Trade & Reference Div.

McEvey, Shane F. Moths & Butterflies. 2001. (Insects & Spiders Ser.). (Illus.). (J). (gr. 4 up). 16.95 (978-0-7910-6598-3(7) , 010555, Chelsea Hse.) Facts On File, Inc.

Meister, Cari. Butterflies. 2001. (Insects Ser.). (Illus.). 24p. (J). (gr. k-6). lib. bdg. 21.35 (978-1-57765-459-9(5) , Checkerboard Library) ABDO Publishing Co.

Milbourne, Anna. Butterfly. 2005. 24p. (J). 9.99 (978-0-7945-1052-7(3) , Usborne) EDC Publishing.

Mitchell, Melanie S. Butterflies. (First Step Nonfiction Ser.). (Illus.). (J). (gr. k-2). 2003. 24p. lib. bdg. 18.60 (978-0-8225-4598-9(5)); 2002. 23p. pap. 3.95 (978-0-8225-4599-6(3) , Lerner Pubns.) Lerner Publishing Group.

Monarch Butterflies, Vol. 3. 2005. (Bugs, Bugs, Bugs Ser.). (YA). (gr. k-3). (978-0-7368-8200-2(6) , Pebble Bks.) Capstone Pr., Inc.

Monarch Butterflies, 6 vols. (gr. k-2). 28.95 (978-0-7368-8240-8(5)) Red Brick Learning.

Morgan, Sally. Butterflies & Moths. 2000. (Looking at Minibeasts Ser.). (Illus.). 32p. (J). (gr. 1-4). lib. bdg. 16.95 (978-1-929298-80-8(3)) Chrysalis Education.

—Butterflies & Other Insects. 2001. (Illus.). 32p. (J). lib. bdg. 24.25 (978-1-930643-42-0(X)) Chrysalis Education.

—From Caterpillar to Butterfly. 2002. (How Things Grow Ser.). (Illus.). 32p. (J). lib. bdg. 24.25 (978-1-930643-88-8(8)) Chrysalis Education.

Morris, Neil & Morris, Ting. Butterfly. 2003. (Illus.). 32p. (J). lib. bdg. 27.10 (978-1-58340-379-2(5)) Smart Apple Media.

Mudd, Maria M. The Butterfly. Smith-Griswold, Wendy, illus. 2001. 14p. (J). (ps-3). 12.95 (978-1-58117-096-2(3) , Intervisual/Piggy Toes) Dalmatian Pr.

Murray, Julie. Butterflies. 2002. (Buddy Book Ser.). (Illus.). 24p. (J). (gr. k-4). lib. bdg. 21.35 (978-1-57765-718-7(7)) ABDO Publishing Co.

Murray, Julie. Monarch Butterflies. 2007. (Life Cycles Ser.). 24p. (J). (gr. k-4). lib. bdg. 21.35 (***978-1-59928-708-9(0)***, Buddy Bks.) ABDO Publishing Co.

Nelson, Sara Elizabeth. Butterflies. 2007. (Nature Watch Ser.). 48p. (J). (gr. 4-8). lib. bdg. 26.60 (***978-0-8225-6766-0(0)***, Lerner Pubns.) Lerner Publishing Group.

Neye, Emily. Butterflies. Broda, Ron, illus. 2000. (All Aboard Reading Ser.). 32p. (J). (ps-3). pap. 3.99 (978-0-448-41966-4(1) , Grosset & Dunlap) Penguin Group (USA) Inc.

—Butterflies. 2000. (gr. k-3). lib. bdg. 11.80 (978-0-613-24447-3(8)); (Illus.). (J). 10.79 (978-0-606-18464-9(3)) Tandem Library Bks.

Nicholls, Judith. Crawly Caterpillar. 2008. (Doodlebops Ser.). 32p. (J). bds. 7.99 (***978-0-545-03026-7(9)***, Cartwheel Bks.) Scholastic, Inc.

Noonan, Diana. The Butterfly. 2002. (Life Cycle Ser.). (Illus.). 32p. (J). (gr. k-2). 23.00 (978-0-7910-6963-9(X) , 104001, Chelsea Hse.) Facts On File, Inc.

Opler, Paul. Butterflies of North America: An Activity & Coloring Book. 2004. 84p. pap. 9.95 (978-1-57098-435-8(2)) Rinehart, Roberts Pubs.

Opler, Paul A. Butterflies East & West: A Book to Color. Strawn, Susan, illus. 1999. 80p. (ps-3). pap. 8.95 (978-1-879373-45-7(9)) Rinehart, Roberts Pubs.

Parker, Victoria. Life As a Butterfly. 2003. (Raintree Sprouts Ser.). (Illus.). 24p. (J). pap. 5.50 (978-1-4109-0654-0(X)) ; lib. bdg. 18.56 (978-1-4109-0628-1(0)) Raintree.

—Life As a Butterfly. 2003. (ps-2). lib. bdg. 13.55 (978-0-613-78263-0(1)) Tandem Library Bks.

Parsonage, Betty. Butterfly Wings. 2003. (Illus.). 50p. 12.95 (978-1-59094-013-6(X) , 159094013X) Jawbone Publishing Corp.

Patent, Dorothy Hinshaw. Fabulous Fluttering Tropical Butterflies. Jubb, Kendahl Jan, illus. 2003. 32p. (J). (gr. 1-5). 17.85 (978-0-8027-8839-9(4)); 16.95 (978-0-8027-8838-2(6)) Walker & Co.

Preston-Mafham, Rod. Butterflies & Moths. 2002. (Secret World Of... Ser.). (Illus.). 48p. (J). lib. bdg. 27.12 (978-0-7398-4984-2(0)) Raintree.

Pringle, Laurence P. An Extraordinary Life: The Story of a Monarch Butterfly. Marstall, Bob, illus. 2000. 64p. (J). (gr. 3-7). pap. 7.95 (978-0-531-07169-4(3) , Orchard Bks.) Scholastic, Inc.

—An Extraordinary Life: The Story of a Monarch Butterfly. 2000. (Illus.). (J). (978-0-606-18330-7(2)) Tandem Library Bks.

Prischmann, Deirdre A. Butterflies. 2005. (Illus.). 24p. (J). (ps-7). lib. bdg. 21.26 (978-0-7368-4335-5(3)) Capstone Pr., Inc.

Pyers. Butterflies, 6, Pack. 2004. (Minibeasts up Close Ser.). pap. 40.50 (978-1-4109-1542-9(5)) Harcourt Schl. Pubs.

Pyers, Greg. Butterflies up Close. (Minibeasts up Close Ser.). (Illus.). 32p. (J). (ps-7). 2005. lib. bdg. 27.50 (978-1-4109-1528-3(X)); 2004. pap. (978-1-4109-1535-1(2)) Harcourt Schl. Pubs.

Pyle, Robert Michael. Butterflies. Hughes, Sarah Anne, illus. 2003. (Peterson Field Guide Coloring Bks.). 64p. pap. 7.95 (978-0-618-30723-4(0)) Houghton Mifflin Co. Trade & Reference Div.

QEB Start Reading & Talking National Book Stores Edition: Life Cycles: from Caterpillar to Butterfly. 2006. (J). per. (978-1-59566-252-1(9)) QEB Publishing Inc.

Rabe, Tish. My, Oh My—A Butterfly! All about Butterflies. Ruiz, Aristides & Mathieu, Joe, illus. 2007. (Cat in the Hat's Learning Library Ser.). 48p. (J). (gr. k-3). lib. bdg. 11.99 (978-0-375-92882-6(0) , Random Hse. Bks. for Young Readers) Random Hse. Children's Bks.

—My, Oh My—a Butterfly! All about Butterflies. Ruiz, Aristides & Mathieu, Joe, illus. 2007. (Cat in the Hat's Learning Library). 48p. (J). (gr. k-3). 8.99 (978-0-375-82882-9(6) , Random Hse. Bks. for Young Readers) Random Hse. Children's Bks.

Rau, Dana Meachen. The Butterfly in the Sky. 2006. (Nature Ser.). (Illus.). 24p. (J). lib. bdg. 22.79 (978-0-7614-2311-9(7) , Benchmark Bks.) Cavendish, Marshall Corp.

—Fly, Butterfly, Fly! 2007. (Go, Critter, Go! Ser.). (Illus.). 23p. (J). (ps-3). lib. bdg. 22.79 (*978-0-7614-2649-3(3) , Benchmark Bks.) Cavendish, Marshall Corp.

—Fly, Butterfly, Fly!/¡Vuela Mariposa, Vuela! 2007. (Go, Critter, Go!/¡Vamos Criaturita, Vamos! Ser.). (SPA & ENG.). 24p. (J). lib. bdg. 22.79 (*978-0-7614-2814-5(3) , Benchmark Bks.) Cavendish, Marshall Corp.

—¡Vuela, Mariposa, Vuela! 2007. (¡Vamos Criaturita, Vamos! Ser.). (SPA.). 24p. (J). lib. bdg. 22.79 (*978-0-7614-2790-2(2) , Benchmark Bks.) Cavendish, Marshall Corp.

The Really Big Butterfly Coloring Book ' A Teaching & Learning Tool. 2004. Orig. Title: Same. (J). per. 7.95 (978-0-9729753-2-2(2)) Really Big Coloring Bks., Inc.

Ring, Elizabeth. Monarch Butterfly of Aster Way. Lee, Katie, illus. (Smithsonian's Backyard Ser.). 32p. (J). (ps-2). 2005. pap. 6.95 (978-1-931465-40-3(1) , S5017); 1999. 15.95 (978-1-56899-568-7(7) , B5017); 1999. 19.95 incl. reel tape (978-1-56899-570-0(9) , BC5017); 1999. 43.95 (978-1-56899-571-7(7)); Incl. toy. 1999. 32.95 (978-1-56899-572-4(5)); Incl. toy. 1999. 36.95 incl. audio (978-1-56899-574-8(1)) Soundprints.

—Monarch Butterfly of Aster Way: Micro Book. Lee, Katie, illus. 1999. (Smithsonian's Backyard Ser.: No. 17). 32p. (J). (ps-2). 4.95 (978-1-56899-569-4(5) , B5067) Soundprints.

—Monarch Butterfly of Aster Way: Micro Edition, Incl. toy. Lee, Katie, illus. 1999. (Smithsonian's Backyard Ser.: Vol. 17). 32p. (J). (ps-2). incl. audio (978-1-56899-575-5(X)) Soundprints.

Rockwell, Anne F. Becoming Butterflies. Halsey, Megan, illus. 32p. (J). 2004. pap. 6.95 (978-0-8027-7686-0(8)); 2002. lib. bdg. 16.85 (978-0-8027-8798-9(3)) Walker & Co.

Romeu, Emma. Un Bosque para la Mariposa Monarca. Sanchez Vigil, Luis Gerardo & Vanden Broeck, Fabricio, illus. 2004. (Coleccion Animales de America). (SPA.). 48p. (J). (gr. 5-8). pap. 7.95 (978-970-29-0515-8(X)) Santillana USA Publishing Co., Inc.

—A Forest for the Monarch Butterfly. Vigil, Luis Gerardo Sanchez & Broeck, Fabricio Vanden, illus. (SPA.). 48p. (J). (gr. 3-5). pap. 7.95 (978-1-59437-844-7(4)) Santillana USA Publishing Co., Inc.

Roop, Connie & Roop, Peter. Millions of Monarchs. Maydak, Michael S., illus. 2003. 30p. (J). (978-0-439-43965-7(5)) Scholastic, Inc.

Rosenblatt, Lynn M., photos by & text. Monarch Magic! Butterfly Activities & Nature Discoveries. Rosenblatt, Lynn M., text. 2000. (Good Times Bks.: Vol. 2). (Illus.). 96p. (J). (gr. 1-7). pap. 12.95 (978-1-885593-23-8(6) , Williamson Bks.) Ideals Pubns.

Royston, Angela. Butterfly. 2002. (Life Cycle of a... Ser.). (Illus.). 32p. (J). (gr. k-2). pap. 6.95 (978-1-57572-473-7(1) , 90462) Heinemann Library.

—Butterfly. 2001. (Illus.). 32p. (J). (ps-ps). lib. bdg. 14.75 (978-0-613-24452-7(4)) Tandem Library Bks.

—La Mariposa. Abello, Patricia, tr. 2003. (Ciclo de la Vida de... Ser.). Tr. of Butterfly. (SPA & ENG., Illus.). 32p. (J). lib. bdg. 22.79 (978-1-4034-3018-2(7)) Heinemann Library.

—La Mariposa. 2003. Tr. of Butterfly. (SPA.). 32p. (J). pap. 6.95 (978-1-4034-3041-0(1)) Heinemann Library.

Running Press Staff. Butterflies. 2000. (Mini Edition Ser.). (Illus.). 96p. 4.95 (978-0-7624-0757-6(3) , Running Pr. Minature Editions) Running Pr. Bk. Pubs.

Rustad, Martha E. H. Butterflies. 2007. (Illus.). 24p. (J). lib. bdg. 19.95 (978-1-60014-075-4(0)) Bellwether Media.

Salariya, David. The Journey of a Butterfly. Sorace, Carolyn, photos by. 2000. (Lifecycles Ser.). (Illus.). 32p. (J). (gr. k-2). 25.50 (978-0-531-14518-0(2) , Watts, Franklin) Scholastic Library Publishing.

Samuel, Anna, ed. Glitter Butterflies Stickers. 2004. (Glitter Stickers Ser.). (Illus.). 2p. 1.50 (978-0-486-43537-4(7)) Dover Pubns., Inc.

Sandved, Kjell B. The Butterfly Alphabet. 1999. (Illus.). 64p. (J). (ps-3). pap. 5.99 (978-0-439-07947-1(0)) Scholastic, Inc.

—The Butterfly Alphabet. 1999. (J). (978-0-606-16930-1(X)) Tandem Library Bks.

Saunders-Smith, Gail. Butterflies. 1998. (J). pap. 13.25 (978-0-516-21232-6(X) , Children's Pr.) Scholastic Library Publishing.

Schaefer, Lola M. Butterflies: Pollinators & Nectar-Sippers. 2001. (Wild World of Animals Ser.). (Illus.). 24p. (J). (gr. 1-2). lib. bdg. 18.60 (978-0-7368-0824-8(8) , Bridgestone Bks.) Capstone Pr., Inc.

Schlaepfer, Gloria G. Butterflies. 2005. (Animalways Ser.). (Illus.). 112p. (J). (gr. 3-7). lib. bdg. (978-0-7614-1745-3(1) , Benchmark Bks.) Cavendish, Marshall Corp.

Scholastic, Inc. Staff. Butterflies: The Hands-On Way to Build Reading Skills! Cooper, Terry, ed. 1999. 6p. pap. 7.95 (978-0-439-04311-3(5)) Scholastic, Inc.

School Specialty Publishing. Butterfly Life Cycle. 2004. (On-File Ser.). 4p. (J). (gr. 1-3). ring bd. 4.99 (978-0-7424-2888-1(5) , Instructional Fair) Schaffer, Frank Pubns.

Schuh, Mari C. Butterflies. 2005. (Bugs, Bugs, Bugs Ser.). 24p. (YA). (gr. k-3). pap. (978-0-7368-3386-8(2) , Pebble Bks.) Capstone Pr., Inc.

—Butterflies. 2003. (Insects Ser.). (Illus.). 24p. (J). (gr. k-1). lib. bdg. 15.93 (978-0-7368-1664-9(X) , Pebble Bks.) Capstone Pr., Inc.

Schwartz, David M. La Mariposa Monarca. Kuhn, Dwight, photos by. 2001. (Springboards into Science Ser.). (SPA., Illus.). 24p. (J). (gr. 1 up). lib. bdg. 20.67 (978-0-8368-2998-3(0)) Stevens, Gareth Inc.

—Monarch Butterfly. Kuhn, Dwight, photos by. 2001. (Springboards into Science Ser.). (Illus.). 24p. (J). (gr. 1 up). lib. bdg. 20.67 (978-0-8368-2979-2(4)) Stevens, Gareth Inc.

Scott, Rose Marie. The Gentle Ones. Scott, Rose Marie, illus. 2003. (Illus.). 60p. (J). lib. bdg. 22.95 (978-1-59098-395-9(5)) Wooster Bk. Co., The.

Scrace, Carolyn. Journey of a Butterfly. 2000. (gr. k-3). lib. bdg. 15.25 (978-0-613-29456-0(4)) Tandem Library Bks.

Shahan, Sherry. The Little Butterfly. 1998. (J). (978-0-606-13964-9(8)) Tandem Library Bks.

Shapiro, Karen. Butterflies, Level 2. Cassels, Jean, illus. 2002. (Hello Reader! Science Ser.). 32p. (J). (gr. k-2). pap. 3.99 (978-0-439-20636-5(7) , Cartwheel Bks.) Scholastic, Inc.

—Butterflies. 2001. (gr. k-3). lib. bdg. 11.80 (978-0-613-50276-4(0)) Tandem Library Bks.

Shaw, Nancy J. Butterflies. (Let's Investigate Ser.). (Illus.). 32p. (J). 2001. (gr. 3). pap. 8.95 (978-0-89812-326-5(7) , Creative Paperbacks); 1998. (ps-3). lib. bdg. (978-0-88682-960-5(7) , Creative Education) Creative Co., The.

Simonson, Ned. Butterflies. 2000. (High Interest Bks.). (Illus.). 48p. (YA). (gr. 7-12). 24.00 (978-0-516-23328-4(9)); pap. 6.95 (978-0-516-23528-8(1)) Scholastic Library Publishing. (Children's Pr.).

Smith, A. G. Beautiful Butterflies Stained Glass Coloring Book. 2003. (Illus.). 16p. (J). (gr. 3). pap. 5.95 (978-0-486-43061-4(8)) Dover Pubns., Inc.

Soffer, Ruth. Butterflies & Flowers to Paint or Color. 2005. 48p. (J). (gr. 3). pap. 4.95 (978-0-486-44496-3(1)) Dover Pubns., Inc.

—Learning about Tropical Butterflies. 2004. 16p. (J). pap. 1.50 (978-0-486-43706-4(X)) Dover Pubns., Inc.

Sorace, Carolyn & Salariya, David. The Journey of a Butterfly. 2000. (Lifecycles Ser.). (Illus.). 32p. (J). (gr. k-2). pap. 6.95 (978-0-531-15417-5(3) , Watts, Franklin) Scholastic Library Publishing.

Spilsbury, Louise. Butterfly. 2005. (Heinemann Read & Learn Ser.). (Illus.). 24p. (J). 20.64 (978-1-4034-6770-6(6)); pap. (978-1-4034-6775-1(7)) Heinemann Library.

Stewart, Melissa. Butterflies. Recher, Andrew, illus. 2007. (Our Wild World Ser.). (J). 48p. (gr. 3-6). 10.95 (978-1-55971-966-7(4)); 48p. (gr. 3-6). pap. 7.95 (978-1-55971-967-4(2)); 47p. (*978-1-4287-3849-2(5)) T&N Children's Publishing. (NorthWord Bks. for Young Readers).

—My Butterfly Book. 2008. 16p. (J). 6.99 (*978-0-06-089980-6(8)) HarperCollins Pubs.

Stewart, Melissa. A Place for Butterflies. Bond, Higgins, illus. 2006. (J). 16.95 (978-1-56145-357-3(9)) Peachtree Pubs., Ltd.

Stidworthy, John. Queen Alexandra's Birdwing: The World's Largest Butterfly. 2007. (SuperSized! Ser.). (Illus.). 24p. (J). lib. bdg. 21.28 (978-1-59716-395-8(3) , 1265940) Bearport Publishing Co., Inc.

Stone, Tanya Lee. Butterflies. 2003. (Wild Wild World Ser.). (Illus.). 24p. (J). 22.45 (978-1-56711-811-7(9) , Blackbirch Pr.) Thomson Gale.

Swinburne, Stephen R. Unbeatable Beaks. Paley, Joan, illus. rev. ed. 1999. 32p. (J). (ps-3). 16.95 (978-0-8050-4802-5(2) , Holt, Henry & Co. Bks. For Young Readers) Holt, Henry & Co.

—Wings of Light: A Migration of Butterflies from the Rainforest to Your Backyard. Hiscock, Bruce, illus. 32p. (J). 15.95 (978-1-59078-082-4(5)) Boyds Mills Pr.

Swinburne, Stephen R. Wings of Light: The Migration of the Yellow Butterfly. Hiscock, Bruce, illus. 2006. (J). (*978-1-4156-6549-7(4)) Boyds Mills Pr.

Taylor, Barbara & Dorling Kindersley Publishing Staff. Butterflies & Moths. 2nd ed. 2004. (Pocket Guides Ser.). (Illus.). 160p. (J). pap. 6.99 (978-0-7566-0204-8(1)) Dorling Kindersley Publishing, Inc.

Thatcher, Rebecca. Threat of the Monarch Butterfly. 2007. (On the Verge of Extinction Ser.). (Illus.). 32p. (J). (gr. 1-4). lib. bdg. 25.70 (*978-1-58415-587-4(6)) Mitchell Lane Pubs., Inc.

Time for Kids Editors. Butterflies! 2006. (Time for Kids Science Scoops Ser.). (Illus.). 32p. (J). 14.99 (978-0-06-078217-7(X)); pap. 3.99 (978-0-06-078213-9(7)) HarperCollins Pubs.

Trumbauer, Lisa. The Life Cycle of a Butterfly. 2002. (Life Cycles Ser.). (Illus.). 24p. (J). (gr. k-1). lib. bdg. 15.93 (978-0-7368-1181-1(8) , Pebble Bks.) Capstone Pr., Inc.

Turnbull, S. Caterpillars & Butterflies. 2004. (Beginners Ser.). 32p. (J). (gr. 1 up). pap. 4.95 (978-0-7945-0378-9(0)); lib. bdg. 12.95 (978-1-58086-506-7(2)) EDC Publishing.

Turnbull, Stephanie. Caterpillars & Butterflies - Internet Referenced (Level 1) 2007. 32p. (J). 4.99 (*978-0-7945-1337-5(9) , Usborne) EDC Publishing.

Underwood, Deborah. Mexico or Bust. 2007. (J). (*978-1-4109-2842-9(X)); (*978-1-4109-2859-7(4)) Steck-Vaughn.

Unstead, Sue. The Beautiful Butterfly Book. Tomblin, Gill, illus. 2005. (Beautiful Bug Ser.). 24p. (J). (ps-ps). spiral bd. 17.95 (978-0-7696-4151-5(2)) School Specialty Publishing.

Upgrade kit dsm-3 Butterflies&moths. (J). 2004. (978-1-59242-526-6(7)); 2003. (978-1-59242-409-2(0)) Delta Education, LLC.

Waiting for Wings. 2004. 29.95 incl. cd-rom (978-1-55592-152-1(3)) Weston Woods Studios, Inc.

Wallace, Karen. Born to Be a Butterfly. 2000. (Dorling Kindersley Readers: Vol. 1). (Illus.). 32p. (J). (gr. 5-3). pap. 3.99 (978-0-7894-5705-9(9)) Dorling Kindersley Publishing, Inc.

—Born to Be a Butterfly. 2000. (Eyewitness Readers Ser.). (J). 10.79 (978-0-606-20117-9(3)) Tandem Library Bks.

—Born to Be Butterfly. 2000. (gr. k-3). lib. bdg. 11.80 (978-0-613-32334-5(3)) Tandem Library Bks.

Wallace, Karen & Dorling Kindersley Publishing Staff. Born to Be a Butterfly. 2000. (Dorling Kindersley Readers: Vol. 1). (Illus.). 32p. (J). (ps-3). 14.99 (978-0-7894-5704-2(0)) Dorling Kindersley Publishing, Inc.

Wallace, Nancy Elizabeth, illus. Fly, Monarch! Fly! 2008. (J). (*978-0-7614-5425-0(X)) Cavendish, Marshall Corp.

Warren, Jean. Butterflies. Cubley, Kathleen, ed. 1998. (Sticker Book Ser.). (Illus.). 32p. (J). (ps). pap. 3.95 (978-1-57029-215-6(9) , WPH 3705, Totline Pubns.) Schaffer, Frank Pubns.

Watts, Barrie. Butterfly. 2003. 32p. (J). lib. bdg. 24.25 (978-1-58340-234-4(9)) Smart Apple Media.

Waxman, Laura Hamilton. Monarch Butterflies. 2003. (gr. k-3). lib. bdg. 14.10 (978-0-613-58930-7(0)) Tandem Library Bks.

Webber, Hiltrud M. Collecting Butterflies & Moths. l.t. ed. 1999. (Ozarkae Ser.: Vol. 2). (Illus.). 35p. (J). spiral bd. 10.95 (978-0-9652173-2-3(9)) HMW Pubns.

Wenger, Shaunda. Watch a Butterfly Grow. 2006. (Early Explorers Ser.). (J). 34.00 (*978-1-4108-6100-9(7)) Benchmark Education Co.

Whalley, Paul. Butterfly & Moth. 2000. (Eyewitness Bks.). (Illus.). 64p. (J). (gr. 4-7). 15.99 (978-0-7894-5832-2(2)) Dorling Kindersley Publishing, Inc.

Whalley, Paul & Dorling Kindersley Publishing Staff. Butterfly & Moth. 2000. (Eyewitness Bks.). (Illus.). 64p. (J). (gr. 4-7). lib. bdg. 19.99 (978-0-7894-6556-6(6)) Dorling Kindersley Publishing, Inc.

Wildlife Education, Ltd. Staff. Butterflies. Meltzer, Davis & Ripper, Chuck, illus. 2000. (Zoobooks Ser.). 18p. (J). pap. 2.95 (978-0-937934-65-4(8)) Wildlife Education, Ltd.

Wildlife Education, Ltd. Staff & Brust, Beth W. Butterflies: Pollinators & Nectar Sippers. Meltzer, Davis & Ripper, Chuck, illus. 2001. (Zoobooks Ser.). 24p. (J). (gr. k-3). 15.95 (978-0-937934-76-0(3)) Wildlife Education, Ltd.

Windsor, Jo. Butterflies: Early Level Satellite Individual Title Six-Packs. (Sails Literacy Ser.). 16p. (gr. 1-2). 27.00 (978-0-7578-2926-0(0)) Rigby Education.

Winer, Yvonne. Butterflies Fly. Lloyd-Jones, Karen, illus. 2001. 32p. (J). (ps-4). 7.95 (978-1-57091-447-8(8)) Charlesbridge Publishing, Inc.

—Butterflies Fly. 2001. (gr. 3-6). lib. bdg. 15.25 (978-0-613-45646-3(7)) Tandem Library Bks.

Winer, Yvonne & Lloyd-Jones, Karen. Butterflies Fly. 2000. (Illus.). 32p. (J). (ps-4). 16.95 (978-1-57091-446-1(X)) Charlesbridge Publishing, Inc.

World Book, Inc. Staff, contrib. by. Butterflies of the United States & Canada. 2004. (World Book's Science & Nature Guides Ser.). (Illus.). 80p. (J). (978-0-7166-4211-4(5)) World Bk., Inc.

—Monarchs & Other Butterflies. 2005. (World Book's Animals of the World Ser.). (Illus.). 64p. (J). (978-0-7166-1271-1(2)) World Bk., Inc.

Zemlicka, Shannon. From Egg to Butterfly. (From Start to Finish Ser.). (J). (gr. k-2). 2003. (Illus.). 24p. lib. bdg. 18.60 (978-0-8225-0713-0(7)); 2002. pap. 4.95 (978-0-8225-0666-9(1)) Lerner Publishing Group.

Ziefert, Harriet. Bugs, Beetles, & Butterflies. Flather, Lisa, illus. 1998. (Easy-to-Read Ser.). 32p. (J). (ps-2). pap. 3.99 (978-0-14-038691-2(2) , Puffin) Penguin Group (USA) Inc.

—Bugs, Beetles, & Butterflies. Flather, Lisa, illus. 1998. (Puffin Easy-to-Read Ser.). 32p. (J). (ps-2). lib. bdg. 10.79 (978-0-606-20458-3(X)); lib. bdg. 11.80 (978-0-613-11368-7(3)) Tandem Library Bks.

BUTTERFLIES—FICTION

Ada, Alma Flor. Rose with Wings. 2000. (gr. k-3). lib. bdg. 17.60 (978-0-613-79393-3(5)) Tandem Library Bks.

Albanell, Pep. El Grito de la Botella. Tobella, Montse, illus. 2004. Tr. of Scream from the Bottle. (SPA.). (J). pap. 7.99 (978-84-236-6701-7(4)) Edebé ESP. *Dist:* Lectorum Pubns., Inc.

Andersen, Hans Christian. IceMaiden & Other Tales. 2006. pap. (*978-1-4068-0421-8(5)) Echo Library.

Andrews, Miriam. The Butterfly's Last Journey. 2001. pap. (*978-1-889733-10-4(5)) Precious Life Bks., Inc.

Araki, Mie. Kitten's Big Adventure. 2005. (Illus.). 40p. (J). 15.00 (978-0-15-216738-7(2)) Harcourt Trade Pubs.

Argiento, Cindy. Doris in Dreamland. 2007. pap. 8.00 (*978-0-8059-7461-4(X)) Dorrance Publishing Co., Inc.

Ashepak, Agnes. Caqelngataq. Nevak, Caroline, illus. l.t. ed. 1999. Tr. of Butterfly. (ESK.). 8p. (J). (gr. k-3). pap. 14.50 (978-1-58084-059-0(0)); pap. 14.50 (978-1-58084-106-1(6)) Lower Kuskokwim Schl. District.

—Haqalikitaq. Nevak, Caroline, illus. l.t. ed. 1999. Tr. of Butterfly. (ESK.). 8p. (J). (gr. k-3). pap. 14.50 (978-1-58084-132-0(5)); pap. 14.50 (978-1-58084-140-5(6)) Lower Kuskokwim Schl. District.

—Saqaliqitaaq. Nevak, Caroline, illus. l.t. ed. 1999. Tr. of Butterfly. (ESK.). 8p. (J). (gr. k-3). pap. 14.50 (978-1-58084-125-2(2)) Lower Kuskokwim Schl. District.

Baer, Julie. Love Me Later. 2005. (Illus.). 28p. (J). (ps-ps). 16.99 (978-1-932188-03-5(7)) Bollix Bks.

Barsy, Kalman. The Crying Crocodile. Gastaldo, Walter, illus. 2004. (Yellow Ser.). (SPA.). 31p. (J). (gr. k-3). pap. 5.95 (978-1-57581-433-9(1)) Santillana USA Publishing Co., Inc.

Belli, Gioconda. The Butterfly Workshop. Erlbruch, Wolf, illus. 2006. 40p. pap. 14.95 (978-1-933372-12-9(5)) Europa Editions, Inc.

Bishop, Gay. Miss Hallberg's Butterfly Garden. Goetzel, Kathy, illus. 2000. 32p. (J). (ps-6). pap. 10.95 (978-0-9676839-0-4(4)) Pipevine Pr.

Blaylock, Kathy. Adventures of Buddy Fairy & Friends. 2007. 48p. 12.95 (*978-1-4137-9195-2(6)) PublishAmerica, Inc.

Book Company Staff & Turner, Jill. Percival the Beautiful Butterfly. 2005. (Sparkle Bks.). (Illus.). 16p. (J). (gr. 4-11). bds. 12.95 (978-1-74047-234-0(9)) Book Co. Publishing Pty, Ltd., The AUS. *Dist:* Penton Overseas, Inc.

Boone, Sheila. Free As a Butterfly. Knox, Susi Grell, illus. 2003. 32p. (J). (ps-3). pap. 7.95 (978-1-891577-80-2(8)) Image Pr., Inc.

—Free As a Butterfly. 2003. (J). pap. 6.95 (978-1-891577-81-9(6)) Images Pr.

Boynton, Cara. Sam's Secret World. 2006. (ENG.). 48p. per. 12.95 (*978-1-4241-4529-4(5)) PublishAmerica, Inc.

Brown, Monica & Ventura, Gabriela Baeza. Butterflies on Carmen Street/Mariposas en la Calle Carmen. Ward, April, illus. 2007. (SPA & ENG.). 32p. (J). (ps-4). 15.95 (*978-1-55885-484-0(3) , Piñata Books) Arte Publico Pr.

Bumpy Slide Books Staff. Things That Fly. Nickelodeon/ Viacom International Staff, ed. 2000. (Blue's Clues: No. 7). (Illus.). 32p. (J). (ps-1). 3.49 (978-1-57973-073-4(6)) Advance Pubs. LLC.

Bunting, Eve. The Butterfly House. Shed, Greg, illus. 1999. 32p. (J). (gr. k-3). pap. 16.95 (978-0-590-84884-8(4)) Scholastic, Inc.

Burke. Buddy Butterfly & His Cousin. 1999. (J). pap. 5.18 (978-0-7398-2396-5(5)) Steck-Vaughn.

Butterfield, Moira. Do Frogs Fly? Canals, Sonia, illus. 2007. (Animal Flappers Bks.). 16p. (J). (gr. k-k). 7.99 (978-0-7641-6027-1(3)) Barron's Educational Series, Inc.

The Butterfly Farm Burglar, 6 vols., Vol. 3. (Woodland Mysteriestm Ser.). 133p. (gr. 3-7). 42.50 (978-0-322-02374-1(2)) Wright Group, The.

Butterfly Journey. 2002. (Backyard Mini Bks.). (Illus.). 32p. (J). (978-1-59069-013-0(3) , H2002) Studio Mouse LLC.

A Butterfly's Tale. 2005. (J). per. (978-1-59700-082-6(5)) Island Heritage Publishing.

Cain, Sheridan. Crunching Munching Caterpillar. Tickle, Jack, illus. 2003. 32p. (J). tchr. ed. 15.95 (978-1-58925-025-3(7) , tiger tales) ME Media LLC.

Carle, Eric. La Oruga Muy Hambrienta. Carle, Eric, illus. 2002. (SPA., Illus.). 24p. (J). bds. 10.99 (978-0-399-23960-1(X) , Philomel) Penguin Group (USA) Inc.

Childers, Leta N. Chasing Butterflies & Finding Rainbows. 1999. (J). (gr. k-3). 6.50 incl. audio (978-1-58495-023-3(4)) DiskUs Publishing.

Churchill & Fuge. Butterfly Kiss. (Illus.). 28p. (J). pap. (978-0-340-68614-0(6) , Hodder & Stoughton) Hodder General Publishing Division.

Collard, Sneed B., III. Butterfly Count. Kratter, Paul, illus. 2002. 32p. (J). (gr. k-3). tchr. ed. 16.95 (978-0-8234-1607-3(0)) Holiday Hse., Inc.

Collicott, Sharleen. Toestomper & the Bad Butterflies. 2003. (Illus.). 32p. (J). (gr. k-3). tchr. ed. 15.00 (978-0-618-14092-3(1)) Houghton Mifflin Co. Trade & Reference Div.

Conley, Deane. Butterflies. Hunt, Christy, ed. Thiele, Marcus, illus. 2000. (Butterfly Tree Ser.: Vol. 2). 32p. (J). (ps-3). 17.00 (978-0-9664329-4-7(0)) Buckhead Pr.

Corning, Spring Mary. Miss Elliot's Girls (Stories of Beasts. 2006. 32.99 (*978-1-4280-2822-7(6)) IndyPublish.com.

Coville, Bruce. The Prince of Butterflies. Clapp, John, illus. (J). 2007. 36p. (gr. 1-4). pap. 7.00 (978-0-15-205854-8(0) , Voyager Bks./Libros Viajeros); 2002. 40p. (gr. k-4). 17.00 (978-0-15-201454-4(3)) Harcourt Children's Bks.

Cox, Judy. Butterfly Buddies. Sims, Blanche, illus. 2001. 96p. (J). (gr. 4-6). tchr. ed. 15.95 (978-0-8234-1654-7(2)) Holiday Hse., Inc.

Crusoe, Kristen. The Maggie Tales: Morgan & the Sneaker Wave. 2007. (Illus.). 20p. pap. 14.95 ***(978-1-59299-286-7(2))*** Inkwater Pr.

Curry, Kelli. Strawberry Shortcake & the Butterfly Garden. 2005. (All Aboard Reading Ser.). (Illus.). 32p. (J). (ps-2). mass mkt. 3.99 (978-0-448-43643-2(4) , Grosset & Dunlap) Penguin Group (USA) Inc.

—Strawberry Shortcake & the Butterfly Garden. Artful Doodlers Limited Staff, illus. 2005. 31p. (J). (ps-ps). lib. bdg. 10.79 (978-0-606-33096-1(8)) Tandem Library Bks.

Davol, Marguerite W. Why Butterflies Go by on Silent Wings. Roth, Robert, illus. 2001. (J). lib. bdg. (978-0-531-33322-8(1) , Orchard Bks.) Scholastic, Inc.

deVries, Maggie. Chance & the Butterfly. Ghent, Cindy, illus. 2002. (Orca Young Readers Ser.). 160p. (J). (gr. 3-6). pap. 4.99 (978-1-55143-208-3(0)) Orca Bk. Pubs. USA.

Donaldson, Julia. Where's My Mom? Scheffler, Axel, illus. 2008. 32p. (J). (ps). 16.99 ***(978-0-8037-3228-5(7)*** , Dial) Penguin Group (USA) Inc.

Edwards, Pamela Duncan. Clara Caterpillar. Cole, Henry, illus. 2001. 40p. (J). (ps-1). 16.99 (978-0-06-028995-9(3)) HarperCollins Pubs.

—Clara Caterpillar. 2004. (ps-2). lib. bdg. 14.15 (978-0-613-84142-9(5)) Tandem Library Bks.

Eggleton, Jill. Yellow Bird: Early Level Satellite Individual Title Six-Packs. (Sails Literacy Ser.). 16p. (gr. 1-2). 27.00 (978-0-7578-2936-9(8)) Rigby Education.

Eisenberg Sasso, Sandy. Butterflies Under Our Hats. 2006. (Illus.). 32p. (J). 16.95 (978-1-55725-474-0(5)) Paraclete Pr., Inc.

Fanelli, Sara. First Flight. 2002. (Illus.). 40p. (J). (gr. k-4). 18.00 (978-0-224-06457-6(6) , Jonathan Cape) Random Hse. Children's Bks. GBR. *Dist:* Trafalgar Square Publishing.

Fontenot, Mary Alice. Clovis Crawfish & Silvie Sulphur. Buckner, Julie Dupre, illus. 2004. (ENG & FRE.). 32p. (J). pap. 15.95 (978-1-56554-864-0(7)) Pelican Publishing Co., Inc.

Francisco, Jimenez. La Mariposa. 2000. Tr. of Butterfly. (J). (978-0-606-19426-6(6)) Tandem Library Bks.

Good Night Sweet Butterflies. 2003. (J). (978-0-9740149-0-6(7)) White Heat Ltd.

Graves, Keith. Three Nasty Gnarlies. Graves, Keith, illus. 2003. (Illus.). 40p. (J). pap. 16.95 (978-0-439-24090-1(5)) Scholastic, Inc.

The Great Caterpillar Adventure. 2002. (J). lib. bdg. 13.95 (978-0-9725485-0-2(5)) Waterfall Ridge.

Grimm, Lana & Bloch, Tania. How Butterbees Came to Bee! 2001. (Illus.). (J). (978-0-9662048-2-7(4)) Bee Unlimited, Inc.

—How Butterbees Came to Bee! Michener, David, illus. 2nd ed. 2001. 48p. 19.95 (978-0-9662048-3-4(2)) Bee Unlimited, Inc.

Grote, Rich. Megan & the Borealis Butterfly. 1999. (Magic Attic Club Ser.). (J). lib. bdg. (978-0-606-16953-0(9)) Tandem Library Bks.

Gudino Kieffer, E. Giraluna (Moonflower) (J). 22.50 (978-950-04-1280-3(2)) Emecé Editores S.A. ARG. *Dist:* AIMS International Bks., Inc.

Haque, Mary Baca. Madalynn the Monarch Butterfly & Her Quest to Michoacan. Jones, Francisco Lancaster, tr. from ENG. du Houx, Emily, illus. 2003. (ENG & SPA.). 64p. pap. 14.00 (978-1-882190-52-2(1)) Polar Bear & Co.

Harcourt School Publishers Staff. The Butterfly Garden Advanced Level. 3rd ed. 2002. (Trophies Reading Program Ser.). (Illus.). pap. 5.10 (978-0-15-323198-8(X)) Harcourt Schl. Pubs.

—Coyote & the Butterflies: Library Edition. 1999. (Collections Ser.). (Illus.). (J). 4.70 (978-0-15-314343-4(6)) Harcourt Schl. Pubs.

—Why Butterflies Were Made On Level. 3rd ed. 2002. (Trophies Reading Program Ser.). (Illus.). pap. 5.10 (978-0-15-323178-0(5)) Harcourt Schl. Pubs.

Harris, Sue. Butterfly Garden. Boey, Stephanie, illus. 2006. 20p. (J). 15.95 (978-0-8118-5247-0(4)) Chronicle Bks. LLC.

Haskins, Lori. Butterfly Fever. Smath, Jerry, illus. 2004. 31p. (J). lib. bdg. 20.00 ***(978-1-4242-1087-9(9))*** Fitzgerald Bks.

—Butterfly Fever. Smath, Jerry, tr. Smath, Jerry, illus. 2004. (Science Solves It! Ser.). (J). pap. 4.99 (978-1-57565-134-7(3)) Kane Pr., The.

Heap, Sue. Four Friends in the Garden. Heap, Sue, illus. 2004. (Illus.). 32p. (J). (gr. k-ps). 15.99 (978-0-7636-2371-5(7)) Candlewick Pr.

Hill, Franklin. Wings of Change. Cheung, Aries, illus. l.t. ed. 2001. 32p. (J). (ps-3). 15.95 (978-0-935699-18-0(X) , 093569918x) Illumination Arts Publishing Co., Inc.

Holabird, Katharine & Lever, Sally-Ann. Angelina & the Butterfly. Craig, Helen, illus. 2006. (Angelina Ballerina Ser.). 24p. (J). (ps-2). 3.99 (978-0-448-44015-6(6) , Grosset & Dunlap) Penguin Group (USA) Inc.

Holland, Diane. Sally Butterfield Goes Fishing! 2005. 49p. pap. 12.95 (978-1-4137-9767-1(9)) PublishAmerica, Inc.

Hood, Susan. Caterpillar Spring, Butterfly Summer. Gévry, Claudine, illus. 2003. 10p. (J). (gr. k-3). bds. 12.99 (978-0-7944-0149-8(X) , Reader's Digest Children's Bks.) Reader's Digest Children's Publishing, Inc.

Horacek, Petr. Butterfly, Butterfly: A Book of Colors. Horacek, Petr, illus. 2007. (Illus.). 16p. (J). (ps-k). 12.99 (978-0-7636-3343-1(7)) Candlewick Pr.

Hoyland, Christa. The Beautiful Butterfly. 2004. (J). (978-0-9759530-4-4(4)) Jostens Bks.

Jantti, Mariana. Becoming Butterflies: The Story of Matilde & Clotilde. 2007. (Little Books for Big Kids Ser.). (Illus.). 32p. (J). pap. 9.95 (978-9974-7960-2-7(4)) Hardenville SA URY. *Dist:* Independent Pubs. Group.

Jarrell, Pamela R. Flitter, Flutter Butterfly Board Book & Felt Puppet Set. Middleton, Mikell, illus. 2005. (J). bds. (978-1-57332-361-1(6)) HighReach Learning, Inc.

Johnston, Tony. Isabel's House of Butterflies. Guevara, Susan, illus. 2003. 32p. (J). (ps-3). 15.95 (978-0-87156-409-2(2)) Sierra Club Bks. for Children.

—Isabel's House of Butterflies. Guevara, Susan, illus. 2005. 32p. pap. 6.95 (978-1-58685-844-5(0)); pap. 7.95 (978-1-57805-128-1(2)) Gibbs Smith, Publisher.

Jorento, Dane, illus. Turtles into Butterflies. 2002. (J). 15.95 (978-0-9643004-1-5(9)) Laughing Peaches Pubns.

Kane, Tracy. Fairy Flight. Kane, Tracy, illus. l.t. ed. 2003. (Fairy Houses Ser.). (Illus.). 40p. (J). (gr. k-3). 15.95 (978-0-9708104-2-7(3)) Light-Beams Publishing.

Kienzle, Patricia Taylor. A Butterfly at the Funeral. 1999. (Illus.). (J). (ps-4). pap. 4.00 (978-1-890798-11-6(8)) Kienzle, Patricia Taylor.

Kipnis, Itzik. The Four Butterflies. Leviant, Curt, tr. from YID. Craft, Dana Duane, illus. 1999. 24p. (J). (ps-3). pap. (978-1-894303-22-4(9)) Raven Rock Publishing.

Kirk, David. Miss Spider: All Pupa'ed Out. 2005. (Miss Spider Ser.). 32p. (J). (ps-2). pap. 3.99 (978-0-448-43802-3(X) , Grosset & Dunlap) Penguin Group (USA) Inc.

Kline, Suzy. Horrible Harry & the Dungeon. 1998. (Horrible Harry Ser.: No. 7). (Illus.). 64p. (J). (gr. 2-4). pap. 3.99 (978-0-14-038620-2(3) , Puffin) Penguin Group (USA) Inc.

Kompelien, Tracy. Monarch Butterfly. Haberstroh, Anne, illus. (Fact & Fiction Ser.). 24p. (J). 2007. 21.35 (978-1-59928-454-5(5)); 2006. (978-1-59928-455-2(3)) ABDO Publishing Co.

Krauss, Ruth. Open House for Butterflies. Sendak, Maurice, illus. 2001. (Sendak Reissues Ser.). 48p. 14.95 (978-0-06-028636-1(9)) HarperCollins Pubs.

Krauss, Ruth & Sendak, Maurice. Open House for Butterflies. 2001. (Sendak Reissues Ser.). (Illus.). 48p. (J). 12.89 (978-0-06-028637-8(7)) HarperCollins Pubs.

Krings, Antoon. Abeja Teresa. 2005. (Bichitos curiosos Ser.). (SPA., Illus.). 32p. (J). 5.95 (978-84-932442-7-9(9)) Blume ESP. *Dist:* Independent Pubs. Group.

Kroll, Virginia L. Butterfly Boy. Suzan, Gerardo, illus. 2003. 32p. (J). (gr. k-2). pap. 8.95 (978-1-59078-055-8(8)) Boyds Mills Pr.

—Butterfly Boy. 2002. (gr. k-3). lib. bdg. 16.40 (978-0-613-59283-3(2)) Tandem Library Bks.

Kulling, Monica. Edgar Badger's Butterfly Day. Twinem, Nancy, illus. 1999. 48p. (J). (gr. 1-5). pap. 4.50 (978-1-57255-604-1(8)) Mondo Publishing.

Laughter in the Wind. 2004. (Illus.). (J). 17.95 (978-0-9753417-0-4(7)) Cheerful Cherub.

Leske, Staci. Butterfly That Loved the Firefly. 2006. 21.95 ***(978-1-4259-7645-3(X));*** pap. 11.95 ***(978-1-4259-7644-6(1))*** AuthorHouse.

Luis y la Mariposa: Individual Title Six-Packs. (Literatura 2000 Ser.). (SPA.). (gr. 2-3). 33.00 (978-0-7635-1263-7(X)) Rigby Education.

Madison, Alan. Velma Gratch & the Way Cool Butterfly. Hawkes, Kevin, illus. 2007. 40p. (J). (ps-3). 16.99 ***(978-0-375-83597-1(0));*** lib. bdg. 19.99 ***(978-0-375-93597-8(5))*** Random Hse. Children's Bks. (Schwartz & Wade Bks.).

—Velma Gratch & the Way Cool Butterfly. Hawkes, Kevin, illus. 2007. (J). (978-0-689-86921-1(5) , Atheneum) Simon & Schuster Children's Publishing.

Margolis, Amy. Butterflies & Magical Wings, 1. 2006. (Illus.). 44p. (J). pap. 16.99 (978-0-9776692-0-2(3)) Margolis, Amy Publishing.

Marks, Kathi. Butterflies are Special: The Most Beautiful Butterfly. 2006. (ENG.). 48p. per. 9.95 ***(978-1-59800-572-1(3))*** Outskirts Press, Inc.

Martin-Larranaga, Ana, illus. Butterfly at Home. 2007. (J). bds. 5.95 (978-1-58925-804-4(5) , tiger tales) ME Media LLC.

—Butterfly in the Garden. 2007. (J). bds. 5.95 (978-1-58925-803-7(7) , tiger tales) ME Media LLC.

—Butterfly in the Town. 2007. (J). bds. 5.95 (978-1-58925-805-1(3) , tiger tales) ME Media LLC.

—Butterfly on the Farm. 2007. (J). bds. 5.95 (978-1-58925-802-0(9) , tiger tales) ME Media LLC.

Mayer, Mercer. Our Friend Sam, Vol. 3. 2002. (Little Critter First Readers Ser.). (Illus.). 24p. (J). (gr. 1-2). pap. 3.95 (978-1-57768-815-0(5)) School Specialty Publishing.

McBratney, Sam. When I'm Big. Jeram, Anita, illus. 2007. (Guess How Much I Love You Ser.). 24p. (J). (gr. k-ps). bds. 7.99 ***(978-0-7636-3546-6(4))*** Candlewick Pr.

McGee, Warner, illus. Diego Saves a Butterfly. 2007. (Go, Diego, Go! Ser.). 24p. (J). pap. 3.99 (978-1-4169-3364-9(6) , Simon Spotlight/Nickelodeon) Simon & Schuster Children's Publishing.

Menase Debora & Wanha Edih. Purple Butterflies. 2006. 24p. 13.50 (978-975-6663-74-5(X)) Citlembik Pubns. TUR. *Dist:* Biblio Distribution.

Merrell, Victoria Jane. The Buffalo & the Butterfly. Bilisoly, Harvey, illus. 2002. 12p. (J). (ps-4). 21.95 (978-0-9717556-0-4(4)) VJM Pubns.

Meserve, Adria. Cleopatra Silverwing. 2005. (Illus.). 32p. (J). pap. 9.99 (978-0-09-943228-9(5) , Red Fox) Random Hse. Children's Bks. GBR. *Dist:* Trafalgar Square Publishing.

—Cleopatra Silverwing. 2005. (Illus.). 32p. (J). 19.95 (978-0-370-32565-1(6)) Random Hse. GBR. *Dist:* Independent Pubs. Group.

Millard, Glenda. Kaito's Cloth. Chapman, Gaye, illus. 2008. 32p. (J). (gr. k). 15.99 ***(978-0-399-24797-2(1)*** , Philomel) Penguin Group (USA) Inc.

Moody, Gloria. Two Beautiful Butterflies. Doering, Kimber, illus. l.t. ed. 2005. 25p. (YA). per. 8.99 (978-1-59879-002-3(1)) Lifevest Publishing, Inc.

Myers, Robert J. When the Monarchs Fly. McGehee, Cricket, illus. 2005. 64p. 11.95 (978-0-945582-76-2(5)) Down The Shore Publishing.

Noyes, Deborah & Haarsma, P. J. Red Butterfly: How a Princess Smuggled the Secret of Silk Out of China. Blackall, Sophie, illus. 2008. (Softwire Ser.). 272p. (J). (gr. 7). 16.99 ***(978-0-7636-2710-2(0))*** Candlewick Pr.

O'Connor, Crystal Ball. Gift/ Book Combo. Hollinger, Valerie Bunch, illus. 2005. (J). 25.00 (978-0-9774038-0-6(7)) Monarch Pubs.

—Jake & the Migration of the Monarch. Hollinger, Valerie Bunch, illus. 2005. 32p. (J). 17.95 (978-0-615-12659-3(6)) Monarch Pubs.

—Jake & the Migration of the Monarch with CD. Hollinger, Valerie Bunch, illus. 2005. (J). audio compact disk 18.95 (978-0-9774038-3-7(1)) Monarch Pubs.

—Jake y la Migraci'on de la Monarca. Brenes-Sotela, Guillermo J. & Quave, Gloria Martinez, trs. from ENG. Hollinger, Valerie Bunch, illus. 2005. (SPA.). (J). 17.95 (978-0-9774038-2-0(3)) Monarch Pubs.

O'Connor, Jane. Fancy Nancy: Bonjour, Butterfly. Glasser, Robin Preiss, illus. 2008. (Fancy Nancy Ser.). 32p. (J). 16.99 ***(978-0-06-123588-7(1));*** lib. bdg. 17.89 ***(978-0-06-123589-4(X))*** HarperCollins Pubs.

O'Flatharta, Antoine. Hurry & the Monarch. So, Meilo, illus. 2005. 40p. (J). (gr. k-3). 14.95 (978-0-375-83003-7(0) , Knopf Bks. for Young Readers) Random Hse. Children's Bks.

O'Neal, Kerry. I Wish I Could Fly/I Can Fly! The Lonely Caterpillar BOOK I & the Lonely Butterfly BOOK II. O'Neal, Kerry, illus. l.t. ed. 2006. (Illus.). 60p. (J). 29.99 ***(978-1-59879-197-6(4));*** per. 17.99 ***(978-1-59879-196-9(6))*** Lifevest Publishing, Inc.

Patterson, Christine. On the Wings of a Butterfly. 2004. 21p. (J). per. 10.68 (978-1-4116-0669-2(8)) Lulu.com.

Penney, Shannon. Mariposa. 2008. (Barbie Fairytopia Ser.). 80p. (J). pap. 3.99 ***(978-0-545-03590-3(2)*** , Scholastic Paperbacks) Scholastic, Inc.

Pinkham, Mark Amaru. Love Me Later. 2005. 202p. 14.95 (978-1-932188-02-8(9)) Adventures Unlimited Pr.

Prida, Isabel Suarez de la. El Caracol de las Mariposas. (Barril Sin Fondo Ser.).Tr. of Shell of the Butterflies. (SPA., Illus.). (J). (gr. 3-5). pap. 8.76 (978-968-6465-76-1(6)) Casa de Estudios de Literatura y Talleres Artisticos Amaquemecan A.C. MEX. *Dist:* Lectorum Pubns., Inc.

Prince, Sarah. Butterfly, the Bird, the Beetle, & Me. 2000. (gr. k-3). lib. bdg. 11.80 (978-0-613-29568-0(4)) Tandem Library Bks.

Priscella the Monarch Butterfly. l.t. ed. 2000. 10p. (J). 5.95 (978-0-9716507-1-8(3)) Foglestories.

Rea, Ba. Monarch! Come Play with Me. Rea, Ba, illus. 2006. (Illus.). 32p. (J). per. 10.95 (978-0-9657472-5-7(5)) Bas Relief Publishing.

Remkiewicz, Frank, illus. Horrible Harry & the Dungeon. 2002. (Horrible Harry Ser.). (J). 11.49 (978-0-7587-0590-7(5)) Book Wholesalers, Inc.

Richards, Kitty. Prilla & the Butterfly Lie. Shimabukuro, Denise, illus. 2007. (Stepping Stone Bks.). 128p. (J). (gr. 1-5). 5.99 (978-0-7364-2419-6(9) , RH/Disney) Random Hse. Children's Bks.

—Prilla & the Butterfly Lie. Shimabukuro, Denise, illus. 2007. (Disney Fairies Ser.). 113p. (J). ***(978-1-4287-2536-2(9))*** Random Hse., Inc.

Robinson, Zan D. Ferdie the Fay Meets Flutterey the Butterfly: A Forest Fable. Maxwell, Jeremy, illus. (Ferdie the Fay Adventure Ser.: No. 1). 52p. (Orig.). (J). (ps-4). (978-0-9635587-4-9(9)) Connors, E. W. Publishing Co.

Ruth, Nick. The Dark Dreamweaver. Concannon, Sue, illus. 2007. (Remin Chronicles: 1). 256p. (J). per. 11.95 ***(978-0-9745603-5-9(9))*** Imaginator Pr.

Ruvalcaba, Carlos. La Mariposa Bailarina. Mora, Francisco, illus. (SPA.). 24p. (J). (gr. 3-5). pap. 10.95 (978-1-56014-617-9(6)) Santillana USA Publishing Co., Inc.

Savage, Derek. Cool Cat Learns Karate. Bustamante, Denny, illus. 2001. (Donny the Dinosaur Ser.: Vol. 1). Tr. of Cool Cat Aprende Karate. (ENG & SPA.). 32p. (J). lib. bdg. 9.95 (978-0-9673000-8-5(8)) Savage Bks.

Schaeffer-Stumpf, Dawn. Fluttah Fluttah Butterfly. 2003. (Illus.). 24p. (J). per. 14.95 (978-0-9747147-0-7(4)) MK Publishing.

Schmauss, Judy Kentor. The Caterpillar. 2006. (Reader's Clubhouse Set A Ser.). (Illus.). 24p. (J). pap. 3.99 (978-0-7641-3286-5(5)) Barron's Educational Series, Inc.

Shahan, Sherry. The Little Butterfly. 1998. (J). (978-0-606-13964-9(8)) Tandem Library Bks.

Shi, Sharon. Once I Saw a Butterfly. Sohn, Catherine Jung, illus. 2000. 15p. (J). (ps-2). pap. 4.99 (978-0-9678636-0-3(0) , B001, Tattootles Bks.) Tattoo Manufacturing.

Smith, Debbie Powell. Eugie's Rainbow. 2000. 21p. (J). pap. 8.99 (978-1-930673-01-4(9)) Childhood Friends, Inc.

Soundar, Chitra. Chasing the Pot of Gold. Amrein, Paul, illus. 2006. 32p. (J). E-Book 5.00 incl. cd-rom ***(978-1-933090-36-8(7))*** Guardian Angel Publishing, Inc.

Steck-Vaughn Staff. Bud Butterfly & Cousin Butterfly. 1999. (Take Me Home Ser.). (Illus.). (J). pap. (978-0-7398-2589-1(5)) Steck-Vaughn.

Stone, Kazuko G. & Keido, Ippo. The Butterfly's Dream: Children's Stories from China. 2003. (Illus.). 32p. 15.95 (978-0-8048-3480-3(6)) Tuttle Publishing.

The Story of the Mexican Jumping Bean, 6 vols. (Multicultural Programs Ser.). 16p. (gr. 1-6). 25.95 (978-0-7802-8312-1(0)) Wright Group, The.

Sundgaard, Arnold & Sundgaard, Carle. The Lamb & the Butterfly. Carle, Eric, illus. 1999. 32p. (J). (ps-1). pap. 16.95 (978-0-531-05779-7(8) , Orchard Bks.) Scholastic, Inc.

Swope, Sam. Gotta Go! Gotta Go! Riddle, Sue, illus. 32p. (J). (ps-3). 2000. 14.00 (978-0-374-32757-6(2) , Farrar, Straus & Giroux (BYR)); 2004. reprint ed. pap. 5.95 (978-0-374-42786-3(0) , Sunburst) Farrar, Straus & Giroux.

Symes, Sally. Caterpillar to Butterfly: A Colorful Adventure. Harmer, Sharon, illus. 2008. 16p. (J). bds. 8.99 ***(978-1-4169-4753-0(1)*** , Little Simon) Simon & Schuster Children's Publishing.

Taylor-Gaines, Lonnetta. Fia & the Butterfly: 7 Stories for Character Education. 2005. 13.00 (978-0-8059-9848-1(9)) Dorrance Publishing Co., Inc.

Tennyson, Michael. Morpha: A Rain Forest Story. Yoswa, Jennifer H., illus. 2002. (CMC Wilderness Kids Ser.). 40p. 14.95 (978-0-9671466-8-3(2)) Colorado Mountain Club Pr., The.

Thierry, Raphael. Green Butterfly: A Superdog Adventure. 2007. (Illus.). 24p. (J). 7.95 ***(978-1-59354-198-9(8))*** Handprint Bks.

Tony & the Butterfly: Individual Title Six-Packs. (Literatura 2000 Ser.). (gr. 2-3). 33.00 (978-0-7635-0243-0(X)) Rigby Education.

Trimble, Marcia. Malinda Martha Meets Mariposa: A Star Is Born. Lund, John, illus. 32p. (J). (gr. k-5). 2000. pap. 7.95 (978-1-891577-58-1(1)); 1999. 15.95 (978-1-891577-57-4(3)) Images Pr.

van Kampen, Vlasta. Marigold's Wings. 2005. (Illus.). 31p. (J). lib. bdg. 24.67 (978-0-8368-4500-6(5)) Stevens, Gareth Inc.

Wagner, Fiona. The Little Cat. 2005. 15p. (J). 9.99 (978-1-4116-5568-3(0)) Lulu.com.

Waiting for Wings. 2004. (J). 24.95 incl. audio (978-1-55592-151-4(5)) Weston Woods Studios, Inc.

Wargin, Kathy-Jo. A Mother's Wish. Roman, Irena, illus. 2006. 32p. (J). 15.99 (978-0-06-057170-2(5)); lib. bdg. 16.89 (978-0-06-057171-9(3)) HarperCollins Pubs.

Webber, Vanessa. Glitterbutterfly. 2005. (Illus.). 4p. (J). bds. 5.95 (978-1-59354-084-5(1)) Handprint Bks.

Webster, Christy. Barbie Mariposa. 2008. (Step into Reading Ser.). (Illus.). 32p. (J). (ps-1). lib. bdg. 11.99 ***(978-0-375-95198-5(9));*** pap. 3.99 ***(978-0-375-85198-8(4))*** Random Hse. Children's Bks. (Random Hse. Bks. for Young Readers).

Wenger, Shaunda. Caterpillar Can't Wait! 2006. (Early Explorers Ser.). (J). 34.00 ***(978-1-4108-6101-6(5))*** Benchmark Education Co.

Wert, Debra L. Caterfly: Mac's Back Struggling to Stay Drug-Free. 1998. (J). (978-0-944576-27-4(3)) Rocky River Pubs., LLC.

West, Annie. The Butterfly Who Wouldn't. 1999. (Illus.). 22p. (J). (ps-1). pap. (978-1-902586-57-1(3)) Mentor Bks.

White, Nancy. Butterfly Battle. Gangloff, Hope, illus. 2003. (Magic School Bus Ser.: Vol. 16). 80p. (J). pap. 4.99 (978-0-439-42936-8(6)) Scholastic, Inc.

Yee, Paul. The Boy in the Attic. 1998. (Illus.). (J). (gr. 2-5). 15.95 (978-0-88899-330-4(7) , Libros Tigrillo) Groundwood Bks. CAN. *Dist:* Transition Vendor.

Yolen, Jane. An Invitation to the Butterfly Ball: A Counting Rhyme. Zalben, Jane Breskin, illus. 2003. 32p. (J). (gr. k-2). pap. 9.95 (978-1-56397-692-6(7)) Boyds Mills Pr.

Young-Robinson, Christine. Isra the Butterfly Gets Caught for Show & Tell. l.t. ed. 2001. 28p. (J). reprint ed. bds. 14.95 (978-0-9706985-0-6(X)) Yoroson Publishing.

Zimmerman, Kathleen. Oscar's First Flight. Feldmeier Sims, Julie & Hartman, John, illus. 2005. 44p. (J). per. 16.95 (978-0-9744330-0-4(4)) Kat Tales Publishing.

Zoehfeld, Kathleen Weidner. Amazon Fever. Bogan, Paulette, illus. 2006. (Road to Reading Ser.). 48p. (J). (gr. 1-4). 11.99 (978-0-307-46407-1(5)); pap. 3.99 (978-0-307-26407-7(6)) Random Hse. Children's Bks. (Random Hse. Bks. for Young Readers).

BUTTONS

Dahl, Michael. Bunches of Buttons: Counting by 10s. Trover, Zachary, illus. 2006. 24p. (J). (ps-2). 22.60 (978-1-4048-1315-1(2)) Picture Window Bks.

Fung, Karen & Butterfield, Moira. Zipper, Buttons & Bows. Utton, Peter, illus. 2000. 12p. (J). (ps-k). 12.95 (978-0-7641-5289-4(0)) Barron's Educational Series, Inc.

Lakeshore Learning Materials Staff, contrib. by. Button Box Kit. 2000. (J). pap. 29.95 (978-1-929255-61-0(6)) Lakeshore Learning Materials.

Warren, Jean. Buttons. Cubley, Kathleen, ed. 1998. (Sticker Book Ser.). (Illus.). 32p. (J). (ps). pap. 3.95 (978-1-57029-216-3(7) , WPH 3706, Totline Pubns.) Schaffer, Frank Pubns.

BUYERS GUIDES

see Consumer Education; Shopping

BY-PRODUCTS

see Waste Products

BYRD, RICHARD EVELYN, 1888-1957

Burleigh, Robert. Black Whiteness: Admiral Byrd Alone in the Antarctic. Krudop, Walter Lyon, illus. 1998. 40p. (J). (gr. 2-7). 17.95 (978-0-689-81299-6(X) , Atheneum) Simon & Schuster Children's Publishing.

Rink, Paul. Admiral Richard Byrd: Alone in the Antarctic. 2006. (Sterling Point Bks.). (Illus.). 192p. (J). 12.95 (978-1-4027-3189-1(2)); pap. 6.95 (978-1-4027-3610-0(X)) Sterling Publishing Co., Inc.

BYRON, GEORGE GORDON BYRON, BARON, 1788-1824

Wills, Karen & Pesta, Duke. Lord Byron. Bloom, Harold, ed. 2003. (Bloom's BioCritiques Ser.). (Illus.). 112p. (gr. 9-13). 35.00 (978-0-7910-6367-5(4) , 000872, Chelsea Hse.) Facts On File, Inc.

BYZANTINE EMPIRE

The Byzantine Empire in the Age of Justinian (NCHS) (YA). (gr. 6-9). spiral bd., tchr.'s planning gde. ed. 11.00 (978-0-382-40980-6(9)) Cobblestone Publishing Co.

The Byzantine Empire in the Age of Justinian (NCHS) Grades 6-9. (J). tchr. ed. 15.50 (978-0-382-40981-3(7)) Cobblestone Publishing Co.

Corrick, James A. The Byzantine Empire. 2006. (World History Ser.). (Illus.). 112p. (J). (gr. 7-10). 32.45 (978-1-59018-837-8(3) , Lucent Bks.) Thomson Gale.

Feldman, Ruth Tenzer. The Fall of Constantinople. 2007. (J). lib. bdg. (*978-0-8225-5918-4(8)) Twenty First Century Bks.

Marston, Elsa. The Byzantine Empire. 2002. (Cultures of the Past Ser.). (Illus.). 80p. (YA). (gr. 5). 29.93 (978-0-7614-1495-7(9) , Benchmark Bks.) Cavendish, Marshall Corp.

Nardo, Don. The Byzantine Empire. 2005. (Life During the Great Civilizations Ser.). (Illus.). 48p. (J). (ps-7). lib. bdg. 24.95 (978-1-4103-0586-2(4) , Blackbirch Pr., Inc.) Thomson Gale.

Stefoff, Rebecca. The Medieval World. 2003. (Illus.). 48p. (J). 27.07 (978-0-7614-1642-5(0) , Benchmark Bks.) Cavendish, Marshall Corp.

BYZANTINE EMPIRE—FICTION

Barrett, Tracy. Anna of Byzantium. 2000. (Illus.). 224p. (YA). (gr. 7-12). pap. 5.99 (978-0-440-41536-7(5) , Laurel Leaf) Random Hse. Children's Bks.

—Anna of Byzantium. 2000. (J). 11.64 (978-0-606-19742-7(7)); (gr. 7-12). lib. bdg. 12.40 (978-0-613-28364-9(3)) Tandem Library Bks.

Paton Walsh, Jill. The Emperor's Winding Sheet. 2004. 256p. (YA). reprint ed. pap. 8.95 (978-1-886910-88-1(X) , Lemniscaat) Boyds Mills Pr.

C

CABEZA DE VACA, ALVAR NUNEZ, 1490?-1557

Johnston, Lissa J. & Nunez Cabeza de Vaca, Alvar. Crossing a Continent: The Incredible Journey of Cabeza de Vaca. 2005. 82p. (J). pap. 9.95 (978-1-57168-183-6(3) , Eakin Pr.) Eakin Pr.

Waldman, Stuart. We Asked for Nothing: The Remarkable Journey of Cabeza de Vaca. McNeely, Tom, illus. 2003. (Great Explorers Ser.). 48p. (J). (gr. 4-8). 19.95 (978-1-931414-07-4(6)) Mikaya Pr.

CABINET OFFICERS

Acker, Kerry. Madeleine Albright. 2004. (Women in Politics Ser.). (Illus.). 120p. 30.00 (978-0-7910-7734-4(9)); 116p. pap. 30.00 (978-0-7910-7998-0(8)) Facts On File, Inc. (Chelsea Hse.).

Anderson, Dale. Elizabeth Dole. 2004. (Women in Politics Ser.). (Illus.). 120p. 30.00 (978-0-7910-7733-7(0)); 104p. pap. 30.00 (978-0-7910-7997-3(X)) Facts On File, Inc. (Chelsea Hse.).

Banting, Erinn. Condoleezza Rice. 2007. (J). (*978-1-59036-639-4(5)); (*978-1-59036-640-0(9)) Weigl Pubs., Inc.

Brown, Warren. Colin Powell: Soldier & Statesman. (Black Americans of Achievement Ser.). (Illus.). 112p. (J). (gr. 6-12). 2005. pap. 13.25 (978-0-7910-8373-4(X)); 2004. 30.00 (978-0-7910-8254-6(7)) Facts On File, Inc. (Chelsea Hse.).

Burgan, Michael. Madeleine Albright. 1998. (Single Titles Ser.: up). (Illus.). 144p. (gr. 7-12). lib. bdg. 24.90 (978-0-7613-0367-1(7) , Millbrook Pr.) Lerner Publishing Group.

Byman, Jeremy. Madam Secretary: The Story of Madeleine Albright. (Notable Americans Ser.). (Illus.). 1998. 96p. (gr. 5 up). 21.95 (978-1-883846-23-7(4)); 2004. 128p. (YA). (gr. 6-12). 23.95 (978-1-931798-34-1(6)) Reynolds, Morgan Inc.

Ditchfield, Christin. Condoleezza Rice: America's Leading Stateswoman. 2006. (Great Life Stories Ser.). (Illus.). 111p. (J). (gr. 5-8). 30.50 (978-0-531-13874-8(7) , Watts, Franklin) Scholastic Library Publishing.

Emert, Phyllis Raybin. Attorneys General: Enforcing the Law. 2005. (Illus.). 176p. (J). (gr. 7 up). lib. bdg. 24.95 (978-1-881508-66-3(8)) Oliver Pr., Inc.

Feinstein, Stephen. Colin Powell. 2007. (African-American Heroes Ser.). (Illus.). 24p. (J). (gr. 1-3). lib. bdg. 21.26 (978-0-7660-2761-9(9) , Enslow Elementary) Enslow Pubs., Inc.

Granger, Stacey. Colin Powell. l.t. ed. 2002. (Real-Life Reader Biography Ser.). (Illus.). 32p. (J). (gr. 3-8). lib. bdg. 15.95 (978-1-58415-144-9(7)) Mitchell Lane Pubs., Inc.

Harmon, Daniel E. Attorney General's Office. 2001. (Your Government Ser.). (Illus.). 64p. (J). (gr. 4-7). 25.00 (978-0-7910-5995-1(2) , Chelsea Hse.) Facts On File, Inc.

—The Secretary of State. 2001. (Your Government Ser.). (Illus.). 64p. (J). (gr. 4-7). 25.00 (978-0-7910-5996-8(0) , Chelsea Hse.) Facts On File, Inc.

Hasday, Judy L. Madeleine Albright: Stateswoman. 1999. (Women of Achievement Ser.). (Illus.). (J). (978-0-606-18035-1(4)) Tandem Library Bks.

Horn, Geoffrey M. Colin Powell. 2004. (Trailblazers of the Modern World Ser.). (Illus.). 48p. (J). pap. 11.95 (978-0-8368-5267-7(2)); (YA). lib. bdg. 30.00 (978-0-8368-5498-5(5)) Stevens, Gareth Inc. (World Almanac Library).

Kramer, Barbara. Madeleine Albright: First Woman Secretary of State. 2000. (People to Know Ser.). (Illus.). 112p. (J). (gr. 6-12). lib. bdg. 26.60 (978-0-7660-1143-4(7)) Enslow Pubs., Inc.

Mattern, Joanne. Attorney General. 2003. (America's Leaders Ser.). (Illus.). 32p. (J). 24.94 (978-1-56711-278-8(1) , Blackbirch Pr., Inc.) Thomson Gale.

Rau, Dana Meachen. Elizabeth Dole: Public Servant & Senator. 2005. (J). (978-0-7565-1583-6(1)) Compass Point Bks.

Scott Ingram. The Secretary of Commerce. 2004. (America's Leaders Ser.). (Illus.). 32p. (J). 23.70 (978-1-4103-0091-1(9) , Blackbirch Pr., Inc.) Thomson Gale.

Strong, Mike. Colin Powell: It Can Be Done! 2002. (High Five Reading Ser.). (Illus.). 48p. (J). (gr. 3-4). lib. bdg. 22.60 (978-0-7368-9551-4(5) , Capstone High-Interest Bks.); pap. (978-0-7368-9529-3(9)) Capstone Pr., Inc.

Strum, Richard. Henry Knox: Washington's Artilleryman. 2006. (Forgotten Heroes of the American Revolution Ser.). (Illus.). 88p. (J). (gr. 5-11). lib. bdg. 23.95 (978-1-59556-013-1(0)) OTTN Publishing.

Strum, Richard M. Henry Knox: Washington's Artilleryman. 2006. (J). pap. (978-1-59556-018-6(1)) OTTN Publishing.

Wellman, Sam. The Cabinet. 2001. (Your Government Ser.). (Illus.). 64p. (J). (gr. 4-7). 25.00 (978-0-7910-5993-7(6) , Chelsea Hse.) Facts On File, Inc.

Wheeler, Jill C. America's Leaders. 2002. (War on Terrorism Ser.). (Illus.). 64p. (J). (gr. 4-8). lib. bdg. 25.65 (978-1-57765-661-6(X) , ABDO & Daughters) ABDO Publishing Co.

—Madeleine Albright. 2002. (Women of the World Ser.). (J). lib. bdg. 21.35 (978-1-57765-316-5(5)) ABDO Publishing Co.

CABINET WORK

see also Woodwork

Feirer, John L. Cabinetmaking & Millwork. 5th ed. 1999. (Illus.). (YA). (gr. 6-12). stu. ed., wbk. ed. 8.68 (978-0-02-675960-1(8)) Glencoe/McGraw-Hill.

CABINS

see Log Cabins

CABOT, JOHN, D. 1498

Anthony, Laurence. John Cabot. 2001. (Great Explorers Ser.). (Illus.). 48p. (J). (gr. 5 up). lib. bdg. 30.00 (978-0-8368-5012-3(2) , World Almanac Library) Stevens, Gareth Inc.

Bastable, Tony. John Cabot. 2003. (Great Explorers Ser.). (Illus.). 48p. (J). (gr. 5 up). pap. 14.60 (978-0-8368-5172-4(2) , World Almanac Library) Stevens, Gareth Inc.

Cabot. (Exploring the World Ser.). 48p. (YA). 8.95 (978-0-7565-1138-8(0)) Compass Point Bks.

Champion, Neil. John Cabot. (Groundbreakers Ser.). (Illus.). 48p. (J). (gr. 5-7). 2002. pap. 8.50 (978-1-58810-370-3(6) , 91095); 2001. lib. bdg. 25.64 (978-1-58810-046-7(4)) Heinemann Library.

Doak, Robin S. Cabot: John Cabot & the Journey to North America. 2003. (Exploring the World Ser.). (Illus.). 48p. (J). (gr. 4 up). lib. bdg. 22.60 (978-0-7565-0420-5(1)) Compass Point Bks.

Great Explorers: Captain James Cook; Christopher Columbus; Ferdinand Magellan; John Cabot, 4 bks. 2002. (Illus.). (J). (gr. 5 up). pap. (978-0-8368-5179-3(X)); lib. bdg. 117.06 (978-0-8368-5019-2(X)) Stevens, Gareth Inc. (World Almanac Library).

Larkin, Tanya. John Cabot. 2001. (Famous Explorers Ser.). (Illus.). 24p. (J). (gr. 3). lib. bdg. 18.75 (978-0-8239-5553-4(2) , PowerKids Pr.) Rosen Publishing Group, Inc., The.

Malam, John. John Cabot. 1999. (Tell Me about Ser.). (Illus.). 24p. (gr. 2-5). lib. bdg. 19.93 (978-1-57505-365-3(9)) Lerner Publishing Group.

Marsh, Carole. John Cabot. 2002. (One Thousand Readers Ser.). (Illus.). 12p. (J). (gr. k-4). 2.95 (978-0-635-01515-0(3) , 15153) Gallopade International.

Mass, Wendy. John Cabot: Early Explorer. 2004. (Explorers! Ser.). (Illus.). 48p. (J). lib. bdg. 23.93 (978-0-7660-2144-0(0)) Enslow Pubs., Inc.

Mattern. Earth's Explorers: John & Sebastian Cabot. 2000. (SPA., Illus.). pap. (978-0-7398-3337-7(5)) Steck-Vaughn.

Mattern, Joanne. The Travels of John & Sebastian Cabot. 1999. (Explorers & Exploration Ser.). (Illus.). 48p. (J). (gr. 4-7). lib. bdg. 22.83 (978-0-7398-1492-5(3)) Raintree.

Morey, Allan. John Cabot. 2003. (Explorers of the Unknown Ser.). (J). pap. (978-1-58417-098-3(0)) Lake Street Pubs.

Petrie, Kristin. John Cabot. 2004. (Explorers Set I Ser.). (J). (gr. k-6). lib. bdg. 22.78 (978-1-59197-593-9(X)) ABDO Publishing Co.

Rice Jr., Earle. John Cabot. 2006. (Profiles in American History Ser.). (Illus.). 48p. (J). (gr. 4-8). lib. bdg. 20.95 (978-1-58415-451-8(9)) Mitchell Lane Pubs., Inc.

Shields, Charles J. John Cabot & the Rediscovery of North America. 2001. (Explorers of New Worlds Ser.). (Illus.). (J). (gr. 4-8). 63p. pap. 25.00 (978-0-7910-6439-9(5)); 64p. 25.00 (978-0-7910-6438-2(7)) Facts On File, Inc. (Chelsea Hse.).

—John Cabot & the Rediscovery of North America. 2002. (gr. 3-6). lib. bdg. 17.60 (978-0-613-65430-2(7)) Tandem Library Bks.

CABOT, JOHN, D. 1498—FICTION

Garfield, Henry. The Lost Voyage of John Cabot. 2004. (Illus.). 320p. (YA). 16.95 (978-0-689-85173-5(1) , Atheneum/Richard Jackson Bks.) Simon & Schuster Children's Publishing.

—The Lost Voyage of John Cabot. l.t. ed. 2004. 326p. 20.95 (978-0-7862-7085-9(3)) Thorndike Pr.

CACTUS

Bailey, Jill. Life in a Desert Cactus. (Microhabitats Ser.). (Illus.). 32p. (J). (ps-ps). 2004. lib. bdg. 24.28 (978-0-7398-6801-0(2)); 2003. pap. 7.50 (978-1-4109-0347-1(8)) Raintree.

—Life in a Desert Cactus. 2003. (gr. k-3). lib. bdg. 15.90 (978-0-613-78241-8(0)) Tandem Library Bks.

Bash, Barbara. Desert Giant: The World of the Saguaro Cactus. Bash, Barbara, illus. 2nd ed. 2002. (Illus.). 28p. (J). reprint ed. pap. 6.95 (978-1-57805-085-7(5)) Sierra Club Bks. for Children.

—Desert Giant: The World of the Saguaro Cactus. 2002. (gr. k-3). lib. bdg. 15.25 (978-0-613-52553-4(1)) Tandem Library Bks.

Benchmark Education Staff, compiled by. Cactus & Canyons & Ecosystems. 2005. spiral bd. 225.00 (*978-1-4108-5806-1(5)) Benchmark Education Co.

—Cactus & Canyons & Regions. 2005. spiral bd. 225.00 (*978-1-4108-5805-4(7)) Benchmark Education Co.

Bernath, Stefen. Cactus Coloring Book. 1998. (Illus.). 48p. (J). pap. 3.95 (978-0-486-24097-8(5)) Dover Pubns., Inc.

Canizares, Susan. Cactus Names. 1998. (Science Emergent Readers Ser.). (J). 3.25 (978-0-590-63871-5(8)) Scholastic, Inc.

Dorling Kindersley Publishing Staff. Cacti & Succulents. 2004. (101 Essential Tips Ser.). (Illus.). 72p. (gr. 12). pap. 5.00 (978-0-7566-0613-8(6)) Dorling Kindersley Publishing, Inc.

Ecton, Ann. Saguaro. Romo, Alberto, tr. Torrisi, Gary, illus. 1999. (Books for Young Learners). (SPA.). 12p. (J). (gr. k-2). pap. 5.00 (978-1-57274-287-1(9)) Owen, Richard C. Pubs., Inc.

Fowler, Allan. Cactuses. (Rookie Read-About Science Ser.). (Illus.). 32p. (J). (gr. 1-2). 2002. pap. 4.95 (978-0-516-25983-3(0)); 2001. 20.50 (978-0-516-21686-7(4)) Scholastic Library Publishing. (Children's Pr.).

—Cactuses. 2001. (gr. k-3). lib. bdg. 12.95 (978-0-613-53975-3(3)) Tandem Library Bks.

Green, Jen. A Saguaro Cactus. 1999. (Small Worlds Ser.). (Illus.). 32p. (J). (gr. 3-4). pap. (978-0-7787-0148-4(4)) Crabtree Publishing Co.

Guiberson, Brenda Z. Cactus Hotel. 2007. (Illus.). 32p. (J). 23.95 (*978-0-8050-8228-9(X) , Holt, Henry & Co. Bks. For Young Readers) Holt, Henry & Co.

Harcourt School Publishers Staff. The Giant of the Desert Below Level. 3rd ed. 2002. (Trophies Reading Program Ser.). (Illus.). pap. 5.10 (978-0-15-323053-0(3)) Harcourt Schl. Pubs.

—The Land of Little Water Below Level. 3rd ed. 2002. (Trophies Reading Program Ser.). (Illus.). pap. 5.10 (978-0-15-323243-5(9)) Harcourt Schl. Pubs.

Morrison, Yvonne. Stuck on Cactus: American Desert Life. 2007. (Shockwave: Life Science & Medicine Ser.). (Illus.). 36p. (J). (gr. 4-6). lib. bdg. 25.00 (*978-0-531-17768-6(8) , Children's Pr.) Scholastic Library Publishing.

Ross-Flanigan, Nancy. Peyote. 2001. (Drug Library). (Illus.). 112p. (YA). (gr. 6-12). pap. 13.26 (978-0-7660-1928-7(4)) Enslow Pubs., Inc.

CAESAR, CAIUS JULIUS, 100-44 B.C.

see Caesar, Julius

CAESAR, JULIUS

Barter, James. Julius Caesar & Ancient Rome in World History. 2001. (In World History Ser.). (Illus.). 128p. (J). (gr. 5-12). lib. bdg. 26.60 (978-0-7660-1461-9(4)) Enslow Pubs., Inc.

Bernier Grand Carmen. Cesar. DIAZ DAVID, illus. 2006. (SPA.). 48p. 16.95 (978-0-7614-5283-6(4)) Cavendish, Marshall Corp.

Crompton, Samuel Willard. Julius Caesar. 2003. (Ancient World Leaders Ser.). (Illus.). 112p. (gr. 6-12). 30.00 (978-0-7910-7220-2(7)); pap. 30.00 (978-0-7910-7494-7(3)) Facts On File, Inc. (Chelsea Hse.).

Firth, Rachel & Parkhouse, Stephen. Julius Caesar. 2007. (Famous Lives Gift Bks). 64p. (J). 8.99 (978-0-7945-1595-9(9) , Usborne) EDC Publishing.

Galford, Ellen. Julius Caesar: The Boy Who Conquered an Empire. 2007. (World History Biographies Ser.). (Illus.). 64p. (J). (gr. 3-7). 17.95 (978-1-4263-0064-6(6)); lib. bdg. 27.90 (978-1-4263-0065-3(4)) National Geographic Society. (National Geographic Children's Bks.).

Gormley, Beatrice. Julius Caesar: Young Statesman. 2006. (Childhood of World Figures Ser.). 256p. (J). pap. 5.99 (978-1-4169-1281-1(9) , Aladdin) Simon & Schuster Children's Publishing.

Greenblatt, Miriam. Julius Caesar & the Roman Republic. 2005. (Rulers & Their Times Ser.). (Illus.). 96p. (J). (gr. 3-7). lib. bdg. 29.93 (978-0-7614-1836-8(9) , Benchmark Bks.) Cavendish, Marshall Corp.

Jeffrey, Gary & Petty, Kate. Julius Caesar: The Life of a Roman General. 2005. (Illus.). 48p. (J). lib. bdg. 26.50 (978-1-4042-0239-9(0) , 1241097) Rosen Publishing Group, Inc., The.

Kent, Zachary. Julius Caesar: Ruler of the Roman World. 2006. (Rulers of the Ancient World Ser.). (Illus.). 160p. (J). lib. bdg. 27.93 (978-0-7660-2563-9(2)) Enslow Pubs., Inc.

Parsons, Jayne, ed. Julius Caesar. 2006. (DK Discoveries Ser.). 48p. (J). pap. 6.99 (978-0-7566-1963-3(7)) Dorling Kindersley Publishing, Inc.

Reid, Struan. Julius Caesar. (Historical Biographies Ser.). 32p. 2003. pap. 7.50 (978-1-58810-999-6(2)); 2002. (Illus.). (J). (gr. 2-4). lib. bdg. 22.79 (978-1-58810-564-6(4)) Heinemann Library.

Ross, Stewart. Big J. Shields, Sue, illus. 32p. pap. 9.99 (978-0-7502-2852-7(0) , Hodder & Stoughton) Hodder General Publishing Division GBR. *Dist:* Trafalgar Square Publishing.

Saunders, Nicholas. The Life of Julius Caesar. 2006. (Stories from History Ser.). 48p. (J). 14.95 (978-0-7696-4717-3(0)); pap. 6.95 (978-0-7696-4697-8(2)) School Specialty Publishing.

Scott, James. Julius Caesar: A Student Response Journal. 2002. 36p. (J). (978-1-58049-939-2(2) , RJ62) Prestwick Hse., Inc.

—Julius Caesar: Activity Pack. 2002. 108p. (J). ring bd. (978-1-58049-620-9(2) , PA0119) Prestwick Hse., Inc.

Thorne, James. Julius Caesar: Conqueror & Dictator. 2003. (Leaders of Ancient Rome Ser.). (Illus.). 112p. (YA). (gr. 5-8). lib. bdg. 31.95 (978-0-8239-3595-6(7) , Rosen Central) Rosen Publishing Group, Inc., The.

Watson, Robert W. A Student's Companion to the Tragedy of Julius Caesar. 1999. stu. ed. 6.96 (978-1-929579-52-5(7) , SG6003) Smarr Pubs.

Whiting, Jim. The Life & Times of Julius Caesar. 2005. (Biography from Ancient Civilizations Ser.). (Illus.). 48p. (J). (ps-7). lib. bdg. 29.95 (978-1-58415-337-5(7)) Mitchell Lane Pubs., Inc.

CAESAR, JULIUS—DRAMA

Edcon Staff. Julius Caesar: Level 5. 2003. 72p. (YA). act. bk. ed. 9.95 (978-1-55576-336-7(7) , EDSC502B) AV Concepts Corp.

CAFETERIAS

see Restaurants

CAILLOU (FICTITIOUS CHARACTER)—FICTION

Caillou. 2003. 32p. pap., wbk. ed. 14.95 incl. cd-rom (978-1-57791-012-1(5)); 32p. pap., wbk. ed. 14.95 incl. cd-rom (978-1-57791-013-8(3)); 32p. pap., wbk. ed. 14.95 incl. cd-rom (978-1-57791-014-5(1)); 32p. pap., wbk. ed. 14.95 incl. cd-rom (978-1-57791-015-2(X)); 32p. pap., wbk. ed. 14.95 incl. cd-rom (978-1-57791-028-2(1)); cd-rom 19.95 (978-1-57791-019-0(2)) Brighter Minds Children's Publishing.

Caillou Coloring Book. 2004. (J). act. bk. ed. (978-0-7666-1101-6(9) , 99430); act. bk. ed. (978-0-7666-1102-3(7) , 99430); act. bk. ed. (978-0-7666-1103-0(5) , 99430); act. bk. ed. (978-0-7666-1104-7(3) , 99430) Modern Publishing.

Chouette. Caillou Goes to Work. rev. ed. 2005. (Abracadabra Ser.).Tr. of Caillou va Travailler. (Illus.). 24p. (J). (ps-1). pap. 4.95 (978-2-89450-548-9(5)) Chouette Publishing CAN. *Dist:* Independent Pubs. Group.

—Caillou Is Sick. rev. ed. 2005. (Abracadabra Ser.).Tr. of Caillou est Malade. (Illus.). 24p. (J). (ps-1). pap. 4.95 (978-2-89450-547-2(7)) Chouette Publishing CAN. *Dist:* Independent Pubs. Group.

Chouette Publishing. Caillou: In My House. Brignaud, Pierre, illus. rev. ed. 2007. (My First Dictionary Ser.). 16p. (J). bds. 12.95 (*978-2-89450-627-1(9)) Chouette Publishing CAN. *Dist:* Independent Pubs. Group.

—Caillou: My Clothes. Brignaud, Pierre, illus. rev. ed. 2008. 24p. (J). bds. 7.95 (*978-2-89450-629-5(5)) Chouette Publishing CAN. *Dist:* Independent Pubs. Group.

—Caillou: My Room. Brignaud, Pierre, illus. rev. ed. 2008. (Caillou Board Bks.). 24p. (J). bds. 7.95 (*978-2-89450-628-8(7)) Chouette Publishing CAN. *Dist:* Independent Pubs. Group.

Hensley, Sarah M. Caillou's Rodeo Day. Storch, Ellen N., illus. 2006. (J). bds. (978-1-57332-375-8(6)) HighReach Learning, Inc.

Johnson, Marion. Caillou: New Shoes. rev. ed. 2008. (Playtime Ser.). (Illus.). 24p. (J). pap. 4.95 (*978-2-89450-634-9(1)) Chouette Publishing CAN. *Dist:* Independent Pubs. Group.

—Caillou Watches Rosie. rev. ed. 2008. (Playtime Ser.). (Illus.). 20p. (J). pap. 4.95 (*978-2-89450-635-6(X)) Chouette Publishing CAN. *Dist:* Independent Pubs. Group.

L'Heureux, Christine. Buenas Noches! 2004. (Caillou Estrella Polar Ser.). (SPA., Illus.). 24p. (J). (ps up). pap. 3.95 (978-1-58728-345-1(X) , Creative Publishing International) Quayside.

—Caillou - I Will Always Love You. Johanson, Sarah Margaret, tr. from FRE. Brignaud, Pierre, illus. 2006. Tr. of Caillou - Je T'aime, Je T'aime. 24p. (J). (ps-1). pap. 7.95 (978-2-89450-551-9(5)) Chouette Publishing CAN. *Dist:* Independent Pubs. Group.

L'Heureux, Christine & Lapierre, Claude. Caillou Treasury Collection. 2003. (North Star Ser.). (Illus.). 148p. (J). pap. 9.99 (978-2-89450-357-7(1)) Chouette Publishing CAN. *Dist:* Independent Pubs. Group.

L'Heureux, Christine, et al. Good Night! Lapierre, Claude, illus. rev. ed. 2000. (J). pap. (978-2-89450-176-4(5)) Chouette Publishing.

Mercier, Johanne & Brignaud, Pierre. Caillou on the Subway. rev. ed. 2006. (Out & about Ser.). (Illus.). 24p. (J). pap. 3.95 (*978-2-89450-584-7(1)) Chouette Publishing CAN. *Dist:* Independent Pubs. Group.

Mullican, Judy. Caillou Plays Dinosaur Hide-and-Seek. Storch, Ellen N., illus. 2006. (J). pap. (978-1-57332-376-5(4)) HighReach Learning, Inc.

Nadeau, Nicole. Caillou - I'm Not Hungry! Brignaud, Pierre, illus. rev. ed. 2005. (Hand in Hand Ser.).Tr. of Caillou - Un Festin Chez Grand-Maman. 24p. (J). (ps-1). pap. 5.95 (978-2-89450-512-0(4)) Chouette Publishing CAN. *Dist:* Independent Pubs. Group.

Nadeau, Nicole & Brignaud, Pierre. Caillou Wakes up at Night. rev. ed. 2008. (Hand in Hand Ser.). (Illus.). 24p. (J). bds. 5.95 (*978-2-89450-643-1(0)) Chouette Publishing CAN. *Dist:* Independent Pubs. Group.

Pleau-Murissi, Marilyn. Caillou the Phone Call. 2003. (ps-2). lib. bdg. 10.10 (978-0-613-85207-4(9)) Tandem Library Bks.

Rechkemmer, Jaime Marie. Caillou's Friends in the Garden. Storch, Ellen N., illus. 2006. (J). pap. (978-1-57332-373-4(X)) HighReach Learning, Inc.

Sanschagrin, Joceline. Caillou - Potty Time. Brignaud, Pierre, illus. rev. ed. 2005. (Hand in Hand Ser.).Tr. of Caillou - Le Pot. 24p. (J). (ps-1). pap. 5.95 (978-2-89450-367-6(9)) Chouette Publishing CAN. *Dist:* Independent Pubs. Group.

—Caillou' at Grandma & Grandpa's. Lapierre, Claude, illus. 2002. 23p. (J). pap. (978-2-89450-296-9(6)) Chouette Publishing.

Sanschagrin, Joceline & Brignaud, Pierre. Caillou: Baby Sister. rev. ed. 2008. (Hand in Hand Ser.). (Illus.). 24p. (J). bds. 5.95 (***978-2-89450-642-4(2)***) Chouette Publishing CAN. *Dist:* Independent Pubs. Group.

Savary, Fabien. Caillou It's Me! 2007. (Lift-the-Flap Book Ser.). 12p. (J). bds. 4.95 (***978-2-89450-619-6(8)***) Chouette Publishing CAN. *Dist:* Independent Pubs. Group.

—Caillou Peek-a-Boo! 2007. (Pull-tab Ser.). 12p. (J). bds. 4.95 (***978-2-89450-621-9(X)***) Chouette Publishing CAN. *Dist:* Independent Pubs. Group.

—Caillou Something Is Missing? 2007. (Pull-tab Ser.). 12p. (J). bds. 4.95 (***978-2-89450-622-6(8)***) Chouette Publishing CAN. *Dist:* Independent Pubs. Group.

—Caillou Where Am I? 2007. (Lift-the-Flap Book Ser.). 12p. (J). bds. 4.95 (***978-2-89450-620-2(1)***) Chouette Publishing CAN. *Dist:* Independent Pubs. Group.

CAKE

The Birthday Cake, 6 Pack. (Rigby Focus Ser.). 16p. (gr. k up). 28.00 (978-0-7578-5534-4(2)) Rigby Education.

The Birthday Cake: Individual Title Six-Packs. (Rigby Focus Ser.). 16p. (gr. k up). 26.00 (978-0-7578-5300-5(5)) Rigby Education.

Cohen, Elaine. Super-Duper Cupcakes: Kids' Creations from the Cupcake Caboose. 2006. (Illus.). 96p. (J). 9.95 (978-1-4027-2174-8(9)) Sterling Publishing Co., Inc.

Cole, Joanna. The Magic School Bus Gets Baked in a Cake: A Book about Kitchen Chemistry. 2002. (Magic School Bus Ser.). (Illus.). (J). 11.45 (978-0-7587-6701-1(3)) Book Wholesalers, Inc.

Crespo, Clare. Hey There, Cupcake! 35 Yummy Fun Cupcake Recipes for All Occasions. Staudenmaier, Eric, photos by. 2004. (Illus.). 80p. (J). 16.95 (978-0-9717935-6-9(5)) Melcher Media.

Hill, Mary. Let's Make a Cake. 2002. (gr. k-3). lib. bdg. 12.95 (978-0-613-58781-5(2)) Tandem Library Bks.

Patchett, Fiona. Children's Bk of Baking. 2007. 96p. (J). 17.99 (978-0-7945-1438-9(3) , Usborne) EDC Publishing.

Rau, Dana Meachen. Cake. 2008. (J). (***978-0-7614-2896-1(8)***) Cavendish, Marshall Bks., Ltd.

Sloan, Peter. Baking a Cake. 1999. (gr. k-3). lib. bdg. 11.80 (978-0-613-30254-8(0)) Tandem Library Bks.

Yeva Corporation Staff, ed. Kidskills: Cooking with Kids Series: Cake Mix Recipes. 2001. (J). spiral bd. 15.95 (978-1-930758-65-0(0) , Yeva Kids) Yeva Corp.

CALAMITIES

see Disasters

CALCULATING MACHINES

see Calculators

CALCULATORS

Here are entered works on present-day calculators as well as on calculators and mechanical computers of pre-1945 vintage. Works on modern electronic computers first developed after 1945 are entered under Computers.

see also Arithmetic; Computers

Advanced Calculator. (J). 2001. pap. 4.95 (978-1-56911-725-5(X)); 1999. pap. 4.95 (978-1-56911-808-5(6)) Learning Resources, Inc.

Bitter. Math Calc Explorer 10-Pk. 2004. (gr. 4-6). suppl. ed. 230.04 (978-0-201-23163-2(8)) Addison-Wesley Educational Pubs., Inc.

Johnson, Rebecca L. Crunching Numbers. 2004. (Math Behind the Science Ser.). (Illus.). 24p. (J). pap. (978-0-7922-4592-6(X)) National Geographic Society.

CALCULUS

Analysis III: Integralrechnung. (Duden Abiturhilfen Ser.). (GER.). 112p. (YA). (gr. 12-13). (978-3-411-70182-7(X)) Bibliographisches Institut & F. A. Brockhaus AG DEU. *Dist:* International Bk. Import Service, Inc.

Anton, Howard. Test Bank to Accompany Calculus Early Transcendentals Combined. 7th ed. 2002. 1009p. (YA). (978-0-471-43498-6(1)) Wiley, John & Sons, Inc.

—Test Bank to Accompany Calculus Late Transcendentals Combined. 7th ed. 2002. 1024p. (YA). (978-0-471-43497-9(3)) Wiley, John & Sons, Inc.

Armstrong, Stephen. Answer Key for Zooming-In Precalculus Explorations with Technology. McMullin, Lin, ed. 2000. 50p. (J). (gr. 9-12). pap. 8.95 (978-1-878621-58-0(0)) D&S Marketing Systems, Inc.

—Zooming in Precalculus Explorations with Technology. McMullin, Lin, ed. 2000. (Illus.). 230p. (J). (gr. 9-12). pap. 19.95 (978-1-878621-56-6(4)) D&S Marketing Systems, Inc.

Aufmann, Richard N., et al. Mathematical Excursions. 2003. 913p. (YA). 119.56 incl. cd-rom (978-0-618-38639-0(4) , 300615) Houghton Mifflin College Div.

Berresford. Applied Calculus: Smarthinking. 3rd ed. 2003. (YA). pap., pap. 135.56 (978-0-618-47664-0(4) , 387971) Houghton Mifflin College Div.

Blitzer, Robert F. Precalculus. 2003. (Homework Booklets Ser.). 72p. (YA). (gr. 8 up). pap. 2.99 (978-1-56822-418-3(4) , Instructional Fair) Schaffer, Frank Pubns.

Blitzer, Robert F. & Bentley, Wayne J. Precalculus. 1999. (100+ Seriestm Ser.). 128p. (YA). (gr. 9-12). pap. 12.99 (978-1-56822-488-6(5) , IF8768) School Specialty Publishing.

Burger. Thinkwell Calculus: Multimedia Package. 4th ed. 2004. 86.66 (978-0-03-036937-7(1)) Holt, Rinehart & Winston.

Calculus 1 with Precalculus. 2002. (YA). (gr. 6-12). (978-0-618-08768-6(0) , 3-31838) McDougal Littell Inc.

Calculus: an Applied Approach: Learning Tools. 6th ed. 2002. (YA). (gr. 6-12). stu. ed. 13.56 incl. cd-rom (978-0-618-21875-2(0) , 360006) Houghton Mifflin College Div.

Calculus from Graphical, Numerical, & Symbolic Points of View: Instructor's Annotated Edition. 2002. (gr. 6-12). (978-0-618-24860-5(9) , 3-90139) McDougal Littell Inc.

Calculus Syllabus & Tests. 1999. 10p. (J). ring bd., suppl. ed. 2.50 (978-1-57896-076-7(2) , 2553, Hewitt Homeschooling Resources) Hewitt Research Foundation, Inc.

Calculus with Analytic Geometry. 7th ed. 2001. (YA). (gr. 11-12). stu. ed. 3.96 incl. cd-rom (978-0-618-21333-7(3) , 332381) Houghton Mifflin College Div.

Calculus with Analytic Geometry. 7th ed. 2002. (gr. 11-12). (978-0-618-14928-5(7) , 3-32364); (978-0-618-14939-1(2) , 3-32375); tchr. ed. (978-0-618-14931-5(7) , 3-32367); tchr. ed. (978-0-618-14932-2(5) , 3-32368); tchr. ed. (978-0-618-14933-9(3) , 3-32369); tchr. ed. (978-0-618-14926-1(0) , 3-32362); instr.'s gde. ed. (978-0-618-14930-8(9) , 3-32366) McDougal Littell Inc.

Calculus Without Tears Vol. 2: Easy Lessons for Learning Calculus for Students from the 4th Grade up - Newton's Apple. 2005. spiral bd. 19.95 net. (978-0-9764138-1-3(7)) Berkeley Science Bks.

Cohen, Don. Calculus for Young People, 2 vols. 2006. (YA). cd-rom 64.95 (978-0-9779493-1-1(1)) Don Cohen-The Mathman.

Cohen, Donald. Calculus by & for Young People - Ages 7, Yes 7 & Up (CD-ROM) 2006. cd-rom 17.95 (978-0-9779493-0-4(3)) Don Cohen-The Mathman.

Flannery, William Davis. Calculus Without Tears Vol. 1: Easy Lessons for Learning Calculus for Students from the 4th Grade up - Constant Velocity Motion. 2004. spiral bd. 14.95 net. (978-0-9764138-0-6(9)) Berkeley Science Bks.

Foerster, Paul A. Calculus Explorations. 1998. 133p. (YA). (gr. 11 up). pap. 24.95 (978-1-55953-311-9(0) , 1559533110) Key Curriculum Pr.

Fogiel, M., ed. The High School Pre-Calculus Tutor'. 2006. (High School Tutors Ser.). (Illus.). 360p. (gr. 9-12). pap. 16.95 (978-0-87891-910-9(4)) Research & Education Assn.

Hostetler, Robert & Larson, Ron. College Algebra. 6th ed. 2003. 675p. (YA). (gr. 11-12). 128.76 incl. cd-rom (978-0-618-38649-9(1) , 332715) Houghton Mifflin College Div.

Hughes-Hallett, Deborah. Test Bank to Accompany Calculus: Single & Multivariable. 3rd ed. 2002. 1040p. (YA). (978-0-471-15024-4(X)) Wiley, John & Sons, Inc.

Larson. Calculus: An Applied Approach Plus Eduspace. 7th ed. 2005. (YA). pap. 125.16 (978-0-618-64497-1(0) , 396114) Houghton Mifflin College Div.

—Calculus: High School. 7th ed. 2001. (YA). (gr. 11-12). stu. ed. 165.96 (978-0-618-14918-6(X) , 332352) Houghton Mifflin College Div.

—Calculus 1 Plus Mathspace Cd Plus Study & Solutions Guide Volume 1 8th Edition. 8th ed. 2005. (YA). pap. 99.56 incl. cd-rom (978-0-618-67418-3(7) , 396560) Houghton Mifflin College Div.

—Calculus Applied Approach Plus Mathspace Cd 7th Edition Plus Eduspace. 7th ed. 2005. (YA). pap. 137.96 incl. cd-rom (978-0-618-69652-9(0) , 396961) Houghton Mifflin College Div.

—Calculus Brief: Applied Approach Plus Mathspace CD Plus Study & Solutions Guide. 7th ed. 2005. (YA). pap. 125.16 incl. cd-rom (978-0-618-66970-7(1) , 396483) Houghton Mifflin College Div.

—Calculus Early Transcendental Functions, Third Edition with Student CD-ROM & CD-ROM Three Point Zero. 3rd ed. 2002. (YA). 151.16 incl. cd-rom, cd-rom (978-0-618-30412-7(6) , 385491) Houghton Mifflin College Div.

—Calculus with Analytic Geometry. 7th ed. 2002. (gr. 11-12). pap., stu. ed. (978-0-618-23973-3(1) , 3-84365) McDougal Littell Inc.

—Calculus with Mathspace, Plus Eduspace 1, Vols. 1&2. 8th ed. 2005. (YA). pap., pap., stu. ed. 175.56 incl. cd-rom (978-0-618-63093-6(7) , 396024) Houghton Mifflin College Div.

—Student Solutions Guide: Used with ... Larson-Calculus: An Applied Approach. 6th ed. 2002. (YA). (gr. 6-12). stu. ed. 40.76 (978-0-618-21872-1(6) , 360003) Houghton Mifflin College Div.

Larson, Roland, et al. Calculus with Analytic Geometry. 6th alt. ed. 1998. 1123p. (YA). 165.96 (978-0-395-88902-2(2) , 331030) Houghton Mifflin College Div.

Larson, Ron & Edwards, Bruce H. Calculus: An Applied Approach. 6th ed. 2002. 715p. (YA). (gr. 6-12). 148.76 incl. cd-rom (978-0-618-22679-5(6) , 360009) Houghton Mifflin College Div.

Larson, Ron, et al. Calculus 1 with Precalculus: A One-Year Course. 2001. (Illus.). 911p. (YA). (gr. 6-12). stu. ed. 121.16 (978-0-618-08760-0(5) , 331830) Houghton Mifflin College Div.

—Calculus of a Single Variable with Learning. 7th ed. 2002. 713p. (YA). (gr. 11-12). 144.36 incl. cd-rom (978-0-618-23974-0(X) , 384366) Houghton Mifflin College Div.

—Interactive Calculus with Analytic Geometry Version 2.0: Calculus with Analytic Geometry. 6th alt. ed. 1998. (YA). (gr. 11-12). cd-rom 85.56 (978-0-395-91102-0(8) , 331065) Houghton Mifflin College Div.

Levy, Benjamin N. & Larson, Ron. Graphing Technology Guide for Calculus & Precalculus. 5th ed. 2000. (YA). (gr. 6-12). 22.36 (978-0-618-07287-3(X) , 330431) Houghton Mifflin College Div.

Maor, Eli. Facts on File Calculus Handbook. (Science Handbook Ser.). (Illus.). 176p. (gr. 9-12). pap. 17.95 (978-0-8160-6229-4(3)) Facts On File, Inc.

McRae, W. David. Calculus Student Activities Book. 2003. (Illus.). stu. ed., per., wbk. ed. (978-1-931680-26-4(4) , Expert Systems for Teachers) Teaching Point, Inc.

Ostebee. Calculus, Volume 1 Chapters 1 to 5, Second Edition & Student Solutions Manual, Volume 1, Second Edition. 2nd ed. 2002. (YA). pap., pap. 73.16 (978-0-618-33121-5(2) , 384875) Houghton Mifflin College Div.

—Single Variable: Calculus from Graphical, Numerical, & Symbolic Points of View. 2nd ed. 2001. (Illus.). 607p. (YA). (gr. 6-12). 140.76 (978-0-618-24788-2(2) , 390083) Houghton Mifflin College Div.

—Student Solutions Manual: Used with ... Ostebee-Calculus from Graphical, Numerical, & Symbolic Points of View. 2nd ed. 2002. (YA). (gr. 6-12). stu. ed. 34.76 (978-0-618-25412-5(9) , 390168); stu. ed. 34.76 (978-0-618-25413-2(7) , 390169) Houghton Mifflin College Div.

Ostebee, Arnold & Zorn, Paul. Navigating Calculus: Used with ... Ostebee-Calculus from Graphical, Numerical, & Symbolic Points of View. 2nd ed. 2001. (YA). cd-rom 37.16 (978-0-618-24976-3(1) , 390161) Houghton Mifflin College Div.

Salas. Test Bank to Accompany Calculus. 9th ed. 2002. 304p. (YA). (978-0-471-27523-7(9)) Wiley, John & Sons, Inc.

School Mathematics Project Staff. SMP 16-19 Pure 3: Vectors & Applications of Calculus. rev. ed. 2002. (School Mathematics Project 16-19 Ser.). (Illus.). 158p. pap. 19.80 (978-0-521-78799-4(8)) Cambridge Univ. Pr.

Single Var Calc Trans 5e Sg. 5th ed. 2003. (C). pap. 37.95 (978-0-534-39331-1(4)) Brooks/Cole.

Ssm Applied Calculus. 3rd ed. 2003. (C). pap. 26.95 (978-0-534-41960-8(7)) Brooks/Cole.

Ssm Multivariable Calc. 3rd ed. 2004. (C). pap. 34.95 (978-0-534-41005-6(7)) Brooks/Cole.

Stewart. Sg Multivariable Calc. 3rd ed. 2005. (C). pap. 26.95 (978-0-534-41006-3(5)) Brooks/Cole.

CALDECOTT MEDAL BOOKS

Bankston, John. Randolph J. Caldecott & the Story of the Caldecott Medal. 2003. (Great Achiever Awards Ser.). (Illus.). 48p. (J). (gr. 4-8). lib. bdg. 29.95 (978-1-58415-200-2(1)) Mitchell Lane Pubs., Inc.

Marcus, Leonard S. A Caldecott Celebration: Seven Artists & their Paths to the Caldecott Medal. 10th ed. 2007. (Illus.). 64p. (J). 19.95 (***978-0-8027-9703-2(2)***) Walker & Co.

—A Caldecott Celebration: Seven Artists & Their Paths to the Caldecott Medal. 10th ed. 2007. 56p. (J). 20.85 (***978-0-8027-9704-9(0)***) Walker & Co.

CALENDARS

see also Almanacs

Brimner, Larry Dane. The Official "M&M's" Book of the Millennium. 1999. (gr. k-3). lib. bdg. 15.25 (978-0-613-88704-5(2)) Tandem Library Bks.

—The Official M&M's' Brand History of the Calendar. Pellaton, Karen E., illus. 2004. 32p. (YA). 16.95 (978-1-57091-431-7(1)); pap. 6.95 (978-1-57091-432-4(X)) Charlesbridge Publishing, Inc.

—The Official M&M's' Brand History of the Calendar. 2002. (gr. 3-6). lib. bdg. 15.25 (978-0-613-90243-4(2)) Tandem Library Bks.

Brothers 2005: A Calendar of Light, Color & a Couple of Cats. 2004. (978-0-9746974-0-6(0)) Schroeder, Robert.

Brown, Angela McHaney. Months of the Year. 2005. (Talking about Time Ser.). (Illus.). 24p. (J). (978-1-4109-1642-6(1)); pap. (978-1-4109-1648-8(0)) Steck-Vaughn.

Burkett, Larry. All about Time: Discovering How the Calendar Affects You. Locke, Gary, illus. 2003. (All about Ser.). 32p. (J). pap., pap. 7.99 (978-0-7814-3788-2(1) , 0781437881) Cook, David C. Publishing Co.

—All about Time: Discovering How the Calendar Affects You. 2003. (gr. 3-6). lib. bdg. 16.45 (978-0-613-74880-3(8)) Tandem Library Bks.

Cooper, Emmett. The One Year Make-It-Stick Devotions. Hickerson, Joel, illus. 2007. 416p. (J). pap. 13.99 (***978-1-4143-1551-5(1)***) Tyndale Hse. Pubs.

Dennen, Sue. Make Your Own Calendar 2001. Dennen, Sue, illus. 2000. (Illus.). 24p. (J). (gr. 1-5). pap. 6.95 (978-0-316-19210-1(4)) Little Brown & Co.

Dusikova, Maja, illus. Up on Rooftop Advent. 2007. 0001p. pap. 6.95 (***978-0-7358-2137-8(2)***) North-South Bks., Inc.

Esparza, Thomas, Jr., prod. Esther's Playhouse, Disk E. 2004. (Illus.). (J). cd-rom (978-1-879817-46-3(2) , Children) Star Light Pr.

Garbo, Beth. Renoir to Matisse: A Calendar Book - 1999. 1998. (Illus.). 106p. spiral bd. 12.95 (978-1-892373-38-0(6) , 38-6) Especially Bks.

George, Lynn. Calendars of Native Americans: Timekeeping Methods of Ancient North America. 2004. (PowerMath Ser.). (Illus.). 32p. (J). lib. bdg. 22.50 (978-0-8239-8994-2(1) , PowerKids Pr.) Rosen Publishing Group, Inc., The.

Goodings, Christina. Around the Year: A Calendar & Counting Rhyme. Lewis, Jan, illus. 2001. 32p. (J). pap. 13.99 (978-0-7459-4451-7(5) , Lion) Lion Hudson plc GBR. *Dist:* Independent Pubs. Group.

Kompelien, Tracy. I Know the Days in Many Ways! (Illus.). 24p. (J). 2007. 19.93 (978-1-59928-531-3(2) , SandCastle); 2006. (978-1-59928-532-0(0)) ABDO Publishing Co.

Kummer, Patricia K. The Calendar. 2005. (Inventions That Shaped the World Ser.). (Illus.). 80p. (J). (gr. 5-8). pap. 9.95 (978-0-531-16720-5(8)); 30.50 (978-0-531-12340-9(5)) Scholastic Library Publishing. (Watts, Franklin).

Leffler, Silke. A Simply Wonderful Christmas: A Literary Advent Calendar. 2006. (Illus.). 144p. (J). 25.00 (978-0-7358-2100-2(3)) North-South Bks., Inc.

Maestro, Betsy. The Story of Clocks & Calendars. Maestro, Giulio, illus. 2004. 48p. (J). (gr. 2 up). pap. 8.99 (978-0-06-058945-5(0) , Harper Trophy) HarperCollins Pubs.

May, Darcy. Old-Time Christmas Village Sticker Advent Calendar. 2000. (Illus.). 4p. (J). (ps-5). 5.95 (978-0-486-41053-1(6)) Dover Pubns., Inc.

Murphy, Patricia J. A Day. (Calendar Ser.). 24p. (J). pap. 5.95 (978-0-7368-5074-2(0)) Capstone Pr., Inc.

—A Day. 2005. (Calendar Ser.). (Illus.). 24p. (J). 15.93 (978-0-7368-3626-5(8) , Pebble Bks.) Capstone Pr., Inc.

—Months. 2005. (Calendar Ser.). (Illus.). 24p. (J). 15.93 (978-0-7368-3628-9(4) , Pebble Bks.) Capstone Pr., Inc.

—A Week. 2005. (Calendar Ser.). (Illus.). 24p. (J). 15.93 (978-0-7368-3627-2(6) , Pebble Bks.) Capstone Pr., Inc.

—A Week. (Calendar Ser.). 24p. (J). pap. 5.95 (978-0-7368-5076-6(7)) Capstone Pr., Inc.

—A Year. (Calendar Ser.). 24p. (J). pap. 5.95 (978-0-7368-5077-3(5)) Capstone Pr., Inc.

—A Year. 2005. (Calendar Ser.). (Illus.). 24p. (J). 15.93 (978-0-7368-3629-6(2) , Pebble Bks.) Capstone Pr., Inc.

Nelson, Robin. A Day. 2005. (First Step Nonfiction Ser.). (Illus.). 24p. (gr. k-2). 17.27 (978-0-8225-0177-0(5)) Lerner Publishing Group.

—Months. 2005. (First Step Nonfiction Ser.). (Illus.). 24p. (gr. k-2). 17.27 (978-0-8225-0179-4(1)) Lerner Publishing Group.

—A Week. 2005. (First Step Nonfiction Ser.). (Illus.). 24p. (gr. k-2). 17.27 (978-0-8225-0178-7(3)) Lerner Publishing Group.

Noble, Marty. Santa's Sticker Advent Calendar. 2000. (Dover Little Activity Bks.). (Illus.). 4p. (J). (ps-5). 4.50 (978-0-486-41055-5(2)) Dover Pubns., Inc.

Randolph, Joanne. All about the Months. 2008. lib. bdg. (***978-1-4042-3769-8(0)*** , PowerKids Pr.) Rosen Publishing Group, Inc., The.

Smith, A. G. What Time Is It? (Illus.). 86p. (Orig.). (YA). (gr. 4-9). pap. 13.95 (978-0-7737-6219-0(1)) Stoddart Kids CAN. *Dist:* Fitzhenry & Whiteside, Ltd.

—What Time Is It? 2000. (Orig.). (gr. 3-6). lib. bdg. 23.40 (978-0-613-81886-5(5)) Tandem Library Bks.

Somervill, Barbara A. The History of the Calendar. 2006. (Timeline Library Ser.). (Illus.). 32p. (J). (gr. 2-6). 27.07 (978-1-59296-436-9(2)) Child's World, Inc.

Sper, Emily. The Kids' Fun Book of Jewish Time. Sper, Emily, illus. 2006. (HEB & ENG., Illus.). 24p. (J). 16.99 (978-1-58023-311-8(2) , 1260461) Jewish Lights Publishing.

Steck-Vaughn Staff. Cool Calendar Skills. 2003. (Illus.). (J). (gr. 2). pap. (978-0-7398-7100-3(5)) Steck-Vaughn.

Studio Mouse. Disney's Winnie the Pooh: Time to Learn: Learn & Carry 4 Books with CD. rev. ed. 2007. 4x20p. 14.99 (***978-1-59069-564-7(X)***) Studio Mouse LLC.

Sweeney, Jacqueline. Prompt a Day! 360 Thought-Provoking Writing Prompts Keyed to Every Day of the School Year. 1998. (Illus.). 112p. (J). 14.95 (978-0-590-18738-1(4)) Scholastic, Inc.

Updike, John. A Child's Calendar. Hyman, Trina Schart, illus. 1999. (Caldecott Honor Book Ser.). 32p. (J). (gr. k-3). 6.95 (978-0-8234-1766-7(2)) Holiday Hse., Inc.

CALHOUN, JOHN C. (JOHN CALDWELL), 1782-1850

Silate, Jennifer. The Calhoun-Randolph Debate on the Eve of the War of 1812: A Primary Source Investigation. 2004. (Great Historic Debates & Speeches Ser.). (Illus.). 64p. (YA). lib. bdg. 29.25 (978-1-4042-0150-7(5)) Rosen Publishing Group, Inc., The.

CALIFORNIA

Abbink, Emily. Missions of the Monterey Bay Area: San Carlos Borromeo de Carmelo, San Juan Bautista, Santa Cruz. 1999. (California Missions Ser.). (Illus.). 80p. (gr. 4-7). pap., lib. bdg. 23.93 (978-0-8225-9835-0(3)) Lerner Publishing Group.

Ansary, Mir Tamim. All Around California: Regions & Resources. 2002. (Heinemann State Studies). (Illus.). 48p. (J). pap. 8.50 (978-1-4034-0556-2(5)); (gr. 3-5). lib. bdg. (978-1-4034-0339-1(2)) Heinemann Library.

Bogue, Gary. Raccoon Next Door: And Other Creatures of the Urban Wilderness. Todd, Chuck, illus. 2003. 196p. pap. 16.95 (978-1-890771-71-3(6)) Heyday Bks.

Brant, Cherie. Legends of Ventura County. 2003. per. 9.99 (978-0-9722936-4-8(7) , Legends1) Del Sol Pubns.

Brown, Vinson. The Californian Wildlife Region. 3rd rev. ed. 2003. (Illus.). 302p. (J). pap. 14.95 (978-0-87961-201-6(0)) Naturegraph Pubs., Inc.

Bruun, Erik & Peterson, Rick. California. 2000. (Illus.). 48p. (J). (gr. 3-7). 9.95 (978-1-57912-100-6(4) , 81100) Black Dog & Leventhal Pubs., Inc.

Burgan, Michael. California. 2002. (It's My State! Ser.). (Illus.). 73p. (J). 27.07 (978-0-7614-1420-9(7) , Benchmark Bks.) Cavendish, Marshall Corp.

California. 2003. (World Almanac Biblioteca de los Estados). (SPA., Illus.). 48p. (J). (gr. 5 up). pap. 11.95 (978-0-8368-5549-4(3) , World Almanac Library) Stevens, Gareth Inc.

California: Grades 4-9. (Teaching with Primary Sources Ser.). (J). tchr. ed., ring bd. 32.95 (978-0-382-40871-7(3)) Cobblestone Publishing Co.

Capstone Press Staff, contrib. by. California. rev. ed. 2002. (One Nation Ser.). (Illus.). 48p. (J). (gr. 3-4). lib. bdg. 22.60 (978-0-7368-1229-0(6) , Bridgestone Bks.) Capstone Pr., Inc.

Ching, Jacqueline. Mission San Rafael Arcangel. 2000. (Missions of California Ser.). (Illus.). 64p. (J). (gr. 4). lib. bdg. 25.50 (978-0-8239-5506-0(0) , PowerKids Pr.) Rosen Publishing Group, Inc., The.

Cooper, Terry, ed. California Missions: Scholastic Technology Activity Folder. 2001. (Instant Internet Activities Folder Ser.). 6p. 3.95 (978-0-439-30957-8(3)) Scholastic, Inc.

Domeniconi, David. G Is for Golden: A California Alphabet. Carroll, Pam, illus. 2002. 40p. (J). (ps-5). 17.95 (978-1-58536-045-1(7)) Sleeping Bear Pr.

C
D

Edgar, Kathleen J. & Edgar, Susan E. Mission San Luis Obispo de Tolosa. 2000. (Missions of California Ser.). (Illus.). 64p. (J). (gr. 4). lib. bdg. 25.50 (978-0-8239-5491-9(9) , PowerKids Pr.) Rosen Publishing Group, Inc., The.

Escott, John. California. 2000. (Oxford Bookworms Factfiles Ser.). (Illus.). 24p. 7.50 (978-0-19-423205-0(0)) Oxford Univ. Pr., Inc.

Fandel, Jennifer. Golden Gate Bridge. 2006. (Modern Wonders of the World Ser.). (Illus.). 32p. (J). 18.95 (***978-1-58341-437-8(1)*** , 1262897, Creative Education) Creative Co., The.

Feinstein, Stephen. Uniquely California. (Heinemann State Studies). (Illus.). 48p. (J). 2003. lib. bdg. (978-1-4034-0344-5(9)); 2002. pap. 8.50 (978-1-4034-0561-6(1)) Heinemann Library.

Furstinger, Nancy. Los Angeles. 2005. (Cities Ser.). (Illus.). 32p. (J). (gr. k-6). lib. bdg. 22.78 (978-1-59197-861-9(0)) ABDO Publishing Co.

Gamble, Adam. Good Night San Diego. Kelly, Cooper, illus. 2006. (Good Night Our World Ser.). 20p. (J). bds. 9.95 (978-0-9777979-6-7(1)) Our World of Books.

Greene, Carol. "C" Is for California. Gorenkamp, Michelle, illus. 2000. (Alpha Flight Bks.). 60p. (J). (ps-3). 17.95 (978-1-892920-27-0(1)) GHB Publishers, LLC.

Guia del Maestro: Gente y Lugares. 2003. (MacMillan/McGraw-Hill. Estudios Sociales Ser.). (ENG & SPA.). (gr. 1 up). (978-0-02-149965-6(9)) Macmillan/McGraw-Hill Schl. Div.

Healton, Sarah. California - So Wondrous to Behold! A History of California in Choral Verse. Newell, Robert, illus. rev. ed. 1998. 40p. (J). (gr. 2-7). pap. 5.00 (978-0-935661-27-9(1)) Riverside Museum Pr.

Heinemann Library Staff, ed. California, 6 bks., Set. 2003. (Heinemann State Studies). (J). (gr. 3-5). lib. bdg. 162.42 (978-1-58810-613-1(6)) Heinemann Library.

Heinrichs, Ann. California. 2002. (This Land Is Your Land Ser.). (Illus.). 48p. (J). (gr. 3 up). lib. bdg. 22.60 (978-0-7565-0308-6(6)) Compass Point Bks.

Herrera, Juan Felipe. Calling the Doves. 2001. Tr. of El Canto De Las Palomos. (SPA.). (gr. 3-6). lib. bdg. 16.40 (978-0-613-34098-4(1)) Tandem Library Bks.

Hines Weaver, Dorothy. California A to Z. Wacker, Kay, illus. 1999. 32p. (J). (ps-1). 6.95 (978-0-87358-682-5(4) , Rising Moon Bks. for Young Readers) Northland Publishing.

—California A to Z. 1999. (J). 13.75 (978-0-606-17023-9(5)) Tandem Library Bks.

Horner, Edith R., ed. California Cities, Towns & Counties 1999. 13th ed. 1999. 608p. pap. 81.00 (978-0-931845-62-8(9)) Morris Publishing.

Ingram, Scott. California. Porras, Carlos & D'Andrea, Patricia, trs. 2003. (World Almanac Biblioteca de los Estados). (SPA., Illus.). 48p. (J). (gr. 5 up). lib. bdg. 30.00 (978-0-8368-5542-5(6) , World Almanac Library) Stevens, Gareth Inc.

—California: The Golden State. 2002. (World Almanac Library of the States). (Illus.). 48p. (J). (gr. 5 up). pap. 14.95 (978-0-8368-5282-0(6)); lib. bdg. 30.00 (978-0-8368-5113-7(7)) Stevens, Gareth Inc. (World Almanac Library).

—California: The Golden State. 2002. (Illus.). 48p. (J). (gr. 4-7). lib. bdg. 24.15 (978-0-613-52334-9(2)) Tandem Library Bks.

Johnson, Michael & Yenne, Bill. Native Tribes of California & the Southwest. 2004. (Native Tribes of North America Ser.). (Illus.). 64p. (J). (gr. 5 up). lib. bdg. 32.67 (978-0-8368-5609-5(0) , World Almanac Library) Stevens, Gareth Inc.

Kavanagh, James. California Trees & Wildflowers: An Introduction to Familiar Species. Leung, Raymond, illus. 2001. (Pocket Naturalist Ser.). 12p. pap. 5.95 (978-1-58355-071-7(2)) Waterford Pr., Ltd.

Kennedy, Teresa. California. 80p. (J). 2008. (From Sea to Shining Sea, Second Ser.). pap. 7.95 (***978-0-531-18801-9(9));*** 2001. (From Sea to Shining Sea Ser.: 2). (Illus.). (gr. 3-5). 30.50 (978-0-516-22309-4(7)) Scholastic Library Publishing. (Children's Pr.).

Koontx, Jayne. California Central Coast Coloring Book. 2005. (J). 8.95 (978-1-930401-35-8(3)) Central Coast Pr.

Labastida, Roberta. My Ancestor's Village. 2003. (Illus.). 32p. (J). 9.95 (978-0-932653-61-1(8)) Sunbelt Pubns., Inc.

Lee, Sally. Arnold Schwarzenegger: From Superstar to Governor. 2006. (People to Know Today Ser.). (Illus.). 128p. (J). lib. bdg. 31.93 (978-0-7660-2625-4(6)) Enslow Pubs., Inc.

Mannis, Celeste Davidson. Snapshots: The Wonders of Monterey Bay. 2006. (Illus.). 32p. (J). (gr. 1). 16.99 (978-0-670-06062-7(3) , Viking Adult) Penguin Group (USA) Inc.

Marsh, Carole. The Big California Reproducible Activity Book. 2004. (Carole Marsh California Bks.). (Illus.). 96p. (J). (gr. 2-6). pap. 9.95 (978-0-7933-9457-9(0)) Gallopade International.

—California Classic Christmas Trivia. 2002. (Carole Marsh California Bks.). (Illus.). 32p. pap. 6.95 (978-0-635-01377-4(0) , 13770); lib. bdg. 21.95 (978-0-635-01378-1(9) , 13789) Gallopade International. (Marsh, Carole Bks.).

—California Current Events Projects: 30 Cool, Activities, Crafts, Experiments & More for Kids to Do to Learn about Your State! 2003. (California Experience Ser.). 32p. (gr. k-8). pap. 5.95 (978-0-635-02024-6(6) , Marsh, Carole Bks.) Gallopade International.

—The California Experience Pocket Guide. 2000. (Carole Marsh California Bks.). (Illus.). 96p. (J). (gr. 3-8). pap. 6.95 (978-0-7933-9447-0(3)) Gallopade International.

—California Geography Projects: 30 Cool, Activities, Crafts, Experiments & More for Kids to Do to Learn about Your State! 2003. (California Experience Ser.). 32p. (gr. k-5). pap. 5.95 (978-0-635-01824-3(1) , Marsh, Carole Bks.) Gallopade International.

—California Government Projects: 30 Cool, Activities, Crafts, Experiments & More for Kids to Do to Learn about Your State! 2003. (California Experience Ser.). 32p. (gr. k-5). pap. 5.95 (978-0-635-01924-0(8) , Marsh, Carole Bks.) Gallopade International.

—California Jeopardy! Answers & Questions about Our State! 2000. (Carole Marsh California Bks.). (Illus.). 32p. (J). (gr. 3-8). pap. 7.95 (978-0-7933-9504-0(6)) Gallopade International.

—California "Jography" A Fun Run Thru Our State! 2000. (Carole Marsh California Bks.). (Illus.). 32p. (J). (gr. 3-8). pap. 7.95 (978-0-7933-9505-7(4)) Gallopade International.

—California Millionaire: Game Book. 2001. (Carole Marsh California Bks.). (Illus.). 32p. (J). (gr. 3-8). pap., act. bk. ed. 9.95 (978-0-635-00026-2(1)) Gallopade International.

—California People Projects: 30 Cool, Activities, Crafts, Experiments & More for Kids to Do to Learn about Your State! 2003. (California Experience Ser.). 32p. (gr. k-5). pap. 5.95 (978-0-635-01974-5(4) , Marsh, Carole Bks.) Gallopade International.

—California Survivor: Game Book. 2001. (Carole Marsh California Bks.). (Illus.). 32p. (J). (gr. 3-8). pap., act. bk. ed. 9.95 (978-0-635-00526-7(3)) Gallopade International.

—California Symbols & Facts Projects: 30 Cool, Activities, Crafts, Experiments & More for Kids to Do to Learn about Your State! 2003. (California Experience Ser.). 32p. (gr. k-5). pap. 5.95 (978-0-635-01873-1(X) , Marsh, Carole Bks.) Gallopade International.

—The Cool California Coloring Book. 2000. (Carole Marsh California Bks.). (Illus.). 32p. (J). (gr. k-2). pap. 3.95 (978-0-7933-9467-8(8)) Gallopade International.

—My First Book about California. 2000. (Carole Marsh California Bks.). (Illus.). 32p. (J). (gr. k-4). pap. 7.95 (978-0-7933-9503-3(8)) Gallopade International.

—My First Pocket Guide California. 2000. (California Experience! Ser.). (Illus.). 96p. (J). (gr. 3-8). 12.95 (978-0-635-01295-1(2) , 12952) Gallopade International.

—The Survivor: A Class Challenge. 2001. (Carole Marsh California Bks.). lib. bdg. 29.95 (978-0-635-00651-6(0)) Gallopade International.

McAuliffe, Emily. California: Facts & Symbols. 1998. (States & Their Symbols Ser.). 24p. (J). lib. bdg. 14.00 (978-0-531-11548-0(8) , Watts, Franklin) Scholastic Library Publishing.

—California Facts & Symbols. rev. ed. 2003. (States & Their Symbols Ser.). 24p. (J). lib. bdg. 19.93 (978-0-7368-2235-0(6)) Capstone Pr., Inc.

McNeil, Niki, et al. HOCPP 1084 California. 2006. spiral bd. 24.00 (***978-1-60308-084-2(8))*** In the Hands of a Child.

—HOCPP 1090 Native Americans of California. 2006. spiral bd. 19.50 (***978-1-60308-090-3(2))*** In the Hands of a Child.

—HOCPP 1098 Disneyland. 2006. spiral bd. 16.00 (***978-1-60308-098-9(8))*** In the Hands of a Child.

Migdale, Lawrence, photos by. A Child's California. 2000. (Illus.). 32p. (YA). (gr. 2-4). 15.95 (978-1-55868-520-8(0) , West Winds Pr.) Graphic Arts Ctr. Publishing Co.

Motoyoshi, Michelle. Filipinos in California. 1999. (California Cultures Ser.). (Illus.). 64p. (J). (gr. 4-8). pap. 14.95 (978-1-884925-92-4(8)) Toucan Valley Pubns., Inc.

—Mexicans in California. 1999. (California Cultures Ser.). (Illus.). 64p. (J). (gr. 4-8). pap. 14.95 (978-1-884925-91-7(X)) Toucan Valley Pubns., Inc.

Nugent, Wendy W. Fantastic Fresno Fun Book: An Educational Activity Book for Kids. Markus, Elisabeth, illus. 1998. 32p. (J). (ps-6). 6.95 (978-0-9666581-0-1(8)) Clover Pubns.

Obregon, Jose M. California. 2005. (Bilingual Library of the United States of America: Set 1). (ENG & SPA., Illus.). 32p. (J). (ps-k). lib. bdg. 22.50 (978-1-4042-3069-9(6) , Buenas Letra) Rosen Publishing Group, Inc., The.

Obregon, José María. California. 2006. (Bilingual Library of the United States of America). (SPA.). (J). lib. bdg. (978-1-4042-3137-5(4) , PowerKids Pr.) Rosen Publishing Group, Inc., The.

Oliver, Rice D. Student Atlas of California. 5th rev. ed. 1999. (Illus.). 66p. (J). (gr. 4-12). pap. 13.00 (978-0-936778-08-2(3)) California Weekly Explorer, Inc.

Orr, Tamra. California. 2007. (America the Beautiful, Third Ser.). (Illus.). 144p. (YA). (gr. 5-8). lib. bdg. 38.00 (***978-0-531-18557-5(5)*** , Children's Pr.) Scholastic Library Publishing.

—California. 2005. (Portraits of the States Ser.). (Illus.). 32p. (J). pap. (978-0-8368-4640-9(0)) Stevens, Gareth Inc.

Orr, Tamra B. California. 2005. (Portraits of the States Ser.). (Illus.). 32p. (J). (ps). lib. bdg. 23.33 (978-0-8368-4621-8(4)) Stevens, Gareth Inc.

Parker, Adam D. People of the California Gold Rush. Tamminga, Jean, illus. 1999. (California Biography Ser.). 64p. (J). (gr. 4-8). pap. 14.95 (978-1-884925-82-5(0)) Toucan Valley Pubns., Inc.

Parker, Janice. A Guide to California. 2000. (American States Ser.). (Illus.). 32p. (J). (gr. 3-7). lib. bdg. 22.60 (978-1-930954-45-8(X)) Weigl Pubs., Inc.

Pascoe, Elaine & Corwin, Jeff. Into Wild California. 2003. (Animal Planet Ser.). (Illus.). 48p. (J). 11.20 (978-1-4103-0178-9(8) , Blackbirch Pr., Inc.) Thomson Gale.

Pearce, Claudia & Worley, Karen E. San Diego Zoo. Bohn, Ken & Garrison, Ron, illus. Bohn, Ken & Garrison, Ron, photos by. 2003. (Great Zoos of the United States Ser.). 24p. (J). lib. bdg. 18.75 (978-0-8239-6321-8(7) , PowerKids Pr.) Rosen Publishing Group, Inc., The.

Pelta, Kathy. California. 2nd rev. exp. ed. (Hello U. S. A. Ser.). (Illus.). 84p. (J). (gr. 3-6). 2003. pap. 6.95 (978-0-8225-4146-2(7)); 2002. 25.26 (978-0-8225-4062-5(2)) Lerner Publishing Group.

Peterson, Sheryl. California. 2008. (J). (***978-1-58341-630-3(7)*** , Creative Education) Creative Co., The.

Pulte, Therese Marie. Laguna Beach: A Visual Souvenir. 2004. (Illus.). 80p. (YA). lib. bdg. (978-0-9746557-0-3(8) , Destination Pubs.) Pulte, Therese Marie.

Quasha, Jennifer. California's Sights & Symbols. 2004. 48p. pap. 8.95 (978-1-4042-8500-2(8)) Rosen Publishing Group, Inc., The.

—How to Draw California's Sights & Symbols. 2002. (Kid's Guide to Drawing America Ser.). (Illus.). 32p. (J). (gr. 3-5). lib. bdg. 25.25 (978-0-8239-6059-0(5) , PowerKids Pr.) Rosen Publishing Group, Inc., The.

Raabe, Emily. The Gold Rush: California or Bust! Individual Title Six-Packs. (On Deck Ser.: Vol. 2). 24p. (gr. 4-5). 35.00 (978-0-7578-5807-9(4)) Rigby Education.

Sacramento Sold C 2005. 2004. 420p. (YA). pap. 17.00 (978-1-58553-963-5(5) , 05GC0019) Entertainment Publications, Inc.

Saeks, Diane Dorrans. California Country Style. Livingston, David Duncan, photos by. 2006. (Illus.). 216p. 40.00 (978-0-8118-5181-7(8)) Chronicle Bks. LLC.

San Diego Gold C 2005. 2004. 388p. (YA). pap. 15.00 (978-1-58553-964-2(3) , 05GC0007) Entertainment Publications, Inc.

Savage, Jeff. California: A MyReportLinks. Com Book. 2003. (States Ser.). (Illus.). 48p. (J). (gr. 4-10). lib. bdg. 25.26 (978-0-7660-5113-3(7) , MyReportLinks.com Bks.) Enslow Pubs., Inc.

Schanzer, Rosalyn. Gold Fever! Tales from the California Gold Rush. 1999. (Illus.). 48p. (J). (gr. 1-4). 17.95 (978-0-7922-7303-5(6) , National Geographic Children's Bks.) National Geographic Society.

Schuh, Mari C. In My State. 2006. (J). (978-0-7368-4240-2(3)) Capstone Pr., Inc.

Schwartz, Linda. California Geodoodles, Grades 4-6: Learning about California Through Step-by-Step Drawings. Armstrong, Beverly, illus. 2000. 64p. (J). pap., tchr. ed. 9.99 (978-0-88160-355-2(4) , LW-394, Learning Works, The) Creative Teaching Pr., Inc.

Sosca. California. 2000. (Switched on Schoolhouse Ser.). (Illus.). (YA). (gr. 7-12). pap. 24.95 incl. cd-rom (978-0-7403-0257-2(4) , SOSCA) Alpha Omega Pubns., Inc.

Steele, Christy. California & the Southwest Join the United States. 2005. (Illus.). 48p. (J). lib. bdg. 30.00 (978-0-8368-5786-3(0) , World Almanac Library) Stevens, Gareth Inc.

Sullivan, Jenna M. & Sullivan, Laura C. Kid's Guide to the National Parks of California & Oregon: Written by Kids for Kids. Sullivan, Jenna M. & Sullivan, Laura C., photos by. Sullivan, P. Deborah, photos by. 2001. (Illus.). 116p. (J). (gr. 6-12). pap. 10.95 (978-1-880062-23-4(2)) E&S Geographic & Information Services.

Tamminga, Jean, illus. California Explorers Fact Cards. 1999. 68p. (J). (gr. 4-8). ring bd. 36.00 (978-1-884925-74-0(X)) Toucan Valley Pubns., Inc.

Turner, Rich, photos by. Delta Skies Fine Art Folio, 2003. (Illus.). (978-0-9762410-4-1(8)) Turner, Rich Photographs.

Weintraub, Aileen. Point Pinos Light: The West Coast's Oldest Continuously Active Lighthouse. 2003. (Great Lighthouses of North America Ser.). (Illus.). 24p. (J). pap. 18.75 (978-0-8239-6173-3(7) , PowerKids Pr.) Rosen Publishing Group, Inc., The.

Zelver, Patricia. Wonderful Towers of Watts. Lessac, Frane, illus. 2005. 32p. (J). pap. 9.95 (978-1-59078-255-2(0)) Boyds Mills Pr.

CALIFORNIA—BIOGRAPHY

Ansary, Mir Tamim. People of California. 2003. (Heinemann State Studies). (Illus.). 48p. (J). (gr. 3-5). lib. bdg. (978-1-4034-0342-1(2)) Heinemann Library.

Dunn, Joeming W. California Gold Rush. Dunn, Ben, illus. 2007. (Graphic History Ser.). 32p. (J). (gr. 3-6). lib. bdg. 27.07 (***978-1-60270-076-5(1)*** , Graphic Planet) Magic Wagon.

Goldsmith, Connie. Lost in Death Valley: The True Story of Four Families in California's Gold Rush. 2001. (Single Titles Ser.: up). (Illus.). 144p. (J). (gr. 7-12). lib. bdg. 24.90 (978-0-7613-1915-3(8) , Millbrook Pr.) Lerner Publishing Group.

Greenlee, Carolyn Wing. Son of South Mountain & Dust. Wing, Thomas W. & Chin, Duncan, illus. 2001. vii, 149p. (J). (978-1-887400-30-5(3)) Earthen Vessel Publishing.

Hill, Julia Butterfly. Legacy of Luna: The Story of A Tree, A Woman & the Struggle to Save the Redwoo. 2001. (gr. 7-12). lib. bdg. 23.45 (978-0-613-50118-7(5)) Tandem Library Bks.

Krakow, Kari. The Harvey Milk Story. Gardner, David, illus. 2002. 32p. (J). 17.95 (978-0-9674468-3-7(X)) Two Lives Publishing.

Little, Jane Braxton. Plumas Sketches. Posner, Sally, illus. 3rd exp. ed. 2002. per. 19.95 net. (978-0-9611886-2-7(6)) Wolf Creek Pr.

Lynetter, Rachel. Julia Butterfly Hill. 2007. (Young Heros Ser.). 64p. (J). (gr. 4-8). 27.45 (***978-0-7377-3628-1(3)*** , Kidhaven) Thomson Gale.

Mahaney, Ian F. Danny Harf: Wakeboarding Champion. 2005. (Extreme Sports Biographies Ser.). (Illus.). 24p. (J). 19.95 (978-1-4042-2743-9(1) , PowerKids Pr.) Rosen Publishing Group, Inc., The.

Marsh, Carole. The California Experience Library State Resource Set. 2001. (California Experience! Ser.). (Illus.). (J). lib. bdg. 100.20 incl. cd-rom (978-0-635-00457-4(7)) Gallopade International.

Murphy, Claire Rudolf. Children of Alcatraz: Growing up on the Rock. 2006. (Illus.). 64p. (J). 18.85 (978-0-8027-9578-6(1)); 17.95 (978-0-8027-9577-9(3)) Walker & Co.

Olson, Nathan. Levi Strauss & Blue Jeans. 2007. (Graphic Library). (Illus.). 32p. (J). (***978-0-7368-9646-7(5))*** Capstone Pr., Inc.

Perissinotto, Giorgio Sabino Antonio, ed. & tr. from SPA. The California Recollections of Angustias de la Guerra Ord: (Occurrences in Hispanic California) Perissinotto, Giorgio Sabino Antonio, tr. 2004. (ENG & SPA.). xxi, 172p. (978-0-88382-157-2(5)) Academy of American Franciscan History.

Run of the Mill: A True Life, Napa Valley Adventure. 2004. (YA). lib. bdg. (978-0-9760276-0-7(7)) Pastime Pubns.

St. Antoine, Sara, ed. The California Coast. 2005. (Stories from Where We Live Ser.). (Illus.). 248p. (J). pap. 10.95 (978-1-57131-653-0(1)) Milkweed Editions.

Tracy, Kathleen. Mariano Guadalupe Vallejo. 2002. (Latinos in American History). (Illus.). 56p. (gr. 4-8). lib. bdg. 29.95 (978-1-58415-152-4(8)) Mitchell Lane Pubs., Inc.

Weber, Terri. Oscar de la Hoya. 2004. (J). pap. (978-1-932724-31-8(1)); lib. bdg. (978-1-932724-30-1(3)) Panda Publishing, L.L.C. (Bios for Kids).

Willis, Linda. Between the Floods: Happy Camp, CA from 1956-1965. 2002. (Illus.). 281p. 14.95 net. (978-0-615-12228-1(0) , 1) Willis' Wiki-up.

Wing, Thomas W. & Greenlee, Carolyn Wing. Son of South Mountain & Dust. BlueWolf, James Don, ed. Chin, Duncan, illus. ltd. ed. 1999. 88p. (J). spiral bd. 19.95 (978-1-887400-27-5(3) , EVB-1020A) Earthen Vessel Production, Inc.

Yen Mah, Adeline. Chinese Cinderella: True Story of an Unwanted Daughter. 2001. (Illus.). 224p. (YA). (gr. 7 up). mass mkt. 6.50 (978-0-440-22865-3(4) , Laurel Leaf) Random Hse. Children's Bks.

CALIFORNIA—FICTION

Ada, Alma Flor. El Vuelo de los Colibries. Jacobson, Judith, illus. 32p. (J). (gr. 3-6). pap. 9.95 (978-1-56492-211-3(1)) Laredo Publishing Co., Inc.

Alcorn, Steve. A Matter of Justice. 2003. (J). (978-1-59426-002-5(8)) Mundania Pr.

Alef, Daniel. Centennial Stories: A Living History of San Francisco. 2nd ed. 2000. (Illus.). 227p. (J). pap. 15.95 (978-0-9700174-2-0(1)) Maxit Publishing, Inc.

Alger, Horatio. Joe's Luck: Or, Always Wide Awake. 2007. 172p. pap. 11.99 (***978-1-4264-6426-3(6));*** 2006. 176p. pap. 13.99 (978-1-4264-0883-0(8)); 2007. 186p. pap. 14.99 (***978-1-4264-6500-0(9));*** 2006. 170p. pap. 16.99 (978-1-4264-0864-9(1)) BiblioBazaar.

—Joe's Luck; Or, Always Wide Awake. 2006. pap. (***978-1-4065-0713-3(X))*** Dodo Pr.

Alger, Horatio. Tom Temple's Career. reprint ed. pap. 79.00 (978-1-4047-3611-5(5)) Classic Textbooks.

—Tom Temple's Career. l.t. ed. 2002. (Illus.). pap. 19.95 (978-1-4115-0422-6(4)); (J). pap. 17.95 (978-1-4115-0057-0(1)) Polyglot Pr., Inc.

Allende, Isabel & Vega, Diego. Young Zorro: The Iron Brand. 2007. 240p. (J). pap. 6.99 (978-0-06-083947-5(3) , Rayo) HarperCollins Pubs.

Alphin, Elaine Marie. Picture Perfect. 2003. (Illus.). 252p. (J). (gr. 7 up). 15.95 (978-0-8225-0535-8(5)) Lerner Publishing Group.

Altman, Linda Jacobs. The Legend of Freedom Hill. Van Wright, Cornelius, illus. 2003. 32p. (J). (978-1-58430-169-1(4)) Lee & Low Bks., Inc.

—The Legend of Freedom Hill. Van Wright, Cornelius & Hu, Ying-Hwa, illus. 2000. 32p. (J). (ps up). 15.95 (978-1-58430-003-8(5)) Lee & Low Bks., Inc.

—The Legend of Freedom Hill. Van Wright, Cornelius et al, illus. 2004. 32p. (J). (ps-k). lib. bdg. 13.75 (978-0-606-30127-5(5)) Tandem Library Bks.

—The Legend of Freedom Hill. 2003. (gr. k-3). lib. bdg. 15.25 (978-0-613-85872-4(7)) Tandem Library Bks.

Anderson, Gary H. Gameplayer: The Genesis Portal. 2006. (J). pap. (***978-0-9778205-5-9(6))*** Helm Publishing.

Anderson, Jean & Lininger, Linda. Calistoga Candlestick Caper. 2000. 124p. (J). (gr. 4 up). pap. 14.95 (978-0-9678605-9-6(8)) InfoHi Publishing.

Anderson, Launi K. Jillian's Discovery. 1999. (Choose the Right Ser.: Bk. 3). 60p. (J). pap. (978-1-57008-673-1(7)) Scribbulations LLC.

Appleton, Victor. The Moving Picture Boys on the Coast or Showing up the Perils of the Deep. 2004. reprint ed. pap. 24.95 (978-1-4179-1612-2(5)) Kessinger Publishing, LLC.

Axelrod, Amy. The News Hounds Catch a Wave: A Geography Adventure. Bowers, Tim, illus. 2001. (J). 13.00 (978-0-689-82410-4(6) , Simon & Schuster Children's Publishing) Simon & Schuster Children's Publishing.

Balmes, Kathy. Thunder on the Sierra. Catapano, Vicki, illus. 2001. (Adventures in America Ser.). 96p. (J). (gr. 3-7). lib. bdg. 14.95 (978-1-893110-10-6(9)) Silver Moon Pr.

Barnes, Steven. Iron Shadows. 2000. (gr. 7-12). lib. bdg. 15.30 (978-0-613-27904-8(2)) Tandem Library Bks.

Barnett, Gary W. Princess of the Lights: Fantasy Adventure. 2007. 324p. 29.95 (***978-0-595-68957-6(4));*** per. 19.95 (***978-0-595-44705-3(8))*** iUniverse, Inc.

Baum, L. Frank. Dorothy & the Wizard in Oz. 2006. pap. 26.99 (***978-1-4219-7695-2(1))*** IndyPublish.com.

Beatty, P. Lupita Manana, 6 vols., Set. 3rd ed. 2000. (J). pap. 29.70 (978-0-13-772484-0(5)) Prentice Hall (Schl. Div.).

Beckler, Bruce. The Secrets of the Green Mansion. l.t. ed. 2004. (Illus.). 240p. (J). per. 13.99 (978-0-9745210-1-5(9)) Myers Publishing Co.

Benson, Linda. Finding Chance. Lane, Nancy, illus. 2006. 112p. (J). (978-1-59336-696-4(5)) Mondo Publishing.

Birney, Betty G. The Princess & the Peabodys. 2007. 256p. (J). lib. bdg. 16.89 (***978-0-06-084721-0(2));*** (gr. 5 up). 15.99 (***978-0-06-084720-3(4))*** HarperCollins Pubs.

Block, Francesca Lia. I Was a Teenage Fairy. 192p. (J). (gr. 7 up). 1998. 14.89 (978-0-06-027748-2(3)); 2000. reprint ed. pap. 7.99 (978-0-06-440862-2(0) , Cotler, Joanna Books) HarperCollins Pubs.

—I Was a Teenage Fairy. 2000. (gr. 7-12). lib. bdg. 16.45 (978-0-613-28529-2(8)); (Illus.). (J). 14.64 (978-0-606-18903-3(3)) Tandem Library Bks.

Boone, Sheila. Free As a Butterfly. Knox, Susi Grell, illus. 2003. 32p. (J). (ps-3). pap. 7.95 (978-1-891577-80-2(8)) Image Pr., Inc.

Boyle, Doe. Otter on His Own: The Story of A Sea Otter. 2002. (gr. k-3). lib. bdg. 15.25 (978-0-613-50226-9(4)) Tandem Library Bks.

Brown, Amanda. Blonde Love. 4th rev. ed. 2007. 224p. (gr. 3-7). pap. 6.99 (978-0-7868-3888-2(4)) Hyperion Pr.

—Vote Blonde. 3rd rev. ed. 2006. 224p. (gr. 3-7). pap. 6.99 (978-0-7868-3887-5(6)) Hyperion Pr.

Buel, Hubert & Erskine, Dorothy Ward. North with de Anza. 2004. (Illus.). 234p. (J). (gr. 6-10). pap. 9.95 (978-0-8263-3631-6(0)) Univ. of New Mexico Pr.

Bulla, Clyde Robert. The Secret Valley. 19.00 (978-0-8446-6997-7(0)) Smith, Peter Pub., Inc.

Bunting, Eve. The Lambkins. Keegan, Jonathan, illus. 2005. 192p. (J). (gr. 5 up). 15.99 (978-0-06-059906-5(5) , Cotler, Joanna Books) HarperCollins Pubs.

—A Sudden Silence. 2007. (Illus.). 144p. (YA). pap. 6.95 (978-0-15-205868-5(0) , Harcourt Paperbacks) Harcourt Children's Bks.

Byrd, Sandra. Change of Heart. 2002. (gr. 3-6). lib. bdg. 13.00 (978-0-613-84506-9(4)) Tandem Library Bks.

—Cross My Heart. 2001. (Hidden Diary Ser.). 112p. (J). (gr. 3-7). reprint ed. pap. 5.99 (978-0-7642-2480-5(8)) Bethany Hse. Pubs.

—Cross My Heart. 2001. (gr. 3-6). lib. bdg. 13.00 (978-0-613-84512-0(9)) Tandem Library Bks.

—Just Between Friends. 2001. (Hidden Diary Ser.). 112p. (J). (gr. 3-7). pap. 4.99 (978-0-7642-2482-9(4)) Bethany Hse. Pubs.

—Pass It On. 2002. (Hidden Diary Ser.: Bk. 5). 112p. (J). pap. 4.99 (978-0-7642-2484-3(0)) Bethany Hse. Pubs.

Cadnum, Michael. Edge. 1999. (Illus.). 144p. (J). (gr. 7-12). 5.99 (978-0-14-038714-8(5) , Puffin) Penguin Group (USA) Inc.

—Edge. 1999. (gr. 7-12). lib. bdg. 14.15 (978-0-613-14695-1(6)) Tandem Library Bks.

Campbell Hale, Janet. The Owl's Song. 1998. 153p. (C). pap. 13.95 (978-0-8263-1861-9(4)) Univ. of New Mexico Pr.

Chambers, Vickie. In the Silence of the Hills. Taylor, LaVonne, ed. (Illus.). (YA). (gr. 9-12). (978-0-9627735-1-8(4)) Excellence Enterprises.

Choldenko, Gennifer. Al Capone Does My Shirts. 240p. 2004. (Illus.). (YA). (gr. 4-6). 16.99 (978-0-399-23861-1(1) , Putnam Juvenile); 2006. (J). (gr. 5). reprint ed. pap. 6.99 (978-0-14-240370-9(9) , Puffin) Penguin Group (USA) Inc.

—Al Capone Does My Shirts. l.t. ed. 2005. 299p. (YA). 22.95 (978-0-7862-8043-8(3)) Thorndike Pr.

Christopher, Matt. Catching Waves. 2006. 128p. (J). (gr. 3-7). pap. 4.99 (978-0-316-05848-3(0)) Little Brown & Co.

Cole, Sheila. The Canyon. 2002. 160p. (J). (gr. 3-7). 15.89 (978-0-06-029496-0(5)) HarperCollins Pubs.

Corman, Dick. Noah Knows. 2006. 183p. (YA). pap. 12.95 (***978-0-9655749-3-8(8)***) Corman Productions.

Corwin, Susan Simon. The Cryptic Cat. Corwin, Stuart, illus. 2006. 99p. (YA). (***978-0-9790632-0-6(5)***) Lucky Duck Designs.

Cruise, Robin. Little Mama Forgets. Dressen-McQueen, Stacey, illus. 2006. 40p. (J). 16.00 (978-0-374-34613-3(5) , Farrar, Straus & Giroux (BYR)) Farrar, Straus & Giroux.

Currier, Katrina Saltonstall. Kai's Journey to Gold Mountain: An Angel Island Story. 2004. 40p. 16.95 (978-0-9667352-7-7(7)); (Illus.). 44p. (J). pap. 10.95 (978-0-9667352-4-6(2)) Angel Island Assoc.

Deal, Paul. Lighting Candles. 2003. 122p. (YA). 20.95 (978-0-595-65804-6(0)); pap. 10.95 (978-0-595-28457-3(4)) iUniverse, Inc.

Dean, Zoey. Blonde Ambition. 2004. (A-List Ser.: No. 3). 240p. (YA). (gr. 9-17). pap. 9.99 (978-0-316-73474-5(8) , Poppy) Little, Brown Bks. for Young Readers.

Deaver, Julie Reece. Night I Disappeared. 2002. 242p. (J). (ps-7). per. 14.15 (978-0-613-60586-1(1)) Tandem Library Bks.

Dixon, Franklin W. Martial Law. 2006. 152p. (J). lib. bdg. 16.92 (***978-1-4242-0389-5(9)***) Fitzgerald Bks.

—Martial Law. 2006. (Illus.). 152p. (J). (978-1-4156-6852-8(3) , Aladdin) Simon & Schuster Children's Publishing.

Dixon, Franklin W. Running on Fumes. 2005. 150p. (J). lib. bdg. 16.92 (***978-1-4242-0384-0(8)***) Fitzgerald Bks.

—Running on Fumes. 2005. (Illus.). 150p. (J). (***978-1-4156-0714-5(1)*** , Aladdin) Simon & Schuster Children's Publishing.

Doyle, Bill. Silenced! The 1969 Journal of Malcolm. Kelleher, Kathie, illus. 2006. 141p. (J). lib. bdg. 18.46 (***978-1-4242-1736-6(9)***) Fitzgerald Bks.

Dubus, Andre, III. House of Sand & Fog. 2000. (gr. 7-12). lib. bdg. 23.45 (978-0-613-36408-9(2)) Tandem Library Bks.

Duey, Kathleen & Bale, Karen. Three of Hearts. 1998. (J). (gr. 3-7). pap. 3.99 (978-0-380-78720-3(2)) HarperCollins Pubs.

Easton, Kelly. The Life History of a Star. 2002. 208p. (YA). pap. 6.99 (978-0-689-85270-1(3) , Simon Pulse) Simon & Schuster Children's Publishing.

—The Life History of a Star. 2002. (gr. 7-12). lib. bdg. 15.30 (978-0-613-60641-7(8)) Tandem Library Bks.

—The Life History of a Star. l.t. ed. 2002. 200p. 22.95 (978-0-7862-4786-8(X)) Thorndike Pr.

Easton, Kelly. White Magic: Spells to Hold You, A Novel. 2007. 208p. (YA). (gr. 7-11). 15.99 (***978-0-375-83769-2(8)***); lib. bdg. 18.99 (***978-0-375-93769-9(2)***) Random Hse. Children's Bks. (Lamb, Wendy).

Ewing, Lynne. Choice. 9th rev. ed. 2003. (Daughters of the Moon Ser.: No. 9). 288p. (gr. 7-17). 9.99 (978-0-7868-0851-9(9) , Volo) Hyperion Bks. for Children.

—Daughters of the Moon. 2000. 160p. (YA). pap. 4.99 (978-0-7868-1409-1(8)); Vol. 2. pap. 4.99 (978-0-7868-1410-7(1)) Disney Pr.

—Moon Demon, Bk. 7. rev. ed. 2002. (Daughters of the Moon Ser.: No. 7). 289p. (J). (gr. 7-17). 9.99 (978-0-7868-0849-6(7) , Volo) Hyperion Bks. for Children.

Faber, Gail & Lasagna, Michele. Clara Rides the Rancho. Faber, Gail, illus. (Whispers Ser.). (Illus.). (J). (gr. 3-7). 2002. 52p. pap., tchr.'s training gde. ed. 10.95 (978-0-936480-17-6(3)); 2001. 185p. 12.95 (978-0-936480-16-9(5)); 2001. 185p. pap. 9.95 (978-0-936480-15-2(7)) Magpie Pubns.

Ferguson, Tina. The Day i Disappeared. 2005. 83p. pap. 14.95 (978-1-4137-9243-0(X)) PublishAmerica, Inc.

Ferreiro-Esteban, Carmen. Two Moon Princess. 2007. 300p. (gr. 5 up). 15.95 (***978-1-933718-12-5(9)***) Tanglewood Pr.

Fitzgerald, Joanne. Yum! Yum! Delicious Nursery Rhymes. 2007. (Illus.). 32p. (J). (ps-1). (***978-1-55041-888-0(2)***) Fitzhenry & Whiteside, Ltd.

Fleischman, Sid. The Giant Rat of Sumatra: Or Pirates Galore. Hendrix, John, illus. 208p. (J). 2005. (gr. 5 up). 15.99 (978-0-06-074238-6(0)); 2006. reprint ed. pap. 5.99 (978-0-06-074240-9(2) , Harper Trophy) HarperCollins Pubs.

Fletcher, Susan. Walk Across the Sea. Jakesevic, Nenad, illus. 2001. 224p. (J). (gr. 5-9). 16.95 (978-0-689-84133-0(7) , Atheneum) Simon & Schuster Children's Publishing.

—Walk Across the Sea. l.t. ed. 2002. 218p. (J). 22.95 (978-0-7862-4439-3(9)) Thorndike Pr.

Fowler, Earlene. Mariner's Compass. 2000. (gr. 7-12). lib. bdg. 15.30 (978-0-613-42752-4(1)) Tandem Library Bks.

Freeman, Martha. The Spy Wore Shades. Date not set. 160p. (YA). (gr. 3 up). pap. 4.99 (978-0-06-440957-5(0)) HarperCollins Pubs.

—The Spy Wore Shades. Cigliano, Bill, illus. 2001. 240p. (J). (gr. 3 up). 15.89 (978-0-06-029270-6(9)) HarperCollins Pubs.

—The Trouble with Babies. Smith, Cat Bowman, illus. 2002. 80p. (J). (gr. 4-6). tchr. ed. 15.95 (978-0-8234-1698-1(4)) Holiday Hse., Inc.

—The Year My Parents Ruined My Life. 1999. (978-0-606-16453-5(7)) Tandem Library Bks.

Frieders, Robert. American Elves - The Yankoos Vol. 1: The Yankoos & Life in the Sonoran Desert. Olin, George & Robinson, Earle, photos by. 1998. (Illus.). 152p. (J). (gr. 4 up). 16.00 (978-0-9639284-6-7(5)) Yankoo Publishing Co.

Friedman, Aimee. Hollywood Hills. 2007. 352p. (J). pap. 8.99 (978-0-439-79282-0(7) , Scholastic Paperbacks) Scholastic, Inc.

Gamble, Adam. Good Night California. Kelly, Cooper, illus. 2008. (Good Night Our World Ser.). 24p. (J). bds. 9.95 (***978-1-60219-021-4(6)***) Our World of Books.

García, Cristina. I Wanna Be Your Shoebox. 2008. 208p. (J). (***978-1-4169-3928-3(8)*** , Simon & Schuster Children's Publishing) Simon & Schuster Children's Publishing.

Garfinkle, Debra. The Band: Trading Guys: Trading Guys. 2007. 256p. (YA). (gr. 12). pap. 9.99 (***978-0-425-21513-5(X)*** , Berkley Trade) Penguin Group (USA) Inc.

Garfinkle, Debra. Storky: How I Lost My Nickname & Won the Girl. 192p. (YA). 2007. (gr. 7 up). pap. 5.99 (978-0-14-240782-0(8) , Puffin); 2005. (gr. 6). 16.99 (978-0-399-24284-7(8) , Putnam Juvenile) Penguin Group (USA) Inc.

Garland, Sherry. Valley of the Moon: The Diary of Maria Rosalia de Milagros, Sonoma Valley, Alta California, 1846. 2001. (Dear America Ser.). (Illus.). 208p. (J). (gr. 4-9). pap. 10.95 (978-0-439-08820-6(8)) Scholastic, Inc.

Gates, Doris. Blue Willow. 2000. (J). (gr. 3-7). 21.25 (978-0-8446-7143-7(6)) Smith, Peter Pub., Inc.

Gehrman, Jody. Confessions of a Triple Shot Betty. 2008. 256p. (J). (gr. 9). 16.99 (***978-0-8037-3247-6(3)*** , Dial) Penguin Group (USA) Inc.

Graham, Rosemary. Thou Shalt Not Dump the Skater Dude & Other Commandments I Have Broken. 2005. 224p. (J). (gr. 7). 16.99 (978-0-670-06017-7(8) , Viking Juvenile) Penguin Group (USA) Inc.

—Thou Shalt Not Dump the Skater Dude (Splashproof Edition) 2007. 1p. (YA). (gr. 7). pap. 6.99 (978-0-14-240836-0(0) , Puffin) Penguin Group (USA) Inc.

Gregory, Kristiana. Seeds of Hope: The Gold Rush Diary of Susanna Fairchild, 1849. 2001. (Dear America Ser.). (Illus.). 176p. (J). (gr. 5-8). pap. 10.95 (978-0-590-51157-5(2)) Scholastic, Inc.

Gunn, Robin Jones. Hold on Tight. 1998. (Sierra Jensen Ser.: Bk. 10). 160p. (YA). (gr. 7-11). pap. (978-1-56179-637-3(9)) Focus on the Family Publishing.

—Hold on Tight. 1998. (Sierra Jensen Ser.: Bk. 10). (gr. 7-12). lib. bdg. 15.30 (978-0-613-82316-6(8)) Tandem Library Bks.

—Take My Hand. 1999. (Sierra Jensen Ser.: Bk. 12). 144p. (YA). (gr. 7-11). pap. 6.99 (978-1-56179-736-3(7)) Bethany Hse. Pubs.

Hamilton, Elizabeth L. Secret of Cachuma Lake. 2001. (Travel Adventure Ser.: Bk. 1). (Illus.). 144p. (YA). per. 9.95 (978-0-9713749-7-3(X)) Quiet Impact, Inc.

Handford, Martin. Where's Waldo in Hollywood? Handford, Martin, illus. 2002. (Where's Waldo? Ser.). (Illus.). 32p. (J). (gr. 1-5). 5.99 (978-0-7636-1919-0(1)) Candlewick Pr.

Harcourt School Publishers Staff. Desert Letters On Level. 3rd ed. 2002. (Trophies Reading Program Ser.). (Illus.). pap. 5.10 (978-0-15-323280-0(3)) Harcourt Schl. Pubs.

—Food for Fun. 3rd ed. 2002. (Trophies English Language Learners Ser.). (Illus.). pap. 5.10 (978-0-15-327835-8(8)) Harcourt Schl. Pubs.

—Gold Rush News Below Level. 3rd ed. 2002. (Trophies Reading Program Ser.). (Illus.). pap. 5.10 (978-0-15-323246-6(3)) Harcourt Schl. Pubs.

—How Will I Get There? 3rd ed. 2002. (Trophies English Language Learners Ser.). (Illus.). pap. 5.10 (978-0-15-327882-2(X)) Harcourt Schl. Pubs.

—Mischa Learns English On Level. 3rd ed. 2002. (Trophies Reading Program Ser.). (Illus.). pap. 5.10 (978-0-15-323162-9(9)) Harcourt Schl. Pubs.

Haskins, Lori. Butterfly Fever. Smath, Jerry, illus. 2004. 31p. (J). lib. bdg. 20.00 (***978-1-4242-1087-9(9)***) Fitzgerald Bks.

—Butterfly Fever. Smath, Jerry, tr. Smath, Jerry, illus. 2004. (Science Solves It! Ser.). (J). pap. 4.99 (978-1-57565-134-7(3)) Kane Pr., The.

Hernandez, David. Suckerpunch. 2008. 224p. (J). 16.99 (***978-0-06-117330-1(4)***); lib. bdg. 17.89 (***978-0-06-117331-8(2)***) HarperCollins Pubs. (HarperTeen).

Hernandez, Natalie. Las Aventuras con Padre Serra. Hernandez, Tony Y., tr. Nolan, Claudia, illus. 1999. (ENG & SPA.). 112p. (Orig.). (J). (gr. 3-8). pap. 9.95 (978-0-9644386-1-3(5)) Santa Ines Pubns.

—Stowaway to California: Adventures with Father Junipero Serra, 3. 2003. (Illus.). 138p. (J). per. 10.95 (978-1-885852-29-8(0)) James Stevenson Pub.

Hernandez, Natalie Nelson. Aventuras Con Padre Serra. 2003. (SPA., Illus.). 112p. (J). per. 10.95 (978-1-885852-30-4(4)) James Stevenson Pub.

—Captain Sutter's Fort: Adventures with John A. Sutter. 2003. (Illus.). 108p. (J). per. 9.95 (978-1-885852-28-1(2)) James Stevenson Pub.

—Captain Sutter's Fort: Adventures with John A. Sutter. 1999. (Illus.). 107p. (J). (gr. 4-6). pap. 9.95 (978-0-9644386-3-7(1)) Santa Ines Pubns.

Herrera, Juan Felipe. Downtown Boy. 2005. 304p. (J). pap. 16.99 (978-0-439-64489-1(5) , Scholastic Pr.) Scholastic, Inc.

—Grandma & Me at the Flea / Los Meros Meros Remateros. Rohmer, Harriet & Cumpiano, Ina, eds. Lucio-Brock, Anita de, illus. 2002. Tr. of Los Meros Meros Remateros. (ENG & SPA.). 32p. (J). (gr. 1 up). 16.95 (978-0-89239-171-4(5)) Children's Bk. Pr.

Hinman, Bonnie. San Francisco Earthquake. 32nd ed. 1998. (American Adventure Ser.: No. 32). (Illus.). (J). (gr. 3-7). pap. 3.97 (978-1-57748-393-9(6)) Barbour Publishing, Inc.

Hiti, Samuel, creator. End Times - Tiempos Finales Vol. 1: English / Spanish. 2004. Orig. Title: Bloody Demon Guts. (Illus.). 128p. (YA). per. 9.95 net. (978-0-9755193-0-1(1)) La Luz comics.

Hobbs, Valerie. Anything but Ordinary. 2007. 176p. (YA). (gr. 7 up). 16.00 (978-0-374-30374-7(6)) Farrar, Straus & Giroux.

—Charlie's Run. 2000. (Illus.). 176p. (YA). (gr. 4-7). 16.00 (978-0-374-34994-3(0) , Farrar, Straus & Giroux (BYR)) Farrar, Straus & Giroux.

—Charlie's Run. 2002. (gr. 3-6). lib. bdg. 14.15 (978-0-613-85722-2(4)) Tandem Library Bks.

—Charlie's Run. l.t. ed. 2001. (Illus.). 166p. (J). (gr. 4-7). 21.95 (978-0-7862-3104-1(1)) Thorndike Pr.

—How Far Would You Have Gotten If I Hadn't Called You Back? 2003. 320p. (J). pap. 5.99 (978-0-439-58396-1(9) , Scholastic Paperbacks) Scholastic, Inc.

—How Far Would You Have Gotten If I Hadn't Called You Back? 2003. (J). (gr. 7-12). lib. bdg. 14.15 (978-0-613-72289-6(2)) Tandem Library Bks.

—Tender. 2001. 256p. (YA). (gr. 7 up). 18.00 (978-0-374-37397-9(3) , Farrar, Straus & Giroux (BYR)) Farrar, Straus & Giroux.

Hogan, Mary. Pretty Face. 2008. 224p. (J). 16.99 (***978-0-06-084111-9(7)***); lib. bdg. 17.89 (***978-0-06-084112-6(5)***) HarperCollins Pubs. (HarperTeen).

Hogan, Mary. The Serious Kiss. 2005. 256p. (J). pap. 7.99 (978-0-06-072208-1(8) , Harper Trophy); (YA). (gr. 7 up). 16.99 (978-0-06-072206-7(1)) HarperCollins Pubs.

Island of the Blue Dolphins. 2004. (Literature Connections Ser.). (Illus.). (gr. 6-12). (978-0-395-87473-8(4) , 2-70833) McDougal Littell Inc.

Jacquemain, Patti. Journey of the Great Bear: Through California's Golden Past. Jacquemain, Patti, illus. 2006. (J). (978-0-929702-10-0(7)) Mission Creek Studios.

James, Larry W. Captain Petey: An Adventure at Sea. Ramos, Violet M., ed. James, Larry W. & Freshman, Floris R., illus. 2003. 28p. pap. 6.99 (978-0-9742154-0-2(6)) Cross Pointe Printing.

Jimenez, Francisco. Breaking Through. 2001. (gr. 7-12). lib. bdg. 15.25 (978-0-613-60762-9(7)) Tandem Library Bks.

Jiménez, Francisco. Breaking Through: A Migrant Child's Journey from the Fields. 2001. (Illus.). 208p. (YA). (gr. 7 up). tchr. ed. 16.00 (978-0-618-01173-5(0)) Houghton Mifflin Co. Trade & Reference Div.

Jimenez, Francisco. Cajas de Carton: Relatos de la Vida Peregrina de un Nino Campesino. 2002. Tr. of Circuit. (SPA.). (gr. 5-8). lib. bdg. 15.25 (978-0-613-89004-5(3)) Tandem Library Bks.

—Senderos Fronterizos. 2002. (SPA.). (gr. 7-12). lib. bdg. 15.25 (978-0-613-60784-1(8)) Tandem Library Bks.

Johnson, Lissa Halls & Wierenga, Kathy. No Lifeguard on Duty, Vol. 8. 2005. (Brio Girls Ser.). 192p. (YA). (gr. 6-11). pap. 7.99 (978-1-58997-081-6(0)) Focus on the Family Publishing.

Johnston, Tony. Angel City. Byard, Carole M., illus. 2006. 40p. (J). (ps). 15.99 (978-0-399-23405-7(5) , Philomel) Penguin Group (USA) Inc.

Juan, Felipe Herrera. Coralito's Bay: Bahia de Coralito. 2004. (SPA & ENG.). 41p. 14.95 (978-0-9742810-0-1(X)) Monterey Bay Sancturary Foundation.

Jukes, Mavis. Expecting the Unexpected. 1999. (J). (978-0-606-15911-1(8)) Tandem Library Bks.

Karr, Kathleen. Exiled: Memoirs of a Camel. 240p. (J). 2006. pap. 6.95 (978-0-7614-5291-1(5)); 2004. 15.95 (978-0-7614-5164-8(1)) Cavendish, Marshall Corp.

Katz, Welwyn W. Whalesinger. 2002. 212p. (YA). pap. 5.95 (978-0-88899-191-1(6)) Groundwood Bks. CAN. *Dist:* Perseus Distribution.

Kchodl, Joseph 'PaleoJoe' & Caszatt-Allen, Wendy. Secret Sabertooth. 2007. (PaleoJoe's Dinosaur Detective Club Ser.: 3). (Illus.). 140p. (J). pap. 6.95 (***978-1-934133-10-1(8)***) Mackinac Island Pr., Inc.

Kehret, Peg. Searching for Candlestick Park. Marchesi, S., illus. 1999. 144p. (J). (gr. 3-7). pap. 5.99 (978-0-14-130366-6(2) , Puffin) Penguin Group (USA) Inc.

—Searching for Candlestick Park. 1999. (978-0-606-17427-5(3)); (gr. 5-8). lib. bdg. 14.15 (978-0-613-23030-8(2)) Tandem Library Bks.

Komaiko, Leah. Malibu Carmie. 2007. 256p. (YA). (gr. 7-11). mass mkt. 5.99 (978-0-440-42014-9(8) , Laurel Leaf) Random Hse. Children's Bks.

Konnikov, Svetlana. Grapette, the Runaway Who Rolled Away. Smishliaev, Anatoli, illus. 2007. (Grapette's Adventures Ser.). 32p. (J). 15.95 (***978-0-9791758-0-0(1)***) Aurora Pubs., Inc.

Koontz, Dean. Ticktock. 2000. (gr. 7-12). lib. bdg. 16.45 (978-0-613-49461-8(X)) Tandem Library Bks.

Korman, Gordon. Hollywood Hustle. 2006. 272p. (gr. 7-17). reprint ed. pap. 5.99 (978-0-7868-0919-6(1)) Hyperion Pr.

—Son of the Mob. l.t. ed. 2005. 253p. 22.95 (978-0-7862-7189-4(2)) Thorndike Pr.

Koss, Amy Goldman. Kailey. Howe, Philip, illus. 2003. (American Girl of Today Ser.). 152p. (J). pap. 6.95 (978-1-58485-591-0(6)) American Girl Publishing, Inc.

—Kailey. 2003. (gr. 3-6). lib. bdg. 15.25 (978-0-613-86379-7(8)) Tandem Library Bks.

Lachtman, Ofelia Dumas. A Good Place for Maggie. 2002. 160p. (YA). pap. 9.95 (978-1-55885-372-0(3) , Piñata Books) Arte Publico Pr.

—A Good Place for Maggie. 2002. (gr. 3-6). lib. bdg. 18.75 (978-0-613-85296-8(6)) Tandem Library Bks.

—The Trouble with Tessa. 122p. (J). (ps-7). pap. 9.95 (978-1-55885-448-2(7) , Piñata Books) Arte Publico Pr.

Lawton, Wendy. Flip Flop. 2004. (Real Tv - Real Transformations Series (Take 2) Ser.). 208p. (J). pap. 10.99 (978-0-8024-5414-0(3)) Moody Pubs.

Lazewnik, Libby. Forever & a Day. 2002. 300p. 18.95 (978-1-56871-265-9(0)) Targum Pr., Inc.

Lazo, Dorina. Children of the San Joaquin Valley. Hires, Josh, photos by. 2005. (Illus.). 35p. (YA). (gr. 7-12). pap. 15.00 (978-0-938911-28-9(7)) Individualized Education Systems/Poppy Lane Publishing.

Lee, Milly. Landed. Choi, Yangsook, illus. 2006. 40p. (J). 16.00 (978-0-374-34314-9(4) , Farrar, Straus & Giroux (BYR)) Farrar, Straus & Giroux.

Lehr, Norma. Haunting at Black Water Cove. 2000. (Illus.). (J). (978-0-606-18311-6(6)) Tandem Library Bks.

Lenhard, Elizabeth. Power of Five. 2004. 158p. (J). lib. bdg. 16.92 (***978-1-4242-0795-4(9)***) Fitzgerald Bks.

Levitin, Sonia. Boom Town. Smith, Cat Bowman, illus. 1998. 32p. (J). (gr. k-4). pap. 16.95 (978-0-531-30043-5(9) , Orchard Bks.) Scholastic, Inc.

Lewman, David. Case of the Missing Gold. 2000. (gr. 3-6). lib. bdg. 11.80 (978-0-613-24494-7(X)) Tandem Library Bks.

Lobdell, Scott. The Hardy Boys #8: Board to Death. Henrique, Paulo, illus. 8th rev. ed. 2007. (Hardy Boys: Undercover Brothers Ser.). 112p. (J). 12.95 (978-1-59707-054-6(8)); pap. 7.95 (978-1-59707-053-9(X)) Papercutz.

Lopez, Jack. In the Break. 2006. (Illus.). 208p. (J). (gr. 7-17). 16.99 (978-0-316-00874-7(5)) Little Brown & Co.

Lowell, Susan. I Am Lavina Cumming. 2005. (Historical Fiction for Young Readers Ser.). (Illus.). 200p. (J). pap. 6.95 (978-1-57131-655-4(8)) Milkweed Editions.

Lupita Manana. 3rd ed. (J). pap., stu. ed. (978-0-13-772500-7(0)) Prentice Hall (Schl. Div.).

Ly, Many. Home Is East. 304p. 2007. (YA). (gr. 7-11). mass mkt. 6.50 (***978-0-440-23900-0(1)*** , Laurel Leaf); 2005. (J). (gr. 5 up). lib. bdg. 17.99 (978-0-385-73223-9(6) , Delacorte Bks. for Young Readers) Random Hse. Children's Bks.

Madison, Mike. No Time to Nap. Peterson, Mary, illus. 2007. (J). (978-1-59714-046-1(5)) Heyday Bks.

Marlow, Susan K. Andrea Carter & the Long Ride Home. 2005. 128p. (J). (ps-7). pap. 7.99 (978-0-8254-3188-3(3)) Kregel Pubns.

Marsh, Carole. The Mystery on the California Mission Trail. 2003. (gr. 3-6). lib. bdg. 14.10 (978-0-613-73039-6(9)) Tandem Library Bks.

Martin, Ann M. Amalia: Diary Three. 2000. (California Diaries: Bk. 14). (Illus.). 144p. (YA). (gr. 6-8). pap. 4.99 (978-0-439-09548-8(4)) Scholastic, Inc.

—Amalia: Diary Three. 1999. (California Diaries: Bk. 14). (Illus.). (YA). (gr. 6-8). (978-0-606-18525-7(9)) Tandem Library Bks.

—Amalia: Diary Two. 1998. (California Diaries: Bk. 9). (Illus.). 10p. (YA). (gr. 6-8). pap. 4.50 (978-0-590-02385-6(3)) Scholastic, Inc.

—Dawn: Diary Three. 1999. (California Diaries: Bk. 11). 144p. (YA). (gr. 6-8). pap. 3.99 (978-0-590-02389-4(6)) Scholastic, Inc.

—Dawn: Diary Three. 1999. (California Diaries: Bk. 11). (J). (978-0-606-16609-6(2)) Tandem Library Bks.

C D

—Dawn: Diary Two. 1998. (California Diaries: Bk. 7). (YA). (gr. 6-8). pap. 4.99 (978-0-590-01846-3(9)) Scholastic, Inc.

—Dawn: Diary Two. 1998. (California Diaries: Bk. 7). (YA). (gr. 6-8). (978-0-606-13238-1(4)) Tandem Library Bks.

—Dawn on the Coast. (Baby-Sitters Club Ser.: No. 23). 10p. (J). (gr. 3-7). pap. 3.95 (978-0-590-42007-5(0)) Scholastic, Inc.

—Ducky. 1998. (California Diaries Ser.: Bk 5). 10p. (YA). (gr. 6-8). pap. 4.50 (978-0-590-29839-1(9)) Scholastic, Inc.

—Ducky: Diary Three. 15th ed. 2000. (California Diaries: Bk. 15). 144p. (YA). (gr. 6-8). pap. 4.99 (978-0-439-09549-5(2) , Scholastic Paperbacks) Scholastic, Inc.

—Ducky: Diary Three. 2000. (California Diaries: Bk. 15). (Illus.). (YA). (gr. 6-8). (978-0-606-18866-1(5)) Tandem Library Bks.

—Ducky: Diary Two. 1998. (California Diaries: Bk. 10). (YA). (gr. 6-8). pap. 71.82 (978-0-590-63083-2(0)) Scholastic, Inc.

—Ducky No. 10: Diary Two. 1998. (California Diaries: Bk. 10). 144p. (YA). (gr. 6-8). pap. 3.99 (978-0-590-02387-0(X)) Scholastic, Inc.

—Maggie: Diary Three. 1999. (California Diaries: Bk. 13). (Illus.). (YA). (gr. 6-8). (978-0-606-18524-0(0)) Tandem Library Bks.

—Maggie: Diary Two. 1998. (California Diaries: Bk. 8). (YA). (gr. 6-8). pap. 3.99 (978-0-590-02383-2(7)) Scholastic, Inc.

—Maggie: Diary Two. 1998. (California Diaries: Bk. 8). (YA). (gr. 6-8). (978-0-606-13239-8(2)) Tandem Library Bks.

—Sunny. 1999. (California Diaries: Bk. 2). (YA). (gr. 6-8). pap. 54.00 (978-0-439-09614-0(6)) Scholastic, Inc.

—Sunny: Diary Three. 1999. (California Diaries: Bk. 12). 160p. (YA). (gr. 6-8). pap. 4.50 (978-0-590-02390-0(X)) Scholastic, Inc.

—Sunny: Diary Three. 1999. (California Diaries: Bk. 12). (Illus.). (YA). (gr. 6-8). (978-0-606-18523-3(2)) Tandem Library Bks.

—Sunny: Diary Two. 1998. (California Diaries: Bk. 6). (YA). (gr. 6-8). pap. 3.99 (978-0-590-29840-7(2)); pap. 71.82 (978-0-590-65607-8(4)) Scholastic, Inc.

—Sunny: Diary Two. 1998. (California Diaries: Bk. 6). (YA). (gr. 6-8). (978-0-606-13237-4(6)) Tandem Library Bks.

Martin, Anne E. Flip Flops for Paige. 2007. (Illus.). 48p. (J). per. 14.99 (***978-1-59879-243-0(1)***) Lifevest Publishing, Inc.

Mayer, Melody. The Nannies: Friends with Benefits. 2006. (Nannies Ser.). 288p. (YA). (gr. 9). pap. 8.95 (978-0-385-73284-0(8)); lib. bdg. 10.99 (978-0-385-90301-1(4)) Random Hse. Children's Bks. (Delacorte Bks. for Young Readers).

—The Nannies: Have to Have It. 2006. (Nannies Ser.). 256p. (YA). (gr. 7). 8.95 (978-0-385-73351-9(8) , Delacorte Bks. for Young Readers) Random Hse. Children's Bks.

—The Nannies: Have to Have It. 2006. (Nannies Novel Ser.). 256p. (YA). (gr. 9). lib. bdg. 10.99 (978-0-385-90366-0(9) , Delacorte Bks. for Young Readers) Random Hse. Children's Bks.

Mayer, Melody. Tainted Love: A Nannies Novel. 2007. (Nannies Ser.). 272p. (gr. 9). (J). lib. bdg. 11.99 (***978-0-385-90367-7(7)***); (YA). 8.99 (***978-0-385-73352-6(6)***) Random Hse. Children's Bks. (Delacorte Bks. for Young Readers).

Mazer, Harry. A Boy No More. 2004. (Illus.). 144p. (J). 16.95 (978-0-689-85533-7(8)) Simon & Schuster Children's Publishing.

McGarrahan, Margaret. Nessie's California Adventures. Wright, Kathleen, illus. 2002. 55p. (J). (gr. k-4). pap. 12.50 (978-0-9672639-2-2(1)) Smith Lane Pubs.

McGinley, Jerry. Joaquin Strikes Back. 1998. 158p. (YA). (gr. 5-10). 18.95 (978-0-936389-58-5(3)) Tudor Pubs., Inc.

Montes, Marisa. A Crazy Mixed-Up Spanglish Day. Cepeda, Joe, illus. 2003. (Get Ready for Gabi Ser.). 128p. (J). pap. 12.95 (978-0-439-51710-2(9) , Scholastic Paperbacks) Scholastic, Inc.

Na, An. Wait for Me. 2007. 192p. (YA). (gr. 7 up). 7.99 (***978-0-14-240918-3(9)*** , Puffin) Penguin Group (USA) Inc.

Nascimbene, Yan. Day in September. 2002. (J). (978-0-89812-328-9(3) , Creative Paperbacks) Creative Co., The.

Nelson, Theresa. Ruby Electric. 272p. (J). 2003. (Illus.). 16.95 (978-0-689-83852-1(2) , Atheneum/Richard Jackson Bks.); 2004. reprint ed. pap. 5.99 (978-0-689-87146-7(5) , Aladdin) Simon & Schuster Children's Publishing.

Noël, Alyson & Quiksilver Entertainment. Laguna Cove. 2006. 224p. (YA). pap. 8.95 (978-0-312-34869-4(X) , St. Martin's Griffin) St. Martin's Pr.

O'Dell, Scott. La Isla de los Delfines Azules. (SPA., Illus.). (YA). (gr. 5-8). (978-1-56137-541-7(1) , NU5722) Noguer y Caralt Editores, S. A. ESP. *Dist:* Lectorum Pubns., Inc.

Okei-san: The Girl from Wakamatsu. 2006. (J). pap. 11.95 (***978-0-9642112-8-5(9)***) Barsotti Bks.

Paraskevas, Betty. Chocolate at the Four Seasons. Paraskevas, Mickey, illus. 2007. 32p. (J). (ps-1). 16.99 (978-0-316-01375-8(7)) Little Brown & Co.

Perez, L. King. First Day in Grapes. Casilla, Robert, illus. 2002. 32p. (J). (gr. 1-3). 16.95 (978-1-58430-045-8(0)) Lee & Low Bks., Inc.

Perrin, Randy, et al. Time Like a River. 2004. 144p. (gr. 5 up). 14.95 (978-1-57143-061-8(X)) RDR Bks.

Pfitsch, Patricia Curtis. Riding the Flume. 2004. (Illus.). 240p. (J). pap. 4.99 (978-0-689-86692-0(5) , Aladdin) Simon & Schuster Children's Publishing.

Phelan, Regina V. They Came Around the Horn; Vol. 5. Champy, Al, illus. l.t. ed. 1999. (History of California for the Young Reader Ser.). 64p. (J). lib. bdg. 15.00 (978-0-87062-292-2(7) , Clark, Arthur H. Co., The) Univ. of Oklahoma Pr.

Pinder, Margaret. But I Don't Want to Be a Movie Star. 2006. 256p. (YA). (gr. 6-12). 15.99 (978-0-525-47634-4(2) , Dutton Juvenile) Penguin Group (USA) Inc.

The Place Beyond the Dust Bowl. 2100th ed. 2002. (Illus.). 223p. pap. 15.95 (978-1-892622-16-7(5)) Bear State Bks.

Pockets Learning Staff. Samantha's California Adventure. 1998. (Illus.). 2p. (ps-1). 15.00 (978-1-888074-91-8(4)) Pockets of Learning.

Preble, Laura. The Queen Geek Social Club. 2006. 336p. (YA). (gr. 12). pap. 9.99 (978-0-425-21164-9(9) , Berkley Trade) Penguin Group (USA) Inc.

Prentice-Hall Staff. The Red Pony. 2nd ed. (J). stu. ed. (978-0-13-717133-0(1)) Prentice Hall (Schl. Div.).

RealBuzz Studios Staff. Let There Be Lighten Up! 2007. (Goofyfoot Gurl Ser.: No. 1). 96p. (YA). pap. 4.97 (978-1-59789-573-6(3) , Barbour Bks.) Barbour Publishing, Inc.

Riefe, Barbara. Amelia Dale Archer Story. 1998. 304p. (YA). (gr. 8 up). 22.95 (978-0-312-86077-6(3) , Forge Bks.) Doherty, Tom Assocs., LLC.

Rio, Adam del & Arroyo, David. Vines of the Earth. Rio, Adam del & Arroyo, David, illus. 2006. (SPA & ENG., Illus.). 27p. (***978-0-9772852-7-3(8)***); pap. (***978-0-9772852-6-6(X)***) Lectura Bks.

The Rise of Death Valley. 2006. (YA). (***978-0-9786681-0-5(3)***) Children's Heart Publishing Co.

Ritter, John H. The Boy Who Saved Baseball. 224p. 2005. (J). (gr. 4). pap. 6.99 (978-0-14-240286-3(9) , Puffin); 2003. (Illus.). (YA). (gr. 5-7). 17.99 (978-0-399-23622-8(8) , Philomel) Penguin Group (USA) Inc.

—The Boy Who Saved Baseball. 2005. 216p. (J). (ps-7). per. 12.64 (978-0-606-33116-6(6)) Tandem Library Bks.

Ritter, John H. Under the Baseball Moon. 2008. 320p. (J). (gr. 6). 6.99 (***978-0-14-241090-5(X)*** , Puffin); 2006. (Illus.). 224p. (YA). (gr. 5). 16.99 (978-0-399-23623-5(6) , Philomel) Penguin Group (USA) Inc.

Rivers, Karen. The Quirky Girls' Guide to Rest Stops & Road Trips. 2007. 256p. (J). pap. 7.95 (978-1-55192-907-1(4) , Polestar Book Pubs.) Raincoast Bk. Distribution CAN. *Dist:* Perseus Distribution.

Roberts, Laura Peyton. Ghost of a Chance. 2006. 208p. (YA). (gr. 7). mass mkt. 5.99 (978-0-553-49498-3(8) , Laurel Leaf) Random Hse. Children's Bks.

—Ghost of a Chance. 1999. (J). (978-0-606-16448-1(0)) Tandem Library Bks.

—The Queen of Second Place. 336p. (gr. 7). 2006. (YA). pap. 5.99 (978-0-440-23871-3(4) , Laurel Leaf); 2005. (J). lib. bdg. 17.99 (978-0-385-90200-7(X) , Delacorte Bks. for Young Readers); 2005. (YA). 15.95 (978-0-385-73162-1(0) , Delacorte Bks. for Young Readers) Random Hse. Children's Bks.

Roberts, Willo Davis. Undercurrents. 2003. (Illus.). 240p. (J). pap. 4.99 (978-0-689-85994-6(5) , Aladdin) Simon & Schuster Children's Publishing.

—Undercurrents. Downey, Mark, illus. 2002. 240p. (J). (gr. 5-8). 16.95 (978-0-689-81671-0(5) , Atheneum) Simon & Schuster Children's Publishing.

—Undercurrents. 2002. (gr. 3-6). lib. bdg. 13.00 (978-0-613-66553-7(8)) Tandem Library Bks.

Roderman, Anna Marie. Two Tales of Courage. 2004. 116p. (YA). pap. 7.95 (978-0-87714-318-5(8)) Denlingers Pubs., Ltd.

Romeyn, Debra. Passage to Monterey. May, Dan, tr. May, Dan, illus. 2003. (Adventures of Juan & Mariano Ser.: No. 1). 39p. (J). pap. 9.95 (978-0-9729016-0-4(4)) Gossamer Bks.

Rosner, Hannah. The Ambulance Club. 2005. 87p. pap. 14.95 (978-1-4137-7492-4(X)) PublishAmerica, Inc.

Ross, Sylvia. Lion Singer. 2005. (Illus.). 33p. (J). (gr. 1-4). 12.95 (978-1-59714-009-6(0) , Great Valley Bks.) Heyday Bks.

Rosten, Carrie. Chloe Leiberman (Sometimes Wong) 2007. 224p. (YA). (gr. 7). pap. 8.99 (978-0-385-73248-2(1) , Delacorte Bks. for Young Readers) Random Hse. Children's Bks.

Rubcic, Michael. Native Soul. 2004. 216p. (Orig.). (J). pap. 14.95 (978-0-9746848-0-2(5)) Native Sun Pr.

Ruiz, Joseph J. Angel on Daniel's Shoulder. 2004. (SPA & ENG., Illus.). 108p. (J). pap. 12.95 (978-0-86534-402-0(7)) Sunstone Pr.

Ryan, Pam Muñoz. Esperanza Renace. Selznick, Bryan, illus. 2002. (SPA.). 272p. (J). (gr. 4-9). pap. 4.99 (978-0-439-39885-5(1) , Scholastic en Espanol) Scholastic, Inc.

—Esperanza Rising. unabr. ed. 2004. (Middle Grade Cassette Librariestm Ser.). 272p. (J). (gr. 4-7). pap. 36.00 incl. audio (978-0-8072-1726-9(3) , S YA 281 SP, Listening Library) Random Hse. Audio Publishing Group.

—Esperanza Rising. (Illus.). (J). (gr. 4-9). 2007. 307p. 5.99 (978-0-439-12042-5(X)); 2000. 272p. pap. 15.95 (978-0-439-12041-8(1) , Scholastic Pr.) Scholastic, Inc.

—Esperanza Rising. 2001. (gr. 5-8). lib. bdg. 13.00 (978-0-613-53807-7(2)) Tandem Library Bks.

—Nacho & Lolita. Rueda, Claudia, illus. 2005. 40p. (J). (ps-3). pap. 16.99 (978-0-439-26968-1(7) , Scholastic Pr.) Scholastic, Inc.

—Riding Freedom. Selznick, Brian, illus. 2007. 144p. (J). (gr. 3-7). mass mkt. 4.99 (978-0-439-08796-4(1) , Scholastic Paperbacks) Scholastic, Inc.

—Riding Freedom. Selznick, Brian, illus. 1999. 138p. per. 11.64 (978-0-606-17445-9(1)) Tandem Library Bks.

—Riding Freedom. 1999. (gr. 3-6). lib. bdg. 13.00 (978-0-613-22765-0(4)) Tandem Library Bks.

—Yo, Naomi Leon. 2005. (SPA.). 272p. (J). (gr. 4-7). pap. 4.99 (978-0-439-75572-6(7) , Scholastic en Espanol) Scholastic, Inc.

Sanchez, Alex. So Hard to Say. 240p. 2004. (J). 15.95 (978-0-689-86564-0(3)); 2006. (Illus.). (YA). reprint ed. pap. 7.99 (978-1-4169-1189-0(8) , Aladdin) Simon & Schuster Children's Publishing.

Sandoval, Victor. Roll over, Big Toben. 128p. (YA). pap. 9.95 (978-1-55885-401-7(0) , Piñata Books) Arte Publico Pr.

Santana, Patricia. Motorcycle Ride on the Sea of Tranquility. 2002. 270p. (YA). 19.95 (978-0-8263-2435-1(5)) Univ. of New Mexico Pr.

Sayles, Carol L. Turn the Turtle Rightside. 2007. 156p. (J). pap. 9.95 (978-1-933255-25-5(0)) DNA Pr.

Schraff, Anne. The Greatest Heroes. 2000. 143p. (J). pap. (978-0-7891-5133-9(2)); (gr. 5-12). lib. bdg. 13.95 (978-0-7807-9271-5(8)) Perfection Learning Corp.

—Memories Are Forever. 1999. 135p. (J). pap. (978-0-7891-4924-4(9)); (gr. 5-12). lib. bdg. 13.95 (978-0-7807-8008-8(6)) Perfection Learning Corp.

Schulte, Elaine L. Daniel Colton Kidnapped. 2002. (Colton Cousins Adventure Ser.: Bk. 4). (Illus.). 138p. (J). (gr. 4-7). 7.49 (978-1-57924-566-5(8)) Jones, Bob Univ. Pr.

—Suzannah Strikes Gold. 2001. (Illus.). 144p. (J). (gr. 4-7). pap. 7.49 (978-1-57924-565-8(X)) Jones, Bob Univ. Pr.

Senate, Richard. Ghosts of the Ojai: California's Most Haunted Valley. 2002. (Illus.). per. 8.95 (978-0-9722936-0-0(4)) Del Sol Pubns.

Shannon, Monica. California Fairy Tales. Millard, C. E., illus. 2004. reprint ed. pap. 30.95 (978-1-4179-4211-4(8)) Kessinger Publishing, LLC.

Sibley, Linda. David Joins the California Gold Rush. 2004. 96p. (***978-0-7891-6002-7(1)***) Perfection Learning Corp.

Simmons, Andrea. What Anna Loves. Capaldi, Gina, illus. 2006. 32p. (J). 15.95 (978-1-59714-044-7(9)) Heyday Bks.

Simmons, Michael. Pool Boy. 2005. 192p. (YA). (gr. 7). reprint ed. pap. 7.95 (978-0-385-73196-6(5) , Delacorte Bks. for Young Readers) Random Hse. Children's Bks.

Simpson, Fiona, ed. Novelization. 2006. 232p. (J). pap. 6.99 (978-0-439-74572-7(1)) Scholastic, Inc.

Singleton, Linda Joy. Last Dance. 2005. (Seer Ser.: Book 2). 264p. pap. 6.99 (978-0-7387-0638-2(8)) Llewellyn Pubns.

—Oh No! UFO! Karre, Andrew, ed. 2004. (Strange Encounters Ser.). 192p. (gr. 8-12). pap. 4.99 (978-0-7387-0579-8(9)) Llewellyn Pubns.

Smith, D. James. The Boys of San Joaquin. 240p. (J). (gr. 3-7). 2006. pap. 5.99 (978-1-4169-1619-2(9) , Aladdin); 2005. (Illus.). 16.99 (978-0-689-87606-6(8) , Atheneum) Simon & Schuster Children's Publishing.

—Probably the World's Best Story about a Dog & the Girl Who Loved Me. 2006. 240p. (J). (gr. 4-7). 15.95 (978-1-4169-0542-4(1)) Simon & Schuster Children's Publishing.

Smith, Stephen D. & Caldwell, Lise. Rivals on the Waves. 2006. 128p. (J). pap. 5.99 (978-0-7847-1470-6(3) , 42141) Standard Publishing.

Snedden, Genevra Sis. Docas the Indian Boy of Santa Clara. 2005. pap. 21.95 (978-1-4179-2695-4(3)) Kessinger Publishing, LLC.

Soto, Gary. The Afterlife: A Novel. 2003. 176p. (J). (gr. 6 up). 17.00 (978-0-15-204774-0(3) , 53597422) Harcourt Children's Bks.

Standiford, Natalie. The Dating Game, No. 1. 2005. 224p. (YA). (gr. 8-17). pap. 9.99 (978-0-316-11040-2(X)) Little Brown & Co.

—Dating Game: Breaking Up Is Really, Really Hard to Do, No. 2. 2005. 224p. (YA). (gr. 8-17). pap. 9.99 (978-0-316-11041-9(8)) Little Brown & Co.

—Dating Game: Can True Love Survive High School?, No. 3. 2005. 224p. (YA). (gr. 8-17). pap. 9.99 (978-0-316-11042-6(6)) Little Brown & Co.

—Ex Rating. 4th rev. ed. 2006. (Dating Game Ser.: No. 4). 224p. (J). (gr. 8-17). pap. 9.99 (978-0-316-15876-3(3)) Little Brown & Co.

—Speed Dating. 5th ed. 2006. (Dating Game Ser.: No. 5). 224p. (J). (gr. 8-17). pap. 9.99 (978-0-316-11530-8(4)) Little Brown & Co.

Stites, Clara. Katya of Fort Ross. 2001. (Illus.). 80p. (J). pap. 8.95 (978-1-56474-379-4(9)) Fithian Pr.

—Lixia of Gold Mountain: A Story of Early California. 2003. (Illus.). 64p. (J). pap. 8.95 (978-1-56474-421-0(3)) Fithian Pr.

—Rosalba of Santa Juanita: A California Story. 2002. (Illus.). 80p. (J). pap. 8.95 (978-1-56474-394-7(2)) Fithian Pr.

Stokes, Phil. Phillip & Dickie. 2004. 384p. (YA). 28.95 (978-0-9744360-0-5(3)) Da Wong Bks.

Taiz, Lincoln. Libra: The Cat Who Saved Silicon Valley. Taiz, Lee, illus. 2002. 326p. (J). pap. 14.95 incl. audio compact disk (978-0-9723044-0-5(1) , AGP-1) Amsea Group, Inc.

Taiz, Lincoln & Taiz, Lee. Libra: The Cat Who Saved Silicon Valley. 2001. (Illus.). 326p. pap. 15.95 (978-0-9723044-1-2(X) , AGP-1) Amsea Group, Inc.

Taylor, Theodore. Lord of the Kill. 2004. 256p. (J). pap. 5.99 (978-0-439-55956-0(1) , Scholastic Paperbacks) Scholastic, Inc.

(Trantham) Rogers Staff. Barefoot in the Cotton Fields of Oklahom. 2005. (Illus.). 123p. pap. 17.95 (978-1-4137-7205-0(6)) PublishAmerica, Inc.

Trevor, Simeon. I'm Going to Fly SomeDay. 2004. 36p. spiral bd. 13.93 (978-1-4116-2072-8(0)) Lulu.com.

Turner, Ginger. Gold Mine! The California Gold Rush Story. 2004. (Illus.). 46p. (J). per. 15.95 (978-0-9742502-2-9(8)) Gossamer Bks., LLC.

Turner, Ginger & Shimpi, Shekhar. Gold Mine! The California Gold Rush Story. 2004. (Illus.). 44p. (J). pap. 15.95 (978-0-9742502-3-6(6)) Gossamer Bks., LLC.

Uchida, Yoshiko. A Jar of Dreams. 1998. (J). pap. 3.95 (978-0-87628-469-8(1)) Ctr. for Applied Research in Education, The.

Uncle Markie. Piglettè & Bobo Christmas in Palm Springs. 2003. (YA). ring bd. 9.95 (978-1-933129-10-5(7)) Studio 403.

—Piglettè & Bobo in Berkeley. 2003. (YA). ring bd. 9.95 (978-1-933129-07-5(7)) Studio 403.

—Piglettè & BoBoTrash Orange County. 2003. (YA). ring bd. 9.95 (978-1-933129-09-9(3)) Studio 403.

Van Dyne, Edith. Aunt Jane's Nieces Out West. 2006. 180p. pap. 14.99 (***978-1-4264-4188-2(6)***); 164p. pap. 11.99 (***978-1-4264-4145-5(2)***) BiblioBazaar.

Van Syckle, A. & Schwartz, Josh. The OC: 'twas the Night Before Chrismukkah. 2005. 206p. (YA). (978-1-4156-3915-3(9)) Scholastic, Inc.

Vega, Diego & Adkins, Jan. Young Zorro (Spanish Edition) El joven Zorro: la marca de Hierro. 2007. (SPA.). 256p. (J). pap. 6.99 (***978-0-06-115378-5(8)*** , Rayo) HarperCollins Pubs.

Vinette, Arnold D. Reid & Danielle's Adventures - 1st Year Breaking in Your New Parents. Vinette, Dorothy V., ed. 2004. 592p. (J). pap. 24.50 (978-1-4149-0005-6(8) , Time Capsule Bks.) Time Capsule eBooks, Inc.

—Reid's Adventures - 1st Year Breaking in Your New Parents. Vinette, Dorothy V., ed. 2004. (J). 576p. 35.99 (978-1-4149-0002-5(3)); 592p. pap. 24.50 (978-1-4149-0004-9(X)) Time Capsule eBooks, Inc. (Time Capsule Bks.).

Wallington, Aury. Secrets. novel ed. 2005. (O. C. Ser.: No. 4). 264p. 6.99 (978-0-439-69632-6(1)) Scholastic, Inc.

Wallington, Aury & Schwartz, Josh. The OC: Bait & Switch. 2005. 163p. (YA). (978-1-4156-2363-3(5)) Scholastic, Inc.

Walls, P. Abby: El oro de California. 2003. (Abby Ser.).Tr. of Abby: California Gold. pap. 6.99 (978-0-7899-0969-5(3)) Editorial Unilit.

Warner Bros Us Staff & Martin, Cory. OC: The Outsider. 2006. (Illus.). 320p. pap. 5.57 (978-0-14-131907-0(0)) Penguin Group (USA) Inc.

Warner, Penny. Mystery of the Haunted Cave. 2001. 102p. (J). (978-0-88166-390-7(5)) Meadowbrook Pr.

Warner, Sally. This Isn't about the Money. 2002. 224p. (J). (gr. 3-6). 15.99 (978-0-670-03574-8(2) , Viking Juvenile) Penguin Group (USA) Inc.

Wasserman, Robin & Pyle, Howard. Lust. 2005. (Seven Deadly Sins Ser.). 256p. (YA). pap. 8.99 (978-0-689-87782-7(X) , Simon Pulse) Simon & Schuster Children's Publishing.

Williams, Patricia de Belloy. Pioneers-1937. 2003. (Illus.). 409p. (J). per. 14.99 (978-1-932176-00-1(4)) Beluga-Duga Pr.

Wilsdon, Christina. Lights! Action! California! Hockerman, Dennis, illus. 2006. 26p. (J). 7.99 (978-1-59939-009-3(4) , Reader's Digest Young Families, Inc.) Reader's Digest Children's Publishing, Inc.

Wilson, Eric G. Disneyland Hostage. 2000. (Illus.). 144p. (J). (gr. 6-8). pap. 4.99 (978-1-55143-174-1(2)) Orca Bk. Pubs. USA.

Windle, Jeanette. Jana's Journal: A Novel for Teens. 2002. 256p. pap. 12.99 (978-0-8254-4117-2(X)) Kregel Pubns.

Wood, Frances M. Daughter of Madrugada. l.t. ed. 2004. 170p. 20.95 (978-0-7862-6142-0(0)) Thorndike Pr.

Yamada, Debbie Leung. Striking It Rich: Treasures from Gold Mountain. Tang, You-shan, illus. l.t. ed. 2004. 128p. (J). (gr. 4-8). pap. 13.95 (978-1-879965-21-8(6)) Polychrome Publishing Corp.

Yee, Lisa. So Totally Emily Ebers. 2008. 304p. (J). 5.99 (978-0-439-83848-1(7) , Levine, Arthur A. Bks.) Scholastic, Inc.

—So Totally Emily Embers. 2007. 304p. (J). (gr. 4-7). pap. 16.99 (978-0-439-83847-4(9) , Levine, Arthur A. Bks.) Scholastic, Inc.

Yep, Laurence. My Name Is America: The Journal of Wongming-chun, A Chinese Miner. 2000. (My Name Is America Ser.). (Illus.). 224p. (J). (gr. 4-8). pap. 10.95 (978-0-590-38607-4(7)) Scholastic, Inc.

Yin. Coolies. Soentpiet, Chris, illus. 2003. 40p. (J). (gr. k-3). pap. 7.99 (978-0-14-250055-2(0) , Puffin) Penguin Group (USA) Inc.

—Coolies. Soentpiet, Chris K., illus. 2001. 1p. (J). (ps-3). 16.99 (978-0-399-23227-5(3) , Philomel) Penguin Group (USA) Inc.

—Coolies. 2003. (gr. 3-6). lib. bdg. 16.45 (978-0-613-62936-2(1)) Tandem Library Bks.

Zarr, Sara. Story of a Girl. 2007. 208p. (J). (gr. 7-17). 16.99 (978-0-316-01453-3(2)) Little Brown & Co.

Zolty, H. Calli the Bear: the Story of a Little Bear Who Explores California & Helps Children Learn about the Golden State. 2006. 56p. pap. 19.98 (978-1-4116-4889-0(7)) Lulu.com.

CALIFORNIA—GOLD DISCOVERIES

Aretha, David. The Gold Rush to California's Riches. 2006. (Wild History of the American West Ser.). (Illus.). 128p. (J). lib. bdg. 33.27 (978-1-59845-012-5(3) , MyReportLinks.com Bks.) Enslow Pubs., Inc.

Blashfield, Jean F. The California Gold Rush. 2000. (We the People Ser.). (Illus.). 48p. (J). (gr. 4 up). lib. bdg. 22.60 (978-0-7565-0041-2(9)) Compass Point Bks.

Brown, Rachel K. Sacramento: Daily Life in Western Mining Town. 2003. (J). pap. (978-1-58417-078-5(6)); lib. bdg. (978-1-58417-015-0(8)) Lake Street Pubs.

Burger, James P. The Quest for California's Gold. 2002. (Library of the Westward Expansion). (Illus.). 24p. (J). (gr. 3). lib. bdg. 19.95 (978-0-8239-5849-8(3) , PowerKids Pr.) Rosen Publishing Group, Inc., The.

The California Gold Rush. 2002. (Illus.). (J). pap. 6.25 (978-0-7398-6174-5(3)) Steck-Vaughn.

Craats, Rennay. Gold Rush. 2003. (Real Life Stories Ser.). (Illus.). 24p. (J). lib. bdg. 15.95 (978-1-59036-078-1(8)) Weigl Pubs., Inc.

Crewe, Sabrina & Uschan, Michael V. The California Gold Rush. 2003. (Events That Shaped America Ser.). (Illus.). 32p. (J). (gr. 3 up). lib. bdg. 24.67 (978-0-8368-3393-5(7)) Stevens, Gareth Inc.

Doeden, Matt. John Sutter & the California Gold Rush. Barnett, Charles, III & Frenz, Ron, illus. 2005. (Graphic Library). 32p. (J). (gr. 3-7). lib. bdg. 25.26 (978-0-7368-4370-6(1)) Capstone Pr., Inc.

Dolan, Edward F., Jr. The California Gold Rush. 2002. (Kaleidoscope - American History Ser.). (Illus.). 48p. (J). 25.64 (978-0-7614-1456-8(8) , Benchmark Bks.) Cavendish, Marshall Corp.

Eagan, Robynne. Gold Rush. Mitchell, Judy, ed. Hierstein, Judith, illus. 2001. (History - Hands On! Ser.). 32p. (J). (gr. 1-4). pap. 6.95 (978-1-57310-304-6(7)) Teaching & Learning Co.

Emert, Phyllis Raybin. California Gold Rush. 1998. (J). (gr. 5-9). pap. 12.00 (978-1-57960-037-2(9)) History Compass, LLC.

Goff, Elizabeth Hudson & Uschan, Michael V. The California Gold Rush. 2006. (Graphic Histories Ser.). (Illus.). (J). pap. (978-0-8368-6254-6(6)); 32p. lib. bdg. 26.00 (978-0-8368-6202-7(3)) Stevens, Gareth Inc. (World Almanac Library).

Green, Carl R. The California Trail to Gold in American History. 2000. (In American History Ser.). (Illus.). 128p. (YA). (gr. 5-12). lib. bdg. 26.60 (978-0-7660-1347-6(2)) Enslow Pubs., Inc.

Harcourt School Publishers Staff. The California Gold Rush: Take-Home Book. 2001. (Collections Ser.). (Illus.). (J). pap. 1.90 (978-0-15-319559-4(2)) Harcourt Schl. Pubs.

—Going for the Gold. 3rd ed. 2002. (Horizons Ser.). (Illus.). (J). pap. 7.30 (978-0-15-333610-2(2)) Harcourt Schl. Pubs.

Isaacs, Sally Senzell. The Gold Rush. 2003. (Illus.). 32p. (J). pap. 7.50 (978-1-4034-4772-2(1)); lib. bdg. 25.65 (978-1-4034-2501-0(9)) Heinemann Library.

Jordan, Shirley. California Gold Rush: Moments in History. 2003. (Cover-To-Cover Books). (Illus.). 64p. (J). pap. (978-0-7891-5554-2(0)); (gr. 4-7). lib. bdg. 17.95 (978-0-7569-0633-7(4)) Perfection Learning Corp.

Kallen, Stuart A. California Gold Country. 2002. (Traveler's Guide To). (Illus.). 112p. (J). 29.95 (978-1-59018-144-7(1)) Thomson Gale.

Kalman, Bobbie. The Gold Rush. 1999. (Life in the Old West Ser.). (Illus.). 32p. (J). (gr. 3-4). pap. (978-0-7787-0111-8(5)); lib. bdg. (978-0-7787-0079-1(8)) Crabtree Publishing Co.

—The Gold Rush. 1999. (Life in the Old West Ser.). (J). (978-0-606-16430-6(8)) Tandem Library Bks.

Kraft, Eric. ¡la fiebre del oro! & Gold Rush! 2005. spiral bd. 84.00 (*978-1-4108-5699-9(2)) Benchmark Education Co.

Lyngheim, Linda. California Gold Rush Projects & Activities. Garber, Phyllis, illus. 1998. (California Junior Heritage Ser.). 56p. (J). (gr. 3-12). pap. 9.95 (978-0-915369-07-2(9)) Langtry Pubns.

Mason, Paul. Panning for Gold. 2007. (J). pap. (*978-1-4109-2865-8(9)) Steck-Vaughn.

—Panning for Gold: Mixtures & Solutions. 2007. (Raintree Fusion: Physical Science Ser.). (Illus.). 32p. (J). lib. bdg. (*978-1-4109-2848-1(9)) Steck-Vaughn.

McCall, Edith. Gold Rush Adventures. 2001. (Adventures on the American Frontier Ser.: Bk. 9). (Illus.). 127p. (J). (gr. 3-6). pap. 9.99 (978-0-89824-310-9(6) , 3106) Royal Fireworks Publishing Co.

Monroe, Judy. The California Gold Rush. 2002. (Let Freedom Ring Ser.). (Illus.). 48p. (J). (gr. 3-4). lib. bdg. 22.60 (978-0-7368-1098-2(6) , Bridgestone Bks.) Capstone Pr., Inc.

O'Donnell, Kerri. The California Gold Rush: Multiplying & Dividing Using Three- & Four-Digit Numbers. 2005. (PowerMath Ser.). (Illus.). 32p. (J). 22.50 (978-1-4042-2934-1(5)); pap. 22.50 (978-1-4042-5131-1(6)) Rosen Publishing Group, Inc., The. (PowerKids Pr.).

Quasha, Jennifer. Gold Rush: Hands-On Projects about Mining the Riches of California. 2001. (Great Social Studies Projects Ser.). (Illus.). 24p. (J). (gr. 3). lib. bdg. 19.95 (978-0-8239-5705-7(5) , PowerKids Pr.) Rosen Publishing Group, Inc., The.

Raabe, Emily. The Gold Rush: California or Bust! 2003. (Reading Power Ser.). (Illus.). 24p. (J). lib. bdg. 17.25 (978-0-8239-6494-9(9) , PowerKids Pr.) Rosen Publishing Group, Inc., The.

Rau, Margaret. The Wells Fargo Book of the Gold Rush. 2003. (Illus.). 143p. (J). (gr. 3-7). reprint ed. 18.00 (978-0-7567-6878-2(0)) DIANE Publishing Co.

Raum, Elizabeth. The California Gold Rush: An Interactive History Adventure. 2008. (You Choose Bks.). 112p. (J). (gr. 3-7). lib. bdg. 27.23 (*978-1-4296-0160-3(4)) Capstone Pr., Inc.

Rivera, Sheila. California Gold Rush. 2005. (American Moments Ser.). (Illus.). 48p. (J). (gr. 4-8). lib. bdg. 25.65 (978-1-59197-281-5(7)) ABDO Publishing Co.

Roop, Connie & Roop, Peter, eds. The Diary of David R. Leeper: Rushing for Gold. 2000. (In My Own Words Ser.). (Illus.). 78p. (J). (gr. 5 up). lib. bdg. 27.07 (978-0-7614-1011-9(2) , Benchmark Bks.) Cavendish, Marshall Corp.

Saffer, Barbara. The California Gold Rush. 2002. (History of the Old West Ser.). (Illus.). 64p. (J). (gr. 5-7). lib. bdg. (978-1-59084-060-3(7)) Mason Crest Pubs.

Schanzer, Rosalyn. Gold Fever! Tales from the California Gold Rush. (Illus.). 48p. (J). 2007. (gr. 4-9). pap. 6.95 (978-1-4263-0040-0(9)); 1999. (gr. 1-4). 17.95 (978-0-7922-7303-5(6)) National Geographic Society. (National Geographic Children's Bks.).

Scholastic, Inc. Staff, contrib. by. Gold Rush. 2002. (Instant Social Studies Activities Folders Ser.). (Illus.). 6p. (J). (gr. 4-8). 3.95 (978-0-439-37082-0(5)) Scholastic, Inc.

Schroeder, Lisa Golden. California Gold Rush Cooking. 2000. (Blue Earth Books). (Illus.). 32p. (J). (gr. 3-4). lib. bdg. 22.60 (978-0-7368-0603-9(2) , Bridgestone Bks.) Capstone Pr., Inc.

Somervill, Barbara A. The Gold Rush: Buried Treasure. 2005. (Trailblazers of the West Ser.). (Illus.). 48p. (J). (ps-7). 24.00 (978-0-516-25129-5(5)); (YA). (gr. 7-12). pap. 6.95 (978-0-516-25099-1(X)) Scholastic Library Publishing. (Children's Pr.).

Thompson, Linda. The California Gold Rush. (Expansion of America Ser.). 48p. 2005. (Illus.). (gr. 4-8). 20.95 (978-1-59515-222-0(9)); 2004. pap. 7.95 (978-1-59515-322-7(5)) Rourke Publishing, LLC.

Uschan, Michael V. The California Gold Rush. 2003. (Landmark Events in American History Ser.). (Illus.). 48p. (J). (gr. 5 up). pap. 14.95 (978-0-8368-5402-2(0)); lib. bdg. 30.00 (978-0-8368-5374-2(1)) Stevens, Gareth Inc. (World Almanac Library).

CALIFORNIA—HISTORY

Abbink, Emily. Monterey Bay Area Missions. 2007. (Exploring California Missions Ser.). (J). 27.93 (*978-0-8225-0887-8(7) , Lerner Pubns.) Lerner Publishing Group.

Alef, Daniel. Centennial Stories: A Living History of San Francisco. 2nd ed. 2000. (Illus.). 227p. (J). pap. 15.95 (978-0-9700174-2-0(1)) Maxit Publishing, Inc.

Altman, Linda Jacobs. California. 2005. (Celebrate the States Ser.). (Illus.). 144p. (J). (gr. 4-7). lib. bdg. 37.07 (978-0-7614-1737-8(0) , Benchmark Bks.) Cavendish, Marshall Corp.

Anderson, Dale. The California Missions. 2002. (Landmark Events in American History Ser.). (Illus.). 48p. (J). (gr. 5 up). lib. bdg. 30.00 (978-0-8368-5339-1(3)); pap. 14.60 (978-0-8368-5353-7(9)) Stevens, Gareth Inc. (World Almanac Library).

Ansary, Mir Tamim. California History. (Heinemann State Studies). (Illus.). 48p. (J). 2003. (gr. 3-5). lib. bdg. (978-1-4034-0340-7(6)); 2002. pap. 8.50 (978-1-4034-0557-9(3)) Heinemann Library.

Baker, Gayle. Cambria: A HarborTown History. 2003. (Illus.). 96p. per. 8.95 (978-0-9710984-2-8(5)) HarborTown Histories.

—Newport Beach: A HarborTown History. 2004. (Illus.). 112p. per. 9.95 (978-0-9710984-3-5(3)) HarborTown Histories.

—Santa Barbara: A HarborTown History. 2003. (Illus.). 96p. per. 8.95 (978-0-9710984-1-1(7)) HarborTown Histories.

Behrens, June. Central Coast Missions in California. 2007. (Exploring California Missions Ser.). (J). 27.93 (*978-0-8225-0897-7(4) , Lerner Pubns.) Lerner Publishing Group.

Binns, Tristan Boyer. Mission San Juan Capistrano. 2002. (Visiting the Past Ser.). (Illus.). 32p. (J). (gr. 5-7). pap. 6.95 (978-1-58810-410-6(9) , 91183) Heinemann Library.

—San Juan Capistrano. 2001. (Visiting the Past Ser.). (Illus.). 32p. (J). (gr. 5-7). lib. bdg. 24.22 (978-1-58810-272-0(6)) Heinemann Library.

Blashfield, Jean F. The California Gold Rush. 2000. (We the People Ser.). (Illus.). 48p. (J). (gr. 4 up). lib. bdg. 22.60 (978-0-7565-0041-2(9)) Compass Point Bks.

Boekhoff, P. M. & Kallen, Stuart A. California. 2001. (Seeds of a Nation Ser.). (Illus.). 48p. (J). (gr. 3-5). 23.70 (978-0-7377-0946-9(4) , LML00902-178532, Kidhaven) Thomson Gale.

Boule, Mary Null. California Native American Tribes: Mohave Tribe, 28 booklets. Liddell, Daniel & Basta, Mary, illus. (California Native American Tribes). 52p. (J). (gr. 3-6). pap. 7.95 (978-1-877599-73-6(5)) Merryant Pubs.

—California's Native American Tribes, 26 vols. Liddell, Daniel & Basta, Mary, illus. 2000. 52p. (J). (gr. 3-6). pap. 108.00 (978-1-877599-23-1(9)) Merryant Pubs.

Brimner, Larry Dane. Angel Island. 2001. (gr. 3-6). lib. bdg. 14.10 (978-0-613-51973-1(6)) Tandem Library Bks.

Britton, Tamara L. Angel Island. 2005. (Illus.). 32p. (J). (gr. k-6). lib. bdg. 22.78 (978-1-59197-832-9(7)) ABDO Publishing Co.

Brower, Pauline. Inland Valley Missions in California. 2007. (Exploring California Missions Ser.). (J). 27.93 (*978-0-8225-0899-1(0) , Lerner Pubns.) Lerner Publishing Group.

Brown, Rachel K. Sacramento: Daily Life in Western Mining Town. 2003. (J). pap. (978-1-58417-078-5(6)) Lake Street Pubs.

California Missions Fact Cards. 2nd rev. ed. 1998. (Illus.). 48p. (J). (gr. 3-6). ring bd. 24.00 (978-1-884925-05-4(7)) Toucan Valley Pubns., Inc.

Campbell, Wallis. Angel Island. 2006. (Illus.). 48p. (J). pap. (978-1-59034-808-6(7)) Mondo Publishing.

Cassanos, Lynda Cohen. Sutter's Fort. 2004. (American Forts & Their Strategic Importance Ser.). (J). (978-1-59084-709-1(1)) Mason Crest Pubs.

Cherny, Robert, et al. Competing Visions: A History of California. 2000. (Illus.). 464p. (YA). 77.16 (978-0-395-95964-0(0) , 310283) Houghton Mifflin College Div.

Coleman, Wim & Perrin, Pat. The Rebellious Californians & the Brave Struggle to Join the Nation. 2006. (Wild History of the American West Ser.). (Illus.). 128p. (J). lib. bdg. 33.27 (978-1-59845-015-6(8) , MyReportLinks.com Bks.) Enslow Pubs., Inc.

Crewe, Sabrina & Uschan, Michael V. The California Gold Rush. 2003. (Events That Shaped America Ser.). (Illus.). 32p. (J). (gr. 3 up). lib. bdg. 24.67 (978-0-8368-3393-5(7)) Stevens, Gareth Inc.

Davis, Rebecca & Sprinkle, Karen. Riverside's History from Its First People to the Present: Third Grade Student Edition. Tobias, Martin & Pratt, Jan, illus. 1998. 141p. (J). (gr. 3-6). pap., stu. ed. 5.00 (978-0-935661-29-3(8)) Riverside Museum Pr.

De Capua, Sarah. California. 2005. (Rookie Espanol: Geografia Ser.). (SPA., Illus.). 32p. (J). (gr. k-2). pap. 5.95 (978-0-516-25513-2(4) , Children's Pr.) Scholastic Library Publishing.

Denis-Huot, Christine. The Zebra: Striped Horse. 1999. (Animal Close-Ups Ser.). (978-0-606-16408-5(1)) Tandem Library Bks.

Dentro de California Salvaje. 2005. (Jeff Corwin Experience Ser.). (ENG & SPA., Illus.). 48p. (J). (ps-7). lib. bdg. 24.95 (978-1-4103-0671-5(2) , Blackbirch Pr., Inc.) Thomson Gale.

Ditchfield, Christin. Spanish Missions. 2006. 48p. (gr. 3-5). (YA). pap. 6.95 (978-0-516-21746-8(1)); (Illus.). (J). 25.00 (978-0-516-22834-1(X)) Scholastic Library Publishing. (Children's Pr.).

Doak, Robin & National Geographic Society Staff. California 1542-1850. 2006. (Voices from Colonial America Ser.). (Illus.). 112p. (J). (gr. 5-9). 21.95 (978-0-7922-6391-3(X)); lib. bdg. 32.90 (978-0-7922-6861-1(X)) National Geographic Society. (National Geographic Children's Bks.).

Dolan, Edward F., Jr. The California Gold Rush. 2002. (Kaleidoscope - American History Ser.). (Illus.). 48p. (J). 25.64 (978-0-7614-1456-8(8) , Benchmark Bks.) Cavendish, Marshall Corp.

Douglas, Julie. Fun Facts & Games: California. Nolte, Larry, illus. 2000. (Fun Facts & Games Ser.). 64p. (J). (ps-3). pap. 5.95 (978-1-892920-22-5(0)) GHB Publishers, LLC.

Doyle, Peter R. Bunker Hill. 1999. (Drums of War Ser.: Vol. 2). 172p. (YA). (gr. 4-12). pap. 7.95 (978-1-887456-08-1(2)) Providence Foundation.

Dunn, Joeming W. California Gold Rush. Dunn, Ben, illus. 2007. (Graphic History Ser.). 32p. (J). (gr. 3-6). lib. bdg. 27.07 (*978-1-60270-076-5(1) , Graphic Planet) Magic Wagon.

Fletcher, Susan. Walk Across the Sea. Jakesevic, Nenad, illus. 2001. 224p. (J). (gr. 5-9). 16.95 (978-0-689-84133-0(7) , Atheneum) Simon & Schuster Children's Publishing.

Fuego en California! Libros Aventuras (Adventure Books) 2000. (MacMillan/McGraw-Hill. Estudios Sociales Ser.). (ENG & SPA.). (gr. 2 up). (978-0-02-148676-2(X)) Macmillan/McGraw-Hill Schl. Div.

Goff, Elizabeth Hudson & Uschan, Michael V. The California Gold Rush. 2006. (Graphic Histories Ser.). (Illus.). (J). pap. (978-0-8368-6254-6(6)); 32p. lib. bdg. 26.00 (978-0-8368-6202-7(3)) Stevens, Gareth Inc. (World Almanac Library).

Green, Carl R. The California Trail to Gold in American History. 2000. (In American History Ser.). (Illus.). 128p. (YA). (gr. 5-12). lib. bdg. 26.60 (978-0-7660-1347-6(2)) Enslow Pubs., Inc.

—The Mission Trails in American History. 2001. (In American History Ser.). (Illus.). 128p. (YA). (gr. 5-12). lib. bdg. 26.60 (978-0-7660-1349-0(9)) Enslow Pubs., Inc.

Heinrichs, Ann. The California Missions. 2002. (We the People Ser.). (Illus.). 48p. (J). (gr. 4 up). lib. bdg. 22.60 (978-0-7565-0208-9(X)) Compass Point Bks.

Herrera, Matthew D. History Guide to Old Mission San Luis Obispo de Tolosa. 2003. (Illus.). 77p. 9.95 (978-0-9723720-1-5(6)) Tixlini Scriptorium, Inc.

Isaacs, Sally Senzell. The Gold Rush. 2003. (Illus.). 32p. (J). pap. 7.50 (978-1-4034-4772-2(1)); lib. bdg. 25.65 (978-1-4034-2501-0(9)) Heinemann Library.

—Life in a California Mission. (Picture the Past Ser.). (Illus.). 32p. (J). 2002. (gr. k-3). pap. 7.50 (978-1-58810-414-4(1) , 91187); 2001. (gr. 2-4). lib. bdg. 21.36 (978-1-58810-249-2(1)) Heinemann Library.

Jacobstein, Bennett. Profiles of the California Governors. 1999. (California Government Ser.). (Illus.). 48p. (J). (gr. 4-10). pap. 14.95 (978-1-884925-98-6(7)) Toucan Valley Pubns., Inc.

Jacobstein, David. California Through the Decades Fact Cards. Yamaguma, Reiko, illus. 1999. 54p. (J). (gr. 4-8). ring bd. 32.00 (978-1-884925-70-2(7)) Toucan Valley Pubns., Inc.

Jaskol, Julie & Lewis, Brian. City of Angels: In & Around Los Angeles. Kleven, Elisa, illus. 1999. 48p. (J). (ps-3). 16.99 (978-0-525-46214-9(7) , Dutton Juvenile) Penguin Group (USA) Inc.

Jordan, Shirley. California Gold Rush: Moments in History. 2003. (Cover-To-Cover Books). (Illus.). 64p. (J). pap. (978-0-7891-5554-2(0)); (gr. 4-7). lib. bdg. 17.95 (978-0-7569-0633-7(4)) Perfection Learning Corp.

Kallen, Stuart A. California Gold Country. 2002. (Traveler's Guide To). (Illus.). 112p. (J). 29.95 (978-1-59018-144-7(1)) Thomson Gale.

Kay, Verla. Rough, Tough Charley. Gustavson, Adam, illus. 2006. 32p. (J). (ps-3). 15.95 (*978-1-58246-184-7(8) , Tricycle Pr.) Ten Speed Pr.

Keremitsis, Eileen. Life in a California Mission. 2002. (Way People Live Ser.). (Illus.). 112p. (J). (gr. 7-10). 29.95 (978-1-59018-159-1(X) , Lucent Bks.) Thomson Gale.

Lemke, Nancy. Southern Coast Missions in California. 2007. (Exploring California Missions Ser.). (J). 27.93 (*978-0-8225-1935-5(6) , Lerner Pubns.) Lerner Publishing Group.

Linse, Barbara B. Live Again Our Mission Past for Kids. Kuska, George & Clark, Cynthia, illus. 2000. (California Mission Ser.). (SPA.). 108p. (J). (gr. 4-7). pap. (978-1-878079-26-8(3)) Arts Pubns.

Little, Jane Braxton. Plumas Sketches. Posner, Sally, illus. 3rd exp. ed. 2002. per. 19.95 net. (978-0-9611886-2-7(6)) Wolf Creek Pr.

Marschner, Janice. California 1850: A Snapshot in Time. 2nd rev. ed. 2001. (Illus.). 275p. lib. bdg. 19.95 (978-0-9677069-4-8(7)) Coleman Ranch Pr.

—California's Arab Americans. 2003. (Illus.). 160p. lib. bdg. 18.95 (978-0-9677069-7-9(1)) Coleman Ranch Pr.

Marsh, Carole. California History Projects: 30 Cool, Activities, Crafts, Experiments & More for Kids to Do to Learn about Your State! 2003. (California Experience Ser.). 32p. (gr. k-5). pap. 5.95 (978-0-635-01774-1(1) , Marsh, Carole Bks.) Gallopade International.

McAuliffe, Emily. California: Facts & Symbols. 1998. (States & Their Symbols Ser.). 24p. (J). lib. bdg. 14.00 (978-0-531-11548-0(8) , Watts, Franklin) Scholastic Library Publishing.

Minch, John, et al. Caminos de Baja California: Geologia y Biologica Para Su Viaje. Minch, Jason, ed. Ledesma Vazquez, Jorge, tr. Minch, Edwin, illus. Minch, John, photos by. 2003. (SPA.). 192p. per. 23.95 (978-0-9631090-2-6(2)) Minch, John & Assocs., Inc.

The Missions of California, 21 bks. Incl. Mission la Purisima Concepcion. Ostrow, Kim. 2000. lib. bdg. 25.50 (978-0-8239-5498-8(6)); Mission Nuestra Senora de la Soledad. Ostrow, Kim. 2000. lib. bdg. 25.50 (978-0-8239-5500-8(1)); Mission San Antonio de Padua. Serafin, Kim. 2000. lib. bdg. 25.50 (978-0-8239-5489-6(7)); Mission San Buenaventura. Margaret, Amy. 2000. lib. bdg. 25.50 (978-0-8239-5496-4(X)); Mission San Carlos Borromeo del Rio Carmela. Edgar, Kathleen J. & Edgar, Susan E. 2000. lib. bdg. 25.50 (978-0-8239-5488-9(9)); Mission San Diego de Alcala. Edgar, Kathleen J. & Edgar, Susan E. 2000. lib. bdg. 25.50 (978-0-8239-5487-2(0)); Mission San Fernando Rey de Espana. Ching, Jacqueline. 2000. lib. bdg. 25.50 (978-0-8239-5503-9(6)); Mission San Francisco de Asis. Edgar, Kathleen J. & Edgar, Susan E. 2000. lib. bdg. 25.50 (978-0-8239-5492-6(7)); Mission San Francisco de Solano. Draper, Allison Stark. 2000. lib. bdg. 25.50 (978-0-8239-5507-7(9)); Mission San Gabriel Arcangel. McGinty, Alice B. 2000. lib. bdg. 25.50 (978-0-8239-5490-2(0)); Mission San Jose de Guadalupe. Margaret, Amy. 2000. lib. bdg. 25.50 (978-0-8239-5495-7(1)); Mission San Juan Bautista. Draper, Allison Stark. 2000. lib. bdg. 25.50 (978-0-8239-5501-5(X)); Mission San Juan Capistrano. Edgar, Kathleen J. & Edgar, Susan E. 2000. lib. bdg. 25.50 (978-0-8239-5493-3(5)); Mission San Luis Obispo de Tolosa. Edgar, Kathleen J. & Edgar, Susan E. 2000. lib. bdg. 25.50 (978-0-8239-5491-9(9)); Mission San Luis Rey de Francia. Quasha, Jennifer. 1999. lib. bdg. 25.50 (978-0-8239-5504-6(4)); Mission San Miguel Arcangel. Edgar, Kathleen J. & Edgar, Nancy A. 2000. lib. bdg. 25.50 (978-0-8239-5502-2(8)); Mission San Rafael Arcangel. Ching, Jacqueline. 2000. lib. bdg. 25.50 (978-0-8239-5506-0(0)); Mission Santa Barbara. Margaret, Amy. 2000. lib. bdg. 25.50 (978-0-8239-5497-1(8)); Mission Santa Clara de Asis. Margaret, Amy. 2000. lib. bdg. 25.50 (978-0-8239-5494-0(3)); Mission Santa Cruz. Ostrow, Kim. 2000. lib. bdg. 25.50 (978-0-8239-5499-5(4)); Mission Santa Ines. Ching, Jacqueline. 2000. lib. bdg. 25.50 (978-0-8239-5505-3(2)); 64p. (J). (gr. 4). (Illus.). Set lib. bdg. 535.50 (978-0-8239-5706-4(3) , MISET, PowerKids Pr.) Rosen Publishing Group, Inc., The.

Montes, Marisa. A Circle of Time. 2002. (Time Travel Mystery Ser.). 272p. (YA). (gr. 6-10). 17.00 (978-0-15-202626-4(6)) Harcourt Children's Bks.

Mosier, Dan L. & Williams, Earle E. History of Tesla: A California Coal Mining Town. 2nd rev. ed. 2002. (Illus.). 360p. per. 29.95 (978-1-889064-08-6(4)) Mines Road Bks.

Murphy, Claire Rudolf. Children of Alcatraz: Growing up on the Rock. 2006. (Illus.). 64p. (J). 18.85 (978-0-8027-9578-6(1)); 17.95 (978-0-8027-9577-9(3)) Walker & Co.

Murray, Julie. California. 2005. (Buddy Book Ser.). (Illus.). 32p. (J). (gr. k-4). lib. bdg. 22.78 (978-1-59197-664-6(2) , Buddy Bks.) ABDO Publishing Co.

Oney, Yannick. First American Colonies. 2004. (World Discovery History Readers Ser.). (Illus.). 32p. (J). pap. (978-0-439-66555-1(8)) Scholastic, Inc.

Perissinotto, Giorgio Sabino Antonio, ed. & tr. from SPA. The California Recollections of Angustias de la Guerra Ord: (Occurrences in Hispanic California) Perissinotto, Giorgio Sabino Antonio, tr. 2004. (ENG & SPA.). xxi, 172p. (978-0-88382-157-2(5)) Academy of American Franciscan History.

Phelan, Regina V. They Came Overland by Train, Vol. 6. Champy, Al, illus. l.t. ed. 1999. (History of California for the Young Reader Ser.). 63p. (J). lib. bdg. 15.00 (978-0-87062-295-3(1) , Clark, Arthur H. Co., The) Univ. of Oklahoma Pr.

Philipp, Cathy. On the Trail Again: Malibu to Santa Barbara, 1. Philipp, Cathy et al, photos by. 2004. (Illus.). 252p. per. (978-0-9655848-1-4(X)) Philipp, Cathy Publishing.

Presnall, Judith Janda. Life on Alcatraz. 2000. (Way People Live Ser.). (Illus.). 112p. (J). (gr. 7-10). 28.70 (978-1-56006-639-2(3) , LML00902-177994, Lucent Bks.) Thomson Gale.

Price, Sean. The Birth of a State: California Missions. 2007. (J). (*978-1-4109-2694-4(X)); pap. (*978-1-4109-2705-7(9)) Steck-Vaughn.

Raum, Elizabeth. Birth & Death of a City. 2006. (Illus.). 32p. (J). (978-1-4109-2597-8(8)); pap. (978-1-4109-2626-5(5)) Steck-Vaughn.

—The California Gold Rush: An Interactive History Adventure. 2008. (You Choose Bks.). 112p. (J). (gr. 3-7). lib. bdg. 27.23 (*978-1-4296-0160-3(4)) Capstone Pr., Inc.

—Fusion: On the Move. 2007. (Illus.). 32p. (J). (*978-1-4062-0480-3(3)); pap. (*978-1-4062-0505-3(2)) Steck-Vaughn.

Reinstedt, Randall A. Tales & Treasures of California's Ranchos. Bergez, John, ed. Greco, Ed, illus. 1999. (History & Happenings of California Ser.). 127p. (J). (gr. 3-6). 14.95 (978-0-933818-29-3(7)) Ghost Town Pubns.

Richter, Glenda. The Stories of Juana Briones: Alta California Pioneer. Heywood, Della, illus. 2002. 64p. (J). (gr. 3-6). 14.95 (978-0-9700379-0-9(2)); pap. 7.95 (978-0-9700379-1-6(0)) Bookhandler Pr.

Rosinsky, Natalie M. California Ranchos. 2006. (We the People Ser.). (Illus.). 48p. (J). (gr. 4-6). 23.93 (978-0-7565-1633-8(1)) Compass Point Bks.

Ryan, Pam Muñoz. Our California. Lopez, Rafael, illus. 2008. (J). lib. bdg. ***(978-1-58089-116-5(0))*** Charlesbridge Publishing, Inc.

Ryan, Pam Muñoz & Lopez, Rafael. Nuestra California. Lopez, Rafael, illus. 2008. (SPA & ENG.). ***(978-1-58089-226-1(4))*** Charlesbridge Publishing, Inc.

Scarbrough, Mary Hertz. A California Mission. 2005. (Daily Life Ser.). (J). (978-0-7377-3090-6(0) , Greenhaven Pr., Inc.) Thomson Gale.

Schanzer, Rosalyn. Gold Fever! Tales from the California Gold Rush. 1999. (Illus.). 48p. (J). (gr. 1-4). 17.95 (978-0-7922-7303-5(6) , National Geographic Children's Bks.) National Geographic Society.

Sherrow, Victoria. San Francisco Earthquake, 1989: Death & Destruction. 1998. (American Disasters Ser.). (Illus.). 48p. (YA). (gr. 4-10). lib. bdg. 23.93 (978-0-7660-1060-4(0)) Enslow Pubs., Inc.

Somervill, Barbara A. The Gold Rush: Buried Treasure. 2005. (Trailblazers of the West Ser.). (Illus.). 48p. (J). (ps-7). 24.00 (978-0-516-25129-5(5)); (YA). (gr. 7-12). pap. 6.95 (978-0-516-25099-1(X)) Scholastic Library Publishing. (Children's Pr.).

Steele, Christy. California & the Southwest Join the United States. 2005. (Illus.). 48p. (J). pap. (978-0-8368-5793-1(3) , World Almanac Library) Stevens, Gareth Inc.

Thompson, Gare. Missions & Ranchos: Early California Life. 2004. (National Geographic Reading Expeditions Ser.). (Illus.). 40p. (J). pap. (978-0-7922-4548-3(2)) National Geographic Society.

—When the Mission Padre Came to the Rancho: The Early California Adventures of Rosalinda & Simon Delgado. 2004. (I Am American Ser.). (Illus.). 40p. (J). (gr. 3-7). pap. 6.99 (978-0-7922-6945-8(4) , National Geographic Children's Bks.) National Geographic Society.

Trahan, Kendra & Hawkins, Dave. Disneyland Detective: An Independent Guide to Discovering Disney's Legend, Lore, & Magic. McKim, Brian & Yamauchi, Karl, illus. 2004. 248p. (gr. 7-12). pap. 19.95 (978-0-9717464-0-4(0)) PermaGrin Publishing.

Uschan, Michael V. The California Gold Rush. 2003. (Landmark Events in American History Ser.). (Illus.). 48p. (J). (gr. 5 up). pap. 14.95 (978-0-8368-5402-2(0)); lib. bdg. 30.00 (978-0-8368-5374-2(1)) Stevens, Gareth Inc. (World Almanac Library).

Van Steenwyk, Elizabeth. The California Missions. 1998. (Illus.). 63p. (J). (gr. 4-7). lib. bdg. 15.25 (978-0-613-53978-4(8)) Tandem Library Bks.

Wagner, Harr. California History for Children: Short Stories from Cabrillo in 1542 to the San Francisco Earthquake. Stevenson, James, ed. 1999. (Illus.). 79p. (J). pap. 8.95 (978-1-885852-12-0(6)) James Stevenson Pub.

Weber, Valerie J. & Anderson, Dale. The California Missions. 2002. (Events That Shaped America Ser.). (Illus.). 32p. (J). (gr. 3 up). lib. bdg. 24.67 (978-0-8368-3223-5(X)) Stevens, Gareth Inc.

Williams, Jack S. The California Presidios. 2004. (American Forts & Their Strategic Importance Ser.). (J). (978-1-59084-711-4(3)) Mason Crest Pubs.

—Craftsmen & Craftswomen. 2004. (People of the California Missions Ser.). (Illus.). 64p. (J). lib. bdg. 25.50 (978-0-8239-6280-8(6) , PowerKids Pr.) Rosen Publishing Group, Inc., The.

Williams, Jack S. & Davis, Thomas L. Padres of the California Mission Frontier. 2004. (People of the California Missions Ser.). (Illus.). 64p. (J). lib. bdg. 25.50 (978-0-8239-6283-9(0) , PowerKids Pr.) Rosen Publishing Group, Inc., The.

—Sailors, Merchants, & Muleteers. 2004. (People of the California Missions Ser.). (Illus.). 64p. (J). lib. bdg. 25.50 (978-0-8239-6282-2(2)) Rosen Publishing Group, Inc., The.

—Soldiers & Their Families of the California Mission Frontier. 2004. (People of the California Missions Ser.). (Illus.). 64p. (J). lib. bdg. 25.50 (978-0-8239-6285-3(7)) Rosen Publishing Group, Inc., The.

—Townspeople & Ranchers of the California Mission Frontier. 2004. (People of the California Missions Ser.). (Illus.). 64p. (J). lib. bdg. 25.50 (978-0-8239-6284-6(9) , PowerKids Pr.) Rosen Publishing Group, Inc., The.

Willis, Linda. Between the Floods: Happy Camp, CA from 1956-1965. 2002. (Illus.). 281p. 14.95 net. (978-0-615-12228-1(0) , 1) Willis' Wiki-up.

CALIFORNIA, UNIVERSITY OF

Epstein, Brad M., ed. UCLA 101: My First Text-Board-Book. l.t. ed. 2004. (My First Text Board Bks.). (Illus.). 20p. (J). bds. 9.95 (978-1-932530-15-5(0)) Michaelson Entertainment.

CALISTHENICS

see Exercise

CALLIGRAPHY

Campbell, Fiona. Calligraphy. 2005. (Illus.). 32p. (J). (gr. 3-6). lib. bdg. 27.10 (978-1-932889-83-3(3) , 1247649) Sea-To-Sea Pubns.

Campbell, Fiona & Watt, Fiona. Calligraphy. 1999. (Arts & Crafts Skills Ser.). (Illus.). 32p. (gr. 3-6). pap. 6.95 (978-0-516-26450-9(8) , Children's Pr.) Scholastic Library Publishing.

Halliday, Peter. Creative Calligraphy: A Do-It-Yourself Guide to Decorative Lettering. Halliday, Peter, illus. 2000. (Illus.). 40p. (J). (gr. 5-8). pap. 5.95 (978-1-85697-539-1(8) , Kingfisher) Houghton Mifflin Co. Trade & Reference Div.

Phillips, Karen. Klutz Lettering. Date not set. 60p. (J). spiral bd. 16.95 (978-1-57054-428-6(X)) Klutz.

Potter, Tony. Calligraphy for Kids: Learn Lettering Skills. Knowles, Patrick, illus. 2006. 48p. (J). 10.99 (978-0-7641-5923-7(2)) Barron's Educational Series, Inc.

Top That Publishing Staff, ed. Calligraphy Skills. (Illus.). 48p. 2005. (978-1-84510-302-6(5)); 2004. (978-1-84510-319-4(X)) Top That! Publishing PLC.

Top That!, creator. Cachet Calligraphy. 2005. (Illus.). 48p. (978-1-84510-510-5(9)) Top That! Publishing PLC.

Watt, Fiona. Calligraphy. 1999. pap. 3.99 (978-0-516-24118-0(4) , Children's Pr.) Scholastic Library Publishing.

Winters, Eleanor. Calligraphy for Kids. (Illus.). 128p. 2007. (J). pap. 9.95 (978-1-4027-3912-5(5)); 2004. 14.95 (978-1-4027-0664-6(2)) Sterling Publishing Co., Inc.

—1-2-3 Calligraphy! Letters & Projects for Beginners & Beyond. 2006. (Illus.). 128p. (gr. 4 up). 14.95 (978-1-4027-1839-7(X) , 1251928) Sterling Publishing Co., Inc.

CALVERT FAMILY

Robinson, J. Dennis. Lord Baltimore: Founders of Maryland. 2006. (Signature Lives Ser.). (Illus.). 112p. (J). (gr. 5-7). 30.60 (978-0-7565-1592-8(0)) Compass Point Bks.

Whiting, Jim. The Maryland Colony: Lord Baltimore. 2007. (Illus.). 48p. (J). lib. bdg. 29.95 ***(978-1-58415-547-8(7))*** Mitchell Lane Pubs., Inc.

CALVIN, JEAN, 1509-1564

Davis, Thomas J. John Calvin. 2004. (Spiritual Leaders & Thinkers Ser.). (Illus.). 120p. (J). (gr. 9-13). 30.00 (978-0-7910-8100-6(1) , Chelsea Hse.) Facts On File, Inc.

McPherson, Joyce. The River of Grace: The Story of John Calvin. Robinson, Jennifer B., illus. 1999. 140p. (YA). (gr. 5-12). pap. 7.95 (978-1-882514-54-0(8)) Greenleaf Pr.

CAMBISTRY

see Weights and Measures

CAMBODIA

Allen, John. Pol Pot. 2005. (History's Villains Ser.). (Illus.). 112p. (J). (gr. 5-7). lib. bdg. 28.70 (978-1-56711-901-5(8) , Blackbirch Pr., Inc.) Thomson Gale.

Canesso, Claudia. Cambodia. 1999. (Major World Nations Ser.). (Illus.). 144p. (YA). (gr. 4-7). 29.95 (978-0-7910-4732-3(6) , Chelsea Hse.) Facts On File, Inc.

De Silva, Dayaneetha. Cambodia. 2000. (Countries of the World Ser.). (Illus.). 96p. (J). (gr. 6 up). lib. bdg. 30.00 (978-0-8368-2322-6(2)) Stevens, Gareth Inc.

Deedrick, Tami. Khmer Empire. 2001. (Ancient Civilizations Ser.). (Illus.). 48p. (J). lib. bdg. 22.83 (978-0-7398-3586-9(6)) Raintree.

—The Khmer Empire. 2000. (Ancient Civilizations Ser.). (Illus.). (J). pap. 7.20 (978-0-7398-4154-9(8)) Steck-Vaughn.

Diep, Bridgette. Trip Through Cambodia. Vaing, Jocelang, illus. 32p. (J). (ps-3). 14.95 (978-0-87592-054-2(3)) Scroll Pr., Inc.

Green, Robert. Cambodia. 2003. (Modern Nations of the World Ser.). (Illus.). 112p. (J). 29.95 (978-1-59018-109-6(3) , Lucent Bks.) Thomson Gale.

Kras, Sara Louise. Cambodia. 2005. (Enchantment of the World, Second Ser.). (Illus.). 144p. (YA). (gr. 5-9). 36.00 (978-0-516-23679-7(2) , Children's Pr.) Scholastic Library Publishing.

Lord, Michelle. A Song for Cambodia. Arihara, Shino, illus. 2008. (J). ***(978-1-60060-139-2(1))*** Lee & Low Bks., Inc.

Max, Jill. Strangers in Black: A Young Boy's Struggle to Survive in Khmer Rouge Cambodia. 2006. (J). pap. (978-0-88092-617-1(1)); lib. bdg. (978-0-88092-616-4(3)) Royal Fireworks Publishing Co.

Nobleman, Marc Tyler. Cambodia. 2002. (Countries of the World Ser.). (Illus.). 126p. (J). (gr. 2-3). 18.60 (978-0-7368-1370-9(5) , Bridgestone Bks.) Capstone Pr., Inc.

Sheehan, Sean & Cooke, Barbara. Cambodia. 2nd ed. 2007. (Cultures of the World Ser.). 144p. (J). lib. bdg. 39.93 (978-0-7614-2071-2(1) , Benchmark Bks.) Cavendish, Marshall Corp.

Taus-Bolstad, Stacy & Goldstein, Margaret J. Cambodia in Pictures. 2nd rev. expurg. ed. 2004. (Visual Geography Ser.). (Illus.). 80p. (J). (gr. 5-12). 27.93 (978-0-8225-1994-2(1)) Lerner Publishing Group.

Yip, Dora & De Silva, Dayaneetha. Welcome to Cambodia. 2001. (Welcome to My Country Ser.). (Illus.). 48p. (J). (gr. 2 up). lib. bdg. 26.00 (978-0-8368-2522-0(5)) Stevens, Gareth Inc.

CAMBODIA—FICTION

Ho, Minfong. The Stone Goddess. 2003. (First Person Fiction Ser.). 208p. (J). (gr. 4-7). pap. 16.95 (978-0-439-38197-0(5) , Orchard Bks.) Scholastic, Inc.

Lipp, Frederick. Running Shoes. Gaillard, Jason, illus. 2008. (J). ***(978-1-58089-175-2(6))*** Charlesbridge Publishing, Inc.

Lord, Michelle. Little Sap & Monsieur Rodin. Hoshino, Felicia, illus. 2006. 32p. (J). (ps-3). 16.95 (978-1-58430-248-3(8)) Lee & Low Bks., Inc.

Ly, Many. Roots & Wings. 2008. 256p. (YA). (gr. 7). lib. bdg. 18.99 ***(978-0-385-90494-0(0)*** , Delacorte Bks. for Young Readers) Random Hse. Children's Bks.

CAMELS

Barnes, Julia. Camels & Llamas at Work. 2006. (Illus.). 32p. (J). 23.33 (978-0-8368-6222-5(8)) Stevens, Gareth Inc.

Los Camellos Tienen Jorobas. 2003. (Enciclopedia Me Pregunto Por Que). (SPA., Illus.). 32p. (J). (gr. 3-5). (978-84-241-2167-9(8) , EV2029) Everest de Ediciones y Distribucion, S.L. ESP. *Dist:* Lectorum Pubns., Inc.

Camels. (Butterfly Collection). 8.95 (978-0-86685-491-7(6) , LDL54E) Librairie du Liban Pubns. FRA. *Dist:* International Bk. Ctr., Inc.

Camels & Their Cousins: Level J, 6 vols. 128p. (gr. 2-3). 40.50 (978-0-7699-0995-0(7)) Shortland Pubns. (U. S. A.) Inc.

Gareth Stevens Publishing Staff, contrib. by. Camels. 2004. (All about Wild Animals Ser.). (J). lib. bdg. 23.33 (978-0-8368-4181-7(6)) Stevens, Gareth Inc.

How the Camel Got his Hump: Level J, 6 vols. 128p. (gr. 2-3). 41.95 (978-0-7699-0991-2(4)) Shortland Pubns. (U. S. A.) Inc.

Jango-Cohen, Judith. Camels. 2004. (Animals, Animals Ser.). (Illus.). 47p. (J). 25.64 (978-0-7614-1750-7(8) , Benchmark Bks.) Cavendish, Marshall Corp.

Macken, JoAnn Early. Camels. 2002. (Weekly Reader Early Learning Library). (Illus.). 24p. (J). (ps up). pap. 7.93 (978-0-8368-3280-8(9)); lib. bdg. 19.33 (978-0-8368-3267-9(1)) Stevens, Gareth Inc. (Weekly Reader Early Learning Library).

Penner, Lucille Recht & Rabe, Tish. Is a Camel a Mammal? 1998. (Cat in the Hat's Learning Library). (Illus.). 48p. (J). (gr. k-3). lib. bdg. 11.99 (978-0-679-97302-7(8) , Random Hse. Bks. for Young Readers) Random Hse. Children's Bks.

Ripple, William John. Camels. 2005. (Desert Animals Ser.). (Illus.). 24p. (J). 15.93 (978-0-7368-3634-0(9) , Pebble Bks.) Capstone Pr., Inc.

Santore, Charles & Carryl, Charles Edward. The Camel's Lament. 2004. (Illus.). 32p. (J). (ps-1). 16.95 (978-0-375-81426-6(4) , Random Hse. Bks. for Young Readers) Random Hse. Children's Bks.

Stevens, Kathryn. Camels. 2007. (New Naturebooks Ser.). 32p. (J). (gr. 1-5). 27.07 ***(978-1-59296-844-2(9))*** Child's World, Inc.

Swan, Erin Pembrey. Camels & Pigs: What They Have in Common. (Animals in Order Ser.). (Illus.). 48p. (J). (gr. 4-6). 2000. pap. 6.95 (978-0-531-16400-6(4)); 1999. 26.50 (978-0-531-11585-5(2)) Scholastic Library Publishing. (Watts, Franklin).

Wexo, John Bonnett. Camels. 2001. (Zoobooks Ser.). (Illus.). 24p. (J). (gr. 1-6). 15.95 (978-1-888153-40-8(7)) Wildlife Education, Ltd.

Wildlife Education, Ltd. Staff & Wexo, John Bonnett. Camels. Orr, Richard, illus. 1999. (Zoobooks Ser.). 18p. (YA). (gr. 5 up). pap. 2.95 (978-0-937934-24-1(0)) Wildlife Education, Ltd.

Windsor, Jo. Camels: Early Level Satellite Individual Title Six-Packs. (Sails Literacy Ser.). 16p. (gr. 1-2). 27.00 (978-0-7578-6509-1(7)) Rigby Education.

Winner, Cherie. Camels. 2007. (Nature Watch Ser.). 48p. (J). (gr. 4-8). lib. bdg. 26.60 ***(978-1-57505-870-2(7)*** , Lerner Pubns.) Lerner Publishing Group.

CAMELS—FICTION

Alsenas, Linas. Peanut. 2007. 32p. (J). (ps-k). pap. 16.99 ***(978-0-439-77980-7(4))*** Scholastic, Inc.

Antieau, Kim. Broken Moon. 2007. 192p. (YA). (gr. 9 up). 15.99 (978-1-4169-1767-0(5) , McElderry, Margaret K.) Simon & Schuster Children's Publishing.

Brandon, Taylor. The Straw That Didn't Break the Camel's Back! Sandow, Paris, illus. 1999. (World's Greatest Children's Bks.). 48p. (J). (gr. k-5). 14.99 (978-1-889945-58-3(7)) Imperius.

Brown, Rachel W. N. Small Camel Follows the Star. Ferri, Giuliano, illus. 2007. 32p. (J). (gr. k-3). 16.95 ***(978-0-8075-7453-9(8))*** Whitman, Albert & Co.

Carr, Fran. Wilbur Wins the Race. 2005. (ENG., Illus.). 111p. pap. ***(978-1-84401-439-2(8))*** Athena Pr.

Christie, Gerschutz. Samuel the Camel & the Lone Star. 2006. 96p. pap. 7.50 ***(978-1-933341-19-4(X))*** CRM.

Davis, Gene. Dromedarius & Camela. 2006. lib. bdg. 18.95 (978-1-59094-115-7(2)) Jawbone Publishing Corp.

Devine, Barbara. Elvis the Camel. Al Fakhri, P., illus. 2002. 31p. 14.95 (978-1-900988-39-1(9)) Interlink Publishing Group, Inc.

Dowell, F. M. C. The Little Palace. 2004. (YA). per. 14.95 (978-1-932205-48-0(9)) Word Association Pubs.

Eduar, Gilles. Dream Journey. Eduar, Gilles, illus. 1999. (Illus.). 32p. (J). (ps-2). pap. 15.95 (978-0-531-30202-6(4) , Orchard Bks.) Scholastic, Inc.

Fontes, Justine & Fontes, Ron. How the Camel Got Its Hump. Motoyama, Keiko, illus. 2001. (Tales from Around the World Ser.). 24p. (J). (gr. k-k). 2.99 (978-0-307-96019-1(6) , Golden Bks.) Random Hse. Children's Bks.

Gauthier, Bertrand & Cote, Genevieve. Adrien n'est Pas un Chameau. 1999. (Premier Roman Ser.). (FRE., Illus.). 64p. (J). (gr. 2-5). pap. (978-2-89021-375-3(7)) Diffusion du livre Mirabel.

Gruelle, Johnny. Raggedy Ann & Andy & the Camel with the Wrinkled Knees. Moerbeek, Kees, illus. ltd. ed. 2003. (Raggedy Ann Ser.). 14p. (J). 150.00 (978-0-689-86370-7(5) , Little Simon) Simon & Schuster Children's Publishing.

Hamilton, K. R. A Freaky Kind of Courage. 2007. (J). ***(978-0-7847-1909-1(8))*** Standard Publishing.

Hanna, Margaret Leis. Canneh, the Reluctant Christmas Camel. Weltner, Dave, illus. l.t. ed. 2003. 26p. (J). 7.95 (978-0-9706654-7-8(4)) Sprite Pr.

Hanson, Sandy. A Camel's Story: A Search for the Messiah. Hanson, Sandy & Delage, Kristi, illus. 2005. 53p. (J). lib. bdg. 21.95 (978-0-9763271-0-3(4)) MK Publishing.

Heyer, Carol. Humphrey's First Christmas. 2007. (Illus.). 32p. (J). (ps-3). 14.99 ***(978-0-8249-5559-5(5)*** , Ideals Children's Bks.) Ideals Pubns.

Johnson, Julia. One Humpy Grumpy Camel. Styles, Emily, illus. 2003. 32p. (J). (gr. 3-6). 15.95 (978-1-900988-75-9(5)) Stacey International Pubs. GBR. *Dist:* Interlink Publishing Group, Inc.

Johnston, Annie Fellows. In the Desert of Waiting the Legend of Camel Back Mountain. 2005. reprint ed. pap. 15.95 (978-1-4179-3370-9(4)) Kessinger Publishing, LLC.

Jones, Christianne C. & Kipling, Rudyard. How the Camel Got Its Hump: A Retelling of the Classic Folktale. Rooney, Ronnie, illus. 2005. (Read-It! Readers Ser.). 32p. (J). (gr. k-3). 18.60 (978-1-4048-1003-7(X)) Picture Window Bks.

Karr, Kathleen. Exiled: Memoirs of a Camel. 240p. (J). 2006. pap. 6.95 (978-0-7614-5291-1(5)); 2004. 15.95 (978-0-7614-5164-8(1)) Cavendish, Marshall Corp.

King-Smith, Dick. Hairy Hezekiah. Bruel, Nick, illus. 2007. 96p. (J). (gr. 2-5). 12.95 ***(978-1-59643-318-2(3))*** Roaring Brook Pr.

Kipling, Rudyard. How the Camel Got His Hump. Raglin, Tim, illus. 2006. (J). (gr. 2-6). 25.65 (978-1-59197-749-0(5)) Spotlight.

Krimm, Rebecca L. Camerella. 1998. (Illus.). 32p. (J). (gr. k-5). 9.95 (978-1-892263-00-1(9)) Rebecca's Hse. Publishing.

Lewin, Betsy. What's the Matter, Habibi? 2004. (Illus.). 32p. (J). (gr. k-3). pap. 6.95 (978-0-618-43242-4(6) , Clarion Bks.) Houghton Mifflin Co. Trade & Reference Div.

Manuel, Lynn. Camels Always Do. Charko, Kasia, illus. 2004. 32p. (J). (ps-2). 16.95 (978-1-55143-284-7(6)); 7.95 (978-1-55143-470-4(9)) Orca Bk. Pubs. USA.

Merkle, Ben & Merkle, Bekah. In a Camel's Eye. Hartranft, Debi, illus. 2000. per. 3.00 (978-1-930710-28-3(3)) Veritas Pr., Inc.

Mills, Joyce C. & Crowley, Richard J. Sammy the Elephant & Mr. Camel: A Story to Help Children Overcome Bedwetting. Pillo, Cary, illus. 2nd ed. 2005. 32p. (J). 14.95 (978-1-59147-247-6(4)); pap. 8.95 (978-1-59147-248-3(2)) American Psychological Assn. (Magination Pr.).

Oppenheim, Shulamith Levey. The Hundredth Name. Hays, Michael, illus. 2003. 32p. (J). (gr. k-2). pap. 9.95 (978-1-56397-694-0(3)) Boyds Mills Pr.

Peterson, M. Helen. Old Camel's First Christmas. 2004. (ENG.). 44p. (J). per. 17.99 (978-1-4141-0215-3(1)) Pleasant Word.

Plante, Raymond. Un Dromadaire Chez Marilou Polaire. Favreau, Marie-Claude, illus. 2003. (Premier Roman Ser.). (FRE.). 64p. (J). (gr. 1-4). pap. (978-2-89021-608-2(X)) Diffusion du livre Mirabel.

Plante, Raymond. Marilou Keeps a Camel. Favreau, Marie-Claude, illus. 2004. 61p. (J). lib. bdg. 12.00 ***(978-1-4242-1232-3(4))*** Fitzgerald Bks.

—Marilou Keeps a Camel. Cummins, Sarah, tr. from FRE. Favreau, Marie-Claude, illus. 2004. (First Novel Ser.). 64p. (J). (gr. 1-5). 4.95 (978-0-88780-634-6(1)); ***(978-0-88780-635-3(X))*** Formac Publishing Co., Ltd. CAN. *Dist:* Casemate Pubs. & Bk. Distributors, LLC.

Prap, Lila. Why? 2005. Orig. Title: Zakaj?. (Illus.). 32p. (J). (ps-ps). 14.95 (978-1-929132-80-5(8)) Kane/Miller Bk. Pubs., Inc.

Rennison, Louise. Away Laughing on a Fast Camel: Even More Confessions of Georgia Nicolson. (Confessions of Georgia Nicolson Ser.). 2004. (Illus.). 288p. (J). lib. bdg. 16.89 (978-0-06-058935-6(3)); 2005. 304p. reprint ed. pap. 7.99 (978-0-06-058936-3(1)) HarperCollins Pubs. (HarperTeen).

Sargent, Dave & Sargent, Pat. Cammie Camel: Endurance, 56 bks, Vol. 42. Lenoir, Jane, illus. 2000. (Animal Pride Ser.). 36p. (J). lib. bdg. 19.95 (978-1-56763-525-6(3)) Ozark Publishing.

Sargent, Dave, et al. Cammie Camel: Endurance, 17, 42. 2000. (Animal Pride Ser.: 42). (Illus.). (J). pap. 6.95 (978-1-56763-526-3(1)) Ozark Publishing.

Simon, Francesca. Camels Don't Ski. Busby, Ailie, illus. 1999. 32p. (ps-3). 14.95 (978-1-899607-59-4(5)) Sterling Publishing Co., Inc.

Taylor, Dan & Taylor, Damon J. Caleb Crosses the Country: A Camel's Tale. Taylor, Damon J., illus. 2004. (God Can Use Me Ser.). 8p. (J). 10.99 (978-0-8254-3870-7(5)) Kregel Pubns.

Thury, Frederick. The Last Straw. van Kampen, Vlasta, illus. 1999. 32p. (J). (ps-3). 15.95 (978-0-88106-152-9(2)) Charlesbridge Publishing, Inc.

Weed, Thurlow R. Camel Fables from the Sailors of the Sudan. 2004. 84p. pap. 15.95 (978-0-7414-2229-3(8)) Infinity Publishing.

CAMERAS

Argus DC 2200 Digital Camera. 2001. (J). cd-rom 9000.00 (978-1-931872-35-5(X)) APTE, Inc.

Argus DC 2200 Digital Camera Lab 5. 2001. (J). cd-rom 9000.00 (978-1-931872-36-2(8)) APTE, Inc.

Argus DC 3510 Digital Camera. 2001. (J). cd-rom 9000.00 (978-1-931872-37-9(6)) APTE, Inc.

Argus DC1500 Digital Camera Lab 10 Lab Pack 10: Education Version. 2002. (J). 769.90 (978-1-931872-34-8(1)) APTE, Inc.

Ballweg, Judy K. KI Pix Digital Gallery: Cameras, Scanners & Computers. 2000. (Illus.). 120p. (J). (gr. k-2). spiral bd. 26.95 (978-1-56484-156-8(1)) International Society for Technology in Education.

Barney Picture Day Camera Book. 2002. (Illus.). (J). 15.98 (978-0-7853-6070-4(0)) Publications International, Ltd.

Berry, Ron. My First Camera Book. Sharp, Chris, illus. 2008. 12p. (J). 8.99 ***(978-0-8249-6722-2(4)*** , Ideals Children's Bks.) Ideals Pubns.

Bodden, Valerie. Photography. 2008. ***(978-1-58341-558-0(0)*** , Creative Education) Creative Co., The.

Hills, Larry. The Camera. 2004. (Fact Finders Ser.). (Illus.). 32p. (J). (gr. 3-5). lib. bdg. 22.60 (978-0-7368-2669-3(6) , Fact Finders) Capstone Pr., Inc.

Lorenz Books Staff, et al. Cameras: Practical Tips & Exciting Projects Inprove Techniques & Understanding. 2000. (Investigations Ser.). (Illus.). 64p. (gr. 3-7). 14.95 (978-0-7548-0455-0(0) , Lorenz Bks.) Anness Publishing GBR. *Dist:* National Bk. Network.

Oxlade, Chris & Morrison, Al. Cameras. 2004. (All about Ser.). (Illus.). 64p. (gr. 3-7). pap. 7.99 (978-1-84215-769-5(8) , Southwater) Anness Publishing GBR. *Dist:* National Bk. Network.

Pobst, Sandy. The Camera. 2005. (Great Inventions Ser.). (Illus.). 48p. (YA). lib. bdg. 30.00 (978-0-8368-5801-3(8) , World Almanac Library) Stevens, Gareth Inc.

Raum, Elizabeth. The History of the Camera. 2007. (J). (*978-1-4034-9647-8(1) ; pap. (*978-1-4034-9653-9(6)) Heinemann Library.

Richter, Joanne. Inventing the Camera. 2006. (Breakthrough Inventions Ser.). (Illus.). 32p. (J). (gr. 3-9). pap. (978-0-7787-2836-8(6)); (978-0-7787-2814-6(5)) Crabtree Publishing Co.

Stefoff, Rebecca. The Camera. 2007. (Great Inventions Ser.). (Illus.). 144p. (YA). (gr. 9 up). lib. bdg. 39.93 (*978-0-7614-2596-0(9) , Benchmark Bks.) Cavendish, Marshall Corp.

Trueit, Trudi Strain. The Camera. 2006. 80p. (gr. 5-8). pap. 9.95 (978-0-531-13900-4(X)); (Illus.). (J). 30.50 (978-0-531-12409-3(6)) Scholastic Library Publishing. (Watts, Franklin).

CAMP COOKING

see Outdoor Cookery

CAMPAIGNS, POLITICAL

see Politics, Practical

CAMPAIGNS, PRESIDENTIAL

see Presidents—United States—Election

CAMPANELLA, ROY, 1921-1993

Adler, David A. Campy: The Story of Roy Campanella. James, Gordon C., illus. 2007. 40p. (J). (gr. 1-4). 15.99 (978-0-670-06041-2(0) , Viking Adult) Penguin Group (USA) Inc.

CAMPING

see also Outdoor Cookery; Outdoor Life; Tents; Wilderness Survival

Armour, Christopher. 40 Daily Devotions. 2004. (Wisdom Ser.). (Illus.). 144p. pap. 7.00 (978-1-882959-55-6(8)) Foxglove Pr.

Bayne, Allan P. & Platford, Gary. Bugs, Sweat & Fears: Beginner's Guide to Wilderness Canoe Camping. Penner, Burton, illus. 1999. 208p. pap. (978-0-88801-234-0(9)) Turnstone Pr.

Beylon, Cathy. At Day Camp. 2005. (Illus.). 32p. (J). (ps-3). pap. 2.95 (978-0-486-44431-4(7)) Dover Pubns., Inc.

Camps & Retreats to Go: Above & Beyond. 2004. spiral bd. 132.00 (978-0-9743687-2-6(5)) Connection.

Carlson, Laurie M. & Dammel, Judith. Kids Camp! Activities for the Backyard or Wilderness. 2003. (Kid's Guide Ser.). (Illus.). 174p. (J). (gr. k-7). pap. 14.95 (978-1-55652-237-6(1)) Chicago Review Pr., Inc.

Ching, Jacqueline. Camping: Have Fun, Be Smart. 2005. (Explore the Outdoors Ser.). (Illus.). 64p. (YA). (gr. 7-12). lib. bdg. 26.50 (978-0-8239-3173-6(0) , EO-CAMP) Rosen Publishing Group, Inc., The.

Davis, James (Jim) W. Out-takes of 55 Years of Camping, 2004. (Illus.). 168p. (YA). per. 5.95 (978-0-9760960-0-9(5)) Davis, James (Jim).

Dewey, Jennifer Owings. Finding Your Way: The Art of Natural Navigation. Trimble, Stephen, photos by. 2001. (Illus.). 64p. (gr. 4-6). lib. bdg. 23.90 (978-0-7613-0956-7(X) , Millbrook Pr.) Lerner Publishing Group.

Dinio-Durkin, Cecilia. Hit the Trail! The Camping Kit for Kids. 1998. (J). pap. 16.95 (978-0-8362-5450-1(3)) Andrews McMeel Publishing.

Drake, Jane & Love, Ann. The Kids Campfire Book. Collins, Heather, illus. unabr. ed. 1998. (Fun for All Seasons Ser.). 128p. (J). (gr. 4-6). (978-1-55074-454-5(2)); (978-1-55074-539-9(5)) Kids Can Pr., Ltd.

Early Bird Books Staff. Going Camping. Date not set. 1.95 (978-0-394-86704-5(1) , Random Hse. Bks. for Young Readers) Random Hse. Children's Bks.

Eckart, Edana. I Can Go Camping. 2003. (Wel-Sports Ser.). (Illus.). 24p. (J). 18.00 (978-0-516-24280-4(6) , Children's Pr.) Scholastic Library Publishing.

Evans, Lynette. Camp Extreme. 2007. (Shockwave: the Human Experience Ser.). (Illus.). 36p. (J). (gr. 4-6). lib. bdg. 25.00 (*978-0-531-17758-7(0) , Children's Pr.) Scholastic Library Publishing.

Gingold, Janet. My Adventure as a Camper: Advanced My Adventure. 2007. 44p. (J). pap. 8.99 (978-1-59092-407-5(X) , Orchard Academy Pr.) Windstorm Creative.

Harris, Carolyn. RV in NZ: How to Spend Your Winters Freedom Camping South—Way South—in New Zealand. 2004. (Illus.). 140p. pap. 17.00 (978-0-9748552-0-2(0)) Marble Mountain Pr.

Harvey, Roger. Caillou Goes Camping. Lapierre, Claude, illus. rev. ed. 2007. (Lift-the-Flap Book Ser.). 20p. (J). pap. 5.95 (*978-2-89450-612-7(0)) Chouette Publishing CAN. *Dist:* Independent Pubs. Group.

The Hiking & Camping Coloring Book. 2004. (J). mass mkt. (978-0-9745863-8-0(2)) Cypress Knees Publishing.

Hood, Susan. Camp Rules! A Cool Camp Journal. 2005. 128p. 12.99 (978-0-88088-197-5(6)) Peter Pauper Pr. Inc.

Hooks, Kristine. Essential Camping for Teens. 2000. (High Interest Bks.). (Illus.). 48p. (YA). (gr. 7-12). 24.00 (978-0-516-23353-6(X)); pap. 6.95 (978-0-516-23553-0(2)) Scholastic Library Publishing. (Children's Pr.).

James, Helen Foster. S Is for S'mores: A Camping Alphabet. Judge, Lita, illus. rev. ed. 2007. 40p. (J). 17.95 (*978-1-58536-302-5(2)) Sleeping Bear Pr.

Keller, Kristin Thoennes. Camping. 2001. (Great Outdoors Ser.). (Illus.). 48p. (J). (gr. 3-4). lib. bdg. 21.26 (978-0-7368-0911-5(2) , Capstone High-Interest Bks.) Capstone Pr., Inc.

Loy, Jessica. Follow the Trail: A Young Person's Guide to the Great Outdoors. rev. ed. 2003. (Illus.). 48p. (J). (gr. 2-7). 18.95 (978-0-8050-6195-6(9) , Holt, Henry & Co. Bks. For Young Readers) Holt, Henry & Co.

Mader, Jan. Let's Go Camping! 2007. (Sports & Activities Ser.). (Illus.). 24p. (J). (ps-1). lib. bdg. 19.93 (978-0-7368-6360-5(5) , Pebble Bks.) Capstone Pr., Inc.

Mason, Bernard Sterling. Boy's Book of Camping & Wood Crafts. 2001. 250p. pap. 19.95 (978-1-58667-072-6(7)) Derrydale Pr., The.

Mason, Paul. Hiking & Camping. 2007. (J). (*978-1-59920-129-0(1)) Smart Apple Media.

More Eternal Camping-Grounds. 2004. (YA). (978-0-9753721-3-5(0)) Fame's Eternal Bks., LLC.

Ruth, Angie. My Adventure Camping. 2006. 44p. (J). 8.99 (978-1-59092-414-3(2) , Orchard Academy Pr.) Windstorm Creative.

Ruurs, Margriet. When We Go Camping. Kiss, Andrew, illus. 32p. (J). (gr. 1). 2004. pap. 7.95 (978-0-88776-685-5(4)); 2001. 14.95 (978-0-88776-476-9(2)) Tundra Bks., Inc./Livres Toundra, Inc. CAN. *Dist:* Random Hse., Inc.

Seeberg, Timothy J. Camping. 2004. (Complete Guides Ser.). (Illus.). 32p. (J). (gr. 1-5). 25.64 (978-1-59296-032-3(4)) Child's World, Inc.

Slade, Suzanne. Let's Go Camping. 2007. (Adventures Outdoors Ser.). (Illus.). 32p. (J). (gr. 4-6). lib. bdg. 23.95 (978-1-4042-3650-9(3) , PowerKids Pr.) Rosen Publishing Group, Inc., The.

Speregen, Devra Newberger. The Ultimate Summer Camp Guide. 2000. (Illus.). 128p. (J). (gr. 3 up). 5.95 (978-1-84207-018-5(5)) Element Children's Bks.

Thoennes Keller, Kristin. Camping. 2008. (J). (*978-1-4296-0815-2(3)) Capstone Pr., Inc.

Tomljanovic, Tatiana. Camping. 2007. (J). (*978-1-59036-657-8(3)); (*978-1-59036-658-5(1)) Weigl Pubs., Inc.

White, Linda. Sleeping in a Sack: Camping Activities for Kids. Lee, Fran, illus. 2000. 64p. (YA). (gr. 2-7). reprint ed. pap. 9.95 (978-0-87905-830-2(7)) Gibbs Smith, Publisher.

Willow Creek Press Staff, ed. What Camping Can Teach Us. 2006. (Illus.). 32p. (J). 12.95 (978-1-59543-290-2(6)) Willow Creek Pr., Inc.

Winner, Cherie. Kids Gone Campin' The Young Camper's Guide to Having More Fun Outdoors. 2006. (Illus.). 96p. pap. 12.95 (978-1-58923-225-9(9) , Creative Publishing International) Quayside.

Zimmermann, Dottie, creator. Interactive Sing-along Big Books Cool Camping Fun. 2007. (J). spiral bd. 12.95 (*978-1-58650-721-3(4)) Super Duper Pubns.

CAMPING—FICTION

Aldridge, Janet. Meadow Brook Girls Afloat. l.t. ed. 2006. 156p. pap. 14.99 (978-1-4264-0859-5(5)) BiblioBazaar.

—Meadow Brook Girls Afloat: Or the Stormy Cruise of the Red Rover. 2006. 160p. pap. 11.99 (978-1-4264-0878-6(1)) BiblioBazaar.

Aldridge, Janet. The Meadow-Brook Girls under Canvas (Ill. 2006. pap. (*978-1-4065-0695-2(8)) Dodo Pr.

Alessi, Patricia E. Rrreggie's Camping Adventure. Slagle, Ronson, illus. 2001. 60p. pap. 9.95 (978-0-615-11920-5(4)) Alessi, Patricia.

Allen, Quinc. The Outdoor Chums: The First Tour of the. 2004. reprint ed. pap. 20.95 (978-1-4191-7642-5(0)) Kessinger Publishing, LLC.

Amelia Bedelia Goes Camping. 2002. (Amelia Bedelia Ser.). (Illus.). (J). 12.34 (978-0-7587-0423-8(2)) Book Wholesalers, Inc.

Amery, Heather. Camping Out. Cartwright, Stephen, illus. 2005. 16p. (J). (ps-17). pap. 5.95 (978-0-7945-0750-3(6) , Usborne) EDC Publishing.

Arensen, Shel. Poachers Beware, Vol. 3. 2003. (Rugendo Rhino Ser.: Vol. 3). 128p. (J). pap. 5.99 (978-0-8254-2039-9(3)) Kregel Pubns.

Auerbach, Annie. Grosse Adventures, the Volume 3: Trouble at Twilight Cave. 2007. (Illus.). 96p. pap. 4.99 (*978-1-59816-051-2(6) , Tokyopop Kids) TOKYOPOP, Inc.

Banks, Steven. Pick a Dad, Any Dad! Moore, Harry, illus. ed. 2005. (Fairly Odd Parents Ser.: 7). 24p. (J). lib. bdg. 15.00 (978-1-59054-804-2(3)) Fitzgerald Bks.

Barbour, Ralph Henry. The Lilac Girl. 2006. (Illus.). pap. (*978-1-4065-0778-2(4)) Dodo Pr.

Barshaw, Ruth McNally. Ellie McDoodle: Have Pen, Will Travel. Barshaw, Ruth McNally, illus. 2007. (Illus.). 176p. (J). (gr. 3-7). 11.95 (*978-1-58234-745-5(X)) Bloomsbury Publishing.

Beasley, David R. Canoe Trip. Milner, Elizabeth B., illus. 2006. 129p. (YA). per. 15.00 (*978-0-915317-21-9(4)) Davus Publishing.

Bent, Ruth. Llama Hiking with Katie. 2000. 28p. (J). (gr. 1-3). pap. 8.00 (978-0-615-11191-9(2)) Sijama Publishing.

Beresford, Elisabeth. Wombles Camping & Cloudberries. (Illus.). 15p. (J). (gr. k-6). pap. (978-0-340-73584-8(8) , Hodder & Stoughton) Hodder General Publishing Division.

Blaine, Chris. Beyond Hocus - Pocus. Blaine, Sally, ed. Goforth, Amanda, illus. 1998. (YA). (gr. 6 up). Vol. 2. 81p. 6.95 (978-1-892250-01-8(2)); Vol. 3. 84p. 6.95 (978-1-892250-02-5(0)) Barnett Educational Supplies, Inc.

Bonehill, Ralph. Four Boy Hunters or the Outing of the Gu. 2006. 78.99 (*978-1-4280-0015-5(1)); pap. 72.99 (*978-1-4280-0023-0(2)) IndyPublish.com.

Bonehill, Ralph. Guns & Snowshoes: Or, the Winter Outing of the Young Hunters. 2006. 160p. pap. 11.99 (978-1-4264-3173-9(2)); 174p. pap. 14.99 (978-1-4264-3208-8(9)) BiblioBazaar.

Bridwell, Norman. Camping Out. Bracken, Carolyn & Edwards, Ken, illus. 2003. (Big Red Reader Ser.). (J). (978-0-439-45810-8(2)) Scholastic, Inc.

Brin, Susannah. Alien Encounter. 2000. (gr. 5-8). lib. bdg. 11.80 (978-0-613-51048-6(8)); (Illus.). (J). 10.75 (978-0-606-20538-2(1)) Tandem Library Bks.

Broekstra, Lorette. Baby Bear Goes Camping. 2004. (Baby Bear Ser.). (Illus.). 32p. (J). 5.99 (978-1-85854-408-3(4)) Brimax Books Ltd. GBR. *Dist:* Byeway Bks.

Brooks, Walter R. Freddy Goes Camping. Wiese, Kurt, illus. 2001. 258p. (J). 23.95 (978-1-58567-177-9(0)) Overlook Pr., The.

—Freddy Goes Camping. 2003. (gr. 3-6). lib. bdg. 16.45 (978-0-613-61624-9(3)) Tandem Library Bks.

Brown, Marc. Arthur Goes to Camp. Brown, Marc, illus. 2002. (Arthur Adventure Ser.). (Illus.). (J). 13.15 (978-0-7587-1972-0(8)) Book Wholesalers, Inc.

Budbill, David. The Bones on Black Spruce Mountain. 2004. 117p. (J). (978-0-9657144-6-4(2)); pap. (978-0-9657144-7-1(0)) Onion River Pr.

—Snowshoe Trek to Otter River. 2005. (J). pap. (978-0-9657144-9-5(7)) Onion River Pr.

Campbell, William W. The Great Hoo-Hah. Sam, Sidewalk, illus. 2000. 48p. (J). (gr. k-5). pap. 6.95 (978-1-58066-059-4(2) , Covered Bridge Pr.) Douglas Charles, Ltd.

Camping Caper: Coloring/Activity Book (English) incl. Stickers. 2007. (Illus.). (J). (*978-1-933934-65-5(4)) Educational Adventures.

Camping Caper: Picture Book (English) 8x8. 2007. (Illus.). (J). (*978-1-933934-64-8(6)) Educational Adventures.

Camping Out: A Shadow Story. (Illus.). 26p. (YA). bds. 7.50 (978-1-56021-387-1(6)) W.J. Fantasy, Inc.

Chancellor, Deborah. Camping Trip. Fairclough, Chris, illus. 2005. (Reading Corner Ser.). 24p. (J). (gr. k-3). lib. bdg. 22.80 (978-1-59771-010-7(5)) Sea-To-Sea Pubns.

Chapman, Allen. Frank Roscoes Secret or the Darewell Chu. 2007. pap. (*978-1-4065-1431-5(4)) Dodo Pr.

Choyce, Lesley. Carrie's Camping Adventure. Thurman, Mark, illus. 2001. (First Novels Ser.: Vol. 17). 64p. (gr. 1-5). (J). (978-0-88780-535-6(3)); 4.95 (978-0-88780-534-9(5)) Formac Publishing Co., Ltd. CAN. *Dist:* Casemate Pubs. & Bk. Distributors, LLC.

Clark, N. Laurie. It's Wesley! The Adirondack Guide. Clark, N. Laurie, illus. 1998. (Illus.). 32p. (J). (gr. k up). per. 14.95 (978-0-9641197-1-0(4)) Clark Pubs.

Clements, Andrew. A Week in the Woods. 2002. 160p. (J). (gr. 4-6). 16.95 (978-0-689-82596-5(X)); 2004. 208p. reprint ed. pap. 5.99 (978-0-689-85802-4(7) , Aladdin) Simon & Schuster Children's Publishing.

—A Week in the Woods. 2003. (Juvenile Ser.). (J). 21.95 (978-0-7862-5016-5(X)) Thorndike Pr.

Cole, Stephen. The Adventures of Mr. Bean. 2002. (Illus.). 64p. (J). pap. 6.99 (978-1-84222-659-9(2)) Carlton Bks., Ltd. GBR. *Dist:* Independent Pubs. Group.

Crisis Maximus! Individual Title Six-Packs. (Bookweb Ser.). 32p. (gr. 6 up). 34.00 (978-0-7578-0902-6(2)) Rigby Education.

Dakin, Glenn & Chapman, Keith. Can We Tell Time? Bob the Builder. 2003. (Illus.). (J). bds. 16.98 (978-0-7853-8809-8(5)) Publications International, Ltd.

Dalmatian Press Staff, ed. Sesame Street: Spooky Sleep-Out. 2006. 24p. pap. 3.50 (978-1-4037-2432-8(6)) Dalmatian Pr.

Davis, Terry. Camping with Dad: The Mystery of Valley Gulch. 2006. (ENG.). 148p. per. 19.95 (*978-1-4241-5659-7(9)) PublishAmerica, Inc.

de Brunhoff, Laurent. Babar's Rescue. 2004. (Illus.). 32p. (J). (ps-3). 16.95 (978-0-8109-4839-6(7)) Abrams, Harry N., Inc.

Denton, P. J. Camping Out. Denos, Julia, illus. 2007. (Sleepover Squad Ser.: No. 2). 96p. (J). pap. 3.99 (978-1-4169-2791-4(3) , Aladdin) Simon & Schuster Children's Publishing.

Dougherty, Terri. The Camping Scare. Thompson, Jeffrey, illus. 2006. (Read-It! Readers Ser.). (J). 19.93 (978-1-4048-2405-8(7)) Picture Window Bks.

Eastman, Peter. Fred & Ted Go Camping. 2005. (Bright & Early Bks.). (Illus.). 48p. (J). (gr. k-3). 8.99 (978-0-375-82965-9(2)); lib. bdg. 12.99 (978-0-375-92965-6(7)) Random Hse. Children's Bks. (Random Hse. Bks. for Young Readers).

Elkins, Stephen. Know God, No Fear. Reisch, Jessie, illus. 2003. 32p. (J). (gr. k-5). 14.99 (978-0-8054-2658-8(2)) B&H Publishing Grp.

Espinosa, Laura & Espinosa, Leo. Otis & Rae & the Grumbling Splunk. Espinosa, Laura & Espinosa, Leo, illus. 2008. 32p. (J). (ps-3). 12.95 (*978-0-618-98206-6(X)) Houghton Mifflin Co.

Evangelista, Beth. Gifted. 192p. (J). 2007. pap. 6.95 (*978-0-8027-9644-8(3)); 2005. (gr. 5-9). 16.95 (978-0-8027-8994-5(3)) Walker & Co.

Farnes, Catherine. Over the Divide. 2001. 146p. (J). (gr. 7-12). 6.49 (978-1-57924-646-4(X)) Jones, Bob Univ. Pr.

—Over the Divide. 2001. (gr. 7-12). lib. bdg. 14.70 (978-0-613-85517-4(5)) Tandem Library Bks.

Figler, Jeanie. Majestic Blue Horses. 1999. (Illus.). (J). 9.95 (978-1-56492-273-1(1)) Laredo Publishing Co., Inc.

Fleck, Earl. Chasing Bears: A Canoe Country Adventure. 2004. (Illus.). 160p. (gr. 7-12). pap. 12.95 (978-0-930100-90-2(5)) Holy Cow! Pr.

—Chasing Fire: Danger in Canoe Country. 2002. (Illus.). 160p. pap. 12.95 (978-0-930100-53-7(0)) Holy Cow! Pr.

Foggo, Cheryl. I Have Been in Danger. Hotchkiss, Conrad & Graham, Heather, illus. 2005. (In the Same Boat Ser.: No. 3). 184p. (J). (gr. 4-6). pap. 7.95 (978-1-55050-185-8(2)) Coteau Bks. CAN. *Dist:* Fitzhenry & Whiteside, Ltd.

Frenette, Liza. Dangerous Falls Ahead: An Adirondack Canoeing Adventure. Gillis, Jane, illus. 2001. (J). pap. 11.95 (978-0-925168-79-5(3)) North Country Bks., Inc.

—Dead End. Gillis, Jane, illus. 2005. x, 65p. (J). (978-1-59531-001-9(0)) North Country Bks., Inc.

Frey, G. Hildegard. The Camp Fire Girls at Camp Keeway-din or. 2006. 41.99 (*978-1-4280-0526-6(9)); pap. 35.99 (*978-1-4280-0521-1(8)) IndyPublish.com.

Garis, Howard Roger. The Curlytops on Star Island or Camping. 2006. 63.99 (*978-1-4280-0922-6(1)); pap. 56.99 (*978-1-4280-0933-2(7)) IndyPublish.com.

Gauthier, Bertrand. Just Me & My Dad, 2 bks. Sylvestre, Daniel, illus. Incl. Zachary in Camping Out. lib. bdg. 19.93 (978-0-8368-1012-7(0)); Zachary in the Winner. lib. bdg. 19.93 (978-0-8368-1009-7(0)); 24p. (J). (gr. 2 up). 1993. (Illus.). Set lib. bdg. 39.86 (978-0-8368-1006-6(6)) Stevens, Gareth Inc.

Gelsey, James. Scooby Doo! & the Zombie's Treasure. 2000. (gr. 3-6). lib. bdg. 11.80 (978-0-613-27677-1(9)) Tandem Library Bks.

Gifaldi, David. Ben, King of the River. Johnson, Layne, illus. 2001. (Concept Book Ser.). 32p. (J). (gr. k-4). 15.95 (978-0-8075-0635-6(4)) Whitman, Albert & Co.

Gold, Becky. Camp Out. Cuan, Sergio, illus. 2000. (Ready-to-Read Ser.). 32p. (J). (ps-3). per. 3.99 (978-0-671-77314-4(3) , Simon & Schuster Children's Publishing) Simon & Schuster Children's Publishing.

—Camp Out. 1999. (gr. k-3). lib. bdg. 11.80 (978-0-613-15743-8(5)) Tandem Library Bks.

Grant, Robert. Jack in the Bush or A Summer on a Salmon River. 2005. pap. 33.95 (978-1-4179-5573-2(2)) Kessinger Publishing, LLC.

Hale, Kathleen. Orlando the Marmalade Cat: A Camping Holiday. 2003. (Illus.). 32p. (J). (gr. 1-5). 20.00 (978-0-7567-6602-3(8)) DIANE Publishing Co.

Hamilton, Elizabeth L. Secret of Cachuma Lake. 2001. (Travel Adventure Ser.: Bk. 1). (Illus.). 144p. (YA). per. 9.95 (978-0-9713749-7-3(X)) Quiet Impact, Inc.

Hanson, Dave. We're Going Camping. McNicholas, Shelagh, illus. 2005. (Reading Corner Ser.). 24p. (J). (gr. k-3). lib. bdg. 22.80 (978-1-59771-015-2(6)) Sea-To-Sea Pubns.

Harcourt School Publishers Staff. The Perfect Ending On Level. 3rd ed. 2002. (Trophies Reading Program Ser.). (Illus.). pap. 5.10 (978-0-15-323188-9(2)) Harcourt Schl. Pubs.

—Robert's Rules Advanced Level. 3rd ed. 2002. (Trophies Reading Program Ser.). (Illus.). (gr. 3). pap. 5.10 (978-0-15-323191-9(2)) Harcourt Schl. Pubs.

Harriot, Ray. More Stories for Around the Campfire. 1998. (J). (gr. 3-10). pap. 7.95 (978-0-9617653-1-6(3)) Campfire Publishing Co.

Hill, David. Take It Easy. 2000. (Illus.). (J). pap. 5.99 (978-0-14-130349-9(2) , Puffin) Penguin Group (USA) Inc.

Hines, Anna Grossnickle, illus. Whistling. 2003. 40p. (J). 16.89 (978-0-06-050236-2(3)) HarperCollins Pubs.

Hiris, Monica. Just Like Mom. Sierra, Holly, illus. 2005. (J). pap. 4.95 (978-1-57874-088-8(6)) Kaeden Corp.

Hodgson, Mona Gansberg. Campout Capers. Sharp, Chris, illus. 1999. (Desert Critter Friends Ser.: Vol. 8). 48p. (J). (ps-2). 4.99 (978-0-570-05482-5(6)) Concordia Publishing Hse.

Hofmeister, Alan, et al. In the Tent. (Reading for All Learners Ser.). (Illus.). (J). pap. (978-1-56861-132-7(3)) Swift Learning Resources.

Holabird, Katharine. Angelina & Henry. Craig, Helen, illus. 2006. 32p. (J). pap. 5.99 (978-0-14-240590-1(6) , Puffin) Penguin Group (USA) Inc.

Honey, Elizabeth. Don't Pat the Wombat. 2001. (gr. 3-6). lib. bdg. 12.40 (978-0-613-36095-1(8)) Tandem Library Bks.

Hopkinson, Deborah. The Long Trail. Farnsworth, Bill, illus. 2004. 76p. (J). (gr. 1-4). lib. bdg. 12.10 (978-1-4176-3246-6(1)) Tandem Library Bks.

Howe, James. Nighty-Nightmare. Morrill, Leslie, illus. 2007. 144p. (J). pap. 5.99 (*978-1-4169-3966-5(0) , Aladdin) Simon & Schuster Children's Publishing.

Howe, James. Pinky & Rex & the Double-Dad Weekend. 2006. (J). (gr. 1-4). 24.21 (978-1-59961-075-7(2)) Spotlight.

Hundal, Nancy. Camping. Deines, Brian, illus. 2002. 32p. (ps-3). (978-1-55041-668-8(5)) Fitzhenry & Whiteside, Ltd.

—Camping. Deines, Brian, illus. 2006. 32p. pap. 7.95 (978-1-55041-686-2(3)) Fitzhenry & Whiteside, Ltd. CAN. *Dist:* F & W Pubns., Inc.

Huneck, Stephen. Sally Goes to the Mountains. 2001. (Illus.). 38p. (J). (ps-3). 17.95 (978-0-8109-4485-5(5)) Abrams, Harry N., Inc.

Jennings, Patrick. The Pup Tent: An Ike & Mem Story. O'Neill, Catharine, illus. 2005. (J). (978-0-8234-1938-8(X)) Holiday Hse., Inc.

Jones, Christianne C. Camping Trip. Demski, James, illus. 2005. (Read-It! Readers Ser.). 24p. (J). (ps). lib. bdg. 18.60 (978-1-4048-1167-6(2)) Picture Window Bks.

Jones, Christianne C., et al. Acampar. Demski, James, illus. 2006. (Read-It! Readers Ser.). (ENG & SPA.). 32p. (J). (ps-3). 19.95 (978-1-4048-1681-7(X)) Picture Window Bks.

Kalar, Bonnie. Neal Camps Out. Spreen, Kathe, illus. Date not set. 12p. (J). (ps-2). pap. (978-1-891619-39-7(X)) Corona Pr.

Klingel, Cynthia Fitterer & Noyed, Robert B. The Amazing Letter F. 2003. (Alphaphonics Ser.). (Illus.). 24p. (J). (ps-2). 21.36 (978-1-59296-096-5(0)) Child's World, Inc.

Kropp, Joseph P. Hickok's Gold. 2006. (J). (*978-1-890905-25-5(9)) Day to Day Enterprises.

Kvasnosky, Laura McGee. Frank & Izzy Set Sail. Kvasnosky, Laura McGee, illus. 2004. (Illus.). 32p. (J). (gr. k-4). 15.99 (978-0-7636-2146-9(3)) Candlewick Pr.

Labatt, Mary. Secret of Sagawa Lake. 2001. (gr. 3-6). lib. bdg. 12.95 (978-0-613-51586-3(2)) Tandem Library Bks.

Lang, Aubrey. Baby Sea Turtle. Lynch, Wayne, photos by. 2007. (Nature Babies Ser.). (Illus.). 32p. (J). (gr. k-3). (*978-1-55041-728-9(2)) Fitzhenry & Whiteside, Ltd.

Leonard Marcia. Mi día de campamento (My Camp-Out) 2007. (Lecturas para niños de verdad - Nivel 1 (Real Kids Readers - Level 1) Ser.). (J). pap. 5.95 (*978-0-8225-7798-0(4) , Ediciones Lerner) Lerner Publishing Group.

Leslie, J. Lawrence. At Whispering Pine Lodge. 2006. 94.99 (*978-1-4219-7396-8(0)); pap. 88.99 (*978-1-4219-7413-2(4)) IndyPublish.com.

Lewman, David. Campfire Funnies. Style Guide Staff, illus. 2006. (SpongeBob SquarePants Ser.). 48p. (J). pap. 3.99 (978-1-4169-1315-3(7) , Simon Spotlight) Simon & Schuster Children's Publishing.

Long, Christopher E. Blackfoot Braves Society: Spirit Totems. Geiger, Michael, illus. 2006. 127p. (J). 12.95 (978-0-9742803-9-4(9) , Actionopolis) Komikwerks, LLC.

Lundy, Charlotte. Thank You, Peter. Waldrep, Evelyn L., ed. Blackley, Mary Beth, illus. 2003. 32p. (gr. k-3). 15.95 (978-0-9670280-8-8(6)) Bay Light Publishing.

Mayer, Mercer. Camping Out. 2002. (Little Critter Ser.). (Illus.). 24p. (J). (ps-k). pap. 3.95 (978-1-57768-806-8(6)) School Specialty Publishing.

—Camping Out. 2001. (ps-2). lib. bdg. 11.80 (978-0-613-79359-9(5)) Tandem Library Bks.

Mazer, Anne. Too Close for Comfort. Gesue, Monica, illus. 2003. (Amazing Days of Abby Hayes Ser.: No. 11). 128p. (J). (gr. 3-6). 4.99 (978-0-439-48273-8(9) , Scholastic Paperbacks) Scholastic, Inc.

—Too Close for Comfort. 2003. (Amazing Days of Abby Hayes Ser.: No. 11). (gr. k-3). lib. bdg. 12.40 (978-0-613-72005-2(9)) Tandem Library Bks.

McCully, Emily Arnold. Monk Camps Out. McCully, Emily Arnold, illus. 2000. (Illus.). 32p. (J). (ps-4). pap. 15.95 (978-0-439-09976-9(5) , Levine, Arthur A. Bks.) Scholastic, Inc.

—Monk Camps Out. 2000. (Illus.). (J). (978-0-439-09977-6(3)) Scholastic, Inc.

Meister, Cari. Tiny Goes Camping. Davis, Rich, illus. 2006. (Viking Easy-To-Read Ser.). 32p. (J). (ps-k). 13.99 (978-0-670-89250-1(5) , Viking Adult) Penguin Group (USA) Inc.

Miller, Dorothy Anne. Stories to Read 'Round the Campfire. 2006. pap. 12.95 (978-1-4137-7554-9(3)) PublishAmerica, Inc.

Moss, Miriam. One Day It Was Wet. 2000. (Cambridge Reading Ser.). (Illus.). 14p. pap. 5.00 (978-0-521-65950-5(7)) Cambridge Univ. Pr.

—One Day It Was Wet: American English Edition. 2000. (Cambridge Reading Ser.). (Illus.). 12p. pap. 5.00 (978-0-521-79529-6(X)) Cambridge Univ. Pr.

Myers, Arthur & Rau, Margaret. Scary Stories for Campfires. 2005. (Illus.). 96p. (ps-7). pap. 5.95 (978-1-4027-2170-0(6)) Sterling Publishing Co., Inc.

No Extras: Individual Title, 6 packs. (Literatura 2000 Ser.). (gr. 1-2). 28.00 (978-0-7635-0103-7(4)) Rigby Education.

Orme, Helen. Wet! 2008. (Siti's Sisters Ser.). 36p. pap. 7.95 (***978-1-84167-688-3(8)***) Ransom Publishing Ltd. GBR. *Dist:* International Publishers Marketing.

Parish, Peggy. Amelia Bedelia Goes Camping. Sweat, Lynn, illus. 2003. (I Can Read Bks.). 64p. (J). (ps-ps). pap. 3.99 (978-0-06-051106-7(0) , Harper Trophy) HarperCollins Pubs.

—Amelia Bedelia Goes Camping. 2003. (gr. k-3). lib. bdg. 11.80 (978-0-613-62664-4(8)) Tandem Library Bks.

Parr, Todd. Otto Goes to Camp. 2004. (Illus.). 24p. (J). (ps-3). 9.95 (978-0-316-73900-9(6)) Little Brown & Co.

Parvensky Barwell, Catherine A. Tommi Goes Camping, 4 vols. Barwell, Matthew W. et al, eds. Parvensky Barwell, Catherine A., illus. 2006. (Illus.). 40p. (J). 14.95 (978-0-9774409-3-1(1) , TL004) ILT Publishing.

Paterson, Brian. Zigby Camps Out. 2003. (Illus.). 32p. (J). (ps). pap. 8.99 (978-0-00-713180-8(1) , HarperCollins Children's Bks.) HarperCollins Pubs. Ltd. GBR. *Dist:* Independent Pubs. Group.

Petersen, P. J. I Hate Camping. 1998. (Puffin Chapters Ser.). (978-0-606-13504-7(9)) Tandem Library Bks.

Pittar, Gill. Milly & Molly Go Camping. 2004. (Illus.). 28p. (978-1-86972-003-2(2)) Milly Molly Bks.

Pringle, Laurence P. Bear Hug. Palmer, Kate Salley, illus. 2003. 32p. (J). (gr. k-2). 15.95 (978-1-56397-876-0(8)) Boyds Mills Pr.

Redenbaugh, Vicki. Skar's Picnic ... A Bear's Tale. Redenbaugh, Vicki, illus. 2005. (Illus.). (J). 14.95 (978-1-59091-034-4(6)) Eastern National.

Reid, Roger. Longleaf. 2006. 136p. (J). 19.95 (978-1-58838-194-1(3) , Junebug Bks.) NewSouth, Inc.

Rey, Margret. Curious George Goes Camping. 1999. (gr. k-3). lib. bdg. 11.80 (978-0-613-21391-2(2)) Tandem Library Bks.

Rey, Margret & Rey, H. A. Curious George & the Dumptruck. Vipah Interactive Staff, illus. 1999. (Curious George Ser.). 24p. (J). (gr. k-3). pap. 3.95 (978-0-395-97836-8(X)) Houghton Mifflin Co. Trade & Reference Div.

—Curious George Goes Camping. 1999. (Curious George Ser.). (Illus.). 24p. (J). (gr. k-3). tchr. ed. 12.95 (978-0-395-97831-3(9)) Houghton Mifflin Co. Trade & Reference Div.

—Curious George Goes Camping. Interactive, Vipah, illus. 1999. (Curious George Ser.). 32p. (J). (gr. k-3). pap. 3.95 (978-0-395-97835-1(1)) Houghton Mifflin Co. Trade & Reference Div.

River Runners: Individual Title Six-Packs. (Action Packs Ser.). 120p. (gr. 3-5). 44.00 (978-0-7635-8398-9(7)) Rigby Education.

Root, Phyllis. Mouse Goes Out. Croft, James, illus. 2002. (Brand New Readers Ser.). (J). (ps-2). 48p. 12.99 (978-0-7636-1351-8(7)); 32p. pap. 5.99 (978-0-7636-1352-5(5)) Candlewick Pr.

Rue, Nancy N. Rough & Rugged Lily. 2002. (Ywof Library). (Illus.). 128p. (J). pap. 5.99 (978-0-310-70260-3(7)) Zonderkidz.

Ruelle, Karen Gray. The Monster in Harry's Backyard. (Holiday House Readers Ser.). (Illus.). 32p. (J). (gr. k-3). 4.95 (978-0-8234-1783-4(2)) Holiday Hse., Inc.

Ruurs, Margriet. When We Go Camping. 2004. lib. bdg. 17.60 (978-0-613-77350-8(0)) Tandem Library Bks.

Rylant, Cynthia. Henry & Mudge & the Starry Night. Stevenson, Sucie, illus. 2002. (Henry & Mudge Ser.). (J). 11.91 (978-0-7587-1272-1(3)) Book Wholesalers, Inc.

—Henry & Mudge & the Starry Night. Stevenson, Sucie, illus. 2002. (Henry & Mudge Ser.). 28.95 incl. audio compact disk (978-1-59112-643-0(6)); pap. 31.95 incl. audio compact disk (978-1-59112-644-7(4)) Live Oak Media.

—Henry & Mudge & the Starry Night. Stevenson, Sucie, illus. 1999. (Henry & Mudge Ser.). 48p. (J). (gr. k-3). pap. 3.99 (978-0-689-82586-6(2) , 076714003996, Aladdin) Simon & Schuster Children's Publishing.

—Poppleton in Spring. Teague, Mark, illus. 2002. (Poppleton Ser.). (J). 11.91 (978-0-7587-1589-0(7)) Book Wholesalers, Inc.

—Poppleton in Spring. Teague, Mark, illus. 1999. (Poppleton Ser.). 48p. (J). (ps-2). pap. 15.95 (978-0-590-84818-3(6) , Blue Sky Pr., The) Scholastic, Inc.

—Poppleton in Spring. 1999. (Poppleton Ser.). (J). (gr. k-3). (978-0-606-16594-5(0)) Tandem Library Bks.

Salisbury, Graham. Night of the Howling Dogs. 2007. 208p. (J). (gr. 3-7). 16.99 (***978-0-385-73122-5(1)***); lib. bdg. 19.99 (***978-0-385-90146-8(1)***) Random Hse. Children's Bks. (Lamb, Wendy).

Schraff, Anne. Who Has Seen the Beast? 2001. (PageTurner Adventure Ser.). 80p. (YA). per. 3.95 (978-1-56254-186-6(2) , SP 1862) Saddleback Educational Publishing.

—Who Has Seen the Beast? 2001. (gr. 7-12). lib. bdg. 11.80 (978-0-613-33243-9(1)) Tandem Library Bks.

Scrimger, Richard. Noses Are Red. 2002. (gr. 3-6). lib. bdg. 16.40 (978-0-613-70897-5(0)) Tandem Library Bks.

—Noses Are Red. 2002. 208p. (J). (gr. 3-7). pap. 7.95 (978-0-88776-590-2(4)) Tundra Bks., Inc./Livres Toundra, Inc. CAN. *Dist:* Random Hse., Inc.

Scripture Teachers: Solomon & Friends Learn about Trusting God. 2003. pap. (***978-0-9712894-2-0(5)***) Lighthouse Christian Products Co.

Seton, Ernest Thompson. Two Little Savages. 2006. pap. 30.99 (***978-1-4280-0828-1(4)***) IndyPublish.com.

Singer, Marilyn. Quiet Night. Manders, John, illus. 2002. 32p. (J). (gr. k-ps). 15.00 (978-0-618-12044-4(0) , Clarion Bks.) Houghton Mifflin Co. Trade & Reference Div.

Singleton, Linda Joy. Oh No! UFO! Karre, Andrew, ed. 2004. (Strange Encounters Ser.). 192p. (gr. 8-12). pap. 4.99 (978-0-7387-0579-8(9)) Llewellyn Pubns.

Spalding, Andrea. An Island of My Own. 2007. 112p. (YA). pap. 11.99 (***978-1-55002-635-1(6)*** , Sandcastle Bks.) Dundurn Group, The CAN. *Dist:* Univ. of Toronto Pr.

Spohn, Kate. Turtle & Snake at Work. 1999. (Puffin Easy-to-Read Ser.). (978-0-606-16823-6(0)) Tandem Library Bks.

—Turtle & Snake Go Camping. 2000. (Easy-to-Read Ser.). (Illus.). 32p. (J). (ps-2). pap. 3.99 (978-0-14-130670-4(X) , Puffin) Penguin Group (USA) Inc.

—Turtle & Snake Go Camping. 2000. (Puffin Easy-to-Read Ser.). (978-0-606-18460-1(0)); lib. bdg. 11.80 (978-0-613-27346-6(X)) Tandem Library Bks.

Stamper, Judith Bauer. A Squeak, a Squeal, & a Screech! Fisher, Cynthia, illus. 1999. (Scholastic At-Home Phonics Reading Program Ser.: Vol. 31). 24p. (J). (978-0-590-68779-9(4)) Scholastic, Inc.

Staunton, Ted. Campfire Morgan. Slavin, Bill, illus. 2007. (First Novel Ser.). 64p. (J). (gr. 2-5). (***978-0-88780-725-1(9)***); 4.95 (***978-0-88780-721-3(6)***) Formac Publishing Co., Ltd. CAN. *Dist:* Casemate Pubs. & Bk. Distributors, LLC.

Steinberg, Laya. Thesaurus Rex Finds a Friend. Harter, Debbie, illus. 2006. (J). (978-1-905236-48-0(4)) Barefoot Bks., Inc.

Stem, Jacqueline. Mystery of the Whispering Walls. 2004. (J). 148p. pap. (978-1-57168-844-6(7)); (Hollow Tree Mystery Ser.: Bk. 6). (Illus.). v, 142p. (978-1-57168-850-7(1) , Eakin Pr.) Eakin Pr.

Stine, R. L. Return to Ghost Camp. 1999. (Goosebumps Series 2000: No. 19). 112p. (gr. 3-7). pap. 3.99 (978-0-590-68523-8(6)) Scholastic, Inc.

Taylor, Leigh. Camptime. Taylor, Leigh, illus. 1999. (Illus.). 64p. (YA). (gr. 7-12). pap. 6.50 (978-0-9660664-1-8(3)) Taylor, Leigh.

Van Draanen, Wendelin. Sammy Keyes & the Wild Things. 2007. (Sammy Keyes Ser.: Bk. 11). 304p. (J). (gr. 5-8). 15.99 (978-0-375-83525-4(3) , Knopf Bks. for Young Readers) Random Hse. Children's Bks.

—Sammy Keyes & the Wild Things. Biggs, Brian, illus. 2007. (Sammy Keyes Ser.: Bk. 11). 304p. (J). (gr. 5-8). lib. bdg. 18.99 (978-0-375-93525-1(8) , Knopf Bks. for Young Readers) Random Hse. Children's Bks.

Van Dusen, Chris. A Camping Spree with Mr. Magee. 2003. (Illus.). 36p. (J). 14.95 (978-0-8118-3603-6(7)) Chronicle Bks. LLC.

Van Valkenburgh, Norman J. Cub Scouts Climb the Tower: Hunter Mountain, 1963. Van Valkenburgh, Russell V., illus. 2000. 46p. (J). pap. 6.00 (978-1-930098-06-0(5)) Purple Mountain Pr., Ltd.

Warner, Penny. Mystery of the Haunted Cave. 2001. 102p. (J). (978-0-88166-390-7(5)) Meadowbrook Pr.

Yep, Laurence. Skunk Scout. 2005. 192p. (gr. 3-7). pap. 5.99 (978-0-7868-1714-6(3)) Hyperion Pr.

Ziefert, Harriet. What's a Vacation? Schumacher, Claire, illus. 2006. 16p. pap. 5.95 (978-1-4027-2400-8(4)) Sterling Publishing Co., Inc.

Zucker, Jonny. A Deck of Monsters. Williams, Anthony, illus. 2008. (J). pap. (***978-1-59889-898-9(1)***); 33p. (YA). (gr. 5-9). lib. bdg. 21.26 (***978-1-59889-846-0(9)***) Stone Arch Bks.

CAMPS

Carpenter, Tracy. Country Fair Camp. 2006. (Camp Ser.). (YA). 59.99 (978-0-7847-1856-8(3) , 40182) Standard Publishing.

—Summer Camp. 2006. (Camp Ser.). (YA). 59.99 (978-0-7847-1649-6(8) , 40181) Standard Publishing.

—Winter Camp. 2006. cd-rom 59.99 (978-0-7847-1892-6(X)) Standard Publishing.

Gish, Sarah. The Summer Book 2006: A Guide to Houston Day Camps & Classes for Kids & Teens. 2006. spiral bd. 12.95 (978-0-9728507-3-5(2)) Gish Creative.

Gleason, Kendall Lione. Wyonegonic: The First 100 Years. 2001. (Illus.). 120p. pap. (978-0-9655584-3-3(6)) Gleason Publishing, Inc.

Northstar Summer Camp Guide - 2001 Edition: Your Number One Summer Camp Resource, 3 vols. 2001st ed. 2000. 300p. per. 36.00 (978-0-9702071-0-4(7)) Northstar Publishing, Inc.

Thurber, Christopher A. & Malinowski, Jon C. Summer Camp Handbook: Everything You Need to Find, Choose & Get Ready for Overnight Camp & Skip the Homesickness. 2000. (Illus.). 247p. (J). pap. 14.95 (978-1-930085-00-8(1)) Perspective Publishing, Inc.

Willson, Sarah. The Summer Camp Survival Guide. 1999. (Nick Reference Ser.). (Illus.). (J). mass mkt. 5.99 (978-0-689-84557-4(X) , Simon Spotlight/Nickelodeon) Simon & Schuster Children's Publishing.

CAMPS—FICTION

Adler, David A. Cam Jansen & the Summer Camp Mysteries: A Super Special. Allen, Joy, illus. 2007. (Cam Jansen Ser.). 128p. (J). 4.99 (978-0-14-240742-4(9) , Puffin); 14.99 (978-0-670-06218-8(9) , Viking Adult) Penguin Group (USA) Inc.

Aldridge, Janet. MeadowBrook Girls under Canvas or Fun an. 2006. 78.99 (***978-1-4280-3182-1(0)***) IndyPublish.com.

Alexander, Nina. The Case of the Haunted Camp. 1998. (New Adventures of Mary-Kate & Ashley Ser.). (Illus.). 85p. (J). (gr. 2-7). pap. 3.99 (978-0-590-29397-6(4)) Scholastic, Inc.

Atungsiri's Ghost & Other Tales. 2002. (J). pap. 5.95 net. (978-0-620-29636-6(4)) African Artistic Ventures.

Bader, Bonnie. Benny the Big Shot Goes to Camp. Warren, Shari, illus. 2003. (All Aboard Reading Station Stop Ser.: No. 2). 32p. (J). (gr. 1-3). pap. 3.99 (978-0-448-42894-9(6) , Grosset & Dunlap) Penguin Group (USA) Inc.

—Benny the Big Shot Goes to Camp. 2003. (gr. k-3). lib. bdg. 11.80 (978-0-613-64019-0(5)) Tandem Library Bks.

Banim, Lisa. Case at Camp Get-Me Outie. 2004. 125p. (J). lib. bdg. 16.92 (***978-1-4242-0680-3(4)***) Fitzgerald Bks.

Bateman, Teresa. Hamster Camp: How Harry Got Fit. Cote, Nancy, illus. 2005. 32p. (J). (gr. k-4). 15.95 (978-0-8075-3139-6(1)) Whitman, Albert & Co.

Bee, Clair. Ten Seconds to Play!, Vol. 12. 1999. (Chip Hilton Sports Ser.). x, 191p. (J). reprint ed. pap. 5.99 (978-0-8054-1994-8(2)) B&H Publishing Grp.

—Ten Seconds to Play! 1999. (gr. 7-12). lib. bdg. 14.15 (978-0-613-90142-0(8)) Tandem Library Bks.

Bennett, Dean. The Late Loon. 2006. (Illus.). 32p. 15.95 (978-0-89272-730-8(6)) Down East Bks.

Bergen, Lara. Candy Apple #8 I've Got A Secret. 2008. (Candy Apple Ser.). 176p. (J). pap. 4.99 (***978-0-545-03427-2(2)***) Scholastic, Inc.

Blumenthal, Deborah. Fat Camp. 2006. 240p. (gr. 12). pap. 9.99 (978-0-451-21865-0(5) , N A L) Penguin Group (USA) Inc.

Bode, N. E. Nobodies. Ferguson, Peter, illus. 2005. 304p. (J). 16.99 (978-0-06-055738-6(9)); lib. bdg. 17.89 (978-0-06-055739-3(7)) HarperCollins Pubs.

Bourgeois, Paulette. Franklin Goes to Day Camp: A Story & Activity Book. Clark, Brenda, illus. (Franklin Ser.). 74p. (J). (ps-3). (978-1-55074-372-2(4)) Kids Can Pr., Ltd.

—Franklin Goes to Day Camp: A Story & Activity Book. Clark, Brenda, illus. 1998. (Franklin Ser.). (J). (ps-3). pap. 4.50 (978-0-590-06828-4(8) , Cartwheel Bks.) Scholastic, Inc.

Bradford, Karleen. Ghost Wolf. Cormack, Allan & Drew-Brook, Deborah, illus. 2005. (Orca Echoes Ser.). 64p. (J). (gr. 2-3). pap. 4.99 (978-1-55143-341-7(9)) Orca Bk. Pubs. USA.

Brady, Jenifer. Buddy Check. 2002. (gr. 7-12). lib. bdg. 32.65 (978-0-613-77905-0(3)) Tandem Library Bks.

Brammer, Deb. Moose. 2006. (YA). (***978-1-59166-722-3(4)***) Jones, Bob Univ. Pr.

Brouwer, Sigmund. Camp Craziness. 2003. (Watch Out for Joel Ser.). (Illus.). 32p. (J). (gr. 1-3). reprint ed. pap. 3.99 (978-0-7642-2582-6(0)) Bethany Hse. Pubs.

—Camp Craziness. 2003. (gr. k-3). lib. bdg. 11.80 (978-0-613-87752-7(7)) Tandem Library Bks.

Brown, Marc. Arthur Goes to Camp. Brown, Marc, illus. 1998. (Arthur Adventure Ser.). (Illus.). 32p. (J). (gr. k-3). pap. 5.95 (978-0-316-11529-2(0)) Little, Brown Bks. for Young Readers.

Buchanan, Paul. Brain Freeze, Vol. 15. 2000. (Misadventures of Willie Plummett Ser.: Vol. 15). 128p. (J). (gr. 3-7). 5.99 (978-0-570-07004-7(X)) Concordia Publishing Hse.

—Brain Freeze. 2000. (gr. 3-6). lib. bdg. 14.15 (978-0-613-72827-0(0)) Tandem Library Bks.

—Dances with Werewolves, Vol. 8. 2000. (Heebie Jeebies Ser.: Vol. 6). 128p. (J). (gr. 3-7). pap. 5.99 (978-0-8054-1982-5(9)) B&H Publishing Grp.

Bunting, Eve. I Don't Want to Go to Camp. Cocca-Leffler, Maryann, illus. 2003. 32p. (J). (ps up). pap. 8.95 (978-1-59078-074-9(4)) Boyds Mills Pr.

—I Don't Want to Go to Camp. 2003. (ps-2). lib. bdg. 17.60 (978-0-613-58326-8(4)) Tandem Library Bks.

Burleigh, Cyril. The Hilltop Boys on the River. 2005. 26.95 (978-1-4218-0327-2(5) , 1st World Library - Literary Society) 1st World Publishing, Inc.

—The Hilltop Boys on the River. 2007. 118p. pap. 10.99 (***978-1-4264-6538-3(6)***) BiblioBazaar.

—The Hilltop Boys on the River. 2006. 77.99 (***978-1-4280-0122-0(0)***); pap. 71.99 (***978-1-4280-0141-1(7)***) IndyPublish.com.

Busby, Cylin. The Campfire Crush: A Choose Your Boyfriend Book. 2007. (Date Him or Dump Him? Ser.). 176p. (J). (gr. 5-8). pap. 6.95 (***978-1-59990-083-4(1)***) Bloomsbury Publishing.

Byrd, Sandra. Change of Heart. 2002. (gr. 3-6). lib. bdg. 13.00 (978-0-613-84506-9(4)) Tandem Library Bks.

Camp Day's. 2003. (J). per. (978-1-57657-955-8(7)) Paradise Pr., Inc.

Campbell, Joanna. Camp Saddlebrook. 1998. (Thoroughbred Ser.: No. 28). 192p. (gr. 4-7). mass mkt. 4.99 (978-0-06-106530-9(7)) HarperCollins Pubs.

Chapman, Brenda. Where Trouble Leads. 2007. (Illus.). 136p. (YA). (gr. 5 up). pap. 8.95 (***978-1-894917-44-5(8)***) Napoleon Publishing/Rendezvous Pr. CAN. *Dist:* AtlasBooks Distribution.

Christelow, Eileen. Jerome Camps Out. 2002. (Illus.). 32p. (J). (gr. k-3). 5.95 (978-0-618-19467-4(3) , Clarion Bks.) Houghton Mifflin Co. Trade & Reference Div.

—Jerome Camps Out. Christelow, Eileen, illus. 1998. (Illus.). 32p. (J). (gr. k-3). tchr. ed. 16.00 (978-0-395-75831-1(9) , Clarion Bks.) Houghton Mifflin Co. Trade & Reference Div.

—Jerome Camps Out. 2002. (gr. k-3). lib. bdg. 14.10 (978-0-613-72915-4(3)) Tandem Library Bks.

Clark, Carol Toledo. Cheii's Sheepcamp. 2005. 16.95 (978-0-533-15141-7(4)) Vantage Pr., Inc.

Clymer, Susan. There's a Frog in My Sleeping Bag. 1998. (Illus.). (J). (gr. 2-5). pap. 3.99 (978-0-590-88026-8(8) , Scholastic Paperbacks) Scholastic, Inc.

Cohn, Arlen D. Camp Wazoo. Cole, Jeff, illus. 2007. 28p. bds. 9.99 (***978-1-57939-353-3(5)***) Andrews McMeel Publishing.

Cole, Brock. The Goats. 2003. 20.75 (978-0-8446-7238-0(6)) Smith, Peter Pub., Inc.

Coyle, Carmela LaVigna. Thank You, Aunt Tallulah. MacPherson, Bruce, illus. 2006. 32p. 15.95 (978-0-87358-891-1(6) , Rising Moon Bks. for Young Readers) Northland Publishing.

Danziger, Paula. There's a Bat in Bunk Five. 2006. (J). 160p. (gr. 5). pap. 5.99 (978-0-14-240681-6(3)); 150p. (***978-1-4156-7491-8(4)***) Penguin Group (USA) Inc. (Puffin).

David, Lawrence. To Catch a Clownosaurus. Gott, Barry, tr. Gott, Barry, illus. 2003. (Horace Splattly Ser.). 160p. (J). pap. 4.99 (978-0-14-250135-1(2) , Puffin) Penguin Group (USA) Inc.

Davis, Tanita S. Summer of Friends. 1999. 128p. (J). 7.99 (978-0-8280-1292-8(X)) Review & Herald Publishing Assn.

Deans, Sis Boulos. Rainy. 2005. 208p. (J). (ps-7). 16.95 (978-0-8050-7831-2(2)) Holt, Henry & Co.

deGroat, Diane. Good Night, Sleep Tight, Don't Let the Bedbugs Bite! deGroat, Diane, illus. 2002. (Illus.). 32p. (J). (gr. k-3). 16.50 (978-1-58717-129-1(5) , SeaStar Bks.) Chronicle Bks. LLC.

Dizard, John & Morgan, Melissa J. Best (Boy)Friend Forever. 2006. (Camp Confidential Ser.: No. 9). 160p. (J). (gr. 4-7). pap. 4.99 (978-0-448-44325-6(2) , Grosset & Dunlap) Penguin Group (USA) Inc.

Drake, Emily. The Magickers. 2002. 384p. reprint ed. mass mkt. 6.99 (978-0-7564-0035-4(X) , D A W Bks., Inc.) Penguin Group (USA) Inc.

Draper, Sharon M. Shadows of Caesar's Creek. Watson, Jesse Joshua, illus. 2006. (Ziggy & the Black Dinosaurs Ser.: No. 3). 128p. (J). pap. 4.99 (978-0-689-87913-5(X) , Aladdin) Simon & Schuster Children's Publishing.

—The Space Mission Adventure. Watson, Jesse Joshua, illus. 2006. (Ziggy & the Black Dinosaurs Ser.: No. 4). 128p. (J). pap. 4.99 (978-0-689-87914-2(8) , Aladdin) Simon & Schuster Children's Publishing.

Durbin, William. Blackwater Ben. 2005. 208p. (gr. 5). 5.99 (978-0-440-42008-8(3) , Yearling) Random Hse. Children's Bks.

Dussling, Jennifer. Gotcha! Nez, John, illus. 2003. (Science Solves It! Ser.). 32p. (J). 4.99 (978-1-57565-124-8(6)) Kane Pr., The.

—Gotcha! 2003. (gr. k-3). lib. bdg. 13.00 (978-0-613-79272-1(6)) Tandem Library Bks.

Dussling, Jennifer. The Longest Yawn. Sims, Blanche, illus. 2005. 32p. (J). lib. bdg. 20.00 (***978-1-4242-1095-4(X)***) Fitzgerald Bks.

—The Longest Yawn. Sims, Blanche, illus. 2006. (Science Solves It! Ser.). 32p. (J). pap. 4.99 (978-1-57565-160-6(2)) Kane Pr., The.

Emerson, Alice. Ruthfielding at Snow Camp. 2002. 216p. pap. 29.95 (978-1-932080-54-4(6)) Ross & Perry, Inc.

Emerson, B. Alice. Betty Gordon at Mountain Camp or the Mys. 2006. 77.99 (***978-1-4280-2604-9(5)***) IndyPublish.com.

Fitzhugh, K. Percy. Tom Slade at Temple Camp. 2007. (ENG.). 136p. 95.99 (***978-1-4280-7410-1(4)***); per. 88.99 (***978-1-4280-7390-6(6)***) IndyPublish.com.

Fitzhugh, Percy. Tom Slade on Mystery Trail. 2006. pap. 12.95 (***978-1-55742-910-0(3)***) Wildside Pr.

Fleming, Denise. Buster Goes to Cowboy Camp. 2008. 40p. (J). 16.95 (***978-0-8050-7892-3(4)***) Holt, Henry & Co.

Freedman, Sharon. Hey Guys: A Story about Going to Day Camp. Nelson, Megan, illus. 2004. 39p. pap. 17.95 (978-1-4137-2422-6(1)) PublishAmerica, Inc.

Frey, Hildegard G. The Camp Fire Girls at School or the Woleho Weavers. 2004. reprint ed. pap. 21.95 (978-1-4191-5575-8(X)); pap. 1.99 (978-1-4192-5575-5(4)) Kessinger Publishing, LLC.

Friedman, Laurie B. Campfire Mallory. Kalis, Jennifer, illus. 2008. (Mallory Ser.). (J). lib. bdg. 15.95 (***978-0-8225-7657-0(0)*** , Carolrhoda Bks.) Lerner Publishing Group.

Gaard, Betty. Jericho Ride. 2003. (Illus.). 165p. (J). pap. (978-1-57924-968-7(X)) Jones, Bob Univ. Pr.

Gallagher, Diana G. Camp Can't: The Complicated Life of Claudia Cristina Cortez. Garvey, Brann, illus. 2008. (J). pap. (****978-1-59889-878-1(7)***); 81p. (gr. 4-8). lib. bdg. 23.93 (****978-1-59889-840-8(X)***) Stone Arch Bks.

Gelman, Steve. Help! I'm Trapped in the First Day of Summer Camp. 1998. (Help! I'm Trapped Ser.). (J). (gr. 4-7). pap. 4.50 (978-0-590-02965-0(7)) Scholastic, Inc.

Gershon, Gina & Gershon, Dann. Camp Creepy Time: The Adventures of Einstein P. Fleet. 2007. 224p. (J). (gr. 5 up). 16.99 (978-0-399-24737-8(8) , Putnam Juvenile) Penguin Group (USA) Inc.

Greenburg, Dan. The Boy Who Cried Bigfoot. 2000. (gr. 3-6). lib. bdg. 13.00 (978-0-613-24401-5(X)) Tandem Library Bks.

Griffin, Adele. Witch Twins at Camp Bliss. Rogers, Jacqueline, illus. 2003. 144p. (gr. 2-6). pap. 5.99 (978-0-7868-1583-8(3)) Hyperion Bks. for Children.

—Witch Twins at Camp Bliss. 2003. (gr. 3-6). lib. bdg. 14.15 (978-0-613-63671-1(6)) Tandem Library Bks.

Gutman, Anne & Hallensleben, Georg. Gaspard at the Seashore. 2002. (Illus.). 32p. (J). (gr. k-3). 9.95 (978-0-375-81118-0(4) , Knopf Bks. for Young Readers) Random Hse. Children's Bks.

Hancock, H. Irving. The High School Boys in Summer Camp. rev. ed. 2006. 216p. 27.95 (978-1-4218-1750-7(0)); pap. 12.95 (978-1-4218-1850-4(7)) 1st World Publishing, Inc. (1st World Library - Literary Society).

Hancock, Irving H. The High School Boys in Summer Camp or T. 2006. 78.99 (****978-1-4219-9926-5(9)***); pap. 72.99 (****978-1-4219-9928-9(5)***) IndyPublish.com.

Hanson, Bonnie Compton. Escape from Camp Porcupine. 2004. (Ponytail Girls Ser.). (Illus.). 192p. (J). pap. 7.99 (978-1-58411-033-0(3) , Legacy Pr.) Rainbow Pubs. & Legacy Pr.

Harcourt School Publishers Staff. Amigos para Siempre On Level. 3rd ed. 2002. (Trofeos Ser.).Tr. of Always Friends. (SPA., Illus.). pap. 6.80 (978-0-15-324088-1(1)) Harcourt Schl. Pubs.

—Around the Campfire Below Level. 3rd ed. 2002. (Trophies Reading Program Ser.). (Illus.). pap. 5.10 (978-0-15-323057-8(6)) Harcourt Schl. Pubs.

—Friends Forever On Level. 3rd ed. 2002. (Trophies Reading Program Ser.). (Illus.). pap. 5.10 (978-0-15-323177-3(7)) Harcourt Schl. Pubs.

—Fun at Camp: Independent Reader. 3rd ed. 2002. (Trophies Reading Program Ser.). (Illus.). (J). pap. 2.90 (978-0-15-325478-9(5)) Harcourt Schl. Pubs.

—A Great Time at Camp Resolve Advanced Level. 3rd ed. 2002. (Trophies Reading Program Ser.). (Illus.). pap. 5.10 (978-0-15-323372-2(9)) Harcourt Schl. Pubs.

—The Mystery of Camp Owana! Take-Home Book. 1999. (Collections Ser.). (Illus.). (J). pap. 1.90 (978-0-15-317274-8(6)) Harcourt Schl. Pubs.

—The Seventh Grade Penny Drive On Level. 3rd ed. 2002. (Trophies Reading Program Ser.). (Illus.). pap. 5.10 (978-0-15-323451-4(2)) Harcourt Schl. Pubs.

—The Thing That Visited Our Camp 5-Pack, Below Level. 3rd ed. 2002. (Trophies Reading Program Ser.). (Illus.). (gr. 1). pap. 20.10 (978-0-15-326818-2(2)) Harcourt Schl. Pubs.

—The Way Home On Level. 3rd ed. 2002. (Trophies Reading Program Ser.). (Illus.). pap. 5.10 (978-0-15-323171-1(8)) Harcourt Schl. Pubs.

Hartinger, Brent. The Order of the Poison Oak. 2006. 240p. (J). reprint ed. pap. 6.99 (978-0-06-056732-3(5) , HarperTeen) HarperCollins Pubs.

Hautzig, Deborah. Little Witch Goes to Camp. 2002. (gr. k-3). lib. bdg. 10.95 (978-0-613-82447-7(4)) Tandem Library Bks.

Heath, Kathy. Camp Crazy Kids. 2006. 157p. pap. 19.95 (978-1-4241-0260-0(X)) PublishAmerica, Inc.

Henry, April. Shock Point. 2006. 192p. (YA). (gr. 6). 16.99 (978-0-399-24385-1(2) , Putnam Juvenile) Penguin Group (USA) Inc.

Higginson, Hadley. Keeker & Pony Camp Catastrophe, Bk. 5. Parrett, Lisa, illus. 2007. 56p. (J). 15.50 (978-0-8118-5596-9(1)) Chronicle Bks. LLC.

—Keeker & the Pony Camp Catastrophe. Parrett, Lisa, illus. 2007. (Keeker & the Sneaky Pony Ser.: Bk. 5). 56p. (J). (gr. k-3). pap. 3.95 (978-0-8118-5597-6(X)) Chronicle Bks. LLC.

Hoff, Syd. Danny & the Dinosaur Go to Camp. Hoff, Syd, illus. 1998. (I Can Read Bks.). (Illus.). 32p. (J). (ps-2). pap. 3.99 (978-0-06-444244-2(6) , Harper Trophy) HarperCollins Pubs.

—Danny & the Dinosaur Go to Camp. 1998. (I Can Read Bks.). (J). (ps-1). 10.79 (978-0-606-13313-5(5)) Tandem Library Bks.

Howe, James. Pinky & Rex Go to Camp. 1999. (gr. k-3). lib. bdg. 11.80 (978-0-7857-0627-4(5)) Tandem Library Bks.

Jacobson, Jennifer Richard. Truly Winnie. Geis, Alissa Imre, illus. 2006. 112p. (J). (gr. 3-5). pap. 5.95 (978-0-618-68954-5(0)) Houghton Mifflin Co.

Johnson, Harriet McBryde. Accidents of Nature. rev. ed. 2006. 240p. (YA). 16.95 (978-0-8050-7634-9(4) , Holt, Henry & Co. Bks. For Young Readers) Holt, Henry & Co.

Johnson, Regan. Hold on to Your Tail: Letters from Camp Lizard. Johnson, Regan, illus. 2007. (Letters From Camp Lizard Ser.). (Illus.). 100p. (J). (gr. 2-7). per. (****978-1-933831-04-6(9)*** , Ready Blade) Blooming Tree Pr.

Jones, Christianne C. Eric No Juega. Demski, James, Jr., illus. 2006. (Read-It! Readers en Espanol Ser.).Tr. of Eric Won't Do It. (SPA.). 32p. (J). (ps-3). 19.95 (978-1-4048-1683-1(6)) Picture Window Bks.

Kasischke, Laura. Boy Heaven. 288p. (J). 2008. pap. 7.99 (****978-0-06-081316-1(4))***; 2006. 16.99 (978-0-06-081314-7(8)); 2006. lib. bdg. 17.89 (978-0-06-081315-4(6)) HarperCollins Pubs. (HarperTeen).

Kaye, Michael. Summer Camp Race of Horror. 2002. 108p. pap. 9.95 (978-0-595-23726-5(6) , Writers Club Pr.) iUniverse, Inc.

Keene, Carolyn. Riding Club Crime. 2003. (gr. 5-8). lib. bdg. 13.00 (978-0-613-65082-3(4)) Tandem Library Bks.

Kindig, Tess Eileen. Camp Bee-A-Champ. 2001. (gr. k-3). lib. bdg. 13.00 (978-0-613-72852-2(1)) Tandem Library Bks.

Kindig, Tess Eileen & Van Severen, Joe. Double Whammy!, Vol. 7. 2001. (Slam Dunk Ser.: Vol. 7). (Illus.). 96p. (J). (gr. 1-4). 4.99 (978-0-570-07143-3(7)) Concordia Publishing Hse.

Klise, Kate. Letters from Camp. Klise, M. Sarah, illus. 2000. 192p. (J). (gr. 4-7). pap. 5.99 (978-0-380-79348-8(2) , Harper Trophy) HarperCollins Pubs.

—Letters from Camp. 2000. (gr. 3-6). lib. bdg. 14.15 (978-0-613-28552-0(2)) Tandem Library Bks.

Koch, Edward T. & Thaler, Pat Koch. Eddie's Little Sister Makes a Splash. Warhola, James, illus. 2007. 32p. (J). (gr. k). 16.99 (978-0-399-24310-3(0) , Putnam Juvenile) Penguin Group (USA) Inc.

Konigsburg, E. L. The Outcasts of 19 Schuyler Place. 304p. 2004. 16.95 (978-0-689-86636-4(4) , Atheneum); 2005. (J). reprint ed. pap. 5.99 (978-0-689-86637-1(2) , Aladdin) Simon & Schuster Children's Publishing.

—The Outcasts of 19 Schuyler Place. l.t. ed. 2004. (Thorndike Press Large Print the Literary Bridge Ser.). 346p. (J). 22.95 (978-0-7862-6483-4(7)) Thorndike Pr.

Krailing, Tessa. Beastly Basil. Phillips, Mike, illus. 2006. 48p. (J). lib. bdg. (****978-1-4048-3113-1(4)***) Picture Window Bks.

Krulik, Nancy E. Camp Rules! John and Wendy Staff, illus. 2007. (Katie Kazoo, Switcheroo Ser.). 160p. (J). pap. 4.99 (978-0-448-44542-7(5) , Grosset & Dunlap) Penguin Group (USA) Inc.

—Get Lost!, No. 6. 2003. (Katie Kazoo, Switcheroo Ser.: No. 6). (Illus.). 80p. (J). (gr. 2-6). pap. 3.99 (978-0-448-43101-7(7) , Grosset & Dunlap) Penguin Group (USA) Inc.

—Get Lost!, No. 6. 2003. (Katie Kazoo, Switcheroo Ser.: No. 6). (gr. 3-6). lib. bdg. 11.80 (978-0-613-60289-1(7)) Tandem Library Bks.

Lasky, Kathryn. Born to Rule. Walton, Tony, illus. 2006. (Camp Princess Ser.: No. 1). 160p. (J). pap. 4.99 (978-0-06-058763-5(6) , Harper Trophy); 15.99 (978-0-06-058761-1(X)) HarperCollins Pubs.

—Marven of the Great North Woods. Hawkes, Kevin, illus. 2002. 48p. (J). (gr. 1-4). pap. 7.00 (978-0-15-216826-1(5) , Voyager Bks./Libros Viajeros) Harcourt Children's Bks.

Lasky, Kathryn. Unicorns? Get Real! 2007. (Camp Princess Ser.: Vol. 2). (Illus.). 160p. (J). pap. 4.99 (****978-0-06-058766-6(0)*** , Harper Trophy) HarperCollins Pubs.

Leblanc, Margaret. Ms. Maddy Comes to Town. 2006. 76p. pap. 14.95 (978-1-4241-4103-6(6)) PublishAmerica, Inc.

Lenhard, Elizabeth. OSS Wilderness. 2003. (gr. 3-6). lib. bdg. 13.00 (978-0-613-68274-9(2)) Tandem Library Bks.

—OSS Wilderness. 2003. (Spykids Adventures Ser.: Vol. 4). 160p. (Orig.). (J). (gr. 3-7). pap. 4.99 (978-0-7868-1718-4(6) , Volo) Hyperion Bks. for Children.

Leslie, J. Lawrence. In Camp on the Big Sunflower. 2006. 24.99 (****978-1-4219-7624-2(2)***); pap. 18.99 (****978-1-4219-7630-3(7)***) IndyPublish.com.

Lewis, Beverly. No Guys Pact. 2003. (Holly's Heart Ser.: Bk. 9). 160p. (YA). (gr. 5-9). pap. 6.99 (978-0-7642-2616-8(9)) Bethany Hse. Pubs.

Lewis, Cynthia C. Dilly's Summer Camp Diary. 2000. 4. (Illus.). 32p. (J). (gr. 2-4). pap. 6.95 (978-0-7613-0990-1(X) , First Avenue Editions) Lerner Publishing Group.

—Dilly's Summer Camp Diary. 1999. (gr. 3-6). lib. bdg. 15.25 (978-0-613-28464-6(X)) Tandem Library Bks.

Littlefield, William. The Circus in the Woods. 2001. 208p. (J). (gr. 4-6). tchr. ed. 15.00 (978-0-618-06642-1(X)) Houghton Mifflin Co. Trade & Reference Div.

London, Jonathan. Froggy Goes to Camp. Remkiewicz, Frank, illus. 2008. (Froggy Ser.). 32p. (J). (ps-k). 15.99 (****978-0-670-01098-1(7)*** , Viking Juvenile) Penguin Group (USA) Inc.

Lupica, Mike. Summer Ball. 2007. 256p. (YA). (gr. 4 up). 17.99 (978-0-399-24487-2(5) , Philomel) Penguin Group (USA) Inc.

Lynch, Chris. Slot Machine. 2003. 21.75 (978-0-8446-7249-6(1)) Smith, Peter Pub., Inc.

Matlin, Marlee. Deaf Child Crossing. (Illus.). 208p. (J). 2004. pap. 4.99 (978-0-689-86696-8(8) , Aladdin); 2002. (gr. 3-6). 15.95 (978-0-689-82208-7(1)) Simon & Schuster Children's Publishing.

—Deaf Child Crossing. 2004. (gr. 3-6). lib. bdg. 13.00 (978-0-613-88068-8(4)) Tandem Library Bks.

Mattern, Joanne. Batter Up! 2005. 40.00 (****978-1-4108-4193-3(6)***) Benchmark Education Co.

Mayer, Mercer. Day at Camp. 2001. (gr. k-3). lib. bdg. 11.80 (978-0-613-67608-3(4)) Tandem Library Bks.

—A Day at Camp, Vol. 2. 2002. (Little Critter First Readers Ser.). (Illus.). 24p. (J). (gr. k-1). pap. 3.95 (978-1-57768-836-5(8)) School Specialty Publishing.

Mays, Stan. Wicked Little Camp Story. 2005. 248p. pap. 14.95 (978-1-59113-674-3(1)) Booklocker.com, Inc.

McKinney, Lorrie J., et al. Camp Jacubbi the Bubble Gummers. Loomis, Larry, illus. 2000. 20p. (J). (ps-6). pap. 9.95 (978-0-9701667-0-8(2)) Jacubbi Enterprises.

McKissack, Patricia C. Miami Makes the Play. 2001. (gr. k-3). lib. bdg. 11.80 (978-0-613-43071-5(9)) Tandem Library Bks.

McKissack, Patricia C. & McKissack, Fredrick L. Miami Jackson Makes the Play. Chesworth, Michael, illus. 2004. (Road to Reading Ser.). 96p. (J). (gr. k-3). pap. 3.99 (978-0-307-26505-0(6) , Random Hse. Bks. for Young Readers) Random Hse. Children's Bks.

—Miami Makes the Play. Chesworth, Michael, illus. 2004. 92p. (J). (gr. 4-7). lib. bdg. 11.19 (978-0-606-32802-9(5)) Tandem Library Bks.

Metzenthen, David. Adrian Goes Out There! 2000. (gr. 7-12). lib. bdg. 12.25 (978-0-613-28720-3(7)) Tandem Library Bks.

Morgan, Melissa J. Alex's Challenge. 2007. 22.78 (978-1-59961-150-1(3)) Spotlight.

—Camp Confidential Vol. 4: Alex's Challenge. 2005. (Camp Confidential Ser.). 160p. (gr. 4-7). mass mkt. 4.99 (978-0-448-43876-4(3) , Grosset & Dunlap) Penguin Group (USA) Inc.

—Golden Girls, No. 16. 2007. (Camp Confidential Ser.). 160p. (J). pap. 4.99 (978-0-448-44541-0(7) , Grosset & Dunlap) Penguin Group (USA) Inc.

—Jenna's Dilemma, No. 2. 2005. (Camp Confidential Ser.). 160p. (J). (gr. 4-7). mass mkt. 4.99 (978-0-448-43738-5(4) , Grosset & Dunlap) Penguin Group (USA) Inc.

—Natalie's Secret, No. 1. 2005. (Camp Confidential Ser.). 160p. (J). (gr. 4-7). mass mkt. 4.99 (978-0-448-43737-8(6) , Grosset & Dunlap) Penguin Group (USA) Inc.

—Over & Out. 2006. (Camp Confidential Ser.: No. 10). 160p. (J). (gr. 4-7). pap. 4.99 (978-0-448-44326-3(0) , Grosset & Dunlap) Penguin Group (USA) Inc.

—Reality Bites, No. 15. 2007. (Camp Confidential Ser.). 160p. (J). pap. 4.99 (978-0-448-44539-7(5) , Grosset & Dunlap) Penguin Group (USA) Inc.

Moss, Marissa. Amelia Takes Command. 1999. (Amelia's Notebooks). (Illus.). 48p. (J). (ps-7). lib. bdg. 12.75 (978-0-606-19868-4(7)) Tandem Library Bks.

Murphy, Stuart J. Grizzly Gazette. 2003. (gr. k-3). lib. bdg. 13.00 (978-0-613-59243-7(3)) Tandem Library Bks.

Myers, Bill. My Life As a Smashed Burrito. 1999. (Incredible Worlds of Wally McDoogle Ser.: No. 1). 128p. (J). (gr. 3-7). pap. 1.99 (978-0-8499-7508-0(5)) Nelson, Thomas Inc.

—My Life As A Smashed Burrito. Mangiat, Jeff, illus. 2005. (Incredible Worlds of Wally McDoogle Ser.: Vol. 1). 128p. (J). 9.99 (978-1-4003-0571-1(3)) Nelson, Thomas Inc.

Naylor, Phyllis Reynolds. Patiently Alice. (Alice Ser.). 256p. (YA). 2004. mass mkt. 5.99 (978-0-689-87073-6(6) , Simon Pulse); 2003. (Illus.). 15.95 (978-0-689-82636-8(2) , Atheneum) Simon & Schuster Children's Publishing.

Nixon, Joan Lowery. Nightmare. 176p. 2005. (J). (gr. 5). 5.50 (978-0-440-23773-0(4) , Yearling); 2003. (YA). (gr. 7). 15.95 (978-0-385-73026-6(8) , Delacorte Bks. for Young Readers); 2003. (YA). (gr. 7). lib. bdg. 17.99 (978-0-385-90151-2(8) , Delacorte Bks. for Young Readers) Random Hse. Children's Bks.

Nolen, Jerdine. Plantzilla Goes to Camp. Catrow, David, illus. 2006. 32p. (J). (gr. k-3). 16.95 (978-0-689-86803-0(0)) Simon & Schuster Children's Publishing.

Novara, Joseph. Wa-Tonka! Camp Cowboys. Lawson, Robert, illus. 2000. 232p. (J). per. 9.95 (978-0-9671978-9-0(9)) Syncopated Pr.

O'Dell, Kathleen. Agnes Parker... Happy Camper? 2005. (Illus.). 160p. (J). (gr. 5-7). 16.99 (978-0-8037-2962-9(6) , Dial) Penguin Group (USA) Inc.

Pascal, Francine. Love & Betrayal & Hold the Mayo. 2003. (Victoria Martin Trilogy: No. 3). (gr. 7-12). lib. bdg. 13.00 (978-0-613-66459-2(0)) Tandem Library Bks.

Penner, Lucille Recht. Clean-Sweep Campers. Billin-Frye, Paige, illus. 2000. (Math Matters Ser.). 32p. (J). (gr. 1-3). pap. 4.95 (978-1-57565-096-8(7)) Kane Pr., The.

—Clean-Sweep Campers. 2000. (Math Matters Ser.). (J). 11.75 (978-0-606-20181-0(5)); lib. bdg. 12.95 (978-0-613-39304-1(X)) Tandem Library Bks.

Pinkwater, Daniel M. Go West. Rash, Andy, illus. 2002. (Fat Camp Commandos Ser.). 96p. (J). (gr. 3-8). pap. 14.95 (978-0-439-29772-1(9) , Scholastic Pr.) Scholastic, Inc.

—Go West. 2003. (gr. 3-6). lib. bdg. 12.40 (978-0-613-62511-1(0)) Tandem Library Bks.

Pyle, Hugh F. Scamper Squirrel Goes to Camp. 2000. (Illus.). 72p. (J). (gr. 4-7). pap. 7.95 (978-0-87398-774-5(8)) Sword of the Lord Pubs.

Quinn, Zoe. Cabin Fever. 2007. (Caped Sixth Grader Ser.). 144p. (J). (gr. 4-7). 5.50 (978-0-440-42082-8(2)); (Illus.). lib. bdg. 11.99 (978-0-385-90307-3(3)) Random Hse. Children's Bks. (Yearling).

Rainsbury, Julie. Crab-Boy Cranc. Evans, Fran, illus. 2000. 48p. pap. 11.95 (978-1-85902-835-3(7)) Beekman Bks., Inc.

Randall, Rod. Welcome to Camp Creeps, Vol. 2. 1998. (Heebie Jeebies Ser.). 144p. (J). (gr. 1-6). pap. 5.99 (978-0-8054-1195-9(X)) B&H Publishing Grp.

Rau, Dana Meachen. Feet. Stromoski, Rick, illus. 2000. (Rookie Reader Espanol Ser.). 24p. (J). (gr. k-2). pap. 4.95 (978-0-516-27042-5(7)); 19.50 (978-0-516-22008-6(X)) Scholastic Library Publishing. (Children's Pr.).

—Feet. 2000. (gr. k-3). lib. bdg. 12.95 (978-0-613-54486-3(2)) Tandem Library Bks.

Reif, Charles Braddock. Toxamok, a Troll at Summer Camp. Ashcraft, Wanda, illus. 1999. 75p. (J). (gr. 4-6). (978-0-9666156-1-6(1)) Keepsake Chronicles.

Reisner, Molly & Ostrow, Kim. Camp SpongeBob. Martinez, Heather, illus. 2004. (SpongeBob SquarePants Ready-To-Read Ser.: Vol. 5). 32p. (J). pap. 3.99 (978-0-689-86593-0(7) , Simon Spotlight/Nickelodeon) Simon & Schuster Children's Publishing.

—Camp Spongebob. Martinez, Heather, illus. ed. 2005. 32p. (J). lib. bdg. 15.00 (978-1-59054-983-4(X)) Fitzgerald Bks.

Reiss, Mike. The Boy Who Looked Like Lincoln. Catrow, David, tr. Catrow, David, illus. 2003. 32p. (J). (ps-6). 10.99 (978-0-8431-0271-0(3) , Price Stern Sloan) Penguin Group (USA) Inc.

—The Boy Who Looked Like Lincoln. Catrow, David, illus. 2006. 32p. (J). (ps). reprint ed. pap. 5.99 (978-0-14-240416-4(0) , Puffin) Penguin Group (USA) Inc.

Riordan, Rick. The Lightning Thief. 2006. (Percy Jackson & the Olympians Ser.: Bk. 1). 392p. (gr. 5 up). reprint ed. pap. 7.99 (978-0-7868-3865-3(5)) Miramax Bks.

—The Sea of Monsters. 2nd rev. ed. 2007. (Percy Jackson & the Olympians Ser.: Bk. 2). 304p. (gr. 5 up). pap. 7.99 (****978-1-4231-0334-9(3)***) Miramax Bks.

—The Sea of Monsters. l.t. ed. 2006. (Percy Jackson & the Olympians Ser.: Bk. 2). (YA). (gr. 5 up). 22.95 (978-0-7862-9074-1(9)) Thorndike Pr.

Roter, Jordan. Camp Rules. 2007. 272p. (YA). (gr. 6-9). 15.99 (978-0-525-47803-4(5) , Dutton Juvenile) Penguin Group (USA) Inc.

Roy, Ron. Detective Camp. Gurney, John Steven, illus. 2006. (A to Z Mysteries Ser.: No. 27). 144p. (J). (gr. 1-4). pap. 4.99 (978-0-375-83534-6(2)); lib. bdg. 11.99 (978-0-375-93534-3(7)) Random Hse. Children's Bks. (Random Hse. Bks. for Young Readers).

Rue, Nancy N. Lily's Church Camp Adventure. 2003. (gr. 3-6). lib. bdg. 13.00 (978-0-613-71663-5(9)) Tandem Library Bks.

—Lily's Church Camp Adventure. 2003. (Ywof Library). 128p. (J). pap. 5.99 (978-0-310-70264-1(X)) Zonderkidz.

Ryan, Sara. Empress of the World. 2003. (gr. 7-12). lib. bdg. 16.45 (978-0-613-67491-1(X)) Tandem Library Bks.

Sachar, Louis. Hoyos. (SPA.). 236p. (YA). (gr. 5-8). (978-84-348-6793-2(1) , SM7975) SM Ediciones ESP. *Dist:* Lectorum Pubns., Inc.

—Hoyos. Abos, Elena, tr. 2nd ed. 2005. (Barco de Vapor Ser.). (SPA., Illus.). 240p. (J). (gr. 4-8). 8.95 (978-84-348-7860-0(7) , SM5090) SM Ediciones ESP. *Dist:* AIMS International Bks., Inc., Lectorum Pubns., Inc., Iaconi, Mariuccia Bk. Imports.

—Hoyos. 2001. (SPA.). (gr. 5-8). lib. bdg. 16.40 (978-0-613-64523-2(5)) Tandem Library Bks.

Sauer, Tammi. Cowboy Camp. Reed, Mike, illus. 2005. 32p. (J). (ps-2). 14.95 (978-1-4027-2224-0(9)) Sterling Publishing Co., Inc.

Schade, Susan. Baseball Camp on the Planet of the Eyeballs. Buller, Jon, illus. 1998. (Step into Reading Step 3 Bks.). (J). (gr. 2-3). (978-0-606-13950-2(8)) Tandem Library Bks.

Schanback, Mindy. Princess from Another Planet. 2005. 254p. (J). (gr. 5-9). 16.95 (978-0-8234-1847-3(2)) Holiday Hse., Inc.

Schraff, Anne. Horse Called Courage. 2001. (gr. 7-12). lib. bdg. 11.80 (978-0-613-32650-6(4)) Tandem Library Bks.

Scorcia, Yvonne M. Cindy Goes to Camp. 1998. 64p. (J). (gr. k-4). pap. 8.00 (978-0-8059-4521-8(0)) Dorrance Publishing Co., Inc.

Scott, Rosanna. Peter & Friends at Camp. Fargo, Todd, illus. l.t. ed. 2006. (Turtle Books). 32p. (J). (gr. k-4). pap. 9.95 (978-0-944727-51-5(4)); lib. bdg. 15.95 (978-0-944727-52-2(2)) Jason & Nordic Pubs. (Turtle Bks.).

Seuling, Barbara. Robert Goes to Camp. Brewer, Paul, illus. 2007. (Robert Bks.). 160p. (J). (gr. 2-4). 16.95 (****978-0-8126-2753-4(9)***) Cricket Bks.

Smallcomb, Pam. Camp Buccaneer. Lichtenheld, Tom, illus. ed. 2005. 58p. (J). lib. bdg. 15.00 (978-1-59054-897-4(3)) Fitzgerald Bks.

—Camp Buccaneer. Lichtenheld, Tom, illus. 2002. (Ready-for-Chapters Ser.). 64p. (J). (gr. 1-3). lib. bdg. 11.89 (978-0-689-84383-9(6) , Aladdin Library) Simon & Schuster Children's Publishing.

Smith, Jane Denitz. Mary by Myself. 1999. (J). (978-0-606-16701-7(3)) Tandem Library Bks.

Snider, Cindy Gay. Finding Anna Bee. Chambers, Mary, illus. 2007. (J). pap. (****978-0-8361-9392-3(X)***) Herald Pr.

Standish, Burt L. Frank Merriwell's Happy Camp. Rudman, Jack, ed. 2003. (Frank Merriwell Ser.). pap. 9.95 (978-0-8373-9140-3(7)) Merriwell, Frank Inc.

Stanley, George Edward. Snake Camp. Lee, Jared D., illus. 2000. (Road to Reading Ser.). 48p. (J). (gr. 2-5). pap. 3.99 (978-0-307-26406-0(8) , Random Hse. Bks. for Young Readers) Random Hse. Children's Bks.

—Snake Camp. 2000. (J). (978-0-606-18927-9(0)); (gr. 3-6). lib. bdg. 11.80 (978-0-613-33066-4(8)) Tandem Library Bks.

Steele, Michael Anthony. The Ghost of Camp Ka Nowato. 1999. (Wishbone Super Mysteries Ser.: No. 2). (J). (gr. 2-5). (978-0-606-19033-6(3)) Tandem Library Bks.

Stem, Jacqueline. The Borrowed Grave. Laronde, Gary, illus. 2001. v, 153p. (J). pap. 11.95 (978-1-57168-556-8(1) , Eakin Pr.) Eakin Pr.

—The Borrowed Grave, Vol. 3. 2001. (Hollow Tree Mystery Ser.). (Illus.). 160p. 16.95 (978-1-57168-451-6(4)) Eakin Pr.

Stern, Ricki. Beryl E. Bean. 2nd ed. 2002. (Beryl E. Bean Ser.). (Illus.). 64p. (J). 14.89 (978-0-06-028772-6(1)) HarperCollins Pubs.

Stewart, Jane L. The Camp Fire Girls at Long Lake. rev. ed. 2006. (ENG.). 140p. 25.95 (978-1-4218-2057-6(9) , 1st World Library - Literary Society) 1st World Publishing, Inc.

—The Camp Fire Girls at Long Lake or Bessie King in Summer Camp. 2004. reprint ed. pap. 15.95 (978-1-4191-5574-1(1)); pap. 1.99 (978-1-4192-5574-8(6)) Kessinger Publishing, LLC.

Stine, R. L. Welcome to Camp Nightmare. 2003. (Goosebumps Ser.). 160p. pap. 4.99 (978-0-439-56846-3(3) , 53657973, Scholastic Paperbacks) Scholastic, Inc.

—Welcome to Camp Nightmare. 2003. (gr. 5-8). lib. bdg. 13.00 (978-0-613-70846-3(6)) Tandem Library Bks.

Swain, Cynthia, told to. At Camp. 2003. (BuildUp Ser.). (J). pap. 22.00 (978-1-4108-0750-2(9)) Benchmark Education Co.

Sykes, Shelley & Szymanski, Lois. The Ghost Comes Out. 2001. (Gettysburg Ghost Gang Ser.: Vol. 1). 96p. (J). pap. 5.95 (978-1-57249-266-0(X) , White Mane Kids) White Mane Publishing Co., Inc.

—Ghost on Board. 2001. (Gettysburg Ghost Gang Ser.: Vol. 2). (Illus.). 96p. (J). pap. 5.95 (978-1-57249-267-7(8) , White Mane Kids) White Mane Publishing Co., Inc.

Thomas, Jeana. How Louie Became a Safety Swimmer: Water Safety. Triefenbach, Lisa, illus. l.t. ed. 2002. (Camp of Champs Ser.: Vol. 2). 24p. (J). (ps-3). pap. 6.95 (978-0-9701118-4-5(3) , 050-002) Charm Pubns., Inc.

Thomas, Jerry D. Mystery at Thunder Mountain. 2003. (Detective Zack Ser.). (Illus.). 132p. (J). pap., pap. 6.99 (978-0-7814-3731-8(8) , 0781437318) Cook, David C. Publishing Co.

—Mystery at Thunder Mountain. 2002. (gr. 3-6). lib. bdg. 14.15 (978-0-613-74878-0(6)) Tandem Library Bks.

Thompson, Lisa. Wild Ideas. Thompson, Lisa & Stapleton, Matthew, illus. 2005. (Read-It! Chapter Bks.). 48p. (J). (ps-k). lib. bdg. 19.95 (978-1-4048-1346-5(2)) Picture Window Bks.

Uncle Markie. Pigletté & Bobo Go to Summer Camp. 2002. 34p. (YA). ring bd. 9.95 (978-1-933129-04-4(2)) Studio 403.

Vandercook, Margaret. The Camp Fire Girls at Sunrise Hill. 2004. reprint ed. pap. 19.95 (978-1-4191-5576-5(8)); pap. 1.99 (978-1-4192-5576-2(2)) Kessinger Publishing, LLC.

Warner, Gertrude Chandler. The Mystery of the Screech Owl. Soileau, Hodges, illus. 2001. 117p. (J). (gr. 2-7). per. 11.80 (978-0-613-35790-6(6)) Tandem Library Bks.

—The Mystery of the Screech Owl, Vol. 16. 2004. (Boxcar Children Special Ser.: No. 16). (Illus.). 144p. (J). (gr. 2-5). 14.95 (978-0-8075-5481-4(2)); pap. 3.95 (978-0-8075-5482-1(0)) Whitman, Albert & Co.

—Summer Camp Mystery. 2001. (gr. 3-6). lib. bdg. 11.80 (978-0-613-35798-2(1)) Tandem Library Bks.

Warner, Gertrude Chandler, creator. The Boxcar Children Summer Special. 2007. (Boxcar Children Mysteries Ser.). 376p. (J). pap. 7.95 (***978-0-8075-0885-5(3)***) Whitman, Albert & Co.

Wedekind, Annie. A Horse of Her Own. 2008. 288p. (J). 16.95 (***978-0-312-36927-9(1)***) Feiwel & Friends.

Weiss, Ellen. My First Day at Camp. Thornburgh, Rebecca McKillip, illus. 1999. (Bank Street Reader Collection). (J). (ps-2). lib. bdg. 22.60 (978-0-8368-2418-6(0)) Stevens, Gareth Inc.

Welch, Ruth. Our Camping Trip: Level G, 6 Packs. (Lighthouse Ser.). 12p. (gr. 1 up). 26.00 (978-0-7578-0840-1(9)) Rigby Education.

Wells, Helen. Cherry Ames, Camp Nurse. 2007. (YA). (***978-0-8261-0417-5(7)***) Springer.

Wetz, Juliann. Boot Camp: A Robbie & Marshall Adventure. 2002. (J). mass mkt. 4.95 (978-0-9716397-1-3(X)) Wetz, Juliann.

Williams, Jacklyn. Happy Birthday, Gus! Cushman, Doug, illus. 2005. (Read-It! Readers Ser.). 32p. (J). (gr. k-3). 18.60 (978-1-4048-0957-4(0)) Picture Window Bks.

Willow Creek Association. 5-G Challenge Spring Quarter Camp Iwanabeagee: Doing Life with God in the Picture. 2004. (Promiseland Ser.). (J). pap. 12.99 (978-0-7441-4293-8(8)) Zonderkidz.

Wilson, Jacqueline. How to Survive Summer Camp. 2002. (J). pap. 29.95 incl. audio (978-0-7540-6250-9(3)) BBC Audiobooks America.

—How to Survive Summer Camp. Heap, Sue, illus. l.t. ed. 2002. 256p. (J). 16.95 (978-0-7540-7808-1(6) , Galaxy Children's Large Print) BBC Audiobooks America.

—My Brother Bernadette. Roberts, David, illus. 2002. (Yellow Bananas Ser.). 48p. (J). (gr. 3-4). pap. (978-0-7787-0986-2(8)); lib. bdg. (978-0-7787-0940-4(X)) Crabtree Publishing Co.

—My Brother Bernadette. 2002. (gr. 3-6). lib. bdg. 12.95 (978-0-613-52884-9(0)) Tandem Library Bks.

Wing, Natasha. The Night Before Summer Camp. Pierce, Mindy, illus. 2007. 32p. (J). pap. 3.99 (978-0-448-44639-4(1) , Grosset & Dunlap) Penguin Group (USA) Inc.

Withers, Pam. Camp Wild. (Orca Currents Ser.). 112p. (J). 2006. lib. bdg. 14.95 (978-1-55143-557-2(8)); 2005. (Illus.). (gr. 4-10). pap. 7.95 (978-1-55143-361-5(3)) Orca Bk. Pubs. USA.

Wojciechowski, Susan. Beany Goes to Camp. Natti, Susanna, illus. ed. 2005. (Beany Ser.). 112p. (J). (gr. 1-4). pap. 4.99 (978-0-7636-2570-2(1)) Candlewick Pr.

CANADA

Barlas, Robert, et al. Welcome to Canada. 1999. (Welcome to My Country Ser.). (Illus.). 48p. (J). (gr. 2 up). lib. bdg. 26.00 (978-0-8368-2394-3(X)) Stevens, Gareth Inc.

Beckett, Harry. Manitoba. 2003. (Eye on Canada Ser.). (Illus.). 32p. (J). pap. 7.95 (978-1-894705-01-1(7)) Weigl Pubs., Inc.

Blades, Heather. Focus on Canada. 2006. (Illus.). 64p. (J). pap. (978-0-8368-6234-8(1)); lib. bdg. 32.67 (978-0-8368-6215-7(5)) Stevens, Gareth Inc. (World Almanac Library).

Boraas, Tracey. Canada. 2001. (Countries & Cultures Ser.). (Illus.). 64p. (J). (gr. 3-4). lib. bdg. 23.93 (978-0-7368-0766-1(7) , Bridgestone Bks.) Capstone Pr., Inc.

Bowers, Vivien. British Columbia. 2nd ed. (Hello Canada Ser.). 72p. pap. (978-1-55041-758-6(4)) Fitzhenry & Whiteside, Ltd.

—British Columbia. 1998. (Hello Canada Ser.). (Illus.). (J). (gr. 3-6). pap. 6.95 (978-0-8225-9797-1(7)) Lerner Publishing Group.

—Crazy about Canada! Amazing Things Kids Want to Know. Eastman, Dianne, illus. 2006. 96p. (J). 28.95 (978-1-897066-47-8(3)); pap. 18.95 (978-1-897066-48-5(1)) Maple Tree Pr. CAN. *Dist:* Perseus Distribution.

—Only in Canada! From the Colossal to the Kooky. Eastman, Dianne, illus. 2002. (Wow Canada! Ser.). 91p. (J). (gr. 3-7). pap. 14.95 (978-1-894379-38-0(1) , Owl Bks.) Maple Tree Pr. CAN. *Dist:* Firefly Bks., Ltd.

—That's Very Canadian! An Exceptionally Interesting Report about All Things Canadian, by Rachel. Eastman, Dianne, illus. 2004. (Wow Canada! Collection). 96p. (J). 28.95 (978-1-897066-04-1(X)); pap. 18.95 (978-1-897066-05-8(8)) Maple Tree Pr. CAN. *Dist:* Perseus Distribution.

—Wow, Canada! Exploring This Land from Coast to Coast. Hobbs, Dan, illus. 1999. (Wow Canada! Ser.). 160p. (J). (gr. 3-7). 29.95 (978-1-895688-93-1(0)); pap. 19.95 (978-1-895688-94-8(9)) Maple Tree Pr. CAN. (Owl Bks.). *Dist:* Firefly Bks., Ltd.

—Wow Canada! Exploring This Land from Coast to Coast. 1999. (gr. 3-6). lib. bdg. 30.35 (978-0-613-88447-1(7)) Tandem Library Bks.

—Wow, Canada! Exploring This Land from Coast to Coast to Coast. Hobbs, Dan & Eastman, Dianne, illus. 160p. 2005. pap. 19.95 (978-1-897066-36-2(8)); 2nd ed. 2007. (J). (gr. 3-7). 29.95 (978-1-897066-94-2(5)); 2nd ed. 2007. (J). (gr. 3-7). pap. 24.95 (978-1-897066-95-9(3)) Maple Tree Pr. CAN. *Dist:* Transition Vendor, Perseus Distribution.

Braun, Eric. Canada in Pictures. 2nd ed. 2003. (Visual Geography Ser.). (Illus.). 80p. (J). (gr. 5-12). 27.93 (978-0-8225-4679-5(5)) Lerner Publishing Group.

Campbell, Kumari. New Brunswick. 1999. (Hello Canada Ser.). 72p. (J). pap. (978-1-55041-268-0(X)) Fitzhenry & Whiteside, Ltd.

Canada. 2006. 24p. 15.95 (***978-1-58341-444-6(4)*** , Creative Education) Creative Co., The.

Canada. 2002. 176p. (J). (gr. 2-5). 15.99 (978-0-7439-3630-9(2) , 3630) Teacher Created Materials, Inc.

Canadian Books Staff. Canadian Scented Book. 2005. 12p. 6.95 (978-0-9762524-5-0(7)) Gimme Gimme Toys & Games Inc.

Canizares, Susan & Berger, Samantha. Canada. 1999. (J). 2.50 (978-0-439-04573-5(8)) Scholastic, Inc.

—Canada. 1999. (ps-2). lib. bdg. 10.95 (978-0-613-21286-1(X)) Tandem Library Bks.

Desaulniers, Kristi L. & Desaulniers, Rob. Canada. 2003. (Modern World Nations Ser.). (Illus.). (gr. 6-12). 150p. 30.00 (978-0-7910-7238-7(X)); 200p. pap. 30.00 (978-0-7910-7501-2(X)) Facts On File, Inc. (Chelsea Hse.).

Dolan, Sean. Canada. 2002. (Steadwell Books World Tour). (Illus.). 48p. (J). lib. bdg. 24.26 (978-0-7398-5533-1(6)) Raintree.

Durbin, William. The Broken Blade. 1998. (Illus.). 176p. (J). (gr. 5-9). reprint ed. 5.50 (978-0-440-41184-0(X) , Yearling) Random Hse. Children's Bks.

Erwin, Vicki B. "C" Is for Canada. Thurman, Mark, illus. 2000. (Alpha Flight Bks.). 60p. (J). (ps-3). 17.95 (978-1-892920-30-0(1)) GHB Publishers, LLC.

Ferry, Steven. Yukon Territory. 2002. (Exploring Canada Ser.). (Illus.). 104p. (J). 29.95 (978-1-59018-053-2(4) , Lucent Bks.) Thomson Gale.

Flowers, Pam. Alone Across the Arctic: One Woman's Epic Journey by Dog Team. 2001. (gr. 5-8). lib. bdg. 25.70 (978-0-613-59797-5(4)) Tandem Library Bks.

Flowers, Pam & Dixon, Ann. Alone Across the Arctic: One Woman's Epic Journey by Dog Team. 2005. (Illus.). 120p. (gr. 5-10). 22.95 (978-0-88240-547-6(0)) Graphic Arts Ctr. Publishing Co.

Frost, Helen. A Look at Canada. Saunders-Smith, Gail, ed. 2002. (Our World Ser.). (Illus.). 24p. (J). (gr. k-1). lib. bdg. 15.93 (978-0-7368-1166-8(4) , Pebble Bks.) Capstone Pr., Inc.

Gall, Timothy L. & Gall, Susan B. Junior Worldmark Encyclopedia of Canadian Provinces. 5th rev. ed. 2007. (J). 67.00 (978-1-4144-1060-9(3) , UXL) Thomson Gale.

—Junior Worldmark Encyclopedia of the Canadian Provinces. 2nd ed. 1999. (Illus.). x, 254p. (J). (gr. 4-7). 49.00 (978-0-7876-3811-5(0) , UXL) Thomson Gale.

Gall, Timothy L. & Gall, Susan B., eds. Junior Worldmark Encyclopedia of the Canadian Provinces. 3rd ed. 2001. (Illus.). 240p. (J). 55.00 (978-0-7876-5386-6(1) , GML00502-173575, UXL) Thomson Gale.

Garrington, Sally. Canada. 2005. (Countries of the World Ser.). 64p. (J). (gr. 6-12). 30.00 (978-0-8160-6009-2(6)) Facts On File, Inc.

Geiger, Beth. Geography of Canada. 2006. (Navigators Ser.). (J). pap. 44.00 (***978-1-4108-6262-4(3)***) Benchmark Education Co.

Ghione, Yvette & Gurth, Per-Henrik. Canada in Colours. 2008. 24p. (***978-1-55453-240-7(X)***) Kids Can Pr., Ltd.

Golden, Nancy. Exploring Canada with the Five Themes of Geography/By Nancy Golden. (Library of the Western Hemisphere). (J). 2005. (Illus.). 24p. 19.95 (978-1-4042-2669-2(9) , PowerKids Pr.); 2004. pap. (978-0-8239-4641-9(X)); 2004. (Illus.). 24p. lib. bdg. (978-0-8239-4629-7(0)) Rosen Publishing Group, Inc., The.

Grabowski, John F. Canada. 1999. (Modern Nations of the World Ser.). (Illus.). 112p. (YA). (gr. 7-10). 27.45 (978-1-56006-520-3(6) , Lucent Bks.) Thomson Gale.

Gray, Shirley W. Canada. 2000. (First Reports). (Illus.). 48p. (J). (gr. 3 up). lib. bdg. 22.60 (978-0-7565-0028-3(1)) Compass Point Bks.

Greenwood, Barbara. The Kids Book of Canada. MacRae, Jock, illus. 1998. 60p. (J). (gr. 4-6). (978-1-55074-315-9(5)) Kids Can Pr., Ltd.

Gurth, Per-Henrik & Bellefontaine, Kim. Canada 123. 2008. 24p. (***978-1-55453-235-3(3)***) Kids Can Pr., Ltd.

Gutsole, Reginald. Discovering Canada. 2000. (Illus.). 64p. (J). (978-0-19-541487-5(X)) Oxford Univ. Pr., Inc.

Hamilton, Janice. Canada. (Country Explorers Ser.). 48p. 2007. (J). (gr. 4-8). lib. bdg. 27.93 (***978-0-8225-7128-5(5)*** , Lerner Pubns.); 1999. (Illus.). (gr. 2-4). lib. bdg. 22.60 (978-1-57505-133-8(8)); 1999. (Illus.). (J). (gr. 3-5). lib. bdg. 22.60 (978-1-57505-108-6(7) , Carolrhoda Bks.) Lerner Publishing Group.

Hancock, Lee. Nunavut. 1999. (Hello Canada Ser.). (J). pap. (978-1-55041-271-0(X)) Fitzhenry & Whiteside, Ltd.

Hancock, Lyn. Nunavut. 2nd rev. ed. (Hello Canada Ser.). 72p. (J). pap. (978-1-55041-760-9(6)) Fitzhenry & Whiteside, Ltd.

Harcourt School Publishers Staff. Canada's French Province. 3rd ed. 2002. (Horizons Ser.). (Illus.). (J). pap. 7.30 (978-0-15-333557-0(2)) Harcourt Schl. Pubs.

Harrison, Ted. O Canada. ed. 2004. (J). (gr. k-3). spiral bd. (978-0-616-03038-7(X)) Canadian National Institute for the Blind/Institut National Canadien pour les Aveugles.

Haugen, Brenda. Canada ABCs: A Book about the People & Places of Canada. Shaw, David, illus. 2004. (Country ABCs Ser.). 32p. (J). (gr. k-5). 23.93 (978-1-4048-0285-8(1)) Picture Window Bks.

Hozy, Penny & Yates, Sarah. Manitoba. 2nd rev. ed. (Hello Canada Ser.). (Illus.). 72p. pap. (978-1-55041-439-4(9)) Fitzhenry & Whiteside, Ltd.

Hughes, Susan. Lester B. Pearson. (Illus.). 64p. (J). (gr. 5 up). pap. (978-1-55041-504-9(2)) Fitzhenry & Whiteside, Ltd.

Kalman, Bobbie. Canada - The Culture. 2nd rev. ed. 2002. (Lands, Peoples & Cultures Ser.). (Illus.). 32p. (J). (gr. 4-5). (978-0-7787-9360-1(5)); pap. (978-0-7787-9728-9(7)) Crabtree Publishing Co.

—Canada - The Land. 2nd rev. ed. 2002. (Lands, Peoples & Cultures Ser.). (Illus.). 32p. (J). (gr. 4-5). (978-0-7787-9358-8(3)); pap. (978-0-7787-9726-5(0)) Crabtree Publishing Co.

—Canada - The People. 2nd rev. ed. 2002. (Lands, Peoples & Cultures Ser.). (Illus.). 32p. (J). (gr. 4-5). (978-0-7787-9359-5(1)); pap. (978-0-7787-9727-2(9)) Crabtree Publishing Co.

—Canada from a to Z. 1999. (gr. 5-8). 18.85 (978-0-7857-1273-2(9)) Tandem Library Bks.

Kaplan, Leslie C. Canada, a Primary Source Guide. 2005. (Countries of the World, a Primary Source Journey Ser.). (J). 19.95 (978-1-4042-2750-7(4) , PowerKids Pr.) Rosen Publishing Group, Inc., The.

Kavanagh, James. Manitoba & Saskatchewan Birds. Leung, Raymond, illus. 1999. (Pocket Naturalist Ser.). (J). 5.95 (978-1-58355-038-0(0)) Waterford Pr., Ltd.

Keeler, Stephen & Little, Catherine. Canada. 2003. (What's it Like to Live in... Ser.). (Illus.). 32p. (J). 16.95 (978-1-57768-878-5(3) , Waterbird Bks.) School Specialty Publishing.

Landau, Elaine. Canada. 2000. (True Bks.). (Illus.). 48p. (J). (gr. 3-5). pap. 6.95 (978-0-516-27021-0(4)); 25.00 (978-0-516-21170-1(6)) Scholastic Library Publishing. (Children's Pr.).

—Canada. 2000. (gr. 3-6). lib. bdg. 15.25 (978-0-613-53982-1(6)) Tandem Library Bks.

Laws, Gordon D. & Laws, Lauren M. The Maritime Provinces. 2003. (Illus.). 112p. (J). 29.95 (978-1-59018-335-9(5) , Lucent Bks.) Thomson Gale.

—The Northwest Territories. 2003. (Exploring Canada Ser.). (Illus.). 112p. (J). 29.95 (978-1-59018-049-5(6) , Lucent Bks.) Thomson Gale.

LeVert, Suzanne. Alberta. 2000. (Canada in the Twenty First Century Ser.). (Illus.). 64p. (J). (gr. 8-12). 18.95 (978-0-7910-6059-9(4) , Chelsea Hse.) Facts On File, Inc.

—British Columbia. 2000. (Canada in the Twenty First Century Ser.). (Illus.). 64p. (J). (gr. 8-12). 18.95 (978-0-7910-6060-5(8) , Chelsea Hse.) Facts On File, Inc.

—Canada: Facts & Figures. 2000. (Canada in the Twenty First Century Ser.). (Illus.). (J). (gr. 8-12). 29.50 (978-0-7910-6062-9(4) , Chelsea Hse.) Facts On File, Inc.

—Dominion of Canada. Sheppard, George, ed. 2000. (Canada in the Twenty First Century Ser.). (Illus.). 64p. (J). 29.50 (978-0-7910-6061-2(6) , Chelsea Hse.) Facts On File, Inc.

—Manitoba. Sheppard, George, ed. 2000. (Canada in the Twenty First Century Ser.). (Illus.). 64p. (J). (gr. 8-12). 25.00 (978-0-7910-6063-6(2) , Chelsea Hse.) Facts On File, Inc.

—New Brunswick. 2000. (Canada in the Twenty First Century Ser.). (Illus.). 64p. (J). (gr. 8-12). 18.95 (978-0-7910-6064-3(0) , Chelsea Hse.) Facts On File, Inc.

—Newfoundland. Sheppard, George, ed. 2000. (Canada in the Twenty First Century Ser.). (Illus.). (J). (gr. 8-12). 18.95 (978-0-7910-6065-0(9) , Chelsea Hse.) Facts On File, Inc.

—Northwest Territories. 2000. (Canada in the Twenty First Century Ser.). (Illus.). (J). (gr. 8-12). 29.50 (978-0-7910-6066-7(7) , Chelsea Hse.) Facts On File, Inc.

—Quebec. 2000. (Canada in the Twenty First Century Ser.). (Illus.). (J). (gr. 8-12). 18.95 (978-0-7910-6070-4(5) , Chelsea Hse.) Facts On File, Inc.

—Saskatchewan. 2000. (Canada in the Twenty First Century Ser.). (Illus.). (J). (gr. 8-12). 25.00 (978-0-7910-6071-1(3) , Chelsea Hse.) Facts On File, Inc.

—Yukon. 2000. (Canada in the Twenty First Century Ser.). (Illus.). 64p. (J). 18.95 (978-0-7910-6072-8(1) , Chelsea Hse.) Facts On File, Inc.

Little, Catherine. Canada. 2002. (Changing Face Of... Ser.). (Illus.). 48p. (J). lib. bdg. 27.12 (978-0-7398-5212-5(4)) Raintree.

A Look at Canada. 2005. (One World, Many Cultures Ser.). (YA). (gr. k-3). (978-0-7368-9362-6(8) , Pebble Bks.) Capstone Pr., Inc.

A Look at Canada, 6 vols. (gr. k-2). 28.95 (978-0-7368-9363-3(6)) Red Brick Learning.

Lutz, Norma Jean. Nunavat. 2000. (Canada in the Twenty First Century Ser.). (Illus.). (J). (gr. 8-12). 29.50 (978-0-7910-6073-5(X) , Chelsea Hse.) Facts On File, Inc.

MacLeod, Elizabeth. The Kids Book of Great Canadians. Mantha, John, tr. Mantha, John, illus. 2004. (Kids Books Of ... Ser.). 64p. (J). (gr. 3-7). (978-1-55337-366-7(9)) Kids Can Pr., Ltd.

Marsh, Carole. America's Important Neighbors: Canada, Mexico & Cuba. 2001. (Here & Now Series!). (Illus.). 48p. (J). (gr. 3-8). pap. 7.95 (978-0-635-00262-4(0)) Gallopade International.

—The Big Canada Reproducible Activity Book! 2001. (Canada Experience! Ser.). (Illus.). 96p. (J). (gr. 2-6). pap., act. bk. ed. 9.95 (978-0-635-00513-7(1)) Gallopade International.

—Canada Coloring Book! 2001. (Canada Experience! Ser.). (Illus.). 32p. (J). (gr. k-3). pap. 3.95 (978-0-635-00517-5(4)) Gallopade International.

—Canada Jeopardy! 2001. (Canada Experience! Ser.). (Illus.). 32p. (J). (gr. 3-8). pap., act. bk. ed. 7.95 (978-0-635-00520-5(4)) Gallopade International.

—Canada "Jography" 2001. (Canada Experience! Ser.). (Illus.). 32p. (J). (gr. 3-8). pap., act. bk. ed. 7.95 (978-0-635-00521-2(2)) Gallopade International.

—Canada Millionaire. 2001. (GameBook Ser.). (Illus.). 32p. (J). (gr. 3-8). pap., act. bk. ed. 9.95 (978-0-635-00702-5(9)) Gallopade International.

—Canada Survivor. 2001. (GameBook Ser.). (Illus.). 32p. (J). (gr. 3-8). pap., act. bk. ed. 9.95 (978-0-635-00698-1(7)) Gallopade International.

—Canada Wheel of Fortune. 2001. (GameBook Ser.). (Illus.). 32p. (J). (gr. 3-8). pap., act. bk. ed. 9.95 (978-0-635-00700-1(2)) Gallopade International.

—My First Book about Canada. 2001. (Canada Experience! Ser.). (Illus.). 32p. (J). (gr. k-4). pap. 7.95 (978-0-635-00519-9(0)) Gallopade International.

—My First Pocket Guide: Canada. 2001. (Canada Experience! Ser.). (Illus.). 96p. (J). (gr. 3-8). pap., act. bk. ed. 6.95 (978-0-635-00512-0(3)) Gallopade International.

—My First Pocket Guide Canada. 2002. (Canada Experience! Ser.). (Illus.). 32p. (J). (gr. 3-9). lib. bdg. 10.95 (978-0-635-01341-5(X) , 1341X) Gallopade International.

—The Survivor: A Class Challenge. 2001. (Canada Experience! Ser.). lib. bdg. 29.95 (978-0-635-00697-4(9)) Gallopade International.

—Wheel of Fortune. 2001. (Canada Experience! Ser.). lib. bdg. 29.95 (978-0-635-00699-8(5)) Gallopade International.

Marx, David F. Canada. 2001. (Rookie Read-About Geography Ser.). (Illus.). 32p. (J). (gr. 1-2). pap. 5.95 (978-0-516-27083-8(4) , Children's Pr.) Scholastic Library Publishing.

—Canada. 2000. (gr. k-3). lib. bdg. 14.10 (978-0-613-53981-4(8)) Tandem Library Bks.

Match Game Staff. Canada Scented Memory Game. 2005. pap. 19.95 (978-0-9762524-1-2(4)) Gimme Gimme Toys & Games Inc.

Mattern, Joanne. Let's Visit Canada: The Metric System. 2004. (PowerMath Ser.). (Illus.). 24p. (J). pap. (978-0-8239-8872-3(4) , PowerKids Pr.) Rosen Publishing Group, Inc., The.

McCarthy, Pat. Canada: A MyReportLinks. com Book. 2004. (Top Ten Countries of Recent Immigrants Ser.). (Illus.). 48p. (J). lib. bdg. 25.26 (978-0-7660-5176-8(5) , MyReportLinks.com Bks.) Enslow Pubs., Inc.

McNamara, Margaret. Canada. 2006. pap. 42.00 (***978-1-4108-6458-1(8)***) Benchmark Education Co.

Meister, Cari. Canada. 2000. (Going Places Ser.). (Illus.). 24p. (J). (gr. k-6). lib. bdg. 21.35 (978-1-57765-028-7(X) , Checkerboard Library) ABDO Publishing Co.

Moore, Christopher. The Big Book of Canada: Exploring the Provences & Territories. Slavin, Bill, illus. 2002. 256p. (J). (gr. 4 up). 29.95 (978-0-88776-457-8(6)) Tundra Bks., Inc./Livres Toundra, Inc. CAN. *Dist:* Random Hse., Inc.

Nations of the World: Canada. (Time Traveler Ser.). 32p. (gr. 3-6). 6.99 (978-0-513-02377-2(1) , TSD23771) Denison, T. S. & Co., Inc.

Nelson, Sheila. Before Canada: First Nations & First Contacts, Prehistory-1523. 2005. (Illus.). 87p. (J). (gr. 3-7). lib. bdg. 21.95 (978-1-4222-0001-8(9) , 1247963) Mason Crest Pubs.

Nickles, Greg & Walker, Niki. Canada. 2000. (Nations of the World Ser.). (Illus.). 128p. (YA). (gr. 6-8). lib. bdg. 34.26 (978-0-8172-5780-4(2)) Raintree.

Oberle, Lora Polack. The Canadian Forces Snowbirds: 431 Air Demonstration Squadron. 2001. (Serving Your Country Ser.). (Illus.). 48p. (J). (gr. 3-4). lib. bdg. 21.26 (978-0-7368-0774-6(8) , Capstone High-Interest Bks.) Capstone Pr., Inc.

Olson, Kay Melchisedech. Canada. 2003. (Many Cultures, One World Ser.). (Illus.). 32p. (J). (gr. 2-3). lib. bdg. 23.93 (978-0-7368-2166-7(X) , Bridgestone Bks.) Capstone Pr., Inc.

Olson, Nathan. Canada: A Question & Answer Book. 2004. (Fact Finders Ser.). (Illus.). 32p. (J). (gr. 3-4). lib. bdg. 22.60 (978-0-7368-2686-0(6)) Capstone Pr., Inc.

Orr, Tamra. Canada. 2006. (Illus.). 40p. (J). (gr. 2-4). pap. 6.95 (978-0-516-24950-6(9) , Children's Pr.) Scholastic Library Publishing.

Orr, Tamra B. Canada. 2005. (to Z Ser.). (Illus.). 40p. (J). (ps-ps). 24.50 (978-0-516-23661-2(X) , Children's Pr.) Scholastic Library Publishing.

Palana, B. J. British Columbia. 2002. (Exploring Canada Ser.). (Illus.). 104p. (J). 29.95 (978-1-59018-046-4(1) , Lucent Bks.) Thomson Gale.

Pang, Guek Cheng. Canada. 2nd ed. 2004. (Cultures of the World Ser.). 144p. (J). 37.07 (978-0-7614-1788-0(5) , Benchmark Bks.) Cavendish, Marshall Corp.

Park, Ted. Taking Your Camera To... Includes: Australia, Brazil, Canada, Egypt, France, Israel, Italy, Japan, Mexico, Panama, Russia, Spain, 12 bks., Set. 2000. (Taking Your Camera to Ser.). (Illus.). (J). (gr. 4-7). 273.96 (978-0-7398-3096-3(1)) Raintree.

Pohl, Kathleen. Looking at Canada. 2007. (J). pap. (*978-0-8368-8175-2(3)); 32p. (gr. 2-4). lib. bdg. 25.27 (*978-0-8368-8168-4(0)) Stevens, Gareth Inc.

Rogers, Barbara Radcliffe & Rogers, Stillman D. Canada. 2000. (Enchantment of the World, Second Ser.). (Illus.). 144p. (YA). (gr. 5-9). 36.00 (978-0-516-21076-6(9) , Children's Pr.) Scholastic Library Publishing.

Rogers, Stillman D. & Rogers, Barbara Radcliffe. Toronto. 2001. (Cities of the World Ser.). (Illus.). 64p. (YA). (gr. 4-9). pap. 9.95 (978-0-516-27169-9(5) , Children's Pr.) Scholastic Library Publishing.

Ruth, Angie. My Adventure in Canada. 2007. 44p. (J). 8.99 (978-1-59092-424-2(X) , Orchard Academy Pr.) Windstorm Creative.

Schemenauer, Elma. Welcome to Canada. 2007. (Welcome to the World Ser.). 32p. (J). (gr. 1-5). 27.07 (*978-1-59296-911-1(9)) Child's World, Inc.

Schwartz, Noa & Beaumont, Mick. Crazy for Canada. Tebbutt, Susan, illus. 1998. 24p. (J). (ps-3). pap. (978-0-9680678-2-6(4)) Tumbleweed Pr.

Shea, Kitty. Teens in Canada. 2007. (J). lib. bdg. (*978-0-7565-3303-8(1)) Compass Point Bks.

Shireman, Myrl. Canada. 1998. (Illus.). 80p. (YA). (gr. 5-8). pap. 9.95 (978-1-58037-076-9(4)) Twain, Mark Media, Inc. Pubs.

Smith, Roger & McIntosh, Marsha. Youth in Prison. 2006. (Incarceration Issues Ser.). (Illus.). 112p. (J). (gr. 7 up). (978-1-59084-990-3(6)) Mason Crest Pubs.

Staunton, Ted. The Dreadful Truth: Canadian Crime. Geoffroi, Remie, illus. 2006. (Dreadful Truth Ser.). 104p. (J). (gr. 3-8). (*978-0-88780-705-3(4)) Formac Publishing Co., Ltd. CAN. *Dist:* Casemate Pubs. & Bk. Distributors, LLC.

Stewart, Mark. The United States & Canada. 2007. (J). pap. (*978-1-4034-9912-7(8)); (Illus.). 64p. (gr. 4-7). lib. bdg. (*978-1-4034-9903-5(9)) Raintree.

Stotksy, Sandra. Canada. 1999. (Major World Nations Ser.). (Illus.). 144p. (YA). (gr. 4-7). 29.95 (978-0-7910-4733-0(4) , Chelsea Hse.) Facts On File, Inc.

Symon, John. The Lobster Kids' Guide to Exploring Ottawa-Hull: 12 Months of Fun. Kirner, Bob, ed. Battuz, Christine, illus. 1999. (Lobster Kids' City Explorers Ser.). 256p. (J). (ps-7). pap. 17.95 (978-1-894222-01-3(6)) Lobster Pr. CAN. *Dist:* Univ. of Toronto Pr.

Thompson, Alexa. Nova Scotia. 1999. (Hello Canada Ser.). (J). pap. (978-1-55041-272-7(8)) Fitzhenry & Whiteside, Ltd.

Tompsett, Norman & Barlas, Robert. Canada. 1998. (Countries of the World Ser.). (Illus.). 96p. (J). (gr. 6 up). lib. bdg. 30.00 (978-0-8368-2123-9(8)) Stevens, Gareth Inc.

Trottier, Maxine. One Is Canada. ed. 2004. (Illus.). (J). (gr. 1-5). spiral bd. (978-0-616-01797-5(9)) Canadian National Institute for the Blind/Institut National Canadien pour les Aveugles.

—One Is Canada. Slavin, Bill, illus. 2000. 32p. (J). pap. (978-0-00-638663-6(6)) HarperCollins Canada, Ltd.

—One Is Canada. Slavin, Bill, illus. 2000. 24p. (J). (ps-5). 17.95 (978-0-00-224556-2(6)) HarperCollins Pubs.

Ulmer, Mike. M Is for Maple: A Canadian Alphabet. Rose, Melanie, illus. 2001. 40p. (J). (ps-3). 19.95 (978-1-58536-051-2(1)) Sleeping Bear Pr.

—M Is for Maple: A Canadian Alphabet. rev. ed. 2007. (Board Ser.). 36p. bds. 7.99 (*978-1-58536-345-2(6)) Sleeping Bear Pr.

—M Is for Maple: A Canadian Alphabet. Rose-Popp, Melanie, illus. rev. ed. 2004. 48p. (J). pap. 10.95 (978-1-58536-235-6(2)) Sleeping Bear Pr.

Walsh, Kieran. Canada. 2005. (Countries in the News Ser.). (Illus.). 24p. (gr. 1-4). 17.95 (978-1-59515-171-1(0)) Rourke Publishing, LLC.

Williams, Brian. Canada. 2007. (National Geographic Countries of the World Ser.). (Illus.). 64p. (J). (gr. 3-5). lib. bdg. 27.90 (978-1-4263-0025-7(5) , National Geographic Children's Bks.) National Geographic Society.

—Guide to Canada. 1998. (World Guides Ser.). (Illus.). 32p. (J). (gr. 2-6). lib. bdg. 21.27 (978-1-884756-40-5(9)) Davidson Titles, Inc.

Zocchi, Judy. In Canada. Brodie, Neale, illus. 2005. (Global Adventures II Ser.). 32p. (J). per. 9.95 (978-1-59646-169-7(1)) Dingles & Co.

—In Canada/en Canada. Brodie, Neale, illus. 2005. (Global Adventures II Ser.).Tr. of En Canada. (ENG & SPA.). 32p. (J). per. 9.95 (978-1-59646-171-0(3)) Dingles & Co.

—In Cuba. Brodie, Neale, illus. 2005. (Global Adventures II Ser.). 32p. (J). per. 9.95 (978-1-59646-161-1(6)) Dingles & Co.

CANADA—BIOGRAPHY

Bailey, Katie. Radisson & Groseilliers: Fur Traders of the North. 2006. (In the Footsteps of Explorers Ser.). (Illus.). 32p. (J). (gr. 3-9). (978-0-7787-2422-3(0) , 1253444) Crabtree Publishing Co.

Bankston, John. Michael J. Fox. l.t. ed. 2002. (Real Life Reader Biography Ser.). (Illus.). 32p. (gr. 3-8). lib. bdg. 24.95 (978-1-58415-128-9(5)) Mitchell Lane Pubs., Inc.

Benge, Janet & Benge, Geoff. Rowland Bingham: Into Africa's Interior. 2003. (Christian Heroes, Then & Now Ser.). (Illus.). 192p. pap. 8.99 (978-1-57658-282-4(5)) YWAM Publishing.

Bogart, Jo Ellen. Capturing Joy: The Story of Maud Lewis. Lang, Mark, illus. 2002. 32p. (J). (gr. 3-7). 16.95 (978-0-88776-568-1(8)) Tundra Bks., Inc./Livres Toundra, Inc. CAN. *Dist:* Random Hse., Inc.

Brown, Don. Mack Made Movies. 2005. (Illus.). 32p. (J). (ps-ps). reprint ed. pap. 6.95 (978-1-59643-091-4(5)) Roaring Brook Pr.

—Mack Made Movies. Brown, Don, illus. rev. ed. 2003. (Illus.). 32p. (J). (ps-4). 16.95 (978-0-7613-1538-4(1)) Roaring Brook Pr.

Butts, Ed. She Dared: True Stories of Heroines, Scoundrels, & Renegades. Collins, Heather, illus. 2005. 121p. (J). (gr. 6-9). lib. bdg. 16.00 (978-0-606-33860-8(8)) Tandem Library Bks.

Butts, Edward. She Dared: True Stories of Heroines, Scoundrels, & Renegades. Collins, Heather, illus. 2005. 128p. (J). (gr. 6-9). pap. 8.95 (978-0-88776-718-0(4)) Tundra Bks., Inc./Livres Toundra, Inc. CAN. *Dist:* Random Hse., Inc.

Conover, David, Sr. Once upon an Island: The Adventures of a Young Couple Who Did Buy Their Dream Island. 2nd ed. 2004. 224p. pap. 17.95 (978-0-9707399-1-9(5) , 425-485-2813) San Juan Publishing.

Cooper, John. Rapid Ray: The Story of Ray Lewis. 2002. (Illus.). 160p. (J). (gr. 5-9). pap. 8.95 (978-0-88776-612-1(9)) Tundra Bks., Inc./Livres Toundra, Inc. CAN. *Dist:* Random Hse., Inc.

Cutler, May Ebbitt. Breaking Free: The Story of William Kurelek. Kurelek, William, illus. 2002. 32p. (J). (gr. 5 up). 17.95 (978-0-88776-617-6(X)) Tundra Bks., Inc./Livres Toundra, Inc. CAN. *Dist:* Random Hse., Inc.

Debon, Nicolas. Four Pictures by Emily Carr. (Illus.). (J). 2007. 32p. pap. 6.95 (*978-0-88899-814-9(7)); 2003. 40p. 15.95 (978-0-88899-532-2(6)) Groundwood Bks. CAN. *Dist:* Perseus Distribution.

Debon, Nicolas. The Strongest Man in the World: Louis Cyr. Debon, Nicolas, illus. 2007. (Illus.). 36p. (J). (gr. 2 up). 17.95 (978-0-88899-731-9(0)) Groundwood Bks. CAN. *Dist:* Perseus Distribution.

Doeden, Matt. Wayne Gretzky. 2007. (J). lib. bdg. (*978-0-8225-7165-0(X)) Twenty First Century Bks.

Dube, Jean-Claude. The Chevalier de Montmagny: First Governor of New France. Rapley, Elizabeth, tr. from FRE. 2004. (FRE., Illus.). 430p. (C). 65.00 (978-0-7766-3028-1(8)) Univ. of Ottawa Pr./Presses de l'Universite d'Ottawa CAN. *Dist:* Univ. of Toronto Pr.

Dublin, Anne. June Callwood: A Life of Action. 2006. (Illus.). 140p. pap. 12.95 (978-1-897187-14-2(9)) Second Story Pr. CAN. *Dist:* Orca Bk. Pubs. USA.

Emery, Joanna. Caring for a Colony: The Story of Jeanne Mance. 2005. (Stories of Canada Ser.). (Illus.). 66p. (J). 16.95 (978-1-894917-07-0(3)) Napoleon Publishing/Rendezvous Pr. CAN. *Dist:* AtlasBooks Distribution.

Friedman, Katherine. Hayden Christensen. 2002. (gr. 7-12). lib. bdg. 15.25 (978-0-613-58699-3(9)) Tandem Library Bks.

Fryer, Mary Beacock. Bold, Brave, & Born to Lead: Major General Isaac Brock & the Canadas. 2004. (Illus.). 200p. pap. 9.99 (978-1-55002-501-9(5)) Dundurn Group, The CAN. *Dist:* Univ. of Toronto Pr.

Hacker, Carlotta. Humanitarians. 1999. (Illus.). 48p. (J). (ps-11). lib. bdg. 17.60 (978-0-613-11656-5(9)) Tandem Library Bks.

—Rebels. 1998. (Illus.). 48p. (J). (ps-11). lib. bdg. 17.60 (978-0-613-12026-5(4)) Tandem Library Bks.

Hunter, Shaun. Visual & Performing Artists. 1999. (Illus.). 48p. (J). (ps-11). lib. bdg. 17.60 (978-0-613-12237-5(2)) Tandem Library Bks.

Janveau, Teri-Lynn & Thompson, Allister. Sailing for Glory: The Story of Angus Walters. Thompson, Samantha, illus. 2006. 72p. (J). 16.95 (978-1-894917-09-4(X)) Napoleon Publishing/Rendezvous Pr. CAN. *Dist:* AtlasBooks Distribution.

Kalman, Bobbie. Canada: The Land. 2002. (gr. 3-6). lib. bdg. 16.40 (978-0-613-52941-9(3)) Tandem Library Bks.

—Canada: The People. 2002. (gr. 3-6). lib. bdg. 16.40 (978-0-613-52942-6(1)) Tandem Library Bks.

Knelman, Martin. Mike's World: The Life of Mike Myers. 2003. (Illus.). 268p. (gr. 5-12). pap. 16.95 (978-1-55297-661-6(0)) Firefly Bks., Ltd.

Konieczny, Vladimir. Struggling for Perfection. 2007. 97p. pap. 15.95 (*978-1-894917-48-3(0)) Napoleon Publishing/Rendezvous Pr. CAN. *Dist:* AtlasBooks Distribution.

Kyi, Tanya Lloyd. Canadian Boys Who Rocked the World. Bagley, Tom, illus. 2007. 126p. (J). (gr. 3-2). pap. 9.95 (978-1-55285-799-1(9) , Walrus Bks.) Whitecap Bks., Ltd. CAN. *Dist:* Firefly Bks., Ltd.

Lewis, Wendy A. Fire on the Water: The Red-hot Career of Superstar Rower Ned Hanlan. 2007. (Recordbooks Ser.). (Illus.). 112p. (J). (gr. 7-12). 8.95 (*978-1-55028-972-5(1)); (*978-1-55028-973-2(X)) Lorimer, James & Co., Ltd., Pubs. CAN. *Dist:* Casemate Pubs. & Bk. Distributors, LLC.

Livesey, Robert. The Rebels. Smith, A. G., illus. 2001. (Discovering Canada Ser.). 90p. (J). (gr. 3-7). 10.95 (978-0-7737-6170-4(5)) Stoddart Kids CAN. *Dist:* Fitzhenry & Whiteside, Ltd.

Lloyd, Tanya. Canadian Girls Who Rocked the World. 2001. (Illus.). 128p. (J). (gr. 3-2). pap. 8.95 (978-1-55285-203-3(2)) Whitecap Bks., Ltd. CAN. *Dist:* Firefly Bks., Ltd.

Manson, Ainslie. Baboo: The Story of Sir John A. MacDonald's Daughter. Wand, Bill, illus. 1998. (J). (ps-4). (978-0-88899-329-8(3)) Groundwood Bks.

—House Calls: The True Story of a Pioneer Doctor. Gerber, Mary Jane, illus. 2001. (J). (gr. 3-7). pap. 15.95 (978-0-88899-446-2(X)) Groundwood Bks. CAN. *Dist:* Transition Vendor.

Marin, Reva. Oscar: The Life & Music of Oscar Peterson. 2003. (Illus.). 144p. (J). (gr. 6 up). 16.95 (978-0-88899-537-7(7)) Groundwood Bks. CAN. *Dist:* Perseus Distribution.

Marsh, Carole. The Canada Experience Library State Resource Set. 2001. (Canada Experience! Ser.). (Illus.). (J). lib. bdg. 100.20 incl. cd-rom (978-0-635-00461-1(5)) Gallopade International.

McMeans, Bonnie. James Cameron. 2002. (Behind the Camera Ser.). (Illus.). 112p. (J). (gr. 6-12). 30.00 (978-0-7910-6713-0(0) , Chelsea Hse.) Facts On File, Inc.

Merritt, Susan E. Her Story II: Women from Canada's Past. 1998. (Illus.). vii, 184p. (YA). pap. (978-1-55125-022-9(5)) Vanwell Publishing, Ltd.

Millar, Ruth E. Saskatchewan Heroes & Rogues. 2004. (Illus.). 240p. (gr. 7 up). pap. 17.95 (978-1-55050-289-3(1)) Coteau Bks. CAN. *Dist:* Fitzhenry & Whiteside, Ltd.

Mudge, Jacqueline. Bret Hart: The Story of the Wrestler They Call "The Hitman" 1999. (Pro Wrestling Legends Ser.). (Illus.). 64p. (YA). (gr. 3 up). 25.00 (978-0-7910-5408-6(X) , Chelsea Hse.) Facts On File, Inc.

Murdico, Suzanne J. Mario Lemieux. 1998. (Overcoming the Odds Ser.). (Illus.). 48p. (J). (gr. 3-8). (978-0-8172-4126-1(4)) Raintree.

—Mario Lemieux. 1998. (Overcoming the Odds Ser.). (Illus.). 48p. (J). (gr. 4-7). pap. 7.95 (978-0-8172-8004-8(9)) Steck-Vaughn.

Murray, Jim, intro. Larry Walker. 1999. (Baseball Legends Ser.). (Illus.). 64p. (YA). (gr. 3-7). 18.65 (978-0-7910-5159-7(5) , Chelsea Hse.) Facts On File, Inc.

Musgrave, Susan. Nerves Out Loud: Critical Moments in the Lives of Seven Teen Girls. 2001. (gr. 7-12). lib. bdg. 18.75 (978-0-613-62398-8(3)) Tandem Library Bks.

Musgrave, Susan, ed. Nerves Out Loud: Critical Moments in the Lives of Seven Teen Girls. 2001. 112p. (YA). (gr. 9 up). 19.95 (978-1-55037-693-7(4)); (Illus.). pap. 9.95 (978-1-55037-692-0(6)) Annick Pr., Ltd. CAN. *Dist:* Firefly Bks., Ltd.

Shardlow, Tom & Wysotski, Chrissie. Mapping the Wilderness: The Story of David Thompson. 2006. (Illus.). 72p. (J). 16.95 (978-0-929141-85-5(7)) Napoleon Publishing/Rendezvous Pr. CAN. *Dist:* AtlasBooks Distribution.

Slade, Arthur G. John Diefenbaker: An Appointment with Destiny. 2001. (Illus.). 181p. (J). pap. (978-0-9688166-0-8(6)) X Y Z Publishing.

Spigelman, Martin. Wilfrid Laurier. 2nd ed. 2000. (Canadians Ser.). (Illus.). 64p. (YA). (gr. 8 up). pap. (978-1-55041-481-3(X)) Fitzhenry & Whiteside, Ltd.

Stinson, Kathy. Cornelia Oberlander: The Art of the Possible. 2008. 96p. 22.95 (*978-0-88776-804-0(0)) Tundra Bks., Inc./Livres Toundra, Inc. CAN. *Dist:* Random Hse. of Canada, Ltd.

Sturgis, James. Adam Beck. (Illus.). 64p. (J). (gr. 5 up). pap. (978-1-55041-828-6(9)) Fitzhenry & Whiteside, Ltd.

Westerhout, Lynn. Making It Home: The Story of Catharine Parr Traill. 2004. (Stories of Canada Ser.). (Illus.). 76p. (J). 16.95 (978-0-929141-90-9(3)) Napoleon Publishing/Rendezvous Pr. CAN. *Dist:* AtlasBooks Distribution.

Wheeler, Jill C. Michael J. Fox. 2001. (Star Tracks Ser.). (Illus.). 64p. (J). (gr. 3-8). lib. bdg. 25.65 (978-1-57765-551-0(6) , ABDO & Daughters) ABDO Publishing Co.

—Shania Twain. 2001. (Star Tracks Ser.). (Illus.). 64p. (J). (gr. 3-8). lib. bdg. 25.65 (978-1-57765-552-7(4) , ABDO & Daughters) ABDO Publishing Co.

Wilner, Barry. Mark Messier. 1999. (Ice Hockey Legends Ser.). (Illus.). 64p. (YA). (gr. 4-7). 12.95 (978-0-7910-4559-6(5) , Chelsea Hse.) Facts On File, Inc.

Wilson, John. Righting Wrongs: The Story of Norman Bethune. 2004. (Stories of Canada Ser.). (Illus.). 65p. (J). (gr. 3-7). 14.95 (978-0-929141-71-8(7)) Napoleon Publishing/Rendezvous Pr. CAN. *Dist:* AtlasBooks Distribution.

Woodcock, George. Gabriel Dumont. 2003. (Canadians Ser.). (Illus.) 64p. pap. (978-1-55041-492-9(5)) Fitzhenry & Whiteside, Ltd.

CANADA—DISCOVERY AND EXPLORATION

see America—Discovery and Exploration

CANADA—FICTION

Aksomitis, Linda. Adeline's Dream. 2006. (From Many Peoples Ser.). 272p. (J). pap. 7.95 (978-1-55050-323-4(5)) Coteau Bks. CAN. *Dist:* F & W Pubns., Inc.

Alma, Ann. Skateway to Freedom. 2008. 136p. (YA). pap. 11.99 (*978-1-55002-719-8(6) , Sandcastle Bks.) Dundurn Group, The CAN. *Dist:* Univ. of Toronto Pr.

Anderson, Dee, retold by. Beaver's New Coat A Pourquoi Tale of Canada's Bungee Indians. l.t. ed. 2002. (Illus.). 24p. (J). pap. 3.00 (978-0-9755934-0-0(4)) Colonel Davenport Historical Foundation.

Arkin, Alan. Cassie Loves Beethoven. l.t. ed. 2003. (Children's Large Print Ser.). 28.95 (978-1-58118-108-1(6)) LRS.

Banerjee, Anjali. Maya Running. 2006. 224p. (YA). (gr. 7). reprint ed. mass mkt. 5.99 (978-0-553-49424-2(4) , Laurel Leaf) Random Hse. Children's Bks.

Bastedo, Jaya. A Winter Walk with Haley. Macintosh, Tessa, illus. Macintosh, Tessa, photos by. l.t. ed. 1999. 24p. (J). (ps-5). pap. (978-1-894303-06-4(7)) Raven Rock Publishing.

Bell, William. Zack. l.t. ed. 2000. (LRS Large Print Cornerstone Ser.). 256p. (YA). (gr. 5-12). lib. bdg. 28.95 (978-1-58118-072-5(1) , 23656) LRS.

—Zack. 2000. (J). (978-0-606-20095-0(9)) Tandem Library Bks.

Bishop, Mary Harelkin. Tunnels of Treachery: Another Moose Jaw Adventure. 2003. (Tunnels of Moose Jaw Adventure Ser.: Vol. 3). (Illus.). 312p. (J). (gr. 5-7). pap. 7.95 (978-1-55050-270-1(0)) Coteau Bks. CAN. *Dist:* Fitzhenry & Whiteside, Ltd.

Blades, Ann. Mary of Mile 18. Blades, Ann, illus. 30th anniv. ed. 2001. (Illus.). 40p. (J). (gr. 1). 16.95 (978-0-88776-581-0(5)) Tundra Bks., Inc./Livres Toundra, Inc. CAN. *Dist:* Random Hse., Inc.

—Too Small. Blades, Ann, illus. 2000. (Illus.). 32p. (J). (ps-3). 15.95 (978-0-88899-400-4(1)) Groundwood Bks. CAN. *Dist:* Perseus Distribution.

Blum, Vicki. Spitt to the Rescue. unabr. ed. 2004. 115p. (J). (gr. 3-6). pap. 7.95 (978-1-932280-59-3(6) , 80596) Granite Publishing & Distribution.

Bo, Ben. The Edge. 2003. (Young Adult Fiction Ser.). 144p. (J). (gr. 9-12). 14.95 (978-0-8225-3307-8(3)) Lerner Publishing Group.

Book, Rick. Necking with Louise. 2004. 168p. (gr. 9 up). pap. 7.95 (978-0-88995-194-5(2)) Red Deer Pr. CAN. *Dist:* Fitzhenry & Whiteside, Ltd.

Bourgeois, Paulette. Postal Workers. LaFave, Kim, illus. 2005. 32p. (J). lib. bdg. 15.38 (*978-1-4242-1192-0(1)) Fitzgerald Bks.

Brandis, Marianne & Brender a Brandis, G. The Tinderbox. 2003. Orig. Title: Fyrtojet. (Illus.). 176p. (J). (gr. 6-9). pap. 9.95 (978-0-88776-626-8(9)) Tundra Bks., Inc./Livres Toundra, Inc. CAN. *Dist:* Random Hse., Inc.

Brennan, Ann. The Hawthorn Bush. 2005. (Illus.). 163p. pap. (*978-0-88887-316-3(6)) Borealis Pr.

Brooks, Bertha. The Big Fishing Trip. 2004. (Illus.). 32p. (J). 12.00 (978-1-58374-086-6(4)) Chicago Spectrum Pr.

Brooks, Martha. Bone Dance. 2005. 184p. (J). (gr. 7-16). pap. 6.95 (978-0-88899-336-6(6)) Groundwood Bks. CAN. *Dist:* Perseus Distribution.

—The Bone Dance. 1999. (J). (978-0-606-16716-1(1)) Tandem Library Bks.

—Mistik Lake. 2007. 224p. (J). (gr. 9 up). 16.00 (*978-0-374-34985-1(1) , Farrar, Straus & Giroux (BYR)) Farrar, Straus & Giroux.

Brooks, Martha. True Confessions of a Heartless Girl. 2003. 192p. (YA). (gr. 9 up). 16.00 (978-0-374-37806-6(1) , Farrar, Straus & Giroux (BYR)) Farrar, Straus & Giroux.

—True Confessions of a Heartless Girl. 2004. 224p. (J). reprint ed. pap. 6.99 (978-0-06-059497-8(7) , HarperTeen) HarperCollins Pubs.

—True Confessions of a Heartless Girl. 2004. 216p. (YA). (gr. 7-12). lib. bdg. 13.64 (978-0-606-32642-1(1)) Tandem Library Bks.

Brouwer, Sigmund. Tiger Threat. 2006. 144p. (J). pap. 8.95 (978-1-55143-639-5(6)) Orca Bk. Pubs. USA.

Brownridge, William Roy. The Moccasin Goalie. Brownridge, William Roy, illus. 2001. (Illus.). 32p. (J). (ps-2). 7.95 (978-1-55143-054-6(1)) Orca Bk. Pubs. USA.

Buffie, Margaret. Who Is Frances Rain? 20th ed. 2007. 184p. pap. (*978-1-55453-209-4(4)) Kids Can Pr., Ltd.

Burkett, Larry. Last Chance for Camp. 2000. (Great Smoky Mountain Storybook Ser.). (Illus.). 32p. (J). (ps-3). 7.99 (978-0-8024-0985-0(7)) Moody Pubs.

Butcher, Kristin. Gramma War. 2001. (gr. 3-6). lib. bdg. 15.25 (978-0-613-45662-3(9)) Tandem Library Bks.

Caraher, Denise Page. The End of Forever: The Story of Mekinges & William Conner. Braulin, Sue Ellen, illus. 2003. 145p. pap. 14.99 (978-1-57860-128-8(2)) Emmis Bks.

Carbone, Elisa. Stealing Freedom. 2001. (Illus.). 272p. (YA). (gr. 5-8). 5.99 (978-0-440-41707-1(4) , Yearling) Random Hse. Children's Bks.

Carter, Anne. Under a Prairie Sky. Daniel, Alan & Daniel, Lea, illus. 2001. 32p. (J). (ps-2). 16.95 (978-1-55143-226-7(9)) Orca Bk. Pubs. USA.

Carter, Anne Laurel. Under a Prairie Sky. Daniel, Alan & Daniel, Lea, illus. 2004. 32p. (J). (ps-2). 7.95 (978-1-55143-282-3(X)) Orca Bk. Pubs. USA.

—Under a Prairie Sky. Daniel, Alan & Daniel, Lea, illus. 2004. 32p. (J). (ps-ps). lib. bdg. 15.15 (978-0-606-30126-8(7)) Tandem Library Bks.

Chan, Gillian. The Carved Box. Fernandez, Laura, illus. 232p. (YA). (gr. 13 up). 2004. (978-1-55337-016-1(3)); 2001. (978-1-55074-895-6(5)) Kids Can Pr., Ltd.

Charles, Norma M. Sophie Sea to Sea: Star Girl's Cross-Canada Adventures! 2005. 152p. (YA). (gr. 3-8). pap., tchr. ed. (978-0-88878-404-9(X) , Sandcastle Bks.) Dundurn Group, The.

Charles, Veronika Martenova. Maiden of the Mist: A Legend of Niagara Falls. 2001. (gr. 3-6). lib. bdg. 15.25 (978-0-613-52136-9(6)) Tandem Library Bks.

Childress, Mildred Tickfer. Esmerelda, the Silly Goose. Zipperer, Susan Johnson, illus. 2004. 64p. (J). lib. bdg. 11.95 (978-1-887774-17-8(3) , Wynden) Canmore Pr.

Citra, Becky. Danger at the Landings. 2002. (Orca Young Readers Ser.). 96p. (J). (gr. 3-6). pap. 4.99 (978-1-55143-232-8(3)) Orca Bk. Pubs. USA.

—Danger at the Landings. 2002. (gr. 3-6). lib. bdg. 13.00 (978-0-613-84753-7(9)) Tandem Library Bks.

—Ellie's New Home. 1999. (Young Reader Ser.). (J). (978-0-606-19475-4(4)) Tandem Library Bks.

—The Freezing Moon. McCallum, Stephen, illus. 2001. (Young Reader Ser.). 112p. (J). (gr. 3-6). pap. 4.99 (978-1-55143-181-9(5)) Orca Bk. Pubs. USA.

—Strawberry Moon, Vol. 5. 2005. (Orca Young Readers Ser.: Book #5). (Illus.). 96p. (J). (gr. 3-6). pap. 5.95 (978-1-55143-367-7(2)) Orca Bk. Pubs. USA.

Crook, Connie Brummel. The Hungry Year. 2001. 201p. (YA). (gr. 5 up). pap. 7.95 (978-0-7737-6206-0(X)) Stoddart Kids CAN. *Dist:* Fitzhenry & Whiteside, Ltd.

—Hungry Year. 2001. (gr. 5-8). lib. bdg. 16.40 (978-0-613-46140-5(1)) Tandem Library Bks.

—Nellie's Victory. 2000. (Illus.). 269p. (YA). (gr. 7-12). mass mkt. 5.95 (978-0-7736-7481-3(0)) Stoddart Kids CAN. *Dist:* Fitzhenry & Whiteside, Ltd.

—Nellie's Victory. 2000. (gr. 7-12). lib. bdg. 14.10 (978-0-613-28980-1(3)) Tandem Library Bks.

—The Perilous Year. 2004. 200p. (J). (gr. 4 up). (978-1-55041-818-7(1)); 2003. 197p. (YA). (978-1-55041-816-3(5)) Fitzhenry & Whiteside, Ltd.

Curwood, James Oliver. Kazan: Father of Baree. 2005. 240p. (YA). (gr. 4-7). pap. 5.95 (978-1-55704-225-5(X)) Newmarket Pr.

Czuchna-Curl, Ardyce. Days of Gold. 2002. (Illus.). 128p. (J). pap. 12.95 (978-0-88196-012-9(8)) Oak Woods Media.

Daher, Anita. Racing for Diamonds. 2007. (Orca Young Readers Ser.). 128p. (J). pap. (*978-1-55143-675-3(2)) Orca Bk. Pubs.

C
D

Dell, Pamela. Half-Breed: A Story of Two Boys During the Klondike Gold Rush. 2003. (Scrapbooks of America Ser.). (Illus.). 48p. (J). (gr. 2-6). 28.50 (978-1-59187-044-9(5)) Child's World, Inc.

Denman, K. L. Mirror Image. 2007. (Orca Currents Ser.). 112p. (YA). (gr. 5 up). pap. (*978-1-55143-665-4(5)); lib. bdg. (*978-1-55143-667-8(1)) Orca Bk. Pubs.

Doyle, Brian. Boy O'Boy. 2005. 162p. (YA). pap. 6.95 (978-0-88899-654-1(3)) Groundwood Bks. CAN. *Dist:* Perseus Distribution.

—Easy Avenue. 2004. 122p. (YA). pap. 6.95 (978-0-88899-605-3(5)) Groundwood Bks. CAN. *Dist:* Perseus Distribution.

—Hey, Dad! 2006. 112p. (J). pap. 6.95 (978-0-88899-708-1(6)) Groundwood Bks. CAN. *Dist:* Perseus Distribution.

—Mary Ann Alice. braille ed. 2003. (J). (gr. 2). spiral bd. (978-0-616-15266-9(3)) Canadian National Institute for the Blind/Institut National Canadien pour les Aveugles.

—Mary Ann Alice. (J). 2002. (gr. 4-8). pap. 12.95 (978-0-88899-454-7(0)); 2nd ed. 2003. 168p. (gr. 9-13). pap. 5.95 (978-0-88899-551-3(2)) Groundwood Bks. CAN. *Dist:* Transition Vendor, Perseus Distribution.

—Mary Ann Alice. 2003. (gr. 3-6). lib. bdg. 14.10 (978-0-613-88583-6(X)) Tandem Library Bks.

—Spud in Winter. 2006. 140p. (J). pap. 5.95 (978-0-88899-755-5(8)) Groundwood Bks. CAN. *Dist:* Perseus Distribution.

—Uncle Ronald. 2004. 138p. (J). pap. 6.95 (978-0-88899-621-3(7)) Groundwood Bks. CAN. *Dist:* Perseus Distribution.

Durbin, William. The Broken Blade. 1998. (J). 11.64 (978-0-606-13228-2(7)) Tandem Library Bks.

Eckert, Allan W. Return to Hawk's Hill. 1998. (Illus.). 160p. (J). (gr. 7-12). 15.95 (978-0-316-21593-0(7)) Little Brown & Co.

—Return to Hawk's Hill. 2000. (978-0-606-17850-1(3)) Tandem Library Bks.

—Return to Hawk's Hill: Sequel to the Newbery Honor-Winning Incident at Hawk's Hill. 2000. 208p. (J). (gr. 7-17). pap. 15.99 (978-0-316-00689-7(0)) Little Brown & Co.

Fairbridge, Lynne. Tangled in Time. 1999. 158p. (J). pap. 8.95 (978-0-921870-69-2(8)) Ronsdale Pr. CAN. *Dist:* Literary Pr. Group of Canada.

Feagan, Robert. Napachee. 2005. 128p. (YA). (gr. 3-8). pap., tchr. ed. (978-0-88878-403-2(1) , Sandcastle Bks.) Dundurn Group, The.

Fleck, Earl. Chasing Bears: A Canoe Country Adventure. 2004. (Illus.). 160p. (gr. 7-12). pap. 12.95 (978-0-930100-90-2(5)) Holy Cow! Pr.

Foggo, Cheryl. One Thing That's True. unabr. ed. 128p. (YA). (gr. 13 up). 2002. (Illus.). (978-1-55074-377-7(5)); 1998. (978-1-55074-411-8(9)) Kids Can Pr., Ltd.

—Sam Finds a Monster. Sarrazin, Marisol, illus. 2004. (Kids Can Read! Ser.). 32p. (J). (gr. k-3). (978-1-55337-351-3(0)) Kids Can Pr., Ltd.

Frost, Helen. The Braid. 2006. (Illus.). 112p. (YA). (gr. 7 up). 16.00 (978-0-374-30962-6(0) , Frances Foster Bks.) Farrar, Straus & Giroux.

Gaetz, Dayle. Something Suspicious in Saskatchewan. 2006. 208p. (J). pap. 7.95 (978-1-55143-565-7(9)) Orca Bk. Pubs. USA.

Gale, Donald. Francie & the Basket Women. 2000. (Illus.). 56p. (J). pap. (978-1-55081-149-0(5)) Breakwater Bks., Ltd.

Garrigue, Sheila. The Eternal Spring of Mr. Ito. 1998. (J). pap. 3.95 (978-0-87628-340-0(7)) Ctr. for Applied Research in Education, The.

Garvie, Maureen McCallum, et al. George Johnson's War. (Illus.). (J). (gr. 7 up). 2003. 224p. pap. 8.95 (978-0-88899-468-4(0)); 2002. 15.95 (978-0-88899-465-3(6)) Groundwood Bks. CAN. *Dist:* Perseus Distribution, Transition Vendor.

Gilmore, Rachna. Roses for Gita. Priestley, Alice, illus. 2004. 24p. (J). (CHI, ENG, TUR, PAN & GUJ.). (978-1-85269-367-1(3)); (GUJ, CHI, ENG, PAN & TUR.). (978-1-85269-369-5(X)) Mantra Publishing, Ltd.

—Roses for Gita. 2001. (gr. k-3). lib. bdg. 16.40 (978-0-613-53301-0(1)) Tandem Library Bks.

—Roses for Gita. Priestley, Alice, illus. 2005. 24p. (J). (gr. 3-6). pap. 7.95 (978-0-88448-224-6(3)) Tilbury Hse. Pubs.

Glaze, Dave. The Light-Fingered Gang. 2006. 196p. (YA). (gr. 4-7). pap. 7.95 (978-1-55050-326-5(X)) Coteau Bks. CAN. *Dist:* F & W Pubns., Inc.

Goodman, Joan Elizabeth. Paradise: A Tale of Survival. 2002. 224p. (J). (gr. 7 up). tchr. ed. 16.00 (978-0-618-11450-4(5)) Houghton Mifflin Co. Trade & Reference Div.

Gostick, Adrian R. Jessica's Search: The Secret of Ballycater Cove. 1998. (J). 1.99 (978-1-57345-436-0(2)) Deseret Bk. Co.

Greeson, Ewell. Aegis. 2003. 436p. (YA). per. 19.95 (978-1-59453-024-1(6) , 1701) Airleaf Publishing & Bookselling.

Griek, Susan Vande. The Art Room. Milelli, Pascal, illus. 2002. 24p. (J). (ps-2). 15.95 (978-0-88899-449-3(4)) Groundwood Bks. CAN. *Dist:* Perseus Distribution.

Gutierrez, Elisa. Picturescape. 2005. (Illus.). 32p. (J). (gr. k). 16.95 (978-1-894965-24-8(8)) Simply Read Bks. CAN. *Dist:* Perseus Distribution.

Halvorson, Marilyn. Let It Go. 2004. 224p. (YA). (gr. 7-9). (978-1-55005-105-6(9)) Fitzhenry & Whiteside, Ltd.

Harcourt School Publishers Staff. Ronda & the Garden of the Gulf On Level. 3rd ed. 2002. (Trophies Reading Program Ser.). (Illus.). pap. 5.10 (978-0-15-323454-5(7)) Harcourt Schl. Pubs.

Harlow, Joan Hiatt. Star in the Storm. 160p. 2005. pap. 2.99 (978-1-4169-0530-1(8)); 2001. (gr. 3-7). mass mkt. 5.99 (978-0-689-84621-2(5)) Simon & Schuster Children's Publishing. (Aladdin).

—Star in the Storm. 2001. (978-0-606-22107-8(7)); (gr. 3-6). lib. bdg. 13.00 (978-0-613-53446-8(8)) Tandem Library Bks.

Harris, Michael. A Forest for Christmas. Orchard, Eric, illus. 2007. 48p. (J). (gr. 2-10). (*978-1-55109-589-9(0)) Nimbus Publishing, Ltd.

Harrison, Troon. Bushel of Light. 2001. (gr. 5-8). lib. bdg. 16.40 (978-0-613-44633-4(X)) Tandem Library Bks.

Hebert-Collins, Sheila. Jean-Paul Hebert Was There. Bergeron, John W., illus. 2004. Tr. of Jean-Paul Hebert Etait La. (ENG & FRE.). 32p. (J). pap. 15.95 (978-1-56554-928-9(7)) Pelican Publishing Co., Inc.

Hemon, Louis. Maria Chapdelaine. Kupesic, Rajka, illus. 2004. 40p. (J). (gr. 3-7). 15.95 (978-0-88776-697-8(8)) Tundra Bks., Inc./Livres Toundra, Inc. CAN. *Dist:* Random Hse., Inc.

Heneghan, James. Torn Away. 2003. 256p. (J). (gr. 4-7). pap. 6.95 (978-1-55143-263-2(3)) Orca Bk. Pubs. USA.

—Torn Away. 2003. (gr. 7-12). lib. bdg. 15.25 (978-0-613-84756-8(3)) Tandem Library Bks.

Henty, G. A. With Wolfe in Canada: The Winning of a Continent. 2001. (Illus.). 353p. (J). (978-0-921100-86-7(8)); pap. (978-0-921100-87-4(6)) Inheritance Pubns.

—With Wolfe in Canada: The Winning of a Continent. (Illus.). 353p. (J). 2000. (gr. 8-12). pap. 14.99 (978-1-887159-30-2(4)); 1998. lib. bdg. 20.99 (978-1-887159-18-0(5)) Preston-Speed Pubns.

Hokenson, Terry. The Winter Road. 2006. 176p. (J). 16.95 (978-1-932425-45-1(4) , Front Street) Boyds Mills Pr.

Holeman, Linda. Raspberry House Blues. 2000. 238p. (J). (gr. 4-7). pr. 15.25 (978-0-613-53300-3(3)) Tandem Library Bks.

—Raspberry House Blues. 2003. 248p. (J). (gr. 6-9). pap. 6.95 (978-0-88776-493-6(2)) Tundra Bks., Inc./Livres Toundra, Inc. CAN. *Dist:* Random Hse., Inc.

Holubitsky, Katherine. Alone at Ninety Foot. 2001. 192p. (J). (gr. 7-12). mass mkt. 6.95 (978-1-55143-204-5(8)) Orca Bk. Pubs. USA.

—Alone at Ninety Foot. 1999. (Illus.). (J). (978-0-606-18327-7(2)) Tandem Library Bks.

Hughes, Monica. Jan on the Trail. Freire, Carlos, illus. 2000. (New First Novels Ser.). 61p. (gr. 1-5). 4.95 (978-0-88780-502-8(7)); (J). (978-0-88780-503-5(5)) Formac Publishing Co., Ltd. CAN. *Dist:* Casemate Pubs. & Bk. Distributors, LLC.

Hunter, Bernice Thurman. The Girls They Left Behind. 2005. (Illus.). 192p. (J). pap. (978-1-55041-927-6(7)) Fitzhenry & Whiteside, Ltd.

Ibbitson, John. Jeremy's War of 1812. 2000. 182p. (J). (gr. 5-9). (978-1-55074-988-5(9)) Kids Can Pr., Ltd.

Jam, Teddy. The Kid Line. Zhang, Ange, illus. 2001. 32p. (J). (gr. k-3). 16.95 (978-0-88899-432-5(X)) Groundwood Bks. CAN. *Dist:* Perseus Distribution.

—The Stoneboat. Zhang, Ange, illus. 2nd ed. 1999. 32p. (J). (ps-2). 15.95 (978-0-88899-368-7(4) , Libros Tigrillo) Groundwood Bks. CAN. *Dist:* Perseus Distribution.

Jenkins Bathe, Bettina. Violet the Pilot in Canada. 2004. (Illus.). 20p. (J). (978-1-4120-3215-5(6)) Trafford Publishing.

Johnston, Julie. Hero of Lesser Causes. pap. 6.95 (978-0-7737-5850-6(X)) Stoddart Kids CAN. *Dist:* Fitzhenry & Whiteside, Ltd.

—Hero of Lesser Causes. 2003. 232p. (J). (gr. 6). pap. 9.95 (978-0-88776-649-7(8)) Tundra Bks., Inc./Livres Toundra, Inc. CAN. *Dist:* Random Hse., Inc.

—Only Outcast. 1999. (gr. 7-12). lib. bdg. 15.25 (978-0-613-28008-2(3)) Tandem Library Bks.

—Susanna's Quill. 2004. 336p. (J). (gr. 6). 18.95 (978-0-88776-706-7(0)) Tundra Bks., Inc./Livres Toundra, Inc. CAN. *Dist:* Random Hse., Inc.

Juby, Susan. Alice, I Think. 2004. 320p. (J). reprint ed. pap. 7.99 (978-0-06-051545-4(7) , HarperTeen) HarperCollins Pubs.

—Alice, I Think. 2000. 224p. (YA). pap. (978-1-894345-12-5(6)) Thistledown Pr., Ltd.

Keeley, Catherine. The Secrets of Phantom Valley. 2003. 101p. (YA). pap. 10.95 (978-0-7414-1831-9(2)) Infinity Publishing.

Kent, Jennifer McGrath. Chocolate River Rescue. 2007. 88p. (J). (gr. 2-5). pap. (*978-1-55109-600-1(5)) Nimbus Publishing, Ltd.

Koops, Sheena. Voice of the Valley. 2006. 208p. (J). pap. 8.95 (978-1-55143-514-5(4)) Orca Bk. Pubs. USA.

Kositsky, Lynne. Claire by Moonlight. 2001. (On Time's Wing Ser.). 224p. (J). pap. 8.95 (978-1-896184-03-6(0)) Roussan Pubs., Inc./Roussan Editeur, Inc. CAN. *Dist:* Orca Bk. Pubs. USA.

—Claire by Moonlight. 2005. 280p. (YA). (gr. 7). pap. 9.95 (978-0-88776-659-6(5)) Tundra Bks., Inc./Livres Toundra, Inc. CAN. *Dist:* Random Hse., Inc.

Kusugak, Michael Arvaarluk. Arctic Stories. Krykorka, Vladyana Langer, illus. 1998. 40p. (J). (gr. k-4). pap. 7.95 (978-1-55037-452-0(4)); lib. bdg. 19.95 (978-1-55037-453-7(2)) Annick Pr., Ltd. CAN. *Dist:* Firefly Bks., Ltd.

—Arctic Stories. 1999. (J). (978-0-606-16482-5(0)) Tandem Library Bks.

Lawson, Julie. White Jade Tiger. rev. ed. 2005. 168p. (YA). (gr. 3-8). reprint ed. pap., tchr. ed. 6.95 (978-0-88878-332-5(9)) Beach Holme Pubs., Ltd. CAN. *Dist:* Literary Pr. Group of Canada.

Leavey, Peggy Dymond. Finding My Own Way. 2004. 173p. (YA). (gr. 8 up). pap. 7.95 (978-0-929141-83-1(0)) Napoleon Publishing/Rendezvous Pr. CAN. *Dist:* Atlas-Books Distribution.

Leavitt, Martine. Heck, Superhero! 2004. 144p. (YA). 16.95 (978-1-886910-94-2(4) , Lemniscaat) Boyds Mills Pr.

Lindy, Elaine L. The Long Winter: A Canadian First Nation Folk Tale. 2002. (Whootie Owl's Test Prep Storytime Ser.). 32p. (J). 4.99 (978-0-9672831-6-6(7)) Whootie Owl International, LLC.

Lindy, Elaine L., creator. The Native American Cinderella: A Canadian First Nation Folk Tale. 2002. (Whootie Owl's Test Prep Storytime Ser.). (J). 4.99 (978-0-9672831-9-7(1)) Whootie Owl International, LLC.

Little, Jean. Birdie for Now. 2002. (gr. 3-6). lib. bdg. 13.00 (978-0-613-53482-6(4)) Tandem Library Bks.

London, Jack. The Call of the Wild. Corvino, Lucy, illus. 2005. (Classic Starts Ser.). 160p. 4.95 (978-1-4027-1274-6(X)) Sterling Publishing Co., Inc.

—Colmillo Blanco. 2003. (Advanced Reading Ser.: Vol. 56). (SPA., Illus.). 268p. (J). (gr. 4-7). 11.95 (978-84-239-9030-6(3)) Espasa Calpe, S.A. ESP. *Dist:* Planeta Publishing Corp., i.b.d., Ltd.

—Colmillo Blanco. 2000. (SPA., Illus.). 280p. (YA). (gr. 7 up). 9.95 (978-84-207-1229-1(9)) Grupo Anaya, S.A. ESP. *Dist:* Libros Sin Fronteras.

—Colmillo Blanco. (SPA.). (J). 8.00 (978-958-04-7143-1(6)) Norma S.A. COL. *Dist:* Distribuidora Norma, Inc.

—Encender un Fuego. Gonzalez Batlle, Jorge, tr. Vogel, Nathaele, illus. 2004. (SPA.). 79p. pap. 12.95 (978-84-95939-52-4(5)) Blume ESP. *Dist:* Independent Pubs. Group.

—White Fang. Andreasen, Dan, illus. 2006. (Classic Starts Ser.). 160p. 4.95 (978-1-4027-2500-5(0)) Sterling Publishing Co., Inc.

—White Fang: The Whole Story. 1999. (Whole Story Ser.). (Illus.). 248p. (J). (gr. 7-12). pap. 18.99 (978-0-670-88480-3(4) , Viking Juvenile) Penguin Group (USA) Inc.

—White Fang: With a Discussion of Resilience. Walker, Karen, illus. 2003. (Values in Action Illustrated Classics Ser.). 191p. (J). (978-1-59203-038-5(6)) Learning Challenge, Inc.

London, Jack & Olmos. Colmillo Blanco. 2004. (SPA.). 280p. pap. 13.95 (*978-84-263-5246-0(4)) Vives, Luis Editorial (Edelvives) ESP. *Dist:* Lectorum Pubns., Inc.

Lottridge, Celia B. Wings to Fly. 2007. 144p. (J). pap. 8.95 (*978-0-88899-844-6(9)) Groundwood Bks. CAN. *Dist:* Perseus Distribution.

Lunn, Janet. Hollow Tree. 1998. 272p. (J). mass mkt. (978-0-676-97143-9(1) , Knopf Canada) Knopf Canada CAN. *Dist:* Random Hse., Inc.

—Laura Secord: A Story of Courage. Newhouse, Maxwell, illus. 2001. 32p. (J). (gr. 3-4). 16.95 (978-0-88776-538-4(6)) Tundra Bks., Inc./Livres Toundra, Inc. CAN. *Dist:* Random Hse., Inc.

MacGregor, Roy. The Ghost of the Stanley Cup. Banning, Gregory C., illus. 1999. (Screech Owls Ser.: No. 11). 128p. (J). (gr. 4-7). mass mkt. 4.95 (978-0-7710-5622-2(2) , Screech Owls) McClelland & Stewart CAN. *Dist:* Random Hse., Inc.

MacIntyre, R. P. & MacIntyre, Wendy. Apart. 2007. 192p. (J). (gr. 8 up). 16.95 (*978-0-88899-750-0(7)) Groundwood Bks. CAN. *Dist:* Perseus Distribution.

Maracle, Lee. Will's Gardens. 2002. (Illus.). 1p. (J). (gr. 7 up). pap. 9.95 (978-1-894778-02-2(2)) Theytus Bks., Ltd. CAN. *Dist:* Orca Bk. Pubs. USA.

Matas, Carol. Rebecca. 2000. (Illus.). 160p. (J). pap. (978-0-439-98718-9(0)) Scholastic, Inc.

—Sparks Fly Upward. 2002. 192p. (YA). (gr. 5-9). 15.00 (978-0-618-15964-2(9) , Clarion Bks.) Houghton Mifflin Co. Trade & Reference Div.

Matheson, Shirlee Smith. Gambler's Daughter. 2008. 144p. (YA). pap. 11.99 (*978-1-55002-718-1(2) , Sandcastle Bks.) Dundurn Group, The CAN. *Dist:* Univ. of Toronto Pr.

McKay, Sharon E. Esther. 2004. 336p. (J). pap. (*978-0-14-331204-8(9)) Penguin Group (Canada).

McNamee, Graham. Acceleration. 2005. 240p. (YA). (gr. 7). reprint ed. pap. 6.50 (978-0-440-23836-2(6) , Laurel Leaf) Random Hse. Children's Bks.

McNicoll, Sylvia. Grave Secrets. l.t. ed. 1999. (Illus.). 176p. (J). (gr. 7-9). pap. 8.95 (978-0-7737-6015-8(6)) Stoddart Kids CAN. *Dist:* Fitzhenry & Whiteside, Ltd.

—Grave Secrets. 1999. (J). 228p. (gr. 3-7). per. 17.60 (978-0-613-28858-3(0)); (978-0-606-19641-3(2)) Tandem Library Bks.

McTighe, Carolyn. The Sakura Tree. Brownlee, Karen, illus. 2008. 32p. (J). (ps-3). 17.95 (*978-0-88995-354-3(6)) Red Deer Pr. CAN. *Dist:* Fitzhenry & Whiteside, Ltd.

Montero, Gloria. Billy Higgins Rides the Freights. 2003. (Adventures in Canada Ser.). (Illus.). 119p. (YA). (gr. 3-8). 7.95 (978-0-88862-579-3(0)) Lorimer, James & Co., Ltd., Pubs. CAN. *Dist:* Casemate Pubs. & Bk. Distributors, LLC.

Montgomery, L. M. Anne of Avonlea. l.t. ed. 2006. (ENG.). pap. (*978-1-4068-3173-3(5)) Echo Library.

—Anne of Avonlea. 2006. (Scholastic Classics Ser.). (Illus.). viii, 239p. (J). 25.00 (978-0-531-16979-7(0) , Watts, Franklin) Scholastic Library Publishing.

—Anne of Green Gables. l.t. ed. 2006. (ENG.). pap. (*978-1-4068-3174-0(3)) Echo Library.

—Anne of Green Gables. Rubio, Mary & Waterson, Elizabeth, eds. 2006. (Norton Critical Edition Ser.). (Illus.). 400p. (C). pap. 9.00 (978-0-393-92695-8(8)) Norton, W. W. & Co., Inc.

—Anne of Green Gables. 2002. (Cageworld Ser.). (Illus.). (J). pap. 9.99 (978-0-14-250102-3(6) , Puffin) Penguin Group (USA) Inc.

—Anne of Green Gables. Howell, Troy, illus. 2002. 256p. (J). 12.99 (978-0-517-22111-2(X) , Gramercy) Random Hse. Value Publishing.

—Anne of Green Gables. 2006. (Scholastic Classics Ser.). (Illus.). viii, 272p. (J). (gr. 9-12). 25.00 (978-0-531-16980-3(4) , Watts, Franklin) Scholastic Library Publishing.

—Anne of Green Gables. 2001. (Children's Classics). (ENG.). 288p. (J). pap. (978-1-85326-139-8(4)) Wordsworth Editions, Ltd.

—The Complete Anne of Green Gables: Anne of Green Gables; Anne of the Island; Anne of Avonlea; Anne of Windy Poplars; Anne's House of Dreams; Anne of Ingleside; Rainbow Valley; Rilla of Ingleside, 8 vols. gif. ed. 1998. (J). (gr. 4-7). mass mkt. 40.43 (978-0-553-60941-7(6) , Starfire) Random Hse. Children's Bks.

—Midnight Madness & Mayhem. Griffin, Jim, illus. 2005. (Story Girl Ser.). 112p. (J). (gr. 3-7). pap. 4.99 (978-0-310-70861-2(3)) Zonderkidz.

—Wedding Wishes & Woes. Griffin, Jim, illus. 2005. (Story Girl#8482; Ser.). 112p. (J). (gr. 3-7). pap. 4.99 (978-0-310-70860-5(5)) Zonderkidz.

—The Winds of Change. 2005. (Story Girl#8482; Ser.). (Illus.). 112p. (J). (gr. 3-7). pap. 4.99 (978-0-310-70862-9(1)) Zonderkidz.

—Winter on the Island. Griffin, Jim, illus. 2005. (Story Girl Ser.). 112p. (J). (gr. 3-7). pap. 4.99 (978-0-310-70859-9(1)) Zonderkidz.

Napoli, Donna Jo. North. 2004. (Illus.). 352p. (J). (gr. 4 up). 16.99 (978-0-06-057987-6(0)); lib. bdg. 17.89 (978-0-06-057988-3(9)) HarperCollins Pubs.

Nicolas, Ron. Northern Lights: A Wilderness Adventure. 2005. 228p. (YA). per. 15.85 (978-0-9770043-2-4(5)) New Global Publishing.

Oke, Janette. Drums of Change: The Story of Running Fawn. 2003. (Classics for Girls Ser.). (Illus.). 176p. (J). 9.99 (978-0-7642-2714-1(9)) Bethany Hse. Pubs.

—The Meeting Place. 1999. (Song of Acadia Ser.: Vol. 1). (gr. 7-12). lib. bdg. 21.10 (978-0-613-23358-3(1)) Tandem Library Bks.

—The Sacred Shore. 2000. (Song of Acadia Ser.: Vol. 2). (gr. 5-8). lib. bdg. 21.10 (978-0-613-55660-6(7)) Tandem Library Bks.

Oxley, MacDonald J. Young Woodsman or Life in the Forests of. 2006. 24.99 (*978-1-4280-3300-9(9)); pap. 18.99 (*978-1-4280-3280-4(0)) IndyPublish.com.

Page, Katherine Hall. Bon Voyage, Christie & Company. (Christie & Company Ser.). (YA). (gr. 6-8). 1999. (Illus.). 10p. pap. 3.99 (978-0-380-78035-8(6)); 1998. 288p. 14.00 (978-0-380-97398-9(7)) HarperCollins Pubs.

Paulsen, Gary. Hatchet. 2002. (Illus.). (J). 14.47 (978-0-7587-0017-9(2)) Book Wholesalers, Inc.

—Hatchet. 1999. 235p. (J). 17.90 (978-0-03-054626-6(5)) Holt, Rinehart & Winston.

—Hatchet. l.t. ed. 2000. (LRS Large Print Cornerstone Ser.). 205p. (YA). (gr. 4-12). lib. bdg. 28.95 (978-1-58118-055-8(1) , 23469) LRS.

—Hatchet. 2003. 151p. (J). 9.99 (978-0-330-31045-1(3) , Pan) Pan Macmillan GBR. *Dist:* Trafalgar Square Publishing.

—Hatchet. 2000. 195p. (J). (gr. 4-6). pap. 4.99 (978-0-8072-8320-2(7) , Listening Library) Random Hse. Audio Publishing Group.

—Hatchet. 2000. (Illus.). 208p. (YA). 17.99 (978-0-689-84092-0(6) , Atheneum/Richard Jackson Bks.) Simon & Schuster Children's Publishing.

—Hatchet. Willis, Drew, illus. 20th ed. 2007. 188p. (J). (gr. 5-9). 19.99 (*978-1-4169-2508-8(2)) Simon & Schuster Children's Publishing.

Paulsen, Gary. Hatchet: With Related Readings. 2004. (EMC Masterpiece Series Access Editions). (J). (978-0-8219-2960-5(7)) EMC/Paradigm Publishing.

Pearce, Jacqueline. The Reunion. 2003. (Orca Young Readers Ser.). (Illus.). 96p. (J). (gr. 3-6). pap. 4.99 (978-1-55143-230-4(7)) Orca Bk. Pubs. USA.

Perkins, Lynne Rae. Pictures from Our Vacation. Perkins, Lynne Rae, illus. 2007. (Illus.). (J). (gr. 2-5). 40p. 16.99 (*978-0-06-085097-5(3)); 32p. lib. bdg. 17.89 (*978-0-06-085098-2(1)) HarperCollins Pubs. (Greenwillow Bks.).

Pugliano-Martin, Carol. Glooscap Makes the Seasons: A Canadian Legend. 2006. spiral bd. 42.00 (*978-1-4108-7159-6(2)) Benchmark Education Co.

Rees, Celia. Sorceress. (Illus.). 352p. (YA). (gr. 9). 2003. pap. 8.99 (978-0-7636-2183-4(8)); 2002. 15.99 (978-0-7636-1847-6(0)) Candlewick Pr.

Reitz, Ric. The Journey of Sir Douglas Fir: A Reader's Musical. Bell, Suzanne, ed. Brewer, David, illus. 1999. 48p. (J). (gr. 2-6). per. 19.95 (978-0-9670160-0-9(2) , Sir Fir Bks. & Music) Sir Fir Enterprises, LLC.

Reynolds, Marilynn. The Prairie Fire. Kilby, Don, illus. 2001. 32p. (J). (ps-2). 6.95 (978-1-55143-175-8(0)) Orca Bk. Pubs. USA.

Richards, David. Soldier Boys. Paquette, Armand, illus. 2004. 256p. mass mkt. (978-1-895449-06-8(5)) Thistledown Pr., Ltd.

Richardson, Faith. Tree Root & River Rat. 2003. (Illus.). 248p. (J). 21.95 (978-0-9744989-4-2(7)); pap. 12.95 (978-0-9744989-5-9(5)) Fox Song Bks.

Rivera, Raquel. Arctic Adventures: Tales from the Lives of Inuit Artists. Marton, Jirina, illus. 2007. 36p. (gr. 3 up). 18.95 (978-0-88899-714-2(0)) Groundwood Bks. CAN. *Dist:* Perseus Distribution.

Sage, Elizabeth. Finding Home. 2002. (Five Star First Edition Women's Fiction Ser.). 225p. (J). 26.95 (978-0-7862-4111-8(X) , Five Star) Thomson Gale.

Schwartz, Virginia Frances. Messenger. 2002. 290p. (J). (gr. 7 up). tchr. ed. 17.95 (978-0-8234-1716-2(6)) Holiday Hse., Inc.

Scrimger, Richard. The Nose from Jupiter. 1998. (Illus.). 156p. (J). (ps-6). per. 16.40 (978-0-613-10237-7(1)) Tandem Library Bks.

—The Nose from Jupiter. 1998. 160p. (J). (gr. 3-7). pap. 7.95 (978-0-88776-428-8(2)) Tundra Bks., Inc./Livres Toundra, Inc. CAN. *Dist:* Random Hse., Inc.

Sherrard, Valerie. Three Million Acres of Flame. 2007. 180p. (YA). pap. 10.99 (*978-1-55002-727-3(1)) , Boardwalk Bks.) Dundurn Group, The CAN. *Dist:* Univ. of Toronto Pr.

Silverthorne, Judith. Dinosaur Hideout. 2003. (Dinosaur Adventure Ser.). 192p. (J). (gr. 4-6). pap. 6.95 (978-1-55050-226-8(3)) Coteau Bks. CAN. *Dist:* Fitzhenry & Whiteside, Ltd.

—The Secret of the Stone House. 2006. (From Many Peoples Ser.). (Illus.). 192p. (J). pap. 7.95 (978-1-55050-325-8(1)) Coteau Bks. CAN. *Dist:* F & W Pubns., Inc.

Skrypuch, Marsha Forchuk. Hope's War. 2004. 200p. pap. 8.99 (978-1-895681-19-2(7) , Boardwalk Bks.) Dundurn Group, The CAN. *Dist:* Univ. of Toronto Pr.

—Silver Threads. Martchenko, Michael, illus. 2004. 32p. (J). (gr. 2-5). (978-1-55041-901-6(3)) Fitzhenry & Whiteside, Ltd.

Spalding, Andrea. The Keeper & the Crows. 1999. (Young Reader Ser.). (Illus.). 128p. (J). (gr. 3-6). pap. 5.95 (978-1-55143-141-3(6)) Orca Bk. Pubs. USA.

—The Keeper & the Crows. 2000. (gr. 3-6). lib. bdg. 12.40 (978-0-613-83717-0(7)) Tandem Library Bks.

—Sarah May & the New Red Dress. ed. 2004. (Illus.). (J). (gr. k-3). spiral bd. (978-0-616-01782-1(0)) Canadian National Institute for the Blind/Institut National Canadien pour les Aveugles.

—Sarah May & the New Red Dress. 2000. (ps-2). lib. bdg. 15.25 (978-0-613-83716-3(9)); (978-0-606-18329-1(9)) Tandem Library Bks.

Stafford, Liliana. Snow Bear. Davis, Lambert, illus. 32p. (J). pap. (978-0-88899-441-7(9)) Groundwood Bks.

—Snow Bear. Davis, Lambert, illus. 2001. 32p. (J). (gr. 1-3). 15.95 (978-0-439-26977-3(6)) Scholastic, Inc.

Stanek, Mary Beth. The Fire Keepers: Mystery at Manitou Beach. Stanek, Mary Beth, illus. Stanek, Linda, photos by. 2003. (J). pap. 20.00 (978-0-9747556-0-1(5)) Stanek, Mary Beth.

Stanley, George Edward. Adam Sharp No. 5: Moose Master. 2004. (gr. k-3). lib. bdg. 11.80 (978-0-613-86694-1(0)) Tandem Library Bks.

Stenhouse, Ted. Across the Steel River. Deines, Brian, illus. 2003. 224p. (YA). (gr. 13 up). (978-1-55337-015-4(5)); (978-1-55074-891-8(2)) Kids Can Pr., Ltd.

—Across the Steel River. 2001. 222p. (YA). (gr. 8-12). per. 15.25 (978-0-613-84417-8(3)) Tandem Library Bks.

Sterling, Shirley. My Name Is Seepeetza. 1998. 126p. (J). (gr. 5-7). pap. 8.95 (978-0-88899-165-2(7) , Libros Tigrillo) Groundwood Bks. CAN. *Dist:* Perseus Distribution.

Stewart, Sharon. Spider's Web. 1998. 160p. (J). (gr. 4-9). pap. 7.95 (978-0-88995-177-8(2)) Red Deer Pr. CAN. *Dist:* Fitzhenry & Whiteside, Ltd.

Stroud, Bettye. The Patchwork Path: A Quilt Map to Freedom. Bennett, Erin Susanne, illus. 2007. 32p. (J). (gr. k-3). pap. 7.99 (*978-0-7636-3519-0(7)) Candlewick Pr.

Stuchner, Joan Betty. The Kugel Valley Klezmer Band. Row, Richard, illus. 2005. 30p. (J). (gr. 2-6). reprint ed. 16.00 (978-0-7567-8605-2(3)) DIANE Publishing Co.

—The Kugel Valley Klezmer Band. Bow, Richard, illus. 2001. 32p. (J). (ps-3). 15.95 (978-1-56656-430-4(1) , Crocodile Bks.) Interlink Publishing Group, Inc.

Sutherland, Robert. Son of the Hounds. 2004. 196p. pap. (978-1-55041-906-1(4)) Fitzhenry & Whiteside, Ltd.

Taylor, Drew Hayden. The Boy in the Treehouse/The Girl Who Loved Her Horses. 2000. 160p. pap. 13.95 (978-0-88922-441-4(2)) Talonbooks, Ltd. CAN. *Dist:* Chicago Distribution Ctr.

Thien, Madeleine. The Chinese Violin. Chang, Joe, illus. 2001. 32p. (J). (gr. k-2). 15.95 (978-1-55285-205-7(9)) Whitecap Bks., Ltd. CAN. *Dist:* Firefly Bks., Ltd.

Thompson, Margaret. Eyewitness. 2000. (Illus.). 190p. (J). (gr. 4-10). pap., tchr. ed. 8.95 (978-0-921870-74-6(4)) Ronsdale Pr. CAN. *Dist:* Literary Pr. Group of Canada.

Trottier, Maxine. By the Standing Stone. 2001. (gr. 3-6). lib. bdg. 16.40 (978-0-613-51481-1(5)) Tandem Library Bks.

—A Circle of Silver. 2000. (Circle of Silver Chronicles Ser.). 216p. (J). (gr. 7-12). pap. 7.95 (978-0-7737-6055-4(5)) Stoddart Kids CAN. *Dist:* Fitzhenry & Whiteside, Ltd.

—Circle of Silver. 2000. (gr. 7-12). lib. bdg. 16.40 (978-0-613-81347-1(2)) Tandem Library Bks.

—Under a Shooting Star. 2002. (Circle of Silver Chronicles Ser.). 212p. (YA). (gr. 5-8). pap. 7.95 (978-0-7737-6228-2(0)) Stoddart Kids CAN. *Dist:* Fitzhenry & Whiteside, Ltd.

Trottier, Maxine & Mantha, John. Storm at Batoche. 2001. (Illus.). 29p. (J). (ps-3). 15.95 (978-0-7737-3248-3(9)) Stoddart Kids CAN. *Dist:* Fitzhenry & Whiteside, Ltd.

Troughton, Ruth. The Artifact. 2003. 106p. pap. 9.95 (978-0-595-30607-7(1)) iUniverse, Inc.

—The Invisible Ones. 2003. 88p. pap. 9.95 (978-0-595-29592-0(4)) iUniverse, Inc.

Ulmer, Michael. The Gift of the Inuksuk. Rose-Popp, Melanie, illus. rev. ed. 2004. 32p. (J). 17.95 (978-1-58536-214-1(X)) Sleeping Bear Pr.

Valgardson, W. D. Frances. (J). (gr. 6-9). 2002. 172p. pap. 5.95 (978-0-88899-397-7(8)); 2000. 190p. 15.95 (978-0-88899-386-1(2)) Groundwood Bks. CAN. *Dist:* Perseus Distribution, Transition Vendor.

Vogelaar, Alie. At Last. . . Margreet!, 5 bks. VanBrugge, J., tr. from DUT. Kramer, K. J., illus. 2002. 123p. (YA). lib. bdg. 10.95 (978-0-9670728-4-5(0)) Early Foundations Pubs.

—What Are Your Plans, Margreet?, 5 bks. VanBrugge, J., tr. from DUT. Kramer, K. J., illus. 2001. 122p. (YA). lib. bdg. 10.95 (978-0-9670728-3-8(2)) Early Foundations Pubs.

Wallace, Ian. Trapper Jack's Missing Toe. 2001. (Illus.). (J). (978-0-7894-7666-1(5)) Dorling Kindersley Publishing, Inc.

—The True Story of Trapper Jack's Left Big Toe. (Illus.). 32p. (J). 18.95 (978-0-88899-415-8(X)) Groundwood Bks. CAN. *Dist:* Transition Vendor.

Walsh, Ann. Beginnings: Stories of Canada's Past. 2005. (Illus.). 228p. (J). pap. 12.95 (978-0-921870-87-6(6)) Ronsdale Pr. CAN. *Dist:* Literary Pr. Group of Canada.

—Your Time, My Time. 2006. 168p. (J). (gr. 3-8). reprint ed. pap., tchr. ed. 5.95 (978-0-88878-219-9(5) , Sandcastle Bks.) Dundurn Group, The CAN. *Dist:* Univ. of Toronto Pr.

Walters, Eric. Caged Eagles. 2001. 256p. (J). (gr. 7-12). pap. 7.95 (978-1-55143-139-0(4)) Orca Bk. Pubs. USA.

—Caged Eagles. 2001. (gr. 7-12). lib. bdg. 16.40 (978-0-613-86415-2(8)) Tandem Library Bks.

—Run. 2005. (Illus.). 224p. (YA). pap. 8.50 (978-0-14-331218-5(9) , Penguin Global) Penguin Group (USA) Inc.

Walters, Eric. Sketches. 2008. 232p. (YA). (gr. 6). 15.99 (*978-0-670-06294-2(4) , Viking Juvenile) Penguin Group (USA) Inc.

Warner, Gertrude Chandler. The Mystery of the Screech Owl. Soileau, Hodges, illus. 2001. 117p. (J). (gr. 2-7). per. 11.80 (978-0-613-35790-6(6)) Tandem Library Bks.

—The Mystery of the Screech Owl, Vol. 16. 2004. (Boxcar Children Special Ser.: No. 16). (Illus.). 144p. (J). (gr. 2-5). 14.95 (978-0-8075-5481-4(2)); pap. 3.95 (978-0-8075-5482-1(0)) Whitman, Albert & Co.

Warren, Bertie. Sammie's Journey to Freedom. 2006. (ENG.). 52p. per. 12.95 (*978-1-4241-5142-4(2)) PublishAmerica, Inc.

Warring, Molly-Ann. Paradise Acres. 2005. 518p. (978-0-88887-312-5(3)) Borealis Pr.

Welvaert, Scott R. The Curse of the Wendigo: An Agate & Buck Adventure. Garvey, Brann, illus. 2007. (Vortex Books). 105p. (J). (gr. 5 up). lib. bdg. 22.60 (978-1-59889-066-2(2)) Stone Arch Bks.

Welvaert, Scott R. The Mosquito King: An Agate & Buck Adventure. Garvey, Brann, illus. 2008. (J). lib. bdg. (*978-1-59889-857-6(4)) Stone Arch Bks.

White Fang Study Guide. 2002. (Illus.). 48p. (YA). per. 17.95 (978-1-56254-536-9(1) , SP5361) Saddleback Educational Publishing.

White, Howard. The Airplane Ride. Guzek, Greta, illus. unabr. ed. 2006. 32p. (J). bds. 14.95 (*978-0-88971-224-9(7)) Harbour Publishing Co., Ltd. CAN. *Dist:* Graphic Arts Ctr. Publishing Co.

Whitehead, Catherine. Skookumchuck. 2002. (Illus.). 156p. (J). (gr. 5-12). pap. 11.95 (978-1-58151-064-5(0)) BookPartners, Inc.

Wieler, Diana. Ranvan: Magic Nation. 1998. 229p. (J). (gr. 7-12). pap. 5.95 (978-0-88899-316-8(1) , Libros Tigrillo) Groundwood Bks. CAN. *Dist:* Transition Vendor.

Williford, Lex. Scribner Anthology of Contemporary Short Fiction. 1999. (978-0-606-18627-8(1)) Tandem Library Bks.

Willson, Sarah. What's with Dad? Marantz, Larissa & DiPaolo, Katharine, illus. 2006. (All Grown Up! Ser.). 32p. (J). pap. 3.99 (978-1-4169-0669-8(X) , Simon Spotlight/Nickelodeon) Simon & Schuster Children's Publishing.

Wilson, Eric G. Vampires of Ottawa. 2001. (Liz Austen Mystery Ser.). (Illus.). 108p. (J). (gr. 3-7). pap. 4.99 (978-1-55143-228-1(5)) Orca Bk. Pubs. USA.

—Vancouver Nightmare: A Tom Austin Mystery. Row, Richard, illus. 2000. (Tom Austin Mysteries Ser.). 112p. (J). pap. 4.99 (978-1-55143-149-9(1)) Orca Bk. Pubs. USA.

Wiseman, Eva. Kanada. 2006. (Illus.). 264p. (J). (gr. 5). pap. 9.95 (978-0-88776-729-6(X)) Tundra Bks., Inc./Livres Toundra, Inc. CAN. *Dist:* Random Hse., Inc.

Woodbury, Mary. Flight of the Tiger Moth. 2007. 224p. (YA). (gr. 7 up). 9.95 (*978-1-55050-364-7(2)) Coteau Bks. CAN. *Dist:* Fitzhenry & Whiteside, Ltd.

Wyeth, Sharon Dennis. Message in the Sky Bk. 3: Corey's Underground Railroad Diary. 2003. (My America Ser.). 112p. (J). pap. 10.95 (978-0-439-37057-8(4) , Scholastic Pr.) Scholastic, Inc.

Wynne-Jones, Tim. The Boy in the Burning House. braille ed. 2003. (J). (gr. 2). spiral bd. (978-0-616-15275-1(2)) Canadian National Institute for the Blind/Institut National Canadien pour les Aveugles.

—The Boy in the Burning House. 2000. (J). (978-0-7894-5621-2(4)) Dorling Kindersley Publishing, Inc.

—The Boy in the Burning House. 2003. 224p. (J). pap. 6.95 (978-0-374-40887-9(4) , Sunburst) Farrar, Straus & Giroux.

—The Boy in the Burning House. pap. 8.95 (978-0-88899-500-1(8)) Groundwood Bks. CAN. *Dist:* Transition Vendor.

—The Boy in the Burning House. 2001. (gr. 7-12). lib. bdg. 14.10 (978-0-613-69045-4(1)) Tandem Library Bks.

—The Boy in the Burning House. l.t. ed. 2002. 332p. (J). 23.95 (978-0-7862-4435-5(6)) Thorndike Pr.

—Lord of the Fries & Other Stories: Other Stories. pap. 9.95 (978-0-88899-274-1(2)) Groundwood Bks. CAN. *Dist:* Transition Vendor.

—Rex Zero & the End of the World. 2007. 186p. (J). (*978-1-4287-3318-3(3)) Farrar, Straus & Giroux.

Wynne-Jones, Tim. A Thief in the House of Memory. 2005. 224p. (YA). 17.00 (978-0-374-37478-5(3) , Nelanie Kroupa Bks.) Farrar, Straus & Giroux.

—A Thief in the House of Memory. l.t. ed. 2006. 235p. (YA). 21.95 (978-0-7862-9022-2(6)) Thorndike Pr.

Yee, Paul. The Jade Necklace. Lin, Grace, illus. 2002. 32p. (J). (ps-3). 15.95 (978-1-56656-455-7(7) , Crocodile Bks.) Interlink Publishing Group, Inc.

—What Happened This Summer. 2006. 128p. (YA). 15.95 (978-1-896580-88-3(2)) Tradewind Bks. CAN. *Dist:* Orca Bk. Pubs. USA.

Zagwyn, Deborah Turney. The Pumpkin Blanket. Zagwyn, Deborah Turney, illus. 2004. (Illus.). 32p. (J). (gr. k-3). 7.95 (978-1-883672-59-1(7) , Tricycle Pr.) Ten Speed Pr.

Zeman, Ludmila. The First Red Maple Leaf. Zeman, Ludmila, illus. 1999. (Illus.). 24p. (J). (gr. k-3). reprint ed. pap. 9.95 (978-0-88776-419-6(3)) Tundra Bks., Inc./Livres Toundra, Inc. CAN. *Dist:* Random Hse., Inc.

CANADA—HISTORY

Bagnall, K. The Little Immigrants. (J). pap. 5.95 (978-0-7736-7342-7(3)) Stoddart Kids CAN. *Dist:* Fitzhenry & Whiteside, Ltd.

Bailey, Katie. Radisson & Groseilliers: Fur Traders of the North. 2006. (In the Footsteps of Explorers Ser.). (Illus.). 32p. (J). (gr. 3-14). pap. (978-0-7787-2458-2(1) , 1253444); (978-0-7787-2422-3(0) , 1253444) Crabtree Publishing Co.

Beckett, Harry. Nunavut. 2003. (Eye on Canada Ser.). 32p. (J). pap. 7.95 (978-1-894705-02-8(5)) Weigl Pubs., Inc.

Bercuson, David. How Canada Became Canada, 10 vols., Set. 2005. (Illus.). 88p. (J). (gr. 5 up). lib. bdg. 219.50 (978-1-4222-0000-1(0) , 1247970) Mason Crest Pubs.

Bruchac, Marge. Malian's Song. Maughan, William, illus. 2006. (Vermont Folklife Center Children's Book Ser.). 36p. 16.95 (978-0-916718-26-8(3)) Univ. Pr. of New England.

Campbell, Kumari. Destination Saint John. 1998. (Port Cities of North America Ser.). (Illus.). 80p. (J). (gr. 6-8). lib. bdg. 23.93 (978-0-8225-2785-5(5)) Lerner Publishing Group.

—New Brunswick. 1998. (Hello Canada Ser.). (Illus.). (J). (gr. 3-6). pap. 6.95 (978-0-8225-9814-5(0)) Lerner Publishing Group.

Campbell, Marjorie Wilkins. The Nor'westers: The Fight for the Fur Trade. 2002. (Illus.). 144p. pap. 12.95 (978-1-894004-97-8(3)) Fifth Hse. Pubs. CAN. *Dist:* Fitzhenry & Whiteside, Ltd.

—The Savage River: Seventy-One Days with Simon Fraser. Delainey, James, illus. 2003. 149p. pap. 11.95 (978-1-894856-24-9(4)) Fifth Hse. Pubs. CAN. *Dist:* Fitzhenry & Whiteside, Ltd.

Corrigan, Jim. Filipino Immigration. 2003. (Changing Face of North America Ser.). (Illus.). 112p. (YA). lib. bdg. (978-1-59084-684-1(2)) Mason Crest Pubs.

Dueck, Adele. Nettie's Journey. 2006. (Illus.). 224p. (J). pap. 7.95 (978-1-55050-322-7(7)) Coteau Bks. CAN. *Dist:* F & W Pubns., Inc.

Duivenvoorden Mitic, Trudy. The Canadians: Mr. Dress-Up Ernie Coombs. 2004. (Illus.). 64p. pap. (978-1-55041-498-1(4)) Fitzhenry & Whiteside, Ltd.

Funk, Jack. Outside, the Women Cried: The Story of the Surrender by Chief Thunderchild's Band of Their Reserve near Delmas, Saskatchewan 1908. 2007. 108p. per. 12.95 (*978-0-595-43557-9(2)) iUniverse, Inc.

Gaines, Jena. Haitian Immigration. 2003. (Changing Face of North America Ser.). (Illus.). 112p. (J). lib. bdg. (978-1-59084-691-9(5)) Mason Crest Pubs.

Gall, Timothy L. & Gall, Susan B. Junior Worldmark Encyclopedia of the Canadian Provinces. 2nd ed. 1999. (Illus.). x, 254p. (J). (gr. 4-7). 49.00 (978-0-7876-3811-5(0) , UXL) Thomson Gale.

Gillis, Jennifer Blizin. Life in New France. 2003. (Picture the Past Ser.). (Illus.). 32p. (J). pap. 6.95 (978-1-4034-4286-4(X)) Heinemann Library.

—Life in New France, Quebec. 2003. (Picture the Past Ser.). (Illus.). 32p. (J). lib. bdg. 24.22 (978-1-4034-3799-0(8)) Heinemann Library.

Grambo, Rebecca L. Digging Canadian History. 2006. (Illus.). 64p. (J). (gr. 2-6). pap. 16.95 (978-1-55285-757-1(3)) Whitecap Bks., Ltd. CAN. *Dist:* Firefly Bks., Ltd.

Granfield, Linda. Pier 21: Gateway to Hope. 2000. (978-0-606-22840-4(3)) Tandem Library Bks.

—Pier 21: Gateway to Hope. 2000. (Illus.). 48p. (J). (gr. 3-8). pap. 12.95 (978-0-88776-517-9(3)) Tundra Bks., Inc./Livres Toundra, Inc. CAN. *Dist:* Random Hse., Inc.

—Pier Twenty-One: Gateway to Hope. 2000. (gr. 3 6). lib. bdg. 22.25 (978-0-613-49399-4(0)) Tandem Library Bks.

Grant, Vicki. The Halifax Citadel. Pilsworth, Graham, tr. Pilsworth, Graham, illus. 2003. (Dreadful Truth Ser.). 80p. (J). (gr. 3-8). (*978-0-88780-599-8(X)) Formac Publishing Co., Ltd. CAN. *Dist:* Casemate Pubs. & Bk. Distributors, LLC.

Gwyn, Richard. The Canadians: Pierre Trudeau. 2004. (Illus.). 64p. pap. (978-1-55041-774-6(6)) Fitzhenry & Whiteside, Ltd.

Hacker, Carlotta. The Kid's Book of Canadian History. Mantha, John, illus. 2002. (Kids Books Of ... Ser.). 72p. (J). (gr. 3-7). (978-1-55074-868-0(8)) Kids Can Pr., Ltd.

Hamilton-Barry, Joann. Boldly Canadian. Clancy, Tom, illus. 1999. 260p. (J). (gr. 3-7). (978-1-55074-520-7(4)) Kids Can Pr., Ltd.

Harcourt School Publishers Staff. Canada/Mexico/Central America: Assignment Program. 2nd ed. 2002. (Horizons Ser.). (gr. k-7). pap. 128.10 (978-0-15-335844-9(0)) Harcourt Schl. Pubs.

—Social Studies: Canada/Latin America. 1999. (Harcourt Brace Social Studies). (Illus.). (gr. k-7). 16.60 (978-0-15-316093-6(4)) Harcourt Schl. Pubs.

Hernandez, Romel. Immigration from Central America. 2004. (Changing Face of North America Ser.). (Illus.). 112p. (YA). lib. bdg. (978-1-59084-688-9(5)) Mason Crest Pubs.

Hodge, Deborah. The Kids Book of Canada's Railway: And How the CPR Was Built. Mantha, John, illus. 2000. 544p. (YA). (gr. 3 up). (978-1-55074-526-9(3)) Kids Can Pr., Ltd.

Honovich, Nancy. Immigration from the Former Yugoslavia. 2003. (Changing Face of North America Ser.). (Illus.). 112p. (YA). lib. bdg. (978-1-59084-690-2(7)) Mason Crest Pubs.

Hughes, Susan. Coming to Canada: Building a Life in a New Land. 2005. (Wow Canada! Collection). (Illus.). 112p. (J). (gr. 4-7). 28.95 (978-1-897066-45-4(7)); pap. 18.95 (978-1-897066-46-1(5)) Maple Tree Pr. CAN. *Dist:* Perseus Distribution.

—Let's Call It Canada: Amazing Stories of Canadian Place Names. Dobson, Clive & Dobson, Jolie, illus. 2003. (Wow Canada! Ser.). 96p. (J). (gr. 3-7). pap. 16.95 (978-1-894379-50-2(0)); lib. bdg. 26.95 (978-1-894379-49-6(7)) Maple Tree Pr. CAN. *Dist:* Firefly Bks., Ltd.

Junior World Mark Encyclopedia of the Nations/States/ Canadian Provinces, 3 vols., Set. 3rd ed. 2001. 455.00 (978-0-7876-4811-4(6)) Thomson Gale.

Kalman, Bobbie. Travel in the Early Days. 2001. (gr. 3-6). lib. bdg. 16.40 (978-0-613-33160-9(5)) Tandem Library Bks.

Kalman, Bobbie & Brady, Deanna. The Woodworkers. Rouse, Bonna, illus. (Colonial People Ser.). 32p. (J). (gr. 3). 2002. (978-0-7787-0744-8(X)); 2001. pap. (978-0-7787-0790-5(3)) Crabtree Publishing Co.

Kalman, Bobbie & Calder, Kate. Travel in the Early Days. 2000. (Historic Communities Ser.). (Illus.). 32p. (J). (gr. 3). pap. (978-0-86505-472-1(X)); lib. bdg. (978-0-86505-442-4(8)) Crabtree Publishing Co.

Kalman, Bobbie & Gleeson, Carrie. Spotlight on Canada. 2007. (Spotlight on My Country Ser.). (Illus.). 32p. (J). (gr. 2-5). pap. (*978-0-7787-3476-5(5)) Crabtree Publishing Co.

Kauffman, Dorothy. Letters from Canada & Mexico. 2005. (Content Area Readers Ser.). (Illus.). 4.95 (978-0-19-430951-6(7)) Oxford Univ. Pr., Inc.

Kizilos, Peter. Quebec: Province Divided. 1999. (World in Conflict Ser.). (Illus.). 104p. (YA). (gr. 7-12). lib. bdg. 25.26 (978-0-8225-3562-1(9) , Lerner Pubns.) Lerner Publishing Group.

Knudsen, Anders. Antoine de la Mothe Cadillac: French Settlements at Detroit & Louisiana. 2006. (In the Footsteps of Explorers Ser.). (Illus.). 32p. (J). (gr. 3-9). (978-0-7787-2429-2(8)); pap. (978-0-7787-2465-0(4)) Crabtree Publishing Co.

Le Sueur, William Dawson. W. l. MacKenzie. reprint ed. 150.00 (978-0-7222-6950-3(1)) Library Reprints, Inc.

Leighton, Douglas. The Canadian Rockies. 2005. (Illus.). 112p. pap. (978-1-55153-233-2(6)) Altitude Publishing Canada Ltd.

Leonetti, Mike. The Greatest Goal. Thompson, Sean, illus. 2002. (Hockey Heroes Ser.). 32p. (J). (ps-3). 15.95 (978-1-55192-318-5(1)) Raincoast Bk. Distribution CAN. *Dist:* Perseus Distribution.

Lingen, Marissa. Chinese Immigration. 2004. (Changing Face of North America Ser.). (Illus.). 112p. (YA). lib. bdg. (978-1-59084-694-0(X)) Mason Crest Pubs.

Livesey, Robert. Defenders. 1999. (gr. 3-6). lib. bdg. 19.90 (978-0-613-20342-5(9)) Tandem Library Bks.

—The Loyal Refugees. Smith, A. G., illus. 1999. (Discovering Canada Ser.). 90p. (J). (gr. 3-7). pap. 10.95 (978-0-7737-6043-1(1)) Stoddart Kids CAN. *Dist:* Fitzhenry & Whiteside, Ltd.

—The Rebels. Smith, A. G., illus. 2001. (Discovering Canada Ser.). 90p. (J). (gr. 3-7). 10.95 (978-0-7737-6170-4(5)) Stoddart Kids CAN. *Dist:* Fitzhenry & Whiteside, Ltd.

Mackay, Claire. The Toronto Story. Wales, Johnny, illus. rev. ed. 2002. 176p. (J). (gr. 5 up). 34.95 (978-1-55037-763-7(9)) Annick Pr., Ltd. CAN. *Dist:* Firefly Bks., Ltd.

Mattern, Joanne. Let's Visit Canada: The Metric System. 2004. (PowerMath Ser.). (Illus.). 24p. (J). lib. bdg. 21.25 (978-0-8239-8967-6(4) , PowerKids Pr.) Rosen Publishing Group, Inc., The.

Maury, Rob. Immigration from the Middle East. 2004. (Changing Face of North America Ser.). (Illus.). 112p. (J). lib. bdg. (978-1-59084-695-7(8)) Mason Crest Pubs.

McNamara, Margaret. Discover Canada. 2006. pap. 39.00 (*978-1-4108-6461-1(8)) Benchmark Education Co.

Moore, Christopher. Champlain. Back, Francis, illus. 2004. 56p. (J). (gr. 3-7). 18.95 (978-0-88776-657-2(9)) Tundra Bks., Inc./Livres Toundra, Inc. CAN. *Dist:* Random Hse., Inc.

Nelson, Sheila. Britain's Canada, 1613-1770. 2005. (Illus.). 87p. (J). (gr. 3-7). lib. bdg. 21.95 (978-1-4222-0003-2(5)) Mason Crest Pubs.

—Canada's Changing Society, 1984-the Present. 2005. (Illus.). 87p. (J). (gr. 3-7). lib. bdg. 21.95 (978-1-4222-0009-4(4) , 1247977) Mason Crest Pubs.

—Conflicts, Changes, & Confederation, 1770-1867. 2005. (Illus.). 87p. (J). (gr. 3-7). lib. bdg. 21.95 (978-1-4222-0004-9(3) , 1247970) Mason Crest Pubs.

—From the Atlantic to the Pacific: Canadian Expansion, 1867-1909. 2005. (Illus.). 87p. (J). (gr. 3-7). lib. bdg. 21.95 (978-1-4222-0005-6(1) , 1247971) Mason Crest Pubs.

—Redefining Canada: A Developing Identity, 1960-1984. 2005. (Illus.). 87p. (J). (gr. 3-7). lib. bdg. 21.95 (978-1-4222-0008-7(6) , 1247976) Mason Crest Pubs.

—The Settlement of New France & Acadia, 1524-1701. 2005. (Illus.). 87p. (J). (gr. 3-7). lib. bdg. 21.95 (978-1-4222-0002-5(7)) Mason Crest Pubs.

Noonan, Sheila Smith. Korean Immigration. 2003. (Changing Face of North America Ser.). (Illus.). 112p. (YA). lib. bdg. (978-1-59084-693-3(1)) Mason Crest Pubs.

Owens, Ann-Maureen, et al. Canada's Maple Leaf: The Story of Our Flag. 1999. (Illus.). 112p. (J). (gr. 3-7). (978-1-55074-516-0(6)) Kids Can Pr., Ltd.

Park, Ted. Canada. 1999. (Taking Your Camera to Ser.). (Illus.). 32p. (J). (gr. 4-7). lib. bdg. 22.83 (978-0-7398-1803-9(1)) Raintree.

Pitt, Steve. To Stand & Fight Together: Richard Pierpoint & the Colored Corps of Upper Canada. 2008. 144p. pap. 17.99 (*978-1-55002-731-0(X)) Dundurn Group, The CAN. *Dist:* Univ. of Toronto Pr.

C
D

Renaud, Anne. A Bloom of Friendship: The Story of the Canadian Tulip Festival. Spires, Ashley, illus. 2005. 24p. pap. (978-1-897073-35-3(6)) Lobster Pr.

Rinker, Kimberly. Immigration from the Dominican Republic. 2003. (Changing Face of North America Ser.). (Illus.). 112p. (J). lib. bdg. (978-1-59084-689-6(3)) Mason Crest Pubs.

Santella, Andrew. Jacques Cartier. 2002. (Groundbreakers Ser.). (Illus.). 48p. (J). (gr. 5-7). lib. bdg. 27.07 (978-1-58810-594-3(6)) Heinemann Library.

Shemie, Bonnie. Ainsi S'est Construit le Canada. Levesque, Suzanne, tr. from ENG. 2002. (FRE & SPA., Illus.). 40p. (J). (gr. 4). 18.95 (978-0-88776-555-1(6) , Livres Toundra) Tundra Bks., Inc./Livres Toundra, Inc. CAN. *Dist:* Random Hse., Inc.

Staunton, Ted. Confederation. Pilsworth, Graham, illus. 2004. (Dreadful Truth Ser.). 80p. (J). (gr. 3-8). ***(978-0-88780-630-8(9))*** Formac Publishing Co., Ltd. CAN. *Dist:* Casemate Pubs. & Bk. Distributors, LLC.

Stotksy, Sandra. Canada. 1999. (Major World Nations Ser.). (Illus.). 144p. (YA). (gr. 4-7). 29.95 (978-0-7910-4733-0(4) , Chelsea Hse.) Facts On File, Inc.

Stubbs, Dave. Our Game: The History of Hockey in Canada. Portnoy, Neal, illus. 2006. 48p. (J). (gr. 3-7). (978-1-897073-27-8(5)) Lobster Pr.

—Our Game: The History of Hockey in Canada. Portnoy, Neal, illus. 2006. 48p. (J). (gr. 3-7). pap. (978-1-897073-46-9(1)) Lobster Pr.

Woodcock, George. Gabriel Dumont. 2003. (Canadians Ser.). (Illus.). 64p. pap. (978-1-55041-492-9(5)) Fitzhenry & Whiteside, Ltd.

Wyatt, Valerie. The Kids Book of Canadian Firsts. Mantha, John, illus. 2001. (Kids Books Of ... Ser.). 56p. (J). (gr. 3-7). (978-1-55074-965-6(X)) Kids Can Pr., Ltd.

Wyeth, Sharon Dennis. Flying Free: Corey's Underground Railroad Diary. 2002. (My America Ser.: Bk. 2). (Illus.). 112p. (J). (gr. 2-5). pap. 10.95 (978-0-439-24443-5(9) , Scholastic Pr.) Scholastic, Inc.

Zelenyi, Alexander. Marquette & Jolliet: Quest for the Mississippi. 2006. (In the Footsteps of Explorers Ser.). (Illus.). 32p. (J). (gr. 3-9). (978-0-7787-2431-5(X)); pap. (978-0-7787-2467-4(0)) Crabtree Publishing Co.

Zocchi, Judy. In Canada. Brodie, Neale, illus. 2005. (Global Adventures II Ser.). 32p. (J). pap. 9.95 (978-1-59646-168-0(3)); lib. bdg. 20.65 (978-1-59646-083-6(0)) Dingles & Co.

—In Canada/en Canada. Brodie, Neale, illus. 2005. (Global Adventures II Ser.).Tr. of En Canada. (ENG & SPA.). 32p. (J). pap. 9.95 (978-1-59646-170-3(5)); lib. bdg. 20.65 (978-1-59646-084-3(9)) Dingles & Co.

Zronik, John Paul. Sieur de La Salle: New World Adventurer. 2005. (In the Footsteps of Explorers Ser.). (Illus.). 32p. (J). (gr. 3-9). (978-0-7787-2413-1(1)) Crabtree Publishing Co.

CANADA—HISTORY—FICTION

Boissery, Beverley. Sophie's Treason. 2006. 224p. (J). pap. 12.99 ***(978-1-55002-642-9(9)*** , Boardwalk Bks.) Dundurn Group, The CAN. *Dist:* Univ. of Toronto Pr.

Chan, Gillian. An Ocean Apart: The Gold Mountain Diary of Chin Mei-Ling. 2004. (Dear Canada Ser.). (Illus.). 217p. (J). pap. (978-0-7791-1353-8(5)) Scholastic Canada, Ltd.

Matas, Carol. Turned Away: The World War II Diary of Devorah Bernstein. 2005. (Dear Canada Ser.). (Illus.). 199p. (J). pap. ***(978-0-439-96946-8(8))*** Scholastic Canada, Ltd.

McDivitt, Barry. The Youngest Spy. 2007. 176p. (J). (gr. 3-9). pap. 10.95 ***(978-1-897235-17-1(8))*** Thistledown Pr., Ltd. CAN. *Dist:* Fitzhenry & Whiteside, Ltd.

Montgomery, L. M. Anne of the Island. Date not set. mass mkt. (978-0-8125-6563-8(0) , Tor Bks.) Doherty, Tom Assocs., LLC.

—Anne of the Island. 2006. (ENG.). pap. ***(978-1-4068-2171-0(3));*** pap. ***(978-1-4068-3175-7(1))*** Echo Library.

—Anne of the Island. 2006. (ENG.). 102.99 ***(978-1-4219-3295-8(4))*** IndyPublish.com.

—Anne of the Island. 2004. reprint ed. pap. 1.99 (978-1-4192-0718-1(0)); pap. 30.95 (978-1-4179-0885-1(8)) Kessinger Publishing, LLC.

—Anne of the Island. (Twelve-Point Ser.). 2001. 240p. lib. bdg. 25.00 (978-1-58287-157-8(4)); 2004. 396p. 26.00 (978-1-58287-640-5(1)) North Bks.

—Anne of the Island. abr. ed. 1998. (Avonlea Ser.: No. 4). 304p. (J). (gr. 5-8). pap. 4.99 (978-0-14-036777-5(2) , Puffin) Penguin Group (USA) Inc.

—Anne of the Island. 2000. (Anne of Green Gables Ser.: Vol. No. 3). (gr. 5-8). 182p. 24.95 (978-1-57646-309-3(5)); 182p. pap. 14.99 (978-1-57646-308-6(7)); 336p. pap. 19.99 (978-1-57646-310-9(9)) Quiet Vision Publishing.

—Anne of the Island. 2001. (gr. 7-12). lib. bdg. 30.40 (978-0-613-79774-0(4)) Tandem Library Bks.

—Anne of the Island Book & Charm. 2005. (Charming Classics). 304p. (J). pap. 6.99 (978-0-06-075859-2(7) , Harper Festival) HarperCollins Pubs.

Trottier, Maxine. Death of My Country: The Plains of Abraham Diary of Geneviève Aubuchon. 2005. (Dear Canada Ser.). (Illus.). 208p. pap. ***(978-0-439-96762-4(7))*** Scholastic Canada, Ltd.

Welvaert, Scott R. The Mosquito King: An Agate & Buck Adventure. Garvey, Brann, illus. 2008. (J). pap. ***(978-1-59889-923-8(6))*** Stone Arch Bks.

Wynne-Jones, Tim. Rex Zero & the End of the World. 2007. (Illus.). 192p. (J). (gr. 3-7). 16.00 (978-0-374-33467-3(5)) Farrar, Straus & Giroux.

Wynne-Jones, Tim. Rex Zero, the King of Nothing. 2008. 224p. (J). 16.95 ***(978-0-374-36259-1(9))*** Farrar, Straus & Giroux.

CANADA—HISTORY—TO 1763 (NEW FRANCE)

Bergen, Lara Rice. The Travels of Sieur de la Salle. 1999. (Explorers & Exploration Ser.). (Illus.). 48p. (J). (gr. 4-7). lib. bdg. 22.83 (978-0-7398-1495-6(8)) Raintree.

Bush, Karen Elizabeth. Marie-Therese Guyon, Mme. Cadillac: First Lady of Detroit. 2001. (Detroit Biography Series for Young Readers). (Illus.). 191p. (J). (gr. 5 up). 27.95 (978-0-8143-2983-2(7) , Great Lakes Bks.) Wayne State Univ. Pr.

Dube, Jean-Claude. The Chevalier de Montmagny: First Governor of New France. Rapley, Elizabeth, tr. from FRE. 2004. (FRE., Illus.). 430p. (C). 65.00 (978-0-7766-3028-1(8)) Univ. of Ottawa Pr./Presses de l'Universite d'Ottawa CAN. *Dist:* Univ. of Toronto Pr.

Englar, Mary. Sieur de la Salle. 2004. (Fact Finders Ser.). (Illus.). 32p. (J). lib. bdg. 22.60 (978-0-7368-2666-2(1)) Capstone Pr., Inc.

Harkins, Susan and William. The Life & Times of Father Jacques Marquette. 2007. (Profiles in American History Ser.). (J). lib. bdg. ***(978-1-58415-528-7(0))*** Mitchell Lane Pubs., Inc.

Harmon, Daniel E. Jacques Cartier & the Exploration of Canada. 2001. (gr. 3-6). lib. bdg. 17.60 (978-0-613-32700-8(4)) Tandem Library Bks.

Livesey, Robert. New France. 1999. (gr. 3-6). lib. bdg. 18.75 (978-0-613-20470-5(0)) Tandem Library Bks.

Maestro, Betsy. The New Americans: Colonial Times, 1620-1689. Maestro, Giulio, illus. 2004. 48p. (J). (gr. 2-5). lib. bdg. 14.19 (978-0-606-30661-4(7)) Tandem Library Bks.

Morganelli, Adrianna. Samuel de Champlain: From New France to Cape Cod. 2005. (In the Footsteps of Explorers Ser.). (Illus.). 32p. (J). (gr. 3-9). (978-0-7787-2414-8(X)); pap. (978-0-7787-2450-6(6)) Crabtree Publishing Co.

Parker, Lewis K. French Colonies in the Americas. 2003. (Reading Power Ser.). (Illus.). 24p. (J). lib. bdg. 17.25 (978-0-8239-6473-4(6) , PowerKids Pr.) Rosen Publishing Group, Inc., The.

Petrie, Kristin. Jacques Cartier. 2004. (Explorers Set I Ser.). (Illus.). 32p. (J). (gr. k-6). lib. bdg. 22.78 (978-1-59197-594-6(8)) ABDO Publishing Co.

—Marquette & Jolliet. 2007. (Illus.). 32p. (J). 22.78 (978-1-59679-745-1(2)) ABDO Publishing Co.

—La Salle. 2007. (Illus.). 32p. (J). 22.78 (978-1-59679-750-5(9)) ABDO Publishing Co.

Thompson, Linda. Los Grandes Lagos. 2005. (ENG & SPA., Illus.). 48p. (J). (978-1-59515-661-7(5)) Rourke Publishing, LLC.

—The Great Lakes. 2006. (Expansion of America II Ser.). (Illus.). 48p. (gr. 4-8). 20.95 (978-1-59515-512-2(0)) Rourke Publishing, LLC.

Worth, Richard. New France, 1534-1763. 2007. (Voices from Colonial America Ser.). (Illus.). 112p. (J). (gr. 5-9). 21.95 ***(978-1-4263-0147-6(2));*** lib. bdg. 32.90 ***(978-1-4263-0148-3(0))*** National Geographic Society. (National Geographic Children's Bks.).

CANADA—HISTORY—1914-1945

Nelson, Sheila. Crisis at Home & Abroad: The Great Depression, World War II, & Beyond, 1929-1959. 2005. (Illus.). 87p. (J). (gr. 3-7). lib. bdg. 21.95 (978-1-4222-0007-0(8) , 1247974) Mason Crest Pubs.

—A Nation Is Born: World War I & Independence, 1910-1929. 2005. (Illus.). 87p. (J). (gr. 3-7). lib. bdg. 21.95 (978-1-4222-0006-3(X) , 1247972) Mason Crest Pubs.

Smith, Robert W. Spotlight on America: The Great Depression. 2006. 48p. pap. 8.99 (978-1-4206-3218-7(3)) Austin & Company, Inc.

CANADA—POLITICS AND GOVERNMENT

Granatstein, Jack L. W. L. MacKenzie King. rev. ed. 2001. (Canadians Ser.). (Illus.). 64p. (978-1-55041-489-9(5)) Fitzhenry & Whiteside, Ltd.

Kizilos, Peter. Quebec: Province Divided. 1999. (World in Conflict Ser.). (Illus.). 104p. (YA). (gr. 7-12). lib. bdg. 25.26 (978-0-8225-3562-1(9) , Lerner Pubns.) Lerner Publishing Group.

Waite, P. B. John A. MacDonald. 2000. (Canadians Ser.). 64p. pap. (978-1-55041-479-0(8)) Fitzhenry & Whiteside, Ltd.

CANADA—ROYAL CANADIAN MOUNTED POLICE

see Royal Canadian Mounted Police

CANADA—SOCIAL LIFE AND CUSTOMS

Auch, Alison. Welcome to Canada. 2002. (Spyglass Books). (Illus.). 24p. (J). (gr. 1 up). lib. bdg. 18.60 (978-0-7565-0372-7(8)) Compass Point Bks.

Cooper, John. Season of Rage: Hugh Burnett & the Struggle for Civil Rights. 2005. (Illus.). 80p. (J). (gr. 5-12). pap. 9.95 (978-0-88776-700-5(1)) Tundra Bks., Inc./Livres Toundra, Inc. CAN. *Dist:* Random Hse., Inc.

Costain, Meredith & Collins, Paul, eds. Welcome to Canada. 2001. (Countries of the World Ser.). (Illus.). 32p. (J). 28.00 (978-0-7910-6873-1(0) , Chelsea Hse.) Facts On File, Inc.

Granfield, Linda. Cowboy: An Album. (J). 9.99 (978-1-55054-230-1(3)) Douglas & McIntyre, Ltd. CAN. *Dist:* Transition Vendor.

Greenwood, Barbara. A Pioneer Christmas: Celebrating in the Backwoods in 1841. Collins, Heather, illus. 2004. 48p. (J). (gr. 4-6). (978-1-55074-955-7(2)); (978-1-55074-953-3(6)) Kids Can Pr., Ltd.

Grolier Educational Staff, contrib. by. Canada. 2003. (Illus.). 32p. (J). (978-0-7172-5790-4(8) , Grolier) Scholastic Library Publishing.

Kalman, Bobbie. Canada: The Culture. 2002. (gr. 3-6). lib. bdg. 16.40 (978-0-613-52940-2(5)) Tandem Library Bks.

Orchard, Andy & Orchard, Clare. Canada. Fairclough, Chris, illus. Fairclough, Chris, photos by. 2004. (Letters from Around the World Ser.). (J). lib. bdg. (978-1-84234-242-8(8) , Cherrytree Books) Evans Publishing Group.

Quigley, Mary. A Visit to Canada. 2003. (Visit to Ser.). (Illus.). 32p. (J). lib. bdg. 22.79 (978-1-4034-0964-5(1)) Heinemann Library.

Zocchi, Judy. In Canada. Brodie, Neale, illus. 2005. (Global Adventures II Ser.). 32p. (J). pap. 9.95 (978-1-59646-168-0(3)); lib. bdg. 20.65 (978-1-59646-083-6(0)) Dingles & Co.

—In Canada/en Canada. Brodie, Neale, illus. 2005. (Global Adventures II Ser.).Tr. of En Canada. (ENG & SPA.). 32p. (J). pap. 9.95 (978-1-59646-170-3(5)); lib. bdg. 20.65 (978-1-59646-084-3(9)) Dingles & Co.

CANADIAN INDIANS

see Indians of North America—Canada

CANADIAN POETRY—COLLECTIONS

Bledsoe, Michele. Hors d'Oeuvres. Schaffer, Kelly & Walton, James W., illus. 1999. 14p. (J). (gr. 1 up). bds. 9.95 (978-0-9653042-1-4(3)) Come & Get It Publishing.

Booth, David. Doctor Knickerbocker & Other Rhymes. ed. 2004. (Illus.). (J). (gr. k-3). spiral bd. (978-0-616-01563-6(1)); spiral bd. (978-0-616-01564-3(X)) Canadian National Institute for the Blind/Institut National Canadien pour les Aveugles.

Fitch, Sheree. If I Had a Million Onions. Yayo, illus. 2006. 63p. (J). (gr. 4-6). (978-1-896580-78-4(5)) Tradewind Bks.

Heidbreder, Robert. Python Play & Other Recipes. Patkau, Karen, illus. 2000. 48p. (ps-2). 14.95 (978-0-7737-3213-1(6)) Stoddart Kids CAN. *Dist:* Fitzhenry & Whiteside, Ltd.

Pittman, Al. Down by Jim Long's Stage: Rhymes for Children & Young Fish. Hall, Pam, illus. rev. ed. 2001. 88p. (J). (978-1-55081-163-6(0)) Breakwater Bks., Ltd.

Stone, Tiffany. Floyd the Flamingo & His Flock of Friends. Shoemaker, Kathryn E., illus. 2006. 64p. (J). 7.95 (978-1-896580-58-6(0)) Tradewind Bks. CAN. *Dist:* Orca Bk. Pubs. USA.

CANAL, ANTONIO, CALLED CANALETTO, 1697-1768

see Canaletto, 1697-1768

CANALETTO, 1697-1768

Rice, Earle, Jr. Canaletto. 2007. (Art Profiles for Kids Ser.). (Illus.). 48p. (J). lib. bdg. 29.95 ***(978-1-58415-561-4(2))*** Mitchell Lane Pubs., Inc.

CANALS

see also Inland Navigation

also names of canals, e.g. Panama Canal; etc.

Anderson, Dale. Building the Panama Canal. 2004. (Landmark Events in American History Ser.). (Illus.). 48p. (J). 11.95 (978-0-8368-5422-0(5)); lib. bdg. 30.00 (978-0-8368-5394-0(6)) Stevens, Gareth Inc. (World Almanac Library).

Bial, Raymond. The Canals: Building America. 2001. (Building America Ser.). (Illus.). 56p. (J). (gr. 4-7). lib. bdg. 27.07 (978-0-7614-1336-3(7) , Benchmark Bks.) Cavendish, Marshall Corp.

Crewe, Sabrina & Anderson, Dale. Building the Panama Canal. 2005. (Events That Shaped America Ser.). (Illus.). 32p. (J). 24.67 (978-0-8368-3413-0(5)) Stevens, Gareth Inc.

Landau, Elaine. Canals. 2001. (True Bks.). (Illus.). 48p. (J). (gr. 3-5). pap. 6.95 (978-0-516-27314-3(0)); 25.00 (978-0-516-22183-0(3)) Scholastic Library Publishing. (Children's Pr.).

—Canals. 2001. (gr. 3-6). lib. bdg. 15.25 (978-0-613-53487-1(5)) Tandem Library Bks.

Mayer, Cassie. Canales. 2007. (SPA & ENG.). (J). pap. ***(978-1-4329-0389-3(6));*** lib. bdg. ***(978-1-4329-0384-8(5))*** Heinemann Library.

—Canals. 2007. (J). ***(978-1-4034-9366-8(9));*** pap. ***(978-1-4034-9370-5(7))*** Heinemann Library.

Oxlade, Chris. Canals. (Building Amazing Structures Ser.). (Illus.). 32p. (J). 2000. (gr. 3-5). lib. bdg. 22.79 (978-1-57572-276-4(3)); 2nd ed. 2005. (978-1-4034-7902-0(X)) Heinemann Library.

Richards, Julie. Canals & Aqueducts. 2003. 32p. (J). lib. bdg. 24.25 (978-1-58340-347-1(7)) Smart Apple Media.

Spangenburg, Ray & Moser, Diane. The Story of America's Canals. 1999. (Illus.). 96p. (J). lib. bdg. 23.95 (978-0-7351-0204-0(X)) Replica Bks.

—The Story of America's Canals: Connecting a Continent. 1999. (Illus.). 82p. (gr. 5-12). reprint ed. pap. 17.00 (978-0-7881-6380-7(9)) DIANE Publishing Co.

CANALS—FICTION

Brandis, Marianne. The Quarter-Pie Window. 2003. (gr. 5-8). lib. bdg. 18.75 (978-0-613-77299-0(7)) Tandem Library Bks.

Hurst, Carol Otis. Through the Lock. 2001. 176p. (J). (gr. 5-9). tchr. ed. 15.00 (978-0-618-03036-1(0) , Walter Lorraine) Houghton Mifflin Co. Trade & Reference Div.

Stacy, Dorothy. Erie Canal Cousins. Stacy, Dorothy, illus. 2007. (Illus.). 110p. (J). per. 9.95 ***(978-0-9792947-0-9(3))*** Blackberry Hill Pr.

CANARIES—FICTION

Foreman, Michael. Cat & Canary. 2004. (Illus.). 32p. (J). pap. 8.99 (978-1-84270-287-1(4)) Andersen GBR. *Dist:* Trafalgar Square Publishing.

Roy, Ron. The Canary Caper. Gurney, John Steven, illus. 1998. (A to Z Mysteries Ser.: No. 3). (J). (gr. k-3). 10.79 (978-0-606-12864-3(6)) Tandem Library Bks.

Scherer, Catherine W. Simon & Barklee in China, Book 1 - the Southeast. 2007. (Another Country Calling Ser.). (J). per. 15.00 (978-0-9714502-6-4(9) , Explorer Media) Simon & Barklee, Inc./ExplorerMedia.

CANARY ISLANDS—FICTION

Baglio, Ben M. Following the Rainbow. 2003. (Dolphin Diaries Ser.: No. 7). (Illus.). 160p. (J). (gr. 3-6). pap. 4.99 (978-0-439-44614-3(7) , Scholastic Paperbacks) Scholastic, Inc.

—Following the Rainbow. 2003. (gr. 3-6). lib. bdg. 12.40 (978-0-613-72206-3(X)) Tandem Library Bks.

CANCER

see also Leukemia

Ackermann, Abigail & Ackermann, Adrienne. Our Mom Has Cancer. 2001. (Illus.). 32p. 12.95 (978-0-944235-31-7(X) , 9780944235317) American Cancer Society, Inc.

—Our Mom Has Cancer. 2002. 32p. pap. 8.95 (978-0-944235-16-4(6) , 9780944235164) McGraw-Hill Cos., The.

Alagna, Magdalena. Everything You Need to Know about Chemotherapy. 2001. (Need to Know Library). (Illus.). 64p. (YA). (gr. 4-6). lib. bdg. 25.25 (978-0-8239-3394-5(6)) Rosen Publishing Group, Inc., The.

American Cancer Society Staff. Because Someone I Love Has Cancer: Kids' Activity Book. 2002. 96p. pap., act. bk. ed. 12.95 (978-0-944235-32-4(8) , 9780944235324) McGraw-Hill Cos., The.

Ammary, Neyal J. In Mommy's Garden: A Book to Help Explain Cancer to Young Children. Risch, Christopher, illus. 2004. 34p. (J). per. 10.95 (978-0-9754221-0-6(3)) Canyon Beach Visual Communications.

Apel, Melanie Ann. Coping with Leukemia. 2005. (Coping Ser.). (Illus.). 192p. (YA). (gr. 7-12). lib. bdg. 26.50 (978-0-8239-3200-9(1)) Rosen Publishing Group, Inc., The.

Armentrout, David & Armentrout, Patricia, trs. Lance Armstrong. 2003. (Discover the Life of a Sports Star Ser.). (Illus.). 24p. (J). 20.64 (978-1-58952-651-8(1)) Rourke Publishing, LLC.

Armstrong, Kristin. Lance Armstrong: The Race of His Life. Call, Ken, illus. 2000. (All Aboard Reading Ser.). 48p. (J). (gr. 2-3). 13.89 (978-0-448-42415-6(0)); (gr. 4-7). pap. 3.99 (978-0-448-42407-1(X)) Penguin Group (USA) Inc. (Grosset & Dunlap).

—Lance Armstrong: The Race of His Life. 2000. (All Aboard Reading Ser.). (J). (978-0-606-20267-1(6)); lib. bdg. 11.80 (978-0-613-31402-2(6)); (Illus.). (J). (978-0-606-20403-3(2)) Tandem Library Bks.

Aronson, Virginia. Everything You Need to Know about Breast Health & Examinations. 2005. (Need to Know Library). (Illus.). 64p. (YA). (gr. 7-12). lib. bdg. 25.25 (978-0-8239-3224-5(9) , NTBRHE) Rosen Publishing Group, Inc., The.

Bankston, John. Lance Armstrong. 2004. (Blue Banner Biography Ser.). (Illus.). 32p. (J). lib. bdg. (978-1-58415-334-4(2)) Mitchell Lane Pubs., Inc.

Benowitz, Stephen I. Cancer. 1999. (Diseases & People Ser.). (Illus.). 128p. (YA). (gr. 6-12). lib. bdg. 26.60 (978-0-7660-1181-6(X)) Enslow Pubs., Inc.

Benson, Michael. Lance Armstrong, Cyclist. 2003. (Ferguson Career Biographies Ser.). (Illus.). 144p. (J). (gr. 6-12). 25.00 (978-0-8160-5479-4(7) , Ferguson Publishing Co.) Facts On File, Inc.

Bozzone, Donna M. Causes of Cancer. 2007. (Biology of Cancer Ser.). 136p. (gr. 9). 31.95 ***(978-0-7910-8819-7(7)*** , Chelsea Hse.) Facts On File, Inc.

Bozzone, Donna M. & St. Michael's College, Library Staff. Cancer Genetics. 2007. (Biology of Cancer Ser.). 136p. (J). (gr. 9). 31.95 (978-0-7910-8818-0(9) , Chelsea Hse.) Facts On File, Inc.

Bridge, Chris. Andrew's Story: A Book about a Boy Who Beat Cancer. Bridge, Chris, illus. 2001. (Meeting the Challenge Ser.). (Illus.). 32p. (J). (gr. 2-4). 21.27 (978-0-8225-2587-5(9) , Lerner Pubns.) Lerner Publishing Group.

Brill, Marlene Targ. Lung Cancer. 2004. (Illus.). 64p. (J). 28.50 (978-0-7614-1802-3(4) , Benchmark Bks.) Cavendish, Marshall Corp.

Caldwell, Wilma R., ed. Cancer Information for Teens: Health Tips about Cancer Awareness, Prevention, Diagnosis, & Treatment. 2004. (Teen Health Ser.). (Illus.). 428p. (J). 65.00 (978-0-7808-0678-8(6)) Omnigraphics, Inc.

Cancer & Modern Science. (Illus.). (YA). (gr. 7-12). 175.50 (978-1-4042-0627-4(2)) Rosen Publishing Group, Inc., The.

Cancer Journal for the Survivor in You. 2004. (YA). spiral bd. 9.50 (978-0-9749216-0-0(2)) Swannee Rivers.

Carter, Elizabeth. Everything You Need to Know about Human Papillomavirus. 2001. (Need to Know Library). (Illus.). 64p. (YA). (gr. 4-6). lib. bdg. 25.25 (978-0-8239-3397-6(0)) Rosen Publishing Group, Inc., The.

Carter, Stephanie & Lederman, JoAnn. Meditapes Six - Fighting Cancer. 1998. (YA). (gr. 7 up). pap. 24.95 incl. audio (978-1-893868-05-2(2)) Meditapes.

Cefrey, Holly. Coping with Cancer. 2000. (Coping Ser.). (Illus.). 128p. (YA). (gr. 7-12). lib. bdg. 26.50 (978-0-8239-2849-1(7) , COCANC) Rosen Publishing Group, Inc., The.

Christopher, Matt. On the Bike with... Lance Armstrong. 2003. (Illus.). 112p. (J). (gr. 5-8). pap. 4.99 (978-0-316-07549-7(3)) Little, Brown Bks. for Young Readers.

—On the Bike with... Lance Armstrong. 2003. (gr. 3-6). lib. bdg. 13.00 (978-0-613-71601-7(9)) Tandem Library Bks.

Clifford, Christine. Our Family Has Cancer, Too! 1998. pap. 6.95 (978-0-8166-4186-4(2)) Univ. of Minnesota Pr.

Cohen, Cindy Klein & Heiney, John T. My Daddy's Cancer. Gordon, Michael J., illus. 1999. 32p. (J). (ps-6). pap. 7.95 (978-0-9656498-1-0(4)) Promise Pubns.

—My Mommy's Cancer. Baseman, Sharon R., ed. Gordon, Michael J., illus. 1999. 32p. (J). pap. 7.95 (978-0-9656498-2-7(2)) Promise Pubns.

Cranston, Lynda. You & Your Cancer: A Child's Guide. 2001. (Illus.). 64p. (J). pap. (978-1-55009-147-2(6)) Decker, B. C. Inc.

Croker, J. M. Helping the Child Understand Cancer: Is My Mother Going to Die? 2002. (Illus.). 44p. (YA). (gr. 4 up). pap. 9.95 (978-0-9719034-0-1(9)) Croker Bks.

Donovan, Sandy. Lance Armstrong. 2005. (Amazing Athletes Ser.). (Illus.). 32p. (J). (gr. 3-4). lib. bdg. 23.93 (978-0-8225-3691-8(9)) Lerner Publishing Group.

Dorfman, Elsa, photos by. No Hair Day. 2004. (Wgbh Specials Ser.). (gr. 7 up). 19.95 (978-1-57807-730-4(3) , WG1205) WGBH Boston Video.

Dreyer, ZoAnn. Teen's Guide to Living with Cancer. 2007. (Teen's Guides). 192p. (J). (gr. 6-12). 34.95 (***978-0-8160-6484-7(9)***) Facts On File, Inc.

Egan, Tracie. Skin Cancer: Current & Emerging Trends in Detection & Treatment. 2005. (Cancer & Modern Science Ser.). (Illus.). 64p. (J). (ps-7). lib. bdg. 29.25 (978-1-4042-0390-7(7)) Rosen Publishing Group, Inc., The.

Ellwood, Nancy. Lance Armstrong: With a Discussion of Determination. 2004. (Values in Action Ser.). (J). (978-1-59203-073-6(4)) Learning Challenge, Inc.

Freedman, Jeri. Lymphoma: Current & Emerging Trends in Detection & Treatment. 2005. (Cancer & Modern Science Ser.). (Illus.). 64p. (J). (ps-7). lib. bdg. 29.25 (978-1-4042-0389-1(3)) Rosen Publishing Group, Inc., The.

Gaines, Ann Graham. Robert Weinberg & the Search for the Cause of Cancer. l.t. ed. 2002. (Unlocking the Secrets of Science Ser.). (Illus.). 56p. (gr. 4-10). lib. bdg. 25.70 (978-1-58415-095-4(5)) Mitchell Lane Pubs., Inc.

Garcia, Kimberly. Lance Armstrong. 2002. (Real-Life Reader Biographies Ser.). (Illus.). 32p. (gr. 3-8). lib. bdg. 15.95 (978-1-58415-125-8(0)) Mitchell Lane Pubs., Inc.

Giddens, Sandra & Giddens, Owen. Coping with Chemotherapy. 2005. (Coping Ser.). (Illus.). 192p. (YA). (gr. 7-12). lib. bdg. 26.50 (978-0-8239-3361-7(X)) Rosen Publishing Group, Inc., The.

Gillie, Oliver. Cancer. 2004. (Just the Facts Ser.). (J). lib. bdg. 27.07 (978-1-4034-5144-6(3)) Heinemann Library.

Gold, John Coopersmith. Cancer. rev. ed. 2001. (Health Watch Ser.). (Illus.). 48p. (YA). (gr. 4-10). lib. bdg. 23.93 (978-0-7660-1652-1(8)) Enslow Pubs., Inc.

Gordon, Melanie Apel. Let's Talk about When Kids Have Cancer. 1999. (Let's Talk Library). 24p. (YA). (gr. 3 up). pap. 6.95 (978-1-56838-274-6(X)) Hazelden Publishing & Educational Services.

—Let's Talk about When Kids Have Cancer. 1999. (Let's Talk Library). (Illus.). 24p. (J). (gr. 3). lib. bdg. 18.75 (978-0-8239-5195-6(2) , PowerKids Pr.) Rosen Publishing Group, Inc., The.

Grabowski, John F. Lance Armstrong. 2005. (People in the News Ser.). (Illus.). 112p. (J). (ps-7). lib. bdg. 32.45 (978-1-59018-711-1(3) , Lucent Bks.) Thomson Gale.

Gravelle, Karen. Teenagers Face to Face with Cancer. 2000. 132p. (YA). (gr. 8-12). pap. 9.95 (978-0-595-15274-2(0) , Backinprint.com) iUniverse, Inc.

Greenfield, Nancy Reuben. When Mommy Had a Mastectomy. Butler, Ralph M., illus. 2005. 40p. (J). (ps-3). 14.95 (978-0-910155-60-1(7)) Bartleby Pr.

Harpham, Wendy Schlessel. Despues del Cancer: Una Guia para su Nueva Vida. Puig, Jose Maria Fabregas, tr. 2000. (SPA.). 418p. pap. 18.95 (978-968-13-3227-3(X)) Editorial Diana, S.A. MEX. *Dist:* Lectorum Pubns., Inc.

Henry, Cynthia S. & Gosselin, Kim. Taking Cancer to School. Dineen, Tom, illus. 2001. (Special Kids in School Ser.: Vol. 8). 32p. (J). pap. 11.95 (978-1-891383-11-3(6)) JayJo Bks., LLC.

Jackson, Mikayla A. Dear Mom, I Am Sor[r]y That You Had to Get Bre[a]st Canser [sic]. 2003. (Illus.). 31p. (J). (978-1-55306-704-7(5)) Essence Publishing.

Johanson, Paula. Breast Cancer Prevention. 2007. (J). lib. bdg. (***978-1-4042-1947-2(1)*** , Rosen Central) Rosen Publishing Group, Inc., The.

Jones, Brenn. Learning about Resilience from the Life of Lance Armstrong. 2002. (Character Building Book Ser.). (Illus.). 24p. (J). (gr. 3). lib. bdg. 18.75 (978-0-8239-5779-8(9) , PowerKids Pr.) Rosen Publishing Group, Inc., The.

Kenny, Paraic & Bozzone, Donna M. Stages of Cancer Development. 2007. (Biology of Cancer Ser.). 136p. (J). (gr. 9). 31.95 (978-0-7910-8825-8(1) , Chelsea Hse.) Facts On File, Inc.

Klein, Nancy C. Healing Images for Children: Teaching Relaxation & Guided Imagery to Children Facing Cancer & Other Serious Illnesses. O'Brien, Staci Leigh, ed. Holden, Matthew, illus. 2001. 280p. (J). pap. 24.95 (978-0-9636027-2-5(1)) Inner Coaching.

Kramer, Barbara. Lance Armstrong: Determined to Beat the Odds. 2005. (Awesome Values in Famous Lives Ser.). (Illus.). 48p. (J). (ps-7). lib. bdg. 23.93 (978-0-7660-2377-2(X) , Enslow Elementary) Enslow Pubs., Inc.

Lamb, Kirsten. Cancer. 2002. (Health Issues Ser.). (Illus.). 64p. (J). (gr. 6-8). lib. bdg. 28.54 (978-0-7398-5219-4(1)) Raintree.

Lance Armstrong. 2004. (J). 27.07 (978-0-7614-1761-3(3)) Cavendish, Marshall Corp.

Lewis, Alaric. When Someone You Love Has Cancer: A Guide to Help Kids Cope. Alley, Robert W., illus. 2005. 32p. (J). per. 7.95 (978-0-87029-395-5(8)) Abbey Pr.

Lewis, Gregg. Dave Dravecky. 2002. (gr. 3-6). lib. bdg. 13.00 (978-0-613-71674-1(4)) Tandem Library Bks.

Lewis, Kristen N. Roses Are Red, Violets Are Blue, I Beat Cancer, So Can You! Lewis, Staci L., illus. 1998. 24p. (J). (978-0-9666212-0-4(4)) Meeko Tin Pr.

Lilleby, Kathryn Ulberg. Stevie's New Blood. Chronick, Chad, illus. 2000. 43p. (J). (gr. k-6). pap. 11.00 (978-1-890504-17-5(3)) Oncology Nursing Society.

Majure, Janet. Breast Cancer. 2000. (Diseases & People Ser.). (Illus.). 128p. (YA). (gr. 6-12). lib. bdg. 26.60 (978-0-7660-1312-4(X)) Enslow Pubs., Inc.

Martin, Carrie & Martin, Chia. The Rainbow Feelings of Cancer: A Book of Children Who Have a Loved One with Cancer. 2001. (Illus.). 32p. wbk. ed. 14.95 (978-1-890772-16-1(X)) Hohm Pr.

Massari, Francesca. Everything You Need to Know about Cancer. 2005. (Need to Know Library). (Illus.). 64p. (YA). (gr. 7-12). lib. bdg. 25.25 (978-0-8239-3164-4(1) , NTCANC) Rosen Publishing Group, Inc., The.

McKinnell, Robert G. & Bozzone, Donna M. Prevention of Cancer. 2008. (Biology of Cancer Ser.). 112p. (gr. 9). 31.95 (***978-0-7910-8827-2(8)*** , Chelsea Hse.) Facts On File, Inc.

Miller, Michelle. I Can Make Healthy Choices: Dog Tales, Cancer Stories for Kids. 2007. 37p. pap. 9.99 (***978-1-58752-261-1(6)***) Timberwolf Pr., Inc.

Moehn, Heather. Everything You Need to Know When Someone You Know Has Leukemia. 2005. (Need to Know Library). (Illus.). 64p. (YA). (gr. 7-12). lib. bdg. 25.25 (978-0-8239-3121-7(8) , NTLEUK) Rosen Publishing Group, Inc., The.

Mooney, Belinda. Cancer. 2007. (At Issue Ser.). (Illus.). 128p. (gr. 10-12). 29.95 (978-0-7377-3411-9(6)); pap. 21.20 (978-0-7377-3412-6(4)) Thomson Gale. (Greenhaven Pr., Inc.).

My Book about Cancer: A Workbook to Help Children Deal with the Diagnosis & Treatment of a Father with Cancer. 2003. (ACE.). (J). 6.00 (978-1-890504-33-5(5) , INPU0546D) Oncology Nursing Society.

Naff, Clay Farris. Cancer 2007. 2007. (Contemporary Issues Companion Ser.). 240p. (gr. 10-12). 36.20 (***978-0-7377-2444-8(7)*** , Greenhaven Pr., Inc.) Thomson Gale.

Nardo, Don. Breast Cancer. 2001. (Diseases & Disorders Ser.). (Illus.). 120p. (YA). (gr. 6-9). 32.45 (978-1-56006-905-8(8) , GML12001-179161, Lucent Bks.) Thomson Gale.

Nelson, Sheila & Walker, Ida. Youth with Cancer: Facing the Shadows. 2008. (J). (***978-1-4222-0139-8(2)***) Mason Crest Pubs.

Peacock, Judith. Breast Cancer. 2001. (Perspectives on Disease & Illness Ser.). (Illus.). 64p. (J). (gr. k-9). lib. bdg. 23.93 (978-0-7368-1028-9(5) , LifeMatters Bks.) Capstone Pr., Inc.

—Hodgkin's Disease. 2000. (Perspectives on Disease & Illness Ser.). (Illus.). 64p. (YA). (gr. 4-6). lib. bdg. 23.93 (978-0-7368-1027-2(7) , LifeMatters Bks.) Capstone Pr., Inc.

Ridddering, Marggie & Riddering, David. Atravesando el Valle. 2005. (SPA.). (YA). 9.95 (978-0-9765977-0-4(5)) Riddering, Marggie.

Riddering, Margie & Riddering, David. Walking through the Valley. 2nd ed. 2005. (YA). 9.95 (978-0-9765977-1-1(3)) Riddering, Marggie.

Ries, Lori Anne. Punk Wig. Eitter-Kono, Erin, illus. 2008. (J). (***978-1-59078-486-0(3)***) Boyds Mills Pr.

Rocha, Toni L. Coping When Someone in Your Family Has Cancer. 2005. (Coping Ser.). (Illus.). 192p. (YA). (gr. 7-12). lib. bdg. 26.50 (978-0-8239-3195-8(1)) Rosen Publishing Group, Inc., The.

Royston, Angela. Cancer. 2005. (What's It Like? Ser.). (Illus.). 32p. (J). (ps-ps). lib. bdg. 24.21 (978-1-4034-5850-6(2)) Heinemann Library.

Schmidt, Rebecca C. My Book about Cancer: A Workbook to Help Children Deal with the Diagnosis & Treatment of a Mother with Cancer. 2003. (J). 6.00 (978-1-890504-36-6(X) , INPU0546M) Oncology Nursing Society.

Shapiro, Dean. Prostate Cancer. 2007. (Diseases & Disorders Ser.). 128p. (gr. 7-10). 31.20 (***978-1-59018-593-3(5)*** , Lucent Bks.) Thomson Gale.

Sheen, Barbara. Ovarian Cancer. 2005. (Diseases & Disorders Ser.). (Illus.). 112p. (YA). (gr. 7-10). lib. bdg. 32.45 (978-1-59018-342-7(8) , Lucent Bks.) Thomson Gale.

Silver, Alex, et al. Our Mom Is Getting Better. 2007. 32p. 14.95 (***978-0-944235-85-0(9)*** , 9780944235850) American Cancer Society, Inc.

Silverman, Alexander E., et al. Our Dad Is Getting Better. 2007. 32p. 14.95 (***978-0-944235-86-7(7)*** , 9780944235867) American Cancer Society, Inc.

Silverstein, Alvin, et al. The Breast Cancer Update. 2007. (Disease Update Ser.). (Illus.). 128p. (J). (gr. 5 up). lib. bdg. 31.93 (***978-0-7660-2747-3(3)***) Enslow Pubs., Inc.

Silverstein, Alvin, et al. Cancer. 2006. (Twenty-First Century Medical Library). (Illus.). 121p. (J). (gr. 7 up). 27.93 (978-0-7613-2833-9(5) , Twenty-First Century Bks.) Lerner Publishing Group.

So, Po-Lin & Bozzone, Donna M. Skin Cancer. 2007. (Biology of Cancer Ser.). 112p. (gr. 9). 31.95 (***978-0-7910-8938-5(X)*** , Chelsea Hse.) Facts On File, Inc.

Stewart, Gail B. Alexandra Scott, Cancer Research Fundraiser. 2006. 64p. (gr. 4-8). 27.45 (978-0-7377-3613-7(5) , Kidhaven) Thomson Gale.

—Teens with Cancer. Franzen, Carl G., photos by. 2001. (Other America Ser.). (Illus.). 96p. (J). (gr. 4-12). lib. bdg. 29.95 (978-1-56006-884-6(1) , LML00902-178207, Lucent Bks.) Thomson Gale.

Stokes, Mark. Prostate Cancer: Current & Emerging Trends in Detection & Treatment. 2005. (Cancer & Modern Science Ser.). (Illus.). 64p. (J). (ps-7). lib. bdg. 29.25 (978-1-4042-0391-4(5)) Rosen Publishing Group, Inc., The.

Stone, Miriam R. At the End of Words: A Daughters Memoir. Franke, Lisa R., illus. 2003. 64p. (J). (gr. 7). 14.00 (978-0-7636-1854-4(3)) Candlewick Pr.

Tanner, Jerome E. & Bozzone, Donna M. Myeloma. 2008. (Biology of Cancer Ser.). 112p. (gr. 9). 31.95 (***978-0-7910-8824-1(3)*** , Chelsea Hse.) Facts On File, Inc.

Tate, M. My Little Life: A Cancer Survivor's Story As Told by Nature. Tate, M., photos by. 2004. (YA). pap. 10.00 (978-0-9761969-0-7(5)) Heads First (1st).

Thomas, Cristine. Can I Catch Cancer? Explaining cancer to Children. Thomas, Cristine, illus. 2007. (Illus.). 44p. (J). 10.95 (***978-0-9778796-9-4(0)***) Brittany's Bks.

Thompson, John. Lance Armstrong. 2001. (Overcoming Adversity Ser.). (Illus.). (J). 100p. pap. 9.95 (978-0-7910-5880-0(8)); 112p. (gr. 5 up). 30.00 (978-0-7910-5879-4(4)) Facts On File, Inc. (Chelsea Hse.).

Torrey, Lisa. Michael's Mommy Has Breast Cancer. Watler, Barbara W., illus. 1999. 40p. (J). (gr. k-5). pap. 10.95 (978-0-9647763-6-4(7)) Hibiscus Pr.

van Dernoot, Peter. Talking with My Treehouse Friends about Cancer. (J). per. 9.95 (978-1-55591-630-5(9)) Fulcrum Publishing.

Victory in the Valleys: A Journey Through the Valleys of Life Including Cancer & Death. 2004. (YA). pap. 12.99 (978-0-9753818-0-9(6)) Victory Pr.

Vogel, Carole Garbuny. Breast Cancer: Questions & Answers for Young Women. 2001. (Single Titles Ser.). (Illus.). 176p. (gr. 7 up). lib. bdg. 25.90 (978-0-7613-1855-2(0) , Twenty-First Century Bks.) Lerner Publishing Group.

Walker, Julie. Lung Cancer: Current & Emerging Trends in Detection & Treatment. 2005. (Cancer & Modern Science Ser.). (Illus.). 64p. (J). (ps-7). lib. bdg. 29.25 (978-1-4042-0388-4(5)) Rosen Publishing Group, Inc., The.

Werther, Scott P. Dr. Jerri Nielsen: Cheating Death in Antarctica. 2003. (High Interest Books Ser.). (Illus.). 48p. (J). 23.00 (978-0-516-24331-3(4) , Children's Pr.) Scholastic Library Publishing.

—Dr. Jerri Nielsen: Cheating Death in Antarctica. 2003. (Illus.). 48p. (J). (gr. 4-7). lib. bdg. 15.25 (978-0-613-67881-0(8)) Tandem Library Bks.

What If. . . . Someone I Love Has Cancer. 2003. (J). per. 19.95 incl. cd-rom (978-0-9676189-1-3(6)) Star Pr., The.

Where's Mom's Hair: A Family's Journey Through Cancer. 2005. (Illus.). 32p. (J). (gr. 1-7). pap. 10.95 (978-1-896764-94-8(0)) Second Story Pr. CAN. *Dist:* Orca Bk. Pubs. USA, Univ. of Toronto Pr.

Wilde, Daxton. I'm a Super Hero. l.t. ed. 2001. (Illus.). 30p. (J). 2.95 net. (978-0-9749834-0-0(3)) Daxton Wilde Fnd.

Wyborny, Sheila. Cancer Treatments. 2005. (Science on the Edge Ser.). (Illus.). 48p. (YA). (gr. 8-12). lib. bdg. 24.95 (978-1-4103-0603-6(8) , Blackbirch Pr., Inc.) Thomson Gale.

Yaffe, Risa Sacks. Once upon a Hopeful Night. Cramer, Troy, illus. 1998. 32p. (J). (gr. k-3). pap. 7.00 (978-1-890504-10-6(6)) Oncology Nursing Society.

Yount, Lisa. Cancer. (Contemporary Issues Companion Ser.). (Illus.). (YA). 2000. 190p. (gr. 10 up). lib. bdg. 24.95 (978-0-7377-0160 9(9) , Greenhaven Pr., Inc.); 1999. 112p. (gr. 6-9). lib. bdg. 29.95 (978-1-56006-363-6(7) , LML00902-177748, Lucent Bks.) Thomson Gale.

CANCER—FICTION

Albert, Louise. Less Than Perfect. 2003. 224p. (J). (gr. 7 up). tchr. ed. 17.95 (978-0-8234-1688-2(7)) Holiday Hse., Inc.

Anderson, Laurie Halse. Say Good-Bye. 2003. (Wild at Heart Ser.). (Illus.). 129p. (J). (gr. 4 up). lib. bdg. 23.33 (978-0-8368-3259-4(0)) Stevens, Gareth Inc.

—Say Good-Bye. 2001. (American Girl Wild at Heart Ser.: Bk. 5). (Illus.). (YA). (978-0-606-21527-5(1)) Tandem Library Bks.

Bauer, Joan. Hope Was Here. 2000. (Illus.). 192p. (J). (gr. 7-12). 16.99 (978-0-399-23142-1(0) , Putnam Juvenile) Penguin Group (USA) Inc.

Bobrow, Laura J. He Listens. 2004. (YA). 9.95 (978-0-9716489-4-4(8)) VisionQuest Ministries.

Borden, Louise. Good Luck, Mrs. K. ! Gustavson, Adam, illus. 2002. 32p. (J). (gr. 1-5). pap. 6.99 (978-0-689-85119-3(7) , Aladdin) Simon & Schuster Children's Publishing.

Buckingham, Dorothea N. Staring down the Dragon. Yasutake, Sarah Wageman, ed. 2003. 204p. (YA). (gr. 7-12). pap. 10.95 (978-0-9724577-3-6(9)) Sydney Pr.

Byrd, Sandra. Red Velvet. 2005. (Friends for a Season Ser.). 256p. (J). (gr. 8-12). pap. 10.99 (978-0-7642-0022-9(4)) Bethany Hse. Pubs.

Caldwell, V. M. Runt: Story of a Boy. 2006. 208p. (J). 16.95 (978-1-57131-662-2(0)); pap. 6.95 (978-1-57131-661-5(2)) Milkweed Editions.

Carney, Karen L. What Is Cancer, Anyway? Explaining Cancer to Children of All Ages. Carney, Karen L., illus. rev. ed. 2001. (Barklay & Eve Ser.: Bk. 5). (Illus.). (J). pap. 6.95 (978-0-9667820-4-2(6)) Dragonfly Publishing.

Crews, Dana-Susan. Our Daddy's Cancer: How We Helped Him Fight. 2007. (J). per. 10.99 (***978-1-60247-409-3(5)***) Tate Publishing & Enterprises, L.L.C.

Duane, Diane. The Wizard's Dilemma. 2002. (Young Wizards Ser.: Bk. 5). 432p. (YA). (gr. 7 up). pap. 6.95 (978-0-15-202460-4(3) , Magic Carpet Bks.) Harcourt Children's Bks.

—The Wizard's Dilemma. 2002. (gr. 5-8). lib. bdg. 15.25 (978-0-613-55225-7(3)) Tandem Library Bks.

Fallon, Kevin A. Rest in Peas: What Does that Mean? 2005. per. 12.95 (978-1-59196-943-3(3)) Instantpublisher.com.

Geller, Rita. Victoria's Smile. 2001. (978-0-606-22172-6(7)) Tandem Library Bks.

Hannigan, Katherine. Ida B: ... And Her Plans to Maximize Fun, Avoid Disaster, & (Possibly) Save the World. 256p. 2004. (J). (gr. 4 up). 16.99 (978-0-06-073024-6(2)); 2004. (gr. 4 up). lib. bdg. 16.89 (978-0-06-073025-3(0)); 2007. reprint ed. pap. 5.99 (978-0-06-073026-0(9) , Harper Trophy) HarperCollins Pubs.

Hershey, Marilyn K. Oncology, Stupology... I Want to Go Home! Boris, Jill M., illus. Blodgea, Randy, photos by. 1999. 32p. (J). (ps-6). pap. 5.00 (978-0-9673550-0-9(1)) Butterfly Pr.

Hobbs, Valerie. Defiance. 2005. 128p. (J). 16.00 (978-0-374-30847-6(0)) Farrar, Straus & Giroux.

—Defiance. l.t. ed. 2006. 147p. 22.95 (978-0-7862-8667-6(9)) Thorndike Pr.

I Can Too! Cancer Kids Can Too Caucasian Series. l.t. ed. 2006. (Illus.). 44p. (J). (978-0-9778796-3-2(1)) Brittany's Bks.

Jablonski, Carla. Thicker Than Water. 2007. 272p. (YA). (gr. 9-12). pap. 8.99 (978-1-59514-123-1(5) , Razorbill) Penguin Group (USA) Inc.

Janover, Caroline D. The Worst Speller in Jr. High. 2001. 208p. (YA). (gr. 4-7). pap. 13.95 (978-0-595-15328-2(3) , Backinprint.com) iUniverse, Inc.

Johnson, Angela. Toning the Sweep. 2002. (J). 13.19 (978-0-7587-0401-6(1)) Book Wholesalers, Inc.

—Toning the Sweep. 2003. 112p. (J). (gr. 7 up). pap. 5.99 (978-0-590-48142-7(8) , Scholastic Paperbacks) Scholastic, Inc.

Karu, Tim, et al. Henry & the White Wolf. Karu, Tyler, illus. 2000. (Illus.). 32p. (J). (ps-3). 12.95 (978-0-7611-2135-0(8) , 12135) Workman Publishing Co., Inc.

Koss, Amy Goldman. Side Effects. 2006. 144p. (YA). 16.95 (***978-1-59643-294-9(2));*** 143p. (J). (***978-1-4287-0203-5(2)***) Roaring Brook Pr.

Latorre, Jose Maria. La Incognita del Volcan. Ibarz, Miguel, illus. 2000. (Periscopio Ser.).Tr. of Mystery of the Volcano. (SPA.). 236p. (YA). (gr. 9 up). (978-84-236-5517-5(2)) Edebé ESP. *Dist:* Baker & Taylor Bks.

Levchuk, Lisa. Everything Beautiful in the World. 2008. (YA). (***978-0-374-32238-0(4)***) Farrar, Straus & Giroux.

Martin, Ann M. On Christmas Eve. 160p. (J). 2007. pap. 5.99 (***978-0-439-74589-5(6)*** , Scholastic Paperbacks); 2006. (Illus.). pap. 15.99 (978-0-439-74588-8(8) , Scholastic) Scholastic, Inc.

Martin, Ann M. Sunny: Diary Three. 1999. (California Diaries: Bk. 12). 160p. (YA). (gr. 6-8). pap. 4.50 (978-0-590-02390-0(X)) Scholastic, Inc.

—Sunny: Diary Three. 1999. (California Diaries: Bk. 12). (Illus.). (YA). (gr. 6-8). (978-0-606-18523-3(2)) Tandem Library Bks.

McDaniel, Lurlene. Dawn Rochelle: Four Novels. 2000. (Dawn Rochelle Ser.). (Illus.). (J). (978-0-606-17994-2(1)) Tandem Library Bks.

—Don't Die, My Love. 2000. (YA). pap. 50.24 incl. audio (978-0-7887-4165-4(9) , 41101) Recorded Bks., LLC.

—Garden of Angels. 2005. 288p. (YA). (gr. 7). pap. 5.50 (978-0-553-49432-7(5) , Laurel Leaf) Random Hse. Children's Bks.

—Letting Go of Lisa. (YA). (gr. 7). 2007. 176p. mass mkt. 6.50 (***978-0-440-23868-3(4)*** , Laurel Leaf); 2006. 192p. 10.95 (978-0-385-73159-1(0) , Delacorte Bks. for Young Readers); 2006. 192p. lib. bdg. 12.99 (978-0-385-90196-3(8) , Delacorte Bks. for Young Readers) Random Hse. Children's Bks.

McDaniel, Lurlene. Raina's Story. 2005. (Angels in Pink Ser.). 208p. (J). (gr. 7). lib. bdg. 12.99 (978-0-385-90194-9(1) , Delacorte Bks. for Young Readers) Random Hse. Children's Bks.

McGraw, Jason. Beating the Odds. 2007. 30p. 47.88 (***978-0-615-13681-3(8)***) McGraw, Jason A.

Miller, Deborah. Bitter Anguish. 2005. 80p. per. (978-1-55306-971-3(4) , Guardian Bks.) Essence Publishing.

Owens, Connie S. Aunt Lucy Has Cancer. 2003. (J). pap. 5.99 (978-1-59317-008-0(4)) Warner Pr. Pubs.

Padian, Maria. Brett McCarthy: Work In Progress. 2008. (J). 288p. (***978-0-375-84675-5(1)); (978-0-375-94675-2(6)***) Knopf, Alfred A. Inc.

Parker, Marjorie Blain. Jasper's Day. Wilson, Janet, illus. 2002. 32p. (J). (gr. k-3). (978-1-55074-957-1(9)) Kids Can Pr., Ltd.

Pearce, Emily Smith. Isabel & the Miracle Baby. 2007. 144p. (YA). (gr. 3 up). 15.95 (***978-1-932425-44-4(6)*** , Front Street) Boyds Mills Pr.

Polacco, Patricia. The Lemonade Club. Polacco, Patricia, illus. 2007. (Illus.). 48p. (J). (gr. 1). 16.99 (***978-0-399-24540-4(5)*** , Philomel) Penguin Group (USA) Inc.

Preller, James. Six Innings: A Game in the Life. 2008. 160p. (J). 16.95 (***978-0-312-36763-3(5)***) Feiwel & Friends.

Rapp, Adam. Under the Wolf, under the Dog. 320p. (YA). (gr. 9). 2007. pap. 8.99 (978-0-7636-3365-3(8)); 2004. 16.99 (978-0-7636-1818-6(7)) Candlewick Pr.

Richter, Jutta. The Summer of the Pike. Brailovsky, Anna, tr. from GER. Buchholz, Quint, illus. 2006. 132p. (J). pap. 6.95 (978-1-57131-672-1(8)); 16.95 (978-1-57131-671-4(X)) Milkweed Editions.

Russell, Laura Okmin. Mommy Has Cancer. Calvert-Weyant, Lynda, illus. 2003. (J). (978-0-7853-6335-4(1)) Publications International, Ltd.

Sauer, Tammi. Dear Jack. 2004. 164p. (YA). mass mkt. 6.99 (***978-0-9753367-0-0(3)***) Onstage Publishing, LLC.

Scott, Liz, et al. Alex & the Amazing Lemonade Stand. Howard, Pam, illus. 2005. 32p. (ps-5). 15.95 (978-0-9753200-0-6(9)) PAJE Publishing Co.

Sherrard, Valerie. Kate. 2004. 200p. pap. 8.99 (978-1-55002-476-0(0)) Dundurn Group, The CAN. *Dist:* Univ. of Toronto Pr.

—Kate. 2003. (gr. 7-12). lib. bdg. 17.60 (978-0-613-88193-7(1)) Tandem Library Bks.

Sinykin, Sheri Cooper. Giving up the Ghost. 2007. 224p. (J). (gr. 4-7). 14.95 (***978-1-56145-423-5(0)*** , Peachtree Junior) Peachtree Pubs., Ltd.

Speltz, Ann. The Year My Mother Was Bald. Sternberg, Kate, illus. 2003. 64p. (YA). (gr. 3-8). 14.95 (978-1-55798-837-9(4)); (ps-8). pap. 8.95 (978-1-55798-888-1(9)) American Psychological Assn. (Magination Pr.).

—Year My Mother Was Bald. 2003. (gr. 3-6). lib. bdg. 17.60 (978-0-613-61137-4(3)) Tandem Library Bks.

Stuart, Duncan. The Whole of the Moon. 200p. (YA). (gr. 8 up). pap. 13.00 (978-1-877135-05-7(4)) Longacre Pr. NZL. *Dist:* Pacific Island Bks.

C
D

Sutherland, Eileen & Sutherland, Maggie. Mom & the Polka-Dot Boo-Boo. 2007. 32p. 14.95 (***978-0-944235-87-4(5)*** , 9780944235874) American Cancer Society, Inc.

Swanson, Julie A. Going for the Record. 2004. 223p. (J). pap. 8.00 (978-0-8028-5273-1(4)) Eerdmans, William B. Publishing Co.

Thomas, Cristine Leeann. I Can Too! Cancer Kids Can Too African American Series. Thomas, Cristine Leeann, illus. 2006. (J). (978-0-9778796-4-9(X)) Brittany's Bks.

Tinkham, Kelly. Hair for Mama. Bates, Amy June, illus. 2007. 32p. (J). (ps-3). 16.99 (978-0-8037-2955-1(3) , Dial) Penguin Group (USA) Inc.

Townsend, Lois Ritter. Our Journey Through Breast Cancer: -a story based on a teacher's journey through breast cancer with her kindergarten Class. 2005. (Illus.). 20p. (J). pap. 6.99 (978-1-933570-93-8(8)) Aardvark Global Publishing.

Turner, Ann. Hard Hit. l.t. ed. 2006. (YA). 21.95 (978-0-7862-8745-1(4)) Thorndike Pr.

Turner, Ann Warren. Hard Hit. 2006. 128p. (J). (gr. 7 up). pap. 16.99 (978-0-439-29680-9(3)) Scholastic, Inc.

Victoria, Lisa, illus. Clara's Gift from the Heart. 2006. (J). 17.95 (978-0-9674602-9-1(8)) Blue Marlin Pubns.

Vigna, Judith. When Eric's Mom Fought Cancer. ed. 2004. (J). (gr. 1-5). spiral bd. (978-0-616-03063-9(0)) Canadian National Institute for the Blind/Institut National Canadien pour les Aveugles.

Wang, An. Anywhere but Here. 2006. 100p. (YA). pap. 9.95 (978-0-88100-140-2(6)) National Writers Pr., The.

Warner, Sally. Sort of Forever. 1998. (J). (gr. 3-6). pap. (978-0-679-88649-5(4) , Random Hse. Bks. for Young Readers) Random Hse. Children's Bks.

—Sort of Forever. 1999. (978-0-606-17153-3(3)) Tandem Library Bks.

Weston, Carol. Melanie Martin Goes Dutch: The Private Diary of My Almost Bummer Summer with Cecily, Matt the Brat, & Vincent van Go Go Go. 2003. (Illus.). 240p. (J). (gr. 3-7). 5.99 (978-0-440-41899-3(2) , Yearling) Random Hse. Children's Bks.

—Melanie Martin Goes Dutch: The Private Diary of My Almost Bummer Summer with Cecily, Matt the Brat, & Vincent van Go Go Go. 2003. (gr. 3-6). lib. bdg. 25.70 (978-0-613-62527-2(7)) Tandem Library Bks.

Wilde, Daxton & Wilde, Sherry. I'm a Superhero. Wilde, Daxton, illus. 2005. (Illus.). 32p. (J). (ps-3). 9.95 (978-1-58685-847-6(5)) Gibbs Smith, Publisher.

Wood, Debra. William Warrior Bear. Blake, Joshua Aaron, illus. l.t. ed. 2005. 30p. (J). per. 12.95 (978-1-59879-001-6(3)) Lifevest Publishing, Inc.

Writers Uniting Against Cancer Staff. The Acorn Gathering: Writers Uniting Against Cancer. 2002. 154p. pap. 11.95 (978-0-595-22788-4(0) , Writers Club Pr.) iUniverse, Inc.

Zinnen, Linda. Holding at Third. 2006. 160p. (YA). (gr. 4). pap. 5.99 (978-0-14-240554-3(X) , Puffin) Penguin Group (USA) Inc.

CANDLES

Candle Making for Kids With Other. 1999. mass mkt. 168.60 (978-0-590-63241-6(8)) Scholastic, Inc.

Check, Laura. Create Your Own Candles: 30 Easy-To-Make Designs. 2004. (Quick Starts for Kids! Ser.). (J). pap. (978-1-885593-52-8(X) , Williamson Bks.) Ideals Pubns.

Constable, David. Funstation Candle Making, 5 vols., Set. 1998. (Funstations Ser.). (Illus.). 48p. (J). (gr. 3-7). 17.95 (978-1-57145-349-5(0) , Silver Dolphin Bks.) Advantage Pubs. Group.

Sadler, Judy Ann. Making Candles. Walker, Tracy, illus. 1998. (Kids Can Do It Ser.). 40p. (J). (gr. 4-6). (978-1-55074-501-6(8)) Kids Can Pr., Ltd.

Tolhurst, Marilyn. Lights & Candles. Date not set. (Sense of History Ser.). (Illus.). 24p. pap. 27.69 (978-0-582-04026-7(4)) Addison-Wesley Longman, Ltd. GBR. *Dist:* Trans-Atlantic Pubns., Inc.

Yonck, Barbara. Candle Crafts. Date not set. (Illus.). (J). (gr. 4-8). lib. bdg. 8.95 (978-0-87460-376-7(5)) Lion Bks.

CANDY

see Confectionery

CANNED GOODS

see Canning and Preserving

CANNING AND PRESERVING

Mecozzi, Maureen. The Uncanny Can. 2007. (Shockwave: Science in Practice Ser.). (Illus.). 36p. (J). (gr. 4-6). lib. bdg. 25.00 (***978-0-531-17584-2(7)*** , Children's Pr.) Scholastic Library Publishing.

Parker, Lewis K. The Inventions of Amanda Jones: The Vacuum Method of Canning & Food Preservation. 2003. (19th Century American Inventors Ser.). (Illus.). 24p. (J). lib. bdg. 17.25 (978-0-8239-6445-1(0) , PowerKids Pr.) Rosen Publishing Group, Inc., The.

CANNON

see Ordnance

CANOES AND CANOEING

Bach, Julie S. Kayaking. 2000. (World of Sports Ser.). (Illus.). 32p. (J). (gr. 4 up). lib. bdg. 16.95 (978-1-887068-56-7(2)) Smart Apple Media.

Bass, Scott. Kayaking. 2005. (Kids' Guides Ser.). (Illus.). 32p. (J). (gr. 1-5). 25.64 (978-1-59296-208-2(4)) Child's World, Inc.

Bayne, Allan P. & Platford, Gary. Bugs, Sweat & Fears: Beginner's Guide to Wilderness Canoe Camping. Penner, Burton, illus. 1999. 208p. pap. (978-0-88801-234-0(9)) Turnstone Pr.

Cooper, Jason. Canoes & Kayaks. 1999. (Boats & Ships Discovery Library). (Illus.). 24p. (J). (gr. 1-4). lib. bdg. 19.27 (978-0-86593-560-0(2)) Rourke Publishing, LLC.

Corral, Kimberly. A Child's Glacier Bay. Corral, Roy, illus. 1998. 32p. (ps up). 15.95 (978-0-88240-503-2(9)) Graphic Arts Ctr. Publishing Co.

De Medeiros, James. Kayaking. 2007. (J). (***978-1-59036-663-9(8)); *978-1-59036-664-6(6)***) Weigl Pubs., Inc.

Draper, Allison Stark. Kayaking: Have Fun, Be Smart. 2005. (Explore the Outdoors Ser.). (Illus.). 64p. (YA). (gr. 7-12). lib. bdg. 26.50 (978-0-8239-3166-8(8) , EOKAYA) Rosen Publishing Group, Inc., The.

Graf, Mike. White-Water Kayaking. 2004. (Great Outdoors Ser.). (Illus.). 48p. (J). 16.95 (978-0-7368-2413-2(8) , Capstone High/Low Bks.) Capstone Pr., Inc.

Lourie, Peter. Erie Canal: Canoeing America's Great Waterway. Lourie, Peter, photos by. 2003. (Illus.). 48p. (J). (gr. 2-5). 17.95 (978-1-56397-669-8(2)) Boyds Mills Pr.

—Erie Canal: Canoeing America's Great Waterway. 2003. (Illus.). 48p. (YA). (gr. 4-6). pap. 10.95 (978-1-56397-764-0(8)) Boyds Mills Pr.

—Yukon River: An Adventure to the Gold Fields of the Klondike. 2003. (Illus.). 48p. (YA). (gr. 4-6). pap. 9.95 (978-1-56397-878-4(4)) Boyds Mills Pr.

—Yukon River: An Adventure to the Gold Fields of the Klondike. 2000. (gr. 3-6). lib. bdg. 18.75 (978-0-613-49402-1(4)) Tandem Library Bks.

Revell, Phil. Kayaking. 1999. (Radical Sports Ser.). 32p. (J). (gr. 5-7). lib. bdg. 24.22 (978-1-57572-943-5(1)) Heinemann Library.

Salas, Laura Purdie. Canoeing. (J). 2008. (***978-1-4296-0816-9(1))***; 2002. (Illus.). 48p. (gr. 3-4). lib. bdg. 21.26 (978-0-7368-1055-5(2) , Capstone High-Interest Bks.) Capstone Pr., Inc.

Slade, Suzanne. Let's Go Canoeing & Kayaking. 2007. (Adventures Outdoors Ser.). (Illus.). 32p. (J). (gr. 4-6). lib. bdg. 23.95 (978-1-4042-3649-3(X) , PowerKids Pr.) Rosen Publishing Group, Inc., The.

Tobin, Jennifer & Tobin, Adriana. ABCs of the BWCAW: A Fun Guide to the Boundary Waters Canoe Area Wilderness. Tobin, Jennifer, photos by. 2003. (Illus.). 60p. (YA). bds. 17.95 (978-0-9742555-0-7(5)) MyHandiwork.

CANOES AND CANOEING—FICTION

Ballantyne, Michael. Blown to Bits or the Lonely Man of Rakat. 2006. 36.99 (***978-1-4280-4221-6(0))***; pap. 30.99 (***978-1-4280-4226-1(1)***) IndyPublish.com.

Ballantyne, R. M. Blown to Bits; or, the Lonely Man of Rak. 2006. pap. (***978-1-4065-0515-3(3)***) Dodo Pr.

Barber-Starkey, Joe. Jason's New Dugout Canoe. Montpellier, Paul, illus. unabr. ed. 32p. (J). (978-1-55017-229-4(8)) Harbour Publishing Co., Ltd.

Berenstain, Stan & Berenstain, Jan. The Berenstain Bear Scouts & the White-Water Mystery. 1999. (Berenstain Bear Scouts Ser.). 32p. (J). (gr. 3-6). pap. 3.50 (978-0-590-56522-6(2)) Scholastic, Inc.

—The Berenstain Bear Scouts & the White-Water Mystery. 1999. (Berenstain Bear Scouts Ser.). (J). (gr. 3-6). (978-0-606-16598-3(3)) Tandem Library Bks.

Brown, Don. Our Time on the River. 2003. 144p. (J). (gr. 7-9). tchr. ed. 15.00 (978-0-618-31116-3(5)) Houghton Mifflin Co. Trade & Reference Div.

Casanova, Mary. One Dog Canoe. Goodrich, Carter, illus. 1999. (978-0-7894-2582-9(3)) Dorling Kindersley Publishing, Inc.

—One-Dog Canoe. Hoyt, Ard, illus. 2003. 32p. (J). (ps-1). 16.50 (978-0-374-35638-5(6) , Farrar, Straus & Giroux (BYR)) Farrar, Straus & Giroux.

Charlie Canoe & Other Boats, Too. 2006. (J). (978-0-9755348-2-3(3)) Kids Life Pr.

Clark, Brenda, illus. Franklin's Canoe Trip. 2002. (Franklin Ser.). 12.40 (978-1-4046-0324-0(7)) Book Wholesalers, Inc.

Drawson, Blair. All along the River. Drawson, Blair, illus. 2003. (Illus.). 36p. (J). (ps-2). 16.95 (978-0-88899-546-9(6)) Groundwood Bks. CAN. *Dist:* Perseus Distribution.

Dygard, Thomas J. River Danger. 1998. 160p. (J). (gr. 7 up). 16.99 (978-0-688-14852-2(2)) HarperCollins Pubs.

Entz, Susan & Galarza, Sheri. How the Canoe Got Its Sail. Hale, Bruce, illus. 1999. (Hawaiian Values Ser.: Vol. 2). 24p. (J). (ps-2). pap. 4.95 (978-1-57306-088-2(7)) Bess Pr., Inc.

Fleck, Earl. Chasing Fire: Danger in Canoe Country. 2002. (Illus.). 160p. pap. 12.95 (978-0-930100-53-7(0)) Holy Cow! Pr.

Frenette, Liza. Dangerous Falls Ahead: An Adirondack Canoeing Adventure. Gillis, Jane, illus. 2001. (J). pap. 11.95 (978-0-925168-79-5(3)) North Country Bks., Inc.

Garner, Ron. One Last Chance: Trapped by a Blowdown. 2007. 240p. (YA). per. 8.95 (***978-1-59193-211-6(4)***) Adventure Pubns., Inc.

Gonzalez, Victoria Ortiz. En Piragua Por el Sella. 1998. (SPA.). (gr. 7-12). lib. bdg. 14.10 (978-0-613-80704-3(9)) Tandem Library Bks.

Graves, Damien. The Deadly Catch. 2008. (Midnight Library: Vol. 8). 176p. (J). pap. 5.99 (***978-0-439-89395-4(X)*** , Scholastic Paperbacks) Scholastic, Inc.

Hobbs, William. Ghost Canoe. 2002. (Illus.). (J). 14.47 (978-0-7587-6516-1(9)) Book Wholesalers, Inc.

—Ghost Canoe. 2004. 195p. (J). (gr. 5-9). pap. 38.00 incl. audio (978-0-8072-0450-4(1) , Listening Library) Random Hse. Audio Publishing Group.

—River Thunder. 1999. (978-0-606-15817-6(0)) Tandem Library Bks.

—Wild Man Island. 192p. (J). (gr. 5 up). 2003. pap. 5.99 (978-0-380-73310-1(2) , Harper Trophy); 2002. (Illus.). 19.99 (978-0-688-17473-6(6)); 2002. (Illus.). lib. bdg. 16.89 (978-0-06-029810-4(3)) HarperCollins Pubs.

Lamberti, B. J. Nelson Paige & the Treasure Trove. 2006. 174p. per. 12.95 (978-1-59886-193-8(X)) Tate Publishing & Enterprises, L.L.C.

Matthews, T. J. The Canoeing Safari. Rheburg, Judy, illus. 2004. (J). (978-0-938978-35-0(7)) Wycliffe Bible Translators.

Nixon-Roulet, Mary F. Kalitan Our Little Alaskan Cousin. 2004. reprint ed. pap. 15.95 (978-1-4191-2838-7(8)); pap. 1.99 (978-1-4192-2838-4(2)) Kessinger Publishing, LLC.

Panagopoulos, Janie Lynn. Mark of the Bear Claw. 2004. (J). 15.95 (978-0-938682-78-3(4)) River Road Pubns., Inc.

Paulsen, Gary. Canoe Days. Paulsen, Ruth Wright, illus. 2001. 32p. (J). (ps-3). reprint ed. pap. 6.99 (978-0-440-41441-4(5) , Dragonfly Bks.) Random Hse. Children's Bks.

Trout, Richard. Sign of the Dragon. 2007. (J). 15.95 (***978-1-58980-476-0(7)***) Pelican Publishing Co., Inc.

Weaver, Jenny. Following the Raven. 2003. 113p. (YA). (gr. 5-8). pap. 14.95 (978-1-878044-91-4(5)) Mayhaven Publishing.

Withers, Pam. Camp Wild. 2006. (Orca Currents Ser.). 112p. (J). lib. bdg. 14.95 (978-1-55143-557-2(8)) Orca Bk. Pubs. USA.

CAPE COD (MASS.)

Clark, Admont G. The Boy Who Saved a Cape Cod Town: And Other Cape Cod Stories. Fraser, Richard, illus. 2006. (YA). pap. 12.95 (978-0-9785766-0-8(8)) On Cape Pubns.

Giambarba, Paul. Cape Cod Light: The Lighthouse at Dangerfield. Giambarba, Paul, illus. 2000. (J). per. 9.95 (978-0-9653283-3-3(3)) On Cape Pubns.

Penta, Mark, creator. Cape Cod Invasion! 2007. 17.95 (***978-1-933212-49-4(7)***) Commonwealth Editions.

Zschock, Martha Day. Journey Around Cape Cod & the Islands from A to Z. Zschock, Martha Day, illus. 1999. (Journey Around Ser.). 32p. (J). 17.95 (978-1-889833-28-6(2)) Commonwealth Editions.

CAPE COD (MASS.)—FICTION

Clark, Mary Higgins. Ghost Ship: A Cape Cod Story. Minor, Wendell, illus. 2007. 40p. (J). (gr. 1-5). 17.99 (978-1-4169-3514-8(2) , Simon & Schuster/Paula Wiseman Bks.) Simon & Schuster Children's Publishing.

Feil, Hila. Blue Moon. 2007. (Illus.). 272p. (YA). pap. 6.95 (978-0-15-205933-0(4) , Harcourt Paperbacks) Harcourt Children's Bks.

Gamble, Adam. Good Night Cape Cod. Andert, John, illus. 2005. (J). bds. 9.95 (978-0-9758502-5-1(3)) On Cape Pubns.

—Good Night Cape Cod. Andert, John, illus. 2007. (Good Night Our World Ser.). 16p. (J). bds. 9.95 (***978-1-60219-004-7(6)***) Our World of Books.

Holland, Robert. The Black Queen. 2003. (Books Boys Want to Read). 220p. (J). pap. 12.00 (978-0-9720922-1-0(8)) Frost Hollow Pubs., LLC.

Johnson, Angela. Looking for Red. 128p. (YA). 2003. (Illus.). pap. 8.95 (978-0-689-86388-2(8) , Simon Pulse); 2002. (gr. 7 up). 15.95 (978-0-689-83253-6(2)) Simon & Schuster Children's Publishing.

—Looking for Red. 2003. (gr. 7-12). lib. bdg. 13.00 (978-0-613-73436-3(X)) Tandem Library Bks.

—Looking for Red. l.t. ed. 2003. 117p. (J). 24.95 (978-0-7862-5603-7(6)) Thorndike Pr.

Murphy, T. M. The Secrets of Belltown. 2001. (Belltown Mystery Ser.: Vol. 1). 176p. (J). (gr. 4-7). pap. 9.95 (978-1-880158-34-0(5)) Townsend, J.N. Publishing.

—The Secrets of Cranberry Beach. 2001. (Belltown Mystery Ser.). (Illus.). 156p. (J). 9.95 (978-1-880158-36-4(1)) Townsend, J.N. Publishing.

—The Secrets of Pilgrim Pond. 2001. (Belltown Mystery Ser.). 144p. (J). (gr. 4-7). pap. 9.95 (978-1-880158-39-5(6)) Townsend, J.N. Publishing.

Nelson, Blake. They Came from Below. 2007. 304p. (YA). (gr. 8 up). 17.95 (***978-0-7653-1423-9(1)*** , Tor Teen) Doherty, Tom Assocs., LLC.

Paratore, Coleen. Catching the Sun. 2010. (J). (978-0-618-45780-9(1)) Houghton Mifflin Co.

—The Cupid Chronicles. 2006. (Wedding Planner's Daughter Ser.). 224p. (J). 15.95 (978-1-4169-0867-8(6) , Simon & Schuster Children's Publishing) Simon & Schuster Children's Publishing.

Paratore, Coleen Murtagh. The Cupid Chronicles. 2008. (Wedding Planner's Daughter Ser.). 224p. (J). pap. 5.99 (***978-1-4169-5484-2(8)*** , Aladdin) Simon & Schuster Children's Publishing.

—The Wedding Planner's Daughter. 2005. (Wedding Planner's Daughter Ser.). 208p. (J). 15.95 (978-0-689-87340-9(9)) Simon & Schuster Children's Publishing.

Paratore, Coleen Murtagh. Willa by Heart. 2008. (Wedding Planner's Daughter Ser.). 240p. (J). 15.99 (***978-1-4169-4076-0(6)***) Simon & Schuster Children's Publishing.

Rue, Nancy N. The Caper. 2000. (Christian Heritage Ser.). (Illus.). 192p. (J). (gr. 3-7). pap. 5.99 (978-1-56179-837-7(1)) Bethany Hse. Pubs.

When Santa Claus Met Sandy Claws: A Cape Cod Christmas Story. 2002. (Illus.). 64p. (978-0-9669240-1-5(0)) Paine Wolf Productions.

Wittlinger, Ellen. Razzle. 2001. (Illus.). 256p. (J). (gr. 7-10). 17.00 (978-0-689-83565-0(5)) Simon & Schuster Children's Publishing.

—Razzle. 2003. (gr. 7-12). lib. bdg. 16.45 (978-0-613-61811-3(4)) Tandem Library Bks.

CAPITAL PUNISHMENT

Day, Nancy. The Death Penalty for Teens: A Pro/Con Issue. 2000. (Hot Pro/Con Issues Ser.). (Illus.). 64p. (YA). (gr. 6-12). lib. bdg. 27.93 (978-0-7660-1370-4(7)) Enslow Pubs., Inc.

Gottfried, Ted. The Death Penalty: Justice or Legalized Murder? 2002. (Single Titles Ser.). (Illus.). 144p. (gr. 7 up). lib. bdg. 24.90 (978-0-7613-2155-2(1) , Twenty-First Century Bks.) Lerner Publishing Group.

Grabowski, John F. The Death Penalty. 1998. (Overview Ser.). (Illus.). 96p. (YA). (gr. 6-9). lib. bdg. 29.95 (978-1-56006-371-1(8) , LML00902-177756, Lucent Bks.) Thomson Gale.

Kerrigan, Michael. Death Row & Capital Punishment. 2003. (Crime & Detection Ser.). (Illus.). 96p. (J). (gr. 7 up). lib. bdg. (978-1-59084-375-8(4)) Mason Crest Pubs.

Marzilli, Alan. Capital Punishment. 2003. (Point/Counterpoint Ser.). (Illus.). 112p. (gr. 9-13). 32.95 (978-0-7910-7369-8(6)) ; pap. 15.95 (978-0-7910-7505-0(2)) Facts On File, Inc. (Chelsea Hse.).

McLane, William. Furman vs. Georgia. 2001. (Famous Trials Ser.). (Illus.). 112p. (J). (gr. 7-10). lib. bdg. 29.95 (978-1-56006-470-1(6) , LML00902-177835, Lucent Bks.) Thomson Gale.

Meister, Deborah. What Catholic Teens Should Know about Capital Punishment. Larkin, Jean, ed. 2003. (What Catholic Teens Should Know Ser.). (Illus.). 8p. (YA). 7.95 (978-0-89837-193-2(7) , 440610) Pflaum Publishing Group.

Roensch, Greg. Furman V. Georgia: Cruel & Unusual Punishment. 2007. (Great Supreme Court Decisions Ser.). 112p. (J). (gr. 5-8). 30.00 (978-0-7910-9382-5(4) , Chelsea Hse.) Facts On File, Inc.

Rooney, Anne. Capital Punishment. 2005. (Face the Facts Ser.). (Illus.). 56p. (J). (gr. 4-6). lib. bdg. 31.36 (978-1-4109-1067-7(9)) Harcourt Schl. Pubs.

Smith, Rich. Eighth Amendment: The Right to Mercy. 2007. (Bill of Rights Ser.). (ENG., Illus.). 32p. (J). (gr. 4-8). lib. bdg. 25.65 (***978-1-59928-920-5(2)*** , ABDO & Daughters) ABDO Publishing Co.

Stearman, Kaye. The Death Penalty. 2007. (J). lib. bdg. (***978-1-4042-3752-0(6)*** , Rosen Central) Rosen Publishing Group, Inc., The.

Stefoff, Rebecca. Furman v. Georgia: Debating the Death Penalty. 2007. (Supreme Court Milestones Ser.). 144p. (J). (gr. 9 up). lib. bdg. 39.93 (***978-0-7614-2583-0(7)*** , Benchmark Bks.) Cavendish, Marshall Corp.

Streissguth, Thomas. The Death Penalty: Debating Capital Punishment. 2002. (Issues in Focus Ser.). (Illus.). 112p. (YA). (gr. 6-12). lib. bdg. 26.60 (978-0-7660-1688-0(9)) Enslow Pubs., Inc.

Symonette, Craig. The Death Penalty. Cannizzo, Karen A., ed. 1999. (Conversations with Teens Ser.). 16p. (YA). pap. 7.95 (978-0-937997-62-8(5) , 3826) Pflaum Publishing Group.

Torr, James D. Problems of Death. 2000. (Opposing Viewpoints Ser.). (Illus.). 189p. (YA). (gr. 10-12). pap. 24.95 (978-0-7377-0349-8(0)); 36.20 (978-0-7377-0350-4(4)) Thomson Gale. (Greenhaven Pr., Inc.).

CAPITALISM

see also Socialism

Downing, David & Tames, Richard. Capitalism. 2003. (Political & Economic Systems Ser.). (Illus.). 64p. (YA). (gr. 5-8). lib. bdg. 28.50 (978-1-4034-0315-5(5)) Heinemann Library.

Grant, R. G. Capitalism. 2001. (Ideas of the Modern World Ser.). (Illus.). 64p. (YA). (gr. 7-9). lib. bdg. 25.69 (978-0-7398-3161-8(5)) Raintree.

—Capitalism. 2001. (Ideas of the Modern World Ser.). (Illus.). 64p. (J). (978-0-7502-2750-6(8)) Steck-Vaughn.

—Protesting Capitalism. 2003. (Ideas of the Modern World Ser.). (Illus.). 64p. (J). lib. bdg. 28.56 (978-0-7398-6414-2(9)) Raintree.

Hess, Karl. Capitalism for Kids: Growing up to Be Your Own Boss. rev. ed. 2006. 196p. (J). pap. 8.95 (978-0-942617-35-1(5)) Bluestocking Pr.

Tillema, Juliana O. The Young Zillionaire's Guide to Producing Goods & Services. 2000. (Be a Zillionaire Ser.). (Illus.). 48p. (YA). (gr. 5-8). lib. bdg. 23.95 (978-0-8239-3260-3(5) , ZIPROD, Rosen Central) Rosen Publishing Group, Inc., The.

CAPITALISTS AND FINANCIERS

Burgan, Michael. J. Pierpont Morgan: Industrialist & Financier. 2006. (J). (978-0-7565-1890-5(3)) Compass Point Bks.

Kishel, Ann-Marie. Cashier. 2007. (First Step Nonfiction Ser.). (J). pap. (978-0-8225-6843-8(8)) Lerner Publishing Group.

Lupo, Tamar. Warren Buffet. 2007. (J). (***978-1-59036-651-6(4)); *978-1-59036-652-3(2)***) Weigl Pubs., Inc.

Mara, Wil. Henry Ford. (Rookie Biographies Ser.). (Illus.). (J). 2004. 31p. (gr. 1-2). pap. 4.95 (978-0-516-27917-6(3)); 2003. 32p. 20.50 (978-0-516-25863-8(X)) Scholastic Library Publishing. (Children's Pr.).

Parker, Lewis K. J. Pierpont Morgan & Wall Street. 2003. (Reading Power Ser.). (Illus.). 24p. (J). lib. bdg. 17.25 (978-0-8239-6449-9(3) , PowerKids Pr.) Rosen Publishing Group, Inc., The.

Ryan, Bernard. Warren Buffett: Financier. 2005. (Ferguson Career Biographies Ser.). (Illus.). 144p. (J). (gr. 6-12). 25.00 (978-0-8160-5894-5(6) , Ferguson Publishing Co.) Facts On File, Inc.

Vickers, Rebecca. Asa Candler: The Founder of Coca-Cola. 2005. (Lives & Times Ser.). (Illus.). 32p. (J). (gr. 1-2). lib. bdg. 24.21 (978-1-4034-6343-2(3)) Heinemann Library.

—Asa Candler: The Man Who Brought Us Coca-Cola. 2005. (Illus.). 32p. pap. (978-1-4034-6357-9(3)) Heinemann Library.

CAPITALIZATION (FINANCE)

see Securities

CAPTAIN UNDERPANTS (FICTITIOUS CHARACTER)—FICTION

Pilkey, Dav. The Adventures of Captain Underpants: An Epic Novel. ed. 2005. (Captain Underpants Ser.: No. 1). (Illus.). 124p. (J). lib. bdg. 15.00 (978-1-59054-680-2(6)) Fitzgerald Bks.

—The Adventures of Captain Underpants: An Epic Novel. 2004. (Captain Underpants Ser.: No. 1). (J). lib. bdg. 19.95 (978-0-439-68434-7(X) , Scholastic, Inc.) Scholastic, Inc.

—Las Aventuras del Capitan Calzoncillos. 2000. (Captain Underpants Ser.: No. 1). (SPA., Illus.). 126p. (J). 10.95 (978-84-348-7047-5(9)) SM Ediciones ESP. *Dist:* Distribooks, Inc.

—Las Aventuras del Capitan Calzoncillos. 2002. (Captain Underpants Ser.: No. 1). (SPA.). 128p. (J). (ps-4). pap. 4.99 (978-0-439-22648-6(1) , SO3077, Scholastic en Espanol) Scholastic, Inc.

—El Capitan Calzoncillos y el Ataque de los Inodoros Parlantes. 2002. (Captain Underpants Ser.). (SPA.). 144p. (J). (ps). pap. 4.99 (978-0-439-31736-8(3) , SO31151, Scholastic en Espanol) Scholastic, Inc.

—El Capitan Calzoncillos y la Furia de la Supermujer Macroelastica. 2003. (Captain Underpants Ser.). (SPA., Illus.). 176p. (J). (gr. 2-5). pap. 4.99 (978-0-439-53820-6(3) , Scholastic en Espanol) Scholastic, Inc.

—The Captain Underpants Set: The Adventures of Captain Underpants; Captain Underpants & the Attack of the Talking Toilets; Captain Underpants & the Invasion of the Incredibly Naughty Cafeteria Ladies from Outer Space; Captain Underpants & the Perilous Plot of Professor Poopypants, 4 vols. 2000. (Captain Underpants Ser.: Nos. 1-4). (J). (gr. 2-5). pap. 19.95 (978-0-439-22700-1(3) , Blue Sky Pr., The) Scholastic, Inc.

—Captain Underpants & the Attack of the Talking Toilets. ed. 2005. (Captain Underpants Ser.: No. 2). (Illus.). 140p. (J). lib. bdg. 15.00 (978-1-59054-657-4(1)) Fitzgerald Bks.

—Captain Underpants & the Attack of the Talking Toilets. (Captain Underpants Ser.: No. 2). (J). 2004. lib. bdg. 19.95 (978-0-439-68436-1(6) , Scholastic, Inc.); 1999. (Illus.). 144p. (gr. 2-5). pap. 16.95 (978-0-590-63136-5(5) , Blue Sky Pr., The) Scholastic, Inc.

—Captain Underpants & the Attack of the Talking Toilets. Pilkey, Dav, illus. 1999. (Captain Underpants Ser.: No. 2). (Illus.). 144p. (J). (gr. 2-5). pap. 4.99 (978-0-590-63427-4(5)) Scholastic, Inc.

—Captain Underpants & the Attack of the Talking Toilets. 1999. (Captain Underpants Ser.: No. 2). (Illus.). (J). (gr. 2-5). 11.64 (978-0-606-15830-5(8)); (gr. 3-6). lib. bdg. 13.00 (978-0-613-11382-3(9)) Tandem Library Bks.

—Captain Underpants & the Big, Bad Battle of the Bionic Booger Boy Pt. 1: The Night of the Nasty Nostril Nuggets. ed. 2005. (Captain Underpants Ser.: No. 6). (Illus.). 176p. (J). lib. bdg. 15.00 (978-1-59054-682-6(2)) Fitzgerald Bks.

—Captain Underpants & the Big, Bad Battle of the Bionic Booger Boy Pt. 1: The Night of the Nasty Nostril Nuggets. Pilkey, Dav, illus. 2003. (Captain Underpants Ser.: Bk. 6). (Illus.). 176p. (J). 4.99 (978-0-439-37610-5(6) , Blue Sky Pr., The) Scholastic, Inc.

—Captain Underpants & the Big, Bad Battle of the Bionic Booger Boy Pt. 2: The Revenge of the Ridiculous Robo-Boogers. Pilkey, Dav, illus. 2003. (Captain Underpants Ser.). (Illus.). 176p. (J). (gr. 3-6). 4.99 (978-0-439-37612-9(2)); pap. 16.95 (978-0-439-37611-2(4)) Scholastic, Inc. (Blue Sky Pr., The).

—Captain Underpants & the Invasion of the Incredibly Naughty Cafeteria Ladies from Outer Space: And the Subsequent Assault of the Equally Evil Lunchroom Zombie Nerds. ed. 2005. (Captain Underpants Ser.: No. 3). (Illus.). 144p. (J). lib. bdg. 15.00 (978-1-59054-681-9(4)) Fitzgerald Bks.

—Captain Underpants & the Invasion of the Incredibly Naughty Cafeteria Ladies from Outer Space: And the Subsequent Assault of the Equally Evil Lunchroom Zombie Nerds. Pilkey, Dav, illus. 1999. (Captain Underpants Ser.: No. 3). (Illus.). 144p. (J). (gr. 2-5). 4.99 (978-0-439-04996-2(2) , Blue Sky Pr., The) Scholastic, Inc.

—Captain Underpants & the Invasion of the Incredibly Naughty Cafeteria Ladies from Outer Space: And the Subsequent Assault of the Equally Evil Lunchroom Zombie Nerds. 1999. (Captain Underpants Ser.: No. 3). (Illus.). 134p. (J). (gr. 2-5). pap. 16.95 (978-0-439-04995-5(4) , Blue Sky Pr., The) Scholastic, Inc.

—Captain Underpants & the Invasion of the Incredibly Naughty Cafeteria Ladies from Outer Space: And the Subsequent Assault of the Equally Evil Lunchroom Zombie Nerds. 1999. (Captain Underpants Ser.: No. 3). (J). (gr. 2-5). 11.64 (978-0-606-17274-5(2)) Tandem Library Bks.

—Captain Underpants & the Perilous Plot of Professor Poopypants. ed. 2005. (Captain Underpants Ser.: No. 4). (Illus.). 156p. (J). lib. bdg. 15.00 (978-1-59054-678-9(4)) Fitzgerald Bks.

—Captain Underpants & the Perilous Plot of Professor Poopypants. 2004. (Captain Underpants Ser.: No. 4). (J). lib. bdg. 19.95 (978-0-439-68440-8(4) , Scholastic, Inc.) Scholastic, Inc.

—Captain Underpants & the Perilous Plot of Professor Poopypants. Pilkey, Dav, illus. 2000. (Captain Underpants Ser.: No. 4). (Illus.). 160p. (J). (gr. 2-5). pap. 4.99 (978-0-439-04998-6(9)); pap. 16.95 (978-0-439-04997-9(0)) Scholastic, Inc. (Blue Sky Pr., The).

—Captain Underpants & the Perilous Plot of Professor Poopypants. 2000. (Captain Underpants Ser.: No. 4). (gr. 3-6). lib. bdg. 13.00 (978-0-613-21289-2(4)); (Illus.). (J). (gr. 2-5). 11.64 (978-0-606-18526-4(7)) Tandem Library Bks.

—Captain Underpants & the Wrath of the Wicked Wedgie Woman. 2004. (Captain Underpants Ser.: No. 5). (J). lib. bdg. 19.95 (978-0-439-68441-5(2) , Scholastic, Inc.) Scholastic, Inc.

—Captain Underpants & the Wrath of the Wicked Wedgie Woman. Pilkey, Dav, illus. 2001. (Captain Underpants Ser.: No. 5). (Illus.). 176p. (J). (gr. 2-5). 4.99 (978-0-439-05000-5(6)) Scholastic, Inc.

—Captain Underpants & the Wrath of the Wicked Wedgie Woman. 2001. (Captain Underpants Ser.: No. 5). (gr. 3-6). lib. bdg. 13.00 (978-0-613-35767-8(1)); (Illus.). (J). 11.64 (978-0-606-21101-7(2)) Tandem Library Bks.

—The Captain Underpants Extra-Crunchy Book O' Fun. 2001. (Captain Underpants Ser.). (gr. 3-6). lib. bdg. 11.80 (978-0-613-32369-7(6)) Tandem Library Bks.

—The Captain Underpants Extra-Crunchy Book O' Fun 'N Games. Pilkey, Dav, illus. 2001. (Captain Underpants Ser.). (Illus.). 96p. (J). (gr. 2-5). mass mkt. 3.99 (978-0-439-26761-8(7)) Scholastic, Inc.

—The First Captain Underpants Collection: Captain Underpants & the Perilous Plot of Professor Poopypants; Captain Underpants & the Invasion of the Incredibly Naughty Cafeteria Ladies from Outer Space; Captain Underpants & the Attack of the Talking Toilets; The Adventures of Captain Underpants. 2004. (Captain Underpants Ser.). (Illus.). (J). 19.96 (978-0-439-69862-7(6)) Scholastic, Inc.

—The Second Captain Underpants Collection: The Adventures of Super Diaper Baby; Captain Underpants & the Big, Bad Battle of the Bionic Booger Boy Part 2; Captain Underpants & the Big, Bad Battle of the Bionic Booger Boy Part 1; Captain Underpants & the Wrath of the Wicked Wedgie Woman. 2004. (Captain Underpants Ser.). (Illus.). 525p. (J). (gr. 3 up). 19.96 (978-0-439-69054-6(4) , Scholastic Paperbacks) Scholastic, Inc.

—The Wrath of the Wicked Wedgie Women. Pilkey, Dav, illus. 2001. (Captain Underpants Ser.: No. 5). (Illus.). 176p. (J). (gr. 2-5). pap. 16.95 (978-0-439-04999-3(7)) Scholastic, Inc.

Pilkey, Dav, illus. The All New Captain Underpants Extra-Crunchy Book O' Fun 2. 2002. (Captain Underpants Ser.). 96p. (J). (gr. 1-5). pap. 3.99 (978-0-439-37608-2(4)) Scholastic, Inc.

—Captain Underpants & the Big, Bad Battle of the Bionic Booger Boy Pt. 1: The Night of the Nasty Nostril Nuggets. 2003. (Captain Underpants Ser.: Bk. 6). 176p. (J). pap. 16.95 (978-0-439-37609-9(2) , Blue Sky Pr., The) Scholastic, Inc.

CAR WHEELS

see Wheels

CARBINES

see Rifles

CARBON

see also Diamonds

Blashfield, Jean F. Carbon. 1999. (Sparks of Life Ser.). (Illus.). 64p. (YA). (gr. 7-8). lib. bdg. 27.12 (978-0-8172-5041-6(7)) Raintree.

Saunders, N. Carbon & the Elements of Group 14. 2003. (Periodic Table Ser.). (Illus.). 64p. (J). pap. 8.95 (978-1-4034-3516-3(2)) Heinemann Library.

—Carbon & the Group 14 Elements. 2003. (Periodic Table Ser.). (Illus.). 64p. (J). lib. bdg. 28.50 (978-1-4034-0873-0(4)) Heinemann Library.

Slade, Suzanne. The Carbon Cycle. 2007. (Illus.). 24p. (J). (978-1-4042-2389-9(4)); pap. (978-1-4042-2199-4(9)); (gr. 4-6). lib. bdg. 21.25 (978-1-4042-3490-1(X)) Rosen Publishing Group, Inc., The. (PowerKids Pr.).

Sparrow, Giles. Carbon. 1999. (Elements Ser.). (Illus.). 32p. (J). (ps-17). lib. bdg. 25.64 (978-0-7614-0878-9(9) , Benchmark Bks.) Cavendish, Marshall Corp.

Summers, Marilee. C Is for Carbon. Wojtko, Kimberlee, illus. 2004. 61p. (J). per. 24.95 (978-0-9753078-0-9(0)) MackStorm Productions, Inc.

Tocci, Salvatore. Carbon. (True Bks.). (J). 2005. (Illus.). 48p. (gr. 3-5). pap. 6.95 (978-0-516-27848-3(7)); 2004. 25.00 (978-0-516-22828-0(5)) Scholastic Library Publishing. (Children's Pr.).

Wu, Ronald W. Carbon. 2005. (Interpreting the Periodic Table Ser.). (Illus.). 48p. (J). (gr. 5-8). lib. bdg. 26.50 (978-1-4042-0155-2(6)) Rosen Publishing Group, Inc., The.

CARCINOMA

see Cancer

CARD GAMES

see Cards

CARD TRICKS

see also Fortune-Telling

Blum, Raymond. Mathemania. Sinclair, Jeff, illus. 2002. 96p. (gr. 3-7). pap. 6.95 (978-1-4027-0125-2(X)) Sterling Publishing Co., Inc.

Card Tricks. 48p. (J). Date not set. 7.98 (978-0-7525-9817-8(1)); 2002. 3.98 (978-0-7525-7635-0(6)) Parragon, Inc.

Card Tricks Kit Kit. 2004. (Illus.). 32p. (J). 8.99 (978-1-58086-455-8(4)); (gr. 2 up). 8.99 (978-1-58086-439-8(2)) EDC Publishing.

Diagram Visual. Super Little Giant Book of Card Tricks. 2007. (Illus.). 288p. (J). pap. 6.95 (***978-1-4027-3902-6(8)**) Sterling Publishing Co., Inc.

Eldin, Peter & Shone, Rob. How to Do Card Tricks. Shone, Rob, illus. 2006. (Most Excellent Book Of- Ser.). (Illus.). 32p. (J). (978-1-59604-126-4(9)) Stargazer Bks.

Ho, Oliver. Card Tricks. Garbot, David, illus. 2005. (Young Magician Ser.). 48p. (J). (ps). pap. 4.95 (978-1-4027-2807-5(7)) Sterling Publishing Co., Inc.

—Young Magician. Garbot, Dave, illus. 2005. 96p. (J). (978-1-4027-2920-1(0) , Sterling/Main St.) Sterling Publishing Co., Inc.

Klingel, Cynthia Fitterer & Noyed, Robert B. Card Tricks. 2002. (Games Around the World Ser.). (Illus.). 32p. (J). (gr. 3 up). lib. bdg. 21.26 (978-0-7565-0190-7(3)) Compass Point Bks.

Longe, Bob. Card Tricks Galore. 1999. (gr. 3-6). lib. bdg. 14.10 (978-0-613-75480-4(8)) Tandem Library Bks.

—A Little Giant Book: Card Tricks. 2007. (Illus.). 360p. (J). pap. 6.95 (***978-1-4027-4988-9(0)**) Sterling Publishing Co., Inc.

Longe, Bob. World's Best Card Tricks. 2003. (Illus.). 128p. (gr. 4-7). pap. 5.95 (978-0-8069-8233-5(0)) Sterling Publishing Co., Inc.

Magic Card Tricks. 2007. (J). 8.99 (***978-0-439-85308-8(7)**) Scholastic, Inc.

Magic Card Tricks. 2004. (Whizz Kits Ser.). (Illus.). 48p. (J). (978-1-84229-943-2(3)) Top That! Publishing PLC.

Tremain, Jon. Amazing Card Tricks. 2007. 128p. (J). (gr. 6 up). 11.99 (978-0-7641-6014-1(1)) Barron's Educational Series, Inc.

World's Greatest Kids Cards & Tricks. 2002. bds. 9.99 (978-1-931918-16-9(3)) Compass Labs.

Zenon, Paul. Cool Card Tricks: Techniques for the Advanced Magician. 2007. (J). (***978-1-4042-1085-1(7)**) Rosen Publishing Group, Inc., The.

—Simple Sleight-Of-Hand: Card & Coin Tricks for the Beginning Magician. 2007. (J). (***978-1-4042-1070-7(9)**) Rosen Publishing Group, Inc., The.

CARDIAC DISEASES

see Heart—Diseases

CARDINALS (BIRDS)

Goldish, Meish. Cardinals & Other Songbirds. World Book, Inc. Staff, ed. 2001. (World Book's Animals of the World Ser.: Set 2). (Illus.). 64p. (J). (978-0-7166-1216-2(X)) World Bk., Inc.

Murray, Julie. Cardinals. 2002. (Buddy Book Ser.). (Illus.). 24p. (J). (gr. k-4). lib. bdg. 21.35 (978-1-57765-704-0(7)) ABDO Publishing Co.

CARDS

see also Card Tricks; Fortune-Telling

Age of Dinosaurs Playing Cards. (Additional Educational Games & Activities for Children Ser.). pap. 5.00 (978-0-88079-709-2(6) , DIN54) U. S. Games Systems, Inc.

Allyson, Jackie. Chris "Jesus" Ferguson. 2008. (J). (***978-1-4222-0218-0(6)**) Mason Crest Pubs.

—Doyle "Texas Dolly" Brunson. 2008. (J). (***978-1-4222-0216-6(X)**) Mason Crest Pubs.

—Gus "The Great Dane" Hansen. 2008. (J). (***978-1-4222-0219-7(4)**) Mason Crest Pubs.

American Education Publishing Staff. Card Games. 2001. (Illus.). 36p. (J). 71.76 (978-1-56189-495-6(8) , 31068, American Education Publishing) School Specialty Publishing.

—Crazy Eights. 2003. (Brighter Child Card Games Ser.). (Illus.). 36p. (J). 2.99 (978-1-56189-456-7(7) , 31039, American Education Publishing) School Specialty Publishing.

—Go Fish. 2003. (Brighter Child Card Games Ser.). (Illus.). 36p. (J). 2.99 (978-1-56189-455-0(9) , 31038, American Education Publishing) School Specialty Publishing.

—Old Maid. 2003. (Brighter Child Card Games Ser.). (Illus.). 36p. (J). 2.99 (978-1-56189-454-3(0) , 31037, American Education Publishing) School Specialty Publishing.

Amery, Heather. Donkey Cards. Cartwright, Stephen, illus. 2004. (Farmyard Tales Card Games Ser.). 52p. (J). 8.95 (978-0-7945-0326-0(8) , Usborne) EDC Publishing.

Bagley, Val. Who Said Book of Mormon Match Game. 2004. 8.95 (978-1-57734-527-5(4)) Covenant Communications, Inc.

—Who Said Match Game: Follow the Prophet. 2004. 9.95 (978-1-59156-058-6(6)) Covenant Communications, Inc.

Bagley, Val Chadwick. Who Said Match Game: Bible Edition. 2004. 9.95 (978-1-57734-847-4(8)) Covenant Communications, Inc.

Barker, Cicely Mary. Flower Fairies Postcard Book. 2002. 64p. (J). pap. 7.99 (978-0-7232-4762-3(5) , Warne) Penguin Group (USA) Inc.

Barry, Sheila Anne, et al. Giant Book of Card Games/Giant Book of Card Tricks: Flip Book. Sterling Publishing Company Staff, ed. (Illus.). 512p. pap. 9.98 (978-1-4027-0467-3(4)) Sterling Publishing Co., Inc.

Blister Pack Staff. Phase 10 Card Game. 7.00 (978-1-57281-141-6(2) , PH8220) U. S. Games Systems, Inc.

Bustamante, Frank & Gray, Dan, eds. The Testimony of Jacob Hollow. Bustamante, Frank et al, illus. alt. ed. 2003. (YA). bds. 19.95 (978-0-9728526-0-9(3)) Third World Games, Inc.

Card Games. 48p. (J). Date not set. 7.98 (978-0-7525-9816-1(3)); 2002. 3.98 (978-0-7525-7631-2(3)) Parragon, Inc.

Cartwright, Stephen, illus. Fairytale Snap. 2005. (Snap Card Games Ser.). 52p. (J). 8.95 (978-0-7945-0905-7(3) , Usborne) EDC Publishing.

Cassidy, Maura A. Go Ask Anyone! 2003. 56p. (YA). mass mkt. (978-0-9742866-4-8(8)) Go Ask Anyone, Inc.

—Go Ask Your Girlfriends! 2003. 56p. (YA). mass mkt. (978-0-9742866-5-5(6)) Go Ask Anyone, Inc.

—Go Ask Your Grandparent! 2003. 56p. (YA). mass mkt. (978-0-9742866-2-4(1)) Go Ask Anyone, Inc.

—Go Ask Your Mother! 2003. 56p. (YA). mass mkt. (978-0-9742866-1-7(3)) Go Ask Anyone, Inc.

—Go Ask Your Teenager! 2003. 56p. (YA). mass mkt. (978-0-9742866-3-1(X)) Go Ask Anyone, Inc.

Chronicle Books Staff, ed. Let's Go! A Nick Jr. Travel Deck. 2004. (Illus.). 30p. (J). 8.95 (978-0-8118-4153-5(7)) Chronicle Bks. LLC.

Crazy Eights. 2005. 2.99 (978-0-7696-4173-7(3) , Brighter Child) School Specialty Publishing.

Daniel, Andy, et al. Bid-It! Card Game. 2003. 9.95 (978-1-929645-17-6(1)) Enginuity, LLC.

—LINX Card Game. 2003. 9.95 (978-1-929645-19-0(8)) Enginuity, LLC.

—Target Card Game. 2nd rev. ed. 1998. (Illus.). (J). (gr. 3). 9.95 (978-1-929645-05-3(8)) Enginuity, LLC.

—Target Card Game. Daniel, Sara Ellen, ed. Daniel, Sara Ellen, illus. 3rd ed. 2000. (J). (gr. 3). 9.95 (978-1-929645-10-7(4)) Enginuity, LLC.

—Target Card Game in a Tin. 2002. 9.95 (978-1-929645-15-2(5) , 1041) Enginuity, LLC.

Danson, Lesley. Princess Snap. Danson, Lesley, illus. 2007. 52p. (J). 8.99 (978-0-7945-1448-8(0) , Usborne) EDC Publishing.

Donaldson, Terry, et al, creators. The Lord of the Rings Tarot Gravity Feed Counter Display. 2004. (Illus.). 108.00 (978-1-57281-162-1(5) , DLR6) U. S. Games Systems, Inc.

Douglas, Vincent & School Specialty Publishing Staff. Go Fish. 2003. (Brighter Child Flash Cards Ser.). (Illus.). 54p. (J). (ps up). 2.99 (978-0-7696-2376-4(X) , Brighter Child) School Specialty Publishing.

—Old Maid. 2003. (Brighter Child Flash Cards Ser.). (Illus.). 54p. (J). (ps up). 2.99 (978-0-7696-2393-1(X) , Brighter Child) School Specialty Publishing.

Easy Addition War. 2005. 2.99 (978-0-7696-4174-4(1) , Brighter Child) School Specialty Publishing.

Edens, Cooper & Abrams, Sheryl. Sweet Dreams: 36 Bedtime Wishes. 2002. (Illus.). 36p. 9.95 (978-0-8118-3312-7(7)) Chronicle Bks. LLC.

Empyrean, Inc. 2004. (YA). 12.99 (978-0-9749460-1-6(X)) Versal Technologies, Inc.

Faidutti, Bruno. Terra: Game. 2004. 25.00 (978-92-3-010870-0(7)) UNESCO Publishing FRA. *Dist:* Renouf Publishing Co., Ltd.

Fitzgerald. Dragon Hunt Card Game. 8.00 (978-1-57281-098-3(X) , WDH66) U. S. Games Systems, Inc.

Flaherty, Patrick. Why Scouting? A Collection of Thoughts & Stories about Our Family's Experiences with the Boy Scout Program. McLaughlin, Pat, ed. 2004. 96p. per. 9.95 (978-0-9724178-6-0(9)) Teckni-Corp, Ltd.

Flaherty, Patrick J. Camping Challenge: Card Game for Campers. 2003. (Illus.). 54p. (YA). mass mkt. 6.95 (978-0-9724178-4-6(2)) Teckni-Corp, Ltd.

Get the Goods Card Game. 8.00 (978-1-57281-081-5(5) , GTG100) U. S. Games Systems, Inc.

Gill, Bill Pojo. Duel Masters. 2004. (Illus.). 80p. pap. 9.95 (978-1-57243-700-5(6)) Triumph Bks.

Golick, Margie. Card Games for Smart Kids. 1998. (Official Mensa Game Bks.). (Illus.). 96p. (gr. 4-7). pap. 5.95 (978-0-8069-4887-4(6)) Sterling Publishing Co., Inc.

Gulliver, A. & Cartwright, S. Snap. 2004. (Treasury of Farmyard Tales Ser.). (J). 8.95 (978-0-7945-0325-3(X)) EDC Publishing.

Harrison, Erica. Monster Snap. Harrison, Erica, illus. 2007. 52p. (J). 8.99 (978-0-7945-1449-5(9) , Usborne) EDC Publishing.

—Pirate Snap. Harrison, Erica, illus. 2007. 52p. (J). 8.99 (978-0-7945-1433-4(2) , Usborne) EDC Publishing.

Hiron. Rhombo Continuo. 12.00 (978-1-57281-110-2(2) , RCT48) U. S. Games Systems, Inc.

Holt, Deloris L. Black History Playing Card Deck: With 52 Portraits of Distinguished Black Americans. Newman, Langley, illus. (History Channel (R) Ser.). 120p. pap. 12.00 (978-1-57281-422-6(5) , HCBH55) U. S. Games Systems, Inc.

Kern Alphabet Card Games. (Illus.). 60.00 (978-1-57281-133-1(1) , DAZ12) U. S. Games Systems, Inc.

Kern, Donna. Animal Alphabet. Kern, Donna, illus. (Illus.). 60.00 (978-1-57281-296-3(6) , DAA12) U. S. Games Systems, Inc.

—Kern Alphabet Card Games. Kern, Donna, illus. (Illus.). 5.00 (978-1-57281-092-1(0) , AZ54) U. S. Games Systems, Inc.

Klutz Press Staff. Card Games 6 W/Display. 2005. (J). 83.70 (978-1-57054-287-9(2)) Klutz.

Landoll Inc. Staff, ed. Arthur Goes Fishing: Fun & Educational Game Cards. 1999. (Learn Along with Arthur Ser.). 36p. (J). (ps-3). ring bd. 2.49 (978-1-56189-516-8(4) , 31153, American Education Publishing) School Specialty Publishing.

Littlefield, Cindy A. Stampede! A Horsin' Around Card Game. 2004. (Illus.). 53p. (J). 9.95 (978-1-58017-582-1(1) , 67582, Storey Kids) Storey Publishing, LLC.

MacColl, Gail. The Book of Card Games for Little Kids. 2000. (Illus.). 128p. (J). (ps up). pap. 12.95 (978-0-7611-0708-8(8) , 10708) Workman Publishing Co., Inc.

Marshall, Todd, illus. Dinosaur Snap - Internet Referenced. 2005. (Snap Card Games Ser.). 50p. (J). 8.95 (978-0-7945-0903-3(7) , Usborne) EDC Publishing.

Match It: A Collection of Index Card Games for Learners of English. 2000. 96p. pap. 18.00 (978-0-86647-132-9(4)) Pro Lingua Assocs., Inc.

Medina, Rick. Humaliens Vol. 5: Milky Way vs. Andromeda, Special Edition. 1999. 200p. (gr. 4-7). pap. 5.99 (978-1-892587-04-6(1)) Dualstar, Inc.

Michaan, Steven. Hans Janner, Sr. Playing Cards: Boxed, Custom Designed, Deluxe Poker-Size Playing Cards. 2006. 11.95 (978-0-9748721-2-4(1)) Fish Decoy.com, Ltd.

Mother Goose Nursery Rhymes I. (Mother Goose Nursery Rhymes Ser.). (Illus.). 5.00 (978-0-88079-647-7(2) , NR541) U. S. Games Systems, Inc.

Moulton, LeArta. Do or Die Playing Cards: Learn Wild Plants & Herbs While You Play Your Favorie Card Games. 2001. (Do or Die Playing Cards). 54p. 9.95 (978-0-935596-23-6(2)) LM Pubns.

Numbers League: Adventures in Addiplication. 2006. (SPA, FRE, GER & ENG.). (J). 19.95 (***978-0-9768848-1-1(X)**) Bent Castle Workshops.

Numbers League Infinity Level Expansion. 2007. (J). 9.95 (***978-0-9768848-3-5(6)**) Bent Castle Workshops.

Ouija Oracle Card Game. 2004. 12.00 (978-1-57281-047-1(5) , OUJ52); 72.00 (978-1-57281-135-5(8) , DOUJ6) U. S. Games Systems, Inc.

Peleg Pete's Deck of Royal Rogues: Pirate Playing Cards. 2007. (YA). (***978-0-9768848-2-8(8)**) Bent Castle Workshops.

Phase 10 Card Game. 7.00 (978-1-57281-140-9(4) , PH9225); 84.00 (978-1-57281-143-0(9) , DPH12) U. S. Games Systems, Inc.

Quinn, Vernon. 50 Card Games for Children. 2005. (J). pap. 14.95 (978-0-911845-18-1(6)) Neumann Pr., The.

Rain Forest Card Games. (Additional Educational Games & Activities for Children Ser.). 10.00 (978-1-57281-307-6(5) , RF48); 60.00 (978-1-57281-338-0(5) , DRF6) U. S. Games Systems, Inc.

Rau, Dana Meachen. Card Games. 2004. (Games Around the World Ser.). 32p. (J). (gr. 3 up). lib. bdg. 22.60 (978-0-7565-0675-9(1)) Compass Point Bks.

Reynolds, Charles. Card Magic. 6.95 (978-1-59093-001-4(0) , Eager Minds Pr.) Warehousing & Fulfillment Specialists, LLC (WFS, LLC).

Richard, Elaine. 10 Critical Thinking Card Games: Easy-to-Play, Reproducible Card & Board Games That Boost Kids' Critical Thinking Skills-and Help Them Succeed on Tests. 2005. (Illus.). 64p. (ps-7). pap. 12.99 (978-0-439-66542-1(6) , Teaching Resources) Scholastic, Inc.

—10 Vocabulary Card Games: Easy-to-Play, Reproducible Card & Board Games That Boost Kids' Vocabulary-and Help Them Succeed on Tests. 2005. (Illus.). 64p. (ps-k). pap. 12.99 (978-0-439-51378-4(2) , Teaching Resources) Scholastic, Inc.

School Specialty Publishing. Go Fish. 2006. (Brighter Child Flash Cards Ser.). 54p. (J). 2.99 (978-0-7696-4839-2(8) , Brighter Child) School Specialty Publishing.

School Zone Publishing Company Staff. Crazy Eights. rev. ed. 1999. (Game Cards Ser.). 56p. (J). 2.79 (978-0-88743-274-3(3) , 05017) School Zone Publishing Co.

—Five-State Rummy. 1999. (Game Cards Ser.). (J). 2.79 (978-0-88743-225-5(5) , 05019) School Zone Publishing Co.

—Readiness Fun. 2000. (Flash Cards 4-Pack Ser.). (J). 12.99 (978-0-88743-816-5(4) , 04033) School Zone Publishing Co.

—Reading Fun. 2000. (Flash Cards 4-Pack Ser.). (J). 12.99 (978-0-88743-814-1(8) , 04031) School Zone Publishing Co.

Seelig, Tina L. Active Earth Cards. 2000. (Illus.). 61p. (J). (gr. k up). 9.95 (978-0-8118-2883-3(2)) Chronicle Bks. LLC.

—Human Body Cards. 2005. (Illus.). 61p. (J). (ps-17). 9.95 (978-0-8118-4671-4(7)) Chronicle Bks. LLC.

—United States Cards. 2005. (Illus.). 61p. (J). (ps-17). 9.95 (978-0-8118-4670-7(9)) Chronicle Bks. LLC.

—Wild Weather Cards: Games for Your Brain. 2000. (Illus.). 61p. (J). (gr. k up). 9.95 (978-0-8118-2882-6(4)) Chronicle Bks. LLC.

Sheinwold, Alfred, et al. The Little Giant Book of Card Games. Sterling Publishing Company Staff, ed. 2003. (Illus.). 352p. pap. 6.95 (978-1-4027-0286-0(8)) Sterling Publishing Co., Inc.

Simons, Rae. Texas Hold'em: The Learning Curve of Life. 2008. (J). (***978-1-4222-0229-6(1)**) Mason Crest Pubs.

Smith, Dan & Nickoloff, Michael, eds. Portable Adventures: 8th Grade. Smith, Dan, illus. 2003. (YA). bds. 12.95 (978-0-9728526-2-3(X)) Third World Games, Inc.

—Portable Adventures: Lair of the Rat King. Smith, Dan, illus. 2003. (YA). bds. 12.95 (978-0-9728526-1-6(1)) Third World Games, Inc.

Smith, Ryan A. Trading Cards: From Start to Finish. Tolle, Gary, photos by. 2005. (Made in the USA Ser.). (Illus.). 32p. (J). (ps-7). lib. bdg. 23.70 (978-1-4103-0374-5(8) , Blackbirch Pr., Inc.) Thomson Gale.

Solamo, Toni Carmine. 4-Unit Blister Pack. (Kids' Classics(R) Ser.). pap. 12.00 (978-1-57281-444-8(6) , CCBP168) U. S. Games Systems, Inc.

Sterling Publishing Co., Inc., ed. A Little Giant Book: Card Games. 2007. (Illus.). 360p. (J). pap. 6.95 (***978-1-4027-4980-3(5)**) Sterling Publishing Co., Inc.

Steven, Michaan. Oscar Peterson Playing Cards: Boxed, Custom-designed, Poker-size Playing Cards. 2006. 11.95 (978-0-9748721-3-1(X)) Fish Decoy.com, Ltd.

Stillinger, Doug. Castles. Klutz Editors, ed. 2005. (Illus.). 28p. (J). spiral bd. 12.95 (978-1-57054-204-6(X)) Klutz.

Stone. Lucky 13 Card Game. 10.00 (978-1-57281-200-0(1) , LK55) U. S. Games Systems, Inc.

Teddy Bear Playig Cards/Games. (Mother Goose Nursery Rhymes Ser.). 72.00 (978-1-57281-134-8(X) , DTB12) U. S. Games Systems, Inc.

Triumph Books Staff. Total Digimon. 2000. (Illus.). 112p. (J). (ps-3). pap. 12.95 (978-1-57243-371-7(X)) Triumph Bks.

Uncle Markie. Piglette Holiday Postcard Series. 2002. 10p. 5.95 (978-0-9633943-5-4(5)) Studio 403.

World's Greatest Kids Cards & Tricks. 2002. bds. 9.99 (978-1-931918-16-9(3)) Compass Labs.

CARDS, GREETING

see Greeting Cards

CARE BEARS (FICTITIOUS CHARACTERS)—FICTION

Ann Ladd, Frances. Care Bears. Johnson, Jay, illus. 2004. (Care Bears Ser.). 80p. (J). pap. 6.99 (978-0-439-66402-8(0)) Scholastic, Inc.

Bright, J. E. Care Bears: What Makes You Happy? Stein, David, illus. 2003. (Care Bears 8x8 Ser.). 24p. (J). (ps-1). pap. 3.50 (978-0-439-45543-5(X)) Scholastic, Inc.

—Care Bears: What Makes You Happy? 2003. (ps-2). lib. bdg. 11.25 (978-0-613-72172-1(1)) Tandem Library Bks.

Care, Bears. Care Bears: Plant A Garden. 2008. 24p. pap. 3.99 (***978-0-545-00908-9(1)** , Scholastic) Scholastic, Inc.

—Caring Bears: Caring Colors. 2008. 5p. bds. 5.99 (***978-0-545-00653-8(8)** , Scholastic) Scholastic, Inc.

Care Bears: It's a Rainbow Day! 2004. (Care Bears). (Illus.). 30p. (J). (978-0-7666-0947-1(2) , 55310) Modern Publishing.

Care Bears Bonus Fun Books. 2004. (Illus.). 40p. (J). 3.99 (978-0-7666-0948-8(0) , 55310) Modern Publishing.

Care Bears Coloring Books. 2004. (J). act. bk. ed. (978-0-7666-0919-8(7) , 99390); act. bk. ed. (978-0-7666-0920-4(0) , 99390); act. bk. ed. 1.29 (978-0-7666-0921-1(9) , 99390); act. bk. ed. (978-0-7666-0922-8(7) , 99390) Modern Publishing.

del Sur, Duendes. ABC: A Book about Letter. 2003. (Care Bears Ser.). (Illus.). 8p. (J). bds. 5.99 (978-0-439-51804-8(0)) Scholastic, Inc.

Flasterstein, Ran. Care Bears: Lullaby. Brighter Minds, illus. 2007. 10p. (J). bds. 12.95 incl. audio compact disk (978-1-57791-303-0(5) , Little Melody Pr.) Brighter Minds Children's Publishing.

Johnson, Jay, illus. King Funshine Bear. 2004. (Care Bears Ser.). 48p. (J). (ps-3). pap. 7.99 (978-0-439-62490-9(8)) Scholastic, Inc.

Ladd, Frances Ann. Care Bears. Johnson, Jay, illus. 2003. (Care Bears Ser.). 24p. (J). pap. 3.50 (978-0-439-45172-7(8)) Scholastic, Inc.

—How Does Your Garden Grow? Johnson, Jay, illus. 2004. (Care Bears Ser.). 32p. (J). 3.99 (978-0-439-54962-2(0)) Scholastic, Inc.

—Journey to Joke-a-Lot. Johnson, Jay, illus. movie tie-in ed. 2004. (Care Bears Ser.). 32p. (J). (gr. 2 up). pap. 3.99 (978-0-439-65102-8(6)) Scholastic, Inc.

Lee, Quilan B. Ositos Cariosos: Special Delivery. 2004. (Care Bears Ser.). 24p. (J). pap. 3.50 (978-0-439-61713-0(8) , Scholastic en Espanol) Scholastic, Inc.

Lee, Quinlan B. Christmas in Care-a-Lot. Johnson, Jay, illus. 2004. (Care Bears Ser.). 16p. (J). (ps-3). pap. 5.99 (978-0-439-66409-7(8)) Scholastic, Inc.

—Phonics: 12 Book Reading Program, 12 vols. 2006. (Illus.). (***978-0-439-78938-7(9)**); (***978-0-439-78939-4(7)**); (***978-0-439-78940-0(0)**); (***978-0-439-78941-7(9)**); (***978-0-439-78942-4(7)**); (***978-0-439-78943-1(5)**); (***978-0-439-78944-8(3)**); (***978-0-439-78945-5(1)**); (***978-0-439-78946-2(X)**); (***978-0-439-78947-9(8)**); (***978-0-439-78948-6(6)**); (***978-0-439-78949-3(4)**) Scholastic, Inc.

Lee, Quinlan B. Trick or Treat. Johnson, Jay, illus. 2004. (Care Bears Ser.). 24p. (J). pap. 3.50 (978-0-439-66398-4(9)) Scholastic, Inc.

O'Ryan, Ellie. Care Bears Christmas Wishes. Moore, Saxton, illus. 2005. (J). (***978-1-4156-8978-3(4)**) Scholastic, Inc.

Pants, S. & Brooke, Samantha. Caring & Sharing. 2007. (Care Bears Ser.). 24p. (J). pap. 3.99 (978-0-439-89468-5(9)) Scholastic, Inc.

Parent, Nancy. Care Bears: Caring Contest. Stein, David, illus. 2003. (Care Bears 8x8 Ser.). 24p. (J). (ps-1). pap. 3.50 (978-0-439-45158-1(2)) Scholastic, Inc.

—Care Bears Caring Contest. 2003. (ps-2). lib. bdg. 11.25 (978-0-613-72160-8(8)) Tandem Library Bks.

—The Day Nobody Shared. Johnson, Jay, illus. 2003. (Care Bears Ser.). 24p. (J). 3.50 (978-0-439-45157-4(4) , Scholastic Paperbacks) Scholastic, Inc.

Sander, Sonia. Busy, Busy, Sunny Day. Stein, David, illus. 2003. (Care Bears Ser.). 24p. (J). pap. 3.50 (978-0-439-53196-2(9)) Scholastic, Inc.

—Care Bears. Johnson, Jay, illus. 2004. (Care Bears Ser.). 8p. (J). bds. 5.99 (978-0-439-54961-5(2)) Scholastic, Inc.

—Care Bears: Find That Rainbow! Sticker Storybook. del Sur, Duendes, illus. 2003. (Care Bears Ser.). 16p. (J). (ps-2). pap. 5.99 (978-0-439-45176-5(0)) Scholastic, Inc.

—Care Bears: Find That Rainbow! Sticker Storybook. 2003. (ps-2). lib. bdg. 14.15 (978-0-613-72161-5(6)) Tandem Library Bks.

—Care BearsTM: Caring Rainbow. Johnson, Jay, illus. 2003. (Care Bears Ser.). 8p. (J). (ps). bds. 5.99 (978-0-439-45178-9(7)) Scholastic, Inc.

—Good Luck Bear's Special Day. 2007. (Care Bears Ser.). 24p. (J). pap. 3.99 (***978-0-439-88858-5(1)**) Scholastic, Inc.

Sander, Sonia. Who's Who? Sticker Storybook. del Sur, Duendes, illus. 2003. (Care Bears Ser.). 16p. (J). 5.99 (978-0-439-45544-2(8)) Scholastic, Inc.

Scholastic, Inc. Staff. Treasury. Swendsen, Silje, ed. 2004. (Care Bears Ser.). 192p. (J). pap. 10.99 (978-0-439-62486-2(X)) Scholastic, Inc.

Spelvin, Justin. My Best Friends. 2006. (Care Bears Ser.). 32p. (J). pap. 3.99 (978-0-439-86232-5(9) , Scholastic) Scholastic, Inc.

Tait, Katie. Catch the Christmas Spirit! 2003. (Care Bears Ser.). (Illus.). 16p. (J). bds. 4.99 (978-0-439-46023-1(9) , Scholastic Paperbacks) Scholastic, Inc.

CAREERS

see Occupations; Professions; Vocational Guidance

see subject headings with the subdivision Vocational Guidance

CAREY, WILLIAM, 1761-1834

Alex, Ben. William Carey. Rava, Giuseppe, illus. 1998. (Heroes of Faith & Courage Ser.). 50p. (gr. 3-12). reprint ed. pap. 7.99 (978-1-884543-15-9(4)) Authentic Media.

Meloche, Renee. William Carey: Bearer of Good News. 2002. (Illus.). 32p. 8.99 (978-1-57658-236-7(1)) YWAM Publishing.

CARIBBEAN AREA

Bentley, Joyce. St. Lucia. 2005. (Illus.). 32p. 18.95 (978-1-59389-227-2(6)) Chrysalis Education.

Blue, Rose & Naden, Corinne J. Exploring Central America, Mexico, & the Caribbean. 2003. (Illus.). 64p. pap. 9.50 (978-1-4109-0334-1(6)) Raintree.

Brooks, Susie. St. Lucia. 2006. (Our Lives, Our World Ser.). (J). (978-1-59389-290-6(X)) Chrysalis Education.

Dixon, Franklin W. The Caribbean Cruise Caper. 1999. (Hardy Boys Mystery Stories Ser.: No. 154). 160p. (J). (gr. 3-6). pap. 4.99 (978-0-671-02549-6(X) , Aladdin) Simon & Schuster Children's Publishing.

Graham, Ian. The Caribbean. 2002. (Country File Ser.). (Illus.). 32p. (J). lib. bdg. 24.25 (978-1-58340-205-4(5)) Smart Apple Media.

Green, Jen. Caribbean Sea & Gulf of Mexico. 2006. (Illus.). 48p. (J). pap. (978-0-8368-6280-5(5)); lib. bdg. 30.00 (978-0-8368-6272-0(4)) Stevens, Gareth Inc. (World Almanac Library).

Henderson, James D., ed. Discovering the Caribbean, 11 vols., Set. (Illus.). 64p. (YA). (gr. 5 up). lib. bdg. (978-1-59084-503-5(X)) Mason Crest Pubs.

Illsley, Linda. The Caribbean. 1999. (Food & Festivals Ser.). (Illus.). 32p. (J). (gr. 1-4). lib. bdg. 25.69 (978-0-8172-5758-3(6)) Raintree.

Katchur, Matthew & Sterngass, Jon. Spanish Settlement in North America. 2006. (Latino American History Ser.). (Illus.). 112p. (J). (gr. 5-8). 35.00 (978-0-8160-6442-7(3) , Chelsea Hse.) Facts On File, Inc.

Kaufman, Cheryl Davidson. Cooking the Caribbean Way. 2nd rev. expurg. ed. 2002. (Easy Menu Ethnic Cookbooks). (Illus.). 72p. (J). (gr. 5-12). 25.26 (978-0-8225-4103-5(3)) Lerner Publishing Group.

Malam, John. You Wouldn't Want to Be a Pirate's Prisoner! Antram, David, illus. 2002. (You Wouldn't Want to Ser.). 32p. (J). (gr. 2-5). 28.50 (978-0-531-14607-1(3)); pap. 9.95 (978-0-531-16368-9(7)) Scholastic Library Publishing. (Watts, Franklin).

—You Wouldn't Want to Be a Pirate's Prisoner! 2002. (gr. 3-6). lib. bdg. 18.75 (978-0-613-53885-5(4)) Tandem Library Bks.

Orr, Tamra. St. Lucia. 2008. (Cultures of the World Ser.). (J). lib. bdg. (***978-0-7614-2569-4(1)** , Benchmark Bks.) Cavendish, Marshall Corp.

Picayo, Mario. A Caribbean Journey from a to Y: Read & Discover What Happened to the Z. Griswold, Earleen, illus. 2007. (J). (***978-0-9725611-8-1(8)** , Campanita Bks.) Editorial Campana.

Popper, Garry. Winston in the Caribbean. Johnson, Andi, illus. 2004. 36p. (ps-7). 4.00 (978-1-84161-061-0(5)) Ravette Publishing, Ltd. GBR. *Dist:* Parkwest Pubns., Inc.

Powell, Jillian. Looking at Caribbean Countries. 2006. (Illus.). 32p. (J). pap. (***978-0-8368-7674-1(1)**); lib. bdg. (***978-0-8368-7667-3(9)**) Stevens, Gareth Inc.

Prevost, John F. Caribbean Sea. 2003. (Oceans & Seas Ser.). (Illus.). 24p. (J). (gr. k-6). lib. bdg. 21.35 (978-1-57765-096-6(4)) ABDO Publishing Co.

Silva Lee, Alfonso. My Island & I: The Nature of the Caribbean. Hayskar, Bonnie J., ed. Lago, Alexis, illus. 32p. (J). 2010. pap. 9.95 (978-1-929165-14-8(5)); 2002. (gr. 2-5). 15.95 (978-1-929165-15-5(3)) PANGAEA.

Temko, Florence. Traditional Crafts from the Caribbean. 2005. (Culture Crafts Ser.). (Illus.). 64p. (gr. 3-8). 23.93 (978-0-8225-2937-8(8)) Lerner Publishing Group.

Waters, Rosa. Bob Marley & the Wailers. 2008. (J). (***978-1-4222-0192-3(9)**) Mason Crest Pubs.

Weintraub, Aileen. Anne Bonny & Mary Read: Fearsome Female Pirates of the 18th-Century. 2002. (Library of Pirates). (Illus.). 24p. (J). (gr. 3). lib. bdg. 18.75 (978-0-8239-5795-8(0) , PowerKids Pr.) Rosen Publishing Group, Inc., The.

Wilson, Amber. Jamaica the Land. 2003. (gr. k-3). lib. bdg. 16.40 (978-0-613-82414-9(8)) Tandem Library Bks.

—Jamaica the People. 2003. (gr. 3-6). lib. bdg. 16.40 (978-0-613-84499-4(8)) Tandem Library Bks.

CARIBBEAN AREA—FICTION

Anderson, Al. Pegasus: Adventures with Bingo Borden. Kurzyca, Krystyna Emilia, illus. 2006. 77p. (J). per. 19.50 (***978-1-887250-46-7(8)**) Agora Pubns., Inc.

Applin, Barbara, ed. Carib Anth Stories for Children 1. 2006. 68p. pap. 11.95 (978-1-4050-3094-6(1)) Macmillan Caribbean GBR. *Dist:* Interlink Publishing Group, Inc.

Baglio, Ben M. Dolphin Diaries: Chasing the Dream. Lawton, Judith, illus. 2003. (Dolphin Diaries: No. 5). 160p. (J). (gr. 3-6). 4.99 (978-0-439-31951-5(X)) Scholastic, Inc.

—Dolphin Diaries: Chasing the Dream. 2003. (gr. 3-6). lib. bdg. 12.40 (978-0-613-72059-5(8)) Tandem Library Bks.

Bjerkvold, Belinda & Stevenson, Robert Louis. Treasure Island. Tod, Lluis M. & Andrada, Javier, illus. 2006. 36p. (J). lib. bdg. (***978-0-8368-7665-9(2)**) Stevens, Gareth Inc.

Buffett, Jimmy & Buffett, Savannah Jane. The Jolly Mon. Davis, Lambert, illus. 2006. 32p. (J). 17.95 (978-0-15-205786-2(2)) Harcourt Children's Bks.

Campbell, Hazel. Juice Box & Scandal. 2nd ed. 2005. (Illus.). 100p. 4.49 (978-976-8184-65-8(5)) Penguin Group (USA) Inc.

Cherry, Lynne. The Sea, the Storm, & the Mangrove Tangle. 2004. (Illus.). 40p. (J). 17.00 (978-0-374-36482-3(6) , Farrar, Straus & Giroux (BYR)) Farrar, Straus & Giroux.

Christie, Agatha. A Caribbean Mystery. 2000. (gr. 5-8). lib. bdg. 14.15 (978-0-613-57191-3(6)) Tandem Library Bks.

Cohen, Miriam. Down in the Subway. Greenberg, Melanie Hope, illus. 2003. 40p. (J). (gr. k-3). pap. 5.95 (978-1-932065-24-4(5)); 15.95 (978-1-932065-08-4(3)) Star Bright Bks., Inc.

Cooke, Trish. Hey Crazy Riddle! Shaw, Hannah, illus. 2006. 96p. pap. 6.95 (978-1-84507-378-7(9)) Lincoln, Frances Ltd. GBR. *Dist:* Perseus Distribution.

Crowe, Carole. Waiting for Dolphins. 2003. 144p. (YA). (gr. 4-6). pap. 9.95 (978-1-59078-073-2(6)); (Illus.). pap. 16.95 (978-1-56397-847-0(4)) Boyds Mills Pr.

—Waiting for Dolphins. 2003. (gr. 3-6). lib. bdg. 18.75 (978-0-613-59368-7(5)) Tandem Library Bks.

Dead Man's Chest. 2007. (Pirates of the Caribbean Ser.). 160p. pap. 4.99 (***978-1-4231-1106-1(0)**) Disney Publishing Worldwide.

Disney Press, ed. Pirates of the Caribbean Film - Box Set. rev. ed. 2007. 496p. (gr. 3-7). pap. 12.99 (***978-1-4231-0926-6(0)**) Disney Pr.

—Pirates of the Caribbean: GN - at Worlds End. rev. ed. 2007. 48p. (gr. 1). pap. 3.99 (***978-1-4231-0449-0(8)**) Disney Pr.

Disney Press Staff. The Curse of Davy Jones. 2nd rev. ed. 2006. (Pirates of the Carribean Ser.). (Illus.). 24p. (ps-1). pap. 3.50 (978-1-4231-0026-3(3)) Disney Pr.

—Dead Man's Chest. 2007. 48p. (ps-3). 12.99 incl. audio compact disk (978-1-4231-0368-4(8)) Disney Pr.

—Dead Man's Chest - Swann Song. 2nd rev. ed. 2006. (Pirates of the Carribean Ser.:). (Illus.). 24p. (ps-1). pap. 3.50 (978-1-4231-0027-0(1)) Disney Pr.

Disney Press Staff, ed. Pirates of the Caribbean: At World's End Storybook. rev. ed. 2007. 48p. (J). (gr. 1-4). 12.99 (***978-1-4231-0918-1(X)**) Disney Pr.

Dorling Kindersley Publishing Staff. Pirates of the Caribbean. 2006. (Ultimate Sticker Bks.). 16p. (J). pap. 6.99 (978-0-7566-2065-3(1)) Dorling Kindersley Publishing, Inc.

—Pirates of the Caribbean Visual Guide. 2006. (Illus.). 80p. (J). 19.99 (978-0-7566-2064-6(3)) Dorling Kindersley Publishing, Inc.

Dorros, Arthur. Isla. Kleven, Elisa, illus. 1999. Orig. Title: The Island. 40p. (J). (ps-1). pap. 6.99 (978-0-14-056505-8(1) , Puffin) Penguin Group (USA) Inc.

—Isla. 1999. Orig. Title: The Island. (J). 12.79 (978-0-606-16810-6(9)); (J). 13.79 (978-0-606-16811-3(7)); lib. bdg. 14.15 (978-0-613-14865-8(7)); (SPA.). lib. bdg. 15.30 (978-0-613-18258-4(8)) Tandem Library Bks.

—La Isla. Kleven, Elisa, illus. 1999. (Picture Puffin Ser.). (SPA.). 40p. (J). (gr. k-3). pap. 6.99 (978-0-14-056541-6(8) , DT8806, Puffin) Penguin Group (USA) Inc.

Edmonds, Lyra. An African Princess. Wilson, Anne, illus. 2004. 32p. (J). (ps-2). 15.99 (978-0-7636-2595-5(7)) Candlewick Pr.

Faye, Thomas. Pirates of the Caribbean: The Secret Files of the East India Trading Company. rev. ed. 2007. 28p. (gr. 8). 19.99 (***978-1-4231-0499-5(4)**) Disney Pr.

Ferris, Aimee. Girl Overboard. 2007. (S. A. S. S. (Students Across the Seven Seas) Ser.). 224p. (YA). (gr. 7). pap. 6.99 (978-0-14-240799-8(2) , Puffin) Penguin Group (USA) Inc.

Fontanez, Edwin. On This Beautiful Island. Fontanez, Edwin, illus. l.t. ed. 2004. (Illus.). 32p. (J). 16.95 (978-0-9640868-6-9(7) , 1241077) Exit Studio.

Gershator, David & Gershator, Phillis. Kallaloo: A Caribbean Tale. Greenseid, Diane, illus. 2005. 32p. (J). 16.95 (978-0-7614-5110-5(2)) Cavendish, Marshall Corp.

Hamilton, Tisha. Piratas del Caribe. el viaje al fin del Mundo: Pirates of the Caribbean: at the World's End. 2007. (Illus.). 38p. (J). 24.95 (***978-970-718-532-6(5)** , Silver Dolphin en Español) Advanced Marketing, S. de R. L. de C. V. MEX. *Dist:* Perseus Distribution.

Hodge, Merle. For the Life of Laetitia. 2003. 21.25 (978-0-8446-7246-5(7)) Smith, Peter Pub., Inc.

Isadora, Rachel. Caribbean Dream. Isadora, Rachel, illus. 2002. (Illus.). 32p. (J). pap. 6.99 (978-0-698-11944-4(4) , Putnam Juvenile) Penguin Group (USA) Inc.

—Caribbean Dream. 2002. (ps-2). lib. bdg. 15.30 (978-0-613-51441-5(6)) Tandem Library Bks.

Kaserman, James F. & Kaserman, Sarah Jane. The Legend of Gasparilla: A Tale for All Ages. 2000. (Illus.). 304p. (J). pap. 14.95 (978-0-9674081-1-8(3)) Pirate Publishing International.

Kidd, Rob. City of Gold. Orpinas, Jean-Paul, illus. 7th rev. ed. 2007. (Pirates of the Caribbean Ser.: Bk. 7). 128p. (gr. 3-7). pap. 4.99 (978-1-4231-0170-3(7)) Disney Pr.

Kidd, Rob. Pirates of the Caribbean: Sins of the Fathers - Jack Sparrows #10. 10th rev. ed. 2007. 144p. (gr. 2-7). pap. 4.99 (***978-1-4231-0455-1(2)**) Disney Pr.

Laurie, Peter. Mauby & the Hurricane. 2007. 56p. pap. 16.00 (***978-1-4050-7718-7(2)**) Macmillan Caribbean GBR. *Dist:* Interlink Publishing Group, Inc.

Lawrence, Iain. The Buccaneers. (Illus.). 256p. (gr. 5-9). 2003. 5.99 (978-0-440-41671-5(X) , Yearling); 2001. 16.95 (978-0-385-32736-7(6) , Delacorte Bks. for Young Readers) Random Hse. Children's Bks.

—The Buccaneers. l.t. ed. 2001. (Illus.). 320p. (J). 23.95 (978-0-7862-3464-6(4)) Thorndike Pr.

—The Castaways. 2007. 256p. (YA). (gr. 7). 15.99 (***978-0-385-73090-7(X)**); lib. bdg. 18.99 (***978-0-385-90112-3(7)**) Random Hse. Children's Bks. (Delacorte Bks. for Young Readers).

Lawrence, Iain. Ghost Boy. 2002. 352p. (YA). (gr. 7). reprint ed. pap. 6.50 (978-0-440-41668-5(X) , Laurel Leaf) Random Hse. Children's Bks.

—Ghost Boy. 2002. (gr. 7-12). lib. bdg. 14.15 (978-0-613-58216-2(0)) Tandem Library Bks.

Lessac, Frane. Island Counting 1 2 3. Lessac, Frane, illus. 2007. (Illus.). 24p. (J). (gr. k-ps). bds. 6.99 (***978-0-7636-3518-3(9)**) Candlewick Pr.

Lessac, Frané. Island Counting 123. 2005. (Illus.). 24p. (J). (gr. k-ps). 12.99 (978-0-7636-1960-2(4)) Candlewick Pr.

Lopez Soria, Marisa. Los Colores de Mateo. Rogowicz, Katarzyna, illus. 2002. (Montana Encantada Ser.). (SPA.). 36p. (J). 7.50 (978-84-241-8029-4(1)) Everest de Ediciones y Distribucion, S.L. ESP. *Dist:* Lectorum Pubns., Inc.

Marcotte, Danielle & Duchesne, Bernard. La Terreur des Mers. 2001. (Roman Jeunesse Ser.). (FRE., Illus.). 96p. (J). pap. 9.95 (978-2-89021-479-8(6)) Diffusion du livre Mirabel.

McCafferty, Catherine. Dead Man's Chest. 2nd rev. ed. 2006. (Pirates of the Carribean Ser.:). (Illus.). 64p. (gr. 2-5). 8.99 (978-1-4231-0025-6(5)) Disney Pr.

Meyer, Kai. Pirate Curse. Crawford, Elizabeth D., tr. from GER. 2006. (Wave Walkers Ser.). 336p. (J). (gr. 5-9). 15.95 (978-1-4169-2421-0(3) , McElderry, Margaret K.) Simon & Schuster Children's Publishing.

Mitchell, Rita Phillips. Hue Boy. Binch, Caroline, illus. 1999. 32p. (J). (gr. k-3). pap. 11.95 (978-0-14-056354-2(7)) Penguin Bks., Ltd. GBR. *Dist:* Trafalgar Square Publishing.

Nestor, Gregg. All Hands on Deck: Become Part of a Caribbean Sailing Adventure. 2005. (Illus.). 72p. (J). (ps-7). pap. 29.00 (978-1-4208-2407-0(4)) AuthorHouse.

Nixon, Joan Lowery. Playing for Keeps. 2003. 208p. (YA). (gr. 7). pap. 5.50 (978-0-440-22867-7(0) , Laurel Leaf) Random Hse. Children's Bks.

—Playing for Keeps. 2003. (gr. 7-12). lib. bdg. 13.55 (978-0-613-64782-3(3)) Tandem Library Bks.

Owen, James A. & Owen, Jeremy. Lost Treasures of the Pirates of the Caribbean: Secret Maps, Legends, & Lore Revealed! Owen, James A., illus. 2007. 32p. (J). 16.99 (978-1-4169-3960-3(1)) Simon & Schuster Children's Publishing.

Platt, Richard. Pirates of the Caribbean Visual Guide: The Complete Visual Guide. 2007. 12p. (J). 19.99 (978-0-7566-2676-1(5)) Dorling Kindersley Publishing, Inc.

Pow, Tom. Captives. 2007. 192p. (YA). 17.95 (***978-1-59643-201-7(2)***) Roaring Brook Pr.

Random House Disney Staff. Pirates of the Caribbean: Dead Man's Chest. 2006. (Illus.). 12p. (J). (ps-1). pap. 6.99 (978-0-7364-2378-6(8) , RH/Disney) Random Hse. Children's Bks.

Redbank, Tennant. Dead Man's Chest - the Chase Is On. 2nd rev. ed. 2006. (Pirates of the Carribean Ser.). 32p. (gr. k-2). pap. 3.99 (978-1-4231-0089-8(1)) Disney Pr.

Sabatini, Rafael. The King's Messenger. 2004. reprint ed. pap. 15.95 (978-1-4191-6824-6(X) ; pap. 1.99 (978-1-4192-6824-3(4)) Kessinger Publishing, LLC.

Santomenna, Joan E. & Santomenna, Marco D. Caribbean Capers. 2003. (Illus.). 144p. (YA). (gr. 3-9). pap. 9.95 (978-0-9643407-2-5(0)) WindSpirit Publishing.

Stevenson, Robert Louis. Off to Sea Bk. 2. Comport, Sally Wern, illus. 2006. (Easy Reader Classics Ser.). 32p. (J). pap. 3.95 (978-1-4027-3298-0(8)) Sterling Publishing Co., Inc.

—Treasure Island. Winter, Milo, illus. 2002. (Illustrated Library for Children). 272p. (J). 12.99 (978-0-517-22114-3(4) , Gramercy) Random Hse. Value Publishing.

—Treasure Island. 2006. (Scholastic Classics Ser.). (Illus.). x, 205p. (J). (gr. 9-12). 25.00 (978-0-531-16961-2(8) , Watts, Franklin) Scholastic Library Publishing.

—Treasure Island Bk. 1: The Treasure Map. Comport, Sally Wern, illus. 2006. (Easy Reader Classics Ser.). 32p. (J). pap. 3.95 (978-1-4027-3297-3(X)) Sterling Publishing Co., Inc.

Stewart, Michael. Pirates of the Caribbean. Evans, Dustin, illus. 2006. 128p. (J). (gr. 3-7). pap. 9.99 (978-0-7868-4714-3(X)) Disney Pr.

Sutherland, T. T. Pirates of the Caribbean 3: Turner. Disney Press Staff, ed. 2007. 24p. (ps-2). pap. 3.99 (***978-1-4231-0376-9(9)***) Disney Pr.

Taylor, Theodore. Cayo. 2001. (SPA.). (gr. 3-6). lib. bdg. 17.05 (978-0-613-44195-7(8)) Tandem Library Bks.

—Timothy of the Cay. 2007. (Illus.). 176p. (YA). pap. 5.95 (978-0-15-206320-7(X) , Harcourt Paperbacks) Harcourt Children's Bks.

Taylor, Theodore & Gonzalez, Tomas. El Cavo. 2000. (SPA., Illus.). 106p. (J). (gr. k-2). 9.50 (978-84-279-3250-0(2) , NG0873) Lectorum Pubns., Inc.

Trimble, Irene. Dead Man's Chest. 2nd novel rev. ed. 2006. (Pirates of the Caribbean Ser.). (Illus.). 160p. (gr. 3-7). pap. 4.99 (978-1-4231-0024-9(7)) Disney Pr.

CARIBOU

Caribou: Individual Title, 6 vols. 16p. (gr. 3 up). 36.00 (978-0-7635-9686-6(8)) Rigby Education.

French, Vivian. Caribou Journey. Flather, Lisa, illus. 2003. (Fantastic Journeys Ser.). 32p. (J). (978-1-84089-216-1(1) , Zero to Ten, Limited) Evans Publishing Group.

Frost, Helen. Caribou. 2006. (Polar Animals Ser.). (Illus.). 24p. (J). (978-0-7368-4245-7(4)) Capstone Pr., Inc.

Hiscock, Bruce. The Big Caribou Herd: Life in the Arctic National Wildlife Refuge. Hiscock, Bruce, illus. 2003. (Illus.). 32p. (J). (gr. 2-4). 16.95 (978-1-59078-010-7(8)) Boyds Mills Pr.

Hodge, Deborah. Deer, Moose, Elk & Caribou. 1999. (J). 12.75 (978-0-606-19013-8(9)) Tandem Library Bks.

—Deer, moose, elk & caribou. 2004. (Kids Can Press Wildlife Ser.). (Illus.). 32p. (J). (gr. k-3). (978-1-55074-667-9(7)) Kids Can Pr., Ltd.

—Deer, moose, elk & caribou. Stephens, Pat, illus. 1998. (Kids Can Press Wildlife Ser.). 32p. (J). (gr. k-3). (978-1-55074-435-4(6)) Kids Can Pr., Ltd.

Miller, Debbie S. A Caribou Journey. 2000. (Illus.). (J). (978-0-606-18255-3(1)) Tandem Library Bks.

Quinlan, Susan E. Caribou. 2005. (Nature Watch Ser.). (Illus.). 48p. (J). (gr. 3-8). lib. bdg. 25.26 (978-1-57505-579-4(1)) Lerner Publishing Group.

Vogel, Julia. Caribou. McGee, John F., illus. 2004. (Our Wild World Ser.). 48p. (J). (gr. 2-5). ring bd. 10.95 (978-1-55971-813-4(7)); pap. 7.95 (978-1-55971-812-7(9)) T&N Children's Publishing. (NorthWord Bks. for Young Readers).

—Caribou. 2002. (gr. 3-6). lib. bdg. 16.40 (978-0-613-55804-4(9)) Tandem Library Bks.

—Polar Animals. McGee, John F., illus. 2004. (Our Wild World Ser.). 192p. (J). (gr. 2-5). ring bd. 16.95 (978-1-55971-832-5(3) , NorthWord Bks. for Young Readers) T&N Children's Publishing.

CARIBOU—FICTION

Coles, Michael Joseph, et al. The Land of Caring Bou. Banks, Timothy, illus. 2006. (J). (978-0-87483-814-5(2)) August Hse. Pubs., Inc.

Root, Phyllis. If You Want to See a Caribou. Meyer, Jim, illus. 2004. 32p. (J). (gr. k-3). tchr. ed. 16.00 (978-0-618-39314-5(5)) Houghton Mifflin Co. Trade & Reference Div.

CARICATURES AND CARTOONS

see Cartoons and Comics

CARILLONS

see Bells

CARLSBAD CAVERNS (N.M.)

Burnham, Brad. Carlsbad Caverns: America's Largest Underground Chamber. 2003. (Famous Caves of the World Ser.). (Illus.). 24p. (J). lib. bdg. 18.75 (978-0-8239-6256-3(3)) Rosen Publishing Group, Inc., The.

Hall, Margaret. Carlsbad Caverns National Park. 2006. (Symbols of Freedom Ser.). (Illus.). 32p. (J). (978-1-4034-7792-7(2)) Heinemann Library.

CARNEGIE, ANDREW, 1835-1919

De Capua, Sarah E. Andrew Carnegie. 2008. (J). lib. bdg. 26.00 (***978-1-60279-067-4(1)***) Cherry Lake Publishing.

Edge, Laura Bufano. Andrew Carnegie. 2004. (Lerner Biographies Ser.). (Illus.). 128p. (J). (gr. 6-12). lib. bdg. 27.93 (978-0-8225-4965-9(4)) Lerner Publishing Group.

Kent, Zachary. Andrew Carnegie: Steel King & Friend to Libraries. 1999. (Historical American Biographies Ser.). (Illus.). 128p. (YA). (gr. 6-12). lib. bdg. 26.60 (978-0-7660-1212-7(3)) Enslow Pubs., Inc.

Parker, Lewis K. Andrew Carnegie & the Steel Industry, 6 vols., Pack. (On Deck Ser.: Vol. 2). 24p. (gr. 4-5). 35.00 (978-0-7578-5847-5(3)) Rigby Education.

—Andrew Carnegie & the Steel Industry. 2003. (Reading Power Ser.). (Illus.). 24p. (J). lib. bdg. 17.25 (978-0-8239-6448-2(5) , PowerKids Pr.) Rosen Publishing Group, Inc., The.

Rau, Dana Meachen. Andrew Carnegie: Captain of Industry. 2005. (Signature Lives Ser.). (Illus.). 112p. (J). (gr. 5-7). (978-0-7565-0995-8(5) , 1244082) Compass Point Bks.

Simon, Charnan. Andrew Carnegie: Builder of Libraries. 1998. (Community Builders Ser.). (Illus.). 48p. (J). (gr. 3-5). pap. 6.95 (978-0-516-26131-7(2) , Children's Pr.) Scholastic Library Publishing.

CARNIVALS

see Festivals

CARNIVOROUS PLANTS

Batten, Mary. Hungry Plants. Mirocha, Paul, illus. 2004. (Step into Reading Ser.). 48p. (J). (gr. 2-4). pap. 3.99 (978-0-375-82533-0(9) , Random Hse. Bks. for Young Readers) Random Hse. Children's Bks.

—Hungry Plants. 2000. (Road to Reading Ser.). (Illus.). (J). 10.79 (978-0-606-20438-5(5)) Tandem Library Bks.

Collard, Sneed B., III. Tough Terminators. 2004. (It's Nature! Ser.). (Illus.). 32p. (J). (gr. 3-6). pap. 7.95 (978-1-55971-633-8(9) , Creative Publishing International) Quayside.

Fowler, Allan. Plants That Eat Animals. 2001. (Rookie Read-About Science Ser.). (Illus.). 32p. (J). (gr. 1-2). pap. 4.95 (978-0-516-27309-9(4)); 19.50 (978-0-516-21683-6(X)) Scholastic Library Publishing. (Children's Pr.).

—Plants That Eat Animals. 2001. (gr. k-3). lib. bdg. 12.95 (978-0-613-54637-9(7)) Tandem Library Bks.

Johnson, Rebecca L. Carnivorous Plants. 2007. (Nature Watch Ser.). (Illus.). 48p. (J). 25.26 (978-0-8225-6563-5(3) , Lerner Pubns.) Lerner Publishing Group.

Kudlinski, Kathleen V. Venus Flytraps. Wexler, Jerome, photos by. 1998. (Early Bird Nature Bks.). (Illus.). 48p. (J). (gr. 2-4). lib. bdg. 25.26 (978-0-8225-3015-2(5) , Lerner Pubns.) Lerner Publishing Group.

Kuhn, Dwight & Pascoe, Elaine. Carnivorous Plants. 2004. (Illus.). 48p. (J). (gr. 2-4). 24.95 (978-1-4103-0309-7(8) , Blackbirch Pr., Inc.) Thomson Gale.

Pascoe, Elaine. How & Why Plants Eat Insects. Kupperstein, Joel, ed. Kuhn, Dwight, photos by. 2000. (How & Why Ser.). (Illus.). 16p. (J). (gr. 1-3). pap. 2.99 (978-1-57471-667-2(0) , 2974) Creative Teaching Pr., Inc.

—Plants Eat Insects. Kuhn, Dwight, photos by. 2002. (Springboards into Science Ser.). (Illus.). 24p. (J). (gr. 1 up). lib. bdg. 20.67 (978-0-8368-3011-8(3)) Stevens, Gareth Inc.

Pike, Katy. Plants That Bite Back. 2005. (Real Deal Ser.). (Illus.). 32p. (J). 18.50 (978-0-7910-8429-8(9) , Chelsea Hse.) Facts On File, Inc.

Platt, Richard. Plants Bite Back! 1999. (Eyewitness Readers). (Illus.). 48p. (J). (gr. 5-3). pap. 3.99 (978-0-7894-4754-8(1)) Dorling Kindersley Publishing, Inc.

—Plants Bite Back! 1999. (J). (978-0-606-18991-0(2)); lib. bdg. 11.80 (978-0-613-22189-4(3)) Tandem Library Bks.

Souza, Dorothy M. Meat-Eating Plants. 2002. (Watts Library). (Illus.). (J). (gr. 5-7). 63p. pap. 8.95 (978-0-531-16222-4(2)); 64p. 25.50 (978-0-531-11980-8(7)) Scholastic Library Publishing. (Watts, Franklin).

—Meat-Eating Plants. 2002. (gr. 3-6). lib. bdg. 17.60 (978-0-613-53835-0(8)) Tandem Library Bks.

Steck-Vaughn Staff. The Meat-Eating Plants Next Door. 2002. pap. (978-0-7398-6149-3(2)) Steck-Vaughn.

Stefoff, Rebecca. Flytrap. 1999. (Living Things Ser.). (Illus.). 32p. (J). (gr. 1-12). lib. bdg. 22.79 (978-0-7614-0445-3(7) , Benchmark Bks.) Cavendish, Marshall Corp.

CAROLS

Amery, H. Christmas Carols. 2004. (Songbooks Ser.). 32p. (J). pap. 6.95 incl. audio (978-0-7945-0600-1(3)) EDC Publishing.

Beall, Pamela Conn & Nipp, Susan Hagen. Away in a Manger. Wittwer, Hala, illus. 2001. (Wee Sing Ser.). 24p. (J). bds. 4.99 (978-0-8431-7707-7(1) , Price Stern Sloan) Penguin Group (USA) Inc.

—Ten Days of Christmas. Wittwer, Hala, illus. 2001. (Wee Sing Ser.). 24p. (J). bds. 4.99 (978-0-8431-7708-4(X) , Price Stern Sloan) Penguin Group (USA) Inc.

—Wee Sing for Christmas. Guida, Liisa & Klein, Nancy, illus. ed. 2002. (Wee Sing Ser.). 64p. (J). pap. 9.99 (978-0-8431-4961-6(2) , Price Stern Sloan) Penguin Group (USA) Inc.

Birmingham, Christian & Dickens, Charles. A Christmas Carol. ed. 2002. (Heirloom Editions Ser.). (Illus.). 56p. 16.95 (978-0-7624-1299-0(2) , Running Pr.) Running Pr. Bk. Pubs.

Blumen, Karen. The Friendly Beasts. Blumen, John, illus. 2004. 30p. (ps-2). 7.99 (978-0-8066-3330-5(1) , 9-3330, Augsburg Bks.) Augsburg Fortress, Pubs.

Bonicatto, Marsha. Christmas Song of the North. Holman, Karlyn, illus. 2001. 32p. (J). (ps-2). pap. 14.95 (978-0-439-16262-3(9)) Scholastic, Inc.

Boys Choir of Harlem Staff. O Holy Night: Christmas with the Boys Choir of Harlem. Ringgold, Faith, illus. 2004. 40p. (J). 18.99 (978-0-06-000979-3(9)); 19.89 (978-0-06-051819-6(7)) HarperCollins Pubs.

Bramley, Henry R. Christmas Carols, New & Old. 2001. 91p. (YA). reprint ed. 88.00 (978-0-7222-6103-3(9)) Library Reprints, Inc.

Chants de Noel. 2000. (Musicontes Ser.).Tr. of Christmas Songs. (FRE.). (J). 24.95 incl. audio (978-2-09-230369-6(4)) Nathan, Fernand FRA. *Dist:* Distribooks, Inc.

Christmas Coloring Fun Christmas Carols. 2004. (J). per. 6.95 (978-1-885920-47-8(4)) Pyramid Publishing, Inc.

de Paola, Tomie. The Friendly Beasts: An Old English Christmas Carol. 1998. (Illus.). 40p. (J). (ps-3). pap. 6.99 (978-0-698-11661-0(5) , Putnam Juvenile) Penguin Group (USA) Inc.

Dickens, Charles. A Christmas Carol. 2001. (gr. 5-8). lib. bdg. 13.00 (978-0-613-63928-6(6)) Tandem Library Bks.

Duncan, Edmondstoune. Story of the Carol. 2001. 253p. (YA). reprint ed. 98.00 (978-0-7222-6104-0(7)) Library Reprints, Inc.

Gibb, Sarah, illus. The Family Treasury of Classic Christmas Carols. 2002. (Courage Children's Ser.). 48p. (J). (gr. 3-6). 9.98 (978-0-7624-1392-8(1) , Courage Bks.) Running Pr. Bk. Pubs.

Griffin, Rachel. Twelve Days of Christmas. 2002. (Illus.). 32p. (J). (gr. k-2). 17.99 incl. audio compact disk (978-1-84148-940-7(9)) Barefoot Bks., Inc.

Hal Leonard Corp., creator. Popular Christmas Carols Coloring Book. 2000. 24p. pap. 6.95 (978-1-57560-367-4(5) , 1575603675) Cherry Lane Music Co.

Illustrated Christmas Story. 2007. 72p. pap. 14.95 (***978-0-8256-3550-2(0)*** , Amsco Music) Music Sales Corp.

Jeffers, Susan. Silent Night. Jeffers, Susan, illus. 2003. (Illus.). 32p. (J). (gr. k). 16.99 (978-0-525-47136-3(7) , Dutton Juvenile) Penguin Group (USA) Inc.

Julian, Alison, illus. The 12 Days of Christmas. 2005. (J). (***978-1-74157-281-0(9)***) Hinkler Bks. Pty, Ltd.

Keats, Ezra Jack & Keats, Ezra Jack. The Little Drummer Boy. 2000. (Illus.). (J). (ps-3). lib. bdg. 15.30 (978-0-613-30008-7(4)) Tandem Library Bks.

Litchfield, Jo, illus. First Book of Christmas Carols. 2004. (First Book of Christmas Carols Ser.). 24p. (J). 9.95 (978-0-7945-0596-7(1) , Usborne) EDC Publishing.

The Little Drummer Boy. 2004. pap. 14.95 incl. audio (978-1-56008-156-2(2)) Weston Woods Studios, Inc.

Long, Sylvia, contrib. by. Sylvia Long's Deck the Hall Bb. 2006. (J). bds. 6.95 (978-0-8118-5387-3(X)) Chronicle Bks. LLC.

Manson, Christopher, illus. Good King Wenceslas. 2004. 25p. (J). (gr. k-4). reprint ed. 15.00 (978-0-7567-8226-9(0)) DIANE Publishing Co.

Moore, Clement C. A Christmas Carol. (Illus.). 12p. (J). 4.95 (978-1-58989-103-6(1)) Thurman Hse., LLC.

National Gallery of Art of London Staff. Hark! the Herald Angels Sing. 2004. (Illus.). 48p. (J). pap. 7.95 (978-1-84507-305-3(3)) Lincoln, Frances Ltd. GBR. *Dist:* Perseus Distribution.

National Gallery of Art Staff. Hark! The Herald Angels Sing: The National Gallery, London. (Illus.). 48p. (J). (gr. k up). 19.99 (978-0-7112-0814-8(X)) Lincoln, Frances Ltd. GBR. *Dist:* Antique Collectors' Club.

Neale, J. M. Good King Wenceslas. Ladwig, Tim, illus. 2005. 32p. (J). (ps-17). 16.00 (978-0-8028-5209-0(2) , Eerdmans Bks For Young Readers) Eerdmans, William B. Publishing Co.

Newsom, Tom, illus. The First Noel. 2006. 14p. (J). (gr. k-4). reprint ed. 8.00 (978-1-4223-5413-1(X)) DIANE Publishing Co.

Nightingale, Sandy. Carols for Children: 22 Favorite Christmas Carols & Songs with Words & Music. 2000. (Illus.). 48p. (YA). (gr. 2 up). pap. (978-0-330-35164-5(8) , Macmillan Children's Bks.) Pan Macmillan.

O Christmas Tree. 32p. (J). (978-0-7853-9382-5(X) , 9642200) Publications International, Ltd.

Okun, Milton, ed. Christmas Carols for Piano Duet. 63p. (YA). pap. 14.95 (978-0-89524-948-7(0) , 02505651) Cherry Lane Music Co.

Omochabako. Joy to the World! Ebina, H., illus. 2006. (JPN.). (J). bds. 9.95 (978-0-8198-3985-5(X)) Pauline Bks. & Media.

Onorati, Henry, et al. The Little Drummer Boy. Rodanas, Kristina, illus. 2001. 32p. (J). (gr. k-3). tchr. ed. 15.00 (978-0-395-97015-7(6) , Clarion Bks.) Houghton Mifflin Co. Trade & Reference Div.

Ringgold, Faith, illus. O Holy Night: Christmas with the Boys Choir of Harlem. 2006. 30p. (J). (gr. 4-8). 19.00 (978-1-4223-5512-1(8)) DIANE Publishing Co.

Running Press Staff. The Christmas Carol Kazoo. 2006. (Illus.). 32p. (J). pap. 6.95 (978-0-7624-2829-8(5) , Running Pr.) Running Pr. Bk. Pubs.

Scholastic, Inc. Staff. Jingle Bells. 2007. (My First Taggies Book Ser.). (Illus.). 8p. (J). 12.99 (***978-0-545-01159-4(0)***) Scholastic, Inc.

Scott, James. A Christmas Carol: A Student Response Journal. 2001. 28p. (YA). (gr. 7-12). wbk. ed. 19.95 (978-1-58049-907-1(4) , RJ24) Prestwick Hse., Inc.

Seymour, Brenda Meredith, illus. First Carols. 2000. (First Books Ser.). 40p. (J). 8.00 (978-0-7188-2827-1(5)) Lutherworth Pr., The GBR. *Dist:* Parkwest Pubns., Inc.

Shaw, M. English Carol Book. 2001. (YA). reprint ed. 150.00 (978-0-7222-6108-8(X)) Library Reprints, Inc.

Spirin, Gennady, illus. We Three Kings. 2007. 24p. (J). (ps-3). 16.99 (978-0-689-82114-1(X)) Simon & Schuster Children's Publishing.

Stern, Leonard & Price, Roger. Christmas Carol Mad Libs: Very Merry Songs & Stories. 2007. (Mad Libs Ser.). 48p. (J). (gr. 3). pap. 3.99 (***978-0-8431-2676-1(0)*** , Price Stern Sloan) Penguin Group (USA) Inc.

Strasser, Myrna. Silent Night, Holy Night: The Story Behind Our Favorite Christmas Carol. Porfirio, Guy, illus. 2004. (Traditions of Faith Ser.). 40p. (J). 15.99 (978-0-310-70672-4(6)) Zonderkidz.

Tada, Joni & Wolgemuth, Bobbie. Christmas Carols for Kid's Heart, Vol. 3. Martinez, Sergio, illus. 2005. (Great Hymns of Our Faith Ser.). 96p. (J). 21.99 incl. audio compact disk (978-1-58134-626-8(3) , Crossway Bibles) Crossway Bks.

Tebbs, Philip & Tebbs, Victoria. Best-Loved Carols. Lush, Debbie, illus. 1999. 48p. (gr. 1-11). 5.00 (978-0-8170-1326-4(1)) Judson Pr.

Trapani, Iza. Jingle Bells. Trapani, Iza, illus. 2005. (Illus.). 32p. (J). (ps). per. 15.95 (978-1-58089-095-3(4)) Charlesbridge Publishing, Inc.

Tyrrell, Frances, illus. The Huron Carol. 2004. 32p. 16.00 (978-0-8028-5263-2(7)) Eerdmans, William B. Publishing Co.

Vojtech, Anna, illus. The Friendly Beasts. 2003. (J). 15.95 (978-0-7358-1764-7(2)); lib. bdg. 16.50 (978-0-7358-1765-4(0)) North-South Bks., Inc.

We Wish You a Merry Christmas. Date not set. 6p. (J). (gr. 1 up). bds. 6.99 (978-0-694-01558-0(X)) HarperCollins Pubs.

Wood, Charles. An Italian Carol Book. 2001. (YA). reprint ed. 150.00 (978-0-7222-6109-5(8)) Library Reprints, Inc.

Yolen, Jane & Stemple, Adam. Sing Noel. Carpenter, Nancy, illus. 2003. 96p. (J). (gr. 4-6). 17.95 (978-1-56397-420-5(7)) Boyds Mills Pr.

CARPENTRY

Here are entered works dealing with the construction of a wooden building or the wooden portion of any building. Works that treat the making and finishing of fine woodwork, such as furniture or interior details, are entered under Cabinet Work.

see also Building; Cabinet Work; Woodwork

Burby, Liza N. A Day in the Life of a Carpenter. 1999. (Kids' Career Library). (Illus.). 24p. (J). (gr. 3). lib. bdg. 18.75 (978-0-8239-5301-1(7) , PowerKids Pr.) Rosen Publishing Group, Inc., The.

Carpenters. 2000. (My Ancestors—My Heroes Ser.: Vol. 47). (J). (gr. 3-4). (978-1-893091-46-7(5)) Parker Publishing Co.

Feirer, John L. & Hutchings. Guide to Residential Carpentry. 1999. (Illus.). (YA). (gr. 6-12). stu. ed. 7.16 (978-0-02-676340-0(0)) Glencoe/McGraw-Hill.

Feirer, John L., et al. Carpentry & Building Construction. 5th ed. 1999. (Illus.). 161p. (YA). (gr. 6-12). pap., stu. ed., wbk. ed. 7.99 (978-0-02-838701-7(5)) Glencoe/McGraw-Hill.

Franchino, Vicky. Carpenters. 2000. (Community Workers Ser.). (Illus.). 32p. (J). (gr. 1 up). lib. bdg. 21.26 (978-0-7565-0006-1(0)) Compass Point Bks.

Freese, Joan. Carpenters. 2006. (Pull Ahead Books). (Illus.). 32p. (J). (ps-7). 22.60 (978-0-8225-2800-5(2) , Lerner Pubns.) Lerner Publishing Group.

Kishel, Ann-Marie. Carpenter. 2007. (First Step Nonfiction Ser.). (J). pap. (978-0-8225-6842-1(X)) Lerner Publishing Group.

Ross, Allison J. & Harrison, Scott. Choosing a Career in Carpentry. 2005. (World of Work Ser.). (Illus.). 64p. (YA). (gr. 7-12). lib. bdg. 25.25 (978-0-8239-3294-8(X)) Rosen Publishing Group, Inc., The.

Simon, Charnan. Uncle Jack Is a Carpenter. Squier, Robert, illus. 2006. (Magic Door to Learning Ser.). 24p. (J). 21.36 (978-1-59296-618-9(7)) Child's World, Inc.

Snyder, Inez. Building Tools. 2002. (Welcome Bks.). (Illus.). 24p. (J). (ps-2). pap. 4.95 (978-0-516-24034-3(X) , Children's Pr.) Scholastic Library Publishing.

Wallner, Rosemary. Construction Carpenter. 2000. (Career Exploration Ser.). (Illus.). 48p. (J). (gr. 3-4). lib. bdg. 21.26 (978-0-7368-0487-5(0) , LifeMatters Bks.) Capstone Pr., Inc.

Weinberger, Kimberly. Home Depot. Miller, Edward, illus. 2002. (J). pap. 3.50 (978-0-439-33296-5(6)) Scholastic, Inc.

Winne, Joanne. A Day with a Carpenter. 2001. (Welcome Bks.). (Illus.). 24p. (J). (ps-2). pap. 4.95 (978-0-516-23061-0(1) , Children's Pr.) Scholastic Library Publishing.

—Day with a Carpenter. 2001. (gr. k-3). lib. bdg. 12.95 (978-0-613-58758-7(8)) Tandem Library Bks.

Yanuck, Debbie L. Carpenters. 2002. (Community Helpers Ser.). (Illus.). 24p. (J). (gr. 1-2). lib. bdg. 18.60 (978-0-7368-1126-2(5) , Bridgestone Bks.) Capstone Pr., Inc.

CARPENTRY—FICTION

Carr, Karen. Clumsy Wally the Handyman. Volodka, Aras, illus. 2000. 32p. (J). pap. (978-0-9701450-9-3(8)) Long Hill Productions, Inc.

Cohn, Diana. Dream Carver. Cordova, Amy, illus. 2002. 40p. (J). (ps-3). 16.95 (978-0-8118-1244-3(8)) Chronicle Bks. LLC.

Down, Reg. The Magic Knot: And other Tangles. 2007. (Illus.). 100p. (J). per. 14.95 (***978-0-9794452-0-0(5)***) Lightly Pr.

Hesse, Karen. Sable. 1998. (YA). (gr. 4 up). (978-0-606-13755-3(6)) Tandem Library Bks.

—Sable. Sewall, Marcia, illus. 1998. 81p. (J). (ps-k). lib. bdg. 16.40 (978-0-613-08689-9(9)) Tandem Library Bks.

Jacob's Gift. 2004. (Max Lucado Ser.). 32p. 19.99 incl. DVD (978-1-4003-0182-9(3)) Nelson, Thomas Inc.

Joslin, Steve. The Working Class Meets the Carpenter. 2004. 25p. (J). pap. 12.99 (978-1-4116-1223-5(X)) Lulu.com.

Klinting, Lars. Harvey the Carpenter. 2005. (Handy Harvey Ser.). (Illus.). 40p. (J). (ps-k). pap. 4.95 (978-0-7534-5912-6(4) , Kingfisher) Houghton Mifflin Co. Trade & Reference Div.

Lucado, Max. Jacob's Gift. Hunt, Robert, illus. 2005. 20p. (J). (ps-2). bds., bds. 15.99 (978-1-4003-0696-1(5)) Nelson, Thomas Inc.

McCaughrean, Geraldine. The Jesse Tree. Willey, Bee, illus. 2005. 93p. (J). (gr. k). 20.00 (978-0-8028-5288-5(2) , Eerdmans Bks For Young Readers) Eerdmans, William B. Publishing Co.

Ruiz-Flores, Lupe. The Woodcutter's Gift/El Regalo del Leñador. Jerome, Elaine, illus. 2007. (SPA & ENG.). 32p. (J). (ps-2). 15.95 ***978-1-55885-489-5(4)** , Piñata Books) Arte Publico Pr.

Singer, Marilyn. Let's Build a Clubhouse. Bush, Timothy, illus. 2006. 32p. (J). (gr. k-3). 16.00 (978-0-618-30670-1(6) , Clarion Bks.) Houghton Mifflin Co. Trade & Reference Div.

Widmer, Kirsten & Buxton, Sarah. Workshops That Work! 2004. 160p. pap. 19.99 (978-0-439-44406-4(3) , Teaching Resources) Scholastic, Inc.

CARPENTRY—TOOLS

Clement, Mark. Kid's Carpenter's Workbook. 2005. (Illus.). (J). 12.95 (978-0-9754212-6-0(3)) CenterLine Media.

Synder, Inez. Building Tools. 2002. (gr. k-3). lib. bdg. 12.95 (978-0-613-58825-6(8)) Tandem Library Bks.

CARRIERS, AIRCRAFT

see Aircraft Carriers

CARROLL, LEWIS, 1832-1898

Cadavid, Jorge. Lewis Carroll -Los Juegos del Lenguaje. 2005. 128p. pap. (978-958-30-1833-6(3)) Panamericana Editorial.

Carpenter, Angelica Shirley. Lewis Carroll: Through the Looking Glass. 2002. (Lerner Long Biographies Ser.). (Illus.). 128p. (J). 27.93 (978-0-8225-0073-5(6) , Lerner Pubns.) Lerner Publishing Group.

CARS (AUTOMOBILES)

see Automobiles

CARS, ARMORED (TANKS)

see Tanks (Military Science)

CARSON, KIT, 1809-1868

Boraas, Tracey. Kit Carson: Mountain Man. 2002. (Let Freedom Ring Ser.). (Illus.). 48p. (J). (gr. 3-4). lib. bdg. 22.60 (978-0-7368-1349-5(7) , Bridgestone Bks.) Capstone Pr., Inc.

Burke, Rick. Kit Carson. 2003. (Illus.). 32p. (J). pap. 6.95 (978-1-4034-4200-0(2)); lib. bdg. 24.22 (978-1-4034-4192-8(8)) Heinemann Library.

Calvert, Patricia. Kit Carson: He Led the Way. 2006. (Great Explorations Ser.). (Illus.). 80p. (J). lib. bdg. 32.79 (978-0-7614-2223-5(4) , Benchmark Bks.) Cavendish, Marshall Corp.

Ellis, Edward Sylvester. The Life of Kit Carson: Hunter, Trapper, Guide, Indian Agent, & Colonel U. S. A. Fitterling, Michael A. et al, illus. 1998. 364p. (J). (gr. 5-12). reprint ed. pap. 14.95 (978-1-890623-04-3(0)) Lost Classics Bk. Co.

Kit Carson. (Exploring the West Biographies Ser.). 48p. (YA). 7.95 (978-0-7368-4510-6(0)) Capstone Pr., Inc.

CARSON, KIT, 1809-1868—FICTION

Osborne, Mary Pope. Adaline Falling Star. unabr. ed. 2004. (Middle Grade Cassette Librariestm Ser.). 176p. (J). (gr. 3-7). pap. 29.00 incl. audio (978-0-8072-1195-3(8) , S YA 319 SP, Listening Library) Random Hse. Audio Publishing Group.

CARSON, RACHEL, 1907-1964

Bank Street Staff & Glimm, Adele. Rachel Carson: Protecting Our Earth. 2000. (Ideas on Trial Ser.). (Illus.). 124p. (C). (gr. 4-7). pap. 8.95 (978-0-07-135742-5(4)) McGraw-Hill Cos., The.

Bruchac, Joseph. Rachel Carson: Preserving a Sense of Wonder. Locker, Thomas, illus. 2004. (Thomas Locker Images of Conservation Ser.). 32p. (J). 17.95 (978-1-55591-482-0(9)) Fulcrum Publishing.

Domblewski, Carol. Citizens Who Made a Difference. 2005. (Navigators Ser.). (J). pap. 38.00 ***978-1-4108-5097-3(8)*** Benchmark Education Co.

Ehrlich, Amy. Rachel: The Story of Rachel Carson. Minor, Wendell, illus. 2008. 32p. (J). pap. 6.00 ***978-0-15-206324-5(2)*** , Voyager Bks./Libros Viajeros) Harcourt Children's Bks.

—Rachel: The Story of Rachel Carson. Minor, Wendell, illus. 2003. 32p. (J). (gr. k-3). 16.00 (978-0-15-216227-6(5) , Silver Whistle) Harcourt Trade Pubs.

Fontes, Justine & Fontes, Ron. Rachel Carson. 2005. (Rookie Biographies(R) Ser.). (Illus.). 32p. (J). (gr. 1-2). 20.50 (978-0-516-25896-6(6) , Children's Pr.) Scholastic Library Publishing.

Fontes, Ron. Rachel Carson. 2005. (Rookie Biographies(R) Ser.). (Illus.). 31p. (J). (gr. 1-2). pap. 4.95 (978-0-516-26819-4(8) , Children's Pr.) Scholastic Library Publishing.

Glimm, Adele. Rachel Carson: Defender of the Environment. 2000. (gr. 3-6). lib. bdg. 17.60 (978-0-613-71540-9(3)) Tandem Library Bks.

Gow, Mary. Rachel Carson: Ecologist & Activist. 2005. (Great Minds of Science Ser.). (Illus.). 128p. (J). (gr. 4-10). lib. bdg. 26.60 (978-0-7660-2503-5(9)) Enslow Pubs., Inc.

Landau, Elaine. Rachel Carson & the Environmental Movement. 2004. (Cornerstones of Freedom Ser.). (Illus.). 48p. (J). 26.00 (978-0-516-24232-3(6) , Children's Pr.) Scholastic Library Publishing.

Levine, Ellen. Rachel Carson. 2007. (Up Close Ser.). 224p. (YA). (gr. 6-9). 15.99 (978-0-670-06220-1(0) , Viking Juvenile) Penguin Group (USA) Inc.

Levine, Ellen. Up Close: Rachel Carson: Rachel Carson. 2008. (Up Close Ser.). 208p. (J). (gr. 6). pap. 6.99 ***978-0-14-241046-2(2)*** , Puffin) Penguin Group (USA) Inc.

Quaratiello, Arlene R. Rachel Carson: A Biography. 2004. (Greenwood Biographies Ser.). (Illus.). 168p. 36.95 (978-0-313-32388-1(7) , GR2388, Greenwood Pr.) Greenwood Publishing Group, Inc.

Rachel Carson, Escritora Y Cientifica. 2003. (Notas Biograficas Ser.). pap. 48.95 (978-0-8136-5886-5(1)) Modern Curriculum Pr.

Rivera, Sheila. Rachel Carson: A Life of Responsibility. 2007. (Pull Ahead Books-Biographies Ser.). (J). 22.60 (978-0-8225-6462-1(9) , Lerner Pubns.) Lerner Publishing Group.

Schlank, Carol Hilgartner & Metzger, Barbara. A Clean Sea: The Rachel Carson Story. Cohen, Judith Love, ed. Katz, David Arthur, illus. 2002. 40p. (J). pap. 9.50 incl. DVD (978-1-880599-62-4(7)) Cascade Pass, Inc.

—A Clean Sea: The Rachel Carson Story. Cohen, Judith Love, ed. Katz, David Arthur, illus. l.t. ed. 2002. 40p. (J). 13.95 (978-1-880599-61-7(9)) Cascade Pass, Inc.

Shea, George. Rachel Carson: Founder of the Environmental Movement. 2005. (Giants of Science Ser.). (Illus.). 64p. (J). (gr. 4-7). lib. bdg. 26.20 (978-1-4103-0568-8(6) , Blackbirch Pr., Inc.) Thomson Gale.

Simon, Charnan. Rachel Carson: Author & Environmentalist. 2003. (Spirit of America). (Illus.). 32p. (J). (gr. 2-6). 27.07 (978-1-59296-011-8(1)) Child's World, Inc.

Tremblay, E. A. Rachel Carson. 2003. (Women in the Science Ser.). (Illus.). 118p. pap. 30.00 (978-0-7910-7520-3(6)); 112p. (gr. 6-12). 30.00 (978-0-7910-7244-8(4)) Facts On File, Inc. (Chelsea Hse.).

CARTER, HOWARD, 1874-1939

Harvey, Gill. Tutankhamun. Tomlins, Karen, illus. 2006. 64p. (J). 8.99 (978-0-7945-1271-2(2) , Usborne) EDC Publishing.

Woods, Michael & Woods, Mary B. The Tomb of King Tutankhamun. 2008. (J). lib. bdg. ***(978-0-8225-7506-1(X))*** Twenty First Century Bks.

Zoehfeld, Kathleen Weidner. The Curse of King Tut's Mummy. Nelson, James, illus. 2007. (Stepping Stones Ser.). 112p. (J). (gr. 1-4). 3.99 (978-0-375-83862-0(7) , Random Hse. Bks. for Young Readers) Random Hse. Children's Bks.

—Curse of King Tut's Mummy. Nelson, James, illus. 2007. (Stepping Stones Ser.). 112p. (J). (gr. 2-4). lib. bdg. 11.99 (978-0-375-93862-7(1) , Random Hse. Bks. for Young Readers) Random Hse. Children's Bks.

CARTER, JIMMY, 1924-

Acker, Kerry. Jimmy Carter. (Major World Leaders Ser.). (Illus.). (gr. 6-12). 2003. 144p. pap. 30.00 (978-0-7910-7523-4(0)); 2002. 112p. 30.00 (978-0-7910-6947-9(8)) Facts On File, Inc. (Chelsea Hse.).

—Jimmy Carter. 2003. (gr. 5-8). lib. bdg. 18.75 (978-0-613-86156-4(6)) Tandem Library Bks.

Gherman, Beverly. Jimmy Carter. 2004. (Presidential Leaders Ser.). (Illus.). 112p. (J). 29.27 (978-0-8225-0816-8(8) , Lerner Pubns.) Lerner Publishing Group.

January, Brendan & Seidman, David. Jimmy Carter: Peacemaker & President. 2004. (Great Life Stories Ser.). (Illus.). 127p. (J). 30.50 (978-0-531-12374-4(X) , Watts, Franklin) Scholastic Library Publishing.

Joseph, Paul. Jimmy Carter. 1999. (United States Presidents Ser.). (Illus.). 32p. (J). (gr. k-6). lib. bdg. 22.78 (978-1-56239-747-0(8) , Checkerboard Library) ABDO Publishing Co.

Kent, Deborah. Jimmy Carter. 2005. (Encyc of Presidents, 2ND Ser.). (Illus.). 112p. (J). (gr. 6-8). 34.00 (978-0-516-22975-1(3) , Watts, Franklin) Scholastic Library Publishing.

Kramer, Barbara. Jimmy Carter: A Life of Service. 2005. (Awesome Values in Famous Lives Ser.). (Illus.). 48p. (J). (ps-7). lib. bdg. 23.93 (978-0-7660-2379-6(6) , Enslow Elementary) Enslow Pubs., Inc.

Margaret, Amy. Jimmy Carter Library & Museum. 2004. (Presidential Libraries Ser.). (Illus.). 24p. (J). lib. bdg. 18.75 (978-0-8239-6271-6(7) , PowerKids Pr.) Rosen Publishing Group, Inc., The.

O'Shei, Tim. Jimmy Carter: A MyReportLinks.com Book. 2002. (Presidents Ser.). (Illus.). 48p. (J). (gr. 4-10). lib. bdg. 25.26 (978-0-7660-5051-8(3) , MyReportLinks.com Bks.) Enslow Pubs., Inc.

Ryan, Bernard. Jimmy Carter: U. S. President & Humanitarian. 2006. 160p. (gr. 6-12). 25.00 (978-0-8160-5903-4(9) , Ferguson Publishing Co.) Facts On File, Inc.

Santella, Andrew. James Earl Carter, Jr. 2002. (Profiles of the Presidents Ser.). (Illus.). 64p. (J). (gr. 4 up). lib. bdg. 23.93 (978-0-7565-0283-6(7)) Compass Point Bks.

Schraff, Anne. Jimmy Carter. 1998. (United States Presidents Ser.). (Illus.). 112p. (YA). (gr. 5-12). lib. bdg. 26.60 (978-0-89490-935-1(5)) Enslow Pubs., Inc.

Slavicek, Louise Chipley. Jimmy Carter. (Great American Presidents Ser.). (Illus.). (gr. 4-8). 2004. 112p. pap. 30.00 (978-0-7910-7790-0(X)); 2003. 100p. 30.00 (978-0-7910-7646-0(6)) Facts On File, Inc. (Chelsea Hse.).

Venezia, Mike. Jimmy Carter. 2008. (Getting to Know the U. S. Presidents Ser.). 32p. (J). pap. 7.95 ***978-0-516-25971-0(7)*** , Children's Pr.) Scholastic Library Publishing.

Venezia, Mike, illus. Jimmy Carter. 2007. 32p. (J). 28.00 ***978-0-516-22643-9(6)*** , Children's Pr.) Scholastic Library Publishing.

Waxman, Laura Hamilton. Jimmy Carter. 2006. (History Makers Bios Ser.). (Illus.). 48p. (J). 26.60 (978-0-8225-5939-9(0) , Lerner Pubns.) Lerner Publishing Group.

Whitelaw, Nancy. Jimmy Carter: President & Peacemaker. 2004. (Twentieth Century Leaders Ser.). (Illus.). 128p. (YA). (gr. 6-12). 23.95 (978-1-931798-18-1(4)) Reynolds, Morgan Inc.

Wilson, Natashya & Natashya, Wilson. How to Draw the Life & Times of James Earl Carter Jr. 2007. (Kid's Guide to Drawing the Presidents of the United States of America Ser.). (Illus.). 32p. (J). 25.25 (978-1-4042-3015-6(7) , PowerKids Pr.) Rosen Publishing Group, Inc., The.

CARTIER, JACQUES, 1491-1557

Blashfield, Jean F. Cartier: Jacques Cartier in Search of the Northwest Passage. 2001. (Exploring the World Ser.). (Illus.). 48p. (J). (gr. 4 up). lib. bdg. 22.60 (978-0-7565-0122-8(9)) Compass Point Bks.

Donaldson-Forbes, Jeff. Jacques Cartier. 2002. (Famous Explorers Ser.). (Illus.). 24p. (J). (gr. 3). lib. bdg. 18.75 (978-0-8239-5834-4(5) , PowerKids Pr.) Rosen Publishing Group, Inc., The.

Harmon, Daniel E. Jacques Cartier & the Exploration of Canada. 2000. (Explorers of the New World Ser.). (Illus.). (J). 63p. (gr. 4-7). pap. 25.00 (978-0-7910-6168-8(X)); 64p. (gr. 8-12). 25.00 (978-0-7910-5958-6(8)) Facts On File, Inc. (Chelsea Hse.).

—Jacques Cartier & the Exploration of Canada. 2001. (gr. 3-6). lib. bdg. 17.60 (978-0-613-32700-8(4)) Tandem Library Bks.

Kjelle, Marylou Morano. Jacques Cartier. 2006. (What's So Great About... ? Ser.). (Illus.). 32p. (J). (gr. 1-4). lib. bdg. (978-1-58415-481-5(0)) Mitchell Lane Pubs., Inc.

Lackey, Jennifer D. B. Jacques Cartier: Exploring the St. Lawrence River. 2006. (In the Footsteps of Explorers Ser.). (Illus.). 32p. (J). (gr. 3-9). pap. (978-0-7787-2466-7(2)); lib. bdg. (978-0-7787-2430-8(1)) Crabtree Publishing Co.

Marsh, Carole. Jacques Cartier. 2002. (One Thousand Readers Ser.). (Illus.). 12p. (J). (gr. k-4). 2.95 (978-0-635-01540-2(4) , 15404) Gallopade International.

Morey, Allan. Jacques Cartier. 2003. (Explorers of the Unknown Ser.). (J). (978-1-58417-038-9(7)); pap. (978-1-58417-101-0(4)) Lake Street Pubs.

Petrie, Kristin. Jacques Cartier. 2004. (Explorers Set I Ser.). (Illus.). 32p. (J). (gr. k-6). lib. bdg. 22.78 (978-1-59197-594-6(8)) ABDO Publishing Co.

CARTOGRAPHY

Here are entered works on the general science of mapmaking, including map projection and the mapping of large areas. Works on the mapping of small areas and the drawing of maps in elementary schools are entered under Map Drawing. Works on cartography applied to a particular subject are entered under that subject subdivided by the subdivision Maps, e.g. Geology—Maps.

see also Map Drawing; Maps

Aberg, Rebecca. Latitud y Longitud. (J). (gr. k-2). 2006. (SPA.). 32sbp. pap. 5.95 (978-0-516-25042-7(6)); 2005. (ENG & SPA., Illus.). 31p. 19.50 (978-0-516-25240-7(2)) Scholastic Library Publishing. (Children's Pr.).

Alter, Judy. Exploring & Mapping the American West. 2001. (gr. 3-6). lib. bdg. 14.10 (978-0-613-52037-9(8)) Tandem Library Bks.

Ashley, Susan. I Can Read a Map. 2004. (Illus.). 24p. (J). pap. (978-0-8368-4331-6(2)); (YA). lib. bdg. 19.33 (978-0-8368-4324-8(X)) Stevens, Gareth Inc.

Ball, Jackie. Mapping Earth. 2004. (Discovery Channel School Science Ser.). (Illus.). 32p. (J). (gr. 5 up). lib. bdg. 24.67 (978-0-8368-3382-9(1)) Stevens, Gareth Inc.

Blevins, Wiley. Maps. 2003. (Compass Point Phonics Readers Ser.). (Illus.). 16p. (J). (gr. 1 up). 13.26 (978-0-7565-0512-7(7)) Compass Point Bks.

Burstein, John. Making Maps: Where's the Party? 2003. (Weekly Reader Early Learning Library). (Illus.). 24p. (J). (gr. 1 up). pap. 7.93 (978-0-8368-3826-8(2) , Weekly Reader Early Learning Library) Stevens, Gareth Inc.

Chancellor, Deborah. Maps & Mapping. 2007. (Science Kids Ser.). (Illus.). 48p. (J). pap. 6.95 ***978-0-7534-6164-8(1)*** , Kingfisher) Houghton Mifflin Co. Trade & Reference Div.

Coupe, Robert. Maps & Our World. 1999. (Explorers Ser.). (Illus.). 32p. (J). (978-0-7699-0486-3(6)) Shortland Pubns. (U. S. A.) Inc.

Deboo, Ana. Mapping the Land & Environment. 2006. (Map Readers Ser.). (Illus.). (J). (978-1-4034-6792-8(7)); 32p. pap. (978-1-4034-6799-7(4)) Heinemann Library.

—Mapping the World. 2006. (Illus.). 32p. (J). (978-1-4034-6789-8(7)); pap. (978-1-4034-6796-6(X)) Heinemann Library.

—Mapping Your Way. 2006. (Map Readers Ser.). (Illus.). 32p. (J). 27.07 (978-1-4034-6790-4(0)); pap. (978-1-4034-6797-3(8)) Heinemann Library.

Fredette, Nathalie & Lafleur, Claude. Our Planet Today. 2001. (Twenty-First Century Science Ser.). (Illus.). 64p. (J). (gr. 5 up). lib. bdg. 32.67 (978-0-8368-5003-1(3) , World Almanac Library) Stevens, Gareth Inc.

Gonzales, Doreen. Are We There Yet? Using Map Scales. 2008. (J). ***978-1-4296-0053-8(5)*** , First Facts) Capstone Pr., Inc.

Grolier Educational Staff, contrib. by. City Maps, 8 vols., Vol. 7. 2002. (Illus.). (J). (978-0-7172-5626-6(X) , Grolier) Scholastic Library Publishing.

—Mapping for Governments, 8 vols., Vol. 6. 2002. (Illus.). (J). (978-0-7172-5625-9(1) , Grolier) Scholastic Library Publishing.

—Mapping for Today & Tomorrow, 8 vols., Vol. 8. 2002. (Illus.). (J). (978-0-7172-5627-3(8) , Grolier) Scholastic Library Publishing.

—Mapping New Lands, 8 vols., Vol. 5. 2002. (Illus.). (J). (978-0-7172-5624-2(3) , Grolier) Scholastic Library Publishing.

—Mapping the World, 8 vols., set. Incl. Vol. 1. Ways of Mapping the World. (978-0-7172-5620-4(0)); Vol. 2. Observation & Measurement. (978-0-7172-5621-1(9)); Vol. 3. Maps for Travelers. (978-0-7172-5622-8(7)); Vol. 4. Navigation. (978-0-7172-5623-5(5)); Vol. 5. Mapping New Lands. (978-0-7172-5624-2(3)); Vol. 6. Mapping for Governments. (978-0-7172-5625-9(1)); Vol. 7. City Maps. (978-0-7172-5626-6(X)); Vol. 8. Mapping for Today & Tomorrow. (978-0-7172-5627-3(8)); (J). 2002. (Illus.). 2002. 239.00 (978-0-7172-5619-8(7) , Grolier) Scholastic Library Publishing.

—Maps for Travelers, 8 vols., Vol. 3. 2002. (Illus.). (J). (978-0-7172-5622-8(7) , Grolier) Scholastic Library Publishing.

—Navigation, 8 vols., Vol. 4. 2002. (Illus.). (J). (978-0-7172-5623-5(5) , Grolier) Scholastic Library Publishing.

—Observation & Measurement, 8 vols., Vol. 2. 2002. (Illus.). (J). (978-0-7172-5621-1(9) , Grolier) Scholastic Library Publishing.

—Ways of Mapping the World, 8 vols., Vol. 1. 2002. (Illus.). (J). (978-0-7172-5620-4(0) , Grolier) Scholastic Library Publishing.

Hall, Margaret. X Marks the Spot. 2006. (Illus.). 32p. (J). pap. (978-1-4109-2629-6(X)); lib. bdg. (978-1-4109-2600-5(1)) Steck-Vaughn.

Harcourt School Publishers Staff. How to Get from Here to There. 3rd ed. 2002. (Illus.). (J). pap. 7.30 (978-0-15-333600-3(5)) Harcourt Schl. Pubs.

Heinrichs, Ann. Gerardus Mercator: Father of Modern Mapmaking. 2007. (Signature Lives Ser.). (J). lib. bdg. 31.93 ***978-0-7565-3312-0(0)*** Compass Point Bks.

Hudak, Heather C. Mapping. 2007. (J). ***978-1-59036-762-9(6)*** ; lib. bdg. ***978-1-59036-761-2(8)*** Weigl Pubs., Inc.

Johnson, Jinny. Maps & Mapping. 2007. (Inside Access Ser.). 32p. (J). 9.95 ***978-0-7534-6062-7(9)*** , Kingfisher) Houghton Mifflin Co. Trade & Reference Div.

Kachur, Matthew. Como hacer un mapa & Making Maps. 2005. spiral bd. 84.00 ***978-1-4108-5693-7(3)*** Benchmark Education Co.

Kennedy, Jan. Map Skills Grade 3. 1999. (Basic Skills Ser.). 48p. (J). (gr. 3-3). pap. 6.99 (978-1-56822-638-5(1) , IF5190) School Specialty Publishing.

Levy, Janey. Mapping America's Westward Expansion: Applying Geographic Tools & Interpreting Maps. 2005. (Critical Thinking in American History Ser.). (Illus.). 48p. (J). (gr. 5-8). lib. bdg. 25.25 (978-1-4042-0416-4(4)) Rosen Publishing Group, Inc., The.

Maps Show Us the Way. (Rosen Real Readers Big Bookstm Ser.). 12p. (J). (gr. 1-2). 31.95 (978-1-4042-6218-8(0)) Rosen Publishing Group, Inc., The.

Morrison, Taylor. The Coast Mappers. 2004. (Illus.). 48p. (J). (gr. 3-5). tchr. ed. 16.00 (978-0-618-25408-8(0) , Walter Lorraine) Houghton Mifflin Co. Trade & Reference Div.

Oleksy, Walter. Maps in History. (Watts Library). (Illus.). 64p. (J). 2003. (gr. 5-7). pap. 8.95 (978-0-531-16633-8(3)); 2002. (gr. 4-6). pap. 25.50 (978-0-531-12028-6(7)) Scholastic Library Publishing. (Watts, Franklin).

Olesky, Walter. Mapping the World. 2002. (gr. 3-6). lib. bdg. 17.60 (978-0-613-59515-5(7)) Tandem Library Bks.

—Maps in History. 2002. (gr. 3-6). lib. bdg. 17.60 (978-0-613-59516-2(5)) Tandem Library Bks.

Ross, Val. The Road to There: Mapmakers & Their Stories. 2003. (Illus.). 152p. (J). (gr. 6-9). 22.95 (978-0-88776-621-3(8)) Tundra Bks., Inc./Livres Toundra, Inc. CAN. *Dist:* Random Hse., Inc.

Ryan, P. Explorers & Mapmakers. 2000. 48p. (J). pap. 13.99 (978-0-237-52231-5(4) , Evans Brothers, Limited) Evans Publishing Group GBR. *Dist:* Independent Pubs. Group.

Sammis, Fran. Mapping Our World - Group 2, 4 bks., Set. Incl. Maps & Mapmaking. lib. bdg. 27.07 (978-0-7614-0367-8(1)); Oceans & Skies. lib. bdg. 27.07 (978-0-7614-0374-6(4)); South America. lib. bdg. 27.07 (978-0-7614-0369-2(8)); 64p. (J). (gr. 4-8). 1999. (Illus.). 2000. Set lib. bdg. 108.29 (978-0-7614-0375-3(2) , Benchmark Bks.) Cavendish, Marshall Corp.

Scott, Janine. Mapping Our World. 2002. (Spyglass Books). (Illus.). 24p. (J). (gr. 1 up). lib. bdg. 18.60 (978-0-7565-0362-8(0)) Compass Point Bks.

Smith, James K. David Thompson. 2001. (Canadians Ser.). (Illus.). 64p. (978-1-55041-493-6(3)) Fitzhenry & Whiteside, Ltd.

Walsh, Kieran. Map Math. 2003. (Illus.). 48p. (J). 29.93 (978-1-58952-379-1(2)) Rourke Publishing, LLC.

Zelon, Helen. The Endeavour SRTM: Mapping the Earth. 2002. (Space Missions Ser.). 24p. (J). lib. bdg. 19.95 (978-0-8239-5775-0(6) , PowerKids Pr.) Rosen Publishing Group, Inc., The.

CARTOONING

Ames, Lee J. Draw 50 Famous Cartoons. 1999. (Illus.). (J). (gr. 3-6). lib. bdg. 17.60 (978-0-8085-3760-1(1)) Tandem Library Bks.

—Draw Fifty Animal 'Toons. 2000. (Illus.). (gr. 3-6). lib. bdg. 17.60 (978-0-613-51068-4(2)) Tandem Library Bks.

Artell, Mike. Cartooning for Kids. 2002. (Illus.). 128p. pap. 9.95 (978-1-4027-0111-5(X)) Sterling Publishing Co., Inc.

—Cartooning for Kids. 2002. (gr. 3-6). lib. bdg. 18.75 (978-0-613-84767-4(9)) Tandem Library Bks.

—Funny Cartooning for Kids. 2006. (Illus.). 352p. (J). (gr. 3-6). 17.95 (978-1-4027-2260-8(5)) Sterling Publishing Co., Inc.

Auerbach, Annie & Heiss, Lori. Lilo & Stitch. 2003. (DMA Learn to Draw Ser.). (Illus.). 32p. (J). pap. 5.95 (978-1-56010-045-4(1)) Foster, Walter Publishing, Inc.

Barnhart, Duane & Barnhart, Angie. Cartooning Basics: Creating the Characters & More. 4th ed. 2004. (Illus.). 88p. (J). per. 12.99 (978-0-9657136-4-1(4) , 1235827) Cartoon Connections Pr.

Barr, Steve. 1-2-3 Draw Cartoon Aircraft: A Step-By-Step Guide. 2005. (Illus.). 64p. (J). pap. 8.99 (978-0-939217-76-2(7)) Peel Productions, Inc.

—1-2-3 Draw Cartoon Animals: A Step-by-Step Guide. 2002. (One-Two-Three Draw Ser.). (Illus.). 64p. (J). (gr. 1). pap. 8.99 (978-0-939217-48-9(1)) Peel Productions, Inc.

—1-2-3 Draw Cartoon Animals: A Step-by-Step Guide. 2002. (gr. k-3). lib. bdg. 17.60 (978-0-613-86905-8(2)) Tandem Library Bks.

—1-2-3 Draw Cartoon Faces: A Step-by-Step Guide. 2002. (One-Two-Three Draw Ser.). (Illus.). 64p. (J). (gr. 1). pap. 8.99 (978-0-939217-47-2(3)) Peel Productions, Inc.

—1-2-3 Draw Cartoon Monsters: A Step-by-Step Guide. 2004. (Illus.). 64p. pap. 8.99 (978-0-939217-74-8(0)) Peel Productions, Inc.

—1-2-3 Draw Cartoon People: A Step-by-Step Guide. 2002. (One-Two-Three Draw Ser.). (Illus.). 64p. (J). (gr. 1). pap. 8.99 (978-0-939217-46-5(5)) Peel Productions, Inc.

—1-2-3 Draw Cartoon People: A Step-by-Step Guide. 2002. (gr. k-3). lib. bdg. 17.60 (978-0-613-89960-4(1)) Tandem Library Bks.

—1-2-3 Draw Cartoon Sea Critters. 2003. (One-Two-Three Draw Ser.). (Illus.). 64p. pap. 8.99 (978-0-939217-72-4(4)) Peel Productions, Inc.

—1-2-3 Draw Cartoon Trucks & Motorcycles: A Step-By-Step Guide. 2005. (Illus.). 64p. (J). pap. 8.99 (978-0-939217-77-9(5)) Peel Productions, Inc.

—1-2-3 Draw Cartoon Wildlife: A Step-by-Step Guide. 2003. (One-Two-Three Draw Ser.). (Illus.). 64p. (J). pap. 8.99 (978-0-939217-70-0(8)) Peel Productions, Inc.

—1-2-3 Draw Cartoon Wildlife: A Step-by-Step Guide. 2003. (gr. k-3). lib. bdg. 17.60 (978-0-613-86900-3(1)) Tandem Library Bks.

Beauvais, Den. Dragonfly Flipz Sampler. 2003. (Illus.). 96p. per. 3.99 (978-0-9745213-0-5(2) , Dragonfly Flipz) Dragonfly Entertainment.

Beginner's Guide to Drawing Cartoons. Date not set. (I Can Draw Ser.). (Illus.). 128p. (J). 7.98 (978-1-4054-0543-0(0)) Parragon, Inc.

Bellen-Berthézène, Cyndie. Cartoon How-To. Workman, Terry & Workman, Lisa, illus. 2005. 48p. (J). (978-0-439-81332-7(8)) Scholastic, Inc.

Bergstrom, Joan M. Lights! Color! Animation! 1999. (Illus.). 181p. (J). (gr. k-6). 29.95 (978-1-931042-01-7(2)) Activities Club, Inc., The.

Blitz, Bruce. Blitz Dynamite Video Drawing: Cartoon Basics. 2007. 56p. (J). 12.95 (***978-0-7624-2864-9(3)*** , Running Pr. Kids) Running Pr. Bk. Pubs.

—Blitz Ultimate Cartooning Kit. 2004. (Illus.). 56p. pap. 19.95 (978-0-7624-1928-9(8) , Running Pr. Kids) Running Pr. Bk. Pubs.

—Bruce Blitz's Toonrific Craft Kit. 2006. (Illus.). 56p. (YA). pap. 19.95 (978-0-7624-1929-6(6) , Running Pr. Kids) Running Pr. Bk. Pubs.

Booth, Scott, illus. How to Draw Superheroes & Super Villains. 2003. 64p. (J). (978-0-439-55133-5(1)) Scholastic, Inc.

Bulloch, Ivan, et al. Cartoons & Animation. 2005. (Illus.). 32p. (J). (gr. 3-7). lib. bdg. 27.10 (978-1-932889-81-9(7) , 1247651) Sea-To-Sea Pubns.

Caldwell, Ben. Fantasy! Cartooning. 2005. (Illus.). 96p. (ps-11). pap. 9.95 (978-1-4027-1612-6(5)) Sterling Publishing Co., Inc.

Cartooning with Toon Takes: Animal Cartoons. 2000. 75p. (J). ring bd. 9.95 (978-1-929456-18-5(2)) Myrtle-Seal Publishing.

Cervone, Tony. Animating the Looney Tunes Way. Foster, Walter T., ed. 2000. (Looney Tunes Collection). (Illus.). 96p. (J). (gr. 3). pap. 14.95 (978-1-56010-303-5(5)) Foster, Walter Publishing, Inc.

Comic Book Creators. 2007. 145.26 (978-1-59928-296-1(8) , ABDO & Daughters) ABDO Publishing Co.

Comikers. Pen & Ink. 2006. (Illus.). 114p. (YA). pap. 19.95 (978-1-56970-917-7(3)) Digital Manga Publishing.

Costello, Bill. Cartooning with Math. Costello, Bill, illus. 1998. (Illus.). 64p. (J). (ps-8). pap. 8.95 (978-1-891905-31-5(7)) Thinkorporated.

Coupe, Peter. A Beginner's Guide to Drawing Comics, Caricatures & Cartoon Strips. Coupe, Peter, illus. 2004. (Illus.). 80p. (YA). (gr. 5-10). reprint ed. pap. 15.00 (978-0-7567-7306-9(7)) DIANE Publishing Co.

Doran, Colleen. Girl to Grrrl Manga. 2006. (Illus.). 128p. pap. 19.99 (978-1-58180-809-4(7) , North Light Bks.) F & W Pubns., Inc.

Dorling Kindersley Publishing Staff & Jurgens, Dan. You Can Draw Marvel Characters. 2006. (You Can Draw Ser.). (Illus.). 96p. (J). ring bd. 19.99 (978-0-7566-1470-6(8) , 1246486) Dorling Kindersley Publishing, Inc.

Drawing Cartoons. 2004. (I-Quest Ser.). (J). (978-1-84229-756-8(2)) Top That! Publishing PLC.

Dunn, Ben. How to Draw Manga. 2004. (Illus.). 344p. (YA). pap. 3.25 (978-1-59412-063-3(3)) Mud Puddle, Inc.

Espinosa, Frank. Draw the Looney Tunes: The Warner Bros. Character Design Manual. Chan, San Wei, illus. 2005. 208p. 40.00 (978-0-8118-5016-2(1)) Chronicle Bks. LLC.

Farris, D. & Brookes. Activators Cartooning. (Illus.). iv, 122p. (J). pap. (978-0-340-71518-5(9) , Hodder & Stoughton) Hodder General Publishing Division.

Ferrer, María, tr. from JPN. Como Dibujar Manga Vol. 1: Personajes. 2004. (SPA., Illus.). 82p. (YA). pap. 20.95 (978-1-59497-038-2(6)) Public Square Bks.

Foster, Walter, ed. Cartooning: Character Design. 2006. (How to Draw & Paint/Art Instruction Program Ser.). (Illus.). 32p. (J). pap. 7.95 (978-1-56010-967-9(X)) Foster, Walter Publishing, Inc.

—Finding Nemo. 2003. (Disney's How to Draw Classic Character Ser.). (Illus.). 32p. (J). pap. 5.95 (978-1-56010-689-0(1)) Foster, Walter Publishing, Inc.

—Scooby-Doo! Step by Step. Musacchia, Vince, illus. 2002. (How to Draw Ser.). 32p. (J). pap. 5.95 (978-1-56010-715-6(4)) Foster, Walter Publishing, Inc.

—Spongebob Squarepants. Martinez, Heather, illus. 2002. (Nick How to Draw Ser.). 32p. (J). pap. 5.95 (978-1-56010-662-3(X)) Foster, Walter Publishing, Inc.

Foster, Walter & Martinez, Heather. How to Draw Wyland's Spouty & Friends. Wyland, ed. 2006. (Wyland HTD Books & Kits Ser.). (Illus.). 32p. (J). pap. 5.95 (978-1-56010-968-6(8)) Foster, Walter Publishing, Inc.

Galea, Mario. Discover Manga Drawing: 30 Easy Lessons for Drawing Guys & Girls. 2006. (Illus.). 96p. pap. 16.99 (978-1-58180-697-7(3) , Impact) F & W Pubns., Inc.

Gilbert, James. Big Jims Ten Years & Still Cartooning. 2005. (J). 9.95 (978-1-59971-024-2(2)) Aardvark Global Publishing.

Glossop, Jennifer. Tattoo You! Color & Make Your Own Temporary Tattoo Designs. Klund, Barbara, illus. 2004. 30p. (J). (gr. k-4). reprint ed. pap. 8.00 (978-0-7567-8260-3(0)) DIANE Publishing Co.

Go Office Staff. How to Draw Manga: Official More How to Draw Manga Illustration Kit, 1. 2004. (Illus.). 126p. 29.99 (978-1-59396-121-3(9)) Diamond Bk. Distributors.

Gray, Peter C. How to Draw Manga Animals. 2006. (Kid's Guide to Drawing Ser.). (Illus.). 32p. (J). (978-1-4042-3329-4(6) , PowerKids Pr.) Rosen Publishing Group, Inc., The.

—How to Draw Manga Female Action Figures. 2006. (Kid's Guide to Drawing Ser.). (Illus.). 32p. (J). lib. bdg. 25.25 (978-1-4042-3327-0(X) , PowerKids Pr.) Rosen Publishing Group, Inc., The.

—How to Draw Manga Heroes & Villains. 2006. (Kid's Guide to Drawing Ser.). (Illus.). 32p. (J). 25.25 (978-1-4042-3330-0(X) , PowerKids Pr.) Rosen Publishing Group, Inc., The.

—How to Draw Manga Male Action Figures. 2006. (Kid's Guide to Drawing Ser.). (Illus.). 32p. (J). lib. bdg. (978-1-4042-3328-7(8) , PowerKids Pr.) Rosen Publishing Group, Inc., The.

—How to Draw Manga Monsters. 2006. (Kid's Guide to Drawing Ser.). (Illus.). 32p. (J). lib. bdg. 25.25 (978-1-4042-3331-7(8) , PowerKids Pr.) Rosen Publishing Group, Inc., The.

—How to Draw Manga Robots. 2006. (Kid's Guide to Drawing Ser.). (Illus.). 32p. (J). lib. bdg. (978-1-4042-3332-4(6) , PowerKids Pr.) Rosen Publishing Group, Inc., The.

Griffin, Georgene & Walker, Karen, illus. How to Draw Funny Faces. 1999. 123p. (J). (978-1-56156-791-1(4)) Kidsbooks, Inc.

Hamilton, Sue. Jack Kirby. 2007. (Comic Book Creators Ser.). (Illus.). 32p. (J). (gr. 3-5). lib. bdg. 24.21 (978-1-59928-298-5(4) , ABDO & Daughters) ABDO Publishing Co.

—Joe Simon. 2007. (Comic Book Creators Ser.). (Illus.). 32p. (J). (gr. 3-5). lib. bdg. 24.21 (978-1-59928-300-5(X) , ABDO & Daughters) ABDO Publishing Co.

—Joe Sinnott. 2007. 24.21 (978-1-59928-299-2(2) , ABDO & Daughters) ABDO Publishing Co.

—John Buscema. 2007. (Illus.). 32p. 24.21 (978-1-59928-297-8(6) , ABDO & Daughters) ABDO Publishing Co.

—John Romita, Sr. 2007. 24.21 (978-1-59928-302-9(6) , ABDO & Daughters) ABDO Publishing Co.

Harat, Christopher. Draw Manga. 2006. 25p. (gr. 5). pap. 16.99 (978-0-9776925-0-7(7)) Loew-Cornell, Inc.

Hart, Christopher. Christopher Hart's Cartoon Studio. 2003. (gr. 3-6). lib. bdg. 16.40 (978-0-613-90861-0(9)) Tandem Library Bks.

—Christopher Hart's Cartoon Studio. 2003. (Illus.). 48p. pap. 7.95 (978-0-8230-0624-3(7)) Watson-Guptill Pubns., Inc.

—Draw Manga! 2003. (gr. 3-6). lib. bdg. 15.25 (978-0-613-76655-5(5)) Tandem Library Bks.

—Draw Manga! 2003. (Xtreme Art Ser.). (Illus.). 64p. 7.95 (978-0-8230-0369-3(8)) Watson-Guptill Pubns., Inc.

—Draw Manga Martial Arts Masters. 2006. 25p. (gr. 8). pap. 16.99 (978-0-9776925-1-4(5)) Loew-Cornell, Inc.

—Draw Manga Monsters. 2005. (Xtreme Art Ser.). (Illus.). 64p. (J). pap. 7.95 (978-0-8230-0372-3(8)) Watson-Guptill Pubns., Inc.

—Draw Manga Super Cute Characters. 2006. 25p. (gr. 8). pap. 16.99 (978-0-9776925-3-8(1)) Loew-Cornell, Inc.

—Draw Manga Teen Characters. 2006. 25p. (gr. 8). pap. 16.99 (978-0-9776925-2-1(3)) Loew-Cornell, Inc.

—How to Draw Amazing Comic Book Characters. 2006. (Illus.). 25p. (gr. 8). pap. 16.99 (978-0-9776925-4-5(X)) Loew-Cornell, Inc.

—How to Draw Cartoon Animals. 2006. (Illus.). 25p. (gr. 6). pap. 16.99 (978-0-9776925-6-9(6)) Loew-Cornell, Inc.

—Kids Draw Angels, Elves, Fairies & More. 2001. (Kids Draw Ser.). (Illus.). 64p. (gr. 1-7). pap. 10.95 (978-0-8230-2627-2(2)) Watson-Guptill Pubns., Inc.

—Kids Draw Manga Monsters! 2007. (Illus.). 64p. (J). pap. 11.95 (***978-0-8230-9840-8(0)***) Watson-Guptill Pubns., Inc.

—Manga Mania: How to Draw Japanese Comics. 2003. (Illus.). 144p. (gr. 5-8). lib. bdg. 30.35 (978-0-613-49336-9(2)) Tandem Library Bks.

—Manga Shoujo. 2005. (Kids Draw Ser.). (Illus.). 64p. (J). pap. 10.95 (978-0-8230-2622-7(1)) Watson-Guptill Pubns., Inc.

Hodge, Anthony. Cartoons. 2004. (J). lib. bdg. 27.10 (978-1-932799-02-6(8)) Stargazer Bks.

How to Draw Cartoons. 2002. 48p. lib. bdg. (978-1-59168-010-9(7)) Flying Rhinoceros, Inc.

Janson, Klaus. DC Comics Guide to Pencilling Comics. 2002. (gr. 7-12). lib. bdg. 30.35 (978-0-613-51207-7(3)) Tandem Library Bks.

Keely, Jack. Beginner's Guide - Cartooning, Bk. 2. Foster, Walter T., ed. 2004. (How to Draw & Paint Ser.). Orig. Title: Step-by-Step Cartooning. (Illus.). 32p. (gr. k-6). pap. 7.95 (978-1-56010-488-9(0)) Foster, Walter Publishing, Inc.

Keely, Jack & Van Osten, Carson. Cartooning, Bk. 1. Foster, Walter T., ed. 2004. (How to Draw & Paint Ser.). Orig. Title: Starting Out in Cartooning. (Illus.). 32p. (gr. k-6). pap. 7.95 (978-1-56010-487-2(2)) Foster, Walter Publishing, Inc.

Kistler, Mark. Gadgets & Gizmos. Kistler, Mark, illus. 2003. (Dare to Draw in 3-D Ser.: Bk. 4). (Illus.). 48p. (J). pap. 4.99 (978-0-439-38075-1(8)) Scholastic, Inc.

—Gadgets & Gizmos. 2003. (gr. 3-6). lib. bdg. 13.00 (978-0-613-72051-9(2)) Tandem Library Bks.

—Monster Mania. 2002. (Dare to Draw in 3-D Ser.: No. 1). (Illus.). 40p. (J). pap. 4.99 (978-0-439-38073-7(1)) Scholastic, Inc.

—Monster Mania. 2002. (gr. 3-6). lib. bdg. 13.00 (978-0-613-72049-6(0)) Tandem Library Bks.

Klutz Editors. Draw the Marvel Heroes. 2007. 94p. (J). (gr. 3 up). pap. 16.95 (***978-1-59174-434-4(2)***) Klutz.

Krefta, Ben. Step-by-Step Manga. 2005. (Step-by-step Manga Ser.). (Illus.). 64p. (J). pap. 6.99 (978-0-439-67706-6(8)) Scholastic, Inc.

Levy, Barbara Soloff. How to Draw Funny Faces. 2002. (Hobbies & Amusements for Children Ser.). (Illus.). 32p. (J). (gr. k-5). pap. 2.95 (978-0-486-42397-5(2)) Dover Pubns., Inc.

Lewis, Sian, et al. Cartwnio gydag Elwyn Ioan. 2005. (978-0-903131-18-6(8)) Urdd Gobaith Cymru.

Lightfoot, Marge. Cartooning for Kids. Lightfoot, Marge, illus. 2005. (Illus.). 64p. 14.95 (978-1-897066-38-6(4)); pap. 6.95 (978-1-897066-26-3(0)) Maple Tree Pr. CAN. *Dist:* Perseus Distribution.

Lim, Ron & Dakota, Heather. How to Draw Manga Extreme. Im, Angela, ed. 2005. (Illus.). 64p. (J). 12.99 (978-0-439-79567-8(2) , Tangerine Pr.) Scholastic, Inc.

Lipsey Edwards, Jennifer. I Love Draw Cartoons! 2007. (My Very Favorite Art Book Ser.). (Illus.). 48p. (J). 9.95 (978-1-57990-819-5(5)) Lark Bks.

Manga University Staff. Manga Without Borders: Japanese Comic Art from All Four Corners of the World. 2006. (ENG & JPN., Illus.). 64p. pap. (978-4-921205-05-8(1) , Manga University) Japanime Co., Ltd.

Marvis, Barbara J. Charles Schulz. 2004. (Robbie Reader Ser.). (Illus.). 32p. (J). (gr. 1-4). lib. bdg. 25.70 (978-1-58415-289-7(3)) Mitchell Lane Pubs., Inc.

Mayne, Don. Draw Your Own Cartoons! 2000. (Quick Starts for Kids! Ser.). (Illus.). 64p. (J). (gr. 3 up). pap. 8.95 (978-1-885593-76-4(7) , Williamson Bks.) Ideals Pubns.

—Draw Your Own Cartoons! 2000. (gr. 3-6). lib. bdg. 17.60 (978-0-613-57600-0(4)) Tandem Library Bks.

McCafferty, Catherine. Princesses. Foster, Walter, ed. 2004. (Disney Learn-to-Draw Ser.). (Illus.). 32p. (J). pap. 5.95 (978-1-56010-699-9(9)) Foster, Walter Publishing, Inc.

Milbourne, A. Drawing Cartoons. 2004. (Art School Ser.). (Illus.). 64p. (J). pap. 8.99 (978-0-7945-0372-7(1)); lib. bdg. 16.95 (978-1-58086-507-4(0)) EDC Publishing.

Miller, Raymond H. Matt Groening. 2005. (Inventors & Creators Ser.). (Illus.). 48p. (gr. 4-8). 26.20 (978-0-7377-3158-3(3) , Greenhaven Pr., Inc.) Thomson Gale.

Miller, Steve & Baugh, Bryan. Scared! How to Draw Fantastic Horror Comic Characters. 2004. (Illus.). 144p. pap. 19.95 (978-0-8230-1664-8(1)) Watson-Guptill Pubns., Inc.

Okum, David. Draw super Heroes. 2005. (Illus.). 64p. pap. 6.99 (978-1-58180-731-8(7) , 1245830, Impact) F & W Pubns., Inc.

—Draw super Manga. 2005. (Illus.). 64p. pap. 6.99 (978-1-58180-732-5(5) , 1245828, Impact) F & W Pubns., Inc.

—Draw super manga Monsters. 2005. (Illus.). 64p. pap. 6.99 (978-1-58180-733-2(3) , 1245829, Impact) F & W Pubns., Inc.

—Manga Fantasy Madness. 2006. (Illus.). 128p. pap. 19.99 (978-1-58180-708-0(2) , 1255708, Impact) F & W Pubns., Inc.

—Manga Madness. 2004. (Illus.). 128p. pap. 19.99 (978-1-58180-534-5(9) , North Light Bks.) F & W Pubns., Inc.

Phelps, Earl R. How to Draw Muticultural Supercharacters. 2000. (Coleccion Mujeres de Palabra Ser.). (SPA., Illus.). 96p. (gr. 3-7). pap. 18.95 (978-1-887627-04-7(9)) Phelps Publishing.

QEB Learn Art National Book Stores Edition: Cartooning. 2006. (J). per. (978-1-59566-279-8(0)) QEB Publishing Inc.

Robins, Deri. Cartooning. 2004. (QEB Learn Art Ser.). (Illus.). 32p. (J). lib. bdg. 18.95 (978-1-59566-044-2(5)) QEB Publishing Inc.

Robins Deri. Cartooning. 2006. (Illus.). 32p. (J). 9.95 (978-1-58728-533-2(9) , 1253681, Two Can Publishing) T&N Children's Publishing.

Roche, Art. Art for Kids: Comic Strips: Create Your Own Comic Strips from Start to Finish. 2007. (Illus.). 112p. 17.95 (978-1-57990-788-4(1)) Lark Bks.

—Cartooning: The Only Cartooning Book You'll Ever Need to Be the Artist You've Always Wanted to Be. 2005. (Art for Kids Ser.). (Illus.). 112p. (J). 17.95 (978-1-57990-623-8(0)) Lark Bks.

Sabatino, Chris. Stick It Notes: 100 Cartoons to Draw & Leave Behind. 2007. (Illus.). 208p. (J). pap. 4.95 (978-1-60059-074-0(8)) Lark Bks.

Sautter, Aaron. How to Draw Comic Heroes. Martin, Cynthia, illus. 2008. (J). (***978-1-4296-0074-3(8)***) Capstone Pr., Inc.

—How to Draw Manga Warriors. Martin, Cynthia, illus. 2008. (J). (***978-1-4296-0078-1(0)***) Capstone Pr., Inc.

Scholastic, Inc. Staff. How to Draw. Simpson, Fiona, ed. 2004. (Justice League Ser.). 32p. (J). pap. 4.99 (978-0-439-57167-8(7)) Scholastic, Inc.

—How to Draw Garfield & the Gang. Polt, Gabrielle, ed. 2004. 32p. (J). pap. 4.99 (978-0-439-63821-0(6)) Scholastic, Inc.

—How to Draw Graphic Novels. Im, Angela, ed. 2004. 24p. (J). (gr. 3 up). pap. 4.99 (978-0-439-66469-1(1)) Scholastic, Inc.

Spilsbury, Richard. Cartoons & Animation. 2006. (Art off the Wall Ser.). (Illus.). 56p. (J). (978-1-4034-8287-7(X)) Heinemann Library.

Stephens, Jay. Heroes! Draw Your Own Superheroes, Gadget Geeks & Other Do-Gooders. 2007. (Illus.). 64p. (J). (gr. 4-6). 12.95 (978-1-57990-934-5(5)) Lark Bks.

Sullivan, Howard J. How to Draw Digimon Digital Monsters, 2 vols. 2000. (Illus.). (J). pap. (978-0-439-28661-9(1)) Scholastic, Inc.

Takarai, Saori & Kardy, Glenn. Manga Moods: Forty Faces + 80 Phrases. 2006. (Illus.). 96p. (YA). (978-4-921205-13-3(2)) Japanime Co., Ltd.

Tatchell, Judy. Ht Draw Cartoons & Caricatures. Round, Graham, illus. rev. ed. 2006. 40p. (J). pap. 5.99 (978-0-7945-1374-0(3) , Usborne) EDC Publishing.

Top That Publishing Staff, ed. Shadow on Wall. 2004. (Wicked Tattoos Ser.). (Illus.). 16p. (J). pap. (978-1-84510-112-1(X)) Top That! Publishing PLC.

Visca, Curt. How to Draw Cartoon Fish. 2003. (Kids Guide to Drawing Ser.). (Illus.). 24p. (J). lib. bdg. 21.25 (978-0-8239-6159-7(1) , PowerKids Pr.) Rosen Publishing Group, Inc., The.

Visca, Curt & Visca, Kelley. How to Draw Cartoon Careers. 2004. (Kid's Guide to Drawing Ser.). (Illus.). 24p. (J). lib. bdg. 21.25 (978-0-8239-6725-4(5) , PowerKids Pr.) Rosen Publishing Group, Inc., The.

—How to Draw Cartoon Holiday Symbols. 2004. (Kid's Guide to Drawing Ser.). (Illus.). 24p. (J). lib. bdg. 21.25 (978-0-8239-6726-1(3) , PowerKids Pr.) Rosen Publishing Group, Inc., The.

—How to Draw Cartoon Insects. 2003. (Kid's Guide to Drawing Ser.). (Illus.). 24p. (J). lib. bdg. 21.25 (978-0-8239-6157-3(5) , PowerKids Pr.) Rosen Publishing Group, Inc., The.

—How to Draw Cartoon Reptiles. 2003. (Kid's Guide to Drawing Ser.). (Illus.). 24p. (J). lib. bdg. 21.25 (978-0-8239-6160-3(5) , PowerKids Pr.) Rosen Publishing Group, Inc., The.

—How to Draw Cartoon Rodents. 2003. (Kid's Guide to Drawing Ser.). (Illus.). 24p. (J). lib. bdg. 21.25 (978-0-8239-6161-0(3) , PowerKids Pr.) Rosen Publishing Group, Inc., The.

—How to Draw Cartoon Spacecraft & Astronauts in Action. 2004. (Kid's Guide to Drawing Ser.). (Illus.). 24p. (J). lib. bdg. 21.25 (978-0-8239-6729-2(8) , PowerKids Pr.) Rosen Publishing Group, Inc., The.

—How to Draw Cartoon Symbols of the United States. 2004. (Kid's Guide to Drawing Ser.). (Illus.). 24p. (J). lib. bdg. 21.25 (978-0-8239-6727-8(1) , PowerKids Pr.) Rosen Publishing Group, Inc., The.

—How to Draw Cartoon Symbols of the Wild West. 2004. (Kid's Guide to Drawing Ser.). (Illus.). 24p. (J). lib. bdg. 21.25 (978-0-8239-6728-5(X) , PowerKids Pr.) Rosen Publishing Group, Inc., The.

—How to Draw Cartoon Vehicles. 2004. (Kid's Guide to Drawing Ser.). (Illus.). 24p. (J). lib. bdg. 21.25 (978-0-8239-6724-7(7) , PowerKids Pr.) Rosen Publishing Group, Inc., The.

Visca, Kelley & Visca, Curt. How to Draw Cartoon Birds. 2003. (Kid's Guide to Drawing Ser.). (Illus.). 24p. (J). lib. bdg. 21.25 (978 0 8239 6156-6(7) , PowerKids Pr.) Rosen Publishing Group, Inc., The.

Woods, Mae. Charles Schulz. 2000. (Children's Authors Ser.). (Illus.). 24p. (J). (gr. k-6). lib. bdg. 21.35 (978-1-57765-425-4(0) , Checkerboard Library) ABDO Publishing Co.

CARTOONS, ANIMATED

see Animated Films

CARTOONS AND COMICS

see also Pictures; Wit And Humor, Pictorial

Abadzis, Nick. Laika Collector's Edition. 2007. (Illus.). 208p. (YA). 29.95 (***978-1-59643-302-1(7)*** , First Second Bks.) Roaring Brook Pr.

Abbott, Wes, illus. & creator. Dogby Walks Alone. Abbott, Wes, creator. 2006. 192p. pap. 9.99 (978-1-59816-582-1(8) , Tokyopop Adult) TOKYOPOP, Inc.

Abnett, Dan & Lanning, Andy. Majestic Bk. 1: While You Were Out. Googe, Neil, illus. 2005. 168p. pap. 12.99 (978-1-4012-0850-9(9)) DC Comics.

Abnett, Dan & Williams, Anthony. This Ghost Is Toast! 2007. (Real Ghostbusters Ser.). (Illus.). 96p. pap. 8.95 (***978-1-84576-143-1(X)***) Titan Bks. Ltd. GBR. *Dist:* Random Hse., Inc.

Abrams, Pete. The Bug, the Witch, & the Robot. 2001. (Sluggy Freelance Ser.: No. 6). 178p. pap. 12.95 (978-1-929462-37-7(9)) Plan Nine Publishing, Inc.

The Adirondack. 2006. (YA). per. (978-1-59872-344-1(8)) Instantpublisher.com.

Agee, Jon. Smart Feller Fart Smeller & Other Spoonerisms. 2006. (Illus.). 64p. (J). (gr. 2-17). 14.95 (978-0-7868-3692-5(X)) Hyperion Bks. for Children.

—Why Did the Chicken Cross the Road? Arnold, Tedd et al, illus. 2006. 40p. (J). (ps-4). 16.99 (978-0-8037-3094-6(2) , Dial) Penguin Group (USA) Inc.

Aikawa, Yu. Dark Edge. (Illus.). (YA). Vol. 4. 2005. 208p. pap. 9.95 (978-1-59796-024-3(1)); Vol. 6. 2006. 200p. pap. 9.95 (978-1-59796-026-7(8)) DrMaster Pubns. Inc.

Aisaka (Character Designs), Koji, et al, illus. Lost War Chronicles, Vol. 2. 2nd rev. ed. 2006. (Mobile Suit Gundam Ser.). pap. 9.99 (978-1-59816-214-1(4), Tokyopop Kids) TOKYOPOP, Inc.

Akamatsu, Ken. A. I. Love You, 8 vols., Vol. 8. Ury, David, tr. from JPN. Akamatsu, Ken, illus. rev. ed. 2005. (Illus.). 224p. (YA). pap. 9.99 (978-1-59182-944-7(5), Tokyopop Adult) TOKYOPOP, Inc.

Aki, Katsu. Psychic Academy, Vol. 8. Aki, Katsu, illus. rev. ed. 2005. (Illus.). 192p. pap. 9.99 (978-1-59532-427-6(5), Tokyopop Adult) TOKYOPOP, Inc.

—Psychic Academy, Vol. 9. 9th rev. ed. 2005. (Illus.). pap. 9.99 (978-1-59532-428-3(3), Tokyopop Adult) TOKYOPOP, Inc.

—Psychic Academy, Vol. 10. Aki, Katsu, illus. 10th rev. ed. 2005. (Illus.). pap. 9.99 (978-1-59532-429-0(1), Tokyopop Adult) TOKYOPOP, Inc.

Akimine, Kamijyo. Samurai Deeper Kyo, Vol. 12. Akimine, Kamijyo, illus. 12th rev. ed. 2005. (Illus.). 192p. pap. 9.99 (978-1-59532-452-8(6), Tokyopop Adult) TOKYOPOP, Inc.

Akimoto, Nami. Miracle Girls, 9 vols. 2002. 192p. Vol. 5. 5th rev. ed. pap. 9.99 (978-1-892213-83-9(4)); Vol. 6. 6th rev. ed. pap. 9.99 (978-1-892213-84-6(2)) TOKYOPOP, Inc.

—Miracle Girls, 9 vols., Vol. 7. Akimoto, Nami, illus. 7th rev. ed. 2003. (Illus.). 192p. (gr. 2 up). pap. 9.99 (978-1-59182-073-4(1)) TOKYOPOP, Inc.

—Miracle Girls, 9 vols. 2003. (Illus.). 192p. (gr. 2 up). Vol. 8. 8th rev. ed. pap. 9.99 (978-1-59182-193-9(2)); Vol. 9. 9th rev. ed. pap. 9.99 (978-1-59182-194-6(0)) TOKYOPOP, Inc.

Akira, Shouko. Times Two. Akira, Shouko, illus. 2005. (Times Two Ser.). (Illus.). 200p. (YA). pap. 9.99 (978-1-59116-736-5(1)) Viz Media.

Akita, Yoshinobu. Orphen, Vol. 5. 2006. (Illus.). 168p. (YA). pap. (978-1-4139-0270-9(7)) ADV Manga.

—Orphen Volume 6. 2006. (Illus.). 168p. (YA). pap. (978-1-4139-0271-6(5)) ADV Manga.

Akiyama, Tamayo, illus. & creator. Secret Chaser. Akiyama, Tamayo, creator. 2006. 192p. pap. 9.99 (978-1-59816-341-4(8), Tokyopop Adult) TOKYOPOP, Inc.

Albano, John, et al. Jonah Hex. DeZuniga, Tony, illus. rev. ed. 2005. (Showcase Presents Ser.: Vol. 1). 528p. (YA). pap. 16.99 (978-1-4012-0760-1(X)) DC Comics.

Alden, Paul. Dungeon Siege: The Battle for Aranna. 2005. (Illus.). 88p. (YA). pap. 6.95 (978-1-59307-425-8(5)) Dark Horse Comics.

Alden, Paul & Bird, Brad. The Incredibles. Eliopoulos, Chris, illus. 2005. 96p. pap. 9.95 (978-1-59307-354-1(2)) Dark Horse Comics.

Alden, Paul, et al. The Imperial Perspective. 2004. 144p. pap. 17.95 (978-1-59307-128-8(0)) Dark Horse Comics.

Alex de Campi & Edo Fuijkschot. Agent Boo, Vol. 1. 2006. (Illus.). 96p. pap. 4.99 (978-1-59816-802-0(9), Tokyopop Kids) TOKYOPOP, Inc.

Alfonsi, Alice. Trust Your Heart. novel rev. ed. 2007. (W. I. T. C. H. Ser.: Bk. 24). 144p. (gr. 3-7). pap. 4.99 (***978-1-4231-0288-5(6)**) Hyperion Pr.

Alfonsi, Alice. A Weakened Heart. rev. ed. 2006. (W. I. T. C. H. Ser.: Bk. 21). 144p. (gr. 3-7). pap. 4.99 (978-0-7868-5595-7(9)) Hyperion Pr.

Alichino POP Display. 2005. pap. 319.68 (978-1-59532-830-4(0), Tokyopop Kids) TOKYOPOP, Inc.

All the Colors of the Earth. 2004. (J). pap. 18.95 incl. audio compact disk (978-1-55592-100-2(0)); pap. 38.75 incl. audio compact disk (978-1-55592-627-4(4)); pap. 32.75 incl. audio (978-1-55592-180-4(9)); pap. 14.95 incl. audio (978-1-55592-050-0(0)) Weston Woods Studios, Inc.

Allred, Laura, illus. The Superman: Madman Hullabaloo! 1998. 96p. (YA). (gr. 7 up). pap. 8.95 (978-1-56971-301-3(4)) Dark Horse Comics.

Amano, Kozue. Aria. 2004. (Illus.). Vol. 2. 194p. (YA). pap. (978-1-4139-0071-2(2)); Vol. 3. 188p. pap. (978-1-4139-0089-7(5)) ADV Manga.

Amano, Shiro. Kingdom Hearts: Chain of Memories, Vol. 2. 2nd rev. ed. 2007. 232p. (gr. 4-7). pap. 9.99 (978-1-59816-638-5(7), Tokyopop Kids) TOKYOPOP, Inc.

Amend, Bill. Encyclopedias Brown & White: A FoxTrot Collection. 2001. (gr. 7-12). lib. bdg. 17.60 (978-0-613-67543-7(6)) Tandem Library Bks.

—Foxtrot: Assembled with Care. 2002. (Illus.). 191p. (gr. 7-12). lib. bdg. 24.55 (978-0-613-67545-1(2)) Tandem Library Bks.

—Think Ifruity: A FoxTrot Collection. 2000. (gr. 7-12). lib. bdg. 18.75 (978-0-613-67586-4(X)) Tandem Library Bks.

Andersen, Hans Christian, illus. Thumbelina. 2004. Tr. of Tommelise. 32p. 3.99 (978-1-894998-17-8(0)) Lake, Jack Productions, Inc. CAN. *Dist:* Hushion Hse. Publishing, Ltd.

Anderson, Andrea Patrice. Heaven's Diary: Our Gift from God. 2006. 37.00 (***978-0-8059-8845-1(9)**) Dorrance Publishing Co., Inc.

Anderson, Brian. The Adventures of Commander Zack Proton & the Warlords of Nibblecheese. Holgate, Doug, illus. 2006. (Adventures of Commander Zack Proton Ser.). 112p. (J). pap. 3.99 (978-1-4169-1365-8(3), Aladdin) Simon & Schuster Children's Publishing.

Andrews, Kaare. Spider-Man Legend of the Spider-Clan, 3 vols. Young, Skott, illus. 2003. (Mangaverse Ser.: Vol. 3). 128p. (YA). pap. 11.99 (978-0-7851-1114-6(X)) Marvel Enterprises, Inc.

Andreyko, Marc. Street Justice. Saiz, Jesus & Palmiotti, Jimmy, illus. 2005. (Manhunter Ser.). 128p. pap. 12.99 (978-1-4012-0728-1(6)) DC Comics.

Annable, Graham. Further Grickle. 2003. 128p. pap. 14.95 (978-1-891867-55-2(5)) Alternative Comics.

Anzai, Nobuyuki. Flame of Recca, Vol. 14. Anzai, Nobuyuki, illus. 2005. (Flame of Recca Ser.). 184p. (YA). pap. 9.99 (978-1-4215-0014-0(0)) Viz Media.

—Flame of Recca. (Flame of Recca Ser.). (YA). Vol. 15. 2005. (Illus.). 200p. pap. 9.99 (978-1-4215-0131-4(7)); Vol. 18. 2006. 208p. pap. 9.99 (978-1-4215-0454-4(5)); Vol. 19. 2006. 208p. pap. 9.99 (978-1-4215-0455-1(3)); Vol. 23. 2007. 192p. pap. 9.99 (978-1-4215-0893-1(1)) Viz Media.

Aoki, Takao. Beyblade. Aoki, Takao, illus. 2004. (Beyblade Ser.). (Illus.). 200p. (YA). pap. 7.99 (978-1-59116-621-4(7)) Viz Media.

—Beyblade. 2006. (Beyblade Ser.). 208p. (YA). Vol. 11. pap. 7.99 (978-1-4215-0437-7(5)); Vol. 12. pap. 7.99 (978-1-4215-0438-4(3)) Viz Media.

—Beyblade: Beyblade Extreme Rotation Shoot, Vol. 2. Aoki, Takao, illus. 2004. (Beyblade Ser.). (Illus.). 192p. (YA). pap. 7.99 (978-1-59116-697-9(7)) Viz Media.

Aoki, Yuya. GetBackers, 21 vols., Vol. 2. Cohen, James, tr. from JPN. Ayamine, Rando, illus. rev. ed. 2004. 216p. pap. 9.99 (978-1-59182-634-7(9), Tokyopop Adult) TOKYOPOP, Inc.

Aragones, Sergio. Sergio Aragones Groo Handbook. 1999. (Illus.). 96p. (YA). (gr. 5 up). pap. 9.95 (978-1-56971-385-3(5)) Dark Horse Comics.

Arai, Kiyoko. Beauty Pop, Vol. 1. 2006. (Beauty Pop Ser.). (Illus.). 200p. (YA). pap. 8.99 (978-1-4215-0575-6(4)) Viz Media.

Arai, Kiyoko. Beauty Pop, Vol. 6. 2007. (Beauty Pop Ser.). 200p. (YA). pap. 8.99 (***978-1-4215-1323-2(4)**) Viz Media.

Araki, Hirohiko. Bizarre Adventure, Vol. 4. 2006. (Jo Joo's Bizarre Adventure Ser.). 208p. (YA). pap. 7.99 (978-1-4215-0653-1(X)) Viz Media.

—Jojo's Bizarre Adventure, Vol. 1. Araki, Hirohiko, illus. 2005. (Jo Joo's Bizarre Adventure Ser.). (Illus.). 192p. (YA). pap. 7.99 (978-1-59116-754-9(X)) Viz Media.

—Jojo's Bizarre Adventure, Vol. 5. 2006. (Jo Joo's Bizarre Adventure Ser.). 208p. (YA). pap. 7.99 (978-1-4215-0654-8(8)) Viz Media.

Archie, 6 bks., Set. 2007. (J). 145.26 (***978-1-59961-257-7(7)**) Spotlight.

Archie in Help Wanted. 2007. (Illus.). 80p. (J). 24.21 (***978-1-59961-258-4(5)**) Spotlight.

Archie in Quiet Please. 2007. (Illus.). 80p. (J). 24.21 (***978-1-59961-260-7(7)**) Spotlight.

Ariyoshi, Kyoko. Swan. Ariyoshi, Kyoko, illus. 2005. (Illus.). (YA). Vol. 4. 200p. pap. 9.99 (978-1-4012-0538-6(0)); Vol. 5. 192p. pap. 9.99 (978-1-4012-0539-3(9)) DC Comics.

Arnold, Adam. Aoi House, Vol. 1. 2006. (Illus.). 192p. (YA). pap. 10.99 (978-1-933164-12-0(3)) Seven Seas Entertainment, LLC.

Arnold, Robyn. Branli Says Bye-Bye to Binky. 2007. 32p. 16.50 (***978-0-615-15292-9(9)**) Robyn Z Moon Publishing.

Aryal, Aimee. Go, Pack, Go! de Angel, Miguel, illus. 2007. (J). 14.95 (***978-1-932888-94-2(2)**) Mascot Bks., Inc.

—Hello, Ralphie! 2007. (J). 14.95 (***978-1-932888-34-8(9)**) Mascot Bks., Inc.

Asamiya, Kia. Silent Bius. 2004. (gr. 7-12). lib. bdg. 22.20 (978-0-613-85851-9(4)) Tandem Library Bks.

Asano, Rin. Tengai-Retrogical, Vol. 1. 2004. (Illus.). 184p. (YA). pap. (978-1-4139-0208-2(1)) ADV Manga.

Ashbe, Jeanne. Cu Cu! 2003. (SPA.). 36p. (978-84-8470-053-1(4)) Corimbo, Editorial S.L.

—Eso No Se Hace! 2003. (SPA.). 32p. (J). 6.80 (978-84-95150-25-7(5)) Corimbo, Editorial S.L. ESP. *Dist:* Lectorum Pubns., Inc.

Asso, B. & Rideau, J. Biggles Recounts: The Falklands War. Spear, Luke, tr. Chauvin, D. & Uderzo, M., illus. 2007. 48p. pap. 9.99 (***978-1-905460-22-9(8)**) CineBook GBR. *Dist:* Biblio Distribution.

Auerbach, Annie. Grosse Adventures, the Volume 3: Trouble at Twilight Cave. 2007. (Illus.). 96p. pap. 4.99 (***978-1-59816-051-2(6)**, Tokyopop Kids) TOKYOPOP, Inc.

Averdonz, N., et al. Advent. 2007. (Z Graphic Novels / Hand of the Morning Star Ser.). 160p. (YA). pap. 9.99 (978-0-310-71369-2(2)) Zonderkidz.

—The Coming Storm. Broome, Mat, illus. 2007. (Z Graphic Novels / Kingdoms#8482;: A Biblical Epic Ser.). 160p. (YA). pap. 9.99 (978-0-310-71353-1(6)) Zonderkidz.

Avery, Fiona & Brooks, Mark. Arana: The Heart of the Spider. 2005. (Spider-Man Ser.). (Illus.). 144p. pap. 7.99 (978-0-7851-1506-9(4)) Marvel Enterprises, Inc.

Ayamine, Rando. GetBackers, 21 vols., Vol. 3. Aoki, Yuya, illus. 3rd rev. ed. 2004. 216p. pap. 9.99 (978-1-59182-635-4(7), Tokyopop Adult) TOKYOPOP, Inc.

—GetBackers, Vol. 4. Kirsch, Alexis, tr. from JPN. Aoki, Yuya, illus. rev. ed. 2004. 216p. pap. 9.99 (978-1-59182-636-1(5), Tokyopop Adult) TOKYOPOP, Inc.

Ayamine, Rando, illus. Getbackers, Vol. 8. 8th rev. ed. 2005. (JPN & ENG.). 200p. pap. 9.99 (978-1-59182-970-6(4), Tokyopop Adult) TOKYOPOP, Inc.

Azuma, Kiyohiko. Azumanga Daioh: The Manga, Vol. 1. 2003. (Illus.). 172p. (YA). pap. 9.99 (978-1-4139-0000-2(3)) A. D. Vision, Inc.

—Azumanga Daioh: The Manga, Vol. 2. 2003. (Illus.). 168p. (YA). pap. (978-1-4139-0023-1(2)) ADV Manga.

Badgett, Wally. Cowboyin' with Earl. 2000. (Book of Earl Ser.: Vol. 10). (Illus.). 96p. (J). per. 10.00 (978-1-892661-11-1(X)) Holmlund Distributing.

Badgett, Wally, creator. Cowboyin' with Earl. 2002. (Book of Earl Ser.: Vol. 12). (Illus.). 96p. per. 12.00 (978-1-892661-13-5(6)) Holmlund Distributing.

Baek, Hye-Kyung. Bring It On, Vol. 2. 2006. (Illus.). 200p. (YA). pap. 10.95 (***978-89-527-4471-5(3)**) ICE Kunion KOR. *Dist:* Diamond Bk. Distributors.

Bailey, Chris. Major Damage, Vol. 1. 2004. 96p. (YA). pap. 14.95 (978-0-9721831-4-7(0)); pap. 29.95 (978-0-9721831-5-4(9)) sky-dog.

Bair, Katie, et al. NHS Hawaii Pocket Manga, Vol. 1. 2006. 144p. (YA). pap. 12.95 (978-0-9768043-1-4(X)) Antarctic Pr., Inc.

Baker, Kyle. King David. 2002. (gr. 7-12). lib. bdg. 30.35 (978-0-613-56474-8(X)) Tandem Library Bks.

Balducci, Rita. Disney Princess Storybook & Movie Projector: Season of Enchantment: Jeweled Collector's Edition. 2007. (RD Innovative Book & Player Format Ser.). 48p. (J). 24.99 (***978-0-7944-1355-2(2)**) Reader's Digest Assn., Inc., The.

Baldwin, Stephen. Spirit Warriors: A Graphic Novel. 2006. Vol. 1. (Illus.). 208p. (YA). pap. 9.99 (978-0-8054-4357-8(6)) B&H Publishing Grp.

—Spirit Warriors: Number Three. Simko, Joe et al, illus. 2007. 208p. (YA). pap. 9.99 (978-0-8054-4356-1(8)) B&H Publishing Grp.

—Spirit Warriors: Number Two. 2007. (Illus.). 208p. (YA). pap. 9.99 (978-0-8054-4355-4(X)) B&H Publishing Grp.

Baltazar, Art & Franco, Aureliani. Patrick the Wolf Boy, Vol. 4. 2007. (Illus.). 144p. pap. 12.99 (978-1-932796-83-4(5)) Devil's Due Publishing, Inc.

Baraou, Anne & Sardon, Vincent. The Skeleton Family: The Neighbors from Elsewhere. 2005. (Illus.). 64p. (978-1-59687-825-9(8), ipicturebooks) ibooks, Inc.

Barasui, illus. & creator. Strawberry Marshmallow: Ichigo Mashimaro. Barasui, creator. 2006. 192p. pap. 9.99 (978-1-59816-494-7(5), Tokyopop Adult) TOKYOPOP, Inc.

Barks, Carl. Uncle Scrooge, Vol. 345. Rockwell, Scott, illus. 2005. 64p. (YA). pap. 6.95 (978-0-911903-88-1(7)) Gemstone Publishing, Inc.

Barks, Carl & Rosa, Don. Donald Duck Adventures: Donald Duck's Atom Bomb/the Duck Who Fell to Earth. 2007. 64p. pap. 8.99 (***978-1-60360-006-4(X)**) Gemstone Publishing, Inc.

Barks, Carl, et al. Uncle Scrooge. 2006. 64p. No. 352. pap. 6.95 (978-1-888472-22-6(7)); No. 353. pap. 6.95 (978-1-888472-16-5(2)) Gemstone Publishing, Inc.

—Uncle Scrooge #349. 2006. 64p. pap. 6.95 (978-1-888472-13-4(8)) Gemstone Publishing, Inc.

—Uncle Scrooge #351. 2006. 64p. pap. 6.95 (978-1-888472-15-8(4)) Gemstone Publishing, Inc.

—Uncle Scrooge #355. 2006. 64p. pap. 6.95 (978-1-888472-24-0(3)) Gemstone Publishing, Inc.

—Uncle Scrooge #356. 2006. 64p. pap. 6.95 (978-1-888472-25-7(1)) Gemstone Publishing, Inc.

—Uncle Scrooge #371. 2007. 64p. pap. 7.99 (***978-1-60360-001-9(9)**) Gemstone Publishing, Inc.

—Uncle Scrooge #372. 2007. 64p. pap. 7.99 (***978-1-60360-002-6(7)**) Gemstone Publishing, Inc.

—Vacation Parade #3. 2006. 80p. pap. 8.95 (978-1-888472-34-9(0)) Gemstone Publishing, Inc.

—Walt Disney's Christmas Parade #5. 2007. 80p. pap. 10.50 (***978-1-60360-005-7(1)**) Gemstone Publishing, Inc.

—Walt Disney's Comics & Stories #684. 2007. 64p. pap. 7.99 (***978-1-888472-95-0(2)**) Gemstone Publishing, Inc.

—Walt Disney's Comics & Stories #685. 2007. 64p. pap. 7.99 (***978-1-888472-96-7(0)**) Gemstone Publishing, Inc.

—Walt Disney's Comics & Stories #686. 2007. 64p. pap. 7.99 (***978-1-888472-97-4(9)**) Gemstone Publishing, Inc.

Baron, Mike, et al. The Last Command: X-Wing Rogue Squadron. (Star Wars Ser.). (Illus.). 144p. (YA). (gr. 7 up). pap. 17.95 (978-1-56971-378-5(2)) Dark Horse Comics.

Barry, Bill. Cargo Smith - Navy Seal: Yamashita's Gold. Barry, O. H., ed. 2002. (Illus.). 64p. (J). pap. 11.95 (978-0-944099-27-8(0)) Bill Barry's Compass Bks.

Baum, L. Frank. The Wizard of Oz. 2006. (J). (gr. 4-8). 24.21 (978-1-59961-120-4(1)) Spotlight.

—Wizard of Oz. Michael, Cavallaro, illus. 2005. (Puffin Graphics Ser.). 176p. (J). (gr. 3). pap. 9.99 (978-0-14-240471-3(3), Puffin) Penguin Group (USA) Inc.

Beatty, Scott. The BatmanTM Handbook: The Ultimate Training Manual. Hahn, David, illus. 2005. 192p. pap. 15.95 (978-1-59474-023-7(2)) Quirk Bks.

—JLA: The Ultimate Guide to the Justice League of America. Stewart, Roger, illus. 2002. (Dc Comics Ser.). 96p. (J). (gr. 3-12). 19.99 (978-0-7894-8893-0(0)) Dorling Kindersley Publishing, Inc.

—Murder in Mind, Vol. 4. Guice, Butch et al, illus. 2004. (Ruse Ser.: Vol. 4). 160p. (YA). pap. 15.95 (978-1-59314-047-2(9)) CrossGeneration Comics, Inc.

—Superman: The Ultimate Guide to the Man of Steel. 2006. (Illus.). 144p. (J). 24.99 (978-0-7566-2067-7(8)) Dorling Kindersley Publishing, Inc.

Beatty, Scott & Dougall, Alastair. The Ultimate Guide to the Amazon Princess. 2003. (Illus.). 144p. (J). 24.99 (978-0-7894-9616-4(X)) Dorling Kindersley Publishing, Inc.

Bedard, Tony. Most Haunted, Vol. 2. Moline, Karl et al, illus. 2004. (Route 666 Traveler Ser.: Vol. 2). 160p. (YA). pap. 9.95 (978-1-59314-055-7(X)) CrossGeneration Comics, Inc.

—Mystic: The Mathemagician, Vol. 6. Lopresti, Aaron et al, illus. 2004. (Mystic Ser.). 160p. (YA). pap. 15.95 (978-1-59314-039-7(8)) CrossGeneration Comics, Inc.

—Route 666 Traveler: Highway of Horror. Moline, Karl et al, illus. 2004. (Route 666 Traveler Ser.). 160p. (YA). pap. 9.95 (978-1-59314-041-0(X)) CrossGeneration Comics, Inc.

Beechen, Adam. UFO! (SpongeBob SquarePants) Saunders, Zina, illus. 2005. (Spongebob Squarepants Ser.). 32p. (J). pap. 3.99 (978-0-689-87202-0(X), Simon Spotlight/Nickelodeon) Simon & Schuster Children's Publishing.

—Wild Thornberrys Survival Guide. 2000. (gr. 3-6). lib. bdg. 10.65 (978-0-613-27582-8(9)) Tandem Library Bks.

Beeuwsaert, Matt. I Got Game. Beeuwsaert, Matt, illus. 2003. (Illus.). 176p. per. 14.95 (978-0-9724358-0-2(8)) Beex Art Bks.

Bell, Christine. Oh No! the Television Won't Work! 2005. (Illus.). 52p. pap. (***978-1-84401-340-1(5)**) Athena Pr.

Belshe, Judy. The Fry Family Goes to Hollywood. 2007. (Illus.). 50p. (J). spiral bd. 10.00 (***978-0-9655530-4-9(3)**) Belshe, Judy.

Bendis, Brian Michael. Avengers Disassembled HC. 2007. (Illus.). 184p. 24.99 (978-0-7851-2294-4(X)) Marvel Enterprises, Inc.

—Blockbuster. Finch, David, illus. 2004. 160p. lib. bdg. 24.35 (978-1-4176-6045-2(7)) Tandem Library Bks.

—Carnage. Bagley, Mark, illus. 2004. 100p. lib. bdg. 24.35 (978-1-4176-6038-4(4)) Tandem Library Bks.

—Cats & Kings. Bagley, Mark, illus. 2004. 184p. lib. bdg. 30.15 (978-1-4176-6035-3(X)) Tandem Library Bks.

—Daredevil, Vol. 5. (Illus.). 256p. 29.99 (978-0-7851-2110-7(2)) Marvel Enterprises, Inc.

—Hollywood. Bagley, Mark, illus. 2004. 100p. lib. bdg. 24.35 (978-1-4176-6037-7(6)) Tandem Library Bks.

—Lowlife, 6 vols. Maleev, Alex, illus. 120p. (YA). 13.99 (978-0-7851-1105-4(0)) Marvel Enterprises, Inc.

—The Murdock Papers. (Illus.). 152p. pap. 14.99 (978-0-7851-1810-7(1)) Marvel Enterprises, Inc.

—New Mutants. Finch, David, illus. 2004. lib. bdg. 24.35 (978-1-4176-6046-9(5)) Tandem Library Bks.

—Secrets & Lies, Vol. 3. (Illus.). 128p. 19.99 (978-0-7851-1939-5(6)) Marvel Enterprises, Inc.

—Sentry. (Illus.). 152p. pap. 14.99 (978-0-7851-1672-1(9)) Marvel Enterprises, Inc.

Bendis, Brian Michael & Bagley, Mark. Ultimate Spider-Man Vol. 11: Carnage. 2004. (Spider-Man Ser.). (Illus.). 144p. pap. 12.99 (978-0-7851-1403-1(3)) Marvel Enterprises, Inc.

Bendis, Brian Michael & Finch, David. The Avengers: Disassembled. (Illus.). 176p. pap. 15.99 (978-0-7851-1482-6(3)) Marvel Enterprises, Inc.

—Ultimate X-Men, Vol. 4. 2005. (X-Men Ser.). (Illus.). 304p. 29.99 (978-0-7851-1251-8(0)) Marvel Enterprises, Inc.

Bendis, Brian Michael & Straczynski, J. Michael. The Road to Civil War. 2007. (Civil War Ser.). (Illus.). 160p. (J). pap. 14.99 (978-0-7851-1974-6(4)) Marvel Enterprises, Inc.

Bendis, Brian Michael, et al. What If... ? Why Not?, Vol. 1. 2005. (Marvel Heroes Ser.). (Illus.). 152p. pap. 16.99 (978-0-7851-1593-9(5)) Marvel Enterprises, Inc.

Benintendi, Stephen F. PowerMark 3-pk Issues 1-3. 2004. (J). 7.95 (978-0-9729135-7-7(2)) PowerMark Productions.

—PowerMark 3-pk Issues 4-6. 2004. (YA). 7.95 (978-0-9729135-8-4(0)) PowerMark Productions.

—PowerMark 3-pk Issues 7-9. 2004. (YA). 7.95 (978-0-9729135-9-1(9)) PowerMark Productions.

—PowerMark Issue 22: Unlikely Heroes. 2004. (YA). 2.95 (978-0-9717876-1-2(1)) PowerMark Productions.

—PowerMark Issue 23: Prodigal. 2004. (YA). 2.95 (978-0-9717876-2-9(X)) PowerMark Productions.

—PowerMark Issue 24: Apocalypse. 2004. (YA). 2.95 (978-0-9717876-3-6(8)) PowerMark Productions.

—PowerMark LightQuest Issue 1: The Hunted. 2004. (YA). 2.95 (978-0-9725121-4-5(4)) PowerMark Productions.

—PowerMark Seeker Series Issue 4: Redemption. 2003. (ENG & SPA.). (J). 1.75 (978-0-9729135-4-6(8)) PowerMark Productions.

—PowerMark Seeker Series Issue 5: Transformation. 2003. (ENG & SPA.). (J). 1.75 (978-0-9729135-5-3(6)) PowerMark Productions.

—PowerMark Seeker Series Issue 6: The Pathway. 2003. (ENG & SPA.). (J). 1.75 (978-0-9729135-6-0(4)) PowerMark Productions.

—PowerMark Series One Autographed Box Set: Issues 1-12. aut. ed. 2003. 50.00 (978-0-9717876-4-3(6)) PowerMark Productions.

Benintendi, Steve. PM Seeker Series # 7 Masquerade: Halloween Edition. 2005. (Illus.). 20p. (J). pap. 7.25 (978-0-9749339-1-7(0)) PowerMark Productions.

—PowerMark Issue 10 5-Pack. 2004. (Powermark Comics Ser.). (Illus.). 32p. pap. 14.75 (978-0-9747026-2-9(5)) PowerMark Productions.

Bennett, Anina. Heartbreakers Superdigest Year 10. 1999. 104p. (YA). pap. 13.95 (978-1-58240-124-9(1)) Image Comics.

Beop-Ryong, Yeo. Chronicles of the Cursed Sword, Vol. 13. Hui-Jin, Park, illus. 13th rev. ed. 2005. 192p. pap. 9.99 (978-1-59532-645-4(6), Tokyopop Adult) TOKYOPOP, Inc.

Bergen, Lara. Phonics Comics: Fearless Four - Level 2. Semple, Dave, illus. 2007. 24p. (J). (gr. 1-17). pap. 3.99 (978-1-58476-564-6(X)) Innovative Kids.

Bernthal, Mark S. Coin Toss. 2005. (Duel Masters Ser.). (Illus.). 64p. (J). (ps-7). pap. 3.99 (978-0-439-73383-0(9)) Scholastic, Inc.

Berrill, Jack. Under the Friday Night Lights! A Gil Thorp Football Collection. 2004. (Illus.). 328p. per. 32.95 (978-0-930099-14-5(1)) Take Five Pubs.

Bersson, Robert & Shoup, Dolores. Stripes & Stars. Bersson, Robert & Trobaugh, Scott, illus. l.t. ed. 2003. 40p. (J). (gr. 1-4). per. 16.95 (978-0-9740585-0-4(5)) Legacy Group Productions, LLC.

Betty & Veronica, 6 bks., Set. 2007. (J). 145.26 (***978-1-59961-264-5(X)**) Spotlight.

Bissette, Steve, et al. The Age of Monsters. 1998. (Godzilla Ser.). (Illus.). 272p. (YA). (gr. 5 up). pap. 17.95 (978-1-56971-277-1(8)) Dark Horse Comics.

A Bit Haywire. 2006. (YA). per. 11.95 (978-0-9777883-5-4(0)) Viper Comics.

Blackman, Haden, et al. Star Wars Vol. 2: Clone Wars Adventures. Barlow, Jeremy et al, eds. 2004. (Illus.). 96p. (YA). pap. 6.95 (978-1-59307-271-1(6)) Dark Horse Comics.

—Victories & Sacrifices Vol. 2. 2003. (Illus.). 112p. (YA). pap. 14.95 (978-1-56971-969-5(1)) Dark Horse Comics.

Blaney, Michael, creator. The Fly Chronicles: Life at the Bottom of the Food Chain. 2005. (YA). pap. 12.95 (978-0-9740567-9-1(0)) Active Images.

Blitz, Bruce. The Big Book of Cartooning, No. 1. 2001. (Illus.). 320p. (J). (gr. 4-7). pap. 16.95 (978-0-7624-0939-6(8) , Running Pr. Kids) Running Pr. Bk. Pubs.

Bloom, Carol A. The Wishing Closet. (Magic Mansion Mystery Ser.: Bk. 2). 124p. (J). (gr. 3-6). 9.99 (978-0-88092-476-4(4)) Royal Fireworks Publishing Co.

Bollers, Karl. Bloom Digest, Vol. 3. 2005. (X-Men Ser.). (Illus.). 144p. (YA). pap. 7.99 (978-0-7851-1473-4(4)) Marvel Enterprises, Inc.

Bones. Wolf's Rain. Lida, Toshitsugu, illus. 2005. (Wolf's Rain Ser.). 184p. (YA). pap. 9.99 (978-1-59116-718-1(3)) Viz Media.

Bowkett, Stephen. Detective Files. Burroughs, Dave, illus. 2008. (J). (*978-1-59889-826-2(4)); pap. (*978-1-59889-882-8(5)) Stone Arch Bks.

Bowser, Milton, illus. Cartoon Stories from the Teachings of Buddha. l.t. ed. 2003. (Cartoon Ser.). (JPN & SPA.). 72p. (YA). 10.00 (978-0-940178-34-2(6) , Buddha 1) Sitare, Ltd.

Boylan, Molly. Elmo & Zoe Fly a Kite, 1. 2005. (Illus.). 32p. (ps-17). pap. 3.99 (978-1-59532-746-8(0) , Tokyopop Kids) TOKYOPOP, Inc.

Braddock, Paige. Jane's World, Vol. 4. 2006. (Illus.). 160p. pap. 15.00 (978-0-9766707-3-5(9)) Girl Twirl Comics.

Brightwood, Laura, illus. I Am A Frog. Brightwood, Laura, . 2007. (J). DVD (*978-1-934409-02-2(2)) 3-C Institute for Social Development.

—King's New Suit. Brightwood, Laura, . 2007. (J). DVD (*978-1-934409-05-3(7)) 3-C Institute for Social Development.

—Lion & Mousie. Brightwood, Laura, . 2007. (J). DVD (*978-1-934409-00-8(6)) 3-C Institute for Social Development.

—Little Freddie & His Whistle. Brightwood, Laura, . 2007. (J). DVD (*978-1-934409-01-5(4)) 3-C Institute for Social Development.

—Look What You've Done. Brightwood, Laura, . 2007. (J). DVD (*978-1-934409-03-9(0)) 3-C Institute for Social Development.

—Wolf under the Bed. Brightwood, Laura, . 2007. (J). DVD (*978-1-934409-04-6(9)) 3-C Institute for Social Development.

—The Woodsman & His Ax. Brightwood, Laura, . 2007. (J). DVD (*978-1-934409-07-7(3)) 3-C Institute for Social Development.

Broadhurst, D. T. The Faringo Kid. 2006. pap. 13.49 (*978-1-4259-1836-1(0)) AuthorHouse.

Brooks, Brian. Oopsy Daisy's Bad Day. Brooks, Brian, illus. 2007. (Illus.). 62p. (J). reprint ed. 13.00 (*978-1-4223-9004-7(7)) DIANE Publishing Co.

Broome, John. All Star Comics. rev. ed. 2004. (Archives Ser.: Vol. 10). (Illus.). 216p. 49.95 (978-1-4012-0159-3(8)) DC Comics.

Broome, John & Fox, Gardner. Green Lantern. Didio, Dan, ed. Kane, Gil, illus. rev. ed. 2005. (Showcase Presents Ser.: Vol. 1). 528p. (YA). pap. 9.99 (978-1-4012-0759-5(6)) DC Comics.

Brubaker, Ed. Fantastic Four: Books of Doom TPB: Books of Doom TPB. 2007. (Illus.). 144p. pap. 14.99 (978-0-7851-1704-9(0)) Marvel Enterprises, Inc.

Bucki, Jo Dee & O'Malley, John. Maya Visits a Hospital: Love Is the Best Medicine, 110 vols. Hicks, Mindy, ed. Matthews, Ashley, illus. l.t. ed. 2007. 32p. (J). per. 4.95 (978-0-9769069-0-2(2)) Maya Ventures & Publishing.

Buckley, James, Jr. Los Asombrosos Poderes de Spider-Man. O'Neill, Cynthia, ed. 2005. (Dk Readers Ser.). (Illus.). 48p. (J). (ps-7). 14.99 (978-0-7566-1500-0(3)) Dorling Kindersley Publishing, Inc.

Buckley, James. Los Asombrosos Poderes de Spider-Man. O'Neill, Cynthia, ed. 2005. (Dk Readers Ser.). (Illus.). 48p. (J). (ps-7). pap. 3.99 (978-0-7566-1499-7(6)) Dorling Kindersley Publishing, Inc.

—Creating the X-Men: How Comic Books Came to Life. 2000. (gr. k-3). lib. bdg. 11.80 (978-0-613-32428-1(5)) Tandem Library Bks.

Bugtime Adventures - Blessing in Disguise. 2005. (J). 3.95 (978-1-933262-26-0(5)) Lightning Bug Flix.

Bui-Quang, Phuong-Mai. Tea Club. 2006. (YA). per. 10.95 (978-1-59971-581-0(3)) Aardvark Global Publishing.

Bulloch, Ivan. Cartoons & Animation. 1999. pap. 3.99 (978-0-516-24117-3(6)); (Illus.). 32p. (J). (gr. 3-6). pap. 6.95 (978-0-516-26342-7(0)) Scholastic Library Publishing. (Children's Pr.).

Burgan, Michael. Hot Iron: The Adventures of a Civil War Powder Boy. Rodríquez, Pedro, illus. 2007. (J). pap. (*978-1-59889-406-6(4)); 56p. (gr. 3-6). 23.93 (*978-1-59889-311-3(4)) Stone Arch Bks.

Burstein, Chaya M. The Kids' Cartoon Bible. 2002. (Illus.). 132p. pap. 17.95 (978-0-8276-0729-3(6)) Jewish Pubn. Society.

Busiek, Kurt. Syndicate Rules, Vol. 17. Garney, Ron, illus. rev. ed. 2005. 200p. pap. 17.99 (978-1-4012-0477-8(5)) DC Comics.

Busiek, Kurt, et al. Avengers Assemble HC, Vol. 3. 2006. (Illus.). 424p. 34.99 (978-0-7851-2130-5(7)) Marvel Enterprises, Inc.

Butch, Hartman. The Fairly Oddparents Vol. 6: Gone Too Far. 2005. (Illus.). 96p. (J). pap. 7.99 (978-1-59532-898-4(X)) TOKYOPOP, Inc.

Cabarga, Leslie & Beck, Jerry. Harvey Comics Classics Volume 1: Casper: Casper. 2007. (Illus.). 480p. pap. 19.95 (*978-1-59307-781-5(5)) Dark Horse Comics.

Cabot, Meg. The Merlin Prophecy. Coronado, Jinky, illus. 2007. (Avalon High Coronation Ser.: No. 1). 208p. (J). (gr. 7 up). pap. 7.99 (*978-0-06-117707-1(5)) TOKYOPOP, Inc.

Cadic, Oliver. Queen Margot. 2007. (Illus.). 52p. pap. 13.95 (*978-1-905460-19-9(8)) CineBook GBR. *Dist:* Biblio Distribution.

Cadic, Olivier & Gheysens, Francois. Queen Margot: The Age of Innocence. Spear, Luke, tr. from FRE. Derenne, Juliette, illus. 2007. 48p. pap. 13.95 (*978-1-905460-10-6(4)) CineBook GBR. *Dist:* Biblio Distribution.

Campbell, Jan-Ives. League of Super Groovy Crimefighters Trade Paperback. Taylor, James et al, illus. 2003. (YA). per. 12.95 (978-0-9744216-0-5(X)) Ancient Studios.

Caniff, Milton. The Complete Terry & the Pirates Vol. 1: 1934 - 1936 a Library of American Comics Original. 2007. 368p. 49.99 (*978-1-60010-100-7(3)) Diamond Bk. Distributors.

Capcom, et al, creators. Devil May Cry. 2006. pap. 7.99 (978-1-59816-450-3(3) , Tokyopop Adult) TOKYOPOP, Inc.

Caple, Kathy. Worm Gets a Job. Caple, Kathy, illus. 2004. (Illus.). 40p. (J). (gr. k-3). 15.99 (978-0-7636-1694-6(X)) Candlewick Pr.

Carew, Kieran. 1 Block Down. Yan, Stan, illus. 2004. 24p. (YA). 2.95 (978-0-9755041-2-3(6)) Squid Works.

Carey, Mike. The Divine Comedy. Gross et al, illus. rev. ed. 2003. (Lucifer Ser.: Bk. 4,Vol. 4). 192p. pap. 17.99 (978-1-4012-0009-1(5)) DC Comics.

—Ultimate X-Men/Fantastic Four TPB. 2006. (Illus.). 152p. pap. 12.99 (978-0-7851-2292-0(3)) Marvel Enterprises, Inc.

Carey, Mike, et al. Mirror Mirror. 2006. (Illus.). 152p. (YA). pap. 16.99 (978-0-7851-1902-9(7)) Marvel Enterprises, Inc.

Carmody, Isobelle. Dreamwalker. Woolman, Steven, illus. 2002. 48p. (YA). (978-0-7344-0007-9(1) , Lothian Bks.) Hachette Livre Australia.

Cartoon Network Staff, contrib. by. Name That Toon: Cartoon Network Triva Book. 2000. (Illus.). 48p. (J). (ps-3). pap. 3.99 (978-0-307-10777-0(9) , Golden Bks.) Random Hse. Children's Bks.

Cartoon Stickers. 2004. (Art Rom Create Your Own... Ser.). (Illus.). 24p. (J). pap. incl. audio compact disk (978-1-84229-737-7(6)) Top That! Publishing PLC.

Casey, Joe & Gerard, Caleb. Full Moon Fever. 2005. (Illus.). 88p. (YA). pap. 12.95 (978-1-932051-35-3(X)) A i T/Planet Lar.

Cassaday, John, et al. Weird Tales. (Hellboy Ser.: Vol. 1). 128p. (YA). pap. 17.95 (978-1-56971-622-9(6)) Dark Horse Comics.

Chadwick, Paul. Darklighter. 2004. (Star Wars Ser.: Vol. 2). 144p. (YA). pap. 17.95 (978-1-56971-975-6(6)) Dark Horse Comics.

—Depths. 2005. (Illus.). 208p. (YA). pap. 12.95 (978-1-59307-343-5(7)) Dark Horse Comics.

Chariton, Dan & Weiss, Stacy. Silver Surfer, Vol. 2. 2005. (Silver Surfer Ser.: Vol. 2). (Illus.). 192p. (YA). pap. 19.99 (978-0-7851-1575-5(7)) Marvel Enterprises, Inc.

Charlip, Remy & Moore, Lilian. Hooray for Me! 2007. (Illus.). 40p. (J). pap. 7.95 (*978-1-58246-201-1(1) , Tricycle Pr.) Ten Speed Pr.

Cheung, Dave. Chugworth Academy, Vol. 1. 2006. (Illus.). 160p. pap. 13.99 (978-1-933164-17-5(4)) Seven Seas Entertainment, LLC.

Chiang, Dean. The Yearning. 2000. (Illus.). 96p. (YA). pap. 10.95 (978-0-943151-11-3(2)) Slave Labor Bks.

Chickasaw Adventures: More than Warriors. 2005. (J). (978-1-4265-0002-2(5)) Layne Morgan Media, Inc.

Chickasaw Adventures: Tears at Fort Coffee. 2004. (J). (978-0-9762904-2-1(1)) Layne Morgan Media, Inc.

Chickasaw Adventures: The Battle of Akia. 2004. (J). (978-0-9762904-1-4(3)) Layne Morgan Media, Inc.

Chickasaw Adventures: The Civil War. 2005. (J). (978-1-4265-0000-8(9)) Layne Morgan Media, Inc.

Chickasaw Adventures: The Making of a Storyteller. 2004. (J). (978-0-9762904-3-8(X)) Layne Morgan Media, Inc.

Chickasaw Adventures: War with the Creeks. 2005. (J). (978-1-4265-0001-5(7)) Layne Morgan Media, Inc.

Chickasaw Adventures No. 1: The Journey Begins. 2004. (J). (978-0-9762904-0-7(5)) Layne Morgan Media, Inc.

Child, Lauren. Hubert Horatio Bartle Bobton-Trent. 2005. (Illus.). 32p. (ps-2). 16.99 (978-0-7868-5485-1(5)) Hyperion Bks. for Children.

Chin, Oliver. 9 of 1: A Window to the World. 2003. (gr. 7-12). lib. bdg. 19.90 (978-0-613-79605-7(5)) Tandem Library Bks.

Ching, Jacqueline. Cloned. 12th rev. ed. 2006. (Kim Possible Ser.: Bk. 12). 80p. (gr. 2-5). pap. 3.99 (978-0-7868-4691-7(7)) Disney Pr.

Ching, Jerry Yu & Onghai, Mike. The Greatest King. Ching, Jerry Yu, illus. 2nd l.t. ed. 2003. (Illus.). 52p. (978-0-9743215-0-9(8)) WebCartoons, LLC.

Chizuru, Mio. The Pirate & the Princess Volume 1: the Timelight Stone: The Timelight Stone. 2007. 110p. (J). pap. 5.99 (*978-1-933164-43-4(3)) Seven Seas Entertainment, LLC.

—The Pirate & the Princess Volume 2: the Red Crystal: The Red Crystal. 2007. 110p. (J). pap. 5.99 (*978-1-933164-44-1(1)) Seven Seas Entertainment, LLC.

Cho, Jerry, et al. Stray Little Devil. 2006. (Illus.). 200p. (YA). pap. 9.95 (978-1-59796-043-4(8)) DrMaster Pubns. Inc.

Chon, Kye Young. Audition: Volume 1, 10 vols. 2006. (Audition Ser.). (Illus.). 176p. pap. 11.99 (978-1-933809-43-4(4)) DramaQueen, L.L.C.

Christantemo. 2004. pap. 32.75 incl. audio (978-1-55592-343-3(7)) Weston Woods Studios, Inc.

Christin, Dominique. Girlz Rock: The Go-Girl Kit with Attitude. Cider Mill Press Staff, ed. gif. ed. 2006. (Magnetic Wisdom Ser.). (Illus.). 96p. pap. 9.95 (978-1-933662-26-8(3)) Cider Mill Pr. Bk. Pubs. LLC.

Chronicle Books LLC Staff. Nickelodeon Nighttime Book. (J). 16.95 (978-0-8118-4628-8(8)) Chronicle Bks. LLC.

Chrono, Nanae. Peacemaker Kurogane, Vol. 1. Forsyth, Amy, tr. 2004. (Illus.). 194p. (YA). pap. (978-1-4139-0161-0(1)) ADV Manga.

—Peacemaker Kurogane, Vol. 2. 2004. (Illus.). 184p. (YA). pap. (978-1-4139-0192-4(1)) ADV Manga.

Ciencin, Scott. Masters of Mayhem. 3rd rev. ed. 2005. (Illus.). 80p. (gr. 2-5). pap. 3.99 (978-0-7868-4689-4(5)) Disney Pr.

Clamp. Angelic Layer, 5 vols. (gr. 2-6). Vol. 1. 2002. (Illus.). 180p. pap. 9.99 (978-1-931514-47-7(X)); Vol. 2 rev. ed. 2002. (Illus.). 180p. pap. 9.99 (978-1-59182-003-1(0)); Vol. 3. 3rd rev. ed. 2002. 192p. (J). pap. 9.99 (978-1-59182-004-8(9)); Vol. 5. rev. ed. 2003. (Illus.). 196p. pap. 9.99 (978-1-59182-152-6(5)) TOKYOPOP, Inc. (Tokyopop Kids).

—The Art of Cardcaptor Sakura, 3 vols., Vol. 1. 2002. 120p. (gr. 2-6). pap. 19.99 (978-1-59182-000-0(6)) TOKYOPOP, Inc.

—Cardcaptor Sakura, Vol. 6. rev. ed. 2005. (Illus.). pap. 9.99 (978-1-59182-883-9(X) , Tokyopop Kids) TOKYOPOP, Inc.

—Cardcaptor Sakura: Master of the Clow, 6 vols. (Illus.). 192p. (gr. 2-6). Vol. 1. 2002. pap. 9.99 (978-1-892213-75-4(3)); Vol. 3. 2003. pap. 9.99 (978-1-892213-77-8(X)); Vol. 4. 2003. pap. 9.99 (978-1-892213-78-5(8)) TOKYOPOP, Inc. (Tokyopop Kids).

—Cardcaptor Sakura Master of the Clow No.01. 2002. (gr. 7-12). lib. bdg. 18.80 (978-0-613-80311-3(6)) Tandem Library Bks.

—Cardcaptor Sakura Master of the Clow No.02. 2002. (gr. 7-12). lib. bdg. 18.80 (978-0-613-80316-8(7)) Tandem Library Bks.

—Magic Knight Rayearth, 2 vols., Vol. 2, Set. 2003. (Illus.). 650p. (gr. 2 up). pap. 29.99 (978-1-59182-091-8(X)) TOKYOPOP, Inc.

—Master of the Clow 5. 2003. (gr. 3-6). lib. bdg. 18.80 (978-0-613-80317-5(5)) Tandem Library Bks.

—Serenade, Vol. 5. 1999. (X/1999 Ser.). (Illus.). 184p. (YA). pap. 15.95 (978-1-56931-407-4(1)) Viz Media.

—X/1999 Vol. 16: Nocturne. Clamp, illus. 2004. (X/1999 Ser.). (Illus.). 184p. (YA). pap. 9.95 (978-1-59116-596-5(2)) Viz Media.

—X/1999 Vol. 17: Suite. Clamp, illus. 2005. (X/1999 Ser.). (Illus.). 176p. (YA). pap. 9.95 (978-1-59116-682-5(9)) Viz Media.

Clamp, creator. Angelic Layer, 5 vols., Vol. 4. rev. ed. 2003. (Illus.). 192p. (gr. 2 up). pap. 9.99 (978-1-59182-086-4(3) , Tokyopop Kids) TOKYOPOP, Inc.

—Legend of Chun Hyang, Vol. 1. 2004. (Illus.). 192p. (gr. 2-5). pap. 9.99 (978-1-59182-763-4(9) , Tokyopop Adult) TOKYOPOP, Inc.

Clamp, ed. Chobits with Figurine. 2003. (Illus.). 96p. pap. 19.99 (978-1-59182-588-3(1)) TOKYOPOP, Inc.

Clamp, illus. & creator. Cardcaptor Sakura, Vol. 5. Clamp, creator. 5th rev. ed. 2005. pap. 9.99 (978-1-59182-882-2(1) , Tokyopop Kids) TOKYOPOP, Inc.

—Rg Veda. Clamp, creator. 2005. pap. 9.99 (978-1-59532-484-9(4) , Tokyopop Adult) TOKYOPOP, Inc.

—Tokyo Babylon, Vol. 7. Clamp, creator. rev. ed. 2005. 160p. pap. 9.99 (978-1-59532-051-3(2) , Tokyopop Adult) TOKYOPOP, Inc.

Clamp, et al. Cardcaptor Sakura: Master of the Clow, 6 vols., Vol. 2. rev. ed. 2002. (Illus.). 192p. (gr. 2-6). pap. 9.99 (978-1-892213-76-1(1) , Tokyopop Kids) TOKYOPOP, Inc.

Claremont, Chris. Days of Future Past. 2004. (X-Men Ser.). (Illus.). 144p. (YA). 19.99 (978-0-7851-1560-1(9)) Marvel Enterprises, Inc.

—Excalibur Classic : Cross-Time Caper Book 1 TPB, Vol. 3. 2007. (Illus.). 216p. pap. 24.99 (978-0-7851-2202-9(8)) Marvel Enterprises, Inc.

—New Mutants Classic, Vol. 1. 2006. (Illus.). 240p. pap. 24.99 (978-0-7851-2194-7(3)) Marvel Enterprises, Inc.

—Wolverine by Claremont & Miller Premiere HC. 2007. (Illus.). 144p. 19.99 (978-0-7851-2329-3(6)) Marvel Enterprises, Inc.

—X-Men. 2005. (Essential Ser.: Vol. 2). (Illus.). 584p. pap. 16.99 (978-0-7851-2007-0(6)) Marvel Enterprises, Inc.

—X-Men: the Dark Phoenix Saga (New Printing) TPB: The Dark Phoenix Saga (New Printing) TPB. 2006. (Illus.). 200p. pap. 24.99 (978-0-7851-2213-5(3)) Marvel Enterprises, Inc.

Claremont, Chris & Lee. X-Men: Mutant Genesis TPB: Mutant Genesis TPB. 2nd ed. 2006. (Illus.). 184p. pap. 19.99 (978-0-7851-2212-8(5)) Marvel Enterprises, Inc.

Claremont, Chris & Milligan, Peter. Decimation: X-Men - the Day after TPB: X-Men - the Day after TPB. 2006. (Illus.). 160p. pap. 15.99 (978-0-7851-1984-5(1)) Marvel Enterprises, Inc.

Clarke, Carol Page. The Cuddly Mogs. 2006. (Illus.). 72p. pap. (*978-1-84401-620-4(X)) Athena Pr.

Clements, Andrew. Lunch Money. Selznick, Brian, illus. l.t. ed. 2005. 231p. (J). (gr. 3-7). 21.95 (978-0-7862-8036-0(0) , Large Print Pr.) Thorndike Pr.

Clopper, Brian. Graham the Gargoyle: Fear of Flying. Clopper, Michelle & Morgan, Katrina, eds. Clopper, Brian, illus. 2000. (Illus.). 108p. (J). (ps-3). pap. 6.95 (978-0-9700659-0-2(6) , Teeny Behemoth Bks.) Topsy Turvy Pubns.

Clueless George Goes to War. 2005. (Illus.). 32p. (J). (ps-3). per. 7.95 (978-0-9744860-5-5(1)) White Horse Bks.

Coffman, Patrick, tr. Vampire Game, Vol. 11. Judal, illus. rev. ed. 2005. 208p. pap. 9.99 (978-1-59532-441-2(0) , Tokyopop Adult) TOKYOPOP, Inc.

Cole, Bob. Power Reading: Comic Book/Dr. Little. Sirrell, Terri, illus. 2005. 36p. (J). (gr. 2-4). vinyl bd. (978-1-883186-77-7(3) , PPSFC1) National Reading Styles Institute, Inc.

—Power Reading: Comic Book/Jungle Book. Connor, Robin, illus. 2005. 62p. (J). (gr. 3 up). vinyl bd. 39.95 (978-1-883186-74-6(9) , PPCLC2) National Reading Styles Institute, Inc.

—Power Reading: Comic Book/Superhero. Ford, David, illus. 2005. 34p. (J). (gr. 2-4). vinyl bd. 29.95 (978-1-883186-79-1(X) , PPSFC2) National Reading Styles Institute, Inc.

—Power Reading: Comic Book/Time Warp. Ford, David, illus. 2005. 36p. (J). (gr. 3-4). vinyl bd. 29.95 (978-1-883186-69-2(2) , PPSFC3) National Reading Styles Institute, Inc.

—Power Reading: Comic Book/Treasure Island. Lee, Ioe, illus. 2005. 70p. (J). (gr. 4-6). vinyl bd. (978-1-883186-78-4(1) , PPCLC3) National Reading Styles Institute, Inc.

—Power Reading: Comic Book/Wizard of OZ. Sirrell, Terri, illus. 2005. 60p. (J). (gr. 3-4). vinyl bd. 39.95 (978-1-883186-80-7(3) , PPCLC1) National Reading Styles Institute, Inc.

Collins, Terry. Spongebob Naturepants. Bond, Clint, illus. 2001. (SpongeBob SquarePants Chapter Bks.: Vol. 7). 64p. (J). (gr. 2-5). pap. 3.99 (978-0-689-84194-1(9) , Simon Spotlight) Simon & Schuster Children's Publishing.

Comic Debris Staff. The Boring Issue. 2005. (Illus.). 48p. (J). pap. 7.95 (978-1-59307-323-7(2)) Dark Horse Comics.

Cook, Greg. Friends Is Friends. 2009. 192p. (YA). pap. 16.95 (978-1-59643-105-8(9)) Roaring Brook Pr.

—Iraq Project. 2009. 192p. (YA). pap. 16.95 (978-1-59643-104-1(0)) Roaring Brook Pr.

Cooke, Darwyn, et al. Spider-Man's Tangled Web, 4 vols., Vol. 4. Cooke, Darwyn et al, illus. 2003. (Spider-Man's Tangled Web Ser.). 176p. (YA). 15.99 (978-0-7851-1064-4(X)) Marvel Enterprises, Inc.

Cosentino, Ralph. Batman. 2008. 40p. (J). (ps). 15.99 (*978-0-670-06255-3(3) , Viking Juvenile) Penguin Group (USA) Inc.

Cosmic Debris Staff. Dark Issue. 2006. (Illus.). 48p. (J). pap. 7.95 (978-1-59307-467-8(0)) Dark Horse Comics.

—The Lost Issue. 2005. (Emily the Strange Ser.: Bk. 2). (Illus.). 48p. (YA). pap. 7.95 (978-1-59307-429-6(8)) Dark Horse Comics.

Cosmic Debris Staff, contrib. by. Emily the Strange: Seeing/Deceiving. 2006. 64p. 12.95 (978-0-8118-5626-3(7)) Chronicle Bks. LLC.

Coy, John. Around the World. Reonegro, Antonio & Lynch, Tom, illus. 2005. 32p. (J). (gr. 1-4). 17.95 (978-1-58430-244-5(5)) Lee & Low Bks., Inc.

Craft, Jerry. Mama's Boyz: Home Schoolin' Because Learning Shouldn't Stop at 3 O'clock!, 2. 2007. (Illus.). 112p. (YA). per. 9.95 (*978-0-9796132-0-3(5)) Mama's Boyz, Inc.

Crane, Stephen. Stephen Crane/the Red Badge of Courage. Carrillo, Fred, illus. 2005. 48p. (gr. 5-8). 25.50 (978-0-7910-9103-6(1)) Facts On File, Inc.

Crilley, Mark. Akiko: Pieces of Gax. Crilley, Mark, illus. 2006. (Illus.). 224p. (gr. 3). lib. bdg. 11.99 (978-0-385-90430-8(4) , Delacorte Bks. for Young Readers) Random Hse. Children's Bks.

—Akiko: Pieces of Gax. Crilley, Mark, illus. 2006. (Illus.). 224p. (J). (gr. 3). 9.95 (978-0-385-73044-0(6) , Delacorte Bks. for Young Readers) Random Hse. Children's Bks.

—Bornstone's Elixir. 2001. (gr. 3-6). lib. bdg. 22.20 (978-0-613-50412-6(7)) Tandem Library Bks.

—Flights of Fancy. exp. ed. 2007. (Illus.). 264p. pap. 24.95 (*978-1-57989-088-9(1)) Sirius Entertainment, Inc.

—Spring. Crilley, Mark, illus. 2007. (Miki Falls Ser.). (Illus.). 176p. (J). (gr. 7 up). pap. 7.99 (*978-0-06-084616-9(X) , HarperTeen) HarperCollins Pubs.

—Summer. Crilley, Mark, illus. 2007. (Miki Falls Ser.). (Illus.). 176p. (J). (gr. 7 up). pap. 7.99 (*978-0-06-084617-6(8) , HarperTeen) HarperCollins Pubs.

Croall, Marie. Sinbad. Hilinski, Clint, illus. 2007. (Graphic Myths & Legends Ser.). 48p. (J). (gr. 4-8). 26.60 (978-0-8225-6375-4(4)) Lerner Publishing Group.

Croall, Marie P. & Lago, Ray, texts. Marwe: Into the Land of the Dead: An East African Folktale. 2007. (Graphic Myths & Legends Ser.). (J). 26.60 (*978-0-8225-7134-6(X) , Graphic Universe) Lerner Publishing Group.

Cronin, Doreen. Wiggle. 2006. (J). (ps-3). 22.78 (978-1-59961-093-1(0)) Spotlight.

Curry, Don, ed. Spider-Man 3 Board Game Book. 2007. 10p. (J). bds. 12.99 (*978-0-696-23411-8(4)) Meredith Bks.

Cuthbert, Jennifer. The Adventures of Lollipop. 2004. 28p. 4.95 (978-0-9732053-0-5(X)) Peppermint Publishing CAN. *Dist:* Hushion Hse. Publishing, Ltd.

Czekaj, Jef. Grampa & Julie: Shark Hunters. 2004. (Illus.). 128p. pap. 14.95 (978-1-891830-52-5(X)) Top Shelf Productions.

Dakin, Glenn & Dorling Kindersley Publishing Staff. Scooby-Doo! The Essential Guide. 2004. (Illus.). 48p. (J). 12.99 (978-0-7566-0300-7(5)) Dorling Kindersley Publishing, Inc.

Dalmatian Press Staff. Disney Ultimate Wipe-off Book. 2006. (Illus.). 10p. (J). bds. 12.99 (978-1-4037-2412-0(1)) Dalmatian Pr.

—Justice League: Big Best Book to Color with Stickers. 2005. (Justice League Ser.). (Illus.). 80p. (J). pap. 3.99 (978-1-4037-0826-7(6)) Dalmatian Pr.

—Justice League: Saving the World. 2005. (Justice League Ser.). (Illus.). 400p. (J). pap. 5.99 (978-1-4037-0537-2(2)) Dalmatian Pr.

—Marked for Fun! Amazing Marker Book. 2004. (Powerpuff Girls Ser.). 48p. (J). pap. 4.99 (978-1-4037-0819-9(3)) Dalmatian Pr.

—Power Rangers: Bright Idea Book to Color. rev. ed. 2003. (Power Rangers Ninja Storm Ser.). (Illus.). 32p. (J). 4.49 (978-1-4037-0442-9(2)) Dalmatian Pr.

—Power Rangers: : Wild Force. 2004. 400p. (J). pap. 5.99 (978-1-4037-0811-3(8)) Dalmatian Pr.

Dark Horse Comics Staff & Burden, Bob. Flaming Carrot's Greatest Hits. 1998. (Flaming Carrot Comics Ser.: No. 3). (Illus.). 216p. (gr. 11 up). pap. 17.95 (978-1-56971-282-5(4)) Dark Horse Comics.

Dark Horse Comics Staff & Manabe, Johji. Drakuun: Shadow of the Warlock. 1999. 160p. (gr. 11 up). pap. 14.95 (978-1-56971-406-5(1)) Dark Horse Comics.

Dark Horse Comics Staff & Sakai, Stan. Daisho. 1998. (Usagi Yojimbo Ser.). 200p. (YA). (gr. 5 up). pap. 14.95 (978-1-56971-292-4(1)) Dark Horse Comics.

Dark Horse Comics Staff & Shirow, Masamune. Dominion: Tank Police. 3rd ed. 2000. (Illus.). 224p. (gr. 11 up). pap. 16.95 (978-1-56971-488-1(6)) Dark Horse Comics.

Dark Horse Comics Staff & Warner, Chris. No World So Dark. 2000. (Ghost Ser.). (Illus.). 136p. (YA). (gr. 9 up). pap. 14.95 (978-1-56971-434-8(7)) Dark Horse Comics.

Darlington, Jeff. Gone with the Windows. 2000. (General Protection Fault Ser.: Vol. 2). 152p. pap. 12.95 (978-1-929462-19-3(0)) Plan Nine Publishing, Inc.

David, Peter. Nothing to Lose. Cross, Chris, illus. 2003. (Captain Marvel Ser.). 144p. (YA). pap. 12.99 (978-0-7851-1104-7(2)) Marvel Enterprises, Inc.

—Peter David, Vol. 3. 2006. (Illus.). 192p. pap. 19.99 (978-0-7851-2095-7(5)) Marvel Enterprises, Inc.

—Wolverine Classic, Vol. 3. 2006. (Illus.). 144p. (YA). pap. 14.99 (978-0-7851-2053-7(X)) Marvel Enterprises, Inc.

David, Peter, et al. The Return of the Worthy. 2007. (Illus.). 160p. pap. 19.95 (***978-1-84576-319-0(X)***) Titan Bks. Ltd. GBR. *Dist:* Random Hse., Inc.

Davidson, Ellen. Goodnight Around the World. Wise, Noreen, ed. Schneider, Rex, illus. 2000. 32p. (J). (ps up). pap. 5.95 (978-1-58584-352-7(0)) Huckleberry Pr.

Davis, Alan. Killraven. Davis, Alan, illus. 2003. (Spider-Man Ser.). (Illus.). 144p. (YA). pap. 16.99 (978-0-7851-1083-5(6)) Marvel Enterprises, Inc.

Davis, Alan, et al, illus. Excalibur Classic Vol. 2: Two-Edged Sword. 2006. 200p. pap. 24.99 (978-0-7851-2201-2(X)) Marvel Enterprises, Inc.

Davis, Daniel M. & Davis, Dawna Jo. Klawberry: Good Girl. Bad World. McClellan, Sara, ed. ltd. ed. 2007. per. 20.00 (***978-0-9774173-3-9(6)***) Steam Crow Pr.

Davis, Jim. Fat Cat, No.1. 2003. (J). (gr. 5-8). lib. bdg. 24.55 (978-0-613-68581-8(4)) Tandem Library Bks.

—Garfield: Sticht Zu. Goetting, Waltraud & Bartoszko, Alexandra, trs. from ENG. (Garfield Ser.: Vol. 10). (GER., Illus.). 128p. (J). pap. 10.95 (978-3-8105-0754-9(7)) Kruger, Wolfgang Verlag, GmbH DEU. *Dist:* Distribooks, Inc., International Bk. Import Service, Inc.

—Garfield at Large: His First Book. 2001. (gr. 5-8). lib. bdg. 18.75 (978-0-613-81056-2(2)) Tandem Library Bks.

—Garfield au Kilo. 2000. (Garfield Ser.: No. 1). Tr. of Garfield by the Pound. (FRE.). (J). 7.95 (978-2-922148-00-8(9)) Presses aventure/Adventure Pr. CAN. *Dist:* AIMS International Bks., Inc.

—Garfield Beefs Up: His 37th Book. 2000. (gr. 5-8). lib. bdg. 19.90 (978-0-613-68578-8(4)) Tandem Library Bks.

—Garfield Benimmt sich Daneben. Goetting, Waltraud & Bartoszko, Alexandra, trs. from ENG. (GER., Illus.). 128p. (J). pap. (978-3-8105-0890-4(X)) Kruger, Wolfgang Verlag, GmbH DEU. *Dist:* International Bk. Import Service, Inc.

—Garfield Blast sich Auf. Goetting, Waltraud & Bartoszko, Alexandra, trs. from ENG. (Garfield Ser.: Vol. 20). (GER., Illus.). 128p. (J). pap. (978-3-8105-0884-3(5)) Kruger, Wolfgang Verlag, GmbH DEU. *Dist:* International Bk. Import Service, Inc.

—Garfield Bleibt sich Treu. Goetting, Waltraud & Bartoszko, Alexandra, trs. from ENG. (Garfield Ser.: Vol.19). (GER., Illus.). 128p. (J). pap. (978-3-8105-0880-5(2)) Kruger, Wolfgang Verlag, GmbH DEU. *Dist:* International Bk. Import Service, Inc.

—Garfield Casse la Croute. 2000. (Garfield Ser.: No. 6). Tr. of Garfield Dishes It Out. (FRE.). (J). 7.95 (978-2-922148-05-3(X)) Presses aventure/Adventure Pr. CAN. *Dist:* AIMS International Bks., Inc.

—Garfield Chef de File. 2000. (Garfield Ser.: No. 4). Tr. of Garfield Hits the Big Time. (FRE.). (J). 7.95 (978-2-922148-03-9(3)) Presses aventure/Adventure Pr. CAN. *Dist:* AIMS International Bks., Inc.

—Garfield Dreht Durch. Goetting, Waltraud & Bartoszko, Alexandra, trs. from ENG. (Garfield Ser.: Vol. 22). (GER., Illus.). 128p. (J). pap. (978-3-8105-0886-7(1)) Kruger, Wolfgang Verlag, GmbH DEU. *Dist:* International Bk. Import Service, Inc.

—Garfield et Ses Amis. 2000. (Garfield Ser.: No. 3). Tr. of Garfield Takes His Licks. (FRE.). (J). 7.95 (978-2-922148-02-2(5)) Presses aventure/Adventure Pr. CAN. *Dist:* AIMS International Bks., Inc.

—Garfield Fait le Plein. 2000. (Garfield Ser.: No. 7). Tr. of Garfield Life in the Fat Lane. (FRE.). (J). 7.95 (978-2-922148-06-0(8)) Presses aventure/Adventure Pr. CAN. *Dist:* AIMS International Bks., Inc.

—Garfield Feeds the Kitty. 2000. (gr. 3-6). lib. bdg. 16.40 (978-0-613-21576-3(1)) Tandem Library Bks.

—Garfield Fou Rire. 2000. (Garfield Ser.: No. 8). Tr. of Garfield Tons of Fun. (FRE.). (J). 7.95 (978-2-922148-07-7(6)) Presses aventure/Adventure Pr. CAN. *Dist:* AIMS International Bks., Inc.

—Garfield Gets Cookin' His 38th Book. 2001. (gr. 5-8). lib. bdg. 18.75 (978-0-613-68582-5(2)) Tandem Library Bks.

—Garfield Halt die Ohren Steif. Goetting, Waltraud & Bartoszko, Alexandra, trs. from ENG. (Garfield Ser.: Vol. 23). (GER., Illus.). 128p. (J). pap. (978-3-8105-0889-8(6)) Kruger, Wolfgang Verlag, GmbH DEU. *Dist:* International Bk. Import Service, Inc.

—Garfield Hangt Ab. Bartoszko, Alexandra, tr. from ENG. (Garfield Ser.: Vol. 32). (GER., Illus.). 128p. (J). pap. (978-3-8105-0918-5(3)) Kruger, Wolfgang Verlag, GmbH DEU. *Dist:* International Bk. Import Service, Inc.

—Garfield Hat Genug. Goetting, Waltraud & Bartoszko, Alexandra, trs. from ENG. (Garfield Ser.: Vol. 18). (GER., Illus.). 128p. (J). pap. (978-3-8105-0833-1(0)) Kruger, Wolfgang Verlag, GmbH DEU. *Dist:* International Bk. Import Service, Inc.

—Garfield Hat Schwein. Bartoszko, Alexandra, tr. from ENG. (Garfield Ser.: Vol. 31). (GER., Illus.). 128p. (J). pap. (978-3-8105-0897-3(7)) Kruger, Wolfgang Verlag, GmbH DEU. *Dist:* International Bk. Import Service, Inc.

—Garfield Haut Rein. Goetting, Waltraud & Bartoszko, Alexandra, trs. from ENG. (Garfield Ser.: Vol. 17). (GER., Illus.). 128p. (J). pap. (978-3-8105-0779-2(2)) Kruger, Wolfgang Verlag, GmbH DEU. *Dist:* International Bk. Import Service, Inc.

—Garfield Hebt Ab. Goetting, Waltraud & Bartoszko, Alexandra, trs. from ENG. (Garfield Ser.: Vol. 16). (GER., Illus.). 128p. (J). pap. (978-3-8105-0776-1(8)) Kruger, Wolfgang Verlag, GmbH DEU. *Dist:* International Bk. Import Service, Inc.

—Garfield Hogs the Spotlight: His 36th Book. 2000. (Garfield Ser.: Vol. 36). (Illus.). 128p. pap. 7.95 (978-0-345-43922-2(8) , Ballantine Bks.) Random House Publishing Group.

—Garfield Hogs the Spotlight: His 36th Book. 2000. (gr. 5-8). lib. bdg. 16.40 (978-0-613-68583-2(0)); (Illus.). (J). 15.50 (978-0-606-17987-4(9)) Tandem Library Bks.

—Garfield ist Spitze. Goetting, Waltraud & Bartoszko, Alexandra, trs. from ENG. (Garfield Ser.: Vol. 11). (GER., Illus.). 128p. (J). pap. (978-3-8105-0757-0(1)) Kruger, Wolfgang Verlag, GmbH DEU. *Dist:* International Bk. Import Service, Inc.

—Garfield Kratzt die Kurve. Goetting, Waltraud & Bartoszko, Alexandra, trs. from ENG. (Garfield Ser.: Vol. 28). (GER., Illus.). 128p. (J). pap. (978-3-8105-0894-2(2)) Kruger, Wolfgang Verlag, GmbH DEU. *Dist:* International Bk. Import Service, Inc.

—Garfield Lasst nicht Locker. Goetting, Waltraud & Bartoszko, Alexandra, trs. from ENG. (Garfield Ser.: Vol. 14). (GER., Illus.). 128p. (J). pap. (978-3-8105-0771-6(7)) Kruger, Wolfgang Verlag, GmbH DEU. *Dist:* International Bk. Import Service, Inc.

—Garfield Legts Drauf An. Goetting, Waltraud & Bartoszko, Alexandra, trs. from ENG. (Garfield Ser.: Vol. 25). (GER.). 128p. (J). pap. (978-3-8105-0891-1(8)) Kruger, Wolfgang Verlag, GmbH DEU. *Dist:* International Bk. Import Service, Inc.

—Garfield Nimmt den Mund Voll. Goetting, Waltraud & Bartoszko, Alexandra, trs. from ENG. (Garfield Ser.: Vol. 21). (GER., Illus.). 128p. (J). pap. (978-3-8105-0885-0(3)) Kruger, Wolfgang Verlag, GmbH DEU. *Dist:* International Bk. Import Service, Inc.

—Garfield Nimmt's Leicht. Bartoszko, Alexandra, tr. from ENG. (Garfield Ser.: Vol. 29). (GER., Illus.). 128p. (J). pap. (978-3-8105-0895-9(0)) Kruger, Wolfgang Verlag, GmbH DEU. *Dist:* International Bk. Import Service, Inc.

—Garfield Out to Lunch: His Twelfth Book. 2006. (Garfield Ser.: Vol. 12). (Illus.). 96p. 10.95 (978-0-345-47562-6(3) , Ballantine Bks.) Random House Publishing Group.

—Garfield Platzt aus allen Naehten. Bartoszko, Alexandra, tr. from ENG. (Garfield Ser.: Vol. 33). (GER., Illus.). 128p. (J). pap. (978-3-8105-0919-2(1)) Kruger, Wolfgang Verlag, GmbH DEU. *Dist:* International Bk. Import Service, Inc.

—Garfield Releve le Defi. 2000. (Garfield Ser.: No. 5). Tr. of Garfield Pulls His Weight. (FRE.). (J). 7.95 (978-2-922148-04-6(1)) Presses aventure/Adventure Pr. CAN. *Dist:* AIMS International Bks., Inc.

—Garfield Riecht den Braten. Bartoszko, Alexandra, tr. from ENG. (Garfield Ser.: Vol. 34). (GER., Illus.). 128p. (J). pap. (978-3-8105-0920-8(5)) Kruger, Wolfgang Verlag, GmbH DEU. *Dist:* International Bk. Import Service, Inc.

—Garfield Spielt auf Zeit. Goetting, Waltraud & Bartoszko, Alexandra, trs. from ENG. (Garfield Ser.: Vol. 13). (GER., Illus.). 128p. (J). pap. (978-3-8105-0759-4(8)) Kruger, Wolfgang Verlag, GmbH DEU. *Dist:* International Bk. Import Service, Inc.

—Garfield Streicht Ein. Goetting, Waltraud & Bartoszko, Alexandra, trs. from ENG. (Garfield Ser.: Vol. 12). (GER., Illus.). 128p. (J). pap. (978-3-8105-0758-7(X)) Kruger, Wolfgang Verlag, GmbH DEU. *Dist:* International Bk. Import Service, Inc.

—Garfield Treasury 9. 1998. (Illus.). (J). pap. (978-0-345-91496-5(1) , Ballantine Bks.) Random House Publishing Group.

—Garfield Voit Grand. 2000. (Garfield Ser.: No. 2). Tr. of Garfield Keeps his Chin up. (FRE.). (J). 7.95 (978-2-922148-01-5(7)) Presses aventure/Adventure Pr. CAN. *Dist:* AIMS International Bks., Inc.

—Garfield Waechst & Gegeiht. Bartoszko, Alexandra, tr. from ENG. (Garfield Ser.: Vol. 30). (GER., Illus.). 128p. (J). pap. (978-3-8105-0896-6(9)) Kruger, Wolfgang Verlag, GmbH DEU. *Dist:* International Bk. Import Service, Inc.

—Garfield Will es Wissen. Goetting, Waltraud & Bartoszko, Alexandra, trs. from ENG. (Garfield Ser.: Vol. 26). (GER., Illus.). 128p. (J). pap. (978-3-8105-0892-8(6)) Kruger, Wolfgang Verlag, GmbH DEU. *Dist:* International Bk. Import Service, Inc.

—Garfield Zeigt die Krallen. Goetting, Waltraud & Bartoszko, Alexandra, trs. from ENG. (Garfield Ser.: Vol. 27). (GER., Illus.). 128p. (J). pap. (978-3-8105-0893-5(4)) Kruger, Wolfgang Verlag, GmbH DEU. *Dist:* International Bk. Import Service, Inc.

—In the Mood for Food. 1998. (Garfield Ser.). (Illus.). (J). pap. (978-0-345-91568-9(2) , Ballantine Bks.) Random House Publishing Group.

—Twelfth Garfield Fat Cat, 3 Packs. 2001. (gr. 5-8). lib. bdg. 19.90 (978-0-613-68627-3(6)) Tandem Library Bks.

DC Comics Staff. Batman Big Color & Activity Book: With Stickers. Meredith Books Staff & Forlini, Victoria, eds. 2005. 64p. (J). pap., act. bk. ed. 2.99 (978-0-696-22721-9(5)) Meredith Bks.

—Batman Jumbo Color & Activity Book. Meredith Books Staff et al, eds. 2005. 400p. (J). pap. 5.99 (978-0-696-22722-6(3)) Meredith Bks.

DC Comics Staff, ed. Batman Classic Book with Activity Kit. 2008. 32p. (J). pap. 14.99 (***978-0-696-23961-8(2)***) Meredith Bks.

De Campi, Alex. Kat & Mouse Volume 3. 2007. (Illus.). 96p. pap. 5.99 (***978-1-59816-550-0(X)*** , Tokyopop Kids) TOKYOPOP, Inc.

Decampi, Alex & Federica Manfredi. Kat & Mouse, Vol. 2. 2007. (Illus.). pap. 5.99 (978-1-59816-549-4(6) , Tokyopop Kids) TOKYOPOP, Inc.

DeFalco, Tom. Avenging Allies, Vol. 3. 2005. (Spider-Man Ser.: Vol. 3). (Illus.). 152p. pap. 7.99 (978-0-7851-1658-5(3)) Marvel Enterprises, Inc.

—Bedeviled. 2006. (Illus.). (J). (gr. 2-6). 21.35 (978-1-59961-027-6(2)) Spotlight.

—Choices. 2006. (Illus.). (J). (gr. 2-6). 21.35 (978-1-59961-028-3(0)) Spotlight.

—Fantastic Four: The Ultimate Guide. 2005. (Illus.). 144p. (YA). (ps-7). 24.99 (978-0-7566-1173-6(3)) Dorling Kindersley Publishing, Inc.

—Fun 'N' Games with the Fantastic Five! 2006. (Illus.). (J). (gr. 2-6). 21.35 (978-1-59961-030-6(2)) Spotlight.

—Legacy... in Black & White. 2006. (Illus.). (J). (gr. 2-6). 21.35 (978-1-59961-029-0(9)) Spotlight.

—Spider-Girl Battles the Deadly Dragon King. 2006. (Illus.). (J). (gr. 2-6). 21.35 (978-1-59961-025-2(6)) Spotlight.

Defalco, Tom. Spider-Man: The Ultimate Guide. 2004. (Illus.). 168p. (J). (gr. 4-10). reprint ed. 25.00 (978-0-7567-7419-6(5)) DIANE Publishing Co.

DeFalco, Tom. Touch of Venom. 2006. (Illus.). (J). (gr. 2-6). 21.35 (978-1-59961-026-9(4)) Spotlight.

—X-Men: Firestar Digest: Firestar Digest. 2006. (Illus.). 104p. pap. 7.99 (978-0-7851-2200-5(1)) Marvel Enterprises, Inc.

DeFalco, Tom & Frenz, Ron. Spider-Girl Presents Avengers Next Vol. 1: Second Coming Digest. 2006. (Illus.). 144p. pap. 7.99 (978-0-7851-2131-2(5)) Marvel Enterprises, Inc.

DeFalco, Tom, et al. Spider-Girl Volume 6: Too Many Spiders! Digest: Too Many Spiders! Digest. 2006. (Illus.). 144p. pap. 7.99 (978-0-7851-2156-5(0)) Marvel Enterprises, Inc.

Defilippis, Nunzio & Weir, Christina. Amazing Agent Luna, Vol. 3. 2006. (Illus.). 192p. (YA). pap. 10.99 (978-1-933164-10-6(7)) Seven Seas Entertainment, LLC.

—Destiny's Hand, Vol. 1. 2006. (Illus.). 192p. (YA). pap. 10.99 (978-1-933164-11-3(5)) Seven Seas Entertainment, LLC.

Defilippis, Nunzio & Weir, Christina. Destiny's Hand Volume 2. 2007. (Illus.). 192p. pap. 10.99 (***978-1-933164-52-6(2)***) Seven Seas Entertainment, LLC.

DeJesus, Melissa, illus. Sokora Refugees, Vol. 1. 2005. (YA). pap. 9.99 (978-1-59532-736-9(3) , Tokyopop Adult) TOKYOPOP, Inc.

Dela Cruz, Arthur. Kissing Chaos Vol. 2: Nonstop Beauty. 2003. (Illus.). 112p. (YA). pap. 11.95 (978-1-929998-64-7(3)) Oni Pr., Inc.

DeMatteis, J. M. & Giffen, Keith. I Can't Believe It's Not the Justice League. Macguire, Kevin, illus. rev. ed. 2005. 144p. pap. 12.99 (978-1-4012-0478-5(3)) DC Comics.

DeMatteis, J. M., et al. Son of the Goblin. 2004. (Spider-Man Ser.). (Illus.). 144p. (YA). 15.99 (978-0-7851-1563-2(3)) Marvel Enterprises, Inc.

Desfile de Walt Disney. (Coleccion Estrella). (SPA., Illus.). 64p. (YA). 14.95 (978-950-11-0008-2(1) , SGM008) Sigmar ARG. *Dist:* Continental Bk. Co., Inc.

Dexter & His Mystery Friend. 2004. (J). per. 15.99 (978-0-9753533-5-6(7)) Golden Eagle Publishing Hse., Inc.

Dexter & Milly the Caterpiller. 2004. (J). per. 15.99 (978-0-9753533-4-9(9)) Golden Eagle Publishing Hse., Inc.

Dexter Rescues Matt the Duckling. 2004. (J). per. 15.99 (978-0-9753533-3-2(0)) Golden Eagle Publishing Hse., Inc.

Dexter the Hamster Gets Lost. 2004. (J). per. 15.99 (978-0-9753533-2-5(2)) Golden Eagle Publishing Hse., Inc.

Dezago, Todd. Captain America: Stars, Stripes, & Spiders! 2006. (Spider-Man Team up Ser.). (Illus.). (J). (gr. 2-6). 21.35 (978-1-59961-010-8(9)) Spotlight.

—Duel with Daredevil! 2006. (Illus.). (J). (gr. 2-6). 21.35 (978-1-59961-013-9(2)) Spotlight.

—Enforcers! 2006. (Illus.). (J). (gr. 2-6). 21.35 (978-1-59961-019-1(1)) Spotlight.

—Fantastic Four: The Chameleon Strikes! 2006. (Spider-Man Team up Ser.). (Illus.). (J). (gr. 2-6). 21.35 (978-1-59961-005-4(1)) Spotlight.

—Fantastic Four: The Menace of Monster Isle! 2006. (Spider-Man Team up Ser.). (Illus.). (J). (gr. 2-6). 21.35 (978-1-59961-006-1(X)) Spotlight.

—Kitty Pryde: Down with the Monsters! 2006. (Spider-Man Team up Ser.). (Illus.). (J). (gr. 2-6). 21.35 (978-1-59961-002-3(7)) Spotlight.

—Man Called Electro! 2006. (Illus.). (J). (gr. 2-6). 21.35 (978-1-59961-021-4(3)) Spotlight.

—Spider-Man & the Terrible Threat of the Living Brain! 2006. (Illus.). (J). (gr. 2-6). 21.35 (978-1-59961-008-5(6)) Spotlight.

—Spidey Strikes Back! 2006. (Illus.). (J). (gr. 2-6). 21.35 (978-1-59961-017-7(5)) Spotlight.

—Storm: Change the Weather. 2006. (Spider-Man Team up Ser.). (Illus.). (J). (gr. 2-6). 21.35 (978-1-59961-003-0(5)) Spotlight.

—Thor: Out of Time! 2006. (Spider-Man Team up Ser.). (Illus.). (J). (gr. 2-6). 21.35 (978-1-59961-004-7(3)) Spotlight.

Dezago, Todd & Raicht, Mike. The Goblin Strikes Digest, Vol. 4. 2004. (Spider-Man Ser.: Vol. 4). (Illus.). 96p. 5.99 (978-0-7851-1549-6(8)) Marvel Enterprises, Inc.

—Spidey Strikes Back!, Vol. 5. 2005. (Spider-Man Ser.). (Illus.). 96p. pap. 5.99 (978-0-7851-1632-5(X)) Marvel Enterprises, Inc.

—Swingtime. 2004. (Spider-Man Ser.: Vol. 3). (Illus.). 96p. (YA). pap. 5.99 (978-0-7851-1548-9(X)) Marvel Enterprises, Inc.

Dgn Production Inc Staff & Lau, Ding Kin. Chinese Hero Tales of the Blood Sword V. 2007. (Illus.). 280p. (YA). pap. 19.95 (***978-1-59796-117-2(5)***) DrMaster Pubns. Inc.

Dickens, Charles. Charles Dickens/A Christmas Carol. Lo Famia, Jon, illus. 2005. 48p. (gr. 5-8). 25.50 (978-0-7910-9108-1(2)) Facts On File, Inc.

—Oliver Twist. Gelev, Penko, illus. 2006. (Graphic Classics Ser.). 48p. (J). (gr. 4-8). 15.99 (978-0-7641-5975-6(5)); pap. 8.99 (978-0-7641-3490-6(6)) Barron's Educational Series, Inc.

Diesslin, Richard L., illus. Knots or Not Scouting Cartoon Collection! Cartoons Celebrating the Fun in Scouting! 2002. cd-rom 24.95 (978-0-9702244-6-0(X)) Diesslin, Richard L.

Dietz, William C. Jedi Knight. 1998. (Star Wars Ser.: Bk. 3). 128p. (YA). 24.95 (978-1-56971-157-6(7)) Dark Horse Comics.

—Soldier for the Empire. 1998. (Star Wars Ser.: Bk. 1). 128p. (YA). pap. 14.95 (978-1-56971-348-8(0)) Dark Horse Comics.

Dietz, William C. & Dorman, Dave. Dark Forces: Jedi Knight. 2004. (Star Wars Ser.). 128p. (YA). (gr. 7 up). pap. 14.95 (978-1-56971-433-1(9)) Dark Horse Comics.

DiPucchio, Kelly. Grace for President. Pham, LeUyen, illus. rev. ed. 2008. 40p. (gr. 7-17). 15.99 (***978-0-7868-3919-3(8)***) Hyperion Pr.

Disney. Boys & Beauty Blunders. 2007. (Hannah Montana Cine-manga Ser.: Vol. 3). 96p. pap. 7.99 (***978-1-4278-0785-4(X)*** , Tokyopop Kids) TOKYOPOP, Inc.

Disney Pixar Staff, creator. Cars. 2006. (Illus.). pap. 7.99 (978-1-59816-481-7(3) , Tokyopop Kids) TOKYOPOP, Inc.

—Cars Jr Cine Manga. 2006. (Illus.). 24p. pap. 3.99 (978-1-59816-483-1(X) , Tokyopop Kids) TOKYOPOP, Inc.

Disney Press, ed. Pirates of the Caribbean: GN - at Worlds End. rev. ed. 2007. 48p. (gr. 1). pap. 3.99 (***978-1-4231-0449-0(8)***) Disney Pr.

Disney Press Staff. Dead Man's Chest. 2007. 48p. (ps-3). 12.99 incl. audio compact disk (978-1-4231-0368-4(8)) Disney Pr.

—Disney Friendship Stories. Disney Storybook Artists Staff, illus. 2006. 304p. (ps-17). 15.99 (978-1-4231-0087-4(5)) Disney Pr.

—Disney's Lilo & Stitch. 2006. (Disney Adventure Ser.: No.1). 96p. (gr. 3-7). pap. 4.99 (978-0-7868-4719-8(0)) Disney Pr.

—Disney's Storybook Collection. Disney Storybook Artists Staff, illus. 2006. 320p. (ps-17). 15.99 (978-1-4231-0073-7(5)) Disney Pr.

—Finding Nemo. 2006. (Disney Junior Graphic Novel Ser.: Vol. 1). (Illus.). 48p. (gr. 1-4). pap. 3.99 (978-1-4231-0140-6(5)) Disney Pr.

—In the Realm of the Never Fairies: The Secret World of Pixie Hollow. 2006. 144p. (gr. 2-17). 18.99 (978-0-7868-4765-5(4)) Disney Pr.

Disney Press Staff, ed. Dead Man's Chest. 2007. 48p. (gr. 1-3). pap. 3.99 (***978-1-4231-0370-7(X)***) Disney Pr.

—Haunted Mansion. 2007. 96p. (gr. 8-17). pap. 9.99 (***978-1-4231-0393-6(9)***) Disney Pr.

Disney Press Staff & Driscoll, Laura. I Love You, My Bunnies. Disney Storybook Artists Staff et al, illus. 2007. 32p. (J). (ps-1). 9.99 (978-1-4231-0078-2(6)) Disney Pr.

Disney Press Staff & King, M. C. Truth or Dare. 4th rev. ed. 2007. (Hannah Montana Ser.: No. 4). 128p. (gr. 3-7). pap. 4.99 (978-1-4231-0277-9(0)) Disney Pr.

Disney Press Staff & Monica, Carol. Princess Mix & Match. Marderosian, Mark, illus. 2006. 12p. (ps-17). 14.99 (978-0-7868-3623-9(7)) Disney Pr.

Disney Press Staff & Richards, Kitty. Goodnight, Thumper! Disney Storybook Artists Staff & Tyminski, Lori, illus. 2007. 16p. (J). (ps-k). 5.99 (978-1-4231-0077-5(8)) Disney Pr.

—My Secret Diary by Ariel. Disney Storybook Artists Staff, illus. 2006. (Disney Princess Ser.). 64p. (ps-2). 14.99 (978-0-7868-4954-3(1)) Disney Pr.

Disney Staff. Crushes & Camping. 2007. (Hannah Montana Cine-manga Ser.: Vol. 2). 96p. pap. 7.99 (***978-1-4278-0282-8(3)*** , Tokyopop Kids) TOKYOPOP, Inc.

—Gorilla, Gorilla. 2006. (Disney Adventure Ser.: Vol. 2). 96p. (gr. 3-7). pap. 4.99 (978-0-7868-4720-4(4)) Disney Pr.

—Secrets & Super Sneaks, Vol. 1. 2007. (Hannah Montana Cine-manga Ser.: Vol. 1). pap. 7.99 (***978-1-4278-0281-1(5)*** , Tokyopop Kids) TOKYOPOP, Inc.

—The Story of Clarabelle Cow. 2004. (Illus.). 96p. (J). 35.00 incl. audio compact disk (978-1-55709-357-8(1)) Applewood Bks.

—The Story of Donald Duck. 2004. (Illus.). 96p. (J). (ps-3). 35.00 incl. audio compact disk (978-1-55709-354-7(7)) Applewood Bks.

—The Story of Mickey Mouse. 2004. (Illus.). 92p. (J). (ps-3). 100.00 incl. audio compact disk (978-1-55709-352-3(0)) Applewood Bks.

—The Story of Minnie Mouse. 2004. (Illus.). 96p. (J). (gr. 1-1). 100.00 (978-1-55709-353-0(9)) Applewood Bks.

—The Story of Pluto the Pup. 2004. (Illus.). 96p. (J). 35.00 incl. audio compact disk (978-1-55709-356-1(3)) Applewood Bks.

Disney Staff, creator. Kim Possible: The New Ron & Mind Games, 4 vols., Vol. 3. 2003. (Illus.). 192p. pap. 7.99 (978-1-59182-243-1(2) , Tokyopop Kids) TOKYOPOP, Inc.

Disney Staff & McCoy, Glenn. Disney's Tall Tails. 2006. (Disney Adventure Ser.: Vol. 3). 96p. (gr. 3-7). pap. 4.99 (978-0-7868-3766-3(7)) Disney Pr.

Disney Staff & Walker, Landry Quinn. Kid Gravity. Jones, Eric, illus. 2006. (Disney Adventure Ser.: Vol. 4). 96p. (gr. 3-7). pap. 4.99 (978-0-7868-3765-6(9)) Disney Pr.

Disney Storybook Artists Staff. Disney Pixar Storybook Collection. 2006. 320p. (ps-17). 15.99 (978-0-7868-3602-4(4)) Disney Pr.

Disney, Walt. The Classics Collection. 2006. (Illus.). 256p. (ps-17). 49.95 (978-0-7868-4902-4(9)) Disney Pr.

Ditama, Bow. Mahoromatic, 4 vols., Vol. 2. 2nd rev. ed. 2004. (Illus.). pap. 9.99 (978-1-59182-730-6(2) , Tokyopop Adult) TOKYOPOP, Inc.

Ditama, Bow, illus. Mahoromatic, Vol. 5. rev. ed. 2005. 184p. pap. 9.99 (978-1-59182-915-7(1) , Tokyopop Adult) TOKYOPOP, Inc.

Ditko, Steve & Gill, Joe. Action Heroes: Captain Atom. rev. ed. 2004. (Archives Ser.: Col. 1). (Illus.). 228p. 49.95 (978-1-4012-0302-3(7)) DC Comics.

Dixon, Chuck. El Cazador. Epting, Stephen, illus. rev. ed. 2007. 144p. (J). (gr. 5 up). pap. 12.99 (***978-1-4231-0927-3(9)***) Hyperion Pr.

—Perdition's Gate, Vol. 6. Eaglesham, Dale et al, illus. 2004. (Sigil Ser.: Vol. 6). 160p. (YA). pap. 15.95 (978-1-59314-048-9(7)) CrossGeneration Comics, Inc.

—Resurrection, Vol. 5. Cariello, Sergio et al, illus. 2004. (Crux Ser.: Vol. 5). 160p. (YA). pap. 15.95 (978-1-59314-053-3(3)) CrossGeneration Comics, Inc.

—Way of the Rat Traveler, Vol. 1. 2003. (Way of the Rat Traveler Ser.). (Illus.). 160p. (YA). pap. 9.95 (978-1-59314-032-8(0)) CrossGeneration Comics, Inc.

Dixon, Dougal. The Discovery of T. Rex. 2006. (Stories from History Ser.). 48p. (J). 14.95 (***978-0-7696-4712-8(X)***); pap. 6.95 (***978-0-7696-4693-0(X)***) School Specialty Publishing.

Dixon, Franklin W. Hardy Boys Starter Set. 2007. (Hardy Boys Ser.). 128p. (J). lthr. 25.98 (***978-0-448-44820-6(3)*** , Grosset & Dunlap) Penguin Group (USA) Inc.

—Pushed. 2007. (Hardy Boys (All New) Undercover Brothers Ser.). 154p. (J). (gr. 3-7). per. 4.99 (***978-1-4169-4802-5(3)*** , Aladdin) Simon & Schuster Children's Publishing.

Dodson Wade, Mary. Christopher Columbus: Famous Explorer. 2007. (Graphic Library). (Illus.). 32p. (J). (***978-0-7368-7905-7(6)*** , 1264941) Capstone Pr., Inc.

Donald Duck Adventures, Vol. 17. 2006. 128p. (YA). pap. 7.95 (978-1-888472-12-7(X)) Gemstone Publishing, Inc.

Donaldson, Julia. Charlie Cook's Favorite Book. Scheffler, Axel, illus. 2008. 32p. (J). (ps-k). pap. 6.99 (***978-0-14-241138-4(8)*** , Puffin) Penguin Group (USA) Inc.

Donobo, Yu. Pita-Ten, 6 vols. rev. ed. 2004. (Illus.). 192p. Vol. 3. pap. 9.99 (978-1-59182-629-3(2)); Vol. 4. pap. 9.99 (978-1-59182-630-9(6)) TOKYOPOP, Inc. (Tokyopop Kids).

Doran, Colleen. A Distant Soil Vol. 4: Coda Limited Edition. ltd. ed. 2006. 164p. (YA). 29.95 (978-1-58240-525-4(5)) Image Comics.

Dorling Kindersley Publishing Staff. Glow-in-the-Dark Marvel Heroes. 2006. (Ultimate Sticker Bks.). 16p. (J). pap. 6.99 (978-0-7566-2002-8(3)) Dorling Kindersley Publishing, Inc.

—Glow-in-the-Dark Spider-Man. 2006. (Ultimate Sticker Bks.). 16p. (J). pap. 6.99 (978-0-7566-1999-2(8)) Dorling Kindersley Publishing, Inc.

—Glow-in-the-Dark X-Men. 2006. (Ultimate Sticker Bks.). 16p. (J). pap. 6.99 (978-0-7566-1998-5(X)) Dorling Kindersley Publishing, Inc.

—X-Men. 2006. (Ultimate Sticker Bks.). 16p. (J). pap. 6.99 (978-0-7566-1997-8(1)) Dorling Kindersley Publishing, Inc.

Dorling Kindersley Publishing Staff, ed. Disney Villains: The Essential Guide. 2004. (Illus.). 48p. (J). 12.99 (978-0-7566-0580-3(6)) Dorling Kindersley Publishing, Inc.

—Star Wars: Clone Wars. 2004. (Ultimate Sticker Bks.). 16p. (J). pap. 6.99 (978-0-7566-0759-3(0)) Dorling Kindersley Publishing, Inc.

Dotrice, Roy, narrated by. The Little Mermaid: Read Along. 2001. (Illus.). 32p. (J). pap. 9.98 incl. audio compact disk (978-0-7634-0799-5(2)) Walt Disney Records.

Dowell, Michael. Moodoo: The Marvelous World of Moodoo. 2005. (Illus.). 128p. (J). per. 13.99 (***978-0-9762454-2-1(6)*** , b-001) Moodoo Productions, Inc.

Dragon Tales. 2005. (Thrillogy Ser.). (Illus.). 48p. (gr. 4-8). 17.50 (978-0-7910-8887-6(1)) Facts On File, Inc.

The Dreamer Who Unlocked the Secrets of the Universe... 2004. (Illus.). 126p. (YA). pap. 11.11 (978-0-9749196-1-4(6)) Don Quixote Publishing Co. Inc.

Drummer Hoff Error. 2004. (J). pap. 18.95 incl. audio compact disk (978-1-55592-409-6(3)); pap. 38.75 incl. audio compact disk (978-1-55592-410-2(7)) Weston Woods Studios, Inc.

Dumas, Alexandre & Pipe, Jim. The Man in the Iron Mask. Gelev, Penko, illus. 2007. (Graphic Classics Ser.). 48p. (J). (gr. 3 up). 15.99 (***978-0-7641-6055-4(9)***); pap. 8.99 (***978-0-7641-3779-2(4)***) Barron's Educational Series, Inc.

Dunfey, Beth, ed. Taz, 4 Pack. 2001. (Looney Tunes Teacher's Pets Ser.). 32p. (J). lthr. 19.80 (978-0-439-31812-9(2) , Scholastic Paperbacks) Scholastic, Inc.

Dunn, Ben. The Agents Pocket Manga. 2004. 136p. (YA). pap. 9.99 (978-1-932453-64-5(4)) Antarctic Pr., Inc.

Dunn, Ben & Dunn, Ben, illus. The Time Machine. 2007. (Graphic Classics). 32p. (J). (gr. 3-6). lib. bdg. 27.07 (***978-1-60270-054-3(0)*** , Graphic Planet) Magic Wagon.

Dunn, Ben & Mallette, Herb. Ninja High School Pocket Manga, Vol. 8. 2006. 144p. (YA). pap. 9.99 (978-0-9768043-2-1(8)) Antarctic Pr., Inc.

Dunn, Joe. The Bombing of Pearl Harbor. Wight, Joseph & Espinosa, Rod, illus. 2007. (Graphic History Ser.). 32p. (J). (gr. 3-6). lib. bdg. 27.07 (***978-1-60270-074-1(5)*** , Graphic Planet) Magic Wagon.

Dunn, Joeming W. & Dunn, Ben, illus. Robin Hood. 2007. (Graphic Classics). 32p. (J). (gr. 3-6). lib. bdg. 27.07 (***978-1-60270-053-6(2)*** , Graphic Planet) Magic Wagon.

—White Fang. 2007. (Graphic Classics). (J). (gr. 3-6). lib. bdg. 27.07 (***978-1-60270-055-0(9)*** , Graphic Planet) Magic Wagon.

Dye, Thomas. Press Badge Blues. 2002. (Newshounds Ser.: 3). pap. 12.95 (978-1-929462-41-4(7)) Plan Nine Publishing, Inc.

Dye, Thomas K. Tonight's Top Story. 2000. (Newshounds Ser.: Vol. 2). 152p. pap. 12.95 (978-1-929462-10-0(7)) Plan Nine Publishing, Inc.

Edginton, Ian. Scarlet Traces. 2003. 88p. (YA). 14.95 (978-1-56971-940-4(3)) Dark Horse Comics.

Egan, Kate, adapted by. Worlds Apart. rev. ed. 2005. (W. I. T. C. H. Ser.: Bk. 14). (Illus.). 144p. (J). (gr. 3-7). pap. 4.99 (978-0-7868-5192-8(9) , Volo) Hyperion Bks. for Children.

Eickhoff, Kim, et al. Bamboo Zoo: Meet Lester Panda & his Friends! 2005. (Bamboo Zoo Ser.: Bk. 1). (Illus.). (J). per. 9.95 (978-0-9774493-0-9(0)) Bamboo Zoo, LLC.

Eisner, Will. The Last Day in Vietnam: A Memory. 2000. (Illus.). 80p. (gr. 11 up). pap. 10.95 (978-1-56971-500-0(9)) Dark Horse Comics.

—Sundiata: A Legend of Africa. 2003. (Illus.). 32p. 7.95 (978-1-56163-340-1(2)) NBM Publishing Co.

Eisner, Will, illus. & retold by. Sundiata: A Legend of Africa. Eisner, Will, retold by. 2003. 32p. (gr. k-3). 15.95 (978-1-56163-332-6(1)) NBM Publishing Co.

Eliot, Jan. The First Collection of the Syndicated Cartoon Strip, No. 1. 2004. 128p. pap. 10.95 (978-0-9674102-2-7(3)) Four Panel Pr.

Ellerton, Sarah. Inverloch, Vol. 1. 2006. (Illus.). 160p. pap. 14.99 (978-1-933164-13-7(1)) Seven Seas Entertainment, LLC.

Ellis, Warren. Mike Deodato Jr. 2004. (Thor Ser.). (Illus.). 184p. (YA). 19.99 (978-0-7851-1408-6(4)) Marvel Enterprises, Inc.

Ellis, Warren & Carey, Mike. Ultimate Fantastic Four, Vol. 2. 2006. (Illus.). 240p. 29.99 (978-0-7851-2058-2(0)) Marvel Enterprises, Inc.

Ellis, Warren & Hairsine, Trevor. Ultimate Galactus: Nightmare. 2005. (Ultimate Galactus: Vol. 1). (Illus.). 120p. pap. 12.99 (978-0-7851-1497-0(1)) Marvel Enterprises, Inc.

Ellis, Warren & Immonen, Stuart. Doom, Vol. 2. 2004. (Fantastic Four Ser.). (Illus.). 144p. pap. 12.99 (978-0-7851-1457-4(2)) Marvel Enterprises, Inc.

Ende, Michael. El Largo Camino Hacia Santa Cruz. Kehn, Regina, illus. (SPA.). 64p. (J). (gr. 3-5). 6.95 (978-84-241-3354-2(4) , EV3073) Everest de Ediciones y Distribucion, S.L. ESP. *Dist:* Lectorum Pubns., Inc.

Endoh, Minari. Dazzle, Vol. 4. 3rd rev. ed. 2006. pap. 9.99 (978-1-59816-094-9(X) , Tokyopop Kids) TOKYOPOP, Inc.

Endoh, Minari, illus. & creator. Dazzle, Vol. 2. Endoh, Minari, creator. 2nd rev. ed. 2006. pap. 9.99 (978-1-59816-093-2(1) , Tokyopop Kids) TOKYOPOP, Inc.

Englehart, Steve & Warner, John. Captain America & the Falcon: Nomad TPB: Nomad TPB. 2007. (Illus.). 192p. pap. 24.99 (978-0-7851-2197-8(8)) Marvel Enterprises, Inc.

Ennis, Garth. The Slavers, Vol. 5. 2006. (Illus.). 144p. pap. 15.99 (978-0-7851-1899-2(3)) Marvel Enterprises, Inc.

Ennis, Garth & Larosa, Lewis. In the Beginning. 2004. (Punisher Ser.). (Illus.). 144p. 14.99 (978-0-7851-1391-1(6)) Marvel Enterprises, Inc.

Erickson, Byron, et al. Mickey Mouse Adventures, Vol. 9. 2006. (Illus.). 128p. (YA). pap. 7.95 (978-1-888472-10-3(3)) Gemstone Publishing, Inc.

Erickson, Byron, et al. Walt Disney's Comics & Stories #687. 2007. 64p. pap. 7.99 (***978-1-888472-98-1(7)***) Gemstone Publishing, Inc.

Erickson, Timothy Ronald. Death's Whisper Recoil, 2. Erickson, Timothy Ronald, illus. 2003. (YA). pap. 14.95 (978-1-59492-001-1(X)) Erickson, Tim.

Escaich, Bertrand & Roque, Caroline. The Rugger Boys: Why Are We Here Again? Spear, Luke, tr. from FRE. 2007. (Illus.). 52p. pap. 9.99 (***978-1-905460-33-5(3)***) CineBook GBR. *Dist:* Biblio Distribution.

Escape from the Comics, 6 Packs. (Bookweb Ser.). 32p. (gr. 4 up). 34.00 (978-0-7635-3723-4(3)) Rigby Education.

Espinosa, Frank. The Journey to the Hidden Sea. (Illus.). 304p. (YA). pap. 19.99 (978-1-58240-585-8(9)) Image Comics.

Espinosa, Rod. Benjamin Franklin. 2007. (Bio-Graphics Ser.). (Illus.). 32p. (J). (gr. 3-6). lib. bdg. 27.07 (***978-1-60270-066-6(4)*** , Graphic Planet) Magic Wagon.

—Courageous Princess Vol. 3: Kingdom of Leptia. 2002. 88p. pap. 12.95 (978-0-9663588-4-1(8)) Antarctic Pr., Inc.

—George Washington. 2007. (Bio-Graphics Ser.). (Illus.). 32p. (J). (gr. 3-6). lib. bdg. 27.07 (***978-1-60270-067-3(2)*** , Graphic Planet) Magic Wagon.

—Peter Pan. 2007. (Graphic Classics). (Illus.). 32p. (J). (gr. 3-6). lib. bdg. 27.07 (***978-1-60270-052-9(4)*** , Graphic Planet) Magic Wagon.

Espinosa, Rod, illus. & adapted by. Moby Dick. Espinosa, Rod, adapted by. 2007. (Graphic Classics). 32p. (J). (gr. 3-6). lib. bdg. 27.07 (***978-1-60270-051-2(6)*** , Graphic Planet) Magic Wagon.

Estes, Max. Coffee & Donuts. 2006. (Illus.). 128p. pap. 10.00 (978-1-891830-80-8(5)) Top Shelf Productions.

Eun-Ah, Park. Sweet & Sensitive, Vol. 2. 2004. 208p. pap. (978-1-4139-0095-8(X)) ADV Manga.

Evans, Marion, Anna Baraitser. Home Number One. 2006. (Illus.). 63p. (YA). pap. (978-0-9529426-7-2(4)) Loki Books Ltd.

Evans, Greg. Dates & Other Disasters: A Luann Collection. 2004. (Illus.). 128p. (J). pap. 10.95 (978-0-7407-4664-2(2)) Andrews McMeel Publishing.

Fackrell, David. Princess, the Collection, Vol. 1. 2005. 78p. pap. 19.99 (978-1-4116-5820-2(5)) Lulu.com.

Faerber, Jay, et al. Captain Universe Universal Heroes. 2006. (Illus.). 136p. (YA). pap. 13.99 (978-0-7851-1857-2(8)) Marvel Enterprises, Inc.

Fajardo, Alexis E. Kid Beowulf. 2nd ed. 2005. (Illus.). 170p. (YA). pap. 14.95 (978-0-9746000-2-4(4) , Kid Beowulf) Lexpress.

Fake, Vol. 8. 2004. (YA). pap. 9.99 (978-1-59182-454-1(0)) TOKYOPOP, Inc.

Falloon, Jane. Thumbelina. Andersen, Hans Christian & Clark, E.C., illus. 2007. Tr. of Tommelise. 48p. (J). (ps-3). pap. 9.99 (***978-1-84458-471-0(2)***) Anova Bks. GBR. *Dist:* Independent Pubs. Group.

Fandel, Jennifer. Louis Pasteur & Pasteurization. Wilson, Keith et al, illus. 2007. 32p. (***978-0-7368-6844-0(5)***) Capstone Pr., Inc.

Farley, Terri. Renegade. 2003. (gr. 5-8). lib. bdg. 13.00 (978-0-613-66731-9(X)) Tandem Library Bks.

Feiffer, Jules. Meanwhile... Feiffer, Jules, illus. 1999. (Michael di Capua Bks.). (Illus.). 32p. (J). (ps-k). pap. 6.99 (978-0-06-205933-8(5)) HarperCollins Pubs.

—Meanwhile... 1999. (978-0-606-17882-2(1)); lib. bdg. 14.15 (978-0-613-22891-6(X)) Tandem Library Bks.

Feldman, Thea. A Kite-Tacular Adventure. rev. ed. 2007. 10p. (ps-1). 12.99 (***978-1-4231-0904-4(X)***) Disney Pr.

Feldstein, Al. The EC Archives Vol. 2: Shock Suspenstories. 2007. (Illus.). 212p. (YA). 49.95 (***978-1-888472-70-7(7)***) Gemstone Publishing, Inc.

—The EC Archives Vol. 2: Weird Science. 2007. (Illus.). 212p. (YA). 49.95 (***978-1-888472-69-1(3)***) Gemstone Publishing, Inc.

Fenton, Sue Fenton, creator. Professor Mel T. Lingual's Coloring Book of Signs: Promoting Language Study & Cultural Awareness. 2005. (Illus.). 58p. (YA). 18.95 (978-0-9762900-2-5(2) , #MFP 114) Madame Fifi Pubns.

Fernandez, Nacho. La nueva era del sueno vol. 2: Los desiertos del Norte: The New Age of Dreams vol. 2: the Deserts of the North. 2007. (SPA.). 48p. 22.95 (***978-1-59497-398-7(9)***) Public Square Bks.

Festival de Walt Disney. (Coleccion Estrella). (SPA., Illus.). 64p. (J). 14.95 (978-950-11-0003-7(0) , SGM003) Sigmar ARG. *Dist:* Continental Bk. Co., Inc.

Finger, Bill, et al. Superman. Swan, Curt, illus. rev. ed. 2005. (Showcase Presents Ser.: Vol. 1). 560p. (YA). pap. 9.99 (978-1-4012-0758-8(8)) DC Comics.

Fingeroth, Danny. The Last Stand: The Junior Novel. 2006. (X Men Ser.). 144p. (J). pap. 4.99 (978-0-06-082208-8(2)) HarperCollins Pubs.

Fisch, Sholly. No Place Like Home. 2000. (gr. k-3). lib. bdg. 10.95 (978-0-613-32901-9(5)) Tandem Library Bks.

Fischer, Steven. The Wonderful, Happy, Cartoony World of Steve & Bluey. Fischer, Steven, illus. 2001. (Illus.). 212p. (YA). (gr. 6-9). pap. 19.05 (978-0-9627367-1-1(6)) Blue Dog Productions, Inc.

Flyboy. 2001. 321p. per. 12.95 (978-0-9711519-0-1(3)) Belt, Robert L.

Foglio, Phil & Foglio, Kaja. Agatha Heterodyne & the Clockwork Princess. 2006. (Girl Genius Ser.: Vol. 5). (Illus.). 112p. (YA). pap. 19.95 (978-1-890856-39-7(8)) Studio Foglio, LLC.

Fontes, Justine & Reader's Digest Staff. Scooby-Doo Mysterious Message Storybook Scooby Clues. 2007. 32p. (J). 12.99 (***978-0-7944-1304-0(8)***) Reader's Digest Assn., Inc., The.

—Scooby-Doo the Haunted Mysteries Storybook & DVD. 2007. (Readers Book & DVD Ser.). 32p. (J). 17.99 (***978-0-7944-1302-6(1)***) Reader's Digest Assn., Inc., The.

Fontes Ron & Fontes, Justine. El caballo de Troya (the Trojan Horse) La caída de Troya (the Fall of Troy) Purcell, Gordon, illus. 2007. (Mitos y leyendas en viñetas (Graphic Myths & Legends) Ser.). (J). pap. 8.95 (***978-0-8225-7970-0(7)*** , Ediciones Lerner) Lerner Publishing Group.

Fontes, Ron & Fontes, Justine. Captured by Pirates. Witt, David, illus. 2007. (Twisted Journeys Ser.). 112p. (J). (gr. 4-7). lib. bdg. 27.93 (***978-0-8225-6201-6(4)*** , Graphic Universe); pap. 7.95 (***978-0-8225-6202-3(2)***) Lerner Publishing Group.

—The Trojan Horse: The Fall of Troy. Purcell, Gordon, illus. 2007. (Graphic Myths & Legends Ser.). 48p. (YA). (gr. 4-9). pap. 8.95 (***978-0-8225-6484-3(X)***) Lerner Publishing Group.

Fontes, Ron, et al. The Trojan Horse: The Fall of Troy. Purcell, Gordon, illus. 2007. (Graphic Myths & Legends Ser.). 48p. (J). 26.60 (978-0-8225-3085-5(6)) Lerner Publishing Group.

Forbes, Jake, ed. Tokyopop Manga Sampler. 2002. (Illus.). 190p. (YA). mass mkt. (978-0-681-88644-5(7) , TOKYOPOP Manga) TOKYOPOP, Inc.

Forlini, Victoria, ed. Batman Begins Stencil Activity Book. 2005. (Illus.). 22p. (J). bds., act. bk. ed. 9.95 (978-0-696-22590-1(5)) Meredith Bks.

Forney, Ellen. Monkey Food: The Complete I was Seven in '75 Collection. Forney, Ellen, illus. 2005. (Illus.). 142p. (YA). reprint ed. pap. 13.00 (978-0-7567-8610-6(X)) DIANE Publishing Co.

Fountain, Bill. Raven: The Sleeping Glass Heart. 2005. (Illus.). 24p. (YA). 5.00 (978-0-9773461-0-3(2)) Level Ground Pr.

Fox, Gardner. The Atom - Archives, Vol. 2. rev. ed. 2003. (Illus.). 216p. 49.95 (978-1-4012-0014-5(1)) DC Comics.

Fox, Gardner, et al. JLA: Greatest Stories Ever Told. Ross, Alex, illus. rev. ed. 2006. 192p. pap. 19.99 (978-1-4012-0932-2(7)) DC Comics.

Freeland, Dar. Urp: Blahg by Dar. Freeland, Dar, illus. 2000. (Illus.). 72p. (YA). per. 12.99 (978-0-9771660-0-8(7)) Freeland, Darlene.

French, Renee. The Soap Lady. French, Renee, illus. 2005. (Illus.). 111p. (J). (gr. 4-8). reprint ed. 20.00 (978-0-7567-9419-4(6)) DIANE Publishing Co.

Friedman, Michael Jan, et al. Convergence. Erwin, Steve et al, illus. 2007. 176p. pap. 22.95 (***978-1-84576-320-6(3)***) Titan Bks. Ltd. GBR. *Dist:* Random Hse., Inc.

Friesen, Christi. Cats, Big & Small: The CF Polymer Clay Sculpture Series Book 4, Vol. 4. 2007. per. 9.95 (978-0-9728177-1-4(9)) Don't Eat Any Bugs Prodns.

—Under the Sea: The CF Sculpture Series Book 3. 2007. 48p. pap. 9.95 (978-0-9728177-0-7(0) , CF Bks.) Don't Eat Any Bugs Prodns.

Friesen, Ray. Another Dirt Sandwich: Some Rambling & Hilarious Exploits of Tbyrd Fearlessness, 2008. (ENG., Illus.). 100p. pap. 12.95 (978-0-9728177-4-5(3)) Don't Eat Any Bugs Prodns.

—Lookit!, Vol. 2. 2004. (YA). per. 4.95 (978-0-9728177-3-8(5)) Don't Eat Any Bugs Prodns.

—Lookit! Vol. 2: Yarg! & Other Stories. 2007. 96p. (J). (gr. 3-6). pap. 11.95 (978-0-9728177-9-0(4)) Don't Eat Any Bugs Prodns.

—Lookit! A Cheese Related Mishap Vol. 1: And Other Stories. 2006. 96p. pap. 8.95 (978-0-9728177-6-9(X)) Don't Eat Any Bugs Prodns.

—RQW, Vol. 3. 2003. (YA). 2.95 (978-0-9728177-2-1(7)) Don't Eat Any Bugs Prodns.

—RQW Comics #1-4 Collection. 2004. (YA). 10.00 (978-0-9728177-5-2(1)) Don't Eat Any Bugs Prodns.

Fujii, Mihona. Gals! 2005. 192p. Vol. 3. (Illus.). pap. 9.99 (978-1-4012-0552-2(6)); Vol. 4. pap. 9.99 (978-1-4012-0553-9(4)) DC Comics.

Fujima, Takuya. Deus Vitae, 3 vols., Vol. 1. 2004. (Illus.). 200p. pap. 9.99 (978-1-59182-769-6(8) , Tokyopop Adult) TOKYOPOP, Inc.

Fujino, Moyamu. The First King Adventure, Vol 1. 2004. (Illus.). 184p. (YA). pap. (978-1-4139-0194-8(8)) ADV Manga.

Fujisawa, Tohru, illus. & compiled by. GTO: Great Teacher Onizuka, 25 vols., Vol. 21. Fujisawa, Tohru, compiled by. rev. ed. 2004. 192p. pap. 9.99 (978-1-59182-455-8(9) , Tokyopop Adult) TOKYOPOP, Inc.

Fujishima, Kosuke. Mara Strikes Back. 2000. (Oh My Goddess! Ser.: Vol. 8). (Illus.). 176p. (J). (gr. 3 up). pap. 14.95 (978-1-56971-449-2(5)) Dark Horse Comics.

—Oh My Goddess! (J). Vol. 1. 2005. 192p. pap. 10.95 (978-1-59307-387-9(9)); Vol. 22. 2006. 176p. pap. 10.95 (978-1-59307-400-5(X)); Vol. 25. 2007. 176p. pap. 10.95 (978-1-59307-644-3(4)) Dark Horse Comics.

—Oh My Goddess! Childhood's End. 2002. (gr. 7-12). lib. bdg. 25.70 (978-0-613-55151-9(6)) Tandem Library Bks.

—Oh My Goddess! Colors. 2007. 192p. (J). pap. 19.95 (978-1-59307-408-1(5)) Dark Horse Comics.

—Oh My Goddess! Devil in Miss Urd. 2001. (gr. 7-12). lib. bdg. 24.55 (978-0-613-55156-4(7)) Tandem Library Bks.

—Oh My Goddess! Fourth Goddess. 2001. (gr. 7-12). lib. bdg. 29.20 (978-0-613-55165-6(6)) Tandem Library Bks.

—Oh My Goddess! Mara Strikes Back. 2000. (gr. 7-12). lib. bdg. 24.55 (978-0-613-55175-5(3)) Tandem Library Bks.

—Oh My Goddess! Ninja Master. 2000. (gr. 7-12). lib. bdg. 23.40 (978-0-613-55182-3(6)) Tandem Library Bks.

—Phantom Racer. 2004. (Oh My Goddess! Ser.: Vol. 18). 256p. pap. 17.95 (978-1-59307-217-9(1)) Dark Horse Comics.

—Terrible Master Urd. Gleason, Alan et al, trs. 1999. (Oh My Goddess! Ser.: Vol. 4). (Illus.). 176p. (J). (gr. 3 up). pap. 14.95 (978-1-56971-369-3(3)) Dark Horse Comics.

Fujita, Maki, illus. & creator. Platinum Garden. Fujita, Maki, creator. 2006. (YA). pap. 9.99 (978-1-59816-361-2(2) , Tokyopop Kids) TOKYOPOP, Inc.

Fumiya, Sato, illus. The Kindaichi Case Files Vol. 13, Pt. 2: Playing the Fool. 2006. 312p. pap. 9.99 (978-1-59532-697-3(9) , Tokyopop Kids) TOKYOPOP, Inc.

Fuqua, Jonathon Scott. Medusas Daughter: A Graphic Novel. Parke, Steven, illus. 2007. (Narrative, Ink Ser.). 128p. (YA). (gr. 10 up). pap. 17.95 (***978-1-933368-92-4(6)***) Counterpoint.

—Medusas Daughter Graphic Novella. Parke, Steven, illus. 2007. (Narrative, Ink Ser.). 64p. (J). (***978-1-933368-93-1(4)***) Counterpoint.

—Medusas Daughter Novel. 2007. (Narrative, Ink Ser.). 192p. (J). (***978-1-933368-91-7(8)***) Counterpoint.

Furuya, Usamaru. Short Cuts, Vol. 1. Furuya, Usamaru, illus. 2002. (Short Cuts Ser.). (Illus.). 136p. (YA). pap. 12.95 (978-1-59116-031-1(6)) Viz Media.

Gaiman, Neil. El Dia Que Cambie a Mi Padre Por Dos Peces de Colores. Ferrer, María, tr. from ENG. 2005. (Single Volume Ser.). (SPA., Illus.). 56p. 28.95 (978-1-59497-076-4(9)) Public Square Bks.

C
D

—Los lobos de la Pared: Wolves in the Walls. 2006. (SPA.). 64p. 22.95 (978-1-59497-222-5(2)) Public Square Bks.
—Marvel 1602 TPB (Quill Award Edition) 2006. (Illus.). 248p. (YA). pap. 19.99 (978-0-7851-2311-8(3)) Marvel Enterprises, Inc.
—The Wolves in the Walls. McKean, Dave, illus. 2005. 56p. reprint ed. pap. 6.99 (978-0-380-81095-6(6) , Harper Trophy) HarperCollins Pubs.
Gallagher, John. Buzzboy Vol. 2: Monsters, Dreams, & Milkshakes. 2004. 144p. pap. 11.95 (978-0-9721831-1-6(6)) sky-dog.
Gallagher, Mike. Sonic the Hedgehog Archives, Vol. 1. 2006. 112p. pap. 7.49 (978-1-879794-20-7(9)) Archie Comic Pubns., Inc.
Gallagher, Mike & DeCesare, Angelo. Sonic the Hedgehog Archives, Vol. 2. 2006. 112p. pap. 7.49 (978-1-879794-21-4(7)) Archie Comic Pubns., Inc.
Gatou, Shouji. Full Metal Panic!, Vol. 7. Tateo, Retsu, illus. 2005. 172p. (YA). pap. 9.99 (978-1-4139-0200-6(6)) A. D. Vision, Inc.
—Full Metal Panic! Tateo, Retsu, illus. (YA). Vol. 2. 2003. 200p. pap. (978-1-4139-0006-4(2)); Vol. 3. 2004. 178p. pap. (978-1-4139-0007-1(0)); Vol. 4. 2004. 160p. pap. (978-1-4139-0039-2(9)) ADV Manga.
—Full Metal Panic!, Vol. 6. Tateo, Retsuo, illus. 2004. 172p. (YA). pap. (978-1-4139-0198-6(0)) ADV Manga.
—Full Metal Panic, Vol. 9. 2006. (Illus.). 184p. (YA). pap. (978-1-4139-0338-6(X)) ADV Manga.
—Full Metal Panic! Film Book. 2003. (JPN & ENG., Illus.). 100p. pap. 19.98 (978-1-4139-0027-9(5)) A. D. Vision, Inc.
—Full Metal Panic! Overload!, Vol. 5. 2006. (Illus.). 200p. (YA). pap. (978-1-4139-0342-3(8)) ADV Manga.
Gatou, Shouji & Kaisyaku. Full Metal Panic!, Vol. 1. 2003. (Illus.). 168p. (YA). pap. (978-1-4139-0001-9(1) , MFP/001) ADV Manga.
Gatou, Shouji & Tateo, Retsu. Full Metal Panic!, Vol. 5. 2004. (Illus.). 168p. (YA). pap. (978-1-4139-0051-4(8)) ADV Manga.
Gavila, Robert. Nisha: Montana. 2004. (YA). 2.25 (978-0-9748466-0-6(0)) Crossover Comics.
Gay, Francis. The Friendship Book. 2005. (Illus.). 180p. 9.95 (978-1-84535-050-5(2)) Thomson, D.C. & Co., Ltd. GBR. *Dist:* APG Sales and Fulfillment.
Gaydos, Nora. Phonics Comics: Pony Tales - Level 1. Hamilton, Pamela, illus. 2007. 24p. (J). (gr. 1-17). pap. 3.99 (978-1-58476-553-0(4)) Innovative Kids.
Gemstone Publishing, creator. Mickey Mouse Adventures, Vol. 6. 2005. (Illus.). 128p. (YA). pap. 7.95 (978-0-911903-71-3(2)) Gemstone Publishing, Inc.
Gerber, Steve, et al. Omega: The Unknown Classic. 2005. (Illus.). 224p. (YA). pap. 29.99 (978-0-7851-2009-4(2)) Marvel Enterprises, Inc.
Gerstein, David. Mickey & the Gang: Classic Stories in Verse. 2005. 360p. pap. 29.99 (978-1-888472-06-6(5)) Gemstone Publishing, Inc.
Gilbert, Michael T., et al. Mickey Mouse Adventures, Vol. 8. 2006. 128p. (YA). pap. 7.95 (978-1-888472-09-7(X)) Gemstone Publishing, Inc.
Gilchrist, Guy. I'm Having a Bad Fur Day. 2001. (Mudpies Ser.: Vol. 1). 128p. pap. 9.95 (978-1-929462-35-3(2)) Plan Nine Publishing, Inc.
Gipi. Garage Band. Spectrum, tr. from FRE. 2007. (Illus.). 128p. (YA). (gr. 7 up). pap. 16.95 (978-1-59643-206-2(3) , First Second Bks.) Roaring Brook Pr.
Girard, Jeremy. The Key to Slumber: The Tales of Slumber. 2005. 201p. pap. 19.95 (978-1-4137-7243-2(9)) PublishAmerica, Inc.
Given, Cate. The Great Pogo Stick. Hill-Peterson, Jodi, illus. 2006. (J). (*978-0-9790057-0-1(1)*) Paws In the Sand Publishing.
Glossop, Jennifer & Russell, Jay. Hypacrosaurus. 1999. (Tiny Perfect Dinosaur Ser.). (Illus.). 32p. 12.95 (978-0-8362-7910-8(7)) Andrews McMeel Publishing.
Glymph, Rikimah. Are You My Friend? 2006. (Illus.). 32p. (J). lib. bdg. 17.95 (*978-1-934190-00-5(4)*) Ocean Front Bk. Publishing, Inc.
Godwin, Parke. Meridian Magic. rev. ed. 2005. (W. I. T. C. H. Graphic Novels Ser.: Bk. 2). (Illus.). 128p. (gr. 3-7). pap. 4.99 (978-0-7868-0974-5(4) , Volo) Hyperion Bks. for Children.
Gokurakuin, Sakurako. FLCL Clear Poster: Haruhara Haruko. 2005. (Illus.). 208p. (YA). pap. 19.99 (978-1-932480-45-0(5)) Broccoli International USA, Inc.
The Golden Bird. rev. ed. 2006. 152p. 26.95 (*978-1-4218-2343-0(8)*); pap. 11.95 (*978-1-4218-2443-7(4)*) 1st World Publishing, Inc. (1st World Library - Literary Society).
Goldman, Steven & Goldman, Dan. Everyman: Be the People. Bucco, Joe, illus. 2004. 96p. per. 6.00 (978-0-9759152-0-2(7)) FWDbks.
Goldsmann, Henri. Secret Agent Spanky Sheep in the mystery of: the Pooperous Pizza Plunderer. 2006. 140p. pap. 11.99 (978-1-4116-8094-4(4)) Lulu.com.
Golightly, Holly. School Bites: Blood Drinking 101, 2. ed. 2005. (Illus.). 64p. (YA). per. (978-0-9745367-3-6(3)) BroadSword Comics/ Jim Balent Studios.
Golightly, Holly, creator. School Bites. 2004. 64p. (YA). per. (978-0-9745367-2-9(5) , SB1A) BroadSword Comics/ Jim Balent Studios.
Gonzales, David. Mijos Handbook. Gonzales, David, illus. 2004. (Mijos Ser.). (Illus.). 80p. (J). (gr. 2-5). pap. 5.99 (978-0-439-56232-4(5) , Scholastic Paperbacks) Scholastic, Inc.
Gorgas, Paula Blais. Little Lost Leprechaun. Taylor, Chet, illus. l.t. ed. 2005. 20p. (J). 17.99 (978-0-9755888-4-0(2)) Dragonfly Publishing, Inc.
Gormon: The Sentinel Awakes. 2004. per. 2.75 (978-0-9762294-0-7(4)) Corbett Features.
Goscinny. Billy the Kid. Morris, illus. 2007. 48p. pap. 11.95 (*978-1-905460-11-3(2)*) CineBook GBR. *Dist:* Biblio Distribution.
Goscinny, R. A Lucky Luke Adventure: Barbed Wire on the Prairie. Spear, Luke, tr. from FRE. Morris, illus. 2007. 48p. pap. 9.99 (*978-1-905460-24-3(4)*) CineBook GBR. *Dist:* Biblio Distribution.
Goscinny, R. A Lucky Luke Adventure Dalton City. Morris, illus. 2007. 48p. pap. 9.99 (*978-1-905460-13-7(9)*) CineBook GBR. *Dist:* Biblio Distribution.
—A Lucky Luke Adventure in the Shadow of the Derricks. Morris, illus. 2007. 48p. pap. 9.99 (*978-1-905460-17-5(1)*) CineBook GBR. *Dist:* Biblio Distribution.
—A Lucky Luke Adventure Jesse James. Morris, illus. 2007. 48p. pap. 9.99 (*978-1-905460-14-4(7)*) CineBook GBR. *Dist:* Biblio Distribution.
Goscinny, René. Asterix & the Cheiftan's Sheild. Uderzo, Albert, illus. 2004. 48p. 12.95 (978-0-7528-6624-6(9)) Orion Bks. Ltd. GBR. *Dist:* Sterling Publishing Co., Inc.
—Asterix & the Goths. Uderzo, Albert, illus. 2004. 48p. 12.95 (978-0-7528-6614-7(1)) Orion Bks. Ltd. GBR. *Dist:* Sterling Publishing Co., Inc.
—Asterix & the Great Crossing. Uderzo, Albert, illus. 2005. 48p. pap. 9.95 (978-0-7528-6648-2(6)) Orion Bks. Ltd. GBR. *Dist:* Sterling Publishing Co., Inc.
—Asterix & the Great Divide. Uderzo, Albert, illus. 2007. 48p. (*978-0-7528-4712-2(0)*) Orion Media.
—Asterix & the Roman Agent. Uderzo, Albert, illus. 2004. 48p. 12.95 (978-0-7528-6632-1(X)) Orion Bks. Ltd. GBR. *Dist:* Sterling Publishing Co., Inc.
—Asterix et les Goths. (FRE.). (J). pap. 21.95 (978-2-01-210003-9(1)) Hachette Groupe Livre FRA. *Dist:* Distribooks, Inc.
—Asterix in Belgium. Uderzo, Albert, illus. 2005. 48p. 12.95 (978-0-7528-6649-9(4)) ; pap. 9.95 (978-0-7528-6650-5(8)) Orion Bks. Ltd. GBR. *Dist:* Sterling Publishing Co., Inc.
—Asterix in Corsica. Uderzo, Albert, illus. 2005. 48p. 12.95 (978-0-7528-6643-7(5)); pap. 9.95 (978-0-7528-6644-4(3)) Orion Bks. Ltd. GBR. *Dist:* Sterling Publishing Co., Inc.
—Asterix le Gaulois. 2005. audio compact disk 45.00 (978-0-320-06624-5(X)) French & European Pubns., Inc.
—Asterix le Gaulois. (FRE.). (J). pap. 21.95 (*978-2-01-210133-3(X)*) Hachette Groupe Livre FRA. *Dist:* Distribooks, Inc.
—Asterix the Legionary. Uderzo, Albert, illus. 2004. 48p. 12.95 (978-0-7528-6620-8(6)) Orion Bks. Ltd. GBR. *Dist:* Sterling Publishing Co., Inc.
—Asterix the Mansions of the Gods. Uderzo, Albert, illus. 2005. 48p. 12.95 (978-0-7528-6638-3(9)) Orion Bks. Ltd. GBR. *Dist:* Sterling Publishing Co., Inc.
—Ma Dalton. 2007. (Illus.). 48p. pap. 9.99 (*978-1-905460-18-2(X)*) CineBook GBR. *Dist:* Biblio Distribution.
Goscinny, René. Obelix & Co. Uderzo, Albert, illus. 2005. 48p. (J). 12.95 (978-0-7528-6651-2(6)) Orion Bks. Ltd. GBR. *Dist:* Sterling Publishing Co., Inc.
Goscinny, René, text. Asterix le Gaulois. (FRE.). pap. 21.95 (978-2-01-210001-5(5)) Hachette Groupe Livre FRA. *Dist:* Distribooks, Inc.
Goscinny, René & Uderzo. Le Tour de Gaule d'Asterix. (Asterix Adventure Ser.). (FRE., Illus.). 48p. pap. 19.95 (978-2-205-00146-4(9)) Dargaud Publishing Co. FRA. *Dist:* Distribooks, Inc.
Goscinny, René & Uderzo, Albert. Asterix & Caesar's Gift. 2005. (Illus.). 48p. pap. 9.95 (978-0-7528-6646-8(X)) Orion Bks. Ltd. GBR. *Dist:* Sterling Publishing Co., Inc.
—Asterix & the Banquet. Uderzo, Albert, illus. 2004. (Illus.). 48p. pap. 9.95 (978-0-7528-6609-3(5)) Orion Bks. Ltd. GBR. *Dist:* Sterling Publishing Co., Inc.
—Asterix & the Cauldron. Uderzo, Albert, illus. 2004. (Illus.). 48p. pap. 9.95 (978-0-7528-6629-1(X)) Orion Bks. Ltd. GBR. *Dist:* Sterling Publishing Co., Inc.
—Asterix & the Chieftain's Shield. Uderzo, Albert, illus. 2004. (Illus.). 48p. pap. 9.95 (978-0-7528-6625-3(7)) Orion Bks. Ltd. GBR. *Dist:* Sterling Publishing Co., Inc.
—Asterix & the Falling Sky. (Illus.). 48p. 2006. pap. 9.95 (978-0-7528-7548-4(5)); 2005. 12.95 (978-0-7528-7301-5(6)) Orion Bks. Ltd. GBR. *Dist:* Sterling Publishing Co., Inc.
—Asterix & the Golden Sickle. Uderzo, Albert, illus. 2004. (Illus.). 48p. pap. 9.95 (978-0-7528-6613-0(3)) Orion Bks. Ltd. GBR. *Dist:* Sterling Publishing Co., Inc.
—Asterix & the Goths. Uderzo, Albert, illus. 2004. (Illus.). 48p. pap. 9.95 (978-0-7528-6615-4(X)) Orion Bks. Ltd. GBR. *Dist:* Sterling Publishing Co., Inc.
—Asterix & the Laurel Wreath. Uderzo, Albert, illus. 2005. (Illus.). 48p. pap. 9.95 (978-0-7528-6637-6(0)) Orion Bks. Ltd. GBR. *Dist:* Sterling Publishing Co., Inc.
—Asterix & the Normans. Uderzo, Albert, illus. 2004. (Illus.). 48p. pap. 9.95 (978-0-7528-6623-9(0)) Orion Bks. Ltd. GBR. *Dist:* Sterling Publishing Co., Inc.
—Asterix & the Roman Agent. Uderzo, Albert, illus. 2004. (Illus.). 48p. pap. 9.95 (978-0-7528-6633-8(8)) Orion Bks. Ltd. GBR. *Dist:* Sterling Publishing Co., Inc.
—Asterix & the Soothsayer. Uderzo, Albert, illus. 2005. (Illus.). 48p. pap. 9.95 (978-0-7528-6642-0(7)) Orion Bks. Ltd. GBR. *Dist:* Sterling Publishing Co., Inc.
—Asterix in Spain. Uderzo, Albert, illus. 2004. (Illus.). 48p. pap. 9.95 (978-0-7528-6631-4(1)) Orion Bks. Ltd. GBR. *Dist:* Sterling Publishing Co., Inc.
—Asterix Omnibus 1. 2008. (Illus.). 144p. 27.95 (*978-0-7528-9154-5(5)*); pap. 19.95 (*978-0-7528-9155-2(3)*) Orion Bks. Ltd. GBR. *Dist:* Sterling Publishing Co., Inc.
—Asterix Omnibus 2. 2008. (Illus.). 144p. 27.95 (*978-0-7528-9156-9(1)*) Orion Bks. Ltd. GBR. *Dist:* Sterling Publishing Co., Inc.
—Asterix Omnibus 2: Three Great Asterix Stories in One Volume. 2008. (Illus.). 144p. per. 19.95 (*978-0-7528-9158-3(8)*) Orion Bks. Ltd. GBR. *Dist:* Sterling Publishing Co., Inc.
—Asterix the Gaul. Uderzo, Albert, illus. 2004. (Illus.). 48p. pap. 9.95 (978-0-7528-6605-5(2)) Orion Bks. Ltd. GBR. *Dist:* Sterling Publishing Co., Inc.
—Asterix the Gladiator. Uderzo, Albert, illus. 2004. (Illus.). 48p. pap. 9.95 (978-0-7528-6611-6(7)) Orion Bks. Ltd. GBR. *Dist:* Sterling Publishing Co., Inc.
—Asterix the Legionary. Uderzo, Albert, illus. 2004. (Illus.). 48p. pap. 9.95 (978-0-7528-6621-5(4)) Orion Bks. Ltd. GBR. *Dist:* Sterling Publishing Co., Inc.
—La Vuelta a la Galia. (SPA.). 48p. 9.95 (978-84-7510-132-3(1)) Grijalbo-Dargaud, S.A. Editores ESP. *Dist:* Distribooks, Inc.
Goscinny, René & Uderzo, M. El Adivino. (SPA., Illus.). (J). 24.95 (978-0-8288-6082-6(3) , S26630) French & European Pubns., Inc.
—Der Arvernerschild. (GER., Illus.). (J). 24.95 (978-0-8288-4914-2(5)) French & European Pubns., Inc.
—La Cizana. (SPA., Illus.). (J). 24.95 (978-0-8288-4961-6(7)) French & European Pubns., Inc.
—El Combate de los Jefes. (SPA., Illus.). (J). 24.95 (978-0-8288-4962-3(5)) French & European Pubns., Inc.
—El Escudo Arverno. (SPA., Illus.). (J). 24.95 (978-0-8288-4965-4(X)) French & European Pubns., Inc.
—Falx Aurea. (LAT., Illus.). (J). 24.95 (978-0-8288-4966-1(8)) French & European Pubns., Inc.
—Das Geschenk Casars. (GER., Illus.). (J). 24.95 (978-0-8288-4967-8(6)) French & European Pubns., Inc.
—Die Goldene Sichel. (GER., Illus.). (J). 24.95 (978-0-8288-4969-2(2)) French & European Pubns., Inc.
—La Gran Travesia. (SPA., Illus.). (J). 24.95 (978-0-8288-5124-4(7)) French & European Pubns., Inc.
—Die Grosse Uberfahrt. (GER., Illus.). (J). 24.95 (978-0-8288-4972-2(2)) French & European Pubns., Inc.
—La Hoz de Oro. (SPA., Illus.). (J). 24.95 (978-0-8288-4973-9(0)) French & European Pubns., Inc.
—Der Kampf der Hauptlinge. (GER., Illus.). (J). 24.95 (978-0-8288-4974-6(9)) French & European Pubns., Inc.
—Der Kupferkessel. (GER., Illus.). (J). 24.95 (978-0-8288-4975-3(7)) French & European Pubns., Inc.
—Los Laureles del Cesar. (SPA., Illus.). (J). 24.95 (978-0-8288-4976-0(5)) French & European Pubns., Inc.
—Die Lorbeeren des Casar. (GER., Illus.). (J). 24.95 (978-0-8288-4978-4(1)) French & European Pubns., Inc.
—Die Normannen. (GER., Illus.). (J). 24.95 (978-0-8288-4980-7(3)) French & European Pubns., Inc.
—El Regalo del Cesar. (SPA., Illus.). (J). 24.95 (978-0-8288-4900-5(5)) French & European Pubns., Inc.
—La Residencia de los Dioses. (SPA., Illus.). (J). 24.95 (978-0-8288-4901-2(3)) French & European Pubns., Inc.
—Der Seher. (GER., Illus.). (J). 24.95 (978-0-8288-5125-1(5)) French & European Pubns., Inc.
—Le Tour de Gaulle. (FRE., Illus.). (J). 24.95 (978-0-8288-4908-1(0)) French & European Pubns., Inc.
—Die Trabantenstadt. (GER., Illus.). (J). 24.95 (978-0-8288-4910-4(2)) French & European Pubns., Inc.
—La Vuelta a la Galia. (SPA., Illus.). (J). 24.95 (978-0-8288-4911-1(0)) French & European Pubns., Inc.
Gotsubo, Masaru. Samurai Champloo, Vol. 2. 2nd rev. ed. 2006. (Illus.). (YA). pap. 9.99 (978-1-59816-215-8(2) , Tokyopop Adult) TOKYOPOP, Inc.
Gownley, Jimmy. Amelia Rules! Vol. 3: Superheroes. 2006. (Illus.). 176p. (J). pap. (978-0-9712169-6-9(7)) Renaissance Pr.
—Amelia Rules! Superheroes. 2006. 176p. (J). (978-0-9712169-7-6(5)) Renaissance Pr.
Graham-Larkin, Debbie. Magic in the Air. 2005. (Graham Cracker Kids Adventure Ser.). (Illus.). (J). pap. 12.95 (978-0-9716475-1-0(8)) Graham Cracker Kids.
Grant, Steven, et al. Ghost Rider Team-up TPB. 2007. (Illus.). 144p. pap. 15.99 (978-0-7851-2257-9(5)) Marvel Enterprises, Inc.
Graphic Mysteries, 6 bks., Set. Incl. Atlantis & Other Lost Cities. Shone, Rob. Eldridge, Jim, illus. (YA). lib. bdg. 29.95 (978-1-4042-0794-3(5)); Bermuda Triangle : Strange Happenings at Sea. West, David. Lacey, Mike, illus. (J). lib. bdg. 29.95 (978-1-4042-0795-0(3)); Bigfoot & Other Strange Beasts. Shone, Rob. Spender, Nick, illus. (J). lib. bdg. 29.95 (978-1-4042-0793-6(7)); Ghosts & Poltergeists : Stories of the Supernatural. West, David. Riley, Terry, illus. (YA). lib. bdg. 29.95 (978-1-4042-0608-3(6)); Loch Ness Monster & Other Lake Mysteries. Jeffrey, Gary. Spender, Nik & Moulder, Bob, illus. (J). lib. bdg. 29.95 (978-1-4042-0796-7(1)); UFOs : Alien Abduction & Close Encounters. Jeffrey, Gary. (J). lib. bdg. 29.95 (978-1-4042-0797-4(X)); (Illus.). 48p. (gr. 5-8). 2005. 2005. Set lib. bdg. 179.70 (978-1-4042-0829-2(1)) Rosen Publishing Group, Inc., The.
Graphic Novel Classics. 2006. (J). (gr. 4-8). 193.68 (978-1-59961-112-9(0)) Spotlight.
Graphic Novel Collection. (Fiction Collections). 304.27 (978-1-59889-041-9(7)) Stone Arch Bks.
Graphic Quest. (Illus.). (YA). (gr. 3 up). lib. bdg. 85.04 (978-1-59889-031-0(X)) Stone Arch Bks.
The Graphix Collection, 3 bks., Set. Incl. Great Cow Race. Smith, Jeff. Hamaker, Steve, illus. 144p. pap. 19.95 (978-0-439-70624-7(6)); Out from Boneville. Smith, Jeff. 144p. pap. 18.95 (978-0-439-70623-0(8)); Queen Bee. Clugston, Chynna. 112p. pap. 16.99 (978-0-439-71572-0(5)); (Illus.). (J). 2005. 2006. 54.89 (978-0-439-79840-2(X) , Graphix) Scholastic, Inc.
Grayson, Devin. Am I Blue. 2006. (X-Men, Evolution Ser.). (Illus.). (J). (gr. 2-6). 21.35 (978-1-59961-052-8(3)) Spotlight.
—Hearing Things. 2006. (X-Men Evolution Ser.). (Illus.). 21.35 (978-1-59961-053-5(1)) Spotlight.
—Lines in the Sand. 2006. (X-Men, Evolution Ser.). (Illus.). (J). (gr. 2-6). 21.35 (978-1-59961-054-2(X)) Spotlight.
—Seeing Clearly. 2006. (X-Men, Evolution Ser.). (Illus.). (J). (gr. 2-6). 21.35 (978-1-59961-055-9(8)) Spotlight.
Greenberg, Dan. Comic-Strip Grammar: 40 Reproducible Cartoons with Engaging Practice Exercises That Make Learning Grammar Fun. 2000. (Illus.). 64p. pap. 10.95 (978-0-439-08681-3(7)) Scholastic, Inc.
—Comic-Strip Math: Mini-Story Problems: 60 Reproducible Cartoons with Dozens of Story Problems. 2000. (Illus.). 48p. (J). pap. 9.95 (978-0-439-04383-0(2)) Scholastic, Inc.
Gregori, Anthony, illus. Meet the ItsIts. l.t. ed. 2007. 40p. (J). lib. bdg. 9.99 (*978-0-9769360-1-5(1)*) Adam Hill Pubns.
Gregory, Deborah. The Cheetah Girls 2. 2006. (Cheetah Girls Ser.: No. 2). 48p. (gr. k-17). pap., pap. 6.99 (978-0-7868-4715-0(8)) Disney Pr.
Greig, Allison. Stacey's Adventures. 2006. (Illus.). 64p. pap. (*978-1-84401-035-6(X)*) Athena Pr.
Groening, Matt. Simpsons Comics Royale. 2001. (Simpsons Comics Ser.). (gr. 5-8). lib. bdg. 24.55 (978-0-613-49364-2(8)) Tandem Library Bks.
—Simpsons Comics Unchained. 2001. (Simpsons Comics Ser.). (gr. 5-8). lib. bdg. 24.55 (978-0-613-51119-3(0)) Tandem Library Bks.
—The Simpson's Treehouse of Horror Heebie-Jeebie Hullabaloo. 1999. (Treehouse of Horror Ser.). (gr. 5-8). lib. bdg. 25.70 (978-0-613-53669-1(X)) Tandem Library Bks.
Groot, Bob de & Turk. The Laughing Thief. 2007. (Illus.). 48p. pap. 9.99 (*978-1-905460-07-6(4)*) CineBook GBR. *Dist:* Biblio Distribution.
—My Dear Wilkinson. 2007. (Illus.). 48p. pap. 9.99 (*978-1-905460-06-9(6)*) CineBook GBR. *Dist:* Biblio Distribution.
Groot, De. Clifton: Black Moon. Spear, Luke, tr. from FRE. Rodrigue, illus. 2007. 48p. pap. 9.99 (*978-1-905460-30-4(9)*) CineBook GBR. *Dist:* Biblio Distribution.
Gruenwald, Mark, et al. Essential Official Handbook of the Marvel Universe - TPB, 3 vols., Vol. 2. deluxe ed. 2006. (Illus.). 480p. pap. 16.99 (978-0-7851-1935-7(3)) Marvel Enterprises, Inc.
—Squadron Supreme: Death of a Universe. 2006. (Illus.). 240p. (YA). pap. 24.99 (978-0-7851-2091-9(2)) Marvel Enterprises, Inc.
Guibert, Emmanuel. Sardine in Outer Space. Watson, Sasha, tr. from FRE. Sfar, Joann, illus. deluxe ed. 2006. (Sardine in Outer Space Ser.). 128p. (J). pap. 12.95 (978-1-59643-126-3(1) , First Second Bks.) Roaring Brook Pr.
—Sardine in Outer Space 3. Brizzi, Elisabeth & Siegel, Alexis, trs. from FRE. Sfar, Joann, illus. 3rd rev. ed. 2007. (Sardine in Outer Space Ser.). 112p. (J). (gr. 1-5). pap. 12.95 (*978-1-59643-128-7(8)* , First Second Bks.) Roaring Brook Pr.
—Space Pirate Sardine in Outer Space. Sfar, Joann, illus. 2008. 64p. (J). pap. 6.99 (*978-0-312-38056-4(9)*) Square Fish.
Guibert, Emmanuel & Sfar, Joann. The Professor's Daughter. 2007. 80p. (YA). pap. 16.95 (978-1-59643-130-0(X) , First Second Bks.) Roaring Brook Pr.
Guigar, Brad J. Dilutions of Grandeur. 2001. (Greystone Inn Ser.). 152p. pap. 12.95 (978-1-929462-25-4(5)) Plan Nine Publishing, Inc.
Guillaume, Robert, narrated by. Lion King: Read Along. 2001. (Illus.). 32p. (J). pap. 9.98 incl. audio compact disk (978-0-7634-0735-3(6)) Walt Disney Records.
Gully, Mario & Hammond, Marc. Reality Bites. 2006. (Illus.). 120p. (YA). pap. 12.99 (978-1-58240-580-3(8)) Image Comics.
Gunderson, Jessica. Fire & Snow: A Tale of the Alaskan Gold Rush. Townsend, Shannon, illus. 2007. (J). 56p. 23.93 (*978-1-59889-310-6(6)*); 47p. pap. (*978-1-59889-405-9(6)*) Stone Arch Bks.
—The Last Rider: The Final Days of the Pony Express. Ocampo Ruiz, José Alfonso, illus. 2007. (J). 56p. 23.93 (*978-1-59889-312-0(2)*); 49p. pap. (*978-1-59889-407-3(2)*) Stone Arch Bks.
Gureke, Mankin. Imperfect Hero, Vol. 3. 2005. (Illus.). 208p. (YA). pap. 9.95 (978-1-59796-094-6(2)) DrMaster Pubns. Inc.
Gureke, Nankin. Imperfect Hero, Vol. 2. 2006. (Illus.). 208p. pap. 9.95 (978-1-58899-247-5(0)) DrMaster Pubns. Inc.
H., Yves & Hermann. Manhattan Beach 1957. 2003. (Illus.). 56p. (YA). (gr. 11 up). 12.95 (978-1-931724-23-4(7)) Diamond Select Toys & Collectibles.
Hadley, Amy. Fool's Gold. 2006. (Illus.). pap. 9.99 (978-1-59816-585-2(2) , Tokyopop Adult) TOKYOPOP, Inc.
Hagiwara, Kazushi. Bastard!! Hagiwara, Kazushi, illus. (Bastard!! Ser.). (YA). Vol. 7. 2005. (Illus.). 192p. pap. 9.99 (978-1-59116-742-6(6)); Vol. 12. 2006. 208p. pap. 9.99 (978-1-4215-0434-6(0)) Viz Media.
Hajime, Kanzaka Rui Araizumi. Slayers, Vol. 5. 2005. (Illus.). 192p. pap. 7.99 (978-1-59532-581-5(6) , Tokyopop Kids) TOKYOPOP, Inc.
Hakoda, Maki. R2, Vol. 1. 2004. (Illus.). 184p. (YA). pap. (978-1-4139-0056-9(9)) ADV Manga.
Hall, Susan', illus. Agent Secret. 2007. (Backyardigans Ser.). 24p. (J). pap. 3.99 (*978-1-4169-3823-1(0)* , Simon Spotlight/Nickelodeon) Simon & Schuster Children's Publishing.
Hama, Larry. Fight to the Death: Battle of Guadalcanal. Elson, Richard & Williams, Anthony, illus. 2007. (Graphic History Ser.). 48p. (J). (gr. 3). pap. 9.95 (978-1-84603-060-4(9)) Osprey Publishing, Ltd. GBR. *Dist:* Random Hse., Inc.
Hamazaki, Tatsuya. . hack //Legend of the Twilight, Volume 1: Kaplan SAT/ACT Vocabulary-Building Manga. Izumi, Rei, illus. 2007. (Kaplan SAT/ACT Score-Raising Manga Ser.). 192p. pap. 9.99 (*978-1-4277-5497-4(7)*) Kaplan Bks.

Hamilton, John. Defending the Nation, 8 vols., Set. Incl. Army. lib. bdg. 22.78 (978-1-59679-754-3(1)); CIA. lib. bdg. 22.78 (978-1-59679-756-7(8)); Coast Guard. lib. bdg. 22.78 (978-1-59679-755-0(X)); FBI. lib. bdg. 22.78 (978-1-59679-757-4(6) , Checkerboard Library); Marine Corps. lib. bdg. 22.78 (978-1-59679-758-1(4) , Checkerboard Library); Navy. lib. bdg. 22.78 (978-1-59679-760-4(6) , Checkerboard Library); Special Forces. lib. bdg. 22.78 (978-1-59679-759-8(2) , Checkerboard Library); (Illus.). 32p. (J). (gr. 3-5). 2007. Set lib. bdg. 182.24 (***978-1-59679-752-9(5)*** , Checkerboard Library) ABDO Publishing Co.

Hamme. Thorgal Child of the Stars. Rosinski, Grzegorz, illus. 2007. 96p. pap. 14.99 (***978-1-905460-23-6(6))*** CineBook GBR. *Dist:* Biblio Distribution.

Haney, Bob & Fox, Gardner. Metamorpho Vol. 1: The Element Man. Fradon, Ramona, illus. rev. ed. 2005. (Showcase Presents Ser.). 560p. (YA). pap. 16.99 (978-1-4012-0762-5(6)) DC Comics.

Hansen, Marc. Ralph Snart Adventures: Comic Collection #2. 2007. (Illus.). 128p. (YA). pap. 14.95 (***978-0-9794643-1-7(5))*** Hansen, Marc Stuff!.

Hansen, Marc. Ralph Snart Adventures: Comic Collection #1. Hansen, Marc, . 2007. (YA). per. 14.95 (***978-0-9794643-0-0(7))*** Hansen, Marc Stuff!.

Hapka, Catherine. Astro Boy Color, Bk. 1. Merkel, Joe F., illus. 2004. (Astro Boy Ser.). 32p. (J). pap., act. bk. ed. 4.99 (978-0-06-072522-8(2) , Harper Festival) HarperCollins Pubs.

—Astro Boy Color & Sticker Book, Bk. 2. Farley, Rick, illus. 2004. (Astro Boy Ser.). 32p. (J). pap. 4.99 (978-0-06-072523-5(0) , Harper Festival) HarperCollins Pubs.

—The Last Stand: Beast Chooses Sides. Gordon, Steven E., illus. 2006. (X Men Ser.). 24p. (J). pap. 3.99 (978-0-06-082202-6(3)) HarperCollins Pubs.

—The Last Stand: Teaming Up. Kirkland, Boyd, illus. 2006. (X Men Ser.). 24p. (J). pap. 3.99 (978-0-06-082201-9(5)) HarperCollins Pubs.

Hardcastle, Michael. My Brother's a Keeper. Moulder, Bob, illus. 2007. (Graphic Quest Ser.). 88p. (J). (***978-1-59889-212-3(6)*** , 1256168) Stone Arch Bks.

Hardy Boys. 2006. (J). (gr. 3-8). 72.63 (978-1-59961-060-3(4)) Spotlight.

Harperfestival. Hulk: The Beast Within. 2003. (gr. 3-6). lib. bdg. 13.00 (978-0-613-85980-6(4)) Tandem Library Bks.

—Hulk: The Hulk Escapes. 2003. (ps-2). lib. bdg. 11.80 (978-0-613-81693-9(5)) Tandem Library Bks.

—Hulk: The Hulk Fights Back. 2003. (gr. 3-6). lib. bdg. 13.00 (978-0-613-81692-2(7)) Tandem Library Bks.

Harras, Bob, et al. Galactic Storm Vol. 1. 2006. (Avengers Ser.). (Illus.). 280p. (YA). pap. 29.99 (978-0-7851-2044-5(0)) Marvel Enterprises, Inc.

Harrison, Emma. A Dictionary of Growl-Licious Lingo. 2006. (Cheetah Chatter Ser.: Bk. 2). 128p. (gr. 2-17). pap. 4.99 (978-0-7868-4716-7(6)) Disney Pr.

Hart, Christopher. Draw Manga! 2003. (gr. 3-6). lib. bdg. 15.25 (978-0-613-76655-5(5)) Tandem Library Bks.

—Draw Manga! 2003. (Xtreme Art Ser.). (Illus.). 64p. 7.95 (978-0-8230-0369-3(8)) Watson-Guptill Pubns., Inc.

—Kids Draw Anime. 2003. (gr. 3-6). lib. bdg. 19.90 (978-0-613-88815-8(4)) Tandem Library Bks.

—Kids Draw Anime. 2002. (Kids Draw Ser.). (Illus.). 64p. (J). (gr. 3-6). pap. 11.95 (978-0-8230-2690-6(6)) Watson-Guptill Pubns., Inc.

Hart, J. J. Zombie Monkey Monster Jamboree. Meugniot, Will, illus. 2006. 141p. (J). 12.95 (978-1-933925-07-3(8) , Actionopolis) Komikwerks, LLC.

Hartzell, Andy. Fox Bunny Funny. 2007. 104p. pap. 10.00 (***978-1-891830-97-6(X))*** Top Shelf Productions.

Hasbro. Dancing in the Clouds Vol. 3. 2006. (My Little Pony Ser.). (Illus.). 32p. pap. 3.99 (978-1-59816-281-3(0) , Tokyopop Kids) TOKYOPOP, Inc.

—G. I. Joe Valor vs. Venom, Vol. 1. (Illus.). 96p. (YA). pap. 7.99 (978-1-59182-816-7(3)) TOKYOPOP, Inc.

Hasbro, creator. Very Minty Christmas. 2005. (Illus.). 32p. pap. 3.99 (978-1-59816-001-7(X) , Tokyopop Kids) TOKYOPOP, Inc.

Haskins, Lori. May I Have This Dance? 2005. 16p. (ps-2). 14.99 (978-0-7868-3608-6(3)) Disney Pr.

Hata, Kenjiro. Hayate the Combat Butler, Volume 2. 2007. (Conversational Ser.). 200p. (YA). pap. 9.99 (978-1-4215-0852-8(4)) Viz Media.

Hayashi, Fumino. Neon Genesis Evangelion: Angelic Days. 2006. 184p. (YA). (Angelic Days Ser.: Vol. 2). (Illus.). pap. (978-1-4139-0348-5(7)); pap. (978-1-4139-0344-7(4)) ADV Manga.

—Neon Genesis Evangelion Vol. 3: Angelic Days. 2006. (Illus.). 184p. (YA). pap. (978-1-4139-0350-8(9)) ADV Manga.

Hazelton, Jack W. Puddlefoot Pete. Hazelton, Jack W., illus. l.t. ed. 2002. (Illus.). 24p. cd-rom 9.95 (978-1-928907-51-0(2)) Jack's Bookshelf, Inc.

Heath, Michael, ed. "Spectator" Cartoon Book. 2004. (Illus.). 96p. pap. 6.99 (978-1-86197-773-1(5)) Profile Bks. Ltd. GBR. *Dist:* Trafalgar Square Publishing.

Hee-Joon, Son. PhD Vol. 3: Phantasy Degree. Hee-Joon, Son, illus. 2005. (Illus.). pap. 9.99 (978-1-59532-319-4(8) , Tokyopop Adult) TOKYOPOP, Inc.

Hee-Joon, Son, illus. & creator. PHD: Phantasy Degree, Vol. 2. Hee-Joon, Son, creator. rev. ed. 2005. 192p. pap. 9.99 (978-1-59532-320-0(1) , Tokyopop Adult) TOKYOPOP, Inc.

Heinberg, Allan. Family Matters. 2006. (Young Avengers Ser.: Vol. 2). (Illus.). 184p. (YA). 22.99 (978-0-7851-2021-6(1)) Marvel Enterprises, Inc.

—Sidekicks. 2006. (Young Avengers Ser.: Vol. 1). (Illus.). 144p. (YA). pap. 14.99 (978-0-7851-2018-6(1)) Marvel Enterprises, Inc.

Heller, Sarah & Reader's Digest Staff. Disney Tinker Bell Music Player & Storybook. 2008. (RD Innovative Book & Player Format Ser.). 36p. (J). 24.99 (***978-0-7944-1300-2(5))*** Reader's Digest Assn., Inc., The.

Hello, Cy! 2007. (J). 14.95 (***978-1-932888-53-9(5))*** Mascot Bks., Inc.

Hello, Phillie Phanatic! 2007. (J). 17.95 (***978-1-932888-85-0(3))*** Mascot Bks., Inc.

Henderson, Felicity. The Adventure Story Picture Bible. 2001. 126p. (J). lib. bdg. 16.95 (978-1-59325-024-9(X)) Word Among Us Pr.

Hergé. Aventures de Tintin au Pays des Soviets. (FRE.). 21.95 (978-2-203-00100-8(3)) Casterman, Editions FRA. *Dist:* Distribooks, Inc.

—Tintín: El cangrejo de las pinzas de Oro. 2007. (SPA., Illus.). 64p. reprint ed. 22.95 (***978-1-59497-346-8(6))*** Public Square Bks.

—Tintín: El cetro de Ottokar. 2007. (SPA., Illus.). 64p. reprint ed. 22.95 (***978-1-59497-345-1(8))*** Public Square Bks.

—Tintín: La isla Negra. 2007. (SPA., Illus.). 64p. reprint ed. 22.95 (***978-1-59497-344-4(X))*** Public Square Bks.

Herge. Tintin & Alph-Art. 2007. (Adventures of Tintin Ser.). 64p. pap. 10.99 (***978-0-316-00375-9(1))*** Little, Brown Bks. for Young Readers.

—Tintin Boxed Set Of 8. 2007. (ps-17). 150.00 (***978-0-316-00668-2(8))*** Little, Brown Bks. for Young Readers.

Hergé. Tintin et le Lac aux Requins. (FRE.). 21.95 (978-2-203-00122-0(4)) Casterman, Editions FRA. *Dist:* Distribooks, Inc.

Herge. Tintin in the Land of the Soviets. 2007. (Adventures of Tintin Ser.). 144p. pap. 10.99 (***978-0-316-00374-2(3))*** Little, Brown Bks. for Young Readers.

Hergé. Le Tresor de Rackham le Rouge. (Tintin Ser.). (FRE., Illus.). 62p. (J). pap. 21.95 (978-2-203-00111-4(9)) Casterman, Editions FRA. *Dist:* Distribooks, Inc.

Hergé, illus. Tintin & Snowy: Album 1. 2006. 68p. (J). pap. 9.99 (978-0-86719-668-9(8)) Last Gasp of San Francisco.

Hermann. Blood Ties. 2000. 56p. (gr. 11 up). pap. 14.95 (978-1-56971-565-9(3)) Dark Horse Comics.

Hibbert, Clare. Meet the X-Men. 2006. (Dk Readers Ser.). (Illus.). 32p. (J). 14.99 (978-0-7566-1927-5(0)); pap. 3.99 (978-0-7566-1928-2(9)) Dorling Kindersley Publishing, Inc.

Higuchi, Daisuke. Whistle! Kokubo, Naomi, tr. from JPN. Higuchi, Daisuke, illus. 2005. (Whistle! Ser.: Vol. 6). (Illus.). 200p. (YA). pap. 7.99 (978-1-59116-836-2(8)) Viz Media.

—Whistle! Higuchi, Daisuke, illus. 2005. (Whistle! Ser.). (YA). Vol. 3. 208p. pap. 7.99 (978-1-59116-692-4(6)); Vol. 7. 200p. pap. 7.99 (978-1-59116-973-4(9)) Viz Media.

—Whistle! On Your Marks, 2. Higuchi, Daisuke, illus. 2004. (Whistle! Ser.). (Illus.). 208p. (YA). pap. 7.99 (978-1-59116-686-3(1)) Viz Media.

—Whistle! Pure Soul, Vol. 5. Higuchi, Daisuke, illus. 2005. (Whistle! Ser.). (Illus.). 208p. (YA). (ps-13). pap. 7.99 (978-1-59116-789-1(2)) Viz Media.

—Whistle! Re-Start, Vol. 4. Higuchi, Daisuke, illus. 2005. (Whistle! Ser.). (Illus.). 200p. (YA). pap. 7.99 (978-1-59116-727-3(2)) Viz Media.

Higuchi, Masakazu. Manga Bible Story-Japanese. 2006. 880p. pap. 38.00 (978-4-264-01798-1(X)) STL Distribution North America.

Higuri, You. Seimaden, Vol. 2. 2005. 180p. (YA). pap. 9.99 (978-1-4012-0700-7(6)) DC Comics.

Hiiragi, Aoi. Baron: The Cat Returns. 2005. (Baron Ser.). (Illus.). 224p. (YA). pap. 9.99 (978-1-59116-956-7(9)) Viz Media.

Hikawa, Kyoko. From Far Away. Hikawa, Kyoko, illus. (From Far Away Ser.). (YA). 1. 2004. (Illus.). 200p. pap. 9.99 (978-1-59116-599-6(7)); Vol. 2. 2005. (Illus.). 184p. pap. 9.99 (978-1-59116-601-6(2)); Vol. 11. 2006. 208p. pap. 9.99 (978-1-4215-0538-1(X)) Viz Media.

—From Far Away, Vol. 12. 2006. (From Far Away Ser.). 208p. (YA). pap. 9.99 (978-1-4215-0539-8(8)) Viz Media.

Hillenburg, Steven. SpongeBob SquarePants: Another Day Another Dollar, Vol. 5. 2004. (Nickelodeon Ser.). (Illus.). 96p. pap. 7.99 (978-1-59532-209-8(4) , Tokyopop Kids) TOKYOPOP, Inc.

Hillenburg, Steven, creator. Movie. 2005. (Cine-Manga Ser.). (Illus.). pap. 7.99 (978-1-59532-089-6(X) , Tokyopop Kids) TOKYOPOP, Inc.

—Spongebob Squarepants Vol. 8: Saves the Day. 2005. (Nickelodeon Ser.). (Illus.). pap. 7.99 (978-1-59532-679-9(0) , Tokyopop Kids) TOKYOPOP, Inc.

Hina. Di Gi Charat Theater - Leave it to Piyoko, 2 vols., Vol. 2. 2005. (Illus.). 208p. pap. 9.99 (978-1-932480-18-4(8)) Broccoli International USA, Inc.

Hinds, Gareth, illus. & adapted by. Beowulf. Hinds, Gareth, adapted by. 2007. 128p. (J). (gr. 3-7). pap. 9.99 (978-0-7636-3023-2(3)); (gr. 5 up). 21.99 (978-0-7636-3022-5(5)) Candlewick Pr.

Hine, David. Mr. M. 2005. (X-Men Ser.: Vol. 1). (Illus.). 144p. (YA). pap. 14.99 (978-0-7851-1444-4(0)) Marvel Enterprises, Inc.

Hino, Hideshi. The Bug Boy No. 2: Hino Horror: A Graphic Novel. Hino, Hideshi, illus. 2005. (Illus.). 204p. (YA). (gr. 4-9). reprint ed. pap. 10.00 (978-0-7567-9709-6(8)) DIANE Publishing Co.

Hirai, Rin. Legendz, Vol. 1. Haruno, Makoto, illus. 2005. (Legendz Ser.). 208p. (YA). pap. 7.99 (978-1-59116-772-3(8)) Viz Media.

—Legendz. Haruno, Makoto, illus. (Legendz Ser.). (YA). Vol. 3. 2005. 224p. pap. 7.99 (978-1-59116-994-9(1)); Vol. 4. 2006. 208p. pap. 7.99 (978-1-4215-0149-9(X)) Viz Media.

Hirano, Toshiki, illus. Shaolin Sisters Vol. 1: Reborn. 2005. 224p. pap. 9.99 (978-1-59532-507-5(7) , Tokyopop Kids) TOKYOPOP, Inc.

Hiroyuki, Tamakoshi, illus. Boys Be Vol. 4: Second Season. rev. ed. 2005. 208p. pap. 9.99 (978-1-59532-102-2(0) , Tokyopop Adult) TOKYOPOP, Inc.

Hiwatari, Saki. Please Save My Earth, Vol. 17. Hiwatari, Saki, illus. 2006. (Please Save My Earth Ser.). 208p. (YA). pap. 9.99 (978-1-4215-0550-3(9)) Viz Media.

—Please Save My Earth, Vol. 18. 2006. (Please Save My Earth Ser.). 208p. (YA). pap. 9.99 (978-1-4215-0551-0(7)) Viz Media.

—Please Save My Earth: Volume 2. 2004. (Please Save My Earth Ser.), (Illus.). (YA). (gr. 7-12). lib. bdg. 18.75 (978-0-613-85852-6(2)) Tandem Library Bks.

Ho, Jason, illus. Frankenstein. 2007. (Graphic Horror Ser.). 32p. (YA). (gr. 5-8). lib. bdg. 27.07 (***978-1-60270-059-8(1)*** , Graphic Planet) Magic Wagon.

Ho, Sohn Eun. Quantum Mistake, Vol. 1. 2004. 192p. (YA). pap. (978-1-4139-0149-8(2)) ADV Manga.

Hoena, B. A. & Harpster, Steve. Invaders from the Great Goo Galaxy. 2007. (Graphic Sparks Ser.). (Illus.). (J). 19.93 (978-1-59889-052-5(2)) Stone Arch Bks.

Hoena, Blake A. Ooze Slingers from Outer Space. Harpster, Steve, illus. 2007. (J). 33p. pap. (***978-1-59889-410-3(2));*** 40p. (gr. 2-4). lib. bdg. 21.26 (***978-1-59889-315-1(7))*** Stone Arch Bks.

Holbrook, Bill. Booth Bunnies. 2002. (Kevin & Kell Ser.). 128p. pap. 12.95 (978-1-929462-26-1(3)) Plan Nine Publishing, Inc.

—Bottom Feeders. 2001. (Safe Havens Ser.: Vol. 3). 160p. pap. 12.95 (978-1-929462-32-2(8)) Plan Nine Publishing, Inc.

—Run Free! 1999. (Kevin & Kell Ser.: Vol. 4). (Illus.). (YA). pap. 12.95 (978-0-9660676-9-9(X)) Plan Nine Publishing, Inc.

Holm, Jennifer L. & Holm, Matthew. Beach Babe! 2006. (Babymouse Ser.). (Illus.). 96p. (J). (gr. 2-5). pap. 5.95 (978-0-375-83231-4(9)); lib. bdg. 12.99 (978-0-375-93231-1(3)) Random Hse. Children's Bks. (Random Hse. Bks. for Young Readers).

—Camp Babymouse. 2007. (Babymouse Ser.: No. 6). 96p. (J). (gr. 2-5). pap. 5.99 (978-0-375-83988-7(7)); lib. bdg. 12.99 (978-0-375-93988-4(1)) Random Hse. Children's Bks. (Random Hse. Bks. for Young Readers).

—Heartbreaker. 2006. (Babymouse Ser.: No. 5). (Illus.). 96p. (J). (gr. 2-5). lib. bdg. 12.99 (978-0-375-93798-9(6) , Random Hse. Bks. for Young Readers) Random Hse. Children's Bks.

—Our Hero. 2005. (Babymouse Ser.). (Illus.). 96p. (J). (gr. 2-5). pap. 5.95 (978-0-375-83230-7(0)); lib. bdg. 12.99 (978-0-375-93230-4(5)) Random Hse. Children's Bks. (Random Hse. Bks. for Young Readers).

—Queen of the World! 2005. (Babymouse Ser.). (Illus.). 96p. (J). (gr. 2-5). pap. 5.95 (978-0-375-83229-1(7)); lib. bdg. 12.99 (978-0-375-93229-8(1)) Random Hse. Children's Bks. (Random Hse. Bks. for Young Readers).

—Rock Star! Holm, Jennifer L. & Holm, Matthew, illus. 2006. (Babymouse Ser.). (Illus.). 96p. (J). (gr. 1-5). pap. 5.95 (978-0-375-83232-1(7) , Random Hse. Bks. for Young Readers) Random Hse. Children's Bks.

—Rock Star! 2006. (Babymouse Ser.). (Illus.). 96p. (J). (gr. 1-5). lib. bdg. 12.99 (978-0-375-93232-8(1) , Random Hse. Bks. for Young Readers) Random Hse. Children's Bks.

Hong, Jihae, tr. Threads of Time, Vol. 5. Young Noh, Mi, illus. rev. ed. 2005. 192p. pap. 9.99 (978-1-59532-036-0(9) , Tokyopop Adult) TOKYOPOP, Inc.

Hongo, Akiyoshi. Digimon, 5 vols., Vol. 3. Sheh, Stephanie, tr. rev. ed. 2003. (Illus.). 164p. (gr. 2 up). pap. 9.99 (978-1-59182-158-8(4)) TOKYOPOP, Inc.

—Digimon, 5 vols., Vol. 1. Yuen Wong Yu, illus. 2003. 164p. (gr. 2 up). pap. 9.99 (978-1-59182-076-5(6)) TOKYOPOP, Inc.

Digimon, 5 vols., Vol. 4. 4th rev. ed. 2003. (Illus.). 164p. (gr. 2 up). pap. 9.99 (978-1-59182-159-5(2)) TOKYOPOP, Inc.

Hooper, Mary. The Haunting of Julia. Gray, Maureen, illus. 2008. (J). (***978-1-59889-827-9(2));*** pap. (***978-1-59889-883-5(3))*** Stone Arch Bks.

Hopkins, David. Emily Edison. Rizy, Brock, illus. 2006. 144p. (YA). (gr. 8 up). per. 12.95 (978-0-9777883-2-3(6)) Viper Comics.

Horowitz, Anthony & Johnston, Antony. Point Blank: the Graphic Novel: The Graphic Novel. Kanako & Yuzuru, illus. 2007. 144p. (J). (gr. 4). pap. 14.99 (***978-0-399-25026-2(3)*** , Philomel) Penguin Group (USA) Inc.

Horowitz, Jeanine. My First Playing Lesson. l.t. ed. 2006. (Illus.). 32p. (J). lib. bdg. (***978-1-934190-04-3(7))*** Ocean Front Bk. Publishing, Inc.

Horumarin. Medaforce! 2003. (gr. 3-6). lib. bdg. 18.75 (978-0-613-81218-4(2)) Tandem Library Bks.

Hoshino, Katsura. D. Gray-Man, Vol. 4. 2007. (D. Gray-man Ser.). 200p. (YA). pap. 7.99 (978-1-4215-1052-1(9)) Viz Media.

Hotta, Yumi. Hikaru No Go, Vol. 3. Hotta, Yumi & Obata, Takeshi, illus. 2005. (Hikaru No Go Ser.). 208p. (YA). pap. 7.95 (978-1-59116-687-0(X)) Viz Media.

—Hikaru No Go, Vol. 7. 2006. (Hikaru No Go Ser.). 208p. (YA). pap. 7.95 (978-1-4215-0641-8(6)) Viz Media.

—Hikaru No Go Vol. 4: Divine Illusions. Obata, Takeshi, illus. 2005. (Hikaru No Go Ser.). 200p. (YA). pap. 7.95 (978-1-59116-688-7(8)) Viz Media.

Howard, Josh. Dead@17: Blood of Saints. Howard, Josh, illus. 2004. 112p. (YA). per. 14.95 (978-0-9754193-1-1(5)) Viper Comics.

Hudlin, Reginald & Romita, John. Bad Mutha. 2006. (Illus.). 96p. pap. 10.99 (978-0-7851-1750-6(4)) Marvel Enterprises, Inc.

Hudson, Don, creator. Gunpowder Girl & the Outlaw Squaw. 2005. (YA). pap. 12.95 (978-0-9766761-0-2(9)) Active Images.

Hui-Jin, Park. Chronicles of the Cursed Sword, 10 vols. Beop-Ryong, Yuy, illus. rev. ed. 2004. 176p. Vol. 6. pap. 9.99 (978-1-59182-423-7(0)); Vol. 7. pap. 9.99 (978-1-59182-424-4(9)) TOKYOPOP, Inc. (Tokyopop Adult).

Hulk. 2003. (J). per. (978-1-57657-856-8(9)) Paradise Pr., Inc.

Hunter-Bone, Maureen & Feldman, Thea. Our World: People, Celebrations, Amazing Discoveries, Places. 2005. (Disney Learning Ser.). (Illus.). 192p. (gr. 1-4). 19.99 (978-0-7868-0936-3(1)) Disney Pr.

Hunter, Derek. Pirate Club Vol. 2: Brainwash Escape Victims. 2006. (Illus.). 144p. (YA). pap. 12.95 (978-1-59362-051-6(9)) Slave Labor Bks.

Hunter, Erin & Jolley, Dan. The Lost Warrior. Barry, James L., illus. 2007. (Warriors Manga Ser.: No. 1). 112p. (J). (gr. 4-6). pap. 6.99 (***978-0-06-124020-1(6))*** TOKYOPOP, Inc.

Hurchalla, Elizabeth, ed. Friends Are Never Far Away. 2005. (Illus.). 32p. (ps-7). pap. 3.99 (978-1-59816-000-0(1) , Tokyopop Kids) TOKYOPOP, Inc.

—Happy Healthy Monsters, Vol. 2. 2005. (Illus.). 32p. (ps-17). pap. 3.99 (978-1-59532-826-7(2) , Tokyopop Kids) TOKYOPOP, Inc.

Husted, Ursula. Making Rain. 2004. 56p. (J). per. 9.95 (978-0-9753225-0-5(8)) Atomic Fruit Pr.

Hwang, Mina. Redmoon. (YA). Vol. 2. 2001. 200p. pap. 11.95 (978-1-58899-094-5(X)); Vol. 3. 2001. 201p. pap. 11.95 (978-1-58899-095-2(8)); Vol. 4. 2002. 201p. pap. 11.95 (978-1-58899-096-9(6)); Vol. 5. 2002. 206p. pap. 11.95 (978-1-58899-097-6(4)) ComicsOne Corp./Dr. Masters.

Hyman, Fracaswell, et al, creators. Romeo! Living Large!, Vol. 1. 2005. (Illus.). 90p. (ps-7). pap., pap. 7.99 (978-1-59532-728-4(2) , Tokyopop Kids) TOKYOPOP, Inc.

Hyperion. Meridian Magic. 2nd ed. 2005. (W. I. T. C. H. Graphic Novels Ser.: Bk. 2). 125p. (J). pap. 4.99 (978-0-7868-5576-6(2) , Volo) Hyperion Bks. for Children.

Hyperion, ed. An Unexpected Return - #8: W. I. T. C. H. Graphic Novel. 8th rev. ed. 2007. 128p. (gr. 3-7). pap. 4.99 (***978-1-4231-0903-7(1))*** Hyperion Pr.

Hyperion Staff. Legends Revealed. rev. ed. 2006. (W. I. T. C. H. Graphic Novels Ser.: Bk. 6). (Illus.). 128p. (gr. 3-7). pap. 4.99 (978-0-7868-4876-8(6)) Hyperion Pr.

—The Other Truth. 19th rev. ed. 2006. (W. I. T. C. H. Ser.: Bk. 19). 144p. (gr. 3-7). pap. 4.99 (978-0-7868-5280-2(1)) Hyperion Pr.

Hyun, You. Faeries' Landing, 13 vols. 2004. (Illus.). Vol. 2. rev. ed. 192p. pap. 9.99 (978-1-59182-610-1(1)); Vol. 3. 3rd rev. ed. pap. 9.99 (978-1-59182-611-8(X)); Vol. 4. rev. ed. 192p. pap. 9.99 (978-1-59182-612-5(8)) TOKYOPOP, Inc. (Tokyopop Adult).

Hyun, You, illus. & creator. Faeries' Landing, Vol. 8. Hyun, You, creator. rev. ed. 2005. 192p. pap. 9.99 (978-1-59532-396-5(1) , Tokyopop Adult) TOKYOPOP, Inc.

Hyung, Kang-Suk & Ah, Shin. Sky Blade Sword of the Heavens, Vol. 1. 2004. 184p. pap. (978-1-4139-0081-1(X)) ADV Manga.

Hyung, Kang Suk & Ah, Shin. Sky Blade Sword of the Heavens, Vol. 2. 2004. 184p. pap. (978-1-4139-0102-3(6)) ADV Manga.

Hyung Kim, Tae, illus. & creator. Planet Blood, Vol. 2. Hyung Kim, Tae, creator. rev. ed. 2005. 200p. pap. 9.99 (978-1-59532-538-9(7) , Tokyopop Adult) TOKYOPOP, Inc.

I-Haun. Real Fake Princess Volume 2. 2006. (Illus.). 200p. (YA). pap. 9.95 (***978-1-59796-080-9(2))*** DrMaster Pubns. Inc.

—Real Fake Princess Volume 3. 2006. 200p. (YA). pap. 9.95 (***978-1-59796-081-6(0))*** DrMaster Pubns. Inc.

—Real/Fake Princess, Vol. 4. 2007. (Illus.). 200p. pap. 9.95 (***978-1-59796-082-3(9))*** DrMaster Pubns. Inc.

I-Huan. Real Fake Princess, Vol. 1. 2006. (Illus.). 200p. (YA). pap. 9.95 (***978-1-59796-079-3(9))*** DrMaster Pubns. Inc.

Ikumi, Mia. Tokyo Mew Mew. 2006. (SPA., Illus.). reprint ed. 6. 192p. pap. 10.95 (978-1-59497-174-7(9)); Vol. 7. 176p. pap. 10.95 (978-1-59497-198-3(6)) Public Square Bks.

—Tokyo Mew Mew a la Mode, Vol. 2. 2nd rev. ed. 2005. (Illus.). (gr. 4-7). pap. 9.99 (978-1-59532-790-1(8) , Tokyopop Kids) TOKYOPOP, Inc.

—Tokyo Mew Mew (en Español) 2006. (SPA., Illus.). reprint ed. Vol. 2. 176p. pap. 10.95 (978-1-59497-170-9(6)); Vol. 3. 176p. pap. 10.95 (978-1-59497-171-6(4)); Vol. 4. 184p. pap. 10.95 (978-1-59497-172-3(2)); Vol. 5. 184p. pap. 10.95 (978-1-59497-173-0(0)) Public Square Bks.

Ikumi, Mia & Yoshida, Reiko. Tokyo Mew Mew (en Español), Vol. 1. 2006. (SPA., Illus.). 176p. reprint ed. pap. 10.95 (978-1-59497-155-6(2)) Public Square Bks.

Ilka, Benjamin Alexander. A Boy & His Shadow. Ilka, Benjamin Alexander, illus. (YA). Pt. 1. 2005. per. 4.95 net. (978-0-9779504-0-9(9)); Pt. 2. 2006. 3.95 net. (978-0-9779504-1-6(7)) Hogan Publishing LLC.

Im, Hye-Young, tr. Dragon Hunter, Vol. 12. Seock Seo, Hong, illus. rev. ed. 2005. 176p. pap. 9.99 (978-1-59182-960-7(7) , Tokyopop Adult) TOKYOPOP, Inc.

Im, Jae Won. The Boss. 2004. 184p. (YA). Vol. 1. pap. (978-1-4139-0069-9(0)); Vol. 2. pap. (978-1-4139-0075-0(5)) ADV Manga.

Impact Books, 10 bks., Set. 2007. (J). (gr. 4-8). 226.00 (***978-1-59889-462-2(5))*** Stone Arch Bks.

In-Soo, Ra & Jae-Hwan, Kim. King of Hell, Vol. 14. 14th rev. ed. 2006. Tr. of Ma-Je. pap. 9.99 (978-1-59816-867-9(3) , Tokyopop Adult) TOKYOPOP, Inc.

C
D

Inagaki, Riichird & Inagaki, Riichiro. Eyeshield 21, Vol. 1. Murata, Yusuke, illus. 2005. (Eyeshield 21 Ser.). 208p. (YA). (gr. 11-17). pap. 7.99 (978-1-59116-752-5(3) , Viz Comics) Viz Media.

Inagaki, Riichiro. Eyeshield 21. (Eyeshield 21 Ser.). (YA). Vol. 5. 2005. (Illus.). 200p. pap. 7.99 (978-1-4215-0113-0(9)); Vol. 8. 2006. 208p. pap. 7.99 (978-1-4215-0637-1(8)); Vol. 9. 2006. (Illus.). 208p. pap. 7.99 (978-1-4215-0638-8(6)) Viz Media.

—Eyeshield 21, Volume 12. 2007. (Eyeshield 21 Ser.). 208p. (YA). pap. 7.99 (978-1-4215-1061-3(8)) Viz Media.

—Eyeshield 21, Volume 13. 2007. (Eyeshield 21 Ser.). 216p. (YA). pap. 7.99 (978-1-4215-1062-0(6)) Viz Media.

Inagaki, Riichiro & Toriyama, Akira. Dragon Ball Z, Vol. 19. Inagaki, Riichiro, illus. 2005. (Dragon Ball Z Ser.). (Illus.). 184p. (YA). (ps-13). pap. 7.95 (978-1-59116-751-8(5)) Viz Media.

Inoue, Kazurou. Midori Days. 2006. (Midori Days Ser.). 208p. (YA). Vol. 6. pap. 9.99 (978-1-4215-0495-7(2)); Vol. 7. pap. 9.99 (978-1-4215-0496-4(0)) Viz Media.

Inoue, Takehiko. Vagabond. Inoue, Takehiko, illus. 2005. (Vagabond Ser.). (Illus.). 200p. (YA). Vol. 18. pap. 9.95 (978-1-59116-642-9(X)); Vol. 19. pap. 9.95 (978-1-59116-643-6(8)); Vol. 20. pap. 9.95 (978-1-59116-583-5(0)) Viz Media.

Inu Yasha: A Feudal Fairy Tale. 2002. Vol. 9. (YA). 23.19 (978-0-7587-9968-5(3)); (Inu Yasha Ser.: Vol. 1). (Illus.). 23.19 (978-1-4046-2212-8(8)); Vol. 10. (Illus.). (J). 23.19 (978-0-7587-9942-5(X)); (Inu Yasha Ser.: Vol. 11). (Illus.). (YA). 23.19 (978-1-4046-2211-1(X)); (Inu Yasha Ser.: Vol. 12). (Illus.). 23.19 (978-1-4046-1626-4(8)); (Inu Yasha Ser.: Vol. 2). (Illus.). 23.19 (978-1-4046-2213-5(6)); (Inu Yasha Ser.: Vol. 3). (Illus.). 23.19 (978-1-4046-2214-2(4)); (Inu Yasha Ser.: Vol. 4). (Illus.). 23.19 (978-1-4046-2215-9(2)); (Inu Yasha Ser.: Vol. 5). (Illus.). (YA). 23.19 (978-1-4046-2208-1(X)); (Inu Yasha Ser.: Vol. 6). (Illus.). (YA). 23.19 (978-1-4046-0206-9(2)); (Inu Yasha Ser.: Vol. 7). (Illus.). 23.19 (978-1-4046-2209-8(8)); (Inu Yasha Ser.: Vol. 8). (Illus.). 23.19 (978-1-4046-2210-4(1)) Book Wholesalers, Inc.

Inui, Sekihiko, illus. & creator. Comic Party, Vol. 5. Inui, Sekihiko, creator. 5th rev. ed. 2006. 248p. pap. 9.99 (978-1-59816-272-1(1) , Tokyopop Adult) TOKYOPOP, Inc.

Isabella, Tony, et al. Champions Classic, Vol. 1. 2006. (Illus.). 208p. pap. 19.99 (978-0-7851-2097-1(1)) Marvel Enterprises, Inc.

Izubuchi, Yukaka. RahXephon Bible. 2003. (JPN & ENG., Illus.). 100p. pap. 19.98 (978-1-4139-0026-2(7)) A. D. Vision, Inc.

Izubuchi, Yutaka. Rahxephon. Momose, Takeaki, illus. 2004. (Rahxephon Ser.). (YA). 192p. pap. 9.95 (978-1-59116-407-4(9)); Vol. 2. 200p. pap. 9.95 (978-1-59116-427-2(3)); Vol. 3. 200p. pap. 9.95 (978-1-59116-428-9(1)) Viz Media.

Izumi, Kaneyoshi. Doubt!, Vol. 1. Izumi, Kaneyoshi, illus. 2005. (Doubt Ser.). (Illus.). 192p. (YA). pap. 9.99 (978-1-59116-908-6(9)) Viz Media.

Izumi, Rei, illus. Hack//AI Buster. 2005. 192p. pap. 7.99 (978-1-59532-869-4(6) , Tokyopop Adult) TOKYOPOP, Inc.

Jackson, Robert, Jr. The Amazing Liberteens. 2004. (YA). per. 9.95 (978-0-9761420-0-3(7)) Jackson, Robert.

Jacobs, Edgar P. Blake & Mortimer the Yellow M. 2007. (Illus.). 48p. pap. 14.45 (***978-1-905460-21-2(X)***) Cine-Book GBR. *Dist:* Biblio Distribution.

Jacobs, Lana. The Last Stand: Coloring & Activity Book & Crayons. Gordon, Steven E., illus. 2006. (X Men Ser.). 32p. (J). pap., act. bk. ed. 4.99 (978-0-06-082210-1(4)) HarperCollins Pubs.

Jacobsen, Allan. To End All Wars, Vol. 1. Lucas, Jorge, illus. 2005. (Marvel Heroes Ser.). 216p. (YA). pap. 19.99 (978-0-7851-1449-9(1)) Marvel Enterprises, Inc.

Jae Hoo, Yoon, creator. In Dream World. 2005. (Illus.). pap. 9.99 (978-1-59532-516-7(6) , Tokyopop Adult) TOKYOPOP, Inc.

Jappa, Anthony Wayne. Jiroboy Chap. 1: The Mechnorganic Kid. 2002. cd-rom 5.00 (978-0-9720694-0-3(2)) Jappamation Studios.

Jarvis, James. Vortigern¿s Machine & the Great Sage of Wisdom. 2006. (Illus.). 48p. pap. 24.00 (978-3-89955-098-6(6)) Die Gestalten Verlag DEU. *Dist:* Prestel Publishing.

Jea-Eun, Kim, illus. Soul to Seoul, Vol. 2. 2nd rev. ed. 2005. 200p. pap. 9.99 (978-1-59532-313-2(9) , Tokyopop Adult) TOKYOPOP, Inc.

Jee-Hyung, Lee. Demon Diary, 7 vols., Vol. 7. Lim, Kara, illus. rev. ed. 2004. 192p. pap. 9.99 (978-1-59182-432-9(X) , Tokyopop Adult) TOKYOPOP, Inc.

Jeeva Raghunath & Nayar, Deeya. Malli: Malli. Nancy Raj, illus. 2005. (HIN & ENG.). 16p. (J). (***978-81-8146-089-9(8)***) Tulika Pubs.

Jenkins, Paul. Decimation: Generation M TPB: Generation M TPB. 2006. (Illus.). 120p. pap. 13.99 (978-0-7851-1958-6(2)) Marvel Enterprises, Inc.

—Here There Be the Monsters, Vol. 3. Scott, Damion, illus. 2004. (Spider-Man Ser.). 144p. (YA). 9.99 (978-0-7851-1333-1(9)) Marvel Enterprises, Inc.

—Trials & Tribulations, 4 vols., Vol. 4. Buckingham, Mark, illus. 2003. (Peter Parker, Spider-Man Ser.: Vol. 4). 128p. (YA). 11.99 (978-0-7851-1150-4(6)) Marvel Enterprises, Inc.

Jensen, Lars, et al. Donald Duck Adventures, Vol. 18. 2006. (Illus.). 128p. (YA). pap. 7.95 (978-1-888472-30-1(8)) Gemstone Publishing, Inc.

Jenson, Jeff. X-Factor. Ranson, Arthur, illus. 2003. (X-Men Ser.: Vol. 1). 96p. (YA). pap. 9.99 (978-0-7851-1016-3(X)) Marvel Enterprises, Inc.

Jeon, Jin-Seok. One Thousand & One Nights Volume 2. 2006. (Illus.). 200p. pap. 10.95 (***978-89-527-4477-7(2)***) ICE Kunion KOR. *Dist:* Diamond Bk. Distributors.

Jeon, Kook Jin. Ruler of the Land, Vol. 2. 2004. 200p. (YA). pap. (978-1-4139-0037-8(2)) ADV Manga.

Jeon, Kook Jin & Yang, Jae Hyun. Ruler of the Land, Vol. 3. 2004. 200p. (YA). pap. (978-1-4139-0057-6(7)) ADV Manga.

Jezo & Jozev. Journal of the Vampire Hunter. 2006. (Illus.). 64p. (YA). pap. 5.95 (***978-1-59796-089-2(6));*** pap. 5.95 (***978-1-59796-088-5(8)***) DrMaster Pubns. Inc.

Jippes, Daan, et al. Walt Disney's Comics & Stories, Vol. 666. 2006. 64p. pap. 6.95 (978-1-888472-19-6(7)) Gemstone Publishing, Inc.

—Walt Disney's Comics & Stories #668. 2006. 64p. pap. 6.95 (978-1-888472-26-4(X)) Gemstone Publishing, Inc.

Job. Yakari & the Beavers. 2007. 48p. pap. 9.99 (***978-1-905460-09-0(0)***) CineBook GBR. *Dist:* Biblio Distribution.

—Yakari & the Grizzly. Jeffrey, Erica, tr. from FRE. Derib, illus. 2007. 48p. pap. 9.99 (***978-1-905460-16-8(3)***) CineBook GBR. *Dist:* Biblio Distribution.

—Yakari & the White Buffalo. Jeffrey, Erica, tr. Derib, illus. 2007. 48p. pap. 9.99 (***978-1-905460-05-2(8)***) Cine-Book GBR. *Dist:* Biblio Distribution.

Job & Derib. Yakari & Great Eagle. 2007. (Illus.). 48p. pap. 9.99 (***978-1-905460-04-5(X)***) CineBook GBR. *Dist:* Biblio Distribution.

Johns, Geoff & Heinberg, Allan. Crisis of Conscience. rev. ed. 2006. (Infinite Crisis Story Ser.: Vol. 18). (Illus.). 126p. pap. 12.99 (978-1-4012-0963-6(7)) DC Comics.

Johnson, Regan. Hold on to Your Tail: Letters from Camp Lizard. Johnson, Regan, illus. 2007. (Letters From Camp Lizard Ser.). (Illus.). 100p. (J). (gr. 2-7). per. (***978-1-933831-04-6(9)*** , Ready Blade) Blooming Tree Pr.

Jolley, Dan. Escape from Pyramid X. Wendt, Matt, illus. 2007. (Twisted Journeys Ser.). 112p. (J). (gr. 4-7). lib. bdg. 27.93 (***978-0-8225-6777-6(6)*** , Graphic Universe); pap. 7.95 (***978-0-8225-6779-0(2)***) Lerner Publishing Group.

—Iron Man: The Movie Storybook. 2008. (Iron Man Ser.). 256p. (J). 6.99 (***978-0-06-082198-2(1)*** , Harper Entertainment) HarperCollins Pubs.

Jones, Bruce. Hulk & Thing: Hard Knocks. Lee, Jae, illus. 2005. (Hulk Ser.). 120p. pap. 13.99 (978-0-7851-1576-2(5)) Marvel Enterprises, Inc.

Jones, Bruce & Austen, Chuck. The Call of Duty Vol. 2: The Precinct, 2 vols. Mandrake, Tom & Zezelj, Danijel, illus. 2003. (Call Ser.). 128p. (YA). pap. 9.99 (978-0-7851-0974-7(9)) Marvel Enterprises, Inc.

Jones, Gerard & Ono, Toshihiro. Pikachu Meets the Press: A Pokemon Newspaper Strip Collection. Benimaru, Ashura, illus. 2001. (Pokemon Ser.). 200p. (YA). (ps up). pap. 9.95 (978-1-56931-576-7(0)) Viz Media.

Jones, Kelley. Kelley Jone's the Hammer. Lewis, Dana & Smith, Toren, trs. 2001. 120p. pap. 12.95 (978-1-56971-340-2(5)) Dark Horse Comics.

Journey into DigiWorld. 1999. (Digimon Tattoo Bks.). (Illus.). 17p. (J). (ps-2). pap. (978-0-7666-0551-0(5)) Modern Publishing.

Jozev. Journal of the Vampire Hunter. 2006. (Illus.). 64p. (YA). pap. 5.95 (978-1-59796-090-8(X)) DrMaster Pubns. Inc.

Jughead with Archie, 6 bks., Set. 2007. (J). 145.26 (***978-1-59961-271-3(2)***) Spotlight.

Jurgens, Dan, et al. Thor Vol. 3: Gods on Earth, 3 vols. Raney, Tom & Bennett, Davis, illus. 2003. (Thor Ser.). 248p. (YA). pap. 21.99 (978-0-7851-1126-9(3)) Marvel Enterprises, Inc.

Kaczmarczyk, Kyle J. The Misadventures of Silent Boy - Volume II: the Stupid Strikes Back. 2005. 52p. (YA). pap. 17.99 (978-1-4116-5231-6(2)) Lulu.com.

Kadokawa. Steel Angel Kurumi, Vol. 3. 2004. 172p. pap. (978-1-4139-0013-2(5)) ADV Manga.

Kadono, Kouhei. Boogiepop & Others. 2006. (Illus.). 250p. pap. 9.99 (978-1-933164-16-8(6)) Seven Seas Entertainment, LLC.

—Boogiepop Doesn't Laugh, Vol. 1. 2006. 192p. pap. 10.99 (978-1-933164-18-2(2)) Seven Seas Entertainment, LLC.

Kaishaku. Steel Angel Kurumi. 2004. Vol. 5. (Illus.). 176p. (YA). pap. (978-1-4139-0078-1(X)); Vol. 6. 192p. pap. (978-1-4139-0099-6(2)); Vol. 8. 184p. pap. (978-1-4139-0152-8(2)) ADV Manga.

Kaisyaku. Steel Angel Kurumi, Vol. 1. 2003. 176p. pap. (978-1-4139-0011-8(9)) ADV Manga.

—Steel Angel Kurumi, Vol. 2. Bertrand, Kay, tr. from JPN. 2004. (Illus.). 172p. (YA). pap. (978-1-4139-0012-5(7)) ADV Manga.

—Steel Angel Kurumi. 2004. (Illus.). (YA). Vol. 7. 180p. pap. (978-1-4139-0117-7(4)); Vol. 9. 188p. pap. (978-1-4139-0153-5(0)) ADV Manga.

Kakinouchi, Narumi. My Codename Is Charmer, Vol. 3. 208p. pap. 12.95 (978-1-932575-08-8(1)) International Comics & Entertainment L.L.C.

Kamio, Yoko. Boys over Flowers, Vol. 11. Kamio, Yoko, illus. 2005. (Boys over Flowers ~ Hana Yori Dango Ser.).Tr. of Hana Yori Dango. (Illus.). 184p. (YA). pap. 9.99 (978-1-59116-747-1(7)) Viz Media.

—Boys over Flowers. (Boys over Flowers Ser.).Tr. of Hana Yori Dango. (YA). Vol. 15. 2005. (Illus.). 192p. pap. 9.99 (978-1-4215-0136-9(8)); Vol. 18. 2006. 208p. pap. 9.99 (978-1-4215-0532-9(0)); Vol. 19. 2006. 208p. pap. 9.99 (978-1-4215-0533-6(9)) Viz Media.

Kaneko, Shinya. Culdcept, Vol. 5. 5th rev. ed. 2006. (Illus.). pap. 9.99 (978-1-59816-553-1(4) , Tokyopop Adult) TOKYOPOP, Inc.

Kanemaki, Tomoco. Kingdom Hearts: Darkness Within. Disney Press Staff, ed. Amano, Shiro, illus. 2nd rev. ed. 2008. 224p. (J). (gr. 4-7). pap. 5.99 (***978-1-4231-0396-7(3)***) Disney Pr.

—Kingdom Hearts: The First Door. Disney Press Staff, ed. Amano, Shiro, illus. 2008. 224p. (J). (gr. 4-7). pap. 5.99 (***978-1-4231-0395-0(5)***) Disney Pr.

Kaneyoshi, Izumi. Doubt!!, Vol. 4. Kaneyoshi, Izumi, illus. 2005. (Doubt Ser.). 192p. (YA). pap. 9.99 (978-1-59116-984-0(4)) Viz Media.

Kang Won, Kim, illus. & creator. The Queen's Knight. Kang Won, Kim, creator. 2005. Vol. 3. 3rd rev. ed. pap. 9.99 (978-1-59532-259-3(0)); Vol. 4. rev. ed. 208p. pap. 9.99 (978-1-59532-260-9(4)) TOKYOPOP, Inc. (Tokyopop Kids).

Kanietzko, Bryan. Avatar, 2 vols., Vol. 1. 2006. (Illus.). pap. 7.99 (978-1-59532-891-5(2) , Tokyopop Kids) TOKYOPOP, Inc.

Kanietzko, Bryan. Avatar Volume 6. 2007. 192p. pap. 7.99 (***978-1-59816-930-0(0)*** , Tokyopop Kids) TOKYOPOP, Inc.

Kanietzko, Bryan & Dimartino, Michael Dante. Avatar. 2007. (Illus.). pap. 7.99 (***978-1-59816-929-4(7));*** 96p. pap. 7.99 (***978-1-59816-928-7(9)***) TOKYOPOP, Inc. (Tokyopop Kids).

Kardy, Glenn. Kanji de Manga, 33 vols., Vol. 3. 2005. (JPN & ENG., Illus.). 112p. (YA). pap. (978-4-921205-04-1(3) , Manga University) Japanime Co., Ltd.

—Kanji de Manga Vol. 2: The Comic Book That Teaches You How to Read Japanese!, 33 vols. 2005. (JPN & ENG., Illus.). 112p. (YA). pap. (978-4-921205-03-4(5)) Japanime Co., Ltd.

Kardy, Glenn & Hattori, Chihiro. Kanji de Manga Vol. 1: The Comic Book That Teaches You How to Read & Write Japanese!, 33 vols. 2005. (Illus.). 112p. (YA). pap. (978-4-921205-02-7(7) , Manga University) Japanime Co., Ltd.

Katayama, Kyoichi. Socrates in Love. Kazui, Kazumi, illus. 2005. (Socrates in Love Ser.: Vol. 1). 192p. (YA). pap. 8.99 (978-1-4215-0199-4(6)) Viz Media.

—Socrates in Love, Vol. 1. Wegmuller, Akemi, tr. from JPN. 2005. (Socrates in Love Ser.). 208p. (YA). 17.99 (978-1-4215-0154-3(6)) Viz Media.

Katschke, Judy. The Adventures of Astro. 2004. (Astro Boy Ser.). (Illus.). 64p. (J). pap. 4.99 (978-0-06-072528-0(1) , Harper Festival) HarperCollins Pubs.

—Duke & Fang, Level 3. Baumann, Marty, illus. 2006. (Phonics Comics Ser.). 24p. (J). (gr. 1-17). pap. 3.99 (978-1-58476-411-3(2) , IKIDS) Innovative Kids.

Katsu, Aki, creator. The Vision of Escaflowne, 8 vols., Vol. 8. 8th rev. ed. 2004. (Illus.). 216p. pap. 9.99 (978-1-59182-453-4(2) , Tokyopop Adult) TOKYOPOP, Inc.

Katsura, Masakazu. Ghost in the Shell 2: Innocence, 4 vols. Katsura, Masakazu, illus. 2005. (Ghost in the Shell 2 Ani-Manga Ser.). 200p. (YA). pap. 39.99 (978-1-59116-829-4(5)) Viz Media.

—Is, Vol. 8. 2006. (I's Ser.). 208p. (YA). pap. 7.99 (978-1-4215-0649-4(1)) Viz Media.

—I's, Vol. 9. 2006. (I's Ser.). 208p. (YA). 7.99 (978-1-4215-0650-0(5)) Viz Media.

—Len's Story, Vol. 15. 2006. (Video Girl Ai Ser.). 208p. (YA). pap. 9.99 (978-1-4215-0295-3(X)) Viz Media.

—Video Girl Ai: Cutting Room, Vol. 6. Katsura, Masakazu, illus. 2005. (Video Girl Ai Ser.). (Illus.). 200p. (YA). pap. 9.99 (978-1-59116-607-8(1)) Viz Media.

Kaulfersch, Ron & Schwark, Mike. Van Von Hunter. 2007. (Kaplan SAT/ACT Score-Raising Manga Ser.: Vol. 1). 192p. pap. 9.99 (***978-1-4277-5494-3(2)***) Kaplan Publishing.

Kawahara, Yumiko. Dolls, 1. Kawahara, Yumiko, illus. 2004. (Dolls Ser.). (Illus.). 200p. (YA). pap. 9.99 (978-1-59116-508-8(3)) Viz Media.

Kawashita, Mizuki. Ichigo 100% (JPN., Illus.). (YA). Vol. 1. 191p. pap. (978-4-08-873304-3(5)); Vol. 2. 188p. pap. (978-4-08-873326-5(6)); Vol. 3. 182p. pap. (978-4-08-873369-2(X)); Vol. 4. 190p. pap. (978-4-08-873412-5(2)); Vol. 5. 187p. pap. (978-4-08-873438-5(6)); Vol. 6. 186p. pap. (978-4-08-873496-5(3)); Vol. 8. 185p. pap. (978-4-08-873537-5(4)); Vol. 9. 180p. pap. (978-4-08-873577-1(3)); Vol. 10. 189p. pap. (978-4-08-873597-9(8)); Vol. 11. 186p. pap. (978-4-08-873629-7(X)); Vol. 12. 190p. pap. (978-4-08-873650-1(8)); Vol. 13. 190p. pap. (978-4-08-873669-3(9)) Shuei-Sha.

Kayser, Eric. Champion: Graphic Novel Series. 3rd ed. 2007. (YA). 2.95 (***978-0-9785605-2-2(3)***) Oasis Studios Inc.

Kayser, Eric, creator. Champion: Graphic Novel Series. (Illus.). (YA). 2007. 28p. 2.95 (***978-0-9785605-4-6(X));*** 2006. 32p. 2.95 (978-0-9785605-0-8(7)); abr. ed. 2007. 28p. 2.95 (***978-0-9785605-3-9(1));*** 2nd abr. ed. 2007. 28p. 2.95 (***978-0-9785605-1-5(5)***) Oasis Studios Inc.

Kelly, Joe. Justice League Elite, Vol. 1. rev. ed. 2005. (Illus.). 208p. pap. 19.99 (978-1-4012-0481-5(3)) DC Comics.

Kelly, Neil. Evil Adversaries. 2007. 48p. (J). 14.99 (978-0-7566-2701-0(X)) Dorling Kindersley Publishing, Inc.

—The World's Greatest Superteam. 2007. 48p. (J). 14.99 (978-0-7566-2700-3(1)); pap. 3.99 (978-0-7566-2699-0(4)) Dorling Kindersley Publishing, Inc.

Kelly, Neil & Beecroft, Simon. Evil Adversaries. 2007. 48p. (J). pap. 3.99 (978-0-7566-2702-7(8)) Dorling Kindersley Publishing, Inc.

Kennedy, Mike & Emberlin, Randy. Dead to Rights. 2002. 64p. (YA). pap. 5.95 (978-1-56971-853-7(9)) Dark Horse Comics.

Kennedy, Mike & Robinson, Roger. Alien vs. Predator: Thrill of the Hunt. 2004. (Illus.). 96p. pap. 6.95 (978-1-59307-257-5(0)) Dark Horse Comics.

Kesel, Barbara. Radiant, Vol. 2. Perez, George et al, illus. 2004. (Solus Ser.: Vol. 2). 160p. (YA). pap. 15.95 (978-1-59314-057-1(6)) CrossGeneration Comics, Inc.

Kibuishi, Kazu. Amulet: Book 1. 2008. 192p. (J). pap. 9.99 (***978-0-439-84681-3(1)*** , Graphix) Scholastic, Inc.

Kibuishi, Kazu, ed. Flight Explorer: Vol. 1. 2008. 112p. pap. 9.95 (***978-0-345-50313-8(9)*** , Villard Bks.) Random House Publishing Group.

Kidd, Ronald. Undercover Kid: Comic Book King. Sklar, Andy, illus. 2007. (All Aboard Mystery Reader Ser.). 48p. (J). pap. 3.99 (***978-0-448-44438-3(0)*** , Grosset & Dunlap) Penguin Group (USA) Inc.

The Kids Guide to Pet Jokes, Rhymes & Riddles: For Kids Who Love Pets. 2006. (J). 7.95 (***978-0-9744749-3-9(2)***) Crazy Pet Pr., The.

Kikuchi, Hideyuki. Demon City Hunter. 2003. (YA). Vol. 1. 216p. pap. (978-1-4139-0003-3(8)); Vol. 2. 208p. pap. (978-1-4139-0025-5(9)) ADV Manga.

—Demon City Shinjuku, Vol. 1. 2003. (JPN & ENG.). 200p. (YA). pap. 9.99 (978-1-4139-0004-0(6)) A. D. Vision, Inc.

—Demon Palace Babylon, Vol. 1. 2003. 216p. (YA). pap. (978-1-4139-0005-7(4)) ADV Manga.

—Figure 17, Vol. 2. 2004. 200p. pap. (978-1-4139-0041-5(0)) ADV Manga.

—Steel Angel Kurumi, Vol. 4. 2004. 172p. pap. (978-1-4139-0059-0(3)) ADV Manga.

Kilby, Janice Eaton. The Code Chronicles: A Time Traveling, Code-Cracking Adventure. Fields, Robert Edward, illus. 2008. 64p. (J). 12.95 (***978-1-57990-926-0(4)***) Lark Bks.

Kim, Mi-Kyung. 11th Cat, Vol. 2. 2006. (Illus.). 200p. (YA). pap. 10.95 (***978-89-527-4473-9(X)***) ICE Kunion KOR. *Dist:* Diamond Bk. Distributors.

—11th Cat, Vol. 3. 2006. (Illus.). 200p. (YA). pap. 10.95 (***978-89-527-4481-4(0)***) ICE Kunion KOR. *Dist:* Diamond Bk. Distributors.

—11th Cat, Vol. 4. 2006. (Illus.). 200p. (YA). pap. 10.95 (***978-89-527-4500-2(0)***) ICE Kunion KOR. *Dist:* Diamond Bk. Distributors.

Kim, Mikyung. 11th Cat: Vol. 1. 2005. (Illus.). 180p. (YA). pap. 10.95 (978-89-527-4461-6(6)) Diamond Bk. Distributors.

Kim, Yoon-Kyung, illus. Id_Entity, Vol. 1. 2005. 200p. pap. 9.99 (978-1-59532-345-3(7) , Tokyopop Adult) TOKYOPOP, Inc.

—Id_Entity, Vol. 2. rev. ed. 2005. 192p. pap. 9.99 (978-1-59532-346-0(5) , Tokyopop Adult) TOKYOPOP, Inc.

Kindt, Matt. Super Spy. 2007. 304p. (YA). pap. 19.95 (***978-1-891830-96-9(1)***) Top Shelf Productions.

King, Frank. Nina & Skeezix: The Problem of the Lost Ring. 2005. pap. 26.95 (978-1-4179-9654-4(4)) Kessinger Publishing, LLC.

King, Peter. Chronicles. 2002. (gr. 7-12). lib. bdg. 14.15 (978-0-613-77868-8(5)) Tandem Library Bks.

King, Peter & McCoy, Mike. Soldier of God. 2002. 32p. (gr. 7 up). Vol. 1. (Illus.). pap. 5.00 (978-0-9715206-3-9(1)); Vol. 2. (YA). pap. 3.00 (978-0-9715206-4-6(X)) Quest Comics.

King, Peter, et al. Chronicles. 2002. 56p. Vol. 1. (Illus.). (gr. 8 up). pap. 6.00 (978-0-9715206-0-8(7)); Vol. 2. (Illus.). (gr. 7 up). pap. 6.00 (978-0-9715206-1-5(5)); Vol. 3. (gr. 7 up). pap. 6.00 (978-0-9715206-2-2(3)) Quest Comics.

Kirby, Jack. Black Panther by Jack Kirby Volume 2 TPB, Vol. 2. 2006. (Illus.). 112p. pap. 19.99 (978-0-7851-2069-8(6)) Marvel Enterprises, Inc.

Kirk, David. Dashing Through the Snow. 2005. (Miss Spider Ser.). (Illus.). 32p. (J). (ps-7). 12.99 (978-0-448-43998-3(0)) Callaway Editions, Inc.

—I Smell the Future: Book & Toy. 2006. (Nova the Robot Ser.). 32p. (J). 14.99 (978-0-448-43995-2(6)) Callaway Editions, Inc.

—The Listening Walk. 2005. (Miss Spider Ser.). (Illus.). 32p. (J). (ps-7). 17.99 (978-0-448-43999-0(9)) Callaway Editions, Inc.

—Nova's Super-Galactic Pop-up. 2005. (Nova the Robot Ser.). (Illus.). 16p. (J). (ps-3). 22.99 (978-0-448-43993-8(X)) Callaway Editions, Inc.

—Wiggle's Squiggles. 2005. (Miss Spider Ser.). (Illus.). 32p. (J). 14.99 (978-0-448-44002-6(4)) Callaway Editions, Inc.

Kirkman, Robert. Freedom Ring, Vol. 4. 2007. (Illus.). 168p. pap. 17.99 (978-0-7851-1990-6(6)) Marvel Enterprises, Inc.

—Genesis Vol. 1. (Illus.). 120p. pap. 12.99 (978-1-58240-572-8(7)) Image Comics.

—Marvel Zombies HC. 2006. (Illus.). 136p. 19.99 (978-0-7851-2277-7(X)) Marvel Enterprises, Inc.

—Masters of the Universe: He-Man's Icons of Evil. Neves, Diogenes & Walker, Cory, illus. 2004. (Masters of the Universe Ser.). 160p. (YA). pap. 9.95 (978-1-59314-040-3(1)) CrossGeneration Comics, Inc.

—The Ultimate Collection. (Illus.). 400p. (YA). 34.95 (978-1-58240-500-1(X)) Image Comics.

Kirshenblatt, Shane. Dorothy Gale - Journey to Oz. 2005. 64p. Vol. 2. 7.99 (978-1-894998-89-5(8)); Vol. 3. 7.99 (978-1-894998-90-1(1)) Lake, Jack Productions, Inc. CAN. *Dist:* Hushion Hse. Publishing, Ltd.

Kishimoto, Masashi. Naruto: The Forest of Death, Vol. 6. Kishimoto, Masashi, illus. 2005. (Naruto Ser.). (Illus.). 192p. (YA). pap. 7.95 (978-1-59116-739-6(6)) Viz Media.

—Naruto Anime Profiles: Episodes 1-37. 2006. (Naruto Anime Profiles Ser.). (YA). pap. 14.99 (978-1-4215-0657-9(2)) Viz Media.

Kishimoto, Seishi. O-Parts Hunter. 2007. (O-Parts Hunter Ser.). 200p. (YA). Vol. 2. pap. 9.99 (978-1-4215-0856-6(7)); Vol. 3. pap. 9.99 (978-1-4215-0857-3(5)) Viz Media.

Kishiro, Yukito. Angel of Redemption, Vol. 5. Kishiro, Yukito, illus. 2nd ed. 2004. (Battle Angel Alita Ser.). (Illus.). 208p. (YA). pap. 9.95 (978-1-59116-276-6(9)) Viz Media.

—Angel of the Innocents, Vol. 2. 2003. (Battle Angel Alita Last Order Ser.). (Illus.). 208p. (YA). pap. 9.95 (978-1-56931-976-5(6)) Viz Media.

—Battle Angel Alita: Last Order, Vol. 5. Kishiro, Yukito, illus. 2005. (Battle Angel Alita Last Order Ser.). (Illus.). 200p. pap. 9.95 (978-1-59116-282-7(3)) Viz Media.

—Battle Angel Alita Last Order Vol. 4: Angel of Protest. Kishiro, Yukito, illus. 2004. (Battle Angel Alita Last Order Ser.: Vol. 4). (Illus.). 200p. (YA). pap. 9.95 (978-1-59116-281-0(5)) Viz Media.

—Battle Angle Alita Vol. 7: Last Order. 2006. (Battle Angel Alita Last Order Ser.). 208p. (YA). pap. 9.99 (978-1-4215-0433-9(2)) Viz Media.

Kishiro, Yukito & Takahashi, Kazuki. Duelist, Vol. 2. Kishiro, Yukito & Takahashi, Kazuki, illus. 2005. (Yu-Gi-Oh! Ser.). 208p. (YA). pap. 7.95 (978-1-59116-716-7(7)) Viz Media.

Klein, Grady. The Snodgrass Conspiracy Bk. 1. collector's ed. 2006. (Lost Colony Ser.). (Illus.). 128p. (YA). 25.00 (978-1-59643-172-0(5) , First Second Bks.) Roaring Brook Pr.

Knaak, Richard A. & Kim, Jae-Hwan. Warcraft Vol. 1: Dragon Hunt : SAT/ACT Vocabulary-Building Manga. 2007. (Kaplan SAT/ACT Score-Raising Manga Ser.). 160p. pap. 9.99 ***978-1-4277-5495-0(0))** Kaplan Publishing.

Kobayashi, Jin. School Rumble, Vol. 1. 2006. (Illus.). 192p. (gr. 11). pap. 10.95 (978-0-345-49147-3(5) , Del Rey) Random House Publishing Group.

Kobayashi, Makoto. Hard Day's Life. 2002. (gr. 5-8). lib. bdg. 17.60 (978-0-613-79093-2(6)) Tandem Library Bks.

—The Ideal Cat Vol. 9. 2004. (What's Michael? Ser.). 88p. pap. 8.95 (978-1-59307-120-2(5)) Dark Horse Comics.

Kochalka, James. Fantastic Butterflies. 2002. (Illus.). 168p. (YA). pap. 14.95 (978-1-891867-18-7(0) , JUN021979) Alternative Comics.

—James Kochalka's Magic Boy & Robot Elf. 2003. (Illus.). 80p. (YA). pap. 9.95 (978-1-891830-33-4(3)) Top Shelf Productions.

Koeppel, Ruth & Reader's Digest Staff. Dora's Special Memories: Storybook & Toy Camera. 2007. (RD Innovative Book & Player Format Ser.). 10p. (J). 21.99 ***(978-0-7944-1294-4(7))** Reader's Digest Assn., Inc., The.

Koge-Donbo. Di Gi Charat Theater - Dejiko's Summer Vacation. Yamashita, Saki, ed. Hina., illus. 2003. (Di Gi Charat Theater Ser.). 176p. pap. 9.99 (978-1-932480-07-8(2) , Broccoli Bks.) Broccoli International USA, Inc.

—Kamichama Karin, Vol. 5. 5th rev. ed. 2006. pap. 9.99 (978-1-59816-186-1(5) , Tokyopop Kids) TOKYOPOP, Inc.

Koge-Donbo, illus. & creator. Pita Ten Official Fan Book, Vol. 2. Koge-Donbo, creator. 2nd rev. ed. 2006. pap. 9.99 (978-1-59816-107-6(5) , Tokyopop Kids) TOKYOPOP, Inc.

Komikwerks. 2003. (Illus.). (YA). Vol. 1. 116p. per. 9.95 (978-0-9742803-0-1(5)); Vol. 2. per. 9.95 (978-0-9742803-1-8(3)) Komikwerks, LLC.

Komorn, Julie & Lenhard, Elizabeth, adapted by. The Light of Meridian. 2004. (W. I. T. C. H. Ser.: Bk. 7). (Illus.). 144p. (J). lib. bdg. 16.92 ***(978-1-4242-0794-7(0))** Fitzgerald Bks.

Koshi, Rikdo. Excel Saga. 2004. (gr. 7-12). lib. bdg. 18.75 (978-0-613-85850-2(6)) Tandem Library Bks.

—Excel Saga. Koshi, Rikdo, illus. 2005. (Excel Saga Ser.). (Illus.). Vol. 10. 200p. (YA). pap. 9.99 (978-1-59116-644-3(6)); Vol. 13. 184p. pap. 9.99 (978-1-4215-0143-7(0)) Viz Media.

Kotecki, Jason. Childhood Returns No. 2: Kim & Jason Annual #2. 2002. per. 13.95 (978-0-9715253-1-3(5)) JBiRD iNK, Ltd.

—Dreaming Big: Kim & Jason Annual #1. 2001. 118p. per. 13.95 (978-0-9715253-0-6(7)) JBiRD iNK, Ltd.

—Stupid Swimming Lessons: Kim & Jason Annual #3. 2004. 134p. per. 13.95 (978-0-9715253-2-0(3)) JBiRD iNK, Ltd.

Kovac, Tommy. Wonderland #1. 2006. (Illus.). 24p. (YA). pap. 3.50 (978-1-59362-039-4(X) , Slave Labor Graphics) Slave Labor Bks.

—Wonderland #2: The Tulgey Wood & the Treacle Well. 2006. (Illus.). 3.50 (978-1-59362-050-9(0)) Slave Labor Bks.

Kreie, Chris. Lost: A Tale of Survival. Smith, Marcus, illus. 2008. (J). ***(978-1-59889-828-6(0)**); pap. ***(978-1-59889-884-2(1))** Stone Arch Bks.

Krensky, Stephen. Bubble Trouble. Pickering, Jimmy, illus. ed. 2005. 32p. (J). lib. bdg. 15.00 (978-1-59054-922-3(8)) Fitzgerald Bks.

Kunkel, Mike. Inheritance. 2003. (gr. k-3). lib. bdg. 30.35 (978-0-613-77882-4(0)) Tandem Library Bks.

Kurkoski, Bettina. My Cat Loki, Vol. 1. 2006. pap. 9.99 (978-1-59816-731-3(6) , Tokyopop Adult) TOKYOPOP, Inc.

Kurtti, Jeff. Disney Villains: The Top Secret Files. 2005. (Illus.). 48p. (gr. k-17). 15.99 (978-0-7868-3603-1(2)) Disney Pr.

Kurtz, Scott. PvP Rides Again, Vol. 3. (Illus.). 144p. pap. 11.95 (978-1-58240-553-7(0)) Image Comics.

Kurumada, Masami. Knights of the Zodiac. 2006. (Knights of the Zodiac Ser.). 208p. (YA). Vol. 14. pap. 7.95 (978-1-4215-0418-6(9)); Vol. 16. pap. 7.95 (978-1-4215-0659-3(9)); Vol. 17. pap. 7.95 (978-1-4215-0660-9(2)) Viz Media.

—Knights of the Zodiac Vol. 4: Saint Seiya, Vol. 8. Kurumada, Masami, illus. 2005. (Knights of the Zodiac Ser.). (Illus.). 192p. (YA). pap. 7.95 (978-1-59116-715-0(9)) Viz Media.

Kusaka, Hidenori. Yellow Caballero: Making Waves. MATO Staff, illus. 1999. (Pokemon Adventures Ser.: Vol. 5). 192p. (YA). pap. 13.95 (978-1-59116-027-4(8)) Viz Media.

—Yellow Caballero: The Seafoam Encounter. MATO Staff, illus. 2002. (Pokemon Adventures Ser.: Vol. 5). 49p. (YA). pap. 4.95 (978-1-56931-726-6(7)) Viz Media.

Kyle, Craig & Yost, Christopher. Childhood's End, Vol. 1. 2006. (Illus.). 104p. (YA). pap. 10.99 (978-0-7851-1831-2(4)) Marvel Enterprises, Inc.

Kyung-ah, Choi, illus. & creator. Snow Drop. Kyung-ah, Choi, creator. 2005. Vol. 8. rev. ed. 208p. pap. 9.99 (978-1-59532-044-5(X)); Vol. 9. 9th rev. ed. 192p. pap. 9.99 (978-1-59532-045-2(8)) TOKYOPOP, Inc. (Tokyopop Adult).

LaRocque, Greg. Crybaby: Extinction. Castillo, Cesar & Burruss, Melissa, illus. 2005. (YA). per. 9.99 (978-1-933570-86-0(5)) Aardvark Global Publishing.

Larsen, Erik, et al. Image Comics. ltd. ed. 2005. 128p. (YA). 75.00 (978-1-58240-257-4(4)) Image Comics.

The Last Draw. 1998. (Comic Book Ser.). (Illus.). (J). (978-0-7652-0300-7(6)) Modern Curriculum Pr.

Lauria, Frank. La Mascara de Zorro. 2000. Tr. of Mask of Zorro. (SPA., Illus.). 176p. (J). 9.95 (978-84-406-8484-4(3)) Ediciones B ESP. *Dist:* Distribooks, Inc.

Lawhead, Stephen R. & Lawhead, Ross. Hero. 2003. (gr. 7-12). lib. bdg. 18.80 (978-0-613-89617-7(3)) Tandem Library Bks.

Lawson, Jim & Dooney, Michael. Paleo: Tales of the Late Cretaceous. 2003. (Illus.). 172p. (YA). reprint ed. pap. 12.95 (978-0-9661985-3-9(0) , Empty Sky) Zeromayo Studios, LLP.

Layman, John S. Armageddon & Son. 2005. (Illus.). 96p. (YA). pap. 9.95 (978-1-932664-33-1(5)) Oni Pr., Inc.

Lee, Bin. One, 5 vols. 2004. (Illus.). 192p. Vol. 2. 3rd rev. ed. pap. 9.99 (978-1-59182-753-5(1)); Vol. 3. 4th rev. ed. pap. 9.99 (978-1-59182-754-2(X)) TOKYOPOP, Inc. (Tokyopop Kids).

Lee, Eun. Antique Gift Shop, Vol. 2. 2005. (Illus.). 180p. (YA). pap. 10.95 ***(978-89-527-4475-3(6))** ICE Kunion KOR. *Dist:* Diamond Bk. Distributors.

Lee, Hana. Heavenly Executioner Chiwoo, Vol. 2. 2006. (Illus.). 180p. (YA). pap. 10.95 ***(978-89-527-4476-0(4))** ICE Kunion KOR. *Dist:* Diamond Bk. Distributors.

Lee, Myung-Jin, creator. Ragnarok Boxed Set Collection, Vol. 1-3. collector's ed. 2003. (Illus.). pap. 29.99 (978-1-59182-591-3(1)) TOKYOPOP, Inc.

Lee, Shi Young. Fantasy Land, Vol. 1. 2004. 192p. (YA). pap. (978-1-4139-0066-8(6)) ADV Manga.

Lee, So-Young, illus. & creator. Arcana, Vol. 4. Lee, So-Young, creator. 4th rev. ed. 2006. pap. 9.99 (978-1-59816-200-4(4) , Tokyopop Kids) TOKYOPOP, Inc.

Lee, Stan. Essential Fantastic Four, Vol. 5. 2006. (Marvel Essentials Ser.). (Illus.). 568p. pap. 16.99 (978-0-7851-2162-6(5)) Marvel Enterprises, Inc.

—Essential Silver Surfer Volume 1 TPB. 2nd ed. 2005. (Illus.). 528p. pap. 16.99 (978-0-7851-2008-7(4)) Marvel Enterprises, Inc.

—The Fantastic Four: Fantastic Four #1-20 & Annual #1. Kirby, Jack, illus. 2005. (Essential Ser.). 544p. (YA). pap. 16.99 (978-0-7851-1828-2(4)) Marvel Enterprises, Inc.

Lee, Stan, et al. John Buscema. 2007. (Marvel Visionaries Ser.). (Illus.). 368p. 34.99 (978-0-7851-2161-9(7)) Marvel Enterprises, Inc.

Lee, Sun-Hee, creator. Neck & Neck, Vol. 5. 5th rev. ed. 2006. (Illus.). 192p. (YA). pap. 9.99 (978-1-59816-099-4(0) , Tokyopop Kids) TOKYOPOP, Inc.

Lee, Young Yuu, creator. Kill Me, Kiss Me, 5 vols., Vol. 4. 4th rev. ed. 2004. (Teen Ser.). (Illus.). 192p. pap. 9.99 (978-1-59182-596-8(2) , Tokyopop Kids) TOKYOPOP, Inc.

Lee, YoungHee. You're So Cool Volume 2. 2007. (Illus.). 200p. (YA). pap. 10.95 ***(978-89-527-4718-1(6))** ICE Kunion KOR. *Dist:* Diamond Bk. Distributors.

Lee, Younghee. You're So Cool Volume 3. 2007. 200p. (YA). pap. 10.95 ***(978-89-527-4874-4(3))** ICE Kunion KOR. *Dist:* Diamond Bk. Distributors.

Left Behind Graphic Novel. 2002. (Left Behind Ser.: Vol. 2). (YA). 14.47 (978-1-4046-2500-6(3)); 14.47 (978-1-4046-2501-3(1)); 14.47 (978-1-4046-2502-0(X)); (YA). 14.47 (978-1-4046-2503-7(8)) Book Wholesalers, Inc.

Left Behind Tribulation Force. 2002. (Left Behind Ser.: Vol. 2). (YA). 14.47 (978-1-4046-2505-1(4)); 14.47 (978-1-4046-2506-8(2)); 14.47 (978-1-4046-2507-5(0)); 14.47 (978-1-4046-2508-2(9)) Book Wholesalers, Inc.

Leitha, Dan. Welcome to Life after Eden. 2003. (YA). per. 12.00 (978-1-893345-15-7(7)) Answers in Genesis Ministries.

Leloup, Roger. Yoko Tsuno: On the Edge of Life. Spear, Luke, tr. from FRE. 2007. (Illus.). 48p. pap. 9.99 ***(978-1-905460-32-8(5))** CineBook GBR. *Dist:* Biblio Distribution.

Lemire, Jeff. Essex County Vol. 1: Tales from the Farm. 2007. (Illus.). 112p. (YA). pap. 9.95 ***(978-1-891830-88-4(0))** Top Shelf Productions.

—Essex County Vol. 2: Ghost Stories. 2007. (Illus.). 112p. (YA). pap. 14.95 ***(978-1-891830-94-5(5))** Top Shelf Productions.

Lenhard, Elizabeth. Different Path. 2004. (W. I. T. C. H. Ser.: Bk. 13). 158p. (J). lib. bdg. 16.92 ***(978-1-4242-0791-6(6))** Fitzgerald Bks.

Lente, Fred Van, et al. Untold Tales of the New Universe TPB. 2006. (Illus.). 152p. pap. 15.99 (978-0-7851-2185-5(4)) Marvel Enterprises, Inc.

Lichtenheld, Tom. What Are You So Grumpy About? 2007. (Illus.). 38p. (J). (ps-1). 6.99 (978-0-316-06589-4(7)) Little Brown & Co.

—What Are You So Grumpy About? Lichtenheld, Tom, illus. 2003. (Illus.). 32p. (J). (ps-17). 15.99 (978-0-316-59236-9(6)) Little, Brown Bks. for Young Readers.

Liefeld, Rob, et al. Wolverine, Vol. 3. 2006. (Illus.). 112p. pap. 12.99 (978-0-7851-2065-0(3)) Marvel Enterprises, Inc.

Lijewski, Christy. Next Exit, Vol. 1. 2006. (Illus.). 168p. (YA). pap. 12.95 (978-1-59362-037-0(3)) Slave Labor Bks.

Limke, Jeff. Isis & Osiris: To the Ends of the Earth. Witt, David, illus. 2007. (Graphic Myths & Legends Ser.). 48p. (YA). (gr. 4-9). pap. 8.95 ***(978-0-8225-6482-9(3))** Lerner Publishing Group.

Limke Jeff. Isis y Osiris (Isis & Osiris) Hasta el fin del mundo (to the Ends of the Earth) Witt, David, illus. 2007. (Mitos y leyendas en viñetas (Graphic Myths & Legends) Ser.). (SPA & ENG.). (J). pap. 8.95 ***(978-0-8225-7971-7(5)** , Ediciones Lerner) Lerner Publishing Group.

Limke, Jeff. King Arthur: Excalibur Unsheathed. Yeates, Thomas, illus. 2007. (Graphic Myths & Legends Ser.). 48p. (YA). (gr. 4-9). pap. 8.95 ***(978-0-8225-6483-6(1))** Lerner Publishing Group.

Limke Jeff. El rey Arturo (King Arthur) La espada Excalibur desenvainada (Excalibur Unsheathed) Yeates, Thomas, illus. 2007. (Mitos y leyendas en viñetas (Graphic Myths & Legends) Ser.). (J). pap. 8.95 ***(978-0-8225-7968-7(5)** , Ediciones Lerner) Lerner Publishing Group.

Limke, Jeff. The Treasure of Mount Fate. Hilinski, Clint, illus. 2007. (Twisted Journeys Ser.). 112p. (J). (gr. 4-7). lib. bdg. 27.93 ***(978-0-8225-6205-4(7)** , Graphic Universe); pap. 7.95 ***(978-0-8225-6206-1(5))** Lerner Publishing Group.

Linsner, Joseph Michael. Three Tiers. (Dawn Ser.: Vol. 3). 176p. (YA). (Illus.). 39.99 (978-1-58240-573-5(5)); 2006. 69.99 (978-1-58240-574-2(3)) Image Comics.

Litchmore, Michael. The MB Force: Heroes at the Best! 2007. 56p. pap. 9.00 ***(978-0-8059-7399-0(0))** Dorrance Publishing Co., Inc.

Lobdell, Scott. Flesh & Blood, 3. 5. (Illus.). 464p. (Orig.). pap. 24.99 (978-1-58240-538-4(7)) Image Comics.

—The Hardy Boys #8: Board to Death. Henrique, Paulo, illus. 8th rev. ed. 2007. (Hardy Boys: Undercover Brothers Ser.). 112p. (J). 12.95 (978-1-59707-054-6(8)); pap. 7.95 (978-1-59707-053-9(X)) Papercutz.

—Malled. Rendon, Daniel, illus. 4th rev. ed. 2006. (Hardy Boys Graphic Novel Ser.: No. 4). 96p. (J). 12.95 (978-1-59707-015-7(7)); pap. 7.95 (978-1-59707-014-0(9)) Papercutz.

—The Opposite Numbers. Rendon, Daniel, illus. 7th rev. ed. 2006. (Hardy Boys Ser.: No. 7). 96p. (J). pap. 7.95 (978-1-59707-034-8(3)) Papercutz.

—The Oppsite Numbers. Rendon, Daniel, illus. 7th rev. ed. 2006. (Hardy Boys Ser.: No. 7). 96p. (J). 12.95 (978-1-59707-035-5(1)) Papercutz.

Lobdell, Scott & Baron, Mike. Kiss Vol. 3: Men & Monsters. 2003. 96p. (YA). pap. 12.95 (978-1-56971-971-8(3)) Dark Horse Comics.

Lobdell, Scott & Nicieza, Fabian. Slayer, Interrupted. 2003. (Angel/Buffy the Vampire Slayer Ser.). 104p. (YA). pap. 12.95 (978-1-59307-011-3(X)) Dark Horse Comics.

Lobdell, Scott & Rendon, Daniel. Hyde & Shriek. 6th rev. ed. 2006. (Hardy Boys Ser.: No. 6). (Illus.). 96p. (J). 12.95 (978-1-59707-029-4(7)); pap. 7.95 (978-1-59707-028-7(9)) Papercutz.

—Identity Theft. 2nd rev. ed. 2005. (Hardy Boys Graphic Novel Ser.: No. 2). (Illus.). 96p. (J). (gr. 3-9). 12.95 (978-1-59707-007-2(6)); pap., pap. 7.95 (978-1-59707-003-4(3)) Papercutz.

—Mad House. 3rd rev. ed. 2005. (Hardy Boys Graphic Novel Ser.: No. 3). (Illus.). 96p. (J). (gr. 3-7). pap., pap. 7.95 (978-1-59707-010-2(6)) Papercutz.

—The Ocean of Osyria. Hernandez, Lea, illus. 2005. (Hardy Boys Graphic Novel Ser.: No. 1). 96p. (J). (gr. 3-9). 12.95 (978-1-59707-005-8(X)); (ps-7). pap. 7.95 (978-1-59707-001-0(7)) Papercutz.

Lobdell, Scott, et al. X-Men: Dreams End. 2004. (X-Men Ser.). (Illus.). 192p. pap. 17.99 (978-0-7851-1551-9(X)) Marvel Enterprises, Inc.

Loeb, Jeph. Blue. Sale, Tim, illus. 2003. (Spider-Man Ser.). 160p. (YA). 21.99 (978-0-7851-1062-0(3)) Marvel Enterprises, Inc.

Lofficier, Randy & Lofficier, Jean-Marc. Robonocchio. Martiniere, Stephan, illus. 2004. (FRE.). 128p. (YA). per. 14.95 (978-1-932983-04-3(X) , Black Coat Pr.) HollywoodComics.com, LLC.

London, Jack. Jack London's The Call of the Wild. 2006. (J). (gr. 4-8). 24.21 (978-1-59961-114-3(7)) Spotlight.

—Jack London/the Call of the Wild. Carrillo, Fred, illus. 2005. 48p. (gr. 5-8). 25.50 (978-0-7910-9104-3(X)) Facts On File, Inc.

London, Jack, et al. Graphic Classics Jack London. 2nd ed. 2006. 144p. (YA). pap. 11.95 (978-0-9746648-8-0(X)) Eureka Productions.

Love One Another. 4.50 (978-0-687-04511-2(8)) Abingdon Pr.

Luke, Eric, et al. Painful Music. 1999. (Ghost Ser.). (Illus.). 96p. (YA). (gr. 9 up). pap. 9.95 (978-1-56971-422-5(3)) Dark Horse Comics.

Lustig, John & Barks, Carl. Donald Duck & Uncle Scrooge: Somewhere in Nowhere. Block, Pat & Rockwell, Scott, illus. 2005. 64p. (YA). pap. 6.95 (978-1-888472-05-9(7)) Gemstone Publishing, Inc.

Lutes, Jason. Houdini: The Handcuff King. Bertozzi, Nick, illus. 2007. 96p. (gr. 5-17). 16.99 ***(978-0-7868-3902-5(3))** Hyperion Pr.

Lyga, Barry. The Astonishing Adventures of Fanboy & Goth Girl. 2007. 320p. (YA). (gr. 9-12). pap. 8.99 ***(978-0-618-91652-8(0))** Houghton Mifflin Co. Trade & Reference Div.

Lyons, Michelle. Trigun Ultimate Fan Guide, Vol. 1, No. 1. 2002. 112p. (YA). pap. 24.95 (978-1-894525-36-7(1)) Guardians of Order CAN. *Dist:* LPC Group.

Ma, Wing Shing. Black Leopard, Vol. 1. 2005. (Illus.). 160p. (YA). pap. 14.95 (978-1-58899-333-5(7)) ComicsOne Corp./Dr. Masters.

—Black Leopard #3. 2005. 160p. (YA). pap. 14.95 (978-1-58899-335-9(3)) ComicsOne Corp./Dr. Masters.

—Black Leopard #4. 2005. 160p. (YA). pap. 14.95 (978-1-58899-336-6(1)) ComicsOne Corp./Dr. Masters.

Macan, Darko. Soldier X. Kordey, Igor, illus. 2003. 144p. (YA). pap. 12.99 (978-0-7851-1013-2(5)) Marvel Enterprises, Inc.

MacCormick, James. The Gemini Solution. Sivertsen, Kirk, illus. 2002. 80p. (YA). per. 4.99 (978-0-9725925-0-5(4)) Comicstories.com.

—West of the Dakotas. Glanzman, Sam, illus. 2002. 80p. (YA). per. 4.99 (978-0-9725925-1-2(2)) Comicstories.com.

Macdonald, Fiona & Stoker, Bram. Dracula. Gelev, Penko, illus. 2007. (Graphic Classics Ser.). 48p. (J). (gr. 3 up). 15.99 ***(978-0-7641-6054-7(0)**); pap. 8.99 ***(978-0-7641-3778-5(6))** Barron's Educational Series, Inc.

MacDonald, Kimber. The Misfits, Level 3. Swain, Wilson, illus. 2006. (Phonics Comics Ser.). 24p. (J). (gr. 1-17). pap. 3.99 (978-1-58476-421-2(X) , IKIDS) Innovative Kids.

—Time Travelers, Level 3. Sisk, Clay, illus. 2006. (Phonics Comics Ser.). 24p. (J). (gr. 1-17). pap. 3.99 (978-1-58476-472-4(4) , IKIDS) Innovative Kids.

Mack, David. Skin Deep. 1999. (Illus.). 112p. (YA). 23.95 (978-1-58240-073-0(3)) Image Comics.

Magic Wand Disney Princess. 2005. (Illus.). 10p. (J). bds. 15.98 (978-1-4127-3537-7(8) , 7263500) Publications International, Ltd.

Mainardi, Alessandro. The Life of Pope John Paul II: In Comics! Maresta, Werner, illus. rev. ed. 2006. 96p. (J). (gr. 4-9). 16.95 (978-1-59707-039-3(4)) Papercutz.

Malbrough, Page. Fire Proves Iron: Grounded Stars. Malbrough, Michael & Fisher, G. W., illus. 2004. 80p. (YA). per. 9.95 (978-0-9758883-0-8(7)) Malbrough, Michael.

Manabe, Johji. Drakuun: Rise of the Dragon Princess. 1998. 168p. (gr. 2 up). pap. 12.95 (978-1-56971-302-0(2)) Dark Horse Comics.

—Drakuun: The Revenge of Gustav. 1999. 160p. (gr. 11 up). pap. 14.95 (978-1-56971-368-6(5)) Dark Horse Comics.

Mandracchia, Charles, 8th, illus. & creator. Showtoonz, Mandracchia, Charles, 8th, creator. 2nd l.t. ed. 2005. 38p. (J). per. 995.00 net. (978-0-9721957-2-0(6) , Mandracchia Bks.) Mandracchia, Charles.

Manfredi, Federica, illus. Kat & Mouse. 2006. (Kat & Mouse Ser.: Vol. 1). pap. 5.99 (978-1-59816-548-7(8) , Tokyopop Kids) TOKYOPOP, Inc.

Mankoff, Robert. The New Yorker Book of Kids Cartoons: And the People Who Live with Them. 2002. (Illus.). 144p. 21.95 (978-1-57660-097-9(1)) Bloomberg Pr.

Mantlo, Bill, et al. Champions Classic, Vol. 2. 2007. (Illus.). 216p. pap. 19.99 (978-0-7851-2098-8(X)) Marvel Enterprises, Inc.

Marathon Team. Spies in Space. 4th rev. ed. 2007. (Totally Spies Ser.: No. 4). (Illus.). 112p. (J). 12.95 (978-1-59707-056-0(4)); pap. 7.95 (978-1-59707-055-3(6)) Papercutz.

March, Julia. Disney Villains. 2004. (Ultimate Sticker Bks.). (Illus.). 16p. (J). pap. 6.99 (978-0-7566-0577-3(6)) Dorling Kindersley Publishing, Inc.

Marini, Enrico & Dufaux, Jean. Rapaces, Vol. 4. 2005. (SPA., Illus.). 56p. pap. 17.95 (978-1-59497-107-5(2)) Public Square Bks.

Markas, Jenny. Scooby-Doo & the Monster of Mexico Jr Novelization. 2003. (gr. k-3). lib. bdg. 13.00 (978-0-613-66378-6(0)) Tandem Library Bks.

Marks, Melanie. Spooky Sara, Level 3. Ball, Victoria, illus. 2006. (Phonics Comics Ser.). 24p. (J). (gr. 1-17). pap. 3.99 (978-1-58476-473-1(2) , IKIDS) Innovative Kids.

—Super Sam. Collins, Daryll, illus. 2006. (Phonics Comics Ser.). 24p. (J). (gr. 1-17). pap. 3.99 (978-1-58476-420-5(1) , IKIDS) Innovative Kids.

Martin, Ann M. Baby Sitter's Club: Kristy's Great Idea. 2006. (Illus.). 192p. (J). pap. 8.99 (978-0-439-73933-7(0) , Graphix) Scholastic, Inc.

—Kristy's Great Idea. 2006. (Baby-Sitters Club Ser.: No. 1). (Illus.). 192p. (J). (gr. 3-7). pap. 16.99 (978-0-439-80241-3(5) , Graphix) Scholastic, Inc.

Martin, Ann M. Mary Anne Saves the Day. 2007. (BSC Graphix Ser.: No. 3). 160p. (J). pap. 8.99 ***(978-0-439-88516-4(7)** , Graphix) Scholastic, Inc.

Marunas, Nathaniel. Manga Claus: The Blade of Kringle. Craddock, Erik, illus. 2006. 80p. (J). (gr. 4-12). 12.99 (978-1-59514-134-7(0) , Razorbill) Penguin Group (USA) Inc.

Marvel. The Art of Marvel Comics, Vol. 2. 2004. (Marvel Heroes Ser.). (Illus.). 128p. 29.99 (978-0-7851-1361-4(4)) Marvel Enterprises, Inc.

Marvel & Kiefer, Kit. Marvel Encyclopedia Vol. 6: Fantastic Four. 2004. (Fantastic Four Ser.). (Illus.). 240p. 29.99 (978-0-7851-1480-2(7)) Marvel Enterprises, Inc.

Marvel, et al. Best of Wolverine, Vol. 1. 2004. (Wolverine Ser.). (Illus.). 320p. 29.99 (978-0-7851-1370-6(3)) Marvel Enterprises, Inc.

Marvel Characters, Inc Staff. X-Men Pop-Up: Marvel True Believers Retro Collection. Repchuck, Caroline, ed. 2007. (Marvel True Believers Ser.). (Illus.). 16p. (J). (gr. k). 24.99 ***(978-0-7636-3462-9(X))** Candlewick Pr.

Marvel Comics Staff. The Incredible Hulk Big Color & Activity Book. Meredith Books Staff & Curry, Don, eds. 2005. 64p. (J). pap., act. bk. ed. 2.99 (978-0-696-22676-2(6)) Meredith Bks.

C D

—Iron Man Big Color & Activity Book with Stickers. Meredith Books Staff, ed. 2008. 64p. (J). pap. 2.99 (978-0-696-22681-6(2)) Meredith Bks.

—Iron Man Jumbo Color & Activity Book. Meredith Books Staff, ed. 2008. 400p. (J). pap. 5.99 (978-0-696-22656-4(1)) Meredith Bks.

—Spider-Man Big Color & Activity Book: With Stickers. Meredith Books Staff & Curry, Don, eds. 2005. 64p. (J). pap., act. bk. ed. 2.99 (978-0-696-22679-3(0)) Meredith Bks.

—X-Men Big Color & Activity Book: With Stickers. Meredith Books Staff & Curry, Don, eds. 2005. 64p. (J). pap., act. bk. ed. 2.99 (978-0-696-22678-6(2)) Meredith Bks.

Marvel Staff. The Clone Trap. 2007. 24p. (J). pap. 3.99 (978-0-696-23477-4(7)) Meredith Bks.

Mary & Joseph a Story of Fai. 2004. pap. 14.99 (978-0-7907-1830-9(8)) Hachette Bk. Group.

Mary Jane. 2006. (J). (gr. 2-6). 85.40 (978-1-59961-036-8(1)) Spotlight.

Marz, Ron. Mystic Traveler: The Demon Queen, Vol. 2. Peterson, Brandon et al, illus. 2004. (Mystic Traveler Ser.). 160p. (YA). pap. 9.95 (978-1-59314-037-3(1)) CrossGeneration Comics, Inc.

—Scion Vol. 6: The Royal Wedding. Cheung, Jim et al, illus. 2004. (Scion Ser.). 160p. (YA). pap. 15.95 (978-1-59314-034-2(7)) CrossGeneration Comics, Inc.

Masami, Tsuda. Kare Kano, Vol. 17. 17th rev. ed. 2005. (Illus.). 192p. pap. 9.99 (978-1-59532-591-4(3) , Tokyopop Kids) TOKYOPOP, Inc.

Masashi, Kishimoto. Zatch Bell. 2004. 192p. pap. 9.95 (978-1-59116-679-5(9)) Viz Media.

Mashima, Hiro. En Espanol, Vol. 5. 2006. (SPA., Illus.). 192p. reprint ed. pap. 10.95 (978-1-59497-179-2(X)) Public Square Bks.

—Rave Master. 2006. (SPA., Illus.). reprint ed. Vol. 7. 200p. pap. 10.95 (978-1-59497-199-0(4)); Vol. 8. 186p. pap. 10.95 (978-1-59497-200-3(1)); Vol. 9. 192p. pap. 10.95 (978-1-59497-201-0(X)) Public Square Bks.

—Rave Master. Vol. 4. pap. 7.99 (978-1-59532-792-5(4)); Vol. 5. (Illus.). 200p. pap. 7.99 (978-1-59532-793-2(2)) TOKYOPOP, Inc.

—Rave Master. Mashima, Hiro, illus. 2005. (Illus.). Vol. 15. rev. ed. 192p. pap. 9.99 (978-1-59532-020-9(2)); Vol. 17. 17th rev. ed. pap. 9.99 (978-1-59532-022-3(9)); Vol. 18. 18th rev. ed. pap. 9.99 (978-1-59532-023-0(7)) TOKYOPOP, Inc. (Tokyopop Kids).

—Rave Master. Vol. 21. 21st rev. ed. 2006. pap. 9.99 (978-1-59532-026-1(1) , Tokyopop Kids); Vol. 22. 22nd rev. ed. 2006. pap. 9.99 (978-1-59532-626-3(X) , Tokyopop Kids); Vol. 23. 2007. pap. 9.99 (978-1-59532-627-0(8) , Tokyopop Kids); Vol. 24. 2007. pap. 9.99 (978-1-59532-628-7(6) , Tokyopop Kids); Vol. 25. 2007. 192p. pap. 9.99 (978-1-59532-629-4(4) , Tokyopop Kids); Vol. 26. 2007. 192p. pap. 9.99 (978-1-59532-630-0(8) , Tokyopop Kids); Vol. 27. 2008. 192p. mass mkt. 9.99 (978-1-59532-631-7(6)); Vol. 28. 2008. pap. 9.99 (978-1-59532-632-4(4)); Vol. 29. 2008. pap. 9.99 (978-1-59532-809-0(2)) TOKYOPOP, Inc.

—Rave Master (En Español) 2006. (SPA., Illus.). reprint ed. Vol. 1. 192p. pap. 10.95 (978-1-59497-175-4(7)); Vol. 2. 192p. pap. 10.95 (978-1-59497-176-1(5)); Vol. 3. 184p. pap. 10.95 (978-1-59497-177-8(3)); Vol. 4. 192p. pap. 10.95 (978-1-59497-178-5(1)); Vol. 6. 200p. pap. 10.95 (978-1-59497-180-8(3)) Public Square Bks.

Mashima, Hiro, illus. Rave Master, Vol. 14. rev. ed. 2005. 200p. pap. 9.99 (978-1-59532-019-3(9) , Tokyopop Kids) TOKYOPOP, Inc.

Mason, Jeff. 9-11: Emergency Relief. 2002. (gr. 7-12). lib. bdg. 24.55 (978-0-613-51101-8(8)) Tandem Library Bks.

Master Warriors. 1999. (Digimon Tattoo Bks.). (Illus.). 17p. (J). (ps-2). pap. (978-0-7666-0552-7(3)) Modern Publishing.

Masters, Anthony. The Haunted Surfboard. Dennis, Peter, illus. 2007. (Graphic Quest Ser.). (J). 88p. (***978-1-59889-215-4(0)*** , 1256167); 80p. (gr. 2-8). lib. bdg. 21.26 (978-1-59889-080-8(8) , 1256167) Stone Arch Bks.

—Hot Air. Perkins, Mike, illus. 2007. (Graphic Trax Ser.). 66p. (J). (gr. 4-8). lib. bdg. 19.93 (978-1-59889-086-0(7)) Stone Arch Bks.

—Raven's Revenge. Dennis, Peter, illus. 2007. (Graphic Quest Ser.). 80p. (J). (gr. 4-8). lib. bdg. 21.26 (978-1-59889-082-2(4)) Stone Arch Bks.

Mathieu, Marc-Antoine. Dead Memory. 2003. 64p. 14.95 (978-1-56971-840-7(7)) Dark Horse Comics.

Matsubara, Hiroaki. More Starlight to Your Heart, Vol 1. 2004. (Illus.). 184p. (YA). pap. (978-1-4139-0206-8(5)) ADV Manga.

Matsumoto, Tomo. Beauty Is the Beast, Vol. 4. 2006. (Beauty Is the Beast Ser.). 208p. (YA). pap. 8.99 (978-1-4215-0354-7(9)) Viz Media.

Matsushita, Yoko. Yami No Matsuei, Vol. 4. Matsushita, Yoko, illus. 2005. (Descendants of Darkness Ser.). (Illus.). 184p. (YA). pap. 9.99 (978-1-59116-702-0(7)) Viz Media.

Matsuura, Tokihiko. Tuxedo Gin, Vol. 10. Matsuura, Tokihiko, illus. 2005. (Tuxedo Gin Ser.). (Illus.). 200p. (YA). pap. 9.95 (978-1-59116-695-5(0)) Viz Media.

Matsuura, Tokihiko & Watsuki, Nobuhiro. Rurouni Kenshin, Vol. 12. Matsuura, Tokihiko & Watsuki, Nobuhiro, illus. 2005. (Rurouni Kenshin Ser.). 200p. (YA). pap. 7.95 (978-1-59116-712-9(4)) Viz Media.

Mattel, creator. Barbie Box - the Enchanted Collection. 2005. (Illus.). 288p. pap. 19.99 (978-1-59816-408-4(2)) TOKYOPOP, Inc.

McAdams Moore, Carol. Phonics Comics: Cave Dave - Level 1. Dammer, Mike, illus. 2007. 24p. (J). (gr. 1-17). pap. 3.99 (978-1-58476-552-3(6)) Innovative Kids.

McAvennie, Mike. Batmobile Owner's Manual. Chasemore, Richard & Su, E. J., illus. 2008. 32p. (J). (gr. 5-12). 24.99 (***978-0-7566-3839-9(9)***) Dorling Kindersley Publishing, Inc.

McBride, Earvin, Jr. Dumbball the Bodybuilder. McBride, Earvin, Jr., illus. unabr. ed. 2002. (Earvin MacBride's Fun Fun Lovable Cartoons Ser.). (Illus.). 123p. (YA). (gr. 7-12). pap. 4.95 (978-1-892511-02-7(9)) MacBride, E. J. Pubn., Inc.

—Earvin MacBride's Fun Fun Lovable Cartoons, 4 vols., Set. McBride, Earvin, Jr., illus. unabr. ed. 2002. (Illus.). (J). (gr. 7-12). pap. 16.95 (978-1-892511-00-3(2)) MacBride, E. J. Pubn., Inc.

McCann, Jesse Leon. Ghastly Giant. del Sur, Duendes, illus. 2003. (Scooby Doo Ser.). 32p. (J). pap. 3.50 (978-0-439-45523-7(5)) Scholastic, Inc.

—Ghastly Giant. 2003. (gr. k-3). lib. bdg. 11.25 (978-0-613-66376-2(4)) Tandem Library Bks.

—Scooby-Doo & the Legend of Vampire Rock. 2003. (gr. 3-6). lib. bdg. 11.25 (978-0-613-58167-7(9)) Tandem Library Bks.

—Scooby-Doo & the Monster of Mexico. 2003. (gr. 3-6). lib. bdg. 11.25 (978-0-613-66377-9(2)) Tandem Library Bks.

McCann, Jesse Leon, et al. The Scrapyard Detectives: Collected Cases Volume 1. 2007. 106p. (J). pap. 5.00 (***978-0-9797193-0-1(5)***) Diversity Foundation, The.

McDonald, Ian. Bruno: Most Wanted. 2000. (Bruno the Bandit Ser.: Vol. 2). 152p. pap. 12.95 (978-1-929462-22-3(0)) Plan Nine Publishing, Inc.

McDonnell, Patrick. Mutts: Tiere sind auch nur Menschen. Dickerhof-Kranz, Susanne, tr. from ENG. (GER., Illus.). 64p. (J). Vol. 1. pap. (978-3-8105-1250-5(8)); Vol. 2. pap. (978-3-8105-1251-2(6)); Vol. 3. pap. (978-3-8105-1252-9(4)); Vol. 4. pap. (978-3-8105-1253-6(2)); Vol. 5. pap. (978-3-8105-1254-3(0)); Vol. 6. pap. (978-3-8105-1255-0(9)) Kruger, Wolfgang Verlag, GmbH DEU. *Dist:* International Bk. Import Service, Inc.

McEown, Pat. Homecoming. 2000. (Illus.). 64p. pap. 7.95 (978-1-56971-405-8(3)) Dark Horse Comics.

McFarlane, Todd & Harmon, Paul. All Beasts Will Show Their Teeth. 2006. (Illus.). 128p. (YA). pap. 12.99 (978-1-58240-588-9(3)) Image Comics.

McGreal, Pat, et al. Donald Duck Adventures, Vol. 19. 2006. (Illus.). 128p. (YA). pap. 7.95 (978-1-888472-31-8(6)) Gemstone Publishing, Inc.

—Mickey Mouse Adventures, Vol. 10. 2006. (Illus.). 128p. (YA). pap. 7.95 (978-1-888472-32-5(4)) Gemstone Publishing, Inc.

McGregor, Don. Drownings. Lima, Sidney, illus. 2nd rev. ed. 2006. (Zorro Graphic Novel Ser.: No. 2). 96p. (J). pap. 7.95 (978-1-59707-018-8(1)) Papercutz.

—Sabre 20th Anniversary. anniv. ed. 1999. (Illus.). 48p. pap. 12.95 (978-1-58240-059-4(8)) Image Comics.

—Vultures! Lima, Sidney, illus. 3rd rev. ed. 2006. (Zorro Graphic Novel Ser.: No. 3). 96p. (J). 12.95 (978-1-59707-021-8(1)); pap. 7.95 (978-1-59707-020-1(3)) Papercutz.

—Zorro: Drownings. Lima, Sidney, illus. 2nd rev. ed. 2006. (Zorro Graphic Novel Ser.: No. 2). 96p. (J). 12.95 (978-1-59707-019-5(X)) Papercutz.

McGregor, Don & Lima, Sidney. Zorro: Flights. 4th rev. ed. 2006. (Zorro Ser.). (Illus.). 96p. (J). 12.95 (978-1-59707-027-0(0)); pap. 7.95 (978-1-59707-026-3(2)) Papercutz.

McJunkin, Jehu David & Wethern, Amelia A. Back on the Farm. l.t. ed. 2006. (Illus.). 100p. (J). 14.95 (978-0-9766124-1-4(0)) Ap Amelia Pr.

McKeever, Sean. Doom with a View. 2007. 21.35 (978-1-59961-208-9(9)) Spotlight.

—Loyalty Thing. 2006. (Illus.). (J). (gr. 2-6). 21.35 (978-1-59961-037-5(X)) Spotlight.

—Money Thing. 2006. (Illus.). (J). (gr. 2-6). 21.35 (978-1-59961-038-2(8)) Spotlight.

—Real Thing. 2006. (Illus.). (J). (gr. 2-6). 21.35 (978-1-59961-039-9(6)) Spotlight.

—Sentinel Vol. 3: Past Imperfect Digest. 2006. (Illus.). 120p. pap. 7.99 (978-0-7851-1914-2(0)) Marvel Enterprises, Inc.

—Trust Thing. 2006. (Illus.). (J). (gr. 2-6). 21.35 (978-1-59961-040-5(X)) Spotlight.

McMullan, Kate & Lemaitre, Pascal. Supercat. 2002. (Illus.). 32p. (J). (ps). bds. 6.95 (978-0-7611-2644-7(9) , 12644) Workman Publishing Co., Inc.

Melville, Herman. Cities of the Fantastic: Brusel. Eisner, Will, illus. 2003. (Cities of the Fantastic Ser.). 120p. 19.95 (978-1-56163-291-6(0)) NBM Publishing Co.

—Herman Melville/Moby Dick. Niño, Alex, illus. 2005. 48p. (gr. 5-8). 25.50 (978-0-7910-9106-7(6)) Facts On File, Inc.

—Moby Dick. 2003. (Illus.). 32p. 7.95 (978-1-56163-294-7(5)) NBM Publishing Co.

—Moby Dick. Eisner, Will, illus. 2003. 32p. (gr. 4-7). 15.95 (978-1-56163-293-0(7)) NBM Publishing Co.

Melville, Herman, et al. Moby Dick. (Classics Illustrated Ser.). (Illus.). 52p. (YA). pap. 4.95 (978-1-57209-003-3(0)) Classics International Entertainment, Inc.

Meredith Books Staff. Superman Returns. Curry, Don, ed. 2007. (I Can Find It Ser.). 24p. (J). pap. 4.99 (***978-0-696-23728-7(8)***) Meredith Bks.

Meredith Books Staff, ed. Batman Sticker Storybook. 2008. 16p. pap. 5.99 (***978-0-696-23960-1(4)***) Meredith Bks.

—Doom in A Box. 2008. 24p. pap. 3.99 (***978-0-696-23956-4(6)***) Meredith Bks.

—Heads or Tails. 2008. 24p. pap. 3.99 (***978-0-696-23959-5(0)***) Meredith Bks.

—Madagascar Activity Book & Floor Puzzle. 10p. (J). bds. 12.95 (978-0-696-22701-1(0)) Meredith Bks.

—Madagascar Stencil Activity Book with Stickers. 22p. (J). bds. 12.95 (978-0-696-22702-8(9)) Meredith Bks.

—Race Against Crime. 2008. 24p. pap. 3.99 (***978-0-696-23958-8(2)***) Meredith Bks.

—Robo-Monster. 2008. 24p. pap. 3.99 (***978-0-696-23957-1(4)***) Meredith Bks.

Meredith Books Staff & Marvel Comics Staff. Fantastic Four Big Color & Activity Book: With Stickers. Curry, Don, ed. 2005. (Illus.). 64p. (J). pap., act. bk. ed. 2.99 (978-0-696-22677-9(4)) Meredith Bks.

—The Incredible Hulk Jumbo Color & Activity Book. Curry, Don, ed. 2005. (Illus.). 400p. (J). (ps-7). pap., act. bk. ed. 5.99 (978-0-696-22654-0(5)) Meredith Bks.

—X-Men Jumbo Color & Activity Book. Curry, Don, ed. 2005. (Illus.). 400p. (J). (ps-7). pap., act. bk. ed. 5.99 (978-0-696-22655-7(3)) Meredith Bks.

Meredith, Randy. Marvel: Mix & Match Storybook. 2006. (Illus.). 8p. spiral bd. 8.95 (978-1-57791-299-6(3) , Penny Candy Pr.) Brighter Minds Children's Publishing.

Meredith, Randy. My First Marvel Super Hero Factbook. 2006. (Marvel Ser.). 5p. (J). bds. 8.95 (***978-1-57791-298-9(5)***) Brighter Minds Children's Publishing.

Metaphrog. Louis: Red Letter Day. 2000. (Illus.). 68p. pap. 15.95 (978-0-9534932-5-8(3)) Diamond Bk. Distributors.

Metroid, 2 vols., Vol. 1. 2005. (Illus.). 192p. (YA). pap. 9.99 (978-1-59182-738-2(8)) TOKYOPOP, Inc.

Mickey Mouse Adventures, Vol. 5. 2005. 128p. (YA). pap. 7.95 (978-0-911903-70-6(4)) Gemstone Publishing, Inc.

Mignola, Mike. The Chained Coffin & Others, Vol. 3. (Hellboy Ser.). (Illus.). 168p. (YA). pap. 17.95 (978-1-59307-091-5(8)) Dark Horse Comics.

—Hellboy: La Mano Derecha del Destino, Abuli, Enrique Sanchez, tr. from ENG. 2004. Orig. Title: Hellboy: the Right Hand of Doom. (SPA., Illus.). 56p. pap. 12.95 (978-1-59497-032-0(7)) Public Square Bks.

—The Right Hand of Doom. 2nd ed. (Hellboy Ser.: Vol. 4). (Illus.). 144p. pap. 17.95 (978-1-59307-093-9(4)) Dark Horse Comics.

—Wake the Devil, Vol. 2. (Hellboy Ser.). (Illus.). 144p. (YA). pap. 17.95 (978-1-59307-095-3(0)) Dark Horse Comics.

Mihara, Mitsukazu. Beautiful People. 2006. (Illus.). pap. 9.99 (978-1-59816-243-1(8) , Tokyopop Adult) TOKYOPOP, Inc.

—Doll, Vol. 1. 2004. (Illus.). 192p. pap. 9.99 (978-1-59182-710-8(8) , Tokyopop Adult) TOKYOPOP, Inc.

Mihara, Mitsukazu, illus. & creator. Doll. Mihara, Mitsukazu, creator. rev. ed. 2005. Vol. 4. 192p. pap. 9.99 (978-1-59532-390-3(2)); Vol. 5. 176p. pap. 9.99 (978-1-59532-391-0(0)) TOKYOPOP, Inc. (Tokyopop Adult).

Millar, Mark. Ultimate Fantastic Four Volume 5: Crossover TPB: Crossover TPB. 2006. (Illus.). 144p. pap. 12.99 (978-0-7851-1802-2(0)) Marvel Enterprises, Inc.

Millar, Mark & Johns, Geoff. The Ultimate Collection, Vol. 1. 2006. (Illus.). 336p. pap. 24.99 (978-0-7851-2187-9(0)) Marvel Enterprises, Inc.

Millar, Mark & Romita, John. Enemy of the State, Vol. 2. 2006. (Illus.). 176p. pap. 16.99 (978-0-7851-1627-1(3)) Marvel Enterprises, Inc.

Miller, Frank. Batman: The Dark Knight Returns. Miller, Frank, illus. 2002. (Illus.). 22.40 (978-1-4046-2249-4(7)) Book Wholesalers, Inc.

—The Big Guy & Rusty the Boy Robot. 2007. (Illus.). 80p. (YA). (gr. 3 up). pap. 14.95 (978-1-56971-201-6(8)) Dark Horse Comics.

Milligan, Peter. Good Omens. Allred, Mike, illus. 2003. (X-Statix Ser.). 128p. (YA). 11.99 (978-0-7851-1059-0(3)) Marvel Enterprises, Inc.

—X-Force: Famous, Mutant & Mortal. Allred, Mike, illus. 2003. (X-Statix Ser.). 352p. (YA). 29.99 (978-0-7851-1023-1(2)) Marvel Enterprises, Inc.

Millionaire, Tony. Sock Monkey: the Inches Incident: The Inches Incident. 2007. 88p. (J). pap. 12.95 (***978-1-59307-842-3(0)***) Dark Horse Comics.

Milton, Fred, et al. Walt Disney's Comics & Stories #670. 2006. 64p. pap. 6.95 (978-1-888472-28-8(6)) Gemstone Publishing, Inc.

Min, Suh Park. Blazin' Barrels, Vol. 2. Park, Min-Seo, illus. 2nd rev. ed. 2005. pap. 9.99 (978-1-59532-559-4(X) , Tokyopop Kids) TOKYOPOP, Inc.

Minsky, Terri, creator. Lizzie Mcguire Box 1. 2005. (Illus.). 384p. pap. 19.99 (978-1-59816-063-5(X) , Tokyopop Kids) TOKYOPOP, Inc.

—Lizzie Mcguire Cine-Manga Vol. 11: In Miranda, Lizzie Does Not Trust & the Longest Yard. 2005. (Illus.). 192p. pap. 7.99 (978-1-59532-282-1(5) , Tokyopop Kids) TOKYOPOP, Inc.

Mitsui-Kids. A Duel on the Dark Side, 3 vols. Shogakukan, ed. 2004. (Teen Ser.). (Illus.). 96p. (J). pap. 7.99 (978-1-59532-064-3(4) , Tokyopop Kids) TOKYOPOP, Inc.

Mitter, Matt. Fisher Price Let's Meet Firefighter Cheryl. SI Artists, illus. 2007. 10p. (J). bds. 6.99 (***978-0-7944-1292-0(0)***) Reader's Digest Assn., Inc., The.

—Fisher Price Let's Meet Police Officer Patrick. SI Artists, illus. 2007. 10p. (J). bds. 6.99 (***978-0-7944-1293-7(9)***) Reader's Digest Assn., Inc., The.

Miyasaka, Kaho. Kare First Love, Vol. 3. Miyasaka, Kaho, illus. 2005. (Kare First Love Ser.). (Illus.). 192p. (YA). pap. 9.99 (978-1-59116-701-3(9)) Viz Media.

—Kare First Love. (Kare First Love Ser.). Vol. 6. 2005. (Illus.). 200p. pap. 9.99 (978-1-4215-0139-0(2)); Vol. 8. 2006. 208p. (YA). pap. 9.99 (978-1-4215-0546-6(0)); Vol. 9. 2006. 208p. (YA). pap. 9.99 (978-1-4215-0547-3(9)) Viz Media.

Miyazaki, Hayao. The Art of Howl's Moving Castle. 2005. (Art of Howl's Moving Castle Ser.). (Illus.). 256p. (YA). pap. 34.99 (978-1-4215-0049-2(3)) Viz Media.

—The Art of Porco Rosso. Searleman, Eric, ed. Miyazaki, Hayao, illus. 2005. (Porco Rosso Ser.). (Illus.). 208p. (YA). 34.99 (978-1-59116-704-4(3)) Viz Media.

—Howl's Moving Castle Film Comic, Vol. 2. 2005. (Howl's Moving Castle Film Comics Ser.). 176p. (YA). pap. 9.99 (978-1-4215-0092-8(2)) Viz Media.

—Howl's Moving Castle Film Comic, Vol. 3. Miyazaki, Hayao, illus. 2005. (Howl's Moving Castle Film Comics Ser.). 176p. (YA). pap. 9.99 (978-1-4215-0093-5(0)) Viz Media.

—Howl's Moving Castle Film Comics, Vol. 1. 2005. (Howl's Moving Castle Film Comics Ser.). (Illus.). 176p. (YA). pap. 9.99 (978-1-4215-0091-1(4)) Viz Media.

—Howls Moving Castle Picture Book. Miyazaki, Hayao, illus. 2005. (Howl's Moving Castle Picture Book Ser.). 184p. (YA). 19.99 (978-1-4215-0090-4(6)) Viz Media.

—Kiki's Delivery Service Film Comic. 2006. (Kiki's Delivery Service Film Comics Ser.). 208p. (YA). Vol. 3. pap. 9.99 (978-1-59116-784-6(1)); Vol. 4. pap. 9.99 (978-1-4215-0595-4(9)) Viz Media.

—Kiki's Delivery Service Picture Book, Vol. 1. 2006. (Kiki's Delivery Service Film Comics Ser.). 208p. (YA). pap. 14.99 (978-1-4215-0596-1(7)) Viz Media.

—Miyazaki's Spirited Away. Miyazaki, Hayao, illus. 2002. (Spirited Away Ser.). (Illus.). 17.51 (978-1-4046-2807-6(X)); 17.51 (978-1-4046-2808-3(8)); 17.51 (978-1-4046-2809-0(6)); 17.51 (978-1-4046-2789-5(8)); 17.51 (978-1-4046-2587-7(9)) Book Wholesalers, Inc.

—Princess Mononoke Film Comics, Vol. 1. 2006. (Princess Mononoke Film Comics Ser.). (YA). 9.99 (978-1-4215-0597-8(5)) Viz Media.

Miyazaki, Hayao, illus. & creator. My Neighbor Totoro Picture Book. Miyazaki, Hayao, creator. 2005. (Art of My Neighbor Totoro Ser.). 152p. (YA). 14.99 (978-1-59116-595-8(4)) Viz Media.

Mizobuchi, Makoto & Uemaya, Michiro. Zoids New Century. 2002. (Zoids Ser.). (Illus.). 200p. (YA). pap. 9.95 (978-1-56931-786-0(0)) Viz Media.

Mizuno, Ryou & Sasameyuki, Jun. Louie the Rune Soldier, Vol. 2. 2004. (Illus.). 168p. (YA). pap. (978-1-4139-0105-4(0)) ADV Manga.

Mizutani, Yuzu. Magical x Miracle. 2006. (Illus.). pap. 9.99 (978-1-59816-328-5(0) , Tokyopop Kids) TOKYOPOP, Inc.

Moeller, Christopher. A League of One. rev. ed. 2002. (Justice League Adventures Ser.). (Illus.). 112p. pap. 14.95 (978-1-56389-923-2(X)) DC Comics.

Moench, Doug, et al. Essential Moon Knight, Vol. 1. 2006. (Illus.). 536p. pap. 16.99 (978-0-7851-2092-6(0)) Marvel Enterprises, Inc.

Monda, Joseph, creator. The Unnaturals. 2007. (Illus.). 32p. (YA). 3.00 (***978-0-615-15138-0(8)***) Wild Mind Creations.

Mongillo, Michael. The Philistine: Anthology/Chronology, 1 book. Zittel, Michael, illus. 2003. 216p. (YA). pap. 24.95 (978-0-9743086-0-9(9)) United Comics.

Monica, Carol. Fisher Price Let's Go on a Class Trip Lift the Flap. SI Artists, illus. 2007. 10p. (J). bds. 8.99 (***978-0-7944-1291-3(2)***) Reader's Digest Assn., Inc., The.

Monsho, Seikaino & Yoshinaga, Aya. Crest of the Stars, 3 vols., Vol. 1. 2004. (Illus.). pap. 9.99 (978-1-59182-857-0(0) , Tokyopop Adult) TOKYOPOP, Inc.

Monsters Inc. Read Along. 2001. (J). pap. 9.98 incl. audio compact disk (978-0-7634-1828-1(5)) Walt Disney Records.

Montes, Graciela. Federico Dice No. (SPA.). 16p. pap. 9.95 (978-950-07-1158-6(3)) Editorial Sudamericana S.A. ARG. *Dist:* Distribooks, Inc.

—Federico Se Hizo Pis. (SPA.). pap. 9.95 (978-950-07-0851-7(5)) Editorial Sudamericana S.A. ARG. *Dist:* Distribooks, Inc.

Moon, Fabio. Ursula. Pinto, Joan De Sola & Pinto, Guilherme, trs. 2004. (Illus.). 72p. pap. 9.95 (978-1-932051-22-3(8)) A i T/Planet Lar.

Mooney, E. S. Mojo & Mini-Mo. 2003. (gr. k-3). lib. bdg. 11.80 (978-0-613-66424-0(8)) Tandem Library Bks.

Moore, B. Clay, et al. Put the Book Back on the Shelf: A Belle & Sebastian Anthology. (Illus.). 144p. (YA). pap. 19.99 (978-1-58240-600-8(6)) Image Comics.

Moore, Perry. Hero. rev. ed. 2007. 432p. (gr. 8 up). 16.99 (***978-1-4231-0195-6(2)***) Hyperion Pr.

Morgan, Richard K. Black Widow: the Things They Say about Her TPB: The Things They Say about Her TPB. 2006. (Illus.). 144p. (YA). pap. 15.99 (978-0-7851-1768-1(7)) Marvel Enterprises, Inc.

Mori, Kotaro. Stray Little Devil. 2006. (Illus.). 200p. (YA). Vol. 2. pap. 9.95 (***978-1-59796-044-1(6)***); Vol. 3. pap. 9.95 (***978-1-59796-045-8(4)***) DrMaster Pubns. Inc.

—Stray Little Devil Volume 4. 2007. (Illus.). 200p. (YA). pap. 9.95 (***978-1-59796-046-5(2)***) DrMaster Pubns. Inc.

Morinaga, Ai. Your & My Secret, Vol.1. 2004. (Illus.). 184p. (YA). pap. (978-1-4139-0143-6(3)) ADV Manga.

Morioka, Hiroyuki. Seikai Trilogy: Banner of the Stars: The Shape of Bonds, 3 vols., Vol. 2. Ono, Toshihiro, illus. rev. ed. 2004. (Seikai Trilogy). 200p. pap. 9.99 (978-1-59182-858-7(9) , Tokyopop Adult) TOKYOPOP, Inc.

Morita, Hiroyuki. The Cat Returns Picture Book. Searleman, Eric, ed. Hiiragi, Aoi, illus. 2007. (Cat Returns Ser.). 112p. (YA). 14.99 (***978-1-4215-1498-7(2)***) Viz Media.

Moriyama, Daisuke. Chrono Crusade. 2004. (Illus.). (YA). Vol. 1. 190p. pap. (978-1-4139-0084-2(4)); Vol. 2. 200p. pap. (978-1-4139-0104-7(2)); Vol. 3. 198p. pap. (978-1-4139-0045-3(3)) ADV Manga.

Morris, Kimberly. Be Mine: Junior Novel. 12th rev. ed. 2005. (That's So Raven Ser.: Vol. 12). (Illus.). 144p. (gr. 3-7). pap. 4.99 (978-0-7868-4695-5(X)) Disney Pr.

—Boyfriend Blues: Junior Novel. 11th rev. ed. 2005. (That's So Raven Ser.: Vol. 11). (Illus.). 144p. (gr. 3-7). pap. 4.99 (978-0-7868-4694-8(1)) Disney Pr.

Morrison, Grant. Riot at Xavier's, 4 vols., Vol. 4. Quitely, Frank, illus. 2003. (New X-Men Ser.: Vol. 4). 120p. (YA). 11.99 (978-0-7851-1067-5(4)) Marvel Enterprises, Inc.

Morrison, Grant & Millar, Mark. Skrull Kill Krew TPB. 2006. (Illus.). 120p. pap. 16.99 (978-0-7851-2120-6(X)) Marvel Enterprises, Inc.

Morse, Scott. Magic Pickle vs. the Egg Poacher. 2008. 144p. (J). pap. 5.99 (***978-0-439-87997-2(3)*** , Graphix) Scholastic, Inc.

Morvan, Jean-David. Artifice/Maximum (in)Security, 67 vols. Buchet, Philippe, illus. 2005. 96p. pap. 14.95 (978-1-56163-420-0(4)) NBM Publishing Co.

Moscowitz, Moshe & Resnick, Yael. The Queen of Persia. Sokoloff, David, illus. 2004. 107p. (***978-1-930925-09-0(3)*** , Shazak Productions) Torah Excel.

Muldrow, Diane. Mickey Big Book. 2000. 48p. (J). 12.99 (978-0-7364-1018-2(X)) Disney Pr.

Murakami, Maki. Gamerz Heaven, Vol. 1. 2004. (Illus.). 184p. (YA). pap. (978-1-4139-0202-0(2)) ADV Manga.

—Gravitation, Vol. 11. Murakami, Maki, illus. rev. ed. 2005. (Illus.). 176p. pap. 9.99 (978-1-59532-414-6(3) , Tokyopop Adult) TOKYOPOP, Inc.

Murakami, Maki, creator. Kimi No Unaji ni Kanpai!, Vol. 1. 2005. (Illus.). pap. 9.99 (978-1-59532-317-0(1) , Tokyopop Adult) TOKYOPOP, Inc.

Murase, Sho & Petrucha, Stefan. The Haunted Dollhouse. 3rd rev. ed. 2005. (Nancy Drew Ser.: No. 3). (Illus.). 96p. (J). (gr. 3-7). 12.95 (978-1-59707-009-6(2)) Papercutz.

Murayama, Wataru. Desert Coral, Vol. 1. Spencer, Tomoe, tr. 2004. (Illus.). 200p. (YA). pap. (978-1-4139-0050-7(X)) ADV Manga.

—Desert Coral, Vol. 2. 2004. (Illus.). 186p. (YA). pap. (978-1-4139-0088-0(7)) ADV Manga.

—Kagerou-Nostalgia, Vol. 1. 2004. 186p. pap. (978-1-4139-0053-8(4)) ADV Manga.

Murozumi, Hikaru & Inokuma, Shinobu. The School of Water Business. (Illus.). (YA). 206p. pap. (978-4-09-153102-5(4)); Vol. 4. 2005. (JPN., 205p. mass mkt. (978-4-09-153104-9(0)); Vol. 5. (JPN., 205p. mass mkt. (978-4-09-153105-6(9)) Shogakukan.

Murphy, Stephen & Murphy, Sonia. The Master's Book. Johnson, Shane L., illus. unabr. ed. 2006. (Teenage Mutant Ninja Turtles Ser.: 1). 64p. (J). pap. 4.99 (978-1-4169-0945-3(1) , Simon Spotlight) Simon & Schuster Children's Publishing.

Myers, Janet Nuzum. Critter Jokes & Riddles. Clegg, Dave, illus. 2007. 96p. (J). pap. 4.95 (***978-1-4027-3865-4(X)***) Sterling Publishing Co., Inc.

Myers, Scott. 101 Dumb Dog Deaths. 2001. pap. 10.00 (978-0-9724047-0-9(8)) Myers, Ralph.

Nagai, Tomohiro & Gatou, Shouji. Full Metal Panic Overload, Vol. 4. 2006. 168p. (YA). pap. (978-1-4139-0340-9(1)) ADV Manga.

Naifeh, Ted. Courtney Crumrin & the Night Things. Jones, James Lucas, ed. 2005. (Illus.). 120p. lib. bdg. 19.00 (978-0-606-33365-8(7)) Tandem Library Bks.

Nakahira, Masahiko. Street Fighter Alpha Volume 1. 2007. (Illus.). 200p. (YA). pap. 12.95 (***978-1-897376-50-8(2)***) URON Entertainment Corp. CAN. *Dist:* Diamond Bk. Distributors.

—Street Fighter Alpha Volume 2. 2007. (Illus.). 200p. (YA). pap. 12.95 (***978-1-897376-51-5(0)***) URON Entertainment Corp. CAN. *Dist:* Diamond Bk. Distributors.

—Street Fighter Sakura Ganbaru! Volume 1. 2007. 200p. (YA). pap. 12.95 (***978-1-897376-52-2(9)***) URON Entertainment Corp. CAN. *Dist:* Diamond Bk. Distributors.

Nakajo, Hisaya. Hana-Kimi. 2007. (Hana-Kimi Ser.). 184p. (YA). Vol. 16. pap. 9.99 (978-1-4215-0991-4(1)); Vol. 17. pap. 9.99 (978-1-4215-0992-1(X)) Viz Media.

Nakayama, Bunjuro. Mahoromatic: Automatic Maiden, 4 vols., Vol. 1. Ditama, Bow, illus. 2004. 192p. pap. 9.99 (978-1-59182-729-0(9) , Tokyopop Adult) TOKYOPOP, Inc.

Nanami, Shingo & Tezuka, Kaname. Kamui, Vol. 7. Seto, Dietrich & Yamashita, Shizuki, eds. Yamashita, Satsuki, tr. O'Leary, Keiran & McDougall, Chris, illus. 2007. (Kamui Ser.). 224p. pap. 9.99 (***978-1-59741-054-0(3)***) Broccoli International USA, Inc.

Nanatsuki, Kyoichi. Project Arms, Vol. 13. Nanatsuki, Kyoichi, illus. 2006. (Project Arms Ser.). 208p. (YA). pap. 9.99 (978-1-4215-0502-2(9)) Viz Media.

Nanten, Yutaka, illus. Cowboy Bebop VI. ed. 2005. 192p. pap. 9.99 (978-1-59816-038-3(9)) TOKYOPOP, Inc.

Naruse, Kaori. Pretear Vol. 2: The New Legend of Snow White. 2004. (Illus.). 198p. (YA). pap. (978-1-4139-0145-0(X)) ADV Manga.

Naruse, Kaori & Satou, Junichi. Pretear Vol. 1: The New Legend of Snow White. 2004. (Illus.). 188p. (YA). pap. (978-1-4139-0144-3(1)) ADV Manga.

Nasu, Yukie. Here Is Greenwood. Nasu, Yukie, illus. 2005. (Here Is Greenwood Ser.). (Illus.). (YA). Vol. 2. 216p. pap. 9.99 (978-1-59116-605-4(5)); Vol. 3. 200p. pap. 9.99 (978-1-59116-606-1(3)) Viz Media.

Nasu, Yukie & Smith, Joe. Here Is Greenwood, 1. Nasu, Yukie, illus. 2004. (Here Is Greenwood Ser.). (Illus.). 208p. (YA). pap. 9.99 (978-1-59116-604-7(7)) Viz Media.

Nelahw, Sam. Got Attitude: Celebrate the Inner Sarcastic You. Cider Mill Press Staff, ed. gif. ed. 2007. (Magnetic Wisdom Ser.). (Illus.). 96p. pap. 9.95 (978-1-933662-28-2(X)) Cider Mill Pr. Bk. Pubs. LLC.

Nelly. Nelly Music Manga. (Illus.). 96p. (J). pap. 7.99 (978-1-59182-834-1(1)) TOKYOPOP, Inc.

Neri, Filippo. Steam Park. Piero, Ruggeri, illus. 2006. 44p. 16.95 (978-1-894965-63-7(9)) Simply Read Bks. CAN. *Dist:* Perseus Distribution.

Netcomics & Lee, Youngran. Click, Vol. 4. 2007. (Click (Netcomics) Ser.). (Illus.). 184p. per. 9.99 (***978-1-60009-204-6(7)***) Netcomics.

News Currents Editors, ed. Editorial Cartoons by Kids 1998. 10th anniv. ed. 1998. (Illus.). 200p. (J). (gr. 4-7). pap. 10.95 (978-1-55933-242-2(5)) Zino Pr. Children's Bks.

Ng, Leandro, illus. Passage 2: HIV/AIDS — First Love. 2005. (1 World Manga Ser.: Vol. 2). 40p. pap. 3.99 (978-0-8213-6406-2(5)) World Bank Pubns.

Nguyen, Taohuu. Mighty Mite 3: Good Mites, Bad Mites. Nguyen, Taohuu, illus. 2007. (J). 14.95 (***978-0-9790302-3-9(4)***) Amazing Factory, The.

Nicieza, Fabian. The Blackburne Covenant. 2003. 104p. pap. 12.95 (978-1-56971-889-6(X)) Dark Horse Comics.

—Bosom Buddies. 2006. (Illus.). 144p. (YA). pap. 14.99 (978-0-7851-1869-5(1)) Marvel Enterprises, Inc.

—Right of Power, Vol. 3. 2006. (Illus.). 184p. pap. 17.99 (978-0-7851-1832-9(2)) Marvel Enterprises, Inc.

Nickel, Scott. Backyard Bug Battle: A Buzz Beaker Brainstorm. Smith, Andy J., illus. 2007. (Graphic Sparks Ser.). 33p. (J). (gr. 2-5). lib. bdg. 19.93 (978-1-59889-054-9(9)) Stone Arch Bks.

—Billions of Bats: A Buzz Beaker Brainstorm. Smith, Andy J., illus. 2007. 33p. (J). pap. (***978-1-59889-408-0(0)***) Stone Arch Bks.

—Curse of the Red Scorpion. Harpster, Steve, illus. 2006. (Graphic Sparks Ser.). 33p. (J). 19.93 (978-1-59889-034-1(4)) Stone Arch Bks.

—Double Trouble. Harpster, Steve, illus. 2007. (J). 40p. (***978-1-59889-314-4(9)***); 33p. pap. (***978-1-59889-409-7(9)***) Stone Arch Bks.

—Night of the Homework Zombies. Harpster, Steve, illus. 2006. (Graphic Sparks Ser.). 33p. (J). 19.93 (978-1-59889-035-8(2)) Stone Arch Bks.

Nickel, Scott. The Super-Powered Sneeze. Harpster, Steve, illus. 2007. 33p. (J). pap. (***978-1-59889-411-0(0)***); (gr. 2-4). lib. bdg. 21.26 (***978-1-59889-316-8(5)***) Stone Arch Bks.

Nickel, Scott & Stone Arch Books (Firm : Afton, Minn.) Staff. Billions of Bats: A Buzz Beaker Brainstorm. Smith, Andy J., illus. 2007. (Buzz Beaker Brainstorm Ser.). 40p. (J). (gr. k-4). lib. bdg. 21.26 (***978-1-59889-313-7(0)***) Stone Arch Bks.

Nickelodeon Staff. Nickelodeon Trivia Book. 2007. (Illus.). 144p. (J). (gr. 1 up). spiral bd. 19.99 (978-0-8118-4924-1(4)) Chronicle Bks. LLC.

Nieves, Miguel, et al. Otazine: Manga of Otaku Generation. Duarte, Nicolas Benjamin, ed. Nieves, Miguel et al, illus. ltd. ed. 2004. 160p. (YA). per. 10.00 (978-0-9770461-0-2(9)) Otakorp, Inc.

Niles, Steve. The War of the Worlds. 2005. (Illus.). 48p. 15.99 (978-1-933239-37-8(9)) Diamond Bk. Distributors.

Niles, Steve, et al. Marvel Monsters. 2006. (Illus.). 224p. 20.99 (978-0-7851-2141-1(2)) Marvel Enterprises, Inc.

Nishimori, Hiroyuki. Cheeky Angel, Vol. 8. 2005. (Cheeky Angel Ser.). 192p. (YA). pap. 9.99 (978-1-59116-979-6(8)) Viz Media.

—Cheeky Angel, Vol. 13. Nishimori, Hiroyuki, illus. 2006. (Cheeky Angel Ser.). 208p. (YA). pap. 9.99 (978-1-4215-0447-6(2)) Viz Media.

—Cheeky Angel, Vol. 14. 2006. (Cheeky Angel Ser.). 208p. (YA). pap. 9.99 (978-1-4215-0448-3(0)) Viz Media.

—Cheeky Angel, Volume 17. 2007. (Cheeky Angel Ser.). 192p. (YA). pap. 9.99 (978-1-4215-0886-3(9)) Viz Media.

Nishiyama, Yuriko, illus. & creator. Dragon Voice, Vol. 4. Nishiyama, Yuriko, creator. rev. ed. 2005. 192p. pap. 9.99 (978-1-59532-122-0(5) , Tokyopop Adult) TOKYOPOP, Inc.

—Rebound, Vol. 13. Nishiyama, Yuriko, creator. rev. ed. 2005. 192p. pap. 9.99 (978-1-59532-618-8(9) , Tokyopop Adult) TOKYOPOP, Inc.

No, Yi-Jung, illus. & creator. Visitor. No, Yi-Jung, creator. 2005. 192p. (YA). pap. 9.99 (978-1-59532-342-2(2) , Tokyopop Adult) TOKYOPOP, Inc.

Nocenti, Ann. Typhoid Mary, 4 vols. Romita, John, Jr., illus. 2003. (Daredevil Legends Ser.: Vol. 4). 224p. (YA). pap. 19.99 (978-0-7851-1041-5(0)) Marvel Enterprises, Inc.

North, Ryan. Dinosaur Comics. North, Ryan, illus. 2005. 112p. 14.99 (978-0-7560-0518-4(3)) Teacher's Discovery.

Nutrition Adventures with the Nutri Gang, Race Day, Issue #1: The Nutri Gang. 2007. (J). 2.99 (***978-0-9792383-0-7(7)***) KJ Pubns.

O'Connor, Eddie, et al. Donald Duck Adventures, Vol. 16. 2006. 128p. (YA). pap. 7.95 (978-1-888472-11-0(1)) Gemstone Publishing, Inc.

O'Donnell, Liam. Blackbeard's Sword: The Pirate King of the Carolinas. Spoor, Mike, illus. 2007. (J). 46p. pap. (***978-1-59889-404-2(8)***); 56p. (gr. 3-5). lib. bdg. 23.93 (***978-1-59889-309-0(2)***) Stone Arch Bks.

—Understanding Photosynthesis with Max Axiom, Super Scientist. 2007. (Graphic Library). (Illus.). 32p. (J). (***978-0-7368-7893-7(9)*** , 1264938) Capstone Pr., Inc.

Oeming, Michael Avon. Thor Blood Oath. 2007. (Illus.). 144p. pap. 14.99 (978-0-7851-1852-7(7)) Marvel Enterprises, Inc.

—Thor: Blood Oath HC: Blood Oath HC. 2006. (Illus.). 144p. 19.99 (978-0-7851-2274-6(5)) Marvel Enterprises, Inc.

Ohashi, Kaoru & Kusunoki, Kei. Diabolo, Vol. 3. rev. ed. 2005. (Illus.). 216p. pap. 9.99 (978-1-59532-594-5(8) , Tokyopop Adult) TOKYOPOP, Inc.

Ohkami, Mineko. Dragon Knights, Vol. 24. 24th rev. ed. 2007. 192p. pap. 9.99 (978-1-59816-797-9(9) , Tokyopop Adult) TOKYOPOP, Inc.

—Dragon Knights. Ohkami, Mineko, illus. (Illus.). 210p. Vol. 12. 2004. lib. bdg. 20.90 (978-1-4176-5944-9(0)); Vol. 14. 2004. lib. bdg. 20.90 (978-1-4176-5945-6(9)); Vol. 16. 2004. lib. bdg. 20.90 (978-1-4176-5946-3(7)); Vol. 18. 2005. lib. bdg. 20.90 (978-1-4176-5947-0(5)) Tandem Library Bks.

Ohkami, Mineko, illus. & creator. Dragon Knights, Vol. 19. Ohkami, Mineko, creator. 19th rev. ed. 2005. 192p. pap. 9.99 (978-1-59182-962-1(3) , Tokyopop Adult) TOKYOPOP, Inc.

Ohnogi, Hiroki. Raxephon Novel, Vol. 1. 2005. 200p. (YA). pap. 7.95 (978-1-59796-000-7(4)) DrMaster Pubns. Inc.

Ohnogi, Hiroshi. Rahxephon Novel. 2006. (Illus.). (YA). Vol. 3. 208p. pap. 7.95 (***978-1-59796-002-1(0)***); Vol. 4. 200p. pap. 7.95 (***978-1-59796-003-8(9)***); Vol. 5. 200p. pap. 7.95 (***978-1-59796-004-5(7)***) DrMaster Pubns. Inc.

Okamoto, Kazuhiro. Translucent Volume 1. 2007. (Illus.). 192p. (J). pap. 9.95 (***978-1-59307-647-4(9)***) Dark Horse Comics.

Okonkwo, Chidi, creator. Destiny, Neo Genesis, Vol. 6. 2004. 32p. (YA). 2.95 (978-0-9758863-5-9(5)) Vizione Productions Inc.

Okuda, Hitoshi. The All New Tenchi Muyo!, Vol. 8. 2006. (All New Tenchi Muyo! Ser.). 208p. (YA). pap. 8.95 (978-1-4215-0315-8(8)) Viz Media.

—No Need for Tenchi! Okuda, Hitoshi, illus. (No Need for Tenchi! Ser.). 184p. (YA). Vol. 1. 2nd ed. 2004. pap. 9.99 (978-1-59116-610-8(1)); Vol. 2. 2005. (Illus.). pap. 9.99 (978-1-59116-611-5(X)) Viz Media.

—No Need for Tenchi!, Vol. 6. 2nd ed. 2006. (No Need for Tenchi! Ser.). 208p. (YA). pap. 9.99 (978-1-4215-0280-9(1)) Viz Media.

—No Need for Tenchil, Vol. 8. 2nd ed. 2006. (No Need for Tenchi! Ser.). 208p. (YA). pap. 9.99 (978-1-4215-0591-6(6)) Viz Media.

Okudo, Hitoshi. The All-New Tenchi Muyo!, Vol. 6. Okudo, Hitoshi, illus. 2005. (All New Tenchi Muyo! Ser.). (Illus.). 184p. (YA). (gr. 8-8). pap. 8.95 (978-1-4215-0011-9(6)) Viz Media.

Olsen, Lauri. Pacific Bound: The Adventures of Lewis & Clark. Toonz Animation, ed. 2005. (Illus.). 44p. (J). 18.95 (978-0-9742502-5-0(2)) Gossamer Bks., LLC.

—Pacific Bound: The Adventures of Lewis & Clark. 2004. (Illus.). 46p. (J). per. 15.95 (978-0-9742502-4-3(4)) Gossamer Bks., LLC.

Olson, Nathan. Theodore Roosevelt: Bear of a President. Martin, Cynthia et al, illus. 2007. (Graphic Library). 32p. (J). (gr. 3-5). pap. 7.95 (***978-0-7368-7901-9(3)*** , 1264944) Capstone Pr., Inc.

Omishi, Ray, illus. Sorcerer Hunters Vol. 2: Authentic Relaunch. rev. ed. 2005. 192p. pap. 9.99 (978-1-59532-495-5(X) , Tokyopop Adult) TOKYOPOP, Inc.

—Sorcerer Hunters Authentic Relaunch. 2005. Vol. 1. 208p. pap. 9.99 (978-1-59532-494-8(1)); Vol. 3. 192p. pap. 9.99 (978-1-59532-496-2(8)) TOKYOPOP, Inc. (Tokyopop Adult).

Onion Head Monster Attacks. 2007. (YA). per. 12.95 (***978-0-9793676-0-1(3)***) Friedrich, Paul.

Onion Head Monster Attacks (XL) 2006. per. 19.99 (***978-0-9793676-3-2(8)***) Friedrich, Paul.

Onion Head Monster Bombastic. 2007. (YA). per. 12.95 (***978-0-9793676-1-8(1)***) Friedrich, Paul.

Onion Head Monster Catastrophic. 2007. per. 12.95 (***978-0-9793676-2-5(X)***) Friedrich, Paul.

Optic Nerve. No. 4. 2002. pap. 2.95 (978-1-894937-34-4(1)); No. 8. 2001. pap. 3.50 (978-1-894937-38-2(4)) Drawn & Quarterly Pubns. CAN. *Dist:* Chronicle Bks. LLC.

Orme, David. Boffin Boy & the Deadly Swarm. 2007. (Boffin Boy Ser.). (Illus.). 36p. pap. 7.95 (***978-1-84167-625-8(X)***) Ransom Publishing Ltd. GBR. *Dist:* International Publishers Marketing.

—Boffin Boy & the Ice Caves of Pluto. 2007. (Boffin Boy Ser.). (Illus.). 36p. pap. 7.95 (***978-1-84167-626-5(8)***) Ransom Publishing Ltd. GBR. *Dist:* International Publishers Marketing.

—Boffin Boy & the Invaders from Space. 2007. (Boffin Boy Ser.). (Illus.). 36p. pap. 7.95 (***978-1-84167-613-5(6)***) Ransom Publishing Ltd. GBR. *Dist:* International Publishers Marketing.

—Boffin Boy & the Lost City. 2007. (Boffin Boy Ser.). (Illus.). 36p. pap. 7.95 (***978-1-84167-617-3(9)***) Ransom Publishing Ltd. GBR. *Dist:* International Publishers Marketing.

—Boffin Boy & the Monsters from the Deep. 2007. (Boffin Boy Ser.). (Illus.). 36p. pap. 7.95 (***978-1-84167-615-9(2)***) Ransom Publishing Ltd. GBR. *Dist:* International Publishers Marketing.

—Boffin Boy & the Quest for Wisdom. 2007. (Boffin Boy Ser.). (Illus.). 36p. pap. 7.95 (***978-1-84167-628-9(4)***) Ransom Publishing Ltd. GBR. *Dist:* International Publishers Marketing.

—Boffin Boy & the Red Wolf. 2007. (Boffin Boy Ser.). (Illus.). 36p. pap. 7.95 (***978-1-84167-616-6(0)***) Ransom Publishing Ltd. GBR. *Dist:* International Publishers Marketing.

—Boffin Boy & the Rock Men. 2007. (Boffin Boy Ser.). (Illus.). 36p. pap. 7.95 (***978-1-84167-624-1(1)***) Ransom Publishing Ltd. GBR. *Dist:* International Publishers Marketing.

—Boffin Boy & the Temples of Mars. 2007. (Boffin Boy Ser.). (Illus.). 36p. pap. 7.95 (***978-1-84167-623-4(3)***) Ransom Publishing Ltd. GBR. *Dist:* International Publishers Marketing.

—Boffin Boy & the Time Warriors. 2007. (Boffin Boy Ser.). (Illus.). 36p. pap. 7.95 (***978-1-84167-622-7(5)***) Ransom Publishing Ltd. GBR. *Dist:* International Publishers Marketing.

—Boffin Boy & the Wizard of Edo. 2007. (Boffin Boy Ser.). (Illus.). 36p. pap. 7.95 (***978-1-84167-614-2(4)***) Ransom Publishing Ltd. GBR. *Dist:* International Publishers Marketing.

Oshima, Towa. High School Girls. 2005. (YA). Vol. 4. 200p. pap. 9.95 (978-1-59796-084-7(5)); Vol. 5. (Illus.). 208p. pap. 9.95 (978-1-59796-058-8(6)) DrMaster Pubns. Inc.

Oshima, Towa & Aikawa, Yu. Dark Edge, Vol. 3. 2005. (Illus.). 208p. (YA). pap. 9.95 (978-1-59796-030-4(6)) DrMaster Pubns. Inc.

Ostrander, John, et al. Star Wars': The Stark Hyperspace War. 2003. (Illus.). 120p. (YA). pap. 12.95 (978-1-56971-985-5(3)) Dark Horse Comics.

Otomo, Katsuhiro. Steamboy Ani-Manga, Vol. 2. 2006. (Steam Boy Ani-Manga Ser.). 192p. (YA). pap. 19.99 (978-1-4215-0494-0(4)) Viz Media.

Page, Frank. Sometimes a Squirrel Is Just a Squirrel. 2005. 106p. pap. 9.99 (978-1-4116-6062-5(5)) Lulu.com.

Palazeti, Toulla. My Name Is Neofytos. Wise, Noreen, ed. Landrie, Don, illus. 2000. (Book-a-Day Collection). 32p. (YA). (ps up). pap. 5.95 (978-1-58584-387-9(3)) Huckleberry Pr.

Palookaville. 2001. pap. 3.75 (978-1-894937-42-9(2)); 2001. pap. 3.75 (978-1-894937-39-9(2)); 2000. pap. 3.75 (978-1-894937-41-2(4)); 1999. pap. 3.75 (978-1-894937-40-5(6)) Drawn & Quarterly Pubns. CAN. *Dist:* Chronicle Bks. LLC.

Parham, Keelan. Let's Toon Caricatures. 2003. (Illus.). 128p. per. 18.95 (978-0-9725638-0-2(6)) Lunar Donut Pr.

Park, Sang-Sun, creator. The Tarot Cafe, Vol. 1. 2005. (Illus.). 184p. (YA). pap. 9.99 (978-1-59532-555-6(7) , Tokyopop Adult) TOKYOPOP, Inc.

Parker, Jeff. The Bird, the Beast & the Lizard. 2007. (X-Men: First Class Ser.). 24p. (J). (gr. 2-6). 21.35 (***978-1-59961-398-7(0)***) Spotlight.

—Come Out & Fight Like a (Molecule) Man. 2007. (Fantastic Four Set II Ser.). 24p. (J). (gr. 2-6). 21.35 (***978-1-59961-388-8(3)***) Spotlight.

—Doom, Where's My Car?! 2007. (Fantastic Four Set II Ser.). 24p. (J). (gr. 2-6). 21.35 (***978-1-59961-389-5(1)***) Spotlight.

—Finding Zemo. 2007. (Avengers Ser.). 24p. (J). (gr. 2-6). 21.35 (***978-1-59961-383-3(2)***) Spotlight.

—Law of the Jungle. 2007. (Fantastic Four Set II Ser.). 24p. (J). (gr. 2-6). 21.35 (***978-1-59961-390-1(5)***) Spotlight.

—The Leader Has a Big Head. 2007. (Avengers Ser.). 24p. (J). (gr. 2-6). 21.35 (***978-1-59961-384-0(0)***) Spotlight.

—A Life of the Mind. 2007. (X-Men: First Class Ser.). (ENG.). 24p. (J). (gr. 2-6). lib. bdg. 21.35 (***978-1-59961-399-4(9)***) Spotlight.

—The Master of Sound. 2007. (Fantastic Four Set II Ser.). 24p. (J). (gr. 2-6). 21.35 (***978-1-59961-391-8(3)***) Spotlight.

—The Masters of Evil. 2007. (Avengers Ser.). 24p. (J). (gr. 2-6). 21.35 (***978-1-59961-385-7(9)***) Spotlight.

—The Replacements. 2007. (Avengers Ser.). 24p. (J). (gr. 2-6). 21.35 (***978-1-59961-386-4(7)***) Spotlight.

—Seeing Red. 2007. (X-Men: First Class Ser.). 24p. (J). (gr. 2-6). 21.35 (***978-1-59961-400-7(6)***) Spotlight.

—X-Men 101. 2007. (X-Men: First Class Ser.). 24p. (J). (gr. 2-6). 21.35 (***978-1-59961-401-4(4)***) Spotlight.

Parker, Jeff, et al. Marvel Romance Redux: Another Kind of Love. 2007. (Illus.). 168p. pap. 13.99 (978-0-7851-2090-2(4)) Marvel Enterprises, Inc.

Pauline Comics Series, 10 bks., Set. Incl. James Alberione Vol. 10 : Hero for the Gospel. Richards, Virginia Helen, ed. Wickenhiser, Mary D., tr. 80p. (gr. 5-9). 1996. pap. 2.95 (978-0-8198-3964-0(7)); Vol. 1. St. Maximilian Kolbe. Laferte, Jean-Marie & Jeanson, Brigitte. Trouve', Marianne L., tr. 32p. (gr. 3-8). 1995. pap. 1.95 (978-0-8198-6978-4(3)); Vol. 3. St. Elizabeth. Lang, Justin & Wehrung, Juliette. Trouve', Marianne L., tr. Retailleau, Jean, illus. 32p. (gr. 3-8). 1995. pap. 1.95 (978-0-8198-6981-4(3) , 332-325); Vol. 4. St. Joan of Arc. Berthier, Rene & Segault, Marie. Trouve', Marianne L., tr. Le Sourd, Bruno, illus. 32p. (gr. 3-8). 1995. pap. 1.95 (978-0-8198-6975-3(9)); Vol. 5. St. Clare of Assisi. Dhombre, Pierre. Trouve', Marianne L., tr. De La Fuente, Victor, illus. 32p. (gr. 3-8). 1995. pap. 1.95 (978-0-8198-6976-0(7)); Vol. 6. St. Martin. Trouve', Marianne L. & Maric, Raymond, trs. Frisano, Pierre & Alluard, Marie, illus. 32p. (gr. 3-8). 1995. pap. 1.95 (978-0-8198-6980-7(5) , 332-324); Vol. 7. St. Bernadette. Berthier, Rene & Sigault, Marie. Trouve', Marianne L., tr. Garel, Roland, illus. 32p. (gr. 3-8). 1995. pap. 1.95 (978-0-8198-6977-7(5)); Vol. 8. St. Vincent de Paul. Garel, Roland. Trouve', Marianne L., tr. 32p. (gr. 3-8). 1995. pap. 1.95 (978-0-8198-6982-1(1)); Vol. 9. St. Bernard of Clairvaux. Monk of Citeaux Staff. Trouve', Marianne L., tr. De La Fuente, Victor, illus. 32p. (gr. 3-8). 1995. pap. 1.95 (978-0-8198-6979-1(1) , 332-323); (J). Set pap. 18.45 (978-0-8198-5903-7(6)) Pauline Bks. & Media.

Peach-Pit. Dear's, Vol. 2. Peach-Pit & Peach-Pit, illus. Peach-Pit, illus. 2nd rev. ed. 2005. (Illus.). pap. 9.99 (978-1-59532-309-5(0) , Tokyopop Adult) TOKYOPOP, Inc.

—Dears, Vol. 3. 3rd rev. ed. 2005. (Illus.). pap. 9.99 (978-1-59532-310-1(4) , Tokyopop Adult) TOKYOPOP, Inc.

—DearS. 2006. Vol. 7. 7th rev. ed. (Illus.). pap. 9.99 (978-1-59816-185-4(7)); Vol. 8. 8th rev. ed. pap. 9.99 (978-1-59816-861-7(4)) TOKYOPOP, Inc. (Tokyopop Adult).

PEACH-PIT. DearS Official Fan Book. 2006. (Illus.). 192p. pap. 9.99 (978-1-59816-493-0(7) , Tokyopop Adult) TOKYOPOP, Inc.

Pearce, Jacqueline. Manga Touch. 2007. (Orca Currents Ser.). 112p. (YA). (gr. 5 up). pap. (***978-1-55143-746-0(5)***); lib. bdg. (***978-1-55143-748-4(1)***) Orca Bk. Pubs.

Pef. Belle lisse poire du prince De. pap. 16.95 (978-2-07-054806-4(0)) Gallimard, Editions FRA. *Dist:* Distribooks, Inc.

Penny, Anne. Scraper. 2006. (Illus.). 56p. pap. (***978-1-84401-921-2(7)***) Athena Pr.

C D

Perry, Fred. Gold Digger Pocket Manga, Vol. 8. 2006. (Illus.). 200p. (YA). pap. 9.99 (978-0-9768043-0-7(1)) Antarctic Pr., Inc.

Pet Robots. 2007. (J). per. 19.95 (978-0-9789168-2-4(4)) Blue Dream Studios.

Peters, Andrew & Player, Stephen. Ed & the Witchblood. 2005. (Illus.). (J). 18.00 (978-0-340-86551-4(2) , Hodder & Stoughton) Hodder General Publishing Division GBR. *Dist:* Trafalgar Square Publishing.

Peters, Andrew Fusek & Player, Stephen. Ed & the River of the Damned. 2005. (Illus.). (J). pap. 9.99 (978-0-340-86637-5(3) , Hodder & Stoughton) Hodder General Publishing Division GBR. *Dist:* Trafalgar Square Publishing.

—Ed & the Witchblood. 2005. (Illus.). (J). pap. 9.99 (978-0-340-86557-6(1) , Hodder & Stoughton) Hodder General Publishing Division GBR. *Dist:* Trafalgar Square Publishing.

Peterson, Brandon & Brereton, Dan. Giant Killer. 2006. (Illus.). 128p. (YA). pap. 14.99 (978-1-58240-539-1(5)) Image Comics.

Peterson, Scott. New Hero in Town. 2000. (gr. k-3). lib. bdg. 10.95 (978-0-613-32879-1(5)) Tandem Library Bks.

—Royally Enchanted Cartoon Tales. 4th rev. ed. 2006. (Disney Princess Ser.: Vol. 44). (Illus.). 192p. (gr. 1-5). 14.99 (978-0-7868-3715-1(2)) Disney Pr.

—Splashtacular Cartoon Tales. 3rd rev. ed. 2006. (Disneys Ser.: Vol. 3). (Illus.). 192p. (gr. 1-17). 14.99 (978-0-7868-3610-9(5)) Disney Pr.

Petrie, Doug. Ring of Fire. 2000. (gr. 7-12). lib. bdg. 18.75 (978-0-613-50992-3(7)) Tandem Library Bks.

Petrucha, Stefan. The Charmed Bracelet. Ross, Vaughn, illus. 2006. (Nancy Drew Ser.). 96p. (J). rev. ed 12.95 (978-1-59707-037-9(8)); 7th rev. ed. pap. 7.95 (978-1-59707-036-2(X)) Papercutz.

—The Girl Who Wasn't There. Murase, Sho, illus. 4th rev. ed. 2006. (Nancy Drew Ser.: No. 4). 96p. (J). 12.95 (978-1-59707-013-3(0)); pap. 7.95 (978-1-59707-012-6(2)) Papercutz.

—Global Warning. Murase, Sho, illus. 8th rev. ed. 2007. (Nancy Drew Ser.: No. 8). 112p. (J). 12.95 (978-1-59707-052-2(1)); pap. 7.95 (978-1-59707-051-5(3)) Papercutz.

Petrucha, Stefan & Murase, Sho. The Demon of River Heights. 2005. (Nancy Drew Ser.: No. 1). (Illus.). 96p. (J). (gr. 3-9). pap. 7.95 (978-1-59707-000-3(9)) Papercutz.

—Demon of River Heights. 2005. (Nancy Drew Ser.: No. 1). (Illus.). 96p. (J). (gr. 3-9). 12.95 (978-1-59707-004-1(1)) Papercutz.

—The Haunted Dollhouse. 3rd rev. ed. 2005. (Nancy Drew Ser.: No. 3). (Illus.). 96p. (J). (gr. 3-7). pap., pap. 7.95 (978-1-59707-008-9(4)) Papercutz.

—Mr. Cheeters Is Missing. 6th rev. ed. 2006. (Nancy Drew Ser.: No. 6). (Illus.). 96p. (J). 12.95 (978-1-59707-031-7(9)); pap. 7.95 (978-1-59707-030-0(0)) Papercutz.

—Writ in Stone. 2nd rev. ed. 2005. (Nancy Drew Ser.: No. 2). (Illus.). 96p. (J). (gr. 3-9). 12.95 (978-1-59707-006-5(8)); pap., pap. 7.95 (978-1-59707-002-7(5)) Papercutz.

Petrucha, Stefan, et al. Mickey Mouse Adventures, Vol. 7. 2006. 128p. (YA). pap. 7.95 (978-0-911903-92-8(5)) Gemstone Publishing, Inc.

Pettinato, Laura. Thirteen Americas: American Revolution & Constitution. Tiwari, Saral, illus. 2004. (J). 18.95 (978-0-9742502-7-4(9)) Gossamer Bks., LLC.

—Thirteen Americas: The Declaration of Independence. Tiwari, Saral, illus. 2nd ed. 2004. (J). lib. bdg. (978-0-9742502-6-7(0)) Gossamer Bks., LLC.

Peyer, Tom. Go Boy 7 Vol. 1: Ready Set Go! 2004. 96p. pap. 12.95 (978-1-56971-937-4(3)) Dark Horse Comics.

Phillips, Samantha. Crow: Part 1, Vol. 1. 2006. (ENG.). 24p. (YA). 3.50 (978-0-9785891-0-3(6) , 0001) MANGA-CANDY, LLC.

Pierce, Terry. Goofy Knock-Knocks. 2005. (Illus.). 96p. pap. 4.95 (978-1-4027-2421-3(7)) Sterling Publishing Co., Inc.

Pilkey, Dav. El Capitan Calzoncillos la Ridicula Historia De. 2008. 176p. (J). pap. 4.99 (*978-0-545-02583-6(4) , Scholastic en Espanol) Scholastic, Inc.

—Captain Underpants & the Attack of the Talking Toilets. ed. 2005. (Captain Underpants Ser.: No. 2). (Illus.). 140p. (J). lib. bdg. 15.00 (978-1-59054-657-4(1)) Fitzgerald Bks.

—Captain Underpants & the Attack of the Talking Toilets. collector's ed. 2007. 144p. (J). pap. 9.99 (*978-0-545-02727-4(6)) Scholastic, Inc.

—Captain Underpants & the Big, Bad Battle of the Bionic Booger Boy Pt. 1: The Night of the Nasty Nostril Nuggets. ed. 2005. (Captain Underpants Ser.: No. 6). (Illus.). 176p. (J). lib. bdg. 15.00 (978-1-59054-682-6(2)) Fitzgerald Bks.

—Captain Underpants & the Preposterous Plight of the Purple Potty People. 2006. 176p. (J). 19.99 (978-0-439-90381-3(5) , Blue Sky Pr., The) Scholastic, Inc.

Pilkey, Dav. Captain Underpants Books 1-4 Boxset. 2007. (J). pap. 19.96 (*978-0-545-02287-3(8) , Blue Sky Pr., The) Scholastic, Inc.

Pipe, Jim. The Race to the South Pole. 2006. (Stories from History Ser.). 48p. (J). 14.95 (*978-0-7696-4722-7(7)); pap. 6.95 (*978-0-7696-4702-9(2)) School Specialty Publishing.

Plaka, Christina. Yonen Buzz. 2006. (Illus.). (YA). pap. 9.99 (978-1-59816-403-9(1) , Tokyopop Adult) TOKYOPOP, Inc.

Plaka, Christina, illus. Yonen Buzz, Vol. 2. 2006. (YA). pap. 9.99 (978-1-59816-404-6(X) , Tokyopop Adult) TOKYOPOP, Inc.

Plan Nine Christmas Annual 2000. 2000. (Christmas Annual Ser.). 100p. pap. 14.95 (978-1-929462-21-6(2)) Plan Nine Publishing, Inc.

PM Seeker Series #8 Jesus, Someone Who Cares. 2005. (J). pap. 2.95 (978-0-9749339-6-2(1)) PowerMark Productions.

Pokemon Advanced. 2005. 39.98 incl. DVD (978-1-4215-0214-4(3)) Viz Media.

Polette, Nancy. Gifted or Goof Off? Fact & Fiction of the Famous. 2004. (J). pap. 11.95 (978-1-931334-23-5(4)) Pieces of Learning.

Ponti, James. Psyched. 10th rev. ed. 2005. (That's So Raven Ser.: Vol. 10). (Illus.). 144p. (gr. 3-7). pap. 4.99 (978-0-7868-4693-1(3)) Disney Pr.

Pope, Paul. Escapo: A Life Affirming Romance Set in a Fin-de-Siecle Circus. 1999. (Illus.). 112p. (YA). pap. 9.95 (978-1-882402-14-4(6)) NBM Publishing Co.

The Power of Friendship. 2005. (W. I. T. C. H. Graphic Novels Ser.: Bk. 1). (Illus.). 128p. (gr. 3-7). pap. 4.99 (978-0-7868-3674-1(1) , Volo) Hyperion Bks. for Children.

PowerMark 3-pk Issues 10-12. 2004. (YA). 7.95 (978-0-9725121-6-9(0)) PowerMark Productions.

PowerMark Issue 1 Vol. 1: The Mission, 3 vols. 2001. 40p. (J). pap. 2.95 (978-0-9705669-0-4(5)) PowerMark Productions.

PowerMark Issue 3 Vol. 1, Issue 3: Under Fire. 2001. 32p. (J). pap. 2.95 (978-0-9705669-2-8(1)) PowerMark Productions.

Price, Roger & Stern, Leonard. Madagascar Mad Libs. 2005. (Illus.). 48p. (J). (gr. 3-7). pap. 3.99 (978-0-8431-1588-8(2) , Price Stern Sloan) Penguin Group (USA) Inc.

Priddy, Joel. Pulpatoon Pilgrimage. 2002. (Illus.). 160p. (gr. 11 up). pap. 12.95 (978-0-9721794-0-9(2)) AdHouse Bks.

Priest, Christopher. Brothers & Keepers. 2005. (Captain America & the Falcon Ser.: Vol. 2). (Illus.). 168p. (YA). pap. 17.99 (978-0-7851-1568-7(4)) Marvel Enterprises, Inc.

Prophesy of Destiny Vol. 1: Fate. 2002. (YA). per. 12.95 (978-0-9722899-0-0(9)) Moonation.

Punch, Monkey, creator. Lupin III Vol. 2: World's Most Wanted. 2nd rev. ed. 2004. (Illus.). 192p. pap. 9.99 (978-1-59532-071-1(7) , Tokyopop Adult) TOKYOPOP, Inc.

Purvis, Leland. Pubo. 2003. 96p. (YA). pap. 9.95 (978-1-56971-970-1(5)) Dark Horse Comics.

Pyle, Kevin C. Blindspot. 2007. (Illus.). (*978-1-4287-3845-4(2)) Holt, Henry & Co.

Quantz, Daniel. Duel to the Death with the Vulture. 2006. (Illus.). (J). (gr. 2-6). 21.35 (978-1-59961-012-2(4)) Spotlight.

—Face-to-Face with the Lizard! 2006. (Illus.). (J). (gr. 2-6). 21.35 (978-1-59961-014-6(0)) Spotlight.

—Marked for Destruction by Dr. Doom! 2006. (Illus.). (J). (gr. 2-6). 21.35 (978-1-59961-015-3(9)) Spotlight.

—Nothing Can Stop the Sandman! 2006. (Illus.). (J). (gr. 2-6). 21.35 (978-1-59961-016-0(7)) Spotlight.

—Unmasked by Doctor Octopus! 2006. (Illus.). (J). (gr. 2-6). 21.35 (978-1-59961-010-8(8)) Spotlight.

The Quest. 2nd ed. 2003. 170p. (YA). per. 10.95 (978-0-9713292-7-0(3)) Aim Higher Bks.

The Quest. 1999. (Dragon Ball Z Tattoo Bks.). (Illus.). 17p. (J). (gr. 1-2). pap. (978-0-7666-0543-5(4)) Modern Publishing.

Quinn, Zoe. The Caped 6th Grader: Lightning Strikes! 2006. (Illus.). 128p. (J). (gr. 4-7). lib. bdg. 11.99 (978-0-385-90306-6(5) , Yearling) Random Hse. Children's Bks.

Quino. Mafalda. (SPA., Illus.). 2003. 88p. (978-950-515-609-2(X)); 2002. 94p. (978-950-515-602-3(2)); 2002. 94p. (978-950-515-603-0(0)); 2002. 94p. (978-950-515-604-7(9)); 2002. 94p. (978-950-515-605-4(7)); 2002. 94p. (978-950-515-606-1(5)); 2002. 94p. (978-950-515-607-8(3)); 2002. 94p. (978-950-515-608-5(1)); 2002. 94p. (978-950-515-610-8(3)); 2002. 94p. (J). (978-950-515-601-6(2)) De La Flor.

—Mafalda. (SPA., Illus.). 94p. 12.95 (978-84-264-4503-2(9)) Editorial Lumen ESP. *Dist:* Distribooks, Inc.

—Mafalda. Quino, illus. 2000. (SPA., Illus.). (J). 94p. 12.95 (978-84-264-4500-1(4)); Vol. 1. 96p. 12.95 (978-84-264-4501-8(2)); Vol. 2. 96p. 12.95 (978-84-264-4502-5(0)); Vol. 3. 94p. 12.95 (978-84-264-4504-9(7)); Vol. 5. 94p. 12.95 (978-84-264-4505-6(5)); Vol. 6. 94p. 12.95 (978-84-264-4506-3(3)); Vol. 7. 94p. 12.95 (978-84-264-4507-0(1)); Vol. 8. 96p. pap. 12.95 (978-84-264-4508-7(X)); Vol. 9. 92p. 12.95 (978-84-264-4509-4(8)) Editorial Lumen ESP. *Dist:* Distribooks, Inc.

Ra, In-Soo. King of Hell, Vol. 13. Kim, Jae-Hwan, illus. 13th rev. ed. 2006. pap. 9.99 (978-1-59816-061-1(3) , Tokyopop Adult) TOKYOPOP, Inc.

Raab, Ben. The Phantom: Death in the Deep Woods. 2005. 120p. (YA). pap. 14.95 (978-1-933076-06-5(2)) Moonstone.

Ragawa, Mirimo. Baby & Me, Vol. 2. Ragawa, Mirimo, illus. 2006. (Baby & Me Ser.). 208p. (YA). pap. 8.99 (978-1-4215-0573-2(8)) Viz Media.

Ragawa, Mirimo. Baby & Me, Vol. 5. Ragawa, Mirimo, illus. 2007. (Baby & Me Ser.). 192p. (YA). pap. 8.99 (*978-1-4215-1008-8(1)) Viz Media.

Raicht, Mike. Grotesque Adventure of the Green Goblin! 2006. (Illus.). (J). (gr. 2-6). 21.35 (978-1-59961-020-7(5)) Spotlight.

—Kraven the Hunter. 2006. (Illus.). (J). (gr. 2-6). 21.35 (978-1-59961-009-2(4)) Spotlight.

—Menace of Mysterio. 2006. (Illus.). (J). (gr. 2-6). 21.35 (978-1-59961-022-1(1)) Spotlight.

—Where Flies the Beetle... ! 2006. (Illus.). (J). (gr. 2-6). 21.35 (978-1-59961-023-8(X)) Spotlight.

Raiku, Makoto. Zatch Bell! Raiku, Makoto, illus. 2005. (Zatch Bell Ser.). (Illus.). (YA). Vol. 1. 192p. pap. 9.99 (978-1-59116-586-6(5)); Vol. 2. 192p. pap. 9.99 (978-1-59116-588-0(1)); Vol. 3. 200p. pap. 9.99 (978-1-59116-590-3(3)) Viz Media.

Raiku, Makoto, contrib. by. Zatchbell!, Vol. 3. 2005. 200p. 9.99 (978-1-4215-0208-3(9)) Viz Media.

Ralph, Brian. Crum Bums. 2007. (Illus.). 208p. (YA). pap. 15.00 (*978-1-60309-002-5(9)) Top Shelf Productions.

Ramirez, David. Minimonsters (En Español) 2004. (SPA., Illus.). 48p. 23.95 (978-1-59497-073-3(4)) Public Square Bks.

Random House Disney Staff. The Race Is On! 2006. (Illus.). 24p. (J). (ps-2). pap. 5.99 (978-0-7364-2438-7(5) , RH/Disney) Random Hse. Children's Bks.

Random House Staff. Super Friends: Flying High. 2008. (Step into Reading Ser.). 32p. (J). (ps-1). lib. bdg. 11.99 (*978-0-375-95208-1(X) , Random Hse. Bks. for Young Readers) Random Hse. Children's Bks.

Rawson, Dave & Van Horn, William. Walt Disney's Comics & Stories, No. 661. 2005. (Illus.). 64p. (YA). (ps-3). pap. 6.95 (978-0-911903-86-7(0)) Gemstone Publishing, Inc.

Reader's Digest Staff. Disney Fairies Tinker Bell & Friends Storybook & Kaleidoscope Viewer. 2007. (RD Innovative Book & Player Format Ser.). 40p. (J). bds. 24.99 (*978-0-7944-1350-7(1)) Reader's Digest Assn., Inc., The.

—Disney Princess My Pod Storybook & Music Player. Disney & Reader's Digest, illus. 2007. (RD Innovative Book & Player Format Ser.). 40p. 24.99 (*978-0-7944-1301-9(3)) Reader's Digest Assn., Inc., The.

—Disney's Little Einsteins Storybook & Viewer. 2007. (RD Innovative Book & Player Format Ser.). 40p. (J). 24.99 (*978-0-7944-1307-1(2)) Reader's Digest Assn., Inc., The.

—Scooby-Doo Magnetic Mystery. 2007. 16p. (J). 14.99 (*978-0-7944-1353-8(6)) Reader's Digest Assn., Inc., The.

Real Bout High School, Vol. 6. 2005. (YA). pap. 9.99 (978-1-59182-523-4(7)) TOKYOPOP, Inc.

RealBuzz Studios Staff. Hits & Misses. 2007. 128p. (YA). No. 1. pap. 4.97 (978-1-59789-569-9(5)); No. 2. pap. 4.97 (978-1-59789-570-5(9)); No. 3. pap. 4.97 (978-1-59789-571-2(7)); No. 4. pap. 4.97 (978-1-59789-572-9(5)) Barbour Publishing, Inc. (Barbour Bks.).

—Let There Be Lighten Up! 2007. (Goofyfoot Gurl Ser.: No. 1). 96p. (YA). pap. 4.97 (978-1-59789-573-6(3) , Barbour Bks.) Barbour Publishing, Inc.

—Saved / Esther Queen of Persia: Life Camera Action Book 3. 2007. 128p. (YA). pap. 4.97 (978-1-59789-579-8(2) , Barbour Bks.) Barbour Publishing, Inc.

—Serenity — Rave-N-Rant, Vol. 4. 2006. (Serenity Ser.: Vol. 4). (Illus.). 96p. (YA). pap. 7.97 (978-1-59310-873-1(7)) Barbour Publishing, Inc.

—Serenity—Basket Case, Vol. 3. 2006. (Serenity Ser.: Vol. 3). (Illus.). 96p. (YA). pap. 7.97 (978-1-59310-872-4(9)) Barbour Publishing, Inc.

—Serenity—New Bad Girl in Town, Vol. 1. 2005. (Serenity Ser.: 1). (Illus.). 96p. (J). pap. 7.97 (978-1-59310-941-7(5)) Barbour Publishing, Inc.

—Serenity—Snow Biz, Vol. 5. 2006. (Serenity Ser.: Vol. 5). (Illus.). 96p. (YA). pap. 7.97 (978-1-59310-874-8(5) , Barbour Bks.) Barbour Publishing, Inc.

—Serenity—Stepping Out, Vol. 2. 2006. (Serenity Ser.: Vol. 2). (Illus.). 96p. (YA). pap. 7.97 (978-1-59310-942-4(3)) Barbour Publishing, Inc.

—Space Cadet vs Drama Queen Terror from the Tarantula Nebula: Life Camera Action Book 1. 2007. 128p. (YA). pap. 4.97 (978-1-59789-577-4(6) , Barbour Bks.) Barbour Publishing, Inc.

—Sunday Best / Crawling from the Wreckage Life Camera Action BK 2: Life Camera Action Book 2. 2007. 128p. (YA). pap. 4.97 (978-1-59789-578-1(4) , Barbour Bks.) Barbour Publishing, Inc.

—When Dolphins Fly. 2007. (Goofyfoot Gurl Ser.: No. 2). 96p. (YA). pap. 4.97 (978-1-59789-574-3(1) , Barbour Bks.) Barbour Publishing, Inc.

Reed, Brian. Ms. Marvel TPB, Vol. 1. 2007. (Illus.). 136p. pap. 14.99 (978-0-7851-1996-8(5)) Marvel Enterprises, Inc.

Reger, Rob & Parker, Buzz. Emily the Strange, Vol. 1. 2006. (SPA., Illus.). 64p. 19.95 (978-1-59497-188-4(9)) Public Square Bks.

—Emily the Strange Vol. 2: El libro Secreto de Las Cosas Extrañas. 2006. (SPA., Illus.). 64p. reprint ed. 19.95 (978-1-59497-189-1(7)) Public Square Bks.

Reis, Erica, illus. Sea Princess Azuri. 2006. 192p. (YA). (gr. 8 up). pap. 4.99 (978-1-59816-401-5(5) , Tokyopop Kids) TOKYOPOP, Inc.

Reisfeld, Randi, ed. Tweety, 4, Pack. 2001. (Looney Tunes Teacher's Pets Ser.). 32p. (J). lthr. 19.80 (978-0-439-31811-2(4) , Scholastic Paperbacks) Scholastic, Inc.

Reit, Seymour, et al. Great Stories of Courage/[adapted by Seymour Reit ; Art by Ernie Colon]. 2006. pap. (*978-0-8368-7933-9(3) , World Almanac Library) Stevens, Gareth Inc.

Remender, Rick. Girl Afraid Vol. 1. (Illus.). 104p. (YA). pap. 12.99 (978-1-58240-543-8(3)) Image Comics.

Rendon, Daniel & Lobdell, Scott. Mad House. 3rd rev. ed. 2005. (Hardy Boys Graphic Novel Ser.: No. 3). (Illus.). 96p. (J). (gr. 3-7). 12.95 (978-1-59707-011-9(4)) Papercutz.

Rennie, Gordon. Glimmer Rats. 2002. 64p. pap. 14.95 (978-1-56971-698-4(6)) Dark Horse Comics.

—Rain Dogs. 2002. 52p. 14.95 (978-1-56971-697-7(8)) Dark Horse Comics.

Rennie, Gordon, et al. Starship Troopers. 1998. (Illus.). 152p. (YA). pap. 14.95 (978-1-56971-314-3(6)) Dark Horse Comics.

Reynolds, Aaron. The Dung Beetle Bandits. Lervold, Eric, illus. 2007. (J). 40p. (*978-1-59889-317-5(3)); 33p. pap. (*978-1-59889-412-7(9)) Stone Arch Bks.

—The Fortune Cookies of Weevil. Lervold, Eric, illus. 2007. 33p. (J). (*978-1-59889-318-2(1)); pap. (*978-1-59889-413-4(7)) Stone Arch Bks.

Rhim, Ju-Yeon. President Dad, Vol. 4. 4th rev. ed. 2005. (Illus.). 192p. pap. 9.99 (978-1-59532-237-1(X) , Tokyopop Kids) TOKYOPOP, Inc.

Ribeiro, Nelson & Gorelick, Victor. Betty & Veronica in Trendsetter. 2007. (Illus.). 80p. (J). 24.21 (978-1-59961-268-3(2)) Spotlight.

Richards, Christopher, illus. King Arthur & the Knights of the Round Table. 2007. (Graphic Revolve Ser.). 63p. (J). (gr. 4-6). lib. bdg. 22.60 (978-1-59889-048-8(4)) Stone Arch Bks.

Richards, Kitty. Bunnies: Thumper Counts to Ten. Disney Storybook Artists Staff et al, illus. 2007. 16p. (J). (ps-k). 5.99 (978-1-4231-0076-8(X)) Disney Pr.

—Disney's Marie. Disney Storybook Artists Staff, illus. 2006. 40p. (ps-2). 14.99 (978-1-4231-0058-4(1)) Disney Pr.

—Meet the Sparkplugs. Simard, Remy, illus. 2006. (Phonics Comics Ser.). 24p. (J). (gr. 1-17). pap. 3.99 (978-1-58476-419-9(8) , IKIDS) Innovative Kids.

—Twisted Tales, Level 3. Juarez, Fernando, illus. 2006. (Phonics Comics Ser.). 24p. (J). (gr. 1-17). pap. 3.99 (978-1-58476-514-1(3) , IKIDS) Innovative Kids.

Ricketts, Mark & Harris, Tony. The Invincible Iron Man': Disassembled. (Illus.). 144p. pap. 14.99 (978-0-7851-1653-0(2)) Marvel Enterprises, Inc.

Rieber, John Ney. G. I. Joe Reloaded Vol. I: In the Name of Patriotism. Lim, Ron & Millet, Jason, illus. 2005. 144p. pap. 12.95 (978-1-932796-23-0(1)) Devil's Due Publishing, Inc.

Rika, Tanaka. Kilala Princess. 20th rev. ed. 2007. (Illus.). pap. 5.99 (*978-1-59816-768-9(5) , Tokyopop Kids) TOKYOPOP, Inc.

Riley, Chuck, narrated by. Atlantis: The Lost Empire Read Along. 2001. (Illus.). 32p. (J). pap. incl. audio compact disk (978-0-7634-0783-4(6)) Walt Disney Records.

Rimmer, Ian. Catch of the Day. Hansen, Jimmy, illus. 2003. 48p. (gr. 2-7). 12.95 (978-1-84023-495-4(4)) Titan Bks. Ltd. GBR. *Dist:* Random Hse., Inc.

Rinaldi, Francis. Brock Lee & the Salad Kids. 2005. 20p. 7.53 (978-1-4116-5552-2(4)) Lulu.com.

Rinaldo, Jessica. Key to the Gate Book 1. 2005. 324p. (YA). pap. 14.98 (978-1-4116-5262-0(2)) Lulu.com.

Risso, Eduardo. Los misterios de la Luna Roja Vol. 1: Mysteries of the Red Moon. 2006. (SPA.). 48p. pap. 16.95 (978-1-59497-162-4(5)) Public Square Bks.

—Mysteries of the Red Moon, Vol. 3. 2006. (SPA.). 48p. pap. 16.95 (978-1-59497-163-1(3)) Public Square Bks.

Robbins, Trina. The Odyssey: A Graphic Classic. 2002. (Read 180 Ser.). (Illus.). 24p. (J). (978-0-439-12336-5(4)) Scholastic, Inc.

Roberts, Scott. Patty Cake & Friends. 2006. 96p. pap. 12.95 (978-1-59362-030-1(6)) Slave Labor Bks.

Rocks!, Misako. Biker Girl. 2006. (Illus.). 160p. (gr. 5-17). pap. 7.99 (978-0-7868-3676-5(8)) Hyperion Pr.

Rocks!, Misako. Rock & Roll Love. Rocks!, Misako, illus. 2007. 112p. (YA). (gr. 6-9). pap. 7.99 (*978-0-7868-3685-7(7)) Hyperion Pr.

Rodi, Robert & Higgins, John. Identity Disc. 2005. (Marvel Heroes Ser.). (Illus.). 120p. pap. 13.99 (978-0-7851-1567-0(6)) Marvel Enterprises, Inc.

Rodi, Robert & Richards, Cliff. Rogue: Going Rogue. 2005. (X-Men Ser.). (Illus.). 144p. pap. 14.99 (978-0-7851-1336-2(3)) Marvel Enterprises, Inc.

Rodriguez, Robert & Roberson, Chris. Shark Boy & Lava Girl Adventures: Return to Planet Drool. Toader, Alex, illus. 2005. (Shark Boy & Lava Girl Adventures Ser.: Book 2). 150p. (J). (978-1-933104-05-8(8)) Troublemaker Publishing, LP.

Rogow, Debbie & Grasmuck, Sherri. Get Real Comics, Vol. 3. Parker, Charley, illus. 1998. 24p. (Orig.). (J). (gr. 4-8). mass mkt. 1.95 (978-1-891103-02-5(4)) Tides Ctr./Collage, The.

Rohmer, Sax, pseud, et al. Adventure Classics, Vol. 12. Pomplun, Tom, ed. 2005. (Graphic Classics Ser.: Vol. 12). (Illus.). 144p. pap. 11.95 (978-0-9746648-4-2(7) , Graphic Classics) Eureka Productions.

Rolt, Molly. The Chocci-Croc & Other Stories. 2006. 64p. pap. (*978-1-84401-890-1(3)) Athena Pr.

Roman, Annette. 1 World Manga. Ng, Leandro, illus. (1 World Manga Ser.). (YA). Vol. 1. 2005. 40p. pap. 3.99 (978-1-4215-0364-6(6)); Vol. 2. 2005. 40p. pap. 3.99 (978-1-4215-0365-3(4)); Vol. 3. 2006. 40p. pap. 3.99 (978-1-4215-0366-0(2)); Vol. 5. 2007. 240p. pap. 3.99 (978-1-4215-1169-6(X)) Viz Media.

Roman, Steven A. Sunn. Lau, Kevin et al, illus. 2003. 192p. (gr. 7). pap. 9.95 (978-1-59687-814-3(2)) ibooks, Inc.

Rosa, Don, et al. Uncle Scrooge #347. 2005. (Illus.). 64p. (YA). pap. 6.95 (978-1-888472-00-4(6)) Gemstone Publishing, Inc.

—Uncle Scrooge #350. 2006. 64p. pap. 6.95 (978-1-888472-14-1(6)) Gemstone Publishing, Inc.

—Uncle Scrooge #354. 2006. 64p. pap. 6.95 (978-1-888472-23-3(5)) Gemstone Publishing, Inc.

Rosado, Maria. Wild Thornberrys Trivia Book. 2000. (gr. 3-6). lib. bdg. 10.65 (978-0-613-27583-5(7)) Tandem Library Bks.

Rose, Simon. The Emerald Curse. Nugent, Cynthia, illus. 2006. 96p. (J). (gr. 3-7). 7.95 (978-1-896580-90-6(4)) Tradewind Bks. CAN. *Dist:* Orca Bk. Pubs. USA.

Rosenberg, Jonathan. Behold the Power of Ignorance Vol. IV: Goats. 2001. (Illus.). 132p. per. 17.95 (978-1-59151-041-3(4)) Point E Publishing.

Rostam, Search for the King: Tales from the Shahnameh. 2007. (Illus.). 32p. (YA). 5.95 (*978-0-9770213-2-1(7)) hyperwerks.

Rowles, Chuck, et al. Drunk & Disorderly Vol. 2: The Drunk Duck Collection. Rowles, Chuck et al, illus. 2004. (YA). per. 14.95 (978-0-9748900-1-4(2)) Drunk Duck Comics.

Runton, Andy. Owly Volume 4. 2007. (Illus.). 120p. pap. 10.00 (*978-1-891830-89-1(9)) Top Shelf Productions.

Ruurs, Margriet. Emma at the Fair. Spurll, Barbara, illus. 2007. 32p. (J). per. ***(978-1-55005-127-8(X))*** Fitzhenry & Whiteside, Ltd.

Sadamoto, Yoshiyuki. Neon Genesis Evangelion. Sadamoto, Yoshiyuki, illus. collector's ed. (Neon Genesis Evangelion Ser.). (YA). 2002. (Illus.). 192p. pap. 15.95 (978-1-56931-400-5(4)); 2002. (Illus.). 192p. pap. 15.95 (978-1-56931-451-7(9)); Vol. 5. 2002. (Illus.). 192p. pap. 15.95 (978-1-56931-647-4(3)); Vol. 9. 2004. 200p. pap. 9.99 (978-1-59116-707-5(8)) Viz Media.

—Neon Genesis Evangelion, Vol. 10. 2007. (Neon Genesis Evangelion Ser.). 200p. (YA). pap. 9.99 (978-1-4215-1160-3(6)) Viz Media.

—Neon Genesis Evangelion Vol. 2. Sadamoto, Yoshiyuki, illus. collector's ed. 2002. (Neon Genesis Evangelion Ser.). (Illus.). 168p. (YA). pap. 15.95 (978-1-56931-344-2(X)) Viz Media.

Saijyo, Shinji. Iron Wok Jan, Vol. 13. 2005. (Illus.). 208p. (YA). pap. 9.95 (978-1-59796-031-1(4)) DrMaster Pubns. Inc.

Saito, Chiho. Revolutionary Girl Utena: The Adolescence of Utena. Saito, Chiho, illus. 2004. (Revolutionary Girl Utena Ser.). (Illus.). 192p. (YA). pap. 9.95 (978-1-59116-500-2(8)) Viz Media.

—To Sprout. Be-Papas, illus. 2003. (Revolutionary Girl Utena Ser.: Vol. 3). 200p. (YA). pap. 9.95 (978-1-56931-812-6(3)) Viz Media.

Saito, Takao. Golgo 13. 2006. (Golgo 13 Ser.). 208p. (YA). Vol. 3. pap. 9.99 (978-1-4215-0462-9(6)); Vol. 4. pap. 9.99 (978-1-4215-0463-6(4)) Viz Media.

Saiyan Stomping. 1999. (Dragon Ball Z Tattoo Bks.). (Illus.). 17p. (J). (gr. 1-2). pap. (978-0-7666-0544-2(2)) Modern Publishing.

Sakai, Stan. Duel at Kitanoji. 2003. (Usagi Yojimbo Ser.). (Illus.). 224p. (YA). pap. 16.95 (978-1-56971-973-2(X)) Dark Horse Comics.

—Travels with Jotaro. 2004. (Usagi Yojimbo Ser.: Vol. 18). (Illus.). 208p. (YA). pap. 15.95 (978-1-59307-220-9(1)) Dark Horse Comics.

—Usagi Yojimbo Vol. 3: Al Filo de la Vida y la Muerte. 2007. (SPA., Illus.). 200p. reprint ed. pap. 15.95 ***(978-1-59497-319-2(9))*** Public Square Bks.

—Usagi Yojimbo Vol. 4: Estaciones. 2007. (SPA., Illus.). 200p. reprint ed. pap. 15.95 ***(978-1-59497-320-8(2))*** Public Square Bks.

—Usagi Yojimbo Vol. 5: Segadora. 2007. (SPA., Illus.). 256p. reprint ed. pap. 17.95 ***(978-1-59497-321-5(0))*** Public Square Bks.

—Usagi Yojimbo Vol. 7: Samurai (en Español) 2007. (SPA., Illus.). 144p. reprint ed. pap. 14.95 ***(978-1-59497-323-9(7))*** Public Square Bks.

—Usagi Yojimbo Volume 21: the Mother of Mountains: The Mother of Mountains. 2007. (Illus.). 184p. (YA). pap. 15.95 ***(978-1-59307-783-9(1))*** Dark Horse Comics.

Salas, Macarena, ed. Baby Donald Makes A Snowfriend/beb Donald Hace un Amigo de Nieve: A Book about Shapes/Un Libro Sobre Las Formas. 2005. (SPA.). 10p. (J). bds. 3.99 (978-0-439-66362-5(8) , Scholastic en Espanol) Scholastic, Inc.

—Disney Bil: Follow Your Nose, Baby Pluto/sigue Tu Nariz, Beb Pluto. 2005. (SPA & ENG.). 10p. (J). bds. 3.99 (978-0-439-66365-6(2) , Scholastic en Espanol) Scholastic, Inc.

—Disney Bil: What Will You Do Today/ qu Vas a Hacer Hoy? 2005. (SPA.). 10p. (J). bds. 3.99 (978-0-439-66368-7(7) , Scholastic en Espanol) Scholastic, Inc.

Salazar, Souther. Destined for Dizzyness. Salazar, Souther, illus. 2005. (Illus.). 48p. pap. 5.95 (978-0-9766848-1-7(0)) Buenaventura Pr.

Salvagnini, Rudy, et al. Uncle Scrooge #370. 2007. 64p. pap. 7.99 ***(978-1-60360-000-2(0))*** Gemstone Publishing, Inc.

Samura, Hiroaki. Blade of the Immortal: On Silent Wings. Lewis, Dana & Smith, Toren, trs. from JPN. 1999. (Blade of the Immortal Ser.). (Illus.). 176p. (YA). (gr. 11 up). pap. 14.95 (978-1-56971-412-6(6)) Dark Horse Comics.

—Last Blood. Lewis, Dana & Smith, Toren, trs. Samura, Hiroaki, illus. 2005. (Illus.). per. 30.15 (978-1-4176-5923-4(8)) Tandem Library Bks.

Sanadura, Hiroyuki. Gunparade March, Vol. 1. 2004. (Illus.). 216p. (YA). pap. (978-1-4139-0035-4(6)) ADV Manga.

Sanami, Matoh. Tenryu: The Dragon Cycle, Vol. 3. 2005. (Illus.). 200p. (gr. 8-12). pap. 9.99 (978-1-4012-0671-0(9)) DC Comics.

Sanders, Fred. Dr. Doctrine's Christian Comix, 4 Vols. 1999. (J). 15.96 (978-0-8308-2240-9(2)) InterVarsity Pr.

Sanderson, Peter. X-Men: The Ultimate Guide. 2006. (Illus.). 192p. (J). 24.99 (978-0-7566-2005-9(8)) Dorling Kindersley Publishing, Inc.

Sanjo, Riku. Beet Vol. 2: The Vandal Buster. 2004. (Beet the Vandel Buster Ser.). (Illus.). 184p. (YA). pap. 7.99 (978-1-59116-691-7(8)) Viz Media.

—Beet the Vandel Buster. Inada, Koji, illus. (Beet the Vandel Buster Ser.). (YA). 2005. 208p. pap. 7.99 (978-1-59116-750-1(7)); 2004. 200p. pap. 7.99 (978-1-59116-690-0(X)) Viz Media.

Sanschagrin, Joceline. Calillow, C'est a Moi! Tipeo, illus. (FRE.). 24p. pap. 11.95 (978-2-89450-281-5(8)) Chouette Publishing CAN. *Dist:* Distribooks, Inc.

Sansom, Erik. Off the Rails. 2000. (Toy Trunk Railroad Ser.: Vol. 2). 152p. pap. 12.95 (978-1-929462-06-3(9)) Plan Nine Publishing, Inc.

Santoro, Lucio, et al. Journey to the Moon: A Roaring, Soaring Ride. 2007. 14p. (J). (ps). 26.99 ***(978-1-4169-4721-9(3)*** , Little Simon) Simon & Schuster Children's Publishing.

Saruwatari, Tetsuya. Tough. Saruwatari, Tetsuya, illus. 2005. (Tough Ser.). (Illus.). Vol. 1. 200p. (YA). pap. 9.99 (978-1-59116-710-5(8)); Vol. 2. 192p. pap. 9.99 (978-1-59116-714-3(0)) Viz Media.

Sasaki, Mutsumi. Happy Lesson, Vol.1. 2004. 170p. pap. (978-1-4139-0021-7(6)) ADV Manga.

Satoru, Akahori. Sorcerer Hunter, Vol. 13. Satoru, Akahori, illus. 13th rev. ed. 2003. (Illus.). 192p. (gr. 11 up). pap. 12.99 (978-1-59182-066-6(9)) TOKYOPOP, Inc.

Satrapi, Marjane. Persépolis (En Español), Vol. 4. Agut, Albert, tr. from FRE. 2005. (SPA., Illus.). 160p. pap. 22.95 (978-1-59497-096-2(3)) Public Square Bks.

Satterwhite, William. Stealth,, Vol. 1. 2005. 44p. (YA). pap. 5.75 (978-1-4116-2395-8(9)) Lulu.com.

Saunders, Catherine. Spider-Man: The Amazing Story. 2006. (Dk Readers Ser.). (Illus.). (J). 1p. pap. 3.99 (978-0-7566-2025-7(2)); 32p. pap. 14.99 (978-0-7566-2026-4(0)) Dorling Kindersley Publishing, Inc.

—Spider-Man's Worst Enemies. 2006. (Dk Readers Ser.). (Illus.). 32p. (J). 14.99 (978-0-7566-2024-0(4)); pap. 3.99 (978-0-7566-2023-3(6)) Dorling Kindersley Publishing, Inc.

Saunders, Nicholas. Gladiators & the Story of the Colosseum. 2006. (Stories from History Ser.). 48p. (J). 14.95 ***(978-0-7696-4704-3(9))*** ; pap. 6.95 ***(978-0-7696-4632-9(8))*** School Specialty Publishing.

—Pizarro & the Incas. 2006. (Stories from History Ser.). 48p. (J). pap. 6.95 ***(978-0-7696-4642-8(5))*** School Specialty Publishing.

Sava, Scott Christian. The Dreamland Chronicles: Collecting the first four issues of the critically acclaimed comic series. : Book One, 6. 2006. (Illus.). 300p. (YA). per. 19.99 net. (978-0-9789168-0-0(8)) Blue Dream Studios.

Scarpa, Romano, et al. Uncle Scrooge, No. 346. 2005. (Illus.). 64p. (YA). (ps-3). pap. 6.95 (978-0-911903-89-8(5)) Gemstone Publishing, Inc.

Schilling, Katherine, tr. Boys Be, Vol. 3. Tamakoshi, Hiroyuki, illus. rev. ed. 2005. 208p. pap. 9.99 (978-1-59532-101-5(2) , Tokyopop Adult) TOKYOPOP, Inc.

Schneider, Dan, creator. Drake & Josh: Match Made in Heaven, Vol. 1. 2005. (Illus.). 90p. (J). (ps-7). pap. 7.99 (978-1-59532-718-5(5) , Tokyopop Kids) TOKYOPOP, Inc.

Schooley, Bob. Kim Possible Cine-Manga: Animal Attraction & All the News, 9 vols., Vol. 5. McCorkle, Mark, illus. 2004. 96p. pap. 7.99 (978-1-59182-568-5(7) , Tokyopop Kids) TOKYOPOP, Inc.

Schultz, Charles M. It's the Easter Beagle, Charlie Brown. 2006. (Illus.). 128p. 4.95 (978-0-7624-2695-9(0) , Running Pr. Minature Editions) Running Pr. Bk. Pubs.

Schulz, Charles M. Alle Achtung. Herbst, Gabriele & Rolle, Ekkehard, trs. from ENG. (Snoopy & die Peanuts Ser.: Vol. 5). (GER., Illus.). 128p. (J). pap. (978-3-8105-1818-7(2)) Kruger, Wolfgang Verlag, GmbH DEU. *Dist:* International Bk. Import Service, Inc.

—Alles Peanuts. Herbst, Gabriele & Rolle, Ekkehard, trs. from ENG. (Snoopy & die Peanuts Ser.: Vol. 26). (GER., Illus.). 96p. (J). pap. (978-3-8105-1871-2(9)) Kruger, Wolfgang Verlag, GmbH DEU. *Dist:* International Bk. Import Service, Inc.

—Allzeit Bereit. Herbst, Gabriele & Rolle, Ekkehard, trs. from ENG. (Snoopy & die Peanuts Ser.: Vol. 35). (GER., Illus.). 96p. (J). pap. (978-3-8105-1891-0(3)) Kruger, Wolfgang Verlag, GmbH DEU. *Dist:* International Bk. Import Service, Inc.

— An der Langen Leine. Herbst, Gabriele & Rolle, Ekkehard, trs. from ENG. (Snoopy & die Peanuts Ser.: Vol. 30). (GER., Illus.). 96p. (J). pap. (978-3-8105-1880-4(8)) Kruger, Wolfgang Verlag, GmbH DEU. *Dist:* International Bk. Import Service, Inc.

—Auf den Hund Gekommen. Herbst, Gabriele & Rolle, Ekkehard, trs. from ENG. (Snoopy & die Peanuts Ser.: Vol. 34). (GER., Illus.). 96p. (J). pap. (978-3-8105-1888-0(3)) Kruger, Wolfgang Verlag, GmbH DEU. *Dist:* International Bk. Import Service, Inc.

—Charlie Brown Christmas. 2001. (gr. k-3). lib. bdg. 14.15 (978-0-613-61753-6(3)) Tandem Library Bks.

—Charlie Brown Christmas, Spec Sales Ed. 2004. 128p. 4.95 (978-0-7624-2289-0(0)) Running Pr. Bk. Pubs.

—Christmas Is Together-Time. 2006. (Peanuts Ser.). (Illus.). 72p. 5.95 (978-1-933662-37-4(9)) Cider Mill Pr. Bk. Pubs. LLC.

—Den Wind im Ruecken. Herbst, Gabriele & Rolle, Ekkehard, trs. from ENG. (Snoopy & die Peanuts Ser.: Vol. 6). (GER., Illus.). 96p. (J). pap. (978-3-8105-1819-4(0)) Kruger, Wolfgang Verlag, GmbH DEU. *Dist:* International Bk. Import Service, Inc.

—Einfach Genial. Herbst, Gabriele & Rolle, Ekkehard, trs. from ENG. (Snoopy & die Peanuts Ser.: Vol. 31). (GER., Illus.). 96p. (J). pap. (978-3-8105-1881-1(6)) Kruger, Wolfgang Verlag, GmbH DEU. *Dist:* International Bk. Import Service, Inc.

—Einfach Unschlagbar. Herbst, Gabriele & Rolle, Ekkehard, trs. from ENG. (Snoopy & die Peanuts Ser.: Vol. 1). (GER., Illus.). 96p. (J). pap. (978-3-8105-1811-8(5)) Kruger, Wolfgang Verlag, GmbH DEU. *Dist:* International Bk. Import Service, Inc.

—Grundlos Gluecklich. Herbst, Gabriele & Rolle, Ekkehard, trs. from ENG. (Snoopy & die Peanuts Ser.: Vol. 37). (GER., Illus.). 96p. (J). pap. (978-3-8105-1893-4(X)) Kruger, Wolfgang Verlag, GmbH DEU. *Dist:* International Bk. Import Service, Inc.

—Gut Aufgelegt. Herbst, Gabriele & Rolle, Ekkehard, trs. from ENG. (Snoopy & die Peanuts Ser.: Vol. 12). (GER., Illus.). 96p. (J). pap. (978-3-8105-1828-6(X)) Kruger, Wolfgang Verlag, GmbH DEU. *Dist:* International Bk. Import Service, Inc.

—Herzlich Unverschaemt. Herbst, Gabriele & Rolle, Ekkehard, trs. from ENG. (Snoopy & die Peanuts Ser.: Vol. 9). (GER., Illus.). 128p. (J). pap. (978-3-8105-1823-1(9)) Kruger, Wolfgang Verlag, GmbH DEU. *Dist:* International Bk. Import Service, Inc.

—Himmel & Hoelle. Herbst, Gabriele & Rolle, Ekkehard, trs. from ENG. (Snoopy & die Peanuts Ser.: Vol. 23). (GER., Illus.). 96p. (J). pap. (978-3-8105-1867-5(0)) Kruger, Wolfgang Verlag, GmbH DEU. *Dist:* International Bk. Import Service, Inc.

—Hoch die Tassen. Herbst, Gabriele & Rolle, Ekkehard, trs. from ENG. (Snoopy & die Peanuts Ser.: Vol. 36). (GER., Illus.). 96p. (J). pap. (978-3-8105-1892-7(1)) Kruger, Wolfgang Verlag, GmbH DEU. *Dist:* International Bk. Import Service, Inc.

—I Need All the Friends I Can Get. 2006. (Peanuts Ser.). (Illus.). 72p. 5.95 (978-1-933662-39-8(5)) Cider Mill Pr. Bk. Pubs. LLC.

—Immer Dabei. Herbst, Gabriele & Rolle, Ekkehard, trs. from ENG. (Snoopy & die Peanuts Ser.: Vol. 27). (GER., Illus.). 96p. (J). pap. (978-3-8105-1872-9(7)) Kruger, Wolfgang Verlag, GmbH DEU. *Dist:* International Bk. Import Service, Inc.

—It's the Easter Beagle, Charlie Brown. 2002. lib. bdg. 14.15 (978-0-613-61781-9(9)) Tandem Library Bks.

—Kaum zu Bremsen. Rolle, Ekkehard, tr. from ENG. (Snoopy & die Peanuts Ser.: Vol. 11). (GER., Illus.). 128p. (J). pap. (978-3-8105-1827-9(1)) Kruger, Wolfgang Verlag, GmbH DEU. *Dist:* International Bk. Import Service, Inc.

—The Many Faces of Snoopy. 2006. (Illus.). 352p. pap. 16.95 (978-0-345-47983-9(1) , Ballantine Bks.) Random House Publishing Group.

—Peanuts: The Grand Piano Book. 2008. 10p. (J). pap. 7.95 ***(978-0-7624-3236-3(5)*** , Running Pr.) Running Pr. Bk. Pubs.

—Peanuts: Where Is Woodstock? 2008. 12p. (J). 7.95 ***(978-0-7624-3238-7(1)*** , Running Pr.) Running Pr. Bk. Pubs.

—Pfoten Hoch! Herbst, Gabriele & Rolle, Ekkehard, trs. from ENG. (Snoopy & die Peanuts Ser.: Vol. 33). (GER., Illus.). 96p. (J). pap. (978-3-8105-1887-3(5)) Kruger, Wolfgang Verlag, GmbH DEU. *Dist:* International Bk. Import Service, Inc.

—Schwer in Fahrt. Herbst, Gabriele & Rolle, Ekkehard, trs. from ENG. (Snoopy & die Peanuts Ser.: Vol. 7). (GER., Illus.). 128p. (J). pap. (978-3-8105-1820-0(4)) Kruger, Wolfgang Verlag, GmbH DEU. *Dist:* International Bk. Import Service, Inc.

—Suppertime. 2006. (Peanuts Ser.). (Illus.). 72p. 5.95 (978-1-933662-38-1(7)) Cider Mill Pr. Bk. Pubs. LLC.

—Voll auf die Schnauze. Herbst, Gabriele & Rolle, Ekkehard, trs. from ENG. (Snoopy & die Peanuts Ser.: Vol. 32). (GER., Illus.). 96p. (J). pap. (978-3-8105-1886-6(7)) Kruger, Wolfgang Verlag, GmbH DEU. *Dist:* International Bk. Import Service, Inc.

—Voll im Griff. Herbst, Gabriele & Rolle, Ekkehard, trs. from ENG. (Snoopy & die Peanuts Ser.: Vol. 13). (GER., Illus.). 128p. (J). pap. (978-3-8105-1829-3(8)) Kruger, Wolfgang Verlag, GmbH DEU. *Dist:* International Bk. Import Service, Inc.

Schwartz, Lew Sayre. Moby Dick: Based on the Novel by Herman Melville. 2002. (gr. 5-8). lib. bdg. 15.25 (978-0-613-70733-6(8)) Tandem Library Bks.

Schwarz, Laurence & KOL (AOL Kids) Staff. Game Over: As Seen on Cartoon Network. 3rd ed. 2006. (Princess Natasha Ser.: No. 3). (Illus.). 80p. (J). (gr. 3-7). pap. 3.99 (978-0-316-15506-9(3)) Little Brown & Co.

Schwarz, Viviane. Shark & Lobster's Amazing Undersea Adventure. Stewart, Joel, illus. 2006. 34p. (J). ***(978-1-4156-8140-4(6))*** Candlewick Pr.

Scion: Blood for Blood. 2002. (Scion Ser.). 28.47 (978-1-4046-1028-6(6)) Book Wholesalers, Inc.

Scott, Prue. Growth Spurt: Zits Sketchbook 2. 1999. (gr. 7-12). lib. bdg. 19.90 (978-0-613-23720-8(X)) Tandem Library Bks.

Seagle, Steven T. Solstice. Norman, Justin, illus. 2005. (YA). pap. 12.95 (978-0-9766761-1-9(7)) Active Images.

Segamu. Sokora Refugees, Vol. 2. DeJesus, Melissa, illus. 2006. (YA). pap. 9.99 (978-1-59816-551-7(8) , Tokyopop Adult) TOKYOPOP, Inc.

Sekarski, Dan. Bemba's Secret Garden. 2006. (Illus.). 57p. (J). per. 16.95 ***(978 0 9790110-0-9(0))*** Tpprince Esquire.

Sentinel. 2007. (J). 128.10 ***(978-1-59961-315-4(8))*** Spotlight.

Seto, Andy. Shaolin Soccer. 2005. (Illus.). 128p. (YA). Vol. 1. pap. 13.95 (978-1-58899-318-2(3)); Vol. 2. pap. 13.95 (978-1-58899-319-9(1)) ComicsOne Corp./Dr. Masters.

Seto, Dietrich, et al, eds. Galaxy Angel Party, Vol. 3. Tajii, Koji, tr. from JPN. Kanan, illus. 2007. (Galaxy Angel Ser.). Orig. Title: Galaxy Angel Anthology. 208p. pap. 9.99 (978-1-932480-28-3(5) , Broccoli Bks. Deluxe) Broccoli International USA, Inc.

Sewell, Anna. Black Beauty. Tanner, Jennifer, illus. 2007. (Graphic Revolve Ser.). 63p. (J). 22.60 (978-1-59889-046-4(8)) Stone Arch Bks.

Sfar, Joann. Klezmer, Collector's Edition: Tales of the Wild East. 2006. (Illus.). 144p. (YA). 25.00 (978-1-59643-210-9(1) , First Second Bks.) Roaring Brook Pr.

Sfar, Joann & Trondheim, Lewis. La Mazmorra: Corazon de Pato. Abuli, Enrique Sanchez, tr. from FRE. 2004. Orig. Title: Le Donjon: Coeur de Canard. (SPA., Illus.). 48p. pap. 16.95 (978-1-59497-057-3(2)) Public Square Bks.

—La Mazmorra: El Cementerio de los Dragones. Abuli, Enrique Sanchez, tr. from FRE. 2004. Orig. Title: Donjon Crepuscule 101: le Cimetiere des Dragons. (SPA., Illus.). 48p. pap. 16.95 (978-1-59497-060-3(2)) Public Square Bks.

—La Mazmorra: La Princesa de los Barbaros. Abuli, Enrique Sanchez, tr. from FRE. 2004. Orig. Title: Donjon Zenith 3: la Princesse des Barbares. (SPA., Illus.). 48p. pap. 16.95 (978-1-59497-059-7(9)) Public Square Bks.

—La Mazmorra: Sortilegios e Infortunios. Abuli, Enrique Sanchez, tr. from FRE. 2005. Orig. Title: Donjon Zenith 4: Sortilege et Avatar. (SPA., Illus.). 48p. pap. 16.95 (978-1-59497-063-4(7)) Public Square Bks.

—La Mazmorra: Un Justiciero en Apuros. Abuli, Enrique Sanchez, tr. from FRE. 2004. Orig. Title: Donjon Potron-minet -98: un Justicier dans L'Ennui. (SPA., Illus.). 48p. (J). pap. 16.95 (978-1-59497-062-7(9)) Public Square Bks.

Shadow Quest. 2002. (Illus.). 20p. 4.00 (978-0-9726100-0-1(6)) EverCross Studios.

Shakespeare, William. MacBeth. 2006. (J). (gr. 3-8). 24.21 (978-1-59961-117-4(1)) Spotlight.

Shakespeare, William & Appignanesi, Richard. Romeo & Juliet. Leong, Sonia, illus. 2007. (Manga Shakespeare Ser.). 208p. (J). (gr. 2-8). pap. 9.95 ***(978-0-8109-9325-9(2)*** , Abrams Bks. for Young Readers) Abrams, Harry N. , Inc.

Shakespeare, William, et al. Hamlet. 2007. (Manga Shakespeare Ser.). 204p. (J). (gr. 2-8). pap. 9.95 ***(978-0-8109-9324-2(4)*** , Abrams Bks. for Young Readers) Abrams, Harry N. , Inc.

Shanower, Eric. Adventures in Oz. Shanower, Eric, illus. 2007. (Illus.). 256p. (J). (gr. 5-7). 75.00 ***(978-1-60010-071-0(6))*** Idea & Design Works, LLC.

Shanower, Eric. Thousand Ships. 2001. (gr. 7-12). lib. bdg. 30.35 (978-0-613-65633-7(4)) Tandem Library Bks.

Shelley, Mary Wollstonecraft. Frankenstein. Cruz, Nardo, illus. 2005. 48p. (gr. 5-8). 25.50 (978-0-7910-9100-5(7)) Facts On File, Inc.

Shelley, Mary Wollstonecraft. Frankenstein. Calero, Dennis, illus. 2008. (J). ***(978-1-59889-830-9(2));*** 72p. pap. ***(978-1-59889-886-6(8))*** Stone Arch Bks.

Shelley, Mary Wollstonecraft & Grant, J. Frankenstein. 144p. (J). lib. bdg. 12.95 (978-1-58086-667-5(0) , Usborne) EDC Publishing.

Shepard, Aaron. Master Man: A Tale of Nigeria. Wisniewski, David, illus. 2001. 32p. (J). (gr. k-3). 15.95 (978-0-688-13783-0(0)) HarperCollins Pubs.

Shepard, Aaron. The Monkey King: A Superhero Tale of China, Retold from the Journey to the West. 2008. (Ancient Fantasy Ser.: 4). 50p. (J). lib. bdg. 15.00 ***(978-0-938497-40-0(5));*** lib. bdg. 6.00 ***(978-0-938497-41-7(3))*** Shepard Pubns. (Skyhook Pr.).

Shigeno, Shuichi. Initial D, Vol. 17. Shigeno, Shuichi, illus. 2005. (Illus.). 212p. lib. bdg. 20.90 (978-1-4176-5264-8(0)) Tandem Library Bks.

Shigeno, Shuichi, illus. & creator. Initial D, Vol. 22. Shigeno, Shuichi, creator. 22nd rev. ed. 2006. 240p. pap. 9.99 (978-1-59182-998-0(4) , Tokyopop Adult) TOKYOPOP, Inc.

Shigeno, Suichi. Initial D, 23 vols., Vol. 11. Kanemitsu, Dan, tr. from JPN. rev. ed. 2004. (Illus.). 240p. pap. 9.99 (978-1-59182-174-8(6) , Tokyopop Adult) TOKYOPOP, Inc.

—Initial D, 23 vols., Vol. 12. 12th rev. ed. 2004. (Illus.). 240p. pap. 9.99 (978-1-59182-462-6(1) , Tokyopop Adult) TOKYOPOP, Inc.

—Initial D, 23 vols., Vol. 13. Papia, Dan, tr. from JPN. rev. ed. 2004. (Illus.). 240p. pap. 9.99 (978-1-59182-463-3(X) , Tokyopop Adult) TOKYOPOP, Inc.

Shimizu, Aki, ed. Suikoden III: The Successor of Fate, Vol. 6. rev. ed. 2005. (Illus.). 180p. (YA). pap. 9.99 (978-1-59532-436-8(4) , Tokyopop Adult) TOKYOPOP, Inc.

Shin, Ji-Sang. Chocolat, Vol. 2. Geo, illus. 2006. 200p. (YA). pap. 10.95 ***(978-89-527-4472-2(1))*** ICE Kunion KOR. *Dist:* Diamond Bk. Distributors.

Shinohara, Chie. Red River, Vol. 8. Shinohara, Chie, illus. 2005. (Red River Ser.). 200p. (YA). pap. 9.99 (978-1-59116-988-8(7)) Viz Media.

—Red River. (Red River Ser.). (YA). Vol. 10. 2005. 192p. pap. 9.99 (978-1-4215-0195-6(3)); Vol. 14. 2006. 208p. pap. 9.99 (978-1-4215-0556-5(8)) Viz Media.

—Red River, Volume 17. 2007. (Red River Ser.). 192p. (YA). pap. 9.99 (978-1-4215-0997-6(0)) Viz Media.

Shiozu, Shuri, creator. Eerie Queerie!, 4 vols., Vol. 4. rev. ed. 2004. (Illus.). 200p. pap. 9.99 (978-1-59182-861-7(9) , Tokyopop Adult) TOKYOPOP, Inc.

Shiro Amano. Kingdom Hearts, 4 vols., Vol. 4. 4th rev. ed. 2006. (Disney Squaresoft Ser.). (Illus.). pap. 5.99 (978-1-59816-220-2(9) , Tokyopop Kids) TOKYOPOP, Inc.

Shirodaira, Kyo & Mizuno, Eita. Spiral. (JPN., Illus.). (YA). Vol. 1. 189p. pap. (978-4-7575-0175-1(7)); Vol. 2. 190p. pap. (978-4-7575-0271-0(0)); Vol. 6. 185p. pap. (978-4-7575-0678-7(3)); Vol. 7. 182p. pap. (978-4-7575-0790-6(9)); Vol. 8. 190p. pap. (978-4-7575-0854-5(9)); Vol. 10. 187p. pap. (978-4-7575-1099-9(3)); Vol. 11. 205p. pap. (978-4-7575-1186-6(8)); Vol. 12. 183p. pap. (978-4-7575-1252-8(X)) Enix Corp.

Shogakukan & Mitsui-Kids, illus. Duel Masters Vol. 3: The Champion of Tomorrow. 2004. (Teen Ser.), 96p. pap. 7.99 (978-1-59532-065-0(2) , Tokyopop Kids) TOKYOPOP, Inc.

Sholly, Pete Von. Pete Von Sholly's Morbid. 2003. (Illus.). 96p. (YA). pap. 14.95 (978-1-59307-028-1(4)) Dark Horse Comics.

Shoujo Pocket Manga #1. 2004. 128p. (YA). pap. 9.99 (978-1-932453-46-1(6)) Antarctic Pr., Inc.

Shue, Ken, intro. The Art of Winnie the Pooh: Disney Artist Celebrate the Silly Old Bear. 2006. (Illus.). 176p. (ps-17). 35.00 (978-1-4231-0252-6(5) , Disney Editions) Disney Pr.

Siegel, Siena Cherson. To Dance: A Ballerina's Graphic Novel. Siegel, Mark, illus. 2006. 64p. (J). (gr. 3-9). 17.95 (978-0-689-86747-7(6) , Atheneum/Richard Jackson Bks.); pap. 9.99 (978-1-4169-2687-0(9) , Aladdin) Simon & Schuster Children's Publishing.

Sigsawa, Keiichi. Kino No Tabi, Vol. 2. 2008. (Illus.). 192p. mass mkt. 9.99 (978-1-59816-456-5(2) , Tokyopop Adult) TOKYOPOP, Inc.

Silver Dolphin en Español Editors. Disney princesas: Felices para Siempre: Disney Princesses: Happily Ever after, Spanish-Language Editon. 2007. (Illus.). 5p. (J). 14.99 ***(978-970-718-448-0(5)*** , Silver Dolphin en Español) Advanced Marketing, S. de R. L. de C. V. MEX. *Dist:* Perseus Distribution.

C
D

—Disney Serie Aprendizaje: Disney Learn to Count. 2005. (SPA., Illus.). 22p. (J). bds. 16.95 (978-970-718-250-9(4) , Silver Dolphin en Español) Advanced Marketing, S. de R. L. de C. V. MEX. *Dist:* Perseus Distribution.

—Disney Serie Aprendizaje: Disney Princesses Learn to Write. 2005. (SPA., Illus.). 22p. (J). bds. 16.95 (978-970-718-248-6(2) , Silver Dolphin en Español) Advanced Marketing, S. de R. L. de C. V. MEX. *Dist:* Perseus Distribution.

—Disney Serie Aprendizaje: Disney Winnie the Pooh Learning Shapes. 2005. (SPA., Illus.). 22p. (J). bds. 16.95 (978-970-718-249-3(0) , Silver Dolphin en Español) Advanced Marketing, S. de R. L. de C. V. MEX. *Dist:* Perseus Distribution.

Simone, Gail. Gus Beezer with Spider-Man. 2006. (Marvelous Adventures of Gus Beezer Ser.). (Illus.). (J). (gr. 2-6). 21.35 (978-1-59961-047-4(7)) Spotlight.

—Gus Beezer with Spider-Man: Along Came a Spidey! 2006. (Marvelous Adventures of Gus Beezer Ser.). (Illus.). (J). (gr. 2-6). 21.35 (978-1-59961-048-1(5)) Spotlight.

—Gus Beezer with the Hulk. 2006. (Marvelous Adventures of Gus Beezer Ser.). (Illus.). (J). (gr. 2-6). 21.35 (978-1-59961-049-8(3)) Spotlight.

—Gus Beezer with the X-Men: X Marks the Mutant. 2006. (Marvelous Adventures of Gus Beezer Ser.). (Illus.). (J). (gr. 2-6). 21.35 (978-1-59961-050-4(7)) Spotlight.

Simonson, Louise, et al. X-Factor. 2007. (Essential Ser.: Vol. 2). (Illus.). 544p. pap. 16.99 (978-0-7851-2099-5(8)) Marvel Enterprises, Inc.

Simonson, Walter. Meltdown, 3 vols. Simonson, Louise et al, illus. 2003. (Wolverine Legends Ser.: Vol. 2). 200p. (YA). 19.99 (978-0-7851-1048-4(8)) Marvel Enterprises, Inc.

Simpson, David. Never Mind Pants. 2000. (Ozy & Millie Ser.: Vol. 2). 152p. pap. 12.95 (978-1-929462-20-9(4)) Plan Nine Publishing, Inc.

Siu-Chong, Ken. Street Fighter, Vol. 1. 2006. (Illus.). 144p. pap. 9.99 (***978-0-9738652-0-2(2)***) URON Entertainment Corp. CAN. *Dist:* Diamond Bk. Distributors.

—Street Fighter Legends Volume 1: Sakura: Sakura. 2007. (Illus.). 128p. pap. 11.95 (***978-0-9781386-4-6(3)***) URON Entertainment Corp. CAN. *Dist:* Diamond Bk. Distributors.

—Street Fighter Volume 2. 2006. (Illus.). 200p. pap. 13.99 (***978-0-9738652-7-1(X)***) URON Entertainment Corp. CAN. *Dist:* Diamond Bk. Distributors.

—Street Fighter Volume 3: Fighter's Destiny: Fighter's Destiny. 2007. 160p. (YA). pap. 13.99 (***978-0-9738652-8-8(8)***) URON Entertainment Corp. CAN. *Dist:* Diamond Bk. Distributors.

Slott, Dan. She-Hulk Volume 4: Laws of Attraction TPB: Laws of Attraction TPB. 2007. (Illus.). 192p. pap. 19.99 (978-0-7851-2218-0(4)) Marvel Enterprises, Inc.

Smart, Jamie. Bear: Immortal. 2004. (Illus.). 144p. pap. 14.95 (978-1-59362-001-1(2)) Slave Labor Bks.

The Smartest Thing. 2004. (YA). (978-0-9762904-8-3(0)) Layne Morgan Media, Inc.

Smarto, Luke, illus. A Donde Te Vas? 2003. 16p. (J). per. 0.75 (978-0-930201-05-0(1)) Frontline Pr.

Smith, Bruce L. Song of Life. l.t. ed. 2006. (Illus.). 32p. (J). lib. bdg. (***978-1-934190-08-1(X)***) Ocean Front Bk. Publishing, Inc.

Smith, Ian. Emily & the Intergalactic Lemonade Stand. 2004. (Illus.). 96p. (gr. 1 up). pap. 12.95 (978-0-943151-96-0(1)) Slave Labor Bks.

Smith, Jeff. Bone: Eyes of the Storm. Smith, Jeff, illus. 2002. (Bone Ser.). (Illus.). 27.19 (978-1-4046-2801-4(0)) Book Wholesalers, Inc.

—Bone: Old Man's Cave. Smith, Jeff, illus. 2002. (Bone Ser.). (Illus.). (YA). 26.06 (978-1-4046-2804-5(5)) Book Wholesalers, Inc.

—Bone: Out from Boneville. Smith, Jeff, illus. 2002. (Illus.). 22.68 (978-1-4046-2251-7(9)) Book Wholesalers, Inc.

—Bone: Out from Boneville. Hamaker, Steve, illus. 2005. (Bone Ser.). 144p. (J). 9.99 (978-0-439-70640-7(8) , Graphix) Scholastic, Inc.

—Bone: The Dragonslayer. Smith, Jeff, illus. 2002. (Bone Ser.). (Illus.). 27.19 (978-1-4046-2802-1(9)) Book Wholesalers, Inc.

—Bone: The Great Cow Race. Smith, Jeff, illus. 2002. (Bone Ser.). (Illus.). (YA). 24.94 (978-1-4046-2800-7(2)) Book Wholesalers, Inc.

—Bone: Treasure Hunters. Smith, Jeff, illus. 2002. (Bone Ser.). (Illus.). (YA). 26.06 (978-1-4046-2806-9(1)) Book Wholesalers, Inc.

—Bone Vol. 7: Ghost Circles. Smith, Jeff, illus. 2002. (Bone Ser.). (Illus.). 27.19 (978-1-4046-2805-2(3)) Book Wholesalers, Inc.

—Bone: Rock Jaw: Master of the Eastern Border. Smith, Jeff, illus. 2002. (Bone Ser.). (Illus.). 24.94 (978-1-4046-2803-8(7)) Book Wholesalers, Inc.

—The Ghost Circles. 2008. 160p. pap. 19.99 (***978-0-439-70629-2(7)*** , Graphix) Scholastic, Inc.

—The Great Cow Race. Hamaker, Steve, illus. 2005. (Bone Ser.: No. 2). 144p. (ps-7). pap. 9.99 (978-0-439-70639-1(4) , Graphix) Scholastic, Inc.

—Out from Boneville. 2005. (Bone Ser.: No. 1). (Illus.). 144p. (J). pap. 18.95 (978-0-439-70623-0(8) , Graphix) Scholastic, Inc.

Smith, Joe & Matsumoto, Taiyo. Blue Spring, Vol. 1. Smith, Joe, illus. 2004. (Blue Spring Ser.). 216p. pap. 9.99 (978-1-59116-645-0(4)) Viz Media.

Smith, Ozzie. Hello, Fredbird! de Angel, Miguel, illus. 2006. 30p. (J). 17.95 (***978-1-932888-83-6(7)***) Mascot Bks., Inc.

Smith, Rick. Shuck Unmasked. 2003. (Illus.). 168p. pap. 14.95 (978-1-891830-47-1(3)) Top Shelf Productions.

Sneaks Q1 2003. 2003. (YA). pap. (978-1-59182-405-3(2)) TOKYOPOP, Inc.

Sneaks Q2 2003. 2003. (YA). pap. (978-1-59182-406-0(0)) TOKYOPOP, Inc.

Sneaks Q3 2003. 2003. (Illus.). (YA). pap. (978-1-59182-407-7(9)) TOKYOPOP, Inc.

Sneaks Q4 2003. 2003. (YA). pap. (978-1-59182-408-4(7)) TOKYOPOP, Inc.

Snider, Brandon T. Cry of the Penguin: Deluxe Sound Storybook. Forlini, Victoria, ed. Staton, Joe & DeCarlo, Mike, illus. 2005. (Batman Ser.). 22p. (J). (ps-3). 15.95 (978-0-696-22736-3(3)) Meredith Bks.

Sniegoski, Tom. Billy Hooten. Powell, Eric, illus. 2007. (Owlboy Ser.). 256p. (J). (gr. 4-7). lib. bdg. 9.99 (***978-0-385-90402-5(9)*** , Yearling) Random Hse. Children's Bks.

—Billy Hooten: Owlboy. Powell, Eric, illus. 2007. (Owlboy Ser.). 256p. (J). (gr. 4-7). 5.99 (***978-0-440-42180-1(2)*** , Yearling) Random Hse. Children's Bks.

So-Yong, Lee. Model, 4 vols., 1. Na, Lauren, tr. from KOR. 2004. (Illus.). 212p. pap. 9.99 (978-1-59182-711-5(6) , Tokyopop Adult) TOKYOPOP, Inc.

—Model, 4 , Vol. 2. rev. ed. 2004. (Illus.). 212p. pap. 9.99 (978-1-59182-712-2(4) , Tokyopop Adult) TOKYOPOP, Inc.

So-Young, Lee. Model, Vol. 6. rev. ed. 2005. (Illus.). 200p. pap. 9.99 (978-1-59532-008-7(3) , Tokyopop Adult) TOKYOPOP, Inc.

Soda, Masahito. Daigo of Fire Company M. Soda, Masahito, illus. 2005. (Firefighter Ser.: Vol. 10). 208p. (YA). pap. 9.95 (978-1-59116-635-1(7)) Viz Media.

—Firefighter! (Firefighter Daigo of Fire Company M Ser.). (YA). Vol. 13. 2005. (Illus.). 200p. pap. 9.95 (978-1-4215-0130-7(9)); Vol. 14. 2006. 208p. pap. 9.95 (978-1-4215-0318-9(2)); Vol. 15. 2006. 208p. pap. 9.95 (978-1-4215-0451-3(0)) Viz Media.

—Firefighter, Vol. 16. 2006. (Firefighter Daigo of Fire Company M Ser.). 208p. (YA). pap. 9.95 (978-1-4215-0452-0(9)) Viz Media.

Sohn, Emily. A Crash Course in Forces & Motion with Max Axiom, Super Scientist. 2007. (Graphic Library). (Illus.). 32p. (J). (***978-0-7368-7890-6(4)*** , 1264931) Capstone Pr., Inc.

Son, Hee-Joon. Id_Entity, Vol. 3. Kim, Yoon-Kyung, illus. 3rd rev. ed. 2005. pap. 9.99 (978-1-59532-347-7(3) , Tokyopop Adult) TOKYOPOP, Inc.

Sorachi, Hideaki. Gin Tama. (JPN., Illus.). (YA). Vol. 1. 202p. pap. (978-4-08-873623-5(0)); Vol. 2. 206p. pap. (978-4-08-873632-7(X)); Vol. 3. 190p. pap. (978-4-08-873653-2(2)); Vol. 4. 186p. pap. (978-4-08-873672-3(9)) Shuei-Sha.

Soundprints. Old Macdonald: And Other Favorites. 2002. (Illus.). 36p. (J). bds. 8.95 (978-1-931465-24-3(X) , Little Soundprints) Soundprints.

—Old MacDonald: And Other Favorites. 2005. (Meet Mother Goose Ser.). (Illus.). 36p. (J). bds. 10.95 incl. audio compact disk (978-1-931465-30-4(4)) Soundprints.

Southey, Robert. Goldilocks & the Three Bears. 2005. (Classics Illustrated Junior Ser.). 32p. 5.99 (978-1-894998-21-5(9)) Lake, Jack Productions, Inc. CAN. *Dist:* Houghton Hse. Publishing, Ltd.

Spider-Man & Friends. 2003. (J). per. (978-1-57657-858-2(5)) Paradise Pr., Inc.

Spiegelman, Art. Big Fat Little Lit. Mouly, Francoise, ed. 2006. (Illus.). 144p. (J). (gr. k). pap. 14.99 (978-0-14-240706-6(2) , Puffin) Penguin Group (USA) Inc.

Spiegelman, Art & Mouly, Francoise. It Was a Dark & Silly Night... Spiegelman, Art & Mouly, Francoise, illus. 2003. (Little Lit Ser.: Vol. 3). (Illus.). 48p. (J). (gr. 1 up). 19.99 (978-0-06-028628-6(8)) HarperCollins Pubs.

—Strange Stories for Strange Kids. Spiegelman, Art, illus. 2001. (Little Lit Ser.). (Illus.). 64p. (J). (ps-3). 19.95 (978-0-06-028626-2(1) , Cotler, Joanna Books) HarperCollins Pubs.

Spiegle, Dan, et al. Historical Adventure. 2006. (Illus.). 56p. pap. (***978-0-8368-7934-6(1)***); (YA). (gr. 4 up). lib. bdg. 29.27 (***978-0-8368-7927-8(9)***) Stevens, Gareth Inc. (World Almanac Library).

SpongeBob Squarepants WOW! Scratchers. 2005. 4p. (J). 6.99 (978-1-59524-031-6(4)) Giddy Up, LLC.

SpongeBob WOW Paper Scribble & Giggle Pad. 2004. 36p. (J). 7.99 (978-1-59524-006-4(3)) Giddy Up, LLC.

SpongeBob WOW! Surprise & Shine. 2005. 4p. (J). 6.99 (978-1-59524-049-1(7)) Giddy Up, LLC.

Spotlight (Firm) Staff, contrib. by. Jughead with Archie in Power Play. 2007. (Illus.). 80p. (J). 24.21 (***978-1-59961-275-1(5)***) Spotlight.

—Laugh with a Test Case. 2007. (Illus.). 80p. (J). 24.21 (***978-1-59961-284-3(4)***) Spotlight.

—Laugh with Mammoth Madness. 2007. (Illus.). 80p. (J). 24.21 (***978-1-59961-281-2(X)***) Spotlight.

—Laugh with Snack Swap. 2007. (Illus.). 80p. (J). 24.21 (***978-1-59961-282-9(8)***) Spotlight.

—Laugh with Stampede. 2007. (Illus.). 80p. (J). 24.21 (***978-1-59961-283-6(6)***) Spotlight.

Spyboy. 2002. (Spyboy Ser.). (Illus.). 18.66 (978-1-4046-2811-3(8)) Book Wholesalers, Inc.

Spyboy: The Deadly Gourmet Affair. 2002. (Spyboy Ser.). (Illus.). 17.62 (978-1-4046-2267-8(5)) Book Wholesalers, Inc.

Spyboy: Trial & Terror. 2002. (Spyboy Ser.). (Illus.). 17.60 (978-1-4046-2810-6(X)) Book Wholesalers, Inc.

Spyboy: Undercover, Underwear! 2002. (Spyboy Ser.). (Illus.). 18.66 (978-1-4046-2812-0(6)) Book Wholesalers, Inc.

Stahnke, Rich. Furious Fist of the Drunken Monkey: Origin of the Species #3. 2007. 2.95 (***978-0-9791192-4-8(3)***) Silent Devil Productions.

Stanley, John. Little Lulu Vol. 14: Queen Lulu. 2007. 240p. pap. 9.95 (978-1-59307-683-2(5)) Dark Horse Comics.

—Little Lulu Explorers, Vol. 15. 2007. 240p. pap. 9.95 (***978-1-59307-684-9(3)***) Dark Horse Comics.

Stanley, John. Little Lulu Volume 13: Too Much Fun: Too Much Fun. 2006. (Illus.). 208p. pap. 9.95 (978-1-59307-621-4(5)) Dark Horse Comics.

Stanton, Andrew, creator. Finding Nemo. 2003. (Illus.). 96p. pap. 7.99 (978-1-59182-758-0(2) , Tokyopop Kids) TOKYOPOP, Inc.

Starlin, Jim. Infinity War. 2006. (Illus.). 400p. (YA). pap. 29.99 (978-0-7851-2105-3(6)) Marvel Enterprises, Inc.

Starlin, Jim & Edelman, Scott. Silver Surfer Rebirth of Thanos. 2006. (Illus.). 224p. pap. (978-0-7851-2046-9(7)) Diamond Bks.

Staton, John, et al. Otazine: Manga of Otaku Generation. Duarte, Nicolas Benjamin, ed. Staton, John et al, illus. 2005. 150p. (YA). per. 10.00 (978-0-9770461-1-9(7)) Otakorp, Inc.

Staub, Rusty. Hello, Mr. Met! Moore, Danny, illus. 2006. (J). 17.95 (***978-1-932888-82-9(9)***) Mascot Bks., Inc.

Steele, Michael. Last Princess of Sparks. 2006. (Winx Club Ser.). (Illus.). 80p. (J). pap. 5.99 (978-0-439-74423-2(7)) Scholastic, Inc.

Steele, Michael Anthony. The Winx Club: Dragon Fire. 2005. (Winx Club Ser.). (Illus.). 80p. (J). 5.99 (978-0-439-69151-2(6)) Scholastic, Inc.

—Winx Club: Hidden Secrets. 2005. (Winx Club Ser.). (Illus.). 112p. (ps-k). 4.99 (978-0-439-74424-9(5)) Scholastic, Inc.

Stein, Erin, ed. Duel Masters Vol. 5: Goblin Gone Wild. Matsumoto, Shigenobu, illus. 2005. 96p. (J). (ps-7). pap. 7.99 (978-1-59532-675-1(8) , Tokyopop Kids) TOKYOPOP, Inc.

—The Incredibles. 2005. (Illus.). pap. 7.99 (978-1-59532-720-8(7) , Tokyopop Kids) TOKYOPOP, Inc.

Steinberg, David. Mac Attack! Smith, Brian, illus. 2008. 96p. (J). (gr. 3-6). pap. 5.99 (***978-0-448-44699-8(5)*** , Grosset & Dunlap) Penguin Group (USA) Inc.

Stern. Hulk, Vol. 1. (Illus.). (J). mass mkt. (978-0-671-00091-2(8) , Pocket) Simon & Schuster.

—Spiderman. (Illus.). (J). mass mkt. (978-0-671-00093-6(4)); Vol. 2. mass mkt. (978-0-671-00087-5(X)) Simon & Schuster. (Pocket).

Stevens, Terry. The Battle at Longshore Causeway. 2006. 64p. pap. (***978-1-84401-751-5(6)***) Athena Pr.

Stevenson, James. The Castaway. Stevenson, James, illus. 2002. (Illus.). 32p. (J). (gr. 2 up). 15.95 (978-0-688-16965-7(1)) HarperCollins Pubs.

—El Tiovivo de Don Ramiro. (Coleccion el Faro Azul). (SPA., Illus.). (J). 8.95 (978-84-348-1852-1(3) , SM005) SM Ediciones ESP. *Dist:* Continental Bk. Co., Inc.

Stevenson, Robert Louis. Kidnapped. Kennedy, Cam, illus. 2007. 64p. (J). (gr. 5). pap. 11.95 (***978-0-88776-843-9(1)***) Tundra Bks., Inc./Livres Toundra, Inc. CAN. *Dist:* Random Hse., Inc.

—Robert Louis Stevenson's Treasure Island: The Graphic Novel. 2005. (Puffin Graphics Ser.). (Illus.). 176p. (978-1-4156-2620-7(0) , Puffin) Penguin Group (USA) Inc.

—Robert Louis Stevenson/Treasure Island. Cruz, Nardo, illus. 2005. 48p. (J). (gr. 5-8). 25.50 (978-0-7910-9107-4(4)) Facts On File, Inc.

—Treasure Island. Gelev, Penko, illus. 2006. (Graphic Classics Ser.). 48p. (J). (gr. 2-6). pap. 8.99 (978-0-7641-3491-3(4)); 15.99 (978-0-7641-5976-3(3)) Barron's Educational Series, Inc.

—Treasure Island. Rebis, Greg, illus. 2007. (Graphic Revolve Ser.). 63p. (J). (gr. 4-6). lib. bdg. 22.60 (978-1-59889-050-1(6)) Stone Arch Bks.

—Treasure Island. Hamilton, Tim, illus. 2005. (Puffin Graphics Ser.). 176p. (J). (gr. 3-7). pap. 10.99 (978-0-14-240470-6(5) , Puffin) Penguin Group (USA) Inc.

Stevenson, Robert Louis & Castle, Mort. Graphic Classics Robert Louis Stevenson. 2004. (Graphic Classics Ser.: 9). (Illus.). 144p. (YA). pap. 9.95 (978-0-9746648-0-4(4) , Graphic Classics) Eureka Productions.

Stierle, Cynthia. Ratatouille Movie Theater Storybook & Movie Projector. Disney, Reader's Digest, Pixar, illus. 2007. (RD Innovative Book & Player Format Ser.). 48p. (J). (ps-4). bds. 24.99 (***978-0-7944-1284-5(X)***) Reader's Digest Assn., Inc., The.

Stine, R. L. Creepy Creatures. 2006. (Goosebumps Ser.). (Illus.). 144p. (J). pap. 16.99 (978-0-439-84124-5(0)); pap. 8.99 (978-0-439-84125-2(9)) Scholastic, Inc. (Graphix).

Stine, R. L. Scary Summer. 2007. (Goosebumps Graphix Ser.: No. 3). 144p. (J). pap. 8.99 (***978-0-439-85782-6(1)***) Scholastic, Inc.

Stoker, Bram. Bram Stoker/Dracula. Redondo, Nestor, illus. 2005. 48p. (gr. 5-8). 25.50 (978-0-7910-9109-8(0)) Facts On File, Inc.

—Dracula. Becky, Cloonan, illus. 2006. (Puffin Graphics Ser.). 176p. (J). (gr. 3). pap. 10.99 (978-0-14-240572-7(8) , Puffin) Penguin Group (USA) Inc.

Stoker, Bram & Mucci, Michael. Dracula. Halliar, Bill, illus. 2008. (All-Action Classics Ser.). 128p. (J). pap. 6.95 (978-1-4027-3152-5(3)) Sterling Publishing Co., Inc.

Stones, Tad & Pascoe, Jim. Hellboy Animated Volume 2: the Judgement Bell: The Judgement Bell. 2007. 80p. (J). pap. 6.95 (***978-1-59307-799-0(8)***) Dark Horse Comics.

Storrie, Paul D. Robin Hood: Outlaw of Sherwood Forest. Yeates, Thomas, illus. 2007. (Graphic Myths & Legends Ser.). 48p. (J). (gr. 4-8). 26.60 (978-0-8225-5964-1(1)) Lerner Publishing Group.

Storrie, Paul D. Terror in Ghost Mansion. Carruthers, Sandy, illus. 2007. (Twisted Journeys Ser.). 112p. (J). (gr. 4-8). pap. 7.95 (***978-0-8225-6778-3(4)*** , Twenty-First Century Bks.) Lerner Publishing Group.

St.Pierre, Joe, creator. Bold Blood. 2005. (YA). per. 5.95 (978-0-9772727-0-9(2)) Astronaut Ink.

Straczynski, J. M. Hyperion. 2006. (Illus.). 120p. pap. 14.99 (978-0-7851-1895-4(0)) Marvel Enterprises, Inc.

Straczynski, J. Michael. Amazing Spider-Man: The Life & Death of Spiders, 4 vols., Vol. 4. Romita, John, Jr., illus. 2003. (Amazing Spider-man Ser.). 120p. (YA). 11.99 (978-0-7851-1097-2(6)) Marvel Enterprises, Inc.

—Best of Spider-Man HC, Vol. 5. 2006. (Illus.). 240p. 29.99 (978-0-7851-2128-2(5)) Marvel Enterprises, Inc.

—Happy Birthday. Romita, John, Jr., illus. 2004. 100p. lib. bdg. 24.35 (978-1-4176-6025-4(2)) Tandem Library Bks.

—Sins Past. Deodato, Mike, Jr., illus. 2005. (Spider-Man Ser.: Vol. 8). 144p. (YA). pap. 12.99 (978-0-7851-1509-0(9)) Marvel Enterprises, Inc.

Straczynski, J. Michael & Frank, Gary. Powers & Principalities, Vol. 2. 2005. (Max Ser.). (Illus.). 144p. 14.99 (978-0-7851-1456-7(4)) Marvel Enterprises, Inc.

Stringer, Lew, creator. Brickman Begins! 2005. (YA). pap. 9.99 (978-0-9740567-8-4(2)) Active Images.

Strong, Jeremy. Krazy Kow Saves the World - Well, Almost. l.t. ed. 2003. (Illus.). 152p. (J). 16.95 (978-0-7540-7841-8(8) , Galaxy Children's Large Print) BBC Audiobooks America.

—Stuff: The Life of a Cool Demented Dude. Armstrong, Matthew S., illus. 2007. 240p. (J). (gr. 7 up). 15.99 (978-0-06-084105-8(2) , HarperTeen) HarperCollins Pubs.

—Stuff: The Life of a Cool Demented Dude. Armstrong, Matthew, illus. 2007. 240p. (J). (gr. 7 up). lib. bdg. 16.89 (978-0-06-084106-5(0) , HarperTeen) HarperCollins Pubs.

The Strongest of Them All. 2003. (J). per. (978-1-57657-862-9(3)) Paradise Pr., Inc.

Sturm, James. Unstable Molecules. Davis, Guy & Sikoryak, Bob, illus. 2003. (Fantastic Four Legends Ser.: Vol. 1). 128p. (YA). pap. 13.99 (978-0-7851-1112-2(3)) Marvel Enterprises, Inc.

Sugisaki, Yukiru. D. N. Angel, Vol. 11. 11th rev. ed. 2006. pap. 9.99 (978-1-59816-810-5(X) , Tokyopop Adult) TOKYOPOP, Inc.

—Lagoon Engine, Vol. 3. 3rd rev. ed. 2005. (Illus.). pap. 9.99 (978-1-59532-803-8(3) , Tokyopop Kids) TOKYOPOP, Inc.

Sullivan, Howard J. How to Draw Digimon Digital Monsters, 2 vols. 2000. (Illus.). (J). pap. (978-0-439-28661-9(1)) Scholastic, Inc.

Sullivan, Stephen D. Iron Man: The Junior Novel. 2008. (Iron Man Ser.). 144p. (J). pap. 4.99 (***978-0-06-082197-5(3)*** , Harper Entertainment) HarperCollins Pubs.

Sumerak, Marc, et al. The Return of Doom, Vol. 3. Doddridge, Joseph, illus. 2005. (Fantastic Four Ser.). 96p. pap. 5.99 (978-0-7851-1622-6(2)) Marvel Enterprises, Inc.

Sumerak, Mark. End of the Rainbow. 2006. (Illus.). (J). (gr. 2-6). 21.35 (978-1-59961-032-0(9)) Spotlight.

—I Know What We Did That Summer. 2006. (Illus.). (J). (gr. 2-6). 21.35 (978-1-59961-033-7(7)) Spotlight.

—Misadventures in Babysitting. 2006. (Illus.). (J). (gr. 2-6). 21.35 (978-1-59961-034-4(5)) Spotlight.

—Vacation of Doom! 2006. (Illus.). (J). (gr. 2-6). 21.35 (978-1-59961-035-1(3)) Spotlight.

Suzuki, Etsuo. Anne Frank. 2006. (Illus.). 160p. pap. 9.95 (978-1-56970-974-0(2)) Digital Manga Publishing.

Swoboda, Annette. El Chupete de Dudu. 2005. (SPA.). (J). bds. 7.99 (978-84-261-3247-5(2)) Juventud, Editorial ESP. *Dist:* Lectorum Pubns., Inc., Iaconi, Mariuccia Bk. Imports.

—Dudu Se Viste. 2005. (SPA.). (J). bds. 8.50 (978-84-261-3243-7(X)) Juventud, Editorial ESP. *Dist:* Lectorum Pubns., Inc.

—Dudu y el Orinal. 2005. (SPA.). (J). bds. 8.50 (978-84-261-3245-1(6)) Juventud, Editorial ESP. *Dist:* Lectorum Pubns., Inc.

Tachibana, Yutaka. Gacchagacha. 2006. (Illus.). pap. 9.99 (978-1-59816-153-3(9) , Tokyopop Kids) TOKYOPOP, Inc.

Tachibana, Yutaka, illus. & creator. Gatcha Gacha. Tachibana, Yutaka, creator. 2nd rev. ed. 2006. pap. 9.99 (978-1-59816-154-0(7) , Tokyopop Kids) TOKYOPOP, Inc.

Tachikawa, Megumi, creator. Dream Saga, Vol. 4. rev. ed. 2005. (Illus.). 208p. pap. 9.99 (978-1-59532-210-4(8) , Tokyopop Kids) TOKYOPOP, Inc.

—Dream Saga, Vol. 5. rev. ed. 2005. (Illus.). 192p. (J). pap. 9.99 (978-1-59532-211-1(6) , Tokyopop Kids) TOKYOPOP, Inc.

Tadano, Kazuko. Kazuko Tadano Portfolio Vol. 6. 2004. (Illus.). 80p. (YA). pap. 14.99 (978-4-7661-1468-3(X)) Diamond Bk. Distributors.

Takahama, Kan. Kinderbook. 2006. 204p. pap. 17.99 (***978-84-933093-9-8(7)***) Ponent Mon, S.L. ESP. *Dist:* Biblio Distribution.

Takahashi, Hiroshi. Worst, Vol. 1. 2004. (Illus.). 208p. (YA). pap. 12.95 (978-1-56970-983-2(1)) Digital Manga Publishing.

Takahashi, Kazuki. The Millennium Puzzle. Takahashi, Kazuki, illus. 2003. (Illus.). 195p. (gr. 5-8). per. 16.40 (978-0-613-67443-0(X)) Tandem Library Bks.

—Monster Fight. Takahashi, Kazuki, illus. 2004. (Illus.). 200p. lib. bdg. 18.55 (978-1-4176-5897-8(5)) Tandem Library Bks.

—Monster World. Takahashi, Kazuki, illus. 2004. (Illus.). 200p. lib. bdg. 18.55 (978-1-4176-5898-5(3)) Tandem Library Bks.

—Yu-Gi-Oh! Vol. 3: Capsule Monster Chess, 3. Sengupta, Anita, tr. Takahashi, Kazuki, illus. 2003. (Yu-Gi-Oh! Ser.). (Illus.). 216p. (YA). pap. 7.95 (978-1-59116-179-0(7)) Viz Media.

—Yu-Gi-Oh! Duelist, Vol. 8. Takahashi, Kazuki, illus. 2005. (Yu-Gi-Oh! Ser.). (Illus.). 224p. (YA). pap. 7.95 (978-1-59116-998-7(4)) Viz Media.

—Yu-Gi-Oh! Duelist: The Player Killer, Vol. 3. Takahashi, Kazuki, illus. 2005. (Yu-Gi-Oh! Ser.). (Illus.). 216p. (YA). (gr. 8-13). pap. 7.95 (978-1-59116-771-6(X)) Viz Media.

—Yu-Gi-Oh! Millennium World, Vol. 3. 2006. (Yu-Gi-Oh! Ser.). 208p. (YA). pap. 7.95 (978-1-4215-0409-4(X)) Viz Media.

—Yu-GI-Oh! Millennium World Vol. 1: The World of Memory. Takahashi, Kazuki, illus. 2005. (Yu-Gi-Oh! Ser.). (Illus.). 192p. (YA). pap. 7.95 (978-1-59116-878-2(3)) Viz Media.

Takahashi, Rumiko. Inu Yasha. Takahashi, Rumiko, illus. 2004. (Illus.). 190p. per. 19.70 (978-1-4176-5276-1(4)); 184p. per. 19.70 (978-1-4176-5272-3(1)) Tandem Library Bks.

—Inu Yasha. 2003. (Illus.). 188p. per. 19.70 (978-1-4176-5645-5(X)) Tandem Library Bks.

—Inu Yasha. Takahashi, Rumiko, illus. 2003. (Illus.). 188p. per. 19.70 (978-1-4176-5646-2(8)); 182p. per. 19.70 (978-1-4176-5274-7(8)); 185p. per. 19.70 (978-1-4176-5273-0(X)); 186p. per. 19.70 (978-1-4176-5271-6(3)); 189p. per. 19.70 (978-1-4176-5648-6(4)); 181p. per. 19.70 (978-1-4176-5082-8(6)) Tandem Library Bks.

—Inu-Yasha. Takahashi, Rumiko, illus. (Inuyasha Ser.). (Illus.). (YA). Vol. 13. 2003. 192p. pap. 8.95 (978-1-56931-808-9(5)); Vol. 19. 2004. 200p. pap. 8.95 (978-1-59116-678-8(0)) Viz Media.

—Inu Yasha: Volume 12. Takahashi, Rumiko, illus. 2004. (Illus.). 200p. lib. bdg. 19.70 (978-1-4176-5992-0(0)) Tandem Library Bks.

—Inu Yasha Ani-Manga. Takahashi, Rumiko, illus. 2004. (Illus.). 206p. per. 21.35 (978-1-4176-6422-1(3)) Tandem Library Bks.

—Inu Yasha Animanga. (Inuyasha Ani-Manga Ser.). (YA). Vol. 13. 2006. 208p. pap. 11.99 (978-1-4215-0252-6(6)); Vol. 15. 2006. 208p. pap. 11.99 (978-1-4215-0482-7(0)); Vol. 16. 2006. 208p. pap. 11.99 (978-1-4215-0483-4(9)); Vol. 19. 2007. 216p. pap. 11.99 (978-1-4215-0903-7(2)); Vol. 20. 2007. 216p. pap. 11.99 (978-1-4215-0904-4(0)) Viz Media.

—Inuyasha, Vol. 20. Takahashi, Rumiko, illus. 2004. (Inuyasha Ser.). (Illus.). 200p. (YA). pap. 8.95 (978-1-59116-626-9(8)) Viz Media.

—Inuyasha, Vol. 29. 2007. (Inuyasha Ser.). 192p. (YA). pap. 8.95 (978-1-4215-0900-6(8)) Viz Media.

—Inuyasha Vol. 19: Demon Box Set. 2004. (Inuyasha Ser.). (Illus.). 192p. pap. 24.99 (978-1-59116-725-9(6)) Viz Media.

—Inuyasha the Movie Ani-Manga: Affections Touching Across Time. Takahashi, Rumiko, illus. 2005. (Inuyasha Ser.). 432p. (YA). pap. 24.99 (978-1-59116-828-7(7)) Viz Media.

—Maison Ikkoku, Vol. 10. Takahashi, Rumiko, illus. 2005. (Maison Ikkoku Ser.). (Illus.). 248p. (YA). pap. 9.95 (978-1-59116-729-7(9)) Viz Media.

—Maison Ikkoku, Vol. 14. 2nd ed. 2005. (Maison Ikkoku Ser.). (Illus.). 240p. (YA). pap. 9.95 (978-1-4215-0142-0(2)) Viz Media.

—Ranma 1/2, Vol. 8. Takahashi, Rumiko, illus. 2004. (Illus.). 196p. (gr. 3-6). lib. bdg. 18.75 (978-0-613-85854-0(9)) Tandem Library Bks.

—Ranma 1/2, Vol. 31. Takahashi, Rumiko, illus. 2005. (Ranma 1/2 Ser.). (Illus.). 200p. (YA). pap. 9.95 (978-1-59116-860-7(0)) Viz Media.

Takahashi, Shin. Saikano, Vol. 4. Takahashi, Shin, illus. 2005. (Saikano Ser.). (Illus.). 248p. (YA). pap. 9.95 (978-1-59116-476-0(1)) Viz Media.

Takanashi, Mitsuba. Crimson Hero. (Crimson Hero Ser.). (YA). Vol. 1. 2005. (Illus.). 192p. pap. 8.99 (978-1-4215-0140-6(6)); Vol. 3. 2006. 208p. pap. 8.99 (978-1-4215-0577-0(0)) Viz Media.

Takao, Ukyou. To Heart. 2004. (Illus.). (YA). Vol. 2. 178p. pap. (978-1-4139-0070-5(4)); Vol. 3. 186p. pap. (978-1-4139-0087-3(9)) ADV Manga.

Takaya, Natsuki. Fruits Basket, Vol. 6. Takaya, Natsuki, illus. 2004. (Illus.). lib. bdg. 20.90 (978-1-4176-5219-8(5)) TOKYOPOP, Inc.

—Fruits Basket. 2005. (Illus.). 191p. per. 20.90 (978-1-4176-5948-7(3)) Tandem Library Bks.

Takaya, Natsuki, illus. Fruits Basket Notebook/Journal. 2005. 128p. 9.99 (978-1-59816-260-8(8) , Tokyopop Adult) TOKYOPOP, Inc.

Takemoto, Novala. Kamikaze Girls. 2006. (Kamikaza Girls Novel Ser.). (Illus.). 208p. (YA). pap. 8.99 (978-1-4215-0268-7(2)) Viz Media.

Tallarico, Tony. How Fire Came to the Indians. 2005. (Classics Illustrated Junior Ser.). 32p. 5.99 (978-1-894998-18-5(9)) Lake, Jack Productions, Inc. CAN. *Dist:* Hushion Hse. Publishing, Ltd.

Tamura, Yumi. Basara. (Basara Ser.). (YA). Vol. 18. 2006. 208p. pap. 9.99 (978-1-4215-0528-2(2)); Vol. 19. 2006. 208p. pap. 9.99 (978-1-4215-0529-9(0)); Vol. 22. 2007. 192p. pap. 9.99 (978-1-4215-0979-2(2)) Viz Media.

—Wild Com. Tamura, Yumi, illus. 2004. (Wild Com Ser.). (Illus.). 192p. (YA). pap. 9.95 (978-1-59116-559-0(8)) Viz Media.

Tan, Shaun. The Arrival. 2007. (J). 128p. (gr. 7 up). pap. 19.99 (978-0-439-89529-3(4)); (978-0-439-89530-9(8)) Scholastic, Inc. (Levine, Arthur A. Bks.).

Tanabe, Yellow. Kekkaishi, Vol. 3. Tanabe, Yellow, illus. 2005. (Kekkaishi Ser.). 192p. (YA). pap. 9.99 (978-1-4215-0067-6(1)) Viz Media.

—Kekkaishi, Vol. 6. 2006. (Kekkaishi Ser.). (Illus.). 208p. (YA). pap. 9.99 (978-1-4215-0487-2(1)) Viz Media.

Tanaka, Yoshiki. Clamp No Kiseki, Vol. 1. Clamp, illus. 2005. 32p. pap. 29.99 (978-1-59532-605-8(7) , Tokyopop Adult) TOKYOPOP, Inc.

Tanemura, Arina. Full Moon. (Full Moon o Sagashite Ser.). (YA). Vol. 4. 2005. (Illus.). 192p. pap. 8.99 (978-1-4215-0125-3(2)); Vol. 5. 2006. 200p. pap. 8.99 (978-1-4215-0266-3(6)) Viz Media.

—O Sagashite. Tanemura, Arina, illus. 2006. (Full Moon o Sagashite Ser.). 200p. (YA). pap. 8.99 (978-1-4215-0397-4(2)) Viz Media.

Tashiro, Takuyo. Najica Blitz Tactics, Vol. 1. 2004. (Illus.). 200p. (YA). pap. (978-1-4139-0018-7(6)) ADV Manga.

Tbd. I Am Iron Man. 2008. (I Can Read Bks.). 32p. (J). pap. 3.99 (***978-0-06-082193-7(0)*** , Harper Trophy) HarperCollins Pubs.

Team Effort. 1999. (Digimon Sticker Activity Bks.) (Illus.). 25p. (J). (ps-2). pap. (978-0-7666-0570-1(1)) Modern Publishing.

Teitelbaum, Michael. Creating the X-Men: How It All Began. 2000. (gr. k-3). lib. bdg. 11.80 (978-0-613-33109-8(5)) Tandem Library Bks.

—La Historia de Spider-Man. 2005. (Dk Readers Ser.). (Illus.). 48p. (J). (ps-7). pap. 3.99 (978-0-7566-1506-2(2)) Dorling Kindersley Publishing, Inc.

—Marvel Heroes Mix & Match. 2007. 12p. (J). bds. 14.99 (978-0-7944-1229-6(7)) Reader's Digest Assn., Inc., The.

—Spider-Man: Amazing Powers. 2001. lib. bdg. 11.80 (978-0-613-43958-9(9)) Tandem Library Bks.

Teitelbaum, Michael & O'Neill, Cynthia. La Historia de Spider-Man. 2005. (Dk Readers Ser.). (Illus.). 48p. (J). (ps-7). 14.99 (978-0-7566-1502-4(X)) Dorling Kindersley Publishing, Inc.

Teitlebaum, Michael. X-Men School. 2006. (Dk Readers Ser.). (Illus.). 48p. (J). 14.99 (978-0-7566-1929-9(7)); pap. 3.99 (978-0-7566-1930-5(0)) Dorling Kindersley Publishing, Inc.

Temple, Bob. The Day Mom Finally Snapped. Harpster, Steve, illus. 2006. (Graphic Sparks Ser.). 33p. (J). 19.93 (978-1-59889-038-9(7)) Stone Arch Bks.

Terasawa, Buichi. Kabuto. 2001. (YA). Vol. 1. 313p. pap. 11.95 (978-1-58899-121-8(0)); Vol. 2. 291p. pap. 11.95 (978-1-58899-122-5(9)) ComicsOne Corp./Dr. Masters.

Tezuka, Osamu. Astro Boy. 2003. (YA). Vol. 19. 208p. pap. 9.95 (978-1-56971-900-8(4)); Vol. 20. 224p. pap. 9.95 (978-1-56971-901-5(2)); Vol. 21. 232p. pap. 9.95 (978-1-56971-902-2(0)); Vol. 22. 216p. pap. 9.95 (978-1-56971-903-9(9)) Dark Horse Comics.

—The Dawn. Tezuka, Osamu, illus. 2003. (Phoenix Ser.: Vol. 1). (Illus.). 344p. (YA). pap. 15.95 (978-1-56931-868-3(9)) Viz Media.

—Nextworld. 2003. (YA). Vol. 1. (Illus.). 160p. pap. 13.95 (978-1-56971-866-7(0)); Vol. 2. 152p. pap. 13.95 (978-1-56971-867-4(9)) Dark Horse Comics.

—Phoenix. 2006. (Phoenix Ser.). 208p. (YA). Vol. 6. pap. 16.99 (978-1-4215-0258-8(5)); Vol. 7. pap. 15.99 (978-1-4215-0517-6(7)); Vol. 8. pap. 15.99 (978-1-4215-0518-3(5)) Viz Media.

—Phoenix Vol. 3: Yamato/Space. Tezuka, Osamu, illus. 2003. (Phoenix Ser.). (Illus.). 336p. (YA). pap. 15.95 (978-1-59116-100-4(2)) Viz Media.

Thomas, John Ira. Zoo Force: Dear Eniko. Smith, Jeremy, illus. 2003. 68p. per. 6.95 (978-0-9743147-1-6(4)) Candle Light Pr.

Thomas, Roy. Rogues in the House & Other Stories. 2003. (Chronicles of Conan Ser.: Vol. 2). 144p. (YA). pap. 15.95 (978-1-59307-023-6(3)) Dark Horse Comics.

—Roy Thomas. 2006. (Marvel Visionaries Ser.). (Illus.). 352p. (YA). 34.99 (978-0-7851-2088-9(2)) Marvel Enterprises, Inc.

Thomas, Roy, et al. Avengers. 2006. (Marvel Essentials Ser.: Vol. 5). (Illus.). 552p. pap. 16.99 (978-0-7851-2087-2(4)) Marvel Enterprises, Inc.

—Essential Classic X-Men, Vol. 2. 2006. (Illus.). 640p. pap. 16.99 (978-0-7851-2116-9(1)) Marvel Enterprises, Inc.

Thompson, Bart A. Mummy. Miroglio, Brian, illus. 2007. (Graphic Horror Ser.). 32p. (YA). (gr. 5-8). lib. bdg. 27.07 (***978-1-60270-061-1(3)*** , Graphic Planet) Magic Wagon.

Thompson, Jill. Scary Godmother. 2005. (Illus.). 48p. pap. 9.95 (978-1-57989-070-4(9)) Sirius Entertainment, Inc.

—Scary Godmother: The Revenge of Jimmy. 2006. (Illus.). 48p. pap. 9.95 (978-1-57989-071-1(7)) Sirius Entertainment, Inc.

—Scary Godmother Vol. 4: The Boo Flu. 2000. (Illus.). 48p. 19.95 (978-1-57989-038-4(5)) Sirius Entertainment, Inc.

Thompson, Jill, creator. Scary Godmother: The Mystery Date. 2004. (Illus.). 48p. pap. 9.95 (978-1-57989-072-8(5)) Sirius Entertainment, Inc.

Thompson, Jill, illus. Magic Trixie. 2008. 96p. (J). pap. 7.99 (***978-0-06-117045-4(3)*** , Harper Trophy) HarperCollins Pubs.

Thompson, Lisa. Wonder Worlds. Thompson, Lisa & Stapleton, Matthew, illus. 2005. (Read-It! Chapter Bks.). 48p. (J). (ps-k). lib. bdg. 19.95 (978-1-4048-1347-2(0)) Picture Window Bks.

Thopmson, Frank. Tim Burton's the Nightmare Before Christmas. 2005. (Illus.). 176p. (J). (gr. 5-17). pap. 8.99 (978-0-7868-3849-3(3)) Disney Pr.

Thor, Son of Asgard. 2007. (J). 128.10 (***978-1-59961-285-0(2)***) Spotlight.

Thoughts Staff. Police Stories: the fight Call. 2005. 16p. 8.99 (978-1-4116-2267-8(7)) Lulu.com.

Tieman, Robert. The Disney Keepsakes. 2005. (Illus.). 64p. (ps-17). 60.00 (978-0-7868-5558-2(4) , Disney Editions) Disney Pr.

Tieri, Frank. Law of the Jungle, 3 vols. Chen, Sean, illus. 2003. (Wolverine Legends Ser.: Vol. 3). 144p. (YA). 12.99 (978-0-7851-1135-1(2)) Marvel Enterprises, Inc.

—Weapon X: The Underground, Vol. 2. Youngquist, Jeff, ed. Jeanty, Georges, illus. 2004. (X-Men Ser.). 184p. pap. 19.99 (978-0-7851-1253-2(7)) Marvel Enterprises, Inc.

Tinder, Jeremy. Cry Yourself to Sleep. 2006. (Illus.). 88p. (YA). pap. 7.00 (978-1-891830-81-5(3)) Top Shelf Productions.

To Wait Is to Win. 2004. (J). (978-0-9762904-7-6(2)) Layne Morgan Media, Inc.

The Tobacco Temptation. (J). 39.50 (978-1-56230-082-1(2)) Syndistar, Inc.

Toda, Yasunari, illus. Gundam Seed Astray R, Vol. 2. 2nd rev. ed. 2005. pap. 9.99 (978-1-59532-577-8(8) , Tokyopop Adult) TOKYOPOP, Inc.

—Gundam Seed Astray R, Vol. 3. rev. ed. 2005. 192p. pap. 9.99 (978-1-59532-578-5(6) , Tokyopop Adult) TOKYOPOP, Inc.

Tokoro, Juzo. Spawn Manga, Vol. 1. (Illus.). 200p. (YA). pap. 9.99 (978-1-58240-571-1(9)) Image Comics.

Tokyopop Staff, creator. Rising Stars of Manga - Uk & Ireland Edition. 2006. (Illus.). 192p. pap. 9.99 (978-1-59816-464-0(3) , Tokyopop Adult) TOKYOPOP, Inc.

Tokyopop Staff, ed. Jackie Chan Adventures: Enter the Dark Hand, 3 vols. 2003. (Illus.). 128p. pap. 7.99 (978-1-59182-402-2(8)) TOKYOPOP, Inc.

—Rising Stars of Manga, Vol. 2. 2003. (Illus.). 192p. pap. 9.99 (978-1-59182-536-4(9) , Tokyopop Adult) TOKYOPOP, Inc.

Tokyopop Staff, illus. Rave Master: The Sound of Thunder, Vol. 3. 2005. 96p. (J). pap. 7.99 (978-1-59532-791-8(6)) TOKYOPOP, Inc.

Tokyopop Staff, prod. Pop Displays - 2005 Air Gear 32 Count Pop Displa, Vol. 11. 2005. (Illus.). pap. 319.68 (978-1-59532-868-7(8)) TOKYOPOP, Inc.

Tolkien, J. R. R., et al. El Hobbit. Diaz, Lorenzo, tr. from ENG. 2004. (SPA., Illus.). 136p. 19.95 (978-1-59497-071-9(8)) Public Square Bks.

Tom & Jerry, 3 vols. 2001. (J). (978-1-58805-142-4(0)) DS-Max USA, Inc.

Tomizawa, Hitoshi. Treasure Hunter 1: Eternal Youth, 3 vols., Vol. 1. Pannone, Frank, ed. Kobayashi, Mayumi, tr. from JPN. Tomizawa, Hitoshi, illus. 2004. Orig. Title: Hizenya Jyubei 2. (Illus.). 200p. pap. 9.99 (978-1-58664-921-0(3) , CMX 65101G, CPM Manga) Central Park Media Corp.

—Treasure Hunter 2: Figurehead of Souls, 3 vols., Vol. 2. Pannone, Frank, ed. Kobayashi, Mayumi, tr. from JPN. Tomizawa, Hitoshi, illus. 2004. Orig. Title: Hizenya Jyubei 2. (Illus.). 200p. pap. 9.99 (978-1-58664-922-7(1) , CMX 65102G, CPM Manga) Central Park Media Corp.

—Treasure Hunter 3: The Last Crusade, 3 vols., Vol. 3. Pannone, Frank, ed. Kobayashi, Mayumi, tr. from JPN. Tomizawa, Hitoshi, illus. 2004. Orig. Title: Hizenya Jyubei 2. (Illus.). 216p. pap. 9.99 (978-1-58664-923-4(X) , CMX 65103G, CPM Manga) Central Park Media Corp.

Tomohiro, Chiba. Gundam Seed Astray, Vol. 2. Kouichi, Tokita, illus. rev. ed. 2004. 192p. (YA). pap. 9.99 (978-1-59182-939-3(9) , Tokyopop Adult) TOKYOPOP, Inc.

Tonka Let's Go! 2004. (J). (978-0-9767179-0-4(5)) ABC Development, Inc.

Tony's Sobering Lesson. (J). 39.50 (978-1-56230-075-3(X)) Syndistar, Inc.

Top That, ed. How to Draw 101 Cartoon Characters. 2005. (Illus.). 48p. (J). pap. (978-1-84510-735-2(7)) Top That! Publishing PLC.

Toriyama, Akira. Dr. Slump. 2006. (Dr. Slump Ser.). 208p. (YA). Vol. 8. pap. 7.99 (978-1-4215-0632-6(7)); Vol. 9. pap. 7.99 (978-1-4215-0633-3(5)) Viz Media.

—Dragon Ball 6. 2001. (gr. 3-6). lib. bdg. 22.20 (978-0-613-55703-0(4)) Tandem Library Bks.

—Dragon Ball 7. 2002. (gr. 3-6). lib. bdg. 22.20 (978-0-613-55704-7(2)) Tandem Library Bks.

—Dragon Ball 8. 2002. (gr. 3-6). lib. bdg. 22.20 (978-0-613-55705-4(0)) Tandem Library Bks.

—Dragon Ball 9. 2002. (gr. 3-6). lib. bdg. 22.20 (978-0-613-55706-1(9)) Tandem Library Bks.

—Dragon Ball Z. Toriyama, Akira, illus. 2004. (Illus.). Vol. 15. 200p. lib. bdg. 18.55 (978-1-4176-5214-3(4)); Vol. 16. 200p. lib. bdg. 18.55 (978-1-4176-5215-0(2)); Vol. 17. 200p. lib. bdg. 18.55 (978-1-4176-5216-7(0)); Vol. 18. lib. bdg. 18.55 (978-1-4176-5213-6(6)) Tandem Library Bks.

—Dragon Ball Z, Vol. 20. Toriyama, Akira, illus. 2005. (Dragon Ball Z Ser.). (Illus.). 192p. (YA). pap. 7.95 (978-1-59116-808-9(2)) Viz Media.

—Dragon Ball Z, Vol. 26. 2006. (Dragon Ball Z Ser.). 208p. (YA). pap. 7.95 (978-1-4215-0636-4(X)) Viz Media.

Torres, Daniel. Tom Vol. 1: Las Aventuras de Tom. 2004. (SPA., Illus.). 48p. 19.95 (978-1-59497-068-9(8)) Public Square Bks.

Torres, J. The Copybook Tales. 2002. 240p. (YA). pap. 19.95 (978-1-929998-39-5(2)) Oni Pr., Inc.

Tow Nakazaki. Et Cetera, Vol. 6. 6th rev. ed. 2005. (Illus.). 192p. pap. 9.99 (978-1-59532-135-0(7) , Tokyopop Kids) TOKYOPOP, Inc.

Toy Box Innovations Staff, creator. Disney Pixar: Finding Nemo/A Bug's Life/Monsters, Inc. unabr. abr. ed. 2005. (Disney's Read along Collection). (J). audio compact disk 14.99 (978-0-7634-1151-0(5)) Walt Disney Records.

Toy Box Productions Staff, Box, creator. Disney's Read Along Collection: Cinderella; Snow White; Sleeping Beauty. unabr. abr. ed. 2005. (Disney Princess Ser.). (J). audio compact disk 14.99 (978-0-7634-1150-3(7)) Walt Disney Records.

Toybox Innovations. Disney Pixar's Toy Story. 2006. (Disney's Read Along Ser.). (Illus.). (J). (ps-3). audio compact disk 7.99 (978-0-7634-2179-3(0)) Walt Disney Records.

ToyBox Innovations, creator. Dead Man's Chest. 2006. (Pirates of the Caribbean (Audio) Ser.). (Illus.). 24p. (J). (ps-3). audio compact disk 7.99 (978-0-7634-2177-9(4)) Walt Disney Records.

—Deep in the Jungle. abr. ed. 2006. (Disney's Read along Collection). (J). (ps-3). pap. 14.99 incl. audio compact disk (978-0-7634-2182-3(0)) Walt Disney Records.

—Disney Cars. 2006. (Disney's Read Along Ser.). (Illus.). 24p. (J). (ps-3). audio compact disk, audio compact disk 7.99 (978-0-7634-2169-4(3)) Walt Disney Records.

—Disney's Chicken Little. 2006. (Disney's Read Along Ser.). (Illus.). 24p. (J). pap. 7.99 incl. audio compact disk (978-0-7634-2170-0(7)) Walt Disney Records.

—Disney's Cinderella. 2006. (Disney's Read Along Ser.). (Illus.). 24p. (J). pap. 7.99 incl. audio compact disk (978-0-7634-2171-7(5)) Walt Disney Records.

—Disney's Finding Nemo. 2006. (Disney's Read Along Ser.). (Illus.). 24p. (J). pap. 7.99 incl. audio compact disk (978-0-7634-2172-4(3)) Walt Disney Records.

—Disney's Lilo & Stitch. 2006. (Disney's Read Along Ser.). (Illus.). 24p. (J). audio compact disk 7.99 (978-0-7634-2173-1(1)) Walt Disney Records.

—Disney's Little Mermaid. 2006. (Disney's Read Along Ser.). (Illus.). 24p. (J). audio compact disk 7.99 (978-0-7634-2174-8(X)) Walt Disney Records.

—Disney's Monsters Inc. 2006. (Disney's Read Along Ser.). (Illus.). 24p. (J). audio, audio compact disk 7.99 (978-0-7634-2175-5(8)) Walt Disney Records.

The Transformation. 2003. (J). per. (978-1-57657-863-6(1)) Paradise Pr., Inc.

Trillo, Carlos. Bird. Bobillo, Juan, illus. 2003. 48p. (YA). (gr. 11 up). 12.95 (978-1-931724-22-7(9)) Diamond Select Toys & Collectibles.

—Video Noire. 2001. (Illus.). 96p. pap. 9.95 (978-1-56971-628-1(5)) Dark Horse Comics.

Trondheim, Lewis. Kaput & Zosky. 2008. 80p. (J). pap. 13.95 (***978-1-59643-132-4(6)*** , First Second Bks.) Roaring Brook Pr.

Trondheim, Lewis. Li'l Santa. Robin, Thierry, illus. 2003. 48p. 14.95 (978-1-56163-335-7(6)) NBM Publishing Co.

Trudell, Devin, illus. 3 Stories. Trudell, Devin, . 2007. (YA). 10.00 (***978-0-9794004-0-7(6)***) Art Night Bks.

Tsuda, Masami. Kare Kano: His & Her Circumstances, Vol. 18. 18th rev. ed. 2005. (Illus.). pap. 9.99 (978-1-59532-592-1(1) , Tokyopop Kids) TOKYOPOP, Inc.

Tsuda, Masami, illus. & creator. Kare Kano, Vol. 15. Tsuda, Masami, creator. rev. ed. 2005. Tr. of Kareshi Kanojo No Jijo. 200p. pap. 9.99 (978-1-59532-589-1(1) , Tokyopop Kids) TOKYOPOP, Inc.

Tsukuba, Sakura. Land of the Blindfolded, Vol. 5. 2005. (Illus.). 200p. (YA). pap. 9.99 (978-1-4012-0528-7(3) , CMX) DC Comics.

Tuazon, Noel & Keating, Scott A., illus. Elk's Run. 2007. 224p. 19.95 (978-0-345-49511-2(X) , Villard Bks.) Random House Publishing Group.

Tucker, Mark. Super Phil. Petete, Christine, illus. 2003. (J). 4.50 (978-1-882440-00-9(5)) God's World Pubns. Inc.

Tunasima, Sirou. Jinki: Extend. 2004. Vol. 1. (Illus.). 186p. pap. (978-1-4139-0052-1(6)); Vol. 2. 184p. pap. (978-1-4139-0090-3(9)) ADV Manga.

Twain, Mark. Mark Twain/the Adventures of Huckleberry Finn. Redondo, Frank, illus. 2005. 48p. (gr. 5-8). 25.50 (978-0-7910-9101-2(5)) Facts On File, Inc.

—Mark Twain/the Adventures of Tom Sawyer. Cruz, E. R., illus. 2005. 48p. (gr. 5-8). 25.50 (978-0-7910-9102-9(3)) Facts On File, Inc.

Uderzo, Albert & Goscinny, René. Asterix & the Actress. 2002. (Asterix Ser.). (Illus.). 48p. pap. 9.95 (978-0-7528-4658-3(2)) Orion Bks. Ltd. GBR. *Dist:* Sterling Publishing Co., Inc.

—Asterix & the Actress. Bell, Anthea & Hockridge, Derek, trs. from FRE. 2001. (Illus.). 48p. (J). (gr. 5). (978-0-7528-4657-6(4)) Orion Media.

—Asterix & the Magic Carpet. 2002. (Asterix Ser.). (Illus.). 48p. pap. 9.95 (978-0-7528-4776-4(7)) Orion Bks. Ltd. GBR. *Dist:* Sterling Publishing Co., Inc.

—Asterix & the Magic Carpet. 2002. (Illus.). 48p. (978-0-7528-4715-3(5)) Orion Media.

Ueda, Miwa. Change of Heart. Yoshimoto, Ray, tr. from JPN. rev. ed. 2003. (Peach Girl Ser.: Vol. 2). (Illus.). 192p. (gr. 7 up). pap. 9.99 (978-1-59182-195-3(9) , Tokyopop Adult) TOKYOPOP, Inc.

—Change of Heart, 1. 2003. (Illus.). 192p. (gr. 7 up). pap. 9.99 (978-1-931514-19-4(4) , Tokyopop Adult) TOKYOPOP, Inc.

Ueda, Miwa, illus. & creator. Peach Girl Authentic, Vol. 4. Ueda, Miwa, creator. 4th rev. ed. 2005. 192p. pap. 9.99 (978-1-59532-174-9(8) , Tokyopop Kids) TOKYOPOP, Inc.

Ueda, Rinko. Tail of the Moon, Volume 4. 2007. (Tail of the Moon Ser.). 200p. (YA). pap. 8.99 (978-1-4215-0816-0(8)) Viz Media.

—Trail of the Moon, Volume 3. 2007. (Tail of the Moon Ser.). 200p. (YA). pap. 8.99 (978-1-4215-0814-6(1)) Viz Media.

Ueyama, Michiro. Chaotic Century. Ueyama, Michiro, illus. (Zoids Ser.). (Illus.). (YA). Vol. 7. 2002. 80p. pap. 5.95 (978-1-56931-766-2(6)); Vol. 8. 2002. 72p. pap. 5.95 (978-1-56931-767-9(4)); Vol. 9. 2002. 72p. pap. 5.95 (978-1-56931-768-6(2)); Vol. 10. 2002. 70p. pap. 5.95 (978-1-56931-857-7(3)); Vol. 11. 2004. 82p. pap. 5.95 (978-1-56931-858-4(1)); Vol. 12. 2003. 72p. pap. 5.95 (978-1-56931-867-6(0)) Viz Media.

Ugawa, Hiroki. Shrine of the Morning Mist. Ukawa, Hiroki, illus. 2006. (YA). pap. 9.99 (978-1-59816-343-8(4) , Tokyopop Kids) TOKYOPOP, Inc.

Umezu, Kazuo. Blood. Umezu, Kazuo, illus. 2002. (Orochi Ser.). (Illus.). 224p. (YA). pap. 16.95 (978-1-56931-787-7(9)) Viz Media.

—The Drifting Classroom, Vol. 8. Roman, Annette, ed. Umezu, Kazuo, illus. 2007. (Drifting Classroom Ser.). 192p. (YA). pap. 9.99 (***978-1-4215-0960-0(1)***) Viz Media.

—Drifting Classroom, Vol. 9. Roman, Annette, ed. Umezu, Kazuo, illus. 2007. (Drifting Classroom Ser.). 192p. (YA). pap. 9.99 (***978-1-4215-0961-7(X)***) Viz Media.

Up in Smoke. 2004. (J). (978-0-9762904-9-0(9)) Layne Morgan Media, Inc.

Urasawa, Naoki. Naoki Urasawa's Monster. (Naoki Urasawa's Monster Ser.). 216p. (YA). Vol. 2. 2006. pap. 9.99 (978-1-4215-0112-3(0)); Vol. 7. 2007. pap. 9.99 (978-1-4215-0500-8(2)) Viz Media.

—Naoki Urasawa's Monster, Volume 1 Vol. 1: Herr Dr Tenma. Urasawa, Naoki, illus. 2006. (Monster Ser.). 224p. (YA). pap. 9.99 (978-1-59116-641-2(1)) Viz Media.

Urrea, Lourdes, et al. Athon Labar. rev. ed. 2006. (Ediciones Castillo Castillo Del Terror Ser.). (SPA.). 136p. (J). (gr. 2-6). pap. 6.95 (978-970-20-0309-0(1)) Castillo, Ediciones, S. A. de C. V. MEX. *Dist:* Macmillan.

—El Dragon Jines. 2005. (Ediciones Castillo Castillo Del Terror Ser.). (SPA.). (J). (gr. 2-6). pap. 7.95 (978-970-20-0357-1(1)) Castillo, Ediciones, S. A. de C. V. MEX. *Dist:* Iaconi, Mariuccia Bk. Imports.

—En Busca de Dracu. 2005. (Ediciones Castillo Castillo Del Terror Ser.).Tr. of Looking for Dracu. (SPA.). (J). (gr. 2-6). pap. 7.95 (978-970-20-0339-7(3)) Castillo, Ediciones, S. A. de C. V. MEX. *Dist:* Iaconi, Mariuccia Bk. Imports.

—Piel de Gallilna. 2005. (Ediciones Castillo Castillo Del Terror Ser.).Tr. of Chicken Bumps. (SPA.). (J). (gr. 2-6). pap. 7.95 (978-970-20-0292-5(3)) Castillo, Ediciones, S. A. de C. V. MEX. *Dist:* Iaconi, Mariuccia Bk. Imports.

—El Secreto Gitano. 2005. (Ediciones Castillo Castillo Del Terror Ser.).Tr. of Gypsy Secret. (SPA.). (J). (gr. 2-6). pap. 7.95 (978-970-20-0310-6(5)) Castillo, Ediciones, S. A. de C. V. MEX. *Dist:* Iaconi, Mariuccia Bk. Imports.

Van Hamme, Jean. Thorgal: La Maga Traicionada. Rosinski, Grzegorz, illus. 2004. Orig. Title: Thorgal vol. 1: la Magicienne Trahie. (SPA.). 48p. pap. 16.95 (978-1-59497-006-1(8)) Public Square Bks.

—Los Tres Ancianos del pais de Aran, Vol. 3. Roskinski, Grzegorz, illus. 2004. Orig. Title: Thorgal Vol. 3: les Trois Vieillards du Pays d'Aran. (SPA.). 48p. pap. 16.95 (978-1-59497-008-5(4)) Public Square Bks.

Van Horn, William & Gilbert, Janet. Uncle Scrooge #348. 2005. 64p. (YA). pap. 6.95 (978-1-888472-01-1(4)) Gemstone Publishing, Inc.

Van Horn, William & Rawson, Dave. Walt Disney's Comics & Stories, No. 662. 2005. (Illus.). 64p. (YA). pap. 6.95 (978-1-888472-02-8(2)) Gemstone Publishing, Inc.

Van Horn, William & Rosa, Don. Walt Disney's Comics & Stories, Vol. 663. 2005. 64p. (YA). pap. 6.95 (978-1-888472-03-5(0)) Gemstone Publishing, Inc.

Van Horn, William, et al. Walt Disney's Comics & Stories. 64p. No. 660. 2005. (Illus.). (YA). pap. 6.95 (978-0-911903-85-0(2)); Vol. 664. 2006. pap. 6.95 (978-1-888472-17-2(0)); Vol. 665. 2006. pap. 6.95 (978-1-888472-18-9(9)); Vol. 667. 2005. pap. 6.95 (978-1-888472-20-2(0)) Gemstone Publishing, Inc.

—Walt Disney's Comics & Stories #669. 2006. 64p. pap. 6.95 (978-1-888472-27-1(8)) Gemstone Publishing, Inc.

—Walt Disney's Comics & Stories #671. 2006. 64p. pap. 6.95 (978-1-888472-29-5(4)) Gemstone Publishing, Inc.

Van Lente, Fred. Breaking up Is Venomous to Do! 2007. (Spider-Man Set III Ser.). 24p. (J). (gr. 2-6). 21.35 (*978-1-59961-393-2(X)) Spotlight.

—Dust-up in Aisle Seven! 2007. (Spider-Man Set III Ser.). 24p. (J). (gr. 2-6). 21.35 (*978-1-59961-394-9(8)) Spotlight.

—Fasion Victims. 2007. (Spider-Man Set III Ser.). 24p. (J). (gr. 2-6). 21.35 (*978-1-59961-395-6(6)) Spotlight.

—World War G. 2007. (Spider-Man Set III Ser.). 24p. (J). (gr. 2-6). 21.35 (*978-1-59961-396-3(4)) Spotlight.

Vaughan, Brian K. Cry Wolf. Kubert, Andy, illus. 2005. 96p. lib. bdg. 19.75 (978-1-4176-6048-3(1)) Tandem Library Bks.

—Escape to New York. 2006. (Runaways Ser.: Vol. 5). (Illus.). 144p. pap. 7.99 (978-0-7851-1901-2(9)) Marvel Enterprises, Inc.

—Magnetic North. 2006. (Illus.). 128p. (YA). pap. 12.99 (978-0-7851-1906-7(X)) Marvel Enterprises, Inc.

—The Tempest. 2004. (X-Men Ser.: Vol. 9). (Illus.). 112p. (YA). 10.99 (978-0-7851-1404-8(1)) Marvel Enterprises, Inc.

—Ultimate X Men, Vol. 5. 2006. (Illus.). 296p. (YA). 29.99 (978-0-7851-2103-9(X)) Marvel Enterprises, Inc.

Vaughan, Brian K. & Kubert, Andy. Cry Wolf, Vol. 10. 2005. (X-Men Ser.). (Illus.). 96p. pap. 8.99 (978-0-7851-1405-5(X)) Marvel Enterprises, Inc.

Vega, Michael, illus. Dark Moon Diary. 2007. 192p. pap. 9.99 (978-1-59532-844-1(0) , Tokyopop Kids) TOKYOPOP, Inc.

Velasco, Francisco Ruiz. Battle Gods: Warriors of the Chaak. 2001. (Illus.). 240p. (YA). pap. 19.95 (978-1-56971-562-8(9)) Dark Horse Comics.

Velez, Ivan. Dead High Yearbook. McVeigh, Mark, ed. 2007. 80p. (YA). (gr. 7 up). 18.99 (978-0-525-47783-9(7) , Dutton Juvenile) Penguin Group (USA) Inc.

Verne, Jules. Journey to the Center of the Earth. Rebis, Greg, illus. 2008. (J). (*978-1-59889-832-3(9)); 72p. pap. (*978-1-59889-888-0(4)) Stone Arch Bks.

Verne, Jules. Jules Verne/Journey to the Center of the Earth. 2005. (Illus.). 48p. (gr. 5-8). 25.50 (978-0-7910-9105-0(8)) Facts On File, Inc.

Vin, Lee. One, 5 vols. rev. ed. 2004. (Illus.). 192p. pap. 9.99 (978-1-59182-752-8(3) , Tokyopop Kids) TOKYOPOP, Inc.

Vin, Lee, illus. Crazy Love Story, Vol. 4. 4th rev. ed. 2005. 192p. pap. 9.99 (978-1-59182-950-8(X) , Tokyopop Kids) TOKYOPOP, Inc.

Visca, Curt & Visca, Kelley. How to Draw Cartoon Crustaceans. 2003. (Kid's Guide to Drawing Ser.). (Illus.). 24p. (J). lib. bdg. 21.25 (978-0-8239-6158-0(3) , PowerKids Pr.) Rosen Publishing Group, Inc., The.

Viz Media Staff. Pokemon Vol. 1: Pikachu & Friends. 2006. (Pokemon 3D Pop Outs Ser.). 5p. (YA). pap. 9.99 (978-1-4215-1002-6(2)) Viz Media.

—Pokemon 3D Pop Outs Vol. 1: Togepi & Friends. 2006. (Pokemon Ser.). 5p. (YA). pap. 9.99 (978-1-4215-1132-0(0)) Viz Media.

Vogler, Christopher. Ravenskull. 2006. (Illus.). 192p. pap. 10.99 (978-1-933164-14-4(X)) Seven Seas Entertainment, LLC.

Volo, creator. The Revealing. 3rd rev. ed. 2005. (W. I. T. C. H. Graphic Novels Ser.: Bk. 3). (Illus.). 128p. (gr. 3-7). pap. 4.99 (978-0-7868-3655-0(5) , Volo) Hyperion Bks. for Children.

Wade, Ellen A. Peanuts' New Friend. Schneider, Rex, illus. 1999. 26p. (J). (gr. 2-4). pap. 8.00 (978-0-9653635-2-5(X)) LNA Publishing.

Wagner, John. Predator vs. Judge Dredd. 1998. (Predator Ser.). (Illus.). 80p. (YA). (gr. 9 up). pap. 9.95 (978-1-56971-345-7(6)) Dark Horse Comics.

Waid, Mark. Enter the Detective. Guice, Butch & Perkins, Mike, illus. 2003. (Ruse Traveler Ser.: Vol. 1). 192p. (YA). (gr. 7 up). pap. 9.95 (978-1-59314-012-0(6)) CrossGeneration Comics, Inc.

—Fantastic Four, Vol. 3. 2005. (Illus.). 256p. (YA). 29.99 (978-0-7851-2011-7(4)) Marvel Enterprises, Inc.

—Imaginauts. Wieringo, Mike, illus. 2003. (Fantastic Four Ser.: Vol. 1). 144p. (YA). pap. 12.99 (978-0-7851-1063-7(1)) Marvel Enterprises, Inc.

—Supreme Justice. 2001. lib. bdg. 28.00 (978-0-613-92134-3(8)) Tandem Library Bks.

Waid, Mark, et al. Terror Incognita. Hitch, Brian, illus. rev. ed. 2002. (Justice League Adventures Ser.: Vol. 9). 144p. pap. 12.99 (978-1-56389-936-2(1)) DC Comics.

Walt Disney Company Staff, creator. Lady & the Tramp. 2006. (Illus.). 32p. pap. 3.99 (978-1-59816-443-5(0) , Tokyopop Kids) TOKYOPOP, Inc.

Walt Disney Records Staff. Disney Princess Holiday: Cinderella So This Is Christmas/Beauty & the Beast One Magical Christmas/Ariel's Christmas under the Sea. unabr. ed. 2005. (Disney's Read along Collection Ser.). (J). audio compact disk 14.99 (978-0-7634-1146-6(9)) Walt Disney Records.

—The Lion King: The Lion King/The Lion King II Simba's Pride/The Lion King the Brightest Star. unabr. ed. 2005. (Disney's Read along Collection Ser.). (J). audio compact disk 14.99 (978-0-7634-1149-7(3)) Walt Disney Records.

—Winnie the Pooh: Winnie the Pooh Springtime with Roo/Pooh's Huffalump Movie/Piglet's Big Movie. unabr. ed. 2005. (Disney's Read along Collection Ser.). (J). audio compact disk 14.99 (978-0-7634-1147-3(7)) Walt Disney Records.

Walter, Dan. Hello, Willie! 2007. (J). 14.95 (*978-1-932888-52-2(7)) Mascot Bks., Inc.

Warren, Adam. Meanwhile. 2003. (Gen 13 Ser.). (Illus.). 160p. pap. 17.95 (978-1-4012-0062-6(1)) DC Comics.

Watanabe, Shinichiro. Cowboy Bebop Film Comic, Vol 1. 2006. (Illus.). 164p. (YA). pap. 10.99 (978-1-59409-532-0(9)) Bandai Entertainment.

Watanabe, Taeko. Kaze Hikaru. (Kaze Hikaru Ser.). (YA). Vol. 2. 2006. 208p. pap. 8.99 (978-1-4215-0581-7(9)); Vol. 4. 2007. 200p. pap. 8.99 (978-1-4215-1017-0(0)) Viz Media.

Watanabe, Yoshitomo, illus. & creator. Beyond the Beyond. Watanabe, Yoshitomo, creator. 2006. pap. 9.99 (978-1-59816-371-1(X) , Tokyopop Kids) TOKYOPOP, Inc.

Watase, Yu. Bandit, 4. Watase, Yu, illus. 2nd ed. 2004. (Fushigi Yugi Ser.). (Illus.). 200p. (YA). pap. 9.95 (978-1-56931-993-2(6)) Viz Media.

—Enemy, Vol. 10. Watase, Yu, illus. 2004. (Illus.). 200p. lib. bdg. 20.85 (978-1-4176-5241-9(1)) Tandem Library Bks.

—Maya. Watase, Yu, illus. 2004. (Illus.). 200p. lib. bdg. 20.85 (978-1-4176-5874-9(6)) Tandem Library Bks.

—Oracle: Vol. 2. Watase, Yu, illus. 2004. (Illus.). 200p. lib. bdg. 20.85 (978-1-4176-5230-3(6)) Tandem Library Bks.

Watase, Yuu. Absolute Boyfriend, Vol. 3. 2007. (Absolute Boyfriend Ser.). (Illus.). 200p. (YA). pap. 8.99 (978-1-4215-1003-3(0)) Viz Media.

—Alice 19th Vol. 1: Lotis Master. Watase, Yuu, illus. 2003. (Alice 19th Ser.). (Illus.). 192p. (YA). pap. 9.95 (978-1-59116-215-5(7)) Viz Media.

—Alice 19th Vol. 2: Inner Heart. JN Productions Staff, tr. 2003. (Alice 19th Ser.). (Illus.). 200p. (YA). pap. 9.95 (978-1-59116-229-2(7)) Viz Media.

—Alice 19th Vol. 6: Blindness. Watase, Yuu, illus. 2004. (Alice 19th Ser.). (Illus.). 200p. (YA). pap. 9.99 (978-1-59116-243-8(2)) Viz Media.

—Ceres, Celestial Legend Vol. 8: Miori. Watase, Yuu, illus. 2004. (Ceres, Celestial Legend Ser.). (Illus.). 200p. (YA). pap. 9.95 (978-1-59116-260-5(2)) Viz Media.

—Chidori. Watase, Yuu, illus. 2nd ed. 2004. (Ceres, Celestial Legend Ser.: Vol. 4). (Illus.). 192p. (YA). pap. 9.95 (978-1-59116-609-2(8)) Viz Media.

—Genbu Kaiden, Vol. 4. Watase, Yuu, illus. 2006. (Fushigi Yugi Ser.). 208p. (YA). pap. 8.99 (978-1-4215-0579-4(7)) Viz Media.

—The Lost Word. Watase, Yuu, illus. 2004. (Alice 19th Ser.). (Illus.). 200p. (YA). pap. 9.99 (978-1-59116-244-5(0)) Viz Media.

Waterson, Bill. Jetzt geht's Rund. Goetting, Waltraud, tr. from ENG. (Calvin & Hobbes Ser.: Vol. 1). (GER., Illus.). 64p. (J). pap. (978-3-8105-0328-2(2)) Kruger, Wolfgang Verlag, GmbH DEU. *Dist:* International Bk. Import Service, Inc.

Watsuki, Nobuhiro. Busou Renkin. (JPN., Illus.). (YA). Vol. 1. 188p. pap. (978-4-08-873557-3(9)); Vol. 3. 182p. pap. (978-4-08-873630-3(3)); Vol. 4. 204p. pap. (978-4-08-873651-8(6)); Vol. 5. 185p. pap. (978-4-08-873670-9(2)) Shuei-Sha.

—Busou Renkin Vol. 2: Fade to Black. (Illus.). 203p. (YA). pap. (978-4-08-873587-0(0)) Shuei-Sha.

—In the 11th Year of Meiji, May 14th. Watsuki, Nobuhiro, illus. 2004. (Illus.). 200p. lib. bdg. 18.55 (978-1-4176-5888-6(6)) Tandem Library Bks.

—Mitsurugi, Master & Student. Watsuki, Nobuhiro, illus. 2005. (Illus.). 200p. lib. bdg. 18.55 (978-1-4176-5890-9(8)) Tandem Library Bks.

—On the East Sea Road. Watsuki, Nobuhiro, illus. 2005. (Illus.). 185p. per. 18.55 (978-1-4176-5889-3(4)) Tandem Library Bks.

—Rurouni Kenshin: Overture to Destruction, Vol. 11. Watsuki, Nobuhiro, illus. 2005. (Rurouni Kenshin Ser.). (Illus.). 192p. (YA). pap. 7.95 (978-1-59116-709-9(4)) Viz Media.

Watterson, Bill. Achtung, Fertig, Los! Goetting, Waltraud, tr. from ENG. (Calvin & Hobbes Ser.: Vol. 8). (GER., Illus.). 64p. (J). pap. (978-3-8105-0336-7(3)) Kruger, Wolfgang Verlag, GmbH DEU. *Dist:* International Bk. Import Service, Inc.

—Alles unter Kontrolle. Goetting, Waltraud, tr. from ENG. (Calvin & Hobbes Ser.: Vol. 3). (GER., Illus.). 64p. (J). pap. (978-3-8105-0330-5(4)) Kruger, Wolfgang Verlag, GmbH DEU. *Dist:* International Bk. Import Service, Inc.

—Auf dem Sprung. Goetting, Waltraud, tr. from ENG. (Calvin & Hobbes Ser.: Bk. 1). (GER., Illus.). 96p. (J). pap. (978-3-8105-0320-6(7)) Kruger, Wolfgang Verlag, GmbH DEU. *Dist:* International Bk. Import Service, Inc.

—Bloss nicht Aergern. Goetting, Waltraud, tr. from ENG. (Calvin & Hobbes Ser.: Bk. 3). (GER., Illus.). 96p. (J). pap. (978-3-8105-0322-0(3)) Kruger, Wolfgang Verlag, GmbH DEU. *Dist:* International Bk. Import Service, Inc.

—La Buena Vida. 2000. (Calvin y Hobbes Ser.: Vol. 12). Tr. of Good Life. (SPA., Illus.). 64p. (J). 6.95 (978-84-406-8543-8(2)) Ediciones B ESP. *Dist:* Distribooks, Inc.

—Calvin & Hobbes: Das Jubilaumsalbum, 10 vols. Bartoszko, Alexandra, tr. from ENG. (Calvin & Hobbes Ser.). (GER., Illus.). 208p. (J). (978-3-8105-0370-1(3)) Kruger, Wolfgang Verlag, GmbH DEU. *Dist:* International Bk. Import Service, Inc.

—Comedores de Gusanos. 2000. (Calvin y Hobbes Ser.: Vol. 11). (SPA., Illus.). 64p. (J). 6.95 (978-84-406-8542-1(4)) Ediciones B ESP. *Dist:* Distribooks, Inc.

—Einfach Umwerfend. Goetting, Waltraud, tr. from ENG. (Calvin & Hobbes Ser.: Vol. 13). (GER., Illus.). 48p. (J). pap. (978-3-8105-0350-3(9)) Kruger, Wolfgang Verlag, GmbH DEU. *Dist:* International Bk. Import Service, Inc.

—Enorm in Form. Goetting, Waltraud, tr. from ENG. (Calvin & Hobbes Ser.: Vol. 9). (GER., Illus.). 64p. (J). pap. (978-3-8105-0340-4(1)) Kruger, Wolfgang Verlag, GmbH DEU. *Dist:* International Bk. Import Service, Inc.

—Feine Freunde. Goetting, Waltraud, tr. from ENG. (Calvin & Hobbes Ser.: Vol. 15). (GER., Illus.). 80p. (J). pap. (978-3-8105-0353-4(3)) Kruger, Wolfgang Verlag, GmbH DEU. *Dist:* International Bk. Import Service, Inc.

—Fix & Fertig. Goetting, Waltraud, tr. from ENG. (Calvin & Hobbes Ser.: Bk. 2). (GER., Illus.). 96p. (J). pap. (978-3-8105-0321-3(5)) Kruger, Wolfgang Verlag, GmbH DEU. *Dist:* International Bk. Import Service, Inc.

—Ganz schoen Daneben. Goetting, Waltraud, tr. from ENG. (Calvin & Hobbes Ser.: Vol. 7). (GER., Illus.). 64p. (J). pap. (978-3-8105-0335-0(5)) Kruger, Wolfgang Verlag, GmbH DEU. *Dist:* International Bk. Import Service, Inc.

—Hay un Tigre en Mi Sopa. 2000. (Calvin y Hobbes Ser.: Vol. 7). Tr. of There's a Tiger in My Soup. (SPA., Illus.). 48p. (J). 6.95 (978-84-406-8250-5(6)) Ediciones B ESP. *Dist:* Distribooks, Inc.

—Immer mit der Ruhe. Goetting, Waltraud, tr. from ENG. (Calvin & Hobbes Ser.: Vol. 4). (GER., Illus.). 64p. (J). pap. (978-3-8105-0331-2(2)) Kruger, Wolfgang Verlag, GmbH DEU. *Dist:* International Bk. Import Service, Inc.

—Immer Voll Drauf. Goetting, Waltraud, tr. from ENG. (Calvin & Hobbes Ser.: Vol. 5). (GER., Illus.). 64p. (J). pap. (978-3-8105-0332-9(0)) Kruger, Wolfgang Verlag, GmbH DEU. *Dist:* International Bk. Import Service, Inc.

—Jetzt Erst Recht. Goetting, Waltraud, tr. from ENG. (Calvin & Hobbes Ser.: Vol. 10). (GER., Illus.). 64p. (J). pap. (978-3-8105-0339-8(8)) Kruger, Wolfgang Verlag, GmbH DEU. *Dist:* International Bk. Import Service, Inc.

—Mach mir den Tiger. Goetting, Waltraud, tr. from ENG. (Calvin & Hobbes Ser.: Vol. 11). (GER., Illus.). 64p. (J). pap. (978-3-8105-0341-1(X)) Kruger, Wolfgang Verlag, GmbH DEU. *Dist:* International Bk. Import Service, Inc.

—Matando el Tiempo. 2000. (Calvin y Hobbes Ser.: Vol. 5). Tr. of Killing Time. (SPA., Illus.). 48p. (J). 6.95 (978-84-406-8047-1(3)) Ediciones B ESP. *Dist:* Distribooks, Inc.

—Memorias de un Seisanero. 2000. (Calvin y Hobbes Ser.: Vol. 9). Tr. of Memories of a Six-Year-Old. (SPA., Illus.). 48p. (J). 6.95 (978-84-406-8505-6(X)) Ediciones B ESP. *Dist:* Distribooks, Inc.

—Munecos de Nieve Suicidas. 2000. (Calvin y Hobbes Ser.: Vol. 3). (SPA., Illus.). 48p. (J). 6.95 (978-84-406-7411-1(2)) Ediciones B ESP. *Dist:* Distribooks, Inc.

—No Me Gusta Tu Cara! 2000. (Calvin y Hobbes Ser.: Vol. 4). Tr. of I Don't Like Your Face!. (SPA., Illus.). 48p. (J). 6.95 (978-84-406-7410-4(4)) Ediciones B ESP. *Dist:* Distribooks, Inc.

—No Quiero Hacer los Deberes! 2000. (Calvin y Hobbes Ser.: Vol. 6). (SPA., Illus.). 48p. (J). 6.95 (978-84-406-8121-8(6)) Ediciones B ESP. *Dist:* Distribooks, Inc.

—Die Phantastischen Zwei. Goetting, Waltraud, tr. from ENG. (Calvin & Hobbes Ser.: Vol. 14). (GER., Illus.). 80p. (J). pap. (978-3-8105-0351-0(7)) Kruger, Wolfgang Verlag, GmbH DEU. *Dist:* International Bk. Import Service, Inc.

—Solo en la Oscuridad. 2000. (Calvin y Hobbes Ser.: Vol. 8). Tr. of Alone in the Dark. (SPA., Illus.). 48p. (J). 6.95 (978-84-406-8249-9(2)) Ediciones B ESP. *Dist:* Distribooks, Inc.

—Steil nach Oben. Goetting, Waltraud, tr. from ENG. (Calvin & Hobbes Ser.: Vol. 6). (GER., Illus.). 64p. (J). pap. (978-3-8105-0333-6(9)) Kruger, Wolfgang Verlag, GmbH DEU. *Dist:* International Bk. Import Service, Inc.

—El Tiempo Esta Loco. 2000. (Calvin y Hobbes Ser.: Vol. 10). (SPA., Illus.). 48p. (J). 6.95 (978-84-406-8541-4(6)) Ediciones B ESP. *Dist:* Distribooks, Inc.

—Tierisch Lyrisch. Goetting, Waltraud, tr. from ENG. (Calvin & Hobbes Ser.: Vol. 12). (GER., Illus.). 64p. (J). pap. (978-3-8105-0349-7(5)) Kruger, Wolfgang Verlag, GmbH DEU. *Dist:* International Bk. Import Service, Inc.

—Die Welt der Wunder. Bartoszko, Alexandra, tr. from ENG. (Calvin & Hobbes Ser.: Vol. 16). (GER., Illus.). 64p. (J). pap. (978-3-8105-0365-7(6)) Kruger, Wolfgang Verlag, GmbH DEU. *Dist:* International Bk. Import Service, Inc.

—Yo Tengo Razon, los Demas Estan Equivocados! 2000. (Calvin y Hobbes Ser.: Vol. 2). (SPA., Illus.). 48p. (J). 6.95 (978-84-406-7412-8(0)) Ediciones B ESP. *Dist:* Distribooks, Inc.

Wax, Wendy. Fairly Odd Funnies. Style Guide Staff, illus. 2005. (Fairly OddParents Ser.). 48p. (J). pap. 3.99 (978-0-689-87599-1(1) , Simon Spotlight) Simon & Schuster Children's Publishing.

—Phonics Comics: Clara the Klutz - Level 2. Mattocks, Tracy & Sullivan, Mary, illus. 2007. 24p. (J). (gr. 1-17). pap. 3.99 (978-1-58476-565-3(8)) Innovative Kids.

Way, Daniel. Ghost Rider Vicious Cycl, Vol. 1. 2007. (Illus.). 120p. pap. 13.99 (978-0-7851-2296-8(6)) Marvel Enterprises, Inc.

—Planet Hulk Prelude. 2006. (Illus.). 144p. pap. 13.99 (978-0-7851-1953-1(1)) Marvel Enterprises, Inc.

—Sabretooth: Open Season. Sears, Bart, illus. 2005. (Wolverine Ser.). 96p. pap. 9.99 (978-0-7851-1507-6(2)) Marvel Enterprises, Inc.

Webb, Mack H., Jr. Danny & the Detention Demons. Espinola, Nicole & Nealon, Eve, illus. l.t. ed. 2007. 52p. (J). per. 15.95 (*978-0-9779576-2-0(4)) Pilinut Pr., Inc.

Weber, Lou, ed. Disney Learning Letters & Words: Sight & Sound Activity. 2005. 64p. (J). 16.98 (978-1-4127-3535-3(1) , 7262500) Publications International, Ltd.

—Disney Princess Look & Find Wipe off 3 Pack. 2004. 72p. (J). spiral bd. 15.98 (978-1-4127-3296-3(4) , 7244700) Publications International, Ltd.

—Disney's Toy Story 2 Look & Find 3 Pack. 2004. 72p. (J). spiral bd. 15.98 (978-1-4127-3295-6(6) , 7244600) Publications International, Ltd.

—Dreamy Stories. 2005. (Disney Princess Ser.). 40p. (J). bds. 12.98 (978-1-4127-3479-0(7) , 7259700) Publications International, Ltd.

Weigel, Jeff. Atomic Ace: (He's Just My Dad) Weigel, Jeff, illus. 2004. (Illus.). 32p. (J). (gr. 1-4). pap. 6.95 (978-0-8075-3217-1(7)) Whitman, Albert & Co.

Weiser, Joey. The Ride Home. 2007. (Illus.). 168p. pap. 8.95 (*978-0-9770304-4-6(X)) AdHouse Bks.

Weisman, Greg. Gargoyles #1. 2006. (Illus.). 24p. (YA). pap. 3.50 (978-1-59362-040-0(3) , Slave Labor Graphics) Slave Labor Bks.

Weiss, Sam. Jesus Plays the Catskills. 2004. 96p. per. 11.95 (978-0-9754699-0-3(8)) Gross, H. H.

Wells, Conrad. The Batman: How to Draw. Albano, Ursula, illus. 2005. (Batman Ser.). 32p. (J). (ps-k). 4.99 (978-0-439-72782-2(0)) Scholastic, Inc.

Wells, H. G. The Invisible Man. Calero, Dennis, illus. 2008. (J). (*978-1-59889-831-6(0)); 72p. pap. (*978-1-59889-887-3(6)) Stone Arch Bks.

—The Time Machine. Ocampo Ruiz, José Alfonso, illus. 2008. (J). (*978-1-59889-833-0(7)); 72p. pap. (*978-1-59889-889-7(2)) Stone Arch Bks.

Wells, Zeb. Spider-Man/Doctor Octopus: Year One. Andrews, Kaare, illus. 2005. (Spider-Man Ser.). 120p. pap. 13.99 (978-0-7851-1532-8(3)) Marvel Enterprises, Inc.

West, Tracey. Game On! 2007. (Yu-gi-oh Ser.: No. 1). (Illus.). 96p. (J). pap. 4.99 (*978-0-439-87394-9(0)) Scholastic, Inc.

—The Night Spies. 2007. (Yu-Gi-Oh Gx Ser.). 96p. (J). pap. 4.99 (*978-0-439-88832-5(8)) Scholastic, Inc.

—Yu-Gi-Oh GX: Jaden's Secret. 2007. 32p. (J). pap. 3.99 (*978-0-439-88838-7(7)) Scholastic, Inc.

—Yu-Gi-Oh Gx Ch Bk #5 Nightshroud's Secret. 2008. 96p. pap. 4.99 (*978-0-545-04406-6(5) , Scholastic) Scholastic, Inc.

—Yu-Gi-Oh Gx Reader #3 Rescue Duel. 2008. 32p. pap. 3.99 (*978-0-439-88840-0(9) , Scholastic) Scholastic, Inc.

What Can I Do. 2002. (J). 4.95 (978-0-9725121-2-1(8)) PowerMark Productions.

Whedon, Joss. Astonishing X-Men, Vol.1. gif. ed. (Illus.). 152p. (YA). pap. 14.99 (978-0-7851-1531-1(5)) Marvel Enterprises, Inc.

—Astonishing X-Men HC Variant, Vol. 1. (Illus.). 320p. 29.99 (978-0-7851-2301-9(6)) Marvel Enterprises, Inc.

—The Gift. 2005. (Illus.). 96p. (YA). (ps-7). pap. 7.99 (978-1-59816-029-1(X) , Tokyopop Adult) TOKYOPOP, Inc.

Wheeler, Lisa. Seadogs Epic Ocean Operetta. Siegel, Mark, illus. 2004. 40p. (J). 17.95 (978-0-689-85689-1(X) , Atheneum/Richard Jackson Bks.) Simon & Schuster Children's Publishing.

Wheeler, Shannon. Too Much Coffee, Man's Parade of Tirade. 1999. (Illus.). 142p. (YA). (gr. 9 up). pap. 12.95 (978-1-56971-437-9(1)) Dark Horse Comics.

When Kingdoms Collide Part 2. 2005. (SPA, JPN, RUS, CHI & HEB.). (YA). 2.50 (978-0-9762842-1-5(9)) Fantasy Prone Comics.

Whitta, Gary. Death, Jr. (Illus.). 144p. pap. 14.99 (978-1-58240-526-1(3)) Image Comics.

Wight, Eric. My Dead Girlfriend. 2007. (Illus.). pap. 9.99 (***978-1-59816-996-6(3)***, Tokyopop Adult) TOKYOPOP, Inc.

Wilkerson, L. Kobie, 3rd, reader. Fred & Mary. 2008. (Illus.). 32p. (J). 24.95 incl. DVD, audio compact disk (***978-0-9796679-0-9(9)***) Gye Nyame Pr.

Williams, Marcia, illus. & retold by. Charles Dickens & Friends: Five Lively Retellings. Williams, Marcia, retold by. 2006. 48p. (J). (gr. 3-7). pap. 7.99 (978-0-7636-3198-7(1)) Candlewick Pr.

Willingham, Bill & Winick, Judd. Day of Vengeance. Churchill, Ian, illus. rev. ed. 2005. 224p. pap. 12.99 (978-1-4012-0840-0(1)) DC Comics.

Windsor-Smith, Barry. Wolverine Weapon X Premiere. 2007. (Illus.). 152p. 19.99 (***978-0-7851-2327-9(X)***) Marvel Enterprises, Inc.

Wingerter, Linda. Home on the Range. 2009. 32p. (J). (ps-3). 14.95 (978-0-316-83202-1(2), Tingley, Megan Bks.) Little, Brown Bks. for Young Readers.

Winick, Judd. Fantastic Voyage. Youngquist, Jeff, ed. Calafiore, Jim, illus. 2004. (Marvel Heroes Ser.). 168p. (YA). 17.99 (978-0-7851-1197-9(2)) Marvel Enterprises, Inc.

—Outsiders Vol. 3: Wanted. rev. ed. 2005. (Illus.). 192p. pap. 14.99 (978-1-4012-0460-0(0)) DC Comics.

Wlodarski, Loran. If a Dolphin Were a Fish. Klein, Laurie Allen, illus. 2007. 1p. (J). 8.95 (***978-1-934359-03-7(3)***) Sylvan Dell Pubng.

Wohl, David, et al. Top Cows Best of Michael Turner. 2005. (Illus.). 240p. (YA). pap. 24.99 (978-1-58240-544-5(1)) Image Comics.

Won, Im Jae. The Boss, Vol. 3. 2004. 184p. (YA). pap. (978-1-4139-0083-5(6)) ADV Manga.

WOO, illus. & creator. Rebirth, Vol. 13. WOO, creator. rev. ed. 2005. 200p. pap. 9.99 (978-1-59532-028-5(8), Tokyopop Adult) TOKYOPOP, Inc.

Woo, Soo Jung. Legend Volume 3. 2007. (Illus.). 200p. (YA). pap. 10.95 (***978-89-527-4712-9(7)***) ICE Kunion KOR. *Dist:* Diamond Bk. Distributors.

—Legend Volume 4. 2007. 200p. (YA). pap. 10.95 (***978-89-527-4871-3(9)***) ICE Kunion KOR. *Dist:* Diamond Bk. Distributors.

—Legend Volume 5. 2007. 200p. (YA). pap. 10.95 (***978-89-527-4883-6(2)***) ICE Kunion KOR. *Dist:* Diamond Bk. Distributors.

Wood, Wally. T. H. U. N. D. E. R. Agents. rev. ed. 2002. (Archives Ser.: Vol. 1). (Illus.). 248p. 49.95 (978-1-56389-903-4(5)) DC Comics.

Wooderson, Philip. Arf & the Metal Detector. MacKeith, Bridget, illus. 2007. (Graphic Trax Ser.). 66p. (J). (gr. 2-8). lib. bdg. 19.93 (978-1-59889-085-3(9)) Stone Arch Bks.

Wooderson, Philip. Guard Dog. Burroughs, Dave, illus. 2008. (J). (***978-1-59889-829-3(9)***); pap. (***978-1-59889-885-9(X)***) Stone Arch Bks.

Woodward, Simon. Brave Dave: The Makings of a Hero. 2006. pap. 12.49 (***978-1-4259-5996-8(2)***) AuthorHouse.

Wyre, Yvonne. The Adventures of Cuthbert the Coal Lorry. 2005. 160p. pap. (***978-1-84401-500-9(9)***) Athena Pr.

Yadate, Hajime. Cowboy Bebop, 2 vols. Kuga, Cain, illus. 2003. pap. 44.99 (978-1-59182-590-6(3)) TOKYOPOP, Inc.

Yagami, Yu. Those Who Hunt Elves, Vol. 1. McGregor, Eiko, tr. 2003. (Illus.). 216p. (YA). pap. (978-1-4139-0014-9(3)) ADV Manga.

—Those Who Hunt Elves. 2004. (YA). Vol. 3 (Illus.). 202p. pap. (978-1-4139-0034-7(8)); Vol. 4. 200p. pap. (978-1-4139-0063-7(1)); Vol. 5. (Illus.). 202p. pap. (978-1-4139-0077-4(1)), Vol. 6. 202p. pap. (978-1-4139-0098-9(4)); Vol. 7. (Illus.). 200p. pap. (978-1-4139-0116-0(6)) ADV Manga.

Yagi, Norihiro. Claymore. 2006. (Claymore Ser.). 208p. (YA). Vol. 2. pap. 7.99 (978-1-4215-0619-7(X)); Vol. 3. pap. 7.99 (978-1-4215-0620-3(3)) Viz Media.

Yago, Norihiro. Claymore. 2007. (Claymore Ser.). 200p. (YA). Vol. 6. pap. 7.99 (978-1-4215-1048-4(0)); Vol. 7. pap. 7.99 (978-1-4215-1049-1(9)) Viz Media.

Yamada, Masaki. Innocence: After the Long Goodbye. 2005. (Ghost in the Shell Novel Ser.: Vol. 1). 264p. (YA). 19.99 (978-1-4215-0156-7(2)) Viz Media.

Yamada, Shutaro. R. O. D, Vol. 3. Yamada, Shutaro, illus. 2006. (Read or Die Ser.). 208p. (YA). pap. 9.99 (978-1-4215-0508-4(8)) Viz Media.

—R. O. D, Vol. 4. 2006. (Read or Die Ser.). 208p. (YA). pap. 9.99 (978-1-4215-0509-1(6)) Viz Media.

Yamashita, Ray, tr. Lupin III Vol. 1: World's Most Wanted. 2004. (Illus.). 240p. pap. 9.99 (978-1-59532-070-4(9), Tokyopop Adult) TOKYOPOP, Inc.

Yamashita, Satsuki, et al, eds. Aquarian Age - Juvenile Orion Illustration Book: Realm of Light. Yamashita, Satsuki, tr. Gokurakuin, Sakurako et al, illus. 2006. (Aquarian Age - Juvenile Orion Ser.). 96p. 19.99 (978-1-59741-108-0(6), Broccoli Bks.) Broccoli International USA, Inc.

Yan, Wing. King of Fighters 2003, Vol. 4. 2008. (Illus.). 128p. (YA). pap. 13.95 (***978-1-59796-010-6(1)***) DrMaster Pubns. Inc.

Yang, Kyung-Il, illus. Blade of Heaven, Vol. 3. rev. ed. 2005. 196p. pap. 9.99 (978-1-59532-329-3(5), Tokyopop Adult) TOKYOPOP, Inc.

Yang, Yuh Jin. Saint Marie, Vol. 1. 2004. (Illus.). 190p. (YA). pap. (978-1-4139-0065-1(8)) ADV Manga.

Yasuhiko, Yoshikazu. Gundam No. 9, No. 10: The Origin. 2004. (gr. 7-12). lib. bdg. 16.40 (978-0-613-88462-4(0)) Tandem Library Bks.

Yatate, Hajime & Tomino, Yoshiyuki, creators. Lost War Chronicles, 2 vols., Vol. 1. 2006. (Mobile Suit Gundam Ser.). (Illus.). 144p. pap. 9.99 (978-1-59816-213-4(6), Tokyopop Kids) TOKYOPOP, Inc.

Yates, Lady. Earthsong, Vol. 1. 2006. (Illus.). 160p. (YA). pap. 14.99 (978-1-933164-15-1(8)) Seven Seas Entertainment, LLC.

Yeates, Thomas, illus. Arthur & Lancelot: The Fight for Camelot. 2007. (Graphic Myths & Legends Ser.). 48p. (J). (gr. 4-8). lib. bdg. 26.60 (***978-0-8225-6296-2(0)***, Graphic Universe) Lerner Publishing Group.

Yeh, Julie. Poppie's Adventures: Serpents in Paradise. Hsu, Jack, illus. 2003. 48p. (J). per. (978-0-9742386-0-9(0)) Way Out Comics.

Yeh, Phil. Dinosaurs Across America. 2007. (Illus.). 32p. (J). (gr. 1-5). 12.95 (***978-1-56163-509-2(X)***) NBM Publishing Co.

Yeo, Ho-Kyung. Honey Mustard, Vol. 4. 4th rev. ed. 2006. (Illus.). pap. 9.99 (978-1-59816-208-0(X), Tokyopop Adult) TOKYOPOP, Inc.

Yeo-Jin, Yang. Saint Marie, Vol. 2. 2004. 184p. (YA). pap. (978-1-4139-0080-4(1)) ADV Manga.

YKids Staff. Albert Einstein. 2007. (Great Figures in History Ser.). 148p. (J). (gr. 4-7). pap. 14.95 (***978-981-05-4944-2(X)***) Youngjin (Singapore) Pte Ltd. SGP. *Dist:* Independent Pubs. Group.

—Daddy Long Legs. 2008. (Manga Literary Classics Ser.). 144p. (J). pap. 14.95 (***978-981-05-7554-0(8)***) Youngjin (Singapore) Pte Ltd. SGP. *Dist:* Independent Pubs. Group.

—Gandhi. 2007. (Great Figures in History Ser.). 148p. (J). (gr. 4-7). pap. 14.95 (***978-981-05-4945-9(8)***) Youngjin (Singapore) Pte Ltd. SGP. *Dist:* Independent Pubs. Group.

—Gulliver's Travels. 2007. (Manga Literary Classics Ser.). 148p. (J). (gr. 4-7). pap. 14.95 (***978-981-05-4941-1(5)***) Youngjin (Singapore) Pte Ltd. SGP. *Dist:* Independent Pubs. Group.

—Leonardo da Vinci. 2008. (Great Figures in History Ser.). 144p. (J). pap. 14.95 (***978-981-05-7555-7(6)***) Youngjin (Singapore) Pte Ltd. SGP. *Dist:* Independent Pubs. Group.

—Little Women. 2007. (Manga Literary Classics Ser.). 148p. (J). (gr. 4-7). pap. 14.95 (***978-981-05-4943-5(1)***) Youngjin (Singapore) Pte Ltd. SGP. *Dist:* Independent Pubs. Group.

—Marie Curie. 2007. (Great Figures in History Ser.). 148p. (J). (gr. 4-7). pap. 14.95 (***978-981-05-4946-6(6)***) Youngjin (Singapore) Pte Ltd. SGP. *Dist:* Independent Pubs. Group.

—Mother Teresa. 2008. (Great Figures in History Ser.). 144p. (J). pap. 14.95 (***978-981-05-7552-6(1)***) Youngjin (Singapore) Pte Ltd. SGP. *Dist:* Independent Pubs. Group.

—Nelson Mandela. 2008. (Great Figures in History Ser.). 144p. (J). (gr. 4-7). pap. 14.95 (***978-981-05-7551-9(3)***) Youngjin (Singapore) Pte Ltd. SGP. *Dist:* Independent Pubs. Group.

—Prince & the Pauper. 2008. (Manga Literary Classics Ser.). 144p. (J). (gr. 4-7). pap. 14.95 (***978-981-05-7553-3(X)***) Youngjin (Singapore) Pte Ltd. SGP. *Dist:* Independent Pubs. Group.

—Treasure Island. 2007. (Manga Literary Classics Ser.). 148p. (J). (gr. 4-7). pap. 14.95 (***978-981-05-4942-8(3)***) Youngjin (Singapore) Pte Ltd. SGP. *Dist:* Independent Pubs. Group.

—20,000 Leagues under the Sea. 2008. (Manga Literary Classics Ser.). 144p. (J). pap. 14.95 (***978-981-05-7556-4(4)***) Youngjin (Singapore) Pte Ltd. SGP. *Dist:* Independent Pubs. Group.

Yoon, Ji-Un. Cynical Orange, Vol. 2. 2006. (Illus.). 200p. (YA). pap. 10.95 (***978-89-527-4478-4(0)***) ICE Kunion KOR. *Dist:* Diamond Bk. Distributors.

Yoshida, Akimi. Banana Fish. (Banana Fish Ser.). (YA). Vol. 14. 2006. 208p. pap. 9.99 (978-1-4215-0524-4(X)); Vol. 15. 2006. 208p. pap. 9.99 (978-1-4215-0525-1(8)); Vol. 18. 2007. 192p. pap. 9.99 (978-1-4215-0876-4(1)) Viz Media.

Yoshida, Akira. Elektra: The Hand. Gossett, Christian, illus. 2005. (Elektra Ser.). 120p. pap. 13.99 (978-0-7851-1594-6(3)) Marvel Enterprises, Inc.

Yoshimoto, Ray, tr. from JPN. Gravitation, Vol. 12. Murakami, Maki, illus. rev. ed. 2005. 192p. pap. 9.99 (978-1-59532-415-3(1), Tokyopop Adult) TOKYOPOP, Inc.

—Tokyo Babylon, Vol. 6. Clamp, illus. rev. ed. 2005. 176p. pap. 9.99 (978-1-59532-050-6(4), Tokyopop Adult) TOKYOPOP, Inc.

Yoshimura, Natsuki. Mystical Prince Yoshida-Kun!, Vol. 1. 2004. (Illus.). 184p. (YA). pap. (978-1-4139-0207-5(3)) ADV Manga.

Yoshizaki, Mine. Sgt. Frog, 6 vols., Vol. 2. Fukami, Yuko, tr. from JPN. rev. ed. 2004. (Illus.). 192p. pap. 9.99 (978-1-59182-704-7(3), Tokyopop Adult) TOKYOPOP, Inc.

—Sgt. Frog, 6 vols., Vol. 3. rev. ed. 2004. (Illus.). 192p. pap. 9.99 (978-1-59182-705-4(1), Tokyopop Adult) TOKYOPOP, Inc.

Yoshizaki, Mine, creator. Sgt. Frog, 6 vols. 2004. (Illus.). Vol. 4. rev. ed. 188p. pap. 9.99 (978-1-59182-706-1(X)); Vol. 5. 5th rev. ed. 192p. pap. 9.99 (978-1-59182-707-8(8)) TOKYOPOP, Inc. (Tokyopop Adult).

Yoshizuki, Kumichi. Someday's Dreamers. 2006. (Illus.). pap. 9.99 (978-1-59816-178-6(4)); 2nd rev. ed. pap. 9.99 (978-1-59816-179-3(2)) TOKYOPOP, Inc. (Tokyopop Kids).

You, Lee Young. Kill Me, Kiss Me, 5 vols. rev. ed. 2004. (Illus.). 192p. Vol. 2. pap. 9.99 (978-1-59182-594-4(6)); Vol. 3. pap. 9.99 (978-1-59182-595-1(4)) TOKYOPOP, Inc. (Tokyopop Kids).

Young Noh, Mi, illus. & creator. Threads of Time, Vol. 4. Young Noh, Mi, creator. rev. ed. 2005. 192p. pap. 9.99 (978-1-59532-035-3(0), Tokyopop Adult) TOKYOPOP, Inc.

Yozaburo, Kanari. Kindaichi Case Files, 10 vols. Fumiya, Sato, illus. 2004. 240p. Vol. 7. 7th rev. ed. pap. 9.99 (978-1-59182-478-7(8)); Vol. 8. 8th rev. ed. pap. 9.99 (978-1-59182-479-4(6)) TOKYOPOP, Inc. (Tokyopop Kids).

—Playing the Fool, Vol. 12. Fumiya, Sato, illus. 12th rev. ed. 2005. 192p. pap. 9.99 (978-1-59532-696-6(0), Tokyopop Kids) TOKYOPOP, Inc.

Yu, Yuen Wong. Digimon, 5 vols., Vol. 2. rev. ed. 2003. (Illus.). 164p. (gr. 2 up). pap. 9.99 (978-1-59182-090-1(1)) TOKYOPOP, Inc.

Yuasa, Kumiko, tr. from JPN. Deus VitaeTM, 3 vols., Vol. 2. rev. ed. 2004. (Illus.). 200p. pap. 9.99 (978-1-59182-770-2(1), Tokyopop Adult) TOKYOPOP, Inc.

Yuichi, Kumakura. Jing: King of Bandits—Twilight Tales, Vol. 5. 5th rev. ed. 2005. (Illus.). 192p. pap. 9.99 (978-1-59532-418-4(6), Tokyopop Kids) TOKYOPOP, Inc.

—Jing Vol. 6: King of Bandits—Twilight Tales, 6 vols. 6th rev. ed. 2005. (Illus.). 192p. pap. 9.99 (978-1-59532-419-1(4), Tokyopop Kids) TOKYOPOP, Inc.

Yuji, Iwahara. Chikyu Misaki, Vol. 1. Yuji, Iwahara, illus. 2005. (Illus.). 196p. (YA). pap. 9.99 (978-1-4012-0799-1(5)) DC Comics.

—Chikyu Misaki, Vol. 2. 2005. 196p. (YA). pap. 9.99 (978-1-4012-0800-4(2)) DC Comics.

Yuki, Kaori. Angel Sanctuary, Vol. 15. 2006. (Angel Sanctuary Ser.). 208p. (YA). pap. 9.99 (978-1-4215-0521-3(5)) Viz Media.

—Angel Sanctuary, Volume 18. 2007. (Angel Sanctuary Ser.). 200p. (YA). pap. 9.99 (978-1-4215-0976-1(8)) Viz Media.

—Godchild, Vol. 4. 2007. (GodChild Ser.). 200p. (YA). pap. 8.99 (978-1-4215-0478-0(2)) Viz Media.

—Shonen. Yuki, Kaori, illus. 2006. (Cain Saga Ser.: Vol. 2). 208p. (YA). pap. 8.99 (978-1-59116-977-2(1)) Viz Media.

Yuki, Kaori, creator. Angel Cage. 2005. (Art of Angel Sanctuary Ser.). 80p. (YA). pap. 19.99 (978-1-4215-0157-4(0)) Viz Media.

Yutenji, Ako, illus. & creator. Liling-PO, Vol. 2. Yutenji, Ako, creator. rev. ed. 2005. 200p. pap. 9.99 (978-1-59532-520-4(4), Tokyopop Adult) TOKYOPOP, Inc.

Zellers, Michelle. Maya's Magic Carpet. 2006. (J). per. 11.95 (978-1-889743-48-6(8)) Robbie Dean Pr.

Zidrou. Ducoboo: In the Corner! Godi, illus. 2007. 48p. pap. 9.99 (***978-1-905460-26-7(0)***) CineBook GBR. *Dist:* Biblio Distribution.

Ziefert, Harriet. Knick-Knack Paddywhack. Bolam, Emily, illus. 2005. 16p. (ps-k). bds. 5.95 (978-1-4027-2292-9(3)) Sterling Publishing Co., Inc.

Zornow, Jeff. Werewolf. Zornow, Jeff, illus. 2007. (Graphic Horror Ser.). (Illus.). 32p. (YA). (gr. 5-8). lib. bdg. 27.07 (***978-1-60270-062-8(1)***, Graphic Planet) Magic Wagon.

Zornow, Jeff, illus. & adapted by. The Legend of Sleepy Hollow. Zornow, Jeff, adapted by. 2007. (Graphic Horror Ser.). 32p. (YA). (gr. 5-8). lib. bdg. 27.07 (***978-1-60270-060-4(5)***, Graphic Planet) Magic Wagon.

60 Years of the Dandy & the Beano 2004. 2003rd ed. 2003. (Illus.). 144p. (978-0-85116-808-1(6)) Thomson, D.C. & Co., Ltd. GBR. *Dist:* APG Sales and Fulfillment.

CARVER, GEORGE WASHINGTON, 1864?-1943

Adler, David A. A Picture Book of George Washington Carver. Brown, Dan, illus. 1999. 32p. (J). (gr. k-3). tchr. ed. 16.95 (978-0-8234-1429-1(9)); pap. 6.95 (978-0-8234-1633-2(X)) Holiday Hse., Inc.

Bolden, Tonya & Field Museum of Natural History Staff. George Washington Carver. 2008. 40p. (J). 18.95 (***978-0-8109-9366-2(X)***, Abrams Bks. for Young Readers) Abrams, Harry N., Inc.

Bowdish, Lynea. George Washington Carver. 2004. (Rookie Biographies Ser.). (J). 32p. (gr. 1-2). pap. 4.95 (978-0-516-24644-4(5)); (Illus.). 31p. 20.50 (978-0-516-23610-0(5)) Scholastic Library Publishing. (Children's Pr.).

Burgan, Michael. George Washington Carver: Scientist, Inventor, & Teacher. 2006. (Signature Lives Ser.). (Illus.). 112p. (J). (978-0-7565-1882-0(2), 1265882) Compass Point Bks.

Carey, Charles W., Jr. George Washington Carver. 1999. (Journey to Freedom Ser.). (Illus.). 40p. (J). (gr. 3-7). 28.50 (978-1-56766-569-7(1)) Child's World, Inc.

Carter, Andy. George Washington Carver. 2000. (gr. 3-6). lib. bdg. 14.10 (978-0-613-79176-2(2)) Tandem Library Bks.

Carter, Andy, et al. George Washington Carver. Paladino, Lance, illus. (On My Own Biographies Ser.). 48p. (J). (gr. 1-3). 2003. 5.95 (978-1-57505-458-2(2)); 2000. lib. bdg. 23.93 (978-1-57505-427-8(2), Carolrhoda Bks.) Lerner Publishing Group.

Chelsea House Publishing Staff. George Washington Carver: Devout Scientist. 1999. (Heroes of the Faith Ser.). 208p. (YA). (gr. 4-7). lib. bdg. 17.95 (978-0-7910-5040-8(8), Chelsea Hse.) Facts On File, Inc.

Compass Point Books, contrib. by. George Washington Carver. (Compass Point Early Biographies Ser.). 32p. (J). pap. 7.95 (978-0-7565-1171-5(2)) Compass Point Bks.

Doeden, Matt. George Washington Carver. 2007. (History Maker Biographies Ser.). (J). 26.60 (***978-0-8225-7605-1(8)***, Lerner Pubns.) Lerner Publishing Group.

Driscoll, Laura. George Washington Carver. Weber, Jill, illus. 2003. (Smart about Scientists Ser.). 32p. (J). (gr. k-5). pap. 5.99 (978-0-448-43243-4(9), Grosset & Dunlap) Penguin Group (USA) Inc.

—George Washington Carver. 2003. (gr. k-3). lib. bdg. 14.15 (978-0-613-72535-4(2)) Tandem Library Bks.

Feinstein, Stephen. Read about George Washington Carver. 2006. (I Like Biographies! Ser.). (Illus.). 24p. (J). lib. bdg. 21.26 (978-0-7660-2597-4(7), Enslow Elementary); (978-0-7660-2897-5(6)) Enslow Pubs., Inc.

Franchino, Vicky. George Washington Carver. 2001. (Compass Point Early Biographies Ser.). (Illus.). 32p. (J). (gr. 2 up). lib. bdg. 21.26 (978-0-7565-0112-9(1)) Compass Point Bks.

George Washington Carver. 2005. (First Biographies Ser.). (YA). (gr. k-3). (978-0-7368-9444-9(6), Pebble Bks.) Capstone Pr., Inc.

Gomez, Rebecca. George Washington Carver. 2003. (First Biographies Ser.). (Illus.). 32p. (J). (gr. k-4). lib. bdg. 22.78 (978-1-57765-944-0(9)) ABDO Publishing Co.

Halvorsen, Lisa. George Washington Carver: Innovator in Agriculture. 2002. (Giants of Science Ser.). (Illus.). 64p. (J). 26.20 (978-1-56711-657-1(4), Blackbirch Pr., Inc.) Thomson Gale.

Kiely Miller, Barbara. George Washington Carver. 2007. (J). pap. (***978-0-8368-8320-6(9)***, Weekly Reader Early Learning Library) Stevens, Gareth Inc.

Kittinger, Jo S. George Washington Carver. 2005. (Scholastic News Nonfiction Readers Ser.). (Illus.). 24p. (J). pap. (978-0-516-24782-3(4)) Children's Pr., Ltd.

—George Washington Carver. 2005. (Scholastic News Nonfiction Readers Ser.). (Illus.). 24p. (J). (gr. 1-2). 19.00 (978-0-516-24939-1(8), Children's Pr.) Scholastic Library Publishing.

Kramer, Barbara. George Washington Carver: Scientist & Inventor. 2002. (African-American Biographies Ser.). (Illus.). 128p. (J). (gr. 6-12). lib. bdg. 26.60 (978-0-7660-1770-2(2)) Enslow Pubs., Inc.

Krensky, Stephen. Man for All Seasons. 2008. 32p. (J). (gr. k-4). lib. bdg. 17.89 (978-0-06-027886-1(2)) HarperCollins Pubs.

—Man for All Seasons. Clay, Wil, illus. 2008. 32p. (J). (gr. k-4). 16.99 (978-0-06-027885-4(4)) HarperCollins Pubs.

Leavitt, Amie. George Washington Carver. 2007. (What's So Great About... ? Ser.). (J). lib. bdg. 25.70 (***978-1-58415-580-5(9)***) Mitchell Lane Pubs., Inc.

MacLeod, Elizabeth. George Washington Carver: An Innovative Life. 2007. (Illus.). 32p. (J). (gr. 3-7). (***978-1-55337-906-5(3)***); (***978-1-55337-907-2(1)***) Kids Can Pr., Ltd.

Marsh, Carole. George Washington Carver. 2002. (One Thousand Readers Ser.). (Illus.). 12p. (J). (gr. k-4). 2.95 (978-0-635-01487-0(4), 14874) Gallopade International.

—The Virginia Reader: George Washington Carver. 2001. (Virginia Experience! Ser.). (Illus.). 12p. (J). (gr. k-5). pap. 2.95 (978-0-635-00354-6(6)) Gallopade International.

McKissack, Patricia C. & McKissack, Fredrick L. George Washington Carver: The Peanut Scientist. rev. ed. 2002. (Great African Americans Ser.). (Illus.). 32p. (J). (gr. 1-4). lib. bdg. 18.60 (978-0-7660-1700-9(1)) Enslow Pubs., Inc.

McMurry Edwards, Linda. George Washington Carver: The Life of the Great American Agriculturist. 2005. (Library of American Lives & Times). (Illus.). 112p. (J). (gr. 4-8). lib. bdg. 31.95 (978-0-8239-6633-2(X)) Rosen Publishing Group, Inc., The.

Miller, Barbara Kiely. George Washington Carver. 2007. (Great Americans Ser.). 24p. (J). (gr. 2-4). lib. bdg. 19.93 (***978-0-8368-8313-8(6)***, Weekly Reader Early Learning Library) Stevens, Gareth Inc.

Miller, Raymond H. George Washington Carver. 2005. (Inventors & Creators Ser.). (Illus.). 48p. (J). (ps-8). lib. bdg. 26.20 (978-0-7377-3160-6(5), Greenhaven Pr., Inc.) Thomson Gale.

Monroe, Judy. George Washington Carver. 2005. (Fact Finders Ser.). (Illus.). 32p. (J). (978-0-7368-4345-4(0)) Capstone Pr., Inc.

Mortensen, Lori. George Washington Carver: Teacher, Scientist, & Inventor. O'Connor, Niamh, illus. 2007. (J). lib. bdg. (***978-1-4048-3725-6(6)***) Picture Window Bks.

Nelson, Robin. George Washington Carver: A Life of Devotion. 2007. (Pull Ahead Books-Biographies Ser.). (J). 22.60 (978-0-8225-6461-4(0), Lerner Pubns.) Lerner Publishing Group.

Olson, Nathan. George Washington Carver: Ingenious Inventor. 2006. (Graphic Library). (Illus.). 32p. (J). 25.26 (978-0-7368-5484-9(3)) Capstone Pr., Inc.

Riley, John B. George Washington Carver: A Photo Biography. 1.t. ed. 2004. (First Biographies Ser.). (Illus.). 24p. (YA). (gr. 5 up). 16.95 (978-1-883846-62-6(5), First Biographies) Reynolds, Morgan Inc.

Rustad, Martha E. H. George Washington Carver. Saunders-Smith, Gail, ed. 2001. (First Biographies Ser.). (Illus.). 24p. (J). (gr. k-1). lib. bdg. 15.93 (978-0-7368-0996-2(1), Pebble Bks.) Capstone Pr., Inc.

Wheeler, Jill C. George Washington Carver. 2003. (Breaking Barriers Ser.). (Illus.). 64p. (J). (gr. 3-8). lib. bdg. 25.65 (978-1-57765-904-4(X)) ABDO Publishing Co.

Wilson, Camilla. George Washington Carver: The Genius Behind the Peanut. 2003. (Scholastic Biography Ser.). (Illus.). 101p. (J). pap. (978-0-439-28722-7(7)) Scholastic, Inc.

CARVER, GEORGE WASHINGTON, 1864?-1943—FICTION

Jackson, Dave & Jackson, Neta. The Forty-Acre Swindle: George Washington Carver. McLaughlin, Catherine R., illus. 2000. (Trailblazer Bks.: Vol. 31). 144p. (J). (gr. 3-7). pap. 6.99 (978-0-7642-2264-1(3)) Bethany Hse. Pubs.

Owens, Vivian W. I Met a Great Man: John Meets Dr. Carver of Tuskegee. Owens, April, ed. Watson, Richard J., illus. unabr. ed. 1998. 64p. (J). (gr. 4-10). pap. 8.95 (978-0-9623839-6-0(1)) Eschar Pubns.

CARVING, WOOD

see Wood-Carving

C D

CASH, JOHNNY, 1932-2003

Neimark, Anne E. Johnny Cash. 2007. (Up Close Ser.). (Illus.). 208p. (J). (gr. 8 up). 15.99 (978-0-670-06215-7(4) , Viking Juvenile) Penguin Group (USA) Inc.

—Johnny Cash: A Twentieth-Century Life. 2007. (Up Close Ser.). (Illus.). 207p. (J). (*978-1-4287-3958-1(0) , Viking Adult) Penguin Group (USA) Inc.

—Up Close: Johnny Cash: Johnny Cash. 2008. (Up Close Ser.). 208p. (J). (gr. 6). pap. 6.99 (*978-0-14-241047-9(0) , Puffin) Penguin Group (USA) Inc.

CASSATT, MARY, 1845-1926

Casey, Carolyn. Mary Cassatt: The Life of an Artist. 2004. (Artist Biographies Ser.). (Illus.). 48p. (J). lib. bdg. 23.93 (978-0-7660-2093-1(2)) Enslow Pubs., Inc.

Ferrara, Cos. Mary Cassatt: The Life & Art of a Genteel Rebel. 2004. (Girls Explore, Reach for the Stars Ser.). (Illus.). 101p. (J). 20.00 (978-0-9749456-3-7(3) , Girls Explore) Girls Explore LLC.

Giesecke, Ernestine. Mary Cassatt. (Heinemann First Library). (Illus.). 32p. (J). 2006. lib. bdg. (*978-1-4034-8493-2(7)); Set 1. 2002. pap. 6.50 (978-1-58810-284-3(X) , 91056) Heinemann Library.

—Mary Cassatt. 2001. (gr. k-3). lib. bdg. 14.75 (978-0-613-89894-2(X)) Tandem Library Bks.

Giesecke, Ernestine, contrib. by. Mary Cassatt. 1999. (Life & Work of. . . Ser.). (Illus.). 32p. (J). (gr. k-2). lib. bdg. 21.36 (978-1-57572-955-8(5)) Heinemann Library.

Harris, Lois V. Mary Cassatt: Impressionist Painter. 2007. 32p. (J). (gr. k-3). 15.95 (*978-1-58980-452-4(X)) Pelican Publishing Co., Inc.

Hoena, Blake A. Mary Cassatt. 2003. (Masterpieces, Artists & Their Works). (Illus.). 24p. (J). lib. bdg. 19.93 (978-0-7368-2229-9(1) , Bridgestone Bks.) Capstone Pr., Inc.

Mattern, Joanne. Mary Cassatt. 2005. (Checkerboard Biography Library). (Illus.). 32p. (J). (gr. k-6). lib. bdg. 22.78 (978-1-59197-840-4(8)) ABDO Publishing Co.

O'Connor, Jane. Mary Cassatt: Family Pictures. Kalis, Jennifer, illus. 2003. (Smart about Art Ser.). 32p. (J). (gr. k-3). 14.89 (978-0-448-43153-6(X)); pap. 5.99 (978-0-448-43152-9(1)) Penguin Group (USA) Inc. (Grosset & Dunlap).

—Mary Cassatt: Family Pictures. 2003. (gr. k-3). lib. bdg. 14.15 (978-0-613-61641-6(3)) Tandem Library Bks.

Streissguth, Thomas. Mary Cassatt: Portrait of an American Impressionist. 1998. (Trailblazers Biographies Ser.). (Illus.). 112p. (J). (gr. 4-7). lib. bdg. 27.93 (978-1-57505-291-5(1) , Carolrhoda Bks.) Lerner Publishing Group.

Sweeney, Joan. Suzette & the Puppy: A Story about Mary Cassatt. Wharton, Jennifer Heyd, illus. 2000. 28p. (J). (ps-3). 14.99 (978-0-7641-5294-8(7)) Barron's Educational Series, Inc.

CASTAWAYS

Beech, Sandy. Isle Be Seeing You. 2005. (Illus.). 179p. (J). (*978-1-4156-1539-3(X) , Aladdin) Simon & Schuster Children's Publishing.

—Weather's Here, Wish You Were Great. 2005. (Illus.). 186p. (J). (*978-1-4156-1165-4(3) , Aladdin) Simon & Schuster Children's Publishing.

—Worst Class Trip Ever. 2005. 173p. (J). (*978-1-4156-0619-3(6) , Aladdin) Simon & Schuster Children's Publishing.

McCully, Emily Arnold. Manjiro: The Boy Who Risked His Life for Two Countries. 2008. (J). (*978-0-374-34792-5(1)) Farrar, Straus & Giroux.

Stevenson, James. The Castaway. Stevenson, James, illus. 2002. (Illus.). 32p. (J). (gr. 2 up). 15.95 (978-0-688-16965-7(1)) HarperCollins Pubs.

CASTLE OF SEVEN TOWERS (IMAGINARY PLACE)—FICTION

Nix, Garth. Aenir. 2001. (Seventh Tower Ser.: Bk. 3). 240p. (J). (ps-7). mass mkt. 5.99 (978-0-439-17684-2(0)) Scholastic, Inc.

—Aenir. 2001. (Seventh Tower Ser.: Bk. 3). 233p. (gr. 3-6). lib. bdg. 13.00 (978-0-613-32247-8(9)) Tandem Library Bks.

—Castle. Rawlings, Steve, illus. 2007. (Seventh Tower Ser.: Bk. 2). 224p. (J). (gr. 3-7). pap. 4.99 (978-0-439-17683-5(2)) Scholastic, Inc.

—The Fall. 2007. (Seventh Tower Ser.: Bk. 1). 208p. (J). (gr. 4-7). pap. 4.99 (978-0-439-17682-8(4)) Scholastic, Inc.

CASTLES

Adams, Brian. Medieval Castles. 2006. (Hallmarks of History Ser.). (Illus.). 32p. (J). (978-1-59604-119-6(6)) Stargazer Bks.

Adams, Simon. Castles & Forts. (Kingfisher Knowledge Ser.). (Illus.). 64p. (J). (gr. 4-6). 2007. pap. 8.95 (*978-0-7534-6119-8(6)); 2003. tchr. ed. 12.95 (978-0-7534-5620-0(6)) Houghton Mifflin Co. Trade & Reference Div. (Kingfisher).

The Age of Castles, 4 bks., Set. 2000. (Illus.). (J). (978-0-7398-4214-0(5)) Raintree.

Alderton, David. Castles & Palaces. (Information Ser.). (Illus.). 32p. (J). 3.25 (978-0-7214-1741-7(8) , Dutton Juvenile) Penguin Group (USA) Inc.

Ball, Jacqueline A. Himeji Castle: Japan's Samurai Past. 2005. (Castles, Palaces, & Tombs Ser.). (J). lib. bdg. 25.27 (978-1-59716-001-8(6)) Bearport Publishing Co., Inc.

Bergin, Mark. Castle. 1999. (Fast Forward Ser.). (Illus.). 32p. (J). (gr. 4-8). pap. 9.95 (978-0-531-15421-2(1)); 29.00 (978-0-531-14571-5(9)) Scholastic Library Publishing. (Watts, Franklin).

—Castle. 1999. (gr. 3-6). lib. bdg. 18.75 (978-0-613-37307-4(3)) Tandem Library Bks.

Bingham, Jane. Great Castle Search. 2005. 32p. (J). pap. 7.95 (978-0-7945-0998-9(3) , Usborne) EDC Publishing.

Bodden, Valerie. Medieval Castles. 2008. (J). (*978-1-58341-561-0(0) , Creative Education) Creative Co., The.

Brooks, Philip. Knights & Castles. Kingfisher Editors, ed. 2001. (Questions & Answers about... Ser.). 40p. (J). (gr. 4-6). pap. 7.95 (978-0-7534-5371-1(1) , Kingfisher) Houghton Mifflin Co. Trade & Reference Div.

Los Castillos Tenian Foso. 2003. (Enciclopedia Me Pregunto Por Que). (SPA., Illus.). 32p. (J). (gr. 3-5). (978-84-241-2175-4(9) , EV2037) Everest de Ediciones y Distribucion, S.L. ESP. *Dist:* Lectorum Pubns., Inc.

Cole, Joanna, et al. Ms. Frizzle's Adventures: Medieval Castle. Degen, Bruce, illus. 2003. (Magic School Bus Ser.). 48p. (J). pap. 15.95 (978-0-590-10820-1(4)) Scholastic, Inc.

Coppendale, Jean. Knights & Castles. Hutchinson, Tim, illus. 2005. (Explore Inside Ser.). 10p. (J). (gr. 4-7). 9.98 (978-0-7624-2319-4(6) , Courage Bks.) Running Pr. Bk. Pubs.

Cox, Phil Roxbee. What Were Castles For? rev. ed. 2004. (Starting Point History Ser.). (Illus.). 32p. (J). pap. 4.99 (978-0-7945-0178-5(8) , Usborne); lib. bdg. 12.95 (978-1-58086-396-4(5)) EDC Publishing.

Dargie, Richard. Castle under Seige. 1998. (Age of Castles Ser.). (Illus.). 48p. (J). (gr. 4-8). pap. 7.95 (978-0-8172-8121-2(5)) Steck-Vaughn.

—Knights & Castles. 1998. (Age of Castles Ser.). (Illus.). 48 p. (J). (gr. 3-7). lib. bdg. 25.69 (978-0-8172-5122-2(7)) Raintree.

—Knights & Castles. 1998. (Age of Castles Ser.). (Illus.). 48p. (J). (gr. 4-8). pap. 7.95 (978-0-8172-8122-9(3)) Steck-Vaughn.

Daynes, Katie. See inside Castles. Hancock, David, illus. 2005. 16p. (J). 12.95 (978-0-7945-1022-0(1) , Usborne) EDC Publishing.

—(See Inside Castles) - Spanish. 2006. 16p. (J). bds. 12.99 (978-0-7460-7383-4(6) , Usborne) EDC Publishing.

Dixon, Philip. Knights & Castles. 2007. (Insiders Ser.). 64p. (J). (gr. 3-7). 16.99 (*978-1-4169-3864-4(8)) Simon & Schuster Children's Publishing.

DK Publishing Staff. Castle. 2007. (Experience Ser.). 64p. (J). (gr. 3-8). 15.99 (978-0-7566-2838-3(5)) Dorling Kindersley Publishing, Inc.

Dorling Kindersley Publishing Staff. Castle. 2004. (Eyewitness Books). 72p. (J). lib. bdg. 19.99 (978-0-7566-0659-6(4)) Dorling Kindersley Publishing, Inc.

—Castle & Knight. 2005. (Ultimate sticker Bks.). 16p. (J). pap. 6.99 (978-0-7566-1455-3(4)) Dorling Kindersley Publishing, Inc.

Dorling Kindersley Publishing Staff, ed. Castle. 2004. (Dk Eyewitness Books Ser.). 72p. (J). 15.99 (978-0-7566-0660-2(8)) Dorling Kindersley Publishing, Inc.

Eastwood, Kay. Life in a Castle. 2003. (Medieval World Ser.). (Illus.). 32p. (J). (gr. 5). pap. (978-0-7787-1343-2(1)); pap. (978-0-7787-1375-3(X)) Crabtree Publishing Co.

Gallagher, Debbie. Palaces, Mansions, & Castles. 2007. (J). (*978-1-59920-151-1(8)) Smart Apple Media.

Gilkerson, Patricia. My Adventure in a Castle. 2006. 44p. (J). 8.99 (978-1-59092-271-2(9) , Orchard Academy Pr.) Windstorm Creative.

Gravett, Christopher. Castle. 2008. (DK Eyewitness Bks.). 72p. (J). (gr. 3-8). 15.99 (*978-0-7566-3769-9(4)) Dorling Kindersley Publishing, Inc.

Hamilton, John. Castles & Dungeons. 2005. (Illus.). 32p. (J). (gr. 4-8). lib. bdg. 24.21 (978-1-59679-335-4(X) , ABDO & Daughters) ABDO Publishing Co.

Hammond, John Hays. The Story of Hammond Castle. 1999. (Learning & Coloring Bks.). (Illus.). 32p. (J). (gr. 2 up). pap. 5.95 (978-1-878452-29-0(0) , Tory Corner Editions) Quincannon Publishing Group.

Harris, Nicholas. Castle. Dennis, Peter, illus. 2001. (Fast Forward Bks.). 24p. (J). (gr. 2 up). 14.95 (978-0-7641-5309-9(9)) Barron's Educational Series, Inc.

Heritage, English. The Very Big Book of Castles. 2006. (Illus.). 23p. pap. 8.00 (*978-1-905624-43-0(3)) English Heritage GBR. *Dist:* Brown, David Bk. Co., The.

Hicks, Peter. How Castles Were Built. (Age of Castles Ser.). (Illus.). 48p. (J). (gr. 4-8). 1999. (978-0-7502-2144-3(5)); 1998. pap. 7.95 (978-0-8172-8119-9(3)) Steck-Vaughn.

Hindley, J. Knights & Castles. 2004. (Time Traveler Ser.). (Illus.). 32p. (J). lthr. 14.95 (978-1-58086-554-8(2)); pap. 6.95 (978-0-7945-0335-2(7)) EDC Publishing.

Hinds, Kathryn. The Castle. 2000. (Life in the Middle Ages Ser.). (Illus.). 80p. (J). (gr. 5 up). lib. bdg. 29.93 (978-0-7614-1007-2(4) , Benchmark Bks.) Cavendish, Marshall Corp.

Jarrow, Gail. A Medieval Castle. 2004. (Great Structures in History Ser.). (Illus.). 48p. (J). (gr. 4-7). 26.20 (978-0-7377-2070-9(0)) Thomson Gale.

Jarvie, Gordon & Whelan, Olwyn. Scottish Castles. 2004. (Scottie Bks.). (Illus.). 41p. (J). (gr. 3-7). pap. 8.95 (978-0-11-494276-2(5)) NMS Enterprises Ltd. - Publishing GBR. *Dist:* Antique Collectors' Club.

Jovinelly, Joann & Netelkos, Jason. The Crafts & Culture of a Medieval Castle. 2006. (Illus.). 47p. (J). (978-1-4042-0760-8(0)) Rosen Publishing Group, Inc., The.

Key Porter Books Staff. Gymboree in a Princess Castle. rev. ed. 2007. (Illus.). 1p. (J). 16.95 (*978-1-55263-923-8(1)) Key Porter Bks. CAN. *Dist:* Perseus Distribution.

Knox, Barbara J. Castle Dracula: Romania's Vampire Home. 2005. (Castles, Palaces, & Tombs Ser.). (Illus.). 32p. (J). lib. bdg. 25.27 (978-1-59716-000-1(8)) Bearport Publishing Co., Inc.

Leonhardt, Alice. Castles. 1999. (Illus.). (J). pap. (978-0-7398-2415-3(5)) Steck-Vaughn.

MacDonald, Fiona. Castles. 2001. (Topic Bks.). (Illus.). 32p. (J). (gr. 2-5). 23.50 (978-0-531-14551-7(4) , Watts, Franklin) Scholastic Library Publishing.

—Castles. 2000. (gr. 3-6). lib. bdg. 15.25 (978-0-613-34107-3(4)) Tandem Library Bks.

—Knights & Castles. 2005. (First Look at History Ser.). (Illus.). 24p. (J). lib. bdg. 22.00 (978-0-8368-4526-6(9)) Stevens, Gareth Inc.

—Knights, Castles, & Warfare in the Middle Ages. 2005. (World Almanac Library of the Middle Ages). (Illus.). 48p. (J). pap. (978-0-8368-5904-1(9)); lib. bdg. 30.00 (978-0-8368-5895-2(6)) Stevens, Gareth Inc. (World Almanac Library).

Martin, Alex. Knights & Castles. 2004. (Picture That! Ser.). (Illus.). 64p. (gr. 3 up). 19.95 (978-1-58728-441-0(3) , Creative Publishing International) Quayside.

McAleavy, Tony. Life in a Medieval Castle. 2003. (English Heritage (Series)). (Illus.). 64p. (J). (gr. 6-12). 22.00 (978-1-59270-005-9(5)) Enchanted Lion Bks., LLC.

Murrell, Deborah. The Best Book of Knights & Castles. 2005. (Best Book of... Ser.). (Illus.). 32p. (J). (gr. k-3). 12.95 (978-0-7534-5935-5(3) , Kingfisher) Houghton Mifflin Co. Trade & Reference Div.

Orme, Helen. Edinburgh Castle: Scotland's Haunted Fortress. 2006. (Castles, Palaces, & Tombs Ser.). (Illus.). 32p. (J). lib. bdg. 25.27 (978-1-59716-248-7(5)) Bearport Publishing Co., Inc.

Osborne, Mary Pope & Osborne, Will. Knights & Castles: A Nonfiction Companion to The Knight at Dawn. Murdocca, Sal, illus. 2000. (Magic Tree House Research Guide Ser.: No. 2). 128p. (J). (gr. k-3). lib. bdg. 11.99 (978-0-375-90297-0(X)); mass mkt. 4.99 (978-0-375-80297-3(5)) Random Hse. Children's Bks. (Random Hse. Bks. for Young Readers).

—Knights & Castles: A Nonfiction Companion to The Knight at Dawn. 2000. (Magic Tree House Research Guide Ser.: No. 2). (J). (gr. k-3). (978-0-606-18857-9(6)); lib. bdg. 13.00 (978-0-613-26101-2(1)) Tandem Library Bks.

Pianini, Michele. Life in a Medieval Castle. Mesturini, Cristina, illus. 2004. 40p. (J). bds. 9.99 (978-0-7641-5751-6(5)) Barron's Educational Series, Inc.

Platt, Richard & Biesty, Stephen. Castle. (Illus.). 32p. (J). pap. 21.95 (978-0-590-24346-9(2)) Scholastic, Inc.

Pratt, Leonie. Knights & Castles Things to Make & Do. Thompson, Josephine Et Al, illus. 2006. 32p. (J). pap. 6.99 (978-0-7945-1355-9(7) , Usborne) EDC Publishing.

Quadrillion Media Staff. Castles, 10th ed. 1999. (J). 12.95 (978-1-58185-011-6(5)) Quadrillion Media LLC.

Rau, Dana Meachen. Bookworms: The Inside Story, 6 bks., Set. Incl. Castle. 32p. lib. bdg. 22.79 (978-0-7614-2272-3(2)); Igloo. 24p. lib. bdg. 22.79 (978-0-7614-2273-0(0)); Log Cabin. 24p. lib. bdg. 22.79 (*978-0-7614-2274-7(9)); Pyramid. 32p. lib. bdg. 22.79 (*978-0-7614-2275-4(7)); Skyscraper. 32p. lib. bdg. 22.79 (978-0-7614-2276-1(5)); Tepee. 32p. lib. bdg. 22.79 (978-0-7614-2277-8(3)); (Illus.). (J). (gr. k-2). 2006. 2006. Set lib. bdg. 136.71 (*978-0-7614-2271-6(4) , Benchmark Bks.) Cavendish, Marshall Corp.

Rau, Dana Meachen. Castle. 2006. (Bookworms Ser.). (Illus.). 32p. (J). lib. bdg. 22.79 (978-0-7614-2272-3(2) , Benchmark Bks.) Cavendish, Marshall Corp.

Reid, Straun. Castle Life. 1998. (Age of Castles Ser.). (Illus.). 48p. (J). (gr. 4-8). pap. 7.95 (978-0-8172-8120-5(7)) Steck-Vaughn.

Reid, Struan. Castle Life. 1998. (Age of Castles Ser.). (Illus.). 48p. (J). (gr. 3-7). lib. bdg. 25.69 (978-0-8172-5119-2(7)) Raintree.

—Castle Life. 1998. (Age of Castles Ser.). (Illus.). 48p. (J). (gr. 4-8). (978-0-7502-2145-0(3)) Steck-Vaughn.

—Castle under Seige. 1998. (Age of Castles Ser.). (Illus.). 48 p. (J). (gr. 3-7). lib. bdg. 25.69 (978-0-8172-5120-8(0)) Raintree.

Sabuda, Robert & Olmon, Kyle. Castle: Medieval Days & Knights. Reinhart, Matthew & Sabin, Tracy, illus. 2006. 6p. (J). 19.99 (978-0-439-54324-8(X) , Orchard Bks.) Scholastic, Inc.

Salley, Victoria. Castles & Knights. Jackson, Rosie, tr. from GER. Ferraro, Andrea, illus. 2001. (Adventures in Architecture Ser.). 30p. (gr. 3-5). 14.95 (978-3-7913-2576-7(0)) Prestel Publishing.

Shuter, Jane. Carisbrooke Castle. 1999. (Visiting the Past Ser.). 32p. (J). (gr. 5-7). lib. bdg. 24.22 (978-1-57572-857-5(5)) Heinemann Library.

—Life in a Medieval Castle. 2005. (Picture the Past Ser.). (Illus.). 32p. (J). (gr. 2-4). lib. bdg. 26.79 (978-1-4034-6445-3(6)); pap. (978-1-4034-6452-1(9)) Heinemann Library.

Simon, Seymour. See More Knights & Castles. 2006. (Illus.). 40p. (J). 14.50 (978-0-8118-5408-5(6)); pap. 3.95 (978-0-8118-5409-2(4)) Chronicle Bks. LLC.

Sims, L. Castles. 2004. (SPA., Illus.). 104p. (J). (gr. 4). pap. 14.95 (978-0-7945-0144-0(3) , Usborne); lib. bdg. 22.95 (978-1-58086-425-1(2)) EDC Publishing.

Smith, A. G. Castles Stained Glass Coloring Book. 2003. (Illus.). 16p. (J). pap. 5.95 (978-0-486-43048-5(0)) Dover Pubns., Inc.

—Medieval Castle. 2002. (Dover Coloring Bks.). (Illus.). 32p. (J). pap. 3.95 (978-0-486-42080-6(9)) Dover Pubns., Inc.

—Medieval Castle Sticker Picture. 1998. (Illus.). (J). 5.95 (978-0-486-40588-9(5)) Dover Pubns., Inc.

Star, Fleur & Dorling Kindersley Publishing Staff. Castle & Knight. 2005. (Eye Wonder Ser.). (Illus.). 48p. (J). 9.99 (978-0-7566-1417-1(1)); lib. bdg. 17.99 (978-0-7566-1418-8(X)) Dorling Kindersley Publishing, Inc.

Steele, Philip. Castles. 1999. (gr. 3-6). lib. bdg. 19.90 (978-0-613-90019-5(7)) Tandem Library Bks.

—I Wonder Why Castles Had Moats & Other Questions about Long Ago. 2004. (I Wonder Why Ser.). (Illus.). 32p. (J). (gr. k-3). pap. 6.95 (978-0-7534-5809-9(8) , Kingfisher) Houghton Mifflin Co. Trade & Reference Div.

—The World of Castles. 2005. (World Of Ser.). (Illus.). 64p. (J). (gr. 4-6). pap. 8.95 (978-0-7534-5834-1(9) , Kingfisher) Houghton Mifflin Co. Trade & Reference Div.

Sterling Publishing Company Staff. Make A Castle. 1999. (Illus.). 12p. (J). (gr. 2-4). pap. 5.95 (978-0-8069-1945-4(0)) Sterling Publishing Co., Inc.

Taylor, Barbara. The Amazing World of Castles: Discover the Fascinating History of Medieval Adventure, Battle & Romance. 2003. (Illus.). 64p. (gr. 3-7). 14.99 (978-0-7548-1206-7(5)) Anness Publishing GBR. *Dist:* National Bk. Network.

—Castles. 2000. (Illus.). 64p. pap. 7.95 (978-1-84215-045-0(6) , Southwater) Anness Publishing GBR. *Dist:* National Bk. Network.

—World of Castles. 2000. (gr. 3-6). lib. bdg. 16.40 (978-0-613-89411-1(1)) Tandem Library Bks.

Turnbull, S. Castles. 2004. (Beginners Ser.). 32p. (J). (gr. 1 up). pap. 4.95 (978-0-7945-0320-8(9)); lib. bdg. 12.95 (978-1-58086-481-7(3)) EDC Publishing.

Turnbull, Stephanie. Castles - Internet Referenced (Level 1) 2007. 32p. (J). 4.99 (978-0-7945-1335-1(2) , Usborne) EDC Publishing.

Waddell, Martin, et al. Crazy Castles. 2007. (I-read Ser.). (Illus.). 40p. pap. (*978-0-521-70474-8(X)) Cambridge Univ. Pr.

White, Graham. Storming a Castle. 2002. (gr. 3-6). lib. bdg. 17.60 (978-0-613-81333-4(2)) Tandem Library Bks.

—Storming A Castle: National Geographic Maze Adventures. 2002. (Illus.). 32p. (J). (gr. 3-7). pap. 8.95 (978-0-7922-6940-3(3) , National Geographic Children's Bks.) National Geographic Society.

White, Matt. Castles: Towers, Dungeons, Moats, & More. 2002. (High Five Reading Ser.). (Illus.). 48p. (J). (gr. 2-3). lib. bdg. 22.60 (978-0-7368-9549-1(3) , Capstone High-Interest Bks.); pap. (978-0-7368-9527-9(2)) Capstone Pr., Inc.

Wilson, Phil, illus. Medieval Castle: A Three Dimensional. 2004. (J). 22.00 (978-1-58117-365-9(2) , Intervisual/Piggy Toes) Dalmatian Pr.

Wright, Rachel. Castles. (Illus.). 32p. (YA). (gr. 3 up). lib. bdg. 27.10 (978-1-932889-04-8(3)) Sea-To-Sea Pubns.

CASTLES—FICTION

Abbott, Tony. The Riddle of Zorfendorf Castle. Merrell, David, illus. 2005. 124p. (J). (ps-k). lib. bdg. 10.79 (978-0-606-33298-9(7)) Tandem Library Bks.

Abbott, Tony. Riddle of Zorfendorf Castle. Merrell, David, illus. 2005. 124p. (J). lib. bdg. 15.38 (*978-1-4242-0310-9(4)) Fitzgerald Bks.

Aber, Linda Williams. The Clue in the Castle Wall. 2004. (Barbie Mystery Ser.: No. 6). 48p. (J). pap. 3.99 (978-0-439-55709-2(7) , Scholastic Paperbacks) Scholastic, Inc.

Alfred the Curious: Individual Chapter Book Title Six-Packs. Vol. 26. 32p. (gr. 3-4). 44.00 (978-0-7635-4476-8(0)) Rigby Education.

Archambault, Lilith R. Cat in the Castle. 2007. 19p. pap. 7.95 (*978-0-533-15622-1(X)) Vantage Pr., Inc.

Ballou, Kathy. The Tracks Out Back. l.t. ed. 2005. (Illus.). 24p. (J). per. 10.00 (978-1-932338-50-8(0)) Lifevest Publishing, Inc.

Bernheimer, Kate. The Girl in the Castle Inside the Museum. Ceccoli, Nicoletta, illus. 2008. 40p. (J). (*978-0-375-83606-0(3) , Schwartz & Wade Bks.) Random Hse. Children's Bks.

Bernston, Lynn, ed. The Castle Keys. 2001. (Illus.). 72p. (YA). (gr. 5 up). 8.00 (978-0-9705459-0-9(8)) Edwards, Lorryann.

Bishop, Phyllis. Tommy Minor & Tiny Major Danger. l.t. ed. 2005. (Illus.). 36p. (J). per. 9.99 (978-1-59879-028-3(5)) Lifevest Publishing, Inc.

Blyton, Enid. Castle of Adventure. 2006. (Adventure Ser.). 288p. (J). pap. 9.99 (*978-0-330-44630-3(4)) Macmillan Publishers Ltd. GBR. *Dist:* Independent Pubs. Group.

Brennan, Herbie. Nuff Said: Another Tale of Bluebell Wood. Collins, Ross, illus. 2002. 128p. (J). (gr. 2-5). 13.95 (978-1-58234-771-4(9) , Bloomsbury Children) Bloomsbury Publishing.

Caballero, Erica. Mount Mole. 2006. pap. 10.00 (*978-1-4257-2301-9(2)) Xlibris Corp.

Chambers, Mark, illus. Build Your Own Fairytale Castle: A Push-Out-and-Play Book. 2008. 12p. (J). bds. 8.95 (*978-0-385-61115-2(3)) Transworld Publishers Ltd. GBR. *Dist:* Independent Pubs. Group.

Clark, CoraMarie. Emily's Magical Journey with Toothena the Tooth Fairy. Lawton, Val, illus. 2007. 32p. (J). (*978-0-9783779-0-8(7)) Strategix Ltd.

Colshorn, Carl & Colshorn, Theodore. The Porridge Pot. Carls, Claudia, illus. 2007. 32p. (J). (ps). 16.99 (*978-0-698-40073-3(9) , Minedition) Penguin Group (USA) Inc.

Cook, Sherry & Johnson, Terri. Quincy Quake. 26. Kuhn, Jesse, illus. l.t. ed. 2006. (Quirkles—Exploring Phonics through Science Ser.: 17). 32p. (J). 7.99 (978-1-933815-16-9(7) , Quirkles, The) Creative 3, LLC.

Cook, Vivian E. Trapped in Haunted Castle. Nelson, Grace I., illus. 1999. (Adventures of Spencer, Private Eye & His Psychic Sister, Tiffany Ser.: No. 5). 58p. (J). (gr. 3-5). pap. 8.95 (978-1-928659-04-4(7)) Two Sisters Publishing.

Coulton, Mia. Danny's Castle. Coulton, Mia, photos by. 2005. (J). 4.95 (978-1-933624-00-6(0)) Maryruth Bks., Inc.

Deary, Terry. The Ghosts of Batwing Castle. l.t. ed. 2005. (Illus.). 88p. (J). pap. incl. audio (978-0-7540-7869-2(8) , CLP 451) BBC Audio.

Deskis, Jane. Arianna & the Missing Princess. 2002. 84p. pap. 14.95 (978-1-59129-556-3(4)) PublishAmerica, Inc.

Doyle, Malachy. The Great Castle of Marshmangle. Hess, Paul, illus. 2003. 32p. (J). pap. 11.00 (978-1-84270-215-4(7)) Andersen GBR. *Dist:* Independent Pubs. Group.

Duey, Kathleen. Castle Avamir. Rayyan, Omar, illus. ed. 2005. 76p. (J). lib. bdg. 15.00 (978-1-59054-899-8(X)) Fitzgerald Bks.

Fairy Tales- Jack & the Beanstalk. 2005. (J). bds. (978-1-4194-0040-7(1)) Paradise Pr., Inc.
French, Allen. The Lost Baron. Wyeth, Andrew, illus. 2001. 320p. (J). (gr. 5-12). reprint ed. pap. 14.95 (978-1-883937-53-9(1) , 53-1) Bethlehem Bks.
Gayzagian, Doris. One White Wishing Stone: A Beach Day Counting Book. 2006. (Illus.). 32p. (J). (ps-1). 16.95 (978-0-7922-5110-1(5)); 25.90 (978-0-7922-5573-4(9)) National Geographic Society. (National Geographic Children's Bks.).
Gelsey, James. Scooby-Doo & the Haunted Castle: Scooby-Doo Y el Castillo Hechizado. 2002. (Scooby-Doo Mysteries Ser.: No. 1). (SPA., Illus.). 64p. (J). (gr. 2-4). mass mkt. 3.99 (978-0-439-40984-1(5) , Scholastic en Espanol) Scholastic, Inc.
—Scooby-Doo y el Castillo Hechizado. 2002. Tr. of Scooby-Doo & the Haunted Castle. (SPA.). (gr. k-3). lib. bdg. 13.00 (978-0-613-82494-1(6)) Tandem Library Bks.
George, Jean Craighead. Tree Castle Island. 2003. 256p. (J). pap. 5.99 (978-0-06-000256-5(5) , Harper Trophy) HarperCollins Pubs.
—Tree Castle Island. 2003. (gr. 3-6). lib. bdg. 14.15 (978-0-613-67007-4(8)) Tandem Library Bks.
Gliori, Debi. Pure Dead Frozen. 2007. (J). (gr. 5). 320p. 15.99 (***978-0-375-83317-5(X)***); 304p. lib. bdg. 18.99 (***978-0-375-93317-2(4)***) Random Hse. Children's Bks. (Knopf Bks. for Young Readers).
—Pure Dead Magic. 2002. (Illus.). 208p. (gr. 5). mass mkt. 6.50 (978-0-440-41849-8(6) , Yearling) Random Hse. Children's Bks.
—Pure Dead Wicked. 2003. 240p. (gr. 5 up). 6.50 (978-0-440-41936-5(0) , Yearling) Random Hse. Children's Bks.
Gralley, Jean. Yonderful's Castle. 2000. (J). 16.95 (978-0-8050-6329-5(3) , Holt, Henry & Co. Bks. For Young Readers) Holt, Henry & Co.
Griffin, Adele. Witch Twins & the Ghost of Glenn Bly. Rogers, Jacqueline, illus. 2005. 128p. (gr. 2-6). pap. 5.99 (978-0-7868-5496-7(0)) Hyperion Bks. for Children.
Hanken, Sandra. Sky Castle. Bergsma, Jody Lynn, illus. 1998. 32p. (ps-3). 15.95 (978-0-935699-14-2(7)) Illumination Arts Publishing Co., Inc.
Harrison, Cora. The Secret of Drumshee Castle. 1998. (Drumshee Timeline Ser.: Bk. 3). (Illus.). 128p. (J). (gr. 3-9). pap. 6.95 (978-0-86327-632-3(6)) Wolfhound Pr. IRL. *Dist:* Interlink Publishing Group, Inc., Irish American Bk. Co.
Hayes, Rosemary. The Magic Sword. 2005. (Cambridge Storybooks Ser.). 32p. pap. 7.00 (978-0-521-67475-1(1)) Cambridge Univ. Pr.
Hepworth, David G. The Picture Stone. 2006. (Illus.). 76p. pap. (***978-1-4120-9053-7(9)***) Trafford Publishing.
Hofer, Nelly & Hofer, Ernst, illus. Clever Katarina: A Tale in Six Parts. 2006. 40p. (J). (gr. 3-5). 17.95 (978-0-88776-764-7(8)) Tundra Bks., Inc./Livres Toundra, Inc. CAN. *Dist:* Random Hse., Inc.
Ibbotson, Eva. The Beasts of Clawstone Castle. Hawkes, Kevin, illus. (J). 2007. 256p. (gr. 3 up). 6.99 (***978-0-14-240931-2(6)*** , Puffin); 2006. 192p. (gr. 5). 16.99 (978-0-525-47719-8(5) , Dutton Juvenile) Penguin Group (USA) Inc.
Johnson, Bob. The Castle of Gallimaufry Bk. 4: The Squatland Chronicles. l.t. ed. 2005. 56p. per. 11.00 (978-1-59453-510-9(8) , 2549) Airleaf Publishing & Bookselling.
Jones, Diana Wynne. Howl's Moving Castle. 2001. 336p. (J). (gr. 5 up). pap. 6.99 (978-0-06-441034-2(X)) HarperCollins Pubs.
Jones, Miranda. Castle Magic. 2006. (Little Genie Ser.). (Illus.). 96p. (J). (gr. 1-3). pap. 4.99 (978-0-440-41976-1(X) , Yearling) Random Hse. Children's Bks.
—Little Genie No. 4: Castle Magic. Calver, David, illus. 2004. 144p. (gr. 1-3). 8.95 (978-0-385-73165-2(5) , Delacorte Bks. for Young Readers) Random Hse. Children's Bks.
Kilworth, Garry. The Castle Storm. 1998. (Welkin Weasels Ser.: No. 2). 388p. (YA). (gr. 9). pap. 11.99 (978-0-552-54547-1(3) , Corgi) Transworld Publishers Ltd. GBR. *Dist:* Independent Pubs. Group.
Kolding, Richard Max. Castles. 1998. (Sticker Stories Ser.). (Illus.). 16p. (J). (ps-1). pap. 4.99 (978-0-448-41861-2(4) , Grosset & Dunlap) Penguin Group (USA) Inc.
Krensky, Stephen. We Just Moved! Di Fiori, Lawrence, illus. 1998. (Hello Reader! Ser.). 32p. (J). pap. 3.99 (978-0-590-33127-2(2)) Scholastic, Inc.
Krossing, Karen. The Castle Key. 2004. (Illus.). 170p. (J). (gr. 3-6). pap. 7.95 (978-0-929141-76-3(8)) Napoleon Publishing/Rendezvous Pr. CAN. *Dist:* AtlasBooks Distribution.
Lamensdorf, Len. The Crouching Dragon. 1999. (Will to Conquer Ser.: Bk. 1). (Illus.). 278p. (YA). (gr. 7-12). 19.95 (978-0-9669741-5-7(8)) SeaScape Pr., Ltd.
Lamere, Jill. The King's Crown. 2007. (Illus.). 5p. (J). 14.95 (***978-0-9772320-2-4(6)***) Minikin Pr.
Lester, Anna. Fairytale Castles. Cascio, Lo & Cristina, Maria, illus. 2007. (Young Reading Series 1 Gift Bks). 48p. (J). 8.99 (***978-0-7945-1679-6(3)*** , Usborne) EDC Publishing.
Love, Ann. Ice Cream at the Castle. 1999. (Child's Play Library). (Illus.). 32p. (J). (gr. k-3). 14.99 (978-0-85953-677-6(7)) Child's Play-International.
—Ice Cream at the Castle. Goffe, Toni, illus. 2001. (J). (gr. k-3). lib. bdg. 17.95 (978-1-56674-291-7(9)) Forest Hse. Publishing Co., Inc.
Mason, Jane B. & Stephens, Sarah Hines. Appley Ever After. 2005. (Princess School Ser.: No. 6). (Illus.). 128p. (J). (ps-7). pap. 4.99 (978-0-439-69814-6(6) , Scholastic Paperbacks) Scholastic, Inc.
Milbourne, Anna. In the Castle. Davies, Benji, illus. 2006. 24p. (J). 9.99 (978-0-7945-1243-9(7) , Usborne) EDC Publishing.
Militzer, Jill. Kizzy's Castle. 2005. 35p. 13.24 (978-1-4116-5538-6(9)) Lulu.com.
Miyazaki, Hayao. The Art of Howl's Moving Castle. 2005. (Art of Howl's Moving Castle Ser.). (Illus.). 256p. (YA). pap. 34.99 (978-1-4215-0049-2(3)) Viz Media.
—Howl's Moving Castle Film Comic, Vol. 2. 2005. (Howl's Moving Castle Film Comics Ser.). 176p. (YA). pap. 9.99 (978-1-4215-0092-8(2)) Viz Media.
—Howl's Moving Castle Film Comic, Vol. 3. Miyazaki, Hayao, illus. 2005. (Howl's Moving Castle Film Comics Ser.). 176p. (YA). pap. 9.99 (978-1-4215-0093-5(0)) Viz Media.
—Howl's Moving Castle Film Comics, Vol. 1. 2005. (Howl's Moving Castle Film Comics Ser.). (Illus.). 176p. (YA). pap. 9.99 (978-1-4215-0091-1(4)) Viz Media.
—Howls Moving Castle Picture Book. Miyazaki, Hayao, illus. 2005. (Howl's Moving Castle Picture Book Ser.). 184p. (YA). 19.99 (978-1-4215-0090-4(6)) Viz Media.
Munsch, Robert N. The Sand Castle Contest. Martchenko, Michael, illus. 2005. 28p. (J). (ps). lib. bdg. 11.19 (978-0-606-33821-9(7)) Tandem Library Bks.
—The Sandcastle Contest. Martchenko, Michael, illus. 2005. 32p. (J). (ps-ps). pap. 3.99 (978-0-439-74865-0(8) , Cartwheel Bks.) Scholastic, Inc.
The Mysterious Castle. 80p. (YA). (gr. 6-12). pap. 10.95 (978-0-8224-3942-4(5)) Globe Fearon Educational Publishing.
Nesbit, E. The Enchanted Castle Book & Charm. 2002. (Charming Classics). 304p. (J). pap. 6.99 (978-0-694-01580-1(6) , Harper Festival) HarperCollins Pubs.
Nimmo, Jenny. Charlie Bone & the Castle of Mirrors. 2005. (Children of the Red King Ser.: Bk. 4). 432p. 9.95 (978-0-439-54528-0(5) , Orchard Bks.) Scholastic, Inc.
Ogilvy, Ian. Measle & the Mallockee. 2006. 384p. (J). 15.99 (978-0-06-058691-1(5)) HarperCollins Pubs.
Osborne, Mary Pope. El Caballero del Alba. 2004. (Coleccion la Casa Del Arbol the Magic Tree House Ser.). (SPA.). (J). pap. 4.95 (978-1-930332-50-8(5)) Lectorum Pubns., Inc.
—Haunted Castle on Hallows Eve. Murdocca, Sal, illus. 2003. (Magic Tree House Ser.: No. 30). 128p. (J). (gr. k-3). 11.95 (978-0-375-82521-7(5)); lib. bdg. 13.99 (978-0-375-92521-4(X)) Random Hse. Children's Bks. (Random Hse. Bks. for Young Readers).
—The Knight at Dawn. unabr. ed. 2004. (Magic Tree House Ser. : No. 2). 66p. (J). (gr. k-3). pap. 17.00 incl. audio (978-0-8072-0331-6(9) , Listening Library) Random Hse. Audio Publishing Group.
Osborne, Mary Pope. The Knight at Dawn Book & CD. Murdocca, Sal, illus. 2008. (Stepping Stone Book(TM) Ser.). (J). (gr. k-3). 9.99 (***978-0-375-84406-5(6)*** , Random Hse. Bks. for Young Readers) Random Hse. Children's Bks.
Page, Jason. Wham Bam Boozle: A Gnastly, Noisy, Stinky Pop-Up Book! Quigley, Sebastian, illus. 2003. 12p. (J). (gr. k-4). reprint ed. 12.00 (978-0-7567-6906-2(X)) DIANE Publishing Co.
Prasadam, Smriti & Finn, Rebecca. My Knight's Castle: Through Play Books. 2008. (Illus.). 12p. (J). bds. 6.95 (***978-0-7475-8813-9(9)***) Bloomsbury Publishing Plc GBR. *Dist:* Independent Pubs. Group.
Prins, Piet. The Haunted Castle. 2006. (Illus.). 139p. (J). pap. (978-1-894666-44-2(5)) Inheritance Pubns.
—The Treasure of Rodensteyn Castle. Kramer, Jaap, illus. 2006. 132p. (J). pap. (978-1-894666-47-3(X)) Inheritance Pubns.
Raintree Steck-Vaughn Staff. El Concurso de Castillos de Arena. 1999. (SPA.). (J). pap., stu. ed. 31.05 (978-0-7398-0765-1(X)) Steck-Vaughn.
Random House Disney Staff. Dream Castle. Harding, Niall, illus. 2005. (Reusable Sticker Book Ser.). 12p. (J). (ps-3). pap. 6.99 (978-0-7364-2305-2(2) , RH/Disney) Random Hse. Children's Bks.
Random House Disney Staff & Winston, Helena. Castle Cleanup! BKN International Staff, illus. 2002. 32p. (J). (ps-k). pap. 3.99 (978-0-7364-1290-2(5) , Golden/Disney) Random Hse. Children's Bks.
Rice, Gloria. The Flying Castle. 2001. (J). pap. 8.00 (978-0-8059-5116-5(4)) Dorrance Publishing Co., Inc.
Richards, Kitty. The Enchanted Castle. Disney Storybook Artists Staff, illus. rev. ed. 2007. (Disney Princess Ser.). 4p. (ps-1). 12.99 (***978-1-4231-0912-9(0)***) Disney Pr.
ROBERTSON, M. P. The Sandcastle. 2008. (Illus.). 32p. (J). pap. 7.95 (***978-1-84507-800-3(4)***) Lincoln, Frances Ltd. GBR. *Dist:* Perseus Distribution.
Rose, Maddy. Adventures of Pinkie: Sandcastle Fun. 2008. 24p. (J). pap. 9.95 (***978-1-86230-492-5(0)***) Transworld Publishers Ltd. GBR. *Dist:* Independent Pubs. Group.
Ross, Jillian. Alissa & the Castle Ghost. Backes, Nick, illus. 2nd ed. 1998. (Stardust Classics). (J). (gr. 2-6). 113p. 12.95 (978-1-889514-07-9(1)); 119p. pap. 5.95 (978-1-889514-08-6(X)) Dolls Corp.
Rossell, Judith. The Haunted Castle of Count Viper: A Spooky Maze Adventure. 2007. (Illus.). 32p. (Orig.). (J). pap. 4.95 (978-1-57990-950-5(7)) Lark Bks.
Roy, Ron. The Deadly Dungeon. Gurney, John Steven, illus. 1998. (A to Z Mysteries Ser.: No. 4). 96p. (gr. k-3). lib. bdg. 11.99 (978-0-679-98755-0(X) , Random Hse. Bks. for Young Readers) Random Hse. Children's Bks.
—The Deadly Dungeon. Gurney, John Steven, illus. 1998. (A to Z Mysteries Ser.: No. 4). 86p. (J). (ps-k). lib. bdg. 11.80 (978-0-613-04817-0(2)) Tandem Library Bks.
Russell, P. Craig. Fairy Tales of Oscar Wilde: The Selfish Giant & the Star Child, Vol. 1. Russell, P. Craig, illus. 2003. (Fairy Tales of Oscar Wilde Ser.: No. 1). (Illus.). 48p. 7.95 (978-1-56163-375-3(5)) NBM Publishing Co.
The Sand Castle. 2007. (J). per. (***978-1-932570-84-7(5)***) Literacy Footprints Inc.
Sanders, Roy E. Land of Pink: From thesNot So Far Ago Series. 2007. (J). 19.99 (***978-1-59879-327-7(6)***) Lifevest Publishing, Inc.
Santillo, LuAnn. I Have Fun. Santillo, LuAnn, ed. 2003. (Half-Pint Kids Readers Ser.). (Illus.). 7p. (J). (ps-1). pap. (978-1-59256-055-4(5)) Half-Pint Kids, Inc.
Schnitzius, Ron. Timecastle. unabr. ed. 2002. 191p. (YA). (gr. 7-12). pap. 8.95 (978-0-9718411-0-9(1)) JumpRope Bks.
Seabrooke, Brenda. Stonewolf. 2004. 240p. (J). (gr. 7 up). tchr. ed. 16.95 (978-0-8234-1848-0(0)) Holiday Hse., Inc.
Sims, Lesley. Castle that Jack Built. Gordon, Mike, illus. 2007. 48p. (J). 8.99 (***978-0-7945-1599-7(1)*** , Usborne) EDC Publishing.
—Enchanted Castle. Marks, Alan, illus. 2007. (Young Reading Series 2 Gift Bks). 64p. (J). 8.99 (***978-0-7945-1347-4(6)*** , Usborne) EDC Publishing.
Sims, Lesley. The Story of Castles. 2004. (Young Reading Series Two Ser.). (Illus.). 64p. (J). (gr. 2 up). pap. 5.95 (978-0-7945-0756-5(5) , Usborne) EDC Publishing.
Smith, M. J. Kevin Murphy Takes on the Father of Lies. 2005. (Illus.). 311p. (J). (gr. 4-8). pap. 10.95 (978-0-9765066-0-7(2)) B & S Publishing Corp.
Stilton, Geronimo. Cat & Mouse in a Haunted House. Wolf, Matt & Keys, Larry, illus. 2004. (Geronimo Stilton Ser.: No. 3). 128p. (J). pap. 6.99 (978-0-439-55965-2(0) , Scholastic Paperbacks) Scholastic, Inc.
—Cat & Mouse in a Haunted House. 2004. (Geronimo Stilton Ser.: No. 3). (gr. 3-6). lib. bdg. 14.15 (978-0-613-72224-7(8)) Tandem Library Bks.
—The Secret of Cacklefur Castle. 2005. (Geronimo Stilton Ser.: No. 22). (Illus.). 111p. (J). (gr. 2-5). lib. bdg. 13.04 (978-0-606-33833-2(0)) Tandem Library Bks.
Stuart, Jon & Stuart, Page J. Whambamboozle. Quigley, Sebastian, illus. 2000. 16p. (J). (gr. 2-5). pap. 11.95 (978-0-688-17175-9(3) , Harper Festival) HarperCollins Pubs.
Sturm auf die Burg. (GER.). (978-3-411-09321-2(8)) Bibliographisches Institut & F. A. Brockhaus AG DEU. *Dist:* i.b.d., Ltd.
Thomas, Micahla F. Anna & Jasmine & the Tale of the Gateway Castle. 2004. (J). 5.99 (978-0-9719727-0-4(2)) Honorable Pr.
Thompson, Colin. Castles. 2006. (Illus.). 32p. (J). (gr. k-2). (978-0-09-188486-4(1) , Hutchinson) Random Hse.
—Castles. 2007. (Illus.). 32p. (J). pap. 9.99 (***978-0-09-943942-4(5)*** , Red Fox) Random Hse. Children's Bks. GBR. *Dist:* Independent Pubs. Group.
Tub Tales: The Castle. 2003. (Illus.). 10p. (J). 6.00 (978-0-9713507-0-0(1) , 841) Panline U.S.A., Inc.
Tunison, Dick. Marley & the Big Stone Castle. Carrel, Dolores W., illus. l.t. ed. 2001. 40p. (J). (gr. k-5). pap. 7.95 (978-0-9707015-0-3(0)) Emmaus Pr.
Vargo, Tim. Unbound: A Tale of Temptation & Terror. 2003. 242p. pap. 12.95 (978-1-930008-04-5(X)) Willowgate Pr.
Warkentin, Karla. Mystery in Medieval Castle. 2004. (Time Stone Travelers Ser.). 144p. (J). pap., pap. 6.99 (978-0-7814-4025-7(4) , 0781440254) Cook, David C. Publishing Co.
Warren, Rick. Made for a Purpose AMS. 2004. (J). 287.82 (978-0-310-60329-0(3)) Zonderkidz.
Weber, Lou, ed. Castle Large Lift-a-Flap. 2005. (Active Minds Ser.). (Illus.). 12p. (J). bds. 7.98 (978-0-7853-9988-9(7) , 7208500) Publications International, Ltd.
Wilson, David Henry. The Castle of Inside Out. unabr. ed. 2003. (Read-Along Ser.). (J). pap. 24.95 incl. audio (978-0-7540-6249-3(X) , Galaxy Children's Large Print) BBC Audiobooks America.
Winthrop, Elizabeth. The Battle for the Castle. 211p. (J). pap. 5.50 (978-0-8072-1501-2(5) , Listening Library) Random Hse. Audio Publishing Group.
Wright, Betty Ren. Crandall's Castle. 2005. 184p. (J). pap. 6.95 (978-0-8234-1978-4(9)) Holiday Hse., Inc.

CASTRO, FIDEL, 1927-

Butts, Ellen R. & Schwartz, Joyce R. Fidel Castro. 2005. (Biography ' Ser.). (Illus.). 112p. (J). 29.27 (978-0-8225-2371-0(X) , Lerner Pubns.); (gr. 6 up). pap. 7.95 (978-0-8225-9524-3(9)) Lerner Publishing Group.
Connolly, Sean. Castro. 2002. (Beginner's Guide Ser.). (Illus.). 96p. (YA). pap. 11.99 (978-0-340-84612-4(7)) Headway GBR. *Dist:* Trafalgar Square Publishing.
Cox, Vicki. Fidel Castro. 2003. (Major World Leaders Ser.). (Illus.). 112p. (gr. 6-12). 30.00 (978-0-7910-7651-4(2) , Chelsea Hse.) Facts On File, Inc.
Gibb, Tom. Fidel Castro: Leader of Cuba's Revolution. 2001. (Famous Lives Ser.). (Illus.). 48p. (J). (gr. 3-7). lib. bdg. 27.12 (978-0-8172-5718-7(7)) Raintree.
Gibb, Tom, contrib. by. Fidel Castro: Leader of Cuba's Revolution. 2001. (Illus.). 48p. (J). (978-0-7502-3046-9(0)) Steck-Vaughn.
January, Brendan. Fidel Castro: Cuban Revolutionary. 2003. (Book Report Biographies Ser.). (Illus.). 112p. (J). 30.50 (978-0-531-11676-0(X) , Watts, Franklin) Scholastic Library Publishing.
Markel, Rita J. Fidel Castro's Cuba. 2007. (Dictatorships Ser.). (Illus.). 160p. (YA). (gr. 9-12). lib. bdg. 38.60 (***978-0-8225-7284-8(2)***) Lerner Publishing Group.
Naden, Corinne J. & Blue, Rose. Fidel Castro & the Cuban Revolution. 2006. (World Leaders Ser.). (Illus.). 144p. (J). (gr. 6-12). lib. bdg. 27.95 (978-1-59935-029-5(7)) Reynolds, Morgan Inc.
Platt, Richard. Fidel Castro. 2003. (20th Century History Makers Ser.). (Illus.). 112p. (J). lib. bdg. 32.85 (978-0-7398-6141-7(7)) Raintree.
Rees, Fran. Fidel Castro, Leader of Communist Cuba. 2006. (Signature Lives Ser.). (Illus.). 112p. (J). (gr. 5-7). 30.60 (978-0-7565-1580-5(7)) Compass Point Bks.
Selsdon, Esther. Fidel Castro. 1999. (Life & Times of Ser.). (Illus.). 48p. (YA). (gr. 5 up). lib. bdg. 28.91 (978-0-7910-4636-4(2) , Chelsea Hse.) Facts On File, Inc.
Woog, Adam. Fidel Castro. 2003. (Importance of Ser.). (Illus.). 112p. (J). 32.45 (978-1-59018-231-4(6) , Lucent Bks.) Thomson Gale.

CAT

see Cats

CAT FAMILY (MAMMALS)

see also Cheetahs; Jaguar; Leopards; Lions; Lynx; Panthers; Pumas; Tigers

Big Cats. 2004. (J). per. 4.99 (978-1-933581-21-7(2)) Byeway Bks.
Bonar, Samantha. Small Wildcats. 2002. (gr. 3-6). lib. bdg. 17.60 (978-0-613-59548-3(3)) Tandem Library Bks.
Clarke, Penny. Big Cats. 2003. (gr. 3-6). lib. bdg. 15.25 (978-0-613-53961-6(3)) Tandem Library Bks.
Group/McGraw-Hill, Wright. Cougar Level: Wildcats Cougar Complete Kit. (Wildcats Ser.). (gr. 2-8). 599.95 (978-0-322-06680-9(8)) Wright Group, The.
—Cougar Level Set: Adventure Journal. (Wildcats Ser.). (gr. 2-8). 31.95 (978-0-322-05788-3(4)) Wright Group, The.
—Creature Talk, 6 vols. (Wildcats Ser.). 32p. (gr. 2-8). (978-0-322-05860-6(0)) Wright Group, The.
—Panther Level: Adventure Journal Set. (Wildcatstm Ser.). (gr. 2-8). 31.95 (978-0-322-05793-7(0)) Wright Group, The.
Harvey, Bev. The Cat Family. 2003. (Animal Families Ser.). (Illus.). 32p. (gr. 2-4). 23.00 (978-0-7910-7541-8(9) , Chelsea Hse.) Facts On File, Inc.
Huggins-Cooper, Lynn. Big Cats. 2006. (J). (978-1-58340-931-2(9)) Smart Apple Media.
Landau, Elaine. Big Cats: Hunters of the Night. 2007. (Animals after Dark Ser.). (Illus.). 32p. (J). (gr. 2-4). lib. bdg. 22.60 (978-0-7660-2770-1(8) , Enslow Elementary) Enslow Pubs., Inc.
Leonhardt. Wild Cats. 1999. (Illus.). pap. 6.20 (978-0-7398-0885-6(0)) Steck-Vaughn.
Mattern, Joanne. Cats Are Night Animals. 2006. (Illus.). 24p. (J). pap. (***978-0-8368-7853-0(1)***); lib. bdg. (***978-0-8368-7846-2(9)***) Stevens, Gareth Inc. (Weekly Reader Early Learning Library).
—Cats Are Night Animals: Los Felinos Son Animales Nocturnos. 2006. (ENG & SPA., Illus.). 24p. (J). pap. (***978-0-8368-8050-2(1)***); lib. bdg. (***978-0-8368-8043-4(9)***) Stevens, Gareth Inc. (Weekly Reader Early Learning Library).
Morgan, Sally. Small Cats. 2004. (J). lib. bdg. (978-1-59389-176-3(8) , Cherrytree Books) Evans Publishing Group.
Nichols, Catherine. Ripley's Big Cats. 2004. (Illus.). 59p. (J). (978-0-439-63361-1(3)) Scholastic, Inc.
Patent, Dorothy Hinshaw. Big Cats. Jubb, Kendahl Jan, illus. 2005. 32p. (J). (gr. 3-6). 17.95 (978-0-8027-8968-6(4)) Walker & Co.
Patent, Dorothy Hinshaw & Jubb, Kendahl Jan. Big Cats. Jubb, Kendahl Jan, illus. 2005. (Illus.). 32p. (J). (gr. 3-6). 18.85 (978-0-8027-8969-3(2)) Walker & Co.
Resnick, Jane Parker. Cats. 2001. (Nature's Wild Ser.). (J). lib. bdg. (978-1-58952-202-2(8)) Rourke Publishing, LLC.
Saign, Geoffrey C. African Cats. 1999. (gr. 5-8). lib. bdg. 15.25 (978-0-613-53899-2(4)) Tandem Library Bks.
Shea, Therese. Wild Cats. 2006. (Illus.). 24p. (J). lib. bdg. (978-1-4042-3522-9(1) , PowerKids Pr.) Rosen Publishing Group, Inc., The.
Sheikh-Miller, J. & Turnbull, S. Big Cats. 2004. (Discovery Program Ser.). (Illus.). 48p. (J). lib. bdg. 16.95 (978-1-58086-467-1(8)) EDC Publishing.
Solway, Andrew. Killer Cats. 2005. (Illus.). 48p. (J). (978-1-4034-6565-8(7)); pap. (978-1-4034-6571-9(1)) Heinemann Library.
Southwater Staff. Big Cats. 2000. (Nature Fact File Ser.). (Illus.). 64p. (gr. 3-7). pap. 7.95 (978-1-84215-232-4(7) , Southwater) Anness Publishing GBR. *Dist:* National Bk. Network.
Waters, Jo. The Wild Side of Pet Cats. 2004. (Raintree Perspectives Ser.). (Illus.). 32p. (J). 7.50 (978-1-4109-1157-5(8)); 25.70 (978-1-4109-1017-2(2)) Harcourt Schl. Pubs.
Wexo, John Bonnett. Big Cats. rev. ed. 2003. (Illus.). 24p. (J). 10.95 (978-1-888153-91-0(1) , Zoo Bks.) Wildlife Education, Ltd.

CAT FAMILY (MAMMALS)—FICTION

Coakley, Lena & Watts, Leslie Elizabeth. On the Night of the Comet. 2004. (Illus.). 32p. (J). (ps-2). 16.95 (978-1-55143-287-8(0) , 1234126) Orca Bk. Pubs. USA.
Sargent, Dave & Sargent, Pat. Bobby Bobcat: Be a Friend, 15 vols., Vol. 10. Huff, Jeane, illus. 2nd rev. ed. 2003. (Animal Pride Ser.: No. 10). 42p. (J). pap. 6.95 (978-1-56763-778-6(7)); lib. bdg. 19.95 (978-1-56763-777-9(9)) Ozark Publishing.
—Dike the Wolf: Teamwork, 56 bks, Vol. 5. Huff, Jeane, illus. 2nd rev. ed. 2003. (Animal Pride Ser.: Vol. 15). 42p. (J). lib. bdg. 19.95 (978-1-56763-767-0(1)) Ozark Publishing.

CAT IN THE HAT (FICTITIOUS CHARACTER)—FICTION

McCann, Jesse Leon. The Cat in the Hat. 2003. (Illus.). 24p. (J). (gr. k-k). 0.33 (978-0-375-82780-8(3) , Golden Bks.) Random Hse. Children's Bks.
Seuss, Dr. The Cat in the Hat. 1999. (Illus.). (J). 12.99 (978-0-679-89267-0(2) , Random Hse. Bks. for Young Readers) Random Hse. Children's Bks.
—The Cat in the Hat. Seuss, Dr., illus. l.t. ed. 2007. (I Can Read It All by Myself). (Illus.). 72p. (J). (gr. k-3). 8.99 (978-0-394-80001-1(X) , Random Hse. Bks. for Young Readers) Random Hse. Children's Bks.

—The Cat in the Hat's Great Big Flap Book. Ruiz, Aristides, illus. 1999. 12p. (J). (gr. k-ps). bds. 11.99 (978-0-679-89360-8(1) , Random Hse. Bks. for Young Readers) Random Hse. Children's Bks.

Universal Dreamworks Pictures Staff. Cat in the Hat: Official Movie Book. 2004. (Illus.). 128p. pap. 12.95 (978-1-57243-609-1(3) , 53846352) Triumph Bks.

CATASTROPHES

see Disasters

CATERPILLARS

see also Butterflies; Moths

Bailey, Jill. How Caterpillars Turn into Butterflies. 1998. (Nature's Mysteries Ser.). (Illus.). 32p. (J). (gr. 3-5). lib. bdg. 22.79 (978-0-7614-0857-4(6) , Benchmark Bks.) Cavendish, Marshall Corp.

Berger, Melvin & Berger, Gilda. Caterpillar to Butterfly. 2004. (Scholastic Readers Ser.). (Illus.). (J). (978-0-439-57483-9(8)) Scholastic, Inc.

Berger, Melvin & Berger, Gilda. Schol True of False #2 Butterflies & Caterpill. 2008. 48p. pap. 4.99 (***978-0-545-00392-6(X)** , Scholastic Reference) Scholastic, Inc.

Caterpillars, Vol. 3. 2005. (Bugs, Bugs, Bugs Ser.). (YA). (gr. k-3). (978-0-7368-8199-9(9) , Pebble Bks.) Capstone Pr., Inc.

Caterpillars, 6 vols. (gr. k-2). 28.95 (978-0-7368-8239-2(1)) Red Brick Learning.

Chappelow, Sarah. Caterpillars. 2005. (Creepy Creatures Ser.). (Illus.). 24p. (J). (978-1-4109-1767-6(3)); (gr. 4-7). pap. 6.00 (978-1-4109-1772-0(X)) Steck-Vaughn.

Coder, Leona G. The Fuzzy Wuzzy Caterpillar. Riphahn, Anna, illus. 1998. (J). (ps-3). 15.95 (978-1-892455-02-4(1)) Desk Top Pubs., Inc.

Frost, Helen. Caterpillars. Saunders-Smith, Gail, ed. 1999. (Butterflies Ser.). (Illus.). 24p. (J). (gr. k-1). lib. bdg. 14.60 (978-0-7368-0228-4(2) , Pebble Bks.) Capstone Pr., Inc.

Ganeri, Anita. Butterflies & Caterpillars. 2007. (J). (***978-1-58340-808-7(8)**) Smart Apple Media.

Ganeri, Anita. From Caterpillar to Butterfly. 2006. (Illus.). 32p. (J). (978-1-4034-7855-9(4)); pap. (978-1-4034-7864-1(3)) Heinemann Library.

Greenaway, Theresa. Caterpillars. 1999. (Minipets Ser.). (Illus.). 32p. (gr. 1-5). pap. 7.95 (978-0-8172-4209-1(0)) Steck-Vaughn.

Harcourt School Publishers Staff. The Very Hungry... 1999. (Collections Ser.). (Illus.). lib. bdg. 18.40 (978-0-15-313415-9(1)) Harcourt Schl. Pubs.

Hartley, Karen, et al. Caterpillar. 2006. (Illus.). 32p. (J). (***978-1-4034-8294-5(2)**); 2nd ed. pap. (***978-1-4034-8307-2(8)**) Heinemann Library.

Hartley, Karen, et al. La Oruga. 2003. (Los Insectos Ser.). (SPA.). 32p. (J). pap. 6.95 (978-1-4034-3033-5(0)) Heinemann Library.

Heiligman, Deborah. From Caterpillar to Butterfly Big Book. Weissman, Bari, illus. 2008. (Let's-Read-and-Find-Out Science Ser.). 32p. (J). pap. 24.99 (***978-0-06-111975-0(X)**) HarperCollins Pubs.

Kalman, Bobbie & Mondor, Lyne. Les Papillons. 2005. (FRE., Illus.). 32p. pap. (978-2-89579-029-7(9)) Crabtree Publishing Co.

Lafford, Stuart & Greenaway, Theresa. Caterpillars. 1999. (Minipets Ser.). (Illus.). 32p. (J). (gr. 1-5). lib. bdg. 25.69 (978-0-8172-5585-5(0)) Raintree.

Latimer, Jonathan P. Caterpillars. 2000. (gr. 3-6). lib. bdg. 14.10 (978-0-613-27766-2(X)); (Illus.). (J). pap. (978-0-606-20597-9(7)) Tandem Library Bks.

Latimer, Jonathan P. & Nolting, Karen Stray. Caterpillars. Wright, Amy Bartlett, illus. 2000. (Peterson Field Guides for Young Naturalists). 48p. (J). (gr. 4-6). tchr. ed. 15.00 (978-0-395-97942-6(0)); pap. 5.95 (978-0-395-97945-7(5)) Houghton Mifflin Co. Trade & Reference Div.

Legg, Gerald & Salariya, David. From Caterpillar to Butterfly. Scrace, Carolyn, illus. 1998. (Life Cycles Ser.). 32p. (J). (gr. k-2). 25.50 (978-0-531-14493-0(3) , Watts, Franklin) Scholastic Library Publishing.

Llewellyn, Claire. Caterpillars. 2002. (gr. k-3). lib. bdg. 12.95 (978-0-613-54113-8(8)) Tandem Library Bks.

Llewellyn, Claire & Watts, Barrie. Caterpillars. 2002. (Minibeasts Ser.). (Illus.). 32p. (J). (gr. k-3). pap. 4.95 (978-0-531-14830-3(0) , Watts, Franklin) Scholastic Library Publishing.

MacRo, Hartley & MacRo, Taylor. Caterpillar. 2002. (Illus.). 32p. (J). (gr. k-2). pap. 6.95 (978-1-58810-321-5(8) , 91032) Heinemann Library.

Mitchell, Melanie S. Butterflies. (First Step Nonfiction Ser.). (Illus.). (J). (gr. k-2). 2003. 24p. lib. bdg. 18.60 (978-0-8225-4598-9(5)); 2002. 23p. pap. 3.95 (978-0-8225-4599-6(3) , Lerner Pubns.) Lerner Publishing Group.

Morgan, Sally. From Caterpillar to Butterfly. 2002. (How Things Grow Ser.). (Illus.). 32p. (J). lib. bdg. 24.25 (978-1-930643-88-8(8)) Chrysalis Education.

Murawski, Darlyne A. Face to Face with Caterpillars. 2007. (Face to Face with Animals Ser.). (Illus.). 32p. (J). (gr. 2-6). 16.95 (978-1-4263-0052-3(2) , National Geographic Children's Bks.) National Geographic Society.

Murowski, Darlyne A. Face to Face with Caterpillars. 2007. (Face to Face with Animals Ser.). (Illus.). 32p. (J). (gr. 2-6). lib. bdg. 25.90 (978-1-4263-0053-0(0) , National Geographic Children's Bks.) National Geographic Society.

Nicholls, Judith. Crawly Caterpillar. 2008. (Doodlebops Ser.). 32p. (J). bds. 7.99 (***978-0-545-03026-7(9)** , Cartwheel Bks.) Scholastic, Inc.

Peterson, Roger T. & Wright, Amy Bartlett. Peterson First Guide to Caterpillars of North America. 2nd ed. 1998. (First Guides). (Illus.). 128p. pap. 5.95 (978-0-395-91184-6(2)) Houghton Mifflin Co. Trade & Reference Div.

Reid, Barbara. Caterpillar to Butterfly. braille ed. 2004. (J). (gr. 1). spiral bd., bds. (978-0-616-03086-8(X)) Canadian National Institute for the Blind/Institut National Canadien pour les Aveugles.

—Caterpillar to Butterfly. 2000. (Illus.). 14p. (J). (ps-3). 6.95 (978-0-00-224007-9(6)) HarperCollins Pubs.

Robinson, W. Wright. How Spiders & Other Silkmakers Build Their Amazing Homes. Calvert, Trudy L., illus. 1999. (Animal Architects Ser.). 64p. (J). (gr. 5-9). 24.95 (978-1-56711-378-5(8) , Blackbirch Pr., Inc.) Thomson Gale.

Rockwell, Anne F. Becoming Butterflies. Halsey, Megan, illus. 32p. (J). 2004. pap. 6.95 (978-0-8027-7686-0(8)); 2002. lib. bdg. 16.85 (978-0-8027-8798-9(3)) Walker & Co.

Ross, Michael Elsohn. Caterpillarology. Erickson, Darren, illus. Grogan, Brian, photos by. 2003. (Backyard Buddies Ser.). 48p. (YA). (gr. 3-5). 6.95 (978-1-57505-434-6(5) , Carolrhoda Bks.) Lerner Publishing Group.

—Caterpillarology. 2000. (gr. 3-6). lib. bdg. 15.25 (978-0-613-79231-8(9)) Tandem Library Bks.

School Specialty Publishing. My Very Best Coloring & Activity Book: Catepillar. 2002. 120p. (J). (gr. k-3). pap. 1.99 (978-0-7696-2788-5(9) , American Education Publishing) School Specialty Publishing.

Taylor, Phillip. La Oruga. 2003. (SPA.). (gr. k-3). lib. bdg. 14.75 (978-0-613-67110-1(4)) Tandem Library Bks.

Trumbauer, Lisa. The Life Cycle of a Butterfly. 2002. (Life Cycles Ser.). (Illus.). 24p. (J). (gr. k-1). lib. bdg. 15.93 (978-0-7368-1181-1(8) , Pebble Bks.) Capstone Pr., Inc.

Turnbull, S. Caterpillars & Butterflies. 2004. (Beginners Ser.). 32p. (J). (gr. 1 up). pap. 4.95 (978-0-7945-0378-9(0)); lib. bdg. 12.95 (978-1-58086-506-7(2)) EDC Publishing.

Turnbull, Stephanie. Caterpillars & Butterflies - Internet Referenced (Level 1) 2007. 32p. (J). 4.99 (***978-0-7945-1337-5(9)** , Usborne) EDC Publishing.

Watts, Barrie. Caterpillars. (Illus.). 32p. (YA). (gr. 2 up). lib. bdg. 27.10 (978-1-932889-18-5(3)) Sea-To-Sea Pubns.

CATERPILLARS—FICTION

Ada, Alma Flor. Rose with Wings. 2000. (gr. k-3). lib. bdg. 17.60 (978-0-613-79393-3(5)) Tandem Library Bks.

Barton, Renee, illus. Amagestic: A Caterpillar's Journey. 2005. Orig. Title: Amagestic. (J). per. 7.99 (978-0-9741864-2-9(2) , 1) NT Publishing, L.L.C.

Book Company Staff. Percival the Baby Caterpillar. 2005. (Illus.). 15p. (J). (gr. 4-11). bds. 12.95 (978-1-74047-608-9(5)) Book Co. Publishing Pty, Ltd., The AUS. *Dist:* Penton Overseas, Inc.

—Percival the Plain Little Caterpillar. Brawley, Helen, illus. 2005. (Sparkle Bks.). 16p. (J). (gr. 4-11). bds. 12.95 (978-1-74047-109-1(1)) Book Co. Publishing Pty, Ltd., The AUS. *Dist:* Penton Overseas, Inc.

Brindle, Susan A., et al. The Little Caterpillar That Finds Jesus (La Oruguita que Encuentra a Jesus) A Parable of the Eucharist (Una Parabola Acerca de la Eucaristia) Emmanuelli Klosterman, Carmen A., tr. Brindle, Susan A. et al, illus. 1999. (Seven Sacraments Ser.). (ENG & SPA.). 72p. (gr. k-10). pap. 9.95 (978-1-889733-08-1(3) , 01011) Precious Life Bks., Inc.

Brothers, J. Adventures of Caterpillar Jones. 1999. (J). pap. 6.95 (978-0-9718774-1-2(6)) Foundation Publishing.

Bruel, Robert O. Bob & Otto. Bruel, Nick, illus. 2007. 32p. (J). (ps-1). 15.95 (978-1-59643-203-1(9)) Roaring Brook Pr.

Cain, Sheridan. The Crunching Munching Caterpillar. Tickle, Jack, illus. 2005. 28p. (J). bds. 6.95 (978-1-58925-757-3(X) , tiger tales) ME Media LLC.

—Crunching Munching Caterpillar. Tickle, Jack, illus. 2003. 32p. (J). tchr. ed. 15.95 (978-1-58925-025-3(7) , tiger tales) ME Media LLC.

—The Crunching Munching Caterpillar Pop-up. Tickle, Jack, illus. 2006. 16p. (J). 15.95 (978-1-58925-771-9(5) , tiger tales) ME Media LLC.

Carle, Eric. Al Dudatu Al Shadidatu Al Gou: The Very Hungry Caterpillar. 2006. 32p. pap. 12.00 (978-977-6171-03-9(6) , 706-007) Al-Balsam Pubng. Hse. EGY. *Dist:* Bookworld Trade, Inc.

—Chenille Qui Fait des Trous. (FRE.). pap. 18.95 (978-2-87142-174-0(9)) Mijade Editions BEL. *Dist:* Distribooks, Inc.

—Count with the Very Hungry Caterpillar. 2006. (World of Eric Carle Ser.). 16p. (J). (ps-1). pap. 4.99 (978-0-448-44420-8(8) , Grosset & Dunlap) Penguin Group (USA) Inc.

—Kleine Raupe Nimmerstatt.Tr. of Very Hungry Caterpillar. (GER., Illus.). pap. 16.95 (978-3-423-07922-8(3)) Deutscher Taschenbuch Verlag GmbH & Co KG DEU. *Dist:* Distribooks, Inc.

—My Very Own Hungry Caterpillar Coloring Book. Carle, Eric, illus. 2003. (Illus.). 32p. (J). 5.99 (978-0-399-24207-6(4) , Philomel) Penguin Group (USA) Inc.

—La Oruga Muy Hambrienta. Carle, Eric, illus. 2002. (SPA., Illus.). 24p. (J). bds. 10.99 (978-0-399-23960-1(X) , Philomel) Penguin Group (USA) Inc.

—The Very Hungry Caterpillar. ed. 2004. (J). (ps-2). spiral bd. (978-0-616-01610-7(7)); spiral bd. (978-0-616-01611-4(5)) Canadian National Institute for the Blind/Institut National Canadien pour les Aveugles.

—The Very Hungry Caterpillar. 2004. (VIE, GUJ, URD, SOM & CHI., Illus.). 23p. (J). (978-1-85269-129-5(8)) Mantra Publishing, Ltd.

—The Very Hungry Caterpillar. 2004. (Illus.). (J). (BEN, ARA, VIE, GUJ & URD.). 23p. 10.95 (978-1-85269-125-7(5)); (GUJ, BEN, VIE, URD & SOM., 23p. 10.95 (978-1-85269-127-1(1)); (SOM., 19p. 10.95 (978-1-85269-128-8(X)) Mantra Publishing, Ltd. GBR. *Dist:* AIMS International Bks., Inc.

—The Very Hungry Caterpillar. Carle, Eric, illus. 2007. 10p. (J). bds. 14.99 incl. audio compact disk (978-0-399-24745-3(9) , Philomel) Penguin Group (USA) Inc.

—The Very Hungry Caterpillar: Board Book & Plush Set. Carle, Eric, illus. 2002. (Illus.). 24p. (J). (ps-1). 16.99 (978-0-399-24205-2(8) , Philomel) Penguin Group (USA) Inc.

—The Very Hungry Caterpillar: Giant Board Book & Plush Package. Carle, Eric, illus. 2001. (Illus.). 24p. (J). 25.99 (978-0-399-23772-0(0) , Philomel) Penguin Group (USA) Inc.

Caterpillar Hides Away. 2003. (Daisy Board Books Ser.). 10p. (J). bds. 9.95 (978-0-7525-8298-6(4)) Parragon, Inc.

Changizi, Mandana S. The Plain Blue Caterpillar. 2000. (Illus.). 16p. (J). (ps-5). pap. 9.95 (978-0-9637240-9-0(6)) Biographical Publishing Co.

Collicott, Sharleen. Toestomper & the Caterpillars. 2002. (Illus.). 32p. (J). (gr. k-3). pap. 5.95 (978-0-618-19675-3(7)) Houghton Mifflin Co. Trade & Reference Div.

—Toestomper & the Caterpillars. Collicott, Sharleen, illus. 1999. (Illus.). 32p. (J). (gr. k-3). tchr. ed. 15.00 (978-0-395-91168-6(0)) Houghton Mifflin Co. Trade & Reference Div.

—Toestomper & the Caterpillars. 2002. (gr. k-3). lib. bdg. 14.10 (978-0-613-90726-2(4)) Tandem Library Bks.

Cooper, Afua. The Red Caterpillar on College Street. Martin, Stephanie, illus. Date not set. 400p. (J). (ps-3). pap. (978-0-920813-87-4(9)) Sister Vision Pr.

Cosgrove, Stephen. Dream Tree. James, Robin, illus. 1999. (J). (978-0-8431-0053-2(2) , Grosset & Dunlap) Penguin Group (USA) Inc.

—Dream Tree. 2002. (gr. k-3). lib. bdg. 13.00 (978-0-613-85014-8(9)) Tandem Library Bks.

Creepy Crawly Caterpillar. 2005. (J). bds. 7.99 (978-1-933200-16-3(2)) Family Bks. at Home.

Dexter & Milly the Caterpiller. 2004. (J). per. 15.99 (978-0-9753533-4-9(9)) Golden Eagle Publishing Hse., Inc.

DiMarco, Carol. Alchemy. 2007. 44p. (J). 8.99 (978-1-59092-219-4(0) , Little Blue Works) Windstorm Creative.

Dychtwald, Ken, et al. Gideon's Dream: A Tale of New Beginnings. Zaboski, Dave & Zaboski, Grace, illus. 2008. 40p. (J). lib. bdg. 17.89 (***978-0-06-143498-3(1)*** HarperCollins Pubs.

Edwards, Pamela Duncan. Clara Caterpillar. Cole, Henry, illus. 2004. 40p. (J). (ps-1). reprint ed. pap. 6.99 (978-0-06-443691-5(8) , Harper Trophy) HarperCollins Pubs.

Ernst, Lisa Campbell. Bubba & Trixie. 2000. (J). (978-0-606-20085-1(1)) Tandem Library Bks.

Galjanic, Lisa. When Caterpillars Grow Up. Hope, Michelle, illus. 2007. (J). 9.95 (978-1-933532-03-5(3)) LSG Pubns.

Galjanic, Lisa. When Series 6 Volume Set, 6. 2007. (Illus.). 100p. (J). 34.95 (***978-1-933532-06-6(8)**) LSG Pubns.

Garnett, Jana. How the Caterpillar Got Its Wings: (How Acknowledging Your Feelings Can Give You Flight) 2003. (Illus.). (J). spiral bd. 19.95 (978-0-9728716-7-9(5)) Journey Pubns., LLC.

Gawade, Akansha A. This Is Who I Am. 2006. (J). pap. 8.00 (978-0-8059-6886-6(5)) Dorrance Publishing Co., Inc.

George, Katie. Stripey the Caterpillar. 1999. (Illus.). 16p. (J). 6.95 (978-1-86233-039-9(5)) Sterling Publishing Co., Inc.

The Great Caterpillar Adventure. 2002. (J). lib. bdg. 13.95 (978-0-9725485-0-2(5)) Waterfall Ridge.

Harcourt School Publishers Staff. The Edge of the Puddle: On Level. 3rd ed. 2002. (Trophies Reading Program Ser.). (Illus.). pap. 5.10 (978-0-15-323003-5(7)) Harcourt Schl. Pubs.

—Trofeos: La Oruga Muy Hambrienta Big Book. 3rd ed. 2002. (SPA., Illus.). pap. 81.90 (978-0-15-332457-4(0)) Harcourt Schl. Pubs.

—500 Isabels On Level. 3rd ed. 2002. (Trophies Reading Program Ser.). (Illus.). pap. 5.10 (978-0-15-323072-1(X)) Harcourt Schl. Pubs.

Hill, Franklin. Wings of Change. Cheung, Aries, illus. l.t. ed. 2001. 32p. (J). (ps-3). 15.95 (978-0-935699-18-0(X) , 093569918x) Illumination Arts Publishing Co., Inc.

Hixson, Jon, et al. Caterpillar Jones & the Adventures of Nut E. Squirrel. 2002. (Mulberry Meadow Ser.: Vol. 2). iv, 184p. (J). (gr. 2-6). pap. 8.95 (978-0-9718774-0-5(8)) Foundation Publishing.

Hood, Susan & Gevry, Claudine. Caterpillar Spring, Butterfly Summer. 2006. 10p. (J). bds. 6.99 (978-0-7944-1217-3(3)) Reader's Digest Assn., Inc., The.

House, Darrell. Miller the Green Caterpillar. Argoff, Patti, illus. l.t. ed. 2005. 32p. 16.95 (978-0-9663276-9-4(1)) Red Engine Pr.

Hover Get's His Wings. 2004. Tr. of Cometin recibe sus alas. (SPA.). 24p. 10.99 (978-1-59185-422-7(9) , Casa Creacion) Strang Communications Co.

J J Brothers & Hixson, Jon. Adventures of Caterpillar Jones. 2nd ed. 2000. (Mulberry Meadow Ser.). 154p. (gr. 4-7). pap. 6.95 (978-1-892714-13-8(2)) Onjinjinkta Publishing.

Jantti, Mariana. Cambio de Planes: El cuento de Matilde y Clotilde. 2007. (Pequenos cuentos para grandes Lectores Ser.). (SPA., Illus.). 32p. (J). pap. 9.95 (978-84-96448-15-5(0)) Hardenville SA URY. *Dist:* Independent Pubs. Group.

Keller, Holly. Farfallina & Marcel. Keller, Holly, illus. (Illus.). 32p. (J). 2002. 16.99 (978-0-06-623932-3(X)); 2005. reprint ed. pap. 6.99 (978-0-06-443872-8(4) , Harper Trophy) HarperCollins Pubs.

—Farfallina & Marcel. 2004. (Illus.). 26p. (J). (ps-ps). lib. bdg. 12.79 (978-0-606-32617-9(0)) Tandem Library Bks.

Kirk, David. Miss Spider: All Pupa'ed Out. 2005. (Miss Spider Ser.). 32p. (J). (ps-2). pap. 3.99 (978-0-448-43802-3(X) , Grosset & Dunlap) Penguin Group (USA) Inc.

Kompelien, Tracy. Monarch Butterfly. Haberstroh, Anne, illus. (Fact & Fiction Ser.). 24p. (J). 2007. 21.35 (978-1-59928-454-5(5)); 2006. (978-1-59928-455-2(3)) ABDO Publishing Co.

Kubler, Annie, illus. The Mixed up Caterpillar. 2006. 24p. (J). 9.99 (978-1-84643-026-8(7)) Child's Play-International.

LaDeane, Symone. The Caterpillar That Would Be A Rainbow. 2007. 24p. (J). per. 11.99 (***978-1-59886-691-9(5)***) Tate Publishing & Enterprises, L.L.C.

Lal, Ranjit. Caterpillar Who Went on a Diet & Other Stories. 2004. (Illus.). 188p. (J). pap. (978-0-14-333593-1(6) , Puffin) Penguin Group (USA) Inc.

Lallouz, Michele. The Adventures of Cali. Nielson, Ginger, illus. 2007. 32p. (J). pap. 9.95 (***978-0-9793004-0-0(1)***) Cali Publishing.

Law, Felicia. The Furry Caterpillar. Philpott, Claire & Radford, Karen, illus. 2006. (J). (978-1-4048-2599-4(1)) Picture Window Bks.

Lawrence, Michael. The Caterpillar That Roared. 2000. (J). (978-0-606-20118-6(1)) Tandem Library Bks.

Lehnert, R. B. The Adventures of Billy Butterfly. Garcia, Marc Khayam, illus. 2003. (J). per. (978-0-9747628-2-1(2)) BKB Group, Inc., The.

Lionni, Leo. The Alphabet Tree. 2004. (Illus.). 40p. (J). (ps-3). reprint ed. 15.95 (978-0-394-81016-4(3) , Knopf Bks. for Young Readers) Random Hse. Children's Bks.

Lucado, Max. Colors. 2004. (Buginnings Ser.: Vol. 2). (Illus.). 24p. (J). 9.99 (978-1-4003-0422-6(9)) Nelson, Thomas Inc.

—Hermie: A Common Caterpillar. 2002. (Max Lucado's Hermie & Friends Ser.). 16p. (J). bds. 6.99 (978-1-4003-0126-3(2)) Nelson, Thomas Inc.

—Hermie y sus Amigos: Atrapado en una cueva Apestosa. 2003. Tr. of Hermie & Friends: Trapped in a Stinky Den. 24p. bds. 4.99 (978-0-88113-781-1(2)) Grupo Nelson.

Lucado, Max, creator. Hermie: A Common Caterpillar. 2005. 32p. (J). pap. 3.99 (978-1-4003-0663-3(9)) Nelson, Thomas Inc.

—Hermie, A Common Caterpillar. 2006. 38p. (J). bds. 12.99 (978-1-4003-0888-0(7)) Nelson, Thomas Inc.

—To Share or Nut to Share. 2006. (Max Lucado's Hermie & Friends Ser.). (Illus.). 24p. (J). bds. 12.99 (978-1-4003-0776-0(7)) Nelson, Thomas Inc.

Lucado, Max & Smith, Brian. Turn. 2005. (Illus.). 160p. 12.99 (978-1-59052-450-3(0) , Multnomah) WaterBrook Pr.

Mala, Rich. The Family Tree. Tasselmyer, Daniel, illus. 2002. 20p. (J). (ps-5). mass mkt. 4.95 (978-0-9704307-2-4(8)) Mala Vision.

Martin, Anne E. Spike the Friendly Caterpillar. McCabb, Jamie, illus. l.t. ed. 2006. 53p. (J). per. 9.99 (978-1-59879-127-3(3)) Lifevest Publishing, Inc.

Marzollo, Jean. Soy una Oruga. Moffatt, Judith, illus. 2002. (Coleccion "Hola, Lector" Ser.). (SPA.). 32p. (J). (ps-1). pap. 3.99 (978-0-439-08697-4(3) , SO5358, Scholastic en Espanol) Scholastic, Inc.

Mayer, Mercer. Little Critter: Just a School Project (Spanish Edition) Tan solo un proyecto Escolar. Mayer, Mercer, illus. 2007. (Little Critter Ser.). (SPA.). 24p. (J). pap. 3.99 (***978-0-06-089241-8(2)** , Rayo) HarperCollins Pubs.

Mayer, Mercer. Our Friend Sam, Vol. 3. 2002. (Little Critter First Readers Ser.). (Illus.). 24p. (J). (gr. 1-2). pap. 3.95 (978-1-57768-815-0(5)) School Specialty Publishing.

McBratney, Sam. The Caterpillow Fight. 2002. (Illus.). (J). 11.23 (978-0-7587-2207-2(9)) Book Wholesalers, Inc.

McBratney, Sam. When I'm Big. Jeram, Anita, illus. 2007. (Guess How Much I Love You Ser.). 24p. (J). (gr. k-ps). bds. 7.99 (***978-0-7636-3546-6(4)***) Candlewick Pr.

McNamee, Barbara Oakley. Kelsey & Seattle. 2007. (J). pap. 15.00 (***978-0-8059-7428-7(8)***) Dorrance Publishing Co., Inc.

Nejime, Shoichi. Bit by Bit. Castles, Heather, illus. 2005. 32p. (J). (ps-k). pap. 7.95 (978-1-55037-906-8(2)); lib. bdg. 19.95 (978-1-55037-907-5(0)) Annick Pr., Ltd. CAN. *Dist:* Firefly Bks., Ltd.

O'Callahan, Jay. Herman & Marguerite: An Earth Story. O'Callahan, Laura, illus. 2003. 36p. (J). pap. 7.95 (978-1-56145-283-5(1)) Peachtree Pubs., Ltd.

—Herman & Marguerite: An Earth Story. 2003. (gr. k-3). lib. bdg. 16.40 (978-0-613-60387-4(7)) Tandem Library Bks.

O'Neal, Kerry. I Wish I Could Fly/I Can Fly! The Lonely Caterpillar BOOK I & the Lonely Butterfly BOOK II. O'Neal, Kerry, illus. l.t. ed. 2006. (Illus.). 60p. (J). 29.99 (***978-1-59879-197-6(4)***); per. 17.99 (***978-1-59879-196-9(6)***) Lifevest Publishing, Inc.

Pedowitz, Laura. Kyla's Search for Wings. 2003. 27p. pap. 14.95 (978-1-4137-0610-9(X)) PublishAmerica, Inc.

Perera, Hilda. Pericopin. (SPA., Illus.). 48p. (J). 7.50 (978-84-241-3272-9(6)) Everest de Ediciones y Distribucion, S.L. ESP. *Dist:* Lectorum Pubns., Inc.

Phillips, Gina & Martin, Stuart. Ants & Caterpillars. 2003. (Busy Bugs Ser.). 12p. (J). bds. 14.95 (978-1-74047-240-1(3)) Book Co. Publishing Pty, Ltd., The AUS. *Dist:* Penton Overseas, Inc.

Raintree Steck-Vaughn Staff. Anda, Oruga, Anda! 1999. (Coleccion en Parejas). (SPA.). (J). pap., stu. ed. 21.50 (978-0-7398-0840-5(0)) Steck-Vaughn.

Reader's Digest Children's Books, creator. Little Cricket & Friends 3 Volume Boxed Set. 2007. (Illus.). 36p. (J). (ps-k). bds., bds. 16.99 (***978-0-7944-1359-0(5)***) Reader's Digest Assn., Inc., The.

Scaglione/Small. Lifes Little Lessons. 2006. pap. 9.95 (978-1-57886-336-5(8)) Rowman & Littlefield Pubs., Inc.

Schield, Allie Schield. Solomon & Lily. Jerome, Barb, illus. 2003. 34p. (J). per. 11.99 (978-0-9743948-0-0(7)) One Little Miracle.

Schmauss, Judy Kentor. The Caterpillar. 2006. (Reader's Clubhouse Set A Ser.). (Illus.). 24p. (J). pap. 3.99 (978-0-7641-3286-5(5)) Barron's Educational Series, Inc.

Shilling, Barbara. The Very Hungry Caterpillar. Chang, Wendy, illus. 1999. (Literature Units Ser.). 48p. (gr. k-3). pap., tchr. ed. 7.99 (978-1-57690-335-3(4), TCA2335) Teacher Created Materials, Inc.

Slusher, Randall. A Day in the Life. 2004. 8p. (J). pap. 6.98 (978-1-4116-1237-2(X)) Lulu.com.

Sommer, Carl. The Ugly Caterpillar. 2003. (Another Sommer-Time Story Ser.). (Illus.). 48p. (J). (gr. 1-4). 16.95 incl. audio compact disk (978-1-57537-515-1(X)); 16.95 incl. audio (978-1-57537-564-9(8)) Advance Publishing, Inc.

—The Ugly Caterpillar. Budwine, Greg, illus. (Another Sommer-Time Story Ser.). 48p. (J). (gr. k-3). 2000. lib. bdg. 16.95 (978-1-57537-058-3(1)); 1999. 9.95 (978-1-57537-015-6(8)) Advance Publishing, Inc.

—The Ugly Caterpillar Read-along, 1 bk. 2003. (Another Sommer-Time Story Ser.). (Illus.). (J). 48p. lib. bdg. 23.95 incl. audio compact disk (978-1-57537-715-5(2)); lib. bdg. 23.95 incl. audio (978-1-57537-765-0(9)) Advance Publishing, Inc.

Southard, Ashley. Maddie. 2006. 10p. 8.01 (978-1-4116-8318-1(8)) Lulu.com.

Steuerwald, Shannon B. From Scrawny to Brawny. 2006. (J). per. 9.95 (978-1-931787-19-2(0)) Fundamental Christian Endeavors.

Sullivan, Jenny. The Caterpillar That Couldn't. 2002. (Illus.). 32p. pap. 12.95 (978-1-84323-071-7(2)) Beekman Bks., Inc.

Swope, Sam. Gotta Go! Gotta Go! Riddle, Sue, illus. 32p. (J). (ps-3). 2000. 14.00 (978-0-374-32757-6(2), Farrar, Straus & Giroux (BYR)); 2004. reprint ed. pap. 5.95 (978-0-374-42786-3(0), Sunburst) Farrar, Straus & Giroux.

Symes, Sally. Caterpillar to Butterfly: A Colorful Adventure. Harmer, Sharon, illus. 2008. 16p. (J). bds. 8.99 ***(978-1-4169-4753-0(1)**, Little Simon) Simon & Schuster Children's Publishing.

Tarbett, Debbie. Ten Wriggly Wiggly Caterpillars. (Illus.). 24p. (J). bds. 19.95 (978-1-84506-027-5(X)) Little Tiger Pr.

Thottam, Meena. The Do or Die Caterpillar. 2006. (J). 3.95 (978-0-9776917-1-5(3), Curcumin Bks.) Davlaw Press.

Tiller, Steve. Henry Hump Born to Fly. Tecosky, Kathryn, ed. Cremeans, Robert, illus. 2002. 32p. (J). (ps-3). 15.95 (978-0-9704597-7-0(7)) MichaelsMind LLC.

University Games Staff. Very Hungrey Caterpillar. 2006. 24p. (J). (978-1-57528-891-8(5)) University Games.

van Kampen, Vlasta. Marigold's Wings. 2005. (Illus.). 31p. (J). lib. bdg. 24.67 (978-0-8368-4500-6(5)) Stevens, Gareth Inc.

Weare, Tim. I'm a Little Caterpillar. Weare, Tim, illus. 2002. (Finger Puppet Pals Ser.). (Illus.). 12p. (J). bds. 6.95 (978-0-439-33867-7(0), Cartwheel Bks.) Scholastic, Inc.

Wenger, Shaunda. Caterpillar Can't Wait! 2006. (Early Explorers Ser.). (J). 34.00 (***978-1-4108-6101-6(5)**) Benchmark Education Co.

Wert, Debra L. Caterfly: Mac's Back Struggling to Stay Drug-Free. 1998. (J). (978-0-944576-27-4(3)) Rocky River Pubs., LLC.

Williams, Julia. The Curious Caterpillar. 2007. pap. 9.00 (***978-0-8059-8949-6(8)**) Dorrance Publishing Co., Inc.

Wilson, George H. The Perils of Cory the Caterpillar. 2008. (Illus.). 50p. (J). 14.99 (***978-0-9778477-0-9(5)**) Storyplus, Inc., A.

CATHARINE, OF ARAGON, QUEEN, CONSORT OF HENRY VIII, KING OF ENGLAND, 1485-1536—FICTION

Meyer, Carolyn. Patience, Princess Catherine. 2004. (Young Royals Ser.). (Illus.). 208p. (YA). 17.00 (978-0-15-216544-4(4), Gulliver Bks.) Harcourt Children's Bks.

CATHEDRALS

Chapman, Lynne F. Cathedrals. 1999. (Designing the Future Ser.). (Illus.). 32p. (J). (gr. 4-7). lib. bdg. (978-0-88682-505-8(9), Creative Education) Creative Co., The.

Jovinelly, Joann & Netelkos, Jason. The Crafts & Culture of a Medieval Cathedral. 2006. (Illus.). 28p. (J). lib. bdg. (978-1-4042-0758-5(9)) Rosen Publishing Group, Inc., The.

Lace, William W. The Medieval Cathedral. 2000. (Building History Ser.). (Illus.). 96p. (J). (gr. 6-9). 32.45 (978-1-56006-720-7(9), Lucent Bks.) Thomson Gale.

CATHER, WILLA, 1873-1947

Ehrlich, Amy. Willa: The Story of Willa Cather. Minor, Wendell, illus. 2006. (J). 16.99 (978-0-689-86573-2(2), Simon & Schuster Children's Publishing) Simon & Schuster Children's Publishing.

Meltzer, Milton. Willa Cather: A Biography. 2008. (J). (***978-0-8225-7604-4(X)**) Twenty First Century Bks.

Raum, Elizabeth. The Story Behind Willa Cather's My Antonia. 2006. (History in Literature Ser.). (Illus.). 56p. (YA). (gr. 7 up). lib. bdg. 32.86 (978-1-4034-8211-2(X)) Heinemann Library.

Steinbauer, Janine. Willa Cather. 2001. (Notebooks Ser.). (YA). (gr. 6 up). 17.95 (978-0-88682-622-2(5), Creative Education) Creative Co., The.

Wooten, Sara McIntosh. Willa Cather: Writer of the Prairie. 1998. (People to Know Ser.). (Illus.). 128p. (YA). (gr. 6-12). lib. bdg. 20.95 (978-0-89490-980-1(0)) Enslow Pubs., Inc.

CATHERINE DE MEDICIS, QUEEN, CONSORT OF HENRY II, KING OF FRANCE, 1519-1589

Somervill, Barbara A. Catherine de Medici: The Power Behind the French Throne. 2006. (Signature Lives Ser.). (Illus.). 112p. (J). (gr. 5-7). 30.60 (978-0-7565-1581-2(5)) Compass Point Bks.

Whitelaw, Nancy. Catherine de Medici & the Protestant Reformation. 2004. (World Leaders Ser.). (Illus.). 160p. (YA). (gr. 6-12). lib. bdg. 26.95 (978-1-931798-26-6(5)) Reynolds, Morgan Inc.

CATHERINE II, EMPRESS OF RUSSIA, 1729-1796

Gibson, Karen Bush. The Life & Times of Catherine the Great. 2005. (Biography from Ancient Civilizations Ser.). (Illus.). 48p. (J). (gr. 4-7). lib. bdg. 29.95 (978-1-58415-347-4(4)) Mitchell Lane Pubs., Inc.

Hatt, Christine. Catherine the Great. 2003. (Judge for Yourself Ser.). (J). (Illus.). 64p. (gr. 5 up). lib. bdg. 30.00 (978-0-8368-5535-7(3)); pap. (978-0-8368-5538-8(8)) Stevens, Gareth Inc. (World Almanac Library).

Whitelaw, Nancy. Catherine the Great & the Enlightenment in Russia. 2004. (World Leaders Ser.). (Illus.). 160p. (YA). (gr. 6-12). lib. bdg. 26.95 (978-1-931798-27-3(3)) Reynolds, Morgan Inc.

CATHERINE, THE GREAT, 1729-1796

see Catherine II, Empress of Russia, 1729-1796

CATHOLIC CHURCH

Adam Woog. Catholic. 2004. (What Makes Me a — ? Ser.). (Illus.). 48p. (J). 26.20 (978-0-7377-2268-0(1), Kidhaven) Thomson Gale.

Alves, Mary E. & Kelley, Patrick, illus. Saint Francis of Assisi: Gentle Revolutionary. rev. ed. 1999. (Encounter the Saints Ser.: No. 4). 120p. (J). (gr. 5-9). pap. 5.95 (978-0-8198-7030-8(7), 332-342) Pauline Bks. & Media.

Amidei, Kathie. Building My Moral Life: Basic Catholic Teachings. Remhof, Beth & Larkin, Jean, eds. Becker, Linda, illus. 2000. (Active Learning for Catholic Kids Ser.). 28p. (J). (gr. 4-6). pap. 7.95 (978-0-937997-88-8(9)) Pflaum Publishing Group.

Amodei, Michael. Send Out Your Spirit: A Confirmation Candidate's Handbook for Faith. 2003. (Send Out Your Spirit Ser.). (Illus.). 256p. (gr. 6-12). 9.95 (978-0-87793-952-8(7)) Ave Maria Pr.

Angell, Carolyn. The Mass: Creative Activities. 2001. (Illus.). 32p. (J). (gr. 1-4). pap. 9.95 (978-1-893757-27-1(7), 27-7) Needer, E.T. Publishing.

Benson, Susan C. Knowing My Church: What Makes Us Catholic. Lynch, Patricia & Larkin, Jean, eds. Lynch, Patricia, illus. 2000. (Active Learning for Catholic Kids Ser.). 28p. (J). (gr. 4-6). pap. 7.95 (978-0-937997-85-7(4)) Pflaum Publishing Group.

—My Catholic Identity: The Marks of the Church & More. Remhof, Beth & Larkin, Jean, eds. Lynch, Patricia, illus. 2000. (Active Learning for Catholic Kids Ser.). 28p. (YA). pap. 7.95 (978-0-937997-92-5(7)) Pflaum Publishing Group.

Bertanzetti, Eileen Dunn. Rich in Love: The Story of Padre Pio of Pietrelcina. 1999. (Weaver Bks.). 72p. (YA). (gr. 6-9). pap. 3.95 (978-0-8198-6470-3(6)) Pauline Bks. & Media.

—Saint Pio of Pietrelcina: Rich in Love. Ritz, Karen, illus. 2002. (Encounter the Saints Ser.: Vol. 13). 120p. (J). pap. 5.95 (978-0-8198-7067-4(6), 332-364) Pauline Bks. & Media.

Buell, Jean. Exploring My Catholic Church: Familiar People, Places & Things. Larkin, Jean, ed. Becker, Linda, illus. 2000. (Active Learning for Catholic Kids Ser.). 28p. (J). (gr. 1-3). pap. 7.95 (978-0-937997-81-9(1)) Pflaum Publishing Group.

Burns, Peggy. Pope John Paul II: Pope for the People. 2000. (Famous Lives Ser.). (Illus.). 48p. (J). (gr. 3-7). lib. bdg. 27.12 (978-0-8172-5714-9(4)) Raintree.

Catholic Child's First Communion Bible. 2000. (J). (ps-3). 12.95 (978-0-88271-014-3(1)); 12.95 (978-0-88271-015-0(X)) Regina Pr., Malhame & Co.

Children's Missalette. 2006. (J). 2.25 (978-1-933178-40-0(X)) Pflaum Publishing Group.

Comiskey, James A. This Is Our Church: A Guide for Children. Powers, James, illus. 2005. 48p. pap. 4.95 (978-0-8146-2597-2(5)) Liturgical Pr.

Essenmacher, Carole. Caring for God's Creation: Precious Gift, Precious Duty. Larkin, Jean, ed. Lynch, Patricia, illus. 2000. (Active Learning for Catholic Kids Ser.). 28p. (J). (gr. 1-3). pap. 7.95 (978-0-937997-82-6(X)) Pflaum Publishing Group.

Ficocelli, Elizabeth. Child's Guide to Reconciliation. Blake, Anne Catharine, tr. Blake, Anne Catharine, illus. 2004. 32p. 9.95 (978-0-8091-6709-8(3), 6709-3) Paulist Pr.

Gaupin, Linda. The Spirit Sets Us Free, Catechist's Guide: Confirmation Preparation for Youth. 1999. (Illus.). 68p. (YA). (gr. 6-9). pap. 16.98 net. (978-0-8215-5702-0(5)) Sadlier, William H. Inc.

Givens, Steve. The Sacrament of Penance for Teens: A Time & Place for Healing. Cannizzo, Karen A., ed. 1999. 30p. (YA). 1.95 (978-0-937997-61-1(7), 4200) Pflaum Publishing Group.

Hailer, Gretchen. Believing in a Media Culture. Zanzig, Thomas, ed. Thiewes, Sam, illus. 2003. (Horizons Program : Level II, Minicourse 1). 52p. (Orig.). (YA). (gr. 10). pap., stu. ed. 9.95 (978-0-88489-390-5(1)) St. Mary's Pr.

Howell, Maria L. Catholicism. 2007. (Religion & Religious Movements Ser.). 240p. (gr. 10-12). 36.20 (978-0-7377-3511-6(2), Greenhaven Pr., Inc.) Thomson Gale.

Hunt, Marigold. A Life of Our Lord for Children. 2003. (Illus.). v, 189p. (J). 14.95 (978-1-928832-64-5(4)) Sophia Institute Pr.

Isca, Kay Lynn. Catholic Etiquette for Children at Mass. 2001. 32p. pap. 1.50 (978-0-87973-123-6(0)) Our Sunday Visitor, Publishing Div.

Javernick, Ellen. God's House. Richards, Virginia Helen, illus. 1999. 32p. (J). (gr. k-4). pap. 3.95 (978-0-8198-3096-8(8), 332-104) Pauline Bks. & Media.

John Paul II, pseud. My Dear Young Friends: Pope John Paul II Speaks to Teens on Life, Love, & Courage. Vitek, John, ed. 2003. 120p. (YA). pap. 6.95 (978-0-88489-724-8(9)) St. Mary's Pr.

Juliana, M., et al, eds. Catholic Children's Treasure Box Vols. 11-20: Commonly Called Simply Treasure Box. Miki, illus. 2nd l.t. rev. ed. 1998. 32p. (J). (ps-3). pap. 35.00 (978-0-89555-582-3(4)) TAN Bks. and Pubs., Inc.

Keane, Michael. What You Will See Inside a Catholic Church. 2003. Tr. of Lo Que Se Puede Ver Dentro de una Iglesia Catolica. (Illus.). 32p. (978-2-89507-357-4(0)) Novalis Publishing.

—What You Will See Inside a Catholic Church. Pepis, Aaron, photos by. 2002. (What You Will See Inside Ser.).Tr. of Lo Que Se Puede Ver Dentro de una Iglesia Catolica. (Illus.). 34p. (J). 17.95 (978-1-893361-54-6(3)) SkyLight Paths Publishing.

Kerry, Margaret Charles, et al. Saint Anthony of Padua: Fire & Light. 1999. (Encounter the Saints Ser.: No. 1). (Illus.). 120p. (YA). (gr. 5-9). pap. 5.95 (978-0-8198-7019-3(6), 332-337) Pauline Bks. & Media.

Kielbasa, Marilyn. Called to Live the Gospel. Zanzig, Thomas, ed. Thiewes, Sam, illus. 2003. (Horizons Program : Level II, Core 3). 96p. (Orig.). (YA). (gr. 10). pap., stu. ed. 19.95 (978-0-88489-406-3(1)) St. Mary's Pr.

—Finding Your Personal Style. Zanzig, Thomas, ed. Thiewes, Sam, illus. 2003. (Horizons Program : Level 1, Minicourse 3). 68p. (Orig.). (YA). (gr. 9). pap., stu. ed. 9.95 (978-0-88489-344-8(8)) St. Mary's Pr.

—Keeping a Journal. Zanzig, Thomas, ed. Thiewes, Sam, illus. 2003. (Horizons Program : Level 1, Minicourse 1). 64p. (Orig.). (YA). (gr. 9). pap., stu. ed. 9.95 (978-0-88489-345-5(6)) St. Mary's Pr.

Koch, Carl. The Catholic Church: Journey, Wisdom, & Mission. 2nd rev. ed. 2003. (High School Textbooks Ser.). (Illus.). 336p. (gr. 11-12). pap. 17.30 (978-0-88489-298-4(0)) St. Mary's Pr.

Lynch, Kelly Ann. He Said Yes: The Story of Father Mychal Judge. 2007. (Illus.). 32p. (J). (gr. k-7). 12.95 (***978-0-8091-6740-1(9)**, 6740-1) Paulist Pr.

Mack, John P. Priests: An Inside Look. 2003. (Illus.). 72p. (J). pap. 6.95 (978-0-88489-720-0(6)) St. Mary's Pr.

Maryknoll Sisters Staff, et al, eds. Catholic Children's Treasure Box. Miki, illus. 2nd ed. 1998. 32p. (J). (ps-3). Vol. 11. pap. 5.00 (978-0-89555-561-8(1), No. 1351); Vol. 12. pap. 5.00 (978-0-89555-562-5(X), No. 1352); Vol. 13. pap. 5.00 (978-0-89555-563-2(8), No. 1353); Vol. 14. pap. 5.00 (978-0-89555-564-9(6), No. 1354); Vol. 15. pap. 5.00 (978-0-89555-565-6(4), No. 1355); Vol. 16. pap. 5.00 (978-0-89555-566-3(2), No. 1356); Vol. 17. pap. 5.00 (978-0-89555-567-0(0), No. 1357); Vol. 18. pap. 5.00 (978-0-89555-568-7(9), No. 1358); Vol. 19. pap. 5.00 (978-0-89555-569-4(7), No. 1359); Vol. 20. pap. 5.00 (978-0-89555-570-0(0), No. 1360) TAN Bks. and Pubs., Inc.

Montessori, Maria. The Mass Explained to Children. 1998. 116p. (J). (gr. 3-9). reprint ed. 14.95 (978-0-912141-61-9(1)) Roman Catholic Bks.

O'Connor, Francine M. ABC's of the Mass: For Children. 1998. pap. 9.95 (978-0-89243-654-5(9)) Liguori Pubns.

O'Dell, Catherine M. & Savitskas, Margaret. Loyola Kids Book of Everyday Prayers. 2004. (Loyola Kids Ser.). (Illus.). 208p. (J). (gr. 3-6). 15.95 (978-0-8294-1509-4(2)) Loyola Pr.

Odell, William. What's Special about Being Catholic? Sawyer, Kieran, ed. 2003. (Developing Faith Ser.). (Illus.). 80p. (gr. 9-12). stu. ed. 7.95 (978-0-87793-568-1(8)) Ave Maria Pr.

Parker. The Vatican. 2003. (Holy Places Ser.). (Illus.). 32p. (J). pap. 6.95 (978-1-4109-0054-8(1)) Raintree.

Questions for God Series. 2006. (J). 54.95 (978-0-9779497-0-0(2)) VirTru Powers.

Singer-Towns, Brian. Deciding As a Christian. Zanzig, Thomas, ed. Thiewes, Sam, illus. 2003. (Horizons Program : Level II, Minicourse 6). 76p. (YA). (gr. 10-11). pap., stu. ed. 9.95 (978-0-88489-407-0(X)) St. Mary's Pr.

Singer-Towns, Brian, ed. Catholic Youth Bible: Pray It, Study It, Live It. 2000. (Illus.). 1576p. (YA). (gr. 7-12). im. lthr. 47.95 (978-0-88489-693-7(5)) St. Mary's Pr.

Snyder, Bernadette McCarver. 131 FUN-damental Facts for Catholic Kids. Sharp, Chris, illus. 2006. (Liguori's Fun Facts Ser.). 144p. (J). per. 9.95 (978-0-7648-1502-7(4)) Liguori Pubns.

Solimini, Joyce. Sacraments: A Way of Life Participant Book. Sawyer, Kieran, ed. 2003. (Developing Faith Ser.). (Illus.). 80p. (gr. 9-12). stu. ed. 6.95 (978-0-87793-587-2(4)) Ave Maria Pr.

Stanton, Sue. Child's Guide to the Mass. Alan, H. M., illus. 2001. 32p. (ps-3). 9.95 (978-0-8091-6682-4(8), 6682-8) Paulist Pr.

Stubna, Kris D. Pocket Catechism for Kids. 2001. (gr. 5-8). lib. bdg. 14.10 (978-0-613-77251-8(2)) Tandem Library Bks.

Suser, Sherry. Confirmation. 2002. 32p. (J). pap. 5.95 (978-1-931709-07-1(6)) Our Sunday Visitor, Publishing Div.

Theisen, Michael. Exploring Catholicism. Zanzig, Thomas, ed. Thiewes, Sam, illus. 2003. (Horizons Program : Vol. Level II, Minicourse 2). 64p. (Orig.). (YA). (gr. 10). pap., stu. ed. 9.95 (978-0-88489-408-7(8)) St. Mary's Pr.

—Ready-to-Go Game Shows (That Teach Serious Stuff) Catholic Teachings & Practices Edition. 2003. (Illus.). 144p. (YA). 19.95 (978-0-88489-757-6(5)) St. Mary's Pr.

Vitek, John. Living the Questions Jesus Asks: A Guide for Teens. 2003. 136p. (YA). per. 6.95 (978-0-88489-782-8(6)) St. Mary's Pr.

Welborn, Amy. Prove It! Church. 2001. (gr. 7-12). lib. bdg. 15.25 (978-0-613-77256-3(3)) Tandem Library Bks.

Wood Lake Books Staff & Novalis Staff. Your Child's Baptism: Roman Catholic. Date not set. 16p. (Orig.). (J). pap. 2.50 (978-2-89088-669-8(7)) Logos Productions, Inc.

Zanzig, Thomas. The Church: It's Wisdom, Works & Worship. Thiewes, Sam, illus. 2003. (Horizons Program : Level II, Core 4). 88p. (YA). (gr. 10-11). pap., stu. ed. 19.95 (978-0-88489-336-3(7)) St. Mary's Pr.

—Jesus: His Message & Mission. Thiewes, Sam, illus. 2003. (Horizons Program : Level 1, Core 2). 88p. (YA). (gr. 9). pap., stu. ed. 19.95 (978-0-88489-337-0(5)) St. Mary's Pr.

CATHOLIC CHURCH—DICTIONARIES

Dyches, Richard W. & Mustachio, Thomas. A Child's First Catholic Dictionary. Holmberg, Ansgar, illus. 2004. 112p. (gr. k-3). 16.95 (978-1-59471-013-1(9)) Ave Maria Pr.

Hunt, Marigold. Schooled by St. Patrick: A Children's Adventure Catechism. 2004. (Illus.). v, 279p. (J). pap. (978-1-928832-92-8(X)) Sophia Institute Pr.

CATHOLIC CHURCH—DOCTRINES

Butler, Brian, et al. Theology of the Body for Teens: Student Workbook. 2006. per. 14.95 (***978-1-932927-86-3(7)**) Ascension Pr.

Gortler, Rosemarie, et al. Little Acts of Grace. 2002. (Illus.). 48p. (J). (gr. k-5). pap. 5.95 (978-0-9707756-7-2(9)) Our Sunday Visitor, Publishing Div.

Knowing Our Catholic Faith: 26 Lessons. 2004. (978-0-8294-1129-4(1)); Vol. 2. (978-0-8294-1130-0(5)); Vol. 3. (978-0-8294-1131-7(3)) Loyola Pr.

Knowing Our Catholic Faith: 32 Lessons. 2004. Vol. 4. (978-0-8294-1132-4(1)); Vol. 5. (978-0-8294-1134-8(8)); Vol. 6. (978-0-8294-1135-5(6)) Loyola Pr.

Knowing Our Catholic Faith: 38 Lessons. 2004. Vol. 7. (978-0-8294-1136-2(4)); Vol. 8. (978-0-8294-1137-9(2)) Loyola Pr.

Knowing Our Catholic Faith: Complete Set, 8 vols. 2004. (978-0-8294-1508-7(4)) Loyola Pr.

Knowlton, Laurie Lazzaro, et al. Catholic Book of Bible Stories. Ettlinger, Doris, illus. 2004. (Bible Storybooks Ser.). 224p. (J). 16.99 (978-0-310-70505-5(3)) Zonderkidz.

Lockman, Vic. Catechism for Young Children Coloring Book. Lockman, Vic, illus. 2003. (Illus.). 24p. (J). (ps-3). (978-0-936175-41-6(9)) Lockman, Vic.

O'Keefe, Susan Heyboer. It's Great to Be Catholic! Kelley, Patrick, illus. 2002. 32p. 10.95 (978-0-8091-6680-0(1), 6680-1) Paulist Pr.

—It's Great to Be Catholic! 2001. (gr. k-3). lib. bdg. 19.90 (978-0-613-75764-5(5)) Tandem Library Bks.

Regina Press Staff, ed. Catholic Bible. 2000. (Illus.). (J). (ps-k). bds. 9.99 (978-0-88271-751-7(0)) Regina Pr., Malhame & Co.

Singer-Towns, Brian & Calderone-Stewart, Lisa-Marie. Bringing Catholic Youth & the Bible Together: Strategies & Activities for Parishes & Schools. 2003. (Illus.). 96p. (YA). (gr. 8-12). pap. 14.95 (978-0-88489-692-0(7)) St. Mary's Pr.

Windley-Daoust, Jerry & Kilmartin, Lorraine. Living Justice & Peace: Catholic Social Teaching in Practice. 2001. 335p. (J). 17.20 (978-0-88489-632-6(3)) St. Mary's Pr.

Wright, Melissa & Curelli, Augusta. My Bible: The Story of God's Love. Curreli, Augusta, illus. 2004. 236p. (J). 24.95 (978-0-8198-4834-5(4), 332-223) Pauline Bks. & Media.

Zanzig, Thomas. Catechist's Guide. 2001. (Confirmed in a Faithful Community Ser.). (Illus.). 370p. spiral bd. 24.95 (978-0-88489-673-9(0)) St. Mary's Pr.

CATHOLIC CHURCH—FICTION

Canales, Viola. The Tequila Worm. 2005. 208p. (YA). (gr. 7 up). 15.95 (978-0-385-74674-8(1), Lamb, Wendy) Random Hse. Children's Bks.

Casanova, Mary. Curse of a Winter Moon. 2000. (gr. 5-8). lib. bdg. 14.15 (978-0-613-68226-8(2)) Tandem Library Bks.

—Curse of the Winter Moon. 2000. 144p. (gr. 3-7). 16.49 (978-0-7868-2475-5(1)) Hyperion Bks. for Children.

—Curse of the Winter Moon. 2002. (Illus.). 144p. (gr. 5-9). pap. 5.99 (978-0-7868-1602-6(3)) Hyperion Paperbacks for Children.

Cormier, Robert. Other Bells for Us to Ring. 2000. (J). (978-0-606-19745-8(1)) Tandem Library Bks.

Hood, Ann. How I Saved My Father's Life (and Ruined Everything Else) 2008. 224p. (J). pap. 16.99 (***978-0-439-92819-9(2)**, Scholastic Pr.) Scholastic, Inc.

Hunt, Marigold. St. Patrick's Summer. 2002. (Illus.). 273p. reprint ed. 21.00 (978-1-930873-71-1(9)) Neumann Pr., The.

Jacobson, Jennifer Richard. Stained. 2005. (Illus.). 208p. (YA). (gr. 8 up). 16.95 (978-0-689-86745-3(X), Atheneum) Simon & Schuster Children's Publishing.

Jennings, Patrick. The Wolving Time. 2003. 208p. (J). pap. 15.95 (978-0-439-39555-7(0)) Scholastic, Inc.

Klise, Kate. Deliver Us from Normal. 2005. 240p. (YA). (gr. 5-9). 16.95 (978-0-439-52322-6(2)) Scholastic, Inc.

—Deliver Us from Normal: Read-Along/Homework Pack. unabr. ed. 2005. (YA). (gr. 5-8). 65.70 incl. audio (978-1-4193-3619-5(3), 42050) Recorded Bks., LLC.

Littman, Sarah. Confessions of a Closet Catholic. 2006. 208p. (J). (gr. 5). reprint ed. pap. 5.99 (978-0-14-240597-0(3), Puffin) Penguin Group (USA) Inc.

Madrigal, Antonio Hernandez. Blanca's Feather. Suzan, Gerardo, illus. 2000. 32p. (gr. k-3). 15.95 (978-0-87358-743-3(X), Rising Moon Bks. for Young Readers) Northland Publishing.

Massi, Jeri. Some Through the Fire, 2 vols. 2003. (Great Stories That Teach Eternal Truths Ser.). 496p. pap. 12.99 (978-0-8024-1513-4(X)) Moody Pubs.

Nobisso, Josephine. El Peso de Una Misa: Un Relato de fe. Szegedi, Katalin, illus. 2003. Orig. Title: The Weight of a Mass a Tale of Faith. (SPA.). 32p. 17.95 (978-0-940112-15-5(9)); pap. 9.95 (978-0-940112-17-9(5)) Gingerbread Hse.

C D

—Weight of a Mass: A Tale of Faith. 2003. (gr. k-3). lib. bdg. 18.75 (978-0-613-70732-9(X)) Tandem Library Bks.

Riordan, Robert. Medicine for Wildcat: A Story of the Friendship between a Menominee Indian & Frontier Priest Samuel Mazzuchelli. 2006. (Illus.). 132p. (YA). per. 14.95 (978-0-9774934-0-1(7)) Sinsinawa Dominicans, Inc.

CATHOLIC CHURCH—HISTORY

Faith Handed On. 2004. (Effective Dre Ser.). pap. (978-0-8294-1497-4(5)) Loyola Pr.

Fisher, James T. Catholics in America. 2000. (Religion in America Ser.). (Illus.). 176p. (YA). (gr. 8 up). reprint ed. 30.00 (978-0-19-511179-8(6)) Oxford Univ. Pr., Inc.

Reformation DBA. 2003. spiral bd. 16.95 (978-1-56004-167-2(6)) Social Studies Schl. Service.

Ross, Mandy. The Vatican. 2003. (Holy Places Ser.). (Illus.). 32p. (J). lib. bdg. 24.28 (978-0-7398-6081-6(X)) Raintree.

Stanton, Sue. Great Women of Faith: Inspiration for Action. 2003. (Illus.). 128p. (J). 12.95 (978-0-8091-4123-4(X), 4123-x) Paulist Pr.

Welborn, Amy. Loyola Kids Book of Heroes: Stories of Catholic Heroes & Saints Throughout History. 2004. (Illus.). 175p. (J). 15.95 (978-0-8294-1584-1(X)) Loyola Pr.

Young Writers Workshop Staff, contrib. by. Kids Explore America's Catholic Heritage. 2001. (Illus.). 192p. (J). pap. 9.95 (978-0-8198-4208-4(7), 332-162) Pauline Bks. & Media.

CATHOLIC LITERATURE

John Paul II, pseud. My Dear Young Friends: Pope John Paul II Speaks to Youth on Life, Love, & Courage. Vitek, John, ed. 2003. (Illus.). 144p. (YA). pap., pap. 9.95 (978-0-88489-748-4(6)) St. Mary's Pr.

Sawyer, Kieran & Amodei, Michael. Confirming Faith: Candidate Book..Faith Development Program for High School Students Preparing to Celebrate the Sacrament of Confirmation with the Support of the Entire Faith Community. Robinson, Katherine, illus. rev. ed. 2003. (Confirming Faith Ser.). 152p. (gr. 9-12). stu. ed. 7.95 (978-0-87793-549-0(1)) Ave Maria Pr.

—Confirming Faith: Director's Manual...Faith Development Program for High School Students Preparing to Celebrate the Sacrament of Confirmation with the Support of the Entire Faith Community. Robinson, Katherine, illus. rev. ed. 2003. (Confirming Faith Ser.). 232p. tchr. ed., spiral bd. 19.95 (978-0-87793-548-3(3)) Ave Maria Pr.

Singer-Towns, Brian, ed. Catholic Youth Bible: Pray It, Study It, Live It. rev. ed. 2003. (Illus.). 1576p. (YA). (gr. 7-12). 37.95 (978-0-88489-667-8(6)); pap. 27.95 (978-0-88489-489-6(4)) St. Mary's Pr.

CATS

Adelman, Beth. Cool Cats. 2007. (Girls Rock! Ser.). 32p. (J). (gr. 1-5). 24.21 (***978-1-59296-865-7(1)***) Child's World, Inc.

Alderton, David. Cat. 2003. (Looking after My Pet Ser.). (Illus.). 24p. (gr. k-4). 7.99 (978-0-7548-1157-2(3)) Anness Publishing GBR. *Dist:* National Bk. Network.

Allen. Ap Lab Manual with Cat Dissection Manual, Set. 2003. (Illus.). 740p. (YA). pap., lab manual ed. (978-0-471-27067-6(9), Wiley) Wiley, John & Sons, Inc.

Alley Cats. (Sails Literacy Ser.). 24p. (gr. 2 up). 27.00 (978-0-7635-6996-9(8)); Pack. 57.00 (978-0-7578-3211-6(3)) Rigby Education.

Alley Cats: 6 Small Books. (Sails Literacy Ser.). 24p. (gr. 2 up). 25.00 (978-0-7578-3187-4(7)) Rigby Education.

Axelrod, Herbert R. Feline Behavior. 1999. (Cats & Dogs). (Illus.). 84p. (YA). (gr. 3-7). 21.95 (978-0-7910-4810-8(1), Chelsea Hse.) Facts On File, Inc.

—Persians. 1999. (Cats & Dogs). (Illus.). 84p. (YA). (ps-k). 21.95 (978-0-7910-4809-2(8), Chelsea Hse.) Facts On File, Inc.

—Skin Care for Cats. 1999. (Cats & Dogs). (Illus.). 84p. (YA). (gr. 3 up). lib. bdg. 21.95 (978-0-7910-4807-8(1), Chelsea Hse.) Facts On File, Inc.

Aylmore, Angela. I Like Cats. 2007. (Illus.). 24p. (J). (978-1-4034-9279-1(4)); (978-1-4034-9270-8(0)) Heinemann Library.

Baillie, Marilyn. My Pet Kitten. Kurisu, Jane, illus. 2005. 32p. (J). (gr. k-3). (978-1-55337-653-8(6)) Kids Can Pr., Ltd.

Barbaresi, Nina. Cats. 2004. (Illus.). 64p. (J). (ps-2). pap. 1.50 (978-0-486-43510-7(5)) Dover Pubns., Inc.

Barge Cat: Second Grade Big Books. (On Our Way to English Ser.). (gr. 2 up). 29.95 (978-0-7578-1423-5(9)) Rigby Education.

Barge Cat: Small Versions of Big Books. (On Our Way to English Ser.). (gr. 2 up). 29.00 (978-0-7578-7234-1(4)) Rigby Education.

Barnes, J. Lou. Cats & Kittens. 2002. (PowerPhonics Ser.). (Illus.). 23p. (J). lib. bdg. (978-0-8239-8248-6(3)) Rosen Publishing Group, Inc., The.

—Cats & Kittens: Learning the Hard C & K Sounds. 2002. (PowerPhonics Ser.). (Illus.). 24p. (J). (gr. 1). lib. bdg. 18.50 (978-0-8239-5903-7(1), PowerKids Pr.) Rosen Publishing Group, Inc., The.

Barnes, Julia. Pet Cats. 2006. (Pet Pals Ser.). (Illus.). 32p. (J). (gr. 2-5). lib. bdg. 23.93 (978-0-8368-6776-3(9)) Stevens, Gareth Inc.

Barret & Allen. El Lince. 2002. (Gatos Salvajes Serie).Tr. of Wild Cats: The Bobcat. (SPA.). 24p. (J). (gr. 3-5). 22.45 (978-1-4103-0010-2(2), Blackbirch Pr., Inc.) Thomson Gale.

Barrett, Jalma. Bobcat. Allan, Larry, photos by. 1998. (Wildcats of North America Ser.). (Illus.). 24p. (J). (gr. 3-6). 24.94 (978-1-56711-257-3(9), Blackbirch Pr., Inc.) Thomson Gale.

—Cougar. Allan, Larry, photos by. 1998. (Wildcats of North America Ser.). (Illus.). 24p. (J). (gr. 3-6). 21.20 (978-1-56711-258-0(7), Blackbirch Pr., Inc.) Thomson Gale.

—Feral Cat. Allan, Larry, photos by. 1998. (Wildcats of North America Ser.). (Illus.). 24p. (J). (gr. 3-6). 22.45 (978-1-56711-260-3(9), Blackbirch Pr., Inc.) Thomson Gale.

Batten, Mary. Wild Cats. Rowe, Michael Langham, illus. 2004. (Step into Reading Ser.). 48p. (J). (gr. 2-4). pap. 3.99 (978-0-375-82551-4(7)); lib. bdg. 11.99 (978-0-375-92551-1(1)) Random Hse. Children's Bks. (Random Hse. Bks. for Young Readers).

—Wild Cats. 2002. (gr. 3-6). lib. bdg. 11.80 (978-0-613-50261-0(2)) Tandem Library Bks.

Baumbusch, Brigitte. Cats in Art. 2005. (Illus.). 32p. (J). lib. bdg. 22.00 (978-0-8368-4444-3(0)) Stevens, Gareth Inc.

Beck, Isabel L., et al. Trophies Kindergarten: Little Cat, Big Cat. 2003. (Trophies Ser.). (gr. k-6). 13.80 (978-0-15-329552-2(X)) Harcourt Schl. Pubs.

Bendon Publishing Intl. Staff. Hello Kitty Sticker W/Poster Book #1705. 2004. 3.99 (978-1-59394-355-4(5)) Bendon Publishing International.

Bennett, Leonie. My Cat's A Mommy! 2006. (I Love Reading Ser.). (Illus.). 24p. (J). lib. bdg. 19.96 (978-1-59716-157-2(8)) Bearport Publishing Co., Inc.

Bessant, Claire. Kittentalk: 50 Ways to Make Friends with Your Kitten. 2006. (Illus.). (J). pap. 4.99 (978-0-340-89376-0(1), Hodder & Stoughton) Hodder General Publishing Division GBR. *Dist:* Trafalgar Square Publishing.

Beylon, Cathy. Cats & Kittens Stained Glass Coloring Book. 2005. (Illus.). 16p. (J). (gr. 1-4). pap. 5.95 (978-0-486-44467-3(8)) Dover Pubns., Inc.

Bicknell, Joanna. Noisy (Touch & Feel) Kitten. 2006. (Touch & Feel Noisy Ser.). (Illus.). 12p. (ps). per., bds. 6.95 (978-1-84610-284-4(7)) Make Believe Ideas GBR. *Dist:* Ingram Pub. Services.

Bidner, Jenni. Is My Cat a Tiger: How Your Cat Compares to Its Wild Cousins. 2007. (Illus.). 64p. 9.95 (978-1-57990-815-7(2)) Lark Bks.

Big Cat, Little Cat: Individual Title Six-Packs. (Rigby Focus Ser.). 16p. (gr. k up). 26.00 (978-0-7578-5285-5(8)); 28.00 (978-0-7578-5519-1(9)) Rigby Education.

Blackaby, Susan. A Cat for You: Caring for Your Cat. DeLage, Charlene, illus. 2004. (Pet Care Ser.). 24p. (C). (gr. k-3). 22.60 (978-1-4048-0115-8(4)) Picture Window Bks.

Bodden, Valerie. Cats. 2006. (Illus.). 24p. (J). 15.95 (978-1-58341-457-6(6), Creative Education) Creative Co., The.

Bonar, Samantha. Small Wild Cats. 2002. (Watts Library). (Illus.). 64p. (J). (gr. 5-7). pap. 25.50 (978-0-531-11965-5(3), Watts, Franklin) Scholastic Library Publishing.

Boss, Kittie. Cat Tails. Mauterer, Erin Marie, illus. 1999. (Books for Young Learners). 8p. (J). (gr. k-2). pap. 5.00 (978-1-57274-139-3(2)) Owen, Richard C. Pubs., Inc.

Bourgeois, Kim. Kitty's First Year: A Record Book & Keepsake. Sarrazin, Marisol, illus. 2000. (Abby & Tess Pet-Sitters Ser.). 22p. (J). pap. 7.95 (978-1-894222-26-6(1)) Lobster Pr. CAN. *Dist:* Univ. of Toronto Pr.

Bozzo, Linda. My First Cat. 2007. (My First Pet Library from the American Humane Association Ser.). (Illus.). 32p. (J). (gr. 1-2). lib. bdg. 22.60 (978-0-7660-2750-3(3), Enslow Elementary) Enslow Pubs., Inc.

Bratun, Katy. Drawing Cats. Bratun, Katy, illus. 2002. (Books & Stuff Ser.). (Illus.). 64p. (J). pap. 7.99 (978-0-448-42595-5(5), Grosset & Dunlap) Penguin Group (USA) Inc.

—Drawing Cats. 2002. (gr. 3-6). lib. bdg. 15.30 (978-0-613-72440-1(2)) Tandem Library Bks.

Buck, Nola. Oh, Cats! Westcott, Nadine Bernard, illus. 1998. (Trophy I Can Read Bks.). 32p. (J). (ps up). pap. 3.99 (978-0-06-444240-4(3), Harper Trophy) HarperCollins Pubs.

The Cat: Individual Title Six-Packs. (Chiquilibros Ser.). (gr. k-1). 23.00 (978-0-7635-0456-4(4)) Rigby Education.

Cat Chat. (Little Book Practice Reader). (J). (978-0-8136-2066-4(X)) Modern Curriculum Pr.

A Cat for You. (Pet Care Ser.). 24p. (J). 7.95 (978-1-4048-0391-6(2)) Picture Window Bks.

Cats. (Eyes on Nature Ser.). 32p. (J). (gr. 1). pap. (978-1-882210-52-7(2)) Action Publishing, Inc.

Cats. (Eyes on Nature Ser.). (Illus.). 32p. (J). (gr. 1 up). 7.95 (978-1-56156-419-4(2)) Kidsbooks, Inc.

Cats - Set III, Set. 2002. (J). (gr. k-6). lib. bdg. 128.10 (978-1-57765-861-0(2)) ABDO Publishing Co.

Cats & Dogs (Gr. PreK-5) 2003. (J). (978-1-58232-018-2(7)) Bryan Hse. Pubs., Inc.

Cats & Kittens Kid Kit. 2003. (Illus.). 32p. 13.95 (978-1-58086-526-5(7)) EDC Publishing.

Cats! Cats! Cats!, Vol. 2. 2005. (Emergent Library: Vol. 1). (YA). (ps-1). 23.94 (978-0-8215-8908-3(3)) Sadlier, William H. Inc.

Cats Have Kittens. (Animals & Their Young Ser.). 24p. (J). 7.95 (978-0-7565-1236-1(0)) Compass Point Bks.

Cats Set IV. 2006. (J). (gr. k-6). 128.10 (978-1-59679-263-0(9), Checkerboard Library) ABDO Publishing Co.

Chat. 1999. (Pocket Pals Ser.). (FRE.). (J). (ps-1). pap. 1.99 (978-0-85953-732-2(3)) Child's Play International Ltd. GBR. *Dist:* Child's Play-International.

Clements, Andrew. Dolores & the Big Fire: A True Story. 2003. (gr. k-3). lib. bdg. 11.80 (978-0-613-61549-5(2)) Tandem Library Bks.

—Ringo Saves the Day! A True Story. 2002. (ps-2). lib. bdg. 11.80 (978-0-613-57581-2(4)) Tandem Library Bks.

Clutton-Brock, Juliet & Dorling Kindersley Publishing Staff. Cat. 2004. (Dk Eyewitness Books Ser.). 72p. (J). 15.99 (978-0-7566-0662-6(4)) Dorling Kindersley Publishing, Inc.

Cole, Lynn. My Cat. 2001. (Pet Pals Ser.). (Illus.). 48p. (J). (gr. 1-5). pap. 8.95 (978-1-55971-792-2(0), NorthWord Bks. for Young Readers) T&N Children's Publishing.

Coppendale, Jean. Kitten. 2004. (QEB You & Your Pet Ser.). (Illus.). 32p. (J). lib. bdg. 18.95 (978-1-59566-050-3(X)) QEB Publishing Inc.

Crisp, Marty. Everything Cat. 2003. (Kids' FAQs Ser.). (Illus.). 64p. (gr. 2-6). 10.95 (978-1-55971-864-6(1)); (YA). pap. 6.95 (978-1-55971-865-3(X)) T&N Children's Publishing. (NorthWord Bks. for Young Readers).

—Everything Cat: What Kids Really Want to Know about Cats. 2003. (gr. 3-6). lib. bdg. 15.25 (978-0-613-71017-6(7)) Tandem Library Bks.

Cutrone, Joy Radle. Why Do Cats Purr? Lapham, Sharon Smith, illus. 2002. 24p. per. 9.95 (978-0-9727585-0-5(X), CatsPurr4-03) Animal Humanity Bks., LLC.

Dalmatian Press Staff. Pretty Kitty: Little Pups Board Book. 2002. (Little Pups Board Bks.). (Illus.). 20p. (J). bds. 2.99 (978-1-57759-633-2(1)) Dalmatian Pr.

Dennis-Bryan, Kim & Dorling Kindersley Publishing Staff. Kitten Care: A Guide for Young Pet Owners. 2004. 48p. (J). 9.99 (978-0-7566-0388-5(9)) Dorling Kindersley Publishing, Inc.

DK Publishing. Puppies & Kittens. 2008. 14p. (J). (ps-k). bds. 5.99 (***978-0-7566-3835-1(6)***) Dorling Kindersley Publishing, Inc.

Doering, Amanda. Cats ABC: An Alphabet Book. 2004. (A+ Alphabet Books). (Illus.). 17p. (J). 22.60 (978-0-7368-2604-4(1), Aplus Bks.) Capstone Pr., Inc.

Dolbear, Emily J. & Primm, E. Russell. Cats Have Kittens. 2001. (Animals & Their Young Ser.). (Illus.). 24p. (J). (gr. 1 up). lib. bdg. 18.60 (978-0-7565-0059-7(1)) Compass Point Bks.

Dora Blat's Cat, 6 vols. 8p. (gr. k-1). 21.50 (978-0-322-02066-5(2)) Wright Group, The.

Dorling Kindersley Publishing Staff. Cat. (Ultimate Sticker Bks.). (J). 2006. 16p. (gr. 8). pap. 6.99 (978-0-7566-2097-4(X)); 2004. 72p. lib. bdg. 19.99 (978-0-7566-0661-9(6)) Dorling Kindersley Publishing, Inc.

—Kitten. (See How They Grow Ser.). (J). (ps-1). 2007. 24p. pap. 3.99 (978-0-7566-3017-1(7)); 2006. 16p. pap. 6.99 (978-0-7566-2101-8(1)) Dorling Kindersley Publishing, Inc.

Dorling Kindersley Publishing Staff & Alderton, David. Cats. 2nd rev. ed. 2003. (DK Pockets Ser.). (Illus.). 128p. (J). pap. 6.99 (978-0-7894-9590-7(2)) Dorling Kindersley Publishing, Inc.

Dorling Kindersley Publishing Staff, et al. Caring for Your Cat. 2003. (101 Essential Tips Ser.). (Illus.). 72p. pap. 5.00 (978-0-7894-9689-8(5)) Dorling Kindersley Publishing, Inc.

Doudna, Kelly. Kittens. l.t. ed. 1999. (Baby Animals Ser.). (Illus.). 24p. (J). (ps-3). lib. bdg. 19.93 (978-1-57765-182-6(0), SandCastle) ABDO Publishing Co.

Draw 50 Cats. 2002. (Draw 50 Ser.). (J). 17.60 (978-0-7587-4162-2(6)) Book Wholesalers, Inc.

Duran Armengol, Teresa. El Gato. 2002. (SPA., Illus.). 24p. (J). 6.50 (978-84-246-1721-9(5)) La Galera, S.A. Editorial ESP. *Dist:* AIMS International Bks., Inc.

Endres, Hollie. Cats. 2007. (Illus.). 24p. (J). lib. bdg. 19.95 (978-1-60014-111-9(0)) Bellwether Media.

Evans, Mark. Kitten. 2001. (ASPCA Pet Care Guides for Kids). (Illus.). (J). (978-0-606-21284-7(1)) Tandem Library Bks.

Fahiner, Paul. Dog & Cat. 2004. (My First Reader Ser.). (Illus.). 29p. (J). (gr. k-1). pap. 3.95 (978-0-516-24626-0(7), Children's Pr.) Scholastic Library Publishing.

Fogle, Bruce. CATalog. 2002. (gr. 3-6). lib. bdg. 28.00 (978-0-613-57710-6(8)) Tandem Library Bks.

Foley, Cate. My Cat. 2001. (My Pets Ser.). (Illus.). 24p. (J). (ps-2). 17.00 (978-0-516-23183-9(9), Children's Pr.) Scholastic Library Publishing.

—My Cat. 2001. (gr. k-3). lib. bdg. 12.95 (978-0-613-58857-7(6)) Tandem Library Bks.

Fordham, Kate. Me & My Kitten. 2006. (Illus.). 80p. (J). (***978-0-439-89293-3(7)***) Scholastic, Inc.

Fowler, Allan. Really Big Cats. Rau, Dana, ed. 1998. (Rookie Read-About Science Ser.). (Illus.). 32p. (J). (gr. 1-2). pap. 4.95 (978-0-516-26367-0(6), Children's Pr.) Scholastic Library Publishing.

—Really Big Cats. 1998. (Rookie Read-About Science Ser.). (Illus.). 32p. (J). (gr. 1-2). 20.50 (978-0-516-20805-3(5), Children's Pr.) Scholastic Library Publishing.

Frattini, Stephane. Face-to-Face with the Cat. Klein, Jean-Louis & Hubert, Marie-Luce, illus. 2004. (Face to Face Ser.). 28p. (J). 9.95 (978-1-57091-454-6(0)) Charlesbridge Publishing, Inc.

Friedman, Carol. Baby Cat Nicky 123. 2005. (Illus.). 24p. (J). (ps-k). per. 7.95 (978-1-57687-273-4(4), PowerHouse Kids) powerHouse Cultural Entertainment, Inc.

Frost, Helen. Cats. 2000. (All about Pets Ser.). (Illus.). 24p. (J). (gr. k-1). lib. bdg. 15.93 (978-0-7368-0655-8(5), Pebble Bks.) Capstone Pr., Inc.

Furstinger, Nancy. American Shorthair Cats. 2006. (Checkerboard Animal Library). (Illus.). 24p. (J). (gr. k-6). 21.35 (978-1-59679-264-7(7), Checkerboard Library) ABDO Publishing Co.

—Calico Cats. 2006. (Checkerboard Animal Library). (Illus.). 24p. (J). (gr. k-6). 21.35 (978-1-59679-265-4(5), Checkerboard Library) ABDO Publishing Co.

—Himalayan Cats. 2006. (Illus.). 24p. (J). (gr. k-6). 21.35 (978-1-59679-266-1(3), Checkerboard Library) ABDO Publishing Co.

—Norwegian Forest Cats. 2006. (Checkerboard Animal Library). (Illus.). 24p. (J). (gr. k-6). 21.35 (978-1-59679-267-8(1), Checkerboard Library) ABDO Publishing Co.

—Somali Cats. 2006. (Checkerboard Animal Library). (Illus.). 24p. (J). (gr. k-6). 21.35 (978-1-59679-268-5(X), Checkerboard Library) ABDO Publishing Co.

—Sphynx Cats. 2006. (Checkerboard Animal Library). (Illus.). 24p. (J). (gr. k-6). 21.35 (978-1-59679-269-2(8), Checkerboard Library) ABDO Publishing Co.

Ganeri, Anita. Cats. 2003. (Heinemann First Library). (Illus.). 32p. (J). pap. (978-1-4034-4269-7(X)) Heinemann Library.

—Cats & Kittens. 2007. (J). (***978-1-58340-807-0(X)***) Smart Apple Media.

Ganeri, Anita. A Pet's Life: Cats. 2003. (Heinemann First Library). (Illus.). 32p. (J). lib. bdg. 22.79 (978-1-4034-3993-2(1)) Heinemann Library.

Gatitos: Individual Title Six-Packs. (Literatura 2000 Ser.). (SPA.). (ps-1). 28.00 (978-0-7635-1195-1(1)) Rigby Education.

Gentle, Victor & Perry, Janet. Big Cats, 6 bks. Incl. Cheetahs. lib. bdg. 22.00 (978-0-8368-3024-8(5)); Cougars. lib. bdg. 22.00 (978-0-8368-3025-5(3)); Leopards. lib. bdg. 22.00 (978-0-8368-3026-2(1)); Lions. lib. bdg. 22.00 (978-0-8368-3027-9(X)); Lynxes. lib. bdg. 22.00 (978-0-8368-3028-6(8)); Tigers. lib. bdg. 22.00 (978-0-8368-3029-3(6)); 24p. (J). (gr. 2 up). (Imagination Library). (Illus.). 2002. Set lib. bdg. 132.00 (978-0-8368-3023-1(7)) Stevens, Gareth Inc.

George, Jean Craighead. How to Talk to Your Cat. Truesdell, Sue & Meisel, Paul, illus. 2000. 40p. (J). (gr. 2-4). 14.99 (978-0-06-027968-4(0)); (ps-4). lib. bdg. 13.89 (978-0-06-027969-1(9)) HarperCollins Pubs.

Gillis, Jennifer Blizin. Cats. 2004. (Heinemann Read & Learn Ser.). (Illus.). 24p. (J). 18.50 (978-1-4034-5051-7(X)); pap. 5.75 (978-1-4034-6019-6(1)) Heinemann Library.

—Los Gatos. 2004. (Las Mascotas de Mi Casa (Pets at My House) Ser.).Tr. of Cats. (ENG & SPA.). 24p. (ps-1). lib. bdg. 20.64 (978-1-4034-6032-5(9)) Heinemann Library.

Goecke, Michael P. Scimitar Cat. 2004. (Prehistoric Animals Set II Ser.). (Illus.). 24p. (J). (gr. k-4). lib. bdg. 21.35 (978-1-57765-977-8(5)) ABDO Publishing Co.

Gunzi, Christiane. The Best Book of Big Cats. (Best Book of... Ser.). 32p. (J). (gr. k-3). 2006. pap. 6.95 (978-0-7534-5986-7(8)); 2001. (Illus.). tchr. ed. 12.95 (978-0-7534-5337-7(1)) Houghton Mifflin Co. Trade & Reference Div. (Kingfisher).

Gutman, Bill. Adopting Pets: How to Choose Your New Best Friend. 2001. (Pet Friends Ser.). (Illus.). 64p. (gr. 4-6). lib. bdg. (978-0-7613-1863-7(1), Millbrook Pr.) Lerner Publishing Group.

Hanson, Anders. Cuddly Cats. Nobens, C. A., illus. 2007. (Perfect Pets Ser.). 24p. (J). (gr. k-3). lib. bdg. 19.93 (***978-1-59928-745-4(5)***, SandCastle) ABDO Publishing Co.

Harcourt School Publishers Staff. A Happy Cat. 3rd ed. 2002. (Trophies English Language Learners Ser.). (Illus.). pap. 5.10 (978-0-15-327647-7(9)) Harcourt Schl. Pubs.

Hart, Joyce. Cats. 2007. (Great Pets Ser.). 48p. (J). lib. bdg. 28.50 (***978-0-7614-2710-0(4)***, Benchmark Bks.) Cavendish, Marshall Corp.

Hazen, Barbara Shook. City Cats, Country Cats. Paparone, Pamela, illus. 1999. (Road to Reading Ser.). 32p. (J). (ps-1). pap. 3.99 (978-0-307-26109-0(3), Random Hse. Bks. for Young Readers) Random Hse. Children's Bks.

Head, Honor. Kittens & Cats. 2007. (QEB Know Your Pet Ser.). (Illus.). 32p. (J). lib. bdg. 19.95 (978-1-59566-217-0(0)) QEB Publishing Inc.

Hendry, Linda. Cat Crafts. unabr. ed. 2004. (Kids Can Do It Ser.). (Illus.). 330p. (J). (gr. 4-6). (978-1-55074-964-9(1)) Kids Can Pr., Ltd.

Higgins, Maria Mihalik. Cats: From Tigers to Tabbies. 1998. (Animal Planet Ser.). (J). (978-0-606-13259-6(7)) Tandem Library Bks.

Hillier, Malcolm & Fogle, Bruce. Cat's Christmas. 2006. 48p. 9.95 (978-0-7566-2260-2(3)) Dorling Kindersley Publishing, Inc.

Hinds, Kathryn. Cats. 1999. (Perfect Pets Ser.). (Illus.). 32p. (J). (gr. 3-5). lib. bdg. 25.64 (978-0-7614-0794-2(4), Benchmark Bks.) Cavendish, Marshall Corp.

Hoare, Ben. Cat. 2006. (Owning a Pet Ser.). (J). (978-1-59771-053-4(9)) Sea-To-Sea Pubns.

Hodge, Deborah. Wild Cats: Cougars, Bobcats & Lynx. Ogle, Nancy Gray, illus. unabr. ed. 2004. (Kids Can Press Wildlife Ser.). 32p. (J). (gr. k-3). (978-1-55074-357-9(0)) Kids Can Pr., Ltd.

Holmen, Lene. Kittens. 2006. (Touch & Sparkle Ser.). (Illus.). 12p. (ps). per., bds. 5.95 (978-1-84610-077-2(1)) Make Believe Ideas GBR. *Dist:* Ingram Pub. Services.

Holub, Joan. Why Do Cats Meow? 2001. (Easy-to-Read Ser.). (Illus.). 48p. (J). (ps-3). 13.99 (978-0-8037-2503-4(5), Dial) Penguin Group (USA) Inc.

—Why Do Cats Meow? DiVito, Anna, illus. 2001. (Easy-to-Read Ser.). 48p. (J). (ps-3). pap. 3.99 (978-0-14-056788-5(7), Puffin) Penguin Group (USA) Inc.

—Why Do Cats Meow? 2001. (gr. k-3). lib. bdg. 11.80 (978-0-613-35606-0(3)) Tandem Library Bks.

Hope. Nursery Rhymes for Cats. 1998. (Illus.). 32p. (J). pap. 11.99 (978-0-553-50720-1(6)) Transworld Publishers Ltd. GBR. *Dist:* Independent Pubs. Group.

Hornidge, Marilis. That Yankee Cat: The Maine Coon Cat. 3rd rev. ed. 2002. (Illus.). 120p. pap. 14.95 (978-0-88448-243-7(X)) Tilbury Hse. Pubs.

Horton-Bussey, Claire, et al. 101 Facts about Kittens. 2001. (One Hundred One Facts about Pets Ser.). (Illus.). 32p. (J). (gr. 3 up). lib. bdg. 23.33 (978-0-8368-2889-4(5)) Stevens, Gareth Inc.

Hosley, Maria. Cats. 2007. (Illus.). 24p. (J). 21.35 (***978-1-59679-801-4(7)***) ABDO Publishing Co.

Huckleberry, Jim. The Christmas Cat. 2005. (Illus.). 24p. (J). per. 9.95 (978-1-59453-750-9(X), 3022, Airleaf Publishing) Airleaf Publishing & Bookselling.

Ireland, Charles E. Toolbox. Diienno, Trish, illus. 2006. (J). (978-1-892142-30-6(9)) Cedar Tree Bks.

Jeffrey, Laura S. Cats: How to Choose & Care for a Cat. 2004. (American Humane Pet Care Library). (Illus.). 48p. (J). lib. bdg. 23.93 (978-0-7660-2516-5(0)) Enslow Pubs., Inc.

Jenkins, Steve. Dogs & Cats. 2007. (Illus.). 40p. (J). (gr. 1-5). 16.00 (***978-0-618-50767-2(1)***) Houghton Mifflin Co. Trade & Reference Div.

Jones, Annie. All about Cats. 2005. (Illus.). 38p. (J). (ps-8). lib. bdg. 28.00 (978-0-7910-8687-2(9) , Chelsea Hse.) Facts On File, Inc.

Kalman, Bobbie. What Is a Cat? 2002. (Science of Living Things Ser.). (Illus.). 32p. (J). (gr. 2-3). (978-0-86505-990-0(X)); pap. (978-0-86505-967-2(5)) Crabtree Publishing Co.

—What Is a Cat? 2003. (gr. 3-6). lib. bdg. 14.10 (978-0-613-52931-0(6)) Tandem Library Bks.

Kalman, Bobbie & Bishop, Amanda. Les Felides. 2003. (FRE., Illus.). 32p. (J). pap. (978-2-89579-006-8(X)) Crabtree Publishing Co.

Kimiko, Mitsuko. El Gato. (SPA.). 10p. (978-84-95150-52-3(2)) Corimbo, Editorial S.L.

The Kittens: KinderConcepts Individual Title Six-Packs. (Kinderstarters Ser.). 8p. (ps-1). 21.00 (978-0-7635-8717-8(6)) Rigby Education.

Kittens & Puppies. 2002. (Three Minute Tales Ser.). 32p. (J). 12.98 (978-0-7525-5467-9(0)) Parragon, Inc.

Knight, K. R. Kitty: Cuddly Pups Board Book. rev. ed. 2002. (Cuddly Pups Board Bks.). (Illus.). 18p. (J). 4.99 (978-1-57759-788-9(5)) Dalmatian Pr.

Landau, Elaine. Your Pet Cat. rev. ed. 2006. (True Book Ser.). (Illus.). 47p. (J). (978-0-531-16766-3(6)) Children's Pr., Ltd.

—Your Pet Cat. 1998. (True Bks.). (Illus.). 48p. (J). (gr. 3-5). pap. 6.95 (978-0-516-26260-4(2) , Children's Pr.) Scholastic Library Publishing.

Lewis, David, contrib. by. Kittens. 1999. (Junior Pet Care Ser.). (Illus.). 48p. (YA). (gr. 4-7). lib. bdg. 18.65 (978-0-7910-4906-8(X) , Chelsea Hse.) Facts On File, Inc.

The Life Cycle of a Cat, Vol. 2. 2005. (Animals, Animals, Animals Ser.). (YA). (gr. k-3). (978-0-7368-3391-2(9) , Pebble Bks.) Capstone Pr., Inc.

Limbacher-Tildes, Phyllis. Calico's Cousins: Cats from Around the World. 1999. (J). 13.75 (978-0-606-16406-1(5)) Tandem Library Bks.

Ling, Mary, ed. The Kitten. 2001. (See How They Grow Ser.). (Illus.). 24p. (J). (ps-3). pap. 4.99 (978-0-7894-7657-9(6)) Dorling Kindersley Publishing, Inc.

Lodien, Jennie, des. Cat Tales. 2004. (Illus.). 48p. (YA). ring bd. 16.95 (978-0-9746341-8-0(2)) Chin & A Pr.

Loves, June. Cats. 2003. (Pets Ser.). (Illus.). 32p. (gr. 2-4). 23.00 (978-0-7910-7548-7(6) , Chelsea Hse.) Facts On File, Inc.

Loxton, Howard. Cats: An Eyewitness 3-D Book. 2004. (Illus.). 58p. (YA). reprint ed. 17.00 (978-0-7567-7414-1(4)) DIANE Publishing Co.

Macken, JoAnn Early. Kittens. 2003. (Let's Read about Pets Ser.). (Illus.). 24p. (J). (ps up). lib. bdg. 19.33 (978-0-8368-3799-5(1)); pap. 7.93 (978-0-8368-3846-6(7)) Stevens, Gareth Inc. (Weekly Reader Early Learning Library).

Magloff, Lisa & Dorling Kindersley Publishing Staff. Kitten. 2005. (Watch me Grow Ser.). (Illus.). 24p. (J). (gr. 5-ps). 7.99 (978-0-7566-1156-9(3)) Dorling Kindersley Publishing, Inc.

Makowski, Robin. Cats Drawing Made Fun. 2005. 32p. pap. 6.45 (978-1-59515-782-9(4)) Rourke Publishing, LLC.

Makowski, Robin Lee. Cats. 2001. (How to Draw Ser.). (Illus.). 32p. (J). (gr. 2-5). lib. bdg. 25.27 (978-1-58952-152-0(8)) Rourke Publishing, LLC.

Markle, Sandra. Outside & Inside Big Cats. 2003. (Outside Inside Ser.). (Illus.). 40p. (J). 17.95 (978-0-689-82299-5(5) , Atheneum) Simon & Schuster Children's Publishing.

Mattern, Joanne. The Abyssinian Cat. 2000. (Learning about Cats Ser.). (Illus.). 48p. (J). (gr. 3-4). lib. bdg. 21.26 (978-0-7368-0564-3(8) , Capstone High-Interest Bks.) Capstone Pr., Inc.

—The American Shorthair Cat. 2002. (Learning about Cats Ser.). (Illus.). 48p. (J). (gr. 3-4). lib. bdg. 21.26 (978-0-7368-1300-6(4) , Capstone High Interest Bks.) Capstone Pr., Inc.

—The Birman Cat. 2001. (Learning about Cats Ser.). (Illus.). 48p. (J). (gr. 3-4). lib. bdg. 21.26 (978-0-7368-0895-8(7) , Capstone High-Interest Bks.) Capstone Pr., Inc.

—The Exotic Cat. 2001. (Learning about Cats Ser.). (Illus.). 48p. (J). (gr. 3-4). lib. bdg. 21.26 (978-0-7368-0896-5(5) , Capstone High-Interest Bks.) Capstone Pr., Inc.

—Learning about Cats, 8 bks. Incl. Abyssinian Cat. 2000. lib. bdg. 21.26 (978-0-7368-0564-3(8)); American Shorthair Cat. 2002. lib. bdg. 21.26 (978-0-7368-1300-6(4)); Birman Cat. 2001. lib. bdg. 21.26 (978-0-7368-0895-8(7)); Exotic Cat. 2001. lib. bdg. 21.26 (978-0-7368-0896-5(5)); Maine Coon Cat. 2000. lib. bdg. 21.26 (978-0-7368-0565-0(6)); Manx Cat. 2002. lib. bdg. 21.26 (978-0-7368-1301-3(2)); Ocicat. 2002. lib. bdg. 21.26 (978-0-7368-1302-0(0)); Oriental Cat. 2002. lib. bdg. 21.26 (978-0-7368-1303-7(9)); Persian Cat. 2000. lib. bdg. 21.26 (978-0-7368-0566-7(4)); Ragdoll Cat. 2001. lib. bdg. 21.26 (978-0-7368-0897-2(3)); Siamese Cat. 2000. lib. bdg. 21.26 (978-0-7368-0567-4(2)); Sphynx Cat. 2001. lib. bdg. 21.26 (978-0-7368-0898-9(1)); 48p. (J). (gr. 3-4). (Illus.). Set lib. bdg. 255.12 (978-0-7368-1304-4(7) , Capstone High-Interest Bks.) Capstone Pr., Inc.

—The Maine Coon Cat. 2000. (Learning about Cats Ser.). (Illus.). 48p. (J). (gr. 3-4). lib. bdg. 21.26 (978-0-7368-0565-0(6) , Capstone High-Interest Bks.) Capstone Pr., Inc.

—The Manx Cat. 2002. (Learning about Cats Ser.). (Illus.). 48p. (J). (gr. 3-4). lib. bdg. 21.26 (978-0-7368-1301-3(2) , Capstone High-Interest Bks.) Capstone Pr., Inc.

—The Ocicat. 2002. (Learning about Cats Ser.). (Illus.). 48p. (J). (gr. 3-4). lib. bdg. 21.26 (978-0-7368-1302-0(0) , Capstone High-Interest Bks.) Capstone Pr., Inc.

—The Oriental Cat. 2002. (Learning about Cats Ser.). (Illus.). 48p. (J). (gr. 3-4). lib. bdg. 21.26 (978-0-7368-1303-7(9) , Capstone High-Interest Bks.) Capstone Pr., Inc.

—The Persian Cat. 2000. (Learning about Cats Ser.). (Illus.). 48p. (J). (gr. 3-4). lib. bdg. 21.26 (978-0-7368-0566-7(4) , Capstone High-Interest Bks.) Capstone Pr., Inc.

—The Ragdoll Cat. 2001. (Learning about Cats Ser.). (Illus.). 48p. (J). (gr. 3-4). lib. bdg. 21.26 (978-0-7368-0897-2(3) , Capstone High-Interest Bks.) Capstone Pr., Inc.

—The Siamese Cat. 2000. (Learning about Cats Ser.). (Illus.). 48p. (J). (gr. 3-4). lib. bdg. 21.26 (978-0-7368-0567-4(2) , Capstone High-Interest Bks.) Capstone Pr., Inc.

—The Sphynx Cat. 2001. (Learning about Cats Ser.). (Illus.). 48p. (J). (gr. 3-4). lib. bdg. 21.26 (978-0-7368-0898-9(1) , Capstone High-Interest Bks.) Capstone Pr., Inc.

Meadows, Graham. Cats. Meadows, Graham, photos by. 1998. (Animals Are Not Like Us Ser.). (Illus.). 24p. (J). (ps up). lib. bdg. 21.26 (978-0-8368-2251-9(X)) Stevens, Gareth Inc.

Milbourne, Anna. Cats (Level 1) - Internet Referenced. 2006. 32p. (J). 4.99 (978-0-7945-1394-8(8) , Usborne) EDC Publishing.

Millard, Anne. Gatitos Juguetones/Playful Kittens. 2005. (Soft-to-touch Bks.). (ENG & SPA., Illus.). 16p. (J). bds. 4.99 (978-0-7566-1202-3(0)) Dorling Kindersley Publishing, Inc.

Miller, M. Cats. 2002. (Pets Ser.). (Illus.). 24p. (J). (gr. k-3). pap. 6.50 (978-1-57572-477-5(4) , 90466) Heinemann Library.

Montardre, Hélène. Little Cats. 2006. (Born to Be Wild Ser.). (Illus.). 24p. (J). lib. bdg. 22.00 (978-0-8368-6162-4(0)) Stevens, Gareth Inc.

Montardre, Helene. El pequeno Gato. 2005. (Quien eres tu? Ser.). 24p. (J). 7.95 (978-84-7864-234-2(X)) Combel Editorial, S.A. ESP. *Dist:* Independent Pubs. Group.

Morgan, Sally. Cats & Other Mammals. 2001. (Illus.). 32p. (J). lib. bdg. 24.25 (978-1-930643-43-7(8)) Chrysalis Education.

—From Kitten to Cat. 2002. (How Things Grow Ser.). (Illus.). 32p. (J). lib. bdg. (978-1-930643-87-1(X)) Chrysalis Education.

Morley, Christine & Orbell, Carole. Mon Chat. 2000. (Me & My Pet Ser.). (FRE., Illus.). 32p. (J). (gr. 2-5). pap. 4.95 (978-1-58728-140-2(6) , Two Can Publishing) T&N Children's Publishing.

Murphy, Chuck. Chuck Murphy's Black Cat, White Cat: A Pop-Up Book of Opposites. 2000. (Illus.). 12p. (J). (gr. k-3). per. (978-0-689-83507-0(8) , Simon & Schuster Children's Publishing) Simon & Schuster Children's Publishing.

Murray, Julie. American Curl Cats. 2005. (Animal Kingdom Set Ii Ser.). (Illus.). 24p. (J). (gr. k-4). lib. bdg. 21.35 (978-1-59197-301-0(5)) ABDO Publishing Co.

—Bombay Cats. 2003. (Checkerboard Animal Library). (Illus.). 24p. (J). (gr. k-6). lib. bdg. 21.35 (978-1-57765-862-7(0)) ABDO Publishing Co.

—Burmese Cats. 2003. (Checkerboard Animal Library). (Illus.). 24p. (J). (gr. k-6). lib. bdg. 21.35 (978-1-57765-865-8(5)) ABDO Publishing Co.

—Cornish Rex Cats. 2003. (Checkerboard Animal Library). (Illus.). 24p. (J). (gr. k-6). lib. bdg. 21.35 (978-1-57765-863-4(9)) ABDO Publishing Co.

—Korat Cats. 2003. (Checkerboard Animal Library). (Illus.). 24p. (J). (gr. k-6). lib. bdg. 21.35 (978-1-57765-864-1(7)) ABDO Publishing Co.

—Ocicat Cats. 2003. (Checkerboard Animal Library). (Illus.). 24p. (J). (gr. k-6). lib. bdg. 21.35 (978-1-57765-866-5(3)) ABDO Publishing Co.

—Persian Cats. 2005. (Animal Kingdom Set Ii Ser.). (Illus.). 24p. (J). (gr. k-4). lib. bdg. 21.35 (978-1-59197-330-0(9)) ABDO Publishing Co.

—Scottish Fold Cats. 2003. (Checkerboard Animal Library). (Illus.). 24p. (J). (gr. k-6). lib. bdg. 21.35 (978-1-57765-867-2(1)) ABDO Publishing Co.

—Siamese Cats. 2002. (Animal Kingdom Ser.). (Illus.). 24p. (J). (gr. k-4). lib. bdg. 21.35 (978-1-57765-644-9(X)) ABDO Publishing Co.

—Tabby Cats. 2002. (Animal Kingdom Ser.). (Illus.). 24p. (J). (gr. k-4). lib. bdg. 21.35 (978-1-57765-645-6(8)) ABDO Publishing Co.

Murray, Thelma & McClanahan Book Company Staff. Kittens. Solomon, Rosiland, illus. 1998. (Storyshapes Ser.). 24p. (J). pap. 2.25 (978-1-56293-908-3(4) , McClanahan Bk.) Learning Horizons, Inc.

Newbery, L. Azul, el Gato de Humo. (Raton de Biblioteca Coleccion). (SPA.). 80p. (J). (gr. 3). 7.95 (978-84-88061-73-7(0)) Serres, Ediciones, S. L. ESP. *Dist:* Lectorum Pubns., Inc.

Neye, Emily. All about Cats & Kittens. Hathon, Elizabeth, illus. 1999. (All Aboard Bks.). 32p. (J). (ps-3). pap. 3.99 (978-0-448-42082-0(1) , Grosset & Dunlap) Penguin Group (USA) Inc.

—All about Cats & Kittens. 1999. (gr. k-3). lib. bdg. 11.25 (978-0-613-21082-9(4)) Tandem Library Bks.

Nicholas, Christopher. Kittens. 2005. (Illus.). 22p. (J). (ps-ps). pap. 5.99 incl. audio compact disk (978-1-58610-933-2(2)) Learning Horizons, Inc.

Nye, Penny. My Cat. Eargle, Michelle, photos by. 1999. (Illus.). (J). (ps-5). pap. 12.00 (978-1-890703-16-5(8) , Bookmates) Penny Laine Papers, Inc.

Old Cat, New Cat: Level I, 6 vols. (Wonder Worldtm Ser.). 16p. 29.95 (978-0-7802-4591-4(1)) Wright Group, The.

Orbell, Carole. Cat. Morley, Christine, illus. rev. ed. 2004. (Me & My Pet Ser.). 32p. (J). (ps-1). pap. 4.95 (978-1-58728-200-3(3) , Two Can Publishing) T&N Children's Publishing.

Page, Gill. I Am Your Kitten. 2004. (gr. 3-6). lib. bdg. 14.10 (978-0-613-74928-2(6)) Tandem Library Bks.

Palika, Liz. What Your Cat Needs. 2000. (gr. 7-12). lib. bdg. 12.95 (978-0-613-33227-9(X)) Tandem Library Bks.

Parker, Steve. 10 Things You Should Know about Big Cats. Borton, Paula, ed. Jackson, Ian, illus. 2004. (10 Things You Should Know Ser.). 24p. (J). 6.99 (978-1-84236-119-1(8)) Miles Kelly Publishing, Ltd. GBR. *Dist:* Independent Pubs. Group.

Penner, Fred. The Cat Came Back. Reichert, Renée, illus. 2005. 32p. (J). (ps-2). 15.95 (978-1-59643-030-3(3)) Roaring Brook Pr.

Perkins, Wendy. Abyssinian Cats. 2008. (J). (***978-1-4296-1214-2(2)*** , Pebble Bks.) Capstone Pr., Inc.

—American Shorthair Cats. 2008. (J). (***978-1-4296-1215-9(0)*** , Pebble Bks.) Capstone Pr., Inc.

—Maine Coon Cats. 2008. (J). (***978-1-4296-1216-6(9))*** Capstone Pr., Inc.

—Manx Cats. 2008. (J). (***978-1-4296-1217-3(7))*** Capstone Pr., Inc.

—Persian Cats. 2008. (J). (***978-1-4296-1218-0(5)*** , Pebble Bks.) Capstone Pr., Inc.

—Siamese Cats. 2008. (J). (***978-1-4296-1219-7(3))*** Capstone Pr., Inc.

Petty, Kate. Cat. 2005. (Illus.). 24p. (J). (gr. 2-5). lib. bdg. 22.80 (978-1-59604-025-0(4)) Stargazer Bks.

Pfloog, Jan. The Kitten Book. Pfloog, Jan, illus. 1999. (Golden Super Shape Book Ser.). (Illus.). 24p. (J). (gr. k). pap. 3.29 (978-0-307-10079-5(0) , 10079, Golden Bks.) Random Hse. Children's Bks.

Phillips, Meredith. Cat Chat. 2004. (Pet's Point of View Ser.). 32p. (J). (gr. 4 up). lib. bdg. 22.60 (978-0-7565-0697-1(2)) Compass Point Bks.

Pickett, Robert & Pickett, Justine, illus. Cat. Pickett, Robert & Pickett, Justine, photos by. 2004. 32p. (J). lib. bdg. 27.10 (978-1-58340-431-7(7)) Smart Apple Media.

Pipe, Jim. Cats. 2007. (J). (***978-1-59604-164-6(1))*** Stargazer Bks.

Pollard, Michael. The Encyclopedia of the Cat. 2002. 384p. (YA). pap. 19.95 (978-0-7525-8275-7(5)) Parragon, Inc.

Pons, Matthew A. Thru the Eyes of a Cat. Spring, Grace J., illus. 1999. 26p. (gr. k-3). pap. 5.95 (978-0-9671807-0-0(8)) New Start Publishing, LLC.

Powell, Jillian. From Kitten to Cat. 2001. (How Do They Grow? Ser.). (Illus.). 32p. (J). lib. bdg. 25.69 (978-0-7398-4424-3(5)) Raintree.

Priddy, Roger. Baby Tales: Katy Cat. rev. ed. 2005. 8p. (J). 6.95 (978-0-312-49539-8(0) , Priddy Bks.) St. Martin's Pr.

—Kittens. 2005. 12p. (J). bds. 0.97 (978-0-312-49615-9(X) , Priddy Bks.) St. Martin's Pr.

Pugliano-Martin, Carol. Cats of the Serengeti. 2003. (Early Connections Ser.). (J). pap. 33.00 (978-1-4108-1068-7(2)) Benchmark Education Co.

Quasha, Jennifer. American Shorthair Cats: Everything about Purchase, Care, Nutrition, Health Care, Behavior & Showing. 2000. (Kids' Cat Library). 24p. (J). (gr. k-4). lib. bdg. 18.75 (978-0-8239-5513-8(3) , PowerKids Pr.) Rosen Publishing Group, Inc., The.

—Maine Coon Cats: Everything about Purchase, Care, Nutrition, Reproduction, Diseases & Behavior. 2000. (Kids' Cat Library). 24p. (J). (gr. k-4). lib. bdg. 18.75 (978-0-8239-5510-7(9) , PowerKids Pr.) Rosen Publishing Group, Inc., The.

—The Manx: The Cat with No Tail. 2000. (Kids' Cat Library). 24p. (J). (gr. k-4). lib. bdg. 18.75 (978-0-8239-5512-1(5) , PowerKids Pr.) Rosen Publishing Group, Inc., The.

—Persian Cats. 2000. (Kids' Cat Library). 24p. (J). (gr. k-4). lib. bdg. 18.75 (978-0-8239-5508-4(7) , PowerKids Pr.) Rosen Publishing Group, Inc., The.

—Siamese Cats. 2000. (Pets Throughout History Ser.). 24p. (J). (gr. k-4). lib. bdg. 18.75 (978-0-8239-5509-1(5) , PowerKids Pr.) Rosen Publishing Group, Inc., The.

Raintree Steck-Vaughn Staff. Gatos, Gatos y Mas Gatos. 1999. (Coleccion en Parejas). (J). pap., stu. ed. 21.50 (978-0-7398-0821-4(4)) Steck-Vaughn.

Rau, Dana Meachen. Guess Who Purrs. 2008. (J). (***978-0-7614-2972-2(7))*** Cavendish, Marshall Bks., Ltd.

—Top 10 Cats for Kids. 2008. (J). (***978-0-7660-3071-8(7))*** Enslow Pubs., Inc.

Rayner, Matthew & BVetMed MRCVS Staff. Cat. Burton, Jane & Greenaway, Frank, photos by. 2004. (I Am Your Pet Ser.). (Illus.). 32p. (J). (gr. 2 up). lib. bdg. 23.33 (978-0-8368-4102-2(6)) Stevens, Gareth Inc.

Repchuk, Caroline. Catopia: A Cat Compendium. Mortimer, Anne, illus. 2007. 32p. (J). (gr. 3-7). 19.99 (***978-0-06-124004-1(4)*** , Tegen, Katherine Bks) HarperCollins Pubs.

Richmond, Marianne R. Goodbye, Lovable Friend: Remembering Your Cat with Affection. 2005. (Illus.). 40p. (YA). 7.95 (978-0-9770000-0-5(1)) Marianne Richmond Studios, Inc.

Riley, Joelle. Pouncing Bobcats. 2002. (Pull Ahead Bks.). (Illus.). 32p. (J). lib. bdg. (978-0-8225-0686-7(6) , Lerner Pubns.) Lerner Publishing Group.

—Pouncing Bobcats. 2003. (gr. k-3). lib. bdg. 14.10 (978-0-613-52482-7(9)) Tandem Library Bks.

Ring, Susan. Caring for Your Cat. 2003. (gr. 3-6). lib. bdg. 16.40 (978-0-613-79819-8(8)) Tandem Library Bks.

—Caring for Your Cat. Kissock, Heather & Marshall, Diana, eds. 2003. (Caring for Your Pet Ser.). (Illus.). 32p. (J). pap. 7.95 (978-1-59036-062-0(1)) Weigl Pubs., Inc.

—Caring for Your Cat. 2002. (Caring for Your Pet Ser.). (Illus.). 32p. (J). lib. bdg. 16.95 (978-1-59036-032-3(X)) Weigl Pubs., Inc.

Robb, Jackie & Stringle, Berny. The Story of Cat. Duncan, Karen & Stringle, Sam, illus. 2004. (Bang on the Door Ser.). 32p. (YA). pap. (978-1-85602-314-6(1)) Chrysalis Children's Bks.

Roca, Nuria. Let's Take Care of Our New Cat. Curto, Rosa M., illus. 2006. (Let's Take Care of Bks.). 36p. (J). (ps-2). pap. 6.99 (978-0-7641-3452-4(3)) Barron's Educational Series, Inc.

Rockwell, Anne F. How Kittens Grow. Date not set. 40p. (J). (ps-1). pap. 15.99 (978-0-06-029103-7(6)); pap. 4.99 (978-0-06-445219-9(0)); lib. bdg. 16.89 (978-0-06-029104-4(4)) HarperCollins Pubs.

Roselin, Sadina. Luckylull. 2003. pap. 6.95 (978-0-533-13246-1(0)) Vantage Pr., Inc.

Ross, Veronica. Cat. 2002. (My First Ser.). (Illus.). 32p. (J). lib. bdg. 24.25 (978-1-930643-72-7(1)) Chrysalis Education.

Rowinski, Kate. Cats in the Dark. Bishop, Bonnie, illus. 1998. 32p. (J). (ps-3). 14.95 (978-0-89272-427-7(7)) Down East Bks.

Royston, Angela. The Kitten. 2001. (978-0-606-22325-6(8)) Tandem Library Bks.

—Kitten. 2004. (J). lib. bdg. 27.10 (978-1-59389-158-9(X)) Chrysalis Education.

Sanders, Cheryl L. Runaway Tigger. Aarvig, Cindy, illus. 2002. 44p. (J). (gr. k-4). pap. 9.95 (978-0-9723394-1-4(8)) Jollyville Pr.

Sanschagrin, Joceline. Caillou & Gilbert. rev. ed. 2006. (Abracadabra Ser.). (Illus.). 24p. (J). pap. 4.95 (***978-2-89450-596-0(5))*** Chouette Publishing CAN. *Dist:* Independent Pubs. Group.

Schaefer, Peggy. More Stories of Cats. 2005. (Illus.). 208p. 12.95 (978-0-8249-4638-8(3)) Ideals Pubns.

Schick-Jacobowitz, Jean & Schick-Pierce, Susan. You're My Friend Beclaws. gif. ed. 2006. (Illus.). 48p. 7.95 (978-1-4022-0739-6(5)) Sourcebooks, Inc.

Schuh, Mari C. Cats on the Farm. 2003. (On the Farm Ser.). (Illus.). 24p. (J). (gr. k-1). lib. bdg. 15.93 (978-0-7368-1660-1(7) , Pebble Bks.) Capstone Pr., Inc.

—Cats on the Farm. (On the Farm Ser.). 24p. (J). pap. 5.95 (978-0-7368-3422-3(2)) Capstone Pr., Inc.

Shores, Erika L. Caring for Your Cat. 2007. (First Facts Ser.). (Illus.). 24p. (J). (978-0-7368-6384-1(2)) Capstone Pr., Inc.

Silverstein, Alvin, et al. Curious Cats. 2003. (What a Pet! Ser.). (Illus.). 48p. (gr. 5-8). lib. bdg. 23.90 (978-0-7613-2512-3(3) , Millbrook Pr.) Lerner Publishing Group.

Simon, Seymour. Cats. Simon, Seymour, illus. (Illus.). (J). (ps-1). Date not set. 32p. pap. 6.99 (978-0-06-446254-9(4)); 2004. 40p. 16.99 (978-0-06-028940-9(6)); 2004. 40p. lib. bdg. 17.89 (978-0-06-028941-6(4)) HarperCollins Pubs.

Sovak, Jan. Learning about Wild Cats. 2003. (Dover Little Activity Bks.). (Illus.). 16p. (J). pap. 1.50 (978-0-486-42638-9(6)) Dover Pubns., Inc.

Spaht-Gill, Janie. Socks. Lambson, Elizabeth, illus. (J). 5.95 (978-0-89868-301-1(7)) ARO Publishing Co.

Spilsbury, Louise & Spilsbury, Richard. Cats. 2006. (Keeping Pets Ser.). (Illus.). 48p. (J). (978-1-4034-7698-2(5)) Heinemann Library.

Squire, Ann O. Bobcats. 2005. (True Bks.). (Illus.). (J). (gr. 3-5). 47p. pap. 6.95 (978-0-516-27931-2(9)); 48p. 25.00 (978-0-516-22791-7(2)) Scholastic Library Publishing. (Children's Pr.).

Standley, Andrew. My Old Cat. 2003. (Illus.). 8p. (J). (978-1-888223-48-4(0)) McMillen Publishing.

Starke, Katherine. Cats & Kittens. rev. ed. 2005. 32p. (J). (gr. 1 up). pap. 5.95 (978-0-7945-0798-5(0) , Usborne) EDC Publishing.

Starke, Katherine & Watt, Fiona. Cats & Kittens. Fox, Christyan, illus. Burton, Jane, photos by. 2006. 30p. (J). pap. (***978-0-439-78492-4(1))*** Scholastic, Inc.

Steck-Vaughn Staff. Early Reader Program Level A: Why Cats Hunt at Night, 6 Pack. 2004. (Illus.). pap. 30.00 (978-0-7398-8153-8(1)) Steck-Vaughn.

Stone, Lynn M. Abyssinian Cats. 1999. (Read All about Cats Ser.). (Illus.). 24p. (J). (gr. 1-4). lib. bdg. 25.64 (978-0-86593-557-0(2)) Rourke Publishing, LLC.

—Bengal Cats. 1999. (Read All about Cats Ser.). (Illus.). 24p. (J). (gr. 1-4). lib. bdg. 25.64 (978-0-86593-554-9(8)) Rourke Publishing, LLC.

—Persian Cats. 1999. (Read All about Cats Ser.). (Illus.). 24p. (J). (gr. 1-3). lib. bdg. 25.64 (978-0-86593-556-3(4)) Rourke Publishing, LLC.

—Ragdoll Cats. 1999. (Read All about Cats Ser.). (Illus.). 24p. (J). (gr. 1-4). lib. bdg. 25.64 (978-0-86593-552-5(1)) Rourke Publishing, LLC.

—Siamese Cats. 1999. (Illus.). 24p. (J). (gr. 1-4). lib. bdg. 25.64 (978-0-86593-555-6(6)) Rourke Publishing, LLC.

Stone, Lynn M., et al, contrib. by. Maine Coon Cats. 1999. (Read All about Cats Ser.). (Illus.). 24p. (J). (gr. 1-4). lib. bdg. 25.64 (978-0-86593-553-2(X)) Rourke Publishing, LLC.

Stonehouse, Bernard. Wild Cats. Camm, Martin, illus. (Animal Watch Ser.). 48p. (J). (gr. 4-9). 16.95 (978-0-8160-3925-8(9) , Checkmark Bks.) Facts On File, Inc.

Submarine Cat. (Buggy Buddies with Flaps Ser.). (Illus.). (YA). bds. 3.00 net. (978-1-56021-391-8(4)) W.J. Fantasy, Inc.

Summer, Paulette. I Am Lucky: The True Story of a Courageous & Inspiring Kitten Born with Disabling Disabilities. Nozik, Ira, photos by. 2000. 64p. (YA). (gr. 5 up). per. 9.95 (978-0-9627610-1-0(X)) Millennium Pubns.

Swanson, Diane. Wild Cats. 1998. (Welcome to the World of Animals Ser.). (Illus.). 32p. (J). (gr. 3 up). lib. bdg. 23.33 (978-0-8368-2217-5(X)) Stevens, Gareth Inc.

Tahta, S. Cats Sticker Book. 2007. 24p. (J). pap. 8.99 (***978-0-7945-1584-3(3)*** , Usborne) EDC Publishing.

Thomas, Peggy. Big Cat Conservation. 2000. (Science of Saving Animals Ser.: 8). (Illus.). 64p. (gr. 5-8). lib. bdg. 25.90 (978-0-7613-3231-2(6) , Twenty-First Century Bks.) Lerner Publishing Group.

C
D

Thomson, Ruth. Cat. 2007. (J). lib. bdg. (*978-1-4042-3710-0(0) , PowerKids Pr.) Rosen Publishing Group, Inc., The.

Tildes, Phyllis L. Calico's Cousins: Cats from Around the World. 1999. (Illus.). 32p. (J). (ps-3). 15.95 (978-0-88106-648-7(6)); pap. 6.95 (978-0-88106-649-4(4)) Charlesbridge Publishing, Inc.

Tildes, Phyllis Limbacher. Calico's Cousins: Cats from Around the World. Tildes, Phyllis Limbacher, illus. 1999. (Illus.). (J). (ps-ps). lib. bdg. 15.25 (978-0-613-16332-3(X)) Tandem Library Bks.

Top That Publishing Staff, ed. Kittens & Cats. 2005. (Illus.). 24p. (978-1-84510-538-9(9)) Top That! Publishing PLC.

Trumbauer, Lisa. The Life Cycle of a Cat. 2002. (Life Cycles Ser.). (Illus.). 24p. (J). (gr. k-1). lib. bdg. 15.93 (978-0-7368-1182-8(6) , Pebble Bks.) Capstone Pr., Inc.

Trumble, Kelly. Cat Mummies. Kubinyi, Laszlo, illus. 1999. 64p. (J). (gr. 4-6). pap. 7.95 (978-0-395-96891-8(7) , Clarion Bks.) Houghton Mifflin Co. Trade & Reference Div.

Tuxworth, Nicola. Kittens. (Illus.). (ps). 2005. 12p. bds. 6.99 (978-0-7548-1333-0(9) , Lorenz Bks.); 2001. 20p. 5.95 (978-0-7548-0942-5(0)) Anness Publishing GBR. *Dist:* National Bk. Network.

—Kittens. 1999. (Very First Picture Bks.). (Illus.). 12p. bds. 4.95 (978-0-7548-0067-5(9)) Anness Publishing, Inc.

—Kittens: A Very First Picture Book. 1999. (Pictures & Words Ser.). (Illus.). 24p. (J). (ps up). lib. bdg. 22.00 (978-0-8368-2273-1(0)) Stevens, Gareth Inc.

Twine, Alice. Kittens. 2008. (J). lib. bdg. (*978-1-4042-4144-2(2) , PowerKids Pr.) Rosen Publishing Group, Inc., The.

—Wild Cats. 2008. (J). lib. bdg. (*978-1-4042-3772-8(0) , PowerKids Pr.) Rosen Publishing Group, Inc., The.

Walker, Niki & Kalman, Bobbie. Los Gatitos. 2005. (SPA., Illus.). 32p. (J). (978-0-7787-8454-8(1)) Crabtree Publishing Co.

—Los Gatitos: Kittens. 2006. (SPA., Illus.). 32p. pap. (978-0-7787-8476-0(2)) Crabtree Publishing Co.

—Kittens. (Pet Care Ser.). (Illus.). 32p. (J). 2004. pap. (978-0-7787-1782-9(8)); 2003. (978-0-7787-1750-8(X)) Crabtree Publishing Co.

Walker, Sarah. Big Cats. Leonard, Sue, ed. 2002. (Eye Wonder Ser.). (Illus.). 48p. (gr. k-3). 9.99 (978-0-7894-8548-9(6)) Dorling Kindersley Publishing, Inc.

Washburn, Lucia, illus. Cats & Kittens. 1998. (Nature Sticker Stories Ser.). 16p. (J). (ps-3). mass mkt. 4.99 (978-0-448-41832-2(0) , Grosset & Dunlap) Penguin Group (USA) Inc.

Waters, Jo. The Wild Side of Pet Cats. 2004. (Raintree Perspectives Ser.). (Illus.). 32p. (J). 7.50 (978-1-4109-1157-5(8)); 25.70 (978-1-4109-1017-2(2)) Harcourt Schl. Pubs.

Watt, Fiona. Kittens. Wells, Rachel, illus. rev. ed. 2005. (Big Touchy Feely Board Books Ser.). 10p. (J). 11.95 (978-0-7945-0891-3(X) , Usborne) EDC Publishing.

Wexo, John Bonnett. Big Cats. 2001. (Zoobooks Ser.). (Illus.). 24p. (J). (gr. 1-6). 15.95 (978-1-888153-38-5(5)) Wildlife Education, Ltd.

Wildlife Education, Ltd. Staff. Big Cats. Meltzer, Davis et al, illus. 2001. (Zoobooks Ser.). 18p. (Orig.). (YA). (gr. 5 up). pap. 2.95 (978-0-937934-04-3(6)) Wildlife Education, Ltd.

Wildlife Education, Ltd. Staff, contrib. by. Cats, Set. 2002. (All about Animals Ser.). (Illus.). (J). (gr. k-6). 16.95 incl. VHS (978-1-888153-87-3(3)) Wildlife Education, Ltd.

Wildlife Education, Ltd. Staff & Wexo, John Bonnett. Little Cats. Orr, Richard & Stuart, Walter, illus. (Zoobooks Ser.). 2001. 24p. (J). 15.95 (978-0-937934-82-1(8)); 1998. 18p. (YA). (gr. 5 up). pap. 2.95 (978-0-937934-16-6(X)) Wildlife Education, Ltd.

Williams, Deborah. Cats. 2004. 12p. (Orig.). (J). (gr. k-3). pap. 4.25 (978-1-57874-081-9(9)) Kaeden Corp.

Wilsdon, Christina. Cats. 2007. (J). (*978-1-59939-128-1(7) , Reader's Digest Young Families, Inc.) Reader's Digest Children's Publishing, Inc.

Winters, Kari, told to. Princess Fiona: My Purrsonal Story. 2003. (YA). pap. 14.95 (978-0-9740980-0-5(0)) shelter-petsink.

World Book, Inc Staff, contrib. by. Siamese & Other Short-Haired Cats. 2007. (World Book's Animals of the World Ser.). (Illus.). 64p. (J). (978-0-7166-1335-0(2)) World Bk., Inc.

Zuffi, Stefano. The Cat in Art. 2007. 360p. 35.00 (*978-0-8109-9328-0(7)) Abrams, Harry N. , Inc.

CATS—FICTION

Aalborg, Gordon. Cat Tracks. l.t. ed. 2005. pap. 13.95 (978-0-9765185-0-1(3) , 800-431-1579) Delphi Bks.

Aardvark, D. Punkin's upside down Day. l.t. ed. 2004. (Illus.). 40p. (J). per. 10.95 (978-0-9755567-0-2(3)) Aardvark's Weedpatch Pr.

Abbott, Jan. Sundance & the Bully. 2002. pap. (978-0-9718565-7-8(5)) Playbooks, Inc.

Abley, Mark. Ghost Cat. Reczuch, Karen, illus. ed. 2004. (J). (gr. k-3). spiral bd. (978-0-616-11091-1(X)); spiral bd. (978-0-616-11092-8(8)) Canadian National Institute for the Blind/Institut National Canadien pour les Aveugles.

—Ghost Cat. Reczuch, Karen, illus. 2001. 32p. (J). (ps-k). 16.95 (978-0-88899-433-2(8)) Groundwood Bks. CAN. *Dist:* Perseus Distribution.

Abrams. Hello Kitty, Hello Christmas! Book & Ornament. 2004. 24p. (gr. 8-17). pap. 9.95 (978-0-8109-5042-9(1)) Abrams, Harry N. , Inc.

Adler, C. S. The No Place Cat. 2002. 160p. (YA). (gr. 5-9). 15.00 (978-0-618-09644-2(2) , Clarion Bks.) Houghton Mifflin Co. Trade & Reference Div.

Adler, David A. Young Cam Jansen & the Spotted Cat Mystery. (Young Cam Jansen Ser.). 32p. (J). (gr. k-3). 2007. 3.99 (*978-0-14-241012-7(8) , Puffin); 2006. (Illus.). 13.99 (978-0-670-06094-8(1) , Viking Juvenile) Penguin Group (USA) Inc.

The Adventures of Ricky Raccoon & Jodi the Cat. 2001. 28p. (J). 7.95 (978-0-9709408-0-3(7)) Pinetree Pubns.

Aigner-Clark, Julie. Cats. 2002. (Baby Einstein Ser.). (Illus.). 20p. (J). (ps-17). bds. 3.99 (978-0-7868-0840-3(3)) Hyperion Bks. for Children.

Aiken, Joan. El Gato Mog.Tr. of Necklace of Raindrops. (SPA.). 104p. (J). 5.95 (978-84-348-1275-8(4)) SM Ediciones ESP. *Dist:* AIMS International Bks., Inc.

Albee, Sarah. Hello, Cat, Hello, Dog. Leigh, Tom, illus. 2006. (Step-By-Step Readers Ser.). (J). pap. (978-1-59939-054-3(X) , Reader's Digest Young Families, Inc.) Reader's Digest Children's Publishing, Inc.

Alcantra, Ricardo. Dog & Cat. Gusti, illus. 1999. 32p. (gr. k-2). lib. bdg. 19.90 (978-0-7613-1420-2(2) , Millbrook Pr.) Lerner Publishing Group.

Aldrich, Thomas Bail. The Story of a Cat. 2006. (Illus.). pap. 19.95 (*978-1-4254-9049-2(2)) Kessinger Publishing, LLC.

Alexander, Heather. Allie Gator's Halloween Hayride. 2006. (Illus.). 24p. (J). pap. 3.95 (978-0-7624-2658-4(6)) Running Pr. Bk. Pubs.

Alexander, Lloyd. The Cat Who Wished to Be a Man. 2000. (Illus.). 128p. (J). (gr. 3-7). pap. 4.99 (978-0-14-130704-6(8) , Puffin) Penguin Group (USA) Inc.

—The Cat Who Wished to Be a Man. 107p. (J). pap. 3.99 (978-0-8072-1505-0(8) , Listening Library) Random Hse. Audio Publishing Group.

—The Cat Who Wished to Be a Man. 2002. (J). (gr. 3-6). 19.75 (978-0-8446-7203-8(3)) Smith, Peter Pub., Inc.

—The Cat Who Wished to Be a Man. 2000. (J). (ps-7). 107p. per. 13.00 (978-0-613-12359-4(X)); (Illus.). 11.64 (978-0-606-18393-2(0)) Tandem Library Bks.

—Dream-of-Jade: The Emperor's Cat. Burkett, D. Brent, illus. 2005. 48p. (J). 16.95 (978-0-8126-2736-7(9)) Cricket Bks.

—How the Cat Swallowed Thunder. Schachner, Judith B., illus. 2003. 40p. (J). (gr. k-4). pap. 6.99 (978-0-14-250003-3(8) , Puffin) Penguin Group (USA) Inc.

—How the Cat Swallowed Thunder. 2003. (gr. k-3). lib. bdg. 15.30 (978-0-613-61632-4(4)) Tandem Library Bks.

—Time Cat: The Remarkable Journeys of Jason & Gareth. Sokol, Bill, illus. rev. ed. 2003. 224p. (J). (gr. 3-7). 16.95 (978-0-8050-7270-9(5) , Holt, Henry & Co. Bks. For Young Readers) Holt, Henry & Co.

—Time Cat: The Remarkable Journeys of Jason & Gareth. 2004. (Illus.). 224p. (J). (gr. 3-3). pap. 6.99 (978-0-14-240107-1(2) , Puffin) Penguin Group (USA) Inc.

—Time Cat: The Remarkable Journeys of Jason & Gareth. l.t. ed. 2003. (Middle Reader Ser.). 255p. (J). 23.95 (978-0-7862-5892-5(6)) Thorndike Pr.

—The Town Cat & Other Tales. Kubinyi, Laszlo, illus. 1998. 128p. (J). (gr. 3-7). reprint ed. pap. 5.99 (978-0-14-130122-8(8) , Puffin) Penguin Group (USA) Inc.

Allen, J. J. Hello Kitty's Fun Friend Day! 2003. (Illus.). 32p. (J). pap. (978-0-439-44917-5(0)) Scholastic, Inc.

Allen, Judy. The Catnapping Cat. Giordano, Philip, illus. 2007. 32p. (J). pap. 9.99 (*978-0-340-90270-7(1)) Hodder General Publishing Division GBR. *Dist:* Independent Pubs. Group.

—Catnapping Cat The. Giordano, Philip, illus. 2007. 32p. (J). (*978-0-340-90269-1(8)) Hodder General Publishing Division.

Allyson, Libby. Scottie Rides the Bus. 2004. 27p. pap. 14.95 (978-1-4137-3298-6(4)) PublishAmerica, Inc.

Almond, David. Kate, the Cat & the Moon. Lambert, Steven, illus. 2005. 32p. (J). (ps-3). 15.95 (978-0-385-74691-5(1) , Doubleday Bks. for Young Readers) Random Hse. Children's Bks.

Alter, Anna. Francine's Day. Alter, Anna, illus. 2003. (Illus.). 32p. (J). lib. bdg. 16.89 (978-0-06-623937-8(0)) HarperCollins Pubs.

Alter, Robert M. & Alter, Jane. How Long till My Soul Gets It Right? 100 Doorways on the Journey to Happiness. 2001. 304p. pap. 14.00 (978-0-06-098749-7(9) , Regan-Books) HarperCollins Pubs.

Alumenda, Stephen. Toko & the Lost Kittens. 2004. (Illus.). 19p. 13.95 (978-9966-25-170-1(7)) Heinemann Kenya, Limited (East African Educational Publishers Ltd E.A.E.P.) KEN. *Dist:* Michigan State Univ. Pr.

Amedick, Deborah. A Cat Named Wellington: His Lessons for Christmas. 1998. (Animal Ser.). (Illus.). 36p. (J). (ps-1). pap. 4.95 (978-1-891210-79-2(3) , CNWXM1) Bartlett Publishing.

Amery, Heather & Cartwright, Stephen. Kitten's Day Out. 2004. (Farmyard Tales Ser.). (Illus.). 16p. (J). (ps). pap. 6.95 (978-0-7945-0065-8(X) , Usborne) EDC Publishing.

Anderson, Laurie Halse. Homeless, Vol. 2. 2007. (Vet Volunteers Ser.). 144p. (J). (gr. 3). pap. 6.99 (978-0-14-240863-6(8) , Puffin) Penguin Group (USA) Inc.

—Homeless. 2003. (Wild at Heart Ser.). (Illus.). 130p. (J). (gr. 4 up). lib. bdg. 23.33 (978-0-8368-3257-0(4)) Stevens, Gareth Inc.

—Homeless. 2000. (American Girl Wild at Heart Ser.: Bk. 2). (Illus.). 138p. (YA). (978-0-606-18359-8(0)) Tandem Library Bks.

—Storm Rescue. 2001. (American Girl Wild at Heart Ser.: Bk. 6). (Illus.). (YA). (978-0-606-21528-2(X)) Tandem Library Bks.

Anderson, Scoular. Stan the Dog & the Crafty Cats. 2006. (Read-It! Chapter Books). (J). 21.26 (978-1-4048-2739-4(0)) Picture Window Bks.

Andrea, Leona. El Club de Las Siete Gatas. 2004. Tr. of Seven Kittens Club. (SPA., Illus.). 176p. (978-84-95618-73-3(7) , Umbriel) Ediciones Urano S. A.

Angus & the Cat. 2004. (J). 24.95 incl. audio (978-0-89719-699-4(6)) Weston Woods Studios, Inc.

Anna, Jennifer. Tonight I Heard the Ghost Cat: A Different Kind of Guardian Angel. Dengate, Patrick, illus. 2000. 44p. (J). (ps-5). 10.99 (978-1-886383-56-2(1) , Little Blue Works) Windstorm Creative.

Anzalone, Karen. Time in a Bottle. 2003. 100p. (YA). pap. 9.00 (978-0-7599-3840-3(7)) Hard Shell Word Factory.

Appelt, Kathi. The Alley Cat's Meow. Goodell, Jon, illus. 2002. 32p. (J). (gr. k-2). 16.00 (978-0-15-201980-8(4)) Harcourt Children's Bks.

Araki, Mie. Kitten's Big Adventure. 2005. (Illus.). 40p. (J). 15.00 (978-0-15-216738-7(2)) Harcourt Trade Pubs.

Archambault, John. Boom Chicka Rock. Chitwood, Suzanne Tanner, illus. 2004. 36p. (J). (ps-2). 15.99 (978-0-399-23587-0(6) , Philomel) Penguin Group (USA) Inc.

Archambault, Lilith R. Cat in the Castle. 2007. 19p. pap. 7.95 (*978-0-533-15622-1(X)) Vantage Pr., Inc.

Archibald, Laura. The Cats of Grand Central. Beckett, Garner, illus. 2004. 30p. 16.95 (978-0-9730951-0-4(5)) Solomon's Signature CAN. *Dist:* Hushion Hse. Publishing, Ltd.

Archway Paperbacks Staff. Salem Goes to Rome. 1998. lib. bdg. 11.80 (978-0-613-73074-7(7)) Tandem Library Bks.

Arenson, Carole L. Boots, the Church Cat. Ledesma, Eric M., illus. 1998. 34p. (Orig.). (J). (ps-2). reprint ed. pap. 15.95 (978-1-929187-12-6(2) , CGBK63) Choristers Guild.

Argabright, Sheila. The Cadillac Cat. 2005. (Illus.). 20p. (J). per. 9.95 (978-1-59453-485-0(3) , Airleaf Publishing) Airleaf Publishing & Bookselling.

Aristocats. (Disney Read-Alongs Ser.). (J). 7.99 incl. audio (978-1-55723-022-5(6)) Walt Disney Home Video.

Arkle, Phyllis. Railway Cat. 2002. (Illus.). 96p. pap. 7.99 (978-0-340-72777-5(2) , Coronet) Hodder General Publishing Division GBR. *Dist:* Trafalgar Square Publishing.

—Railway Cat & the Ghost. (Illus.). 56p. (J). pap. 6.99 (978-0-340-69993-5(0) , Hodder & Stoughton) Hodder General Publishing Division GBR. *Dist:* Trafalgar Square Publishing.

Arlette, Joan. Maybe, Molly & Must-Be-Red. 1998. (Illus.). 8p. (J). (ps-5). mass mkt. 7.00 (978-0-9700121-0-4(1) , 001) Light Years Ahead.

Armstrong, Alan W. Whittington. 2006. (Illus.). 208p. (J). (gr. 3-7). pap. 6.50 (978-0-375-82865-2(6) , Yearling) Random Hse. Children's Bks.

—Whittington. Schindler, S. D., illus. 2005. 208p. (J). (gr. 3-7). 14.95 (978-0-375-82864-5(8)); lib. bdg. 16.99 (978-0-375-92864-2(2)) Random Hse. Children's Bks. (Random Hse. Bks. for Young Readers).

Arnold, Katya R., illus. & retold by. Me Too! Two Small Stories about Small Animals. Arnold, Katya R., retold by. 2000. 32p. (J). (gr. k-3). tchr. ed. 15.95 (978-0-8234-1483-3(3)) Holiday Hse., Inc.

Arrington, Aileen. Camp of the Angel. 2003. 154p. (YA). (gr. 5). 16.99 (978-0-399-23882-6(4) , Philomel) Penguin Group (USA) Inc.

Aryal, Aimee. Hello Wildcat! Cooper, Blair, illus. 2004. (J). 19.95 (978-1-932888-33-1(0)) Mascot Bks., Inc.

As Orange As Marmalade: Tan naranja como Mermelada. 2007. (ENG & SPA.). (J). per. 10.00 (*978-0-9749876-8-2(9)) Doggie In The Window Pubns.

Asare, Meshack. Cat in Search of a Friend. 1999. Tr. of Die Katze Sucht Sich Einen Freund. pap. (978-9988-550-18-9(9)) Sub-Saharan Pubs. & Traders.

—Chipo & the Bird on the Hill: A Tale of Ancient Zimbabwe. 2002. (Illus.). 35p. (J). (ps-7). pap. (978-9988-550-44-8(8)) Sub-Saharan Pubs. & Traders.

Asch, Frank. Here Comes the Cat! Vagin, Vladimir, illus. 2004. (Bookshelf Ser.). (J). pap. 5.99 (978-0-439-66942-9(1)) Scholastic, Inc.

—Monsieur Saguette & His Baguette. Asch, Frank, illus. 2006. (Illus.). 32p. 6.95 (978-1-55337-978-2(0)) Kids Can Pr., Ltd. CAN. *Dist:* Wybel Marketing Group.

Asch, Frank. Mrs. Marlowe's Mice. Asch, Devin, illus. 2007. 32p. (J). (gr. k-4). (*978-1-55453-022-9(9)) Kids Can Pr., Ltd.

Asch, Frank & Asch, Devin. Mr. Maxwell's Mouse. Asch, Frank & Asch, Devin, illus. 2005. (Illus.). 32p. (J). (gr. k-4). (978-1-55337-486-2(X)) Kids Can Pr., Ltd.

Ashcroft, Eagle. Nibs Goes to London. 2007. 104p. pap. 11.00 (*978-1-60047-075-2(0)) Wasteland Pr.

Atkinson, Sally. The Tales of Tango Bk. II: The Sticky Situation. Metzel, Lee, illus. 1998. 32p. (J). (gr. k-4). 14.95 (978-0-9653034-1-5(1)) Tango's Grove Publishing.

Auerbach, Annie. Most World Records. 2000. (gr. 3-6). lib. bdg. 11.80 (978-0-613-26278-1(6)) Tandem Library Bks.

Aunt Nina & Her Nephews & Nieces. 2004. (J). 24.95 incl. audio (978-1-56008-160-9(0)) Weston Woods Studios, Inc.

Averill, Esther. The Hotel Cat: A Jenny's Cat Club Book. Averill, Esther, illus. 2005. (New York Review Children's Collection Ser.). (Illus.). 180p. (J). 17.95 (978-1-59017-159-2(4) , NYR Children's Collection) New York Review of Bks., Inc., The.

—Jenny's Moonlight Adventure. 32p. (J). pap. 12.95 (978-0-553-15145-9(2)) Bantam Bks.

—Jenny's Moonlight Adventure. Averill, Esther, illus. 2005. (New York Review Children's Collection). (Illus.). 32p. (J). (ps-ps). pap. 12.95 (978-1-59017-160-8(8) , NYR Children's Collection) New York Review of Bks., Inc., The.

—The School for Cats: A Jenny's Cat Club Book. Averill, Esther, illus. 2005. (New York Review Children's Collection Ser.). 32p. (J). (ps-17). 12.95 (978-1-59017-173-8(X) , NYR Children's Collection) New York Review of Bks., Inc., The.

Averill, Esther H. Fire Cat. 2000. (I Can Read Bks.). (Illus.). (J). (ps-1). 6.93 (978-0-06-020195-1(9) , 076859) HarperCollins Pubs.

—The Fire Cat. Averill, Esther H., illus. 2002. (Illus.). (J). 12.34 (978-0-7587-6092-0(2)) Book Wholesalers, Inc.

—Jenny & the Cat Club: A Collection of Favorite Stories about Jenny Linsky. Averill, Esther H., illus. 2003. (New York Review Children's Collection Ser.). (Illus.). 176p. (J). pap. 16.95 (978-1-59017-047-2(4) , NYR Children's Collection) New York Review of Bks., Inc., The.

Averill, Esther Holden. Captains of the City Streets: A Jenny's Cat Club Book. 2005. (New York Review Children's Collection Ser.). (Illus.). 164p. (J). 17.95 (978-1-59017-174-5(8) , NYR Children's Collection) New York Review of Bks., Inc., The.

—Jenny Goes to Sea. Averill, Esther Holden, illus. 2005. (New York Review Children's Collection). (Illus.). 140p. (J). (ps-17). reprint ed. pap. 17.95 (978-1-59017-155-4(1) , NYR Children's Collection) New York Review of Bks., Inc., The.

—Jenny's Birthday Book. Averill, Esther Holden, illus. 2005. (New York Review Children's Collection). (Illus.). 44p. (J). (ps-ps). reprint ed. pap. 15.95 (978-1-59017-154-7(3) , NYR Children's Collection) New York Review of Bks., Inc., The.

Avi. Ragweed. Howard, E., ed. Floca, Brian, illus. 2000. (Tales from Dimwood Forest Ser.). 224p. (J). (gr. 3-7). pap. 5.99 (978-0-380-80167-1(1)) HarperCollins Pubs.

—Ragweed. Floca, Brian, illus. 1999. (Avon Camelot Bks.). 192p. (J). (gr. 3-7). 16.99 (978-0-380-97690-4(0)) HarperCollins Pubs.

—Ragweed. 2000. (978-0-606-18714-5(6)); (gr. 3-6). lib. bdg. 14.15 (978-0-613-26699-4(4)) Tandem Library Bks.

Ayme, Marcel. Los Cuentos Del Gato: Encaramado 1. 2003. (SPA.). 192p. 4.99 (978-968-16-7060-3(4)) Fondo de Cultura Economica USA.

Babbitt, Natalie. Elsie Times Eight. Babbitt, Natalie, illus. 2005. (Illus.). 26p. (J). (gr. k-4). reprint ed. 16.00 (978-0-7567-9640-2(7)) DIANE Publishing Co.

Babson, Marian. The Multiple Cat. 1999. mass mkt. (978-0-312-97041-3(2) , St. Martin's Paperbacks) St. Martin's Pr.

Bachelet, Gilles. My Cat, the Silliest Cat in the World. 2006. (Illus.). 24p. (J). (ps-3). 16.95 (978-0-8109-4913-3(X)) Abrams, Harry N. , Inc.

Bachelet, Gilles. When the Silliest Cat Was Small. Bachelet, Gilles, illus. 2007. (FRE & ENG., Illus.). 32p. (J). (ps-3). 16.95 (*978-0-8109-9415-7(1) , Abrams Bks. for Young Readers) Abrams, Harry N. , Inc.

Baglio, Ben M. Cat Crazy. 2000. (Animal Ark Pets Ser.: No. 13). (Illus.). 128p. (J). (gr. 2-5). pap. 3.99 (978-0-439-05170-5(3)) Scholastic, Inc.

—Cat in the Crypt. Baum, Ann, illus. 2002. (Animal Ark Hauntings Ser.: No. 2). 144p. (J). pap. 3.99 (978-0-439-34407-4(7)) Scholastic, Inc.

—Cats at the Campground. Baum, Ann, illus. 2004. (Animal Ark Hauntings Ser.: No. 32). 144p. (J). mass mkt. 3.99 (978-0-439-34393-0(3)) Scholastic, Inc.

—Kitten in the Candy Corn. 2006. (Animal Ark Hauntings Ser.). (Illus.). 144p. (J). pap. 3.99 (978-0-439-68758-4(6)) Scholastic, Inc.

—Kitten in the Cold. McNicholas, Shelagh, illus. 1999. (Animal Ark Ser.). 144p. (J). (gr. 3-5). pap. 3.99 (978-0-439-09698-0(7)) Scholastic, Inc.

—Kitten in the Cold. 1999. (gr. 3-6). lib. bdg. 11.80 (978-0-613-21870-2(1)) Tandem Library Bks.

—The Kitten That Won First Prize & Other Animal Stories. Gregory, Jenny, illus. 2000. (Animal Ark Special Ser.: No. 1). 160p. (J). (gr. 4-7). pap. 3.99 (978-0-439-09703-1(7)) Scholastic, Inc.

—Kittens in the Cold. McNicholas, Shelagh, illus. 1999. (Animal Ark Ser.). (J). (gr. 3-5). (978-0-606-19926-1(8)) Tandem Library Bks.

—Kittens in the Kitchen. McNicholas, Shelagh, illus. 1998. (Animal Ark Ser.: No. 1). 160p. (J). (gr. 3-5). pap. 3.99 (978-0-590-18749-7(X)) Scholastic, Inc.

—Kittens in the Kitchen. McNicholas, Shelagh, illus. 1998. (Animal Ark Ser.: No. 1). (J). (gr. 3-5). (978-0-606-13129-2(9)) Tandem Library Bks.

—Kitty in the Candy Hearts. 2007. (Illus.). 147p. (J). pap. (*978-0-439-87119-8(0)) Scholastic, Inc.

—Runaway Rascal. 2006. (Illus.). 157p. (J). (*978-0-439-79250-9(9)) Scholastic, Inc.

Baglio, Ben M. Tabby in the Tub. Gregory, Jenny, illus. 2003. (Animal Ark Ser.: Bk. 29). 144p. (J). 3.99 (978-0-439-34390-9(9) , Scholastic Paperbacks) Scholastic, Inc.

—Tabby in the Tub. 2002. (gr. 3-6). lib. bdg. 11.80 (978-0-613-63350-5(4)) Tandem Library Bks.

Bahous, Sally. Sitti & the Cats: A Tale of Friendship. Malick, Nancy, illus. 2001. 32p. (gr. 3-6). 13.95 (978-1-879373-61-7(0)) Rinehart, Roberts Pubs.

Baker, Barbara. Digby & Kate 1-2-3. Winborn, Marsha, illus. 2004. (Dutton Easy Reader Ser.). 48p. (J). (gr. 1-4). 14.99 (978-0-525-46854-7(4) , Dutton Juvenile) Penguin Group (USA) Inc.

—Digby & Kate & the Beautiful Day. Winborn, Marsha, illus. 2004. (Easy-to-Read Ser.). 48p. (J). (gr. 1-4). pap. 3.99 (978-0-14-240035-7(1) , Puffin) Penguin Group (USA) Inc.

—Digby & Kate & the Beautiful Day. 2004. (gr. k-3). lib. bdg. 11.80 (978-0-613-86706-1(8)) Tandem Library Bks.

BAKER, E. D. Story of kitten Cuckoo. 2007. 32p. 15.95 (*978-1-933572-04-8(3)) Centro Bks., LLC.

Baker, Leslie A. Paris Cat. Baker, Leslie A., illus. 1999. (Illus.). 32p. (J). (ps-3). 15.95 (978-0-316-07309-7(1)) Little Brown & Co.

Balcerek, Tom. The Cat & the Christmas Tree. 2006. (ENG.). 28p. per. 15.00 (*978-1-4259-7334-6(5)) AuthorHouse.

Balloon Books Staff, ed. Callie Cat Learns about Opposites. 2000. (Balloon Ser.). (Illus.). 12p. (J). (ps). bds. 4.95 (978-0-8069-2921-7(9)) Sterling Publishing Co., Inc.

—Small Cat, Smaller Cat. 2003. (Animal Bring-Along Bks.). (Illus.). 16p. (J). bds. 3.50 (978-0-8069-8066-9(4) , Balloon Bks.) Sterling Publishing Co., Inc.

Bampton, Bob. Animal Friends Little Kitten Board Book. 1999. 7.95 (978-1-58185-221-9(5)) Quadrillion Media LLC.

Banks, Kate. The Cat Who Walked Across France. Hallensleben, Georg, illus. 2004. 40p. (J). 16.00 (978-0-374-39968-9(9) , Farrar, Straus & Giroux (BYR)) Farrar, Straus & Giroux.

Banks, Steven. Catdog Undercover. 2000. (gr. 3-6). lib. bdg. 11.80 (978-0-613-21308-0(4)) Tandem Library Bks.

—Space Oddity. 2000. (gr. 3-6). lib. bdg. 11.80 (978-0-613-27021-2(5)) Tandem Library Bks.

Bannister, Bram. Rupert, the Alien & the Bank Robbery. 2007. 56p. per. 8.95 (*978-0-595-44839-5(9)) iUniverse, Inc.

Baraba, Joseph Frank. Dusty. 2006. 59p. pap. 12.95 (978-1-4241-2018-5(7)) PublishAmerica, Inc.

Barbaresi, Nina, illus. The Tale of Tom Kitten: A Story about Good Behavior. 2006. (J). 6.99 (978-1-59939-002-4(7)) Reader's Digest Young Families, Inc.

Barbey, Beatrice. Meow Said the Mouse. Ames, Philippe, illus. 2005. 40p. (J). 15.00 (978-1-888375-49-7(3)) Parallax Pr.

Barbo, Maria S. Hello Kitty, Ice-Skating Princess. 2005. 32p. (*978-0-439-68070-7(0)) Scholastic, Inc.

Barnes, Emma. The Thief of Bracken Farm. 2007. (J). lib. bdg. 16.95 (*978-1-59566-338-2(X)) QEB Publishing Inc.

Barnes, Peter W. & Barnes, Cheryl Shaw. Nat, Nat, the Nantucket Cat Goes to the Beach. Arciero, Susan, illus. 2001. 32p. 15.95 (978-1-893622-05-0(3) , VSP Bks.) Vacation Spot Publishing.

Barnes, Peter W. & Barnes, Cheryl Shaw. Where's Nat? A Nat, Nat, the Nantucket Cat Adventure Book. Arciero, Susan, illus. 2007. 32p. (J). 17.95 (*978-1-893622-19-7(3) , VSP Bks.) Vacation Spot Publishing.

Baronian, Jean-Baptiste. Figaro: The Cat Who Snored. Kinder, Martina, illus. 2004. 32p. (J). pap. 7.95 (978-1-929132-53-9(0)) Kane/Miller Bk. Pubs., Inc.

Barrick, Linda Richardson. Cat Tales. 2001. (Illus.). per. 9.95 (978-1-59094-005-1(9)) Jawbone Publishing Corp.

Barsy, Kalman. The Three Castaways. Perez-Moliere, Marnie, illus. 2004. (Orange Ser.). (SPA.). 40p. (J). (gr. 3-5). pap. 5.95 (978-1-57581-469-8(2)) Santillana USA Publishing Co., Inc.

Basore, Polly M. Santa's Stray. Williams, Carlene H., illus. 2004. 32p. (J). per. (978-0-9771749-2-8(1)) AngelBooks.

Bastet - Evaluation Guide: Evaluation Guide. 2006. (J). (978-1-55942-400-4(1)) Marsh Media.

Bastet - Teaching Guide. 2000. (J). 17.95 (978-1-55942-175-1(4)) Marsh Media.

Bauer, Marion Dane. Christmas in the Forest. Hearn, Diane Dawson, illus. (Holiday House Reader Ser.). 48p. (J). (gr. k-3). tchr. ed. 15.95 (978-0-8234-1371-3(3)) Holiday Hse., Inc.

Bauer, Steven. A Cat of a Different Color. Raglin, Tim, illus. 2001. 197p. (J). (ps-7). per. 11.15 (978-0-606-21103-1(9)) Tandem Library Bks.

Beames, Margaret. Night Cat. Hitchcock, Sue, illus. 2003. 40p. (J). (gr. k-2). pap. 15.95 (978-0-439-38576-3(8) , Orchard Bks.) Scholastic, Inc.

Beardsley, Martyn. Five Naughty Kittens. East, Jacqueline, illus. 2005. (Reading Corner Ser.). 24p. (J). (gr. k-3). lib. bdg. 22.80 (978-1-59771-006-0(7)) Sea-To-Sea Pubns.

Bechtold, Lisze. Edna's Tale. 2001. (Illus.). 32p. (J). (gr. k-3). tchr. ed. 15.00 (978-0-618-09164-5(5)) Houghton Mifflin Co. Trade & Reference Div.

Bednar, Martin. Sandy's Vision. 2006. (J). lib. bdg. 19.95 (*978-1-933732-15-2(6) , Bear Hug Bks.) MidAmerica Publishing Co.

Beechen, Adam. Cat's Meow. 2001. (gr. k-3). lib. bdg. 11.25 (978-0-613-43922-0(8)) Tandem Library Bks.

Behmer, Arlene M. The Moving Van: Oh, No, Not Again! 2003. (J). pap. 9.00 (978-0-8059-9280-9(4) , RoseDog Bks.) Dorrance Publishing Co., Inc.

Bell, Alia R. The Capers of Coco, a City Kitty. 2002. (Illus.). 28p. per. (978-1-931456-41-8(0)) Athena Pr.

Bell, Clare. Clan Ground. 2007. 272p. (YA). (gr. 7). pap. 7.99 (978-0-14-240812-4(3) , Puffin) Penguin Group (USA) Inc.

—Ratha & Thistle-Chaser: The Third Book of the Named. 2007. 272p. (YA). (gr. 7). 8.99 (*978-0-14-240944-2(8) , Puffin) Penguin Group (USA) Inc.

—Ratha's Challenge: The Fourth Book of the Named. 2007. 272p. (YA). (gr. 7). 8.99 (*978-0-14-240915-2(4) , Puffin) Penguin Group (USA) Inc.

—Ratha's Courage. 2007. 256p. (J). (gr. 7). 18.99 (*978-0-670-06170-9(0) , Viking Juvenile) Penguin Group (USA) Inc.

Bell, Clare. Ratha's Creature. 2007. 272p. (YA). (gr. 7). pap. 7.99 (978-0-14-240843-8(3) , Puffin) Penguin Group (USA) Inc.

Benator, Eileen B. A Ballet for Bobcat. Benator, Seth, illus. l.t. ed. 2005. 32p. (J). (ps-2). 15.95 (978-0-9748478-7-0(9)) Lion's Tale Press, L.L.C.

Bensen, Rosie. Fessie the Eddy School Cat. Reid, Abby, illus. 1999. iii, 24p. pap. 5.95 (978-0-9668325-0-1(7)) Bensen, Rosie.

Bentley, Dawn. Calico Kitties. Winston, Jeannie, illus. 1999. (Cuddly Cloth Book Ser.). 8p. (J). bds. 9.95 (978-1-58117-043-6(2) , Intervisual/Piggy Toes) Dalmatian Pr.

—Cat Nap: A Counting Book. Nagy, Krisztina, illus. 1999. 10p. (J). (ps-3). 9.95 (978-1-58117-033-7(5) , Intervisual/Piggy Toes) Dalmatian Pr.

Berenstain, Stan & Berenstain, Jan. The Berenstain Bears' New Kitten. Berenstain, Stan, illus. 2007. (I Can Read Bks.). 32p. (J). 15.99 (*978-0-06-058356-9(8)); pap. 3.99 (*978-0-06-058357-6(6) , Harper Trophy) HarperCollins Pubs.

Berg, Idabelle L. Adventures of a Cool Cat: More Journals of Blackie "Ice" Berg. Berg, Idabelle L., illus. 2001. (Illus.). 192p. (J). (gr. 6 up). 22.95 (978-0-9677583-4-3(3)) Quixote Pubns.

Bergeron, Joe. Cosmic Cat. 2005. 50p. pap. 14.99 (978-1-4116-6246-9(6)) Lulu.com.

Bergman, Tamar. Where Is? Modan, Rutu, illus. 2002. 24p. (J). (gr. k-3). tchr. ed. 15.00 (978-0-618-09539-1(X) , Walter Lorraine) Houghton Mifflin Co. Trade & Reference Div.

Bernstein, Margery. That Cat! Handelman, Dorothy, photos by. 1998. (Real Kids Readers Ser.). (Illus.). 32p. (gr. k-2). (J). pap. 4.99 (978-0-7613-2044-9(X)); lib. bdg. 18.90 (978-0-7613-2019-7(9)) Lerner Publishing Group. (Millbrook Pr.).

Berry, Lynne. The Curious Demise of a Contrary Cat. LaMarca, Luke, illus. 2006. 40p. (J). (ps-2). 12.95 (978-1-4169-0211-9(2)) Simon & Schuster Children's Publishing.

Berry, W. Douglas. Cat Tales. 2005. (Illus.). 112p. (YA). per. 10.99 (978-0-9766449-4-1(0)) Global Authors Pubns.

Bersson, Robert & Shoup, Dolores. Stripes & Stars. Bersson, Robert & Trobaugh, Scott, illus. l.t. ed. 2003. 40p. (J). (gr. 1-4). per. 16.95 (978-0-9740585-0-4(5)) Legacy Group Productions, LLC.

Beware of the Cat! 3-in-1 Package. (Sails Literacy Ser.). 24p. (gr. 1 up). 57.00 (978-0-7578-3204-8(0)) Rigby Education.

Beware of the Cat! 6 Small Books. (Sails Literacy Ser.). 24p. (gr. 1 up). 25.00 (978-0-7578-3180-5(X)) Rigby Education.

Beware of the Cat! Big Book Only. (Sails Literacy Ser.). 24p. (gr. 1 up). 27.00 (978-0-7635-5927-4(X)) Rigby Education.

Bilgrami, Shaheen. Cozy Kitten. Lake, Emma, illus. 2002. (Animal Snuggles Ser.). 8p. (J). bds. 7.95 (978-1-4027-0207-5(8)) Sterling Publishing Co., Inc.

Biller, Maxim & Hein, Sybille. Poppy's Biggest Wish. 2006. (Illus.). 32p. (ps). 17.99 (978-0-7475-8236-6(X) , Bloomsbury Children) Bloomsbury Publishing Plc GBR. *Dist:* Independent Pubs. Group.

Bingham, Deanne Lee. Andrew, Catch That Cat! 1999. (First Flight Ser.). (Illus.). 46p. (J). (978-1-55041-411-0(9)) Fitzhenry & Whiteside, Ltd.

Bingham, Deanne Lee & LaFave, Kim. Andrew, Catch That Cat! 1999. (First Flight Ser.). (Illus.). 46p. (J). pap. (978-1-55041-413-4(5)) Fitzhenry & Whiteside, Ltd.

Birdsall, Jeanne. The Penderwicks on Gardam Street. 2008. 320p. (J). (gr. 3-7). 15.99 (*978-0-375-84090-6(7) , Knopf Bks. for Young Readers) Random Hse. Children's Bks.

Bistricean, Karen. The Adventures of Fergus & Lady: Home Sweet Home. Bistricean, Claudius, illus. 2006. (J). (978-0-9786975-1-8(0)) Fergus & Lady Publishing.

—The Adventures of Fergus & Lady: The Beginning. Bistricean, Claudius, illus. 2006. (J). (978-0-9786975-0-1(2)) Fergus & Lady Publishing.

Black Cat Goes Away, 6 Pack. (Sails Literacy Ser.). (gr. 1-2). 36.00 (978-0-7578-4001-2(9)) Rigby Education.

Black Cat Stays Out, 6 vols., Pack. (Sails Literacy Ser.). (gr. 1-2). 36.00 (978-0-7578-6725-5(1)) Rigby Education.

Blackstone, Stella. Cleo & Caspar. Mockford, Caroline, illus. 24p. (J). (gr. k-2). 2002. bds. 6.99 (978-1-84148-973-5(5)); 2001. 14.99 (978-1-84148-440-2(7)) Barefoot Bks., Inc.

—Cleo in the Snow. Mockford, Caroline, illus. 2002. 24p. (J). (gr. k-2). 14.99 (978-1-84148-951-3(4)) Barefoot Bks., Inc.

—Cleo on the Move. Mockford, Caroline, illus. 2002. 24p. (J). (gr. k-2). 14.99 (978-1-84148-898-1(4)) Barefoot Bks., Inc.

—Cleo the Cat. Mockford, Caroline, illus. 24p. (J). (ps-2). 2001. bds. 6.99 (978-1-84148-427-3(X)); 2000. 14.99 (978-1-84148-259-0(5)) Barefoot Bks., Inc.

—Cleo's Alphabet Book. Mockford, Caroline, illus. 32p. (J). 2004. pap. 5.99 (978-1-84148-165-4(3)); 2003. 15.99 (978-1-84148-008-4(8)) Barefoot Bks., Inc.

—Cleo's Color Book. Mockford, Caroline, illus. 2006. 0032p. (J). 15.99 (978-1-905236-30-5(1)) Barefoot Bks., Inc.

—Come Here, Cleo! Mockford, Caroline, illus. 2001. 24p. (J). (ps-2). bds. 6.99 (978-1-84148-423-5(7)); 14.99 (978-1-84148-329-0(X)) Barefoot Bks., Inc.

—Where's the Cat? Harter, Debbie, illus. 2003. 24p. (J). (gr. k-2). bds. 6.99 (978-1-84148-607-9(8)) Barefoot Bks., Inc.

Blair, Eric. El Gato con Botas: Version del Cuento de los Hermanos Grimm. Ouren, Todd, illus. 2006. (Read-It! Readers en Espanol Ser.).Tr. of Puss in Boots: A Retelling of the Grimm's Fairy Tale. (SPA.). 32p. (J). (ps-3). 19.95 (978-1-4048-1635-0(6)) Picture Window Bks.

Blat, the Alley Cat: Early Level Satellite Individual Title Six-Packs. (Sails Literacy Ser.). 16p. (gr. 1-2). 27.00 (978-0-7578-3157-7(5)) Rigby Education.

Blissman, Rodger J. Spookster the Halloween Cat. 2004. 85p. (J). (gr. 3-7). pap. 5.99 (978-0-9745895-0-3(0)) Oxfordshire Publishing Co.

Blunt, Edna M. Margie the Cat. pap. 6.95 (978-0-681-02740-4(1)) Booklines Hawaii, Ltd.

Blyton, Enid. Birthday Kitten. (Illus.). (J). 95p. pap. 4.95 (978-0-09-924100-3(5)); 190p. pap. 5.95 (978-0-09-977930-8(7)) Random Hse. GBR. *Dist:* Trafalgar Square Publishing.

—Mr Pink-Whistle Interferes. (Illus.). 112p. (J). pap. 7.99 (978-0-7475-3859-2(X)) Bloomsbury Publishing Plc GBR. *Dist:* Trafalgar Square Publishing.

Boada, Francesc & Perrault, Charles. Puss in Boots: A Bilingual Book. Merino, Jose Luis, illus. tr. from CAT. Merino, Jose Luis, illus. 2004. Tr. of El Gato con Botas. (ENG & SPA.). 32p. (J). pap. 6.95 (978-0-8118-3924-2(9)) Chronicle Bks. LLC.

Boada, Francesc, et al. Puss in Boots: A Bilingual Book. 2004. Tr. of El Gato con Botas. (ENG & SPA., Illus.). 32p. (J). (gr. k-3). 14.95 (978-0-8118-3923-5(0)) Chronicle Bks. LLC.

Bolam, Emily, illus. Cat. 2003. (Chunky Pet Bks.). 14p. (J). bds. 5.99 (978-0-7641-5609-0(8)) Barron's Educational Series, Inc.

Boland, Janice. I Meowed. Mauterer, Erin Marie, illus. 2000. (Books for Young Learners). 12p. (J). pap. 5.00 (978-1-57274-252-9(6)) Owen, Richard C. Pubs., Inc.

Boldizsar, Anneliese. How to Make Friends. Boldizsar, Anneliese, illus. 2000. (Illus.). 59p. pap. (978-0-7541-0916-7(X)) Minerva Pr. GBR. *Dist:* Unity Distribution.

Bonnell, Kris. The Big Hungry Cat. 2006. (J). 3.95 (*978-1-933727-33-2(0)) Reading Reading Bks., LLC.

—Louis Is Hungry. 2005. (J). 3.75 (978-1-933727-09-7(8)) Reading Reading Bks., LLC.

—That Cat! 2005. (J). 3.75 (978-1-933727-17-2(9)) Reading Reading Bks., LLC.

—Where Can Louis Sleep? 2007. (J). 3.95 (*978-1-933727-57-8(8)) Reading Reading Bks., LLC.

—Where Is the Big Cat? 2007. (J). 3.95 (*978-1-933727-62-2(4)) Reading Reading Bks., LLC.

Booth, Crystal. Introducing Tucker. 2005. 49p. pap. 12.95 (978-1-4137-8934-8(X)) PublishAmerica, Inc.

Borlenghi, Patricia. Chaucer the Cat & the Animal Pilgrims. 2001. (Illus.). 77p. (J). pap. 16.99 (978-0-7475-4790-7(4)) Bloomsbury Publishing Plc GBR. *Dist:* Independent Pubs. Group.

Boss, Kittie. Rabos de Gato. Romo, Alberto, tr. Mauterer, Erin Marie, illus. 1999. (Books for Young Learners).Tr. of Cat Tails. (SPA.). 8p. (J). (gr. k-2). pap. 5.00 (978-1-57274-345-8(X) , A2893) Owen, Richard C. Pubs., Inc.

Bott, Elizabeth. Vinnie in Egypt. Frosini, Guido & Cecchetti, Alessandra, illus. l.t. ed. 2000. (Laugh & Learn Travel Ser.: No. 1). 54p. (J). (gr. k-8). 15.95 (978-0-9704678-0-5(X)) Pageturner Bks.

—Vinnie in France. Frosini, Guido & Cecchetti, Alessandra, illus. 2001. (Vinnie Ser.: Vol. 2). 54p. (YA). (gr. 5 up). 15.95 (978-0-9704678-1-2(8)) Pageturner Bks.

Bradford, Karleen. You Can't Rush a Cat. Watts, Leslie Elizabeth, illus. 2004. 32p. (J). (ps-2). 7.95 (978-1-55143-283-0(8)) Orca Bk. Pubs. USA.

—You Can't Rush a Cat. Watts, Leslie Elizabeth, tr. Watts, Leslie Elizabeth, illus. 2003. 32p. (J). (ps-2). 16.95 (978-1-55143-247-2(1)) Orca Bk. Pubs. USA.

Bradman, Tony. Flora the Fairy. 2005. (Green Bananas Ser.). (Illus.). 48p. (J). (ps). pap. (978-0-7787-1038-7(6)) Crabtree Publishing Co.

—A Goodnight Kind of Feeling. Scruton, Clive, illus. 1998. 32p. (J). (ps-k). tchr. ed. 15.95 (978-0-8234-1351-5(9)) Holiday Hse., Inc.

Brantley, Steven & Brantley, Judi S. The Throwaway Cat. Holt, Del, illus. 1998. 48p. (J). (ps-3). 16.95 (978-1-892570-00-0(9)) Spring Hse. Bks.

Brasch, R. Cat's Pyjamas. 1998. 304p. pap. 12.95 (978-0-207-18970-8(6)) HarperCollins Pubs. AUS. *Dist:* Consortium Bk. Sales & Distribution.

Braun, Lilian Jackson. The Cat Who Saw Stars. 2000. lib. bdg. 15.30 (978-0-613-21306-6(8)) Tandem Library Bks.

—The Cat Who Smelled a Rat. 2002. (gr. 5-8). lib. bdg. 15.30 (978-0-613-51533-7(1)) Tandem Library Bks.

Bresnan, Lynn. Vincent: The Magnificent Cat. 2005. 213p. pap. 19.95 (978-1-4137-7459-7(8)) PublishAmerica, Inc.

Brett, Jan. Annie & the Wild Animals. 2006. (Illus.). 17p. (J). (gr. k-3). bds. 7.95 (978-0-618-74786-3(9)) Houghton Mifflin Co. Trade & Reference Div.

—Comet's Nine Lives. Brett, Jan, illus. 2002. (Illus.). (J). 23.64 (978-0-7587-2268-3(0)) Book Wholesalers, Inc.

—Comet's Nine Lives. 2001. (Illus.). 32p. (J). (ps-3). pap. 6.99 (978-0-698-11894-2(4) , Putnam Juvenile) Penguin Group (USA) Inc.

—Comet's Nine Lives. 2001. (gr. k-3). lib. bdg. 15.30 (978-0-613-35918-4(6)); (Illus.). (J). 13.79 (978-0-606-21119-2(5)) Tandem Library Bks.

Brian, James. Catkid Book #4 Three's A Crowd. 2008. 96p. pap. 3.99 (*978-0-439-88857-8(3) , Scholastic Paperbacks) Scholastic, Inc.

Bridwell, Norman. The Cat & the Bird in the Hat. Bridwell, Norman, illus. 2000. (Hello Reader! Ser.). (Illus.). 32p. (J). (ps-3). pap. 3.99 (978-0-439-15433-8(2)) Scholastic, Inc.

—The Cat & the Bird in the Hat. 2000. (Hello Reader! Ser.). (Illus.). (J). (978-0-606-18531-8(3)) Tandem Library Bks.

Brighter Vision Publishing Staff. Mittens. 1999. (Stick'n Learn Stories Ser.). (Illus.). (J). (ps-1). pap. 2.50 (978-1-55254-070-1(7)) Brighter Vision Pubns.

Brimner, Larry Dane. Cat on Wheels. Peterson, Mary, illus. 2003. 32p. (J). (gr. k-2). 15.95 (978-1-56397-747-3(8)) Boyds Mills Pr.

—Cats! Payne, Tom, illus. 2001. (Rookie Reader Espanol Ser.). 24p. (J). (gr. k-2). pap. 4.95 (978-0-516-27075-3(3) , Children's Pr.) Scholastic Library Publishing.

—Cats! Payne, Tom, illus. 2001. 23p. (J). (ps-3). lib. bdg. 12.95 (978-0-613-54114-5(6)) Tandem Library Bks.

Brookes, Diane. The Story of Spot, the School Cat. Lewis, Stephen, illus. l.t. ed. 1999. 16p. (J). (ps-3). pap. (978-1-894303-02-6(4)) Raven Rock Publishing.

Brooks, Dawn Marie. Cat-Ice. 2004. 175p. pap. 13.95 (978-0-7414-2240-8(9)) Infinity Publishing.

Brooks, Felicity. The Missing Cat. 2000. (gr. k-3). lib. bdg. 14.10 (978-0-613-67567-3(3)) Tandem Library Bks.

Brooks, Felicity & Litchfield, Jo. The Missing Cat. 2004. (Easy Reading Ser.). (Illus.). 96p. (J). (ps-3). lib. bdg. 13.95 (978-1-58086-226-4(8)) EDC Publishing.

Brooks, Ron. Oscar y la Gata de Medianoche. 2nd ed. 2002. (Rosa y Manzana Ser.). (SPA.). 32p. (J). (978-84-89804-05-0(2)) Loguez Ediciones ESP. *Dist:* Lectorum Pubns., Inc.

Broome, Errol. Missing Mem. 2003. (gr. 3-6). lib. bdg. 13.00 (978-0-613-61801-4(7)) Tandem Library Bks.

Brown, Celease N. & Mubarak, Enoch. The Color Orange. 2004. (Illus.). 32p. (978-1-55306-742-9(8) , Guardian Bks.) Essence Publishing.

Brown, George MacKay. The Six Lives of Fankle the Cat. 2002. (Kelpies Ser.). (Illus.). 160p. pap. 10.00 (978-0-86315-403-4(4)) Floris Bks. GBR. *Dist:* SteinerBooks, Inc.

Brown, Marc. Buster Baxter, Cat Saver. ed. 2005. (Arthur Chapter Bks.: Bk. 19). (Illus.). 58p. (J). lib. bdg. 15.00 (978-1-59054-736-6(5)) Fitzgerald Bks.

Brown, Margaret Wise. The Color Kittens. Provensen, Alice & Provensen, Martin, illus. 2003. (Little Golden Book Classics). 24p. (J). (gr. k-k). 2.99 (978-0-307-02141-0(6) , Golden Bks.) Random Hse. Children's Bks.

—A Pussycat's Christmas. 2002. (Illus.). (J). 14.43 (978-0-7587-3470-9(0)) Book Wholesalers, Inc.

—A Pussycat's Christmas. Mortimer, Anne, illus. 1998. 32p. (J). (ps up). pap. 6.99 (978-0-06-443466-9(4) , Harper Trophy) HarperCollins Pubs.

—A Pussycat's Christmas. 1998. (ps-2). lib. bdg. 14.10 (978-0-613-81428-7(2)) Tandem Library Bks.

Brown, Ruth. A Dark, Dark Tale. Brown, Ruth, illus. 2002. (Illus.). (J). 14.04 (978-0-7587-2348-2(2)) Book Wholesalers, Inc.

Brown, Tricia. Groucho's Eyebrows. Lavallee, Barbara, tr. Lavallee, Barbara, illus. 2005. 32p. 15.95 (978-0-88240-556-8(X)) Graphic Arts Ctr. Publishing Co.

Browning, Dave. Marvin Measures Up. 2000. (Illus.). 12p. (J). (ps-3). pap. 6.95 (978-0-688-17734-8(4)) HarperCollins Pubs.

—Marvin Weighs In. 2000. (Illus.). 12p. (J). (ps-3). pap. 6.95 (978-0-688-17735-5(2) , Harper Festival) HarperCollins Pubs.

Bruel, Nick. Bad Kitty. Bruel, Nick, illus. 2005. (Illus.). 40p. (J). (ps-3). 15.95 (978-1-59643-069-3(9)) Roaring Brook Pr.

—Bad Kitty Cat-Nipped Edition. 2007. (Illus.). 40p. (J). 16.95 (*978-1-59643-299-4(3)) Roaring Brook Pr.

—Poor Puppy. 2007. (Illus.). 40p. (J). (ps up). 16.95 (*978-1-59643-270-3(5)) Roaring Brook Pr.

Bruzzone, Catherine. Lucy the Cat at the Farm: La Gatita Lucia en la Granja. Martin, Rosa Maria, tr. from ENG. Beaton, Clare, illus. 2005. (Bilingual Picture Strip Bks.). (SPA & ENG.). 24p. (J). pap. 4.95 (978-0-7641-3150-9(8)) Barron's Educational Series, Inc.

—Lucy the Cat in Town: La Gatita Lucia en la Cuidad. Martin, Rosa Maria, tr. Beaton, Clare, illus. 2005. (Bilingual Picture Strip Bks.). (SPA & ENG.). 24p. (J). pap. 4.95 (978-0-7641-3149-3(4)) Barron's Educational Series, Inc.

Bryan, Jennifer. The Different Dragon. Hosler, Danamarie, illus. 2006. (J). pap. 10.95 (978-0-9674468-6-8(4)) Two Lives Publishing.

Buck, Nola. Oh, Cats! Westcott, Nadine Bernard, illus. 1998. (Trophy I Can Read Bks.). 32p. (J). (ps up). pap. 3.99 (978-0-06-444240-4(3) , Harper Trophy) HarperCollins Pubs.

—Oh, Cats! 1998. (My First I Can Read Bks.). (J). (ps-k). (978-0-606-13005-9(5)) Tandem Library Bks.

Buhler, Cynthia von, illus. The Cat Who Wouldn't Come Inside: A True Story. 2006. 40p. (J). (ps-k). 16.00 (978-0-618-56314-2(8)) Houghton Mifflin Co.

Bunting, Eve. Hey Diddle Diddle, the Cat Plays the Fiddle. 2002. 24p. (J). (ps up). 9.95 (978-0-694-01434-7(6)) HarperCollins Pubs.

Bunting, Eve. Mouse Island. Catalano, Dominic, illus. 2008. (J). (*978-1-59078-447-1(2)) Boyds Mills Pr.

Burghardt, Frances. Pushie the Kitten-Cat. 2000. (J). pap. 8.00 (978-0-8059-4857-8(0)) Dorrance Publishing Co., Inc.

Burnford, Sheila. The Incredible Journey. unabr. ed. 2004. 145p. (J). (gr. 5-9). pap. 29.00 incl. audio (978-0-8072-8322-6(3) , YA162SP, Listening Library) Random Hse. Audio Publishing Group.

Burstein, Chaya M. Hanukkah Cat. Henn, Judy Hanks, illus. 2003. 32p. (J). (ps-3). pap. 6.95 (978-1-58013-029-5(1)) Kar-Ben Publishing.

Butler, John, illus. If You See a Kitten. 2003. 24p. (J). 13.95 (978-1-56145-108-1(8)) Peachtree Pubs., Ltd.

Butler, Philippa. Pawprints in Time. (Illus.). 32p. (J). pap. 9.95 (978-0-14-056240-8(0)) Penguin Bks., Ltd. GBR. *Dist:* Trafalgar Square Publishing.

Byrne. Mad Mags: Purr. (Illus.). 80p. (J). 7.95 (978-0-14-130042-9(5)) Penguin Bks., Ltd. GBR. *Dist:* Trafalgar Square Publishing.

Cabrera, Jane. Cat's Colors. Cabrera, Jane, illus. 2000. (Picture Puffin Ser.). (Illus.). 32p. (J). (ps-1). pap. 6.99 (978-0-14-056487-7(X) , Puffin) Penguin Group (USA) Inc.

—Cat's Colors. 2000. (gr. k-3). lib. bdg. 15.30 (978-0-613-28438-7(0)); (Illus.). (J). 13.79 (978-0-606-18835-7(5)) Tandem Library Bks.

—Kitty's Cuddles. Cabrera, Jane, illus. 2007. (Illus.). 26p. (J). (ps-k). 16.95 (*978-0-8234-2066-7(3)) Holiday Hse., Inc.

—Pram Race. 2004. (Popcorn & Banana Bob Ser.). 32p. 15.99 (*978-0-689-86058-4(7)) Simon & Schuster, Ltd. GBR. *Dist:* Independent Pubs. Group.

C D

Calhoun, Mary. Blue-Ribbon Henry. Ingraham, Erick, illus. 1999. 40p. (J). (gr. k-3). 16.00 (978-0-688-14674-0(0)) HarperCollins Pubs.

—Henry the Christmas Cat. Ingraham, Erick, illus. 2004. 32p. (J). (ps-3). 15.99 (978-0-688-16560-4(5)); lib. bdg. 16.89 (978-0-688-16561-1(3)) HarperCollins Pubs.

—Henry the Sailor Cat. 1998. 12.75 (978-0-606-13474-3(3)) Tandem Library Bks.

—High-Wire Henry. 2000. (YA). pap. 33.00 incl. audio (978-0-7887-4175-3(6) , 41090) Recorded Bks., LLC.

—Hot-Air Henry. unabr. ed. 2000. (YA). pap. 23.20 incl. audio (978-0-7887-3846-3(1) , 41044X4) Recorded Bks., LLC.

—The House of Thirty Cats. 2002. (Lost Treasures Ser.: No. 7). 288p. (gr. 3-7). pap. 4.99 (978-0-7868-1692-7(9)) Disney Pr.

—House of Thirty Cats. 2002. (gr. 3-6). lib. bdg. 13.00 (978-0-613-75027-1(6)) Tandem Library Bks.

Cameron, Kathleen. The Chicken Without a Coop. 2003. (Illus.). (J). 14.95 (978-1-882897-71-1(4)) Lost Coast Pr.

Campoy, F. Isabel, et al. Celebra Kwanzaa con Botitas y Sus Gatitos. Docampo, Valeria, illus. 2006. (J). (978-1-59820-123-9(9)) Santillana USA Publishing Co., Inc.

—Celebrate Kwanzaa with Boots & Her Kittens. Docampo, Valeria, illus. 2006. 31p. (J). (978-1-59820-135-2(2)) Santillana USA Publishing Co., Inc.

Canas, José. El Gato Que Quiso Volar Alto. (SPA.). 84p. (J). (gr. 3-5). 9.50 (978-84-241-3370-2(6)) Everest de Ediciones y Distribucion, S.L. ESP. *Dist:* Lectorum Pubns., Inc.

Canning, Sean. The Cat That Loves to Eat. Canning, Erin, ed. Canning, Sean, illus. 2005. (J). 9.95 (978-0-9773134-0-2(9)) SP Family Productions, LLC.

Capatti, Bérénice. Klimt & His Cat. Monaco, Octavia, illus. 2005. 40p. (J). 18.00 (978-0-8028-5282-3(3)) Eerdmans, William B. Publishing Co.

Capelli, Katie, et al. Molly, the Super Cat, in Chicago. 2000. (J). pap. 6.95 (978-0-533-13406-9(4)) Vantage Pr., Inc.

Caple, Kathy. Hillary to the Rescue. Caple, Kathy, illus. 2003. (Picture Bks.). (Illus.). 32p. (J). (ps-3). 15.95 (978-1-57505-420-9(5) , Carolrhoda Bks.) Lerner Publishing Group.

—Starring Hillary. Caple, Kathy, illus. 2003. (Picture Bks.). (Illus.). 28p. (J). (ps-3). 15.95 (978-1-57505-261-8(X) , Carolrhoda Bks.) Lerner Publishing Group.

Capucilli, Alyssa Satin. Biscuit Wants to Play. Schories, Pat, illus. 2001. (My First I Can Read Bks.). 32p. (J). (ps-k). 15.99 (978-0-06-028069-7(7)); lib. bdg. 15.89 (978-0-06-028070-3(0)) HarperCollins Pubs.

—Biscuit Wants to Play. 2002. (gr. k-3). lib. bdg. 11.80 (978-0-613-44508-5(2)) Tandem Library Bks.

—Little Spotted Cat. Andreasen, Dan, illus. 2005. 32p. (J). (ps-ps). 14.99 (978-0-8037-2692-5(9) , Dial) Penguin Group (USA) Inc.

—Mrs. McTats & Her Houseful of Cats. Rankin, Joan, illus. 32p. (J). 2004. 6.99 (978-0-689-86991-4(6) , Aladdin); 2001. 17.99 (978-0-689-83185-0(4) , McElderry, Margaret K.) Simon & Schuster Children's Publishing.

Carle, Eric. Have You Seen My Cat? Carle, Eric, illus. 2002. (Illus.). (J). 15.53 (978-0-7587-2706-0(2)) Book Wholesalers, Inc.

Carlow, Emma. Flora the Fairy. Carlow, Emma, illus. 2005. (Green Bananas Ser.). (Illus.). 48p. (J). (978-0-7787-1022-6(X)) Crabtree Publishing Co.

—Kitty Princess & the Newspaper Dress. Dickinson, Trevor, illus. 2003. 32p. (J). (ps-1). 16.99 (978-0-7636-2077-6(7)) Candlewick Pr.

Carman, Debby. I'm Maximum Cat That's a Fact. 2006. (J). (978-0-9777340-2-3(1)) Faux Paw Media Group.

—Kittywimpuss, Got Game. 2006. (J). (978-0-9777340-4-7(8)) Faux Paw Media Group.

—The Nutcracker Cats of the Kremlin. 2006. (J). (978-0-9777340-7-8(2)) Faux Paw Media Group.

—Purrlonia's Lullaby. 2006. (J). (978-0-9777340-1-6(3)) Faux Paw Media Group.

Carmody, Isobelle. Magic Night. Lee, Declan, illus. 2007. (Picture Book Ser.). 40p. (J). (ps-1). 16.99 (***978-0-375-83918-4(6)***); lib. bdg. 19.99 (***978-0-375-93918-1(0)***) Random Hse. Children's Bks. (Random Hse. Bks. for Young Readers).

Carpenter, Christopher, illus. Lilly's Heart: The Veterinary Clinic Cases Series. 2006. 32p. (J). per. 9.95 (978-0-9766641-0-9(0)) Ichabod Ink.

Carter, Noelle. Where Is the Rainbow? A Color Flap Book. Carter, Noelle, illus. 2004. (Illus.). 14p. (J). bds. 6.99 (978-0-689-86026-3(9) , Little Simon) Simon & Schuster Children's Publishing.

Cartwright, Stephen & Zeff, Claudia. Find the Kitten. 2000. (Kid Kits Ser.). (Illus.). 10p. (J). (ps). 10.95 (978-0-88110-802-6(2)) EDC Publishing.

Cassidy, Anne. Jasper & Jess. Hall, Francois, illus. 2004. (Read-It! Readers Ser.). 32p. (C). (gr. k-3). 18.60 (978-1-4048-0061-8(1)) Picture Window Bks.

Castelli, Jeanette. The cats on the Moon / Los gatos en la Luna. 2005. 48p. pap. (978-958-30-1767-4(1)) Panamericana Editorial.

Cat & Dog Talk: Individual Title Six-Packs. (Sails Literacy Ser.). (gr. 1-2). 36.00 (978-0-7578-4021-0(3)) Rigby Education.

Cat & Rat Fall Out: Individual Title Six-Pack Pouch - Level K. (Lighthouse Ser.). 16p. (gr. 2 up). 28.00 (978-0-7578-0870-8(0)) Rigby Education.

Cat Concert: Individual Title Six-Packs. (Literatura 2000 Ser.). (gr. 2-3). 33.00 (978-0-7635-0163-1(8)) Rigby Education.

The Cat-Flap Trap: Individual Title Six-Packs. (Story Steps Ser.). (gr. k-2). 32.00 (978-0-7635-9824-2(0)) Rigby Education.

Cat in the Hen House: KinderConcepts Individual Title Six-Packs. (Kinderstarters Ser.). 8p. (ps-1). 21.00 (978-0-7635-8728-4(1)) Rigby Education.

Cat on the Move. (Early Intervention Levels Ser.). 21.30 (978-0-7362-0364-7(8)) Hampton-Brown Bks.

Cat Stepped Out. 2002. 32p. 16.95 (978-1-930758-64-3(2) , Yeva Kids) Yeva Corp.

Catalanotto, Peter. Kitten Red, Yellow, Blue. Catalanotto, Peter, illus. 2005. (Illus.). 32p. (J). 15.95 (978-0-689-86562-6(7) , Atheneum/Richard Jackson Bks.) Simon & Schuster Children's Publishing.

Catch Me, Cat: Early Level Satellite Individual Title Six-Packs. (Sails Literacy Ser.). 16p. (gr. 1-2). 27.00 (978-0-7578-2907-9(4)) Rigby Education.

Cats & Other Stories: Individual Title Six-Pack. (Story Steps Ser.). (gr. k-2). 48.00 (978-0-7635-9848-8(8)) Rigby Education.

Cats, Cats & More Cats. 2008. (J). 14.95 (978-1-933872-30-8(6)) Lima Bear Pr LLC, The.

Cecil, Laura. Cunning Cat Stories. Clark, Emma Chichester, illus. 2003. 80p. (J). 24.00 (978-1-86205-376-2(6) , Pavilion Bks., Ltd.) Anova Bks. GBR. *Dist:* Trafalgar Square Publishing.

—Cunning Cat Tales. Clark, Emma Chichester, illus. 2006. 71p. (J). (gr. k-4). reprint ed. pap. 17.00 (978-1-4223-5013-3(4)) DIANE Publishing Co.

Charlie & the Kitten. 2006. (Charlie's Great Adventures: 5). (Illus.). 96p. (J). per. 5.95 (978-0-9702546-5-6(0)) GoodyGoody Bks.

Charlie Moves to Arizona Vol. 2: Charlie's Great Adventure. 2001. 88p. (J). per. 5.95 (978-0-9702546-9-6(5)) GoodyGoody Bks.

Charlie's Great Adventure: The Hilarious Tale of Life Through a Cat's Eyes. 2000. 112p. per. 6.95 (978-0-9702546-4-1(4)) GoodyGoody Bks.

Charlotte Latin School Staff. Ann & the Kitten. Sher, illus. 2001. 32p. (J). per. 4.95 (978-0-9707920-6-8(9)) Charlotte's Storybooks.

Le Chat Botte.Tr. of Puss in Boots. (FRE.). 48p. pap. 12.95 incl. audio compact disk (978-2-89558-062-1(6)) Coffragants CAN. *Dist:* Penton Overseas, Inc.

Le Chat Botte. 2000. Tr. of Puss in Boots. (FRE., Illus.). 32p. (J). 13.95 (978-2-09-202100-2(1)) Nathan, Fernand FRA. *Dist:* Distribooks, Inc.

Chato & the Party Animals. 2004. 29.95 incl. audio compact disk (978-1-55592-703-5(3)); 24.95 incl. audio (978-1-55592-693-9(2)); pap. 14.95 incl. audio (978-1-55592-687-8(8)) Weston Woods Studios, Inc.

Chato Y Su Cena. 2004. (J). pap. 32.75 incl. audio (978-1-55592-342-6(9)) Weston Woods Studios, Inc.

Chato's Kitchen. 2004. (J). 24.95 incl. audio (978-0-7882-0696-2(6)); pap. 18.95 incl. audio compact disk (978-1-55592-386-0(0)); pap. 18.95 incl. audio compact disk (978-1-55592-389-1(5)); pap. 38.75 incl. audio compact disk (978-1-55592-388-4(7)); pap. 38.75 incl. audio compact disk (978-1-55592-390-7(9)); pap. 32.75 incl. audio (978-1-55592-202-3(3)); pap. 32.75 incl. audio (978-1-55592-203-0(1)); (SPA.). pap. 14.95 incl. audio (978-0-7882-0134-9(4)); pap. 14.95 incl. audio (978-0-7882-0697-9(4)) Weston Woods Studios, Inc.

Chausse, Sylvie. Trent-Six Chats de Marie. 2000. Tr. of Marie T's 36 Cats. (FRE.). (J). 19.95 (978-2-86726-897-7(4)) Editions Milan FRA. *Dist:* AIMS International Bks., Inc.

Cherrington, Janelle. Tale of Two Catdogs. 2000. (gr. 3-6). lib. bdg. 11.80 (978-0-613-27166-0(1)) Tandem Library Bks.

Chichester-Clark, Emma, illus. Cunning Cat Tales. 2004. 80p. (J). pap. 12.50 (978-1-84365-023-2(1)) Chrysalis Children's Bks. GBR. *Dist:* Trafalgar Square Publishing.

Child, Lauren. Que Lata de Rata. 2002. (Illus.). (J). (SPA.). 32p. 17.95 (978-84-8488-058-5(3)); (CAT & SPA., 26p. (978-84-8488-059-2(1)) Serres, Ediciones, S. L. ESP. *Dist:* Lectorum Pubns., Inc.

Childers, Leta N. The Window to Summer. 1999. (J). 6.50 incl. audio (978-1-58495-024-0(2)) DiskUs Publishing.

Chin, Oliver Clyde. Harriet's Hairballs. Crawford, Gregory, tr. Crawford, Gregory, illus. 2003. 32p. (J). 15.95 (978-1-58394-078-5(2) , Frog Ltd.) North Atlantic Bks.

Choukas, Nita & Tyler, Gillian. Bayberry & Beau. 2006. (Illus.). 112p. (J). 15.95 (978-1-933392-35-6(5)) Chelsea Green Publishing.

Christensen, Nancy. Good Night, Little Kitten. 2004. (My First Reader Ser.). (Illus.). 29p. (J). (gr. k-1). pap. 3.95 (978-0-516-24628-4(3) , Children's Pr.) Scholastic Library Publishing.

—Good Night, Little Kitten. Hockerman, Dennis, illus. 2003. (My First Reader Ser.). 32p. (J). 18.50 (978-0-516-22926-3(5) , Children's Pr.) Scholastic Library Publishing.

Christian, Cheryl. Where's the Kitten? (Korean) Dwight, Laura, photos by. 2004. (KOR., Illus.). 12p. (J). bds. 5.50 (978-1-932065-78-7(4)) Star Bright Bks., Inc.

—Where's the Kitten? (Simplified Chinese) Dwight, Laura, photos by. 2004. (CHI., Illus.). 12p. (J). bds. 5.50 (978-1-932065-66-4(0)) Star Bright Bks., Inc.

—Where's the Kitten? (Traditional Chinese) Dwight, Laura, photos by. 2004. (CHI., Illus.). 12p. (J). bds. 5.50 (978-1-932065-60-2(1)) Star Bright Bks., Inc.

—Where's the Kitten? (Vietnamese) Dwight, Laura, photos by. 2004. (VIE., Illus.). 12p. (J). bds. 5.50 (978-1-932065-72-5(5)) Star Bright Bks., Inc.

—Where's the Kitten?/¿Donde esta el Bebé? Bilingual Edition. Dwight, Laura, photos by. 2004. (SPA & ENG., Illus.). 12p. (J). bds. 5.50 (978-1-932065-54-1(7) , 718-784-9112) Star Bright Bks., Inc.

—Where's the Kitten?/Kote Ti Chat la Ye? Dwight, Laura, photos by. 2005. (CRP., Illus.). 12p. (J). (ps). per. 5.50 (978-1-59572-028-3(6)) Star Bright Bks., Inc.

Christian, Mary Blount. If Not for the Calico Cat. Serra, Sebastia, illus. 2007. 32p. (J). 16.99 (978-0-525-47779-2(9) , Dutton Juvenile) Penguin Group (USA) Inc.

Christmas Comes to Silver Lake. 2000. 10p. (J). pap. 5.95 (978-0-9706322-0-3(7)) Silver Lake Mill.

Chronicle Books LLC Staff. Hide-and-Seek Big Trucks & Diggers! 2008. 8p. (J). bds. 6.99 (978-0-8118-5203-6(2)) Chronicle Bks. LLC.

Cizmich, Marilyne. Sonia, the Church Cat. 2007. (Illus.). 28p. (J). per. 9.99 (***978-1-60247-096-5(0)***) Tate Publishing & Enterprises, L.L.C.

Clairmont, Patsy. Tails from the Pantry: Soccer. 2005. (Tails from the Pantry Ser.). (Illus.). 32p. (J). 9.99 (978-1-4003-0562-9(4)) Nelson, Thomas Inc.

Clairmont, Patsy. 5 Cheesy Stories: About Friendship, Bravery, Bullying, & More. 2007. (Tails from the Pantry Ser.). 144p. (J). 14.99 (***978-1-4003-1042-5(3)***) Nelson, Thomas Inc.

Clanchy, Kate. Our Cat Henry Comes to the Swings. Bird, Jemima, illus. 2007. 32p. (J). (ps-1). 16.00 (***978-1-56148-563-5(2)***) Good Bks.

—Our Cat Henry Comes to the Swings. (Illus.). 32p. (978-0-19-279122-1(2)) Oxford Univ. Pr., Inc.

Clanchy, Kate & Bird, Jemima. Our Cat Henry Comes to the Swings. (Illus.). 32p. (978-0-19-272557-8(2)) Oxford Univ. Pr., Inc.

Clark Jordan Sarah. Bossqueen Little Bigbark & Sentinel Pup. 2006. 144p. (J). 5.95 (978-1-58246-170-0(8) , Tricycle Pr.) Ten Speed Pr.

Clark, Patricia Nikolina. In the Shadow of the Mammoth. LeTourneau, Anthony Alex, illus. 2005. (J). 14.99 (978-0-9674602-8-4(X)) Blue Marlin Pubns.

Clark, Seneca & Giardi, Sandy. The Yellowest Yellow Lab. Decedue, Julie, illus. 2005. 32p. (J). 10.95 (978-0-9767276-2-0(5)) Three Bean Pr.

Clarke, Gus. Nervous Norris. 2002. (Illus.). 64p. (J). pap. (978-1-84270-049-5(9)) Andersen.

—Scratch N' Sniff. 1998. (Illus.). 27p. (J). pap. 9.95 (978-0-86264-810-7(6)) Andersen GBR. *Dist:* Trafalgar Square Publishing.

Clements, Andrew. Temple Cat. 2001. (J). (978-0-606-21484-1(4)); lib. bdg. 14.10 (978-0-613-35581-0(4)) Tandem Library Bks.

Clements, Andrew & Beier, Ellen. Ringo Saves the Day! A True Story. 2002. (Pets to the Rescue Ser.). 32p. (J). pap. 3.99 (978-0-689-83439-4(X) , Aladdin) Simon & Schuster Children's Publishing.

Clineff, Jeff. Too Many Kitties. Movshina, Marina, illus. 2007. 22p. (J). E-Book 9.95 incl. cd-rom (***978-1-933090-45-0(6)***) Guardian Angel Publishing, Inc.

Clineff, Jeff. Too Many Kitties. Movshina, Marina, illus. 2007. (ESK.). 24p. (J). 9.95 (978-1-933090-10-8(3)) Guardian Angel Publishing, Inc.

Coakley, Lena & Watts, Leslie Elizabeth. On the Night of the Comet. 2004. (Illus.). 32p. (J). (ps-2). 16.95 (978-1-55143-287-8(0) , 1234126) Orca Bk. Pubs. USA.

Coatsworth, Elizabeth. The Cat Who Went to Heaven. Ward, Lynd, illus. 2002. (J). 13.40 (978-0-7587-0177-0(2)) Book Wholesalers, Inc.

—Cat Who Went to Heaven. Craig, Daniel & Vitale, Raoul, illus. 2008. 96p. (J). pap. 4.99 (***978-1-4169-4973-2(9)*** , Aladdin) Simon & Schuster Children's Publishing.

Coatsworth, Elizabeth. Gata Que Se Fue Para el Cielo. (SPA.). (YA). 8.95 (978-958-04-1530-5(7) , NR4853) Norma S.A. COL. *Dist:* AIMS International Bks., Inc., Distribuidora Norma, Inc., Lectorum Pubns., Inc.

Cocca-Leffler, Maryann. Calling All Cats: All Aboard Picture Reader. 2004. (All Aboard Books Ser.). (Illus.). 32p. (J). (ps-1). mass mkt. 3.99 (978-0-448-43369-1(9) , Grosset & Dunlap) Penguin Group (USA) Inc.

Coffey, Maria. A Cat Adrift. Fernandes, Eugenie, illus. 2002. (Teelo's Adventures Ser.). 32p. (J). (gr. 1-2). pap. 6.95 (978-1-55037-726-2(4)); lib. bdg. 18.95 (978-1-55037-727-9(2)) Annick Pr., Ltd. CAN. *Dist:* Firefly Bks., Ltd.

—Cat Adrift. 2002. (gr. k-3). lib. bdg. 15.25 (978-0-613-63025-2(4)) Tandem Library Bks.

—A Seal in the Family. Fernandes, Eugenie, illus. 1999. 32p. (J). (ps-2). lib. bdg. 17.95 (978-1-55037-581-7(4)) Annick Pr., Ltd. CAN. *Dist:* Firefly Bks., Ltd.

Cole, Kathryn. Pawluk. 2004. 48p. pap. 12.95 (978-1-4137-5477-3(5)) PublishAmerica, Inc.

Collins, Tom. Perfect Bone. 1999. (gr. 3-6). lib. bdg. 11.80 (978-0-613-22168-9(0)) Tandem Library Bks.

Colors All Day. (J). 26.20 (978-0-8136-8399-7(8)); 59.50 (978-0-8136-7918-1(4)); 1998. pap. (978-0-8136-8292-1(4)) Modern Curriculum Pr.

Come & Play Cat. 2000. (J). (978-1-58453-126-5(6)) Pioneer Valley Educational Pr., Inc.

Coniglio, John. The Cat Who Slept All Day: What Happens While the Cat Sleeps. Key, Pamela, illus. 2006. 24p. (J). per. 2.99 (978-1-59958-004-3(7)) Journey Stone Creations, LLC.

Connors, Jerrold. Now, Louie! Connors, Jerrold, illus. 2006. (Illus.). 40p. (J). 12.99 (978-0-9721416-1-1(8)) Alligator Boogaloo.

Cooper, Clare. Cat of Morfa. 1998. 128p. (J). (gr. 4-12). pap. 14.95 (978-0-8464-4907-2(2)) Beekman Bks., Inc.

—One Day on Morfa. 2001. 112p. pap. 12.95 (978-1-85902-946-6(9)) Beekman Bks., Inc.

Cooper, Elisha. Magic Thinks Big. Cooper, Elisha, illus. 2004. (Illus.). 32p. (J). (ps up). 14.99 (978-0-06-058164-0(6)); lib. bdg. 15.89 (978-0-06-058165-7(4)) HarperCollins Pubs.

Cooper, Helen. Delicious! A Pumpkin Soup Story. 2007. (Illus.). 32p. (J). (ps-3). 16.00 (***978-0-374-31756-0(9)*** , Farrar, Straus & Giroux (BYR)) Farrar, Straus & Giroux.

—A Pipkin of Pepper. 2005. (Illus.). 32p. (J). (ps-ps). 16.00 (978-0-374-35953-9(9)) Farrar, Straus & Giroux.

—Pumpkin Soup. Cooper, Helen, illus. 1999. (Illus.). 32p. (J). (ps-3). 16.00 (978-0-374-36164-8(9) , Farrar, Straus & Giroux (BYR)) Farrar, Straus & Giroux.

Cooper, Ilene. Lucy on the Loose. Harvey, Amanda, illus. 2000. (Road to Reading Ser.). 80p. (J). (gr. 2-5). pap. 3.99 (978-0-307-26508-1(0) , Golden Bks.) Random Hse. Children's Bks.

—Lucy on the Loose. 2000. (J). (978-0-606-18929-3(7)) Tandem Library Bks.

Cope-Robinson, Lyn. Cat Tails. Cope-Robinson, Lyn, illus. l.t. ed. 2003. (Illus.). 32p. (J). lib. bdg. (978-1-887774-14-7(9) , Wynden) Canmore Pr.

Copeland, Walter. The Black Cat Book. Robinson, Charles, illus. 2002. 48p. (J). (ps-3). pap. 8.00 (978-1-883211-61-5(1) , Green Tiger Pr.) Laughing Elephant.

Coplans, Peta. Cat & Dog. 2000. (Illus.). (J). pap. (978-0-14-056140-1(4) , Puffin) Penguin Group (USA) Inc.

Coppel, Chris. Far from Burden Dell. 2005. 286p. (J). pap. 4.95 (978-0-9746481-6-3(7)) Brown Barn Bks.

Copycats. 2001. (ps-2). lib. bdg. 9.80 (978-0-613-32425-0(0)) Tandem Library Bks.

Corder, Zizou. Lionboy. (Lionboy Trilogy : Bk. 1). (Illus.). (gr. 3-6). 2003. 288p. (J). 15.99 (978-0-8037-2982-7(0) , Dial); 2004. 304p. (YA). reprint ed. pap. 7.99 (978-0-14-240226-9(5) , Puffin) Penguin Group (USA) Inc.

—Lionboy: The Chase. 2005. (Lionboy Trilogy : Bk. 2). (Illus.). 288p. (J). (gr. 3-7). pap. 6.99 (978-0-14-240454-6(3) , Puffin) Penguin Group (USA) Inc.

—Lionboy: The Chase. Van Deelen, Fred, illus. 2004. (Lionboy Trilogy Ser.: Bk. 2). 272p. (J). (gr. 5). 15.99 (978-0-8037-2984-1(7) , Dial) Penguin Group (USA) Inc.

—Truth. 2006. (Lionboy Trilogy : Bk. 3). 240p. (J). (gr. 3). pap. 6.99 (978-0-14-240705-9(4) , Puffin) Penguin Group (USA) Inc.

Cosgrove, Stephen. Catundra. James, Robin, illus. ed. 2001. (Serendipity Bks.). 32p. (J). pap. 4.99 (978-0-8431-7684-1(9) , Price Stern Sloan) Penguin Group (USA) Inc.

—Catundra. 2001. (gr. k-3). lib. bdg. 13.00 (978-0-613-88240-8(7)) Tandem Library Bks.

Cosy Cat. 2005. (J). bds. 6.99 (978-0-9753127-5-9(8)) Family Bks. at Home.

County Studio Staff. Katie: The Mischievous Kitten. 16p. (J). bds. (978-0-7554-1095-8(5)) Grandreams Bks., Inc.

Cousineau-Peiffer, Trisha. Have You Ever Heard of a Rainbow Farm. Everett-Hawkes, Bonnie, illus. 2006. 32p. (J). 12.95 (***978-0-9792084-1-6(6)***) Dream Ridge Pr.

—Have You Ever Heard of a Rainbow Farm: The Missing Color Kittens. Everett-Hawkes, Bonnie, illus. 2007. 48p. (J). per. 15.95 (***978-0-9792084-2-3(4)***) Dream Ridge Pr.

Cox, Judy. Cool Cat, School Cat. Sims, Blanche, illus. 2002. 96p. (J). (gr. 4-6). tchr. ed. 15.95 (978-0-8234-1714-8(X)) Holiday Hse., Inc.

Cox, Judy. One Is a Feast for Mouse. Ebbeler, Jeffrey, illus. 2008. (J). (***978-0-8234-1977-7(0)***) Holiday Hse., Inc.

Cox, Phil Roxbee. Fat Cat on A Mat. Cartwright, Stephen, illus. rev. ed. 2006. 16p. (J). pap. 6.99 (978-0-7945-1502-7(9) , Usborne) EDC Publishing.

Cox, Phil Roxbee & Cartwright, S. Fat Cat on a Mat. 2004. (Phonics Board Bks.). 10p. (J). 4.95 (978-0-7945-0059-7(5) , Usborne) EDC Publishing.

—Ted's Shed, Toad Makes a Road, Fat Cat on a Mat & Sam Sheep Can't Sleep. 2004. (Easy Words to Read Ser.). (Illus.). 16p. (J). (gr. 1 up). pap. 9.95 (978-0-7945-0245-4(8) , Usborne) EDC Publishing.

Coxon, Michele. The Cat Who Found His Way Home. 2005. (Illus.). 32p. (J). (ps-ps). pap. (978-1-903285-21-3(6)) Happy Cat Bks.

—The Cat Who Found His Way Home. 2000. (Illus.). 32p. (ps-1). 13.95 (978-1-899248-88-9(9)) Happy Cat Bks. GBR. *Dist:* Star Bright Bks., Inc.

—The Cat Who Lost His Purr. 2000. (Illus.). 32p. (J). (ps up). pap. 14.95 (978-1-899248-98-8(6)) Happy Cat Bks. GBR. *Dist:* Star Bright Bks., Inc.

—Catch up, Little Cheetah: A Lift-the-Flap Book. 2000. (Illus.). 32p. (J). (ps). 13.95 (978-1-899248-23-0(4)) Happy Cat Bks. GBR. *Dist:* Star Bright Bks., Inc.

—Catch up, Little Cheetah: A Lift-the-Flap Book. Coxon, Michele, illus. 1999. (Illus.). 20p. (J). (ps-k). pap. 5.95 (978-1-887734-63-9(5)) Star Bright Bks., Inc.

—Le Has Dado de Comer Al Gato?/Have You Fed the Cat? Coxon, Michele, illus. 2004. (SPA & ENG., Illus.). 40p. (J). 15.95 (978-1-59572-001-6(4)); pap. 5.95 (978-1-59572-002-3(2)) Star Bright Bks., Inc.

—Have You Fed the Cat? Coxon, Michele, illus. 2004. (Illus.). 40p. (J). 15.95 (978-1-932065-90-9(3)) Star Bright Bks., Inc.

—Have You Fed the Cat? 2004. (Illus.). 40p. (J). pap. 5.95 (978-1-932065-91-6(1)) Star Bright Bks., Inc.

—Kitten Finds a Home. 2002. (Illus.). 16p. (J). 13.95 (978-1-903285-23-7(2)); pap. 5.95 (978-1-903285-22-0(4)) Happy Cat Bks. GBR. *Dist:* Star Bright Bks., Inc.

—Kitten's Adventure. 2000. (Illus.). 32p. (J). (ps-3). 13.95 (978-1-899248-01-8(3)) Happy Cat Bks. GBR. *Dist:* Star Bright Bks., Inc.

—Kitten's Adventure. Coxon, Michele, illus. 1998. (Happy Cat Bks.). (Illus.). 32p. (J). (ps-k). bds. 5.50 (978-1-887734-38-7(4)) Star Bright Bks., Inc.

Coxon, Michèle. Kitten's Adventure / As Aventuras do Gatinho (bilingual) Coxon, Michèle, illus. 2006. (POR, SPA & ENG., Illus.). 32p. (J). pap. 6.00 (978-1-59572-047-4(2)) Star Bright Bks., Inc.

—Kitten's Adventure / Las aventuras del Gatito. Coxon, Michèle, illus. 2006. (SPA., Illus.). 32p. (J). pap. (978-1-59572-048-1(0)) Star Bright Bks., Inc.

Coxon, Michele. Where's My Kitten? (Illus.). 16p. (J). pap. 5.95 (978-1-903285-02-2(X)) Happy Cat Bks. GBR. *Dist:* Star Bright Bks., Inc.

Crabb, June Kesslar. Spooky: The Little Mischief Maker. 2007. 30p. pap. 7.95 (***978-0-533-15612-2(2)***) Vantage Pr., Inc.

Crackers. abr. ed. 2002. (J). (gr. k-3). 26.90 incl. audio (978-0-8045-6886-9(3)) Spoken Arts, Inc.

Crawford, Gregory, illus. Mr. Meow Visits the Shelter. 2007. 32p. pap. (978-1-58394-120-1(7) , Frog Ltd.) North Atlantic Bks.

Crebbin, June. A Cat for Tom. 2005. (Cambridge Storybooks Ser.). 32p. pap. 7.00 (978-0-521-67471-3(9)) Cambridge Univ. Pr.

Cregar, Elyse. Feline Online: What Happens When a Smart Cat Surfs the Internet? 2001. 149p. (J). (gr. 2-7). pap. 8.95 (978-0-9621292-1-6(6)) Tamerac Publishing Co.

Crimi, Carolyn. Tessa's Tip-Tapping Toes. Carrington, Marsha Gray, illus. 2002. 32p. (J). (ps-2). pap. 16.95 (978-0-439-31768-9(1) , Orchard Bks.) Scholastic, Inc.

Croteau-Fleury, Marie-Danielle. Fred's Midnight Prowler. Cummins, Sarah, tr. from FRE. St. Aubin, Bruno, illus. 2000. (First Novels Ser.). 64p. (gr. 1-5). 4.95 (978-0-88780-522-6(1)) Formac Publishing Co., Ltd. CAN. *Dist:* Casemate Pubs. & Bk. Distributors, LLC.

Croteau-Fleury, Marie-Danielle & St. Aubin, Bruno. Le Chat de Mes Reves. 2001. (FRE., Illus.). 64p. (J). pap. (978-2-89021-503-0(2)) Diffusion du livre Mirabel.

Croteau-Fleury, Marie-Danielle, et al. Fred's Midnight Prowler. Cummins, Sarah, tr. from FRE. Derome, Pierre-Andre & St. Aubin, Bruno, illus. 2000. (First Novels Ser.). 64p. (J). (gr. 1-5). (978-0-88780-523-3(X)) Formac Publishing Co., Ltd. CAN. *Dist:* Casemate Pubs. & Bk. Distributors, LLC.

Croteau, Marie-Danielle. Fred & the Mysterious Letter. Cummins, Sarah, tr. from FRE. St-Aubin, Bruno, illus. 2005. (First Novel Ser.). 64p. (J). (gr. 2-5). (***978-0-88780-689-6(9));*** 4.95 (978-0-88780-688-9(0)) Formac Publishing Co., Ltd. CAN. *Dist:* Casemate Pubs. & Bk. Distributors, LLC.

—Fred's Midnight Prowler. 2001. (gr. k-3). lib. bdg. 11.80 (978-0-613-87995-8(3)) Tandem Library Bks.

—Mon Chat Est un Oiseau de Nuit. St. Aubin, Bruno, illus. 2001. (Premier Roman — Special Editions Ser.). (FRE.). 64p. (J). (gr. 1-4). pap. (978-2-89021-505-4(9)) Diffusion du livre Mirabel.

Crotty, Martha. Hong Kong Kitty. Thurn, Gwen & Thurn, David Ryan, illus. 2005. (J). per. 14.00 (978-0-9766017-0-8(2)) Ironcreek Pr.

Cuddly Kittens First Number Fun. 2002. (J). bds. 4.98 (978-0-7525-8864-3(8)) Parragon, Inc.

Cummings. Ferdinand: The Bottle-Headed Cat. 2004. 124p. per. 11.95 (978-1-59453-280-1(X) , 2093) Airleaf Publishing & Bookselling.

Curry, Peter. Millie at Home. 2004. (First Words with Millie Ser.). (Illus.). 12p. (J). bds. 3.99 (978-1-85854-508-0(0)) Brimax Books Ltd. GBR. *Dist:* Byeway Bks.

—Millie Goes Driving. 2004. (First Words with Millie Ser.). (Illus.). 12p. (J). bds. 3.99 (978-1-85854-506-6(4)) Brimax Books Ltd. GBR. *Dist:* Byeway Bks.

—Millie Goes Shopping. 2004. (First Words with Millie Ser.). (Illus.). 12p. (J). bds. 3.99 (978-1-85854-505-9(6)) Brimax Books Ltd. GBR. *Dist:* Byeway Bks.

—Millie in the Garden. 2004. (First Words with Millie Ser.). (Illus.). 12p. (J). bds. 3.99 (978-1-85854-507-3(2)) Brimax Books Ltd. GBR. *Dist:* Byeway Bks.

Cushman, Doug. A Pirate Cat's Dream. Date not set. (J). (978-0-8050-6603-6(9) , Holt, Henry & Co. Bks. For Young Readers) Holt, Henry & Co.

—Space Cat. Cushman, Doug, illus. (I Can Read Bks.). (Illus.). 32p. (J). 2006. pap. 3.99 (978-0-06-008967-2(9) , Harper Trophy); 2004. 15.99 (978-0-06-008965-8(2)); 2004. lib. bdg. 16.89 (978-0-06-008966-5(0)) HarperCollins Pubs.

Cutchin, Marcia, illus. Feathers: A Jewish Tale from Eastern Europe. 2005. 32p. (gr. 2-5). 16.95 (978-0-87483-755-1(3) , 1249133) August Hse. Pubs., Inc.

Czernecki, Stefan. If You Give a Cat a Cupcake. Date not set. 32p. (J). (ps-2). 15.99 (978-0-06-026683-7(X)) HarperCollins Pubs.

Dahl, Michael. Frog Pajama Party. Schultz, Sara, illus. 2005. (Read-It! Readers Ser.). 32p. (J). (ps). lib. bdg. 18.60 (978-1-4048-1170-6(2)) Picture Window Bks.

Dahlstrom, Halene. Raven Cove Mystery: A Rennie of Alaska Mystery. 2005. 12.95 (978-1-59433-001-8(8)) Publication Consultants.

Daines, McKay. The Cats of Storm Mountain. Daines, Cameron, illus. 2003. 294p. (YA). 28.95 (978-0-9749467-1-9(0)); pap. 17.99 (978-0-9749467-0-2(2)) Shine Publishing Hse.

Dale, Jenny. Bob the Bouncy Kitten. Hellard, Susan, illus. 2000. (Kitten Friends Ser.: Vol. 2). (J). 10.79 (978-0-606-19718-2(4)) Tandem Library Bks.

—Felix the Fluffy Kitten. 2000. (gr. 3-6). lib. bdg. 11.80 (978-0-613-31184-7(1)) Tandem Library Bks.

—Leo the Lucky Kitten, No. 5. 2001. (Illus.). (J). (978-0-606-20755-3(4)) Tandem Library Bks.

—Nell the Naughty Kitten, No. 4. 2001. (Kitten Friends Ser.). (Illus.). (J). (978-0-606-20754-6(6)) Tandem Library Bks.

—Star the Snowy Kitten. Hellard, Susan, illus. 2000. (Kitten Friends Ser.: Vol. 3). (J). (978-0-606-19719-9(2)) Tandem Library Bks.

Dalmatian Press Staff. Three Little Kittens: Best Loved Stories Collection. 2004. (Illus.). 160p. (J). 5.99 (978-1-4037-0750-5(2)) Dalmatian Pr.

—Winifred Witch & Her Very Own Cat. 2002. (Illus.). 24p. (J). (gr. k-5). pap. 2.99 (978-1-57759-363-8(4)) Dalmatian Pr.

—Winifried Witch & Her Very Own Cat. 2005. (Illus.). 12p. (J). bds. 4.99 (978-1-4037-1494-7(0)) Dalmatian Pr.

Dalton, Pamela. The Millionaire Cat. Heeger, Marilyn, illus. 2004. 96p. (J). 20.00 (978-0-7188-2853-0(4)) Lutherworth Pr., The GBR. *Dist:* Parkwest Pubns., Inc.

Daniels, Lucy. Kitten Crowd. Howard, Paul, illus. 1999. (Animal Ark Pets Ser.: No. 2). 128p. (J). (gr. 3-6). pap. 3.99 (978-0-439-05159-0(2)) Scholastic, Inc.

Dann, Colin. Copycat. 1999. 165p. mass mkt. 8.95 (978-0-09-921212-6(9)) Random Hse. GBR. *Dist:* Trafalgar Square Publishing.

Danziger, Paula. The Cat Ate My Gymsuit. 1998. (J). 12.64 (978-0-606-13091-2(8)) Tandem Library Bks.

—The Cat Ate My Gymsuit. l.t. ed. 2005. 174p. pap. 10.95 (978-0-7862-7267-9(8) , Large Print Pr.) Thorndike Pr.

A Dark, Dark Tale. 2004. (J). pap. 18.95 incl. audio compact disk (978-1-55592-804-9(8)); pap. 38.75 incl. audio compact disk (978-1-55592-821-6(8)); pap. 32.75 incl. audio (978-1-55592-192-7(2)) Weston Woods Studios, Inc.

Daugherty, George. Acrobat Cats. Schields, Gretchen, illus. 2002. (Sagwa, the Chinese Siamese Cat Ser.: No. 1). 32p. (J). (ps-3). pap. 3.99 (978-0-439-42873-6(4)) Scholastic, Inc.

Davies, Nicola. Stories from Abergelli Street. 2002. (Illus.). 48p. pap. 11.95 (978-1-84323-075-5(5)) Beekman Bks., Inc.

Davis, Anne. Bud & Gabby. Davis, Anne, illus. 2006. (Illus.). 32p. (J). 15.99 (978-0-06-075350-4(1)); lib. bdg. 16.89 (978-0-06-075351-1(X)) HarperCollins Pubs.

Davis, David. Jazz Cats. Galey, Chuck, illus. 2001. 32p. (J). (gr. 2-4). pap. 15.95 (978-1-56554-859-6(0)) Pelican Publishing Co., Inc.

Davis, Jim. Fat Cat, No.1. 2003. (J). (gr. 5-8). lib. bdg. 24.55 (978-0-613-68581-8(4)) Tandem Library Bks.

—Garfield: Sticht Zu. Goetting, Waltraud & Bartoszko, Alexandra, trs. from ENG. (Garfield Ser.: Vol. 10). (GER., Illus.). 128p. (J). pap. 10.95 (978-3-8105-0754-9(7)) Kruger, Wolfgang Verlag, GmbH DEU. *Dist:* Distribooks, Inc., International Bk. Import Service, Inc.

—Garfield au Kilo. 2000. (Garfield Ser.: No. 1). Tr. of Garfield by the Pound. (FRE.). (J). 7.95 (978-2-922148-00-8(9)) Presses aventure/Adventure Pr. CAN. *Dist:* AIMS International Bks., Inc.

—Garfield Beefs Up: His 37th Book. 2000. (gr. 5-8). lib. bdg. 19.90 (978-0-613-68578-8(4)) Tandem Library Bks.

—Garfield Benimmt sich Daneben. Goetting, Waltraud & Bartoszko, Alexandra, trs. from ENG. (GER., Illus.). 128p. (J). pap. (978-3-8105-0890-4(X)) Kruger, Wolfgang Verlag, GmbH DEU. *Dist:* International Bk. Import Service, Inc.

—Garfield Bigger Than Life. 2002. (Illus.). 96p. (gr. 5-8). per. 18.75 (978-0-613-68579-5(2)) Tandem Library Bks.

—Garfield Blast sich Auf. Goetting, Waltraud & Bartoszko, Alexandra, trs. from ENG. (Garfield Ser.: Vol. 20). (GER., Illus.). 128p. (J). pap. (978-3-8105-0884-3(5)) Kruger, Wolfgang Verlag, GmbH DEU. *Dist:* International Bk. Import Service, Inc.

—Garfield Bleibt sich Treu. Goetting, Waltraud & Bartoszko, Alexandra, trs. from ENG. (Garfield Ser.: Vol.19). (GER., Illus.). 128p. (J). pap. (978-3-8105-0880-5(2)) Kruger, Wolfgang Verlag, GmbH DEU. *Dist:* International Bk. Import Service, Inc.

—Garfield Casse la Croute. 2000. (Garfield Ser.: No. 6). Tr. of Garfield Dishes It Out. (FRE.). (J). 7.95 (978-2-922148-05-3(X)) Presses aventure/Adventure Pr. CAN. *Dist:* AIMS International Bks., Inc.

—Garfield Chef de File. 2000. (Garfield Ser.: No. 4). Tr. of Garfield Hits the Big Time. (FRE.). (J). 7.95 (978-2-922148-03-9(3)) Presses aventure/Adventure Pr. CAN. *Dist:* AIMS International Bks., Inc.

—Garfield Dreht Durch. Goetting, Waltraud & Bartoszko, Alexandra, trs. from ENG. (Garfield Ser.: Vol. 22). (GER., Illus.). 128p. (J). pap. (978-3-8105-0886-7(1)) Kruger, Wolfgang Verlag, GmbH DEU. *Dist:* International Bk. Import Service, Inc.

—Garfield et Ses Amis. 2000. (Garfield Ser.: No. 3). Tr. of Garfield Takes His Licks. (FRE.). (J). 7.95 (978-2-922148-02-2(5)) Presses aventure/Adventure Pr. CAN. *Dist:* AIMS International Bks., Inc.

—Garfield Fait le Plein. 2000. (Garfield Ser.: No. 7). Tr. of Garfield Life in the Fat Lane. (FRE.). (J). 7.95 (978-2-922148-06-0(8)) Presses aventure/Adventure Pr. CAN. *Dist:* AIMS International Bks., Inc.

—Garfield Feeds the Kitty. 2000. (gr. 3-6). lib. bdg. 16.40 (978-0-613-21576-3(1)) Tandem Library Bks.

—Garfield Fou Rire. 2000. (Garfield Ser.: No. 8). Tr. of Garfield Tons of Fun. (FRE.). (J). 7.95 (978-2-922148-07-7(6)) Presses aventure/Adventure Pr. CAN. *Dist:* AIMS International Bks., Inc.

—Garfield Halt die Ohren Steif. Goetting, Waltraud & Bartoszko, Alexandra, trs. from ENG. (Garfield Ser.: Vol. 23). (GER., Illus.). 128p. (J). pap. (978-3-8105-0889-8(6)) Kruger, Wolfgang Verlag, GmbH DEU. *Dist:* International Bk. Import Service, Inc.

—Garfield Hangt Ab. Bartoszko, Alexandra, tr. from ENG. (Garfield Ser.: Vol. 32). (GER., Illus.). 128p. (J). pap. (978-3-8105-0918-5(3)) Kruger, Wolfgang Verlag, GmbH DEU. *Dist:* International Bk. Import Service, Inc.

—Garfield Hat Genug. Goetting, Waltraud & Bartoszko, Alexandra, trs. from ENG. (Garfield Ser.: Vol. 18). (GER., Illus.). 128p. (J). pap. (978-3-8105-0833-1(0)) Kruger, Wolfgang Verlag, GmbH DEU. *Dist:* International Bk. Import Service, Inc.

—Garfield Hat Schwein. Bartoszko, Alexandra, tr. from ENG. (Garfield Ser.: Vol. 31). (GER., Illus.). 128p. (J). pap. (978-3-8105-0897-3(7)) Kruger, Wolfgang Verlag, GmbH DEU. *Dist:* International Bk. Import Service, Inc.

—Garfield Hebt Ab. Goetting, Waltraud & Bartoszko, Alexandra, trs. from ENG. (Garfield Ser.: Vol. 16). (GER., Illus.). 128p. (J). pap. (978-3-8105-0776-1(8)) Kruger, Wolfgang Verlag, GmbH DEU. *Dist:* International Bk. Import Service, Inc.

—Garfield Hogs the Spotlight: His 36th Book. 2000. (gr. 5-8). lib. bdg. 16.40 (978-0-613-68583-2(0)) Tandem Library Bks.

—Garfield ist Spitze. Goetting, Waltraud & Bartoszko, Alexandra, trs. from ENG. (Garfield Ser.: Vol. 11). (GER., Illus.). 128p. (J). pap. (978-3-8105-0757-0(1)) Kruger, Wolfgang Verlag, GmbH DEU. *Dist:* International Bk. Import Service, Inc.

—Garfield Kratzt die Kurve. Goetting, Waltraud & Bartoszko, Alexandra, trs. from ENG. (Garfield Ser.: Vol. 28). (GER., Illus.). 128p. (J). pap. (978-3-8105-0894-2(2)) Kruger, Wolfgang Verlag, GmbH DEU. *Dist:* International Bk. Import Service, Inc.

—Garfield Lasst nicht Locker. Goetting, Waltraud & Bartoszko, Alexandra, trs. from ENG. (Garfield Ser.: Vol. 14). (GER., Illus.). 128p. (J). pap. (978-3-8105-0771-6(7)) Kruger, Wolfgang Verlag, GmbH DEU. *Dist:* International Bk. Import Service, Inc.

—Garfield Legts Drauf An. Goetting, Waltraud & Bartoszko, Alexandra, trs. from ENG. (Garfield Ser.: Vol. 25). (GER.). 128p. (J). pap. (978-3-8105-0891-1(8)) Kruger, Wolfgang Verlag, GmbH DEU. *Dist:* International Bk. Import Service, Inc.

—Garfield Nimmt den Mund Voll. Goetting, Waltraud & Bartoszko, Alexandra, trs. from ENG. (Garfield Ser.: Vol. 21). (GER., Illus.). 128p. (J). pap. (978-3-8105-0885-0(3)) Kruger, Wolfgang Verlag, GmbH DEU. *Dist:* International Bk. Import Service, Inc.

—Garfield Nimmt's Leicht. Bartoszko, Alexandra, tr. from ENG. (Garfield Ser.: Vol. 29). (GER., Illus.). 128p. (J). pap. (978-3-8105-0895-9(0)) Kruger, Wolfgang Verlag, GmbH DEU. *Dist:* International Bk. Import Service, Inc.

—Garfield Out to Lunch: His Twelfth Book. 2006. (Garfield Ser.: Vol. 12). (Illus.). 96p. 10.95 (978-0-345-47562-6(3) , Ballantine Bks.) Random House Publishing Group.

—Garfield Platzt aus allen Naehten. Bartoszko, Alexandra, tr. from ENG. (Garfield Ser.: Vol. 33). (GER., Illus.). 128p. (J). pap. (978-3-8105-0919-2(1)) Kruger, Wolfgang Verlag, GmbH DEU. *Dist:* International Bk. Import Service, Inc.

—Garfield Releve le Defi. 2000. (Garfield Ser.: No. 5). Tr. of Garfield Pulls His Weight. (FRE.). (J). 7.95 (978-2-922148-04-6(1)) Presses aventure/Adventure Pr. CAN. *Dist:* AIMS International Bks., Inc.

—Garfield Riecht den Braten. Bartoszko, Alexandra, tr. from ENG. (Garfield Ser.: Vol. 34). (GER., Illus.). 128p. (J). pap. (978-3-8105-0920-8(5)) Kruger, Wolfgang Verlag, GmbH DEU. *Dist:* International Bk. Import Service, Inc.

—Garfield Spielt auf Zeit. Goetting, Waltraud & Bartoszko, Alexandra, trs. from ENG. (Garfield Ser.: Vol. 13). (GER., Illus.). 128p. (J). pap. (978-3-8105-0759-4(8)) Kruger, Wolfgang Verlag, GmbH DEU. *Dist:* International Bk. Import Service, Inc.

—Garfield Streicht Ein. Goetting, Waltraud & Bartoszko, Alexandra, trs. from ENG. (Garfield Ser.: Vol. 12). (GER., Illus.). 128p. (J). pap. (978-3-8105-0758-7(X)) Kruger, Wolfgang Verlag, GmbH DEU. *Dist:* International Bk. Import Service, Inc.

—Garfield Treasury 9. 1998. (Illus.). (J). pap. (978-0-345-91496-5(1) , Ballantine Bks.) Random House Publishing Group.

—Garfield Voit Grand. 2000. (Garfield Ser.: No. 2). Tr. of Garfield Keeps his Chin up. (FRE.). (J). 7.95 (978-2-922148-01-5(7)) Presses aventure/Adventure Pr. CAN. *Dist:* AIMS International Bks., Inc.

—Garfield Waechst & Gegeiht. Bartoszko, Alexandra, tr. from ENG. (Garfield Ser.: Vol. 30). (GER., Illus.). 128p. (J). pap. (978-3-8105-0896-6(9)) Kruger, Wolfgang Verlag, GmbH DEU. *Dist:* International Bk. Import Service, Inc.

—Garfield Will es Wissen. Goetting, Waltraud & Bartoszko, Alexandra, trs. from ENG. (Garfield Ser.: Vol. 26). (GER., Illus.). 128p. (J). pap. (978-3-8105-0892-8(6)) Kruger, Wolfgang Verlag, GmbH DEU. *Dist:* International Bk. Import Service, Inc.

—Garfield Zeigt die Krallen. Goetting, Waltraud & Bartoszko, Alexandra, trs. from ENG. (Garfield Ser.: Vol. 27). (GER., Illus.). 128p. (J). pap. (978-3-8105-0893-5(4)) Kruger, Wolfgang Verlag, GmbH DEU. *Dist:* International Bk. Import Service, Inc.

—In the Mood for Food. 1998. (Garfield Ser.). (Illus.). (J). pap. (978-0-345-91568-9(2) , Ballantine Bks.) Random House Publishing Group.

—K-Niner: Dog of Doom. 1998. (Garfield's Pet Force Ser.: Vol. 3). (J). (gr. 3-7). pap. 4.50 (978-0-590-05944-2(0)) Scholastic, Inc.

—Menace of the Nutanator. 1998. (Garfield's Pet Force Ser.: No. 4). (Illus.). (J). (gr. 3-7). pap. 4.50 (978-0-590-05945-9(9)) Scholastic, Inc.

—Pie-Rat's Revenge. 1998. (Garfield's Pet Force Ser.: Vol. 2). (Illus.). (J). (gr. 3-7). pap. 4.50 (978-0-590-05909-1(2)) Scholastic, Inc.

—Twelfth Garfield Fat Cat, 3 Packs. 2001. (gr. 5-8). lib. bdg. 19.90 (978-0-613-68627-3(6)) Tandem Library Bks.

Davis, Ruth Barton. A Story from Home Featuring... Zoro, a Cat. 1999. (Illus.). 40p. (C). pap. (978-0-9623785-1-5(8)) Pilgrim Way Pr., The.

Davis, Sharon. The Adventures of Capitol Kitty: An Almost True Story. San Souci, Daniel & Soucie, Daniel, illus. 2002. 32p. (J). pap. 4.99 (978-0-439-40305-4(7)) Scholastic, Inc.

Davis, Sharon & San Souci, Daniel. The Adventures of Capitol Kitty: An Almost True Story. San Souci, Daniel, illus. 2002. (Illus.). 32p. (J). 14.95 (978-0-439-45069-0(1)) Scholastic, Inc.

Davoll, Barbara. Saved by the Bell. Hockerman, Dennis, illus. 1999. (Christopher Churchmouse Classics Ser.). 24p. (J). (ps-3). 7.99 (978-0-8024-4934-4(4)) Moody Pubs.

Day, Kimberly. The Cat Who Went Back in Time. 1998. (Illus.). 24p. (J). (gr. 2-3). pap. 7.00 (978-0-8059-4269-9(6)) Dorrance Publishing Co., Inc.

Day, Nancy Raines. A Kitten's Year. Mortimer, Anne, illus. 2002. (J). 23.98 (978-0-7587-2937-8(5)) Book Wholesalers, Inc.

—A Kitten's Year. Mortimer, Anne, illus. 32p. (J). (ps-4). 2001. pap. 5.95 (978-0-06-443863-6(5) , Harper Trophy); 2000. 16.99 (978-0-06-027230-2(9)) HarperCollins Pubs.

de Paola, Tomie. Tom. de Paola, Tomie, illus. 2002. (Illus.). (J). 13.19 (978-0-7587-3827-1(7)) Book Wholesalers, Inc.

De Regniers, Beatrice Schenk. So Many Cats! Weiss, Ellen, illus. 2002. 32p. (J). (gr. k-3). pap. 9.95 incl. audio (978-0-618-21254-5(X) , Clarion Bks.) Houghton Mifflin Co. Trade & Reference Div.

Deary, Terry. The Magic & the Mummy. Flook, Helen, illus. 2005. (Read-It! Chapter Bks.). 64p. (J). (ps-k). lib. bdg. 19.95 (978-1-4048-1271-0(7)) Picture Window Bks.

DeGross, Monalisa. Donavan's Word Jar. Hanna, Cheryl, illus. 1998. (Trophy Chapter Bks.). 80p. (J). (gr. 2-5). pap. 4.99 (978-0-06-442089-1(2) , Harper Trophy) HarperCollins Pubs.

Delval, Marie-Helene. Mama Pata Cuenta a Sus Pequeqos. Courtin, Thierry, illus. 2002. (Palabras Menudas Ser.).Tr. of Mother Duck Counts to Her Young. (SPA.). 14p. (ps). 4.95 (978-84-7864-516-9(0)) Combel Editorial, S.A. ESP. *Dist:* Independent Pubs. Group.

DePrisco, Dorothea. Willie & Buster Take the Train. Ansley, Frank, illus. 2003. (Stories to Share Ser.). 10p. (J). 10.95 (978-1-58117-183-9(8) , Intervisual/Piggy Toes) Dalmatian Pr.

DeRosier, Cher. The Plight of the Jelly Bean. Contreras, Gilbert, illus. 2005. (J). (978-1-891685-50-7(3)) Dearborn Publishing.

Devine, Robert. Barney of the Serengeti. 2006. 22p. 9.99 (978-1-4116-7294-9(1)) Lulu.com.

Dexter & Missy the Kitten. 2004. (J). per. 15.99 (978-0-9753533-1-8(4)) Golden Eagle Publishing Hse., Inc.

Dick Whittington: Individual Title, 6 packs. 32p. (gr. 3 up). 37.00 (978-0-7635-9681-1(7)) Rigby Education.

Dickson, Louise. Vanishing Cat. 2002. (gr. 3-6). lib. bdg. 15.25 (978-0-613-53331-7(3)) Tandem Library Bks.

Diederich, Ellen Jean. Where's Petunia? 2003. (Illus.). 32p. (J). per. 18.99 (978-0-9728654-0-1(3)) Givinity Pr.

DiGenti, Victor. Windrusher. 2006. 292p. per. 15.95 (978-0-9767291-4-3(8)) Ocean Publishing.

Dioverti, Silvia. Gato Embotado y Enamorado. Rodriguez, Idana, illus. (SPA.). (J). pap. 7.60 (978-980-01-0832-1(7)) Monte Avila Editores Latinoamericana CA VEN. *Dist:* Lectorum Pubns., Inc.

Distler, Christine A. Pegasus: The Introduction. 2005. 84p. pap. 11.95 (978-1-59113-763-4(2)) Booklocker.com, Inc.

Dodd, Lynley. Hairy Maclary from Donaldson's Dairy. Dodd, Lynley, illus. 2000. (Gold Star First Readers Ser.). (Illus.). 32p. (J). (gr. 1 up). lib. bdg. 21.26 (978-0-8368-2688-3(4)) Stevens, Gareth Inc.

—Hairy Maclary from Donaldson's Dairy. 2005. (Illus.). 36p. (J). 5.95 (978-1-58246-059-8(0) , Tricycle Pr.) Ten Speed Pr.

—Hairy Maclary Scattercat. Dodd, Lynley, illus. 2000. (Gold Star First Readers Ser.). (Illus.). 32p. (J). (gr. 1 up). lib. bdg. 22.00 (978-0-8368-2689-0(2)) Stevens, Gareth Inc.

—Hairy Maclary Scattercat. 2005. (Illus.). 32p. (J). 5.95 (978-1-58246-095-6(7) , Tricycle Pr.) Ten Speed Pr.

—Hairy Maclary's Caterwaul Caper. Dodd, Lynley, illus. 2000. (Gold Star First Readers Ser.). (Illus.). 32p. (J). (gr. 1 up). lib. bdg. 22.00 (978-0-8368-2690-6(6)) Stevens, Gareth Inc.

—Hairy Maclary's Showbusiness. 2006. (Illus.). 32p. (J). 5.95 (***978-1-58246-208-0(9)*** , Tricycle Pr.) Ten Speed Pr.

—Scarface Claw. Dodd, Lynley, illus. 2002. (Gold Star First Readers Ser.). (Illus.). 32p. (J). (gr. 1 up). lib. bdg. 22.00 (978-0-8368-3161-0(6)) Stevens, Gareth Inc.

—Slinky Malinki. Dodd, Lynley, illus. 2001. (Gold Star First Readers Ser.). (Illus.). 32p. (J). (gr. 1 up). lib. bdg. 22.00 (978-0-8368-2784-2(8)) Stevens, Gareth Inc.

—Slinky Malinki. 2005. (Illus.). 32p. (J). reprint ed. 5.95 (978-1-58246-148-9(1) , Tricycle Pr.) Ten Speed Pr.

—Slinky Malinki Catflaps. Dodd, Lynley, illus. 1999. (Gold Star First Readers Ser.). (Illus.). 32p. (J). (gr. 1 up). lib. bdg. 22.00 (978-0-8368-2249-6(8)) Stevens, Gareth Inc.

—Slinky Malinki Catflaps. 2006. (Illus.). 0032p. (J). pap. 5.95 (978-1-58246-175-5(9) , Tricycle Pr.) Ten Speed Pr.

—Slinky Malinki, Open the Door. Dodd, Lynley, illus. 2001. (Gold Star First Readers Ser.). (Illus.). 32p. (J). (gr. 1 up). lib. bdg. 22.00 (978-0-8368-2785-9(6)) Stevens, Gareth Inc.

—Slinky Malinki, Open the Door. 2006. (Illus.). 0032p. (J). pap. 5.95 (978-1-58246-176-2(7) , Tricycle Pr.) Ten Speed Pr.

Dodson, Emma. Very Important Idea The. 2007. (Illus.). 32p. 19.95 (***978-0-340-87808-8(8));*** pap. 9.95 (***978-0-340-87809-5(6)***) Hodder Children's Division GBR. *Dist:* Independent Pubs. Group.

Dolezal, Margaret. Smokey's Odyssey. 1998. 64p. (YA). (gr. 7 up). 12.00 (978-0-8059-4317-7(X)) Dorrance Publishing Co., Inc.

Donlon, Diane Youngblood. Like a Cat: Creep, Sleep, Pounce, & Peek. . . Suhr, James W., illus. 2003. 32p. (J). 16.95 (978-0-9720427-2-7(5)) OLLY Publishing Co.

C D

Doran, Susan. Hannah & the Street Cats. Scott, Sarah, illus. 2007. 212p. (YA). per. 14.95 (*978-1-933002-47-7(6)) PublishingWorks.

Dorling Kindersley Publishing Staff, contrib. by. Kitten. 1999. (Touch & Feel Ser.). (Illus.). 12p. (J). (ps-k). bds. 6.99 (978-0-7894-3990-1(5)) Dorling Kindersley Publishing, Inc.

Dorling Kindersley Publishing Staff, ed. Kittens. 2004. (Dk Picture Stickers Ser.). 16p. (J). pap. 3.99 (978-0-7566-0559-9(8)) Dorling Kindersley Publishing, Inc.

Dow, Jill. Molly's Supper. (Windy Edge Farm Ser.). (Illus.). (J). 2004. 26p. pap. 7.95 (978-1-84507-251-3(0)); 2001. 32p. pap. (978-0-7112-1776-8(9)) Lincoln, Frances Ltd. GBR. *Dist:* Perseus Distribution, Transition Vendor.

Downey, Glen. Ice Journey. Brucker, Glenn, illus. 2007. 48p. (J). lib. bdg. 23.08 (*978-1-4242-1618-5(4)) Fitzgerald Bks.

Downey, Lynn. Matilda's Humdinger. Bowers, Tim, illus. 2006. 40p. (J). (gr. k-4). 15.95 (978-0-375-82403-6(0)); lib. bdg. 17.99 (978-0-375-92403-3(5)) Random Hse. Children's Bks. (Knopf Bks. for Young Readers).

Doyle, Malachy. Albert & Sarah Jane. 2007. (J). lib. bdg. 16.95 (*978-1-59566-336-8(3)) QEB Publishing Inc.

Doyle, Malachy. Storm Cats. Trotter, Stuart, illus. 2002. 32p. (J). (ps-1). 15.95 (978-0-689-84464-5(6) , McElderry, Margaret K.) Simon & Schuster Children's Publishing.

Drew, Rosa. Cat & Dog Go Shopping, Vol. 4476. Kupperstein, Joel, ed. Leary, Catherine, illus. 1998. (Learn to Read Math Ser.). 16p. (J). pap. 2.75 (978-1-57471-383-1(3) , 4476) Creative Teaching Pr., Inc.

Duckworth, Liz. Ragtail Remembers. Barnes, Jeff, illus. 2002. (J). (978-1-56123-163-8(0)) Centering Corp.

Dumbleton, Mike. Cat. Smith, Craig, illus. 2008. 32p. (J). 15.95 (*978-1-933605-73-9(1)) Kane/Miller Bk. Pubs., Inc.

Duncan, Lois. I Walk at Night. Johnson, Steve & Fancher, Lou, illus. 2000. 32p. (J). (ps-3). 15.99 (978-0-670-87513-9(9) , Viking Juvenile) Penguin Group (USA) Inc.

Dunn, Carolyn. A Cat's Gotta Do...What a Cat's Gotta Do. 2001. (J). lib. bdg. 16.00 (978-0-689-82626-9(5) , Simon & Schuster Children's Publishing) Simon & Schuster Children's Publishing.

Dunn, Opal. Leo le Chat Comes to School: A First French Story. Gale, Cathy, illus. 2006. (ENG & FRE.). 24p. (J). 15.95 (*978-1-84507-403-6(3)) Lincoln, Frances Ltd. GBR. *Dist:* Perseus Distribution.

Dunn, Opal & Gale, Cathy. El Gato Leo Comes to Play! A First Spanish Story. 2004. (ENG & SPA., Illus.). 24p. (J). 7.95 (978-1-84507-336-7(3)) Lincoln, Frances Ltd. GBR. *Dist:* Perseus Distribution.

Durant, Kathy. The Grand Cat. Hunt, Judith A., illus. 2000. per. 3.00 (978-1-930710-33-7(X)) Veritas Pr., Inc.

Duvall, Deborah L. Rabbit Goes to Kansas. 2007. (Illus.). 32p. (J). (gr. 1 up). 16.95 (*978-0-8263-4181-5(0)) Univ. of New Mexico Pr.

DuVall, Nell. The Bucket. Less, Sally, illus. 2000. 32p. (J). 7.95 (978-0-9706654-1-6(5)) Sprite Pr.

East, Jacqueline, illus. Kitten. 2007. (Wiggle-Waggles Ser.). 8p. (J). (ps). bds. 4.99 (*978-0-7641-6073-8(7)) Barron's Educational Series, Inc.

Ebl, Donna. The Adventures of Salamander Sam. 2004. (J). pap. 9.00 (978-0-8059-6165-2(8)) Dorrance Publishing Co., Inc.

Edmiston, Jim, illus. The Emperor Who Hated Yellow. 1999. 32p. (J). (ps-k). 14.95 (978-1-902283-39-5(2)) Barefoot Bks., Inc.

Edwards, Becky. My Cat Charlie. Armitage, David, illus. 2000. 32p. (J). 19.99 (978-0-7475-4465-4(4)) Bloomsbury Publishing Plc GBR. *Dist:* Independent Pubs. Group.

Edwards, Julie Andrews. Little Bo in France. Cole, Henry, illus. 2002. 128p. (gr. 2-17). 19.49 (978-0-7868-2540-0(5)) Hyperion Pr.

—Little Bo in France: The Further Adventures of Bonnie Boadicea. Cole, Henry, illus. 2004. 117p. (J). (gr. k-4). reprint ed. 19.00 (978-0-7567-8163-7(9)) DIANE Publishing Co.

Edwards, Julie Andrews & Cole, Henry. Little Bo: The Story of Bonnie Boadicea. 2006. (Illus.). 89p. (J). (gr. k-4). reprint ed. 17.00 (978-1-4223-5481-0(4)) DIANE Publishing Co.

Egan, Tim. Roasted Peanuts. 2006. (Illus.). 32p. (J). (gr. k-3). 16.00 (978-0-618-33718-7(0)) Houghton Mifflin Co.

Eggleton, Jill. Cat & Dog: Emergent Level Satellite Individual Title Six-Packs. (Sails Literacy Ser.). (gr. k-1). 27.00 (978-0-7578-7915-9(2)) Rigby Education.

—Cat Party: Emergent Level Satellite Individual Title Six-Packs. McGrath, Raymond, illus. (Sails Literacy Ser.). (gr. k-1). 27.00 (978-0-7578-7916-6(0)) Rigby Education.

—Crumpet, the Cat: 3-in-1 Package. Hawley, Kelvin, illus. (Sails Literacy Ser.). 24p. (gr. 1 up). 57.00 (978-0-7578-8619-5(1)) Rigby Education.

—Crumpet, the Cat: 6 Small Books. Hawley, Kelvin, illus. (Sails Literacy Ser.). 24p. (gr. 1 up). 25.00 (978-0-7578-7731-5(1)) Rigby Education.

—Crumpet, the Cat: Big Book Only. Hawley, Kelvin, illus. (Sails Literacy Ser.). 24p. (gr. 1 up). 27.00 (978-0-7578-6203-8(9)) Rigby Education.

Egielski, Richard. Slim & Jim. Egielski, Richard, illus. 2005. (Illus.). 37p. (J). (gr. k-4). reprint ed. 16.00 (978-0-7567-8936-7(2)) DIANE Publishing Co.

Ehlert, Lois. Feathers for Lunch. Ehlert, Lois, illus. 2002. (Illus.). (J). 14.04 (978-0-7587-2487-8(X)) Book Wholesalers, Inc.

—Top Cat. Ehlert, Lois, illus. 2001. (Illus.). 36p. (J). (ps-2). pap. 7.00 (978-0-15-202425-3(5) , Voyager Bks./Libros Viajeros) Harcourt Children's Bks.

—Top Cat. 1998. (Illus.). 40p. (J). (ps-5). 17.00 (978-0-15-201739-2(9)) Harcourt Children's Bks.

Einhorn, Edward. A Very Improbable Story. Gustavson, Adam, illus. 2007. (J). (*978-1-57091-871-1(6)); pap. (*978-1-57091-872-8(4)) Charlesbridge Publishing, Inc.

Eldridge, Les. Santa's Cat. Eldridge, Les & Casey, James, illus. 2003. 24p. (J). (978-1-877338-03-8(6)) Steele Roberts Publishing Ltd.

Elliott, John C. Ri Ra: An Adventure Begins. 2006. 48p. pap. 12.95 (978-1-4241-2771-9(8)) PublishAmerica, Inc.

Ellis, A. G. A Trellis for Mr. Ellis: Or How I Saved the World from Global Warming. Ellis, A. G. & Deaton, T. K., illus. l.t. ed. 2002. 32p. (J). per. 8.95 (978-0-9717451-1-7(0) , Louisa May Allcat Children's Bks.) Allcat Pr.

Elschner, Geraldine. Mark's Messy Room. Myngheer, Charise, tr. from GER. Junge, Alexandra, illus. 2006. 32p. (J). (ps-3). 16.99 (978-0-698-40047-4(X) , Minedition) Penguin Group (USA) Inc.

Emm, David. Madison Meets the Minister. Bedrick, Jeff, illus. 2006. 48p. (J). 14.95 (978-1-889658-42-1(1)) STL Distribution North America.

Entara Ltd. Staff, photos by. Piggley Helps Out. 2006. (Ready-To-Read Ser.). 24p. (J). pap. 3.99 (978-0-689-87614-1(9) , Simon Spotlight) Simon & Schuster Children's Publishing.

Equipo Staff. Este No Es Mi Gatito. 2004. Tr. of That's Not My Kitten. (SPA., Illus.). 12p. (J). (ps). 7.95 (978-0-7460-4513-8(1)) EDC Publishing.

—El Gato. 2000. (SPA., Illus.). 12p. (J). (ps-k). 7.95 (978-84-488-0893-8(2)) Beascoa, Ediciones S.A. ESP. *Dist:* Distribooks, Inc., Lectorum Pubns., Inc.

Erickson, John R. The Case of the Haystack Kitties. Holmes, Gerald L., illus. 1998. (Hank the Cowdog Ser.: No. 30). 144p. (J). (gr. 2-5). 14.99 (978-0-670-88437-7(5) , Viking Juvenile); Vol. 30. pap. 4.99 (978-0-14-130406-9(5) , Puffin) Penguin Group (USA) Inc.

—The Case of the Haystack Kitties. 1999. (Hank the Cowdog Ser.: No. 30). (gr. 3-6). lib. bdg. 13.00 (978-0-613-07442-1(4)) Tandem Library Bks.

—The Case of the Missing Cat. Holmes, Gerald L., illus. (Hank the Cowdog Ser.: No. 15). 144p. (J). (gr. 2-5). 2000. 14.99 (978-0-670-88422-3(7) , Viking Juvenile); 1998. pap. 4.99 (978-0-14-130391-8(3) , Puffin) Penguin Group (USA) Inc.

—The Case of the Missing Cat. 1999. (Hank the Cowdog Ser.: No. 15). (gr. 3-6). lib. bdg. 13.00 (978-0-8335-6828-1(0)) Tandem Library Bks.

—The Case of the Twisted Kitty. Holmes, Gerald L., illus. 2004. (Hank the Cowdog Ser.: No. 43). 131p. (J). lib. bdg. 17.00 (*978-1-4242-1600-0(1)) Fitzgerald Bks.

—The Case of the Twisted Kitty, Vol. 43. Holmes, Gerald L., tr. Holmes, Gerald L., illus. 2004. (Hank the Cowdog Ser.: No. 43). 144p. (J). pap. 4.99 (978-0-14-240041-8(6) , Puffin) Penguin Group (USA) Inc.

—The Case of the Vampire Cat. Holmes, Gerald L., illus. 1998. (Hank the Cowdog Ser.: No. 21). 144p. (J). (gr. 2-5). 14.99 (978-0-670-88428-5(6) , Viking Juvenile); Vol. 21. pap. 4.99 (978-0-14-130397-0(2) , Puffin) Penguin Group (USA) Inc.

Estes, Eleanor. Miranda the Great. Ardizzone, Edward, illus. 2005. 96p. (J). (ps-7). 16.00 (978-0-15-205405-2(7)); pap. 5.95 (978-0-15-205411-3(1)) Harcourt Trade Pubs.

—Pinky Pye. Ardizzone, Edward, illus. 2000. 272p. (YA). (gr. 3-7). pap. 6.00 (978-0-15-202565-6(0) , Odyssey Classics); (gr. 4-7). 17.00 (978-0-15-202559-5(6)) Harcourt Children's Bks.

—Pinky Pye. 2000. (J). (978-0-606-20042-4(8)); (J). (978-0-606-20170-4(X)); (gr. 3-6). lib. bdg. 14.15 (978-0-613-30671-3(6)) Tandem Library Bks.

Farish, Terry. The Cat Who Liked Potato Soup. Root, Barry, illus. 40p. (J). (gr. 1). 2007. pap. 6.99 (978-0-7636-3297-7(X)); 2003. 16.99 (978-0-7636-0834-7(3)) Candlewick Pr.

Farley, Terri. Challenger. 2003. (gr. 5-8). lib. bdg. 13.00 (978-0-613-66694-7(1)) Tandem Library Bks.

Fearnley, Jan. Billy Tibble Moves Out! Fearnley, Jan, illus. 2006. (Illus.). 29p. (J). (gr. k-4). reprint ed. 16.00 (978-1-4223-5557-2(8)) DIANE Publishing Co.

Fehlner, Paul. Dog & Cat. Chambliss, Maxie, illus. 2003. (My First Reader Ser.). 32p. (J). 18.50 (978-0-516-22924-9(9) , Children's Pr.) Scholastic Library Publishing.

Feldman, Thea. Hello Kitty, Hello Family! Hirashima, Jean, illus. 2002. 6p. (J). (ps-ps). bds. 6.95 (978-0-8109-5693-3(4)) Abrams, Harry N. , Inc.

—Hello Kitty, Hello Friends! Hirashima, Jean, illus. 2002. 6p. (J). (ps-ps). bds. 6.95 (978-0-8109-5692-6(6)) Abrams, Harry N. , Inc.

—My Magnetic Shapes & Colors: Flo & Zip's Busy Day. 2007. 8p. bds. 9.95 (978-1-932915-38-9(9)) Sandvik Innovations, LLC.

Ferro, Ursula. Tanny's Meow. Huff, Ariella, illus. 2005. 51p. (J). pap. 12.95 (978-0-9766006-0-2(9)) Marti Bks.

Fielder, Barbara L. Missy, the Kitty, Plays Hide & Go Seek. (Illus.). 17p. (J). 6.95 (978-0-9639986-5-1(X)) Fielder Group.

—Missy, the Kitty, Visits the Veterinarian. (Illus.). 15p. (J). 6.95 (978-0-9639986-7-5(6)) Fielder Group.

—Treats for Missy, the Kitty. (Illus.). 13p. (J). 6.95 (978-0-9639986-4-4(1)) Fielder Group.

Fielder, Barbara L. & Broady, Brianna. Missy, the Kitty, Learns about Sharing. (Illus.). 13p. (J). 6.95 (978-0-9639986-2-0(5)) Fielder Group.

—Missy, the Mischievous Kitty. (Illus.). 17p. (J). 6.95 (978-0-9639986-3-7(3)) Fielder Group.

—Missy, the Patriotic Kitty. (Illus.). 11p. (J). 6.95 (978-0-9639986-1-3(7)) Fielder Group.

Findlay, Lisa. Puss in Boots. Bowers, Tim, illus. 2008. (J). pap. (*978-0-375-84671-7(9)); 48p. lib. bdg. 11.99 (*978-0-375-94671-4(3)) Random Hse., Inc.

Fine, Anne. El Diario de un Gato Asesino. Ortega, Damian, illus. 2000. (la Orilla Del Viento Ser.). (SPA.). 46p. (J). (ps-13). reprint ed. pap. 5.99 (978-968-16-5674-4(1) , 113) Fondo de Cultura Economica USA.

—The Diary of a Killer Cat. Cox, Steve, illus. 2006. 64p. (J). 15.00 (978-0-374-31779-9(8)) Macmillan.

—The Return of the Killer Cat. Cox, Steve, illus. 2007. 80p. (J). (gr. 3-5). 16.00 (978-0-374-36248-5(3) , Farrar, Straus & Giroux (BYR)) Farrar, Straus & Giroux.

Finn, Mitch. NASCAR: Cat Racer's Race Day. Reiter, Cheryl, ed. Hogan, Jayne, illus. 2000. 12p. (J). (ps). mass mkt. 9.99 (978-1-887327-45-9(2)) Ertl Co., Inc.

Fish, Mister, illus. Snerfy Cat Meets Prancy Finch. Fish, Mister, . 2007. 80p. (J). 14.99 (*978-0-9794753-0-6(9)) Children's Classic Book Pubs.

Flanagan, Alice K. Cats: The Sound of Short A. 1999. (Wonder Books Phonics: Vowels Ser.). (Illus.). 24p. (J). (ps-3). 21.36 (978-1-56766-691-5(4)) Child's World, Inc.

The Flat Hat: KinderReaders Individual Title Six-Packs. (Kinderstarters Ser.). 8p. (ps-1). 21.00 (978-0-7635-8662-1(5)) Rigby Education.

Fleming, Denise. Mama Cat Has Three Kittens. Fleming, Denise, illus. 2002. (Illus.). (J). 15.49 (978-1-4046-4054-2(1)) Book Wholesalers, Inc.

—Mama Cat Has Three Kittens. rev. ed. 2002. (Illus.). 32p. (J). (ps-k). pap. 7.95 (978-0-8050-7162-7(8) , Holt, Henry & Co. Bks. For Young Readers) Holt, Henry & Co.

—Mama Cat Has Three Kittens. Fleming, Denise, illus. rev. ed. 1998. (Illus.). 32p. (J). (ps-k). 16.95 (978-0-8050-5745-4(5) , Holt, Henry & Co. Bks. For Young Readers) Holt, Henry & Co.

—Mama Cat Has Three Kittens. 2002. (ps-2). lib. bdg. 15.25 (978-0-613-51377-7(0)) Tandem Library Bks.

Florek, Amy. Silly Beulah! l.t. ed. 2006. (Illus.). 21p. (J). 15.95 (978-1-59879-158-7(3)); per. 9.99 (978-1-59879-138-9(9)) Lifevest Publishing, Inc.

Follow the Paw Prints: Small Book. (Pebble Soup Explorations Ser.). 16p. (ps up). 5.00 (978-0-7635-7042-2(7)) Rigby Education.

Fontaine, Anne. Ocho Loved Flowers. Heavner, Obadinah, illus. 2007. 48p. (J). (gr. k-3). 14.95 (*978-0-9789174-0-1(5)); pap. 6.95 (*978-0-9789174-1-8(3)) Stoneleigh Pr.

Ford, Bernette. Ballet Kitty. Williams, Sam, illus. 2007. 32p. (J). (ps-1). 14.95 (*978-1-905417-56-8(X)) Boxer Bks., Ltd. GBR. *Dist:* Sterling Publishing Co., Inc.

Ford, Sandy Lee, illus. Gullah, the Nawleans Cat Meets Katrina. 2007. 32p. (J). (*978-0-9793637-0-2(5)) Hart Street Pubs.

Fordham, Kate. Me & My Kitten. 2007. 80p. (J). (gr. 2-5). pap. 9.99 (*978-0-439-92964-6(4)) Scholastic, Inc.

Foreman, Michael. Cat & Canary. 2004. (Illus.). 32p. (J). pap. 8.99 (978-1-84270-287-1(4)) Andersen GBR. *Dist:* Trafalgar Square Publishing.

—Cat in the Manger. rev. ed. 2001. (Illus.). 32p. (J). (ps-3). 17.95 (978-0-8050-6677-7(2) , Holt, Henry & Co. Bks. For Young Readers) Holt, Henry & Co.

—Cat on the Hill. (Illus.). 32p. (J). 2005. pap. 8.99 (*978-1-84270-471-4(0)); 2003. 16.00 (978-1-84270-282-6(3)) Andersen GBR. *Dist:* Independent Pubs. Group.

Fox, Diane & Fox, Christyan. Raton, Que Te Pilla el Gato! 2003. (ENG & SPA., Illus.). 20p. pap. 11.95 (978-84-7864-693-7(0)) Combel Editorial, S.A. ESP. *Dist:* Independent Pubs. Group.

Fox, Mem. A Cat Called Kite. Slack, Michael H., illus. 2008. (J). (*978-0-15-204909-6(6)) Harcourt Trade Pubs.

Fox, Paula. One-Eyed Cat. Meltzer, Erika, illus. 2000. 224p. (J). (gr. 5-9). pap. 5.99 (978-0-689-83970-2(7) , Aladdin) Simon & Schuster Children's Publishing.

—One-Eyed Cat. 2000. (gr. 5-8). lib. bdg. 13.00 (978-0-613-33717-5(4)) Tandem Library Bks.

Frahm, Amelia. Tickles Tabitha's Cancer-Tankerous Mommy. Schultz, Elizabeth, illus. 2001. 32p. (J). (gr. k-4). pap. 9.95 (978-0-9705752-0-3(3) , 1068755) Nutcracker Publishing Co.

Franca, Mary. Rabo de Gato. Franca, Eliardo, illus. 2002. Tr. of Cat's Tail. (SPA.). (J). pap. 4.95 (978-980-257-015-7(X) , EK7928) Ekare, Ediciones VEN. *Dist:* Lectorum Pubns., Inc.

Franco, Betsy. Clever Calculator Cat. Perks, Anne-Marie, illus. 1999. 32p. (J). (gr. 2-4). pap. 8.50 (978-0-914534-19-8(X) , 124) Stokes Publishing Co., Inc.

Frank, Lucy. Just Ask Iris. 2003. (Illus.). 224p. (J). pap. 4.99 (978-0-689-84454-6(9) , Aladdin) Simon & Schuster Children's Publishing.

—Just Ask Iris. 2003. (gr. 5-8). lib. bdg. 13.00 (978-0-613-66417-2(5)) Tandem Library Bks.

Franklin, Rosalind. Clemo the Cornish Cat. Coomber, Eva, illus. 2006. 32p. (J). (978-1-905363-08-7(7) , Diggory Pr. Ltd.) Meadow Bks.

Freeman, Kathie. Catwalk: A Feline Odyssey. 2003. 236p. per. 11.95 (978-0-9742062-3-3(7)) McPugh, Kathleen.

Freeman, Martha. Mrs. Wow Never Wanted a Cow. Salerno, Steven, illus. 2006. 48p. (J). (gr. k-3). 8.99 (978-0-375-83418-9(4)); lib. bdg. 11.99 (978-0-375-93418-6(9)) Random Hse. Children's Bks. (Random Hse. Bks. for Young Readers).

—Mrs. Wow Never Wanted a Cow. Salerno, Steven, illus. 2006. (J). (978-0-375-83419-6(2)) Random Hse., Inc.

—The Trouble with Babies. Smith, Cat Bowman, illus. 2002. 80p. (J). (gr. 4-6). tchr. ed. 15.95 (978-0-8234-1698-1(4)) Holiday Hse., Inc.

—The Trouble with Cats. Smith, Cat Bowman, illus. 2000. 80p. (J). (gr. 4-6). tchr. ed. 15.95 (978-0-8234-1479-6(5)) Holiday Hse., Inc.

—Who Stole Halloween? 224p. (J). (ps-7). 16.95 (978-0-8234-1962-3(2)) Holiday Hse., Inc.

Frees, Jessie Lynch. Jackie Winquackey & Her 43 Cats Go to Hollywood. Gebr, Jaroslav, illus. 2005. 32p. (J). 14.99 (978-0-9760553-0-3(9)) Tizbit Books, LLC.

French, Fiona. Jamil's Clever Cat. 2002. (Illus.). 32p. (J). 22.95 (978-0-7112-1209-1(0)) Lincoln, Frances Ltd. GBR. *Dist:* Raincoast Bk. Distribution.

—Jamil's Clever Cat: A Folk Tale from Bengal. French, Fiona, illus. 1999. (Illus.). 32p. (J). (ps-3). 13.95 (978-1-887734-72-1(4)) Star Bright Bks., Inc.

—Jamils Clever Cat: A Folk Tale from Bengal. 2006. (Illus.). 32p. (J). pap. 7.95 (978-1-84507-518-7(8)) Lincoln, Frances Ltd. GBR. *Dist:* Perseus Distribution.

French, Vivian. A Cat in a Coat. Williams, Lisa, illus. 2005. (Lightning Readers Ser.). 32p. (J). (gr. k-k). pap. 3.95 (978-0-7696-4029-7(X) , Gingham Dog Pr.) School Specialty Publishing.

—Cat in a Coat. Bartlett, Alison, illus. 2005. 32p. (J). (ps-k). lib. bdg. 11.15 (978-0-606-33583-6(8)) Tandem Library Bks.

—Detective Dan. Bartlett, Alison, illus. 2006. (Read-It! Chapter Books). 48p. (J). (gr. 2-4). 19.95 (978-1-4048-1659-6(3)) Picture Window Bks.

—Un Gato Con Chaqueta. Williams, Lisa, illus. 2005. (Lightning Readers Ser.). 32p. (J). (gr. k-k). pap. 3.95 (978-0-7696-4069-3(9) , Gingham Dog Pr.) School Specialty Publishing.

—I Love You, Grandpa. Kubick, Dana, illus. 2004. 32p. (J). (ps up). 15.99 (978-0-7636-2520-7(5)) Candlewick Pr.

—Morris & the Cat Flap. 2002. (Roaring Good Reads Ser.). (Illus.). 64p. (J). pap. 7.99 (978-0-00-714161-6(0)) HarperCollins Pubs. Ltd. GBR. *Dist:* Independent Pubs. Group.

—Morris the Mouse Hunter. 2003. (Roaring Good Reads Ser.). (Illus.). 64p. (J). pap. 7.99 (978-0-00-714732-8(5)) HarperCollins Pubs. Ltd. GBR. *Dist:* Independent Pubs. Group.

—Present for Mom. Kubick, Dana, illus. 32p. (J). (ps up). 2002. 13.99 (978-0-7636-1587-1(0)); 2005. reprint ed. pap. 5.99 (978-0-7636-2692-1(9)) Candlewick Pr.

Frenkel, Yetti. Libby & the Cat. Frenkel, Yetti, illus. 2005. (Illus.). 32p. 16.95 (978-0-9749006-2-9(1)) Snow Tree Bks.

—Trudy & the Captain's Cat. Frenkel, Yetti, illus. 2005. (Illus.). 32p. 16.95 (978-0-9749006-1-2(3)) Snow Tree Bks.

Friday, Stormy. Signal's Airport Adventure. Saroff, Phyllis, illus. 2006. (J). 14.95 (*978-0-9717047-5-6(9)) Bay Media, Inc.

Friebert, Judith M. The Flying Cats: Oliver & Jimmy. 2003. (Illus.). 16p. (Orig.). (J). (ps-6). pap. (978-0-9744852-0-1(9)) Sandner-Petersen International Bks.

Friedman, Carol. Nicky the Jazz Cat. 2004. (Illus.). 32p. (J). (ps-3). 16.95 (978-0-9726092-0-3(2)) Dominick Pictures.

—Nicky the Jazz Cat. Friedman, Carol, illus. 2005. (Illus.). 32p. (J). 16.95 (978-1-57687-248-2(3) , PowerHouse Kids) powerHouse Cultural Entertainment, Inc.

—Nicky's Jazz Christmas. 2006. (Illus.). 32p. (J). 16.95 (978-1-57687-341-0(2)) powerHouse Cultural Entertainment, Inc.

Friedman, Mel. Kitten Castle. 2001. (gr. k-3). lib. bdg. 12.95 (978-0-613-39335-5(X)); (Illus.). (J). (978-0-606-20753-9(8)) Tandem Library Bks.

Friedman, Mel, et al. Kitten Castle. 2001. (Math Matters Ser.). (Illus.). 32p. (J). (gr. k-2). pap. 4.95 (978-1-57565-103-3(3)) Kane Pr., The.

Friel, Maeve. Felix on the Move. Blake, Beccy, illus. 2004. (Read-It! Readers Ser.). 32p. (C). (gr. k-3). 18.60 (978-1-4048-0055-7(7)) Picture Window Bks.

Friend, Catherine. The Perfect Nest. Manders, John, illus. 2007. (J). (ps-2). 40p. 16.99 (978-0-7636-2430-9(6)); (*978-1-4287-3697-9(2)) Candlewick Pr.

Fuks, Menuhah & Tager, Gavriella. Smile with Avigayil #2: Avigayil & the Black Cat. Haas, Esti, illus. 2006. (ENG.). 64p. (J). 12.95 (*978-1-932443-58-5(4)) Judaica Pr., Inc., The.

Futterer, Kurt. Emile. Gray, Bronwen et al, trs. from GER. Futterer, Ralf, illus. 2004. (J). 17.95 (978-1-931561-95-2(8)) MacAdam/Cage Publishing, Inc.

Fuzz & the Glass Eye: Individual Title Six-Packs. (Action Packs Ser.). 120p. (gr. 3-5). 44.00 (978-0-7635-8421-4(5)) Rigby Education.

Ga'g, Wanda. Millions of Cats. 2000. (J). pap. 12.95 incl. audio Weston Woods Studios, Inc.

Gag, Wanda. Millions of Cats. gif. ed. 2006. 32p. (J). (ps). pap. 7.99 (978-0-14-240708-0(9) , Puffin) Penguin Group (USA) Inc.

Galdone, Paul, retold by. King of the Cats. unabr. ed. 2001. (J). (gr. k-4). pap. 16.90 incl. audio (978-0-8045-6517-2(1) , 6517) Spoken Arts, Inc.

Gallyp, Tracy. King Cat. Gallyp, Tracy, illus. 2006. (Illus.). 32p. (J). (978-0-9749145-8-9(4)) Mackinac Island Pr., Inc.

Gambill, Glenda Colleen. Ringo, the Amazing Cat. Dove, Pauline, illus. 2003. (J). pap. 14.00 (978-0-8059-5908-6(4)) Dorrance Publishing Co., Inc.

Gangas, Patricia. Cats Everywhere. MacDonald, Bruce, illus. 2000. (Books for Young Learners). 12p. (J). pap. 5.00 (978-1-57274-253-6(4)) Owen, Richard C. Pubs., Inc.

Gantos, Jack. Back to School for Rotten Ralph. Rubel, Nicole, illus. (Rotten Ralph Ser.). 40p. (J). (ps-3). 2000. pap. 6.99 (978-0-06-443705-9(1) , Harper Trophy); Bk. 1. 1998. 14.89 (978-0-06-027532-7(4)) HarperCollins Pubs.

—Back to School for Rotten Ralph. 2000. 12.75 (978-0-606-22184-9(0)); (gr. 3-6). lib. bdg. 14.10 (978-0-613-30974-5(X)) Tandem Library Bks.

—Best in Show for Rotten Ralph: A Rotten Ralph Rotten Reader. Rubel, Nicole, illus. 2005. (Rotten Ralph Reader Ser.: No. 4). 48p. (J). 15.00 (978-0-374-36358-1(7) , Farrar, Straus & Giroux (BYR)) Farrar, Straus & Giroux.

—Practice Makes Perfect for Rotten Ralph: A Rotten Ralph Rotten Reader. Rubel, Nicole, illus. 2002. (Rotten Ralph Rotten Readers Ser.). 48p. (J). (ps-2). 15.00 (978-0-374-36356-7(0) , Farrar, Straus & Giroux (BYR)) Farrar, Straus & Giroux.

—Rotten Ralph Feels Rotten: A Rotten Ralph Rotten Reader. Rubel, Nicole, tr. Rubel, Nicole, illus. 2004. (Rotten Ralph Rotten Readers Ser.). 48p. (J). 15.00 (978-0-374-36357-4(9) , Farrar, Straus & Giroux (BYR)) Farrar, Straus & Giroux.

—Rotten Ralph Helps Out. Rubel, Nicole, illus. unabr. ed. 2006. (Readalongs for Beginning Readers Ser.). (J). (gr. k-3). 24.95 incl. audio (978-1-59519-678-1(1)); 28.95 incl. audio compact disk (978-1-59519-679-8(X)); pap. 16.00 incl. audio (978-1-59519-674-3(9)); pap. 18.95 incl. audio compact disk (978-1-59519-675-0(7)); Set. pap. 29.95 incl. audio (978-1-59519-676-7(5)); Set. pap. 31.95 incl. audio compact disk (978-1-59519-677-4(3)) Live Oak Media.

—Rotten Ralph Helps Out: A Rotten Ralph Rotten Reader. Rubel, Nicole, illus. (Rotten Ralph Rotten Readers Ser.). 48p. (J). 2004. pap. 5.95 (978-0-374-46355-7(7) , Sunburst); 2001. (gr. 1-3). 15.00 (978-0-374-36355-0(2) , Farrar, Straus & Giroux (BYR)) Farrar, Straus & Giroux.

—Untitled Rotten Ralph Reader. Date not set. (Rotten Ralph Reader Ser.: No. 5). (J). (978-0-374-36354-3(4)); (Illus.). (978-0-374-36353-6(6)) Farrar, Straus & Giroux. (Farrar, Straus & Giroux (BYR)).

—Wedding Bells for Rotten Ralph. Rubel, Nicole, illus. 1999. (Rotten Ralph Ser.: Vol. 2). (J). (ps-3). 40p. 15.99 (978-0-06-027533-4(2)); Bk. 2. 32p. 14.89 (978-0-06-027534-1(0)) HarperCollins Pubs.

Gardner, Wendy. Naughty Naughty Keifer. Gardner, Wendy, illus. 2002. (Naughty Naughty Pets Ser.). (Illus.). 32p. (ps-17). 10.99 (978-0-7868-0886-1(1)) Hyperion Bks. for Children.

Gardner, Wendy Ann. Yes, a Cat Named Marty Cohen. 2002. (Naughty Naughty Pets Ser.). (Illus.). 32p. (ps-17). 10.99 (978-0-7868-0887-8(X)) Hyperion Bks. for Children.

Garland, Michael. Angel Cat. Garland, Michael, illus. 1998. (Illus.). 32p. (J). (gr. k-3). 15.95 (978-1-56397-726-8(5)) Boyds Mills Pr.

Garretson, Jerri. Imagicat. Dollar, Diane A., illus. 2000. 160p. (J). (gr. 3-5). pap. 6.95 (978-0-9659712-2-5(8)) Ravenstone Pr.

El Gato, 6 Packs. (Chiquilibros Ser.). (SPA.). (gr. k-1). 23.00 (978-0-7635-8622-5(6)) Rigby Education.

El Gato Libertad 13: Leveled Books. 2001. (McGraw-Hill. Lectura Ser.). (ENG & SPA.). (gr. 2 up). (978-0-02-188062-1(X)) Macmillan/McGraw-Hill Schl. Div.

Gauthier, Gail. A Girl, a Boy, & a Monster Cat. Cepeda, Joe, illus. 2007. 96p. (J). (gr. 2-4). 14.99 (978-0-399-24689-0(4) , Putnam Juvenile) Penguin Group (USA) Inc.

Gauthier, Gail. A Girl, A Boy, & Three Robbers. Cepeda, Joe, illus. 2008. 64p. (J). (gr. 1-3). 14.99 (***978-0-399-24690-6(8)*** , Putnam Juvenile) Penguin Group (USA) Inc.

Gay, Marie-Louise. Caramba. 2005. (Illus.). 40p. (ps-7). 16.95 (978-0-88899-667-1(5)) Groundwood Bks. CAN. *Dist:* Perseus Distribution.

Gee, Genese. The Story of Jack, Sprat, & the Backpack. Gee, Genese, illus. (Illus.). 20p. (J). (ps-1). 2002. 14.99 (978-0-9719935-1-8(3)); 2001. pap. 10.49 (978-0-9719935-0-1(5)) Gee, Genese Celeste.

Gelman, Rita Golden. Hello, Cat, You Need a Hat. 1999. (Hello Reader! Ser.). (Illus.). (J). (978-0-606-18557-8(7)) Tandem Library Bks.

George, Olivia. Copy Cat. Hudson, Brett, illus. (My First Reader Ser.). (J). (gr. k-1). 2005. 32p. pap. 3.95 (978-0-516-25113-4(9)); 2004. 18.50 (978-0-516-24679-6(8)) Scholastic Library Publishing. (Children's Pr.).

Geras, Adele. Callie's Kitten: The Cats of Cuckoo Square. 2003. (gr. k-3). lib. bdg. 11.80 (978-0-613-85703-1(8)) Tandem Library Bks.

—Family Files. Ross, Tony, illus. 1998. (Fabulous Fantoras Ser.: Vol. 1). 144p. (J). (gr. 3-7). 14.00 (978-0-380-97547-1(5)) HarperCollins Pubs.

—Picasso Perkins: The Cats of Cuckoo Square. Ross, Tony, illus. 2002. 96p. (J). (gr. 1-4). pap. 3.99 (978-0-440-41815-3(1) , Yearling) Random Hse. Children's Bks.

—Picasso Perkins: The Cats of Cuckoo Square. 2002. (gr. k-3). lib. bdg. 11.80 (978-0-613-85702-4(X)) Tandem Library Bks.

Geringer, Lucy T. Rhymes & Times of Cleo-cat-tra. Kollock, Bernardita Cox, illus. 2002. 34p. (J). (ps-1). pap. 8.95 (978-0-9719483-0-3(5)) Cleo Cat Bks.

—Rhymes & Times of Cleo-cat-tra. Kollock, Bernardita Cox, illus. l.t. ed. 2000. (Cleo-Cat-Tra Easy-to-Read Book Ser.). 28p. (J). (ps-2). pap. 7.95 (978-0-9600962-7-5(2)) Displays for Schls., Inc.

Gerowin, Sean. Catte au Lait & the Big Hurricane. 2005. 36p. (J). 8.99 (978-1-4116-5157-9(X)) Lulu.com.

Gerstein, Mordicai, illus. Three Samurai Cats: A Story from Japan. 2003. 32p. (J). (gr. k-3). 6.95 (978-0-8234-1877-0(4)) Holiday Hse., Inc.

—Three Samurai Cats: A Story from Japan. 2004. (J). (978-0-439-69256-4(3)) Scholastic, Inc.

Gibbel, Mark. Oh, Harry! Massini, Sarah, illus. rev. ed. 2003. 32p. (J). (ps-2). 15.95 (978-0-8050-6851-1(1) , Holt, Henry & Co. Bks. For Young Readers) Holt, Henry & Co.

Giff, Patricia Reilly. El Gato "Vinagrete" 2000. (SPA.). (YA). (gr. 1 up). 3.95 (978-0-922852-51-2(0)) AIMS International Bks., Inc.

—Kidnap at the Catfish Cafe. Cravath, Lynne W., illus. 2000. (Adventures of Minnie & Max Ser.: Vol. 1). 80p. (J). (gr. 2-6). pap. 4.99 (978-0-14-130821-0(4) , Puffin) Penguin Group (USA) Inc.

—Kidnap at the Catfish Cafe. Cravath, Lynne, illus. 1998. 80p. (J). (gr. 2-6). 13.99 (978-0-670-88180-2(5) , Viking Juvenile) Penguin Group (USA) Inc.

—Kidnap at the Catfish Cafe. 2000. (gr. 3-6). lib. bdg. 13.00 (978-0-613-25875-3(4)); (Illus.). (J). 11.79 (978-0-606-18384-0(1)) Tandem Library Bks.

—Mary Moon Is Missing. Cravath, Jill & Cravath, Lynne, illus. 2000. (Adventures of Minnie & Max Ser.: Vol. 2). 80p. (J). (gr. 2-6). pap. 4.99 (978-0-14-130823-4(0) , Puffin) Penguin Group (USA) Inc.

—Mary Moon Is Missing. 2000. (gr. 3-6). lib. bdg. 11.80 (978-0-613-26156-2(9)); (Illus.). (J). 10.79 (978-0-606-18385-7(X)) Tandem Library Bks.

Giles, Susan. Caribbean Cats. Giles, Susan, illus. 2003. (Meet the Author Ser.). (Illus.). 16p. (J). pap. 5.00 net. (978-1-57274-662-6(9) , 2728) Owen, Richard C. Pubs., Inc.

Gilkey, Gail. Happy Cat. 1998. (Illus.). 32p. (J). (ps-k). pap. 4.95 (978-0-9662983-0-7(6)) Windy Hill Pr.

Gill, Amber. Joseph's Summer. 2006. 71p. pap. 14.95 (978-1-4241-0122-1(0)) PublishAmerica, Inc.

Gill, Janet. Basket Weaver & Catches Many Mice. Choi, Yangsook, illus. 2005. 30p. (J). (gr. k-4). reprint ed. 19.00 (978-0-7567-9420-0(X)) DIANE Publishing Co.

Gilmer, Evelyn. Maggie: The Beagle with a Broken Tail. 2007. (J). per. 6.99 (***978-1-60247-310-2(2)***) Tate Publishing & Enterprises, L.L.C.

Glaser, Byron. Hello Kitty, Hello Color! Higashi, Sandra, photos by. 2006. (Illus.). 23p. (J). (ps-3). reprint ed. 13.00 (978-1-4223-5491-9(1)) DIANE Publishing Co.

Glaser, Higashi, illus. Hello Kitty, Hello USA! A Celebration of All Fifty States. 2006. 55p. (J). (gr. k-4). reprint ed. 13.00 (978-1-4223-5624-1(8)) DIANE Publishing Co.

Glaser, Higashi & Higashi/Glaser Design Inc. Staff. Hello Kitty Hello Beauty! Style Kit. 2006. 16p. (J). (ps-3). 14.95 (978-0-8109-4946-1(6) , Abrams Bks. for Young Readers) Abrams, Harry N. , Inc.

Gleasner, Diana C. Popoki's Incredible Adventure at the Volcano. Winton, Andrea E., illus. 1999. (J). (978-0-9651185-5-2(X)) Gleasner, Bill & Diana Inc.

Gleb... the Terrible! 2004. (Illus.). 36p. pap. 15.00 (978-0-9761041-1-7(3)) Celstumo Publishing.

Godwin, Laura. The Best Fall of All. Chapman, Jane, illus. 2002. (Happy Honey Ser.). 32p. (J). pap. 3.99 (978-0-689-84763-9(7) , Aladdin); 14.95 (978-0-689-84713-4(0) , McElderry, Margaret K.) Simon & Schuster Children's Publishing.

—Best Fall of All. 2002. (ps-2). lib. bdg. 11.80 (978-0-613-57495-2(8)) Tandem Library Bks.

—Happy & Honey. Chapman, Jane, illus. 2001. (Happy Honey Ser.: Vol. 1). 32p. (J). pap. 3.99 (978-0-689-84235-1(X) , Aladdin) Simon & Schuster Children's Publishing.

—Happy & Honey. 2001. (gr. k-3). lib. bdg. 11.80 (978-0-613-36968-8(8)); (Illus.). (J). 10.79 (978-0-606-22029-3(1)) Tandem Library Bks.

—Happy & Honey: Honey Helps. 2001. (gr. k-3). lib. bdg. 11.80 (978-0-613-36969-5(6)) Tandem Library Bks.

—Happy Christmas, Honey. 2002. (ps-2). lib. bdg. 11.80 (978-0-613-57505-8(9)) Tandem Library Bks.

—Honey Helps. Chapman, Jane, illus. 2001. (Happy Honey Ser.: Vol. 2). 32p. (J). pap. 3.99 (978-0-689-84234-4(1) , Aladdin) Simon & Schuster Children's Publishing.

—Honey Helps. 2001. (Illus.). (J). 10.79 (978-0-606-22030-9(5)) Tandem Library Bks.

Godwin, Laura & Chapman, Jane. Happy Christmas, Honey! 2002. (Ready-to-Read Ser.). (Illus.). 32p. (J). 14.95 (978-0-689-84714-1(9) , McElderry, Margaret K.) Simon & Schuster Children's Publishing.

Goldsberry, Booty. Scaredy-Cat, I'm Not. 2007. (Illus.). 40p. pap. 9.95 (***978-0-9792875-0-3(2)***) Goldsberry, Booty.

Goldsboro, Bobby. Jonah & the Whale/Daniel & the Lion's Den, Vol. 2. Stewart, Toni D., illus. 2003. (Adventures of Cheze & Kwackers Ser.: Bk. 2). 48p. (J). (gr. k-3). pap. 8.95 (978-1-889658-28-5(6)) New Canaan Publishing Co. LLC.

—Noah & the Ark/David & Goliath. Stewart, Toni D., illus. 2003. (Adventures of Cheze & Kwackers Ser.: Bk. 1). 48p. (J). (gr. k-3). pap. 8.95 (978-1-889658-27-8(8)) New Canaan Publishing Co. LLC.

Gollub, Matthew. The Twenty-Five Mixtec Cats. Martinez, Leovigildo, illus. 2004. 32p. (J). pap. 6.95 (978-1-889910-29-1(5)) Tortuga Pr.

Gollub, Matthew W. The Twenty-five Mixtec Cats. Martinez, Leovigildo, illus. rev. ed. 2004. 32p. (J). 15.95 (978-1-889910-28-4(7)) Tortuga Pr.

Gomez, Rebecca. Happy Easter, Hello Kitty! 2005. (Illus.). 32p. (***978-0-439-67637-3(1)***) Scholastic, Inc.

Goodhart, Pippa. Fire Cat. Hurst, Philip, illus. 2005. (Red Go Bananas Ser.). 48p. (J). pap. (978-0-7787-2697-5(5)) Crabtree Publishing Co.

Goodhart, Pippa & Hurst, Philip. Fire Cat. 2005. (Red Go Bananas Ser.). (Illus.). 48p. (J). lib. bdg. (978-0-7787-2675-3(4)) Crabtree Publishing Co.

Grant, Joan. Cat & Fish. Curtis, Neil, illus. 2005. 32p. (J). 16.95 (978-1-894965-14-9(0)) Simply Read Bks. CAN. *Dist:* Perseus Distribution.

Grant, Joan & Curtis, Neil. Cat & Fish Go to See. 2006. (Illus.). 32p. (J). 16.95 (978-1-894965-39-2(6)) Simply Read Bks. CAN. *Dist:* Perseus Distribution.

Gravdahl, John. Curious Catwalk. 2003. (Illus.). (J). (gr. k-5). 16.95 (978-0-9678577-8-7(3)) Propeller Pr.

Graves, Sue. Fat Cat. 2007. (Fun with Phonics Ser.). 20p. (J). pap. 4.99 (***978-0-439-02552-2(4)***) Scholastic, Inc.

Gray, Nigel. My Dog, My Cat, My Mama, & Me! Graham, Bob, illus. 2007. 24p. (J). (gr. k-ps). 8.99 (***978-0-7636-3639-5(8)***) Candlewick Pr.

Gray, Sondra. According to Punkin. 2006. 82p. per. 8.95 (978-1-59886-436-6(X)) Tate Publishing & Enterprises, L.L.C.

Graziani, Maria. A Black Cat on Halloween: Un Gato Negro en Dia de Brujas. Elejalde, Eliana, illus. l.t. ed. 2004. (SPA.). 23p. (J). 7.00 (978-0-9762361-1-5(7)) Ed. Acespanish S.A.C.- Lima, Peru.

Green, Jonathan, illus. Amadeus, the Leghorn Rooster. 2004. (J). 17.95 (978-0-87844-174-7(3)) Sandlapper Publishing Co., Inc.

Greene, Carol. The Cat & the Bear. 2005. 32p. (J). pap. (978-0-7868-1175-5(7)) Hyperion Bks. for Children.

—Where Is That Cat? 1999. 32p. (J). 14.99 (978-0-7868-0611-9(7)) Hyperion Bks. for Children.

Greene, Vivien. Laurel for Libby: A Facsimile Edition of a Small Story Book Written for Graham Greene by his Wife, Vivien. 2006. (Illus.). 40p. 12.00 (978-1-85124-350-1(X)) Bodleian Library GBR. *Dist:* Chicago Distribution Ctr.

Greenhut, Elyse. The Littlest Kitten. 2003. 33p. pap. 14.95 (978-1-59286-986-2(6)) PublishAmerica, Inc.

Gregory, Jillian Louise. Dobbs Dog Detective: Operation Fido & Fifi. 2003. 67p. pap. 11.95 (978-1-4137-0644-4(4)) PublishAmerica, Inc.

Gregory, Valiska. The Mystery of the Grindlecat. 2003. (Illus.). 32p. (J). 18.99 (978-1-57860-142-4(8)); pap. 9.99 (978-1-57860-141-7(X)) Emmis Bks.

Gretz, Susanna. Riley & Rose in the Picture. Gretz, Susanna, illus. 2005. (Illus.). 32p. (J). (gr. k-3). 16.99 (978-0-7636-2681-5(3)) Candlewick Pr.

Grimes, Nikki. When Gorilla Goes Walking. Evans, Shane, illus. 2007. 32p. (J). (ps-3). pap. 16.99 (978-0-439-31770-2(3) , Orchard Bks.) Scholastic, Inc.

Grizzle, Charles R. Cats Mysterioso: True Tales Odd & Puzzling. l.t. ed. 2001. (Illus.). 140p. (J). pap. 9.95 (978-0-9644033-3-8(1)) Plateau Pubns.

Groce, Michelle. Jasper. Duis, Laura, illus. 2005. 178p. 11.95 (978-0-9760963-1-3(5)); 2003. 174p. (J). 17.95 (978-0-9708972-6-8(X)) Novello Festival Pr.

Group/McGraw-Hill, Wright. The Klutzy Cat: Level N, 6 vols. 128p. (gr. 3-6). 36.95 (978-0-322-05882-8(1)) Wright Group, The.

Grow, Kathy K. & Varvel, Lois H. The Day Bridger Got His Name. Clay, Nancy, illus. 2002. 40p. (J). pap. 10.95 (978-0-9704839-1-1(0)) Vintage Point Pr.

Grow, Mary L. Chester Meets the Walker House Ghost, No. 1. Richel, Jean - Marc, illus. 2000. 72p. (Orig.). (J). (gr. 8-12). pap. 12.00 (978-0-9700777-0-7(X)) Studio 17.

Gullihur, Mary Ann. Seven Cool Cats. Faust, Richard, illus. 1998. 8p. (J). (gr. k-2). pap. 3.75 (978-1-880612-81-1(X) , Seedling Pubns.) Continental Pr., Inc.

Hacker, Marie. The Cute & Curious Cleo. 1998. (Illus.). 40p. (J). (gr. k-3). pap. 8.00 (978-0-8059-4408-2(7)) Dorrance Publishing Co., Inc.

Hacking, Norm. When Cats Go Wrong. Nugent, Cynthia, illus. 2006. 32p. (J). pap. 9.95 (978-1-55192-917-0(1)) Raincoast Bk. Distribution CAN. *Dist:* Perseus Distribution.

Hafner, Marylin. Molly & Emmett's Surprise Garden. 2003. (Molly & Emmett Ser.). (Illus.). 32p. (J). (ps up). 12.95 (978-1-57768-895-2(3) , Cricket) School Specialty Publishing.

Hahn, Mary Downing. Witch Catcher. 2006. 240p. (J). (gr. 4-6). 16.00 (978-0-618-50457-2(5) , Clarion Bks.) Houghton Mifflin Co. Trade & Reference Div.

Hale, Bruce. Pirates of Underwhere. Hillman, Shane, illus. 2008. (Underwhere Ser.). 160p. (J). 15.99 (***978-0-06-085127-9(9)***); lib. bdg. 16.89 (***978-0-06-085128-6(7)***) HarperCollins Pubs.

—Prince of Underwhere. Hillman, Shane, illus. 2008. (Underwhere Ser.). 176p. (J). lib. bdg. 16.89 (***978-0-06-085125-5(2)***); (gr. 3-7). 15.99 (***978-0-06-085124-8(4)***) HarperCollins Pubs.

Hale, Kathleen. Orlando the Marmalade Cat: A Camping Holiday. 2003. (Illus.). 32p. (J). (gr. 1-5). 20.00 (978-0-7567-6602-3(8)) DIANE Publishing Co.

Halstead, Jayce N. The True Legend of White Crow: Adventures of the Fudge Sisters. Twomey-Lange, Marianna, photos by. 2004. (Illus.). 80p. (J). per. 7.95 (978-0-9749046-3-4(5)) Aarow Pr.

Hamilton, Elizabeth L. Christopher Cat's Character Club. 2003. (Character Critters Ser.: No. 1). (Illus.). 32p. (J). (ps-3). per. 5.95 (978-0-9713749-2-8(9) , Character-in-Action) Quiet Impact, Inc.

Hancasky, Carrie A. Curiosity Kitty. 2002. 24p. 14.95 (978-1-56167-762-7(0)) American Literary Pr.

Hanson, Dave. What Now, Puss? Langley, Jonathan, illus. 2005. (Reading Corner Ser.). 24p. (J). (gr. k-3). lib. bdg. 22.80 (978-1-59771-001-5(6)) Sea-To-Sea Pubns.

Hanson, Mary Elizabeth. How to Save Your Tail: If You Are a Rat Nabbed by Cats Who Really Like Stories about Magic Spoons, Wolves with Snout-Warts, Big Hairy Chimney Trolls—And Cookies Too. Hendrix, John, illus. 2007. 112p. (J). (gr. 1-5). 15.99 (978-0-375-83755-5(8) , Schwartz & Wade Bks.) Random Hse. Children's Bks.

—How to Save Your Tail: If You Are a Rat Nabbed by Cats Who Really Like Stories about Magic Spoons, Wolves with Snout-Warts, Big Hairy Chimney Trolls—and Cookies Too. 2007. (Illus.). 112p. (J). (gr. 1-5). lib. bdg. 18.99 (978-0-375-93755-2(2) , Schwartz & Wade Bks.) Random Hse. Children's Bks.

Hapka, Cathy. Clue School: The Case of the Missing Cat, Level 4. Torrey, Richard, illus. 2006. (innovativeKids readers ser.: level 4). 32p. (J). (gr. 2-17). pap., pap. 6.99 (978-1-58476-479-3(1) , IKIDS) Innovative Kids.

Harcourt School Publishers Staff. The Art of Being a Cat Advanced Level. 3rd ed. 2002. (Trophies Reading Program Ser.). (Illus.). pap. 5.10 (978-0-15-323292-3(7)) Harcourt Schl. Pubs.

—A Birthday Basket: Library Book. 1999. (Collections Ser.). (Illus.). pap. 14.90 (978-0-15-313402-9(X)) Harcourt Schl. Pubs.

—The Cat Has Escaped in Steerage Level D: Library Edition. 2001. (Collections Ser.). (Illus.). pap. 12.10 (978-0-15-314407-3(6)) Harcourt Schl. Pubs.

—Cat in Boots 5-Pack, On Level. 3rd ed. 2002. (Trophies Reading Program Ser.). (Illus.). (gr. 1). pap. 20.10 (978-0-15-326841-0(7)) Harcourt Schl. Pubs.

—A Day with Wiggles: Take-Home Book. 1999. (Collections Ser.). (Illus.). (J). pap. 1.90 (978-0-15-317202-1(9)) Harcourt Schl. Pubs.

—Go Cat! Below Level. 3rd ed. 2002. (Trophies Reading Program Ser.). (Illus.). (J). (gr. 1). pap. 3.20 (978-0-15-322940-4(3)) Harcourt Schl. Pubs.

—The Guest That Forgot to Leave: Take-Home Book. 2001. (Collections Ser.). (Illus.). (J). pap. 1.90 (978-0-15-319494-8(4)) Harcourt Schl. Pubs.

—The Guest That Forgot to Leave Below Level. 3rd ed. 2002. (Trophies Reading Program Ser.). (Illus.). pap. 5.10 (978-0-15-323232-9(3)) Harcourt Schl. Pubs.

—El Invitado Que No Se Fue Below Level. 3rd ed. 2002. (Trofeos Ser.). (SPA., Illus.). pap. 6.80 (978-0-15-324143-7(8)) Harcourt Schl. Pubs.

—Jasper's Beanstalk: Little Book. 2000. (Collections Ser.). (Illus.). (J). pap. 10.20 (978-0-15-314504-9(8)) Harcourt Schl. Pubs.

—Lost! Take-Home Book. 1999. (Collections Ser.). (Illus.). (J). pap. 1.90 (978-0-15-317246-5(0)) Harcourt Schl. Pubs.

—My Cats: Below Level. 3rd ed. 2002. (Trophies Reading Program Ser.). (Illus.). (J). (gr. 1). pap. 4.10 (978-0-15-322957-2(8)) Harcourt Schl. Pubs.

—My Cats 5-Pack, Below Level. 3rd ed. 2002. (Illus.). (gr. 1). pap. 20.10 (978-0-15-326807-6(7)) Harcourt Schl. Pubs.

—Not a Cat: Take-Home Book. 1999. (Collections Ser.). (Illus.). (J). pap. 1.90 (978-0-15-317192-5(8)) Harcourt Schl. Pubs.

—Pat the Cat: On Level. 3rd ed. 2002. (Trophies Reading Program Ser.). (Illus.). (J). pap. 3.20 (978-0-15-322974-9(8)) Harcourt Schl. Pubs.

—Pepe Finds His Home Below Level. 3rd ed. 2002. (Trophies Reading Program Ser.). (Illus.). pap. 5.10 (978-0-15-323064-6(9)) Harcourt Schl. Pubs.

—That's My Shot Below Level. 3rd ed. 2002. (Trophies Reading Program Ser.). (Illus.). pap. 5.10 (978-0-15-323138-4(6)) Harcourt Schl. Pubs.

—This & That: Library Book. 1999. (Collections Ser.). (Illus.). pap. 13.60 (978-0-15-313406-7(2)) Harcourt Schl. Pubs.

—Trofeos Below Level: Tito, Eso No! 3rd ed. 2002. (SPA., Illus.). (J). (gr. 1). pap. 3.50 (978-0-15-323851-2(8)) Harcourt Schl. Pubs.

—Trofeos On Level: El Gato/Botas. 3rd ed. 2002. (SPA., Illus.). pap. 5.50 (978-0-15-323902-1(6)) Harcourt Schl. Pubs.

—Trofeos On Level: Pepe. 3rd ed. 2002. (SPA., Illus.). pap. 6.80 (978-0-15-324081-2(4)) Harcourt Schl. Pubs.

—What Can Matt Do? Advanced Level. 3rd ed. 2002. (Trophies Reading Program Ser.). (Illus.). (J). pap. 3.70 (978-0-15-323008-0(8)) Harcourt Schl. Pubs.

Harjo, Joy. The Good-Luck Cat. Lee, Paul, illus. 2000. 32p. (J). (gr. 1-4). 17.00 (978-0-15-232197-0(7)) Harcourt Children's Bks.

Harper, Anita. It's Not Fair! McQuillan, Mary, illus. 2007. 32p. (J). (ps-k). 16.95 (***978-0-8234-2094-0(9)***) Holiday Hse., Inc.

Harper, Charise Mericle. Fashion Kitty. 2005. (Illus.). 96p. (gr. 3-7). pap. 8.99 (978-0-7868-5134-8(1)) Hyperion Pr.

Harper, Dan. Telling Time with Big Mama Cat. Moser, Barry & Moser, Cara, illus. 1998. 36p. (J). (ps-3). 16.00 (978-0-15-201738-5(0)) Harcourt Children's Bks.

Harper, Jessica. I'm Not Going to Chase the Cat Today! 2000. (Illus.). 32p. (J). (ps-3). 15.89 (978-0-688-17637-2(9)) HarperCollins Pubs.

—I'm Not Going to Chase the Cat Today! Dupont, Lindsay Harper, illus. 2000. 32p. (J). (ps-3). 15.95 (978-0-688-17636-5(4)) HarperCollins Pubs.

HarperEntertainment Staff. Li'l Pet Hospital No.3: The Very Rainy Day. 2003. (gr. k-3). lib. bdg. 11.80 (978-0-613-86273-8(2)) Tandem Library Bks.

Harris, Joan. Moving Day: An Alfie & Roxy Adventure. Santeramo, Rich, illus. 2007. 16p. (J). 12.95 (***978-0-9796994-9-8(5)***) TRIAD Publishing Group.

Harris, Lee. Never Let Your Cat Make Lunch for You. Tilley, Debbie, illus. 2004. 24p. (J). (ps-2). 12.95 (978-1-883672-80-5(5) , Tricycle Pr.) Ten Speed Pr.

Harris, Peter & Weir, Doffy. Bottomley at the Cattery. 1998. (Illus.). 32p. (J). pap. 5.95 (978-0-7641-0667-5(8)) Barron's Educational Series, Inc.

Harris, Rita & Long, Paul. The 19 Cats of Alabama. 2004. 35p. pap. 17.95 (978-1-4137-3006-7(X)) PublishAmerica, Inc.

Harris, Robin. Marmalade & the Magic Birds. 2001. (Illus.). 32p. (J). (ps-1). 15.99 (978-1-84148-316-0(8)) Barefoot Bks., Inc.

Harris, Sue. Butterfly Garden. Boey, Stephanie, illus. 2006. 20p. (J). 15.95 (978-0-8118-5247-0(4)) Chronicle Bks. LLC.

Hartley, Susan. Kit & Kim. 2003. (StartUp Ser.). (J). pap. 22.00 (978-1-4108-0712-0(6)) Benchmark Education Co.

—Pop & the Fat Cat. 2003. (StartUp Ser.). (J). pap. 22.00 (978-1-4108-0701-4(0)) Benchmark Education Co.

Hartmann, Jennifer. Kristofur Kitty: Crossing the Street. 2003. (J). pap. 8.00 (978-0-8059-5388-6(4)) Dorrance Publishing Co., Inc.

Harvey, Jayne. Cat Show. Petrosino, Tamara, illus. 2003. (All Aboard Math Reader Station Stop Ser.). 48p. (J). (ps-2). pap. 3.99 (978-0-448-43112-3(2) , Grosset & Dunlap) Penguin Group (USA) Inc.

—Cat Show. 2003. (gr. k-3). lib. bdg. 11.80 (978-0-613-64030-5(6)) Tandem Library Bks.

Hassett, Ann & Hassett, John. Cat up a Tree. 2003. (Illus.). 32p. (J). (gr. k-3). pap. 5.95 (978-0-618-33524-4(2) , Walter Lorraine) Houghton Mifflin Co. Trade & Reference Div.

Hassett, John & Hassett, Ann. Cat up a Tree. 1998. (Illus.). 32p. (J). (gr. k-3). tchr. ed. 16.00 (978-0-395-88415-7(2) , Walter Lorraine) Houghton Mifflin Co. Trade & Reference Div.

Hassett, John & Hassett, Ann. The Nine Lives of Dudley Dog. 2008. 32p. (J). (gr. k-3). 16.00 (***978-0-618-81153-3(2)***) Houghton Mifflin Co.

Haworth, Margaret. Jarry, Garry Palas: Cat Tail Stories. Haworth, Margaret, photos by. l.t. ed. 2003. (Books That Help Ser.: Vol. 3). (Illus.). 34p. (J). (gr. 1-6). pap. 9.95 (978-0-9740313-5-4(6)) Haworth, Margaret.

—Oh Holly Dallig: Cat Tail Stories. Haworth, Margaret, photos by. l.t. ed. 2003. (Books That Help Ser.: Vol. 3). (Illus.). 34p. (J). (gr. 1-6). pap. 9.95 (978-0-9740313-4-7(8)) Haworth, Margaret.

Haydel, Catherine. Uno the Cat & Hurricane Katrina. 2006. 18.00 (978-0-8059-7341-9(9)) Dorrance Publishing Co., Inc.

Hazelton, Jamie. The Grandest Adventure of Captain Goldeneears. Hazelton, Jamie, illus. 2001. 14p. 5.00 net. (978-0-9715792-0-0(2)) Fables & Tails.

Hazen, Barbara Shook. City Cats, Country Cats. 1999. (ps-2). lib. bdg. 11.80 (978-0-613-27770-9(8)) Tandem Library Bks.

Hearn, Diane Dawson. Bad Luck Boswell. 1999. (J). (978-0-606-17312-4(9)) Tandem Library Bks.

Hearn, Michael Patrick. The Porcelain Cat. Dillon, Leo & Dillon, Diane, illus. 2004. 32p. (J). (ps-ps). 16.95 (978-0-689-03592-0(6) , Milk & Cookies) ibooks, Inc.

Heflick, LaMonte. The Story of Ninja Cat. 2004. 64p. pap. 3.99 (978-1-56175-905-7(8)) Remedia Pubns.

Heinz, Brian J. The Alley Cat. Blair, June H., illus. l.t. ed. 2002. 32p. (J). 14.95 (978-0-936335-05-6(X)); pap. 6.95 (978-0-936335-06-3(8)) Ballyhoo BookWorks, Inc.

—The Barnyard Cat. Blair, June H., illus. 2000. 32p. (J). (gr. k-4). 14.95 (978-0-936335-04-9(1)) Ballyhoo BookWorks, Inc.

—The Barnyard Cat. l.t. ed. 2003. (Illus.). 32p. (J). pap. 6.96 (978-0-936335-07-0(6)) Ballyhoo BookWorks, Inc.

Helberg, Shirley H. The Kitty-Cat Who Wanted to Fly. Helberg, Shirley H., illus. 1999. (Illus.). 54p. (J). (gr. k-2). mass mkt. (978-0-7392-0165-7(4) , PO3118) Morris Publishing.

Helmer, Diana Star. The Cat Who Came for Tacos. Escriva, Vivi, illus. 2003. 32p. (J). (gr. 1-3). 15.95 (978-0-8075-5106-6(6)) Whitman, Albert & Co.

Helmer, Marilyn. Fog Cat. ed. 2004. (Illus.). (J). (gr. k-3). spiral bd. (978-0-616-03039-4(8)) Canadian National Institute for the Blind/Institut National Canadien pour les Aveugles.

—Fog Cat. Mombourquette, Paul, illus. 32p. (J). (gr. k-3). 2001. (978-1-55337-097-0(X)); 2000. (978-1-55074-791-1(6)); 1999. (978-1-55074-460-6(7)) Kids Can Pr., Ltd.

—Mr. McGratt & the Ornery Cat. Gourbault, Martine, illus. unabr. ed. 2002. 32p. (J). (gr. k-3). (978-1-55337-162-5(3)) Kids Can Pr., Ltd.

—Three Cat & Mouse Tales. Masse, Josee, illus. 2004. (Once-upon-a-Time Ser.). 32p. (J). (gr. k-3). (978-1-55074-943-4(9)) Kids Can Pr., Ltd.

Helmer, Marilyn & Gourbault, Martine. Mr. McGratt & the Ornery Cat. 1999. (Illus.). 32p. (J). (gr. k-3). (978-1-55074-564-1(6)) Kids Can Pr., Ltd.

Henderson, Kathy. Tabby Cat's Secret. 2003. (Illus.). 36p. pap. 9.95 (978-0-7112-1883-3(8)) Lincoln, Frances Ltd. GBR. *Dist:* Transition Vendor.

Henderson, Kathy & Winter, Susan. Tabby Cat's Secret. 2004. (Illus.). 32p. (J). pap. 9.95 (978-1-84507-270-4(7)) Lincoln, Frances Ltd. GBR. *Dist:* Perseus Distribution.

Henkes, Kevin. Kitten's First Full Moon. Henkes, Kevin, illus. 2004. 40p. (J). (ps-k). 16.99 (978-0-06-058828-1(4)); lib. bdg. 16.89 (978-0-06-058829-8(2)) HarperCollins Pubs.

—La Primera Luna Llena de Gatita. Henkes, Kevin, illus. 2006. Orig. Title: Kitten's First Full Moon. (SPA.). 32p. (J). 16.99 (978-0-06-087223-6(3)) HarperCollins Pubs.

Henry, Marguerite. Benjamin West & His Cat Grimalkin. Dennis, Wesley, illus. 2000. 160p. (J). per. 14.95 (978-0-9705618-0-0(6)) Bradford Pr.

Henry, Steve. Nobody Asked Me! 2001. (Illus.). 32p. (J). (ps-k). 14.95 (978-0-688-17865-9(0)) HarperCollins Pubs.

Henry, T. K. Rickey & Rachel, the Cats without Tails & Their Awesome Adventure. 2007. 40p. (J). pap. 8.00 (***978-0-8059-7224-5(2)***) Dorrance Publishing Co., Inc.

Herman, Gail. Meet Trouble. 2002. lib. bdg. 11.80 (978-0-613-64069-5(1)) Tandem Library Bks.

—Pizza Cats. 2000. (Ready-to-Read Ser.). (Illus.). 31p. (J). (ps-3). per. (978-0-671-77316-8(X) , Simon & Schuster Children's Publishing) Simon & Schuster Children's Publishing.

Herman, Gail & Hughes, Francine. Cats & Dogs. 2001. (Illus.). 32p. (J). (gr. k-3). pap. 3.50 (978-0-439-22573-1(6)) Scholastic, Inc.

Hesse, Karen. The Cats in Krasinski Square. Watson, Wendy, illus. 2004. 32p. (J). (gr. 2-5). pap. 16.95 (978-0-439-43540-6(4) , Scholastic Pr.) Scholastic, Inc.

Heurtelou, Maude. Istwa Chat ak Sourit. Louissaint, Louis, illus. 1999. Tr. of Cat & Mouse. (CRP.). 24p. (J). (gr. 3-5). pap. 19.00 incl. audio (978-1-881839-90-3(7)) Educa Vision.

Hickey, Tony & Myler, Terry. Flip 'n' Flop & the Movies. 1998. 112p. pap. 7.95 (978-1-901737-05-9(5)) Anvil Bks., Ltd. IRL. *Dist:* Dufour Editions, Inc.

Hicks, Barbara Jean. The Secret Life of Walter Kitty. Santat, Dan, illus. 2007. (J). lib. bdg. (***978-0-375-03196-0(0)***) Knopf, Alfred A. Inc.

—The Secret Life of Walter Kitty. Santat, Dan, illus. 2007. 40p. (J). (gr. k-3). 16.99 (978-0-375-83196-6(7)); lib. bdg. 18.99 (978-0-375-93196-3(1)) Random Hse. Children's Bks. (Knopf Bks. for Young Readers).

Hicks Brooks, Kathy. Cuddles at Home Series: Cuddles in the Kitchen. 2006. (Illus.). 28p. pap. 15.95 (978-1-59299-208-9(0)) Inkwater Pr.

Hiebert, Elfrieda H. & Juel, Connie. The Cat That Broke the Rules. (Little Book Practice Reader Ser.). (J). (978-0-8136-0967-6(4)) Modern Curriculum Pr.

—My Cat. (Little Book Practice Reader Ser.). (J). (978-0-8136-0680-4(2)) Modern Curriculum Pr.

—That Cat. (Little Book Practice Reader Ser.). (J). (978-0-8136-0941-6(0)) Modern Curriculum Pr.

Higashi, Sandra & Higashi/Glaser Design Inc. Staff. Hello Kitty, Hello School! Kit: Includes Finger Puppets, Mini Book, & Stage. Hirashima, Jean, illus. 2003. (Hello Kitty Ser.). 16p. (J). (ps-3). 12.95 (978-0-8109-4596-8(7)) Abrams, Harry N. , Inc.

—Hello Kitty's Graduation Day. Hirashima, Jean, illus. 2004. 24p. (J). (ps-3). 12.95 (978-0-8109-4818-1(4)) Abrams, Harry N. , Inc.

Higashi/Glaser Design Inc. Staff. Hello Kitty, Hello Christmas! Higashi/Glaser Design Inc. Staff, illus. 2002. (Illus.). 24p. (J). (ps-3). 12.95 (978-0-8109-3543-3(0) , 53229572) Abrams, Harry N. , Inc.

—Hello Kitty, Hello Love! 2005. (Illus.). 24p. (J). (ps-3). bds. 6.95 (978-0-8109-5754-1(X) , Abrams Bks. for Young Readers) Abrams, Harry N. , Inc.

—Hello Kitty, Hello Love! Red Heart Secret Drawer Locked Diary. 2005. 128p. 12.95 (978-0-8109-8807-1(0) , Abrams Gifts and Stationery) Abrams, Harry N. , Inc.

—Hello Kitty Hello Nature! Explorer Kit. 2007. 16p. (J). (ps-3). 14.95 (***978-0-8109-9365-5(1)***) Abrams, Harry N. , Inc.

Higashi/Glaser Design Inc. Staff. Hello Kitty, Hello USA! 2005. (Illus.). 56p. (J). (ps-3). 12.95 (978-0-8109-5772-5(8) , Abrams Bks. for Young Readers) Abrams, Harry N. , Inc.

Higashi/Glaser Design Inc. Staff, illus. Hello Kitty, Hello World! 2000. 32p. (J). (ps-3). 12.95 (978-0-8109-3443-6(4)) Abrams, Harry N. , Inc.

Hiiragi, Aoi. Baron: The Cat Returns. 2005. (Baron Ser.). (Illus.). 224p. (YA). pap. 9.99 (978-1-59116-956-7(9)) Viz Media.

Hill, Merle Roddy. Kitty Goes Splash. Diez-Luckie, Cathy, illus. 2005. 12p. (J). pap. 5.00 (978-1-57274-823-1(0) , 2171, Bks. for Young Learners) Owen, Richard C. Pubs., Inc.

Hill, Sandi. Detective Dog & the Search for Cat, Vol. 4415. Kupperstein, Joel, ed. Leary, Catherine, illus. 1998. (Learn to Read Social Studies). 16p. (J). (ps-2). pap. 2.75 (978-1-57471-338-1(8) , 4415) Creative Teaching Pr., Inc.

Hill, Susan. Stuart at the Library. Halverson, Lydia, illus. 2001. (I Can Read Bks.). 32p. (J). (ps-1). pap. 3.99 (978-0-06-444303-6(5) , Harper Trophy); Bk. 1. 15.99 (978-0-06-029538-7(4)); Bk. 1. 15.89 (978-0-06-029632-2(1)) HarperCollins Pubs.

—Stuart Hides Out. Halverson, Lydia, illus. 2001. (I Can Read Bks.). 32p. (J). (ps-3). pap. 3.99 (978-0-06-444301-2(9) , Harper Trophy); Bk. 1. 14.95 (978-0-06-029536-3(8)); Bk. 1. 14.89 (978-0-06-029634-6(8)) HarperCollins Pubs.

—Stuart Hides Out. 2001. (gr. k-3). lib. bdg. 11.80 (978-0-613-35577-3(6)) Tandem Library Bks.

Hillert, Margaret. The No-Tail Cat: Or, I Like What I Am. 2004. (Illus.). 32p. (J). (978-1-59577-025-7(9)) Starfall Education.

—The No-Tail Cat or, I Like What I Am, 5 bks. 2005. (Illus.). 32p. (J). 6.95 (978-1-59577-024-0(0)) Starfall Education.

Himler, Ronald. Six Is So Much Less Than Seven. Himler, Ronald, illus. 2002. (Illus.). 40p. (J). 16.95 (978-1-887734-91-2(0)) Star Bright Bks., Inc.

Hinkes, Enid. Police Cat. Rasmussen, Wendy, illus. 2005. 32p. (J). (gr. k-3). 15.95 (978-0-8075-5758-7(7)) Whitman, Albert & Co.

Hobbs, Leigh. Old Tom, Man of Mystery. 2005. (Illus.). 32p. (J). (gr. k-2). per. 16.95 (978-1-56145-346-7(3)) Peachtree Pubs., Ltd.

—Old Tom's Guide to Being Good. Hobbs, Leigh, illus. 2006. 96p. (gr. 1-3). pap. 3.99 (978-0-7868-5694-7(7)) Hyperion Pr.

Hobbs, Leigh, illus. Old Tom's Holiday. 2004. 32p. (J). 16.95 (978-1-56145-316-0(1)) Peachtree Pubs., Ltd.

Hoberman, Mary Ann. One of Each. Priceman, Marjorie, illus. 2000. 32p. (J). (ps-3). pap. 7.99 (978-0-316-36644-1(7)) Little, Brown Bks. for Young Readers.

—One of Each. Priceman, Marjorie, illus. 2000. (J). (ps-ps). lib. bdg. 14.10 (978-0-613-30077-3(7)) Tandem Library Bks.

—One of Each. 2000. (978-0-606-22189-4(1)) Tandem Library Bks.

—The Two Sillies. Cravath, Lynne W., illus. 2004. 28p. (J). (ps-2). reprint ed. 16.00 (978-0-7567-7869-9(7)) DIANE Publishing Co.

Hobrecker, Ginny. Magic Memories of Mutts & More. 2006. 49p. per. 8.95 (***978-1-59824-371-0(3)***) E-BookTime LLC.

Hochenauer, Mary & Hochenauer-Fox, Lois. Sunny & Wondrous, Cat Cousins. 2006. (J). 15.95 (978-0-9778005-0-6(4)) Gnatcatcher Children'S Bks.

Hodgkins, Fran. The Cat of Strawberry Hill: A True Story. Sochor, Lesia, illus. 2005. (ps-3). 15.95 (978-0-89272-684-4(9)) Down East Bks.

Hogg, Gary. Look What the Cat Dragged In. Wohnoutka, Mike, illus. 2005. 32p. (J). (ps). 15.99 (978-0-525-46984-1(2) , Dutton Juvenile) Penguin Group (USA) Inc.

Hoh, Molly. Creating the Purrfect Tale. 2004. 179p. pap. 19.95 (978-1-4137-4443-9(5)) PublishAmerica, Inc.

Hollaway, David. The Three Little Figs: A Fruity Tale of Mischief & Trickery. 2006. (J). per. 17.95 (978-1-933211-00-8(8)) Quackenworth Publishing.

Holm, Jennifer & Hamel. To Scratch a Thief. Weinman, Brad, illus. 2005. (Stink Files Ser.: Bk.2). 144p. pap. 4.99 (978-0-06-052984-0(9) , Harper Trophy) HarperCollins Pubs.

Holm, Jennifer L. & Hamel. To Scratch a Thief. Weinman, Brad, illus. 2004. (Stink Files, Dossier Ser.: No. 2). 144p. (J). 14.99 (978-0-06-052982-6(2)) HarperCollins Pubs.

Holm, Jennifer L. & Hamel, Jonathan. The Postman Always Brings Mice. Weinman, Brad, illus. 2004. (Stink Files, Dossier Ser.). 144p. (J). 14.99 (978-0-06-052979-6(2)); lib. bdg. 15.89 (978-0-06-052980-2(6)) HarperCollins Pubs.

—You Only Have Nine Lives. Weinman, Brad, illus. 144p. (J). 2007. (Stink Files, Dossier Ser.: No. 3). pap. 4.99 (978-0-06-052987-1(3)); 2005. (Stink Files Ser.). lib. bdg. 15.89 (978-0-06-052986-4(5)); 2005. (Stink Files Ser.: No. 3). 14.99 (978-0-06-052985-7(7)) HarperCollins Pubs.

Holmes, Efner. Christmas Cat. 2002. (gr. 3-6). lib. bdg. 14.15 (978-0-8335-6642-3(3)) Tandem Library Bks.

Holmes, Linda. Jazz & Sam. 2002. (Reading Explosion Beginner Readers: Book 2). 32p. (J). pap. 9.95 (978-1-57921-445-6(2)) WinePress Publishing.

Holub, Joan. Lost & Found in Jumpstart Town. del Sur, Duendes, illus. 2000. (Jumpstart Workbooks). 32p. (J). (ps-k). pap. 3.99 (978-0-439-08789-6(9)) Scholastic, Inc.

—Scat Cats! Davis, Rich, illus. 2001. (Viking Easy-to-Read Ser.). 32p. (J). (gr. k-2). pap. 3.99 (978-0-14-130905-7(9) , Puffin) Penguin Group (USA) Inc.

—Scat Cats! 2001. (Puffin Easy-to-Read Ser.). (Illus.). (J). (978-0-606-21412-4(7)) Tandem Library Bks.

—Scat, Cats! 2001. (ps-2). lib. bdg. 11.80 (978-0-613-35620-6(9)) Tandem Library Bks.

Hood, Susan. Meet Trouble! Anastas, Margaret, ed. Stephenson, Kristina, illus. 2001. (First Friends, First Readers Ser.). 32p. (J). (ps-1). pap. 3.99 (978-0-448-42455-2(X) , Grosset & Dunlap) Penguin Group (USA) Inc.

—Meet Trouble! 2001. (First Friends, First Readers Ser.). (Illus.). (J). (978-0-606-21325-7(2)) Tandem Library Bks.

Hooper, Meredith. Celebrity Cat: With Paintings from Art Galleries Around the World. Willey, Bee, illus. 2006. 40p. 15.95 (978-1-84507-290-2(1)) Lincoln, Frances Ltd. GBR. *Dist:* Perseus Distribution.

Hope, Laura Lee. Freddie & Flossie & the Train Ride. Pyle, Chuck, illus. 2005. (Ready-To-Read Ser.). 32p. (J). (ps-ps). pap. 3.99 (978-1-4169-0269-0(4) , Aladdin) Simon & Schuster Children's Publishing.

—Freddie & Flossie & the Train Ride. 2006. (Ready-To-Read Ser.). (J). (ps-2). 21.35 (978-1-59961-097-9(3)) Spotlight.

Hope, Laura Lee. The Story of a China Cat. 2007. (ENG.). 72p. per. 87.99 (***978-1-4280-7317-3(5)***) IndyPublish.com.

Horn, Emily. Excuse Me... Are You a Witch? Pawlak, Pawel, illus. 32p. (J). 2005. pap. 6.95 (978-1-58089-103-5(9)); 2004. 15.95 (978-1-58089-093-9(8)) Charlesbridge Publishing, Inc.

Hosta, Dar. Mavis & Her Marvelous Mooncakes. 2006. (Illus.). (J). (ps-1). lib. bdg. 17.95 (***978-0-9721967-2-7(2)***) Brown Dog Bks.

Howe, Deborah & Howe, James. A Rabbit-Tale of Mystery. unabr. ed. 2004. (Bunnicula Ser.). 98p. (J). (gr. 3-7). pap. 29.00 incl. audio (978-0-8072-8204-5(9) , YYA139SP, Listening Library) Random Hse. Audio Publishing Group.

Howe, James. Bonicula: Una Historia de Misterio Conejil. 2000. Tr. of Bunnicula. (SPA.). (gr. 3-6). lib. bdg. 14.15 (978-0-613-85443-6(8)) Tandem Library Bks.

—Bunnicula & Friends: Hot Fudge. Mack, Jeff, illus. 2004. 42p. (J). lib. bdg. 15.00 (***978-1-4242-1149-4(2)***) Fitzgerald Bks.

—Bunnicula Strikes Again! 2004. (Bunnicula Ser.). 116p. (J). (gr. 3-7). pap. 29.00 incl. audio (978-0-8072-8213-7(8) , Listening Library) Random Hse. Audio Publishing Group.

—Bunnicula Strikes Again! Daniel, Alan, illus. 2007. (Bunnicula Ser.). 144p. (J). pap. 5.99 (***978-1-4169-3968-9(7)***, Aladdin) Simon & Schuster Children's Publishing.

—Bunnicula Strikes Again! 2001. (Bunnicula Ser.). (gr. 3-6). lib. bdg. 13.00 (978-0-613-49480-9(6)); (Illus.). (J). 11.64 (978-0-606-21090-4(3)) Tandem Library Bks.

—The Celery Stalks at Midnight. unabr. ed. 2004. (Bunnicula Ser.). 111p. (J). (gr. 3-7). pap. 29.00 incl. audio (978-0-8072-8357-8(6) , YA173SP, Listening Library) Random Hse. Audio Publishing Group.

—The Celery Stalks at Midnight. Morrill, Leslie H., illus. 2006. (Bunnicula Ser.). 144p. (J). pap. 4.99 (978-1-4169-2814-0(6) , Aladdin) Simon & Schuster Children's Publishing.

—The Celery Stalks at Midnight. 2002. (Bunnicula Ser.). (gr. 3-6). lib. bdg. 13.00 (978-0-613-50190-3(X)) Tandem Library Bks.

—Horace & Morris, but Mostly Delores. 2003. (Live Oak Readalong Ser.). (Illus.). (J). pap. 16.95 incl. audio (978-1-59112-241-8(4)) Live Oak Media.

—Hot Fudge. Mack, Jeff, illus. 2006. (Bunnicula & Friends Ser.). 48p. (J). pap. 3.99 (978-0-689-85750-8(0) , Aladdin) Simon & Schuster Children's Publishing.

—Hot Fudge. Mack, Jeff, tr. Mack, Jeff, illus. 2004. (Bunnicula & Friends Ser.). 48p. (J). 14.95 (978-0-689-85725-6(X) , Atheneum) Simon & Schuster Children's Publishing.

—Houndsley & Catina. Gay, Marie-Louise, illus. 2006. 48p. (J). (gr. k-2). 14.99 (978-0-7636-2404-0(7)) Candlewick Pr.

—Houndsley & Catina. Gay, Marie-Louise, illus. 2007. (Candlewick Sparks Ser.). 48p. (J). (gr. k-2). pap. 4.99 (978-0-7636-3293-9(7)) Candlewick Pr.

—Houndsley & Catina & the Birthday Surprise. Gay, Marie-Louise, illus. 2006. 48p. (J). (gr. k-3). 14.99 (978-0-7636-2405-7(5)) Candlewick Pr.

—Houndsley & Catina & the Birthday Surprise. Gay, Marie-Louise, illus. 2007. 48p. (J). (gr. k-3). pap. 4.99 (***978-0-7636-3640-1(1)***) Candlewick Pr.

—Howliday Inn. Munsinger, Lynn, illus. 2nd ed. 2006. 224p. (J). pap. 5.99 (978-1-4169-2815-7(4) , Aladdin) Simon & Schuster Children's Publishing.

—Howliday Inn. 2001. (Bunnicula Ser.). 11.64 (978-0-606-22105-4(0)) Tandem Library Bks.

—Nighty-Nightmare. unabr. ed. 2004. (Bunnicula Ser.). 128p. (J). (gr. 3-7). pap. 29.00 incl. audio (978-0-8072-8397-4(5) , YA201SP, Listening Library) Random Hse. Audio Publishing Group.

—Nighty-Nightmare. Morrill, Leslie, illus. 2007. 144p. (J). pap. 5.99 (***978-1-4169-3966-5(0)***, Aladdin) Simon & Schuster Children's Publishing.

—Pinky & Rex & the Just-Right Pet. 2002. (gr. k-3). lib. bdg. 11.80 (978-0-613-45091-1(4)) Tandem Library Bks.

—Rabbit-Cadabra! Daniel, Alan, illus. 1999. (Bunnicula & Friends Ser.). 48p. (J). (gr. k-3). pap. 5.95 (978-0-688-16699-1(7)) HarperCollins Pubs.

—Rabbit-Cadabra! Mack, Jeff, illus. 2006. (Bunnicula & Friends Ser.: Vol. 4). 48p. (J). 14.95 (978-0-689-85727-0(6) , Atheneum) Simon & Schuster Children's Publishing.

—Rabbit-cadabra! Mack, Jeff, illus. 2007. (Bunnicula & Friends Ser.). 48p. (J). pap. 3.99 (***978-0-689-85752-2(7)***, Aladdin) Simon & Schuster Children's Publishing.

—Return to Howliday Inn. Daniel, Alan, illus. 2007. (Bunnicula Ser.). 192p. (J). pap. 5.99 (***978-1-4169-3967-2(9)***, Aladdin) Simon & Schuster Children's Publishing.

—Scared Silly. Mack, Jeff, illus. (Bunnicula & Friends Ser.). (J). 2006. 40p. pap. 3.99 (978-0-689-85751-5(9) , Aladdin); 2005. 48p. 14.95 (978-0-689-85726-3(8) , Atheneum) Simon & Schuster Children's Publishing.

—The Vampire Bunny. Mack, Jeff, illus. 2005. (Bunnicula & Friends Ser.). 48p. (J). pap. 3.99 (978-0-689-85749-2(7) , Aladdin) Simon & Schuster Children's Publishing.

Hsu, Stacey W. Old Mo. Ritter, Adam, illus. 2006. (Rookie Reader Skill Set Ser.). 32p. (J). (gr. k-2). 19.50 (978-0-516-24981-0(9) , Children's Pr.) Scholastic Library Publishing.

Hsu, Stacey W. & Ritter, Adam. Old Mo. 2006. (Rookie Reader Ser.). (Illus.). 32p. (J). pap. 4.95 (978-0-516-24762-5(X) , Children's Pr.) Scholastic Library Publishing.

Hudelhoff, Allen H. Cats & Kids. 2002. 2. (Illus.). 32p. pap. 4.99 (978-0-7613-1783-8(X) , Millbrook Pr.) Lerner Publishing Group.

—Cats & Kids. Green, Anne Canevari, illus. 2002. (Silly Millies Ser.). 32p. (J). (gr. k-2). pap. 4.99 (978-0-7613-2668-7(5) , Millbrook Pr.) Lerner Publishing Group.

—Cats & Kids. 2002. (gr. k-3). lib. bdg. 13.00 (978-0-613-55805-1(7)) Tandem Library Bks.

Hughes, Shirley. Alfie & the Birthday Surprise. 1998. (Illus.). 32p. (J). (ps-1). 16.00 (978-0-688-15187-4(6)) HarperCollins Pubs.

—Alfie & the Birthday Surprise. 2007. (Illus.). 32p. (J). pap. 8.95 (***978-0-09-920862-4(8)***, Red Fox) Random Hse. Children's Bks. GBR. *Dist:* Independent Pubs. Group.

—Alfie & the Birthday Surprise. Hughes, Shirley, illus. 1999. (Illus.). 30p. (J). 9.99 (978-1-58048-086-4(1)) Sandvik Publishing.

Humphrey, 6 Packs. (Action Packs Ser.). 104p. (gr. 3-5). 44.00 (978-0-7635-8403-0(7)) Rigby Education.

Hunter, Erin. A Dangerous Path. 2004. (Warriors Ser.: Bk. 5). 336p. (J). (gr. 5 up). 16.99 (978-0-06-000006-6(6)); lib. bdg. 17.89 (978-0-06-052564-4(9)) HarperCollins Pubs.

—Dark River. 2008. (Warriors Ser.: Bk. 2). 352p. (J). lib. bdg. 17.89 (***978-0-06-089206-7(4)***); (gr. 5 up). 16.99 (***978-0-06-089205-0(6)***) HarperCollins Pubs.

—The Darkest Hour. (Warriors Ser.: Bk. 6). (Illus.). (J). 2006. 315p. (***978-1-4156-2257-5(4)***, Avon Bks.); 2005. 336p. pap. 6.99 (978-0-06-052585-9(1)); 2004. 336p. (gr. 5 up). 15.99 (978-0-06-000007-3(4)); 2004. 336p. (gr. 5 up). lib. bdg. 17.89 (978-0-06-052584-2(3)) HarperCollins Pubs.

—Dawn. 2006. (Warriors Ser.: Bk. 3). 352p. (J). pap. 6.99 (978-0-06-074457-1(X) , Harper Trophy); (Illus.). 15.99 (978-0-06-074455-7(3)); (Illus.). lib. bdg. 17.89 (978-0-06-074456-4(1)) HarperCollins Pubs.

—Fire & Ice. (Warriors Ser.: Bk. 2). 336p. (gr. 5 up). 2004. (Illus.). pap. 6.99 (978-0-06-052559-0(2)); 2003. (J). 16.99 (978-0-06-000003-5(1)); 2003. (J). lib. bdg. 17.89 (978-0-06-052556-9(8)) HarperCollins Pubs.

—Firestar's Quest. 2008. (Warriors Ser.). 544p. (J). pap. 7.99 (***978-0-06-113167-7(9)***) HarperCollins Pubs.

—Firestar's Quest. Chalk, Gary, illus. 2007. (Warriors Ser.). 528p. (J). (gr. 5 up). lib. bdg. 18.89 (*978-0-06-113166-0(0)); 17.99 (*978-0-06-113164-6(4)) HarperCollins Pubs.

—Forest of Secrets. (Warriors Ser.: Bk. 3). 336p. (J). (gr. 5 up). 2004. pap. 6.99 (978-0-06-052561-3(4)); 2003. (Illus.). 16.99 (978-0-06-000004-2(X)); 2003. (Illus.). lib. bdg. 17.89 (978-0-06-052560-6(6)) HarperCollins Pubs.

—Into the Wild. (Warriors Ser.: Bk. 1). 288p. (J). 2007. pap. 2.99 (978-0-06-128420-5(3) , Harper Trophy); 2003. (gr. 5 up). 16.99 (978-0-06-000002-8(3)) HarperCollins Pubs.

—The Lost Warrior. 2007. (Warriors Manga Ser.: No. 1). (J). (*978-0-06-124061-4(3)) HarperCollins Pubs.

—Midnight. (Warriors Ser.: Bk. 1). (J). 2006. 336p. pap. 6.99 (978-0-06-074451-9(0)); 2005. (Illus.). 320p. (gr. 5 up). lib. bdg. 16.89 (978-0-06-074450-2(2)); 2005. (Illus.). 320p. (gr. 5 up). 16.99 (978-0-06-074449-6(9)) HarperCollins Pubs.

—Moonrise. 2005. (Warriors Ser.: Bk. 2). (Illus.). 304p. (YA). (gr. 5 up). 15.99 (978-0-06-074452-6(9)) HarperCollins Pubs.

—Rising Storm. (Warriors Ser.: Bk. 4). 336p. (J). (gr. 5 up). 2005. pap. 6.99 (978-0-06-052563-7(0)); 2004. lib. bdg. 17.89 (978-0-06-052562-0(2)); 4. 2004. 16.99 (978-0-06-000005-9(8)) HarperCollins Pubs.

—Rising Storm. 2005. (Warriors Ser.: Bk. 4). (Illus.). 315p. (J). (gr. 5-9). lib. bdg. 13.04 (978-0-606-33340-5(1)) Tandem Library Bks.

—The Sight. (Warriors Ser.: Bk. 1). (J). 2008. 400p. pap. 6.99 (*978-0-06-089204-3(8) , Harper Trophy); 2007. 384p. 16.99 (*978-0-06-089201-2(3)); 2007. 384p. lib. bdg. 17.89 (*978-0-06-089203-6(X)) HarperCollins Pubs.

—Starlight. (Warriors Ser.: Bk. 4). (J). 2007. 320p. pap. 6.99 (978-0-06-082762-5(9) , Harper Trophy); 2006. 336p. 16.99 (978-0-06-082758-8(0)); 2006. 336p. lib. bdg. 17.89 (978-0-06-082760-1(2)) HarperCollins Pubs.

—Sunset. 2007. (Warriors Ser.: Bk. 6). (Illus.). (J). 303p. (gr. 5-9). per. 6.99 (*978-0-06-082771-7(8) , Harper Trophy); 320p. 16.99 (978-0-06-082769-4(6)); 320p. lib. bdg. 17.89 (978-0-06-082770-0(X)) HarperCollins Pubs.

—Twilight. (Warriors Ser.: Bk. 5). (J). 2007. 352p. pap. 6.99 (*978-0-06-082767-0(X) , Harper Trophy); 2006. (Illus.). 336p. 16.99 (978-0-06-082764-9(5)); 2006. (Illus.). 336p. lib. bdg. 16.89 (978-0-06-082766-3(1)) HarperCollins Pubs.

—Warriors Set: Into the Wild; Fire & Ice; Forest of Secrets; Rising Storm; A Dangerous Path; The Darkest Hour. 2007. (Warriors Ser.: Bks. 1-6). (J). pap. 36.99 (*978-0-06-147793-5(1) , Harper Trophy) HarperCollins Pubs.

—Warriors Boxed Set: Rising Storm; A Dangerous Path; The Darkest Hour. 2007. (Warriors Ser.: Bks. 4-6). (J). pap. 19.99 (*978-0-06-128452-6(1) , Harper Trophy) HarperCollins Pubs.

—Warriors Field Guide: Secrets of the Clans. 2007. (Warriors Ser.). (J). 144p. 15.99 (*978-0-06-123903-8(8)); 176p. lib. bdg. 16.89 (*978-0-06-123904-5(6)) HarperCollins Pubs.

Hunter, Erin & Jolley, Dan. The Lost Warrior. Barry, James L., illus. 2007. (Warriors Manga Ser.: No. 1). 112p. (J). (gr. 4-6). pap. 6.99 (*978-0-06-124020-1(6)) TOKYOPOP, Inc.

Hurd, Clement. The Merry Chase. 2005. (Illus.). 32p. (J). 15.95 (978-0-8118-4967-8(8)) Chronicle Bks. LLC.

Hussain, Jean. Cat Chat Anyone? 2001. 35p. (J). per. 8.95 (978-0-7414-0583-8(0)) Infinity Publishing.

Hutchins, Hazel. TJ & the Cats. 2002. (Illus.). 105p. (J). (gr. 2-7). lib. bdg. 13.00 (978-0-613-53571-7(5)) Tandem Library Bks.

Hutchins, Hazel J. Robyn's Best Idea. Cathcart, Yvonne, illus. 2001. (First Novels Ser.: Vol. 20). 62p. (gr. 1-5). (J). (978-0-88780-531-8(0)); 4.95 (978-0-88780-530-1(2)) Formac Publishing Co., Ltd. CAN. Dist: Casemate Pubs. & Bk. Distributors, LLC.

—TJ & the Cats. 2002. (Orca Young Readers Ser.). (Illus.). 108p. (J). (gr. 3-6). pap. 5.95 (978-1-55143-205-2(6)) Orca Bk. Pubs. USA.

Iddon, Joan. Daffodil Is My Cat. 2000. (J). (gr. k-2). 6.95 (978-0-533-13181-5(2)) Vantage Pr., Inc.

Ikumi, Mia. Tokyo Mew Mew (en Español), Vol. 4. 2006. (SPA., Illus.). 184p. reprint ed. pap. 10.95 (978-1-59497-172-3(2)) Public Square Bks.

Illsley, Amber Jo. Reilly - a Dreadful Adorable Cat. Webster, Christopher Lee, photos by. 2000. (Illus.). 116p. (J). pap. 6.95 (978-0-87714-664-3(0)) Denlingers Pubs., Ltd.

I'm Gronk & I'm Green. 2006. (J). (978-0-9777340-0-9(5)) Faux Paw Media Group.

Impey, Rose. Wanda Witch & the Wobbly Fang. Mcewen, Katharine, illus. 2006. (Scholastic Reader Level 3 Ser.). 32p. (J). pap. 3.99 (978-0-439-78450-4(6) , Cartwheel Bks.) Scholastic, Inc.

—Wanda Witch & Too Many Frogs. McEwen, Katharine, illus. 2006. (Scholastic Reader Ser.). 32p. (J). pap. 3.99 (978-0-439-78451-1(4) , Cartwheel Bks.) Scholastic, Inc.

Inches, Alison. My Visit with Periwinkle. Levy, David B., illus. ed. 2005. 22p. (J). lib. bdg. 15.00 (978-1-59054-970-4(8)) Fitzgerald Bks.

—My Visit with Periwinkle. Levy, David B., illus. 2003. (Ready-to-Read Ser.). 24p. (J). pap. 3.99 (978-0-689-85230-5(4) , Simon Spotlight/Nickelodeon) Simon & Schuster Children's Publishing.

—My Visit with Periwinkle. 2003. (gr. k-3). lib. bdg. 11.80 (978-0-613-58161-5(X)) Tandem Library Bks.

Inches, Alison, adapted by. Piggley Helps Out: Jakers! 2006. (Illus.). 24p. (J). lib. bdg. 15.00 (*978-1-4242-1553-9(6)) Fitzgerald Bks.

Ioan, Elwyn. Ici'r Ddol A'r Cathod Nadolig. 2005. (WEL., Illus.). 36p. pap. (978-0-86243-361-1(4)) Y Lolfa.

Ives, Bob. The Three Ants & the Cat. Fairy, Meg, illus. 2003. 40p. (J). (978-1-920832-07-0(6)) Four Heads Publishing Group Pty, Ltd.

Jack Stanley. The Coaster Cats Go to the Amusement Park. Breuer, Paul, illus. 2006. 19p. (J). pap. 5.99 (*978-0-9776284-0-7(X)) Forbes Literary Ltd. Inc.

Jackson, Leona Novy. The Littlest Christmas Kitten. Dupre, Kelly, illus. 2005. 32p. (J). 16.00 (978-0-930643-18-8(6) , 1250560) Images Unlimited.

Jacobsen, Annie. The Terrible Troll Cat. Hanson, Susan Jo, illus. 2006. (J). 16.95 (978-0-9778276-0-2(7)) Pickled Herring Pr.

Jaffe, Michele. Bad Kitty. 2007. 304p. (J). (gr. 7 up). pap. 8.99 (*978-0-06-078110-1(6) , HarperTeen) HarperCollins Pubs.

James, Brian. I'm No Fraidy Cat. Woodman, Ned, illus. 2007. (Catkid Ser.: Bk. 1). 96p. (J). pap. 3.99 (*978-0-439-88854-7(9)) Scholastic, Inc.

—Yucky Puppy Love. 2007. (Catkid Ser.). 96p. (J). pap. 3.99 (*978-0-439-88856-1(5) , Scholastic Paperbacks) Scholastic, Inc.

Jamieson-Brown, Heather. I Can't Find Bongo Kitty! Savage, Carol, illus. 2002. 16p. (J). 7.00 (978-0-9721946-1-7(4)) Paraclete Publishing.

Jane, Pamela. Milo & the Greatest Trick Ever! Johnson, Meredith, ed. Johnson, Meredith, illus. 2002. 32p. (J). 13.95 (978-1-59034-187-2(2)); (gr. 1-3). pap. 13.95 (978-1-59034-184-1(8)) Mondo Publishing.

Janelle-Engle, Terry. Fraidy Cat's Nightmare. 1999. (Illus.). 28p. (J). mass mkt. (978-0-7541-0864-1(3)) Minerva Pr. GBR. Dist: Unity Distribution.

Janovitz, Marilyn. We Love Christmas! 32p. (J). 9.95 (978-1-59014-126-7(1)); (Illus.). pap. 3.50 (978-1-59014-125-0(3)) Night Sky Bks.

Jarman, Julia. The Time-Travelling Cat & the Aztec Sacrifice. 2006. (Illus.). 164p. (J). (978-1-84270-516-2(4)) Andersen.

—The Time-Travelling Cat & the Egyptian Goddess. 2007. (Time-Travelling Cat Ser.). 112p. (J). (gr. 4-7). per. 7.95 (*978-1-84270-521-6(0)) Andersen GBR. Dist: Independent Pubs. Group.

—The Time-Travelling Cat & the Egyptian Goddess. l.t. ed. 2005. (Illus.). 156p. (J). pap. incl. audio (978-0-7540-7873-9(6) , CLP 454) BBC Audio.

—The Time-Travelling Cat & the Roman Eagle. (Illus.). 160p. (J). 16.95 (978-0-86264-861-9(0)) Andersen GBR. Dist: Trafalgar Square Publishing.

—The Time-Travelling Cat & the Tudor Treasure. 2007. 144p. (J). (gr. 4-7). 7.95 (*978-1-84270-616-9(0)) Andersen GBR. Dist: Independent Pubs. Group.

—The Time-Travelling Cat & the Tudor Treasure. l.t. ed. 2005. (J). pap. (978-1-4056-6005-1(8)) BBC Audio.

—Time Travelling Cat, the & the Roman. l.t. ed. 2006. pap. 16.95 (978-1-4056-6069-3(4)) BBC Audio GBR. Dist: BBC Audiobooks America.

Jarvis, Robin. The Alchemist's Cat. 2006. 304p. (YA). pap. 6.95 (978-0-8118-5450-4(7)) Chronicle Bks. LLC.

Jasper the Cat. 2003. (Chunky Animal Shaped Boards Ser.). (J). 10p. bds. 9.95 (978-0-7525-7854-5(5)); (Illus.). bds. 1.98 (978-0-7525-7775-3(1)) Parragon, Inc.

Jasper the Cat Chapter Set 1. 2004. (J). (978-1-58453-287-3(4)) Pioneer Valley Educational Pr., Inc.

Jeffries, Alison. Sam & the Bag. Andreasen, Dan, illus. 2004. (Green Light Readers Level 1 Ser.). 24p. (J). 12.95 (978-0-15-205152-5(X)); pap. 3.95 (978-0-15-205151-8(1)) Harcourt Children's Bks. (Green Light Readers).

Jenkins, Emily. Cinco Criaturas. Cortes, Eunice, tr. Bogacki, Tomek, illus. 2003. (Picture Bks.).Tr. of Five Creatures. (SPA.). (J). (978-970-690-648-9(7)) Planeta Mexicana Editorial S. A. de C. V.

—Love You When You Whine. Ruzzier, Sergio, illus. 2006. 32p. (J). 15.00 (978-0-374-34652-2(6)) Farrar, Straus & Giroux.

Jenkins, Emily & Bogacki, Tomek. Five Creatures. 2005. (Illus.). 32p. (J). (ps-ps). reprint ed. pap. 5.95 (978-0-374-42328-5(8) , Sunburst) Farrar, Straus & Giroux.

Jennings, Linda. Nine Naughty Kittens. Church, Caroline Jayne, illus. 1999. 20p. (J). (ps-1). 14.95 (978-1-888444-62-9(2)) Little Tiger Pr.

Jennings, Patrick. Faith & the Rocket Cat, Vol. 1. 1999. 240p. (gr. 3-7). pap. 4.99 (978-0-590-11005-1(5)) Scholastic, Inc.

Jennings, Patti. The Fleecy Kitty. 2003. (Fleecy Friends Ser.). (Illus.). 10p. (J). (ps). 9.99 (978-0-8431-7787-9(X) , Price Stern Sloan) Penguin Group (USA) Inc.

Jerome, Kate Boehm. Miniature Golf Madness. 2005. (Illus.). 32p. (J). 15.95 (978-0-9769087-3-9(5)) Vertical Connect Pr.

Jewell, Nancy Geller. Five Little Kittens. Sayles, Elizabeth, illus. 2004. 32p. (J). (ps-1). pap. 4.95 (978-0-618-43241-7(8) , Clarion Bks.) Houghton Mifflin Co. Trade & Reference Div.

Johansen, K. V. Pippin & Pudding. Lum, Bernice, illus. unabr. ed. 2002. (Pippin & Mabel Ser.). 32p. (J). (gr. k-3). (978-1-55074-631-0(6)) Kids Can Pr., Ltd.

—Pippin & Pudding. 2001. (ps-2). lib. bdg. 14.10 (978-0-613-57114-2(2)) Tandem Library Bks.

Johns, Barbara L. The Cat in the Candle Factory. Stich, Carolyn R., illus. 2005. 32p. (J). 15.00 (978-0-9762862-0-2(3)) Steeple Ridge Publications.

Johnson, David, illus. The Boy Who Drew Cats. 2007. (J). 25.65 (978-1-59961-305-5(0)) ABDO Publishing Co.

Johnson, Jane. The Secret Country. Stower, Adam, illus. 336p. (J). 2007. (Eidolon Chronicles Ser.). pap. 5.99 (*978-1-4169-3815-6(X) , Aladdin); 2006. (Chronicles of Eidolon Ser.: Bk. 1). (gr. 3-7). 14.95 (978-1-4169-0712-1(2)) Simon & Schuster Children's Publishing.

Johnson, Janet L. The Ritz Carlton Cat. l.t. ed. 1999. (Illus.). 12p. pap. 18.95 (978-0-9673389-0-3(5)) Johnson, Janet L.

Johnson, Kimberly P. Not Again, Mr. Cat! Smith, Landa, illus. 2003. 36p. (gr. k-3). 14.95 (978-1-57197-362-7(1)) Pentland Pr., Inc.

Johnson, Linda Rene'. Prissy, Where Are You? 2004. 37p. pap. 17.95 (978-1-4137-3009-8(4)) PublishAmerica, Inc.

Johnson, Paul Brett. Mr. Persnickety & Cat Lady. Johnson, Paul Brett, illus. 2000. (Illus.). 32p. (J). (ps-2). 16.99 (978-0-531-33283-2(7)); pap. 15.95 (978-0-531-30283-5(0)) Scholastic, Inc. (Orchard Bks.).

Johnson, Sandi. Cats on Vacation. Brundige, Britt, illus. 1999. 12p. (J). (ps-6). spiral bd. 6.99 (978-1-929063-46-8(6) , 146) Moons & Stars Publishing For Children.

—Dingbat: El Gato Voluntario. Johnson, Britt, ed. Short, Elizabeth, tr. from ENG. Trevinio, Juan, illus. l.t. ed. 2003. Orig. Title: Dingbat the Wayward Cat. (SPA.). 14p. (J). (gr. k-5). spiral bd. 4.99 (978-1-929063-85-7(7) , 326) Moons & Stars Publishing For Children.

Johnston, Tony. Cat, What Is That? Minor, Wendell, illus. 2001. 32p. (J). 15.95 (978-0-06-027742-0(4)); lib. bdg. 16.89 (978-0-06-027743-7(2)) HarperCollins Pubs.

Jolin, Dominique. Peek-a-Boo, Deecee! Perkes, Carolyn, tr. from FRE. Jolin, Dominique, illus. 2001. (Deecee Ser.). (Illus.). 14p. (J). bds. (978-1-894363-53-2(1)) Dominique & Friends.

Jones, Carl L., Sr. Joint Jerome Jones. 2004. (Illus.). 56p. (YA). pap. 12.99 (978-0-9748266-0-8(X)) Grampa Jones's Publishing Co.

Jones, Nancy. The Grandpaws. 2005. 57p. pap. 12.95 (978-1-4137-4778-2(7)) PublishAmerica, Inc.

Jones, Shelley. Sooty. 2000. (gr. k-3). lib. bdg. 11.80 (978-0-613-29751-6(2)) Tandem Library Bks.

Jones, Stephen. Scratch the Boatyard Cat. 2004. (Illus.). 56p. (J). pap. 18.95 (978-0-9718303-9-4(8)) Flat Hammock Pr.

Joosse, Barbara M. Nugget & Darling. Truesdell, Sue, illus. 2001. 32p. (J). (gr. k-3). 5.95 (978-0-618-11141-1(7) , Clarion Bks.) Houghton Mifflin Co. Trade & Reference Div.

Jordan, Sarah Clark. The BossQueen, Little BigBark, & the Sentinel Pup. 2004. (Illus.). 144p. (J). 14.95 (978-1-58246-115-1(5) , Tricycle Pr.) Ten Speed Pr.

Jude, Tracey. Mr. Topaz Takes a Walk. 2005. 43p. (J). spiral bd. 16.99 (978-1-4116-5691-8(1)) Lulu.com.

Kalar, Bonnie. The Cat & the Ant. Spreen, Kathe, illus. 1998. 8p. (J). (ps-2). pap. (978-1-891619-02-1(0)) Corona Pr.

Kaplan, Sheldon A. The Great Snuggleypuss. 2000. (Illus.). 22p. (J). 12.95 (978-0-9677993-3-9(3)) Kaplan, Sheldon A. & Assocs,.

Karlin, Nurit. The Fat Cat Sat on the Mat. Karlin, Nurit, illus. 1998. (I Can Read Bks.). (Illus.). 32p. (J). (ps-1). pap. 3.99 (978-0-06-444246-6(2)) HarperCollins Pubs.

—The Fat Cat Sat on the Mat. 1998. (I Can Read Bks.). (J). (ps-1). 10.79 (978-0-606-13379-1(8)) Tandem Library Bks.

Karon, Jan & Cecka, Melanie. Violet Goes to the Country. McCully, Emily Arnold, illus. 2007. 36p. (J). (ps). 16.99 (*978-0-670-06181-5(6) , Viking Juvenile) Penguin Group (USA) Inc.

Karon, Jan, et al. Violet Comes to Stay. McCully, Emily Arnold, illus. 2006. (Mitford Ser.). 36p. (J). (gr. k). 15.99 (978-0-670-06073-3(9) , Viking Juvenile) Penguin Group (USA) Inc.

Keats, Ezra Jack. Hi, Cat! Keats, Ezra Jack, illus. 2002. (Illus.). (J). 22.72 (978-0-7587-6792-9(7)) Book Wholesalers, Inc.

—Hi, Cat! Keats, Ezra Jack, illus. unabr. ed. 1998. (Illus.). (J). (gr. k-3). 25.95 incl. audio (978-0-87499-180-2(3)) Live Oak Media.

—Hi, Cat! Keats, Ezra Jack, illus. 1999. (Illus.). 40p. (J). (ps-3). 15.99 (978-0-670-88546-6(0) , Viking Juvenile) Penguin Group (USA) Inc.

—Kitten for a Day. Keats, Ezra Jack, illus. 2002. (Illus.). (J). 14.04 (978-1-4046-0836-8(2)) Book Wholesalers, Inc.

—Kitten for a Day. Keats, Ezra Jack, illus. 2002. (Illus.). 32p. (J). pap. 6.99 (978-0-14-230054-1(3) , Puffin) Penguin Group (USA) Inc.

—Pet Show. 2001. (ps-2). lib. bdg. 15.30 (978-0-613-44246-6(5)) Tandem Library Bks.

Keehn, Sally M. Gnat Stokes & the Foggy Bottom Swamp Queen. 2005. 160p. (YA). (gr. 5-7). 16.99 (978-0-399-24287-8(2) , Philomel) Penguin Group (USA) Inc.

Keene, Carolyn. The Kitten Caper. Jones, Jan Naimo, illus. 2005. 72p. (J). lib. bdg. 15.00 (*978-1-4242-0916-3(1)) Fitzgerald Bks.

Keens-Douglas, Richardo. The Miss Meow Pageant. Lafrance, Marie, illus. 1998. 32p. (J). (ps-2). pap. 6.95 (978-1-55037-536-7(9)); lib. bdg. 16.95 (978-1-55037-537-4(7)) Annick Pr., Ltd. CAN. Dist: Firefly Bks., Ltd.

Keep, Richard. A Thump from Upstairs: Starring Mr. Boo & Max. Keep, Richard, illus. 2005. (Illus.). 36p. (J). (ps-ps). 15.95 (978-1-56145-348-1(X)) Peachtree Pubs., Ltd.

Kehret, Peg. Spy Cat. 192p. (J). 2004. (gr. 3 up). pap. 5.99 (978-0-14-240151-4(X) , Puffin); 2003. (gr. 5-6). 15.99 (978-0-525-47046-5(8) , Dutton Juvenile) Penguin Group (USA) Inc.

—The Stranger Next Door. (J). 2003. (Illus.). 176p. (gr. 3-7). pap. 5.99 (978-0-14-250178-8(6) , Puffin); 2002. 160p. (gr. 4-8). 15.99 (978-0-525-46829-5(3) , Dutton Juvenile) Penguin Group (USA) Inc.

—The Stranger Next Door. 2003. (gr. 5-8). lib. bdg. 14.15 (978-0-613-82994-6(8)) Tandem Library Bks.

—Trapped. 2006. 192p. (J). (gr. 5). 16.99 (978-0-525-47728-0(4) , Dutton Juvenile) Penguin Group (USA) Inc.

Keller, Holly. A Bed Full of Cats. 2003. (Green Light Readers Level 2 Ser.). (Illus.). 24p. (J). 11.95 (978-0-15-204876-1(6)); pap. 3.95 (978-0-15-204836-5(7)) Harcourt Children's Bks. (Green Light Readers).

Kellogg, Steven. Rose for Pinkerton. 2002. (ps-2). lib. bdg. 15.30 (978-0-613-43641-0(5)) Tandem Library Bks.

Kelly, Martin & Adamac, Matt. Three Little Kittens. (Illus.). 6p. (J). 4.95 (978-1-59766-24-6(6)) Handprint Bks.

Kennedy, Joe. Lucy Goes to the Country. Canemaker, John, illus. 2004. (Alyson Wonderland Ser.). 32p. (ps-k). 15.95 (978-1-55583-428-9(0) , Alyson Wonderland) Alyson Pubns.

Kerr, Judith. Goodbye, Mog. 2003. (Illus.). 32p. (J). pap. 9.99 (978-0-00-714969-8(7)) HarperCollins Pubs. Ltd. GBR. Dist: Independent Pubs. Group.

—Goodbye, Mog. Kerr, Judith, illus. 2002. (Illus.). 32p. (J). 17.99 (978-0-00-714968-1(9)) HarperCollins Pubs. Ltd. GBR. Dist: Trafalgar Square Publishing.

—Mog & Bunny. Kerr, Judith, illus. 2005. (Illus.). 32p. (J). (ps-7). pap. 9.99 (978-0-00-717130-9(7)) HarperCollins Pubs. Ltd. GBR. Dist: Trafalgar Square Publishing.

—Mog & Me. 2002. (Illus.). 18p. (J). bds. 5.99 (978-0-00-138416-3(3)) HarperCollins Pubs. Ltd. GBR. Dist: Trafalgar Square Publishing.

—Mog & the Granny. (Illus.). 32p. (J). 17.99 (978-0-00-198176-8(5)); pap. 9.99 (978-0-00-664592-4(5)) HarperCollins Pubs. Ltd. GBR. Dist: Trafalgar Square Publishing.

—Mog & the Vet. (Illus.). 32p. (J). 19.99 (978-0-00-198211-6(7)); pap. 9.99 (978-0-00-664620-4(4)) HarperCollins Pubs. Ltd. GBR. Dist: Trafalgar Square Publishing.

—Mog Baby. 2005. (Illus.). 32p. (J). pap. 7.99 (978-0-00-717132-3(3)) HarperCollins Pubs. Ltd. GBR. Dist: Independent Pubs. Group.

—Mog Collection, 6 vols. Kerr, Judith, illus. 2007. 1p. (J). (gr. k-2). pap., pap., pap. 35.00 (*978-0-00-725944-1(1)) HarperCollins Pubs. Ltd. GBR. Dist: Independent Pubs. Group.

—Mog in Dark. 2006. (Illus.). 48p. (J). (ps). pap. 9.99 (978-0-00-717133-0(1) , HarperCollins Children's Bks.) HarperCollins Pubs. Ltd. GBR. Dist: Independent Pubs. Group.

—Mog in the Dark. (Illus.). 48p. (J). pap. 9.99 (978-0-00-662774-6(9)) HarperCollins Pubs. Ltd. GBR. Dist: Trafalgar Square Publishing.

—Mog in the Garden. Kerr, Judith, illus. 2003. (Illus.). 16p. (J). pap. 6.99 (978-0-00-137476-8(1)) HarperCollins Pubs. Ltd. GBR. Dist: Independent Pubs. Group.

—Mog on Fox Night. (Illus.). 32p. (J). pap. 9.99 (978-0-00-664501-6(1)); 2004. pap. 7.99 (978-0-00-717136-1(6)) HarperCollins Pubs. Ltd. GBR. Dist: Trafalgar Square Publishing, Independent Pubs. Group.

—Mog the Forgetful Cat. Kerr, Judith, illus. 2005. (Illus.). 40p. (J). (ps). 7.99 (978-0-00-722895-9(3) , HarperCollins Children's Bks.) HarperCollins Pubs. Ltd. GBR. Dist: Independent Pubs. Group.

—Mog the Forgetful Cat. 30th anniv. ed. 2000. (Illus.). 40p. (J). (ps-2). 19.99 (978-0-00-195507-3(1)) HarperCollins Pubs. Ltd. GBR. Dist: Independent Pubs. Group.

—Mog the Forgetful Cat: Book & Toy Gift Set. 2005. (Illus.). 40p. (J). (ps). 16.99 (978-0-00-721134-0(1) , HarperCollins Children's Bks.) HarperCollins Pubs. Ltd. GBR. Dist: Independent Pubs. Group.

—Mog Vee Ee Tee. 2005. (Illus.). 32p. (J). (ps). pap. 9.99 (978-0-00-717128-6(5) , HarperCollins Children's Bks.) HarperCollins Pubs. Ltd. GBR. Dist: Independent Pubs. Group.

—Mog's Amazing Birthday Caper. (Illus.). 48p. (J). 2005. pap. 8.99 (978-0-00-717131-6(5)); 2002. pap. 8.99 (978-0-00-663383-9(8)) HarperCollins Pubs. Ltd. GBR. Dist: Independent Pubs. Group.

—Mog's Bad Thing. 2004. (Illus.). 32p. (J). pap. 8.99 (978-0-00-664755-3(3) , HarperSport) HarperCollins Pubs. Ltd. GBR. Dist: Independent Pubs. Group.

—Mog's Christmas. Kerr, Judith, illus. 2005. (Illus.). 32p. (J). (ps-3). pap. 9.99 (978-0-00-717135-4(8)) HarperCollins Pubs. Ltd. GBR. Dist: Trafalgar Square Publishing.

—Mog's Christmas. (Illus.). 2004. 28p. 7.95 (978-0-00-716705-0(9)); 2005. 32p. 14.00 (978-0-00-719366-0(1)) HarperCollins Pubs. Ltd. GBR. Dist: Trafalgar Square Publishing, Independent Pubs. Group.

—Mog's Christmas. l.t. ed. 2001. (Illus.). 32p. (J). (ps-2). 8.99 (978-0-00-664146-9(6)) Headline Bk. Publishing GBR. Dist: Trafalgar Square Publishing.

—Mog's Family of Cats. 2003. (Illus.). 18p. (J). pap. 6.99 (978-0-00-138415-6(5)) HarperCollins Pubs. Ltd. GBR. Dist: Independent Pubs. Group.

—Mog's Kittens. Kerr, Judith, illus. 2002. (Illus.). 16p. (J). pap. 6.99 (978-0-00-136000-6(0)) HarperCollins Pubs. Ltd. GBR. Dist: Independent Pubs. Group.

Kerr, Judith. Twinkles, Arthur & Puss. Kerr, Judith, illus. 2007. (Illus.). 40p. 22.95 (*978-0-00-725446-0(6)) HarperCollins Pubs. Ltd. GBR. Dist: Independent Pubs. Group.

Kerr, Judith, illus. Mog & the Granny. 2005. 32p. (J). (ps-7). pap. 9.99 (978-0-00-717127-9(7)) HarperCollins Pubs. Ltd. GBR. Dist: Trafalgar Square Publishing.

—Mog Time: Six Stories about Mog. 2005. 208p. (J). 24.99 (978-0-00-719360-8(2)) HarperCollins Pubs. Ltd. GBR. Dist: Trafalgar Square Publishing.

Kettner, Christine. Oliver Cat on Planet B. Kettner, Christine, illus. 2003. (Illus.). 48p. (J). (gr. 1-3). 15.99 (978-0-525-47094-6(8) , Dutton Juvenile) Penguin Group (USA) Inc.

Khalsa, Dayal Kaur. Green Cat. 2002. (Illus.). 24p. (J). (gr. k-3). 14.95 (978-0-88776-586-5(6)) Tundra Bks., Inc./Livres Toundra, Inc. CAN. Dist: Random Hse., Inc.

—Snow Cat. 1999. (gr. k-3). lib. bdg. 18.80 (978-0-613-71032-9(0)) Tandem Library Bks.

Kim, Mi-Kyung. 11th Cat, Vol. 2. 2006. (Illus.). 200p. (YA). pap. 10.95 (*978-89-527-4473-9(X)) ICE Kunion KOR. Dist: Diamond Bk. Distributors.

—11th Cat, Vol. 3. 2006. (Illus.). 200p. (YA). pap. 10.95 (*978-89-527-4481-4(0)) ICE Kunion KOR. Dist: Diamond Bk. Distributors.

C D

—11th Cat, Vol. 4. 2006. (Illus.). 200p. (YA). pap. 10.95 (***978-89-527-4500-2(0)***) ICE Kunion KOR. *Dist:* Diamond Bk. Distributors.

Kim, Mikyung. 11th Cat: Vol. 1. 2005. (Illus.). 180p. (YA). pap. 10.95 (978-89-527-4461-6(6)) Diamond Bk. Distributors.

Kimmel, Eric A. When Mindy Saved Hanukkah. McClintock, Barbara, illus. 2005. 32p. (J). (ps-3). pap. 5.99 (978-0-439-76990-7(6) , Scholastic Paperbacks) Scholastic, Inc.

King-Smith, Dick. The Catlady. 80p. (J). 2007. (gr. 1-4). 5.50 (***978-0-440-42031-6(8)*** , Yearling); 2006. (Illus.). (gr. 2-5). lib. bdg. 17.99 (978-0-375-92985-4(1) , Knopf Bks. for Young Readers) Random Hse. Children's Bks.

—The Catlady. Eastwood, John, illus. 2006. 80p. (J). (gr. 2-5). 15.95 (978-0-375-82985-7(7) , Knopf Bks. for Young Readers) Random Hse. Children's Bks.

—The Nine Lives of Aristotle. Graham, Bob, illus. 2003. 80p. (J). (gr. 1-4). 14.99 (978-0-7636-2260-2(5)) Candlewick Pr.

—Three Terrible Trins. 105p. (J). pap. 4.99 (978-0-8072-1482-4(5) , Listening Library) Random Hse. Audio Publishing Group.

Kirk, Daniel. Rex Tabby: Cat Detective. (Illus.). 144p. (J). 2005. (gr. 2-5). pap. 3.99 (978-0-439-45287-8(2) , Scholastic Paperbacks); 2004. pap. 9.95 (978-0-439-45286-1(4) , Orchard Bks.) Scholastic, Inc.

Kirkpatrick, June. Barn Kitty. Peterson, Lori, illus. l.t. ed. 1999. 32p. (J). (ps-3). pap. 10.95 (978-0-9660239-5-4(1)) Azro Pr., Inc.

Kitamura, Satoshi. El Bano de Gato. 2001. (SPA.). 114p. (J). (978-84-207-8949-1(6)) Grupo Anaya, S.A. ESP. *Dist:* Lectorum Pubns., Inc.

—Gato Busca un Amigo. 2000. Tr. of Cat Finds a Friend. (SPA., Illus.). 114p. (J). 9.95 (978-84-207-8948-4(8)) Grupo Anaya, S.A. ESP. *Dist:* Distribooks, Inc., Lectorum Pubns., Inc.

—Gato Tiene Sueno. 1998. (SPA., Illus.). (J). (ps). per. (978-968-16-5537-2(0)) Fondo de Cultura Economica MEX. *Dist:* Lectorum Pubns., Inc.

—Gato Tiene Sueno. 2000. (SPA., Illus.). 14p. (J). 9.95 (978-84-207-8103-7(7)) Grupo Anaya, S.A. ESP. *Dist:* Distribooks, Inc.

—Me & My Cat? Kitamura, Satoshi, illus. 2000. (Illus.). 40p. (J). (ps-3). 16.00 (978-0-374-34906-6(1) , Farrar, Straus & Giroux (BYR)) Farrar, Straus & Giroux.

—Me & My Cat? 2005. (Illus.). 40p. (J). reprint ed. pap. 6.95 (978-0-374-44796-0(9) , Sunburst) Farrar, Straus & Giroux.

Kitten. (Buggy Buddies Ser.). (Illus.). (J). (ps). bds. (978-1-56021-350-5(7) , 201) W.J. Fantasy, Inc.

Kitten chased a Fly 6 Packs. Individual Title. (gr. 1-2). 22.00 (978-0-7635-9163-2(7)) Rigby Education.

Kittens. 2002. (Three Minute Tales Ser.). 32p. (J). 5.98 (978-0-7525-3833-4(0)); 7.95 (978-0-7525-5539-3(1)) Parragon, Inc.

Kittens: Individual Title Six-Packs. (Literatura 2000 Ser.). (ps-1). 28.00 (978-0-7635-0033-7(X)) Rigby Education.

Kitten's House. Date not set. (Illus.). (J). bds. 4.98 (978-1-4054-0786-1(7)) Parragon, Inc.

Kitten's New Friend. 2002. 10p. (J). bds. 2.50 (978-1-56021-397-0(3)) W.J. Fantasy, Inc.

Kitty Heaven's in the Sky! 2004. (J). 4.95 (***978-0-9791362-1-4(0)***) Tony Tales.

The Kitty with the Racoon Tail. 2006. (J). per. (***978-0-9772425-7-3(9)***) BLPH, Inc.

Klein, Abby. Halloween Fraidy-Cat. McKinley, John, illus. 2006. (Ready, Freddy! Ser.: No. 8). 96p. (J). pap. 3.99 (978-0-439-78457-3(3) , Blue Sky Pr., The) Scholastic, Inc.

Kleven, Elisa. The Wishing Ball. 2006. (Illus.). 32p. (J). 16.00 (978-0-374-38449-4(5)) Farrar, Straus & Giroux.

Kline, Suzy. Horrible Harry & the Goog. Remkiewicz, Frank, illus. 64p. (J). (gr. 2). 2006. pap. 3.99 (978-0-14-240728-8(3) , Puffin); 2005. 13.99 (978-0-670-05992-8(7) , Viking Juvenile) Penguin Group (USA) Inc.

Kneen, Maggie. Halloween Kittens. Kneen, Maggie, illus. 2004. (Illus.). 20p. (J). 15.95 (978-0-8118-4228-0(2)) Chronicle Bks. LLC.

Knoll, Anne. The Secret Life of Thomas Bradford. 1998. 155p. (J). 9.99 (978-0-88092-421-4(7) , 4217) Royal Fireworks Publishing Co.

Kobayashi, Makoto. The Ideal Cat Vol. 9. 2004. (What's Michael? Ser.). 88p. pap. 8.95 (978-1-59307-120-2(5)) Dark Horse Comics.

Koda-Callan, Elizabeth. Cat Next Door. Koda-Callan, Elizabeth, illus. 2005. (Illus.). 48p. (J). (ps-ps). 9.95 (978-0-7611-3829-7(3) , 13829) Workman Publishing Co., Inc.

Kojima, Naomi. Singing Shijimi Clams. Kojima, Naomi, illus. 2006. (Illus.). 32p. (J). 15.95 (978-1-933605-12-8(X)) Kane/Miller Bk. Pubs., Inc.

Koontz, Robin Michal. Why a Dog? By A. Cat. 2000. (Hello Reader! Ser.). (978-0-606-18892-0(4)) Tandem Library Bks.

Krailing, Tessa. The Cat Burglar. Lewis, Jan & Eastwood, John, illus. 1998. (Petsitters Club Ser.: No. 2). 96p. (J). (gr. 2-5). pap. 4.99 (978-0-7641-0570-8(1)) Barron's Educational Series, Inc.

—El Ladron de Gatos. (Club de las Mascotas Coleccion). (SPA.). 96p. (J). (gr. 3). (978-84-88061-89-8(7)) Serres, Ediciones, S. L. ESP. *Dist:* Lectorum Pubns., Inc.

Kreloff, Elliot, illus. I'm Going to Read (Level 2): Tic & Tac Clean Up. 2007. (I'm Going to Read Ser.). 32p. (J). pap. 3.95 (978-1-4027-4243-9(6)) Sterling Publishing Co., Inc.

—No More TV, Sleepy Cat. 2005. (I'm Going to Read Ser.). 28p. (J). (ps-k). pap., pap. 3.95 (978-1-4027-2508-1(6)) Sterling Publishing Co., Inc.

Krensky, Stephen. Fraidy Cats. Lewin, Betsy, illus. 2004. 32p. (J). lib. bdg. 15.00 (978-1-59054-383-2(1)) Fitzgerald Bks.

Krensky, Stephen. Snack Attack. Curtis, Stacy, illus. 2008. (Ready-to-Reads Ser.). 32p. (J). pap. 3.99 (***978-1-4169-0238-6(4)***); lib. bdg. 13.89 (***978-1-4169-0239-3(2)***) Simon & Schuster Children's Publishing. (Aladdin).

Kroll, Jeri. A Coat of Cats. James, Ann, illus. 32p. pap. (978-0-7344-0118-2(3) , Lothian Bks.) Hachette Livre Australia.

Kroll, Jeri & James, Ann. A Coat of Cats. (Illus.). 32p. (978-0-85091-953-0(3) , Lothian Bks.) Hachette Livre Australia.

Krulik, Nancy E. Cat's Big Night. 1999. Tr. of Dog Behind Bars. (gr. 3-6). lib. bdg. 11.80 (978-0-613-21313-4(0)) Tandem Library Bks.

Kuper, Peter. Theo & the Blue Note. Kuper, Peter, illus. 2006. (Illus.). 32p. (J). (ps). 15.99 (978-0-670-06137-2(9) ; Viking Juvenile) Penguin Group (USA) Inc.

Kurkoski, Bettina. My Cat Loki, Vol. 1. 2006. pap. 9.99 (978-1-59816-731-3(6) , Tokyopop Adult) TOKYOPOP, Inc.

Kuskin, Karla. So, What's It Like to Be a Cat? Lewin, Betsy, illus. (J). 2008. 40p. 6.99 (***978-0-689-85930-4(9)*** , Aladdin); 2005. 32p. 15.95 (978-0-689-84733-2(5) , Atheneum) Simon & Schuster Children's Publishing.

Kuskin, Karla. The Upstairs Cat. Fine, Howard, illus. 2003. 32p. (J). (gr. k-3). 5.95 (978-0-618-31676-2(0) , Clarion Bks.) Houghton Mifflin Co. Trade & Reference Div.

Kwon, Yoon-duck. My Cat Copies Me. Kwon, Yoon-duck, illus. 2007. (Illus.). 32p. (J). (ps-2). 15.95 (978-1-933605-26-5(X)) Kane/Miller Bk. Pubs., Inc.

La Borde, Roger & Biddulph, Robert. Hello Kitty, Hello Love! 2003. (Illus.). 24p. (J). (ps-3). 12.95 (978-0-8109-8538-4(1)) Abrams, Harry N. , Inc.

Lacy, Ann. Minsty's Amazing Journey. 2004. 92p. (J). per. 9.95 (978-0-9939965-34-2(8)) Macedon Production Co.

Laden, Nina. Romeow & Drooliet. 2005. (Illus.). 44p. (J). 16.95 (978-0-8118-3973-0(7)) Chronicle Bks. LLC.

Lakin, Patricia. Clarence the Copy Cat. Manders, John, illus. 2007. 32p. (J). (ps-3). pap. 6.99 (978-0-440-41725-5(2) , Dragonfly Bks.) Random Hse. Children's Bks.

Lambert, Marilyn. Franny & Roxxy. 1999. (J). (gr. k-3). pap. 6.95 (978-0-533-12820-4(X)) Vantage Pr., Inc.

LaMear, Arline. Lewis & Clark, the Astoria Cats. Goza, Benjamin, illus. 2002. 32p. (J). (gr. 3-7). pap. 9.95 (978-0-9720394-0-6(6)) Lucky Cat Publishing.

Landalf, Helen. The Secret Night World of Cats. Rimland, Mark, illus. 1998. 32p. (J). (gr. k-3). pap. 16.95 (978-1-57525-117-2(5)) Smith and Kraus Publishers, Incorporated.

Landau, Emily Fisher, et al. Mishoo, Cosmopolitan Cat. 2000. (Illus.). (J). (978-0-87427-125-6(8)) Whitney Museum of American Art.

Lander, C. F. Willow: A Magical Cat. 2002. 108p. pap. 13.95 (978-1-59286-096-8(6)) PublishAmerica, Inc.

—Willow & the Ice Fairies. 2004. 88p. pap. 14.95 (978-1-4137-1638-2(5)) PublishAmerica, Inc.

Landstrom, Olof & Landstrom, Lena. Boo & Baa Have Company. Sandin, Joan, tr. from SWE. 2006. (Illus.). 40p. (J). 15.00 (978-91-29-66546-8(9)) R & S Bks. SWE. *Dist:* Macmillan.

Langley, Jonathan. Missing! Langley, Jonathan, illus. 2000. (Illus.). 32p. (J). (ps-k). 15.95 (978-0-7614-5078-8(5) , Cavendish Children's Bks.) Cavendish, Marshall Corp.

—Missing! 2007. (Illus.). 32p. (J). pap. 7.95 (***978-1-84507-740-2(7)***) Lincoln, Frances Ltd. GBR. *Dist:* Perseus Distribution.

Langreuter, Jutta & Hebrock, Andrea. Belly Buttons. 1999. (Illus.). 32p. (J). (ps-2). 12.95 (978-0-7641-5216-0(5)) Barron's Educational Series, Inc.

Larsen, Alison. Birds Don't Say 'Bow ¿ Wow!' 2006. (Illus.). 28p. (J). per. 12.95 (978-1-59453-937-4(5) , Airleaf Publishing) Airleaf Publishing & Bookselling.

Lascaro, Ruth. Bed Full of Cats. 1999. (Green Light Readers Ser.). (978-0-606-17485-5(0)) Tandem Library Bks.

Lashley, Beverly. One Can Never Have Too Many Cats!! Morrow, Jason, illus. 2006. (J). (978-0-9786835-0-4(1)) Two Tired Teachers Connection, Inc., The.

LaTondre, Richard. Grandpa's Cat. 2006. 9.00 (***978-0-8059-7343-3(5)***) Dorrance Publishing Co., Inc.

Lauber, Patricia. Purrfectly Purrfect: Life at the Acatemy. Lewin, Betsy, illus. 2000. 80p. (J). (gr. 3-7). 15.89 (978-0-06-029209-6(1)); 15.95 (978-0-688-17299-2(7)) HarperCollins Pubs.

The Laughing Lavender Field. 2005. (J). 5.00 (978-0-9765731-0-4(5)) DTJ, LLC.

Laurie, Peter. Mauby & the Hurricane. 2007. 56p. pap. 16.00 (***978-1-4050-7718-7(2)***) Macmillan Caribbean GBR. *Dist:* Interlink Publishing Group, Inc.

Lawson, Janet. Audrey & Barbara. Lawson, Janet, illus. 2002. (Illus.). 32p. (J). (ps-3). 13.95 (978-0-689-83896-5(4) , Atheneum) Simon & Schuster Children's Publishing.

Lawson, Julie. The Klondike Cat. Mombourquette, Paul, illus. 2002. 32p. (J). (gr. k-3). (978-1-55337-013-0(9)) Kids Can Pr., Ltd.

—Klondike Cat. Mombourquette, Paul, illus. 2004. 32p. (J). (gr. k-3). (978-1-55337-766-5(4)) Kids Can Pr., Ltd.

Lazo, Caroline. Someday When My Cat Can Talk. Brooker, Kyrsten, illus. 2008. 32p. (J). (ps-3). lib. bdg. 19.99 (***978-0-375-93754-5(4)*** , Schwartz & Wade Bks.) Random Hse. Children's Bks.

Lazo, Caroline Evensen. Someday When My Cat Can Talk. Brooker, Kyrsten, illus. 2008. 32p. (J). (***978-0-375-83754-8(X)*** , Schwartz & Wade Bks.) Random Hse. Children's Bks.

Le Guin, Ursula K. Catwings. Schindler, S. D., illus. 1999. (Catwings Ser.: No. 1). 39p. (J). (gr. 1-4). pap. 3.95 (978-0-531-07110-6(3) , Orchard Bks.) Scholastic, Inc.

—Catwings. 2003. (Catwings Ser.: No. 1). (gr. 3-6). lib. bdg. 11.80 (978-0-613-70842-5(3)) Tandem Library Bks.

—Catwings Return. 2003. (Catwings Ser.: No. 2). (gr. 3-6). lib. bdg. 11.80 (978-0-613-65072-4(7)) Tandem Library Bks.

—Jane on Her Own. Schindler, S. D., illus. 1999. (Catwings Ser.: No. 4). 48p. (J). (gr. 1-4). 15.99 (978-0-531-33133-0(4) , Orchard Bks.) Scholastic, Inc.

—Jane on Her Own. 2003. (Catwings Ser.: No. 4). (gr. k-3). lib. bdg. 11.80 (978-0-613-85117-6(X)) Tandem Library Bks.

—Wonderful Alexander & the Catwings. (Catwings Ser.: No. 3). (gr. k-3). 2003. lib. bdg. 11.80 (978-0-613-85116-9(1)); 1999. (978-0-606-17403-9(6)) Tandem Library Bks.

Leaney, Cindy. Rainy Day Play. Whitehouse, Patty, ed. King, Sue & Wilks, Peter, illus. 2004. (Friendly Phonics Ser.). 24p. (J). lib. bdg. 14.95 (978-1-59054-047-3(6)) Fitzgerald Bks.

LeapFrog Staff, compiled by. Casey Cat Has a Hat. 2001. (J). (ps-2). spiral bd. 10.95 (978-1-58605-032-0(X)) LeapFrog Enterprises, Inc.

Lear, Edward. Buho y la Gatita.Tr. of Owl & the Cat. (SPA., Illus.). 32p. (J). 14.95 (978-84-261-3023-5(2)) Juventud, Editorial ESP. *Dist:* AIMS International Bks., Inc.

Leatham, Alan D. Four Cats, Five Monkeys, Absurd Birds & Other Fanciful Stuff. 2006. 108p. pap. 16.95 (***978-1-4241-0692-9(3)***) PublishAmerica, Inc.

Lee, Meredith Meade. Sissy & Smooch: A Tale of a Kitten & Her Angel. Tidey, Joel, illus. 2000. (J). (ps-3). 39.95 (978-0-9706254-0-3(5)) Meredith International, LLC.

Lefèvre, A. M. Pws Esgid Uchel. 2005. (WEL., Illus.). 10p. (978-0-86381-647-5(9)) Gwasg Carreg Gwalch.

Lement, Wendy. Keri Tarr: Cat Detective. Burrows, Jeffrey Scott, illus. 2004. 80p. pap. 9.95 (978-1-891369-52-0(0)) Breakaway Bks.

Lenhard, Elizabeth. Cats & Dogs. 2001. (Illus.). 144p. (J). (gr. 2-5). pap. 4.99 (978-0-439-22569-4(8)) Scholastic, Inc.

LePage, Deborah. Scary Stories to Tell Your Pet: The Kitty Man. 2003. 108p. pap. 13.95 (978-1-59286-878-0(9)) PublishAmerica, Inc.

Lesynski, Loris. Catmagic. Lesynski, Loris, illus. 1998. (Illus.). 32p. (J). (ps-2). pap. 5.95 (978-1-55037-532-9(6)); lib. bdg. 15.95 (978-1-55037-533-6(4)) Annick Pr., Ltd. CAN. *Dist:* Firefly Bks., Ltd.

Levack, Joseph, photos by. Picture Me Three Little Kittens. 1999. (Picture Me Ser.). (Illus.). 10p. (J). (ps up). bds. 4.99 (978-1-57151-549-0(6)) Playhouse Publishing.

Lewin, Betsy. Cat Count. rev. ed. 2003. (Illus.). 32p. (J). (ps-2). 14.95 (978-0-8050-6747-7(7) , Holt, Henry & Co. Bks. For Young Readers) Holt, Henry & Co.

Light, Steve. Rocking Horse: A Press-Out & Play Book. Hirashima, Jean, illus. 2002. (Hello Kitty, Hello Playtime! Ser.). 8p. (J). (ps-1). 8.95 (978-0-8109-1233-5(3)) Abrams, Harry N. , Inc.

Lindi, Nkululeko. Three Fat Cats: Luvale Version. Sakapaji, tr. 2001. (Illus.). 8p. pap. 0.45 (978-0-521-01551-6(0)) Cambridge Univ. Pr.

—Three Fat Cats: Silozi Version. Mwendende, tr. 2001. (Illus.). 8p. pap. 0.45 (978-0-521-01552-3(9)) Cambridge Univ. Pr.

Lipp, Frederick J. That Cat Is Not for Sale. Bruce, Britta, illus. 1998. 24p. (J). (ps-3). pap. 5.99 (978-0-9664248-0-5(8)) Sloane Pubns.

Lisi, Charlotte. I Am Special. Ortega, David, illus. 2006. 16p. (J). (***978-1-4120-8911-1(5)***) Trafford Publishing.

Little, Jean. The Birthday Girl. Lawrason, June, illus. 2004. 64p. (J). lib. bdg. 20.00 (***978-1-4242-1256-9(1)***) Fitzgerald Bks.

Little Kitten. 2003. (Goodnight Mr. Moon Ser.). (Illus.). (J). bds. 2.98 (978-0-7525-4743-5(7)) Parragon, Inc.

Little Kitten, Big Cat: First Grade Big Books. (On Our Way to English Ser.). (gr. 1 up). 29.95 (978-0-7578-1511-9(1)) Rigby Education.

Little Kitten, Big Cat: Small Versions of Big Books. (On Our Way to English Ser.). (gr. 1 up). 29.00 (978-0-7578-7227-3(1)) Rigby Education.

Lloyd, Sam. Mr. Pusskins: A Love Story. Lloyd, Sam, illus. 2006. (Illus.). 32p. (J). (ps-3). 14.95 (978-1-4169-2517-0(1) , Atheneum) Simon & Schuster Children's Publishing.

Lobel, Anita. Nini Here & There. Lobel, Anita, illus. 2007. 32p. (J). (ps-2). 16.99 (978-0-06-078767-7(8)); (Illus.). lib. bdg. 17.89 (978-0-06-078768-4(6)) HarperCollins Pubs.

—One Lighthouse, One Moon. Lobel, Anita, illus. 2000. (Illus.). 48p. (J). (ps up). 16.99 (978-0-688-15539-1(1)) HarperCollins Pubs.

Long, Olivia. Too Many Kittens. Long, Olivia, illus. Date not set. (Pets & Their People Ser.). (Illus.). 32p. (J). (ps-4). (978-1-880042-09-0(6)) Shelf-Life Bks.

Louise, T. Paula. The Baggage Comes to Town. 2002. (Illus.). 32p. (J). (gr. 1-5). pap. 7.99 (978-0-9719775-0-1(X)) Idea & Design Works, LLC.

Lucas, Celia. Madoc's Prickly Problem. 2000. (Illus.). 132p. pap. 11.95 (978-1-85902-777-6(6)) Beekman Bks., Inc.

Lueck, Andrew. Chicabee. 2006. 32p. 16.95 (978-0-9774547-0-9(3)) Lueck Studios.

Luke, Deanna. Marky & the Cat. Chambers, Lynne, illus. 2000. (Marky Ser.: Vol. No. 2). 40p. (J). (gr. 2-7). 8.95 (978-1-928777-06-9(6) , BOW Bks.) Blessing Our World, Inc.

—Marky & the Cat: Story Book. 2001. (Marky Ser.: Vol. 2). (J). cd-rom 5.95 (978-1-928777-21-2(X) , BOW Bks.) Blessing Our World, Inc.

—Marky & the Cat Electronic Coloring Book. Chambers, Lynne, illus. 2001. (Marky Ser.: Vol. 2). (J). cd-rom 3.95 (978-1-928777-15-1(5) , BOW Bks.) Blessing Our World, Inc.

Lum, Bernice, illus. Pippin & Pudding. 2002. (Pippin Ser.). 32p. (J). (gr. k-3). (978-1-55337-418-3(5)) Kids Can Pr., Ltd.

Lundy, Charlotte. Thank You, Jesus. Waldrep, Evelyn L., ed. Claremont, Heather, illus. 2003. 32p. (gr. k-3). 15.95 (978-0-9670280-1-9(9)) Bay Light Publishing.

Lyon, George Ella. A Traveling Cat. Johnson, Paul Brett, illus. 1998. 32p. (J). (gr. k-4). 16.99 (978-0-531-33102-6(4) , Orchard Bks.) Scholastic, Inc.

Maccarone, Grace. What Is That? Said the Cat. Scherer, Jeffrey, illus. 2004. 32p. (J). lib. bdg. 15.00 (978-1-59054-662-8(8)) Fitzgerald Bks.

MacDonald, Alan. Scaredy Mouse. Warnes, Tim, illus. (J). (ps-k). 2007. 18p. bds. 6.95 (***978-1-58925-827-3(4)***); 2002. 32p. tchr. ed. 14.95 (978-1-58925-018-5(4)) ME Media LLC. (tiger tales).

Macfarlane, Stuart & Macfarlane, Linda. The Secret Diary of Adrian Cat. 2006. 286p. (YA). (gr. 5-8). 24.95 (978-1-933255-23-1(4)) DNA Pr.

MacKinnon, Debbie. Find Kitty! Sieveking, Anthea, photos by. 1999. (Illus.). 10p. (J). (978-0-7112-0921-3(9)) Lincoln, Frances Ltd. GBR. *Dist:* Antique Collectors' Club.

MacLachlan, Patricia. Who Loves Me? Shepherd, Amanda, illus. 2005. 40p. (J). (ps-3). lib. bdg. 15.89 (978-0-06-027977-6(X)); 14.99 (978-0-06-027976-9(1)) HarperCollins Pubs. (Cotler, Joanna Books).

MacLachlan, Patricia & MacLachlan, Emily. Bittle. Yaccarino, Dan, illus. 2004. 40p. (J). (ps-3). 16.99 (978-0-06-000961-8(6)); lib. bdg. 16.89 (978-0-06-000962-5(4)) HarperCollins Pubs. (Cotler, Joanna Books).

MacLennan, Cathy. Chicky Chicky Chook Chook. MacLennan, Cathy, illus. 2007. (Illus.). 32p. (J). (ps-1). 12.95 (978-1-905417-40-7(3)) Boxer Bks., Ltd. GBR. *Dist:* Sterling Publishing Co., Inc.

Maitland, Barbara. The Bookstore Burglar. 2001. (Easy-to-Read Ser.). (Illus.). (J). 10.79 (978-0-606-21079-9(2)) Tandem Library Bks.

—Bookstore Burglar. 2001. (gr. k-3). lib. bdg. 11.80 (978-0-613-35609-1(8)) Tandem Library Bks.

—Bookstore Valentine. 2002. (gr. k-3). lib. bdg. 11.80 (978-0-613-64398-6(4)) Tandem Library Bks.

Malak, Annabel, illus. Puss 'n Boots. 2000. (Classic Stories Ser.). 48p. (J). audio, audio compact disk (978-2-921997-85-0(1)) Coffragants.

Mallat, Kathy. Trouble on the Tracks. 2001. (Illus.). 24p. (J). (ps-2). lib. bdg. 16.85 (978-0-8027-8773-6(8)) Walker & Co.

—Trouble on the Tracks. Mallat, Kathy, illus. 2001. (Illus.). 24p. (J). (ps-2). 15.95 (978-0-8027-8771-2(1)) Walker & Co.

Maltbie, P. I. Picasso & Minou. Estrada, Pau, illus. 2005. 32p. (J). 15.95 (978-1-57091-620-5(9)) Charlesbridge Publishing, Inc.

Mariconda, Barbara. Turn the Cup Around. 1998. (978-0-606-13878-9(1)) Tandem Library Bks.

Marlow, Herb. The Lost Kitten. Head, Pat, illus. 2003. 16p. (J). 19.95 (978-1-893595-34-7(X)) Four Seasons Bks., Inc.

Marlow, Layn. The Witch with a Twitch. Dreidemy, Joelle, illus. 2005. 32p. (J). (ps-ps). 15.95 (978-1-58925-052-9(4) , tiger tales) ME Media LLC.

—Witch with a Twitch. Dreidemy, Joelle, illus. 2006. 32p. (J). pap. 6.95 (978-1-58925-400-8(7) , tiger tales) ME Media LLC.

Marois, Andri. Le Chat Botti New York. ed. 2004. (FRE., Illus.). (J). (gr. k-3). spiral bd. (978-0-616-07263-9(5)) Canadian National Institute for the Blind/Institut National Canadien pour les Aveugles.

Marr, Ella J. The Adventures of Curtis & Grammy. 2006. 57p. pap. 12.95 (***978-1-4241-4743-4(3)***) PublishAmerica, Inc.

Marrero, Carla. The Magical Cat. 2006. (Illus.). 28p. (J). 16.95 (***978-1-59299-232-4(3)***) Inkwater Pr.

Martin, Ann M. Karen's Black Cat. 1998. (Baby-Sitters Little Sister Ser.: No. 102). (J). (gr. 3-7). pap. 3.99 (978-0-590-50054-8(6)) Scholastic, Inc.

—Leo the Magnificat. 2000. (Illus.). (J). (978-0-606-18573-8(9)) Tandem Library Bks.

Martin, Bill, Jr. Fire! Fire! Said Mrs. Mcguire. Radunsky, Vladimir, illus. 2006. 32p. (J). 16.00 (978-0-15-205725-1(0) , Gulliver Bks.) Harcourt Children's Bks.

Martin, David. All for Pie, Pie for All. Gorbachev, Valeri, illus. 2006. 32p. (J). (ps-k). 15.99 (978-0-7636-2393-7(8)) Candlewick Pr.

Marzollo, Jean. Ten Cats Have Hats. 99th ed. 1999. (Signatures Ser.). (Illus.). (gr. 1). pap. 14.30 (978-0-15-310845-7(2)) Harcourt Schl. Pubs.

—Thanksgiving Cats. 1999. (978-0-606-17282-0(3)) Tandem Library Bks.

Mass, Wendy. A Mango-Shaped Space. 2005. 240p. (J). (gr. 5-8). pap. 6.99 (978-0-316-05825-4(4)) Little Brown & Co.

Masson, J. Moussaieff. The Cat Who Came in from the Cold: A Fable. 2004. 107p. (978-0-345-47867-2(3) , Ballantine Bks.) Random House Publishing Group.

Master, Angel Michael. She Is a Gift from Jah. 2003. (Illus.). pap. 13.00 (978-0-8059-5967-3(X)) Dorrance Publishing Co., Inc.

Masurel, Claire. A Cat & a Dog. Kolar, Bob, illus. 2003. 32p. (J). (ps). pap. 6.95 (978-0-7358-1780-7(4)) North-South Bks., Inc.

—A Cat & a Dog BB W/sound. 2007. (J). bds. 11.95 (978-0-7358-2118-7(6)) North-South Bks., Inc.

—Cat & Dog Bilingual BB W/sou. 2007. (J). bds. 11.95 (978-0-7358-2114-9(3)) North-South Bks., Inc.

—Un Gato y un Perro. Antreasyan, Andres, tr. Kolar, Bob, illus. 2003. Tr. of Cat & a Dog. (SPA & ENG.). 32p. (J). (ps). pap. 6.95 (978-0-7358-1784-5(7)) ; 13.95 (978-0-7358-1835-4(5)) North-South Bks., Inc.

—That Bad, Bad Cat! Kelley, True, illus. 2002. (All Aboard Reading Ser.). 32p. (J). pap. 3.99 (978-0-448-42622-8(6) , Grosset & Dunlap) Penguin Group (USA) Inc.

—That Bad, Bad Cat! Kelley, True, illus. 2002. 32p. (J). (ps-1). lib. bdg. 11.80 (978-0-613-43645-8(8)) Tandem Library Bks.

Matson, Laurie. Jaz-O & 'G' in Key West. Matson, Laurie, illus. l.t. ed. 2003. (Illus.). (J). 4.95 (978-0-9673704-5-3(0)) Seastory Pr.

Matsutani, Miyoko. Peek-a-Boo. Segawa, Yasuo, illus. 2006. 20p. (J). 10.95 (978-1-74126-047-2(7)) R.I.C. Pubns. AUS. *Dist:* SCB Distributors.

—Smiley Face. Segawa, Yasuo, illus. 2006. 20p. (J). 10.95 (978-1-74126-045-8(0)) R.I.C. Pubns. AUS. *Dist:* SCB Distributors.

Maxwell, Corey. The Careless Kittensitters. Turnbaugh, Paul & Vitale, Steve, illus. 2000. (Paw Island Presents...Ser.). 32p. (J). (gr. k-3). 12.95 (978-1-890145-05-7(X) , Paw Island Entertainment, Inc.) PetCare, Inc.

Mayer, Mercer. The Great Cat Chase. 2003. (Illus.). (J). pap. (978-1-57768-357-5(9)) School Specialty Publishing.

Mayerhofer, Felix. Horace the Great Harmonica King. MacFarlane, John, illus. 2006. 31p. (J). per. 16.95 (***978-1-60002-255-5(3)*** , 4313, Airleaf Publishing) Airleaf Publishing & Bookselling.

Mayne, William. Pandora. Blech, Dietlind, illus. 2001. (SPA.). 32p. (J). (gr. k-3). (978-84-89675-63-6(5) , ZZ0542) Zendrera Zariquiey, Editorial ESP. *Dist:* Lectorum Pubns., Inc.

McBride, Anthony & McBride, Autumn. The Lost Cat. 2007. (Illus.). pap. 11.00 (***978-1-56411-540-9(2)*** , CB Publishing & Design) UBUS Communications Systems.

McCann, Jesse Leon. The Case of the Karate Kitty-Nappers. 2000. (Illus.). 57p. (J). (ps-3). pap. 3.99 (978-0-439-20654-9(5)) Scholastic, Inc.

—The Case of the Karate Kitty-Nappers. 2000. (Ace Ventura Chapter Bk.: Vol. 1). (J). 10.79 (978-0-606-19525-6(4)) Tandem Library Bks.

—The Cat in the Hat. 2003. (Illus.). 24p. (J). (gr. k-k). 0.33 (978-0-375-82780-8(3) , Golden Bks.) Random Hse. Children's Bks.

McCarthy, Margaret. The Cat Did Not Know. 2006. pap. 10.20 (978-1-85390-923-8(8)) Veritas Pubns. IRL. *Dist:* STL Distribution North America.

McCarty, Peter. Fabian Escapes. rev. ed. 2007. (Illus.). 40p. (J). (ps-1). 16.95 (***978-0-8050-7713-1(8)*** , Holt, Henry & Co. Bks. For Young Readers) Holt, Henry & Co.

—Hondo & Fabian. McCarty, Peter, illus. rev. ed. 2002. (Illus.). 32p. (J). (ps-1). 16.95 (978-0-8050-6352-3(8) , Holt, Henry & Co. Bks. For Young Readers) Holt, Henry & Co.

—Hondo & Fabian. 2007. (Illus.). 32p. (J). pap. 6.95 (***978-0-312-36747-3(3)***) Square Fish.

—Hondo & Fabian. unabr. ed. 2006. (Illus.). (J). (ps-3). 24.95 incl. audio (978-0-439-84905-0(5) , WHRA688); 29.95 incl. audio compact disk (978-0-439-84906-7(3) , WHCD688) Weston Woods Studios, Inc.

McDermott, Michael. Jingle Cats. 2004. (Illus.). 32p. (J). 12.99 (978-1-4003-0469-1(5)); 9.99 (978-1-4003-0471-4(7)) Nelson, Thomas Inc.

McDonnell, Patrick. The Gift of Nothing. 2005. (Illus.). 52p. (J). (ps-1). 14.99 (978-0-316-11488-2(X)) Little Brown & Co.

—Hug Time. 2007. (Illus.). 48p. (J). (ps-1). 14.99 (***978-0-316-11494-3(4)***) Little Brown & Co.

—Hug Time. 2007. 14.99 (***978-0-316-02373-3(6)***) Little, Brown Bks. for Young Readers.

—I Want to Be the Kitty, Vol. 8. 2003. (Illus.). 128p. pap. 10.95 (978-0-7407-3305-5(2)) Andrews McMeel Publishing.

—Just Like Heaven: A Mutts Children's Book. 2006. (Illus.). 44p. (J). (ps-1). 14.99 (978-0-316-11493-6(6)) Little Brown & Co.

McDoogle, Farrah & Mathieu, Joe. Music Player. 2007. (RD Innovative Book & Player Format Ser.). 40p. (J). 24.99 (***978-0-7944-1363-7(3)***) Reader's Digest Assn., Inc., The.

McElroy, Roland. Jibicle & Cokie: Friends at Last. 2006. (J). pap. (978-0-9673917-1-7(7)) McElroy & Assocs.

McFarland, Lyn Rossiter. Widget. McFarland, Jim, illus. ed. 2004. (J). (ps-k). spiral bd. (978-0-616-11121-5(5)); spiral bd. (978-0-616-11122-2(3)) Canadian National Institute for the Blind/Institut National Canadien pour les Aveugles.

—Widget. McFarland, Jim, illus. 2001. 32p. (J). (ps-1). 16.00 (978-0-374-38428-9(2) , Farrar, Straus & Giroux (BYR)) Farrar, Straus & Giroux.

—Widget. McFarland, Jim, illus. 2006. 32p. (J). pap. 5.95 (978-0-374-48386-9(8)) Macmillan.

—Widget & the Puppy. McFarland, Jim, illus. 2004. 32p. (J). 16.00 (978-0-374-38429-6(0) , Farrar, Straus & Giroux (BYR)) Farrar, Straus & Giroux.

McGraw, Sheila. Pussycats Everywhere! McGraw, Sheila, illus. 2000. (Illus.). 32p. (J). (gr. k-3). pap. 6.95 (978-1-55209-348-1(4)); lib. bdg. 19.95 (978-1-55209-346-7(8)) Firefly Bks., Ltd.

McGuinness-Kelly, Tracy-Lee. Bad Cat. McGuinness-Kelly, Tracy-Lee, illus. 2006. (Illus.). 29p. (J). (gr. k-4). reprint ed. 16.00 (978-0-7567-9823-9(X)) DIANE Publishing Co.

McKay, Hilary. There's a Dragon Downstairs. Harvey, Amanda, tr. Harvey, Amanda, illus. 2005. 32p. (J). 16.95 (978-0-689-86774-3(3) , McElderry, Margaret K.) Simon & Schuster Children's Publishing.

McKay, Sindy. We Both Read-Too Many Cats. Johnson, Meredith, illus. 2003. (We Both Read Ser.). 44p. (J). (gr. k up). 7.99 (978-1-891327-49-0(6)); pap. 3.99 (978-1-891327-50-6(X)) Treasure Bay, Inc.

McKendry, Sam. Curious Kitties: A Colors Book. Mitchell, Melanie, illus. 2005. 16p. (J). 9.95 (978-1-58117-417-5(9) , Intervisual/Piggy Toes) Dalmatian Pr.

McKinlay, Penny. Flabby Tabby. Teckentrup, Britta, illus. 2005. 32p. (J). 15.95 (978-1-84507-090-8(9)) Lincoln, Frances Ltd. GBR. *Dist:* Perseus Distribution.

McKinley, Cheryl. The Mouse in the Bathtub. Alexander, Colin, illus. 2005. (ENG.). 32p. (J). (ps). per. 18.00 (978-1-4208-2555-8(0)) AuthorHouse.

McLaren, Chesley. Zat Cat! A Haute Couture Tail. McLaren, Chesley, illus. 2002. (Illus.). 40p. (J). (ps-3). pap. 16.95 (978-0-439-27316-9(1) , Scholastic Pr.) Scholastic, Inc.

McLellan, Stephanie Simpson. The Chicken Cat. Cassidy, Sean, illus. 2001. (gr. k-3). 36p. (J). (978-1-55041-531-5(X)); 40p. (J). pap. (978-1-55041-673-2(1)); 40p. (978-1-55041-677-0(4)) Fitzhenry & Whiteside, Ltd.

McManaway, Mary Elizabeth Siske. Prince's Cat Tale. 2006. pap. 7.95 (978-0-533-15229-2(1)) Vantage Pr., Inc.

McMullan, Kate. Supercat to the Rescue. (J). 55.60 (978-0-7611-3234-9(1) , 23234) Workman Publishing Co., Inc.

—Supercat to the Rescue. Lemaitre, Pascal, illus. 2003. 32p. (J). bds. 6.95 (978-0-7611-2734-5(8) , 12734) Workman Publishing Co., Inc.

McMullan, Kate & Lemaitre, Pascal. Supercat. 2002. (Illus.). 32p. (J). (ps). bds. 6.95 (978-0-7611-2644-7(9) , 12644) Workman Publishing Co., Inc.

MCP Staff. The Big Cat, 6 bks., set, Level 4, Bk. 2. 2003. (J). (ps-3). 24.50 (978-0-8136-2373-3(1)) Modern Curriculum Pr.

McPhail, David M. & O'Connor. The Sled: Fox & Rabbit Stories. 1999. (First Flight Ser.). (Illus.). 32p. (J). (ps-k). pap. (978-1-55041-517-9(4)) Fitzhenry & Whiteside, Ltd.

McPherson, Christopher. Mama Cat. 2003. (J). per. 9.95 (978-1-932205-79-4(9)) Word Association Pubs.

McPherson, Dottie. Kizzi's Special Friends. 2003. (Illus.). (J). 14.95 (978-0-9724979-0-9(0) , Advocate Hse.) A Cappela Publishing.

McQuade, Jacqueline. Touch the Kitty. 2002. (Baby Animals to Touch & Feel! Ser.). (Illus.). 10p. (J). bds. 6.99 (978-0-439-33942-1(1) , Cartwheel Bks.) Scholastic, Inc.

Meggs, Libby Phillips. Go Home! The True Story of James the Cat. Meggs, Libby Phillips, illus. 2000. (Illus.). 32p. (J). (gr. k-3). pap. 6.95 (978-0-8075-2976-8(1)) Whitman, Albert & Co.

Meister, Cari. Catch That Cat! Brooks, David J., illus. 2000. (Rookie Reader Espanol Ser.). 24p. (J). (gr. k-2). pap. 4.95 (978-0-516-26541-4(5) , Children's Pr.) Scholastic Library Publishing.

Mentink, Jarrett W. Alley the Cat. Carlson, Patrick W., illus. l.t. ed. 2002. 44p. (J). 14.95 (978-0-9723314-0-1(9)) Kids in the Clouds.

Meyers, Susan. Kittens! Kittens! Kittens! Walker, David, illus. 2007. (J). (ps-1). 32p. 15.95 (978-0-8109-1218-2(X)); (***978-1-4287-3986-4(6)***) Abrams, Harry N. , Inc. (Abrams Bks. for Young Readers).

Mgrdichian, Teri. The Cat's Meow. McGlinchey, Gertie, illus. 2006. (J). 19.95 (978-1-933002-14-9(X)) PublishingWorks.

Mighty Fine, Inc. Staff. French Kitty in Kitty Goes to Paris. 2003. (Illus.). 48p. 12.95 (978-0-8109-4447-3(2)) Abrams, Harry N. , Inc.

—French Kitty in Las Vegas Pair-a-Dice. 2005. (Illus.). 56p. 12.95 (978-0-8109-5861-6(9)) Abrams, Harry N. , Inc.

Miller, Alan. The Litluns & the Golden Spider Web. 2005. 61p. pap. 12.95 (978-1-4137-6444-4(4)) PublishAmerica, Inc.

Miller, Jessel. Calico Cat. Miller, Jessel, illus. 1999. (Illus.). 24p. (J). (ps-3). 20.00 (978-0-9660381-8-7(5)) Jessel Gallery.

Miller, Sara Swan. Cat in the Bag. Mahan, Benton, illus. 2001. (Rookie Reader Espanol Ser.). (J). 32p. (gr. k-2). pap. 4.95 (978-0-516-27292-4(6)); 31p. (gr. 1-2). 19.50 (978-0-516-22014-7(4)) Scholastic Library Publishing. (Children's Pr.).

—Cat in the Bag. 2001. (gr. k-3). lib. bdg. 12.95 (978-0-613-54112-1(X)) Tandem Library Bks.

—La Gatita en la Maleta. Mahan, Benton, illus. 2001. (Rookie Reader Espanol Ser.). (SPA.). 32p. (J). (gr. k-2). 19.50 (978-0-516-22355-1(0) , Children's Pr.) Scholastic Library Publishing.

—Three More Stories You Can Read to Your Cat. Kelley, True, illus. 2002. 48p. (J). (gr. k-3). 15.00 (978-0-618-11035-3(6)) Houghton Mifflin Co. Trade & Reference Div.

—Three Stories You Can Read to Your Cat. Kelley, True, illus. 1999. 48p. (J). (gr. 4-6). pap., pap. 5.95 (978-0-395-95752-3(4)) Houghton Mifflin Co. Trade & Reference Div.

—Three Stories You Can Read to Your Cat. 1999. (978-0-606-16539-6(8)) Tandem Library Bks.

—Three Stories You Can Read to Your Teddy Bear. Kelley, True, tr. Kelley, True, illus. 2004. 48p. (J). (gr. k-3). tchr. ed. 15.00 (978-0-618-30397-7(9)) Houghton Mifflin Co. Trade & Reference Div.

Miller, Virginia. Ten Red Apples: A Bartholomew Bear Counting Book. 2002. (Illus.). 32p. (J). (ps-k). 13.99 (978-0-7445-9280-1(1)) Candlewick Pr.

Min, Laura. Las Gallinas de la Senora Sato, Level 1. Ada, Alma Flor, tr. Huang, Benrei, illus. 2003. (Dejame Leer Ser.). (SPA.). 8p. (J). (ps-3). 6.50 (978-0-673-36298-8(1) , Good Year Bks.) Celebration Pr.

Minarik, Else Holmelund. Cat & Dog. Langdo, Bryan, illus. 2005. (My First I Can Read Bks.). 32p. (J). (ps up). 14.99 (978-0-06-074247-8(X)); lib. bdg. 15.89 (978-0-06-074248-5(8)) HarperCollins Pubs.

Minolli Skupinski, Teresa. The Courtship of Leonora: A Fable about Gentle Hearts & Timeless Values. 2005. (Illus.). 88p. (J). 19.95 (978-0-9753326-0-3(0)) Villa Serena Publishing.

Minou: Evaluation Guide. 2006. (J). (978-1-55942-416-5(8)) Marsh Media.

Mishica, Clare. A Friend for Fraidy Cat. Caldwell, Lise, ed. Wagoner, Bill, illus. rev. ed. 1998. (Happy Day Bks.). 24p. (J). (ps-2). 2.49 (978-0-7847-0831-6(2) , 24-04261, Bean Sprouts) Standard Publishing.

Mitra, Annie. Chloe's Sunny Day. 1998. (Chloe Weather Board Bks.). (Illus.). 14p. (J). bds. 5.95 (978-1-86233-031-3(X)) Sterling Publishing Co., Inc.

Mlodinow, Leonard & Mlodinow, M. Costello. Titanic Cat. Nash, Josh, illus. 2004. (Einstein Elementary Ser.). 64p. (J). pap. 3.99 (978-0-439-53774-2(6) , Cartwheel Bks.) Scholastic, Inc.

Mockford, Caroline, illus. Cleo the Cat. (J). 12.99 (978-1-84148-458-7(X)) Barefoot Bks., Inc.

Moglia, Amy. Alfalfa Kitty. 20th ed. 2003. (Illus.). 30p. (J). spiral bd. 12.95 (978-0-9622500-3-3(1)) Clements, Jehan.

Moncomble, Gérard. The Nine Lives of the Cat. Arinouchkine, Andreï, illus. 2005. 32p. 16.95 (978-1-59687-189-2(X) , Milk & Cookies) ibooks, Inc.

Moncomble, Gerard. Pippin. Devos, Xavière, illus. 2006. 32p. (J). (ps-2). 15.95 (978-0-7358-2062-3(7)) North-South Bks., Inc.

Moncomble, Gerard & Arinouchkine, Andrei. The Nine Lives of the Cat. 2005. (Illus.). 32p. (J). 16.95 (978-0-689-04637-7(5) , Milk & Cookies) ibooks, Inc.

Monkman, Olga. Gatos. Zecchin, Feliciano G., illus. 2001. Tr. of Cats. (SPA.). 61p. (J). per. (978-950-07-1989-6(4)) Editorial Sudamericana S.A.

Monks, Lydia. The Cat Barked? 2001. (J). 12.79 (978-0-606-21102-4(0)) Tandem Library Bks.

Montana, Scarlett. Lunch with a Blue Kitty. Montana, Scarlett, illus. 2007. (Illus.). 41p. (J). pap. (***978-0-9796814-0-0(5)***) Blue Kitty, The.

Montardre, Helene. The Cat & the Dog. 2003. (Illus.). 8p. (J). bds. 7.95 (978-1-58728-483-0(9) , Two Can Publishing) T&N Children's Publishing.

Montgomery, Rutherford G. Rufus. Nenninger, J. D., illus. 2004. (Classic Ser.). 138p. (gr. 4-7). pap. 12.95 (978-0-87004-405-2(2)) Caxton Pr.

Monty, the Missing Cat. 2001. (J). (978-1-58453-170-8(3)) Pioneer Valley Educational Pr., Inc.

Moon, Catherine R. & Everette, Maureen C. The Adventures of NanaCat & Her Children: Someone New. Richardson, Kara, illus. 2004. 32p. (J). per. 6.95 (978-0-930507-02-2(9)) Currier Davis Publishing.

Mooney, Margaret. Cat & Dog. 2001. (gr. k-3). lib. bdg. 11.80 (978-0-613-33346-7(2)) Tandem Library Bks.

Moore, Stephen. Skin & Bone. mass mkt. 8.99 (978-0-340-70455-4(1) , Hodder & Stoughton) Hodder General Publishing Division GBR. *Dist:* Trafalgar Square Publishing.

Mora, Pat. A Birthday Basket for Tia. 1998. (J). pap. 4.99 (978-0-87628-395-0(4)) Ctr. for Applied Research in Education, The.

—Una Cesta de Cumpleanos para Tia Abuela. Lang, Cecily, illus. (SPA.). (J). (gr. k-2). pap. 3.16 net. (978-0-395-78817-2(X) , HMS088) Houghton Mifflin Co.

Moran, Alex. Come Here, Tiger. 2001. (Green Light Readers Ser.). (Illus.). (J). (978-0-606-21118-5(7)) Tandem Library Bks.

—Come Here, Tiger! Ernst, Lisa Campbell, illus. 2003. (Green Light Readers Level 1 Ser.). 24p. (J). 11.95 (978-0-15-204820-4(0)); pap. 3.95 (978-0-15-204860-0(X)) Harcourt Children's Bks. (Green Light Readers).

—Come Here, Tiger! 2001. (ps-2). lib. bdg. 11.80 (978-0-613-64473-0(5)) Tandem Library Bks.

—Sam & Jack: Three Stories. 2001. (gr. k-3). lib. bdg. 11.80 (978-0-613-64590-4(1)) Tandem Library Bks.

Moray-Williams, Ursula & Williams, Ursula Moray. The Further Adventures of Gobbolino & the Little Wooden Horse. Howard, Paul, illus. 2002. (Kingfisher Modern Classics Ser.). 240p. (J). (gr. k-3). tchr. ed. 15.95 (978-0-7534-5495-4(5) , Kingfisher) Houghton Mifflin Co. Trade & Reference Div.

Morgan, Michaela. Silly Sausage & the Little Visitor. Shulman, Dee, illus. 2006. (Read-It! Chapter Books). (J). 21.26 (978-1-4048-2735-6(8)) Picture Window Bks.

—Silly Sausage & the Spooks. Shulman, Dee, illus. 2006. (Read-It! Chapter Books). (J). 21.26 (978-1-4048-2736-3(6)) Picture Window Bks.

Morgan, Palo. Cat Balloon. 2006. (Illus.). 32p. (J). (ps). 16.95 (978-1-894965-35-4(3)) Simply Read Bks. CAN. *Dist:* Perseus Distribution.

Morita, Hiroyuki. The Cat Returns Picture Book. Searleman, Eric, ed. Hiiragi, Aoi, illus. 2007. (Cat Returns Ser.). 112p. (YA). 14.99 (***978-1-4215-1498-7(2)***) Viz Media.

Morpurgo, Michael. The Amazing Story of Adolphus Tips. 2006. 208p. (J). (gr. 2-5). 16.99 (978-0-439-79661-3(X) , Scholastic Pr.) Scholastic, Inc.

Moser, Cherry. Backyard Adventures. 2005. 51p. pap. 12.95 (978-1-4137-6202-0(6)) PublishAmerica, Inc.

Mouse Works Staff. Beauty & the Beast & The Aristocats, 2 vols. 75th anniv. ed. 1998. (Illus.). (ps-3). (978-0-7364-0092-3(3)) Mouse Works.

Mr. Meow. Mr. Meow's Amazing Alphabet Adventure. Crawford, Gregory, illus. 2004. 32p. (J). pap. (978-1-58394-098-3(7) , Frog Ltd.) North Atlantic Bks.

Mueller, Pamela Bauer. Rain City Cats. Weiler, Naomi M., illus. 2000. 125p. (J). (gr. 2-8). pap. 6.00 (978-0-9685097-1-5(1)) Pinata Publishing.

Mulligan, Frank. Cookie & Curley. Myler, Terry, illus. 2003. (Chimp Ser.). 64p. (YA). (gr. k up). pap. 8.95 (978-1-901737-38-7(1)) Anvil Bks., Ltd. IRL. *Dist:* Dufour Editions, Inc.

—Cookie the Cat. 2002. 64p. (YA). (gr. k up). pap. 7.95 (978-1-901737-34-9(9)) Anvil Bks., Ltd. IRL. *Dist:* Dufour Editions, Inc.

Muncy, Brenda. Truly Lucky. 2006. (ENG.). 32p. per. 16.49 (***978-1-4259-6289-0(0)***) AuthorHouse.

Munoz, Isabel. Eric & Julieta: Where Is Eric?/Donde Esta Eric? Mazali, Gustavo, illus. 2006. (ENG & SPA.). 24p. (J). pap. 3.50 (978-0-439-78371-2(2)) Scholastic, Inc.

Murphy, Stephen, et al. The Secret. S. I. International Staff & Ostrom, Bob, illus. 2004. (Teenage Mutant Ninja Turtles Ser.). 32p. (J). pap. 3.99 (978-0-689-86965-5(7) , Simon Spotlight) Simon & Schuster Children's Publishing.

Murphy, Stuart J. Pepper's Journal: A Kitten's First Year. Winborn, Marsha, illus. 2000. (Trophy Picture Bk.). 40p. (J). (gr. 1 up). pap. 5.99 (978-0-06-446723-0(6) , Harper Trophy) HarperCollins Pubs.

—Pepper's Journal: A Kitten's First Year. 2000. (Math Start Ser.). (978-0-606-18711-4(1)); lib. bdg. 13.00 (978-0-613-22167-2(2)) Tandem Library Bks.

Murray, Carol. Jenny's Socks. Burris, Priscilla, tr. Burris, Priscilla, illus. 2004. (Rookie Reader Ser.). 31p. (J). 19.50 (978-0-516-25899-7(0) , Children's Pr.) Scholastic Library Publishing.

—Jennys Socks. Burris, Priscilla, illus. 2004. (Rookie Reader Skill Set Ser.). 32p. (J). (gr. k-2). pap. 4.95 (978-0-516-26826-2(0) , Children's Pr.) Scholastic Library Publishing.

Murray, Guillermo. Que, Miedo! rev. ed. 2006. (Castillo del Terror Ser.). (SPA.). 112p. (J). (gr. 2-6). pap. 6.95 (978-970-20-0338-0(5)) Castillo, Ediciones, S. A. de C. V. MEX. *Dist:* Macmillan.

Murray, Joe. The Enormous Mister Schmupsle. 2003. (Illus.). 32p. (J). 16.95 (978-1-931290-53-1(9)) Tallfellow Pr.

Mustaine Hettinger, Cynthia. Boomerang, the Farm Cat. Ramsey, Jayne, illus. 2004. (Electra's Acres Ser.: 4). 32p. (J). per. 14.95 (978-0-9746330-5-3(4)) Anton Berkshire Publishing.

My Black Cat. 2003. (J). (978-1-58453-145-6(2)) Pioneer Valley Educational Pr., Inc.

My Cat: Individual Title Six-Pack Pouch - Level B. (Lighthouse Ser.). 12p. (gr. k-1). 24.00 (978-0-7578-0812-8(3)) Rigby Education.

My Cat Sam Set B: Individual Title Six-Packs. (gr. k-3). 29.00 (978-0-7635-0535-6(8)) Rigby Education.

My Crazy Christmas Catastrophe Cat. 2003. (Illus.). 22p. (J). 9.95 (978-0-9744751-1-0(4)) Timothy Lane Pr.

My Name Is Boots: A Cat's Tale. 2003. (Illus.). 55p. (J). (978-0-9742277-0-2(6)) Hargroves Publishing Co.

Myers, Christopher. Black Cat. Myers, Christopher, illus. 2002. (Illus.). (J). 26.13 (978-0-7587-0341-5(4)) Book Wholesalers, Inc.

—Black Cat. 2001. (J). incl. audio (978-0-8045-6863-0(4) , 6863) Spoken Arts, Inc.

Myers, Christopher A. Black Cat. Myers, Christopher A., illus. 1999. (Illus.). 40p. (J). (gr. k-3). pap. 16.95 (978-0-590-03375-6(1)) Scholastic, Inc.

Myers, Walter Dean. Three Swords for Granada. Speirs, John, illus. 2002. 112p. (J). (gr. 4-6). tchr. ed. 15.95 (978-0-8234-1676-9(3)) Holiday Hse., Inc.

The Mystery of the Clever Cat: Second Grade Guided Reading Level J. (On Our Way to English Ser.). (gr. 2 up). 34.50 (978-0-7578-7091-0(0)) Rigby Education.

Nadimi, Suzan. The Hungry Cat, Downie, Christopher, illus. l.t. ed. 2005. (PER.). 32p. 5.95 net. (978-0-9764947-0-6(1)) Nur Pubns.

Nagda, Ann Whitehead. The Perfect Cat-Sitter. Roth, Stephanie, illus. 2007. 96p. (J). (gr. 2-6). 15.95 (***978-0-8234-2112-1(0)***) Holiday Hse., Inc.

Nanette. Tootie the Green Kitten. 2004. (Life on Granny's Farm Ser.). (J). 12.95 (978-0-9741269-7-5(7)) St. Bernard Publishing, LLC.

Napthine, Margaret. The Kittens Thomas & Tut. Lovejoy, Brenda, illus. 2006. (J). per. 16.00 (978-0-9763993-2-2(6) , Ithaca Pr.) Authors & Artists Publishers of New York, Inc.

Nation, Kay. Jamie Learns to Love. 2006. pap. 10.00 (***978-1-4257-0534-3(0)***) Xlibris Corp.

Naughty Kitten: Set B Individual Title, 6 Packs. (Smart Start Ser.). (gr. k-1). 23.00 (978-0-7635-0420-5(3)) Rigby Education.

Naylor, Phyllis Reynolds. Carlotta's Kittens. Daniel, Alan, illus. 2005. (Cat Pack Ser.). 144p. (J). pap. 5.99 (978-0-689-87405-5(7) , Aladdin) Simon & Schuster Children's Publishing.

—Danny's Desert Rats. 1999. 11.15 (978-0-606-17630-9(6)) Tandem Library Bks.

—The Grand Escape. Daniel, Alan, illus. 2005. (Cat Pack Ser.). 160p. (J). pap. 4.99 (978-0-689-87407-9(3) , Aladdin) Simon & Schuster Children's Publishing.

—The Healing of Texas Jake. Daniel, Alan, illus. 2005. (Cat Pack Ser.). 128p. (J). pap. 4.99 (978-0-689-87406-2(5) , Aladdin) Simon & Schuster Children's Publishing.

—Patches & Scratches. Ramsey, Marcy, illus. 2007. (Simply Sarah Ser.). 80p. (J). (gr. 2-4). 14.99 (***978-0-7614-5347-5(4)***) Cavendish, Marshall Corp.

Naylor, Phyllis Reynolds. Polo's Mother. Daniel, Alan, illus. (Cat Pack Ser.). 176p. (J). 2006. pap. 5.99 (978-0-689-87404-8(9) , Aladdin); 2005. 15.95 (978-0-689-86555-8(4) , Atheneum) Simon & Schuster Children's Publishing.

Neuhaus, Eve. Journey to Mythaca. 2006. 347p. (YA). per. 16.95 (***978-1-59594-101-5(0)*** , Wingspan Pr.) Wingspan Publishing.

Neville, Emily Cheney. It's Like This, Cat. 2002. (Illus.). (J). 14.47 (978-0-7587-0195-4(0)) Book Wholesalers, Inc.

—It's Like This, Cat. 1999. (J). 9.95 (978-1-56137-101-3(7)) Novel Units, Inc.

Newberry. Marshmallow. 2008. 32p. (J). 17.89 (***978-0-06-072487-0(0)***) HarperCollins Pubs.

Newberry, Clare Turlay. Marshmallow. Newberry, Clare Turlay, illus. 2008. 32p. (J). 16.99 (***978-0-06-072486-3(2)***) HarperCollins Pubs.

Newell, Jeff. Skimper-Scamper. Hranilovich, Barbara J., illus. 2005. (Green Light Readers Level 2 Ser.). 24p. (J). 12.95 (978-0-15-205166-2(X)); pap. 3.95 (978-0-15-205165-5(1)) Harcourt Children's Bks. (Green Light Readers).

Newman, Barbara Johansen. Tex & Sugar: A Big City Kitty Ditty. Newman, Barbara Johansen, illus. 2007. (Illus.). 32p. (J). (gr. k-2). 14.95 (978-1-4027-3887-6(0)) Sterling Publishing Co., Inc.

Newman, Leslea. The Best Cat in the World. Himler, Ronald, illus. 32p. (J). 2006. pap. 8.00 (978-0-8028-5294-6(7) , Eerdmans Bks For Young Readers); 2004. (gr. 1-4). 16.00 (978-0-8028-5252-6(1)) Eerdmans, William B. Publishing Co.

—Cats, Cats, Cats! Oller, Erika, illus. 2001. 32p. (J). (ps-1). 16.00 (978-0-689-83077-8(7)) Simon & Schuster Children's Publishing.

—Cats, Cats, Cats! 2001. (978-0-606-22791-9(1)) Tandem Library Bks.

Newman, Lesléa. Cats, Cats, Cats! Oller, Erika, illus. 2004. 32p. (J). reprint ed. pap. 6.99 (978-0-689-86697-5(6) , Aladdin) Simon & Schuster Children's Publishing.

Newsome, Jill. Night Walk. Munoz, Claudio, illus. 2003. (J). (gr. k-3). 15.00 (978-0-618-32458-3(5) , Clarion Bks.) Houghton Mifflin Co. Trade & Reference Div.

Newton, Suzanne. Purro & the Prattleberries. 1998. 144p. (J). (gr. 2-6). pap. 5.00 (978-0-9664376-4-5(0)) Green Ridge Bks.

Nicoll, Helen, et al. Meg y Mog Juegan Al Escondite. Pienkowski, Jan, illus. 2005. (SPA.). 12p. (ps-k). bds. 14.95 (978-84-666-1819-9(8)) Ediciones B ESP. *Dist:* Independent Pubs. Group.

Nimmo, Jenny. Charlie Bone & the Hidden King. 2006. (Children of the Red King Ser.: Bk. 5). 464p. (J). 9.95 (978-0-439-54530-3(7) , Orchard Bks.) Scholastic, Inc.

Nishimura, Kae. Dinah! 2004. 32p. 14.00 (978-0-618-33613-5(3) , Clarion Bks.) Houghton Mifflin Co. Trade & Reference Div.

—Dinah! A Cat Adventure. 2004. (Illus.). 32p. (J). (gr. k-3). 14.00 (978-0-618-33612-8(5) , Clarion Bks.) Houghton Mifflin Co. Trade & Reference Div.

Nodset, Joan L. Come Here, Cat. Date not set. 40p. (J). 15.99 (978-0-06-028081-9(0)) HarperCollins Pubs.

—Come Here, Cat. Kellogg, Steven, illus. Date not set. 40p. (J). 16.89 (978-0-06-028082-6(4)) HarperCollins Pubs.

Norris, L. Wayne. The Adventures of Ricky Raccoon & Jodi the Cat with Boomer. l.t. ed. 2003. (Illus.). 36p. (J). pap. (978-0-9709408-1-0(5)) Pinetree Pubns.

Norton, Miriam. The Kitten Who Thought He Was a Mouse. 2008. (Little Golden Book Ser.). (Illus.). 24p. (J). (gr. k-k). 2.99 ***(978-0-375-84822-3(3)*** , Golden Bks.) Random Hse. Children's Bks.

Nostlinger, Christine. Un Gato No Es un Cojin. Campos, Angel, illus. 2003. (SPA.). 60p. (J). (gr. 3-5). pap. 10.95 (978-968-19-0548-4(2)) Santillana USA Publishing Co., Inc.

Nowiki, Boszenna. Why Some Cats are Rascals. No. 2. 2006. 224p. pap. 9.95 (978-0-9727328-5-7(3)); No. 3. 2007. 208p. pap. 9.95 (978-0-9727328-6-4(1)) Healthy Life Pr., Inc.

—Why Some Cats are Rascals, Book 1. 2007. (Illus.). 140p. pap. 8.95 (978-0-9727328-2-6(9)) Healthy Life Pr., Inc.

Numeroff, Laura Joffe. If You Give a Cat a Cupcake. Bond, Felicia, illus. 1999. 32p. (J). (ps-2). 15.89 (978-0-06-026684-4(8)) HarperCollins Pubs.

—If You Give a Cat a Cupcake: Book & Doll. Bond, Felicia, illus. Date not set. (J). 19.99 (978-0-694-01431-6(1)) HarperCollins Pubs.

Nunes, Lygia Bojunga. El Sofa Estampado. (SPA.). 184p. (YA). (gr. 5-8). (978-84-239-2748-7(2) , EC2752) Espasa Calpe, S.A. ESP. *Dist:* Lectorum Pubns., Inc.

Oates, Joyce Carol. Come Meet Muffin! Graham, Mark, illus. 1998. 32p. (ps-1). 18.00 (978-0-88001-556-1(X)) HarperCollins Pubs.

—Naughty Cherie. Graham, Mark, illus. 2008. (J). 40p. 17.89 (978-0-06-074359-8(X)); 32p. 16.99 (978-0-06-074358-1(1)) HarperCollins Pubs.

—Where Is Little Reynard? Graham, Mark, illus. 2003. 32p. (J). 16.89 (978-0-06-029583-7(X)) HarperCollins Pubs.

Ochiltree, Dianne. Cats Add Up! Dunn-Ramsey, Marcy, illus. 1998. (Hello Reader! Math Ser.). 48p. (J). (gr. 1-3). pap. 3.99 (978-0-590-12005-0(0)) Scholastic, Inc.

Ocker, Christa Holder. Smitten the Kitten. 2006. (J). per. ***(978-1-59872-713-5(3))*** Instantpublisher.com.

O'Conner, Hugh, creator. Marlin the Cat. 2002. 30p. per. 12.99 (978-0-9707914-9-8(6)) Litterateur Pubns., Inc.

O'Connor, Ilett. Daniel's Visit to the Zoo & Katrina's off to See the World. Khan, Alisha, illus. unabr. ed. 2002. 42p. (J). (ps-5). pap. 12.00 (978-0-9717003-4-5(6)) O'Connor, Ilett K.

O'Donnell, Liam. Baxter Needs a Home. Hynes, Robert, illus. 2005. (Pet Tales Ser.). 32p. (J). (ps-2). 2.95 (978-1-59249-298-5(3) , 1B015); 4.95 incl. cd-rom (978-1-59249-297-8(5) , 1B013) Soundprints.

—Lucy & the Busy Boat. Hynes, Robert, illus. 2005. (Pet Tales Ser.). 32p. (J). (ps-2). 2.95 (978-1-59249-296-1(7) , 1B021) Soundprints.

Oh, Jiwon. Mr. Monkey's Classroom. Oh, Jiwon, illus. 2005. (Illus.). 32p. (J). (ps-2). lib. bdg. 15.89 (978-0-06-055722-5(2)) HarperCollins Pubs.

O'Herron, Mary. A Letter from Marty: Grandma & Grandpa's Cat. O'Herron, Mary, illus. 2004. (Illus.). 32p. (J). (ps-1). pap. 8.95 (978-0-9664732-4-7(8)) Countinghouse Pr., Inc.

Oke, Janette. The Prodigal Cat. Munger, Nancy, illus. 2000. (Animal Friends Ser.). 64p. (Orig.). (J). (gr. 1-5). reprint ed. pap. 6.99 (978-0-7642-2406-5(9)) Bethany Hse. Pubs.

—The Prodigal Cat. 2000. (Orig.). (gr. 3-6). lib. bdg. 14.15 (978-0-613-82428-6(8)) Tandem Library Bks.

Oldfield, J. Home Farm Twins Christmas Mystery. (Illus.). 124p. (J). pap. 8.99 (978-0-340-72682-2(2) , Hodder & Stoughton) Hodder General Publishing Division GBR. *Dist:* Trafalgar Square Publishing.

Oller, Erika. The Cabbage Soup Solution. Oller, Erika, illus. 2004. (Illus.). 32p. (J). (ps-1). 15.99 (978-0-525-47005-2(0) , Dutton Juvenile) Penguin Group (USA) Inc.

Olsen, Sylvia. Murphy & Mousetrap. 2005. (Orca Young Readers Ser.). (Illus.). 128p. (J). (gr. 3-6). pap. 5.95 (978-1-55143-344-8(3)) Orca Bk. Pubs. USA.

O'Malley, Kevin. Herbert Fieldmouse, Secret Agent. 2003. (Illus.). 32p. (J). pap. (978-1-59336-043-6(6)); (gr. 1-6). 15.95 (978-1-59336-042-9(8)) Mondo Publishing.

Ortiz, Carolyn. Cat's Got My Tongue! 2006. (ENG., Illus.). 40p. per. 13.90 (978-1-4208-7851-6(4)) AuthorHouse.

Ostrowski-Young, Lori. Aboo & Sidekick. 2007. (YA). per. 6.99 ***(978-1-59886-753-4(9))*** Tate Publishing & Enterprises, L.L.C.

Owen, Vi. Found a Tiny, Injured Kitten - A True Story. O'Connell, Pat, illus. Breese, Toni, photos by. 2000. 33p. (J). (ps). pap. 13.95 (978-0-9653334-2-9(6)) Owen, V.

Page, Gail. How to Be a Good Dog. Page, Gail, illus. 2007. (Illus.). 32p. (J). (ps-3). pap. 6.95 ***(978-1-59990-151-0(X)*** , Bloomsbury Children) Bloomsbury Publishing.

—How to Be a Good Dog. 2006. (Illus.). 32p. (J). 15.95 (978-1-58234-683-0(6) , Bloomsbury Children) Bloomsbury Publishing.

Paine, Penelope C. Time for Horatio. Maeno, Itoko, illus. 2001. 48p. (J). per. 17.95 (978-0-9707944-7-5(9)) Paper Posie.

Palatini, Margie. Cats Hanukkah. 2006. (978-0-06-052637-5(8)); lib. bdg. (978-0-06-052638-2(6)) HarperCollins Canada, Ltd.

Palmer, Barbara A. Finding Fido the Feline: Flip Book with American Sign Language. Palmer, Barbara A., illus. 2004. (J). bds. 11.99 (978-0-9728228-1-7(X)) Palmer, Barbara A.

—The Journey of Cattail. Palmer, Barbara A., illus. 2004. (Illus.). 26p. (J). 16.95 (978-0-9728228-0-0(1)) Palmer, Barbara A.

Papa Piccolo: Evaluation Guide. 2006. (J). 17.95 (978-1-55942-419-6(2)) Marsh Media.

Parish, Herman. Amelia Bedelia & the Cat. Sweat, Lynn, illus. 2008. 48p. (J). 16.99 ***(978-0-06-084349-6(7));*** lib. bdg. 17.89 ***(978-0-06-084350-2(0))*** HarperCollins Pubs. (Greenwillow Bks.).

Parish, Peggy. The Cats' Burglar. 1998. (J). (978-0-606-13258-9(9)) Tandem Library Bks.

Parker, Ant. Ginger. 2000. (Illus.). 32p. (J). (ps-1). pap. 5.95 (978-1-57255-429-0(0)) Mondo Publishing.

—Wake up, Ginger. Parker, Ant, illus. 2001. (Illus.). 32p. (J). (ps-1). pap. 5.95 (978-1-58653-853-8(5)) Mondo Publishing.

Parnal, Peter. Gato Salvaje. Enriquez, Luis F., illus. 1998. (SPA.). 150p. (YA). (ps-ps). pap. 6.99 (978-968-16-4464-2(6)) Fondo de Cultura Economica MEX. *Dist:* Continental Bk. Co., Inc.

Partis, Joanne. Try Counting Sheep. 2007. (Illus.). (J). (ps-k). bds. 12.95 ***(978-0-7696-5342-6(1)*** , Gingham Dog Pr.) School Specialty Publishing.

Pasnak, William. The Ginger Princess. 2006. (Streetlights Ser.). 96p. (J). (gr. 2-5). 7.95 ***(978-1-55028-952-7(7))*** Lorimer, James & Co., Ltd., Pubs. CAN. *Dist:* Casemate Pubs. & Bk. Distributors, LLC.

Paterson, Aileen. Maisie Bites the Big Apple. Paterson, Aileen, illus. 2002. (Illus.). 32p. (J). pap. (978-1-871512-69-4(7)) Glowworm Bks., Ltd.

—Maisie Goes to a Wedding. Paterson, Aileen, illus. 2000. (Illus.). 32p. (J). (gr. 1-3). pap. (978-1-871512-54-0(9)) Glowworm Bks., Ltd.

—Maisie Goes to Hollywood. Paterson, Aileen, illus. 2001. (Illus.). 32p. (J). (ps-3). pap. (978-1-871512-40-3(9)) Glowworm Bks., Ltd.

—Maisie Loves Paris. Paterson, Aileen, illus. 2001. (Illus.). 32p. (J). pap. (978-1-871512-05-2(0)) Glowworm Bks., Ltd.

—Maisie's Merry Christmas. Paterson, Aileen, illus. 2001. (Illus.). 32p. (J). pap. (978-1-871512-46-5(8)) Glowworm Bks., Ltd.

Patterson, Francine. Koko's Kitten. 1999. (Illus.). (J). (gr. k-3). lib. bdg. 13.00 (978-0-8085-8825-2(7)) Tandem Library Bks.

Peacock, Carol Anto. Pilgrim Cat. Ettlinger, Doris, illus. 2004. 32p. (J). (gr. 2-5). 16.95 (978-0-8075-6532-2(6)) Whitman, Albert & Co.

Pearl, Alyson J. Josie & Friends. 2007. (J). per. 9.99 ***(978-1-60247-115-3(0))*** Tate Publishing & Enterprises, L.L.C.

Pedersen, Janet. Pino & the Signora's Pasta. Pedersen, Janet, illus. 2005. (Illus.). 32p. (J). (ps-3). 16.99 (978-0-7636-2396-8(2)) Candlewick Pr.

Pelham, David. Applebee's Colors. 2006. (Illus.). 16p. (J). 12.95 (978-0-7624-2647-8(0) , Running Pr.) Running Pr. Bk. Pubs.

—Applebee's Shapes. 2006. (Illus.). 16p. (J). 12.95 (978-0-7624-2648-5(9) , Running Pr.) Running Pr. Bk. Pubs.

Pemberton, Bonnie. The Cat Master. 2007. 259p. (YA). (gr. 5-9). 16.99 ***(978-0-7614-5340-6(7))*** Cavendish, Marshall Corp.

Penner, Lucille Recht. Where's That Bone? Adams, Lynn, illus. 2005. (Math Matters Ser.). 32p. (ps). pap. 4.95 (978-1-57565-097-5(5)) Kane Pr., The.

—Where's That Bone? 2000. (Math Matters Ser.). (J). (978-0-606-20183-4(1)); lib. bdg. 12.95 (978-0-613-39374-4(0)) Tandem Library Bks.

Perez, Vivian. Stolen Stories for My Nieces. 2007. (ENG.). 68p. per. 12.95 ***(978-1-4241-6679-4(9))*** PublishAmerica, Inc.

The Perils of Pink Cat. 2004. (Illus.). 36p. pap. 15.00 (978-0-9761041-2-4(1)) Celstumo Publishing.

Perkins, Lynne Rae. The Broken Cat. Perkins, Lynne Rae, illus. 2002. (Illus.). 32p. (J). (ps-1). 16.99 (978-0-06-029263-8(6)) HarperCollins Pubs.

—The Broken Cat. 2002. (Illus.). 32p. (J). (ps-1). 16.89 (978-0-06-029264-5(4)) HarperCollins Pubs.

Perrault, Charles. Puss in Boots. Arthur, Malcolm, tr. Marcellino, Fred, illus. 1998. (J). (ps-17). lib. bdg. 17.60 (978-0-613-10524-8(9)) Tandem Library Bks.

Peters, Mike. Grimmy's Cat Tails. 2001. 128p. mass mkt. 4.99 (978-0-8125-6491-4(X) , Tor Bks.) Doherty, Tom Assocs., LLC.

Peterson, Jim. Kitten Tales. 2006. (ENG.). 76p. per. 14.95 ***(978-1-4241-4448-8(5))*** PublishAmerica, Inc.

Peterson, Jim. Kittens in the Mall. 2006. 76p. pap. 14.95 (978-1-4241-2604-0(5)) PublishAmerica, Inc.

Peutrell, Ann. No More Fleas. 1999. 28p. (J). (ps-2). 7.95 (978-0-7641-5213-9(0)) Barron's Educational Series, Inc.

Picture Me Three Little Kittens Mini. 2002. 10p. (J). (ps up). bds. 2.99 (978-1-57151-554-4(2)) Playhouse Publishing.

Pilkey, Dav. Dragon y el Gato Panzon. 1999. (Dragon's Tales Ser.: Bk. 4). (SPA., Illus.). 48p. (J). (gr. 1-3). pap. 7.50 (978-980-257-218-2(7)) Ekare, Ediciones VEN. *Dist:* Kane/Miller Bk. Pubs., Inc., Lectorum Pubns., Inc.

—Dragon y el Gato Panzon. 2000. (Dragon's Tales Ser.: Bk. 4). (Illus.). (J). 14.75 (978-0-606-20639-6(6)) Tandem Library Bks.

—Dragon's Fat Cat. Pilkey, Dav, illus. 2002. (Dragon's Tales Ser.: Bk. 4). (Illus.). (J). 13.79 (978-0-7587-0543-3(3)) Book Wholesalers, Inc.

—Kat Kong. Pilkey, Dav, illus. 2002. (Illus.). (J). 14.04 (978-0-7587-2923-1(5)) Book Wholesalers, Inc.

—Kat Kong. 2003. (Illus.). 32p. (J). 14.00 (978-0-15-204951-5(7)); pap. 5.95 (978-0-15-204950-8(9) , Harcourt Paperbacks) Harcourt Children's Bks.

—Kat Kong. 2003. (gr. k-3). lib. bdg. 12.95 (978-0-613-71635-2(3)) Tandem Library Bks.

—'Twas the Night Before Christmas: The Wrath of Mrs. Claus. 1999. (J). (978-0-590-12073-9(5) , Blue Sky Pr., The) Scholastic, Inc.

Pinkwater, Daniel M. Rainy Morning. Pinkwater, Jill, illus. 1999. (Pinkwater Ser.: Vol. 1). 32p. (J). (gr. k-3). 16.00 (978-0-689-81143-2(8) , Atheneum) Simon & Schuster Children's Publishing.

Piper, Sophie. Little Kitten's Friendship Book. Massey, Jane, illus. 2006. 64p. (J). pap. 6.99 (978-0-7459-4710-5(7) , Lion) Lion Hudson plc GBR. *Dist:* Independent Pubs. Group.

Pirotta, Saviour & Marks, Alan. The Enchanted Gazelle. 2007. (J). ***(978-1-59771-081-7(4))*** Sea-To-Sea Pubns.

Pitts, Constance. Chulita the Blind Cat. 2007. (Illus.). 48p. (J). ***(978-0-9652902-2-7(0))*** Beevinwood, Inc.

The Playful Kitten. 2003. (J). per. (978-1-57657-888-9(7)) Paradise Pr., Inc.

Playing with my Cat. 2000. (J). (978-1-58453-093-0(6)) Pioneer Valley Educational Pr., Inc.

Pliszka, Jodi. Bella & Gizmo's Adventures — the Hairless Sphynx Cats. 2005. (Illus.). 30p. (J). per. 18.95 (978-1-933449-27-2(6)) Nightengale Pr.

Polacco, Patricia. Mrs. Katz & Tush. Polacco, Patricia, illus. 2002. (Illus.). (J). 14.79 (978-0-7587-3191-3(4)) Book Wholesalers, Inc.

Pollitz, Edith Elizabeth. Carrie. 2004. 43p. pap. 19.95 (978-1-4137-3355-6(7)) PublishAmerica, Inc.

The Porcelain Cat. 2004. 32p. 16.95 (978-1-59687-175-5(X) , Milk & Cookies) ibooks, Inc.

Posner, Fran. Halloween Makes Me Batty! 2007. (Illus.). 12p. (J). (gr. k-k). bds. 3.99 ***(978-0-7364-2458-5(X)*** , Golden Bks.) Random Hse. Children's Bks.

Potter, Beatrix. Conte de Tom Chaton. pap. 18.95 (978-2-07-054700-5(0)) Gallimard, Editions FRA. *Dist:* Distribooks, Inc.

—My Tom Kitten Cloth Book. 1999. (Illus.). 10p. (J). (ps). pap. 4.99 (978-0-7232-0021-5(1) , Warne) Penguin Group (USA) Inc.

—The Tale of Samuel Whiskers: Or the Roly-Poly Pudding. Potter, Beatrix, illus. 2002. (Illus.). 15.23 (978-1-4046-2497-9(X)) Book Wholesalers, Inc.

—The Tale of Tom Kitten, No. 8. 2002. (Illus.). 64p. (J). 6.99 (978-0-7232-4777-7(3) , Warne) Penguin Group (USA) Inc.

—The Tale of Tom Kitten. (Illus.). 12p. 4.95 (978-1-58989-273-6(9)) Thurman Hse., LLC.

—The Tale of Tom Kitten: A Sticker Story Book. 2008. (Potter Ser.). 24p. (J). (ps). 5.99 ***(978-0-7232-6288-6(8)*** , Warne) Penguin Group (USA) Inc.

—The Tale of Tom Kitten: Adapted from the Original. 2003. (Illus.). 32p. (J). 3.99 (978-0-7232-4720-3(X) , Warne) Penguin Group (USA) Inc.

—Tom Kitten. 2007. (Potter Shaped Board Book Ser.). 12p. (J). bds. 3.99 (978-0-7232-5857-5(0) , Warne) Penguin Group (USA) Inc.

Potter, Tony. Find the String Kitten. 1998. (J). (ps). 9.95 (978-1-902553-03-0(9)) Grimond FRA. *Dist:* Continental Enterprises Group, Inc. (CEG).

Poulin, Stephane. Catch That Cat! Poulin, Stephane, illus. 2003. (Illus.). 24p. (J). (gr. k-3). pap. 6.95 (978-0-88776-642-8(0)) Tundra Bks., Inc./Livres Toundra, Inc. CAN. *Dist:* Random Hse., Inc.

—Peux-Tu Attraper Josephine? 2003. (FRE & SPA., Illus.). 24p. (J). (gr. k-3). pap. 6.95 (978-0-88776-643-5(9) , Livres Toundra) Tundra Bks., Inc./Livres Toundra, Inc. CAN. *Dist:* Random Hse., Inc.

—Where's That Cat? Poulin, Stephane, illus. 2003. (Illus.). 24p. (J). (gr. k-3). pap. 6.95 (978-0-88776-644-2(7)) Tundra Bks., Inc./Livres Toundra, Inc. CAN. *Dist:* Random Hse., Inc.

Powell, Richard. GTI Kitten. Holt, Emma, illus. 2003. (Whizzy Wheels Bks.). 20p. (J). bds. 4.95 (978-0-7641-5588-8(1)) Barron's Educational Series, Inc.

—Kitty's Tail. Davis, Caroline, illus. 2003. (Animal Tails Ser.). 10p. (J). 3.95 (978-1-58925-673-6(5) , tiger tales) ME Media LLC.

Pratchett, Terry. The Amazing Maurice & His Educated Rodents. 2003. 368p. (YA). (gr. 7 up). pap. 6.99 (978-0-06-001235-9(8)) HarperCollins Pubs.

—The Amazing Maurice & His Educated Rodents. 2003. (gr. 5-8). lib. bdg. 15.30 (978-0-613-65757-0(8)) Tandem Library Bks.

Prentice, Amy. Mouser Cats' Story. 2004. reprint ed. pap. 15.95 (978-1-4191-3542-2(2)); pap. 1.99 (978-1-4192-3542-9(7)) Kessinger Publishing, LLC.

Preston, Mary Lou. Do You Know What Wildcats Do at School in P. E. Class? Wildcat's First Day in Class. 2006. (J). pap. 8.00 (978-0-8059-7013-5(4)) Dorrance Publishing Co., Inc.

Price, Robin. Catligula, 8 vols. 2006. (Spartapuss Tales Ser.). 192p. (J). pap. 14.95 (978-0-9546576-1-1(6)) Mogzilla GBR. *Dist:* Independent Pubs. Group.

—Die Clawdius, Vol. 3. 2007. (Spartapuss Tales Ser.). 192p. (J). pap. 14.95 ***(978-0-9546576-8-0(3))*** Mogzilla GBR. *Dist:* Independent Pubs. Group.

Price, Robin. I Am Spartapuss. 2006. (Spartapuss Tales Ser.). 192p. (J). pap. 14.95 (978-0-9546576-0-4(8)) Mogzilla GBR. *Dist:* Independent Pubs. Group.

Priceman, Marjorie. My Nine Lives by Clio. 2001. (J). 26.95 incl. audio (978-0-8045-6866-1(9) , 6866) Spoken Arts, Inc.

Pringle, Laurence P. Naming the Cat. Potter, Katherine, illus. 1999. 32p. (J). (gr. k-3). 15.95 (978-0-8027-8621-0(9)) Walker & Co.

Prowense, Mary J. Amy Goes Country. 2007. (ENG.). 136p. per. 19.95 ***(978-1-4241-5519-4(3))*** PublishAmerica, Inc.

Prymak, Leonid. Adventures of Siberian Cat Katerina. 2002. 108p. (J). pap. 9.95 (978-0-595-22497-5(0) , Writers Club Pr.) iUniverse, Inc.

Pueppke. Fuzzy the Cat & his Vacation in Gatlinburg. 2000. (Illus.). 89p. (YA). per. 6.99 (978-0-9678352-2-8(4)) FUZZY DREAMS, Inc.

Pueppke, M. D. Even Fuzzier Logic, Fuzzy the Cat Digs Deeper. 2004. (Illus.). 166p. (YA). per. 9.99 (978-0-9678352-3-5(2)) FUZZY DREAMS, Inc.

—Fuzzy the Cat & His Adventures in St. Augustine. 1999. 48p. (J). pap. 6.99 (978-0-9678352-0-4(8)) FUZZY DREAMS, Inc.

Pulver, Robin. Christmas for a Kitten. Johnson, Layne, illus. (Albert Whitman Prairie Bks.). 32p. (J). (gr. k-3). 2005. pap. 6.95 (978-0-8075-1154-1(4)); 2003. 16.95 (978-0-8075-1151-0(X)) Whitman, Albert & Co.

Puss in Boots. 2002. (Classic Tales Mini Bks.). (Illus.). 32p. (J). (978-1-59069-035-2(4) , T1004); incl. audio compact disk (978-1-59069-102-1(4) , T1104) Studio Mouse LLC.

Puss-in-Boots: Individual Title Six-Packs. 32p. (gr. 2 up). 37.00 (978-0-7635-9220-2(X)) Rigby Education.

Q. T. Pie's Rescue Adventure. 2003. (Illus.). 36p. (J). (ps-6). mass mkt. 4.99 (978-0-9670875-3-5(8) , 313-533-7383) SanPaul Group, LLC, The.

Quinlan, Heather. Silly Cat. Sterling Publishing Company Staff, ed. 2003. (Illus.). 14p. (J). bds. 4.95 (978-1-4027-0970-8(6)) Sterling Publishing Co., Inc.

Quinones, Juan Carlos. The Gang under the Tree. Montanez, Nivea Ortiz, illus. 2004. (Purple Ser.). (SPA.). 44p. (J). (gr. 3-5). pap. 5.95 (978-1-57581-439-1(0)) Santillana USA Publishing Co., Inc.

—La Pandilla Bajo el Arbol. 2003. (SPA.). (gr. 3-6). lib. bdg. 14.10 (978-0-613-79282-0(3)) Tandem Library Bks.

Quiroga, Luis Alberto. Chiquita. (SPA.). pap. 8.95 (978-950-07-1987-2(8)) Editorial Sudamericana S.A. ARG. *Dist:* Distribooks, Inc.

Radzinski, Kandy. What Cats Want for Christmas. rev. ed. 2007. (Holiday Ser.). 32p. (J). 16.95 ***(978-1-58536-340-7(5))*** Sleeping Bear Pr.

Rainey, L. E. Sad Sam, Glad Sam. 2006. (Illus.). 32p. (J). 16.95 (978-0-9785521-0-7(5)) Shoetree Publishers, Inc.

Raintree Steck-Vaughn Staff. Huellas de Gato. 1999. (Coleccion en Parejas). (SPA.). (J). pap., stu. ed. 21.50 (978-0-7398-0820-7(6)) Steck-Vaughn.

—Wild Cats. 1999. (Illus.). (J). pap. 35.60 (978-0-7398-0916-7(4)) Steck-Vaughn.

Ramage, Jan. Eyes in the Night. Peterson, Laura, illus. 2006. 32p. pap. 15.25 (978-1-920694-67-8(6)) Univ. of Western Australia Pr. AUS. *Dist:* International Specialized Bk. Services.

Randall, Marilyn Mae. The Three Wives of Hero the Second. Heavner, Jodi, illus. 2004. (J). per. 14.99 (978-0-9713589-7-3(4)) Ubaviel's Gifts.

Randell, Beverley & Bruere, Julian, contrib. by. Mimosa y el Arbol, 6 vols., Pack. (Coleccion Pm Ser.).Tr. of Tabby in the tree. (SPA.). 16p. (gr. 1 up). 26.00 (978-0-7578-3015-0(3)) Rigby Education.

Rankin, Joan. Scaredy Cat. 1999. (978-0-606-16292-0(5)) Tandem Library Bks.

Raschka, Chris. Like Likes Like. 2001. (Illus.). 32p. (J). (ps-k). pap. 6.95 (978-0-7894-8189-4(8)) Dorling Kindersley Publishing, Inc.

—Like Likes Like. 2001. (978-0-606-22361-4(4)) Tandem Library Bks.

Rau, Dana Meachen. Sweet Pea: Escape in the Garden. Hannon, Holly, illus. 2006. (J). ***(978-1-58987-200-4(2))*** Kindermusik International.

Rea, Monique. Toulouse the Moose. 2003. (J). 3.50 (978-1-891030-30-7(2)) Paragon Agency, The.

Rea, Monique F. The Original Story of Toulouse the Moose & His Friends: Book & CD. 2007. (J). ***(978-0-9788926-2-3(3))*** Trails of Discovery.

Redman-Waldeyer, Christine. Around the World with Rosalie. Adams, Marcella Ryan, illus. 2003. pap. 9.00 (978-0-8059-6185-0(2)) Dorrance Publishing Co., Inc.

Redmond, Diane. Scoop Saves the Day. 2001. (ps-2). lib. bdg. 11.25 (978-0-613-51323-4(1)) Tandem Library Bks.

Reeg, Cynthia. Kitty Kerplunking: Preposition Fun. Movshina, Marina, illus. 2006. 24p. (J). E-Book 9.95 incl. cd-rom (978-1-933090-27-6(8)) Guardian Angel Publishing, Inc.

—Kitty Kerplunking: Preposition Fun. l.t. ed. 2006. (ENG., Illus.). 24p. (J). 11.95 (978-1-933090-29-0(4)) Guardian Angel Publishing, Inc.

Reeves, Claire. Adventures of Boots the One Eyed Cat. 2003. (Illus.). 32p. (J). 15.95 (978-0-9743048-1-6(6)) LTI Publishing.

Reinen, Judy. Meow: A Day in the Life of Cats. Reinen, Judy, illus. 2001. (Illus.). 32p. (J). (gr. k-3). 13.95 (978-0-316-83342-4(8)) Little, Brown Bks. for Young Readers.

Ricci, Christine. The Halloween Cat. Saunders, Zina, illus. 2004. (Dora the Explorer Ser.). 24p. (J). pap. 3.99 (978-0-689-86799-6(9), Simon Spotlight/Nickelodeon) Simon & Schuster Children's Publishing.

Richter, Jutta. The Cat, or, How I Lost Eternity. Brailovsky, Anna, tr. from GER. 2007. (Illus.). 80p. (J). (gr. 3 up). 14.00 (***978-1-57131-676-9(0)***) Milkweed Editions.

Rifkin, L. The Nine Lives of Romeo Crumb: Life One. 2005. 311p. (J). (gr. 6-8). 16.95 (978-0-9743221-0-0(5)) Stratford Road Pr., Ltd.

Rifkin, L. & Hartman, Kurt. The Nine Lives of Romeo Crumb: Life Three. 2006. (Illus.). 276p. 16.95 (978-0-9743221-2-4(1)) Stratford Road Pr., Ltd.

Rigby Education Staff. Cargo Cat. (Sails Literacy Ser.). (Illus.). 16p. (gr. 1-2). 27.00 (978-0-7635-9915-7(8), 699158C99) Rigby Education.

—The Cat Show. (Sails Literacy Ser.). (Illus.). 16p. (gr. k-1). 27.00 (978-0-7635-9881-5(X), 698819C99) Rigby Education.

—Cat's Diary. (Sails Literacy Ser.). (Illus.). 16p. (gr. 2-3). 27.00 (978-0-7635-9937-9(9), 699379C99) Rigby Education.

—Custard's Cat Flap. (Sails Literacy Ser.). (Illus.). 16p. (gr. 1-2). 27.00 (978-0-7635-9903-4(4), 699034C99) Rigby Education.

—The Daily Meow. (Sails Literacy Ser.). (Illus.). 16p. (gr. 2-3). 27.00 (978-0-7635-9940-9(9), 6997409C99) Rigby Education.

—The Happy House. (Sails Literacy Ser.). (Illus.). 16p. (gr. 1-2). 27.00 (978-0-7635-9908-9(5), 699085C99) Rigby Education.

—McGinty's Friend. (Sails Literacy Ser.). (Illus.). 16p. (gr. 2-3). 27.00 (978-0-7635-9947-8(6), 699476C99) Rigby Education.

—The Old Cat. (Sails Literacy Ser.). (Illus.). 16p. (gr. 1-2). 27.00 (978-0-7635-9932-4(8)) Rigby Education.

—Silly Cat. (Sails Literacy Ser.). (Illus.). 16p. (gr. k-1). 27.00 (978-0-7635-9876-1(3), 698763C99) Rigby Education.

—The Space Cat. (Sails Literacy Ser.). (Illus.). 16p. (gr. 2-3). 27.00 (978-0-7635-9949-2(2), 699492C99) Rigby Education.

Riordan, James. My G-r-r-r-reat Uncle Tiger. Ayliffe, Alex, illus. 2000. (Accelerated Reader Ser.). 32p. (J). (ps-1). pap. 6.95 (978-1-56145-228-6(9), Q17614) Peachtree Pubs., Ltd.

—My G-R-R-R-Reat Uncle Tiger. Ayliffe, Alex, illus. 2000. (ps-1). lib. bdg. 15.25 (978-0-613-82659-4(0)) Tandem Library Bks.

Rip Squeak & His Friends Discover the Treasure. 2003. Tr. of Rip Squeak y Sus Amigos Descubren un Tesoro. per. 16.95 (978-0-9672422-5-5(8)) Rip Squeak, Inc.

Rizzati, Lorella. Hello Kitty. 2001. (Portable Pets Ser.). (Illus.). 12p. (J). (ps-ps). bds. 6.95 (978-0-8109-5680-3(2)) Abrams, Harry N., Inc.

Robbins, Beth. Tom, Ally & the Babysitter. Stuart, Jon, illus. 2001. (It's OK! Ser.). 24p. (J). (ps-k). pap. 3.95 (978-0-7894-7426-1(3), D K Ink) Dorling Kindersley Publishing, Inc.

—Tom, Ally, & the New Baby. Stuart, Jon, illus. 2001. (It's OK! Ser.). 24p. (J). (ps-k). pap. 3.95 (978-0-7894-7430-8(1), D K Ink) Dorling Kindersley Publishing, Inc.

—Tom & Ally Visit the Doctor: American Edition. Stuart, Jon, illus. 2001. (It's OK! Ser.). 24p. (J). (ps-k). pap. 3.95 (978-0-7894-7428-5(X), D K Ink) Dorling Kindersley Publishing, Inc.

—Tom's First Day at School. Stuart, Jon, illus. 2001. (It's OK! Ser.). 24p. (J). (ps-k). pap. 3.95 (978-0-7894-7422-3(0), D K Ink) Dorling Kindersley Publishing, Inc.

Robbins, Beth & Stuart, Jon. Tom's First Haircut. 2001. (It's OK! Ser.). (Illus.). 24p. (J). (ps-k). pap. 3.95 (978-0-7894-7424-7(7), D K Ink) Dorling Kindersley Publishing, Inc.

Roberts, Bethany. Cat Skidoo. Alley, R. W., tr. Alley, R. W., illus. rev. ed. 2004. 32p. (J). 16.95 (978-0-8050-6710-1(8), Holt, Henry & Co. Bks. For Young Readers) Holt, Henry & Co.

Roberts, Dina. Thirty Cats. 2003. 162p. (YA). pap. 12.95 (978-0-595-29775-7(7)) iUniverse, Inc.

Robertson, Susan, illus. Little Kitten. 2002. 8p. (J). (ps). per. 6.99 (978-1-57755-502-5(3)) Allied Publishing.

Robeson, K. S. Chloe, Bia & the Little People: Tales from Wind Creek Book Three. 2003. (Tales from Wind Creek Ser.: 3). 104p. (J). pap. 8.95 (978-0-9723530-4-5(6)) Falcor Bks.

Robison, Peggy. Prince Cody Meets A Monster. Clay, Doris, illus. 2004. 40p. (J). 9.95 (978-0-9708395-7-2(X)) Legacy Publishing Services, Inc.

—Prince Cody Runs Ahead of the Hurricane. Clay, Doris, illus. 2005. 64p. (J). per. 9.95 (978-0-9764982-7-8(8)) Legacy Publishing Services, Inc.

Robledo, Honorio. Nico Visita la Luna. Robledo, Honorio, illus. 2001. (SPA., Illus.). 32p. (J). 15.95 (978-0-938317-62-3(8)) Cinco Puntos Pr.

Rocha, Ruth. El Gato Borba. 2001. Tr. of Borba, the Cat. (SPA.). 48p. (J). 5.95 (978-84-348-2473-7(6)) SM Ediciones ESP. *Dist:* AIMS International Bks., Inc.

Rockwell, Anne F. Katie Catz Makes a Splash. Meisel, Paul, illus. 2003. (Good Sports Ser.). 40p. (J). (ps-1). 15.99 (978-0-06-028441-1(2)) HarperCollins Pubs.

—Katie Catz Swims at Last. Meisel, Paul, illus. 1999. 32p. (J). (ps-1). pap. 5.95 (978-0-06-446740-7(6)) HarperCollins Pubs.

Roe, E. T. Fun & Frolic. 2004. reprint ed. pap. 15.95 (978-1-4191-2129-6(4)); pap. 1.99 (978-1-4192-2129-3(9)) Kessinger Publishing, LLC.

Rohmann, Eric. The Cinder-Eyed Cats. 2001. 40p. (J). (gr. k-3). pap. 6.99 (978-0-440-41743-9(0), Dragonfly Bks.) Random Hse. Children's Bks.

—The Cinder-Eyed Cats. 2001. 13.79 (978-0-606-22187-0(5)) Tandem Library Bks.

Rohmann, Eric. A Kitten Tale. 2008. (J). (***978-0-517-70915-3(5)***); lib. bdg. (***978-0-517-70916-0(3)***) Knopf, Alfred A. Inc.

Romano, Melora. Meow, What Now? Christian, Sara, illus. 1998. 12p. (J). (gr. k-2). pap. 3.75 (978-1-880612-78-1(X), Seedling Pubns.) Continental Pr., Inc.

Ronan, Anne M. Muffles in New York. 1999. (Illus.). 32p. (J). (ps-4). pap. 8.00 (978-1-930248-00-7(8)) Polka Dot Pr. Corp., The.

Root, Phyllis. Here Comes Tabby Cat. McEwen, Katharine, illus. 2000. (Brand New Readers Ser.). 32p. (J). (ps-2). pap. 5.99 (978-0-7636-0772-2(X)) Candlewick Pr.

—Hey, Tabby Cat! McEwen, Katharine, illus. 2000. (Brand New Readers Ser.). 1p. (J). (ps-2). pap. 5.99 (978-0-7636-0800-2(9)) Candlewick Pr.

—Lucia & the Light. GrandPré, Mary, illus. 2006. 40p. (J). (gr. k-3). 16.99 (978-0-7636-2296-1(6)) Candlewick Pr.

Rosario, Joann. Puddy Cat & the Chick Muck. Rosario, Joann, illus. 2004. (Illus.). 15p. (J). (ps-5). pap. 10.00 (978-0-9758746-3-9(2), 1246169) J.G.R. Enterprises.

A Rose for Pinkerton. 2004. (J). 24.95 incl. audio (978-0-7882-0644-3(3)); pap. 14.95 incl. audio (978-0-7882-0643-6(5)) Weston Woods Studios, Inc.

Rosen, Michael. Lovely Old Roly. Lamont, Priscilla, illus. 2004. (J). 25p. (978-0-7112-1488-0(3)); 32p. pap. 7.95 (978-1-84507-144-8(1)) Lincoln, Frances Ltd. GBR. *Dist:* Transition Vendor, Perseus Distribution.

Ross, Eileen. The Halloween Showdown. Reed, Lynn R., illus. 1999. 32p. (J). (gr. k-3). tchr. ed. 15.95 (978-0-8234-1395-9(0)) Holiday Hse., Inc.

Ross, Tony. Quiero un Gato (I Want a Cat) (SPA.). 28p. (J). 17.95 (978-84-233-1999-2(7)) Ediciones Destino ESP. *Dist:* AIMS International Bks., Inc.

Rostoker-Gruber, Karen. Bandit. Nguyen, Vincent, illus. 2008. (J). (***978-0-7614-5382-6(2)***) Cavendish, Marshall Corp.

Rowinski, Kate. Cats in the Dark. Bishop, Bonnie, illus. 1998. 32p. (J). (ps-3). 14.95 (978-0-89272-427-7(7)) Down East Bks.

Rowland, Patty. Marvelous Max, the Mansion Mouse. Rasmussen, Wendy, tr. Rasmussen, Wendy, illus. 2003. 32p. (J). 17.95 (978-0-9649934-4-0(9)) Norfleet Pr., Inc.

Roxbee-Cox, Phil. Find the Kitten. 2007. (Find-its Board Bks). 12p. (J). bds. 6.99 (***978-0-7945-1803-5(6)***, Usborne) EDC Publishing.

Roy, Claude. Chat qui parlait malgre Lui. pap. 14.95 (978-2-07-051422-9(6)) Gallimard, Editions FRA. *Dist:* Distribooks, Inc.

Ruby, Laura. The Wall & the Wing. (J). 2007. 352p. (gr. 5 up). pap. 6.99 (***978-0-06-075257-6(2)***, Eos); 2006. 336p. 16.99 (978-0-06-075255-2(6)) HarperCollins Pubs.

Rudisill, J. J., et al, illus. Scaredy Cats. 1999. (Wimzie's House Bks.). 24p. (J). pap. 3.99 (978-0-88724-518-3(8), CD-4842) Carson-Dellosa Publishing Co., Inc.

Ruelle, Karen Gray. April Fool! (Illus.). 32p. (J). (gr. k-3). 4.95 (978-0-8234-1780-3(8)) Holiday Hse., Inc.

—Dear Tooth Fairy. (Illus.). 32p. (J). 14.95 (978-0-8234-1929-6(0)); 4.95 (978-0-8234-1984-5(3)) Holiday Hse., Inc.

—Easter Egg Disaster: A Harry & Emily Adventure. (Illus.). 32p. (J). (gr. k-3). tchr. ed. 14.95 (978-0-8234-1806-0(5)) Holiday Hse., Inc.

—Just in Time for New Year'S! A Harry & Emily Adventure. (Illus.). 32p. (J). tchr. ed. 14.95 (978-0-8234-1841-1(3)) Holiday Hse., Inc.

—Just in Time for New Year'S! A Harry & Emily Adventure. Ruelle, Karen Gray, illus. (Holiday House Readers Ser.). (Illus.). 32p. (J). pap. 4.95 (978-0-8234-1842-8(1)) Holiday Hse., Inc.

Rumford, James. Calabash Cat. 2003. (ENG & ARA., Illus.). 32p. (J). (gr. k-3). 16.00 (978-0-618-22423-4(8)) Houghton Mifflin Co. Trade & Reference Div.

Rylant, Cynthia. Boris. 2005. (Illus.). 80p. (YA). 16.00 (978-0-15-205412-0(X)) Harcourt Children's Bks.

—The Case of the Climbing Cat. Karas, G. Brian, illus. (High-Rise Private Eyes Ser.: No. 2). 48p. (J). 2001. (ps-3). pap. 3.99 (978-0-06-444307-4(8), Harper Trophy); 2000. (gr. 1 up). 14.89 (978-0-688-16309-9(2)) HarperCollins Pubs.

—The Case of the Climbing Cat. 2001. (High-Rise Private Eyes Ser.: No. 2). (J). (ps-3). 10.79 (978-0-606-22320-1(7)) Tandem Library Bks.

—El Caso del Gato Escalador.Tr. of Case of the Climbing Cat. (SPA.). (J). 7.95 (978-958-04-7076-2(6)) Norma S.A. COL. *Dist:* Distribuidora Norma, Inc.

—The Eagle. McDaniels, Preston, illus. 2004. (Lighthouse Family Ser.). 64p. (J). 14.95 (978-0-689-86243-4(1)) Simon & Schuster Children's Publishing.

—The Eagle. McDaniels, Preston, illus. 2005. (Lighthouse Family Ser.). 64p. (J). pap. 3.99 (978-0-689-86311-0(X), Aladdin) Simon & Schuster Children's Publishing.

—Moonlight: The Halloween Cat. Sweet, Melissa, illus. 2003. 32p. (J). (ps-k). 14.99 (978-0-06-029711-4(5)); lib. bdg. 16.89 (978-0-06-029712-1(3)) HarperCollins Pubs.

—Mr. Putter & Tabby Catch the Cold. Howard, Arthur, illus. (Mr. Putter & Tabby Ser.). 44p. (J). 2003. pap. 5.95 (978-0-15-204760-3(3), Harcourt Paperbacks); 2002. (gr. 1-4). 15.00 (978-0-15-202414-7(X)) Harcourt Children's Bks.

—Mr. Putter & Tabby Feed the Fish. 2002. (Mr. Putter & Tabby Ser.). (Illus.). (J). 13.15 (978-0-7587-9914-2(4)) Book Wholesalers, Inc.

—Mr. Putter & Tabby Feed the Fish. Howard, Arthur, illus. (Mr. Putter & Tabby Ser.). 44p. (J). (gr. 1-4). 2002. pap. 5.95 (978-0-15-216366-2(2), Harcourt Paperbacks); 2001. 15.00 (978-0-15-202408-6(5)) Harcourt Children's Bks.

—Mr. Putter & Tabby Feed the Fish. 2001. (Mr. Putter & Tabby Ser.). (gr. k-3). lib. bdg. 14.10 (978-0-613-44315-9(2)) Tandem Library Bks.

—Mr. Putter & Tabby Fly the Plane. Howard, Arthur, illus. 2002. (Mr. Putter & Tabby Ser.). (J). 13.15 (978-0-7587-0681-2(2)) Book Wholesalers, Inc.

—Mr. Putter & Tabby Make a Wish. 2005. (Illus.). 38p. (J). lib. bdg. 20.00 (***978-1-4242-1954-4(X)***) Fitzgerald Bks.

—Mr. Putter & Tabby Make a Wish. Howard, Arthur, illus. 2006. (Mr. Putter & Tabby Ser.). 44p. (J). pap. 5.95 (978-0-15-205443-4(X), Harcourt Paperbacks) Harcourt Children's Bks.

—Mr. Putter & Tabby Make a Wish. Howard, Arthur, illus. 2005. (Mr. Putter & Tabby Ser.). 44p. (J). (ps-2). 14.00 (978-0-15-202426-0(3)) Harcourt Trade Pubs.

—Mr. Putter & Tabby Paint the Porch. Howard, Arthur, illus. 2001. (Mr. Putter & Tabby Ser.). 44p. (J). (gr. 1-4). pap. 5.95 (978-0-15-202474-1(3), Harcourt Paperbacks) Harcourt Children's Bks.

—Mr. Putter & Tabby Paint the Porch. Rylant, Cynthia & Howard, Arthur, illus. 2000. (Mr. Putter & Tabby Ser.). 44p. (J). (gr. k-3). 13.00 (978-0-15-201787-3(9)) Harcourt Children's Bks.

—Mr. Putter & Tabby Paint the Porch. 2001. (Mr. Putter & Tabby Ser.). (978-0-606-22609-7(5)); lib. bdg. 14.10 (978-0-613-46257-0(2)) Tandem Library Bks.

—Mr. Putter & Tabby Pour the Tea. Howard, Arthur, illus. 2002. (Mr. Putter & Tabby Ser.). (J). 13.15 (978-0-7587-0684-3(7)) Book Wholesalers, Inc.

—Mr. Putter & Tabby Ride the Bike. 2002. (Illus.). (J). (978-0-15-202432-1(8)) Harcourt Trade Pubs.

—Mr. Putter & Tabby Row the Boat. Howard, Arthur, illus. 2002. (Mr. Putter & Tabby Ser.). (J). 13.15 (978-0-7587-0685-0(5)) Book Wholesalers, Inc.

—Mr. Putter & Tabby Run the Race. Howard, Arthur, illus. 2008. (Mr. Putter & Tabby Ser.). 44p. (J). 15.00 (***978-0-15-206069-5(3)***) Harcourt Trade Pubs.

—Mr. Putter & Tabby See the Stars. Howard, Arthur, illus. 2008. (Mr. Putter & Tabby Ser.). 44p. (J). pap. 5.95 (***978-0-15-206366-5(8)***, Harcourt Paperbacks) Harcourt Children's Bks.

—Mr. Putter & Tabby See the Stars. Howard, Arthur, illus. 2007. (Mr. Putter & Tabby Ser.). 44p. (J). (gr. 1-4). 14.00 (***978-0-15-206075-6(8)***) Harcourt Trade Pubs.

—Mr. Putter & Tabby Spin the Yarn. Howard, Arthur, illus. 2007. (Mr. Putter & Tabby Ser.). 44p. (J). pap. 5.95 (***978-0-15-206095-4(2)***, Harcourt Paperbacks) Harcourt Children's Bks.

—Mr. Putter & Tabby Spin the Yarn. Howard, Arthur, illus. 2006. (Mr. Putter & Tabby Ser.). 44p. (J). (gr. k-2). 14.00 (978-0-15-205067-2(1)) Harcourt Trade Pubs.

—Mr. Putter & Tabby Stir the Soup. Howard, Arthur, illus. (Mr. Putter & Tabby Ser.). 44p. (J). 2004. pap. 5.95 (978-0-15-205058-0(2), Harcourt Paperbacks); 2003. 14.00 (978-0-15-202637-0(1)) Harcourt Children's Bks.

—Mr. Putter & Tabby Take the Train. Howard, Arthur, illus. 2002. (Mr. Putter & Tabby Ser.). (J). 13.15 (978-0-7587-0686-7(3)) Book Wholesalers, Inc.

—Mr. Putter & Tabby Take the Train. Howard, Arthur, illus. (Mr. Putter & Tabby Ser.). 44p. (J). (gr. 1-4). 2000. pap. 5.95 (978-0-15-202389-8(5), Harcourt Paperbacks); 1998. 14.00 (978-0-15-201786-6(0)) Harcourt Children's Bks.

—Mr. Putter & Tabby Take the Train. 1999. (Mr. Putter & Tabby Ser.). (J). (gr. 1 up). pap., stu. ed. 30.00 incl. audio (978-0-7887-2988-1(8), 40870) Recorded Bks., LLC.

—Mr. Putter & Tabby Toot the Horn. Howard, Arthur, illus. 2002. (Mr. Putter & Tabby Ser.). (J). 13.15 (978-0-7587-0687-4(1)) Book Wholesalers, Inc.

—Mr. Putter & Tabby Walk the Dog. Howard, Arthur, illus. 2002. (Mr. Putter & Tabby Ser.). (J). 13.15 (978-0-7587-0688-1(X)) Book Wholesalers, Inc.

—Mr. Putter & Tabby Write the Book. Howard, Arthur, illus. 2004. (Mr. Putter & Tabby Ser.). 44p. (J). 14.00 (978-0-15-200241-1(3)) Harcourt Children's Bks.

—Mr. Putter & Tabby Write the Book. Howard, Arthur, illus. 2005. (Mr. Putter & Tabby Ser.). 44p. (J). (ps). pap., pap. 5.95 (978-0-15-200242-8(1)) Harcourt Trade Pubs.

Rylant, Cynthia. Puppy Mudge Finds a Friend. Stevenson, Sucie, illus. 2005. (Puppy Mudge Ser.). (J). (***978-1-4156-3675-6(3)***, Aladdin) Simon & Schuster Children's Publishing.

Rylant, Cynthia & McDaniels, Preston. The Storm. 2003. (Lighthouse Family Ser.). (Illus.). 80p. (J). pap. 3.99 (978-0-689-84882-7(X), Aladdin) Simon & Schuster Children's Publishing.

Rymas-Loomis, Cathy. Calamity Clancey: The Calamity Cat from Kalvesta Kansas. 2007. 40p. per. 12.97 (***978-1-932344-85-1(3)***) Thornton Publishing.

Rymond, Lynda Gene. Oscar & the Mooncats. Ceccoli, Nicoletta, illus. 2007. 40p. (J). (gr. k-3). 16.00 (***978-0-618-56316-6(4)***) Houghton Mifflin Co.

Sachs, Marilyn. The Four Ugly Cats in Apartment 3D. Litzinger, Rosanne, illus. 2003. (Ready-for-Chapters Ser.). 80p. (J). pap. 3.99 (978-0-689-86353-0(5), Aladdin) Simon & Schuster Children's Publishing.

Sachs, Marilyn & Litzinger, Rosanne. The Four Ugly Cats in Apartment 3D. 2002. (Illus.). 80p. (J). (gr. 3-5). 15.00 (978-0-689-84581-9(2), Atheneum/Richard Jackson Bks.) Simon & Schuster Children's Publishing.

Sacre, Antonio. The Barking Mouse. Aguirre, Alfredo, illus. 2003. 32p. (J). (gr. k-3). 15.95 (978-0-8075-0571-7(4)) Whitman, Albert & Co.

Said, S. F. The Outlaw Varjak Paw. McKean, Dave, illus. 2007. 272p. (J). (gr. 3-7). 6.50 (978-0-440-42172-6(1), Yearling) Random Hse. Children's Bks.

—Varjak Paw. McKean, Dave, illus. 2003. (J). (gr. k-7). 256p. 16.95 (978-0-385-75019-6(6)); 256p. lib. bdg. 18.99 (978-0-385-75030-1(7)); 259p. (978-0-385-60415-4(7)) Random Hse. Children's Bks. (Fickling, David Bks.).

Salas, Macarena, ed. La Ratita Presumida / the Conceited Little Rat. 2006. (Bilingual Tales Ser.). 24p. (J). pap. 3.50 (978-0-439-77379-9(2), Scholastic en Espanol) Scholastic, Inc.

Salmassian, Jennifer. Sally Saves the Mice. 2007. (J). per. 0.01 net. (***978-1-60402-115-8(2)***) Independent Pub.

—Sally the Firefighter. 2007. (J). per. 0.01 net. (***978-1-60402-164-6(0)***) Independent Pub.

Saltzberg, Barney. I Love Cats. Saltzberg, Barney, illus. 2005. (Super Sturdy Picture Book Ser.). (Illus.). 24p. (J). (ps-17). 8.99 (978-0-7636-2588-7(4)) Candlewick Pr.

Samarrippas, Gloria. In Search for Lucky's Lost Toys. 2006. 17.00 (***978-0-8059-7329-7(X)***) Dorrance Publishing Co., Inc.

Sampson, Fay. Pangur Ban, the White Cat, Vol. 2. 2002. 160p. (J). (gr. 5-8). pap. 7.99 (978-0-7459-4763-1(8), Lion) Lion Hudson plc GBR. *Dist:* Independent Pubs. Group.

—Shape-Shifter: The Naming of Pangur Ban. 2002. (Illus.). 160p. (J). (gr. 5-8). pap. 7.99 (978-0-7459-4762-4(X), Lion) Lion Hudson plc GBR. *Dist:* Independent Pubs. Group.

Samuels, Barbara. Dolores Meets Her Match. 2007. (Dolores Ser.). (Illus.). 32p. (J). (ps-3). 16.00 (***978-0-374-31758-4(5)***, Farrar, Straus & Giroux (BYR)) Farrar, Straus & Giroux.

Samuels, Barbara. Dolores on Her Toes. Samuels, Barbara, illus. 2003. (Dolores Ser.). (Illus.). 40p. (J). 16.50 (978-0-374-31818-5(2), Farrar, Straus & Giroux (BYR)) Farrar, Straus & Giroux.

Samuels, Barbara & Dorling Kindersley Publishing Staff. Aloha, Dolores. 2000. (Melanie Kroupa Bks.). (Illus.). 32p. (J). (ps-2). 15.95 (978-0-7894-2508-9(4)) Dorling Kindersley Publishing, Inc.

San Souci, Robert D. The White Cat. Spirin, Gennady, illus. 2000. 32p. (J). (ps-3). pap. 6.95 (978-0-531-07170-0(7), Orchard Bks.) Scholastic, Inc.

—The White Cat. 2000. (978-0-606-18336-9(1)) Tandem Library Bks.

Sander, Sonia. Sagwa: Festival of Lanterns. Thompson Brothers Staff, illus. 2003. (Sagwa, the Chinese Siamese Cat Ser.). 32p. (J). (ps-3). pap. 3.99 (978-0-439-45179-6(5)) Scholastic, Inc.

—Sagwa: Sagwa's Lucky Bat. George, Chris, illus. 2003. (Sagwa, the Chinese Siamese Cat Ser.). 64p. (J). (ps-3). 2.99 (978-0-439-45181-9(7)) Scholastic, Inc.

Sanderson, Ruth. Papa Gatto: An Italian Fairy Tale. Sanderson, Ruth, illus. 1999. (Illus.). 32p. (J). (ps-3). pap. 5.95 (978-0-316-77112-2(0)) Little Brown & Co.

Sang, Franchesca Ho, compiled by. Wisdom of Kittens. 2006. (Illus.). 128p. (J). (978-1-59258-252-5(4)) Hylas Publishing.

Santillo, LuAnn. The Cat. Santillo, LuAnn, ed. 2003. (Half-Pint Kids Readers Ser.). (Illus.). 7p. (J). (ps-1). pap. (978-1-59256-066-0(0)) Half-Pint Kids, Inc.

Santoro, Scott. Farm-Fresh Cats. Santoro, Scott, illus. 2006. (Illus.). 32p. (J). 15.99 (978-0-06-078178-1(5)); lib. bdg. 16.89 (978-0-06-078179-8(3)) HarperCollins Pubs.

Sarduy, Severo. Gatico-Gatico. Gomez, Patricio, illus. (Literary Encounters Ser.). (SPA.). (J). (gr. 3-5). pap. (978-968-494-062-8(9), CI1124) Centro de Informacion y Desarrollo de la Comunicacion y la Literatura MEX. *Dist:* Lectorum Pubns., Inc.

Sargent, Dave & Sargent, David, Jr. Tin Wren: Be Nice, 19, 19. Lenoir, Jane, illus. 2003. (Feather Tales Ser.: No. 19). 42p. (J). pap. 6.95 (978-1-56763-756-4(6)) Ozark Publishing.

—Tom Turkey: Don't Bully, 19, 20. Lenoir, Jane, illus. 2003. (Feather Tales Ser.: 20). 42p. (J). pap. 6.95 (978-1-56763-758-8(2)) Ozark Publishing.

Sargent, Dave & Sargent, Pat. Cat Who Barked, 10, 18. Robinson, Laura, illus. 2004. (Learn to Read Ser.: 10). 18p. (J). pap. 9.95 (978-1-56763-832-5(5)); lib. bdg. 19.95 (978-1-56763-831-8(7)) Ozark Publishing.

—Cat Who Barked/el gato que Ladro, 10, 18. Robinson, Laura, illus. 2004. (Learn to Read Ser.: 10). (ENG & SPA.). 18p. (J). pap. 9.95 (978-1-56763-996-4(8)); lib. bdg. 19.95 (978-1-56763-995-7(X)) Ozark Publishing.

—Little Big Cat, 10, 16. Robinson, Laura, illus. 2004. (Learn to Read Ser.: 10). 18p. (J). pap. 9.95 (978-1-56763-828-8(7)); lib. bdg. 19.95 (978-1-56763-827-1(9)) Ozark Publishing.

—Little Big Cat/Gato pequeño y Grande, 10, 16. Robinson, Laura, illus. 2004. (Learn to Read Ser.: 10). (ENG & SPA.). 18p. (J). pap. 9.95 (978-1-56763-992-6(5)) Ozark Publishing.

—Little Big Cat/Gato Pequeño y Grande, 10 vols., Vol. 16. Robinson, Laura, illus. 2004. (Learn to Read Ser.: 10). Tr. of Gato Pequeno y Grande. (ENG & SPA.). 18p. (J). (gr. k-2). lib. bdg. 19.95 (978-1-56763-991-9(7)) Ozark Publishing.

—Samone the Siamese: Lazybones!, 56 vols., 36. Huff, Jeane, illus. 2001. (Animal Pride Ser.: Vol. 36). 36p. (J). lib. bdg. 19.95 (978-1-56763-388-7(9)) Ozark Publishing.

C
D

Sarmonpol, Paulette. Where Are My Onions? Vignale, Silvia, illus. 2000. 32p. (J). (ps-3). (978-1-896580-08-1(4)); pap. (978-1-896580-32-6(7)) Tradewind Bks.

Satrapi, Marjane. Monsters Are Afraid of the Moon. 2006. (Illus.). 32p. (J). 15.95 (978-1-58234-744-8(1) , Bloomsbury Children) Bloomsbury Publishing.

Satterfield, Barbara. Tomias the Cat. 2000. (Illus.). 30p. (J). (gr. 2-6). pap. 9.99 (978-0-9725941-0-3(8)) Milligan Bks., Inc.

Saul, Carol P. Barn Cat. Azarian, Mary, illus. 2002. (J). 21.66 (978-0-7587-2036-8(X)) Book Wholesalers, Inc.

—Barn Cat: A Counting Book. Azarian, Mary, illus. 2000. (J). 12.75 (978-0-606-19836-3(9)) Tandem Library Bks.

Saunders, Marshall. Pussy BlackFace or the Story of A Kitten. 2006. (Illus.). pap. 31.95 (*978-1-4254-9478-0(1)*) Kessinger Publishing, LLC.

Savage, Derek. Cool Cat Goes to Hollywood. Bustamante, Denny, illus. 2001. (Cool Cat Ser.: Vol. 2). 32p. (J). pap. 9.95 (978-0-9673000-4-7(5)) Savage Bks.

—Cool Cat Goes to New York. Bustamante, Denny, illus. 2001. (Cool Cat Ser.: Vol. 4). 32p. (J). pap. 9.95 (978-0-9673000-6-1(1)) Savage Bks.

—Cool Cat Goes to Texas. Bustamante, Denny, illus. 2001. (Cool Cat Ser.: Vol. 3). 32p. (J). pap. 9.95 (978-0-9673000-5-4(3)) Savage Bks.

—Cool Cat Is a Cool Cat. Bustamante, Denny, illus. 2001. (Cool Cat Ser.: Vol. 1). 32p. (J). pap. 9.95 (978-0-9673000-3-0(7)) Savage Bks.

Say, Allen. Allison. 2004. (Illus.). 32p. (J). (ps-ps). lib. bdg. 13.75 (978-0-606-32838-8(6)) Tandem Library Bks.

Scamell, Ragnhild. Fat Cats. 2000. (Illus.). 64p. (J). 13.99 (978-0-86264-979-1(X)) Andersen GBR. *Dist:* Independent Pubs. Group.

Scammell, Ragnhild. Wish Come True Cat. Hansen, Gaby, illus. 2001. 28p. (J). (ps-2). 13.95 (978-0-7641-5392-1(7)) Barron's Educational Series, Inc.

Schachner, Judith B. The Grannyman. 2003. (Illus.). 32p. (J). (gr. k-3). pap. 6.99 (978-0-14-250062-0(3) , Puffin) Penguin Group (USA) Inc.

—The Grannyman. unabr. ed. 2000. (YA). pap. 32.99 incl. audio (978-0-7887-3640-7(X) , 41005X4) Recorded Bks., LLC.

—The Grannyman. 1999. (gr. k-3). lib. bdg. 15.30 (978-0-613-68241-1(6)) Tandem Library Bks.

Schachner, Judith Byron. Skippyjon Jones & the Big Dig. 2007. 32p. (J). (ps). 16.99 (*978-0-525-47884-3(1)* , Dutton Juvenile) Penguin Group (USA) Inc.

Schachner, Judy. Skippy Jon Jones. Schachner, Judy, illus. 2005. (Illus.). 32p. (J). reprint ed. pap. 5.99 (978-0-14-240403-4(9) , Puffin) Penguin Group (USA) Inc.

—Skippyjon Jones. 2007. (Puffin Storytime Ser.). 32p. (J). (ps). pap. 9.99 (978-0-14-240872-8(7) , Puffin) Penguin Group (USA) Inc.

—Skippyjon Jones: Color Crazy. 2007. 12p. (J). (ps). pap. 6.99 (978-0-525-47782-2(9) , Dutton Juvenile) Penguin Group (USA) Inc.

—Skippyjon Jones: Up & Down. 2007. 12p. (J). (ps). pap. 6.99 (978-0-525-47807-2(8) , Dutton Juvenile) Penguin Group (USA) Inc.

—Skippyjon Jones & the Treasure Hunt. 2008. 16p. (J). (ps-1). 9.99 (*978-0-448-44817-6(3)* , Grosset & Dunlap) Penguin Group (USA) Inc.

—Skippyjon Jones Book & Toy Set. Schachner, Judy, illus. 2007. 32p. (J). (ps). 14.99 (*978-0-525-47774-7(8)* , Dutton Juvenile) Penguin Group (USA) Inc.

—Skippyjon Jones in Mummy Trouble. Schachner, Judy, illus. 2006. (Illus.). 36p. (J). (ps). 16.99 (978-0-525-47754-9(3) , Dutton Juvenile) Penguin Group (USA) Inc.

—Skippyjon Jones in the Doghouse. 2008. (Puffin Storytime Ser.). 10p. (J). (ps). 9.99 (*978-0-14-241041-7(1)* , Puffin) Penguin Group (USA) Inc.

—Skippyjon Jones in the Doghouse. Schachner, Judy, illus. 2007. 32p. (J). pap. 6.99 (978-0-14-240749-3(6) , Puffin) Penguin Group (USA) Inc.

—Skippyjon Jones in the Doghouse. Wilhelm, James J., ed. Schachner, Judy, illus. 2005. (Illus.). 32p. (J). (ps). 16.99 (978-0-525-47297-1(5) , Dutton Juvenile) Penguin Group (USA) Inc.

Schachner, Judy. A Surprise for Mama. 2008. 16p. (J). (ps-1). pap. 5.99 (*978-0-448-44816-9(5)* , Grosset & Dunlap) Penguin Group (USA) Inc.

Schade, Susan. Cat on Ice. 2001. (Road to Reading Ser.). (Illus.). (J). 10.79 (978-0-606-20596-2(9)) Tandem Library Bks.

Schade, Susan & Buller, Jon. Cat on the Mat. 1998. (Step into Reading Ser.: Vol. 2). (Illus.). 32p. (J). (ps-1). pap. 3.99 (978-0-307-26207-3(3) , Random Hse. Bks. for Young Readers) Random Hse. Children's Bks.

—Cat on the Mat. 1998. (Illus.). 32p. (J). (ps-ps). lib. bdg. 11.80 (978-0-613-16623-2(X)) Tandem Library Bks.

Schaefer, Lola M. Follow Me, Mittens. Hartung, Susan Kathleen, illus. 2007. (My First I Can Read Bks.). 32p. (J). (ps-2). 15.99 (*978-0-06-054665-6(4)*); lib. bdg. 16.89 (*978-0-06-054666-3(2)*) HarperCollins Pubs.

—Mittens. Hartung, Susan Kathleen, illus. 2007. (My First I Can Read Bks.). 32p. (J). pap. 3.99 (*978-0-06-054661-8(1)* , Harper Trophy) HarperCollins Pubs.

—What's That, Mittens? Hartung, Susan Kathleen, illus. 2008. (My First I Can Read Bks.). 32p. (J). 16.99 (*978-0-06-054662-5(X)*); lib. bdg. 17.89 (*978-0-06-054663-2(8)*) HarperCollins Pubs.

Schaenen, Inda. All the Cats of Cairo. 2007. 232p. (J). (gr. 5-10). pap. 8.95 (*978-0-9768126-5-4(7)*) Brown Barn Bks.

Scheunemann, Pam. Cat Tails. Chawla, Neena, illus. 2006. (Fact & Fiction Ser.). 24p. (J). pap. (978-1-59679-928-8(5)); (gr. 1-3). 21.35 (978-1-59679-927-1(7) , Sandcastle) ABDO Publishing Co.

Schietinger-Cachina, Daryl A. Pat & Pat the Cat & Rat. Schietinger-Cachina, Daryl A., illus. 1999. (Illus.). 8p. (J). (ps-5). pap. 5.00 (978-1-928641-00-1(8)) Daryl Ann Pubns.

Schindel, John. Busy Kitties. Franzen, Sean, photos by. 2004. (Illus.). 20p. (J). bds. 6.95 (978-1-58246-130-4(9) , Tricycle Pr.) Ten Speed Pr.

Schlein, Miriam. The Way Mothers Are. 2000. (978-0-606-18777-0(4)) Tandem Library Bks.

—The Way Mothers Are. Lasker, Joe, illus. 2003. (Concept Book Ser.). 32p. (J). (ps-2). pap. 6.95 (978-0-8075-8690-7(0)) Whitman, Albert & Co.

—Way Mothers Are. 2000. (ps-2). lib. bdg. 15.25 (978-0-613-28691-6(X)) Tandem Library Bks.

Schmidt, Annie M. G. Miaou. 2004. (FRE.). 224p. (J). pap. (978-2-89021-705-8(1)) Diffusion du livre Mirabel.

Schofield, Brent R. Hairballs & Sticky Things. 2003. 120p. pap. 10.95 (978-0-595-27470-3(6)) iUniverse, Inc.

Scholastic, Inc. Staff. Ataque de Gato! 2004. (Shrek Ser.). Orig. Title: Cat Attack!. (SPA., Illus.). 24p. (J). pap. 3.99 (978-0-439-63200-3(5) , Scholastic en Espanol) Scholastic, Inc.

—Hello Kitty: My Show-&-Tell Day. 1998. (Sanrio Ser.). (Illus.). 24p. (J). (ps-1). pap. 3.95 (978-0-590-55822-8(6) , Cartwheel Bks.) Scholastic, Inc.

Scholastic, Inc. Staff & Daugherty, George. Princess Sheegwa. Schields, Gretchen, illus. 2002. (Sagwa, the Chinese Siamese Cat Ser.: No. 2). 32p. (J). pap. 3.99 (978-0-439-42880-4(7)) Scholastic, Inc.

Scholastic, Inc. Staff & Hernandez-Rosenblatt, Jason. Batman: The Purr-fect Crime. Burchett, Rick, illus. 2004. (Batman Ser.: No. 4). 40p. (J). 3.99 (978-0-439-47100-8(1) , Cartwheel Bks.) Scholastic, Inc.

School Zone Publishing Company Staff & Vinje, Marie. The Cat That Sat, Level 1. 1999. (Start to Read! Ser.). (Illus.). 32p. (J). (ps-3). pap. 3.95 (978-0-88743-432-7(0) , 06084) School Zone Publishing Co.

Schories, Pat, illus. Biscuit Wants to Play. 2002. (Biscuit Ser.). (J). 11.87 (978-0-7587-8903-7(3)) Book Wholesalers, Inc.

Schubert, Ingrid & Schubert, Dieter. My Hero. 2005. (Illus.). 40p. (J). (gr. 1-3). (978-1-932425-10-9(1) , Lemniscaat) Boyds Mills Pr.

Schuepbach, Lynnette. Cat Time. 2006. 28p. pap. 12.95 (978-0-9759613-2-2(2)) Creative Sources.

Schurr, Cathleen. The Shy Little Kitten. Tenggren, Gustaf, illus. deluxe ed. Date not set. (J). (ps-2). reprint ed. (978-1-929566-57-0(3)) Cronies.

—The Shy Little Kitten. Tenggren, Gustaf, illus. 1999. (Little Golden Bks.). 24p. (J). (gr. k-k). 2.99 (978-0-307-00145-0(8) , 98103, Golden Bks.) Random Hse. Children's Bks.

—The Shy Little Kitten: Classic Edition. Tenggren, Gustaf, illus. Date not set. (J). (ps-1). reprint ed. (978-1-929566-51-8(4)) Cronies.

Schwaeber, Barbie. Princess Lucky Kitten. Huerta, Catherine, illus. 2007. 32p. 4.95 (*978-1-59249-675-4(X)*) Soundprints.

Schwaeber, Barbie Heit. Princess A Lucky Kitten. Huerta, Catherine, illus. 2007. 32p. 2.95 (*978-1-59249-676-1(8)*) Soundprints.

Segal, Lore. The Story of Mrs. Lovewright & Purrless Her Cat. Zelinsky, Paul O., illus. 2005. 40p. (J). pap. 6.99 (978-0-689-87328-7(X) , Aladdin); reprint ed. 16.95 (978-0-689-87327-0(1) , Atheneum/Anne Schwartz Bks.) Simon & Schuster Children's Publishing.

Seidler, Tor. Toes. Beddows, Eric, illus. 176p. (J). 2004. (gr. 3 up). 15.99 (978-0-06-054099-9(0) , Geringer, Laura Book); 2004. (gr. 3 up). lib. bdg. 16.89 (978-0-06-054100-2(8) , Geringer, Laura Book); 2006. reprint ed. pap. 5.99 (978-0-06-054101-9(6) , Harper Trophy) HarperCollins Pubs.

Seki, Sunny, illus. & retold by. The Tale of the Lucky Cat. Seki, Sunny, retold by. 2007. (JPN & ENG.). (J). (*978-0-9669437-5-7(9)*) East West Discovery Pr.

Selden, George. The Cricket in Times Square. Williams, Garth, illus. 2008. 144p. (J). pap. 6.99 (*978-0-312-38003-8(8)*) Square Fish.

Selden, George. Harry Kitten & Tucker Mouse. Williams, Garth, illus. 2001. (Chester Cricket Ser.). 80p. (J). (gr. 3-6). reprint ed. pap. 5.95 (978-0-374-42895-2(6) , Sunburst) Farrar, Straus & Giroux.

—Harry Kitten & Tucker Mouse. 2001. (gr. 3-6). lib. bdg. 14.10 (978-0-613-85136-7(6)) Tandem Library Bks.

Sepulveda, Luis. Gaviota y del Gato. 9th ed. 2003. (SPA.). 144p. (978-968-7723-11-2(4) , 6020) Tusquests Editores Mexico, S.A. de C.V.

—The Story of a Seagull & the Cat Who Taught Her to Fly. Peden, Margaret Sayers, tr. from SPA. Sheban, Chris, illus. Tr. of Historia de una Gaviota y del Gato Que le Enseano a Volar. 128p. (J). 2003. (gr. 3-6). pap. 15.95 (978-0-439-40186-9(0)); 2006. reprint ed. pap. 5.99 (978-0-439-40187-6(9)) Scholastic, Inc. (Levine, Arthur A. Bks.).

Seto, Dietrich, et al, eds. Galaxy Angel Party, Vol. 3. Tajii, Koji, tr. from JPN. Kanan, illus. 2007. (Galaxy Angel Ser.). Orig. Title: Galaxy Angel Anthology. 208p. pap. 9.99 (978-1-932480-28-3(5) , Broccoli Bks. Deluxe) Broccoli International USA, Inc.

Seuss, Dr. The Cat in the Hat. 1999. (Illus.). (J). 12.99 (978-0-679-89267-0(2) , Random Hse. Bks. for Young Readers) Random Hse. Children's Bks.

—The Cat in the Hat. Seuss, Dr., illus. l.t. ed. 2007. (I Can Read It All by Myself). (Illus.). 72p. (J). (gr. k-3). 8.99 (978-0-394-80001-1(X) , Random Hse. Bks. for Young Readers) Random Hse. Children's Bks.

—The Cat in the Hat Book & CD. 2005. (Illus.). 64p. (J). (gr. k-3). pap. 9.95 incl. audio compact disk (978-0-375-83492-9(3) , Random Hse. Bks. for Young Readers) Random Hse. Children's Bks.

—The Cat in the Hat Comes Back. 2006. (Illus.). 64p. (J). (gr. k-3). 9.95 (978-0-375-87538-0(7) , Random Hse. Bks. for Young Readers) Random Hse. Children's Bks.

—The Cat in the Hat's Great Big Flap Book. Ruiz, Aristides, illus. 1999. 12p. (J). (gr. k-ps). bds. 11.99 (978-0-679-89360-8(1) , Random Hse. Bks. for Young Readers) Random Hse. Children's Bks.

—Cattus Petasatus. Tunberg, Jennifer Morrish & Tunberg, Terence O., trs. from ENG. 2000. Tr. of Cat in the Hat. (LAT., Illus.). 80p. (YA). (ps-3). 20.00 (978-0-86516-472-7(X)); 26.00 (978-0-86516-471-0(1)) Bolchazy-Carducci Pubs.

—¡El Gato con Sombrero Viene de Nuevo! Canetti, Yanitzia, tr. from ENG. 2004. (SPA., Illus.). 63p. (ps-1). 8.99 (978-1-930332-43-0(2)) Lectorum Pubns., Inc.

—Gatola da Cartola. pap. 23.95 (978-85-7406-085-9(2)) Schwarcz, Editora Ltda, Companhia das Letrinhas BRA. *Dist:* Distribooks, Inc.

Seymour, Jane & Keach, James. And Then There Were Three. Planer, Geoffrey, illus. 2007. (This One & That One Ser.: Vol. 5). 32p. 12.99 (978-1-932431-09-4(8) , Angel Gate) Left Field Ink.

—Boing! No Bouncing on the Bed. Planer, Geoffrey, illus. 2007. (This One & That One Ser.: Vol. 1). 32p. 12.99 (978-1-932431-06-3(3) , Angel Gate) Left Field Ink.

—Splat! The Tale of a Colorful Cat. Planer, Geoffrey, illus. 2007. (This One & That One Ser.: Vol. 2.). 32p. 12.99 (978-1-932431-07-0(1) , Angel Gate) Left Field Ink.

—What's for Lunch? Fried Pies & Roast Cake. Planer, Geoffrey, illus. 2003. (This One & That One Ser.: Vol. 5). (ENG.). 32p. 12.99 (978-1-932431-10-0(1) , Angel Gate) Left Field Ink.

—Yum! A Tale of Two Cookies. Planer, Geoffrey, illus. 2nd ed. 2003. (This One & That One Ser.: Vol. 3). 32p. 12.99 (978-1-932431-08-7(X) , Angel Gate) Left Field Ink.

Shah, Indries. The Farmer's Wife/la Esposa Del Granjero. Santiago, Rose Mary, illus. 2003. (SPA & ENG.). (J). 6.95 (978-1-883536-34-3(0) , FAWI3, Hoopoe Bks.) ISHK.

Shahan, Sherry. Cool Cats Counting. Barragan, Paula, illus. 2005. (ENG & SPA.). 24p. (gr. k-2). 16.95 (978-0-87483-757-5(X)) August Hse. Pubs., Inc.

Shanklin, Sandra, told to. Tales of Cat Canyon. 2005. (Illus.). 143p. pap. 12.95 (978-0-9632459-2-2(9)) Great Plains Pr.

Sheldon, Dyan. Clara & Buster Go Moondancing. 2001. (978-0-606-22329-4(0)) Tandem Library Bks.

Shepard, Aaron. King o' the Cats. Sorra, Kristin, illus. 2004. 32p. (J). 16.95 (978-0-689-82082-3(8) , Atheneum) Simon & Schuster Children's Publishing.

A Shoe, 6 Packs. (Sails Literacy Ser.). 16p. (gr. k up). 27.00 (978-0-7635-4417-1(5)) Rigby Education.

Shoo, Shoo, Shoo! & Other Stories, 6 Packs. (Story Steps Ser.). (gr. k-2). 48.00 (978-0-7635-9604-0(3)) Rigby Education.

Shortridge, Retha. Baby & Meow. 2004. 42p. per. 12.83 (978-1-4116-1085-9(7)) Lulu.com.

Shreve, Susan Richards. Ghost Cats. 1999. 162p. (J). (gr. 3-7). pap. 14.95 (978-0-590-37131-5(2) , Levine, Arthur A. Bks.) Scholastic, Inc.

—Ghost Cats. 2001. (Illus.). (J). (978-0-606-21211-3(6)) Tandem Library Bks.

Shulman, Mark. Big Cat. Chambers, Sally, illus. 2004. 8p. (J). bds. 6.95 (978-1-58925-737-5(5) , tiger tales) ME Media LLC.

—El Gato Grande. Chambers, Sally, illus. 2004. (Todo cambia Ser.). (SPA.). 8p. 12.95 (978-84-7864-822-1(4)) Combel Editorial, S.A. ESP. *Dist:* Independent Pubs. Group.

Shumsky, Andrea L. Send the Cat to Jamaica. 1999. (Illus.). 32p. pap. (978-0-9628921-4-1(9)) Book Street Pr.

Silver, Pattie, illus. Kitty's Barn. 2005. 12p. (J). bds. 9.95 (978-1-58117-385-7(7) , Intervisual/Piggy Toes) Dalmatian Pr.

Silverhardt, Lauryn. A contar con Blue (Counting with Blue) Style Guide Staff, illus. 2005. (Blue's Clues Ser.). (SPA.). 14p. (J). bds. 4.99 (978-0-689-87748-3(X) , Libros Para Ninos) Simon & Schuster Children's Publishing.

Silvestri, Noelle. Boomer & Lillibeth's Hairy Tale. Kiplinger Pandy, Lori, illus. l.t. ed. 2002. 27p. per. 7.99 (978-1-932338-02-7(0)) Lifevest Publishing, Inc.

Simmie, Lois. El Gato Ya Se Va. Nugent, Cynthia, illus. 2000. (Primeras Lecturas Coleccion). (SPA.). 36p. (J). (gr. 1). pap. 7.50 (978-980-257-250-2(0)) Ekare, Ediciones VEN. *Dist:* Lectorum Pubns., Inc.

—Mister Got to Go & Arnie. Nugent, Cynthia, illus. 2004. 32p. pap. 6.95 (978-1-55192-636-0(9)) Raincoast Bk. Distribution CAN. *Dist:* Perseus Distribution.

Simmonds, Posy. Baker Cat. (Illus.). 32p. (J). pap. 8.99 (*978-0-09-945596-7(X)* , Red Fox) Random Hse. Children's Bks. GBR. *Dist:* Trafalgar Square Publishing.

—Baker Cat. 2004. (Illus.). 32p. 19.99 (*978-0-224-07004-1(5)*) Transworld Publishers Ltd. GBR. *Dist:* Independent Pubs. Group.

Simon, Charnan. Luna the Wake up Cat. 2006. (Rookie Reader Skill Set Ser.). (Illus.). 32p. (J). (gr. k-2). 19.50 (978-0-531-12087-3(2) , Children's Pr.) Scholastic Library Publishing.

—Luna the Wake-Up Cat. Huang, Benrei, illus. 2007. (Rookie Reader Ser.). 31p. (J). pap. (*978-0-531-12489-5(4)*) Children's Pr., Ltd.

Simon, Charnan. Sam's Pet. Bialke, Gary, illus. 2000. (Rookie Reader Skill Set Ser.). 32p. (J). (gr. k-2). pap. 4.95 (978-0-516-26553-7(9) , Children's Pr.) Scholastic Library Publishing.

—Sam's Pet. Bialke, Gary, illus. 2000. 31p. (J). (ps-3). lib. bdg. 12.95 (978-0-613-54642-3(3)) Tandem Library Bks.

Simonson, Audrey. Where Is Your Mousey? 2006. (ENG.). 40p. per. 22.65 (*978-1-4134-0270-4(4)*) Xlibris Corp.

Simsich, Steven & Maval Publishing Inc. Staff. Jim, the Heavy Cat. 2001. (Illus.). 32p. (J). (ps-3). pap. 7.50 (978-1-884083-71-6(4)) Maval Publishing, Inc.

Singer, Marilyn. Cats to the Rescue: True Tales of Heroic Felines. Cassels, Jean, illus. rev. ed. 2006. 160p. (J). 16.95 (978-0-8050-7433-8(3) , Holt, Henry & Co. Bks. For Young Readers) Holt, Henry & Co.

Skelton, Mora. The Baritone Cat. Wilson, Janet, illus. 2001. 30p. (J). (ps-3). 7.95 (978-0-7737-6204-6(3)) Stoddart Kids CAN. *Dist:* Fitzhenry & Whiteside, Ltd.

Slater, Teddy & Boyd, Aaron. Black Cat Creeping: A Lucky Cat Story. 2005. (Illus.). 24p. (J). (ps-ps). 6.95 (978-1-4027-1979-0(5)) Sterling Publishing Co., Inc.

Sleigh, Barbara. Carbonel: The King of Cats. Drummond, V. H., illus. 2004. 216p. (J). reprint ed. 16.95 (978-1-59017-126-4(8) , NYR Children's Collection) New York Review of Bks., Inc., The.

Smalley, Roger. Big Cat Trouble. Shaw, Charles, illus. 2005. (J). (978-1-933248-13-4(0)) World Quest Learning.

Smath, Jerry. Sammy Salami. 2007. (Illus.). 32p. (J). (gr. 1-3). 15.95 (*978-0-8109-9350-1(3)* , Abrams Bks. for Young Readers) Abrams, Harry N. , Inc.

Smiley, Norene. That Stripy Cat. Anderson, Tara, illus. 2007. 32p. (J). (ps-1). (*978-1-55005-164-3(4)*) Fitzhenry & Whiteside, Ltd.

Smith, David, told to. The Cart. 2003. (J). pap. 8.00 (978-0-8059-5745-7(6)) Dorrance Publishing Co., Inc.

Smith, Jay F. A Day to Remember: A Sam & Coco Story. Smith, Jay F., illus. 2005. (Illus.). 32p. (J). (978-0-9764719-0-5(6)) MiceWorks.

Smith, Jill & Diller, Howard. Nat the Fat Cat. 2006. (Illus.). 91p. (J). pap. (978-1-933873-00-8(0)) Apodixis Pr.

—Nat the Fat Cat: Workbook. 2006. (Illus.). 80p. (J). pap. (978-1-933873-01-5(9)) Apodixis Pr.

Smith, Linda. Mrs. Crump's Cat. Roberts, David, illus. 2006. 32p. (J). (ps-3). 16.99 (978-0-06-028302-5(5)); lib. bdg. 17.89 (978-0-06-443551-2(2)) HarperCollins Pubs.

Smith, Linda Jane. A Tale of Two Kitties. 2001. (Illus.). 48p. (J). (ps-3). 19.95 (978-0-8230-5055-0(6)) Watson-Guptill Pubns., Inc.

Smith, Maggie. Desser the Best Ever Cat. Smith, Maggie, illus. 2003. (Illus.). 40p. (J). (gr. k-3). pap. 6.99 (978-0-440-41774-3(0) , Dragonfly Bks.) Random Hse. Children's Bks.

—Desser the Best Ever Cat. 2003. (gr. k-3). lib. bdg. 15.30 (978-0-613-62976-2(X)) Tandem Library Bks.

Smith, Maggie Caldwell. Tommy Wilson, Junior Veterinarian: The Case of the Orphaned Bobcat. Heyer, Carol & White, Charlotte L., illus. 2006. (J). per. 7.95 (978-0-9788391-1-6(0)) Magpie Pr., Pine Mtn Club, CA.

Smith Novelty Company Staff. Clyde the Cable Car. 2006. (J). pap. 9.95 (978-1-59099-076-6(5)) Smith Novelty Co., Inc.

Smith, Philip D. & Day-Bivins, Pat. Little Tom Meets Mr Jonah. Brooks, Donna, illus. 2000. 32p. (ps-3). 15.95 (978-1-886864-16-0(0)) Golden Anchor Pr.

Snyder, Zilpha Keatley. The Witches of Worm. 2006. 22.00 (978-0-8446-7290-8(4)) Smith, Peter Pub., Inc.

Sollinger, Emily & Ken Karp Photography Staff. Let's Play, Baby! 2006. (Baby Nick Jr Ser.). (Illus.). 10p. (J). bds. 9.99 (978-1-4169-1209-5(6) , Simon Spotlight/Nickelodeon) Simon & Schuster Children's Publishing.

Soloman, Debra. Jasper & His Magical Tail. 2004. 13p. (J). pap. 9.79 (978-1-4116-1841-1(6)) Lulu.com.

Sommer, Carl. If Only I Were. . ., 1 bk. 2003. (Another Sommer-Time Story Ser.). (Illus.). 48p. (J). 16.95 incl. audio compact disk (978-1-57537-502-1(8)); (gr. 1-4). 16.95 incl. audio (978-1-57537-551-9(6)) Advance Publishing, Inc.

Sophie Maye. 2000. (Illus.). 20p. (J). (gr. k-3). pap. 10.00 (978-0-9679561-1-4(0)); 18.00 (978-0-9679561-0-7(2)) Debbie-Lou Productions.

Sorensen, Susan & Whims, Joette. Kit-Cat's Time-Travel Adventure: The Story of the National Day of Prayer. Young, Woody, illus. 2001. 152p. (J). (gr. 3-6). pap. 7.99 (978-0-939513-69-7(2)) Joy Publishing.

Soto, Gary. Chato & the Party Animals. Guevara, Susan, illus. 25.95 incl. audio (978-1-59112-460-3(3)); 28.95 incl. audio compact disk (978-1-59112-920-2(6)); pap. 37.95 incl. audio (978-1-59112-461-0(1)); pap. 39.95 incl. audio compact disk (978-1-59112-921-9(4)) Live Oak Media.

—Chato & the Party Animals. 2005. (J). pap. 18.95 incl. audio compact disk (978-1-59112-919-6(2)); (Illus.). pap. 16.95 incl. audio (978-1-59112-459-7(X)) Live Oak Media.

—Chato & the Party Animals. Guevara, Susan, illus. 2000. (SPA.). 32p. (J). (ps-3). 16.99 (978-0-399-23159-9(5) , Putnam Juvenile) Penguin Group (USA) Inc.

—Chato & the Party Animals. 2004. (gr. k-3). lib. bdg. 15.30 (978-0-613-89799-0(4)) Tandem Library Bks.

—Chato & the Party Animals. Guevara, Susan, illus. 2004. (J). (ps-ps). lib. bdg. 13.79 (978-0-606-29661-8(1)) Tandem Library Bks.

—Chato & the Party Animals. Guevara, Susan, illus. 2004. 32p. (J). (gr. k-3). reprint ed. pap. 6.99 (978-0-14-240032-6(7) , Puffin) Penguin Group (USA) Inc.

—Chato Goes Cruisin' Guevara, Susan, tr. Guevara, Susan, illus. 2005. 32p. (J). (ps-3). 16.99 (978-0-399-23974-8(X) , Putnam Juvenile) Penguin Group (USA) Inc.

—Chato Goes Cruisin' Guevara, Susan, illus. 2007. 32p. (J). (ps). pap. 6.99 (978-0-14-240810-0(7) , Puffin) Penguin Group (USA) Inc.

—Chato y Los Amigos Pachangueros. 2004. (SPA.). (gr. k-3). lib. bdg. 16.45 (978-0-613-82998-4(0)) Tandem Library Bks.

—Chato's Kitchen. 2002. (Live Oak Readalong Ser.). (Illus.). (J). pap. 16.95 incl. audio (978-1-59112-205-0(8)); pap. 18.95 incl. audio compact disk (978-1-59112-336-1(4)) Live Oak Media.

—Chato's Kitchen. Guevara, Susan, illus. 2002. 25.95 incl. audio (978-1-59112-206-7(6)); 28.95 incl. audio compact disk (978-1-59112-528-0(6)); pap. 37.95 incl. audio (978-1-59112-207-4(4)); pap. 39.95 incl. audio compact disk (978-1-59112-527-3(8)) Live Oak Media.

—Chato's Kitchen; Chato Y Su Cena. Guevara, Susan, illus. 2002. pap. 33.95 incl. audio (978-1-59112-208-1(2)) Live Oak Media.

Spanyol, Jessica. Carlo & the Really Nice Librarian. Spanyol, Jessica, illus. 2004. (Illus.). 32p. (J). (gr. k-k). 15.99 (978-0-7636-2526-9(4)) Candlewick Pr.

Speare, Elizabeth George. Calico Captive. 2001. 288p. (YA). (gr. 5-9). tchr. ed. 16.00 (978-0-618-15075-5(7)); pap. 6.95 (978-0-618-15076-2(5)) Houghton Mifflin Co. Trade & Reference Div.

Spicer, Lin. Faerie Baby. 2006. pap. (***978-1-84426-384-4(3)***) Upfront Publishing Ltd.

Spinelli, Eileen. Callie Cat, Ice Skater. Kennedy, Anne, illus. 2007. 32p. (J). (gr. 1-4). 16.95 (***978-0-8075-1042-1(4)***) Whitman, Albert & Co.

—Hero Cat. McAllister Stammen, Jo Ellen, illus. 2006. 32p. (J). 16.95 (978-0-7614-5223-2(0)) Cavendish, Marshall Corp.

—Kittycat Lullaby. Mortimer, Anne, illus. 2001. 32p. (J). 13.49 (978-0-7868-2400-7(X)) Disney Pr.

—Kittycat Lullaby. Mortimer, Anne, illus. 2001. 32p. (ps-1). 14.99 (978-0-7868-0458-0(0)) Hyperion Bks. for Children.

—Moe McTooth: An Alley Cat's Tale. Bronson, Linda, illus. 2003. 32p. (J). (gr. k-3). tchr. ed. 15.00 (978-0-618-11760-4(1), Clarion Bks.) Houghton Mifflin Co. Trade & Reference Div.

Spohn, Kate. Dog & Cat Shake a Leg. 2000. 32p. (J). pap. 3.99 (978-0-14-038374-4(3), Puffin) Penguin Group (USA) Inc.

St. John, Patricia. Friska My Friend & the Other Kitten. 2003. (Illus.). 192p. 6.49 (978-1-85999-312-5(5)) Scripture Union GBR. *Dist:* Gabriel Resources.

Stadler, John. Catilda. Stadler, John, illus. 2003. (Illus.). 32p. (J). (ps-k). 16.95 (978-0-689-84728-8(9), Atheneum/Richard Jackson Bks.) Simon & Schuster Children's Publishing.

—The Cats of Mrs. Calamari. Stadler, John, illus. 1999. (Illus.). 32p. (J). (ps-1). pap. 5.95 (978-0-531-07140-3(5), Orchard Bks.) Scholastic, Inc.

—The Cats of Mrs. Calamari. 1999. (Illus.). (J). (978-0-606-18332-1(9)) Tandem Library Bks.

Staffier, Jane Sarah. Casey & the Boston Freedom Trail. Staffier, Jane Sarah, illus. l.t. ed. 1999. (Beacon Hill Ser.: No. 2). (Illus.). 28p. (J). (gr. k-7). spiral bd. 9.95 (978-1-928895-01-5(8)) B.A.B., Ltd.

—Casey the Beacon Hill Cat Coloring Book Adventures, 4 vols., Set. Staffier, Jane Sarah, illus. l.t. ed. 2001. 130p. (J). (ps-7). pap. 32.95 (978-1-928895-04-6(2)) B.A.B., Ltd.

—Casey's Day at the Beach. Staffier, Jane Sarah, illus. l.t. ed. 1999. (Casey the Beacon Hill Cat Ser.). (Illus.). 28p. (J). (gr. k-5). spiral bd. 9.95 (978-1-928895-00-8(X)) B.A.B., Ltd.

—Casey's History of the World: Or "Roots" Casey. l.t. ed. 1999. (Casey the Beacon Hill Cat Ser.: Vol. 4). 32p. (J). (gr. k-5). spiral bd. 9.95 (978-1-928895-03-9(4)) B.A.B., Ltd.

—The Tale of Casey's Tail... A Happy Ending. 1999. (Casey the Beacon Hill Cat Ser.: Vol. 3). 33p. (J). spiral bd. (978-1-928895-02-2(6)) B.A.B., Ltd.

Stahl, Mary L. Accumulating Cats. (Illus.). 56p. (J). (gr. k-6). (978-1-886075-09-2(3)) Grass Root Enterprises.

Stainton, Sue. Chocolate Cat. 2007. (Illus.). 32p. (J). lib. bdg. 17.89 (***978-0-06-057246-4(9)***) HarperCollins Pubs.

—Chocolate Cat. Mortimer, Anne, illus. 2007. 32p. (J). (ps-2). 16.99 (***978-0-06-057245-7(0)***) HarperCollins Pubs.

—I Love Cats. Mortimer, Anne, illus. 2007. 24p. (J). (ps-k). 15.99 (978-0-06-085154-5(6)); lib. bdg. 16.89 (978-0-06-085156-9(2)) HarperCollins Pubs.

—The Lighthouse Cat. Mortimer, Anne, illus. 2004. 32p. (J). (ps-2). 15.99 (978-0-06-009604-5(7)) HarperCollins Pubs.

—Santa's Snow Cat. Mortimer, Anne, illus. 32p. (J). 2007. pap. 6.99 (***978-0-06-000540-5(8)***, Harper Trophy); 2001. 15.99 (978-0-06-623827-2(7)) HarperCollins Pubs.

—Santa's Snow Kitten. Mortimer, Anne, illus. 2008. (J). (***978-0-06-082714-4(9)***); lib. bdg. (***978-0-06-082715-1(7)***) HarperCollins Pubs.

—Snow Cat. 2000. (Illus.). 32p. (J). pap. 15.99 (978-0-7868-0692-8(3)) Hyperion Bks. for Children.

—Snow Cat: Santa's Littlest Cat. Mortimer, Anne, illus. 2000. (J). (978-0-7868-4437-1(X)) Hyperion Bks. for Children.

Staman, A. Louise. Rupert & the Bag. Adams, Rich, illus. 2006. (J). 11.99 (***978-0-9787263-0-0(8)***) Tiger Iron Pr.

Stanek, Gerald R. Sarah 'n' Dippity. Stanek, Joyce Huntington, illus. 2004. 28p. (J). 14.95 (978-0-9747417-0-3(1)) Shiver Hill Bks.

Starke, Ruth. Chomps: Catland: Can Rose pull off her purrfect Plan? 2007. 96p. (J). pap. 3.95 (***978-0-7624-2925-7(9)***, Running Pr. Kids) Running Pr. Bk. Pubs.

Steck-Vaughn Staff. Cats: Red & Every Cat. 1998. (Illus.). (J). pap. (978-0-8172-8634-7(9)) Steck-Vaughn.

Steele, Michael. A Tale of Two Kitties. novel movie tie-in ed. 2006. (Garfield's A Tail of Two Kitties Ser.). 112p. (J). pap. 4.99 (978-0-439-87395-6(9)) Scholastic, Inc.

Steffen, Tim & Thornton, Susan. The Adventures of Baby Cat in Cherry Grove: Home Sweet Home. 2006. (Illus.). (J). per. 15.00 (978-0-9779518-0-2(4)) Baby Cat Books.

Steffen, Tim & Thornton, Susan Ann. The Adventures of Baby Cat in Cherry Grove: Finding Faith. Thornton, Susan Ann, illus. 2007. (Illus.). 50p. (J). per. 12.00 (***978-0-9779518-1-9(2)***) Baby Cat Books.

Steingold, Rita Whitman. A Kitten Followed Me Home. 2001. (Jellybean Bks.). (Illus.). (J). (ps). (978-0-375-80667-4(9), Random Hse. Bks. for Young Readers) Random Hse. Children's Bks.

Stephenson, Nancy. The Three Little Kittens. Faris, Eva, illus. l.t. ed. 2003. 30p. (J). per. 7.99 (978-1-932338-13-3(6)) Lifevest Publishing, Inc.

Sterling Publishing Co., Inc. Naughty Kitten: A Touch & Feel Adventure. 2005. (Illus.). 16p. (J). 12.95 (978-1-4027-2454-1(3)) Sterling Publishing Co., Inc.

Sternberg, Demetria. Hey, What's Going on down There? 2005. 23p. pap. 14.95 (978-1-4137-3806-3(0)) PublishAmerica, Inc.

Stevens, Janet & Stevens Crummel, Susan. My Big Dog. Stevens, Janet, illus. 2005. (Illus.). 40p. (J). (gr. k-k). 12.95 (978-0-375-83297-0(1)); lib. bdg. 14.99 (978-0-375-93297-7(6)) Random Hse. Children's Bks. (Golden Bks.).

Stewaart, Toni D., illus. The Man, the Hat, & the Cat. 1999. 13p. (Orig.). (J). (gr. k-2). pap. 2.50 (978-1-889658-02-5(2)) New Canaan Publishing Co. LLC.

Stewart, Dana. God Made My Kitten. Stewart, Jennifer, ed. Haantz, Carol, illus. 1999. (Tall Shape Board Bks.). 10p. (J). (ps-1). 4.99 (978-0-7847-0962-7(9), 04302, Bean Sprouts) Standard Publishing.

Stewart, Linda. The Maltese Kitten: A Sam the Cat Mystery. 2002. 135p. (J). (gr. 4-7). pap. 10.95 (978-0-9675073-8-5(3)) Cheshire House Bks.

Stilton, Geronimo. Attack of the Bandit Cats. Wolf, Matt, illus. 2004. (Geronimo Stilton Ser.: No. 8). 115p. (J). lib. bdg. 10.00 (***978-1-4242-0277-5(9)***) Fitzgerald Bks.

Stilton, Geronimo. Cat & Mouse in a Haunted House. 2004. (Geronimo Stilton Ser.: No. 3). (gr. 3-6). lib. bdg. 14.15 (978-0-613-72224-7(8)) Tandem Library Bks.

Stockham, Jess, et al, illus. Puss in Boots. 2007. 24p. pap. 5.99 (***978-1-84643-075-6(5)***) Child's Play International Ltd. GBR. *Dist:* Child's Play-International.

Stokes, Carolyn Ashe. Multy: The Search to Belong. . . a Story of Hope. 2003. pap. 9.00 (978-0-8059-5679-5(4)) Dorrance Publishing Co., Inc.

Stolz, Mary. Casebook of a Private (Cat's) Eye. Levy, Pamela R., illus. 1999. 128p. (J). (gr. 4-7). 14.95 (978-0-8126-2650-6(8)) Cricket Bks.

Story Lady. The House of the Seven Cats: An Adventure. 2001. 132p. pap. 10.95 (978-0-595-20681-0(6), Writers Club Pr.) iUniverse, Inc.

Strom, Kellie. Sadie the Air Mail Pilot. 2007. 32p. (J). (gr. k-3). 16.99 (***978-0-385-75027-1(7)***); lib. bdg. 19.99 (***978-0-385-75041-7(2)***) Random Hse. Children's Bks. (Fickling, David Bks.).

Strong, Frances Dinkins. Pat, the Cat. Lee, Linda, illus. 2003. 24p. (J). pap. (978-0-9720267-1-0(1)) Learning Abilities Bks.

Stutson, Caroline. Pirate Pup. Rayevsky, Robert, illus. 2005. 32p. (J). 15.95 (978-0-8118-4239-6(8)) Chronicle Bks. LLC.

Su, Lucy. Make a Picnic. Su, Lucy, illus. 2003. (Kitten & Baby Kitten Ser.). (Illus.). 32p. (YA). (978-1-85602-445-7(8)) Chrysalis Children's Bks.

—Make Cards. Su, Lucy, illus. 2003. (Kitten & Baby Kitten Ser.). (Illus.). 32p. (YA). (978-1-85602-446-4(6)) Chrysalis Children's Bks.

—Play Dressing Up. Su, Lucy, illus. 2003. (Kitten & Baby Kitten Ser.). (Illus.). 42p. (J). bds. (978-1-85602-463-1(6)) Chrysalis Children's Bks.

—Play Hide & Seek. Su, Lucy, illus. 2003. (Kitten & Baby Kitten Ser.). (Illus.). 42p. (J). pap. (978-1-85602-538-6(1)) Chrysalis Children's Bks.

—Say Good Morning. Su, Lucy, illus. 2003. (Kitten & Baby Kitten Ser.). (Illus.). 42p. (J). bds. (978-1-85602-466-2(0)) Chrysalis Children's Bks.

—Say Good Night. Su, Lucy, illus. 2003. (Kitten & Baby Kitten Ser.). (Illus.). 42p. (J). bds. (978-1-85602-537-9(3)) Chrysalis Children's Bks.

Suzuki, Genevieve A. The Original Poi Cats on Oahu. 2005. 40p. 13.95 (978-1-56647-718-5(2)) Mutual Publishing LLC.

Sweeney, Joan. Bijou, Bonbon, & Beau: The Kittens Who Danced for Degas. Wu, Leslie, illus. 2002. 26p. (J). pap. 6.95 (978-0-8118-3486-5(7)) Chronicle Bks. LLC.

Taber, Tory & Taber, Norman. Rufus at Work. 2005. (Illus.). 32p. (J). (ps-2). 16.95 (978-0-8027-8984-6(6)) Walker & Co.

Tabuas, Mireya. Gato Encerrado. Keller, Cristina, illus. (SPA.). (J). pap. (978-980-01-0880-2(7)) Monte Avila Editores Latinoamericana CA VEN. *Dist:* Lectorum Pubns., Inc.

Taiz, Lincoln. Libra: The Cat Who Saved Silicon Valley. Taiz, Lee, illus. 2002. 326p. (J). pap. 14.95 incl. audio compact disk (978-0-9723044-0-5(1), AGP-1) Amsea Group, Inc.

Taiz, Lincoln & Taiz, Lee. Libra: The Cat Who Saved Silicon Valley. 2001. (Illus.). 326p. pap. 15.95 (978-0-9723044-1-2(X), AGP-1) Amsea Group, Inc.

A Tale of Three Amigos: Cat Detectives. 2002. (Cat Detectives Present Ser.: Vol. 2). (Illus.). 88p. (J). per. 6.99 (978-0-9706062-3-5(0)) Aloha Publications.

Talley, Linda. Bastet. Maeno, Itoko, illus. (Key Concepts in Personal Development Ser.). 2001. 32p. pap., tchr. ed. 89.95 incl. VHS (978-1-55942-176-8(2), 9390K3); 2000. 30p. (J). 89.95 incl. VHS (978-1-55942-161-4(4)) Marsh Media.

Talone, Augusto. The Adventures of Max & Sandy: Three Short Stories about a Yellow Labrador Retriever Named Max & a Simese House Cat Named Sandy, Who Solve Mysteries. 2006. 96p. (J). pap. 11.99 (978-1-59977-005-5(9)) Annotation Pr.

Tan, Amy. Sagwa, the Chinese Siamese Cat. Schields, Gretchen, illus. 2001. 40p. (J). 6.99 (978-0-689-84617-5(7), Aladdin) Simon & Schuster Children's Publishing.

—Sagwa, the Chinese Siamese Cat. 2001. (978-0-606-22103-0(4)) Tandem Library Bks.

Tattum, Stephan. The Mad Cat. 2nd ed. 2005. (J). 4.95 (978-1-59792-001-8(0)) F.A.S.T. Learning LLLC.

Teague, Mark. Detective LaRue: Letters from the Investigation. Teague, Mark, illus. 2004. (Detective Larue Ser.). (Illus.). 32p. (J). (ps-3). pap. 15.95 (978-0-439-45868-9(4), Scholastic Pr.) Scholastic, Inc.

—Larue para Alcalde: Cartas de la Campana: Cartas de la Campana. 2008. (Larue for Mayor Ser.). 32p. (J). pap. 4.99 (***978-0-545-02214-9(2)***, Scholastic en Espanol) Scholastic, Inc.

—The Letters from the Campaign. 2008. (Larue for Mayor Ser.). 32p. (J). pap. 16.99 (***978-0-439-78315-6(1)***, Blue Sky Pr., The) Scholastic, Inc.

Ted in a Red Bed Kid Kit. (Kid Kits Ser.). (Illus.). 10p. (J). 11.95 (978-1-58086-416-9(3)); 2004. bds. 9.95 (978-1-58086-404-6(X)) EDC Publishing.

Teeters, Peggy. The Cat with No Tail. Howland, Naomi, illus. 1999. (Books for Young Learners). 16p. (J). (gr. k-2). pap. 5.00 (978-1-57274-218-5(6)) Owen, Richard C. Pubs., Inc.

Temple, Philip & Gaskin, Chris. The Story of the Kakapo. rev. ed. 2000. (Illus.). 32p. (J). (gr. 1-5). pap. 9.95 (978-1-877135-34-7(8)) Longacre Pr. NZL. *Dist:* Pacific Island Bks.

Testa, F. Cat & Mouse & Something to Do. 1998. (Illus.). 25p. (J). 19.99 (978-0-86264-799-5(1)) Andersen GBR. *Dist:* Independent Pubs. Group.

Thaler, Mike. My Cat Is Going to the Dogs. 1999. (gr. k-3). lib. bdg. 11.25 (978-0-613-76303-5(3)) Tandem Library Bks.

There's a Cat in God's Tree! 1999. (Peek-In Board Book Ser.). (Illus.). 10p. (J). (ps-k). bds. 4.99 (978-0-7847-1081-4(3), 04287, Bean Sprouts) Standard Publishing.

Thomas, Frances. Polly's Absolutely Worst Birthday Ever. Gardner, Sally, illus. 2003. 96p. (gr. 1-4). lib. bdg. 16.99 (978-0-385-90122-2(4), Delacorte Bks. for Young Readers) Random Hse. Children's Bks.

Thomas, Jan. What Will Fat Cat Sit On? 2007. (Illus.). 40p. (J). (ps-k). 12.95 (***978-0-15-206051-0(0)***) Harcourt Children's Bks.

Thomas, Shelley Moore. Take Care, Good Knight. Meisel, Paul, illus. 2006. 36p. (J). (ps). 15.99 (978-0-525-47695-5(4), Dutton Juvenile) Penguin Group (USA) Inc.

Thomas, Valerie. Winnie the Witch. Paul, Korky, illus. 2007. 32p. (J). (ps-3). 14.99 (***978-0-06-117312-7(6)***) HarperCollins Pubs.

Thompson, Elissa. Tryin' Ryan. 2006. (J). 15.00 (978-0-9787341-0-7(6)) Aidan's Butterfly Pubns.

Thompson, Patricia Parrott. Chocolate & Her Meow. 2003. pap. 12.00 (978-0-8059-5774-7(X)) Dorrance Publishing Co., Inc.

Thompson, Richard. The Follower. Springett, Martin, illus. 2000. 28p. (J). (gr. k-4). (978-1-55041-532-2(8)) Fitzhenry & Whiteside, Ltd.

—There Is Music in a Pussy Cat. Hartmann, Barbara, illus. 1999. (First Flight Ser.). 32p. (J). pap. (978-1-55041-513-1(1)); (978-1-55041-511-7(5)) Fitzhenry & Whiteside, Ltd.

Thomson, Pat. The Badcat Gang. Phillips, Mike, illus. 2006. 48p. (J). lib. bdg. (***978-1-4048-3112-4(6)***) Picture Window Bks.

—Cat Baby. Shulman, Dee, illus. 2006. (Read-It! Chapter Books). 64p. (J). lib. bdg. (***978-1-4048-3123-0(1)***, 1265800) Picture Window Bks.

—Drat That Fat Cat! Busby, Ailie, illus. 2003. (J). (ps up). 40p. pap. 15.95 (978-0-439-47195-4(8)); (978-0-439-47196-1(6), Levine, Arthur A. Bks.) Scholastic, Inc.

Thomson, Pat. It's So Unfair. Allen, Jonathan, illus. 2007. 32p. (J). pap. 9.95 (***978-1-84270-594-0(6)***) Andersen GBR. *Dist:* Independent Pubs. Group.

Tiger Tales Staff. Little Kitty. Finn, Rebecca, illus. 2005. (Cuddly Cuffs Ser.). 6p. (J). 6.95 (978-1-58925-760-3(X), tiger tales) ME Media LLC.

Tildes, Phyllis L. Calico's Curious Kittens. 2003. (Illus.). 32p. (J). 16.95 (978-1-57091-511-6(3)); pap. 6.95 (978-1-57091-512-3(1)) Charlesbridge Publishing, Inc.

—Calico's Curious Kittens. 2003. (gr. k-3). lib. bdg. 15.25 (978-0-613-89443-2(X)) Tandem Library Bks.

Timbers, James. Salmon & Fuzz in Helping a Friend. 2004. 30p. pap. 14.95 (978-1-4137-2602-2(X)) PublishAmerica, Inc.

Time-Life Books Editors. Scaredy Cat: A Book about Being Brave. 1998. (Big Comfy Couch Ser.). (Illus.). 32p. (J). 5.95 (978-0-7370-1000-8(2)) Time-Life Inc.

Timmy: Individual Title Six-Packs. (Literatura 2000 Ser.). (gr. 1-2). 28.00 (978-0-7635-0067-2(4)) Rigby Education.

Titus, Eve. Anatole & the Cat. 2006. 40p. (J). (gr. k-4). 14.95 (978-0-375-83902-3(X), Knopf Bks. for Young Readers) Random Hse. Children's Bks.

—Anatole & the Cat. Galdone, Paul, illus. 2006. 40p. (J). (gr. k-4). 16.99 (978-0-375-93902-0(4), Knopf Bks. for Young Readers) Random Hse. Children's Bks.

Tom Pouce. 2000. (Musicontes Ser.).Tr. of Tom Thumb. (FRE.). (J). 24.95 incl. audio (978-2-09-230442-6(9)) Nathan, Fernand FRA. *Dist:* Distribooks, Inc.

Tomaszewski, Suzanne Lyon. Samuel's Exeter Walkabout. Dionne, Nina, illus. 2003. 37p. (J). (978-0-9744855-0-8(0)) Gold Charm Publishing, LLC.

Tomkins, Jasper. Catwalk. 2004. (Illus.). 48p. (J). 15.95 (978-1-57061-421-7(0)) Sasquatch Bks.

Tomlinson, Jill. Cat Wanted to Go Home - Picture Boo. Howard, Paul, illus. 2004. 32p. (J). (ps). pap. 9.99 (978-1-4052-1873-3(8)) Egmont Bks., Ltd. GBR. *Dist:* Independent Pubs. Group.

—Cat Wanted to Go Home - Picture Boo. 2008. (Illus.). 32p. (J). pap. 14.00 (***978-1-4052-3251-7(X)***) Egmont Bks., Ltd. GBR. *Dist:* Independent Pubs. Group.

Tomlinson, Jill. The Cat Who Wanted to Go Home. Howard, Paul, illus. (J). (ps-2). 2006. 32p. 17.99 (978-1-4052-0600-6(4)); 2005. 96p. reprint ed. pap. 6.99 (978-1-4052-1080-5(X)) Egmont Bks., Ltd. GBR. *Dist:* Independent Pubs. Group, Trafalgar Square Publishing.

Tomonari, Itsuko. The Adventures of Meow Meow & Friends. 2003. (Illus.). 82p. per. 15.95 (978-1-59405-012-1(0)) New Age World Publishing.

Tomos, Angharad. Diwrnod Golchi. 2005. (WEL., Illus.). 48p. pap. (978-0-86243-115-0(8)) Y Lolfa.

—Jam Poeth. 2005. (WEL., Illus.). 48p. pap. (978-0-86243-145-7(X)) Y Lolfa.

—Mali Meipen. 2005. (WEL., Illus.). 48p. pap. (978-0-86243-104-4(2)) Y Lolfa.

Trimble, Marcia. A Name for Kitty. Lapuyade, Gloria, illus. 2000. 32p. (J). (ps-2). 15.95 (978-1-891577-63-5(8)); pap. 7.95 (978-1-891577-64-2(6)) Images Pr.

Trondheim, Lewis. McConey Vol. 2: The Hoodoodad. 1998. (Fantagraphics Ser.). (Illus.). 48p. (gr. 10 up). pap. 10.95 (978-1-56097-338-6(2)) Fantagraphics Bks.

The Trouble with Oatmeal: Individual Chapter Book Title Six-Packs. Vol. 26. 32p. (gr. 3-4). 44.00 (978-0-7635-4477-5(9)) Rigby Education.

Tuato'o, Jackie. Our Mom, the Human. 2004. (Illus.). 20p. (J). per. 19.95 (978-1-932373-89-9(6)) Cedar Hill Publishing.

Tucker, Ellen. Cats in the Belfry. 2004. (YA). per. (978-1-932496-21-5(1)) Penman Publishing, Inc.

Tudor, Tasha. Corgiville Fair. Tudor, Tasha, illus. 1998. (Illus.). 48p. (J). (ps-17). 17.99 (978-0-316-85312-5(7)) Little Brown & Co.

Tukan, Jaytoe Anthony, Sr. In the Kingdom of Animals: Kitty Cat Had a Dream, Vol. 2. 2002. (J). per. 9.95 (978-0-9665909-2-0(9)) Kalawantis Publishing Services, Inc.

—Kitty cat had a Dream: Kingdom without a King. 2005. (J). per. 19.95 (978-0-9665909-7-5(X)) Kalawantis Publishing Services, Inc.

Tukan, Jaytoe Anthony, Sr., text. In the Kingdom of Animals: Kitty Cat Had a Dream, Vol. 1. 2002. (J). per. 9.95 (978-0-9665909-1-3(0)) Kalawantis Publishing Services, Inc.

Turner, Ann. Pumpkin Cat. Bates, Amy June, illus. 2004. 32p. (ps-2). 15.99 (978-0-7868-0494-8(7)) Hyperion Pr.

Turner, Dona. My Cat Pearl. 2007. (J). bds. 13.95 (***978-1-59692-229-7(X)***) MacAdam/Cage Publishing, Inc.

Turner, Sandy. Cool Cat, Hot Dog. Turner, Sandy, illus. 2005. (Illus.). 48p. (J). (ps-ps). 16.95 (978-0-689-84946-6(X), Atheneum) Simon & Schuster Children's Publishing.

The Two Foolish Cats: Individual Title Six-Packs. (Literatura 2000 Ser.). (gr. 2-3). 33.00 (978-0-7635-0190-7(5)) Rigby Education.

Umansky, Kaye. I Don't Like Gloria! Chamberlain, Margaret, illus. 2007. 32p. (J). (ps-1). 15.99 (978-0-7636-3202-1(3)) Candlewick Pr.

Ungerer, Tomi. Keine Kuss fur Mutler. 2000. Tr. of No Kiss for Mother. (GER.). (J). pap. 15.95 (978-3-257-25018-3(5)) Diogenes Verlag AG CHE. *Dist:* Distribooks, Inc.

—No Kiss for Mother. 1998. (Illus.). 40p. (J). (ps-3). pap. 5.95 (978-1-57098-208-8(2)) Rinehart, Roberts Pubs.

Universal Dreamworks Pictures Staff. Cat in the Hat: Official Movie Book. 2004. (Illus.). 128p. pap. 12.95 (978-1-57243-609-1(3), 53846352) Triumph Bks.

Unwin, Pippa. Tomcat Takes a Walk. 1998. (Illus.). 32p. (J). (ps-1). 17.95 (978-0-86264-705-6(3)) Andersen GBR. *Dist:* Trafalgar Square Publishing.

Ure, Jean. Snow Kittens. 1999. (We Love Animals Bks.). (Illus.). 160p. (J). (gr. 4-7). pap. 3.95 (978-0-7641-0970-6(7)) Barron's Educational Series, Inc.

Vail, Rachel. Over the Moon. Nash, Scott, illus. 32p. (J). (ps-2). 2001. pap. 5.95 (978-0-531-07184-7(7)); 1998. 16.99 (978-0-531-33068-5(0)); 1998. pap. 15.95 (978-0-531-30068-8(4)) Scholastic, Inc. (Orchard Bks.).

Van Draanen, Wendelin. Sammy Keyes & the Psycho Kitty Queen. 2006. (Sammy Keyes Ser.: Bk. 9). (Illus.). 320p. (J). (gr. 5-8). 5.99 (978-0-440-41910-5(7), Yearling) Random Hse. Children's Bks.

—Sammy Keyes & the Psycho Kitty Queen. Yaccarino, Dan, illus. 2006. (Sammy Keyes Ser.: Bk. 9). 293p. (J). (***978-1-4156-6951-8(1)***, Yearling) Random Hse. Children's Bks.

—Sammy Keyes & the Psycho Kitty Queen. 2004. (Sammy Keyes Ser.: Bk. 9). (Illus.). 304p. (J). (gr. 5-8). 15.95 (978-0-375-82349-7(2)); lib. bdg. 17.99 (978-0-375-92349-4(7)) Random Hse. Children's Bks. (Knopf Bks. for Young Readers).

van Ommen, Sylvia. Jellybeans. 2006. (Illus.). 56p. (J). pap. 8.95 (978-1-55643-632-1(7)) North Atlantic Bks.

Vaniko, K. L. Why the Dog Chases the Cat & the Cat C. 2006. 30.99 (***978-1-59926-863-7(9)***) Xlibris Corp.

Varon, Sara. Chicken & Cat. 2006. (Illus.). 40p. (J). (ps-3). pap. 16.99 (978-0-439-63406-9(7), Scholastic Pr.) Scholastic, Inc.

Veldkamp, Debby. Quake! Six Point Five: The Cat Survived. Van Den Berg, Helen, illus. 2004. (J). lib. bdg. 16.95 (978-1-930401-25-9(6)) Central Coast Pr.

Ventura, Antonio. Lucas y el Ruisenor. Angela-Lago, illus. 2005. (SPA.). 24p. (J). (ps-ps). pap. 6.99 (978-980-257-285-4(3)) Ekare, Ediciones VEN. *Dist:* Lectorum Pubns., Inc., Iaconi, Mariuccia Bk. Imports.

C
D

Villar Liebana, Luisa. El Misterio de la Gata Maga. 2005. (Investigator Big Ears Ser.). (SPA., Illus.). 72p. (J). (gr. 2-3). 8.95 (978-84-348-9423-5(8)) SM Ediciones ESP. *Dist:* Iaconi, Mariuccia Bk. Imports.

Violet, Claire. Alley Cat. 2002. (Books for Young Learners). (Illus.). 8p. (J). pap. 5.00 (978-1-57274-523-0(1) , 2121) Owen, Richard C. Pubs., Inc.

Viorst, Judith. The Tenth Good Thing about Barney. Cruz, Ray, illus. 2002. (J). 13.40 (978-0-7587-3778-6(5)) Book Wholesalers, Inc.

Viscardi, Dolly. All Around Cats, , Brooks, David, illus. 2004. 32p. (gr. k-3). 15.95 (978-1-55971-072-5(1) , NorthWord Bks. for Young Readers) T&N Children's Publishing.

Voake, Charlotte. Ginger Finds a Home. Voake, Charlotte, illus. 2003. (Illus.). 40p. (J). (ps-2). 15.99 (978-0-7636-1999-2(X)) Candlewick Pr.

Vrombaut, A. Tiger Trail. 2002. (Illus.). 32p. (J). (978-0-340-77928-6(4) , Hodder & Stoughton) Hodder General Publishing Division.

Vrombaut, An. Tiger Trail. 2003. (Illus.). 32p. (J). pap. 8.99 (978-0-340-77929-3(2)) Headway GBR. *Dist:* Trafalgar Square Publishing.

Waber, Bernard. Lyle at Christmas. Waber, Bernard, illus. 2002. (Lyle the Crocodile Ser.). (Illus.). (J). 23.40 (978-0-7587-3058-9(6)) Book Wholesalers, Inc.

—Lyle at Christmas. 2003. (Lyle the Crocodile Ser.). (Illus.). 48p. (J). (gr. k-3). pap. 5.95 (978-0-618-38002-2(7) , Walter Lorraine) Houghton Mifflin Co. Trade & Reference Div.

—Lyle at Christmas. Waber, Bernard, illus. 1998. (Lyle the Crocodile Ser.). (Illus.). 48p. (J). (gr. k-3). tchr. ed. 16.00 (978-0-395-91304-8(7) , Walter Lorraine) Houghton Mifflin Co. Trade & Reference Div.

Waber, Bernard & Waber, Bernard. Lyle at Christmas. Waber, Bernard, illus. 2003. (Lyle the Crocodile Ser.). (Illus.). 48p. (J). (ps-3). lib. bdg. 14.10 (978-0-613-88087-9(0)) Tandem Library Bks.

Waddell, Martin. Who Do You Love. Ashforth, Camilla, illus. 2004. 24p. (J). (gr. k-ps). bds. 6.99 (978-0-7636-2565-8(5)) Candlewick Pr.

Waddington-Feather, John. Quill's Adventures in Mereful. 2004. 87p. pap. 14.95 (978-1-4137-1632-0(6)) PublishAmerica, Inc.

Wagener, Gerda. Hay un Raton en Casa! 2002. Tr. of There's a Mouse in the House!. (SPA.). (gr. k-3). lib. bdg. 14.10 (978-0-613-73551-3(X)) Tandem Library Bks.

Wagner, Fiona. The Little Cat. 2005. 15p. (J). 9.99 (978-1-4116-5568-3(0)) Lulu.com.

Wallace, Bill. Goosed! Rogers, Jacqueline, illus. 2002. 128p. (J). (gr. 4-6). tchr. ed. 16.95 (978-0-8234-1757-5(3)) Holiday Hse., Inc.

—Goosed! Rogers, Jacqueline, illus. 2004. 128p. (J). pap. 4.99 (978-0-689-86681-4(X) , Aladdin) Simon & Schuster Children's Publishing.

Wallace, Carol. Flying Flea, Callie & Me. 1999. (gr. 3-6). lib. bdg. 13.00 (978-0-613-84533-5(1)) Tandem Library Bks.

Wallace, Carol & Wallace, Bill. The Flying Flea, Callie & Me. 1999. (Gray Cat Ser.: Vol. 1). 96p. (J). (gr. 3-6). pap. 4.99 (978-0-671-03968-4(7) , Aladdin) Simon & Schuster Children's Publishing.

—The Flying Flea, Callie & Me. 1999. (Illus.). (J). 11.79 (978-0-606-18368-0(X)) Tandem Library Bks.

Wallace, Karen. Clever Cat. Axworthy, Ann, illus. 2004. (Read-It! Readers Ser.). 32p. (C). (gr. k-3). 18.60 (978-1-4048-0560-6(5)) Picture Window Bks.

—My Cat's Secret. Ling, Mary, ed. 2001. (Readers Ser.). (Illus.). 32p. (J). (ps-3). pap. 3.99 (978-0-7894-7876-4(5)) Dorling Kindersley Publishing, Inc.

—My Cat's Secret. 2001. (978-0-606-22328-7(2)); lib. bdg. 11.80 (978-0-613-43943-5(0)) Tandem Library Bks.

Wallace, Karen & Dorling Kindersley Publishing Staff. My Cat's Secret. 2001. (Dk Readers Ser.). (Illus.). 32p. (J). (ps-3). 12.99 (978-0-7894-7875-7(7)) Dorling Kindersley Publishing, Inc.

Wallace, Nikki. Stubby & the Puppy Pack. 2000. (Illus.). 96p. (J). (gr. 4-7). pap. 3.99 (978-0-671-02589-2(9) , Aladdin) Simon & Schuster Children's Publishing.

—Stubby & the Puppy Pack. 2000. (gr. 3-6). lib. bdg. 11.80 (978-0-613-34025-0(6)) Tandem Library Bks.

—Stubby & the Puppy Pack to the Rescue. Gurney, John Steven, illus. 144p. (J). 2003. pap. 4.99 (978-0-7434-2695-4(9) , Aladdin); 2002. (gr. 3-6). 16.00 (978-0-7434-2694-7(0)) Simon & Schuster Children's Publishing.

—Stubby & the Puppy Pack to the Rescue. 2003. (gr. 3-6). lib. bdg. 13.00 (978-0-613-66546-9(5)) Tandem Library Bks.

Walsh, Paton Jill. Pepi & the Secret Names. French, Fiona, illus. 2004. 32p. (J). pap. 8.95 (978-1-84507-351-0(7)) Lincoln, Frances Ltd. GBR. *Dist:* Perseus Distribution.

Walton, Rick. The Remarkable Friendship of Mr. Cat & Mr. Rat. McCue, Lisa, illus. 2006. 32p. (J). (ps-3). 14.99 (978-0-399-23899-4(9) , Putnam Juvenile) Penguin Group (USA) Inc.

Ward, Cindy. Cookie's Week. de Paola, Tomie, illus. 2004. 34p. (J). (ps-1). bds. 6.99 (978-0-399-24325-7(9) , Putnam Juvenile) Penguin Group (USA) Inc.

Waring, Geoff. Oscar & the Frog: A Book about Growing. Waring, Geoff, illus. 2007. (Illus.). 32p. (J). (ps). 11.99 (***978-0-7636-3558-9(8)***) Candlewick Pr.

—Oscar & the Moth: A Book about Light & Dark. Waring, Geoff, illus. 2007. (Illus.). 32p. (J). (ps). 11.99 (***978-0-7636-3559-6(6)***) Candlewick Pr.

Warner, Sunny. The Moon Quilt. 2001. (Illus.). 32p. (J). (gr. k-3). tchr. ed. 15.00 (978-0-618-05583-8(5) , Walter Lorraine) Houghton Mifflin Co. Trade & Reference Div.

Waters, Michael. Dumdickle & Tweedy: A Tail of Two Cats. 2006. 16p. (J). 10.30 (978-1-4116-6734-1(4)) Lulu.com.

Watkins, Dawn L. Nantucket Cats. Bonge, Lynn E., illus. 1998. 32p. (J). (ps-1). pap. 5.49 (978-0-89084-975-0(7)) Jones, Bob Univ. Pr.

Watson, Jacqueline. Mattie-Jo-Calico. 2003. 109p. pap. 16.95 (978-1-59286-920-6(3)) PublishAmerica, Inc.

Watson, T. E. The Man Who Spoke with Cats. Ferchaud, Steve, illus. 2006. (J). lib. bdg. 18.95 (978-1-58478-019-9(3) , Highland Children's Pr.) Heather & Highlands Publishing.

Watt, Fiona. That's Not My Kitten. Wells, Rachel, illus. rev. ed. 2006. 10p. (J). bds. 7.99 (978-0-7945-1266-8(6) , Usborne) EDC Publishing.

Watt, Melanie. Chester. Watt, Melanie, illus. 2007. (Illus.). 32p. (J). (ps-3). (***978-1-55453-140-0(3)***) Kids Can Pr., Ltd.

Weaver, Tess. Cat Jumped In! McCully, Emily Arnold, illus. 2007. 32p. (J). (ps-1). 16.00 (***978-0-618-61488-2(5)*** , Clarion Bks.) Houghton Mifflin Co. Trade & Reference Div.

Weaver, Tess. Opera Cat. Wesson, Andrea, illus. 2002. 32p. (J). (gr. k-3). 15.00 (978-0-618-09635-0(3) , Clarion Bks.) Houghton Mifflin Co. Trade & Reference Div.

Webb, Beth. Fleabag & the Fire Cat. 1998. (Fleabag Ser.). 176p. (J). pap. 8.99 (978-0-7459-3846-2(9) , Lion) Lion Hudson plc GBR. *Dist:* Independent Pubs. Group.

Weigelt, Udo. Spring Fever. 2005. (Illus.). 32p. (J). (ps up). 15.95 (978-0-7358-2033-3(3)) North-South Bks., Inc.

Weiss, David & Weiss, Bobbi J. G. Cat Attack! Storybook with Stickers. 2004. (Shrek 2 Ser.). (Illus.). 24p. (J). pap. 3.99 (978-0-439-53851-0(3)) Scholastic, Inc.

Weiss, David Cody. Kitty Cornered. 2000. (Sabrina, the Teenage Witch: No. 13). (Illus.). 64p. (J). (gr. 2-5). per. (978-0-671-77336-6(4) , Simon & Schuster Children's Publishing) Simon & Schuster Children's Publishing.

Welchert, Kathleen. Sir Reginald Armitage Iv: The All-Around. 2005. 62p. pap. 12.95 (978-1-4137-5674-6(3)) PublishAmerica, Inc.

Welling, Peter J. Darlene Halloween & the Great Chicago Fire. Welling, Peter J., illus. 2007. 32p. (J). (gr. k-3). 15.95 (***978-1-58980-479-1(1)***) Pelican Publishing Co., Inc.

Welling, Peter J. Joe Van der Katt & the Grat Picket Fence. 2005. (Illus.). 32p. (J). 15.95 (978-1-58980-281-0(0)) Pelican Publishing Co., Inc.

Wells, Rosemary. Make New Friends. Wheeler, Jody, illus. 2003. (Yoko & Friends School Days Ser.: Bk. 11). 32p. (gr. k-2). pap. 3.99 (978-0-7868-1536-4(1)); 9.99 (978-0-7868-0730-7(X)) Hyperion Bks. for Children. (Volo).

—Make New Friends. Wheeler, Jody, illus. 2003. 31p. (J). (ps-ps). lib. bdg. 11.80 (978-0-613-74980-0(4)) Tandem Library Bks.

—Mama, Don't Go! 2001. (Yoko & Friends School Days Ser.: No. 1). (Illus.). 32p. (gr. k-2). 9.99 (978-0-7868-0720-8(2) , Volo) Hyperion Bks. for Children.

—Mama, Don't Go! 2001. (J). (978-0-606-22546-5(3)); lib. bdg. 11.80 (978-0-613-53276-1(7)) Tandem Library Bks.

—McDuff's Wild Romp. Jeffers, Susan, illus. 2005. 32p. (ps-k). 9.99 (978-0-7868-1930-0(8)) Hyperion Bks. for Children.

—Practice Makes Perfect. Wheeler, Jody, illus. 2002. (Yoko & Friends School Days Ser.: Bk. 10). 32p. (gr. k-2). pap. 3.99 (978-0-7868-1531-9(0)); 9.99 (978-0-7868-0725-3(3)) Disney Pr.

—Practice Makes Perfect. 2002. (gr. k-3). lib. bdg. 11.80 (978-0-613-74979-4(0)) Tandem Library Bks.

—Read Me a Story. Wheeler, Jody & Nez, John, illus. 2002. (Yoko & Friends School Days Ser.: Bk. 8). 32p. (gr. k-2). pap. 3.99 (978-0-7868-1533-3(7) , Volo) Hyperion Bks. for Children.

—The School Play. Wheeler, Jody, illus. 2001. (Yoko & Friends School Days Ser.: No. 2). 32p. (gr. k-2). 9.99 (978-0-7868-0721-5(0)); pap. 3.99 (978-0-7868-1527-2(2)) Hyperion Bks. for Children. (Volo).

—The School Play. 2001. (J). (978-0-606-22547-2(1)) Tandem Library Bks.

—When I Grow Up. Wheeler, Jody, illus. 2003. (Yoko & Friends School Days Ser.: Bk. 12). 32p. (gr. k-2). 9.99 (978-0-7868-0731-4(8) , Volo) Hyperion Bks. for Children.

—Yoko. 1998. (Illus.). 32p. (ps-2). 14.95 (978-0-7868-0395-8(9)) Hyperion Pr.

—Yoko's Paper Cranes. Wells, Rosemary, illus. 2001. (Illus.). 32p. (ps-2). 15.99 (978-0-7868-0737-6(7)) Hyperion Bks. for Children.

West, C. Marmaduke: The Magic Cat. 1999. (Illus.). 64p. (J). pap. 7.95 (978-0-340-72663-1(6) , Hodder & Stoughton) Hodder General Publishing Division GBR. *Dist:* Trafalgar Square Publishing.

—Marmaduke the Magic Cat 1. (Illus.). 64p. (J). pap. (978-0-340-66094-2(5) , Hodder & Stoughton) Hodder General Publishing Division.

West, Tracey. Me & My Robot: The Show-and-Tell Show Off. Revell, Cindy, illus. 2003. (All Aboard Reading Ser.). 32p. (J). (ps-2). pap. 3.99 (978-0-448-43251-9(X) , Grosset & Dunlap) Penguin Group (USA) Inc.

—Me & My Robot: The Show-and-Tell Show-Off. Revell, Cindy, illus. 2003. (All Aboard Math Reader Station Stop 1 Ser.). 48p. (J). (ps-2). pap. 3.99 (978-0-448-42895-6(4) , Grosset & Dunlap) Penguin Group (USA) Inc.

—Me & My Robot No.2: The Show-and-Tell Show-off. 2003. (ps-2). lib. bdg. 11.80 (978-0-613-72529-3(8)); lib. bdg. 11.80 (978-0-613-64065-7(9)) Tandem Library Bks.

Westall, Robert & Geldert, Bill. David & the Kittens. (Illus.). 32p. (J). pap. (978-0-340-74380-5(8) , Hodder Children's Books) Hodder Children's Division.

Weston, Martha. Cats Are Like That. Weston, Martha, illus. (Holiday House Reader Ser.). (Illus.). 32p. (J). (gr. k-3). tchr. ed. 15.95 (978-0-8234-1419-2(1)) Holiday Hse., Inc.

What Tommy Did: Individual Title, 6 packs. (Literatura 2000 Ser.). (gr. 1-2). 28.00 (978-0-7635-0152-5(2)) Rigby Education.

Wheatley, Marylou. Calypso & Strange Lands. 2004. 119p. pap. 16.95 (978-1-4137-1012-0(3)) PublishAmerica, Inc.

Wheeler, Lisa. Castaway Cats. Goembel, Ponder, illus. 2006. 32p. (J). (ps-2). 16.95 (978-0-689-86232-8(6) , Atheneum) Simon & Schuster Children's Publishing.

Where Is the Cat? Kindergarten Guided Reading Level A. (On Our Way to English Ser.). (gr. k up). 27.75 (978-0-7578-7000-2(7)) Rigby Education.

Where's the Kitten? (English/Russian) 2004. (RUS., Illus.). 12p. (J). bds. 5.50 (978-1-932065-84-8(9)) Star Bright Bks., Inc.

Who Stole Mole Hill? 2001. pap. 5.95 (978-0-9706322-1-0(5)) Silver Lake Mill.

Wicke, Ed. Nicklus. Warne, Tom, illus. 2004. 192p. (J). per. (978-0-9677652-4-2(2) , BlacknBlue Pr. UK) Blacknblue Pr.

Wiggins, VeraLee. Thor the Thunder Cat 1999. (Julius & Friends Ser.: Vol. 6). (J). (gr. 1-5). 6.99 (978-0-8163-1703-5(8)) Pacific Pr. Publishing Assn.

Wild, Robyn. Benjamin's Basket. Cullen, Elizabeth, illus. 1999. (J). (ps-4). 12.95 (978-0-944576-17-5(6)) Rocky River Pubs., LLC.

Williams, John. Smokie Forever. 2003. 74p. (J). pap. 8.95 (978-0-595-29340-7(9)) iUniverse, Inc.

Williams, Rozanne Lanczak. Cat Can't Write: A Cat & Dog Story. Maio, Barbara, ed. Leary, Catherine, illus. 2006. (Learn to Write Ser.). (J). 16p. pap. 1.99 (978-1-59198-293-7(6) , 6187); per. 6.99 (***978-1-59198-344-6(4)***) Creative Teaching Pr., Inc.

—Cat's Fairy Tale: A Cat & Dog Story. Maio, Barbara, ed. Leary, Catherine, illus. 2006. (Learn to Write Ser.). (J). 16p. pap. 2.99 (978-1-59198-294-4(4) , 6191); per. 6.99 (***978-1-59198-348-4(7)***) Creative Teaching Pr., Inc.

Willis, Jeanne & Ross, Tony. Dr. Xargle's Book of Earth Tiggers. 2001. (Illus.). 32p. (J). pap. 9.99 (978-1-84270-054-9(5)) Andersen GBR. *Dist:* Independent Pubs. Group.

Wilson, Budge. Fear of Angelina Domino. 2000. (gr. k-3). lib. bdg. 16.40 (978-0-613-34707-5(2)) Tandem Library Bks.

Wilson, Karen Collett. Pogonip Magic. Zerga, Susan A., illus. 2002. 40p. (J). (ps-3). 14.95 (978-0-9722570-0-8(4)) Snowbound Bks.

Wilson, Karma. Sleepyhead. Segal, John, illus. 2006. 32p. (J). (ps-2). 15.95 (978-1-4169-1241-5(X) , McElderry, Margaret K.) Simon & Schuster Children's Publishing.

Wilson-Max, Ken. Happy Cat, Me! A Slide-the-Spot Book of Animals. Stojic, Manya & Hamilton, Allen, illus. 2005. 10p. (J). (gr. k-4). reprint ed. 10.00 (978-0-7567-9364-7(5)) DIANE Publishing Co.

Wise, D. Rudd & Wise, Rachel. The Three Little Orphan Kittens. Gottschalk, Deana, illus. 2006. (J). 15.95 (978-0-9786276-0-7(1)) Mentzer Printing Ink.

Wishinsky, Frieda. Give Maggie a Chance. Griffiths, Dean, illus. 2004. 32p. (J). (gr. k-2). pap. (978-1-55041-704-3(5)) Fitzhenry & Whiteside, Ltd.

Woelfle, Gretchen. Katje, the Windmill Cat. Bayley, Nicola, illus. 2006. 32p. (J). (ps). pap. 6.99 (978-0-7636-2089-9(0)) Candlewick Pr.

Wohlford, Martha Crikelair. Splash: The Staniel Cay Cat. 2006. (J). per. 21.95 (***978-0-9787981-0-9(4)***) Serenity Pr.

Wojtusik, Elizabeth. Kitty Up! Yoshikawa, Sachiko, illus. 2008. (J). (978-0-8037-3045-8(4) , Dial) Penguin Group (USA) Inc.

Wolff, Nancy. It's Time for School with Tallulah. 2007. (Illus.). 40p. (J). (ps-3). 16.95 (***978-0-8050-7962-3(9)***) Holt, Henry & Co.

Wood, Audrey. Princess, the Dragon & Scaredy Cats. (J). audio 10.97 (978-0-85953-375-1(1)) Child's Play-International.

—Scaredy Cats. Wood, Audrey, illus. 2005. (Illus.). 32p. (J). pap. 7.99 (978-1-904550-48-8(7)) Child's Play-International.

—The Wheels on the Bus. 2001. (Illus.). 16p. (J). (ps-3). 19.99 (978-0-85953-895-4(8)) Child's Play-International.

Wood, David & Leroux, Gaston. The Phantom Cat of the Opera. Day, Peters, illus. 2001. 40p. (J). (gr. 2-5). 16.95 (978-0-8230-4018-6(6)) Watson-Guptill Pubns., Inc.

Wood, Jakki. Never Say Boo to a Goose! Beaton, Clare, illus. 2002. 24p. (J). (gr. k-2). 14.99 (978-1-84148-255-2(2)) Barefoot Bks., Inc.

Wood, Jane Roberts. Mocha the Real Doctor. 2004. (Illus.). 32p. 14.95 (978-1-931721-30-1(0)) Bright Sky Pr.

Wood, Steve. The Courageous Cats' Club. l.t. ed. 2005. 144p. (J). pap. (978-0-7540-7926-2(0) , CLP 482) BBC Audio.

Wood, Steve & Fox, Woody. Courageous Cats Compete. 2006. (Illus.). 144p. (J). (gr. 3-4). pap. 8.99 (978-0-7459-6011-1(1) , Lion Children's) Lion Hudson plc GBR. *Dist:* Independent Pubs. Group.

Woods, Noah. Tom Cat. 2004. (Illus.). 32p. (J). (ps-2). lib. bdg. 16.99 (978-0-375-92497-2(3) , Random Hse. Bks. for Young Readers) Random Hse. Children's Bks.

The World of Jacky Blue & Other Cats. 2004. (Illus.). 40p. pap. 15.00 (978-0-9761041-0-0(5)) Celstumo Publishing.

Wormell, Mary. Why Not? 2003. lib. bdg. 14.10 (978-0-613-59763-0(X)) Tandem Library Bks.

Worth, Bonnie. The Cat in the Hat: Cooking with the Cat. Moroney, Christopher, illus. 2003. (Step into Reading Ser.). 32p. (J). (ps-1). lib. bdg. 11.99 (978-0-375-92494-1(9) , Random Hse. Bks. for Young Readers) Random Hse. Children's Bks.

—Cooking with the Cat. Moroney, Christopher, illus. 2003. (Step into Reading Ser.). 32p. (J). (ps-1). pap. 3.99 (978-0-375-82494-4(4) , 53560581, Random Hse. Bks. for Young Readers) Random Hse. Children's Bks.

Yager, Jan. The Cantaloupe Cat: A Picture Book. Lyman, Mitzi, illus. 1999. 32p. (J). (ps-k). 15.95 (978-1-889262-12-3(9)) Hannacroix Creek Bks., Inc.

Yanowski, Barbara. Sam the Hero Cat. 2002. (Illus.). 48p. lib. bdg. 12.99 (978-0-9715699-0-4(8)) Lucky Duck Pr., Inc.

Yates, Janet Lee. Skeeter Bug Loves Sarah. 2007. (ENG.). 88p. per. 11.99 (***978-1-4141-0820-9(6)***) Pleasant Word.

Yolen, Jane. Soft House. Halperin, Wendy Anderson, illus. 2005. 32p. (J). (ps-2). 15.99 (978-0-7636-1697-7(4)) Candlewick Pr.

Yoon, Salina. Black Cat. Yoon, Salina, illus. 2004. (Illus.). 10p. (J). bds. 5.99 (978-0-689-85393-7(9) , Little Simon) Simon & Schuster Children's Publishing.

Yost-Filgate, Susan. Rip Squeak & His Friends Discover the Treasure. Filgate, Leonard, illus. 2005. 32p. (J). 16.95 (978-0-9672422-2-4(3)) Rip Squeak, Inc.

Young, L. H. The Christmas Kitten. 2007. 43p. pap. 7.95 (***978-0-533-15732-7(3)***) Vantage Pr., Inc.

Zabrosky, Joseph. Rudy Cazootie, 3 vols., 4 bks. l.t. ed. 2005. (Illus.). 32p. (J). per. (978-0-9768831-2-8(0)) Elohim Bks.

Zaikine, Zak. A Mother's Love. Zaikine, Zak & O'Keefe, Karin, eds. deluxe ed. 2005. Vol. 2. (Illus.). 42p. (J). 24.95 (978-0-934290-01-2(6)) Moon Valley Productions.

Zendarski, Cherie. What Bird? Zendarski, Cherie, illus. 2006. (Illus.). 30p. (J). per. 14.95 (***978-1-934138-00-7(2)*** , 459-007) Bouncing Ball Bks., Inc.

Ziefert, Harriet. Cat Goes Fiddle-i-Fee. Bolam, Emily, illus. 2005. 16p. bds. 5.95 (978-1-4027-2293-6(1)) Sterling Publishing Co., Inc.

—Nicky's Noisy Night. Brown, Richard, illus. 2003. 7p. (ps). bds. 6.95 (978-1-929766-79-6(3)) Blue Apple Bks.

—No Kiss for Grandpa. Boon, Emilie, illus. 2001. 32p. (J). (ps-k). pap. 12.95 (978-0-531-30328-3(4) , Orchard Bks.) Scholastic, Inc.

—Thank You, Nicky! Brown, Richard, illus. 2002. 7p. (ps). bds. 6.95 (978-1-929766-73-4(4)) Blue Apple Bks.

—Tic & Tac. Kreloff, Elliot, illus. 2006. (I'm Going to Read Ser.). 48p. (J). pap. 3.95 (978-1-4027-3432-8(8)) Sterling Publishing Co., Inc.

—Where's Nicky's Easter Egg? Brown, Richard, illus. 2003. 7p. bds. 6.95 (978-1-929766-80-2(7)) Blue Apple Bks.

Ziefert, Harriet & Cohen, Santiago. Kitty Says Meow. Cohen, Santiago, illus. 2002. (Illus.). 14p. (J). bds. 5.99 (978-0-448-42608-2(0) , Grosset & Dunlap) Penguin Group (USA) Inc.

Zuhdi, Darla. A South Sea Adventure, Vol. 4. 2005. (Cat Detectives Present Ser.: 4). (Illus.). 104p. (J). per. 6.99 (978-0-9706062-6-6(5)) Aloha Publications.

CATS—HABITS AND BEHAVIOR

George, Jean Craighead. How to Talk to Your Cat. Truesdell, Sue & Meisel, Paul, illus. 40p. (J). 2003. (gr. 1-3). pap. 6.99 (978-0-06-000622-8(6) , Harper Trophy); 2000. (gr. 2-4). 14.99 (978-0-06-027968-4(0)); 2000. (ps-4). lib. bdg. 13.89 (978-0-06-027969-1(9)) HarperCollins Pubs.

—How to Talk to Your Cat. 2003. (gr. 3-6). lib. bdg. 14.15 (978-0-613-62958-4(2)) Tandem Library Bks.

Rogala, Jennifer. My Pet Cat at Home in the Wild. 2007. 32p. (J). per. 12.95 (***978-1-58939-962-4(5)***) Virtualbookworm.com Publishing, Inc.

Zumbusch, Amelie von. Dangerous Cats, 6 bks., Set. Incl. Cheetahs : World's Fastest Cats. lib. bdg. 21.25 (978-1-4042-3630-1(9) , PowerKids Pr.); Jaguars : World's Strongest Cats. lib. bdg. 21.25 (978-1-4042-3628-8(7) , PowerKids Pr.); Leopards : Silent Stalkers. lib. bdg. 21.25 (978-1-4042-3633-2(3) , PowerKids Pr.); Lions : King of the Beasts. lib. bdg. 21.25 (978-1-4042-3631-8(7)); Tigers : World's Largest Cats. lib. bdg. 21.25 (978-1-4042-3632-5(5)); (Illus.). 24p. (J). (gr. k-5). 2007. 2007. Set lib. bdg. 127.50 (***978-1-4042-3600-4(7)***) Rosen Publishing Group, Inc., The.

CATS—HISTORY

Fineran, John J., 3rd, ed. The Traditional Siamese & Classic Siamese Cat: A Complete History of the Breed, 2003. (Illus.). 980p. per. 85.00 (978-0-9746554-0-6(6) , 1) Tullycrine, LLC.

Quasha, Jennifer. Siamese Cats. 2000. (Pets Throughout History Ser.). 24p. (J). (gr. k-4). lib. bdg. 18.75 (978-0-8239-5509-1(5) , PowerKids Pr.) Rosen Publishing Group, Inc., The.

Trumble, Kelly. Cat Mummies. Kubinyi, Laszlo, illus. 1999. 64p. (J). (gr. 4-6). pap. 7.95 (978-0-395-96891-8(7) , Clarion Bks.) Houghton Mifflin Co. Trade & Reference Div.

CATS—PICTORIAL WORKS

Aigner-Clark, Julie. Gatos. 2004. (Baby Einstein Ser.). (SPA., Illus.). 20p. (J). bds. 3.95 (978-970-718-157-1(5) , Silver Dolphin en Español) Advanced Marketing, S. de R. L. de C. V. MEX. *Dist:* Perseus Distribution.

Cats & Kittens Sticker Activity Book. 2003. (Illus.). 12p. (J). 2.98 (978-1-4054-1178-3(3)) Parragon, Inc.

Darling, Kathy. ABC Cats. Darling, Tara, photos by. 1998. (Illus.). 32p. (J). (ps-3). 15.95 (978-0-8027-8666-1(9)); lib. bdg. 16.85 (978-0-8027-8667-8(7)) Walker & Co.

Foster, Walter, ed. Cats & Kittens. Fisher, Diana, illus. 2004. (Draw & Color Ser.). 40p. (J). pap. 4.95 (978-1-56010-834-3(4)) Foster, Walter Publishing, Inc.

Green, John. World of Cats to Paint or Color. 2007. 48p. pap. 4.95 (***978-0-486-46233-2(1)***) Dover Pubns., Inc.

Millard, Anne. Kitten Games. 2001. (Soft-to-Touch Bk.). (Illus.). 18p. (J). (ps-3). bds. 4.99 (978-0-7894-7400-1(X)) Dorling Kindersley Publishing, Inc.

Murawski, Laura. How to Draw Cats. 2001. (Kid's Guide to Drawing Ser.). (Illus.). 24p. (J). (gr. 3). lib. bdg. 21.25 (978-0-8239-5549-7(4) , PowerKids Pr.) Rosen Publishing Group, Inc., The.

Quasha, Jennifer. The Sphynx: The Hairless Cat. 2000. (Kids' Cat Library). 24p. (J). (gr. k-4). lib. bdg. 18.75 (978-0-8239-5511-4(7) , PowerKids Pr.) Rosen Publishing Group, Inc., The.

Rosen, Michael J., ed. Purr: Children's Book Illustrators Brag about Their Cats. 2003. (Illus.). 42p. (J). (gr. 3-7). reprint ed. 22.00 (978-0-7567-6794-5(6)) DIANE Publishing Co.

Soffer, Ruth. The Cat Lovers' Coloring Book. 2007. (Illus.). 32p. pap. 3.95 (***978-0-486-46200-4(5)***) Dover Pubns., Inc.

Sterling Publishing Company Staff. Katie Cat Super. abr. ed. 2000. (Balloon Ser.). (Illus.). 8p. (J). (ps-1). pap. 4.95 (978-0-8069-2765-7(8) , Balloon Bks.) Sterling Publishing Co., Inc.

Watt, Fiona & Wells, Rachel. Gatitos. 2004. (SPA.). 10p. (J). 11.95 (978-0-7460-5091-0(7)) EDC Publishing.

Wild Cats & Other Dangerous Predators. 2002. (Wild, Wild World Ser.). 32p. (J). 9.95 (978-0-7525-4682-7(1)) Parragon, Inc.

CATS—POETRY

Bibisi, Carole. Tails of American Bronte: A Cat's View of Life. 2007. (Illus.). 32p. (***978-1-59849-026-8(5)***) Peanut Butter Publishing.

Crawley, Dave. Cat Poems. Petrosino, Tamara, illus. 2004. 32p. (J). 15.95 (978-1-59078-287-3(9) , Wordsong) Boyds Mills Pr.

Farjeon, Eleanor. Cats Sleep Anywhere. 1999. (J). (978-0-606-16690-4(4)) Tandem Library Bks.

Florian, Douglas. Mammalabilia. 2004. (Illus.). 48p. (J). reprint ed. pap. 7.00 (978-0-15-205024-5(8) , Voyager Bks./Libros Viajeros) Harcourt Children's Bks.

Kirk, Daniel. Cat Power. rev. ed. 2007. 48p. (J). (gr. 3-7). 15.99 (***978-1-4231-0081-2(6)***) Hyperion Pr.

Kuskin, Karla. Toots the Cat: Poems. Bechtold, Lisze, illus. 2005. 32p. (J). 16.95 (978-0-8050-6841-2(4) , Holt, Henry & Co. Bks. For Young Readers) Holt, Henry & Co.

Leopold, Niki Clark. K Is for Kitten. Jeffers, Susan, illus. 2002. 32p. (J). 15.99 (978-0-399-23563-4(9) , Putnam Juvenile) Penguin Group (USA) Inc.

Linch, Tanya. The Three Little Kittens. Linch, Tanya, illus. 2001. (Illus.). 32p. (J). (ps-k). (978-1-86233-204-1(5) , Gullane Children's Bks.) Pinwheel.

Lindi, Nkululeko. Three Fat Cats. Rankin, Joan, illus. 1999. (Cambridge Reading Ser.). 10p. pap., pap. 19.00 (978-0-521-66705-0(4)) Cambridge Univ. Pr.

Turner, Nancy Byrd. When It Rained Cats & Dogs. Jerome, Karen A., illus. rev. ed. 2000. 24p. (J). (ps-1). 14.95 (978-0-9665564-1-4(0)) Meadow Geese Pr.

Waters, Fiona, ed. Cat in the Dark & Other Cat Poems. Williams, Sophy, illus. 2001. 32p. (J). (gr. k-5). pap. 8.99 (978-0-7112-1476-7(X)) Lincoln, Frances Ltd. GBR. *Dist:* Transition Vendor.

Waters, Fiona & Williams, Sophy. Cat in the Dark. 2004. (Illus.). 32p. (J). pap. 7.95 (978-1-84507-177-6(8)) Lincoln, Frances Ltd. GBR. *Dist:* Perseus Distribution.

CATS—TRAINING

Axelrod, Herbert R. The Myth & Magic of Cats. 1999. (Cats & Dogs). (Illus.). 84p. (YA). (gr. 3 up). 19.95 (978-0-7910-4808-5(X) , Chelsea Hse.) Facts On File, Inc.

CATTLE

see also Cows; Dairying; Livestock; Veterinary Medicine

Cattle, 6 Pack. 16p. (gr. 2 up). 36.00 (978-0-7635-9214-1(5)) Rigby Education.

Cooper, Jason. Calf to Cow. 2003. (Rourke Discovery Library). (Illus.). 24p. (J). 20.64 (978-1-58952-690-7(2)) Rourke Publishing, LLC.

Dalgleish, Sharon. Cattle. 2005. (Farm Animals Ser.). (Illus.). 32p. (J). (gr. 2-4). 23.00 (978-0-7910-8270-6(9) , Chelsea Hse.) Facts On File, Inc.

Hudak, Heather C. Cattle. 2006. (J). (978-1-59036-422-2(8)); (978-1-59036-429-1(5)) Weigl Pubs., Inc.

Macken, JoAnn Early. Cows. 2004. (Animals That Live on the Farm Ser.). (Illus.). 24p. (J). pap. (978-0-8368-4279-1(0)); (YA). lib. bdg. 19.33 (978-0-8368-4272-2(3)) Stevens, Gareth Inc.

Stockland, Patricia M. In the Cattle Yard. Ouren, Todd, illus. 2007. (Barnyard Buddies Ser.). 24p. (J). (ps-2). lib. bdg. 25.65 (***978-1-60270-022-2(2)*** , Looking Glass Library) Magic Wagon.

Stone, Lynn M. Cows Have Calves. 2000. (Animals & Their Young Ser.). (Illus.). 24p. (J). (gr. 1 up). lib. bdg. 18.60 (978-0-7565-0001-6(X)) Compass Point Bks.

—Texas Longhorn. 2003. (Animals in U.S. History Ser.). (Illus.). 24p. (J). 25.64 (978-1-58952-702-7(X)) Rourke Publishing, LLC.

Thomas, Heather Smith. Your Calf: A Kid's Guide to Raising & Showing Beef & Dairy Calves. 2003. (Illus.). 186p. (J). (gr. 4-7). pap. 14.95 (978-0-88266-947-2(8) , 66947) Storey Publishing, LLC.

Top That Publishing Staff, ed. Wacky Bull. 2004. (Wacky Animals Ser.). (Illus.). 10p. (J). pap. (978-1-84510-085-8(9)) Top That! Publishing PLC.

Webber, Desiree Morrison. Bone Head: Story of the Longhorn. Shropshire, Sandy, illus. 2003. 74p. (J). 16.95 (978-1-57168-763-0(7)); pap. 9.95 (978-1-57168-750-0(5)) Eakin Pr. (Eakin Pr.).

Wolfman, Judy. Life on a Cattle Farm. Winston, David Lorenz, photos by. 2005. (Life on a Farm Ser.). (Illus.). 48p. (gr. 2-5). lib. bdg. 23.93 (978-1-57505-516-9(3)) Lerner Publishing Group.

CATTLE—FICTION

Bester, Maryanne. The Cool Nguni. Bester, Shayle, illus. 2007. 24p. (J). pap. 12.00 (***978-1-77009-264-8(1)***) Jacana Media ZAF. *Dist:* Independent Pubs. Group.

Davis, David. Texas Zeke & the Longhorn. Stacey, Alan, illus. 2006. 32p. (J). 15.95 (978-1-58980-348-0(5)) Pelican Publishing Co., Inc.

Dearen, Patrick. On the Pecos Trail. 2001. (gr. 3-6). lib. bdg. 17.60 (978-0-613-83166-6(7)) Tandem Library Bks.

—On the Pecos Trail. 2001. (Lone Star Heroes Ser.). 128p. (gr. 4-7). pap. 8.95 (978-1-55622-830-8(9) , Republic of Texas Pr.) Wordware Publishing, Inc.

Gébler, Carlo. The Bull Raid. 2006. 402p. (J). (gr. 7-9). 22.95 (978-1-4052-1255-7(1)) Egmont Bks., Ltd. GBR. *Dist:* Independent Pubs. Group.

Ibbotson, Eva. The Beasts of Clawstone Castle. Hawkes, Kevin, illus. (J). 2007. 256p. (gr. 3 up). 6.99 (***978-0-14-240931-2(6)*** , Puffin); 2006. 192p. (gr. 5). 16.99 (978-0-525-47719-8(5) , Dutton Juvenile) Penguin Group (USA) Inc.

Kahn, Lisa. The Calf Who Fell in Love with a Wolf: And Other Calf Stories from Round Top, Texas. von Schweinitz, Helga, tr. from GER. 1999. (J). (978-1-57168-346-5(1) , Eakin Pr.) Eakin Pr.

Kamau, G. Why Beetles Roll Cowdung. 2004. 18p. 13.95 (978-9966-25-167-1(7)) Heinemann Kenya, Limited (East African Educational Publishers Ltd E.A.E.P.) KEN. *Dist:* Michigan State Univ. Pr.

Lewis, Preston. They Called Me Old Blue: Or How I Helped Charles Goodnight Invent the Chuck Wagon. 2001. (Illus.). 188p. 17.95 (978-1-57168-493-6(X)); 12.95 (978-1-57168-636-7(3)) Eakin Pr.

Read, Nicholas. Saving Emily. Klem, Ellen, illus. 2004. (Young Readers Ser.). 150p. (J). (gr. 5 up). pap. 16.00 (978-1-57392-897-7(6) , Pyr Bks.) Prometheus Bks., Pubs.

Roach, Joyce Gibson. Horned Toad Canyon. 2004. (Illus.). 48p. 17.95 (978-1-931721-01-1(7)) Bright Sky Pr.

CAVE DRAWINGS

Litwin, Laura Baskes. Diego Rivera: Legendary Mexican Painter. 2005. (Latino Biography Library). (Illus.). 128p. (J). (gr. 6-13). lib. bdg. 31.93 (978-0-7660-2486-1(5)) Enslow Pubs., Inc.

The Mural, 6 vols. (Multicultural Programs Ser.). 16p. (gr. 1-3). 24.95 (978-0-7802-9207-9(3)) Wright Group, The.

Patent, Dorothy Hinshaw. Mystery of the Lascaux Cave. 1998. (Frozen in Time Ser.). (Illus.). 64p. (J). (gr. 5-9). lib. bdg. 28.50 (978-0-7614-0784-3(7)) Cavendish, Marshall Corp.

Walkup, Nancy Elizabeth & Stephens, Pamela Geiger, contrib. by. Take 5: Murals Prints Portfolio & Guide. 2001. (Take Five Art Ser.). 5p. (gr. 5 up). pap. 44.00 (978-1-56290-226-1(1)) Crystal Productions.

CAVE DWELLERS—FICTION

de Paola, Tomie. Little Grunt & the Big Egg: A Prehistoric Fairy Tale. 2007. 29.95 incl. audio compact disk (***978-0-8045-4158-9(2)***) Spoken Arts, Inc.

DePaola, Tomie. Little Grunt & the Big Egg: A Prehistoric Fairy Tale. 2006. 32p. (J). (ps-3). 16.99 (978-0-399-24529-9(4)) Penguin Group (USA) Inc.

French, Vivian. Te Presento al Mamut!, Level P. Williams, Lisa, illus. 2006. (Lightning Readers Ser.). (SPA.). 32p. (J). pap. 3.95 (978-0-7696-4217-8(9) , Gingham Dog Pr.) School Specialty Publishing.

French/Williams, Vivian/Lisa. Meet the Mammoth! 2005. (Illus.). 32p. (J). lib. bdg. 9.00 (***978-1-4242-0881-4(5)***) Fitzgerald Bks.

Mason, Jane. Flinstones in Viva Rock Vegas: Flinstones Movie Storybook. 2000. (Illus.). 32p. (J). (ps-3). pap. 5.99 (978-0-439-17304-9(3)) Scholastic, Inc.

McIntyre, A. Margaret. Cave Boy of the Age of Stone. 2006. pap. 87.99 (***978-1-4280-3996-4(1)***) IndyPublish.com.

Penguin Books Staff. The Flintstones in Viva Rock Vegas, Level 2. 2001. (Illus.). 32p. (C). pap. 9.00 (978-0-582-45190-2(6)) Longman Publishing Group.

Perkins, Lucy Fitch. The Cave Twins. (J). 19.95 (978-0-89190-467-0(0)) Amereon LTD.

CAVELL, EDITH LOUISA, 1865-1915

Batten, Jack. Silent in an Evil Time: The Brave War of Edith Cavell. 2007. 144p. (YA). (gr. 5 up). pap. 16.95 (***978-0-88776-737-1(0)***) Tundra Bks., Inc./Livres Toundra, Inc. CAN. *Dist:* Random Hse., Inc.

CAVELL, EDITH LOUISA, 1865-1915—FICTION

Farenhorst, Christine. A Cup of Cold Water: The Compassion of Nurse Edith Cavell. 2007. (J). pap. (***978-1-59638-026-4(8)***) P & R Publishing.

CAVES

Allman, Toney. Life in a Cave. 2004. (Ecosystems Ser.). (Illus.). 48p. (J). (gr. 4-7). 26.20 (978-0-7377-3014-2(5) , Greenhaven Pr., Inc.) Thomson Gale.

Arnott, Leslie. Underground Worlds. 2005. (Real Deal-Red Plus Ser.). (Illus.). 32p. (gr. 4-8). 19.00 (978-0-7910-8897-5(9)) Facts On File, Inc.

Aulenbach, Nancy Holler, et al. Exploring Caves: Journeys into the Earth. 2001. (Illus.). 64p. (J). (gr. 3-7). 17.95 (978-0-7922-7721-7(X) , National Geographic Children's Bks.) National Geographic Society.

Banting, Erinn. Caves. 2006. (J). (978-1-59036-437-6(6)); (Illus.). 32p. (gr. 4-6). lib. bdg. 26.00 (978-1-59036-436-9(8)) Weigl Pubs., Inc.

Brimner, Larry Dane. Caves. 2001. (True Bks.). (Illus.). 48p. (J). (gr. 3-5). pap. 6.95 (978-0-516-27189-7(X) , Children's Pr.) Scholastic Library Publishing.

—Caves. 2001. (Illus.). 47p. (J). (ps-7). lib. bdg. 15.25 (978-0-613-54115-2(4)) Tandem Library Bks.

—Caving: Exploring Limestone Caves. 2001. (Sports Library). (Illus.). 64p. (J). (gr. 5-7). 25.50 (978-0-531-20318-7(2) , Watts, Franklin) Scholastic Library Publishing.

—Caving: Exploring Limestone Caves. 2001. (gr. 5-8). lib. bdg. 17.60 (978-0-613-51623-5(0)) Tandem Library Bks.

Burnham, Brad. Kazumura Cave: The World's Longest Lava Tube. 2003. (Famous Caves of the World Ser.). (Illus.). 24p. (J). lib. bdg. 18.75 (978-0-8239-6261-7(X) , PowerKids Pr.) Rosen Publishing Group, Inc., The.

—Qumran Caves: Hiding Place for the Dea Sea Scrolls. 2003. (Famous Caves of the World Ser.). (Illus.). 24p. (J). lib. bdg. 18.75 (978-0-8239-6259-4(8) , PowerKids Pr.) Rosen Publishing Group, Inc., The.

Caves Learning about the Earth. 2006. (Illus.). 24p. (J). (gr. k-2). 18.50 (***978-0-531-17886-7(2)***) Scholastic Library Publishing.

Costain, Meredith. Science Chapters: into the Earth: The Story of Caves. 2006. (National Geographic Science Chapters Ser.). (Illus.). 48p. (gr. 1-4). 17.90 (978-0-7922-5950-3(5) , National Geographic Children's Bks.) National Geographic Society.

Creature Color & Discover Cave Life. (Illus.). 28p. (J). (gr. 1-8). reprint ed. (978-1-881469-41-4(7)) Safari, Ltd.

Crowther, Robert. Deep down under Ground: A Pop-up Book of Amazing Facts & Feats. Crowther, Robert, illus. 2004. (Illus.). 18p. (J). (gr. 3-8). reprint ed. pap. 22.00 (978-0-7567-7179-9(X)) DIANE Publishing Co.

Las Cuevas. (Coleccion Tierra Viva).Tr. of Caves. (SPA.). (YA). (gr. 5-8). pap. (978-84-348-3264-0(X)) SM Ediciones.

Dark Zones: Individual Title Six-Packs. 32p. (gr. 5 up). 44.00 (978-0-7578-0993-4(6)) Rigby Education.

Davis, Wendy. Limestone Cave. 1998. (Habitats Ser.). (Illus.). 32p. (J). (gr. 2-3). pap. 6.95 (978-0-516-20371-3(1) , Children's Pr.) Scholastic Library Publishing.

Delafosse, Claude & Jeunesse, Gallimard. Caves Hidden World. Heliadore, illus. 2000. (First Discovery Book Ser.). 24p. (J). (ps-3). 12.95 (978-0-439-10680-1(X) , Scholastic Reference) Scholastic, Inc.

Faulkner, Rebecca. Beneath the Surface. 2007. (J). (***978-1-4329-0110-3(9)***); pap. (***978-1-4329-0116-5(8)***) Heinemann Library.

Gaff, Jackie. Stalactities Hang down & Other Questions about Caves. 2003. (I Wonder Why Ser.). (Illus.). 32p. (J). (gr. k-3). 11.95 (978-0-7534-5573-9(0) , Kingfisher) Houghton Mifflin Co. Trade & Reference Div.

Galko, Francine. Cave Animals. 2003. (Animals in Their Habitats Ser.). (Illus.). 32p. (J). (gr. k-2). lib. bdg. 21.36 (978-1-4034-0176-2(4)); pap. 6.95 (978-1-4034-0433-6(X)) Heinemann Library.

—Cave Animals. 2003. (gr. k-3). lib. bdg. 14.75 (978-0-613-45720-0(X)) Tandem Library Bks.

Gallagher, Debbie. Cave & Underground Homes. 2007. (J). (***978-1-59920-155-9(0)***) Smart Apple Media.

Gallant, Roy A. Limestone Caves. 1998. (First Bks.). 64p. (J). (Illus.). (gr. 5-7). pap. 6.95 (978-0-531-15910-1(8)); (gr. 4-7). 23.00 (978-0-531-20293-7(3)) Scholastic Library Publishing. (Watts, Franklin).

Green, Emily K. Caves. 2006. (Blastoff! Readers Ser.). (Illus.). 24p. (J). lib. bdg. 16.95 (978-1-60014-034-1(3)) Bellwether Media.

Hanson, Jeanne K. & Hanson, Erik. Caves. 2007. (Extreme Earth Ser.). 168p. (J). (gr. 6-12). 35.00 (978-0-8160-5917-1(9) , Chelsea Hse.) Facts On File, Inc.

Harcourt School Publishers Staff. Caves: Take Home Book. 1999. (Signatures Ser.). (Illus.). (J). (gr. 6). pap. 1.90 (978-0-15-313967-3(6)) Harcourt Schl. Pubs.

—Horizons: Wyandotte Cave. 3rd ed. 2002. (Illus.). pap. 5.60 (978-0-15-333496-2(7)) Harcourt Schl. Pubs.

Harrison, David L. Cave Detectives: Unraveling the Mystery of an Ice Age Cave. McCann, Lisa, illus. Biamonte, Edward, photos by. 2007. 48p. (J). (gr. 4-6). 15.95 (978-0-8118-5006-3(4)) Chronicle Bks. LLC.

—Caves: Mysteries Beneath Our Feet. Nathan, Cheryl, illus. 2003. (Earthworks Ser.). 32p. (J). (gr. k-2). 15.95 (978-1-56397-915-6(2)) Boyds Mills Pr.

Howes, Chris. Caving. 2002. (Radical Sports Ser.). (Illus.). 32p. (J). (gr. 5-7). lib. bdg. 25.64 (978-1-58810-626-1(8)) Heinemann Library.

Johnson, Rebecca L. Peering into Darkness. 2003. (National Geographic Reading Expeditions Ser.). (Illus.). 32p. (J). (978-0-7922-8451-2(8)) National Geographic Society.

Jones, Veda Boyd. Caves. Durney, Ryan, photos by. 1999. 8p. (J). (gr. k-2). pap. 3.75 (978-1-880612-97-2(6) , Seedling Pubns.) Continental Pr., Inc.

Kerbo, Ronal C. The Hidden World of Caves: A Children's Guide to the Underground Wilderness. 2002. (Illus.). 48p. (J). pap. 10.00 (978-1-879961-18-0(0)) National Speleological Society, Inc.

Lindop, Laurie. Cave Sleuths. 2006. (Science on the Edge Ser.). (Illus.). 80p. (J). (gr. 5 up). 27.93 (978-0-7613-2702-8(9) , Twenty-First Century Bks.) Lerner Publishing Group.

Llewellyn, Claire. Caves. 2000. (Heinemann First Library). (Illus.). 32p. (J). (gr. k-2). lib. bdg. 21.36 (978-1-57572-202-3(X)) Heinemann Library.

—Caves. 2000. (gr. k-3). lib. bdg. 14.75 (978-0-613-45721-7(8)) Tandem Library Bks.

Llewellyn, Claire, et al. Caves. 2002. (Geography Starts Ser.). (Illus.). 32p. (J). (gr. k-2). pap. 6.95 (978-1-58810-968-2(2) , 91451) Heinemann Library.

Lynette, Rachel. Caves. 2005. (Wonders of the World Ser.). (Illus.). 48p. (J). (gr. 4-8). 26.20 (978-0-7377-2645-9(8) , Greenhaven Pr., Inc.) Thomson Gale.

Marchant, Ian. Crypts, Caves, & Tunnels of London. 2004. (... . of London Ser.). (Illus.). 96p. 8.99 (978-1-904153-04-7(6)) Watling St., Ltd. GBR. *Dist:* Trafalgar Square Publishing.

Mayer, Cassie. Caves. 2006. (Illus.). 24p. (J). (978-1-4034-8434-5(1)); pap. (978-1-4034-8440-6(6)) Heinemann Library.

McFall, Christie. America Underground. McFall, Christie, illus. 2004. (Illus.). 80p. (J). (gr. 4-8). reprint ed. 14.00 (978-0-7567-7712-8(7)) DIANE Publishing Co.

Nadeau, Isaac. Caves. 2006. (Illus.). 24p. (J). lib. bdg. (978-1-4042-3128-3(5) , PowerKids Pr.) Rosen Publishing Group, Inc., The.

Niz, Ellen Sturm. Caves. 2005. (Illus.). 24p. (J). (ps-7). lib. bdg. 21.26 (978-0-7368-4307-2(8)) Capstone Pr., Inc.

Oliver, Clare. Life in a Cave. 2002. (Microhabitats Ser.). (Illus.). 32p. (J). lib. bdg. 25.69 (978-0-7398-4330-7(3)) Raintree.

Patent, Dorothy Hinshaw. Mystery of the Lascaux Cave. 1998. (Frozen in Time Ser.). (Illus.). 64p. (J). (gr. 5-9). lib. bdg. 28.50 (978-0-7614-0784-3(7)) Cavendish, Marshall Corp.

Rau, Dana Meachen. Caves. 2007. (Wonders of Nature Ser.). 32p. (J). lib. bdg. 22.79 (***978-0-7614-2665-3(5)*** , Benchmark Bks.) Cavendish, Marshall Corp.

—Caves/Las Cuevas. 2007. (Wonders of Nature/Maravillas de la Naturaleza Ser.). (SPA & ENG.). 32p. (J). lib. bdg. 22.79 (***978-0-7614-2828-2(3)*** , Benchmark Bks.) Cavendish, Marshall Corp.

—Las Cuevas. 2007. (Maravillas de la Naturaleza Ser.). (SPA.). 32p. (J). lib. bdg. 22.79 (***978-0-7614-2804-6(6)*** , Benchmark Bks.) Cavendish, Marshall Corp.

Schuh, Mari C. What Are Caves? Saunders-Smith, Gail, ed. 2002. (Earth Features Ser.). (Illus.). 24p. (J). (gr. k-1). lib. bdg. 15.93 (978-0-7368-1169-9(9) , Pebble Bks.) Capstone Pr., Inc.

Siebert, Diane. Cave. McLoughlin, Wayne, illus. 2000. 32p. (J). (ps-3). 16.95 (978-0-688-16447-8(1)) HarperCollins Pubs.

Taylor, Peter Lane & Nicola, Christos. The Secret of Priest's Grotto: A Holocaust Survival Story. 2007. 64p. (gr. 5 up). (YA). pap. 8.95 (***978-1-58013-261-9(8)***); (J). 18.95 (978-1-58013-260-2(X)) Kar-Ben Publishing.

Todd, Anne M. Caving Adventures. 2001. (Dangerous Adventures Ser.). (Illus.). 48p. (J). (gr. 3-4). lib. bdg. 21.26 (978-0-7368-0905-4(8) , Capstone High-Interest Bks.) Capstone Pr., Inc.

Walker, Sally M. Caves. 2007. (Early Bird Earth Science Ser.). (J). 26.60 (***978-0-8225-6734-9(2)*** , Lerner Pubns.) Lerner Publishing Group.

What Are Caves?, 6 vols., Vol. 2. 2005. (Earth & Outer Space Ser.). (gr. k-2). 28.95 (978-0-7368-3273-1(4)) Red Brick Learning.

World's Top Ten, 8 vols., Set. 1999. (Illus.). (gr. 3-6). 127.84 (978-0-8172-4349-4(6)) Raintree.

CAVES—FICTION

Abbott, Tony. In the Ice Caves of Krog. Adams, Gil, illus. 2003. (Secrets of Droon Ser.: No. 20). 128p. mass mkt. 3.99 (978-0-439-56040-5(3) , Scholastic Paperbacks) Scholastic, Inc.

—In the Ice Caves of Krog. 2003. (gr. 3-6). lib. bdg. 11.80 (978-0-613-66360-1(8)) Tandem Library Bks.

Anderson, Max Elliot. Secret of Abbott's Cave. 2005. 144p. pap. 10.95 (978-0-9752880-0-9(8)) Baker Trittin Pr.

Anzai, Nobuyuki. Flame of Recca, Vol. 23. 2007. (Flame of Recca Ser.). 192p. (YA). pap. 9.99 (978-1-4215-0893-1(1)) Viz Media.

Appleton, Victor. Tom Swift in the Caves of Ice. 1998. (Tom Swift Original Ser.: No. 8). (J). (gr. 3-7). lib. bdg. 18.95 (978-1-56723-021-5(0)) Yestermorrow, Inc.

Barry, Dave & Pearson, Ridley. Cave of the Dark Wind: A Never Land Adventure. Call, Greg, illus. 2007. 176p. (gr. 3 up). 9.99 (978-0-7868-3790-8(X)) Hyperion Bks. for Children.

Black, Holly & DiTerlizzi, Tony. Spiderwick Chronicles Set: The Field Guide, the Seeing Stone, Lucinda's Secret, the Ironwood Tree, the Wrath of Mulgarath. DiTerlizzi, Tony, illus. movie tie-in ed. 2008. (Spiderwick Chronicles). 672p. (J). 49.99 (***978-1-4169-5016-5(8)***) Simon & Schuster Children's Publishing.

Bowman, Robert. The Three Vests: The New Brilliants. 2003. 224p. (J). pap. 7.95 (978-0-9713530-2-2(6)) Smart & Smarter Publishing.

Carothers, Daniella. Over the Valley. 2007. 148p. pap. 17.95 (***978-1-59299-291-1(9)***) Inkwater Pr.

Clark, Malcolm. Bounty's Cave. 2007. (ENG.). 156p. per. 19.95 (***978-1-932762-82-2(5)***) Elderberry Press, Inc.

Coleman, Michael. Weirdo's War. 1998. (Illus.). 192p. (J). (gr. 4-8). pap. 16.95 (978-0-531-30103-6(6) , Orchard Bks.) Scholastic, Inc.

Dadey, Debbie & Jones, Marcia Thornton. Mrs. Jeepers' Secret Cave. Gurney, John Steven, illus. 1998. (Adventures of the Bailey School Kids Super Special Ser.: No. 3). 128p. (J). (gr. 2-4). pap. 4.99 (978-0-590-11712-8(2) , Scholastic Paperbacks) Scholastic, Inc.

Deal, Paul. Lighting Candles. 2003. 122p. (YA). 20.95 (978-0-595-65804-6(0)); pap. 10.95 (978-0-595-28457-3(4)) iUniverse, Inc.

DiTerlizzi, Tony & Black, Holly. The Ironwood Tree. (Spiderwick Chronicles: Bk. 4). 128p. (J). 2004. (Illus.). (gr. 1-5). 10.99 (978-0-689-85939-7(2)); 2008. 10.99 (***978-1-4169-5020-2(6)***) Simon & Schuster Children's Publishing.

—The Ironwood Tree. l.t. ed. 2006. (Spiderwick Chronicles: Bk. 4). 90p. (YA). (gr. 2 up). 23.95 (978-0-7862-8583-9(4)) Thorndike Pr.

Douglas, Vincent. The Lion King - Cave Secret. 2002. (Disney Parent & Child Read Together Ser.). (Illus.). 40p. (ps-k). 4.99 (978-1-57768-735-1(3)) School Specialty Publishing.

Dreyer, Ellen. The Glow Stone. 2006. 186p. (J). 15.95 (978-1-56145-370-2(6) , Peachtree Junior) Peachtree Pubs., Ltd.

Eaton, Anthony. The Girl in a Cave. Danalis, John, illus. 2004. 128p. (Orig.). (J). pap. 14.95 (978-0-7022-3437-8(0)) Univ. of Queensland Pr. AUS. *Dist:* International Specialized Bk. Services.

C D

Ferris, Jean. Underground. 2007. (Illus.). 176p. (J). (gr. 7 up). 16.00 (***978-0-374-37243-9(8)*** , Farrar, Straus & Giroux (BYR)) Farrar, Straus & Giroux.

Freeman, Martha. The Spy Wore Shades. Date not set. 160p. (YA). (gr. 3 up). pap. 4.99 (978-0-06-440957-5(0)) HarperCollins Pubs.

—The Spy Wore Shades. Cigliano, Bill, illus. 2001. 240p. (J). (gr. 3 up). 15.89 (978-0-06-029270-6(9)) HarperCollins Pubs.

Gelsey, James. Chill-Out Scooby-Doo. 2007. (Scooby-Doo Video Tie-In Novelization Ser.). 64p. (J). pap. 3.99 (***978-0-439-91595-3(3)***) Scholastic, Inc.

Gelsey, James, et al. Chill-Out Scooby-Doo. 2007. (Scooby-Doo 8x8 Video Tie-In Ser.). 24p. (J). pap. 3.99 (***978-0-439-91597-7(X)***) Scholastic, Inc.

Harcourt School Publishers Staff. The Perfect Ending On Level. 3rd ed. 2002. (Trophies Reading Program Ser.). (Illus.). pap. 5.10 (978-0-15-323188-9(2)) Harcourt Schl. Pubs.

Hays, Anna Jane. The Secret of the Circle K Cave. Smath, Jerry, illus. 2006. (Science Solves It! Ser.). 32p. (J). (gr. k-3). pap. 4.99 (978-1-57565-189-7(0)) Kane Pr., The.

Herald, James M. Mystery Cave: Mystery Cave in Mystery Hill. 2000. (Illus.). 90p. (J). (gr. 1-7). pap. 15.00 (978-0-9648236-7-9(5)) Herald Source, Inc.

Higman, Anita. The Living Darkness: Texas Caves. 2nd ed. 2003. (Illus.). xiii, 93p. (J). (978-1-57168-783-8(1) , Eakin Pr.) Eakin Pr.

Hobbs, William. Wild Man Island. 192p. (J). (gr. 5 up). 2003. pap. 5.99 (978-0-380-73310-1(2) , Harper Trophy); 2002. (Illus.). 19.99 (978-0-688-17473-6(6)); 2002. (Illus.). lib. bdg. 16.89 (978-0-06-029810-4(3)) HarperCollins Pubs.

—Wild Man Island. 2003. (gr. 5-8). lib. bdg. 14.15 (978-0-613-61741-3(X)) Tandem Library Bks.

The Ice Cave: Level 3, 6 vols. (Fluency Strand Ser.). (gr. 4-8). 45.00 (978-1-4045-1220-7(9)) Wright Group, The.

Jones, Maurice. Welcome Home Little Bear. Currey, Anna, illus. 1998. 28p. (J). (ps-1). 13.95 (978-0-7641-5081-4(2)) Barron's Educational Series, Inc.

Kenny, Kathryn. The Mystery at Bob-White Cave. Frame, Paul, illus. 2005. (Trixie Belden Ser.: Vol. 11). 256p. (J). (gr. 3-7). lib. bdg. 9.99 (978-0-375-93051-5(5) , Random Hse. Bks. for Young Readers) Random Hse. Children's Bks.

Knight. Dead Beckoning. (Thumbprint Mysteries Ser.). 32.86 (978-0-8092-0421-2(5)) McGraw-Hill/Contemporary.

Law, Felicia. Rumble Meets Eli Elephant. 2005. (Read-It! Readers Ser.). (Illus.). 32p. (J). (ps-k). lib. bdg. 18.60 (978-1-4048-1332-8(2)) Picture Window Bks.

—Rumble Meets Shelby Spider. 2005. (Read-It! Readers Ser.). (Illus.). 32p. (J). (ps-k). lib. bdg. 18.60 (978-1-4048-1286-4(5)) Picture Window Bks.

—Rumble the Dragon's Cave. 2005. (Read-It! Readers Ser.). (Illus.). 32p. (J). (ps-k). lib. bdg. 18.60 (978-1-4048-1353-3(5)) Picture Window Bks.

Marsh, Carole. Dear Bats: The Creepy Cave Caper. 2007. (Postcard Mysteries Ser.). 128p. (J). (gr. 2-9). 14.95 (***978-0-635-06398-4(0)*** , Marsh, Carole Family CD-Rom); pap. 5.99 (***978-0-635-06342-7(5)***) Gallopade International.

McMullan, Kate. Class Trip to the Cave of Doom. Basso, Bill, illus. 2003. (Dragon Slayers' Academy Ser.: No. 3). 112p. (J). (gr. 1-4). pap. 4.99 (978-0-448-43110-9(6) , Grosset & Dunlap) Penguin Group (USA) Inc.

—Class Trip to the Cave of Doom. 2006. (Dragon Slayers' Academy Ser.: No. 3). (J). (gr. 1-6). 24.21 (978-1-59961-123-5(6)) Spotlight.

—Class Trip to the Cave of Doom. 2003. (Dragon Slayers' Academy Ser.: No. 3). (gr. 3-6). lib. bdg. 13.00 (978-0-613-72615-3(4)) Tandem Library Bks.

Mehnert, Robert. Spelunkers. 2003. (gr. 7-12). lib. bdg. 21.70 (978-0-613-77919-7(3)) Tandem Library Bks.

Mitchell, Betsy. Journey to the Bottomless Pit: The Story of Stephen Bishop & Mammoth Cave. 2004. (Illus.). 128p. (J). (gr. 3-7). 15.99 (978-0-670-05908-9(0) , Viking Juvenile) Penguin Group (USA) Inc.

Nimmo, Jenny. Charlie Bone & the Beast. 2007. (Children of the Red King Ser.: Bk. 6). 464p. (J). 10.99 (***978-0-439-84665-3(X)*** , Orchard Bks.) Scholastic, Inc.

Parr, A. L. The Mysterious Cave: Includes Audio Cassette, Coloring Pad & Crayons. Holman, Laura, illus. 1998. 16p. (J). (gr. k-4). pap. 12.50 incl. audio (978-0-9662994-1-0(8)) Adventure Meadow.

Ransom, Candice F. Danger at Sand Cave. Schofield, Den, illus. (On My Own History Ser.). 2005. 48p. (gr. 2-5). pap. 23.93 (978-1-57505-454-4(X)); 2000. 47p. (J). (gr. 1-4). lib. bdg. (978-1-57505-379-0(9) , Carolrhoda Bks.) Lerner Publishing Group.

—Danger at Sand Cave. 2000. (gr. k-3). lib. bdg. 14.10 (978-0-613-68228-2(9)) Tandem Library Bks.

Rau, Dana Meachen. Explore in a Cave. 2000. (Adventurers Ser.). (Illus.). 24p. (J). (gr. k-2). lib. bdg. 19.27 (978-1-57103-318-5(1)) Rourke Publishing, LLC.

Roy, Sandy & Roy, Pat. Jonathan Park & the Secret of the Hidden Cave. 1999. (Illus.). 112p. (J). (gr. 5-9). pap. 8.99 (978-0-89051-263-0(9)) Master Bks.

The Secret Hideaway: Individual Title, 6 packs. 16p. (gr. 2 up). 35.00 (978-0-7635-9376-6(1)) Rigby Education.

Sell, Jeff. The Quarry Cave. 2006. 51p. pap. 12.95 (978-1-4241-1188-6(9)) PublishAmerica, Inc.

Sibley, Jerry. The Adventures of Harley Earle. 2006. 170p. 25.95 (978-1-59824-230-0(X)); per. 12.95 (978-1-59824-229-4(6)) E-BookTime LLC.

Siler, D. Danger Cave. 2006. 76p. pap. 14.95 (978-1-4241-4335-1(7)) PublishAmerica, Inc.

Stellinga, Mark. Buster Boogernose & the Secret Cave. 2007. (J). per. 9.95 (***978-0-9796421-8-0(3)***) Stellinga, Mark.

Ungerer, Tomi. The Mellops Go Spelunking. Ungerer, Tomi, illus. 1998. (Illus.). 32p. (J). (gr. k-4). pap. 5.95 (978-1-57098-228-6(7)) Rinehart, Roberts Pubs.

Urquhart, John. Liza & the Riddling Cave. 1999. 54p. (J). pap. 7.00 (978-0-87602-367-9(7)) Anchorage Pr.

Watson, Richard A. In the Dark Cave. Norman, Dean, illus. 2005. 40p. (J). (ps-ps). pap. 5.95 (978-1-59572-038-2(3)) Star Bright Bks., Inc.

Weathers, Anah D. Secrets of the Cave. Weathers, Luther, illus. Weathers, Luther, photos by. unabr. ed. 2000. (Treasures from the Past Ser.). x, 104p. (J). (gr. 4-8). pap. 7.98 (978-0-9702584-0-3(2)) Creative Services.

Wilson, N. D. Leepike Ridge. 2007. (Illus.). 240p. (J). (gr. 3-7). 15.99 (978-0-375-83873-6(2)); lib. bdg. 18.99 (978-0-375-93873-3(7)) Random Hse. Children's Bks. (Random Hse. Bks. for Young Readers).

—Leepike Ridge. 2007. (Illus.). 224p. (J). pap. (978-0-375-83874-3(0)) Random Hse., Inc.

Wormell, Chris. The Wild Girl. Wormell, Chris, illus. 2006. (Illus.). 32p. (J). 17.00 (978-0-8028-5311-0(0) , Eerdmans Bks For Young Readers) Eerdmans, William B. Publishing Co.

CD-ROMS

Cole, John O. Plugged in to English: English & Language Arts Activities for the Computer Lab. Thurston Miller, Cheryl, ed. 2003. (Illus.). 144p. pap. 28.95 (978-1-877673-60-3(9) , PI-BWK03) Cottonwood Pr., Inc.

CELLS

see also DNA; Embryology; Protozoa

Allman, Toney. Stem Cells. 2005. (Great Medical Discoveries Ser.). (Illus.). 128p. (J). (gr. 4-7). lib. bdg. 29.95 (978-1-59018-772-2(5) , Lucent Bks.) Thomson Gale.

Baeuerle, Patrick A. & Landa, Norbert. The Cell Works: Microexplorers. 1999. (Microexplorers Ser.: No. 4). (Illus.). 42p. lib. bdg. 18.95 (978-1-56674-235-1(8)) Forest Hse. Publishing Co., Inc.

—How the Y Makes the Guy: Microexplorers. 1999. (Microexplorers Ser.: No. 4). (Illus.). 42p. (J). (gr. k up). lib. bdg. 18.95 (978-1-56674-236-8(6)) Forest Hse. Publishing Co., Inc.

Balkwill, Fran. SuperCell. Rolph, Mic, illus. 2002. (Making Sense of Science Ser.). 32p. (J). pap. (978-1-85578-093-4(3)) Portland Pr., Ltd.

Balkwill, Fran & Rolph, Mic. Enjoy Your Cells. 2001. (Enjoy Your Cells Ser.: Vol. 1). (Illus.). 32p. (J). 13.95 (978-0-87969-612-5(5)); pap. 8.95 (978-0-87969-584-2(6)) Cold Spring Harbor Laboratory Pr.

Belval, Brian, ed. Stem Cell Research. 2005. (Critical Anthologies of Nonfiction Writing Ser.). 176p. (J). (978-1-4042-0540-6(3)) Rosen Publishing Group, Inc., The.

Black, Laura. The Stem Cell Debate: The Ethics & Science Behind the Research. 2006. (Issues in Focus Today Ser.). (Illus.). 128p. (J). lib. bdg. 31.93 (978-0-7660-2545-5(4)) Enslow Pubs., Inc.

Building Blocks of Science: Understanding Cells & DNA Teacher's Guide (Firsthand Learning) 2007. ring bd. (***978-0-89278-338-0(9)***) Carolina Biological Supply Co.

Building Blocks of Science: Understanding Cells & DNA Unit Kit (Firsthand Learning) 2007. ring bd. (***978-0-89278-433-2(4)***) Carolina Biological Supply Co.

La Celula, el Origen de la Vida. (Coleccion Mundo Invisible). (SPA.). (YA). (gr. 5-8). pap. 8.00 (978-958-04-3223-4(6)) Norma S.A. COL. *Dist:* Distribuidora Norma, Inc., Lectorum Pubns., Inc.

Design Cell Guide. 3rd rev. ed. 2004. 178p. pap. (978-0-86657-505-8(7)) Lab-Volt Systems, Inc.

Diagram Group. Cells & Genetics. 2005. (Illus.). 112p. (J). (978-0-8160-5980-5(2)) Facts On File, Inc.

DuPrau, Jeanne. Cells. 2001. (Kidhaven Science Library). (Illus.). 48p. (J). (gr. 3-5). 23.70 (978-0-7377-0647-5(3) , LML00102-178557, Kidhaven) Thomson Gale.

Ellis, Catherine. Cars & Trucks. 2007. (Mega Military Machines Ser.). (Illus.). 24p. (J). (gr. k-5). lib. bdg. 21.25 (978-1-4042-3669-1(4)) Rosen Publishing Group, Inc., The.

Favor, Lesli J. Eukaryotic & Prokaryotic Cell Structures: Understanding Cells with & Without a Nucleus. 2004. (Library of Cells). (Illus.). 48p. (YA). lib. bdg. 25.25 (978-1-4042-0323-5(0)) Rosen Publishing Group, Inc., The.

Forman, Lillian. Stem Cell Research. 2007. (Essential Viewpoints Ser.). (ENG., Illus.). 112p. (YA). (gr. 7-9). lib. bdg. 32.79 (***978-1-59928-864-2(8)*** , Essential Library) ABDO Publishing Co.

Freedman, Jeri. America Debates Stem Cell Research. 2007. (J). (***978-1-4042-1928-1(5)***) Rosen Publishing Group, Inc., The.

French, Cathy. Las células & Cells. 2005. spiral bd. 88.00 (***978-1-4108-5726-2(3)***) Benchmark Education Co.

Ganeri, Anita. Cells & Life Systems. 2000. (Life Processes Ser.). (Illus.). 32p. (J). lib. bdg. 21.95 (978-1-57572-471-3(5)) Heinemann Library.

George, Michael. Cells. 2002. (LifeViews Ser.). (J). (978-0-89812-372-2(0) , Creative Paperbacks) Creative Co., The.

—Cells: Building Blocks of Life. 2002. (LifeViews Ser.). (Illus.). 32p. (J). lib. bdg. (978-1-58341-245-9(X) , Creative Education) Creative Co., The.

Green, Jen. Cells & Reproduction. 2005. (Illus.). 32p. (J). (gr. 3-7). lib. bdg. 27.10 (978-1-59604-052-6(1)) Stargazer Bks.

Hil, Mcgraw. Gr 6 Cells Grwth & Rep S. 2000. (McGraw-Hill Science Ser.). (gr. 6 up). (978-0-02-278232-0(X)) Macmillan/McGraw-Hill Schl. Div.

—Trfpaswak Cells Grwth & 2000. (McGraw-Hill Science Ser.). (gr. 6 up). (978-0-02-277653-4(2)) Macmillan/McGraw-Hill Schl. Div.

Holly Wallace. Cells & Systems. 2nd ed. 2006. (Life Processes Ser.). (Illus.). 32p. (J). pap. (***978-1-4034-8851-0(7)***) Heinemann Library.

Holt, Rinehart and Winston Staff. Cells: Item Listing, Group C. 2nd ed. 2001. (Holt Science & Technology Ser.). pap. 11.26 (978-0-03-065511-1(0)) Holt, Rinehart & Winston.

—Cells in Action: Chapter Resources: Tennessee Edition. 3rd ed. 2003. (Holt Science & Technology Ser.). pap. 11.40 (978-0-03-069133-1(8)) Holt, Rinehart & Winston.

—Holt Science & Technology Chapter 3: Life Science: Cells - Basic Units. 5th ed. 2004. (Illus.). pap. 12.86 (978-0-03-030171-1(8)) Holt, Rinehart & Winston.

—Holt Science & Technology Chapter 4: Life Science: The Cell in Action. 5th ed. 2004. (Illus.). pap. 12.86 (978-0-03-030176-6(9)) Holt, Rinehart & Winston.

Johnson, Rebecca L. Looking at Cells. 2003. (National Geographic Reading Expeditions Ser.). (Illus.). 32p. (J). pap. (978-0-7922-8868-8(8)) National Geographic Society.

Johnson, Rebecca L. Mighty Animal Cells. Desrocher, Jack, illus. 2007. (Microquests Ser.). 48p. (J). (gr. 3-5). lib. bdg. 29.27 (***978-0-8225-7137-7(4)*** , Millbrook Pr.) Lerner Publishing Group.

Lewin, Benjamin, ed. Cells. 2003. (Discovery Channel School Science Ser.). (Illus.). 32p. (J). (gr. 5 up). lib. bdg. 24.67 (978-0-8368-3367-6(8)) Stevens, Gareth Inc.

The Library of Cells, 6 bk. set. 2005. (YA). (gr. 7-12). lib. bdg. 151.50 (978-1-4042-0379-2(6)) Rosen Publishing Group, Inc., The.

Light, Douglas W. Cells, Tissue, & Skin. 2003. (Your Body, How It Works). (Illus.). 112p. (J). (gr. 9-13). 31.95 (978-0-7910-7708-5(X) , Chelsea Hse.) Facts On File, Inc.

Lokere, Jillian. Cells: An Anthology of Current Thought. 2005. (Contemporary Discourse in the Field of Biology Ser.). (Illus.). 224p. (J). (ps-7). lib. bdg. 30.60 (978-1-4042-0398-3(2)) Rosen Publishing Group, Inc., The.

Marzilli, Alan. Stem Cell Research & Cloning. 2006. (Point/Counterpoint Ser.). (Illus.). 144p. (J). (gr. 9). 32.95 (978-0-7910-9230-9(5) , Chelsea Hse.) Facts On File, Inc.

Modules: Life Science; Cells & Heredity PE. 2005. (gr. 6-12). (978-0-618-33427-8(0) , 2-01015) McDougal Littell Inc.

Modules: Physical Science; Cells & Heredity Unit. 2005. (gr. 6-12). lab manual ed. (978-0-618-43722-1(3) , 2-01215) McDougal Littell Inc.

Morgan, Sally. Cells & Cell Function. 2005. (Life Science In-Depth Ser.). (Illus.). 64p. (J). (978-1-4034-7520-6(2)); pap. (978-1-4034-7528-2(8)) Heinemann Library.

—From Microscopes to Stem Cell Research: Discovering Regenerative Medicine. 2006. (Chain Reactions Ser.). (Illus.). 64p. (YA). (gr. 6-9). lib. bdg. 34.29 (978-1-4034-8836-7(3)) Heinemann Library.

Panno, Joseph. Stem Cell Research. (New Biology Ser.). 192p. (gr. 6-12). pap. 18.95 (978-0-8160-6931-6(X) , Checkmark Bks.) Facts On File, Inc.

Rainis, Kenneth G. Cell & Microbe Science Fair Projects Using Microscopes, Mold, & More. 2005. (Biology! Best Science Projects Ser.). (Illus.). 128p. (J). (gr. 6-12). lib. bdg. 26.60 (978-0-7660-2369-7(9)) Enslow Pubs., Inc.

Romano, Amy. Cell Specialization & Reproduction: Understanding How Cells Divide & Differentiate. 2004. (Library of Cells). (Illus.). 48p. lib. bdg. 25.25 (978-1-4042-0322-8(2)) Rosen Publishing Group, Inc., The.

Rushworth, Gary. Body Systems: Human Cells. 2005. (Navigators Ser.). (J). pap. 42.00 (***978-1-4108-5086-7(2)***) Benchmark Education Co.

Sakany, Lois. Cell Regulation: Understanding How Cell Functions. Growth, & Division are Regulated. 2004. (Library of Cells). (Illus.). 48p. (J). lib. bdg. 25.25 (978-1-4042-0321-1(4)) Rosen Publishing Group, Inc., The.

Sherman, Josepha. How Do We Know the Nature of the Cell? 2005. (Great Scientific Questions & the Scientists Who Answered Them Ser.). (Illus.). 112p. (J). (gr. 7-12). lib. bdg. 26.50 (978-1-4042-0072-2(X)) Rosen Publishing Group, Inc., The.

Silverstein, Alvin & Silverstein, Virginia. Cells. 2002. (Science Concepts Ser.). (Illus.). 64p. (gr. 5-8). lib. bdg. 26.90 (978-0-7613-2254-2(X) , Twenty-First Century Bks.) Lerner Publishing Group.

Snedden, Robert. Cell Division & Genetics. 2003. (Cells & Life Ser.). (Illus.). 48p. (gr. 6-8). (J). lib. bdg. 27.86 (978-1-58810-672-8(1)); (YA). pap. 8.50 (978-1-58810-934-7(8)) Heinemann Library.

—Cells & Life. 2003. (Illus.). (YA). (gr. 6-8). lib. bdg. 167.16 (978-1-58810-466-3(4)) Heinemann Library.

—The World of the Cell: Life on a Small Scale. 2003. (Cells & Life Ser.). (Illus.). 48p. (gr. 6-8). (J). lib. bdg. 27.86 (978-1-58810-676-6(4)); (YA). pap. 8.50 (978-1-58810-938-5(0)) Heinemann Library.

Stewart, Melissa. Cell Biology. 2007. (J). lib. bdg. (***978-0-8225-6603-8(6)***) Twenty First Century Bks.

Stille, Darlene R. Animal Cells: Smallest Units of Life. 2006. (Illus.). 48p. (J). pap. (***978-0-7565-1761-8(3)*** , 1253130) Compass Point Bks.

—Animal Cells: The Smallest Units of Life. 2006. (Exploring Science Ser.). (Illus.). 48p. (J). (gr. 5-7). 25.27 (978-0-7565-1616-1(1) , 1253130) Compass Point Bks.

—Cells. 2007. (J). pap. (***978-0-8368-8446-3(9)***); 48p. (gr. 5-8). lib. bdg. 26.60 (***978-0-8368-8437-1(X)***) Stevens, Gareth Inc.

Stille, Darlene R. Plant Cells: The Building Blocks of Plants. 2006. (Exploring Science Ser.). (Illus.). 48p. (J). (gr. 5-7). 25.27 (978-0-7565-1619-2(6)) Compass Point Bks.

Viegas, Jennifer. Cell Functions: Understanding How Cells Work. 2004. (Library of Cells). (Illus.). 48p. (YA). lib. bdg. 25.25 (978-1-4042-0320-4(6)) Rosen Publishing Group, Inc., The.

—Stem Cell Research. 2005. (Library of Future Medicine). (Illus.). 64p. (YA). (gr. 7-12). lib. bdg. 26.50 (978-0-8239-3669-4(4)) Rosen Publishing Group, Inc., The.

Wallace, Holly. Cells & Systems. 2006. (Life Processes Ser.). (Illus.). 32p. (J). (***978-1-4034-8844-2(4)***) Heinemann Library.

CELLS, ELECTRIC

see Electric Batteries

CELTIC LEGENDS

see Legends, Celtic

CELTS

Grant, Neil. Everyday Life of the Celts. Cappon, Manuela, illus. 2003. (Uncovering History Ser.). 46p. (J). lib. bdg. 19.95 (978-1-58340-252-8(7)) Smart Apple Media.

Lassieur, Allison. The Celts. 2001. (Lost Civilizations Ser.). (Illus.). 96p. (J). (gr. 6-9). 29.95 (978-1-56006-756-6(X) , LML00902-178104, Lucent Bks.) Thomson Gale.

MacDonald, Fiona. Find Out about the Celts: What Life Was Like for the Warlike Tribes of Ancient Europe. 2003. (Find Out about...Ser.). (Illus.). 64p. pap. 7.99 (978-1-84215-693-3(4) , Southwater) Anness Publishing GBR. *Dist:* National Bk. Network.

Pratt, Leonie. Celts - Internet Referenced (Level 2) 2007. 32p. (J). 4.99 (978-0-7945-1580-5(0) , Usborne) EDC Publishing.

CELTS—FOLKLORE

Artzybasheff, Boris & Bock, Vera. Celtic Wonder Tales & Other Stories. 2001. (Illus.). 224p. (J). pap. 19.99 (978-0-86315-350-1(X)) Floris Bks. GBR. *Dist:* Steiner-Books, Inc.

MacUistin, Liam. Celtic Magic Tales. 2000. (Classic Celtic Tales Ser.). (Illus.). 96p. (YA). (gr. 5 up). pap. 6.95 (978-0-86278-341-9(0)) O'Brien Pr., Ltd., The IRL. *Dist:* Independent Pubs. Group.

—Celtic Tales of Enchantment. 2002. (Illus.). 93p. pap. 7.95 (978-0-86278-692-2(4)) O'Brien Pr., Ltd., The IRL. *Dist:* Independent Pubs. Group.

Matthews, Caitlin. Celtic Memories. Whelan, Olwyn, illus. 2003. 80p. (J). 19.99 (978-1-84148-097-8(5)) Barefoot Bks., Inc.

Matthews, John. Classic Celtic Fairy Tales. Daniels, Ian, illus. 1999. 208p. (gr. 4-7). pap. 14.95 (978-0-7137-2783-8(7)) Blandford Pr. GBR. *Dist:* Sterling Publishing Co., Inc.

CEMETERIES

Greene, Meg. Rest in Peace: A History of American Cemeteries. 2008. (J). lib. bdg. (***978-0-8225-3414-3(2)***) Twenty First Century Bks.

MacDonald, Fiona & Millard, Anne. Mummies & Tombs. 2000. (World Of... Ser.). (Illus.). 64p. (gr. 3-7). pap. 7.95 (978-1-84215-231-7(9) , Southwater) Anness Publishing GBR. *Dist:* National Bk. Network.

Perl, Lila & Heweston, Nicholas. Dying to Know: About Death, Funeral Customs, & Final Resting Places. 2001. (Single Titles Ser.). (Illus.). 96p. (gr. 5-7). lib. bdg. 25.90 (978-0-7613-1564-3(0) , Millbrook Pr.) Lerner Publishing Group.

CEMETERIES—FICTION

Bell, Albert A., Jr. The Secret of the Lonely Grave. 2007. 160p. pap. 8.95 (***978-1-932158-79-3(0)*** , Claystone Bks.) Ingalls Publishing Group, Inc.

Breslin, Theresa. Whispers in the Graveyard. 2004. 128p. (J). pap. 8.99 (978-0-7497-4480-9(4)) Egmont Bks., Ltd. GBR. *Dist:* Trafalgar Square Publishing.

Charest, Jocelyne. La Loi du Talion. Fil & Julie, illus. 2004. (FRE.). 145p. (YA). 8.95 (978-2-922565-85-0(8)) Editions de la Paix CAN. *Dist:* World of Reading, Ltd.

Dahl, Michael. The Eye in the Graveyard. Garvey, Brann, illus. 2007. (J). 40p. (***978-1-59889-328-1(9)***); 33p. pap. (***978-1-59889-423-3(4)***) Stone Arch Bks.

Gaiman, Neil. Graveyard. 2008. 192p. (J). 17.99 (***978-0-06-053092-1(8)***); lib. bdg. 18.89 (***978-0-06-053093-8(6)***) HarperCollins Pubs.

Joosse, Barbara M. Dead Guys Talk: A Wild Willie Mystery. Truesdell, Sue & Carter, Abby, illus. 2006. 112p. (J). (gr. 3-5). 15.00 (978-0-618-30666-4(8) , Clarion Bks.) Houghton Mifflin Co. Trade & Reference Div.

Leonard, Rebecca JoAnne. Adirondack Halloween: A Spooky Tale in the North Country. 2006. 48p. (J). pap. 7.95 (***978-1-4327-0139-0(8)***) Outskirts Press, Inc.

Pratchett, Terry. Johnny & the Dead. 224p. (J). 2007. pap. 5.99 (978-0-06-054190-3(3) , Harper Trophy); 2006. 15.99 (978-0-06-054188-0(1)); 2006. (gr. 5-7). lib. bdg. 16.89 (978-0-06-054189-7(X)) HarperCollins Pubs.

Price, Charlie. Dead Connection. 2006. 240p. (YA). 16.95 (978-1-59643-114-0(8)) Roaring Brook Pr.

—Dead Connection. 2008. 256p. (YA). pap. 7.99 (***978-0-312-37966-7(8)***) Square Fish.

Roy, Ron. The Zombie Zone. Gurney, John Steven, illus. 2005. (A to Z Mysteries Ser.: No. 26). 96p. (J). (gr. k-3). pap. 3.99 (978-0-375-82483-8(9)); (gr. 1-4). lib. bdg. 11.99 (978-0-375-92483-5(9)) Random Hse. Children's Bks. (Random Hse. Bks. for Young Readers).

—The Zombie Zone. Gurney, John Steven, illus. 2005. (A to Z Mysteries Ser.: No. 26). 85p. (J). (gr. k-3). lib. bdg. 11.19 (978-0-606-33238-5(3)) Tandem Library Bks.

Watson Martin, JoAn. Goodnight Mrs. Dinglewall. Sleep Tight! 2006. (YA). per. (978-0-9777996-0-2(3)) Great American Pr.,The.

CENSORSHIP

Burns, Kate. Fighters Against Censorship. 2003. (History Makers Ser.). (Illus.). 112p. (J). 29.95 (978-1-59018-340-3(1) , Lucent Bks.) Thomson Gale.

Center for Learning Network Staff. Censorship. 2000. (Social Studies Ser.). 109p. (YA). tchr. ed., spiral bd. 20.95 (978-1-56077-642-0(0)) Ctr. for Learning, The.

Hinds, Maurene J. John Steinbeck: Banned, Challenged, & Censored. 2008. (Authors of Banned Books Ser.). (Illus.). 160p. (YA). (gr. 9-12). lib. bdg. 34.60 (***978-0-7660-2688-9(4)***) Enslow Pubs., Inc.

Houle, Michelle M. Mark Twain: Banned, Challenged, & Censored. 2008. (Authors of Banned Books Ser.). (Illus.). 160p. (YA). (gr. 9-12). lib. bdg. 34.60 (***978-0-7660-2689-6(2)***) Enslow Pubs., Inc.

Karolides, Nicholas J. Literature Suppressed on Political Grounds. rev. ed. 2006. (Banned Books Ser.). 640p. (gr. 9). 50.00 (978-0-8160-6270-6(6)) Facts On File, Inc.

MacDonald, Joan Vos. J. K. Rowling: Banned, Challenged, & Censored. 2008. (Authors of Banned Books). (Illus.). 160p. (YA). (gr. 9-12). lib. bdg. 34.60 (978-0-7660-2687-2(6)) Enslow Pubs., Inc.

McClellan, Marilyn. Madeleine L'Engle: Banned, Challenged, & Censored. 2008. (Authors of Banned Books Ser.). (Illus.). 160p. (YA). (gr. 9-12). lib. bdg. 34.60 (***978-0-7660-2708-4(2)***) Enslow Pubs., Inc.

Steele, Philip. Censorship. 1998. (Moral Dilemmas Ser.). (Illus.). 64p. 24.95 (978-0-237-51878-3(3) , Evans Brothers, Limited) Evans Publishing Group GBR. *Dist:* Independent Pubs. Group.

Steffens, Bradley. Censorship. rev. ed. 2004. (Overview Ser.). (Illus.). 112p. (gr. 7-10). 29.95 (978-1-59018-187-4(5) , Lucent Bks.) Thomson Gale.

CENSORSHIP—FICTION

Crutcher, Chris. The Sledding Hill. 2005. 240p. (J). (gr. 7 up). 16.99 (978-0-06-050243-0(6)); lib. bdg. 17.89 (978-0-06-050244-7(4)) HarperCollins Pubs.

—Sledding Hill. 2006. 256p. (J). pap. 6.99 (978-0-06-050245-4(2) , HarperTeen) HarperCollins Pubs.

—The Sledding Hill. l.t. ed. 2005. 181p. (YA). 20.95 (978-0-7862-8091-9(3)) Thorndike Pr.

Garden, Nancy. The Year They Burned the Books. 1999. 256p. (YA). (gr. 7-12). 17.00 (978-0-374-38667-2(6) , Farrar, Straus & Giroux (BYR)) Farrar, Straus & Giroux.

Selzer, Adam. How to Get Suspended & Influence People. 2007. 192p. (J). (gr. 7). 15.99 (978-0-385-73369-4(0) , Delacorte Bks. for Young Readers) Random Hse. Children's Bks.

CENTIPEDES

Dahl, Michael. Speed, Speed Centipede! Counting by 10s. Trover, Zachary, illus. 2006. 24p. (J). (ps-2). 22.60 (978-1-4048-1316-8(0)) Picture Window Bks.

Dickmann, Nancy. Centipedes. 2005. (Creepy Creatures Ser.). (Illus.). 24p. (J). (978-1-4109-1768-3(1)); pap. (978-1-4109-1773-7(8)) Steck-Vaughn.

Greenaway, Theresa. Centipedes & Millipedes. Fairclough, Chris, illus. 1999. (Minipets Ser.). 32p. (J). (gr. 1-5). lib. bdg. 25.69 (978-0-7398-1829-9(5)) Raintree.

—Centipedes & Millipedes. 2000. (Minipets Ser.). (Illus.). 32p. (J). (gr. 1-5). pap. 7.95 (978-0-7398-2194-7(6)) Steck-Vaughn.

—Centipedes & Millipedes. 2000. (gr. 3-6). lib. bdg. 17.85 (978-0-613-74066-1(1)) Tandem Library Bks.

Hall, Margaret. Centipedes. 2006. (Pebble Plus Ser.). 24p. (J). (978-0-7368-5348-4(0) , Pebble Bks.) Capstone Pr., Inc.

Hartley, Karen, et al. Centipede. (Bug Bks.). 32p. pap. 6.95 (978-1-4034-3323-7(2)); 2006. (Illus.). (J). (***978-1-4034-8295-2(0));*** 1999. (Illus.). (J). lib. bdg. 21.36 (978-1-57572-796-7(X)); 2nd ed. 2006. (Illus.). (J). pap. (***978-1-4034-8308-9(6)***) Heinemann Library.

Povey, Karen D. Centipede. 2004. (Bugs Ser.). (J). 24.95 (978-0-7377-1766-2(1) , Greenhaven Pr., Inc.) Thomson Gale.

CENTIPEDES—FICTION

Banks, Lynne Reid. Harry the Poisonous Centipede: A Story to Make You Squirm. Ross, Tony, illus. l.t. ed. 2005. 176p. (J). pap. (978-0-7540-6148-9(5) , CLP 341) BBC Audio.

—Harry the Poisonous Centipede: A Story to Make You Squirm. Ross, Tony, illus. 1998. 128p. (J). (gr. 3-7). pap., pap. 5.99 incl. audio (978-0-380-72734-6(X) , Harper Trophy) HarperCollins Pubs.

—Harry the Poisonous Centipede: A Story to Make You Squirm. (J). (gr. 1-3). 118p. pap. 4.50 (978-0-8072-1523-4(6)); 1998. pap. 23.00 incl. audio (978-0-8072-7997-7(8) , YA962SP) Random Hse. Audio Publishing Group. (Listening Library).

—Harry the Poisonous Centipede Goes to Sea. Ross, Tony, illus. 2006. 208p. (J). 15.99 (978-0-06-077548-3(3)); lib. bdg. 16.89 (978-0-06-077549-0(1)) HarperCollins Pubs.

—Harry the Poisonous Centipede's Big Adventure: Another Story to Make You Squirm. l.t. ed. 2005. (Illus.). 176p. (J). pap. (978-0-7540-6197-7(3) , CLP 388) BBC Audio.

—Harry the Poisonous Centipede's Big Adventure: Another Story to Make You Squirm. Ross, Tony, illus. 2001. 192p. (J). (ps-1). 14.95 (978-0-06-029139-6(7)); (gr. 4-7). 14.89 (978-0-06-029394-9(2)) HarperCollins Pubs.

Ghigna, Charles. One Hundred Shoes. Staake, Bob, illus. 2002. (Road to Reading Ser.: Vol. 2). 32p. (J). (ps-2). pap. 3.99 (978-0-375-82178-3(3) , Random Hse. Bks. for Young Readers) Random Hse. Children's Bks.

—One Hundred Shoes. 2002. (ps-2). lib. bdg. 11.80 (978-0-613-89788-4(9)) Tandem Library Bks.

Itoh, Shimpei. Hyper Dolls, Vol. 5. 2003. (Illus.). 208p. pap. 15.95 (978-1-929090-67-9(6)) International Comics & Entertainment L.L.C.

Ross, Tony. Centipede's One Hundred Shoes. rev. ed. 2003. (Illus.). 32p. (J). (ps-2). 16.95 (978-0-8050-7298-3(5) , Holt, Henry & Co. Bks. For Young Readers) Holt, Henry & Co.

Siegel, Phil. Simon the Daredevil Centipede: He Learned to Skate - & Much, Much More. Caiarelli, Alisa, illus. 1998. 28p. (J). pap. 8.95 (978-0-932991-58-4(0) , Different Bks.) Place In The Woods, The.

Snyder, Susan. The Very Stubborn Centipede. McCabe, Susan, ed. Johanson, Anna, illus. 2005. 24p. (J). (ps-ps). 9.95 (978-0-9767163-0-3(5)) Kotzig Publishing, Inc.

Top That!, ed. Millie the Millipede. Elliot, Rebecca, illus. 2007. 20p. (J). (ps). bds. 10.99 (***978-1-84666-274-4(5)*** , Tide Mill Pr.) Top That! Publishing PLC GBR. *Dist:* Random Hse., Inc.

CENTRAL AMERICA

Bianchi, John-Paul. World Through Words: Central & South America. 2000. (gr. 5-8). lib. bdg. 24.50 (978-0-613-45700-2(5)) Tandem Library Bks.

Bianchi, John-Paul, ed. Central & South America. 2001. (World in Focus Ser.). (YA). (gr. 5 up). 64p. pap., suppl. ed. 16.20 (978-1-56711-349-5(4) , Blackbirch Pr., Inc.); 32p. pap., act. bk. ed. 11.20 (978-1-56711-351-8(6)) Thomson Gale.

Bramwell, Martyn. Central & South America. 2000. (World in Maps Ser.). (Illus.). 40p. (YA). (gr. 5-12). lib. bdg. 23.93 (978-0-8225-2912-5(2) , Lerner Pubns.) Lerner Publishing Group.

Cowley, Joy. The Red-Eyed Tree Frog. Bishop, Nic, illus. 1999. (J). pap. (978-0-590-87176-1(5)); 32p. pap. 16.95 (978-0-590-87175-4(7)) Scholastic, Inc.

Cox, Vicki. Oscar Arias Sanchez: Bringing Peace to Central America. 2007. (Modern Peacemakers Ser.). (Illus.). 128p. (YA). (gr. 9 up). 30.00 (***978-0-7910-8999-6(1)*** , Chelsea Hse.) Facts On File, Inc.

Fowler, Allan. Central America. 2002. (Rookie Read-About Geography Ser.). (J). (978-0-516-22235-6(X) , Children's Pr.) Scholastic Library Publishing.

Franklin, Sharon, et al. Mexico & Central America: Understanding Geography & History Through Art. 1999. (Artisans Around the World Ser.). (Illus.). 48p. (J). (gr. 4-8). lib. bdg. 27.12 (978-0-7398-0121-5(X)) Raintree.

Harcourt School Publishers Staff. Social Studies: Central America. 2000. (Harcourt Brace Social Studies). (Illus.). (gr. k-7). pap. 33.90 (978-0-15-317435-3(8)) Harcourt Schl. Pubs.

Miller, Debra A. Belize. 2005. (Modern Nations of the World Ser.). (Illus.). 112p. (YA). (gr. 7-10). lib. bdg. 29.95 (978-1-59018-726-5(1) , Lucent Bks.) Thomson Gale.

Parker, Edward. Central America. 1999. (Country Fact Files Ser.). (Illus.). 48p. (J). (gr. 4-8). lib. bdg. 27.12 (978-0-8172-5406-3(4)) Raintree.

Schwartz, Eric. Central American Immigrants to the United States: Refugees from Unrest. 2005. (Illus.). 112p. (J). (ps-7). lib. bdg. (978-1-59084-929-3(9)) Mason Crest Pubs.

Shields, Charles J. Belize. 2002. (Let's Discover Central America Ser.). (Illus.). 64p. (J). (gr. 5-7). lib. bdg. (978-1-59084-092-4(5)) Mason Crest Pubs.

CENTRAL AMERICA—ANTIQUITIES

Kirkpatrick, Naida. The Maya. 2003. (Understanding People in the Past Ser.: Set. 3). (J). pap. 8.95 (978-1-4034-0606-4(5)); (Illus.). 64p. pap. 28.50 (978-1-4034-0386-5(4)) Heinemann Library.

CENTRAL AMERICA—HISTORY

Ackroyd, Peter. Cities of Blood. 2005. (Voyages through Time Ser.). (Illus.). 144p. (J). (gr. 4-7). pap. 9.99 (978-0-7566-1367-9(1)) Dorling Kindersley Publishing, Inc.

Allman, Barbara. Central & South America. Bianchi, John-Paul, ed. 2001. (World in Focus Ser.). (Illus.). 80p. (J). (gr. 5 up). pap. 17.45 (978-1-56711-347-1(8) , Blackbirch Pr., Inc.) Thomson Gale.

—World in Focus: Central & South America. 2000. (gr. 5-8). lib. bdg. 26.00 (978-0-613-45649-4(1)) Tandem Library Bks.

Blue, Rose & Naden, Corinne J. Exploring Central America, Mexico, & the Caribbean. 2003. (Illus.). 64p. pap. 9.50 (978-1-4109-0334-1(6)) Raintree.

Chin-Lee, Cynthia. A Es para Decir Americas. 1999. (978-0-606-17568-5(7)) Tandem Library Bks.

Chin-Lee, Cynthia & De la Pena, Terri. A Es para Decir America's. Sanchez, Enrique O., illus. 1999. (SPA.). 32p. (J). (gr. k-4). pap. 6.95 (978-0-531-07134-2(0) , Orchard Bks.) Scholastic, Inc.

Ganeri, Anita & Barber, Nicola. Central America. 2005. (Illus.). 44p. (J). (gr. 6-9). lib. bdg. 29.95 (978-1-58340-609-0(3)) Smart Apple Media.

Harcourt School Publishers Staff. Canada/Mexico/Central America. 2nd ed. (Horizons Ser.). (gr. k-7). 2003. (Illus.). act. bk. ed. 11.00 (978-0-15-335841-8(6)); 2002. pap., tchr. ed., act. bk. ed. 26.70 (978-0-15-335843-2(2)) Harcourt Schl. Pubs.

—Canada/Mexico/Central America: Assignment Program. 2nd ed. 2002. (Horizons Ser.). (gr. k-7). pap. 128.10 (978-0-15-335844-9(0)) Harcourt Schl. Pubs.

Hernandez, Romel. Immigration from Central America. 2004. (Changing Face of North America Ser.). (Illus.). 112p. (YA). lib. bdg. (978-1-59084-688-9(5)) Mason Crest Pubs.

Hesse, Joseph M. Central America: CA1 - Spanish Version. 1999. (Geography Capsules Ser.). 90p. (YA). (gr. 7-12). 62.00 (978-1-885888-20-4(1)) Global Awareness Publishing Co.

—Central America: CA2 - English Version. 1999. (Geography Capsules Ser.). 90p. (YA). (gr. 7-12). 62.00 (978-1-885888-21-1(X)) Global Awareness Publishing Co.

—Central America: CA3 - Spanish-English Version. 1999. (Geography Capsules Ser.). 110p. (YA). (gr. 7-12). 78.00 (978-1-885888-22-8(8)) Global Awareness Publishing Co.

—Central America: CA4 - Social Studies Version. 1999. (Geography Capsules Ser.). 90p. (YA). (gr. 7-12). 74.00 (978-1-885888-23-5(6)) Global Awareness Publishing Co.

Petersen, Christine. The Iran-Contra Scandal. 2004. (Cornerstones of Freedom Ser.). (Illus.). 48p. (J). 26.00 (978-0-516-24228-6(8) , Children's Pr.) Scholastic Library Publishing.

Tunica, Nicky. South & Central America. 2001. (Cambridge Junior History Ser.). (Illus.). 48p. pap. 7.00 (978-0-521-77645-5(7)) Cambridge Univ. Pr.

CENTRAL EUROPE

see Europe, Central

CENTRAL STATES

see Middle West

CEPEDA, ORLANDO, 1937-

Markusen, Bruce. The Orlando Cepeda Story. 2001. (Illus.). 144p. (YA). (gr. 4 up). 16.95 (978-1-55885-333-1(2) , Piñata Books) Arte Publico Pr.

CEREBRAL PALSY

Anderson, Mary Elizabeth. Taking Cerebral Palsy to School. Gosselin, Kim, ed. Dineen, Tom, illus. 2000. (Special Kids in School Ser.: Vol. 6). 32p. (J). (gr. k-5). pap. 11.95 (978-1-891383-08-3(6)) JayJo Bks., LLC.

Bjorklund, Ruth. Cerebral Palsy. 2006. (Health Alert Ser.). (Illus.). 64p. (J). lib. bdg. 31.36 (978-0-7614-2209-9(9) , Benchmark Bks.) Cavendish, Marshall Corp.

Gilman, Laura Anne. Coping with Cerebral Palsy. 2005. (Coping Ser.). (Illus.). 192p. (YA). (gr. 7-12). lib. bdg. 26.50 (978-0-8239-3150-7(1)) Rosen Publishing Group, Inc., The.

Gold, John Coopersmith. Cerebral Palsy. 2001. (Health Watch Ser.). (Illus.). 48p. (YA). (gr. 4-10). lib. bdg. 23.93 (978-0-7660-1663-7(3)) Enslow Pubs., Inc.

Gray, Susan Heinrichs. Living with Cerebral Palsy. 2002. (Living Well: Chronic Conditions Ser.). (Illus.). 32p. (J). (gr. 2-6). 27.07 (978-1-56766-101-9(7)) Child's World, Inc.

Nixon, Shelley. From Where I Sit: Making My Way with Cerebral Palsy, Vol. 1. 1999. 144p. (YA). (gr. 7-12). pap. 4.99 (978-0-590-39584-7(X)) Scholastic, Inc.

—From Where I Sit: Making My Way with Cerebral Palsy. 1999. (Illus.). (J). (978-0-606-18549-3(6)) Tandem Library Bks.

Peacock, Judith. Cerebral Palsy. 1999. (Perspectives on Disease & Illness Ser.). (Illus.). 64p. (J). (gr. 4-6). lib. bdg. 23.93 (978-0-7368-0280-2(0) , LifeMatters Bks.) Capstone Pr., Inc.

Pincus, Dion. Everything You Need to Know about Cerebral Palsy. 2005. (Need to Know Library). (Illus.). 64p. (YA). (gr. 7-12). lib. bdg. 25.25 (978-0-8239-2960-3(4) , NTCEPA) Rosen Publishing Group, Inc., The.

Sheen, Barbara. Cerebral Palsy. 2003. (Illus.). 96p. (J). 32.45 (978-1-59018-038-9(0) , Lucent Bks.) Thomson Gale.

CEREBRAL PALSY—FICTION

Card, C. Fran. Ceana Has CP. 2007. 16.95 (***978-0-615-13125-2(5)***) Partners Bk. Distributing, Inc.

Guzman, Lila. Green Slime & Jam. Guzman, Lila, illus. 2001. (Illus.). v, 168p. (J). pap. 11.95 (978-1-57168-555-1(3) , Eakin Pr.) Eakin Pr.

—Green Slime & Jam. Guzman, Jenny, illus. 2001. 174p. 16.95 (978-1-57168-483-7(2)) Eakin Pr.

Hiner, Danielle E. Mommy Can I Play with Tommy? Based on Joseph Hiner, a boy with Cerebral Palsy. 2004. 25p. pap. 14.95 (978-1-4137-2677-0(1)) PublishAmerica, Inc.

Johnson, Harriet McBryde. Accidents of Nature. rev. ed. 2006. 240p. (YA). 16.95 (978-0-8050-7634-9(4) , Holt, Henry & Co. Bks. For Young Readers) Holt, Henry & Co.

Koertge, Ronald. Stoner & Spaz. 176p. (YA). (gr. 9-12). 2002. 15.99 (978-0-7636-1608-3(7)); 2004. reprint ed. pap. 6.99 (978-0-7636-2150-6(1)) Candlewick Pr.

Lears, Laurie. Nathan's Wish: A Story about Cerebral Palsy. Schuett, Stacey, illus. 2005. 32p. (J). (gr. 1-4). 15.95 (978-0-8075-7101-9(6)) Whitman, Albert & Co.

Mikaelsen, Ben. Petey. 1998. 256p. (gr. 5-17). 15.95 (978-0-7868-0426-9(2)) Disney Pr.

—Petey. 2000. 256p. (gr. 5-17). pap. 5.99 (978-0-7868-1336-0(9)) Hyperion Bks. for Children.

—Petey. 2000. (978-0-606-17561-6(X)); (gr. 5-8). lib. bdg. 14.15 (978-0-613-15072-9(4)) Tandem Library Bks.

Roesti, Delores. Mareena Maree Mulligan & the Flying Wheel Chair: Book 1: School Days. 2007. 81p. pap. 9.95 (***978-0-7414-4048-8(2)***) Infinity Publishing.

Sachar, Louis. Small Steps. (YA). 2008. 288p. (gr. 7). pap. 8.99 (***978-0-385-73315-1(1));*** 2006. 272p. (gr. 5). 16.95 (978-0-385-73314-4(3)); 2006. 272p. (gr. 7). lib. bdg. 19.99 (978-0-385-90333-2(2)) Random Hse. Children's Bks. (Delacorte Bks. for Young Readers).

—Small Steps. rev. l.t. ed. 2006. 339p. 23.95 (978-0-7862-8297-5(5)) Thorndike Pr.

Trueman, Terry. Cruise Control. 2004. 160p. (J). 15.99 (978-0-06-623960-6(5)); lib. bdg. 16.89 (978-0-06-623961-3(3)) HarperCollins Pubs.

—Stuck in Neutral. 128p. (J). (gr. 5 up). 2001. pap. 7.99 (978-0-06-447213-5(2) , HarperTeen); 2000. (Illus.). lib. bdg. 16.89 (978-0-06-028518-0(4)) HarperCollins Pubs.

—Stuck in Neutral. 2001. (gr. 7-12). lib. bdg. 15.30 (978-0-613-44419-4(1)) Tandem Library Bks.

Vaughn Zimmer, Tracie. Reaching for Sun. 2007. 144p. (J). (gr. 7 up). 14.95 (978-1-59990-037-7(8) , Bloomsbury Children) Bloomsbury Publishing.

Wait, Lea. Finest Kind. 2006. 256p. (J). 16.95 (978-1-4169-0952-1(4) , McElderry, Margaret K.) Simon & Schuster Children's Publishing.

Willis, Wren. Why Is My Name September? 2005. 155p. pap. 11.39 (978-1-4116-6534-7(1)) Lulu.com.

CEREMONIES

see Etiquette; Manners and Customs; Rites and Ceremonies

CERTAINTY

see Belief and Doubt; Probabilities

CERVANTES SAAVEDRA, MIGUEL DE, 1547-1616

Aller, Eduardo Murias, et al. Cervantes: Un Escritor en Busca de la Libertad. 2006. (SPA., Illus.). (J). (gr. 6-8). 9.60 (978-84-316-7840-1(2) , W33552) Vicens-Vives, Editorial, S.A. ESP. *Dist:* Lectorum Pubns., Inc.

Parker, Barbara Keevil & Parker, Duane F. Miguel de Cervantes. 2003. (Great Hispanic Heritage Ser.). (Illus.). 112p. (J). (gr. 6-12). 30.00 (978-0-7910-7252-3(5) , Chelsea Hse.) Facts On File, Inc.

CEYLON

see Sri Lanka

CEZANNE, PAUL, 1839-1906

Burleigh, Robert. Paul Cezanne: A Painter's Journey. 2006. (Illus.). 32p. (J). (gr. k-4). 17.95 (978-0-8109-5784-8(1)) Abrams, Harry N. , Inc.

Connolly, Sean. Paul Cezanne. 1999. (Life & Work of. . . Ser.). (Illus.). 32p. (J). (gr. k-2). lib. bdg. 21.36 (978-1-57572-957-2(1)) Heinemann Library.

—Paul Cezanne. 2000. (gr. k-3). lib. bdg. 14.75 (978-0-613-60915-9(8)) Tandem Library Bks.

Connolly, Sean. Paul Cézanne. 2006. (Heinemann First Library). (Illus.). 32p. (J). lib. bdg. (***978-1-4034-8495-6(3)***) Heinemann Library.

Harris, Nathaniel. Paul Cezanne. 2003. (Artists in Their Time Ser.). (Illus.). 48p. (J). 23.50 (978-0-531-12242-6(5)); (gr. 5-7). pap. 6.95 (978-0-531-16646-8(5)) Scholastic Library Publishing. (Watts, Franklin).

—Paul Cezanne. 2003. (Illus.). 46p. (gr. 5-8). lib. bdg. 15.25 (978-0-613-59535-3(1)) Tandem Library Bks.

Mis, Melody S. Paul Cezanne. 2008. (J). lib. bdg. (***978-1-4042-3842-8(5)*** , PowerKids Pr.) Rosen Publishing Group, Inc., The.

Soni, Jaymee & Schubert, Charles. A Kid at Art - Paul Cezanne. 2003. (J). pap. 14.99 (978-0-9743760-0-4(0)) Little Noggin LLC.

Tracy, Kathleen. Paul Cézanne. 2007. (Art Profiles for Kids Ser.). (Illus.). 48p. (J). lib. bdg. 29.95 (***978-1-58415-565-2(5)***) Mitchell Lane Pubs., Inc.

Venezia, Mike. Paul Cezanne. 1998. (Getting to Know the World's Greatest Artists Ser.). (Illus.). 32p. (J). (gr. 3-4). 27.00 (978-0-516-20762-9(8) , Children's Pr.) Scholastic Library Publishing.

CHAGALL, MARC, 1887-1985

Hopler, Brigitta. Marc Chagall: Life Is a Dream. 1998. (Adventures in Art Ser.). (Illus.). 30p. (gr. 3-6). 14.95 (978-3-7913-1986-5(8)) Prestel Publishing.

Landmann, Bimba, illus. I Am Marc Chagall. 2006. (Eerdmans Books for Young Readers). 40p. (J). 18.00 (978-0-8028-5305-9(6) , Eerdmans Bks For Young Readers) Eerdmans, William B. Publishing Co.

Markel, Michelle. Dreamer from the Village: The Story of Marc Chagall. Lisker, Emily, illus. 2005. 40p. (J). 17.95 (978-0-8050-6373-8(0) , Holt, Henry & Co. Bks. For Young Readers) Holt, Henry & Co.

Mason, Antony. Marc Chagall. 2004. (Lives of the Artists Ser.). (Illus.). 48p. (J). pap. 11.95 (978-0-8368-5654-5(6)); lib. bdg. 30.00 (978-0-8368-5649-1(X)) Stevens, Gareth Inc. (World Almanac Library).

Mattern, Joanne. Marc Chagall. 2005. (Checkerboard Biography Library). (Illus.). 32p. (J). (gr. k-6). lib. bdg. 22.78 (978-1-59197-841-1(6)) ABDO Publishing Co.

Venezia, Mike. Marc Chagall. 2000. (Getting to Know the World's Greatest Artists Ser.). (Illus.). 32p. (J). (gr. 3-4). pap. 6.95 (978-0-516-27041-8(9)); 27.00 (978-0-516-21055-1(6)) Scholastic Library Publishing. (Children's Pr.).

—Marc Chagall. 2000. (gr. 3-6). lib. bdg. 15.25 (978-0-613-37447-7(9)) Tandem Library Bks.

Welton, Jude. Marc Chagall. 2003. (Artists in Their Time Ser.). (Illus.). 48p. (J). 23.50 (978-0-531-12235-8(2)); (gr. 5-7). pap. 6.95 (978-0-531-16645-1(7)) Scholastic Library Publishing. (Watts, Franklin).

—Marc Chagall. 2003. (gr. 5-8). lib. bdg. 15.25 (978-0-613-59517-9(3)) Tandem Library Bks.

CHAIRS

Cappetta, Cynthia. Chairs, Chairs, Chairs! Stromoski, Rick, illus. 1999. (Rookie Reader Skill Set Ser.). 32p. (J). (gr. k-2). pap. 4.95 (978-0-516-26474-5(5) , Children's Pr.) Scholastic Library Publishing.

—Chairs, Chairs, Chairs! 1999. (gr. k-3). lib. bdg. 12.95 (978-0-613-37308-1(1)) Tandem Library Bks.

Evangelista, Gloria. Ignacio's Chair. Morrison, Cathy, illus. 2002. 32p. (gr. 3-4). 17.95 (978-1-55591-966-5(9)) Fulcrum Publishing.

Ridley, Sarah. A Wooden Chair. 2006. (Illus.). 32p. (J). lib. bdg. 23.33 (978-0-8368-6296-6(1)) Stevens, Gareth Inc.

CHAIRS—FICTION

Bertram, Debbie & Bloom, Susan. The Best Place to Read. Garland, Michael, illus. 2003. 32p. (J). (ps-1). 14.95 (978-0-375-82293-3(3) , Random Hse. Bks. for Young Readers) Random Hse. Children's Bks.

Bloom, Susan & Bertram, Debbie. The Best Place to Read. Garland, Michael, illus. 2007. 32p. (J). (ps-3). pap. 6.99 (978-0-375-83757-9(4) , Dragonfly Bks.) Random Hse. Children's Bks.

A Chair for My Mother. 1998. (J). 3.95 (978-0-439-04431-8(6)) Scholastic, Inc.

Clyde, Addie Mae. Charlie the Chair. 2006. (J). per. 10.95 (***978-1-59872-694-7(3)***) Instantpublisher.com.

Hutchins, Pat. Happy Birthday, Sam. Hutchins, Pat, illus. 2005. (Illus.). (J). (gr. k-3). pap. 16.95 incl. audio (978-0-87499-287-8(7)) BBC Audiobooks America.

C D

James, Betsy. My Chair. DePalma, Mary Newell, tr. DePalma, Mary Newell, illus. 2004. (J). 40p. pap. 16.95 (978-0-439-44421-7(7)); pap. (978-0-439-44422-4(5)) Scholastic, Inc. (Levine, Arthur A. Bks.).

Keats, Ezra Jack. Peter's Chair. 2001. (Illus.). 40p. (J). (gr. k-3). pap. 6.95 (978-1-931016-07-0(0) , MHC-07-0) Minnesota Humanities Commission.

—Peter's Chair. Keats, Ezra Jack, illus. 1998. (Illus.). 40p. (J). (ps-3). 15.99 (978-0-670-88064-5(7) , Viking Juvenile); pap. 6.99 (978-0-14-056441-9(1) , Puffin) Penguin Group (USA) Inc.

—Peter's Chair. Keats, Ezra Jack, illus. 1998. (Picture Puffin Ser.). (Illus.). (978-0-606-13701-0(7)) Tandem Library Bks.

—Peter's Chair. (J). (ps-3). pap. 12.95 incl. audio Weston Woods Studios, Inc.

—Peter's Chair. 2006. 32p. (J). (ps-ps). bds. 6.99 (978-0-670-06190-7(5) , Viking Juvenile) Penguin Group (USA) Inc.

Keffer, Ann. The Seventh Chair. 2007. 76p. (J). per. 8.95 (***978-0-595-45917-9(X)***) iUniverse, Inc.

Kouyama, Yoshiko. The Giving Chair. Kakimoto, Kozo, illus. 2006. 32p. (J). 14.95 (978-1-74126-432-6(4)) R.I.C. Pubns. AUS. *Dist:* SCB Distributors.

Lanteigne, Helen. The Seven Chairs. Kovalski, Maryann, illus. 1998. 32p. (J). (ps-2). 14.95 (978-0-531-30110-4(9) , Orchard Bks.) Scholastic, Inc.

Magoun, James. There's a Bear in My Chair. Magnuson, Diana, illus. 2004. 20p. (J). (gr. k-3). pap. 4.95 (978-1-57874-080-2(0)) Kaeden Corp.

Mahy, Margaret. Down the Back of the Chair. Dunbar, Polly, illus. 2006. 32p. (J). (gr. k-3). 16.00 (978-0-618-69395-5(5) , Clarion Bks.) Houghton Mifflin Co. Trade & Reference Div.

Manuel, Lynn. The Trouble with Tilly Trumble. Greenseid, Diane, illus. 2006. 32p. (J). (ps-3). 16.95 (978-0-8109-5972-9(0)) Abrams, Harry N. , Inc.

Martin, S. R. Vanish. 1999. (Insomniacs Ser.: No. 6). 80p. (YA). (gr. 7-12). pap. 2.99 (978-0-439-04426-4(X)) Scholastic, Inc.

McIntosh, C. Ruth Bay & the Minotaur. 2004. 91p. pap. 14.95 (978-1-4137-4811-6(2)) PublishAmerica, Inc.

Morabito, Fabio. Gerardo y la Cama. Cardemil, Carmen, illus. 2003. (SPA.). (978-968-494-087-1(4) , CI31141) Centro de Informacion y Desarrollo de la Comunicacion y la Literatura MEX. *Dist:* Lectorum Pubns., Inc.

Morris, Gilbert. Spell of the Crystal Chair. 2000. (gr. 7-12). lib. bdg. 14.15 (978-0-613-88611-6(9)) Tandem Library Bks.

Niland, Deborah. Annie's Chair. Niland, Deborah, illus. 2005. (Illus.). 32p. (J). (***978-0-670-04249-4(8)***) Penguin Group Australia.

—Annie's Chair. 2006. (Illus.). 32p. (J). 17.85 (978-0-8027-8083-6(0)); 16.95 (978-0-8027-8082-9(2)) Walker & Co.

Niland, Deborah. When I Was a Baby. Niland, Deborah, illus. 2007. (Illus.). 24p. (J). (ps). pap. 4.99 (***978-1-933605-49-4(9)***) Kane/Miller Bk. Pubs., Inc.

Santucci, Barbara. Abby's Chairs. Santini, Debrah L., illus. 2004. 32p. 16.00 (978-0-8028-5205-2(X)) Eerdmans, William B. Publishing Co.

Suen, Anastasia. Helping Sophia. Ebbeler, Jeffrey, illus. 2007. (Main Street School - Kids with Character Ser.). 32p. (J). (ps-4). lib. bdg. 27.07 (***978-1-60270-030-7(3)*** , Looking Glass Library) Magic Wagon.

Wilkowski, Susan. The Bad Luck Chair. 2007. (Illus.). 96p. (J). (gr. 3-5). 15.99 (978-0-525-47794-5(2) , Dutton Juvenile) Penguin Group (USA) Inc.

Williams, Vera B. A Chair for My Mother: Ib Lub Rooj Rua Kuv Nam/Ib Lub Rooj Rau Kuv Niam. Williams, Vera B., illus. 2001. 32p. (J). pap. 6.95 (978-1-931016-03-2(8) , MHC-03-8) Minnesota Humanities Commission.

—Un Sillon para Mi Mama. Williams, Vera B., illus. unabr. ed. 2004. (SPA., Illus.). (J). (gr. k-2). pap. 16.95 incl. audio (978-0-87499-335-6(0) , LK6260) Live Oak Media.

Yolen, Jane. Baby Bear's Chairs. Sweet, Melissa, illus. 2005. 40p. (J). (ps). 16.00 (978-0-15-205114-3(7)) Harcourt Children's Bks.

CHAKA, ZULU CHIEF, 1787-1828—FICTION

Tellem, Sundiata. Chaka Goes to Nambia. 2005. (Illus.). 24p. (J). per. 8.99 (978-1-932338-73-7(X)) Lifevest Publishing, Inc.

—Chaka Goes to S. Africa. 2005. (Illus.). 24p. (J). per. 8.99 (978-1-932338-74-4(8)) Lifevest Publishing, Inc.

—Meet Chaka Tellem. 2005. (Illus.). 24p. (J). per. 8.99 (978-1-932338-75-1(6)) Lifevest Publishing, Inc.

CHAMBERLAIN, WILT, 1936-1999

Greenberger, Robert. Wilt Chamberlain. 2002. (Basketball Hall of Famers Ser.). (Illus.). 112p. (YA). (gr. 5-8). lib. bdg. 29.25 (978-0-8239-3486-7(1) , Rosen Central) Rosen Publishing Group, Inc., The.

CHAMELEONS

Baker, Sue. Chameleons. Hatfield, Richard, illus. 2000. 32p. (J). 12.99 (978-0-85953-564-9(9)) Child's Play-International.

—Chameleons (Misunderstood) Hatfield, Richard, illus. 2000. 32p. (J). 6.99 (978-0-85953-609-7(2)) Child's Play-International.

Cowley, Joy. Chameleon, Chameleon. Bishop, Nic, illus. Bishop, Nic, photos by. 2005. 32p. (J). pap. 16.95 (978-0-439-66653-4(8)) Scholastic, Inc.

Deiters, Jim & Deiters, Erika. Chameleons. 2001. (Animals of the Rain Forest Ser.). (Illus.). 32p. (YA). lib. bdg. 22.83 (978-0-7398-4681-0(7)) Raintree.

Engfer, Leeanne. My Pet Lizards. King, Andy, photos by. 1999. (All about Pets Ser.). (Illus.). 64p. (gr. 2-6). lib. bdg. 22.60 (978-0-8225-2263-8(2)) Lerner Publishing Group.

Glaser, Jason. Chameleons. 2006. (Illus.). 24p. (J). (978-0-7368-5420-7(7)) Capstone Pr., Inc.

Jenkins, Martin. Chameleons Are Cool. Shields, Sue, illus. 2001. (Read & Wonder Ser.). 32p. (J). (ps up). pap. 6.99 (978-0-7636-1139-2(5)) Candlewick Pr.

—Chameleons Are Cool. 2001. (gr. k-3). lib. bdg. 14.15 (978-0-613-35916-0(X)); (Illus.). (J). 12.79 (978-0-606-21106-2(3)) Tandem Library Bks.

Knudsen, Michelle. Colorful Chameleons! 2001. (Step into Reading Ser.). (Illus.). (J). 10.79 (978-0-606-21117-8(9)) Tandem Library Bks.

Labella, Susan. Chameleons & Other Animals with Amazing Skin. 2005. (Scholastic News Nonfiction Readers Ser.). (Illus.). 24p. (J). (gr. 1-2). 19.00 (978-0-516-24925-4(8) , Children's Pr.) Scholastic Library Publishing.

Lockwood, Sophie. Chameleons. 2006. (World of Reptiles Ser.). (Illus.). 40p. (J). (gr. 2-6). 29.93 (978-1-59296-543-4(1)) Child's World, Inc.

Miller, Jake. The Chameleon. 2003. (Lizard Library). (Illus.). 24p. (J). lib. bdg. 18.75 (978-0-8239-6417-8(5) , PowerKids Pr.) Rosen Publishing Group, Inc., The.

Whiting, Jim. Care for a Pet Chameleon. 2007. (How to Convince Your Parents You Can ... Ser.). (Illus.). 32p. (J). (gr. 1-4). lib. bdg. 25.70 (***978-1-58415-605-5(8)***) Mitchell Lane Pubs., Inc.

CHAMPLAIN, SAMUEL DE, 1567-1635

Faber, Harold. Samuel de Champlain, Explorer of Canada. 2003. (Great Explorations Ser.). (J). 29.93 (978-0-7614-1608-1(0) , Benchmark Bks.) Cavendish, Marshall Corp.

Hurwicz, Claude. Samuel de Champlain. 2001. (Famous Explorers Ser.). (Illus.). 24p. (J). (gr. 3). lib. bdg. 18.75 (978-0-8239-5559-6(1) , PowerKids Pr.) Rosen Publishing Group, Inc., The.

Kline, Trish. Samuel de Champlain. 2001. (Illus.). 24p. (J). (gr. 1-4). lib. bdg. 20.64 (978-1-58952-070-7(X)) Rourke Publishing, LLC.

Marsh, Carole. Samuel de Champlain. 2002. (One Thousand Readers Ser.). (Illus.). 12p. (J). (gr. k-4). 2.95 (978-0-635-01525-9(0) , 15250) Gallopade International.

Mattern. Earth's Explorers: Samuel de Champlain. 2000. (SPA., Illus.). pap. (978-0-7398-3339-1(1)) Steck-Vaughn.

Mattern, Joanne. The Travels of Samuel de Champlain. 1999. (Explorers & Exploration Ser.). (Illus.). 48p. (J). (gr. 4-7). lib. bdg. 22.83 (978-0-7398-1494-9(X)) Raintree.

Morganelli, Adrianna. Samuel de Champlain: From New France to Cape Cod. 2005. (In the Footsteps of Explorers Ser.). (Illus.). 32p. (J). (gr. 3-9). (978-0-7787-2414-8(X)); pap. (978-0-7787-2450-6(6)) Crabtree Publishing Co.

Sonneborn, Liz. Samuel de Champlain. 2001. (Exploration Library). (Illus.). 64p. (J). (gr. 5-7). 25.50 (978-0-531-11978-5(5) , Watts, Franklin) Scholastic Library Publishing.

CHAMPLAIN, LAKE—FICTION

Arnosky, Jim. Little Champ. Arnosky, Jim, illus. 2001. (J). pap. 6.95 (978-0-9657144-5-7(4)) Onion River Pr.

CHAMPOLLION, JEAN FRANCOIS, 1790-1832

Rumford, James. Seeker of Knowledge: The Man Who Deciphered Egyptian Hieroglyphs. (Illus.). 32p. (J). (gr. k-3). 2003. pap. 6.95 (978-0-618-33345-5(2)); 2000. tchr. ed. 16.00 (978-0-395-97934-1(X)) Houghton Mifflin Co. Trade & Reference Div.

—Seeker of Knowledge: The Man Who Deciphered Egyptian Hieroglyphs. 2000. (gr. k-3). lib. bdg. 15.25 (978-0-613-60835-0(6)) Tandem Library Bks.

CHANGE, SOCIAL

see Social Change

CHANTIES

see Sea Songs

CHAPLIN, CHARLIE, 1889-1977

Turk, Ruth. Charlie Chaplin: Genius of the Silent Screen. 1999. (Lerner Biographies Ser.). (Illus.). 128p. (gr. 6-12). lib. bdg. 27.93 (978-0-8225-4957-4(3)) Lerner Publishing Group.

CHAPMAN, JOHN, 1774-1845

see Appleseed, Johnny, 1774-1845

CHARACTER EDUCATION

see Moral Education

CHARACTERS AND CHARACTERISTICS IN LITERATURE

see also African Americans in Art; Children in Literature and Art

Dunham, M. L. Disney's Junior Encyclopedia of Animated Characters: Including Characters from Your Favorite Disney Pixar Films. 2004. (Illus.). 192p. (gr. 2-6). 17.99 (978-0-7868-3434-1(X) , Disney Editions) Disney Pr.

Hamilton, Sue L. Captain America. 2006. (978-1-59679-979-0(X)) ABDO Publishing Co.

—The Incredible Hulk. 2006. (978-1-59679-981-3(1)) ABDO Publishing Co.

—Spider-Man. 2006. (978-1-59679-982-0(X)) ABDO Publishing Co.

—X-Men. 2006. (978-1-59679-984-4(6)) ABDO Publishing Co.

Jweid, Rosann & Rizzo, Margaret. Building Character Through Literature: A Guide for Middle School Readers. 2001. (Illus.). 240p. (gr. 7-8). 39.50 (978-0-8108-3951-9(2)) Scarecrow Pr., Inc.

Mouser, David B. Harry Potter's Muggles Guide to Magic. deluxe l.t. ed. 2001. 80p. (J). lib. bdg. 15.95 (978-1-929771-04-2(5)) H P Pubns., LTD.

Ross, Kathy. Crafts from Your Favorite Childrens Stories. 2001. (gr. k-3). lib. bdg. 17.60 (978-0-613-45174-1(0)) Tandem Library Bks.

Sage, Alison & Tolkien, J. R. R. The Lord of the Rings: The Fellowship of the Ring Photo Guide. 2001. (Illus.). 48p. (J). (gr. 4-6). pap. 9.95 (978-0-618-19558-9(0)) Houghton Mifflin Co. Trade & Reference Div.

CHARADES

Foxx, Kylie. Pajama Parties: Wacky Charades. Ledesma, Sophie, illus. 2001. 16p. tchr. ed. 7.95 (978-0-7611-2357-6(1) , 12357) Workman Publishing Co., Inc.

CHARITY

Craats, Rennay. United Way. 2002. (International Organizations Ser.). (Illus.). 32p. (J). lib. bdg. 16.95 (978-1-59036-022-4(2)) Weigl Pubs., Inc.

Levchuck, Caroline M. Learning about Charity from the Life of Princess Diana. 1999. (Character Building Book Ser.). (Illus.). 24p. (J). (gr. 3). lib. bdg. 18.75 (978-0-8239-5344-8(0) , PowerKids Pr.) Rosen Publishing Group, Inc., The.

Nault, Jennifer. Save the Children. 2002. (International Organizations Ser.). (Illus.). 32p. (J). lib. bdg. 16.95 (978-1-59036-021-7(4)) Weigl Pubs., Inc.

Organizaciones de Ayuda Series, 6 bks., Set. 2003. (Organizaciones de Ayuda Ser.). (SPA & ENG., Illus.). (J). 103.50 (978-0-8239-6918-0(5) , Buenas Letra) Rosen Publishing Group, Inc., The.

Uschan, Michael V. Matt Dalio: China Care Founder. 2007. (Young Heroes Ser.). (Illus.). 64p. (J). (gr. 4-8). 27.45 (***978-0-7377-3670-0(4)*** , Kidhaven) Thomson Gale.

Zeiler, Freddi. A Kid's Guide to Giving. Schumaker, Ward, illus. 2006. 208p. (J). (gr. 7-17). 9.99 (978-1-58476-489-2(9) , IKIDS) Innovative Kids.

CHARLEMAGNE, 742-814

Bhote, Themina. Charlemagne: Life & Times of an Early Medieval Emperor. 2004. (Medieval Leaders Ser.). (Illus.). 112p. (J). lib. bdg. 31.95 (978-1-4042-0161-3(0)) Rosen Publishing Group, Inc., The.

Gelfand, Dale Evva. Charlemagne. 2003. (Ancient World Leaders Ser.). (Illus.). 112p. (gr. 6-12). 30.00 (978-0-7910-7224-0(X) , Chelsea Hse.) Facts On File, Inc.

Greenblatt, Miriam. Charlemagne & the Early Middle Ages. 2002. (Rulers & Their Times Ser.). (Illus.). 80p. (J). (gr. 8-12). 29.93 (978-0-7614-1487-2(8) , Benchmark Bks.) Cavendish, Marshall Corp.

MacDonald, Fiona. Charlemagne. 2000. (World in the Time of... Ser.). (Illus.). 48p. (J). (gr. 4-7). 22.95 (978-0-7910-6030-8(6) , Chelsea Hse.) Facts On File, Inc.

Schlesinger, Arthur M., Jr., intro. Ancient World Leaders. (Illus.). (gr. 6-12). lib. bdg. (978-0-7910-8056-6(0) , Chelsea Hse.) Facts On File, Inc.

Sypeck, Jeff. The Holy Roman Empire & Charlemagne in World History. 2002. (In World History Ser.). (Illus.). 128p. (YA). (gr. 5-12). lib. bdg. 26.60 (978-0-7660-1901-0(2)) Enslow Pubs., Inc.

Whiting, Jim. The Life & Times of Charlemagne. 2005. (Biography from Ancient Civilizations Ser.). (Illus.). 48p. (J). (gr. 4-8). lib. bdg. 29.95 (978-1-58415-346-7(6)) Mitchell Lane Pubs., Inc.

CHARLES 1ST, KING OF GREAT BRITAIN, 1600-1649

Abbott, Jacob. History of King Charles the Second of en. 2006. pap. (***978-1-4065-0357-9(6)***) Dodo Pr.

CHARLES 2ND, KING OF GREAT BRITAIN, 1630-1685

Abbot, Jacob. History of King Charles the Second of England. 2005. 204p. pap. 12.95 (978-1-4218-0152-0(3)); 27.95 (978-1-4218-0052-3(7)) 1st World Publishing, Inc. (1st World Library - Literary Society).

CHARLESTON (S.C.)

Baldwin, William. Charleston My Picture Guide to a Holy City. Baldwin, Aaron et al, eds. 2003. per. 24.95 (978-0-9740091-1-7(3)) Village Museum.

Burgan, Michael. Fort Sumter. 2006. (We the People Ser.). (Illus.). 48p. (J). (gr. 4-6). 23.93 (978-0-7565-1629-1(3)) Compass Point Bks.

Colbert, Nancy A. The Firing on Fort Sumter: A Splintered Nation Goes to War. 2004. (First Battles Ser.). (Illus.). 112p. (J). (gr. 6-12). 23.95 (978-1-883846-51-0(X) , First Biographies) Reynolds, Morgan Inc.

Crewe, Sabrina & Uschan, Michael V. Fort Sumter: The Civil War Begins. 2005. (Events That Shaped America Ser.). (Illus.). 32p. (J). lib. bdg. 24.67 (978-0-8368-3414-7(3)) Stevens, Gareth Inc.

Paterson Chappell, Ruth. All 'Bout Charleston. Wroth, Dean, illus. 1998. 54p. (J). 14.95 (978-0-87844-144-0(1)) Sandlapper Publishing Co., Inc.

Shipwreck Search: Discovery of the H. L. Hunley. 2007. (J). pap. 5.95 (***978-0-8225-6449-2(1)*** , First Avenue Editions) Lerner Publishing Group.

Vierow, Wendy. Shots Fired at Fort Sumter. 2004. (Headlines from History Ser.). (Illus.). 24p. (J). lib. bdg. 19.95 (978-0-8239-6220-4(2)) Rosen Publishing Group, Inc., The.

Walker, Sally M. Shipwreck Search: Discovery of the H. L. Hunley. Verstraete, Elaine, illus. 2006. (On My Own Science Ser.). 48p. (J). (gr. 2-4). lib. bdg. 25.26 (978-1-57505-878-8(2) , Millbrook Pr.) Lerner Publishing Group.

CHARLESTON (S.C.)—FICTION

Asim, Jabari. The Road to Freedom: A Story of the Reconstruction. 2004. (Jamestown's American Portraits Ser.). (Illus.). 136p. (J). (gr. 5-7). pap. 4.95 (978-0-7696-3432-6(X) , Waterbird Bks.) School Specialty Publishing.

Brouwer, Sigmund. Legend of the Gilded Saber. 2002. (gr. 3-6). lib. bdg. 14.15 (978-0-613-89740-2(4)) Tandem Library Bks.

Clary, Margie Willis. Make It Three: The Story of the CSS H. L. Hunley, Civil War Submarine. Rickenbaker, Becky, illus. 2001. 110p. (J). 9.95 (978-0-87844-158-7(1)) Sandlapper Publishing Co., Inc.

Curtis, Alice Turner. Yankee Girl at Fort Sumter. Caley, Isabel & Calley, Isabel W., illus. 2004. (Yankee Girl Ser.). 204p. (J). (gr. 4-7). per. 9.95 (978-1-55709-525-1(6)) Applewood Bks.

—A Yankee Girl at Fort Sumter. 2005. 26.95 (978-1-4218-0301-2(1)); 180p. pap. 11.95 (978-1-4218-0401-9(8)) 1st World Publishing, Inc. (1st World Library - Literary Society).

—A Yankee Girl at Fort Sumter. 2006. pap. 71.99 (***978-1-4219-9790-2(8)***) IndyPublish.com.

Curtis, Alice Turner. Yankee Girl at Fort Sumter. 2004. reprint ed. pap. 19.95 (978-1-4191-9516-7(6)); pap. 1.99 (978-1-4192-9516-4(0)) Kessinger Publishing, LLC.

Curtis, Turner Alice. Yankee Girl at Fort Sumter. 2006. 62.99 (***978-1-4280-2477-9(8)***) IndyPublish.com.

Hogan, Stephen. Johnny Lynch: Patriot Drummerboy. rev. ed. 2007. (J). (***978-0-9795474-0-9(7)***) KAM Publishing.

—Johnny Lynch: Road to Camden. 2007. (J). (***978-0-9795474-1-6(5)***) KAM Publishing.

Jasper, Mark. Good Night Charleston. Kelly, Cooper, illus. 2007. (Good Night Our World Ser.). 20p. (J). bds. 9.95 (***978-1-60219-022-1(4)***) Our World of Books.

Lavender, William. Just Jane: A Daughter of England Caught in the Struggle of the American Revolution. 2005. (Great Episodes Ser.). 336p. (YA). pap. 6.95 (978-0-15-205472-4(3) , Gulliver Bks.) Harcourt Children's Bks.

Love, D. Anne. Three Against the Tide. 2000. (978-0-606-18909-5(2)) Tandem Library Bks.

McCLure, Beverly Stowe. Listen to the Ghost. 2005. (J). per. 16.95 (978-1-933353-51-7(1) , Paladin Timeless) Twilight Times Bks.

Rue, Nancy N. The Escape. 1998. (Christian Heritage Ser.). 192p. (J). (gr. 3-7). pap. 5.99 (978-1-56179-639-7(5)) Bethany Hse. Pubs.

—The Hostage. 1998. (Christian Heritage Ser.). 208p. (J). (gr. 3-7). pap. 5.99 (978-1-56179-638-0(7)) Bethany Hse. Pubs.

Smith, Sally. Rosebud Roams Charleston: A Child 's Clippity-Clop Guide to the City. 1999. (Illus.). (J). (978-0-933101-19-7(8)) Legacy Pubns.

Stroll with Mr. Emmett: A Walk Through Charleston. 2004. (J). lib. bdg. 15.95 (978-0-9759346-0-9(0)) Mr. Emmett Publishing.

Thompson, Laura J. Joseph's Charleston Adventure. Thompson, Laura J., illus. 1998. (Illus.). 28p. (J). (ps-4). 16.95 (978-0-9607854-1-4(8)) Junior League of Charleston, South Carolina, Inc.

Weathers, Andrea. Hermy the Hermit Crab Goes Shopping. Thames, Bob, illus. 2001. 40p. (J). 15.99 (978-0-933101-20-3(1)) Legacy Pubns.

CHARLOTTE, CONSORT OF MAXIMILIAN, EMPEROR OF MEXICO, 1840-1927

Torres, Elizar. Maximiliam & Carlota, Emperor & Empress of Mexico 1864-1867. Torres, Anna Marie, ed. Vargas, Adriana, tr. Martinez, Adela, illus. 2000. (ENG & SPA.). 65p. (YA). (gr. 3-7). pap. 7.49 (978-0-9678599-1-0(3)) EP PUBS.

CHARMS

Bracken, Thomas. Good Luck Symbols & Talismans. 1999. (Looking Into the Past Ser.). (Illus.). 64p. (YA). lib. bdg. 19.75 (978-0-7910-4683-8(4) , Chelsea Hse.) Facts On File, Inc.

Bruce, Marie. Everyday Spells for a Teenage Witch. 2002. (Illus.). 160p. 14.95 (978-0-572-02770-4(2)) Foulsham, W. Co., Ltd. GBR. *Dist:* APG Sales and Fulfillment.

Manoy, Lauren. Where to Park Your Broomstick: A Teen's Guide to Witchcraft. 2002. (Illus.). 320p. pap. 13.00 (978-0-684-85500-4(3) , Fireside) Simon & Schuster.

Naylor, Caroline. Beauty Trix for Cool Chix: Easy-to-Make Lotions, Potions, & Spells to Bring out a Beautiful You. 2003. (Cool Chix Ser.). (Illus.). 96p. (gr. 5 up). pap. 9.95 (978-0-8230-6957-6(5)) Watson-Guptill Pubns., Inc.

Wood, Jamie. The Teen Spell Book: Magick for Young Witches. 2004. (Illus.). 304p. 12.95 (978-1-58761-115-5(5) , Celestial Arts Publishing Company) Ten Speed Pr.

CHARTOGRAPHY

see Map Drawing; Maps

CHASE, THE

see Hunting

CHATEAUX

see Castles

CHAUCER, GEOFFREY, D. 1400

Childress, Diana. Chaucer's England. 2000. (Illus.). xvii, 137p. (YA). (gr. 7-12). pap. 25.00 (978-0-208-02489-3(1) , Linnet Bks.) Shoe String Pr., Inc.

Hubbard-Brown, Janet. Chaucer: Celebrated Poet & Author. 2005. (Makers of the Middle Ages & Renaissance Ser.). (Illus.). 144p. (J). (gr. 4-8). 30.00 (978-0-7910-8635-3(6) , Chelsea Hse.) Facts On File, Inc.

CHAUCER, GEOFFREY, D. 1400—CRITICISM

Chaucer, Geoffrey. The General Prologue to the Canterbury Tales. Allen, Valerie & Kirkham, David M., eds. 1999. (Cambridge School Chaucer Ser.). (Illus.). 96p. pap., stu. ed. 13.00 (978-0-521-59508-7(8)) Cambridge Univ. Pr.

CHAVEZ, CESAR, 1927-1993

Apte, Sunita. Cesar Chavez: We Can Do It! 2005. (Defining Moments Ser.). (Illus.). 32p. (J). (gr. 3-7). lib. bdg. 25.27 (978-1-59716-073-5(3)) Bearport Publishing Co., Inc.

Auster, Michael A. They Led the Way. 2005. (Yellow Umbrella Ser.). (J). (978-0-7368-5315-6(4)); (Illus.). 16p. (978-0-7368-5279-1(4)) Capstone Pr., Inc.

Braun, Eric. Cesar Chavez: Fighting for Farmworkers. Roland, Harry et al, illus. 2005. (Graphic Library). 32p. (J). (gr. 3-7). lib. bdg. 25.26 (978-0-7368-4631-8(X)) Capstone Pr., Inc.

Brown, Jonatha A. Cesar Chavez. (People We Should Know Ser.). (J). 2006. 24p. pap. 5.95 (978-0-8368-4766-6(0)); 2006. 24p. lib. bdg. 19.33 (978-0-8368-4759-8(8)); 2005. (Illus.). 24p. pap. (978-0-8368-4752-9(0)); 2005. (Illus.). 24p. lib. bdg. 19.33 (978-0-8368-4745-1(8)); 2004. (Illus.). 48p. (gr. 5 up). pap. 11.95 (978-0-8368-5257-8(5) , World Almanac Library); 2004. (Illus.). 48p. (gr. 5 up). lib. bdg. 30.00 (978-0-8368-5097-0(1) , World Almanac Library) Stevens, Gareth Inc.

Cesar Chavez. (Photo Illustrated Biographies Ser.). 24p. (J). 6.95 (978-0-7368-8425-9(4)); Vol. 3. 2005. (YA). (978-0-7368-8110-4(7) , Pebble Bks.) Capstone Pr., Inc.

Cesar Chavez. (Compass Point Early Biographies Ser.). 32p. (J). 7.95 (978-0-7565-1166-1(6)) Compass Point Bks.

Cesar Chavez: Fighter in the Fields, 6 vols. (gr. 4 up). 49.95 (978-0-7368-9539-2(6) , High Five) Red Brick Learning.

Cesar Chavez 2: Leveled Books. 2001. (McGraw-Hill. Lectura Ser.). (ENG & SPA.). (gr. 4 up). (978-0-02-188202-1(9)) Macmillan/McGraw-Hill Schl. Div.

Charlesworth, Eric. Easy Reader Biographies: Cesar Chavez: A Leader for Change. 2007. 16p. pap. 2.99 ***(978-0-439-77416-1(0)*** , Teaching Resources) Scholastic, Inc.

Collins, David R. Cesar Chavez. 2005. (Just the Facts Biographies Ser.). (Illus.). 112p. (J). (gr. 6-12). 27.93 (978-0-8225-2248-5(9)) Lerner Publishing Group.

Cruz, Barbara C. Cesar Chavez: A Voice for Farmworkers. 2005. (Latino Biography Library). (Illus.). 128p. (J). (gr. 6-13). lib. bdg. 31.93 (978-0-7660-2489-2(X)) Enslow Pubs., Inc.

Davis, Barbara J. The National Grape Boycott: A Victory for Farmworkers. 2007. (J). lib. bdg. ***(*978-0-7565-2454-8(7))*** Compass Point Bks.

Davis, Lucile. Cesar Chavez. Schon, Isabel, ed. Ferrer, Martín Luis Guzman, tr. from ENG. 1998. (Biografías Ilustradas con Fotografías Ser.). (SPA., Illus.). 24p. (J). (gr. 2-3). lib. bdg. 18.60 (978-1-56065-808-5(8) , CAP2791, Bridgestone Bks.) Capstone Pr., Inc.

del Castillo, Richard Griswold. César Chavez: La lucha por la Justicia. Colin, Jose Juan, tr. from ENG. Accardo, Anthony, illus. 2001. (Hispanic Civil Rights Ser.). (ENG & SPA.). 32p. (J). (ps-3). 15.95 (978-1-55885-324-9(3) , Piñata Books) Arte Publico Pr.

Domblewski, Carol. Citizens Who Made a Difference. 2005. (Navigators Ser.). (J). pap. 38.00 ***(*978-1-4108-5097-3(8))*** Benchmark Education Co.

Ebon Research Systems Staff. Dare to Be... A Hero Vol. 3: Cesar Chavez. l.t. ed. 2003. Tr. of Atrevete Ser... Un Heroe Cesar Chavez. (ENG & SPA., Illus.). 16p. (J). 3.99 (978-0-9648313-6-0(8)) Ebon Research Systems Publishing, LLC.

Eddy, Susan. Cesar Chavez. (Rookie Biographies Ser.). (Illus.). (J). 2004. 31p. (gr. 1-2). pap. 4.95 (978-0-516-27923-7(8)); 2003. 32p. 20.50 (978-0-516-25882-9(6)) Scholastic Library Publishing. (Children's Pr.).

Feinstein, Stephen. Lee sobre César Chavez/Read about Cesar Chavez. 2006. (I Like Biographies! Bilingual Ser.). (ENG & SPA., Illus.). 24p. (J). (gr. 1-3). lib. bdg. 21.26 (978-0-7660-2744-2(9) , Enslow Elementary) Enslow Pubs., Inc.

—Read about Cesar Chavez. 2004. (I Like Biographies Ser.!). (Illus.). 24p. (J). lib. bdg. 21.26 (978-0-7660-2296-6(X)) Enslow Pubs., Inc.

Gaines, Ann Graham. Cesar E. Chavez: The Fight for Farm Workers' Rights. 2003. (Proud Heritage-The Hispanic Library). (Illus.). 40p. (J). (gr. 3-7). 28.50 (978-1-56766-209-2(9)) Child's World, Inc.

Gotsch, Patrice. Cesar Chavez: Changing Lives. Arreola, Gil, illus. 2005. 19p. (J). pap. ***(*978-1-55501-780-4(0))*** Ballard & Tighe Pubs.

Guzman, Lila & Guzman, Rick. César Chavez: Fighting for Fairness. 2006. (Famous Latinos Ser.). (Illus.). 32p. (J). lib. bdg. 22.60 (978-0-7660-2370-3(2) , Enslow Elementary) Enslow Pubs., Inc.

Guzman, Lila & Guzman, Rick. César Chavez: La lucha por lo Justo. 2007. (Latinos Famosos Ser.). (SPA., Illus.). 32p. (J). (gr. 3-4). lib. bdg. 22.60 ***(*978-0-7660-2679-7(5)*** , Enslow Elementary) Enslow Pubs., Inc.

Haugen, Brenda. Cesar Chavez: Crusader for Social Change. 2007. (J). lib. bdg. ***(*978-0-7565-3321-2(X))*** Compass Point Bks.

Houle, Michelle M. Caesar Chavez. 2002. (People Who Made History Ser.). (Illus.). 200p. (YA). (gr. 9-12). pap. 24.95 (978-0-7377-1299-5(6)); lib. bdg. 36.20 (978-0-7377-1298-8(8)) Thomson Gale. (Greenhaven Pr., Inc.).

Krull, Kathleen. Cosechando Esperanza: La Historia de Cesar Chavez. Campoy, F. Isabel & Ada, Alma Flor, trs. Morales, Yuyi, illus. 2004. (SPA.). 48p. (J). pap. 7.00 (978-0-15-205169-3(4) , Voyager Bks./Libros Viajeros) Harcourt Children's Bks.

—Harvesting Hope: The Story of Cesar Chavez. Morales, Yuyi, illus. 2003. 48p. (J). (gr. 3-6). 17.00 (978-0-15-201437-7(3)) Harcourt Children's Bks.

Krull, Kathleen & Morales, Yuyi. Cosechando Esperanza: La Historia de Cesar Chavez. Ada, Alma Flor & Campoy, F. Isabel, trs. from ENG. Morales, Yuyi, illus. 2003. (SPA., Illus.). 48p. (J). 17.00 (978-0-15-204755-9(7) , Voyager Bks./Libros Viajeros) Harcourt Children's Bks.

Marcovitz, Hal. Cesar Chavez. 2003. (Great Hispanic Heritage Ser.). (Illus.). 112p. (gr. 6-12). 30.00 (978-0-7910-7253-0(3)); pap. 30.00 (978-0-7910-7515-9(X)) Facts On File, Inc. (Chelsea Hse.).

Marsh, Carole. Cesar Chavez. 2002. (One Thousand Readers Ser.). (Illus.). 12p. (J). (gr. k-4). 2.95 (978-0-635-01566-2(8) , 15668) Gallopade International.

Matthews, J. L. & Rasinski, Timothy V. Cesar Chavez: Fighter in the Fields. 2002. (High Five Reading Ser.). (Illus.). 48p. (J). (gr. 2-3). lib. bdg. 22.60 (978-0-7368-9550-7(7) , Capstone High-Interest Bks.); pap. 16.95 (978-0-7368-9528-6(0)) Capstone Pr., Inc.

McLeese, Don. Cesar E. Chavez. 2003. (Rourke Discovery Library). (Illus.). 24p. (gr. 2-5). 14.95 (978-1-58952-285-5(0)) Rourke Publishing, LLC.

Olmstead. Cesar Chavez. (Hispanic-American Biographies Ser.). 2005. pap. 9.50 (978-1-4109-1595-5(6)); 2005. pap. 34.20 (978-1-4109-1600-6(6)); Pack. 2004. (Illus.). pap. 51.30 (978-1-4109-1192-6(6)) Harcourt Schl. Pubs.

Olmstead, Mary. Cesar Chavez. 2004. (Hispanic-American Biographies Ser.). (Illus.). 64p. (J). pap. 9.50 (978-1-4109-0916-9(6)) Harcourt Schl. Pubs.

—Cesar Chavez. 2004. (Hispanic-American Biographies Ser.). (Illus.). 64p. (J). (gr. 4-6). 32.86 (978-1-4109-0710-3(4)) Raintree.

Paths: Jose Marti, Frida Kahlo, Cesar Chavez. 2001. (Gateways to the Sun Ser.). (J). (gr. 3-4). lib. bdg. 14.95 (978-1-58105-573-3(0)) Santillana USA Publishing Co., Inc.

Rinaldo, Denise. Cesar Chavez: With a Discussion of Compassion. 2003. (Values in Action Ser.). (J). (978-1-59203-064-4(5)) Learning Challenge, Inc.

Roman, Michelle. Becoming Cesar Chavez. Ballis, George, photos by. 2002. (ENG & SPA., Illus.). 48p. (J). (gr. 1-6). pap. 8.95 (978-0-938911-21-0(X)) Individualized Education Systems/Poppy Lane Publishing.

Schaefer, Lola M. Cesar Chavez. Saunders-Smith, Gail, ed. 1998. (Famous Americans Ser.). (Illus.). 24p. (J). (gr. k-1). lib. bdg. 15.93 (978-0-7368-0109-6(X) , Pebble Bks.) Capstone Pr., Inc.

Schumacher, Tyler. Cesar Chavez: Champion of Workers. 2006. (Fact Finders Ser.). (Illus.). 32p. (J). (978-0-7368-5436-8(3) , Fact Finders) Capstone Pr., Inc.

Seidman, David. Cesar Chavez: Labor Leader. 2004. (Great Life Stories Ser.). (Illus.). 127p. (J). 30.50 (978-0-531-12319-5(7) , Watts, Franklin) Scholastic Library Publishing.

Shea, Kitty. Cesar Chavez: Leader of Migrant Farm Workers. 2004. (Compass Point Early Biographies Ser.). (Illus.). 32p. (J). (gr. 1-3). lib. bdg. 21.26 (978-0-7565-0793-0(6)) Compass Point Bks.

Slade, Suzanne. Cesar Chavez: Champion & Voice of Farmworkers. Thompson, Jeffrey, illus. 2007. (J). lib. bdg. ***(*978-1-4048-3724-9(8))*** Picture Window Bks.

Soto, Gary. Cesar Chavez: A Hero for Everyone. Lohstoeter, Lori, illus. 2003. (Milestone Ser.). 80p. (J). pap. 3.99 (978-0-689-85922-9(8) , Aladdin) Simon & Schuster Children's Publishing.

—Cesar Chavez: A Hero for Everyone. 2003. (gr. 3-6). lib. bdg. 11.80 (978-0-613-90718-7(3)) Tandem Library Bks.

Tello, Jerry. Let's Read About— César Chavez. Marchesi, Stephen, illus. 2004. (Scholastic First Biographies Ser.). (J). pap. (978-0-439-68051-6(4)) Scholastic, Inc.

Thompson, E. L. Cesar Chavez, with Profiles of Terence V. Powderly & Dolores Huerta. 2006. (Biographical Connections Ser.). (Illus.). 112p. (J). (978-0-7166-1827-0(3)) World Bk., Inc.

Wadsworth, Ginger. Cesar Chavez. Schroeder, Mark, illus. 2005. (Yo Solo - Biografias (on My Own - Biographies) Ser.). (SPA.). 48p. (J). (ps-ps). pap. 5.95 (978-0-8225-3125-8(9)) Lerner Publishing Group.

—Cesar Chavez. Schroder, Mark, illus. 2005. (Yo Solo (On My Own) Ser.). (SPA.). 48p. (J). (ps-7). lib. bdg. 23.93 (978-0-8225-3124-1(0) , Ediciones Lerner) Lerner Publishing Group.

—Cesar Chavez. 2005. (On My Own Biography Ser.). (Illus.). 48p. (J). 25.26 (978-1-57505-652-4(6) , Carolrhoda Bks.) Lerner Publishing Group.

—Cesar Chavez. Schroder, Mark, illus. 2005. 48p. (J). (gr. 1-3). pap. 5.95 (978-1-57505-826-9(X)) Lerner Publishing Group.

Wheeler, Jill C. Cesar Chavez. 2003. (Breaking Barriers Ser.). (Illus.). 64p. (J). (gr. 3-8). lib. bdg. 25.65 (978-1-57765-905-1(8)) ABDO Publishing Co.

Young, Jeff C. Cesar Chavez. 2007. (American Workers Ser.). 160p. (YA). (gr. 5-8). lib. bdg. 27.95 (978-1-59935-036-3(X)) Reynolds, Morgan Inc.

Zannos, Susan. Cesar Chavez. 1998. (Real-Life Reader Biographies Ser.). (Illus.). 32p. (J). (gr. 4-7). lib. bdg. 15.95 (978-1-883845-71-1(8)) Mitchell Lane Pubs., Inc.

CHECKERS

Alvarez, Michel J., creator. WonderCheckers - Checkers Kit for Kids: Featuring Unique Prize-fillable Pieces, Incentive Charts & Motivational Stickers - plus 3D Tic-Tac-Toe. 2005. (J). 17.95 (978-0-9771787-2-8(2)) Wonder Chess LLC.

Cardie, John P. How to Beat Granddad at Checkers. 2007. (J). per. 15.95 ***(*978-1-59879-390-1(X))*** Lifevest Publishing, Inc.

CHEERS AND CHEERLEADING

Cheerleading: Individual Title Six-Packs. (On Deck Ser.). 24p. (gr. 4-5). 35.00 (978-0-7578-1021-3(7)) Rigby Education.

Cheerleading for Fun! (For Fun Ser.). 48p. (YA). 8.95 (978-0-7565-1152-4(6)) Compass Point Bks.

Crossingham, John. Cheerleading in Action. Rouse, Bonna, illus. Crabtree, Marc, photos by. 2003. 32p. (J). (ps-7). lib. bdg. 15.25 (978-0-613-59060-0(0)) Tandem Library Bks.

—Porristas en Accion. Rouse, Bonna, illus. Crabtree, Marc, photos by. 2005. (Deportes en Accion Ser.). (SPA & ENG.). 32p. (J). (gr. 3-4). (978-0-7787-8575-0(0)); (gr. 6-9). pap. (978-0-7787-8621-4(8)) Crabtree Publishing Co.

Crossingham, John & Rouse, Bonna. Cheerleading in Action. 2003. (Sports in Action Ser.). (Illus.). 32p. (J). (gr. 1-4). (978-0-7787-0333-4(9)); pap. (978-0-7787-0353-2(3)) Crabtree Publishing Co.

Emmer, Rae. Cheerleading. 2002. (Reading Power Ser.). (Illus.). 24p. (J). (gr. 1). lib. bdg. 17.25 (978-0-8239-5965-5(1) , PowerKids Pr.) Rosen Publishing Group, Inc., The.

—Porristas. 2004. (Actividades Escolares Ser.). (SPA & ENG., Illus.). 24p. (J). lib. bdg. 17.25 (978-0-8239-6899-2(5) , Buenas Letra) Rosen Publishing Group, Inc., The.

Gruber, Beth. Cheerleading for Fun. 2004. (Activities for Fun Ser.). (Illus.). 48p. (J). (gr. 3 up). lib. bdg. 21.26 (978-0-7565-0584-4(4)) Compass Point Bks.

Jones, Jen. Cheer All-Stars. 2008. (J). ***(*978-1-4296-1346-0(7))*** Capstone Pr., Inc.

—Cheer Basics: Rules to Cheer By. 2005. (J). 22.60 (978-0-7368-4359-1(0)) Capstone Pr., Inc.

—Cheer Chants & Signs. 2008. (J). ***(*978-1-4296-1347-7(5))*** Capstone Pr., Inc.

—Cheer Competitions. 2008. (J). ***(*978-1-4296-1348-4(3))*** Capstone Pr., Inc.

—Cheer Essentials: Uniforms & Equipment. 2005. (Illus.). 32p. (J). 22.60 (978-0-7368-4360-7(4)) Capstone Pr., Inc.

—Cheer Professionals. 2008. (J). ***(*978-1-4296-1349-1(1))*** Capstone Pr., Inc.

—Cheer Skills: Beginning Tumbling & Stunting. 2005. (Illus.). 32p. (J). 22.60 (978-0-7368-4358-4(2)) Capstone Pr., Inc.

—Cheer Spirit: Revving up the Crowd. 2005. (Illus.). 32p. (J). 22.60 (978-0-7368-4362-1(0)) Capstone Pr., Inc.

—Cheer Squad: Building Spirit & Getting Along. 2005. (Illus.). 32p. (J). 22.60 (978-0-7368-4363-8(9)) Capstone Pr., Inc.

—Cheer Tryouts: Tips for Making the Cut. 2005. (Illus.). 32p. (J). 22.60 (978-0-7368-4361-4(2) , 1244021) Capstone Pr., Inc.

—Cheerleading. 2005. (Illus.). (J). (gr. 3-4). lib. bdg. 151.56 (978-0-7368-4426-0(0)) Capstone Pr., Inc.

Maurer, Tracy. Cheerleading Gear. 2006. (Jump & Shout Ser.). (Illus.). 48p. (gr. 4-8). 20.95 (978-1-59515-502-3(3)) Rourke Publishing, LLC.

Maurer, Tracy Nelson. The Cheerleaders. 2006. (Jump & Shout Ser.). (Illus.). 48p. (gr. 4-8). 20.95 (978-1-59515-498-9(1)) Rourke Publishing, LLC.

—Cheerleading Practice. 2006. (Jump & Shout Ser.). (Illus.). 48p. (gr. 4-8). 20.95 (978-1-59515-503-0(1)) Rourke Publishing, LLC.

—Cheerleading Skills. 2006. (Jump & Shout Ser.). (Illus.). 48p. (gr. 4-8). 20.95 (978-1-59515-500-9(7)) Rourke Publishing, LLC.

—Competitive Cheerleading. 2006. (Jump & Shout Ser.). (Illus.). 48p. (gr. 4-8). 20.95 (978-1-59515-501-6(5)) Rourke Publishing, LLC.

—School Cheerleading. 2006. (Jump & Shout Ser.). (Illus.). 48p. (gr. 4-8). 20.95 (978-1-59515-499-6(X)) Rourke Publishing, LLC.

McCoy, Lisa. Cheerleading. 2003. (Sports Injuries Ser.). (Illus.). 64p. (J). lib. bdg. (978-1-59084-628-5(1)) Mason Crest Pubs.

Peters, Craig. Chants, Cheers, & Jumps. 2003. (Let's Go Team Ser.). (Illus.). 64p. (J). (gr. 5 up). lib. bdg. (978-1-59084-535-6(8)) Mason Crest Pubs.

—Cheerleading Stars. 2003. (Let's Go Team Ser.). (Illus.). 64p. (J). (gr. 5 up). lib. bdg. (978-1-59084-533-2(1)) Mason Crest Pubs.

—Competitive Cheerleading. 2003. (Let's Go Team Ser.). (Illus.). 64p. (J). (gr. 5 up). lib. bdg. (978-1-59084-532-5(3)) Mason Crest Pubs.

—Techniques of Cheerleading. 2003. (Let's Go Team Ser.). (Illus.). 64p. (J). (gr. 5 up). lib. bdg. (978-1-59084-530-1(7)) Mason Crest Pubs.

—Techniques of Dance for Cheerleading. 2003. (Let's Go Team Ser.). (Illus.). 64p. (J). (gr. 5 up). lib. bdg. (978-1-59084-531-8(5)) Mason Crest Pubs.

Rusconi, Ellen. Cheerleading. 2001. (After School Ser.). (Illus.). (J). 48p. (gr. 7-12). 23.00 (978-0-516-23148-8(0)); 48p. (gr. 7-12). pap. 6.95 (978-0-516-29552-7(7)); lib. bdg. (978-0-516-23251-5(7)) Scholastic Library Publishing. (Children's Pr.).

Scott, Kieran. Ultimate Cheerleading. 1998. (Illus.). 64p. (J). (gr. 5-9). pap. 8.95 (978-0-590-38651-7(4)) Scholastic, Inc.

Szwast, Ursula. Cheerleading. 2004. (Get Going! Hobbies Ser.). (Illus.). 32p. (J). 27.79 (978-1-4034-6116-2(3)); pap. 7.50 (978-1-4034-6123-0(6)) Heinemann Library.

Valliant, Doris. The History of Cheerleading. 2003. (Let's Go Team Ser.). (Illus.). 64p. (J). (gr. 5 up). lib. bdg. (978-1-59084-534-9(X)) Mason Crest Pubs.

Wells, Don. Cheerleading. 2005. (For the Love of Sports Ser.). (Illus.). 24p. (J). (ps-6). lib. bdg. 24.45 (978-1-59036-295-2(0)); pap. 6.95 (978-1-59036-299-0(3)) Weigl Pubs., Inc.

101 Best Cheers. 2004. (J). per. 4.95 (978-1-932855-06-7(8)) becker&mayer! books.

CHEETAHS

Aaseng, Nathan. The Cheetah. 2000. (Endangered Animals & Habitats Ser.). (Illus.). 96p. (YA). (gr. 4-12). 27.45 (978-1-56006-680-4(6) , Lucent Bks.) Thomson Gale.

Albee, Sarah & Delaney, Kate. Cheetahs. 2007. (J). ***(*978-1-59939-118-2(X)*** , Reader's Digest Young Families, Inc.) Reader's Digest Children's Publishing, Inc.

Barfuss, Matto H. My Cheetah Family. 1999. (Photo Bks.). (Illus.). 48p. (J). (gr. 3-6). lib. bdg. (978-1-57505-377-6(2) , Carolrhoda Bks.) Lerner Publishing Group.

The Cheetah: Individual Title Six-Packs. (On Deck Ser.). 24p. (gr. 4-5). 35.00 (978-0-7578-1064-0(0)) Rigby Education.

Clarke, Ginjer L. Cheetah Cubs: Station Stop 2. Washburn, Lucia, illus. 2007. 48p. (J). pap. 3.99 (978-0-448-44361-4(9) , Grosset & Dunlap) Penguin Group (USA) Inc.

Claybourne, Anna. Cheetah. 2003. (Natural World Ser.). (Illus.). 48p. (J). lib. bdg. 27.14 (978-0-7398-6056-4(9)) Raintree.

Cole, Melissa S. Cheetahs. 2001. (Wild Cats of the World Ser.). (Illus.). 24p. (J). (gr. 3-6). 22.45 (978-1-56711-449-2(0) , Blackbirch Pr., Inc.) Thomson Gale.

Cooper, Jason. Cheetahs. 2002. (Rourke Discovery Library). (Illus.). 24p. (J). lib. bdg. 20.64 (978-1-58952-401-9(2)) Rourke Publishing, LLC.

Denis-Huot, Christine & Denis-Huot, Michel. The Cheetah. 2004. (Animal Close-Ups Ser.). (Illus.). 28p. (J). pap. 6.95 (978-1-57091-626-7(8)) Charlesbridge Publishing, Inc.

Eckart, Edana. Cheetah. 2005. (Welcome Bks.). (Illus.). 24p. (ps-2). (J). pap. 4.95 (978-0-516-25163-9(5)); 18.00 (978-0-516-25052-6(3)) Scholastic Library Publishing. (Children's Pr.).

Estigarribia, Diana. Cheetahs. 2004. (Animals, Animals Ser.). (Illus.). 46p. (J). 25.64 (978-0-7614-1749-1(4) , Benchmark Bks.) Cavendish, Marshall Corp.

Feeney, Kathy, et al. Wild Animals: Explore the Fascinating Worlds Of. . . McGee, John F., illus. 2000. 192p. (J). pap. (978-1-55971-741-0(6) , NorthWord Bks. for Young Readers) T&N Children's Publishing.

Gentle, Victor & Perry, Janet. Cheetahs. 2002. (Big Cats Ser.). (Illus.). 24p. (J). (gr. 2 up). lib. bdg. 22.00 (978-0-8368-3024-8(5)) Stevens, Gareth Inc.

Grimbly, Shona. Cheetahs. 1999. (Endangered! Ser.). (Illus.). 32p. (J). (gr. 3-5). lib. bdg. 25.64 (978-0-7614-0319-7(1) , Benchmark Bks.) Cavendish, Marshall Corp.

El Guepardo: Individual Title Six-Packs. (On Deck en Espanol Ser.).Tr. of Cheetah. (SPA.). 24p. (gr. 4-5). 35.00 (978-0-7578-6435-3(X)) Rigby Education.

Hansen, Rosanna. Caring for Cheetahs: My African Adventure. 2007. (Illus.). 32p. (J). (gr. 3-5). 16.95 (978-1-59078-387-0(5)) Boyds Mills Pr.

Harkrader, Lisa. The Cheetah: A MyReportLinks. com Book. 2005. (Endangered & Threatened Animals Ser.). (Illus.). 48p. (J). lib. bdg. 25.26 (978-0-7660-5065-5(3) , MyReportLinks.com Bks.) Enslow Pubs., Inc.

Hopcraft, Xan. How It Was with Dooms: A True Story from Africa. Hopcraft, Carol Cawthra, illus. 2000. 64p. (J). (ps-3). pap. 9.99 (978-0-689-83539-1(6) , Aladdin) Simon & Schuster Children's Publishing.

—How It Was with Dooms: A True Story from Africa. 2000. (Illus.). (J). (978-0-606-17923-2(2)) Tandem Library Bks.

Lantier-Sampon, Patricia & MacPherson, Winnie. The Wonder of Cheetahs. McGee, John F., illus. 2001. (Animal Wonders Ser.). 48p. (J). (gr. 1 up). lib. bdg. 26.00 (978-0-8368-2763-7(5)) Stevens, Gareth Inc.

Latta, Jan. Charlie the Cheetah. 2006. (Illus.). 24p. (J). pap. ***(*978-0-8368-7774-8(8));*** lib. bdg. ***(*978-0-8368-7767-0(5))*** Stevens, Gareth Inc.

Levine, Michelle. Cheetahs. 2007. (Pull Ahead Books). (Illus.). 32p. (J). 22.60 (978-0-8225-5933-7(1) , Lerner Pubns.) Lerner Publishing Group.

—Speedy Cheetahs. 2006. (Pull Ahead Books). (Illus.). 32p. (J). pap. 5.95 (978-0-8225-6510-9(2) , First Avenue Editions) Lerner Publishing Group.

MacPherson, Winnie. Cheetah Magic for Kids. McGee, John F., illus. 1999. (Animal Magic for Kids Ser.). 48p. (J). (gr. 3 up). lib. bdg. 26.00 (978-0-8368-2631-9(0)) Stevens, Gareth Inc.

—Cheetahs for Kids. 1998. (Wildlife for Kids Ser.). (Illus.). 48p. (J). (gr. 4-7). pap. 6.95 (978-1-55971-665-9(7) , NorthWord Bks. for Young Readers) T&N Children's Publishing.

Markert, Jenny. Cheetahs. 2006. (New Naturebooks). (Illus.). 32p. (J). (gr. 1-5). 27.07 (978-1-59296-632-5(2)) Child's World, Inc.

Middleton, Don. Cheetahs. 1999. (PowerKids Readers Ser.). 24p. (J). (gr. k-4). lib. bdg. 18.75 (978-0-8239-5212-0(6) , PowerKids Pr.) Rosen Publishing Group, Inc., The.

Murray, Julie. Cheetahs. 2005. (Animal Kingdom Set Ii Ser.). (Illus.). 24p. (J). (gr. k-4). lib. bdg. 21.35 (978-1-59197-305-8(8)) ABDO Publishing Co.

Nagda, Ann Whitehead. Cheetah Math: Learning about Division from Baby Cheetahs. rev. ed. 2007. (Illus.). 32p. (J). (gr. 2-5). 16.95 ***(*978-0-8050-7645-5(X))*** Holt, Henry & Co.

Paige, Joy. The Cheetah: World's Fastest Land Animal. 2002. (Reading Power Ser.). (Illus.). 24p. (J). (gr. 1). lib. bdg. 17.25 (978-0-8239-5959-4(7) , PowerKids Pr.) Rosen Publishing Group, Inc., The.

—El Guepardo: El Animal Terrestre Mas Veloz Del Mundo. 2004. (Campeones Del Mundo Animal Ser.). (SPA & ENG., Illus.). 24p. (J). (gr. 3-6). lib. bdg. 17.25 (978-0-8239-6892-3(8) , Buenas Letra) Rosen Publishing Group, Inc., The.

Parker, Barbara Keevil. Cheetahs. 2005. (Early Bird Nature Bks.). (Illus.). 48p. (J). (gr. 2-4). lib. bdg. 25.26 (978-0-8225-3053-4(8)) Lerner Publishing Group.

Pohl, Kathleen. Cheetahs. 2007. (J). pap. ***(*978-0-8368-8225-4(3));*** 24p. lib. bdg. 19.93 ***(*978-0-8368-8218-6(0))*** Stevens, Gareth Inc. (Weekly Reader Early Learning Library).

—Cheetahs; Guepardos. 2007. (SPA & ENG.). (J). pap. ***(*978-0-8368-8239-1(3)*** , Weekly Reader Early Learning Library) Stevens, Gareth Inc.

—Cheetahs/Guepardos. 2007. (Animals I See at the Zoo/ Animales que Veo en el Zoologico Ser.). (SPA & ENG.). 24p. (J). (gr. k-2). lib. bdg. 19.93 ***(*978-0-8368-8232-2(6)*** , Weekly Reader Early Learning Library) Stevens, Gareth Inc.

Prudom, Sharla. Jambo! Cheetah. Prudom, Sharla, photos by. 2002. (Jambo! Ser.). (SWA & ENG., Illus.). 11p. (J). cd-rom 12.50 (978-1-931792-27-1(5)) E-Digital Bks., LLC.

Robinson, Claire & St. Pierre, Stephanie. Cheetahs. 2002. (In the Wild Ser.). (Illus.). 24p. (J). (gr. k-2). pap. 6.95 (978-1-58810-379-6(X) , 91099) Heinemann Library.

Schlaepfer, Gloria G. Cheetahs. 2001. (Animalways Ser.). (Illus.). 112p. (J). (gr. 5 up). lib. bdg. 31.36 (978-0-7614-1266-3(2) , Benchmark Bks.) Cavendish, Marshall Corp.

Squire, Ann O. Cheetahs. 2005. (True Bks.). (Illus.). (J). (gr. 3-5). 47p. pap. 6.95 (978-0-516-27932-9(7)); 48p. 25.00 (978-0-516-22792-4(0)) Scholastic Library Publishing. (Children's Pr.).

Stephanie, St Pierre. Cheetahs. 2001. (In the Wild Ser.). (Illus.). 24p. (J). (ps-3). lib. bdg. 21.36 (978-1-58810-106-8(1)) Heinemann Library.

Stille, Darlene R. Cheetahs. 2004. (First Reports). (Illus.). 48p. (J). (gr. 3 up). lib. bdg. 22.60 (978-0-7565-0576-9(0)) Compass Point Bks.

Sullivan, Jody. Cheetahs: Spotted Speedsters. 2002. (Wild World of Animals Ser.). (Illus.). 24p. (J). (gr. 1-3). lib. bdg. 18.60 (978-0-7368-1393-8(4) , Bridgestone Bks.) Capstone Pr., Inc.

Theodorou, Rod. Cheetah. (Animals in Danger Ser.). (Illus.). 32p. (J). (gr. k-2). 2002. pap. 6.95 (978-1-58810-363-5(3) , 91075); 2001. lib. bdg. 21.36 (978-1-57572-269-6(0)) Heinemann Library.

Vogel, Elizabeth. Cheetahs. 2002. (PowerKids Readers Ser.). (Illus.). 24p. (J). (gr. 1). lib. bdg. 16.00 (978-0-8239-6023-1(4) , PowerKids Pr.) Rosen Publishing Group, Inc., The.

Welsbacher, Anne. Cheetahs. 2000. (Wild Cats Ser.). (Illus.). 24p. (J). (gr. k-6). lib. bdg. 21.35 (978-1-57765-087-4(5) , Checkerboard Library) ABDO Publishing Co.

Wildlife Education, Ltd. Staff, et al. Cheetahs. Stuart, Walter et al, illus. 2000. (Zoobooks Ser.). (J). 24p. 15.95 (978-0-937934-77-7(1)); 18p. pap. 2.95 (978-0-937934-67-8(4)) Wildlife Education, Ltd.

Zumbusch, Amelie von. Cheetahs. 2007. (Safari Animals Ser.). (Illus.). 24p. (J). (gr. k-3). lib. bdg. 21.25 (978-1-4042-3614-1(7) , 1266066, PowerKids Pr.) Rosen Publishing Group, Inc., The.

—Cheetahs: World's Fastest Cats. 2007. (Dangerous Cats Ser.). (Illus.). 24p. (J). (gr. k-5). lib. bdg. 21.25 (978-1-4042-3630-1(9) , PowerKids Pr.) Rosen Publishing Group, Inc., The.

CHEMICAL ANALYSIS

see Chemistry, Analytic

CHEMICAL BONDS

Cesa, Irene, ed. Chemical Bonding, 24 vols., Vol. 5. 2004. (ChemTopic Labs Ser.: 5). (Illus.). (YA). per. 12.95 (978-1-877991-73-8(2)) Flinn Scientific, Inc.

Holt, Rinehart and Winston Staff. Chemical Bonding: Chapter Resources: Tennessee Edition. 3rd ed. 2003. (Holt Science & Technology Ser.). pap. 11.40 (978-0-03-069181-2(8)) Holt, Rinehart & Winston.

—Holt Science & Technology Chapter 13: Physical Science: Chemical Bonding. 5th ed. 2004. (Illus.). pap. 12.86 (978-0-03-030406-4(7)) Holt, Rinehart & Winston.

Video Education Australasia Pt, prod. Chemical Bonding: Inner Forces. (YA). cd-rom 149.95 (978-0-7365-1248-0(9)) Films Media Group.

CHEMICAL ELEMENTS

see also Periodic Law

Baldwin. Compounds, Mixtures, & Solutions. 2004. (Matter & Materials Ser.). (Illus.). pap. 8.50 (978-1-4109-0937-4(9)) Raintree.

—Mixtures, Compounds & Solutions 6 Packs. 2004. (Matter & Materials Ser.). (Illus.). pap. 45.90 (978-1-4109-0944-2(1)) Raintree.

—Nonmetals. 2004. (Matter & Materials Ser.). (Illus.). pap. 8.50 (978-1-4109-0939-8(5)) Raintree.

—Nonmetals 6-Pack. 2004. (Matter & Materials Ser.). (Illus.). pap. 45.90 (978-1-4109-0946-6(8)) Raintree.

Baldwin, Carol. Metals. 2004. (Material Matters (Freestyle Express) Ser.). (Illus.). 48p. (YA). (gr. 6-9). 22.00 (978-1-4109-0551-2(9)) Raintree.

—Mixtures, Compounds & Solutions. 2004. (Matter & Materials Ser.). (Illus.). 48p. 28.56 (978-1-4109-0550-5(0)) Raintree.

—Mixtures, Compounds & Solutions. 2005. (J). (978-1-4109-1677-8(4)); pap. (978-1-4109-1684-6(7)) Steck-Vaughn.

—Non-Metals. 2005. (Illus.). 48p. (J). (978-1-4109-1673-0(1)); pap. (978-1-4109-1680-8(4)) Steck-Vaughn.

—Nonmetals. 2004. (Matter & Materials Ser.). (Illus.). 48p. 28.56 (978-1-4109-0552-9(7)) Raintree.

Barber, Ian. Sorting the Elements: The Periodic Table at Work. 2008. (J). ***978-1-60044-607-8(8))** Rourke Publishing, LLC.

Blashfield, Jean F. Sparks of Life, 12 bks., Set. Incl. Calcium. (YA). 1999. lib. bdg. 27.12 (978-0-8172-5040-9(9)); Carbon. (YA). 1999. lib. bdg. 27.12 (978-0-8172-5041-6(7)); Chlorine. (J). 2001. lib. bdg. 27.12 (978-0-7398-4358-1(3)); Hydrogen. (YA). 1999. lib. bdg. 27.12 (978-0-8172-5038-6(7)); Iron & the Trace Elements. (J). 2001. lib. bdg. 27.12 (978-0-7398-4359-8(1)); Magnesium. (J). 2001. lib. bdg. 27.12 (978-0-7398-4360-4(5)); Nitrogen. (YA). 1999. lib. bdg. 27.12 (978-0-8172-5039-3(5)); Oxygen. (YA). 1999. lib. bdg. 27.12 (978-0-8172-5037-9(9)); Phosphorus. (J). 2001. lib. bdg. 27.12 (978-0-7398-3450-3(9)); Potassium. (J). 2001. lib. bdg. 27.12 (978-0-7398-3451-0(7)); Sodium. (YA). 1999. lib. bdg. 27.12 (978-0-8172-5042-3(5)); Sulfur. (J). 2001. lib. bdg. 27.12 (978-0-7398-3452-7(5)); 64p. (gr. 7-8). (Illus.). 2001. Set lib. bdg. 325.44 (978-0-7398-4362-8(1)) Raintree.

Brandolini, Anita J. Fizz, Bubble & Flash! Element Explorations & Atom Adventures for Hands-On Science Fun! 2004. (Kids Can Bks.). (Illus.). 128p. (J). pap. 12.95 (978-1-885593-83-2(X) , Williamson Bks.) Ideals Pubns.

Cooper, Chris. Arsenic. 2006. (Elements Ser.). (Illus.). 32p. (J). lib. bdg. 28.50 (978-0-7614-2203-7(X) , Benchmark Bks.) Cavendish, Marshall Corp.

Cooper, Sharon Katz & Compass Point Books Staff. The Periodic Table: Mapping the Elements. 2006. 48p. (J). (978-0-7565-1961-2(6)) Compass Point Bks.

Dingle, Adrian & Kingfisher Editors. The Periodic Table: Elements with Style! Basher, Simon, illus. 2007. 128p. (J). (gr. 5 up). pap. 8.95 (978-0-7534-6085-6(8) , Kingfisher) Houghton Mifflin Co. Trade & Reference Div.

The Elements, 4 bks., Gorup 8. Incl. Boron. Beatty, Richard. lib. bdg. (978-0-7614-1921-1(7)); Chromium. Lepora, Nathan. lib. bdg. (978-0-7614-1920-4(9)); Radioactive Elements. Jackson, Tom. lib. bdg. (978-0-7614-1923-5(3)); Zinc. Gray, Leon. lib. bdg. (978-0-7614-1922-8(5)); (Illus.). 32p. (J). (gr. 3-7). 2005. (978-0-7614-1919-8(5) , Benchmark Bks.) Cavendish, Marshall Corp.

The Elements - Group 2, 4 bks., Set. Incl. Calcium. Farndon, John. lib. bdg. 25.64 (978-0-7614-0888-8(6)); Gold. Angliss, Sarah. lib. bdg. 25.64 (978-0-7614-0887-1(8)); Hydrogen. Farndon, John. lib. bdg. 25.64 (978-0-7614-0886-4(X)); Magnesium. Uttley, Colin. lib. bdg. 25.64 (978-0-7614-0889-5(4)); 32p. (J). (gr. 3-5). (Illus.). 2000. 102.57 (978-0-7614-0885-7(1) , Benchmark Bks.) Cavendish, Marshall Corp.

The Elements - Group 7, 4 Bks, Set. 2004. (J). 102.57 (978-0-7614-1810-8(5)) Cavendish, Marshall Corp.

The Elements Group 9, 4 bks., Set. Incl. Arsenic. Cooper, Chris. 2006. lib. bdg. 28.50 (978-0-7614-2203-7(X)); Cobalt. Watt, Susan. 2007. lib. bdg. 28.50 ***978-0-7614-2200-6(5));** Lithium. Jackson, Tom. 2007. lib. bdg. 28.50 ***978-0-7614-2199-3(8));** Molybdenum. Lepora, Nathan. 2007. lib. bdg. 28.50 ***978-0-7614-2201-3(3));** (Illus.). 32p. (J). 2007. Set lib. bdg. 114.00 ***978-0-7614-2197-9(1)** , Benchmark Bks.) Cavendish, Marshall Corp.

Gareth Stevens Publishing Staff, contrib. by. Elements. 2003. (Discovery Channel School Science Ser.). (Illus.). 32p. (J). (gr. 5 up). lib. bdg. 24.67 (978-0-8368-3357-7(0)) Stevens, Gareth Inc.

Hasan, Heather. Fluorine. 2006. (Understanding the Elements of the Periodic Table Ser.). (Illus.). 48p. (YA). (gr. 5-8). lib. bdg. 26.50 (978-1-4042-1005-9(9)) Rosen Publishing Group, Inc., The.

Jackson, Tom. Lithium. 2007. (Elements Ser.). (Illus.). 32p. (J). lib. bdg. 28.50 ***978-0-7614-2199-3(8)** , Benchmark Bks.) Cavendish, Marshall Corp.

Jackson, Tom. Radioactive Elements. 2005. (Elements Ser.). (Illus.). 32p. (J). (gr. 3-7). lib. bdg. (978-0-7614-1923-5(3) , Benchmark Bks.) Cavendish, Marshall Corp.

Johanson, Paula. Cobalt. 2008. (J). ***978-1-4042-1410-1(0))** Rosen Publishing Group, Inc., The.

Kjelle, Marylou Morano. The Properties of Salts. 2007. (Library of Physical Science). (Illus.). 24p. (J). pap. (978-1-4042-2172-7(7)); lib. bdg. (978-1-4042-3425-3(X)) Rosen Publishing Group, Inc., The. (PowerKids Pr.).

Knapp, Brian J. Elements, 3 vols. Woodroffe, David & Hardy, David A., illus. 2001. (J). 168p. 129.00 (978-0-7172-5675-4(8)); Set. 840p. 299.00 (978-0-7172-5674-7(X)) Scholastic Library Publishing. (Grolier).

Kroutil Artists, creator. The Elements & Their Electron Configurations: Build the Atoms from Actinum to Zirconium. 2004. (Illus.). 144p. per. 24.95 (978-1-932689-01-3(X)) EDGEucation Publishing.

Lepora, Nathan. Molybdenum. 2007. (Elements Ser.). (Illus.). 32p. (J). lib. bdg. 28.50 ***978-0-7614-2201-3(3)** , Benchmark Bks.) Cavendish, Marshall Corp.

Lew, Kristi. Argon. 2008. ***978-1-4042-1409-5(7))** Rosen Publishing Group, Inc., The.

Miller, Ron. The Elements: What You Really Want to Know. 2006. (Worlds Beyond Ser.). (Illus.). 136p. (J). (gr. 8-12). 29.27 (978-0-7613-2794-3(0) , Millbrook Pr.) Lerner Publishing Group.

Morgan, Sally. From Greek Atoms to Quarks: Discovering Atoms. 2007. (Chain Reactions Ser.). (Illus.). 64p. (YA). (gr. 6-9). lib. bdg. 34.29 ***978-1-4034-9551-8(3))** Heinemann Library.

Oxlade, Chris. Elements & Compounds. 2nd ed. 2007. (Chemicals in Action Ser.). 48p. (J). (gr. 6-8). lib. bdg. 22.00 ***978-1-4329-0052-6(8))** Heinemann Library.

Roza, Greg. Calcium. 2007. (J). ***978-1-4042-1963-2(3))** Rosen Publishing Group, Inc., The.

Saucerman, Linda. Hydrogen: The Fuel for Life. 2005. (Interpreting the Periodic Table Ser.). (Illus.). 48p. (J). (gr. 5-8). lib. bdg. 26.50 (978-1-4042-0156-9(4)) Rosen Publishing Group, Inc., The.

Saunders, N. Aluminum & the Elements of Group 13. 2003. (Periodic Table Ser.). (Illus.). 64p. (J). lib. bdg. (978-1-4034-1661-2(3)) Heinemann Library.

—Calcium & the Alkaline Earth Metals. 2003. (Periodic Table Ser.). (Illus.). 64p. (J). pap. 8.95 (978-1-4034-3515-6(4)); lib. bdg. 28.50 (978-1-4034-0872-3(6)) Heinemann Library.

—Fluorine & the Halogens. 2003. (Periodic Table Ser.). (Illus.). 64p. (J). lib. bdg. (978-1-4034-1662-9(1)) Heinemann Library.

—Gold & the Elements of Groups. 2003. (Periodic Table Ser.). (Illus.). 64p. (J). lib. bdg. 28.50 (978-1-4034-0871-6(8)) Heinemann Library.

—Gold & the Elements of Groups 8 to 12. 2003. (Periodic Table Ser.). (Illus.). 64p. (J). pap. 8.95 (978-1-4034-3517-0(0)) Heinemann Library.

—Hydrogen. 2003. (Periodic Table Ser.). (Illus.). 64p. (J). lib. bdg. (978-1-4034-1663-6(X)) Heinemann Library.

—Nitrogen & the Elements of Group 15. 2003. (Periodic Table Ser.). (Illus.). 64p. (J). lib. bdg. (978-1-4034-1664-3(8)) Heinemann Library.

—Tungsten & the Elements of Groups 3 to 7. 2003. (Periodic Table Ser.). (Illus.). 64p. (J). pap. 8.95 (978-1-4034-3518-7(9)); lib. bdg. 28.50 (978-1-4034-0876-1(9)) Heinemann Library.

—Uranium & the Rare Earth Metals. 2003. (Periodic Table Ser.). (Illus.). 64p. (J). lib. bdg. (978-1-4034-1666-7(4)) Heinemann Library.

Saunders, Nigel. Sodium & the Alkali Metals. 2003. (Periodic Table Ser.). (Illus.). 64p. (J). lib. bdg. (978-1-4034-1665-0(6)) Heinemann Library.

Slade, Suzanne. Elements & the Periodic Table. 2007. (Library of Physical Sciences). (Illus.). 24p. (J). (978-1-4042-2355-4(X)); pap. (978-1-4042-2165-9(4)); (gr. 3-6). lib. bdg. 21.25 (978-1-4042-3418-5(7)) Rosen Publishing Group, Inc., The. (PowerKids Pr.).

—The Elements Common to Most Living Organisms. 2007. (Library of Physical Sciences). (J). (978-1-4042-2361-5(4)); (Illus.). 24p. pap. (978-1-4042-2171-0(9)); (Illus.). 24p. lib. bdg. (978-1-4042-3424-6(1)) Rosen Publishing Group, Inc., The. (PowerKids Pr.).

Solway, Andrew. A History of Super Science: Atoms & Elements. 2005. (Illus.). 32p. (J). (978-1-4109-1951-9(X)); (gr. 3-5). lib. bdg. 28.21 (978-1-4109-1920-5(X)) Steck-Vaughn.

Sparks of Life: Includes: Phosphorus; Potassium; Sulfur, 3 bks., Set. 2001. (Illus.). (J). (gr. 4-7). lib. bdg. 81.36 (978-0-7398-3453-4(3)) Raintree.

Spilsbury, Louise & Spilsbury, Richard. Elements & Compounds. 2007. (Illus.). 32p. (J). (978-1-4034-9343-9(X)); lib. bdg. (978-1-4034-9338-5(3)) Heinemann Library.

St. Pierre, Stephanie. Elements & Compounds. 2002. (Chemicals in Action Ser.). (Illus.). 48p. (J). (gr. 6-8). lib. bdg. 25.64 (978-1-58810-196-9(7)) Heinemann Library.

Strom, Laura Layton. Grab a Seat at the Periodic Table: A Chemical Mystery. 2007. (Shockwave: Earth & Physical Science Ser.). (Illus.). 36p. (J). (gr. 4-6). lib. bdg. 25.00 ***978-0-531-17793-8(9)** , Children's Pr.) Scholastic Library Publishing.

Swertka, Albert. The Elements: A Mini Guide to the Periodic Table. 2007. 128p. 4.95 (978-0-7624-2985-1(2) , Running Pr. Miniature Editions) Running Pr. Bk. Pubs.

Tocci, Salvatore. Chlorine. (J). 2006. 48p. (gr. 3-5). pap. 6.95 (978-0-516-25574-3(6)); 2005. (Illus.). 47p. (ps-7). 25.00 (978-0-516-23698-8(9)) Scholastic Library Publishing. (Children's Pr.).

—Mercury. 2006. 48p. (J). (gr. 3-5). pap. 6.95 (978-0-516-25576-7(2) , Children's Pr.) Scholastic Library Publishing.

—The Periodic Table. (True Bks.). (J). 2005. (Illus.). 48p. (gr. 3-5). pap. 6.95 (978-0-516-27852-0(5)); 2004. 25.00 (978-0-516-22833-4(1)) Scholastic Library Publishing. (Children's Pr.).

—Silicon. (J). 2006. 48p. (gr. 3-5). pap. 6.95 (978-0-516-25577-4(0)); 2005. (Illus.). 47p. (ps-7). 25.00 (978-0-516-23701-5(2)) Scholastic Library Publishing. (Children's Pr.).

—Sodium. (J). 2006. 48p. (gr. 3-5). pap. 6.95 (978-0-516-25578-1(9)); 2005. (Illus.). 47p. (ps-7). 25.00 (978-0-516-23702-2(0)) Scholastic Library Publishing. (Children's Pr.).

—Zinc. 2006. 48p. (J). (gr. 3-5). pap. 6.95 (978-0-516-25579-8(7) , Children's Pr.) Scholastic Library Publishing.

Watt, Susan. Cobalt. 2007. (Elements Ser.). (Illus.). 32p. (J). lib. bdg. 28.50 ***978-0-7614-2200-6(5)** , Benchmark Bks.) Cavendish, Marshall Corp.

—Zirconium. 2007. (Elements Ser.). 32p. (J). lib. bdg. 28.50 ***978-0-7614-2688-2(4)** , Benchmark Bks.) Cavendish, Marshall Corp.

Zannos, Susan. Dmitri Mendeleyev & the Periodic Table. 2004. (Uncharted, Unexplored, & Unexplained Ser.). (Illus.). 48p. (J). (gr. 4-8). lib. bdg. 29.95 (978-1-58415-267-5(2)) Mitchell Lane Pubs., Inc.

CHEMICAL INDUSTRIES

Here are entered works about industries based mainly on chemical processes. Works on the manufacture of chemicals as such are entered under Chemicals.

see also names of industries, e.g. Paper Making and Trade; etc.

Bryan, Nichol. Bhopal: Chemical Plant Accident. 2003. (Environmental Disasters Ser.). (Illus.). 48p. (gr. 5 up). (YA). lib. bdg. 30.00 (978-0-8368-5503-6(5)); (J). pap. 11.95 (978-0-8368-5510-4(8)) Stevens, Gareth Inc. (World Almanac Library).

—Love Canal: Pollution Crisis. 2003. (Environmental Disasters Ser.). (Illus.). 48p. (YA). (gr. 5 up). lib. bdg. 30.00 (978-0-8368-5508-1(6) , World Almanac Library) Stevens, Gareth Inc.

Riddle, John. Bhopal. 2002. (Great Disasters, Reforms & Ramifications Ser.). 112p. (J). 30.00 (978-0-7910-6741-3(6) , Chelsea Hse.) Facts On File, Inc.

CHEMICALS

see also Chemical Industries

Baldwin, Carol. Mixtures, Compounds & Solutions. 2004. (Matter & Materials Ser.). (Illus.). 48p. 28.56 (978-1-4109-0550-5(0)) Raintree.

—Mixtures, Compounds & Solutions. 2005. (J). (978-1-4109-1677-8(4)); pap. (978-1-4109-1684-6(7)) Steck-Vaughn.

Kain, Kathleen E. Surprise Explosions: The Science Spiders(TM) Make Chemicals React. 1999. (Illus.). 32p. (J). (gr. k-3). pap. 5.95 (978-1-892221-02-5(0) , RW0562) Ranch Works.

Kerrigan, Michael. Biological & Germ Warfare Protection. 2002. (Rescue & Prevention Ser.). (Illus.). 96p. (J). (gr. 7 up). lib. bdg. (978-1-59084-411-3(4)) Mason Crest Pubs.

Maddocks, Steven. Chemical & Biological Warfare. 2003. (Face the Facts Ser.). (J). lib. bdg. 28.56 (978-0-7398-6847-8(0)) Raintree.

Oxlade, Chris. Chemicals in Action, 6 bks., Set. (gr. 6-8). 2002. (YA). lib. bdg. 153.84 (978-1-58810-200-3(9)); 2nd ed. 2007. lib. bdg. 132.00 ***978-1-4329-0056-4(0))** Heinemann Library.

Oxlade, Chris. Elements & Compounds. 2nd ed. 2007. (Chemicals in Action Ser.). 48p. (J). (gr. 6-8). lib. bdg. 22.00 ***978-1-4329-0052-6(8))** Heinemann Library.

Richards, Jon. Chemicals & Reactions. 2008. (J). lib. bdg. ***978-1-4042-3906-7(5))** Rosen Publishing Group, Inc., The.

Snedden, Robert. Changing Materials. 2002. (Material World Ser.). (Illus.). 32p. (YA). (gr. 6-8). lib. bdg. 24.22 (978-1-58810-069-6(3)) Heinemann Library.

Trueit, Trudi Strain. Gunpowder. 2005. (Inventions That Shaped the World Ser.). (Illus.). 80p. (J). 30.50 (978-0-531-12371-3(5) , Watts, Franklin) Scholastic Library Publishing.

Whyman, Kathryn. Everyday Chemicals. Nevett, Louise, illus. 2004. (J). lib. bdg. (978-1-932799-23-1(0)) Stargazer Bks.

CHEMISTRY

see also Biochemistry; Color; Explosives; Fire; Pharmacy; Poisons

also headings beginning with the word Chemical

Ace Academics, ed. Chemistry: A Whole Course in a Box! 2007. (Exambusters Ser.). 384p. (gr. 7 up). 12.95 (978-1-881374-93-0(9) , Exambusters) Ace Academics, Inc.

Acs & American Chemical Society Staff. Activities Workbook for Chemistry in the Community. 4th ed. 2001. 243p. pap. 12.95 (978-0-7167-3920-3(8)) Freeman, W. H. & Co.

Active Chemistry. 2002. tchr. ed., per. (978-1-58591-114-1(3)); stu. ed., bds. (978-1-58591-113-4(5)) It's About Time, Herff Jones Education Diiv.

Allgemeine Chemie. 2nd ed. (Duden Abiturhilfen Ser.). (GER.). 112p. (YA). (gr. 12-13). (978-3-411-04622-5(8)) Bibliographisches Institut & F. A. Brockhaus AG DEU. *Dist:* International Bk. Import Service, Inc.

Baldwin. Acids & Bases, 6, Pack. 2004. (Matter & Materials Ser.). (Illus.). pap. 45.90 (978-1-4109-0942-8(5)) Raintree.

—Chemical Reactions. 2004. (Matter & Materials Ser.). (Illus.). pap. 8.50 (978-1-4109-0936-7(0)) Raintree.

—Chemical Reactions 6-Pack. 2004. (Matter & Materials Ser.). pap. 45.90 (978-1-4109-0943-5(3)) Raintree.

Baldwin, Carol. Acids & Bases. 2004. (Matter & Materials Ser.). (Illus.). 48p. (gr. 6-8). (J). pap. 8.50 (978-1-4109-0935-0(2)); (YA). 22.00 (978-1-4109-0548-2(9)) Raintree.

—Acids & Bases. 2005. (Illus.). 48p. (J). (gr. 4-6). lib. bdg. 31.43 (978-1-4109-1676-1(6)) Steck-Vaughn.

—Acids & Bases. 2005. (Illus.). 48p. (J). (978-1-4109-1683-9(9)) Steck-Vaughn.

—Chemical Reactions. 2004. (Matter & Materials Ser.). (Illus.). 48p. 28.56 (978-1-4109-0549-9(7)) Raintree.

—Chemical Reactions. 2005. (Illus.). 48p. (J). (978-1-4109-1681-5(2)); (978-1-4109-1674-7(X)) Steck-Vaughn.

Barber, Jacqueline. Chemical Reactions. Bergman, Lincoln & Fairwell, Kay, eds. Baker, Lisa H. & Craig, Rose, illus. Barber, Jacqueline et al, photos by. rev. ed. 1998. (Great Explorations in Math & Science Ser.). 40p. (YA). (gr. 6-8). pap. 9.00 (978-0-924886-06-5(4) , GEMS) Univ. of California, Berkeley, Lawrence Hall of Science.

—Of Cabbages & Chemistry. Bergman, Lincoln & Fairwell, Kay, eds. Bevilacqua, Carol & Klofkorn, Lisa, illus. Hoyt, Richard, photos by. rev. ed. 2003. (Great Explorations in Math & Science Ser.). 80p. (J). (gr. 4-8). pap., tchr. ed. 10.50 (978-0-924886-28-7(5) , GEMS) Univ. of California, Berkeley, Lawrence Hall of Science.

Bauldock, Gerald, Sr., et al. Kids for Chemistry. 2002. (YA). pap. 24.95 net. (978-0-9621728-1-6(2)) B-Dock Pr.

Baxter, Roberta. Chemical Reaction. 2004. (KidHaven Science Library). (Illus.). 48p. (J). (gr. 4-7). 26.20 (978-0-7377-2072-3(7)) Thomson Gale.

Beatty, Richard. Boron. 2005. (Elements Ser.). (Illus.). 32p. (J). (gr. 3-7). lib. bdg. (978-0-7614-1921-1(7) , Benchmark Bks.) Cavendish, Marshall Corp.

Beech, Linda Ward. The Magic School Bus Gets Baked in a Cake: A Book about Kitchen Chemistry. Duchesne, Lucie, tr. from ENG. Degen, Bruce, illus. (Magic School Bus Ser.). (FRE.). 32p. (J). (gr. 1-4). pap. 5.99 (978-0-590-24660-6(7)) Scholastic, Inc.

Bell, Suzanne. Drugs, Poisons, & Chemistry. 2008. (Essentials of Forensic Science Ser.). 176p. (gr. 6-12). 35.00 (978-0-8160-5510-4(6)) Facts On File, Inc.

Benchmark Education Staff, compiled by. Chemistry. 2006. spiral bd. 159.00 ***978-1-4108-7134-3(7))** Benchmark Education Co.

Bergethon, Peter R. Atoms & Elements Pt. I: An Introduction to Chemistry, Student Science Journal. 2000. (Illus.). 58p. (YA). (gr. 5-8). pap. (978-1-58447-055-7(0)) Symmetry Learning Systems.

Blashfield, Jean F. Chlorine. 2001. (Sparks of Life Ser.). (Illus.). 64p. (J). (gr. 7-8). lib. bdg. 27.12 (978-0-7398-4358-1(3)) Raintree.

—Magnesium. 2001. (Sparks of Life Ser.). (Illus.). 64p. (J). (gr. 7-8). lib. bdg. 27.12 (978-0-7398-4360-4(5)) Raintree.

—Phosphorus. 2001. (Sparks of Life Ser.). (Illus.). 64p. (J). (gr. 7-8). lib. bdg. 27.12 (978-0-7398-3450-3(9)) Raintree.

—Potassium. 2001. (Sparks of Life Ser.). (Illus.). 64p. (J). (gr. 7-8). lib. bdg. 27.12 (978-0-7398-3451-0(7)) Raintree.

Brian, Sarah Jane. Forensics: Chemistry & Crime. 2006. (Navigators Ser.). (J). pap. 42.00 ***978-1-4108-6234-1(8))** Benchmark Education Co.

Cambridge Educational, prod. Chemical Changes Hybrid Lb. (YA). cd-rom 222.50 (978-0-7365-4341-5(4)) Films Media Group.

—Patterns in Chemistry Hyb Lb. (YA). cd-rom 222.50 (978-0-7365-4355-2(4)) Films Media Group.

Carberry, Edward. General Chemistry Laboratory Manual, 6th ed. 2002. (Illus.). 158p. (C). 38.95 (978-1-888833-07-2(6)) MGLS, Inc.

Cesa, Irene, ed. Chemical Bonding, 24 vols., Vol. 5. 2004. (ChemTopic Labs Ser.: 5). (Illus.). (YA). per. 12.95 (978-1-877991-73-8(2)) Flinn Scientific, Inc.

—Chemical Reactions. 2004. (ChemTopic Labs Ser.: 6). (YA). per. 12.95 (978-1-877991-74-5(0)) Flinn Scientific, Inc.

—Solubility & Solutions. 2004. (ChemTopic Labs Ser.: No. 12). (YA). per. 12.95 (978-1-877991-80-6(5)) Flinn Scientific, Inc.

A Chef's Laboratory: Individual Title Six-Packs. (Bookweb Ser.). 32p. (gr. 6 up). 34.00 (978-0-7578-0912-5(X)) Rigby Education.

Chemie. (Duden-Schuelerduden Ser.). (GER., Illus.). 442p. (YA). (978-3-411-05383-4(6)) Bibliographisches Institut & F. A. Brockhaus AG DEU. *Dist:* International Bk. Import Service, Inc.

Chemist. (Science Ser.). (J). incl. audio NewSound, LLC.

Cobb, Allan B. Cadmium. 2007. (Elements Ser.). 32p. (J). lib. bdg. 28.50 (***978-0-7614-2686-8(8)***, Benchmark Bks.) Cavendish, Marshall Corp.

Cole, Joanna. The Magic School Bus Meets the Rot Squad: A Book about Decomposition. 2002. (Magic School Bus Ser.). (J). 11.45 (978-0-7587-6507-9(X)) Book Wholesalers, Inc.

Cooke, Andy & Martin, Jean, eds. Spectrum Chemistry Class. 2004. (Spectrum Key Stage 3 Science Ser.). (Illus.). 182p. pap. 15.00 (978-0-521-54922-6(1)) Cambridge Univ. Pr.

Coulter, Shirley. Chemistry. Date not set. (Science Fair Ser.). 48p. (J). (gr. 3-6). lib. bdg. 22.60 (978-1-57103-427-4(7)) Rourke Publishing, LLC.

Cullen, Katherine. Chemistry: The People Behind the Science. 2005. (Pioneers in Science Ser.). (Illus.). 192p. (gr. 6-12). 29.95 (978-0-8160-5462-6(2)) Facts On File, Inc.

Demmin, Peter E. Multiple-Choice & Free-Response Questions in Preparation for the AP Chemistry Examination. 4th ed. 2000. (Illus.). 225p. (J). (gr. 9-12). pap. 19.95 (978-1-878621-59-7(9)) D&S Marketing Systems, Inc.

—Students Solutions Manual to Accompany Multiple-Choice & Free-Response Questions in Preparation for the AP Chemistry Examination. 4th ed. 2000. (J). (gr. 9-12). pap. 14.95 (978-1-878621-60-3(2)) D&S Marketing Systems, Inc.

Diagram Group. The Facts on File Chemistry Handbook. 2nd rev. ed. 2006. (Science Handbook Ser.). 272p. (gr. 6-12). 35.00 (978-0-8160-5878-5(4)) Facts On File, Inc.

Diagram Group Staff. Chemistry: An Illustrated Guide to Science. 2006. (Science Visual Resources Ser.). (Illus.). 208p. (YA). (gr. 6-12). 49.50 (978-0-8160-6163-1(7)) Facts On File, Inc.

Discovering French, Nouveau! Blanc: Activites Pour Tous, Level 2. 2003. (978-0-618-29912-6(2)) McDougal Littell Inc.

DK Publishing Staff. It's Elementary! Put the Crackle in Chemistry. 2007. 96p. (J). (gr. 2-5). 15.99 (978-0-7566-2666-2(8)) Dorling Kindersley Publishing, Inc.

Earth Science, Physics, Chemistry for 21st Century Kit. 2000. bds. (978-1-58591-121-9(6)) It's About Time, Herff Jones Education Diiv.

Earth Science, Physics, Chemistry for the 21st Century. 2002. tchr. ed., per. (978-1-58591-120-2(8)); stu. ed., bds. (978-1-58591-119-6(4)) It's About Time, Herff Jones Education Diiv.

Ebbing. Essential General Chemistry. 2nd ed. 2005. (YA). stu. ed. 7.96 incl. cd-rom (978-0-618-57733-0(5) , 314495) Houghton Mifflin College Div.

—Student Solutions Manual: Used with ... Ebbing-General Chemistry. 8th ed. 2004. (YA). stu. ed. 58.36 (978-0-618-39945-1(3) , 314454) Houghton Mifflin College Div.

—Study Guide: Used with ... Ebbing-General Chemistry. 8th ed. 2004. (YA). stu. ed. 55.56 (978-0-618-39943-7(7) , 314452) Houghton Mifflin College Div.

Ebbing, Darrell & Gammon, Steven D. General Chemistry: Text with Media Guide for Students. 8th ed. 2004. 1062p. (YA). 171.96 incl. cd-rom (978-0-618-44796-1(2) , 314466) Houghton Mifflin College Div.

The Elements - Group 1, 4 bks., Set. Incl. Carbon. Sparrow, Giles. (ps-17). 1999. lib. bdg. 25.64 (978-0-7614-0878-9(9)); Iron. Sparrow, Giles. (gr. 3-5). 1998. lib. bdg. 25.64 (978-0-7614-0880-2(0)); Nitrogen. Farndon, John. (gr. 3-5). 1999. lib. bdg. 25.64 (978-0-7614-0877-2(0)); Oxygen. Farndon, John. (gr. 3-5). 1999. lib. bdg. 25.64 (978-0-7614-0879-6(7)); 32p. (J). (Illus.). 1999. Set lib. bdg. 102.57 (978-0-7614-0876-5(2) , Benchmark Bks.) Cavendish, Marshall Corp.

Farndon, John. Calcium. 2000. (Elements Ser.). (Illus.). 32p. (J). (gr. 3-5). lib. bdg. 25.64 (978-0-7614-0888-6(6) , Benchmark Bks.) Cavendish, Marshall Corp.

Fluids & Solutions Chemistry: Integrated Physics & Chemistry /Algebra I Insturctional Unit. 2003. (Region IV ESC Resources for Mathematics & Science Ser.). stu. ed., per. (978-1-932524-71-0(1)) Region IV Education Service Ctr.

Gareth Stevens Publishing Staff, contrib. by. Chemistry. 2003. (Discovery Channel School Science Ser.). (Illus.). 32p. (J). (gr. 5 up). lib. bdg. 24.67 (978-0-8368-3355-3(4)) Stevens, Gareth Inc.

Gore, Bryson. Chemistry: Flames Are Stored Sunlight. 2005. (Illus.). 32p. (J). (gr. 3-7). lib. bdg. 27.10 (978-1-59604-066-3(1)) Stargazer Bks.

Gray, Leon. Iodine. 2004. (J). 25.64 (978-0-7614-1812-2(1) , Benchmark Bks.) Cavendish, Marshall Corp.

—Zinc. 2005. (Elements Ser.). (Illus.). 32p. (J). (gr. 3-7). lib. bdg. (978-0-7614-1922-8(5) , Benchmark Bks.) Cavendish, Marshall Corp.

Gribben, Peter & Cassidy, Marta. Cambridge HSC Chemistry Study Guide. 2003. (Cambridge HSC Study Guides). (Illus.). 256p. pap. 10.95 (978-0-521-54001-8(1)) Cambridge Univ. Pr.

Griffith, Dave. Chemistry. 1999. (YA). pap., stu. ed., wbk. ed. 15.00 (978-1-886998-03-2(5)) Pasco Scientific.

Grundlagen der Chemie. (Duden-Schuelerhilfen Ser.). (GER.). 109p. (YA). (gr. 8-10). (978-3-411-05931-7(1)) Bibliographisches Institut & F. A. Brockhaus AG DEU. *Dist:* International Bk. Import Service, Inc.

Handwerker, Mark J. Ready-to-Use Chemistry Activities for Grades 5-12. 2000. (Secondary Science Curriculum Activities Library: Vol. 2). (Illus.). 256p. (J). pap. 27.50 (978-0-13-029108-0(0) , Addison Wesley) Benjamin-Cummings Publishing Co.

Haugen, David M. Hydrogen. 2006. (Fueling the Future Ser.). (Illus.). 144p. (gr. 10-12). 34.95 (978-0-7377-3592-5(9) , Greenhaven Pr., Inc.) Thomson Gale.

Hixson, Bryce. Le Boom Du Jour. Hixson, Bryce, illus. 2002. (Illus.). (J). per. 14.95 (978-0-9660965-7-6(6)) Loose In The Lab.

Holman, John S. & Stone, Phil. Chemistry. 2nd ed. 2001. (Nelson Science Ser.). (Illus.). 314p. (YA). pap., stu. ed. 36.50 (978-0-7487-6239-2(6)) Nelson Thornes Ltd. GBR. *Dist:* Trans-Atlantic Pubns., Inc.

Holt, Rinehart and Winston Staff. Chemical Compounds: Chapter Resources: Tennessee Edition. 3rd ed. 2003. (Holt Science & Technology Ser.). pap. 11.40 (978-0-03-069183-6(4)) Holt, Rinehart & Winston.

—Chemical Reaction: Chapter Resources: Tennessee Edition. 3rd ed. 2003. (Holt Science & Technology Ser.). pap. 11.40 (978-0-03-069182-9(6)) Holt, Rinehart & Winston.

—Chemistry: Chapter Resource File. 6th ed. 2006. No. 1. pap. 11.73 (978-0-03-041432-9(6)); No. 2. pap. 11.73 (978-0-03-041433-6(4)); No. 3. pap. 11.73 (978-0-03-041434-3(2)); No. 4. pap. 11.73 (978-0-03-041437-4(7)); No. 5. pap. 11.73 (978-0-03-041438-1(5)); No. 6. pap. 11.73 (978-0-03-041439-8(3)); No. 7. pap. 11.73 (978-0-03-041442-8(3)); No. 8. pap. 11.73 (978-0-03-041443-5(1)); No. 9. pap. 11.73 (978-0-03-041444-2(X)); No. 10. pap. 11.73 (978-0-03-041447-3(4)); No. 11. pap. 11.73 (978-0-03-041448-0(2)); No. 12. pap. 11.73 (978-0-03-041449-7(0)); No. 13. pap. 11.73 (978-0-03-041452-7(0)); No. 14. pap. 11.73 (978-0-03-041453-4(9)); No. 15. pap. 11.73 (978-0-03-041454-1(7)); No. 16. pap. 11.73 (978-0-03-041457-2(1)); No. 17. pap. 11.73 (978-0-03-041458-9(X)); No. 18. pap. 11.73 (978-0-03-041459-6(8)); No. 19. pap. 11.73 (978-0-03-041462-6(8)); No. 20. pap. 11.73 (978-0-03-041463-3(6)) Harcourt Schl. Pubs.

—Holt Chemistry: Enhanced Online Edition. 4th ed. 2004. 17.26 (978-0-03-037154-7(6)) Holt, Rinehart & Winston.

—Holt Chemistry: Strategies & Practice Answer Key. 4th ed. 2004. (Illus.). pap. 6.00 (978-0-03-020479-1(8)) Holt, Rinehart & Winston.

—Holt Chemistry: Strategies & Practice for Reading: New York Edition. 5th ed. Date not set. (Chemistry Ser.). pap. 12.80 (978-0-03-074139-5(4)) Holt, Rinehart & Winston.

—Holt Chemistry Chptr. 5: Ionic Compounds. 4th ed. Date not set. pap. 11.20 (978-0-03-068127-1(8)) Holt, Rinehart & Winston.

—Holt Chemistry Chptr. 6: Covalent Bonds. 4th ed. Date not set. pap. 11.20 (978-0-03-068128-8(6)) Holt, Rinehart & Winston.

—Holt Chemistry Chptr. 7: Molecules/Chemical Compositions. 4th ed. Date not set. pap. 11.20 (978-0-03-068131-8(6)) Holt, Rinehart & Winston.

—Holt Chemistry Chptr. 8: Chemical Equations/Reactions. 4th ed. Date not set. pap. 11.20 (978-0-03-068132-5(4)) Holt, Rinehart & Winston.

—Holt Chemistry Chptr. 10: Causes of Change. 4th ed. Date not set. pap. 11.20 (978-0-03-068134-9(0)) Holt, Rinehart & Winston.

—Holt Chemistry Chptr. 11: States of Matter & Forces. 4th ed. Date not set. pap. 11.20 (978-0-03-068136-3(7)) Holt, Rinehart & Winston.

—Holt Chemistry Chptr. 13: Solutions. 4th ed. Date not set. pap. 11.20 (978-0-03-068138-7(3)) Holt, Rinehart & Winston.

—Holt Chemistry Chptr. 14: Chemical Equilibrium. 4th ed. Date not set. pap. 11.20 (978-0-03-068139-4(1)) Holt, Rinehart & Winston.

—Holt Chemistry Chptr. 15: Acids & Bases. 4th ed. Date not set. pap. 11.20 (978-0-03-068141-7(3)) Holt, Rinehart & Winston.

—Holt Chemistry Chptr. 16: Reaction Rates. 4th ed. Date not set. pap. 11.20 (978-0-03-068142-4(1)) Holt, Rinehart & Winston.

—Holt Chemistry Chptr. 17: Oxidation/Reduction. 4th ed. Date not set. pap. 11.20 (978-0-03-068143-1(X)) Holt, Rinehart & Winston.

—Holt Chemistry Chptr. 18: Nuclear Chemistry. 4th ed. Date not set. pap. 11.20 (978-0-03-068144-8(8)) Holt, Rinehart & Winston.

—Holt Chemistry 2 Chptr. 3: Atoms & Molecules. 4th ed. Date not set. pap. 11.20 (978-0-03-068124-0(3)) Holt, Rinehart & Winston.

—Holt Chemistry 2 Chptr. 4: The Periodic Table. 4th ed. Date not set. pap. 11.20 (978-0-03-068126-4(X)) Holt, Rinehart & Winston.

—Holt Chemistry 2 Chptr. 9: Stoichiometry. 4th ed. Date not set. pap. 11.20 (978-0-03-068133-2(2)) Holt, Rinehart & Winston.

—Holt Science & Technology Chapter 14: Physical Science: Chemical Reactions. 5th ed. 2004. (Illus.). pap. 12.86 (978-0-03-030411-8(3)) Holt, Rinehart & Winston.

—Holt Science & Technology Chapter 15: Physical Science: Chemical Compounds. 5th ed. 2004. (Illus.). pap. 12.86 (978-0-03-030412-5(1)) Holt, Rinehart & Winston.

—Modern Chemistry: Strategies & Practice: Readings in Science - Louisiana Edition. 2nd ed. 2002. pap. 13.86 (978-0-03-071232-6(7)) Holt, Rinehart & Winston.

—Standard Test Preparation Workbook: South Carolina Edition - Chemistry. 2nd ed. 2002. (J). pap. 11.00 (978-0-03-069038-9(2)) Holt, Rinehart & Winston.

Husting, Chad. Chemistry Student Labs & Activities. 2003. (Illus.). stu. ed., per., wbk. ed. (978-1-931680-32-5(9) , Expert Systems for Teachers) Teaching Point, Inc.

Integrated Physics & Chemistry, Chapter 1, Activities. 2005. (Illus.). 22p. (YA). pap. 5.00 (978-1-59476-173-7(6)) Paradigm Accelerated Curriculum.

Integrated Physics & Chemistry Chapter 1, Text. 2005. Orig. Title: (Key Topics. (Illus.). 34p. (YA). pap. 7.00 (978-1-59476-161-4(2)) Paradigm Accelerated Curriculum.

Integrated Physics & Chemistry, Chapter 10, Activities. 2005. (Illus.). 32p. (YA). pap. 5.00 (978-1-59476-182-9(5)) Paradigm Accelerated Curriculum.

Integrated Physics & Chemistry, Chapter 10, Text. 2005. (Illus.). 68p. (YA). pap. 7.00 (978-1-59476-170-6(1)) Paradigm Accelerated Curriculum.

Integrated Physics & Chemistry, Chapter 11, Activities. 2005. (Illus.). 40p. (YA). pap. 5.00 (978-1-59476-183-6(3)) Paradigm Accelerated Curriculum.

Integrated Physics & Chemistry, Chapter 11, Text. 2005. (Illus.). 64p. (YA). pap. 7.00 (978-1-59476-171-3(X)) Paradigm Accelerated Curriculum.

Integrated Physics & Chemistry, Chapter 12, Activities. 2005. (Illus.). 32p. (YA). pap. 5.00 (978-1-59476-184-3(1)) Paradigm Accelerated Curriculum.

Integrated Physics & Chemistry, Chapter 12, Text. 2005. (Illus.). 66p. (YA). pap. 7.00 (978-1-59476-172-0(8)) Paradigm Accelerated Curriculum.

Integrated Physics & Chemistry, Chapter 2, Activities. 2005. (Illus.). 42p. (YA). pap. 5.00 (978-1-59476-174-4(4)) Paradigm Accelerated Curriculum.

Integrated Physics & Chemistry, Chapter 2, Text. 2005. (Illus.). 66p. (YA). pap. 7.00 (978-1-59476-162-1(0)) Paradigm Accelerated Curriculum.

Integrated Physics & Chemistry, Chapter 3 Activities. 2005. (Illus.). 32p. (YA). pap. 5.00 (978-1-59476-175-1(2)) Paradigm Accelerated Curriculum.

Integrated Physics & Chemistry, Chapter 3, Text. 2005. (Illus.). 66p. (YA). pap. 7.00 (978-1-59476-163-8(9)) Paradigm Accelerated Curriculum.

Integrated Physics & Chemistry, Chapter 4, Text. 2005. (Illus.). 64p. (YA). pap. 7.00 (978-1-59476-164-5(7)) Paradigm Accelerated Curriculum.

Integrated Physics & Chemistry, Chapter 5, Activities. 2005. (Illus.). 32p. (YA). pap. 5.00 (978-1-59476-177-5(9)) Paradigm Accelerated Curriculum.

Integrated Physics & Chemistry, Chapter 5, Text. 2005. (Illus.). 64p. (YA). pap. 7.00 (978-1-59476-165-2(5)) Paradigm Accelerated Curriculum.

Integrated Physics & Chemistry, Chapter 6, Activities. 2005. (Illus.). 32p. (YA). pap. 5.00 (978-1-59476-178-2(7)) Paradigm Accelerated Curriculum.

Integrated Physics & Chemistry, Chapter 6, Text. 2005. (Illus.). 64p. (YA). pap. 7.00 (978-1-59476-166-9(3)) Paradigm Accelerated Curriculum.

Integrated Physics & Chemistry, Chapter 7, Activities. 2005. (Illus.). 32p. (YA). pap. 5.00 (978-1-59476-179-9(5)) Paradigm Accelerated Curriculum.

Integrated Physics & Chemistry, Chapter 7, Text. 2005. (Illus.). 66p. (YA). pap. 7.00 (978-1-59476-167-6(1)) Paradigm Accelerated Curriculum.

Integrated Physics & Chemistry, Chapter 8, Activities. 2005. (Illus.). 32p. (YA). pap. 5.00 (978-1-59476-180-5(9)) Paradigm Accelerated Curriculum.

Integrated Physics & Chemistry, Chapter 8, Text. 2005. (Illus.). 64p. (YA). pap. 7.00 (978-1-59476-168-3(X)) Paradigm Accelerated Curriculum.

Integrated Physics & Chemistry, Chapter 9, Activities. 2005. (Illus.). 32p. (YA). pap. 5.00 (978-1-59476-181-2(7)) Paradigm Accelerated Curriculum.

Integrated Physics & Chemistry, Chapter 9, Text. 2005. (Illus.). 68p. (YA). pap. 7.00 (978-1-59476-169-0(8)) Paradigm Accelerated Curriculum.

Integrated Physics & Chemistry, Full Course Kit, 25 bks. 2005. (Illus.). 7969p. (YA). 169.00 (978-1-59476-187-4(6)) Paradigm Accelerated Curriculum.

Integrated Physics & Chemistry, Teacher's Resource Kit with CD. 2005. (Illus.). 439p. (YA). pap. 25.00 (978-1-59476-185-0(X)) Paradigm Accelerated Curriculum.

Introductory Chemistry: Complete Solutions Guide. 5th ed. 2004. (gr. 6-12). (978-0-618-30532-2(7) , 3-70778) McDougal Littell Inc.

Introductory Chemistry: Test Item File. 5th ed. 2004. (gr. 6-12). (978-0-618-30535-3(1) , 3-70780) McDougal Littell Inc.

Jackson, Tom. Radioactive Elements. 2005. (Elements Ser.). (Illus.). 32p. (J). (gr. 3-7). lib. bdg. (978-0-7614-1923-5(3) , Benchmark Bks.) Cavendish, Marshall Corp.

Johnson, Rebecca L. Acids & Bases. 2004. (National Geographic Reading Expeditions Ser.). (Illus.). 32p. (J). pap. (978-0-7922-4582-7(2)) National Geographic Society.

—Chemical Changes. 2004. (National Geographic Reading Expeditions Ser.). (Illus.). 32p. (J). pap. (978-0-7922-4583-4(0)) National Geographic Society.

Kain, Kathleen E. What Can I Do? The Science Spider-s(TM) Learn Acid-Base Chemistry. 1999. (Illus.). 32p. (J). (gr. k-3). pap. 5.95 (978-1-892221-04-9(7) , RW0564) Ranch Works.

Keller, Rebecca. Real Science-4-Kids Chemistry Level I. l.t. ed. 2004. (Illus.). 72p. 24.95 (978-0-9749149-0-9(8)) Gravitas Pubns., Inc.

Lepora, Nathan. Chromium. 2005. (Elements Ser.). (Illus.). 32p. (J). (gr. 3-7). lib. bdg. (978-0-7614-1920-4(9) , Benchmark Bks.) Cavendish, Marshall Corp.

Lew, Kristi. Chemical Reactions. 2007. (Essential Chemistry Ser.). 128p. (gr. 6-12). 35.00 (***978-0-7910-9531-7(2)***, Chelsea Hse.) Facts On File, Inc.

Lister, Ted & Renshaw, Janet. Chemistry for Advanced Level Course. 4th ed. 2000. (Illus.). 80p. (YA). (gr. 11 up). pap., stu. ed. 24.00 (978-0-7487-4465-7(7)) Nelson Thornes Ltd. GBR. *Dist:* Trans-Atlantic Pubns., Inc.

—New Understanding Chemistry for Advanced Level. 3rd ed. 1999. (Illus.). 688p. (YA). (gr. 11 up). pap. 79.50 (978-0-7487-3958-5(0)) Nelson Thornes Ltd. GBR. *Dist:* Trans-Atlantic Pubns., Inc.

Mahase, Compton & Morris, Mark. CXC Revision Guide for Chemistry. 2nd rev. ed. 2007. 86p. pap. 9.50 (978-0-521-69296-0(2)) Cambridge Univ. Pr.

McCarthy, Anne S. Methods of Analysis & Detection. 2nd ed. 2001. (Cambridge Advanced Sciences Ser.). (Illus.). 64p. pap. 12.00 (978-0-521-78724-6(6)) Cambridge Univ. Pr.

McGraw-Hill Staff. Chemistry. 2nd ed. 2004. (Glencoe Science Ser.). stu. ed. 20.64 (978-0-07-861767-6(7) , 9780078617676) Glencoe/McGraw-Hill.

—Chemistry: Concepts & Applications. 2004. stu. ed. 91.96 (978-0-07-861798-0(7) , 9780078617980) Glencoe/McGraw-Hill.

McNeil, Niki, et al. HOCPP 1109 Foundations for Chemistry. 2006. spiral bd. 23.00 (***978-1-60308-109-2(7)***) In the Hands of a Child.

Menetrez, Marc Yves, et al. Encyclopedia of Environmental Studies. 3rd rev. ed. 2008. (Science Encyclopedia Ser.). 800p. (gr. 9). 150.00 (***978-0-8160-6511-0(X)***) Facts On File, Inc.

Milner, Bryan, et al, eds. Core Science 1: Key Concepts. 1998. (Core Science Ser.). (Illus.). 302p. pap. 30.00 (978-0-521-58850-8(2)) Cambridge Univ. Pr.

—Core Science 2: Consolidation. 1998. (Core Science Ser.). (Illus.). 244p. pap. 24.00 (978-0-521-58849-2(9)) Cambridge Univ. Pr.

Mitchell, David. The Wonders of Waldorf Chemistry: Notes from a Teacher's Notebook. Odermatt, Brian, illus. 2004. 250p. (gr. 7-9). per. 22.00 (978-1-888365-16-0(1)) Assn. of Waldorf Schls. of North America Pubns. (AWSNA).

Modules: Physical Science; Chemical Interactions. 2005. (gr. 6-12). lab manual ed. (978-0-618-43723-8(1) , 2-01216) McDougal Littell Inc.

Modules: Physical Science; Chemical Interactions PE. 2005. (gr. 6-12). (978-0-618-33438-4(6) , 2-01025) McDougal Littell Inc.

Moje, Steven W. Cool Chemistry: Great Experiments with Simple Stuff. 2001. (Illus.). (J). (978-0-606-21122-2(5)) Tandem Library Bks.

Myers. Holt Chemistry: Online Edition Upgrade. 4th ed. 2004. 31.93 (978-0-03-037174-5(0)); 7.93 (978-0-03-037217-9(8)) Holt, Rinehart & Winston.

—Holt Chemistry: Premier Online Edition. 6th ed. 2005. 19.93 (978-0-03-040067-4(8)) Holt, Rinehart & Winston.

Newmark, Ann & Buller, Laura. Chemistry. 2005. (Dk eyewitness Bks.). (Illus.). 72p. (J). lib. bdg. 19.99 (978-0-7566-1394-5(9)); (gr. 4-7). 15.99 (978-0-7566-1385-3(X)) Dorling Kindersley Publishing, Inc.

Newton, David E. Chemistry & the Environment. 2007. (New Chemistry Ser.). 240p. (gr. 6-12). 35.00 (978-0-8160-5273-8(5)) Facts On File, Inc.

—The New Chemistry Set. 2007. (New Chemistry Ser.). 192p. (gr. 6-12). 210.00 (978-0-8160-5272-1(7)) Facts On File, Inc.

Norman, Penny. Science One Two Three Chemistry. Einstein, Ann, ed. 2005. 15.95 (978-1-886978-66-9(2)) Norman & Globus, Inc.

Olmsted. Ctb - Ibm to Accompany Chemistry. 3rd ed. 2002. (YA). (978-0-471-44347-6(6) , Wiley) Wiley, John & Sons, Inc.

—Ctb - Mac to Accompany Chemistry. 3rd ed. 2002. (YA). (978-0-471-44351-3(4) , Wiley) Wiley, John & Sons, Inc.

—Test Bank to Accompany Chemistry. 3rd ed. 2002. 192p. (YA). (978-0-471-20498-5(6)) Wiley, John & Sons, Inc.

Oxlade, Chris, et al, eds. Illustrated Dictionary of Chemistry. 2nd rev. ed. 2004. (Illustrated Dictionaries Ser.). (Illus.). 128p. (J). (gr. 7 up). pap. 12.95 (978-0-7460-3794-2(5)) EDC Publishing.

Parker, Steve. Chemicals & Change. 2004. (Science View Ser.). (Illus.). 32p. (J). (gr. 4-8). 28.00 (978-0-7910-8212-6(1) , Chelsea Hse.) Facts On File, Inc.

Parratore, Phil. Hands-On Chemistry. 2001. (Cool, Awesome, Simple Science Ser.). (Illus.). 64p. (J). pap. 9.99 (978-0-88724-652-4(4) , CD-7323) Carson-Dellosa Publishing Co., Inc.

The People, Places & Principles of Integrated Physics & Chemistry. 2000. (YA). (gr. 7-12). Vol. 1. stu. ed., spiral bd. (978-1-928629-18-4(0)); Vol. 2. stu. ed., spiral bd. (978-1-928629-19-1(9)); Vol. 3. stu. ed., spiral bd. (978-1-928629-20-7(2)); Vol. 4. stu. ed., spiral bd. (978-1-928629-21-4(0)) Paradigm Accelerated Curriculum.

The People, Places & Principles of Integrated Physics & Chemistry: Activities, Quizzes & Tests. 2000. (YA). (gr. 7-12). Vol. 1. spiral bd. (978-1-928629-22-1(9)); Vol. 2. spiral bd. (978-1-928629-23-8(7)); Vol. 3. spiral bd. (978-1-928629-24-5(5)); Vol. 3. spiral bd. (978-1-928629-25-2(3)) Paradigm Accelerated Curriculum.

Phelan, Gary. Chemistry in the Kitchen. 2006. (Navigators Ser.). (J). pap. 42.00 (***978-1-4108-6232-7(1)***) Benchmark Education Co.

Pinna, Simon de. Chemical Reactions. 2006. pap. (***978-0-8368-8093-9(5)***); lib. bdg. (***978-0-8368-8084-7(6)***) Stevens, Gareth Inc.

C D

Ramsden, E. N. A-Level Chemistry. 4th ed. 2000. (Illus.). 784p. (YA). (gr. 11 up). pap. 69.50 (978-0-7487-5299-7(4)) Nelson Thornes Ltd. GBR. *Dist:* Trans-Atlantic Pubns., Inc.

Ratcliff, Brian, et al. Chemistry 1. 2000. (Cambridge Advanced Sciences Ser.). (Illus.). 224p. pap. 26.00 (978-0-521-78778-9(5)) Cambridge Univ. Pr.

Romano, Nicholas & Cameron, Philip. Chemistry: Physical Setting STAReview. 2002. (ENG., Illus.). 396p. (YA). per. 15.95 (978-0-935487-75-6(1) , STAReviews) N&N Publishing Co., Inc.

Romero, Libby. Discover Forensic Chemistry. 2006. pap. 39.00 (***978-1-4108-6503-8(7)***) Benchmark Education Co.

—Forensic Chemistry. 2006. pap. 42.00 (***978-1-4108-6500-7(2)***) Benchmark Education Co.

—Kitchen Chemistry. 2006. pap. 39.00 (***978-1-4108-6498-7(7)***) Benchmark Education Co.

Ryan, Lawrie. Advanced Chemistry for You. 2000. (Illus.). 472p. (YA). (gr. 11 up). pap. 62.50 (978-0-7487-5297-3(8)) Nelson Thornes Ltd. GBR. *Dist:* Trans-Atlantic Pubns., Inc.

—Chemistry for You. 2nd rev. ed. 2001. (Illus.). 400p. pap. 36.50 (978-0-7487-6234-7(5)) Nelson Thornes Ltd. GBR. *Dist:* Trans-Atlantic Pubns., Inc.

Ryan, Lawrie, et al. Chemistry. 2003. (Illus.). 72p. pap. (978-0-7487-6800-4(9)) Nelson Thornes Ltd.

Saunders, N. Chemical Reactions. 2007. (J). lib. bdg. (***978-1-4042-3751-3(8)***) Rosen Publishing Group, Inc., The.

Science Stories Foss Spanish Mixtures & Solutions EA CR05. 2005. (J). (978-1-59242-594-5(1)) Delta Education, LLC.

Sganga, Francis T. Essential Chemistry for Gifted Students: Preparation for High School Chemistry, Grades 4-8. 2003. (Illus.). 75p. spiral bd. 18.00 net. (978-0-910609-44-9(6)) Gifted Education Pr.

Simple Chemistry. 2002. (ScienceWorks for Kids Ser.). (Illus.). (J). (gr. 4-6). pap. 9.99 (978-1-55799-834-7(5) , EMC878) Evan-Moor Educational Pubs.

Slade, Roger. Cambridge Checkpoints VCE Chemistry Unit 3 2005. 2004. (Cambridge Checkpoints Ser.). 184p. pap., stu. ed. 11.35 (978-0-521-60818-3(X)) Cambridge Univ. Pr.

—Cambridge Checkpoints VCE Chemistry Unit 4 2005. 2004. (Cambridge Checkpoints Ser.). 160p. pap., stu. ed. 11.50 (978-0-521-61146-6(6)) Cambridge Univ. Pr.

Slade, Suzanne. The Nitrogen Cycle. 2007. (Cycles in Nature Ser.). (Illus.). 24p. (J). (gr. 4-6). lib. bdg. 21.25 (978-1-4042-3491-8(8) , PowerKids Pr.) Rosen Publishing Group, Inc., The.

Smith, A. & Clarke, P. Mixtures & Compounds. 2004. (Library of Science Ser.). 64p. (J). lib. bdg. 17.95 (978-1-58086-377-3(9)) EDC Publishing.

Solway, Andrew. From Gunpowder to Laser Chemistry: Discovering Chemical Reactions. 2007. (Illus.). 64p. (J). (***978-1-4034-9552-5(1)***) Heinemann Library.

Solway, Andrew. A History of Super Science: Atoms & Elements. 2005. (Illus.). 32p. (J). (978-1-4109-1951-9(X)); (gr. 3-5). lib. bdg. 28.21 (978-1-4109-1920-5(X)) Steck-Vaughn.

Spencer. Chemistry Structure 2E with Chemistry a Guided Inq Uiry 2E Set. 6th ed. 2002. (YA). (978-0-471-26645-7(0)) Wiley, John & Sons, Inc.

Spilsbury, Louise & Spilsbury, Richard. Chemical Reactions. 2007. (Illus.). 32p. (J). (978-1-4034-9342-2(1)); lib. bdg. (978-1-4034-9337-8(5)) Heinemann Library.

—Mixtures & Solutions. 2007. (Illus.). 32p. (J). (978-1-4034-9344-6(8)); lib. bdg. (978-1-4034-9339-2(1)) Heinemann Library.

Stille, Darlene R. Chemical Change: From Fireworks to Rust. 2005. (Exploring Science Ser.). (Illus.). 48p. (J). (gr. 5-7). (978-0-7565-1256-9(5)) Compass Point Bks.

Stwertka, Albert. A Guide to the Elements. rev. ed. 2003. (Illus.). 238p. (J). (gr. 6-10). reprint ed. pap. 23.00 (978-0-7567-6738-9(5)) DIANE Publishing Co.

—A Guide to the Elements. 2nd rev. ed. 2002. (Illus.). 248p. (YA). (gr. 6 up). reprint ed. pap. 19.95 (978-0-19-515027-8(9)); 37.50 (978-0-19-515026-1(0)) Oxford Univ. Pr., Inc.

Thomas, Isabel. Fireworks! 2006. (Illus.). 32p. (J). (978-1-4109-2589-3(7)) Steck-Vaughn.

Tilley, Eurona Earl. Acids & Bases. 2007. 128p. 35.00 (***978-0-7910-9550-8(9)*** , Chelsea Hse.) Facts On File, Inc.

Tocci, Salvatore. Chlorine. (J). 2006. 48p. (gr. 3-5). pap. 6.95 (978-0-516-25574-3(6)); 2005. (Illus.). 47p. (ps-7). 25.00 (978-0-516-23698-8(9)) Scholastic Library Publishing. (Children's Pr.).

Townsend, John. Crazy Chemistry. 2006. (Illus.). 56p. (J). (978-1-4109-2378-3(9)); pap. (978-1-4109-2383-7(5)) Steck-Vaughn.

Video Education Australasia Pt, prod. Chemical Bonding: Inner Forces. (YA). cd-rom 149.95 (978-0-7365-1248-0(9)) Films Media Group.

Watt, Susan. Chlorine. 2001. (Elements Ser.). (Illus.). 32p. (J). (gr. 3-5). lib. bdg. 25.64 (978-0-7614-1272-4(7) , Benchmark Bks.) Cavendish, Marshall Corp.

—Lead. 2001. (Elements Ser.). (Illus.). 32p. (J). (gr. 3-5). lib. bdg. 25.64 (978-0-7614-1273-1(5) , Benchmark Bks.) Cavendish, Marshall Corp.

—Mercury. 2004. (J). 25.64 (978-0-7614-1814-6(8) , Benchmark Bks.) Cavendish, Marshall Corp.

Whyman, Kathryn. Everyday Chemicals. Nevett, Louise, illus. 2004. (J). lib. bdg. (978-1-932799-23-1(0)) Stargazer Bks.

Wright, John D. Fire & Explosives. 2007. (Forensic Evidence Ser.). (Illus.). 96p. (gr. 6 up). 39.95 (***978-0-7656-8117-1(X)***) Sharpe, M.E. Inc.

Young, June. Look How It Changes! 2006. 32p. (YA). (gr. 1-2). pap. 4.95 (978-0-516-28178-0(X) , Children's Pr.) Scholastic Library Publishing.

Zumdahl. Chemistry Plus Media Guide Update Plus Study & Solutions Guide 6th Edition. 6th ed. 2005. (YA). pap., pap. 171.96 (978-0-618-69648-2(2) , 396960) Houghton Mifflin College Div.

—Introductory Chemistry: Student Support Package. 5th ed. 2003. (YA). (gr. 6-12). cd-rom 3.96 (978-0-618-38803-5(6) , 370781) Houghton Mifflin College Div.

Zumdahl, Steven S. Chemistry. 5th ed. 2000. (YA). stu. ed. 54.36 (978-0-395-98586-1(2) , 370603) Houghton Mifflin College Div.

—Chemistry. 6th ed. 2003. (gr. 6-12). stu. ed. 131.56 (978-0-618-30802-6(4) , 3-70508) McDougal Littell Inc.

—Hardcover Text: Introductory Chemistry: Media Update. 5th ed. 2003. 573p. (YA). (gr. 6-12). 123.96 (978-0-618-30501-8(7) , 370771) Houghton Mifflin College Div.

—Hardcover Text with Student Support Package: Introductory Chemistry. 5th ed. 2003. 573p. (YA). (gr. 6-12). 123.96 incl. cd-rom (978-0-618-39305-3(6) , 370789) Houghton Mifflin College Div.

—Introduction to Chemistry: A Foundation. 4th ed. 1999. (Illus.). 685p. (YA). 128.36 (978-0-395-95536-9(X) , 370700) Houghton Mifflin College Div.

—Introductory Chemistry: A Foundation. 4th ed. 2000. (Illus.). (YA). (978-0-395-95540-6(8)) Houghton Mifflin Co.

—Introductory Chemistry: A Foundation: Text with Student Support Package. 5th ed. 2003. 648p. (YA). (gr. 6-12). stu. ed. 128.36 incl. cd-rom (978-0-618-34342-3(3) , 370786) Houghton Mifflin College Div.

—Introductory Chemistry Interactive CD-ROM with Printed Media Activities Package: Used with ... Zumdahl-Introductory Chemistry: A Foundation; Zumdahl-Introductory Chemistry; Zumdahl-Basic Chemistry. 5th ed. 2003. (YA). (gr. 6-12). cd-rom 35.16 (978-0-618-30540-7(8) , 370782) Houghton Mifflin College Div.

—Introductory Chemistry Paperback with Student Supplement Package. 5th ed. 2003. (YA). pap., stu. ed. 128.36 incl. cd-rom (978-0-618-40076-8(1) , 386354) Houghton Mifflin College Div.

—Solutions Guide: Used with ... Zumdahl-Introductory Chemistry: A Foundation; Zumdahl-Introductory Chemistry; Zumdahl-Basic Chemistry. 5th ed. 2003. (YA). (gr. 6-12). 42.36 (978-0-618-30530-8(0) , 370777) Houghton Mifflin College Div.

—Study Guide: Used with ... Zumdahl-Introductory Chemistry: A Foundation; Zumdahl-Introductory Chemistry; Zumdahl-Basic Chemistry. 5th ed. 2003. (YA). (gr. 6-12). stu. ed. 45.96 (978-0-618-30527-8(0) , 370775) Houghton Mifflin College Div.

—World of Chemistry. 2001. (YA). (gr. 6-12). stu. ed. 90.86 (978-0-618-13496-0(4) , 377643) Houghton Mifflin College Div.

CHEMISTRY, ANALYTIC

Lister, T., compiled by. Chemistry at the Races: The Work of the Horseracing Forensic Laboratory. 2002. (Illus.). 45p. pap. 14.95 (978-0-85404-385-9(3) , 0854043853) Royal Society of Chemistry, The GBR. *Dist:* Springer.

CHEMISTRY, BIOLOGICAL

see Biochemistry

CHEMISTRY—DICTIONARIES

Usborne Books Staff, ed. Illustrated Dictionary of Chemistry. rev. ed. 2004. (Illustrated Dictionaries Ser.). (Illus.). 128p. (J). (gr. 7 up). lib. bdg. 20.95 (978-1-58086-282-0(9)) EDC Publishing.

CHEMISTRY—EXPERIMENTS

Arnold, Nick & De Saulles, Tony. Esa Caotica Quimica. De Saulles, Tony, tr. 2003. (Coleccion Esa Horrible Cienca). (SPA., Illus.). 158p. (YA). (978-84-272-2052-2(9) , ML8312) Molino, Editorial ESP. *Dist:* Lectorum Pubns., Inc.

Epp, Diane N. Product Testing: The Chemistry of Ice Cream. 2001. 94p. (J). 12.95 (978-1-883822-25-5(4)) Terrific Science Pr.

Farndon, John. Chemicals. 2002. (Science Experiments Ser.). (J). 25.64 (978-0-7614-1466-7(5) , Benchmark Bks.) Cavendish, Marshall Corp.

Gardner, Robert. Chemistry Projects with a Laboratory You Can Build. 2007. (Build-a-Lab! Science Experiments Ser.). (Illus.). 128p. (J). (gr. 5). lib. bdg. 31.93 (978-0-7660-2805-0(4)) Enslow Pubs., Inc.

—Chemistry Science Fair Projects Using Acids, Bases, Metals, Salts, & Inorganic Stuff. 2004. (Chemistry! Best Science Projects Ser.). (Illus.). 128p. (J). lib. bdg. 26.60 (978-0-7660-2210-2(2)) Enslow Pubs., Inc.

—Science Project Ideas about Kitchen Chemistry. rev. ed. 2002. (Science Project Ideas Ser.). (Illus.). 128p. (J). (gr. 4-9). lib. bdg. 26.60 (978-0-7660-1706-1(0)) Enslow Pubs., Inc.

—Science Projects about Kitchen Chemistry. 1999. (Science Projects Ser.). (Illus.). 128p. (YA). (gr. 6-12). lib. bdg. 26.60 (978-0-89490-953-5(3)) Enslow Pubs., Inc.

Gardner, Robert & Conklin, Barbara Gardner. Chemistry Science Fair Projects Using French Fries, Gumdrops, Soap, & Other Organic Stuff. 2004. (Chemistry! Best Science Projects Ser.). (Illus.). 128p. (J). lib. bdg. 26.60 (978-0-7660-2211-9(0)) Enslow Pubs., Inc.

Hall, James & Zumdahl. Introductory Chemistry in the Laboratory: Used with ... Zumdahl-Basic Chemistry; Zumdahl-Introductory Chemistry; Zumdahl-Introductory Chemistry: A Foundation. 5th ed. 2003. (YA). (gr. 6-12). 74.76 (978-0-618-30528-5(9) , 370776) Houghton Mifflin College Div.

Kain, Kathleen E. Surprise Explosions: The Science Spiders(TM) Make Chemicals React. 1999. (Illus.). 32p. (J). (gr. k-3). pap. 5.95 (978-1-892221-02-5(0) , RW0562) Ranch Works.

Loesching, Louis V., et al, illus. Chemistry Experiments. 2005. 128p. (gr. 4-7). pap. 5.95 (978-1-4027-2159-5(5)) Sterling Publishing Co., Inc.

McGraw-Hill Staff. Glencoe Science: Chemistry. 2004. pap., stu. ed., lab manual ed. 8.64 (978-0-07-866919-4(7) , 9780078669194) Glencoe/McGraw-Hill.

Mebane, Robert C. & Rybolt, Thomas R. Adventures with Atoms & Molecules: Chemistry Experiments for Young People. 1998. (Adventures with Science Ser.). (Illus.). (YA). (gr. 4-9). Bk. I. 82p. pap. 11.93 (978-0-7660-1224-0(7)); Bk. II. 96p. pap. 11.93 (978-0-7660-1225-7(5)); Bk. III. 96p. pap. 11.93 (978-0-7660-1226-4(3)); Bk. IV. 96p. pap. 11.93 (978-0-7660-1227-1(1)); Bk. V. 96p. pap. 11.93 (978-0-7660-1228-8(X)) Enslow Pubs., Inc.

Oxlade, Chris. Changing Materials. 2007. (J). 32p. pap. (***978-0-7787-3648-6(2)); (*978-0-7787-3638-7(5))*** Crabtree Publishing Co.

—Chemistry. Fairclough, Chris, illus. 1998. (Science Projects Ser.). 48p. (J). (978-0-7502-2160-3(7)) Steck-Vaughn.

—Joining Materials. 2007. 32p. pap. (***978-0-7787-3649-3(0)***) Crabtree Publishing Co.

—Mixing & Separating. 2007. 32p. pap. (***978-0-7787-3650-9(4)***) Crabtree Publishing Co.

—Shaping Materials. 2007. 32p. pap. (***978-0-7787-3651-6(2)***) Crabtree Publishing Co.

Rillero, Peter. Totally Gross Chemistry. Simard, Remy, illus. 1999. (Creative Activity Kit Ser.). 32p. (J). (978-0-7853-3582-5(X)) Publications International, Ltd.

Rompella, Natalie. Chemistry. 2007. (J). (***978-1-4034-7914-3(3)***) Heinemann Library.

School Specialty Publishing. Chemistry. 2004. (Hands-on Experiments Ser.). 80p. (J). (gr. k-2). pap. 10.99 (978-0-7424-2746-4(3) , IFG99234); (gr. 3-5). pap. 10.99 (978-0-7424-2747-1(1) , IFG99233) School Specialty Publishing.

Science & Technology for Children BOOKS: Chemical Tests. 2007. (J). (***978-1-933008-41-7(5)***) National Science Resources Ctr.

Science & Technology for Children BOOKS: Chemical Tests Set. 2007. (J). 127.60 (***978-1-933008-45-5(8)***) National Science Resources Ctr.

VanCleave, Janice Pratt. Janice VanCleave's Microscopes & Magnifying Lenses: Mind-Boggling Chemistry & Biology Experiments You Can Turn into Science Fair Projects. 2002. (Janice Vancleave Ser.). (Illus.). (J). 19.72 (978-0-7587-4631-3(8)) Book Wholesalers, Inc.

CHEMISTRY—HISTORY

Kjelle, Marylou. Antoine Lavoisier: Father of Modern Chemistry. 2004. (Uncharted, Unexplored, & Unexplained Ser.). (Illus.). 48p. (J). (gr. 4-8). lib. bdg. 29.95 (978-1-58415-309-2(1)) Mitchell Lane Pubs., Inc.

CHEMISTRY, INDUSTRIAL

see Chemical Industries

CHEMISTRY, INORGANIC

see also Metals

Thomas, Michelle. Sodium. 2005. (Understanding the Elements of the Periodic Table Ser.). (Illus.). 48p. (J). (gr. 5-8). lib. bdg. 26.50 (978-1-4042-0160-6(2)) Rosen Publishing Group, Inc., The.

CHEMISTRY, MEDICAL AND PHARMACEUTICAL

see also Drugs; Materia Medica; Pharmacy; Poisons

Kendrick, Karolyn. Chemistry in Medicine. 2006. (Navigators Ser.). (J). pap. 42.00 (***978-1-4108-6233-4(X)***) Benchmark Education Co.

Romero, Libby. Medical Chemistry. 2006. pap. 39.00 (***978-1-4108-6499-4(5)***) Benchmark Education Co.

CHEMISTRY, ORGANIC

Brown, William H. Student Solutions Guide to Accompany Introduction to Organic Chemistry. 2nd ed. 1999. 304p. (C). pap., stu. ed. 50.00 (978-0-03-026009-4(4)) Saunders College Publishing.

Chappell, Rachel M. What's Going on in the Compost Pile? A Book about Systems. 2008. (J). (***978-1-60044-541-5(1)***) Rourke Publishing, LLC.

Ege. Study Guide: Used with ... Ege-Organic Chemistry: Structure & Reactivity. 5th ed. 2003. (YA). stu. ed. 97.16 (978-0-618-31810-0(0) , 316091) Houghton Mifflin College Div.

Hart, Harold. Organische Chemie. 2nd ed. (Duden Abiturhilfen Ser.). (GER.). 112p. (YA). (gr. 12-13). (978-3-411-70862-8(X)) Bibliographisches Institut & F. A. Brockhaus AG DEU. *Dist:* International Bk. Import Service, Inc.

Hart Organic Chemistry: A Short Course. 11th ed. 2003. (gr. 6-12). (978-0-618-21546-1(8) , 3-22519) McDougal Littell Inc.

Holt, Rinehart and Winston Staff. Holt Chemistry Chptr. 19: Carbon & Organics. 4th ed. Date not set. pap. 11.20 (978-0-03-068129-5(4)) Holt, Rinehart & Winston.

Kunststoffe, Farbstoffe, Waschmittel. (Duden Abiturhilfen Ser.). (GER.). 96p. (YA). (gr. 12-13). (978-3-411-04511-2(6)) Bibliographisches Institut & F. A. Brockhaus AG DEU. *Dist:* International Bk. Import Service, Inc.

MacCormack, Harry. A Catechism for the Children of De-Light. 2001. (Illus.). 288p. per. 19.95 (978-0-9649573-2-9(9)) Touchstone Adventures.

CHEMISTRY, PHARMACEUTICAL

see Chemistry, Medical and Pharmaceutical

CHEMISTRY, PHYSICAL AND THEORETICAL

see also Atoms; Crystallography; Electrochemistry; Molecules; Nuclear Physics; Periodic Law; Polymers and Polymerization; Radiochemistry; Thermodynamics

Holt, Rinehart and Winston Staff. Holt Science & Technology Chapter 4: Physical Science: Elements, Compounds, & Mixtures. 5th ed. 2004. (Illus.). pap. 12.86 (978-0-03-030371-5(0)) Holt, Rinehart & Winston.

Kjelle, Marylou Morano. Mixtures & Compounds. 2007. (Library of Physical Sciences). (J). (978-1-4042-2357-8(6)); (Illus.). 24p. pap. (978-1-4042-2167-3(0)); (Illus.). 24p. (gr. 3-6). lib. bdg. 21.25 (978-1-4042-3420-8(9)) Rosen Publishing Group, Inc., The. (PowerKids Pr.).

CHEMISTRY, PHYSIOLOGICAL

see Biochemistry

CHEMISTRY—TABLES, ETC.

Holt, Rinehart and Winston Staff. Holt Science & Technology Chapter 12: Physical Science: Periodic Table. 5th ed. 2004. (Illus.). pap. 12.86 (978-0-03-030404-0(0)) Holt, Rinehart & Winston.

Wu, Ronald W. Carbon. 2005. (Interpreting the Periodic Table Ser.). (Illus.). 48p. (J). (gr. 5-8). lib. bdg. 26.50 (978-1-4042-0155-2(6)) Rosen Publishing Group, Inc., The.

CHEMISTRY—VOCATIONAL GUIDANCE

Cohen, Judith Love. You Can Be A Chemist. Katz, David A., illus. l.t. ed. 2005. Orig. Title: You Can Be A Woman Chemist. 40p. (J). per. 7.00 (978-1-880599-71-6(6)) Cascade Pass, Inc.

—You Can Be A Woman Chemist. Katz, David A., illus. l.t. ed. 2005. 40p. (J). 13.95 (978-1-880599-72-3(4)) Cascade Pass, Inc.

CHEMISTS

see also Chemistry—Vocational Guidance

African-American Chemical Engineers. 2000. (My Ancestors—My Heroes Ser.: Vol. 42). (J). (gr. 3-4). (978-1-893091-41-2(4)) Parker Publishing Co.

Birch, Beverley. Marie Curie: Courageous Pioneer in the Study of Radioactivity. 2000. (Giants of Science Ser.). (Illus.). 64p. (J). (gr. 5-8). 24.95 (978-1-56711-333-4(8) , Blackbirch Pr., Inc.) Thomson Gale.

Cobb, Vicki. Marie Curie. 2008. (DK Biography Ser.). 128p. (J). (gr. 3-8). 14.99 (***978-0-7566-3832-0(1));*** pap. 4.99 (***978-0-7566-3831-3(3)***) Dorling Kindersley Publishing, Inc.

Conley, Kate A. Joseph Priestly & the Discovery of Oxygen. 2005. (Uncharted, Unexplored, & Unexplained Ser.). (Illus.). 48p. (J). (gr. 4-8). lib. bdg. 29.95 (978-1-58415-367-2(9)) Mitchell Lane Pubs., Inc.

Evernden, Margery. The Experimenters: Twelve Great Chemists. 2001. (Illus.). 200p. (J). (gr. 6-12). pap. 19.95 (978-1-888105-49-0(6)) Avisson Pr., Inc.

Frost, Helen. We Need Pharmacists. 2004. (Helpers in Our Community Ser.). (Illus.). 24p. (J). lib. bdg. 15.93 (978-0-7368-2575-7(4) , Pebble Bks.) Capstone Pr., Inc.

Fullick, Ann. Marie Curie. (Groundbreakers Ser.). 48p. (J). (gr. 5-7). 2002. (Illus.). pap. 8.50 (978-1-58810-994-1(1) , 91469); 2000. lib. bdg. 25.64 (978-1-57572-374-7(3)) Heinemann Library.

Gaines, Ann Graham. Wallace Carothers & the Story of DuPont Nylon. 2002. (Unlocking the Secrets of Science Ser.). (Illus.). 56p. (gr. 4-10). lib. bdg. 17.95 (978-1-58415-097-8(1)) Mitchell Lane Pubs., Inc.

Gogerly, Liz. Marie Curie. 2001. (Scientists Who Made History Ser.). (Illus.). 48p. (J). lib. bdg. 27.12 (978-0-7398-4413-7(X)) Raintree.

Guidici, Cynthia. Mario Molina. 2006. (Biografías Hispanoamericanas Ser.). (Illus.). 64p. (J). (978-1-4109-2131-4(X)); pap. (978-1-4109-2138-3(7)) Steck-Vaughn.

Hager, Tom. Linus Pauling: And the Chemistry of Life. 1998. (Oxford Portraits in Science Ser.). (Illus.). 144p. (YA). (gr. 7 up). 30.00 (978-0-19-510853-8(1)) Oxford Univ. Pr., Inc.

Healy, Nick. Marie Curie. 2005. (Genius Ser.). (Illus.). 48p. (gr. 5-9). 21.95 (978-1-58341-332-6(4) , Creative Education) Creative Co., The.

Kahn, Jetty. Women in Chemistry Careers. 1999. (Short Biographies Ser.). (Illus.). 48p. (J). (gr. 3-4). lib. bdg. 22.60 (978-0-7368-0315-1(7) , Bridgestone Bks.) Capstone Pr., Inc.

—Women in Chemistry Careers. 1999. (Illus.). 48p. (J). (gr. 3-7). pap. 19.93 (978-0-516-21882-3(4) , Children's Pr.) Scholastic Library Publishing.

Kepnes, Caroline. Stephen Crane. 2004. (Classic Storytellers Ser.). (Illus.). 48p. (J). (gr. 4-8). lib. bdg. 20.95 (978-1-58415-272-9(9)) Mitchell Lane Pubs., Inc.

Kjelle, Marylou. Antoine Lavoisier: Father of Modern Chemistry. 2004. (Uncharted, Unexplored, & Unexplained Ser.). (Illus.). 48p. (J). (gr. 4-8). lib. bdg. 29.95 (978-1-58415-309-2(1)) Mitchell Lane Pubs., Inc.

—John Dalton & the Atomic Theory. 2004. (Uncharted, Unexplored, & Unexplained Ser.). (Illus.). 48p. (J). (gr. 4-8). lib. bdg. 29.95 (978-1-58415-308-5(3)) Mitchell Lane Pubs., Inc.

Lassieur, Allison. Marie Curie: A Scientific Pioneer. 2003. (Great Life Stories Ser.). (Illus.). 112p. (J). 30.50 (978-0-531-12270-9(0) , Watts, Franklin) Scholastic Library Publishing.

MacLeod, Elizabeth. Marie Curie: A Brillant Life. 2005. (Snapshots Ser.). (Illus.). 32p. (YA). (gr. 3-7). (978-1-55337-571-5(8)); (978-1-55337-570-8(X)) Kids Can Pr., Ltd.

McCormick, Lisa Wade. Marie Curie. 2006. (Rookie Biographies Ser.). (Illus.). 32p. (J). (gr. 1-2). 20.50 (978-0-516-25040-3(X) , Children's Pr.) Scholastic Library Publishing.

McLeese, Don. Marie Curie. (Rourke Discovery Library). (Illus.). 24p. 2006. (gr. 2-5). 14.95 (978-1-59515-431-6(0)); 2005. (SPA & ENG., (978-1-59515-671-6(2)) Rourke Publishing, LLC.

Miller, Connie Colwell. Marie Curie & Radioactivity. Larson, Scott & Heike, Mark, illus. 2007. (Graphic Library). 32p. (J). 25.26 (978-0-7368-6486-2(5)); pap. (***978-0-7368-7521-9(2)***) Capstone Pr., Inc.

Ogilvie, Marilyn Bailey. Marie Curie: A Biography. 2004. (Greenwood Biographies Ser.). (Illus.). 184p. 36.95 (978-0-313-32529-8(4) , GR2529, Praeger Pubs.) Greenwood Publishing Group, Inc.

Orr, Tamra. Marie Curie. 2003. (World Was Never the Same Ser.). (J). pap. (978-1-58417-263-5(0)); lib. bdg. (978-1-58417-262-8(2)) Lake Street Pubs.

Pasachoff, Naomi E. Linus Pauling: Advancing Science, Advocating Peace. 2004. (Nobel Prize-Winning Scientists Ser.). (Illus.). 128p. (J). lib. bdg. 26.60 (978-0-7660-2130-3(0)) Enslow Pubs., Inc.

Poynter, Margaret. Marie Curie: Discoverer of Radium. rev. ed. 2007. (Great Minds of Science Ser.). (Illus.). 112p. (J). lib. bdg. 31.93 (978-0-7660-2795-4(3)) Enslow Pubs., Inc.

Santella, Andrew. Marie Curie. 2001. (Trailblazers of the Modern World Ser.). (Illus.). 48p. (J). (gr. 5 up). pap. 14.95 (978-0-8368-5221-9(4)); lib. bdg. 30.00 (978-0-8368-5061-1(0)) Stevens, Gareth Inc. (World Almanac Library).

Schaefer, Lola M. & Schaefer, Wyatt S. Marie Curie. 2004. (First Biographies Ser.). 24p. (J). lib. bdg. 15.93 (978-0-7368-2084-4(1) , Pebble Bks.) Capstone Pr., Inc.

Sherman, Josepha. Henry Cavendish & the Discovery of Hydrogen. 2005. (Uncharted, Unexplored, & Unexplained Ser.). (Illus.). 48p. (J). (gr. 4-8). lib. bdg. 29.95 (978-1-58415-368-9(7)) Mitchell Lane Pubs., Inc.

Solway, Andrew. A History of Super Science: Atoms & Elements. 2005. (Illus.). 32p. (J). (978-1-4109-1951-9(X)); (gr. 3-5). lib. bdg. 28.21 (978-1-4109-1920-5(X)) Steck-Vaughn.

Tracy, Kathleen. Pierre & Marie Curie & the Discovery of Radium. 2004. (Uncharted, Unexplored, & Unexplained Ser.). (Illus.). 48p. (J). (gr. 4-8). lib. bdg. 29.95 (978-1-58415-310-8(5)) Mitchell Lane Pubs., Inc.

Waxman, Laura Hamilton. Marie Curie. 2004. (History Maker Bios Ser.). (Illus.). 48p. (J). 26.60 (978-0-8225-0300-2(X) , Lerner Pubns.) Lerner Publishing Group.

Whiting, Jim. Otto Hahn & the Story of Nuclear Fission. 2003. (Unlocking the Secrets of Science Ser.). (Illus.). 56p. (gr. 4-10). lib. bdg. 25.70 (978-1-58415-204-0(4)) Mitchell Lane Pubs., Inc.

Wishinsky, Frieda. Manya's Dream: A Story of Marie Curie. Lamontagne, Jacques, illus. 2003. 32p. (J). (gr. 3-6). 19.95 (978-1-894379-53-3(5)); pap. 6.95 (978-1-894379-54-0(3)) Maple Tree Pr. CAN. *Dist:* Firefly Bks., Ltd.

Yount, Lisa. Antoine Lavoisier: Founder of Modern Chemistry. 2008. (J). ***978-0-7660-3011-4(3));** 2001. (Illus.). 128p. (YA). (gr. 4-10). pap. 13.26 (978-0-7660-1865-5(2)) Enslow Pubs., Inc.

Zannos, Susan. Dmitri Mendeleyev & the Periodic Table. 2004. (Uncharted, Unexplored, & Unexplained Ser.). (Illus.). 48p. (J). (gr. 4-8). lib. bdg. 29.95 (978-1-58415-267-5(2)) Mitchell Lane Pubs., Inc.

—Linus Pauling & the Chemical Bond. 2003. (Unlocking the Secrets of Science Ser.). (Illus.). 56p. (gr. 4-10). lib. bdg. 25.70 (978-1-58415-123-4(4)) Mitchell Lane Pubs., Inc.

CHEMOTHERAPY

see also Antibiotics

Alagna, Magdalena. Everything You Need to Know about Chemotherapy. 2001. (Need to Know Library). (Illus.). 64p. (YA). (gr. 4-6). lib. bdg. 25.25 (978-0-8239-3394-5(6)) Rosen Publishing Group, Inc., The.

Ballard, Carol. From Cowpox to Antibiotics: Discovering Vaccines & Medicines. 2006. (Chain Reactions Ser.). (Illus.). 62p. (YA). (gr. 6-9). lib. bdg. 34.29 (978-1-4034-8839-8(8)) Heinemann Library.

Bonnice, Sherry. Drug Therapy & Premenstrual Disorders. 2003. (Encyclopedia of Psychiatric Drugs & Their Disorders Ser.). (Illus.). 128p. (J). lib. bdg. (978-1-59084-572-1(2)) Mason Crest Pubs.

Bonnice, Sherry & Hoard, Carolyn. Drug Therapy & Cognitive Disorders. 2003. (Encyclopedia of Psychiatric Drugs & Their Disorders Ser.). (Illus.). 128p. (J). lib. bdg. (978-1-59084-562-2(5)) Mason Crest Pubs.

Brinkerhoff, Shirley. Drug Therapy & Anxiety Disorders. 2003. (Encyclopedia of Psychiatric Drugs & Their Disorders Ser.). (Illus.). 128p. (J). lib. bdg. (978-1-59084-561-5(7)) Mason Crest Pubs.

—Drug Therapy & Childhood & Adolescent Disorders. 2003. (Encyclopedia of Psychiatric Drugs & Their Disorders Ser.). (Illus.). 128p. (J). lib. bdg. (978-1-59084-563-9(3)) Mason Crest Pubs.

—Drug Therapy & Eating Disorders. 2003. (Encyclopedia of Psychiatric Drugs & Their Disorders Ser.). (Illus.). 128p. (J). lib. bdg. (978-1-59084-565-3(X)) Mason Crest Pubs.

—Drug Therapy & Obsessive-Compulsive Disorders. 2003. (Encyclopedia of Psychiatric Drugs & Their Disorders Ser.). (Illus.). 128p. (J). lib. bdg. (978-1-59084-569-1(2)) Mason Crest Pubs.

—Drug Therapy & Personality Disorders. 2003. (Encyclopedia of Psychiatric Drugs & Their Disorders Ser.). (Illus.). 128p. (J). lib. bdg. (978-1-59084-571-4(4)) Mason Crest Pubs.

—Drug Therapy & Schizophrenia. 2003. (Encyclopedia of Psychiatric Drugs & Their Disorders Ser.). (Illus.). 128p. (J). lib. bdg. (978-1-59084-574-5(9)) Mason Crest Pubs.

—Drug Therapy & Substance-Related Disorders. 2003. (Encyclopedia of Psychiatric Drugs & Their Disorders Ser.). (Illus.). 128p. (J). lib. bdg. (978-1-59084-577-6(3)) Mason Crest Pubs.

Carter, Stephanie & Lederman, JoAnn. Meditapes Seven - Chemotherapy Comfort. 1998. (YA). (gr. 7 up). pap. 24.95 incl. audio (978-1-893868-06-9(0)) Meditapes.

Esherick, Joan. Drug Therapy & Mood Disorders. 2003. (Encyclopedia of Psychiatric Drugs & Their Disorders Ser.). (Illus.). 128p. (J). lib. bdg. (978-1-59084-568-4(4)) Mason Crest Pubs.

Esherick, Joan, frwd. Drug Therapy & Sleep Disorders. 2003. (Encyclopedia of Psychiatric Drugs & Their Disorders Ser.). (Illus.). 128p. (J). lib. bdg. (978-1-59084-576-9(5)) Mason Crest Pubs.

Giddens, Sandra & Giddens, Owen. Coping with Chemotherapy. 2005. (Coping Ser.). (Illus.). 192p. (YA). (gr. 7-12). lib. bdg. 26.50 (978-0-8239-3361-7(X)) Rosen Publishing Group, Inc., The.

Libal, Autumn. Drug Therapy & Dissociative Disorders. 2003. (Encyclopedia of Psychiatric Drugs & Their Disorders Ser.). (Illus.). 128p. (J). lib. bdg. (978-1-59084-564-6(1)) Mason Crest Pubs.

—Drug Therapy & Impulse Control Disorders. 2003. (Encyclopedia of Psychiatric Drugs & Their Disorders Ser.). (Illus.). 128p. (J). lib. bdg. (978-1-59084-566-0(8)) Mason Crest Pubs.

Libal, Joyce. Drug Therapy for Mental Disorders Caused by a Medical Condition. 2003. (Encyclopedia of Psychiatric Drugs & Their Disorders Ser.). (Illus.). 128p. (J). lib. bdg. (978-1-59084-567-7(6)) Mason Crest Pubs.

Vitale, Ann E. Drug Therapy & Sexual Disorders. 2003. (Encyclopedia of Psychiatric Drugs & Their Disorders Ser.). (Illus.). 128p. (J). lib. bdg. (978-1-59084-575-2(7)) Mason Crest Pubs.

CHENNAULT, CLAIRE LEE, 1890-1958

Rice, Earle, Jr. Claire Chennault. 2003. (Famous Flyers Ser.). (Illus.). 112p. (gr. 6-12). 30.00 (978-0-7910-7217-2(7)); pap. 30.00 (978-0-7910-7499-2(4)) Facts On File, Inc. (Chelsea Hse.).

Rice, Earle. Claire Chennault: Flying Tigers. 2003. (gr. 5-8). lib. bdg. 18.75 (978-0-613-65196-7(0)) Tandem Library Bks.

CHESS

Alvarez, Michel J. WonderChess - Chess Kit for Kids: Featuring unique, prize-fillable pieces & 3D illustrated lesson Book. Scauzillo, Tony, illus. Thyrion, Marie-Noelle, photos by. 2004. 54p. (J). pap. 19.95 (978-0-9771787-0-4(6)) Wonder Chess LLC.

—WonderChess - Chess Kit for Kids - Deluxe Edition in Tin: Featuring, unique prize fillable pieces & 3D illustrated lesson Book, 1. Scauzillo, Tony, illus. Thyrion, Marie-Noelle, photos by. 2005. 54p. (J). 29.95 (978-0-9771787-1-1(4)) Wonder Chess LLC.

Basman, Michael. Chess for Kids. 2006. 48p. (J). pap. 6.99 (978-0-7566-1807-0(X)) Dorling Kindersley Publishing, Inc.

—Chess for Kids. Ling, Mary, ed. 2001. (Illus.). 48p. (J). (gr. 4-7). 12.99 (978-0-7894-6540-5(X)) Dorling Kindersley Publishing, Inc.

Breutigam-Duden, Martin. Schachturnier: Knifflige Situationen aus Beruehmten Partien. (Pocket-Quizspiel Ser.). (Illus.). 56p. bds. (978-3-411-09411-0(7)) Bibliographisches Institut & F. A. Brockhaus AG DEU. *Dist:* i.b.d., Ltd.

Callick, Paul. Chess Master. Teviotdale, Martin, illus. 2001. (Mini-Maestro Ser.). 48p. (J). (gr. 1-3). 7.95 (978-0-439-21927-3(2)) Scholastic, Inc.

Cardo, Horacio. The Story of Chess. Cardo, Horacio, illus. 1998. (Illus.). 48p. (gr. 3-12). 16.95 (978-0-7892-0250-5(6)) Abbeville Pr., Inc.

Castor, H. Starting Chess. 2004. (First Skills Ser.). (Illus.). 32p. (J). (gr. k-3). pap. 4.95 (978-0-7945-0115-0(X) , Usborne); lthr. 12.95 (978-1-58086-435-0(X)) EDC Publishing.

Chandler, Murray. Chess Tactics for Kids. 2003. (Illus.). 128p. reprint ed. 14.95 (978-1-901983-99-9(4)) Gambit Pubns., Ltd. GBR. *Dist:* Perseus Distribution.

—How to Beat Your Dad at Chess. 1998. (Illus.). 127p. 14.95 (978-1-901983-05-0(6)) Gambit Pubns., Ltd. GBR. *Dist:* Perseus Distribution.

Chandler, Murray & Milligan, Helen. Chess for Children. 2004. (Illus.). 112p. 22.95 (978-1-904600-06-0(9)) Gambit Pubns., Ltd. GBR. *Dist:* Perseus Distribution.

Chess Attack. 2004. (Formula Fun Ser.). (Illus.). 48p. (J). pap. (978-1-84229-582-3(9)) Top That! Publishing PLC.

Cohen, Steve M. The Opening 8 (for You & Your Parents) 2nd l.t. ed. 2002. (Illus.). 359p. (J). 46.30 (978-0-9721087-1-3(8)) UPSCL (Unofficial Penisnula Scholastic Chess League, Inc.).

Dalby, E. Complete Book of Chess. 2004. (Chess Guides). (Illus.). 96p. (J). lthr., act. bk. ed. 25.95 (978-1-58086-517-3(8)) EDC Publishing.

Dalby, Elizabeth. The Usborne Internet-Linked Complete Book of Chess. 2005. (Illus.). 96p. (J). pap. (978-0-439-78711-6(4)) Scholastic, Inc.

Keene, Raymond. Learn Chess Fast with Other. 2001. (gr. 3-6). lib. bdg. 16.40 (978-0-613-88214-9(8)) Tandem Library Bks.

Keene, Raymond & Stewart, Nancy K. Learn Chess Fast: The Fun Way to Start Smart & Master the Game. Munro, Roxie, illus. 2004. 72p. 7.95 (978-0-9704729-4-6(3)) Bright Sky Pr.

—Learn Chess Fast Gift Set: Book & Kit. Munro, Roxie, illus. 2004. 72p. (gr. 3). 19.95 (978-0-9704729-5-3(1)) Bright Sky Pr.

Khmelnitsky, Igor. Chess Exam & Training Guide: Rate yourself & learn how to Improve. 2004. (Illus.). 318p. per. 24.95 (978-0-9754761-2-3(2)) IamCoach.com Publishing.

Kidder, Harvey. Ajedrez Infantil. Osorio, Sergio, illus. 2005. Tr. of Chess for Children. (SPA.). 128p. (YA). (gr. 2). pap. (978-968-403-315-3(X)) Selector, S.A. de C.V.

King, Daniel. Chess. 2004. (From First Moves to Checkmate Ser.). 64p. (J). (gr. 4-8). 8.95 (978-0-7534-5820-4(9) , Kingfisher) Houghton Mifflin Co. Trade & Reference Div.

—Chess: From First Moves to Checkmate. 2001. (Illus.). 68p. (J). (gr. 4-6). tchr. ed. 16.95 (978-0-7534-5387-2(8) , Kingfisher) Houghton Mifflin Co. Trade & Reference Div.

—Chess Box Set: From First Moves to Checkmate. 2004. 64p. (J). (gr. 4-6). 14.95 (978-0-7534-5814-3(4) , Kingfisher) Houghton Mifflin Co. Trade & Reference Div.

MacDonald, Daniel & Escobar, Michael. Chess for Kids! Everything You Need to Learn & Play. 2003. 64p. (gr. 3 up). pap. 15.95 (978-1-58062-990-4(3)) Adams Media Corp.

Macenulty, David. The Chess Kid's Book of Checkmate. 2004. (McKay Chess Library for Kids). (Illus.). 208p. pap. 10.95 (978-0-8129-3594-3(2) , Random Hse. Puzzles & Games) Random Hse. Information Group.

—Chess Kid's Book of Tactics. 2003. (gr. 3-6). lib. bdg. 19.90 (978-0-613-76171-0(5)) Tandem Library Bks.

—The Chess Kid's Book of Tactics. 2003. (McKay Chess Library for Kids). (Illus.). 176p. pap. 10.95 (978-0-8129-3509-7(8) , Random Hse. Puzzles & Games) Random Hse. Information Group.

Powell, Michael. Play Chess! Knight, Kevin, illus. 2005. 48p. (J). 14.95 (978-1-4027-2840-2(9)) Sterling Publishing Co., Inc.

Rau, Dana Meachen. Chess. 2004. (Games Around the World Ser.). 32p. (J). (gr. 3 up). lib. bdg. 22.60 (978-0-7565-0674-2(3)) Compass Point Bks.

Roza, Greg. Checkmate! The Game of Chess: Applying Strategies from Simpler Problems to Complex Problems. 2004. (PowerMath Ser.). (Illus.). 32p. (J). lib. bdg. 22.50 (978-0-8239-8996-6(8) , PowerKids Pr.) Rosen Publishing Group, Inc., The.

—The Game of Chess: Learning to Apply Strategies from Simpler Problems to More Complex Problems. 2004. (PowerMath Ser.). (Illus.). 32p. (J). lib. bdg. (978-0-8239-8925-6(9) , PowerKids Pr.) Rosen Publishing Group, Inc., The.

Schneider, Stephen A. Chess Basics. (J). 2002. 114p. per. 22.50 (978-0-9729456-0-8(1)); 2005. (ENG.). per. 22.50 (978-0-9729456-6-0(0)) Championship Chess.

—Endgame Strategies 1. 2003. (Illus.). per. 22.50 (978-0-9729456-4-6(4)) Championship Chess.

Schneider, Stephen A. Endgame Strategies 1: 2nd Edition. 2nd ed. 2005. 195p. (J). per., act. bk. ed. 24.50 ***978-0-9729456-7-7(9))** Championship Chess.

Scholastic, Inc. Staff, et al. How to Play Chess! Tactics, Traps, & Tips for Beginners. Rath, Robert, illus. 2004. 48p. (J). pap. 8.99 (978-0-439-55129-8(3) , Tangerine Pr.) Scholastic, Inc.

Seirawan, Yasser. Competitive Chess for Kids: (Includes Chess Clock) 1998. (Illus.). 64p. (J). (gr. 3 up). 13.95 (978-0-7641-7186-4(0)) Barron's Educational Series, Inc.

Snyder, Robert M. Unbeatable Chess Lessons for Juniors. 2003. (Illus.). 272p. 15.95 (978-0-8129-3511-0(X) , Random Hse. Puzzles & Games) Random Hse. Information Group.

—Unbeatable Chess Lessons for Juniors. 2003. (gr. 5-8). lib. bdg. 25.70 (978-0-613-76170-3(7)) Tandem Library Bks.

—Winning Chess Tournaments for Juniors. 2004. (Illus.). 208p. pap. 14.95 (978-0-8129-3635-3(3) , Random Hse. Puzzles & Games) Random Hse. Information Group.

Summerscale, Claire. Chess. 2006. (Illus.). 72p. (J). 16.99 (978-0-7566-2147-6(X)) Dorling Kindersley Publishing, Inc.

Watt, Fiona. Complete Book of Chess. 2004. (Chess Guides). (Illus.). 96p. (J). pap., act. bk. ed. 17.95 (978-0-7945-0371-0(3) , Usborne) EDC Publishing.

Williams, Gareth. Chess: An Easy-to-Follow Illustrated Guide to Playing This Popular Game of Skill. 2002. (Illus.). 64p. (J). pap. 9.98 (978-0-7525-5965-0(6)) Parragon, Inc.

CHESS—FICTION

Bailey, Len. Clabbernappers. 2005. (Illus.). 224p. (J). 17.95 (978-0-7653-0981-5(5) , Tor Bks.) Doherty, Tom Assocs., LLC.

Bontempelli, Massimo. The Chess Set in the Mirror. Gilson, Estelle, tr. from ITA. 2007. (Illus.). 120p. (YA). (gr. 5 up). pap. 9.95 (978-1-58988-031-3(5)) Dry, Paul Bks., Inc.

Cool Moves: Individual Chapter Book Title Six-Pack. Vol. 29. 32p. (gr. 5 up). 44.00 (978-0-7578-0976-7(6)) Rigby Education.

DeLaCroix, Alice. How to Survive a Totally Boring Summer. Fisher, Cynthia, illus. 2007. 96p. (J). (gr. 1-4). 16.95 ***978-0-8234-2024-7(8))** Holiday Hse., Inc.

Freymann-Weyr, Garret. The Kings Are Already Here. 2003. 160p. (YA). (gr. 7). tchr. ed. 15.00 (978-0-618-26363-9(2)) Houghton Mifflin Co. Trade & Reference Div.

Mahony, Mary. Stand Tall, Harry. Pasternack, Susan, ed. Larkin, Catherine, illus. 2002. 200p. (J). (gr. 4). pap. 14.95 (978-0-9658879-2-2(8)) Redding Pr.

Morpurgo, Michael. Black Queen. Ross, Tony, illus. 2000. (Young Corgi Ser.). 96p. (J). pap. 7.99 (978-0-552-54645-4(3) , Corgi) Transworld Publishers Ltd. GBR. *Dist:* Independent Pubs. Group.

Neri, G. Chess Rumble. Watson, Jesse Joshua, illus. 2007. 64p. (J). (gr. 3-7). 18.95 ***978-1-58430-279-7(8))** Lee & Low Bks., Inc.

Wong, Janet S. Alex & the Wednesday Chess Club. Schuett, Stacey, illus. 2004. 40p. (J). 16.95 (978-0-689-85890-1(6) , McElderry, Margaret K.) Simon & Schuster Children's Publishing.

CHESTER CRICKET (FICTITIOUS CHARACTER)—FICTION

Selden, George. The Cricket in Times Square. Williams, Garth, illus. 2002. (J). 14.47 (978-0-7587-0252-4(3)) Book Wholesalers, Inc.

—The Cricket in Times Square. Williams, Garth, illus. 1999. (Chester Cricket Ser.). 32p. (J). (gr. 3-6). 9.95 (978-1-56137-396-3(6)) Novel Units, Inc.

—The Cricket in Times Square. Williams, Garth, illus. (Chester Cricket Ser.). 151p. (J). (gr. 3-6). pap. 5.50 (978-0-8072-8311-0(8) , Listening Library) Random Hse. Audio Publishing Group.

—The Cricket in Times Square. unabr. ed. 2004. (Chester Cricket Ser.). 151p. (J). (gr. 3-7). pap. 29.00 incl. audio (978-0-8072-8310-3(X) , S YA 158 SP, Listening Library) Random Hse. Audio Publishing Group.

—The Cricket in Times Square. 1998. (Chester Cricket Ser.). (J). (gr. 3-6). pap. 3.95 (978-0-439-04463-9(4)) Scholastic, Inc.

—The Old Meadow. 2000. (Chester Cricket Ser.). (J). (gr. 3-6). (978-0-606-20135-3(1)) Tandem Library Bks.

CHET GECKO (FICTITIOUS CHARACTER)—FICTION

Hale, Bruce. The Big Nap. Hale, Bruce, illus. (Chet Gecko Mystery Ser.: No. 4). (Illus.). (J). 2002. 132p. (ps-7). pap. 4.95 (978-0-15-202479-6(4) , Harcourt Paperbacks); 2001. 128p. (gr. 3-7). 15.00 (978-0-15-202521-2(9)) Harcourt Children's Bks.

—The Big Nap: From the Tattered Casebook of Chet Gecko, Private Eye. 2002. (Chet Gecko Mystery Ser.: No. 4). (J). (gr. 3-6). lib. bdg. 12.95 (978-0-613-50549-9(2)) Tandem Library Bks.

—The Chameleon Wore Chartreuse: A Chet Gecko Mystery. Hale, Bruce, illus. 2000. (Chet Gecko Mystery Ser.: No. 1). (Illus.). 112p. (J). (gr. 2-5). 14.00 (978-0-15-202281-5(3)) Harcourt Children's Bks.

—The Chameleon Wore Chartreuse: A Chet Gecko Mystery. 2001. (Chet Gecko Mystery Ser.: No. 1). (J). (gr. 3-6). lib. bdg. 12.95 (978-0-613-35450-9(8)); (Illus.). 11.60 (978-0-606-21105-5(5)) Tandem Library Bks.

—Farewell, My Lunchbag: A Chet Gecko Mystery. 2002. (Chet Gecko Mystery Ser.: No. 3). (Illus.). 132p. (ps-7). pap. 4.95 (978-0-15-202629-5(0) , Harcourt Paperbacks) Harcourt Children's Bks.

—Farewell, My Lunchbag: A Chet Gecko Mystery. Hale, Bruce, illus. 2001. (Chet Gecko Mystery Ser.: No. 3). (Illus.). 128p. (J). (gr. 3-7). 15.00 (978-0-15-202275-4(9)) Harcourt Children's Bks.

—Farewell, My Lunchbag: A Chet Gecko Mystery. 2002. (Chet Gecko Mystery Ser.: No. 3). (J). (gr. 3-6). lib. bdg. 12.95 (978-0-613-49734-3(1)) Tandem Library Bks.

—The Hamster of the Baskervilles: A Chet Gecko Mystery. (Chet Gecko Mystery Ser.: No. 5). (Illus.). (J). 2003. 144p. (gr. 3-7). pap. 4.95 (978-0-15-202509-0(X) , Harcourt Paperbacks); 2002. 132p. (gr. 4-7). 14.00 (978-0-15-202503-8(0)) Harcourt Children's Bks.

—The Malted Falcon: A Chet Gecko Mystery. (Chet Gecko Mystery Ser.: No. 7). (Illus.). (J). (gr. 3-7). 2004. 132p. pap. 4.95 (978-0-15-216712-7(9) , Harcourt Paperbacks); 2003. 128p. 14.00 (978-0-15-216706-6(4)) Harcourt Children's Bks.

—The Malted Falcon: A Chet Gecko Mystery. 2004. (Chet Gecko Mystery Ser.: No. 7). (J). (gr. 3-6). lib. bdg. 12.95 (978-0-613-71645-1(0)) Tandem Library Bks.

—Murder, My Tweet: A Chet Gecko Mystery. (Chet Gecko Mystery Ser.: No. 10). (Illus.). (J). (gr. 3-6). 2005. 132p. pap. 4.95 (978-0-15-205219-5(4) , Harcourt Paperbacks); 2004. 136p. 15.00 (978-0-15-205012-2(4)) Harcourt Children's Bks.

—The Mystery of Mr. Nice. 2001. (Chet Gecko Mystery Ser.: No. 2). (J). (gr. 3-7). lib. bdg. 12.95 (978-0-613-35466-0(4)) Tandem Library Bks.

—This Gum for Hire: A Chet Gecko Mystery. (Chet Gecko Mystery Ser.: No. 6). (Illus.). (J). (gr. 3-7). 2003. 144p. pap. 4.95 (978-0-15-202497-0(2) , Harcourt Paperbacks); 2002. 136p. 15.00 (978-0-15-202491-8(3)) Harcourt Children's Bks.

—This Gum for Hire: A Chet Gecko Mystery. 2003. (Chet Gecko Mystery Ser.: No. 6). (J). (gr. 3-6). lib. bdg. 12.95 (978-0-613-59895-8(4)) Tandem Library Bks.

CHICAGO (ILL.)

Adams, Colleen. A Weekend in the City: Adding & Subtracting Times to the Nearest Minute. 2004. (PowerMath Ser.). (Illus.). 24p. (J). lib. bdg. (978-0-8239-8897-6(X) , PowerKids Pr.) Rosen Publishing Group, Inc., The.

Avis, Ed. The Lobster Kids' Guide to Exploring Chicago. Battuz, Christine, illus. 2001. (Lobster Kids' City Explorers Ser.). 237p. (J). (ps-3). pap. 12.95 (978-1-894222-40-2(7)) Lobster Pr. CAN. *Dist:* Univ. of Toronto Pr.

Brent, Lynnette R. Chicago. 2002. (Illus.). 32p. (J). pap. 6.95 (978-1-4034-0703-0(7)); (gr. 3-5). lib. bdg. 24.22 (978-1-4034-0013-0(X)) Heinemann Library.

Carole Marsh. Chicago Coloring & Activity Book. 2004. (City Bks.). 24p. (gr. k-5). pap. 3.95 (978-0-635-02227-1(3)) Gallopade International.

Chicago Gold C 2005. 2004. 452p. (YA). pap. 15.00 (978-1-58553-949-9(X) , 05GC0006) Entertainment Publications, Inc.

Crimi, Carolyn. Kidding Around Chicago: What to Do, Where to Go & How to Have Fun in Chicago. 2nd ed. 2000. (Kidding Around! Ser.). (Illus.). 144p. (gr. 1-5). pap. 8.95 (978-1-56261-587-1(4)) Avalon Travel Publishing.

Dorling Kindersley Publishing Staff. Top 10 Chicago: Eyewitness Top 10 Travel Guides. 2004. (Eyewitness Travel Guides). (Illus.). 128p. pap. 12.00 (978-0-7566-0031-0(6)) Dorling Kindersley Publishing, Inc.

Furstinger, Nancy. Chicago. 2005. (Cities Ser.). (Illus.). 32p. (J). (gr. k-6). lib. bdg. 22.78 (978-1-59197-857-2(2)) ABDO Publishing Co.

Gamble, Adam. Good Night Chicago. Veno, Joe, illus. 2006. (Good Night Our World Ser.). 20p. (J). bds. 9.95 (978-0-9777979-2-9(9)) Our World of Books.

Murray, Julie. Sears Tower. 2005. (Buddy Book Ser.). (Illus.). 24p. (J). (gr. k-4). lib. bdg. 21.35 (978-1-59197-508-3(5)) ABDO Publishing Co.

Neri, Greg. Yummy: The Last Days of a Southside Shorty. DuBurke, Randy, illus. 2007. (J). (978-1-58430-266-7(6)); pap. (978-1-58430-267-4(4)) Lee & Low Bks., Inc.

Nobleman, Marc Tyler. Chicago. 2004. (Great Cities of the World Ser.). (Illus.). 48p. (J). pap. 15.93 (978-0-8368-5196-0(X)); (YA). lib. bdg. 30.00 (978-0-8368-5036-9(X)) Stevens, Gareth Inc. (World Almanac Library).

Roop, Peter & Roop, Connie. A City. 1999. (Walk Around Ser.). (Illus.). 32p. (J). (gr. 1-3). lib. bdg. 21.36 (978-1-57572-129-3(5)) Heinemann Library.

Segal, Robin. ABC in Chicago. 2007. 32p. (J). 12.95 (***978-0-9719697-8-0(7)***) Murray Hill Bks., LLC.

Stein, R. Conrad. The Great Chicago Fire. 2005. (Cornerstones of Freedom Ser.). (Illus.). 48p. (J). 26.00 (978-0-516-23640-7(7) , Children's Pr.) Scholastic Library Publishing.

CHICAGO (ILL.)—FICTION

Alger, Horatio. Mark Manning's Mission: The Story of a Shoe Factory Boy. unabr. ed. 2002. (Polyglot Press Alger Ser.). (Illus.). (J). pap. 17.95 (978-1-4115-0022-8(9)) Polyglot Pr., Inc.

Andracki, Zenon. Dear Ashley: A Middle Grade Novel. 2006. (ENG.). 84p. per. 14.95 (***978-1-4241-6168-3(1)***) PublishAmerica, Inc.

Augustyn, Heather. Chi-Town Coyote. 2005. 215p. pap. 12.59 (978-1-4116-3365-0(2)) Lulu.com.

Balliett, Blue. The Wright 3. Helquist, Brett, illus. (J). 2007. 352p. (gr. 4-7). pap. 6.99 (***978-0-439-69368-4(3)*** , Scholastic Paperbacks); 2006. 272p. pap. 16.99 (978-0-439-69367-7(5) , Scholastic Pr.) Scholastic, Inc.

—The Wright 3. l.t. ed. 2006. 334p. (YA). 23.95 (978-0-7862-9024-6(2)) Thorndike Pr.

Belton, Sandra. Store-Bought Baby. 2006. 256p. (J). 15.99 (978-0-06-085086-9(8)); lib. bdg. 16.89 (978-0-06-085087-6(6)) HarperCollins Pubs.

Brown, Marc. Buster on the Town. 2005. (Postcards from Buster Ser.). (Illus.). 32p. (J). (gr. 1-4). pap. 3.99 (978-0-316-00107-6(4)) Little, Brown Bks. for Young Readers.

Capelli, Katie, et al. Molly, the Super Cat, in Chicago. 2000. (J). pap. 6.95 (978-0-533-13406-9(4)) Vantage Pr., Inc.

Center for Learning Network Staff. The House on Mango Street: Curriculum Unit. 2005. (Novel Ser.). (YA). tchr. ed., spiral bd. 19.95 (978-1-56077-783-0(4)) Ctr. for Learning, The.

Cisneros. The House on Mango Street. 2000. (J). 12.81 (978-0-07-243517-7(8) , McGraw-Hill Humanities, Social Sciences & World Languages) McGraw-Hill Higher Education.

Coalson, Eleanor Akin. Hannah & Emma Go to Chicago (Via CSX) Coalson, Eleanor Akin, illus. 2005. (Illus.). 18p. (J). 12.95 (978-1-56167-899-0(6)) American Literary Pr.

Codell, Esmé Raji. Sahara Special. (gr. 3-7). 2004. 192p. (J). pap. 5.99 (978-0-7868-1611-8(2)); 2003. (Illus.). 208p. (J). lib. bdg. 16.49 (978-0-7868-2627-8(4)); 2003. (Illus.). 192p. 15.99 (978-0-7868-0793-2(8)) Hyperion Bks. for Children.

—Sahara Special. 2003. (gr. 3-6). lib. bdg. 14.10 (978-0-613-65611-5(3)) Tandem Library Bks.

—Vive la Paris! 2006. 224p. (J). (gr. 3-7). 15.99 (978-0-7868-5124-9(4)) Hyperion Pr.

Du Jardin, Rosamond. Young & Fair. 2003. (YA). pap. 12.95 (978-1-930009-79-0(8) , 800-691-7779) Image Cascade Publishing.

Duey, Kathleen & Bale, Karen A. Fire, Chicago, 1871. 1998. (Survival! Ser.: No. 4). (J). (gr. 4-7). (978-0-606-13828-4(5)) Tandem Library Bks.

Ferber, Edna. So Big. 2000. (gr. 7-12). lib. bdg. 22.25 (978-0-613-29347-1(9)) Tandem Library Bks.

Finley, Martha. Elsie at the Worlds Fair. 2006. 78.99 (***978-1-4280-3168-5(5)***) IndyPublish.com.

Greenburg, Dan. My Grandma, Major League Slugger. Davis, Jack E., illus. 2001. (Zack Files Ser.: No. 24). 64p. (J). (gr. 2-5). pap. 4.99 (978-0-448-42550-4(5) , Grosset & Dunlap) Penguin Group (USA) Inc.

—My Grandma, Major League Slugger. 2001. (gr. 3-6). lib. bdg. 13.00 (978-0-613-58376-3(0)) Tandem Library Bks.

Hawley, Richard. Paul & Juliana: A Novel. 2003. 188p. (YA). 19.95 (978-1-890862-33-6(9)) Bancroft Pr.

Hechtman, Betty Jacobson, Jr. & Brown Barn Books Staff. Blue Schwartz & Nefertiti's Necklace: A Mystery with Recipes. 2006. 152p. (J). (gr. 5-9). pap. 8.95 (978-0-9768126-3-0(0)) Brown Barn Bks.

Hoobler, Dorothy & Hoobler, Thomas. The 1920s: Luck. Hoffman, Robin, illus. 2000. (Century Kids Ser.). 160p. (J). (gr. 5-8). lib. bdg. 22.90 (978-0-7613-1602-2(7) , Twenty-First Century Bks.) Lerner Publishing Group.

Jenkins, Jerry B. & Fabry, Chris. Windy City Danger. 2006. (Red Rock Mysteries Ser.). 246p. (J). pap. 5.99 (978-1-4143-0150-1(2)) Tyndale Hse. Pubs.

Jenkins, John L. & Weaver, Mark W. City of Lies. Morales, Steven P., illus. 1998. (Century War Chronicles: Vol. 2). 160p. (YA). (gr. 6 up). per. 7.95 (978-1-888565-04-1(7) , Reconciliation Pr.) Trinity Rivers Publishing, Inc.

King, Katina. Ride Wit' Me. 2006. 144p. (J). pap. 12.00 (***978-0-9724003-8-1(9)***) Power Play Media.

Lamstein, Sarah. Hunger Moon. 2004. (Illus.). 112p. (YA). 15.95 (978-1-932425-05-5(5) , Lemniscaat) Boyds Mills Pr.

Lenhard, Elizabeth. It's a Purl Thing. (YA). 2006. 288p. (gr. 7). pap. 6.99 (978-0-14-240695-3(3) , Puffin); 2005. (Illus.). 272p. (gr. 6-10). 16.99 (978-0-525-47622-1(9) , Dutton Juvenile) Penguin Group (USA) Inc.

—Knit Two Together. 272p. (gr. 7). 2008. (YA). pap. 7.99 (***978-0-14-241013-4(6)*** , Puffin); 2006. (J). 16.99 (978-0-525-47764-8(0) , Dutton Juvenile) Penguin Group (USA) Inc.

—Knitwise. 2007. 272p. (YA). (gr. 7). 16.99 (***978-0-525-47838-6(8)*** , Dutton Juvenile) Penguin Group (USA) Inc.

Lockwood, Cara. Wuthering High. 2006. (Bard Academy Ser.: No. 1). 272p. pap. 9.95 (978-1-4165-2475-5(4) , MTV) Simon & Schuster.

Lollino, Jessica. Little Lily Mays & the Daddy Dilemma. Kendrick-TaZiyah, Brandi, illus. 2006. (Little Lily Mays Ser.: vol. 1). 32p. (J). per. 20.00 (978-0-9712383-1-2(6)) Culture Connection, The.

Marsh, Carole. The Mystery of the Chicago Dinosaurs. 2003. lib. bdg. 14.10 (978-0-613-73040-2(2)) Tandem Library Bks.

Martino, Carmela. Rosa, Sola. 2005. 256p. (J). (gr. 4-7). 15.99 (978-0-7636-2395-1(4)) Candlewick Pr.

McKissack, Patricia C. Color Me Dark: The Diary of Nellie Lee Love, the Great Migration North, Chicago, Illinois, 1919. 2000. (Dear America Ser.). (J). 9.95 (978-0-439-26653-6(X)) Scholastic, Inc.

—Color Me Dark: The Diary of Nellie Lee Love, the Great Migration North, Chicago, Illinois, 1919. 2000. (Dear America Ser.). (Illus.). 224p. (J). (gr. 4-9). pap. 10.95 (978-0-590-51159-9(7)) Scholastic, Inc.

McNeece, Alexander. Sam Iver: Imminent Threat. 2007. 140p. per. 11.95 (***978-0-595-43260-8(3)***) iUniverse, Inc.

Naylor, Phyllis Reynolds. Cuckoo Feathers. Ramsey, Marcy Dunn, illus. 2006. 96p. (J). 14.95 (978-0-7614-5285-0(0)) Cavendish, Marshall Corp.

Nixon, Joan Lowery. Land of Promise. l.t. ed. 2001. (Ellis Island Stories Ser.). 169p. (J). (gr. 4 up). lib. bdg. 23.33 (978-0-8368-2812-2(7)) Stevens, Gareth Inc.

Peck, Richard. Fair Weather. 2001. (Illus.). 160p. (J). (gr. 4-8). 16.99 (978-0-8037-2516-4(7) , Dial) Penguin Group (USA) Inc.

—Fair Weather. 2004. 146p. (J). (gr. 5-9). pap. 36.00 incl. audio (978-0-8072-2038-2(8) , Listening Library) Random Hse. Audio Publishing Group.

Pinkwater, Daniel M. The Education of Robert Nifkin. ed. 2005. 192p. (YA). (gr. 7). pap. 6.99 (978-0-618-55208-5(1) , Graphia) Houghton Mifflin Co. Trade & Reference Div.

Poyner, James R. Toy-Maker's Apprentice. 2006. 68p. (YA). per. 12.00 (***978-1-60002-282-1(0)*** , 4145, Airleaf Publishing) Airleaf Publishing & Bookselling.

Price, Dianne D. Enemy in the House: The Story of a Young Friendship Born of War in America. 2003. 123p. pap. 14.95 (978-1-59286-483-6(X)) PublishAmerica, Inc.

Raintree Steck-Vaughn Staff. Simon's Big Challenge. 1999. (Illus.). (J). pap. 35.60 (978-0-7398-0909-9(1)) Steck-Vaughn.

Raskin, Ellen. Westing Game. 2003. 182p. (J). lib. bdg. 15.00 (***978-1-4242-2271-1(0)***) Fitzgerald Bks.

Robinet, Harriette Gillem. Children of the Fire. 2001. (Illus.). 144p. (J). (gr. 3-7). pap. 5.99 (978-0-689-83968-9(5) , Aladdin) Simon & Schuster Children's Publishing.

—Children of the Fire. 2001. (J). 11.64 (978-0-606-20601-3(9)); (gr. 3-6). lib. bdg. 13.00 (978-0-613-33685-7(2)) Tandem Library Bks.

—Missing from Haymarket Square. 2003. (Illus.). 142p. (J). pap. 4.99 (978-0-689-85490-3(0) , Aladdin) Simon & Schuster Children's Publishing.

—Missing from Haymarket Square. 2003. (gr. 5-8). lib. bdg. 13.00 (978-0-613-61643-0(X)) Tandem Library Bks.

Rue, Nancy N. The Pursuit. 2000. (Christian Heritage Ser.). 192p. (J). (gr. 3-7). pap. 5.99 (978-1-56179-856-8(8)) Bethany Hse. Pubs.

—Pursuit. 2000. (gr. 3-6). lib. bdg. 14.15 (978-0-613-86405-3(0)) Tandem Library Bks.

—The Stunt. 1999. (Christian Heritage Ser.). 208p. (J). (gr. 3-7). pap. 5.99 (978-1-56179-833-9(9)) Bethany Hse. Pubs.

Schreiber, Mark. Starcrossed. 2007. 336p. (J). (gr. 9 up). pap. 8.95 (978-0-7387-1001-3(6) , Flux) Llewellyn Pubns.

Showalter, Gena. Black Listed. 2007. 256p. pap. 9.95 (***978-1-4165-3225-5(0)*** , MTV) Simon & Schuster.

Simmons, Michael. Vandal. 2006. 176p. (YA). 16.95 (978-1-59643-070-9(2)) Roaring Brook Pr.

Sinclair, Upton. Jungle. 2001. (gr. 7-12). lib. bdg. 14.10 (978-0-613-46082-8(0)) Tandem Library Bks.

Sinclair, Upton, et al. The Jungle. (Classics Illustrated Ser.). (Illus.). 52p. (YA). pap. 4.95 (978-1-57209-025-5(1)) Classics International Entertainment, Inc.

Smith, Jennifer E. The Comeback Season. 2008. 256p. (YA). 15.99 (***978-1-4169-3847-7(8)*** , Simon & Schuster Children's Publishing) Simon & Schuster Children's Publishing.

Steck-Vaughn Staff. Simon's Big Challenge/Over-Comming Challenges: The Life of Charles F. Bolden Jr. 1999. (Take Me Home Ser.). (J). pap. 11.30 (978-0-7398-0944-0(X)) Steck-Vaughn.

Thill, Mary Kay. Wablenica: The Tale of a Lakotah Orphan. 2004. 240p. (J). per. (978-0-9743908-0-2(1) , 1232791) Balance Bks., Inc.

TJ & the Mysterious Stranger. 2004. (J). bds. 16.95 (978-0-9710487-2-0(X)) Highlights of Chicago Pr.

Wacker, Mary Langley. Landmarks. 2002. 211p. (gr. 8-12). pap. 19.95 (978-1-59129-374-3(X)) PublishAmerica, Inc.

Walsh, Alice. Pomiuk, Prince of the North. Whitehead, Jerry, illus. 2006. 64p. (J). pap., tchr. ed. 6.95 (978-0-88878-447-6(3) , Sandcastle Bks.) Dundurn Group, The CAN. *Dist:* Univ. of Toronto Pr.

Warner, Gertrude Chandler. The Windy City Mystery. Tang, Charles, illus. 1998. 120p. (J). (ps-7). per. 11.80 (978-0-613-09091-9(8)) Tandem Library Bks.

Warner, Gertrude Chandler, creator. The Windy City Mystery. Vol. 10. 1998. (Boxcar Children Special Ser.: No. 10). (Illus.). 144p. (J). (gr. 2-5). 14.95 (978-0-8075-5447-0(2)); pap. 4.50 (978-0-8075-5448-7(0)) Whitman, Albert & Co.

Wartik, David J. The Vonnesta Project. 2006. 140p. (J). (gr. 3-6). pap. 12.95 (978-1-59113-938-6(4)) Booklocker-.com, Inc.

Welling, Peter J. Darlene Halloween & the Great Chicago Fire. Welling, Peter J., illus. 2007. 32p. (J). (gr. k-3). 15.95 (***978-1-58980-479-1(1)***) Pelican Publishing Co., Inc.

Woodson, J. L. The Things I Could Tell You! Malone, Susan Mary et al, eds. collector's ed. 2003. 206p. pap. 14.95 (978-0-9702699-6-6(X)) Macro Publishing Group.

Yaroslavskaya, Lyudmila. The Great Lakes Legends & Fairy Tales. 2006. (ENG & RUS., Illus.). (J). per. (***978-0-9791248-0-8(8)***) Yaroslavskaya, Lyudmila.

Zuehlke, Karen. Welcome to Janie's World. 2006. (ENG.). 76p. per. 14.95 (***978-1-4241-4587-4(2)***) PublishAmerica, Inc.

CHICAGO (ILL.)—HISTORY

Balcavage, Dynise. Chicago Fire of 1871. 2000. (Great Disasters Ser.). (Illus.). 128p. (J). (gr. 4-7). 21.95 (978-0-7910-5269-3(9) , Chelsea Hse.) Facts On File, Inc.

Brexel, Bernadette. The Knights of Labor & the Haymarket Riot: The Fight for an Eight-Hour Workday. 2003. (America's Industrial Society in the 19th Century Ser.). (Illus.). 32p. (J). pap. (978-0-8239-4283-1(X)) Rosen Publishing Group, Inc., The.

Burgan, Michael. The Haymarket Square Tragedy. 2005. (We the People Ser.). (Illus.). 48p. (J). (gr. 4-6). 23.93 (978-0-7565-1265-1(4)) Compass Point Bks.

Chicago Historical Society Staff. ABC History Mystery. 2001. (Illus.). 64p. (J). 14.95 (978-0-913820-23-0(7)) Chicago Historical Society.

Dybwad, G. L. & Bliss, Joy V. White City Recollections: The Illustrated 1893 Diary of Friend Pitts Williams' Trip to the World's Columbian Exposition. 2nd ed. 2003. (Illus.). 180p. per. 18.95 (978-0-9631612-2-2(9)) Book Stops Here.

Fireside, Bryna J. The Haymarket Square Riot Trial: A Headline Court Case. 2002. (Headline Court Cases Ser.). (Illus.). 128p. (YA). (gr. 6-12). lib. bdg. 26.60 (978-0-7660-1761-0(3)) Enslow Pubs., Inc.

Gutner, Howard. The Chicago Fire. 2002. (Illus.). 16p. (J). (978-0-439-35168-3(5)) Scholastic, Inc.

Hurd, Owen. Chicago History for Kids: Triumphs & Tragedies of the Windy City Includes 21 Activities. 2007. (For Kids Ser.). (Illus.). 192p. (YA). (gr. 4-9). pap. 14.95 (***978-1-55652-654-1(7)***) Chicago Review Pr., Inc.

Marsh, Carole. Jean Baptiste Pointe du Sable. 2002. (One Thousand Readers Ser.). (Illus.). 12p. (J). (gr. k-4). 2.95 (978-0-635-01556-3(0) , 15560) Gallopade International.

Massie, Elizabeth. The Great Chicago Fire, 1871. 1999. (Illus.). (J). (978-0-606-18370-3(1)) Tandem Library Bks.

McHugh, Janet. The Great Chicago Fire. 2007. (Code Red Ser.). (Illus.). 32p. (J). lib. bdg. 25.27 (978-1-59716-360-6(0)) Bearport Publishing Co., Inc.

Murphy, Jim. The Great Fire. 2006. 144p. (J). pap. 8.99 (978-0-439-20307-4(4) , Scholastic Paperbacks) Scholastic, Inc.

Nobleman, Marc Tyler. The Great Chicago Fire. 2005. (We the People Ser.). (Illus.). 48p. (J). (gr. 4-6). (978-0-7565-1263-7(8) , 1244096) Compass Point Bks.

Olson, Kay Melchisedech. The Great Chicago Fire of 1871. Miller, Phil & Barnett, Charles, illus. 2006. (Graphic Library). 32p. (J). (978-0-7368-5480-1(0)) Capstone Pr., Inc.

Stein, R. Conrad. The Great Chicago Fire. 2007. (Cornerstones of Freedomtrade;, Second Ser.). 48p. (J). pap. 5.95 (***978-0-531-18766-1(7)*** , Children's Pr.) Scholastic Library Publishing.

VandeCreek, Drew E. The Great Chicago Fire. 2007. (Essential Events Ser.). (ENG., Illus.). 112p. (YA). (gr. 8-12). lib. bdg. 32.79 (***978-1-59928-851-2(6)*** , Essential Library) ABDO Publishing Co.

Yancey, Diane. Al Capone's Chicago. 2003. (Travel Guide to Ser.). (Illus.). 112p. (J). 29.95 (978-1-59018-248-2(0) , Lucent Bks.) Thomson Gale.

CHICAGO BEARS (FOOTBALL TEAM)

Chicago Bears Staff. Chicago Bears: NFL Today. CWC Sports Inc., ed. 1998. (NFL Team Yearbooks Ser.). 32p. (J). (gr. 1-12). pap. 9.99 (978-1-891613-03-6(0)) Everett Sports Publishing & Marketing.

Frisch, Aaron. Chicago Bears. 2005. (Super Bowl Champions Ser.). (Illus.). 24p. (J). (gr. 1-4). 16.95 (978-1-58341-381-4(2) , Creative Education) Creative Co., The.

—Chicago Bears, the History. 2004. (NFL Today Ser.). (Illus.). 32p. 18.95 (978-1-58341-291-6(3) , Creative Education) Creative Co., The.

Stewart, Mark & Aikens, Jason. The Chicago Bears. 2008. (J). (***978-1-59953-121-2(6)***) Norwood Hse. Pr.

CHICAGO CUBS (BASEBALL TEAM)

Aryal, Aimee. Let's Go Cubs. de Angel, Miguel, illus. 2007. (J). 17.95 (***978-1-932888-84-3(5)***) Mascot Bks., Inc.

Epstein, Brad M. Chicago Cubs 101: My first Team-board-book. l.t. ed. 2007. (101—My First Text-Board Books). (Illus.). 22p. (J). bds. 10.95 (***978-1-932530-77-3(0)*** , 101 Bk.) Michaelson Entertainment.

Frisch, Aaron. Chicago Cubs. 2002. (J). pap. 5.95 (978-0-89812-337-1(2) , Creative Paperbacks); (Illus.). 32p. (978-1-58341-203-9(4) , Creative Education) Creative Co., The.

Goodman, Michael E. The History of the Chicago Cubs. 1998. (Baseball, the Great American Game Ser.). (Illus.). 32p. (YA). (gr. 3-12). pap. 21.30 (978-0-88682-903-2(8) , Creative Education) Creative Co., The.

Klein, Frederick C. For the Love of the Cubs: An A to Z Primer for Cubs Fans of All Ages. Anderson, Mark, illus. 2003. 36p. (J). 16.95 (978-1-57243-545-2(3)) Triumph Bks.

Klein, Fredrick. For Love of the Cubs: An A-to-Z Primer for Fans of All Ages. 2nd ed. 2004. (Illus.). 48p. 16.95 (978-1-57243-646-6(8)) Triumph Bks.

Layden, Joe. Heroe del Jonron: La Historia de Sammy Sosa, 1 vol. 1998. (SPA., Illus.). 58p. (J). (gr. 2-9). pap. 3.99 (978-0-439-07758-3(3)) Scholastic, Inc.

Omoth, Tyler. The Story of the Chicago Cubs. 2007. (J). (***978-1-58341-482-8(7)*** , Creative Education) Creative Co., The.

Stewart, Mark. The Chicago Cubs. 2006. (Team Spirit Ser.). (Illus.). 48p. (J). lib. bdg. 25.27 (978-1-59953-001-7(5)) Norwood Hse. Pr.

Stewart, Mark. Chicago Cubs. 2008. 48p. pap. 9.95 (***978-1-60357-008-4(X)***) Norwood Hse. Pr.

CHICAGO WHITE SOX (BASEBALL TEAM)

Elish, Dan. The Black Sox Scandal of 1919. 2006. (Cornerstones of Freedom Ser.). 48p. (J). (978-0-516-23631-5(8)) Children's Pr., Ltd.

Epstein, Brad M. Chicago White Sox 101: My first Team-board-book. l.t. ed. 2007. (101—My First Text-Board Books). (Illus.). 22p. (J). bds. 10.95 (***978-1-932530-98-8(3)*** , 101 Bk.) Michaelson Entertainment.

Grabowski, John F. Chicago White Sox. 2002. (Illus.). 112p. (J). 29.95 (978-1-56006-938-6(4) , Lucent Bks.) Thomson Gale.

O'Hearn, Michael. The Story of the Chicago White Sox. 2007. (J). (***978-1-58341-483-5(5)*** , Creative Education) Creative Co., The.

Pellowski, Michael. The Chicago Black Sox Baseball Scandal. 2003. (Headline Court Cases Ser.). (Illus.). 128p. (J). (gr. 6-12). lib. bdg. 26.60 (978-0-7660-2044-3(4)) Enslow Pubs., Inc.

Rambeck, Richard. The History of the Chicago White Sox. 1998. (Baseball, the Great American Game Ser.). (Illus.). 32p. (YA). (gr. 3-12). pap. 21.30 (978-0-88682-904-9(6) , Creative Education) Creative Co., The.

Stewart, Mark. Chicago White Sox. 2008. 48p. pap. 9.95 (***978-1-60357-000-8(4)***) Norwood Hse. Pr.

—Los White Sox de Chicago. Kalmanovitz, Manuel, tr. from ENG. 2007. (Team Spirit Ser.). (SPA.). (J). lib. bdg. 25.27 (***978-1-59953-101-4(1)***) Norwood Hse. Pr.

Stewart, Wayne. Chicago White Sox. 2002. 32p. (J). pap. 5.95 (978-0-89812-338-8(0) , Creative Paperbacks); (Illus.). (978-1-58341-204-6(2) , Creative Education) Creative Co., The.

CHICKEN POX

Caso, Laura M. Chicken Pox Explosion! Caso, Adolph, ed. 2000. (Illus.). 10p. (J). (gr. 2-6). pap. 7.95 (978-0-8283-2054-2(3)) Branden Bks.

Glaser, Jason. Chicken Pox. 2005. (First Facts Ser.). (Illus.). 24p. (J). (gr. 1-3). 21.26 (978-0-7368-4288-4(8)) Capstone Pr., Inc.

Gordon, Sharon. Chickenpox. 2002. (Rookie Read-About Health Ser.). (Illus.). 32p. (J). (gr. k-2). pap. 5.95 (978-0-516-26871-2(6)); 20.50 (978-0-516-22567-8(7)) Scholastic Library Publishing. (Children's Pr.).

—Chickenpox. 2002. (gr. k-3). lib. bdg. 14.10 (978-0-613-50672-4(3)) Tandem Library Bks.

Plumb, Jennifer. Everything You Need to Know about Chicken Pox & Shingles. 2001. (Need to Know Library). (Illus.). 64p. (YA). (gr. 4-6). lib. bdg. 25.25 (978-0-8239-3323-5(7)) Rosen Publishing Group, Inc., The.

Royston, Angela. Chicken Pox. 2001. (It's Catching Ser.). (Illus.). 32p. (J). (gr. k-2). lib. bdg. 21.36 (978-1-58810-226-3(2)) Heinemann Library.

Silverstein, Alvin, et al. Chicken Pox & Shingles. 1998. (Diseases & People Ser.). (Illus.). 128p. (YA). (gr. 6-12). lib. bdg. 26.60 (978-0-89490-715-9(8)) Enslow Pubs., Inc.

—Chickenpox. 2001. (My Health Ser.). (Illus.). 48p. (J). (gr. 3-5). pap. 6.95 (978-0-531-13970-7(0)); 25.50 (978-0-531-11782-8(0)) Scholastic Library Publishing. (Watts, Franklin).

CHICKEN POX—FICTION

Bottner, Barbara. Marsha Makes Me Sick. 1999. (J). (978-0-606-16139-8(2)) Tandem Library Bks.

Brown, Marc. Arthur's Chicken Pox. Brown, Marc, illus. 2002. (Arthur Adventure Ser.). (Illus.). (J). 13.15 (978-0-7587-1978-2(7)) Book Wholesalers, Inc.

—Arthur's Chicken Pox. Brown, Marc, illus. 1999. (Arthur Adventure Ser.). (Illus.). 30p. (J). (ps-k). bds. 5.95 (978-0-316-11953-5(9)) Little, Brown Bks. for Young Readers.

—Arthur's Chicken Pox. 1998. (Arthur Adventure Ser.). 32p. (J). (ps-3). 9.95 (978-0-316-11947-4(4)) Little, Brown Bks. for Young Readers.

—Arturo Tiene Varicela. Sarfatti, Esther, tr. from ENG. 2001. (SPA., Illus.). (J). (gr. k-2). pap. 6.95 (978-1-930332-00-3(9) , LC30182) Lectorum Pubns., Inc.

—Arturo Tiene Varicela. 2001. 13.75 (978-0-606-22646-2(X)); (SPA.). lib. bdg. 15.25 (978-0-613-64340-5(2)) Tandem Library Bks.

Cazet, Denys. Grandpa Spanielson's Chicken Pox Stories No. 1: The Octopus. Cazet, Denys, illus. 2005. (I Can Read Bks.). (Illus.). 48p. (J). (ps-3). lib. bdg. 16.89 (978-0-06-051089-3(7)) HarperCollins Pubs.

—Octopus. Cazet, Denys, illus. 2005. (I Can Read Bks.). (Illus.). 48p. (J). (ps-3). 15.99 (978-0-06-051088-6(9)) HarperCollins Pubs.

—Octopus No. 1: Grandpa Spanielson's Chicken Pox Stories. Cazet, Denys, illus. 2006. (I Can Read Bks.). 48p. (J). pap. 3.99 (978-0-06-051092-3(7) , Harper Trophy) HarperCollins Pubs.

—Shrunken Head. Cazet, Denys, illus. 2008. (I Can Read Bks.: No. 3). 48p. (J). pap. 3.99 (***978-0-06-073015-4(3)*** , Harper Trophy) HarperCollins Pubs.

Cazet, Denys. Shrunken Head No. 3: Grandpa Spanielson's Chicken Pox Stories. Cazet, Denys, illus. 2007. (I Can Read Bks.). (Illus.). 48p. (J). (gr. k-2). 15.99 (978-0-06-073013-0(7)); lib. bdg. 16.89 (978-0-06-073014-7(5)) HarperCollins Pubs.

Crandall, Sharon Olexa. Sick Bay. Kemp, Sue, illus. 2001. 24p. (J). pap. 14.95 incl. audio compact disk (978-0-9662378-5-6(4)) Astoria Productions.

Danziger, Paula. You Can't Eat Your Chicken Pox, Amber Brown. (Amber Brown Ser.: No. 2). 101p. (J). (gr. 3-6). pap. 3.50 (978-0-8072-1290-5(3) , Listening Library) Random Hse. Audio Publishing Group.

—You Can't Eat Your Chicken Pox, Amber Brown. Ross, Tony, illus. 2006. (Amber Brown Ser.). 112p. (J). (gr. 2). pap. 4.99 (978-0-14-240629-8(5) , Puffin) Penguin Group (USA) Inc.

Dealey, Erin. Goldie Locks Has Chicken Pox. ed. 2004. (Illus.). (J). (gr. k-3). spiral bd. (978-0-616-14572-2(1)); spiral bd. (978-0-616-14573-9(X)) Canadian National Institute for the Blind/Institut National Canadien pour les Aveugles.

—Goldie Locks Has Chicken Pox. Wakiyama, Hanako, illus. 40p. (J). 2002. 17.99 (978-0-689-82981-9(7) , Atheneum); 2005. reprint ed. 6.99 (978-0-689-87610-3(6) , Aladdin) Simon & Schuster Children's Publishing.

Fine, Anne. Poor Monty. Evans, Kevin, illus. 2004. 32p. 18.00 (978-1-4052-0161-2(4)) Egmont Bks., Ltd. GBR. *Dist:* Trafalgar Square Publishing.

Montano, Josie. Chicken Pox. . . Yuck! 2005. (Illus.). 160p. pap. (978-0-7344-0335-3(6) , Lothian Bks.) Hachette Livre Australia.

Thomas, Frances. Polly's Absolutely Worst Birthday Ever. Gardner, Sally, illus. 2003. 96p. (gr. 1-4). lib. bdg. 16.99 (978-0-385-90122-2(4) , Delacorte Bks. for Young Readers) Random Hse. Children's Bks.

CHICKENPOX

see Chicken Pox

CHICKENS

Barbé-Julien, Colette. Little Chickens. 2006. (Born to Be Wild Ser.). (Illus.). 23p. (J). lib. bdg. 22.00 (978-0-8368-6163-1(9)) Stevens, Gareth Inc.

Barnes, J. Lou. Chicks & Chickens: Learning the CH Sound. (PowerPhonics Ser.). (Illus.). (J). 2002. 24p. (gr. 1). lib. bdg. 18.50 (978-0-8239-5923-5(6)); 2001. 23p. pap. 26.40 (978-0-8239-8268-4(8)) Rosen Publishing Group, Inc., The. (PowerKids Pr.).

Chicken & Egg. 2003. (J). 36.95 (978-0-8136-9274-6(1)) Modern Curriculum Pr.

Chickens: Individual Title Six-Packs. 16p. (gr. 2 up). 36.00 (978-0-7635-9215-8(3)) Rigby Education.

Chickens Have Chicks. (Animals & Their Young Ser.). 24p. (J). 7.95 (978-0-7565-1237-8(9)) Compass Point Bks.

Chickens on the Farm, 6 vols. (gr. k-2). 28.95 (978-0-7368-9228-5(1)) Red Brick Learning.

Chicks. 2003. (Three Minute Tales Ser.). 32p. (J). 5.98 (978-0-7525-8915-2(6)); 7.95 (978-0-7525-4759-6(3)) Parragon, Inc.

Dalgleish, Sharon. Chickens. 2005. (Farm Animals Ser.). (Illus.). 32p. (J). (gr. 2-4). 23.00 (978-0-7910-8274-4(1) , Chelsea Hse.) Facts On File, Inc.

Damerow, Gail. Your Chickens: A Kid's Guide to Raising & Showing. Steege, Gwen & Driggs, Lorin, eds. 2003. (Storey's Your Ser.). (Illus.). 157p. (Orig.). (J). (gr. 4-7). pap. 14.95 (978-0-88266-823-9(4) , 66823) Storey Publishing, LLC.

Dorling Kindersley Publishing Staff. Chick. 2007. (See How They Grow Ser.). 24p. (J). (ps-1). pap. 3.99 (978-0-7566-3015-7(0)) Dorling Kindersley Publishing, Inc.

Doubleday Entertainment USA - Chickens: Down on the Farm. 2006. (J). per. 6.95 (978-1-59566-226-2(X)) QEB Publishing Inc.

Eckard, Leslie. Which Came First, the Chicken or the Egg? Sakaguchi, Judy, illus. 2001. 25p. (J). (gr. k-3). 11.99 (978-0-8054-2167-5(X)) B&H Publishing Grp.

Feldman, Thea. Who You Callin' Chicken? Green-Armytage, Stephen, photos by. 2003. (Illus.). 32p. (J). (ps-3). 14.95 (978-0-8109-4593-7(2)) Abrams, Harry N. , Inc.

Ganeri, Anita. From Egg to Chicken. 2006. (Heinemann First Library). (Illus.). 32p. (J). (978-1-4034-7867-2(8)); (978-1-4034-7858-0(9)) Heinemann Library.

Gibbons, Gail. Chicks & Chickens. 2003. (Illus.). 32p. (gr. k-3). (J). pap. 6.95 (978-0-8234-1939-5(8)); tchr. ed. 16.95 (978-0-8234-1700-1(X)) Holiday Hse., Inc.

Godwin, Sam. The Hen Can't Help It: A First Look at the Life Cycle of a Chicken. Abel, Simone, illus. 2004. (First Look Science Ser.). 32p. (C). (gr. k-3). 22.60 (978-1-4048-0653-5(9)) Picture Window Bks.

Green, Emily K. Chickens. 2007. (Illus.). 24p. (J). lib. bdg. 16.95 (978-1-60014-064-8(5)) Bellwether Media.

—Chickens. 2007. (Blastoff! Readers Ser.). 24p. (J). (gr. k-2). 18.50 (***978-0-531-17550-7(2)*** , Children's Pr.) Scholastic Library Publishing.

Havard, Christian. Face-to-Face with the Chicken. 2004. (Face-to-Face Ser.). (Illus.). 28p. (J). 9.95 (978-1-57091-455-3(9)) Charlesbridge Publishing, Inc.

Hibbert, Clare. Life of a Chicken. 2004. (Raintree Perspectives Ser.). (Illus.). 32p. (J). lib. bdg. 25.70 (978-1-4109-0536-9(5)) Raintree.

—The Life of a Chicken. 2004. (Illus.). pap. 7.50 (978-1-4109-0924-4(7)) Raintree.

—The Life of a Chicken 6-Pack. 2004. (Illus.). pap. 40.50 (978-1-4109-0931-2(X)) Raintree.

Hudak, Heather C. Chickens. 2006. (J). (978-1-59036-423-9(6)); (978-1-59036-430-7(9)) Weigl Pubs., Inc.

Jennings, Patti, illus. Fleecy Chick. 2003. (Fleecy Friends Ser.). 10p. (J). (ps). 9.99 (978-0-8431-7785-5(3) , Price Stern Sloan) Penguin Group (USA) Inc.

Kishel, Ann-Marie. Chickens & Chicks: By Ann-Marie Kishel. 2006. (First Step Nonfiction Ser.). (Illus.). 8p. (J). lib. bdg. (978-0-8225-5648-0(0) , Lerner Pubns.) Lerner Publishing Group.

Life Cycle of a Chicken. 2002. 21.95 (978-1-58810-140-2(1) , 91021) Heinemann Library.

The Life Cycle of a Chicken, Vol. 2. 2005. (Animals, Animals, Animals Ser.). (YA). (gr. k-3). (978-0-7368-3392-9(7) , Pebble Bks.) Capstone Pr., Inc.

Ling, Mary, ed. Chick. 2001. (See How They Grow Ser.). (Illus.). 24p. (J). (ps-3). pap. 5.99 (978-0-7894-7654-8(1)) Dorling Kindersley Publishing, Inc.

Macken, JoAnn Early. Chickens. 2004. (Animals That Live on the Farm Ser.). (Illus.). 24p. (J). pap. (978-0-8368-4278-4(2)); (YA). lib. bdg. 19.33 (978-0-8368-4271-5(5)) Stevens, Gareth Inc.

—Chickens: Las Gallinas. 2004. (ENG & SPA., Illus.). 24p. (J). pap. (978-0-8368-4292-0(8)); lib. bdg. 19.33 (978-0-8368-4285-2(5)) Stevens, Gareth Inc.

Madian. Bald-Headed Chicken. (J). (gr. k-2). 75.00 (978-0-669-13449-0(X)) Houghton Mifflin Co. (Schl. Div.).

Miller, Heather. My Chickens. 2000. (Welcome Bks.). (Illus.). 24p. (J). (ps-2). 17.00 (978-0-516-23105-1(7) , Children's Pr.) Scholastic Library Publishing.

Miller, Sara Swan. Chickens. 2000. (True Bks.). (Illus.). 48p. (J). (gr. 3-5). 25.00 (978-0-516-21576-1(0) , Children's Pr.) Scholastic Library Publishing.

—Chickens. 2000. (gr. 3-6). lib. bdg. 15.25 (978-0-613-54121-3(9)) Tandem Library Bks.

Murray, Julie. Chickens. (Life Cycles Ser.). 24p. (J). (gr. k-4). 2007. lib. bdg. 21.35 (***978-1-59928-704-1(8)*** , Buddy Bks.); 2002. (Illus.). lib. bdg. 21.35 (978-1-57765-649-4(0)) ABDO Publishing Co.

Nelson, Robin. From Egg to Chicken. 2003. (J). pap. 4.95 (978-0-8225-4733-4(3) , Lerner Pubns.); (Illus.). 24p. lib. bdg. 18.60 (978-0-8225-4662-7(0)) Lerner Publishing Group.

Parker, Victoria. Life as a Chicken. 2003. (Raintree Sprouts Ser.). (Illus.). 24p. (J). pap. 5.50 (978-1-4109-0656-4(6)); lib. bdg. 18.56 (978-1-4109-0630-4(2)) Raintree.

—Life as a Chicken. 2003. (ps-2). lib. bdg. 13.55 (978-0-613-78200-5(3)) Tandem Library Bks.

Patchett, Fiona. Eggs & Chicks. 2004. (Beginners Ser.). (Illus.). 32p. (J). (gr. 1 up). pap. 4.95 (978-0-7945-0166-2(4) , Usborne); lib. bdg. 12.95 (978-1-58086-482-4(1)) EDC Publishing.

Patchett, Fiona. Eggs & Chicks - Internet Referenced (Level 1) 2007. 32p. (J). 4.99 (***978-0-7945-1342-9(5)*** , Usborne) EDC Publishing.

Los Pollitos Dicen Pio. 2005. 5.99 (978-84-263-4738-1(X)) Vives, Luis Editorial (Edelvives) ESP. *Dist:* Lectorum Pubns., Inc.

Powell, Jillian. From Chick to Chicken. 2001. (How Do They Grow? Ser.). (Illus.). 32p. (J). lib. bdg. 25.69 (978-0-7398-4427-4(X)) Raintree.

Roche, Hannah. Have You Ever Seen a Chicken Hatch? 1998. (Lifecycle Spirals Ser.). (Illus.). 16p. (J). (ps-1). spiral bd. (978-1-84089-004-4(5) , 868221Q, Zero to Ten, Limited) Evans Publishing Group.

Royston, Angela. Chick. 2004. (J). lib. bdg. 27.10 (978-1-59389-162-6(8)) Chrysalis Education.

—Chick. 2001. (J). (978-0-606-22322-5(3)) Tandem Library Bks.

—Chicken. 2002. (Life Cycle of a... Ser.). (Illus.). 32p. (J). (gr. k-2). pap. 6.95 (978-1-57572-474-4(X) , 90463) Heinemann Library.

—El Pollo. Abello, Patricia, tr. from ENG. 2003. (Ciclo de la Vida de... Ser.).Tr. of Chicken. (SPA & ENG., Illus.). 32p. (J). lib. bdg. 22.79 (978-1-4034-3017-5(9)) Heinemann Library.

—El Pollo. 2003. Tr. of Chicken. (SPA.). 32p. (J). pap. 6.95 (978-1-4034-3040-3(3)) Heinemann Library.

Schuh, Mari C. Chickens on the Farm. 2001. (On the Farm Ser.). (Illus.). 24p. (J). (gr. k-1). lib. bdg. 15.93 (978-0-7368-0991-7(0) , Pebble Bks.) Capstone Pr., Inc.

—Chickens on the Farm. (On the Farm Ser.). 24p. (J). pap. 5.95 (978-0-7368-9142-4(0)) Capstone Pr., Inc.

Schwartz, David M. Chicken. Kuhn, Dwight, photos by. 2001. (Springboards into Science Ser.). (Illus.). 24p. (J). (gr. 1 up). lib. bdg. 20.67 (978-0-8368-2971-6(9)) Stevens, Gareth Inc.

Sklansky, Amy E. Where Do Chicks Come From? Paparone, Pam, illus. 2005. (Let's-Read-and-Find-Out Science Ser.). 40p. (J). (ps-1). 15.99 (978-0-06-028892-1(2)) HarperCollins Pubs.

—Where Do Chicks Come From? Paparone, Pamela, illus. 2005. (I Can Read Bks.). 40p. (J). (ps-1). pap. 5.99 (978-0-06-445212-0(3)) HarperCollins Pubs.

—Where Do Chicks Come From? Paparone, Pam, illus. 2005. (I Can Read Science Bks.). 40p. (J). (ps-1). lib. bdg. 16.89 (978-0-06-028893-8(0)) HarperCollins Pubs.

Stockland, Patricia M. In the Chicken Coop. Ouren, Todd, illus. 2007. (Barnyard Buddies Ser.). 24p. (J). (ps-2). lib. bdg. 25.65 (***978-1-60270-023-9(0)*** , Looking Glass Library) Magic Wagon.

Stone, Lynn M. Chickens Have Chicks. 2000. (Animals & Their Young Ser.). (Illus.). 24p. (J). (gr. 1 up). lib. bdg. 18.60 (978-0-7565-0000-9(1)) Compass Point Bks.

Thomson, Ruth. Chicken. 2007. (J). lib. bdg. (***978-1-4042-3715-5(1)*** , PowerKids Pr.) Rosen Publishing Group, Inc., The.

Trumbauer, Lisa. The Life Cycle of a Chicken. 2002. (Life Cycles Ser.). (Illus.). 24p. (J). (gr. k-1). lib. bdg. 15.93 (978-0-7368-1183-5(4) , Pebble Bks.) Capstone Pr., Inc.

Wolfman, Judy. Life on a Chicken Farm. Winston, David Lorenz, illus. Winston, David Lorenz, photos by. 2004. (Life on a Farm Ser.). 48p. (J). (gr. 2-5). lib. bdg. 23.93 (978-1-57505-191-8(5)) Lerner Publishing Group.

Zollman, Pam. A Chick Grows Up. 2005. (Scholastic News Nonfiction Readers Ser.). (Illus.). 24p. (J). (gr. 1-2). 19.00 (978-0-516-24944-5(4) , Children's Pr.) Scholastic Library Publishing.

CHICKENS—FICTION

Ada, Alma Flor. Daniel's Pet. Karas, G. Brian, illus. 2003. (Green Light Readers Level 1 Ser.). 24p. (J). 11.95 (978-0-15-204825-9(1)); pap. 3.95 (978-0-15-204865-5(0)) Harcourt Children's Bks. (Green Light Readers).

—Daniel's Pet. 2002. (ps-2). lib. bdg. 11.80 (978-0-613-64481-5(6)) Tandem Library Bks.

Ada, Alma Flor. Daniel's Pet: Daniel y Su Mascota. Karas, G. Brian, illus. 2008. (Green Light Readers Level 1 Ser.). (SPA & ENG.). 28p. (J). 12.95 (***978-0-15-206237-8(8)***); pap. 3.95 (***978-0-15-206243-9(2)***) Harcourt Trade Pubs.

Allard, Harry. Starlight Goes to Town. Booth, George, illus. 2007. (J). (978-0-374-37187-6(3)) Farrar, Straus & Giroux.

Allen, Jonathan. Chicken Licken: A Wickedly Funny Flap Book. 2000. (Illus.). 17p. (J). 15.95 (978-0-385-40669-7(X)) Transworld Publishers Ltd. GBR. *Dist:* Trafalgar Square Publishing.

Alonso, Fernando. La Gallina Paulina (The Little Red Hen) (Superbks./Superlibros). (SPA., Illus.). 16p. (J). (gr. k-3). pap. 6.95 (978-0-88272-465-2(7)) Santillana USA Publishing Co., Inc.

—The Little Red Hen (La Gallina Paulina) Gimeno, J. M., illus. 16p. (J). (gr. k-3). pap. 6.95 (978-0-88272-468-3(1)) Santillana USA Publishing Co., Inc.

Amato, Mary. The Chicken of the Family. Durand, Delphine, illus. 2008. 32p. (J). (ps). 16.99 (978-0-399-24196-3(5) , Putnam Juvenile) Penguin Group (USA) Inc.

Andersen, Hans Christian. For Sure! for Sure! White, Mus, tr. from DAN. Czernecki, Stefan, illus. 2006. 29p. (J). (gr. k-4). reprint ed. 17.00 (978-1-4223-5208-3(0)) DIANE Publishing Co.

Apperley, Dawn. Hello Little Chicks. Apperley, Dawn, illus. 2000. (Hello Bks.). (Illus.). 12p. (J). bds. 3.95 (978-1-86233-181-5(2)) David & Charles Children's Bks. GBR. *Dist:* Sterling Publishing Co., Inc.

Arnold, Katya R., illus. & retold by. Me Too! Two Small Stories about Small Animals. Arnold, Katya R., retold by. 2000. 32p. (J). (gr. k-3). tchr. ed. 15.95 (978-0-8234-1483-3(3)) Holiday Hse., Inc.

Arnold, Tedd. The Twin Princes. Arnold, Tedd, illus. 2007. (Illus.). 32p. (J). (ps-2). 16.99 (978-0-8037-2696-3(1) , Dial) Penguin Group (USA) Inc.

—The Twin Princes. 2007. (Illus.). (J). (***978-1-4287-3971-0(8)*** , Dial) Penguin Group (USA) Inc.

Artful Doodlers Limited Staff, illus. It's Absolutely True. 2006. (Famous Fables Ser.). (J). 6.99 (978-1-59939-029-1(9)) Reader's Digest Young Families, Inc.

Atkins, Darrin E. Cooked Chickens Falling from the Sky: And Other Illustrated Children's Stories. Durr, Michael, illus. 2002. 148p. (J). pap. 11.95 (978-0-595-21988-9(8) , Writers Club Pr.) iUniverse, Inc.

Attema, Martha. The Paper Wagon. Ross, Graham, illus. 2005. 61p. (J). lib. bdg. 20.00 (***978-1-4242-1260-6(X)***) Fitzgerald Bks.

Auch, Mary Jane. Chickarella. Auch, Herm, tr. Auch, Herm, illus. 2005. 32p. (J). 16.95 (978-0-8234-1804-6(9)) Holiday Hse., Inc.

—The Easter Egg Farm. Auch, Mary Jane, illus. (Illus.). 36p. (J). (gr. k-3). tchr. ed. 17.95 (978-0-8234-0917-4(1)) Holiday Hse., Inc.

—Peeping Beauty. Auch, Mary Jane, illus. 2002. (Illus.). (J). 15.47 (978-0-7587-3385-6(2)) Book Wholesalers, Inc.

Auch, Mary Jane. The Plot Chickens. 2008. (J). (***978-0-8234-2087-2(6)***) Holiday Hse., Inc.

Auch, Mary Jane & Auch, Herm. Souperchicken. 2003. (Illus.). 32p. (J). (gr. k-3). reprint ed. pap. 6.95 (978-0-8234 1829-9(4)) Holiday Hse., Inc.

Auch, Mary Jane & Auch, Herm, illus. Beauty & the Beaks: A Turkey's Cautionary Tale. 2007. 32p. (J). (ps-3). 16.95 (978-0-8234-1990-6(8)) Holiday Hse., Inc.

—I Was a Third Grade Bodyguard. 2003. 80p. (J). (gr. 4-6). tchr. ed. 15.95 (978-0-8234-1775-9(1)) Holiday Hse., Inc.

Auth, Tony, illus. The Hoboken Chicken Emergency. 2007. 101p. (J). (gr. 1-4). per. 4.99 (***978-1-4169-2810-2(3)*** , Aladdin) Simon & Schuster Children's Publishing.

Backstein, Karen. Little Chick's Easter Surprise. McQueen, Lucinda, illus. 2005. 8p. (J). bds. 1.99 (978-0-439-69728-6(X) , Cartwheel Bks.) Scholastic, Inc.

Barbot, Daniel. Rosaura en Bicicleta. Fuenmayor, Morella, illus. 2005. (SPA.). 23p. (J). (ps-2). reprint ed. pap. 14.00 (978-0-7567-8947-3(8)) DIANE Publishing Co.

Barkaw, Henniette. Don't Cry Sly: Big Book English Only. Johnson, Richard, illus. 2004. (J). pap. (978-1-85269-999-4(X)) Mantra Publishing, Ltd.

Baxter, Nicola. Baby Chicks Day. Boey, Stephanie, illus. 2000. 12p. (J). (ps). bds. 4.99 (978-0-689-82963-5(9) , Little Simon) Simon & Schuster Children's Publishing.

Baxter, Nicola & Caviezel, Giovanni. Baby Chicks Day. Pagnoni, Roberta, illus. 2003. 12p. (J). bds. 4.99 (978-0-689-85247-3(9) , Little Simon) Simon & Schuster Children's Publishing.

Beckerman, Menucha. Avi & Chavi & the Lonely Chick. Peleg, Tirza, illus. 2002. (My Middos World Ser.: Vol. 12). 22p. (J). 11.95 (978-1-931681-29-2(5)) Israel Bk. Shop.

Berggren, Jeff. Chicken Cherries. Hansen, Tammy A., ed. Berggren, Jeff, illus. l.t. ed. 2005. (Illus.). 32p. (J). per. 14.95 (978-0-9755033-0-0(8)) Deep Dish Design.

Bertha Bantam. 2003. (J). 9.99 (978-0-9740847-7-0(8)) GiGi Bks.

Black, Andy. Little Joe's Big Race. Archbold, Tim, illus. 2004. (Read-It! Readers Ser.). 32p. (C). (gr. k-3). 18.60 (978-1-4048-0063-2(8)) Picture Window Bks.

Blackaby, Susan. Hatching Chicks. Muehlenhardt, Amy Bailey, illus. 2004. (Read-It! Readers Classroom Tales Ser.). 32p. (C). (gr. k-3). 18.60 (978-1-4048-0585-9(0)) Picture Window Bks.

Blanc, Esther Silverstein & Eagle, Godeane. Long Johns for a Small Chicken. Dixon, Tennessee, illus. 2003. (J). 16.95 (978-1-884244-23-0(8)) Volcano Pr.

Bogan, Paulette. Goodnight Lulu. 2005. 32p. (YA). pap. 6.95 (978-1-58234-983-1(5) , Bloomsbury Children) Bloomsbury Publishing.

—Goodnight Lulu. Bogan, Paulette, illus. 2003. (Illus.). 32p. (J). (ps-1). 15.95 (978-1-58234-803-2(0) , Bloomsbury Children) Bloomsbury Publishing.

Book Company Staff. Who Am I: Chick. 2003. (Board Bks.). (Illus.). (J). bds. 10.95 (978-1-74047-307-1(8)) Book Co. Publishing Pty, Ltd., The AUS. *Dist:* Penton Overseas, Inc.

Branford, Henrietta. Six Chicks. Elfezzani, Thierry, illus. 2005. 24p. (J). pap. 8.99 (978-0-00-664767-6(7)) HarperCollins Pubs. Ltd. GBR. *Dist:* Trafalgar Square Publishing.

Brett, Jan. Daisy Comes Home. Brett, Jan, illus. 2002. (Illus.). (J). 23.64 (978-1-4046-0028-7(0)) Book Wholesalers, Inc.

—Daisy Comes Home. Brett, Jan, illus. (Illus.). 32p. (J). (ps-3). 2002. 16.99 (978-0-399-23618-1(X) , Putnam Juvenile); 2005. reprint ed. pap. 6.99 (978-0-14-240270-2(2) , Puffin) Penguin Group (USA) Inc.

—Hedgie's Surprise. Brett, Jan, illus. 2004. (Illus.). 30p. (J). (gr. k-4). reprint ed. 17.00 (978-0-7567-7704-3(6)) DIANE Publishing Co.

—Hedgie's Surprise. 2001. (J). (gr. k-3). incl. audio (978-0-8045-6883-8(9) , 6883) Spoken Arts, Inc.

Brown, Jo. Hoppity Skip Little Chick. 2005. (Illus.). 32p. (J). 15.95 (978-1-58925-045-1(1) , tiger tales) ME Media LLC.

Brown, Kenneth. The Scarecrow's Hat. 2001. (Illus.). 32p. (J). (ps-1). 15.95 (978-1-56145-240-8(8) , Q25024) Peachtree Pubs., Ltd.

Bunting, Eve. Hurry! Hurry! Mack, Jeff, illus. 2007. 40p. (J). (ps-1). 16.00 (978-0-15-205410-6(3)) Harcourt Trade Pubs.

Butler, Dori. Detective Cluck & the Missing Hens. 2005. 22.00 (***978-1-4108-4192-6(8)***) Benchmark Education Co.

Caleca, James Renny. Hope, the Wonder Chicken. 2003. (J). 18.00 (978-0-8059-5028-1(1)) Dorrance Publishing Co., Inc.

Cameron, Edith. Chicken Licken: A Children's Cantata. Cameron, Edith, illus. 2004. (J). 17.95 (978-1-57665-121-6(5)) Muggli Graphics.

Cameron, Kathleen. The Chicken Without a Coop. 2003. (Illus.). (J). 14.95 (978-1-882897-71-1(4)) Lost Coast Pr.

Capriola, Arlene & Swenson, Rigmor. Chicken Licken. Mastry, Cherisse, ed. Burns, Kathy, illus. 1998. (Once upon a Time Ser.). (J). (gr. k-2). pap., wbk. ed. incl. audio (978-1-57022-171-2(5)) ECS Learning Systems, Inc.

—The Little Red Hen. Mastry, Cherisse, ed. Burns, Kathy, illus. 1998. (Once upon a Time Ser.). (J). (gr. k-2). pap., wbk. ed. 12.95 incl. audio (978-1-57022-175-0(8)) ECS Learning Systems, Inc.

Cazet, Denys. Elvis the Rooster Almost Goes to Heaven. Cazet, Denys, illus. 2004. (I Can Read Bks.). (Illus.). 48p. (J). (gr. k-3). pap. 3.99 (978-0-06-000502-3(5) , Harper Trophy) HarperCollins Pubs.

—Elvis the Rooster Almost Goes to Heaven. Cazet, Denys, illus. unabr. ed. 2006. (Readalongs for Beginning Readers Ser.). (Illus.). (J). (gr. k-3). 25.95 incl. audio (978-1-59519-686-6(2)); 28.95 incl. audio compact disk (978-1-59519-687-3(0)); pap. 16.95 incl. audio (978-1-59519-682-8(X)); pap. 18.95 incl. audio compact disk (978-1-59519-683-5(8)); Set. pap. 29.95 incl. audio (978-1-59519-684-2(6)); Set. pap. 31.95 incl. audio compact disk (978-1-59519-685-9(4)) Live Oak Media.

—Minnie & Moo: Minnie & Moo & the Musk of Zorro. Cazet, Denys, illus. 2002. (Live Oak Readalong Ser.). (Illus.). (J). pap. 18.95 incl. audio compact disk (978-1-59112-388-0(7)) Live Oak Media.

—Minnie & Moo: The Night Before Christmas. Cazet, Denys, illus. (Readalongs for Beginning Readers Ser.). (Illus.). 2005. (J). pap. 16.95 incl. audio (978-1-59112-883-0(8)); 2004. 25.95 incl. audio (978-1-59112-884-7(6)) Live Oak Media.

—Minnie & Moo & the Musk of Zorro. Cazet, Denys, illus. 2002. (Minnie & Moo Ser.). (Illus.). (J). 11.49 (978-0-7587-6205-4(4)) Book Wholesalers, Inc.

—Minnie & Moo & the Musk of Zorro. Cazet, Denys, illus. 2002. (Live Oak Readalong Ser.). (Illus.). (ps-3). (J). pap. 16.95 incl. audio (978-0-87499-918-1(9)); 28.95 incl. audio compact disk (978-1-59112-589-1(8)); pap. 31.95 incl. audio compact disk (978-1-59112-588-4(X)) Live Oak Media.

—Minnie & Moo & the Musk of Zorro. 2000. (ps-2). lib. bdg. 11.80 (978-0-613-32838-8(8)); (Illus.). (J). (978-0-606-22032-3(1)) Tandem Library Bks.

Cazet, Denys & Dorling Kindersley Publishing Staff. Minnie & Moo & the Musk of Zorro. 2000. (Illus.). 48p. (J). (gr. 1-3). pap. 3.99 (978-0-7894-2653-6(6)); (gr. 5-3). 12.99 (978-0-7894-2652-9(8)) Dorling Kindersley Publishing, Inc.

Chaconas, Dori. Coriander the Contrary Hen. Carrington, Marsha Gray, illus. 2007. 32p. (J). (gr. k-4). spiral bd. 15.95 (978-1-57505-749-1(2) , Carolrhoda Bks.) Lerner Publishing Group.

Chambers, Angela. Follow That Chicken! Abel, Simone, illus. 2001. (Pinwheel Ser.). 10p. (J). bds. 3.95 (978-0-8069-0310-1(4)) Sterling Publishing Co., Inc.

C D

Charlie Chicken goes to Playgroup. 2004. (Play Pals Ser.). (Illus.). 12p. (J). bds. (978-1-84229-639-4(6)) Top That! Publishing PLC.

Chen, Zhiyuan & Chen, Chih-Yuan. The Featherless Chicken. 2006. (Illus.). 40p. (J). 16.95 (978-0-9762056-9-2(6)) Heryin Publishing Corp.

Chick & Go. 2004. (J). per. (978-1-57657-516-1(0)) Paradise Pr., Inc.

Chicken Licken: Set C Individual Title Six-Packs. (gr. k-3). 29.00 (978-0-7635-0541-7(2)) Rigby Education.

Chicken Little. 2004. (J). pap. 18.95 incl. audio compact disk (978-1-55592-391-4(7)); pap. 18.95 incl. audio compact disk (978-1-55592-393-8(3)); pap. 38.75 incl. audio compact disk (978-1-55592-392-1(5)); pap. 38.75 incl. audio compact disk (978-1-55592-394-5(1)); pap. 32.75 incl. audio (978-1-55592-204-7(X)); pap. 32.75 incl. audio (978-1-55592-205-4(8)) Weston Woods Studios, Inc.

Chickens Aren't Only. 1998. (J). pap. 3.95 (978-0-439-04439-4(1)) Scholastic, Inc.

The Chicks are Hatching. 2002. (J). (978-1-58453-176-0(2)); (978-1-58453-144-9(4)) Pioneer Valley Educational Pr., Inc.

Claire Freedman Staff, et al. Squabble & Squawk. 2006. (Illus.). 32p. (ps). pap. 9.99 (978-0-689-87308-9(5)) Simon & Schuster, Ltd. GBR. *Dist:* Independent Pubs. Group.

Clynes, Kate. Little Red Hen & Wheat. 2004. (Illus.). (J). (978-1-84444-058-0(3)) Mantra Publishing, Ltd.

Coerr, Eleanor. The Josefina Story Quilt: Josefina y la colcha de Retazos. Degen, Bruce, illus. 2006. (I Can Read Bks.). (SPA.). 64p. (J). pap. 3.99 (978-0-06-088713-1(3)) HarperCollins Pubs.

Come & Meet Lola: A Very Special Chicken That Will Capture the Hearts of Children of All Ages! (Englishspanish Story Book Ser.).Tr. of Ven a Conocer a Lola.... (ENG & SPA.). 32p. (J). 13.95 (978-1-931398-51-0(8)) Me+Mi Publishing.

Couvillon, Jacques. The Chicken Dance. 2007. 336p. (YA). (gr. 5 up). 16.95 (***978-1-59990-043-8(2)*** , Bloomsbury Children) Bloomsbury Publishing.

Cowley, Joy. Chicken Feathers. Elliott, David W., illus. 2008. 160p. (J). (gr. 3-6). 15.99 (***978-0-399-24791-0(2)*** , Philomel) Penguin Group (USA) Inc.

Cox, Phil Roxbee. Hen's Pens. Cartwright, Stephen, illus. rev. ed. 2006. 16p. (J). pap. 6.99 (978-0-7945-1506-5(1) , Usborne) EDC Publishing.

Cox, Phil Roxbee & Cartwright, Stephen. Hen's Pens. 2004. (Easy Words to Read Ser.). (Illus.). 16p. (J). (gr. 1 up). pap. 6.95 (978-0-7945-0113-6(3) , Usborne) EDC Publishing.

—Ted's Shed. 2004. (Phonics Board Bks.). (Illus.). 10p. (J). 4.95 (978-0-7945-0304-8(7) , Usborne) EDC Publishing.

Coxe, Molly. Big Egg. Coxe, Molly, illus. 2002. (Illus.). (J). 11.91 (978-0-7587-6028-9(0)) Book Wholesalers, Inc.

Curry, Don, ed. The Little Red Hen. 2006. (My Turn! Your Turn! Ser.). (ENG.). 24p. (J). pap. 3.99 (978-0-696-22887-2(4)) Meredith Bks.

Czernecki, Stefan. Huevos Rancheros. 2001. (SPA., Illus.). 32p. (J). (ps-3). 15.95 (978-1-56656-429-8(8)) Interlink Publishing Group, Inc.

Czernecki, Stefan, illus. Huevos Rancheros. 2002. (SPA.). 32p. (J). (ps-3). 15.95 (978-1-56656-428-1(X)) Interlink Publishing Group, Inc.

Dalmatian Press Staff. Little Chick: Soft Spot Board Book. 2002. (Soft Spot Bks.). (Illus.). 10p. (J). bds. 3.99 (978-1-57759-652-3(8)) Dalmatian Pr.

Daly, Niki. Welcome to Zanzibar Road. 2006. (Illus.). 40p. (J). (gr. k-3). 16.00 (978-0-618-64926-6(3) , Clarion Bks.) Houghton Mifflin Co. Trade & Reference Div.

—What's Cooking, Jamela? Daly, Niki, illus. 2001. (Jamela Ser.). (Illus.). 32p. (J). (ps-2). 16.95 (978-0-374-35602-6(5) , Farrar, Straus & Giroux (BYR)) Farrar, Straus & Giroux.

Daniel, Claire. The Chick That Wouldn't Hatch. 1999. (Green Light Readers Ser.). (Illus.). (J). (978-0-606-18170-9(9)) Tandem Library Bks.

—Chick That Wouldn't Hatch. 1999. (gr. k-3). lib. bdg. 11.80 (978-0-613-63269-0(9)) Tandem Library Bks.

Davenier, Christine. Leon & Albertine. Barth, Dominic, tr. 1998. (Illus.). 32p. (J). (ps-1). pap. 15.95 (978-0-531-30072-5(2) , Orchard Bks.) Scholastic, Inc.

David, Lawrence, ed. Chicken Run: Action-Packed Storybook. Barnes, Tom, photos by. 2005. (Illus.). 48p. (gr. k-4). reprint ed. pap. 8.00 (978-0-7567-9472-9(2)) DIANE Publishing Co.

Davidson, Susanna. Little Red Hen. Postgate, Daniel, illus. 2006. 48p. (J). 8.99 (978-0-7945-1375-7(1) , Usborne) EDC Publishing.

Davies, Gill & Freeman, Tina. Happy Hen. 2004. (Tales from Yellow Barn Farm Ser.). (Illus.). 24p. (J). 3.99 (978-1-85854-323-9(1)) Brimax Books Ltd. GBR. *Dist:* Byeway Bks.

The Day the Sky Fell Down: Individual Title Six-Pack Pouch - Level I. (Lighthouse Ser.). 16p. (gr. 1 up). 26.00 (978-0-7578-0857-9(3)) Rigby Education.

De La Garza, David. The Great, Great, Great Chicken War. 2007. (Illus.). 48p. (J). (ps-3). 15.95 (***978-0-9795266-0-2(4)***) Anchorage Foundation Pr.

DeJong, Meindert. Y Entonces Llego un Perro. (SPA.). 144p. (YA). (gr. 5-9). (978-84-279-3220-3(0) , NG3490) Noguer y Caralt Editores, S. A. ESP. *Dist:* Lectorum Pubns., Inc.

Delval, Marie-Helene. A Gallinita le Gustan los Colores. Courtin, Thierry, illus. 2002. (Palabras Menudas Ser.).Tr. of Little Chicken Likes Colors. (SPA.). 14p. (ps). 5.95 (978-84-7864-514-5(4)) Combel Editorial, S.A. ESP. *Dist:* Independent Pubs. Group.

Denchfield, Nick. Charlie Chick. Parker, Ant, illus. 2007. 14p. (J). (ps). 10.95 (978-0-15-206013-8(8) , Red Wagon Bks.) Harcourt Children's Bks.

Diakite, Penda. I Lost My Tooth in Africa. Diakite, Baba Wague, illus. 2006. 32p. (J). (ps-3). pap. 16.99 (978-0-439-66226-0(5) , Scholastic Pr.) Scholastic, Inc.

Disney Book Club Staff. Henny Penny & Big Bad Wolf. 1999. (J). lib. bdg. (978-0-394-94008-3(3) , Random Hse. Bks. for Young Readers) Random Hse. Children's Bks.

Disney Press Staff, creator. Sticky Situations: A Sticker Activity Storybook. 2005. (Disney's Chicken Little Ser.). (Illus.). 12p. (ps-17). 14.99 (978-0-7868-3646-8(6)) Disney Pr.

Don't Cry Sly. 2004. (J). E-Book incl. cd-rom (978-1-84444-457-1(0)) Mantra Publishing, Ltd.

Dorros, Arthur. City Chicken. Date not set. 40p. (J). (ps-1). pap. 5.99 (978-0-06-443587-1(3)) HarperCollins Pubs.

—City Chicken. Cole, Henry, illus. 2003. 40p. (J). (ps-3). 16.89 (978-0-06-028483-1(8)) HarperCollins Pubs.

Doudna, Kelly. Rooster Combs. Haberstroh, Anne, illus. 2006. (Fact & Fiction Ser.). 24p. (J). 21.35 (978-1-59679-965-3(X) , SandCastle); pap. (978-1-59679-966-0(8)) ABDO Publishing Co.

Dowell, Frances O'Roark. Chicken Boy. Krause, George, photos by. 2007. 208p. (J). (gr. 5 up). pap. 5.99 (978-1-4169-3482-0(0) , Aladdin) Simon & Schuster Children's Publishing.

—Chicken Boy. 2005. (Illus.). 208p. (J). 15.95 (978-0-689-85816-1(7) , Atheneum) Simon & Schuster Children's Publishing.

—Chicken Boy. l.t. ed. 2006. 169p. (YA). 22.95 (978-0-7862-8280-7(0)) Thorndike Pr.

Downard, Barry, illus. Carla's Famous Traveling Feather & Fur Show. 2006. 32p. 16.95 (978-1-59687-171-7(7)) ibooks, Inc.

Dunbar, Joyce. A Chick Called Saturday. Granstrom, Brita, illus. 2004. 32p. (J). 16.00 (978-0-8028-5260-1(2)) Eerdmans, William B. Publishing Co.

Dunrea, Olivier. Hanne's Quest. 2006. (Illus.). 96p. (J). (gr. 3). 16.99 (978-0-399-24216-8(3) , Philomel) Penguin Group (USA) Inc.

—Painter Who Loved Chickens. 1998. (978-0-606-13693-8(2)) Tandem Library Bks.

Educa Vision, Inc., Staff. Papiyon. (CRP., Illus.). 21p. (YA). (gr. 3 up). pap. 7.50 (978-1-58432-059-3(1)) Educa Vision.

Elliott, David. One Little Chicken: A Counting Book. Long, Ethan, illus. 2007. 24p. (J). (ps-k). 16.95 (***978-0-8234-1983-8(5)***) Holiday Hse., Inc.

Elschner, Geraldine. The Easter Chick. Junge, Alexandra, illus. 2006. 32p. (J). reprint ed. 6.95 (978-0-7358-2076-0(7)) North-South Bks., Inc.

Equipo Staff. El Pollito. 2000. (SPA., Illus.). 12p. (J). (ps-k). 7.95 (978-84-488-0891-4(6)) Beascoa, Ediciones S.A. ESP. *Dist:* Distribooks, Inc., Lectorum Pubns., Inc.

Erickson, John R. The Case of the Tender Cheeping Chickies. Holmes, Gerald L., illus. 2005. (Hank the Cowdog Ser.: No. 47). 129p. (J). lib. bdg. 17.00 (***978-1-4242-1605-5(2)***) Fitzgerald Bks.

Ethier, Vicki. Papa & the Hen. Ethier, Vicki, illus. 2004. (Illus.). 36p. (J). 7.00 (978-1-928972-12-9(8)) Critter Pubns.

Evans, Paul. The Adventures of Little Chick. Robinson, Laura, illus. 2001. 36p. (J). (gr. 1-6). lib. bdg. 14.95 (978-0-9705727-7-6(8)) Coastal Publishing Carolina, Inc.

Faulkner, Keith. Good Morning, Chick! 2004. (Illus.). 14p. (J). bds. 4.99 (978-0-8431-0650-3(6) , Price Stern Sloan) Penguin Group (USA) Inc.

Finch, Mary. The Little Red Hen & the Ear of Wheat. Bell, Elisabeth, illus. 2001. (ps-ps). lib. bdg. 14.15 (978-0-613-34332-9(8)) Tandem Library Bks.

First Chick Stories. (J). Date not set. (Illus.). bds. 9.98 (978-0-7525-9171-1(1)); 2002. 47p. bds. 9.95 (978-0-7525-7039-6(0)) Parragon, Inc.

Foreman, Michael. Chicken Licken. (Illus.). 32p. (J). 19.95 (978-0-86264-847-3(5)) Andersen GBR. *Dist:* Trafalgar Square Publishing.

Fowler. Little Chick's Big Adventure. 2000. (Illus.). 18p. (J). 10.95 (978-0-385-40728-1(9)) Transworld Publishers Ltd. GBR. *Dist:* Trafalgar Square Publishing.

Fox, Mem. Hattie & the Fox. 2002. (Illus.). (J). 15.53 (978-0-7587-2704-6(6)) Book Wholesalers, Inc.

—Hattie & the Fox. Mullins, Patricia, illus. 2005. (Stories to Go! Ser.). 32p. (J). 4.99 (978-1-4169-0308-6(9) , Aladdin) Simon & Schuster Children's Publishing.

Freedman, Claire & Shearing, Leonie. Squabble & Squawk. 2006. (Illus.). 32p. (J). (ps). 19.95 (978-0-689-87307-2(7)) Simon & Schuster, Ltd. GBR. *Dist:* Independent Pubs. Group.

French, Vivian. The Daddy Goose Treasury. Collins, Ross, illus. 2006. 96p. (J). pap. 18.99 (978-0-439-79608-8(3) , Chicken Hse., The) Scholastic, Inc.

Friend, Catherine. The Perfect Nest. Manders, John, illus. 2007. (J). (ps-2). 40p. 16.99 (978-0-7636-2430-9(6)); (***978-1-4287-3697-9(2)***) Candlewick Pr.

Galdone, Paul. The Little Red Hen. 2006. (Illus.). 40p. (J). (ps-k). 25.00 (978-0-618-83684-0(5)) Houghton Mifflin Co. Trade & Reference Div.

—The Little Red Hen. Galdone, Paul, illus. (J). (ps-k). pap. 12.95 incl. audio Weston Woods Studios, Inc.

Gardner, Wendy. Heedley Pecked Me in the Eye. Gardner, Wendy, illus. 2002. (Naughty Naughty Pets Ser.). (Illus.). 32p. (ps-17). 10.99 (978-0-7868-0885-4(3)) Hyperion Bks. for Children.

Gavin, Jamila. Fine Feathered Friend. Williams, Dan, illus. 2002. (Yellow Bananas Ser.). 48p. (J). (gr. 3-4). pap. (978-0-7787-0985-5(X)); lib. bdg. (978-0-7787-0939-8(6)) Crabtree Publishing Co.

—Fine Feathered Friend. 2002. (gr. 3-6). lib. bdg. 12.95 (978-0-613-52842-9(5)) Tandem Library Bks.

Gernhart, Cyndi. The Adventures of Gertrude Mccluck, Chicken in Charge Vol. 1: The Missing Eggs, 4 vols. Gernhart, Carlie, illus. l.t. ed. 2005. 32p. (J). 8.00 (978-0-9778240-1-4(2)) Prairie Winds Publishing.

—The Adventures of Gertrude Mccluck, Chicken in Charge Vol. 2: The Great Crate Mystery, 4 vols. Gernhart, Carlie, illus. l.t. ed. 2005. 40p. (J). 8.00 (978-0-9778240-2-1(0)) Prairie Winds Publishing.

—The Adventures of Gertrude Mccluck, Chicken in Charge Vol. 3: The Yellow-Eyed Pond Monster, 4 vols. Gernhart, Carlie, illus. l.t. ed. 2005. 52p. (J). 8.00 (978-0-9778240-3-8(9)) Prairie Winds Publishing.

—The Adventures of Gertrude Mccluck, Chicken in Charge Vol. 4: A Midwinter Light's Dream, 4 vols. Gernhart, Carlie, illus. l.t. ed. 2006. 52p. (J). 8.00 (978-0-9778240-4-5(7)) Prairie Winds Publishing.

—Gertrude Sees... On the Farm. Gernhart, Cyndi et al, illus. l.t. ed. 2006. 20p. (J). 8.00 (978-0-9778240-0-7(4)) Prairie Winds Publishing.

Gibbons, Alan. Chicken. l.t. ed. 2005. 152p. (Orig.). (J). pap. (978-0-7540-7917-0(1) , CLP 476) BBC Audio.

Ginsburg, Mirra. The Chick & the Duckling. 2002. (Illus.). (J). 14.47 (978-0-7587-2221-8(4)) Book Wholesalers, Inc.

Golden Books Staff. Chicken Little. 2001. (Illus.). 24p. pap. 3.29 (978-0-307-85813-9(8) , Golden Bks.) Random Hse. Children's Bks.

—The Little Red Hen. 2004. (Illus.). 26p. (J). (gr. k-ps). bds. 4.99 (978-0-375-82773-0(0) , Golden Bks.) Random Hse. Children's Bks.

Goodnight, Little Bug & Wheres the Chick? 2005. (J). bds. 19.99 (978-0-9767325-8-7(0)) Toy Quest.

The Goose, the Chick & the Duck. 1998. (Fisher-Price Phonics Storybooks Ser.: Vol. 4). (Illus.). (J). pap. (978-0-7666-0173-4(0) , Honey Bear Bks.) Modern Publishing.

Gorbachev, Valeri. Chicken Chickens Go to School. Gorbachev, Valeri, illus. 2003. (Illus.). (J). (ps-1). 28p. 15.95 (978-0-7358-1600-8(X)); 32p. 16.50 (978-0-7358-1767-8(7)) North-South Bks., Inc.

Graham, Bob. Queenie, One of the Family. Graham, Bob, illus. 2001. (Illus.). 32p. (J) (gr. k-3). pap. 6.99 (978-0-7636-1400-3(9)) Candlewick Pr.

—Queenie, One of the Family. 2001. (gr. k-3). lib. bdg. 14.15 (978-0-613-74724-0(0)) Tandem Library Bks.

Grant, Judyann. Chicken Said Cluck. Date not set. (My First I Can Read Bks.). (J). lib. bdg. 16.89 (978-0-06-028724-5(1)) HarperCollins Pubs.

—My First I Can Read. Truesdell, Sue, illus. 2002. (My First I Can Read Bks.). 32p. (J). (ps up). 12.95 (978-0-06-028723-8(3)) HarperCollins Pubs.

Graves, Sue. Jen the Hen. 2007. (Fun with Phonics Ser.). 20p. (J). pap. 4.99 (***978-0-439-02553-9(2)***) Scholastic, Inc.

Gray, Kes. Cluck O'Clock. McQuillan, Mary, tr. McQuillan, Mary, illus. 2004. 32p. (J). (gr. k-3). tchr. ed. 16.95 (978-0-8234-1809-1(X)) Holiday Hse., Inc.

Hagemann, Bernhard. Charlie Gallina Ciega. (Torre de Papel Ser.). (SPA., Illus.). (J). 7.95 (978-958-04-5032-0(3)) Norma S.A. COL. *Dist:* Distribuidora Norma, Inc.

Hall, Nancy Abraham & Syverson-Stork, Jill. Los Pollitos Dicen/The Baby Chicks Sing. Chorao, Kay, illus. 1999. (SPA.). 32p. (J). (ps-2). pap. 5.99 (978-0-316-33852-3(4)) Little Brown & Co.

Hallmark, Hazel. A Little White Hen Called "RolyPoly" 1999. (Illus.). 15p. (J). pap. 8.00 (978-1-930002-01-2(7)) I & L Publishing.

Halls, Kelly Milner. I Bought a Baby Chicken. Brooks, Karen Stormer, illus. 2003. 32p. (J). (ps up). 14.95 (978-1-56397-800-5(8)) Boyds Mills Pr.

Happy Hen. 2006. (J). per. 3.99 (978-1-934004-15-9(4)) Byeway Bks.

Harchy, Atelier Philippe, illus. Chicken Little: A Tale about Common Sense. 2006. (J). 6.99 (978-1-59939-019-2(1) , Reader's Digest Young Families, Inc.) Reader's Digest Children's Publishing, Inc.

Harcourt School Publishers Staff. Next Time: Take-Home Book. rev. ed. 2001. (Collections Ser.: Bk. 12). (Illus.). (J). pap. 1.90 (978-0-15-319070-4(1)) Harcourt Schl. Pubs.

Harrison, David L. Dylan the Eagle-Hearted Chicken. Brooks, Karen Stormer, illus. 2003. 32p. (J). (gr. k-2). 15.95 (978-1-56397-982-8(9)) Boyds Mills Pr.

Harry, Rebecca, illus. Little Chick. 2006. (Noisy Farm Babies Ser.). 8p. (J). bds. 5.99 (978-0-7641-5935-0(6)) Barron's Educational Series, Inc.

Hartley, Susan. Mem the Hen. 2003. (StartUp Ser.). (J). pap. 22.00 (978-1-4108-0706-9(1)) Benchmark Education Co.

Harvey, Ken. Life in the Fridge: The Eggsters Story. Hermes, Mary Sue, illus. 2002. 32p. (J). (ps-k). 12.95 (978-1-930093-17-1(9)) Brookfield Reader, Inc., The.

Helakoski, Leslie. Big Chickens. Cole, Henry, illus. 32p. (J). (ps). 2008. pap. 6.99 (***978-0-14-241057-8(8)*** , Puffin); 2006. 15.99 (978-0-525-47575-0(3) , Dutton Juvenile) Penguin Group (USA) Inc.

—Big chickens Fly the Coop. Cole, Henry, illus. 2008. 32p. (J). (ps). 15.99 (***978-0-525-47915-4(5)*** , Dutton Juvenile) Penguin Group (USA) Inc.

Hillert, Margaret. Not I, Not I: The Little Red Hen Retold. Magnuson, Diana, illus. rev. exp. ed. 2007. (Beginning to Read Ser.). 32p. (J). lib. bdg. (978-1-59953-052-9(X)) Norwood Hse. Pr.

Himmelman, John. Chickens to the Rescue. 2006. (Illus.). 32p. (J). (ps-3). 16.95 (978-0-8050-7951-7(3)) Holt, Henry & Co.

Hoadley, Jo. Miss Creant: The Adventures of a little Red Hen. l.t. ed. 2004. (Illus.). 127p. (J). per. 15.99 (978-0-9765088-0-9(X)) Billy Jo Bks.

How the Chick Tricked the Fox. (Little Book Practice Reader Ser.). (J). (978-0-8136-0821-1(X)) Modern Curriculum Pr.

Howarth, Daniel, illus. The Chicken Who Saved Christmas. 2004. 32p. (J). 12.95 (978-1-4027-1625-6(7)) Sterling Publishing Co., Inc.

The Hungry Chickens: Individual Title Six-Packs. (Literatura 2000 Ser.). (gr. 1-2). 28.00 (978-0-7635-0136-5(0)) Rigby Education.

Hunt, Helen, narrated by. Chicken Little. unabr. ed. 1998. (J). (ps-4). 24.95 incl. audio (978-0-7882-0673-3(7) , HRA372) Weston Woods Studios, Inc.

Hutchins, Pat. Bumpety Bump! Hutchins, Pat, illus. 2006. (Illus.). 32p. (J). 15.99 (978-0-06-055999-1(3)); lib. bdg. 16.89 (978-0-06-056000-3(2)) HarperCollins Pubs.

—Rosie's Walk. Hutchins, Pat, illus. 32p. (J). 2002. mass mkt. 1.00 (978-0-689-85548-1(6)); 2nd ed. 2005. (Illus.). 4.99 (978-1-4169-0835-7(8)) Simon & Schuster Children's Publishing. (Aladdin).

—Rosie's Walk. 2nd ed. 2005. (Stories to Go! Ser.). (Illus.). (J). (***978-1-4156-3112-6(3)*** , Aladdin) Simon & Schuster Children's Publishing.

Hutchins, Pat. We're Going on a Picnic! Hutchins, Pat, illus. 2002. (Illus.). 32p. (J). 16.99 (978-0-688-16799-8(3)) HarperCollins Pubs.

Jean-Jacques, Nirvah. Fefe ak Kikit. 2001. 20p. (J). 8.50 (978-1-58432-123-1(7)) Educa Vision.

Johansen, Hanna. Henrietta & the Golden Egg. Barrett, John S., tr. from GER. Bhend-Zaugg, Kathi, illus. 2002. Tr. of Vom Huhnchen das Goldene Eier Legen Wollte. 64p. (J). 16.95 (978-1-56792-210-3(4)) Godine, David R. Pub.

—Henrietta & the Golden Eggs. Barrett, John S., tr. from GER. 2004. (Illus.). 64p. (J). pap. 9.95 (978-1-56792-288-2(0)) Godine, David R. Pub.

Johnson, James & Meade, Tina. Tales from the Coop. 1998. (Illus.). 130p. (J). (gr. 3-7). pap. 9.00 (978-1-883207-03-8(7)) Sohn, Mark F. Pubns.

Johnson, Richard. Little Red Hen & the Grains. 2005. (ENG & KOR., Illus.). 32p. (J). pap. 12.95 (978-1-84444-210-2(1)) Mantra Lingua GBR. *Dist:* Mantra Publishing, Ltd.

—Little Red Hen & the Grains of Wheat: Big Book English Only. 2004. (Illus.). (J). (978-1-84444-298-0(5)) Mantra Publishing, Ltd.

Johnson, Richard, illus. Don't Cry, Sly! 2004. 24p. (J). (TAM, CZE, VIE, SPA & GUJ.). pap. (978-1-85269-649-8(4)); (TAM, CZE, VIE, SPA & GUJ.). pap. (978-1-85269-650-4(8)); (TAM, CZE, VIE, SPA & GUJ.). pap. (978-1-85269-651-1(6)); (TAM, CZE, VIE, SPA & GUJ.). pap. (978-1-85269-652-8(4)); (TAM, CZE, VIE, SPA & GUJ.). pap. (978-1-85269-653-5(2)); (TAM, CZE, VIE, SPA & GUJ.). pap. (978-1-85269-655-9(9)); (TAM, CZE, VIE, SPA & GUJ.). pap. (978-1-85269-656-6(7)); (TAM, CZE, VIE, SPA & GUJ.). pap. (978-1-85269-657-3(5)); (TAM, CZE, VIE, SPA & GUJ.). pap. (978-1-85269-658-0(3)); (TAM, CZE, VIE, SPA & GUJ.). pap. (978-1-85269-659-7(1)); (TAM, CZE, VIE, SPA & GUJ.). pap. (978-1-85269-660-3(5)); (TAM, CZE, VIE, SPA & GUJ.). pap. (978-1-85269-661-0(3)); (TAM, CZE, VIE, SPA & GUJ.). pap. (978-1-85269-662-7(1)); (CZE, TAM, VIE, SPA & GUJ.). pap. (978-1-85269-663-4(X)); (TAM, CZE, VIE, SPA & GUJ.). pap. (978-1-85269-670-2(2)); (TAM, CZE, VIE, SPA & GUJ.). pap. (978-1-85269-671-9(0)); (TAM, CZE, VIE, SPA & GUJ.). pap. (978-1-85269-813-3(6)) Mantra Publishing, Ltd.

Johnston, Tony. Chicken in the Kitchen. Taylor, Eleanor, illus. 2005. 32p. (J). 15.95 (978-0-689-85641-9(5) , Simon & Schuster Children's Publishing) Simon & Schuster Children's Publishing.

Jones, Christianne C. La Gallinita Roja. Magnuson, Natalie, illus. 2006. (Read-It! Readers en Espanol Ser.).Tr. of Little Red Hen. (SPA.). 32p. (J). (ps-3). 19.95 (978-1-4048-1650-3(X)) Picture Window Bks.

Jumbo & Mrs. Hen's Eggs. 2004. (J). per. 15.99 (978-0-9744205-1-6(4)) Golden Eagle Publishing Hse., Inc.

Kelley, Ellen A. My Life As a Chicken. Slack, Michael H., illus. 2007. 40p. (J). (ps-2). 16.00 (978-0-15-205306-2(9)) Harcourt Trade Pubs.

Kellogg, Steven. Pollita Pequenita. Kellogg, Steven, illus. 2001. (SPA., Illus.). 32p. (J). (gr. k-3). 12.95 (978-84-241-3331-3(5) , EV3845) Everest de Ediciones y Distribucion, S.L. ESP. *Dist:* Lectorum Pubns., Inc.

Kellogg, Steven, illus. & narrated by. Chicken Little. Kellogg, Steven, narrated by. unabr. ed. 1998. (J). (ps-4). pap. 14.95 incl. audio (978-0-7882-0678-8(8) , PRA372) Weston Woods Studios, Inc.

Keylocke, Andrew, illus. Hasty Hetty. 2004. (Crazy Racers Ser.). 12p. (J). bds. 4.95 (978-0-7641-5746-2(9)) Barron's Educational Series, Inc.

Khan, Rukshana. Silly Chicken. Kyong, Yunmee, illus. 2005. 32p. (J). (ps-3). 15.99 (978-0-670-05912-6(9) , Viking Juvenile) Penguin Group (USA) Inc.

King-Smith, Dick. Funny Frank. Eastwood, John, illus. 2003. 112p. (gr. 2-5). pap. 5.50 (978-0-440-41880-1(1) , Yearling) Random Hse. Children's Bks.

—Funny Frank. Roth, Roger & Eastwood, John, illus. 2002. 112p. (J). (gr. 2-5). 14.95 (978-0-375-81460-0(4) , Knopf Bks. for Young Readers) Random Hse. Children's Bks.

—Funny Frank. 2003. (gr. 3-6). lib. bdg. 13.00 (978-0-613-72193-6(4)) Tandem Library Bks.

Korman, Gordon. The Chicken Doesn't Skate. 1998. 192p. (J). (gr. 4-8). pap. 4.50 (978-0-590-85301-9(5)) Scholastic, Inc.

Kromhout, Rindert. Little Donkey & the Babysitter. Martens, Marianne, tr. from DUT. Van Haeringen, Annemarie, illus. 2006. 32p. (J). 15.95 (978-0-7358-2057-9(0)) North-South Bks., Inc.

Lagonegro, Melissa. Don't Be a Chicken! 2006. (Step into Reading Ser.). (Illus.). 32p. (J). (ps-2). pap. 3.99 (978-0-7364-2356-4(7) , RH/Disney) Random Hse. Children's Bks.

Lagonegro, Melissa & Random House Disney Staff. Don't Be a Chicken! 2006. (Step into Reading Ser.). (Illus.). 32p. (J). (ps-2). lib. bdg. 11.99 (978-0-7364-8048-2(X) , RH/Disney) Random Hse. Children's Bks.

Lambert, Patricia. The Blue Ribbon Chicken. 2005. 36p. (J). pap. 14.93 (978-1-4116-6163-9(X)) Lulu.com.

Lana Araucana: Our Easter Chick. 2000. (Illus.). 16p. (J). (gr. k-2). pap. 5.95 (978-0-9646370-1-6(4)) Redbud Pr.

Landstrom, Lena. Four Hens & a Rooster. Sandin, Joan, tr. from SWE. Landstrom, Olof, illus. 2005. 28p. (J). (ps-4). 16.00 (978-91-29-66336-5(9)) R & S Bks. SWE. *Dist:* Macmillan.

Lansing, Richard, Jr. The Brown Mud Chickens. Lansing, Randy, illus. 2000. 48p. per. 6.00 (978-0-9661844-6-4(7)) Purple Gorilla, LLC, The.

Law, Felicia. Rumble Meets Milly the Maid. Pak, Yoon Mi, illus. 2007. (Read-It! Readers Ser.). (J). 19.93 (978-1-4048-1341-0(1)) Picture Window Bks.

Lawrence, John. This Little Chick. Lawrence, John, illus. (Illus.). (gr. k-ps). 2006. 24p. (YA). bds. 6.99 (978-0-7636-2882-6(4)); 2002. 32p. (J). 15.99 (978-0-7636-1716-5(4)) Candlewick Pr.

Leland, Debbie. The Little Prairie Hen. Ann Hollis Rife, illus. 2003. 32p. (J). lib. bdg. 14.95 (978-0-9667086-3-9(6)) Wildflower Run.

Lin, Grace. Olvina Flies. Lin, Grace, illus. rev. ed. 2003. (Illus.). 32p. (J). (ps-2). 15.95 (978-0-8050-6711-8(6) , Holt, Henry & Co. Bks. For Young Readers) Holt, Henry & Co.

—Olvina Swims. rev. ed. 2007. (Illus.). 32p. (J). (ps-2). 16.95 (978-0-8050-7661-5(1)) Holt, Henry & Co.

The Little Red Hen. (Ladybird Bks.). (ARA., Illus.). 52p. (J). 4.95 (978-0-86685-203-6(4) , LDL158) International Bk. Ctr., Inc.

The Little Red Hen. (Ladybird Bks.). (ARA., Illus.). 14.95 incl. audio (978-0-86685-211-1(5) , LDL122C) Librairie du Liban Pubns. FRA. *Dist:* International Bk. Ctr., Inc.

Little Red Hen & the Grains of Wheat. 2004. (J). (ALB & ENG.). (978-1-84444-594-3(1)); (ARA & ENG.). (978-1-84444-595-0(X)); (BEN & ENG.). (978-1-84444-596-7(8)); (CHI & ENG.). (978-1-84444-597-4(6)); (CHI & ENG.). (978-1-84444-598-1(4)); (CRO & ENG.). (978-1-84444-599-8(2)); (ENG & PER.). (978-1-84444-600-1(X)); (ENG & FRE.). (978-1-84444-601-8(8)); (ENG & GRE.). (978-1-84444-602-5(6)); (ENG & GUJ.). (978-1-84444-603-2(4)); (ENG & HIN.). (978-1-84444-604-9(2)); (ENG & ITA.). (978-1-84444-605-6(0)); (ENG & JPN.). (978-1-84444-606-3(9)); (ENG & KOR.). (978-1-84444-607-0(7)); (ENG & KUR.). (978-1-84444-608-7(5)); (ENG & PAN.). (978-1-84444-609-4(3)); (ENG & POL.). (978-1-84444-610-0(7)); (ENG & POR.). (978-1-84444-612-4(3)); (ENG & RUS.). (978-1-84444-613-1(1)); (ENG & SOM.). (978-1-84444-614-8(X)); (ENG & SPA.). (978-1-84444-615-5(8)); (ENG & TAG.). (978-1-84444-616-2(6)); (ENG & TAM.). (978-1-84444-617-9(4)); (ENG & TUR.). (978-1-84444-618-6(2)); (ENG & URD.). (978-1-84444-619-3(0)); (ENG & VIE.). (978-1-84444-620-9(4)) Mantra Publishing, Ltd.

Little Red HenGrains. 2004. (J). cd-rom (978-1-84444-462-5(7)) Mantra Publishing, Ltd.

Losordo, Stephen. Cow Moo Me. Conteh-Morgan, Jane, illus. 1998. (Growing Tree Ser.). 16p. (J). (ps up). 5.95 (978-0-694-01108-7(8) , Harper Festival) HarperCollins Pubs.

Lustig, Loretta, illus. The Little Red Hen: A Tale about Co-operation. 2006. (J). 6.99 (978-1-59939-018-5(3) , Reader's Digest Young Families, Inc.) Reader's Digest Children's Publishing, Inc.

MacLennan, Cathy. Chicky Chicky Chook Chook. MacLennan, Cathy, illus. 2007. (Illus.). 32p. (J). (ps-1). 12.95 (978-1-905417-40-7(3)) Boxer Bks., Ltd. GBR. *Dist:* Sterling Publishing Co., Inc.

Madrigal, Antonio Hernandez. Blanca's Feather. Suzan, Gerardo, illus. 2000. 32p. (gr. k-3). 15.95 (978-0-87358-743-3(X) , Rising Moon Bks. for Young Readers) Northland Publishing.

Maguire, Gregory. Crabby Cratchitt. Glass, Andrew, illus. 2000. 32p. (J). (gr. k-3). tchr. ed. 15.00 (978-0-395-60485-4(0) , Clarion Bks.) Houghton Mifflin Co. Trade & Reference Div.

Manning, Mick. Cock-a-Doodle-Hooooooo! Granstrom, Brita, illus. 2007. 28p. (J). (ps-2). 16.95 (***978-1-56148-568-0(3)***) Good Bks.

Marshall, James. Wings: A Tale of Two Chickens. 2003. (Illus.). 32p. (J). (gr. k-3). 6.95 (978-0-618-31659-5(0)) Houghton Mifflin Co. Trade & Reference Div.

Martin, Bill, Jr. Chicken Chuck. Salerno, Steven, illus. 2001. 40p. (J). (ps-3). pap. 7.95 (978-1-58837-017-4(8)) Winslow Pr.

Martin, Jacqueline Briggs. Chicken Joy on Redbean Road: A Bayou Country Romp. Sweet, Melissa, illus. 2007. 32p. (J). (gr. 3-5). 17.00 (978-0-618-50759-7(0)) Houghton Mifflin Co.

Martín Larrañaga, Ana. Pepo & Lolo & the Red Apple. 2004. (Super Sturdy Picture Bookstm Ser.). (Illus.). 24p. (J). (gr. k-ps). 8.99 (978-0-7636-2036-3(X)) Candlewick Pr.

—Pepo & Lolo Are Friends. 2004. (Super Sturdy Picture Bookstm Ser.). (Illus.). 24p. (J). (gr. k-ps). 8.99 (978-0-7636-1982-4(5)) Candlewick Pr.

Mathers, Petra. Lottie's New Beach Towel. Mathers, Petra, illus. 2001. (Illus.). 32p. (J). (ps-3). 6.99 (978-0-689-84441-6(7) , Aladdin) Simon & Schuster Children's Publishing.

—Lottie's New Beach Towel. 1998. (Illus.). 32p. (J). (ps-3). 15.00 (978-0-689-81606-2(5) , Atheneum/Anne Schwartz Bks.) Simon & Schuster Children's Publishing.

—Lottie's New Beach Towel. 2001. (gr. k-3). lib. bdg. 14.15 (978-0-613-37157-5(7)); (Illus.). (J). (978-0-606-21306-6(6)) Tandem Library Bks.

McMillan, Bruce. How the Ladies Stopped the Wind. Gunnella, illus. 2007. 32p. (J). (gr. k-3). 16.00 (***978-0-618-77330-5(4)***) Houghton Mifflin Co.

McMillan, Bruce. The Problem with Chickens. Gunnella, illus. 2005. 32p. (J). (gr. k-3). 16.00 (978-0-618-58581-6(8) , Walter Lorraine) Houghton Mifflin Co. Trade & Reference Div.

McOmber, Rachel B., ed. McOmber Phonics Storybooks: A Red Hen. rev. ed. (Illus.). (J). (978-0-944991-25-1(4)) Swift Learning Resources.

—McOmber Phonics Storybooks: Hen Pox. rev. ed. (Illus.). (J). (978-0-944991-28-2(9)) Swift Learning Resources.

McQueen, Lucinda. Little Chick's Easter Surprise. 1999. (Illus.). 10p. (J). (ps-1). pap. 3.50 (978-0-590-64985-8(X)) Scholastic, Inc.

McQueen, Lucinda. Little Red Hen, Library Edition. 2007. (J). 18.95 (***978-0-545-00511-1(6)***) Scholastic, Inc.

Mcqueen, Lucinda. Little Red Hen, The (Readalong) 2007. audio compact disk (***978-0-545-00507-4(8)***) Scholastic, Inc.

Michael & the Chicks. 2005. (J). (978-1-58453-295-8(5)) Pioneer Valley Educational Pr., Inc.

Miles, Betty. Sky is Falling, Level 1. 1998. (Ready-to-Read Ser.). (978-0-606-13777-5(7)) Tandem Library Bks.

Minters, Frances. Chicken for a Day. 2000. (Illus.). (J). 10.79 (978-0-606-18489-2(9)) Tandem Library Bks.

Montardre, Helene. Hen & Chick. 2004. (Turn & Learn Ser.). (Illus.). 8p. (J). (ps up). bds. 7.95 (978-1-58728-480-9(4) , Two Can Publishing) T&N Children's Publishing.

Morgan, Nicola. Chicken Friend. 2005. 160p. (J). (gr. 4-7). 15.99 (978-0-7636-2735-5(6)) Candlewick Pr.

The Mother Goose Caper. 2005. (J). (978-1-932570-46-5(2)) Literacy Footprints Inc.

Nanette. Little Red. 2004. (Life on Granny's Farm Ser.). (J). 12.95 (978-0-9741269-1-3(8)) St. Bernard Publishing, LLC.

Nash, Margaret. The Bossy Rooster. Moseng, Elisabeth, illus. 2004. (Read-It! Readers Ser.). 32p. (C). (gr. k-3). 18.60 (978-1-4048-0051-9(4)) Picture Window Bks.

—Hetty's New Hat. Impey, Martin, illus. 2005. (Reading Corner Ser.). 24p. (J). (gr. k-3). lib. bdg. 22.80 (978-1-59771-007-7(5)) Sea-To-Sea Pubns.

Naylor, Phyllis Reynolds. The Great Chicken Debacle. 96p. 2005. (YA). (gr. 4-8). pap. 5.95 (978-0-7614-5148-8(X)); 2001. (Illus.). (J). (gr. 3-7). 14.95 (978-0-7614-5095-5(5) , Cavendish Children's Bks.) Cavendish, Marshall Corp.

—The Great Chicken Debacle. 2003. (gr. 3-6). lib. bdg. 14.10 (978-0-613-82436-1(9)) Tandem Library Bks.

Nerette-Louis, Liliane. Zenga. 2001. (CRP.). (J). (gr. 3-5). 8.50 (978-1-58432-043-2(5)); (Illus.). 16p. pap. 8.50 (978-1-58432-087-6(7)) Educa Vision.

Newton, Jill. Peek-a-Boo, Mama! 2007. (Illus.). 20p. (ps). bds. 8.95 (***978-1-59354-628-1(9)***) Blue Apple Bks.

Nostlinger, Christine. Juanito Habichuela y Otros Cuentos. (Torre de Papel Ser.). (SPA.). (J). (gr. 4 up). 8.95 (978-958-04-4533-3(8)) Norma S.A. COL. *Dist:* Distribuidora Norma, Inc.

Numeroff, Laura Joffe. The Chicken Sisters. Collicott, Sharleen, illus. 2002. 28.95 incl. audio compact disk (978-1-59112-533-4(2)); pap. 39.95 incl. audio compact disk (978-1-59112-532-7(4)); (J). pap. 18.95 incl. audio compact disk (978-1-59112-310-1(0)) Live Oak Media.

—The Chicken Sisters. abr. ed. 2002. (Live Oak Readalong Ser.). (Illus.). (J). pap. 16.95 incl. audio (978-0-87499-890-0(5)) Live Oak Media.

—The Chicken Sisters. Collicott, Sharleen, illus. abr. ed. 2002. (J). pap., tchr.'s planning gde. ed. 37.95 incl. audio (978-0-87499-892-4(1)); 25.95 incl. audio (978-0-87499-891-7(3)) Live Oak Media.

—The Chicken Sisters. Collicott, Sharleen, illus. 1999. (J). (ps-ps). lib. bdg. 15.30 (978-0-613-11404-2(3)) Tandem Library Bks.

Nunez, Marisa. The Featherless Chicken. Thomassen, Hellen, illus. 2003. 32p. (J). 14.95 (978-84-95730-36-7(7)) Kalandraka Catalunya, Edicions, S.L. ESP. *Dist:* Independent Pubs. Group.

Nwapa-Ibuaka, Njideka. Tales from Animal Kingdom. unabr. ed. 2003. (Illus.). 40p. (gr. 2-5). pap. 7.95 (978-0-9661598-4-4(5)) Ekwike Bks. & Publishing.

O'Brien, Claire. Barn Party. Archbold, Tim, illus. 2005. 46p. (J). (ps-ps). lib. bdg. 10.75 (978-0-606-33661-1(3)) Tandem Library Bks.

Okereke, Laurence. Barry & Big Joe. 2007. (Illus.). 20p. (J). spiral bd. (***978-0-9795739-0-3(4)***) Dion's Pubn.

Old MacDonald's Hens. 2002. 16p. (J). pap. 2.98 (978-0-7525-7059-4(5)) Parragon, Inc.

O'Malley, Kevin. Gimme Cracked Corn & I Will Share. O'Malley, Kevin, illus. 2007. (Illus.). 32p. (J). (gr. k-3). 17.85 (***978-0-8027-9685-1(0)***); 16.95 (***978-0-8027-9684-4(2)***) Walker & Co.

Once upon a Time Spanish Version-Chicken Little. 2005. (J). (978-1-57022-558-1(3)) ECS Learning Systems, Inc.

Once upon a Time Spanish Version-the Little Red Hen. 2005. (J). (978-1-57022-561-1(3)) ECS Learning Systems, Inc.

O'Neil, Sarah. Looking after Chicks. 2000. (gr. k-3). lib. bdg. 11.80 (978-0-613-29688-5(5)) Tandem Library Bks.

Ormerod, Jan. Story of Chicken Licken: Level 4, Green, 7 vols. Ormerod, Jan, illus. 2nd ed. 1999. (Reading Together Ser.). (Illus.). 32p. (J). pap. (978-0-7636-0871-2(8)) Candlewick Pr.

Palatini, Margie. Three French Hens. Egielski, Richard, illus. 2005. 40p. (ps-3). 15.99 (978-0-7868-5167-6(8)) Hyperion Pr.

Park, Barbara. Junie B. Jones Has a Peep in Her Pocket. unabr. ed. 2004. (Junie B. Jones Ser.: No. 15). 80p. (J). (gr. k-3). pap. 17.00 incl. audio (978-0-8072-0336-1(X) , Listening Library) Random Hse. Audio Publishing Group.

—Junie B. Jones Has a Peep in Her Pocket. Brunkus, Denise, illus. 2000. (Junie B. Jones Ser.: No. 15). 80p. (J). (gr. k-3). lib. bdg. 11.99 (978-0-375-90040-2(3)); pap. 3.99 (978-0-375-80040-5(9)) Random Hse. Children's Bks. (Random Hse. Bks. for Young Readers).

Peg the Hen. 2004. (Illus.). (J). (978-1-59577-002-8(X)) Starfall Education.

Perez, Amada Irma. Nana's Big Surprise/¡Nana, Que Sorpresa! Gonzalez, Maya Christina, tr. Gonzalez, Maya Christina, illus. 2007. (ENG & SPA.). 32p. (J). (gr. 1-2). 16.95 (978-0-89239-190-5(1)) Children's Bk. Pr.

Petre, Wanda E. The Watch Chicken: The Legend of Russell the Rooster & His Friend Hortense. 2006. 36p. (J). pap. 9.93 (978-1-4116-9990-8(4)) Lulu.com.

Pierola, Mabel, illus. La Lechera / the Milkmaid. 2006. (Bilingual Tales Ser.). 24p. (J). pap. 3.50 (978-0-439-77377-5(6) , Scholastic en Espanol) Scholastic, Inc.

Pinkney, Jerry, illus. The Little Red Hen. 2006. 32p. (J). (ps-2). 16.99 (978-0-8037-2935-3(9) , Dial) Penguin Group (USA) Inc.

Pinkwater, Daniel M. The Artsy Smartsy Club. Pinkwater, Jill, illus. 2005. 176p. (J). 16.89 (978-0-06-053558-2(X)); 15.99 (978-0-06-053557-5(1)) HarperCollins Pubs.

Pinkwater, Daniel M. The Hoboken Chicken Emergency. Auth, Tony, illus. 2007. 112p. (J). (gr. 1-4). 16.99 (***978-1-4169-2809-6(X)***, Atheneum) Simon & Schuster Children's Publishing.

—The Hoboken Chicken Emergency. 1999. (gr. 3-6). lib. bdg. 13.00 (978-0-7857-9893-4(5)) Tandem Library Bks.

Plouff, Amy. Chicken & His Friends Learn How to Prepare for a Pandemic. 2008. (Chicken & His Friends Ser.). 48p. (J). 9.95 (***978-1-933255-40-8(4)***) DNA Pr.

—Chicken & His Friends Learn How You Get & Prevent the Flu. 2008. (Chicken & His Friends Ser.). 48p. (J). bds. 9.95 (***978-1-933255-39-2(0)***) DNA Pr.

Polacco, Patricia. Chicken Sunday. 1998. (Illus.). 32p. (J). (gr. k-3). reprint ed. pap. 7.99 (978-0-698-11615-3(1) , Putnam Juvenile) Penguin Group (USA) Inc.

Pollack, Pam & Belviso, Meg. Chickens on the Move. Adams, Lynn, illus. 2002. (Math Matters Ser.). 32p. (J). pap. 4.95 (978-1-57565-113-2(0)) Kane Pr., The.

Pollack, Pamela & Belviso, Meg. Chickens on the Move. Adams, Lynn, illus. 2002. 32p. (J). (ps-3). lib. bdg. 12.95 (978-0-613-53491-8(3)) Tandem Library Bks.

Potter, Marian. The Little Red Hen & Other Stories to Color. Miller, J. P. & Gergely, Tibor, illus. 2007. (Super Coloring Book Ser.). 96p. (J). (ps-2). 2.99 (978-0-375-83535-3(0) , Golden Bks.) Random Hse. Children's Bks.

Powell, Richard. Curious Chick. Martín Larrañaga, Ana, illus. 2001. 10p. bds. 5.95 (978-1-58925-662-0(X) , tiger tales) ME Media LLC.

Prami, S. & Schmid, S. One Two Three Pull! Bb. 2006. (Illus.). 16p. (J). 7.95 (978-0-7358-2098-2(8)) North-South Bks., Inc.

Price, Hugh. The Truth at Last about the Little Red Hen. Lowe, Isabel, illus. 2003. 16p. (J). pap. (978-1-877228-19-3(2)) Steele Roberts Publishing Ltd.

Punter, Russell. Chicken Licken. Kronheimer, Ann, illus. 2007. 48p. (J). 8.99 (***978-0-7945-1546-1(0)***, Usborne) EDC Publishing.

Random House Disney Staff. Chicken Little. 2006. (Disney Read-Aloud Board Books). (Illus.). 24p. (J). (gr. k-k). bds. 4.99 (978-0-7364-2290-1(0) , RH/Disney) Random Hse. Children's Bks.

—Chicken Little: The Junior Novelization. 2005. (Illus.). 128p. (J). (gr. 3-7). 4.99 (978-0-7364-2292-5(7) , RH/Disney) Random Hse. Children's Bks.

—Meet the Misfits! Chicken Little. 2005. (Illus.). 12p. (J). (ps-2). pap. 6.99 (978-0-7364-2299-4(4) , RH/Disney) Random Hse. Children's Bks.

Reader's Digest Editors. Who Does God Love? 2004. (Small Miracles Ser.: No. 3). 10p. (J). 6.99 (978-1-4003-0316-8(8)) Nelson, Thomas Inc.

Reynolds, Aaron. Chicks & Salsa. Bogan, Paulette, illus. 32p. (J). (ps-3). 2007. pap. 6.95 (***978-1-59990-099-5(8)***, Bloomsbury Children); 2005. 16.95 (978-1-58234-972-5(X)) Bloomsbury Publishing.

Rhoda, the Run Away Chicken. 2006. (J). per. 14.95 (***978-0-9754591-1-9(2)***) Cubby Hole Tales.

Rigby Education Staff. Everything Changes: Little Red Riding Hood. (Pebble Soup Explorations Ser.). 16p. (ps up). 5.00 (978-0-7635-7051-4(6)) Rigby Education.

—The House Sitters. (Sails Literacy Ser.). (Illus.). 16p. (gr. 1-2). 27.00 (978-0-7635-9914-0(X) , 699149C99) Rigby Education.

Robb, Thelma-Jane & Dorling Kindersley Publishing Staff. Chicken Little. Saunders, Catherine, ed. 2005. (Ultimate sticker Bks.). (Illus.). 16p. (J). (ps-7). pap. 6.99 (978-0-7566-1170-5(9)) Dorling Kindersley Publishing, Inc.

Robert Rose Incorporated Staff. Chicken. 1998. (Robert Rose's Favorite Ser.). (Illus.). 96p. pap. 7.95 (978-1-896503-53-0(5)) Rose, Robert Inc. CAN. *Dist:* Firefly Bks., Ltd.

Rooster Trouble: Early Level Satellite Individual Title Six-Packs. (Sails Literacy Ser.). 16p. (gr. 1-2). 27.00 (978-0-7578-3156-0(7)) Rigby Education.

Rosario, Joann. Puddy Cat & the Chick Muck. Rosario, Joann, illus. 2004. (Illus.). 15p. (J). (ps-5). pap. 10.00 (978-0-9758746-3-9(2) , 1246169) J.G.R. Enterprises.

Ross, Graham, illus. The Paper Wagon: A Folktale from Friesland. 2005. (Orca Echoes Ser.). 64p. (J). (gr. 2-3). pap. 4.99 (978-1-55143-356-1(7)) Orca Bk. Pubs. USA.

Russell, Naomi. Nikki, Rooster & Chick-a-Biddy. 1998. (Illus.). 100p. (J). 15.00 (978-0-89904-761-4(0)); pap. 10.00 (978-0-89904-762-1(9)) Crumb Elbow Publishing.

Ruurs, Margriet. Emma at the Fair. Spurll, Barbara, illus. (J). 2007. 32p. per. (***978-1-55005-127-8(X)***); 2005. 24p. (978-1-55005-126-1(1)) Fitzhenry & Whiteside, Ltd.

Ruurs, Margriet. Emma's Cold Day. 2003. (Illus.). 24p. (J). pap. (978-1-55005-076-9(1)) Fitzhenry & Whiteside, Ltd.

—Emma's Cold Day. Spurll, Barbara, illus. 2002. 24p. (J). (ps-3). 16.95 (978-0-7737-3314-5(0)) Stoddart Kids CAN. *Dist:* Fitzhenry & Whiteside, Ltd.

—Emma's Cold Day. 2004. (gr. k-3). lib. bdg. 16.40 (978-0-613-70722-0(2)) Tandem Library Bks.

Santillo, LuAnn. The Chick. Santillo, LuAnn, ed. 2003. (Half-Pint Kids Readers Ser.). (Illus.). 7p. (J). (ps-1). pap. (978-1-59256-059-2(8)) Half-Pint Kids, Inc.

Sato & Futamata, Eigoro. Pio-pio. 2005. (SPA., Illus.). 40p. (J). (gr. k-2). 15.95 (978-84-8470-041-8(0)) Corimbo, Editorial S.L. ESP. *Dist:* Iaconi, Mariuccia Bk. Imports.

Schami, Rafik. Alberto Y Lila. 2002. (SPA.). (gr. k-3). lib. bdg. 15.25 (978-0-613-51103-2(4)) Tandem Library Bks.

Schmauss, Judy Kentor. Ted Saw an Egg. 2006. (Reader's Clubhouse Set A Ser.). (Illus.). 24p. (J). pap. 3.99 (978-0-7641-3283-4(0)) Barron's Educational Series, Inc.

Shah, Idries. The Silly Chicken. Jackson, Jeff, illus. 32p. (J). 2005. pap. 6.99 (978-1-883536-50-3(2)); 2000. 17.00 (978-1-883536-19-0(7) , SICH1) ISHK. (Hoopoe Bks.).

—The Silly Chicken/el Pollo Bobo. Wirkala, Rita, tr. Jackson, Jeff, illus. 2005. 32p. (J). (ps-ps). 18.00 (978-1-883536-37-4(5) , Hoopoe Bks.) ISHK.

Shannon, George. Secret Chicken Club. 2005. (Illus.). 40p. (J). 16.50 (978-1-59354-128-6(7)); 15.95 (978-1-59354-118-7(X)) Handprint Bks.

—Tippy-Toe Chick, Go! Dronzek, Laura, illus. 2003. 32p. (J). lib. bdg. 16.89 (978-0-06-029824-1(3)); 16.99 (978-0-06-029823-4(5)) HarperCollins Pubs.

Shea, Bob. New Socks. 2007. (Illus.). 48p. (J). (ps-1). 12.99 (978-0-316-01357-4(9)) Little Brown & Co.

Shoo, Shoo, Shoo! & Other Stories, 6 Packs. (Story Steps Ser.). (gr. k-2). 48.00 (978-0-7635-9604-0(3)) Rigby Education.

Sidjanski, Brigitte & Burg, Sarah. Little Chicken & Little Fox. 2006. 32p. (J). (ps-3). 16.99 (978-0-698-40044-3(5) , Minedition) Penguin Group (USA) Inc.

Silver Dolphin en Español Editors. Magical Magnets: Chicken Little. 2006. (SPA., Illus.). 8p. (J). bds. 12.95 (978-970-718-318-6(7)) Advantage Pubs. Group.

Silverman, Erica. When the Chickens Went on Strike. Trueman, Matthew, illus. 2005. 32p. (J). pap. 6.99 (978-0-14-240279-5(6) , Puffin) Penguin Group (USA) Inc.

Sly Fox & Little Red Hen: Individual Title Six-Packs. 32p. (gr. 2 up). 37.00 (978-0-7635-9221-9(8)) Rigby Education.

Smith, Margie Fulton. Chicken Kate's Visit to Church. 2006. 9.00 (978-0-8059-9071-3(2)) Dorrance Publishing Co., Inc.

Sommer, Carl. Proud Rooster & Little Hen. 2003. (Another Sommer-Time Story Ser.). (Illus.). 48p. (J). (gr. 1-4). 16.95 incl. audio compact disk (978-1-57537-510-6(9)); 16.95 incl. audio (978-1-57537-559-5(1)) Advance Publishing, Inc.

—Proud Rooster & Little Hen. Budwine, Greg, illus. (Another Sommer-Time Story Ser.). 48p. (J). (gr. k-3). 2000. lib. bdg. 16.95 (978-1-57537-060-6(3)); 1999. 9.95 (978-1-57537-010-1(7)) Advance Publishing, Inc.

—The Sly Fox & the Chicks. 2003. (Another Sommer-Time Story Ser.). (Illus.). 48p. (J). 16.95 incl. audio compact disk (978-1-57537-504-5(4)); (gr. 1-4). 16.95 incl. audio (978-1-57537-553-3(2)) Advance Publishing, Inc.

—The Sly Fox & the Chicks. James, Kennon, illus. 2000. (Another Sommer-Time Story Ser.). 48p. (J). (gr. k-3). lib. bdg. 16.95 (978 1 57537-062-0(X)), 9.95 (978-1-57537-004-0(2)) Advance Publishing, Inc.

Sophie's Chicken: 6 Small Books. (gr. k-3). 24.00 (978-0-7635-6232-8(7)) Rigby Education.

Spafford, Suzy. Witzy & Zoom-Zoom. Spafford, Suzy, illus. 1998. (Illus.). 32p. (J). (ps). 14.95 (978-0-9643588-1-2(6)) Suzy's Zoo.

Speceal, Edetha. The Lost Egg & Other Stories. 2006. 144p. pap. (***978-1-84401-644-0(7)***) Athena Pr.

Spengler, Kenneth. Little Red Hen Gets Help. Spengler, Margaret, illus. 2007. (Green Light Readers Level 2 Ser.). 24p. (J). (gr. k-2). 12.95 (***978-0-15-206195-1(9)***); pap. 3.95 (***978-0-15-206189-0(4)***) Harcourt Children's Bks. (Green Light Readers).

Stenmark, Victoria. The Singing Chick. Cecil, Randy, illus. rev. ed. 1999. 32p. (J). (ps-1). 15.95 (978-0-8050-5255-8(0) , Holt, Henry & Co. Bks. For Young Readers) Holt, Henry & Co.

Stevens, Janet. Cook-a-Doodle-Doo! Stevens, Janet, illus. 2002. (Illus.). (J). 22.55 (978-0-7587-2272-0(9)) Book Wholesalers, Inc.

Stevens, Janet & Crummel, Susan Stevens. Cook-a-Doodle-Doo! 2001. (J). (gr. k-3). 27.95 incl. audio (978-0-8045-6865-4(0) , 6865) Spoken Arts, Inc.

Stewart, Maddie. Peg. Willey, Bee, illus. 2001. (Blue Bananas Ser.). 48p. (J). (gr. 1-2). (978-0-7787-0841-4(1)); pap. (978-0-7787-0887-2(X)) Crabtree Publishing Co.

—Peg. 2002. (gr. k-3). lib. bdg. 12.95 (978-0-613-52895-5(6)) Tandem Library Bks.

Stiegemeyer, Julie. Merry Christmas, Cheeps! Baicker-McKee, Carol, illus. 2007. 24p. (J). (ps). 9.95 (978-1-59990-064-3(5)) Bloomsbury Publishing.

Stine, R. L. Chicken Chicken. rev. ed. 2007. (Goosebumps Ser.). 144p. (J). pap. 4.99 (978-0-439-89113-4(2)) Scholastic, Inc.

Stoeke, Janet Morgan. A Friend for Minerva Louise. Stoeke, Janet Morgan, illus. 2002. (Minerva Louise Ser.). (Illus.). (J). 23.40 (978-0-7587-2537-0(X)) Book Wholesalers, Inc.

—A Friend for Minerva Louise. 2001. (Illus.). (J). 12.79 (978-0-606-21201-4(9)) Tandem Library Bks.

—Minerva Louise. 2001. (J). (978-0-606-21330-1(9)) Tandem Library Bks.

—Minerva Louise & the Colorful Eggs. 2006. (Illus.). 24p. (J). (ps). 15.99 (978-0-525-47633-7(4) , Dutton Juvenile) Penguin Group (USA) Inc.

—Minerva Louise & the Red Truck. Stoeke, Janet Morgan, illus. 2002. (Illus.). 32p. (J). (ps-1). 14.99 (978-0-525-46909-4(5) , Dutton Juvenile) Penguin Group (USA) Inc.

—Minerva Louise at the Fair. Stoeke, Janet Morgan, illus. 2002. (Minerva Louise Ser.). (Illus.). 14.21 (978-1-4046-1705-6(1)) Book Wholesalers, Inc.

Stoeke, Janet Morgan. A Minerva Louise Christmas. 2007. 24p. (J). (ps). 15.99 (***978-0-525-47857-7(4)*** , Dutton Juvenile) Penguin Group (USA) Inc.

Sykes, Julie. Dora's Chicks. Chapman, Jane, illus. 2004. 32p. (J). pap. 6.95 (978-1-58925-386-5(8)); 14.95 (978-1-58925-015-4(X)) ME Media LLC. (tiger tales).

—Dora's Eggs. Chapman, Jane, illus. (J). 2007. bds. 6.95 (978-1-58925-801-3(0)); 2002. 32p. 5.95 (978-1-58925-365-0(5)) ME Media LLC. (tiger tales).

—Dora's Eggs. 2002. (gr. k-3). lib. bdg. 14.10 (978-0-613-56323-9(9)) Tandem Library Bks.

Tafuri, Nancy. Five Little Chicks. Tafuri, Nancy, illus. 2006. (Illus.). 32p. (J). (ps-k). 14.95 (978-0-689-87342-3(5)) Simon & Schuster Children's Publishing.

Tanen, Sloane. C Is for Coco: A Little Chick's First Book of Letters. Hagen, Stefan, illus. Hagen, Stefan, photos by. 2007. 24p. (J). (ps). 6.95 (978-1-59990-071-1(8)) Bloomsbury Publishing.

—Coco All Year Round. Hagen, Stefan, photos by. 2006. (Illus.). 32p. (J). 15.95 (978-1-58234-709-7(3) , Bloomsbury Children) Bloomsbury Publishing.

—Coco Counts: A Little Chick's First Book of Numbers. Hagen, Stefan, illus. Hagen, Stefan, photos by. 2007. 24p. (J). (ps). 6.95 (***978-1-59990-072-8(6)***) Bloomsbury Publishing.

Tanen, Sloane. Where Is Coco Going? Hagen, Stefan, photos by. 2004. (Illus.). 32p. (J). 14.95 (978-1-58234-951-0(7) , Bloomsbury Children) Bloomsbury Publishing.

Thomas, Dylan. Iona'r Iar. 2005. (WEL., Illus.). 33p. (978-0-86243-434-2(3)) Y Lolfa.

Thompson, Lauren. Wee Little Chick. Butler, John, illus. 2008. (Wee Little Ser.). 32p. (J). 14.99 (***978-1-4169-3468-4(5)***) Simon & Schuster Children's Publishing.

Tomlinson, Jill. The Hen Who Wouldn't Give Up. Howard, Paul, illus. 2005. 96p. (J). reprint ed. pap. 6.99 (978-1-4052-1083-6(4)) Egmont Bks., Ltd. GBR. *Dist:* Trafalgar Square Publishing.

Toy Box Productions Staff, Box, creator. Disney's Instant Classics: Chicken Little/Lilo & Stitch/Brother Bear. unabr. abr. ed. 2005. (Disney's Read along Collection). (Illus.). (J). audio compact disk 14.99 (978-0-7634-1148-0(5)) Walt Disney Records.

ToyBox Innovations, creator. Disney's Chicken Little. 2006. (Disney's Read Along Ser.). (Illus.). 24p. (J). pap. 7.99 incl. audio compact disk (978-0-7634-2170-0(7)) Walt Disney Records.

Two Little Chicks: KinderReaders, 6 Packs. (Kinderstarters Ser.). 8p. (ps-1). 21.00 (978-0-7635-8646-1(3)) Rigby Education.

Valentina, Marina. Lost in the Roses. Valentina, Marina, illus. 2007. 24p. (J). (ps-1). 14.95 (***978-1-60108-014-1(X)***) Red Cygnet Pr.

Varon, Sara. Chicken & Cat. 2006. (Illus.). 40p. (J). (ps-3). pap. 16.99 (978-0-439-63406-9(7) , Scholastic Pr.) Scholastic, Inc.

Vitale, Jill. Freddie the Free-Range Chicken. 2006. (J). 12.95 (***978-0-9767269-5-1(5)*** , Kids Ahead Bks.) World Ahead Media.

—Freddie the Free-Range Chicken. Boddy, Joe, illus. 2006. 32p. (J). 15.95 (978-0-8343-0256-3(X)) World Almanac Bks.

Wallen, Virginia. Amanda: Duck or Chicken? 2007. 17.00 (***978-0-8059-8828-4(9)***) Dorrance Publishing Co., Inc.

Walt Disney Productions Staff. Chicken Little. Phillips, Elizabeth, ed. Tyminski, Lori & Walt Disney Productions Staff, illus. 2005. (Little Golden Book Ser.). 24p. (J). (gr. k-k). 2.99 (978-0-7364-2333-5(8) , Golden/Disney) Random Hse. Children's Bks.

—Little Town Heroes. Walt Disney Productions Staff, illus. 2005. (Illus.). 64p. (J). (ps-2). pap. 3.99 (978-0-7364-2332-8(X) , Golden/Disney) Random Hse. Children's Bks.

—Wish upon a Star. Walt Disney Productions Staff, illus. 2005. (Illus.). 32p. (J). (ps-2). pap. 3.99 (978-0-7364-2330-4(3) , Golden/Disney) Random Hse. Children's Bks.

Ward, Beck & Morris, Alison. Mama Hen & Her Baby Chicks 1, 2, 3. Sweeten, Sami, illus. 2003. 10p. (J). 14.95 (978-0-689-85660-0(1) , Little Simon) Simon & Schuster Children's Publishing.

Ward, Nick. Farmer George & the Lost Chick. 2001. (Illus.). 32p. (J). (ps-k). pap. 8.99 (978-1-86205-412-7(6) , Pavilion Bks., Ltd.) Anova Bks. GBR. *Dist:* Trafalgar Square Publishing.

Waring, Richard. La Gallina Hambrienta. Church, Caroline Jayne, illus. 2005. (SPA.). 24p. (J). (ps-ps). 17.99 (978-84-261-3339-7(8)) Juventud, Editorial ESP. *Dist:* Lectorum Pubns., Inc., Iaconi, Mariuccia Bk. Imports.

—Hungry Hen. Church, Caroline Jayne, illus. 2002. 24.00 (978-1-4046-0466-7(9)) Book Wholesalers, Inc.

—Hungry Hen. Church, Caroline Jayne, illus. 2001. 32p. (J). (ps-1). 16.99 (978-0-06-623880-7(3)) HarperCollins Pubs.

—Hungry Hen. 1998. (J). (978-0-385-32608-7(4) , Dell Books for Young Readers) Random Hse. Children's Bks.

Wattenberg, Jane, illus. & retold by. Henny-Penny. Wattenberg, Jane, retold by. 2001. (J). (gr. k-3). 26.90 incl. audio (978-0-8045-6877-7(4)) Spoken Arts, Inc.

Weber, Lou, ed. Chicken Little. 2005. 10p. (J). bds. 7.98 (978-1-4127-3365-6(0) , 7251500) Publications International, Ltd.

—Chicken Little Interactive. 2005. 24p. (J). 15.98 (978-1-4127-3553-7(X) , 7254800) Publications International, Ltd.

—Chicken Little Look & Find. 2005. 24p. (J). 7.98 (978-1-4127-3469-1(X) , 7260200) Publications International, Ltd.

Wells, Rosemary. Max Counts His Chickens. Wells, Rosemary, illus. 2007. (Illus.). 32p. (J). (ps). 15.99 (978-0-670-06222-5(7) , Viking Juvenile) Penguin Group (USA) Inc.

—Max's Chocolate Chicken. Wells, Rosemary, illus. 2002. (Max the Bunny Ser.). (Illus.). (J). 13.19 (978-0-7587-3110-4(8)) Book Wholesalers, Inc.

—Max's Chocolate Chicken. Wells, Rosemary, illus. 2000. (Max & Ruby Ser.). (Illus.). 32p. (J). (gr. k-2). pap. 5.99 (978-0-14-056672-7(4) , Puffin) Penguin Group (USA) Inc.

—Max's Chocolate Chicken. 1999. (Max & Ruby Ser.). (Illus.). 32p. (J). (gr. k-2). 16.99 (978-0-670-88713-2(7) , Viking Juvenile) Penguin Group (USA) Inc.

—Max's Chocolate Chicken. 2000. (Max & Ruby Ser.). (J). (gr. k-2). 12.10 (978-0-606-18431-1(7)) Tandem Library Bks.

Wiggin, Kate Douglas. A Village Stradivarius. 2004. reprint ed. pap. 1.99 (978-1-4179-9941-5(1)) Kessinger Publishing, LLC.

Wiles, Deborah. Love, Ruby Lavender. (Illus.). (J). 2001. 200p. (gr. 3-7). 16.00 (978-0-15-202314-0(3)); 2005. 228p. reprint ed. pap. 5.95 (978-0-15-205478-6(2)) Harcourt Children's Bks. (Gulliver Bks.).

—Love, Ruby Lavender. 2004. 216p. (J). (gr. 3-7). pap. 36.00 incl. audio (978-0-8072-2096-2(5) , Listening Library) Random Hse. Audio Publishing Group.

Willever, Lisa Funari & Funari, Lorraine. The Easter Chicken. Overman, Emma, illus. 2001. 32p. (ps-3). 9.95 (978-0-9679227-6-8(3) , 329-002) Franklin Mason Pr.

Wolf, Jackie. Picture Me Peek-A-Boo Farm. 2002. (Peek-a-Boo Ser.). (Illus.). 10p. (J). (ps up). bds. 4.99 (978-1-57151-595-7(X)) Playhouse Publishing.

Wolff, Ashley. The Baby Chicks Are Singing/Los Pollitos Dicen: Sing along in English & Spanish!/Vamos a cantar junto en ingles y Espanol! Wolff, Ashley, illus. 2005. (ENG & SPA., Illus.). 22p. (J). (ps-k). bds. 6.99 (978-0-316-06732-4(6)) Little, Brown Bks. for Young Readers.

Woods, John, Jr., illus. The Sky Is Falling: Little Chicken Charlie. 2004. 120p. (J). 17.50 (978-1-889191-05-8(1)) Clove Pubns.

Wormell, Christopher. A Number of Animals. 2003. (Illus.). 24p. (J). (ps-3). pap. 7.95 (978-0-89812-384-5(4) , Creative Paperbacks) Creative Co., The.

Wu, Liz. Rosa Farm. Phelan, Matt, illus. 2006. 144p. (J). (gr. 2-7). 15.95 (978-0-375-83681-7(0)); lib. bdg. 17.99 (978-0-375-93681-4(5)) Random Hse. Children's Bks. (Knopf Bks. for Young Readers).

Young-Robinson, Christine. Chicken Wing, 2nd ed. 2005. (Illus.). 32p. (J). per. 9.95 (978-0-9706985-1-3(8)) Yoroson Publishing.

Zephaniah, Benjamin. Funky Chickens. (Illus.). 96p. (J). 9.95 (978-0-14-037945-7(2)) Penguin Bks., Ltd. GBR. *Dist:* Trafalgar Square Publishing.

Zilis, Tom, illus. The Little Red Hen: Read Well Level K Unit 20 Storybook. 2003. (Read Well Level K Ser.). 20p. (J). (978-1-57035-691-9(2) , 55600) Sopris West Educational Services.

Zobel-Nolan, Allia. Little Chick. Weidner, Teri, illus. 2000. (Fluffy Tales Ser.). 12p. (ps-k). 6.99 (978-0-7847-0889-7(4) , 03699, Bean Sprouts) Standard Publishing.

CHIEF JUSTICES

see Judges

CHIHUAHUA (DOG BREED)

Gray, Susan H. Chihuahuas. 2007. (Domestic Dogs Ser.). 32p. (J). (gr. k-4). 27.07 (978-1-59296-773-5(6)) Child's World, Inc.

Miller, Connie Colwell. Chihuahuas. 2007. (Illus.). 24p. (J). 15.93 (978-0-7368-6326-1(5)) Capstone Pr., Inc.

Temple, Bob. Chihuahuas. l.t. ed. 2000. (Dogs Ser.). (Illus.). 24p. (J). (gr. k-6). lib. bdg. 21.35 (978-1-57765-419-3(6) , Checkerboard Library) ABDO Publishing Co.

CHILD, LYDIA MARIA, 1802-1880

Kenschaft, Lori J. Lydia Maria Child: The Quest for Racial Justice. 2002. (Oxford Portraits Ser.). (Illus.). 128p. (YA). 28.00 (978-0-19-513257-1(2)) Oxford Univ. Pr., Inc.

CHILD ABUSE

see also Child Sexual Abuse

Almond, Lucinda. Child Abuse. 2006. (Current Controversies Ser.). (Illus.). 244p. (gr. 10-12). 24.95 (978-0-7377-2475-2(7)); pap. 36.20 (978-0-7377-2474-5(9)) Thomson Gale. (Greenhaven Pr., Inc.).

Buchanan, Jane. Three Kinds of Touches. Young, Alice Pixley, illus. 1999. 82p. (J). (ps-5). 15.95 (978-0-615-11183-4(1)) Pennsylvania Coalition Against Rape.

—Three Kinds of Touches. braille ed. 1999. 11p. (J). (ps-5). 15.95 (978-0-615-11184-1(X)) Pennsylvania Coalition Against Rape.

Cavaciuti, Susan. Someone Hurt Me. Cavaciuti, Susan, illus. 2004. (Illus.). 222p. pap. 8.95 (978-1-890995-20-1(7) , Vital Health Publishing) Square One Publishers.

Chaiet, Donna. Safe Zone: A Kid's Guide to Personal Safety. 1998. (Illus.). (J). (978-0-606-15824-4(3)) Tandem Library Bks.

Copen, Lynn M. & Pucci, Linda M. Finding Your Way: What Happens When You Tell about Abuse. 2000. (Interpersonal Violence). (Illus.). 72p. pap. 13.95 (978-0-7619-2183-7(4) , 86546) SAGE Pubns., Inc.

Dudley, William. Child Abuse. 2007. (Introducing Issues with Opposing Viewpoints Ser.). (Illus.). 144p. (gr. 7-10). 33.70 (***978-0-7377-3803-2(0)*** , Greenhaven Pr., Inc.) Thomson Gale.

Giacobello, John. You & Violence in Your Family. 2005. (Family Matters Ser.). (Illus.). 48p. (J). (gr. 5-8). lib. bdg. 23.95 (978-0-8239-3353-2(9)) Rosen Publishing Group, Inc., The.

Goldentyer, Debra. Child Abuse. 1998. (Preteen Pressures Ser.). (Illus.). 48p. (J). (gr. 4-8). lib. bdg. 25.69 (978-0-8172-5032-4(8)) Raintree.

Hyde, Margaret O. Missing & Murdered Children. 1998. (Impact Bks.). (Illus.). 112p. (YA). (gr. 9-12). 25.00 (978-0-531-11384-4(1) , Watts, Franklin) Scholastic Library Publishing.

MacGregor, Cynthia. Ten Steps to Staying Safe. 1999. (Abduction Prevention Library). (Illus.). 24p. (J). (gr. 3). lib. bdg. 18.75 (978-0-8239-5248-9(7) , PowerKids Pr.) Rosen Publishing Group, Inc., The.

Marlowe, Carole. Finding Safety: Boundaries for Teenagers. 1999. (gr. 7-12). lib. bdg. 19.80 (978-0-613-79599-9(7)) Tandem Library Bks.

Nadelson, Carol C. & Reinburg, Claire E., eds. Child Abuse & Neglect: Examining the Psychological Components. 1999. (Encyclopedia of Psychological Disorders Ser.). 88p. (YA). (gr. 7 up). 35.00 (978-0-7910-4955-6(8) , Chelsea Hse.) Facts On File, Inc.

Newman, Shirlee Petkin. Child Slavery in Modern Times. (Watts Library). (Illus.). 64p. (J). (gr. 5-7). 2001. pap. 8.95 (978-0-531-16540-9(X)); 2000. 25.50 (978-0-531-11696-8(4)) Scholastic Library Publishing. (Watts, Franklin).

Penney, Betty. Tell Your Mother. 2004. 32p. (J). pap. 8.95 (978-0-9631975-4-2(1)) Morgan, E. A.

Rein, Mei Ling, et al, eds. Child Abuse: Betraying a Trust. 10th ed. 1999. (Reference Ser.). (Illus.). 136p. (J). (gr. 9-12). pap. 32.00 (978-1-57302-091-6(5)) Thomson Gale.

Rogers, Barbara. Screams from Childhood. 2004. 272p. per. 19.95 (978-0-9719097-2-4(5)) Barabara Pr.

Rosen, Marvin. Dealing with the Effects of Rape & Incest. 2002. (Focus on Family Matters Ser.). (Illus.). 64p. (J). (gr. 5 up). 25.00 (978-0-7910-6693-5(2) , Chelsea Hse.) Facts On File, Inc.

Spelman, Cornelia Maude. Your Body Belongs to You. 2000. (978-0-606-18778-7(2)) Tandem Library Bks.

—Your Body Belongs to You. Weidner, Teri, illus. 2003. (Concept Book Ser.). 24p. (J). (ps-1). pap. 6.95 (978-0-8075-9473-5(3)) Whitman, Albert & Co.

Star, Jig. High School Soap Opera. 2002. 230p. (YA). pap. 14.95 (978-0-595-26196-3(5) , Writers Club Pr.) iUniverse, Inc.

Stevens, Dylan. Wooded Sanctuary. 2004. 136p. (YA). pap. 13.95 (978-0-595-31093-7(1)) iUniverse, Inc.

Stewart, Gail B. Child Abuse. 2002. (Understanding Issues Ser.). (Illus.). 48p. (J). (gr. 3-5). 26.20 (978-0-7377-1280-3(5) , Kidhaven) Thomson Gale.

Tubbs, Janet. Child Abuse. 2000. (Spud Packs Ser.). 16p. (J). pap. 19.95 (978-1-881185-12-3(5)) Arcadia Pr.

Wasserman, Burt G. Feeling Good Again: A Workbook for Children Aged 6 & up Who've Been Sexually Abused. Bear, Euan, ed. 1998. 288p. (J). (gr. k up). pap., wbk. ed. 16.00 (978-1-884444-51-7(2) , WP068) Safer Society Pr.

Wood, Ira. How to Stay Safe at Home & On-Line. 2002. (Reading Room Collection). (Illus.). 24p. (J). lib. bdg. 18.75 (978-0-8239-3722-6(4)) Rosen Publishing Group, Inc., The.

Yen Mah, Adeline. Falling Leaves: The True Story of an Unwanted Chinese Daughter. 1999. (gr. 7-12). lib. bdg. 23.45 (978-0-613-16929-5(8)) Tandem Library Bks.

CHILD ABUSE—FICTION

Alexander, Tonia. Sometimes I Forget to Breathe. 2nd ed. 2005. (YA). (978-0-9770550-0-5(0)) Head On Dialogue Publishing.

Alger, Horatio. Phil the Fiddler. 2006. pap. (***978-1-4068-0667-0(6)***) Echo Library.

Alphin, Elaine Marie. Counterfeit Son. 2002. 192p. (YA). pap. 5.99 (978-0-14-230147-0(7) , Puffin) Penguin Group (USA) Inc.

—Counterfeit Son. 2002. (gr. 7-12). lib. bdg. 14.15 (978-0-613-45254-0(2)) Tandem Library Bks.

Bakas, Demetra. Black-Eyed Susan: A Story of Hope for Children & Families. Powell, Cheryl, illus. 2000. 32p. (J). (gr. 1-8). pap. 7.95 (978-1-929208-02-9(2) , Happy Tales Pr.) Creation of Celebration, Inc.

—Black-Eyed Susan Set: A Story of Hope for Children & Families. Powell, Cheryl, illus. 2000. (J). (gr. 1-8). pap. 9.95 incl. audio (978-1-929208-04-3(9) , Happy Tales Pr.) Creation of Celebration, Inc.

Cassidy, Anne. Looking for JJ. 2007. (Illus.). 336p. (YA). (gr. 9 up). 17.00 (***978-0-15-206190-6(8)***) Harcourt Children's Bks.

Citra, Becky. Runaway. 2003. (Young Reader Ser.). (Illus.). 96p. (J). (gr. 3-6). pap. 4.99 (978-1-55143-276-2(5)) Orca Bk. Pubs. USA.

Clifton, Lucille. One of the Problems of Everett Anderson. Grifalconi, Ann, illus. rev. ed. 2001. 32p. (J). (gr. k-3). 16.95 (978-0-8050-5201-5(1) , Holt, Henry & Co. Bks. For Young Readers) Holt, Henry & Co.

Cross, Gillian. The Black Room: The Lost. 2006. (Dark Ground Ser.). 256p. (YA). (gr. 6). 16.99 (978-0-525-47487-6(0) , Dutton Juvenile) Penguin Group (USA) Inc.

Crutcher, Chris. Chinese Handcuffs. 2004. 304p. (J). pap. 7.99 (978-0-06-059839-6(5) , HarperTeen) HarperCollins Pubs.

D'Adamo, Francesco. Iqbal. Leonori, Ann, tr. 2005. 128p. (J). (ps-7). reprint ed. pap. 4.99 (978-1-4169-0329-1(1) , Aladdin) Simon & Schuster Children's Publishing.

D'Adamo, Francesco & Leonori, Ann. Iqbal Vol. 5: A Novel. 2003. (Illus.). 128p. (J). 15.95 (978-0-689-85445-3(5) , Atheneum) Simon & Schuster Children's Publishing.

—Iqbal Vol. 5: A Novel. l.t. ed. 2004. 138p. (J). 20.95 (978-0-7862-6385-1(7)) Thorndike Pr.

Davis, Diane. Algo Anda Mal en Mi Casa: Un Libro Acerca de Las Peleas de Los Padres. Jones, Cynthia, tr. from ENG. Megale, Marina, illus. 1998. (Children's Safety Bks.). (SPA.). 40p. (J). (ps-3). pap. 5.95 (978-1-884734-40-3(5)) Parenting Pr., Inc.

Deans, Sis Boulos. Racing the Past. 2005. 160p. (J). (gr. 3-9). reprint ed. pap. 5.99 (978-0-14-240308-2(3) , Puffin) Penguin Group (USA) Inc.

Dessen, Sarah. Lock & Key. 2008. 432p. (YA). (gr. 7). 18.99 (***978-0-670-01088-2(X)*** , Viking Juvenile) Penguin Group (USA) Inc.

Draper, Sharon M. Forged by Fire. 2002. (Illus.). (J). 13.40 (978-0-7587-0354-5(6)) Book Wholesalers, Inc.

—Forged by Fire. l.t. ed. 2006. 199p. pap. 10.95 (978-0-7862-8358-3(0)) Thorndike Pr.

—Forged by Fire No. 2: Hazelwood High Trilogy. l.t. ed. 2005. 199p. 21.95 (978-0-7862-7417-8(4)) Thorndike Pr.

Ellerbee, Linda. Girl Reporter Stuck in Jam! 2000. (Get Real Ser.: No. 3). (Illus.). 224p. (J). (gr. 3-7). 14.89 (978-0-06-028247-9(9)) HarperCollins Pubs.

—Girl Reporter Stuck in Jam! 2000. (gr. 3-6). lib. bdg. 12.40 (978-0-613-25334-5(5)); (Get Real Ser.: No. 3). (Illus.). (J). (978-0-606-18901-9(7)) Tandem Library Bks.

Felin, M. Sindy. Touching Snow. 2007. 240p. (YA). (gr. 7 up). 16.99 (978-1-4169-1795-3(0) , Atheneum) Simon & Schuster Children's Publishing.

Flinn, Alex. Breathing Underwater. 272p. (J). 2002. (gr. 5 up). pap. 8.99 (978-0-06-447257-9(4)); 2001. (Illus.). (gr. 8 up). 18.99 (978-0-06-029198-3(2)) HarperCollins Pubs.

—Breathing Underwater. unabr. ed. 2004. (Young Adult Cassette Librariestm Ser.). 272p. (J). (gr. 7 up). pap. 36.00 incl. audio (978-0-8072-0992-9(9) , S YA 346 SP, Listening Library) Random Hse. Audio Publishing Group.

—Breathing Underwater. 2002. (gr. 7-12). lib. bdg. 16.45 (978-0-613-60383-6(4)) Tandem Library Bks.

—Nothing to Lose. 2004. 288p. (J). 16.99 (978-0-06-051750-2(6)); lib. bdg. 17.89 (978-0-06-051751-9(4)) HarperCollins Pubs. (HarperTeen).

Greenburg, Dan. Claws. 2007. 208p. (YA). (gr. 3-7). 5.99 (978-0-375-83411-0(7) , Yearling) Random Hse. Children's Bks.

Griffin, Adele. Sons of Liberty. 1998. 230p. (gr. 5-17). pap. 4.95 (978-0-7868-1300-1(8)) Disney Pr.

Grossman, Linda Sky. A Tale Worth Telling. Bockus, Petra, illus. 2002. (I'm a Great Little Kid Ser.). 24p. pap. 4.95 (978-1-896764-60-3(6)); (gr. 3 up). 11.95 (978-1-896764-62-7(2)) Second Story Pr. CAN. *Dist:* Orca Bk. Pubs. USA.

Hahn, Mary Downing. Following My Own Footsteps. 1998. (Camelot Bks.). 192p. (J). (gr. 3-7). reprint ed. pap. 4.95 (978-0-380-72990-6(3)) HarperCollins Pubs.

Harmon, Michael B. The Last Exit to Normal. 2008. (YA). (***978-0-375-84098-2(2)***); lib. bdg. (***978-0-375-94098-9(7)***) Knopf, Alfred A. Inc.

Harrison, Marie Joseph. Mosanna & Me. 2003. 160p. pap. 12.95 (978-0-916251-62-8(4)) Sunbelt Pubns., Inc.

—Mosanna & Me. 2003. (gr. 7-12). lib. bdg. 22.20 (978-0-613-89684-9(X)) Tandem Library Bks.

Hernandez, David. Suckerpunch. 2008. 224p. (J). 16.99 (***978-0-06-117330-1(4)***); lib. bdg. 17.89 (***978-0-06-117331-8(2)***) HarperCollins Pubs. (HarperTeen).

Hixson, Nancy E. Distorted Vision. 1999. 90p. (J). pap. 15.95 (978-0-936389-62-2(1)) Tudor Pubs., Inc.

Howe, James. The Watcher. 1999. 192p. (YA). (gr. 7-12). pap. 8.99 (978-0-689-82662-7(1) , 076714008007, Simon Pulse) Simon & Schuster Children's Publishing.

—The Watcher. 1999. (978-0-606-16319-4(0)) Tandem Library Bks.

—Watcher. (gr. 7-12). 2001. lib. bdg. 13.00 (978-0-613-18288-1(X)); 1999. lib. bdg. 16.45 (978-0-613-73278-9(2)) Tandem Library Bks.

Irgens, Barbara E. Finding the Way. 2001. 187p. (YA). pap. 14.95 (978-1-930580-06-0(1) , Luminary Media Group) Pine Orchard, Inc.

—Finding the Way. 2001. (gr. 7-12). lib. bdg. 24.55 (978-0-613-80418-9(X)) Tandem Library Bks.

Jacobson, Jennifer Richard. Stained. 208p. (YA). (gr. 8 up). 2005. (Illus.). 16.95 (978-0-689-86745-3(X) , Atheneum); 2006. reprint ed. pap. 6.99 (978-1-4169-1337-5(8) , Simon Pulse) Simon & Schuster Children's Publishing.

Johnson, D. C. & Turner, Sandra. Let's Be Friends. Johnson, D. C. & Johnson, Darnell, illus. 2007. (J). per. 9.95 (***978-1-933556-66-6(8)***) Publishers' Graphics, L.L.C.

Jonsberg, Barry. Dreamrider. 2008. 256p. (J). (gr. 9). lib. bdg. 18.99 (***978-0-375-94457-4(5)*** , Knopf Bks. for Young Readers) Random Hse. Children's Bks.

Kehoe, Patricia. Algo Paso 'y Me Da Miedo Decirlo: Un Libro Para Jovenes Victimas Del Abuso. Jones, Cynthia, tr. from ENG. Deach, Carol, illus. 1998. (Children's Safety Bks.).Tr. of Something Happened & I'm Scared to Tell. (SPA.). 32p. (J). (ps-3). pap. 5.95 (978-1-884734-39-7(1)) Parenting Pr., Inc.

Klass, David. You Don't Know Me. 2001. 272p. (YA). (gr. 7 up). 18.00 (978-0-374-38706-8(0) , Farrar, Straus & Giroux (BYR)) Farrar, Straus & Giroux.

—You Don't Know Me. 2002. (gr. 7-12). lib. bdg. 15.30 (978-0-613-53336-2(4)) Tandem Library Bks.

Klassen, Heather. I Don't Want to Go to Justin's House Anymore. Jepson, Beth, illus. 1999. 32p. (gr. k-7). 6.95 (978-0-87868-724-4(6) , 7246) Child Welfare League of America, Inc.

Littleton, Mark. Sarah's Secret. 2001. (Ally OConnor Adventures Ser.: Vol. 2). 112p. (J). (gr. 4-7). pap. 5.99 (978-0-8010-4489-2(8)) Baker Bks.

Lowry, Lois. Gossamer. 2006. 144p. (J). (gr. 5). 16.00 (978-0-618-68550-9(2)) Houghton Mifflin Co.

—Gossamer. 2008. 160p. (J). (gr. 4-7). pap. 6.99 (***978-0-385-73416-5(6)*** , Delacorte Bks. for Young Readers) Random Hse. Children's Bks.

—Gossamer. l.t. ed. 2006. 151p. (YA). 23.95 (978-0-7862-8947-9(3)) Thorndike Pr.

Masterman-Smith, Virginia. First Mate Tate. 2000. (Illus.). 160p. (J). (gr. 5-9). 14.95 (978-0-7614-5075-7(0) , Cavendish Children's Bks.) Cavendish, Marshall Corp.

Mazer, Norma Fox. When She Was Good. 2000. 240p. (J). (gr. 7-12). pap. 16.95 (978-0-590-13506-1(6)) Scholastic, Inc.

—When She Was Good. 2000. (978-0-606-18615-5(8)) Tandem Library Bks.

McCaffrey, Anne. Acorna: The Unicorn Girl. 2001. (Acorna Ser.). lib. bdg. 15.90 (978-0-613-55549-4(X)) Tandem Library Bks.

Mikaelsen, Ben. Touching Spirit Bear. 2001. 256p. (J). (gr. 5 up). 16.99 (978-0-380-97744-4(3)) HarperCollins Pubs.

—Touching Spirit Bear. l.t. ed. 2004. 305p. pap. 10.95 (978-0-7862-6351-6(2)) Thorndike Pr.

Miller, Deborah. Bitter Anguish. 2005. 80p. per. (978-1-55306-971-3(4) , Guardian Bks.) Essence Publishing.

Olson, Gretchen. Call Me Hope. 2007. 288p. (J). (gr. 3-7). 15.99 (***978-0-316-01236-2(X)***) Little Brown & Co.

—Call Me Hope: A Novel. 2007. 272p. (J). (***978-1-4287-4131-7(3)***) Little Brown & Co.

Pamer, Rosey. Para el Abuso: La palabra asociada al Abuso. 2006. 17.00 (978-0-8059-7330-3(3)) Dorrance Publishing Co., Inc.

Pokeberry, P. J. The Huckenpuck Papers: The Tales of a Family's Secret & a Young Girls Search for Self-Esteem. 2003. (Illus.). 87p. (J). pap. 8.95 (978-0-943962-03-0(X)) Viewpoint Pr.

Rapp, Adam & Boyds Mills Press Staff. Little Chicago. 1998. 256p. (YA). 16.95 (978-1-886910-72-0(3) , Lemniscaat) Boyds Mills Pr.

Reynolds, Marilyn. Telling. rev. ed. 2003. (True-To-Life Series from Hamilton High Ser.). 192p. (J). (gr. 7-12). reprint ed. pap. 8.95 (978-1-885356-03-1(X) , 5603X) Morning Glory Pr., Inc.

Schnur, Steven. Hannah & Cyclops. 2000. 108p. (gr. 4-7). pap. 9.95 (978-0-595-00634-2(5) , Backinprint.com) iUniverse, Inc.

Scieszka, Jon. Nos Vemos, Gladiador.Tr. of See you later, gladiator. (SPA.). (J). 7.95 (978-958-04-6484-6(7)) Norma S.A. COL. *Dist:* Distribuidora Norma, Inc.

Shaw, Susan. The Boy from the Basement. 208p. (gr. 7). 2006. (YA). pap. 6.99 (978-0-14-240546-8(9) , Puffin); 2004. (J). 16.99 (978-0-525-47223-0(1) , Dutton Juvenile) Penguin Group (USA) Inc.

Shea, Pegi Deitz. The Carpet Boy's Gift. Morin, Leane, illus. 2005. 40p. (J). (gr. 3-6). 16.95 (978-0-88448-248-2(0)) Tilbury Hse. Pubs.

Stahler, David, Jr. Doppelganger. 2006. 272p. (J). 16.99 (978-0-06-087232-8(2)); lib. bdg. 17.89 (978-0-06-087233-5(0)) HarperCollins Pubs.

Swindells, Robert. Abomination! 2008. 208p. (YA). pap. 9.95 (***978-0-552-55588-3(6)***) Transworld Publishers Ltd. GBR. *Dist:* Independent Pubs. Group.

Toten, Teresa. Game. 2001. (gr. 7-12). lib. bdg. 16.40 (978-0-613-60557-1(8)) Tandem Library Bks.

Voigt, Cynthia. Dicey's Song. l.t. ed. 2002. (Tillerman Cycle Ser.: Bk. 2). 370p. (YA). lib. bdg. 35.95 (978-1-58118-106-7(X) , 25790) LRS.

Warwick, J. M. An Open Vein. 2007. (YA). per. 12.95 (978-1-933963-96-9(4)) Grove Creek Publishing, LLC.

Werlin, Nancy. The Rules of Survival. 2008. 288p. (YA). (gr. 12). pap. 7.99 (***978-0-14-241071-4(3)*** , Puffin); 2006. 276p. (J). (gr. 7). 16.99 (978-0-8037-3001-4(2) , Dial) Penguin Group (USA) Inc.

Wetter, Bruce. The Boy with the Lampshade on His Head. 2004. (Illus.). 304p. (J). 16.95 (978-0-689-85032-5(8) , Atheneum) Simon & Schuster Children's Publishing.

White, Ruth. Tadpole. 2003. 208p. (J). (gr. 4-8). 16.00 (978-0-374-31002-8(5) , Farrar, Straus & Giroux (BYR)) Farrar, Straus & Giroux.

—Tadpole. 2004. 208p. (gr. 5). 5.99 (978-0-440-41979-2(4) , Yearling) Random Hse. Children's Bks.

—Tadpole. l.t. ed. 2003. 201p. (J). 24.95 (978-0-7862-5813-0(6)) Thorndike Pr.

Whittenberg, Allison. Life Is Fine. 2008. 192p. (YA). (gr. 7). 15.99 (***978-0-385-73480-6(8)*** , Delacorte Bks. for Young Readers) Random Hse. Children's Bks.

Williams, Carol Lynch. The True Colors of Caitlynne Jackson. 1998. (J). (978-0-606-13873-4(0)) Tandem Library Bks.

Wright, Julie. My Not-So-Fairytale Life. 2005. 256p. (YA). pap. 15.95 (978-1-59038-476-3(8)) Deseret Bk. Co.

CHILD AND PARENT

see Parent and Child

CHILD ARTISTS

Here are entered works on children as artists and on works of art by children.

see also Finger Painting

Touba, Jacquiline, et al. Nepal: Chandra Bahadur Ale's Painting: Simple Living. 2001. (Young Artists of the World Ser.). (Illus.). 24p. (J). (ps-3). lib. bdg. 19.95 (978-0-8239-5103-1(0) , PowerKids Pr.) Rosen Publishing Group, Inc., The.

CHILD BIRTH

see Childbirth

CHILD DEVELOPMENT

see also Child Psychology; Child Rearing; Children—Growth

Abraham, Adam E. I Am My Body, Not! Litster, Marie, illus. 2000. 60p. (J). (gr. 1-6). lib. bdg. 19.95 (978-0-9700209-1-8(0) , Phaelos Bks.) Phaelos Publishing.

Aigner-Clark, Julie. 365 Days of Baby Einstein. 2003. (Illus.). 176p. (ps-17). 16.99 (978-0-7868-1908-9(1) , Disney Editions) Disney Pr.

Bradford-Vernon, Jennifer R. How to Be Your Child's First Teacher: Insights for Parent Involvement. 2003. (Illus.). 176p. (gr. k-1). 14.99 (978-1-56822-998-0(4) , IF27018) School Specialty Publishing.

Burrill, Richard L. Somewhere Behind the Eyes: Images in the Moon & in the Stars Aha! Miskey, Tom et al, illus. 1998. 100p. (YA). (gr. 9-12). pap. 19.95 (978-1-878464-05-7(1)) Anthro Co., The.

Chamberlain, Catherine. Basic Concept Workbook. 2006. (Illus.). 168p. (J). per. 34.95 (978-0-7606-0655-1(2)) LinguiSystems, Inc.

Cook, Kerri Beth. The Wannabe Honeybee. Cook, Kerri Beth, illus. 2002. (Illus.). 50p. (J). (ps-2). pap. 12.95 (978-0-9719300-0-1(7)) KBCottontop Publishing.

Cross Training Vol. 4: Growing Up!, 3 bks., Set. 1998. 200p. (YA). (gr. 7-9). pap. 99.99 incl. VHS (978-1-57405-027-1(3) , Cross Training) CharismaLife Pubs.

Daniel, Becky. The Playful Child: 130+ Quick Brain-Boosting Activities for 5- & 6-Year Olds. 2000. (Illus.). 176p. (Orig.). (J). (ps-1). pap. 14.99 (978-1-56822-956-0(9) , IF19623-E4, Instructional Fair) Schaffer, Frank Pubns.

—The Playful Preschooler: 130+ Quick Brain-Boosting Activities for 3- & 4-Year-Olds. 2000. (Growing & Learning Ser.). (Illus.). 176p. (J). (gr. 4 up). pap. 14.99 (978-1-56822-955-3(0) , IF19622) School Specialty Publishing.

—The Playful Toddler: 130+ Quick Brain-Boosting Activities for 18 to 36 Months. 2000. (Growing & Learning Ser.). (Illus.). 176p. (J). (gr. 4 up). pap. 16.99 (978-1-56822-954-6(2) , IF19621) School Specialty Publishing.

Espeland, Pamela & Verdick, Elizabeth. Helping Out & Staying Safe: The Empowerment Assets. 2004. (Adding Assets Series for Kids: Bk. 2). (Illus.). 80p. (J). (gr. 3-7). pap. 9.95 (978-1-57542-161-2(5)) Free Spirit Publishing, Inc.

Growing Up! ldr.'s ed. 1998. (Cross Training Ser.: Vol. 4). 64p. (YA). (gr. 7-9). pap. 15.00 incl. VHS (978-1-57405-028-8(1)) CharismaLife Pubs.

Halpin, Mikki. It's Your World—If You Don't Like It, Change It: Activism for Teenagers. 2004. 304p. (YA). pap. 8.99 (978-0-689-87448-2(0) , Simon Pulse) Simon & Schuster Children's Publishing.

Harris. Tell Me about Me Stories. 1999. (J). 19.99 (978-0-7868-0409-2(2)) Hyperion Pr.

Lee, Quinlan B. Barney Follow Me. McKee, Darren, illus. 2004. (Barney Ser.). 6p. (J). bds. 5.99 (978-0-439-62496-1(7)) Scholastic, Inc.

—Color My World! McKee, Darren, illus. 2004. (Barney Ser.). 6p. (J). bds. 5.99 (978-0-439-62500-5(9)) Scholastic, Inc.

—Hello Day! McKee, Darren, illus. 2004. (Barney Ser.). 6p. (J). bds. 5.99 (978-0-439-62497-8(5)) Scholastic, Inc.

—I Can Do It. McKee, Darren, illus. 2004. (Barney Ser.). 6p. (J). bds. 5.99 (978-0-439-62498-5(3)) Scholastic, Inc.

Mackenzie, Carine. Esther Colouring Book. 16p. (J). pap., act. bk. ed. 1.50 (978-1-85792-827-3(X) , Christian Focus) Christian Focus Pubns. GBR. *Dist:* Riverside.

Markova, Dawna. Como Desarrollar la Inteligencia de Sus Hijos.Tr. of How to Develop Your Child's. (SPA.). (J). 8.98 (978-968-403-887-5(9)) Selector, S.A. de C.V. MEX. *Dist:* AIMS International Bks., Inc.

Marks, James Lynn. Education Through Creation, 8 bks. Incl. I Am a Goal Setter. pap. 9.95 (978-0-9706412-4-3(9) , 1005); I Am Special. pap. 9.95 (978-0-9706412-1-2(4) , 1002); I Can Think. pap. 9.95 (978-0-9706412-3-6(0) , 1004); I Have an Idea! pap. 9.95 (978-0-9706412-0-5(6) , 1001); I Love to Give. pap. 9.95 (978-0-9706412-2-9(2) , 1003); Opposites. pap. 9.95 (978-0-9706412-6-7(5) , 1007); That's Bad... No, That's Good (What Does Your Child Think) pap. 9.95 (978-0-9706412-5-0(7) , 1006); You Did a Great Job Honey! pap. 9.95 (978-0-9706412-7-4(3) , 1008); 16p. (J). (ps-6). (Education Through Creation Ser.). (Illus.). 2000. Set pap. 79.95 (978-0-9706412-8-1(1) , 1009) Seventh Sun Productions.

—I Am a Goal Setter. 2000. (Education Through Creation Ser.: Bk. 5). (Illus.). 16p. (J). (ps-6). pap. 9.95 (978-0-9706412-4-3(9) , 1005) Seventh Sun Productions.

—I Am Special. 2000. (Education Through Creation Ser.: Bk. 2). (Illus.). 16p. (J). (ps-6). pap. 9.95 (978-0-9706412-1-2(4) , 1002) Seventh Sun Productions.

—I Can Think. 2000. (Education Through Creation Ser.: Bk. 4). (Illus.). 16p. (J). (ps-6). pap. 9.95 (978-0-9706412-3-6(0) , 1004) Seventh Sun Productions.

McAlpine, Margaret. Working with Children. 2004. (My Future Career Ser.). (Illus.). 64p. lib. bdg. 26.00 (978-0-8368-4241-8(3)) Stevens, Gareth Inc.

Mokhemar, Mary Ann. Just for Kids Interactive Auditory Processing Pictures Manual. 2006. (J). 0.00 (978-0-7606-0665-0(X)) LinguiSystems, Inc.

Mulstay, Linda Muratore. Autism & PDD Answering Questions, Level 1. 2006. (J). per. 29.95 (978-0-7606-0673-5(0)) LinguiSystems, Inc.

Muratore, Linda Mulstay. Autism & PDD Answering Questions, Level 2. 2006. (J). per. 29.95 (978-0-7606-0674-2(9)) LinguiSystems, Inc.

Murkoff, Heidi. What to Expect Kids, No. 9. 2001. (J). (978-0-694-01329-6(3) , Harper Festival) HarperCollins Pubs.

Paonessa, Mary. Growth & Development with Friends, 8 vols. 3rd rev. ed. 2003. (Human Growth & Development Ser.). (Illus.). 41p. (J). (gr. 5 up). pap. 9.00 (978-0-9711721-0-4(2) , 388) Paon Pubns.

—Growth & Development with Friends & Family, 8 vols. 3rd rev. ed. 2003. (Human Growth & Development Ser.). (Illus.). 64p. (J). (gr. 6 up). pap. 11.00 (978-0-9711721-2-8(9) , 390) Paon Pubns.

Shakarian, Lorraine & Huggins, Pat. Helping Kids Handle Conflict (Intermediate Version) Teaching Self-control. 2003. (ASSIST Program Ser.). (Illus.). 564p. spiral bd. (978-1-57035-818-0(4) , 235 CONINT) Sopris West Educational Services.

Steps to Healthy Touching: Activities to Help Kids Understand & Control Their Problems with Touching. 2nd ed. 2003. (Illus.). 128p. (J). per. 12.95 (978-1-55864-138-9(6)) JIST Publishing.

Tal, Ronit. A Different Story Bk. 1: From Birth to Six Months. 2000. (Illus.). 14p. (J). (978-965-7096-00-0(6)) A Different Story, Ltd.

Thomas, Tyren Scott. The Sun. Phillips, Rick, illus. 2005. (ENG.). 28p. (J). (ps-3). per. 20.25 (978-1-4208-5722-1(3)) AuthorHouse.

Traugh, Steven & Traugh, Susan. Mother Goose Brain Boost: Using Music & Movement to Teach Cognitive Skills. Cernek, Kim, ed. Tom, Darcy & Grayson, Rick, illus. 2006. 80p. pap. 19.99 (978-1-59198-234-0(0) , 2224) Creative Teaching Pr., Inc.

The Weaver Curriculum. 2004. (gr. k-12). Vol. 1. 145.00 (978-1-58095-842-4(7) , WV001, Weaver); Vol. 2. 145.00 (978-1-58095-843-1(5) , WV002, Weaver); Vol. 3. 145.00 (978-1-58095-844-8(3) , WV003, Lifepac); Vol. 4. 145.00 (978-1-58095-845-5(1) , WV004, Lifepac); Vol. 5. 145.00 (978-1-58095-846-2(X) , WV005, Weaver) Alpha Omega Pubns., Inc.

Whitcombe, Renee Raab. Look Who's Going to Be a Big Brother. 2003. (Illus.). 24p. (J). 24.95 (978-0-9741882-1-8(2)) Budding Family Publishing.

—Look Who's Going to Be a Big Sister. 2003. (Illus.). 24p. (J). 24.95 (978-0-9741882-0-1(4)) Budding Family Publishing.

2003 (Guide) Book for Starlight Bands & Sunshine Bands. pap. (978-1-58942-115-8(9)) R.H. Boyd Publishing Corp.

CHILD LABOR

see Children—Employment

CHILD MOLESTING

see Child Sexual Abuse

CHILD PSYCHOLOGY

see also Child Rearing

Andrews, Beth. I Miss You! A Military Kid's Book about Deployment. 2007. 56p. (J). pap. 12.00 (***978-1-59102-534-4(6)***) Prometheus Bks., Pubs.

Berry, Joy. Tough Situations. 2005. (Winning skills series, get over It! Ser.). (Illus.). 48p. (J). 3.95 (978-1-57687-279-6(3) , PowerHouse Kids) powerHouse Cultural Entertainment, Inc.

Berry, Joy Wilt. A Book about Interrupting. 2005. (Illus.). (J). (978-0-7172-8599-0(5)) Scholastic, Inc.

Burns, Peggy. Playground Survival. 2004. (Kids' Guides Ser.). (Illus.). 32p. (J). (gr. 1-4). lib. bdg. 25.64 (978-1-4109-0572-7(1)) Raintree.

Canizares, Susan & Betsey, Chessen. Two Can Do It! 1999. (ps-2). lib. bdg. 10.10 (978-0-613-22540-3(6)) Tandem Library Bks.

Canizares, Susan & Chessen, Betsey. Two Can Do It! 1999. (Social Studies Emergent Readers). (J). 2.50 (978-0-439-04559-9(2)) Scholastic, Inc.

chuta, edith N. Straight Talk to Troubled Kids: Finding Wisdom Underneath Our Pains. 2007. 76p. per. 10.95 (***978-0-595-43778-8(8)***) iUniverse, Inc.

Clark, Jan. Family Survival. 2004. (Illus.). 32p. (J). lib. bdg. 25.64 (978 1 4109 0569-7(1)) Raintree.

Craig, Dave. Bad Attitude: A Sure Way to Look Rather Silly! 2005. (Illus.). 44p. (YA). spiral bd. 7.50 (978-1-59721-003-4(X)) Paperbacks for Educators.

—Cheating: A Sure Way to Become Untrustworthy! 2005. (Illus.). 44p. (YA). spiral bd. 7.50 (978-1-59721-002-7(1)) Paperbacks for Educators.

—Lying: A Sure Way to Destroy Your Credibility! 2005. (J). spiral bd. 7.50 (978-1-59721-001-0(3)) Paperbacks for Educators.

—Stealing: A Sure Way to Make Life Miserable! 2005. (YA). spiral bd. 7.50 (978-1-59721-000-3(5)) Paperbacks for Educators.

Curso Practico de Expresion Corporal: Psicomotricidad Infantil, 3 vols. 2002. Tr. of Practical Course in Bodily Expression: Child Psycho-Motor Development. (SPA., Illus.). 192p. 54.00 (978-84-494-2011-5(3) , GML07104-186027) Oceano Grupo Editoria, S.A. ESP. *Dist:* Thomson Gale.

Day, Roger. Being Mad, Being Glad. 2004. (Kids' Guides Ser.). (Illus.). 32p. (J). (gr. 1-4). lib. bdg. 25.64 (978-1-4109-0570-3(5)) Raintree.

Do, Elisa Shipon-Blum. Understanding Katie: A Day in the Life Of. Salus, Diane, illus. 2003. 28p. (J). (ps up). pap. (978-0-9714800-3-2(6)) Selective Mutism Anxiety Research & Treatment Ctr.

Haisha, Lisa. Whispers from Children's Hearts. 2005. (978-0-9771404-0-4(7)) Risa Publications.

Hubble, Joan. Understanding Anorexia Nervosa. 1999. (Teen Eating Disorder Prevention Library). 144p. (gr. 7-12). pap. 6.95 (978-1-56838-260-9(X)) Hazelden Publishing & Educational Services.

Jackson, Ellen B. Sometimes Bad Things Happen. Rotner, Shelley, illus. 2002. 32p. (ps-1). pap. 7.95 (978-0-7613-1734-0(1) , Millbrook Pr.) Lerner Publishing Group.

Kent, Susan. The Let's Talk Library, Set 8 (Accelerated Reader) Yourself & Others, 6 bks. Incl. Let's Talk about Being a Good Friend. lib. bdg. 18.75 (978-0-8239-5419-3(6)); Let's Talk about Feeling Nervous. lib. bdg. 18.75 (978-0-8239-5420-9(X)); Let's Talk about Living with a Grandparent. lib. bdg. 18.75 (978-0-8239-5421-6(8)); Let's Talk about Needing Extra Help in School. lib. bdg. 18.75 (978-0-8239-5422-3(6)); Let's Talk about Stuttering. lib. bdg. 18.75 (978-0-8239-5423-0(4)); Let's Talk about When You Have Trouble Going to Sleep. lib. bdg. 18.75 (978-0-8239-5424-7(2)); 24p. (J). (gr. 3). (Illus.). 2000. Set lib. bdg. 103.50 (978-0-8239-7008-7(6) , PowerKids Pr.) Rosen Publishing Group, Inc., The.

Lamb-Shapiro, Jessica. Sometimes I Don't Like to Talk: But Sometimes I Can't Keep Quiet. Morris, Robin C., illus. 2002. (J). pap. 15.95 (978-1-58815-045-5(3)) Childswork/Childsplay.

Michaels, P. J. My Listening Friend: A Story about the Benefits of Counseling. Dewdney, Anna, illus. 2001. 57p. (J). pap. 13.50 (978-1-58815-043-1(7)) Childswork/ Childsplay.

Mundy, Michaelene. Mad Isn't Bad: A Child's Book about Anger. Alley, R. W., illus. 1999. (Elf-Help Books for Kids). 32p. (J). (ps-3). pap. 5.95 (978-0-87029-331-3(1) , 20106) Abbey Pr.

Nadelson, Carol C. & Reinburg, Claire E., eds. Sibling Rivalry: Relational Disorders Between Brothers & Sisters. 1999. (Encyclopedia of Psychological Disorders Ser.). (Illus.). 88p. (YA). (gr. 4-7). 35.00 (978-0-7910-4952-5(3) , Chelsea Hse.) Facts On File, Inc.

Peltier, Sylvia M. Nanny & I. Peltier, Sylvia M., illus. 2003. (Illus.). 32p. (YA). (ps up). 16.95 (978-0-9724394-0-4(4)) Sylables.

Peters, Diane. Procrastination: Deal with it all in good Time. Tankard, Jeremy, illus. 2006. (Deal with It Ser.). 32p. (J). (gr. 4-8). pap. 12.95 (***978-1-55028-947-3(0)***) Lorimer, James & Co., Ltd., Pubs. CAN. *Dist:* Casemate Pubs. & Bk. Distributors, LLC.

Potts, Kimberly. What's Your Mood? A Good Day, Bad Day, In-Between Day Book. 2005. (Illus.). 160p. (J). pap. 8.95 (978-1-59337-217-0(5)) Adams Media Corp.

Price, Elizabeth. Divorce & Teens: When a Family Splits Apart. 2004. (Teen Issues Ser.). (Illus.). 64p. (J). lib. bdg. 22.60 (978-0-7660-1670-5(6)) Enslow Pubs., Inc.

Ratcliffe, Jane. Sometimes I Get Sad: But Now I Know What Makes Me Happy. Morris, Robin C., illus. 2002. (J). pap. 15.95 (978-1-58815-046-2(1)) Childswork/ Childsplay.

Ring, Susan. Needs & Wants. 2003. (Yellow Umbrella Books). (Illus.). 16p. (J). (gr. 1). lib. bdg. 14.60 (978-0-7368-2028-8(0) , Pebble Bks.) Capstone Pr., Inc.

Rotner, Shelley & Kelly, Sheila M. Good-Byes. Rotner, Shelley, photos by. 2002. (Contemporary Issues for Young Children Ser.). (Illus.). 32p. (gr. k-3). lib. bdg. 22.90 (978-0-7613-1752-4(X) , Millbrook Pr.) Lerner Publishing Group.

Schmidt, Deborah. Understanding Bulimia Nervosa. 1999. (Teen Eating Disorder Prevention Library). 144p. (gr. 7-12). pap. 6.95 (978-1-56838-261-6(8)) Hazelden Publishing & Educational Services.

Simmons, Rachel. Odd Girl Speaks Out. 2004. (gr. 7-12). lib. bdg. 15.10 (978-0-613-70533-2(5)) Tandem Library Bks.

Stenson, Lila & Stenson, Anna. Daddy, up & Down: Sisters Grieve the Loss of Their Daddy. Ferre', Heidi, ed. Biddix, Cheryl L., illus. 2002. 32p. (J). per. 16.95 (978-0-9658061-1-4(1)) Peaceful Village Publishing.

Stewart, Gail B. Phobias. 2000. (Diseases & Disorders Ser.). (Illus.). 120p. (YA). (gr. 6-9). 32.45 (978-1-56006-726-9(8) , GML12001-178175, Lucent Bks.) Thomson Gale.

Weill, Sabrina Solin. We're Not Monsters: Teens Speak Out about Teens in Trouble. 2002. (gr. 7-12). lib. bdg. 15.25 (978-0-613-71899-8(2)) Tandem Library Bks.

Wells, Donna. Live Aware, Not in Fear: The 411 After 9-11. 2002. (gr. 7-12). lib. bdg. 18.75 (978-0-613-51313-5(4)) Tandem Library Bks.

Wells, Donna K. & Morris, Bruce C. Live Aware, Not in Fear: The 411 after 9-11, A Book for Teens. 2002. (Illus.). 120p. pap. 9.95 (978-0-7573-0013-4(8)) Health Communications, Inc.

Wilde, Jerry. More Hot Stuff to Help Kids Chill Out: The Anger & Stress Management Book. 2001. (Illus.). 85p. (YA). (gr. 5-12). pap. 9.95 (978-0-9657610-3-1(7)) LGR Publishing, Inc.

Williams, Julie. Pyromania, Kleptomania, & Other Impulse-Control Disorders. 2002. (Diseases & People Ser.). (Illus.). 128p. (YA). (gr. 6-12). lib. bdg. 26.60 (978-0-7660-1899-0(7)) Enslow Pubs., Inc.

Zimmerman, Jill. Picture Perfect: What You Need to Feel Better about Your Body. 2007. 256p. (YA). pap. 14.95 (***978-0-7573-0607-5(1)***) Health Communications, Inc.

CHILD REARING

Here are entered works on the principles and techniques of raising children. Works on the psycho-social interaction between parents and their minor children are under Parent and Child.

see also Babysitters; Moral Education; Problem Children

Bass, Joseph L. A Little Handbook on Babies: A Handbook for Parents/ A Handbook for Grandparents. 1998. IV, 46p. (YA). pap. 4.25 (978-0-9669359-0-5(X)) Downhome Enterprise, L. L. C., The.

DeGaetano, Gloria. Parenting Well in a Media Age: Keeping Our Kids Human. 2004. 272p. (J). pap. 18.95 (978-1-932181-12-8(1)) Personhood Pr.

Dickerson, Julie G. Helping Children Understand Series. 1998. (Illus.). 96p. (Orig.). (J). (gr. k-6). pap. 21.95 (978-0-9646576-0-1(0)) Cherubic Pr.

The Don't Bully Me Book: A Hands-On Guide for Children & Grown-Ups. 2001. (J). per. 18.95 (978-1-931413-36-7(3)) Fundcraft Publishing.

Duhaime, Edmund. Discipline Required. 2004. 56p. (J). per. 9.95 (978-1-151-67843-0(0)) American Literary Pr.

Gellman, Marc. Someday You'll Thank Me for This! And Other Annoying (But True) Life Lessons. Tilley, Debbie, illus. 2007. 144p. (J). (gr. 3-7). 12.99 (***978-0-316-01234-8(3)***) Little, Brown Bks. for Young Readers.

Hanson, Marci J., et al. On My Best Behavior. 2001. (Me, Too! Ser.). (Illus.). 24p. pap. 19.95 (978-1-55766-513-3(3) , 5133) Brookes, Paul H. Publishing Co.

Henry, Debra. Best Behavior: A Celebration of Good Manners for Our African-American Children. Deal, David, photos by. 2004. (J). per. 15.00 (978-0-9758611-0-3(7)) Black Society Pages, Inc.

Hurt, Laurie S. What I Think I Want to Be. (J). (gr. k-3). 14.95 (978-0-9729403-0-6(8)) Marshall, George Publishing.

Keller, Kristin Thoennes. Parenting a Toddler. 2000. (Skills for Teens Who Parent Ser.). (Illus.). 64p. (J). (gr. 4-6). lib. bdg. 23.93 (978-0-7368-0703-6(9) , LifeMatters Bks.) Capstone Pr., Inc.

—Parenting an Infant. 2000. (Skills for Teens Who Parent Ser.). (Illus.). 64p. (J). (gr. 4-6). lib. bdg. 23.93 (978-0-7368-0702-9(0) , LifeMatters Bks.) Capstone Pr., Inc.

—Skills for Teens Who Parent, 4 bks. Incl. Disciplining Young Children. lib. bdg. 23.93 (978-0-7368-0701-2(2)); Health Care for Infants & Toddlers. lib. bdg. 23.93 (978-0-7368-0704-3(7)); Parenting a Toddler. lib. bdg. 23.93 (978-0-7368-0703-6(9)); Parenting an Infant. lib. bdg. 23.93 (978-0-7368-0702-9(0)); 64p. (J). (gr. 4-6). 2000. (Illus.). Set lib. bdg. 95.72 (978-0-7368-0718-0(7) , LifeMatters Bks.) Capstone Pr., Inc.

Kennedy-Moore, Eileen. What about Me? Twelve Ways to Get Your Parents' Attention (Without Hitting Your Sister) Katayama, Mits, illus. 2005. 32p. (J). (ps-3). 14.95 (978-1-884734-86-1(3)) Parenting Pr., Inc.

Lindsay, Jeanne Warren. The Challenge of Toddlers: For Teen Parents - Parenting Your Child from One to Three. Crawford, David, photos by. 3rd ed. 2004. (Teen Pregnancy & Parenting Series Ser.). 224p. (J). 18.95 (978-1-932538-07-6(0)); pap. 12.95 (978-1-932538-06-9(2)) Morning Glory Pr., Inc.

—Teen Dads. 1999. (J). (gr. 7-12). lib. bdg. 22.20 (978-0-7857-2434-6(6)) Tandem Library Bks.

—Teen Dads: Rights, Responsibilities & Joys. 2nd rev. ed. 2000. (Teen Pregnancy & Parenting Ser.). (Illus.). 224p. (J). pap. 12.95 (978-1-885356-68-0(4)) Morning Glory Pr., Inc.

—Your Baby's First Year: A Guide for Teenage Parents. Blum, Carole, photos by. 3rd ed. 2004. (Teen Pregnancy & Parenting Series Ser.). 224p. (J). 18.95 (978-1-932538-04-5(6)); pap. 12.95 (978-1-932538-03-8(8)) Morning Glory Pr., Inc.

Roark, Walter. Keeping Your Grandkids Alive till Their Ungrateful Parents Arrive: The Guide for Fun-Loving Granddads. Snape, Jason, illus. 2004. 192p. (J). pap. 15.95 (978-0-9707937-2-0(3)) Clearing Skies Pr.

Sanschagrin, Joceline. Caillou, Help Mommy. CINAR Animation Staff & Sévigny, Eric, illus. adapted rev. ed. 2006. (Lift-the-Flap Cinar Ser.). 20p. (J). pap. 5.95 (978-2-89450-524-3(8)) Chouette Publishing CAN. *Dist:* Independent Pubs. Group.

CHILD SEXUAL ABUSE

Copen, Lynn M. & Pucci, Linda M. Finding Your Way: What Happens When You Tell about Abuse. 2000. (Interpersonal Violence). (Illus.). 72p. pap. 13.95 (978-0-7619-2183-7(4) , 86546) SAGE Pubns., Inc.

Foltz, Linda Lee. Kids Helping Kids Break the Silence of Sexual Abuse. 2003. 144p. (J). 21.95 (978-0-9637966-8-4(2)); (YA). pap. 14.95 (978-0-9637966-9-1(0)) Lighthouse Point Pr.

Lehman, Carolyn. Strong at the Heart: How It Feels to Heal from Sexual Abuse. 2005. (Illus.). 176p. (YA). (gr. 8-12). 18.00 (978-0-374-37282-8(9) , Farrar, Straus & Giroux (BYR)) Farrar, Straus & Giroux.

MacGregor, Cynthia. Staying Safe by Saying No. 1999. (Abduction Prevention Library). (Illus.). 24p. (J). (gr. 3). lib. bdg. 18.75 (978-0-8239-5252-6(5) , PowerKids Pr.) Rosen Publishing Group, Inc., The.

—Stranger Danger. 1999. (Abduction Prevention Library). (Illus.). 24p. (J). (gr. 3). lib. bdg. 18.75 (978-0-8239-5247-2(9) , PowerKids Pr.) Rosen Publishing Group, Inc., The.

Marcy-Webster, Susan & Phillips, Emily. If I Tell. 2006. (Illus.). 32p. (J). pap. 3.95 (978-1-55864-178-5(5) , K1785, KIDSRIGHTS) JIST Publishing.

Pancella, Peggy. Your Own Safety. 2004. (Heinemann First Library). (Illus.). 32p. (J). 6.95 (978-1-4034-4938-2(4)); lib. bdg. 22.79 (978-1-4034-4929-0(5)) Heinemann Library.

Porett, Jane. When I Was Little Like You. 1999. (Illus.). (ps-3). 6.95 (978-0-87868-794-7(7) , 7947) Child Welfare League of America, Inc.

Sherman, Joanne. Because It's My Body. Gurney, John Steven, illus. 2002. (Keep 'Em Safe Ser.). 32p. (J). (ps-2). per. 14.95 (978-0-9711735-0-7(8)) S.A.F.E. for Children Publishing, LLC.

—Because It's My Body! Keep 'Em Safe Series: Anxiety-Free Learning for Children. Gurney, John Steven, illus. 2006. 40p. (J). 18.95 (978-0-9711735-9-0(1)) S.A.F.E. for Children Publishing, LLC.

CHILD SEXUAL ABUSE—FICTION

Block, Francesca Lia. I Was a Teenage Fairy. 192p. (J). (gr. 7 up). 1998. 14.89 (978-0-06-027748-2(3)); 2000. reprint ed. pap. 7.99 (978-0-06-440862-2(0) , Cotler, Joanna Books) HarperCollins Pubs.

—I Was a Teenage Fairy. 2000. (gr. 7-12). lib. bdg. 16.45 (978-0-613-28529-2(8)); (Illus.). (J). 14.64 (978-0-606-18903-3(3)) Tandem Library Bks.

Cumbie, Patricia. Where People Like Us Live. 2008. 224p. (J). 16.99 (***978-0-06-137597-2(7)***); lib. bdg. 17.89 (***978-0-06-137598-9(5)***) HarperCollins Pubs. (Geringer, Laura Book).

Grossman, Linda Sky. Sam Speaks Out. Bockus, Petra, illus. 24p. pap. 4.95 (978-1-896764-57-3(6)); 2002. 11.95 (978-1-896764-59-7(2)) Second Story Pr. CAN. *Dist:* Orca Bk. Pubs. USA.

Hurwin, Davida Wills. Circle the Soul Softly. 2006. 176p. (J). 15.99 (978-0-06-077505-6(X)); lib. bdg. 16.89 (978-0-06-077506-3(8)) HarperCollins Pubs.

Johnson, Tim. Never So Green. 2002. 240p. (YA). 18.00 (978-0-374-35509-8(6) , Farrar, Straus & Giroux (BYR)) Farrar, Straus & Giroux.

Ledwon, Peter. Mia's Secret. Ledwon, Peter & Mets, Marilyn, illus. 2006. 24p. (J). (ps-3). pap. 7.95 (978-0-88776-801-9(6) , Anchor) Knopf Publishing Group.

Mazer, Norma Fox. The Missing Girl. 2008. 288p. (J). 16.99 (***978-0-06-623776-3(9)***); lib. bdg. 17.89 (***978-0-06-623777-0(7)***) HarperCollins Pubs. (HarperTeen).

Nathanson, Laura. El Problema de los Miercoles. (SPA.). 160p. (YA). (gr. 5-8). (978-84-279-3181-7(6) , NG3677) Noguer y Caralt Editores, S. A. ESP. *Dist:* Lectorum Pubns., Inc.

—El Problema de los Miercoles. 2001. (SPA.). (gr. 5-8). lib. bdg. 17.60 (978-0-613-80655-8(7)) Tandem Library Bks.

Rapp, Adam. 33 Snowfish. Ering, Timothy Basil, illus. 2006. 192p. (YA). (gr. 10). pap. 6.99 (978-0-7636-2917-5(0)) Candlewick Pr.

Rapp, Adam & Boyds Mills Press Staff. Little Chicago. 1998. 256p. (YA). 16.95 (978-1-886910-72-0(3) , Lemniscaat) Boyds Mills Pr.

Voigt, Cynthia. When She Hollers. 2003. 192p. (J). (gr. 7 up). pap. 5.99 (978-0-590-46715-5(8) , Scholastic Paperbacks) Scholastic, Inc.

Weeks, Sarah. Jumping Scratch. 2008. 192p. (J). pap. 5.99 (***978-0-06-054111-8(3)*** , Geringer, Laura Book) HarperCollins Pubs.

Weeks, Sarah. Jumping the Scratch. 2006. (Illus.). 176p. (J). 15.99 (978-0-06-054109-5(1)); lib. bdg. 16.89 (978-0-06-054110-1(5)) HarperCollins Pubs. (Geringer, Laura Book).

Woodson, Jacqueline. I Hadn't Meant to Tell You This. 2006. (YA). 176p. (gr. 4). 17.99 (978-0-399-24499-5(9) , Putnam Juvenile); 128p. (gr. 7). pap. 5.99 (978-0-14-240555-0(8) , Puffin) Penguin Group (USA) Inc.

CHILD STUDY

see Child Development; Child Psychology

CHILD WELFARE

Here are entered works on the aid, support, and protection of children, by the state or by private welfare organizations.

see also Children—Employment; Children—Health and Hygiene; Children—Hospitals; Foster Home Care; Juvenile Delinquency; Playgrounds

Berry, Joy. Mine & Yours: Human Rights for Kids. Richardson, Nicole, illus. 2005. 46p. (J). (gr. 3-7). pap. 8.95 (978-1-57687-260-4(2) , PowerHouse Kids) powerHouse Cultural Entertainment, Inc.

Duckworth, Katie. Health. 2004. (Children's Rights Ser.). (J). lib. bdg. 27.10 (978-1-58340-420-1(1)) Smart Apple Media.

Katella-Cofrancesco, Kathy. Children's Causes. 1998. (Celebrity Activists Ser.). (Illus.). 64p. (gr. 5-8). lib. bdg. 25.90 (978-0-7613-3013-4(5) , Twenty-First Century Bks.) Lerner Publishing Group.

Lamanno, Angela. Imagine. 2000. (Illus.). 24p. (ps-3). pap. 6.95 (978-0-87868-744-2(0) , 7440, Child & Family Pr.) Child Welfare League of America, Inc.

Libal, Joyce. Somebody Hear Me Crying: Youth in Protective Services. 2004. (Youth with Special Needs Ser.). (Illus.). 128p. (J). lib. bdg. (978-1-59084-739-8(3)) Mason Crest Pubs.

Morris, Kimberly & Burke, Kathleen. Just for Now: Kids & the People of the Court. Sansevero, Tony, illus. 2007. 48p. (J). (gr. k-4). 16.95 (***978-0-9754953-9-1(9)***) Child Advocates, Inc.

Parry, Ann. Save the Children. 2005. (Humanitarian Organizations Ser.). (Illus.). 32p. (J). (gr. 4-8). lib. bdg. 22.95 (978-0-7910-8816-6(2) , Chelsea Hse.) Facts On File, Inc.

Strom, Laura Layton. Don't Try This at Home: Avoiding Extreme Behaviors. 2007. (Shockwave: Science in Practice Ser.). 36p. (J). pap. 6.95 (***978-0-531-18773-9(X)***); (Illus.). (gr. 4-6). lib. bdg. 25.00 (***978-0-531-17573-6(1)***) Scholastic Library Publishing. (Children's Pr.).

Weekley, Randy/ J. Strangers Bullies Safety & More... A How to Guide to Child Safety. 2nd ed. 2007. (Illus.). 48p. (J). per. 9.99 (***978-0-9777457-9-1(1)***) Privacy Trust Group, The.

CHILDBIRTH

see also Pregnancy

Bauer, Marion Dane. If You Were Born a Kitten. Stammen, JoEllen McAllister, illus. 1999. 32p. (J). (gr. k-3). per. 16.00 (978-0-689-82725-9(3) , Simon & Schuster Children's Publishing) Simon & Schuster Children's Publishing.

—If You Were Born a Kitten. 2001. (Illus.). (J). 13.79 (978-0-606-20719-5(8)) Tandem Library Bks.

Brown, Margaret Wise. A Child Is Born: Picture Book. Cooper, Floyd, illus. 2003. 22p. (J). (ps-ps). 6.99 (978-0-7868-1840-2(9)) Hyperion Bks. for Children.

Buck, Nola. How a Baby Grows. 1998. (Growing Tree Ser.). (Illus.). 14p. (J). (ps up). bds. 5.95 (978-0-694-00873-5(7) , Harper Festival) HarperCollins Pubs.

Butler, Dori Hillestad. My Mom's Having a Baby! Thompson, Carol, illus. 32p. (J). 2007. pap. 6.95 (***978-0-8075-5348-0(4)***); 2005. 16.95 (978-0-8075-5344-2(1)) Whitman, Albert & Co.

¿De Donde Vienen los Bebes? (Coleccion Primeros Pasos en la Ciencia). (SPA., Illus.). (J). (gr. 1-3). pap. (978-950-724-218-2(X) , LMA8221) Lumen ARG. *Dist:* Lectorum Pubns., Inc.

Dineen, Jacqueline. Births. 2001. (Ceremonies & Celebrations Ser.). (Illus.). 32p. (J). (ps-3). lib. bdg. 25.69 (978-0-7398-3267-7(0)) Raintree.

Fields, Jennifer. Choosing a Career as a Nurse-Midwife. 2005. (World of Work Ser.). (Illus.). 64p. (YA). (gr. 7-12). lib. bdg. 25.25 (978-0-8239-3293-1(1)) Rosen Publishing Group, Inc., The.

Flegal, Daphna. A Baby Is Coming. 2002. (J). 5.00 (978-0-687-09649-7(9)) Abingdon Pr.

Frasier, Debra. On the Day You Were Born. 2005. (Illus.). 40p. (J). (ps-ps). 18.95 (978-0-15-205567-7(3)) Harcourt Children's Bks.

—On the Day You Were Born: A Photo Journal. 2001. (Illus.). 16p. (J). spiral bd. 9.95 (978-0-15-202172-6(8)) Harcourt Trade Pubs.

God's Gift - A Baby Girl. 1998. 6.95 (978-0-88271-540-7(2) , 10339) Regina Pr., Malhame & Co.

Goggin, Sherri. Dear Kate. 2007. (Illus.). 160p. 16.95 (***978-1-58818-133-6(2)***) Hill Street Pr., LLC.

Grimes, Janice D. Before You Were Born - Our Wish for A Baby: Version 1: in Vitro Fertilization. 2004. (Illus.). 18p. (J). 14.97 (978-0-9755028-0-8(8)) X, Y, & Me LLC.

Harris, Robie H. It's NOT the Stork! A Book about Girls, Boys, Babies, Bodies, Families & Friends. Emberley, Michael, illus. 2006. 64p. (J). (ps-3). 16.99 (978-0-7636-0047-1(4)) Candlewick Pr.

Herman, John. One Winter's Night. Dillon, Leo & Dillon, Diane, illus. 2003. 40p. (J). (ps-3). 16.99 (978-0-399-23418-7(7) , Philomel) Penguin Group (USA) Inc.

Iannucci, Lisa. Birth Defects. 2000. (Diseases & People Ser.). (Illus.). 128p. (YA). (gr. 6-12). lib. bdg. 26.60 (978-0-7660-1186-1(0)) Enslow Pubs., Inc.

Knight, Margy Burns. Welcoming Babies. O'Brien, Anne Sibley, illus. 2003. 32p. (J). (ps-4). lib. bdg. 15.15 (978-0-606-22818-3(7)) Tandem Library Bks.

Miller, Michaela. Reproduction & Growth. 2005. (Exploring the Human Body Ser.). (Illus.). 32p. (J). (gr. 4-7). lib. bdg. 24.95 (978-0-7377-3021-0(8) , Greenhaven Pr., Inc.) Thomson Gale.

Nixon, Joan Lowery. Before Your Were Born. 2nd sensormatic ed. 2006. per. 10.95 (978-1-59276-219-4(0)) Our Sunday Visitor, Publishing Div.

Nystrom, Carolyn. Before I Was Born. rev. ed. 2007. 40p. pap. 9.99 (978-1-60006-014-4(5)) NavPress Publishing Group.

Robert, Naima Bint. Welcome to the World, Baby. Brazell, Derek, illus. 2005. 32p. (J). (ENG & ALB.). pap. 12.95 (978-1-84444-268-3(3)); (ENG & ARA.). pap. 12.95 (978-1-84444-269-0(1)); (ENG & BEN.). pap. 12.95 (978-1-84444-270-6(5)); (ENG & CHI.). pap. 12.95 (978-1-84444-271-3(3)); (ENG & CHI.). pap. 12.95 (978-1-84444-272-0(1)); (CRO, ENG & SER.). pap. 12.95 (978-1-84444-273-7(X)); (ENG, PER & FAR.). pap. 12.95 (978-1-84444-274-4(8)); (ENG & FRE.). pap. 12.95 (978-1-84444-275-1(6)); (ENG & GER.). pap. 12.95 (978-1-84444-276-8(4)); (ENG & GUJ.). pap. 12.95 (978-1-84444-278-2(0)); (ENG & HIN.). pap. 12.95 (978-1-84444-279-9(9)); (ENG & ITA.). pap. 12.95 (978-1-84444-280-5(2)); (JPN & ENG.). pap. 12.95 (978-1-84444-281-2(0)); (ENG & KOR.). pap. 12.95 (978-1-84444-282-9(9)); (ENG & PAN.). pap. 12.95 (978-1-84444-283-6(7)); (ENG & POL.). pap. 12.95 (978-1-84444-284-3(5)); (POR & ENG.). pap. 12.95 (978-1-84444-285-0(3)); (ENG, RUM & ROM.). pap. 12.95 (978-1-84444-286-7(1)); (RUS & ENG.). pap. 12.95 (978-1-84444-287-4(X)); (ENG & SOM.). pap. 12.95 (978-1-84444-288-1(8)); (ENG & SPA.). pap. 12.95 (978-1-84444-289-8(6)); (ENG & SWA.). pap. 12.95 (978-1-84444-290-4(X)); (ENG & TUR.). pap. 12.95 (978-1-84444-293-5(4)); (ENG & URD.). pap. 12.95 (978-1-84444-295-9(0)); (ENG & VIE.). pap. 12.95 (978-1-84444-296-6(9)); (YOR & ENG.). pap. 12.95 (978-1-84444-297-3(7)); (SHO & ENG.). pap. 12.95 (978-1-84444-450-2(3)); (ENG, KOR & KUR.). pap. 12.95 (978-1-84444-633-9(6)) Mantra Lingua GBR. *Dist:* Mantra Publishing, Ltd.

Robert, Naima Bint & Petrova-Browning, Nina. Welcome to the World, Baby. Brazell, Derek, illus. 2005. (ENG & BUL.). 32p. (J). pap. 12.95 (978-1-84444-721-3(9)) Mantra Lingua GBR. *Dist:* Mantra Publishing, Ltd.

Showers, Paul. How a Baby Begins. 40p. (J). (gr. k-4). Date not set. lib. bdg. 16.89 (978-0-06-025413-1(0)); 1999. pap. 4.95 (978-0-06-445140-6(2)) HarperCollins Pubs.

Spirn, Michele Sobel. Birth. 1998. (World Celebrations & Ceremonies Ser.). (Illus.). 24p. (J). (gr. 3-5). 22.45 (978-1-56711-277-1(3) , Blackbirch Pr., Inc.) Thomson Gale.

Vv. Maravilla de la Vida. (SPA.). 266p. (J). 10.00 (978-84-342-1466-8(0)) Parramon Ediciones S.A. ESP. *Dist:* Distribuidora Norma, Inc.

Welcome to the World, Baby. 2004. (J). (ALB & ENG.). (978-1-84444-621-6(2)); (ARA & ENG.). (978-1-84444-622-3(0)); (BEN & ENG.). (978-1-84444-623-0(9)); (CHI & ENG.). (978-1-84444-624-7(7)); (CHI & ENG.). (978-1-84444-625-4(5)); (CRO & ENG.). (978-1-84444-626-1(3)); (ENG & PER.). (978-1-84444-627-8(1)); (ENG & FRE.). (978-1-84444-645-2(X)); (ENG & GRE.). (978-1-84444-628-5(X)); (ENG & GUJ.). (978-1-84444-629-2(8)); (ENG & HIN.). (978-1-84444-630-8(1)); (ENG & ITA.). (978-1-84444-631-5(X)); (ENG & JPN.). (978-1-84444-632-2(8)); (ENG & KUR.). (978-1-84444-634-6(4)); (ENG & PAN.). (978-1-84444-635-3(2)); (ENG & POL.). (978-1-84444-636-0(0)); (ENG & POR.). (978-1-84444-637-7(9)); (ENG & RUS.). (978-1-84444-638-4(7)); (ENG & SOM.). (978-1-84444-639-1(5)); (ENG & SPA.). (978-1-84444-640-7(9)); (ENG & TAM.). (978-1-84444-641-4(7)); (ENG & TUR.). (978-1-84444-642-1(5)); (ENG & URD.). (978-1-84444-643-8(3)); (ENG & VIE.). (978-1-84444-644-5(1)) Mantra Publishing, Ltd.

White, Mia, creator. On the day you were Born: Everything that has Breath. White, Mia, . 2006. per. 20.00 (978-0-9703419-2-1(X) , Love Buddies) MW International, Belle Lumiere.

CHILDBIRTH—FICTION

Allan, Nicholas. Where Willy Went. 2005. (Illus.). 32p. (J). (ps-3). 15.95 (978-0-375-83030-3(8)); lib. bdg. 17.99 (978-0-375-93030-0(2)) Random Hse. Children's Bks. (Knopf Bks. for Young Readers).

Butler, Dori Hillestad. Alexandra Hopewell, Labor Coach. 2005. 136p. (J). (gr. 3-6). 15.95 (978-0-8075-0242-6(1)) Whitman, Albert & Co.

Curtis, Jamie Lee. Cuentame Otra Vez la Noche en Que Naci. Cornell, Laura, illus. 1999. (SPA.). (J). (gr. 1-2). 14.95 (978-1-880507-63-6(3) , LC4416) Lectorum Pubns., Inc.

Doman, Regina. Mi Angelito en las aquas. 2006. (SPA.). 46p. pap. 6.95 (***978-1-933184-22-7(1)***) Sophia Institute Pr.

Grigg, Diane. A Baby Couldn't Do This. 2004. pap. 7.95 (978-0-533-14555-3(4)) Vantage Pr., Inc.

Hathaway, Barbara. Missy Violet & Me. 2004. 112p. (J). (gr. 3-5). tchr. ed. 15.00 (978-0-618-37163-1(X)) Houghton Mifflin Co. Trade & Reference Div.

Overend, Jenni. Hola Bebe. Vivas, Julie, illus. 2001. (SPA.). 32p. (J). (978-980-257-254-0(3)) Ekare, Ediciones.

Paulsen, Gary. The Quilt. 2005. (Illus.). 96p. (J). (gr. 3-7). 5.50 (978-0-440-22936-0(7) , Yearling) Random Hse. Children's Bks.

CHILDREN

see also Child Development

Adamson, Heather. School in Many Cultures. 2008. (J). (***978-1-4296-0021-7(7)***) Capstone Pr., Inc.

Ajmera, Maya. Ser Nino. 2000. (SPA.). (ps-2). lib. bdg. 15.25 (978-0-613-51267-1(7)) Tandem Library Bks.

Alexander, Florence & Alexander, Stanley. Come with Me & See... Children of the World. l.t. ed. 2003. (ENG & SPA., Illus.). 32p. (J). 9.99 (978-0-9648313-9-1(2)) Ebon Research Systems Publishing, LLC.

Ancona, George, photos by. Cuban Kids. 2000. (Illus.). 40p. (J). (gr. 2-6). 15.95 (978-0-7614-5077-1(7) , Cavendish Children's Bks.) Cavendish, Marshall Corp.

Anderson, Debby. Every Child Everywhere. 2007. 32p. (J). pap. 9.99 (***978-1-58134-862-0(2)***) Crossway Bks.

Baby. 2005. (Illus.). 64p. (978-0-7853-5221-1(X) , 3426000) Publications International, Ltd.

Barakat, Ibtisam. Tasting the Sky: A Palestinian Childhood. 2007. (Illus.). 192p. (YA). (gr. 7 up). 16.00 (978-0-374-35733-7(1)) Farrar, Straus & Giroux.

Barraclough, Sue. Your Own Safety. 2007. (J). (***978-1-4034-9858-8(X)***); pap. (***978-1-4034-9865-6(2)***) Heinemann Library.

Bennett, Howard J. Lions Aren't Scared of Shots: A Story for Children about Visiting the Doctor. Weber, M. S., illus. 2006. 32p. (J). (ps-1). 14.95 (978-1-59147-473-9(6) , 441A473); pap. 8.95 (978-1-59147-474-6(4) , 441A474) American Psychological Assn. (Magination Pr.).

Bottoms, James "Bud". Kid Ethics: From A to Z. 2006. (J). per. 12.95 (***978-0-9794863-0-2(0)***) Summerland Publishing.

—Kid Ethics 2: From A to Z. 2007. (J). per. 12.95 (***978-0-9794863-1-9(9)***) Summerland Publishing.

Brownlie Bojang, Ali. Nigeria. 2007. (J). (***978-1-84234-466-8(8)***) Cherrytree Pubns., Inc.

Burns, Marilyn. Brown Paper School Book: I Am Not a Short Adult. 2007. 128p. (J). pap. 12.99 (978-0-316-05979-4(X)) Little Brown & Co.

Busby, Sian. A Wonderful Little Girl: The True Story of Sarah Jacob, the Welsh Fasting Girl. 2004. (Illus.). 144p. pap. 11.00 (978-1-904095-70-5(4)) Short Bks., Ltd. GBR. *Dist:* Independent Pubs. Group.

Canfield, Jack L., et al. Chicken Soup for the Child's Soul Character-Building Stories to Read with Kids. 2007. 288p. (J). pap. 14.95 (***978-0-7573-0589-4(X)***) Health Communications, Inc.

Castle, Caroline. For Every Child: The UN Convention on the Rights of the Child in Words & Pictures. ed. 2004. (J). (gr. k-3). spiral bd. (978-0-616-14617-0(5)); spiral bd. (978-0-616-14618-7(3)) Canadian National Institute for the Blind/Institut National Canadien pour les Aveugles.

Champion, Gina. Anna & Her Mommy. Mitchell, Nanci, illus. 2005. 36p. (J). (gr. k-6). pap. 10.00 (978-1-884363-20-7(2)) Odenwald Pr.

Children around the World. 2005. (J). per. 8.95 (978-1-59566-138-8(7)) QEB Publishing Inc.

Children in Crisis, 6 Vols. 180.00 (978-0-8368-5956-0(1)) Stevens, Gareth Inc.

A Child's Day - Group 1, 5 bks., Set. Incl. Child's Day in a Brazilian Village. Campos, Maria de Fatima. lib. bdg. 25.64 (978-0-7614-1221-2(2)); Child's Day in a Chinese City. So, Sungwan. lib. bdg. 25.64 (978-0-7614-1224-3(7)); Child's Day in a Ghanaian City. Provencal, Francis & McNamara, Catherine. lib. bdg. 25.64 (978-0-7614-1223-6(9)); Child's Day in a Russian City. Ilyin, Andrey. lib. bdg. 25.64 (978-0-7614-1222-9(0)); Child's Day in an Indian Village. Das, Prodeepta. lib. bdg. 25.64 (978-0-7614-1220-5(4)); 32p. (J). (gr. k-2). (Illus.). 2001. 128.21 (978-0-7614-1219-9(0) , Benchmark Bks.) Cavendish, Marshall Corp.

Chrisp, Peter. Ancient Greece. 2006. (Google E Guides). (Illus.). 96p. (J). 17.99 (978-0-7566-1956-5(4)) Dorling Kindersley Publishing, Inc.

Dorling Kindersley Publishing Staff. A Life Like Mine. 2005. 128p. (J). (gr. 8). pap. 12.99 (978-0-7566-1803-2(7)) Dorling Kindersley Publishing, Inc.

Elliott, Lynne. Children & Games in the Middle Ages. 2004. (Medieval World Ser.). (Illus.). 32p. (J). (978-0-7787-1349-4(0)); pap. (978-0-7787-1381-4(4)) Crabtree Publishing Co.

Fisher, Teresa. France. Johnstone, Andy, photos by. 2005. (Letters from Around the World Ser.). (Illus.). 32p. (J). (gr. 3-7). lib. bdg. (978-1-84234-250-3(9) , Cherrytree Books) Evans Publishing Group.

Frankel Hauser, Jill. The Kids Guide to Becoming the Best You Can Be! Developing 5 Traits You Need to Achieve Your Personal Best. 2006. (Illus.). 128p. (J). pap. 12.95 (978-0-8249-6788-8(7) , Williamson Bks.) Ideals Pubns.

Goalec, Francois. Frederico: A Child of Brazil. 2005. (Children of the World Ser.). (Illus.). 24p. (J). (gr. 2-4). 22.45 (978-1-4103-0294-6(6) , Blackbirch Pr., Inc.) Thomson Gale.

Hall, Kirsten. Kids in Sports: A Chapter Book. (True Tales Ser.). (J). 2005. (Illus.). 48p. (gr. 2-4). pap. 4.95 (978-0-516-24685-7(2)); 2004. 22.50 (978-0-516-23733-6(0)) Scholastic Library Publishing. (Children's Pr.).

Hall, Margaret. Your Allowance. 2007. (J). ***978-1-4034-9817-5(2));** pap. (***978-1-4034-9822-9(9))** Heinemann Library.

Hauser, Jill Frankel. The Kids Guide to Becoming the Best You Can Be. 2006. 128p. (J). 16.95 (978-0-8249-6789-5(5) , Williamson Bks.) Ideals Pubns.

Hess, Ingrid. Sleep in Peace. 2007. 40p. (J). pap. (***978-0-8361-9381-7(4))** Herald Pr.

Hufford, Deborah. Scrapbooking: Keep Your Memories Special. 2005. (Snap Books Craft Ser.). (Illus.). 32p. (J). (gr. 3-5). 22.60 (978-0-7368-4387-4(6)) Capstone Pr., Inc.

Hunter, Rebecca. Growing up in the Forties. 2003. (Illus.). 32p. pap. (978-0-7502-3434-4(2) , Hodder Wayland) Hodder Children's Division.

—Growing up in the Thirties. 2003. (Illus.). 32p. pap. (978-0-7502-3433-7(4) , Hodder Wayland) Hodder Children's Division.

I Am. Date not set. 8p. (J). (gr. k-2). pap. 3.75 (978-1-58323-016-9(5) , Seedling Pubns.) Continental Pr., Inc.

Irving, L. T. An Amadan's Odyssey. Irving, R. J. & Irving, Hank, illus. Irving, Hank, photos by. 2000. 115p. (J). pap. 15.00 (978-0-9678217-0-2(3)) Battler Pr., The.

Jackson, Ellen B. Turn of the Century: Eleven Centuries of Children & Change. Ellis, Jan Davey, illus. 2003. 32p. pap. 7.95 (978-0-88106-370-7(3)) Charlesbridge Publishing, Inc.

Kehoe, Stasia Ward. Kids in Their Communities, 6 bks. Incl. I Live at a Military Post. lib. bdg. 18.75 (978-0-8239-5441-4(2)); I Live in a City. lib. bdg. 18.75 (978-0-8239-5437-7(4)); I Live in a Town. lib. bdg. 18.75 (978-0-8239-5440-7(4)); I Live in the Mountains. lib. bdg. 18.75 (978-0-8239-5442-1(0)); I Live on a Farm. lib. bdg. 18.75 (978-0-8239-5438-4(2)); I Live on an Island. lib. bdg. 18.75 (978-0-8239-5439-1(0)); 24p. (J). (gr. 3). (Illus.). 2000. Set lib. bdg. 103.50 (978-0-8239-7010-0(8) , PowerKids Pr.) Rosen Publishing Group, Inc., The.

Kelley, Michelle. Just Like You. 2007. (J). (978-1-59515-934-2(7)) Rourke Publishing, LLC.

Lebovics, Dania. Baby Chronicles: My Very Own Story: From Pre-Natal to Pre-School. Quach, Lam, illus. 2000. 72p. spiral bd. 19.95 (978-0-9699203-7-3(7)) Kiddy Chronicles Publishing CAN. *Dist:* Firefly Bks., Ltd.

Levete, Sarah. Taking Care of Myself. 2007. (***978-1-59604-151-6(X))** Stargazer Bks.

Loewen, Nancy. Save, Spend, or Donate? A Book about Managing Money. Fitzpatrick, Brad, illus. 2004. (Money Matters Ser.). 24p. (J). 22.60 (978-1-4048-0952-9(X)) Picture Window Bks.

Lynch, Emma. Brazil. 2005. (We're from Ser.). (Illus.). 32p. (J). (ps-ps). pap. 7.60 (978-1-4034-5811-7(1)) Heinemann.

—We're from Indonesia. 2005. (We're from Ser.). (Illus.). 32p. (J). pap. (978-1-4034-5813-1(8)); lib. bdg. (978-1-4034-5804-9(9)) Heinemann.

—We're from Italy. 2005. (Heinemann First Library). (Illus.). 32p. (J). (978-1-4034-5805-6(7)); pap. (978-1-4034-5814-8(6)) Heinemann.

—We're from Pakistan. 2005. (We're from Ser.). (J). lib. bdg. 24.21 (978-1-4034-5807-0(3)) Heinemann.

MacKall, Dandi Daley. Kids' Rules for Life: A Guide to Life's Journey from Those Just Starting Out. 2003. (Illus.). 176p. pap. 8.95 (978-1-57071-909-7(8)) Sourcebooks, Inc.

Mahmout, Ulfet & Thompson, Alan. My Life Story. 2004. (CZE, SPA, SER, URD & SOM., Illus.). 34p. (J). (978-1-85269-840-9(3)); (978-1-85269-845-4(4)); (978-1-85269-850-8(0)); (978-1-85269-855-3(1)); (978-1-85269-860-7(8)); (978-1-85269-870-6(5)); (978-1-85269-875-1(6)); (978-1-85269-880-5(2)); (978-1-85269-890-4(X)); (978-1-85269-895-9(0)) Mantra Publishing, Ltd.

—My Life Story: L'historie de Ma Vie. 2004. (CZE, SPA, SER, URD & SOM., Illus.). 34p. (J). (978-1-85269-865-2(9)) Mantra Publishing, Ltd.

Mattern, Joanne. Eating Lunch at School: El Almuerzo en la Escuela. 2006. (ENG & SPA., Illus.). 24p. (J). pap. (978-0-8368-7365-8(3)); lib. bdg. (978-0-8368-7358-0(0)) Stevens, Gareth Inc. (Weekly Reader Early Learning Library).

—Getting Ready for School: Me Preparo para Ir a la Escuela. 2006. (ENG & SPA., Illus.). 24p. (J). pap. (978-0-8368-7366-5(1)); lib. bdg. (978-0-8368-7359-7(9)) Stevens, Gareth Inc. (Weekly Reader Early Learning Library).

—Going to School: De Camino a la Escuela. 2006. (ENG & SPA., Illus.). 24p. (J). pap. (978-0-8368-7367-2(X)); lib. bdg. (978-0-8368-7360-3(2)) Stevens, Gareth Inc. (Weekly Reader Early Learning Library).

—Playing at School: Juego en la Escuela. 2006. (ENG & SPA., Illus.). 24p. (J). pap. (978-0-8368-7369-6(6)); lib. bdg. (978-0-8368-7362-7(9)) Stevens, Gareth Inc. (Weekly Reader Early Learning Library).

—Staying Safe on the School Bus. 2006. (Illus.). 24p. pap. (***978-0-8368-7802-8(7));** lib. bdg. (***978-0-8368-7795-3(0))** Stevens, Gareth Inc. (Weekly Reader Early Learning Library).

—Staying Safe on the School Bus: La Seguridad en el Autobs Escolar. 2006. (J). pap. (***978-0-8368-8067-0(6));** lib. bdg. (***978-0-8368-8060-1(9))** Stevens, Gareth Inc. (Weekly Reader Early Learning Library).

Miller, Jake. Who's Who in a Rural Community. 2005. (Communities at Work Ser.). (Illus.). 24p. (J). (gr. 2-4). lib. bdg. 19.95 (978-1-4042-2787-3(3) , PowerKids Pr.) Rosen Publishing Group, Inc., The.

Minden, Cecilia. Investing: Making Your Money Work for You. 2008. (J). lib. bdg. 25.26 (***978-1-60279-003-2(5))** Cherry Lake Publishing.

Moss, Marissa. Amelia's School Survival Guide. Moss, Marissa, illus. 2006. (Amelia's Notebooks). (Illus.). 64p. (J). (gr. 2-5). 9.95 (978-1-4169-0915-6(X) , Simon & Schuster Children's Publishing) Simon & Schuster Children's Publishing.

Mumford, Sally & Mackinnon, Debbie. What If. 2000. (Illus.). 192p. pap. 13.99 (978-0-09-185609-0(4)) Random Hse. GBR. *Dist:* Independent Pubs. Group.

Murray, Kirsty. What Kids Are Made Of: True Stories of Young Rescuers, Rulers & Rebels. 2000. (Illus.). 160p. (J). (gr. 1-6). pap. 7.95 (978-1-55652-414-1(5)) Chicago Review Pr., Inc.

Olson, Karen W. Healthy Choices, Healthy Lives. Hamelin, Marie-Micheline, illus. 2006. 20p. (J). pap. 10.95 (978-1-894778-31-2(6)) Theytus Bks., Ltd. CAN. *Dist:* Orca Bk. Pubs. USA.

Parker, Victoria. Greece. 2005. (Illus.). 32p. (J). (ps-7). lib. bdg. 24.21 (978-1-4034-5784-4(0)) Heinemann.

—We're from Greece. 2005. (Illus.). 32p. (J). pap. 7.25 (978-1-4034-5791-2(3)) Heinemann.

Rayner, Amanda, ed. A Life Like Mine. 2002. (Illus.). 128p. (J). (gr. 4-7). 24.99 (978-0-7894-8859-6(0)) Dorling Kindersley Publishing, Inc.

Ries, Lori Anne. Punk Wig. Eitter-Kono, Erin, illus. 2008. (J). (***978-1-59078-486-0(3))** Boyds Mills Pr.

Rivers, Ruth, illus. Thank You Prayers. 2003. 32p. (J). 7.99 (978-0-7459-4650-4(X) , Lion) Lion Hudson plc GBR. *Dist:* Independent Pubs. Group.

Roca, Nuria. Boys & Girls of the World: From One End... to the Other. Curto, Rosa Maria, illus. 2002. (From ... to Ser.). 36p. (J). (ps-1). pap. 7.99 (978-0-7641-2141-8(3)) Barron's Educational Series, Inc.

Ross, Michael Elsohn. Children of Ireland. Rigau, Felix, photos by. 2001. (World's Children Ser.). (Illus.). 48p. (J). (gr. 3-6). lib. bdg. (978-1-57505-521-3(X) , Carolrhoda Bks.) Lerner Publishing Group.

—Children of Puerto Rico. Rigau, Felix, illus. Rigau, Felix, photos by. 2001. (World's Children Ser.). 48p. (J). (gr. 3-6). lib. bdg. (978-1-57505-522-0(8) , Carolrhoda Bks.) Lerner Publishing Group.

Rotner, Shelley & Kelly, Sheila M. Good-Byes. Rotner, Shelley, photos by. 2002. (Contemporary Issues for Young Children Ser.). (Illus.). 32p. (gr. k-3). lib. bdg. 22.90 (978-0-7613-1752-4(X) , Millbrook Pr.) Lerner Publishing Group.

Senker, Cath. Spain. 2004. (Letters from Around the World Ser.). (J). (978-1-84234-249-7(5) , Cherrytree Books) Evans Publishing Group.

Senker, Cath. The USA. 2007. (J). (***978-1-84234-464-4(1))** Cherrytree Pubns., Inc.

Spallone, Joseph. Children Are Children: Y2K-01 Edition. 2000. (Illus.). 30p. (J). (gr. 3-8). 14.95 (978-0-9660227-6-6(9)) CTM Publishing.

Tames, Richard. Children. 2002. (People in the Past Ser.). (Illus.). 48p. (J). pap. (978-1-4034-0513-5(1)) Heinemann Library.

Tankard, Fiona. Italy. 2004. (Letters from Around the World Ser.). (J). lib. bdg. (978-1-84234-247-3(9) , Cherrytree Books) Evans Publishing Group.

Townsend, John. Freaky Fashion & Foul Food. 2006. (Raintree Freestyle Ser.). (Illus.). 48p. (J). (978-1-4109-1869-7(6)) Steck-Vaughn.

Wan, Guofang. Virtually True: Questioning Online Media. 2007. (Fact Finders Ser.). (Illus.). 32p. (J). (***978-0-7368-7863-0(7)** , 1264914) Capstone Pr., Inc.

Waryncia, Lou & Hale, Sarah Elder. Young Heroes of the North & South. 2005. (Civil War Ser.). (Illus.). 48p. (J). 17.95 (978-0-8126-7901-4(6)) Cobblestone Publishing Co.

Waryncia, Lou, et al. If I Were a Kid in Ancient Rome. 2007. (Children of the Ancient World Ser.). (Illus.). 32p. (J). 17.95 (978-0-8126-7930-4(X)) Cricket Bks.

Watad, Mahmoud. Agnostic Reader. 2007. (Illus.). 220p. pap. 19.00 (***978-1-59102-535-1(4))** Prometheus Bks., Pubs.

Wilkins, Verna A. Children Around the World. 2004. (QEB Start Reading Ser.). (Illus.). 24p. (J). lib. bdg. 15.95 (978-1-59566-010-7(0)) QEB Publishing Inc.

Wilson. Investigating Childhood in Tudor England. (Illus.). 32p. (J). pap. 8.95 (978-0-7078-0335-7(7)) National Trust, Aylesbury GBR. *Dist:* Trafalgar Square Publishing.

Yonge, Charlotte M. Little Lucy's Wonderful Globe. 2004. reprint ed. pap. 1.99 (978-1-4192-3079-0(4)) Kessinger Publishing, LLC.

CHILDREN—ADOPTION

see Adoption

CHILDREN—AFRICA

Brownlie, Alison. Kenya. 2004. (Letters from Around the World Ser.). (Illus.). 32p. (J). (978-1-84234-252-7(5) , Cherrytree Books) Evans Publishing Group.

Dalton, David. Living in a Refugee Camp: Carbino's Story. 2005. (Illus.). 48p. (J). lib. bdg. 30.00 (978-0-8368-5960-7(X) , World Almanac Library) Stevens, Gareth Inc.

Davidson, Avelyn. A Day in the Life of an African Village. 2007. (Shockwave: People & Communities Ser.). (Illus.). 36p. (J). (gr. 4-6). lib. bdg. 25.00 (***978-0-531-17748-8(3)** , Children's Pr.) Scholastic Library Publishing.

Gioanni, Alain. Arafat: A Child of Tunisia. 2005. (Children of the World Ser.). (Illus.). 24p. (J). (gr. k-3). 22.45 (978-1-4103-0289-2(X) , Blackbirch Pr., Inc.) Thomson Gale.

Giraud, Hervé. Leila: A Tuareg Child. Rey, Jean-Charles, photos by. 2005. (Children of the World Ser.). (Illus.). 24p. (J). (gr. k-3). 22.45 (978-1-4103-0545-9(7) , Blackbirch Pr., Inc.) Thomson Gale.

Kabana, Joni. Torina's World: A Child's Life in Madagascar. 2007. (Illus.). 52p. 14.95 (***978-0-9794771-4-0(X))** Arnica Publishing, Inc.

Nicolotti, Muriel. Kuntai: A Masai Child. 2005. (Children of the World Ser.). (Illus.). 24p. (J). (gr. k-3). 22.45 (978-1-4103-0290-8(3) , 1244126, Blackbirch Pr., Inc.) Thomson Gale.

Onwu, Jackie. Children of Africa: Restoring the Village. 2000. (Illus.). 142p. (J). pap. 6.95 (978-1-890569-28-0(3)) General Board of Global Ministries, The United Methodist Church.

Onyefulu, Ifeoma. One Big Family: Sharing Life in an African Village. Onyefulu, Ifeoma, illus. 2006. (Illus.). 32p. pap. 7.95 (978-1-84507-686-3(9)) Lincoln, Frances Ltd. GBR. *Dist:* Perseus Distribution.

Pedlar, Paige. Who Will Cuddle Them When They Sleep? 2004. 24p. (J). (978-1-55306-790-0(8)) Essence Publishing.

Senker, Cath. South Africa. Bennett, Peter, photos by. 2005. (Letters from Around the World Ser.). (Illus.). 32p. (J). (gr. 3-7). lib. bdg. (978-1-84234-354-8(8) , Cherrytree Books) Evans Publishing Group.

Shoveller, Herb. Ryan & Jimmy: And the Well in Africa That Brought Them Together. 2006. (Illus.). 56p. (J). (gr. 3-7). (978-1-55337-967-6(5)) Kids Can Pr., Ltd.

Waryncia, Lou, et al. If I Were a Kid in Ancient Egypt: Children of the Ancient World. 2007. (Children of the Ancient World Ser.). (Illus.). 32p. (J). 17.95 (978-0-8126-7932-8(6)) Cricket Bks.

Wilkinson, Brenda. Under the Baobob Tree: Children of Africa. Feelings, Tom, illus. 2000. 35p. (J). pap. 4.00 (978-1-890569-19-8(4) , 2872) General Board of Global Ministries, The United Methodist Church.

CHILDREN—ASIA

Brooks, Susie. Bangladesh. 2005. (Our Lives, Our World Ser.). (Illus.). 32p. (J). (gr. 3-7). lib. bdg. 27.10 (978-1-59389-231-9(4)) Chrysalis Education.

—India. 2006. (Our Lives, Our World Ser.). (Illus.). (J). (978-1-59389-288-3(8)) Chrysalis Education.

Brownlie, Alison. Japan. 2004. (Letters from Around the World Ser.). (J). (978-1-84234-256-5(8) , Cherrytree Books) Evans Publishing Group.

Castelain, Celine & Liutkus, Aurelien. Asha: A Child of the Himalayas. 2005. (Children of the World Ser.). (Illus.). 24p. (J). (gr. k-3). 22.45 (978-1-4103-0286-1(5) , Blackbirch Pr., Inc.) Thomson Gale.

Giraud, Hervé. Basha: A Hmong Child. Rey, Jean-Charles, photos by. 2005. (Children of the World Ser.). (Illus.). 24p. (J). (gr. k-3). 22.45 (978-1-4103-0547-3(3) , Blackbirch Pr., Inc.) Thomson Gale.

—Kradji: A Child of Cambodia. Rey, Jean-Charles, photos by. 2005. (Children of the World Ser.). (Illus.). 24p. (J). (gr. k-3). 22.45 (978-1-4103-0548-0(1) , Blackbirch Pr., Inc.) Thomson Gale.

Holmes, Jimmy, illus. & photos by. In a Vietnamese City. Holmes, Jimmy, photos by. Morgan, Tom, photos by. 2002. (Child's Day Ser.). 32p. (J). 25.64 (978-0-7614-1409-4(6) , Benchmark Bks.) Cavendish, Marshall Corp.

Lynch, Emma. We're from Pakistan. 2005. 32p. (J). pap. 7.60 (978-1-4034-5816-2(2)) Heinemann Library.

Parker, Victoria. India. 2005. (We're from Ser.). (Illus.). 32p. (J). (gr. k-2). lib. bdg. 25.36 (978-1-4034-5785-1(9)) Heinemann.

—We're from India. 2005. (We're from Ser.). (Illus.). 32p. (J). pap. (978-1-4034-5792-9(1)) Heinemann.

—We're from Japan. 2005. (Illus.). 32p. (J). (978-1-4034-5786-8(7)); pap. (978-1-4034-5793-6(X)) Heinemann.

Rey, Jean-Charles. Avinesh: A Child of the Ganges. 2005. (Children of the World Ser.). (Illus.). 24p. (J). (gr. k-3). 22.45 (978-1-4103-0287-8(3) , Blackbirch Pr., Inc.) Thomson Gale.

CHILDREN—AUSTRALIA

Parker, Victoria. We're from Australia. 2005. (We're from Ser.). (Illus.). 32p. (J). pap. (978-1-4034-5789-9(1)) Heinemann.

Parker, Victoria & Parker, Vic. Australia. 2005. (We're from Ser.). (Illus.). 32p. (J). (ps-ps). lib. bdg. 25.36 (978-1-4034-5782-0(4)) Heinemann.

Sallis, Eva, et al. Dark Dreams: Australian Refugee Stories by Young Writers Aged 11-20 Years. 2004. 224p. (Orig.). (J). pap. 17.95 (978-1-86254-629-5(0)) Wakefield Pr. Pty, Ltd. AUS. *Dist:* Independent Pubs. Group.

CHILDREN—BOOKS AND READING

Here are entered works on the reading interests of children, or lists of books read by or recommended for children. Collections of works published for children are entered under Children's Literature.

Andersen, Hans Christian. The Constant Tin Soldier. (World of Words Ser.). (J). (gr. k-3). pap. 10.00 incl. audio Spoken Arts, Inc.

Archambault, John & Plummer, David. Baseball Cards & Piggy Banks: Counting Dimes & Dollars. Hamaguchi, Carla, ed. Leary, Catherine, illus. 2001. (Rockin' Readers Ser.). 16p. (J). (gr. k-4). pap. 2.99 (978-1-57471-765-5(0)) Creative Teaching Pr., Inc.

Beech, Linda Ward. Ready-to-Go Reproducibles: Analogies. 2002. 48p. (J). (gr. 2-3). 8.95 (978-0-439-27172-1(X)); (Illus.). (J). (gr. 4-5). pap. 8.95 (978-0-439-27173-8(8)); (Illus.). (YA). (gr. 6-8). pap. 8.95 (978-0-439-27174-5(6)) Scholastic, Inc.

Beginning Readers: Alpha. 2001. (Classroom Libraries). (SPA., Illus.). (J). 106.00 (978-1-58105-895-6(0)); (J). (gr. 2). 94.95 (978-1-58105-898-7(5)); (J). (gr. 3). 94.95 (978-1-58105-901-4(9)); (J). (gr. 4). 102.00 (978-1-58105-904-5(3)); (J). (gr. 5). 111.95 (978-1-58105-907-6(8)); (J). (gr. 6). 103.95 (978-1-58105-910-6(8)); (YA). (gr. 7-8). 99.95 (978-1-58105-913-7(2)) Santillana USA Publishing Co., Inc.

Beginning Readers: Alpha & Beta. 2001. (Classroom Libraries). (SPA., Illus.). (J). 198.95 (978-1-58105-897-0(7)); (J). (gr. 2). 180.00 (978-1-58105-900-7(0)); (J). (gr. 3). 175.95 (978-1-58105-903-8(5)); (J). (gr. 4). 179.95 (978-1-58105-906-9(X)); (J). (gr. 5). 200.00 (978-1-58105-909-0(4)); (J). (gr. 6). 196.95 (978-1-58105-912-0(4)); (YA). (gr. 7-8). 188.95 (978-1-58105-915-1(9)) Santillana USA Publishing Co., Inc.

Beginning Readers: Beta. 2001. (Classroom Libraries). (SPA., Illus.). (J). 103.00 (978-1-58105-896-3(9)); (J). (gr. 2). 95.00 (978-1-58105-899-4(3)); (J). (gr. 3). 90.00 (978-1-58105-902-1(7)); (J). (gr. 4). 86.95 (978-1-58105-905-2(1)); (J). (gr. 5). 98.95 (978-1-58105-908-3(6)); (J). (gr. 6). 102.95 (978-1-58105-911-3(6)); (YA). (gr. 7-8). 98.95 (978-1-58105-914-4(0)) Santillana USA Publishing Co., Inc.

Briefing Associates Staff. This Is BRIEF! Or Starting Preschool & Homeschool Children Reading Naturally - at Once. Khaiphus, Kosta Demetrius, ed. Brown, Linnea, illus. 2004. 136p. (ps-1). pap. 24.95 (978-0-9706105-0-8(5)) BR:IEFing Assocs. of New England.

Brimner, Larry Dane. The Long Way Home. Sirrell, Terry, illus. 2001. (Rookie Reader Skill Set Ser.). 32p. (J). (gr. k-2). pap. 4.95 (978-0-516-27078-4(8) , Children's Pr.) Scholastic Library Publishing.

Carpas, Jackie. Learning Through Literature. 2004. (Illus.). 128p. (J). per. 11.99 (978-0-88724-260-1(X) , CD-0584) Carson-Dellosa Publishing Co., Inc.

Chanko, Pamela. Fresh & Fun: Dozens of Instant & Irresistible Ideas & Activities from Creative Teachers Across the Country. 2001. (Fresh & Fun Ser.). 32p. pap. 8.95 (978-0-439-21610-4(9)) Scholastic, Inc.

Cole, Robert & Alphin, Elaine Marie. Power Reading: Power Pak 8A. Ford, David, illus. 2002. 81p. (YA). (gr. 1-8). pap. 129.95 incl. audio (978-1-883186-11-1(0) , PP08A) National Reading Styles Institute, Inc.

Cole, Robert & Larkin, Barbara. Power Reading: Power Pak 7A. Ford, David, illus. 2002. 81p. (YA). (gr. 1-7). pap. 129.95 incl. audio (978-1-883186-10-4(2) , PP07A) National Reading Styles Institute, Inc.

Collins, Carolyn Strom & Eriksson, Christina Wyss. Inside the Secret Garden: A Treasury of Crafts, Recipes, & Activities. Tudor, Tasha, illus. 2004. 130p. (J). (gr. 2-8). reprint ed. 25.00 (978-0-7567-7630-5(9)) DIANE Publishing Co.

Dutton, Sandra. Power Reading: Power Pak Primer B. Conner, Robin, illus. 2002. 80p. (J). (gr. k-2). pap. 129.95 incl. audio (978-1-883186-13-5(7) , PP0PB) National Reading Styles Institute, Inc.

Dutton, Sandra & Conner, Robin. Power Reading: Power Pak Primer A. 2002. (Illus.). 80p. (J). (gr. k-2). pap. 129.95 incl. audio (978-1-883186-12-8(9) , PP0PA) National Reading Styles Institute, Inc.

Favorite Children's Authors & Illustrators, 8 vols. 2nd ed. 2006. 368.00 (***978-1-59187-065-4(8))** Tradition Publishing Co.

Fulk, Virginia. Learning to Listen - Listening to Learn. Harvey, Gayle S., illus. 1999. (Kids' Stuff Ser.). 80p. (J). (ps-3). pap. 9.95 (978-0-86530-413-0(0) , IP 413-0) Incentive Pubns., Inc.

Gayle-Evans, Guda. An Annotated Bibliography of Multi-Cultural Literature for Children Three to Ten Years. 2004. (Mellen Studies in Children's Literature: Vol. 6). (Illus.). 204p. 109.95 (978-0-7734-6474-2(3)) Mellen, Edwin Pr., The.

Glasscock, Sarah. Immigration: Five Short Plays for the Classroom with Background Information, Writing Prompts, & Creative Activities. 1999. (Illus.). 64p. (J). 10.95 (978-0-590-64458-7(0)) Scholastic, Inc.

Glassman, Peter. Oz: The Hundredth Anniversary Celebration. 2000. (J). lib. bdg. 19.89 (978-0-06-029219-5(9)) HarperCollins Pubs.

Graham, Leland & McCoy, Isabelle. Building Proofreading Skills. Montgomery, Tama & Quinn, Anna, eds. Drayton, Marta, illus. 1999. 96p. (J). (gr. 5-8). pap. 10.95 (978-0-86530-410-9(6) , IP 410-6) Incentive Pubns., Inc.

The Great Southwest Activity Book. 2004. (Illus.). 56p. (J). act. bk. ed. 7.95 (978-0-87358-844-7(4) , Rising Moon Bks. for Young Readers) Northland Publishing.

The Great Yellowstone Grand Teton Glacier Activity Book. 2004. (Illus.). 56p. (J). act. bk. ed. 7.95 (978-0-87358-860-7(6) , Rising Moon Bks. for Young Readers) Northland Publishing.

Hall, Kirsten & Christensen-Hall, Nancy. Fiction: My First Reader. 2004. (Illus.). 350.00 (978-0-516-29718-7(X)) Scholastic Library Publishing.

Harcourt School Publishers Staff. Changing Patterns Level 3-1. 3rd ed. 2003. (Trophies Ser.). (Illus.). (J). (gr. 3 up). pupil's gde. ed. 46.70 (978-0-15-322476-8(2)) Harcourt Schl. Pubs.

—Library Books Collection Moving. 2nd ed. 2002. pap. 80.30 (978-0-15-337373-2(3)) Harcourt Schl. Pubs.

Harris, Julie, narrated by. The Constant Tin Soldier. unabr. ed. 2001. (World of Words Ser.). (J). (gr. k-3). pap. 22.00 incl. audio (978-0-8045-6703-9(4) , 6500-C/10) Spoken Arts, Inc.

—The Fairies. unabr. ed. 2001. (World of Words Ser.). (J). (gr. k-3). pap. 10.00 incl. audio (978-0-8045-6608-7(9) , 6500-H) Spoken Arts, Inc.

—Puss in Boots. unabr. ed. 2001. (World of Words Ser.). (J). (gr. k-3). pap. 22.00 incl. audio (978-0-8045-6704-6(2) , 6500-D/10) Spoken Arts, Inc.

—Rumpelstiltskin. unabr. ed. 2001. (J). (gr. k-3). pap. 10.00 incl. audio (978-0-8045-6606-3(2) , 6500-F); pap. 22.00 incl. audio (978-0-8045-6706-0(9) , 6500-F/10) Spoken Arts, Inc.

Harris, Julie, reader. Puss in Boots. unabr. ed. (World of Words Ser.). (J). (gr. k-3). pap. 10.00 incl. audio (978-0-8045-6604-9(6) , SAC 6500D) Spoken Arts, Inc.

Herman, Gail. The Best Book Ever! 1999. (Fairy School Ser.). (Illus.). (J). 10.79 (978-0-606-21629-6(4)) Tandem Library Bks.

Hill, Char-Lee L. 5th Grade. 1999. (Practice & Learn Ser.). (J). (gr. 5). pap. 18.99 (978-1-57690-722-1(8)) Teacher Created Materials, Inc.

Hinchey, Donald. 5-Minute Messages & More: Children's Lessons for Any Occasion. Kershner, Jan, ed. 1998. (Illus.). 96p. (J). (gr. k-6). pap. 15.99 (978-0-7644-2038-2(0) , Flagship Church Resources) Group Publishing, Inc.

Isbell, Rebecca & Raines, Shirley C. Tell It Again! Easy to Tell Stories with Activities for Young Children. 2004. (Tell It Again Ser.). (Illus.). 192p. (ps-3). pap. 14.95 (978-0-87659-200-7(0) , 19628) Gryphon Hse., Inc.

James, Diane. Time to Wake Up! Bulloch, Ivan, illus. 2004. (My Turn Ser.). 12p. (J). (ps-k). bds. 6.95 (978-1-58728-338-3(7) , Two Can Publishing) T&N Children's Publishing.

Johnson, Lois Walfrid. You're Worth More Than You Think. rev. ed. 1999. (Let's Talk about It Stories for Kids Ser.). 176p. (J). (gr. 3-8). pap. 7.99 (978-1-55661-651-8(1)) Bethany Hse. Pubs.

Lieberman, Lillian. Starting Points for Language Arts. Barr, Marilynn G., illus. 1999. 128p. (J). (gr. 1-3). pap. 14.95 (978-1-57612-069-9(4) , MM2082) Monday Morning Bks., Inc.

—Starting Points for Reading. Barr, Marilynn G., illus. 1999. 128p. (J). (gr. 1-3). pap. 14.95 (978-1-57612-068-2(6) , MM2083) Monday Morning Bks., Inc.

Little House Readers Club. 2000. (J). (978-0-06-028855-6(8)) HarperCollins Pubs.

Littlejohn, Carolyn & Thomas, Cathlyn. Keep Talking That Book: Booktalks to Promote Reading, 2000. (Professional Growth Ser.: Vol. 2). (Illus.). 155p. 36.95 (978-0-938865-92-6(7)) Linworth Publishing, Inc.

Pebble Books Mixed, 1 vol., Set. 1998. (Illus.). (J). (gr. k-2). pap. (978-0-516-29775-0(9) , Children's Pr.) Scholastic Library Publishing.

Perera, Hilda & Fraga, Mana F. La Pata Pita. 2001. (J). wbk. ed. 7.95 (978-0-8056-0136-7(8)) Minerva Bks., Ltd.

—La Pata Pita Vuelve. (SPA.). (J). 7.95 (978-0-8056-0140-4(6)); 2001. 5.95 (978-0-8056-0141-1(4)) Minerva Bks., Ltd.

Primm, E. Russell. Favorite Children's Authors & Illustrators. 2nd ed. 2006. (J). (978-1-59187-057-9(7)); (978-1-59187-058-6(5)); (978-1-59187-059-3(3)); (978-1-59187-060-9(7)); (978-1-59187-061-6(5)); (978-1-59187-062-3(3)); (978-1-59187-063-0(1)); (978-1-59187-064-7(X)) Tradition Publishing Co.

Rabe, Tish. There's a Map in My Lap! Ruiz, Aristides, illus. 2002. (Cat in the Hat's Learning Library Ser.). 48p. (J). (gr. k-3). lib. bdg. 12.99 (978-0-375-91099-9(9) , Random Hse. Bks. for Young Readers) Random Hse. Children's Bks.

—There's a Map in My Lap! All about Maps. Ruiz, Aristides, illus. 2002. (Cat in the Hat's Learning Library). 48p. (J). (gr. k-3). 8.99 (978-0-375-81099-2(4) , Random Hse. Bks. for Young Readers) Random Hse. Children's Bks.

Read Aloud: Alpha. 2001. (Classroom Libraries). (SPA., Illus.). (J). 120.00 (978-1-58105-769-0(5)) Santillana USA Publishing Co., Inc.

Read Aloud: Alpha & Beta. 2001. (SPA., Illus.). (J). 224.00 (978-1-58105-894-9(2)) Santillana USA Publishing Co., Inc.

Read Aloud: Beta. 2001. (Classroom Libraries). (SPA., Illus.). (J). 115.95 (978-1-58105-818-5(7)) Santillana USA Publishing Co., Inc.

Reid, Rob. Storytime Slam! 15 Lesson Plans for Preschool & Primary Story Programs. 2006. (Illus.). 85p. (J). pap. 16.95 (*978-1-932146-52-3(0)* , Upstart Bks.) Highsmith Inc.

Responding to Literature. 912p. (YA). (gr. 8). 52.95 (978-0-8219-1364-2(6) , 35456) EMC/Paradigm Publishing.

Rice, Dona Herweck. Practice & Learn: What Every 4th Grader Needs to Know to Ensure Success in School. Bauer, Larry, illus. 1999. 304p. (J). (gr. 4). pap., act. bk. ed. 14.95 (978-1-57690-714-6(7) , TCA2714) Teacher Created Materials, Inc.

Roberts, Russell. John Newbery & the Story of the Newbery Medal. 2003. (Great Achiever Awards Ser.). (Illus.). 48p. (J). (gr. 4-8). lib. bdg. 29.95 (978-1-58415-201-9(X)) Mitchell Lane Pubs., Inc.

Sanchez, Mireia. En el Suelo. 2002. (Caballo Alado Ser.). (SPA & ENG., Illus.). 24p. 5.95 (978-84-7864-421-6(0)) Combel Editorial, S.A. ESP. *Dist:* Independent Pubs. Group.

Saunders, Mary C. Spread Your Wings & Fly! An Origami Fold-&-Tell. McGregor, Carla M., illus. 2000. 48p. (J). (978-0-9662892-1-3(8)) Possibilities W/MCSS (Mary Chloe Schoolcraft Saunders).

Scholastic, Inc. Staff & Jacobson, Jennifer. The Big Book of Reproducible Graphic Organizers: 50 Great Templates to Help Kids Get More Out of Reading. 2003. (Illus.). 112p. pap. 12.95 (978-0-590-37884-0(8)) Scholastic, Inc.

Schon, Isabel. Recommended Books in Spanish for Children & Young Adults: 1996 Through 1999. 4th ed. 2001. (Studies in Young Adult Literature). (Illus.). 376p. 52.00 (978-0-8108-3840-6(0)) Scarecrow Pr., Inc.

Shiotsu, Vicky. Phonics Puzzles & Games. 2001. (Gifted & Talented Ser.: Vol. 2). (Illus.). 64p. (J). (gr. 1-3). pap. 4.95 (978-0-7373-0579-1(7)); (ps-1). pap. 4.95 (978-0-7373-0581-4(9)) Lowell Hse. Juvenile.

Sullivan, Mary. 101 Thematic Poems for Emergent Readers: Playful Rhymes & Easy Activities that Build Early Reading Skills. 1999. 16p. (J). pap. 12.95 (978-0-590-96733-4(9)) Scholastic, Inc.

Toussaint, Pamela. Great Books for African Americans. 1999. (J). (978-0-606-17070-3(7)) Tandem Library Bks.

Trussell-Cullen, Alan. Guided Reading Set. 2001. (SPA., Illus.). (J). Level M. 56.95 (978-1-58105-929-8(9)); Level N. 45.95 (978-1-58105-930-4(2)); Level O. 31.95 (978-1-58105-931-1(0)); Level P. 59.95 (978-1-58105-932-8(9)); Level Q. 35.95 (978-1-58105-933-5(7)); Level S. 34.95 (978-1-58105-935-9(3)) Santillana USA Publishing Co., Inc.

Uhlig, Susan. Things Little Kids Need to Know. Wharton, Jennifer Heyd, illus. 2000. 32p. (J). (ps-3). 16.00 (978-0-9611872-9-3(8)) Our Child Pr.

Waxman, Sydell. Believing in Books: The Story of Lillian Smith. Gallinger, Patty & Milkau, Liz, illus. 2004. (Stories of Canada Ser.). 83p. (J). (gr. 4-7). 14.95 (978-0-929141-77-0(6)) Napoleon Publishing/Rendezvous Pr. CAN. *Dist:* AtlasBooks Distribution.

Webber, Desiree & Shropshire, Sandy. The Kids' Book Club: Lively Reading & Activities for Grades 1-3. Shropshire, Sandy, illus. 2001. (Illus.). 252p. (J). (gr. 1-3). pap. 35.00 (978-1-56308-818-6(5) , LU8185) Libraries Unlimited, Inc.

World Book, Inc. Staff, contrib. by. Baby's First Book: A Book of Learning: Featuring Selections from Childcraft— the How & Why Library. 2003. (Illus.). 95p. (J). (978-0-7166-0364-1(0)) World Bk., Inc.

CHILDREN—CANADA

Orchard, Andy & Orchard, Clare. Canada. Fairclough, Chris, illus. Fairclough, Chris, photos by. 2004. (Letters from Around the World Ser.). (J). lib. bdg. (978-1-84234-242-8(8) , Cherrytree Books) Evans Publishing Group.

CHILDREN—CARE AND HYGIENE

see Children—Health and Hygiene

CHILDREN—CHARITIES, PROTECTION, ETC.

see Child Welfare

CHILDREN—CHINA

Kids Like Me in China. 2002. 44p. 18.00 (978-0-9638472-6-3(0)) Yeong & Yeong Bk. Co.

Lynch, Emma. China (We're From) 2005. (Heinemann First Libary Ser.). (Illus.). 32p. (J). lib. bdg. (978-1-4034-5803-2(0)) Heinemann Library.

—We're from China. 2005. (J). pap. (978-1-4034-5812-4(X)) Heinemann Library.

Warycnia, Lou, et al. If I Were a Kid in Ancient China: Children of the Ancient World. 2007. (Children of the Ancient World Ser.). (Illus.). 32p. (J). 17.95 (978-0-8126-7931-1(8)) Cricket Bks.

CHILDREN, DELINQUENT

see Juvenile Delinquency

CHILDREN—DISCIPLINE

see Child Rearing

CHILDREN—DISEASES

see also Children—Hospitals

also names of diseases e.g. Diptheria; etc.

Abbott, Marcia. My Face. Abbott, Barbara, ed. Westdal, Jamie, photos by. 1998. (Illus.). 44p. (J). (gr. 1-5). 12.50 (978-0-9666097-0-7(0)) Forward Face.

Bennett, Howard J. It Hurts When I Poop! A Story for Children Who Are Scared to Use the Potty. Weber, M. S., illus. 2007. 32p. (J). (ps-1). 14.95 (*978-1-4338-0130-3(2)* , 4418001); pap. 8.95 (*978-1-4338-0131-0(0)* , 4418002) American Psychological Assn. (Magination Pr.).

Bowman-Kruhm, Mary. Everything You Need to Know about Down Syndrome. rev. ed. 2005. (Need to Know Library). (Illus.). 64p. (YA). (gr. 4-6). lib. bdg. 25.25 (978-0-8239-3767-7(4)) Rosen Publishing Group, Inc., The.

Bowman-Kruhm, Mary, ed. Everything You Need to Know about Down Syndrome. 1999. (Need to Know Library). (Illus.). 64p. (YA). (gr. 4-6). lib. bdg. 25.25 (978-0-8239-2949-8(3) , NTDOSY) Rosen Publishing Group, Inc., The.

Brill, Marlene Targ. Tourette Syndrome. 2002. (Medical Library). (Illus.). 112p. (gr. 7 up). lib. bdg. 26.90 (978-0-7613-2101-9(2) , Twenty-First Century Bks.) Lerner Publishing Group.

Burstein, John. Staying Well. McGinnis, Ben, illus. Pinchbeck, Chris, photos by. 2006. (Slim Goodbody's Good Health Guides Ser.). 32p. (J). (gr. 2-4). lib. bdg. 25.27 (*978-0-8368-7744-1(6)*) Stevens, Gareth Inc.

Chara, Kathleen A., et al. Allergy Busters: A Story for Children with Autism or Related Spectrum Disorders Struggling with Allergies. 2004. (Illus.). 48p. (J). pap. (978-1-84310-782-8(1)) Kingsley, Jessica Ltd.

Cranston, Lynda. You & Your Cancer: A Child's Guide. 2001. (Illus.). 64p. (J). pap. (978-1-55009-147-2(6)) Decker, B. C. Inc.

Culbert, Timothy & Kajander, Rebecca. Be the Boss of Your Pain: Self-Care for Kids. 2007. (Be the Boss of Your Body Ser.). (Illus.). 64p. (J). (gr. 4-7). 6.95 (*978-1-57542-254-1(9)*) Free Spirit Publishing, Inc.

Dowell, Andrea C. & Rokke, Kathi R. Miguel & Sarah: Close Friends & Cystic Fibrosis. Madden, Randi, illus. l.t. ed. 1999. 22p. (J). (gr. k-4). pap. 8.00 (978-0-9644972-1-4(2)) Children's Hospitals & Clinics.

Ehrlich, Fred & Ziefert, Harriet. You Can't Take Your Body to a Repair Shop. Haley, Amanda, illus. 2007. 36p. pap. 6.95 (*978-1-59354-625-0(4)*) Handprint Bks.

Fall, Guy. Everything You Need to Know about Juvenile Arthritis. 2005. (Need to Know Library). (Illus.). 64p. (YA). (gr. 4-6). lib. bdg. 25.25 (978-0-8239-3614-4(7)) Rosen Publishing Group, Inc., The.

Health Matters. 2005. (First Facts Ser.). (Illus.). (J). (gr. 1-2). lib. bdg. 127.56 (978-0-7368-4412-3(0)) Capstone Pr., Inc.

Heelan, Jamee Riggio. Rolling Along: The Story of Taylor & His Wheelchair. Simmonds, Nicola, illus. 2000. (Rehabilitation Institute of Chicago Learning Book Ser.). 32p. (J). (gr. 1-5). 14.95 (978-1-56145-219-4(X)) Peachtree Pubs., Ltd.

Henry, Cynthia S. Taking Cystic Fibrosis to School. Gosselin, Kim, ed. Dineen, Tom, illus. 2000. (Special Kids in School Ser.: Vol. 7). 32p. (J). (gr. k-5). pap. 11.95 (978-1-891383-09-0(4)) JayJo Bks., LLC.

Huegel, Kelly. Young People & Chronic Illness: True Stories, Help & Hope. Bratvold, Gretchen & Verdick, Elizabeth, eds. 1998. (Illus.). 208p. (YA). (gr. 5-9). pap. 14.95 (978-1-57542-041-7(4)) Free Spirit Publishing, Inc.

Liddle, Sharon. Eli - the Bi-Polar Bear. Maximilian Press Staff, ed. Garnvin, Rebecka, illus. deluxe ed. 2003. 76p. (J). (gr. 1-4). 29.95 (978-1-930211-49-0(X)) Maximilian Pr. Pubs.

Llewellyn, Claire. Arthritis. 2001. (Illus.). 32p. (J). lib. bdg. 24.25 (978-1-929298-99-0(4)) Chrysalis Education.

McIntosh, Kenneth & Livingston, Phyllis. Youth with Impulse-Control Disorders: On the Spur of the Moment. 2008. (*978-1-4222-0147-3(3)*) Mason Crest Pubs.

Partner, Daniel. Disorders First Diagnosed in Childhood. 2000. (Encyclopedia of Psychological Disorders Ser.). (Illus.). 88p. (J). (gr. 7 up). 35.00 (978-0-7910-5312-6(1) , Chelsea Hse.) Facts On File, Inc.

Perry, Mignon Marie, text. Look at Me I Had Surgery, A Child's Personalized Guide Through the Perioperative Process. 2006. 28p. (J). 3.00 (978-1-59971-891-0(X)) Aardvark Global Publishing.

Powell, Jillian. Zack has Asthma. 2004. (Like Me Like You Ser.). (Illus.). 32p. (gr. 2-4). 23.00 (978-0-7910-8181-5(8) , Chelsea Hse.) Facts On File, Inc.

Rosaler, Maxine. Cystic Fibrosis. 2006. (Genetic Diseases & Disorders Ser.). (Illus.). 64p. (YA). (gr. 6-8). lib. bdg. 26.50 (978-1-4042-0696-0(5)) Rosen Publishing Group, Inc., The.

Royston, Angela. Using a Wheelchair. 2005. (What's It Like? Ser.). (Illus.). 32p. (J). lib. bdg. 24.21 (978-1-4034-5853-7(7)) Heinemann Library.

Schaefer, Lola M. Some Kids Wear Leg Braces. 2008. (J). (*978-1-4296-0813-8(7)*) Capstone Pr., Inc.

Townsend, John. Nasty Bugs & Ghastly Medicine. 2006. (Illus.). 48p. (978-1-4109-1868-0(8)) Steck-Vaughn.

Walker, Julie. Tay-Sachs Disease. 2006. (Genetic Diseases & Disorders Ser.). (Illus.). 64p. (J). (978-1-4042-0697-7(3)) Rosen Publishing Group, Inc., The.

CHILDREN—DISEASES—FICTION

Alvarado, Carol, illus. Harry's Last Wish: A Story about Forever. 1999. 32p. (J). pap. 19.95 incl. audio (978-0-944963-20-3(X)) Glastonbury Pr.

Bateman, Claire Boudreaux. This Little Light of Mine. Alexander, Katie Norwood, illus. ed. 2005. 32p. (J). per. 18.50 (978-0-9706732-2-0(1)) Shell Beach Publishing, LLC.

Bennett, Cherie. Zink: The Myth, the Legend, the Zebra. unabr. ed. 2000. (YA). (gr. 3 up). pap., stu. ed. 59.95 incl. audio (978-0-7887-4197-5(7) , 41100) Recorded Bks., LLC.

Benz, S. M. Harry's Last Wish: A Story about Forever. Alvarado, Carol, illus. 2007. (ENG.). 32p. (J). 24.95 (978-0-944963-23-4(4)) Glastonbury Pr.

Blume, Judy. Deenie. 143p. (YA). (gr. 7 up). pap. 3.99 (978-0-8072-1360-5(8) , Listening Library) Random Hse. Audio Publishing Group.

Clarke, Gus. Betty's Not Well Today. 2004. (Illus.). 32p. pap. 8.95 (978-1-84270-173-7(8)) Andersen GBR. *Dist:* Trafalgar Square Publishing.

Eudes-Pascal, Elisabeth, illus. Raffi's Animal Rescue. 2007. (First Novel Ser.). 64p. (J). (gr. 2). 4.95 (*978-0-88780-740-4(2)*) Formac Publishing Co., Ltd. CAN. *Dist:* Casemate Pubs. & Bk. Distributors, LLC.

Gleitzman, Morris. Two Weeks with the Queen. l.t. ed. 2002. 192p. (J). 16.95 (978-0-7540-7816-6(7) , Galaxy Children's Large Print) BBC Audiobooks America.

Hamilton, Patricia Birdsong. Why do you Walk Funny? l.t. ed. 2006. (Ataxia: A Lifestyle Change). 38p. (J). 16.95 (978-1-889826-91-2(X)) Scripts Publishing.

Harrison, Troon. Aaron's Awful Allergies. Fernandes, Eugenie, illus. unabr. ed. 2002. 32p. (J). (gr. k-3). (978-1-55074-422-4(4)) Kids Can Pr., Ltd.

Hull, Maureen. The View from a Kite. 2007. (Illus.). 320p. (YA). (gr. 10 up). pap. (*978-1-55109-591-2(2)* , Vagrant Pr.) Nimbus Publishing, Ltd.

Kelley, Ann. The Burying Beetle. 2007. 192p. per. 16.95 (978-1-84282-099-5(0)) Luath Pr. Ltd. GBR. *Dist:* Ingram Pub. Services.

Kent, Deborah. Don't Cry for Yesterday. Young, Sandy, illus. 2002. (Why Me? Ser.: Vol. 3). 192p. (YA). (gr. 7-10). pap. 4.99 (978-0-7434-0033-6(X) , Simon Pulse) Simon & Schuster Children's Publishing.

—Don't Cry for Yesterday. 2002. (gr. 5-8). lib. bdg. 13.00 (978-0-613-74125-5(0)) Tandem Library Bks.

—Living with a Secret. 2001. (gr. 7-12). lib. bdg. 13.00 (978-0-613-74124-8(2)) Tandem Library Bks.

Krumrey, Melanie. Bagels, Buddy, & Me: A Story about Gluten Intolerance & Celiac Disease. 2007. (Illus.). 40p. (YA). per. 14.95 (*978-0-9797703-0-2(0)*) Mustard Seed Pr.

Laird, Elizabeth & Davidson, Roz. Jungle School. Sim, David, illus. 2006. (Green Bananas Ser.). 48p. (J). (gr. k-2). (978-0-7787-1026-4(2)) Crabtree Publishing Co.

Maccarone, Grace. I Have a Cold. Lewin, Betsy, illus. 1999. (Hello Reader! Ser.: Level 1). 32p. (J). (ps-3). pap. 3.99 (978-0-590-39638-7(2) , Cartwheel Bks.) Scholastic, Inc.

—Itchy, Itchy Chicken Pox. Lewin, Betsy, illus. 2004. 32p. (J). lib. bdg. 15.00 (978-1-59054-660-4(1)) Fitzgerald Bks.

Martin, Ann M. Karen's Chicken Pox. 1999. (Baby-Sitters Little Sister Ser.: No. 114). (Illus.). 112p. (J). (gr. 3-7). pap. 3.99 (978-0-590-52382-0(1)) Scholastic, Inc.

McCurty, Darlene M. I'm Special Too. 2003. 55p. (J). (gr. 4-8). pap. 6.95 (978-0-913543-27-6(6)) African American Images.

McDaniel, Lurlene. Until Angels Close My Eyes. 1998. (Angels Trilogy: No. 3). 256p. (YA). (gr. 7-12). pap. 5.50 (978-0-553-57115-8(X) , Laurel Leaf) Random Hse. Children's Bks.

—Until Angels Close My Eyes. 1998. (Angels Trilogy: No. 3). (978-0-606-13884-0(6)) Tandem Library Bks.

Romansky, Sally Rosenberg. Invincible. Ott, Margot Janet, illus. 2006. (J). pap. 8.95 (978-0-9723729-4-7(6)) Imagination Stage, Inc.

Sicherer, Scott H. Andrew & Maya Learn about Food Allergies. Munoz-Furlong, Anne, ed. Taylor, Alyssa C. & Furlong, Mariel Christine, illus. 2000. 36p. (J). (gr. 2-8). pap. 8.00 (978-1-882541-16-4(2)) Food Allergy & Anaphylaxis Network.

Stark, Teri. Alison's Helmet. 2005. (J). per. 12.50 (978-1-933570-46-4(6)) Aardvark Global Publishing.

Weeks, Sarah. Get Well Soon, or Else! 2006. 144p. (J). pap. 4.99 (978-0-439-57470-9(6)) Scholastic, Inc.

Zevy, Aaron. Once upon a Breath: The Story of a Wolf, 3 Pigs & Asthma. 1998. (J). pap. 6.99 (978-0-9680678-1-9(6)) Tumbleweed Pr.

CHILDREN—EDUCATION

see Education, Elementary

CHILDREN, EMOTIONALLY DISTURBED

see Problem Children

CHILDREN—EMPLOYMENT

see also Newsboys

Bartoletti, Susan Campbell. Growing up in Coal Country. 1999. (Illus.). 128p. (J). (gr. 4-6). pap. 7.95 (978-0-395-97914-3(5)) Houghton Mifflin Co. Trade & Reference Div.

—Kids on Strike! (Illus.). 208p. (J). (gr. 4-6). 2003. pap. 9.95 (978-0-618-36923-2(6)); 1999. tchr. ed. 20.00 (978-0-395-88892-6(1)) Houghton Mifflin Co. Trade & Reference Div.

—Kids on Strike! 2003. (gr. 5-8). lib. bdg. 17.60 (978-0-613-90473-5(7)) Tandem Library Bks.

Blatt, Jessica. The Teen Girl's Gotta-Have-It Guide to Money: Getting Smart about Making It, Saving It, & Spending It! Frenette, Cynthia, illus. 2007. (Teen Girl's Gotta-Have-It Guides). 96p. (YA). pap. 8.95 (*978-0-8230-1727-0(3)*) Watson-Guptill Pubns., Inc.

Chambers, Catherine. Living As a Child Laborer: Mehboob's Story. 2005. (Children in Crisis Ser.). (Illus.). 48p. (J). (gr. 6-9). lib. bdg. 30.00 (978-0-8368-5958-4(8) , World Almanac Library) Stevens, Gareth Inc.

Child Labor in America. (Teaching with Primary Sources Ser.: Vol. 3). (YA). (gr. 4-9). ring bd. 28.95 (978-0-942389-23-4(9)) Cobblestone Publishing Co.

Freedman, Russell. Kids at Work: Lewis Hine & the Crusade Against Child Labor. Hine, Lewis, photos by. 1998. (Illus.). 112p. (J). (gr. 4-6). pap. 9.95 (978-0-395-79726-6(8) , Clarion Bks.) Houghton Mifflin Co. Trade & Reference Div.

Gourley, Catherine. Good Girl Work. 1999. (Single Titles Ser.: up). (Illus.). 96p. (gr. 7 up). lib. bdg. 26.90 (978-0-7613-0951-2(9) , Millbrook Pr.) Lerner Publishing Group.

Greenwood, Barbara. Factory Girl. 2007. (Illus.). 136p. (J). (*978-1-55337-648-4(X)*) Kids Can Pr., Ltd.

Herumin, Wendy. Child Labor Today: A Human Rights Issue. 2007. (Issues in Focus Today Ser.). (Illus.). 104p. (J). (gr. 6). lib. bdg. 31.93 (*978-0-7660-2682-7(5)*) Enslow Pubs., Inc.

Koestler-Grack, Rachel A. The Story of Mother Jones. 2004. (Breakthrough Biographies Ser.). (Illus.). 32p. (gr. 3-5). 23.00 (978-0-7910-7316-2(5) , Chelsea Hse.) Facts On File, Inc.

Miller, Connie Colwell. Mother Jones: Labor Leader. Erwin, Steve & Barnett, Charles, illus. 2007. (Graphic Library). 32p. (J). 25.26 (978-0-7368-5487-0(8)); (*978-0-7368-9662-7(7)*) Capstone Pr., Inc.

Miller, Raymond H. Jhalak Man Tamang: Slave Labor Whistleblower. 2006. (Young Heroes Ser.). (Illus.). 64p. (J). (gr. 4-8). lib. bdg. 27.45 (978-0-7377-3616-8(X) , Kidhaven) Thomson Gale.

Newman, Shirlee Petkin. Child Slavery in Modern Times. (Watts Library). (Illus.). 64p. (J). (gr. 5-7). 2001. pap. 8.95 (978-0-531-16540-9(X)); 2000. 25.50 (978-0-531-11696-8(4)) Scholastic Library Publishing. (Watts, Franklin).

Roberts-Davis, Tanya. We Need to Go to School: Voices of the Rugmark Children. 2003. (Illus.). 48p. (J). (gr. 5 up). pap. 7.95 (978-0-88899-426-4(5)) Groundwood Bks. CAN. *Dist:* Perseus Distribution.

Robinson, Tony. Worst Childrens Jobs in History. 2005. (Illus.). 112p. pap. 13.95 (***978-0-330-44286-2(4)***) Macmillan Publishers Ltd. GBR. *Dist:* Independent Pubs. Group.

Saller, Carol. Working Children. 1998. (Picture the American Past Ser.). (Illus.). 48p. (gr. 2-5). lib. bdg. 22.60 (978-1-57505-276-2(8)) Lerner Publishing Group.

Scott, Janine. Kids Have Rights Too! (Shockwave: the Human Experience Ser.). (J). 2008. 32p. pap. 6.95 (***978-0-531-18838-5(8)***); 2007. (Illus.). 36p. (gr. 4-6). lib. bdg. 25.00 (***978-0-531-17763-1(7)***) Scholastic Library Publishing. (Children's Pr.).

Stearman, Kaye. Child Labor. 2003. (Face the Facts Ser.). 56p. (J). pap. 8.95 (978-1-4109-0338-9(9)); lib. bdg. 28.56 (978-0-7398-6848-5(9)) Raintree.

—Child Labor. 2003. (gr. 5-8). lib. bdg. 17.60 (978-0-613-78303-3(4)) Tandem Library Bks.

Townsend, John. Weary Work & Lousy Leisure. 2006. (Raintree Freestyle Ser.). (Illus.). 48p. (J). (978-1-4109-1870-3(X)) Steck-Vaughn.

CHILDREN—EUROPE

Brooks, Susie. Greece. 2006. (Our Lives, Our World Ser.). (J). (978-1-59389-287-6(X)) Chrysalis Education.

Gerstein, Mordicai. The Wild Boy. 2002. (gr. k-3). lib. bdg. 14.10 (978-0-613-71934-6(4)) Tandem Library Bks.

Mcdonald, Blaisdell. Gerda in Sweden. 2006. 32.99 (***978-1-4280-1764-1(X)***) IndyPublish.com.

Middleton, Haydn & Tames, Richard. Ancient Greek Children. 2002. (People in the Past Ser.). 64p. (J). (gr. 4-7). pap. 8.50 (978-1-4034-0131-1(4) , 91636) Heinemann Library.

Tames, Richard. Ancient Greek Children. 2002. (People in the Past Ser.). (Illus.). 48p. (J). (gr. 4-6). lib. bdg. 27.07 (978-1-58810-639-1(X)) Heinemann Library.

—Ancient Roman Children. (People in the Past Ser.). (Illus.). 48p. (J). 2003. (gr. 4-6). lib. bdg. 27.07 (978-1-58810-634-6(9)); 2002. pap. 7.95 (978-1-4034-0518-0(2)) Heinemann Library.

Warynica, Lou, et al. If I Were a Kid in Ancient Greece. 2007. (Children of the Ancient World Ser.). (Illus.). 32p. (J). 17.95 (978-0-8126-7929-8(6)) Cricket Bks.

Williams, Brian. Ancient Roman Children. 2002. (gr. 3-6). lib. bdg. 17.05 (978-0-613-85909-7(X)) Tandem Library Bks.

CHILDREN—EUROPE—FICTION

Jarvis, Martin & Crompton, Richmal. William & the Hidden Treasure & Other Stories, No. 2. Ross, Tony, illus. 2003. (Meet Just William Ser.). 81p. (J). pap. 8.99 (978-0-330-39100-9(3) , Pan) Pan Macmillan GBR. *Dist:* Trafalgar Square Publishing.

—William's Day off & Other Stories, No. 6. Ross, Tony, illus. 2003. (Meet Just William Ser.). 83p. (J). pap. 8.99 (978-0-330-39099-6(6) , Pan) Pan Macmillan GBR. *Dist:* Trafalgar Square Publishing.

CHILDREN—FICTION

A. B. Publishing Staff. In the Twilight. 1998. (J). (gr. 4-7). pap. 6.95 (978-1-881545-90-3(3)) A B Publishing.

Adamek, Maurine Reynolds. I'll Do Better Tomorrow, I Promise. Schubert, Annalee, illus. 2nd ed. 1998. 32p. (J). (gr. 1-6). reprint ed. pap. 6.99 (978-0-9669581-0-2(1)) Dreyer Pr.

Adebayo, Yinka. Big Diss. 1999. (Drummond Hill Crew Ser.). 187p. (978-1-874509-68-4(9)) X Pr., The.

—Glamma Kids. 1999. (Drummond Hill Crew Ser.). 185p. (978-1-874509-67-7(0)) X Pr., The.

—Ragga to Riches. 1999. 187p. (J). (978-1-874509-69-1(7)) X Pr., The.

Alger, Horatio. Paul the Peddler. rev. ed. 2006. (ENG.). 232p. 27.95 (978-1-4218-2090-3(0) , 1st World Library - Literary Society) 1st World Publishing, Inc.

Alger Jr. Horatio Staff. Herbert Carter's Legacy. rev. ed. 2006. 264p. 28.95 (978-1-4218-1756-9(X)); pap. 13.95 (978-1-4218-1856-6(6)) 1st World Publishing, Inc. (1st World Library - Literary Society).

Andrew, Alice, et al. Cin'at (Roe) Sparck, Carole C., illus. l.t. ed. 1999. (ESK.). 8p. (J). (gr. k-3). pap. 6.00 (978-1-58084 153 5(8)) Lower Kuskokwim Schl. District.

—Meluk (Roe) Sparck, Carole C., illus. l.t. ed. 1999. (ESK.). 8p. (J). (gr. k-3). pap. 6.00 (978-1-58084-104-7(6)) Lower Kuskokwim Schl. District.

—Roe. Sparck, Carole C., illus. l.t. ed. 1999. 8p. (J). (gr. k-3). pap. 6.00 (978-1-58084-103-0(1)) Lower Kuskokwim Schl. District.

Applegate, Katherine. The Reunion. 1999. (Animorphs Ser.: No. 30). (J). (978-0-606-16657-7(2)) Tandem Library Bks.

Argay, Melissa Ann. A Day in the Life of Francis. Argay, Melissa Ann, illus. 2000. (World as Francis Knows It Ser.). (Illus.). 22p. (J). (ps). (978-0-9679664-0-3(X)) Chosen Collections.

Armstrong, Robb. Large & in Charge. Smith, Bruce, illus. 1999. (Patrick's Pals Ser.: No. 7). 96p. (J). (gr. 2-7). pap. 3.99 (978-0-06-107073-0(4)) HarperCollins Pubs.

Atkins, Jeannine. Preparadas... Listas... Ya! ed. 2004. (SPA., Illus.). (J). (gr. k-3). spiral bd. (978-0-616-07274-5(0)) Canadian National Institute for the Blind/Institut National Canadien pour les Aveugles.

—Preparadas... Listas... Ya! Sarfatti, Esther, tr. from ENG. Lee, Hector Viveros, illus. 1998. (SPA.). 32p. (J). (gr. 1-3). 15.95 (978-1-880000-77-9(6) , LW(8473)); pap. 6.95 (978-1-880000-78-6(4) , LW(8474)) Lee & Low Bks., Inc.

Atkins, Jill. She Had to Leave Home. There Was No Other Way... Lawrie, Robin, illus. 2001. (Go for It! Ser.). 127p. pap. 9.99 (978-0-237-52332-9(9) , Evans Brothers, Limited) Evans Publishing Group GBR. *Dist:* Independent Pubs. Group.

August Imagination Letter 98. 1998. (978-0-689-00662-3(4) , Simon & Schuster Children's Publishing) Simon & Schuster Children's Publishing.

Backstein, Karen. Los Seis Ciegos y el Elefante. Mitra, Annie, illus. 1999. (Coleccion "Hola, Lector" Ser.). (SPA.). 48p. (J). (gr. 1-3). pap. 3.99 (978-0-439-06338-8(8) , SO0352, Scholastic en Espanol) Scholastic, Inc.

Badowich, D. M. Mine. Chapman, Chris, illus. 1999. 16p. (J). (ps-3). pap. (978-1-894303-19-4(9)) Raven Rock Publishing.

Baggette, Susan K. Jonathan Goes to the Post Office. Moriarty, William J., photos by. 1998. (Jonathan Adventures Ser.). (Illus.). 16p. (J). (ps-k). bds. 5.95 (978-0-9660172-5-0(0)) Brookfield Reader, Inc., The.

Baker, Barbara. Third Grade Is Terrible. Shepherd, Roni, illus. 1999. (Puffin Chapters Ser.). 112p. (J). (gr. 2-5). reprint ed. pap. 4.99 (978-0-14-130103-7(1) , Puffin) Penguin Group (USA) Inc.

Ballantyne, Michael. Blown to Bits or the Lonely Man of Rakat. 2006. 36.99 (***978-1-4280-4221-6(0));*** pap. 30.99 (***978-1-4280-4226-1(1))*** IndyPublish.com.

Barkow, Henriette. That's My Mum. Brazell, Derek, illus. 2004. (CZE, VIE, SPA, GUJ & PER.). 24p. (J). (978-1-85269-597-2(8)); (978-1-85269-598-9(6)); (978-1-85269-599-6(4)); (978-1-85269-601-6(X)); (978-1-85269-602-3(8)); (978-1-85269-603-0(6)); (978-1-85269-604-7(4)); (978-1-85269-605-4(2)); (978-1-85269-606-1(0)); (978-1-85269-608-5(7)); (978-1-85269-609-2(5)); (978-1-85269-628-3(1)); (978-1-85269-802-7(0)); (978-1-85269-803-4(9)); (978-1-85269-804-1(7)) Mantra Publishing, Ltd.

Barkow, Henriette & Brazell, Derek. That's My Mum: Ajo Eshte Nena Ime. 2004. (CZE, VIE, SPA, GUJ & PER., Illus.). 24p. (J). (978-1-85269-596-5(X)) Mantra Publishing, Ltd.

Beaumont, Karen. Move Over, Rover! Dyer, Jane, illus. 2006. 40p. (J). (ps-2). 16.00 (978-0-15-201979-2(0)) Harcourt Trade Pubs.

Beechen, Adam. Two Promises Too Many. 2000. (gr. 3-6). lib. bdg. 11.80 (978-0-613-31850-1(1)) Tandem Library Bks.

Bellingham, Brenda. Storm Child. 2003. (Sports Stories Ser.). 124p. (gr. 3-8). 6.95 (978-0-88862-793-3(9)) Lorimer, James & Co., Ltd., Pubs. CAN. *Dist:* Casemate Pubs. & Bk. Distributors, LLC.

Benenfeld, Rikki. I Go to the Doctor. Benenfeld, Rikki, illus. 2004. (Illus.). (J). lib. bdg. 9.95 (978-1-929628-15-5(3)) Hachai Publishing.

Benjamin, A. H. Podria Haber Sido Peor. Mlawer, Teresa, tr. Warnes, Tim, illus. 2001. (SPA.). (J). (gr. k-2). pap. 8.95 (978-1-930332-19-5(X) , LC7240) Lectorum Pubns., Inc.

Bertollini, Regina. For the Love of Ferny. 2001. (Illus.). 40p. (J). (ps-5). pap. 8.99 (978-0-9713468-0-2(1)) Little Bit Pubns.

Bestmann, Mark. The Only True & Incredible Me. 1998. 24p. (J). 12.99 (978-0-89900-819-6(4)) College Pr. Publishing Co., Inc.

Betancourt, Jeanne. We've Got Spirit! 1999. (Cheer USA Ser.). (J). pap. 36.00 (978-0-439-11748-7(8)) Scholastic, Inc.

Blanchard, Marlene. Wannabe, Wannabe, Wannabe. Blanchard, Marlene, illus. 1999. (Illus.). 40p. pap. 6.95 (978-0-7392-0238-8(3) , PO3284) Morris Publishing.

Blume, Judy. Tales of a Fourth Grade Nothing. 2002. (Fudge Ser.). (Illus.). (J). 13.40 (978-0-7587-6609-0(2)) Book Wholesalers, Inc.

—Tales of a Fourth Grade Nothing. 1999. (Fudge Ser.). (J). 11.95 (978-1-56137-709-1(0)) Novel Units, Inc.

—Tales of a Fourth Grade Nothing. 2004. (Fudge Ser.). 144p. (gr. 12). mass mkt. 5.99 (978-0-425-19379-2(9) , Berkley) Penguin Group (USA) Inc.

Blyton, Enid. Bimbo & Topsy. 2000. (Enid Blyton's Happy Days Ser.). (Illus.). 156p. (J). (gr. 1-4). pap. 6.95 (978-0-7475-3220-0(6)) Bloomsbury Publishing Plc GBR. *Dist:* Trafalgar Square Publishing.

Boone, Sheila. Free As a Butterfly. Knox, Susi Grell, illus. 2003. 32p. (J). (ps-3). pap. 7.95 (978-1-891577-80-2(8)) Image Pr., Inc.

Boullosa, Carmen. Solo para Muchachos. Martinez, Enrique, illus. 2003. (SPA.). 60p. (J). (gr. 4-7). 11.95 (978-968-19-0325-1(0)) Aguilar, Altea, Taurus, Alfaguara, S.A. de C.V MEX. *Dist:* Santillana USA Publishing Co., Inc.

Bowler, Tim. Firmament. 2004. (Illus.). 320p. (YA). 16.95 (978-0-689-86161-1(3) , McElderry, Margaret K.) Simon & Schuster Children's Publishing.

Boynton, Sandra. The Going to Bed Book. Boynton, Sandra, illus. 2006. 14p. (J). 12.95 (978-1-4169-2794-5(8) , Little Simon) Simon & Schuster Children's Publishing.

Bradman, Tony. The Sandal. Dupasquier, Philippe, illus. 32p. (J). (gr. 1-3). pap. 9.99 (978-0-86264-843-5(2)) Andersen GBR. *Dist:* Trafalgar Square Publishing.

Bray, Jeannine D. Rabbie. Kenyatta, Imani, ed. Mitchell, Denise B., illus. 1998. 56p. (J). (gr. k-6). 14.95 (978-1-886580-68-8(5)) Pinnacle-Syatt Pubns.

Brisley, Joyce Lankester. More Milly-Molly-Mandy. 1999. (Story Collections). 224p. (J). (gr. k-3). 13.95 (978-0-7534-5334-6(7) , Kingfisher) Houghton Mifflin Co. Trade & Reference Div.

Brisson, Pat. Bertie's Picture Day. Bluthenthal, Diana Cain, illus. rev. ed. 2000. 80p. (J). (gr. 1-3). 16.00 (978-0-8050-6281-6(5) , Holt, Henry & Co. Bks. For Young Readers) Holt, Henry & Co.

Britton, Susan. The Treekeepers. 2003. 256p. (J). (gr. 4-7). 16.99 (978-0-525-46944-5(3) , Dutton Juvenile) Penguin Group (USA) Inc.

Brooke, Lauren. One Day You'll Know. 2001. (Heartland Ser.: No. 6). 208p. mass mkt. 4.99 (978-0-439-13035-6(2)) Scholastic, Inc.

—One Day You'll Know. 2001. (gr. 3-6). lib. bdg. 13.00 (978-0-613-43859-9(0)) Tandem Library Bks.

Brooke, William J. A Is for AARRGH! 1999. (Illus.). 256p. (J). (gr. 5 up). 15.95 (978-0-06-023393-8(1)) HarperCollins Pubs.

Brookes, Diane. All Alone. Timmins, Ann, illus. 1999. (J). (ps-3). pap. (978-0-9683640-9-3(8)) Raven Rock Publishing.

Brooks, Walter R. Freddy the Pied Piper. Wiese, Kurt, illus. 2002. 253p. (J). (gr. 3). 23.95 (978-1-58567-226-4(2)) Overlook Pr., The.

Brown, Marc. D. W. All Wet. Brown, Marc, illus. 2002. (D. W. Ser.). (Illus.). (J). 13.15 (978-0-7587-2325-3(3)) Book Wholesalers, Inc.

—D. W. Flips! Brown, Marc, illus. 2002. (D. W. Ser.). (Illus.). (J). 13.15 (978-0-7587-2326-0(1)) Book Wholesalers, Inc.

—D. W., Go to Your Room! Brown, Marc, illus. 1999. (D. W. Ser.). (Illus.). 32p. (J). (ps-1). 13.95 (978-0-316-10905-5(3)) Little, Brown Bks. for Young Readers.

Brown, Margaret Wise. Another Important Book. Raschka, Chris, illus. (Joanna Cotler Bks.). 32p. (J). (ps-k). 1999. lib. bdg. 16.89 (978-0-06-026283-9(4) , Cotler, Joanna Books); 1999. 16.99 (978-0-06-026282-2(6) , Cotler, Joanna Books); 2006. reprint ed. pap. 6.99 (978-0-06-443785-1(X) , Harper Trophy) HarperCollins Pubs.

Bruchac, Joseph. Children of the Longhouse. 1998. (Illus.). 160p. (J). (gr. 3-7). pap. 5.99 (978-0-14-038504-5(5) , Puffin) Penguin Group (USA) Inc.

—Children of the Longhouse. 1998. 12.64 (978-0-606-13268-8(6)) Tandem Library Bks.

Bulla, Clyde Robert. The Chalk Box Kid. Allen, Thomas B., illus. 2002. (J). 11.91 (978-0-7587-6051-7(5)) Book Wholesalers, Inc.

Byars, Betsy. Bingo Brown y el Lenguaje del Amor. 2003. (Survival Ser.). (SPA.). (J). (gr. 4-5). pap. 10.95 (978-84-239-7152-7(X) , EC5211) Espasa Calpe, S.A. ESP. *Dist:* Planeta Publishing Corp.

—Las Preguntas de Bingo Brown. Gatagan, T., illus. 2nd ed. 2003. (Espasa Juvenil Ser.: Vol. 15). (SPA.). 186p. (J). (gr. 7 up). (978-84-239-8862-4(7) , EC4398) Espasa Calpe, S.A. ESP. *Dist:* Lectorum Pubns., Inc.

Caffrey-Kira, Albina. The Bear Who Loves Apples. 2006. 25.00 (978-0-8059-9128-4(X)) Dorrance Publishing Co., Inc.

Callella, Trisha. I Try to Be a Good Person, Vol. 4414. Kupperstein, Joel, ed. Jarrett, Michael, photos by. 1998. (Learn to Read Social Studies). (Illus.). 16p. (J). (ps-2). pap. 2.75 (978-1-57471-337-4(X) , 4414) Creative Teaching Pr., Inc.

—Numbers All Around Me, Vol. 4470. Kupperstein, Joel, ed. 1998. (Learn to Read Math Ser.). (Illus.). 16p. (J). pap. 2.75 (978-1-57471-377-0(9) , 4470) Creative Teaching Pr., Inc.

Candlewick Press Staff, ed. Pop Pop Pop. 2000. (Illus.). (J). bds. 4.99 (978-0-7636-1184-2(0)) Candlewick Pr.

Carignan, Michael J. The First Witness. Fuller, Ann, illus. 1998. (J). (ps-6). mass mkt. 4.95 (978-1-892589-00-2(1)) Madjec Jet Publishing Co.

Carlson-Mineau, Anita L. Adventures in Yooperland: Those Happy Days of Childhood. Hendershot, Nancy, ed. Stillwagon, Mary F., illus. 1998. 31p. (J). (gr. 4-6). pap. 11.95 (978-0-9662539-0-0(6)) Books By Anita.

Carson, Carole. Remembering When I Was Young, 2 vols. Kenfield, Peggy, illus. gif. ed. 2006. 92p. (J). 24.95 (978-0-9766030-6-1(3)) Hound Pr.

Case, Margaret. Imagine If You Can. 1999. (Illus.). 60p. (J). (gr. 1-5). pap. 4.99 (978-1-893181-12-0(X) , Lagesse Stevens) Martell Publishing Co.

Caso, Laura M. Chicken Pox Explosion! Caso, Adolph, ed. 2000. (Illus.). 10p. (J). (gr. 2-6). pap. 7.95 (978-0-8283-2054-2(3)) Branden Bks.

Cast, John. Children of the Sun. 1999. (Illus.). 24p. (J). (ps-3). 3.99 (978-0-85953-933-3(4)) Child's Play-International.

Castle, Caroline, adapted by. Para Todos los Ninos - Unicef. 2001. Tr. of For Every Child. (SPA.). 40p. (J). (978-980-257-273-1(X) , EK31557) Ekare, Ediciones.

Chambers, Veronica. Double Dutch: A Celebration of Jump Rope, Rhyme, & Sisterhood. 2002. (Illus.). 72p. (gr. 3-17). 18.99 (978-0-7868-0512-9(9) , Jump at the Sun) Hyperion Bks. for Children.

Cheng, Christopher C. One Child. Woolman, Steven, illus. 2000. 32p. (J). (ps-1). 14.95 (978-1-56656-330-7(5) , Crocodile Bks.) Interlink Publishing Group, Inc.

Chetwin, Grace. Briony's ABC of Abominable Children. Roberts, Claire, illus. 1998. (J). pap. 20.00 (978-0-9649349-4-8(9) , Rivet Bks.) Feral Pr., Inc.

Chouette. Caillou Goes to Work. rev. ed. 2005. (Abracadabra Ser.). Tr. of Caillou va Travailler. (Illus.). 24p. (J). (ps-1). pap. 4.95 (978-2-89450-548-9(5)) Chouette Publishing CAN. *Dist:* Independent Pubs. Group.

Christian, Cheryl. Donde esta el Bebé? Fiol, María A., tr. Dwight, Laura, photos by. 2000. (Photoflaps Ser.). (SPA., Illus.). 12p. (J). (ps). bds. 5.50 (978-1-887734-26-4(0)) Star Bright Bks., Inc.

—Donde Esta el Gatito? Fiol, María A., tr. from ENG. Dwight, Laura, photos by. 2000. (Photoflaps Ser.). (SPA., Illus.). 12p. (J). (ps). bds. 5.50 (978-1-887734-28-8(7)) Star Bright Bks., Inc.

—How Many? 2001. (Photoflaps Ser.). (Illus.). 12p. (J). (ps). bds. 5.50 (978-1-887734-66-0(X)) Star Bright Bks., Inc.

—Where Does It Go? 2001. (Photoflaps Ser.). (Illus.). 12p. (J). (ps). bds. 5.50 (978-1-887734-65-3(1)) Star Bright Bks., Inc.

—Y Ahora, Qué Pasara? Fiol, María A., tr. from ENG. Dwight, Laura, photos by. 2000. (Photoflaps Ser.). (SPA., Illus.). 12p. (J). (ps). bds. 5.50 (978-1-887734-27-1(9)) Star Bright Bks., Inc.

Clarke, Judith. The Lost Day. rev. ed. 1999. 160p. (gr. 7-12). 16.95 (978-0-8050-6152-9(5) , Holt, Henry & Co. Bks. For Young Readers) Holt, Henry & Co.

Cohen, Miriam. Wah! Wah! A Backpack Baby Story. l.t. ed. 2001. (Backpack Baby Stories Ser.). (Illus.). 12p. (J). (ps). bds. 5.95 (978-1-887734-81-3(3)) Star Bright Bks., Inc.

Cole, Babette. The Slimy Book. 2003. (Illus.). 32p. (J). (gr. k-3). pap. 9.99 (978-0-09-943426-9(1) , Red Fox) Random Hse. Children's Bks. GBR. *Dist:* Trafalgar Square Publishing.

Colombo, Corey, et al. Candle in the Window. Stolz, Claudia M., ed. unabr. ed. 1999. 64p. (J). (gr. 3-6). 5.00 (978-0-918761-08-8(5)); pap. 2.50 (978-0-918761-07-1(7)) Miami Univ. Pubns.

Conley, Deane. Angelino. Hunt, Christy, ed. Thiele, Marcus, illus. 2000. (Butterfly Tree Ser.: Vol. 1). 32p. (J). (ps-3). 17.00 (978-0-9664329-2-3(4)) Buckhead Pr.

Conrad, Pam. Staying Nine. 1999. (Illus.). (J). (gr. 3-6). lib. bdg. 13.00 (978-0-8335-6162-6(6)) Tandem Library Bks.

Cosby, Bill. Hooray for the Dandelion Warriors! Honeywood, Varnette P., illus. 1999. (Little Bill Books for Beginning Readers Ser.). (J). (gr. 1-3). pap. 47.88 (978-0-439-13496-5(X)); 40p. (gr. k-3). pap. 15.95 (978-0-590-52191-8(8) , Cartwheel Bks.) Scholastic, Inc.

—Hooray for the Dandelion Warriors! 1999. (gr. k-3). lib. bdg. 11.80 (978-0-613-21717-0(9)); (Illus.). (J). 10.79 (978-0-606-18561-5(5)) Tandem Library Bks.

—The Worst Day of My Life. Honeywood, Varnette P., illus. 1999. (Little Bill Books for Beginning Readers Ser.). 40p. (J). (gr. k-3). pap. 3.99 (978-0-590-52175-8(6)); pap. 3.99 (978-0-590-52190-1(X)) Scholastic, Inc. (Cartwheel Bks.).

—The Worst Day of My Life. 1999. (Little Bill Books for Beginning Readers Ser.). (J). (gr. k-3). (978-0-606-18618-6(2)) Tandem Library Bks.

C D

Cosgrove, Stephen. Feather Fin. James, Robin, illus. ed. 2003. (Serendipity Ser.). 32p. (J). (gr. k-5). pap. 4.99 (978-0-8431-0493-6(7) , Price Stern Sloan) Penguin Group (USA) Inc.

—Feather Fin. 2003. (gr. k-3). lib. bdg. 13.00 (978-0-613-81851-3(2)) Tandem Library Bks.

The Crayon Caper. 2000. 32p. pap. 2.75 (978-0-8341-1854-6(8)) Beacon Hill Pr. of Kansas City.

Crosby, Ruthann. Miracle in the Glass: To Save a Life Is to Save the World. Cook, Richard, illus. l.t. ed. 1998. 48p. (J). (gr. 3-6). pap. 14.95 (978-1-888125-26-9(8)) Publication Consultants.

Curtis, Jamie Lee. When I Was Little. 2000. (Illus.). 32p. (J). (ps-3). 15.95 incl. audio (978-0-06-028258-5(4)) HarperCollins Pubs.

Cutler, Jane. Guttersnipe. Date not set. (J). (978-0-374-32813-9(7) , Farrar, Straus & Giroux (BYR)) Farrar, Straus & Giroux.

Cyrkozuch, Alonda. The Lovell Legend. Meurlot, Donny G., illus. 1999. 28p. (J). (ps-12). pap. 5.95 (978-1-929098-00-2(6) , 01) Story Teller, The.

Dandridge, Derrick M. The Maple Kids Go to the Zoo. l.t. ed. 1999. (Maple Kids Ser.). (Illus.). 32p. (ps-2). pap. 5.00 (978-1-928694-01-4(2)) Modern Star Bks.

—The Original Maple Kids. l.t. ed. 1999. (Maple Kids Ser.). (Illus.). 28p. (ps-2). pap. 5.00 (978-1-928694-00-7(4)) Modern Star Bks.

Danziger, Paula. Everyone Else's Parents Said Yes. 1998. (Matthew Martin Ser.: No. 1). 128p. (J). (gr. 4-7). pap. 5.99 (978-0-698-11687-0(9) , Putnam Juvenile) Penguin Group (USA) Inc.

Davies, Rocky. Harvey Happy Bee. 2005. (Bee Attitude Board Books). (Illus.). (J). (978-1-59156-775-2(0)) Covenant Communications.

Davis, Dawn Schumacher, illus. & abr. Ginger Wants a Cracker. Davis, Dawn Schumacher, abr. 1999. 24p. (YA). (gr. 4-12). 10.95 (978-1-879318-06-9(7)) August Rose Publishing.

Davis, Mildred. Child in My Heart. 1998. pap. 5.95 (978-0-9652894-8-1(6)) GA Publishing.

De Aragon, Ray J. Dodo the Bird & Other Stories. Calles, Rosa M., illus. 105p. (Orig.). (J). (gr. 1-12). pap. 5.95 (978-0-932906-21-2(4)) Pan-American Publishing Co.

De Gross, Monalisa. Steal Away. 1999. (J). (978-0-7868-0161-9(1)) Hyperion Pr.

Delton, Judy. A Big Box of Memories. 2000. (Pee Wee Scouts Ser.: No. 40). (J). (gr. 2-5). (978-0-606-18788-6(X)) Tandem Library Bks.

Derrick, Patricia. Farley the Ferret of Farkleberry Farm. 2007. 32p. 18.95 (978-1-933818-12-2(3)) Animalations.

Deshpande, Chris. Diwali. 1998. (Celebrations Ser.). (Illus.). 32p. (gr. 5-7). pap. 4.95 (978-0-7136-4082-3(0) , 93345) A & C Black GBR. *Dist:* Consortium Bk. Sales & Distribution.

DiGiacomo, Anthony W. Rachel's Stories for Tough Kids. DiGiacomo, Anthony W., illus. 1998. (Illus.). 30p. (J). (gr. 1-4). pap. 7.95 (978-1-58265-001-2(2)) Orphan Pr.

Dines, Carol. Talk to Me: Stories & a Novella. 1999. (978-0-606-16451-1(0)) Tandem Library Bks.

Doggy Heaven's in the Sky! 2004. (J). 4.95 (***978-0-9791362-0-7(2)***) Tony Tales.

Donnell, Frances. Goblins Will Be Seen: When it's time for Halloween. Hebert, Catherine, ed. Merchant, Donna, illus. 2005. 38p. (J). per. 16.95 incl. audio compact disk (978-0-9770893-0-7(4)) 2 Donn Bks.

Dorros, Arthur. Isla. Kleven, Elisa, illus. 1999. Orig. Title: The Island. 40p. (J). (ps-1). pap. 6.99 (978-0-14-056505-8(1) , Puffin) Penguin Group (USA) Inc.

—Isla. 1999. Orig. Title: The Island. (J). 12.79 (978-0-606-16810-6(9)); (J). 13.79 (978-0-606-16811-3(7)); lib. bdg. 14.15 (978-0-613-14865-8(7)); (SPA.). lib. bdg. 15.30 (978-0-613-18258-4(8)) Tandem Library Bks.

—La Isla. Kleven, Elisa, illus. 1999. (Picture Puffin Ser.). (SPA.). 40p. (J). (gr. k-3). pap. 6.99 (978-0-14-056541-6(8) , DT8806, Puffin) Penguin Group (USA) Inc.

Duchesne, Christiane. Edmond et Amandine. ed. 2004. (FRE., Illus.). (J). (ps-3). spiral bd. (978-0-616-11143-7(6)) Canadian National Institute for the Blind/Institut National Canadien pour les Aveugles.

Duffey, Betsy. Hey, New Kid! 1998. (Puffin Chapters Ser.). (Illus.). 96p. (J). (gr. 2-5). pap. 4.99 (978-0-14-038439-0(1) , Puffin) Penguin Group (USA) Inc.

—Hey, New Kid! 2000. (YA). pap. 22.24 incl. audio (978-0-7887-4173-9(X) , 41093) Recorded Bks., LLC.

—Hey, New Kid! Thompson, Ellen, illus. 1998. 89p. (J). (ps-k). lib. bdg. 13.00 (978-0-613-07966-2(3)) Tandem Library Bks.

—Virtual Cody. Thompson, Ellen, illus. 1999. (Puffin Chapters for Readers on the Move Ser.). 96p. (J). (gr. 2-5). pap. 4.99 (978-0-14-130350-5(6) , Puffin) Penguin Group (USA) Inc.

—Virtual Cody. 1999. (Puffin Chapters Ser.). (978-0-606-16774-1(9)); (gr. 3-6). lib. bdg. 11.80 (978-0-613-18287-4(1)) Tandem Library Bks.

Dulaney, Kim. Maya's Magic. Beck, Sherman, illus. 1999. (Fuzzy-Feeling Bks.). (J). (ps-3). pap. 8.25 (978-1-891636-04-2(9) , 1003) Unique Expression.

Dulaney, Kim L. My Best. Beck, Sherman, illus. 1999. (Fuzzy-Feeling Bks.). (J). (gr. 1-4). pap. 8.25 (978-1-891636-05-9(7) , 1006) Unique Expression.

Edwards, Pamela Duncan, et al. Barefoot: Escape on the Underground Railroad. Cole, Henry, illus. 1999. 32p. (J). (gr. k-4). pap. 6.99 (978-0-06-443519-2(9) , Harper Trophy) HarperCollins Pubs.

Edwards, Richard. Copy Me, Copycub. Winter, Susan, illus. 1999. (J). lib. bdg. 16.01 (978-0-06-028571-5(0)) HarperCollins Pubs.

—The Forest Child. Malone, Peter, illus. 2004. 28p. (J). reprint ed. 15.00 (978-0-7567-7850-7(6)) DIANE Publishing Co.

Elliott, Ruth & Elliott, David. The Richest Kid in the Poor House. Elliott, Ruth, illus. l.t. ed. 1999. (Illus.). 68p. (J). (ps-6). 19.95 (978-0-9668747-9-2(X)); pap. 14.95 (978-0-9668747-8-5(1)) Partnership Publishing.

Emberley, Rebecca. Three Cool Kids. 1998. (Illus.). 32p. (J). (ps-3). pap. 5.95 (978-0-316-23519-8(9)) Little Brown & Co.

—Three Cool Kids. 1998. (J). (978-0-606-13847-5(1)) Tandem Library Bks.

Ende, Michael. Momo. Ende, Michael, illus. 2003. (SPA., Illus.). 256p. (J). (gr. 8-12). pap. 13.95 (978-968-19-0255-1(6)) Santillana USA Publishing Co., Inc.

Farber, Erica. Ooey Gooey. 1998. (Step into Reading Step 1 Bks.). (J). (ps-1). (978-0-606-13966-3(4)) Tandem Library Bks.

Farias, Juan. Algunos Ninos, Tres Perros y Mas. 10th ed. 1998. (Espasa Juvenil Ser.: Vol. 34). (SPA., Illus.). 94p. (gr. 3-5). 6.95 (978-84-239-8885-3(6) , EC3387) i.b.d., Ltd.

Fermaglich, Molly. It's Only Me. 2000. (Illus.). 160p. (J). (gr. 4-7). 14.95 (978-0-06-028229-5(0)); lib. bdg. 14.89 (978-0-06-028230-1(4)) HarperCollins Pubs.

Fernandes, Eugenie. A Difficult Day. Fernandes, Eugenie, illus. unabr. ed. 1999. (Illus.). 32p. (J). (gr. k-3). (978-0-921103-17-2(4)) Kids Can Pr., Ltd.

Finley, Martha. Elsie's Children, Vol. 6. (Elsie Bks.: Bk. 6). 320p. (gr. 7-12). pap. 5.95 (978-1-58182-069-0(0)) Cumberland Hse. Publishing.

—Elsie's Children. 1998. (Elsie Bks.: Vol. 6). 229p. (J). (gr. 7-12). pap. 6.99 (978-1-888306-39-2(4) , Full Quart Pr.) Holly Hall Pubns., Inc.

—Elsie's Young Folks, Vol. 25. (Elsie Bks.: Vol. 25). 320p. (gr. 4-7). pap. 5.95 (978-1-58182-180-2(8)) Cumberland Hse. Publishing.

—Elsie's Young Folks. unabr. ed. 1999. (Elsie Dinsmore Collection: vol. 25). (J). reprint ed. 15.00 (978-1-889128-25-2(2)) Mantle Ministries.

—Mildred's New Daughter. unabr. ed. 1999. (Mildred Keith Collection: Vol. 7). (J). reprint ed. 14.00 (978-1-889128-37-5(6)) Mantle Ministries.

Firmin, Josie. My Week. Firmin, Josie, illus. 2001. (Illus.). 12p. (J). (gr. k-k). 6.99 (978-0-7636-1548-2(X)) Candlewick Pr.

First & Foremost. 1998. (Eyewitness Fun Fax Inserts Ser.). (Illus.). (J). (gr. 4-8). pap. 2.95 (978-0-7894-3012-0(6)) Dorling Kindersley Publishing, Inc.

Flam, Chanie. By Myself. (Goldie Gold Board Book Ser.: Vol. 5). (Illus.). (J). (ps-1). bds. 4.95 (978-1-58330-029-9(5)) Feldheim Pubs.

Fleischman, Sid. El Nino Que Pagaba el Pato. 2003. (SPA., Illus.). 112p. (J). (gr. 5-8). pap. 12.95 (978-968-19-1044-0(3)) Santillana USA Publishing Co., Inc.

Fluharty, Jeff & McAndrew, Kelly. I Can't Talk Now, I'm Busy Writing Nothing. 2003. 123p. (J). (gr. 2-6). pap. 9.95 (978-1-878044-60-0(5)) Mayhaven Publishing.

Fritz, Jean. The Great Little Madison. 1998. (J). 12.64 (978-0-606-12956-5(1)) Tandem Library Bks.

Galloway, Priscilla. Snake Dreamer. 2000. (978-0-606-18109-9(1)) Tandem Library Bks.

Gantos, Jack. Jack Adrift: Fourth Grade Without a Clue. 2003. (Jack Henry Ser.). (Illus.). 208p. (J). 16.00 (978-0-374-39987-0(5) , Farrar, Straus & Giroux (BYR)) Farrar, Straus & Giroux.

—Jack Adrift: Fourth Grade Without a Clue. l.t. ed. 2004. 226p. (J). 22.95 (978-0-7862-6387-5(3)) Thorndike Pr.

—The Love Curse of the Rumbaughs. 2006. 192p. (YA). (gr. 7 up). 17.00 (978-0-374-33690-5(3) , Farrar, Straus & Giroux (BYR)) Farrar, Straus & Giroux.

Gardeski, Christina Mia. All Kinds of Kids. McMahon, Bob, illus. 2002. (Rookie Reader Espanol Ser.). 24p. (J). (gr. k-2). pap. 4.95 (978-0-516-27381-5(7) , Children's Pr.) Scholastic Library Publishing.

—All Kinds of Kids. 2002. (gr. k-3). lib. bdg. 12.95 (978-0-613-53791-9(2)) Tandem Library Bks.

Gavin, Jamila. Star Child on Clark Street. 1998. (Cambridge Reading Ser.). (Illus.). 96p. pap. 12.00 (978-0-521-47624-9(0)) Cambridge Univ. Pr.

Gebhard, Wilfried. What Eddie Can Do. Gebhard, Wilfried, illus. 2004. (Illus.). 32p. (J). 15.95 (978-1-929132-60-7(3)) Kane/Miller Bk. Pubs., Inc.

Gellman, Marc & Hartman, Thomas. Lost & Found: A Kid's Book for Living Through Loss. Tilley, Debbie, illus. 1999. 176p. (J). (gr. 3 up). 15.99 (978-0-688-15752-4(1)) HarperCollins Pubs.

George, Lindsay B. Around the World. George, Lindsay B., illus. 1999. (Who's Been Here? Ser.). (Illus.). 48p. (J). (gr. k-3). 17.99 (978-0-688-15268-0(6)) HarperCollins Pubs.

George's Story. Date not set. (J). pap. (978-1-58453-041-1(3)) Pioneer Valley Educational Pr., Inc.

Gibbons, Alan. Edge. 2006. 192p. (J). pap. 11.99 (***978-1-84255-094-6(2)***) Orion Publishing Group, Ltd. GBR. *Dist:* Independent Pubs. Group.

Gilbert, Barbara. Stone Water. 2004. 176p. (YA). pap. 7.95 (978-1-886910-12-6(X) , Lemniscaat) Boyds Mills Pr.

Gill, Janie S. Just Like You. Lambson, Elizabeth, illus. Date not set. pap. 3.95 (978-0-89868-429-2(3)); 1999. 23p. (J). lib. bdg. 10.95 (978-0-89868-428-5(5)) ARO Publishing Co.

Girdwain, Grace. With These Hands: For All the Children Around the World. 2000. (Illus.). 48p. (J). pap. 8.00 (978-0-8059-4911-7(9)) Dorrance Publishing Co., Inc.

Glassman, Miriam. Box Top Dreams. 1999. (J). 10.64 (978-0-606-15910-4(X)) Tandem Library Bks.

Goble, Paul. Lost Children. 1998. (978-0-606-13582-5(0)) Tandem Library Bks.

Golden Books Staff. Full Circle. 2000. (Golden Book Ser.). (Illus.). 84p. (J). (ps-3). pap. 2.99 (978-0-307-25713-0(4) , 25713, Golden Bks.) Random Hse. Children's Bks.

Golenbock, Peter. Hank Aaron: Brave in Every Way. Lee, Paul, illus. 2001. 32p. (J). (gr. 1-4). 16.00 (978-0-15-202093-4(4) , Gulliver Bks.) Harcourt Children's Bks.

Gonzalez, Lucia M. El Gallo de Bodas. Delacre, Lulu, illus. 1999. (ENG & SPA.). 32p. (J). (ps-2). pap. 5.99 (978-0-439-06757-7(X)) Scholastic, Inc.

Goss, Mini. When Mum Was Little. Goss, Mini, illus. 2004. (Illus.). 32p. (J). 15.95 (978-1-929132-64-5(6)) Kane/Miller Bk. Pubs., Inc.

Grannell, Cynthia. The Chairs Where Pam & Sam Sit. Munson, Deborah, illus. 1998. 16p. (J). (ps-k). pap. 5.95 (978-0-9655442-9-0(X)) Business Word, The.

Greenburg, Dan. Now You See Me... Now You Don't, Vol. 12. Davis, Jack E., illus. 1998. (Zack Files Ser.: No. 12). 64p. (J). (gr. 2-5). pap. 4.99 (978-0-448-41738-7(3) , Grosset & Dunlap) Penguin Group (USA) Inc.

Greene, Bette. Morning Is a Long Time Coming. 1999. 272p. (YA). (gr. 7-12). reprint ed. pap. 6.99 (978-0-14-130635-3(1) , Puffin) Penguin Group (USA) Inc.

—Morning Is a Long Time Coming. 2002. 20.25 (978-0-8446-7207-6(6)) Smith, Peter Pub., Inc.

—Morning Is a Long Time Coming. 1999. (978-0-606-17421-3(4)); (gr. 7-12). lib. bdg. 15.30 (978-0-613-22897-8(9)) Tandem Library Bks.

—Philip Hall Likes Me, I Reckon Maybe. l.t. ed. 2003. (Children's Large Print Ser.). (J). 28.95 (978-1-58118-107-4(8)) LRS.

—Philip Hall Likes Me, I Reckon Maybe. Lilly, Charles, illus. 1999. (Puffin Newbery Library). 144p. (J). (gr. 3-7). pap. 5.99 (978-0-14-130312-3(3) , Puffin) Penguin Group (USA) Inc.

—Philip Hall Likes Me, I Reckon Maybe. 1999. (gr. 3-6). lib. bdg. 14.15 (978-0-8085-3871-4(3)) Tandem Library Bks.

Greenes, Carol, et al. Spatial Sense. 2003. (Illus.). 60p. (J). (ps-3). 16.95 (978-0-7690-0014-5(2)) Seymour, Dale Pubns.

Grenville, Bruce, et al. Gathie Falk. 2000. (Illus.). (978-1-55054-745-0(3)) Douglas & McIntyre, Ltd.

Gugler, Laurel Dee. Facing the Day. Betteridge, Deirdre, illus. 1999. 24p. (J). (gr. k-ps). lib. bdg. 15.95 (978-1-55037-577-0(6)) Annick Pr., Ltd. CAN. *Dist:* Firefly Bks., Ltd.

Gutman, Dan. The Kid Who Ran for President. 2000. 176p. (J). (gr. 4-7). pap. 4.99 (978-0-590-93988-1(2)) Scholastic, Inc.

Haddix, Margaret Peterson. Takeoffs & Landings. 2003. (gr. 3-6). lib. bdg. 13.00 (978-0-613-61821-2(1)) Tandem Library Bks.

Hahn, Mary Downing. Following My Own Footsteps. 1998. (J). (978-0-606-13394-4(1)) Tandem Library Bks.

Hale, Beverly A. The Happiness Box. Kimmel, David, illus. 1998. 20p. (J). (ps-6). 8.00 (978-1-893687-03-5(1)) Yard Dog Pr.

Hall, Frostie. Dread Champions of the King: The Humble Beginning. 2004. (Dread Champions of the King Ser.: Bk. 1). 96p. (J). per. (978-1-55306-836-5(X)) Essence Publishing.

Hamilton, Virginia. Dustland. 1998. (Justice Cycle Ser.: Bk. 2). 214p. (YA). (gr. 6-12). pap. 4.50 (978-0-590-36217-7(8)) Scholastic, Inc.

—Dustland. 1998. (Justice Cycle Ser.). (978-0-606-12927-5(8)) Tandem Library Bks.

Hargreaves, Roger. Little Miss Bossy. 1998. (Mr. Men & Little Miss Ser.). (Illus.). 32p. (J). (gr. k up). pap. 3.99 (978-0-8431-7423-6(4) , Price Stern Sloan) Penguin Group (USA) Inc.

—Little Miss Star. 1999. (Mr. Men & Little Miss Ser.). (Illus.). 32p. (J). (gr. k up). pap. 3.99 (978-0-8431-7512-7(5) , Price Stern Sloan) Penguin Group (USA) Inc.

—Little Miss Trouble. 1998. (Mr. Men & Little Miss Ser.). (Illus.). 32p. (J). (gr. k-3). pap. 3.99 (978-0-8431-7426-7(9) , Price Stern Sloan) Penguin Group (USA) Inc.

—Mr. Impossible. 1998. (Mr. Men & Little Miss Ser.). (Illus.). 32p. (J). (gr. k up). pap. 3.99 (978-0-8431-7420-5(X) , Price Stern Sloan) Penguin Group (USA) Inc.

—Mr. Lazy. 1999. (Mr. Men & Little Miss Ser.). (Illus.). 32p. (J). pap. 3.99 (978-0-8431-7509-7(5) , Price Stern Sloan) Penguin Group (USA) Inc.

—Mr. Messy. 1998. (Mr. Men & Little Miss Ser.). (Illus.). 32p. (J). (gr. k up). pap. 3.99 (978-0-8431-7421-2(8) , Price Stern Sloan) Penguin Group (USA) Inc.

Hargreaves, Roger & Hargreaves, Roger. Mr. Tickle. Hargreaves, Roger, illus. 1998. (Mr. Men & Little Miss Ser.). (Illus.). 32p. (J). (gr. k up). pap. 3.99 (978-0-8431-7422-9(6) , Price Stern Sloan) Penguin Group (USA) Inc.

Hartmetz, Richard S. Hurray For Marvin. Dodge, Daniel, illus. 2002. 143p. (gr. 4-7). pap. 11.95 (978-0-595-21562-1(9) , Writers Club Pr.) iUniverse, Inc.

Havel, Katherine Jean. Two Houses, Two Homes... Special Me! Marcus, Tina, illus. 1998. 32p. (J). (ps-5). 17.95 (978-0-9666964-0-0(9)) Special Me!.

Hawkins, E. B. Disco Fever. 2004. 176p. (YA). pap. 8.99 (978-0-689-83755-5(0)) Simon & Schuster, Ltd. GBR. *Dist:* Independent Pubs. Group.

Hazell, Rebecca. The Barefoot Book of Heroic Children. Cann, Helen, illus. 2000. 96p. (J). (gr. 4-7). 19.95 (978-1-902283-23-4(6)) Barefoot Bks., Inc.

Heath, Kristina. Mama's Little One. Heath, Kristina, illus. 2nd rev. ed. 1998. (Illus.). 28p. (J). (ps up). pap. 10.00 (978-0-935790-05-4(5)) Muh-He-Con-Neew Pr.

Hemenway, Michele & Buchanan, Sara A. The Magic Forest, 2 vols., Set. Dobson, David, ed. unabr. ed. 1998. 72p. (J). (ps-6). pap. 24.95 incl. audio (978-1-57895-022-5(8) , Bridge Resources) Curriculum Publishing, Presbyterian Church (U. S. A.).

Henkes, Kevin. Oh! Dronzek, Laura, illus. 1999. 24p. (J). (ps-k). 14.89 (978-0-688-17054-7(4)) HarperCollins Pubs.

Hesse, Karen. Lejos del Polvo. 1999. (SPA., Illus.). 216p. (J). (gr. 4-7). 9.95 (978-84-241-5928-3(4) , EV2448) Everest de Ediciones y Distribucion, S.L. ESP. *Dist:* Lectorum Pubns., Inc.

Hoberman, Mary Ann. And to Think That We Thought That We'd Never Be Friends. 1999. (J). lib. bdg. 18.99 (978-0-679-99240-0(5)) Knopf, Alfred A. Inc.

—And to Think We Thought We'd Never. 1999. (J). 17.00 (978-0-679-89240-3(0)) Knopf, Alfred A. Inc.

Hoff, Syd. The Lighthouse Children. Hoff, Syd, illus. 2002. (Illus.). (J). 12.34 (978-0-7587-6180-4(5)) Book Wholesalers, Inc.

Hofmeister, Alan, et al. The Bat. (Reading for All Learners Ser.). (Illus.). (J). (978-1-56861-126-6(9)) Swift Learning Resources.

—Meet Mit. (Reading for All Learners Ser.). (Illus.). (J). pap. (978-1-56861-079-5(3)) Swift Learning Resources.

—The Men. (Reading for All Learners Ser.). (Illus.). (J). pap. (978-1-56861-116-7(1)) Swift Learning Resources.

—Mit Is Wet. (Reading for All Learners Ser.). (Illus.). (J). pap. (978-1-56861-108-2(0)) Swift Learning Resources.

—Sam Is Mad. (Reading for All Learners Ser.). (Illus.). (J). pap. (978-1-56861-087-0(4)) Swift Learning Resources.

—See It. (Reading for All Learners Ser.). (Illus.). (J). pap. (978-1-56861-080-1(7)) Swift Learning Resources.

—See Mat. (Reading for All Learners Ser.). (Illus.). (J). pap. (978-1-56861-078-8(5)) Swift Learning Resources.

—See Them. (Reading for All Learners Ser.). (Illus.). (J). pap. (978-1-56861-107-5(2)) Swift Learning Resources.

—Sell the Shell. (Reading for All Learners Ser.). (Illus.). (J). pap. (978-1-56861-104-4(8)) Swift Learning Resources.

—Sid. (Reading for All Learners Ser.). (Illus.). (J). pap. (978-1-56861-088-7(2)) Swift Learning Resources.

—Sit on It. (Reading for All Learners Ser.). (Illus.). (J). pap. (978-1-56861-081-8(5)) Swift Learning Resources.

—Smash It. (Reading for All Learners Ser.). (Illus.). (J). (978-1-56861-136-5(6)) Swift Learning Resources.

—To the Den. (Reading for All Learners Ser.). (Illus.). (J). (978-1-56861-138-9(2)) Swift Learning Resources.

—Up the Path. (Reading for All Learners Ser.). (Illus.). (J). pap. (978-1-56861-134-1(X)) Swift Learning Resources.

—Up We Go. (Reading for All Learners Ser.). (Illus.). (J). pap. (978-1-56861-129-7(3)) Swift Learning Resources.

—Was It Wet? (Reading for All Learners Ser.). (Illus.). (J). pap. (978-1-56861-114-3(5)) Swift Learning Resources.

—We Will See. (Reading for All Learners Ser.). (Illus.). (J). pap. (978-1-56861-089-4(0)) Swift Learning Resources.

—Who Am I? (Reading for All Learners Ser.). (Illus.). (J). pap. (978-1-56861-096-2(3)) Swift Learning Resources.

Hood, Susan. The Big Bag Big Book. 1998. (J). (ps-1). pap. 14.99 (978-0-679-88448-4(3) , Random Hse. Bks. for Young Readers) Random Hse. Children's Bks.

—Lets Jump In! 1999. (ps-2). lib. bdg. 11.80 (978-0-613-25948-4(3)) Tandem Library Bks.

Hope. Laughing Day. Anders, Tim, ed. Warner, Curt, illus. 1998. (Life Lessons Ser.). 40p. (J). (ps-3). 15.95 (978-1-885624-50-5(6)) Alpine Publishing.

Howard, Arthur. When I Was Five. Howard, Arthur, illus. 2002. (Illus.). (J). 13.19 (978-0-7587-3975-9(3)) Book Wholesalers, Inc.

—When I Was Five. 1999. (Illus.). 40p. (J). (ps-3). pap. 6.00 (978-0-15-202099-6(3) , Harcourt Paperbacks) Harcourt Children's Bks.

—When I Was Five. 1999. (gr. k-3). lib. bdg. 14.15 (978-0-613-19539-3(6)) Tandem Library Bks.

Hoye, Regena. Ala Voom, Vol. 1. Hoye, Regena, illus. 1998. (Illus.). 65p. (J). (ps-6). 12.00 (978-0-9636906-0-9(4)) Ishnuvu Publishing Co.

Hudelhoff, Allen H. Cats & Kids. 2002. 2. (Illus.). 32p. pap. 4.99 (978-0-7613-1783-8(X) , Millbrook Pr.) Lerner Publishing Group.

—Cats & Kids. Green, Anne Canevari, illus. 2002. (Silly Millies Ser.). 32p. (J). (gr. k-2). pap. 4.99 (978-0-7613-2668-7(5) , Millbrook Pr.) Lerner Publishing Group.

—Cats & Kids. 2002. (gr. k-3). lib. bdg. 13.00 (978-0-613-55805-1(7)) Tandem Library Bks.

Hutchins, Pat. Don't Get Lost! Hutchins, Pat, illus. 2004. (Illus.). 32p. (J). lib. bdg. 16.89 (978-0-06-055997-7(7)) HarperCollins Pubs.

—The Doorbell Rang. Hutchins, Pat, illus. 2005. (Illus.). (J). (ps-4). pap. 16.95 incl. audio (978-0-87499-774-3(7)) BBC Audiobooks America.

—The Doorbell Rang. Hutchins, Pat, illus. 2001. (Illus.). pap. 33.95 incl. audio (978-0-87499-776-7(3)); (J). 25.95 incl. audio (978-0-87499-775-0(5)) Live Oak Media.

Igneri, David S. The Boy & Girl Who Hated History. Wigley, Audrey Watson, illus. deluxe ed. 2000. 60p. (J). (gr. 3-9). 19.50 (978-1-57529-084-3(7)) Kabel Pubs.

Ihebereme, Chidozie . N. Dad Says Write. 2007. per. (***978-1-59872-954-2(3)***) Instantpublisher.com.

I'm Thankful Each Day. 2003. 24p. (J). bds. 6.95 (978-0-8249-4238-0(8)) Ideals Pubns.

Irgens, Barbara. An Anthology for Children. 2005. 108p. pap. 16.95 (978-1-4137-8254-7(X)) PublishAmerica, Inc.

Isadora, Rachel. Peekaboo Morning. Isadora, Rachel, illus. 2002. (Illus.). 32p. (J). (ps-1). 15.99 (978-0-399-23602-0(3) , Putnam Juvenile) Penguin Group (USA) Inc.

Jam, Teddy. Ttum. Chan, Harvey, illus. 2001. (Charlotte Stories). 110p. (J). (gr. 2-4). pap. 5.95 (978-0-88899-374-8(9)) Groundwood Bks. CAN. *Dist:* Perseus Distribution.

Jenkins, Steve. Looking Down. 2003. (Illus.). 32p. (J). (gr. k-3). pap. 5.95 (978-0-618-31098-2(3)) Houghton Mifflin Co. Trade & Reference Div.

—Looking Down. 2003. (gr. k-3). lib. bdg. 14.10 (978-0-613-60775-9(9)) Tandem Library Bks.

Jiménez, Francisco. The Circuit: Stories from the Life of a Migrant Child. 1999. Tr. of Cajas de Carton. (Illus.). 128p. (J). (gr. 5-9). tchr. ed. 16.00 (978-0-395-97902-0(1)) Houghton Mifflin Co. Trade & Reference Div.

Jinkins, Lisa Heath. Too High - First Reader: And J. Otter Noodle Stories. 1999. (Illus.). 24p. (J). bds. 2.99 (978-0-7364-0043-5(5)) Mouse Works.

Joekay, Eliza, et al. Ayagciqiartukut (We Are Going) Sparck, Amy, illus. l.t. ed. 1999. (ESK.). 8p. (J). (gr. k-3). pap. 6.00 (978-1-58084-150-4(3)) Lower Kuskokwim Schl. District.

—Ayagtukut (We Are Going) Sparck, Amy, illus. l.t. ed. 1999. (ESK.). 8p. (gr. k-3). pap. 6.00 (978-1-58084-096-5(5)) Lower Kuskokwim Schl. District.

—We Are Going. Sparck, Amy, illus. l.t. ed. 1999. 8p. (J). (gr. k-3). pap. 6.00 (978-1-58084-095-8(7)) Lower Kuskokwim Schl. District.

Johnny's Light. 1998. (PNI Healing Stories for Children Ser.). 16p. (J). (gr. k-6). 6.95 (978-1-893351-04-2(1)) Asclepian Pr.

Johns, Michael-Anne. Five: Backstage Pass. 1999. (Illus.). 48p. (gr. 5-9). pap. 5.99 (978-0-439-08797-1(X)) Scholastic, Inc.

—Five: Backstage Pass. 1999. (gr. 3-6). lib. bdg. 14.15 (978-0-613-16934-9(4)) Tandem Library Bks.

Johnson, Barbara. The Pepperoni Parade & the Power of Prayer: A Book about Prayer. Frazier, Victoria Ponikvar, illus. 1999. (Geranium Lady Ser.: Vol. 3). 32p. (J). (ps-2). 4.97 (978-0-8499-5950-9(0)) Nelson, Thomas Inc.

Johnson, Cynthia. Twenty Wiggly Toes. Kaleda, Valri Blasi, illus. 1998. 16p. (J). (ps). pap. 5.95 (978-0-9655442-4-5(9)) Business Word, The.

Johnson, Danielle. Fluffy. Thatch, Nancy R., ed. 1999. (Books for Students by Students). (Illus.). 29p. (J). (ps-3). lib. bdg. 15.95 (978-0-933849-74-7(5)) Landmark Editions, Inc.

Jones, Ayaprun L. I Am. Brunk, Cara, illus. l.t. ed. 1999. 20p. (J). (gr. k-3). pap. 25.00 (978-1-58084-070-5(1)) Lower Kuskokwim Schl. District.

Kairaiuak, Agnes, et al. Assikenqurraanka (My Favorite Things) Kairaiuak, Agnes et al, illus. l.t. ed. 1999. (ESK.). 8p. (J). (gr. k-3). pap. 6.00 (978-1-58084-161-0(9)) Lower Kuskokwim Schl. District.

—My Favorite Things. Kairaiuak, Agnes et al, illus. l.t. ed. 1999. 8p. (J). (gr. k-3). pap. 6.00 (978-1-58084-160-3(0)) Lower Kuskokwim Schl. District.

—Piniqapiaranka Cangssagqt (My Favorite Things) (Cupig) Kairaiuak, Agnes et al, illus. l.t. ed. 1999. (ESK.). 8p. (J). (gr. k-3). pap. 6.00 (978-1-58084-162-7(7)) Lower Kuskokwim Schl. District.

Kessler, Leonard. Last One in Is a Rotten Egg. Kessler, Leonard, illus. 2002. (Illus.). (J). 11.91 (978-0-7587-6178-1(3)) Book Wholesalers, Inc.

—Last One in Is a Rotten Egg. 1999. (gr. k-3). lib. bdg. 11.80 (978-0-8335-4944-0(8)) Tandem Library Bks.

Kid in the Red Jacket. 1999. (J). 9.95 (978-1-56137-635-3(3)) Novel Units, Inc.

King, Frank. Tee Tee Peetum. 2003. (Illus.). 48p. (J). pap. 14.95 (978-1-878044-65-5(6)) Mayhaven Publishing.

King-Smith, Dick. The Cuckoo Child. rev. ed. 1999. 128p. (gr. 2-6). pap. 4.99 (978-0-7868-1351-3(2)) Hyperion Pr.

Kitty Heaven's in the Sky! 2004. (J). 4.95 (***978-0-9791362-1-4(0)***) Tony Tales.

Kjelgaard, Jim. Irish Red. 1999. (J). (gr. 3-6). lib. bdg. 13.55 (978-0-8085-5413-4(1)) Tandem Library Bks.

Knights, Harry B. Angel's Star. 2006. (J). lib. bdg. 20.00 (978-0-9632248-8-0(3)) Synergetic Pubns., Inc.

Komorn, Julie. Chat, Chat, Chat. 2000. (Illus.). 96p. (J). (gr. 3-7). pap. 4.50 (978-0-439-14772-9(7)) Scholastic, Inc.

Kroll, Virginia L. On the Way to Kindergarten. Schlossberg, Elisabeth, illus. 2006. 32p. (J). (ps). 15.99 (978-0-399-24168-0(X) , Putnam Juvenile) Penguin Group (USA) Inc.

Ladybird Books Staff. 1,2,3. 1998. (First Steps Ser.). (Illus.). 32p. (J). 2.50 (978-0-7214-1875-9(9) , Dutton Juvenile) Penguin Group (USA) Inc.

Lambert, Martha. I Won't Get Lost. (Illus.). 32p. (J). (ps-2). Date not set. 5.99 (978-0-06-443679-3(9)); 2003. lib. bdg. 16.89 (978-0-06-028961-4(9)) HarperCollins Pubs.

Langley, Noel. The Land of Green Ginger. Ardizzone, Edward, illus. 2007. 176p. (J). (gr. 3 up). pap. 10.95 ***(978-1-56792-333-9(X))*** Godine, David R. Pub.

Levine, Gail Carson. The Wish. 2001. 208p. (J). (gr. 7 up). pap. 5.99 (978-0-06-447361-3(9) , Harper Trophy) HarperCollins Pubs.

—The Wish. unabr. ed. 2004. 208p. (J). (gr. 3-7). pap. 36.00 incl. audio (978-0-8072-8747-7(4) , Listening Library) Random Hse. Audio Publishing Group.

Lewis, Audrey N. Dreamseeker Wish Keeper. Lewis, Audrey N., illus. 1998. (Illus.). 32p. (J). pap. 7.95 (978-0-9668406-0-5(7)) Dreamseekers.

Lewis, Beverly. The Cul-de-Sac Kids Boxed Set: Tarantula Toes; Green Gravy; Backyard Bandit Mystery; Tree House Trouble; the Creepy Sleep-Over; & the Great TV Turn-Off. 1998. (Cul-de-Sac Kids Ser.: Vols. 13-18). 480p. (J). (gr. 2-5). pap. 23.99 (978-0-7642-8258-4(1) , 258258) Bethany Hse. Pubs.

Lichtenheld, Tom. What Are You So Grumpy About? 2007. (Illus.). 38p. (J). (ps-1). 6.99 (978-0-316-06589-4(7)) Little Brown & Co.

Lionni, Leo. Nadarin. 1998. (SPA., Illus.). 32p. (J). (ps-3). 7.95 (978-84-264-4650-3(7) , LUM6507) Lectorum Pubns., Inc.

Lohans, Alison. Skateboard Kids. 1999. (Early Chapters Bks.). 78p. (J). (gr. 1-4). pap. 4.95 (978-1-896184-64-7(2)) Roussan Pubs., Inc./Roussan Editeur, Inc. CAN. *Dist:* Orca Bk. Pubs. USA.

Lujan, Jorge Elias & Quintana, Georgina. Mas allade mi brazo. 2002. (SPA., Illus.). 24p. (J). (ps-k). 14.95 (978-0-88899-464-6(8)) Groundwood Bks. CAN. *Dist:* Perseus Distribution.

Lunn, Janet. The Umbrella Party. 1998. (Illus.). (J). (ps-k). 14.95 (978-0-88899-298-7(X)) Groundwood Bks. CAN. *Dist:* Transition Vendor.

MacDonald, Betty Bard, ed. Mrs. Piggle-Wiggle's Bad Table-Manners Cure. Whatley, Bruce, illus. 2000. (Mrs. Piggle-Wiggle Adventure Ser.). (J). 12.95 (978-0-06-027632-4(0)); 12.89 (978-0-06-027633-1(9)) HarperCollins Pubs.

MacHado, Ana Maria. El Perro del Cerro y la Rana de la Sabana. 1998. (SPA., Illus.). 28p. (J). (ps-k). pap. 14.95 (978-980-257-021-8(4)) Ekare, Ediciones VEN. *Dist:* AIMS International Bks., Inc., Kane/Miller Bk. Pubs., Inc., Lectorum Pubns., Inc.

MacKall, Dandi Daley. Meets the Jigsaw Kids, Vol. 7. 1999. (Puzzle Club Ser.: Vol. 7). 80p. (J). (gr. 1-5). pap. 4.99 (978-0-570-05475-7(3)) Concordia Publishing Hse.

Malley, Gemma. The Declaration. 2007. 320p. (J). (gr. 5 up). 16.95 ***(978-1-59990-119-0(6))*** Bloomsbury Publishing.

Maloney, Peter & Zekauskas, Felicia. Lose That Tooth! 2005. (Illus.). 32p. (J). ***(978-0-439-67639-7(8))*** Scholastic, Inc.

Marie, Evelyn. Sasha, That's Me. Stewart, Todd W., illus. 1999. 48p. (YA). (gr. 4 up). pap. 4.75 (978-1-890579-01-2(7)) Berry Bks.

Martin, Jane Read & Marx, Patricia. Now I Will Never Leave the Dinner Table. Chast, Roz, illus. 1999. (Trophy Picture Bk.). 40p. (J). (gr. k-4). pap. 5.95 (978-0-06-443556-7(3)) HarperCollins Pubs.

Mascari, Johnny. My Light @ Night. Taff, Rebecca, ed. Ott, Derek, illus. 2000. 32p. (J). (ps up). 15.95 (978-1-930413-00-9(9)) Mascari & Co.

Mast, Edward. Wolf Child: The Correction of Joseph. 1999. 54p. (J). pap. 7.00 (978-0-87602-368-6(5)) Anchorage Pr.

Masurel, Claire. Good Night! Henry, Marie H., illus. 1999. 26p. (J). (ps-k). bds. 6.95 (978-0-8118-2461-3(6)) Chronicle Bks. LLC.

Matcheck, Diane. Untitled Novel. 2009. (978-0-374-38041-0(4) , Farrar, Straus & Giroux (BYR)) Farrar, Straus & Giroux.

Matsuura, Richard & Matsuura, Ruth. Kalani & Primo. Chao, Linus, illus. (J). 8.95 (978-1-887916-03-5(2)) Orchid Isle Publishing Co.

Maxwell, E. J. Double Play. 2000. (Moffatts on the Road Ser.: No. 2). (Illus.). 112p. (J). (gr. 3-7). pap. 4.99 (978-0-439-13687-7(3)) Scholastic, Inc.

Mayo-Smith, Ian. The Children's Aviary. 1998. (Illus.). 42p. (J). (gr. 3 up). pap. 7.95 (978-1-56549-950-8(6) , Frog Bks.) Kumarian Pr., Inc.

Mazzeo Zocchi, Judy. Conflict. Vannozzi, Don, illus. 2000. (Paulie & Sasha Ser.). 32p. (J). (gr. k-4). 23.00 (978-1-891997-05-1(X)) Dingles & Co.

McCafferty, Catherine. Picture Me Grown-up. Levack, Joseph, photos by. 1999. (Picture Me Ser.). (Illus.). 10p. (J). (ps-2). bds. 6.99 (978-1-57151-576-6(3)) Playhouse Publishing.

McDalton, Magdalena, et al. I Want to Take It Home. Sparck, Carole C., illus. l.t. ed. 1999. 8p. (J). (gr. k-3). pap. 6.00 (978-1-58084-101-6(5)) Lower Kuskokwim Schl. District.

—Ut'rucugaqa. Sparck, Carole C., illus. l.t. ed. 1999. Tr. of I Want to Take It Home. (ESK.). 8p. (J). (gr. k-3). pap. 6.00 (978-1-58084-148-1(1)) Lower Kuskokwim Schl. District.

—Ut'rucugyaaqaqa. Sparck, Carole C., illus. l.t. ed. 1999. Tr. of I Want to Take It Home. (ESK.). 8p. (J). (gr. k-3). pap. 6.00 (978-1-58084-102-3(3)) Lower Kuskokwim Schl. District.

McDaniel, Lurlene. If I Should Die Before I Wake. 2005. (Illus.). 128p. (gr. 6-12). pap. 4.99 (978-1-58196-009-9(3)) Lerner Publishing Group.

—One Last Wish: Three Novels: Mother, Help Me Live; Let Him Live; Sixteen & Dying, 3 vols. in 1. 1998. (One Last Wish Ser.). 448p. (YA). (gr. 5-12). mass mkt. 7.50 (978-0-553-57142-4(7) , Laurel Leaf) Random Hse. Children's Bks.

McGee, Sherry. AppleLonia "I Like to Read" Johnson, S., illus. 1999. (Applekid's Chapter Bks.). 12p. (J). (gr. k-6). pap. 4.99 (978-0-9673591-0-6(4)) Apple Bk. Ctr.

McGrath, Barbara Barbieri & Mazzola, Frank, Jr. Kellogg's Froot Loops Counting Fun Book. 2000. (Illus.). 16p. (J). (ps up). 5.99 (978-0-694-01506-1(7) , Harper Festival) HarperCollins Pubs.

McIntyre, Agnes, et al. Angliller (Growing Up) Curtis, Katie, illus. l.t. ed. 1999. (ESK.). 8p. (J). (gr. k-3). pap. 6.00 (978-1-58084-152-8(X)) Lower Kuskokwim Schl. District.

—Anglillra Ac'uruunam (Growing Up) Curtis, Katie, illus. l.t. ed. 1999. (ESK.). 8p. (J). (gr. k-3). pap. 6.00 (978-1-58084-100-9(7)) Lower Kuskokwim Schl. District.

—Growing Up. Curtis, Katie, illus. l.t. ed. 1999. 8p. (J). (gr. k-3). pap. 6.00 (978-1-58084-099-6(X)) Lower Kuskokwim Schl. District.

McLeod, G. Ho-Nikon. 2003. 192p. pap. 14.95 (978-1-878044-58-7(3)) Mayhaven Publishing.

Merrell, Patrick. Pipsqueaks! Maze Party. 1999. (Read with Me Cartwheel Bks.). (Illus.). 32p. (ps-1). pap. 3.25 (978-0-590-03713-6(7)) Scholastic, Inc.

Merriam, Eve. Bam Bam Bam. 1998. (978-0-606-13179-7(5)) Tandem Library Bks.

Miles, Betty. The Real Me. 2000. 140p. (YA). (gr. 4-7). pap. 9.95 (978-0-595-00489-8(X)) iUniverse, Inc.

Miller, Dorothy Reynolds. The Clearing. 1998. (978-0-606-13279-4(1)) Tandem Library Bks.

Miller, Margaret. Now I'm Big. Date not set. (Illus.). 32p. (YA). (gr. 5 up). pap. 5.95 (978-0-06-050299-7(1)) HarperCollins Pubs.

Miller, Sara Swan. Better Than TV. 1998. (First Choice Chapter Book Ser.). (J). (978-0-606-13199-5(X)) Tandem Library Bks.

Milne, A. A. & Le Mair, Henriette W. Gallery of Children. 2003. (Illus.). 80p. 16.00 (978-0-7232-4666-4(1) , Penguin Global) Penguin Group (USA) Inc.

Mitchell, Adrian. Maudie & the Green Children. Hamann, Sigune, illus. 2000. 32p. (J). (gr. k-4). pap. 6.95 (978-1-896580-34-0(3)) Tradewind Bks. CAN. *Dist:* Tricycle Pr.

Modesitt, Jeanne. Mama, If You Had a Wish. 1999. (J). (978-0-606-16286-9(0)) Tandem Library Bks.

Moore, Ishbel L. Daughter. 216p. (YA). (gr. 13 up). 1999. (978-1-55074-535-1(2)); 2002. (Illus.). (978-1-55074-537-5(9)) Kids Can Pr., Ltd.

Morris, Helen. Can You Do This? Chikoyak, Andrew J. & Nevak, Caroline, illus. l.t. ed. 1999. 8p. (J). (gr. k-3). pap. 14.50 (978-1-58084-154-2(6)) Lower Kuskokwim Schl. District.

—Kuaten-qa Pituten? Chikoyak, Andrew J. & Nevak, Caroline, illus. l.t. ed. 1999. Tr. of Can you Do This?. (ESK.). 8p. (J). (gr. k-3). pap. (978-1-58084-156-6(2)) Lower Kuskokwim Schl. District.

—Waten-qaa Piyagngauten? (Can You Do This?) Chikoyak, Andrew J. & Nevak, Caroline, illus. l.t. ed. 1999. (ESK.). 8p. (J). (gr. k-3). pap. (978-1-58084-155-9(4)) Lower Kuskokwim Schl. District.

Moss, Miriam. Don't Forget I Love You. Currey, Anna, illus. 2003. 32p. (J). (ps-2). 15.99 (978-0-8037-2920-9(0) , Dial) Penguin Group (USA) Inc.

Mullican, Judy. Me! Me! Magnificent Me! Carroll, Ken, Jr., illus. l.t. ed. 1998. (Little Bks.). 8p. (J). (ps-k). pap. 10.95 (978-1-57332-108-2(7)); pap. 10.95 (978-1-57332-109-9(5)) HighReach Learning, Inc.

Namioka, Lensey. An Ocean Apart, a World Away. 2003. 208p. (YA). (gr. 7). pap. 5.99 (978-0-440-22973-5(1) , Laurel Leaf) Random Hse. Children's Bks.

Nesbit, E. Phoenix & the Carpet. 2006. pap. ***(978-1-4068-3504-5(8))*** Echo Library.

Nix, Garth. Shade's Children. 1998. 352p. (YA). (gr. 7 up). pap. 7.99 (978-0-06-447196-1(9) , Harper Trophy) HarperCollins Pubs.

No One Like You. 2000. (Sweet Dreams Ser.). 32p. (J). 9.95 (978-1-84250-159-7(3) , Bright Sparks) Parragon, Inc.

Norman, Tyler & Perez, Jose S. The Banjoman/El Hombre del Banjo. Perez, Jose S., illus. 2004. (ENG & SPA., Illus.). 32p. (J). 12.95 (978-1-57072-292-9(7)) Overmountain Pr.

Numeroff, Laura Joffe. What Daddies Do Best. Munsinger, Lynn, illus. 2003. (Classic Board Bks.). 22p. (J). bds. 6.99 (978-0-689-85973-1(2) , Little Simon) Simon & Schuster Children's Publishing.

Nye, Naomi Shihab. What Have You Lost? 2001. 224p. (YA). (gr. 7 up). pap. 10.99 (978-0-380-73307-1(2) , HarperTeen) HarperCollins Pubs.

O'Brien, Frances. Sheer Bliss. 2006. (ENG.). 144p. per. ***(978-1-905886-32-6(2))*** Troubador Publishing Ltd.

O'Loughlin, Larry. Breaking the Silence. 2001. 170p. (YA). pap. 7.95 (978-0-86327-836-5(1)) Interlink Publishing Group, Inc.

O'Malley, Kevin. Velcome. 1999. (gr. k-3). lib. bdg. 15.25 (978-0-613-30176-3(5)) Tandem Library Bks.

—Velcome. O'Malley, Kevin, illus. 1999. (Illus.). 32p. (J). (gr. k-3). reprint ed. pap. 7.95 (978-0-8027-7568-9(3)) Walker & Co.

Orr, Wendy. Peeling the Onion. 1999. (Laurel-Leaf Bks.). 176p. (YA). (gr. 7-12). mass mkt. 5.50 (978-0-440-22773-1(9) , Laurel Leaf) Random Hse. Children's Bks.

—Peeling the Onion: A Gripping Story, Told with Honesty & Biting Humour. 1999. (978-0-606-15918-0(5)); (gr. 7-12). lib. bdg. 13.00 (978-0-613-15339-3(1)) Tandem Library Bks.

Overstreet, Marcia Cate. A Day at Gramma's. 2001. (Illus.). 48p. 14.99 (978-0-8254-3471-6(8)) Kregel Pubns.

Owen. Say Cheese. 2000. (Illus.). 62p. (J). pap. 4.95 (978-0-552-52975-4(3)) Transworld Publishers Ltd. GBR. *Dist:* Trafalgar Square Publishing.

Oxenbury, Helen. Clap Hands. Oxenbury, Helen, illus. 1999. (Oxenbury Board Bks.). (Illus.). 10p. (J). (ps-k). bds. 6.99 (978-0-689-81984-1(6) , Little Simon) Simon & Schuster Children's Publishing.

—Tickle, Tickle. Oxenbury, Helen, illus. 1999. (Board Books Ser.). (Illus.). 10p. (J). (ps-k). pap. 6.99 (978-0-689-81986-5(2) , Little Simon) Simon & Schuster Children's Publishing.

Pak, Soyung. Dear Juno. Hartung, Susan Kathleen, illus. 1999. 32p. (J). (ps-2). 17.99 (978-0-670-88252-6(6) , Viking Juvenile) Penguin Group (USA) Inc.

Pancheri, Jan. The Little Angel. 2000. (Illus.). 32p. (J). (gr. 2-4). pap. 9.99 (978-0-09-926442-2(0)) Random Hse. GBR. *Dist:* Trafalgar Square Publishing.

Paterson, Katherine. Un Puente Hasta Terabithia. (SPA.). 122p. (YA). (gr. 5-8). 8.50 (978-84-279-3249-4(9) , NG0834) Noguer y Caralt Editores, S. A. ESP. *Dist:* Lectorum Pubns., Inc.

—Un Puente Hasta Terabithia. (SPA.). (YA). (gr. 5-8). 7.96 net. (978-1-56137-540-0(3) , NU5721) Novel Units, Inc.

Pausacker, Jenny. Get a Life. (Livewire Ser.). 126p. (YA). (gr. 6-9). pap. 8.99 (978-0-7043-4925-4(6)) Women's Pr., Ltd., The GBR. *Dist:* Trafalgar Square Publishing.

Peanuts. Date not set. 5.95 (978-0-89868-353-0(X)) ARO Publishing Co.

Percy, Graham, illus. The Pied Piper of Hamelin. l.t. ed. 2001. (SPA.). 28p. (ps-3). incl. audio compact disk (978-84-8214-085-8(X) , 1622) Peralt Montagut.

—The Pied Piper of Hamelin. l.t. ed. 2001. 28p. (J). (ps-3). 8.99 incl. audio (978-84-86154-38-7(3)) Peralt Montagut ESP. *Dist:* imaJen, Inc.

Perry, Louise K. & Perry, Charles E. The Treasure on Orchard Hill. 1999. 292p. pap. 12.95 (978-0-7392-0446-7(7) , PO3730) Nethope Publishing.

Peters. Revenge of the Snobs. 1998. 128p. (YA). (gr. 3-7). 13.95 (978-0-316-70603-2(5)) Little Brown & Co.

Piano, Maureen & Sykes, Christine. When Flamingos Fly. 2006. 44p. (J). 12.99 (978-1-59092-362-7(6) , Orchard Academy Pr.) Windstorm Creative.

Pierce, Tamora. Tris's Book. 1999. (Circle of Magic Ser.: No. 1). (gr. 5-8). lib. bdg. 13.00 (978-0-613-22952-4(5)); (Illus.). (J). (978-0-606-21813-9(0)) Tandem Library Bks.

Piper, Molly. Skatepark Scrapbook. 1998. 42p. (J). (gr. 4-12). pap. 5.95 (978-1-891360-03-9(5)) Little Deer Pr.

Raintree Steck-Vaughn Staff. Every Monday. 2000. (Illus.). (J). pap. 19.24 (978-0-8172-6452-9(3)) Steck-Vaughn.

Rand, Gloria. Little Flower. Alley, R. W., illus. rev. ed. 2002. 32p. (J). (gr. k-3). 16.95 (978-0-8050-6480-3(X) , Holt, Henry & Co. Bks. For Young Readers) Holt, Henry & Co.

Rau, Dana Meachen. My Special Space. 2004. (Rookie Reader Espanol Ser.). (Illus.). 31p. (J). (gr. k-2). pap. 4.95 (978-0-516-27788-2(X) , Children's Pr.) Scholastic Library Publishing.

Ready Reader Staff. Just Like Us: Short U, 6 bks., set, Level A. 2003. (J). (ps-3). 24.50 (978-0-8136-2023-7(6)) Modern Curriculum Pr.

Rey, H. A. Anybody at Home? rev. ed. 1998. (Illus.). 22p. (J). (gr. k-ps). pap. 5.95 (978-0-395-90692-7(X)) Houghton Mifflin Co. Trade & Reference Div.

Richards, Martha. Dizzy Days: My Amazing 13th Summer. Wise, Noreen, ed. 2002. (Lemonade Collection). 256p. (YA). (gr. 5 up). pap. 13.95 (978-1-58584-285-8(0)) Huckleberry Pr.

Roberts, Ken. Hiccup Champion of the World. (J). pap. 595.00 (978-0-88899-233-8(5)) Groundwood Bks. CAN. *Dist:* Transition Vendor.

Rochford, Bailey. Bailey's Tale. Stevens, John, illus. 1999. (YA). pap. (978-1-886618-01-5(1)) Rochford & Assocs., Inc.

Rollins, Pamela L. Straight & Narrow. Reeck, Karen Ann L., ed. Pryor, Donald, illus. 2000. 70p. (YA). (gr. 5-9). pap. 15.00 (978-0-9678627-0-5(1)) C.W.R. Publishing.

Romeu, Emma. Gregorio y el Mar. 2003. Tr. of Gregory & the Sea. (SPA., Illus.). 151p. (J). (gr. 5-8). pap. 15.95 (978-968-19-0316-9(1)) Santillana USA Publishing Co., Inc.

—Gregorio y el Mar. 1998. Tr. of Gregory & the Sea. (SPA.). (gr. 5-8). lib. bdg. 18.75 (978-0-613-82208-4(0)) Tandem Library Bks.

Rosen, Michael. You Wait till I'm Older Than You. (Illus.). 128p. (J). 7.95 (978-0-14-038014-9(0)) Penguin Bks., Ltd. GBR. *Dist:* Trafalgar Square Publishing.

Rosenfeld, Dina. On the Ball. Nodel, Norman, illus. 1998. (Yossi & Laibel Ser.). (J). 9.95 (978-0-922613-83-0(4)) Hachai Publishing.

Ross, Andrea. Big Surprise Day. Ross, Andrea, illus. 2000. (Illus.). 25p. (J). pap. 9.95 (978-1-887683-09-8(7)) Storybook Pr. & Productions.

Rowan, Paula S. Remember This. Mueller-Brown, Julie, illus. 1998. (World Tree Ser.). (J). (gr. 2-5). 18.95 (978-0-9654682-5-1(9)) Savannah College of Art & Design.

Rowinski, Kate. Cats in the Dark. Bishop, Bonnie, illus. 1998. 32p. (J). (ps-3). 14.95 (978-0-89272-427-7(7)) Down East Bks.

Rylant, Cynthia. Henry & Mudge under the Yellow Moon. Stevenson, Sucie, illus. unabr. ed. 1998. (Henry & Mudge Ser.). (J). (gr. k-3). 25.95 incl. audio (978-0-87499-446-9(2)) Live Oak Media.

Sanders, Stephanie. The Ingredients of A. Q. T. Pie. Pauling, Galen T., illus. 1999. 12p. (J). (ps-6). pap. 3.50 (978-0-9670875-0-4(3)) SanPaul Group, LLC, The.

Savoie, Jacques & Cote, Genevieve. La Plus Populaire du Monde. 2002. (Roman Jeunesse Ser.). (Illus.). 96p. (YA). (gr. 4-7). pap. (978-2-89021-323-4(4)) Diffusion du livre Mirabel.

Scarry, Richard. Coches y Cacharros. 1998. (Zagadki Rossiiskoi Istorii Ser.). (SPA., Illus.). 76p. (J). (ps-1). (978-84-08-01683-0(0)) GeoPlaneta, Editorial, S. A.

Schotter, Roni. Nothing Ever Happens on 90th Street. Brooker, Kyrsten, illus. 1999. 32p. (J). (gr. k-5). pap. 6.99 (978-0-531-07136-6(7) , Orchard Bks.) Scholastic, Inc.

—Nothing Ever Happens on 90th Street. 1999. (gr. k-3). lib. bdg. 14.10 (978-0-613-22888-9(0)) Tandem Library Bks.

Schwartz, Amy. Oma & Bobo. 1998. (978-0-606-13675-4(4)) Tandem Library Bks.

Scimone, Diana. Adventures with Pawpaw: China. Wiedemer, Leah, illus. 2003. 32p. (J). 8.95 (978-0-9729507-0-1(2)) Peapod Publishing, Inc.

Scruggs, Sandy. Oda al Perro Bombo. Chavez-Davalos, Laura, tr. 1999. (SPA., Illus.). 48p. (J). (gr. 4-7). pap. 11.95 (978-0-9660239-8-5(6)) Azro Pr., Inc.

Senack, J. Elaine. Memories of a Monarch. Senack, J. Elaine, illus. 2002. 32p. (J). pap. 7.95 (978-0-9712552-0-3(2)) House Finch Pr.

—Memories of a Monarch. Senack, J. Elaine, illus. 2000. (Book-a-Day Collection). (Illus.). 32p. (YA). (ps). pap. 5.95 (978-1-58584-362-6(8)) Huckleberry Pr.

The Seven Little Kids. 2005. (J). (978-1-58453-305-4(6)) Pioneer Valley Educational Pr., Inc.

Shahan, Sherry. The Little Seed. 1999. (J). pap. 3.25 (978-0-679-89131-4(5) , Random Hse. Bks. for Young Readers) Random Hse. Children's Bks.

Shank, Ned N. Sanyasin's First Day. Stock, Catherine, illus. 1999. (Accelerated Reader Bks.). 32p. (J). (gr. k-3). 15.95 (978-0-7614-5055-9(6) , Cavendish Children's Bks.) Cavendish, Marshall Corp.

Sharmat, Marjorie Weinman. Lost My Shoe. 2000. (J). (978-0-15-202008-8(X)) Harcourt Trade Pubs.

Sidney, Margaret. Five Little Peppers & How They Grew. 2007. 410p. (J). (gr. 4-7). 19.95 (978-1-55709-591-6(4)) Applewood Bks.

Skrypuch, Marsha Forchuk. The Hunger. 2004. (Illus.). 144p. pap. 7.99 (978-1-895681-16-1(2) , Boardwalk Bks.) Dundurn Group, The CAN. *Dist:* Univ. of Toronto Pr.

Smile. 1999. (J). pap. 3.95 (978-1-57560-348-3(9)) Cherry Lane Music Co.

Smith, Doris Buchanan. A Taste of Blackberries. 74p. (J). pap. 4.95 (978-0-8072-1266-0(0) , Listening Library) Random Hse. Audio Publishing Group.

Sommer, Carl. Light Your Candle. 2003. (Another Sommer-Time Story Ser.). (Illus.). 48p. (J). (gr. k-4). lib. bdg. 23.95 incl. audio compact disk (978-1-57537-768-1(3)); 16.95 incl. audio (978-1-57537-567-0(2)); 16.95 incl. audio compact disk (978-1-57537-518-2(4)); lib. bdg. 23.95 incl. audio compact disk (978-1-57537-718-6(7)) Advance Publishing, Inc.

—Light Your Candle. James, Kennon, illus. 2000. (Another Sommer-Time Story Ser.). 48p. (J). (ENG.). (gr. 1-4). 9.95 (978-1-57537-019-4(0)); (ps-4). lib. bdg. 16.95 (978-1-57537-068-2(9)) Advance Publishing, Inc.

Soros, Barbara. La Cancion de la Abuelita (Grandmother's Song) Sarfatti, Ester, tr. Morris, Jackie, illus. 2000. (SPA.). 32p. (J). (gr. 2-4). pap. 6.99 (978-1-84148-218-7(8) , BFP30477) Barefoot Bks., Inc.

Spaht-Gill, Janie. Pigouts. Reese, Bob, illus. 1998. 24p. (J). (ps-3). 5.95 (978-0-89868-317-2(3)) ARO Publishing Co.

Sprecher, John. Eric & the Angrrry Frog, Vol. 2. Forrest, James, illus. l.t. ed. Date not set. (Special Kids "Special Message" Book Ser.). 32p. (J). (gr. k-4). pap. 10.00 (978-1-892186-01-0(2)) Anythings Possible, Inc.

Stoehr, Shelley. Weird on the Outside. 2003. 224p. (YA). pap. 16.95 (978-0-595-26953-2(2) , Backinprint.com) iUniverse, Inc.

Stone, Susheila. Eid-ul-fitr. 2004. (Illus.). 32p. pap. 4.95 (978-0-7136-4083-0(9) , 93344) A & C Black GBR. *Dist:* Consortium Bk. Sales & Distribution.

Strasser, Todd. Can't Get There from Here. 208p. (YA). 2005. pap. 5.99 (978-0-689-84170-5(1) , Simon Pulse); 2004. 16.95 (978-0-689-84169-9(8)) Simon & Schuster Children's Publishing.

Stutson, Caroline. Star Comes Home. 1998. (J). (gr. 2-5). 12.95 (978-1-58021-051-5(1)) Benefactory, Inc., The.

Suen, Anastasia. Recien Nacido. Mendo, Miguel Angel, tr. from ENG. Chang, Chih-Wei, illus. 2000. (SPA.). 18p. (J). (ps-k). bds. 6.95 (978-1-880000-87-8(3)) Lee & Low Bks., Inc.

Sunderland, Margot & Hancock, Nicky. Willy & the Wobbly House: A Story for Children Who Are Anxious or Obsessional. Armstrong, Nicky, tr. Armstrong, Nicky, illus. 28p. pap. (978-0-86388-498-6(9) , 002-5058) Speechmark Publishing Ltd.

Sussex, Lucy. Altered Voices. 1999. 162p. pap. 4.99 (978-0-590-60365-2(5)) Scholastic, Inc.

Sykes, Julie. Shhh! Warnes, Tim, illus. 1999. 14p. (J). (ps-1). bds. 6.95 (978-1-888444-74-2(6)) Little Tiger Pr.

Sykes, Shelley. For Mike. 2000. (978-0-606-17835-8(X)) Tandem Library Bks.

Tang, Charles, illus. The Cereal Box Mystery. 1998. (Boxcar Children Ser.: No. 65). (J). (gr. 2-5). 10.60 (978-0-606-13214-5(7)) Tandem Library Bks.

Tarantino, Christine. Sparkles. 1998. (Illus.). 28p. (J). (ps-2). spiral bd. 5.00 (978-1-887480-88-8(9)) Words of Light International Publishing.

Tate, Eleanora E. Don't Split the Pole: Tales of down-Home Folk Wisdom. 1999. (J). (978-0-606-15815-2(4)) Tandem Library Bks.

Taylor, Sean. Purple Class & the Flying Spider. Bate, Helen, illus. 2006. 96p. (J). pap. 7.95 (978-1-84507-627-6(3)) Lincoln, Frances Ltd. GBR. *Dist:* Perseus Distribution.

TenNapel, Doug & Koelsch, Mike. Tuna Fish Tuesday. 1998. (Strange Kid Chronicles: No. 2). 80p. (J). (gr. 2-5). pap. 3.99 (978-0-590-05955-8(6)) Scholastic, Inc.

There Is a Place That Makes Your Face. 1998. (PNI Healing Stories for Children Ser.). 10p. (J). (gr. k-6). 6.95 (978-1-893351-00-4(9)) Asclepian Pr.

Thomas, Pat & Harker, Lesley. Stop Picking on Me: A First Look at Bullying. 2000. (First Look at Bks.). (Illus.). 32p. (J). (ps-3). pap. 6.95 (978-0-7641-1461-8(1)) Barron's Educational Series, Inc.

Thomassie, Tynia. Feliciana Feydra LeRoux: A Cajun Tall Tale. Smith, Cat Bowman, illus. 1998. 32p. (J). (ps-3). pap. 4.95 (978-0-316-84459-8(4)) Little Brown & Co.

Thury, Frederick. The Last Straw. van Kampen, Vlasta, illus. 1998. 26p. (J). (ps up). (978-1-55263-022-8(6)) Key Porter Bks.

Tillman, Nancy. On the Night You Were Born, 1. l.t. ed. 2005. (Illus.). 32p. (J). 17.95 (978-0-9765761-0-5(4)) Darling Pr. LLC.

Todd, Barbara. Roger Gets Carried Away. Roge, illus. 2005. 32p. (J). (ps-2). pap. 7.95 (978-1-55037-898-6(8)); lib. bdg. 19.95 (978-1-55037-899-3(6)) Annick Pr., Ltd. CAN. *Dist:* Firefly Bks., Ltd.

Torres, Leyla. El Sancocho del Sabado: Saturday Sancocho. Torres, Leyla, illus. 1999. (SPA., Illus.). 32p. (J). (ps-3). pap. 5.95 (978-0-374-42085-7(8) , Mirasol/Libros Juveniles) Farrar, Straus & Giroux.

—Saturday Sancocho. Torres, Leyla, illus. 1999. (Illus.). 32p. (J). (ps-3). pap. 6.95 (978-0-374-46451-6(0) , Sunburst) Farrar, Straus & Giroux.

Toten, Teresa. The Onlyhouse. 1998. (Northern Lights Young Novels Ser.). 112p. (J). (gr. 5-8). pap. 7.95 (978-0-88995-137-2(3)) Red Deer Pr. CAN. *Dist:* Fitzhenry & Whiteside, Ltd.

Trouble with Tuck. 1999. (J). 9.95 (978-1-56137-614-8(0)) Novel Units, Inc.

Troughton, Joanna. Tiger Child. (Illus.). 32p. (J). pap. 11.95 (978-0-14-038238-9(0)) Penguin Bks., Ltd. GBR. *Dist:* Trafalgar Square Publishing.

Truss, J. Jasmin. 2000. (J). (gr. 4-7). pap. (978-0-88899-185-0(1)) Groundwood Bks.

Vail, Emily Blake. The Grey Ghost of the Pharaoh. Barbra K. Mudd, illus. 2004. 176p. (YA). per. 8.99 (978-0-935087-27-7(3)) Wright Publishing, Inc.

Vail, Rachel. Not That I Care: Morgan. 1999. (Friendship Ring Ser.: No. 3). 240p. (J). (gr. 4-8). pap. 3.99 (978-0-439-08763-6(5)) Scholastic, Inc.

Varela, Gabrielle Charbonnet & Tiernan, Cate. Eclipse. 2002. (Sweep Ser.: 12). 192p. (YA). pap. 6.99 (978-0-14-230110-4(8) , Puffin) Penguin Group (USA) Inc.

Viorst, Judith. Super-Completely & Totally the Messiest. Glasser, Robin Preiss, illus. 2004. 32p. (J). pap. 6.99 (978-0-689-86617-3(8) , Aladdin) Simon & Schuster Children's Publishing.

Voake, Charlotte. Ginger. Voake, Charlotte, illus. 2002. (Illus.). (J). 14.79 (978-0-7587-2592-9(2)) Book Wholesalers, Inc.

—Ginger. Voake, Charlotte, illus. 2000. (Illus.). 40p. (J). (ps-2). pap. 6.99 (978-0-7636-0788-3(6)) Candlewick Pr.

—Ginger. 2000. (ps-2). lib. bdg. 15.30 (978-0-613-28496-7(8)) Tandem Library Bks.

Voss, Gisela. Picnics of New England: Recipes to Inspire & Paintings to Enchant. 1998. (Illus.). 72p. (J). (ps-3). 14.95 (978-0-87846-408-1(5)) Museum of Fine Arts, Boston.

Wallace, Bill. Running Wild: Upchuck & the Rotten Willy. 1998. (Upchuck & the Rotten Willy Ser.). (Illus.). 112p. (J). (gr. 4-7). pap. 5.99 (978-0-671-01415-5(3) , Aladdin) Simon & Schuster Children's Publishing.

Waterstone, Rachel. The Much Too Loved Quilt. Webster, Marnie, illus. 1999. 24p. (J). (gr. k-4). 13.95 (978-1-890326-15-9(1)) First Story Pr.

Weatherill, Steve. Good Night Goz. 1999. (Baby Goz Bks.). (Illus.). 16p. (J). (ps). pap. 7.99 (978-0-7112-1020-2(9)) Lincoln, Frances Ltd. GBR. *Dist:* Transition Vendor.

Weber, Lenora Mattingly. The Beany Malone Set, 14 bks., Set. Howe, Gertrude, illus. 1999. (Collection of the Beany Malone Ser.). (J). pap. 167.30 (978-1-930009-08-0(9)) Image Cascade Publishing.

—Make a Wish for Me. 1999. (Beany Malone Ser.). 286p. (J). reprint ed. pap. 12.95 (978-0-9639607-8-8(4)) Image Cascade Publishing.

Weninger, Brigitte. Dany, Mira lo Que Has Hecho! 1999. (gr. k-3). (SPA.). lib. bdg. 15.25 (978-0-613-81373-0(1)); 13.75 (978-0-606-17631-6(4)) Tandem Library Bks.

Wiggins, Everett. The Glitter Machine. 1999. 9p. (J). (ps-6). 6.00 (978-0-9677274-0-0(5)) BlacKat Publishing.

Wignall, Mike. Homer & Olivia: Handles Teasing & Overcome Friendship Problems. Miele, Bob, illus. 1998. 50p. (J). (gr. 2-5). pap. 10.95 (978-1-57543-062-1(2)) MAR*CO Products, Inc.

Wilhelm, Hans. Chico Valiente Como Yo. (SPA.). 32p. (J). 13.95 (978-84-261-2658-0(8)) Juventud, Editorial ESP. *Dist:* AIMS International Bks., Inc.

Williams, Cynthia G. Enid & the Great Idea. Harper, Betty, illus. 2000. (Our Neighborhood Ser.). 32p. (J). (ps-5). 11.99 (978-0-8054-1886-6(5)) B&H Publishing Grp.

Williamson Kids Can!, 6 bks. Incl. Hands Around the World. Milord, Susan. Milord, Susan, illus. 160p. 1999. lib. bdg. 25.26 (978-0-8368-2231-1(5)); Kids Create! Carlson, Laurie M. Trezzo-Braren, Loretta, illus. 160p. 1999. lib. bdg. 25.26 (978-0-8368-2232-8(3)); Kids' Multicultural Art Book. Terzian, Alexandra M. 160p. 1999. lib. bdg. 25.26 (978-0-8368-2233-5(1)); Kids' Nature Book. Milord, Susan. 144p. 1997. lib. bdg. 25.26 (978-0-8368-1967-0(5)); Kids' Science Book : Creative Experiences for Hands-on Fun. Hirschfeld, Robert & White, Nancy. 144p. 1997. lib. bdg. 25.26 (978-0-8368-1968-7(3)); Kids' Wildlife Book. Shedd, Warner. 144p. 1997. lib. bdg. 25.26 (978-0-8368-1969-4(1)); (J). (gr. 3 up). (Illus.). Set lib. bdg. 151.60 (978-0-8368-2255-7(2)) Stevens, Gareth Inc.

Wilson, Jacqueline. The Suitcase Kid. 2001. (Yearling Book Ser.). (Illus.). 32p. 9.95 (978-0-440-86311-3(2) , Corgi) Transworld Publishers Ltd. GBR. *Dist:* Trafalgar Square Publishing.

—Suitcase Kid. 1998. (978-0-606-13823-9(4)) Tandem Library Bks.

Wilson, Nancy Hope. Becoming Felix. 1998. 192p. (J). (gr. 3-7). pap. 3.99 (978-0-380-72945-6(8)) HarperCollins Pubs.

Winthrop. Trade. 1999. (J). pap. 1.00 (978-0-316-94751-0(2)) Little Brown & Co.

Wishinsky, Frieda. Each One Special. Zimmermann, H. Werner, illus. 1999. 32p. (J). (ps-3). 14.95 (978-1-55143-122-2(X)) Orca Bk. Pubs. USA.

Wynne-Jones, Tim. The Maestro. 1998. (J). (978-0-606-13587-0(1)) Tandem Library Bks.

Zamorano, Ana. A Comer! Vivas, Julie, illus. 1999. (SPA.). 32p. (J). (gr. k-1). pap. 5.99 (978-0-439-07191-8(7) , SO3216, Scholastic en Espanol) Scholastic, Inc.

Zemach, Margot. Siempre Puede Ser Peor. Marcuse, Aida E., tr. Zemach, Margot, illus. 1999. (SPA., Illus.). 32p. (J). (ps-3). pap. 6.95 (978-0-374-46459-2(6) , FS4436, Mirasol/Libros Juveniles) Farrar, Straus & Giroux.

—Siempre Puede Ser Peor. 1999. (SPA.). (gr. k-3). lib. bdg. 15.25 (978-0-613-22935-7(5)) Tandem Library Bks.

Zidrou. Ducoboo: In the Corner! Godi, illus. 2007. 48p. pap. 9.99 (***978-1-905460-26-7(0)***) CineBook GBR. *Dist:* Biblio Distribution.

CHILDREN—FOREIGN COUNTRIES

Berry, Joy. Mine & Yours: Human Rights for Kids. Richardson, Nicole, illus. 2005. 46p. (J). (gr. 3-7). pap. 8.95 (978-1-57687-260-4(2) , PowerHouse Kids) powerHouse Cultural Entertainment, Inc.

Blackbirch Press Staff, contrib. by. Ituko: An Inuit Child. 2005. (Children of the World Ser.). (Illus.). 24p. (gr. k-3). 22.45 (978-1-4103-0282-3(2) , Blackbirch Pr., Inc.) Thomson Gale.

Churba, Amy. Children of the Earth. Paltrow, Bob, illus. 1998. 32p. (J). (ps-3). 15.95 (978-0-9662777-0-8(8)) Pleiades Publishing.

Gioanni, Alain. Thanassis: A Child of Greece. 2005. (Children of the World Ser.). (Illus.). 24p. (J). (gr. k-3). 22.45 (978-1-4103-0284-7(9) , Blackbirch Pr., Inc.) Thomson Gale.

Hollyer, Beatrice. Let's Eat: What Children Eat Around the World. rev. ed. 2004. (Illus.). 48p. (J). 16.95 (978-0-8050-7322-5(1) , Holt, Henry & Co. Bks. For Young Readers) Holt, Henry & Co.

Kaltenhauser, Bettina & van Swol-Ulbrich, Hilly. When Abroad - Do As the Local Children Do: Ori's Guide for Young Expats. 2004. (Illus.). 112p. (J). pap. 15.95 (978-90-5594-262-6(6)) Cyan Communications GBR. *Dist:* Independent Pubs. Group.

Leventhal, Debra. What Is Your Language? 1998. (Picture Puffin Ser.). (J). (978-0-606-13901-4(X)) Tandem Library Bks.

CHILDREN—FOREIGN COUNTRIES—FICTION

DeLoach, Sylvia & Massey, Barbara. A Country for Katie. 1998. (Child Like Me Ser.). 32p. (J). (gr. 1-6). pap. 6.99 (978-1-56309-259-6(X) , N987106) New Hope Pubs.

CHILDREN—GREAT BRITAIN

Chrisp, Peter. The Middle Ages. rev. ed. 2004. (Come & Discover My World Ser.). (Illus.). 32p. (gr. 2-5). (J). pap. 7.95 (978-1-58728-069-6(8)); 14.95 (978-1-58728-063-4(9)) T&N Children's Publishing. (Two Can Publishing).

—The Middle Ages. 2000. (My World Ser.). (Illus.). (J). (978-0-606-21950-1(1)) Tandem Library Bks.

Foreman, Michael. After the War was Over. 2007. (Illus.). 96p. (J). pap. 16.99 (***978-1-84365-088-1(6)***) Anova Bks. GBR. *Dist:* Independent Pubs. Group.

Fox, Anne L. & Abraham-Podietz, Eva. Ten Thousand Children: True Stories Told by Children Who Escaped the Holocaust on the Kindertransport. 1998. (Illus.). 128p. (J). (gr. 4-7). pap. 12.95 (978-0-87441-648-0(5)) Behrman Hse., Inc.

Jackson, Ellen B. Turn of the Century. Ellis, Jan Davey, illus. 1998. 32p. (J). (gr. 2-7). 17.95 (978-0-88106-369-1(X)) Charlesbridge Publishing, Inc.

Ross, Michael Elsohn. Children of Northern Ireland. Rigau, Felix, photos by. 2000. (World's Children Ser.). (Illus.). 48p. (J). (gr. 3-6). (978-1-57505-433-9(7) , Carolrhoda Bks.) Lerner Publishing Group.

Stalcup, Ann. On the Home Front: Growing up in Wartime England. 1998. (Illus.). xvi, 91p. (J). (gr. 3-6). lib. bdg. 19.50 (978-0-208-02482-4(4) , Linnet Bks.) Shoe String Pr., Inc.

CHILDREN—GROWTH

Allen, Jeffrey S. & Klein, Roger J. Ready, Set, R. E. L. A. X. A Research-Based Program of Relaxation, Learning, & Self-Esteem for Children. Watts, Julie C. & Holden, Matthew, illus. 2003. 204p. (J). (ps-8). pap. 23.95 (978-0-9636027-0-1(5)) Inner Coaching.

Angliss, Sarah. The Production Line: Reproduction & Growing Up. 1999. (Human Machine Ser.). (Illus.). 32p. (J). lib. bdg. 16.95 (978-1-929298-20-4(X)) Chrysalis Education.

Douglas, Ann. Baby Science: How Babies Really Work! Desputeaux, Helene, illus. 2004. 32p. (J). (gr. k-4). reprint ed. pap. 7.00 (978-0-7567-8455-3(7)) DIANE Publishing Co.

—Baby Science: How Babies Really Work! Desputeaux, Helene, illus. 1998. 32p. (J). (ps-3). 18.95 (978-1-895688-83-2(3)); pap. 6.95 (978-1-895688-84-9(1)) Maple Tree Pr. CAN. (Owl Bks.). *Dist:* Firefly Bks., Ltd.

Liddell, Sharen & Cathcart, Yvonne. Being Big. (FRE., Illus.). (J). pap. 7.99 (978-0-590-24378-0(0)) Scholastic, Inc.

Madaras, Lynda. On Your Mark, Get Set, Grow! A "What's Happening to My Body?" Book for Younger Boys. Gilligan, Paul, illus. 2008. 128p. (YA). 22.00 (***978-1-55704-780-9(4)***); pap. 12.00 (***978-1-55704-781-6(2)***) Newmarket Pr.

Madaras, Lynda. Ready, Set, Grow! A What's Happening to My Body? Book for Younger Girls. Davick, Linda, tr. Davick, Linda, illus. 2003. 128p. (YA). (gr. 3 up). pap. 12.00 (978-1-55704-565-2(8) , Newmarket Shooting Scripts) Newmarket Pr.

—Ready, Set, Grow! A What's Happening to My Body? Book for Younger Girls. 2003. (gr. 3-6). lib. bdg. 21.10 (978-0-613-68537-5(7)) Tandem Library Bks.

Marzollo, Jean. How Kids Grow. Sheehan, Nancy, illus. 1998. 32p. (J). (ps-2). pap. 3.25 (978-0-590-45062-1(X)) Scholastic, Inc.

McManus, Valerie Rainon. A Look in the Mirror: Freeing Yourself from the Body Image Blues. 2004. 110p. pap. 14.95 (978-0-87868-897-5(8) , 8978, Child & Family Pr.) Child Welfare League of America, Inc.

Meredith, S. Growing Up. 56p. (J). lib. bdg. 15.95 (978-1-58086-754-2(5) , Usborne) EDC Publishing.

Meredith, Susan. Growing Up. 2004. (Facts of Life Ser.). 56p. (J). pap. 7.95 (978-0-7945-0764-0(6) , Usborne) EDC Publishing.

O'Brien-Palmer, Michelle. Watch Me Grow: Fun Ways to Learn about Cells, Bones, Muscles, Joints. Lee, Fran, illus. 1999. 144p. (J). (gr. k-4). pap. 14.95 (978-1-55652-367-0(X)) Chicago Review Pr., Inc.

Parker, Steve. Tell Me How Does My Body Fit Together? And More about the Human Body. 2004. (Illus.). 32p. (J). pap. (978-1-84458-058-3(X)) Chrysalis Children's Bks.

Thomasson, Merry F. Hey, Look at Me! Baby Days. Kopald, Sue-Anne, illus. (Hey, Look at Me! Ser.). (J). (978-1-882607-06-8(6)) Merrybooks & More.

CHILDREN—HEALTH AND HYGIENE

Here are entered general works on the physical care of children. Works limited to their physical care in school are entered under School Hygiene.

see also Babysitters; Children—Diseases; Children—Hospitals; Health Education; Nurses and Nursing; School Nursing

Adamson, Heather. A Day in the Life of a Child Care Worker. 2003. (First Facts Ser.). (Illus.). 24p. (J). 15.95 (978-0-7368-2504-7(5)) Capstone Pr., Inc.

Amos, Janine. Hospital. Green, Gwen, illus. Hampton, Angela, photos by. 2002. (Separations Ser.). 32p. (J). (gr. 3 up). lib. bdg. 23.33 (978-0-8368-3091-0(1)) Stevens, Gareth Inc.

Becker, Lynne, creator. Me Too Mommy. 2004. (J). spiral bd. 11.95 (978-0-9748889-0-3(7)) Lynne Ellen, Inc.

Benett, Janet M. IJustWantTo SLEEP for KIDS. Kater, Mary, ed. Linke, Donald Q., Jr., illus. 2005. (J). 56.97 net. (978-0-9744357-0-1(8)) IJustWantToSleep, Inc.

Birch. Head Lice up Close 6 Pack. 2004. pap. 40.50 (978-1-4109-1154-4(3)) Harcourt Schl. Pubs.

A Boy's Guide to Growing up. 2005. (Illus.). tchr. ed. 22.95 (978-1-55942-210-9(6)) Marsh Media.

Child Care Careers (AVA) 2001. (YA). pap. 6.00 (978-1-57078-012-7(9)); pap. 8.00 (978-1-57078-013-4(7) , CEV00013) C E V Multimedia, Ltd.

Cox, Judith. The Wellness Tree. Rogers, Denny, illus. 2003. 32p. (J). (gr. k-4). 19.95 (978-1-878044-29-7(X)) Mayhaven Publishing.

Demuth, Patricia B. Look! My Tooth Is Loose! 2002. (gr. k-3). lib. bdg. 15.30 (978-0-613-72490-6(9)) Tandem Library Bks.

Dollar, Ellen Painter. Growing up with OI: A Guide for Children. 2001. (J). pap. 10.00 (978-0-9642189-2-5(5)) Osteogenesis Imperfecta Foundation.

Dorling Kindersley Publishing Staff, ed. Baby & Child Safety. 2004. (Johnson's Everyday Babycare Ser.). (Illus.). 64p. pap. 8.00 (978-0-7566-0568-1(7)) Dorling Kindersley Publishing, Inc.

Duckworth, Katie. Health. 2004. (Children's Rights Ser.). (J). lib. bdg. 27.10 (978-1-58340-420-1(1)) Smart Apple Media.

Ehrlich, Fred & Ziefert, Harriet. You Can't Take Your Body to a Repair Shop. Haley, Amanda, illus. 2007. 36p. pap. 6.95 (***978-1-59354-625-0(4)***) Handprint Bks.

EMP International Inc., Staff. Be Cool-Play It Safe (Video & Book Set for Hearing Impaired) A Children's Safety Video & Accompanying Activity Book. 1999. (Illus.). 24p. (J). (ps-4). wbk. ed. 19.95 incl. VHS (978-0-940430-92-1(4)) EMP International.

Englehart. Early Childhood Health & Safety Curriculum. 1999. 80p. (J). (gr. k-2). pap. 10.99 (978-0-513-02375-8(5) , TSD23755, Instructional Fair) Schaffer, Frank Pubns.

Galvin, Matthew. Clouds & Clocks: A Story for Children Who Soil. Weber, M. S., illus. 2nd ed. 2007. 32p. (J). (ps-3). 14.95 (***978-1-59147-733-4(6)***); pap. 8.95 (***978-1-59147-734-1(4)***) American Psychological Assn. (Magination Pr.).

Glaser, Jason. Food Allergies. 2007. (First Facts Ser.). (Illus.). 24p. (J). 21.26 (978-0-7368-6391-9(5)) Capstone Pr., Inc.

Good Health. 1999. (SmartReader Ser.). (J). pap., tchr. ed. 19.95 incl. audio (978-0-7887-0125-2(8) , 79313T3) Recorded Bks., LLC.

Gorman, Jacqueline Laks. Dentist/El Dentista. Acosta, Tatiana & Gutiérrez, Guillermo, trs. 2002. (Weekly Reader Early Learning Library). (SPA & ENG., Illus.). 24p. (J). (ps up). lib. bdg. 19.33 (978-0-8368-3307-2(4) , Weekly Reader Early Learning Library) Stevens, Gareth Inc.

Gorman, Jacqueline Laks & Macken, JoAnn Early. Dentist/El Dentista. Coffey, Colleen & Carrillo, Consuelo, trs. Andersen, Gregg, photos by. 2002. (Weekly Reader Early Learning Library). (ENG & SPA., Illus.). 24p. (J). (ps up). pap. 5.95 (978-0-8368-3341-6(4) , Weekly Reader Early Learning Library) Stevens, Gareth Inc.

Harcourt School Publishers Staff. Trofeos Advanced Level: Nos Visita el Medico. 3rd ed. 2002. (SPA., Illus.). pap. 6.80 (978-0-15-323941-0(7)) Harcourt Schl. Pubs.

Harris-Johnson, Debrah. African-American Teenagers Guide to Personal Growth, Health, Saftey, Sex An. 2001. (gr. 7-12). lib. bdg. 30.35 (978-0-613-90283-0(1)) Tandem Library Bks.

Health Watch, 14 bks., Set. Incl. Alzheimer's Disease. Gold, Susan Dudley. (YA). 2000. lib. bdg. 23.93 (978-0-7660-1650-7(1)); Arthritis. Gold, Susan Dudley. (YA). 2001. lib. bdg. 23.93 (978-0-7660-1659-0(5)); Asthma. Gold, Susan Dudley. (J). 2000. lib. bdg. 23.93 (978-0-7660-1656-9(0)); Attention Deficit Disorder. Gold, Susan Dudley. (YA). 2000. lib. bdg. 23.93 (978-0-7660-1657-6(9)); Bipolar Disorder & Depression. Gold, Susan Dudley. (YA). 2000. lib. bdg. 23.93 (978-0-7660-1654-5(4)); Cancer. Gold, John Coopersmith. (YA). 2001. lib. bdg. 23.93 (978-0-7660-1652-1(8)); Cerebral Palsy. Gold, John Coopersmith. (YA). 2001. lib. bdg. 23.93 (978-0-7660-1663-7(3)); Cystic Fibrosis. Gold, Susan Dudley. (YA). 2000. lib. bdg. 23.93 (978-0-7660-1655-2(2)); Diabetes. Semple, Carol McCormick. (YA). 2000. lib. bdg. 23.93 (978-0-7660-1660-6(9)); Epilepsy. Dudley, Mark Edward. (YA). 2001. lib. bdg. 23.93 (978-0-7660-1661-3(7)); Heart Disease. Gold, John Coopersmith. (YA). 2000. lib. bdg. 23.93 (978-0-7660-1653-8(6)); Multiple Sclerosis. Gold, Susan Dudley. (YA). 2001. lib. bdg. 23.93 (978-0-7660-1658-3(7)); Muscular Dystrophy. Burnett, Gail Lemley. (YA). 2000. lib. bdg. 23.93 (978-0-7660-1651-4(X)); Sickle Cell Disease. Gold, Susan Dudley. (YA). 2001. lib. bdg. 23.93 (978-0-7660-1662-0(5)); 48p. (gr. 4-10). (Illus.). Set lib. bdg. 265.30 (978-0-7660-1606-4(4)) Enslow Pubs., Inc.

Hulme, Janet A. Bladder & Bowel Issues for Kids: A Handy Guide for Kids Ages 4-12. 2003. (Illus.). 92p. pap. 14.95 (978-1-928812-05-0(8) , 4000-07) Phoenix Publishing.

J. G. Ferguson Publishing Company Staff, contrib. by. Careers in Focus: Child Care. 2006. (Careers in Focus Ser.). (Illus.). 176p. (J). (gr. 6-12). 29.95 (978-0-8160-6565-3(9) , Ferguson Publishing Co.) Facts On File, Inc.

Keller, Kristin Thoennes. Health Care for Infants & Toddlers. 2000. (Skills for Teens Who Parent Ser.). (Illus.). 64p. (J). (gr. 4-6). lib. bdg. 23.93 (978-0-7368-0704-3(7) , LifeMatters Bks.) Capstone Pr., Inc.

Leeper, Angela. I Care. 2004. (You & Me Ser.). (J). (978-1-4034-6082-0(5)) Heinemann Library.

Lorig, Steffanie. Oodles de Doodles. 2005. Orig. Title: Oodles of Doodles. (SPA., Illus.). 48p. (YA). (gr. 2 up). 10.95 (978-0-9715240-3-3(3)) Art With Heart Press.

Masoff, Joy. The Boo Boo Book. Dickason, Jack, illus. 2006. 20p. (J). 9.95 (978-1-57990-710-5(5)) Lark Bks.

Mattern, Joanne. Eating Lunch at School. 2006. 24p. (J). pap. (978-0-8368-6791-6(2)); lib. bdg. (978-0-8368-6784-8(X)) Stevens, Gareth Inc.

—I Use Math at the Doctor's: Uso Las Matematicas en el Médico. 2005. (Illus.). 24p. (SPA.). pap. (978-0-8368-6006-1(3)); (ENG & SPA., lib. bdg. 19.33 (978-0-8368-5999-7(5)) Stevens, Gareth Inc.

McAlpine, Margaret. Working with Children. 2004. (My Future Career Ser.). (Illus.). 64p. lib. bdg. 26.00 (978-0-8368-4241-8(3)) Stevens, Gareth Inc.

McCoy, Kathy & Wibbelsman, Charles. Growing & Changing: A Handbook for Preteens. rev. ed. 2003. (Illus.). 224p. (gr. 12). pap. 14.95 (978-0-399-52898-9(9) , Perigee Trade) Penguin Group (USA) Inc.

McGrath, Tom. When You're Sick or in the Hospital: Healing Help for Kids. McGrath, Tom & Alley, R. W., illus. 2002. (Elf-Help Books for Kids). (J). per. 6.95 (978-0-87029-367-2(2)) Abbey Pr.

Minden, Cecilia. Lunch by the Numbers. 2008. (J). lib. bdg. 25.26 (***978-1-60279-012-4(4)***) Cherry Lake Publishing.

Montanari, Donata. Children Around the World. Montanari, Donata, illus. (Illus.). 32p. (J). (gr. k-3). 2004. (978-1-55337-684-2(6)); 2001. (978-1-55337-064-2(3)) Kids Can Pr., Ltd.

Nelson, Robin. Staying Safe in Emergencies. 2006. (Pull Ahead Books). (Illus.). 32p. (J). 22.60 (978-0-8225-3391-7(X) , Lerner Pubns.) Lerner Publishing Group.

Nygard, Bonnie, et al. Wow! Cody Investigates the World of Wellness. 2005. (World of Wellness Health Education Ser.). (Illus.). 88p. 19.00 (978-0-7360-6230-5(0)) Human Kinetics Pubs.

—Wow! Ruby Explores the World of Wellness. 2005. (World of Wellness Health Education Ser.). (Illus.). 88p. 19.00 (978-0-7360-6229-9(7)) Human Kinetics Pubs.

—Wow! Ruby Learns about the World of Wellness. 2005. (World of Wellness Health Education Ser.). (Illus.). 88p. 19.00 (978-0-7360-6228-2(9)) Human Kinetics Pubs.

—Wow! Sydney Travels Through the World of Wellness. 2005. (World of Wellness Health Education Ser.). (Illus.). 88p. 19.00 (978-0-7360-6232-9(7)) Human Kinetics Pubs.

—Wow! T.J.'s Adventures in the World of Wellness. 2005. (World of Wellness Health Education Ser.). (Illus.). 88p. 19.00 (978-0-7360-6231-2(9)) Human Kinetics Pubs.

Nygard, Bonnie K., et al. Wow! Ruby Learns about the World of Wellness: Big Book - Orange Level. 2005. (World of Wellness Health Education Ser.). (Illus.). 40p. 79.00 (978-0-7360-5757-8(9)) Human Kinetics Pubs.

—Wow! Sydney Travels Through the World of Wellness: Student Book - Purple Level. 2005. (World of Wellness Health Education Ser.). (Illus.). 88p. pap. 12.00 (978-0-7360-5580-2(0)) Human Kinetics Pubs.

Petty, Kate. Going to the Dentist. 2007. (J). (***978-1-59604-158-5(7)***) Stargazer Bks.

Quinlan, Kathryn A. Child Care Worker. (Careers Without College Ser.). 48p. pap. 6.95 (978-0-7368-8541-6(2) , LifeMatters Bks.) Capstone Pr., Inc.

Rabe, Tish. Oh the Things You Can Do That Are Good for You. Ruiz, Aristides, illus. 2001. (Cat in the Hat's Learning Library). 48p. (J). (gr. k-3). lib. bdg. 11.99 (978-0-375-91098-2(0) , Random Hse. Bks. for Young Readers) Random Hse. Children's Bks.

—Oh the Things You Can Do That Are Good for You! All About Staying Healthy. Ruiz, Aristides, illus. 2001. (Cat in the Hat's Learning Library). 48p. (J). (gr. k-3). 8.99 (978-0-375-81098-5(6) , Random Hse. Bks. for Young Readers) Random Hse. Children's Bks.

Radabaugh, Melinda Beth. Going to the Dentist. 2003. (First Time Ser.). (Illus.). 24p. (J). pap. 5.50 (978-1-4034-0467-1(4)); lib. bdg. 18.50 (978-1-4034-0228-8(0)) Heinemann Library.

—Going to the Doctor. 2003. (First Time Ser.). (J). pap. 5.50 (978-1-4034-0468-8(2)); (Illus.). 24p. lib. bdg. 18.50 (978-1-4034-0229-5(9)) Heinemann Library.

Royston, Angela. Get Some Rest! 2003. (Illus.). 32p. (J). pap. (978-1-4034-4451-6(X)) Heinemann Library.

—Keep Healthy! 2003. (Illus.). 32p. pap. 6.95 (978-1-4034-4450-9(1)); (J). lib. bdg. (978-1-4034-4441-7(2)) Heinemann Library.

—Staying Healthy. 2004. (My Amazing Body Ser.). (Illus.). 32p. 25.70 (978-1-4109-0484-3(9)) Raintree.

Sacks, Janet. The Human Body. Smith, Jan, illus. 2004. (Magic Color Bks.). 12p. (J). 9.95 (978-1-4027-1214-2(6)) Sterling Publishing Co., Inc.

Salzmann, Mary Elizabeth. Being Active. 2004. (Healthy Habits Ser.). (Illus.). 23p. (J). (ps-3). lib. bdg. 19.93 (978-1-59197-550-2(6)) ABDO Publishing Co.

—Healthy Habits. 2004. (Illus.). (J). (ps-3). lib. bdg. 119.58 (978-1-59197-549-6(2) , SandCastle) ABDO Publishing Co.

Schaefer, Lola M. What Is Good for You? 2007. (J). (978-1-59515-926-7(6)) Rourke Publishing, LLC.

Sears, William, et al. You Can Go to the Potty. Andriani, Renee W., illus. 2002. 32p. (J). (ps-ps). 12.99 (978-0-316-78888-5(0)) Little, Brown Bks. for Young Readers.

Silverstein, Alvin, et al. Headaches. 2002. (My Health Ser.). (Illus.). 48p. (J). (gr. 3-5). pap. 6.95 (978-0-531-16561-4(2) , Watts, Franklin) Scholastic Library Publishing.

Simon, Charnan. My Mother Is a Doctor. Girouard, Patrick, illus. 2006. (Magic Door to Learning Ser.). 24p. (J). (gr. k-2). 21.36 (978-1-59296-620-2(9)) Child's World, Inc.

Snyder, Inez. Doctor Tools. 2002. (Welcome Bks.). 24p. (J). (ps-2). pap. 4.95 (978-0-516-24036-7(6) , Children's Pr.) Scholastic Library Publishing.

Spilsbury, Louise. Why Should I Wash My Hair? And Other Questions about Healthy Skin & Hair. 2003. (Body Matters Ser.). (Illus.). 32p. (J). lib. bdg. 16.95 (978-1-4034-4685-5(7)) Heinemann Library.

Stuhring, Celeste & Stuhring, Glen T. Kid Sitter Basics: A Handbook for Babysitters. Young and Company Staff, ed. 4th ed. 1999. 104p. (YA). (gr. 5-11). pap. 12.95 (978-0-9676448-6(1)) Kid Safety Plus.

Take Care of Your Skin, Hair & Nails! With Annie Funelli & the Funsters. 2003. (Lessons for a Healthy Childhood Ser.). (J). (gr. k-3). instr.'s gde. ed. 69.95 (978-1-55942-195-9(9) , 9236V9) Marsh Media.

Townsend, John. Nasty Bugs & Ghastly Medicine. 2006. (Illus.). 48p. (978-1-4109-1868-0(8)) Steck-Vaughn.

Vogel, Elizabeth. A Lavarse Las Manos! 2004. (Limpieza y Salud Todo el Dia Ser.). (SPA & ENG., Illus.). 24p. (J). lib. bdg. 16.00 (978-0-8239-6619-6(4) , Buenas Letra) Rosen Publishing Group, Inc., The.

—Let's Exercise. 2001. (PowerKids Readers Ser.). (Illus.). 24p. (J). (gr. 1). lib. bdg. 16.00 (978-0-8239-5687-6(3) , PKEXER, PowerKids Pr.) Rosen Publishing Group, Inc., The.

—Let's Exercise = a Hacer Ejercicio. 2004. (Limpieza y salud todo el Dia Ser.). (ENG & SPA., Illus.). 24p. (J). lib. bdg. 16.00 (978-0-8239-6615-8(1) , Buenas Letra) Rosen Publishing Group, Inc., The.

Walker, Linda. Living after Chernobyl: Ira's Story. 2005. (Illus.). 48p. (YA). (gr. 6-9). lib. bdg. 30.00 (978-0-8368-5957-7(X) , World Almanac Library) Stevens, Gareth Inc.

Williams, Julie. Skin & Nails: Care Tips for Girls. Banner, Shawn, illus. 2003. (American Girl Library). 64p. pap. 9.95 (978-1-58485-793-8(5)) American Girl Publishing, Inc.

World Book, Inc. Staff, contrib. by. Eating for Health, 5 vols., Vol. 3. 2002. (Illus.). (J). (978-0-7166-6703-2(7)) World Bk., Inc.

—Looking Your Best, 5 vols., Vol. 2. 2002. (Illus.). (J). (978-0-7166-6702-5(9)) World Bk., Inc.

—Recognizing Your Emotions, 5 vols., Vol. 5. 2002. (Illus.). (J). (978-0-7166-6705-6(3)) World Bk., Inc.

—Stayin in Shape, 5 vols., Vol. 1. 2002. (Illus.). (J). (978-0-7166-6701-8(0)) World Bk., Inc.

—Understanding Sexuality, 5 vols., Vol. 4. 2002. (Illus.). (J). (978-0-7166-6704-9(5)) World Bk., Inc.

CHILDREN—HOSPITALS

see also Child Welfare; Children—Diseases

Jaworski, Anna M. My Brother Needs an Operation. Ball, Linda, illus. 1998. 57p. (J). (ps-5). 20.00 (978-0-9652508-2-5(2)) Baby Hearts Pr.

CHILDREN—MANAGEMENT

see Child Rearing

CHILDREN—NORTH AMERICA

Murphy, Claire Rudolf & Haigh, Jane G. Children of the Gold Rush. 1999. (Illus.). 96p. (YA). (gr. 3-7). pap. 14.95 (978-1-57098-257-6(0)) Rinehart, Roberts Pubs.

CHILDREN—PICTORIAL WORKS

Ajmera, Maya. To Be a Kid. 2000. (J). (978-0-606-19334-4(0)); 1999. lib. bdg. 15.25 (978-0-613-30161-9(7)) Tandem Library Bks.

Ajmera, Maya & Ivanko, John D. To Be a Kid. (Illus.). 32p. (J). 2004. bds. 6.95 (978-1-57091-371-6(4)); 2004. pap. 6.95 (978-0-88106-842-9(X)); 1999. 16.95 (978-0-88106-841-2(1)) Charlesbridge Publishing, Inc.

Ajmera, Maya & Versola, Anna Rhesa. Children from Australia to Zimbabwe. (Illus.). 2004. 64p. (YA). 19.95 (978-1-57091-478-2(8)); 2001. (J). pap. (978-1-57091-479-9(6)) Charlesbridge Publishing, Inc.

Brecon, Connah. Tomorrow. 2005. (Illus.). 32p. (978-0-7344-0730-6(0) , Lothian Bks.) Hachette Livre Australia.

Carlson, Laurie M. Kids Create! Trezzo-Braren, Loretta, illus. 1999. (Williamson Kids Can! Ser.). 160p. (J). (gr. 3 up). lib. bdg. 25.26 (978-0-8368-2232-8(3)) Stevens, Gareth Inc.

Dorling Kindersley Publishing Staff, ed. Bebé / Baby. 2004. (Stroller Books Ser.).Tr. of Bebe. (SPA.). 16p. (J). bds. 4.99 (978-0-7566-0628-2(4)) Dorling Kindersley Publishing, Inc.

Griffin, Starla. Girl, 13: A Global Snapshot of Generation E. 2004. (Illus.). 240p. (J). pap. (978-1-59258-112-2(9)) Hylas Publishing.

Hollyer, Beatrice. Wake up, World! A Day in the Life of Children Around the World. rev. ed. 1999. (Illus.). 48p. (J). (gr. 1-4). 17.95 (978-0-8050-6293-9(9) , Holt, Henry & Co. Bks. For Young Readers) Holt, Henry & Co.

Milord, Susan. Hands Around the World. Milord, Susan, illus. 1999. (Williamson Kids Can! Ser.). (Illus.). 160p. (J). (gr. 3 up). lib. bdg. 25.26 (978-0-8368-2231-1(5)) Stevens, Gareth Inc.

Popper, Garry. Winston in the Caribbean. Johnson, Andi, illus. 2004. 36p. (ps-7). 4.00 (978-1-84161-061-0(5)) Ravette Publishing, Ltd. GBR. *Dist:* Parkwest Pubns., Inc.

Seuss, Dr. My Book about Me: By Me, Myself. Seuss, Dr., illus. 2002. (Illus.). (J). 22.40 (978-0-7587-3204-0(X)) Book Wholesalers, Inc.

Simon, Norma. All Kinds of Children. Paterson, Diane, illus. 1999. (Concept Book Ser.). 32p. (J). (ps-2). 16.95 (978-0-8075-0281-5(2)) Whitman, Albert & Co.

Steckel, Richard & Steckel, Michele, photos by. The Milestones Project: Celebrating Childhood Around the World. 2004. (Illus.). 64p. (J). 17.95 (978-1-58246-132-8(5) , Tricycle Pr.) Ten Speed Pr.

Steckel, Richard & Steckel, Michele, photos by. Milestones Project: Celebrating Childhood Around the World. 2007. (Illus.). 64p. (J). pap. 12.95 (***978-1-58246-228-8(3)*** , Tricycle Pr.) Ten Speed Pr.

Swinburne, Stephen R. Go, Go, Go! Kids on the Move. Swinburne, Stephen R., photos by. 2003. (Illus.). 32p. (J). (gr. k-2). 15.95 (978-1-59078-022-0(1)); pap. 8.95 (978-1-59078-038-1(8)) Boyds Mills Pr.

—Go, Go, Go! Kids on the Move. 2002. (ps-2). lib. bdg. 17.60 (978-0-613-79878-5(3)) Tandem Library Bks.

CHILDREN—PSYCHOLOGY

see Child Psychology

CHILDREN—RELIGIOUS LIFE

Arthur, Patti T. A Sacrament of Holy Communion: A Study Guide for Young People. 1999. (Illus.). 16p. (gr. 5). pap. 4.75 (978-0-7880-1351-5(3)) CSS Publishing Co.

Beeke, Joel R. & Boorsma, Heidi. God's Alphabet for Life. Tenelshof, Tim, illus. 2000. 65p. (J). (ps-4). pap. 3.00 (978-1-892777-19-5(3)) Reformation Heritage Bks.

Bernice, Janet. Tiny Talks: I Will Follow God's Plan for Me, Vol. 5. 2004. (YA). pap. 7.95 (978-1-55517-815-4(4) , Cedar Fort, Inc.) Cedar Fort, Inc./CFI Distribution.

Brandt, Catharine. We Light the Candles: Devotions Related to Family Use of the Advent Wreath. 2004. 40p. 5.99 (978-0-8066-1544-8(3) , 10-15443, Augsburg Bks.) Augsburg Fortress, Pubs.

Clawson, Jan. Baptism—My Promise to Jesus: Girl. 1998. (Illus.). 24p. pap. 5.98 (978-0-88290-617-1(8) , 1301G) Horizon Pubs. & Distributors, Inc.

Dillon, Sally Pierson. Hugs from Jesus: 180 Devotions & Worship Activities for Preschoolers. 2001. (Illus.). (J). (978-0-8280-1567-7(8)) Review & Herald Publishing Assn.

Ellis, Gwen & Fitchwell, Jennifer. Our Daily Bread. 2006. (Illus.). 10p. (J). bds. 9.99 (978-0-7847-1852-0(0)) Standard Publishing.

Engelhardt, Lisa O. Right & Wrong & Being Strong: A Kid's Guide. Alley, R. W., illus. 2001. (Elf-Help Books for Kids). 32p. (J). per. 5.95 (978-0-87029-352-8(4)) Abbey Pr.

Esquinaldo, Virginia. Baby, Come to Church! Esquinaldo, Virginia, illus. 2005. (Illus.). (J). 5.95 (978-0-8198-1164-6(5) , 332-027) Pauline Bks. & Media.

Fields, Doug & Eastman, Brett. Connecting Your Heart to Others: 6 Small Group Sessions on Fellowship. 2003. (Life Together Ser.). 144p. pap., stu. ed. 7.99 (978-0-310-25334-1(9)) Zondervan.

—Growing to Be Like Jesus: 6 Small Group Sessions on Discipleship. 2003. (Life Together Ser.). 144p. pap., stu. ed. 7.99 (978-0-310-25335-8(7)) Zondervan.

—Starting to Go Where God Wants You to Be: 6 Small Group Lessons on Beginning Life Together. 2003. (Life Together Ser.). 144p. pap., stu. ed. 7.99 (978-0-310-25333-4(0)) Zondervan.

Grimbol, William R. Jesus in Your Backpack: A Teen's Guide to Spiritual Wisdom Without Religious Judgment. 2007. 256p. pap. 14.95 (978-1-56975-608-9(2)) Ulysses Pr.

Halverson, Delia Touchton. Oak Street Chonicles & the Good News: Everyday Life & Christian Faith. Dotts, M. Franklin, ed. (Illus.). 48p. (Orig.). (J). pap., tchr. ed. 4.95 (978-0-687-75340-6(6)) Abingdon Pr.

Holmes, Andy. Biblia para Mi. Voltz, Ralph, illus. 2004. Tr. of Bible for Me. (SPA.). 24p. 9.99 (978-0-88113-785-9(5)) Grupo Nelson.

Kamann, Donna. Single Life: An Inside Look. 2003. (Vocations (Winona, Minn.) Ser.). 88p. (YA). pap. 6.95 (978-0-88489-723-1(0)) St. Mary's Pr.

Kids Helping Kids. 1999. 48p. (J). No. 3. 12.90 (978-0-7814-0112-8(7)); No. 4. 12.99 (978-0-7814-0114-2(3)) Cook, David C. Publishing Co.

Livingstone Corporation Staff. Revolution Devotional: 90 Daily Devotions for Guys. 2006. (Invert Ser.). 224p. pap. 12.99 (978-0-310-26706-5(4)) Zondervan.

Lucado, Max. He Chose You. 2002. (Illus.). 192p. (J). (gr. 5-9). pap. 10.99 (978-0-8499-7789-3(4)) Nelson, Thomas Inc.

Malone, Alicia. What God Can't Do Just Can't Be Done. Hendrick, Patric J. & Acey-Hendrick, Betty, illus. Hendrick, Patric J. & Acey-Hendrick, Betty, photos by. 1998. 66p. (YA). (gr. 9 up). pap. 9.95 (978-1-884242-82-3(0)) Multicultural Pubns.

McDowell, Josh & Johnson, Kevin. The Great Treasure Quest: Discovering the Purpose of the Bible. 2006. 160p. (J). pap. 10.99 (978-1-932587-85-2(3)) Green Key Bks.

Missions Moments. 2005. pap. 12.99 (978-1-56309-943-4(8)) Woman's Missionary Union.

Nagel, Bernadette, illus. Celebrating My Confirmation: A Remembrance Book. 2001. 48p. (J). 17.95 (978-0-8198-1571-2(3) , 332-051) Pauline Bks. & Media.

Nappa, Tony & Nappa, Mike. Lunch Box Promises: Over 75 Tear-Out Notes with Promises from God's Word. 2000. (Illus.). 160p. (J). (gr. k-6). pap. 7.99 (978-0-7847-1181-1(X) , 04326) Standard Publishing.

O'Keefe, Susan Heyboer. It's Great to Be Catholic! Kelley, Patrick, illus. 2002. 32p. 10.95 (978-0-8091-6680-0(1) , 6680-1) Paulist Pr.

—It's Great to Be Catholic! 2001. (gr. k-3). lib. bdg. 19.90 (978-0-613-75764-5(5)) Tandem Library Bks.

Power Twins Handbook Volume One. 2006. (J). spiral bd. (***978-0-9742355-1-6(2)***) Brda, Tracy.

Publications International Staff, contrib. by. Count Your Blessings 123. 2001. (My Wipe-Off Book Ser.). (Illus.). (J). (978-0-7853-5103-0(5)) Publications International, Ltd.

Ritsi, Rene. Mwangi: Journey of Faith. Thorpe, Cameron, illus. 2004. 32p. 17.95 (978-1-888212-67-9(5)) Conciliar Pr.

Roark, Candice. Adolescent God. 1999. 96p. (YA). (gr. 8 up). pap. 8.99 (978-0-9677184-0-8(6)) Roark, Candice.

Sanders, Thomas. When Can I? Questions Preschoolers Ask in Their First Steps Toward Faith. Thorkelson, Gregg, illus. 2002. 48p. (J). (ps-2). 9.99 (978-0-8054-2162-0(9)) B&H Publishing Grp.

Setzer, Lee Ann. Tiny Talks #6: I will Trust in Heavenly Father & His Son, Jesus Christ-Their Promises are Sure, Vol. 6. 2005. (YA). pap. 7.99 (978-1-55517-889-5(8) , Cedar Fort, Inc.) Cedar Fort, Inc./CFI Distribution.

Shannon, Ellen & Hart, Corinne. We Ask Forgiveness: A Young Child's Book for Reconciliation. Benner, Patti, illus. 2007. 28p. 4.95 (***978-0-86716-845-7(5)***) St. Anthony Messenger Pr. & Franciscan Communications.

Simmons, Justine & Papp, Robert. God, Can You Hear Me? 2007. (Illus.). 32p. (ps-4). 16.99 (978-0-06-115397-6(4) , Amistad) HarperCollins Pubs.

Skinas, John Kosmas. Getting to Know God. 2005. (Illus.). (***978-1-888212-73-0(X)***) Conciliar Pr.

Strang Communications Company Staff, ed. Ages 4-5 Activities: Winter 2001/2002. 2002. (J). (ps-k). pap., act. bk. ed. 2.99 (978-1-57405-900-7(9)) CharismaLife Pubs.

—Ages 4-5 Resources: Winter 2001/2002. 2002. (J). (ps-k). pap. 10.99 (978-1-57405-901-4(7)) CharismaLife Pubs.

—Ages 4-5 Take Home Papers: Winter 2001/2002. 2002. (J). (ps-k). pap. 13.49 (978-1-57405-902-1(5)) CharismaLife Pubs.

—Ages 4-5 Teaching Pictures: Winter 2001/2002. 2002. (J). (ps-k). pap. 10.99 (978-1-57405-904-5(1)) CharismaLife Pubs.

—Grades 1-2 Resources: Winter 2001/2002. 2002. (J). (gr. 1-2). pap. 2.99 (978-1-57405-905-2(X)); pap. 10.99 (978-1-57405-906-9(8)) CharismaLife Pubs.

—Grades 1-2 Teaching Pictures: Winter 2001/2002. 2002. (J). (gr. 1-2). pap. 10.99 (978-1-57405-909-0(2)) CharismaLife Pubs.

—Kidz Chat: Winter 2001/2002. 2002. (J). pap. 13.49 (978-1-57405-912-0(2)) CharismaLife Pubs.

Tetz, RosAnne C. Love Letters from Jesus: The 27 Fundamental Beliefs for Preschoolers. 2000. (Illus.). 180p. (J). 12.99 (978-0-8280-1516-5(3) , 127-100) Review & Herald Publishing Assn.

Thomas Nelson Publishing Staff, contrib. by. New Explorer's Study Bible. 1998. (Illus.). 1472p. (J). (gr. 3-7). 24.99 (978-0-7852-0552-4(7) , 1422) Nelson, Thomas Inc.

Thurman, Debbie. Hold My Heart: A Teen's Journal for Healing & Personal Growth. 2004. 112p. pap. 10.95 (978-0-9676289-2-9(X)) Cedar Hse. Pubs.

—Sheer Faith: A Teen's Journey to Godly Growth. 2004. 112p. pap. 10.95 (978-0-9676289-3-6(8)) Cedar Hse. Pubs.

Tyndale Kids Staff, Kids. One Year Book of Devotions for Girls. 2002. (gr. 3-6). lib. bdg. 22.25 (978-0-613-76865-8(5)) Tandem Library Bks.

World Book, Inc. Staff, contrib. by. Birth & Growing up Celebrations. 2002. (World Book's Celebrations & Rituals Around the World Ser.). (Illus.). 44p. (J). (978-0-7166-5010-2(X)) World Bk., Inc.

Yaconelli, Mike. A Gift for My Daughter. 2nd ed. 2002. (Illus.). 64p. (J). pap. 6.99 (978-0-7459-4786-0(7) , Lion) Lion Hudson plc GBR. *Dist:* Independent Pubs. Group.

—A Gift for My Grandchild. 2nd ed. 2002. (Illus.). 64p. (J). pap. 6.99 (978-0-7459-4788-4(3) , Lion) Lion Hudson plc GBR. *Dist:* Independent Pubs. Group.

CHILDREN—SOUTH AMERICA

Cameron, Sara. Out of War: True Stories from the Frontlines of the Children's Movement for Peace. 2001. (Illus.). 192p. (J). (gr. 7 up). pap. 15.95 (978-0-439-29721-9(4)) Scholastic, Inc.

DeLoach, Sylvia & Massey, Barbara. Partners in Peru. 1998. (Child Like Me Ser.). 32p. (J). (gr. 1-4). per. 6.99 (978-1-56309-258-9(1) , N987105) New Hope Pubs.

Fajardo, Sara Andrea. In a Peruvian City. 2002. (Child's Day Ser.). (Illus.). 32p. (J). 15.95 (978-0-7614-1408-7(8) , Benchmark Bks.) Cavendish, Marshall Corp.

Hynson, Colin. Living on the Street: Hamilton's Story. 2005. (Children in Crisis Ser.). (Illus.). 48p. (J). (gr. 6-9). lib. bdg. 30.00 (978-0-8368-5961-4(8) , World Almanac Library) Stevens, Gareth Inc.

Lynette, Rachel. Ana Dodson: Advocate for Peruvian Orphanages. 2007. (Young Heroes Ser.). (Illus.). 64p. (J). (gr. 4-8). 24.95 (***978-0-7377-3865-0(0)*** , Kidhaven) Thomson Gale.

CHILDREN—TRAINING

see Child Rearing

CHILDREN—UNITED STATES

Andrews, Beth. I Miss You! A Military Kid's Book about Deployment. 2007. 56p. (J). pap. 12.00 (***978-1-59102-534-4(6)***) Prometheus Bks., Pubs.

Billitteri, Thomas J. The Gault Case: Legal Rights for Young People. 2000. (Landmark Supreme Court Cases Ser.). (Illus.). 128p. (YA). (gr. 6-12). lib. bdg. 26.60 (978-0-7660-1340-7(5)) Enslow Pubs., Inc.

Bolden, Tonya. Tell All the Children Our Story: Memories & Mementos of Being Young & Black in America. 2002. (Illus.). 128p. (J). (gr. 5-17). 24.95 (978-0-8109-4496-1(0)) Abrams, Harry N. , Inc.

Botones para el General Washington (Buttons for General Washington) 2006. (J). pap. 5.95 (978-0-8225-6617-5(6) , Ediciones Lerner) Lerner Publishing Group.

Buckley, Susan Washburn & Leacock, Elspeth. Kids Make History: A New Look at America's Story. Jones, Randy, illus. 2006. 48p. (J). (gr. 4-6). 17.00 (978-0-618-22329-9(0)) Houghton Mifflin Co.

Burgan, Michael. The American Newsboy. 2006. (Illus.). 48p. (J). lib. bdg. (978-0-7565-2458-6(X)) Compass Point Bks.

Center for Learning Network Staff. America's Children. 2000. 99p. (YA). (gr. 9-12). spiral bd. 20.95 (978-1-56077-633-8(1)) Ctr. for Learning, The.

Clayton, Lawrence. Coping with a Drug-Abusing Parent. 2003. (C). per. 34.95 (978-0-9709523-6-3(8)) Clayro Corp.

Cohen, Laura. The Gault Case & Young People's Rights: Debating Supreme Court Decisions. 2006. (Debating Supreme Court Decisions Ser.). (Illus.). 128p. (J). lib. bdg. 26.60 (978-0-7660-2476-2(8)) Enslow Pubs., Inc.

Diouf, Sylviane A. Growing up in Slavery. 2001. (Growing Up in... Ser.). (Illus.). 96p. (J). (gr. 5-8). lib. bdg. 25.90 (978-0-7613-1763-0(5) , Millbrook Pr.) Lerner Publishing Group.

Ehrlich, Amy, ed. When I Was Your Age Vol. 2: Original Stories about Growing Up. 2006. (Illus.). 187p. (YA). (gr. 8-11). reprint ed. 17.00 (978-1-4223-5199-4(8)) DIANE Publishing Co.

Embry-Litchman, Kristin. Secrets! Of a Los Alamos Kid 1946-1953. Ebinger, Virginia N., ed. 2001. (Illus.). 111p. (J). (gr. 4-9). pap. 12.95 (978-0-941232-27-2(1)) Los Alamos Historical Society.

Freedman, Russell. Children of the Great Depression. 2005. (Illus.). 128p. (J). (gr. 5-8). 20.00 (978-0-618-44630-8(3) , Clarion Bks.) Houghton Mifflin Co. Trade & Reference Div.

Gold, Susan Dudley. In Re Gault: Do Minors Have the Same Rights As Adults? 2007. (Supreme Court Milestones Ser.). 144p. (YA). (gr. 9 up). lib. bdg. 39.93 (978-0-7614-2584-7(5) , Benchmark Bks.) Cavendish, Marshall Corp.

Harness, Cheryl. Our Colonial Year. Harness, Cheryl, illus. 2005. (Illus.). 40p. (J). (ps-2). 16.95 (978-0-689-83479-0(9) , Simon & Schuster Children's Publishing) Simon & Schuster Children's Publishing.

Hemmel, David Lee & Knutson, Janette C. Alexis' Island: Growing up in the Tropical Paradise of Key West. 2006. (J). per. 14.95 (978-0-9745637-2-5(2)) Duval Publishing.

Hoose, Phillip M. We Were There, Too! Young People in U. S. History. 2000. (J). 25.00 (978-0-7894-2587-4(4)) Dorling Kindersley Publishing, Inc.

—We Were There, Too! Young People in U. S. History. 2001. (Illus.). 276p. (J). (gr. 4-7). 28.00 (978-0-374-38252-0(2) , Farrar, Straus & Giroux (BYR)) Farrar, Straus & Giroux.

Jackson, Ellen B. Turn of the Century. Ellis, Jan Davey, illus. 1998. 32p. (J). (gr. 2-7). 17.95 (978-0-88106-369-1(X)) Charlesbridge Publishing, Inc.

Kilgour, Mary Cameron. Me May Mary. 2004. 200p. (J). pap. 13.95 (978-1-58760-018-0(8) , Child & Family Pr.) Child Welfare League of America, Inc.

Kirkpatrick, Katherine. The Snow Baby: The Arctic Childhood of Robert E. Peary's Daring Daughter. 2006. (Illus.). 48p. (J). 16.95 (978-0-8234-1973-9(8)) Holiday Hse., Inc.

Kule, Elaine A. Beginning Again: Immigrating to America. Thermes, Jennifer, illus. 2006. 40p. (978-1-59137-473-2(1)) Options Publishing.

Lauck, Jennifer. Blackbird: A Childhood Lost & Found. 2001. (gr. 7-12). lib. bdg. 23.45 (978-0-613-45167-3(8)) Tandem Library Bks.

Lemke, Donald B. The Schoolchildren's Blizzard. Hoover, Dave & Barnett, Charles, illus. 2008. (J). (***978-1-4296-0157-3(4)***) Capstone Pr., Inc.

Lynette, Rachel. Ana Dodson: Advocate for Peruvian Orphanages. 2007. (Young Heroes Ser.). (Illus.). 64p. (J). (gr. 4-8). 24.95 (***978-0-7377-3865-0(0)*** , Kidhaven) Thomson Gale.

MacElroy, Mary H. Work & Play in Colonial Days. reprint ed. 150.00 (978-0-7222-6600-7(6)) Library Reprints, Inc.

McHugh, Michael J., et al. A Child's Story of America. 2nd ed. 1998. (Illus.). 202p. (J). (gr. 3-5). pap. 8.95 (978-1-930092-93-8(8) , CLP79945) Christian Liberty Pr.

C D

Miller, Brandon Marie. Growing up in Revolution & the New Nation, 1775 to 1800. 2003. (Our America Ser.). (Illus.). 64p. (J). (gr. 4-7). lib. bdg. 26.60 (978-0-8225-0078-0(7)) Lerner Publishing Group.

Murphy, Claire Rudolf. Children of Alcatraz: Growing up on the Rock. 2006. (Illus.). 64p. (J). 18.85 (978-0-8027-9578-6(1)); 17.95 (978-0-8027-9577-9(3)) Walker & Co.

Murray, Margaret Cox. A-Z Children of Maine. 1999. (Illus.). 15p. (J). (ps-5). pap. 6.95 (978-0-9665140-1-8(7)) Rainbow Pr.

Nelson, Julie. Families Change: A Book for Children Experiencing Termination of Parental Rights. Gallagher, Mary, illus. 2006. (Kids Are Important Ser.). 32p. (J). pap. 9.95 (978-1-57542-209-1(3)) Free Spirit Publishing, Inc.

—Kids Are Important: A Book for Young Children in Foster Care. 2003. (Illus.). (J). (978-0-9743826-1-6(2)) Lifetrack Resources.

Nicodemus, Laura Konger. Grandma's Onion Patch, 4 vols. Nicodemus, Laura Konger, illus. 2002. (Illus.). 16p. (J). (gr. 1-4). 3.99 (978-0-9722216-3-4(8)) Grandma's Stories, Inc.

Parker, Victoria. Mexico. 2005. (We're from Ser.). (Illus.). 32p. (J). (gr. 3-7). lib. bdg. 24.21 (978-1-4034-5787-5(5)) Heinemann.

—We're from Mexico. 2005. (We're from Ser.). (Illus.). 32p. (J). pap. 7.25 (978-1-4034-5794-3(8)) Heinemann.

Pettifor, Bonnie & Petit, Charles E. Weeks vs. United States: Illegal Search & Seizure. 2000. (Landmark Supreme Court Cases Ser.). (Illus.). 128p. (YA). (gr. 6-12). lib. bdg. 26.60 (978-0-7660-1341-4(3)) Enslow Pubs., Inc.

Roop, Peter & Roop, Connie. Botones para el General Washington (Buttons for General Washington) Hanson, Peter E., illus. 2006. (Yo Solo - Historia (on My Own - History) Ser.). (SPA.). 48p. (J). (gr. 2-4). lib. bdg. 25.26 (978-0-8225-6261-0(8) , Ediciones Lerner) Lerner Publishing Group.

Smith, Charles R., Jr. & La Raso, Carlo. I Am America. 2003. (Illus.). 32p. (J). (gr. k-3). pap. 14.95 (978-0-439-43179-8(4) , Cartwheel Bks.) Scholastic, Inc.

CHILDREN—UNITED STATES—FICTION

Franklin, Kristine L. Cuss. 2007. (Illus.). 320p. (J). (gr. 5-8). 6.99 (***978-0-7636-2362-3(8)***) Candlewick Pr.

CHILDREN, VAGRANT

Gerstein, Mordicai. The Wild Boy. Gerstein, Mordicai, illus. 2002. (Illus.). 40p. (J). pap. 5.95 (978-0-374-48396-8(5) , Sunburst) Farrar, Straus & Giroux.

Martin, Norman R. Orphans on the River: Little Red, White & Mississippi Rivers Were Their Home. Mullins, Judy C., ed. 1998. (Illus.). 113p. (YA). pap. 10.00 (978-0-9646489-7-5(0)) Martain Pubs.

CHILDREN IN ART

see Children in Literature and Art

CHILDREN IN LITERATURE AND ART

Bloom, Harold, ed. & tr. The House on Mango Street. Bloom, Harold, tr. 2003. (Bloom's Guides Ser.). (Illus.). 80p. (gr. 9-13). 30.00 (978-0-7910-7565-4(6) , Chelsea Hse.) Facts On File, Inc.

Buchanan, Ben. My Year with Harry Potter: How I Discovered My Own Magical World. 2001. (Illus.). 112p. (ps-3). 12.95 (978-1-930051-50-8(6)) Lantern Bks.

Micklethwait, Lucy. Children: A First Art Book. 2006. (First Art Book Ser.). (Illus.). 24p. 14.95 (978-1-84507-116-5(6)) Lincoln, Frances Ltd. GBR. *Dist:* Perseus Distribution.

CHILDREN'S BOOKS

see Children's Literature

CHILDREN'S CRUSADE, 1212—FICTION

Janasik, Steven M. A Journey of Innocents. 1999. (Illus.). 340p. 25.95 (978-0-9659417-2-3(8)); pap. 16.95 (978-0-9659417-3-0(6)) Century Pr.

McDonnell, Kathleen. 1212: Year of the Journey. 2006. (Illus.). 288p. (J). (gr. 5-9). pap. 7.95 (978-1-897187-11-1(4)) Second Story Pr. CAN. *Dist:* Orca Bk. Pubs. USA.

CHILDREN'S DISEASES

see Children—Diseases

CHILDREN'S HOSPITALS

see Children—Hospitals

CHILDREN'S LIBRARIES

see Libraries, Children's; School Libraries

CHILDREN'S LITERATURE

Here are entered collections of works of a cross-genre nature, e.g., Poetry and Prose. Works on the reading interests of children, and or lists of books read by or recommended for children are entered under Children—Books and Reading.

see also Caldecott Medal Books; Children—Books and Reading; Fairy Tales; Libraries, Children's; Picture Books; Plays; Poetry; Stories

Ada, Alma Flor & Campoy, F. Isabel. Anton Pirulero. (Literature Collection of Puertas Al Sol Ser.). (SPA.). 32p. (J). (gr. k-6). pap. 12.95 (978-1-59437-703-7(0)) Santillana USA Publishing Co., Inc.

Adams, Carol J., et al. Journey to Gameland: How to Make a Board Game from Your Favorite Children's Book. 2001. (Illus.). 112p. 12.95 (978-1-930051-51-5(4)) Lantern Bks.

Adams, David. One, Two, Three: A Collection of Songs, Verses, Riddles, & Stories for Children of Grades 1- 3. Mitchell, David, ed. 2003. (J). per. 14.95 (978-1-888365-35-1(8)) Assn. of Waldorf Schls. of North America Pubns. (AWSNA).

Adil, Janeen R. Dr. Seuss. 2004. (Robbie Reader Ser.). (Illus.). 32p. (J). (gr. 1-4). lib. bdg. 25.70 (978-1-58415-288-0(5)) Mitchell Lane Pubs., Inc.

Ancona, George. Self Portrait. Ancona, George, photos by. 2006. (Meet the Author Ser.). (Illus.). 32p. (J). 14.95 (978-1-57274-860-6(5) , 733, Meet the Author) Owen, Richard C. Pubs., Inc.

Andersen, Hans Christian. Fairy Tales from Hans Andersen. Kingsland, L. W., tr. from DAN. Birkett, Rachel, illus. 2001. (Oxford Story Collections). 240p. (YA). suppl. ed. 14.50 (978-0-19-275010-5(0)) Oxford Univ. Pr., Inc.

—Favorite Tales from Hans Christian Andersen. 2001. (Illus.). 192p. (J). 24.95 (978-0-86315-347-1(X)) Floris Bks. GBR. *Dist:* SteinerBooks, Inc.

—Hans Christian Andersen: Illustrated Fairy Tales, Vol. 1. 2001. (Illus.). 416p. 29.95 (978-87-7247-279-9(0)) Scandinavia Publishing Hse. DNK. *Dist:* National Bk. Network.

Armstrong, Robb. Got Game? Smith, Bruce, illus. 1998. (Patrick's Pals Ser.: No. 3). 96p. (J). (gr. 2-7). mass mkt. 3.99 (978-0-06-107069-3(6) , Harper Entertainment) HarperCollins Pubs.

Arnosky, James. Whole Days Outdoors: An Autobiographical Album. Arnosky, Deanna, photos by. 2006. (Meet the Author Ser.). (Illus.). 32p. (J). 14.95 (978-1-57274-859-0(1) , 734, Meet the Author) Owen, Richard C. Pubs., Inc.

Ballesteros, Xose & Villan, Oscar. The Little White Rabbit. 2002. (Illus.). 32p. (J). 14.95 (978-84-95730-19-0(7)) Kalandraka Catalunya, Edicions, S.L. ESP. *Dist:* Independent Pubs. Group.

Banting, Erinn. Mary Pope Osbourne. 2007. (My Favorite Writer Ser.). (978-1-59036-483-3(X)); lib. bdg. (978-1-59036-482-6(1)) Weigl Pubs., Inc.

Bauld, Jane Scoggins, et al. Come to the Gathering. Woodward, Debbie et al, illus. unabr. ed. 1998. v, 85p. (J). (gr. k-4). per. 12.95 (978-0-9651123-2-1(2) , PyroWriters) Allen, Evelyn W.

Beechen, Adam. Two Promises Too Many. 2000. (gr. 3-6). lib. bdg. 11.80 (978-0-613-31850-1(1)) Tandem Library Bks.

Bennett, William J., ed. The Children's Book of Hearth & Home. Hague, Michael, illus. 2002. ix, 100p. (J). (978-0-385-90849-8(0) , Children's Pr.) Scholastic Library Publishing.

Berne, Emma Carlson. Laura Ingalls Wilder. 2007. (Essential Lives Ser.). (ENG., Illus.). 112p. (J). (gr. 6-8). lib. bdg. 32.79 (***978-1-59928-843-7(5)*** , Essential Library) ABDO Publishing Co.

Betteridge, Barbara Dawson. Whittle Your Ears. Mitchell, David S., ed. 2005. (J). per. 12.00 (978-1-888365-68-9(4)) Assn. of Waldorf Schls. of North America Pubns. (AWSNA).

Bradford, Jumanne. Preserving a Young Generation. 2005. Vol. 1. 87p. pap. 24.99 (978-1-4116-4015-3(2)); Vol. 2. 94p. pap. 24.99 (978-1-4116-4154-9(X)) Lulu.com.

Brine, M. D. Our Little Ones. 2005. pap. 34.95 (978-1-4179-9715-2(X)) Kessinger Publishing, LLC.

Carlson, Cheryl. Dr. Seuss. 2005. (First Biographies Ser.). (Illus.). 24p. (J). 15.93 (978-0-7368-3639-5(X) , Pebble Bks.) Capstone Pr., Inc.

Carver Middle School, compiled by. Voices from the Middle: Stepping into the Real World. Carver Middle School, . 2004. 224p. (YA). per. 9.99 (978-0-9749811-3-0(3) , Sonship Pr.) 21st Century Pr.

Classic Stories: Read-Together Treasury. 2003. (Illus.). 95p. (J). 12.98 (978-0-7853-7230-1(X)) Publications International, Ltd.

Cox, Susan Soon-Keum, ed. Voices from Another Place: A Collection of Works from a Generation Born in Korea. 1999. 152p. (J). pap. 12.00 (978-0-9638472-4-9(4)) Yeong & Yeong Bk. Co.

Coy, Steven & Dooda, Ian, eds. BOOM! for Real: Anthology of Poetry, Prose, & Pictures (Volume One 2005) 2005. (Illus.). 134p. (YA). per. 10.00 (978-0-9743235-4-1(3)) Better Non Sequitur.

Dafydd, Myrddin ap. Syniad Da Iawn! 2005. (WEL., Illus.). 195p. (978-0-86381-641-3(X)) Gwasg Carreg Gwalch.

Draze, Dianne. Junior Literature Companion. 2005. 64p. (Orig.). 11.95 (978-1-59363-084-3(0)) Prufrock Pr.

Fain, David. Spongebob Squarepants Trivia Book. 2000. (SpongeBob SquarePants Ser.). (Illus.). 48p. (J). (gr. 1-4). pap. 3.99 (978-0-689-84018-0(7) , Simon Spotlight) Simon & Schuster Children's Publishing.

—Spongebob Squarepants Trivia Book. 2000. (gr. 3-6). lib. bdg. 10.65 (978-0-613-31745-0(9)) Tandem Library Bks.

Falling for the Story. 2nd ed. 2004. (J). per. 9.95 (978-0-9759524-0-5(4)) Northern Virginia Writing Project.

Florian, Douglas. See for Your Self. Florian, Douglas & Taplinger, Lee, photos by. 2005. (Meet the Author Ser.). (Illus.). 32p. (J). 14.95 (978-1-57274-821-7(4) , 731) Owen, Richard C. Pubs., Inc.

Franco, Betsy, ed. Things I Have to Tell You: Poems & Writing by Teenage Girls. Nickles, Nina, photos by. 2001. (Illus.). 80p. (YA). (gr. 7 up). 15.99 (978-0-7636-0905-4(6)) Candlewick Pr.

Gamboa, Norma & Soberon, Cecilia. Literatura para el Jardin de Ninos (Literature for Young Children) (SPA., Illus.). 207p. (J). (gr. k-2). pap. 19.95 (978-968-416-858-9(6) , 684B) Fernandez USA Publishing.

Gap, April. Rocky Memories. Wheeler, Arloa, illus. 2000. (WeWrite Kids! Ser.: No. 33). 50p. (J). (gr. 3-6). pap. 3.95 (978-1-57635-009-6(6)) WeWrite LLC.

The Giver. 1998. 44p. (YA). 11.95 (978-1-56137-717-6(1) , NU7171SP) Novel Units, Inc.

Green, Phyllis A. The Barn. 1998. 36p. (J). 11.95 (978-1-58130-556-2(7) , NU5567SP) Novel Units, Inc.

Harcourt School Publishers Staff. Living Colors Anthology. 99th ed. 1999. (Signatures Ser.). (Illus.). (gr. 2). 51.20 (978-0-15-310107-6(5)) Harcourt Schl. Pubs.

—Times of Discovery. 2001. (Collections Ser.). (Illus.). (gr. 6). 68.70 (978-0-15-312051-0(7)) Harcourt Schl. Pubs.

—Touch a Dream. 2002. (Collections Ser.). (Illus.). (gr. 4). 68.40 (978-0-15-312048-0(7)) Harcourt Schl. Pubs.

—Touch a Dream: Texas Edition. 2002. (Collections Ser.). (Illus.). (gr. 4). 86.80 (978-0-15-314989-4(2)) Harcourt Schl. Pubs.

—Voices & Reflections: Standard Anthology. 95th ed. 1998. (Treasury of Literature Ser.). (Illus.). (gr. 8). 83.20 (978-0-15-301238-9(2)) Harcourt Schl. Pubs.

—Warm Friends Anthology Level 3. 99th ed. 1999. (Signatures Ser.). (Illus.). 36.00 (978-0-15-310629-3(8)) Harcourt Schl. Pubs.

Harris, Laurie Lanzen. Biography for Beginners: All Authors. 2005. (Illus.). 300p. (978-1-931360-31-9(6)) Favorable Impressions.

Holt, Rinehart and Winston Staff. Preparation & Construct Response: Elemental Literature. 3rd ed. 2003. (J). pap. 12.20 (978-0-03-068278-0(9)) Holt, Rinehart & Winston of Canada, Ltd. CAN. *Dist:* Harcourt Canada, Ltd.

—Preparation & Construction Response: Elemental Literature. 3rd ed. 2003. (J). pap. 12.20 (978-0-03-068277-3(0)); pap. 12.20 (978-0-03-068281-0(9)) Holt, Rinehart & Winston of Canada, Ltd. CAN. *Dist:* Harcourt Canada, Ltd.

—Preparation & Constructive Response: Elemental Literature. 3rd ed. 2003. (J). pap. 12.20 (978-0-03-068282-7(7)); pap. 12.20 (978-0-03-068283-4(5)) Holt, Rinehart & Winston of Canada, Ltd. CAN. *Dist:* Harcourt Canada, Ltd.

Hume, Lotta Carswell. Favorite Children's Stories from China & Tibet. Koon-Chiu, Lo, illus. 2004. 112p. 16.95 (978-0-8048-3586-2(1)) Tuttle Publishing.

Jones, Allan Frewin. Ghostlight, Vol. 8. 2003. 176p. (J). mass mkt. 6.99 (978-0-330-39239-6(5) , Pan) Pan Macmillan GBR. *Dist:* Trafalgar Square Publishing.

Kaur, Prabhjot. Daddoo's Day Out. 2004. (Illus.). 24p. (J). pap. (978-81-87649-94-6(1)) Katha.

Kimmel, Eric A. Tuning Up: A Visit with Eric Kimmel. Childers, Basil, photos by. 2005. (Meet the Author Ser.). (Illus.). 32p. (J). 14.95 (978-1-57274-822-4(2) , 732) Owen, Richard C. Pubs., Inc.

Kirk, Daniel. Moondogs. 1999. (Illus.). 1p. (J). (ps-3). 16.99 (978-0-399-23128-5(5) , Putnam Juvenile) Penguin Group (USA) Inc.

Kurtz, Jane. Jane Kurtz & You. 2007. (Author & YOU Ser.: No. 8). (Illus.). 204p. 35.00 (978-1-59158-295-3(4) , LU2954) Libraries Unlimited, Inc.

Kutscher, Marc, ed. Revolution of the Undertones: A Teen Anthology, 2004. 240p. (YA). per. 14.95 (978-0-9745493-0-9(4)) Scrap Paper Pr.

Lappi, Megan. Will Hobbs. 2007. (My Favorite Writer Ser.). (J). pap. (978-1-59036-489-5(9)); lib. bdg. (978-1-59036-488-8(0)) Weigl Pubs., Inc.

Lee, J. Marie. 4Jellybean Junction. 2003. 125p. (J). per. 19.95 (978-1-59196-326-4(5)) Instantpublisher.com.

Lindgren, Alan. The Courage of the Flame: Ballads, Sonnets & Other Gardens of Poetry with Prose Writings. Lindgren, Alan, ed. 2003. 196p. (YA). pap. 12.95 (978-0-9721429-8-4(3)) Sun Sings Pubns.

Living in the Sixth Dimension. 1999. 100p. (J). (gr. 1-9). pap. 9.95 (978-0-9648757-1-5(3) , Pince Nez Pr.) Pince-Nez Pr.

Locker, Thomas. Home: A Journey Through America. 2000. (Illus.). 32p. (J). (gr. 2-5). pap. 7.00 (978-0-15-202452-9(2) , Voyager Bks./Libros Viajeros) Harcourt Children's Bks.

—Home: A Journey Through America. 1998. (Illus.). 32p. (J). (gr. 1-5). 16.00 (978-0-15-201473-5(X) , Silver Whistle) Harcourt Trade Pubs.

—Home: A Journey Through America. 2000. (978-0-606-20325-8(7)); (gr. 3-6). lib. bdg. 14.15 (978-0-613-30476-4(4)) Tandem Library Bks.

Mandl, Dave & Wilson, Peter L., eds. Wild Children: A Zine for Kids. Date not set. (Illus.). 64p. 5.00 (978-0-936756-83-7(7)) Autonomedia.

Marcovitz, Hal. Bruce Coville. 2005. (Who Wrote That? Ser.). (Illus.). 128p. (J). (gr. 6-12). 30.00 (978-0-7910-8656-8(9) , Chelsea Hse.) Facts On File, Inc.

Marcovitz, Hal. Pat Mora. 2007. (Who Wrote That? Ser.). 136p. (J). (gr. 6-12). 30.00 (***978-0-7910-9528-7(2)*** , Chelsea Hse.) Facts On File, Inc.

Marcus, Leonard S. Side by Side: Five Favorite Picture-Book Teams Go to Work. 2001. (Illus.). 64p. (J). (gr. 3 up). 22.95 (978-0-8027-8778-1(9)) Walker & Co.

Marlin Elementary Students, creator. Marlin Anthology: Exploring Our Horizons as Writers. 2006. per. 19.95 (978-0-9768391-8-7(0)) Pen & Publish Inc.

Marsh, Valerie. Stories That Stick: Quick & Easy Storyboard Tales. Luzadder, Patrick K., illus. 2002. 80p. (J). (gr. k-5). pap. 15.95 (978-1-57950-068-9(4) , Upstart Bks.) Highsmith Inc.

Marshall, Chris. Warfare in the Medieval World. 1999. (History of Warfare Ser.). (Illus.). 80p. (YA). (gr. 7-12). lib. bdg. 29.97 (978-0-8172-5443-8(9)) Raintree.

McGraw-Hill Staff. Glencoe Literature: The Reader's Choice, Course 1, Grade 6. 2001. stu. ed. 89.32 (978-0-07-825105-4(2) , 9780078251054) Glencoe/McGraw-Hill.

—Glencoe Literature: The Reader's Choice, Course 3, Grade 8. 2001. stu. ed. 89.32 (978-0-07-825107-8(9) , 9780078251078) Glencoe/McGraw-Hill.

Meyer, John. TeenInk: Our Voices, Our Visions. 2000. (gr. 7-12). lib. bdg. 22.20 (978-0-613-30777-2(1)) Tandem Library Bks.

Milam, Mary Kay. Meet Zippyr the Zebra-Key. Alabata, Sam V., illus. 2nd ed. 1999. 24p. (J). (ps-k). reprint ed. pap. 15.95 (978-1-58597-008-7(5)) Leathers Publishing.

Montgomery, Janice. Inside Stories Bk. 1: Study Guides for Children's Literature. 2005. 104p. stu. ed. 13.95 (978-1-59363-077-5(8)) Prufrock Pr.

—Inside Stories Bk. 2: Study Guides for Children's Literature. 2005. 96p. stu. ed. 13.95 (978-1-59363-078-2(6)) Prufrock Pr.

—Inside Stories Bk. 3: Study Guides for Children's Literature. 2005. 96p. 13.95 (978-1-59363-079-9(4)) Prufrock Pr.

—Inside Stories Bk. 4: Study Guides for Children's Literature. 2005. 96p. 13.95 (978-1-59363-080-5(8)) Prufrock Pr.

—Inside Stories Vol. 5: Study Guides for Children's Literature. 2005. 96p. stu. ed. 13.95 (978-1-59363-081-2(6)) Prufrock Pr.

Mountain View Elementary School, compiled by. Vegetable Medley for the Mind. 2003. 264p. per. 15.00 (978-0-9740321-1-5(5)) Open Bk. Publishing.

Murray, Jennifer. 'Twas a Dark & Stormy Night... Why Writers Write. 2007. (Shockwave: Life Stories Ser.). (Illus.). 36p. (J). (gr. 4-6). lib. bdg. 25.00 (***978-0-531-17773-0(4)*** , Children's Pr.) Scholastic Library Publishing.

Otfinoski, Steven. Time to Share. 2000. (gr. 3-6). lib. bdg. 11.80 (978-0-613-31820-4(X)) Tandem Library Bks.

Potter. The Narnia Atlas. 2000. 124p. (YA). (gr. 3 up). pap. 18.95 (978-0-06-443485-0(0)) HarperCollins Pubs.

Primm, E. Russell. Favorite Children's Authors & Illustrators. 2nd ed. 2006. (J). (978-1-59187-057-9(7)); (978-1-59187-058-6(5)); (978-1-59187-059-3(3)); (978-1-59187-060-9(7)); (978-1-59187-061-6(5)); (978-1-59187-062-3(3)); (978-1-59187-063-0(1)); (978-1-59187-064-7(X)) Tradition Publishing Co.

Purslow, Neil. R.L. Stine/Neil Purslow. 2007. (My Favorite Writer Ser.). (J). (978-1-59036-487-1(2)); lib. bdg. (978-1-59036-486-4(4)) Weigl Pubs., Inc.

Pyle, Howard. The Book of Pirates. Pyle, Howard, illus. 2000. (Illus.). 320p. (J). (gr. 5-8). pap. 12.95 (978-0-486-41304-4(7)) Dover Pubns., Inc.

Raintree Steck-Vaughn Staff. Get Hooked on Books: Arkansas Edition, 26 bks., Set. 2003. (Illus.). 666.88 (978-1-4109-0160-6(2)) Raintree.

Reid, Rob. Storytime Slam! 15 Lesson Plans for Preschool & Primary Story Programs. 2006. (Illus.). 85p. (J). pap. 16.95 (***978-1-932146-52-3(0)*** , Upstart Bks.) Highsmith Inc.

Risby, Bonnie. Literature Companion. 2005. 64p. 11.95 (978-1-59363-086-7(7)) Prufrock Pr.

Ruffin, Frances E. Meet Cynthia Rylant. 2006. (About the Author Ser.). (Illus.). 24p. (J). lib. bdg. (978-1-4042-3131-3(5) , PowerKids Pr.) Rosen Publishing Group, Inc., The.

Sanchez, Miriam & Fernandez, Federico. Where Did Moon Lose Her Laughter? 2002. (Illus.). 32p. (J). 14.95 (978-84-95730-20-6(0)) Kalandraka Catalunya, Edicions, S.L. ESP. *Dist:* Independent Pubs. Group.

Scholastic Classics, 20 bks., Set. Incl. Adventures of Sherlock Holmes. Doyle, Arthur Conan. v, 256p. (YA). (gr. 9-12). 25.00 (978-0-531-16977-3(4)); Adventures of Tom Sawyer. Twain, Mark. (Illus.). vi, 219p. (J). (gr. 9-12). 25.00 (978-0-531-16978-0(2)); Anne of Avonlea. Montgomery, L. M. (Illus.). viii, 239p. (J). 25.00 (978-0-531-16979-7(0)); Anne of Green Gables. Montgomery, L. M. (Illus.). viii, 272p. (J). (gr. 9-12). 25.00 (978-0-531-16980-3(4)); Black Beauty. Sewell, Anna. x, 203p. (J). (gr. 9-12). 25.00 (978-0-531-16981-0(2)); Call of the Wild & Selected Short Stories. London, Jack. (Illus.). iv, 260p. (J). (gr. 9-12). 25.00 (978-0-531-16982-7(0)); Christmas Carol & Other Stories. Dickens, Charles. iv, 197p. (YA). (gr. 9-12). 25.00 (978-0-531-16983-4(9)); Dr. Jekyll & Mr. Hyde : And Other Stories of the Supernatural. Stevenson, Robert Louis. iv, 143p. (J). (gr. 9-12). 25.00 (978-0-531-16985-8(5)); Invisible Man. Wells, H. G. viii, 146p. (J). (gr. 9-12). 25.00 (978-0-531-16988-9(X)); Kidnapped. Stevenson, Robert Louis. viii, 213p. (J). (gr. 9-12). 25.00 (978-0-531-16990-2(1)); Little Princess : The Story of Sara Crewe. Burnett, Frances Hodgson. v, 178p. (J). (gr. 9-12). 25.00 (978-0-531-16991-9(X)); Peter Pan. Barrie, J. M. (Illus.). v, 140p. (J). (gr. 9-12). 25.00 (978-0-531-16993-3(6)); Pride & Prejudice. Austen, Jane. v, 354p. (YA). (gr. 9-12). 25.00 (978-0-531-16994-0(4)); Raven & Other Poems & Stories. Poe, Edgar Allan. (Illus.). viii, 142p. (YA). (gr. 9-12). 25.00 (978-0-531-16995-7(2)); Secret Garden : A Young Reader's Edition of the Classic Story. Burnett, Frances Hodgson. vi, 222p. (J). (gr. 9-12). 25.00 (978-0-531-16960-5(X)); Treasure Island. Stevenson, Robert Louis. (Illus.). x, 205p. (J). (gr. 9-12). 25.00 (978-0-531-16961-2(8)); War of the Worlds. Wells, H. G. xi, 182p. (J). (gr. 9-12). 25.00 (978-0-531-16963-6(4)); White Fang. London, Jack. v, 206p. (J). (gr. 9-12). 25.00 (978-0-531-16964-3(2)); Wuthering Heights. Brontë, Emily. (Illus.). iv, 307p. (YA). (gr. 9-12). 25.00 (978-0-531-16965-0(0)); 20,000 Leagues under the Sea. Verne, Jules. viii, 322p. (YA). (gr. 9-12). 25.00 (978-0-531-16962-9(6)); 2006. , Watts, Franklin (Illus.). 2007. 500.00 (***978-0-531-12475-8(4)***) Scholastic Library Publishing.

Schon, Isabel. Recommended Books in Spanish for Children & Young Adults: 1996 Through 1999. 4th ed. 2001. (Studies in Young Adult Literature). (Illus.). 376p. 52.00 (978-0-8108-3840-6(0)) Scarecrow Pr., Inc.

Simon, Seymour. From Paper Airplanes to Outer Space. Crews, Nina, photos by. 2000. (Meet the Author Ser.). (Illus.). 32p. (J). (gr. 2-5). 14.95 (978-1-57274-374-8(3) , 725) Owen, Richard C. Pubs., Inc.

Small, Roberta Lee. Down by the Pond. 2005. 116p. (J). pap. 9.95 (978-1-4116-5949-0(X)) Lulu.com.

Smith, Michael T. I Want to Be in the Show! Norden, Carolyn, illus. 2000. (Blue's Clues Ser.: Vol. 5). 24p. (J). (ps-k). pap. 3.50 (978-0-689-83812-5(3) , Simon Spotlight/Nickelodeon) Simon & Schuster Children's Publishing.

Spencer, Gwynne. What's Cooking in Children's Literature. 2001. (Professional Growth Ser.). (Illus.). 160p. 36.95 (978-1-58683-005-2(8)) Linworth Publishing, Inc.

Tabori-Fried, Natasha, ed. A Little Box of Christmas. (Illus.). 144p. 16.95 (978-1-932183-86-3(8) , Welcome Bks.) Welcome Enterprises, Inc.

Tabori, Lena. The Little Big Book for Moms. Tabori, Lena & Wong, Alice, eds. (Illus.). 352p. 24.95 (978-0-941807-41-8(X) , Welcome Bks.) Welcome Enterprises, Inc.

Thaler, Mike. Imagination. Shahan, Sherry & Shahan, Sherry, photos by. 2002. (Meet the Author Ser.). (Illus.). 32p. (J). (gr. 2-5). 14.95 (978-1-57274-598-8(3) , 728) Owen, Richard C. Pubs., Inc.

Thompson, Joel. Shortcuts: And Other Stories That Teach Christian Values. 2003. (Clubzone Kids Ser.). (Illus.). 80p. (J). pap. 5.99 (978-0-8010-4510-3(X)) Baker Bks.

Time-Life Books Editors. Time-Life Early Learning Program Series, 8 bks., Set. Incl. Guess Who? A Lift-the-Flap Animal Book. (Illus.). 20p. (ps-2). 1990. (978-0-8094-9250-3(4)); How Many Hippos? A Mix-&-Match Counting Book. (Illus.). 40p. (ps-2). 1990. (978-0-8094-9258-9(X)); Picture-Perfect Planet. 1992. (978-0-8094-9319-7(5)); Purple Parrots Eating Carrots : A Rebus Reader. Kagan, Neil, ed. (Illus.). 64p. (ps-2). 1991. (978-0-8094-9262-6(8)); Secret Forest : A Lift-the-Flap Nature Book. Kagan, Neil, ed. (Illus.). 20p. (gr. 3-7). 1991. (978-0-8094-9275-6(X)); Voyage of the Micronauts : A Book about the Human Body. Fallow, Allan, ed. Cooke, Tom, illus. 64p. (ps-2). 1992. 16.95 (978-0-8094-9295-4(4)); (J). 1999. 16.95 o.s.i (978-0-8094-9379-1(9)) Time-Life, Inc.

Vaux, F. B. Domestic Pleasures or the Happy Fire Side Illustrated by Interesting Conversations. 2004. reprint ed. pap. 20.95 (978-1-4191-1640-7(1)); pap. 1.99 (978-1-4192-1640-4(6)) Kessinger Publishing, LLC.

Wheeler, Jill C. Mary Pope Osborne. 2007. (Children's Authors Ser.). (Illus.). 24p. (J). 21.35 (978-1-59679-764-2(9)) ABDO Publishing Co.

Where the Red Fern Grows. 1998. 44p. (YA). 11.95 (978-1-56137-497-7(0) , NU4970SP) Novel Units, Inc.

Wong, Janet S. Before It Wriggles Away. Lindsay, Anne, photos by. 2006. (Meet the Author Ser.). (Illus.). 32p. (J). 14.95 (978-1-57274-861-3(3) , 735, Meet the Author) Owen, Richard C. Pubs., Inc.

Young Scribes Staff. Unlock the Secrets of Exeter: The Young Scribes of Exeter, NH. l.t. ed. 2004. (Illus.). 172p. (J). pap. 15.00 (978-0-9744803-9-8(8)) PublishingWorks.

Younge, Jewel Sophia, creator. Pg-13. 2006. (Illus.). 29p. (YA). 10.00 (978-0-9788158-0-6(7)) Sweet Potato Brown.

Zimmer, Kyle, frwd. Jane Yolen. 2005. (Who Wrote That? Ser.). (Illus.). 126p. (J). (gr. 6-12). lib. bdg. 30.00 (978-0-7910-8660-5(7) , Chelsea Hse.) Facts On File, Inc.

CHILDREN'S LITERATURE—BIBLIOGRAPHY

Children's Authors - Set II, Set. Incl. Beverly Cleary. Meister, Cari. lib. bdg. 21.35 (978-1-57765-480-3(3)); H. A. Rey. Meister, Cari. lib. bdg. 21.35 (978-1-57765-481-0(1)); J. K. Rowling. Meister, Cari. lib. bdg. 21.35 (978-1-57765-482-7(X)); Marc Brown. Woods, Mae. lib. bdg. 21.35 (978-1-57765-111-6(1)); R. L. Stine. Meister, Cari. lib. bdg. 21.35 (978-1-57765-484-1(6)); Shel Silverstein. Meister, Cari. lib. bdg. 21.35 (978-1-57765-483-4(8)); 24p. (J). (gr. k-6). 2001. (Illus.). 2001. Set lib. bdg. 128.10 (978-1-57765-502-2(8) , Checkerboard Library) ABDO Publishing Co.

Crew, Hilary. Women Engaged in War in Literature for Youth: A Guide to Resources for Children & Young Adults. 2007. 324p. pap. 51.00 ***(*978-0-8108-4929-7(1))*** Scarecrow Pr., Inc.

Favorite Children's Authors & Illustrators, 8 vols. 2nd ed. 2006. 368.00 ***(*978-1-59187-065-4(8))*** Tradition Publishing Co.

Findlay, Diane. Characters with Character: Using Children's Literature in Character Education. 2001. (Illus.). 88p. (J). (gr. k-5). pap. 16.95 (978-1-57950-064-1(1) , Up start Bks.) Highsmith Inc.

Gayle-Evans, Guda. An Annotated Bibliography of Multi-Cultural Literature for Children Three to Ten Years. 2004. (Mellen Studies in Children's Literature: Vol. 6). (Illus.). 204p. 109.95 (978-0-7734-6474-2(3)) Mellen, Edwin Pr., The.

Jweid, Rosann & Rizzo, Margaret. Building Character Through Literature: A Guide for Middle School Readers. 2001. (Illus.). 240p. (gr. 7-8). 39.50 (978-0-8108-3951-9(2)) Scarecrow Pr., Inc.

CHILDREN'S LITERATURE—HISTORY AND CRITICISM

Belle Prater's Boy. 1998. 44p. (YA). 11.95 (978-1-58130-558-6(3) , NU5583SP) Novel Units, Inc.

Chippendale, Lisa A. Triumph of the Imagination: The Story of Writer J. K. Rowling. 2001. (Overcoming Adversity Ser.). (Illus.). 112p. (J). (gr. 4-8). 30.00 (978-0-7910-6312-5(7) , Chelsea Hse.) Facts On File, Inc.

Colson, Mary. The Story Behind Anne Holm's I Am David. 2006. (History in Literature Ser.). (Illus.). 56p. (YA). (gr. 7 up). lib. bdg. 32.86 (978-1-4034-8204-4(7)) Heinemann Library.

Czerneda, Julie E., ed. Stardust. Normand, Jean-Pierre, illus. 2001. (Tales from the Wonder Zone Ser.). 128p. (J). (gr. 4 up). pap. 11.95 (978-1-55244-018-6(4)) Trifolium Bks., Inc. CAN. *Dist:* Fitzhenry & Whiteside, Ltd.

Dennis, Mary L. & Millin, Kathleen. A Day No Pigs Would Die. 1998. 36p. (YA). 11.95 (978-1-56137-394-9(X) , NU394XSP) Novel Units, Inc.

Gale Research Staff. Children's Literature Review, Vol. 64. 2000. 300p. (C). (ps-3). 215.00 (978-0-7876-3229-8(5)) Thomson Gale.

Gamble, Nikki. Favourite Classic Writers. (Illus.). 32p. pap. (978-0-7502-4286-8(8) , Hodder Wayland) Hodder Children's Division.

Glassman, Peter. Oz: The Hundredth Anniversary Celebration. 2000. (J). lib. bdg. 19.89 (978-0-06-029219-5(9)) HarperCollins Pubs.

Golding, Robert. Lord of the Flies. 2002. (YA). 14.00 (978-0-7587-5197-3(4)) Book Wholesalers, Inc.

Gresh, Lois H. The Truth Behind A Series of Unfortunate Events: Eyeballs, Leeches, Hypnotism, & Orphans—Exploring Lemony Snicket's World. rev. ed. 2004. (Illus.). 208p. (J). 11.95 (978-0-312-32703-3(X) , St. Martin's Paperbacks) St. Martin's Pr.

Hunsicker, Ranelda Mack. Black Beauty: A Guide for Teachers & Students. 2002. (Classics for Young Readers Ser.). 64p. (J). pap. 6.99 (978-0-87552-732-1(9)) P & R Publishing.

I Am the Cheese. 1998. 40p. (J). 11.95 (978-1-58130-581-4(8) , NU5818SP) Novel Units, Inc.

Island of the Blue Dolphins. 1998. 40p. (J). 11.95 (978-1-56137-489-2(X) , NU489XSP) Novel Units, Inc.

Krupp, Edwin C. Rainbow & You. 2000. (J). pap., stu. ed. (978-0-688-18032-4(9) , Harper Trophy) HarperCollins Pubs.

McElroy, Lisa Tucker & Cobb, Abby. Meet My Grandmother: She's a Children's Book Author. Benjamin, Joel, photos by. 2001. (Grandmothers at Work Ser.). (Illus.). 32p. (gr. 2-4). lib. bdg. 22.90 (978-0-7613-1972-6(7) , Millbrook Pr.) Lerner Publishing Group.

Novel Units, Inc. Staff. Mr. Popper's Penguins. 1998. 44p. (J). 9.95 (978-1-56137-177-8(7) , NU1777) Novel Units, Inc.

—My Side of the Mountain. 1998. 44p. (YA). 11.95 (978-1-56137-494-6(6) , NU4946SP) Novel Units, Inc.

—Number the Stars. 1998. 44p. (J). stu. ed. 11.95 (978-1-56137-605-6(1) , NU6051SP) Novel Units, Inc.

Roberts, Russell. John Newbery & the Story of the Newbery Medal. 2003. (Great Achiever Awards Ser.). (Illus.). 48p. (J). (gr. 4-8). lib. bdg. 29.95 (978-1-58415-201-9(X)) Mitchell Lane Pubs., Inc.

CHILDREN'S READING

see Children's Literature; Reading

CHILE

Blomquist, Christopher. Chile, a Primary Source Guide. 2005. (Countries of the World, a Primary Source Journey Ser.). (Illus.). 24p. (J). 19.95 (978-1-4042-2751-4(2) , PowerKids Pr.) Rosen Publishing Group, Inc., The.

Crooker, Richard A. Chile. 2004. (Modern World Nations Ser.). (Illus.). 120p. (gr. 6-12). 30.00 (978-0-7910-7912-6(0) , Chelsea Hse.) Facts On File, Inc.

DiPiazza, Francesca. Chile in Pictures. 2nd ed. 2007. (Visual Geography Ser.). (Illus.). 80p. (J). (gr. 5-12). 27.93 (978-0-8225-6587-1(0) , Twenty-First Century Bks.) Lerner Publishing Group.

Dwyer, Christopher. Chile. 1999. (Major World Nations Ser.). (Illus.). 144p. (YA). (gr. 4-7). lib. bdg. 21.95 (978-0-7910-4734-7(2) , Chelsea Hse.) Facts On File, Inc.

Harcourt School Publishers Staff. Social Studies: Argentina, Chile, Paraguay & Uruguay. 2000. (Harcourt Brace Social Studies). (Illus.). (gr. k-7). pap. 33.90 (978-0-15-317433-9(1)) Harcourt Schl. Pubs.

Holiday, Jane. Exploring Chile with the Five Themes of Geography. 2005. (Library of the Western Hemisphere). (Illus.). 24p. (J). 19.95 (978-1-4042-2677-7(X) , PowerKids Pr.); pap. (978-0-8239-4637-2(1)) Rosen Publishing Group, Inc., The.

Klingel, Cynthia Fitterer & Noyed, Robert B. Chile. 2002. (First Reports). (Illus.). 48p. (J). (gr. 3 up). lib. bdg. 22.60 (978-0-7565-0183-9(0)) Compass Point Bks.

Kwek, Karen. Welcome to Chile. 2004. (Welcome to My Country Ser.). (Illus.). 48p. (J). (gr. 2 up). lib. bdg. 26.00 (978-0-8368-2558-9(6)) Stevens, Gareth Inc.

Martinez, Renee Russo. Chile. 2002. (Countries of the World Ser.). (Illus.). 96p. (J). (gr. 6 up). lib. bdg. 30.00 (978-0-8368-2358-5(3)) Stevens, Gareth Inc.

McNair, Sylvia. Chile. 2000. (Enchantment of the World, Second Ser.). (Illus.). 144p. (J). (gr. 5-9). 36.00 (978-0-516-21007-0(6) , Children's Pr.) Scholastic Library Publishing.

Morrison, Marion. Chile. 2006. (Countries of the World Ser.). 64p. (J). (gr. 6-12). 30.00 (978-0-8160-6014-6(2)) Facts On File, Inc.

Rau, Dana Meachen. Chile. 2006. (Discovering Cultures Ser.). 48p. (J). lib. bdg. 28.50 (978-0-7614-1988-4(8) , Benchmark Bks.) Cavendish, Marshall Corp.

Roraff, Susan. Chile. 1998. (Festivals of the World Ser.). (Illus.). 32p. (J). (gr. 3 up). lib. bdg. 24.67 (978-0-8368-2012-6(6)) Stevens, Gareth Inc.

Schaffer, David. Chile. 2004. (Modern Nations of the World Ser.). (Illus.). 112p. (YA). (gr. 7-12). lib. bdg. 29.95 (978-1-59018-322-9(3) , Lucent Bks.) Thomson Gale.

Selby, Anna. Argentina, Chile, Paraguay, Uruguay. 1999. (Country Fact Files Ser.). (Illus.). 48p. (J). (gr. 4-8). lib. bdg. 27.12 (978-0-8172-5408-7(0)) Raintree.

Shields, Charles J. Chile. 2003. (Discovering South America Ser.). (Illus.). 64p. (J). (gr. 5 up). lib. bdg. (978-1-59084-287-4(1)) Mason Crest Pubs.

Spengler, Kremena. Chile. 2005. (Fact Finders Ser.). (Illus.). 32p. (J). 22.60 (978-0-7368-3748-4(5)) Capstone Pr., Inc.

Weber, Valerie. I Come from Chile. 2006. (Illus.). 24p. (J). pap. (978-0-8368-7241-5(X)); lib. bdg. (978-0-8368-7234-7(7)) Stevens, Gareth Inc. (Weekly Reader Early Learning Library).

Winter, J. Kohen & Roraff, S. Chile. 2nd ed. 2001. (Cultures of the World Ser.). (Illus.). 144p. (gr. 5 up). lib. bdg. 37.07 (978-0-7614-1360-8(X) , Benchmark Bks.) Cavendish, Marshall Corp.

CHILE—FICTION

Bondoux, Anne-Laure. The Killer's Tears. Maudet, Y., tr. 176p. (YA). (gr. 7). 2007. pap. 8.99 (978-0-385-73384-7(4)); 2006. (Illus.). 15.95 (978-0-385-73293-2(7)); 2006. (Illus.). lib. bdg. 17.99 (978-0-385-90314-1(6)) Random Hse. Children's Bks. (Delacorte Bks. for Young Readers).

Diaz-Guerra, Francisco. Mi Pequeno Maestro. 2001. (YA). (978-956-240-304-7(1)) Arrayan Editores S.A.

Hidalgo, Hector, ed. Chile en Cuentos. 2001. (YA). (978-956-240-346-7(7)) Arrayan Editores S.A.

Morel, Alicia. La Conquista del Rocio. 2001. (J). (978-956-240-302-3(5)) Arrayan Editores S.A.

—Los Viajeros Invisibles. 2002. (J). (978-956-240-360-3(2)) Arrayan Editores S.A.

Rand, Gloria & Rand, Ted. A Pen Pal for Max. rev. ed. 2005. (Illus.). 32p. (J). (gr. 4-7). 16.95 (978-0-8050-7586-1(0) , Holt, Henry & Co. Bks. For Young Readers) Holt, Henry & Co.

Thomas, Maria Jose. Bravo, Rosina. Munoz, Claudio, illus. 2006. Tr. of Bravo, Rosina!. (SPA.). (J). (gr. 4-5). 10.40 (978-980-257-242-7(X) , EK33833) Ekare, Ediciones VEN. *Dist:* Lectorum Pubns., Inc.

CHILLS AND FEVER

see Malaria

CHIMES

see Bells

CHIMPANZEES

Albee, Sarah. Chimpanzees. 2006. (J). (978-1-59939-062-8(0) , Reader's Digest Young Families, Inc.) Reader's Digest Children's Publishing, Inc.

Banks, Martin. Chimpanzee. 2000. (Natural World Ser.). (Illus.). 48p. (J). (gr. 4-7). pap. 9.95 (978-0-7398-1817-6(1)) Steck-Vaughn.

—Chimpanzee: Habitats, Life Cycles, Food Chains, Threats. 2000. (Natural World Ser.). (Illus.). 48p. (J). (gr. 3-7). lib. bdg. 27.12 (978-0-7398-1062-0(6)) Raintree.

Bardhan-Quallen, Sudipta. Up Close: Jane Goodall: Jane Goodall. 2008. (Up Close Ser.). 208p. (YA). (gr. 6). 16.99 ***(*978-0-670-06263-8(4)*** , Viking Juvenile) Penguin Group (USA) Inc.

Bow, Patricia. Chimpanzee Rescue: Changing the Future for Endangered Wildlife. 2004. (Firefly Animal Rescue Ser.). (Illus.). 64p. (J). (gr. 5-8). 19.95 (978-1-55297-909-9(1)); pap. 9.95 (978-1-55297-908-2(3)) Firefly Bks., Ltd.

Briscoe, Diana. Jane Goodall: Finding Hope in the Wilds of Africa. 2004. (High Five Reading Ser.). (J). (978-0-7368-3851-1(1)); 23.93 (978-0-7368-3879-5(1)) Capstone Pr., Inc.

Chessen, Betsey & Chanko, Pamela. Jane Goodall & Her Chimpanzees. 1999. (Social Studies Emergent Readers). (J). 2.50 (978-0-439-04576-6(2)) Scholastic, Inc.

—Jane Goodall & Her Chimpanzees. 1999. (ps-2). lib. bdg. 10.10 (978-0-613-21797-2(7)) Tandem Library Bks.

Dennard, Deborah. Chimpanzees. McGee, John F., illus. 2004. (Our Wild World Ser.). 48p. (J). (gr. 2-5). ring bd. 10.95 (978-1-55971-846-2(3)); pap. 7.95 (978-1-55971-845-5(5)) T&N Children's Publishing. (NorthWord Bks. for Young Readers).

—Chimpanzees. 2003. (gr. 3-6). lib. bdg. 16.40 (978-0-613-67955-8(5)) Tandem Library Bks.

Donovan. Chimpanzees. 2002. pap. (978-0-7398-5808-0(4)) Steck-Vaughn.

Donovan, Sandy. Chimpanzees. 2002. (Animals of the Rain Forest Ser.). (Illus.). 32p. (YA). lib. bdg. 22.83 (978-0-7398-5370-2(8)) Raintree.

Dorman, Clive & Dorman, Helen. Okomi Enjoys His Outings, Vol. 5. Hutchings, Tony, illus. 2004. (Okomi Stories Ser.). 24p. (J). pap. 4.95 (978-1-58469-055-9(0)) Dawn Pubns.

Ehrlich, Fred. Does a Panda Go to School? Bolam, Emily, illus. 2003. (Early Experiences Ser.). 32p. 10.95 (978-1-59354-017-3(5)) Blue Apple Bks.

Feinstein, Stephen. The Chimpanzee: Help Save This Endangered Species! 2007. (Saving Endangered Species Ser.). (Illus.). 128p. (J). lib. bdg. 33.27 (978-1-59845-039-2(5) , MyReportLinks.com Bks.) Enslow Pubs., Inc.

Fetty, Margaret. Chimpanzees. 2006. (Smart Animals! Ser.). (Illus.). 32p. (J). lib. bdg. 25.27 (978-1-59716-159-6(4)) Bearport Publishing Co., Inc.

Frost, Helen. Chimpanzees. Saunders-Smith, Gail, ed. 2002. (Rain Forest Animals Ser.). (Illus.). 24p. (J). (gr. k-1). lib. bdg. 15.93 (978-0-7368-1455-3(8) , Pebble Bks.) Capstone Pr., Inc.

Garduno, Joseph A. Moe. 2000. (Illus.). 228p. (YA). pap. 19.95 (978-0-9608806-3-8(1)) Associated Pubns.

Gareth Stevens Publishing Staff, contrib. by. Chimpanzees. 2004. (All about Wild Animals Ser.). (Illus.). 32p. (J). (gr. 2 up). lib. bdg. 23.33 (978-0-8368-4171-8(9)) Stevens, Gareth Inc.

Goodall, Jane. The Chimpanzees I Love: Saving Their World & Ours. 2001. (Illus.). 80p. (J). (gr. 3 up). pap. 18.95 (978-0-439-21310-3(X) , Levine, Arthur A. Bks.) Scholastic, Inc.

—In the Shadow of Man. 2000. (gr. 7-12). lib. bdg. 24.60 (978-0-613-45778-1(1)) Tandem Library Bks.

—With Love: Ten Heartwarming Stories of Chimpanzees in the Wild. Marks, Alan, illus. 1998. 44p. (J). (gr. 1-5). 15.95 (978-1-55858-911-7(2)) North-South Bks., Inc.

—With Love: Ten Heartwarming Stories of Chimpanzees in the Wild. 2003. (gr. 3-6). lib. bdg. 15.25 (978-0-613-81369-3(3)) Tandem Library Bks.

Goodridge, Catherine. Jane Goodall. ed. 2004. (SPA.). (J). pap. 5.00 (978-1-4108-2426-4(8) , A24268) Benchmark Education Co.

Greenberg, Daniel A. Chimpanzees. 2000. (Animals Animals Ser.). (Illus.). 48p. (J). (gr. 3-5). lib. bdg. 25.64 (978-0-7614-1165-9(8) , Benchmark Bks.) Cavendish, Marshall Corp.

Head, Honor. What's It Like to Be a Baby Chimp? Nichols, Matthew, illus. 1998. (Baby Animals Ser.). 32p. (gr. k-3). lib. bdg. 20.90 (978-0-7613-1253-6(6) , Millbrook Pr.) Lerner Publishing Group.

Hilliard, Richard, illus. Ham, the Astrochimp. 2007. 32p. (J). (gr. 4-7). 16.95 ***(*978-1-59078-459-4(6))*** Boyds Mills Pr.

Jacobs, Liza. Chimpanzees. 2003. (Wild Wild World Ser.). (Illus.). 24p. (J). 23.70 (978-1-4103-0031-7(5) , Blackbirch Pr., Inc.) Thomson Gale.

Johnson, Jinny. Chimp. 1999. (Wild Baby Animals Ser.). (Illus.). 16p. (ps-k). 4.99 (978-0-7681-0187-4(5) , McClanahan Bk.) Learning Horizons, Inc.

—Chimp. Ch'en-Ling, illus. Murrell, Simon, photos by. 2001. (Busy Baby Animals Ser.). 16p. (J). (ps up). lib. bdg. 19.33 (978-0-8368-2921-1(2)) Stevens, Gareth Inc.

—Chimpanzee. 2006. (Illus.). 32p. (J). (978-1-58340-900-8(9)) Smart Apple Media.

Kalman, Bobbie & Dyer, Hadley. Les Chimpanzés. rev. ed. 2007. (FRE., Illus.). 32p. (J). (gr. 2-3). pap. ***(*978-2-89579-128-7(7))*** Editions Banjo.

Kalman, Bobbie & Dyer, Hadley. Endangered Chimpanzees. 2005. (Earth's Endangered Animals Ser.). (Illus.). 32p. (J). (gr. 3-5). (978-0-7787-1859-8(X)); (ps-k). pap. (978-0-7787-1905-2(7)) Crabtree Publishing Co.

Kane, Karen. Chimpanzees. Ellis, Gerry, illus. Ellis, Gerry, photos by. 2005. (Early Bird Nature Bks.). (J). 25.26 (978-0-8225-2418-2(X) , Lerner Pubns.) Lerner Publishing Group.

Kendell, Patricia. Chimpanzees. 2002. (In the Wild Ser.). (Illus.). 32p. (J). lib. bdg. 25.69 (978-0-7398-4904-0(2)) Raintree.

Kittinger, Jo S. Jane Goodall. 2005. (Scholastic News Nonfiction Readers Ser.). (Illus.). 24p. pap. (978-0-516-24783-0(2)) Children's Pr., Ltd.

—Jane Goodall. 2005. (Scholastic News Nonfiction Readers Ser.). (Illus.). 24p. (J). (gr. 1-2). 19.00 (978-0-516-24940-7(1) , Children's Pr.) Scholastic Library Publishing.

Krohn, Katherine E. Jane Goodall: Animal Scientist. 2006. (Graphic Library). (Illus.). 32p. (J). 25.26 (978-0-7368-5485-6(1)) Capstone Pr., Inc.

Leavitt, Amie. Care for a Pet Chimpanzee. 2007. (How to Convince Your Parents You Can ... Ser.). (Illus.). 32p. (J). (gr. 1-4). lib. bdg. 25.70 ***(*978-1-58415-607-9(4))*** Mitchell Lane Pubs., Inc.

Lockwood, Sophie. Chimpanzees. 2008. (World of Mammals Ser.). 40p. (J). (gr. 2-6). 29.93 ***(*978-1-59296-927-2(5))*** Child's World, Inc.

Martin, Patricia. Chimpanzees. 2000. (gr. 3-6). lib. bdg. 15.25 (978-0-613-37309-8(X)) Tandem Library Bks.

Martin, Patricia A. Fink. Chimpanzees. 2000. (True Bks.). (Illus.). 48p. (J). (gr. 3-5). pap. 6.95 (978-0-516-27013-5(3) , Children's Pr.) Scholastic Library Publishing.

Murray, Julie. Chimpanzees. 2002. (Buddy Book Ser.). (Illus.). 24p. (J). (gr. k-4). lib. bdg. 21.35 (978-1-57765-713-2(6)) ABDO Publishing Co.

Nagda, Ann Whitehead & Bickel, Cindy. Chimp Math: Learning about Time from a Baby Chimpanzee. rev. ed. 2002. (Illus.). 32p. (J). (gr. 2-5). 17.95 (978-0-8050-6674-6(8) , Holt, Henry & Co. Bks. For Young Readers) Holt, Henry & Co.

Petty, Kate. Chimpanzees. 2004. (J). lib. bdg. 22.80 (978-1-932799-41-5(9)) Stargazer Bks.

Pingry, Patricia A. & Sharp, Chris. Baby Chimpanzee. 2003. (San Diego Zoo Animal Library: Vol. 2). (Illus.). 24p. (J). bds. 6.95 (978-0-8249-6530-3(2)) Ideals Pubns.

Povey, Karen D. Chimpanzees. 2002. (Endangered Animals & Habitats Ser.). (Illus.). 112p. (J). (gr. 4-12). 27.45 (978-1-56006-918-8(X) , Lucent Bks.) Thomson Gale.

Robinson, Claire. Chimpanzees. (Illus.). 24p. (gr. k-2). 2002. (J). pap. 6.95 (978-1-57572-464-5(2) , 90454); 1998. lib. bdg. 21.36 (978-1-57572-136-1(8)) Heinemann Library.

—Chimpanzees. 2001. (Illus.). 24p. (J). (ps-ps). lib. bdg. 15.25 (978-0-613-24558-6(X)) Tandem Library Bks.

Schaefer, Lola M. Jane Goodall. (First Biographies Ser.). 24p. (J). pap. 5.95 (978-0-7368-5085-8(6)) Capstone Pr., Inc.

Schaefer, Lola M. & Schaefer, Wyatt S. Jane Goodall. 2004. (First Biographies Ser.). 24p. (J). lib. bdg. 15.93 (978-0-7368-2083-7(3) , Pebble Bks.) Capstone Pr., Inc.

Shores, Erika L. Chimpanzees: Living in Communities. 2004. (Wild World of Animals Ser.). (Illus.). 24p. (J). lib. bdg. 21.26 (978-0-7368-2613-6(0) , Bridgestone Bks.) Capstone Pr., Inc.

Spilsbury, Louise & Spilsbury, Richard. A Troop of Chimpanzees. 2003. (Animal Groups Ser.). (Illus.). 32p. pap. 6.95 (978-1-4034-3288-9(0)); (J). lib. bdg. 24.22 (978-1-4034-0746-7(0)) Heinemann Library.

Wildlife Education, Ltd. Staff & Elwood, Ann. Chimpanzees. 1999. (Zoobooks Ser.). (Illus.). 18p. (J). pap. 2.95 (978-0-937934-61-6(5)) Wildlife Education, Ltd.

Woronoff, Kristen. Jane Goodall: Animal Scientist. 2002. (Famous Women Juniors Ser.). (Illus.). 32p. (J). (gr. 3-5). 23.70 (978-1-56711-585-7(3) , Blackbirch Pr., Inc.) Thomson Gale.

CHIMPANZEES—FICTION

Alborough, Jez. Yes. Alborough, Jez, illus. 2006. (Illus.). 40p. (J). (ps). 15.99 (978-0-7636-3183-3(3)) Candlewick Pr.

Anderson, Dawn. Chimpance, Como Yo ! 2006. (Illus.). (J). 15.95 (978-0-9786570-1-7(2)) Opposable Thumb Pr.

—Chimpanzee, Like Me! 2006. (Illus.). (J). 15.95 (978-0-9786570-0-0(4)) Opposable Thumb Pr.

Andreae, Giles. Chimpanzees of Happytown. 2006. 32p. (J). pap. 16.99 (978-0-439-83768-2(5) , Orchard Bks.) Scholastic, Inc.

Anholt, Catherine & Anholt, Laurence. Chimp & Zee's Animals. 2007. (Chimp & Zee Ser.). (Illus.). 22p. (J). bds. 3.95 (***978-1-84507-728-0(8)***) Lincoln, Frances Ltd. GBR. *Dist:* Perseus Distribution.

—Chimp & Zee's Clothes. 2007. (Chimp & Zee Ser.). (Illus.). 22p. (J). bds. 3.95 (***978-1-84507-729-7(6)***) Lincoln, Frances Ltd. GBR. *Dist:* Perseus Distribution.

—Chimp & Zee's Noisy Book. 2008. (Chimp & Zee Ser.). (Illus.). 8p. (J). 5.95 (***978-1-84507-804-1(7)***) Lincoln, Frances Ltd. GBR. *Dist:* Perseus Distribution.

—Monkey about with Chimp & Zee. 2008. (Chimp & Zee Ser.). (Illus.). 8p. (J). 5.95 (***978-1-84507-803-4(9)***) Lincoln, Frances Ltd. GBR. *Dist:* Perseus Distribution.

—Play. 2007. (Chimp & Zee Ser.). (Illus.). 22p. (J). bds. 3.95 (***978-1-84507-746-4(6)***) Lincoln, Frances Ltd. GBR. *Dist:* Perseus Distribution.

Anholt, Laurence & Anholt, Catherine. Chimp & Zee: Words & Pictures. 2006. (Chimp & Zee Ser.). (Illus.). 32p. (J). (ps). 15.95 (978-1-84507-375-6(4)) Lincoln, Frances Ltd. GBR. *Dist:* Perseus Distribution.

Beechen, Adam. Best Valentine. 2001. (gr. k-3). lib. bdg. 11.25 (978-0-613-43917-6(1)) Tandem Library Bks.

Bow, Patricia. Chimpanzee Rescue: Changing the Future for Endangered Wildlife. 2004. (Illus.). 64p. (J). (gr. k-9). lib. bdg. 16.60 (978-0-606-33844-8(6)) Tandem Library Bks.

Browne, Anthony. I Like Books. Browne, Anthony, illus. 2004. (Super Sturdy Picture Books Ser.). (Illus.). 24p. (J). (gr. k). 8.99 (978-0-7636-2162-9(5)) Candlewick Pr.

—Willy the Dreamer. 1998. (J). 16.99 (978-0-7636-0617-6(0)) Candlewick Pr.

—Willy the Wizard. 2003. (gr. k-3). lib. bdg. 14.15 (978-0-613-63757-2(7)) Tandem Library Bks.

Dickinson, Peter. Eva. 2005. 220p. (YA). (gr. 7-12). 21.50 (978-0-8446-7274-8(2), 3589) Smith, Peter Pub., Inc.

Dorman, Clive. Okomi: The New Baby. 2001. (ps-2). lib. bdg. 12.95 (978-0-613-79611-8(X)) Tandem Library Bks.

Dorman, Clive & Dorman, Helen. Okomi Wakes up Early, Vol. 6. Hutchings, Tony, illus. 2004. (Sharing Nature with Children Book Ser.). 24p. (J). pap. 4.95 (978-1-58469-056-6(9)) Dawn Pubns.

—Okomi Wanders Too Far, Vol. 8. Hutchings, Tony, illus. 2004. (Sharing Nature with Children Book Ser.). 24p. (J). pap. 4.95 (978-1-58469-058-0(5)) Dawn Pubns.

Dorman, Helen. Okomi & the Tickling Game. 2001. (ps-2). lib. bdg. 12.95 (978-0-613-79614-9(4)) Tandem Library Bks.

—Okomi Climbs a Tree. 2001. (ps-2). lib. bdg. 12.95 (978-0-613-79613-2(6)) Tandem Library Bks.

—Okomi Plays in the Leaves. 2001. (ps-2). lib. bdg. 12.95 (978-0-613-79607-1(1)) Tandem Library Bks.

Dorman, Helen & Dorman, Clive. Okomi & the Tickling Game, Vol. 2. Hutchings, Tony, illus. 2004. (Sharing Nature with Children Book Ser.: 2). 24p. (J). pap. 4.95 (978-1-58469-046-7(1)) Dawn Pubns.

—Okomi Climbs a Tree, Vol. 4. Hutchings, Tony, illus. 2004. (Sharing Nature with Children Book Ser.: 4). 24p. (J). pap. 4.95 (978-1-58469-045-0(3)) Dawn Pubns.

—Okomi Plays in the Leaves, Vol. 3. Hutchings, Tony, illus. 2004. (Sharing Nature with Children Book Ser.: 3). 24p. (J). pap. 4.95 (978-1-58469-047-4(X)) Dawn Pubns.

—Okomi, the New Baby. Hutchings, Tony, illus. 2004. (Sharing Nature with Children Book Ser.: 1). 24p. (J). pap. 4.95 (978-1-58469-044-3(5)) Dawn Pubns.

Faulkner, Keith. Charlie Chimp's Christmas: A Pop-up Extravaganza of Festive Friends. Lambert, Jonathan, illus. 2006. 12p. (J). (ps-3). reprint ed. 10.00 (978-1-4223-5446-9(6)) DIANE Publishing Co.

Goodall, Jane. Rickie & Henri: A True Story. Marks, Alan, illus. 2004. 32p. (J). (ps). 15.99 (978-0-698-40002-3(X), Minedition) Penguin Group (USA) Inc.

Harry, Rebecca, illus. Little Chimp. 2007. (Noisy Jungle Babies Ser.). 8p. (J). bds. 5.99 (978-0-7641-6034-9(6)) Barron's Educational Series, Inc.

Hoban, Lillian. Arthur's Back to School Day. Hoban, Lillian, illus. 64th ed. 1998. (I Can Read Bks.). (Illus.). 48p. (J). (ps-3). pap. 3.99 (978-0-06-444245-9(4), Harper Trophy) HarperCollins Pubs.

—Arthur's Back to School Day. Hoban, Lillian, illus. 1998. (Illus.). (J). (ps-ps). lib. bdg. 11.80 (978-0-613-11282-6(2)) Tandem Library Bks.

—Arthur's Birthday Party. Hoban, Lillian, illus. 1999. (I Can Read Bks.). (Illus.). 64p. (J). (gr. k-4). 14.89 (978-0-06-027799-4(8)); 14.95 (978-0-06-027798-7(X)) HarperCollins Pubs.

—Arthur's Funny Money. Hoban, Lillian, illus. 2002. (Arthur the Chimpanzee Ser.). (Illus.). (J). 12.34 (978-0-7587-5985-6(1)) Book Wholesalers, Inc.

—Arthur's Halloween Costume. Hoban, Lillian, illus. 2002. (Arthur the Chimpanzee Ser.). (Illus.). (J). 12.30 (978-0-7587-5553-7(8)) Book Wholesalers, Inc.

—Arthur's Honey Bear. Hoban, Lillian, illus. 2002. (Arthur the Chimpanzee Ser.). (Illus.). (J). 11.91 (978-0-7587-5986-3(X)) Book Wholesalers, Inc.

—Arthur's Loose Tooth. Hoban, Lillian, illus. 2002. (Arthur the Chimpanzee Ser.). (Illus.). (J). 11.37 (978-0-7587-5987-0(8)) Book Wholesalers, Inc.

—Arthur's Pen Pal. Hoban, Lillian, illus. 2002. (Arthur the Chimpanzee Ser.). (Illus.). (J). 12.34 (978-0-7587-5989-4(4)) Book Wholesalers, Inc.

—Arthur's Prize Reader. Hoban, Lillian, illus. 2002. (Arthur the Chimpanzee Ser.). (Illus.). (J). 12.30 (978-0-7587-5554-4(6)) Book Wholesalers, Inc.

Kilaka, John. Fresh Fish: A Tale from Tanzania. 2005. (Illus.). 32p. (J). 16.95 (978-0-88899-656-5(X)) Groundwood Bks. CAN. *Dist:* Perseus Distribution.

Knudtsen, Ken. My Monkey's Name Is Jennifer. 2003. (Illus.). 152p. (gr. 11 up). pap. 15.95 (978-0-943151-71-7(6)) Slave Labor Bks.

London, Jonathan. Zack at the Dentist. Medoff, Jack, illus. 2004. 32p. (J). pap. 3.50 (978-0-439-53776-6(2), Cartwheel Bks.) Scholastic, Inc.

Mundis, Hester. My Chimp Friday: The Nana Banana Chronicles. 176p. (J). 2004. pap. 4.99 (978-0-689-87326-3(3), Aladdin); 2002. (Illus.). (gr. 4-6). 16.00 (978-0-689-83837-8(9)) Simon & Schuster Children's Publishing.

Napoli, Donna Jo & Furrow, Eva. Bobby the Bold. Hoyt, Ard, illus. 2006. 32p. (J). (ps-12). 16.99 (978-0-8037-2990-2(1), Dial) Penguin Group (USA) Inc.

Oram, Hiawyn. The Wrong Overcoat. Birchall, Mark, illus. 2000. (Picture Bks.). 32p. (J). (ps-3). lib. bdg. 15.95 (978-1-57505-453-7(1), Carolrhoda Bks.) Lerner Publishing Group.

Ostrow, Kim. Darwin's Family Tree. 2001. (gr. k-3). lib. bdg. 11.80 (978-0-613-35602-2(0)) Tandem Library Bks.

Rey, H. A. & Rey, Margret. Curious George & the Birthday Surprise. Weston, Martha, illus. 2003. 24p. (J). (gr. k-3). 12.95 (978-0-618-34688-2(0)); pap. 3.95 (978-0-618-34687-5(2)) Houghton Mifflin Co. Trade & Reference Div.

—Curious George Visits the Library. Weston, Martha, illus. 2003. (Curious George Ser.). 24p. (J). (gr. k-3). pap. 3.95 (978-0-618-06568-4(7)) Houghton Mifflin Co.

Rorby, Ginny. Hurt Go Happy. 2007. 272p. (J). 5.99 (***978-0-7653-5304-7(0)***, Starscape) Doherty, Tom Assocs., LLC.

Stahnke, Rich. Furious Fist of the Drunken Monkey: Origin of the Species #3. 2007. 2.95 (***978-0-9791192-4-8(3)***) Silent Devil Productions.

Thorpe, Kiki. Snowbound. 2000. (gr. k-3). lib. bdg. 11.80 (978-0-613-31727-6(0)) Tandem Library Bks.

—Trouble with Darwin. 2001. (gr. k-3). lib. bdg. 14.15 (978-0-613-43965-7(1)) Tandem Library Bks.

Watson, Richard Jesse. The Boy Who Went Ape. Watson, Benjamin James, illus. 2008. (J). pap. (***978-0-590-47966-0(0)***) Blue Sky Pr.

CHINA

Anderson, Dale. Ancient China. 2005. (History in Art Ser.). (Illus.). 48p. (J). lib. bdg. 29.93 (978-1-4109-0519-2(5)) Steck-Vaughn.

Armentrout, David & Armentrout, Patricia. Treasures from China. 2000. (Treasures from the Past Ser.). (Illus.). 48p. (J). (gr. 4-8). lib. bdg. 29.93 (978-1-55916-288-3(0)) Rourke Publishing, LLC.

Asher, Sandy. China. 2002. (Discovering Cultures Ser.). (Illus.). 48p. (J). 25.64 (978-0-7614-1179-6(8), Benchmark Bks.) Cavendish, Marshall Corp.

Baldwin, Robert F. Daily Life in Ancient & Modern Beijing. Webb, Ray, illus. 1999. (Cities Through Time Ser.). 64p. (J). (gr. 5-12). 25.26 (978-0-8225-3214-9(X)) Lerner Publishing Group.

Behnke, Alison. China in Pictures. 2nd rev. ed. 2003. (Visual Geography Ser.). (Illus.). 80p. (J). (gr. 5-12). 27.93 (978-0-8225-0370-5(0)) Lerner Publishing Group.

Bowden, Rob. The Yangtze. 2003. (River Journey Ser.). (Illus.). 48p. (J). lib. bdg. 28.56 (978-0-7398-6074-8(7)) Raintree.

Bramwell, Neil D. Ancient China: A MyReportLinks. com Book. 2004. (Civilizations of the Ancient World Ser.). (Illus.). 48p. (J). lib. bdg. 25.26 (978-0-7660-5184-3(6), MyReportLinks.com Bks.) Enslow Pubs., Inc.

Brown, Don. Far Beyond the Garden Gate: Alexandra David-Neel's Journey to Lhasa. Brown, Don, illus. 2002. (Illus.). 32p. (J). (gr. k-3). tchr. ed. 16.00 (978-0-618-08364-0(2)) Houghton Mifflin Co. Trade & Reference Div.

Caper, William. India & China. 2005. (Navigators Ser.). (J). pap. 44.00 (***978-1-4108-5112-3(5)***) Benchmark Education Co.

Charley, Catherine. China. 1998. (Country Fact Files Ser.). (Illus.). 48p. (J). (gr. 4-8). lib. bdg. 27.12 (978-0-8172-5410-0(2)) Raintree.

China, 6 vols. (gr. 2-5). 36.95 (978-0-7368-8171-5(9)) Red Brick Learning.

Costain, Meredith & Collins, Paul. Welcome to China. 2001. (Countries of the World Ser.). (Illus.). 32p. (J). (gr. 4 up). 28.00 (978-0-7910-6548-8(0), 010202, Chelsea Hse.) Facts On File, Inc.

Dean, Arlan. Terra-Cotta Soldiers: Army of Stone. 2005. (High Interest Bks.). (Illus.). 48p. (YA). (gr. 7-12). pap. 6.95 (978-0-516-25093-9(0), Children's Pr.) Scholastic Library Publishing.

Dramer, Kim. People's Republic of China. (Enchantment of the World, Second Ser.). (Illus.). 144p. 2006. (J). 36.00 (978-0-516-24867-7(7)); 1999. (YA). (gr. 5-9). 36.00 (978-0-516-21077-3(7)) Scholastic Library Publishing. (Children's Pr.).

—The Yellow River. 2001. (World of Water Ser.). (Illus.). 64p. (J). (gr. 5-7). 25.50 (978-0-531-11855-9(X), Watts, Franklin) Scholastic Library Publishing.

—Yellow River. 2001. (gr. 3-6). lib. bdg. 17.60 (978-0-613-37600-6(5)) Tandem Library Bks.

Enderlein, Cheryl L. Celebrating Birthdays in China. 1998. (Birthdays Around the World Ser.). (Illus.). 24p. (J). (gr. k-3). lib. bdg. 14.00 (978-0-531-11546-6(1), Watts, Franklin) Scholastic Library Publishing.

Fields, Catherine. China. 2000. (Nations of the World Ser.). (Illus.). 128p. (YA). (gr. 6-8). lib. bdg. 34.26 (978-0-8172-5781-1(0)) Raintree.

Flanagan, Alice K. Chinese New Year. Zhurkina, Svetlana, illus. 2003. (Holidays & Festivals Ser.). 32p. (J). (gr. 3 up). lib. bdg. 22.60 (978-0-7565-0479-3(1)) Compass Point Bks.

Fontes, Justine & Fontes, Ron. China. 2004. (to Z Ser.). (J). (gr. 2-4). pap. 6.95 (978-0-516-26807-1(4), Children's Pr.) Scholastic Library Publishing.

Friedman, Mel. China. 2007. (True Booktrade;: Geography: Countries Ser.). 48p. (J). spiral bd. 26.00 (***978-0-531-16852-3(2)***, Children's Pr.) Scholastic Library Publishing.

Frost, Helen. A Look at China. Saunders-Smith, Gail, ed. 2001. (Our World Ser.). (Illus.). 24p. (J). (gr. k-1). lib. bdg. 15.93 (978-0-7368-0983-2(X), Pebble Bks.) Capstone Pr., Inc.

—A Look at China. 2005. (One World, Many Cultures Ser.). 24p. (YA). (gr. k-3). pap. (978-0-7368-9418-0(7), Pebble Bks.) Capstone Pr., Inc.

Goddard, Carole. China. 2004. (Countries of the World Ser.). (Illus.). 64p. (J). (gr. 6-12). 30.00 (978-0-8160-5506-7(8)) Facts On File, Inc.

Goh, Sui Noi & Lim, Bee Iing. Welcome to China. 1999. (Welcome to My Country Ser.). (Illus.). 48p. (J). (gr. 2 up). lib. bdg. 26.00 (978-0-8368-2395-0(8)) Stevens, Gareth Inc.

Green, Jen. National Geographic Countries of the World: China. 2006. (Illus.). 64p. (J). (gr. 5). 27.90 (978-0-7922-6180-3(1), National Geographic Children's Bks.) National Geographic Society.

Harcourt School Publishers Staff. Changing the Face of China. 3rd ed. 2002. (Horizons Ser.). (Illus.). (J). pap. 7.30 (978-0-15-333640-9(4)) Harcourt Schl. Pubs.

Harvey, Miles. Look What Came from China. 1999. (Look What Came from Ser.). (Illus.). 32p. (J). (gr. 2-4). pap. 6.95 (978-0-531-15936-1(1), Watts, Franklin) Scholastic Library Publishing.

Hatt, Christine. Beijing. 1999. (World Cities Ser.). (Illus.). 48p. (J). (gr. 2-6). lib. bdg. 16.95 (978-1-929298-28-0(5)) Chrysalis Education.

Higgenbottom, Trevor. China. 2000. 64p. (YA). (gr. 6-8). lib. bdg. 27.07 (978-1-57572-420-1(0)) Heinemann Library.

Higginbottom, Trevor & White, Tony. China. 1999. (Illus.). 64p. (J). pap. 27.07 (978-1-58810-190-7(8)) Heinemann Library.

Hill, Valerie. China. 2002. (Ask about Asia Ser.). (Illus.). 48p. (J). (gr. 4 up). lib. bdg. (978-1-59084-199-0(9)) Mason Crest Pubs.

Holland, Lorien. China: A Travel Adventure. 2006. (Illus.). 112p. 19.95 (978-0-7946-0319-9(X), PeriplusEdition) Tuttle Publishing.

Houghton, Gillian. China: A Primary Source Cultural Guide. 2005. (Primary Sources of World Cultures Ser.). (Illus.). 128p. (J). (gr. 4-8). lib. bdg. 34.60 (978-1-4042-2908-2(6)) Rosen Publishing Group, Inc., The.

Italia, Bob. China. 2001. (Countries Ser.). (Illus.). 40p. (J). (gr. k-6). lib. bdg. 22.78 (978-1-57765-492-6(7), Checkerboard Library) ABDO Publishing Co.

Jenner, Caryn. Welcome to China. 2008. (Dk Readers Ser.). 48p. (J). (gr. 2-4). 14.99 (***978-0-7566-3752-1(X)***); pap. 3.99 (***978-0-7566-3753-8(8)***) Dorling Kindersley Publishing, Inc.

Kalman, Bobbie. China: The Culture. 2001. (gr. 3-6). lib. bdg. 16.40 (978-0-613-32395-6(5)) Tandem Library Bks.

—China: The Land. 2001. (gr. 3-6). lib. bdg. 16.40 (978-0-613-32396-3(3)) Tandem Library Bks.

—China: The People. 2001. (gr. 3-6). lib. bdg. 16.40 (978-0-613-32397-0(1)) Tandem Library Bks.

—China - The Culture. 2nd rev. ed. 2000. (Lands, Peoples & Cultures Ser.). (Illus.). 32p. (J). (gr. 4-5). (978-0-7787-9380-9(X)); pap. (978-0-7787-9748-7(1)) Crabtree Publishing Co.

—China - The Land. 2nd rev. ed. 2000. (Lands, Peoples & Cultures Ser.). (Illus.). 32p. (J). (gr. 4-5). (978-0-7787-9378-6(8)); pap. (978-0-7787-9746-3(5)) Crabtree Publishing Co.

—China - The People. 2nd rev. ed. 2000. (Lands, Peoples & Cultures Ser.). (Illus.). 32p. (J). (gr. 4-5). (978-0-7787-9379-3(6)); pap. (978-0-7787-9747-0(3)) Crabtree Publishing Co.

Keeler, Stephen. China. 2002. (Changing Face Of... Ser.). (Illus.). 48p. (J). lib. bdg. 27.12 (978-0-7398-5214-9(0)) Raintree.

A Look at China, 6 vols. (gr. k-2). 28.95 (978-0-7368-9419-7(5)) Red Brick Learning.

March, Michael. China. 2003. (Country Files Ser.). 32p. (J). lib. bdg. 24.25 (978-1-58340-236-8(5)) Smart Apple Media.

—Guide to China. 1998. (World Guides Ser.). (Illus.). 32p. (J). (gr. 2-6). lib. bdg. 21.27 (978-1-884756-41-2(7)) Davidson Titles, Inc.

Marx, David F. Chinese New Year. 2002. (Rookie Read-About Holidays Ser.). (Illus.). 32p. (J). (gr. 1-2). pap. 5.95 (978-0-516-27375-4(2), Children's Pr.) Scholastic Library Publishing.

—Chinese New Year. 2002. (gr. k-3). lib. bdg. 14.10 (978-0-613-54125-1(1)) Tandem Library Bks.

Mason, Antony. China: The New Superpower?: A Look at the Way the World Is Today. 2007. (Issues of the World Ser.). (Illus.). 48p. (J). (***978-1-59604-092-2(0)***, 1262573) Stargazer Bks.

McNeil, Niki, et al. HOCPP 1113 Ancient China. 2006. spiral bd. 20.00 (***978-1-60308-113-9(5)***) In the Hands of a Child.

Michels, Dia L. Look What I See! Where Can I Be? Visiting China. Bowles, Michael J. N., photos by. 2003. (Look What I See! Where Can I Be? Ser.: Vol. 5). (Illus.). 32p. 16.95 (978-1-930775-15-2(6)) Platypus Media, L.L.C.

Minnis. Ancient China. 2004. (Raintree Perspectives Ser.). (Illus.). 32p. (J). 26.36 (978-1-4109-0619-9(1)) Harcourt Schl. Pubs.

Morris, Noelle. China. 2002. (Steadwell Books World Tour). (Illus.). 48p. (J). lib. bdg. 24.26 (978-0-7398-5534-8(4)) Raintree.

Noi, Goh Sui. China. Lee, Dinah, ed. 1998. (Countries of the World Ser.). (Illus.). 96p. (J). (gr. 6 up). lib. bdg. 30.00 (978-0-8368-2124-6(6)) Stevens, Gareth Inc.

O'Connell, Kim A. China: A MyReportLinks. com Book. 2004. (Top Ten Countries of Recent Immigrants Ser.). (Illus.). 48p. (J). lib. bdg. 25.26 (978-0-7660-5240-6(0), MyReportLinks.com Bks.) Enslow Pubs., Inc.

Olson, Kay Melchisedech. China. 2003. (Many Cultures, One World Ser.). (Illus.). 32p. (J). (gr. 2-3). lib. bdg. 23.93 (978-0-7368-1531-4(7), Bridgestone Bks.) Capstone Pr., Inc.

Olson, Nathan. China: A Question & Answer Book. 2004. (Fact Finders Ser.). (Illus.). 32p. (J). lib. bdg. 22.60 (978-0-7368-2687-7(4)) Capstone Pr., Inc.

Park. Taking Your Camera To..., 6 vols., Set 3. 2000. pap. (978-0-7398-4136-5(X)) Steck-Vaughn.

Park, Ted. Taking Your Camera To..., Set 3. 2000. pap., tchr. ed. (978-0-7398-4135-8(1)) Steck-Vaughn.

—Taking Your Camera to China. Sloan, Frank, ed. 2001. (Taking Your Camera to Ser.). (Illus.). 32p. (J). (gr. 4-7). lib. bdg. 22.83 (978-0-7398-3568-5(8)) Raintree.

—Taking Your Camera to China. 2000. (Illus.). pap. (978-0-7398-4130-3(0)) Steck-Vaughn.

Pilon, Pascal & Thomas, Elisabeth. We Live in China. Duffet, Sophie, illus. 2006. (Kids Around the World Ser.). 48p. (J). (gr. 3-7). 15.95 (978-0-8109-5735-0(3), Abrams Bks. for Young Readers) Abrams, Harry N., Inc.

Popper, Garry. Li & Lilly May in China. Johnson, Andi, illus. 2004. 36p. (ps-7). 4.00 (978-1-84161-057-3(7)) Ravette Publishing, Ltd. GBR. *Dist:* Parkwest Pubns., Inc.

Powell, Jillian. Looking at China. 2008. (J). pap. (***978-0-8368-8176-9(1)***); 32p. (gr. 2-4). lib. bdg. 25.27 (***978-0-8368-8169-1(9)***) Stevens, Gareth Inc.

Richardson, Adele. China. 2006. (My First Look at Countries Ser.). (Illus.). 24p. (J). (gr. 1-2). lib. bdg. 15.95 (978-1-58341-445-3(2), Creative Education) Creative Co., The.

—Great Wall of China. 2005. (Ancient Wonders of the World Ser.). (Illus.). 32p. (gr. 4-7). 18.95 (978-1-58341-356-2(1), Creative Education) Creative Co., The.

Riehecky, Janet. China. (Country Explorers Ser.). 48p. 2007. (J). (gr. 4-8). lib. bdg. 27.93 (***978-0-8225-7129-2(3)***, Lerner Pubns.); 1999. (Illus.). (gr. 2-4). 22.60 (978-1-57505-140-6(0)); 1999. (Illus.). (J). (gr. 3-5). lib. bdg. 22.60 (978-1-57505-115-4(X), Carolrhoda Bks.) Lerner Publishing Group.

Robinson, Fay. Chinese New Year - A Time for Parades, Family & Friends. 2001. (Finding Out about Holidays Ser.). (Illus.). 48p. (J). (gr. 1-4). lib. bdg. 23.93 (978-0-7660-1631-6(5)) Enslow Pubs., Inc.

Roop, Peter. China. 2003. (gr. k-3). lib. bdg. 14.75 (978-0-613-84978-4(7)) Tandem Library Bks.

Roop, Peter & Roop, Connie. A Visit to China. (Visit to Ser.). 32p. pap. 6.50 (978-1-4034-4145-4(6)) Heinemann Library.

Roza, Greg. A Primary Source Guide to China. 2003. (Countries of the World : A Primary Source Journey Ser.). (Illus.). 24p. (J). pap. (978-0-8239-8075-8(8)); lib. bdg. 19.95 (978-0-8239-6591-5(0)) Rosen Publishing Group, Inc., The. (PowerKids Pr.).

Ruth, Angie. My Adventure in China. 2007. 44p. (J). 8.99 (978-1-59092-425-9(8), Orchard Academy Pr.) Windstorm Creative.

Ryan, Patrick. Welcome to China. 2007. (Welcome to the World Ser.). 32p. (J). (gr. 1-5). 27.07 (***978-1-59296-912-8(7)***) Child's World, Inc.

Schlesinger, Arthur M., Jr. Touring China Eighty Years Ago. Isreal, Fred L., ed. 1999. (Cultural & Geographical Exploration Ser.). (Illus.). 144p. (gr. 5 up). 21.95 (978-0-7910-5448-2(9), Chelsea Hse.) Facts On File, Inc.

Schroeder, Holly. China ABCs: A Book about the People & Places of China. Yesh, Jeff, illus. 2004. (Country ABCs Ser.). 32p. (J). (gr. k-5). 23.93 (978-1-4048-0180-6(4)) Picture Window Bks.

Sebag-Montefiore, Hugh. China. 2007. (DK Eyewitness Bks.). 72p. (J). (gr. 3-8). 15.99 incl. cd-rom (978-0-7566-2976-2(4)); lib. bdg. 19.99 (978-0-7566-2975-5(6)) Dorling Kindersley Publishing, Inc.

Sherman, Josepha. Your Travel Guide to Ancient China. 2005. (Passport to History Ser.). (Illus.). 96p. 26.60 (978-0-8225-3073-2(2)) Lerner Publishing Group.

Shuter, Jane. Ancient China. 2007. (Time Travel Guides Ser.). (Illus.). 64p. (YA). (gr. 5-8). lib. bdg. 34.29 (***978-1-4109-2729-3(6)***) Raintree.

—Ancient China. 2007. (Illus.). 64p. (J). (***978-1-4109-2736-1(9)***) Steck-Vaughn.

Shuter, Jane. The Ancient Chinese. 1999. (History Opens Windows Ser.). (Illus.). (J). 14.30 (978-0-606-21974-7(9)) Tandem Library Bks.

Shuter, Jane & Taylor, Pat. The Ancient Chinese, Set 1. 1999. (History Opens Windows Ser.). 32p. (J). (gr. 2-4). pap. (978-1-57572-594-9(0)) Heinemann Library.

Sinnott, Susan. China. 2000. (First Reports). (Illus.). 48p. (J). (gr. 3 up). lib. bdg. 22.60 (978-0-7565-0029-0(X)) Compass Point Bks.

So, Sungwan. A Child's Day in a Chinese City. 2001. (Child's Day Ser.). (Illus.). 32p. (J). (gr. k-2). lib. bdg. 25.64 (978-0-7614-1224-3(7), Benchmark Bks.) Cavendish, Marshall Corp.

—Shanyi Goes to China. 2006. (Children Return to their Roots Ser.). (Illus.). 40p. 15.95 (978-1-84507-470-8(X)) Lincoln, Frances Ltd. GBR. *Dist:* Perseus Distribution.

Stefoff, Rebecca. Asian Empires. 2004. (Illus.). 48p. (J). 27.07 (978-0-7614-1643-2(9), Benchmark Bks.) Cavendish, Marshall Corp.

Stone, Lynn M. The Land of China. 2000. (China Ser.). (Illus.). 24p. (J). (gr. 1-4). lib. bdg. 19.27 (978-1-55916-318-7(6)) Rourke Publishing, LLC.

—The People of China. 2000. (China Ser.). (Illus.). 24p. (J). (gr. 1-4). lib. bdg. 19.27 (978-1-55916-319-4(4)) Rourke Publishing, LLC.

—Provinces & Cities of China. 2000. (Illus.). 24p. (J). (gr. 1-4). lib. bdg. 19.27 (978-1-55916-320-0(8)) Rourke Publishing, LLC.

—Wonders of China. 2000. (China Ser.). (Illus.). 24p. (J). (gr. 1-4). lib. bdg. 19.27 (978-1-55916-322-4(4)) Rourke Publishing, LLC.

Stotksy, Sandra. China. 1999. (Major World Nations Ser.). (Illus.). 144p. (J). (gr. 4-7). 29.95 (978-0-7910-4735-4(0) , Chelsea Hse.) Facts On File, Inc.

Streissguth, Thomas. China in the 21st Century: A New World Power. 2008. (Issues in Focus Today Ser.). (Illus.). 104p. (J). (gr. 6 up). lib. bdg. 31.93 (*978-0-7660-2684-1(1)) Enslow Pubs., Inc.

Taking Your Camera To... Includes: Argentina, China, Germany, India, South Africa, Vietnam, 6 bks., Set. 2001. (Taking Your Camera to Ser.). (Illus.). (J). (gr. 4-7). 136.98 (978-0-7398-3573-9(4)) Raintree.

Teichmann, Iris. China. 2007. (J). (*978-1-59920-015-6(5)) Smart Apple Media.

Thompson, Stuart & Shui, Amy. China. 1999. (Food & Festivals Ser.). (Illus.). 32p. (J). (gr. 1-4). lib. bdg. 25.69 (978-0-8172-5757-6(8)) Raintree.

Tull, Mary, et al. Northern Asia: Understanding Geography & History Through Art. 1999. (Artisans Around the World Ser.). (Illus.). 48p. (J). (gr. 4-8). lib. bdg. 27.12 (978-0-7398-0119-2(8)) Raintree.

Walker, Kathryn. Shanghai. 2005. (Great Cities of the World Ser.). (Illus.). 48p. (J). pap. (978-0-8368-5206-6(0)); (YA). lib. bdg. 30.00 (978-0-8368-5046-8(7)) Stevens, Gareth Inc. (World Almanac Library).

Wang, Jianwei, ed. China, 10 vols. 2005. (Illus.). 112,144p. 249.50 (978-1-59084-821-0(7)) Mason Crest Pubs.

Wang, Tao. China. 2000. (Exploration Into... Ser.). (Illus.). 48p. (J). (gr. 4-7). 25.00 (978-0-7910-6021-6(7) , Chelsea Hse.) Facts On File, Inc.

Waterlow, Julia. China. 2000. (We Come from Ser.). (Illus.). 32p. (J). (gr. 1-4). lib. bdg. 25.69 (978-0-8172-5219-9(3)) Raintree.

—The Yangtze. 2003. (Great Rivers of the World Ser.). (Illus.). 48p. (gr. 5 up). (J). pap. 14.95 (978-0-8368-5454-1(3)); (YA). lib. bdg. 30.00 (978-0-8368-5447-3(0)) Stevens, Gareth Inc. (World Almanac Library).

Whitefield, Gary T. China. Gritzner, Charles F., ed. 2003. (Modern World Nations Ser.). (Illus.). 200p. (gr. 6-12). lib. bdg. 24.95 (978-0-7910-6930-1(3) , Chelsea Hse.) Facts On File, Inc.

Whiteford, Gary T. China. Gritzner, Charles F., ed. 2005. (Modern World Nations Ser.). (Illus.). 147p. (J). (gr. 6-12). lib. bdg. 30.00 (978-0-7910-8661-2(5) , Chelsea Hse.) Facts On File, Inc.

Zemlicka, Shannon. Colors of China. Porter, Janice Lee, illus. 2003. (Colors of the World Ser.). 24p. (J). (gr. 1-4). 5.95 (978-1-57505-563-3(5)) Lerner Publishing Group.

—Colors of China. 2001. (gr. k-3). lib. bdg. 14.10 (978-0-613-79238-7(6)) Tandem Library Bks.

CHINA—BIOGRAPHY

Demi. Su Dongpo: Chinese Genius. 2006. (Illus.). 56p. (J). (gr. 2-5). 24.00 (978-1-58430-256-8(9)) Lee & Low Bks., Inc.

Donovan, Sandra. Madame Chiang Kai-Shek: Face of Modern China. 2006. (J). (978-0-7565-1886-8(5)) Compass Point Bks.

Haski, Pierre & Ma, Yan. The Diary of Ma Yan: The Struggles & Hopes of a Chinese Schoolgirl. Appignanesi, Lisa & Yanping, He, trs. from CHI. 2005. (Illus.). 176p. (J). (gr. k-17). 15.99 (978-0-06-076496-8(1)) HarperCollins Pubs.

Holt, Rinehart and Winston Staff. The Red Scarf Girl. 2nd ed. 2002. pap., stu. ed. 13.20 (978-0-03-066278-2(8)) Holt, Rinehart & Winston.

Jiang, Cheng A. Empress of China Zhongguo De Nu Huangdi: Wu Ze Tian. Xu, De Y., illus. 1998. 32p. (J). (gr. 3-6). pap. 7.95 (978-1-878217-31-8(3)) Victory Pr.

Jiang, Ji-Li. Red Scarf Girl: A Memoir of the Cultural Revolution. 1998. 304p. (J). (gr. 5 up). pap. 6.99 (978-0-06-446208-2(0) , Harper Trophy) HarperCollins Pubs,

Li, Richard T. The Golden Lotus: Life of a Bound-Feet Peasant Mother in the Chinese Cultural Revolution. 2004. (Illus.). 140p. (YA). pap. 7.95 (978-0-9675988-3-3(4)) Li, Richard T.

Liao, Yan. Famous People of China. 2005. (History & Culture of China Ser.). (Illus.). 119p. (J). lib. bdg. (978-1-59084-826-5(8)) Mason Crest Pubs.

Macdonald, Fiona & Geyer, Flora. Mao Zedong: The Rebel Who Led a Revolution. 2007. (World History Biographies Ser.). (Illus.). 64p. (J). (gr. 3-7). 17.95 (978-1-4263-0062-2(X)); lib. bdg. 27.90 (978-1-4263-0063-9(8)) National Geographic Society. (National Geographic Children's Bks.).

Marx, Christy. Jet Li. 2005. (Martial Arts Masters Ser.). (Illus.). 112p. (YA). (gr. 7-12). lib. bdg. 25.25 (978-0-8239-3519-2(1)) Rosen Publishing Group, Inc., The.

Pancella, Peggy. Qin Shi Huangdi. 2003. (Historical Biographies Ser.). (Illus.). 32p. (J). pap. 7.50 (978-1-4034-3712-9(2)); lib. bdg. 22.79 (978-1-4034-3704-4(1)) Heinemann Library.

Shea, Therese. Yao Ming: International Basketball Star. 2006. (Tony Stead Nonfiction Independent Reading Collection). (J). pap. (978-1-4042-5538-8(9)) Rosen Publishing Group, Inc., The.

Smit, Anika. Taxi. 2006. (ENG.). 168p. per. (*978-1-4251-0019-3(8)) Trafford Publishing.

Stewart, Whitney. Deng Xiaoping: Leader in a Changing China. 2005. (Lerner Biographies Ser.). (Illus.). 128p. (gr. 6-12). 27.93 (978-0-8225-4962-8(X)) Lerner Publishing Group.

Stone, Amy. Jackie Chan. 2006. (Today's Superstars). (Illus.). 32p. (J). (gr. 5 up). lib. bdg. 23.93 (*978-0-8368-7648-2(2)) Stevens, Gareth Inc.

Yan, Ma. The Diary of Ma Yan: The Life of a Chinese School Girl. Haski, Pierre, ed. 2006. (Illus.). 208p. reprint ed. pap. 22.00 (978-1-4223-5712-5(0)) DIANE Publishing Co.

Yen Mah, Adeline. Falling Leaves: The True Story of an Unwanted Chinese Daughter. 1999. (gr. 7-12). lib. bdg. 23.45 (978-0-613-16929-5(8)) Tandem Library Bks.

CHINA—FICTION

Ahern, Carolyn L. Tino Turtle Travels to Beijing, China. 2008. (J). 17.95 incl. audio compact disk (*978-0-9793158-4-8(0)) Tino Turtle Travels, LLC.

Alexander, Lloyd. Dream-of-Jade: The Emperor's Cat. Burkett, D. Brent, illus. 2005. 48p. (J). 16.95 (978-0-8126-2736-7(9)) Cricket Bks.

Andersen, Hans Christian. The Nightingale. Oleynikov, Igor, illus. 2007. Tr. of Nattergalen. 40p. (J). 16.50 (978-1-933327-31-0(6)); 15.95 (978-1-933327-30-3(8)) Purple Bear Bks., Inc.

—El Ruisenor. Mitchell, Stephen, ed. Fischer, Maite Rodriguez, tr. Ibattouline, Bagram, illus. 2004. (SPA.). 48p. 15.95 (978-84-95939-25-8(8)) Blume ESP. *Dist:* Independent Pubs. Group.

—El Ruisenor. (SPA.). 32p. (J). (gr. 2-3). 12.95 (978-84-233-1567-3(3)) Ediciones Destino ESP. *Dist:* Lectorum Pubns., Inc., Planeta Publishing Corp.

Anna, Jennifer. Year of the Dragon: The Complete Story Experience Edition. Brandon, Theresa, illus. 2nd exp. ed. 2005. (Turtle's Back Bks.). 100p. (J). (ps-6). pap. 14.99 (978-1-883573-18-8(1) , Little Blue Works) Windstorm Creative.

Bass, L. G. The Outlaws of Moonshadow Marsh No. 1, Bk.1: The Sign of Qin. 2004. (Illus.). 400p. (gr. 5-17). 17.99 (978-0-7868-1918-8(9)) Hyperion Bks. for Children.

—The Outlaws of Moonshadow Marsh the Sign of Qin, Bk. 1. 2006. 400p. (gr. 5-17). reprint ed. pap. 7.99 (978-0-7868-5566-7(5)) Hyperion Pr.

—Sign of the Qin. l.t. ed. 2004. 513p. 23.95 (978-0-7862-6772-9(0) , Large Print Pr.) Thorndike Pr.

Bouchard, Dave. Dragon of Heaven: Memoirs of the Last Empress of China. Huang, Zhong-Yang, illus. 2003. 96p. 26.95 (978-1-55192-525-7(7)) Raincoast Bk. Distribution CAN. *Dist:* Perseus Distribution.

Bouchard, David. The Great Race - The Legend of the Chinese Zodiac. ed. 2004. (J). (gr. k-3). spiral bd. (978-0-616-01430-1(9)) Canadian National Institute for the Blind/Institut National Canadien pour les Aveugles.

Brett, Jan. Daisy Comes Home. Brett, Jan, illus. 2002. (Illus.). (J). 23.64 (978-1-4046-0028-7(0)) Book Wholesalers, Inc.

—Daisy Comes Home. Brett, Jan, illus. (Illus.). 32p. (J). (ps-3). 2002. 16.99 (978-0-399-23618-1(X) , Putnam Juvenile); 2005. reprint ed. pap. 6.99 (978-0-14-240270-2(2) , Puffin) Penguin Group (USA) Inc.

Buck, Pearl S. A House Divided. 2004. 304p. (C). reprint ed. pap. 12.95 (978-1-55921-340-0(X) , Asphodel Pr.) Moyer Bell.

Capone, Deb. Families Are Forever. 2004. (J). 16.95 (*978-0-9728666-6-8(3)) As Simple As That Publishing.

Carling, Amelia Lau. La Tienda de Mama y Papa. Carling, Amelia Lau, illus. 2003. (Illus.). 32p. (J). (ps-3). (SPA & ENG.). 16.95 (978-0-88899-538-4(5) , Libros Tigrillo); (ENG & SPA., pap. 6.95 (978-0-88899-547-6(4)) Groundwood Bks. CAN. *Dist:* Perseus Distribution.

Cha, Louis. Heaven Sword & Dragon Sabre, 25 vols., Vol. 1. Young, Stuart, tr. from CHI. 2002. (Illus.). 120p. (YA). pap. 13.95 (978-1-58899-183-6(0)) ComicsOne Corp./Dr. Masters.

—Heaven Sword & Dragon Sabre, 25 vols. (Illus.). (YA). Vol. 3. 2002. 120p. pap. 13.95 (978-1-58899-185-0(7)); Vol. 4. 2003. 120p. pap. 13.95 (978-1-58899-186-7(5)); Vol. 5. 2003. 120p. pap. 13.95 (978-1-58899-187-4(3)); Vol. 6. 2003. 120p. (gr. 8 up). pap. 13.95 (978-1-58899-198-0(9)); Vol. 7. 2003. 160p. pap. 14.95 (978-1-58899-241-3(1)) ComicsOne Corp./Dr. Masters.

Chapman, Mary Beth & Chapman, Steven Curtis. Shaoey & Dot: A Trip to Dr. Betterbee. 2005. 20p. (J). 6.99 (978-1-4003-0568-1(3)) Nelson, Thomas Inc.

—Shaoey & Dot: Back in A Bug's Blink. 2005. 20p. (J). 6.99 (978-1-4003-0569-8(1)) Nelson, Thomas Inc.

—Shaoey & Dot: Thunder & Lightning Bugs. 2005. 20p. (J). 6.99 (978-1-4003-0570-4(5)) Nelson, Thomas Inc.

—Shoey & Dot: A Thunder & Lightning Bug Story. Chapman, Jim, illus. 2006. 32p. (J). 10.99 (978-1-4003-0743-2(0)) Nelson, Thomas Inc.

Chapman, Steven Curtis & Chapman, Mary Beth. Shaoey & Dot: Bug Meets Bundle. 2004. (Illus.). 32p. (J). 16.99 (978-1-4003-0482-0(2)) Nelson, Thomas Inc.

Chen, Da. Wandering Warrior. 2004. 336p. (J). (gr. 5). pap. 5.99 (978-0-440-23771-6(8) , Laurel Leaf) Random Hse. Children's Bks.

Cheng, Andrea. Shanghai Messenger. Young, Ed, illus. 2005. 40p. (J). (ps-7). 17.95 (978-1-58430-238-4(0)) Lee & Low Bks., Inc.

Ch'iao, Xiao. Patti & the Weegors. (Illus.). 32p. (J). pap. 4.99 (978-1-85792-557-9(2) , Christian Focus) Christian Focus Pubns. GBR. *Dist:* Riverside.

Chin, Oliver Clyde. The Year of the Rat: Tales from the Chinese Zodiac. Alcorn, Miah, illus. 2008. (Tales from the Chinese Zodiac Ser.). 36p. (J). 15.95 (*978-1-59702-011-4(7)) Immedium.

Cipriano, A. G. Bertie. 1999. 294p. (YA). (gr. 6-12). pap. 5.99 (978-0-9672074-0-7(1)) Gold Lace Publishing, LLC.

Compestine, Ying Chang. Boy Dumplings. Yamasaki, James, illus. 2007. (J). (978-0-8234-1955-5(X)) Holiday Hse., Inc.

—Revolution Is Not a Dinner Party. 2007. 256p. (YA). (gr. 5 up). 16.95 (*978-0-8050-8207-4(7) , Holt, Henry & Co. Bks. For Young Readers) Holt, Henry & Co.

Compestine, Ying Chang. The Story of Noodles. Xuan, Yong-Sheng, illus. 2002. 32p. (J). (gr. k-3). tchr. ed. 16.95 (978-0-8234-1600-4(3)) Holiday Hse., Inc.

Conlogue, Ray. Shen & the Treasure Fleet. 2007. (Illus.). 256p. (J). (gr. 6-12). 21.95 (*978-1-55451-104-4(6)); pap. 11.95 (*978-1-55451-103-7(8)) Annick Pr., Ltd. CAN. *Dist:* Firefly Bks., Ltd.

Coste, Marion. Finding Joy. Chen, Yong, illus. 2006. 32p. (J). (gr. 1-3). 16.95 (978-1-59078-192-0(9)) Boyds Mills Pr.

Crilley, Mark. Rogmasher Rampage. 2007. (Billy Clikk Ser.). 224p. (J). (gr. 4-7). 5.99 (978-0-440-41955-6(7) , Yearling) Random Hse. Children's Bks.

Czernecki, Stefan. Paper Lanterns. 2004. (Illus.). 32p. (J). (ps-13). pap. 6.95 (978-1-57091-411-9(7)) Charlesbridge Publishing, Inc.

—Paper Lanterns. Czernecki, Stefan, illus. 2001. (Illus.). 32p. (J). (ps-3). 15.95 (978-1-57091-410-2(9)) Charlesbridge Publishing, Inc.

Demi. The Empty Pot. 2007. (Illus.). 32p. (J). pap. 23.95 (*978-0-8050-8227-2(1) , Holt, Henry & Co. Bks. For Young Readers) Holt, Henry & Co.

—The Girl Who Drew a Phoenix. 2008. (J). (*978-1-4169-5347-0(7) , McElderry, Margaret K.) Simon & Schuster Children's Publishing.

Demi. The Greatest Power. Demi, illus. 2004. (Illus.). 40p. (J). 19.95 (978-0-689-84503-1(0) , McElderry, Margaret K.) Simon & Schuster Children's Publishing.

Demi, illus. The Magic Pillow. 2008. (J). (*978-1-4169-2470-8(1) , McElderry, Margaret K.) Simon & Schuster Children's Publishing.

Dickins, Rosie. Dragon Painter. Nez, John, illus. 2006. 48p. (J). 8.99 (978-0-7945-1275-0(5) , Usborne) EDC Publishing.

—Emperor & the Nightingale. Philpot, Graham, illus. 2007. (First Reading Level 4 Ser.). 48p. (J). 8.99 (*978-0-7945-1614-7(9) , Usborne) EDC Publishing.

—Monkey King. Ovani, Germano, illus. 2007. (Young Reading Series 1 Gift Bks). 48p. (J). 8.99 (*978-0-7945-1593-5(2) , Usborne) EDC Publishing.

Dorros, Arthur & Dorros, Alex. Numero Uno. Guevara, Susan, illus. 2007. 32p. (J). (ps-3). 16.95 (*978-0-8109-5764-0(7)) Abrams, Harry N. , Inc.

Doyle, Bill. Iced! The 2007 Journal of Nick Fitzmorgan. Simpson, Philomena, illus. 2006. 133p. (J). lib. bdg. 18.46 (*978-1-4242-1734-2(2)) Fitzgerald Bks.

Edwards, Hazel. Duty Free. 100p. (YA). pap. (978-0-7344-0334-6(8) , Lothian Bks.) Hachette Livre Australia.

Flack, Marjorie. The Story about Ping. Flack, Marjorie, illus. 2002. (Illus.). (J). 11.06 (978-0-7587-3710-6(6)) Book Wholesalers, Inc.

—The Story of Ping. Wiese, Kurt, illus. 2000. (Reading Railroad Bks.). 32p. (J). (ps-3). pap. 3.99 (978-0-448-42165-0(8) , Grosset & Dunlap) Penguin Group (USA) Inc.

Foster, Thomas. Travel Buddies: Robby & Sammy Visit China. 2006. (J). pap. 12.00 (978-1-890306-93-9(2)) Warwick Hse. Publishing.

Fritz, Jean. Homesick: My Own Story. Tomes, Margot, illus. 1999. 192p. (J). (gr. 3-7). pap. 5.99 (978-0-698-11782-2(4) , Putnam Juvenile) Penguin Group (USA) Inc.

—Homesick: My Own Story. 1999. (J). 12.64 (978-0-606-16799-4(4)) Tandem Library Bks.

Fritz, Jean & Margot, Tomes. Homesick. 2007. (Puffin Modern Classics Ser.). 176p. (J). (gr. 3). pap. 6.99 (978-0-14-240761-5(5) , Puffin) Penguin Group (USA) Inc.

Fu, Shelley. Hoyi the Archer & other Classic Chinese Tales. Abboreno, Joseph F. & Fu, Sherwin, illus. 2005. 144p. (J). (gr. 4-8). reprint ed. 22.00 (978-0-7567-9713-3(6)) DIANE Publishing Co.

Geis, Patricia. Pequeno Bouyei. 2005. (Ninos y ninas del mundo Ser.). (SPA., Illus.). 32p. (J). 5.95 (978-84-7864-881-8(X)) Combel Editorial, S.A. ESP. *Dist:* Independent Pubs. Group.

Gelsey, James. Chill-Out Scooby-Doo. 2007. (Scooby-Doo Video Tie-In Novelization Ser.). 64p. (J). pap. 3.99 (*978-0-439-91595-3(3)) Scholastic, Inc.

Gelsey, James, et al. Chill-Out Scooby-Doo. 2007. (Scooby-Doo 8x8 Video Tie-In Ser.). 24p. (J). pap. 3.99 (*978-0-439-91597-7(X)) Scholastic, Inc.

Gilbert, Marcie. Zee: Adventure One: Borrowing China. Krebs, Patricia, illus. l.t. ed. 2006. 48p. (J). per. 16.99 (978-0-9771566-0-3(5)) Librujas.

Gower, Catherine. Long-Long's New Year: A Story about the Chinese Spring Festival. Zhihong, He, illus. 2004. 32p. 16.95 (978-0-8048-3666-1(3)) Tuttle Publishing.

Grindley, Sally. Spilled Water. 2004. 224p. (J). 15.95 (978-1-58234-937-4(1) , Bloomsbury Children) Bloomsbury Publishing.

Harcourt School Publishers Staff. Happy Chinese New Year! Below Level. 3rd ed. 2002. (Trophies Reading Program Ser.). (Illus.). pap. 5.10 (978-0-15-323065-3(7)) Harcourt Schl. Pubs.

Hathorn, Libby. The River. Wong, Stanley, illus. 2003. 40p. 28.95 (978-1-86366-516-2(1)) Curriculum Corporation AUS. *Dist:* Cheng & Tsui Co.

Heaton, Caroline. Yi-Min & the Elephants: A Tale of Ancient China. Vyner, Tim, illus. 2004. 32p. (J). pap. 7.95 (978-1-84507-146-2(8)) Lincoln, Frances Ltd. GBR. *Dist:* Perseus Distribution.

Hergé. The Blue Lotus. (Illus.). (J). 19.95 (978-0-8288-5480-1(7)) French & European Pubns., Inc.

—El Loto Azul.Tr. of Blue Lotus. (SPA., Illus.). 62p. (J). 19.95 (978-0-8288-5049-0(6)) French & European Pubns., Inc.

—El Loto Azul. (Tintin Ser.).Tr. of Blue Lotus. (SPA.). 64p. (J). 14.95 (978-84-261-1418-1(0)) Juventud, Editorial ESP. *Dist:* Distribooks, Inc.

—Le Lotus Bleu. 1999. (Tintin Ser.).Tr. of Blue Lotus. (FRE.). (J). (gr. 4-7). 21.95 (978-2-203-00104-6(6)) Casterman, Editions FRA. *Dist:* Distribooks, Inc.

—Le Lotus Bleu.Tr. of Blue Lotus. (FRE.). (J). (gr. 2-9). 19.95 (978-0-8288-5050-6(X)) French & European Pubns., Inc.

Hill, Elizabeth Starr. Bird Boy. 2003. (gr. 3-6). lib. bdg. 14.10 (978-0-613-71735-9(X)) Tandem Library Bks.

—Chang & the Bamboo Flute. Liu, Lesley, illus. 2002. 64p. (J). (gr. 3 up). 15.00 (978-0-374-31238-1(9) , Farrar, Straus & Giroux (BYR)) Farrar, Straus & Giroux.

Hong, Chen Jian. La Leyenda De la Cometa. (SPA.). 32p. (978-84-95150-29-5(8)); (978-84-95150-39-4(5)) Corimbo, Editorial S.L.

Hood, Douglas. The Stone Hat. Simonton, Tom, illus. 2005. 16p. (J). pap. 5.00 (978-1-57274-754-8(4) , 2784, Bks. for Young Learners) Owen, Richard C. Pubs., Inc.

I-Haun. Real Fake Princess Volume 2. 2006. (Illus.). 200p. (YA). pap. 9.95 (*978-1-59796-080-9(2)) DrMaster Pubns. Inc.

—Real Fake Princess Volume 3. 2006. 200p. (YA). pap. 9.95 (*978-1-59796-081-6(0)) DrMaster Pubns. Inc.

—Real/Fake Princess, Vol. 4. 2007. (Illus.). 200p. pap. 9.95 (*978-1-59796-082-3(9)) DrMaster Pubns. Inc.

I-Huan. Real Fake Princess, Vol. 1. 2006. (Illus.). 200p. (YA). pap. 9.95 (*978-1-59796-079-3(9)) DrMaster Pubns. Inc.

Kurita, Miwa. China Tells How the World Began! Matsutani, Miyoko, ed. Mitsukuri, Saoko, illus. 2006. (Asian Folktales Retold Ser.). 32p. 16.95 (978-0-89346-944-3(0)) Consortium Bk. Sales & Distribution.

Kurita, Miwa & Matsutani, Miyoko. Chinese Fables Remembered. Mitsukuri, Saoko, illus. 2006. (Asian Folktales Retold Ser.). 32p. 16.95 (978-0-89346-945-0(9)) Consortium Bk. Sales & Distribution.

Lattimore, Eleanor Frances. Little Pear. 2006. (Illus.). 128p. (J). 16.00 (978-0-15-205496-0(0)) Harcourt Trade Pubs.

—Little Pear. Lattimore, Eleanor Frances, illus. 2006. (Illus.). 128p. (J). (gr. 1-5). pap. 5.95 (978-0-15-205502-8(9)) Harcourt Trade Pubs.

—Little Pear & His Friends. 2006. (Illus.). 144p. (J). 16.00 (978-0-15-205484-7(7)) Harcourt Trade Pubs.

—Little Pear & His Friends. Lattimore, Eleanor Frances, illus. 2006. (Illus.). 144p. (J). (gr. 1-5). pap. 5.95 (978-0-15-205490-8(1)) Harcourt Trade Pubs.

Lee, Milly. Landed. Choi, Yangsook, illus. 2006. 40p. (J). 16.00 (978-0-374-34314-9(4) , Farrar, Straus & Giroux (BYR)) Farrar, Straus & Giroux.

Levinson, Robin. Reyna & the Jade Star. 2006. (Illus.). (J). per. 12.00 (978-0-9773673-1-3(2)) Gali Girls, Inc.

Lewis, Elizabeth Foreman. Young Fu of the Upper Yangtze. Low, William, illus. 2007. 320p. (J). pap. (*978-0-8050-8105-3(4)); (YA). 17.95 (*978-0-8050-8113-8(5)) Holt, Henry & Co.

—Young Fu of the Upper Yangtze. Low, William, illus. 2008. 320p. (J). pap. 6.99 (*978-0-312-38007-6(0)) Square Fish.

Li, Yao-Wen & Kendall, Carol. Sweet & Sour: Tales from China. Felts, Shirley, illus. 2007. 112p. (J). (gr. 4-6). pap. 6.95 (978-0-618-75245-4(5) , Clarion Bks.) Houghton Mifflin Co. Trade & Reference Div.

Lin, Grace. Kite Flying. (Illus.). 32p. (J). (ps-3). 2004. pap. 6.99 (978-0-553-11254-2(6) , Dragonfly Bks.); 2002. 14.95 (978-0-375-81520-1(1) , Knopf Bks. for Young Readers) Random Hse. Children's Bks.

Literature Connections English: Dragonwings. 2004. (gr. 6-12). (978-0-395-77136-5(6) , 2-70214) McDougal Littell Inc.

Louis, Catherine. Liu & the Bird Journey Chinese Calligraphy. 2006. (Illus.). 40p. (J). 16.95 (978-0-7358-2050-0(3)) North-South Bks., Inc.

Low, Vicki. First Emperor. Mayhew, Sara E., illus. 2007. 48p. (J). lib. bdg. 23.08 (*978-1-4242-1626-0(5)) Fitzgerald Bks.

Ma, Wing Shing. Storm Riders Vol. 1: Invading Sun. 2003. (Illus.). 128p. 9.95 (978-1-58899-359-5(0)) ComicsOne Corp./Dr. Masters.

MacLeod, Jean. At Home in This World: A China Adoption Story. 2003. (Illus.). 32p. (J). lib. bdg. 15.95 (978-0-9726244-1-1(4)) EMK Pr.

Mah, Adeline Yen. Chinese Cinderella & the Secret Dragon Society. (Illus.). 256p. (J). 2006. pap. 5.99 (978-0-06-056736-1(8) , Harper Trophy); 2005. (gr. 5 up). 15.99 (978-0-06-056734-7(1)) HarperCollins Pubs.

Marsh, Carole. The Mystery on the Great Wall of China. 2006. 144p. (gr. 3-5). 14.95 (*978-0-635-06209-3(7)); pap. 5.95 (*978-0-635-06205-5(4)) Gallopade International.

Matott, Justin. When I Was a Boy... I Dreamed. Ludy, Mark, illus. 2004. 32p. (J). 17.00 (978-0-9664276-2-2(9)) Green Pastures Publishing, Inc.

McCaughrean, Geraldine. The Kite Rider. 2002. (gr. 7-12). lib. bdg. 15.30 (978-0-613-68440-8(0)) Tandem Library Bks.

McCloskey, John J. Warrior Ching. 2006. 179p. pap. 19.95 (978-1-4241-2389-6(5)) PublishAmerica, Inc.

McCully, Emily Arnold. Beautiful Warrior: The Legend of the Nun's Kung Fu. McCully, Emily Arnold, illus. 2nd ed. 1998. (Illus.). 40p. (J). (ps-3). pap. 19.99 (978-0-590-37487-3(7)) Scholastic, Inc.

McLean, Jacqueline. Grace from China. 2003. 179p. (J). 16.00 (978-0-9638472-8-7(7)) Yeong & Yeong Bk. Co.

Millhouse, Jackie. The Tiger & the General. Girouard, Patrick, illus. 2007. (J). (*978-1-932911-32-9(4)) World Tribune Pr.

Mowll, Joshua. Operation Red Jericho. Heller, Julek et al, illus. 2005. (Guild Trilogy Ser.: Bk. 1). 288p. (YA). (gr. 7-8). 15.99 (978-0-7636-2634-1(1)) Candlewick Pr.

—Operation Red Jericho: The Guide of Specialists Book 1. Heller, Julek & Puttapipat, Niroot, illus. 2007. 288p. (J). (gr. 5). pap. 8.99 (*978-0-7636-3475-9(1)) Candlewick Pr.

Mowll, Joshua. Operation Typhoon Shore. Mowll, Joshua et al, illus. 2006. (Guild of Specialists Ser.). 288p. (YA). (gr. 5 up). 15.99 (978-0-7636-3122-2(1)) Candlewick Pr.

My Trip to China. 2004. (J). ring bd. 4.50 (978-0-9762740-6-3(X)) Smart Smiles Co., The.

Namioka, Lensey. An Ocean Apart, a World Away. 2003. (gr. 7-12). lib. bdg. 13.55 (978-0-613-72264-3(7)) Tandem Library Bks.

—Ties That Bind, Ties That Break. 2000. 160p. (YA). (gr. 7 up). pap. 5.99 (978-0-440-41599-2(3) , Laurel Leaf) Random Hse. Children's Bks.

—Ties That Bind, Ties That Break. 2000. (gr. 7-12). lib. bdg. 13.00 (978-0-613-28377-9(5)) Tandem Library Bks.

Napoli, Donna Jo. Bound. 192p. (YA). 2004. (Illus.). (gr. 6 up). 16.95 (978-0-689-86175-8(3) , Atheneum); 2006. (gr. 7 up). reprint ed. pap. 5.99 (978-0-689-86178-9(8) , Simon Pulse) Simon & Schuster Children's Publishing.

Nash, Deborah. Made in China. (Illus.). 32p. (J). 2006. pap. 7.95 (978-1-84507-120-2(4)); 2004. 15.95 (978-1-84507-043-4(7)) Lincoln, Frances Ltd. GBR. *Dist:* Perseus Distribution.

National Textbook Company Staff, contrib. by. El Ruiseñor de la China. 2000. Tr. of Nightingale of China. (ENG & SPA.). (J). (978-0-658-01026-2(3) , National Textbook Co.) McGraw-Hill/Contemporary.

Neville, Emily C. The China Year. 1999. 256p. (J). pap. 4.95 (978-0-06-440407-5(2)) HarperCollins Pubs.

Noyes, Deborah. Red Butterfly: How a Princess Smuggled the Secret of Silk Out of China. Blackall, Sophie, illus. 2007. 32p. (J). (gr. 1-5). 16.99 (***978-0-7636-2400-2(4))** Candlewick Pr.

Noyes, Deborah & Haarsma, P. J. Red Butterfly: How a Princess Smuggled the Secret of Silk Out of China. Blackall, Sophie, illus. 2008. (Softwire Ser.). 272p. (J). (gr. 7). 16.99 (***978-0-7636-2710-2(0))** Candlewick Pr.

Okimoto, Jean Davies & Aoki, Elaine Mei. The White Swan Express: A Story about Adoption. So, Meilo, illus. 2002. 32p. (J). (gr. k-3). tchr. ed. 16.00 (978-0-618-16453-0(7) , Clarion Bks.) Houghton Mifflin Co. Trade & Reference Div.

Osborne, Mary Pope. Day of the Dragon King, Vol. 14. unabr. ed. 2004. (Magic Tree House Ser. : No. 14). 68p. (J). (gr. k-3). pap. 17.00 incl. audio (978-0-8072-0783-3(7) , S FTR 242 SP, Listening Library) Random Hse. Audio Publishing Group.

—Day of the Dragon King. Murdocca, Sal, illus. 1998. (Magic Tree House Ser.: No. 14). 96p. (J). (gr. k-3). lib. bdg. 11.99 (978-0-679-99051-2(8)); 14th ed. pap. 3.99 (978-0-679-89051-5(3)) Random Hse. Children's Bks. (Random Hse. Bks. for Young Readers).

—Day of the Dragon King. Murdocca, Sal, illus. 1998. (Magic Tree House Ser. : No. 14). (J). (gr. k-3). 10.79 (978-0-606-13958-8(3)) Tandem Library Bks.

Pacilio, V. J. Ling Cho & his Three Friends. Cook, Scott, illus. 2000. 32p. (J). (ps-3). 16.00 (978-0-374-34545-7(7) , Farrar, Straus & Giroux (BYR)) Farrar, Straus & Giroux.

Partridge, Elizabeth. Oranges on Golden Mountain. Sogabe, Aki, illus. 2003. 36p. (J). pap. 6.99 (978-0-14-250033-0(X) , Puffin) Penguin Group (USA) Inc.

—Oranges on Golden Mountain. 2003. (gr. k-3). lib. bdg. 15.30 (978-0-613-61651-5(0)) Tandem Library Bks.

Pferdehirt, Julia, et al. Hudson Taylor: Shanghaied to China. 2000. (Trailblazer Bks.). (Illus.). 24p. (J). pap., stu. ed. 4.99 (978-0-7642-2344-0(5)) Bethany Hse. Pubs.

Pilegard, Virginia Walton. The Warlord's Alarm. Debon, Nicholas, illus. 2006. 32p. (J). 15.95 (978-1-58980-378-7(7)) Pelican Publishing Co., Inc.

—The Warlord's Fish. Debon, Nicolas, illus. 2002. 32p. (J). 15.95 (978-1-56554-964-7(3)) Pelican Publishing Co., Inc.

—The Warlord's Kites. Debon, Nicolas, illus. 2004. 432p. (J). pap. 15.95 (978-1-58980-180-6(6)) Pelican Publishing Co., Inc.

—The Warlord's Messengers. Debon, Nicolas, illus. 2005. 32p. (J). (gr. 1-4). 15.95 (978-1-58980-271-1(3)) Pelican Publishing Co., Inc.

—The Warlord's Puppeteers. Debon, Nicolas, illus. 2003. (Warlord Ser.: 4). 32p. (J). pap. 14.95 (978-1-58980-077-9(X)) Pelican Publishing Co., Inc.

—The Warlord's Puzzle. Debon, Nicolas, illus. 2000. 32p. (J). (ps-4). 15.95 (978-1-56554-495-6(1)) Pelican Publishing Co., Inc.

Poole, Amy Lowry, illus. & retold by. The Pea Blossom. Poole, Amy Lowry, retold by. 2006. 32p. reprint ed. 6.95 (978-0-8234-2018-6(3)) Holiday Hse., Inc.

Poole, Amy Lowry & Andersen, Hans Christian. The Pea Blossom. 2005. (Illus.). 32p. (J). (ps-3). 16.95 (978-0-8234-1864-0(2)) Holiday Hse., Inc.

Porte, Barbara Ann. Ma Jiang & the Orange Ants. Cannon, Annie, illus. 2000. 32p. (J). 17.99 (978-0-531-33241-2(1) , Orchard Bks.) Scholastic, Inc.

Potter, Beatrix. Conte de Pierre Lapin. (FRE.). pap. 18.95 (978-2-07-054698-5(5)) Gallimard, Editions FRA. *Dist:* Distribooks, Inc.

Ransome, Arthur. Missee Lee. 2002. (Swallows & Amazons Ser.). (Illus.). 352p. (J). pap. 14.95 (978-1-56792-196-0(5)) Godine, David R. Pub.

Roome, Diana Reynolds & Daly, Jude. The Elephant's Pillow. 2007. (Illus.). 32p. pap. 7.95 (***978-1-84507-798-3(9))** Lincoln, Frances Ltd. GBR. *Dist:* Perseus Distribution.

Ruby, Lois. Shanghai Shadows. 2006. 256p. (J). (gr. 7 up). 16.95 (978-0-8234-1960-9(6)) Holiday Hse., Inc.

Rumford, James. Cloudmakers. 2006. (Illus.). 32p. (J). (gr. k-3). pap. 6.95 (978-0-618-68951-4(6)) Houghton Mifflin Co.

Russell, Ching Yeung. Child Bride. 136p. 2003. (YA). (gr. 4-6). pap. 9.95 (978-1-59078-024-4(8)); 1999. (Illus.). (J). (gr. 3-7). 15.95 (978-1-56397-748-0(6)) Boyds Mills Pr.

—Moon Festival. 2003. (gr. k-3). lib. bdg. 17.60 (978-0-613-59335-9(9)) Tandem Library Bks.

Santore, Charles. The Silk Princess. 2007. (J). (***978-0-375-83664-0(0));** 40p. lib. bdg. (***978-0-375-93664-7(5))** Random Hse. Children's Bks.

Scherer, Catherine W. Simon & Barklee in China, Book 1 - the Southeast. 2007. (Another Country Calling Ser.). (J). per. 15.00 (978-0-9714502-6-4(9) , Explorer Media) Simon & Barklee, Inc./ExplorerMedia.

—Simon & Barklee in China, Book 2 - the Mountains. 2008. (Another Country Calling Ser.). (J). per. 15.00 (978-0-9714502-7-1(7) , Explorer Media) Simon & Barklee, Inc./ExplorerMedia.

—Simon & Barklee in China, Book 3 - the North. 2008. (Another Country Calling Ser.). (J). per. 15.00 (978-0-9714502-8-8(5) , Explorer Media) Simon & Barklee, Inc./ExplorerMedia.

Schlesinger, Marian C. San Bao & His Adventures in Peking. 2nd ed. 1998. (Illus.). 75p. (J). (gr. 3-7). reprint ed. pap. 15.00 (978-0-9645809-1-6(8)) Gale Hill Bks.

Schotz, Leo D. Rooftop. 2005. (Illus.). 32p. (J). 15.95 (978-0-9741319-7-9(0)) 4N Publishing LLC.

Scimone, Diana. Adventures with Pawpaw: China. Wiedemer, Leah, illus. 2003. 32p. (J). 8.95 (978-0-9729507-0-1(2)) Peapod Publishing, Inc.

Sellier, Marie. Legend of the Chinese Dragon. Louis, Catherine, illus. 2008. 40p. (J). (ps). 15.95 (***978-0-7358-2152-1(6))** North-South Bks., Inc.

Shepard, Aaron. The Magic Brocade: A Tale of China. Xiao Jun Li, illus. 2000. 32p. (J). (gr. 3-7). 16.95 (978-1-57227-064-0(0)) Pan Asia Pubns. (USA), Inc.

—The Magic Brocade: A Tale of China. Araujo, Frank P., tr. Xiao Jun Li, illus. 2000. (ENG & SPA.). 32p. (J). (gr. 3-7). 16.95 (978-1-57227-065-7(9)) Pan Asia Pubns. (USA), Inc.

—The Magic Brocade: A Tale of China. Chen, Isabella, tr. from ENG. Xiao Jun Li, illus. 2000. (ENG & CHI.). 32p. (J). (gr. 3-7). 16.95 (978-1-57227-066-4(7)) Pan Asia Pubns. (USA), Inc.

—The Magic Brocade: A Tale of China. Vu, Khanh Yen, tr. Xiao Jun Li, illus. 2000. (ENG & VIE.). 32p. (J). (gr. 3-7). 16.95 (978-1-57227-067-1(5)) Pan Asia Pubns. (USA), Inc.

—Monkey: A Superhero Tale of China, Retold from the Journey to the West. 2005. 48p. (J). lib. bdg. 15.00 (978-0-938497-25-7(1)); (YA). pap. 6.00 (978-0-938497-26-4(X)) Shepard Pubns. (Skyhook Pr.).

Shepard, Aaron. The Monkey King: A Superhero Tale of China, Retold from the Journey to the West. 2008. (Ancient Fantasy Ser.: 4). 50p. (J). lib. bdg. 15.00 (***978-0-938497-40-0(5));** lib. bdg. 6.00 (***978-0-938497-41-7(3))** Shepard Pubns. (Skyhook Pr.).

Snyder, Lavinia Branca. The Treasure of Lodian: The Kyss Family Mysteries. 2003. (Illus.). (J). mass mkt. (978-1-932233-68-1(7)) Aurora Libris Corp.

Stoeke, Janet Morgan. Waiting for May. Stoeke, Janet Morgan, illus. 2007. 32p. (J). (gr. k). pap. 5.99 (978-0-14-240853-7(0) , Puffin) Penguin Group (USA) Inc.

Stone, Kazuko G. & Keido, Ippo. The Butterfly's Dream: Children's Stories from China. 2003. (Illus.). 32p. 15.95 (978-0-8048-3480-3(6)) Tuttle Publishing.

The Story about Ping. 2004. 24.95 incl. audio (978-0-89719-688-8(0)); pap. 32.75 incl. audio (978-1-55592-313-6(5)); pap. 32.75 incl. audio (978-1-55592-314-3(3)); pap. 14.95 incl. audio (978-1-56008-076-3(0)) Weston Woods Studios, Inc.

A Story about Ping. 2004. (J). pap. 14.95 incl. audio (978-1-55592-857-5(9)) Weston Woods Studios, Inc.

Talley, Linda. Thank You, Meiling. Maeno, Itoko, illus. 1999. (Key Concepts in Personal Development Ser.). 32p. (J). (gr. k-4). 16.95 (978-1-55942-118-8(5) , 7666) Marsh Media.

Thank You, Meiling: Evaluation Guide. 2006. (J). (978-1-55942-423-3(0)) Marsh Media.

Top That Publishing Staff, ed. Chinese Myst. 2004. (Wicked Tattoos Ser.). (Illus.). 16p. (J). pap. (978-1-84510-108-4(1)) Top That! Publishing PLC.

Trout, Richard. Sign of the Dragon. 2007. (J). 15.95 (***978-1-58980-476-0(7))** Pelican Publishing Co., Inc.

Tseng, Grace. White Tiger, Blue Serpent. Tseng, Jean & Tseng, Mou-Sien, illus. 1999. 32p. (J). (ps-3). 16.00 (978-0-688-12515-8(8)) HarperCollins Pubs.

Tsubakiyama, Margaret. Mei-Mei Loves the Morning. Van Wright, Cornelius & Hu, Ying-Hwa, illus. 1999. 32p. (J). (ps-3). 15.95 (978-0-8075-5039-7(6)) Whitman, Albert & Co.

Tucker, Kathy. The Seven Chinese Sisters. Lin, Grace, illus. 2003. 32p. (J). (gr. k-3). 16.95 (978-0-8075-7309-9(4)) Whitman, Albert & Co.

Wallace, Barbara Brooks. Can Do, Missy Charlie. 2000. (Illus.). 228p. (YA). (gr. 4-7). pap. 14.95 (978-0-595-09574-2(7) , Backinprint.com) iUniverse, Inc.

Walsh, Ann. By the Skin of His Teeth. 2005. (Illus.). 144p. (YA). pap., tchr. ed. 6.95 (978-0-88878-448-3(1)) Beach Holme Pubs., Ltd. CAN. *Dist:* Literary Pr. Group of Canada.

Wang, Xiaohong. One Year in Beijing. Lin, Grace, illus. 2006. 32p. (J). (ps-3). 16.95 (***978-0-9747302-5-7(4))** Chinasprout, Inc.

Warner, Gertrude Chandler. Mystery in the Fortune Cookie. 2003. (gr. 3-6). lib. bdg. 11.80 (978-0-613-75713-3(0)) Tandem Library Bks.

Watase, Yu. Oracle: Vol. 2. Watase, Yu, illus. 2004. (Illus.). 200p. lib. bdg. 20.85 (978-1-4176-5230-3(6)) Tandem Library Bks.

Whelan, Gloria. Chu Ju's House. 240p. (J). 2004. (gr. 5 up). 16.99 (978-0-06-050724-4(1)); 2004. (gr. 5 up). lib. bdg. 17.89 (978-0-06-050725-1(X)); 2005. reprint ed. pap. 5.99 (978-0-06-050726-8(8) , Harper Trophy) HarperCollins Pubs.

Wilkinson, Carole. Garden of the Purple Dragon. 2007. 368p. (gr. 3-7). 16.99 (***978-1-4231-0338-7(6))** Hyperion Pr.

Wilson, Barbara Ker & So, Meilo. Wishbones: A Folk Tale from China. (Illus.). 32p. (J). (ps-2). pap. 9.99 (978-0-7112-1415-6(8)) Lincoln, Frances Ltd. GBR. *Dist:* Transition Vendor.

Wulffson, Don L. The Golden Rat. 2007. 176p. (J). 16.95 (***978-1-59990-000-1(9))** Bloomsbury Publishing.

Xiong, Kim. The Little Stone Lion. 2006. (Illus.). 40p. (J). 15.95 (978-0-9762056-1-6(0)) Heryin Publishing Corp.

Yang, Belle. Always Come Home to Me. Yang, Belle, illus. 2007. (Illus.). 32p. (J). (ps-3). 16.99 (***978-0-7636-2899-4(9))** Candlewick Pr.

Yang, Belle & Williams, Marcia. Archie's War. Williams, Marcia, illus. 2007. (Illus.). 48p. (J). (gr. 3-7). 17.99 (***978-0-7636-3532-9(4))** Candlewick Pr.

Ye, Ting-Xing. Share the Sky. Langlois, Suzane, illus. 1999. 32p. (J). (ps-2). lib. bdg. 17.95 (978-1-55037-579-4(2)) Annick Pr., Ltd. CAN. *Dist:* Firefly Bks., Ltd.

—Share the Sky. 1999. (gr. k-3). lib. bdg. 15.25 (978-0-613-26907-0(1)) Tandem Library Bks.

—Throwaway Daughter. 2004. 320p. mass mkt. 5.99 (978-0-7704-2921-8(1) , Seal Bks) Doubleday Canada, Ltd. CAN. *Dist:* Random Hse., Inc.

Yee, Paul. The Jade Necklace. Lin, Grace, illus. 2006. 29p. (J). (gr. 4-8). reprint ed. 16.00 (978-1-4223-5135-2(1)) DIANE Publishing Co.

—The Jade Necklace. Lin, Grace, illus. 2002. 32p. (J). (ps-3). 15.95 (978-1-56656-455-7(7) , Crocodile Bks.) Interlink Publishing Group, Inc.

Yen Mah, Adeline. Chinese Cinderella Boy Knight, Vol. 2. 2006. (978-0-06-056737-8(6)); lib. bdg. (978-0-06-056738-5(4)) HarperCollins Canada, Ltd.

Yi, Hu Yong. Good Morning China. 2007. (Illus.). 32p. (J). (ps-1). 16.95 (***978-1-59643-240-6(3))** Roaring Brook Pr.

Yin. Coolies. Soentpiet, Chris, illus. 2003. 40p. (J). (gr. k-3). pap. 7.99 (978-0-14-250055-2(0) , Puffin) Penguin Group (USA) Inc.

—Coolies. Soentpiet, Chris K., illus. 2001. 1p. (J). (ps-3). 16.99 (978-0-399-23227-5(3) , Philomel) Penguin Group (USA) Inc.

—Coolies. 2003. (gr. 3-6). lib. bdg. 16.45 (978-0-613-62936-2(1)) Tandem Library Bks.

Young, Ed. Beyond the Great Mountains: A Visual Poem about China. 2005. (Illus.). 36p. (J). 17.95 (978-0-8118-4343-0(2)) Chronicle Bks. LLC.

—My Mei Mei. Young, Ed, illus. 2006. (Illus.). 40p. (J). (gr. 1). 16.99 (978-0-399-24339-4(9) , Philomel) Penguin Group (USA) Inc.

Young, Ed & Adams, Tracey. The Lost Horse: A Chinese Folktale. 2004. (Illus.). 32p. (J). pap. 6.00 (978-0-15-205023-8(X) , Voyager Bks./Libros Viajeros) Harcourt Children's Bks.

Zaugg, Sandra L. Alice Says Goodbye. 2005. (Illus.). 95p. (J). pap. (978-0-8163-2049-3(7)) Pacific Pr. Publishing Assn.

—The Man in the Blue Skirt. 2005. (Illus.). 95p. (J). pap. (978-0-8163-2055-4(1)) Pacific Pr. Pubns.

—A Prayer for Mother. 2005. (Illus.). 95p. (J). (978-0-8163-2056-1(X)) Pacific Pr. Pubns.

CHINA—HISTORY

Allan, Tony. Ancient China. 2007. (Cultural Atlas for Young People Ser.). (Illus.). 96p. (YA). (gr. 5-8). 35.00 (***978-0-8160-6827-2(5)** , Chelsea Hse.) Facts On File, Inc.

—The Long March: The Making of Communist China. 2001. (Point of Impact Ser.). (Illus.). 32p. (J). (gr. 5-7). lib. bdg. 24.22 (978-1-58810-073-3(1)) Heinemann Library.

—The Rise of Modern China. 2002. (20th-Century Perspectives Ser.). (Illus.). 48p. (J). (gr. 5-7). lib. bdg. 27.07 (978-1-58810-661-2(6)); Set 2. pap. 7.95 (978-1-58810-921-7(6) , 91512) Heinemann Library.

Ancient China, 6 vols. (gr. 2-5). 36.95 (978-0-7368-4618-9(2)) Red Brick Learning.

Ancient China. (Early Civilization Ser.). 64p. (YA). 7.95 (978-0-7368-4547-2(X)) Capstone Pr., Inc.

Ancient China: Individual Title Six-Packs. (Rigby Infoquest Ser.). (gr. 5 up). 37.00 (978-0-7578-6495-7(3)) Rigby Education.

Anderson, Dale. Chinese Americans. 2006. (World Almanac Library of American Immigration). (Illus.). 47p. (J). pap. (978-0-8368-7321-4(1)); lib. bdg. (978-0-8368-7308-5(4)) Stevens, Gareth Inc. (World Almanac Library).

Armentrout, David & Armentrout, Patricia. China. 2003. (Illus.). 32p. (J). 28.50 (978-1-58952-719-5(4)) Rourke Publishing, LLC.

Art, Suzanne Strauss. The Story of Ancient China. Art, Suzanne Strauss, illus. 2001. 176p. (gr. 6-9). pap. 14.95 (978-0-9656557-8-1(4)) Pemblewick Pr.

Bailey, Linda. Adventures in Ancient China. Slavin, Bill, illus. 2004. (Good Times Travel Agency Ser.). 48p. (J). (gr. 4-6). (978-1-55337-454-1(1)); (978-1-55337-453-4(3)) Kids Can Pr., Ltd.

—Adventures in Ancient China. 2003. (gr. 3-6). lib. bdg. 17.60 (978-0-613-70943-9(8)) Tandem Library Bks.

Benchmark Education Staff. China Long Ago. 2005. 2.00 (***978-1-4108-4668-6(7))** Benchmark Education Co.

Bingham, Jane. Tiananmen Square. 2004. (Days That Shook the World Ser.). (Illus.). 47p. (J). lib. bdg. 28.56 (978-0-7398-6649-8(4)) Raintree.

Binns, Tristan Boyer. Ancient Chinese. 2006. (978-0-7565-1647-5(1)) Compass Point Bks.

Bjorklund, Ruth. Projects about Ancient China. 2006. (Hands-On History Ser.). (Illus.). 48p. (J). (gr. 4-6). lib. bdg. 29.93 (978-0-7614-2257-0(9) , Benchmark Bks.) Cavendish, Marshall Corp.

Blue, Rose, et al. Ancient China. 2006. (National Geographic Explores Ser.). (Illus.). 64p. (J). (gr. 3-7). 23.95 (978-0-7922-7783-5(X) , National Geographic Children's Bks.) National Geographic Society.

Bo, Zhiyue. The History of Modern China. 2004. (Illus.). 143p. (J). lib. bdg. (978-1-59084-830-2(6)) Mason Crest Pubs.

Brannon, Barbara. Discover Ancient China. 2005. 39.00 (***978-1-4108-5162-8(1))** Benchmark Education Co.

Brownlie Bojang, Ali. China. 2006. (Destination Detectives Ser.). 48p. (J). pap. (978-1-4109-2342-4(8)); lib. bdg. (978-1-4109-2331-8(2)) Steck-Vaughn.

Burnham, Brad. Caves of the Thousand Buddhas: Treasure House of Chinese Art. 2003. (Famous Caves of the World Ser.). (Illus.). 24p. (J). lib. bdg. 18.75 (978-0-8239-6260-0(1)) Rosen Publishing Group, Inc., The.

Byrne, Paul J. The Chinese Revolution: The Rise of Communism. 2006. 96p. (J). (978-0-7565-2006-9(1)) Compass Point Bks.

Campbell, Wallis. Angel Island. 2006. (Illus.). 48p. (J). pap. (978-1-59034-808-6(7)) Mondo Publishing.

Challen, Paul C. Life in Ancient China. 2004. (Peoples of the Ancient World Ser.). (Illus.). 32p. (J). (978-0-7787-2037-9(3)) Crabtree Publishing Co.

Childress, Diana. Marco Polo's Travels in China. 2006. (Pivotal Moments in History Ser.). 160p. (YA). (gr. 9-12). lib. bdg. 38.60 (978-0-8225-5903-0(X) , Twenty-First Century Bks.) Lerner Publishing Group.

Cole, Joanna. Ms. Frizzle's Adventures: Imperial China. 30th anniv. ed. 2008. (Magic School Bus Ser.). 40p. (J). pap. 6.99 (***978-0-590-10823-2(9)** , Scholastic Pr.) Scholastic, Inc.

Conklin, Wendy. China * India * Mesopotamia * Africa: All-in-One Resource with Background Information, Map Activities, Simulations & Games, & a Read-Aloud Play to Support Comprehension & Critical Thinking in Social Studies. 2006. (Ancient Civilizations Ser.). 96p. pap. 13.99 (978-0-439-53993-7(5) , Teaching Resources) Scholastic, Inc.

Cotterell, Arthur & Buller, Laura. Ancient China. 2005. (Dk eyewitness Bks.). (Illus.). 72p. (J). lib. bdg. 19.99 (978-0-7566-1391-4(4)) Dorling Kindersley Publishing, Inc.

—Ancient China. Hills, Alan & Brightling, Geoff, photos by. 2005. (Dk eyewitness Bks.). (Illus.). 72p. (J). (gr. 4-7). 15.99 (978-0-7566-1382-2(5)) Dorling Kindersley Publishing, Inc.

Crane, Carol. D Is for Dancing Dragon: A China Alphabet. Wang, Zong-Zhou, illus. rev. ed. 2006. 48p. (J). (gr. 1-5). 17.95 (978-1-58536-273-8(5)) Sleeping Bear Pr.

Deady, Kathleen W. & Dubois, Muriel L. Ancient China. 2004. (Illus.). 48p. (J). 17.95 (978-0-7368-2466-8(9) , Bridgestone Bks.) Capstone Pr., Inc.

Deedrick, Tami. China. Sloan, Frank, ed. 2001. (Ancient Civilizations Ser.). (Illus.). 48p. (J). (gr. 4-7). lib. bdg. 22.83 (978-0-7398-3580-7(7)) Raintree.

—China. 2000. (Ancient Civilizations Ser.). (Illus.). (J). pap. (978-0-7398-4150-1(5)) Steck-Vaughn.

DuTemple, Lesley A. The Great Wall of China. 2003. (Great Building Feats Ser.). (Illus.). 96p. (J). (gr. 5-9). 27.93 (978-0-8225-0377-4(8)) Lerner Publishing Group.

Exploring China, 6 vols. (Book2WebTM Ser.). (gr. 4-8). 36.50 (978-0-322-02991-0(0)) Wright Group, The.

Ganeri, Anita. Legacies from Ancient China. 1999. (Legacies Ser.). (Illus.). 32p. (J). (gr. 4-7). lib. bdg. 16.95 (978-1-929298-51-8(X)) Chrysalis Education.

Gassos, Dolores. China. 2005. (Ancient Civilizations Ser.). (Illus.). 31p. (J). (gr. 4-8). lib. bdg. 28.00 (978-0-7910-8476-2(0) , Chelsea Clubhouse) Facts On File, Inc.

Gay, Kathlyn. The Chinese Nationalist Revolution. 2008. (J). lib. bdg. (***978-0-8225-7601-3(5))** Twenty First Century Bks.

Gay Kathlyn. Mao Zedong's China. 2007. (Dictatorships Ser.). (Illus.). 160p. (YA). (gr. 9-12). lib. bdg. 38.60 (***978-0-8225-7285-5(0)** , Twenty-First Century Bks.) Lerner Publishing Group.

Glencoe McGraw-Hill Staff & McGraw-Hill - Jamestown Education Staff. Jamestown's Early Civilizations: Chinese Life. 2001. (gr. 5-12). pap. 11.96 (978-0-8092-9490-9(7) , 9780809294909) Jamestown.

Greenberger, Robert. The Technology of Ancient China. 2005. (Technology of the Ancient World Ser.). (Illus.). 48p. (J). (978-1-4042-0558-1(6)) Rosen Publishing Group, Inc., The.

Greenhaven Staff. China. 2002. (gr. 7-12). lib. bdg. 33.25 (978-0-613-73949-8(3)) Tandem Library Bks.

Guile, Melanie. China. 2003. (Illus.). 32p. (J). lib. bdg. 25.70 (978-1-4109-0468-3(7)) Raintree.

Hammond, Paula. China & Japan. 2002. (Cultures & Costumes Ser.). (Illus.). 64p. (J). (gr. 7 up). lib. bdg. (978-1-59084-436-6(X)) Mason Crest Pubs.

Hardwick, Susan. China: World-Wise Kids Guides. 2004. 96p. (978-1-59258-094-1(7)) Hylas Publishing.

Hatt, Christine. Mao Zedong. 2003. (Judge for Yourself Ser.). (Illus.). 64p. (J). (gr. 5 up). lib. bdg. 30.00 (978-0-8368-5536-4(1)); pap. (978-0-8368-5539-5(6)) Stevens, Gareth Inc. (World Almanac Library).

Hibbert, Clare. Chinese Art & Culture. 2005. (What About...? Ser.). (Illus.). 56p. (J). (gr. 5-9). lib. bdg. 29.99 (978-1-4109-1107-0(1)) Raintree.

Hirsch, E. D., ed. Ancient China. 2003. tchr. ed. 9.95 (978-0-7690-5044-7(1)); stu. ed. 49.95 (978-0-7690-2950-4(7)) Pearson Learning.

Hollihan-Elliot, Sheila. Ancient Civiliztion of China. 2005. (History & Culture of China Ser.). (Illus.). 144p. (J). lib. bdg. 24.95 (978-1-59084-822-7(5)) Mason Crest Pubs.

Holmes, Burton. Peking. Schlesinger, Arthur M., Jr. & Isreal, Fred L., eds. 1999. (World 100 Years Ago Ser.). (Illus.). 144p. (YA). (gr. 4-7). lib. bdg. 29.95 (978-0-7910-4666-1(4) , Chelsea Hse.) Facts On File, Inc.

—Peking. Israel, Fred L. & Schlesinger, Arthur M., Jr., eds. 1998. (World 100 Years Ago Ser.). (Illus.). 132p. (YA). (gr. 5 up). pap. 19.95 (978-0-7910-4667-8(2) , Chelsea Hse.) Facts On File, Inc.

Holt, Rinehart and Winston Staff. The Red Scarf Girl. 2nd ed. 2002. pap., stu. ed. 13.20 (978-0-03-066278-2(8)) Holt, Rinehart & Winston.

Hunt, Norman Bancroft. Living in Early China & Japan. 2007. (Living in the Ancient World Ser.). 96p. (gr. 6-12). 35.00 (978-0-8160-6342-0(7)) Facts On File, Inc.

Immell, Myra H. The Han Dynasty. 2002. (Lost Civilizations Ser.). (Illus.). 112p. (J). (gr. 6-9). 27.45 (978-1-59018-096-9(8) , Lucent Bks.) Thomson Gale.

Jesse, Denise, et al. Inside the Great Wall: A Journey to the Middle Kingdom: An Interactive Curriculum Unit for Social Studies. 1998. (Illus.). (gr. 4-8). 79.95 (978-1-885360-16-8(9)) Demco, Inc.

Jiang, Cheng A. Empress of China Zhongguo De Nu Huangdi: Wu Ze Tian. Xu, De Y., illus. 1998. 32p. (J). (gr. 3-6). 14.95 (978-1-878217-32-5(1)); pap. 7.95 (978-1-878217-31-8(3)) Victory Pr.

Jiang, Ji-Li. Red Scarf Girl: A Memoir of the Cultural Revolution. 1998. 304p. (J). (gr. 5 up). pap. 6.99 (978-0-06-446208-2(0) , Harper Trophy) HarperCollins Pubs.

—Red Scarf Girl with Connections: A Memoir of the Cultural Revolution. 2001. (HRW Library). xvii, 329p. (J). (978-0-03-066277-5(X)) Holt, Rinehart & Winston.

Kleeman, Terry & Barrett, Tracy. Student Study Guide to the Ancient Chinese World. 2005. (World in Ancient Times Ser.). 64p. (YA). 9.95 (978-0-19-522164-0(8)) Oxford Univ. Pr., Inc.

Kleeman, Terry F. & Barrett, Tracy. The Ancient Chinese World. 2005. (World in Ancient Times Ser.). (Illus.). 176p. 32.95 (978-0-19-517102-0(0)) Oxford Univ. Pr., Inc.

Krebs, Laurie. We're Riding on a Caravan: An Adventure on the Silk Road. Cann, Helen, illus. 2005. 32p. (J). 16.99 (978-1-84148-343-6(5)) Barefoot Bks., Inc.

Landau, Elaine. Exploring Ancient China with Elaine Landau. 2005. (Exploring Ancient Civilizations with Elaine Landau Ser.). (Illus.). 48p. (J). (gr. 4-7). lib. bdg. 23.93 (978-0-7660-2338-3(9) , Enslow Elementary) Enslow Pubs., Inc.

Li, Moying. Snow Falling in Spring: Growing up in China During the Cultural Revolution. 2008. 192p. (YA). 16.00 (***978-0-374-39922-1(0)***) Farrar, Straus & Giroux.

Lin, Zhimin. China under Reform. 2005. (History & Culture of China Ser.). (Illus.). 144p. (YA). lib. bdg. 24.95 (978-1-59084-823-4(3)) Mason Crest Pubs.

Luh, Shu Shin. People of China. 2005. (History & Culture of China Ser.). (Illus.). 127p. lib. bdg. (978-1-59084-831-9(4)) Mason Crest Pubs.

Malaspina, Ann. The Chinese Revolution & Mao Zedong in World History. 2004. (In World History Ser.). (Illus.). 128p. (J). lib. bdg. 26.60 (978-0-7660-1935-5(7)) Enslow Pubs., Inc.

Mann, Elizabeth. The Great Wall: The Story of 4,000 Miles of Earth & Stone That Turned a Nation into a Fortress. Witschonke, Alan, illus. (Wonders of the World Book Ser.). 48p. (J). 2006. (gr. 4-8). pap. 9.95 (978-1-931414-12-8(2)); 2003. (ps up). 22.95 (978-0-9650493-2-0(9)) Mikaya Pr.

Martell, Hazel Mary. Imperial China, 221 B. C. to A. D. 1294. 1999. (Looking Back Ser.). (Illus.). 64p. (J). (gr. 6-9). 19.98 (978-0-8172-5425-4(0)) Raintree.

McCulloch, Julie. China. (Illus.). 48p. (J). 2002. (gr. 4-6). (978-1-58810-386-4(2) , 91136); 2001. (gr. 3-5). lib. bdg. 25.64 (978-1-58810-152-5(5)) Heinemann Library.

Medieval China DBA. 2002. spiral bd. 16.95 (978-1-56004-141-2(2)) Social Studies Schl. Service.

Minnis. You Are in Ancient China. 2004. (Raintree Perspectives Ser.). (Illus.). 32p. (J). pap. 7.50 (978-1-4109-1011-0(3)); pap. 40.50 (978-1-4109-1016-5(4)) Harcourt Schl. Pubs.

Morley, Jacqueline. You Wouldn't Want to Work on the Great Wall of China. Antram, David, illus. 2006. 32p. (J). (gr. 2-5). pap. 9.95 (978-0-531-12449-9(5) , Watts, Franklin) Scholastic Library Publishing.

—You Wouldn't Want to Work on the Great Wall of China! Defenses You'd Rather Not Build. Antram, David, illus. 2006. (You Wouldn't Want To Ser.). 32p. (J). (gr. 2-5). 28.50 (978-0-531-12424-6(X) , Watts, Franklin) Scholastic Library Publishing.

Morris, Ann. Grandma Lai Goon Remembers: A Chinese-American Family Story. Linenthal, Peter, illus. 2002. (What Was It Like, Grandma? Ser.). 32p. (gr. k-3). lib. bdg. 22.90 (978-0-7613-2314-3(7) , Millbrook Pr.) Lerner Publishing Group.

—Grandma Lai Goon Remembers: A Chinese-American Family Story. 2002. (gr. k-3). lib. bdg. 16.40 (978-0-613-56395-6(6)) Tandem Library Bks.

Naden, Corinne, et al. Ancient China. 2006. (National Geographic Explores Ser.). (Illus.). 64p. (gr. 3-7). 27.90 (978-0-7922-7856-6(9) , National Geographic Children's Bks.) National Geographic Society.

Naden, Corinne J. Ancient Chinese & the Great Wall of China. 2003. (J). pap. (978-1-58417-313-7(0)); lib. bdg. (978-1-58417-312-0(2)) Lake Street Pubs.

Nardo, Don. The Song Dynasty. 2003. (Life During the Great Civilizations Ser.). (Illus.). 48p. (J). (gr. 3-5). 24.95 (978-1-4103-0056-0(0) , Blackbirch Pr., Inc.) Thomson Gale.

O'Donnell, Kerri. The Great Wall of China. 2003. (Reading Room Collection). (Illus.). 24p. (J). lib. bdg. 18.75 (978-0-8239-3715-8(1)) Rosen Publishing Group, Inc., The.

Pancella, Peggy. Qin Shi Huangdi. 2003. (Historical Biographies Ser.). (Illus.). 32p. (J). pap. 7.50 (978-1-4034-3712-9(2)); lib. bdg. 22.79 (978-1-4034-3704-4(1)) Heinemann Library.

Parramon Staff. China. 2006. (SPA.). 32p. (J). (gr. 6-8). 10.40 (978-84-342-2737-8(1) , PR33930) Parramon Ediciones S.A. ESP. *Dist:* Lectorum Pubns., Inc.

Patent, Dorothy Hinshaw. The Incredible Story of China's Buried Warriors. 2000. (Frozen in Time Ser.). (Illus.). (J). (gr. 5-9). lib. bdg. 27.07 (978-0-7614-0783-6(9) , Benchmark Bks.) Cavendish, Marshall Corp.

Perfect-Miller, Suzanne. Peoples/Dynasties of Ancient China. 1999. 156p. (J). spiral bd. 14.99 (978-0-945984-59-7(6) , Zephyr Pr.) Chicago Review Pr., Inc.

Perl, Lila. To the Golden Mountain: The Chinese Who Built the Transcontinental Railroad. 2002. (Great Journeys Ser.). (Illus.). 112p. (J). 32.79 (978-0-7614-1324-0(3) , Benchmark Bks.) Cavendish, Marshall Corp.

Pluckrose, Henry. China. 1999. (gr. k-3). lib. bdg. 15.25 (978-0-613-54124-4(3)) Tandem Library Bks.

Reid, Struan. Marco Polo. (Groundbreakers Ser.). 48p. (J). (gr. 5-7). 2002. pap. 8.50 (978-1-58810-371-0(4) , 91097); 2001. (Illus.). lib. bdg. 25.64 (978-1-58810-047-4(2)) Heinemann Library.

Ross, Frank. Oracle Bones, Stars, & Wheelbarrows: Ancient Chinese Science & Technology. (gr. 5-8). lib. bdg. 15.25 (978-0-8335-6082-7(4)) Tandem Library Bks.

Ross, Stewart. Ancient China. 2006. (Tales of the Dead Ser.). (Illus.). 32p. (J). 14.99 (978-0-7566-2076-9(7) , 1254333) Dorling Kindersley Publishing, Inc.

Ryall, Michael. China Long Ago. 2005. 39.00 (***978-1-4108-4620-4(2)***) Benchmark Education Co.

Schomp, Virginia. The Ancient Chinese. (People of the Ancient World Ser.). (Illus.). 112p. (J). 2005. (gr. 6-8). pap. 9.95 (978-0-531-16737-3(2)); 2004. 30.50 (978-0-531-11817-7(7)) Scholastic Library Publishing. (Watts, Franklin).

Shuter, Jane. Ancient China. 2004. (Excavating the Past Ser.). (Illus.). 48p. (J). (gr. 4-6). lib. bdg. 31.43 (978-1-4034-5995-4(9)) Heinemann Library.

—The Ancient Chinese. 2007. (Illus.). 32p. (J). (***978-1-4034-8809-1(6)***) Heinemann Library.

Shuter, Jane. Ancient Chinese Art. (Art in History Ser.). 32p. 2003. pap. 6.95 (978-1-4034-4015-0(8)); 2001. (Illus.). (J). (gr. 4-6). lib. bdg. 24.22 (978-1-58810-090-0(1)) Heinemann Library.

Slavicek, Louise Chipley. The Great Wall of China. 2004. (Arbitrary Borders Ser.). (Illus.). 112p. (YA). (gr. 9-13). 35.00 (978-0-7910-8019-1(6) , Chelsea Hse.) Facts On File, Inc.

—Mao Zedong. 2003. (Great Military Leaders of the Twentieth Century Ser.). (Illus.). 112p. (J). (gr. 6-12). 30.00 (978-0-7910-7407-7(2) , Chelsea Hse.) Facts On File, Inc.

Steele, Philip. Ancient China. 2002. (Illus.). 64p. pap. 7.95 (978-1-84215-616-2(0)) Anness Publishing GBR. *Dist:* National Bk. Network.

Steele, Philip & MacDonald, Fiona. Swords & Samurai: The Ancient Warrior Culture of the East. 2004. (Illus.). 128p. pap. 17.99 (978-1-84215-954-5(2) , Southwater) Anness Publishing GBR. *Dist:* National Bk. Network.

Stewart, Gail B. The Han Dynasty. 2004. (Life During the Great Civilizations Ser.). (Illus.). 48p. (J). (gr. 3-5). 24.95 (978-1-56711-737-0(6) , Blackbirch Pr., Inc.) Thomson Gale.

Sylvester, Diane. Ancient China. VanBlaricum, Pam, ed. Hillam, Corbin & Ciccarelli, Gary, illus. 2006. (Museum Ser.). 64p. pap. 13.99 (978-0-88160-389-7(9) , LW444, Learning Works, The) Creative Teaching Pr., Inc.

Tracy, Kathleen. The Life & Times of Confucius. 2004. (Biography from Ancient Civilizations Ser.). (Illus.). 48p. (J). (gr. 4-8). lib. bdg. 29.95 (978-1-58415-246-0(X)) Mitchell Lane Pubs., Inc.

Webster, Christine. Great Wall. 2007. (J). (***978-1-59036-723-0(5)); (*978-1-59036-724-7(3))*** Weigl Pubs., Inc.

Wilkinson, Philip. Chinese Myth: A Treasury of Legends, Art, & History. 2007. (World of Mythology Ser.). (Illus.). 96p. (YA). (gr. 6 up). 35.95 (***978-0-7656-8103-4(X)***) Sharpe, M.E. Inc.

Yu, Chun. Little Green: Growing up During the Chinese Cultural Revolution. 2005. (Illus.). 128p. (J). 15.95 (978-0-689-86943-3(6) , Simon & Schuster Children's Publishing) Simon & Schuster Children's Publishing.

Zhang, Ange, illus. Red Land, Yellow River: A Story from the Cultural Revolution. 2004. 56p. (J). 19.95 (978-0-88899-489-9(3)) Groundwood Bks. CAN. *Dist:* Perseus Distribution.

CHINA—HISTORY—BOXER REBELLION, 1899-1901

Langellier, John P. Uncle Sam's Little Wars: The Spanish-American War, Philippine Insurrection & Boxer Rebellion. 2001. (G. I. Ser.). (Illus.). 80p. (J). 27.50 (978-0-7910-6674-4(6) , Chelsea Hse.) Facts On File, Inc.

Zdrok, Jodie L. 1880-1900 (Events That Changed the World) 2004. (gr. 10-12). 22.45 (978-0-7377-2038-9(7) , Greenhaven Pr., Inc.) Thomson Gale.

CHINA—POLITICS AND GOVERNMENT

Hatt, Christine. Mao Zedong. 2003. (Judge for Yourself Ser.). (Illus.). 64p. (J). pap. (978-0-8368-5539-5(6) , World Almanac Library) Stevens, Gareth Inc.

Yu, Bin. Government of China. 2005. (History & Culture of China Ser.). (Illus.). 111p. (J). lib. bdg. (978-1-59084-829-6(2)) Mason Crest Pubs.

CHINA—SOCIAL LIFE AND CUSTOMS

Anderson, Jameson. History & Activities of Ancient China. 2006. (Hands-On Ancient History Ser.). (Illus.). 32p. pap. (978-1-4034-7930-3(5)); (J). (gr. 3-6). lib. bdg. 28.21 (978-1-4034-7922-8(4)) Heinemann Library.

Challen, Paul C. Life in Ancient China. 2004. (Peoples of the Ancient World Ser.). (Illus.). 32p. (J). pap. (978-0-7787-2067-6(5)) Crabtree Publishing Co.

Chinese New Year, Vol. 2. 2005. (One World, Many Cultures Ser.). (YA). (gr. k-3). (978-0-7368-9426-5(8) , Pebble Bks.) Capstone Pr., Inc.

Conyers, Karen Elizabeth. Teens in China. 2007. (Global Connections Ser.). (Illus.). 96p. pap. (***978-0-7565-2068-7(1)*** , 1265891) Compass Point Bks.

Demi, Hitz. Happy New Year! Kung-hsi Fa-ts'ai! 1999. (J). (978-0-606-17343-8(9)) Tandem Library Bks.

Drew, Rosa. Celebrating Chinese New Year: Nick's New Year. 1999. (ps-2). lib. bdg. 10.65 (978-0-613-34116-5(3)) Tandem Library Bks.

Glencoe McGraw-Hill Staff & McGraw-Hill - Jamestown Education Staff. Jamestown's Early Civilizations: Chinese Life. 2001. (gr. 5-12). pap. 11.96 (978-0-8092-9490-9(7) , 9780809294909) Jamestown.

Greenblatt, Miriam. Han Wu Di & Ancient China. 2005. (Rulers & Their Times Ser.). (Illus.). 80p. (J). (gr. 3-7). lib. bdg. 29.93 (978-0-7614-1835-1(0) , Benchmark Bks.) Cavendish, Marshall Corp.

Happy New Year: Kung-Hsi Fa-Ts'ai! 1999. (Illus.). (J). (ps-ps). lib. bdg. 15.30 (978-0-613-21676-0(8)) Tandem Library Bks.

Heinrichs, Ann. Chinese New Year. Huang, Benrei, illus. 2006. (Holidays, Festivals, & Celebrations Ser.). 32p. (J). (gr. k-4). 22.79 (978-1-59296-572-4(5)) Child's World, Inc.

Hitz, Demi. Happy, Happy Chinese New Year! 2003. (Illus.). 24p. (J). (ps-3). 8.95 (978-0-375-82642-9(4) , Crown Books For Young Readers) Random Hse. Children's Bks.

Hughes, Monica. My Chinese New Year. 2005. (Illus.). (J). 24p. (gr. 2-4). lib. bdg. 21.36 (978-1-4109-0778-3(3)); pap. (978-1-4109-0783-7(X)) Steck-Vaughn.

Kule, Elaine A. Celebrate Chinese New Year. 2006. (Celebrate Holidays Ser.). (Illus.). 104p. (J). lib. bdg. 31.93 (978-0-7660-2577-6(2)) Enslow Pubs., Inc.

Lakeshore Learning Materials Staff, contrib. by. Chinese Year Celebration Kit. 2000. (J). pap. 29.95 (978-1-929255-85-6(3)) Lakeshore Learning Materials.

Li, Richard T. The Golden Lotus: Life of a Bound-Feet Peasant Mother in the Chinese Cultural Revolution. 2004. (Illus.). 140p. (YA). pap. 7.95 (978-0-9675988-3-3(4)) Li, Richard T.

Lin, Zhimin. China under Reform. 2005. (History & Culture of China Ser.). (Illus.). 144p. (YA). lib. bdg. 24.95 (978-1-59084-823-4(3)) Mason Crest Pubs.

Lynch, Emma. China (We're From) 2005. (Heinemann First Libary Ser.). (Illus.). 32p. (J). lib. bdg. (978-1-4034-5803-2(0)) Heinemann Library.

—We're from China. 2005. (J). pap. (978-1-4034-5812-4(X)) Heinemann Library.

Minnis. Ancient China. 2004. (Raintree Perspectives Ser.). (Illus.). 32p. (J). 26.36 (978-1-4109-0619-9(1)) Harcourt Schl. Pubs.

Morris, Ting. Ancient China. 2006. (Arts & Crafts of Ser.). (Illus.). 32p. (J). (978-1-58340-914-5(9) , 1262690) Smart Apple Media.

Pirotta, Saviour. Chinese New Year. 2007. (J). lib. bdg. (978-1-4042-3709-4(7) , PowerKids Pr.) Rosen Publishing Group, Inc., The.

Rau, Margaret. Young Women in China. 2001. (Illus.). 168p. (YA). pap. 11.95 (978-0-595-16033-4(6)) iUniverse, Inc.

Sheen, Barbara. Foods of China. 2006. (Taste of Culture Ser.). 64p. (J). (gr. 3-6). 27.45 (978-0-7377-3031-9(5) , Greenhaven Pr., Inc.) Thomson Gale.

Simonds, Nina, et al. Moonbeams, Dumplings & Dragon Boats: A Treasury of Chinese Holiday Tales, Activities & Recipes. So, Meilo, illus. 2002. 80p. (J). (gr. 4-7). 21.00 (978-0-15-201983-9(9)) Harcourt Children's Bks.

So, Sungwan. A Child's Day in a Chinese City. 2001. (Child's Day Ser.). (Illus.). 32p. (J). (gr. k-2). lib. bdg. 25.64 (978-0-7614-1224-3(7) , Benchmark Bks.) Cavendish, Marshall Corp.

Stepanchuk, Carol. Exploring Chinatown: A Children's Guide to Chinese Culture. Wong, Leland, illus. 2003. 64p. (gr. 4-8). 22.95 (978-1-881896-25-8(0) , EXCH) Pacific View Pr.

Stewart, Gail B. The Han Dynasty. 2004. (Life During the Great Civilizations Ser.). (Illus.). 48p. (J). (gr. 3-5). 24.95 (978-1-56711-737-0(6) , Blackbirch Pr., Inc.) Thomson Gale.

Temko, Florence. Traditional Crafts from China. Gooch, Randall, illus. 2005. (Culture Crafts Ser.). 64p. (gr. 3-8). 23.93 (978-0-8225-2939-2(4)) Lerner Publishing Group.

Thompson, Stuart, et al. Chinese Cookbook. 2001. (Holiday Cookbooks from Around the World). (Illus.). 32p. (J). lib. bdg. 25.69 (978-0-7398-3262-2(X)) Raintree.

Waryncia, Lou, et al. If I Were a Kid in Ancient China: Children of the Ancient World. 2007. (Children of the Ancient World Ser.). (Illus.). 32p. (J). 17.95 (978-0-8126-7931-1(8)) Cricket Bks.

Yen Mah, Adeline. Chinese Cinderella: The True Story of an Unwanted Daughter. 2001. (gr. 7-12). lib. bdg. 14.15 (978-0-613-34012-0(4)) Tandem Library Bks.

Yu, Chun. Little Green: Growing up During the Chinese Cultural Revolution. 2005. (Illus.). 128p. (J). 15.95 (978-0-689-86943-3(6) , Simon & Schuster Children's Publishing) Simon & Schuster Children's Publishing.

Zhang, Elizabeth Yuan. The Middle Kingdom As We Saw: My Journey to China In 2004. l.t. ed. 2005. (Illus.). 272p. (YA). 29.98 (978-1-933361-04-8(2)) Lexington Pubs.

Zocchi, Judy. On Chinese New Year. Wallis, Rebecca, illus. 2005. (Holiday Happenings Ser.). 32p. (J). pap. 9.95 (978-1-59646-188-8(8)); lib. bdg. 20.65 (978-1-891997-55-6(6)) Dingles & Co.

—On Chinese New Year/el Año Nuevo Chino. Wallis, Rebecca, illus. 2005. (Holiday Happenings Ser.).Tr. of Año Nuevo Chino. (ENG & SPA.). 32p. (J). pap. 9.95 (978-1-59646-190-1(X)); lib. bdg. 20.65 (978-1-891997-56-3(4)) Dingles & Co.

Zucker, Jonny. Lanterns & Firecrackers: A Chinese New Year Story. Cohen, Jan Barger, illus. 2004. (Festival Time! Ser.). 24p. (J). pap. 6.95 (978-0-7641-2668-0(7)) Barron's Educational Series, Inc.

CHINA (PORCELAIN)

see Porcelain

CHINAWARE

see Porcelain

CHINCHILLAS

Handford, Tom. Chinchillas. 2003. (Keeping Unusual Pets Ser.). (Illus.). 48p. (J). (gr. 3-5). lib. bdg. 25.64 (978-1-4034-0280-6(9)) Heinemann Library.

Hudak, Heather C. Caring for Your Chinchilla. 2006. (J). pap. (978-1-59036-467-3(8)); lib. bdg. (978-1-59036-466-6(X)) Weigl Pubs., Inc.

CHINCHILLAS—FICTION

Golden Books Staff. Hop to It! Zalme, Ron, illus. 2006. (Color Plus Chunky Crayons Ser.). 32p. (J). (ps-2). pap. 3.99 (978-0-375-83589-6(X) , Golden Bks.) Random Hse. Children's Bks.

CHINESE

The Origin of Chinese, 1. l.t. ed. 2004. (CHI., Illus.). 60p. (J). (978-0-9752775-1-5(0) , 0-9752775-1-0) Unitrust Design.

CHINESE—CALIFORNIA—FICTION

Yep, Laurence. The Case of the Lion Dance. 1998. (Chinatown Mystery Ser.: Vol. 2). 224p. (J). (gr. 3-7). 15.89 (978-0-06-024448-4(8)) HarperCollins Pubs.

CHINESE—UNITED STATES

Ditchfield, Christin. Sports Great Michael Chang. 1999. (Sports Great Bks.). (Illus.). 64p. (YA). (gr. 4-10). lib. bdg. 22.60 (978-0-7660-1223-3(9)) Enslow Pubs., Inc.

Hoyt-Goldsmith, Diane. Celebrating Chinese New Year. Migdale, Lawrence, photos by. (Illus.). 32p. (J). (gr. 4-6). pap. 6.95 (978-0-8234-1520-5(1)) Holiday Hse., Inc.

Olson, Kay Melchisedech. Chinese Immigrants, 1850-1900. 2001. (Blue Earth Books). (Illus.). 32p. (J). (gr. 3-4). lib. bdg. 22.60 (978-0-7368-0793-7(4) , Bridgestone Bks.) Capstone Pr., Inc.

Wing, Thomas W. & Greenlee, Carolyn Wing. Son of South Mountain & Dust. BlueWolf, James Don, ed. Chin, Duncan, illus. ltd. ed. 1999. 88p. (J). spiral bd. 19.95 (978-1-887400-27-5(3) , EVB-1020A) Earthen Vessel Production, Inc.

CHINESE—UNITED STATES—FICTION

Blakeslee, Ann R. A Different Kind of Hero. 2005. 144p. (YA). pap. 5.95 (978-0-7614-5147-1(1)) Cavendish, Marshall Corp.

Heisel, Sharon E. Precious Gold, Precious Jade. 2000. 192p. (J). (gr. 7 up). tchr. ed. 16.95 (978-0-8234-1432-1(9)) Holiday Hse., Inc.

Joy Luck Club. 1999. (YA). 11.95 (978-1-56137-895-1(X)) Novel Units, Inc.

Lin, Grace. The Ugly Vegetables. 2001. (Illus.). 32p. (J). pap. 6.95 (978-1-57091-491-1(5)) Charlesbridge Publishing, Inc.

—The Ugly Vegetables. Lin, Grace, illus. 1999. (Illus.). 32p. (J). (ps-3). 15.95 (978-0-88106-336-3(3)) Charlesbridge Publishing, Inc.

—The Ugly Vegetables. 2001. (978-0-606-22628-8(1)) Tandem Library Bks.

Look, Lenore. Henry's First-Moon Birthday. Heo, Yumi, illus. 2001. 40p. (J). (ps-2). 16.99 (978-0-689-82294-0(4) , Atheneum/Anne Schwartz Bks.) Simon & Schuster Children's Publishing.

Meeting Half Way. 1999. (SmartReader Ser.). (J). Level 1. pap., tchr. ed. 19.95 incl. audio (978-0-7887-1157-2(1) , 79418T3); Level 2. pap., tchr. ed. 19.95 incl. audio (978-0-7887-0123-8(1) , 79311T3) Recorded Bks., LLC.

Namioka, Lensey. An Ocean Apart, a World Away. 2003. (gr. 7-12). lib. bdg. 13.55 (978-0-613-72264-3(7)) Tandem Library Bks.

—Yang the Second & Her Secret Admirers. De Kiefte, Kees, illus. 1998. 144p. (J). (gr. 3-7). 15.95 (978-0-316-59731-9(7)) Little Brown & Co.

Wallace, Ian. Chin Chiang & the Dragon's Dance. 1998. (Illus.). 32p. (J). (ps-2). pap. 5.95 (978-0-88899-167-6(3)) Groundwood Bks. CAN. *Dist:* Perseus Distribution.

Wallace, Ian, illus. Chin Chiang & the Dragon's Dance. 1998. 32p. (J). (ps-2). 19.95 (978-0-88899-020-4(0)) Groundwood Bks. CAN. *Dist:* Perseus Distribution.

Yep, Laurence. The Imp That Ate My Homework. 2000. 11.75 (978-0-606-17671-2(3)) Tandem Library Bks.

CHINESE AMERICANS

Anderson, Dale. Chinese Americans. 2008. (J). (***978-1-60044-611-5(6)***) Rourke Publishing, LLC.

—Chinese Americans. 2006. (World Almanac Library of American Immigration). (Illus.). 47p. (J). pap. (978-0-8368-7321-4(1)); lib. bdg. (978-0-8368-7308-5(4)) Stevens, Gareth Inc. (World Almanac Library).

Ashley, Susan. Yo-Yo Ma. 2004. (Trailblazers of the Modern World Ser.). (Illus.). 48p. (J). pap. 11.99 (978-0-8368-5266-0(4)); (YA). lib. bdg. 30.00 (978-0-8368-5497-8(7)) Stevens, Gareth Inc. (World Almanac Library).

Behnke, Alison. Chinese in America. 2005. (In America Ser.). (Illus.). 80p. (J). (gr. 5-8). lib. bdg. 27.93 (978-0-8225-4695-5(7)) Lerner Publishing Group.

Boyer Binns, Tristan. Chinese Americans. (We Are America Ser.). (Illus.). 32p. (J). 2003. (gr. 2-4). lib. bdg. (978-1-4034-0162-5(4)); 2002. pap. 6.95 (978-1-4034-0417-6(8)) Heinemann Library.

Broida, Marian. Projects about American Immigrants from China. 2005. (Hands-On History Ser.). (Illus.). 48p. (J). (978-0-7614-1978-5(0) , Benchmark Bks.) Cavendish, Marshall Corp.

Bryan, Nichol. Chinese Americans. 2004. (One Nation Set II Ser.). (Illus.). 32p. (J). (gr. k-6). lib. bdg. 22.78 (978-1-59197-525-0(5)) ABDO Publishing Co.

Campbell, Wallis. Angel Island. 2006. (Illus.). 48p. (J). pap. (978-1-59034-808-6(7)) Mondo Publishing.

Chin, Steven A. Dragon Parade: A Chinese New Year Story. 2000. (J). 12.80 (978-0-606-19075-6(9)) Tandem Library Bks.

Chippendale, Lisa A. Yo-Yo Ma: A Cello Superstar Brings Music to the World. 2004. (People to Know Ser.). (Illus.). 112p. (J). lib. bdg. 26.60 (978-0-7660-2286-7(2)) Enslow Pubs., Inc.

Darraj, Susan Muaddi. Amy Tan. 2007. (Asian Americans of Achievement Ser.). 112p. (gr. 6-12). 30.00 (978-0-7910-9269-9(0) , Chelsea Hse.) Facts On File, Inc.

Deiters, Erika & Deiters, Jim. The Chinese Community in America. 2003. (J). lib. bdg. (978-1-58417-027-3(1)) Lake Street Pubs.

Flanagan, Alice K. Angel Island. 2005. (We the People Ser.). (Illus.). 48p. (J). (gr. 4-6). (978-0-7565-1261-3(1)) Compass Point Bks.

Gatto, Kimberly. Michelle Kwan: Champion on Ice. 1998. (Sports Achievers Biographies Ser.). (Illus.). 64p. (J). (gr. 4-9). lib. bdg. (978-0-8225-3669-7(2)); pap. 5.95 (978-0-8225-9830-5(2)) Lerner Publishing Group. (LernerSports).

Goodridge, Catherine. Michelle Kwan. ed. 2004. (SPA.). (J). pap. 5.00 (978-1-4108-2428-8(4) , A24284) Benchmark Education Co.

Greenlee, Carolyn Wing. Son of South Mountain & Dust. Wing, Thomas W. & Chin, Duncan, illus. 2001. vii, 149p. (J). (978-1-887400-30-5(3)) Earthen Vessel Publishing.

Gritter, Marissa. The Chinese Americans. 2002. (Welcome to America Ser.). (Illus.). 64p. (J). (gr. 4-7). lib. bdg. (978-1-59084-108-2(5)) Mason Crest Pubs.

Harcourt School Publishers Staff. In Two Worlds Advanced Level. 3rd ed. 2002. (Trophies Reading Program Ser.). (Illus.). pap. 5.10 (978-0-15-323192-6(0)) Harcourt Schl. Pubs.

Hill, Anne E. Michelle Kwan. 2004. (Sports Heroes & Legends Ser.). (Illus.). 112p. (J). (gr. 6-12). lib. bdg. 27.93 (978-0-8225-1795-5(7)) Lerner Publishing Group.

Isaacs, Sally Senzell. Life in San Francisco's Chinatown. 2003. (Picture the Past Ser.). (Illus.). 32p. (J). (gr. 2-4). lib. bdg. 22.79 (978-1-58810-692-6(6)); pap. 7.50 (978-1-4034-0524-1(7)) Heinemann Library.

Kaplan, Leslie C. Chinese New Year. 2004. (Library of Holidays). (Illus.). 24p. (J). lib. bdg. 18.75 (978-0-8239-6658-5(5) , PowerKids Pr.) Rosen Publishing Group, Inc., The.

Kite, Lorien. The Chinese. 2000. (We Came to North America Ser.). (Illus.). 32p. (J). (gr. 4). (978-0-7787-0188-0(3)) Crabtree Publishing Co.

—Chinese. 2000. (gr. 3-6). lib. bdg. 17.60 (978-0-613-27769-3(4)) Tandem Library Bks.

—The Chinese: We Came to North America. 2006. (Illus.). 32p. (J). (gr. 4-8). reprint ed. 19.00 (978-0-7567-9904-5(X)) DIANE Publishing Co.

Koh, Frances M. A China Adoption Story: Mommy, Why Do We Look Different? O'Brien, Anne Sibley, illus. 2000. 24p. (J). (gr. 1-2). lib. bdg. 15.95 (978-0-9606090-9-3(1)) EastWest Pr.

Kwan, Michelle. Michelle Kwan: My Book of Memories. 1998. (Illus.). (J). (gr. 4-7). pap. 5.99 (978-0-590-45980-0(6)) Scholastic, Inc.

—Michelle Kwan Chapterbook. 2000. 64p. (J). pap. 4.99 (978-0-7868-1383-4(0)) Disney Pr.

—Michelle Kwan, Heart of a Champion: An Autobiography. 1998. (978-0-606-13607-5(X)) Tandem Library Bks.

Lashnits, Tom. Maya Lin. 2007. (Asian Americans of Achievement Ser.). 128p. (YA). (gr. 6-10). lib. bdg. 30.00 (978-0-7910-9268-2(2) , Chelsea Hse.) Facts On File, Inc.

Lingen, Marissa. Chinese Immigration. 2004. (Changing Face of North America Ser.). (Illus.). 112p. (YA). lib. bdg. (978-1-59084-694-0(X)) Mason Crest Pubs.

MacMillan, Dianne M. Chinese New Year. 2008. (Best Holiday Books Ser.). 48p. (J). (gr. 3-4). lib. bdg. 23.93 (***978-0-7660-3038-1(5)***) Enslow Pubs., Inc.

Martin, Michael. Chinese Americans. 2003. (Immigrants in America Ser.). (Illus.). 112p. (gr. 6-12). 30.00 (978-0-7910-7126-7(X)); pap. 13.25 (978-0-7910-7513-5(3)) Facts On File, Inc. (Chelsea Hse.).

McGinty, Alice B. Meet Laurence Yep. 2003. (About the Author Ser.). (Illus.). 24p. (J). lib. bdg. 18.75 (978-0-8239-6410-9(8) , PowerKids Pr.) Rosen Publishing Group, Inc., The.

Miller, Raymond H. Michelle Kwan. 2003. (Stars of Sports Ser.). (Illus.). 48p. (J). 26.20 (978-0-7377-1540-8(5) , Greenhaven Pr., Inc.) Thomson Gale.

Monique, Tahiera. Annihilator of Innocense. 2002. 256p. 25.95 (978-0-9713953-0-5(6)) Tavine'ra Publishing, LLC.

O'Connell, Kim A. China: A MyReportLinks. com Book. 2004. (Top Ten Countries of Recent Immigrants Ser.). (Illus.). 48p. (J). lib. bdg. 25.26 (978-0-7660-5240-6(0) , MyReportLinks.com Bks.) Enslow Pubs., Inc.

Paprocki, Sherry. Michelle Kwan. 2000. (Women Who Win Ser.). (Illus.). 64p. (J). (gr. 4-7). 25.00 (978-0-7910-5792-6(5) , Chelsea Hse.) Facts On File, Inc.

Perl, Lila. To the Golden Mountain: The Chinese Who Built the Transcontinental Railroad. 2002. (Great Journeys Ser.). (Illus.). 112p. (J). 32.79 (978-0-7614-1324-0(3) , Benchmark Bks.) Cavendish, Marshall Corp.

Raatma, Lucia. Chinese Americans. 2002. (Spirit of America: Our Cultural Heritage Ser.). (Illus.). 32p. (J). (gr. 2-6). 27.07 (978-1-56766-149-1(1)) Child's World, Inc.

Shields, Charles J. Amy Tan. 2001. (Women of Achievement Ser.). (Illus.). 116p. (J). pap. 30.00 (978-0-7910-5890-9(5)); 112p. (YA). (gr. 5 up). 30.00 (978-0-7910-5889-3(1)) Facts On File, Inc. (Chelsea Hse.).

Stepanchuk, Carol. Exploring Chinatown: A Children's Guide to Chinese Culture. Wong, Leland, illus. 2003. 64p. (gr. 4-8). 22.95 (978-1-881896-25-8(0) , EXCH) Pacific View Pr.

Stone, Amy. Maya Lin. 2003. (Raintree Biographies Ser.). (Illus.). 32p. (J). lib. bdg. 25.70 (978-0-7398-6863-8(2)) Raintree.

—Maya Lin. 2003. (gr. 3-6). lib. bdg. 15.90 (978-0-613-78165-7(1)) Tandem Library Bks.

Teitlebaum, Michael. Chinese Immigrants. 2004. (Immigration to the United States Ser.). (Illus.). 96p. (J). (gr. 4-9). 35.00 (978-0-8160-5687-3(0)) Facts On File, Inc.

Thornton, Jeremy. The Gold Rush: Chinese Immigrants Come to America (1848-1882) 2004. (Primary Sources of Immigration & Migration in America Ser.). (Illus.). 24p. (J). lib. bdg. 19.95 (978-0-8239-6833-6(2) , PowerKids Pr.) Rosen Publishing Group, Inc., The.

—The Gold Rush: Chinese Immigrants Come to America, 1848-1882. 2004. (Primary Sources of Immigration & Migration in America Ser.). (Illus.). 24p. (J). lib. bdg. (978-0-8239-8959-1(3) , PowerKids Pr.) Rosen Publishing Group, Inc., The.

Wallner, Rosemary. Michelle Kwan. 2001. (Sports Heroes Ser.). (Illus.). 48p. (J). (gr. 3-4). lib. bdg. 21.26 (978-0-7368-0779-1(9) , Capstone High-Interest Bks.) Capstone Pr., Inc.

Wilner, Barry. Michelle Kwan: Star Figure Skater. 2001. (Sports Reports). (Illus.). 104p. (YA). (gr. 4-10). lib. bdg. 26.60 (978-0-7660-1504-3(1)) Enslow Pubs., Inc.

Wong, Li Keng. Good Fortune: My Journey to Gold Mountain. 2006. (Illus.). 144p. (J). (gr. 3-7). 14.95 (978-1-56145-367-2(6)) Peachtree Pubs., Ltd.

Yen Mah, Adeline. Chinese Cinderella: The True Story of an Unwanted Daughter. 2001. (gr. 7-12). lib. bdg. 14.15 (978-0-613-34012-0(4)); (Illus.). (J). 12.64 (978-0-606-21108-6(X)) Tandem Library Bks.

CHINESE AMERICANS—FICTION

Campoy, F. Isabel & Ada, Alma Flor. Celebrate Chinese New Year with the Fong Family. Castro, Mima, illus. 2006. (Stories to Celebrate Ser.). 31p. (J). (978-1-59820-126-0(3)) Santillana USA Publishing Co., Inc.

Campoy, F. Isabel, et al. Celebra el Ano Nuevo Chino con la Familia Fong. Castro, Mima, illus. 2006. (J). (978-1-59820-114-7(X) , Alfaguara) Santillana USA Publishing Co., Inc.

Chen, Pauline. Peiling & the Chicken-Fried Christmas. 2007. 160p. (J). (gr. 3-6). 15.95 (***978-1-59990-122-0(6)***) Bloomsbury Publishing.

Cheng, Andrea. Goldfish & Chrysanthemums. Chang, Michelle, illus. 2003. 32p. (J). 16.95 (978-1-58430-057-1(4)) Lee & Low Bks., Inc.

—Grandfather Counts. 2000. (gr. k-3). lib. bdg. 15.25 (978-0-613-65692-4(X)) Tandem Library Bks.

—Honeysuckle House. 2004. 136p. (YA). 16.95 (978-1-886910-99-7(5) , Lemniscaat) Boyds Mills Pr.

—The Key Collection. Choi, Yangsook, illus. rev. ed. 2003. 128p. (J). (gr. 3-6). 16.95 (978-0-8050-7153-5(9) , Holt, Henry & Co. Bks. For Young Readers) Holt, Henry & Co.

—Shanghai Messenger. Young, Ed, illus. 2005. 40p. (J). (ps-7). 17.95 (978-1-58430-238-4(0)) Lee & Low Bks., Inc.

Chetin, Helen. Angel Island Prisoner 1922. Harvey, Catherine, tr. Lee, Jan, illus. 2002. (CHI.). 64p. (J). 8.95 (978-0-9667352-3-9(4)) Angel Island Assoc.

Chinn, Karen. Sam y el Dinero de la Suerte. Van Wright, Cornelius, illus. 2003. Tr. of Sam & the Lucky Money. (SPA.). (J). (978-1-58430-167-7(8)); (978-1-58430-168-4(6)) Lee & Low Bks., Inc.

—Xiaoshan Di Ya Shui Qian: Sam & the Lucky Money. Van Wright, Cornelius & Hu, Ying-Hwa, illus. 2002. (CHI.). (J). 16.95 (978-1-58430-084-7(1)); pap. 6.95 (978-1-58430-085-4(X)) Lee & Low Bks., Inc.

Culver, Carol. Rich Girl: A BFF Novel. 2008. 240p. pap. 9.99 (***978-0-425-21915-7(1)*** , Berkley Trade) Penguin Group (USA) Inc.

Cummings, Mary. Three Names of Me. Wang, Lin, illus. 2006. (J). 15.95 (978-0-8075-7903-9(3)) Whitman, Albert & Co.

Currier, Katrina Saltonstall. Kai's Journey to Gold Mountain: An Angel Island Story. 2004. 40p. 16.95 (978-0-9667352-7-7(7)); (Illus.). 44p. (J). pap. 10.95 (978-0-9667352-4-6(2)) Angel Island Assoc.

Dell, Pamela. A Song for Sung Li: A Story of the 1906 San Francisco Earthquake. 2002. (Scrapbooks of America Ser.). (Illus.). 48p. (J). (gr. 2-6). 28.50 (978-1-59187-015-9(1)) Child's World, Inc.

Fletcher, Susan. Walk Across the Sea. Jakesevic, Nenad, illus. 224p. (J). 2003. pap. 11.95 (978-0-689-85707-2(1) , Aladdin); 2001. (gr. 5-9). 16.95 (978-0-689-84133-0(7) , Atheneum) Simon & Schuster Children's Publishing.

—Walk Across the Sea. 2003. (gr. 3-6). lib. bdg. 13.00 (978-0-613-62227-1(8)) Tandem Library Bks.

—Walk Across the Sea. l.t. ed. 2002. 218p. (J). 22.95 (978-0-7862-4439-3(9)) Thorndike Pr.

Headley, Justina Chen. Girl Overboard. 2008. 352p. (J). (gr. 7-17). 16.99 (***978-0-316-01130-3(4)***) Little Brown & Co.

Jordan, Sherryl. The Hunting of the Last Dragon. 2002. 192p. (J). (gr. 7 up). 15.99 (978-0-06-028902-7(3)); 15.89 (978-0-06-028903-4(1)) HarperCollins Pubs.

Kim, Kenneth H. Half & Half. 2000. (gr. 7-12). lib. bdg. 11.80 (978-0-613-51051-6(8)) Tandem Library Bks.

Lavender, William. Aftershocks. 2006. (Illus.). 352p. (YA). 17.00 (978-0-15-205882-1(6)) Harcourt Children's Bks.

Lee, Huy Voun, ed. In the Snow. rev. ed. 2000. (Illus.). 32p. (J). (ps). pap. 7.95 (978-0-8050-6579-4(2) , Holt, Henry & Co. Bks. For Young Readers) Holt, Henry & Co.

Lee, Huy Youn, ed. In the Snow. 2000. (Illus.). (J). (ps-ps). lib. bdg. 15.25 (978-0-613-30516-7(7)) Tandem Library Bks.

Lee, Milly. Earthquake. Choi, Yangsook, illus. 2006. 32p. (J). reprint ed. pap. 6.95 (978-0-374-41946-2(9)) Macmillan.

—Landed. Choi, Yangsook, illus. 2006. 40p. (J). 16.00 (978-0-374-34314-9(4) , Farrar, Straus & Giroux (BYR)) Farrar, Straus & Giroux.

—Nim & the War Effort. Choi, Yangsook, illus. 2002. 40p. (J). pap. 6.95 (978-0-374-45506-4(6) , Sunburst) Farrar, Straus & Giroux.

—Nim & the War Effort. 2002. (gr. 3-6). lib. bdg. 14.10 (978-0-613-53846-6(3)) Tandem Library Bks.

Lin, Grace. Bringing in the New Year. 2008. 32p. (J). (***978-0-375-83745-6(0)***); lib. bdg. (***978-0-375-93745-3(5)***) Knopf, Alfred A. Inc.

—Fortune Cookie Fortunes. (Illus.). 32p. (J). (gr. k-3). 2006. pap. 6.99 (978-0-440-42192-4(6) , Dragonfly Bks.); 2004. 15.95 (978-0-375-81521-8(X) , Knopf Bks. for Young Readers); 2004. lib. bdg. 17.99 (978-0-375-91521-5(4) , Knopf Bks. for Young Readers) Random Hse. Children's Bks.

—Ugly Vegetables. 2001. (gr. k-3). lib. bdg. 15.25 (978-0-613-79134-2(7)) Tandem Library Bks.

Look, Lenore. Love As Strong As Ginger. Johnson, Stephen T., illus. 1999. 32p. (J). (gr. 1-4). 16.99 (978-0-689-81248-4(5) , Atheneum/Anne Schwartz Bks.) Simon & Schuster Children's Publishing.

—Ruby Lu, Brave & True. 2004. (Illus.). 104p. (J). lib. bdg. 15.00 (***978-1-4242-0914-9(5)***) Fitzgerald Bks.

—Ruby Lu, Brave & True. Wilsdorf, Anne, illus. 2006. (Ready-for-Chapters Ser.). 112p. (J). pap. 3.99 (978-1-4169-1389-4(0) , Aladdin) Simon & Schuster Children's Publishing.

—Ruby Lu, Empress of Everything. Wilsdorf, Anne, illus. 2007. 164p. (J). (gr. 1-5). per. 4.99 (***978-1-4169-5003-5(6)*** , Aladdin) Simon & Schuster Children's Publishing.

Look, Lenore. Uncle Peter's Amazing Chinese Wedding. Heo, Yumi, illus. 2006. 40p. (J). (ps-3). 16.95 (978-0-689-84458-4(1) , Atheneum/Anne Schwartz Bks.) Simon & Schuster Children's Publishing.

Look, Lenore & Wilsdorf, Anne. Ruby Lu, Brave & True. 2004. (Illus.). 176p. (J). (gr. 1-2). 15.95 (978-0-689-84907-7(9) , Atheneum/Anne Schwartz Bks.) Simon & Schuster Children's Publishing.

Louie, Therese On. Raymond's Perfect Present. Wang, Suling, illus. 2002. (J). (gr. 2-4). 16.95 (978-1-58430-055-7(8)) Lee & Low Bks., Inc.

Mak, Kam. Chinatown. Date not set. 32p. (J). (gr. k-3). pap. 5.99 (978-0-06-443732-5(9)) HarperCollins Pubs.

—My Chinatown: One Year in Poems. Mak, Kam, illus. 2001. (Illus.). 32p. (J). (gr. k-3). 16.99 (978-0-06-029190-7(7)) HarperCollins Pubs.

Marsden, Carolyn & Loh, Virginia Shin-Mui. The Jade Dragon. 2006. 176p. (J). (gr. 2-5). 15.99 (978-0-7636-3012-6(8)) Candlewick Pr.

Martin, Nora. Flight of the Fisherbird. 2003. (Illus.). 200p. (J). 16.95 (978-1-58234-814-8(6) , Bloomsbury Children) Bloomsbury Publishing.

McDonald, Megan. Happy New Year, Julie, Bk. 3. McAliley, Susan, illus. 2007. 88p. (YA). (gr. 3 up). 12.95 (***978-1-59369-292-6(7)***) American Girl Publishing, Inc.

—Happy New Year, Julie, Bk. 3. McAliley, Susan & Hunt, Robert, illus. 2007. 88p. (YA). (gr. 3 up). pap. 6.95 (***978-1-59369-291-9(9)***) American Girl Publishing, Inc.

Namioka, Lensey. April & the Dragon Lady. 2007. (Illus.). 224p. (YA). pap. 6.95 (***978-0-15-205669-8(6)*** , Harcourt Paperbacks) Harcourt Children's Bks.

—Half & Half. 2004. 144p. (gr. 3-7). pap. 5.50 (978-0-440-41890-0(9) , Yearling) Random Hse. Children's Bks.

—Mismatch. 224p. (gr. 5-9), 2007. (YA). mass mkt. 6.50 (978-0-440-23879-9(X) , Laurel Leaf); 2006. (J). 15.95 (978-0-385-73183-6(3) , Delacorte Bks. for Young Readers) Random Hse. Children's Bks.

Partridge, Elizabeth. Oranges on Golden Mountain. Sogabe, Aki, illus. 2003. 36p. (J). pap. 6.99 (978-0-14-250033-0(X) , Puffin) Penguin Group (USA) Inc.

—Oranges on Golden Mountain. 2003. (gr. k-3). lib. bdg. 15.30 (978-0-613-61651-5(0)) Tandem Library Bks.

Platt, Randall Beth. The Likes of Me. 2001. (J). (978-0-606-21296-0(5)) Tandem Library Bks.

Rosten, Carrie. Chloe Leiberman (Sometimes Wong) 2007. 224p. (YA). (gr. 7). pap. 8.99 (978-0-385-73248-2(1) , Delacorte Bks. for Young Readers) Random Hse. Children's Bks.

Roth, Susan L. Happy Birthday Mr. Kang. 2001. (Illus.). 32p. (J). (ps-3). 16.95 (978-0-7922-7723-1(6) , National Geographic Children's Bks.) National Geographic Society.

Shemin, Craig. Families Are Forever. McCoy, John, illus. l.t. ed. 2004. 34p. 9.95 (978-0-9728666-1-3(2) , 1) As Simple As That Publishing.

Stites, Clara. Lixia of Gold Mountain: A Story of Early California. 2003. (Illus.). 64p. (J). pap. 8.95 (978-1-56474-421-0(3)) Fithian Pr.

Thong, Roseanne. Gai See: What You Can See in Chinatown. Choi, Yangsook, illus. 2007. 40p. (J). (ps-3). 16.95 (***978-0-8109-9337-2(6)*** , Abrams Bks. for Young Readers) Abrams, Harry N. , Inc.

—One Is a Drummer: A Book of Numbers. Lin, Grace, illus. 2004. 40p. (J). 14.95 (978-0-8118-3772-9(6)) Chronicle Bks. LLC.

—Red Is a Dragon. Lin, Grace, illus. 2001. 40p. (J). 15.95 (978-0-8118-3177-2(9)) Chronicle Bks. LLC.

—Round Is a Mooncake: A Book of Shapes. Lin, Grace, illus. 2000. 40p. (J). (ps-k). 14.95 (978-0-8118-2676-1(7)) Chronicle Bks. LLC.

Wong, Benedict Norbert. Lo & Behold. Wong, Benedict Norbert, illus. l.t. ed. 2003. (Illus.). 38p. (gr. 1 up). 16.95 (978-0-9728192-0-6(7) , LOBE) Taiji Arts Publishing.

—Lo & Behold: A Boy & His Dragon. 2004. (Illus.). 44p. (J). (gr. 1-12). 8.95 (978-0-9728192-4-4(X)) Taiji Arts Publishing.

—Lo & Behold: Good Enough to Eat. Wong, Benedict Norbert, illus. l.t. ed. 2003. (Illus.). 40p. (J). (gr. 1-12). 16.95 (978-0-9728192-1-3(5) , 1002LB) Taiji Arts Publishing.

—Lo & Behold: The Millennia Just Roll By. 2004. (Illus.). 40p. (J). (gr. 1-12). 16.95 (978-0-9728192-3-7(1)) Taiji Arts Publishing.

Wong, Janet S. Apple Pie Fourth of July. Chodos-Irvine, Margaret, illus. 40p. (J). 2006. pap. 7.00 (978-0-15-205708-4(0) , Voyager Bks./Libros Viajeros); 2002. 17.00 (978-0-15-202543-4(X)) Harcourt Children's Bks.

Wong, Joyce Lee. Seeing Emily. 288p. (J). 2007. (gr. 5-10). pap. 6.95 (***978-0-8109-9258-0(2)*** , Amulet Bks.); 2005. (Illus.). (gr. 7-11). 16.95 (978-0-8109-5757-2(4) , Abrams Bks. for Young Readers) Abrams, Harry N. , Inc.

Yamada, Debbie Leung. Striking It Rich: Treasures from Gold Mountain. Tang, You-shan, illus. l.t. ed. 2004. 128p. (J). (gr. 4-8). pap. 13.95 (978-1-879965-21-8(6)) Polychrome Publishing Corp.

Yamate, Sandra S. & Yao, Carolina, illus. Char Siu Bao Boy. 2004. 32p. (J). (gr. k-3). pap. 15.95 (978-1-879965-19-5(4)) Polychrome Publishing Corp.

Yang, Belle. Hannah Is My Name. Yang, Belle, illus. 2004. (Illus.). 40p. (J). (gr. k-4). 16.99 (978-0-7636-2223-7(0)) Candlewick Pr.

Yang, Belle. Hannah Is My Name: A Young Immigrant's Story. Yang, Belle, illus. 2007. (Illus.). 32p. (J). (gr. k-4). pap. 6.99 (***978-0-7636-3521-3(9)***) Candlewick Pr.

Yang, Dori Jones. The Secret Voice of Gina Zhang. 2000. (978-0-606-21790-3(8)) Tandem Library Bks.

Yang, Gene Luen. American Born Chinese. Pien, Lark, illus. rev. ed. 2006. 240p. (J). pap. 17.95 (978-1-59643-152-2(0) , First Second Bks.) Roaring Brook Pr.

—American Born Chinese, Collector's Edition. rev. ed. 2006. 240p. (J). 29.95 (978-1-59643-208-6(X) , First Second Bks.) Roaring Brook Pr.

Yee, Lisa. Millicent Min, Girl Genius. 2003. 256p. (YA). (gr. 5-8). 16.95 (978-0-439-42519-3(0) , Levine, Arthur A. Bks.) Scholastic, Inc.

—Stanford Wong Flunks Big Time. 2005. (Illus.). 304p. (J). (gr. 5-7). pap. 16.99 (978-0-439-62247-9(6) , Levine, Arthur A. Bks.) Scholastic, Inc.

Yee, Paul. What Happened This Summer. 2006. 128p. (YA). 15.95 (978-1-896580-88-3(2)) Tradewind Bks. CAN. *Dist:* Orca Bk. Pubs. USA.

Yep, Laurence. The Amah. 2001. (gr. 7-12). lib. bdg. 14.15 (978-0-613-35896-5(1)) Tandem Library Bks.

—Angelfish. 2001. 1p. (J). (gr. 5 up). 16.99 (978-0-399-23041-7(6) , Putnam Juvenile) Penguin Group (USA) Inc.

—Child of the Owl. (J). pap., stu. ed. (978-0-13-053125-4(1)) Prentice Hall (Schl. Div.).

—Child of the Owl. 8.97 (978-0-13-437497-0(5)) Prentice Hall PTR.

—Cockroach Cooties. 2001. 144p. (gr. 3-7). pap. 5.99 (978-0-7868-1338-4(5)) Hyperion Bks. for Children.

—Cockroach Cooties. 2001. (gr. 3-6). lib. bdg. 14.15 (978-0-613-45730-9(7)) Tandem Library Bks.

—The Cook's Family. 1998. (J). (978-0-03-992907-7(8)) Holt, Rinehart & Winston.

—The Cook's Family. 1999. (J). (978-0-606-18932-3(7)) Tandem Library Bks.

—Dream Soul. (J). (gr. 3-7). 2002. 256p. pap. 6.99 (978-0-06-440788-5(8)); 2000. (Illus.). 224p. 16.89 (978-0-06-028390-2(4)) HarperCollins Pubs.

—Dream Soul. 2002. (gr. 3-6). lib. bdg. 15.30 (978-0-613-85146-6(3)) Tandem Library Bks.

—The Earth Dragon Awakes: The San Francisco Earthquake Of 1906. 2006. (Illus.). 128p. (J). (gr. 3-7). 14.99 (978-0-06-027524-2(3)); lib. bdg. 15.89 (978-0-06-027525-9(1)) HarperCollins Pubs.

—The Earth Dragon Awakes: The San Francisco Earthquake Of 1906. 2008. 128p. (J). pap. 5.99 (***978-0-06-000846-8(6)*** , Harper Trophy) HarperCollins Pubs.

—The Magic Paintbrush. Wang, Suling, illus. 2003. 96p. (J). (gr. 3-7). pap. 4.99 (978-0-06-440852-3(3)) HarperCollins Pubs.

—The Magic Paintbrush. 2003. (gr. 3-6). lib. bdg. 13.00 (978-0-613-65808-9(6)) Tandem Library Bks.

—My Name Is America: The Journal of Wongming-chun, A Chinese Miner. 2000. (My Name Is America Ser.). (Illus.). 224p. (J). (gr. 4-8). pap. 10.95 (978-0-590-38607-4(7)) Scholastic, Inc.

—Skunk Scout. 2005. 192p. (gr. 3-7). pap. 5.99 (978-0-7868-1714-6(3)) Hyperion Pr.

—Tiger Magic. 2006. (Tiger's Apprentice Ser.). 288p. (J). 16.99 (978-0-06-001019-5(3)); lib. bdg. 17.89 (978-0-06-001020-1(7)) HarperCollins Pubs.

—Tiger's Apprentice. 2005. 184p. (J). lib. bdg. 24.62 (***978-1-4242-0449-6(6)***) Fitzgerald Bks.

—Tiger's Apprentice. 2005. 184p. (J). (gr. k-9). per. 12.64 (978-0-606-33327-6(4)) Tandem Library Bks.

—The Tiger's Apprentice. 2005. (Tiger's Apprentice Ser.: Bk. 1). 208p. (J). (gr. 5 up). reprint ed. pap. 5.99 (978-0-06-001015-7(0) , Harper Trophy) HarperCollins Pubs.

—Tiger's Blood. 2005. (Tiger's Apprentice Ser.: Bk. 2). 240p. (J). (gr. 5 up). 15.99 (978-0-06-001016-4(9)); lib. bdg. 16.89 (978-0-06-001017-1(7)) HarperCollins Pubs.

—Tiger's Blood. 2006. (Tiger's Apprentice Ser.: Bk. 2). 240p. (J). pap. 5.99 (978-0-06-001018-8(5) , Harper Trophy) HarperCollins Pubs.

—The Traitor: Golden Mountain Chronicles: 1885. (Golden Mountain Chronicles). 320p. (J). (gr. 5 up). 2004. pap. 6.99 (978-0-06-000831-4(8) , Harper Trophy); 2003. 17.99 (978-0-06-027522-8(7)) HarperCollins Pubs.

—When the Circus Came to Town. Wang, Suling, illus. 2001. 128p. (J). (ps-1). 14.99 (978-0-06-029325-3(X)); lib. bdg. 15.89 (978-0-06-029326-0(8)) HarperCollins Pubs.

—When the Circus Came to Town. 2004. (gr. 3-6). lib. bdg. 14.15 (978-0-613-86716-0(5)) Tandem Library Bks.

Yep, Laurence & Yep, Laurence. The Case of the Goblin Pearls. 1998. 179p. (J). (ps-7). per. 14.15 (978-0-613-04692-3(7)) Tandem Library Bks.

—When the Circus Came to Town. Wang, Suling, illus. 2004. 128p. (J). (ps-k). pap. 5.99 (978-0-06-440965-0(1) , Harper Trophy) HarperCollins Pubs.

Yin. Brothers. Soentpiet, Chris, illus. 2006. 32p. (J). (gr. k). 16.99 (978-0-399-23406-4(3) , Philomel) Penguin Group (USA) Inc.

—Coolies. Soentpiet, Chris, illus. 2003. 40p. (J). (gr. k-3). pap. 7.99 (978-0-14-250055-2(0) , Puffin) Penguin Group (USA) Inc.

—Coolies. Soentpiet, Chris K., illus. 2001. 1p. (J). (ps-3). 16.99 (978-0-399-23227-5(3) , Philomel) Penguin Group (USA) Inc.

—Coolies. 2003. (gr. 3-6). lib. bdg. 16.45 (978-0-613-62936-2(1)) Tandem Library Bks.

Young, Ed. My Mei Mei. Young, Ed, illus. 2006. (Illus.). 40p. (J). (gr. 1). 16.99 (978-0-399-24339-4(9) , Philomel) Penguin Group (USA) Inc.

CHINESE LANGUAGE

Amery, Heather. First Thousand Words in Chinese - Internet Linked. Cartwright, Stephen, illus. 2007. 64p. (J). 12.99 (978-0-7945-1550-8(9) , Usborne) EDC Publishing.

Berlitz Publishing Staff, creator. Chinese Mandarin. 2006. (Berlitz Flash Cards Ser.). (CHI & ENG.). 50p. 8.95 (978-981-246-977-9(X)) Berlitz Publishing.

Berlitz Publishing Staff, ed. Chinese Mandarin. 2007. (Lift the Flap Ser.). (CHI & ENG., Illus.). 12p. bds. 7.95 (***978-981-268-036-5(5)***) APA Publications Services SGP. *Dist:* Langenscheidt Pubs Inc.

Buddhist Text Translation Society Staff, contrib. by. Standards for Students: Instructions in Virtue from the Chinese Heritage = [Di Zi Gui]. 2003. (ENG & CHI., Illus.). 41p. (J). (978-0-88139-489-4(0)) Buddhist Text Translation Society.

Carole Marsh. Ho Lee Chow! 2004. (Little Linguist Ser.). 32p. 29.95 (978-0-635-02443-5(8)) Gallopade International.

—Ho Lee Chow! Chinese for Kids. 2004. (Little Linguist Ser.). 32p. (gr. 2-6). pap. 5.95 (978-0-635-02435-0(7)) Gallopade International.

Chang, MacKerras, et al. Hanyu for Beginning Students. 2005. (CHI & ENG.). (YA). (gr. 7-9). tchr. ed., per. 22.50 (978-0-582-90869-7(8)); per. 22.50 (978-0-582-90870-3(1)) Pearson Education Australia AUS. *Dist:* Cheng & Tsui Co.

Chang, Peter & Mackerras, Alyce. Hanyu for Beginning Students. 2005. (Illus.). (YA). (gr. 7-9). 184p. per. 35.99 (978-0-582-87003-1(8)); 96p. per., act. bk. ed. 22.50 (978-0-582-90868-0(X)) Pearson Education Australia AUS. *Dist:* Cheng & Tsui Co.

—Hanyu for Beginning Students Character Writing Book. 2005. (CHI & ENG., Illus.). 40p. (YA). (gr. 7-9). per., wbk. ed. 22.50 (978-0-582-91050-8(1)) Pearson Education Australia AUS. *Dist:* Cheng & Tsui Co.

—Hanyu for Intermediate Students. 2005. (CHI & ENG., Illus.). (YA). 120p. (gr. 10-12). per., act. bk. ed. 22.99 (978-0-7339-1368-6(7)); 216p. (gr. 7-10). per. 39.99 (978-0-582-80087-8(0)); 132p. (gr. 7-10). per., act. bk. ed. 31.99 (978-0-582-80086-1(2)) Pearson Education Australia AUS. *Dist:* Cheng & Tsui Co.

—Hanyu for Intermediate Students: Character Writing Book. 2005. (CHI & ENG., Illus.). 54p. (YA). (gr. 7-10). per., wbk. ed. 11.99 (978-0-582-80084-7(6)) Pearson Education Australia AUS. *Dist:* Cheng & Tsui Co.

Chang, Peter, et al. Hanyu for Intermediate Students, Stage 3. rev. ed. 1999. (CHI & ENG.). (YA). (gr. 10-12). pap., tchr. ed. 100.00 (978-0-88727-339-1(4)) Cheng & Tsui Co.

—Hanyu for Intermediate Students Stage 3. rev. ed. 1999. (CHI & ENG.). (YA). (gr. 10-12). pap., stu. ed. 43.99 (978-0-88727-335-3(1)) Cheng & Tsui Co.

—Hanyu for Senior Students, Stage 4. rev. ed. 1999. (Hanyu Ser.). (CHI & ENG.). (YA). (gr. 11-13). pap., act. bk. ed. 22.99 (978-0-88727-325-4(4)) Cheng & Tsui Co.

Chinn, Karen. Xiaoshan Di Ya Shui Qian: Sam & the Lucky Money. Van Wright, Cornelius & Hu, Ying-Hwa, illus. 2002. (CHI.). (J). 16.95 (978-1-58430-084-7(1)); pap. 6.95 (978-1-58430-085-4(X)) Lee & Low Bks., Inc.

Corbeil, Jean-Claude, et al. Milet Bilingual Visual Dictionary. 2005. (CHI & ENG., Illus.). 232p. (gr. 1-3). pap. 29.95 (978-1-84059-258-0(3)) Milet Publishing.

DK Publishing Staff. Get Talking Chinese. 2007. 128p. (J). pap. 12.99 (978-0-7566-2902-1(0)) Dorling Kindersley Publishing, Inc.

Dong, Li. Tuttle Learner's Chinese-English Dictionary. 2005. (ENG & CHI.). 384p. pap. 29.95 (978-0-8048-3552-7(7)) Tuttle Publishing.

Fine, Jil. Writing in Ancient China. 2003. (Writing in the Ancient World Ser.). (Illus.). 24p. (J). lib. bdg. 17.25 (978-0-8239-6510-6(4)) Rosen Publishing Group, Inc., The.

Fredlein, Shumang & Fredlein, Paul. Ni Hao. 2005. (C & T Asian Language Ser.). (CHI & ENG., Illus.). 3. 128p. (gr. 7-11). pap., tchr. ed. 59.95 (978-0-646-22330-8(5)); Vol. 1. 76p. (gr. 5-9). pap., tchr. ed. 59.95 (978-0-646-06658-5(7)) Cheng & Tsui Co.

Fuhua, Liu, et al. Chinese Paradise. 2005. (CHI & ENG.). (J). (gr. 4-6). 175p. tchr. ed. 17.95 incl. audio compact disk (***978-7-5619-1441-0(5)*** , CHPAI1); Vol. 1. 36p. stu. ed. 10.95 incl. audio compact disk (***978-7-5619-1439-7(3)*** , CHPA1A); Vol. 1. 26p. wbk. ed. 8.95 incl. audio compact disk (***978-7-5619-1440-3(7)*** , CHPAW1A); Vol. 2. 36p. stu. ed. 10.95 incl. audio compact disk (***978-7-5619-1443-4(1)*** , CHPA2A); Vol. 3. 42p. wbk. ed. 11.95 incl. audio compact disk (***978-7-5619-1437-3(7)*** , CHPAW3A) Beijing Language & Culture University Press, China CHN. *Dist:* China Bks. & Periodicals, Inc.

—Chinese Paradise 3, Vol. 3. 2005. (CHI & ENG.). 44p. (J). (gr. 4-6). stu. ed. 11.95 incl. audio compact disk (***978-7-5619-1436-6(9)*** , CHPA3A) Beijing Language & Culture University Press, China CHN. *Dist:* China Bks. & Periodicals, Inc.

Greenfield Educational Center Staff. Comprehensive & Effective Learning of Chinese Characters. 2000. (CHI., Illus.). 64p. (J). Bk. 1. 18.99 (978-962-583-281-4(5)); Bk. 2. 18.99 (978-962-583-282-1(3)) Greenfield Enterprises, Ltd. HKG. *Dist:* Cheng & Tsui Co.

Hippocrene Books, ed. Chinese Children's Picture Dictionary: English-Chinese/Chinese-English. 2006. (Illus.). 114p. pap. 14.95 (978-0-7818-1161-3(9)) Hippocrene Bks., Inc.

Hippocrene Books Firm Staff, contrib. by. Hippocrene Children's Illustrated Chinese (Mandarin) Dictionary: English-Chinese, Chinese-English. 2001. (Children's Illustrated Foreign Language Dictionaries Ser.). (CHI & ENG., Illus.). 94p. (gr. k-5). pap. 11.95 (978-0-7818-0848-4(0)) Hippocrene Bks., Inc.

Hippocrene Books Staff. Hippocrene Children's Illustrated Chinese Dictionary: English-Chinese/Chinese-English. 2000. (CHI & ENG., Illus.). 94p. (J). (gr. k-5). 14.95 (978-0-7818-0834-7(0)) Hippocrene Bks., Inc.

HOP, LLC. Hooked on Chinese. 2006. 99.99 (978-1-933863-86-3(2)) HOP, LLC.

I Can Write Chinese, Vol. 1. 1999. pap. 3.95 (978-981-01-1064-2(2)) European Language Institute ITA. *Dist:* Distribooks, Inc.

Karapetian, Marjam. Bilingual Content Dictionary: English to Mandarin Chinese. 2004. (CHI & ENG.). 4.95 (978-0-9768053-0-4(8)); 4.95 (978-0-9768053-1-1(6)); 9.95 (978-0-9768053-2-8(4)); 13.95 (978-0-9768053-4-2(0)); 15.95 (978-0-9768053-5-9(9)) WizdomInc.

—Bilingual Content Dictionary: English to Mandarin Chinese: Social Studies - American History Through 1776. 2004. (CHI & ENG.). 14.95 (978-0-9768053-3-5(2)) WizdomInc.

Kids Stuff Chinese. 2007. (J). 22.95 (***978-0-9789152-1-6(6)***) Chou-Chou Pr.

Krach, Maywan Shen & Wang, Maychi Shen. I Love China: A Companion Book to D Is for Doufu. Tang, You-shan, illus. 2000. 32p. (J). (ps-5). pap. 10.95 (978-1-885008-15-2(5)) Shen's Bks.

Lee, Huy Voun. 1, 2, 3, Go! rev. ed. 2001. (ENG & CHI., Illus.). 32p. (J). (ps-4). 17.95 (978-0-8050-6205-2(X) , Holt, Henry & Co. Bks. For Young Readers) Holt, Henry & Co.

Lin, Wendy. Chinese for Children. 2002. (Illus.). (J). pap. (978-0-9715058-7-2(X)) Creative World Enterprise, Inc.

Ma, Yamin & Li, Xinying. Chinese Made Easy, Bk. 2. 2001. 200p. wbk. ed. 26.95 (978-962-04-2051-1(9)) Cheng & Tsui Co.

Mandy & Pandy say ni Hao Ma? Teach kids Chinese the fun & easy Way. 2007. (J). bds. 9.95 (***978-0-9758805-7-9(8)***) River Pointe Pubns.

My First Chinese Words, Bks. 1-18, Set. 1. 2001. 8p. (J). (ps-5). pap. 24.95 (978-962-978-060-9(7)); pap. 24.95 (978-962-978-022-7(4)) Better Chinese Limited HKG. *Dist:* Shen's Bks.

My First Chinese Words: Better Chinese, Bks. 19-36, Set. 2. 2001. 8p. (J). (ps-5). pap. 24.95 (978-962-978-079-1(8)); pap. 24.95 (978-962-978-043-2(7)) Better Chinese Limited HKG. *Dist:* Shen's Bks.

National Taiwan Normal University Staff. Practical Audio-Visual Chinese Vol. 3: B. 2004. (CHI & ENG.). (gr. k up). pap., tchr. ed. 12.95 (978-957-09-1244-9(8)) Cheng Chung Bk. Co., Ltd. TWN. *Dist:* Cheng & Tsui Co.

National Taiwan Normal University Staff, compiled by. A Practical Audio-Visual Chinese: A. 2004. (CHI & ENG.). (gr. k up). pap. 35.00 (978-957-09-1238-8(3)) Cheng Chung Bk. Co., Ltd. TWN. *Dist:* Cheng & Tsui Co.

—Practical Audio-Visual Chinese Vol. 3: B. 2004. (gr. k up). (CHI & ENG.). pap. 32.00 (978-957-09-1236-4(7)); (CHI & ENG.). pap. 35.00 (978-957-09-1239-5(1)); Vol. 2. (ENG & CHI.). pap., tchr. ed. 14.95 (978-957-09-1243-2(X)) Cheng Chung Bk. Co., Ltd. TWN. *Dist:* Cheng & Tsui Co.

Qing, Zheng. Find Out about China: Learn Chinese Words & Phrases & about Life in China. Hutchinson, Tim, illus. 2006. (Find Out about Bks.). 64p. (J). (gr. 3 up). spiral bd. 12.99 (978-0-7641-5952-7(6)) Barron's Educational Series, Inc.

The Rosetta Stone Language Library: Chinese Level 2. 2005. (J). (gr. 1 up). cd-rom 239.00 (978-1-883972-70-7(1)) Fairfield Language Technologies.

SISA CHINESE CULTURE CENTER, compiled by. Fun Chinese for Kids. 2004. (CHI & ENG.). 180p. 79.95 (978-7-80052-929-0(0) , FUCHKI) Sinolingua CHN. *Dist:* China Bks. & Periodicals, Inc.

Tan, Huay Peng. Fun with Chinese Characters 1: The Straits Times Collection, 3 vols. 2003. (ENG & CHI., Illus.). 176p. 14.95 (978-1-932457-00-1(3) , FUCHC1) China Bks. & Periodicals, Inc.

—Fun with Chinese Characters 2 Vol. 2: The Straits Times Collection, 3 vols., Vol. 2. 2003. (ENG & CHI., Illus.). 176p. 14.95 (978-1-932457-01-8(1) , FUCHC2) China Bks. & Periodicals, Inc.

—Fun with Chinese Characters 3 Vol. 3: The Straits Times Collection, 3 vols., Vol. 3. 2003. (ENG & CHI., Illus.). 176p. 14.95 (978-1-932457-02-5(X) , FUCHC3) People's Literature Publishing Hse. CHN. *Dist:* China Bks. & Periodicals, Inc.

Tian, Long. Federal Revision Units: Chinese Language for Secondary 1 (Express) 1999. (CHI.). 100p. pap. 8.99 (978-981-01-7713-3(5)) Federal Pubns. (S) Pte Ltd. SGP. *Dist:* Cheng & Tsui Co.

—Federal Revision Units: Chinese Language for Secondary 2 (Express) 1999. (CHI.). 100p. pap. 8.99 (978-981-01-7712-6(7)) Federal Pubns. (S) Pte Ltd. SGP. *Dist:* Cheng & Tsui Co.

—Federal Test Papers: Chinese Language for Secondary 1 (Express Course) 1999. (CHI.). 100p. pap. 8.99 (978-981-01-7719-5(4)) Federal Pubns. (S) Pte Ltd. SGP. *Dist:* Cheng & Tsui Co.

—Federal Test Papers: Chinese Language for Secondary 2 (Express Course) 1999. (CHI.). 100p. pap. 8.99 (978-981-01-7720-1(8)) Federal Pubns. (S) Pte Ltd. SGP. *Dist:* Cheng & Tsui Co.

Wee, Jessie. Dongdong. Mei, Kwan Shan, illus. 2000. (Dongdong Ser.). (CHI.). 64p. (J). (gr. k-3). pap. 9.99 (978-981-01-1151-9(7)) Federal Pubns. (S) Pte Ltd. SGP. *Dist:* Cheng & Tsui Co.

—Dongdong He Peng You. Mei, Kwan Shan, illus. 2000. (Dongdong Ser.). (CHI.). 64p. (J). (gr. k-3). pap. 9.99 (978-981-01-1153-3(3)) Federal Pubns. (S) Pte Ltd. SGP. *Dist:* Cheng & Tsui Co.

Writing in Ancient China, 6 Packs. (On Deck Ser.: Vol. 2). 24p. (gr. 4-5). 35.00 (978-0-7578-5866-6(X)) Rigby Education.

Xuan, Yong-Sheng. The Dragon Lover & Other Chinese Proverbs. Xuan, Yong-Sheng, illus. 1999. (CHI & ENG., Illus.). 32p. (J). 16.95 (978-1-885008-11-4(2)) Shen's Bks.

Yamin, M. & Xinying, L. Chinese Made Easy Bk. 1: Characters & Roman. 2004. (CHI & ENG.). 200p. pap., wbk. ed. 21.95 (978-962-04-2041-2(1) , CMEW1) Joint Publishing Co. HKG. *Dist:* China Bks. & Periodicals, Inc.

Yamin, Ma. Chinese Made Easy for Kids. 2005. (CHI & ENG.). 144p. pap., wbk. ed. 12.95 (978-962-04-2470-0(0) , CMEKW1); Vol. 2. pap., wbk. ed. 12.95 (978-962-04-2499-1(9) , CMEKW2); Vol. 3. pap., wbk. ed. 12.95 (978-962-04-2520-2(0) , CMEKW3); Vol. 4. pap., wbk. ed. 12.95 (978-962-04-2524-0(3) , CMEKW4) Joint Publishing Co. HKG. *Dist:* China Bks. & Periodicals, Inc.

—Chinese Made Easy for Kids: Text Book. 2005. (CHI & ENG.). 128p. pap. 19.95 incl. audio compact disk (978-962-04-2469-4(7) , CMEKT1); Vol. 2. pap. 19.95 incl. audio compact disk (978-962-04-2498-4(0) , CMEKT2); Vol. 3. pap. 19.95 incl. audio compact disk (978-962-04-2519-6(7) , CMEKT3); Vol. 4. pap. 19.95 incl. audio compact disk (978-962-04-2523-3(5) , CMEKT4) Joint Publishing Co. HKG. *Dist:* China Bks. & Periodicals, Inc.

Yan, Hua. Federal Test Papers: Chinese Language for Primary 1. 1999. (CHI., Illus.). 100p. (J). pap. 8.95 (978-981-01-6115-6(8)) Federal Pubns. (S) Pte Ltd. SGP. *Dist:* Cheng & Tsui Co.

—Federal Test Papers: Chinese Language for Primary 2. 1999. (CHI., Illus.). 100p. (J). pap. 8.95 (978-981-01-6116-3(6)) Federal Pubns. (S) Pte Ltd. SGP. *Dist:* Cheng & Tsui Co.

—Federal Test Papers: Chinese Language for Primary 3. 1999. (CHI., Illus.). 100p. pap. 8.95 (978-981-01-6122-4(0)) Federal Pubns. (S) Pte Ltd. SGP. *Dist:* Cheng & Tsui Co.

—Federal Test Papers: Chinese Language for Primary 4. 1999. (CHI., Illus.). 100p. (J). pap. 8.95 (978-981-01-6123-1(9)) Federal Pubns. (S) Pte Ltd. SGP. *Dist:* Cheng & Tsui Co.

—Federal Test Papers: Chinese Language for Primary 5. 1999. (CHI., Illus.). 100p. (J). pap. 8.95 (978-981-01-6129-3(8)) Federal Pubns. (S) Pte Ltd. SGP. *Dist:* Cheng & Tsui Co.

—Federal Test Papers: Chinese Language for Primary 6. 1999. (CHI., Illus.). 100p. (J). pap. 8.95 (978-981-01-6136-1(0)) Federal Pubns. (S) Pte Ltd. SGP. *Dist:* Cheng & Tsui Co.

Yao, Tao-chung, et al. Integrated Chinese. 2003. (CHI & ENG., Illus.). (gr. k up). pap. 160.00 incl. audio compact disk (978-0-88727-406-0(4)) Cheng & Tsui Co.

Zeng, Sunny. Ni Hao Little Friends: Learn Chinese. 2003. (CHI & ENG.). (ps-3). 27.95 (978-0-9707332-0-7(8) , NIHALI1) Chinasprout, Inc.

—Ni Hao Little Friends 2: Chinese with Chinasprout, Vol. 2. 2003. (CHI & ENG.). (ps-3). 27.95 (978-0-9707332-4-5(0) , NIHALI2) Chinasprout, Inc.

CHINESE LITERATURE

Writing in Ancient China, 6 Packs. (On Deck Ser.: Vol. 2). 24p. (gr. 4-5). 35.00 (978-0-7578-5866-6(X)) Rigby Education.

CHIPMUNKS

Bastian, Lois Brunner. Chipmunk Family. 2000. (Wildlife Conservation Society Bks.). (Illus.). 48p. (J). (gr. 4-6). 24.50 (978-0-531-11683-8(2) , Watts, Franklin) Scholastic Library Publishing.

—Chipmunk Family. 2000. (gr. 3-6). lib. bdg. 15.25 (978-0-613-34138-7(4)) Tandem Library Bks.

Boring, Mel. Rabbits, Squirrels & Chipmunks. Garrow, Linda, illus. 1999. (Young Naturalist Field Guides Ser.). 40p. (J). (gr. 3 up). lib. bdg. 24.67 (978-0-8368-2146-8(7)) Stevens, Gareth Inc.

Harcourt School Publishers Staff. Chipmunks Do What Chipmunks Do Below Level. 3rd ed. 2002. (Trophies Reading Program Ser.). (Illus.). pap. 5.10 (978-0-15-323043-1(6)) Harcourt Schl. Pubs.

—What Chipmunks Do: Take-Home Book. 1999. (Collections Ser.). (Illus.). (J). pap. 1.90 (978-0-15-317219-9(3)) Harcourt Schl. Pubs.

Piehl, Janet. Chattering Chipmunks. 2005. (Pull Ahead Bks.). (J). 22.60 (978-0-8225-2420-5(1) , Lerner Pubns.) Lerner Publishing Group.

Swedeen, Staci. How the Chipmunk Got It's Stripes. 2004. (Reader's Theater Ser.). (J). pap. 22.00 (978-1-4108-0800-4(9)) Benchmark Education Co.

Whitehouse, Patricia. Chipmunks. 2003. (Heinemann Read & Learn Ser.). (Illus.). 24p. (J). pap. 5.75 (978-1-4034-4328-1(9)); lib. bdg. 18.50 (978-1-4034-4319-9(X)) Heinemann Library.

CHIPMUNKS—FICTION

Addabbo, Carole. Dina the Deaf Dinosaur. Valentine, illus. 1998. 32p. (J). (ps-5). 19.95 (978-1-889262-04-8(8)) Hannacroix Creek Bks., Inc.

Bailey, Arthur Scott. Sleepy-Time Tales: The Tale of Sandy Chi. 2006. pap. (***978-1-4065-0451-4(3)***) Dodo Pr.

Bailey, Arthur Scott. The Tale of Sandy Chipmunk. 2004. reprint ed. pap. 15.95 (978-1-4191-8480-2(6)); pap. 1.99 (978-1-4192-8480-9(0)) Kessinger Publishing, LLC.

Berenstain, Stan & Berenstain, Jan. The Berenstain Bears & the Baby Chipmunk. Berenstain, Stan, illus. 2005. (Illus.). 32p. (J). lib. bdg. 13.85 (***978-1-4242-0817-3(3)***) Fitzgerald Bks.

—The Berenstain Bears & the Baby Chipmunk. Berenstain, Stan & Berenstain, Jan, illus. 2005. (Berenstain Bears Ser.). (Illus.). 32p. (J). pap. 3.99 (978-0-06-058413-9(0)); 15.99 (978-0-06-058412-2(2)) HarperCollins Pubs.

Chipmunk's Busy Day. 2002. (Backyard Mini Bks.). (Illus.). 32p. (J). (978-1-59069-014-7(1) , H2003) Studio Mouse LLC.

Driscoll, Laura. Beck & the Great Berry Battle. Clarke, Judith, illus. 2006. (Stepping Stone Bks.). 128p. (J). (gr. 2-4). 5.99 (978-0-7364-2373-1(7) , RH/Disney) Random Hse. Children's Bks.

Finn, Perdita. Alvin & the Chipmunks. 2007. (Alvin & the Chipmunks Ser.). 144p. (J). pap. 4.99 (***978-0-06-145064-8(2)*** , Harper Entertainment) HarperCollins Pubs.

Hall, Kirsten. Busy Chipmunk. Phillips, Cary, illus. 2001. (My First Hello Reader! Ser.). (J). pap. (978-0-439-31703-0(7) , Cartwheel Bks.) Scholastic, Inc.

Johnson, Kimberly P. The Adventures of the Itty Bitty Spider & the Itty Bitty Mouse. 2004. (Illus.). 31p. (gr. k-2). 14.95 (978-1-57197-236-1(6)) Pentland Pr., Inc.

Martin, Martha M. Chipper, the Heroic Chipmunk. Matzen, Deon C., illus. 2004. 32p. (J). (ps-3). 16.95 (978-0-9758580-0-4(9)) M & B Publishing.

Michalak, Jamie. Larry & Rita. Newton, Jill, illus. 2007. (Brand New Readers Ser.). 1p. (J). (ps-2). pap. 5.99 (***978-0-7636-2964-9(2)***) Candlewick Pr.

Milord, Susan. If I Could. Denise, Christopher, illus. 2008. 32p. (J). (gr. k-1). 15.99 (978-0-7636-2348-7(2)) Candlewick Pr.

Otto, Carolyn B., et al. Big Box of Backyard Animals, 4 bks., Set. Sherrow, Victoria et al, illus. 2002. (Big Box of Board Bks.). 10p. (J). (ps-k). bds. (978-1-59069-177-9(6)) Studio Mouse LLC.

Piehl, Janet. Chattering Chipmunks. 2005. (Pull Ahead Bks.). 32p. (J). (gr. k-2). pap. 5.95 (978-0-8225-2439-7(2)) Lerner Publishing Group.

Rylant, Cynthia. Thimbleberry Stories. Kneen, Maggie, illus. 2006. 64p. (J). reprint ed. pap. 7.00 (978-0-15-205645-2(9) , Harcourt Paperbacks) Harcourt Children's Bks.

Sargent, Dave & Sargent, Pat. Chip Chipmunk: Tattletale, 56 vols., 25. Huff, Jeane, illus. 2001. (Animal Pride Ser.: Vol. 25). 36p. (J). lib. bdg. 19.95 (978-1-56763-366-5(8)) Ozark Publishing.

—Ellie Elephant: Grudge, 56 vols., 45. Lenoir, Jane, illus. 2001. (Animal Pride Ser.: Vol. 45). 36p. (J). lib. bdg. 19.95 (978-1-56763-531-7(8)) Ozark Publishing.

Sargent, Dave, et al. Ellie Elephant: Grudge, 17 bks, 45. 2000. (Animal Pride Ser.: 45). (Illus.). 42p. (J). pap. 6.95 (978-1-56763-532-4(6)) Ozark Publishing.

Schade, Susan. Faradawn. Buller, Jon, illus. 2007. (Fog Mound Ser.: No. 2). 208p. (J). (gr. 3-7). 15.99 (978-0-689-87686-8(6)) Simon & Schuster Children's Publishing.

—Travels of Thelonious. Buller, Jon, illus. 2007. (Fog Mound Ser.: No. 1). 224p. (J). (gr. 3-7). pap. 7.99 (978-0-689-87685-1(8) , Simon & Schuster Children's Publishing) Simon & Schuster Children's Publishing.

Schade, Susan & Buller, Jon. The Travels of Thelonious. 2006. (Fog Mound Ser.: No. 1). (Illus.). 224p. (J). (gr. 3-7). 14.95 (978-0-689-87684-4(X)) Simon & Schuster Children's Publishing.

See Catalogue Staff. Alvin & the Chipmunks: Meet the Chipmunks. 2007. (I Can Read Bks.). 32p. (J). pap. 3.99 (***978-0-06-145063-1(4)*** , Harper Trophy) HarperCollins Pubs.

—Family Matters. 2007. (Alvin & the Chipmunks Ser.). 24p. (J). pap. 3.99 (***978-0-06-145062-4(6)*** , Harper Entertainment) HarperCollins Pubs.

Smith, Nicole. Chad the Allergic Chipmunk: A Children's Story of Nut Allergies. 2006. (Illus.). (J). per. 11.95 (978-1-58628-054-3(6)) Allergic Child Publishing Group.

Swedeen, Staci. Como la ardilla listada obruvo sus marcas & How the Chipmunk Got Its Stripes. 2005. spiral bd. 76.00 (***978-1-4108-5788-0(3)***) Benchmark Education Co.

CHISHOLM TRAIL

Sanford, William R. The Chisholm Trail in American History. 2000. (Illus.). 112p. (YA). (gr. 5-12). lib. bdg. 26.60 (978-0-7660-1345-2(6)) Enslow Pubs., Inc.

C D

Stein, R. Conrad & Santella, Andrew. The Chisholm Trail. 1998. (Cornerstones of Freedom Ser.). (Illus.). 32p. (J). (gr. 4-6). pap. 5.95 (978-0-516-26225-3(4) , Children's Pr.) Scholastic Library Publishing.

CHISHOLM TRAIL—FICTION

Rogers, Lisa Waller. Get along Little Dogies: The Chisholm Trail Diary of Hallie Lou Wells. 2001. (Lone Star Journals: Vol. 1). (Illus.). 174p. (J). (gr. 4-7). 14.50 (978-0-89672-446-4(8)) Texas Tech Univ. Pr.

—Get along, Little Dogies: The Chisholm Trail Diary of Hallie Lou Wells, South Texas 1878. 2001. (Lone Star Journals). (Illus.). 174p. (J). (gr. 4-7). 8.95 (978-0-89672-448-8(4)) Texas Tech Univ. Pr.

Sargent, Dave & Sargent, Pat. Flash: Speed Counts. Lenoir, Jane, illus. 2001. (Saddle Up Ser.). 36p. (J). pap. 6.95 (978-1-56763-614-7(4)); lib. bdg. 22.60 (978-1-56763-613-0(6)) Ozark Publishing.

CHIVALRY

see also Arthur, King; Civilization, Medieval; Crusades; Feudalism; Heraldry; Knights and Knighthood

Allen, Debbie. Brothers of the Knight. Sherry, Toby, ed. Nelson, Kadir A., illus. 1999. 40p. (J). (gr. k-4). 16.99 (978-0-8037-2488-4(8) , Dial) Penguin Group (USA) Inc.

CHIVALRY—FICTION

Cervantes Saavedra, Miguel de. Don Quixote. Marshall, Michael J., ed. abr. ed. 1999. (Core Classics Ser.: Vol. 6). (Illus.). 264p. (J). (gr. 4-6). pap. 7.95 (978-1-890517-10-6(0)) Core Knowledge Foundation.

—Don Quixote of the Mancha. 1999. (Everyman's Library Children's Classics). (Illus.). 256p. (gr. 8-12). 14.95 (978-0-375-40659-1(X) , Everyman's Library) Knopf Publishing Group.

Kimmel, Eric A. Don Quixote & the Windmills. Fisher, Leonard Everett, illus. 2004. 32p. (J). 16.00 (978-0-374-31825-3(5) , Farrar, Straus & Giroux (BYR)) Farrar, Straus & Giroux.

Matthews, John. The Barefoot Book of Knights. Manna, Giovanni, illus. 2002. 80p. (J). (gr. 4-7). 19.99 (978-1-84148-064-0(9)) Barefoot Bks., Inc.

Morris, Gerald. The Squire's Tale. 1998. (Squire's Tales Ser.). 224p. (J). (gr. 5-9). tchr. ed. 16.00 (978-0-395-86959-8(5)) Houghton Mifflin Co. Trade & Reference Div.

Pyle, Howard. Men of Iron. (J). 25.95 (978-0-8488-1131-0(3)) Amereon LTD.

CHOCOLATE

see also Cocoa

Burleigh, Robert. Chocolate: Riches from the Rainforest. 2002. (Illus.). 40p. (J). (gr. 1-5). 16.95 (978-0-8109-5734-3(5)) Abrams, Harry N. , Inc.

Chocolate! Individual Title Six-Packs. (Action Packs Ser.). 120p. (gr. 3-5). 44.00 (978-0-7635-8427-6(4)) Rigby Education.

Crump, A. K., ed. Chocolate French: Recipes, Language, & Directions to Francais Au Chocolat. 2004. (Illus.). 192p. (gr. 10). pap. 19.95 (978-0-9674898-4-1(9)) TCB-Cafe Publishing.

How Chocolate Is Made: Individual Title Six-Pack Pouch - Level K. (Lighthouse Ser.). 16p. (gr. 2 up). 28.00 (978-0-7578-0869-2(7)) Rigby Education.

Jones, Carol. Chocolate. 2002. (From Farm to You Ser.). (Illus.). 32p. (gr. 4-8). 28.00 (978-0-7910-7008-6(5) , Chelsea Hse.) Facts On File, Inc.

Kropf, Dorothy. A Chocolate Discovery! Kropf, Dorothy, photos by. 2000. (Illus.). 32p. (J). (ps-3). 15.95 (978-0-9675463-0-8(3)) Miles Publishing.

Llewellyn, Claire. Chocolate. 1998. (What's for Lunch? Ser.). (Illus.). 32p. (J). (gr. k-2). pap. 6.95 (978-0-516-26218-5(1) , Children's Pr.) Scholastic Library Publishing.

—Chocolate. 2005. (Illus.). 24p. (YA). (gr. 1 up). lib. bdg. 22.80 (978-1-932889-40-6(X)) Sea-To-Sea Pubns.

MacLeod, Elizabeth. Chock Full of Chocolate. Bradford, June, illus. 2005. 40p. (J). (gr. 3). (978-1-55337-763-4(X)); (978-1-55337-762-7(1)) Kids Can Pr., Ltd.

Markle, Sandra. Smart about Chocolate. Harper, Charise Mericle, illus. (Smart about History Ser.). 32p. (J). (gr. k-5). 2005. 14.89 (978-0-448-43566-4(7)); 2004. pap. 5.99 (978-0-448-43480-3(6)) Penguin Group (USA) Inc. (Grosset & Dunlap).

Morganelli, Adrianna. The Biography of Chocolate. 2005. (How Did That Get Here? Ser.). (Illus.). 32p. (J). (gr. 3-9). (978-0-7787-2481-0(6)); pap. (978-0-7787-2517-6(0)) Crabtree Publishing Co.

Nelson, Robin. From Cocoa Bean to Chocolate. 2003. (Start to Finish Ser.). (Illus.). 24p. (J). (gr. k-2). lib. bdg. 18.60 (978-0-8225-4665-8(5)) Lerner Publishing Group.

Pellaton, Karen E., illus. The Official M&M's' Brand History of Chocolate. 2004. 32p. (YA). (gr. 1-9). 16.95 (978-1-57091-448-5(6)); pap. 6.95 (978-1-57091-449-2(4)) Charlesbridge Publishing, Inc.

Pickering, Robin. I Like Chocolate. 2000. (Welcome Bks.). (Illus.). 24p. (J). (ps-2). 17.00 (978-0-516-23083-2(2) , Children's Pr.) Scholastic Library Publishing.

—I Like Chocolate. 2000. (gr. k-3). lib. bdg. 12.95 (978-0-613-52085-0(8)) Tandem Library Bks.

Pirotta, Saviour. Chocolate. 2003. (Starters Ser.). 24p. (J). lib. bdg. 21.35 (978-1-58340-264-1(0)) Smart Apple Media.

Polin, Caryn J. & Dorling Kindersley Publishing Staff. The Story of Chocolate. 2005. (Dk Readers Ser.). 48p. (J). 14.99 (978-0-7566-0991-7(7)); Level 3. (gr. 5). pap. 3.99 (978-0-7566-0992-4(5)) Dorling Kindersley Publishing, Inc.

Royston, Angela. Chocolate. 2005. (How Are Things Made? Ser.). (Illus.). 32p. (J). tchr. ed. (978-0-431-05046-1(5)); pap. (978-0-431-05053-9(8)) Heinemann Library.

—How Is Chocolate Made? 2005. (How Are Things Made? Ser.). (Illus.). 32p. (J). (gr. k-2). lib. bdg. 24.21 (978-1-4034-6641-9(6)); pap. 7.60 (978-1-4034-6648-8(3)) Heinemann Library.

Snyder, Inez. Beans to Chocolate. 2003. (Welcome Bks.). (Illus.). 24p. (J). (ps-2). 18.00 (978-0-516-24269-9(5) , Children's Pr.); pap. 4.95 (978-0-516-24361-0(6) , Watts, Franklin) Scholastic Library Publishing.

—Beans to Chocolate. 2003. (gr. k-3). lib. bdg. 12.95 (978-0-613-59582-7(3)) Tandem Library Bks.

Van Loon, Joan & Gate, Gabriel. The Chocolate Lovers: A Children's Story & Cookbook. Stewart, Chantal, illus. 2001. 32p. 14.95 (978-1-55285-233-0(4)) Whitecap Bks., Ltd. CAN. *Dist:* Graphic Arts Ctr. Publishing Co.

Woods, Samuel G. Chocolate: From Start to Finish. Zucker, Gale, photos by. 1999. (Made in the U. S. A. Ser.). (Illus.). 32p. (J). (gr. 3-6). 23.70 (978-1-56711-391-4(5) , Blackbirch Pr., Inc.) Thomson Gale.

CHOICE OF BOOKS

see Books and Reading

CHOICE OF PROFESSION

see Vocational Guidance

CHOPIN, FREDERIC, 1810-1849

Aljure, Luis Carlos. Frédéric Chopin -el Espíritu de la Musica. 2005. 116p. pap. (978-958-30-1722-3(1)) Panamericana Editorial.

Cencetti, Greta. Chopin. 2002. (Classic Composers Ser.). (Illus.). 40p. (J). incl. audio compact disk (978-1-59069-093-2(1) , T2103) Studio Mouse LLC.

—Chopin: Getting to Know Your Classical Composers. 2002. (Classic Composers Ser.). (Illus.). 32p. (978-1-59069-026-0(5) , T2003) Studio Mouse LLC.

Finck, Henry Theophilus. Chopin & Other Musical Essays. 2001. 273p. (YA). reprint ed. 98.00 (978-0-7222-5379-3(6)) Library Reprints, Inc.

Jonson, George C. A. A Handbook of Chopin's Works, Giving a Detailed Account of All the Compositions of Chopin, Short Analysis for the Piano Student, & Critical Quotations from the Writings of Well-Known Musical Authors. 2d ed. 2001. 287p. (YA). reprint ed. 98.00 (978-0-7222-5382-3(6)) Library Reprints, Inc.

Karasowski, Maurycy. Frederic Chopin: His Life & Letters, 2 vols., set. 2001. (YA). reprint ed. 250.00 (978-0-7222-5383-0(4)) Library Reprints, Inc.

Kelley, Edgar S. Chopin, The Composer: His Structural Art & Its Influence on Contemporaneous Music. 2001. 190p. (YA). reprint ed. 88.00 (978-0-7222-5384-7(2)) Library Reprints, Inc.

Kleczynski, Jan. The Chopin's Greater Works: Preludes, Ballads, Nocturnes, Polonaises, Mazurkas. 2001. 115p. (YA). reprint ed. 88.00 (978-0-7222-5385-4(0)) Library Reprints, Inc.

Malaspina, Ann. Frédéric Chopin: Expressive Poet of the Piano. 2006. (Lives & Times of the Great Composers of the World Ser.). (J). lib. bdg. (978-1-4042-0723-3(6)) Rosen Publishing Group, Inc., The.

Page, F. B. Chopin. 2001. (YA). reprint ed. 150.00 (978-0-7222-5390-8(7)) Library Reprints, Inc.

Summerer, Eric Michael. Frederic Chopin. 2006. (Primary Source Library of Famous Composers). (Illus.). 32p. (J). 21.95 (978-1-4042-2769-9(5) , PowerKids Pr.) Rosen Publishing Group, Inc., The.

Uminska, Zofia. Chopin, the Child & the Lad. 2001. 91p. (YA). reprint ed. 88.00 (978-0-7222-5392-2(3)) Library Reprints, Inc.

Venezia, Mike. Frederic Chopin. (Getting to Know the World's Greatest Composers Ser.). (Illus.). 32p. (J). (gr. 3-4). 2000. pap. 6.95 (978-0-516-26534-6(2)); 1999. 27.00 (978-0-516-21588-4(4)) Scholastic Library Publishing. (Children's Pr.).

—Frederic Chopin. 1999. (gr. k-3). lib. bdg. 15.25 (978-0-613-37351-7(0)) Tandem Library Bks.

Vernon, Roland. Chopin: Introducing. 2000. (Introducing Composers Ser.). (Illus.). 32p. (J). (gr. 4-7). 21.95 (978-0-7910-6039-1(X) , Chelsea Hse.) Facts On File, Inc.

Wheeler, Opal. Frederic Chopin, Son of Poland Later Years. Price, Christine, illus. 2007. 160p. (J). per. 12.95 (***978-1-933573-09-0(0)***, 4717) Zeezok Publishing.

Whelller, Opal. Frederic Chopin, Son of Poland, Early Years. Price, Christine, illus. 2007. 160p. (J). per. 12.95 (***978-1-933573-11-3(2)***, 4716) Zeezok Publishing.

Whiting, Jim. The Life & Times of Frederic Chopin. 2004. (Masters of Music Ser.). (Illus.). 48p. (gr. 4-8). lib. bdg. 20.95 (978-1-58415-245-3(1)) Mitchell Lane Pubs., Inc.

Wilcox, Judy. Ferderic Chopin, Son of Poland, Early & Later Years Study Guide. 2007. (Illus.). 40p. (J). 9.95 (***978-1-933573-12-0(0)***, 4718) Zeezok Publishing.

CHORAL SPEAKING

Burke. Choral Reading. 1999. (Illus.). (J). (gr. 2-3). pap. (978-0-7398-1312-6(9)); (gr. 4-5). pap. (978-0-7398-1313-3(7)) Steck-Vaughn.

CHOREOGRAPHY

see Ballet; Dance

CHRIST

see Jesus Christ

CHRISTENING

see Baptism

CHRISTIAN ART AND SYMBOLISM

see also Bible—Pictorial Works; Church Architecture; Jesus Christ—Art

also subdivision Art under various subjects, e.g. Jesus Christ—Art

Bulletin Board Set - Christian Symbols. 2004. (J). (gr. k-6). 9.99 (978-0-7647-0993-7(3)) School Specialty Publishing.

Christian Symbols Shapes Stickers - Christian Symbols. 2004. (gr. k-6). 2.25 (978-0-7647-0994-4(1)) School Specialty Publishing.

Gospel Light Staff. Christian Symbols: Coloring & Activities Book. 1999. pap. 1.00 (978-0-8307-2471-0(0)) Gospel Light Pubns.

Jones, Lois S. The Development of Christian Symbolism, 4 vols.; set. Jones, Preston, ed. Date not set. (Development of Christian Symbolism Ser.). (YA). (gr. 10-12). pap. incl. VHS (978-1-882238-01-9(X)) Swan-Jones Production.

CHRISTIAN BIOGRAPHY

see also Apostles; Clergy; Missionaries; Monasticism and Religious Orders; Pilgrims (New Plymouth Colony); Popes; Saints

Alex, Ben. Dietrich Bonhoeffer. Cosimo, Musio, illus. 1998. (Heroes of Faith & Courage Ser.). 50p. (gr. 3-12). reprint ed. 7.99 (978-1-884543-18-0(9)) Authentic Media.

Allen, Raymond E. From Jesus to Santa Claus. Headings, Wade, photos by. 2000. 16p. (J). (ps-7). pap. 4.95 (978-0-9703697-0-3(0)) True To The Word, LLP.

Ayers, Samuel J. Kenneth Wyatt: From the Pulpit to the Paintbrush. 2001. (Illus.). 32p. (J). (gr. 3-8). 14.00 (978-0-9667681-4-5(0)) Hermosa Creations.

Bates, Alice. For All Time: The Story of Ann Judson. 1998. 48p. (J). (gr. 1-6). pap. 6.95 (978-1-56309-257-2(3) , N987102) Woman's Missionary Union.

Benge, Janet. Nicolaus Ludwig von Zinzendorf: First Fruit. 2005. (Christian Heroes Ser.). (J). pap. 8.99 (978-1-57658-262-6(0)) YWAM Publishing.

Benge, Janet & Benge, Geoff. Clarence Jones: Mr. Radio. 2005. (Christian Heroes, Then & Now Ser.). (J). pap. 8.99 (978-1-57658-343-2(0)) YWAM Publishing.

—Peligro en la Selva: La Vida de Nate Saint. 2005. (SPA.). 189p. pap. 8.99 (978-1-57658-317-3(1)) YWAM Publishing.

—Persecucion en Holanda: La Vida de Corrie Ten Boom. 2005. (SPA.). 208p. pap. 8.99 (978-1-57658-338-8(4)) YWAM Publishing.

—Rachel Saint a Star in the Jungle. 2005. (Christian Heroes, Then & Now Ser.). (Illus.). 207p. (J). (gr. 4-7). pap. 8.99 (978-1-57658-337-1(6)) YWAM Publishing.

Benge, Janet Hazel. George Mueller. 1999. (Christian Heroes Ser.). 208p. pap. 8.99 (978-1-57658-145-2(4)) YWAM Publishing.

Benge, Janet Hazel & Benge, Geoffrey Francis. Adoniram Judson: Bound for Burma. 2000. (Christian Heroes Ser.: Vol. 12). 232p. (gr. 5-9). pap. 8.99 (978-1-57658-161-2(6)) YWAM Publishing.

—Amy Carmichaell: A Unit Study Curriculum Guide. 2000. (Christian Heroes Ser.). 64p. (gr. 5-9). 8.99 (978-1-57658-185-8(3)) YWAM Publishing.

—Cameron Townsend: Good News in Every Language. 2000. (Christian Heroes Ser.: Vol. 13). 224p. (gr. 5-9). pap. 8.99 (978-1-57658-164-3(0)) YWAM Publishing.

—Eric Liddell: A Unit Study Curriculum Guide. 2000. (Christian Heroes Ser.). 64p. (gr. 5-9). 8.99 (978-1-57658-182-7(9)) YWAM Publishing.

—Gladys Aylward: A Unit Study Curriculum Guide. 2000. (Christian Heroes Ser.). 64p. (gr. 5-9). 8.99 (978-1-57658-184-1(5)) YWAM Publishing.

—Lottie Moon. 2000. (Christian Heroes Ser.). 208p. (gr. 5-9). pap. 8.99 (978-1-57658-188-9(8)) YWAM Publishing.

—Nate Saint: A Unit Study Curriculum Guide. 2000. (Christian Heroes Ser.). 64p. (gr. 5-9). 8.99 (978-1-57658-187-2(X)) YWAM Publishing.

Bert, Ruth J. Everyone Called Her Sister Sarah. 2004. (ENG., Illus.). 32p. (J). pap. 4.99 (978-1-928915-62-1(0)) Evangel Publishing Hse.

Catherwood, Christopher. Martyn Lloyd-Jones: From Wales to Westminster. 1999. (Trail Blazers Ser.). 160p. (J). (gr. 4-7). mass mkt. 5.99 (978-1-85792-349-0(9) , Christian Focus) Christian Focus Pubns. GBR. *Dist:* Riverside.

Chelsea House Publishing Staff. Heroes of the Faith. 1998. (J). 179.50 (978-0-7910-5050-7(5) , Chelsea Hse.) Facts On File, Inc.

Collins, David R. Servant to the Slaves: The Story of Henriette Delille. 2000. (Weaver Bks.). 68p. (J). (gr. 7-9). pap. 3.95 (978-0-8198-7039-1(0)) Pauline Bks. & Media.

Davenport, John. C. S. Lewis. 2003. (Who Wrote That? Ser.). (Illus.). 112p. (gr. 6-12). 30.00 (978-0-7910-7620-0(2) , Chelsea Hse.) Facts On File, Inc.

Driscoll, Chris. God's Little Flower: The Story of St. Therese of Lisieux. Kelley, Patrick, illus. 2001. 32p. (J). (ps-3). 13.95 (978-1-929039-05-0(0)) Ambassador Bks., Inc.

Eddy, Susan. Mother Teresa. 2004. (Rookie Biographies Ser.). (Illus.). 31p. (J). (gr. 1-2). pap. 4.95 (978-0-516-27922-0(X) , Children's Pr.) Scholastic Library Publishing.

Esther, Gulshan & Sangster, Thelma. The Torn Veil: The Best-Selling Story of Gulshan Esther. 2004. pap. 9.99 (978-0-310-25688-5(7)) Zondervan.

Finn, Francis J. Harry Dee: Or, Working It Out. 2000. 284p. (YA). (gr. 5-8). reprint ed. pap. 9.00 (978-0-89555-672-1(3) , 1756) TAN Bks. and Pubs., Inc.

—Percy Wynn: or Making a Boy of Him. 2000. 248p. (YA). (gr. 5-8). reprint ed. pap. 9.00 (978-0-89555-671-4(5) , 1756) TAN Bks. and Pubs., Inc.

—Tom Playfair: or Making a Start. 2000. 255p. (YA). (gr. 5-8). reprint ed. pap. 9.00 (978-0-89555-670-7(7) , 1755) TAN Bks. and Pubs., Inc.

Francen, Mike. I Have a Dream. O'Hay, Rochelle, ed. 1999. (Illus.). 72p. (YA). (gr. 7). pap. 4.00 (978-1-888079-24-1(6) , FWO Bks.) Francen World Outreach.

Glavich, Mary Kathleen. Saint Julie Billiart: The Smiling Saint. Bentley, James, illus. 2001. (Encounter the Saints Ser.: Vol. 11). 120p. (J). pap. 5.95 (978-0-8198-7050-6(1) , 332-352) Pauline Bks. & Media.

Gormley, Beatrice. C. S. Lewis: The Man Behind Narnia. 2nd ed. 2005. (Illus.). 180p. (YA). (gr. 8-12). pap. 12.00 (978-0-8028-5301-1(3) , Eerdmans Bks For Young Readers) Eerdmans, William B. Publishing Co.

Granfield, Linda. Amazing Grace: The Story of the Hymn. braille ed. 2004. (Illus.). (J). (gr. 2-4). spiral bd. (978-0-616-01661-9(1)) Canadian National Institute for the Blind/Institut National Canadien pour les Aveugles.

Here's My Heart Lord. 2003. (YA). per. (978-1-55630-522-1(2)) Brentwood Communications Group.

Howat, Irene. George Muller: The Children's Champion. 2000. (Trail Blazers Ser.). 192p. (J). (gr. 4-7). mass mkt. (978-1-85792-549-4(1) , Christian Focus) Christian Focus Pubns.

Jackson, Dave & Jackson, Neta. Hero Tales. 2005. (Illus.). 192p. (J). (gr. 1-7). pap. 12.99 (978-0-7642-0079-3(8)); pap. 12.99 (978-0-7642-0080-9(1)) Bethany Hse. Pubs.

Jackson, Dave & Neta. Hero Tales, Vol. 4. 2006. 192p. (J). pap. 12.99 (978-0-7642-0081-6(X)) Bethany Hse. Pubs.

Kent, Deborah. Dorothy Day: Friend to the Forgotten. 2004. (Illus.). 187p. (J). pap. 12.00 (978-0-8028-5265-6(3)) Eerdmans, William B. Publishing Co.

Latham, Frank. Jed Smith: Trail Blazer of the West. McHugh, Michael J., ed. Murch, Frank, illus. 2003. 121p. pap. 6.95 (978-1-930367-86-9(4)) Christian Liberty Pr.

Lewis, Gregg. Dave Dravecky. 2002. (gr. 3-6). lib. bdg. 13.00 (978-0-613-71674-1(4)) Tandem Library Bks.

Lewis, Gregg & Lewis, Deborah S. Joni Eareckson Tada. 2002. (Today's Heroes Ser.). (Illus.). 112p. (J). pap. 4.99 (978-0-310-70300-6(X)) Zonderkidz.

Littleton, Mark. Baseball. 2002. (gr. 3-6). lib. bdg. 14.15 (978-0-613-71665-9(5)) Tandem Library Bks.

—Baseball. 2002. (Illus.). 112p. (J). pap. 5.99 (978-0-310-70291-7(7)) Zonderkidz.

Matimore, P. Henry. Heroes of God's Church. Boog, Michel, illus. Date not set. 286p. (YA). (gr. 5-8). reprint ed. 21.00 (978-0-911845-44-0(5)) Neumann Pr., The.

McHugh, Michael. Giant of the Western Trail: The Missionary Life of Father Peter de Smet. 2003. (Illus.). 181p. (J). reprint ed. 19.00 (978-1-930873-80-3(8)) Neumann Pr., The.

Meloche, Renee. Cameron Townsend: Planting God's Word. Pollard, Bryan, illus. 2004. (Heroes for Young Readers Ser.). 32p. (J). 6.99 (978-1-57658-241-1(8)) YWAM Publishing.

—Jim Elliot: A Light for God. Pollard, Bryan, illus. 2004. (Heroes for Young Readers Ser.). 32p. (J). 8.99 (978-1-57658-235-0(3)) YWAM Publishing.

—Jonathan Goforth: Never Give Up. Pollard, Bryan, illus. 2004. (Heroes for Young Readers Ser.). 32p. (J). 6.99 (978-1-57658-242-8(6)) YWAM Publishing.

—Lottie Moon: A Generous Offering. Pollard, Bryan, illus. 2004. (Heroes for Young Readers Ser.). 32p. (J). 6.99 (978-1-57658-243-5(4)) YWAM Publishing.

Miller, Amos J. Amish Miller Twins Amos & Andy: Childhood & Young Adult Years. 2002. 215p. per. 11.95 (978-0-9721583-9-8(1)) Twin Rose Publishing.

Mohan, Claire J. The Young Life of St. Maria Faustina. Robbins, Jane, illus. 2000. (Young Life Ser.). 114p. (gr. 5-8). pap. 10.95 (978-0-944203-36-1(1)) Marian Pr.

Morrett, John J. Saints I Have Known & Known About. 2003. 117p. (YA). pap. 12.95 (978-0-7414-1435-9(X)) Infinity Publishing.

Muldoon, Kathleen M. Little Book of Saints, 2 bks. Mattozzi, Patricia R., illus. 2005. 24p. (J). Vol. 2. pap. 3.95 (978-0-8198-4511-5(6) , 332-187); Vol. l. pap. 3.95 (978-0-8198-4510-8(8) , 332-186) Pauline Bks. & Media.

Parker, Victoria. C.S. Lewis. 2006. (Illus.). 48p. (J). pap. (978-1-4034-7339-4(0)); lib. bdg. (978-1-4034-7336-3(6)) Heinemann Library.

Pinkney, Gloria Jean, et al. In the Forest of Your Remembrance: Thirty-Three Goodly News Tellings for the Whole Family. Pinkney, Jerry & Pinkney, Brian, illus. Pinkney, Myles C., photos by. 2001. 128p. (J). 16.99 (978-0-8037-2643-7(0) , Dial) Penguin Group (USA) Inc.

Ruiz, Miguel. Prompted by Providence: A Slice from the Life-Adventure of Juan. 2001. 154p. (YA). per. 7.50 net. (978-0-9650557-4-1(4)) Michigan State Univ., Julian Samora Research Institute.

Sayers, Susan. Adventurers: Year A. 2000. (Living Word Living Water Ser.). (Illus.). 144p. (YA). (gr. 6-9). pap. 24.95 (978-1-58595-097-3(1)) Twenty-Third Pubns./Bayard.

—Adventurers: Year B. 2000. (Living Word Living Water Ser.). 144p. (YA). (gr. 6-9). pap. 24.95 (978-1-58595-101-7(3)) Twenty-Third Pubns./Bayard.

—Explorers: Year A. 2000. (Living Word Living Water Ser.). (Illus.). 152p. (J). (gr. 1-5). pap. 24.95 (978-1-58595-096-6(3)) Twenty-Third Pubns./Bayard.

—Explorers: Year B. 2000. (Living Word Living Water Ser.). 152p. (J). (gr. 1-5). pap. 24.95 (978-1-58595-100-0(5)) Twenty-Third Pubns./Bayard.

—Seekers: Year A. 2000. (Living Word Living Water Ser.). (Illus.). 144p. (J). (ps-k). pap. 24.95 (978-1-58595-095-9(5)) Twenty-Third Pubns./Bayard.

Shaw, Maura D. Dorothy Day: A Catholic Life of Action. Marchesi, Stephen, illus. 2004. (Spiritual Biographies for Young Readers Ser.). 32p. (J). 12.99 (978-1-59473-011-5(3)) SkyLight Paths Publishing.

Sweet, Michael, frwd. Stryper: Loud 'n Clear: An Authorized Biography by Dale Erickson & Jesse Sturdevant. 2001. 230p. (J). per. 20.00 (978-0-9710608-0-7(0)) Endgame Entertainment.

Then and Now Staff. Jonathan Goforth. 2000. (Christian Heroes Ser.). 208p. (gr. 5-9). pap. 8.99 (978-1-57658-174-2(8)) YWAM Publishing.

Thorp, Annie E. J. So Very Rosemary. 2000. (Illus.). 32p. (ps-3). pap. 7.99 (978-0-8254-3846-2(2)) Kregel Pubns.

Tinling, Christine I. Heroes of the Cross, All for Jesus, Vol. 8. (J). pap. 5.99 (978-0-88019-162-3(7)) Schmul Publishing Co., Inc.

Walling, Regis M. & Rupp, N. Daniel, eds. The Diary of Bishop Frederic Baraga: First Bishop of Marquette, Michigan. Gregorich, Joseph & Prud'Homme, Paul, trs. from GER. 2001. (Illus.). 344p. pap. 23.95 (978-0-8143-2999-3(3)) Wayne State Univ. Pr.

Walsh, Kay. John Paton, a South Sea Island Rescue. 160p. (J). mass mkt. 5.99 (978-1-85792-852-5(0) , Christian Focus) Christian Focus Pubns. GBR. *Dist:* Riverside.

Wellman, Sam. Billy Graham: The Great Evangelist. 1999. (Heroes of the Faith Ser.). (Illus.). 208p. (YA). (gr. 4-7). 14.95 (978-0-7910-5031-6(9) , Chelsea Hse.) Facts On File, Inc.

Windeatt, Mary Fabyan & Ignatz, Marie. Vocabulary Quiz Workbook: Based on 6 Great Saints' Lives by Mary Fabyan Windeatt. Lester, Mary Frances, ed. 2003. (J). pap., wbk. ed. 21.00 (978-0-89555-743-8(6) , 1841) TAN Bks. and Pubs., Inc.

Wright, Chris. An Incubating Miracle. Taylor, Minnie, ed. 2004. 107p. (J). per. 12.95 (978-1-930908-30-7(X) , AGB/me) AGB Publishing.

Yolen, Jane. Friend: The Story of George Fox & the Quakers. 2nd ed. 2005. (Illus.). xii, 179p. (J). (978-1-888305-41-8(X)) Quaker Press of Friends General Conference.

Young, Joan H. Would You Dare?. Young, Joan H., illus. 2nd ed. 2004. (Illus.). 87p. (YA). reprint ed. 6.00 (978-0-9765432-0-6(6)) Bks. Leaving Footprints.

CHRISTIAN DOCTRINE

see Theology

CHRISTIAN EDUCATION

see Religious Education

CHRISTIAN ETHICS

Birky, Joy. Bully Bill. Thompson, Chad, illus. 2007. (J). (ps-k). pap. 12.99 (***978-0-8361-9382-4(2)***) Herald Pr.

Christian Morality. 2004. (Effective Dre Ser.). pap. (978-0-8294-1061-7(9)) Loyola Pr.

God's Action Plan. 96p. (YA). (gr. 6-8). stu. ed. 10.95 (978-0-570-09800-3(9) , 22-2485) Concordia Publishing Hse.

Jordan, Anne. Perspectives on Religious Issues. 2003. (Illus.). 160p. pap., stu. ed. (978-0-7487-7255-1(3)) Nelson Thornes Ltd.

Karl Marx & Christian Ethics. 2nd l.t. ed. 2000. 401p. (C). pap. 29.00 (978-0-9712616-0-0(1)) Arts Colony Pubs.

Lessons in Responsibility for Boys: Level One. 2007. (YA). per. 18.95 (***978-0-9792446-0-5(9)***) Messiah Publishing - Pearables.

Lessons in Responsibility for boys Level Two. 2007. (YA). per. 18.95 (***978-0-9792446-1-2(7)***) Messiah Publishing - Pearables.

Lessons in Responsibility for Girls: Level One. 2006. Orig. Title: Home Economics for Home Schoolers Level One. (J). per., pupil's gde. ed. 18.95 (***978-0-9792446-2-9(5)***) Messiah Publishing - Pearables.

Lessons in Responsibility for Girls: Level Three, 3. 2005. Orig. Title: Home Economics for Home Schoolers Level Three. (J). per., pupil's gde. ed. (***978-0-9792446-4-3(1)***) Messiah Publishing - Pearables.

Lessons in Responsibility for Girls: Level Two, 2. 2006. Orig. Title: Home Economics for Home Schoolers Level Two. (J). per., pupil's gde. ed. 18.95 (***978-0-9792446-3-6(3)***) Messiah Publishing - Pearables.

CHRISTIAN LIFE

see also Christian Ethics; Faith; Prayer; Religious Education; Spiritual Life

A Sister of Notre Dame. True Stories for First Communicants. 2003. (Illus.). 83p. (J). reprint ed. (978-1-930873-89-6(1)) Neumann Pr., The.

Abadie, M. J. Goddess in Every Girl: Develop Your Teen Feminine Power. 2002. (gr. 7-12). lib. bdg. 24.55 (978-0-613-90527-5(X)) Tandem Library Bks.

ABCs of Christian Character Ac. 2004. pap. 4.99 (978-0-7647-0568-7(7)) School Specialty Publishing.

Abingdon. Choosing Jesus. 2004. (gr. 6-8). stu. ed. 5.00 (978-0-687-02185-7(5)); 12.00 (978-0-687-02195-6(2)) Abingdon Pr.

—In a Dilemma: Living Your Faith Through the Tough Stuff. 2003. (gr. 6-8). pap., stu. ed. 5.00 (978-0-687-02138-3(3)); 12.00 (978-0-687-02148-2(0)) Abingdon Pr.

—Man with a Mission. 2004. pap., stu. ed. 5.00 (978-0-687-02145-1(6)) Abingdon Pr.

—Promises for Girls Living Faithfully with God & Neighbor. 2006. 64p. 4.00 (978-0-687-49385-2(4)) Abingdon Pr.

—Promises for Guys Living Faithfully with God & Neighbour. 2006. 64p. 4.00 (978-0-687-49375-3(7)) Abingdon Pr.

—Promises Leader's Guide Living Faithfully with God & Neighbor. 2006. 64p. 12.00 (978-0-687-49577-1(6)) Abingdon Pr.

—Reel to Real Vol. 4, No. 1: Making the Most of the Movies with Youth. 2000. 32p. (YA). (gr. 8-12). 10.00 (978-0-687-03358-4(6)) Abingdon Pr.

—Reel to Real Vol. 4, No. 2: Making the Most of the Movies with Youth. 2004. 32p. pap. 10.00 (978-0-687-03348-5(9)) Abingdon Pr.

Above & Beyond Quiet Time Guide. 2004. 1.95 (978-0-9743687-3-3(3)) Connection.

Abraham, Adam E. I Am Spirit! Litster, Marie, illus. deluxe ed. 2001. 80p. (YA). (gr. 8 up). lib. bdg. 22.95 (978-0-9700209-3-2(7) , Phaelos Bks.) Phaelos Publishing.

Abraham, Ken. Armed & Dangerous: Straight Answers from the Bible. 2003. (Value Book Ser.). 96p. (YA). pap. 0.99 (978-1-58660-733-3(2) , Barbour Bks.) Barbour Publishing, Inc.

Abraham, Ken & Fitzgerald, Annie. Dear God, It's Me Again. 2003. (Dear God Kids Ser.). (Illus.). 12p. (J). 4.99 (978-0-8254-2648-3(0)) Kregel Pubns.

—Dear God, Thank You for Friends. 2003. (Dear God Kids Ser.). (Illus.). 12p. (J). 4.99 (978-0-8254-2647-6(2)) Kregel Pubns.

—Dear God, Thanks for Making Me Special! 2003. (Dear God Kids Ser.). (Illus.). 12p. (J). 4.99 (978-0-8254-2649-0(9)) Kregel Pubns.

The Action Principles, Catholic Edition: Create a Life of Purpose, Passion, Prosperity & Peace. 2004. 144p. pap. 6.00 (978-1-884864-20-9(1)) American Success Institute, Inc.

Adams, M.H. Small Means & Great Ends (Illustrated. 2006. pap. (***978-1-4065-0478-1(5)***) Dodo Pr.

Adams, Patricia E. Journeying to the Road Called Oneness: An Inductive Study on Intimacy with God. 2006. (One Heart Ser.: Vol. 2). (Illus.). 175p. pap. 19.95 (978-0-9700976-1-3(1) , Shekinah Publishing Hse.) Shekinah Publishing Hse.

—With Oneness of Heart: An Inductive Study on Intimacy with God Vol. 1 of the One Heart Series, 4 vols., Vol. 1. 2004. (One Heart Ser.: Vol. 1). (Illus.). 175p. (gr. 7 up). pap. 19.95 (978-0-9700976-0-6(3) , Shekinah Publishing Hse.) Shekinah Publishing Hse.

Adivina Lo Que Es: Individual 6-packs, Level 4. 2003. 23.95 (978-0-673-57868-6(2)) Celebration Pr.

Air-tistry: Effective Storytelling with Balloons in Ministry. 2001. 50p. pap. 8.50 (978-0-9708486-0-4(9)) Air To The Kingdom.

Air to the Kingdom Balloon Entertainers Workshop Lecture Notes. 2nd ed. 2001. 28p. pap. 3.50 (978-0-9708486-2-8(5)) Air To The Kingdom.

Alex, N. L. Smile All the While. l.t. ed. 2005. (Illus.). 16p. (J). 4.99 (978-0-9766080-0-4(6)) Joe Girl Ink.

Allen, Holly. Following the Cloud: Kid's Slot Material. 2001. (J). 12.97 (978-1-880828-09-0(X)) Touch Pubns.

—Following the Cloud Together: Children's Church Book. 2001. (J). 17.97 (978-1-880828-08-3(1)) Touch Pubns.

Allen Innovations and Initiatives Staff. Prosperity Seeds from the B.O.S.S.! (The Book of Scriptural Seeds. 2001. 48p. (YA). (gr. 7 up). pap. 3.50 (978-0-9708859-0-6(3)) Allen Innovations & Initiatives/AII.

Ameiss, Bill. Love, Sex, & God. 1998. (gr. 7-12). lib. bdg. 19.95 (978-0-613-72727-3(4)) Tandem Library Bks.

American Literature Student Edition: Encouraging Thoughtful Christians to Be World Changers. 2002. (YA). stu. ed. 30.50 (978-0-9725890-0-0(7)) For Such A Time As This Ministries.

Amidei, Kathie. How to Build Relationships: Self, Family, Peers, Authorities. Lynch, Patricia & Larkin, Jean, eds. Lynch, Patricia, illus. 2000. (Active Learning for Catholic Kids Ser.). 28p. (YA). (gr. 7-9). pap. 7.95 (978-0-937997-89-5(7)) Pflaum Publishing Group.

Amos Copelan, Ashley. Thank You God. Senesi, Susan, illus. 1999. 32p. (J). (ps-3). pap. 9.95 (978-1-56167-532-6(6) , Shooting Star Edition) American Literary Pr.

Anderson, Debby. Jesus Is Coming Back! Anderson, Debby, illus. 2005. (Illus.). 32p. (J). (ps-2). pap. 9.99 (978-1-58134-743-2(X) , Crossway Bibles) Crossway Bks.

—Let's Talk about Heaven. 2003. (Illus.). 32p. (J). (ps-2). 12.99 (978-0-7814-3077-7(1) , 0781430771) Cook, David C. Publishing Co.

Anderson, John W. Straight the Highway: The Life Story of Petar & Hannah. 2007. 432p. per. 26.95 (***978-0-595-43876-1(8)***) iUniverse, Inc.

Anderson, Nancy Munger, illus. What Would Jesus Do? 2000. 30p. (J). 5.99 (978-0-310-70166-8(X)) Zondervan.

Anderson, Neil T. Beta Starter Kit. 2004. (Beta Discipleship Ser.). 99.99 (978-0-8307-3384-2(1) , Gospel Light) Gospel Light Pubns.

Angel Prophecies: For Spiritual Architects of the Future. 2000. 192p. (J). per. 15.95 (978-0-9679973-8-4(0)) Landon Pubns.

Angola/Portuguese Book of Hope: International Pictorial Edition (Youth) 2000. (Book of Life Ser.). (J). mass mkt. (978-1-890525-22-4(7)) Book of Hope International.

Angola/Portuguese Your Book of Hope: Early Elementary Edition. 2000. (Book of Life Ser.). 32p. (J). mass mkt. (978-1-890525-31-6(6)) Book of Hope International.

Anonymous. Aunt Harding's Keepsakes or the Two Bibles. 2004. reprint ed. pap. 15.95 (978-1-4191-0822-8(0)); pap. 1.99 (978-1-4192-0822-5(5)) Kessinger Publishing, LLC.

Anonymous. Catechism of Familiar Things. 2006. pap. (***978-1-4068-0491-1(6)***) Echo Library.

Anthony, Kitty. The King's Castles. 2004. 112p. (ps-3). pap. 7.99 (978-0-85151-777-3(3)) Banner of Truth, The.

Appelbaum, Barbara G. & Marchant, Peter, told to. Angie's Story. 2003. (YA). 25.95 (978-0-9710686-4-3(X)); per. 15.95 (978-0-9710686-5-0(8)) Jewish Community Federation of Rochester, NY, Inc.

Arch Books Staff. The Good Shepherd. 1998. (Arch Bks.). (Illus.). 16p. (J). (gr. k-4). pap. 1.99 (978-0-570-07551-6(3) , 59-1524GJ) Concordia Publishing Hse.

Armbrecht, Doug, compiled by. Quiet Time Prepack for Families (Quiet Time Devotionals), 21. 2006. (Illus.). (YA). per. 347.79 (978-1-931235-53-2(8) , gbookpack) Word of Life Fellowship, Inc.

Armstrong, Moses K. Orthodox Christian Alphabet Coloring Book. Date not set. 35p. (J). (gr. k-3). pap. 5.00 (978-1-879038-45-5(5) , 9013) Synaxis Pr.

Arnold, Judy K. Introduction to K. E. Y. S. 2000. 36p. (J). (gr. k-6). pap. 7.77 (978-1-57921-297-1(2)) WinePress Publishing.

Arrowood Press Staff. Jesus Teaches Me Caring. 1999. (Arch Bks.). (Illus.). 80p. (J). (ps-3). 7.99 (978-0-88486-230-7(5) , Arrowood Pr.) BBS Publishing Corp.

Arthur, Kay & Arndt, Janna. Boy, Have I Got Problems. 2003. (Discover-4-Yourself for Kids Ser.). 140p. (J). pap. 8.99 (978-1-888655-74-2(7)) Precept Ministries.

Artz, Tom. What It Means to Be a Catholic, 6 booklets. 1998. (Illus.). (YA). (gr. 9-13). pap., stu. ed. 7.45 (978-0-89837-159-8(7)) Pflaum Publishing Group.

Auer, Jim. Handbook for Today's Catholic Teen. 2004. (YA). pap. 3.95 net. (978-0-7648-1173-9(8)) Liguori Pubns.

AULT, Jane M., concept. Heart Connections: Finding Joy through Openness with God. 2003. (Illus.). 128p. (YA). 11.95 (978-0-9708129-4-0(9) , HC01012004-01) Franklin Publishing.

Aventurate Dia A Dia. 2004. (SPA.). pap. 7.50 (978-0-311-40067-6(1)) Casa Bautista de Publicaciones.

Baaumbach, Gerard F., creator. Sadlier We Believe. 2003. (Sadlier We Believe Religion Ser.). (J). per. (978-0-8215-5500-2(6) , Sadlier) Sadlier, William H. Inc.

Baby Blessings Staff. God Made Me Book W/Plush. 2006. 6p. 12.99 (978-0-7847-1501-7(7) , 04152) Standard Publishing.

Bacchiocchi, Samuele. Hal Lindsey's Prophetic Jigsaw Puzzle: Five Predictions That Failed! 6th deluxe ed. 1998. (Biblical Perspectives Ser.: Vol. 3). 150p. (YA). pap. 20.00 (978-1-930987-02-9(1)) Biblical Perspectives.

Bagley, Val. My Little Book about Joseph. 2004. (Illus.). (J). bds. 9.95 (978-1-57734-729-3(3)) Covenant Communications, Inc.

Bagley, Val Chadwick. My Missionary Book. 2004. pap. 3.95 (978-1-57734-518-3(5) , 01114182) Covenant Communications, Inc.

—Sunday Is a Special Day. 2004. 9.95 (978-1-57734-831-3(1)) Covenant Communications, Inc.

Baker, Harold S. Just a Man in Preacher's Clothing: One Man's Journey to Share His Faith. 2001. 143p. per. 9.95 (978-0-9714196-0-5(4)) Washburn Design & Consulting, Inc.

Baker, Tim. Live It Loud: Devotions for Teens. 2003. (Live It Ser.). 208p. (YA). pap. 10.99 (978-0-8007-5880-6(3)) Baker Publishing Group.

—Live It Now: Devotions for Teens. 2006. (Live It Ser.). 192p. (YA). pap. 10.99 (978-0-8007-5882-0(X)) Revell.

—Live It Real: Devotions for Teens. 2007. (Live It Ser.). 192p. (YA). pap. 11.99 (978-0-8007-5883-7(8)) Revell.

—Live It Strong: Devotions for Teens. 2003. (Live It Ser.: Vol. 2). 208p. (YA). pap. 10.99 (978-0-8007-5881-3(1)) Baker Publishing Group.

Balfour, R. C., III. Fishing for the Abundant Life 2 Journey to Faith. 2004. (gr. 9 up). 26.00 (978-1-889574-21-9(X)) Sentry Pr., Inc.

Banks, Calvin J. Beginning Conversations with God: A Prayer & Spiritual Journal for Children. Hayden, Seito & Chandler, Alton, illus. (J). (ps-3). pap. 14.95 (978-1-877804-14-4(2)) Chandler/White Publishing Co.

Banks, Lois. Learn Your ABC's God's Way. 2006. (J). per. 9.95 (***978-1-933556-24-6(2)***) Publishers' Graphics, L.L.C.

Banner, Horace. Amazon Adventures. (Illus.). 96p. (J), pap. 5.99 (978-1-85792-440-4(1) , Christian Focus) Christian Focus Pubns. GBR. *Dist:* Riverside.

Barbour Books Staff, illus. Choosing Humility. 2001. 96p. (J). (gr. 3-5). pap. 7.99 (978-0-9703069-1-3(1)) Train-Up A Child, LLC.

Barkey, Tom. By the Grace of God - Wealth. 2000. 79p. (YA). pap. 9.95 (978-1-929571-03-1(8)) Power Living Ministries.

—Grace: God's Favor to Succeed. 2000. 200p. (YA). pap. 13.99 (978-1-929571-00-0(3)) Power Living Ministries.

—Healing Grace. 2000. 104p. (YA). pap. 9.95 (978-1-929571-01-7(1)) Power Living Ministries.

Barrington Jones, Barbara & Thomas, Janet. Dear Barbara: Answers to the Most-Asked Questions from Teenage Girls. 1998. (YA). pap. 13.95 (978-1-57345-369-1(2)) Deseret Bk. Co.

Bartel, Blaine. Little Black Book on Dreaming for Your Future. 2004. 80p. pap. 4.99 (978-1-57794-627-4(8)) Harrison Hse., Inc.

—Little Black Book on How to Win a Friend to Christ. 2004. 80p. pap. 4.99 (978-1-57794-628-1(6)) Harrison Hse., Inc.

Basic Friendship Curriculum: Year 1. (YA). (gr. 5 up). stu. ed. 13.25 (978-1-56212-728-2(4) , 300120, Faith Alive Christian Resources) CRC Pubns.

Basic Friendship Curriculum: Year 2. (YA). (gr. 5 up). stu. ed. 13.25 (978-1-56212-733-6(0) , 300220, Faith Alive Christian Resources) CRC Pubns.

Bass, Samuel. The Power of Youth: Understanding the Power of Youth God's Way. 2000. 80p. (YA). per. (978-0-9671417-5-6(3)) BibleScope.

Baumbach, Gerard F. Sadlier We Believe. 2003. (J). (gr. 1). per., tchr.'s training gde. ed. (978-0-8215-5411-1(5)); (gr. 2). per., tchr.'s training gde. ed. (978-0-8215-5412-8(3)); (gr. 3). per., tchr.'s training gde. ed. (978-0-8215-5413-5(1)); (gr. 4). per., tchr.'s training gde. ed. (978-0-8215-5414-2(X)); (gr. 6). per., tchr.'s training gde. ed. (978-0-8215-5416-6(6)) Sadlier, William H. Inc. (Sadlier).

—Sadlier We Believe, Catechist's Guide. 2003. (J). (gr. 6). per. 42.75 (978-0-8215-5516-3(2) , Sadlier) Sadlier, William H. Inc.

—Sadlier We Believe, Parish Edition: God's Law Guides Us. 2003. (J). (gr. 4). per. (978-0-8215-5504-0(9) , Sadlier) Sadlier, William H. Inc.

—Sadlier We Believe, Parish Edition: Jesus Shares God's Life. 2003. (J). (gr. 2). per. (978-0-8215-5502-6(2) , Sadlier) Sadlier, William H. Inc.

—Sadlier We Believe, Parish Edition: We Are God's People. 2003. (J). (gr. 6). per. (978-0-8215-5506-4(5) , Sadlier) Sadlier, William H. Inc.

—Sadlier We Believe, School Edition: God Loves Us. 2003. (Sadlier We Believe Religion Ser.). (J). (gr. 1). per. (978-0-8215-5401-2(8) , Sadlier) Sadlier, William H. Inc.

—Sadlier We Believe, School Edition: We Are God's People. 2003. (J). (gr. 6). per. (978-0-8215-5406-7(9) , Sadlier) Sadlier, William H. Inc.

Baumbach, Gerard F., creator. Sadlier We Believe. 2003. (J). per., tchr.'s training gde. ed. (978-0-8215-5410-4(7)); (gr. 3). per., tchr.'s training gde. ed. (978-0-8215-5503-3(0)); (gr. 5). per., tchr.'s training gde. ed. (978-0-8215-5415-9(8)) Sadlier, William H. Inc. (Sadlier).

—Sadlier We Believe, Catechist's Guide. 2003. (J). per. (978-0-8215-5510-1(3)); (gr. 2). per. (978-0-8215-5512-5(X)); (gr. 3). per. (978-0-8215-5513-2(8)); (gr. 4). per. (978-0-8215-5514-9(6)); (gr. 5). per. (978-0-8215-5515-6(4)); (gr. 6). per. (978-0-8215-5405-0(0)) Sadlier, William H. Inc. (Sadlier).

—Sadlier We Believe, Parish Edition: God Loves Us. 2003. (J). (gr. 1). per. (978-0-8215-5501-9(4) , Sadlier) Sadlier, William H. Inc.

—Sadlier We Believe, Parish Edition: We Are the Church. 2003. (J). (gr. 3). per. (978-0-8215-5403-6(4) , Sadlier) Sadlier, William H. Inc.

—Sadlier We Believe, Parish Edition: We Meet Jesus in the Sacraments. 2003. (J). (gr. 5). per. (978-0-8215-5505-7(7) , Sadlier) Sadlier, William H. Inc.

—Sadlier We Believe, School Edition: God Loves Us. 2003. (J). (gr. 1). per. (978-0-8215-5420-3(4) , Sadlier) Sadlier, William H. Inc.

—Sadlier We Believe, School Edition: God's Law Guides Us. 2003. (J). (gr. 4). per. (978-0-8215-5404-3(2) , Sadlier) Sadlier, William H. Inc.

—Sadlier We Believe, School Edition: Jesus Shares God's Life. 2003. (J). (gr. 2). per. (978-0-8215-5402-9(6) , Sadlier) Sadlier, William H. Inc.

Becker, Leah B. & Beck, Carol. My Grandma's Angels. 2000. 48p. (J). (ps-3). 12.00 (978-1-57921-308-4(1)) WinePress Publishing.

Becker, Mary Lee, contrib. by. Living Our Faith God: Revelation & Relationship. 2002. (Living Our Faith Ser.). (Illus.). 112p. pap., stu. ed. 8.95 (978-0-15-900488-3(8)) Harcourt Religion Pubs.

—Living Our Faith Morality: Challenges & Choices. 2002. (Living Our Faith). (Illus.). 112p. pap. 8.95 (978-0-15-900512-5(4)) Harcourt Religion Pubs.

Becoming a Girl of Faith: According to God's Word. l.t. ed. 2004. 90p. (YA). 12.95 (978-0-9764304-2-1(8)) Girls of Faith.

Beers, Ron & Beers, Gilbert. Young Believer Instant Message: Instant Messages for Real Life. 2004. 256p. (J). pap. 5.99 (978-1-4143-0042-9(5)) Tyndale Hse. Pubs.

Beginnings: Student Devotional. 2000. (J). (978-1-931548-12-0(9)) InQuest Ministries, Inc.

Belonging to God. ed. 1998. (J). 6.95 (978-0-664-50056-6(0)) Geneva Pr.

Benge, Janet & Benge, Geoff. William Booth: Soup, Soap, & Salvation. 2002. 208p. pap. 8.99 (978-1-57658-258-9(2)) YWAM Publishing.

Benge, Janet Hazel. Christian Heroes: Then & Now, 2 vols., Vol. 1-2. 1999. 208p. (J). pap. 6.99 (978-1-57658-173-5(X)) YWAM Publishing.

Benge, Janet Hazel & Benge, Geoffrey Francis. Betty Greene. 2000. (Christian Heroes Ser.). 200p. (gr. 5-9). pap. 8.99 (978-1-57658-152-0(7)) YWAM Publishing.

Berger, Alison J. Where Is Jesus? 2001. 16p. (J). (gr. 3-7). pap. 2.00 (978-1-58595-146-8(3)) Twenty-Third Pubns./Bayard.

Berger, Mary J. Jesus Lives in Us: Activity Book. 96p. (J). (gr. 5). pap. 2.50 (978-0-8198-3931-2(0)) Pauline Bks. & Media.

Berry, Ron. God Loves... Sharp, Chris, illus. 2006. 10p. (J). (ps). 8.95 (978-0-8249-6682-9(1) , Ideals Children's Bks.) Ideals Pubns.

Berry, Sharon. Wisdomquest, Vol. 2. 2001. (J). (gr. 1-6). stu. ed. 9.95 (978-0-633-01003-4(0)) LifeWay Christian Resources.

Berube, Holly & Muggli, Glorianne. I Love the Temple. 2004. act. bk. ed. 8.95 (978-1-57665-107-0(X)) Muggli Graphics.

Betler, Jason. I Have Decided: Beginning Your New life with Jesus. 2004. 36p. (978-0-9761415-0-1(7)) Nations Hope, Inc., The.

Beveridge, Amy. God Bless America. Fletcher, Rusty & Julien, Terry, illus. 2006. 16p. (J). pap. 1.99 (978-0-7847-1806-3(7) , 04188) Standard Publishing.

—God Bless America. Fletcher, Rusty, illus. 2006. 16p. (J). pap. 1.99 (978-0-7847-1509-3(2) , 22136) Standard Publishing.

Bible Activities for Kids. 2004. pap. 1.50 (978-0-87162-937-1(2)) Warner Pr. Pubs.

Bible Crafts & More: Ages 6-8. 2005. (Illus.). 160p. (J). (ps-3). pap. 15.99 (978-0-7847-1786-8(9) , 02275) Standard Publishing.

Bible Visuals International, compiled by. Be the One! the Todd Beamer Story. 2004. (Illus.). (J). cd-rom, audio compact disk (978-1-932381-93-1(7) , 5010-CD) Bible Visuals International, Inc.

—Discovering God's Ways Vol. 17: Old Testament. 2005. (Illus.). (J). pap. (978-1-932381-77-1(5) , 2017) Bible Visuals International, Inc.

—Living by Faith: New Testament Volume 38. 2006. (Illus.). (J). pap. (978-1-932381-28-3(7) , 1038) Bible Visuals International, Inc.

—Living the Christian Life Volume 23: New Testament. 2006. (Illus.). (J). pap. (978-1-932381-52-8(X) , 1023) Bible Visuals International, Inc.

Bick, Margaret & Ecker, Catherine. Alive in the Spirit. 2006. pap. 15.95 (978-1-56854-604-9(1) , AISCPL) Liturgy Training Pubns.

C
D

—Alive in the Spirit, Family Book. 2006. (YA). pap. 7.95 (978-1-56854-603-2(3) , AISCPF) Liturgy Training Pubns.

—Come, Spirit of God. 2006. pap. 15.95 (978-1-56854-602-5(5) , CSGCPL) Liturgy Training Pubns.

—Come, Spirit of God, Family Book. 2006. (J). pap. 7.95 (978-1-56854-601-8(7) , CSGCPF) Liturgy Training Pubns.

The Big Book of Christian Growth. (Big Book Ser.). 176p. (gr. 1-6). 19.99 (978-0-8307-2586-1(5) , Gospel Light) Gospel Light Pubns.

The Big Book of Service Projects. (Big Book Ser.). 176p. (gr. 1-6). pap. 19.99 (978-0-8307-2633-2(0) , Gospel Light) Gospel Light Pubns.

Big Idea, Inc. Staff & Kenney, Cindy. God Loves You Very Much. Ballinger, Bryan, illus. 2003. 18p. 6.99 (978-0-310-70623-6(8)) Zondervan.

Biscontin, Chino. A Friend Named Jesus. (Illus.). 64p. 10.95 (978-1-875570-66-9(7)) St Pauls Pubns. AUS. *Dist:* Alba Hse.

Bishop, Jennie. Jesus Must Be Really Special. Wummer, Amy, illus. 2006. (Heritage Builders Ser.). 32p. (J). 14.99 (978-0-7847-1379-2(0) , 04029) Standard Publishing.

Bishop, Jennie & Henson, Susan. Life Lessons from the Squire & the Scroll (Squire & the Scroll) 2005. 65p. (J). pap. 9.99 (***978-0-940110-67-0(9)***) Life Action Publishing.

Blackburn, Barbara. The Life Project: A Manual for Leaders - Forming Christian Attitudes Toward Grief & Loss - Ages 11-13. 2000. 48p. (Orig.). (YA). (gr. 6-8). pap. 8.95 (978-0-7648-0634-6(3) , Liguori Lifespan) Liguori Pubns.

—The Life Project: A Manual for Leaders - Forming Christian Attitudes Toward Grief & Loss - Ages 5-7. 2000. 56p. (Orig.). (J). (gr. k-2). pap. 8.95 (978-0-7648-0632-2(7) , Liguori Lifespan) Liguori Pubns.

—The Life Project: A Manual for Leaders - Forming Christian Attitudes Toward Grief & Loss - Ages 8-10. 2000. (Illus.). 48p. (Orig.). (J). (gr. 3-5). pap. 8.95 (978-0-7648-0633-9(5) , Liguori Lifespan) Liguori Pubns.

Blackwell, Muriel F. How Do I Become a Christian? Harper, Betty, illus. 2000. 48p. (J). (gr. 3 up). 7.99 (978-0-8054-2378-5(8)) B&H Publishing Grp.

Blundell, Trevor & Thalia. On the Way for 11 - 14's. 96p. (J). Vol. 2. pap. 11.99 (978-1-85792-705-4(2)); Vol. 3. pap. 11.99 (978-1-85792-706-1(0)) Christian Focus Pubns. GBR. (Christian Focus). *Dist:* Riverside.

Bob Jones University Press Staff. A Servants Heart: Bible Truths 2 St Worktext. 3rd ed. 2000. pap. 15.00 (978-1-57924-213-8(8)) Jones, Bob Univ. Pr.

Boelhower, Gary & Boelhower, Patricia. Following Jesus: Basic Moral Teaching, 6 bks. 1998. (Illus.). (YA). (gr. 7-10). stu. ed. 6.95 (978-0-89837-215-1(1)) Pflaum Publishing Group.

Boelts, Maribeth. With My Mom, with My Dad: A Book about Divorce. Bladholm, Cheri, illus. 2004. (Helping Kids Heal Ser.). 32p. (J). 9.99 (978-0-310-70644-1(0)) Zonderkidz.

Bohlmann, Katherine. Grandpa, Is There a Heaven? Erickson, David, illus. 2001. 32p. (J). (ps-2). 14.99 (978-0-570-07136-5(4)) Concordia Publishing Hse.

Bolanos, Roxana, creator. Miracles of Jesus. l.t. ed. 2002. (Illus.). 5p. (J). pap. 24.95 (978-0-9729001-5-7(2)) Quiltown.

Bolet de Fernandez, Silvia. Amigos en la Buenas y en las Malas. 2000. Tr. of Friends in Good Times & Bad. (SPA.). 160p. pap. 7.99 (978-0-8297-2573-5(3)) Vida Pubs.

Bookworks Staff. Jesus Wants Me for a Sunbeam. 2002. (Baby Blessings Ser.). 12p. (J). 7.99 (978-0-7847-1359-4(6)) Standard Publishing.

Bordon, Dave. Truth: Seeing Black & White in a Gray World. 2006. 208p. (YA). pap. 9.97 (978-1-59789-104-2(5)) Barbour Publishing, Inc.

Bostrom & Kucharik. Como Es Dios? (What Is God Like?) 2000. (Little Hearts Ser.). (SPA.). (J). 8.99 (978-0-7899-0857-5(3) , 497776) Editorial Unilit.

Bottke, Allison Gappa & Gemmen, Heather. Jingles & Joy. 1999. (God Allows U Turns Ser.). (Illus.). 32p. (J). pap. 5.99 (978-0-7814-3970-1(1) , 0781439701) Cook, David C. Publishing Co.

—Laughter & Love. 1999. (God Allows U Turns Ser.). (Illus.). 32p. (J). pap. 5.99 (978-0-7814-3969-5(8) , 0781439698) Cook, David C. Publishing Co.

—Picnics & Peace. 2003. (God Allows U-Turns Kids Ser.). (Illus.). 32p. (J). pap. 5.99 (978-0-7814-3971-8(X) , 078143971X) Cook, David C. Publishing Co.

Bound by Blessing. 2004. (J). 15.00 (978-0-9749263-0-8(2)) Artists Looking Ahead.

Bowler, Kathryn C. & Osborne, Rick. I Want to Know, Sam's Club: About God, Jesus, the Bible & Prayer. 2001. 168p. (J). 27.99 (978-0-310-70242-9(9)) Zonderkidz.

Bozanich, Dennis, et al, contrib. by. Jesus: Student. 2000. (Living Our Faith). 112p. (J). pap. 8.95 (978-0-15-900494-4(2)) Harcourt Religion Pubs.

—Sacraments: Student. 2001. (Living Our Faith). 112p. (YA). pap. 8.95 (978-0-15-900506-4(X)) Harcourt Religion Pubs.

Branon, Dave. Undefeated: Catching Inspiration & Hope Thrown by Athletes of Integrity. 2006. 176p. (J). pap. 10.99 (978-0-7642-0293-3(6)) Bethany Hse. Pubs.

Braswell, Steve, et al. Ships: The Relationships of Life. 2000. 144p. (J). stu. ed., per. 8.65 (978-1-929784-26-4(0)) Positive Action For Christ.

Bratcher, Jeryl L. A-b-c bible Book. 2006. (ENG.). 32p. per. 15.99 (***978-1-4208-8505-7(7)***) AuthorHouse.

Bratton, Heidi, photos by. Little Ways to Give God Praise. 2000. (Walking with God Board Bks.). (Illus.). 16p. (ps-k). bds. 5.95 (978-0-8091-6661-9(5) , 6661-5) Paulist Pr.

Bratton, Heidi, told to. Let's Hear It for the Fruits of the Spirit. 2003. 32p. (J). 7.95 (978-1-931709-85-9(8)) Our Sunday Visitor, Publishing Div.

Brazil/Portuguese Book of Hope: Children's Version Animated (NIV) 2000. (Book of Life Ser.). mass mkt. (978-1-890525-18-7(9)) Book of Hope International.

Brazil/Portuguese Book of Hope: Youth Version (NIV) 2000. (Book of Life Ser.). mass mkt. (978-1-890525-17-0(0)) Book of Hope International.

Brazil/Portuguese Your Book of Hope: Early Elementary Edition. 2000. (Book of Life Ser.). 32p. (J). mass mkt. (978-1-890525-27-9(8)) Book of Hope International.

Brazzale, Debi Little. What Difference Does It Make? Faith Answers for Kids. 2003. (Illus.). 96p. (J). (gr. 3). pap., pap. 8.99 (978-0-7814-3701-1(6) , 0781437016) Cook, David C. Publishing Co.

Brennan, Gerald. The Good Bad Boy. 2002. 128p. (J). reprint ed. 16.00 (978-1-930873-54-4(9)); pap. 12.00 (978-1-930873-55-1(7)) Neumann Pr., The.

Brewer, Janet N. In God's Image. Watkins, Virginia, ed. Pullen, Pip, illus. Carr, Geoffrey, photos by. 1998. 32p. (J). (ps-1). stu. ed. 14.99 (978-1-57895-055-3(4)) Bridge Resources.

Brewer, Michael. Gotta Have God 2: Ages 10-12. Heiser, Aline, illus. 2005. (Gotta Have God Ser.). 238p. (J). spiral bd. 12.99 (978-1-58411-059-0(7) , Legacy Pr.) Rainbow Pubs. & Legacy Pr.

Bright, et al. Building an Active Faith, Bk. 4. 2004. pap. 18.99 (978-1-56399-154-7(3)) NewLife Pubns.

Brighter Vision Publishing Staff. Caring. 2000. (Character Counts Ser.). (Illus.). (J). pap. 2.75 (978-1-55254-218-7(1)) Brighter Vision Pubns.

—Character Counts. 2000. (Illus.). (J). pap. 3.99 (978-1-55254-220-0(3)) Brighter Vision Pubns.

—Citizenship. 2000. (Character Counts Ser.). (Illus.). (J). pap. 2.75 (978-1-55254-219-4(X)) Brighter Vision Pubns.

—Fairness. 2000. (Character Counts Ser.). (Illus.). (J). pap. 2.75 (978-1-55254-217-0(3)) Brighter Vision Pubns.

—Respect. 2000. (Character Counts Ser.). (Illus.). (J). pap. 2.75 (978-1-55254-215-6(7)) Brighter Vision Pubns.

—Responsibility. 2000. (Character Counts Ser.). (Illus.). (J). pap. 2.75 (978-1-55254-216-3(5)) Brighter Vision Pubns.

—Trustworthiness. 2000. (Character Counts Ser.). (Illus.). (J). pap. 2.75 (978-1-55254-214-9(9)) Brighter Vision Pubns.

Broadly Graded Niv Extra. 2002. (YA). (978-0-633-08797-5(1)) LifeWay Christian Resources.

Brolsma, Jody, ed. Pray & Play Bible for Young Children. 2004. (Illus.). 176p. (Orig.). (ps). pap. 19.99 (978-0-7644-2024-5(0) , Flagship Church Resources) Group Publishing, Inc.

Brotherton, Marcus. Split: A Graphic Reality Check for Teens Dealing with Divorce. 2006. 64p. pap. 7.00 (978-1-59052-716-0(X) , Multnomah) WaterBrook Pr.

Broussard, Cleola. Inspirational Thoughts to & from the Master: Tender, Humble, Obedient, Uttering, Glory, Hopeful, Thankful, & Salvation. 2003. (Illus.). 98p. per. 12.95 (978-1-930908-25-3(3) , 1) AGB Publishing.

Brown, Mark. Tommy Books: Faith, 10 vols. Mekis, Pete, illus. l.t. ed. 2005. 24p. (J). 12.99 (978-0-9762690-0-7(7)) Tommy Bks. Pubng.

—Tommy Books: Kings, 10 vols. Mekis, Pete, illus. l.t. ed. 2005. 24p. (J). 12.99 (978-0-9762690-4-5(X)) Tommy Bks. Pubng.

—Tommy Books Vol. 2: Love, 10 vols. Mekis, Pete, illus. l.t. ed. 2005. 24p. (J). 12.99 (978-0-9762690-1-4(5)) Tommy Bks. Pubng.

—Tommy Books Vol. 3: Too Busy, 10 vols. Mekis, Pete, illus. l.t. ed. 2005. 24p. (J). 12.99 (978-0-9762690-2-1(3)) Tommy Bks. Pubng.

—Tommy Books Vol. 4: Praise, 10 vols. Mekis, Pete, illus. l.t. ed. 2005. 20p. (J). 12.99 (978-0-9762690-3-8(1)) Tommy Bks. Pubng.

Broyles, Anne. Signs at the Crossroads. 2004. 48p. pap., stu. ed. 6.50 (978-0-687-05860-0(0)) Abingdon Pr.

Bruinsma, Sheryl. How to Eat an Orange: And More Lessons for Kids. 2001. (FaithBuilders for Kids Ser.: Vol. 4). 96p. (J). (ps-3). reprint ed. pap. 4.99 (978-0-8010-6348-0(5) , Object Lessons) Baker Bks.

Brundage, George. Vamos a la misa. 2006. pap. 4.75 (***978-0-89942-799-7(5)***) Catholic Bk. Publishing Corp.

Bruno, Bonnie. God Thought of Everything Strange & Slimy. Brown, Kevin, illus. 2006. 128p. (YA). (gr. 3-6). pap. 8.99 (978-0-7847-1448-5(7) , 04084) Standard Publishing.

—God Thought of Everything Weird & Wacky. Brown, Kevin, illus. 2006. 128p. (YA). (gr. 3-6). pap. 8.99 (978-0-7847-1447-8(9) , 04083) Standard Publishing.

Brusselmans, Christiane, et al. Sunday: Book of Readings Adapted for Children Year C, Year C. 176p. (J). 49.95 (978-0-929496-91-7(4)) Treehaus Communications, Inc.

Bryant, Stephen, et al. Has God Called You to Ministry? 2005. 107p. (gr. 9 up). pap. 5.95 (978-1-885273-04-8(5)) First Century Publishing.

Buchanan, Kathy. Want More? Love. 2004. 160p. (YA). spiral bd., spiral bd. 14.99 (978-1-58997-119-6(1)) Focus on the Family Publishing.

Buchanan, Paul & Randall, Rod. The Misadventures of Willie Plummet Set. (Misadventures of Willie Plummet Ser.). (J). 114.99 (978-0-7586-0012-7(7)) Concordia Publishing Hse.

Buell, Jean. Welcome Children! A Beginner's Mass Book. Larkin, Jean K., ed. 2004. (Illus.). 36p. (J). 3.95 (978-0-89837-174-1(0) , 3504) Pflaum Publishing Group.

Bulthuis, Lenae. It's Me, Jesus: My Prayer Diary. 1999. (Other Resources Ser.). (Illus.). 175p. (J). (gr. 2-6). 8.25 (978-1-56212-504-2(4) , 160455, Faith Alive Christian Resources) CRC Pubns.

Bundschuh, Rick. Heartburn: Blazing Hot Worship - A Six-Session Study of the Psalms. Reeves, Dale, ed. 1999. (Illus.). 80p. (YA). pap. 14.99 (978-0-7847-0930-6(0) , 23316) Standard Publishing.

Bundschuh, Rick & Highway Visual Staff. The Perfect Life? Sin, the Soul & Kingdom Living. ldr.'s ed. 2005. (Highway Visual Curriculum Ser.). (Illus.). 80p. pap. 4.99 (978-0-310-25839-1(1)) Zondervan.

Bundschuh, Rick, et al. Secret Power for Girls Video Devotionals. 2003. (YA). 19.99 incl. VHS (978-0-310-24771-5(3)) Zondervan.

Burgen, Jim. What's the Big Deal about My Parents? Reeves, Dale, ed. 2006. (What's the Big Deal Ser.). 160p. (gr. 7 up). pap. 10.99 (978-0-7847-1252-8(2) , 23335) Standard Publishing.

BURNS, J. I. M. Addicted to God: 50 days to a more powerful relationship with God. 2007. 164p. pap. 12.99 (978-0-8307-4303-2(0) , Regal Bks.) Gospel Light Pubns.

Burns, Jim. Tough Problems, Real Solutions. 181p. pap. 10.99 (978-0-8307-3508-2(9) , Regal Bks.) Gospel Light Pubns.

Burns, Jim & DeVries, Mike. Fresh Ideas 11: Hot Topics. 136p. 17.99 (978-0-8307-2921-0(6) , Gospel Light) Gospel Light Pubns.

Busch, Melinda Kay. God Calls Abraham... God Calls You! Dorenkamp, Michelle, illus. 2003. (Arch Bks.). (ENG.). 16p. (J). (gr. k-4). 1.99 (978-0-7586-0502-3(1)) Concordia Publishing Hse.

Bussard, Paula. Come to a Critter County Party: Children Critter County Activity Book - Discover How You Can Honor Jesus. Kenney, Cindy, ed. Maurice, Dan, illus. 1999. (Celebrate Jesus! Ser.). 64p. (J). 7.00 (978-1-57849-176-6(2)) Mainstay Church Resources.

Busy People. Date not set. 16p. (J). pap., act. bk. ed. 2.99 (978-1-871676-74-7(6) , Christian Focus) Christian Focus Pubns. GBR. *Dist:* Riverside, Spring Arbor Distributors, Inc.

Butcher, Sam. Precious Moments Devotional for Girls. 2005. (Illus.). 192p. (J). (ps-ps). spiral bd. 9.99 (978-1-4003-0596-4(9)) Nelson, Thomas Inc.

Butcher, Sam, illus. My Friend Forever. 2000. (Precious Moments Seasons of Faith Ser.). 32p. (J). (ps-3). 5.99 (978-0-7852-5552-9(4)) Nelson, Thomas Inc.

—Precious Moments: Angel Kisses & Snuggle Time Prayers with Dolly. 2003. 8.40 (978-0-7180-0575-7(9)) Nelson, Thomas Inc.

—Precious Moments: Angel Kisses & Snuggle Time Prayers with Teddy Bear. 2003. 8.40 (978-0-7180-0567-2(8)) Nelson, Thomas Inc.

—Precious Moments: Small Hands Bible with Lavender Bible Cover. 2003. 12.84 (978-0-7180-0570-2(8)) Nelson, Thomas Inc.

Butt, Kyle. How Do You Know the Bible Is from God? 2002. (Illus.). 40p. 10.95 (978-0-932859-46-4(1)) Apologetics Pr., Inc.

—A Matter of Fact: A Look at More Evidence for Christianity. 2002. 160p. pap. 10.95 (978-0-932859-47-1(X)) Apologetics Pr., Inc.

Byrd, Sandra. Girl Talk: 61 Questions from Girls Like You. 2001. (Girls Like You Ser.). 128p. (J). (gr. 3-7). pap. 7.99 (978-0-7642-2492-8(1)) Bethany Hse. Pubs.

—A Growing up Guide: What Girls Like You Want to Know. 2003. (Girls Like You Ser.). (Illus.). 126p. (J). pap. 8.99 (978-0-7642-2752-3(1)) Bethany Hse. Pubs.

Bytheway, John. Are Your Standards Fences or Guardrails? 2003. (Illus.). xiv, 97p. (J). pap. (978-1-57008-990-9(6)) Deseret Bk. Co.

—A Crash Course in Teenage Survival: What I Wish I'd Known in High School, the First & Second Semesters. 2001. (Illus.). 346p. (YA). pap. 15.95 (978-1-57345-930-3(5)) Scribbulations LLC.

Caduto, Michael J. A Child of God: Stories of Jesus & Stewardship Activities for Children. Tyrol, Adelaide, illus. 2005. 48p. (J). 16.95 (978-0-8091-6726-5(3) , 6726-3) Paulist Pr.

Calderone-Stewart, Lisa-Marie. Life Works & Faith Fits: True Stories for Teens. 2003. 112p. (YA). pap. 9.95 (978-0-88489-547-3(5)) St. Mary's Pr.

Caldwell, Lise. Donut Forget! Burris, Priscilla, illus. 1999. 48p. (J). (ps-2). pap. 2.49 (978-0-7847-0993-1(9) , 22063, Bean Sprouts) Standard Publishing.

—God's Animal Friends. Dubin, Jill, illus. 1999. (Coloring Bks.). 16p. (J). (ps-3). pap. 1.99 (978-0-7847-0875-0(4) , 22067) Standard Publishing.

Campbell, June M. & Campbell, Joe Bill. Thank You, God, for Who I Am. 2001. 32p. pap. 4.75 (978-0-8189-0849-1(1)) Alba Hse.

—Thank You, God, for Who I Am. Date not set. (Illus.). viii, 36p. (J). 8.95 (978-0-9665389-1-5(9)) Spring Hollow Bks., LLC.

Campbell, Patsy. Pray Work Win! 2004. 112p. pap. 7.99 (978-0-89114-360-4(2)) Baptist Publishing Hse.

Campher, Jerome C. The Path of Purpose: Walking in God's Plan for Your Life. 2003. 36p. (YA). 6.95 (978-0-9747956-4-5(X)) Greenwood, Lori Ministries, Inc.

Camps & Retreats to Go: Above & Beyond. 2004. spiral bd. 132.00 (978-0-9743687-2-6(5)) Connection.

Canfield, Jack L. & Hansen, Mark V. Chicken Soup for the Tween's Soul Collection. 2005. 539p. (YA). 19.95 (978-0-7573-0386-9(2)) Health Communications, Inc.

Canfield, Jack L., et al. Chicken Soup for the Kid's Soul 2: Read Aloud or Read Alone Character-Building Stories for Kids Ages 6-10. 2006. (Illus.). 200p. (J). pap. 14.95 (978-0-7573-0405-7(2)) Health Communications, Inc.

Cannizzo, Karen, ed. Confirmation: Confirming My Commitment to Christ/Candidate Edition. 2003. (Hi-Time Ser.). (Illus.). 64p. (YA). pap. 7.95 (978-0-89837-172-7(4) , 1790) Pflaum Publishing Group.

Carignan, Michael J. The First Witness. Fuller, Ann, illus. 1998. (J). (ps-6). mass mkt. 4.95 (978-1-892589-00-2(1)) Madjec Jet Publishing Co.

Caring. 2002. (Precious Moments Ser.). (Illus.). 11p. (J). (ps-k). bds. 4.99 (978-1-57759-378-2(2)) Dalmatian Pr.

Carlsen, Derek. Faith & Courage Commentary on Acts. 2004. 544p. per. 12.95 (978-1-930367-98-2(8) , CLP80091) Christian Liberty Pr.

Carlson, Melody. Don't Worry about Tomorrow. Regan, Susan, illus. 2004. (Just Like Jesus Said Ser.). 32p. (J). (ps-5). 12.99 (978-0-8054-2386-0(9)) B&H Publishing Grp.

—I Can Count on God, Vol. 2. Banks, Yvette, illus. 1999. (Big Board Books for Little Kids). 20p. (ps-3). 9.99 (978-1-58134-071-6(0) , Crossway Bibles) Crossway Bks.

—The Lost Lamb. Bjorkman, Steve, illus. 1999. 40p. (ps-3). 9.99 (978-1-58134-072-3(9) , Crossway Bibles) Crossway Bks.

—Piercing Proverbs: Wise Words for Today's Generation. 2002. 96p. pap. 7.99 (978-1-57673-895-5(7) , Multnomah) WaterBrook Pr.

Carmack, Bob. Box of Letters: 93 Days of Devotions for Teens. 2000. 192p. (YA). (gr. 8-12). pap. 9.95 (978-1-57921-307-7(3)) WinePress Publishing.

Carmody, Michael A. Life with Jesus: Bible Study Workbook. 2003. 32p. (YA). pap. 10.00 (978-0-910487-54-2(5)) Royalty Publishing Co.

Caro, Henri. My First Little Gospel Book. 2002. 52p. 2.95 (978-1-58595-219-9(2)) Twenty-Third Pubns./Bayard.

—My First Little Mass Book. 2002. 52p. 2.95 (978-1-58595-217-5(6)) Twenty-Third Pubns./Bayard.

—My First Little Scripture Book. 2002. 52p. 2.95 (978-1-58595-218-2(4)) Twenty-Third Pubns./Bayard.

Caron, Judith A. Images of God. 2000. (Conversations with Teens Ser.). 16p. (YA). pap. 7.95 (978-0-937997-94-9(3)) Pflaum Publishing Group.

Carpenter, Tracy. Country Fair Camp. 2006. (Camp Ser.). (YA). 59.99 (978-0-7847-1856-8(3) , 40182) Standard Publishing.

Carr, Dan. God I Need to Talk Hurting Oth. 2004. 16p. (J). 99.00 (978-0-7586-0517-7(X)) Concordia Publishing Hse.

—God I Need to Talk Paying Atte. 2004. 16p. (J). 99.00 (978-0-7586-0518-4(8)) Concordia Publishing Hse.

Cartwright, Deanna Vincent. Disciple's Diary Student Book. 2nd ed. 2004. (J). spiral bd. 14.99 (978-0-9752605-1-7(0)) LOGOS System Assocs.

Case, Steve. Everything Counts: A Year's Worth of Devotions on Radical Living. 2003. (Invert Ser.). (Illus.). 384p. (YA). pap. 14.99 (978-0-310-25408-9(6)) Zondervan.

Cassel, Katrina. The Christian Girl's Guide to Being Your Best. 2004. (Illus.). 206p. (J). pap. 9.99 (978-1-58411-035-4(X) , Legacy Pr.) Rainbow Pubs. & Legacy Pr.

Cassel, Katrina L. The Junior High Survival Manual. 1998. 128p. (YA). (gr. 8-12). 7.99 (978-0-570-05062-9(6)) Concordia Publishing Hse.

—Junior High Survival Manual. 1998. (gr. 7-12). lib. bdg. 16.45 (978-0-613-72804-1(1)) Tandem Library Bks.

Center for Learning Staff. Faith & Belief. 2007. (Religion Ser.). 124p. (YA). spiral bd. 18.95 (***978-1-56077-845-5(8)***) Ctr. for Learning, The.

—Justice & Peace. 2007. (Religion Ser.). 124p. (YA). spiral bd. 18.95 (***978-1-56077-795-3(8)***) Ctr. for Learning, The.

Chesterton, Chris & Ward, David T. 77 Talks for Cyberspace Kids: Messages from the Truth Zone for 8-12s. 2003. (Illus.). 288p. (gr. 3-7). pap. 12.99 (978-1-85424-598-4(8) , Monarch Bks.) Lion Hudson plc GBR. *Dist:* Kregel Pubns.

Chick, Jack T. The Little Princess. 1999. (Illus.). 24p. (J). pap. 0.14 (978-0-7589-0045-6(7)) Chick Pubns., Inc.

A Child's Book of the Rosary. 2006. (J). 3.95 (978-1-933178-38-7(8)) Pflaum Publishing Group.

A Child's Missal. 2004. per. 17.95 (978-0-9741748-1-5(5)) Patmos, Inc.

Choices: On the Road. ldr.'s ed. (Ministry to Adolescent's Program Ser.). (Illus.). 72p. (978-0-85910-804-1(X)) Australian Church Resources.

Christ Our Life: Confirmation-Confirmed in the Spirit; Parish-Catechist Manual. 2004. (978-0-8294-0906-2(8)) Loyola Pr.

Christ Our Life: God Cares for Us. 2004. (gr. 2 up). stu. ed. (978-0-8294-1655-8(2)) Loyola Pr.

Christ Our Life: God Cares for Us; Parish-Catechist Manual. 2004. (gr. 2 up). (978-0-8294-1659-6(5)) Loyola Pr.

Christ Our Life: God Guides Us. 2004. (gr. 4 up). stu. ed. (978-0-8294-1539-1(4)) Loyola Pr.

Christ Our Life: God Guides Us; Parish-Catechist Manual. 2004. (gr. 4 up). (978-0-8294-1661-9(7)) Loyola Pr.

Christ Our Life: God Loves Us. 2004. (gr. k up). stu. ed. (978-0-8294-1656-5(0)) Loyola Pr.

Christ Our Life: God Loves Us; Parish-Catechist Manual. 2004. (gr. k up). (978-0-8294-1657-2(9)) Loyola Pr.

Christ Our Life: We Believe. 2004. (gr. 3 up). stu. ed. (978-0-8294-1548-3(3)) Loyola Pr.

Christ Our Life: We Believe; Parish-Catechist Manual. 2004. (gr. 3 up). (978-0-8294-1660-2(9)) Loyola Pr.

Christ Our Life: We Worship. 2004. (gr. 5 up). stu. ed. (978-0-8294-1547-6(5)) Loyola Pr.

Christian Life & Work-Guide. 2003. (YA). pap. 4.99 (978-1-56364-711-6(7)) Vision Video.

The Christian Soldier. (Pict-O-Graph Ser.). (Illus.). (J). 10.99 (978-0-7847-1016-6(3) , 02266) Standard Publishing.

The Christian Student Compass: KJV Monthly Version with Book of Proverbs. 2003. (YA). spiral bd. (978-0-9725804-2-7(5)) Salt Pubs.

Christianity 201. ldr.'s ed. 1998. (Cross Training Ser.: Vol. 2). 76p. (YA). (gr. 10-12). pap. 15.00 incl. VHS (978-1-57405-016-5(8)) CharismaLife Pubs.

Christ's Passionate Life Series, 2 bks., 12 booklets. 2005. (YA). per. 29.95 (978-0-9772313-3-1(X)) Covenant Support Network.

Church, Jayne, illus. Little Donkey. 1999. (Waggy Tales Ser.). 10p. (ps up). 6.99 (978-0-7847-1115-6(1) , 03523, Bean Sprouts) Standard Publishing.

Cintron, Carlos Juan, Sr., ed. Mis Primeros Pasos: Red de Niños. deluxe l.t. ed. 2005. (SPA., Illus.). 85p. (J). 12.00 (978-0-9765828-5-4(6)) Ed. Vida Abundante.

Clark, Chap. Next Time I Fall in Love: How to Handle Sex, Intimacy, & Feelings in Dating Relationships. 2004. 144p. pap. 18.00 (978-1-59244-684-1(1) , Wipf and Stock) Wipf & Stock Pubs.

Clark, Jerusha & Henslin, Earl. Inside A Cutter's Mind. 2007. 176p. pap. 12.99 (978-1-60006-054-0(4) , Th1nk Bks.) NavPress Publishing Group.

Clark, Leonard, Sr. The Power God Gave Leonard. 2004. (J). pap. 6.95 (978-0-533-13375-8(0)) Vantage Pr., Inc.

Clark, Lilian. I Belong to God. 2000. (Illus.). 109p. (J). (gr. 1-8). reprint ed. 16.00 (978-0-930873-20-9(4)) Neumann Pr., The.

Clark, Sondra. You Can Change Your World! Creative Ways to Volunteer & Make a Difference. 2003. (gr. 7-12). lib. bdg. 17.60 (978-0-613-75303-6(8)) Tandem Library Bks.

Clarkson, Clay. Our 24 Family Ways (Classic) Color-in Book. 2002. (Illus.). 32p. (J). pap. 6.95 (978-1-888692-11-2(1)) Whole Heart Ministries.

Claussen, Janet. Biblical Women: Exploring Their Stories with Girls. 2003. 120p. (YA). pap. 24.95 (978-0-88489-699-9(4)) St. Mary's Pr.

Clere, Jodi Rae. Youth on Mission Vol. 6: Beyond Belief! 2000. 128p. (YA). (gr. 11-12). pap. 15.99 (978-1-56309-345-6(6)) Woman's Missionary Union.

Cloninger, Claire. More E-Mail from God for Teens. 1999. 256p. pap., pap. 13.99 (978-1-58919-931-6(6) , 1589199316) Cook, David C. Publishing Co.

Cloninger, Claire & Cloninger, Andy. E-Mail from God for Kids. 2001. (E-Mail from God Ser.). 256p. pap., pap. 13.99 (978-1-58919-996-5(0) , 1589199960) Cook, David C. Publishing Co.

Coblenz, John. Viata Familiei Crestine (Christian Family Living) Brinzei, Daniel, ed. Brinzei, Daniel, tr. from ENG. (SPA.). 272p. (YA). pap. (978-1-885270-02-3(X)) Christian Aid Ministries.

Colkmire, Lance. Know It, Live It: Helping Kids Embrace Pentecostal Teachings. 2004. (Illus.). (J). per. 9.99 (978-0-87148-468-0(4)) Pathway Pr.

Come to God's Party: Learning Tool. 2004. (978-0-8066-6479-8(7)) Augsburg Fortress, Pubs.

Comics: Take-Home Papers. 2001. (Planet 56 Ser.). (J). (gr. 5-7). (978-0-8307-2276-1(9)) Gospel Light Pubns.

Comley, Kathlyn. My Sugar Bear. Piatt, Robert, illus. 2004. (J). bds. 9.99 (978-1-4183-0001-2(2)) Christ Inspired, Inc.

Community of Christ Staff. Power & Light for Kids - Kidsbook. 2005. (YA). 5.95 (978-0-8309-1147-9(2)); 5.95 (978-0-8309-1141-7(3) , 0830911413) Herald Publishing Hse.

Conditt, Margaret K. Gifts from God: What Our Dogs Teach Us about God's Love. 2007. 64p. pap. 16.99 (***978-1-57921-883-6(0)***) WinePress Publishing.

Coniaris, Anthony M. The Nicene Creed for Young People. 2004. 112p. (J). (gr. 6-9). pap. 14.95 (978-1-880971-91-8(7)) Light & Life Publishing Co.

El Constructor de Dios (God's Builder) 2000. (SPA.). (J). pap. 1.29 (978-1-56063-704-2(8) , 497735) Editorial Unilit.

Cook, Billie Montgomery. The Real Deal: A Spiritual Guide for Black Teen Girls. 2004. 144p. 13.00 (978-0-8170-1458-2(6)) Judson Pr.

Cook, David Fuller, ed. A Balanced Approach to Long Life & Vitality for Christians: As Used in Fitness, Wellness, Clinical Weight Loss, & Cardiac Rehabilitation Programs. 2003. (Illus.). 105p. spiral bd. 33.95 (978-0-9741629-4-2(9)) Cook, David.

Copeland, Gloria. Go with the Flow Booklet. 2004. pap. 1.00 (978-1-57794-331-0(7)) Harrison Hse., Inc.

Cory, Diane. God & Me! 2: Ages 6-9, 3 vols. 2004. (Illus.). 238p. (J). spiral bd. 12.99 (978-1-58411-055-2(4) , Legacy Pr.) Rainbow Pubs. & Legacy Pr.

—Gotta Have God 2: Ages 6-9. Heiser, Aline, illus. 2005. (Gotta Have God Ser.). 238p. (J). spiral bd. 12.99 (978-1-58411-058-3(9) , Legacy Pr.) Rainbow Pubs. & Legacy Pr.

Couch, Bob. Weekday Early Education Administrative Guide. 2000. (J). 19.95 (978-0-633-00396-8(4)) LifeWay Christian Resources.

Courtney, Claudia. Saved by Faith: Noah & the Ark. 1998. (ps-2). lib. bdg. 10.65 (978-0-613-72652-8(9)) Tandem Library Bks.

Courtney, Vicki. TeenVirtue: Real Issues, Real Life. 2005. (Illus.). 160p. (YA). pap. 14.99 (978-0-8054-3056-1(3)) B&H Publishing Grp.

Courtney, Vicki. TeenVirtue Confidential: Your Questions Answered about Guys, God, & Getting Older. 2007. (Illus.). 160p. (YA). pap. 14.99 (***978-0-8054-4192-5(1)*** , B&H Bks.) B&H Publishing Grp.

Cowie, Sarah. The Abbot & I (As Told by Josie the Cat) Selby, Sarah, illus. 2002. 24p. pap. 8.95 (978-1-888212-25-9(X) , 005197) Conciliar Pr.

Crain, Michael. What Catholic Teens Should Know about Retaliation. Larkin, Jean K., ed. 2004. (What Catholic Teens Should Know Ser.). (Illus.). 8p. (YA). 7.95 (978-0-89837-238-0(0) , 440910) Pflaum Publishing Group.

Crawfird, Donald W. Is This a Test Lord? Prayers, Reflections & Celebrations of a Stroke Survivor, Offering Hope & Healing. 2004. per. 12.95 (978-0-9763933-0-6(1)) Heartfelt Bks.

Crawford, Kathleen. My Communion Book: A Child's Guide to Holy Communion. Cameron, Craig, illus. 2nd ed. 2006. 32p. pap. 10.00 (***978-0-7151-4946-1(6)***) Church Hse. Pubng. GBR. *Dist:* Church Publishing, Inc.

Crews, June T. Can Anyone Fix My Broken Heart? Hope for Children of Divorce. 2000. (Illus.). 32p. (Orig.). (J). (ps-3). pap. 6.99 (978-1-57921-228-5(X)) WinePress Publishing.

Crook, Carol. The Church. abr. ed. 1998. (YA). (gr. 10 up). pap. 5.00 incl. audio (978-0-939399-24-6(5)) Books of Truth.

—Gifts of the Holy Spirit: The Nine Power Gifts. 2000. (Illus.). 223p. (YA). (gr. 10 up). stu. ed., spiral bd. 42.25 (978-0-939399-52-9(0)) Books of Truth.

—Gifts of the Holy Spirit Pt. II: The Five-Fold Ministries. 2000. 162p. (YA). (gr. 10 up). stu. ed., spiral bd. 33.50 (978-0-939399-53-6(9)) Books of Truth.

—How to Be Led by God, 4 vols. 1999. (YA). (gr. 5 up). 20.00 incl. audio (978-0-939399-25-3(3)) Books of Truth.

Cunningham, Brian J. Lessons for the Trail of Life Conversations Starters for Parents & Children. 1999. 80p. (J). pap. 5.00 (978-1-55833-223-2(5)) National Catholic Educational Assn.

Custom Curricul Staff. Can I Really Have a Relationship with God? 2004. (Custom Curriculum Ser.). 256p. pap., pap. 19.99 (978-0-7814-4090-5(4) , 0781440904) Cook, David C. Publishing Co.

—Does God Love You No Matter What? 2004. (Custom Curriculum Ser.). 256p. pap., pap. 19.99 (978-0-7814-4085-1(8) , 0781440858) Cook, David C. Publishing Co.

—Does the Bible Have Any Answers? 2004. (Custom Curriculum Ser.). 256p. pap., pap. 19.99 (978-0-7814-4092-9(0) , 0781440920) Cook, David C. Publishing Co.

—What about Sex, Drugs, And... ? 2004. (Custom Curriculum Ser.). 256p. pap., pap. 19.99 (978-0-7814-4093-6(9) , 0781440939) Cook, David C. Publishing Co.

—What, Me Holy? 2004. (Custom Curriculum Ser.). 256p. pap., pap. 19.99 (978-0-7814-4091-2(2) , 0781440912) Cook, David C. Publishing Co.

—Would Jesus Really Do That? 2004. (Custom Curriculum Ser.). 256p. pap., pap. 19.99 (978-0-7814-4087-5(4) , 0781440874) Cook, David C. Publishing Co.

Custom Curriculum Staff. Can I Really Know Jesus? 2004. (Custom Curriculum Ser.). 256p. pap., pap. 19.99 (978-0-7814-4084-4(X) , 078144084X) Cook, David C. Publishing Co.

Daddy, Where Are You? 2005. (YA). per. 10.00 (978-0-9773356-0-2(7)) Divine Ministry of North Florida, Inc.

Dahlstrom, Kathryn. Hate Fighters. Date not set. (Good News Club Ser.). (J). (gr. 4-11). pap. 4.99 (978-1-55976-832-0(0)) CEF Pr.

Dall, Jeanette & Washington, Linda. God & Me! 2: Ages 10-12, 3 vols. 2004. (Illus.). 238p. (J). spiral bd. 12.99 (978-1-58411-056-9(2) , Legacy Pr.) Rainbow Pubs. & Legacy Pr.

Dall, Jeanette, et al. My Time with God Vol. 1: 150 Ways to Start Your Own Quiet Time. 2000. (Heritage Builders Ser.). 208p. (YA). (gr. 3-7). pap. 8.99 (978-1-56179-802-5(9)) Focus on the Family Publishing.

Dalmatian Press Staff. Joy/Orange. (Fruit of the Spirit Inspirational Ser.). (J). pap. (978-1-4037-0823-6(1)) Dalmatian Pr.

—Kindness/Grapes. (Fruit of the Spirit Inspirational Ser.). (J). pap. (978-1-4037-0824-3(X)) Dalmatian Pr.

—Love/Pear. (Fruit of the Spirit Inspirational Ser.). (J). pap. (978-1-4037-0825-0(8)) Dalmatian Pr.

—Thank You Jesus. 2004. pap. 49.00 (978-1-4037-0231-9(4)) Dalmatian Pr.

Dandridge, Michael E. The Divine Spark. 2002. 120p. 23.95 (978-0-9717868-8-2(7)) WordWright.biz, Inc.

Darcy-Berube, Francoise & Berube, John Paul. Growing up a Friend of Jesus: A Guide to Discipleship for Children. 2003. (Illus.). 128p. (978-2-89507-041-2(5)) Novalis Publishing.

—Growing up a Friend of Jesus: A Guide to Discipleship for Children. 2000. (Illus.). 128p. (J). (gr. 3-6). 17.95 (978-0-86716-401-5(8)) St. Anthony Messenger Pr. & Franciscan Communications.

Dateno, Maria Grace. My First Missal. Esquinaldo, Virginia, illus. 2006. 48p. (J). pap. 3.95 (978-0-8198-4842-0(5)) Pauline Bks. & Media.

David C. Cook. Families, the Environment, Sports & Competition. 2003. (Domain 456 Ser.). 128p. (J). (gr. 4-6). pap., pap. 15.99 (978-0-7814-5514-5(6) , 0781455146) Cook, David C. Publishing Co.

—God's Fruit. 2003. (My Jesus Pocket Bks.). (Illus.). 32p. (J). (gr. 5-3). pap., pap. 8.90 (978-1-55513-132-6(8) , 1555131328) Cook, David C. Publishing Co.

—Substance Abuse, Communicating with Others, Who Is Jesus? 2003. (Domain 456 Ser.). 128p. (J). (gr. 4-6). pap., pap. 15.99 (978-0-7814-5519-0(7) , 0781455197) Cook, David C. Publishing Co.

Davidson, Alice Joyce. God Loves Baby. Abel, Simone, illus. 2000. (Baby Blessings Ser.). 8p. (ps-k). 15.99 (978-0-7847-1187-3(9) , 04327) Standard Publishing.

—Jesus & the Children. 1999. 12p. 3.99 (978-0-310-97601-1(4)) Zondervan.

Davis, Mary J. My Answer Journal: What Kids Wonder about God & the Bible. 2004. (Journals Just for Kids Ser.). (Illus.). 136p. (J). (gr. 4-7). pap. 9.99 (978-1-885358-72-1(5) , Legacy Pr.) Rainbow Pubs. & Legacy Pr.

—My Prayer Journal: A Keepsake for Kids Who Love the Lord. 1998. (Journals Just for Kids Ser.). (Illus.). 144p. (J). (gr. 4-7). pap. 9.99 (978-1-885358-37-0(7) , LP46841, Legacy Pr.) Rainbow Pubs. & Legacy Pr.

A Day with Samuel. (Two Great Ways to Share God's Love Ser.). 16p. (ps-k). 15.00 (978-0-570-00313-7(X)) Concordia Publishing Hse.

Dayton, Howard & Dayton, Beverly. The Secret of Handling Money God's Way. 2003. (Leading Young Hearts & Minds to God Ser.). 144p. (J). pap. 13.99 (978-0-8024-3154-7(2)) Moody Pubs.

DC Talk Staff. Vive Como un Loco por Jesus. 2004. (SPA.). 9.99 (978-0-88419-901-4(0) , Casa Creacion) Strang Communications Co.

De Sturtz, Mari. God Is. 2004. (ENG & SPA.). 32p. 1.99 (978-0-7586-0292-3(8)) Concordia Publishing Hse.

de Vries, Dirk. Life Skills. 2000. (Attitude Ser.: Vol. 2). 136p. (YA). (gr. 7-12). pap. 14.95 (978-1-889108-43-8(X)) Living the Good News.

Deboy, James J., et al. Growing in Love 1: Called to Communion with God, Who Is Love, Level 1. 2002. (Growing in Love Ser.). (Illus.). 64p. (J). (ps-ps). pap., stu. ed., act. bk. ed. 3.95 (978-0-15-900559-0(0)) Harcourt Religion Pubs.

—Growing in Love 2: Incarnational, Level 2. 2002. (Growing in Love Ser.). (Illus.). 64p. (J). (ps-ps). pap., stu. ed. 3.95 (978-0-15-900565-1(5)) Harcourt Religion Pubs.

—Growing in Love Kindergarten: Created in God's Image, Level K. 2002. (Growing in Love Ser.). (Illus.). 64p. (J). (ps-ps). pap., stu. ed., act. bk. ed. 3.95 (978-0-15-900553-8(1)) Harcourt Religion Pubs.

DeBoy, Jim, et al, contrib. by. Growing in Love, Level 4. 2000. (Growing in Love Ser.). 48p. (J). pap., stu. ed. 7.25 (978-0-15-950666-0(2)) Harcourt Religion Pubs.

del Buono, Barbara. Come Holy Spirit: A Guide to Confirming Faith in the Roman Catholic Church. 2001. 156p. pap. 17.95 (978-0-9605698-3-0(9)) Ellingsworth Pr., LLC.

Delgatto, Laurie. Hey God, What Now? Biblical Assurance for Life's Questions. 2003. 158p. (YA). per. 9.95 (978-0-88489-793-4(1)) St. Mary's Pr.

Dent, Jenny. God Loves Us All. (Illus.). 32p. (J). (gr. k-9). 17.95 (978-0-85487-051-6(2)) White Eagle Publishing Trust GBR. *Dist:* DeVorss & Co.

Developing a Christian World View. 2002. (YA). stu. ed. 7.85 (978-1-931548-11-3(0)) InQuest Ministries, Inc.

DeVries, John. J Force to the Rescue: A Kids Musical Discovering the Ultimate Truth. 2004. 112p. 7.99 (978-0-8341-7405-4(7) , MB-935) Lillenas Publishing Co.

DeVries, Mike & Murphy, Troy. Exodus: The Sacred Journey. 2003. (No Limits Ser.). 112p. (YA). pap. 12.99 (978-0-8341-5005-8(0)) Beacon Hill Pr. of Kansas City.

Dicks, Ian & Watton, Nick, illus. God's Earth Forces. 1999. (Zoomers Ser.). 4p. (J). (gr. 3-7). 2.99 (978-0-7847-1123-1(2) , 03533, Bean Sprouts) Standard Publishing.

—God's Fantastic Frogs. 1999. (Zoomers Ser.). 4p. (J). (gr. 3-7). 2.99 (978-0-7847-1124-8(0) , 03534, Bean Sprouts) Standard Publishing.

—God's Solar System. 1999. (Zoomers Ser.). 4p. (J). (gr. 3-7). 2.99 (978-0-7847-1121-7(6) , 03531, Bean Sprouts) Standard Publishing.

Diedrich, Jeff. Talkin' Trash: Truth about the Tongue. 2000. (Hotshots Ser.: Vol. 8). 36p. (J). pap. 10.25 (978-1-929784-47-9(3)) Positive Action For Christ.

Dietrich, Julie. God Chose You. McCain, Kevin, illus. 2000. (ENG.). 32p. (J). (ps-1). 7.99 (978-0-570-07115-0(1)) Concordia Publishing Hse.

Dillon, Sally Pierson. Hugs from Jesus: 180 Devotions & Worship Activities for Preschoolers. 2001. (Illus.). (J). (978-0-8280-1567-7(8)) Review & Herald Publishing Assn.

DiMarco, Hayley. Mean Girls Gone: A Spiritual Guide to Getting Rid of Mean. 2005. (Illus.). 160p. (YA). (gr. 7-9). pap. 11.99 (978-0-8007-3056-7(9)) Revell.

DiMarco, Michael. The Man Manual: Mastering the Moves, Power-Ups, & Pitfalls to Becoming a Real Man. 2007. 192p. pap. 12.99 (978-0-8007-3150-2(6)) Revell.

Dingwall, Cindy. Bible Verse Fun with Kids: 300+ Ideas & Activities to Help Children Learn & Live Scripture. 2004. (Illus.). 192p. pap. 21.00 (978-0-687-04514-3(2)) Abingdon Pr.

Diocese of San Bernardino Staff. My Quinceanera Student Bk: Bilingual Formation Program & Remembrance Book. 120p. pap. 9.95 (978-0-8198-4850-5(6) , 332-228) Pauline Bks. & Media.

Dios me ama/libro para Colorear. 1998. Tr. of God Loves Me/Coloring book. pap. 1.69 (978-1-56063-992-3(X)) Editorial Unilit.

Disciple Helps: Spiritual Journal for Students. 2004. (J). (gr. 7-12). 2.25 (978-0-633-19381-2(X)) LifeWay Christian Resources.

Disciple III. stu. ed. 30.00 (978-0-687-76254-5(5)) Abingdon Pr.

Dobson, Danae. Let's Talk! Good Stuff for Girlfriends about God, Guys, & Growing Up. 2003. (gr. 7-12). lib. bdg. 22.25 (978-0-613-76820-7(5)) Tandem Library Bks.

—Let's Talk! Good Stuff for Girlfriends about God, Guys, & Growing Up. 2003. 208p. (YA). pap. 12.99 (978-0-8423-0818-2(0)) Tyndale Hse. Pubs.

Dockrey, Karen. MissionsQuest Devotional Book: Character Questions. 1998. (MissionsQuest Ser.). 113p. (J). (gr. 10). pap. 9.95 (978-1-56309-263-3(8) , W986123) Woman's Missionary Union.

Dodds, Bill. Ride of Your Life: A Catholic Road Trip for Teens. 2002. (gr. 7-12). lib. bdg. 17.60 (978-0-613-79052-9(9)) Tandem Library Bks.

Dominic, Sister M. Little Nellie of Holy God 1903-1908. Vianney, Sister John, illus. 2006. (J). 8.00 (978-0-89555-834-3(3) , 2120) TAN Bks. and Pubs., Inc.

Donahoe, Sydney. Christian Virtues Made Fun & Easy!, Grades 1 - 2. 1999. (Bible Lessons to Grow By Ser.). 64p. pap. 6.99 (978-1-56822-815-0(5) , In Celebration) Schaffer, Frank Pubns.

—Christian Virtues Made Fun & Easy!, Grades 3 - 4. 1999. (Bible Lessons to Grow By Ser.). 64p. pap. 6.99 (978-1-56822-816-7(3) , In Celebration) Schaffer, Frank Pubns.

Donahue, Laurie. God's Plan My Response. Rittenhouse, Ralph, ed. 2003. (Illus.). 100p. pap. 9.99 (978-0-9718306-0-8(6)) LifeSong Pubs.

Doney. El Gorrion Muy Preocupado.Tr. of Very Worried Sparrow. (SPA.). (J). (978-950-841-003-0(5)) Editorial Unilit.

Dorcy, Mary Jean. Hunters of Souls. 1999. (Illus.). 112p. (YA). (gr. 4 up). 18.00 (978-0-911845-87-7(9)) Neumann Pr., The.

Dorn, Patrick Rainville. Is Jesus Here? Van Fleet, Douglas, illus. 2002. 32p. (J). pap. 6.95 (978-0-8198-3685-4(0) , 332-138) Pauline Bks. & Media.

Dougherty, Chris. I Must Become Less: Making More Room in. 2006. 63p. pap. 12.95 (978-1-4241-3393-2(9)) PublishAmerica, Inc.

Doughten, Russell S., Jr., et al. Share Your Faith Seminar Workbook. 2000. (Illus.). 120p. (YA). (gr. 7). pap. 11.95 (978-1-888568-56-1(9)) Doughten, Russ Films, Inc.

Dowds, Mark. Exploring Christianity. 2003. (gr. 7-12). lib. bdg. 16.45 (978-0-613-89616-0(5)) Tandem Library Bks.

Dredge, Kath. Living 4 God. 2001. (Illus.). 72p. 3.99 (978-1-903087-28-2(7)) DayOne Pubns. GBR. *Dist:* Gabriel Resources.

Drivdahl, Cheryl Miller. We Are Fire! Resource Manual: Discipleship Activities & Prayer Experiences for Teens. Singer-Towns, Brian, ed. 2003. (Illus.). 32p. (YA). pap. 12.95 (978-0-88489-639-5(0)) St. Mary's Pr.

Duncan, George T., Jr. Walking with God, Intimately, As Your Father. 2004. (C). per. 10.95 (978-0-9752665-0-2(0)) Peace B Still Ministries Pr.

Dunlap, Irene. True Stories from the Real Lives of Real Teenagers. 2004. (gr. 7-12). lib. bdg. 22.25 (978-0-613-86014-7(4)) Tandem Library Bks.

Dunlap, Irene, ed. True Vol. 1: Real Stories about God Showing up in the Lives of Teens. 2004. (Invert Ser.). (Illus.). 352p. (YA). pap. 12.99 (978-0-310-25268-9(7)) Zondervan.

Dunn, Sean. Velocity: Moving to a Solid Faith. 2003. (gr. 7-12). lib. bdg. 17.60 (978-0-613-75305-0(4)) Tandem Library Bks.

Durback, Christina Bigatel. FAQs about Confirmation: What You Want to Know. Larkin, Jean, ed. Becker, Linda, illus. 2000. 16p. (YA). (gr. 7-12). pap. 3.95 (978-0-937997-80-2(3)) Pflaum Publishing Group.

Dyrud, Loiell O. & Furman, Leola Dyrud. Each for the Other, All for Christ: Missionaries to Madagascar Rev. Amos & Ovidie Dyrud. 2004. (Illus.). 320p. per. 15.00 net. (978-0-9759598-0-0(8)) Pony Rock Pr.

Eastman, Curtis. Extreme Talk Youth Devotional. 2004. pap. 9.99 (978-1-57794-590-1(5)) Harrison Hse., Inc.

Eckel, Mark. Timeless Truth: An Apologetic for the Reliability, Authenticity, & Authority of the Bible. 2000. (Enabling Educators Ser.). pap., stu. ed. 18.45 (978-1-58331-130-1(0) , 7065) Assn. of Christian Schls. International.

Editorial Portavoz Staff. Manual de Exploracion, Vol. 6. 2004. (Sabio Y Prudente Ser.).Tr. of Exploration Manual #6. (SPA.). 96p. (YA). (gr. 2-7). stu. ed. 3.99 (978-0-8254-0943-1(8) , Editorial Portavoz) Kregel Pubns.

Editorial Vida Staff. Ambassador-Student (Russian) Vol. 6, Bk. 2: Russian Sunday School. Life Publishers International Staff, tr. from SPA. 2000. Orig. Title: El Embajador. Alumno. (RUS.). 61p. (YA). stu. ed. (978-0-7361-0203-2(5)) Life Pubs. International.

Educational Publishing Concept Staff. Party Time, Critter County Activity Center: Children's CD-ROM. 1999. (Celebrate Jesus! 2000 50-Day Spiritual Adventure Ser.). (J). (ps-2). cd-rom 15.00 (978-1-57849-177-3(0)) Mainstay Church Resources.

Eller, T. Suzanne. Real Teens, Real Issues: What Every Parent Needs to Know. 2004. 288p. pap., pap. 14.99 (978-0-7814-4058-5(0) , 0781440580) Cook, David C. Publishing Co.

Elliot, Betsy Rosen. The One Year Book of Fun & Active Devotions for Kids. Crump, Lil, illus. 2000. 384p. (J). pap. 12.99 (978-0-8423-1976-8(X)) Tyndale Hse. Pubs.

Elliot, Elisabeth. Passion & Purity: Learning to Bring Your Love Life under Christ's Control. 2nd ed. 2002. 192p. (gr. 13 up). pap. 11.99 (978-0-8007-5818-9(8)) Revell.

—Taking Flight: Wisdom for Your Journey. 2001. (Illus.). 112p. (YA). (gr. 11-13). pap. 5.99 (978-0-8010-6357-2(4)) Baker Bks.

Elliott, Beverley & Witherow, Wendy. Violets Life Lessons: Growing Toward God. 2007. (Life of Faith Ser.). 168p. (YA). pap., stu. ed. 12.99 (978-1-928749-62-2(3)) Mission City Pr., Inc.

Elliott, Sharon Norris. What? Teenagers in the Bible? 2003. (gr. 7-12). lib. bdg. 22.25 (978-0-613-82117-9(3)) Tandem Library Bks.

Ellis, Gwen. The Christmas Flower. Hansen, Clint, illus. 2005. 32p. (J). 9.99 (978-1-59185-728-0(7)) Strang Communications Co.

Elmer, Robert & Strobel, Lee. Off My Case for Kids: 12 Stories to Help You Defend Your Faith. 2006. (Illus.). 96p. (J). pap. 7.99 (978-0-310-71199-5(1)) Zonderkidz.

Engelhardt, Lisa O. Right & Wrong & Being Strong: A Kid's Guide. Alley, R. W., illus. 2001. (Elf-Help Books for Kids). 32p. (J). per. 5.95 (978-0-87029-352-8(4)) Abbey Pr.

England, Don. God, Are You Really There? (YA). pap., stu. ed. 7.99 (978-0-89098-105-4(1)) Twentieth Century Christian Bks.

English Your Book of Hope: Early Elementary Edition. 2000. (Book of Life Ser.). 32p. (J). mass mkt. (978-1-890525-28-6(6)) Book of Hope International.

Esquinaldo, Virginia. Baby, Come to Church! Esquinaldo, Virginia, illus. 2005. (Illus.). (J). 5.95 (978-0-8198-1164-6(5) , 332-027) Pauline Bks. & Media.

Un Establo Prestado (A Borrowed Stable) (SPA.). (J). (978-0-7899-0873-5(5) , 496232) Editorial Unilit.

Ethridge, Shannon & Arterburn, Stephen. Every Young Woman's Battle: Guarding Your Mind, Heart, & Body in a Sex-Saturated World. 2004. (Illus.). 240p. pap. 13.99 (978-1-57856-856-7(0) , WaterBrook Pr.) WaterBrook Pr.

—Every Young Woman's Battle Workbook: How to Pursue Purity in a Sex-Saturated World. 2004. 112p. pap., wbk. ed. 7.99 (978-1-57856-855-0(2) , WaterBrook Pr.) WaterBrook Pr.

Evans, Joyce Ann. Frootbearer a Granny Goodness Day. 2006. (ENG.). 32p. per. 13.99 (***978-1-4259-7301-8(9)***) AuthorHouse.

Every Day of Advent, Cycle C: A Book of Activites for Children. 2003. (J). pap. 2.95 net. (978-0-7648-1081-7(2)) Liguori Pubns.

Every Day of Lent: A Book of Activities for Children, Cycle C. 2003. (J). pap. 3.95 net. (978-0-7648-1080-0(4)) Liguori Pubns.

Ewald, Thomas. The Fruit of the Spirit. 2003. 48p. (J). 5.99 (978-0-88724-138-3(7)); 5.99 (978-0-88724-139-0(5)); 5.99 (978-0-88724-140-6(9)) Carson-Dellosa Publishing Co., Inc.

Exploring God's Word: Grade 1 - Student Materials. (Voyages Ser.). 10.95 (978-0-570-00259-8(1) , 57-0111) Concordia Publishing Hse.

Exploring God's Word: Grade 2 - Student Materials. (Voyages Ser.). 10.95 (978-0-570-00264-2(8) , 57-0211) Concordia Publishing Hse.

Exploring God's Word: Grade 3 - Student Materials. (Voyages Ser.). (Illus.). 10.95 (978-0-570-00269-7(9) , 57-0311) Concordia Publishing Hse.

Farah, Gregg. Fruit of the Spirit. Powell, Kara Eckmann, ed. 2000. (Pulse Ser.: No. 11). 96p. (gr. 6-9). 14.99 (978-0-8307-2547-2(4) , Gospel Light) Gospel Light Pubns.

FBS 1st & 2Nd Graders Leader Pack. 2000. 16.00 (978-0-633-04563-0(2)) LifeWay Christian Resources.

FBS 1st & 2nd Graders Learner Guide. 2005. 1.70 (978-0-633-17764-5(4)); 2005. 1.70 (978-0-633-17566-5(8)); 2004. 1.70 (978-0-633-17372-2(X)); 2004. 1.70 (978-0-633-08316-8(X)); 2004. 1.70 (978-0-633-08064-8(0)); 2003. 1.65 (978-0-633-07691-7(0)) LifeWay Christian Resources.

Fearon, Sister Mary. Sacraments: Reproducible Activities. 1999. (God's Gift Ser.). (Illus.). 32p. (J). (gr. 4-8). 9.95 (978-1-893757-00-4(5) , 01) Needer, E.T. Publishing.

Fears, Melissa. Thank God It's Sunday. 2004. (J). per. 6.95 (978-0-89315-413-4(X)) Lambert Bk. Hse., Inc.

Feinberg, Margaret. Text Messages from God for Girls Only. 2007. (Instant Messages Ser.). 160p. (J). pap. 9.99 (978-1-59379-038-7(4)) White Stone Bks.

Feinberg, Margaret & Gillespie, Natalie. Text Messages from God for Guys Only. 2007. (Instant Messages Ser.). 160p. (J). pap. 9.99 (978-1-59379-039-4(2)) White Stone Bks.

Fengler, Fred & Varnum, Todd. Manifesting Your Heart's Desire, Bk. 2. 2002. 216p. per. 15.95 (978-0-9641305-3-1(X)) Heartlight.

Ferguson, Sinclair B. Big Book of Questions & Answers: A Family Guide to the Christian Faith. 2003. (gr. k-3). lib. bdg. 21.10 (978-0-613-80048-8(6)) Tandem Library Bks.

Ficocelli, Elizabeth. Child's Guide to First Holy Communion. Blake, Anne Catharine, illus. 2003. 32p. 9.95 (978-0-8091-6708-1(5) , 3708-5) Paulist Pr.

—Child's Guide to the Seven Sacraments. Blake, Anne Catharine, illus. 2005. 32p. (J). 9.95 (978-0-8091-6723-4(9) , 6723-9) Paulist Pr.

Fields, Doug & Eastman, Brett. Beginning in Jesus: 6 Small Group Sessions on the Life of Christ. 2005. (Experiencing Christ Together Student Edition Ser.). 176p. (J). pap. 7.99 (978-0-310-26644-0(0)) Zondervan.

—Connecting Your Heart to Others: 6 Small Group Sessions on Fellowship. 2003. (Life Together Ser.). 144p. pap., stu. ed. 7.99 (978-0-310-25334-1(9)) Zondervan.

—Growing to Be Like Jesus: 6 Small Group Sessions on Discipleship. 2003. (Life Together Ser.). 144p. pap., stu. ed. 7.99 (978-0-310-25335-8(7)) Zondervan.

—Serving Others in Love: 6 Small Group Sessions on Ministry. 2003. (Life Together Ser.). 144p. pap., stu. ed. 7.99 (978-0-310-25336-5(5)) Zondervan.

—Sharing Your Story & God's Story: 6 Small Group Sessions on Evangelism. 2003. (Life Together Ser.). 144p. pap., stu. ed. 7.99 (978-0-310-25337-2(3)) Zondervan.

—Starting to Go Where God Wants You to Be: 6 Small Group Lessons on Beginning Life Together. 2003. (Life Together Ser.). 144p. pap., stu. ed. 7.99 (978-0-310-25333-4(0)) Zondervan.

—Surrendering Your Life to Honor God: 6 Small Group Sessions on Worship. 2003. (Life Together Ser.). 144p. pap., stu. ed. 7.99 (978-0-310-25338-9(1)) Zondervan.

Fiesta! Fire-Up! Youth Leader Guide. 2006. 63p. (J). pap. 14.99 (978-0-7644-2960-6(4)) Group Publishing, Inc.

The Fighting Marriage. 2004. (Focus on the Family Marriage Ser.).Tr. of El Conflicto en el Matrimonio. 80p. 7.99 (978-0-8307-3149-7(0) , Gospel Light) Gospel Light Pubns.

Fillmore, Charles. Los Doce Poderes del Hombre. 4th ed. 1998. (Biblioteca Clasica de Unity Ser.).Tr. of Twelve Powers of Man. (SPA.). 234p. reprint ed. 14.95 (978-0-87159-223-1(1) , 270, Unity Bks. & Multimedia) Unity Schl. of Christianity.

Firm Foundations Child Edition. 2004. 49.95 (978-1-890040-02-4(9)); 5.95 (978-1-890040-03-1(7)) New Tribes Mission, Inc.

First Eucharist Certificate (Spanish) 2004. (SPA., Illus.). 1p. (J). pap. 9.95 (978-0-89837-243-4(7) , 972110) Pflaum Publishing Group.

Fischer, Carl. Celebrating the Liturgical Year: Special Seasons, Special Feasts. Larkin, Jean, ed. Lynch, Patricia, illus. 1999. (Active Learning for Catholic Kids Ser.). 28p. (J). pap. 7.95 (978-0-937997-50-5(1)) Pflaum Publishing Group.

—Days of Faith: Student Planner & Assignment Book/ Intermediate Teacher Supplement. 2005. (J). (978-1-933178-04-2(3)) Pflaum Publishing Group.

—Days of Faith Assignment Book & Student Planner. Homberg, Ansgar, illus. 2003. 108p. (J). spiral bd. 4.99 (978-0-89837-232-8(1) , 9804) Pflaum Publishing Group.

—Exploring the Sacraments: Celebrating with Jesus. Larkin, Jean, ed. Qvick, Larissa, illus. 1999. 28p. (J). (gr. 4-6). pap. 7.95 (978-0-937997-51-2(X)) Pflaum Publishing Group.

—First Eucharist Certificate. 2004. (Together in Jesus Ser.). (Illus.). (J). pap. 9.95 (978-0-937997-74-1(9) , 922110) Pflaum Publishing Group.

Fisher, Patrica A. I Want to Live. Fisher, Patrica A., ed. Fisher, Patrica A., illus. 2004. (Illus.). 200p. (YA). 14.99 (978-0-9677231-5-0(9)) ITSMEEE Industries.

FitzPatrick, Bill. The Catholic Action Principles: Creating Positive Conversations. 2004. 160p. pap. 20.00 (978-1-884864-21-6(X)) American Success Institute, Inc.

Flanagan, Anne. Come to Jesus: A Kids' Book for Eucharistic Adoration. Cleary, Janice, illus. 2006. (J). 4.50 (978-0-8198-1577-4(2)) Pauline Bks. & Media.

Flanagan, Anne J. Jesus Walks with Us: Activity Book. 85p. (J). (gr. 4). pap. 2.25 (978-0-8198-3928-2(0)) Pauline Bks. & Media.

Flanagan, Anne Joan. Miracles of Jesus: Coloring Book. Keating, Elizabeth A., illus. 2001. (J). 1.95 (978-0-8198-4812-3(3)) Pauline Bks. & Media.

Flinn, Frank. Encyclopedia of Catholicism. (Encyclopedia of World Religions Ser.). 704p. (gr. 9). pap. 21.95 (***978-0-8160-7335-1(X)*** , Checkmark Bks.) Facts On File, Inc.

Flynn, Dale, ed. Quiet Time One-Year Daliy Devotionals for Students in Grades 7-12 (Quiet Time Devotionals), 1. 2006. 240p. (YA). per. 15.99 (978-1-931235-51-8(1) , TQT) Word of Life Fellowship, Inc.

Flynn, Dale, et al. Won by One. rev. ed. 2002. (Teen Pressure Points Ser.). (Illus.). (YA). (gr. 7-12). pap. 8.95 (978-1-931235-38-9(4)) Word of Life Fellowship, Inc.

Flynn, Leslie B. 19 Gifts of the Spirit. rev. ed. 2003. 240p. reprint ed. pap., pap. 12.99 (978-1-56476-337-2(4) , 1564763374) Cook, David C. Publishing Co.

Fold 'n Tell, 3 vols. (Illus.). (gr. 1-4). Set 1. 6.00 (978-0-570-05527-3(X) , 54-1037); Set 2. 6.00 (978-0-570-05528-0(8) , 54-1038) Concordia Publishing Hse.

For Heaven's Sake: A Weekly Collection of Saintly Inspiration. 2004. (YA). 17.50 (978-0-9752874-0-8(0)) Lange-Patton, Lorraine.

Forrest, Donna B. 180 Days of Character. Madden, Elizabeth, illus. 1998. 180p. (J). (gr. k-12). pap. 8.95 (978-1-889636-10-8(X) , B002) Youthlight, Inc.

Francen, Mike. The Call of God. O'Hay, Rochelle, ed. 1999. (Illus.). 119p. (YA). (gr. 7). pap. 8.00 (978-1-888079-11-1(8) , FWO Bks.) Francen World Outreach.

—No One Ever Walks Alone. O'Hay, Rochelle, ed. 1999. (Illus.). 47p. (YA). (gr. 7). pap. 5.00 (978-1-888079-26-5(6) , FWO Bks.) Francen World Outreach.

Francis. More Saints of the Eucharist. 2006. (J). 2.50 (***978-0-9778570-1-2(8)***) MOS, Inc.

Frank, Schaffer. Fruit of the Spirit Lessons And. 2002. 64p. (C). pap. 7.99 (978-0-7424-0277-5(0)) School Specialty Publishing.

Franklin, Kirk. How Do Alligators Praise the Lord. Carrier, Jason, illus. 2005. 24p. (J). 11.99 (978-1-59185-209-4(9) , Charisma Kids) Strang Communications Co.

Freed, Shirley Ann & Moon, Louise. In Heaven I Will. Morelan, Bill, ed. Harrell, Rob, illus. l.t. ed. 2002. 16p. (J). (gr. 1-2). pap. 3.99 (978-1-58938-025-7(8)) Concerned Communications.

Freeman, Criswell. When Bad Things Happen. 2003. pap. 4.99 (978-1-4041-8458-9(9)) Nelson, Thomas Inc.

Freeman, Emily. When Hope Is Gone. 2004. (YA). audio compact disk 6.95 (978-1-887938-42-6(7)) Sound Concepts, Inc.

Freeman, Laurence. A Simple Way: The Path of Christian Meditation. 2004. 43p. (YA). pap. 9.95 (978-0-9725627-6-8(1)) Medio Media Publishing.

Friedrich, Eliza. Play Pray & Hooray. 2004. 128p. 10.99 (978-0-7586-0117-9(4)) Concordia Publishing Hse.

Friends: On the Road. ldr.'s ed. (Ministry to Adolescent's Program Ser.). (Illus.). 64p. (978-0-85910-802-7(3) , 23-0802) Australian Church Resources.

Friends of Jesus. Date not set. (Illus.). 16p. (J). 2.99 (978-1-871676-71-6(1)) Christian Focus Pubns. GBR. *Dist:* Riverside, Spring Arbor Distributors, Inc.

Frist Eucharist: Activities for Primary Grades. 2005. (Illus.). 32p. (J). 9.95 (978-1-933178-10-3(8) , 3450) Pflaum Publishing Group.

From Raindrops to Rainbows. 2004. (J). cd-rom 95.00 (978-0-9745631-1-4(0)) Kremer Pubns, Inc.

Frost, Marie. One!Two! & You. 2004. (Pencil Fun Bks.: Vol. 1). 16p. (J). (ps-k). pap., pap. 9.90 (978-1-55513-977-3(9) , 1555139779) Cook, David C. Publishing Co.

Fruitful Lives Kids' Sermons & Object Talks. 112p. 16.99 (978-0-8307-2858-9(9) , Gospel Light) Gospel Light Pubns.

Funkhouser, Sandi. The DoorKeeper: In the King's Presence. 2005. (YA). per. 9.95 (978-0-9771204-0-6(6)) Three Sisters Communication, LLC.

Fushek, Dale & Dodds, Bill. The Ride of Your Life: A Catholic Road Trip. 2002. 136p. pap. 8.99 (978-1-56955-317-6(3) , Servant Bks.) St. Anthony Messenger Pr. & Franciscan Communications.

G-Force. (J). (gr. 1-6). 2004. DVD, cd-rom 29.95 (978-0-633-09412-6(9)); 2004. DVD, cd-rom 29.95 (978-0-633-09499-7(4)); 2003. DVD, cd-rom 29.95 (978-0-633-09406-5(4)); 2003. DVD, cd-rom 29.95 (978-0-633-09935-0(X)) LifeWay Christian Resources.

G-Force Family. (J). (gr. 1-6). 2004. cd-rom 9.95 (978-0-633-09409-6(9)); 2004. cd-rom 9.95 (978-0-633-09411-9(0)); 2003. cd-rom 9.95 (978-0-633-09410-2(2)); 2003. cd-rom 9.95 (978-0-633-09125-5(1)) LifeWay Christian Resources.

G-Force Powercel Cards for Older Children. (J). (gr. 4-6). 2004. 10.95 (978-0-633-09438-6(2)); 2004. 10.95 (978-0-633-09433-1(1)); 2003. 10.95 (978-0-633-09437-9(4)); 2003. 10.95 (978-0-633-09122-4(7)) LifeWay Christian Resources.

G-Force Powercel Cards for Younger Children. (J). (gr. 1-3). 2004. 10.95 (978-0-633-09434-8(X)); 2004. 10.95 (978-0-633-09432-4(3)); 2003. 10.95 (978-0-633-09436-2(6)); 2003. 10.95 (978-0-633-09124-8(3)) LifeWay Christian Resources.

G-Force Visual Pack. (J). (gr. 1-6). 2004. 29.95 (978-0-633-09408-9(0)); 2004. 29.95 (978-0-633-09407-2(2)); 2003. 29.95 (978-0-633-09405-8(6)); 2003. 29.95 (978-0-633-09123-1(5)) LifeWay Christian Resources.

Gaither, Gloria. I Am a Promise: I Can Be Anything God Wants Me to Be. Stephenson, Kristina, illus. 2002. 40p. (J). 14.99 (978-0-310-70075-3(2)) Zonderkidz.

Gallery, Philip D. Can You Find Followers of Jesus? Introducing Your Child to Disciples. Harlow, Janet L., illus. 2000. (Search & Learn Bks.). 40p. (J). (gr. k-5). 15.95 (978-0-86716-388-9(7)) St. Anthony Messenger Pr. & Franciscan Communications.

—Can You Find Saints? Introducing Your Child to Holy Men & Women. Harlow, Janet L., tr. Harlow, Janet L., illus. 2003. (J). 41p. (gr. 2-4). 16.95 (978-0-86716-487-9(5)); 40p. (978-2-89507-437-3(2)) St. Anthony Messenger Pr. & Franciscan Communications.

Ganeri, Anita. Christian Festivals Through the Year. 2003. (Year of Festivals Ser.). 30p. (J). lib. bdg. 24.25 (978-1-58340-370-9(1)) Smart Apple Media.

Gangwer, Rosalie M. & Heffernan, Mary A., texts. Jesus Loves Us. 143p. (gr. 1). pap. 6.50 (978-0-8198-3918-3(3)) Pauline Bks. & Media.

Garland, Ric. Forgiveness Mini Series. Slonim, David, illus. 2001. (Teen Pressure Points Ser.). (YA). (gr. 7-12). pap. 8.95 (978-1-931235-14-3(7)) Word of Life Fellowship, Inc.

Gebauer, Roland. Lass. Bladholm, Cheri, illus. 2004. 32p. 12.99 (978-0-8254-2694-0(4)) Kregel Pubns.

Geisler, Norman L. & Holden, Joseph. Living Loud: Defending Your Faith. 2004. (TruthQuest Ser.). (Illus.). 176p. (gr. 7-12). pap. 9.99 (978-0-8054-2482-9(2)) B&H Publishing Grp.

Geisler, Ruth. It's a Great, Awful, In-Between Day: Devotions for Young Readers. 2003. (Illus.). 112p. (J). (gr. 1-4). 9.99 (978-0-7586-0124-7(7)) Concordia Publishing Hse.

George, Elizabeth. God's Wisdom for Little Girls: Virtues & Fun from Proverbs 31. 2000. (Illus.). 48p. (J). (ps-3). 15.99 (978-0-7369-0427-8(1)) Harvest Hse. Pubs.

—Una Joven Conforme al Corazon de Dios. 2003. pap. 8.99 (978-0-7899-1139-1(6)) Editorial Unilit.

—A Young Woman after God's Own Heart. 2003. (gr. 7-12). lib. bdg. 17.60 (978-0-613-73734-0(2)) Tandem Library Bks.

—A Young Woman after God's Own Heart: A Teen's Guide to Friends, Faith, Family, & the Future. 2003. 224p. (YA). pap. 9.99 (978-0-7369-0789-7(0) , 6907890) Harvest Hse. Pubs.

George, Jim & George, Elizabeth. God's Wisdom for Little Boys: Character-Building Fun from Proverbs. 2002. (Illus.). 48p. 15.99 (978-0-7369-0824-5(2)) Harvest Hse. Pubs.

Gerali, Steve. How to Stay Christian in High School. 2004. 128p. pap. 11.99 (978-1-57683-424-4(7)) NavPress Publishing Group.

Gerlitz, Menachem. Return to the Heavenly City. 91p. (YA). pap. 5.95 (978-1-56062-085-3(4)) CIS Communications, Inc.

Gibbons, Casey Hartley. A Girl's Life with God. 2006. 160p. pap. 8.99 (978-1-56309-757-7(5) , N034115) New Hope Pubs.

Gibbons, Joyce. What God Has Made! 2004. 35p. pap. 17.95 (978-1-4137-3566-6(5)) PublishAmerica, Inc.

Gibson, Cay. Catholic Mosaic: Living the Liturgical Year with Literature, an Illustrated Book Study for Children. Decaen, Rose, ed. 2006. (J). spiral bd. 38.95 (978-0-9766386-6-7(5)) Hillside Education.

Gibson, D. Doug. Good As New - Leaders Guide: A Child's Guide to Becoming A Christian. 2000. 46p. (J). pap. 9.99 (978-0-89900-832-5(1)) College Pr. Publishing Co., Inc.

—Good As New - Student Workbook: A Child's Guide to Becoming A Christian. 2000. (Illus.). 32p. (J). pap. 7.99 (978-0-89900-835-6(6)) College Pr. Publishing Co., Inc.

Gibson, Timmy J. It's Cool to Be a Christian. 2001. 50p. (YA). 2.49 (978-0-9715018-0-5(7)) Cool Pubs.

Gieser, Sherry. Opening Gifts: Marriage & Holy Orders. 2003. 32p. (J). per. (978-1-931709-73-6(4)) Our Sunday Visitor, Publishing Div.

Giles, Doug. Do You Have a Pit Bull Attitude? Phillips, Penny, ed. 1998. (Illus.). 111p. pap. 9.95 (978-0-9667501-0-2(1)) Clash Ministries.

—Do You Have a Pit Bull Attitude? unabr. ed. 2001. (YA). 14.95 incl. audio compact disk (978-0-9667501-2-6(8)) Clash Ministries.

—Ruling in Babylon: Effective Christian Influence in Godless Environments. unabr. ed. 2001. (YA). 19.95 incl. audio compact disk (978-0-9667501-3-3(6)) Clash Ministries.

Giombi, Gary. Finding God Through Prayer: A Backpack Journal for Teens. Cannizzo, Karen A., ed. 2004. 48p. (YA). 6.95 (978-0-89837-196-3(1) , 3524) Pflaum Publishing Group.

The Giving Marriage. 2004. (Focus on the Family Marriage Ser.).Tr. of La Abnegacion en el Matrimonio. 80p. 7.99 (978-0-8307-3151-0(2) , Gospel Light) Gospel Light Pubns.

Gledhill, Steve. Summer Sizzler: Paul. Reichard, Don, ed. 2002. (YA). (gr. 8-12). pap. 8.95 (978-1-931235-48-8(1)) Word of Life Fellowship, Inc.

God & Me, 2 vols., Vol. 2. 2001. (J). per. 10.99 (978-1-57782-151-9(3)) Discipleship Pubns. International.

God in My Life. 2004. (Faith 4 Life Ser.). 48p. 14.99 (978-0-7644-2471-7(8) , Flagship Church Resources) Group Publishing, Inc.

God Rules, 2 vols., Vol. 2. 2001. (J). per. 11.00 (978-1-57782-158-8(0)) Discipleship Pubns. International.

God's Girls: Groovy Coloring Book with Crayons. 2003. (Groovy Coloring Bks.). (Illus.). 32p. (J). 3.99 (978-1-57759-887-9(3)) Dalmatian Pr.

God's Good Plan for Joseph. (Two Great Ways to Share God's Love Ser.). 16p. (ps-k). 15.00 (978-0-570-00255-0(9)) Concordia Publishing Hse.

God's People Celebrate Kids Time Kit. 2004. (KidsTime Ser.). (Illus.). (gr. 1-6). 139.99 (978-0-8307-2541-0(5) , Gospel Light) Gospel Light Pubns.

God's Promise to Every Boy & Girl. 2003. (J). 4.95 (978-0-9745324-1-7(X)) Kingdom Publishing Group, Inc.

God's Purpose for Me. 2004. (Faith 4 Life Ser.). 48p. 14.99 (978-0-7644-2497-7(1) , Flagship Church Resources) Group Publishing, Inc.

God's Ten Commandments. (Two Great Ways to Share God's Love Ser.). 16p. (ps-k). 15.00 (978-0-570-00257-4(5)) Concordia Publishing Hse.

God's Word on Giving. (YA). (978-0-7673-9388-1(0)) LifeWay Christian Resources.

Going Through Tough Times. 2004. (Faith 4 Life Ser.). 48p. 14.99 (978-0-7644-2469-4(6) , Flagship Church Resources) Group Publishing, Inc.

Goode, Rosemary. Always His Choice. 2001. 228p. (YA). pap. 14.95 (978-0-595-19921-1(6)) iUniverse, Inc.

Gorler, Rosemarie & Piscitelli, Donna. Just Like Mary. Sternhagen, Mimi, illus. 2003. 48p. (J). 5.95 (978-1-931709-79-8(3)) Our Sunday Visitor, Publishing Div.

Gorrell, Nancy. Beginning with God: A Family Guide to the Christian Faith. 1999. (I Can Know God Ser.: Vol. 1). (Illus.). 40p. (J). (ps-3). (978-1-85792-453-4(3) , Christian Focus) Christian Focus Pubns.

—Living with God. (I Can Know God Ser.). (Illus.). 72p. (J). 10.99 (978-1-85792-532-6(7) , Christian Focus) Christian Focus Pubns. GBR. *Dist:* Riverside.

—Meeting with God. (I Can Know God Ser.). 54p. (J). 10.99 (978-1-85792-531-9(9) , Christian Focus) Christian Focus Pubns. GBR. *Dist:* Riverside.

Gospel Light: Student Activity Pages. 2001. (Movers & Shakers Ser.). (J). (ps-k). stu. ed. (978-0-8307-2262-4(9)); Set. (gr. 1-3). stu. ed. (978-0-8307-2264-8(5)); Set. (ps). (978-0-8307-2258-7(0)) Gospel Light Pubns.

Gospel Light: Student Guide. 2001. (Network 34 Ser.). (J). (gr. 3-4). stu. ed. (978-0-8307-2104-7(5)); (gr. 5-7). (978-0-8307-2274-7(2)) Gospel Light Pubns.

Gospel Light Publications Staff. Whole-Life Stewardship for Kids. 2000. (Illus.). (J). 20.00 (978-0-8307-2506-9(7)) Gospel Light Pubns.

Gospel Light Staff. Kidventures! Take-Home Papers. 2001. (Kids on the Rock Ser.). (J). (gr. 1-3). pap. 3.00 (978-0-8307-2296-9(3)); Set. (978-0-8307-2265-5(3)) Gospel Light Pubns.

—Love, My Future, Sharing My Faith: Student Guide. 2001. (Planet 56 Ser.). (J). (gr. 5-7). pap. 3.00 (978-0-8307-2305-8(6)) Gospel Light Pubns.

Gothmann, Bill. Discovering Christ's Church: From the Bible & Those Taught by the Apostles. 2002. pap. 8.95 (978-0-9717919-0-9(2)) Poimen Pr.

GP4U: God's Plan for You. (J). 16.00 (978-0-8307-2406-2(0)) Gospel Light Pubns.

Grades 1-2 Activity Fall 2002. 2002. pap. 3.29 (978-1-59185-020-5(7)) CharismaLife Pubs.

Grades 1-2 Activity Winter 2002-03. 2002. pap. 3.29 (978-1-59185-107-3(6)) CharismaLife Pubs.

Grades 1-2 Resource Fall 2002. 2002. pap. 12.99 (978-1-59185-021-2(5)) CharismaLife Pubs.

Grades 1-2 Resource Winter 2002. 2002. pap. 12.99 (978-1-59185-108-0(4)) CharismaLife Pubs.

Grades 5-6 Activity Winter 2002-03. 2002. pap. 3.29 (978-1-59185-098-4(3)) CharismaLife Pubs.

Grades 5-6 Resource Winter 2002-03. 2002. pap. 12.99 (978-1-59185-099-1(1)) CharismaLife Pubs.

Great Big Books. ldr.'s ed. (978-0-687-05326-1(9)) Abingdon Pr.

Great Expectations: Death & Resurrection, HIV & AIDS. 2000. (Connect Ser.: Vol. 7). (YA). 20.00 (978-0-687-72148-1(2)) Abingdon Pr.

Greenwood, Lori. The Genesis Generation: Discover the Power of Unity Between the Sexes — in the Church & in the Home. 2001. 112p. (YA). per. 6.95 (978-0-9747956-0-7(7)) Greenwood, Lori Ministries, Inc.

—The Vision Link: 60 Keys to Fulfilling Your Future. 2003. (YA). 6.95 (978-0-9747956-1-4(5)) Greenwood, Lori Ministries, Inc.

Grimbol, William R. Jesus in Your Backpack: A Teen's Guide to Spiritual Wisdom Without Religious Judgment. 2007. 256p. pap. 14.95 (978-1-56975-608-9(2)) Ulysses Pr.

Group Publishing Staff. 5-Minute Devotions for Youth Ministry. 2002. (gr. 7-12). lib. bdg. 25.75 (978-0-613-74873-5(5)) Tandem Library Bks.

Growing As God's Child Booklet. 2004. 5.99 (978-0-8307-2342-3(0) , Gospel Light) Gospel Light Pubns.

Growing in Love. 2000. (Growing in Love Ser.). (J). Level 3. 48p. pap., stu. ed. 7.25 (978-0-15-950657-8(3)); Level 5. 64p. pap., stu. ed. 7.75 (978-0-15-950667-7(0)) Harcourt Religion Pubs.

Growing in Love: Bilingual. 2000. (Growing in Love Ser.). 64p. (J). Level 1. pap., stu. ed., act. bk. ed. 3.95 (978-0-15-900470-8(5)); Level 2 pap., stu. ed. 3.95 (978-0-15-900476-0(4)); Level K. pap., act. bk. ed. 3.95 (978-0-15-900464-7(0)) Harcourt Religion Pubs.

Growing in Love: Student Text, Level 6. 2000. (Growing in Love Ser.). 64p. (J). pap. 7.75 (978-0-15-950668-4(9)) Harcourt Religion Pubs.

Growing up in Christ: 52 Bible Lessons from the New Testament. 2006. 320p. (YA). (gr. 3-7). 29.99 (978-0-7847-1182-8(8) , 42080) Standard Publishing.

Gustafon, Karen. Mongolia Cries Out for Prayer: Will You Be the One to Answer the Cry? 2004. 32p. (J). bds. 15.95 (978-1-59298-080-2(5)) Beaver's Pond Pr., Inc.

Gustafson, Janie. Advent ABCs: Reproducible Activities. 1999. (God's Gift Ser.). (Illus.). 32p. (J). (gr. k-3). pap. 9.95 (978-1-893757-02-8(1) , 04) Needer, E.T. Publishing.

Haapala, Christine. Speak, Lord, I am Listening. Muller, Gus, illus. 2001. 48p. (J). (ps-7). pap. 8.00 (978-0-9703996-2-5(6)) Suffering Servant Scriptorium.

—Speak Lord I am Listening: A Rosary Book. Maller, Gus, illus. 2nd rev. ed. 2001. 64p. (J). (gr. k-6). pap. 12.00 (978-0-9703996-7-0(7) , 888-652-9494) Suffering Servant Scriptorium.

Hagerman, Nancy. Guess Who's Special. 2005. (ENG.). 36p. per. 15.99 (978-1-4141-0435-5(9)) Pleasant Word.

Hahn, Jennifer, compiled by. The Bible Promise Book for Teens. 2003. (Inspirational Library). 256p. (gr. 8-13). pap. 4.99 (978-1-58660-716-6(2)) Barbour Publishing, Inc.

Haidle, Helen. Comfort for a Child's Heart. 2001. 90p. 9.99 (978-0-310-70126-2(0)) Zondervan.

—Comfort for a Child's Heart: The 23rd Psalm & Bible Promises. Haidle, David, illus. 1999. 96p. (ps-1). 9.99 (978-1-57673-569-5(9) , Multnomah) WaterBrook Pr.

Hakes, Matthew. What Catholic Teens Should Know about Ecstacy. Larkin, Jean, ed. 2003. (What Catholic Teens Should Know Ser.). (Illus.). 8p. (YA). 7.95 (978-0-89837-188-8(0) , 440110) Pflaum Publishing Group.

—What Catholic Teens Should Know about Going to War. Larkin, Jean, ed. 2003. (What Catholic Teens Should Know Ser.). (Illus.). 8p. (YA). 7.95 (978-0-89837-190-1(2) , 440310) Pflaum Publishing Group.

—What Catholic Teens Should Know about What Muslims Believe. Larkin, Jean K., ed. 2004. (What Catholic Teens Should Know Ser.). (Illus.). 8p. (YA). 7.95 (978-0-89837-241-0(0) , 440810) Pflaum Publishing Group.

—What Catholic Teens Should Know When Scandal Hits the Church. Larkin, Jean, ed. 2003. (What Catholic Teens Should Know Ser.). (Illus.). 8p. (YA). 7.95 (978-0-89837-192-5(9) , 440510) Pflaum Publishing Group.

Hale, Mabel. Beautiful Girlhood: A Timeless Guide for Christian Adolescense. 2001. (gr. 7-12). lib. bdg. 12.95 (978-0-613-79648-4(9)) Tandem Library Bks.

Hale, Mable. Beautiful Girlhood. 2001. (Inspirational Library). 224p. pap. 4.99 (978-1-58660-260-4(8)) Barbour Publishing, Inc.

Hall-Smith, Rachel. Tlk 2 Me. (Illus.). 32p. (J). pap. 1.50 (978-1-85792-822-8(9) , Christian Focus) Christian Focus Pubns. GBR. *Dist:* Riverside.

Hamby, Joe & Kluever, Karen Trogdon. Gear for the Road. 2003. 48p. pap., stu. ed. 6.50 (978-0-687-02618-0(0)); 80p. pap. 12.00 (978-0-687-02598-5(2)) Abingdon Pr.

Hamilton, Bethany. Ask Bethany: FAQ's: Surfing, Faith & Friends. 2007. (Soul Surfe Ser.). (Illus.). 192p. (J). pap. 9.99 (978-0-310-71227-5(0)) Zonderkidz.

Hamilton, Dennis Stephen. Higher Ground. 2004. per. 12.95 (978-0-9653904-6-0(2)) DCTS Publishing.

—We Shall Come Rejoicing: Improving Your Service. 2001. 120p. (YA). per. 8.95 (978-0-9653904-3-9(8)) DCTS Publishing.

Hamilton, Kersten. Laylie's Daring Quest. 2005. (Life of Faith Ser.). 224p. (YA). 12.99 (978-1-928749-35-6(6)) Zonderkidz.

Hamrick, Frank. Bread: For Hungry Christians. 2000. (Christian Growth Ser.: Vol. 3). 56p. (J). pap. 3.85 (978-1-929784-41-7(4)) Positive Action For Christ.

—Mighty Through God. 2002. (YA). stu. ed. (978-1-929784-97-4(X)) Positive Action For Christ.

Hamrick, Frank & Dean, Jerry. Meat: For Growing Christians. 2000. (Christian Growth Ser.: Vol. 2). 56p. (J). pap. 3.85 (978-1-929784-23-3(6)) Positive Action For Christ.

—Milk: For New Christians. 2000. (Christian Growth Ser.: Vol. 1). 48p. (J). pap. 3.85 (978-1-929784-48-6(1)) Positive Action For Christ.

Handford, Elizabeth Rice. Those Kids in Proverbsville. 2000. 93p. (J). (gr. 4-7). pap. 3.95 (978-0-87398-823-0(X)) Sword of the Lord Pubs.

Hanna, Robert C. The Dickens Family Gospel: A Family Devotional Guide Based on the Christian Teachings of Charles Dickens. 1998. (Illus.). 152p. (J). pap. 14.99 (978-1-885358-36-3(9) , DB46721, Legacy Pr.) Rainbow Pubs. & Legacy Pr.

Harder Tangvald, Christine. I Can Pray. Stewart, Jennifer, ed. Garris, Norma, illus. 1999. (Patty Cake Devotions Ser.). 14p. (J). (ps). bds. 3.99 (978-0-7847-0979-5(3) , 04293, Bean Sprouts) Standard Publishing.

—Jesus' Little Lamb. Stewart, Jennifer, ed. Garris, Norma, illus. 1999. (Patty Cake Devotions Ser.). 14p. (J). (ps). bds. 3.99 (978-0-7847-0978-8(5) , 04292, Bean Sprouts) Standard Publishing.

Hardwick, John. We're Going on a Jungle Jamboree! A Five-Day Holiday Club Plan, Complete & Ready-to-Run. 2005. (Illus.). 64p. (J). pap. (978-1-84101-253-7(X) , Barnabas) Bible Reading Fellowship.

Hare, Eric B. Clever Queen. 2001. 96p. reprint ed. pap. 11.95 (978-1-57258-211-8(1)) TEACH Services, Inc.

Harper, Vicky. Selah, Vol. 1. 2003. pap. 10.00 (978-0-9746997-0-7(5)) Little Bookstore Who Could, The.

Harrast, Tracy. Adivina Que: Historias de la Biblia. Sharp, Alice & Sharp, Paul, illus. 2005. 192p. (J). (ps-k). 10.99 (978-0-8297-4448-4(7)) Vida Pubs.

Harris, Janice L. & Lisech, Howard. Discovering Christlike Habits: CHRISTIAN SCHOOL Edition: Student Workbook - Snyder, Barb, ed. 2006. (Illus.). 252p. spiral bd. 19.95 (978-1-930547-60-5(9)) Deeper Roots Pubns. & Media.

Harris, Janice L., et al. Discovering Christ-Like Habits: HOME SCHOOL Edition: Student Workbook - Snyder, Barb, ed. 2006. (Illus.). 250p. spiral bd. 19.95 (978-1-930547-53-7(6)) Deeper Roots Pubns. & Media.

Harris, Lisa, illus. VBS-Fiesta-Cuaderno Biblico Elemental (Group's Fiesta! Where Kids Are Fired Up about Jesus) 2006. 11p. (J). pap. 0.99 (978-0-7644-3199-9(4)) Group Publishing, Inc.

Hartman, Jack & Hartman, Judy. Exchange Your Worries for God's Perfect Peace. 2003. 436p. per. 12.00 (978-0-915445-09-7(3) , Lamplight Ministries, Inc.) Lamplight Pubns.

Harvey, Edwin, et al. Asking Father. 2001. (RUM & RUS., Illus.). 120p. (J). 6.00 (978-1-932774-16-0(5)) Christian, Harvey Pubs. Inc.

Haskins, Amanda. God Is My Daddy. l.t. ed. 2006. (Illus.). 26p. (J). per. 11.99 (***978-1-59879-279-9(2)***) Lifevest Publishing, Inc.

Hatfield, Ron. Love Notes from God. Boehm, Annette, ed. 2004. (YA). 7.95 (978-0-9754117-0-4(5)) Butterfly Bk. Makers.

Hatfield, Tyrel S. & Hatfield, Justin R. Fix your eyes on Jesus. Hatfield, Tyrel S., illus. 2005. (Illus.). 108p. (J). spiral bd. 150.00 (978-0-9766703-0-8(5)) Little Acorn LLC.

Hathaway, Jeff. Masterpiece. 2007. (J). per. 7.99 (***978-1-59886-929-3(9)***) Tate Publishing & Enterprises, L.L.C.

Hawkins, Chad S. Youth & the Temple. 2002. (Illus.). vii, 136p. (J). pap. 12.95 (978-1-57008-846-9(2)) Scribbulations LLC.

Head, Heno, Jr. God Made Our Bodies. Ring, Laura, ed. Fletcher, Rusty, illus. 1999. (Happy Day Bks.). 24p. (J). (ps-2). 2.49 (978-0-7847-1084-5(8) , 04280, Bean Sprouts) Standard Publishing.

Heffernan, Eileen. Fifty-Seven Stories of Saints. Rizzo, Jerry, illus. 2003. (J). 552p. pap. 16.95 (978-0-8198-2674-9(X) , 332-094); 549p. (978-0-8198-2675-6(8)) Pauline Bks. & Media.

Helms, Selah & Thompson, Susan. Small Talks on Big Questions Vol. 2: A Historical Companion to the Children's Catechism, 2 vols. Whitney, Caffy, illus. 2003. 192p. 26.99 (978-1-894400-05-3(4)) Joshua Pr., Inc. CAN. *Dist:* Gabriel Resources.

Henderson, Susan & White, Emily. Raising the Roof: Destination Reality. 2003. (YA). pap. 14.99 (978-0-89265-967-8(X)) Randall Hse. Pubns.

Henkel, Vernon & Tweed, Sean, illus. God Is Omniscient Vol. 28: Old Testament. 2003. 30p. (J). pap. (978-1-932381-01-6(5) , 2028) Bible Visuals International, Inc.

Henley, Karyn. God Is with Me All the Time. (Children's Ministry Folders). (Illus.). 8p. (ps-k). 2.99 (978-0-7847-0680-0(8) , 42230) Standard Publishing.

—Hablame de Dios. Erickson, David L., illus. 2005. 20p. (J). (gr. 4-7). 8.99 (978-1-59185-825-6(9) , Charisma Kids) Strang Communications Co.

—I am Kind to My Friends. (Children's Ministry Folders). (Illus.). 8p. (ps-k). 2.99 (978-0-7847-0679-4(4) , 42229) Standard Publishing.

—I Give. (Children's Ministry Folders). (Illus.). 8p. (ps-k). 2.99 (978-0-7847-0675-6(1) , 42225) Standard Publishing.

—I Grow. (Children's Ministry Folders). (Illus.). 8p. (ps-k). 2.99 (978-0-7847-0662-6(X) , 42212) Standard Publishing.

—I Help. (Children's Ministry Folders). (Illus.). 8p. (ps-k). 2.99 (978-0-7847-0666-4(2) , 42216) Standard Publishing.

—I Listen. (Children's Ministry Folders). (Illus.). 8p. (ps-k). 2.99 (978-0-7847-0673-2(5) , 42223) Standard Publishing.

—I Obey My Parents. (Children's Ministry Folders). (Illus.). 8p. (ps-k). 2.99 (978-0-7847-0664-0(6) , 42214) Standard Publishing.

—I Praise God. (Children's Ministry Folders). (Illus.). 8p. (ps-k). 2.99 (978-0-7847-0661-9(1) , 42211) Standard Publishing.

—I Pray. (Children's Ministry Folders). (Illus.). 8p. (ps-k). 2.99 (978-0-7847-0660-2(3) , 42210) Standard Publishing.

—I Say Thank-You. (Children's Ministry Folders). (Illus.). 8p. (ps-k). 2.99 (978-0-7847-0674-9(3) , 42224) Standard Publishing.

—I Share. (Children's Ministry Folders). (Illus.). 8p. (ps-k). 2.99 (978-0-7847-0665-7(4) , 42215) Standard Publishing.

—I Take Care of My Body. (Children's Ministry Folders). (Illus.). 8p. (ps-k). 2.99 (978-0-7847-0663-3(8) , 42213) Standard Publishing.

—I Take Care of My Pets. (Children's Ministry Folders). (Illus.). 8p. (ps-k). 2.99 (978-0-7847-0676-3(X) , 42226) Standard Publishing.

—I Take Care of My Room. (Children's Ministry Folders). (Illus.). 8p. (ps-k). 2.99 (978-0-7847-0678-7(6) , 42228) Standard Publishing.

—I Take Care of the Earth. (Children's Ministry Folders). (Illus.). 8p. (ps-k). 2.99 (978-0-7847-0677-0(8) , 42227) Standard Publishing.

—I Trust God at Night. (Children's Ministry Folders). (Illus.). 8p. (ps-k). 2.99 (978-0-7847-0667-1(0) , 42217) Standard Publishing.

—I Trust God When It Rains. (Children's Ministry Folders). (Illus.). 8p. (ps-k). 2.99 (978-0-7847-0668-8(9)) Standard Publishing.

—Making Peace: The Foundation for Living in Fellowship. Koehler, Ed, illus. 2002. (Foundations Curriculum). 96p. (J). (gr. 3-6). 12.99 (978-0-7847-1369-3(3) , 42070) Standard Publishing.

—Salvation: The Foundation for Living with God. Eichenberger, Jim, ed. Koehler, Ed, illus. 2000. (Foundations Curriculum). 96p. (YA). (gr. 3-6). 12.99 (978-0-7847-1215-3(8) , 42064) Standard Publishing.

—Stewardship: The Foundation for Reflecting God. Koehler, Ed, illus. 2002. (Foundations Curriculum). 96p. (J). (gr. 3-6). 12.99 (978-0-7847-1368-6(5) , 42069) Standard Publishing.

—Tell Me about God. Erickson, David, illus. 2005. 24p. (J). 9.99 (978-1-59185-616-0(7) , Charisma Kids) Strang Communications Co.

Henley, Karyn F. Love Trumps Karma: Uncovering the Truth You Know You Know. 2005. 152p. (YA). per. 12.99 (978-0-9743197-8-0(3) , Karyn Henley Resources) Child Sensitive Communication, LLC.

Heroes for Today. 2006. 16p. (J). pap. 1.99 (978-0-7847-1587-1(4) , 22134) Standard Publishing.

Hershberger, Michele. What Gives? Using God's Money. 1998. (Fast Lane Bible Studies Ser.). 52p. (YA). (gr. 7-9). pap. 9.95 (978-0-87303-334-3(5)) Faith & Life Pr.

Hesselgrave, David J. Planting Churches Cross-Culturally: North America & Beyond. 2nd rev. ed. 2000. (Illus.). 352p. (C). (gr. 13 up). reprint ed. pap. 29.99 (978-0-8010-2222-7(3)) Baker Academic.

Higgs, Liz Curtis. The Pumpkin Patch Parable. 2006. 32p. (J). 7.99 (978-1-4003-0846-0(1)) Nelson, Thomas Inc.

—The Pumpkin Patch Parable: The Parable Series. 2005. 32p. (J). pap. 3.99 (978-1-4003-0668-8(X)) Nelson, Thomas Inc.

Hill, Brenda. Messages of God Written in Rhyme. 2005. 57p. pap. 12.95 (978-1-4137-9480-9(7)) PublishAmerica, Inc.

Hilsman, Lenora & Eberhart, Connie. Affirmations for the Soul. Hilsman, Lenora, ed. 2000. 108p. (YA). (gr. 5 up). pap. 11.95 (978-0-9703305-0-5(2)) Hilsman, Lenora N. & Connie Eberhart.

Hilton, Marilyn Copley. The Christian Girl's Guide to Your Mom. 2004. (Illus.). 176p. (J). pap. 9.99 (978-1-58411-045-3(7) , Legacy Pr.) Rainbow Pubs. & Legacy Pr.

Hinthorn, Aletha. Simply Trusting. l.t. ed. (Satisfied Heart Topical Bible Study Ser.). 158p. (YA). 25.95 (978-0-7862-7552-6(9)) Thorndike Pr.

Hobbs, Ruth K., compiled by. Happy Hearts. 1999. (Illus.). 324p. (J). (gr. 2). 7.95 (978-0-87813-935-4(4)) Christian Light Pubns., Inc.

Hodgson, Mona Gansberg. How Did Bible Heroes Pray? Gillett, Hallie, illus. 2005. (YA). 10.99 (978-0-8254-2778-7(9)) Kregel Pubns.

Hoeksema, Gertrude. Show Me Thy Ways. Steenholdt, Jeff, illus. 2000. ii, 72p. (J). (gr. 5-6). reprint ed. stu. ed., wbk. ed., vinyl bd. 5.95 (978-0-916206-45-1(9)) Reformed Free Publishing Assn.

Hoffman, Janet T. God Is Calling You: And Other Things My Granddad Taught Me. 2002. (Illus.). 128p. pap. 6.99 (978-1-56309-709-6(5) , N027111) New Hope Pubs.

Holder, Greg. God's World. 1998. (Baby Board Bks.). (Illus.). 6p. (J). (ps). bds. 3.99 (978-0-7847-0839-2(8) , 03479, Bean Sprouts) Standard Publishing.

Holder, Greg, ed. God's Animals. 1998. (Baby Board Bks.). (Illus.). 6p. (J). (ps). bds. 3.99 (978-0-7847-0840-8(1) , 03480, Bean Sprouts) Standard Publishing.

Holder, Mig. All Safe On Board. 2004. (Illus.). 32p. 11.99 (978-0-8254-7289-3(X)) Kregel Pubns.

Holl, Kristi. Girlz Rock: Devotions for You. 2005. (Faithgirlz Ser.). 192p. (J). pap. 9.99 (978-0-310-70899-5(0)) Zonderkidz.

Holmes, Andy. Growing with Jesus: 100 Daily Devotionals. 2006. 224p. (J). pap. 12.99 (978-1-4003-0882-8(8)) Nelson, Thomas Inc.

Home Pages. 2001. (Network 34 Ser.). (J). (gr. 3-4). (978-0-8307-2105-4(3)) Gospel Light Pubns.

Honey for a Child's Heart. 2001. (978-1-930871-75-5(9) , Family Christian Pr.) Family Christian Stores, Inc.

Honor Books Publishing Staff. El Librito de Instrucciones de Dios para Jovenes. 1999. (God's Little Instruction Bks.).Tr. of God's Little Instruction Book for Couples. (SPA.). (J). pap. 4.99 (978-0-7899-0547-5(7) , 498351) Editorial Unilit.

—El librito de instrucciones de Dios para Ninos # 2. 2001. (God's Little Instructions Ser.).Tr. of God's Little Instruction Book for Kids # 2. pap. 4.99 (978-0-7899-0989-3(8)) Editorial Unilit.

Honoring God. 2003. per. (978-1-55630-841-3(8)) Brentwood Communications Group.

Horne, Douglas V., ed. & compiled by. The Christian Leaders Home Discipleship Hymnbook. Horne, Douglas V., compiled by. 2004. 15.00 (978-0-9753133-0-5(4)) Home Discipleship Pr.

Horner, Sammy. Talk Sense. (Illus.). 64p. (J). pap. 3.99 (978-1-85792-757-3(5) , Christian Focus) Christian Focus Pubns. GBR. *Dist:* Riverside.

How the Church Grew: Student Guide. 80p. stu. ed. 10.95 (978-0-7586-0472-9(6)) Concordia Publishing Hse.

Howat, Irene. Ten Boys Who Made History. 160p. (J). pap. 5.99 (978-1-85792-836-5(9) , Christian Focus) Christian Focus Pubns. GBR. *Dist:* Riverside.

—Ten Girls Who Made History. 160p. (J). pap. 5.99 (978-1-85792-837-2(7) , Christian Focus) Christian Focus Pubns. GBR. *Dist:* Riverside.

Hudson. God Gave Me. pap. 1.59 (978-0-687-05393-3(5)) Abingdon Pr.

Hudson, Wade. God Smiles When. 2004. (Illus.). 16p. 8.00 (978-0-687-02580-0(X)) Abingdon Pr.

Hudson, Wonderland D. The Believer under Fire 40-Day Devotional & Journal: Daily Inspiration for People Who Love Jesus That Are Going Through the Times of Fiery Trial & Testing. 2003. per. 14.99 (978-0-9744733-4-5(0)) Good Works Publishing Hse.

Humphrey, Art & Humphrey, Pat. Don't Sweat It: Ask Art & Pat. Butler, Tad, illus. pap. 11.95 (978-0-9712305-0-7(1)) Heart Path Publishing.

Hunnicutt, Nathan W. & Farris, James W. Responsible Teenz. 2002. 65p. (YA). per. (978-0-9740232-0-5(5)) Hunnicutt Farris Publishing.

Hunt, Angela Elwell. Keeping Your Life Together When Your Parents Pull Apart: A Teen's Guide to Survi. 2000. (gr. 7-12). lib. bdg. 19.90 (978-0-613-86214-1(7)) Tandem Library Bks.

—Now That He's Asked You Out: Straight Talk for Girls. 2000. (gr. 7-12). lib. bdg. 18.75 (978-0-613-84102-3(6)) Tandem Library Bks.

Hunt, E. Marlene. Every Apple. Hunt, E. Marlene, illus. l.t. ed. 2003. (Illus.). 12p. pap. 10.00 (978-1-893555-45-7(3)) Grace Publishing.

Hunt, T. W. The Mind of Christ Korean Edition. 1999. (YA). 13.95 (978-0-7673-9988-3(9)) LifeWay Christian Resources.

Husted, Russell. Hey Mom, What about Dinosaurs? 2000. (Illus.). 240p. (J). pap. 12.95 (978-1-57921-234-6(4)) WinePress Publishing.

Hyles, Jack. Science of the Christian Life, Vol. 1. 2003. per. (978-0-9745499-5-8(9)) Hyles Pubns.

I Can Be More Like Jesus. 2006. 12.99 (978-1-56309-916-8(0)) Woman's Missionary Union.

I Can Do It! 2003. 9.99 (978-1-56309-626-6(9)) Woman's Missionary Union.

I Can Give. 2003. 9.99 (978-1-56309-625-9(0)) Woman's Missionary Union.

IBS Staff & Zondervan. NVI Biblia Aventura. 2004. (SPA.). 792p. pap. 24.99 (978-0-8297-3231-3(4)) Vida Pubs.

La Iglesia (The Church) Quarter 3, Level 3. (Caminando con Jesus (Walking with Jesus) Series A). (SPA.). (J). (gr. 3-4). stu. ed. 3.50 (978-0-570-05151-0(7) , 16-3813) Concordia Publishing Hse.

In God's Image: Young Children & Sexuality, Guide for Congregations. 7.99 (978-1-57895-057-7(0)) Bridge Resources.

In God's Image: Young Children & Sexuality, Parent's Guide. 6.99 (978-1-57895-056-0(2)) Bridge Resources.

India/Hindi Book of Hope. (J). 2002. 1.00 net. (978-1-931940-04-7(5)); 2001. 32p. mass mkt. (978-1-890525-99-6(5)) Book of Hope International.

Ingraham, Ronald H. There Is No Telling What God Can Do If You Believe: A 21st Century Spiritual Awakening. 2001. (Illus.). 176p. (YA). (gr. 10 up). mass mkt. 13.95 (978-0-9678741-1-1(4)) R I C C Productions.

Inspirational Press Staff. He Is Risen. 1999. (Arch Bks.). (Illus.). 80p. (J). (ps-3). 7.99 (978-0-88486-229-1(1) , Arrowood Pr.) BBS Publishing Corp.

Invading the Lost World, Grades 7-9. 1998. 64p. pap., tchr. ed. 15.00 incl. VHS (978-1-57405-312-8(4)) CharismaLife Pubs.

Irwin, James. Destination Moon. 15th anniv. ed. 2004. 52p. 16.00 (978-1-929241-98-9(4)) STL Distribution North America.

Is There Life after High School? 2004. (Faith 4 Life Ser.). 48p. 14.99 (978-0-7644-2467-0(X) , Flagship Church Resources) Group Publishing, Inc.

Isca, Kay Lynn. Catholic Etiquette for Children at Mass. 2001. 32p. pap. 1.50 (978-0-87973-123-6(0)) Our Sunday Visitor, Publishing Div.

Issues: On the Road. ldr.'s ed. (Ministry to Adolescent's Program Ser.). (Illus.). 72p. (978-0-85910-798-3(1) , 23-0798) Australian Church Resources.

Jackson, James, illus. Dancing with David. Date not set. 24p. (J). (978-1-887399-02-9(X)) Colbert Hse., The.

Jacobs, Sheila. It's my Life. 176p. (YA). mass mkt. 5.99 (978-1-85792-835-8(0) , Christian Focus) Christian Focus Pubns. GBR. *Dist:* Riverside.

Jacobson, Lisa & Jacobson, Matt. The Amazing Beginning of You. 2004. (Illus.). 32p. (J). pap. 6.99 (978-0-310-70925-1(3)) Zonderkidz.

Jarrell, Jane & Saathoff, Deborah. Off to Work We Go. 2004. 50p. (ps up). pap., act. bk. ed. 6.99 (978-0-8054-0823-2(1)) B&H Publishing Grp.

Jeffery, P. Growing Up: Issues Ben Faces as a Christian Teenager. 2004. (Illus.). 48p. (978-0-85234-528-3(3)) Evangelical Pr.

Jeffs, Stephanie & Tulip, Jenny. My First Find Out about Series. 2004. (ps up). (978-0-8294-1735-7(4)) Loyola Pr.

Jenkins, J. B. & LaHaye, Tim. A Traves del Fuego. 1999. (Dejados Atras los Chicos Ser.: No. 3). (SPA.). (J). (gr. 4-7). pap. 4.99 (978-0-7899-0556-7(6) , 497522) Editorial Unilit.

—Segunda Oportunidad. 1999. (Dejados Atras los Chicos Ser.: No. 2). (SPA.). (J). (gr. 4-7). pap. 4.99 (978-0-7899-0555-0(8) , 497521) Editorial Unilit.

Jenkins, Jerry B. & LaHaye, Tim. Golpe de Muerte. 2001. (Dejados Atras los Chicos Ser.: Vol. 8). (SPA.). (J). (gr. 4-7). pap. 4.99 (978-0-7899-0838-4(7)) Spanish Hse. Distributors.

C
D

—Wildfire! Into the Great Tribulation. 2003. (Left Behind Ser.: Bk. 27). 160p. (J). mass mkt. 5.99 (978-0-8423-5791-3(2)) Tyndale Hse. Pubs.

Jesus: On the Road. ldr.'s ed. (Ministry to Adolescent's Program Ser.). (Illus.). 64p. (978-0-85910-800-3(7)) Australian Church Resources.

Jesus Company: Bible Time. 30p. (gr. 4 up). stu. ed. 9.00 (978-0-570-00672-5(4) , 22-2775) Concordia Publishing Hse.

Jesus Company: Bible Time, Grade 5. 30p. (gr. 5 up). stu. ed. 9.00 (978-0-570-00678-7(3) , 7.99) Concordia Publishing Hse.

Jesus Company: Friendship. 32p. (J). (gr. 4). 10.99 (978-0-570-00675-6(9) , 22-2778); (gr. 5). 10.99 (978-0-570-00681-7(3) , 22-2784); (gr. 6). 10.99 (978-0-570-00687-9(2) , 22-2790) Concordia Publishing Hse.

Jesus Company: Service. 32p. (J). (gr. 4). 10.99 (978-0-570-00676-3(7) , 22-2779); (gr. 5). 10.99 (978-0-570-00682-4(1) , 22-2785); (gr. 6). 10.99 (978-0-570-00688-6(0) , 22-2791) Concordia Publishing Hse.

Jesus Company: Witness. 32p. (J). (gr. 4). 12.99 (978-0-570-00677-0(5) , 22-2780); (gr. 5). 12.99 (978-0-570-00683-1(X) , 22-2786); (gr. 6). 12.99 (978-0-570-00689-3(9) , 22-2792) Concordia Publishing Hse.

Jesus Company: Worship. 32p. (J). (gr. 4). 10.99 (978-0-570-00674-9(0) , 22-2777); (gr. 5). 10.99 (978-0-570-00680-0(5) , 22-2783); (gr. 6). 10.99 (978-0-570-00686-2(4) , 22-2789) Concordia Publishing Hse.

Jesus Company: Worship, Friendship, Service & Witness, 4 bks., Set. (gr. 4 up). 40.00 (978-0-570-00690-9(2) , 22-2794); (gr. 5 up). 40.00 (978-0-570-00691-6(0) , 22-2795); (gr. 6 up). 40.00 (978-0-570-00692-3(9) , 22-2796) Concordia Publishing Hse.

Jesus, el Cristo (Jesus, the Christ) Quarter 2, Level 2. (Caminando con Jesus (Walking with Jesus) Series B). (SPA.). (J). (gr. 1-2). stu. ed. 3.50 (978-0-570-05136-7(3) , 16-2912) Concordia Publishing Hse.

A Jesus Kind of Life. 2004. (YA). per. 12.00 (978-0-9747189-8-9(X)) LightHouse Pr.

Jesus Loves Us. 2004. (Orig.). pap. 3.95 (978-0-7647-0570-0(9)) School Specialty Publishing.

Jesus' Message for the Church. 2003. (YA). lib. bdg. 7.99 (978-0-9729477-1-8(X)) Morningstar Christian Chapel.

Jesus Te Ama Libro.Tr. of Jesus Loves You. (SPA.). (J). 1.69 (978-0-7899-0532-1(9) , 498795) Editorial Unilit.

Jingling, Kathy, ed. Barnabas & His Great Mission for Christ. Tobar, Malena, illus. 2003. (SPA.). 198p. (J). spiral bd. 8.00 (978-1-931984-40-9(9) , 2002-00E1) RDM.

—Bernabe y su Gran Mision pro Cristo. Oyola, Milta, tr. from ENG. Tobar, Malena, illus. 2003. Tr. of Barnabas & his Great Mission for Christ. (SPA.). 191p. (J). spiral bd. 8.00 (978-1-931984-41-6(7) , 2002-00S1) RDM.

John Paul II, pseud. For the Children: Words of Love & Inspiration from His Holiness Pope John Paul II. 2000. (Illus.). 32p. (J). (gr. 4-7). pap. 16.95 (978-0-439-14902-0(9) , Scholastic Reference) Scholastic, Inc.

Johnson, Gregg. Bedroom Bible College Manual: BBC Manual. 2004. 123p. pap. 20.00 (978-0-9766930-0-0(3)) Movement Makers International.

Johnson, Jeannette. Against All Odds: A Story of the Miraculous Gift of Life. Krindler, Dorian, ed. 2002. 113p. per. 10.95 (978-0-9676367-1-9(X)) Heart Warming Hse.

Johnson, Kevin. Total Devotion: 365 Days to Hang Tight with Jesus. 2004. 384p. (J). reprint ed. pap. 13.99 (978-0-7642-2884-1(6)) Bethany Hse. Pubs.

Johnson, Kevin W. Stick Tight: Glue Yourself to Godly Friends. 2001. (Early Teen Discipleship Ser.). 128p. (J). pap. 7.99 (978-0-7642-2434-8(4)) Bethany Hse. Pubs.

Johnson, Lois Walfrid. You Are Wonderfully Made. 1999. (Let's Talk about It Stories for Kids Ser.). (Illus.). 176p. (J). (gr. 3-8). pap. 7.99 (978-1-55661-654-9(6)) Bethany Hse. Pubs.

Johnson, Marsha Deveaux. Power Angel on Assignment. 2001. (Power Angel Ser.: Vol. 1). (Illus.). 48p. (J). (gr. 1-7). 14.95 (978-0-9702959-8-9(7)) Jawbone Publishing Corp.

Johnston, Kurt & Oestreicher, Mark. My School. 2007. 144p. (J). pap. 9.99 (***978-0-310-27882-5(1)**) Zondervan.

Johnstone, Jill. Tu Puedes Cambiar Al Mundo (You Can Change the World) (SPA.). 126p. (J). (978-1-56063-726-4(9)) Editorial Unilit.

Jones, James. Following Jesus. Davies, Taffy, illus. 2005. 64p. (J). pap. (978-1-84101-203-2(3) , Barnabas) Bible Reading Fellowship.

Jones, Mary Alice. I'm Growing, Too. 2004. pap. 5.99 (978-1-4037-0540-2(2)) Dalmatian Pr.

Jones, Stan And Brenna & Jones, Brenna. The Story of Me (Revised) 2007. 48p. pap. 9.99 (978-1-60006-013-7(7)) NavPress Publishing Group.

Jones, Tony. Divine Intervention. 2006. 160p. pap. 12.99 (978-1-60006-059-5(5) , Th1nk Bks.) NavPress Publishing Group.

Joseph, E. T. Larry Light up Sneakers. 2004. 25p. pap. 14.95 (978-1-4137-3335-8(2)) PublishAmerica, Inc.

Joseph-Samuel, Dennese H. God Is H. I. T. S. Happily Interested in Teenager's Services. 2004. (YA). per. 15.95 (978-0-9747543-1-4(5)) Kids Children & Teens World 2000 & Beyond.

Joss, Jan. Starting Line. 2000. (Illus.). 176p. (J). (ps-1). pap. 20.95 (978-0-89084-976-7(5) , 109363) Jones, Bob Univ. Pr.

The Journey. 2004. (YA). pap., stu. ed. 5.00 (978-0-9749186-1-7(X)) Revivalist Pr., The.

Joy, Donald M. Becoming a Man: A Celebration of Sexuality, Responsibility & the Christian Young Man. 2nd ed. 2001. (ENG.). 125p. pap. 12.99 (978-1-928915-18-8(3)) Evangel Publishing Hse.

Junior Cross Training, Vol. 8. Incl. Invading the Lost World, Grades 7-9. 64p. 1998. pap., tchr. ed. 15.00 incl. VHS (978-1-57405-312-8(4)); 1998. 99.99 (978-1-57405-309-8(4)) CharismaLife Pubs.

Karr, Leona, compiled by. Make Way for Miracles. 2004. 140p. per. 14.95 (978-0-9761694-0-6(1)) Venture Publishing.

Kast, Michael. What's in Your Locker? 30 Daily Devotions. Reeves, Dale, ed. 2001. 160p. (J). (gr. 7 up). 10.99 (978-0-7847-1253-5(0)) Standard Publishing.

Kaster, Jeffrey. What Catholic Teens Should Know about Homosexuality. Larking, Jean K., ed. 2004. (What Catholic Teens Should Know Ser.). (Illus.). 8p. (YA). 7.95 (978-0-89837-236-6(4) , 441010) Pflaum Publishing Group.

Kaster, Jeffrey & Kaster, Liz. What Catholic Teens Should Know about How Far to Go. Larkin, Jean, ed. 2003. (What Catholic Teens Should Know Ser.). (Illus.). 8p. (YA). 7.95 (978-0-89837-191-8(0) , 440410) Pflaum Publishing Group.

Katie. The Sunday Alphabet of Animals. 1998. (Illus.). 112p. (J). (ps-3). 10.00 (978-1-57683-089-5(6)) NavPress Publishing Group.

Kearns, Becky Lockhart. The Prodical Son: Luke 15:11-32 for Children. Hillam, Corbin, illus. 2005. (ENG.). 16p. (J). (ps-ps). 1.99 (978-0-7586-0591-7(9)) Concordia Publishing Hse.

Keene, Michael. Christian Life. 2000. (Illus.). 80p. (J). (gr. 6-9). pap. 17.95 (978-0-7487-5287-4(0)) Nelson Thornes Ltd. GBR. *Dist:* Trans-Atlantic Pubns., Inc.

Keener, Joan N. God's the One Who Thought of It First. Ring, Laura, ed. Carpenter, Stephen, illus. 1998. (Happy Day Bks.). 24p. (J). (ps-2). pap. 2.49 (978-0-7847-0832-3(0) , 04262, Bean Sprouts) Standard Publishing.

Kelley, Gail & Hershberger, Carol. Come Mime with Me: A Guide to Preparing Scriptural Dramas for Children. 2003. (Illus.). 104p. (YA). (gr. 1 up). 16.00 (978-0-89390-089-2(3)) Resource Pubns., Inc.

Kenney, Cindy & Peterson, Doug. VeggieTales Family Devotional. 2005. (Illus.). 224p. (gr. 4-7). 14.99 (978-1-59145-261-4(9)) Nelson, Thomas Inc.

Kenney, Cindy, et al. Peas & Thank You! 2003. (Big Idea Bks.). 12p. 4.99 (978-0-310-70540-6(1)) Zonderkidz.

Khoury, Robin. Answers for New Christians: What Kids Need to Know about Sin, Salvation, Baptism & More. Corley, Paula & Thompson, John, eds. Corley, Stuart, illus. 1999. (Learn & Color Ser.). 64p. (J). (ps-6). pap. 9.95 (978-0-9667147-9-1(2)) Little Light Pr.

KID's Forecast for Life. 2005. 20.99 (978-1-59781-647-2(7)) Xulon Pr., Inc.

Kids in the Word. 2002. pap. 69.99 (978-1-59185-157-8(2)) CharismaLife Pubs.

Kids in the Word Manual. 2002. pap. 10.00 (978-1-59185-151-6(3)) CharismaLife Pubs.

Kids in the Word Transparencies. 2002. 29.99 (978-1-59185-153-0(X)) CharismaLife Pubs.

Kids in Word Cover. 2002. pap. 0.00 (978-1-59185-163-9(7)) CharismaLife Pubs.

The Kids Prayed & God Arrived. 2004. (YA). (978-1-59581-083-0(8)) Brentwood Communications Group.

Kielbasa, Marilyn & Theisen, Michael. Taking Charge: Managing Life's Struggles. Zanzig, Thomas, ed. Thiewes, Sam, illus. 2003. (Horizons Program : Level II, Minicourse 4). (Orig.). (YA). (gr. 10). 264p. pap., stu. ed. 50.00 (978-0-88489-389-9(8)); 80p. pap., stu. ed. 9.95 (978-0-88489-382-0(0)) St. Mary's Pr.

Kingsbury, Karen. A Treasury of Miracles for Teens: True Stories of God's Presence Today. 2003. 192p. 12.95 (978-0-446-52962-4(1)) FaithWords.

Kintaro, Marino. Jesus Opened My Eyes. 2005. (Illus.). 337p. per. 15.95 (978-1-932338-93-5(4)) Lifevest Publishing, Inc.

Kitch, Anne E. What We Do in Church: An Anglican Child's Activity Book. Perez, Dorothy, illus. 2004. 48p. pap. 7.00 (978-0-8192-2105-6(8)) Morehouse Publishing.

Kitch, Anne E. What We Do in Lent: A Child's Activity Book. Perez, Dorothy Thompson, illus. 2007. 48p. 8.00 (***978-0-8192-2278-7(X)**) Morehouse Publishing.

Kittel, Vernette. Student Daily Devotional: 365 Days. 2003. 388p. (J). pap. 19.99 (978-1-57921-682-5(X)) Pleasant Word.

Kizer, Drew. Make Your Stand. 2004. (YA). per. 10.00 (978-0-9725894-1-3(4)) Riddle Creek Publishing.

Klammer, Lynn. God & Me! 2: Ages 2-5, 3 vols. 2004. (Illus.). 238p. (J). spiral bd. 12.99 (978-1-58411-054-5(6) , Legacy Pr.) Rainbow Pubs. & Legacy Pr.

—Gotta Have God 2: Ages 2-5, 3. Heiser, Aline, illus. 2005. (Gotta Have God Ser.). 238p. (J). spiral bd. 12.99 (978-1-58411-057-6(0) , Legacy Pr.) Rainbow Pubs. & Legacy Pr.

Kluever, Karen T. Friends for the Journey. 2004. pap., stu. ed. 6.00 (978-0-687-02698-2(9)); pap. 10.00 (978-0-687-02668-5(7)) Abingdon Pr.

Knight 6 Personal Growth Planbook: Extreme Quest. 2003. (Illus.). 48p. (J). pap. 4.95 (978-1-59312-047-4(8)) North American Mission Board, SBC.

Knowing Our Catholic Faith: 26 Lessons. 2004. (978-0-8294-1129-4(1)); Vol. 2. (978-0-8294-1130-0(5)); Vol. 3. (978-0-8294-1131-7(3)) Loyola Pr.

Knowing Our Catholic Faith: 32 Lessons. 2004. Vol. 4. (978-0-8294-1132-4(1)); Vol. 5. (978-0-8294-1134-8(8)); Vol. 6. (978-0-8294-1135-5(6)) Loyola Pr.

Knowing Our Catholic Faith: 38 Lessons. 2004. Vol. 7. (978-0-8294-1136-2(4)); Vol. 8. (978-0-8294-1137-9(2)) Loyola Pr.

Knowing Our Catholic Faith: Complete Set, 8 vols. 2004. (978-0-8294-1508-7(4)) Loyola Pr.

Koch, Carl. Creating a Christian Lifestyle. 2nd ed. 2003. (Illus.). 320p. (gr. 11-12). pap. 17.30 (978-0-88489-358-5(8)) St. Mary's Pr.

Koch, Carl, ed. Finding Hope: Stories by Teenagers. 2003. (Stories by Teenagers Ser.: Vol. 3). (Illus.). 136p. (YA). pap. 7.95 (978-0-88489-524-4(6)) St. Mary's Pr.

Kokmeyer, Verna. Object Talks for Any Day. 2nd rev. ed. 2006. (Object Talks Ser.). 48p. (YA). (gr. 1-7). pap. 6.99 (978-0-7847-1265-8(4) , 02845) Standard Publishing.

—Object Talks for Special Occasions. 2nd rev. ed. 2006. (Object Talks Ser.). 48p. (YA). (gr. 1-7). pap. 6.99 (978-0-7847-1269-6(7) , 02830) Standard Publishing.

Kraeuter, Tom. Living Beyond the Ordinary: Developing an Extraordinary Relationship with God. 2000. 176p. (J). pap. 9.99 (978-1-883002-71-8(0)) Emerald Bks.

Kramer, Jim. A Gift from Rex: Guiding Children Through Life & Loss. 2001. 32p. (J). pap. 14.95 (978-1-890676-63-6(2)) Beaver's Pond Pr., Inc.

Kubiak, Shannon. God Called a Girl: How Mary Changed Her World — And You Can Too. 2005. 176p. (J). reprint ed. pap. 11.99 (978-0-7642-0029-8(1)) Bethany Hse. Pubs.

Kucharik, E. Bendiciones Sencillas. 2002. (Little Hearts Ser.).Tr. of Simple Blessings. bds. 4.99 (978-0-7899-0727-1(5)) Editorial Unilit.

—Lluvia o Sol. 2002. (Little Hearts Ser.).Tr. of Rain or Shine. bds. 4.99 (978-0-7899-0692-2(9)) Editorial Unilit.

Kunkel, Jeff, ed. What Scares Me & What I Do about It: Stories & Pictures by Sunday School Kids. 2004. (Illus.). 48p. 12.99 (978-0-8066-4558-2(X) , Augsburg Bks.) Augsburg Fortress, Pubs.

Kunzinger, Bob. The Infant: A Tale from Prague. 2005. 85p. pap. 12.00 (978-0-9725110-4-9(0)) All Nations Pr.

Kutz-Mellem, Sharon. Honest Talk about Eating Disorders. 2000. 28p. (YA). (978-1-57895-096-6(1)) Bridge Resources.

Kuyper, Vicki J. Jesus Speaks to Teens: Not Your Ordinary Meditations on the Word of Jesus. 2004. (Jesus Speaks Ser.). (Illus.). 192p. (J). 14.99 (978-0-7642-2866-7(8)) Bethany Hse. Pubs.

Lackner, Paul M. Memoirs of a Diocesan Priest. 2002. 128p. (Orig.). pap. 22.50 (978-0-939332-28-1(0)) Pohl, J. Assocs.

Lad 1 Personal Growth Planbook: Clue Chasers. 2003. (Illus.). 48p. (J). pap. 4.95 (978-1-59312-042-9(7)) North American Mission Board, SBC.

Lad 2 Personal Growth Planbook: Everglade Explorers. 2003. (Illus.). 48p. (J). pap. 4.95 (978-1-59312-043-6(5)) North American Mission Board, SBC.

Lad 3 Personal Growth Planbook: Rawhide Wranglers. 2003. (Illus.). 48p. (J). pap. 4.95 (978-1-59312-044-3(3)) North American Mission Board, SBC.

Lamar, Melvin. The Call to Be Different. 2003. (YA). per. 12.99 (978-0-9716068-2-1(X)) Lamar, Melvin Productions, Inc.

Lamplighter Staff. Boys of Grit Who Became Men Of. 2004. 16.00 (978-1-58474-026-1(4)) Cornerstone Family Ministries/Lamplighter Publishing.

—Stephen Soldier of the Cross. 2004. 17.00 (978-1-58474-032-2(9)) Cornerstone Family Ministries/Lamplighter Publishing.

Lancaster, Donna. The Short & Tall of It. 2002. 157p. per. 14.95 (978-0-9717868-0-6(1)) WordWright.biz, Inc.

Larkin, Jean. Days of Faith: Student Planner & Assignment Book/Primary Teacher Supplement 2005-2006. 2005. (J). (978-1-933178-06-6(X) , 9816) Pflaum Publishing Group.

Larkin, Jean & O'Connor, Francine. First Reconciliation: Activities for Primary Grades. Larkin, Jean, ed. 2005. (Illus.). 32p. (J). 9.95 (978-1-933178-09-7(4) , 3451) Pflaum Publishing Group.

Larkin, Jean K., ed. Growing Through Relationships: Activities for Junior High, 4 vols. 2002. (Ready Resources for Catholic Teens (For Junior High) Ser.). 32p. (YA). 14.95 (978-0-89837-222-9(4) , P2R2) Pflaum Publishing Group.

—Living a Moral Life: Activities for Junior High, 4 vols. 2002. (Ready Resources for Catholic Teens (For Junior High) Ser.). 32p. (YA). 14.95 (978-0-89837-220-5(8) , P2M2) Pflaum Publishing Group.

—Oraciones y Guias para Jovenes Catolicos. 2004. (SPA.). 28p. (J). 2.25 (978-0-89837-197-0(X) , 4659) Pflaum Publishing Group.

Larson, Tammy, illus. Count Your Blessings at the Beach. 2000. 32p. (J). act. bk. ed. (978-0-9718083-3-1(3)) Three Angels Broadcasting Network.

—God's Way to Health & Happiness. 2001st ed. 2001. (J). act. bk. ed. (978-0-9718083-4-8(1)) Three Angels Broadcasting Network.

Lauria, David C. The Alphabet God's Way. Lauria, David C., illus. 1999. (Illus.). 56p. (J). (ps-6). pap. 12.00 (978-0-9676600-0-4(9)) Lauria, David C.

Lawrence, Ava. A Button for a Crown. Ford, Christina, illus. l.t. ed. 2003. 84p. (J). 14.95 (978-0-9651048-4-5(2)) Papillon Publishing.

Layton, Dian. The Young God Chasers: The King & His Kingdom. 2001. ring bd. 119.99 (978-0-9677402-5-6(8)) Mercy Place, Inc.

Lechner, Diane, et al, texts. Jesus Comes to Us. 143p. (J). (gr. 2). pap. 6.50 (978-0-8198-3921-3(3)) Pauline Bks. & Media.

LeCompte, Teresa. Journey Through the New Testament. 2002. (Illus.). 203p. (YA). (gr. 8-12). pap., stu. ed. 15.95 (978-0-15-900679-5(1)) Harcourt Religion Pubs.

Lee, Kenneth M. God's Help Now! Self-Help Devotional for Finding God's Solutions for Problems. 2001. 146p. (YA). (gr. 9 up). pap. 12.95 (978-0-9711850-0-5(X)) Lee, Kenneth M.

Lee, Witness. The Building Work of God. 2001. 144p. (J). (gr. 6). per. 7.75 (978-0-7363-1460-2(1) , 04-901-001) Living Stream Ministry.

—Como Guiar a los Jovenes. 2001. Tr. of How to Lead the Young People. (SPA.). 37p. (gr. 6). 1.00 (978-0-7363-1366-7(4) , 18-085-002) Living Stream Ministry.

—The Conclusion of the New Testament: Messages 265-275. 2000. 98p. (J). (gr. 6). per. 6.00 (978-0-7363-0152-7(6) , 10-046-001) Living Stream Ministry.

—El Constructor de las Columnas. 2001. Tr. of Builder of the Pillars. (SPA.). 53p. (gr. 6). 1.00 (978-0-7363-1297-4(8) , 18-093-002) Living Stream Ministry.

—Dios, la Educacion y el Caracter. 2001. Tr. of God, Education, & Character. (SPA.). 9p. (gr. 6). 1.00 (978-0-7363-1367-4(2) , 18-094-002) Living Stream Ministry.

—The Economy of God & the Mystery of the Transmission of the Divine Trinity. 2000. 167p. (J). (gr. 6). per. 8.50 (978-0-7363-0851-9(2) , 04-053-001) Living Stream Ministry.

—En Cuanto al Recobro del Senor. 2001. Tr. of Concerning the Lord's Recovery. (SPA.). 92p. (J). (gr. 6). per. 5.50 (978-0-7363-1351-3(6) , 08-006-002) Living Stream Ministry.

—Estudio-Vida de Exodo Vol. 1: Mensajes 1-22. 1998. (SPA.). 246p. (J). (gr. 6). per. 12.00 (978-1-57593-398-6(5) , 10-153-002) Living Stream Ministry.

—Estudio-Vida de Exodo Vol. 3: Mensajes 42-63. 1998. Tr. of Life-Study of Exodus: Messages 42-63. (SPA.). 256p. (J). (gr. 6). per. 12.50 (978-1-57593-400-6(0) , 10-155-002) Living Stream Ministry.

—The Furtherance of the New Way for the Lord's Recovery. 2001. 97p. (J). (gr. 6). per. 6.75 (978-0-7363-1282-0(X) , 12-901-001) Living Stream Ministry.

—God, Education & Character. 2001. 9p. (gr. 6). 1.00 (978-0-7363-1336-0(2) , 18-094-001) Living Stream Ministry.

—God's Salvation in Life. 2001. 69p. (J). (gr. 6). per. 3.50 (978-0-7363-1145-8(9) , 07-927-001) Living Stream Ministry.

—The Holy Word for Morning Revival: Crystallization-Study of Revelation. 2000. (J). (gr. 6). Vol. 3. 136p. 7.00 (978-0-7363-0816-8(4) , 13-099-011); Vol. 4. 109p. 7.00 (978-0-7363-0817-5(2) , 13-100-001) Living Stream Ministry.

—The Holy Word for Morning Revival: Crystallization-Study of the New Jerusalem, Vol. 1. 2000. 136p. (J). (gr. 6). per. 7.00 (978-0-7363-0982-0(9) , 13-127-001) Living Stream Ministry.

—The Holy Word for Morning Revival: Matthew 1:1-7:29, Vol. 1. 2000. 71p. (J). (gr. 6). 6.00 (978-0-7363-1108-3(4) , 13-133-001) Living Stream Ministry.

—The Holy Word for Morning Revival: Matthew 8:1-13:52, Vol. 2. 2000. 90p. (J). (gr. 6). 6.00 (978-0-7363-1109-0(2) , 13-134-001) Living Stream Ministry.

—The Holy Word for Morning Revival: New Revival—Becoming the New Jerusalem. 2000. 109p. (J). (gr. 6). 7.00 (978-0-7363-0926-4(8) , 13-126-001) Living Stream Ministry.

—The Holy Word for Morning Revival: New Revival—Living the Life of a God-Man. 2000. 109p. (J). (gr. 6). 7.00 (978-0-7363-1162-5(9) , 13-138-001) Living Stream Ministry.

—Life-Study of Philippians, 3 vols., Set. 2000. 547p. (J). per. 25.75 (978-0-7363-0912-7(8) , 10-275-001) Living Stream Ministry.

—Life-Study of Philippians Vol. 3: Messages 43-62. 2000. 172p. (J). (gr. 6). per. 10.25 (978-0-7363-0911-0(X) , 10-193-001) Living Stream Ministry.

—A Living of Mutual Abiding with the Lord in Spirit. 2000. 108p. (J). (gr. 6). per. 6.75 (978-0-7363-0806-9(7) , 07-072-001) Living Stream Ministry.

—The Lord's Recovery of Eating. 2000. 42p. (J). (gr. 6). per. 5.25 (978-0-7363-0990-5(X) , 07-080-001) Living Stream Ministry.

—Nuestra Juventud: Un Precioso Tesoro para el Senor. 2001. Tr. of Treasuring the Teenage Years for the Lord. (SPA.). 11p. (gr. 6). 1.00 (978-0-7363-1398-8(2) , 18-095-002) Living Stream Ministry.

—La Palabra Santa para el Avivamiento Matutino: Mateo 13:53-21:22, Vol. 3. 2001. Tr. of Holy Word for Morning Revival: Matthew 13:53-21:22. (SPA.). 83p. (J). (gr. 6). per. 6.00 (978-0-7363-1141-0(6) , 13-135-002) Living Stream Ministry.

—La Palabra Santa para el Avivamiento Matutino: Mateo 21:23-28:20, Vol. 4. 2001. Tr. of Holy Word for Morning Revival: Matthew 21:23-28:20. (SPA.). 83p. (J). (gr. 6). per. 6.00 (978-0-7363-1142-7(4) , 13-136-002) Living Stream Ministry.

—La Palabra Santa para el Avivamiento Matutino: Mover de Dios en Su Recobro Segn se Presenta en Ezequiel, Vol. 2. 1998. (SPA.). 66p. (J). (gr. 6). 4.50 (978-0-7363-0388-0(X) , 13-082-002) Living Stream Ministry.

—Practical Lessons on the Experience of Life. 2001. 236p. (J). (gr. 6). per. 10.00 (978-0-7363-1241-7(2) , 07-081-001) Living Stream Ministry.

—La Propagacion de la Verdad en el Recobro del Snor. 1999. Tr. of Propogation of the Truth in the Lord's Recovery. (SPA.). 36p. (J). (gr. 6). per. 1.50 (978-0-7363-0636-2(6) , 20-116-002) Living Stream Ministry.

—The Pure Heart. 2001. 110p. (J). (gr. 6). per. 6.75 (978-0-7363-1339-1(7) , 07-960-001) Living Stream Ministry.

—The Pursuit of a Christian. 2001. 86p. (J). (gr. 6). per. 6.50 (978-0-7363-1277-6(3) , 13-939-001) Living Stream Ministry.

—The Revelation & Vision of God. 2000. 188p. (J). (gr. 6). per. 8.75 (978-0-7363-1119-9(X) , 15-907-001) Living Stream Ministry.

—Serving in the Meetings & in the Gospel. 2000. 96p. (J). (gr. 6). per. 6.50 (978-0-7363-0909-7(8) , 11-021-001) Living Stream Ministry.

—El Significado del Candelero de Oro. 2001. Tr. of Ultimate Significance of the Golden Lampstand. (SPA.). 88p. (J). (gr. 6). per. 6.50 (978-0-7363-1338-4(9) , 07-069-002) Living Stream Ministry.

—The Spirit & the Service in Spirit. 2001. 115p. (J). (gr. 6). per. 7.25 (978-0-7363-1159-5(9) , 14-905-001) Living Stream Ministry.

—Subjective Experience of the Indwelling Christ. 2000. 106p. (J). (gr. 6). per. 6.75 (978-0-7363-1144-1(0) , 07-930-001) Living Stream Ministry.

—Treasuring the Teenage Years for the Lord. 2001. 10p. (gr. 6). 1.00 (978-0-7363-0856-4(3) , 18-095-001) Living Stream Ministry.

LeFever, Marlene. Flowers from God: Thank-You Notes for Sunday School Teachers. 2002. 64p. pap., pap. 1.99 (978-0-7814-3891-9(8) , 0781438918) Cook, David C. Publishing Co.

Legacy. 7.50 (978-0-8054-5927-2(8)) B&H Publishing Grp.

Legacy Press Staff. God & Me! Devotions for Girls. 1998. (God & Me! Ser.). (Illus.). 238p. (J). (ps-k). spiral bd. 12.99 (978-1-885358-61-5(X) , LP46821); spiral bd. 12.99 (978-1-885358-60-8(1) , LP46822) Rainbow Pubs. & Legacy Pr. (Legacy Pr.).

—God's Girls! Fun & Faith for Ages 9-12. 2004. (God's Girls Ser.: Vol. 1). (Illus.). (J). (gr. 4-7). 176p. pap. 12.99 (978-1-58411-020-0(1)); Vol. 2. 192p. pap. 12.99 (978-1-58411-021-7(X)) Rainbow Pubs. & Legacy Pr. (Legacy Pr.).

—Gotta Have God: Devotions for Boys. 2004. (Gotta Have God Ser.). (Illus.). 238p. (J). (gr. 1-4). spiral bd. 12.99 (978-1-885358-97-4(0)); (gr. 5-7). spiral bd. 12.99 (978-1-885358-98-1(9)); (ps-k). spiral bd. 12.99 (978-1-885358-96-7(2)) Rainbow Pubs. & Legacy Pr. (Legacy Pr.).

Legette, C. F. You'll Never Teach an Old Dog a New Trick. Legette, C. F., illus. l.t. ed. 2002. (Illus.). 36p. per. 14.95 (978-0-9722212-1-4(2)) CALs Ltd.

Leichner, Jeannine Timko. Making Things Right: The Sacrament of Reconciliation. Davidson, Kevin, illus. 2005. 70p. pap. 6.95 (978-1-59276-157-9(7)) Our Sunday Visitor, Publishing Div.

Leigh, Beverly. Adventure Club Preschool: The Champion's Journey. Abboreno, Joseph, illus. 2001. 42p. (J). pap., stu. ed. 19.99 (978-0-935797-44-2(0)) Harvest Pubns.

Leininger, Tracy. Nothing Can Separate Us: The Story of Nan Harper. 2nd ed. 2000. (Illus.). 64p. (J). mass mkt. 15.99 (978-0-9724287-1-2(2)) His Seasons.

Leitch, Wayne. The Way of Assurance. 2006. pap. (978-1-882701-99-5(2)) Gospel Folio Pr.

Lessons in Responsibility for Boys: Level One. 2007. (YA). per. 18.95 (***978-0-9792446-0-5(9)***) Messiah Publishing - Pearables.

Lessons in Responsibility for boys Level Two. 2007. (YA). per. 18.95 (***978-0-9792446-1-2(7)***) Messiah Publishing - Pearables.

Lessons in Responsibility for Girls: Level One. 2006. Orig. Title: Home Economics for Home Schoolers Level One. (J). per., pupil's gde. ed. 18.95 (***978-0-9792446-2-9(5)***) Messiah Publishing - Pearables.

Lessons in Responsibility for Girls: Level Three, 3. 2005. Orig. Title: Home Economics for Home Schoolers Level Three. (J). per., pupil's gde. ed. (***978-0-9792446-4-3(1)***) Messiah Publishing - Pearables.

Lessons in Responsibility for Girls: Level Two, 2. 2006. Orig. Title: Home Economics for Home Schoolers Level Two. (J). per., pupil's gde. ed. 18.95 (***978-0-9792446-3-6(3)***) Messiah Publishing - Pearables.

Let There Be Light: Choices, Uniqueness, Wild, Wonderful Water. 2000. (Connect Ser.: Vol. 6). (YA). 20.00 (978-0-687-72147-4(4)) Abingdon Pr.

Let's Practice Faith: Bible Story Flipbook. 2004. (Firelight Ser.). (gr. 3-4). 4.99 (978-0-8066-6512-2(2)) Augsburg Fortress, Pubs.

Let's Practice Faith: Bible Story Magazine. 2004. (Firelight Ser.). (gr. 5-6). 4.99 (978-0-8066-6514-6(9)) Augsburg Fortress, Pubs.

Let's Practice Faith: Bible Storybook. 2004. (Firelight Ser.). (gr. 1-2). 4.99 (978-0-8066-6510-8(6)) Augsburg Fortress, Pubs.

Let's Practice Faith: Learning Tool. 2004. (978-0-8066-6504-7(1)) Augsburg Fortress, Pubs.

Let's Practice Faith, Ages 2-3: Bible Story Album. 2004. (Firelight Ser.). (ps-k). 4.99 (978-0-8066-6508-5(4)) Augsburg Fortress, Pubs.

Let's Shine Jesus' Light on Halloween. 2006. 16p. (J). pap. 1.99 (978-0-7847-1531-4(9) , 04360) Standard Publishing.

Let's Show God's Love on Valentine's Day. 2006. (J). 16p. pap. 1.99 (978-0-7847-1722-6(2) , 04183); 24p. bds. 7.99 (978-0-7847-1385-3(5) , 04050) Standard Publishing.

Level K Spanish Family Resources. 2000. (Growing in Love Ser.). 32p. pap. 3.95 (978-0-15-950701-8(4)) Harcourt Religion Pubs.

Levey, Michael. The Book of the Holy Light. 2004. 204p. 17.95 (978-1-59540-987-4(4) , Sunstar Publishing) 1st World Publishing, Inc.

Lewellen, LaRose. A Grasp on Reality: Breaking It down for Our Teens. 2007. 124p. per. 12.95 (***978-0-595-43828-0(8)***) iUniverse, Inc.

Lewis, Carole. Everyday Victory for Everyday People. 2004. (First Place Bible Studies). 232p. pap. 19.99 (978-0-8307-2865-7(1) , Gospel Light) Gospel Light Pubns.

—First Place Group Starter Kit. 2004. 179.99 (978-0-8307-3369-9(8) , Gospel Light) Gospel Light Pubns.

—Giving Christ First Place. 2004. (First Place Bible Studies). 224p. pap. 19.99 (978-0-8307-2864-0(3) , Gospel Light) Gospel Light Pubns.

—Life That Wins. 2004. (First Place Bible Studies). 224p. pap. 19.99 (978-0-8307-2924-1(0) , Gospel Light) Gospel Light Pubns.

—Life under Control. 2004. (First Place Bible Studies). 224p. pap. 19.99 (978-0-8307-2930-2(5) , Gospel Light) Gospel Light Pubns.

—Living the Legacy. 2004. (First Place Bible Studies). 240p. pap. 19.99 (978-0-8307-2928-9(3) , Gospel Light) Gospel Light Pubns.

—Making Wise Choices. 2004. (First Place Bible Studies). 208p. pap. 19.99 (978-0-8307-3081-0(8) , Gospel Light) Gospel Light Pubns.

—Seeking God's Best. 2004. (First Place Bible Studies). 208p. pap. 19.99 (978-0-8307-2925-8(9) , Gospel Light) Gospel Light Pubns.

Lewis, Gregg & Lewis, Deborah S. Joni Eareckson Tada. 2002. (Today's Heroes Ser.). (Illus.). 112p. (J). pap. 4.99 (978-0-310-70300-6(X)) Zonderkidz.

Lewis, Helen M. & Lewis, Meharry H. The Church of the Living God, the Pillar & Ground of the Truth, Inc - Eighty-Fifth Anniversary Yearbook, 1. 2002. 180p. 30.00 (978-0-910003-12-4(2)) New & Living Way Publishing Co.

Leys, Lucas & Zondervan. 151 Encuentros con el Rey. 2002. (Youth Specialties Ser.). 192p. pap. 9.99 (978-0-8297-3791-2(X)) Vida Pubs.

Libby, Larry. Someday Heaven. McLoughlin, Wayne, illus. 2001. 40p. (J). 12.99 (978-0-310-70105-7(8)) Zonderkidz.

Libro de Actividades. 2004. (Sabio Y Prudente Ser.).Tr. of Activity Book. (SPA.). 48p. (J). 3.25 (978-0-8254-0924-0(1) , Editorial Portavoz) Kregel Pubns.

Libro de Colorear, Vol. 2. 2004. (Sabio Y Prudente Ser.).Tr. of Coloring Book. (SPA.). 32p. (J). pap. 2.50 (978-0-8254-0929-5(2) , Editorial Portavoz) Kregel Pubns.

The Life of Grace: Revised Grade 7. 2005. (J). pap., stu. ed. 12.95 (978-0-89870-910-0(5)); pap., act. bk. ed. 6.95 (978-0-89870-900-1(8)) Ignatius Pr.

Life Publishers, tr. from SPA. Explorer-Student Vol. 6 Bk. 1: Russian Sunday School, 2000. Orig. Title: El Explorador. Alumno. (RUS.). 48p. (YA). pupil's gde. ed. (978-0-7361-0205-6(1)) Life Pubs. International.

—Explorer-Student Vol. 6 Bk. 2: Russian Sunday School, 2000. Orig. Title: El Explorador. Alumno. (RUS.). 48p. (YA). pupil's gde. ed. (978-0-7361-0206-3(X)) Life Pubs. International.

Life Publishers International Staff. Mis Amigos Alumno Vol. 9, Tomo 3: March to May 2000. 1999. (SPA., Illus.). 32p. (J). (gr. 1-3). pap. (978-0-7361-0108-0(X)) Life Pubs. International.

—Mis Amigos Alumno Vol. 9, Tomos 4: June to August 2000. 1999. (SPA., Illus.). 32p. (J). (gr. 1-3). pap. (978-0-7361-0109-7(8)) Life Pubs. International.

Life Publishers International Staff, tr. from SPA. Ambassador-Student (Russian) Vol. 1, Bk. 1: Russian Sunday School, March-May 1998, 1998. Orig. Title: El Embajador. Alumno. (RUS., Illus.). 48p. (YA). (gr. 10-12). stu. ed. (978-1-890219-87-1(8)) Life Pubs. International.

Life Togerher Sunday School, Winter 2005-06: Class Kit. 2005. (J). 11.99 (978-0-8066-5199-6(7)) Augsburg Fortress, Pubs.

Life Together Sunday School Starter Kit: Leader Guide. 2004. (gr. 7 up). (978-0-8066-5091-3(5)); (978-0-8066-5104-0(0)) Augsburg Fortress, Pubs.

Life Together Sunday School Starter Kit: Learner Resources. 2004. (978-0-8066-5069-2(9)); (978-0-8066-5082-1(6)); (978-0-8066-5095-1(8)); (gr. 1-3). (978-0-8066-5072-2(9)); (gr. 1-3). (978-0-8066-5085-2(0)); (gr. 1-3). (978-0-8066-5098-2(2)); (gr. 4-6). (978-0-8066-5075-3(3)); (gr. 4-6). (978-0-8066-5088-3(5)); (gr. 4-6). (978-0-8066-5101-9(6)) Augsburg Fortress, Pubs.

Life Together, Winter 2005: Lower Elementary Leader Guide. 2005. (J). (gr. 1-3). mass mkt. (978-0-8066-5204-7(7)) Augsburg Fortress, Pubs.

Life Together, Winter 2005: Lower Elementary Learner. 2005. (J). (gr. 1-3). mass mkt. 4.99 (978-0-8066-5203-0(9)) Augsburg Fortress, Pubs.

Life Together, Winter 2005: Pre-Elementary Leader Guide. 2005. (J). (gr. k-2). mass mkt. (978-0-8066-5201-6(2)) Augsburg Fortress, Pubs.

Life Together, Winter 2005: Upper Elementary Learner. 2005. (J). (gr. 4-6). mass mkt. 4.99 (978-0-8066-5206-1(3)) Augsburg Fortress, Pubs.

Life's Journey: A Clear Mind & A Clean Heart, 1 book. 2004. per. (978-0-9752994-0-1(9)) Carroll, Sherry.

Light for My Path for Teens. 2007. 256p. pap. 5.97 (***978-1-59789-864-5(3)***) Barbour Publishing, Inc.

Lilly, Melinda. Pilgrim. 2002. (People of the Middle Ages Ser.). (Illus.). 32p. (J). lib. bdg. 26.60 (978-1-58952-230-5(3)) Rourke Publishing, LLC.

Lindquist, N. J. & Lindquist, Mark E. The New You: Welcome to Your Changed Life. Frank, Kevin, illus. 2000. 103p. (YA). spiral bd. 7.95 (978-1-891793-67-7(5)) High Impact Publishing.

Lingo, Susan. Clip-'n-Snip Object Talks: 25 Cool & Clever Messages Kids Snip from Paper! 2006. 64p. (YA). 11.99 (978-0-7847-1604-5(8) , 42082) Standard Publishing.

—Fold-'n-Hold Object Talks: 25 Cool & Clever Messages Kids Fold from Paper! 2006. 64p. (YA). 11.99 (978-0-7847-1603-8(X) , 42081) Standard Publishing.

Lingo, Susan L. Quick-Quiz Talk Starters: 30 Fast 'n Fun Quizzes - & More - to Get Kids Talking about God & Faith. 2006. 128p. (YA). (gr. 5-7). 15.99 (978-0-7847-1370-9(7) , 42100) Standard Publishing.

Lisech, Howard, et al. Rooted & Grounded (Student Workbook) A Guide for Spiritual Growth Curriculum. Madsen, Rick, ed. Bosacker, Julie & Beckett, Mary Ann, illus. 1999. 270p. (gr. 11-12). stu. ed., per., wbk. ed. 23.95 (978-1-930547-48-3(X)) Deeper Roots Pubns. & Media.

Litchford, David O. Nephi Was an Eagle. unabr. ed. 2004. (Illus.). 46p. (YA). (gr. 5-10). pap. 5.95 (978-1-932280-60-9(X) , 8060X) Granite Publishing & Distribution.

Living Christ's Passionate Life Guidebook. 2005. (YA). per. (978-0-9772313-1-7(3)) Covenant Support Network.

Living for God. (Precious Moments Ser.). (J). 11.99 (978-1-55976-181-9(4)) CEF Pr.

Living in Christ. 304p. stu. ed. 17.95 (978-0-7586-0467-5(X)); 80p. stu. ed., wbk. ed. 10.95 (978-0-7586-0468-2(8)) Concordia Publishing Hse.

Living the Good News Staff. Growing a Grateful, Generous Heart Children's Papers Grades 3-4: Stewardship Resources for Children andTheir Families. 2003. (Illus.). 16p. 2.95 (978-1-931960-19-9(4)) Living the Good News.

—Growing a Grateful, Generous Heart Children's Papers Grades 1-2: Stewardship Resources for Children & Their Families. 2003. (Illus.). 16p. 2.95 (978-1-931960-18-2(6)) Living the Good News.

—Growing a Grateful, Generous Heart Children's Papers Grades 5-6: Stewardship Resources for Children & Their Families. 2003. (Illus.). 16p. 2.95 (978-1-931960-20-5(8)) Living the Good News.

—Growing a Grateful, Generous Heart Children's Papers Preschool/Kindergarten: Stewarship Resources for Children & Their Families. 2003. (Illus.). 16p. 2.95 (978-1-931960-17-5(8)) Living the Good News.

Living the Good News Staff, prod. First Eucharist & Beyond Child's Book: Ongoing Initiation into Communion with Christ. rev. ed. 2005. 32p. (J). 4.95 (978-1-931960-34-2(8)) Living the Good News.

Lockett, Hazel. Youth Devotional & Study Guide Book. 2000. 177p. (YA). (gr. 7 up). pap. 10.00 (978-0-9678877-1-5(2)) Lockett, Hazel.

Lookadoo, Justin. 97: Random Thoughts about Life, Love & Relationships. 2007. (Illus.). 224p. (YA). pap. 14.99 (978-0-8007-3163-2(8)) Revell.

Lookadoo, Justin & DiMarco, Hayley. The Dateable Rules: A Guide to the Sexes. 2004. (Illus.). 176p. (YA). reprint ed. pap. 11.99 (978-0-8007-5915-5(X)) Revell.

Lotz, Louis. The Sweet Life: A Taste of God in the Ordinary. 2004. 139p. pap. (978-0-916466-08-4(6)) Reformed Church Pr., Reformed Church in America.

Loving - Caring - Sharing - Praying, 4 bks., Set. 2002. (Illus.). (J). (ps-1). bds. 9.99 (978-1-57759-591-5(2)) Dalmatian Pr.

Lucado, Max. En el ojo de la Tormenta. 2003. (SPA.). 288p. pap. 12.99 (978-0-88113-721-7(9)) Grupo Nelson.

—Facing Your Giants: Teen Edition. 2007. (Illus.). 208p. (J). pap. 10.99 (978-1-4003-1000-5(8)) Nelson, Thomas Inc.

—He Chose You. 2002. (Illus.). 192p. (J). (gr. 5-9). pap. 10.99 (978-0-8499-7789-3(4)) Nelson, Thomas Inc.

Lucas, Lawrence R. Purity. 2003. 56p. per. 5.95 (978-0-9715916-1-5(X)) Lucas Co.

Luce, Ron. Live God Loud. 2000. (Illus.). 180p. (gr. 8-12). pap. 13.98 (978-0-8499-4281-5(0)) Nelson, Thomas Inc.

Luke - Journeys Pack. 2000. (J). pap. 9.49 (978-0-06-449200-3(1) , Harper Trophy) HarperCollins Pubs.

Lumpkin, Kenya. Quechning the Fire: Many Waters Cannont Quench Love. Lee, Mykle & Shefield, April, eds. 2007. (YA). 21.95 (978-0-9744929-2-6(2)) Leeway Pubs.

Lynn, Debbie. Angel George Series James Needs a Miracle. Norberg, Ken, illus. 2006. (J). 15.95 (978-0-9771318-9-1(0)) Hope Harvest Publishing.

Macdonald, Fiona. Religion. 2003. (Culture Encyclopedia Ser.). (Illus.). 40p. (J). (gr. 5 up). lib. bdg. (978-1-59084-482-3(3)) Mason Crest Pubs.

MacDonald, Mindy. 7 Days of Creation. 2004. (GodCounts Ser.). 24p. (J). bds. 10.99 (978-1-59052-408-4(X) , Multnomah Kidz) WaterBrook Pr.

—9 Fruits Alive. 2004. (God Counts Ser.). 24p. (J). bds. 10.99 (978-1-59052-382-7(2) , Multnomah Kidz) WaterBrook Pr.

Mackall, Dandi D. For God So Loved the World. Selivanova, Elen, illus. 2007. 32p. (J). (ps-2). 12.99 (978-1-59145-524-0(3)) Nelson, Thomas Inc.

Mackall, Dandi Daley. The Armor of God. Harris, Jenny B., illus. 2006. 36p. (J). 9.99 (978-0-7847-1820-9(2)) Standard Publishing.

MacKall, Dandi Daley. Friend from Galilee. Gilchrist, Jan Spivey, illus. 2004. 40p. 9.99 (978-0-8066-4586-5(5) , Augsburg Bks.) Augsburg Fortress, Pubs.

—Jesus in Me. Harris, Jenny, illus. 2006. 36p. (J). 9.99 (978-0-7847-1534-5(3) , 04159) Standard Publishing.

MacKall, Dandi Daley & Kucharik, Elena. Birthday Blessings. 2001. (Little Blessings Ser.). (Illus.). 32p. (J). (ps-k). bds. 6.99 (978-0-8423-3957-5(4)) Tyndale Hse. Pubs.

Mackenzie, Carine. God Is Everywhere. 16p. (J). pap., act. bk. ed. 1.50 (978-1-85792-637-8(4) , Christian Focus) Christian Focus Pubns. GBR. *Dist:* Riverside.

—God Is Faithful. 16p. (J). pap., act. bk. ed. 1.50 (978-1-85792-638-5(2) , Christian Focus) Christian Focus Pubns. GBR. *Dist:* Riverside.

—God Knows Everything. 16p. (J). pap., act. bk. ed. 1.50 (978-1-85792-636-1(6) , Christian Focus) Christian Focus Pubns. GBR. *Dist:* Riverside.

—God Never Changes. 16p. (J). pap., act. bk. ed. 1.50 (978-1-85792-635-4(8) , Christian Focus) Christian Focus Pubns. GBR. *Dist:* Riverside.

—Going to the Doctor. 16p. (J). pap. 3.99 (978-1-85792-548-7(3) , Christian Focus) Christian Focus Pubns. GBR. *Dist:* Riverside.

—Our Loving God. 40p. (J). pap. 6.99 (978-1-85792-419-0(3) , Christian Focus) Christian Focus Pubns. GBR. *Dist:* Riverside.

—Our New Baby. 16p. (J). pap. 3.99 (978-1-85792-547-0(5) , Christian Focus) Christian Focus Pubns. GBR. *Dist:* Riverside.

MacKenzie, Catherine. Feelings. 2000. 16p. (J). (ps-3). (978-1-85792-565-4(3) , Christian Focus) Christian Focus Pubns.

—God Is King. 2000. (Illus.). 48p. (J). (ps-3). pap. (978-1-85792-544-9(0) , Christian Focus) Christian Focus Pubns.

—Hearing. 2000. 16p. (J). (ps-3). (978-1-85792-563-0(7) , Christian Focus) Christian Focus Pubns.

Mackenzie, Catherine. My 1st Experiences: Going to School. 16p. (J). pap. 3.99 (978-1-85792-663-7(3) , Christian Focus) Christian Focus Pubns. GBR. *Dist:* Riverside.

—My 1st Experiences: Our New Home. (Illus.). 16p. (J). pap. 3.99 (978-1-85792-664-4(1) , Christian Focus) Christian Focus Pubns. GBR. *Dist:* Riverside.

—My God Is So Big. (Illus.). 40p. (J). pap. 5.99 (978-1-85792-739-9(7) , Christian Focus) Christian Focus Pubns. GBR. *Dist:* Riverside.

MacKenzie, Catherine. Sight. 2000. 16p. (J). (ps-3). (978-1-85792-562-3(9) , Christian Focus) Christian Focus Pubns.

—Touch. 2000. 16p. (J). (ps-3). (978-1-85792-560-9(2) , Christian Focus) Christian Focus Pubns.

Maclead, Norman. The Gold Thread. Clarkson, Clay, ed. unabr. ed. 1999. (Illus.). 120p. (J). (gr. 3-8). reprint ed. 13.95 (978-1-888692-06-8(5)) Whole Heart Ministries.

Madise, Muriel. My Little Christian Alphabet Book: The ABC's of Christianity. 2002. (Illus.). 32p. (J). 15.95 (978-0-9714994-0-9(3)) MiracleLand Publishers.

Magee, Kanika A. M. Today I Got Saved, 1 book. Thomas, Sonya, illus. 2003. 20p. (J). 10.00 net. (978-0-9748834-0-3(9)) Ebenezer A.M.E. Church.

Magnisi, Sabrina. Miss Sabrina's Learn the Hail Mary As You Color the Rosary: A Guide for Children 6 - 9 & Up! Magnisi, Sabrina & Magnisi, Angelica, illus. 2005. 104p. (J). per. (978-1-933593-30-2(X)) Puarose Publishing.

Mahan, Asa & Hills, Aaron Merritt. Food for Lambs; Or, Leading Children to Christ. Friedrich, Richard, ed. 2003. 134p. per. 6.00 (978-1-932370-03-4(X) , 009) Alethea In Heart.

Mahany, Patricia Shely. Hurry up, Noah. Derico, Laura, ed. Julien, Terry, illus. 2000. (Happy Day Bks.). 24p. (J). (ps-2). 2.49 (978-0-7847-1062-3(7) , 04335, Bean Sprouts) Standard Publishing.

Mally, Sarah. Bright Lights Discipleship Notebook. 2003. (Illus.). (YA). ring bd. 50.00 net. (978-0-9719405-1-2(7)) Tomorrow's Forefathers, Inc.

Manousos, Demetrius. Know Your Mass. Burbank, Addison, illus. 2006. 96p. (YA). per. 14.95 (***978-1-892331-44-1(6)***) Angelus Pr.

Manz Simon, Mary. First Virtues for Toddlers. 2006. 256p. (J). 12.99 (978-0-7847-1848-3(2)) Standard Publishing.

Marrying Right. 2003. (YA). (978-0-9740142-0-3(6)) Five Star Christian Pubns.

Marshall, Mark. God Knows What It's Like to Be a Teenager: Teen Life & the Psalms. 2002. (gr. 7-12). lib. bdg. 24.55 (978-0-613-77808-4(1)) Tandem Library Bks.

Martin, Kim. Because You Were Here. Martin, Kim, illus. 2000. (Illus.). 24p. (J). (ps-6). pap. 5.95 (978-0-615-11533-7(0)) Martin Graphics.

Martin, Michael. TruthQuest Follywood VBS Kit. 2005. cd-rom 99.00 (978-0-9709763-9-0(9)) Return To The Word.

Martin, Michael Heidi. TruthQuest TrueRassic Park VBS Kit. 2002. cd-rom (978-0-9709763-2-1(1)) Return To The Word.

—TruthQuest Weekly Worship Launcher Package. 2002. cd-rom 50.00 (978-0-9709763-3-8(X)) Return To The Word.

Martinez, Mary Ann. 6 Disciplinas Espirituales: Expande las dimensiones de tu relacion con Dios. 2005. (SPA.). 227p. per. 12.00 (978-0-9763015-0-9(4)) Marcasa Bks.

Martos, Joseph. Sacraments: Celebrations of God's Life. 2001. (Illus.). 248p. (YA). per. (978-0-15-901106-5(X)) Harcourt Religion Pubs.

Marxhausen, Joanne. Heaven is a Wonderful Place. Marxhausen, Ben & Koehler, Ed, illus. 2nd ed. 2004. 48p. (J). (ps-4). 7.99 (978-0-7586-0681-5(8)) Concordia Publishing Hse.

Mary Slessor. 2004. 174p. (J). pap. 6.99 (978-1-932307-25-2(7) , Ambassador-Emerald, International) Emerald Hse. Group, Inc.

Maselli, Christopher P. N. Secret of the Firm Foundations Ages 8-12: 12 Mystery Stories to Solve Using the Foundations of Our Faith. 2006. 48p. pap. (978-1-59441-384-1(3)) Carson-Dellosa Publishing Co., Inc.

—Smarter than the Average Pair Ages 8-12: 12 Mystery Stories to Solve Using Wisdom from Proverbs. 2006. 48p. pap. (978-1-59441-383-4(5)) Carson-Dellosa Publishing Co., Inc.

The Mass: Catholics Worship & Celebrate. 1998. (Illus.). (YA). (gr. 7-10). pap., stu. ed. 7.45 (978-0-89837-211-3(9)) Pflaum Publishing Group.

Mass & Sacraments: Celebrating Our Catholic Life. 1998. (Illus.). (YA). (gr. 9-13). stu. ed. 7.45 (978-0-89837-161-1(9)) Pflaum Publishing Group.

Massey, Barbara & DeLoach, Sylvia. Tell Me about God. 1998. (Missions & Me Ser.). (Illus.). 16p. (J). (ps-k). pap. 7.99 (978-1-56309-256-5(5) , W988104) Woman's Missionary Union.

The Masterpiece Marriage. 2004. (Focus on the Family Marriage Ser.).Tr. of La obra Maestra del matrimonio. 72p. 7.99 (978-0-8307-3120-6(2) , Gospel Light) Gospel Light Pubns.

Maxwell, John C. Biblioteca Electronica Caribe Edicion de Liderazgo. 2003. (SPA.). cd-rom 39.99 (978-0-89922-632-3(9)) Grupo Nelson.

—Leading As a Friend. 2001. (PowerPak Collection Ser.). 88p. (J). pap. 3.99 (978-0-8499-7727-5(4)) Nelson, Thomas Inc.

—Leading in Your Youth Group. 2001. 88p. (J). pap. 3.99 (978-0-8499-7726-8(6)) Nelson, Thomas Inc.

Mc Cleary, Donece M. Children's Liturgical Calendar. 2005. (Illus.). 16p. pap., act. bk. ed. 4.95 (978-0-8091-6725-8(5) , 6725-5) Paulist Pr.

McAstocker, David. The Carpenter. 2001. 109p. reprint ed. 17.00 (978-1-930873-34-6(4)) Neumann Pr., The.

McCarty, Diane Bischoff. My First Holy Communtion: A non-Denonimational Program for Preparing young Children to receive Communion for the first Time. 2006. (Illus.). 61p. (J). (978-0-9712124-2-8(2)) Angel Heart Children's Pr.

McCaughrean, Geraldine & Ross, Tony. Dédalo e Icaro; El Rey Midas. Ross, Tony, tr. 2nd ed. 2005. (Mythology Series Collection Mitos Ser.). (SPA., Illus.). 50p. (J). (gr. 2-3). 9.95 (978-84-348-6431-3(2)) SM Ediciones ESP. *Dist:* Iaconi, Mariuccia Bk. Imports.

McConnell, Clem. I Speak to Myself: Encouraging Words for Children. McConnell, Clem, illus. 2007. (Illus.). 32p. (J). per. 5.00 (***978-0-9673490-0-8(1)***) Positive Strokes.

McCottrell-Wade, Cheri C. If You Are Who You Say You Are... Line up with the Word. l.t. ed. 2002. 112p. (YA). per. 20.00 (978-0-9715945-3-1(8)) El-Shaddai Productions.

McCreight, Jacqueline. The Drill Team. 2000. 28p. (YA). pap. 12.00 (978-1-893555-16-7(X)) Grace Publishing.

McDaniel, Karell. Spiritual Agriculture: Such Is the Kingdom of God. 1999. (YA). pap. (978-0-7392-0399-6(1) , PO3625) Morris Publishing.

McDonald, Arthur. Ye Must Be Born Again. 2004. 52p. (978-0-9762892-0-3(2)) Bible Facts Pr.

McDowell, Josh & Pitts, Cindy Ann. Is the Bible Personally from God? Leader's Guide. 2006. 65p. (J). 12.99 (978-1-932587-94-4(2)) Green Key Bks.

McDowell, Josh & Stewart, Ed. Friendship 911 Collection: My Friend Is Struggling With... Conflicts with Others. 2000. (Friendship 911 Ser.). (Illus.). 64p. (gr. 8-12). pap. 7.98 (978-0-8499-3795-8(7)) Nelson, Thomas Inc.

—Friendship 911 Collection: My Friend Is Struggling With... Finding True Love. 2000. (Friendship 911 Ser.). (Illus.). 64p. (gr. 8-12). pap. 7.98 (978-0-8499-3793-4(0)) Nelson, Thomas Inc.

—Friendship 911 Collection: My Friend Is Struggling with... Knowing God's Will. 2000. (Friendship 911 Ser.). (Illus.). 64p. (gr. 8-12). pap. 7.98 (978-0-8499-3798-9(1)) Nelson, Thomas Inc.

McDowell, Josh D. Belief Matters Video Series Curriculum Kit. 2003. (Beyond Belief Campaign Ser.). 149.99 (978-0-8423-8018-8(3)) Tyndale Hse. Pubs.

—The Revolt Video Series Curriculum Kit. 2003. (Beyond Belief Campaign Ser.). 99.99 (978-0-8423-8016-4(7)) Tyndale Hse. Pubs.

McDowell, Sean. Ethix. 2006. 160p. pap. 9.99 (978-0-8054-4050-8(X)) B&H Publishing Grp.

McDowell, Sean. Eti-K: Como destacarse en un mundo en Caos. 2007. 176p. (YA). pap. 8.99 (***978-0-8054-4452-0(1)*** , B&H Bks.) B&H Publishing Grp.

McGrade, Francis & Juliana, M., Sr. I Believe. 2001. (J). reprint ed. 22.00 (978-1-930873-35-3(2)) Neumann Pr., The.

McIntee, Ross. The WAY of Salvation. 2006. 12p. (J). pap. (978-1-897117-12-5(4)) Gospel Folio Pr.

McNaney, Lowell & Lambert, Andy. Fuel for the Journey. 2003. (Illus.). (YA). pap. 15.00 (978-1-930154-11-7(9)) Whitline Ink, Inc.

McNulty, Edward N. Let's Go to the Movies for Young Adults: Alternative Studies for Christian Growth. Patton, Vincent, ed. 2000. 16p. 5.95 (978-1-57895-028-7(7)) Curriculum Publishing, Presbyterian Church (U. S. A.).

—Let's Go to the Movies for Younger & Older Youth: Alternative Studies for Christian Growth. Patton, Vincent, ed. 1999. 16p. (YA). (gr. 7 up). 5.95 (978-1-57895-029-4(5)) Curriculum Publishing, Presbyterian Church (U. S. A.).

Meadows, James L. God Speaks to Today's Teenagers. (YA). Vol. I. pap. 5.50 (978-0-89098-375-1(5)); Vol. II. pap. 5.50 (978-0-89098-376-8(3)) Twentieth Century Christian Bks.

Meaker, Dennis. Following Jesus. 2003. (Bible Studies for Senior High). (Illus.). 96p. pap. 8.00 (978-0-687-06548-6(8)) Abingdon Pr.

Mecham, Janeal A. If Jesus Came to Our House. unabr. ed. 2001. (Illus.). (J). 12.95 (978-1-930980-32-7(9) , 80329) Granite Publishing & Distribution.

Medina, Sarah. A Day to Remember. Brecknell, Annie, illus. 41p. pap. 8.99 (978-0-7459-4770-9(0) , Lion) Lion Hudson plc GBR. *Dist:* Trafalgar Square Publishing.

Meet Herman. 2004. (J). 3.64 (978-1-56870-508-8(5)) Ron-Jon Publishing, Inc.

A Meeting in the Ladies Room: Life Lessons for My Little Sisters in Christ. 2004. (YA). (978-0-9759008-0-2(3)) Nu-Nature.

Meister, Deborah. What Catholics Teens Should Know If Pregnant & Panicked. Larkin, Jean K., ed. 2004. (What Catholic Teens Should Know Ser.). (Illus.). 8p. (YA). 7.95 (978-0-89837-237-3(2) , 440710) Pflaum Publishing Group.

Meloche, Renee. Mary Slessor: Courage in Africa. 2002. (Illus.). 32p. 8.99 (978-1-57658-237-4(X)) YWAM Publishing.

—William Carey: Bearer of Good News. 2002. (Illus.). 32p. 8.99 (978-1-57658-236-7(1)) YWAM Publishing.

Memories of My Baptism, Boy. 1998. (gr. 3). 9.95 (978-1-57734-271-7(2) , 01113313) Covenant Communications, Inc.

Menconi, Al. Full Tilt Media Challenge: 30 Day Devotional Guide. 2004. 200p. (YA). per. 20.00 (978-0-942925-10-4(6)) New Song Publishing Co.

Mercadante, Frank. Positively Dangerous: Live Loud, Be Real, Change the World. 2003. 117p. (YA). 9.95 (978-0-88489-790-3(7)) St. Mary's Pr.

Merlino, John. What Do I Do Now That I'm New: Christian Basics for Kidz Who Want to Follow Jesus. 2002. pap. 5.95 (978-0-9724820-0-4(8)) Paraclete Publishing, Inc.

Metaxas, Eric. Amazing Grace: William Wilberforce & the Heroic Campaign to End Slavery. 2007. 304p. 21.95 (978-0-06-117300-4(2) , Harper San Francisco) HarperCollins Pubs.

Meyer, Joyce & Hafer, Todd. Battlefield of the Mind for Teens: Winning the Battle in Your Mind. 2006. 176p. pap. 10.99 (978-0-446-69764-4(8)) FaithWords.

Meyer, Joyce & Moore, Karen. Battlefield of the Mind for Kids. 2006. (Illus.). 192p. pap. 10.99 (978-0-446-69125-3(9)) FaithWords.

Meyer, Por Joyce. Battlefield of the Mind for Kids. 2006. Tr. of La Batalla de la Mente para Ninos. (SPA.). 128p. pap. 9.99 (978-1-59185-475-3(X)) Strang Communications Co.

Mi Dios es Amor (My God Is Love) Quarter 2, Level 1. (Caminando con Jesus (Walking with Jesus) Series A). (SPA.). (J). (ps-k). stu. ed. 3.50 (978-0-570-05108-4(8) , 16-1812) Concordia Publishing Hse.

Miles, Ted. Respect for Others. Cannizzo, Karen A., ed. 2000. (Conversations with Teens Ser.). (YA). pap. 7.95 (978-0-937997-69-7(2)) Pflaum Publishing Group.

Miller. 7 Things Christians Don't Do Student. 2005. 5.50 (978-0-687-35004-9(2)) Abingdon Pr.

Miller, Doris W. Seven Advent Programs for Children. 2002. 56p. per. 12.95 (978-0-7880-1911-1(2)) CSS Publishing Co.

Miller, Janet. Cut, Color & Paste: God's Creatures. 2004. (Illus.). 96p. (J). (ps-2). 11.95 (978-1-885358-81-3(4)) Rainbow Pubs. & Legacy Pr.

Mills, Ron. A Rock Is My Brother. Padgett, Jim, illus. 1999. 48p. (J). (ps-3). pap. 3.95 (978-0-687-08438-8(5)) Abingdon Pr.

Mirolovich, Nancy, ed. A Sacred History for Children. Marr, Tatiana, tr. Moustardas, Gabriella, illus. 2001. 160p. (J). 25.00 (978-1-928920-03-8(9)) St. John of Kronstadt Pr., The.

La Mision (The Mission) Quarter 2, Level 3. (Caminando con Jesus (Walking with Jesus) Series A). (SPA.). (J). stu. ed. 3.50 (978-0-570-05150-3(9)) Concordia Publishing Hse.

Mission City Press Inc. Staff. Dear Elsie. 2001. (Elsie Dinsmore). 208p. (YA). (gr. 5-9). 12.99 (978-1-928749-55-4(0)) Zonderkidz.

Mission City Press Staff. Dear Millie. 2003. (Life of Faith Ser.). 160p. (YA). 12.99 (978-1-928749-59-2(3)) Zonderkidz.

—Millie's Daily Diary: A Personal Journal for Girls. 2002. (Life of Faith Ser.). 192p. (YA). 14.99 (978-1-928749-56-1(9)) Zonderkidz.

—Millie's Life Lessons: Adventures in Trusting God. 2002. (Life of Faith Ser.). 168p. (YA). (gr. 5-9). pap. 12.99 (978-1-928749-57-8(7)) Zonderkidz.

Missler, Nancy. The Choice: Hypocrisy or Real Christianity. 2001. 176p. (YA). per. 5.95 (978-0-9760994-0-6(3)) King's High Way Ministries, Inc., The.

Mitchell, Stephen. Jesus: What He Really Said & Did. 2003. (gr. 7-12). lib. bdg. 15.30 (978-0-613-71515-7(2)) Tandem Library Bks.

Mittelberg, Mark, et al. Becoming a Contagious Christian Youth Edition: Communicating Your Faith in a Style That Fits You. 2001. (Evangelism Ser.). (J). pap. 89.99 incl. VHS, cd-rom (978-0-310-23769-3(6) , 139180); 128p. pap., stu. ed. 8.99 (978-0-310-23773-0(4) , 139182) Zondervan.

The Model Marriage. 2004. (Focus on the Family(R) Marriage Ser.).Tr. of El Modelo para el Matrimonio. 72p. 7.99 (978-0-8307-3150-3(4) , Gospel Light) Gospel Light Pubns.

Mongtomery Gibson, Jane. In Olden Days. Mongtomery Gibson, Jane, illus. 2005. (YA). bds. 8.99 (978-1-4183-0042-5(X)) Christ Inspired, Inc.

—My Heart Goes with You. Mongtomery Gibson, Jane, illus. 2005. (J). bds. 8.99 (978-1-4183-0029-6(2)) Christ Inspired, Inc.

Mongtomgery Gibson, Jane. Angels Long. Mongtomgery Gibson, Jane, illus. 2005. (YA). bds. 8.99 (978-1-4183-0035-7(7)) Christ Inspired, Inc.

Montgomery Gibson, Jane. God's Little Boy. Montgomery Gibson, Jane, illus. 2005. (YA). bds. 8.99 (978-1-4183-0034-0(9)) Christ Inspired, Inc.

—God's Little Girl. Montgomery Gibson, Jane, illus. 2005. (YA). bds. 8.99 (978-1-4183-0045-6(4)) Christ Inspired, Inc.

—I Touched Jesus Today. Montgomery Gibson, Jane, illus. 2005. (YA). bds. 8.99 (978-1-4183-0027-2(6)) Christ Inspired, Inc.

—I'll Tell You in Heaven. Montgomery Gibson, Jane, illus. 2005. (YA). bds. 8.99 (978-1-4183-0043-2(8)) Christ Inspired, Inc.

—The Inner Soul. Montgomery Gibson, Jane, illus. 2005. (YA). bds. 8.99 (978-1-4183-0049-4(7)) Christ Inspired, Inc.

—The Keeper of Lost & Found. Montgomery Gibson, Jane, illus. 2005. (YA). bds. 8.99 (978-1-4183-0052-4(7)) Christ Inspired, Inc.

—A Little Bit Gone. Montgomery Gibson, Jane, illus. 2005. (YA). bds. 8.99 (978-1-4183-0037-1(3)) Christ Inspired, Inc.

—Mama's Wings. Montgomery Gibson, Jane, illus. 2005. (YA). bds. 8.99 (978-1-4183-0050-0(0)) Christ Inspired, Inc.

—Measure My Heart. Montgomery Gibson, Jane, illus. 2005. (YA). bds. 8.99 (978-1-4183-0023-4(3)) Christ Inspired, Inc.

—Shiny Pants. Montgomery Gibson, Jane, illus. 2005. (YA). bds. 8.99 (978-1-4183-0032-6(2)) Christ Inspired, Inc.

—Through Jesus Eyes. Montgomery Gibson, Jane, illus. 2005. (J). bds. 8.99 (978-1-4183-0024-1(1)) Christ Inspired, Inc.

Moore, Beth, ed. A Heart for Jesus. 2004. Tr. of Un corazon para Jesus. (SPA.). 24p. 8.99 (978-1-59185-420-3(2) , Casa Creacion) Strang Communications Co.

Moore, Karen. Hi God, Let's Talk about My Life. Wummer, Amy, illus. 2006. 128p. (YA). pap. 8.99 (978-0-7847-1246-7(8) , 42173) Standard Publishing.

Moran, Mary Y. & Flanagan, Anne J. Jesus Comes to Us: Activity Book. 80p. (J). (gr. 2). pap. 2.25 (978-0-8198-3922-0(1)) Pauline Bks. & Media.

—Jesus Loves Us: Activity Book. 80p. (J). (gr. 1). pap. 2.25 (978-0-8198-3919-0(1)) Pauline Bks. & Media.

Morgan, Hayley & Lookadoo, Justin. The Dirt on Dating: A Dateable Book. 2005. (Dirt Ser.). 120p. (YA). (gr. 10-12). pap. 9.99 (978-0-8007-5917-9(6)) Revell.

—The Dirt on Drugs: A Dateable Book. 2005. (Dirt Ser.). (Illus.). 112p. (YA). (gr. 10-12). pap. 9.99 (978-0-8007-5919-3(2)) Revell.

Mothers. 7.50 (978-0-8054-5972-2(3)) B&H Publishing Grp.

Mueller, Steve, ed. First Reconciliation & Beyond Child Book: Growing in Friendship with Christ. 2005. (Illus.). 32p. (J). pap. 4.95 (978-1-931960-32-8(1)) Living the Good News.

Mueller, Virginia. What Is Faith? Kolding, Richard Max, illus. rev. ed. 2001. (Happy Day Bks.). 24p. (J). (ps-2). 2.49 (978-0-7847-1218-4(2) , Bean Sprouts) Standard Publishing.

Muggli, Glorianne. Articles of Faith. 1999. (Activity Bks.). (Illus.). 92p. (J). pap., act. bk. ed. 7.95 (978-1-57665-061-5(8)) Muggli Graphics.

—Rebel & the Doctor. Muggli, Glorianne, illus. 2004. (J). 4.95 (978-1-57665-112-4(6)) Muggli Graphics.

—2006 Children's Program - I Will Trust in Heavenly Father & in His Son Jesus Christ: Their Promises Are Sure. 2005. (J). pap. 5.95 (978-1-57665-129-2(0)) Muggli Graphics.

—2006 Monthly Theme Posters - I Will Trust in Heavenly Father & in His Son Jesus Christ: Their Promises Are Sure. 2005. (J). pap. 8.95 (978-1-57665-128-5(2)) Muggli Graphics.

—2006 Primary Theme Book - I Will Trust in Heavenly Father & in His Son Jesus Christ: Their Promises Are Sure. 2005. (J). pap. 11.95 (978-1-57665-126-1(6)) Muggli Graphics.

—2006 Song Visual Aids Book - I Will Trust in Heavenly Father & in His Son Jesus Christ: Their Promises Are Sure. 2005. (J). pap. 8.95 (978-1-57665-127-8(4)) Muggli Graphics.

Mullins, Amy. I'm Reverent When- Bagley, Val Chadwick, illus. 2005. ("Move-About" Book Ser.). (J). (978-1-59156-951-0(6)) Covenant Communications.

Munger, Robert Boyd & Nystrom, Carolyn. My Heart - Christ's Home: Retold for Children. 2001. 32p. pap. 1.50 (978-0-87784-050-3(4)) InterVarsity Pr.

Munson, Jared. Courageous Witness: A Teenager Shares Jesus. 2003. (Illus.). 88p. 8.95 (978-0-8309-1069-4(7)) Herald Publishing Hse.

Murray, Mary. Just Mom & Me Having Tea: A Fun Bible Study for Mothers & Daughters. 2001. (Illus.). 128p. (gr. 4-7). pap. 9.99 (978-0-7369-0426-1(3)) Harvest Hse. Pubs.

Murrie, Diana & Withers, Margaret. Communion Cube. 2006. (Illus.). 9p. 12.00 (***978-0-7151-4976-8(8)***) Church Hse. Pubng. GBR. *Dist:* Church Publishing, Inc.

Mustard Seed International Staff, prod. Share Your Faith Seminar with Book & Video & Other & Workbook. 2000. (YA). (gr. 7). 189.95 (978-1-888568-54-7(2)) Doughten, Russ Films, Inc.

My Beloved. 7.50 (978-0-8054-5913-5(8)) B&H Publishing Grp.

Myers, Bill. Encounter. 2002. (gr. 3-6). lib. bdg. 13.00 (978-0-613-76884-9(1)) Tandem Library Bks.

—The Guardian: Is Every Spirit from Heaven? 2001. (Forbidden Doors Ser.: Vol. 5). 176p. (J). (gr. 5-9). mass mkt. 4.99 (978-0-8423-3992-6(2)) Tyndale Hse. Pubs.

Nagel, Bernadette, illus. Celebrating My Confirmation: A Remembrance Book. 2001. 48p. (J). 17.95 (978-0-8198-1571-2(3) , 332-051) Pauline Bks. & Media.

Nardo, Don. Catholicism. 2005. (Religions of the World Ser.). (Illus.). 112p. (YA). (gr. 7-10). lib. bdg. 29.95 (978-1-59018-632-9(X) , Lucent Bks.) Thomson Gale.

Nav Press Staff. Nuestra Esperanza en Cristo. 2000. Tr. of Our Hope in Christ. (SPA., Illus.). 48p. (YA). pap. 3.99 (978-0-311-13662-9(1) , Editorial Mundo Hispano) Casa Bautista de Publicaciones.

Neal, Connie & Neal, Casey. Hey! This Is Me: Journal. 2001. (Ywof Library). (Illus.). 192p. (J). pap. 12.99 (978-0-310-70162-0(7)) Zonderkidz.

Nee, Watchman. Consagracion. 1998. (Mensajes Para Creyentes Nuevos Ser.).Tr. of Consecration. (SPA & ESP.). 11p. (gr. 6). 2.00 (978-1-57593-447-1(7) , 13-107-002) Living Stream Ministry.

—El Espiritu Santo y la Realidad. 2001. Tr. of Holy Spirit & Reality. (SPA & ESP.). 50p. (gr. 6). 5.50 (978-0-7363-0701-7(X) , 07-910-002) Living Stream Ministry.

—God's Eternal Plan. 2001. 57p. (gr. 6). 5.50 (978-0-7363-0627-0(7) , 08-046-001) Living Stream Ministry.

—God's Overcomers. 1999. 159p. (gr. 6). 16.00 (978-0-7363-0433-7(9) , 07-067-901) Living Stream Ministry.

—The Holy Spirit & Reality. 2001. 53p. (gr. 6). 5.50 (978-0-7363-0628-7(5) , 07-910-001) Living Stream Ministry.

—The Messenger of the Cross. 1998. 44p. (J). (gr. 6). 2.50 (978-0-87083-605-3(6) , 07-033-001) Living Stream Ministry.

—El Plan Eterno de Dios. 2001. Tr. of God's Eternal Plan. (SPA & ESP.). 58p. (gr. 6). 5.50 (978-0-7363-0415-3(0) , 08-046-002) Living Stream Ministry.

—The Sinners' Friend. 2001. (Salvation Ser.). 10p. (gr. 6). 1.00 (978-0-7363-1207-3(2) , 18-087-001) Living Stream Ministry.

Nelson Word Publishing Group Staff. Hand in Hand with Jesus: A Bible Verse for Every Day, to Help Me Live a Better Way. 2000. (Jesus in My Pocket Ser.). (Illus.). 64p. (J). (ps-3). pap. (978-0-7852-0026-0(6)) Nelson/Word Canada.

—Jesus is My Superhero: A Bible Verse for Every Day, to Help Me Live a Better Way, 2000. (Jesus in My Pocket Ser.). (Illus.). 64p. (J). (ps-3). pap. (978-0-7852-0022-2(3)) Nelson/Word Canada.

—My Bible Talks to Me: A Bible Verse for Every Day, to Help Me Live a Better Way, 2000. (Jesus in My Pocket Ser.). (Illus.). 64p. (J). (ps-3). pap. (978-0-7852-0023-9(1)) Nelson/Word Canada.

—Proverbs to Grow By: A Bible Verse for Every Day, to Help Me Live a Better Way. 2000. (Jesus in My Pocket Ser.). (Illus.). 64p. (J). (ps-3). pap. (978-0-7852-0025-3(8)) Nelson/Word Canada.

Neuberger, Anne E. Blessed Kateria & the Cross in the Forest. 2003. 32p. (J). 7.95 (978-1-931709-66-8(1)) Our Sunday Visitor, Publishing Div.

The New First Mass Book: Padded Girls Set. (J). 10.50 (978-0-89942-756-0(1) , B808/42W, Resurrection Pr.) Catholic Bk. Publishing Corp.

The New My First Mass Book: Leatherette Boys Set. (J). lthr. 8.25 (978-0-89942-755-3(3) , B808/67B, Resurrection Pr.) Catholic Bk. Publishing Corp.

The New My First Mass Book: Leatherette Girls Set. (J). lthr. 8.25 (978-0-89942-754-6(5) , B808/67W, Resurrection Pr.) Catholic Bk. Publishing Corp.

The New Saint Joseph Children's Missal: Padded Girls Set. (J). 10.50 (978-0-89942-742-3(1) , B806/42W, Resurrection Pr.) Catholic Bk. Publishing Corp.

Nicholas, Mother Andrea, compiled by. My Little Orthodox Christian Feast Days Activity Book. 2005. (J). spiral bd. 6.95 (978-0-9773579-0-1(2)) St. Nicholas Monastery.

Nigerian/English Book of Hope: International Pictorial Edition (Youth) 2000. (Book of Life Ser.). 64p. (J). mass mkt. (978-1-890525-32-3(4)) Book of Hope International.

Noonan, Robert, et al. Three Weavers Plus Companion: A Father's Guide to Guarding His Daughter's Purity. 2004. 120p. pap. 13.95 (978-0-9700273-5-1(4)) Pumpkin Seed Pr.

Norris, David A. Lasting Success: Quality Decisions, Relationships & Untamed Emotions. 2003. (Illus.). 256p. per. (978-0-943177-12-0(X) , 0-943177-12-x) Heartland Foundation, Inc.

Norvell, Walter. Fundamentals: Web Wise:-) (J). (gr. 6 up). (978-0-633-05796-1(7)) LifeWay Christian Resources.

Nussbaum, Melissa Musick. My First Holy Communion: Sunday Mass & Daily Prayers. Montenegro, Laura, illus. 2002. 64p. (J). 12.00 (978-1-56854-252-2(6)) Liturgy Training Pubns.

Nystrom, Carolyn. Before I Was Born. rev. ed. 2007. 40p. pap. 9.99 (978-1-60006-014-4(5)) NavPress Publishing Group.

Nystrom, Jennifer. Favorite Bible Children: Grades 1 & 2. 2004. (Illus.). 96p. (J). (gr. 1-2). pap. 11.95 (978-1-885358-77-6(6)) Rainbow Pubs. & Legacy Pr.

—Favorite Bible Children: Grades 3 & 4. 2004. (Illus.). 96p. (J). (gr. 3-4). pap. 11.95 (978-1-885358-78-3(4)) Rainbow Pubs. & Legacy Pr.

Oaks, Robert C. Believe! Helping Youth Learn to Trust in the Lord. 2003. (Illus.). xiii, 126p. (J). pap. 14.95 (978-1-59038-203-5(X)) Deseret Bk. Co.

O'Boyle, Neil. Seriously Extreme. 2005. (Illus.). 208p. pap. 11.99 (978-1-85078-446-3(9)) Authentic Media.

O'Connell, Frances H. Giving & Growing: A Student's Guide for Service Projects. Stamschror, Robert P., ed. Mediawerks Staff, illus. 2003. 80p. (YA). (gr. 7-12). 4.25 (978-0-88489-224-3(7)) St. Mary's Pr.

O'Connor, Francine M. ABC's of the Mass: For Children. 1998. pap. 9.95 (978-0-89243-654-5(9)) Liguori Pubns.

—Handbook for Today's Catholic Children. 2002. 64p. pap. 2.95 net. (978-0-7648-1013-8(8)) Liguori Pubns.

—The Sacraments: Walking with Jesus. Larkin, Jean, ed. Lynch, Patricia & Qvick, Larissa, illus. 1999. (Active Learning for Catholic Kids Ser.). 28p. (J). (gr. 1-3). pap. 7.95 (978-0-937997-53-6(6) , 3402) Pflaum Publishing Group.

—We Worship & Pray: The Mass & Traditional Catholic Prayers. Larkin, Jean, ed. Lynch, Patricia, illus. 1999. (Active Learning for Catholic Kids Ser.). 28p. (J). (gr. 4-6). pap. 7.95 (978-0-937997-55-0(2)) Pflaum Publishing Group.

Oestreicher, Mark & Johnston, Kurt. My Faith. 2006. (Invert Middle School Survival Ser.). 80p. (J). pap. 9.99 (978-0-310-27382-0(X)) Zondervan.

—My Family. 2006. (Invert / Middle School Survival Ser.). (Illus.). 144p. (J). pap. 9.99 (978-0-310-27430-8(3)) Zondervan.

Ogbonnaya, A. Okechukwu. Master Stroke: Living in Victory with Jesus, 2 vols. 2001. (Discipleship Training Ser.). 128p. pap., stu. ed. 7.95 (978-0-940955-68-4(7) , 6-5310) UMI (Urban Ministries, Inc.).

Olla, Debbie. Retreats for Teens: Planning Strategies & Teen-Tested Models. Cannizzo, Karen A., ed. 2004. (Youth Ministry Resource Library). 96p. pap. 19.95 (978-0-937997-78-9(1) , 797) Pflaum Publishing Group.

Ollila, Les. Top Priority: Manna. 2002. (YA). ring bd. (978-1-929784-94-3(5)) Positive Action For Christ.

One Room Sunday School Fall: Resource Kit. (Illus.). 52.00 (978-0-687-03622-6(4)) Abingdon Pr.

One Room Sunday School Spring: Resource Kit. (Illus.). 52.00 (978-0-687-03629-5(1)) Abingdon Pr.

One Room Sunday School Winter: Resource Kit. (Illus.). 52.00 (978-0-687-03619-6(4)) Abingdon Pr.

O'Neal, Ted. Making Christmas Count: A Kid's Guide to Keeping the Season Sacred. Alley, R. W., illus. 2006. (AFA.). (J). per. 7.95 (978-0-87029-401-3(6)) Abbey Pr.

Orthodox Woodriver District Baptist Association Staff. Treasured Talents in God's Time. Fisher, Suzanne, ed. Wesley, Robert B., illus. l.t. unabr. ed. 1999. (WeWrite Kids! Ser.: Vol. 42). 39p. (YA). (gr. 4-12). pap. 3.95 (978-1-57635-024-9(X)) WeWrite LLC.

Osborne, Rick. Amazing & Unexplainable Things in the Bible. 2004. (gr. 3-6). lib. bdg. 16.45 (978-0-613-71656-7(6)) Tandem Library Bks.

—God Quest: Dare to Live the Adventure. Close, Alan, illus. 2005. (2:52 Soul Gear Ser.). (J). pap. 7.99 (978-0-310-70868-1(0)) Zonderkidz.

—I Want To Know about the Fruit of the Spirit. 1999. (I Want to Know Ser.). (Illus.). 32p. (J). 9.99 (978-0-310-22096-1(3)) Zondervan.

Osborne, Rick & Bowler, K. Christie. I Want to Know about God: Who God Is, What He Does & Why He Cares about Me. 1998. (I Want to Know Ser.). (Illus.). 32p. (J). (gr. 2-5). 9.99 (978-0-310-22090-9(4)) Zondervan.

—I Want to Know about Prayer. 1998. (I Want to Know Ser.). 32p. (J). 9.99 (978-0-310-22091-6(2)) Zondervan.

Osborne, Rick & Strauss, Ed. Amazing & Unexplainable Things in the Bible. 2004. (2:52 Ser.). (Illus.). 128p. (J). pap. 7.99 (978-0-310-70653-3(X)) Zonderkidz.

—Bible Angels & Demons. 2004. (2:52 Ser.). (Illus.). 112p. (J). pap. 7.99 (978-0-310-70775-2(7)) Zonderkidz.

Osbourne, John. I Want to Know about the Holy Spirit. 1998. (Illus.). 32p. (YA). (gr. 7-10). 9.99 (978-0-310-22093-0(9)) Zondervan.

Osei-Bonsu, Patrick. Run to Win: Releasing the Champion Within You. 2004. (YA). 7.00 (978-0-9747956-3-8(1)) Greenwood, Lori Ministries, Inc.

Our Goal & Our Guides. (YA). (gr. 9-12). 17.00 (978-1-931555-41-8(9)) Our Lady of Victory Schl.

Our Life in the Church: Revised Grade 8 Activity Book. 2005. (J). pap. 6.95 (978-0-89870-901-8(6)) Ignatius Pr.

Our Life in the Church: Revised Grade 8 Student Book. 2005. (J). pap. 12.95 (978-0-89870-911-7(3)) Ignatius Pr.

Pablo y Silas. (Libros Arco (Spanish Arch(R) Books) Ser.).Tr. of Paul & Silas. (SPA.). 24p. (J). 2.49 (978-0-7586-0496-5(3)) Concordia Publishing Hse.

Page 4 Personal Growth Planbook: Mission Max. 2003. (Illus.). 48p. (J). pap. 4.95 (978-1-59312-045-0(1)) North American Mission Board, SBC.

Palau, Luis & Halliday, Steve. High Definition Life: Trading Life's Good for God's Best. 2005. (Illus.). 256p. pap., stu. ed. 14.99 (978-0-8007-3053-6(4)) Revell.

Palmer, Alison. Walking the Path of Faith: More Fun Character-Building Activities for LDS Children - a Companion Volume to Planting Seeds of Faith. 2004. (J). per. 9.99 (978-0-88290-764-2(6) , Horizon Pubs.) Cedar Fort, Inc./CFI Distribution.

Parker, Sherri. Let's Seek God's Word Together. 2004. (J). spiral bd. 5.18 (978-1-56870-544-6(1)) RonJon Publishing, Inc.

Parks, Kathy, illus. My Goodnight Bedtime With Nightlight. 2006. 18p. (J). bds. 8.99 (978-0-7847-1520-8(3) , 04414) Standard Publishing.

Parmer, Paul. Overcoming that "After-Camp Spiritual Dive" Date not set. 10p. (YA). (gr. 3 up). pap. (978-1-884838-17-0(0)) Walterick Pubs., Inc.

Parry, Alan. The First Seven Days. Parry, Linda, illus. 2004. (ps-3). 9.00 (978-0-687-04910-3(5)) Abingdon Pr.

Parry, L. Jesus Hace Amigos (Jesus Makes Friends) (SPA.). (J). 1.99 (978-0-7899-0537-6(X) , 495666) Editorial Unilit.

—Jesus Llama a Sus Discipulos (Jesus Calls His Disciples) (SPA.). (J). 1.99 (978-0-7899-0538-3(8) , 495665) Editorial Unilit.

Parry, L. & Parry, A. Siguiendo la Estrella Actividades.Tr. of Follow the Star Activity Book. (SPA.). (J). 9.99 (978-1-56063-834-6(6) , 497746) Editorial Unilit.

Passey, Marion. My Tiny Book of Joseph Smith. 2004. (Illus.). (J). 5.95 (978-1-59038-243-1(9)) Deseret Bk. Co.

Pastore, Vicki, illus. The Apostle' Creed. 2007. 32p. (J). (gr. k-3). pap. 7.95 (978-0-8091-6738-8(7) , 6738-8) Paulist Pr.

Patricia, St John. A Young Person's Guide to Knowing God. 2000. 240p. (J). (978-1-85792-600-2(5)) Christian Focus Pubns.

Pedersen, Mary Jo, et al. More Than Meets the Eye: Finding God in the Creases & Folds of Family Life. 2003. 160p. (YA). pap. 14.95 (978-0-88489-594-7(7)) St. Mary's Pr.

Perkins, Greg. Un Ninito Los Guiaba. 2005. (Illus.). 16p. (J). (gr. 4-7). 8.99 (978-1-59185-826-3(7) , Charisma Kids) Strang Communications Co.

Perry, Janice Kapp. I'm Trying to Be Like Jesus. Abts, Stacey, illus. 2003. (J). (978-1-57008-843-8(8)) Scribbulations LLC.

Perry, Jason & Keels, Steve. You Are Not Your Own: Living Loud for God. 2004. (TruthQuest Ser.). 144p. (gr. 7 up). pap. 12.99 (978-0-8054-2591-8(8)) B&H Publishing Grp.

Petersen, Randy, et al. The Real Deal: Student Journal. 1998. (Nineteen Ninety Nine Fifty-Day Spiritual Adventure Ser.). (Illus.). 80p. (YA). 7.00 (978-1-57849-107-0(X)) Mainstay Church Resources.

Peterson, Tracie. King of Hearts. 1999. mass mkt. 0.99 (978-1-57748-432-5(0)) Barbour Publishing, Inc.

Petrea, Janice. Just Clowning Around: Sharing God's Love Through Love & Laughter. 1998. (Illus.). 96p. (J). (gr. 7-12). pap. 10.95 (978-1-56309-237-4(9) , W986101) Woman's Missionary Union.

Pettiford, Sherry Lynn. Don't Miss This End Time Move of God: From the Awakenings Series... Awakenings: the Cost. l.t. ed. 2001. 140p. per. (978-0-9715945-0-0(3)) El-Shaddai Productions.

Phillips, Stanley C. Christian Gospel, Doctrine & Experience Simply Put. 2000. v, 152p. (YA). pap. 5.00 (978-0-9706376-1-1(6)) Predestinarian, The.

Pilavachi, Mike. Soul Survivor: Finding Passion & Purpose in the Dry Places. 2004. (Illus.). 120p. 10.99 (978-0-8307-3324-8(8) , Gospel Light) Gospel Light Pubns.

A Pilgrim's Journal. 2001. 32p. (YA). pap. 3.00 (978-0-88489-750-7(8)) St. Mary's Pr.

Pingry, Patricia. The Story of the Star Spangled Banner. 2005. 28p. (J). bds. 6.95 (978-0-8249-6567-9(1)) Ideals Pubns.

Pingry, Patricia A. The Power of Faith for Teens: True Stories. 2004. (Illus.). 160p. pap. 9.95 (978-0-8249-4622-7(7)) Ideals Pubns.

Plans & Pluses, Vol. 5. 2003. (J). 19.95 (978-0-633-09930-5(9)) LifeWay Christian Resources.

Plante, Patty. Joy for Jesus: Doing God's Word, 4. 2004. (Joy for Jesus Ser.: 4). 88p. (J). ring bd. 24.95 (978-1-889723-42-6(8)) Family Harvest Church.

Plum, Joan. I Am Special Four Year Old Child's. 5th ed. 2003. 112p. (J). pap., act. bk. ed. 9.95 (978-1-931709-20-0(3)) Our Sunday Visitor, Publishing Div.

Pockets Learning Staff. Good Samaritan Book. 1998. (Illus.). 8p. (ps up). 35.00 (978-1-888074-97-0(3)) Pockets of Learning.

Podwal, Mark. Jerusalem Sky: Stars, Crosses & Crescents. Podwal, Mark, illus. 2005. (Illus.). 32p. (J). (gr. k-12). 15.95 (978-0-385-74689-2(X) , Doubleday Bks. for Young Readers) Random Hse. Children's Bks.

Pohle & Dowley. Maqueta del Templo de Salomon. 2003. Tr. of Solomon's Temple Model. (SPA.). pap. 9.99 (978-0-7899-1127-8(2)) Editorial Unilit.

Poole, Susie. Always near Me. 2004. (Illus.). 26p. (J). 6.99 (978-0-310-70821-6(4)) Zonderkidz.

—A Time for Everything. 2004. (Illus.). 26p. (J). 6.99 (978-0-310-70822-3(2)) Zonderkidz.

Poor Man's Heaven: Living for the Goodness of God. 2002. 136p. per. 10.00 (978-0-9712585-7-0(0)) JuDe Publishing.

Portavoz Editorial Staff & Sabio Y Prudente Ministries Staff. Manual de Exploracion, Vol. 4. 1999. (Sabio & Prudente Ser.: Vol. 4). (SPA.). 64p. (YA). pap. 3.99 (978-0-8254-0939-4(X) , Editorial Portavoz) Kregel Pubns.

Poteet, Michael S. The Screwtape Letters. 2001. 88p. (J). stu. ed., ring bd. 14.99 (978-1-58609-178-1(6)) Progeny Pr.

Powell, Kara Eckmann. Life at School, Vol. 7. 2000. (Pulse Ser.). (Illus.). 96p. 14.99 (978-0-8307-2508-3(3) , Gospel Light) Gospel Light Pubns.

Powell, Kara Eckmann & Johnson, Mike, eds. Peer Pressure. 2001. (Pulse Ser.: 13). 96p. (gr. 6-9). 14.99 (978-0-8307-2549-6(0) , Gospel Light) Gospel Light Pubns.

Powell, Rebecca. Wise up! Experience the Power of Proverb. 2005. 210p. pap. 19.95 (978-1-4141-0399-0(9)) Pleasant Word.

Power & Light for Kids: Kidsbook. 5.95 (978-0-8309-1076-2(X)); 5.95 (978-0-8309-1080-9(8)); 5.95 (978-0-8309-1085-4(9)) Herald Publishing Hse.

Power & Light for Young Kids. 8.95 (978-0-8309-1096-0(4)); 8.95 (978-0-8309-1097-7(2)); 2005. (YA). pap. 8.95 (978-0-8309-1134-9(0)) Herald Publishing Hse.

Power Pak of Games. 1998. 112p. (J). tchr. ed., per. 12.99 (978-1-57405-000-4(1)) CharismaLife Pubs.

PowerXpress - Journey to Bethlehem Unit. 2004. 115.00 (978-0-687-00578-9(7)) Abingdon Pr.

Pozdol, MaryBeth. Prison to Palace. Leonard, Erskine, illus. 2004. 189p. (J). ring bd. 29.95 (978-1-889723-43-3(6)) Family Harvest Church.

Priddy Books Staff. God Made Me & God Made Us, 2 bks. bds. 15.95 (978-0-312-49161-1(1) , Priddy Bks.) St. Martin's Pr.

Primeros pasitos misioneros (First Steps, Spanish) 2004. pap. 12.99 (978-1-56309-930-4(6)) Woman's Missionary Union.

Prokop, Lori. Jesus Teenager: How to Be the Coolest Kid Around. 2000. (Illus.). (YA). pap. 9.95 (978-1-929737-00-0(9)) Who You Are International, Inc.

Quantrell, Angie. I Can Pray. Reeves, Rhonda, ed. 2000. 32p. (J). (ps). 9.99 (978-1-56309-352-4(9)) Woman's Missionary Union.

Quine, David. Answers for Difficult Days: Surviving the Storm of Secularism. 1998. 48p. (YA). (gr. 7 up). pap. 5.95 (978-0-9656512-1-9(5)) Cornerstone Curriculum Project.

Radecki, Francisco. The Family Catechism. 2005. (Illus.). 120p. (J). 19.95 (978-0-9715061-1-4(6)) St. Joseph Media.

Ramshaw, Gail. Every Day & Sunday, Too. Jarret, Judy, illus. 2004. 44p. 15.99 (978-0-8066-2334-4(9) , 10-23349, Augsburg Bks.) Augsburg Fortress, Pubs.

Rathbun, Frankie Beathard. Ten Kids & a Teacher: Memories from a One Room School. 2006. 132p. (J). pap. 14.99 (978-1-4141-0582-6(7)) Pleasant Word.

Reams, Clyde. Stories by the Fire. 2006. 31p. 10.99 (978-1-4116-7711-1(0)) Lulu.com.

Reed, Judy. Christian Conflict Resol WWJD. 2003. 64p. (C). pap. 7.99 (978-0-7647-0963-0(1)) School Specialty Publishing.

—Sharing My Beliefs: Discovering Real-Life Witnesses. 2004. (Faith Rules Ser.). 96p. (J). pap. 4.99 (978-0-7424-2837-9(0) , In Celebration) Schaffer, Frank Pubns.

Reeg, Cynthia. Gifts from God. Roberts, MarySue, photos by. 2007. (Illus.). (J). 28p. 10.95 ***(978-1-933090-33-7(2));*** 30p. E-Book 5.00 incl. cd-rom ***(978-1-933090-34-4(0))*** Guardian Angel Publishing, Inc.

Reeves. Day by Day Bible Daily Devotions for Reading with Children. 2005. 376p. pap. 16.95 (978-1-56563-521-0(3)) Hendrickson Pubs., Inc.

Reeves, Eira. Dios Te Ama.Tr. of God Loves You. (SPA.). (J). 1.89 (978-0-7899-0477-5(2) , 498668) Editorial Unilit.

Reeves, Rhonda. Families Are Special. 2000. (Missions & Me Ser.). (Illus.). 16p. (J). (ps). 7.99 (978-1-56309-312-8(X)) Woman's Missionary Union.

Regina Press Staff. Catholic Baby's First Prayers. 1999. (J). (ps-k). 10.99 (978-0-88271-715-9(4)) Regina Pr., Malhame & Co.

—Thank You, God. 1999. 4.95 (978-0-88271-672-5(7)) Regina Pr., Malhame & Co.

Reichard, Don. Word of Life Champion QuietTime. 2002. (Illus.). (J). (gr. 10-12). pap. 6.95 (978-1-931235-44-0(9)) Word of Life Fellowship, Inc.

—Word of Life Preschool Quiet Time, 5 vols. 2002. (Illus.). (J). pap. 11.95 (978-1-931235-45-7(7)) Word of Life Fellowship, Inc.

—Word of Life Quiet Time Supplement. 2002. pap. 6.95 (978-1-931235-41-9(4)) Word of Life Fellowship, Inc.

Reichard, Don, ed. Word of Life Challenger Quiet Time. (J). (gr. 1-2). 2002. (Illus.). pap. 6.95 (978-1-931235-42-6(2)); 2001. pap. 6.95 (978-1-931235-09-9(0)) Word of Life Fellowship, Inc.

—Word of Life Conqueror Quiet Time. (J). (gr. 3-4). 2002. (Illus.). pap. 6.95 (978-1-931235-43-3(0)); 2001. pap. 6.95 (978-1-931235-10-5(4)) Word of Life Fellowship, Inc.

—Word of Life Preschool Quiet Time, 5 vols. 2001. (J). (ps). pap. 11.95 (978-1-931235-12-9(0)) Word of Life Fellowship, Inc.

Rice, Wayne & Zondervan. Read This Book or You're Grounded! A Secret Guide to Surviving Home. 2003. (Studentware Ser.). (Illus.). 160p. (J). pap. 9.99 (978-0-310-25049-4(8)) Zondervan.

Riddle, John. Lintball Leo: The Battle of Right & Wrong (2:52 Soul Gear) 2007. 128p. pap. 8.99 (978-0-310-70875-9(3)) Zonderkidz.

Rieder, Ruth. Angels Watching over Me. Comer, Wes, illus. 2002. (J). (ps-5). 6.00 (978-0-9674360-5-0(2)) Rieder, Ruth.

—God's Jewels. Comer, Wes, illus. 2002. (J). (ps-5). 6.00 (978-0-9674360-9-8(5)) Rieder, Ruth.

—Kingdom Clothing. Comer, Wes, illus. 2002. (J). (ps-5). 6.00 (978-0-9674360-7-4(9)) Rieder, Ruth.

—Marble Palaces or Painted Beams. Comer, Wes, illus. 2002. (J). (ps-5). 6.00 (978-0-9674360-8-1(7)) Rieder, Ruth.

Ring, Laura, ed. Favorite Christmas Carols Happy Day Book. Paris, Pat, illus. 1999. (Happy Day Bks.). 24p. (ps-2). 2.49 (978-0-7847-1085-2(6) , 04281, Bean Sprouts) Standard Publishing.

Rise up & Sing. 2nd ed. 2000. (J). 296p. pap. 4.95 (978-1-57992-034-0(9)); 736p. 59.95 (978-1-57992-036-4(5)); 296p. 6.95 (978-1-57992-035-7(7)) Oregon Catholic Pr.

Robins, Jeannie. College Roadmap: Your Guide to Becoming A Freshman in Life. Grimes, Liz & Lindemann, Kara, eds. 2004. (Illus.). 160p. (YA). pap. 14.95 (978-0-9755370-0-8(8)) ReSource Guides, Inc.

Robinson, Helen Lee, ed. Guide's Greatest Sabbath Stories. 2004. (Review Kids Ser.). 144p. (J). pap. 10.99 (978-0-8280-1814-2(6) , 79-978) Review & Herald Publishing Assn.

Robinson, Ruth-Ann. My Heavenly Happys & My Secretly Sads: A Childs Workbook. 1999. (Illus.). 56p. (J). (gr. 3-10). pap. 20.00 (978-1-929010-01-1(X)) Epiphany Pr.

Roche, Aloysius. A Bedside Book of Saints. 2001. reprint ed. 18.00 (978-1-930873-28-5(X)) Neumann Pr., The.

Rock, Lois. Al Final del Dia. Rawlings, Louise, illus. (Coleccion Luz de Noche). (SPA.). (J). (gr. k-3). (978-84-236-5039-2(1)) Edebé ESP. *Dist:* Lectorum Pubns., Inc.

—La Gran Noticia. Rawlings, Louise, illus. (Coleccion Luz de Noche). (SPA.). (J). (gr. k-3). (978-84-236-4917-4(2)) Edebé ESP. *Dist:* Lectorum Pubns., Inc.

—Todos los Dias Contigo. Rawlings, Louise, illus. (Coleccion Luz de Noche). (SPA.). (J). (gr. k-3). (978-84-236-4916-7(4)) Edebé ESP. *Dist:* Lectorum Pubns., Inc.

Rodriguez, Orlando. Estudiante. 2004. (Sabio Y Prudente Ser.).Tr. of Student. (SPA.). 64p. (YA). Vol. 2. pap. 3.99 (978-0-8254-0935-6(7)); Vol. 3. pap. 3.99 (978-0-8254-0937-0(3)) Kregel Pubns. (Editorial Portavoz).

—Maestro, Vol. 3. 2004. (Sabio Y Prudente Ser.).Tr. of Teacher. (SPA.). 64p. (YA). pap. 4.99 (978-0-8254-0936-3(5) , Editorial Portavoz) Kregel Pubns.

Rodriguez, Orlando & Sabio Y Prudente Ministries Staff. Estudiante, Vol. 5. 2000. (Sabio Y Prudente Ser.).Tr. of Student. (SPA.). 64p. (YA). pap. 3.99 (978-0-8254-0941-7(1) , Editorial Portavoz) Kregel Pubns.

—Maestro. (Sabio Y Prudente Ser.).Tr. of Teacher. (SPA.). 64p. (YA). Vol. 2. 2004. pap. 4.99 (978-0-8254-0934-9(9)); Vol. 5. 2000. pap. 4.99 (978-0-8254-0940-0(3)) Kregel Pubns. (Editorial Portavoz).

—Paquete completo no 1 el jardin del Eden. 2001. (Sabio Y Prudente Ser.).Tr. of Complete Package #1 Garden of Eden. (SPA.). (J). pap. 24.95 (978-0-8254-0976-9(4) , Editorial Portavoz) Kregel Pubns.

—Paquete completo no 2 abel y Cain. 2002. (Sabio Y Prudente Ser.).Tr. of Complete Package #2 Cain & Abel. (SPA.). (J). pap. 24.99 (978-0-8254-0969-1(1) , Editorial Portavoz) Kregel Pubns.

Roseman, Kenneth D. Until the Messiah Comes. 2004. (Do-It-Yourself Jewish Adventure Ser.). (Illus.). 145p. (gr. 4-6). pap. 11.95 (978-0-8074-0706-6(2) , 140073) URJ Pr.

Ross & Guymon-King. Primary Partners. 2004. cd-rom 11.95 (978-1-57734-691-3(2)) Covenant Communications, Inc.

—Primary Partners: Faith in God: We Love Activity Days. 2004. cd-rom 12.95 (978-1-59156-344-0(5)) Covenant Communications, Inc.

—Super Little Singers. 2004. pap. 12.95 (978-1-59156-163-7(9)); cd-rom 12.95 (978-1-59156-164-4(7)) Covenant Communications, Inc.

Ross, Mary & Guymon, Jennette. Primary Partners Vol. 2: Nursery-Age 3. 2004. (ps-3). pap. 9.95 (978-1-57734-185-7(6) , 01113208) Covenant Communications, Inc.

Ross, Michael & Edmondson, Jeff. Radically Plugged In: High-Voltage Devotionals to Ground Your Faith. 1998. (Illus.). 136p. (gr. 8-12). pap. 11.99 (978-0-8341-1707-5(X)) Beacon Hill Pr. of Kansas City.

Rottmann, Erik. A Meal for Many: My Gift for Jesus. Paris, Pat, illus. 2003. (Arch Bks.). (ENG.). 16p. (J). (gr. k-4). 1.99 (978-0-7586-0377-7(0)) Concordia Publishing Hse.

Roxborough, Judy A. Convicted by Faith: The Life & Martydom of Mercedes Prat, Stj. adapted ed. 2002. 60p. pap. 3.95 (978-0-9638041-6-7(2)) Society of St. Teresa of Jesus.

Rue, Nancy N. The Beauty Book: It's a God Thing. Mach, Steven, illus. 2000. (Young Women of Faith Library Ser.). 104p. (J). pap. 7.99 (978-0-310-70014-2(0)) Zondervan.

—The Blurry Rules Book: It's a God Thing. 2001. (Ywof Library). 96p. (J). pap. 7.99 (978-0-310-70152-1(X)) Zondervan.

—The Buddy Book: It's a God Thing. 2001. (Ywof Library Ser.). (Illus.). 128p. (J). (gr. 3-7). pap. 7.99 (978-0-310-70064-7(7)) Zonderkidz.

—The Santa Fe Years. 2002. (Christian Heritage Ser.: No. 5). (Illus.). 112p. (J). pap. 7.99 (978-1-56179-897-1(5)) Bethany Hse. Pubs.

—The Values & Virtues Book: It's a God Thing! 2002. (Ywof Library). (Illus.). 112p. (J). pap. 7.99 (978-0-310-70257-3(7)) Zondervan.

—The Walk-the-Walk Book: It's a God Thing! Boyer, Lyn, illus. 2003. (YWOF Library). 128p. (J). pap. 7.99 (978-0-310-70259-7(3)) Zonderkidz.

—The Year 'Round Holiday Book: It's a God Thing! 2002. (Ywof Library). (Illus.). 112p. (J). pap. 7.99 (978-0-310-70256-6(9)) Zonderkidz.

Rue, Nancy N. & Rue, Marijean. Beauty Lab. 2007. (Faithgirlz!#8482; Ser.). 144p. (J). pap. 7.99 (978-0-310-71276-3(9)) Zonderkidz.

Ruffin, Debera. Rejoice Evermore. 2002. (Illus.). 32p. (J). (gr. k-5). 14.99 (978-0-9716240-6-1(2) , 130-001, Christian Living Bks.) Pneuma Life Publishing, Inc.

Russell, Bob & Russell, Rusty. The Power of One Another: Developing Christian Relationships. 2004. 144p. (J). stu. ed. 7.99 (978-0-7847-7199-0(5) , 09419) Standard Publishing.

Sabio Y Prudente Ministries. Marcadores No 1-32. 2004. (Sabio Y Prudente Ser.).Tr. of Bookmarks (32 assorted) #1-32. (SPA.). 7.50 (978-0-8254-0948-6(9) , Editorial Portavoz) Kregel Pubns.

—Nuevos Marcadoresx No 33-64. 1999. (Sabio Y Prudente Ser.).Tr. of New Bookmarks (32 assorted) #33-64. (SPA.). 7.50 (978-0-8254-0975-2(6) , Editorial Portavoz) Kregel Pubns.

The Sacraments. 2004. (Exploring Luther's Small Catechism Ser.). (gr. 5-6). 2.99 (978-0-8066-6786-7(9)) Augsburg Fortress, Pubs.

Sacraments & Prayer, 6 booklets. 1998. (Illus.). (YA). (gr. 7-10). stu. ed. 12.95 (978-0-89837-213-7(5)) Pflaum Publishing Group.

Sadlier Team Staff. Coming to God, Catechist's Annotated Guide: Keystone Parish Edition. 1998. (Coming to Faith Program Ser.). (Illus.). 344p. (J). (gr. 1). pap. 32.76 net. (978-0-8215-4371-9(7)) Sadlier, William H. Inc.

—Coming to God's World, Catechist's Annotated Guide: Keystone Parish Edition. 1998. (Coming to Faith Program Ser.). (Illus.). 368p. (J). (gr. 6). pap. 32.76 net. (978-0-8215-4376-4(8)) Sadlier, William H. Inc.

—Coming to Jesus, Catechist's Annotated Guide: Keystone Parish Edition. 1998. (Coming to Faith Program Ser.). (Illus.). 344p. (J). (gr. 2). pap. 32.76 net. (978-0-8215-4372-6(5)) Sadlier, William H. Inc.

Sadlier We Believe Review & Resource Book. 2003. (J). (gr. 1). per. (978-0-8215-5421-0(2) , Sadlier) Sadlier, William H. Inc.

Sanders, DeAnna. Mission Quest Journal: Quest Reflections. 1998. (MissionsQuest Ser.). (Illus.). 118p. (J). (gr. 11). pap. 9.95 (978-1-56309-262-6(X) , W986124) Woman's Missionary Union.

Sanders, Fred. Dr. Doctrine's Christian Comix, 4 Vols. 1999. (J). 15.96 (978-0-8308-2240-9(2)) InterVarsity Pr.

Sanders, Nancy I. Adventures with Colors. 1998. (Archy's Activity Bks.). (Illus.). 16p. (J). (ps-2). pap. 3.99 (978-0-570-05079-7(0)) Concordia Publishing Hse.

—Adventures with Letters. 1998. (Archy's Activity Bks.). (Illus.). 16p. (J). (ps-2). pap. 3.99 (978-0-570-05080-3(4)) Concordia Publishing Hse.

—Adventures with Numbers. 1998. (Archy's Activity Bks.). (Illus.). 16p. (J). (ps-2). pap. 3.99 (978-0-570-05078-0(2)) Concordia Publishing Hse.

Savelle, Jerry. Don't Let Go of Your Dreams. Date not set. mass mkt. 3.99 (978-0-88144-171-0(6)) Victory Graphics & Media.

Schambach, R. W., frwd. This Charge, This Generation: Could This Be the Generation That Brings about Change in the Earth? 2005. 208p. per. 14.99 (978-0-9763800-0-9(5) , 10) Orison Pubs.

School of the Bible for Kids: The Most High God. 2003. (ENG & GER.). 238p. ring bd. 79.95 (978-0-9767647-3-1(3)) Kids in Ministry International.

School of the Holy Spirit for Kids. 2002. (ENG & GER.). 199p. ring bd. 74.95 (978-0-9767647-2-4(5)) Kids in Ministry International.

Schtick & God's Funny Ways, Is Life Fair? The Point of the Parables. 2000. (Connect Ser.: Vol. 10). (YA). 20.00 (978-0-687-72661-5(1)) Abingdon Pr.

Schultz, Thom & Schultz, Joani. Children's Ministry Kit. 2005. pap. 59.99 incl. DVD (978-0-7644-2890-6(X)) Group Publishing, Inc.

Scrimshire, Hazel. God's Special Day. 16p. (J). pap. (978-1-85792-354-4(5) , Christian Focus) Christian Focus Pubns. GBR. *Dist:* Riverside.

—God's Special Name. 16p. (J). pap. (978-1-85792-353-7(7) , Christian Focus) Christian Focus Pubns. GBR. *Dist:* Riverside.

—Love Mum & Dad. 16p. (J). pap. (978-1-85792-355-1(3) , Christian Focus) Christian Focus Pubns. GBR. *Dist:* Riverside.

—Love Others. 16p. (J). pap. (978-1-85792-356-8(1) , Christian Focus) Christian Focus Pubns. GBR. *Dist:* Riverside.

—A Special Promise. 16p. (J). pap. (978-1-85792-357-5(X) , Christian Focus) Christian Focus Pubns. GBR. *Dist:* Riverside.

—Thanks, God. 16p. (J). pap. (978-1-85792-360-5(X) , Christian Focus) Christian Focus Pubns. GBR. *Dist:* Riverside.

—This Belongs To. 16p. (J). pap. (978-1-85792-358-2(8) , Christian Focus) Christian Focus Pubns. GBR. *Dist:* Riverside.

—Too Many Toys. (God's Little Guidebooks Ser.). 16p. (J). pap. (978-1-85792-352-0(9) , Christian Focus) Christian Focus Pubns. GBR. *Dist:* Riverside.

Scully, Michael. Reaching Teens Through Film. Cannizzo, Karen A., ed. 2002. (Jesus in Modern Media Ser.: Volume 9). (YA). per. 19.95 (978-0-89837-177-2(5) , 3702) Pflaum Publishing Group.

—Reaching Teens Through Film & Music. Cannizzo, Karen A., ed. 2001. (Jesus in Modern Media Ser.: Vol. 2001-2002). 96p. (YA). pap. 19.95 (978-0-89837-176-5(7)) Pflaum Publishing Group.

—Reaching Teens Through Film & Music. 1999. (Jesus in Modern Media Ser.: Vol. 2000). 128p. (YA). pap. 19.95 (978-0-937997-60-4(9) , 3700) Pflaum Publishing Group.

Scully, Michael & Donovan, Patrick. Reaching Teens Through Film, Vol. 11. Cannizzo, Karen A., ed. 2004. (Jesus in Modern Media Ser.: 11). 104p. (YA). per. 21.95 (978-0-89837-195-6(3) , 3704) Pflaum Publishing Group.

Scully, Michael & Donovan, Patrick J. Reaching Teens Through Film, Vol. 10. Cannizzo, Karen, ed. 2003. (Jesus in the Media Ser.: 10). 88p. (YA). per. 19.95 (978-0-89837-187-1(2) , 3703) Pflaum Publishing Group.

Seek to Find Jesus. 2004. (gr. 4-6). 5.95 (978-0-7647-0429-1(X)) School Specialty Publishing.

Seirei to Anata. 2004. (JPN.). (YA). ring bd. 14.00 (978-0-9673342-5-7(X)) Saints Of Glory Church.

Share Your Faith Instructional Manual. 2000. (Illus.). 31p. (YA). pap. 9.95 (978-1-888568-55-4(0)) Doughten, Russ Films, Inc.

Sharing Your Faith. 2004. (Faith 4 Life Ser.). 48p. 14.99 (978-0-7644-2466-3(1) , Flagship Church Resources) Group Publishing, Inc.

Shellenberger, Susie. Bloom: A Girl's Guide to Growing Up. 2003. (Illus.). 232p. (YA). pap. 17.99 (978-1-58997-061-8(6)) Focus on the Family Publishing.

—Secret Power for Girls: Identity, Security, & Self-Respect in Troubling Times. 2003. (Invert / Secret Power Bible Studies for Girls Ser.). 176p. (YA). pap. 9.99 (978-0-310-24972-6(4)) Zondervan.

—Secret Power to Joy, Becoming a Star, & Great Hair Days: Study on the Book of Philippians. 2005. (Invert / Secret Power Bible Studies for Girls Ser.). (Illus.). 128p. (YA). pap. 9.99 (978-0-310-25678-6(X)) Zondervan.

Shining Star. Fruit of the Spirit Crafts & M. 2001. 48p. (C). pap. 7.99 (978-0-7647-0497-0(4)) School Specialty Publishing.

Shoemaker, Tim. Reboot Your Brain: Byte-Sized Devotions for Boys. Baumann, Marty, illus. 2004. 160p. (J). (gr. 3-6). pap. 7.99 (978-0-310-70719-6(6)) Zonderkidz.

Short, William J. Poverty & Joy: The Franciscan Tradition. 1999. (Traditions of Christian Spirituality Ser.). 144p. (J). pap. 15.00 (978-1-57075-295-7(8)) Orbis Bks.

Shouting in the Hush Arbor Student Handbook Younger Elementary. 2.50 (978-0-687-32602-0(8)) Abingdon Pr.

Shouting in the Hush Arbor Teen Leader. 9.00 (978-0-687-32732-4(6)) Abingdon Pr.

Shouting in the Hush Arbor Teen Student Handbook. 4.00 (978-0-687-32742-3(3)) Abingdon Pr.

Show Me the Road. 12.00 (978-0-687-05431-2(1)) Abingdon Pr.

Siciliano, Terry. Beyond a Reasonable Doubt: Evidence for Christianity. 2nd rev. ed. 2001. 166p. (YA). (gr. 7 up). pap. 11.95 (978-0-9710199-4-2(0)) truthpress.com.

Signing God's Word: Wisdom. 2005. 64p. (J). per. 7.99 (978-1-59441-080-2(1) , CD-204007) Carson-Dellosa Publishing Co., Inc.

Simon, Mary Manz. Follow That Star. 1998. (Hear Me Read Bible Stories Ser.). (Illus.). 24p. (J). (ps-3). 20.00 (978-0-570-05076-6(6)) Concordia Publishing Hse.

—Jesus Always Helps Us. 1999. (Hear Me Read Bible Stories Ser.). (Illus.). 96p. (J). (ps-3). 6.99 (978-0-88486-233-8(X) , Arrowood Pr.) BBS Publishing Corp.

—My Happy Birthday: And the True Story of God's Love for Me. 2006. 12p. (J). bds. 10.99 (978-0-7847-1519-2(X) , 04383) Standard Publishing.

—Send a Baby. 1998. (Hear Me Read Bible Stories Ser.). (Illus.). 24p. (J). (ps-3). 20.00 (978-0-570-05074-2(X)) Concordia Publishing Hse.

—Too Tall Too Small. 1998. (Hear Me Read Bible Stories Ser.). (Illus.). 24p. (J). (ps-1). 20.00 (978-0-570-05075-9(8)) Concordia Publishing Hse.

—What Next? 1998. (Hear Me Read Bible Stories Ser.). (Illus.). 24p. (J). (ps-3). 20.00 (978-0-570-05077-3(4)) Concordia Publishing Hse.

Simpson, Amy. Feelings & Emotions. Powell, Kara Eckmann, ed. 2000. (Pulse Ser.: No. 12). 96p. (gr. 6-9). 14.99 (978-0-8307-2548-9(2) , Gospel Light) Gospel Light Pubns.

Sirois, Celia M. Jesus Is the Promise, Vol. 6. 70p. (J). (gr. 6). 2.25 (978-0-8198-3934-3(5)) Pauline Bks. & Media.

Sisters of the Immaculate Heart Staff. My Mass Book. 2002. (Illus.). 79p. (J). reprint ed. 12.00 (978-1-930873-45-2(X)) Neumann Pr., The.

Site Guide. 2004. (J). 14.99 (978-0-7847-7182-2(0) , 09402) Standard Publishing.

Skits Guide. 2004. 24p. (J). 9.99 (978-0-7847-7210-2(X) , 09438) Standard Publishing.

Slattery, Kathryn. If I Could Ask God Anything: Awesome Bible Answers for Curious Kids. 2001. (Illus.). 288p. (gr. 4-7). pap. 12.99 (978-1-59145-411-3(5)) Nelson, Thomas Inc.

Slaughter, Nathan E. & Lewis, Kevin. Clear Perceptions. 2nd ed. 2003. 118p. per. 9.00 (978-0-9746463-2-9(6)) Sabyr Pr.

—Fresh Foundations. 3rd rev. ed. 2003. 116p. per. 9.00 (978-0-9746463-1-2(8)) Sabyr Pr.

—Pure Reflections. 3rd ed. 2003. 116p. per. 9.00 (978-0-9746463-3-6(4)) Sabyr Pr.

Smalley, Gary. The Passionate Marriage. 2004. (Focus on the Family Marriage Ser.). 72p. 7.99 (978-0-8307-3152-7(0) , Gospel Light) Gospel Light Pubns.

Smarto, Luke, illus. Where Are You Headed? 2002. 16p. (J). per. 0.75 net. (978-0-930201-02-9(7)) Frontline Pr.

Smith, Brenda J. Where Did Mommy Go? A Spiritual Tool to Help Children Grow from Grief to Peace. Smith, Brenda J. & Cloud, Olivia, eds. Smith, Brock R. & Smith, Raissa B., illus. 2004. Orig. Title: Listed Above. 52p. (gr. 3-12). pap. 16.95 (978-0-9744549-0-0(7)) Tall Through Bks.

Smith, Louis. Sexual Sins of the Bible: Everything You Want to Know, but Wouldn't Ask! 2004. 200p. pap. 14.99 (978-0-9744519-1-6(6)) Smith, Kasper.

Smith, Marvin L. Revelation Made Plain: The Mysteries Unraveled, the Triumphant Christians. 1999. (Illus.). 80p. pap. 9.00 (978-1-882581-21-4(0)) Campbell Road Pr.

Snyder, Bernadette McCarver. 130 Fun Facts from God's Wonder-Filled World. Sharp, Chris, illus. 2002. 144p. (J). pap. 12.95 (978-0-7648-0925-5(3) , 54528) Liguori Pubns.

So You Want to Be a Wise Guy. 136p. pap. 15.99 (978-0-8307-2917-3(8) , Gospel Light) Gospel Light Pubns.

Solo Dios Salva (Only God Saves) Quarter 3, Level 3. (Caminando con Jesus (Walking with Jesus) Series B). (SPA.). (J). (gr. 3-4). stu. ed. 3.50 (978-0-570-05154-1(1) , 16-3913) Concordia Publishing Hse.

Soul Survivor Guide to Service Projects. 2004. 96p. 19.99 (978-0-8307-3529-7(1) , Gospel Light) Gospel Light Pubns.

Soul Survivor Guide to Youth Ministry. 2004. 96p. 19.99 (978-0-8307-3530-3(5) , Gospel Light) Gospel Light Pubns.

Soul Survivor Prayer Ministry How to Pray for Others. 2004. 72p. 5.99 (978-0-8307-3527-3(5) , Gospel Light) Gospel Light Pubns.

Spanish Book of Hope: Revised Children's Edition. 2000. 32p. (J). mass mkt. (978-1-890525-23-1(5)) Book of Hope International.

Spanish House Inc. Staff. El Libro para Todo un Ano Devocionales para Ninos (The One Year Book of Devotions for Kids) 2000. (SPA.). (J). (gr. 4-7). pap. 12.99 (978-0-7899-0645-8(7) , 497518) Editorial Unilit.

Spanish House Inc. Staff, ed. La Historia de Maria (Mary's Story) 2000. (SPA., Illus.). (J). pap. 8.99 (978-0-7899-0613-7(9) , 495055) Editorial Unilit.

Spanish Messianic Edition: Youth Book. 2000. mass mkt. (978-1-890525-29-3(4)) Book of Hope International.

Spanish Your Book of Hope: Early Elementary Edition. 2000. (Book of Life Ser.). 32p. (J). mass mkt. (978-1-890525-26-2(X)) Book of Hope International.

A Special Purpose. 2006. (Illus.). (J). ring bd. 9.99 net. (978-0-9786031-5-1(X)) Hosannah Pubns.

Special Times. (Bulletin Board Jumbo Cutouts Ser.). (Illus.). 96p. (J). 9.99 (978-0-7847-0553-7(4) , 02590) Standard Publishing.

Spiritual Gifts. 2002. 7.99 (978-1-56390-046-4(7)); 3rd ed. per. 12.99 (978-1-56390-024-2(6)) Global Univ.

Spiritual Gifts. 2003. (Learn It, Live It Bible Studiestm Ser.). 80-112p. pap. 39.99 (978-0-7644-2559-2(5) , Flagship Church Resources) Group Publishing, Inc.

Spiritual Gifts Student Book. 2003. (Learn It, Live It Bible Studiestm Ser.). 80-112p. pap. 7.99 (978-0-7644-2671-1(0) , Flagship Church Resources) Group Publishing, Inc.

A Splash of Welcome Water. 2004. 5.99 (978-0-8066-3848-5(6)) Augsburg Fortress, Pubs.

Squire 5 Personal Growth Planbook: Daring Depths. 2003. (Illus.). 48p. (J). pap. 4.95 (978-1-59312-046-7(X)) North American Mission Board, SBC.

St. James, Rebecca. 40 Days with God: A Devotional Journey. rev. ed. 2006. 112p. pap. 12.99 (978-0-7847-1274-0(3) , 23338) Standard Publishing.

St. John, Patricia. The Safe Place. (Illus.). 24p. (J). 9.99 (978-1-85792-779-5(6) , Christian Focus) Christian Focus Pubns. GBR. *Dist:* Riverside.

Stafford, Lonnie. I'm a Child of God: Songs & Activities for Preschool Choirs & School Programs. Tyree, Debra, ed. 2004. 96p. 20.00 (978-0-687-09762-3(2)) Abingdon Pr.

Standard Publishing Staff. New Baby's Nativity. 1999. (Baby's First Bible Collection). (Illus.). 8p. (J). (ps). 10.99 (978-0-7847-0909-2(2) , 03990, Bean Sprouts) Standard Publishing.

Standard Publishing Staff, creator. Believe God's Son. 2006. (God Rocks Bible Toons Ser.). (YA). 39.99 (978-0-7847-1643-4(9) , 24233) Standard Publishing.

—Bible Crafts & More: Ages 3-6. 2005. (Illus.). 159p. (J). (ps-3). pap. 15.99 (978-0-7847-1784-4(2) , 02273) Standard Publishing.

—Stand Strong in the Lord. 2006. (God Rocks Bible Toons Ser.). cd-rom 39.99 (978-0-7847-1645-8(5)) Standard Publishing.

Stanley, Andy. Am I Good Enough? Preparing for Life's Final Exam. 2005. (LifeChange Bks.). 96p. (YA). 9.99 (978-1-59052-467-1(5) , Multnomah) WaterBrook Pr.

Stanley, Andy & Hall, Stuart. The Seven Checkpoints for Youth Leaders: Seven Principles Every Teenager Needs to Know. 2001. 272p. 16.99 (978-1-58229-177-2(2)) Simon & Schuster.

—The Seven Checkpoints Student Journal: Seven Principles Every Teenager Needs to Know. 2001. 206p. (YA). (gr. 7-12). pap. 14.99 (978-1-58229-178-9(0) , Howard Bks.) Simon & Schuster.

Stanley, Barb. What Catholics Teens Should Know When Dating Turns Violent. Larkin, Jean K., ed. 2004. (What Catholic Teens Should Know Ser.). (Illus.). 8p. (YA). 7.95 (978-0-89837-239-7(9) , 441210) Pflaum Publishing Group.

Stanley, Mandy, illus. Lift & Look Daniel. 2005. 8p. (J). (ps-ps). per. 7.99 (978-0-7847-1751-6(6) , 04377) Standard Publishing.

Stanley, Robin. I Can Be a Good Sport. Harpster, Steve & Julien, Terry, illus. 2006. (Happy Day Summer Titles Ser.). 16p. (J). pap. 1.99 (978-0-7847-1808-7(3) , 04190) Standard Publishing.

Starburst Publishers Staff. Bible Bytes for Teens: A Study-Devotional for Logging In to God's Word. 2001. (Illus.). 284p. (gr. 8 up). pap. 13.99 (978-1-892016-49-2(4)) Starburst Pubs.

Steele, Blake. Radical Forgiveness: A Handbook for Spiritual Growth. 2003. (Spiritual Vision Ser.). (Illus.). 112p. 12.95 (978-87-7247-263-8(4)) Scandinavia Publishing Hse. DNK. *Dist:* National Bk. Network.

Steuerwald, Shannon. A Proverb a Day to Keep the Naughties Away. 2002. (YA). spiral bd. 8.95 (978-1-931787-10-9(7)) Fundamental Christian Endeavors.

Stevens, Margaret M. Stepping Stones for Boys & Girls. Stevens, David S., illus. 2003. 32p. (gr. 5 up). 5.95 (978-0-87516-248-5(7)) DeVorss & Co.

Stewart, Charlie. Blue. Wilson, Phil, illus. 2005. 10p. (J). (ps). per. 6.99 (978-0-7847-1755-4(9) , 04381) Standard Publishing.

—Green. Wilson, Phil, illus. 2005. 10p. (J). (ps-ps). per. 6.99 (978-0-7847-1756-1(7) , 04720) Standard Publishing.

—Orange. Wilson, Phil, illus. 2005. 10p. (J). (ps-ps). per. 6.99 (978-0-7847-1754-7(0) , 04380) Standard Publishing.

—Purple. Wilson, Phil, illus. 2005. 10p. (J). (ps-ps). per. 6.99 (978-0-7847-1757-8(5) , 04721) Standard Publishing.

—Red. Wilson, Phil, illus. 2005. 10p. (J). (ps-ps). per. 6.99 (978-0-7847-1752-3(4) , 04378) Standard Publishing.

—Yellow. Wilson, Phil, illus. 2005. 10p. (J). (ps-ps). per. 6.99 (978-0-7847-1753-0(2) , 04379) Standard Publishing.

Stewart, Jennifer, ed. Fun in God's Seasons. Marlin, Kathy, illus. 1999. 48p. (J). (ps-2). pap. 2.49 (978-0-7847-0991-7(2) , 20061, Bean Sprouts) Standard Publishing.

—Prayers & Praises. Dubin, Jill, illus. 1999. 48p. (J). (ps-2). 2.99 (978-0-7847-0985-6(8) , 22055, Bean Sprouts) Standard Publishing.

Stickler, LeeDell & Newman, Judy. Downright Upright. 2001. 112p. pap. 14.00 (978-0-687-04890-8(7)) Abingdon Pr.

Stiegemeyer, Julie. Colors I See in Church. Mitter, Kathy, illus. 2002. (ENG.). 20p. (J). bds. 4.99 (978-0-7586-0029-5(1)) Concordia Publishing Hse.

—Things I See in Church. Mitter, Kathy, illus. 2003. (ENG.). 20p. (J). bds. 4.99 (978-0-7586-0357-9(6)) Concordia Publishing Hse.

—Things I See in Church. Mitter, Kathryn, illus. 1999. 16p. (J). (ps-k). 6.00 (978-0-570-05489-4(3) , 56-1952GJ) Concordia Publishing Hse.

Stiegemeyer, Julie & Mitter, Kathy. Things I Do in Church. 2003. (ENG., Illus.). 20p. (J). bds. 4.99 (978-0-7586-0126-1(3)) Concordia Publishing Hse.

Stinnett, Leia A. In the Mirror I See, God's Reflection Within Me: A Workbook for Teenagers. Date not set. (Little Angel Bks.). (Illus.). (YA). (gr. 6-12). pap. (978-1-880737-19-4(1)) Crystal Journeys Publishing.

Stott, Darrel E. Gods Joy Can Make A Difference. l.t. ed. 2003. (Illus.). 52p. 5.00 (978-0-9755564-1-2(X)) Compassion Outreach Ministry.

Stowell, Charles J. Dios Comprende (God Understands) 1998. (SPA.). (J). bds. 2.99 (978-0-7899-0513-0(2) , 498772) Editorial Unilit.

—Dios Dio (God Gave) 1998. (SPA.). (J). bds. 2.99 (978-0-7899-0515-4(9) , 498774) Editorial Unilit.

Strack, Jay. Identity Theft: The Thieves Who Want to Rob Your Future. 2006. 128p. (YA). pap. 7.99 (978-1-4185-0594-3(3)) Nelson, Thomas Inc.

—Leadership Rocks: Becoming a Student of Influence. 2006. 128p. (YA). pap. 7.99 (978-1-4185-0593-6(5)) Nelson, Thomas Inc.

Strack, Jay & Edwards, David. Life: How to Get There from Here: Student Leadership University Study Guide Series. 2006. 128p. (YA). pap. 7.99 (978-1-4185-0599-8(4)) Nelson, Thomas Inc.

Strack, Jay & Land, Richard. Mercury Rising: 8 Issues That Are Too Hot to Handle: Student Leadership University Study Guide Series. 2006. 128p. (YA). pap. 7.99 (978-1-4185-0592-9(7)) Nelson, Thomas Inc.

Stripling, Joe. See You in Heaven. Carroll, Joan, ed. Hunter, Charlene, illus. Date not set. (Sunday School Two Thousand Ser.). 38p. (J). pap. 12.95 (978-1-881223-07-8(8)) Zulema Enterprises.

Strobel, Lee. The Case for Faith for Kids. 2006. (Illus.). 96p. (J). pap. 7.99 (978-0-310-71146-9(0)) Zonderkidz.

Strobel, Lee & Vogel, Jane. The Case for Faith. 2002. (Evangelism Ser.). (Illus.). 112p. (YA). pap., stu. ed. 8.99 (978-0-310-24188-1(X) , 230034) Zondervan.

Stubna, Kris D. Pocket Catechism for Kids. 2001. (gr. 5-8). lib. bdg. 14.10 (978-0-613-77251-8(2)) Tandem Library Bks.

Stuff to Know When Cults Come Knocking. (Other Beliefs Ser.). (YA). pap., stu. ed. 8.95 (978-1-59255-196-5(3) , 130530); pap. 16.50 (978-1-59255-197-2(1) , 130535) CRC Pubns. (Faith Alive Christian Resources).

Sturtz, Maria. God Gave Me. 2004. 32p. (J). 1.79 (978-0-7586-0105-6(0)) Concordia Publishing Hse.

—God Is. 2004. 32p. (J). 1.79 (978-0-7586-0104-9(2)) Concordia Publishing Hse.

Sub FBS 1st-2Nd Graders Learner Guide. 9.15 (978-0-633-05036-8(9)) LifeWay Christian Resources.

Sub FBS 1st & 2Nd Graders. ldr.'s ed. 18.95 (978-0-633-05035-1(0)); 79.35 (978-0-633-05072-6(5)) LifeWay Christian Resources.

Sub FBS 3rd-4th Graders. ldr.'s ed. 18.95 (978-0-633-05037-5(7)) LifeWay Christian Resources.

Sub FBS 3rd & 4th Graders. ldr.'s ed. 79.35 (978-0-633-05074-0(1)) LifeWay Christian Resources.

Sub FBS 3rd & 4th Graders Learner Guide. 9.15 (978-0-633-05038-2(5)) LifeWay Christian Resources.

Sub FBS Preschool Bible Fun. 8.28 (978-0-633-05132-7(2)) LifeWay Christian Resources.

Sublett, Kit. After Camp: Beginning the Christian Adventure. 2003. (YA). pap. 3.95 (978-0-9758577-0-0(3)) Whitecaps Media.

Sundet, Marie. "I Am Always with You" Jesus Promises in the Lord's Supper. Hardel, Richard A. et al, eds. 1998. 28p. (J). (gr. 2-4). pap. 8.50 (978-1-889407-25-8(9)) Youth & Family Institute, The.

Surprises! Take-Home Papers, Set. 2001. (Movers & Shakers Ser.). (J). (ps). (978-0-8307-2260-0(2)) Gospel Light Pubns.

The Surprising Marriage. 2004. (Focus on the Family Marriage Ser.).Tr. of La Expectacion en el Matrimonio. 80p. 7.99 (978-0-8307-3153-4(9) , Gospel Light) Gospel Light Pubns.

The Surrendered Christian Athlete. 2001. 140p. (YA). per. 9.95 (978-1-890306-34-2(7)) Warwick Hse. Publishing.

Suzanne, Rentz. Daughters of Heaven Devotional. 2004. pap. 12.99 (978-1-57794-560-4(3)) Harrison Hse., Inc.

Swain. Calling You. 2005. (Illus.). 96p. (J). (978-0-8192-8142-5(5)) Morehouse Publishing.

Swain, Claudia. What's a Girl to Do? 2004. 128p. pap. 6.99 (978-1-56309-440-8(1)) New Hope Pubs.

Swiggart, Carolyn. Shades of Gray: The Clay & McAllister Family of Bryan County Georgia During the Plantation Years. 1999. (Illus.). 189p. (J). (ps-2). 25.95 (978-1-881907-12-1(0)) Two Bytes Publishing.

A Sword in My Hand. 2004. (YA). 12.00 (978-0-9747189-6-5(3)) LightHouse Pr.

Sytsma, Mary & Vogel, Jane. Questions Worth Asking: A Study of the Heidelberg Catechism, Year 1. 2001. (Reformed Faith Ser.). (gr. 9-10). stu. ed. 18.50 (978-1-56212-782-4(9) , 130150); 272p. tchr. ed. 20.95 (978-1-56212-781-7(0) , 130155) CRC Pubns. (Faith Alive Christian Resources).

Szabo, Grable. Holy Donuts: Impacting Schools for Christ. 2005. pap. 9.99 (978-1-59781-155-2(6)) Xulon Pr., Inc.

Tabori, Lena & Wong, Alice. The Little Big Book for God's Children. (Little Big Book Ser.: Vol. 7). (Illus.). 352p. 24.95 (978-0-941807-55-5(X) , Welcome Bks.) Welcome Enterprises, Inc.

Taking Godly Care of My Body. 2005. 80p. (J). per. 9.99 (978-1-59441-081-9(X) , CD-204008) Carson-Dellosa Publishing Co., Inc.

Taking Godly Care of My Money. 2005. 80p. (J). per. 9.99 (978-1-59441-082-6(8) , CD-204009) Carson-Dellosa Publishing Co., Inc.

Tangvald, Christine Harder. Playtime Devotions: Sharing Bible Moments with Your Baby or Toddler. Schmitz, Tamara, illus. 2006. (Heritage Builders Ser.). 36p. (J). 15.99 (978-0-7847-1361-7(8) , 04024) Standard Publishing.

Tardif, Cathy & Sloan, Andrew. The Power of One Another. ldr.'s ed. 2004. 64p. (J). 12.99 (978-0-7847-7198-3(7) , 09418) Standard Publishing.

Tassi, Peter. The Beauty Within: A Celebration of Teenage Life & Faith. 1999. 112p. (Orig.). (YA). pap. 6.95 (978-1-889108-49-0(9)) Living the Good News.

Taylor, Caroline. Lord God Made Us All. Longfoot, Stephanie, illus. 2004. 10p. (My First Prayers Ser.). 10p. (J). bds. 3.99 (978-1-85854-243-0(X)) Brimax Books Ltd. GBR. *Dist:* Byeway Bks.

Taylor, David. Eternal Vision: Seeing Life from Heaven's Perspective. 2005. (Illus.). 341p. pap. 12.00 (978-0-9762933-0-9(7)) Taylor Publishing Grp.

Taylor, Jeannie. Together Forever. 2000. 32p. (J). 14.99 (978-1-929125-22-7(4) , Multnomah) WaterBrook Pr.

Taylor, Jeannie St. John. You Wouldn't Love Me If You Knew. 2004. (Illus.). 32p. 17.00 (978-0-687-07325-2(1)) Abingdon Pr.

Taylor, Kenneth N. Right Choices. Shoemaker, Kathryn E., illus. 1999. 64p. (J). 12.99 (978-0-8423-5299-4(6)) Tyndale Hse. Pubs.

Teen 2 Teen. 2004. (J). (gr. 7-12). stu. ed. 2.69 (978-0-7847-7185-3(5) , 09435) Standard Publishing.

Teen Teacher. 2004. (Illus.). 64p. (J). (ps-k). tchr. ed. 11.99 (978-0-7847-7191-4(X) , 09412) Standard Publishing.

Teen Visuals/Learning Resources. 2004. (Illus.). (J). (ps-k). 11.99 (978-0-7847-7197-6(9) , 09417) Standard Publishing.

Tenney, Tommy. God Chasers for Kids. 2005. 96p. 11.99 (978-0-7684-2165-1(9)) Destiny Image Pubs.

Terrell, Charles. Hey, God, Let's Talk! Teaching Children about Prayer. 2004. (Illus.). 64p. (gr. 4-6). pap. 5.00 (978-0-687-08351-0(6)) Abingdon Pr.

Tesoros Escondidos Vol. 3: Libro para ninos. 2000. pap. (978-1-57697-934-1(2)) United Bible Societies/ Americas Service Ctr.

Theisen, Michael & Bradbury-Haehl, Nora. ScriptureWalk Senior High: Youth Themes. 2003. (ScriptureWalk Ser.). 96p. (YA). (gr. 8-12). pap. 19.95 (978-0-88489-608-1(0)) St. Mary's Pr.

Thiele, Christine. What Catholic Teens Should Know about Suicide. Larkin, Jean K., ed. 2004. (What Catholic Teens Should Know Ser.). (Illus.). 8p. (YA). 7.95 (978-0-89837-240-3(2) , 441110) Pflaum Publishing Group.

Thomas, Daniel D. Prophecies of Life. 2004. (YA). per. 9.95 (978-0-9761604-0-3(4)) Life Line Publishing.

Thomas, Erika & Treg, Mccoy, illus. Petey Yikes! A very, very true story about a homeless little blue bird in New York City. 2006. (J). **(*978-0-9789642-0-7(9))** Times Square Church.

Thomas, Jerry D. What We Believe: Helping Children Understand the Beliefs of the Seventh-Day Adventist Church. 2006. (J). (978-0-8163-2167-4(1)) Pacific Pr. Publishing Assn.

Thomas, John & Thomas, Danita. Inventos de Dimensiones Bíblicas para Niños. 2007. (Illus.). 80p. (J). pap. 14.99 **(*978-0-8054-4499-5(8)** , B&H Bks.) B&H Publishing Grp.

Thomas, Mack. What Would Jesus Pray? A Story to Change the World. 2006. 160p. (J). 12.99 (978-1-59052-738-2(0) , Multnomah) WaterBrook Pr.

Thompson, Robb. Excellence in Ministry. 2nd ed. 2003. 176p. per. 10.00 (978-1-889723-36-5(3)) Family Harvest Church.

Thorne, Rick. The Hidden Secrets of Jesus & Other Revelations. 2004. (Illus.). 268p. (YA). pap. 19.95 (978-0-937327-04-3(2)) Soul Pubns.

Through God's Eyes. 2005. per. (978-1-59581-169-1(9)) Brentwood Communications Group.

Through God's Eyes. 2004. spiral bd. 16.99 (978-0-87808-359-6(6)) Carey, William Library Pubs.

Thurman, Debbie. A Teen's Guide to Christian Living: Practical Answers to Tough Questions about God & Faith. 2003. (gr. 7-12). lib. bdg. 22.20 (978-0-613-74575-8(2)) Tandem Library Bks.

Timothy Grows in God's Word. (Two Great Ways to Share God's Love Ser.). 16p. (ps-k). 15.00 (978-0-570-00314-4(8)) Concordia Publishing Hse.

Titles of the Triune God: Studies in Divine Self-Revelation. 2004. 190p. pap. 19.95 (978-0-9752843-0-8(4)) Capstone Bks.

Tm412 All Terrain Student Book. 2004. (J). (gr. 7-12). 5.95 (978-0-633-01998-3(4)) LifeWay Christian Resources.

Tnt Ministries Staff. On the Way 11 - 14's, Vol. 4. 96p. (J). pap. 11.99 (978-1-85792-707-8(9) , Christian Focus) Christian Focus Pubns. GBR. *Dist:* Riverside.

Toinette, Jim, et al, contrib. by. Growing in Love: Student Text. 2000. (Growing in Love Ser.). 80p. (J). Level 7. pap. 7.95 (978-0-15-950669-1(7)); Level 8. pap. 7.95 (978-0-15-950670-7(0)) Harcourt Religion Pubs.

Tomlin, Carolyn. More Alike Than Different. Reeves, Rhonda, ed. 2000. (Illus.). 32p. (J). (ps). 9.99 (978-1-56309-351-7(0)) Woman's Missionary Union.

Tomlin, Rudolph P. All about Us! From My Perspective. Tomlin, Renata R., ed. 1999. (Illus.). 160p. (C). mass mkt. 10.00 (978-1-882581-22-1(9)) Campbell Road Pr.

Tomlinson, Elisa. True Reflection: A Girls' Guide to Identity in Christ. 2004. 96p. (YA). (978-0-9758989-0-1(6)) Eternity Pr.

Tommy Books: Fear, 10 vols. l.t. ed. 2005. (Illus.). 24p. (J). 12.99 (978-0-9762690-5-2(8)) Tommy Bks. Pubng.

Tommy Books: Forgiveness, 10 vols. l.t. ed. 2005. (Illus.). 24p. (J). 12.99 (978-0-9762690-6-9(6)) Tommy Bks. Pubng.

Tommy Books: Grace & Mercy, 10 Vols. l.t. ed. 2005. (Illus.). 24p. (J). 12.99 (978-0-9762690-8-3(2)) Tommy Bks. Pubng.

Tommy Books: Thank You, 10 vols. l.t. ed. 2005. (Illus.). 24p. (J). 12.99 (978-0-9762690-9-0(0)) Tommy Bks. Pubng.

Tommy Books: Who Am I, 10 vols. l.t. ed. 2005. (Illus.). 24p. (J). 12.99 (978-0-9762690-7-6(4)) Tommy Bks. Pubng.

Topliff, Delores. Whoosh. l.t. ed. 2007. (Illus.). 34p. (J). 9.95 **(*978-0-9769031-1-6(3))** Verona (Bk.) Publishing, Inc.

Totally Lent! A Child's Journey to Easter 2007. 2006. (J). 5.95 (978-1-933178-46-2(9)) Pflaum Publishing Group.

Totally Lent! A Kid's Journey to Easter 2007. 2006. (J). 5.95 (978-1-933178-45-5(0)) Pflaum Publishing Group.

Totally Lent! A Teen's Journey to Easter 2007. 2006. (J). 5.95 (978-1-933178-44-8(2)) Pflaum Publishing Group.

Totilo, Rebecca Park. The Christian Kids' Gardening Guide: Cool Stuff for You to Make & Grow. 2004. (Illus.). 168p. (J). pap. 12.99 (978-1-58411-034-7(1) , Legacy Pr.) Rainbow Pubs. & Legacy Pr.

Touching the Hand of Jesus. 2002. per. 12.50 (978-0-9700985-2-8(9)) HLH Ministries.

Tough Issues. ldr.'s ed. 1998. (Cross Training Ser.: Vol. 3). 64p. (YA). (gr. 10-12). pap. 15.00 incl. VHS (978-1-57405-026-4(5)) CharismaLife Pubs.

Trebi-Ollennu, Flora. My Daily Walk: Discover the Life of Jesus. Barker, Peter, ed. 2005. 384p. 19.95 (978-1-894718-04-2(6)) Amerley Treb Bks. CAN. *Dist:* Biblio Distribution.

Trent, John. Super Hero Swamp. Finger, Matthew, illus. 2007. 64p. (J). (ps-3). 14.99 (978-1-59145-487-8(5)) Nelson, Thomas Inc.

Triplett, Donald & Eiland, Marie. Castle Club: ... Children walking in the way of the Lord, 2 vols., Vol. 12. RDM, tr. from SPA. 2003. Orig. Title: Club Castillo Manual del Maestro. (Illus.). 156p. spiral bd. 7.00 (978-1-931984-93-5(X) , 2003-00E1) RDM.

—Castle Club: Children Walking in the Way of the Lord, 2 vols., Vol. 22. RDM, tr. 2003. Orig. Title: Club Castillo Manual del Estudiante. (SPA., Illus.). 82p. (J). spiral bd. 4.00 (978-1-931984-78-2(6) , 2004-00E1) RDM.

Tripp, Terry. Growing in God's Word. 2004. (J). lib. bdg. (978-0-9673093-4-7(4)) Song Revival Fellowship & Ministries.

True God, True Man. 2004. (Effective Dre Ser.). pap. (978-0-8294-1499-8(1)) Loyola Pr.

Trummel, D. Pauline. A Reformed Baptist Sunday School Curriculum: New Testament Survey, Year 1, Semester 1. Nichols, Gregory G., ed. 2001. (Illus.). 160p. (J). ring bd. 25.00 (978-1-889520-18-6(7)) Truth For Eternity Ministries.

—A Reformed Baptist Sunday School Curriculum: New Testament Survey, year 1, Semester 2. Nichols, Gregory G., ed. 2002. (Illus.). 160p. (J). ring bd. 25.00 (978-1-889520-19-3(5)) Truth For Eternity Ministries.

—A Reformed Baptist Sunday School Curriculum: New Testament Survey, year 2 Semester 1. Nichols, Gregory G., ed. 2003. (Illus.). 160p. (J). ring bd. 25.00 (978-1-889520-20-9(9)) Truth For Eternity Ministries.

—A Reformed Baptist Sunday School Curriculum: New Testament Survey, year 2 Semester 2. Nichols, Gregory G., ed. 2004. (Illus.). 160p. (J). ring bd. 25.00 (978-1-889520-21-6(7)) Truth For Eternity Ministries.

TruthQuest Discipleship Series Pt. 1: Becoming A Christian. 2002. (J). (978-0-9709763-7-6(2)) Return To The Word.

Tween Time. 24.00 (978-0-687-34263-1(5)) Abingdon Pr.

Tyndale House Publishers Staff. The One Year Book of Devotions for Boys. 2000. (One Year Book of Devotions for Kids Ser.). (Illus.). 400p. (YA). (gr. 4-7). per. 12.99 (978-0-8423-3620-8(6)) Tyndale Hse. Pubs.

Tyndale House Publishers Staff, contrib. by. Mind over Media. 2001. (Life on the Edge Ser.). (Illus.). 176p. (YA). pap. 8.99 (978-1-56179-870-4(3)) Focus on the Family Publishing.

Tyndale Kids Staff, Kids. One Year Book of Devotions for Girls. 2002. (gr. 3-6). lib. bdg. 22.25 (978-0-613-76865-8(5)) Tandem Library Bks.

Ulmer, Louise. Good Friday. Sandland, Reg, illus. 2004. (Arch Books). (ENG.). 16p. (J). 1.99 (978-0-7586-0638-9(9)) Concordia Publishing Hse.

Understanding the Gift in Your Pastor. 2005. per. 10.99 (978-0-9765809-0-4(X)) Garing, Bernard.

Unruly Emotions. 1998. (Cross Training Ser.: Vol. 1). 64p. (YA). (gr. 10-12). pap., tchr. ed. 15.00 incl. VHS (978-1-57405-010-3(9)) CharismaLife Pubs.

Upthegrove, C. S. The Wait... the Power... the Evidence... Miracles That Followed the Angelic Visit, 2003. 23.99 (978-0-9716523-6-1(8)) Hope Harvest Publishing.

Van Dyke, Jan. Living Like a King's Kid. Van Order, Laura & VonSeggen, Jon, illus. rev. ed. 2003. 77p. (J). spiral bd. 30.00 (978-1-58302-249-8(X)) One Way St., Inc.

Van Dyken, Harry. Covenantal Catechism Bk. 6: The Epistles & Revelation. 2000. 133p. (YA). (gr. 6-8). pap. 6.95 (978-0-9705251-6-1(8)) Line of Promise Pr.

Van Impe, Rexella & Derenge, Willa. With Jesus, Forever! 2002. (Illus.). (J). (ps-2). 8.95 (978-1-884137-08-2(3)) Van Impe, Jack Ministries.

Van Impe, Rexella & Shelton, Patty. Whoosh! I Want to Go Up! 2001. (Illus.). (J). (ps-2). 8.95 (978-1-884137-07-5(5)) Van Impe, Jack Ministries.

VBS-Fiesta-Hot Tots! Infants, Toddlers, & Twos: Leader Manual (Group's Fiesta! Where Kids. 2006. pap. 14.99 (978-0-7644-2959-0(0)) Group Publishing, Inc.

VBS-Fiesta-Maraca Munchies: Leader Manual (Group's Fiesta! Where Kids Are Fired Up about Jesus) 2006. pap. 9.99 (978-0-7644-2953-8(1)) Group Publishing, Inc.

Vereb, Jerome M. & John Paul II. Every Child a Light: The Pope's Message to Young People. 2003. (Illus.). 48p. (YA). (gr. 2-4). 16.95 (978-1-56397-090-0(2)) Boyds Mills Pr.

Video Zoom Box: Videolympics. 1998. 156p. (J). (gr. 1-6). ring bd. 164.99 incl. audio, VHS, sl. (978-1-57405-104-9(0)) CharismaLife Pubs.

Vidrine, Beverly Barras. Easter Day Alphabet. Lyne, Alison Davis, illus. 2003. 32p. (J). (gr. k-3). pap. 7.95 (978-1-58980-076-2(1)) Pelican Publishing Co., Inc.

Viola, Frank. Forbidden Affection: Letters to a Brokenhearted Christian on Surrendering Love. 2000. 80p. (YA). (gr. 11 up). pap. 6.00 (978-0-9666657-2-7(4)) Present Testimony Ministry.

Viviendo como un Hijo del Rey. 2004. (SPA.). (J). spiral bd. 30.00 (978-1-58302-255-9(4)) One Way St., Inc.

Vladimirov, Artemy. The Path to Confession: A Book for Family Reading Presented to Orthodox Children. Skotina, G. A., illus. 2000. 128p. (J). 22.95 (978-0-916700-55-3(0)) Christ the Saviour Brotherhood Publishing.

Wade, Connie Morgan. Bible Songs & Action Rhymes: Ages 3-6. 2005. (Illus.). 224p. (J). (ps-3). pap. 15.99 (978-0-7847-1781-3(8) , 24190) Standard Publishing.

Walker, Joni. Apostles Creed. Walker, Joni, illus. 2005. (Follow & Do Ser.). (Illus.). 32p. (J). 6.99 (978-0-7586-0802-4(0)) Concordia Publishing Hse.

—Confession - Follow & Do. 2005. (Follow & Do Ser.). (Illus.). 23p. (J). 6.99 (978-0-7586-0808-6(X)) Concordia Publishing Hse.

—Follow & Do Books: The Lord's Prayer. Walker, Joni, illus. 2004. (Follow & Do Ser.). (Illus.). 32p. (J). 6.99 (978-0-7586-0678-5(8)) Concordia Publishing Hse.

—Jesus Knows Me. Walker, Joni, illus. 2003. (ENG., Illus.). 14p. (J). (ps-k). bds. 4.99 (978-0-7586-0507-8(2)) Concordia Publishing Hse.

—Jesus Loves Me. Walker, Joni, illus. 2006. (ENG., Illus.). 20p. (J). bds. 4.99 (978-0-7586-0914-4(0)) Concordia Publishing Hse.

—The Lord's Supper - Follow & Do. 2005. (Follow & Do Ser.). (Illus.). 23p. (J). 6.99 (978-0-7586-0801-7(2)) Concordia Publishing Hse.

Walsch, Neale Donald. Conversations with God for Teens. 2002. 368p. (J). pap. 7.99 (978-0-439-31389-6(9)) Scholastic, Inc.

—The Little Soul & the Sun. Riccio, Frank, illus. 1998. 32p. (ps-3). 17.95 (978-1-57174-087-8(2)) Hampton Roads Publishing Co., Inc.

Warburton, Olivia & White, Jayne. For Your First Holy Communion. Mitchell, Ian, illus. 2004. 48p. pap. 16.99 (978-0-7459-4682-5(8) , Lion) Lion Hudson plc GBR. *Dist:* Independent Pubs. Group.

Warfield, Barbara J. Basic Christian Life Skills for Teens Vol. 1: Light It up - Living as Children of Light. Jones, Stephanie, illus. 1999. 40p. (YA). (gr. 6-12). stu. ed. 2.00 (978-1-929127-02-3(2)) N His Will Ministries.

Warner Press Staff. What Can I Do for Jesus? 1999. (Illus.). (J). pap. 3.95 (978-0-87162-864-0(3)) Warner Pr. Pubs.

Washington, Linda. Promise Kids on the Promise Path: Children's Journal. 1998. (Nineteen Ninety Nine Fifty-Day Spiritual Adventure Ser.). (Illus.). 64p. (J). 7.00 (978-1-57849-108-7(8)) Mainstay Church Resources.

Washington, Linda & Dall, Jeanette. Favorite Bible Children: Ages 4 & 5. 2004. (Illus.). 96p. (J). pap. 11.95 (978-1-885358-76-9(8)) Rainbow Pubs. & Legacy Pr.

Watson, Charles D. Christianity for Fools: A Simple Understanding of the Christian Faith. 2004. 143p. (YA). lib. bdg. 12.95 (978-0-9678519-2-1(0)) Abounding Love Ministries, Inc.

Weaver, Roger. Holy Eucharist for the Children of God. 2003. pap. 8.95 (978-0-9709575-5-9(6)) Singing River Pubns.

Webb, Becky. Andy's Book. 2000. 375p. (J). spiral bd. 16.00 (978-1-57892-054-9(X)) Prayer Point Pr.

Webster, Jennifer. Kamitono Chatto: Oinori No Nikki. 2003. (JPN.). E-Book 11.99 (978-0-9706360-4-1(0)) Webster, Jennifer Hope.

Webster, Jennifer Hope. Chat with God: Prayer Journal. 2nd ed. 2002. (Chat with God: Vol. 1). spiral bd., wbk. ed. 11.99 (978-0-9706360-1-0(6)) Webster, Jennifer Hope.

—Diario de Oracion: La Jornada Espiritual Que Dura Por Toda la Eternida. 2003. (SPA.). (YA). E-Book 11.99 (978-0-9706360-2-7(4)) Webster, Jennifer Hope.

—Molitvennyi Dnevnik: Molitvennoe Pyteshestve Prodolzhaetsya Vechno. . . Chekulaeva, Tatiana, tr. 2003. (RUS.). (J). E-Book 11.99 (978-0-9706360-6-5(7)) Webster, Jennifer Hope.

Weiss, N. E. According to Plan. (YA). (gr. 7-8). 144p. stu. ed. (978-0-85910-315-2(3) , 23-0562); 65p. stu. ed., wbk. ed. (978-0-85910-317-6(X) , 23-0563) Australian Church Resources.

Welborn, Amy. Loyola Kids Book of Heroes: Stories of Catholic Heroes & Saints Throughout History. 2004. (Illus.). 175p. (J). 15.95 (978-0-8294-1584-1(X)) Loyola Pr.

Welborn-Step-by-Step Childrens Church. (Illus.). (J). (978-0-687-39335-0(3)) Abingdon Pr.

Welch, Michael, Sr. Why You Can Do God's Will. Butler, Latrica, ed. 2004. 108p. per. 12.99 (978-0-9753773-0-7(2)) MCW Publishing.

Welch, Michael Eric, Sr. What the Devil Do Not Want You to Know... 2005. per. (978-0-9753773-1-4(0)) MCW Publishing.

Wenig, Laurin J. Getting to Know Jesus, 6 booklets. 1998. (Illus.). (YA). (gr. 7-10). pap., stu. ed. 7.45 (978-0-89837-209-0(7)) Pflaum Publishing Group.

Wesbrooks, Linda. The New You: Lessons for Teenage Girls. (YA). pap. 7.99 (978-0-89098-406-2(9)) Twentieth Century Christian Bks.

Wesemann, Tim. The Book of Cool: Cool Questions, Cooler Answers. 2004. (2:52 / Soul Gear#482; Ser.). (Illus.). 112p. (J). (gr. 3-6). 7.99 (978-0-310-70696-0(3)) Zonderkidz.

What Would Jesus Do? 2. (Illus.). 16p. (J). pap. 1.50 (978-0-87162-806-0(6) , E4511) Warner Pr. Pubs.

What Would Jesus Do? An Activity Book about Biblical Values. (Illus.). 16p. (J). pap. 1.50 (978-0-87162-700-1(0) , E4509) Warner Pr. Pubs.

Whelan, Barbara. Always Be Children for Jesus. 2006. pap. 11.99 **(*978-1-4259-6879-3(1))** AuthorHouse.

When You Graduate Revised. 80.00 (978-0-687-45045-9(4)) Abingdon Pr.

Where Was God September 11? There Is an Answer. 2003. (YA). (978-0-9740898-0-5(X)) Orchid Publishing Co.

White, Ellen G. Amazing Love, Vol. 1. 2nd ed. 1999. 80p. (YA). pap. 9.95 (978-1-883012-79-3(1)) Remnant Pubns.

White, Emily, compiled by. Hot Links Creative Ways to Connect Kids to Christ. 2002. (YA). pap. 14.99 (978-0-89265-591-5(7)) Randall Hse. Pubns.

Whitfield, Laurie A. & Cammarata, Robert P. Taking Care of God's Gifts Stewardship: A Way of Life Grades 3-5. 2003. 48p. (J). pap. 2.95 (978-1-59276-020-6(1)); pap. 24.95 (978-1-59276-040-4(6)) Our Sunday Visitor, Publishing Div.

—Taking Care of God's Gifts Stewardship: A Way of Life Grades K-2. 2003. 48p. (J). pap. 2.95 (978-1-59276-019-0(8)); pap. 24.95 (978-1-59276-039-8(2)) Our Sunday Visitor, Publishing Div.

Whitlock, Matt. Fleas & Thank You. 2004. (Matt Whitlock Ser.). (Illus.). 36p. (J). (gr. 4-7). 12.99 (978-0-7814-4062-2(9) , 0781440629) Cook, David C. Publishing Co.

—Hear No Weevil. 2004. (Matt Whitlock Ser.). (Illus.). 36p. (J). (gr. 4-7). 12.99 (978-0-7814-4063-9(7) , 0781440637) Cook, David C. Publishing Co.

Who Am I with Others? (Christian Character Development Ser.). 64p. (YA). (gr. 8-12). pap. 16.99 (978-0-7644-2127-3(1)) Group Publishing, Inc.

Wholistic Health Student. 1.25 (978-0-687-37395-6(6)) Abingdon Pr.

Why Christmas Trees Aren't Perfect. 129.50 (978-0-687-45364-1(X)) Abingdon Pr.

Why I Believe in Jesus: A Finish-the-Picture Coloring Book. (Illus.). 16p. (J). pap. 1.50 (978-0-87162-814-5(7) , E6027) Warner Pr. Pubs.

Widenhouse, Kathy. The Christian Girl's Guide to Friendship. 2004. (Illus.). 192p. (J). pap. 9.99 (978-1-58411-043-9(0) , Legacy Pr.) Rainbow Pubs. & Legacy Pr.

Wilde, Gary, et al. Handling Conflict. 2003. (Faith 4 Life Ser.). (Illus.). 48p. 14.99 (978-0-7644-2494-6(7) , Flagship Church Resources) Group Publishing, Inc.

Wilkinson, Bruce & Thomas, Mack. A Life God Rewards: Guys Only. ltd. ed. 2006. 96p. bds. 9.99 (978-1-60142-002-2(1) , Multnomah Kidz) WaterBrook Pr.

Will, Julianne M. Stations of the Cross for Children. Mattozzi, Patricia, illus. 2005. 32p. (J). (ps-ps). pap. 3.95 (978-1-59276-153-1(4)) Our Sunday Visitor, Publishing Div.

Williams, Alex. Holy Spy: Student Ministry in Eastern Europe. 2004. (Illus.). 208p. (J). pap. (978-1-85792-906-5(3)) Christian Focus Pubns. GBR. *Dist:* Riverside.

Williams, Carla. Fold & Do. 2004. 54p. (gr. 2-4). 12.99 (978-0-570-05287-6(4)) Concordia Publishing Hse.

—Little Hands Fold & Do. 2004. 54p. (ps-1). 12.99 (978-0-570-05286-9(6)) Concordia Publishing Hse.

Williamson, Wendy. Christian Martial Arts 101. 2004. per. 17.95 (978-0-9721328-2-4(1)); per. 15.95 (978-0-9721328-1-7(3)) Agapy Publishing.

Willow Creek Association. 5-G Impact Spring Quarter Small Group Leader's Guidebook: Doing Life with God in the Picture. 2004. (Promiseland Ser.). 80p. (J). 9.99 (978-0-7441-2562-7(6)) Zonderkidz.

Wilson, Jean. Evangelist to the World: The Story of Billy Graham. 2nd ed. 2004. (Stories of Faith & Fame Ser.). 96p. (J). (gr. 4-7). pap. 6.00 (978-0-7188-2782-3(1)) Lutherworth Pr., The GBR. *Dist:* Parkwest Pubns., Inc.

Wilson, Jenny. Why Do Christians Do What They Do? 96p. (J). pap. 5.99 (978-1-85792-782-5(6)) Christian Focus Pubns. GBR. *Dist:* Riverside.

Winzer, Nikki. Somali. 2002. per. 9.95 (978-0-9724387-0-4(X)) Heavenly Treasures.

Witherspoon Press Staff, contrib. by. Belonging to God: A First Catechism. 2003. (J). (978-1-57153-036-3(3) , Witherspoon Pr.) Curriculum Publishing, Presbyterian Church (U. S. A.).

Wood, Charles M., II. Living the Good Life: Surviving in the 21st Century. 2003. 160p. per. 13.95 (978-0-9724867-0-5(4)) Woodland Pr. LLC.

Words to Live By. 2004. (In Celebration Coloring & Activity Book Ser.). 32p. (J). pap. 1.99 (978-0-7647-1027-8(3) , In Celebration) Schaffer, Frank Pubns.

Working with God. (Precious Moments Ser.). (J). 11.99 (978-1-55976-183-3(0)); pap. 9.99 (978-1-55976-184-0(9)) CEF Pr.

World Changers. ldr.'s ed. 1998. (Cross Training Ser.: Vol. 2). 64p. (YA). (gr. 10-12). pap. 15.00 incl. VHS (978-1-57405-017-2(6)) CharismaLife Pubs.

Wright, Ben. Top Priority: Manna 2. 2003. (YA). ring bd. (978-0-9719491-8-8(2)) Positive Action For Christ.

WWJD: What Would Jesus Do? (Illus.). 16p. (J). pap. 1.50 (978-0-87162-833-6(3) , E6021) Warner Pr. Pubs.

Yaconelli, Mike. Devotion: A Raw Truth Journal for Following Jesus. 2004. (Invert Ser.). (Illus.). 80p. (YA). pap. 10.99 (978-0-310-25559-8(7)) Zondervan.

Yorks, Julia. The Kid's Guide to New Hope. 1999. (Illus.). 40p. 5.95 (978-0-9671987-0-5(4)) Simply Kid's Publishing.

Yoshiike, Yoshitaka. A Christmas Interview: Reporting Live from Bethlehem! Tsuchiya, Fujio, illus. 2005. 32p. (J). (ps-ps). pap. 7.95 (978-0-8198-1572-9(1)) Pauline Bks. & Media.

You Can't Run Away from You: A Young Man's Journey to Himself. 2004. (Illus.). 188p. (YA). per. 15.00 (978-0-9755616-0-7(X)) Darnell Publishing.

Younger Children. (Illus.). 8.00 (978-0-687-04975-2(X)) Abingdon Pr.

Youngs, Bettie B. Living the Ten Commandments in New Times: A Book for Teens. 2004. 304p. (YA). pap. 12.95 (978-0-7573-0128-5(2)) Health Communications, Inc.

Youth For Christ. 3Story' Evangelism Training Curriculum Kit: God's Story, My Story, Your Story. 2007. (3Story' Ser.). pap. 99.99 incl. DVD (978-0-310-27370-7(6)) Zondervan.

Youth Specialties Staff. The Next Level: Youth Leader Curriculum Kit. 1999. pap. 79.99 (978-0-310-22984-1(7)) Zondervan.

Ytreeide, Arnold. Bartholomew's Passage. 2004. 168p. pap. 12.99 (978-0-8307-3383-5(3) , Regal Bks.) Gospel Light Pubns.

—Jotham's Journey. 2004. 168p. pap. 12.99 (978-0-8307-3448-1(1) , Regal Bks.) Gospel Light Pubns.

Zanzig, Thomas. Growing in Wisdom, Age & Grace. Thiewes, Sam, illus. 2003. (Horizons Program : Vol. 1). 78p. (YA). (gr. 9 up). pap. 19.95 (978-0-88489-339-4(1)) St. Mary's Pr.

Zobel Nolan, Allia. Are You There God? A Book about Faith. 2006. (Illus.). 32p. (J). bds. 9.99 (978-0-7944-1144-2(4)) Reader's Digest Assn., Inc., The.

Zondervan. God's Words of Life for Teens. 2000. (God's Words for Life Gift Bks.). 208p. 12.99 (978-0-310-98075-9(5)) Inspirio.

—3 Story Curriculum for Students: God's Story, My Story, Your Story. 2007. 96p. (YA). pap. 7.99 (978-0-310-27374-5(9)) Zondervan.

10 Mandamientos. 2004. 15.95 (978-1-56814-614-0(0)) CCC of America.

50 Crosses Charted for Needlepoint: Christian Symbols Book II. 2004. spiral bd. 39.95 (978-0-9760188-0-3(2)) Roberts, Michele.

100 Days with God. 2004. per. 7.00 (978-0-9762014-0-3(2)) L'Edge Pr.

101 Faith Builders: For Kids. 2004. 64p. (J). pap. 7.99 (978-0-7647-0986-9(0)) School Specialty Publishing.

1,2,3 Numeros de la Biblia: Libro para ninos. 2000. pap. (978-1-57697-833-7(8)) United Bible Societies/ Americas Service Ctr.

CHRISTIAN LIFE—FICTION

AB Publishing Staff. Peep Behind the Scenes. 2004. pap. 5.95 (978-1-881545-95-8(4)) A B Publishing.

ABC of the New Testament. 2005. (J). bds. 8.95 (978-0-9741748-4-6(X)) Patmos, Inc.

Adams, Michelle Medlock. Sister for Sale. Brooks, Karen Stormer, illus. 2004. 28p. (J). pap. 4.99 (978-0-310-70820-9(6)) Zonderkidz.

—Sister for Sale. 2002. (Illus.). 32p. 7.99 (978-0-310-70254-2(2)) Zondervan.

Adee, Donna J. Miriam & Timothy Face Life, Vol. 3. Babcock, Marci, illus. 2000. 384p. (J). pap. 12.95 (978-0-9654272-3-4(4)) Harvest Pubns.

Adler, Tzivia. The Sefer Torah Parade. Perez, Ito Esther, illus. 2005. (J). pap. 11.95 (978-1-929628-26-1(9)) Hachai Publishing.

Aidinoff, Elsie V. The Garden. 2004. (Illus.). 416p. (J). lib. bdg. 17.89 (978-0-06-055606-8(4), HarperTeen) HarperCollins Pubs.

Alcorn, Randy & Ben-Ami, Doran. Wait until Then. 2007. (Illus.). 32p. (J). 14.99 (978-1-4143-1041-1(2), Tyndale Kids) Tyndale Hse. Pubs.

Alsbrooks, Stephanie. The Ten Commandments. Meier, Paul, illus. 2005. (J). bds. 9.99 (978-1-4183-0064-7(0)) Christ Inspired, Inc.

Amadeo, Diana M. My Baby Sister Is a Preemie. Bladholm, Cheri, illus. 2005. (Helping Kids Heal Ser.). 32p. (J). 9.99 (978-0-310-70867-4(2)) Zonderkidz.

Amado, Elisa. Cousins. Garay, Luis, tr. Garay, Luis, illus. 2004. 32p. (J). 16.95 (978-0-88899-459-2(1)) Groundwood Bks. CAN. *Dist:* Perseus Distribution.

—Primas. Iribarren, Elena & Iribarren, Leopoldo, trs. from ENG. Garay, Luis, illus. 2004. (SPA & ENG.). 32p. (J). 16.95 (978-0-88899-548-3(2)) Groundwood Bks. CAN. *Dist:* Perseus Distribution.

The American Adventure. 1999. (Illus.). 144p. (J). (gr. 3). 127.60 (978-0-7910-4917-4(5), Chelsea Hse.) Facts On File, Inc.

American Tract Society Staff. Step by Step or Tidy's Way to Freedom. 2006. 50.99 (*978-1-4219-8162-8(9)); pap. 44.99 (*978-1-4219-8160-4(2)) IndyPublish.com.

Anderson, Andrea Patrice. Heaven's Diary: Our Gift from God. 2006. 37.00 (*978-0-8059-8845-1(9)) Dorrance Publishing Co., Inc.

Anderson, Mary Elizabeth. It's Me Again, God. 2003. 120p. pap. 9.95 (978-1-889658-25-4(1)) New Canaan Publishing Co. LLC.

Anderson, Max Elliot. North Woods Poachers. 2004. 144p. pap. 10.95 (978-0-9729256-8-6(6), Tweener Pr.) Baker Trittin Pr.

Andrews, Andy. The Young Traveler's Gift: Seven Decisions That Determine Personal Success. 2004. 160p. (YA). pap. 12.99 (978-1-4003-0427-1(X)) Nelson, Thomas Inc.

Andrews, Miriam. The Butterfly's Last Journey. 2001. pap. (*978-1-889733-10-4(5)) Precious Life Bks., Inc.

Angeles: Redemption/Redencion. 2004. (Angeles Ser.).Tr. of Angels. (SPA., Illus.). 48p. pap. 4.99 (978-0-8054-2839-1(9)) B&H Publishing Grp.

Angeles: The Secret/el Secreto. 2004. (Angeles Ser.).Tr. of Angels. (SPA., Illus.). 48p. pap. 4.99 (978-0-8054-2833-9(X)) B&H Publishing Grp.

Angeles: The Sin/el Pecado. 2004. (Angeles Ser.).Tr. of Angels. (SPA., Illus.). 48p. pap. 4.99 (978-0-8054-2838-4(0)) B&H Publishing Grp.

Annie, Johnston. Three Weavers. 2004. 11.00 (978-1-58474-021-6(3)) Cornerstone Family Ministries/Lamplighter Publishing.

Anonymous. Theobald the Iron Hearted or Love to Ene. 2004. reprint ed. pap. 15.95 (978-1-4191-8941-8(7)) Kessinger Publishing, LLC.

Anya@Russia. Com. 2004. 32p. pap. 3.99 (978-0-8341-2087-7(9)) Beacon Hill Pr. of Kansas City.

Aprile, Michael Dante & Aprile, Elizabeth Anne, illus. The Character of Elsie Dinsmore. 2001. 176p. (J). pap. 8.95 (978-1-58182-201-4(4)) Cumberland Hse. Publishing.

Archer, James. Travelling Light. 2005. 43p. spiral bd. 20.98 (978-1-4116-4011-5(X)) Lulu.com.

Arensen, Shel. The Carjackers, Vol. 2. 2003. (Rugendo Rhino Ser.). 128p. pap. 5.99 (978-0-8254-2042-9(3)) Kregel Pubns.

—The Poison Arrow Tree. 2003. (Rugendo Rhino Ser.). (Illus.). 128p. (J). pap. 5.99 (978-0-8254-2041-2(5)) Kregel Pubns.

Arenson, Carole L. Boots, the Church Cat. Ledesma, Eric M., illus. 1998. 34p. (Orig.). (J). (ps-2). reprint ed. pap. 15.95 (978-1-929187-12-6(2), CGBK63) Choristers Guild.

Arruda, Suzanne M. A Stocking for Jesus. Ogden, Betina, illus. 2005. (J). pap. 7.95 (978-0-8198-7076-6(5), 332-372) Pauline Bks. & Media.

Arterburn, Stephen & Hunt, Angela Elwell. Noah. 2004. (Young Believer on Tour Ser.). (J). pap. 3.99 (978-0-8423-8337-0(9)) Tyndale Hse. Pubs.

—Paige. 2004. (Young Believer on Tour Ser.). (J). pap. 3.99 (978-0-8423-8338-7(7)) Tyndale Hse. Pubs.

—Shane. 2004. (Young Believer on Tour Ser.). (J). pap. 3.99 (978-0-8423-8339-4(5)) Tyndale Hse. Pubs.

—Taz. 2004. (Young Believer on Tour Ser.). (J). pap. 3.99 (978-0-8423-8340-0(9)) Tyndale Hse. Pubs.

Auer, Chris. The Chinese Puzzle Box. 2005. 128p. (J). pap. 4.99 (978-0-310-70872-8(9)) Zonderkidz.

—Cory & the Bully: A Book about Respecting One Another. Bladholm, Cheri, illus. 2005. (Helping Kids Heal Ser.). 32p. (J). 9.99 (978-0-310-70900-8(8)) Zonderkidz.

—The Forgotten Room. 2005. 128p. (J). pap. 4.99 (978-0-310-70873-5(7)) Zonderkidz.

—Hidden in Plain Sight. 2005. (Illus.). 128p. (J). pap. 4.99 (978-0-310-70870-4(2)) Zonderkidz.

Averdonz, N., et al. Advent. 2007. (Z Graphic Novels / Hand of the Morning Star Ser.). 160p. (YA). pap. 9.99 (978-0-310-71369-2(2)) Zonderkidz.

—The Coming Storm. Broome, Mat, illus. 2007. (Z Graphic Novels / Kingdoms#8482;: A Biblical Epic Ser.). 160p. (YA). pap. 9.99 (978-0-310-71353-1(6)) Zonderkidz.

Baden, Robert. Joseph Forgives His Brothers: Genesis 37, 39-45 for Children. Sharp, Chris, illus. 2005. (ENG.). 16p. (J). (ps-ps). 1.99 (978-0-7586-0456-9(4)) Concordia Publishing Hse.

Bain, Sherry. Benjamin Gets Saved. 1998. (Illus.). 100p. (J). pap. 9.95 (978-1-889448-23-7(0)) Great House Publishers Grp., Inc., The.

Ballard, Curt. A Child of the Veil. 2001. 126p. (J). pap. 7.99 (978-1-889893-64-8(1)) Emerald Hse. Group, Inc.

Barry, Rick. Gunner's Run. 2007. (YA). (*978-1-59166-761-2(5)) Jones, Bob Univ. Pr.

Barth, Jeff. The Homesteaders. Barth, Marge, ed. 2002. (Illus.). 304p. pap. (978-1-891484-04-9(4)) Barth Family Ministries.

Batson, Wayne Thomas. The Door Within: The Door Within Trilogy - Book One. 2007. 336p. (J). pap. 9.99 (*978-1-4003-1011-1(3)) Nelson, Thomas Inc.

—The Final Storm. 2006. (Door Within Trilogy: Bk. 3). (Illus.). 320p. (J). 16.99 (978-1-4003-0783-8(X)) Nelson, Thomas Inc.

—Isle of Swords. 2007. 352p. (J). 16.99 (*978-1-4003-1018-0(0)) Nelson, Thomas Inc.

—The Rise of the Wyrm Lord: The Door Within Trilogy - Book Two. 2007. 336p. (J). pap. 9.99 (*978-1-4003-1012-8(1)) Nelson, Thomas Inc.

Baudouin-Croix, Marie. Saint Anthony of Padua: Proclaimer of the Good News. Keefe, Maryellen, tr. from FRE. Curelli, Augusta, illus. 1999. (Along the Paths of the Gospel Ser.). 74p. (J). (gr. 2-5). 6.95 (978-0-8198-7016-2(1), 332-336) Pauline Bks. & Media.

Beale, Fleur. I Am Not Esther. 2004. 256p. (gr. 7-17). reprint ed. pap. 6.99 (978-0-7868-1673-6(2)) Hyperion Bks. for Children.

Beeke, Joel & Kleyn, Diana. How God Used a Thunderstorm. Anderson, Jeff, illus. (Building on the Rock Ser.). 176p. (J). pap. (978-1-85792-815-0(6), Christian Focus) Christian Focus Pubns. GBR. *Dist:* Riverside.

Bell, C. A O G Bk. 1: Army of God. 2005. 108p. pap. 16.95 (978-1-4137-8130-4(6)) PublishAmerica, Inc.

Bell, Shirley. Boys on the Make. 2007. 54p. 12.95 (*978-1-4241-6575-9(X)) PublishAmerica, Inc.

Bender, Carrie. Chestnut Ridge Acres. 2001. 288p. (J). 24.95 (978-0-7862-3416-5(4), Five Star) Thomson Gale.

Bender, Esther. Elisabeth & the Windmill. 2003. (Lemon Tree Ser.). 112p. (J). (gr. 3-7). pap. 6.99 (978-0-8361-9204-9(4)) Herald Pr.

—Virginia & the Tiny One. Keenan, Joy Dunn, illus. 1998. (Lemon Tree Ser.: Vol. 2). 104p. (J). (gr. 3-7). pap. 6.99 (978-0-8361-9090-8(4)) Herald Pr.

Bennett, James W. Faith Wish. 2003. 160p. (J). (gr. 7 up). tchr. ed. 16.95 (978-0-8234-1778-0(6)) Holiday Hse., Inc.

Benson, Amber. Ghosts of Albion: Initiation. (J). 17.00 (978-1-931555-18-0(4)) Our Lady of Victory Schl.

Berenstain, Michael, et al. The Berenstain Bears & the Golden Rule. 2008. (J). pap. (*978-0-310-71247-3(5)) Zonderkidz.

—The Berenstain Bears Go to Sunday School. 2008. (J). pap. (*978-0-310-71248-0(3)) Zonderkidz.

—The Berenstain Bears Say Their Prayers. 2008. (J). pap. (*978-0-310-71246-6(7)) Zonderkidz.

Bergren, Lisa Tawn. God Gave Us Two. Bryant, Laura J., illus. 2001. 40p. (J). 9.99 (978-1-57856-507-8(3), WaterBrook Pr.) WaterBrook Pr.

—God Gave Us You. Bryant, Laura J., illus. 2000. 40p. (J). (ps-k). 10.99 (978-1-57856-323-4(2), WaterBrook Pr.) WaterBrook Pr.

Berndt, Ted. Search for the City. 2001. 100p. (YA). pap. 10.95 (978-1-58275-059-0(9), Segen Bks.) Black Forest Pr.

Bernthal, Mark & Exclaim Entertainment Staff. Boz/Good Morning Boz. Jeffords, Brandon, illus. 2006. (BOZ#8482; Ser.). 14p. (J). 4.99 (978-0-310-71207-7(6)) Zondervan.

—Boz/Good Night Boz. Jeffords, Brandon, illus. 2006. (BOZ#8482; Ser.). 14p. (J). 4.99 (978-0-310-71206-0(8)) Zondervan.

—God Loves Your Nose. McKee, Darren, illus. 2006. (BOZ#8482; Ser.). 12p. (J). 5.99 (978-0-310-71152-0(5)) Zonderkidz.

Bertola, Ann Marie, et al, contrib. by. Four in the Afternoon. 2003. 118p. pap. 11.99 (978-0-9743661-0-4(2)) Circle Pr.

Bethers, Linda, retold by. Christmas Oranges. 2004. 13p. pap. 3.95 (978-1-57734-546-6(0), 01114387) Covenant Communications, Inc.

Bibee, John. The Mystery of the Widow's Watch Bk. 8. 1999. (Home School Detectives Ser.). (Illus.). (J). 18.99 (978-0-8308-8661-6(3)) InterVarsity Pr.

Biggar, Joan R. Trapped at Haunted Canyon. 1998. (Megan Parnell Mysteries Ser.: Vol. 4). 160p. (J). (gr. 5-9). 5.99 (978-0-570-05069-8(3), 56-1893) Concordia Publishing Hse.

Billingsley, ReShonda Tate. Nothing but Drama. 2006. 288p. pap. 9.95 (978-1-4165-2560-8(2), Pocket) Simon & Schuster.

Bishop, Jennie. The Squire & the Scroll Coloring Book. 2005. (J). pap. 1.79 (*978-1-59317-085-1(8)) Warner Pr. Pubs.

Bishop, Jennie & Henson, Susan. Life Lessons from the Princess & the Kiss. 2004. 8.99 (*978-0-940110-52-6(0)) Life Action Publishing.

Bjorkman, Steve. The Flyaway Kite. Bjorkman, Steve, illus. 2000. (Illus.). 40p. (J). (ps-3). 9.99 (978-1-57856-264-0(3), WaterBrook Pr.) WaterBrook Pr.

Blake, Anne Catharine. Sheep Share. 2001. (ENG., Illus.). 20p. (J). (ps-k). bds. 4.99 (978-0-570-07167-9(4)) Concordia Publishing Hse.

Blake, Chris & Charismalife. Hover Get's His Wings. 2004. 24p. (J). (gr. k-3). 9.99 (978-1-59185-452-4(0), Charisma Kids) Strang Communications Co.

—I'm Just the Right Size. 2004. (Illus.). 24p. (J). (gr. k-3). 9.99 (978-1-59185-461-6(X), Charisma Kids) Strang Communications Co.

Blasdell, Jim & Blasdell, Wendy. God Help Us to Be Good: But Don't Let Us Miss Out on Any Fun: A Teenager's Prayer. 2004. 157p. (YA). pap. 19.95 (978-1-4137-3128-6(7)) PublishAmerica, Inc.

Bly, Stephen A. Danger at Deception Pass. 1998. (gr. 7-12). lib. bdg. 13.00 (978-0-613-77372-0(1)) Tandem Library Bks.

—The Secret of the Old Rifle. 2004. (Lewis & Clark Squad Ser.: No. 2). 160p. (gr. 4-9). 4.99 (978-0-89107-940-8(8)) Crossway Bks.

—Treachery at the River Canyon. 2004. (Lewis & Clark Squad Ser.: No.3). 160p. (YA). (gr. 4-9). 4.99 (978-0-89107-941-5(6)) Crossway Bks.

Boelts, Maribeth. Sarah's Grandma Goes to Heaven: A Book about Grief. Bladholm, Cheri, illus. 2004. (Helping Kids Heal Ser.). 32p. (J). 9.99 (978-0-310-70656-4(4)) Zonderkidz.

—Why Did You Bring Home a New Baby? A Book about Becoming a Sibling. Bladholm, Cheri, illus. 2006. 32p. (J). 9.99 (978-0-310-70901-5(6)) Zonderkidz.

Boger-Bass, Vallerie. The Mustard Seed: A Christian Promise. Boger-Bass, Vallerie, illus. 2003. 40p. pap. 10.00 (978-0-8059-5640-5(9)) Dorrance Publishing Co., Inc.

Boling, Ruth. Mouse Tales Vol. 1: Advent-Christmas-Epiphany. Carrier, Tracy, illus. 2005. 80p. (J). 14.95 (978-0-664-22705-0(8)) Westminster John Knox Pr.

Bollback, Anthony G. Rescue at Cripple Creek, Vol. 4. 1999. (Jack & Jill Mysteries Ser.). 135p. (J). pap. 7.95 (978-1-885729-18-7(9)) Toccoa Falls College Pr.

Bolton, Eddie. Winning the Prize. 2007. 20p. 9.99 (*978-0-7847-2102-5(5)) Standard Publishing.

Bond, Douglas. Guns of Thunder. 2007. (J). 11.99 (978-1-59638-013-4(6)) P & R Publishing.

—Hostage Lands. 2006. 248p. (YA). per. 9.99 (978-1-59638-027-1(6)) P & R Publishing.

—King's Arrow. Bird, Matthew, illus. 2003. (Crown & Covenant Ser.). 208p. (J). per. 10.99 (978-0-87552-743-7(4)) P & R Publishing.

—Rebel's Keep. Bird, Matthew, illus. 2004. (Crown & Covenant Ser.). 285p. (J). per. 9.99 (978-0-87552-744-4(2)) P & R Publishing.

Bookworks Staff, creator. Lee y Juega: El Arca de Noé. 2004. (SPA.). 20p. (J). bds. 4.99 (978-0-88113-668-5(9)) Grupo Nelson.

—Lee y Juega: En el Principio. 2004. (SPA., Illus.). 20p. (J). bds. 4.99 (978-0-88113-666-1(2)) Grupo Nelson.

—Lee y Juega: La Historia de Moisés. 2004. (SPA., Illus.). 20p. (J). bds. 4.99 (978-0-88113-669-2(7)) Grupo Nelson.

—Lee y Juega: Los Milagros de Jesus. 2004. (SPA., Illus.). 20p. (J). bds. 4.99 (978-0-88113-667-8(0)) Grupo Nelson.

Boonstra, Jean Elizabeth. Going Home. 2004. 95p. (J). (978-0-8163-2019-6(5)) Pacific Pr. Publishing Assn.

—A New Life down Under. 2004. 95p. (J). (978-0-8163-2017-2(9)) Pacific Pr. Publishing Assn.

—Secrets & Friends. 2004. 95p. (J). (978-0-8163-2021-9(7)) Pacific Pr. Publishing Assn.

—A Wedding in Avondale. 2004. 95p. (J). (978-0-8163-2018-9(7)) Pacific Pr. Publishing Assn.

Borntrager, Mary Christner. Polly. l.t. ed. 2002. 165p. (J). 25.95 (978-0-7862-4030-2(X)) Thomson Gale.

Bostrom, Kathleen Long. The Day Scooter Died: A Book about the Death of a Pet. Bladholm, Cheri, illus. 2005. (Helping Kids Heal Ser.). 32p. (J). 9.99 (978-0-310-70902-2(4)) Zonderkidz.

—Sunrise Hill. Johnson, Rick, illus. 2004. 32p. (J). 14.99 (978-0-310-70508-6(8)) Zonderkidz.

—Waiting for Christmas: A Story about the Advent Calendar. Natchev, Alexi, illus. 2006. (Traditions of Faith Ser.). 40p. (J). 15.99 (978-0-310-71015-8(4)) Zonderkidz.

—When Pete's Dad Got Sick: A Book about Chronic Illness. Bladholm, Cheri, illus. 2004. (Helping Kids Heal Ser.). 32p. (J). 9.99 (978-0-310-70655-7(6)) Zonderkidz.

Botts, Mary L., illus. Taylor's Halloween. l.t. ed. 1999. 16p. (J). (gr. k-6). pap. 3.99 (978-0-9668891-1-6(8)) Teach My Children Pubns.

Bowen, Connie. Yo Creo en Mi. 1999. Tr. of I Believe in Me. (SPA.). 64p. (J). (ps up). pap. 12.95 (978-0-87159-226-2(6), 296) Unity Schl. of Christianity.

Bower, Gary. Wyatt's Wagon: Including Others. Velker, Kay, ed. Bower, Jan, illus. l.t. ed. 2001. (Thinking of Others: Vol. 2). 32p. (J). lib. bdg. 16.95 (978-0-9704621-1-4(5)) Storybook Meadow Publishing.

Bowman, Crystal. Boxes, Boxes Everywhere. Schettle, Jane, illus. (J). 2004. 20p. 4.99 (978-0-310-70815-5(X)); 2001. 24p. 6.99 (978-0-310-70062-3(0)) Zonderkidz.

—Jake Goes Fishing. Maizel, Karen, illus. 2007. (I Can Read!). 32p. (J). pap. 3.99 (*978-0-310-71454-5(0)) Zonderkidz.

—My Cowboy Boots. Johnson, Meredith, illus. 2004. 20p. (J). pap. 4.99 (978-0-310-70813-1(3)) Zonderkidz.

—My Cowboy Boots. 2002. 24p. 6.99 (978-0-310-70253-5(4)) Zondervan.

Bowman, Crystal. My Happy Pumpkin. 2007. (Illus.). 14p. (J). 6.99 (*978-0-310-71160-5(6)) Zonderkidz.

Boxes, Bridges, & Bread Crumbs (2000-2001 Children's Reading Book) 2000. 32p. (J). pap. 2.75 (978-0-8341-1855-3(6)) Beacon Hill Pr. of Kansas City.

Brammer, Deb. Moose. 2006. (YA). (*978-1-59166-722-3(4)) Jones, Bob Univ. Pr.

Brammer, Deb. Two Sides to Everything. 2003. (Illus.). 151p. (J). (978-1-59166-166-5(8)) Jones, Bob Univ. Pr.

Brande, Robin. Evolution, Me & Other Freaks of Nature. 2007. 272p. (gr. 7). (J). lib. bdg. 18.99 (*978-0-375-94349-2(8)); (YA). 15.99 (*978-0-375-84349-5(3)) Random Hse. Children's Bks. (Knopf Bks. for Young Readers).

Brandenburg, Claire. The Monk Who Grew Prayer. 2003. 32p. 9.95 (978-1-888212-66-2(7)) Conciliar Pr.

Brantley, Judi S. Camille's Crossroad. Ferguson, Martha-Elizabeth, illus. 1999. 48p. (J). (gr. 4-8). 16.95 (978-1-892570-02-4(5)) Spring Hse. Bks.

Brantley, Steven & Brantley, Judi S. The Throwaway Cat. Holt, Del, illus. 1998. 48p. (J). (ps-3). 16.95 (978-1-892570-00-0(9)) Spring Hse. Bks.

Brian's All-Star Day. 2004. 32p. pap. 3.99 (978-0-8341-2089-1(5)) Beacon Hill Pr. of Kansas City.

Bridges, Charlene. Tell me a Story. 2004. (J). per. 9.95 (978-1-59352-062-5(X)) Christian Services Publishing.

Bright, et al. Beginning the Christian Adventure, Bk. 1. 2004. pap. 18.99 (978-1-56399-151-6(9)) NewLife Pubns.

—Discover Our Awesome God, Bk. 2. 2004. pap. 18.99 (978-1-56399-152-3(7)) NewLife Pubns.

Brinkerhoff, Shirley. Balancing Act. 1998. (Nikki Sheridan Ser.: Vol. 4). 208p. (J). (gr. 9-12). pap. 5.99 (978-1-56179-559-8(3)) Bethany Hse. Pubs.

—Mysterious Love. 1998. (Nikki Sheridan Ser.: Bk. 2). 192p. (J). (gr. 4-7). pap. (978-1-56179-485-0(6)) Focus on the Family Publishing.

—Second Choices. 2000. (Nikki Sheridan Ser.: Vol. 6). (Illus.). 160p. (YA). (gr. 9-13). pap. 5.99 (978-1-56179-880-3(0)) Bethany Hse. Pubs.

—Second Choices. 2000. (gr. 7-12). lib. bdg. 14.15 (978-0-613-82302-9(8)) Tandem Library Bks.

—Tangled Web. 2000. (Nikki Sheridan Ser.: Vol. 5). 176p. (J). (gr. 9-12). pap. 5.99 (978-1-56179-737-0(5)) Bethany Hse. Pubs.

—Tangled Web. 2000. (gr. 7-12). lib. bdg. 14.15 (978-0-613-84406-2(8)) Tandem Library Bks.

Brodeur, Tom. Regina Silsby's Phantom Militia. 2005. (Illus.). 267p. (J). (ps-7). 7.49 (978-1-59166-385-0(7)) Jones, Bob Univ. Pr.

Brooks, Linda Grace. The Asquinn Twins & Where the Trail Forks. 2005. 119p. pap. 16.95 (978-0-7414-2445-7(2)) Infinity Publishing.

Brouwer, Sigmund. Alien Pursuit. 2000. (gr. 5-8). lib. bdg. 13.00 (978-0-613-76892-4(2)) Tandem Library Bks.

—The Angel & the Cross. 2005. (Guardian Angel Ser.). 168p. (gr. 3-7). pap. 7.99 (978-0-7369-0296-0(1)) Harvest Hse. Pubs.

—The Angel & the Ring: A Supernatural Adventure. 2005. (Guardian Angel Ser.). 165p. (J). (ps-7). pap. 7.99 (978-0-7369-0294-6(5)) Harvest Hse. Pubs.

—The Angel & the Sword: A Supernatural Adventure. 2005. (Guardian Angel Ser.). 172p. (J). (ps-7). pap. 7.99 (978-0-7369-0293-9(7)) Harvest Hse. Pubs.

—Barbarians from the Isle. 2002. (Winds of Light Ser.). 202p. (YA). pap. 5.99 (978-1-55305-033-9(9)) Cygnet Publishing Group, Inc./Coolreading.com CAN. *Dist:* Orca Bk. Pubs. USA.

—Camp Craziness. 2003. (Watch Out for Joel Ser.). (Illus.). 32p. (J). (gr. 1-3). reprint ed. pap. 3.99 (978-0-7642-2582-6(0)) Bethany Hse. Pubs.

—Camp Craziness. 2003. (gr. k-3). lib. bdg. 11.80 (978-0-613-87752-7(7)) Tandem Library Bks.

—Countdown. 2001. (gr. 5-8). lib. bdg. 13.00 (978-0-613-76821-4(3)) Tandem Library Bks.

—Fly Trap. 2003. (Watch Out for Joel Ser.). (Illus.). 32p. (J). (gr. 1-3). pap. 3.99 (978-0-7642-2583-3(9)) Bethany Hse. Pubs.

—Fly Trap. 2003. (gr. k-3). lib. bdg. 11.80 (978-0-613-87753-4(5)) Tandem Library Bks.

—Hammerhead. 2001. (gr. 3-6). lib. bdg. 13.00 (978-0-613-76893-1(0)) Tandem Library Bks.

—Last Stand. 2002. (gr. 3-6). lib. bdg. 13.00 (978-0-613-76883-2(3)) Tandem Library Bks.

—Legend of the Gilded Saber. 2002. (gr. 3-6). lib. bdg. 14.15 (978-0-613-89740-2(4)) Tandem Library Bks.

—Manchurian Sector. 2002. (gr. 3-6). lib. bdg. 13.00 (978-0-613-76880-1(9)) Tandem Library Bks.

—Mission 10: Last Stand. 2002. (Mars Diaries Ser.: Mission 10). 144p. (J). mass mkt. 4.99 (978-0-8423-5634-3(7)) Tyndale Hse. Pubs.

—Mission 2: Alien Pursuit. 2000. (Mars Diaries Ser.: Mission 2). (Illus.). 144p. (J). (gr. 5-9). mass mkt. 4.99 (978-0-8423-4305-3(9)) Tyndale Hse. Pubs.

—Mission 9: Manchurian Sector. 2002. (Mars Diaries Ser.: Mission 9). 160p. (J). mass mkt. 4.99 (978-0-8423-5633-6(9)) Tyndale Hse. Pubs.

—Moon Racer. 2001. (gr. 5-8). lib. bdg. 13.00 (978-0-613-76814-6(0)) Tandem Library Bks.

—Mystery Pennies. 2003. (Watch Out for Joel Ser.). (Illus.). 32p. (J). pap. 3.99 (978-0-7642-2584-0(7)) Bethany Hse. Pubs.

—Oxygen Level Zero Level Zero. 2000. (gr. 5-8). lib. bdg. 10.65 (978-0-613-76779-8(9)) Tandem Library Bks.

—Sole Survivor. 2001. (gr. 3-6). lib. bdg. 13.00 (978-0-613-76817-7(5)) Tandem Library Bks.

—Strunk Soup. 2003. (Watch Out for Joel Ser.). (Illus.). 32p. (J). pap. 3.99 (978-0-7642-2585-7(5)) Bethany Hse. Pubs.

—Time Bomb. 2000. (gr. 5-8). lib. bdg. 13.00 (978-0-613-76816-0(7)) Tandem Library Bks.

—Wings of an Angel. 2004. (Winds of Light Ser.). 214p. (YA). pap. 5.99 (978-1-55305-032-2(0)) Cygnet Publishing Group, Inc./Coolreading.com CAN. *Dist:* Orca Bk. Pubs. USA.

—Wings of an Angel. 2002. (gr. 5-8). lib. bdg. 14.15 (978-0-613-84971-5(X)) Tandem Library Bks.

Brown, Brian & Melrose, Andrew. The Storykeepers. 2000. (Storykeepers' Ser.). 128p. pap., tchr. ed. 26.99 (978-0-310-23674-0(6)) Zonderkidz.

Brown, Fletch. Street Boy. 3rd ed. 2005. 140p. reprint ed. pap. 5.99 (978-1-884543-64-7(2)) Authentic Media.

Brown, Janet Allison, et al. David & Goliath. Durantz, Summer, illus. 2003. (Inspirational Collection). 24p. (J). pap. 3.99 (978-0-7696-3127-1(4) , Brighter Child) School Specialty Publishing.

—The First Christmas. Durantz, Summer, illus. 2003. (Inspirational Collection). 24p. (J). pap. 3.99 (978-0-7696-3128-8(2) , Brighter Child) School Specialty Publishing.

—Noah's Ark. Durantz, Summer, illus. 2003. (Inspirational Collection). 24p. (J). pap. 3.99 (978-0-7696-3125-7(8) , Brighter Child) School Specialty Publishing.

Brumett, Jonas O. The Weavus Family Storybook. Matera, Francis, illus. l.t. ed. 1999. 64p. (J). (gr. k-2). pap. 16.95 incl. audio compact disk (978-1-892812-50-6(9)) Froginhood & Friends, Inc.

Buchanan, Kathy Wierenga & Johnson, Lissa Halls. When Stars Fall, Vol. 11. 2005. (Brio Girls Ser.). 208p. (YA). pap. 7.99 (978-1-58997-090-8(X)) Focus on the Family Publishing.

Buchanan, Paul. Ask Willie. 1999. (gr. 3-6). lib. bdg. 14.15 (978-0-613-72656-6(1)) Tandem Library Bks.

—Brain Freeze, Vol. 15. 2000. (Misadventures of Willie Plummett Ser.: Vol. 15). 128p. (J). (gr. 3-7). 5.99 (978-0-570-07004-7(X)) Concordia Publishing Hse.

—Brain Freeze. 2000. (gr. 3-6). lib. bdg. 14.15 (978-0-613-72827-0(0)) Tandem Library Bks.

—Dances with Werewolves, Vol. 8. 2000. (Heebie Jeebies Ser.: Vol. 6). 128p. (J). (gr. 3-7). pap. 5.99 (978-0-8054-1982-5(9)) B&H Publishing Grp.

—Dog Days, Vol. 14. 1999. (Misadventures of Willie Plummett Ser.: Vol. 14). (Illus.). 128p. (J). (gr. 3-7). 5.99 (978-0-570-07054-2(6)) Concordia Publishing Hse.

—Dog Days. 1999. (gr. 3-6). lib. bdg. 14.15 (978-0-613-72786-0(X)) Tandem Library Bks.

—Don't Rock the Float. 2000. (gr. 3-6). lib. bdg. 14.15 (978-0-613-72843-0(2)) Tandem Library Bks.

—Hail to the Chump, Vol. 9. 1998. (Misadventures of Willie Plummett Ser.: Vol. 9). 128p. (J). (gr. 3-7). 5.99 (978-0-570-05088-9(X)) Concordia Publishing Hse.

—Heads I Win, Tails You Lose. 1999. (gr. 3-6). lib. bdg. 14.15 (978-0-613-72655-9(3)) Tandem Library Bks.

—House Divided. 2001. (gr. 3-6). lib. bdg. 14.15 (978-0-613-72848-5(3)) Tandem Library Bks.

—Lock-in. 2001. (gr. 3-6). lib. bdg. 14.15 (978-0-613-72847-8(5)) Tandem Library Bks.

—Return to Terror Cove. 2001. (Heebie Jeebies Ser.: Vol. 10). 138p. (J). (gr. 3-7). pap. 5.99 (978-0-8054-2333-4(8)) B&H Publishing Grp.

—Stuck on You, 1, Vol. 13. 1999. (Misadventures of Willie Plummett Ser.: Vol. 13). (Illus.). 128p. (J). (gr. 3-7). 5.99 (978-0-570-07052-8(X)) Concordia Publishing Hse.

—Stuck on You. 1999. (gr. 3-6). lib. bdg. 14.15 (978-0-613-72785-3(1)) Tandem Library Bks.

—Tidal Wave, Vol. 7. 1998. (Misadventures of Willie Plummett Ser.: Vol. 7). 128p. (J). (gr. 3-7). 5.99 (978-0-570-05086-5(3)) Concordia Publishing Hse.

—Uncle from Another Planet. 1999. (Heebie Jeebies Ser.: Vol. 4). 144p. (YA). pap. 5.99 (978-0-8054-1650-3(1)) B&H Publishing Grp.

—Wild Ride on Bigfoot Mountain, Vol. 6. 1999. (Heebie Jeebies Ser.: No. 6). (Illus.). 153p. (J). (gr. 8-12). pap. 5.99 (978-0-8054-1975-7(6)) B&H Publishing Grp.

Buchanan, Paul & Randall, Rod. Ask Willie, Vol. 12. 1999. (Misadventures of Willie Plummett Ser.: Bk. 12). 128p. (J). (gr. 3-7). 5.99 (978-0-570-05478-8(8) , 56-1941GJ) Concordia Publishing Hse.

—Don't Rock the Float, Vol. 17. 2001. (Misadventures of Willie Plummett Ser.: Vol. 17). (Illus.). 128p. (J). (gr. 3-7). 5.99 (978-0-570-07125-9(9)) Concordia Publishing Hse.

—Face the Music, Vol. 18. 2001. (Misadventures of Willie Plummett Ser.: Vol. 18). (Illus.). 128p. (J). (gr. 3-7). 5.99 (978-0-570-07126-6(7)) Concordia Publishing Hse.

—Heads I Win, Tails You Lose, Vol. 11. 1999. (Misadventures of Willie Plummett Ser.: Bk. 11). 128p. (J). (gr. 3-7). 5.99 (978-0-570-05477-1(X) , 56-1940GJ) Concordia Publishing Hse.

—A House Divided, Vol. 20. 2001. (Misadventures of Willie Plummett Ser.: Vol. 20). (Illus.). 128p. (J). (gr. 3-7). 5.99 (978-0-570-07131-0(3)) Concordia Publishing Hse.

—Lock-In, Vol. 19. 2001. (Misadventures of Willie Plummett Ser.: Vol. 19). 128p. (J). (gr. 3-7). 5.99 (978-0-570-07130-3(5)) Concordia Publishing Hse.

—The Monopoly, Vol. 10. 1998. (Misadventures of Willie Plummett Ser.: Vol. 10). 128p. (J). (gr. 3-7). 5.99 (978-0-570-05089-6(8)) Concordia Publishing Hse.

Buckley, Ray. Christmas Moccasins. Buckley, Ray, illus. 2003. (Illus.). 32p. 18.00 (978-0-687-02738-5(1)) Abingdon Pr.

Bunyan, John. The Pilgrim's Progress, No. 1. 2004. pap. 9.99 (978-0-88270-938-3(0)) Bridge-Logos Pubs.

—The Pilgrim's Progress. 2005. (Illus.). 191p. (J). (978-1-84550-102-0(0) , Christian Focus) Christian Focus Pubns.

Burge, Kenneth Dean. Lena's Star. Burge, Deborah Lynn, illus. l.t. ed. 2001. 36p. (J). per. 10.00 (978-0-9715953-0-9(5) , Verner Publishing) Verner Advertising, LLC.

Burkart, Jeffrey E., retold by. The Hidden Prince. 2003. (Illus.). 32p. (J). 9.99 incl. audio compact disk (978-0-570-07174-7(7)) Concordia Publishing Hse.

Burt, William D. The Golden Wood: The King of the Trees, Bk. III. 2002. 288p. per. 14.95 (978-1-57921-466-1(5)) WinePress Publishing.

Byers, Reggie, illus. & creator. Kidz of the KING Bk. 1: There's No Egg Scuse for Doing Violence! Byers, Reggie, creator. 2002. 32p. (J). 4.95 (978-0-9721164-0-4(0)) Sheepdog Publishing.

Byrd, Sandra. Change of Heart. 2002. (gr. 3-6). lib. bdg. 13.00 (978-0-613-84506-9(4)) Tandem Library Bks.

—Chopstick. 2005. (Friends for a Season Ser.). 240p. (J). (gr. 8-12). pap. 10.99 (978-0-7642-0021-2(6)) Bethany Hse. Pubs.

—Cross My Heart. 2001. (Hidden Diary Ser.). 112p. (J). (gr. 3-7). reprint ed. pap. 5.99 (978-0-7642-2480-5(8)) Bethany Hse. Pubs.

—Cross My Heart. 2001. (gr. 3-6). lib. bdg. 13.00 (978-0-613-84512-0(9)) Tandem Library Bks.

—Island Girl. 2005. (Friends for A Season Ser.). 240p. (J). reprint ed. pap. 10.99 (978-0-7642-0020-5(8)) Bethany Hse. Pubs.

—Just Between Friends. 2001. (Hidden Diary Ser.). 112p. (J). (gr. 3-7). pap. 4.99 (978-0-7642-2482-9(4)) Bethany Hse. Pubs.

—Make a Wish. 2001. (Hidden Diary Ser.). 112p. (J). (gr. 3-7). reprint ed. pap. 5.99 (978-0-7642-2481-2(6)) Bethany Hse. Pubs.

—Pass It On. 2002. (Hidden Diary Ser.: Bk. 5). 112p. (J). pap. 4.99 (978-0-7642-2484-3(0)) Bethany Hse. Pubs.

—Pass It On. 2002. (gr. 3-6). lib. bdg. 13.00 (978-0-613-84505-2(6)) Tandem Library Bks.

—Red Velvet. 2005. (Friends for a Season Ser.). 256p. (J). (gr. 8-12). pap. 10.99 (978-0-7642-0022-9(4)) Bethany Hse. Pubs.

Cabbage, Betty, text. Betty & the Devil's Bottle. 2005. (Illus.). 52p. (J). (978-1-59799-000-4(0)) Deaf Missions.

Carlson, Melody. Bad Connection. 2006. 256p. pap. 11.99 (978-1-59052-692-7(9) , Multnomah) WaterBrook Pr.

—Becoming Me. 2000. (Diary of a Teenage Girl Ser.: Bk. 1). (Illus.). 256p. (YA). pap. 12.99 (978-1-57673-735-4(7) , Multnomah) WaterBrook Pr.

—Beyond Reach. 2007. (Secret Life Samantha Mcgregor Ser.). 258p. (YA). pap. 11.99 (978-1-59052-693-4(7) , Multnomah Fiction) WaterBrook Pr.

—Beyond Reach: A Novel. 2007. 250p. (YA). ***(978-1-4287-2412-9(5)*** , Multnomah) WaterBrook Pr.

—Bright Purple. 2006. 224p. (YA). pap. 12.99 (978-1-57683-950-8(8) , Th1nk Bks.) NavPress Publishing Group.

—Burnt Orange: Color Me Wasted. 2005. 207p. (YA). pap. 12.99 (978-1-57683-533-3(2)) NavPress Publishing Group.

—Dark Blue: Color Me Lonely. 2004. 196p. (J). pap. 12.99 (978-1-57683-529-6(4)) NavPress Publishing Group.

—Diary of a Teenage Girl - It's My Life: Diary Number 2. 2002. (gr. 7-12). lib. bdg. 22.25 (978-0-613-88463-1(9)) Tandem Library Bks.

—Faded Denim. 2006. 224p. (YA). pap. 12.99 (978-1-57683-537-1(5) , Th1nk Bks.) NavPress Publishing Group.

—Fool's Gold: Color Me Consumed. 2005. 222p. (YA). (gr. 7-12). pap. 12.99 (978-1-57683-534-0(0)) NavPress Publishing Group.

—Forgive Others. Reagan, Susan Joy, illus. 2004. (Just Like Jesus Said Ser.). 32p. (J). (ps-5). 12.99 (978-0-8054-2385-3(0)) B&H Publishing Grp.

—Hi, I'm Blackbeary: The Fruit of the Spirit Is Peace. Mahan, Ben, illus. 2004. (Beary Patch Bears Ser.). 96p. bds. 6.99 (978-1-58134-182-9(2)) Crossway Bks.

—I Do. 2005. (Diary of a Teenage Girl Ser.). 272p. (YA). pap. 12.99 (978-1-59052-320-9(2) , Multnomah) WaterBrook Pr.

—It's My Life: Diary Number 2. 2002. (Diary of a Teenage Girl Ser.: Bk. 2). 252p. (J). pap. 12.99 (978-1-59052-053-6(X) , Multnomah Fiction) WaterBrook Pr.

—Kenzie's Story. 2004. (Degrees of Betrayal Ser.). 304p. (YA) pap. 9.99 (978 1-4143-0002-3(6)) Tyndale Hse. Pubs.

—Love Your Neighbor. Reagan, Susan Joy, illus. 2004. (Just Like Jesus Said Ser.). 32p. (J). (ps-5). 12.99 (978-0-8054-2383-9(4)) B&H Publishing Grp.

—Moon White. 2007. 224p. (YA). pap. 12.99 (978-1-57683-951-5(6) , Th1nk Bks.) NavPress Publishing Group.

—Notes from a Spinning Planet—Ireland. 2006. 256p. (YA). pap. 12.99 (978-1-4000-7144-9(5) , WaterBrook Pr.) WaterBrook Pr.

—Notes from a Spinning Planet—Papua, New Guinea. 2007. (Notes from a Spinning Planet Ser.). 240p. (YA). pap. 12.99 (978-1-4000-7145-6(3) , WaterBrook Pr.) WaterBrook Pr.

—On My Own. 2002. (gr. 7-12). lib. bdg. 22.25 (978-0-613-85855-7(7)) Tandem Library Bks.

—On My Own: Diary Number 4. 2002. (Diary of a Teenage Girl Ser.: Bk. 4). 300p. (J). pap. 12.99 (978-1-59052-017-8(3) , Multnomah) WaterBrook Pr.

—Project, Girl Power. 2007. (Faithgirlz!#8482; / Girls of 622 Harbor View Ser.). 144p. (J). pap. 6.99 (978-0-310-71186-5(X)) Zonderkidz.

—Project, Mystery Bus. 2007. (Faithgirlz!#8482; / Girls of 622 Harbor View Ser.). 144p. (J). pap. 6.99 (978-0-310-71187-2(8)) Zonderkidz.

—Project, Rescue Chelsea. 2007. (Faithgirlz!#8482; / Girls of 622 Harbor View Ser.). 144p. (J). pap. 6.99 (978-0-310-71188-9(6)) Zonderkidz.

—Project, Take Charge. 2007. (Faithgirlz!#8482; / Girls of 622 Harbor View Ser.). 144p. (J). pap. 6.99 (978-0-310-71189-6(4)) Zonderkidz.

—Road Trip, No. 7. 2003. (Diary of a Teenage Girl Ser.). 304p. pap. 12.99 (978-1-59052-142-7(0) , Multnomah) WaterBrook Pr.

—Secretly Do Good Deeds. Reagan, Susan Joy, illus. 2004. (Just Like Jesus Said Ser.). 32p. (J). (ps-5). 12.99 (978-0-8054-2384-6(2)) B&H Publishing Grp.

—Sold Out. 2003. (gr. 7-12). lib. bdg. 22.25 (978-0-613-86368-1(2)) Tandem Library Bks.

—Sold Out: Diary Number 6. 2003. (Diary of a Teenage Girl Series, Book Six Ser.). 288p. pap. 12.99 (978-1-59052-141-0(2) , Multnomah) WaterBrook Pr.

—When the Creepy Things Come Out! Reagan, Susan Joy, illus. 2003. 32p. (J). (ps-5). 12.99 (978-0-8054-2687-8(6)) B&H Publishing Grp.

Carlyle, Linda Porter. A Child's Steps to Jesus. 2007. (J). ***(978-0-8163-2205-3(8))*** Pacific Pr. Publishing Assn.

Carr, Jon & Carr, Debra. Harry the Hippo. 2004. 6.00 (978-1-59089-724-9(2)) Creflo Dollar Ministries Pubns.

Carroll, Michael & Elmer, Robert, eds. Eat My Martian Dust: Finding God among Aliens, Droids, & Mega Moons. 2005. (Illus.). 256p. (YA). pap. 12.99 (978-0-8010-4528-8(2)) Baker Bks.

Carson, Diana Pastora. All the Muchos in the World: A Special Story about Love. Pruitt, Ginny, illus. 2006. 32p. (J). pap. 8.95 (978-0-8198-0779-3(6)) Pauline Bks. & Media.

Carty, Jay, et al. O. Whillikers in the Hall of Champions. 2000. (Illus.). 112p. (J). pap. 13.00 (978-0-8307-2634-9(9) , Gospel Light) Gospel Light Pubns.

Castleberry, Stephen B., Sr. & Castleberry, Susie L. Weighty Matters. 2003. (Farm Mystery Ser.). 155p. (YA). per. 8.50 (978-1-891907-13-5(1)) Castleberry Farms Pr.

Celebrate God's Harvest. 28p. (J). 3.29 (978-0-7847-1022-7(8)) Standard Publishing.

Chapell, Bryan. I'll Love You Anyway & Always. Jonke, Tim, illus. 2005. 32p. 15.99 (978-1-58134-306-9(X) , Crossway Bibles) Crossway Bks.

Chapman, Steven Curtis. The Great Adventure: A Very Special Story for Children. Colton, Ellie, illus. 2001. (Dove Award Signature Ser.). 32p. (J). (gr. k up). 14.99 (978-0-8054-2399-0(0)) B&H Publishing Grp.

Charlie's Be Kind Day. 2006. 16p. (J). pap. 1.99 (978-0-7847-1689-2(7) , 02991) Standard Publishing.

Cherrington, Sharnett Felicia. Bitter Sweet. 2005. (YA). per. 12.95 (978-1-933570-70-9(9)) Aardvark Global Publishing.

Ch'iao, Xiao. Patti & the Weegors. (Illus.). 32p. (J). pap. 4.99 (978-1-85792-557-9(2) , Christian Focus) Christian Focus Pubns. GBR. *Dist:* Riverside.

Chidley, Howard J. FiftyTwo Story Talks to Boys & Girls D. 2007. pap. ***(978-1-4065-1446-9(2))*** Dodo Pr.

Chief White Hair's Secret. 2004. 54p. pap. 6.99 (978-0-8341-2091-4(7)) Beacon Hill Pr. of Kansas City.

Childhood's Years. 144p. (J). mass mkt. 5.99 (978-1-85792-713-9(3) , Christian Heritage) Christian Focus Pubns. GBR. *Dist:* Riverside.

Christian, Focus. God's Zoo TNT Ministries. Charnick, Tim, illus. 2005. 96p. pap. (978-1-84550-069-6(5) , Christian Focus) Christian Focus Pubns.

Clark, Laura Shipp & Shipp, Dave. The Donut Repair Club Helps Out. Caldwell, Lise, ed. Burris, Priscilla, illus. 1999. (Happy Day Bks.). 24p. (J). (ps-2). pap. 2.49 (978-0-7847-1089-0(9) , 04285, Bean Sprouts) Standard Publishing.

Cloud, Tori & Thomas Nelson Publishing Staff. Sophie & Sam: When to Say Yes & When to Say No. Valentine, Becky, illus. 2006. 128p. (gr. 4-7). 14.99 (978-1-59145-299-7(6)) Nelson, Thomas Inc.

Cobblekids Staff. Making Melody W/Your Heart Pri. 2004. 11.95 (978-1-931737-01-2(0)) Lollipop Publishing, LLC.

Coelho, Paulo. Veronika deschliesst zu Sterb. pap. 22.95 (978-3-257-23305-6(1)) Diogenes Verlag AG CHE. *Dist:* Distribooks, Inc.

Coffee, Karen. God, Do You Love Me? Hardison, Buist, illus. 2007. 32p. (ps-1). 14.00 ***(978-0-687-49270-1(X))*** Abingdon Pr.

The Coin. 2000. 112p. (J). pap. 6.50 (978-0-9658730-1-7(3)) Drew Publishing Co.

Coleman, Charles G. The Shining Sword. 2006. (Illus.). (J). per. 9.95 (978-1-933573-05-2(8) , 3372) Zeezok Publishing.

Collins, Chris. A Mary Little Christmas. Brimer, Molly, illus. l.t. ed. 2002. 32p. (J). lib. bdg. (978-0-9722799-0-1(3)) Words of Grace, Inc.

Colton, Ellie, illus. Thank You: A Very Special Story for Children. 2001. (Dove Award Signature Ser.). 32p. (J). (gr. k up). 14.99 (978-0-8054-2400-3(8)) B&H Publishing Grp.

Coman, Carolyn. Tell Me Everything. 2006. 160p. (YA). pap. 6.95 (978-0-374-40005-7(9) , Farrar, Straus & Giroux (BYR)) Farrar, Straus & Giroux.

Comley, Kathryn. That's How I Found God. Lane, Ranae, illus. 2004. (J). bds. 9.99 (978-1-4183-0014-2(4)) Christ Inspired, Inc.

Comrie, Margaret S. The Heroes of Castle Bretten. 2003. (Illus.). 229p. (J). (978-1-894666-65-7(8)) Inheritance Pubns.

Concordia Publishing Staff. Noah's Ark Activity Set. 1999. (Aloha Cove Ser.: Vol. 13). (Illus.). (J). (ps-2). 12.99 (978-0-570-05567-9(9)) Concordia Publishing Hse.

Condie, Allyson B. Yearbook. 2006. 208p. (YA). pap. 14.95 (978-1-59038-690-3(6)) Deseret Bk. Co.

Cooney, Caroline B. A Friend at Midnight. 2006. 192p. (YA). (gr. 7). 15.95 (978-0-385-73326-7(7) , Delacorte Bks. for Young Readers) Random Hse. Children's Bks.

—A Friend at Midnight. 2006. 192p. (YA). 15.95 (978-1-4000-7208-8(5) , WaterBrook Pr.) WaterBrook Pr.

Cousain, Hattie M. When I Was Little. (J). 8.95 (978-0-9640459-0-3(7)) Cole's, C. Consultant & Pubns.

Crabtree, Dianne. On the Road to Royalty. 2005. 222p. (YA). pap. 14.95 (978-1-932898-32-3(8) , 98328) Spring Creek Bk. Co.

Craner, Kathy. Nibbles the Rabbit Has a Good Habit. 1998. (Illus.). (J). (ps-2). pap. 12.95 (978-0-7880-1404-8(8) , Fairway Pr.) CSS Publishing Co.

Craven, Tracy Leininger. Life of Faith/Kathleens Drought. 2007. (Life of Faith': Kathleen Mckenzie Ser.). 160p. (YA). pap. 6.99 (978-1-928749-27-1(5)) Mission City Pr., Inc.

Crew, Linda. Brides of Eden: A True Story Imagined. (gr. 5 up). 2003. 256p. (J). pap. 6.99 (978-0-06-447217-3(5)); 2001. (Illus.). 240p. (YA). 15.89 (978-0-06-028751-1(9)) HarperCollins Pubs.

The Cross & the Spy (2000-2001 Children's Reading Book) 2000. 80p. (J). pap. 6.90 (978-0-8341-1858-4(0)) Beacon Hill Pr. of Kansas City.

Crouch, Cheryl Lynne. Chosen Girls/Backstage Pass. 2007. (Chosen Girls' Ser.). 144p. (J). pap. 3.99 (978-0-310-71267-1(X)) Zonderkidz.

Cunning, Concord. Scripture Sleuth 3. 2004. pap. 8.95 (978-1-885904-39-3(8)) Focus Publishing.

Cunningham, Elaine. Missing in Madagascar. 2006. 32p. 4.50 (978-0-8341-2230-7(8)) Beacon Hill Pr. of Kansas City.

Curley, Marianne. Los Elegidos. 2003. (SPA.). 208p. (978-84-7888-577-0(3) , 1952) Emece Editores.

Dacey, Richard. Spinner McClock & the Christmas Visit. Gillett, Hallie, illus. 2004. 32p. (J). 13.95 (978-1-929039-24-1(7)) Ambassador Bks., Inc.

Dahlstrom, Kathryn. Peppy's Rescue. Date not set. (Good News Club Ser.). (J). (gr. 4-11). pap. 4.99 (978-1-55976-826-9(6)) CEF Pr.

Daniel, Holdsworth. Baby Love Comes to the Rescue. 1999. (Heartland Ser.). (Illus.). 32p. (J). (ps-2). 3.99 (978-0-570-05499-3(0)) Concordia Publishing Hse.

—Goodness the Paramedic & the Oily Rags, Vol. 1. 1999. (Heartland Ser.). (Illus.). 32p. (J). (ps-2). 3.99 (978-0-570-05498-6(2)) Concordia Publishing Hse.

—Joy the Clown Strengthens Heartland, Vol. 1. 1999. (Heartland Ser.). (Illus.). 32p. (J). (ps-2). 3.99 (978-0-570-05497-9(4)) Concordia Publishing Hse.

—Kiddie Kindness & the Good News, Vol. 1. 1999. (Heartland Ser.). (Illus.). 32p. (J). (ps-2). 3.99 (978-0-570-05463-4(X)) Concordia Publishing Hse.

David C. Cook. The Beginning. 2003. (My Jesus Pocket Bks.). (Illus.). 32p. (J). (gr. 5-3). pap., pap. 8.90 (978-1-55513-092-3(5) , 1555130925) Cook, David C. Publishing Co.

—God Made Everything with Love, Set. 2007. (Land of Milk & Honey Ser.). (J). (ps). bds. 9.99 ***(978-1-4347-0007-0(0))*** Cook, David C. Publishing Co.

—Little Hearts, Little Hands Prayer Set. 2007. (Land of Milk & Honey Ser.). 16p. (J). (ps). bds. 9.99 ***(978-1-4347-0008-7(9))*** Cook, David C. Publishing Co.

Davina. Mr. G - Are You Listening? Kat's Diary. 2003. 96p. (J). pap. 7.99 (978-0-7459-4841-6(3) , Lion) Lion Hudson plc GBR. *Dist:* Independent Pubs. Group.

Davis, Bryan. The Tears of a Dragon, 2005. (Dragons in Our Midst Ser.: 4). 363p. (J). (gr. 7-12). pap. 14.99 (978-0-89957-173-7(5)) AMG Pubs.

Davis, Cynthia. Chrysalis. 2002. (gr. 7-12). lib. bdg. 18.75 (978-0-613-77940-1(1)) Tandem Library Bks.

Davis, Dean. The Dangerous Journey of Sherman the Sheep. 2005. (Illus.). 160p. (J). pap. 9.99 (978-0-9759619-2-6(6)) CLADACH Publishing.

Davis, Holly. Thankful Together. Sokolova, Valerie, illus. 2006. 36p. (J). 5.99 (978-0-7847-1436-2(3) , 04077) Standard Publishing.

Davis, L. Mitchell. Mouse Adventures: The Tale of Micah Mouse. 2007. 32p. per. 13.99 ***(978-1-59886-655-1(9))*** Tate Publishing & Enterprises, L.L.C.

Davis, Susan. I'm Adopted, You're Adopted: Welcome to God's Family. 2007. (ENG.). 79p. (J). (gr. 1-4). per. 8.99 ***(978-0-8127-0434-1(7))*** Autumn Hse. Publishing Co.

Davis, Susan Page. Sarah's Long Ride. 2007. 173p. (J). ***(978-1-59166-737-7(2))*** Jones, Bob Univ. Pr.

Davis, Tanita S. Summer of Friends. 1999. 128p. (J). 7.99 (978-0-8280-1292-8(X)) Review & Herald Publishing Assn.

Davoll, Barbara. Christopher & His Family. Hockerman, Dennis, illus. 2003. (Christopher Churchmouse Ser.). 128p. (J). 14.99 (978-0-8423-5735-7(1)) Tyndale Hse. Pubs.

—Christopher & His Friends. Hockerman, Dennis, illus. 2003. (Christopher Churchmouse Ser.). 128p. (J). 14.99 (978-0-8423-5734-0(3)) Tyndale Hse. Pubs.

—Saved by the Bell. Hockerman, Dennis, illus. 1999. (Christopher Churchmouse Classics Ser.). 24p. (J). (ps-3). 7.99 (978-0-8024-4934-4(4)) Moody Pubs.

—A Sunday Surprise. Hockerman, Dennis, illus. 1999. (Christopher Churchmouse Classics Ser.). 24p. (J). (ps-3). 7.99 (978-0-8024-4935-1(2)) Moody Pubs.

—To London to See the Queen. Hockerman, Dennis, illus. 1999. (New Christopher Churchmouse Adventures Ser.: Vol. 4). 24p. (J). (ps-3). 9.99 (978-0-8024-5399-0(6)) Moody Pubs.

Dawson, Herbert. A Faithful Boy's Influence & Ears for Little Gleaners. unabr. ed. 1998. (Children's Heritage Ser.). (Illus.). 148p. (J). (ps-6). pap. 6.98 (978-1-58339-106-8(1) , D6) Triangle Pr.

de Paola, Tomie. Pascual & the Kitchen Angels. de Paola, Tomie, illus. 2006. (Illus.). 32p. (J). pap. 5.99 (978-0-14-240536-9(1) , Puffin) Penguin Group (USA) Inc.

—Pascual & the Kitchen Angels. 2004. (Illus.). 32p. (J). (ps-3). 16.99 (978-0-399-24214-4(7) , Putnam Juvenile) Penguin Group (USA) Inc.

de Troyes, Chretien. Perceval: King Arthur's Knight of the Holy Grail. Spirin, Gennadii, illus. 2007. 38p. (J). (gr. 4 up). 16.99 (978-0-7614-5339-0(3)) Cavendish, Marshall Corp.

De Villiers Family. The Best Bad Day. De Villiers Family, illus. 2006. (Illus.). 40p. (J). 9.99 (978-1-4000-7296-5(4) , WaterBrook Pr.) WaterBrook Pr.

—The Long Shortcut. 2006. (Sprout Growing with God Ser.). (Illus.). 40p. (J). 9.99 (978-1-4000-7195-1(X) , WaterBrook Pr.) WaterBrook Pr.

—Purple Spot Sickness. 2006. (Sprout Growing with God Ser.). (Illus.). 40p. (J). 9.99 (978-1-4000-7196-8(8) , WaterBrook Pr.) WaterBrook Pr.

—Splish, Splash, Splat. De Villiers Family, illus. 2006. (Illus.). 40p. (J). 9.99 (978-1-4000-7295-8(6) , WaterBrook Pr.) WaterBrook Pr.

Denney, Jim. Invasion of the Time Troopers, Vol. 3. 2002. (Time Benders Ser.). 144p. (J). (gr. 3-7). pap. 5.99 (978-1-4003-0041-9(X)) Nelson, Thomas Inc.

Dennis, Jeanne Gowen & Seifert, Sheila. Escape! Hohn, David, tr. Hohn, David, illus. 2003. (Strive to Thrive Ser.). 96p. (J). pap., pap. 5.99 (978-0-7814-3895-7(0) , 0781438950) Cook, David C. Publishing Co.

Dennis, Rainey. Beyond Knowing. 2004. 10.99 (978-1-56399-208-7(6)) NewLife Pubns.

Derico, Laura. All God¿s Bugs. Smith, Matt, illus. 2007. (Happy Day Bks.). (J). 1.99 (***978-0-7847-1933-6(0)**) Standard Publishing.

Deseret Book Company Staff, contrib. by. A Story to Tell: The Classic Book of Virtues for Children. 2nd ed. 2004. 508p. (J). 16.95 (978-1-59038-359-9(1)) Deseret Bk. Co.

Devore, David Y. Tessie, ed. Happy Birthday to Me. 2004. Tr. of Feliz cumpleanos a mi!. (SPA.). 24p. 8.99 (978-1-59185-421-0(0) , Casa Creacion) Strang Communications Co.

Devries, Douglas. Matt Bugs Me. 2005. 132p. pap. 13.99 (978-1-4141-0451-5(0)) Pleasant Word.

Dobinson, Tony. The Crossing. 2006. 160p. pap. 10.00 (978-1-84427-003-3(3)) STL Distribution North America.

Dobson, Danae, et al. Parables for Kids: Eight Contemporary Stories Based on Best Loved Bible Parables. 2005. 96p. (J). pap. 12.99 (978-1-4143-0274-4(6)) Tyndale Hse. Pubs.

Doney, Meryl. The Very Worried Sparrow. Hansen, Gaby, illus. 2008. (J). 12.95 (***978-0-8198-8038-3(8)**) Pauline Bks. & Media.

Don't Do That, Dexter! 2006. 16p. (J). pap. 1.99 (978-0-7847-1690-8(0) , 02992) Standard Publishing.

Dooley, Phyllis & Duncan, Alice Faye. Christmas Soup. Gilchrist, Jan Spivey, illus. 2005. 32p. (J). (ps-3). 15.99 (978-0-310-70930-5(X)) Zonderkidz.

Douglas, Bond. Duncan's War. 2002. (Crown & Covenant Ser.). (Illus.). 277p. (J). per. 10.99 (978-0-87552-742-0(6)) P & R Publishing.

Dowley, Tim. El Viaje Especial del Burrito - Donkey's Special Ride. (Serie Libros de Carton - Board Bks.). pap. (978-1-56063-956-5(3)) Editorial Unilit.

Doyle, Dennis M. & Doyle, Patrick J. Rumors at School. 2001. (Illus.). 88p. (J). (gr. 4-9). 7.95 (978-0-8091-6686-2(0) , 6700-x) Paulist Pr.

Dreyer, Nicole E. Joseph's Christmas Story. Ebert, Len, illus. 2004. (ENG.). 16p. (J). 1.99 (978-0-570-07577-6(7)) Concordia Publishing Hse.

Dulaney, Kim. I Love Me! 1998. 9.95 (978-1-891636-02-8(2)) Unique Expression.

Dunckel, Mona. Escape. 1999. 101p. (J). (gr. 1-2). pap. 6.49 (978-1-57924-068-4(2) , 113100) Jones, Bob Univ. Pr.

Dunlop, Ed. Escape to Liechtenstein. 2003. 152p. (J). (gr. 4-7). 7.49 (978-1-59166-013-2(0)) Jones, Bob Univ. Pr.

—The Incredible Rescues. Halverson, Tom, illus. 2003. 166p. (J). (gr. 4-7). 7.49 (978-1-59166-012-5(2)) Jones, Bob Univ. Pr.

—The Search for the Silver Eagle. Halverson, Tom, illus. 2003. 159p. (J). (gr. 4-7). 7.49 (978-1-59166-014-9(9)) Jones, Bob Univ. Pr.

—Sherlock Jones: The Assassination Plot. 2004. 116p. (J). (978-1-59166-315-7(6)) Jones, Bob Univ. Pr.

—Sherlock Jones: The Missing Diamond. 2004. 109p. (J). (978-1-59166-316-4(4)) Jones, Bob Univ. Pr.

—Sherlock Jones: The Willoughby Bank Robbery. 2004. 96p. (J). (978-1-59166-314-0(8)) Jones, Bob Univ. Pr.

Durrant, George D. The Christmas Marble: A Christmas Story. 2004. 70p. (J). 4.95 (978-1-55517-824-6(3) , Bonneville Bks.) Cedar Fort, Inc./CFI Distribution.

Durrant, Lynda. The Sun, the Rain, & the Apple Seed: A Novel of Johnny Appleseed's Life. 2003. 208p. (J). (gr. 5-9). tchr. ed. 15.00 (978-0-618-23487-5(X) , Clarion Bks.) Houghton Mifflin Co. Trade & Reference Div.

Edwards, Carol. Jacy Meets Betsy: Jacy's Search for Jesus Book II. Frey, Daniel, illus. 2006. 32p. (J). 15.95 (978-0-9755314-1-9(7)) Majestic Publishing, LLC.

Eglin, Lorna. A Boy of Two Worlds. 2006. 208p. mass mkt. (978-1-84550-126-6(8)) Christian Focus Pubns.

Eileen, Pamela & Eileen, Angela. No Wrong Turns. 2004. (Illus.). 18p. (J). 18.25 (978-0-9753902-0-7(1)) TYL Publishing.

Elkins, Stephen. Ebony & Ivory: Discovering 10 Keys to Racial Harmony. Reisch, Jessie, illus. 2003. 32p. (J). (gr. k up). 14.99 incl. audio compact disk (978-0-8054-2674-8(4)) B&H Publishing Grp.

—God Is in Control. Colton, Ellie, illus. 2002. (Dove Award Signature Ser.). 32p. (J). (gr. k up). 14.99 (978-0-8054-2402-7(4)) B&H Publishing Grp.

—Know God, No Fear. Reisch, Jessie, illus. 2003. 32p. (J). (gr. k-5). 14.99 (978-0-8054-2658-8(2)) B&H Publishing Grp.

—Testify to Love: A Very Special Story for Children. Colton, Ellie, illus. 2002. (Dove Award Signature Ser.). 32p. (J). (gr. k up). 14.99 (978-0-8054-2416-4(4)) B&H Publishing Grp.

Elliott, Ann. GypsyBridge Friends: The Vine. 2003. 40p. pap. 12.95 (978-0-9721825-0-8(0)) Open Vision Entertainment Corp.

Elmer, Robert. About-Face Space Race. 2001. (AstroKids Ser.). (Illus.). 112p. (J). (gr. 2-6). pap. 4.99 (978-0-7642-2360-0(7)) Bethany Hse. Pubs.

—Candy Bombers. 2006. (Wall Ser.: Bk. 1). 160p. (J). pap. 6.99 (978-0-310-70943-5(1)) Zonderkidz.

—The Great Galaxy Goof. 2000. (Astrokids Ser.: Vol. 1). (Illus.). 112p. (J). (gr. 2-6). pap. 5.99 (978-0-7642-2356-3(9)) Bethany Hse. Pubs.

—Miko's Muzzy Mess. 2001. (SpaceKids Ser.: Vol. 4). (Illus.). 112p. (J). (gr. 2-6). pap. 4.99 (978-0-7642-2359-4(3)) Bethany Hse. Pubs.

—Miko's Muzzy Mess. 2001. (gr. 3-6). lib. bdg. 13.00 (978-0-613-85064-3(5)) Tandem Library Bks.

—Wired Wonder Woof. 2001. (SpaceKids Ser.: Vol. 3). (Illus.). 112p. (J). (gr. 2-6). pap. 4.99 (978-0-7642-2358-7(5)) Bethany Hse. Pubs.

—Wired Wonder Woof. 2001. (gr. 3-6). lib. bdg. 13.00 (978-0-613-82426-2(1)) Tandem Library Bks.

—The Zero-G Headache. 2000. (Astrokids Ser.: Vol. 2). (Illus.). 112p. (J). (gr. 2-6). pap. 4.99 (978-0-7642-2357-0(7)) Bethany Hse. Pubs.

Elster, Jean Alicia. I Have a Dream, Too! Tadgell, Nicole, illus. 2002. (Joe Joe in the City Ser.: No. 2). 32p. (gr. 1-5). 12.00 (978-0-8170-1397-4(0)) Judson Pr.

Emm, David. Madison Meets the Minister. Bedrick, Jeff, illus. 2006. 48p. (J). 14.95 (978-1-889658-42-1(1)) STL Distribution North America.

Evangel - the Smallest Angel. 2006. (J). (***978-0-9790210-0-8(6)**) Evening Star Enterprise, Inc.

Evans, Lauralee. The King's Heir. 2006. (YA). (***978-1-55517-865-9(0)** , Bonneville Bks.) Cedar Fort, Inc./CFI Distribution.

Evers, Lynda. JJ & the Angel Academy: Evil Emerges. 2002. 112p. (YA). (gr. 4-10). pap. 7.95 (978-0-9709772-1-2(2)) Angel & Me Publishing.

—JJ & the Hand of God Bk 1: The Beginning. 2001. 105p. (YA). (gr. 4-10). pap. 7.95 (978-0-9709772-0-5(4)) Angel & Me Publishing.

Farenhorst, Christine. A Cup of Cold Water: The Compassion of Nurse Edith Cavell. 2007. (J). pap. (***978-1-59638-026-4(8)**) P & R Publishing.

Farnes, Catherine. Out of Hiding. 2000. 174p. (YA). (gr. 9 up). pap. 6.49 (978-1-57924-329-6(0) , 122085) Jones, Bob Univ. Pr.

—Out of Hiding. 2000. (gr. 7-12). lib. bdg. 14.70 (978-0-613-83927-3(7)) Tandem Library Bks.

—The Slide. 2003. 128p. (J). 6.49 (978-1-57924-967-0(1)) Jones, Bob Univ. Pr.

—Snowblind. 2004. 108p. (J). (978-1-59166-329-4(6)) Jones, Bob Univ. Pr.

—The Way of Escape. 2000. (J). 166p. (gr. 8-12). pap. 6.49 (978-1-57924-453-8(X)); (Illus.). 157p. (gr. 9 up). 6.49 (978-1-57924-454-5(8) , 126599) Jones, Bob Univ. Pr.

The Fijiboat Adventure. 2004. 56p. pap. 6.99 (978-0-8341-2092-1(5)) Beacon Hill Pr. of Kansas City.

Finley, Judith S. As the Waters Cover the Sea: A Visit to the Seashore. Fleet, Eric C., photos by. l.t. ed. 1998. (Caitlyn & Eryn Ser.: No. 1). (Illus.). 20p. (J). (gr. k-2). pap. 6.00 (978-0-9665424-0-0(1)) Master Design, The.

Finley, Martha. Elsie & Her Loved Ones, Vol. 27. (Elsie Bks.: Vol. 27). 320p. (gr. 4-7). pap. 5.95 (978-1-58182-183-3(2)) Cumberland Hse. Publishing.

—Elsie & Her Namesakes, Vol. 28. (Elsie Bks.: Vol. 28). 320p. (gr. 4-7). pap. 5.95 (978-1-58182-184-0(0)) Cumberland Hse. Publishing.

—Elsie at Ion, Vol. 19. (Elsie Bks.: Vol. 19). 320p. (gr. 4-7). pap. 5.95 (978-1-58182-171-0(9)) Cumberland Hse. Publishing.

—Elsie at Nantucket, Vol. 10. 2000. (Elsie Bks.: Vol. 10). 272p. (J). (gr. 4-7). pap. 5.95 (978-1-58182-102-4(6)) Cumberland Hse. Publishing.

—Elsie at Nantucket. 1998. (Elsie Bks.: Vol. 10). (J). (gr. 7-12). pap. 6.99 (978-1-888306-46-0(7)) Holly Hall Pubns., Inc.

—Elsie at Nantucket A Sequel to Elsies Ne. 2006. 34.99 (***978-1-4280-2289-8(9)**) IndyPublish.com.

—Elsie at the Worlds Fair. 2006. 78.99 (***978-1-4280-3168-5(5)**) IndyPublish.com.

—Elsie at the World's Fair, Vol. 20. (Elsie Bks.: Vol. 20). 320p. (gr. 4-7). pap. 5.95 (978-1-58182-172-7(7)) Cumberland Hse. Publishing.

—Elsie at Viamede, Vol. 18. (Original Elsie Classics Ser.: Vol. 18). 320p. (gr. 4-7). pap. 5.95 (978-1-58182-114-7(X)) Cumberland Hse. Publishing.

—Elsie Books, Vols. 1-4. 1998. (J). (gr. 7-12). pap. 24.99 (978-1-888306-61-3(0)) Holly Hall Pubns., Inc.

—Elsie Dinsmore. 2006. (ENG.). pap. 13.95 (***978-1-4218-3092-6(2)**) 1st World Publishing, Inc.

—Elsie's Endless Wait. 224p. 2006. (Life of Faith Ser.). (J). pap. 7.99 (978-1-928749-80-6(1)); Bk. 1. 1999. (Elsie Dinsmore: Bk. 1). (Illus.). (YA). (gr. 5-9). 12.99 (978-1-928749-01-1(1)) Zonderkidz.

—Elsies Girlhood. 2006. 27.99 (***978-1-4280-2220-1(1)**) IndyPublish.com.

—Elsie's Girlhood: A Sequel to Elsie Dinsmore & Elsie's Holidays at Roselands. l.t. ed. 2006. 296p. pap. 17.99 (***978-1-4264-3884-4(2)**) BiblioBazaar.

—Elsie's Great Hope, Vol. 8. 2006. (Life of Faith': Elsie Dinsmore Ser.). 224p. (J). pap. 7.99 (978-1-928749-87-5(9)) Zonderkidz.

—Elsie's Impossible Choice, Bk. 2. Williams, Scott, illus. 1999. (Elsie Dinsmore: Bk. 2). 238p. (YA). (gr. 5-9). 12.99 (978-1-928749-02-8(X)) Zonderkidz.

—Elsie's Impossible Choice, Vol. 2. 2006. (Life of Faith': Elsie Dinsmore Ser.). 224p. (J). pap. 7.99 (978-1-928749-81-3(X)) Zonderkidz.

—Elsie's Journey on Inland Waters, Vol. 21. (Elsie Bks.: Vol. 21). 320p. (gr. 4-7). pap. 5.95 (978-1-58182-174-1(3)) Cumberland Hse. Publishing.

—Elsie's Kith & Kin. 1998. (Elsie Bks.: Vol. 12). pap. 6.99 (978-1-888306-48-4(3)) Holly Hall Pubns., Inc.

—Elsies Kith & Kin. 2006. 79.99 (***978-1-4280-2573-8(1)**) IndyPublish.com.

—Elsie's Kith & Kin, Vol. 12. (Elsie Bks.: Vol. 12). 320p. (gr. 4-7). pap. 5.95 (978-1-58182-105-5(0)) Cumberland Hse. Publishing.

—Elsies Motherhood. 2006. 79.99 (***978-1-4280-2607-0(X)**) IndyPublish.com.

—Elsie's New Life, Bk. 3. Williams, Scott, illus. Grisco, Michelle, photos by. 1999. (Elsie Dinsmore: Bk. 3). 232p. (YA). (gr. 5-9). 12.99 (978-1-928749-03-5(8)) Zonderkidz.

—Elsie's New Life, Vol. 3. 2006. (Life of Faith': Elsie Dinsmore Ser.). 224p. (J). pap. 7.99 (978-1-928749-82-0(8)) Zonderkidz.

—Elsie's New Relations, Vol. 9. (Elsie Bks.: Vol. 9). 320p. (gr. 4-7). pap. 5.95 (978-1-58182-101-7(8)) Cumberland Hse. Publishing.

—Elsie's New Relations. 1998. (Elsie Bks.: Vol. 9). (J). (gr. 7-12). pap. 6.99 (978-1-888306-45-3(9)) Holly Hall Pubns., Inc.

—Elsie's Stolen Heart, Vol. 4. 2006. (Life of Faith': Elsie Dinsmore Ser.). 224p. (J). pap. 7.99 (978-1-928749-83-7(6)) Zonderkidz.

—Elsie's Tender Mercies, Vol. 7. 2006. (Life of Faith': Elsie Dinsmore Ser.). 224p. (J). pap. 7.99 (978-1-928749-86-8(0)) Zonderkidz.

—Elsie's Troubled Times, Vol. 6. 2006. (Life of Faith': Elsie Dinsmore Ser.). 224p. (J). pap. 7.99 (978-1-928749-88-2(7)) Zonderkidz.

—Elsie's True Love. 224p. Bk. 5. 2000. (Elsie Dinsmore: Bk. 5). (YA). (gr. 5-9). 12.99 (978-1-928749-05-9(4)); Vol. 5. 2006. (Life of Faith': Elsie Dinsmore Ser.). (J). pap. 7.99 (978-1-928749-84-4(4)) Zonderkidz.

—Elsies Vacation & after Events. 2006. 42.99 (***978-1-4280-2122-8(1)**); pap. 35.99 (***978-1-4280-2125-9(6)**) IndyPublish.com.

—Elsie's Vacation & After Events, Vol. 17. (Original Elsie Classics Ser.: Vol. 17). 320p. (gr. 4-7). pap. 5.95 (978-1-58182-113-0(1)) Cumberland Hse. Publishing.

—Elsie's Womanhood. 2006. 80.99 (***978-1-4280-3133-3(2)**) IndyPublish.com.

—Millie's Courageous Days, Bk. 2. 2001. (Life of Faith Ser.). 224p. (YA). (gr. 5-9). 12.99 (978-1-928749-10-3(0)) Zonderkidz.

—Millie's Faithful Heart, Bk. 4. Mission City Press Staff, ed. 2002. (Life of Faith Ser.: Vol. Bk. 4). (Illus.). 224p. (J). 12.99 (978-1-928749-12-7(7)) Zonderkidz.

—Millie's Grand Adventure, Bk. 6. 2002. (Life of Faith Ser.: Bk. 6). 224p. (YA). (gr. 5-9). 12.99 (978-1-928749-14-1(3)) Zonderkidz.

—Millie's Remarkable Journey, Bk. 3. Mission City Press Staff, ed. 2002. (Life of Faith Ser.: Vol. 3). (Illus.). 224p. (J). 12.99 (978-1-928749-11-0(9)) Zonderkidz.

—Millie's Steadfast Love, Bk. 5. 2002. (Life of Faith Ser.: Bk. 5). 224p. (YA). (gr. 5-9). 12.99 (978-1-928749-13-4(5)) Zonderkidz.

—Millie's Unsettled Season, Bk. 1. 2001. (Life of Faith Ser.). (Illus.). 224p. (J). (gr. 5-9). 12.99 (978-1-928749-09-7(7)) Zonderkidz.

—The Two Elsies, Vol. 11. (Elsie Bks.: Vol. 11). 320p. (gr. 4-7). pap. 5.95 (978-1-58182-104-8(2)) Cumberland Hse. Publishing.

—The Two Elsies. 2000. (Elsie Books: Vol. 11). 206p. (J). mass mkt. 5.99 (978-1-931343-02-2(0)) Hibbard Pubns., Inc.

—The Two Elsies. 1998. (Elsie Bks.: Vol. 11). (J). (gr. 7-12). pap. 6.99 (978-1-888306-47-7(5)) Holly Hall Pubns., Inc.

—Violet's Bold Mission, Bk. 4. 2004. (Life of Faith Ser.: Bk. 4). 224p. (YA). (gr. 5-8). 12.99 (978-1-928749-20-2(8)) Vida Pubs.

—Violet's Perplexing Puzzles, Bk. 5. 2005. (Life of Faith Ser.). 224p. (YA). 12.99 (978-1-928749-21-9(6)) Zonderkidz.

—Violet's Turning Point, Bk. 3. 2004. (Life of Faith Ser.). 224p. (YA). 12.99 (978-1-928749-19-6(4)) Zonderkidz.

Finley, Martha & Hamilton, Kersten. Life of Faith Collection. 2006. (Life of Faith' Ser.). 992p. (J). pap. 14.99 (978-1-928749-85-1(2)) Mission City Pr., Inc.

Finley, Martha & Mission City Press Staff. Millie Keith, 4 vols., Boxed Set 1-4. 2002. (Life of Faith Ser.). 224p. (YA). 44.99 (978-1-928749-65-3(8)) Mission City Pr., Inc.

—Violet's Amazing Summer, Bk. 2. 2004. (Life of Faith Ser.). 224p. (YA). 12.99 (978-1-928749-18-9(6)) Zonderkidz.

—Violet's Hidden Doubts, Bk. 1. 2004. (Life of Faith Ser.: Bk. 1). 224p. (YA). 12.99 (978-1-928749-17-2(8)) Zonderkidz.

Fletcher, Lois A. Hamburger? Holy Cow! 2000. (Illus.). 1698p. (J). (gr. 4-6). pap. 7.95 (978-0-89827-210-9(6)) Wesleyan Publishing Hse.

Fletcher, Susan. Walk Across the Sea. Jakesevic, Nenad, illus. 224p. (J). 2003. pap. 11.95 (978-0-689-85707-2(1) , Aladdin); 2001. (gr. 5-9). 16.95 (978-0-689-84133-0(7) , Atheneum) Simon & Schuster Children's Publishing.

—Walk Across the Sea. 2003. (gr. 3-6). lib. bdg. 13.00 (978-0-613-62227-1(8)) Tandem Library Bks.

—Walk Across the Sea. l.t. ed. 2002. 218p. (J). 22.95 (978-0-7862-4439-3(9)) Thorndike Pr.

Flying Rhinoceros Productions. The Horned Avenger: The Battle Against VonBoredom! 2005. 64p. (J). 9.99 (978-1-4003-0662-6(0)) Nelson, Thomas Inc.

Focus On The Family Staff. Hero of Hoppers Landing. 2002. (J). 12.99 incl. VHS (978-0-310-70507-9(X)) Zonderkidz.

Forever Friends. 2002. (Illus.). 32p. 16.95 (978-1-931290-12-8(1) , Smallfellow Pr.) Tallfellow Pr.

Foster, Teresa. Big Busy Fire Engine. 1999. (Window Board Bks.). (Illus.). 14p. (J). (ps-k). bds. 4.99 (978-0-7847-0989-4(0) , 03786, Bean Sprouts) Standard Publishing.

Framke, Jilly. Prayer Power: With Nehemiah the Praying Mantis. 2007. (J). pap. 14.99 (***978-1-60247-304-1(8)**) Tate Publishing & Enterprises, L.L.C.

Frank, Christian M. Catholic (Reluctantly) 2007. (YA). pap. 11.95 (***978-1-928832-99-7(7)**) Sophia Institute Pr.

Freedman, Georgene. The Olive Tree. 2nd num. ed. 2006. (J). per. 12.95 (978-0-9771322-1-8(8)) Simpatico Bks.

Freer, Jeannette. When Harry Met the Potter. 2007. 76p. (J). per. 9.99 (***978-1-933899-72-5(7)**) Holy Fire Publishing.

Fremont, Walter & Young, Susan W. Rambunctious Rattler. 1999. 138p. (J). (gr. 4-7). pap. 7.49 (978-1-57924-262-6(6) , 121483) Jones, Bob Univ. Pr.

Fruits from Faith. 2006. (Illus.). 24p. (J). 12.95 (978-0-9777041-1-8(4)) Third Dimension Publishing.

G Studios & Crouch, Cheryl. Double-Booked. 2007. (Chosen Girls' Ser.). 144p. (J). pap. 6.99 (978-0-310-71268-8(8)) Zonderkidz.

—Solo Act. 2007. (Chosen Girls' Ser.). 144p. (J). pap. 6.99 (978-0-310-71270-1(X)) Zonderkidz.

—Unplugged. 2007. (Chosen Girls' Ser.). 144p. (J). pap. 6.99 (978-0-310-71269-5(6)) Zonderkidz.

Gaard, Betty. Jericho Ride. 2003. (Illus.). 165p. (J). pap. (978-1-57924-968-7(X)) Jones, Bob Univ. Pr.

—The Theft. 2000. 190p. (YA). (gr. 7 up). pap. 6.49 (978-1-57924-375-3(4) , 124487) Jones, Bob Univ. Pr.

Gaffney, Sean. Larry Boy y el Emperador de la Envidia. 2003. (Big Idea Bks.).Tr. of Larry Boy & the Emperoro of Envy. (SPA.). 96p. (J). pap. 4.99 (978-0-8297-3748-6(0)) Vida Pubs.

—Larryboy & the Sinister Snow Day. 2003. (Illus.). 96p. pap. 4.99 (978-0-310-70561-1(4)) Zonderkidz.

Gail, Cornelia. Juvey. 2007. 153p. (YA). per. 14.95 net. (***978-0-9674454-4-1(2)**) Girls In Da Game Publishing.

Gaither, Gloria & Hranilovich, Barbara. My Father's Angels. Hranilovich, Barbara, illus. 1999. (Illus.). 32p. (J). (ps-3). 14.99 (978-0-310-23104-2(3)) Zonderkidz.

Garza, Ray. Captain Christian. 2007. (J). pap. 9.95 (***978-0-9795680-3-9(X)**) Believers Publishing.

Gateley, Edwina. God Goes to Church. 1999. (Illus.). (J). pap. 8.95 (978-0-940147-48-5(3)) Source Bks.

Geisert, Bonnie. Lessons. 2005. 192p. (J). (gr. 4-6). 15.00 (978-0-618-47899-6(X) , Walter Lorraine) Houghton Mifflin Co. Trade & Reference Div.

Gemmen, Heather. Quit Looking at Me! Lagares, Luciano, illus. 2003. (Tough Stuff for Kids Ser.). 32p. (J). pap., pap. 5.99 (978-0-7814-3852-0(7) , 0781438527) Cook, David C. Publishing Co.

Gibson, Kari Smalley. Mooki & the Too-Proud Peacock. 2002. 40p. 12.99 (978-0-310-70303-7(4)) Zondervan.

A Gift for Tania (2000-2001 Children's Reading Book) A Gift for Anna. 2000. 32p. pap. 2.75 (978-0-8341-1856-0(4)) Beacon Hill Pr. of Kansas City.

Gilge-Barnes, Jeanette. City-Kid Farmer. 2000. 128p. (J). (gr. 5-7). pap. 4.95 (978-0-9679371-6-8(7)) WinePress Publishing.

—Growing-Up Summer. Hauge, Carl, illus. 2000. (J). (gr. 5-7). pap. 9.99 (978-0-9679371-8-2(3)) WinePress Publishing.

Gilson, Jamie. Stink Alley. 2002. 192p. (J). (gr. 3 up). 15.95 (978-0-688-17864-2(2)); lib. bdg. 15.89 (978-0-06-029217-1(2)) HarperCollins Pubs.

Ginolfi, Arthur. Tiny Snowflake Picture Book. Max, Louise Reinoehl, illus. 2003. 32p. (J). 7.99 (978-1-4003-0205-5(6)) Nelson, Thomas Inc.

Gire, Ken. Treasure in an Oatmeal Box: The Story of a Special Boy & the People Who Loved. 2000. (gr. 3-6). lib. bdg. 13.00 (978-0-613-74893-3(X)) Tandem Library Bks.

Glenn, Sharlee Mullins. One in a Billion. Hoffman-Bayles, Rachel, illus. 2000. (J). (978-1-929281-06-0(4)) Cornerstone Publishing & Distribution, Inc.

God Made You Special. 2006. (J). 16p. pap. 1.99 (978-0-7847-1692-2(7) , 02994); (Illus.). 24p. bds. 6.99 (978-0-7847-1399-0(5) , 04059) Standard Publishing.

Godfrey, Jan. The Lost Sheep. Saunderson, Chris, illus. 2001. (J). (ps-3). 5.00 (978-0-687-04930-1(X)) Abingdon Pr.

Gowen, Jeanne. Matts Fantastic Electronic Com. 2004. 11.99 (978-0-8254-2695-7(2)) Kregel Pubns.

Goza, Shelly. Mr. Meme. Gil, Rodolpho, illus. 2005. (J). bds. 9.99 (978-1-4183-0077-7(2)) Christ Inspired, Inc.

Graham, Christine. When Pioneer Wagons Rumbled West. Meidell, Sherry, illus. 1998. 32p. (J). (ps-3). 14.95 (978-1-57345-272-4(6) , Shadow Mountain) Deseret Bk. Co.

Grant, Larry. I See Greatness. Byers, Reggie, illus. 1998. 48p. (Orig.). (J). (ps-4). pap. 8.95 (978-1-889851-04-4(3)) SolidGumboWorks.

Grant, Nancy. Maggie & the Backyard Helpers. 2006. (ENG.). 60p. per. 12.95 (***978-1-4241-4373-3(X)**) PublishAmerica, Inc.

The Great Bundingle Race: A Lesson in Pride. 2002. (J). 14.95 (978-1-886185-14-2(X)) Mosley Publishing Group.

Greene, Rhonda Gowler. Sing Praise. Broxon, Janet, illus. 2005. 32p. (J). (ps-3). pap. 16.99 (978-0-8066-5120-0(2) , Augsburg Bks.) Augsburg Fortress, Pubs.

Gregory, Kristiana. Journey of Faith. 2003. (gr. 3-6). lib. bdg. 13.00 (978-0-613-72119-6(5)) Tandem Library Bks.

Grote, JoAnn A. The American Revolution. Wallenta, Adam, illus. 1999. (American Adventure Ser.: No. 11). (J). (gr. 3-7). (978-0-7910-5591-5(4) , Chelsea Hse.) Facts On File, Inc.

—Danger in the Harbor: Grain Riots Threaten Boston. 1999. (American Adventure Ser.: No. 6). (Illus.). 144p. (J). (gr. 3-7). lib. bdg. 15.95 (978-0-7910-5046-0(7) , Chelsea Hse.) Facts On File, Inc.

Grovet, Heather. Beanie, the Horse That Wasn't a Horse. 2004. 95p. (J). (978-0-8163-2053-0(5)) Pacific Pr. Publishing Assn.

—Good As Gold: Discovering What Is Really Important. 2007. (Illus.). 95p. (J). (***978-0-8163-2166-7(3)***) Pacific Pr. Publishing Assn.

—A Perfect Star. 2007. (Illus.). 95p. (J). (***978-0-8163-2164-3(7)***) Pacific Pr. Publishing Assn.

—Petunia the Ugly Pug. 2002. (Julius & Friends Ser.: Vol. 7). (Illus.). 94p. (J). 6.99 (978-0-8163-1871-1(9)) Pacific Pr. Publishing Assn.

—Prince Prances Again. 2001. (Julius & Friends Ser.: Bk. 9). (Illus.). 94p. (J). 6.99 (978-0-8163-1807-0(7)) Pacific Pr. Publishing Assn.

Grovet, Heather. Zippitty Do Dah: Trusting God in Troubles Great & Small. 2007. (Illus.). 95p. (J). (***978-0-8163-2165-0(5)***) Pacific Pr. Publishing Assn.

Gunn, Robin Jones. As You Wish. 2000. (Christy & Todd: Bk. 2). (Illus.). 320p. (gr. 7-12). pap. 12.99 (978-0-7642-2273-3(2)) Bethany Hse. Pubs.

—As You Wish. 2000. (Christy & Todd: Bk. 2). (gr. 7-12). lib. bdg. 21.10 (978-0-613-86638-5(X)) Tandem Library Bks.

—Christy Miller Collection: A Time to Cherish; Sweet Dreams; A Promise Is Forever, Vol. 4. 2006. (Christy Miller Ser.: Bks. 10-12). 496p. 14.99 (978-1-59052-587-6(6) , Multnomah Fiction) WaterBrook Pr.

—Christy Miller Collection: Summer Promise; A Whisper & a Wish; Yours Forever, Vol. 1. 2005. (Christy Miller Ser.: Bks. 1-3). 496p. (J). 14.99 (978-1-59052-584-5(1) , Multnomah Fiction) WaterBrook Pr.

—Christy Miller Collection: Surprise Endings; Island Dreamer; A Heart Full of Hope, Vol. 2. 2006. (Christy Miller Ser.: Bks. 4-6). 496p. (J). 14.99 (978-1-59052-585-2(X) , Multnomah Fiction) WaterBrook Pr.

—Christy Miller Collection: True Friends; Starry Night; Seventeen Wishes, Vol. 3. 2006. (Christy Miller Ser.: Bks. 7-9). 480p. (J). 14.99 (978-1-59052-586-9(8) , Multnomah Fiction) WaterBrook Pr.

—Christy Miller Mix: Island Dreamer; A Heart Full of Hope; True Friends; Starry Night. 1999. (Christy Miller Ser.: Bks. 5-8). (J). (gr. 7-12). pap. 27.99 (978-1-56179-723-3(5)) Bethany Hse. Pubs.

—Christy Miller Mix: Seventeen Wishes; A Time to Cherish; Sweet Dreams; A Promise Is Forever. 1999. (Christy Miller Ser.: Bks. 9-12). 160p. (YA). (gr. 7-12). pap. 27.99 (978-1-56179-770-7(7)) Bethany Hse. Pubs.

—Close Your Eyes. 1998. (Sierra Jensen Ser.: Bk. 4). 144p. (YA). (gr. 7-11). pap. (978-1-56179-487-4(2)) Focus on the Family Publishing.

—Closer Than Ever. 1999. (Sierra Jensen Ser.: Bk. 11). 160p. (YA). (gr. 7-11). pap. 6.99 (978-1-56179-722-6(7)) Bethany Hse. Pubs.

—Don't You Wish. 1998. (Sierra Jensen Ser.: Bk. 3). (Illus.). 144p. (YA). (gr. 7-11). pap. (978-1-56179-486-7(4)) Focus on the Family Publishing.

—A Heart Full of Hope. rev. ed. 1999. (Christy Miller Ser.: Bk. 6). 160p. (YA). (gr. 7-12). pap. 6.99 (978-1-56179-719-6(7)) Bethany Hse. Pubs.

—Hold on Tight. 1998. (Sierra Jensen Ser.: Bk. 10). 160p. (YA). (gr. 7-11). pap. (978-1-56179-637-3(9)) Focus on the Family Publishing.

—Hold on Tight. 1998. (Sierra Jensen Ser.: Bk. 10). (gr. 7-12). lib. bdg. 15.30 (978-0-613-82316-6(8)) Tandem Library Bks.

—I Promise. 2007. (Christy & Todd: Bk. 3). 288p. reprint ed. pap. 12.99 (978-0-7642-2274-0(0)) Bethany Hse. Pubs.

—I Promise. 2001. (Christy & Todd: Bk. 3). (gr. 7-12). lib. bdg. 21.10 (978-0-613-82922-9(0)) Tandem Library Bks.

—In Your Dreams. 1998. (Sierra Jensen Ser.: Bk. 2). 144p. (Orig.). (YA). (gr. 7-11). pap. (978-1-56179-444-7(9)) Focus on the Family Publishing.

—In Your Dreams. 1998. (Sierra Jensen Ser.: Bk. 2). (Orig.). (gr. 7-12). lib. bdg. 15.30 (978-0-613-86409-1(3)) Tandem Library Bks.

—Island Dreamer. rev. ed. 1999. (Christy Miller Ser.: Bk. 5). 176p. (J). (gr. 7-12). pap. 6.99 (978-1-56179-718 9(9)) Bethany Hse. Pubs.

—Now Picture This. 1998. (Sierra Jensen Ser.: Bk. 9). 176p. (YA). (gr. 7-11). pap. (978-1-56179-636-6(0)) Focus on the Family Publishing.

—Only You, Sierra. 1998. (Sierra Jensen Ser.: Bk. 1). 176p. (J). (gr. 7-11). pap. 6.99 (978-1-56179-370-9(1)) Bethany Hse. Pubs.

—Open Your Heart. 1998. (Sierra Jensen Ser.: Bk. 7). 160p. (YA). (gr. 7-11). pap. (978-1-56179-562-8(3)) Focus on the Family Publishing.

—Sierra Jensen Collection: Close Your Eyes; Without a Doubt; With This Ring, Vol. 2. 2006. (Sierra Jensen Ser.: Bks. 4-6). 496p. (J). 14.99 (978-1-59052-589-0(2) , Multnomah Fiction) WaterBrook Pr.

—Sierra Jensen Collection: Hold on Tight; Closer Than Ever; Take My Hand, Vol. 4. 2006. (Sierra Jensen Ser.: Bks. 10-12). 464p. (J). 14.99 (978-1-59052-591-3(4) , Multnomah Fiction) WaterBrook Pr.

—Sierra Jensen Collection: Only You; Sierra, In Your Dreams; Don't You Wish, Vol. 1. 2006. (Sierra Jensen Ser.: Bks. 1-3). 432p. (J). 14.99 (978-1-59052-588-3(4) , Multnomah Fiction) WaterBrook Pr.

—Sierra Jensen Collection: Open Your Heart; Time Will Tell; Now Picture This, Vol. 3. 2006. (Sierra Jensen Ser.: Bks. 7-9). 480p. (J). 14.99 (978-1-59052-590-6(6) , Multnomah Fiction) WaterBrook Pr.

—Sierra Jensen Series: Now Picture This; Hold on Tight; Closer Than Ever; Take My Hand. 1999. (Sierra Jensen Ser.: Bks. 9-12). (YA). (gr. 7-11). pap. 27.99 (978-1-56179-839-1(8)) Bethany Hse. Pubs.

—Starry Night. rev. ed. 1999. (Christy Miller Ser.: Bk. 8). 160p. (YA). (gr. 7-12). pap. 6.99 (978-1-56179-721-9(9)) Bethany Hse. Pubs.

—Take My Hand. 1999. (Sierra Jensen Ser.: Bk. 12). 144p. (YA). (gr. 7-11). pap. 6.99 (978-1-56179-736-3(7)) Bethany Hse. Pubs.

—Time Will Tell. 1998. (Sierra Jensen Ser.: Bk. 8). 160p. (YA). (gr. 7-11). pap. (978-1-56179-568-0(2)) Focus on the Family Publishing.

—True Friends. rev. ed. 1999. (Christy Miller Ser.: Bk. 7). 160p. (YA). (gr. 7-12). pap. 6.99 (978-1-56179-720-2(0)) Bethany Hse. Pubs.

—Whispers. 2004. (Glenbrooke Ser.: Bk. 2). 288p. pap. 12.99 (978-1-59052-192-2(7) , Multnomah) WaterBrook Pr.

—With This Ring. 1998. (Sierra Jensen Ser.: Bk. 6). 160p. (J). (gr. 7-11). pap. (978-1-56179-540-6(2)) Focus on the Family Publishing.

—Without a Doubt. 1998. (Sierra Jensen Ser.: Bk. 5). 160p. (YA). (gr. 7-11). pap. (978-1-56179-519-2(4)) Focus on the Family Publishing.

Gurley, Nan. What Color Is Love: A Parable of God's Gifts. Farnsworth, Bill, illus. 2005. 32p. (J). 14.99 (978-0-310-70888-9(5)) Zonderkidz.

Haddix, Margaret Peterson. Leaving Fishers. (YA). 262p. (gr. k up). pap. 4.50 (978-0-8072-1541-8(4)); 1999. (gr. 5 up). pap. 37.00 incl. audio (978-0-8072-8122-2(0) , YA109SP) Random Hse. Audio Publishing Group. (Listening Library).

—Leaving Fishers. 1999. (J). (978-0-606-16313-2(1)) Tandem Library Bks.

Hadley, Caroline. Woodside or Look Listen & Learn. 2007. pap. 87.99 (***978-1-4280-5242-0(9)***) IndyPublish.com.

—Woodside; or, Look, Listen & Learn. 2007. (ENG., Illus.). 80p. per. (***978-1-4065-1557-2(4)***) Dodo Pr.

Hadnot, Victor. The Wheels of God. 2003. 140p. (YA). pap. 11.95 (978-0-595-27507-6(9)) iUniverse, Inc.

Hafer, Todd. Cody's Varsity Rush. 2005. (Spirit of the Game, Sports Fiction Ser.). (Illus.). 144p. (J). (gr. k-17). pap. 4.99 (978-0-310-70794-3(3)) Zonderkidz.

—Full Court Press. 2004. (Spirit of the Game, Sports Fiction Ser.). 144p. (J). (gr. 3-6). pap. 4.99 (978-0-310-70668-7(8)) Zonderkidz.

—Goal-Line Stand. Lucado, Max, ed. 2004. (Spirit of the Game, Sports Fiction Ser.). 144p. (J). (gr. 3-6). pap. 4.99 (978-0-310-70669-4(6)) Zonderkidz.

—Split Decision. 2005. (Spirit of the Game, Sports Fiction Ser.). (Illus.). 144p. (J). (gr. 5). pap. 4.99 (978-0-310-70796-7(X)) Zonderkidz.

—Three-Point Play. 2005. (Spirit of the Game, Sports Fiction Ser.). 144p. (J). (ps-7). pap. 4.99 (978-0-310-70795-0(1)) Zonderkidz.

—Ultimate Challenge. 2005. (Spirit of the Game, Sports Fiction Ser.). (Illus.). 144p. (J). (gr. 5). pap. 4.99 (978-0-310-70797-4(8)) Zonderkidz.

Halfmann, Janet. Best Friends. Mada Design Staff, illus. 2005. (Davey & Goliath Color & Activity Ser.: No. 1). 32p. (J). pap. 3.99 (978-0-439-69833-7(2) , Scholastic Paperbacks) Scholastic, Inc.

—Davey & Goliath: Finders Keepers. Mada Design Staff, illus. 2005. (Davey & Goliath Color & Activity Ser.: No. 2). 32p. (J). pap. 3.99 (978-0-439-69834-4(0) , Scholastic Paperbacks) Scholastic, Inc.

—The Winner. Mada Design Staff, illus. 2005. (Davey & Goliath Ser.: No. 4). 32p. (J). pap. 4.99 (978-0-439-74440-9(7) , Scholastic Paperbacks) Scholastic, Inc.

Hall, Frostie. Dread Champions for the King, Book 2: For the King! 2006. 112p. per. (978-1-55452-044-2(4)) Essence Publishing.

—Dread Champions of the King: The Humble Beginning. 2004. (Dread Champions of the King Ser.: Bk. 1). 96p. (J). per. (978-1-55306-836-5(X)) Essence Publishing.

Hall, Frostie. The Humble Beginning. 2004. (ENG.). 95p. pap. (***978-1-55306-838-9(6)***) Essence Publishing.

Hall, S.C. Turns of Fortune & Other Tales. 2007. (ENG.). 116p. per. (***978-1-4065-1586-2(8)***) Dodo Pr.

Halter, Pam. Beatrice Loses Her Doll. Sponaugle, Kim, tr. Sponaugle, Kim, illus. 2001. 32p. (J). 6.99 (978-0-570-07117-4(8)) Concordia Publishing Hse.

Hambrick, Sharon. Arby Jenkins Meets His Match. Thompson, Del, illus. 2000. 120p. (J). (gr. 4-7). 7.49 (978-1-57924-461-3(0)) Jones, Bob Univ. Pr.

—Arby Jenkins, Ready to Roll. 1998. 150p. (J). (gr. 4-7). pap. 7.49 (978-0-89084-958-3(7)) Jones, Bob Univ. Pr.

—The Year of Abi Crim. 2000. (Illus.). 118p. (J). (gr. 4-7). pap. 7.49 (978-1-57924-374-6(6) , 124255) Jones, Bob Univ. Pr.

Hamel, Mike. The Sword & the Flute: Matterhorn, the Brave Series. 2007. 176p. (J). pap. 12.99 (978-0-89957-833-0(0)) AMG Pubs.

—Talis Hunters: Matterhorn, the Brave Series, Vol. 2. 2007. 176p. (J). pap. 12.99 (978-0-89957-834-7(9)) AMG Pubs.

Hamilton, Bethany. Surfer Girl Rise above 90 Day Devotional. 2007. (Soul Surfer#8482; Ser.). 192p. (J). pap. 9.99 (978-0-310-71226-8(2)) Zonderkidz.

Hamilton, Bethany & Bundschuh, Rick. Burned. 2007. (Soul Surfer#8482; Ser.). (Illus.). 144p. (J). pap. 6.99 (978-0-310-71223-7(8)) Zonderkidz.

—Clash. 2007. (Soul Surfer#8482; Ser.). (Illus.). 144p. (J). pap. 6.99 (978-0-310-71222-0(X)) Zonderkidz.

Hamilton, K. R. Caleb, Son of None. 2007. (J). pap. (978-0-7847-1859-9(8)) Standard Publishing.

Hamilton, K. R. A Freaky Kind of Courage. 2007. (J). (***978-0-7847-1909-1(8)***) Standard Publishing.

Hamilton, Kersten. The Battle of Trickum County. 2007. (Caleb Pascal & the Peculiar People Ser.). 141p. (J). per. 6.99 (***978-0-7847-1910-7(1)***) Standard Publishing.

—A Gathering of Brothers. 2007. (Caleb Pascal & the Peculiar People Ser.). 143p. (J). per. 6.99 (***978-0-7847-1911-4(X)***) Standard Publishing.

Hansen, Eric. Great White Judgment. Moody, Julie, illus. 2005. (YA). bds. 9.99 (978-1-4183-0059-3(4)) Christ Inspired, Inc.

Harder Tangvald, Christine. Jesus is...for Me! 2000. (for Me! Bks.). (Illus.). 24p. (J). (ps-2). pap. 4.99 (978-0-7642-2338-9(0)) Bethany Hse. Pubs.

—Someone I Love Died. 2003. (Please Help Me God Ser.). (Illus.). 24p. (J). (ps up). 9.99 (978-1-55513-490-7(4) , 1555134904) Cook, David C. Publishing Co.

Hardy, LeAnne. Between Two Worlds: A Novel. 2003. 160p. pap. 6.99 (978-0-8254-2793-0(2)) Kregel Pubns.

—The Wooden Ox: A Novel. 2002. 192p. (gr. 4-8). pap. 6.99 (978-0-8254-2794-7(0)) Kregel Pubns.

Hare, Eric B. Curse Proof. 2007. (Illus.). 95p. (J). (***978-0-8163-2208-4(2)***) Pacific Pr. Publishing Assn.

Hare, Sharon C. Poppy's Clouds. Landing, Alex, illus. 1998. 20p. (J). pap. 10.00 (978-1-885938-16-9(0)) Cathedral Foundation Pr.

Harley, Jason. Journey to the Light. 2003. 270p. (J). 22.95 (978-1-929642-47-2(4)) Literally Speaking Publishing Hse.

Hart, Chrissi. Under the Grapevine: A Miracle by St. Kendeas of Cyprus. 2006. 32p. 15.95 (***978-1-888212-84-6(5)***) Conciliar Pr.

Hartman, Bob. Cheer up, Chicken! Spoor, Mike, illus. 2002. 32p. (ps-3). 8.99 (978-0-8066-4364-9(1) , Augsburg Bks.) Augsburg Fortress, Pubs.

—Cheer up, Chicken! Spoor, Mike, illus. 2002. 32p. (J). (ps-2). 9.99 (978-0-7459-3725-0(X) , Lion) Lion Hudson plc GBR. *Dist:* Independent Pubs. Group.

Hartman, Robert & Hird, Nancy E. Silly Stories: 3 Fun-to-Read-Aloud Stories with a Message. Caldwell, Lise, ed. Kolding, Richard Max & Stiles, Andy, illus. 1999. (Read-Aloud Stories Ser.). 24p. (J). (ps-3). 5.99 (978-0-7847-0820-0(7) , 03722, Bean Sprouts) Standard Publishing.

Heaps, Kelly S. & Dunn, Susan. Sheldon: The Story of What Would Jesus Do. Lindgren, Renae & Lindgren, Sam, illus. 1999. (Holy Bear's Travel Ser.). 32p. (J). (gr. k-5). pap. 7.95 (978-1-885628-32-9(3)) Buckaroo Bks.

Heimerdinger, Chris. The Warriors of Cumorah, Vol. 8. 2004. (Tennis Shoes Adventure Ser.). xi, 394p. pap. 14.95 (978-1-57734-922-8(9)) Covenant Communications, Inc.

Hemphill, Helen. Long Gone Daddy. 2006. 176p. (J). 16.95 (978-1-932425-38-3(1) , Lemniscaat) Boyds Mills Pr.

Henderson, Patti & Golden Books Staff. A Blessing from Above. Edge, Elizabeth, illus. 2004. (Little Golden Book Ser.). 24p. (J). (gr. k-k). 2.99 (978-0-375-82866-9(4) , Golden Bks.) Random Hse. Children's Bks.

Henley, Karyn. Marvy Gets the Thumps. 2004. 88p. (J). 10.99 (978-1-4003-0389-2(3)) Nelson, Thomas Inc.

—Monday, Tuesday, Oopsday! 2004. 88p. (J). 10.99 (978-1-4003-0294-9(3)) Nelson, Thomas Inc.

—Pot Luck Supper. 2004. 88p. (J). 10.99 (978-1-4003-0388-5(5)) Nelson, Thomas Inc.

Hergenrader, Christina. Dangerous Roads. 2004. 224p. (J). 6.99 (978-0-7586-0715-7(6)) Concordia Publishing Hse.

—Double Shift. 2004. 208p. (J). 6.99 (978-0-7586-0716-4(4)) Concordia Publishing Hse.

—Lies & Deceptions. 2003. (Novel Devotions Ser.). 176p. (YA). 6.99 (978-0-7586-0229-9(4)) Concordia Publishing Hse.

—Lies & Deceptions. 2003. (gr. 7-12). lib. bdg. 15.30 (978-0-613-74602-1(3)) Tandem Library Bks.

—Temptations. 2003. (Novel Devotions Ser.). 176p. (YA). 6.99 (978-0-7586-0230-5(8)) Concordia Publishing Hse.

—Temptations. 2003. (gr. 7-12). lib. bdg. 15.30 (978-0-613-74603-8(1)) Tandem Library Bks.

Hermes, Patricia. Calling Me Home. (J). 1999. 448p. pap. 3.99 (978-0-380-79100-2(5) , Harper Trophy); 1998. 144p. (gr. 4-7). 15.00 (978-0-380-97451-1(7)) HarperCollins Pubs.

—Calling Me Home. 1999. (Illus.). (J). (978-0-606-17961-4(5)) Tandem Library Bks.

Hernandez, David. Land of the Pharaohs. 2003. (Adventures of Toby Digz Ser.). (Illus.). 96p. (J). pap. 5.99 (978-1-4003-0195-9(5)) Nelson, Thomas Inc.

Hickey, Sally. Empty Shoes. 2004. 139p. (YA). per. 7.95 (978-1-931742-59-7(6) , MountainView) Treble Heart Bks.

Higgs, Liz Curtis. The Parable of the Lily. 10th anniv. ed. 2007. 32p. (J). 7.99 (978-1-4003-0844-6(5)) Nelson, Thomas Inc.

—The Pine Tree Parable: Special Edition. 2006. 32p. (J). 7.99 (978-1-4003-0847-7(X)) Nelson, Thomas Inc.

—The Pine Tree Parable: The Parable Series. 2005. 32p. (J). pap. 3.99 (978-1-4003-0685-5(X)) Nelson, Thomas Inc.

Highstreet, Harry. Melanie Ann. 2005. 118p. pap. 16.95 (978-1-4137-8946-1(3)) PublishAmerica, Inc.

Hill, Karen. Ava, the One & Only. Roos, Maryn, illus. 2005. 24p. (J). 9.99 (978-1-4169-0511-0(1) , Little Simon) Simon & Schuster Children's Publishing.

—Ava, the One & Only. Roos, Maryn, illus. 2005. 24p. (J). pap. 3.99 (978-1-4169-0316-1(X)) Simon & Schuster, Inc.

—Grandmother's Book of Promises. 2002. 48p. (J). 17.95 (978-1-57856-579-5(0)) Random Hse., Inc.

—Grandmother's Book of Promises. Clar, David Austin, illus. 2000. 48p. (J). (ps-2). 9.99 (978-1-57856-221-3(X) , WaterBrook Pr.) WaterBrook Pr.

—I Am Good at Being Me. Graef, Renee, illus. 2005. 24p. (J). 3.99 (978-1-4169-0319-2(4)); 9.99 (978-1-4169-0512-7(X)) Simon & Schuster Children's Publishing. (Little Simon).

—Owen's Walk. Thompson, Carol, illus. 2006. 32p. (J). 14.99 (978-1-4003-0694-7(9)) Nelson, Thomas Inc.

—The Something Wonderful: A Christmas Story. Reagan, Susan, illus. 2005. 36p. (J). (ps-3). pap. 15.99 (978-1-58134-732-6(4) , Crossway Bibles) Crossway Bks.

—We're All God's Creatures. Johnson, Steve & Fancher, Lou, illus. 2006. 14p. (J). 9.99 (978-1-4169-2516-3(3) , Little Simon Inspirations) Simon & Schuster Children's Publishing.

—What Makes God Smile? O'Neill, Philomena, illus. 2005. 24p. (J). 3.99 (978-1-4169-0318-5(6)) Simon & Schuster.

—What Makes God Smile? O'Neill, Philomena, illus. 2005. 24p. (J). 9.99 (978-1-4169-0514-1(6) , Little Simon) Simon & Schuster Children's Publishing.

Hinds, David. Beat Depression. 2001. 208p. pap. 13.99 (978-0-340-78536-2(5) , Hodder & Stoughton) Hodder General Publishing Division GBR. *Dist:* Trafalgar Square Publishing.

Hinds, Ruth McNaughton. Puppy & I. 2006. (J). per. 7.95 (978-0-9764232-2-5(7)) River City Pr.

Hinman, Bonnie. Earthquake in Cincinnati: Disaster Changes Life Forever, 1999. (American Adventure Ser.: No. 14). 144p. (J). (gr. 3-7). lib. bdg. 15.95 (978-0-7910-5589-2(2) , Chelsea Hse.) Facts On File, Inc.

Hird, Nancy E. & Mishica, Clare. Sports Stories: 3 Fun-to-Read-Aloud Stories with a Message. Estes, Kathleen et al, illus. 1999. (Read-Aloud Stories Ser.). 24p. (J). (ps-3). 5.99 (978-0-7847-0819-4(3) , 03729, Bean Sprouts) Standard Publishing.

Hodgson, Mona Gansberg. Clubhouse Surprises. Sharp, Chris, illus. 1999. (Desert Critter Friends Ser.: Vol. 6). 48p. (J). (ps-2). 4.99 (978-0-570-05082-7(0) , 56-1906GJ) Concordia Publishing Hse.

—Clubhouse Surprises. 1998. (ps-2). lib. bdg. 13.00 (978-0-613-72809-6(2)) Tandem Library Bks.

—Crabby Critters. 2000. (Desert Critter Friends Ser.: Vol. 11). (Illus.). 48p. (J). (ps-2). 4.99 (978-0-570-07074-0(0)) Concordia Publishing Hse.

—Crabby Critters. 2000. (ps-2). lib. bdg. 13.00 (978-0-613-72793-8(2)) Tandem Library Bks.

—Desert Critter Friends Set, 12 vols. (Desert Critter Friends Ser.). (J). 54.99 (978-0-7586-0007-3(0)) Concordia Publishing Hse.

—Desert Detectives. Sharp, Chris, illus. 1999. (Desert Critter Friends Ser.: Vol. 5). 48p. (J). (ps-2). 4.99 (978-0-570-05083-4(9) , 56-1907GJ) Concordia Publishing Hse.

—Desert Detectives. 1998. (ps-2). lib. bdg. 13.00 (978-0-613-72810-2(6)) Tandem Library Bks.

—Goofy Glasses. 2000. (ps-2). lib. bdg. 13.00 (978-0-613-72834-8(3)) Tandem Library Bks.

—I Wonder Who Hung the Moon in the Sky. 1999. (I Wonder Ser.). (Illus.). 32p. (J). (ps-2). 6.99 (978-0-570-05067-4(7)) Concordia Publishing Hse.

—Jumping Jokers. 1999. (Desert Critter Friends Ser.: Vol. 7). (Illus.). 48p. (J). (ps-2). 4.99 (978-0-570-05481-8(8)) Concordia Publishing Hse.

—Jumping Jokers. 1999. (ps-2). lib. bdg. 13.00 (978-0-613-72657-3(X)) Tandem Library Bks.

—Sour Snacks. Sharp, Chris, illus. 1998. (Desert Critter Friends Ser.: Vol. 3). 48p. (J). (ps-2). 4.99 (978-0-570-05070-4(7) , 56-1894) Concordia Publishing Hse.

—Sour Snacks. 1998. (ps-2). lib. bdg. 13.00 (978-0-613-72806-5(8)) Tandem Library Bks.

—Spelling Bees. 2000. (Desert Critter Friends Ser.: Vol. 12). (Illus.). 48p. (J). (ps-2). 4.99 (978-0-570-07075-7(9)) Concordia Publishing Hse.

—Spelling Bees. 2000. (ps-2). lib. bdg. 13.00 (978-0-613-72788-4(6)) Tandem Library Bks.

—Sticky Statues. 2000. (Desert Critter Friends Ser.: Vol. 9). (Illus.). 48p. (J). (ps-2). 4.99 (978-0-570-07010-8(4)) Concordia Publishing Hse.

—Sticky Statues. 2000. (ps-2). lib. bdg. 13.00 (978-0-613-72833-1(5)) Tandem Library Bks.

Hodgson, Mona Gansberg & Sharp, Chris. Goofy Glasses. 2000. (Desert Critter Friends Ser.: Vol. 10). (Illus.). 48p. (J). (ps-2). 4.99 (978-0-570-07011-5(2)) Concordia Publishing Hse.

Holl, Kristi. Chat Freak. 2004. 128p. (J). pap. 5.99 (978-1-4003-0326-7(5)) Nelson, Thomas Inc.

—Chick Chat: More Devotions for Girls. 2006. (Faithgirlz Ser.). (Illus.). 192p. (J). pap. 9.99 (978-0-310-71143-8(6)) Zonderkidz.

Holl, Kristi D. Chat Freak. 2005. (TodaysGirls.com Ser.: Vol. 6). 144p. (J). (gr. 4-7). pap. 5.99 (978-1-4003-0760-9(0)) Nelson, Thomas Inc.

Holland, Gretchen. Because He Loves Me. 2005. (J). 8.99 (978-0-9768340-0-7(6)) Holland, Gretchen.

Holm, H. R. Against an Amber Sky. 2007. viii, 214p. (J). (***978-1-55517-991-5(6)***) Cedar Fort, Inc./CFI Distribution.

Hood, Karen Jean Matsko. Adventures of My Dentist & the Tooth Fairy Christian Adventures in Learning Book: Christian Educational Learning Series. 2005. (J). spiral bd. 15.95 (978-1-59210-393-5(6)); cd-rom 13.95 (978-1-59649-329-2(1)) Whispering Pine Pr., Inc.

—Adventures of My Dentist & the Tooth Fairy Christian Adventures in Learning Books: Christian Educational Learning Series. 2005. (J). 15.95 (978-1-59210-392-8(8)) Whispering Pine Pr., Inc.

—Children Far & Wide: A Daily Journal. 2003. (YA). 15.95 (978-1-59434-041-3(2)); cd-rom 13.95 (978-1-59434-043-7(9)) Whispering Pine Pr., Inc.

Horrocks, Anita. Almost Eden. 2006. 288p. (J). (gr. 5-9). pap. 9.95 (978-0-88776-742-5(7)) Tundra Bks., Inc./ Livres Toundra, Inc. CAN. *Dist:* Random Hse., Inc.

Houselander, Caryll. Catholic Tales for Boys & Girls. 2003. Orig. Title: Terrible Farmer Timson (New York: Sheed & Ward, 1957). (Illus.). 160p. (J). pap. 11.95 (978-1-928832-74-4(1)) Sophia Institute Pr.

—More Catholic Tales for Boys & Girls. 2003. Orig. Title: Inside the Ark: & Other Stories (New York: Sheed & Ward, 1956). (Illus.). v, 150p. (J). pap. 10.95 (978-1-928832-84-3(9)) Sophia Institute Pr.

Hover Get's His Wings. 2004. Tr. of Cometin recibe sus alas. (SPA.). 24p. 10.99 (978-1-59185-422-7(9) , Casa Creacion) Strang Communications Co.

Howell, David. Swan Songs-in Search of the Staffstone. 2005. per. 13.99 (978-1-59781-002-9(9)) Xulon Pr., Inc.

Hronas, Georgia. Tell Us a Story, Grandma: More of Grandma's Orthodox Spiritual Stories. 2005. 130p. (J). (gr. 3-7). pap. 12.95 (978-1-880971-93-2(3)) Light & Life Publishing Co.

Hubler, Marsha. Skye's Final Test, Vol. 6. 2005. (Keystone Stables Ser.). (Illus.). 112p. (J). pap. 4.99 (978-0-310-70799-8(4)) Zonderkidz.

—Teamwork at Camp Tioga. 2005. (Keystone Stables Ser.). (Illus.). 128p. (J). pap. 4.99 (978-0-310-70575-8(4)) Zonderkidz.

—Trouble Times Two. 2005. (Keystone Stables Ser.). (Illus.). 128p. (J). pap. 4.99 (978-0-310-70574-1(6)) Zondervan.

—The Trouble with Skye. 2004. (Keystone Stables Ser.: No. 1). 144p. (J). pap. 4.99 (978-0-310-70572-7(X)) Zonderkidz.

—A True Test for Skye. 2004. (Keystone Stables Ser.). (Illus.). 144p. (J). pap. 4.99 (978-0-310-70573-4(8)) Zonderkidz.

—The Winning Summer. 2005. (Keystone Stables Ser.: Bk. 5). (Illus.). 144p. (J). pap. 4.99 (978-0-310-70798-1(6)) Zonderkidz.

Huff, Barb. Backup Singer. 2003. (gr. 7-12). lib. bdg. 11.80 (978-0-613-79646-0(2)) Tandem Library Bks.

—Perfect Girl. 2003. (gr. 3-6). lib. bdg. 11.80 (978-0-613-79653-8(5)) Tandem Library Bks.

Hughes, Lynn Gordon. To Live a Truer Life: A Story of the Hopedale Community. Lindro, illus. 2003. 32p. (J). 20.00 (978-0-9725017-2-9(X)) Blackstone Editions.

Hughes, Marilynn. The Former Angel - A Children's Tale. 2003. 22p. 9.94 (978-1-4116-1712-4(6)) Lulu.com.

Hunt, Angela. The True Princess. 2005. (Illus.). 32p. (J). 9.99 (978-1-59185-633-7(7)) Strang Communications Co.

Hunt, Angela Elwell. The Deadly Chase. 2000. (Colonial Captives Ser.: Vol. 2). 192p. (gr. 4-7). pap. 12.95 (978-0-595-08997-0(6) , Backinprint.com) iUniverse, Inc.

—Sleeping Rose. Gillies, Chuck, illus. 1998. 32p. (J). (ps-3). 14.99 (978-0-8499-5847-2(4)) Nelson, Thomas Inc.

Hunt, Angela Elwell & Arterburn, Stephen. Josiah. 2004. (Young Believer on Tour Ser.). (J). pap. 3.99 (978-0-8423-8335-6(2)) Tyndale Hse. Pubs.

—Liane. 2004. (Young Believer on Tour Ser.). (J). pap. 3.99 (978-0-8423-8336-3(0)) Tyndale Hse. Pubs.

Hunt, Susan & Hunt, Richie. Discovering Jesus in Exodus, Vol. 2. 2005. (Illus.). 176p. pap. 16.99 (978-1-58134-453-0(8) , Crossway Bibles) Crossway Bks.

Huskins, T. A. I Am a Whosoever. 2006. 62p. pap. 12.95 (978-1-4241-0308-9(8)) PublishAmerica, Inc.

Hutchens, Paul. The Battle of the Bees. rev. ed. 1999. (Sugar Creek Gang Ser.: No. 32). (J). (gr. 4-7). 144p. 4.99 (978-0-8024-7035-5(1)); 112p. 4.99 (978-0-8024-7036-2(X)) Moody Pubs.

—The Blue Cow. rev. ed. 1998. (Sugar Creek Gang Ser.: No. 30). 144p. (J). (gr. 4-7). 4.99 (978-0-8024-7034-8(3)) Moody Pubs.

—The Brown Box Mystery. rev. ed. 1998. (Sugar Creek Gang Ser.: No. 27). 128p. (J). (gr. 4-7). 4.99 (978-0-8024-7031-7(9)) Moody Pubs.

—The Bull Fighter. rev. ed. 1998. (Sugar Creek Gang Ser.: No. 20). 128p. (J). (gr. 4-7). 4.99 (978-0-8024-7024-9(6)) Moody Pubs.

—The Ghost Dog. 1998. (gr. 3-6). lib. bdg. 13.00 (978-0-613-90866-5(X)) Tandem Library Bks.

—The Green Tent Mystery. rev. ed. 1998. (Sugar Creek Gang Ser.: No. 19). 128p. (J). (gr. 8-12). 4.99 (978-0-8024-7023-2(8)) Moody Pubs.

—The Green Tent Mystery. 1998. (gr. 7-12). lib. bdg. 13.00 (978-0-613-90323-3(4)) Tandem Library Bks.

—Locked in the Attic. rev. ed. 1999. (Sugar Creek Gang Ser.: No. 35). 96p. (J). (gr. 4-7). 4.99 (978-0-8024-7039-3(4)) Moody Pubs.

—Locked in the Attic. 1999. (gr. 3-6). lib. bdg. 13.00 (978-0-613-90556-5(3)) Tandem Library Bks.

—SCG Set Books: The Hilarious Adventures of a Gang of Boys & Their Friends from Sugar Creek. rev. ed. (Sugar Creek Gang Ser.). (J). 1999. 640p. 24.99 (978-0-8024-6999-1(X)); 1998. 832p. 24.99 (978-0-8024-6998-4(1)); 1998. 784p. 24.99 (978-0-8024-6997-7(3)) Moody Pubs.

—The Sugar Creek Gang, Vols. 13-18. rev. ed. 1998. (Sugar Creek Gang Ser.). 640p. (J). (gr. 4-7). 24.99 (978-0-8024-6996-0(5)) Moody Pubs.

—The Timber Wolf. rev. ed. 1998. (Sugar Creek Gang Ser.: No. 21). 128p. (J). (gr. 4-7). 4.99 (978-0-8024-7025-6(4)) Moody Pubs.

—The Timber Wolf. 1998. (gr. 3-6). lib. bdg. 13.00 (978-0-613-90325-7(0)) Tandem Library Bks.

—The Trapline Thief. rev. ed. 1998. (Sugar Creek Gang Ser.: No. 29). 144p. (J). (gr. 4-7). 4.99 (978-0-8024-7033-1(5)) Moody Pubs.

—The Treasure Hunt. 1998. (gr. 3-6). lib. bdg. 13.00 (978-0-613-90127-7(4)) Tandem Library Bks.

—The Watermelon Mystery. rev. ed. 1998. (Sugar Creek Gang Ser.: No. 28). 160p. (J). (gr. 4-7). 4.99 (978-0-8024-7032-4(7)) Moody Pubs.

—The Watermelon Mystery. 1998. (gr. 3-6). lib. bdg. 13.00 (978-0-613-88823-3(5)) Tandem Library Bks.

—Western Adventure. rev. ed. 1998. (Sugar Creek Gang Ser.: No. 22). 128p. (J). (gr. 4-7). 4.99 (978-0-8024-7026-3(2)) Moody Pubs.

—Western Adventure. 1998. (gr. 3-6). lib. bdg. 13.00 (978-0-613-90865-8(1)) Tandem Library Bks.

—The White Boat Rescue. 1998. (gr. 3-6). lib. bdg. 13.00 (978-0-613-90326-4(9)) Tandem Library Bks.

Iakovos-Dalalakis, Helen. Nicholas Wins the Prize 1: Young Nicholas Experiences the Sacrament of Confession. Gabrili, Alexandra, illus. 2003. 28p. (J). (gr. 2-6). pap. 13.95 (978-1-880971-82-6(8)) Light & Life Publishing Co.

Idle, Molly Schaar. If I Had a Nickel... 2005. (Illus.). 32p. (ps-3). 14.00 (978-0-687-32549-8(8)) Abingdon Pr.

—Pennies from Heaven. 2006. (Illus.). 32p. (ps-3). 14.00 (978-0-687-49505-4(9)) Abingdon Pr.

I'm Just the Right Size. 2004. Tr. of Soy del tamano correcto!. (SPA.). 24p. 8.99 (978-1-59185-423-4(7) , Casa Creacion) Strang Communications Co.

Imbody, Amy E. Snug As a Bug. Gordon, Mike, illus. (Mothers of Preschoolers Ser.). (J). 2004. 28p. pap. 4.99 (978-0-310-70819-3(2)); 2001. 32p. 7.99 (978-0-310-70063-0(9)) Zonderkidz.

Ingrassia, Michelle. The Wisdom Bench. 2006. 72p. pap. 9.99 (978-1-4141-0452-2(9)) Pleasant Word.

Inny. Epiphany Rose-the Message. 2006. pap. 8.99 (***978-1-60034-097-0(0)**) Xulon Pr., Inc.

It's Good Sunday. 2004. (J). bds. 15.95 (978-0-9743394-1-2(5)) More Pr.

Jackson, Beverly Lozier. Mommy, Is God a Super Hero? 2007. (J). per. 7.99 (***978-1-59886-903-3(5)**) Tate Publishing & Enterprises, L.L.C.

Jackson, Dave. Roundup of the Street Rovers. 2001. (gr. 3-6). lib. bdg. 14.15 (978-0-613-82920-5(4)) Tandem Library Bks.

—Sinking the Dayspring: John G. Paton. 2001. (gr. 3-6). lib. bdg. 14.15 (978-0-613-82919-9(0)) Tandem Library Bks.

Jackson, Dave & Jackson, Neta. Exiled to the Red River: Chief Spokane Garry. 2003. (Trailblazer Bks.). (Illus.). 144p. (J). pap. 6.99 (978-0-7642-2235-1(X)) Bethany Hse. Pubs.

—The Mayflower Secret: Governor William Bradford. Jackson, Julian & McLaughlin, Catherine R., illus. 1998. (Trailblazer Bks.: Vol. 26). 160p. (J). (gr. 3-7). pap. 6.99 (978-0-7642-2010-4(1)) Bethany Hse. Pubs.

—Risking the Forbidden Game: Maude Cary. Gavitt, Anne, illus. 2002. (Trailblazers Ser.). 160p. (J). (gr. 3-7). pap. 6.99 (978-0-7642-2234-4(1)) Bethany Hse. Pubs.

—Roundup of the Street Rovers: Charles Loring Brace. Gavitt, Anne, illus. 2001. (Trailblazer Bks.: Vol. 36). 160p. (J). (gr. 3-7). reprint ed. pap. 6.99 (978-0-7642-2269-6(4)) Bethany Hse. Pubs.

Jacobs, Sheila. A Different Life. 2000. 144p. (YA). (gr. 4-7). mass mkt. (978-1-85792-590-6(4) , Christian Focus) Christian Focus Pubns.

—A Life Worth Living. 176p. (YA). mass mkt. 5.99 (978-1-85792-730-6(3) , Christian Focus) Christian Focus Pubns. GBR. *Dist:* Riverside.

Jamieson-Brown, Heather. I Can't Find Bongo Kitty! Savage, Carol, illus. 2002. 16p. (J). 7.00 (978-0-9721946-1-7(4)) Paraclete Publishing.

Jansma, S. L. Journey Through a Jewel. 2000. 288p. (J). (gr. 7-12). pap. 15.99 (978-1-892435-05-7(5) , C055) Covenant Publishing, Inc.

—Journey Through a Jewel. 1999. (gr. 7-12). lib. bdg. 25.75 (978-0-613-80322-9(1)) Tandem Library Bks.

Jeapes, Ben. New World Order. 2006. 448p. (YA). (gr. 7). mass mkt. 6.50 (978-0-553-49491-4(0) , Laurel Leaf) Random Hse. Children's Bks.

Jenkins, Jerry B. Crash at Cannibal Valley. 2006. (AirQuest Adventures Ser.). 160p. (J). pap. 6.99 (978-0-310-71347-0(1)) Zonderkidz.

—Disaster in the Yukon, Bk. 3. 2006. (AirQuest Adventures Ser.). (Illus.). 160p. (J). pap. 6.99 (978-0-310-71345-6(5)) Zonderkidz.

—Uplink from the Underground: Showtime for Vicki. 2002. (Left Behind Ser.: Bk. 24). (gr. 5-8). lib. bdg. 14.15 (978-0-613-59222-0(0)) Tandem Library Bks.

—War of the Dragon: Miracles in the Air. 2003. (Left Behind Ser.: Bk. 32). (gr. 5-8). lib. bdg. 14.15 (978-0-613-76890-0(6)) Tandem Library Bks.

Jenkins, Jerry B. & Fabry, Chris. Canyon Echoes. 2005. (Tyndale Kids Ser.). 240p. (J). pap. 5.99 (978-1-4143-0147-1(2)) Tyndale Hse. Pubs.

—Dead End. 2006. (Red Rock Mysteries Ser.). 256p. (J). pap. 5.99 (978-1-4143-0154-9(5) , Tyndale Kids) Tyndale Hse. Pubs.

—Double Fault. 2005. (Tyndale Kids Ser.). 272p. (J). pap. 5.99 (978-1-4143-0146-4(4)) Tyndale Hse. Pubs.

—Grave Shadows. 2005. (Red Rock Mysteries Ser.). (Illus.). 240p. (J). pap. 5.99 (978-1-4143-0144-0(8)) Tyndale Hse. Pubs.

—Hidden Riches. 2006. (Tyndale Kids Ser.). 272p. (J). pap. 5.99 (978-1-4143-0152-5(9)) Tyndale Hse. Pubs.

—Hollywood Holdup. 2006. (Red Rock Mysteries Ser.). 224p. (J). pap. 5.99 (978-1-4143-0151-8(0)) Tyndale Hse. Pubs.

—Instant Menace. 2006. (Tyndale Kids Ser.). 256p. (J). pap. 5.99 (978-1-4143-0148-8(0)) Tyndale Hse. Pubs.

—Missing Pieces. 2005. (Red Rock Mysteries Ser.). (Illus.). 224p. (J). (ps-7). pap. 5.99 (978-1-4143-0142-6(1)) Tyndale Hse. Pubs.

—Phantom Writer. 2005. (Red Rock Mysteries Ser.). 256p. (J). pap. 5.99 (978-1-4143-0145-7(6)) Tyndale Hse. Pubs.

—Stolen Secrets. 2005. (Red Rock Mysteries Ser.). (Illus.). 224p. (J). (ps-7). pap. 5.99 (978-1-4143-0141-9(3)) Tyndale Hse. Pubs.

—Wild Rescue. 2005. (Red Rock Mysteries Ser.). 256p. (J). (ps-7). pap. 5.99 (978-1-4143-0143-3(X)) Tyndale Hse. Pubs.

—Wind Chill. 2006. (Tyndale Kids Ser.). 240p. (J). pap. 5.99 (978-1-4143-0153-2(7) , Tyndale Kids) Tyndale Hse. Pubs.

—Windy City Danger. 2006. (Red Rock Mysteries Ser.). 246p. (J). pap. 5.99 (978-1-4143-0150-1(2)) Tyndale Hse. Pubs.

Jenkins, Jerry B. & LaHaye, Tim. Battling the Commander: The Hidden Cave. 2001. (Left Behind Ser.: Bk. 15). (Illus.). 152p. (J). (gr. 5-9). mass mkt. 5.99 (978-0-8423-4296-4(6)) Tyndale Hse. Pubs.

—The Beast Arises: Unveiling the Plan. 2003. (Left Behind Ser.: Bk. 26). 160p. (J). mass mkt. 5.99 (978-0-8423-5790-6(4)) Tyndale Hse. Pubs.

—Busted! The Young Trib Force Faces Pressure. 2000. (Left Behind Ser.: Bk. 7). (Illus.). 128p. (J). (gr. 4-7). mass mkt. 5.99 (978-0-8423-4327-5(X)) Tyndale Hse. Pubs.

—Darkening Skies: Judgment of Ice. 2001. (Left Behind Ser.: Bk. 18). 176p. (J). (gr. 4-7). mass mkt. 5.99 (978-0-8423-4312-1(1)) Tyndale Hse. Pubs.

—Death at the Gala: History in the Making. 2003. (Left Behind Ser.: Bk. 25). 176p. (J). mass mkt. 5.99 (978-0-8423-5789-0(0)) Tyndale Hse. Pubs.

—Death Strike: The Young Trib Force Faces War. 2000. (Left Behind Ser.: Bk. 8). (Illus.). 144p. (J). (gr. 4-7). mass mkt. 5.99 (978-0-8423-4328-2(8)) Tyndale Hse. Pubs.

—Earthquake! The Young Trib Force Faces Disaster. 2000. (Left Behind Ser.: Bk. 12). (YA). 12.64 (978-0-606-21865-8(3)) Tandem Library Bks.

—Earthquake! The Young Trib Force Faces Disaster. 2000. (Left Behind Ser.: Bk. 12). (Illus.). 152p. (J). (gr. 4-7). mass mkt. 5.99 (978-0-8423-4332-9(6)) Tyndale Hse. Pubs.

—Escape from New Babylon: Discovering New Believers. 2002. (Left Behind Ser.: Bk. 22). (gr. 3-6). lib. bdg. 14.15 (978-0-613-59298-7(0)) Tandem Library Bks.

—Escape from New Babylon: Discovering New Believers. 2002. (Left Behind Ser.: Bk. 22). 125p. (J). mass mkt. 5.99 (978-0-8423-4316-9(4)) Tyndale Hse. Pubs.

—Escape to Masada: Joining Operation Eagle. 2003. (Left Behind Ser.: Bk. 31). (J). mass mkt. 5.99 (978-0-8423-5801-9(3)) Tyndale Hse. Pubs.

—Facing the Future: Four Kids Face Earth's Last Days Together. 1998. (Left Behind Ser.: Bk. 4). 150p. (J). (gr. 4-7). per. 14.15 (978-0-613-33291-0(1)) Tandem Library Bks.

—Facing the Future: Four Kids Face Earth's Last Days Together. 1998. (Left Behind Ser.: Bk. 4). (Illus.). 160p. (J). (gr. 4-7). mass mkt. 5.99 (978-0-8423-2196-9(9)) Tyndale Hse. Pubs.

—Fire from Heaven: Deceiving the Enemy. 2001. (Left Behind Ser.: Bk. 16). (Illus.). 160p. (J). (gr. 5-9). mass mkt. 5.99 (978-0-8423-4297-1(4)) Tyndale Hse. Pubs.

—Heat Wave: Surviving the Fourth Bowl Judgment. 2004. (Left Behind Ser.: Bk. 37). 208p. (J). mass mkt. 5.99 (978-0-8423-8347-9(6)) Tyndale Hse. Pubs.

—Horsemen of Terror: The Unseen Judgment. 2002. (Left Behind Ser.: Bk. 23). (gr. 5-8). lib. bdg. 14.15 (978-0-613-59200-0(X)) Tandem Library Bks.

—Hunted. 2005. (Left Behind Ser.). 480p. (YA). (gr. 7-17). 14.99 (978-1-4143-0272-0(X)) Tyndale Hse. Pubs.

—Into the Storm: The Search for Secret Documents. 2000. (Left Behind Ser.: Bk. 11). 149p. (J). (gr. k-9). lib. bdg. 12.64 (978-0-606-21867-2(X)); (gr. 5-8). lib. bdg. 14.15 (978-0-613-33301-6(2)) Tandem Library Bks.

—Into the Storm: The Search for Secret Documents. 2000. (Left Behind Ser.: Bk. 11). (Illus.). 160p. (J). (gr. 4-7). mass mkt. 5.99 (978-0-8423-4331-2(8)) Tyndale Hse. Pubs.

—Judgment Day: Into Raging Waters. 2001. (Left Behind Ser.: Bk. 14). (gr. 5-8). lib. bdg. 14.15 (978-0-613-33304-7(7)) Tandem Library Bks.

—Judgment Day: Into Raging Waters. 2001. (Left Behind Ser.: Bk. 14). (Illus.). 144p. (J). (gr. 4-7). mass mkt. 5.99 (978-0-8423-4295-7(8)) Tyndale Hse. Pubs.

—Left Behind: The Kids Collection 5, 6 vols., Bks. 25-30, Set. 2003. (Left Behind Ser.). (J). mass mkt. 32.94 (978-0-8423-8712-5(9)) Tyndale Hse. Pubs.

—Left Behind Bks. 36-40, Set: The Kids Collection 7, 5 vols. 2004. (Left Behind Ser.: Bks. 36-45). (J). mass mkt. 27.45 (978-0-8423-8714-9(5)) Tyndale Hse. Pubs.

—Murder in the Holy Place: Carpathia's Deadly Deception. 2003. (Left Behind Ser.: Bk. 30). (gr. 5-8). lib. bdg. 14.15 (978-0-613-76888-7(4)) Tandem Library Bks.

—Nicolae High: The Young Trib Force Goes Back to School. 1999. (Left Behind Ser.: Bk. 5). (gr. 5-8). lib. bdg. 14.15 (978-0-613-33309-2(8)) Tandem Library Bks.

—Nicolae High: The Young Trib Force Goes Back to School. 1999. (Left Behind Ser.: Bk. 5). (Illus.). 144p. (J). (gr. 4-7). mass mkt. 5.99 (978-0-8423-4325-1(3)) Tyndale Hse. Pubs.

—On the Run: The Kids Are on the Run. 2000. (Left Behind Ser.: Bk. 10). 160p. (J). (gr. k-9). lib. bdg. 12.64 (978-0-606-21868-9(8)); (gr. 5-8). lib. bdg. 14.15 (978-0-613-33310-8(1)) Tandem Library Bks.

—The Perils of Love: Breaking Through the Darkness. 2004. (Left Behind Ser.: Bk. 38). 208p. (J). mass mkt. 5.99 (978-0-8423-8348-6(4)) Tyndale Hse. Pubs.

—Pursued, Bk. 2. 2003. (Left Behind Ser.). (YA). (gr. 5-8). 14.99 (978-0-8423-8352-3(2)) Tyndale Hse. Pubs.

—The Rise of False Messiahs: Carpathia's Evil Tricks. 2004. (Left Behind Ser.: No. 35). 208p. (J). (gr. 5-9). mass mkt. 5.99 (978-0-8423-5805-7(6)) Tyndale Hse. Pubs.

—The Road to War: Facing the Guillotine. 2004. (Left Behind Ser.: Bk. 39). 208p. (J). mass mkt. 5.99 (978-0-8423-8349-3(2)) Tyndale Hse. Pubs.

—The Search: The Struggle to Survive. 2000. (Left Behind Ser.: Bk. 9). 159p. (J). (gr. k-9). lib. bdg. 12.64 (978-0-606-21869-6(6)); (gr. 5-8). lib. bdg. 14.15 (978-0-613-33315-3(2)) Tandem Library Bks.

—Second Chance: Four Kids Face Earth's Last Days Together. 1998. (Left Behind Ser.: Bk. 2). 160p. (J). (gr. 4-7). pap. 5.99 (978-0-8423-2194-5(2)) Tyndale Hse. Pubs.

—Secrets of New Babylon: The Search for an Impostor. 2002. (Left Behind Ser.: Bk. 21). 152p. (J). mass mkt. 5.99 (978-0-8423-4315-2(6)) Tyndale Hse. Pubs.

—Shaken. 2005. (Left Behind Ser.). 384p. (YA). 14.99 (978-1-4143-0268-3(1)) Tyndale Hse. Pubs.

—The Showdown: Behind Enemy Lines. 2001. (Left Behind Ser.: Bk. 13). 132p. (J). (ps-7). lib. bdg. 12.64 (978-0-606-22119-1(0)) Tandem Library Bks.

—The Showdown: Behind Enemy Lines. 2001. (Left Behind Ser.: Bk. 13). (Illus.). 152p. (J). (gr. 4-7). pap. 5.99 (978-0-8423-4294-0(X)) Tyndale Hse. Pubs.

—Taken Bk. 1. 2003. (Left Behind Ser.). (YA). (gr. 5-8). 14.99 (978-0-8423-8351-6(4)) Tyndale Hse. Pubs.

—Terror in the Stadium: Witnesses under Fire. 2001. (Left Behind Ser.: Bk. 17). 176p. (J). (gr. 4-7). mass mkt. 5.99 (978-0-8423-4299-5(0)) Tyndale Hse. Pubs.

—Through the Flames. 1998. (Left Behind Ser.: Bk. 3). 143p. (J). (gr. k-9). per. 14.15 (978-0-613-23517-4(7)) Tandem Library Bks.

—Through the Flames. 1998. (Left Behind Ser.: Bk. 3). (Illus.). 160p. (J). (gr. 4-7). pap. 5.99 (978-0-8423-2195-2(0)) Tyndale Hse. Pubs.

—Triumphant Return: The New Jerusalem. 2004. (Left Behind Ser.: Bk. 40). 224p. (J). mass mkt. 5.99 (978-0-8423-8350-9(6)) Tyndale Hse. Pubs.

—The Underground: The Young Trib Force Fights Back. 1999. (Left Behind Ser.: Bk. 6). (gr. 5-8). lib. bdg. 14.15 (978-0-613-33319-1(5)) Tandem Library Bks.

—The Underground: The Young Trib Force Fights Back. 1999. (Left Behind Ser.: Bk. 6). (Illus.). 128p. (J). (gr. 4-7). mass mkt. 5.99 (978-0-8423-4326-8(1)) Tyndale Hse. Pubs.

—The Vanishings: Four Kids Face Earth's Last Days Together. 1998. (Left Behind Ser.: Bk. 1). 160p. (J). (gr. 4-7). pap. 5.99 (978-0-8423-2193-8(4)) Tyndale Hse. Pubs.

—War of the Dragon: Miracles in the Air. 2003. (Left Behind Ser.: Bk. 32). (J). mass mkt. 5.99 (978-0-8423-5802-6(1)) Tyndale Hse. Pubs.

Jenkins, Jerry B. & Perrodin, John. Demons Bluff. 2007. 288p. (YA). (gr. 4-7). 9.99 (978-1-59145-397-0(6)) Nelson, Thomas Inc.

—The Tattooed Rats. 2006. 288p. (YA). (gr. 8-12). 9.97 (978-1-59145-396-3(8)) Nelson, Thomas Inc.

Jenkins, Jerry B., et al. Deceived. 2005. (Left Behind Ser.). 384p. (YA). 14.99 (978-1-4143-0270-6(3)) Tyndale Hse. Pubs.

—Ominous Choices. 2004. (Tyndale Kids Ser.). 208p. (J). pap. 5.99 (978-0-8423-5807-1(2)) Tyndale Hse. Pubs.

—On the Run: The Kids Are on the Run. 2000. (Left Behind Ser.: Bk. 10). (Illus.). 176p. (J). (gr. 4-7). mass mkt. 5.99 (978-0-8423-4330-5(X)) Tyndale Hse. Pubs.

—Protected. 2005. (Left Behind Ser.). 432p. (YA). 14.99 (978-1-4143-0271-3(1)) Tyndale Hse. Pubs.

—The Search: The Struggle to Survive. 2000. (Left Behind Ser.: Bk. 9). (Illus.). 176p. (J). (gr. 4-7). mass mkt. 5.99 (978-0-8423-4329-9(6)) Tyndale Hse. Pubs.

—Stung. 2004. (Left Behind Ser.: Bk. 5). 384p. (YA). (gr. 5-8). 14.99 (978-0-8423-8355-4(7)) Tyndale Hse. Pubs.

JJ & God's Warrior Force: Purple Hearts. 2002. 112p. (YA). (gr. 4-10). pap. 7.95 (978-0-9709772-2-9(0)) Angel & Me Publishing.

John, P. El Lugar Seguro. 2004. Tr. of Safe place, The. 8.99 (978-0-7899-1181-0(7)) Editorial Unilit.

Johnson, Barbara. Super-Scrumptious Jelly Donuts Sprinkled with Hugs: A Book about Hugs. 1998. (Geranium Lady Ser.). (Illus.). 32p. (J). (ps-2). 4.97 (978-0-8499-5848-9(2)) Nelson, Thomas Inc.

—The Tasty Taffy Tale & Super-Stretching the Truth: A Book about Honesty. Frazier, Victoria Ponikvar, illus. 1999. (Geranium Lady Ser.: Vol. 4). 32p. (J). (ps-2). 4.97 (978-0-8499-5951-6(9)) Nelson, Thomas Inc.

—The Upside-down Frown & Splashes of Joy: A Book about Joy. 1998. (Geranium Lady Ser.). (Illus.). 32p. (J). (ps-2). 4.97 (978-0-8499-5844-1(X)) Nelson, Thomas Inc.

Johnson, J. Renee. Timber! A Tale in Which a Son Learns to Honor His Parents. Zarrinnaal, Laura Nienhaus, illus. 2000. (Stories to Grow By Ser.). 19p. (J). 3.95 (978-1-56822-593-7(8) , Instructional Fair) Schaffer, Frank Pubns.

Johnson, Lissa Halls. Bad Girl Days, Vol. 12. 2005. (Brio Girls Ser.). 192p. (YA). pap. 7.99 (978-1-58997-091-5(8)) Focus on the Family Publishing.

—Stuck in the Sky. 2005. (Brio Girls Ser.). 192p. (YA). (gr. 7-11). pap. 7.99 (978-1-56179-951-0(3)) Focus on the Family Publishing.

Johnson, Lissa Halls & Lambert, David. Opportunity Knocks Twice, Vol. 3. 2005. (Brio Girls Ser.). 192p. (YA). pap. 7.99 (978-1-56179-953-4(X)) Focus on the Family Publishing.

Johnson, Lissa Halls & Vogel, Jane. Going Crazy till Wednesday, Vol. 10. 2005. (Brio Girls Ser.: Bk. 10). (Illus.). 192p. (YA). pap. 7.99 (978-1-58997-089-2(6)) Focus on the Family Publishing.

—Grasping at Moonbeams, Vol. 6. 2005. (Brio Girls Ser.). 192p. (YA). pap. 7.99 (978-1-58997-052-6(7)) Focus on the Family Publishing.

Johnson, Lissa Halls & Wierenga, Kathy. Croutons for Breakfast, Vol. 7. 2005. (Brio Girls Ser.). (Illus.). 192p. (YA). (gr. 6-11). pap. 7.99 (978-1-58997-080-9(2)) Focus on the Family Publishing.

Johnson, Lois Walfrid. Heart of Courage. 2005. (Viking Quest Ser.). (Illus.). 240p. (J). pap. 7.99 (978-0-8024-3115-8(1)) Moody Pubs.

—Mystery of the Silver Coins, Vol. 2. 2003. (Viking Quest Ser.: Vol. 2). (Illus.). 208p. (J). pap. 7.99 (978-0-8024-3113-4(5)) Moody Pubs.

—Raiders from the Sea. 2003. (Viking Quest Ser.). (Illus.). 208p. (J). (gr. 4-7). pap. 7.99 (978-0-8024-3112-7(7)) Moody Pubs.

—Raider's Promise. 2006. (Raiders from the Sea Ser.). (Illus.). 304p. (J). pap. 8.99 (978-0-8024-3116-5(X)) Moody Pubs.

Johnson, P. Mysterious Signal. 1998. (Riverboat Adventures Ser.: Vol. 5). (Illus.). 176p. (J). (gr. 3-8). pap. 5.99 (978-1-55661-355-5(5)) Bethany Hse. Pubs.

Jones, Brenda. Kids Sunday Notes: I Will Follow God's Plan for Me. l.t. ed. 2004. 100p. (J). 7.95 (978-1-57636-168-9(3)) SunRise Publishing.

Jones, Jennifer B. In Between. 2007. 208p. (YA). pap. 12.99 (978-1-60006-098-4(6) , Th1nk Bks.) NavPress Publishing Group.

Jones, Nathan Smith. The Boy Who Ate America. Nelson, Carey, illus. 2007. 32p. (J). (ps-3). 16.95 (***978-1-59038-814-3(3)*** , Shadow Mountain) Deseret Bk. Co.

Jones, Veda Boyd. Adventure in the Wilderness: The Journey to Cincinnati's Frontier, 1999. (American Adventure Ser.: No. 13). (Illus.). 143p. (J). (gr. 3-7). 11.95 (978-0-7910-5587-8(6) , Chelsea Hse.) Facts On File, Inc.

Jones, Veda Boyd. Emma's Secret: The Cincinnati Epidemic. 2005. (Sisters in Time Ser.). 141p. (J). (***978-1-4156-0074-0(0)***) Barbour Publishing, Inc.

Jordan, Sherryl. Secret Sacrament. 2001. (Illus.). 352p. (J). (gr. 7 up). 17.89 (978-0-06-028905-8(8)) HarperCollins Pubs.

—Secret Sacrament. 2000. (gr. 7-12). lib. bdg. 15.30 (978-0-613-68539-9(3)) Tandem Library Bks.

Jordan, Stephanie. Is the Moon God's? Houston, Melissa, illus. 2005. (J). bds. 9.99 (978-1-4183-0062-3(4)) Christ Inspired, Inc.

Joseph's Hands. 2007. (J). 12.99 (***978-0-9792258-8-8(4)***) Bezalel Bks.

Kaplan, Gloria. Pappou, Where Are You? Olavarria, Hector, illus. 2002. 112p. (YA). per. 11.99 (978-1-889732-28-2(1) , Key-A-Teese Production) Word For Word Publishing Co.

—Ride the White Horse. 2004. (YA). per. 8.99 (978-1-889732-48-0(6) , A & E Sivells Pubns.) Word For Word Publishing Co.

Karst, Patrice. Papi, Mami Que Es Dios? rev. ed. 1999. (SPA.). 78p. 11.95 (978-958-96144-6-4(9)) Centauro Publishing.

Katula, Bob. Larryboy y el Atroz Ataque de los Tapones de Cerilla Afonica. 2003. Tr. of Larryboy & the Awful Earwax Attacks. (SPA.). 94p. (J). pap. 4.99 (978-0-8297-3749-3(9)) Vida Pubs.

Keeling, Annie E. Andrew Golding A Tale of the Great Plague. 2004. reprint ed. pap. 15.95 (978-1-4191-0694-1(5)); pap. 1.99 (978-1-4192-0694-8(X)) Kessinger Publishing, LLC.

Keeling, E. Annie. Andrew Golding (a Tale of the Great Plag. 2006. 40.99 (***978-1-4280-0516-7(1)***); pap. 34.99 (***978-1-4280-0515-0(3)***) IndyPublish.com.

Keep Trying, Travis! 2006. 16p. (J). pap. 1.99 (978-0-7847-1705-9(2) , 04166) Standard Publishing.

Keffer, Lois. Fancy the Filly's Not Selfish or Silly. 1999. (J). 9.99 (978-1-57673-442-1(0)) Zondervan.

Keffer, Lois & Haidle, Helen. Ripples Raccoon Shares His Balloon. Spengler, Ken, illus. 1999. (Read-To-Me Puppet Buddies Ser.: Vol. 9). 24p. (J). (ps-1). 9.99 (978-1-57673-438-4(2) , Multnomah) WaterBrook Pr.

Kelby, Tom. Nathaniel's Journey: Journey Through the Great Woods. 2nd ed. 2000. (Illus.). 50p. (J). (978-1-930914-01-8(6)) Hands to the Plow, Inc.

—Nathaniel's Journey: The King's Armory. Yaeger, Mark, illus. 2003. (J). per. (978-1-930914-04-9(0)) Hands to the Plow, Inc.

Kelley, Nancy J. The Whispering Rod: A Tale of Old Massachusetts. 2002. 160p. (J). lib. bdg. 17.95 (978-1-57249-248-6(1) , White Mane Kids) White Mane Publishing Co., Inc.

Kelly, Clint. Escape Underground. 2001. (KidWitness Tales Ser.). 128p. (J). (gr. 3-8). pap. 5.99 (978-1-56179-964-0(5)) Bethany Hse. Pubs.

—Escape Underground. 2001. (gr. 5-8). lib. bdg. 14.15 (978-0-613-85882-3(4)) Tandem Library Bks.

Kelly, Stephen M. Symbala's River. 2006. (YA). lib. bdg. 6.99 (978-1-4276-0237-4(9)) Aardvark Global Publishing.

Kelly, Theresa. Aloha Cove Set, 7 vols. (Aloha Cove Ser.). (YA). 39.99 (978-0-7586-0005-9(4)) Concordia Publishing Hse.

—Dream a Little Dream, Vol. 7. 2000. (Aloha Cove Ser.: Vol. 7). (Illus.). 272p. (J). (gr. 7-11). 5.99 (978-0-570-07072-6(4)) Concordia Publishing Hse.

—Dream a Little Dream. 2000. (gr. 7-12). lib. bdg. 14.15 (978-0-613-72787-7(8)) Tandem Library Bks.

—Forget Me Not, Vol. 5. 2000. (Aloha Cove Ser.: Vol. 5). (Illus.). 272p. (YA). (gr. 7-11). 5.99 (978-0-570-07033-7(3)) Concordia Publishing Hse.

—Forget Me Not. 2000. (gr. 7-12). lib. bdg. 14.15 (978-0-613-72782-2(7)) Tandem Library Bks.

—Good-Bye Is Not Forever. 2000. (Aloha Cove Ser.: Vol. 8). 272p. (J). (gr. 7-11). pap. 5.99 (978-0-570-07073-3(2)) Concordia Publishing Hse.

—Living on Nothing Atoll. 1999. (Aloha Cove Ser.: Vol. 1). (Illus.). 272p. (YA). (gr. 8-12). 5.99 (978-0-570-05483-2(4)) Concordia Publishing Hse.

—Living on Nothing Atoll. 1999. (gr. 7-12). lib. bdg. 14.15 (978-0-613-72659-7(6)) Tandem Library Bks.

—Place in the Heart. 1999. (gr. 7-12). lib. bdg. 14.15 (978-0-613-72783-9(5)) Tandem Library Bks.

—A Place in the Heart, Vol. 6. 2000. (Aloha Cove Ser.: Vol. 6). (Illus.). 272p. (YA). (gr. 7-11). 5.99 (978-0-570-07034-4(1)) Concordia Publishing Hse.

—Seaside High, Vol. 2. 1999. (Aloha Cove Ser.: Vol. 2). (Illus.). 272p. (YA). (gr. 8-12). 5.99 (978-0-570-05484-9(2)) Concordia Publishing Hse.

—Seaside High. 1999. (gr. 7-12). lib. bdg. 14.15 (978-0-613-72660-3(X)) Tandem Library Bks.

—Stand by Me, Vol. 4. 1999. (Aloha Cove Ser.: Vol. 4). (Illus.). 272p. (YA). (gr. 8-12). 5.99 (978-0-570-05486-3(9)) Concordia Publishing Hse.

—Stand by Me. 1999. (gr. 7-12). lib. bdg. 14.15 (978-0-613-72785-3(1)) Tandem Library Bks.

—Tomorrow I'll Miss You, Vol. 3. 1999. (Aloha Cove Ser.: Vol. 3). (Illus.). 272p. (YA). (gr. 8-12). 5.99 (978-0-570-05485-6(0)) Concordia Publishing Hse.

—Tomorrow I'll Miss You. 1999. (gr. 7-12). lib. bdg. 14.15 (978-0-613-72575-0(1)) Tandem Library Bks.

Kennedy, Pamela. Moving Day for Sam. Petrov, Anton, illus. 2007. 32p. (J). (gr. k-3). 8.99 (***978-0-8249-5558-8(7)*** , GPKids) Ideals Pubns.

Kenney, Cindy. An Easter Carol. 2004. (Illus.). 48p. 12.99 (978-0-310-70673-1(4)) Zonderkidz.

—God Is Bigger Than the Boogie Man: And Other Bedtime Stories. Hardin, Greg & Vann, Robert, illus. 2002. 40p. 12.99 (978-0-310-70465-2(0)) Zonderkidz.

—A Very Veggie Family Adventure. 2002. (Illus.). (J). pap. 19.99 (978-0-310-70464-5(2)) Zonderkidz.

—Where Is God When I'm Scared? 2004. (Illus.). 22p. bds. 4.99 (978-0-310-70784-4(6)) Zonderkidz.

—3-2-1 Penguins! Family Adventures. 2003. (Illus.). 96p. (J). pap. 9.99 (978-0-310-70694-6(7)) Zonderkidz.

Kenney, Cindy & Big Idea, Inc. Staff. A Knight to Remember. 2005. (Big Idea Bks.). (Illus.). 40p. (gr. k-3). 9.99 (978-0-310-70730-1(7)) Zonderkidz.

Kent, Renee Holmes. Adventures in Misty Falls, Vol. 8. 2004. (Adventures in Misty Falls Ser.: Vol. 8). (Illus.). 100p. (gr. 4-7). pap. 4.99 (978-1-56309-456-9(8) , N017104) Woman's Missionary Union.

—Best Friends Forever?, Vol. 2. 2004. (Adventures in Misty Falls Ser.: Bk. 2). (Illus.). 100p. (gr. 4-7). pap. 4.99 (978-1-56309-734-8(6) , N007117) New Hope Pubs.

—Cassie, You're a Winner! 2004. (Adventures in Misty Falls Ser.: Vol. 1). (Illus.). 100p. (gr. 4-7). pap. 2.99 (978-1-56309-735-5(4) , N007116) New Hope Pubs.

—Girl Talk, Vol. 7. 2004. (Adventures in Misty Falls Ser.: Vol. 7). (Illus.). 100p. (J). (gr. 4-7). pap. 4.99 (978-1-56309-455-2(X) , N017103) New Hope Pubs.

—J. J. Navajo Princess, Vol. 3. 2004. (Adventures in Misty Falls Ser.: Vol. 3). (Illus.). 100p. (gr. 4-7). pap. 4.99 (978-1-56309-763-8(X) , N007105) New Hope Pubs.

—Robyn to the Rescue, Vol. 5. 2004. (Adventures in Misty Falls Ser.: Vol. 5). (Illus.). 100p. (J). (gr. 4-7). pap. 4.99 (978-1-56309-451-4(7) , N007109) New Hope Pubs.

—Tell the Truth, Cassie, Vol. 6. 2004. (Adventures in Misty Falls Ser.: Vol. 6). (Illus.). 100p. (J). (gr. 4-7). pap. 4.99 (978-1-56309-452-1(5) , N007110) New Hope Pubs.

Kenworthy, Sukalaya. Hmong Means Free. 2004. 49p. pap. 12.95 (978-1-4137-2364-9(0)) PublishAmerica, Inc.

Kerl, Mary. The Secret: A Christian Novel for Middle Readers. 2002. 137p. pap. 19.95 (978-1-59129-907-3(1)) PublishAmerica, Inc.

Kherdian, David. The Revelations of Alvin Tolliver. 2001. 104p. (J). (gr. 3 up). pap. 7.95 (978-1-57174-255-1(7)) Hampton Roads Publishing Co., Inc.

Kid's Kindness Christian Adventures in Learning Book. 2005. (J). 15.95 (978-1-59210-419-2(3)) Whispering Pine Pr., Inc.

Kieda, Alan. No Fair! A Tale in Which Monty Learns Contentment. Myers, Darcy, illus. 2000. (Stories to Grow By Ser.). 19p. (J). 3.95 (978-1-56822-596-8(2) , Instructional Fair) Schaffer, Frank Pubns.

Kieper, Rienhold Richard. Tomahawk. 2004. 19p. (J). pap. 10.00 (978-0-9719284-2-8(8)) Blue Thunder One, Inc.

Kimchi & Komoshins. 2004. 56p. pap. 6.99 (978-0-8341-2090-7(9)) Beacon Hill Pr. of Kansas City.

Kindig, Tess. Luv @ First Site. 2004. 128p. (J). pap. 5.99 (978-1-4003-0325-0(7)) Nelson, Thomas Inc.

Kindig, Tess Eileen. Camp Bee-A-Champ. 2001. (gr. k-3). lib. bdg. 13.00 (978-0-613-72852-2(1)) Tandem Library Bks.

—Double Whammy!, Vol. 8. 2001. (Slam Dunk Ser.: Vol. 8). 96p. (J). (gr. 1-4). 4.99 (978-0-570-07142-6(9)) Concordia Publishing Hse.

—Gimme an A. 2000. (gr. k-3). lib. bdg. 13.00 (978-0-613-72795-2(9)) Tandem Library Bks.

—Gimme an "A", Vol. 5. 2000. (Slam Dunk Ser.: Vol. 5). (Illus.). 96p. (J). (gr. 1-4). 4.99 (978-0-570-07091-7(0)) Concordia Publishing Hse.

—March Mania, Vol. 6. 2000. (Slam Dunk Ser.: Vol. 6). 96p. (J). (gr. 1-4). 4.99 (978-0-570-07092-4(9)) Concordia Publishing Hse.

—March Mania. 2000. (gr. k-3). lib. bdg. 13.00 (978-0-613-72796-9(7)) Tandem Library Bks.

—Muggsy Makes an Assist. 2000. (Slam Dunk Ser.: Vol. 3). 96p. (J). (gr. 1-4). Vol. 3. (Illus.). 4.99 (978-0-570-07018-4(X)); Vol. 4. 4.99 (978-0-570-07019-1(8)) Concordia Publishing Hse.

—Muggsy Makes an Assist. 2000. (gr. k-3). lib. bdg. 13.00 (978-0-613-72906-2(4)) Tandem Library Bks.

—Slam Dunk Set, 8 vols. (Slam Dunk Ser.). (J). 38.99 (978-0-7586-0014-1(3)) Concordia Publishing Hse.

—Spider Mcghee & the Hoopla. 2000. (gr. k-3). lib. bdg. 13.00 (978-0-613-72840-9(8)) Tandem Library Bks.

—Spider McGhee & the Hoopla, Vol. 2. 2000. (Slam Dunk Ser.: Vol. 2). (Illus.). 96p. (J). (gr. 1-4). 4.99 (978-0-570-07017-7(1)) Concordia Publishing Hse.

Kindig, Tess Eileen & Van Severen, Joe. Double Whammy!, Vol. 7. 2001. (Slam Dunk Ser.: Vol. 7). (Illus.). 96p. (J). (gr. 1-4). 4.99 (978-0-570-07143-3(7)) Concordia Publishing Hse.

King, Peter. Chronicles. 2002. (gr. 7-12). lib. bdg. 14.15 (978-0-613-77868-8(5)) Tandem Library Bks.

King, Peter & McCoy, Mike. Soldier of God, Vol. 1. 2002. (Illus.). 32p. (gr. 7 up). pap. 5.00 (978-0-9715206-3-9(1)) Quest Comics.

King, Peter, et al. Chronicles. 2002. 56p. Vol. 1. (Illus.). (gr. 8 up). pap. 6.00 (978-0-9715206-0-8(7)); Vol. 2. (Illus.). (gr. 7 up). pap. 6.00 (978-0-9715206-1-5(5)); Vol. 3. (gr. 7 up). pap. 6.00 (978-0-9715206-2-2(3)) Quest Comics.

King, Robert A. The Song of the Temple Stones. Vandervoort, Gene, illus. 1999. 16p. (J). (gr. 1-4). pap. 4.95 (978-0-8198-7017-9(X)) Pauline Bks. & Media.

—The Three Lumps of Clay. Vandervoort, Gene, illus. 1999. 16p. (J). (gr. 1-4). pap. 4.95 (978-0-8198-7399-6(3)) Pauline Bks. & Media.

The King's Daughter & Other Stories Fo. 2006. 78.99 (***978-1-4142-5874-4(7)***); pap. 71.99 (***978-1-4219-9992-0(7)***) IndyPublish.com.

Kirkman, Robert. Genesis Vol. 1. (Illus.). 120p. pap. 12.99 (978-1-58240-572-8(7)) Image Comics.

Kjellberg, B. Abe: A Farm Boy. 2006. (J). per. (978-0-912868-07-3(4)) Kjellberg, Inc.

—Apple Acres: The Farm. 2006. (J). per. 7.95 (***978-0-912868-10-3(4)***) Kjellberg, Inc.

—Courtnee: A Farm Girl. 2005. (Illus.). 84p. (J). per. 7.95 (978-0-912868-06-6(6)) Kjellberg, Inc.

—Sandy: A City Girl. 2005. (Illus.). 94p. (J). per. 7.95 (978-0-912868-08-0(2) , 8080) Kjellberg, Inc.

Klassen, Kirsten L. Katelyn's Affection. 2004. 280p. pap. 11.99 (978-0-8361-9281-0(8)) Herald Pr.

Knoche, Keith. Radio QHJ? Libro de Diversion. 2000. 12p. 11.99 (978-5-550-02992-3(8)); 7.99 (978-5-550-02993-0(6)) Faith Factory.

Knoche, Keith & Wood, Jeff. Buck to the Rescue. 20p. (gr. k-7). 2001. 14.99 (978-5-550-02994-7(4)); 2000. pap. 11.99 incl. audio (978-5-550-02995-4(2)) Faith Factory.

—WWJD? Radio Felt Set. 2002. pap. 8.99 (978-5-550-00772-3(X)) Faith Factory.

Knowlton, Laurie. N 2 Deep. 2004. 128p. (J). pap. 5.99 (978-1-4003-0327-4(3)) Nelson, Thomas Inc.

Koehne, Troy. Death of a Martyr. 2003. 138p. (YA). pap. 11.95 (978-0-595-28031-5(5)) iUniverse, Inc.

Koenig, Albert. Wood, Hay, & Pigs. Compton, Donna, illus. 2005. (J). 8.99 (978-1-4183-0078-4(0)) Christ Inspired, Inc.

Kosciesza, Ida. Family at Number 5. 2001. (gr. 7-12). lib. bdg. 23.40 (978-0-613-74551-2(5)) Tandem Library Bks.

Krohn, Genendel. Who Is the Builder? Pelleg, Tirtsa, illus. 32p. 13.99 (978-1-58330-515-7(7)) Feldheim Pubs.

Kuijer, Guus. The Book of Everything. Nieuwenhuizen, John, tr. from DUT. 2006. 112p. (J). (gr. 4-7). pap. 16.99 (978-0-439-74918-3(2) , Levine, Arthur A. Bks.) Scholastic, Inc.

Kuijer, Guus & Nieuwenhuizen, John. The Book of Everything. 2006. ix, 101p. (J). 16.99 (978-0-439-74919-0(0) , Levine, Arthur A. Bks.) Scholastic, Inc.

LaHaye, Tim & Jenkins, Jerry B. Attack of Apollyon: Revenge of the Locusts. 2002. (Left Behind Ser.: Bk. 19). 176p. (J). mass mkt. 5.99 (978-0-8423-4313-8(X)) Tyndale Hse. Pubs.

—El Clandestino. 2000. (Dejados Atras los Chicos Ser.: Vol. 6). (SPA.). (J). (gr. 4-7). pap. 4.99 (978-0-7899-0724-0(0)) Spanish Hse. Distributors.

—A Dangerous Plan: Race Against Time. 2002. (Left Behind Ser.: Bk. 20). 176p. (J). mass mkt. 5.99 (978-0-8423-4314-5(8)) Tyndale Hse. Pubs.

—Dejados Atras. 2003. (Left Behind Ser.).Tr. of Left Behind. (SPA., Illus.). 48p. 4.99 (978-0-8054-2843-8(7)); Vol. 2. pap. 4.99 (978-0-8054-2847-6(X)); Vol. 3. 4.99 (978-0-8054-2844-5(5)) B&H Publishing Grp.

—Despojado. 2001. (Dejados Atras los Chicos Ser.: Vol. 7). (SPA.). (J). (gr. 4-7). pap. 4.99 (978-0-7899-0837-7(9)) Spanish Hse. Distributors.

—Left Behind Bks. 1-6, Set: The Kids Collection 1, 6 vols. 1999. (Left Behind Ser.). 175p. (J). (gr. 4-7). mass mkt. 32.94 (978-0-8423-0907-3(1)) Tyndale Hse. Pubs.

—Left Behind Bks. 7-12, Set: The Kids Collection 2, 6 vols. 2001. (Left Behind Ser.). (Illus.). 175p. (YA). mass mkt. 32.94 (978-0-8423-5747-0(5)) Tyndale Hse. Pubs.

—Left Behind Bks. 13-18, Set: The Kids Collection 3, 6 vols. 2001. (Left Behind Ser.). (Illus.). 175p. (YA). mass mkt. 32.94 (978-0-8423-5748-7(3)) Tyndale Hse. Pubs.

—Left Behind Bks. 19-24, Set: The Kids Collection 4, 6 vols. 2002. (Left Behind Ser.). 175p. (J). mass mkt. 32.94 (978-0-8423-7447-7(7)) Tyndale Hse. Pubs.

—Secundaria Nicolas. 2000. (Dejados Atras los Chicos Ser.: Vol. 5). (SPA.). (J). (gr. 4-7). pap. 4.99 (978-0-7899-0723-3(2)) Spanish Hse. Distributors.

Lamplighter Staff. Tales of the Restoration. 2004. 20.00 (978-1-58474-056-8(6)) Cornerstone Family Ministries/ Lamplighter Publishing.

—Teddys Button Hardcover. 2004. 15.00 (978-1-58474-027-8(2)) Cornerstone Family Ministries/Lamplighter Publishing.

—Tom Gillies. 2004. 16.00 (978-1-58474-048-3(5)) Cornerstone Family Ministries/Lamplighter Publishing.

—Tom Watkins Mistake. 2004. 15.00 (978-1-58474-034-6(5)) Cornerstone Family Ministries/Lamplighter Publishing.

Lamson, Sharon. The Roach Rangers Cross Panic Pier: A Story about Courage. Barry, Bruce, illus. 2006. (Bug Rangers Ser.). 24p. (J). pap. 6.99 (978-0-310-71006-6(5)) Zonderkidz.

Lamson, Sharon E. Roach Approach/Squiggz Rides Storm. Barry, Bruce, illus. 2006. 40p. (J). pap. 4.99 (978-0-310-71384-5(6)) Zondervan.

—Roach Ranger Danger at Coaster Cliffs: A Story about Obedience. Barry, Bruce, illus. 2006. (Bug Rangers#8482; Ser.). 28p. (J). 4.99 (978-0-310-71197-1(5)) Zonderkidz.

—Superhero Powers at Muscle Beach: A Story about Giving Credit Where Credit Is Due. Barry, Bruce, illus. 2006. 28p. (J). 4.99 (978-0-310-71198-8(3)) Zonderkidz.

The Land of Havala. 2006. 64p. pap. 6.99 (978-1-59185-910-9(7) , Creation Hse.) Strang Communications Co.

Lane, L. E. The Mysterious Golden Seed. l.t. ed. 2004. 144p. (J). pap. (978-0-9746867-0-7(0)) Christian Visionary Communications.

Lawton, Wendy. Changing Faces: Real TV, Take 1. 2004. (Real Tv - Real Transformations Series (Take 1) Ser.). 224p. (J). pap. 10.99 (978-0-8024-5413-3(5)) Moody Pubs.

—Flip Flop. 2004. (Real Tv - Real Transformations Series (Take 2) Ser.). 208p. (J). pap. 10.99 (978-0-8024-5414-0(3)) Moody Pubs.

—Less Is More: Real TV, Take 3. 2005. (Real Tv Ser.). 192p. (J). pap. 10.99 (978-0-8024-5415-7(1)) Moody Pubs.

—Shadow of His Hand: A Story Based on the Life of Holocaust Survivor Anita Dittman. 2004. (Daughters of the Faith Ser.). 160p. (J). pap. 6.99 (978-0-8024-4074-7(6)) Moody Pubs.

—The Tinker's Daughter: A Story Based on the Life of Mary Bunyan. 2002. (Daughters of the Faith Ser.). 144p. (YA). pap. 6.99 (978-0-8024-4099-0(1)) Moody Pubs.

Layton, Dian. Adventures in the Kingdom: In Search of Wanderer. 2001. (J). pap. 4.99 (978-0-9677402-8-7(2)) Mercy Place, Inc.

—Rescued from the Dragon. 2005. (Illus.). 64p. (J). (gr. 2-5). pap. 4.99 (978-0-9677402-2-5(3)) Destiny Image Pubs.

—Seeker's Great Adventure. 2005. (Illus.). 64p. (J). (gr. 2-5). pap. 4.99 (978-0-9677402-1-8(5)) Destiny Image Pubs.

Le Feuvre, Amy. Harebell's Friend. 2004. (Golden Inheritance Ser.: Vol. 8). (Illus.). 140p. (J). pap. (978-0-921100-84-3(1)) Inheritance Pubns.

—Teddy's Button. 2002. (Golden Inheritance Ser.: Vol. 6). (Illus.). 93p. (J). (978-0-921100-83-6(3)) Inheritance Pubns.

—Teddy's Button. 2004. reprint ed. pap. 15.95 (978-1-4191-5094-4(4)); pap. 1.99 (978-1-4192-5094-1(9)) Kessinger Publishing, LLC.

Lecomte, Eva. Paula the Waldensian. 2004. reprint ed. pap. 21.95 (978-1-4191-4044-0(2)); pap. 1.99 (978-1-4192-4044-7(7)) Kessinger Publishing, LLC.

Lee, Janice G. The Adventures of Chewy & Tonk. 2003. (Illus.). 40p. (J). per. (978-1-55306-599-9(9) , Guardian Bks.) Essence Publishing.

Lee, Quinlan B. LarryBoy & the Bad Apple. Franchesco!, illus. 2006. (VeggieTales Ser.). 32p. (J). act. bk. ed. 3.99 (978-1-4169-3985-6(7) , Simon Scribbles) Simon & Schuster Children's Publishing.

Lefeuvre, Amy. Probable Sons. 2004. reprint ed. pap. 15.95 (978-1-4191-4306-9(9)); pap. 1.99 (978-1-4192-4306-6(3)) Kessinger Publishing, LLC.

Left Behind Graphic Novel. 2002. 14.47 (978-1-4046-2499-3(6)) Book Wholesalers, Inc.

Lehman, Sheryle. Shelter Me Safe: The Story of a Young Girls Struggle in Finding Christ in Her Life. 2002. (Illus.). 253p. (YA). (gr. 6 up). pap. 8.95 (978-1-890050-65-8(2)) Carlisle Pr.- Walnut Creek.

Leininger, Tracy M. A Light Kindled: The Story of Pricilla Mullins. 2nd ed. 2000. (Illus.). 64p. (J). mass mkt. 15.99 (978-0-9724287-2-9(0)) His Seasons.

—A Light Kindled: The Story of Priscilla Mullins. Pulley, Kelly & Reed, Lisa, illus. 2000. 63p. (J). 16.00 (978-1-929241-18-7(6)) Vision Forum, Inc., The.

Leman, Kevin. My Youngest, There's No One Like You. Leman, Kevin, II, illus. 2005. 32p. (J). 12.99 (978-0-8007-1831-2(3)) Revell.

Lepp, Royden. Barnabas Goes Swimming. 2008. 32p. (J). pap. 3.99 (***978-0-310-71584-9(9)***) Zondervan.

—God Loves You Barnbas. 2008. 32p. (J). pap. 3.99 (***978-0-310-71587-0(3)***) Zondervan.

—Happy Birthday Barnabas. 2008. 32p. (J). pap. 3.99 (***978-0-310-71586-3(5)***) Zondervan.

Leppard, Lois Gladys. Mandie & the Cherokee Legend. 2007. (Mandie Bks.: No. 2). 144p. (J). (gr. 4-7). reprint ed. mass mkt. 5.99 (978-0-87123-321-9(5)) Bethany Hse. Pubs.

—Mandie & the Hidden Past. 2003. (Mandie Bks.). 160p. (J). mass mkt. 5.99 (978-0-7642-2641-0(X)) Bethany Hse. Pubs.

—Mandie & the Hidden Past. 2003. (gr. 5-8). lib. bdg. 13.00 (978-0-613-85057-5(2)) Tandem Library Bks.

—Mandie & the Missing Schoolmarm. 2004. (Mandie Bks.). 160p. (J). mass mkt. 5.99 (978-0-7642-2642-7(8)) Bethany Hse. Pubs.

—Mandie & the Night Thief, Vol. 37. 2003. (Mandie Bks.). (Illus.). 160p. (J). mass mkt. 5.99 (978-0-7642-2640-3(1)) Bethany Hse. Pubs.

—Mandie & the Night Thief. 2003. (gr. k-3). lib. bdg. 13.00 (978-0-613-84504-5(8)) Tandem Library Bks.

—Mandie Books Pack, 36-40. 2004. (Mandie Bks.). 800p. (J). mass mkt. 29.99 (978-0-7642-9123-4(8)) Bethany Hse. Pubs.

—The Mysterious Teacher. 2003. 160p. (J). mass mkt. 4.99 (978-1-889893-98-3(6) , Ambassador-Emerald, International) Emerald Hse. Group, Inc.

—New Horizons. 2006. (Mandie Ser.). (Illus.). 224p. (J). pap. 10.99 (978-0-7642-2932-9(X)) Bethany Hse. Pubs.

LeRoye, Dee. Crossfire. 2003. 137p. (YA). per. 5.99 (978-0-9727056-0-8(0)) Dakota Rose.

LeSourd, Nancy. Liberty Letters: The Personal Correspondence of Elizabeth Walton & Abigail Matthews. 2003. (Liberty Letters#8482; Ser.). (Illus.). 256p. (J). 9.99 (978-0-310-70351-8(4)) Zonderkidz.

—Liberty Letters: The Personal Correspondence of Emma Edmonds & Mollie Turner, Civil War Spies, 1862. 2004. (Liberty Letters Ser.). 224p. (J). 9.99 (978-0-310-70352-5(2)) Zonderkidz.

—Liberty Letters: The Personal Correspondence of Hannah Brown & Sarah Smith. 2003. (Liberty Letters Ser.). (Illus.). 192p. (J). 9.99 (978-0-310-70350-1(6)) Zonderkidz.

LeSourd, Nancy & Farnsworth, Bill. Christy- Christmastime at Cutter Gap. Farnsworth, Bill, illus. 2003. (Illus.). (J). (gr. k-3). 15.99 (978-0-310-70571-0(1)) Zonderkidz.

Lewin, Terry. God Remembered Us. Gumm, Susan Kathleen, illus. 2006. 36p. (J). per. 19.00 (***978-0-9771482-1-9(1)*** , Ithaca Pr.) Authors & Artists Publishers of New York, Inc.

Lewis, Beverly. Annika's Secret Wish. Querin, Pamela, illus. 2004. 32p. (J). 16.99 (978-0-7642-2940-4(0)) Bethany Hse. Pubs.

—Best Friend, Worst Enemy. rev. ed. 2001. (Holly's Heart Ser.: Bk. 1). 160p. (YA). (gr. 6-9). pap. 6.99 (978-0-7642-2500-0(6)) Bethany Hse. Pubs.

—Better Than Best. 2000. (Girls Only (Go!) Ser.: Vol. 6). (Illus.). 128p. (J). (gr. 3-8). pap. 6.99 (978-1-55661-641-9(4)) Bethany Hse. Pubs.

—Big Bad Beans. 2000. (Cul-de-Sac Kids Ser.: Vol. 22). (Illus.). 80p. (J). (gr. 2-5). pap. 3.99 (978-0-7642-2127-9(2)) Bethany Hse. Pubs.

—California Crazy. 2002. (Holly's Heart Ser.: Bk. 5). 160p. (YA). pap. 6.99 (978-0-7642-2504-8(9)) Bethany Hse. Pubs.

—Eight Is Enough. 2003. (Holly's Heart Ser.: Bk. 13). (Orig.). (gr. 5-8). lib. bdg. 14.15 (978-0-613-87240-9(1)) Tandem Library Bks.

—Freshman Frenzy. 2003. (Holly's Heart Ser.: Bk. 11). (Illus.). 160p. (YA). pap. 6.99 (978-0-7642-2618-2(5)) Bethany Hse. Pubs.

—Good-Bye, Dressel Hills. 2002. (Holly's Heart Ser.: Bk. 7). 160p. (YA). pap. 6.99 (978-0-7642-2506-2(5)) Bethany Hse. Pubs.

—The Granny Game. 1999. (Cul-de-Sac Kids Ser.: Vol. 20). (Illus.). 80p. (J). (gr. 2-5). pap. 3.99 (978-0-7642-2125-5(6)) Bethany Hse. Pubs.

—It's a Girl Thing. 2003. (Holly's Heart Ser.: Bk. 14). 160p. (Orig.). (YA). pap. 6.99 (978-0-7642-2621-2(5)) Bethany Hse. Pubs.

—It's a Girl Thing. 2003. (Holly's Heart Ser.: Bk. 14). (Orig.). (gr. 5-8). lib. bdg. 14.15 (978-0-613-87241-6(X)) Tandem Library Bks.

—Little White Lies. 2003. (Holly's Heart Ser.: Bk. 10). 160p. (YA). (gr. 5-9). reprint ed. pap. 6.99 (978-0-7642-2617-5(7)) Bethany Hse. Pubs.

—Mystery Letters. 2003. (Holly's Heart Ser.: Bk. 12). (Illus.). 160p. (YA). reprint ed. pap. 6.99 (978-0-7642-2619-9(3)) Bethany Hse. Pubs.

—Mystery Mutt. 2000. (Cul-de-Sac Kids Ser.: Vol. 21). (Illus.). 80p. (J). (gr. 2-5). pap. 3.99 (978-0-7642-2126-2(4)) Bethany Hse. Pubs.

—No Guys Pact. 2003. (Holly's Heart Ser.: Bk. 9). 160p. (YA). (gr. 5-9). pap. 6.99 (978-0-7642-2616-8(9)) Bethany Hse. Pubs.

—A Perfect Match. 1999. (Girls Only (Go!) Ser.: Vol. 3). (gr. 3-6). lib. bdg. 14.15 (978-0-613-23419-1(7)) Tandem Library Bks.

—Photo Perfect. 2001. (Girls Only (Go!) Ser.: Vol. 7). 128p. (J). (gr. 4-7). pap. 6.99 (978-1-55661-642-6(2)) Bethany Hse. Pubs.

—Piggy Party. 1999. (Cul-de-Sac Kids Ser.: Vol. 19). (Illus.). 80p. (J). (gr. 2-5). pap. 3.99 (978-0-7642-2124-8(8)) Bethany Hse. Pubs.

—Second-Best Friend. 2002. (Holly's Heart Ser.: Bk. 6). 160p. (YA). pap. 6.99 (978-0-7642-2505-5(7)) Bethany Hse. Pubs.

—Secret Summer Dreams. rev. ed. 2001. (Holly's Heart Ser.: Bk. 2). 144p. (YA). (gr. 6-9). pap. 6.99 (978-0-7642-2501-7(4)) Bethany Hse. Pubs.

—Shadows Beyond the Gate. 2000. (Summerhill Secrets Ser.: Vol. 10). 144p. (J). (gr. 6-9). pap. 6.99 (978-1-55661-876-5(X)) Bethany Hse. Pubs.

—Star Status. 2002. (Girls Only (Go!) Ser.: Vol. 8). 128p. (J). reprint ed. pap. 6.99 (978-1-55661-643-3(0)) Bethany Hse. Pubs.

—Straight-A Teacher. 2002. (Holly's Heart Ser.: Bk. 8). 160p. (YA). pap. 6.99 (978-0-7642-2615-1(0)) Bethany Hse. Pubs.

—Windows on the Hill. 1999. (Summerhill Secrets Ser.: Vol. 9). 144p. (J). (gr. 6-9). pap. 6.99 (978-1-55661-875-8(1)) Bethany Hse. Pubs.

Lewis, Beverly & Querin, Pamela. Annika's Secret Wish. 2006. (Illus.). 32p. (J). (gr. k-4). reprint ed. 15.00 (978-0-7567-9876-5(0)) DIANE Publishing Co.

Lewis, C. S. Los Cuatro Amigos. (Coleccion Pequenos Clasicos). (SPA.). 24p. (gr. k-3). (J). (978-84-246-2532-0(3) , GL7952); 2003. (978-84-246-1923-7(4) , GL30509) La Galera, S.A. Editorial ESP. *Dist:* Lectorum Pubns., Inc.

Lewis, Richard. The Flame Tree. 2004. (Illus.). 288p. (YA). 16.95 (978-0-689-86333-2(0)) Simon & Schuster Children's Publishing.

Liebig, Nelda Johnson. Carrie & the Boarding House. 2005. 128p. (J). pap. 10.95 (978-1-883953-35-5(9)) Midwest Traditions, Inc.

Lienas, Gemma. Callejon Slin Salida. 2003. (SPA.). 112p. (978-84-348-5285-3(3) , SM7488) SM Ediciones ESP. *Dist:* Lectorum Pubns., Inc.

Liggitt, Ed, Sr. Color Me Christian: A Greek Legionnaire's Story. 2004. 76p. pap. 14.95 (978-1-4137-1504-0(4)) PublishAmerica, Inc.

Lindquist, N. J. More Than Friends Vol. 4: Circle of Friends. 2004. (Circle of Friends Ser.: 4). 224p. pap. 9.95 (978-0-9685495-5-1(1)) That's Life! Communications CAN. *Dist:* STL Distribution North America.

Lingo, Susan. My Little Good Night Storybook. Parks, Kathy, illus. 2006. 108p. (J). 6.99 (978-0-7847-1849-0(0)) Standard Publishing.

Linko, G. J. Allie's Answers. 2004. (Seekers Ser.). 5.99 (978-0-8066-4179-9(7) , Augsburg Bks.) Augsburg Fortress, Pubs.

—Ben's Big Break. 2004. (Seekers Ser.: No. 4). 108p. 5.99 (978-0-8066-4185-0(1) , Augsburg Bks.) Augsburg Fortress, Pubs.

—Frank's Fear. 2004. (Seekers Ser.: No. 6). 108p. 5.99 (978-0-8066-4187-4(8) , Augsburg Bks.) Augsburg Fortress, Pubs.

—Rebecca's Return. 2004. (Seekers Ser.). 5.99 (978-0-8066-4181-2(9) , Augsburg Bks.) Augsburg Fortress, Pubs.

—Rebecca's Return: Topical Study. 2004. (Seekers Ser.). 3.99 (978-0-8066-4184-3(3)) Augsburg Fortress, Pubs.

—Tess's Touchstone. 2004. (Seekers Ser.: No. 5). 108p. 5.99 (978-0-8066-4189-8(4) , Augsburg Bks.) Augsburg Fortress, Pubs.

Little Farm down the Lane, Bk. III. 2005. pap. 10.99 (978-1-59781-702-8(3)) Xulon Pr., Inc.

Little Lambs: Reproducible Student Materials. (Midweek Curriculum Ser.). 64p. (ps-k). stu. ed. 17.00 (978-0-570-00791-3(7)) Concordia Publishing Hse.

Littleton, Mark. Hoofbeats on the Trail. 2002. (Ally OConnor Adventures Ser.: Vol. 3). 128p. (J). (gr. 4-7). pap. 5.99 (978-0-8010-6427-2(9)) Baker Bks.

—Sarah's Secret. 2001. (Ally OConnor Adventures Ser.: Vol. 2). 112p. (J). (gr. 4-7). pap. 5.99 (978-0-8010-4489-2(8)) Baker Bks.

—Tracks in the Sand. 2001. (Ally OConnor Adventures Ser.: Vol. 1). 128p. (J). (gr. 4-7). pap. 5.99 (978-0-8010-4490-8(1)) Baker Bks.

Llorente, Pilar Molina. Aura Gris. (SPA.). 192p. (YA). (gr. 5-8). (978-84-216-0993-4(9) , BU3870) Bruño, Editorial ESP. *Dist:* Lectorum Pubns., Inc.

Loesch, Joe. Holy Moses: As Told by God's Animals. Cox, Brian T., illus. abr. l.t. ed. 2001. (Bible Stories for Kids Ser.: Vol. 8). 60p. (J). pap. 14.95 incl. audio (978-1-887729-81-9(X)) Toy Box Productions.

—Holy Moses: As Told by God's Animals. Hutchinson, Cheryl, ed. Cox, Brian T., illus. unabr. ed. 2001. (Bible Stories for Kids Ser.). 60p. (gr. k-5). reprint ed. 16.95 incl. audio compact disk (978-1-932332-08-7(1)) Toy Box Productions.

—Holy Moses: As Told by God's Animals. Cox, Brian T., illus. unabr. l.t. ed. 2001. (Bible Stories for Kids Ser.: Vol. 8). 60p. (J). pap. 16.95 incl. audio compact disk (978-1-887729-82-6(8)) Toy Box Productions.

—Lions, Lions Everywhere: The Story of Daniel as told by God's Animals. Hutchinson, Cheryl, ed. Cox, Brain T., illus. 2004. (Bible Stories for Kids Ser.). (J). bds. 16.95 incl. audio compact disk (978-1-932332-24-7(3)) Toy Box Productions.

LoisKeffer. God Is There Little Bear. 2007. (Sleepytime Stories Ser.). 24p. (J). bds. 6.99 (978-0-7814-4351-7(2) , 0781443512) Cook, David C. Publishing Co.

London, Victoria. Lucy & the Liberty Quilt. collector's ed. 2001. (Gifted Girls Ser.: Bk. 1). 64p. (J). (gr. 2-7). per. 7.95 (978-0-9714776-0-5(4)) Sparklesoup Studios, Inc.

Losier, Dave. Fred's Prayer Machine. 2002. (Illus.). 152p. (J). pap. 11.95 (978-1-929039-07-4(7)) Ambassador Bks., Inc.

Lough, Loree. Fire by Night: The Great Fire Devastates Boston. 1999. (American Adventure Ser.: No. 4). 144p. (J). (gr. 3-7). lib. bdg. 15.95 (978-0-7910-5044-6(0) , Chelsea Hse.) Facts On File, Inc.

Love Is. 2004. lib. bdg. 15.30 (978-0-613-86963-8(X)) Tandem Library Bks.

Loyola, Mother Mary. The King of the Golden City: An Allegory for Children. Davis, John Watson, illus. 2nd ed. 2005. 128p. (J). per. (978-0-9764691-0-0(3)) Little Way Pr.

Loyola, Mother Mary. The King of the Golden City Study Edition, an Allegory for Children. 2007. 180p. (J). per. 18.95 (***978-1-934185-03-2(5)***) Biblio Resource Pubn.

Lozano, Neal. Can God See Me in the Dark? Hatke, Ben, illus. 2007. (J). (***978-1-883551-45-2(5)*** , Maple Corners Press) Attic Studio Publishing Hse.

Lucado, Max. Because I Love You. Heinze, Mitchell, illus. 2005. 28p. (ps-k). bds. 6.99 (978-1-58134-273-4(X) , Crossway Bibles); 1999. 32p. (gr. 1-3). 15.99 (978-0-89107-992-7(0)) Crossway Bks.

—Buzby & the Grumble Bees. 2007. (Max Lucado's Hermie & Friends Ser.). 38p. (J). bds. 12.99 (***978-1-4003-0913-9(1)***) Nelson, Thomas Inc.

—Colors. 2004. (Buginnings Ser.: Vol. 2). (Illus.). 24p. (J). 9.99 (978-1-4003-0422-6(9)) Nelson, Thomas Inc.

—Coming Home. 2007. (Illus.). 32p. (J). 15.99 (***978-1-58134-756-2(1)***) Crossway Bks.

—Flo the Lyin' Fly. 2004. (Max Lucado's Hermie & Friends Ser.). 24p. (J). bds. 6.99 (978-1-4003-0417-2(2)) Nelson, Thomas Inc.

—Hermie: A Common Caterpillar. 2002. (Max Lucado's Hermie & Friends Ser.). 16p. (J). bds. 6.99 (978-1-4003-0126-3(2)) Nelson, Thomas Inc.

—Hermie y sus Amigos: Atrapado en una cueva Apestosa. 2003. Tr. of Hermie & Friends: Trapped in a Stinky Den. 24p. bds. 4.99 (978-0-88113-781-1(2)) Grupo Nelson.

—Just in Case You Ever Wonder. 2007. 24p. (J). 15.99 (978-1-4003-0878-1(X)); 2000. (Illus.). 16p. (YA). bds. 6.99 (978-0-8499-7509-7(3)) Nelson, Thomas Inc.

—Just in Case You Ever Wonder - No Jacket. 2005. 32p. 9.99 (978-1-4003-0740-1(6)) Nelson, Thomas Inc.

—The Oak Inside the Acorn. Angelini, George, illus. 2006. 48p. (J). 16.99 (978-1-4003-0601-5(9)) Nelson, Thomas Inc.

—Tell Me the Story. DiCianni, Ron, illus. 2nd ed. 2005. 59p. (J). 16.99 (978-1-58134-523-0(2) , Crossway Bibles) Crossway Bks.

—With You All the Way. Gillies, Chuck, illus. 2005. Orig. Title: Song of the King. 31p. (J). (ps-3). 15.99 (978-1-58134-210-9(1) , Crossway Bibles) Crossway Bks.

—You Are Mine. 2004. (Max Lucado's Wemmicks Ser.). 24p. (J). bds. 6.99 (978-1-4003-0415-8(6)) Nelson, Thomas Inc.

—You Are Special. Martinez, Sergio, illus. rev. ed. 2007. 32p. 19.99 (***978-1-58134-894-1(0)***) Crossway Bks.

—You Are Special. 2004. (Max Lucado's Wemmicks Ser.). 24p. (J). bds. 6.99 (978-1-4003-0414-1(8)) Nelson, Thomas Inc.

—You Are Special: A Story for Everyone. Martinez, Sergio, illus. gif. ed. 2005. (Wemmicks Ser.). 46p. (ps-3). 10.99 (978-1-58134-405-9(8) , Crossway Bibles) Crossway Bks.

Lucado, Max, creator. Hermie, A Common Caterpillar. 2006. 38p. (J). bds. 12.99 (978-1-4003-0888-0(7)) Nelson, Thomas Inc.

—To Share or Nut to Share. 2006. (Max Lucado's Hermie & Friends Ser.). (Illus.). 24p. (J). bds. 12.99 (978-1-4003-0776-0(7)) Nelson, Thomas Inc.

—Webster, la Aranita Miedosa. 2005. (Max Lucado's Hermie & Friends Ser.: Vol. 3). (SPA.). 48p. (J). 10.99 (978-0-88113-691-3(3)) Grupo Nelson.

Lucado, Max & Max Lucado's Hermie and Friends Staff. Buzby, la Abeja Mal Portada. 2005. (Max Lucado's Hermie & Friends Ser.: Vol. 4). (SPA.). 48p. (J). 10.99 (978-0-88113-864-1(9)) Grupo Nelson.

Lucado, Max & Schmidt, Troy. Flo, the Lyin' Fly. 2005. 32p. (J). pap. 3.99 (978-1-4003-0664-0(7)) Nelson, Thomas Inc.

—Webster, the Scaredy Spider. 2005. 32p. (J). pap. 3.99 (978-1-4003-0665-7(5)) Nelson, Thomas Inc.

Luchsinger, Dena Fox. Sometimes Smart Is Good: A Veces Es Bueno Ser Listo. Jerome, Karen A., illus. 2007. 32p. (J). (ps). 16.00 (978-0-8028-5215-1(7) , Eerdmans Bks For Young Readers) Eerdmans, William B. Publishing Co.

Lundy, Charlotte. Thank You, Ruth & Naomi. Waldrep, Evelyn L., ed. Sagasti, Miriam, illus. 2004. 32p. (gr. k-4). 15.95 (978-0-9741817-0-7(6)) Bay Light Publishing.

Lutz, Norma Jean. Carrie's Courage: Battling the Powers of Bigotry. 2005. (Sisters in Time Ser.). 144p. (J). pap. 4.97 (978-1-59310-656-0(4)) Barbour Publishing, Inc.

—Elise the Actress: Climax of the Civil War. 2005. (Sisters in Time Ser.). 141p. (J). (***978-1-4156-0075-7(9)***) Barbour Publishing, Inc.

—Escape from Slavery: A Family's Fight for Freedom. 1999. (American Adventure Ser.: No. 16). 144p. (J). (gr. 3-7). 11.95 (978-0-7910-5590-8(6) , Chelsea Hse.) Facts On File, Inc.

—Maggie's Choice: Jonathan Edwards & the Great Awakening. 1999. (American Adventure Ser.: No. 8). (Illus.). 144p. (J). (gr. 3-7). lib. bdg. 15.95 (978-0-7910-5048-4(3) , Chelsea Hse.) Facts On File, Inc.

—Trouble on the Ohio River: Drought Shuts Down a City, 1999. (American Adventure Ser.: No. 15). 144p. (J). (gr. 3-7). lib. bdg. 15.95 (978-0-7910-5588-5(4) , Chelsea Hse.) Facts On File, Inc.

MacDonald, George. At the Back of the North Wind. 1998. (Twelve-Point Ser.). 280p. reprint ed. lib. bdg. 25.00 (978-1-58287-015-1(2)) North Bks.

MacDonald, George. Ranald Bannerman's Boyhood. 2006. 63.99 (***978-1-4280-3039-8(5)***) IndyPublish.com.

MacDonald, Mindy. My Bible Storybook. 2005. (GodCounts Ser.). (Illus.). 24p. (J). bds. 14.99 (978-1-59052-410-7(1) , Multnomah Kidz) WaterBrook Pr.

MacGregor, Rob. Prophecy Rock. 1998. (J). (978-0-606-13725-6(4)) Tandem Library Bks.

MacHado, Ana Maria. Todo Al Mismo Tiempo Ahora. 2001. (SPA.). lib. bdg. 16.95 (978-0-613-83564-0(6)) Tandem Library Bks.

MacKall, Dandi Daley. All the King's Horses, Vol. 8. 2001. (Horsefeathers Ser.: Vol. 8). (Illus.). 192p. (J). (gr. 7-11). 5.99 (978-0-570-07129-7(1)) Concordia Publishing Hse.

—All the King's Horses. 2001. (gr. 7-12). lib. bdg. 14.15 (978-0-613-72846-1(7)) Tandem Library Bks.

—The Cinnamon Lake-Ness Monster. 1998. (Cinnamon Lake Mysteries Ser.: Vol. 7). 80p. (J). (gr. 1-4). 5.99 (978-0-570-05336-1(6) , 12-3384) Concordia Publishing Hse.

—Eager Star. 2002. (Winnie the Horse Gentler Ser.: Bk. 2). (Illus.). 208p. (J). (gr. 4-7). mass mkt. 5.99 (978-0-8423-5543-8(X)) Tyndale Hse. Pubs.

Mackall, Dandi Daley. A Gaggle of Geese & a Clutter of Cats. Hohn, David, illus. 2007. (Dandilion Rhymes Ser.). 32p. (J). (ps-3). 9.99 (***978-1-4000-7204-0(2)*** , WaterBrook Pr.) WaterBrook Pr.

—Grace Notes. 2006. (Faithgirlz Ser.). (Illus.). 128p. (J). pap. 6.99 (978-0-310-71093-6(6)) Zonderkidz.

—Grace under Pressure. 2007. (Faithgirlz!#8482; / Blog On! Ser.). 128p. (J). pap. 6.99 (978-0-310-71263-3(7)) Zonderkidz.

MacKall, Dandi Daley. Home Is Where Your Horse Is, Vol. 6. 2000. (Horsefeathers Ser.: Vol. 6). (Illus.). 192p. (J). (gr. 7-11). 5.99 (978-0-570-07087-0(2)) Concordia Publishing Hse.

—Home Is Where Your Horse Is. 2000. (gr. 7-12). lib. bdg. 14.15 (978-0-613-72790-7(8)) Tandem Library Bks.

—Horse Angels, Vol. 5. 2000. (Horsefeathers Ser.: Vol. 5). (Illus.). 192p. (J). (gr. 7-11). 5.99 (978-0-570-07086-3(4)) Concordia Publishing Hse.

—Horse Angels. 2000. (gr. 7-12). lib. bdg. 14.15 (978-0-613-72789-1(4)) Tandem Library Bks.

—Horse Cents, Vol. 2. 2000. (Horsefeathers Ser.: Vol. 2). 192p. (J). (gr. 7-11). 5.99 (978-0-570-07007-8(4)) Concordia Publishing Hse.

—Horse Cents. 2000. (gr. 7-12). lib. bdg. 14.15 (978-0-613-72830-0(0)) Tandem Library Bks.

—Horse of a Different Color, Vol. 4. 2000. (Horsefeathers Ser.: Vol. 4). 192p. (YA). (gr. 7-11). 5.99 (978-0-570-07009-2(0)) Concordia Publishing Hse.

—Horse of a Different Color. 2000. (gr. 7-12). lib. bdg. 14.15 (978-0-613-72832-4(7)) Tandem Library Bks.

—Horse Whispers in the Air, Vol. 3. 2000. (Horsefeathers Ser.: Vol. 3). 192p. (YA). (gr. 7-11). 5.99 (978-0-570-07008-5(2)) Concordia Publishing Hse.

—Horse Whispers in the Air. 2000. (gr. 7-12). lib. bdg. 14.15 (978-0-613-72831-7(9)) Tandem Library Bks.

—Horsefeathers. 2000. (Horsefeathers Ser.: Vol. 1). (Illus.). 192p. (YA). (gr. 7-11). 5.99 (978-0-570-07006-1(6)) Concordia Publishing Hse.

—Horsefeathers. 2000. (gr. 7-12). lib. bdg. 14.15 (978-0-613-72829-4(7)) Tandem Library Bks.

—Horsefeathers Mystery, Vol. 7. 2001. (Horsefeathers Ser.: Vol. 7). (Illus.). 192p. (J). (gr. 7-12). 5.99 (978-0-570-07128-0(3)) Concordia Publishing Hse.

—Horsefeathers Set, 8 vols. 2004. (YA). 44.99 (978-0-7586-0009-7(7)) Concordia Publishing Hse.

Mackall, Dandi Daley. Just Jazz Bk. 3: Blog On! 2006. (Faithgirlz Ser.). (Illus.). 128p. (J). pap. 6.99 (978-0-310-71095-0(2)) Zonderkidz.

—Love, Annie. 2006. (Faithgirlz Ser.: Bk. 2). 128p. (J). pap. 6.99 (978-0-310-71094-3(4)) Zonderkidz.

MacKall, Dandi Daley. Made for a Purpose. Dibley, Glin, illus. 2004. 40p. (J). 15.99 (978-0-310-70953-4(9)) Zonderkidz.

—The Presidential Mystery. 1999. (Cinnamon Lake Mysteries Ser.: Vol. 8). 80p. (J). (ps-2). 5.99 (978-0-570-05354-5(4) , 12-3405GJ) Concordia Publishing Hse.

Mackall, Dandi Daley. Storm Rising Bk. 4: Blog On! 2006. (Faithgirlz Ser.). (Illus.). 128p. (J). pap. 6.99 (978-0-310-71096-7(0)) Zonderkidz.

—The Treetops Are Whispering. Nguyen, Vincent, illus. 2007. 16p. (J). 8.99 (978-1-4169-1496-9(X) , Little Simon Inspirations) Simon & Schuster Children's Publishing.

—Upsetting Annie. 2007. (Faithgirlz!#8482; / Blog On! Ser.). 128p. (J). pap. 6.99 (978-0-310-71264-0(5)) Zonderkidz.

MacKall, Dandi Daley. Wild Thing. 2002. (Winnie The Horse Gentler Ser.: 1). (Illus.). 192p. (J). mass mkt. 5.99 (978-0-8423-5542-1(1)) Tyndale Hse. Pubs.

MacKall, Dandi Daley & Kucharik, Elena. God Created Me! A Memory Book of Baby's First Year. 2002. (Little Blessings Ser.). (Illus.). 64p. 18.99 (978-0-8423-3958-2(2)) Tyndale Hse. Pubs.

Mackenzie, Catherine. I Can Say to God, I Love You. 10p. (J). 3.99 (978-1-85792-692-7(7) , Christian Focus) Christian Focus Pubns. GBR. *Dist:* Riverside.

—I Can Say to God, I'm Sorry. 10p. (J). 3.99 (978-1-85792-689-7(7) , Christian Focus) Christian Focus Pubns. GBR. *Dist:* Riverside.

—I Can Say to God, Thank You. 10p. (J). 3.99 (978-1-85792-690-3(0) , Christian Focus) Christian Focus Pubns. GBR. *Dist:* Riverside.

MacLean, Christine Kole. How It's Done. 2006. 336p. (J). (gr. 9 up). 15.95 (978-0-7387-1029-7(6) , Flux) Llewellyn Pubns.

Macleod, Norman. The Gold Thread. 2002. 15.95 (978-1-888692-08-2(1)) Whole Heart Ministries.

MacMullen, Grace Rice. A Reward for Jerry. 2000. 96p. (J). (gr. 3-7). pap. 2.95 (978-0-87398-707-3(1)) Sword of the Lord Pubs.

Maines, David. Tales of the Resistance. 2004. 20.00 (978-1-58474-053-7(1)) Cornerstone Family Ministries/ Lamplighter Publishing.

Maizel, Karen, illus. Jake Helps Out. 2007. (I Can Read!). 32p. (J). pap. 3.99 (***978-0-310-71457-6(5)***) Zonderkidz.

—Jake Plays Ball. 2007. (I Can Read!). 32p. (J). pap. 3.99 (***978-0-310-71455-2(9)***) Zonderkidz.

—Jake's Brave Night. 2007. (I Can Read!). 32p. (J). pap. 3.99 (***978-0-310-71456-9(7)***) Zonderkidz.

Malak, Annabel. L' Alchimiste. Beaudoin, Marie-Jose, illus. Tr. of Alchemist. (FRE.). (J). audio, audio compact disk 14.95 (978-2-921997-29-4(0)) Coffragants CAN. *Dist:* Penton Overseas, Inc.

Malanga, Tara & O'Keefe, Susan Heyboer. Sleepy Angel's First Bedtime Story. 2000. (Illus.). 32p. (ps-2). 9.95 (978-0-8091-6670-1(4) , 6670-4) Paulist Pr.

Malison, Anna. Through Thick & Thin. 2006. (ENG.). 136p. per. (978-1-897117-14-9(0)) Gospel Folio Pr.

Mangum, Erynn. Miss Match. 2007. 336p. pap. 12.99 (978-1-60006-095-3(1) , Th1nk Bks.) NavPress Publishing Group.

Mangum, Kay Lynn. When the Bough Breaks. 2007. 352p. (YA). pap. 15.95 (***978-1-59038-748-1(1)***) Deseret Bk. Co.

Manning, Brennan. The Boy Who Cried Abba: A Parable of Trust & Acceptance. 2001. 85p. (J). pap. 13.95 (978-1-879290-19-8(7) , PageMill Pr.) Council Oak Bks.

Margallo, Ramon. The MANGER, the CROSS, & the EMPTY TOMB Christian Apologetics for Young Readers: A Short Story. 2006. 108p. pap. 9.99 (978-1-4116-5751-9(9)) Lulu.com.

Marlow, Susan K. Andrea Carter & the Long Ride Home. 2005. 128p. (J). (ps-7). pap. 7.99 (978-0-8254-3188-3(3)) Kregel Pubns.

Marston, Hope Irvin. Against the Tide: The Valor of Margaret Wilson. 2007. (J). pap. (***978-1-59638-061-5(6)***) P & R Publishing.

Martin. The Cobbler. 1998. 32p. (J). (ps-2). (978-0-7459-3815-8(9)) Cook, David C. Publishing Co.

Martin, LaJoyce. The Silver Ghost. 2004. (Illus.). 161p. (J). pap. 9.99 (978-1-56722-643-0(4)) Word Aflame Pr.

Martini, T. J. Christmas Lost & Found. Kiejna, Magdalenea, illus. 2007. (J). per. 15.99 (***978-0-9705018-7-5(0)***) Wings, Inc.

Maryon, Laura. Mittens, Mittens & More Mittens! Callahan, Pat, illus. 1998. 32p. (J). (ps-1). pap. 11.99 (978-1-57921-138-7(0)) WinePress Publishing.

Maselli, Christopher P. N. Attack of the Tremendous Truth! Ages 8-12: 12 Mystery Stories to Solve Using the Teachings of Jesus. 2006. 48p. pap. (978-1-59441-385-8(1)) Carson-Dellosa Publishing Co., Inc.

—Dangerous Encounters Bk. 5: Tangled Truths & Twisted Tales—Exposed! 2003. (Illus.). 128p. (J). pap. 4.99 (978-0-310-70664-9(5)) Zonderkidz.

—Double-Take: Things Are Not What They Seem. 2002. (2:52 Soul Gear Ser.). (Illus.). 128p. (J). pap. 4.99 (978-0-310-70339-6(5)) Zonderkidz.

—Escape from Jungle Island. 1998. (Commander Kellie & the Superkids' Early Adventures Ser.). (J). pap. (978-1-57562-217-0(3)) Copeland, Kenneth Pubns.

—The Gifts from Outer Space Ages 8-12: 12 Mystery Stories to Solve Using Spiritual Gifts. 2006. 48p. pap. (978-1-59441-386-5(X)) Carson-Dellosa Publishing Co., Inc.

—Hot Pursuit Bk. 6: Steer Clear of Golden Opportunities. 2003. 128p. (J). pap. 4.99 (978-0-310-70665-6(3)) Zonderkidz.

—In Pursuit of the Enemy. 1998. (Commander Kellie & the Superkids' Early Adventures Ser.). (J). pap. (978-1-57562-218-7(1)) Copeland, Kenneth Pubns.

—The Mysterious Presence. 1998. (Commander Kellie & the Superkids' Early Adventures Ser.). pap. (978-1-57562-215-6(7)) Copeland, Kenneth Pubns.

—Power Play: Beware of Broken Promises. 2003. (2:52 Soul Gear Ser.). (Illus.). 128p. (J). pap. 4.99 (978-0-310-70341-9(7)) Zonderkidz.

—The Quest for the Second Half. 1998. (Commander Kellie & the Superkids' Early Adventures Ser.). (J). pap. (978-1-57562-216-3(5)) Copeland, Kenneth Pubns.

Maselli, Christopher P. N. The Runaway Mission. 2004. 104p. (***978-1-57562-805-9(8)***) Copeland, Kenneth Pubns.

Maselli, Christopher P. N. & Zondervan. Reality Shift: They Changed the Future. 2002. (Illus.). 144p. (J). pap. 4.99 (978-0-310-70338-9(7)) Zonderkidz.

Maslyn, Stacie K. B. Mad Maddie Maxwell. 2004. (ps-2). lib. bdg. 13.00 (978-0-613-71695-6(7)) Tandem Library Bks.

—Mad Maddie Maxwell. Schettle, Jane, illus. 2004. 24p. (J). pap. 4.99 (978-0-310-70817-9(6)) Zonderkidz.

—Mad Maddie Maxwell. 2000. (Illus.). 24p. (J). 7.99 (978-0-310-23207-0(4)) Zondervan.

Mason, Phil & Watts, Murray. Children on the Loose. 2001. (Monarch Humor Bks.). (Illus.). 96p. pap. 3.99 (978-0-8254-5996-2(6)) Kregel Pubns.

Massi, Jeri. Some Through the Fire, 2 vols. 2003. (Great Stories That Teach Eternal Truths Ser.). 496p. pap. 12.99 (978-0-8024-1513-4(X)) Moody Pubs.

Max Lucado's Hermie & Friends. Milo, the Mantis Who Wouldn't Pray. 2007. (Max Lucado's Hermie & Friends Ser.). 38p. (J). bds. 12.99 (978-1-4003-0873-6(9)) Nelson, Thomas Inc.

McCaughrean, Geraldine. Pilgrim's Progress. Cockcroft, Jason, illus. 112p. (J). pap. 16.99 (978-0-340-72754-6(3)); 144p. mass mkt. 9.99 (978-0-340-84410-6(8)) Hodder General Publishing Division GBR. (Hodder & Stoughton). *Dist:* Trafalgar Square Publishing.

McConnaughhay, JoDee. Be Brave, Anna! God Helps Me When I'm Afraid. Caldwell, Lise, ed. Dubin, Jill, illus. 1999. (Happy Day Bks.). 24p. (J). (ps-2). 2.49 (978-0-7847-0895-8(9), 04268, Bean Sprouts) Standard Publishing.

—Tell the Truth, Tyler! Ring, Laura, ed. Urbanovic, Jackie, illus. 1999. (Happy Day Bks.). 24p. (J). (ps-2). 2.49 (978-0-7847-1048-7(1), 04278, Bean Sprouts) Standard Publishing.

McCusker, Paul. Arin's Judgment. 2005. (Adventures in Odyssey Passages Ser.). 192p. (J). pap. 7.99 (978-1-58997-168-4(X)) Focus on the Family Publishing.

—Danger Lies Ahead. 2006. (Adventures in Odyssey Ser.: No. 2). 336p. (J). pap. 13.99 (978-1-58997-329-9(1)) Focus on the Family Publishing.

—Darien's Rise. 2005. (Adventures in Odyssey Passages Ser.). 208p. (J). pap. 7.99 (978-1-58997-167-7(1)) Focus on the Family Publishing.

—Draven's Defiance. 2006. (Adventures in Odyssey Passages Ser.). 192p. (J). pap. 7.99 (978-1-58997-177-6(9)) Focus on the Family Publishing.

—Fendar's Legacy. 2006. (Adventures in Odyssey Passages Ser.). 192p. (J). pap. 7.99 (978-1-58997-178-3(7)) Focus on the Family Publishing.

—Point of No Return. 2006. (Adventures in Odyssey Bks.). 336p. (J). pap. 13.99 (978-1-58997-332-9(1)) Focus on the Family Publishing.

McCutchan, Betty. First Things First. 2001. 96p. (J). pap. 9.95 (978-1-57736-247-0(0)) Providence Hse Pubs.

McDaniel, Lurlene. Angel of Hope. 2000. (Mercy Trilogy). 240p. (YA). (gr. 7-12). pap. 4.99 (978-0-553-57148-6(6), Laurel Leaf) Random Hse. Children's Bks.

—Holly's Story. 2005. (Angels in Pink Ser.). 224p. (gr. 7). (YA). 10.95 (978-0-385-73158-4(2)); (J). lib. bdg. 12.99 (978-0-385-90195-6(X)) Random Hse. Children's Bks. (Delacorte Bks. for Young Readers).

—Raina's Story. (Angels in Pink Ser.). 208p. (gr. 7). 2006. (YA). pap. 6.50 (978-0-440-23866-9(8), Laurel Leaf); 2005. (J). lib. bdg. 12.99 (978-0-385-90194-9(1), Delacorte Bks. for Young Readers) Random Hse. Children's Bks.

—Until Angels Close My Eyes. 1998. (Angels Trilogy: No. 3). 256p. (YA). (gr. 7-12). pap. 5.50 (978-0-553-57115-8(X), Laurel Leaf) Random Hse. Children's Bks.

—Until Angels Close My Eyes. 1998. (Angels Trilogy: No. 3). (978-0-606-13884-0(6)) Tandem Library Bks.

McDowell, Josh. Deceivers Book for Youth. 2003. (gr. 7-12). lib. bdg. 19.95 (978-0-613-76719-4(5)) Tandem Library Bks.

McDowell, Josh & Hostetler, Bob. The Truth Twisters. 2006. 170p. (YA). pap. 11.99 (978-1-932587-84-5(5)) Green Key Bks.

McKnight, Penny. Nix. 2006. (Illus.). 84p. (J). (978-1-59166-610-3(4)) Jones, Bob Univ. Pr.

McLernon, Carol M. Overlooking Stoneybrook. 1998. 80p. (J). (gr. 6-9). pap. 8.00 (978-1-57502-864-4(6), PO2356) Morris Publishing.

Mead, David. Ark Angels: Play & Pray. Penton Overseas, Inc. Staff, ed. Currant, Gary, illus. 2006. 16p. (J). (gr. 3-8). bds. 9.95 (978-1-59125-746-2(8), Penton Kids) Penton Overseas, Inc.

Medina, Tony. Christmas Makes Me Think. Cox, Chandra, illus. 2001. 32p. (J). (gr. 1-7). (978-1-58430-024-3(8)) Lee & Low Bks., Inc.

Merkel, Ruth. Hannah's Girls: Ann. 2006. 112p. (J). pap. 9.99 (***978-0-8280-1951-4(7)***) Review & Herald Publishing Assn.

—Hannah's Girls: Grace, 6. 2006. (Illus.). 128p. (J). pap. 9.99 (***978-0-8280-1953-8(3)***) Review & Herald Publishing Assn.

—Hannah's Girls: Marilla, 6 bks. 2006. (Illus.). 144p. (J). pap. 9.99 (***978-0-8280-1952-1(5)***) Review & Herald Publishing Assn.

—Hannah's Girls: Ruthie. 2007. 144p. (J). pap. 9.99 (***978-0-8280-1954-5(1)***) Review & Herald Publishing Assn.

Metaxas, Eric. God Made You Special. 2002. (Big Idea Books Ser.). (Illus.). 18p. bds. 6.99 (978-0-310-70466-9(9)) Zondervan.

Metzger, Kenneth. The Potter's Perfect Piece. 2007. 48p. (J). 19.99 (***978-1-57921-876-8(8)***) WinePress Publishing.

Meyer, Jane. The Man & the Vine. 2006. (Illus.). 32p. (J). 18.00 (978-0-88141-315-1(1)) St. Vladimir's Seminary Pr.

Miller, Christian. The Champagne Sandwich. l.t. ed. 2003. (Isis Hardcover Ser.). (Illus.). 240p. (J). 32.50 (978-0-7531-6887-5(1)) ISIS Large Print Bks. GBR. *Dist:* Ulverscroft Large Print Bks., Ltd.

Miller, David. Heat 16. 2003. 110p. (YA). pap. 9.95 (978-0-595-27424-6(2), Mystery & Suspense Pr.) iUniverse, Inc.

Miller, Gary & Miller, Lynda. The Adventures of Bob & Betty. 2006. (J). spiral bd. (978-1-933594-92-7(6)) Faith Baptist Church Publns.

Miller, Mary. Where Angels Sing. 1998. (Illus.). pap. 7.50 (978-1-884377-04-4(1)) Green Pastures Pr.

Miller, Paula. One-Eyed Jack. Forrest, Chris, illus. 144p. (J). 2007. per. 8.95 (978-0-9769417-0-5(8)); 2006. 13.95 (978-0-9718348-8-0(1)) Blooming Tree Pr.

Milliman, Linda & Soles, Gail. Briny the Starfish. 2002. (Illus.). 26p. (J). (ps-4). pap. 15.00 (978-0-9717603-0-1(6)) Isaiah's Promise Publishing Co.

Mills, Charles. The Bandit of Benson Park. 2003. (Honors Club Story Ser.: Vol. 1). 127p. (J). (978-0-8163-1977-0(4)) Pacific Pr. Pubns.

—The Great Sleepy-Time Stew Rescue. 2004. (Honors Club Story Ser.: Vol. 4). (Illus.). 127p. (J). (978-0-8163-2009-7(8)) Pacific Pr. Publishing Assn.

—The Secret of Scarlett Cove. 2004. (Honors Club Story Ser.: Bk. 3). 127p. (J). (978-0-8163-1999-2(5)) Pacific Pr. Publishing Assn.

—Storm on Shadow Mountain. 2003. 127p. (J). (978-0-8163-1993-0(6)) Pacific Pr. Publishing Assn.

—The Truth Trackers. 2001. 144p. (YA). pap. 7.99 (978-0-8280-1462-5(0)) Review & Herald Publishing Assn.

—Wings over Oshkosh. 2005. (Honors Club Story Ser.: Vol. 5). 127p. (J). (978-0-8163-2089-9(6)) Pacific Pr. Publishing Assn.

Mills, Claudia. Perfectly Chelsea. Rogers, Jacqueline, illus. 2004. 128p. (J). 16.00 (978-0-374-31244-2(3), Farrar, Straus & Giroux (BYR)) Farrar, Straus & Giroux.

Mills, Omar K. Mote-Beam Theory. 2001. (gr. 7-12). lib. bdg. 25.70 (978-0-613-79866-2(X)) Tandem Library Bks.

Mishica, Clare & Keefer, Mikal. Surprising Stories: 3 Fun-to-Read-Aloud Stories with a Message. Girouard, Patrick et al, illus. 1999. (Read-Aloud Stories Ser.). 24p. (J). (ps-3). 5.99 (978-0-7847-0969-6(6), 03730, Bean Sprouts) Standard Publishing.

Mission City Press, adapted by. Violet Travilla Boxed Set Books 1-4. 2004. (Life of Faith Ser.). 240p. (YA). 44.99 (978-1-928749-67-7(4)) Zondervan.

Mission City Press Inc. Staff. Elsie's Daily Diary: A Personal Journal for Girls. 2001. (Elsie Dinsmore). 192p. (YA). (gr. 5-9). 14.99 (978-1-928749-50-9(X)) Zonderkidz.

Mission City Press Inc. Staff & Debeasi, Elizabeth. Elsie's Life Lessons: Walking in the Fruit of the Spirit. 2001. (Elsie Dinsmore). (Illus.). 160p. (J). (gr. 5-9). pap. 12.99 (978-1-928749-51-6(8)) Zonderkidz.

Mission City Press Staff. Millie's Reluctant Sacrifice, Bk. 7. 2003. (Life of Faith Ser.). 224p. (YA). 12.99 (978-1-928749-15-8(1)) Zonderkidz.

Mitzo Thompson, Kim. Inspirational, 2 Packs. 2006. (Read & Sing along Board Books with CDs Ser.). 36p. (J). bds., bds. 14.98 incl. audio compact disk (978-0-7696-4593-3(3)) School Specialty Publishing.

Montgomery Gibson, Jane. Don't Renege! It's Just an Egg! Montgomery Gibson, Jane, illus. 2005. (J). bds. 8.99 (978-1-4183-0036-4(5)) Christ Inspired, Inc.

—Jesus' Bread. Montgomery Gibson, Jane, illus. 2005. (J). bds. 8.99 (978-1-4183-0028-9(4)) Christ Inspired, Inc.

Montgomery, Bobbie. Fruit Tramp Kids. 2000. (Pathfinder Junior Book Club Ser.). 143p. (J). (gr. 4-7). pap. 6.99 (978-0-8280-1422-9(1)) Review & Herald Publishing Assn.

Montgomery Gibson, Jane. Claire, Claire! Wash Your Hair! Montgomery Gibson, Jane, illus. 2005. (J). bds. 8.99 (978-1-4183-0044-9(6)) Christ Inspired, Inc.

—Gracie Got Glasses. Montgomery Gibson, Jane, illus. 2005. (J). bds. 8.99 (978-1-4183-0039-5(X)) Christ Inspired, Inc.

—How Do You Clean a Ballerina? Montgomery Gibson, Jane, illus. 2005. (J). bds. 8.99 (978-1-4183-0020-3(9)) Christ Inspired, Inc.

—Jesus Smith or Jones. Montgomery Gibson, Jane, illus. 2005. (YA). bds. 8.99 (978-1-4183-0031-9(4)) Christ Inspired, Inc.

—Mabel at the Table. Montgomery Gibson, Jane, illus. 2005. (J). bds. 8.99 (978-1-4183-0041-8(1)) Christ Inspired, Inc.

—Maggie Makeup. Montgomery Gibson, Jane, illus. 2005. (J). bds. 9.99 (978-1-4183-0030-2(6)) Christ Inspired, Inc.

—Pink Potatoes. Montgomery Gibson, Jane, illus. 2005. (J). bds. 8.99 (978-1-4183-0038-8(1)) Christ Inspired, Inc.

—Sit down, Clown! Montgomery Gibson, Jane, illus. 2005. (J). bds. 8.99 (978-1-4183-0040-1(3)) Christ Inspired, Inc.

Moore, Stephanie Perry. Absolutely Worthy, Vol. 4. 2003. (Laurel Shadrach Ser.: Vol. 4). 192p. (YA). pap. 6.99 (978-0-8024-4038-9(X)) Moody Pubs.

—Absolutely Worthy. 2003. (gr. 7-12). lib. bdg. 15.30 (978-0-613-90338-7(2)) Tandem Library Bks.

—Equally Yoked, Vol. 3. 2003. (Laurel Shadrach Ser.: Vol. 3). 192p. (YA). pap. 6.99 (978-0-8024-4037-2(1)) Moody Pubs.

—Equally Yoked. 2003. (gr. 7-12). lib. bdg. 15.30 (978-0-613-90874-0(0)) Tandem Library Bks.

—Finally Sure, Vol. 5. 2004. (Laurel Shadrach Ser.). 208p. (YA). pap. 6.99 (978-0-8024-4039-6(8)) Moody Pubs.

—God Can Work It Out. 2007. (Illus.). 144p. (YA). pap. 11.99 (978-0-7369-1919-7(8)) Harvest Hse. Pubs.

—The Payton Skky Series. 2002. (Payton Skky Ser.). 904p. (YA). pap. 29.97 (978-0-8024-4046-4(0)) Moody Pubs.

—Purity Reigns. 2002. (Laurel Shadrach Ser.: Vol. 1). 240p. (YA). pap. 6.99 (978-0-8024-4035-8(5)) Moody Pubs.

—Purity Reigns. 2002. (gr. 7-12). lib. bdg. 15.30 (978-0-613-90559-6(8)) Tandem Library Bks.

—Saved Race, Vol. 3. 2001. (Payton Skky Ser.). 160p. (YA). (gr. 7-13). pap. 6.99 (978-0-8024-4238-3(2)) Moody Pubs.

—Saved Race. 2001. (gr. 7-12). lib. bdg. 15.30 (978-0-613-88831-8(6)) Tandem Library Bks.

—Surrendered Heart. 2002. (gr. 7-12). lib. bdg. 15.30 (978-0-613-84490-1(4)) Tandem Library Bks.

—Totally Free, Vol. 2. 2002. (Laurel Shadrach Ser.: Vol. 2). 208p. (YA). pap. 6.99 (978-0-8024-4036-5(3)) Moody Pubs.

—Totally Free. 2002. (gr. 3-6). lib. bdg. 15.30 (978-0-613-90336-3(6)) Tandem Library Bks.

—True Friends. 2005. (Carmen Browne Ser.). 128p. (YA). pap. 5.99 (978-0-8024-8172-6(8)) Moody Pubs.

Moroney, Tracey, illus. Follow the Star. 1999. (Christmas Bible Play Bks.). 18p. (ps-k). 5.99 (978-0-7847-1050-0(3), 03998, Bean Sprouts) Standard Publishing.

Morris, Gilbert. Dixie & Dolly. 1998. (Dixie Morris Animal Adventure Ser.: No. 3). 160p. (J). (gr. 4-7). pap. 5.99 (978-0-8024-3365-7(0)) Moody Pubs.

—Dixie & Sandy. 1998. (Dixie Morris Animal Adventure Ser.: No. 4). 128p. (Orig.). (J). (gr. 4-7). pap. 5.99 (978-0-8024-3366-4(9)) Moody Pubs.

—Dixie & Stripes. 1998. (Dixie Morris Animal Adventure Ser.: No. 2). 128p. (J). (gr. 4-7). pap. 5.99 (978-0-8024-3364-0(2)) Moody Pubs.

—The Spell of the Crystal Chair. 2000. (Seven Sleepers the Lost Chronicles Ser.: Vol. 1). (Illus.). 160p. (J). (gr. 7-12). pap. 5.99 (978-0-8024-3667-2(6)) Moody Pubs.

—Temptations of Pleasure Island. 2000. (gr. 3-6). lib. bdg. 14.15 (978-0-613-86933-1(8)) Tandem Library Bks.

—Too Smart Jones & the Cat's Secret: A Gilbert Morris Mystery. 2000. (Gilbert Morris Mysteries Ser.: Vol. 6). (Illus.). 124p. (J). (gr. 2-7). pap. 5.99 (978-0-8024-4030-3(4)) Moody Pubs.

—Too Smart Jones & the Disappearing Dogs: A Gilbert Morris Mystery. 2000. (Gilbert Morris Mysteries Ser.: Vol. 3). (Illus.). 128p. (J). (gr. 4-7). pap. 5.99 (978-0-8024-4027-3(4)) Moody Pubs.

—Too Smart Jones & the Pool Party Thief: A Gilbert Morris Mystery. 1999. (Gilbert Morris Mysteries Ser.: Vol. 1). (Illus.). 115p. (J). (gr. 2-7). pap. 5.99 (978-0-8024-4025-9(8)) Moody Pubs.

—Too Smart Jones & the Stolen Bicycle: A Gilbert Morris Mystery. 2000. (Gilbert Morris Mysteries Ser.: Vol. 9). (Illus.). 133p. (J). (gr. 4-7). pap. 5.99 (978-0-8024-4031-0(2)) Moody Pubs.

—Victims of Nimbo. 2000. (gr. 3-6). lib. bdg. 14.15 (978-0-613-88614-7(3)) Tandem Library Bks.

Muller, Mindy. Allie's Answers. ldr.'s ed. 2004. (Seekers Ser.). 3.99 (978-0-8066-4182-9(7)) Augsburg Fortress, Pubs.

Murphy, Elspeth Campbell & Bernal, Richard. Fifteen Flamingos. 2000. (Illus.). 32p. (J). (ps-k). 12.99 (978-0-7642-2201-6(5)) Bethany Hse. Pubs.

Murray, Mary. Larry Lights the Way. 2003. (Big Idea Bks.). 40p. 9.99 (978-0-310-70674-8(2)) Zonderkidz.

—A Picture That! Jonah. 2003. (Illus.). 24p. (J). pap. 6.99 (978-0-310-70470-6(7)) Zonderkidz.

Murray, Mary & Vischer, Lisa. Junior & Laura Share the Year Together. 2003. (Big Idea Bks.). 12p. 4.99 (978-0-310-70541-3(X)) Zonderkidz.

Muschla, Gary Robert. Crusader. 2006. (YA). pap. (978-0-88092-491-7(8)) Royal Fireworks Publishing Co.

Myers, Bill. Baseball for Breakfast: The Story of a Boy Who Hated to Wait. Riccio, Frank, illus. 2005. 29p. (J). (gr. 4-8). reprint ed. 15.00 (978-0-7567-9248-0(7)) DIANE Publishing Co.

—The Curse. 2002. (Forbidden Doors Ser.: Vol. 7). 176p. (J). mass mkt. 4.99 (978-0-8423-5739-5(4)) Tyndale Hse. Pubs.

—Eli. 2000. (gr. 3-6). lib. bdg. 22.25 (978-0-613-51822-2(5)) Tandem Library Bks.

—The Encounter. 2002. (Forbidden Doors Ser.: Vol. 6). 160p. (J). mass mkt. 4.99 (978-0-8423-5738-8(6)) Tyndale Hse. Pubs.

—The Haunting: The Forces of Heaven Battle the Presence of Evil. 2001. (Forbidden Doors Ser.: Vol. 4). 192p. (J). (gr. 5-9). mass mkt. 4.99 (978-0-8423-3991-9(4)) Tyndale Hse. Pubs.

—The House That Went Ker-Splat! The Parable of the Wise & Foolish Builder. Smith, Andy J., illus. 2008. (J). (***978-0-310-71220-6(3)***) Zonderkidz.

—My Life as a Belching Baboon with Bad Breath. 2006. (Incredible Worlds of Wally McDoogle Ser.). pap. 6.99 (978-1-4003-0907-8(7)) Nelson, Thomas Inc.

—My Life As a Broken Bungee Cord. Mangiat, Jeff, illus. 2005. (Incredible Worlds of Wally McDoogle Ser.: Vol. 3). 128p. (J). 9.99 (978-1-4003-0573-5(X)) Nelson, Thomas Inc.

—My Life as a Cowboy Cowpie, Vol. 19. 2001. (Incredible Worlds of Wally McDoogle Ser.: No. 19). 128p. (J). (gr. 3-7). pap. 6.99 (978-0-8499-5990-5(X)) Nelson, Thomas Inc.

—My Life As a Haunted Hamburger, Hold the Pickles. 2006. (Incredible Worlds of Wally McDoogle Ser.: No. 27). 128p. (J). pap. 6.99 (978-1-4003-0636-7(1)) Nelson, Thomas Inc.

—My Life as a Human Hairball, Vol. 15. 1998. (Incredible Worlds of Wally McDoogle Ser.: No. 15). 128p. (J). (gr. 3-7). pap. 6.99 (978-0-8499-4024-8(9)) Nelson, Thomas Inc.

—My Life as a Human Hockey Puck. Mangiat, Jeff, illus. 2005. (Incredible Worlds of Wally McDoogle Ser.: Vol. 7). 128p. (J). (ps-7). 9.99 (978-1-4003-0639-8(6)) Nelson, Thomas Inc.

—My Life as a Screaming Skydiver, Vol. 14. 1998. (Incredible Worlds of Wally McDoogle Ser.: No. 14). (Illus.). 128p. (J). (gr. 3-7). pap. 6.99 (978-0-8499-4023-1(0)) Nelson, Thomas Inc.

—My Life As a Smashed Burrito. 1999. (Incredible Worlds of Wally McDoogle Ser.: No. 1). 128p. (J). (gr. 3-7). pap. 1.99 (978-0-8499-7508-0(5)) Nelson, Thomas Inc.

—My Life As A Smashed Burrito. Mangiat, Jeff, illus. 2005. (Incredible Worlds of Wally McDoogle Ser.: Vol. 1). 128p. (J). 9.99 (978-1-4003-0571-1(3)) Nelson, Thomas Inc.

—My Life as a Splatted Flat Quarterback. 2006. (Incredible Worlds of Wally McDoogle Ser.). pap. 6.99 (978-1-4003-0906-1(9)) Nelson, Thomas Inc.

—My Life As a Stupendously Stomped Soccer Star. 2006. (Incredible Worlds of Wally McDoogle Ser.). 128p. (J). pap. 6.99 (978-1-4003-0635-0(3)) Nelson, Thomas Inc.

—My Life as a Torpedo Test Target. Mangiat, Jeff, illus. 2005. (Incredible Worlds of Wally McDoogle Ser.: Vol. 6). 128p. (J). (ps-7). 9.99 (978-1-4003-0638-1(8)) Nelson, Thomas Inc.

—My Life as Alien Monster Bait. Mangiat, Jeff, illus. 2005. (Incredible Worlds of Wally McDoogle Ser.: Vol. 2). 128p. (J). (ps-7). 9.99 (978-1-4003-0572-8(1)) Nelson, Thomas Inc.

—My Life as Crocodile Junk Food. Mangiat, Jeff, illus. 2005. (Incredible Worlds of Wally McDoogle Ser.). 128p. (J). 9.99 (978-1-4003-0613-8(2)) Nelson, Thomas Inc.

—My Life as Dinosaur Dental Floss. Mangiat, Jeff, illus. 2005. (Incredible Worlds of Wally McDoogle Ser.). 128p. (J). 9.99 (978-1-4003-0614-5(0)) Nelson, Thomas Inc.

—My Life As Invisible Intestines (with Intense Indigestion), Vol. 20. 2001. (Incredible Worlds of Wally McDoogle Ser.). 128p. (J). (gr. 3-7). pap. 6.99 (978-0-8499-5991-2(8)) Nelson, Thomas Inc.

—Phantom of the Haunted Church. 1998. (Bloodhounds, Inc. Ser.: Vol. 3). (Illus.). 128p. (J). (gr. 3-8). pap. 5.99 (978-1-55661-892-5(1)) Bethany Hse. Pubs.

—The Scream. 2002. (Forbidden Doors Ser.: 9). 176p. (J). mass mkt. 4.99 (978-0-8423-5741-8(6)) Tyndale Hse. Pubs.

—Sky Surfing Skateboarder, Vol. 21. 2002. (Incredible Worlds of Wally McDoogle Ser.). (Illus.). 128p. (J). (gr. 3-7). pap. 6.99 (978-0-8499-5992-9(6)) Nelson, Thomas Inc.

—The Society: Who Can Overcome the Powers of Darkness? 2001. (Forbidden Doors Ser.: Vol. 1). 160p. (J). (gr. 5-9). mass mkt. 4.99 (978-0-8423-3987-2(6)) Tyndale Hse. Pubs.

—Society: Who Can Overcome the Powers of Darkness? 2001. (gr. 5-8). lib. bdg. 10.65 (978-0-613-76838-2(8)) Tandem Library Bks.

—Spell. 2001. (gr. 5-8). lib. bdg. 13.00 (978-0-613-76839-9(6)) Tandem Library Bks.

—The Spell: Who Really Holds the Power? 2001. (Forbidden Doors Ser.: Vol. 3). 176p. (J). (gr. 5-9). mass mkt. 4.99 (978-0-8423-3989-6(2)) Tyndale Hse. Pubs.

Myers, Bill. Stink Bug Saves the Day! The Parable of the Good Samaritan. Smith, Andy J., illus. 2008. (J). (***978-0-310-71219-0(X)***) Zonderkidz.

Myers, Bill & Riordan, James. The Cards. 2003. (Forbidden Doors Ser.: Vol. 12). 192p. (J). mass mkt. 5.99 (978-0-8423-7185-8(0), 75 7185-0) Tyndale Hse. Pubs.

Myers, Bill & Wimbish, Dave. I Want My Mummy. 2000. (Bloodhounds, Inc. Ser.: Vol. 8). (Illus.). 128p. (J). (gr. 3-8). pap. 5.99 (978-1-55661-492-7(6)) Bethany Hse. Pubs.

Myers, Bill & Wimbish, David. Mystery of the Melodies from Mars. 2002. (Bloodhounds, Inc. Ser.: No. 11). 128p. (J). pap. 5.99 (978-0-7642-2623-6(1)) Bethany Hse. Pubs.

—Room with a Boo. 2002. (Bloodhounds Inc Ser.). 128p. (J). pap. 5.99 (978-0-7642-2624-3(X)) Bethany Hse. Pubs.

C
D

Myers, Martha. Nibbles, the Mostly Mischievous Monkey. 2003. (Julius & Friends Ser.: Vol. 10). (Illus.). 91p. (J). 6.99 (978-0-8163-1947-3(2)) Pacific Pr. Publishing Assn.

Mykowski, Michelle. Explore God's Forest. Ring, Laura, ed. Mykowski, Michelle, illus. 1999. (Shaped Paperback Bks.). (Illus.). 24p. (J). (ps-1). pap. 3.99 (978-0-7847-0900-9(9) , 03790, Bean Sprouts) Standard Publishing.

Myra, Harold Lawrence. Thanksgiving: What Makes It Special? Kurisu, Jane, illus. 2002. 32p. (J). (ps-3). 7.99 (978-1-4003-0006-8(1)) Nelson, Thomas Inc.

The Mystery of Veggie Island. 2003. (Big Idea Bks.). (978-0-310-70744-8(7)) Zondervan.

Narvaez, Concha Lopez. Endrina y el Secreto del Peregrino. (SPA.). 280p. (YA). (gr. 5-8). 7.60 (978-84-239-2785-2(7)); 16th ed. 2003. (Illus.). 206p. pap. (978-84-239-5899-3(X)) Espasa Calpe, S.A. ESP. *Dist:* Lectorum Pubns., Inc.

Nelson, Kadir A. He's Got the Whole World in His Hands. Nelson, Kadir A., illus. 2005. (Illus.). 32p. (J). (ps). 16.99 (978-0-8037-2850-9(6) , Dial) Penguin Group (USA) Inc.

Nelson, Kelly. Boreal, Dragon of the North. 2005. 68p. (YA). pap. 9.99 (978-1-4141-0292-4(5)) Pleasant Word.

Nelson, Sherrie. The Boy of Color. Cantrell, Jaquese, illus. 2006. 32p. (J). 12.99 (978-1-4003-0910-8(7)) Nelson, Thomas Inc.

Nesbit, Jeffrey Asher. Ryun's Story. 2004. (Degrees of Betrayal Ser.). 320p. (YA). pap. 9.99 (978-1-4143-0003-0(4)) Tyndale Hse. Pubs.

Newth, Mette. The Dark Light. Ingwersen, Faith, tr. 2004. 256p. (YA). reprint ed. pap. 6.95 (978-0-374-41688-1(5) , Sunburst) Farrar, Straus & Giroux.

Nicole, Karen. Bible Tells Me About. 1998. (Illus.). 32p. (J). (ps-3). pap. 1.11 (978-0-8280-0913-3(9)) Review & Herald Publishing Assn.

—I Like to Talk to God. 1998. (Illus.). 31p. (J). (ps-3). pap. 6.99 (978-0-8280-0912-6(0)) Review & Herald Publishing Assn.

Nobisso, Josephine. El Peso de Una Misa: Un Relato de fe. Szegedi, Katalin, illus. 2003. Orig. Title: The Weight of a Mass a Tale of Faith. (SPA.). 32p. 17.95 (978-0-940112-15-5(9)); pap. 9.95 (978-0-940112-17-9(5)) Gingerbread Hse.

—The Weight of a Mass: A Tale of Faith. Szegedi, Katalin, illus. 2002. (SPA.). 32p. (J). (gr. k-5). 17.95 (978-0-940112-09-4(4)); pap. 9.95 (978-0-940112-10-0(8)) Gingerbread Hse.

—Weight of a Mass: A Tale of Faith. 2003. (gr. k-3). lib. bdg. 18.75 (978-0-613-70732-9(X)) Tandem Library Bks.

Nolan, Han. If I Should Die Before I Wake. 2003. 312p. (YA). pap. 6.95 (978-0-15-204679-8(8) , Harcourt Paperbacks) Harcourt Children's Bks.

—Send Me down a Miracle. 2003. 276p. (YA). pap. 6.95 (978-0-15-204680-4(1)) Harcourt Children's Bks.

—Send Me down a Miracle. 2003. (gr. 7-12). lib. bdg. 15.25 (978-0-613-59926-9(8)) Tandem Library Bks.

—When We Were Saints. (YA). 2005. 312p. pap. 6.95 (978-0-15-205322-2(0) , Harcourt Paperbacks); 2003. (Illus.). 304p. 17.00 (978-0-15-216371-6(9) , 53586153) Harcourt Children's Bks.

Norman, Thelma G. A Wife Called Tommie. 2005. 226p. (J). per. 12.95 (978-1-57258-295-8(2)) TEACH Services, Inc.

Nowack, JoAnne Chitwood. A Horse Called Saskatoon. 2001. 128p. (J). pap. (978-0-8280-1562-2(7)) Review & Herald Publishing Assn.

—A Horse Called Tamarindo. 2001. (Horse Called Ser.: Vol. 5). (Illus.). 144p. (J). pap. 7.99 (978-0-8280-1499-1(X)) Review & Herald Publishing Assn.

Nye, Julie & Nye, Julie. Scout: The Secret at les Cheneaux. 2007. (Illus.). 160p. (YA). per. (***978-0-9767762-1-5(9)***) Fieldstone Hill Pr.

O'Day, Joseph E. I Like Snow! Foster, Ron, illus. 2006. 28p. (J). pap. (***978-1-929039-37-1(9)***) Ambassador Bks., Inc.

—I Like Sunshine! Foster, Ron, illus. 2007. (J). (***978-1-929039-41-8(7)***) Ambassador Bks., Inc.

—I Like Wind! Foster, Ron, illus. 2007. (J). (***978-1-929039-42-5(5)***) Ambassador Bks., Inc.

O'Hearn, Audrey. Me & Luke. 2005. 148p. (J). pap. 6.95 (978-0-88899-066-2(9)) Groundwood Bks. CAN. *Dist:* Perseus Distribution.

Oirich, Alan. The Amnesia Countdown. Randall, Ron, illus. 2003. (Jewish Hero Corps. Ser.: 1). 24p. (J). pap. 3.95 (978-1-932443-06-6(1) , JHC1, Shayach Comics) Judaica Pr., Inc., The.

Oke, Janette. Drums of Change: The Story of Running Fawn. 2003. (Classics for Girls Ser.). (Illus.). 176p. (J). 9.99 (978-0-7642-2714-1(9)) Bethany Hse. Pubs.

—Making Memories. Bladholm, Cheri, illus. 1999. 32p. (J). (ps-3). 14.99 (978-0-7642-2190-3(6)) Bethany Hse. Pubs.

—The Meeting Place. 1999. (Song of Acadia Ser.: Vol. 1). (gr. 7-12). lib. bdg. 21.10 (978-0-613-23358-3(1)) Tandem Library Bks.

Oneal, Katherine. Family Series Silly Family. 2008. (J). (***978-0-310-70987-9(3)***) Zonderkidz.

Orr, Ebert Charles. Food for the Lambs or Helps for Young Ch. 2006. 77.99 (***978-1-4280-1237-0(0)***); pap. 70.99 (***978-1-4280-1235-6(4)***) IndyPublish.com.

Osborn, Susan Titus. Parables in Action Set, 8 vols. (Parables in Action Ser.). (J). 38.99 (978-0-7586-0013-4(5)) Concordia Publishing Hse.

Osborne, Susan Titus. Dog Paws & Sandy Claws. Durrell, Julie, illus. 2001. (Parables in Action Ser.: Vol. 8). 48p. (J). (ps-2). 4.99 (978-0-570-07140-2(2)) Concordia Publishing Hse.

—Flip-Flop Fishing. Durrell, Julie, illus. 2001. (Parables in Action Ser.: Vol. 7). 48p. (J). (ps-2). 4.99 (978-0-570-07139-6(9)) Concordia Publishing Hse.

Otte, Wanda. Hidden Secrets of the Knob. 2007. (ENG.). 228p. (J). per. 17.99 (***978-1-4141-0810-0(9)***) Pleasant Word.

Owens, Jim. New Allegory. 2006. (J). per. 12.00 (***978-0-9769132-4-5(0)***) Capri Publishing.

Owens, Roberta R., compiled by. Faith in Children: Stories from Faith-Based Children's Centers. Owens, Roberta R., . 2007. (Illus.). 264p. pap. 34.95 (***978-1-57736-385-9(X)*** , Providence Hse. Pubs.) Providence Hse Pubs.

Palmer, Adam. Mooch. 2006. 272p. pap. 12.99 (978-1-60006-047-2(1) , Th1nk Bks.) NavPress Publishing Group.

Pansy. Divers Women. 2006. 41.99 (***978-1-4280-1450-3(0)***); pap. 35.99 (***978-1-4280-1459-6(4)***) IndyPublish.com.

—Ester Ried. 2006. 33.99 (***978-1-4219-7826-0(1)***); pap. 27.99 (***978-1-4219-7828-4(8)***) IndyPublish.com.

—Ester Ried yet Speaking. 2006. 64.99 (***978-1-4280-3032-9(8)***) IndyPublish.com.

Pansy (Isabella M. Alden). Tip Lewis & His Lamp. 2006. 112p. pap. (978-1-84702-198-4(0)) Echo Library.

Pantelides, Sherry. It's Red Like Me! A Story about the Blood of Jesus. Perez, Debi, illus. 2007. (J). lib. bdg. 12.99 (***978-0-9771076-0-5(4)***) Lacey Productions.

Parra, Jen. Princess Shannon & the Yellow Moon. Meier, Paul, illus. 2004. (J). bds. 9.99 (978-1-4183-0012-8(8)) Christ Inspired, Inc.

Parrott, Leslie. Marshmallow Clouds. Taylor, Terry, illus. 2003. 32p. (J). 12.99 (978-0-310-70349-5(2)) Zonderkidz.

Parry, Alan. Progress of the Pilgrim Mouse: An Adaption of the Pilgrim's Progress. Parry, Linda, illus. 2000. 64p. (J). (ps-3). pap. 9.99 (978-0-8024-2930-8(0)) Moody Pubs.

Parry, Linda. Bramble Forgets. Parry, Alan, illus. 1998. (Honey Bear Ser.). 28p. (J). pap. 4.99 (978-0-8054-1791-3(5)) B&H Publishing Grp.

—Where's Pipkin? Parry, Alan, illus. 1998. (Honey Bear Ser.). 28p. (J). pap. 4.99 (978-0-8054-1788-3(5)) B&H Publishing Grp.

Paterson, Katherine. Preacher's Boy. 2001. 192p. (J). (gr. 5 up). pap. 5.99 (978-0-06-447233-3(7) , Harper Trophy) HarperCollins Pubs.

—Preacher's Boy. 1999. (Illus.). 176p. (J). (gr. 5-9). tchr. ed. 15.00 (978-0-395-83897-6(5) , Clarion Bks.) Houghton Mifflin Co. Trade & Reference Div.

—Preacher's Boy. 2001. (gr. 5-8). lib. bdg. 12.95 (978-0-613-34906-2(7)) Tandem Library Bks.

Pavlicin, Karen. Perch, Mrs. Sackets, & Crow's Nest. 2007. (J). 160p. 16.95 (***978-1-934617-00-7(8)***); pap. (***978-1-934617-01-4(6)***) Elva Resa Publishing, LLC. (Alma Little).

Pearson, Carol Lynn. A Christmas Thief: A Novel. 2003. 67p. 14.95 (978-0-8294-1764-7(8)) Loyola Pr.

Peck, Lisa J. A Challenge for Brittany. 1999. (Choose the Right Ser.: Bk. 2). 60p. (J). pap. (978-1-57008-664-9(8)) Scribbulations LLC.

Peck, Lisa J. A Challenge for Brittany: CTR Club - Book One, 4 bks. 2005. (J). pap. 6.95 (***978-0-9749241-5-1(6)***) Golden Wings Enterprises.

Peckham, Lori, ed. Guide's Greatest Mystery Stories. 2007. 160p. (J). pap. 11.99 (***978-0-8280-2038-1(8)***) Review & Herald Publishing Assn.

Penning, L. & Nelson, Marietjie. The Hero of Spionkop. 2006. (Illus.). 166p. (YA). pap. (978-1-894666-92-3(5)) Inheritance Pubns.

—The Lion of Modderspruit. 2004. (Illus.). 142p. (YA). pap. (978-1-894666-91-6(7)) Inheritance Pubns.

Perdew, Suzanne, et al. The Mystery of the Abandoned Lighthouse. 2001. (Shoebox Kids Ser.: Bk. 12). (Illus.). 93p. (J). (978-0-8163-1819-3(0)) Pacific Pr. Publishing Assn.

Peretti, Frank. Hangman's Curse: The Veritas Project - Volume 1. 2008. 352p. (YA). mass mkt. 7.99 (***978-1-4003-1016-6(4)***) Nelson, Thomas Inc.

—Nightmare Academy: The Veritas Project - Volume 2. 2008. 352p. (YA). mass mkt. 7.99 (***978-1-4003-1017-3(2)***) Nelson, Thomas Inc.

Peretti, Frank E. The Deadly Curse of Toco-Rey. 2005. (Cooper Kids Adventure Ser.: Vol. 6). 160p. (J). pap. 6.99 (978-1-4003-0575-9(6)) Nelson, Thomas Inc.

—Hangman's Curse. movie tie-in ed. 2003. (Veritas Project Ser.). 312p. (YA). pap. 9.99 (978-1-4003-0371-7(0)) Nelson, Thomas Inc.

—Hangman's Curse. 2003. (gr. 3-6). lib. bdg. 18.80 (978-0-613-77934-0(7)) Tandem Library Bks.

—Mayday at Two Thousand Five Hundred. 2005. (Cooper Kids Adventure Ser.: Vol. 8). 144p. (J). pap. 6.99 (978-1-4003-0577-3(2)) Nelson, Thomas Inc.

—Nightmare Academy. 2003. (Veritas Project Ser.). 320p. (YA). pap. 8.99 (978-1-4003-0340-3(0)) Nelson, Thomas Inc.

—Nightmare Academy. 2003. (gr. 3-6). lib. bdg. 17.60 (978-0-613-77930-2(4)) Tandem Library Bks.

—The Secret of the Desert Stone. 2005. (Cooper Kids Adventure Ser.: Vol. 5). 160p. (J). pap. 6.99 (978-1-4003-0574-2(8)) Nelson, Thomas Inc.

Peretz, I. L. The Seven Good Years: And Other Stories of I. L. Peretz. Hautzig, Esther, tr. Ray, Deborah K., illus. 2004. (ENG & YID.). 96p. (J). pap. 9.95 (978-0-8276-0771-2(7)) Jewish Pubn. Society.

Perrotti, P. Joseph & the Prodigal Son. 2005. 74p. pap. 14.95 (978-1-4137-5491-9(0)) PublishAmerica, Inc.

Perry Moore, Stephanie. Finally Sure. 2004. (gr. 3-6). lib. bdg. 15.30 (978-0-613-90337-0(4)) Tandem Library Bks.

Perry-Moore, Stephanie. Happy Princess. 2007. (Carmen Browne Ser.). 128p. pap. 5.99 (978-0-8024-8171-9(X) , Lift Every Voice) Moody Pubs.

—Perfect Joy. 2006. (Carmen Browne Ser.). 112p. pap. 5.99 (978-0-8024-8170-2(1) , Lift Every Voice) Moody Pubs.

Perry Moore, Stephanie. Surrendered Heart: Living for God Is Challenging. 2002. (Payton Skky Ser.: Vol. 5). 192p. (YA). pap. 6.99 (978-0-8024-4240-6(4)) Moody Pubs.

Peterson, Doug. Larryboy & the Abominable Trashman! 2003. Vol. 8. (Illus.). 96p. pap. 4.99 (978-0-310-70652-6(1)) Zonderkidz.

—LarryBoy & the Mudslingers. Big Idea Design Staff, illus. 2006. (Big Idea Books). 32p. (J). 9.99 (978-0-310-71149-0(5)) Zonderkidz.

—Larryboy in the Amazing Brain-Twister. 2003. Vol. 7. (Illus.). 96p. pap. 4.99 (978-0-310-70651-9(3)) Zonderkidz.

—Larryboy Versus the Volcano. 2004. (Illus.). 96p. pap. 4.99 (978-0-310-70728-8(5)) Zonderkidz.

Pferdehirt, Julia, et al. Amy Carmichael: The Hidden Jewel. 2000. (Trailblazer Bks.). (Illus.). 24p. (J). pap., stu. ed. 4.99 (978-0-7642-2345-7(3)) Bethany Hse. Pubs.

Piper, Noel. Most of All Jesus Loves You. Anderson, Debby, illus. 2005. 24p. (J). 9.99 (978-1-58134-630-5(1) , Crossway Bibles) Crossway Bks.

Pisaturn, Angela. A Gift for Abigail. 1998. 54p. (J). pap. (978-1-57502-940-5(5) , P02580) Morris Publishing.

Pistole, Katy. Flying High. 2003. (Illus.). 126p. (J). 7.99 (978-0-8163-1942-8(1)) Pacific Pr. Pubns.

—The Palomino. 2002. (Sonrise Farm Ser.). (Illus.). 128p. (J). 7.99 (978-0-8163-1863-6(8)) Pacific Pr. Publishing Assn.

—Stolen Gold, Vol. 2. 2002. (Illus.). 127p. (J). pap. 7.99 (978-0-8163-1882-7(4)) Pacific Pr. Publishing Assn.

PM Seeker Series #8 Jesus, Someone Who Cares. 2005. (J). pap. 2.95 (978-0-9749339-6-2(1)) PowerMark Productions.

Pogue, Carolyn. After the Beginning. Kyle, Margaret, illus. 2006. 32p. 18.95 (***978-1-896836-83-6(6)***) Northstone Publishing, Inc. CAN. *Dist:* Pilgrim Pr., The/United Church Pr.

Polk, James. God Rules. 2003. pap. 11.00 (978-0-8059-9231-1(6) , RoseDog Bks.) Dorrance Publishing Co., Inc.

—Mr. & Mrs. Love & the Neighborhood Children. 2003. pap. 11.00 (978-0-8059-9232-8(4) , RoseDog Bks.) Dorrance Publishing Co., Inc.

Poth, Karen & Big Ideas Inc. Staff. Larry Aprende a Escuchar. 2004. (Big Idea Bks.). 12p. (J). 5.99 (978-0-8297-4300-5(6)) Vida Pubs.

Potter, George. The Wisemen of Bountiful. Harmon, Glenn, illus. 2005. per. 11.99 (978-1-55517-814-7(6) , Cedar Fort, Inc.) Cedar Fort, Inc./CFI Distribution.

PowerMark Issue 11 Vol. 1, Issue 11: Trojan Horse. 2001. 32p. (J). pap. 2.95 (978-0-9713412-0-7(6)) PowerMark Productions.

PowerMark Issue 12 Vol. 1, Issue 12: Redemption. 2001. 32p. (J). pap. 2.95 (978-0-9713412-1-0(4)) PowerMark Productions.

PowerMark Issue 13 Vol. 1, Issue 13: Standing Tall. 2002. 32p. (J). pap. 2.95 (978-0-9713412-2-7(2)) PowerMark Productions.

Powermark Issue 14 Vol. 2, Issue 14: Sinister Plans. 2002. 32p. (J). pap. 2.95 (978-0-9713412-3-4(0)) PowerMark Productions.

PowerMark Issue 15 Vol. 1, Issue 15: Break Out. 2002. 32p. (J). pap. 2.95 (978-0-9713412-4-1(9)) PowerMark Productions.

PowerMark Issue 16 Vol. 1, Issue 16: Sacrifice. 2002. 32p. (J). pap. 2.95 (978-0-9713412-5-8(7)) PowerMark Productions.

PowerMark Issue 17 Vol. 1, Issue 17: My Brother's Keeper. 2002. 32p. (J). pap. 2.95 (978-0-9713412-6-5(5)) PowerMark Productions.

PowerMark Issue 18 Vol. 2, Issue 18: Playing with Fire. 2002. 32p. (J). pap. 2.95 (978-0-9713412-7-2(3)) PowerMark Productions.

PowerMark Issue 19 Vol. 1, Issue 19: The Den. 2002. 32p. (J). pap. 2.95 (978-0-9713412-8-9(1)) PowerMark Productions.

PowerMark Issue 20 Vol. 1, Issue 20: Redeemer. 2002. 32p. (J). pap. 2.95 (978-0-9713412-9-6(X)) PowerMark Productions.

A Prayer for Owen Meany: Response Journal. 2003. 28p. (YA). (978-1-58049-982-8(1) , RJ82) Prestwick Hse., Inc.

Price, Matt. Out on a Limb. 2006. 32p. 4.50 (978-0-8341-2229-1(4)) Beacon Hill Pr. of Kansas City.

Prickle Says I'm Sorry. 2006. 16p. (J). pap. 1.99 (978-0-7847-1697-7(8) , 02999) Standard Publishing.

Prins, Piet. Stefan Derksen's Polar Adventure. 2004. (Illus.). 237p. (J). pap. (978-1-894666-67-1(4)) Inheritance Pubns.

Pryor, Dave, illus. Go Rest, Young Man. 2001. (Little Dogs on the Prairie Ser.). 64p. (J). (gr. 1-4). pap. 4.99 (978-0-8499-7650-6(2)) Nelson, Thomas Inc.

—Lonesome Duck. 2001. (Little Dogs on the Prairie Ser.). 64p. (J). (gr. 1-4). pap. 4.99 (978-0-8499-7651-3(0)) Nelson, Thomas Inc.

Pulley, Kelly. The Beginner's Bible Lion's Big Sleepover Daniel's Scary Night. 2007. (Beginner's Bible' Ser.). 20p. (J). 6.99 (978-0-310-71387-6(0)) Zondervan.

Pulley, Kelly, illus. The Donkey's Big Find. 2007. (Beginner's Bible' Ser.). 20p. (J). 6.99 (978-0-310-71388-3(9)) Zondervan.

Puppets & Pockets from Paper Plates. (Illus.). 48p. (J). (ps-5). pap. 5.95 (978-0-87162-630-1(6) , E4603) Warner Pr. Pubs.

Ramos, Peregrina. The Little Clay Jar = la Vasijita de Barro. Graham, Dennis, illus. 2006. Tr. of vasijita de Barro. (SPA & ENG.). (J). per. 15.95 (978-0-9788381-0-2(6)) Word Gift Pubns.

Randall, Rod. Along Came a Spider. 2000. (Heebie Jeebies Ser.: Vol. 7). 138p. (J). (gr. 3-7). pap. 5.99 (978-0-8054-1981-8(0)) B&H Publishing Grp.

Randau, Rod. Piranha Picnic. 2001. (Heebie Jeebies Ser.: Vol. 9). 138p. (J). (gr. 3-7). pap. 5.99 (978-0-8054-2332-7(X)) B&H Publishing Grp.

Ravasio, Tom. Shekinah, Lord of the Horses: The Birth. 2004. 96p. (J). per. (978-1-55306-763-4(0) , Guardian Bks.) Essence Publishing.

Rawady, Ed. Everywhere & Everything: A Spiritual Story about the First Dream. Cordaro, Joseph, illus. 1998. 48p. (YA). (gr. 3 up). 18.95 (978-0-9662194-0-1(6)) Table 12 Publishing.

Reader's Digest Editors. Fuzzy Little Lamb. 2004. (Small Miracles Ser.: No. 2). 10p. (J). 5.99 (978-1-4003-0315-1(X)) Nelson, Thomas Inc.

—Who Does God Love? 2004. (Small Miracles Ser.: No. 3). 10p. (J). 6.99 (978-1-4003-0316-8(8)) Nelson, Thomas Inc.

RealBuzz Studios Staff. Come & Play: Goofyfoot Gurl Vol 3. 2007. 96p. (YA). pap. 4.97 (***978-1-59789-575-0(X)***) Barbour Publishing, Inc.

—Girl Overboard Frankensteins Monster: Life Camera Action Book 4. 2007. 128p. (YA). pap. 4.97 (978-1-59789-580-4(6) , Barbour Bks.) Barbour Publishing, Inc.

—Saved / Esther Queen of Persia: Life Camera Action Book 3. 2007. 128p. (YA). pap. 4.97 (978-1-59789-579-8(2) , Barbour Bks.) Barbour Publishing, Inc.

—Serenity — Rave-N-Rant, Vol. 4. 2006. (Serenity Ser.: Vol. 4). (Illus.). 96p. (YA). pap. 7.97 (978-1-59310-873-1(7)) Barbour Publishing, Inc.

—Serenity—Basket Case, Vol. 3. 2006. (Serenity Ser.: Vol. 3). (Illus.). 96p. (YA). pap. 7.97 (978-1-59310-872-4(9)) Barbour Publishing, Inc.

—Serenity—New Bad Girl in Town, Vol. 1. 2005. (Serenity Ser.: 1). (Illus.). 96p. (J). pap. 7.97 (978-1-59310-941-7(5)) Barbour Publishing, Inc.

—Serenity—Snow Biz, Vol. 5. 2006. (Serenity Ser.: Vol. 5). (Illus.). 96p. (YA). pap. 7.97 (978-1-59310-874-8(5) , Barbour Bks.) Barbour Publishing, Inc.

—Serenity—Stepping Out, Vol. 2. 2006. (Serenity Ser.: Vol. 2). (Illus.). 96p. (YA). pap. 7.97 (978-1-59310-942-4(3)) Barbour Publishing, Inc.

—Serenity—You Shall Love..., Vol. 6. 2006. 96p. (YA). pap. 7.97 (978-1-59310-875-5(3) , Barbour Bks.) Barbour Publishing, Inc.

—Sunday Best / Crawling from the Wreckage Life Camera Action BK 2: Life Camera Action Book 2. 2007. 128p. (YA). pap. 4.97 (978-1-59789-578-1(4) , Barbour Bks.) Barbour Publishing, Inc.

Redeker, Kent. Larryboy—The Good, the Bad, & the Eggly. 2003. (Big Idea Bks.). 96p. pap. 4.99 (978-0-310-70650-2(5)) Zonderkidz.

—Larryboy & the Yodel Napper. 2003. (Illus.). 96p. pap. 4.99 (978-0-310-70562-8(2)) Zonderkidz.

Redeker, Kent, et al. Larryboy in the Attack of Outback Jack. 2003. (Big Idea Bks.). 96p. pap. 4.99 (978-0-310-70649-6(1)) Zonderkidz.

Reece, Colleen L. The Mayflower Adventure. 1999. (American Adventure Ser.: No. 1). 144p. (J). (gr. 3-7). lib. bdg. 15.95 (978-0-7910-5041-5(6) , Chelsea Hse.) Facts On File, Inc.

—Mysterious Monday. l.t. ed. 2001. (Christian Mystery Ser.). 192p. (J). 23.95 (978-0-7862-3068-6(1)) Thorndike Pr.

—Saturday Scare. l.t. ed. 2002. (Juli Scott, Super Sleuth Ser.). (Illus.). 211p. (J). 24.95 (978-0-7862-3195-9(5)) Thomson Gale.

—Secrets of the Sea. 2000. (Illus.). 112p. (J). pap. 6.99 (978-0-8280-1390-1(X)) Review & Herald Publishing Assn.

—Thursday Trials. 1998. (Juli Scott, Super Sleuth Ser.: Bk. 4). 176p. (J). (gr. 4-10). pap. 2.97 (978-1-57748-180-5(1)) Barbour Publishing, Inc.

—Thursday Trials. l.t. ed. 2001. (Juli Scott, Super Sleuth Ser.). (Illus.). 204p. (J). 23.95 (978-0-7862-3201-7(3)) Thorndike Pr.

—Trouble on Tuesday. l.t. ed. 2001. (Thorndike Christian Mystery Ser.). (Illus.). 192p. (J). 23.95 (978-0-7862-3178-2(5)) Thorndike Pr.

—Wednesday Witness. l.t. ed. 2001. (Juli Scott, Super Sleuth Ser.). (Illus.). 189p. (J). 23.95 (978-0-7862-3202-4(1)) Thorndike Pr.

Reed, Stephanie. Across the Wide River: A Novel. 2004. 176p. (J). pap. 9.99 (978-0-8254-3576-8(5)) Kregel Pubns.

Reese, Della. God Inside of Me. Buchanan, Yvonne, illus. 2005. 30p. (J). (gr. 4-8). reprint ed. 16.00 (978-0-7567-9366-1(1)) DIANE Publishing Co.

—God Inside of Me. Buchanan, Yvonne, illus. 1999. 32p. (J). lib. bdg. 16.49 (978-0-7868-2395-6(X) , Jump at the Sun) Hyperion Bks. for Children.

Reeve, Penny. Find the Animals: God Made Something Beautiful. (Illus.). 16p. (J). pap. 3.99 (978-1-85792-774-0(5) , Christian Focus) Christian Focus Pubns. GBR. *Dist:* Riverside.

—Find the Animals: God Made Something Clever. (Illus.). 16p. (J). pap. 3.99 (978-1-85792-771-9(0) , Christian Focus) Christian Focus Pubns. GBR. *Dist:* Riverside.

—Find the Animals: God Made Something Quick. (Illus.). 16p. (J). pap. 3.99 (978-1-85792-773-3(7)) Christian Focus Pubns. GBR. *Dist:* Riverside.

—Find the Animals: God Made Something Strong. (Illus.). 16p. (J). pap. 3.99 (978-1-85792-772-6(9) , Christian Focus) Christian Focus Pubns. GBR. *Dist:* Riverside.

Reeves, Nancy Christine, et al. Adventures of the God Detectives. 2006. (Illus.). 94p. (J). pap. 6.95 (***978-1-55145-542-6(0)***) Wood Lake Bks., Inc. CAN. *Dist:* Pilgrim Pr., The/United Church Pr.

Reggie to the Rescue. 2004. 32p. pap. 3.99 (978-0-8341-2088-4(7)) Beacon Hill Pr. of Kansas City.

Regina Press Staff. Good Shepherd. 1999. (J). (ps-3). 4.95 (978-0-88271-673-2(5)) Regina Pr., Malhame & Co.

Reinertson, Debbie. Whose Nose? Whose Toes? Clark, Bill, illus. 1999. 16p. (J). (ps). bds. 4.99 (978-0-570-05490-0(7), 56-1953GJ) Concordia Publishing Hse.

Reiter, Douglas. Back to School in Cedar Heights. 2006. 79p. pap. 14.95 (978-1-4137-9058-0(5)) PublishAmerica, Inc.

Rennie, C. Goal Behind the Curtain. Date not set. 176p. (YA). mass mkt. 4.99 (978-1-871676-47-1(9), Christian Focus) Christian Focus Pubns. GBR. *Dist:* Riverside, Spring Arbor Distributors, Inc.

Repp, Gloria. Booklinks, Level 2. 1998. 149p. (J). (gr. 4-7). pap. 7.49 (978-1-57924-000-4(3), 106484) Jones, Bob Univ. Pr.

—Charlie. 2002. (Illus.). 147p. (J). (gr. 4-7). 7.49 (978-1-57924-817-8(9)) Jones, Bob Univ. Pr.

—Mik-Shrok. 1998. 133p. (J). (gr. 4-7). pap. 7.49 (978-1-57924-069-1(0), 113902) Jones, Bob Univ. Pr.

—The Mystery of the Indian Carvings. Pelicano, Christopher J., illus. 2002. 118p. (J). (gr. 4-7). pap. 7.49 (978-1-57924-726-3(1)) Jones, Bob Univ. Pr.

—Trouble at Silver Pines Inn. 1998. lib. bdg. 14.70 (978-0-613-86050-5(0)) Tandem Library Bks.

—Zebra 77. Schuppert, David, illus. 2002. (Adventures of an Arctic Missionary Ser.). 156p. (J). (gr. 4-7). 7.49 (978-1-57924-930-4(2)) Jones, Bob Univ. Pr.

Rhone, Alexus D. Premature Pleasures. 2001. 224p. (YA). (gr. 6 up). 16.95 (978-0-9708688-0-0(4)) Unshackled Publishing.

Rich, Elaine Sommers. Hannah Elizabeth. Kennedy, Paul Edward, illus. 2002. 174p. pap. 21.00 (978-1-57910-923-3(3), Resource Pubns.) Wipf & Stock Pubs.

Richardson, Arleta. Looking for Home. 2001. (gr. 3-6). lib. bdg. 14.15 (978-0-613-74903-9(0)) Tandem Library Bks.

—Still More Stories from Grandma's Attic, 1. rev. ed. 2003. (Grandma's Attic Ser.). (Illus.). 144p. (J). (gr. 12-8). pap., pap. 6.99 (978-0-7814-3270-2(7), 0781432707) Cook, David C. Publishing Co.

Richardson, Faith. Angel Walker. 2003. Orig. Title: The Sea, the Song & the Trumpetfish. (Illus.). 172p. (J). 19.95 (978-0-9744989-2-8(0)); pap. 12.95 (978-0-9744989-3-5(9)) Fox Song Bks.

Rispin, Karen. Tianna the Terrible. 2002. 104p. (J). pap. 6.99 (978-1-58586-789-9(6)) ereads.com.

Rizzo, Kay D. Bells & Whistles. 2003. 96p. (J). (978-0-8163-1984-8(7)) Pacific Pr. Publishing Assn.

—Old Friends & New. 2003. 96p. (J). (978-0-8163-1975-6(8)) Pacific Pr. Publishing Assn.

—Wagon Train West. 2003. 96p. (J). (978-0-8163-1986-2(3)) Pacific Pr. Publishing Assn.

Rizzo, Kay D. & Ferree, Dennis. The Not-So-Secret Mission. 2003. 96p. (J). (978-0-8163-1966-4(9)) Pacific Pr. Publishing Assn.

Robeson, Randy. Knee Deep in the Soup: And Other Stupid Stories. Robeson, Jerry, ed. Longanecker, Michael, illus. 1998. 128p. (YA). pap. 10.95 (978-1-891879-00-5(6)) Shiloh Publishing Hse., Inc.

Roddy, Lee. Risking the Dream. 2000. (Between Two Flags Ser.: Vol. 6). (Illus.). 176p. (J). (gr. 6-9). pap. 5.99 (978-0-7642-2030-2(6)) Bethany Hse. Pubs.

Rogers, Kayron Upton. Oh Little Speck of Love, So Deep in My Heart. 2000. 36p. (J). pap. 7.95 (978-1-57921-321-3(9)) WinePress Publishing.

Ross, Michael. Tribe: A Warrior's Heart. 2004. (Breakaway Devotional Ser.). 208p. (YA). pap. 13.99 (978-1-58997-118-9(3)) Focus on the Family Publishing.

Ross, Michael & Koehler, Manfred. Tribe: A Warrior's Battles. 2006. 192p. (YA). per. 14.99 (978-1-58997-188-2(4)) Focus on the Family Publishing.

Roth, Susan L. Grandpa Blows His Penny Whistle until the Angels Sing. 2001. (Illus.). 40p. (J). (gr. 3-5). 16.99 (978-1-84148-247-7(1)) Barefoot Bks., Inc.

Rottmann, Erik. Barabbas Goes Free. Kitchel, JoAnn E., illus. 2003. (Arch Bks.). (ENG.). 16p. (J). 1.99 (978-0-570-07582-0(3)) Concordia Publishing Hse.

Rue, Nancy. Sophie Loses the Lead, Vol. 11. 2006. (Faithgirlz! Ser.). 144p. (J). pap. 6.99 (978-0-310-71026-4(X)) Zonderkidz.

—Sophie Loves Jimmy, Vol. 10. 2006. (Faithgirlz Ser.). 144p. (J). pap. 6.99 (978-0-310-71025-7(1)) Zonderkidz.

—Sophie Tracks a Thief, Vol. 8. 2005. (Faithgirlz Ser.). (Illus.). 144p. (J). pap. 6.99 (978-0-310-71023-3(5)) Zonderkidz.

—Sophie's Encore, Vol. 12. 2006. (Faithgirlz! Ser.). (Illus.). 144p. (J). pap. 6.99 (978-0-310-71027-1(8)) Zonderkidz.

Rue, Nancy N. The Accused. 1998. (Christian Heritage Ser.). (Illus.). 224p. (J). (gr. 3-7). pap. 5.99 (978-1-56179-398-3(1)) Bethany Hse. Pubs.

—The Ally. 1998. (Christian Heritage Ser.). 192p. (J). (gr. 3-7). pap. (978-1-56179-561-1(5)) Focus on the Family Publishing.

—Ask Lily. 2001. (Young Women of Faith Library). 144p. (J). pap. 5.99 (978-0-310-23254-4(6)) Zonderkidz.

—The Caper. 2000. (Christian Heritage Ser.). (Illus.). 192p. (J). (gr. 3-7). pap. 5.99 (978-1-56179-837-7(1)) Bethany Hse. Pubs.

—The Choice. 2002. (Christian Heritage Ser.). 192p. (Orig.). (J). pap. (978-1-56179-896-4(7)) Focus on the Family Publishing.

—Christian Heritage Series: The Chicago Years Boxed Set: The Trick; The Chase; The Capture; The Stunt; The Caper; The Pursuit, 6 vols., Set. 2000. (Christian Heritage Ser.). (J). (gr. 3-7). pap. 35.99 (978-1-56179-877-3(0)) Bethany Hse. Pubs.

—The Discovery. 2001. (Christian Heritage Ser.). (Illus.). 192p. (J). (gr. 3-7). pap. (978-1-56179-862-9(2)) Focus on the Family Publishing.

—Do I Have to Paint You a Picture. 1998. (gr. 7-12). lib. bdg. 15.25 (978-0-613-88736-6(0)) Tandem Library Bks.

—The Escape. 1998. (Christian Heritage Ser.). 192p. (J). (gr. 3-7). pap. 5.99 (978-1-56179-639-7(5)) Bethany Hse. Pubs.

—False Friends & True Strangers. 2004. (Invert / 'Nama Beach High Ser.). 192p. (J). pap. 6.99 (978-0-310-25180-4(X)) Zondervan.

—Here's Lily! 2000. (Young Women of Faith Library). (Illus.). 136p. (J). pap. 5.99 (978-0-310-23248-3(1)) Zonderkidz.

—Here's Lily. 2003. pap. 2.99 (978-0-310-70590-1(8)) Zondervan.

—Horse Crazy Lily. 2003. (gr. 3-6). lib. bdg. 13.00 (978-0-613-71715-1(5)) Tandem Library Bks.

—Horse Crazy Lily. 2003. (Young Women of Faith Ser.). 128p. (J). pap. 5.99 (978-0-310-70263-4(1)) Zonderkidz.

—The Hostage. 1998. (Christian Heritage Ser.). 208p. (J). (gr. 3-7). pap. 5.99 (978-1-56179-638-0(7)) Bethany Hse. Pubs.

—The Invasion. 1998. (Christian Heritage Ser.). 192p. (J). (gr. 3-7). pap. (978-1-56179-541-3(0)) Focus on the Family Publishing.

—Invasion. 1998. (gr. 3-6). lib. bdg. 14.15 (978-0-613-85284-5(2)) Tandem Library Bks.

—Lights, Action, Lily! 2002. (Ywof Library Ser.). 128p. (J). pap. 5.99 (978-0-310-70249-8(6)) Zonderkidz.

—Lily & the Creep. 2001. (gr. 3-6). lib. bdg. 13.00 (978-0-613-71718-2(X)) Tandem Library Bks.

—Lily & the Creep. 2001. (Ywof Library). (Illus.). 128p. (J). (gr. 3-7). pap. 5.99 (978-0-310-23252-0(X)) Zonderkidz.

—Lily Rules! 2002. (gr. 3-6). lib. bdg. 13.00 (978-0-613-71708-3(2)) Tandem Library Bks.

—Lily Rules!, No. 8. 2002. (Ywof Library). (Illus.). 128p. (J). pap. 5.99 (978-0-310-70250-4(X)) Zonderkidz.

—Lily Speaks! 2002. (Ywof Library). (Illus.). 128p. (J). pap. 5.99 (978-0-310-70262-7(3)) Zonderkidz.

—Lily the Rebel. 2001. (Ywof Library Ser.: No. 6). (Illus.). 128p. (J). pap. 5.99 (978-0-310-23255-1(4)) Zonderkidz.

—Lily's Church Camp Adventure. 2003. (gr. 3-6). lib. bdg. 13.00 (978-0-613-71663-5(9)) Tandem Library Bks.

—Lily's Church Camp Adventure. 2003. (Ywof Library). 128p. (J). pap. 5.99 (978-0-310-70264-1(X)) Zonderkidz.

—Lily's in London: It's a God Thing! 2003. (gr. 3-6). lib. bdg. 13.00 (978-0-613-71688-8(4)) Tandem Library Bks.

—Lily's in London: It's a God Thing! 2003. (Ywof Library Ser.). 160p. (J). pap. 5.99 (978-0-310-70554-3(1)) Zonderkidz.

—Lily's Passport to Paris. 2003. (Ywof Library). 160p. (J). pap. 5.99 (978-0-310-70555-0(X)) Zonderkidz.

—Lily's Ultimate Party. 2001. (gr. 3-6). lib. bdg. 13.00 (978-0-613-71719-9(8)) Tandem Library Bks.

—The Mirage. 2001. (Christian Heritage Ser.). (Illus.). 192p. (J). (gr. 3-7). pap. 5.99 (978-1-56179-863-6(0)) Bethany Hse. Pubs.

—The Misfit. 1998. (Christian Heritage Ser.). 192p. (J). (gr. 3-7). pap. (978-1-56179-560-4(7)) Focus on the Family Publishing.

—The Mission. 2001. (Christian Heritage Ser.). 192p. (J). (gr. 3-8). pap. (978-1-56179-894-0(0)) Focus on the Family Publishing.

—The Pursuit. 2000. (Christian Heritage Ser.). 192p. (J). (gr. 3-7). pap. 5.99 (978-1-56179-856-8(8)) Bethany Hse. Pubs.

—Pursuit. 2000. (gr. 3-6). lib. bdg. 14.15 (978-0-613-86405-3(0)) Tandem Library Bks.

—Rough & Rugged Lily. 2002. (Ywof Library). (Illus.). 128p. (J). pap. 5.99 (978-0-310-70260-3(7)) Zonderkidz.

—Samaritan. 1998. (gr. 3-6). lib. bdg. 14.15 (978-0-613-88494-5(9)) Tandem Library Bks.

—The Secret. 1998. (Christian Heritage Ser.). 192p. (Orig.). (J). (gr. 3-7). pap. (978-1-56179-443-0(0)) Focus on the Family Publishing.

—Sophie & the Scoundrels, Bk. 3. Chen, Grace, illus. 2005. (Faithgirlz Ser.). 128p. (J). pap. 6.99 (978-0-310-70758-5(7)) Zonderkidz.

—Sophie Breaks the Code, Vol. 7. 2005. (Faithgirlz Ser.). (Illus.). 144p. (J). pap. 6.99 (978-0-310-71022-6(7)) Zonderkidz.

—Sophie Flakes Out, Vol. 9. 2006. (Faithgirlz Ser.). (Illus.). 128p. (J). pap. 6.99 (978-0-310-71024-0(3)) Zonderkidz.

—Sophie's First Dance?, Vol. 5. Chen, Grace, illus. 2005. (Faithgirlz Ser.). 128p. (J). pap. 6.99 (978-0-310-70760-8(9)) Zonderkidz.

—Sophie's Irish Showdown. Chen, Grace, illus. 2005. (Faithgirlz Ser.). 128p. (J). pap. 6.99 (978-0-310-70759-2(5)) Zonderkidz.

—Sophie's Secret, Vol. 2. 2004. (Faithgirlz Ser.). (Illus.). 128p. (J). pap. 6.99 (978-0-310-70757-8(9)) Zonderkidz.

—Sophie's Stormy Summer, Vol. 6. Chen, Grace, illus. 2005. (Faithgirlz Ser.). 128p. (J). pap. 6.99 (978-0-310-70761-5(7)) Zonderkidz.

—Sophie's World. 2004. (Faithgirlz Ser.). (Illus.). 128p. (J). pap. 6.99 (978-0-310-70756-1(0)) Zonderkidz.

—The Stand. 2001. (Christian Heritage Ser.). 192p. (J). (gr. 3-8). pap. (978-1-56179-893-3(2)) Focus on the Family Publishing.

—The Struggle. 2002. (Christian Heritage Ser.). 192p. (J). pap. 5.99 (978-1-56179-895-7(9)) Bethany Hse. Pubs.

—The Stunt. 1999. (Christian Heritage Ser.). 208p. (J). (gr. 3-7). pap. 5.99 (978-1-56179-833-9(9)) Bethany Hse. Pubs.

—The Thief. 1998. (Christian Heritage Ser.). 192p. (J). (gr. 3-7). pap. (978-1-56179-479-9(1)) Focus on the Family Publishing.

—The Threat. 1998. (Christian Heritage Ser.). 208p. (J). (gr. 3-7). pap. (978-1-56179-566-6(6)) Focus on the Family Publishing.

—Totally Unfair. 2005. (Invert / 'Nama Beach High Ser.). 160p. (YA). pap. 6.99 (978-0-310-25183-5(4)) Zondervan.

Rue, Nancy N. & Youth Specialties Staff. New Girl in Town. 2004. (Invert / 'Nama Beach High Ser.: No. 1). 176p. (J). pap. 6.99 (978-0-310-24399-1(8)) Zondervan.

Rushford, Patricia H. The Secret of Ghost Island. 2007. 128p. pap. 6.99 (***978-0-8024-6255-8(3)***) Moody Pubs.

—The Trouble with Max. 2007. 128p. pap. 6.99 (***978-0-8024-6253-4(7)***) Moody Pubs.

Rylant, Cynthia. A Fine White Dust. l.t. ed. 2005. 148p. 21.95 (978-0-7862-7306-5(2), Large Print Pr.) Thorndike Pr.

Samantha Stays Safe. 2006. 16p. (J). pap. 1.99 (978-0-7847-1696-0(X), 02998) Standard Publishing.

Sampson, Michael R. Caddie the Golf Dog. Cooper, Floyd, illus. 2000. 32p. (J). 14.99 (978-0-8499-5823-6(7)) Nelson, Thomas Inc.

Sanchez, Alex. The God Box. 2007. 272p. (YA). (gr. 7 up). 16.99 (***978-1-4169-0899-9(4)***, Simon & Schuster Children's Publishing) Simon & Schuster Children's Publishing.

Sanders, Nancy I. Hidden Treasure. 2000. (Parables in Action Ser.: Vol. 2). (Illus.). 48p. (J). (ps-2). 4.99 (978-0-570-07013-9(9)) Concordia Publishing Hse.

—Hidden Treasure. 2000. (ps-2). lib. bdg. 13.00 (978-0-613-72836-2(X)) Tandem Library Bks.

—Lost & Found. 2000. (Parables in Action Ser.: Vol. 1). (Illus.). 48p. (J). (ps-2). 4.99 (978-0-570-07012-2(0)) Concordia Publishing Hse.

—Lost & Found. 2000. (ps-2). lib. bdg. 13.00 (978-0-613-72835-5(1)) Tandem Library Bks.

Sandrof, George. Me, a Hero? 2000. (Illus.). 77p. (J). (ps up). pap. 7.99 (978-1-58930-006-4(8)) Selah Publishing Group, LLC.

Schadler, Cherie D. & Jones, Ann Biedenharn. When the Rain Came Down in Bayou Town! 2000. (Illus.). 32p. (J). (ps-3). 15.95 (978-1-56554-680-6(6)) Pelican Publishing Co., Inc.

Schneider, Richard H. The Blue Angel Ornament: A Story of Love & Loyalty. Davis, Florence S., illus. 32p. (ps up). 2004. 17.00 (978-0-687-08181-3(5)); 2000. (J). 6.99 (978-0-687-09571-1(9)) Abingdon Pr.

Schneider, Richard H. The Lighthouse Boy: A Story of Courage. Petrov, Anton, illus. 2007. 32p. (J). (ps-3). pap. 8.99 (***978-0-8249-5557-1(9)***, Guideposts) Ideals Pubns.

Schofield, S. M. Race to Eagle Mountain. 2007. (ENG.). 184p. (J). per. 16.99 (***978-1-4141-0814-8(1)***) Pleasant Word.

Schulte, Elaine. Suzannah & the Secret Coins. 2001. (gr. 3-6). lib. bdg. 14.70 (978-0-613-85515-0(9)) Tandem Library Bks.

Schulte, Elaine L. Daniel Colton Kidnapped. 2002. (Colton Cousins Adventure Ser.: Bk. 4). (Illus.). 138p. (J). (gr. 4-7). 7.49 (978-1-57924-566-5(8)) Jones, Bob Univ. Pr.

—Daniel Colton under Fire. 2001. (Illus.). 137p. (J). (gr. 4-7). pap. 7.49 (978-1-57924-564-1(1)) Jones, Bob Univ. Pr.

—Suzannah & the Secret Coins. 2001. (Colton Cousins Adventure Ser.). (Illus.). 130p. (J). (gr. 4-7). 7.49 (978-1-57924-563-4(3)) Jones, Bob Univ. Pr.

—Suzannah Strikes Gold. 2001. (Illus.). 144p. (J). (gr. 4-7). pap. 7.49 (978-1-57924-565-8(X)) Jones, Bob Univ. Pr.

Schwed, Michael J. A Prayer for Jeremy. 2002. 108p. (J). pap. 9.95 (978-0-595-21863-9(6), Writers Club Pr.) iUniverse, Inc.

Scott. Heinle Rdg Lib Ivanhoe. Date not set. (C). pap. (978-0-7593-9879-5(8), Thomson Learning) CENGAGE Learning.

Scott, Lori Z. Megan Rose has Ants in Her Pants. 2007. 96p. (J). pap. 4.99 (***978-0-7847-2105-6(X)***) Standard Publishing.

Scripture Teachers: Solomon & Friends Learn about Forgiveness. 2003. pap. (***978-0-9712894-1-3(7)***) Lighthouse Christian Products Co.

Scripture Teachers: Solomon & Friends Learn about Prayer. 2003. pap. (***978-0-9712894-0-6(9)***) Lighthouse Christian Products Co.

Scripture Teachers: Solomon & Friends Learn about Trusting God. 2003. pap. (***978-0-9712894-2-0(5)***) Lighthouse Christian Products Co.

Seagrove, John K. Noah, Noah, Build an Ark. 1998. 300p. (Orig.). (YA). per. 15.00 (978-0-9647633-2-6(X)) Kendall Publishing.

Shands, Linda I. White Water. 2001. (Wakara of Eagle Lodge Ser.).Tr. of Juv033010. (Illus.). 176p. (YA). (gr. 7-9). pap. 5.99 (978-0-8007-5772-4(6), Spire) Revell.

—Wild Fire. 2001. (Wakara of Eagle Lodge Ser.: Vol. 1). (Illus.). 176p. (J). (gr. 7-9). pap. 5.99 (978-0-8007-5746-5(7)) Revell.

Shaw, Wendy M. How Much Do I Love You? Hemby, Margaret, illus. 2006. (J). 14.95 (***978-0-9788398-1-9(1)***) Jostens Bks.

Sheets, Scott & Vanover, Howard. A Day at the Ball Park-Book 1 of the Wannabe Kids Series. 2007. 16p. (J). per. 9.99 (***978-1-59886-792-3(X)***) Tate Publishing & Enterprises, L.L.C.

Sherwood, Mary Marth. The History of Lucy Clare. 2004. reprint ed. pap. 15.95 (978-1-4191-6620-4(1)) Kessinger Publishing, LLC.

Sherwood, Mary Martha. The History of Lucy Clare. 2004. reprint ed. pap. 1.99 (978-1-4192-6620-1(9)) Kessinger Publishing, LLC.

Siegrist, Bonnie. Little Farm down the Lane -Book IV. 2007. pap. 10.99 (***978-1-60034-912-6(9)***) Xulon Pr., Inc.

Simon, Mary Manz. Bear Obeys. Clearwater, Linda & Couri, Kathy, illus. 2006. (First Virtues for Toddlers Ser.). 20p. (J). 5.99 (978-0-7847-1416-4(9), 04068) Standard Publishing.

Singletary, Mabel Elizabeth. Something to Jump About! 2008. 150p. pap. 5.99 (***978-0-8024-2252-1(7)***) Moody Pubs.

Sisters of Notre Dame Staff. First Communion Days. 2002. (Illus.). 96p. (J). reprint ed. 12.00 (978-1-930873-44-5(1)) Neumann Pr., The.

Sites, Terry A. While You're Asleep. Huddleston, Christine, illus. 1998. 32p. (J). (ps-2). pap. 4.95 (978-0-8198-8292-9(5), 332-403) Pauline Bks. & Media.

—While You're Asleep. 1998. (ps-2). lib. bdg. 12.95 (978-0-613-76562-6(1)) Tandem Library Bks.

Smith, Debra. Hattie Marshall & the Dangerous Fire. 2007. 144p. (J). pap. 7.95 (***978-1-58980-492-0(9)***) Pelican Publishing Co., Inc.

Smith, Debra West. Hattie Marshall & the Prowling Panther. 2005. 144p. (J). 6.95 (978-1-56554-940-1(6)) Pelican Publishing Co., Inc.

Smith, Goerky. Danger Follows. 1999. 98p. (YA). (gr. 7 up). pap. 6.49 (978-1-57924-070-7(4), 109835) Jones, Bob Univ. Pr.

Smith, Michael & Smith, Debbie. Where's Whitney? 2000. 32p. 12.99 (978-0-310-20717-7(7)) Zondervan.

Smith, Simon. Bodge Plants a Seed: A Retelling of the Parable of the Sower. 2004. (Clay Pot Parables Ser.). (Illus.). 32p. (J). 9.99 (978-0-310-70662-5(9)) Zonderkidz.

—Stumpy Stomps Off: A Retelling of the Parable of the Prodigal Son. 2004. (Clay Pot Parables Ser.). (Illus.). 32p. (J). 9.99 (978-0-310-70660-1(2)) Zonderkidz.

Smith, Stephen. Game on Boxed Set Series for Boys. 2006. 512p. (J). 19.99 (978-0-7847-1990-9(X)) Standard Publishing.

Smith, Stephen & Caldwell, Lise. Full Court Pressure. 2006. (Game on for Girls Ser.). 128p. (J). pap. 5.99 (978-0-7847-1730-1(3), 42147) Standard Publishing.

—Spiked. 2006. (Game on for Girls Ser.). 128p. (J). pap. 5.99 (978-0-7847-1731-8(1), 42148) Standard Publishing.

—Strike Three. 2006. (Game on for Girls Ser.). 128p. (J). pap. 5.99 (978-0-7847-1729-5(X), 42146) Standard Publishing.

Smith, Stephen D. & Caldwell, Lise. High Hurdles. 2006. 128p. (J). pap. 5.99 (978-0-7847-1439-3(8), 42144) Standard Publishing.

—Rivals on the Waves. 2006. 128p. (J). pap. 5.99 (978-0-7847-1470-6(3), 42141) Standard Publishing.

Smith, Todd Aaron. Cow Makes a Difference. Smith, Todd Aaron, illus. 2001. (Cows Adventure Ser.). (Illus.). 32p. (ps-2). 7.99 (978-0-8010-4475-5(8)) Baker Bks.

—The Scarecrow & the Spider. 2005. (Illus.). 32p. (J). 9.99 (978-1-4003-0550-6(0)) Nelson, Thomas Inc.

Snedeker, Caroline. Downright Dencey. Barney, Maginel Wright, illus. 2003. (Young Adult Library). 274p. (YA). pap. 11.95 (978-1-883937-79-9(5)) Bethlehem Bks.

Snelling, Lauraine. Class Act. 2000. (High Hurdles Ser.: No. 10). 176p. (J). (gr. 6-9). pap. 5.99 (978-0-7642-2038-8(1)) Bethany Hse. Pubs.

—Return to Red River, Vols. 1-3. 2003. (Return to Red River Ser.). (Illus.). 960p. pap. 38.99 (978-0-7642-9046-6(0)) Bethany Hse. Pubs.

Snider, Cindy Gay. Finding Anna Bee. Chambers, Mary, illus. 2007. (J). pap. (***978-0-8361-9392-3(X)***) Herald Pr.

Somerville, Scott. Olympus: It's Not Just a Game. 2000. (J). per. 12.95 (978-1-56857-083-9(X)) Noble Publishing Assocs.

Sowards, Ben, illus. Christmas Oranges. 2004. 32p. 17.95 (978-1-59156-098-2(5)) Covenant Communications, Inc.

Spafford, Jeannie. Dance of Life: Lord of the Dance. 2003. 124p. (YA). pap. 11.99 (978-1-57921-566-8(1)) Pleasant Word.

Spangenberg, Greg. A Christmas Eve Victory: The Adventures of Churchy Church Mouse & His Cousin Tootsie. Lodwick, Sarah, illus. l.t. ed. 2006. 34p. (J). 16.99 (978-1-59879-140-2(0)) Lifevest Publishing, Inc.

Speck, Nancy. Secret of the Hidden Room. Thomas, Jerry D., ed. Ford, Mark, illus. 1999. (Shoebox Kids Ser.: Vol. 9). 93p. (J). pap. 6.99 (978-0-8163-1682-3(1)) Pacific Pr. Publishing Assn.

Spirin, Gennadii, illus. Perceval: King Arthur's Knight of the Holy Grail. 2007. 36p. (J). (***978-1-4287-3696-2(4)***, Cavendish Children's Bks.) Cavendish, Marshall Corp.

Sproul, R. C. The Lightlings. Gerard, Justin, illus. 2006. (J). (***978-1-56769-078-1(5)***) Reformation Pubs.

St. Clair, Patrick. The Blue Rose. 2000. 32p. 14.95 (978-1-930458-04-8(5)) North Star Pubns.

—Walk until You Find Him. 2000. 32p. (J). pap. 8.95 (978-1-930458-03-1(7)) North Star Pubns.

St. John, Patricia. Friska My Friend & the Other Kitten. 2003. (Illus.). 192p. 6.49 (978-1-85999-312-5(5)) Scripture Union GBR. *Dist:* Gabriel Resources.

St John, Patricia. A Home for Virginia. Smith, Helen, illus. 2005. 24p. (J). (ps-7). per. (978-1-85792-961-4(6), Christian Focus) Christian Focus Pubns.

St. John, Patricia. Secret of the Fourth Candle. rev. ed. 2003. (Illus.). 94p. 6.49 (978-1-85999-511-2(X)) Scripture Union GBR. *Dist:* Gabriel Resources.

—Star of Light. 2002. (Illus.). 160p. (YA). pap. 6.99 (978-0-8024-6577-1(3)) Moody Pubs.

—The Tanglewoods' Secret. Rees, Gary, illus. 2001. 224p. (J). pap. 6.99 (978-0-8024-6576-4(5)) Moody Pubs.

—Treasures of the Snow. Rees, Gary, illus. 2001. 240p. (J). pap. 7.99 (978-0-8024-6575-7(7)) Moody Pubs.

—The Victor. 2003. 176p. 6.49 (978-0-86201-139-0(6)) Scripture Union GBR. *Dist:* Gabriel Resources.

St. Paul, Mary. Meet Your Angel: A Book for Little Catholics to Color & Keep. 2005. 61p. (J). pap. 6.00 (978-0-911845-06-8(2)) Neumann Pr., The.

C D

—Talking to God: A Book for Little Catholics to Color & Keep. 2005. (J). pap. 6.00 (978-0-911845-07-5(0)) Neumann Pr., The.

Stahl, Hilda. Big Trouble for Roxie. 2003. (Best Friends Ser.: No. 2). 160p. (YA). (gr. 4-7). pap. 4.99 (978-0-89107-658-2(1)) Crossway Bks.

Stanley, Andy. Go Fish Study Guide: Because of What's on the Line. 2005. 96p. pap. 9.99 (978-1-59052-548-7(5), Multnomah) WaterBrook Pr.

Stanley, Robin. Vacation Time. Fletcher, Rusty & Julien, Terry, illus. 2006. (Happy Day Summer Titles Ser.). 16p. (J). pap. 1.99 (978-0-7847-1828-5(8), 04191) Standard Publishing.

Stannard, Russell. WWW Here-I-Am. 2002. (gr. 7-12). lib. bdg. 18.75 (978-0-613-84233-4(2)) Tandem Library Bks.

—www.Here-I-Am. Pugh, Jonathan, illus. 2002. 160p. (gr. 5-8). 9.95 (978-1-890151-85-0(8)) Templeton Foundation Pr.

Steele, Michael Anthony. Boz/Boz Says Wiggle Your Ears BB. Johnson, Jay, illus. 2007. (BOZ#8482; Ser.). 20p. (J). 6.99 (978-0-310-71400-2(1)) Zondervan.

Steele, Michael Anthony & Exclaim Entertainment Staff. God Gives You Friends: With Boz the Bear. McKee, Darren, illus. 2006. (Boz Ser.). 12p. (J). 5.99 (978-0-310-71153-7(3)) Zonderkidz.

Steinagle, Michael, illus. On the Wings of the West Wind. 2005. 14.99 (978-1-58134-372-4(8), Crossway Bibles) Crossway Bks.

Stephen, Smith. Fourth & Long. 2006. 128p. (J). pap. 5.99 (978-0-7847-1471-3(1), 42142) Standard Publishing.

Stevans, Joy. Hugs in a Lunch Box. Stanley, Robin, ed. 2006. (Heritage Builders Ser.). 176p. (YA). pap. 8.99 (978-0-7847-1363-1(4), 04023); (J). pap. 8.99 (978-0-7847-1362-4(6), 04022) Standard Publishing.

Stiegemeyer, Julie. Thanksgiving: A Harvest Celebration. Benoit, Renne, illus. 2006. (ENG.). 32p. (J). pap. 6.99 (978-0-7586-0916-8(7)) Concordia Publishing Hse.

Stoks, Peggy. Sonido de las Aguas. 2000. (Reunited Ser.: Vol. 4). (SPA.). (J). (gr. 8-12). mass mkt. 3.99 (978-0-7899-0805-6(0)) Spanish Hse. Distributors.

The Story of Christian. 2005. (Illus.). (J). per. 995.00 (978-0-9762911-1-4(8), Ameeramac Bks.) Ameeramac Reporting, Inc.

Strauss, Ed. Devotions to Make You Stronger: A 90- Day Devotional. 2007. (2:52 Ser.). 192p. (J). pap. 9.99 (978-0-310-71311-1(0)) Zonderkidz.

Streib, Sally. Octopus Encounter. 2007. (J). ***978-0-8163-2210-7(4))*** Pacific Pr. Publishing Assn.

Stretton, Hesba. Cassy. Hymper, W. & Stacey, W. S., illus. 2006. (Golden Inheritance Ser.: Vol. 9). 117p. (J). pap. (978-0-921100-94-2(9)) Inheritance Pubns.

—Jessica's First Prayer. 2004. reprint ed. pap. 15.95 (978-1-4191-2751-9(9)); pap. 1.99 (978-1-4192-2751-6(3)) Kessinger Publishing, LLC.

—Little Meg's Children. 2000. (Golden Inheritance Ser.: Vol. 5). (Illus.). 88p. (J). pap. (978-0-921100-92-8(2)) Inheritance Pubns.

—Little Meg's Children. (Early Children's Bks.). (J). reprint ed. 15.00 (978-0-384-56160-1(8)) Johnson Reprint Corp.

—Lost Gip. 2003. (Golden Inheritance Ser.: Vol. 7). (Illus.). 121p. (J). (978-0-921100-93-5(0)) Inheritance Pubns.

Stuyvesant, Carolyn. Storytime in Africa. 2002. (Illus.). (J). Bk. 1. 64p. pap. (978-1-883012-03-8(1)); Bk. 2. 96p. pap. (978-1-883012-04-5(X)) Remnant Pubns.

Sumpolec, Sarah Anne. The Alliance. 2004. (Becoming Beka Ser.). 256p. (YA). pap. 12.99 (978-0-8024-6452-1(1)) Moody Pubs.

—Encore. 2006. (Becoming Beka Ser.). 272p. (J). pap. 12.99 (978-0-8024-6458-3(0)) Moody Pubs.

—The Passage. 2005. (Becoming Beka Ser.). 256p. (J). pap. 12.99 (978-0-8024-6453-8(X)) Moody Pubs.

Swan, S. Annie. Thankful Rest (a Tale) 2006. 77.99 ***(978-1-4219-9988-3(9));*** pap. 70.99 ***(978-1-4142-5872-0(0))*** IndyPublish.com.

Tada, Joni Eareckson. Meanest Teacher. 2001. (gr. 3-6). lib. bdg. 14.15 (978-0-613-81758-5(3)) Tandem Library Bks.

—Mission Adventure. 2001. (gr. 3-6). lib. bdg. 14.15 (978-0-613-89086-1(8)) Tandem Library Bks.

Tada, Joni Eareckson & Jensen, Steve. The Meanest Teacher. 2005. (Darcy & Friends Ser.). 144p. (gr. 3-6). pap. 5.99 (978-1-58134-256-7(X), Crossway Bibles) Crossway Bks.

—The Mission Adventure. 2005. (Darcy & Friends Ser.). 143p. (gr. 3-6). pap. 5.99 (978-1-58134-257-4(8), Crossway Bibles) Crossway Bks.

—Tell Me the Promises. Dicanni, Ron, illus. 2004. 48p. (gr. 5-7). 17.99 (978-0-89107-904-0(1)) Crossway Bks.

Tate, Elizabeth Dawn. On My Front Porch Swing. 2007. per. 7.99 ***(978-1-60247-402-4(8))*** Tate Publishing & Enterprises, L.L.C.

Tatum, Gwen. K. C.'s Light: I Was Born from a Light. 1999. (Illus.). 32p. (J). pap. 8.00 (978-0-8059-4728-1(0)) Dorrance Publishing Co., Inc.

—K. C.'s Light: I Was Born from a Light. Mallard-Howard, Sabrina, illus. 1998. 32p. (J). (gr. k-6). pap. 9.95 (978-0-9664727-0-7(5)) TNT Publishing.

Taylor, Damon J., et al. En Busca de Tesoros: Cuatro Historias Maravillosas para Jovenes. 2003. (Mis Calcetines Ser.). (SPA.). 120p. pap. 7.99 (978-0-8254-1720-7(1), Editorial Portavoz) Kregel Pubns.

Taylor, Dan & Taylor, Damon J. Caleb Crosses the Country: A Camel's Tale. Taylor, Damon J., illus. 2004. (God Can Use Me Ser.). 8p. (J). 10.99 (978-0-8254-3870-7(5)) Kregel Pubns.

Taylor, Helen. Little Pilgrim's Progress: From John Bunyan's Classic. 2006. 336p. pap. 7.99 (978-0-8024-4924-5(7)) Moody Pubs.

Taylor, Jeannie. Am I Praying? 2003. (Illus.). 32p. (J). 12.99 (978-0-8254-3723-6(7)) Kregel Pubns.

Taylor, Jeannie St. John. Am I Trusting? 2004. 560p. (ps-3). 12.99 (978-0-8254-3721-2(0)) Kregel Pubns.

Teague, Raymond. Shadow's Stand. Archambault, Matthew, illus. 2001. 123p. (J). (gr. 3-6). pap. 10.95 (978-0-87159-265-1(7)) Unity Schl. of Christianity.

Tell Me a Story III. 2005. (J). per. 9.95 (978-1-59352-142-4(1)) Christian Services Publishing.

Tessie & Devore, David. Happy Birthday to Me. 2005. (Charisma Kids Ser.). (Illus.). 24p. (J). (gr. k-3). 9.99 (978-1-59185-207-0(2)) Strang Communications Co.

Thank You, God. 2003. (Illus.). 28p. (J). (ps-k). bds. 7.95 (978-0-8249-5457-4(2)) Ideals Pubns.

Thigpen, Meredith. Saving Nidia. 2007. (J). 17.99 ***(978-1-59886-814-2(4))*** Tate Publishing & Enterprises, L.L.C.

Thomas, Jacquelin. Divine Confidential. 2007. 272p. pap. 9.95 (978-1-4165-2719-0(2), Pocket) Simon & Schuster.

Thomas, Jerry D. Danger at Dinosaur Camp. 2002. (Detective Zack Ser.). (Illus.). 132p. (J). pap., pap. 6.99 (978-0-7814-3732-5(6), 0781437326) Cook, David C. Publishing Co.

—Danger at Dinosaur Camp. 2002. (gr. 3-6). lib. bdg. 14.15 (978-0-613-74879-7(4)) Tandem Library Bks.

—Mystery at Thunder Mountain. 2003. (Detective Zack Ser.). (Illus.). 132p. (J). pap., pap. 6.99 (978-0-7814-3731-8(8), 0781437318) Cook, David C. Publishing Co.

—Mystery at Thunder Mountain. 2002. (gr. 3-6). lib. bdg. 14.15 (978-0-613-74878-0(6)) Tandem Library Bks.

—The Red Hat Mystery. Odell, Lad, illus. 2003. (Detective Zack Ser.). 132p. (J). pap., pap. 6.99 (978-0-7814-3802-5(0), 0781438020) Cook, David C. Publishing Co.

—The Secrets in the Sand. Odell, Lad, illus. 2003. (Detective Zack Ser.). 132p. (J). pap., pap. 6.99 (978-0-7814-3803-2(9), 0781438039) Cook, David C. Publishing Co.

—Shoebox Kids Bible Stories, Vol. 4. 2002. (Illus.). 128p. (J). pap. 7.99 (978-0-8163-1949-7(9)) Pacific Pr. Publishing Assn.

—Shoebox Kids Bible Stories, Vol. 5. Justinen, Kim, illus. 2003. 128p. (J). 7.99 (978-0-8163-1971-8(5)) Pacific Pr. Publishing Assn.

Thompson, Joel. Critter Sitters: And Other Stories That Teach Christian Values. 2003. (ClubZone Kids Ser.). (Illus.). 80p. (J). pap. 5.99 (978-0-8010-4511-0(8)) Baker Bks.

—Shortcuts: And Other Stories That Teach Christian Values. 2003. (Clubzone Kids Ser.). (Illus.). 80p. (J). pap. 5.99 (978-0-8010-4510-3(X)) Baker Bks.

Threatt, Cedric Lanier, Sr. Different, but the Same. 2005. (J). 15.95 (978-0-9720543-2-4(4)) Threatt, Cedric L.

Tiller, Steve. Boat & Wind. Tecosky, Kathryn, ed. Cremeans, Robert, illus. 2002. 28p. (J). (ps-3). 15.95 (978-0-9704597-8-7(5)) MichaelsMind LLC.

—Connected at the Heart. Tecosky, Kathryn, ed. Cremeans, Robert, illus. 2001. (Adventures with Little Angels Ser.). 32p. (J). (ps-3). per. 7.95 (978-0-9704597-3-2(4)) MichaelsMind LLC.

—Connected at the Heart. Cremeans, Robert, illus. 2001. (Adventures with Little Angels Ser.). 36p. (J). (ps-3). 14.95 (978-0-9704597-2-5(6)) MichaelsMind LLC.

Trauscht, John. The Goody-Good Glasses. Trauscht, John & Moore, Michael, illus. 2006. (VeggieTales Ser.). 12p. (J). bds. 7.99 (978-1-4169-4063-0(4), Little Simon Inspirations) Simon & Schuster Children's Publishing.

Treasure Quest Guide. 2004. pap. 5.99 (978-1-56309-913-7(6)) Woman's Missionary Union.

Trent, John T. The Treasure Tree: Helping Kids Get along & Enjoy Each Other. 1998. (Illus.). 112p. (J). (ps-3). 15.99 (978-0-8499-5849-6(0)) Nelson, Thomas Inc.

Trevor, Meriol. Sun Slower Sun Faster. Ardizzone, Edward, illus. 2nd ed. 2004. 290p. (J). pap. 12.95 (978-1-883937-41-6(8)) Bethlehem Bks.

Tullos, Matt. Deleting the Net Threat. 1999. (Summit High Ser.: No. 4). 144p. (J). (gr. 7-9). pap. 4.99 (978-0-8054-1766-1(4)) B&H Publishing Grp.

—Processing the Computer Conspiracy. 1998. (Summit High Ser.: Vol. 2). 144p. (Orig.). (J). (gr. 7-9). pap. 4.99 (978-0-8054-0181-3(4)) B&H Publishing Grp.

—Wild Lies & Secret Truth. 1999. (Summit High Ser.: Vol. 3). 144p. (J). (gr. 7-9). pap. 4.99 (978-0-8054-1765-4(6)) B&H Publishing Grp.

—Wrong Turn in the Fast Lane. 1998. (Summit High Ser.). 144p. (Orig.). (J). (gr. 7-9). pap. 4.99 (978-0-8054-0180-6(6)) B&H Publishing Grp.

—Wrong Turn in the Fast Lane. 1998. (Orig.). (gr. 7-12). lib. bdg. 14.15 (978-0-613-90148-2(7)) Tandem Library Bks.

Two Nisse in Santaland. 2004. (J). bds. 12.95 (978-0-942684-21-6(4)) Wordshed.

Van Dyke, Tony & Van Dyke, Tracey. Ricky & Friends at Sunday School. Preston, Felicia, illus. 2002. (Encouraging African-Americans in Their Walk Ser.). 64p. (J). pap. 5.99 (978-0-8024-0901-0(6)) Moody Pubs.

Van Oss, Laura. Indigo's Gift: Does Indigo Have a Secret Gift? Wolf, Claudia, illus. 2006. 24p. (J). per. 2.99 (978-1-59958-003-6(9)) Journey Stone Creations, LLC.

Varela, Gabrielle Charbonnet & Tiernan, Cate. Strife. 2002. (Sweep Ser.: Vol. 9). 192p. (YA). (gr. 9 up). pap. 6.99 (978-0-14-230107-4(8), Puffin) Penguin Group (USA) Inc.

Veggietales. God Is Bigger! 2007. (Veggie Tales Gift Book Ser.). 32p. (J). 7.99 (978-1-4165-3384-9(2), Howard Bks.) Simon & Schuster.

—I Can Be Your Friend. 2007. (Veggie Tales Gift Book Ser.). 32p. (J). 7.99 (978-1-4165-3383-2(4), Howard Bks.) Simon & Schuster.

—My Day. 2005. (Veggie Tales Gift Book Ser.). 32p. (J). 7.99 (978-1-4165-3385-6(0), Howard Bks.) Simon & Schuster.

—Where My Hairbrush? 2005. (Veggie Tales Gift Book Ser.). 32p. (J). 7.99 (978-1-4165-3386-3(9), Howard Bks.) Simon & Schuster.

Vela, Natalie. Jesus & Me: Best Friends. 2001. (J). pap. 3.29 (978-3-905332-60-5(4)) Aurora Production AG CHE. *Dist:* Activated Ministries.

—Jesus & Me: Tons of Fun. 2001. (J). pap. 3.29 (978-3-905332-83-4(3)) Aurora Production AG CHE. *Dist:* Activated Ministries.

Vernon, Louise A. Peter & the Pilgrims. Eitzen, Allan, illus. 2nd ed. 2002. 128p. (YA). (gr. 4-9). 7.99 (978-0-8361-9226-1(5)) Herald Pr.

Vischer, Phil. A Snoodle's Tale. 2004. (Illus.). 48p. 8.99 (978-0-310-70751-6(X)) Zonderkidz.

Vogel, Jane & Johnson, Lissa Halls. Fast Forward to Normal, Vol. 2. 2005. (Brio Girls Ser.). 192p. (YA). (gr. 7-11). pap. 7.99 (978-1-56179-952-7(1)) Focus on the Family Publishing.

Vogel, Jane, et al. Good-Bye to All That, Vol. 5. 2005. (Brio Girls Ser.). 192p. (YA). pap. 7.99 (978-1-58997-051-9(9)) Focus on the Family Publishing.

Vroom, Angela. Airplane Letters to God. l.t. ed. 2004. (Illus.). 24p. (J). pap. 8.50 (978-0-9762935-0-7(1)) Perkins Crawford.

Walburg, Lori. The Legend of the Candy Cane Keepsake Book. Bernardin, James, illus. 2002. 40p. (J). 14.99 (978-0-310-70535-2(5)) Zondervan.

—The Legend of the Easter Egg. 2004. (Illus.). 26p. (J). bds. 6.99 (978-0-310-70785-1(4)) Zonderkidz.

—The Legend of the Easter Egg. Bernardin, James, illus. 1999. 32p. (J). 15.99 (978-0-310-22447-1(0)) Zonderkidz.

Wallace, Ian & De Brebeuf, Jean. The Huron Carol. Middleton, Jesse Edgar, tr. from FRE. 2006. (Illus.). 32p. 16.95 (978-0-88899-711-1(6)) Groundwood Bks. CAN. *Dist:* Perseus Distribution.

Wallace, Lee. Rapture Ready. 2005. 152p. pap. 19.95 (978-1-4137-5982-2(3)) PublishAmerica, Inc.

Walley, Chris. The Dark Foundations. 2006. (Lamb among the Stars Ser.). (Illus.). 560p. (YA). 19.99 (978-1-4143-0767-1(5), Thirsty(?)) Tyndale Hse. Pubs.

Walls, Pamela June. Quest for Treasure. Tribbles, Jean-Paul, illus. 2000. (Abby & the South Seas Adventures Ser.: No. 2). 224p. (J). (gr. 3-7). mass mkt. 5.99 (978-0-8423-3627-7(3)) Tyndale Hse. Pubs.

—Trouble in Tahiti. 2002. (gr. 3-6). lib. bdg. 14.15 (978-0-613-76806-1(X)) Tandem Library Bks.

—Trouble in Tahiti. 2002. (Abby & the South Seas Adventures Ser.: Vol. 7). 208p. (J). mass mkt. 5.99 (978-0-8423-3632-1(X)) Tyndale Hse. Pubs.

Walsh, Sheila. Gigi, No. 4. 2007. (Gigi, God's Little Princess Ser.). (Illus.). 32p. (J). 12.99 (978-1-4003-0804-0(6)) Nelson, Thomas Inc.

—Gigi & the Perfect Christmas Gift. 2006. (Gigi, God's Little Princess Ser.). (Illus.). 32p. (J). 12.99 (978-1-4003-0801-9(1)) Nelson, Thomas Inc.

—Gigi, God's Little Princess. Johnson, Meredith, illus. 2005. 32p. (J). 12.99 (978-1-4003-0529-2(1)) Nelson, Thomas Inc.

—The Mystery of Magillicuddy's Gold. 2007. (Will, God's Mighty Warrior Ser.). 32p. (J). 12.99 ***(978-1-4003-1028-9(8))*** Nelson, Thomas Inc.

—The Purple Ponies. Johnson, Meredith, illus. 2008. (Gigi, God's Little Princess Ser.). 32p. (J). 12.99 ***(978-1-4003-1124-8(1))*** Nelson, Thomas Inc.

Walsh, Sheila. The Royal Tea Party. 2006. (Gigi, God's Little Princess Ser.). (Illus.). 32p. (J). 12.99 (978-1-4003-0800-2(3)) Nelson, Thomas Inc.

Walton, O. F. Christie's Old Organ or Home, Sweet Home. 2005. reprint ed. pap. 22.95 (978-0-7661-9430-4(2)) Kessinger Publishing, LLC.

—Little Faith. 2002. (Illus.). 95p. 14.00 (978-1-929241-52-1(6)) Vision Forum, Inc., The.

—A Peep Behind the Scenes: A Little Girl's Journey of Discovery. 1999. 256p. (J). mass mkt. (978-1-85792-524-1(6), Christian Heritage) Christian Focus Pubns.

—Saved at Sea: A Young Boy in a Dramatic Rescue. (Illus.). 144p. (J). mass mkt. 5.99 (978-1-85792-795-5(8), Christian Heritage) Christian Focus Pubns. GBR. *Dist:* Riverside.

Walton, Van. From the Pound to the Palace. 2006. (ENG., Illus.). 32p. per. 15.99 (978-1-4141-0579-6(7)) Pleasant Word.

Warburton, Carol. Edge of Night: A Novel. 2004. (Illus.). 278p. pap. 14.95 (978-1-59156-013-5(6)) Covenant Communications, Inc.

Warner Press Staff. Divorce Comes to Our House. 2003. pap. (978-1-59317-009-7(2)) Warner Pr. Pubs.

—Princess & the Kiss: A Story of God's Gift of Purity. 2000. (J). (ps-3). 9.95 (978-0-87162-868-8(6)) Warner Pr. Pubs.

Warren, Rick. Made for a Purpose AMS. 2004. (J). 287.82 (978-0-310-60329-0(3)) Zonderkidz.

Watkins, Dawn L. Jenny Wren. 2000. (J). (gr. 3-7). pap. 14.98 incl. audio (978-0-89084-909-5(9), 100065) Jones, Bob Univ. Pr.

Weaver, Lisa D. Praying with Our Feet. Hess, Ingrid, illus. 2005. 40p. (J). pap. 12.99 (978-0-8361-9306-0(7)) Herald Pr.

Weaver, Will. Full Service. 2005. 240p. (YA). (gr. 9). 17.00 (978-0-374-32485-8(9), Farrar, Straus & Giroux (BYR)) Farrar, Straus & Giroux.

Wehrheim, Carol A. The Word & Picture Books Set 2: For Year C/A, 6 vols. Incl. Baby for Sarah. Frank, Betsy, illus. bds. 4.95 (978-0-8298-1197-1(4)); God's Good World. Frank, Betsy, illus. bds. 4.95 (978-0-8298-1196-4(6)); Good News for Jesus' Friends. James, Betsy, illus. bds. 4.95 (978-0-8298-1195-7(8)); Jesus Visits Zacchaeus. James, Betsy, illus. bds. 4.95 (978-0-8298-1193-3(1)); Lost & Found. James, Betsy, illus. bds. 4.95 (978-0-8298-1192-6(3)); Three Visitors for Jesus. James, Betsy, illus. bds. 4.95 (978-0-8298-1194-0(X)); 12p. (J). (ps). 1997. (Word & Picture Bks.). 29.70 (978-0-8298-1191-9(5)) Pilgrim Pr., The/United Church Pr.

—The Word & Picture Books Set 3: For Year A/B, 6 vols. Incl. Boy Shares Food. James, Betsy, illus. bds. 4.95 (978-0-8298-1229-9(6)); Church People. Frank, Betsy, illus. bds. 4.95 (978-0-8298-1228-2(8)); God Is Our Home. Frank, Betsy, illus. bds. 4.95 (978-0-8298-1199-5(0)); Helping Others. Frank, Betsy, illus. bds. 4.95 (978-0-8298-1225-1(3)); Meet Simeon & Anna. Frank, Betsy, illus. bds. 4.95 (978-0-8298-1226-8(1)); Welcome Jesus! Frank, Betsy, illus. bds. 4.95 (978-0-8298-1227-5(X)); 12p. (J). (ps). 1997. (Word & Picture Bks.). 29.70 (978-0-8298-1198-8(2)) Pilgrim Pr., The/United Church Pr.

Wetherell, Elizabeth. Wide Wide World Volume I. 2006. 99.99 ***(978-1-4280-5026-6(4));*** pap. 92.99 ***(978-1-4280-5023-5(X))*** IndyPublish.com.

—Wide Wide World Volume Ii. 2006. 99.99 ***(978-1-4280-5041-9(8));*** pap. 93.99 ***(978-1-4280-5049-5(3))*** IndyPublish.com.

Weyland, Jack. Ashley & Jen. 2000. (Illus.). 287p. (YA). 16.95 (978-1-57345-803-0(1)) Deseret Bk. Co.

—Emily. 1999. (J). 16.95 (978-1-57345-576-3(8)) Deseret Bk. Co.

Wheeler, Joe. The Candle in the Forest: And Other Christmas Stories Children Love. 2007. 96p. 16.99 ***(978-1-4165-4219-3(1)***, Howard Bks.) Simon & Schuster.

Wheeler, Joe L. The Candle in the Forest: And Other Christmas Stories Children Love. 2007. (J). ***(978-1-58229-707-1(X)***, Howard Bks.) Simon & Schuster.

Wheeler, Kathryn. Finders Keepers! A Tale in Which Robby Stops Stealing & Starts Giving. Sharp, Dan, illus. 2000. (Stories to Grow By Ser.). 19p. (J). (978-0-7424-0011-5(5), Instructional Fair) Schaffer, Frank Pubns.

—No Room for Neighbors: A Tale in Which Two Strangers Become Friends. Myers, Darcy, illus. 2000. (Stories to Grow By Ser.). 19p. (J). 3.95 (978-1-56822-594-4(6), Instructional Fair) Schaffer, Frank Pubns.

—Patty Saves the Day! A Tale in Which Patty Discovers Her True Gift. Myers, Darcy, illus. 2000. (Stories to Grow By Ser.). 19p. (J). (978-0-7424-0012-2(3), Instructional Fair) Schaffer, Frank Pubns.

—The Suspicious Stranger: A Tale in Which Kindness Is Repaid. Anderson, Julie, illus. 1999. (Stories to Grow By Ser.). 20p. (C). 3.99 (978-1-56822-592-0(X), Instructional Fair) Schaffer, Frank Pubns.

—Tunnel 2000: A Tale in Which Edgar Finds Joy in Living. Sharp, Dan, illus. 2000. (Stories to Grow By Ser.). 19p. (J). 3.95 (978-1-56822-597-5(0), Instructional Fair) Schaffer, Frank Pubns.

When Quiet Comes. 2005. (YA). per. 14.95 (978-0-9769815-0-3(5)) DesertStar Communications, LLC.

White, Julie Ellison. Friends Forever. 2001. (Fast Lane Bible Studies Ser.). 52p. (YA). (gr. 7-9). pap. 9.95 (978-0-8361-9188-2(9)) Herald Pr.

White, Tim. A Single Heart. 2006. 193p. pap. 19.95 (978-1-4137-9418-2(1)) PublishAmerica, Inc.

Wierenga, Kathy & Johnson, Lissa Halls. Double Exposure, Vol. 4. 2005. (Brio Girls Ser.). 192p. (YA). pap. 7.99 (978-1-56179-954-1(8)) Focus on the Family Publishing.

Willcox, James. Pixie Howard: Her Adventures in Faith. 2004. 116p. pap. 16.95 (978-1-4137-2499-8(X)) PublishAmerica, Inc.

Williams, Carol Lynch. The Golden Trail: Tish, Booke One, Latter Day Girls Collection. 2000. (J). pap. (978-0-88290-694-2(1)) Cornerstone Publishing & Distribution, Inc.

—Laura's Box of Treasures. 1999. (Choose the Right Ser.: Bk. 1). 61p. (J). pap. (978-1-57008-674-8(5)) Scribbulations LLC.

—Victoria's Courage. 1998. (Latter-Day Daughters Ser.). (J). 5.95 (978-1-57345-434-6(6)) Deseret Bk. Co.

Williams, D. Disillusions. 2005. 164p. pap. 19.95 (978-1-4137-7187-9(4)) PublishAmerica, Inc.

Williams, M. C. No where to be Found: Time Is Short. l.t. ed. 2006. 38p. per. 3.65 (978-1-59879-099-3(4)) Lifevest Publishing, Inc.

Williamson, Joanne S. God King: A Story in the Days of King Hezekiah. 2002. (Living History Library). (Illus.). 212p. (J). pap. 13.95 (978-1-883937-73-7(6), 73-6) Bethlehem Bks.

Wilson, Heather Gemmen. Lydia Barnes & the Blood Diamond Treasure. 2007. (J). ***(978-0-89827-350-2(1))*** Wesleyan Publishing Hse.

Wilson, Lou Ellen. Josiah. 2003. pap. 9.95 (978-0-533-14341-2(1)) Vantage Pr., Inc.

Wilson, Michelle L. Nash Happy from Cloud 9: The Unassigned Mission. 2007. 24p. (J). pap. 8.99 ***(978-1-59886-979-8(5))*** Tate Publishing & Enterprises, L.L.C.

Wilson, Pauline Hutchens & Dengler, Sandy. The Case of the Cold Turkey. 2001. (New Sugar Creek Gang Ser.: Vol. #3). (Illus.). 144p. (J). 5.99 (978-0-8024-8663-9(0)) Moody Pubs.

—The Case of the Dinosaur in the Desert, Vol. 4. 2001. (New Sugar Creek Gang Ser.: Vol. #4). (Illus.). 144p. (J). 5.99 (978-0-8024-8664-6(9)) Moody Pubs.

—The Case of the Monster in the Creek. 2001. (New Sugar Creek Gang Ser.: Vol. 6). 144p. (J). 5.99 (978-0-8024-8666-0(5)) Moody Pubs.

—The Case of the Red Hot Possum: The New Sugar Creek Gang. 2001. (New Sugar Creek Gang Ser.). 144p. (J). (gr. 2-8). 5.99 (978-0-8024-8661-5(4)) Moody Pubs.

Windle, Jeanette. Jana's Journal. 2002. (gr. 7-12). lib. bdg. 22.25 (978-0-613-88253-8(9)) Tandem Library Bks.

—Jana's Journal: A Novel for Teens. 2002. 256p. pap. 12.99 (978-0-8254-4117-2(X)) Kregel Pubns.

—Secret of the Dragon Mark, Vol. 5. 2002. (Parker Twins Ser.: No. 5). 160p. (gr. 3-8). pap. 5.99 (978-0-8254-4149-3(8)) Kregel Pubns.

Wingfield, Al. Come! See! With Little Becky Anne. Ramey, Lisa L., illus. Ramey, Lisa L., photos by. 2000. 16p. (J). (ps-3). pap. 7.95 (978-1-930260-01-6(6)) CTS Family Pr.

—The Twins in the Green Forest. Ramey, Lisa L., illus. Ramey, Lisa L., photos by. 2000. 18p. (J). (ps-3). pap. 7.95 (978-1-930260-02-3(4)) CTS Family Pr.

Winston, Pat. Earl the Emu Discovers God's Greatest Gift. Warren, Steve, illus. l.t. ed. 2002. (Earl the EMU Ser.). 24p. (J). per. 14.95 (978-0-9702821-3-2(3)) Light Way Pubns., The.

Wiseman, Gale. How Mr. Branch Got A New Name. 2007. (J). per. 9.99 (***978-1-59886-811-1(X))** Tate Publishing & Enterprises, L.L.C.

Wood, Christine. Runaway Rabbit. 2000. (gr. 3-6). lib. bdg. 14.15 (978-0-613-89222-3(4)) Tandem Library Bks.

Wood, Lena. The Ancient Omen. 2006. 192p. (J). pap. 6.99 (978-0-7847-1590-1(4) , 42152) Standard Publishing.

—The Angel of Fire. 2006. 192p. (J). pap. 6.99 (978-0-7847-1530-7(0)) Standard Publishing.

—Carpet of Bones. 2006. (Illus.). 192p. (J). pap. 6.99 (978-0-7847-1535-2(1)) Standard Publishing.

—Elijah Creek & the Armor of Gift Set. 2006. 576p. (J). Bks. 1-3. 17.99 (978-0-7847-1966-4(7)); Bks. 4-6. 17.99 (978-0-7847-1967-1(5)) Standard Publishing.

—The Haunted Soul, Vol. 5. 2005. (Elijah Creek & the Armor of God Ser.: 5). (Illus.). 189p. (J). (gr. 3-7). pap. 6.99 (978-0-7847-1760-8(5) , 42155) Standard Publishing.

—The Path of Shadows, Vol. 4. 2005. (Elijah Creek & the Armor of God Ser.: 4). (Illus.). 189p. (J). (gr. 3-7). pap. 6.99 (978-0-7847-1759-2(1) , 42154) Standard Publishing.

—The Raven's Curse. 2006. 192p. (J). pap. 6.99 (978-0-7847-1592-5(0) , 42153) Standard Publishing.

—The Severed Head. 2006. 192p. (J). pap. 6.99 (978-0-7847-1583-3(1) , 42151) Standard Publishing.

Wordshop Editorial Staff. Twink 'n' Twinkle: The Beginning. 1999. (Illus.). 28p. (J). (ps-4). 19.95 (978-0-9668469-0-4(7)) WordSHOP, Inc.

Wright, Caleb E. Marcus Blair A Story of Provincial Times. 2006. pap. 22.95 (***978-1-4286-6303-9(7))** Kessinger Publishing, LLC.

Wright, Julie. My Not-So-Fairytale Life. 2005. 256p. (YA). pap. 15.95 (978-1-59038-476-3(8)) Deseret Bk. Co.

Wright, Lani, ed. Trying Times. 2001. (Being There Ser.: Bk. 2). 40p. (YA). (gr. 9-12). pap. 15.95 (978-0-8361-9183-7(8)) Herald Pr.

Yates, Alma J. Sammy's Song: A Novel. 2005. 272p. (J). (***978-1-59156-945-9(1))** Covenant Communications.

Yeager, Barbara. Confirmation. 2006. 21.95 (***978-1-4259-7010-9(9));** pap. 12.00 (***978-1-4259-7009-3(5))** AuthorHouse.

Yoder, Mary Elizabeth. More Story Times with Grandma. 2000. 235p. (J). (gr. k-5). mass mkt. 4.25 (978-0-87813-591-2(X)) Christian Light Pubns., Inc.

Yoder, Wanda M. In Memory of Michael. 1998. (Hammond Cousins Ser.: Vol. 3). (Illus.). 176p. (YA). (gr. 4 up). pap. 5.95 (978-0-87813-577-6(4)) Christian Light Pubns., Inc.

Yorks, Sharon Lene. The Twin Who Wins. 2002. (Cloverleaf Ser.: Bk. 1). (Illus.). 224p. (J). (gr. 6 up). mass mkt. 5.99 (978-0-9720132-0-8(2)) Tumbleweed Publishing.

Young, Cleous. The Prophetic Artist. 2006. (J). per. 9.95 (978-1-882185-75-7(7)) Cornerstone Publishing, Inc.

Youngberg, Norma R. Jungle Thorn. 2000. (Illus.). 112p. (J). reprint ed. per. 8.95 (978-1-57258-157-9(3) , 945-6024) TEACH Services, Inc.

—Miracle of the Song. 2000. (Illus.). 188p. (J). (gr. 3-6). reprint ed. per. 11.95 (978-1-57258-187-6(5) , 945-6049) TEACH Services, Inc.

Younger, Marshal. The Last Days of Eugene Meltsner. 2000. (Adventures in Odyssey Ser.). (Illus.). 96p. (J). (gr. 3-7). pap. 4.99 (978-1-56179-911-4(4)) Focus on the Family Publishing.

—The Last Days of Eugene Meltsner. 2000. (Adventures in Odyssey Ser.). (Illus.). (J). pap. (978-0-8423-4048-9(3)) Tyndale Hse. Pubs.

Youree, Barbara. Senegal Sleuths. 2006. 56p. 7.75 (978-0-8341-2226-0(X)) Beacon Hill Pr. of Kansas City.

Yoxen, Jackie. Hannah's Sunday Hats. Francis, Lauren, illus. l.t. ed. 2006. 32p. (J). 19.95 (***978-1-59879-184-6(2))** Lifevest Publishing, Inc.

Zalben, Jane Breskin. Light. Zalben, Jane Breskin, illus. 2007. (Illus.). 40p. (J). (gr. k-4). 17.99 (***978-0-525-47827-0(2)** , Dutton Juvenile) Penguin Group (USA) Inc.

Zaugg, Sandra L. The Rock Slide Rescue. Ford, Mark, illus. 1998. (Shoebox Kids Ser.: Vol. 8). 91p. (J). (gr. 2-5). pap. 6.99 (978-0-8163-1387-7(3)) Pacific Pr. Publishing Assn.

Zondervan. Junior, el Esparragos. 2004. (SPA.). 18p. (J). 3.99 (978-0-8297-4416-3(9)) Zondervan.

Zondervan. VeggieTales' Two Compartment Activity Cover. 2007. 16.99 (***978-0-310-81216-6(X))** Zondervan.

Zondervan & Focus on the Family Staff. Froggy World: Where All Your Dreams Come True. 2003. (J). 12.99 incl. VHS (978-0-310-70569-7(X)) Zonderkidz.

CHRISTIAN SCIENCE

Parsons, Cynthia. The Discoverer, Mary Baker Eddy. Longyear Museum Staff, photos by. 2000. (Illus.). 132p. (J). (gr. 4-8). 20.00 (978-1-892286-00-0(9)) Vermont Schoolhouse Pr., The.

CHRISTIAN SYMBOLISM

see Christian Art and Symbolism

CHRISTIANITY

see also Church; God; Jesus Christ; Missions; Protestantism; Reformation; Theology

also names of Christian churches and sects (e.g. Catholic church; Huguenots; etc.) and headings beginning with the words Christian and Church

Alcorn, Randy. Tell Me about Heaven. Dicianni, Ron, illus. 2007. 48p. (J). pap. 19.99 (***978-1-58134-853-8(3))** Crossway Bks.

Anderson, Carolyn B. Heaven Is a Real Place. 2007. 73p. per. 8.95 (***978-1-59824-512-7(0))** E-BookTime LLC.

Anglican Church of Canada Staff. The Gift of Life: Children's Book for the Eucharist from Life in the Eucharist Program. 56p. pap. 5.50 (978-0-919891-62-3(4) , 1275) Anglican Bk. Centre CAN. *Dist:* Forward Movement Pubns.

—Life in the Eucharist: A Communion Program for Children. 64p. pap., stu. ed. 8.95 (978-0-919891-46-3(2) , 1315) Anglican Bk. Centre CAN. *Dist:* Forward Movement Pubns.

Anonymous. Grandes Verdades para Niños Pequeños. Foce, Natalia, tr. from ENG. 2004. Orig. Title: Great Truths for Little Children. (SPA., Illus.). 115p. (J). pap. (978-1-932789-10-2(3)) Editorial Sendas Antiguas, LLC.

Ark & the Dove. (YA). (gr. 9-12). 19.00 (978-1-931555-43-2(5)) Our Lady of Victory Schl.

Arthur, Kay. Lord, I Want to Know You. 2006. (Lord Ser.). 210p. (YA). pap. 13.99 (978-1-888655-14-8(3)) Precept Ministries.

Arthur, Patti T. A Sacrament of Holy Communion: A Study Guide for Young People. 1999. (Illus.). 16p. (gr. 5). pap. 4.75 (978-0-7880-1351-5(3)) CSS Publishing Co.

Ausburg. The Story of the Advent Wreath. 2004. 12p. 1.50 (978-0-8066-2525-6(2) , Augsburg Bks.) Augsburg Fortress, Pubs.

Bahr, Ann Marie B. Christianity. 2004. (Religions of the World Ser.). (Illus.). 150p. (gr. 9-13). 35.00 (978-0-7910-7856-3(6) , Chelsea Hse.) Facts On File, Inc.

Baker, Rod. Real Healing for Kids. 2005. (Real Life Ser.). 32p. (J). (gr. 1-4). mass mkt. 1.99 (978-1-57794-708-0(8)) Harrison Hse., Inc.

—Real Power for Kids. 2005. (Real Life Ser.). 32p. (J). (gr. 1-4). mass mkt. 1.99 (978-1-57794-707-3(X)) Harrison Hse., Inc.

Barnes, Trevor. Christianity: Worship, Festivals, & Ceremonies from Around the World. Kingfisher Editors, ed. 2005. (World Faiths Ser.). (Illus.). 40p. (J). (gr. 5-9). pap., pap. 6.95 (978-0-7534-5880-8(2) , Kingfisher) Houghton Mifflin Co. Trade & Reference Div.

Barry, John F. One Faith, One Lord: A Study of Basic Catholic Belief. 4th ed. 2001. (J). per. (978-0-8215-2207-3(8) , Sadlier) Sadlier, William H. Inc.

Blanck, Ryan. Engaging the Media: Equipping Young People to Think Critically & Make Biblical Decisions about Entertainment. 2003. 122p. (YA). pap. 12.95 (978-0-595-30143-0(6)) iUniverse, Inc.

Bob, Schultz. Boyhood & Beyond. 2004. pap. 10.99 (978-1-883934-09-5(5)) Great Expectations Bk. Co.

Boling, Ruth L. Come Worship with Me: A Journey Through the Church Year. Carrier, Tracey Dahle, illus. 2004. (Mouse Bks.: Vol. 2). 43p. (ps-3). 19.95 (978-0-664-50045-0(5)) Westminster John Knox Pr.

Boshoff, Penny. God & Me: 365 Daily Devotions. 2005. (Illus.). 380p. (J). (ps-7). 14.95 (978-1-905051-78-6(6)) Make Believe Ideas GBR. *Dist:* Ingram Pub. Services.

Broadberry, Richard St L. Thinking about Christianity. 2000. (gr. 7-12). lib. bdg. 18.80 (978-0-613-84080-4(1)) Tandem Library Bks.

Brown, Alan. Christianity. (Illus.). 64p. (YA). (gr. 4 up). lib. bdg. 29.95 (978-1-59389-131-2(8)) Chrysalis Education.

—Christianity. 2006. (QEB World of Faiths Ser.). (Illus.). 32p. (J). lib. bdg. 19.95 (978-1-59566-207-1(3)) QEB Publishing Inc.

—Christianity. 2005. (World Religions Ser.). (Illus.). 58p. (J). (gr. 4-12). pap. 12.95 (978-1-55285-651-2(8) , Walrus Bks.) Whitecap Bks., Ltd. CAN. *Dist:* Firefly Bks., Ltd.

—Jesus & Christianity. 2002. (Great Religious Leaders Ser.). (Illus.). 48p. (J). lib. bdg. 28.50 (978-1-58340-221-4(7)) Smart Apple Media.

Burke, Spencer. Making Sense of Church: Eavesdropping on Emerging Conversations about God, Community, & Culture. 2003. 174p. pap. 16.99 (978-0-310-25499-7(X)) Zondervan.

Card, Michael. Sleep Sound in Jesus: Gentle Lullabies for Little Ones & Inspirational Devotions for Parents. 2nd ed. 2003. (Illus.). 36p. wbk. ed. 15.99 (978-0-7369-1219-8(3)) Harvest Hse. Pubs.

Chapman, Gillian. Celebrations Make & Do. 2004. 32p. (J). 7.99 (978-0-7586-0585-6(4)) Concordia Publishing Hse.

Cho, David Yonggi. 45 Años de Esperanza. 2004. 260p. pap. 9.99 (978-987-557-061-0(3)) Vida Pubs.

Christ Our Life: God Is Good. 2004. (gr. 1 up). stu. ed. (978-0-8294-1549-0(1)) Loyola Pr.

Christ Our Life: God Is Good; Parish-Catechist Manual. 2004. (gr. 1 up). (978-0-8294-1658-9(7)) Loyola Pr.

Christian Focus Publishing Staff. On the Way for 3 - 9's Vol. 7: Christmas, Service & the Promised Messiah. 2000. (On the Way Ser.: Vol. 7). 88-104p. (J). pap. (978-1-85792-327-8(8) , Christian Focus) Christian Focus Pubns.

Christianity 101. 1998. (Cross Training Ser.: Vol. 1). 80p. (YA). (gr. 10-12). pap., tchr. ed. 15.00 incl. VHS (978-1-57405-008-0(7)) CharismaLife Pubs.

Christianity 201. ldr.'s ed. 1998. (Cross Training Ser.: Vol. 2). 76p. (YA). (gr. 10-12). pap. 15.00 incl. VHS (978-1-57405-016-5(8)) CharismaLife Pubs.

Christianity 301. ldr.'s ed. 1998. (Cross Training Ser.: Vol. 3). 72p. (YA). (gr. 10-12). pap. 15.00 incl. VHS (978-1-57405-024-0(9)) CharismaLife Pubs.

Come to God's Party: Learning Tool. 2004. (978-0-8066-6479-8(7)) Augsburg Fortress, Pubs.

Crouser, Brad. What's My Excuse for Not Being a Christian? 12 Myths of Christianity 12 Myths of Christianity. 2004. 160p. (YA). pap. 13.95 (978-0-9724867-5-0(5)) Woodland Pr. LLC.

Darcy-Berube, Francoise & Berube, John Paul. Growing up a Friend of Jesus: A Guide to Discipleship for Children. 2003. (Illus.). 128p. (978-2-89507-041-2(5)) Novalis Publishing.

—Growing up a Friend of Jesus: A Guide to Discipleship for Children. 2000. (Illus.). 128p. (J). (gr. 3-6). 17.95 (978-0-86716-401-5(8)) St. Anthony Messenger Pr. & Franciscan Communications.

Davies, Valerie. Dia a Dia. 2000. Orig. Title: Day by Day. (SPA.). (J). (ps-3). (978-0-7899-0536-9(1) , 495658) Editorial Unilit.

de Talamo, Edith G., tr. Oraciones para los Pequenitos. Stevenson, Peter, illus. 2000. (Baby's First Ser.).Tr. of Prayers for Little Ones. (SPA.). 20p. (J). (ps-k). bds. 10.99 (978-0-7899-0744-8(5) , 493779) Editorial Unilit.

DeVries, Douglas. Enticed by Gold. 2005. 17.00 (978-1-877721-07-6(7)); pap. 12.00 (978-1-877721-08-3(5)) Jade Ram Publishing.

Dillon, Sally. Michael Asks Why Kids Activity Book. Augustin, Nina, illus. 2000. 77p. (J). pap. 1.99 (978-0-8163-1793-6(3)) Pacific Pr. Publishing Assn.

Doerfler-Dall, Mary. Hands on Faith: 66 Projects, Activities & Crafts for Children. 2003. 128p. (gr. 2-6). tchr. ed., spiral bd. 17.95 (978-0-87793-739-5(7)) Ave Maria Pr.

Donahue, Laurie & Phillipps, Paul. The Lord's Supper... Let's Get Ready! Palmer, Scott, illus. 2005. 96p. pap. 9.99 (978-0-9718306-6-0(5)) LifeSong Pubs.

Dowds, Mark. Exploring Christianity. 2003. (gr. 7-12). lib. bdg. 16.45 (978-0-613-89616-0(5)) Tandem Library Bks.

Drury, Keith W, ed. Successful Youth Mentoring Bk. 2: 24 Practical Sessions to Impact Kids' Lives, 1999. 144p. (YA). (gr. 8-12). pap. 16.99 (978-0-7644-2136-5(0)) Group Publishing, Inc.

Editorial Portavoz Staff & Sabio Y Prudente Ministries Staff. Mas Que Vencedores, Vol. 4. 2002. (Sabio Y Prudente Ser.).Tr. of More Than Conquerors #4. (SPA.). 64p. (YA). (gr. 8-13). pap. 4.99 (978-0-8254-0947-9(0) , Editorial Portavoz) Kregel Pubns.

Elkins, Stephen. First Steps in Faith. Colton, Ellie, illus. 2006. 32p. (J). 9.99 (978-0-8054-2662-5(0)) B&H Publishing Grp.

Explorations in Social Studies & Faith. (J). (gr. 1-2). 15.99 (978-0-570-00740-1(2) , 22-2828); (J). (gr. 3-4). 15.99 (978-0-570-00746-3(1) , 22-2834); (J). (gr. 5-6). 15.99 (978-0-570-00752-4(6) , 22-2840); (YA). (gr. 7-8). 15.99 (978-0-570-00758-6(5) , 22-2846) Concordia Publishing Hse.

Explorations in Social Studies & Faith: Early Childhood. (J). 15.99 (978-0-570-00734-0(8) , 22-2822) Concordia Publishing Hse.

Fennewald, Rebecca Greene. Who Are You God? 2005. 65p. per. 8.95 (***978-1-59824-353-6(5))** E-BookTime LLC.

Francen, Mike. We Cannot Deny It. 1999. 62p. (YA). per. 6.00 (978-1-888079-03-6(7)) Francen World Outreach.

Fun with Foster Kids Christian Adventures in Learning. 2005. (J). per. 19.95 (978-1-59649-469-5(7)); cd-rom 19.95 (978-1-59649-177-9(9)) Whispering Pine Pr., Inc.

Fun with Foster Kids Christian Adventures in Learning - English / Spanish Bilingual Translation. 2005. (J). 19.95 (978-1-59649-490-9(5)); spiral bd. 19.95 (978-1-59649-491-6(3)); per. 19.95 (978-1-59649-489-3(1)); cd-rom 19.95 (978-1-59649-492-3(1)) Whispering Pine Pr., Inc.

Fun with Foster Kids Christian Educational Curriculum. 2005. (J). spiral bd. 19.95 (978-1-59649-175-5(2)); per. 19.95 (978-1-59649-470-1(0)); cd-rom 19.95 (978-1-59649-176-2(0)) Whispering Pine Pr., Inc.

Fun with Foster Kids Educational Curriculum Book - English / Spanish Bilingual Translation. 2005. (J). 19.95 (978-1-59649-485-5(9)); spiral bd. 19.95 (978-1-59649-486-2(7)); per. 19.95 (978-1-59649-484-8(0)); cd-rom 19.95 (978-1-59649-487-9(5)) Whispering Pine Pr., Inc.

Fun with Foster Kids Educational Curriculum Student Edition. 2005. (J). per. 29.95 (978-1-59649-468-8(9)); cd-rom 19.95 (978-1-59649-169-4(8)) Whispering Pine Pr., Inc.

Ganeri, Anita. Christian Stories. Phillips, Rachael, illus. 2001. (Storyteller Ser.). 30p. (YA). 22.00 (978-0-237-52035-9(4) , Evans Brothers, Limited) Evans Publishing Group GBR. *Dist:* Independent Pubs. Group.

—Christianity. 2006. (This Is My Faith Bks.). 32p. (J). (gr. 1-4). pap. 4.99 (978-0-7641-3473-9(6)); 11.99 (978-0-7641-5963-3(1)) Barron's Educational Series, Inc.

Ganeri, Martin & Ganeri, Anita. Christian Prayer & Worship. 2007. (J). (***978-1-59771-091-6(1))** Sea-To-Sea Pubns.

Gibson, Lynne. Christianity. 2003. (Living Religions Ser.). (Illus.). 62p. (J). lib. bdg. 28.56 (978-0-7398-6383-1(5)) Raintree.

Glass, John. Amrach & the Paraclete. 2005. 186p. (YA). pap. 9.99 (978-1-85078-556-9(2)) Authentic Media.

God's Big Pictur-Book. ldr.'s ed. 2004. (KidsTime Ser.). 488p. (gr. 1-6). 39.99 (978-0-8307-2349-2(8) , Gospel Light) Gospel Light Pubns.

God's Big Picture: Bible Time Line. 2004. (KidsTime Ser.). (gr. 1-6). 19.99 (978-0-8307-2347-8(1) , Gospel Light) Gospel Light Pubns.

God's People Celebrate: Leader's Guide. 2004. (KidsTime Ser.). (gr. 1-6). 39.99 (978-0-8307-2529-8(6) , Gospel Light) Gospel Light Pubns.

Gortler, Rosemarie & Piscitelli, Donna. The Mass Book for Children. Sternhagen, Mimi, illus. 2004. 48p. per. 5.95 (978-1-59276-075-6(9)) Our Sunday Visitor, Publishing Div.

Groenboom, Roger, et al. The Light of the World Is Jesus. (Walk with Me Ser.). (gr. k-8). 12.95 (978-1-59255-172-9(6) , 017010, Faith Alive Christian Resources) CRC Pubns.

Guia Catolica Para Los Creyentes Mas Pequenos. 2003. (J). pap. 3.95 net. (978-0-7648-1042-8(1)) Liguori Pubns.

Hartney, Chris, et al. Livewire Investigates Christianity. 2004. (Livewires Ser.). (Illus.). 32p. pap. 4.10 (978-0-521-60110-8(X)) Cambridge Univ. Pr.

Hendrick, Kathy. One Faith, Onr Lord, Review & Resource Book. 4th ed. 2001. (J). (978-0-8215-2209-7(4) , Sadlier) Sadlier, William H. Inc.

Hendricks, Kathy & Hutchinson, Gloris. One Faith, One Lord, Catechist's Guide. 4th ed. 2001. (J). per. (978-0-8215-2208-0(6) , Sadlier) Sadlier, William H. Inc.

Hill, Karen. All God's Creatures. Johnson, Steven & Fancher, Lou, illus. 2005. 14p. (J). 9.99 (978-0-689-87819-0(2) , Little Simon Inspirations) Simon & Schuster Children's Publishing.

Hilliker, Amy Warren. Little One, God Loves You. Thompson, Carol, illus. 2004. 12p. (J). 6.99 (978-0-310-70971-8(7)) Zondervan.

—Little One, God Made You. Thompson, Carol, illus. 2004. 12p. (J). 6.99 (978-0-310-70959-6(8)) Zondervan.

Hipps, Amelia. Islam, Christianity, Judaism. 2003. (Introducing Islam Ser.). (Illus.). 112p. (J). lib. bdg. (978-1-59084-698-8(2)) Mason Crest Pubs.

Hoehn, Roxy. God's Adventurers. 2006. pap. 7.99 (978-0-8163-2148-3(5)) Pacific Pr. Publishing Assn.

Hunt, Marigold. A Life of Our Lord for Children. 2003. (Illus.). v, 189p. (J). 14.95 (978-1-928832-64-5(4)) Sophia Institute Pr.

Icelandic Sheepdog Adventures in Learning Book. 2005. (J). 19.95 (978-1-59210-344-7(8)) Whispering Pine Pr., Inc.

Icelandic Sheepdog Hood Christian Educational Curriculum Book. 2005. (J). 19.95 (978-1-59210-389-8(8)) Whispering Pine Pr., Inc.

Illustrated Catechism for Little Children. 2005. (J). pap. 9.95 (978-1-930873-43-8(3)) Neumann Pr., The.

Jacobs, Sheila. Something to Shout About. 1999. 160p. (YA). (gr. 4-8). mass mkt. 5.99 (978-1-85792-488-6(6) , Christian Focus) Christian Focus Pubns. GBR. *Dist:* Riverside.

Joel's First Ski Trip. 2005. (J). 24.95 (978-1-59649-171-7(X)); per. 19.95 (978-1-59649-172-4(8)) Whispering Pine Pr., Inc.

Johnson, Sarah Knights. Meet Jesus. 2000. (Illus.). 40p. (J). (ps-3). pap. (978-1-85792-584-5(X) , Christian Focus) Christian Focus Pubns.

Jones, Carolyn. Who Am I, Really? 2000. (Christian Character Development Ser.). (YA). (gr. 8-12). pap. 16.99 (978-0-7644-2132-7(8)) Group Publishing, Inc.

Joslin, Mary. The Story of the Cross: The Stations of the Cross for Children. Newey, Gail, illus. 2006. 48p. pap. 9.99 (***978-0-7459-4672-6(0))** Lion Hudson plc GBR. *Dist:* Independent Pubs. Group.

—The Story of the Cross: The Stations of the Cross for Children. Newey, Gail, illus. 2004. 94p. 15.95 (978-0-8294-1819-4(9)) Loyola Pr.

Juettner, Marie. Jehovah's Witness. 2005. (What Makes Me A ? Ser.). (Illus.). 48p. (J). (gr. 4-8). lib. bdg. 26.20 (978-0-7377-3084-5(6) , Kidhaven) Thomson Gale.

Keane, Michael. Lo Que Se Puede Ver Dentro de una Iglesia Catolica. Cuesta, Elizabeth & Cuesta, Rogelio, trs. from ENG. Pepis, Aaron, photos by. 2002. (SPA., Illus.). 32p. (J). 16.95 (978-1-893361-66-9(7)) SkyLight Paths Publishing.

Keene, Michael. Jesus of Nazareth. 2000. (Illus.). 80p. (J). (gr. 6-9). pap. 17.95 (978-0-7487-5286-7(2)) Nelson Thornes Ltd. GBR. *Dist:* Trans-Atlantic Pubns., Inc.

Kendall, R. T. Between the Times: Malachi: God's Last Prophet of the Old Testament. 2004. 208p. pap. (978-1-85792-792-4(3) , Christian Focus) Christian Focus Pubns.

Kendig, Ellen J. Children's Book of Table Blessings. Saroff, Phyllis V., illus. 2001. 48p. (J). (gr. k-3). 6.95 (978-0-8091 6689-3(5) , 6689-5) Paulist Pr.

Kids' Kindness Adventures in Learning Book. 2005. (J). 19.95 (978-1-59210-330-0(8)) Whispering Pine Pr., Inc.

Kids' Kindness Educational Curriculum Book. 2005. (J). 19.95 (978-1-59210-333-1(2)) Whispering Pine Pr., Inc.

KidsTime: God's Big Picture Kit. 2004. (gr. k-3). 139.99 (978-0-8307-2345-4(5) , Gospel Light) Gospel Light Pubns.

Lee, Witness. Abiding in the Lord to Enjoy His Life. 2000. 96p. (J). (gr. 6). per. 6.50 (978-0-7363-0834-2(2) , 07-931-001) Living Stream Ministry.

—The Conclusion of the New Testament: Messages 265-275. 2000. 98p. (J). (gr. 6). per. 6.00 (978-0-7363-0152-7(6) , 10-046-001) Living Stream Ministry.

—Dead to Law but Living to God. 2001. 68p. (J). (gr. 6). per. 5.75 (978-0-7363-1453-4(9) , 07-967-001) Living Stream Ministry.

—The Economy of God & the Mystery of the Transmission of the Divine Trinity. 2000. 167p. (J). (gr. 6). per. 8.50 (978-0-7363-0851-9(2) , 04-053-001) Living Stream Ministry.

—The Enjoyment of Christ for His Increase. 2000. 46p. (J). (gr. 6). 5.50 (978-0-7363-0809-0(1) , 07-073-001) Living Stream Ministry.

—The Holy Word for Morning Revival: Crystallization-Study of the New Jerusalem, Vol. 1. 2000. 136p. (J). (gr. 6). per. 7.00 (978-0-7363-0982-0(9) , 13-127-001) Living Stream Ministry.

—The Holy Word for Morning Revival: Matthew 8:1-13:52, Vol. 2. 2000. 90p. (J). (gr. 6). 6.00 (978-0-7363-1109-0(2) , 13-134-001) Living Stream Ministry.

—The Holy Word for Morning Revival: New Revival—Becoming the New Jerusalem. 2000. 109p. (J). (gr. 6). 7.00 (978-0-7363-0926-4(8) , 13-126-001) Living Stream Ministry.

—The Holy Word for Morning Revival: New Revival—Living the Life of a God-Man. 2000. 109p. (J). (gr. 6). 7.00 (978-0-7363-1162-5(9)) , 13-138-001) Living Stream Ministry.

—Life-Study of Philippians, 3 vols., Set. 2000. 547p. (J). per. 25.75 (978-0-7363-0912-7(8) , 10-275-001) Living Stream Ministry.

—Life-Study of Philippians Vol. 3: Messages 43-62. 2000. 172p. (J). (gr. 6). per. 10.25 (978-0-7363-0911-0(X) , 10-193-001) Living Stream Ministry.

—Living Christ. 2000. 40p. (J). (gr. 6). 5.25 (978-0-7363-1037-6(1) , 07-950-001) Living Stream Ministry.

—The Lord's Recovery of Eating. 2000. 42p. (J). (gr. 6). per. 5.25 (978-0-7363-0990-5(X) , 07-080-001) Living Stream Ministry.

—Subjective Experience of the Indwelling Christ. 2000. 106p. (J). (gr. 6). per. 6.75 (978-0-7363-1144-1(0) , 07-930-001) Living Stream Ministry.

—The Work of the Holy Spirit. 1999. 80p. (J). (gr. 6). per. 6.25 (978-0-7363-0663-8(3) , 07-051-001) Living Stream Ministry.

Leichner, Jeannine T. Joy, Joy the Mass. (Illus.). 30p. (J). (gr. 1-3). 5.95 (978-0-87973-350-6(0)) Our Sunday Visitor, Publishing Div.

Let's Practice Faith: Learning Tool. 2004. (978-0-8066-6504-7(1)) Augsburg Fortress, Pubs.

Leunk, Thea. What's up with the Church down the Street? 2002. (Other Beliefs Ser.). (YA). stu. ed. 8.75 (978-1-56212-784-8(5) , 130520, Faith Alive Christian Resources) CRC Pubns.

Libby, Larry. Someday Heaven. McLoughlin, Wayne, illus. 2001. 40p. (J). 12.99 (978-0-310-70105-7(8)) Zonderkidz.

Life Publishers International Staff. El Explorado Alumno Vol. 9, Tomo 3: March to May 2000. 1999. (SPA., Illus.). 48p. (YA). (gr. 7-9). pap. (978-0-7361-0116-5(0)) Life Pubs. International.

—El Explorado Alumno Vol. 9, Tomo 4: June to August 2000. 1999. (SPA., Illus.). 48p. (YA). (gr. 7-9). pap. (978-0-7361-0117-2(9)) Life Pubs. International.

—El Explorador Maestro Vol. 9, Tomos 3y4: March to August 2000. 1999. (SPA., Illus.). 112p. (YA). (gr. 7-9). pap. (978-0-7361-0118-9(7)) Life Pubs. International.

—Primeros Pasos I Trabajo Manual: June to August 2000. 1999. (SPA.). 16p. (J). pap. (978-0-7361-0101-1(2)) Life Pubs. International.

—Primeros Pasos I Trabajo Manual: March to May 2000. 1999. (SPA., Illus.). 16p. (J). pap. (978-0-7361-0100-4(4)) Life Pubs. International.

—Primeros Pasos II Trabajo Manual: June to August 2000. 1999. (SPA., Illus.). 16p. (J). (ps-k). pap. (978-0-7361-0105-9(5)) Life Pubs. International.

—Primeros Pasos II Trabajo Manual: March to May 2000. 1999. (SPA.). 16p. (J). (ps-k). pap. (978-0-7361-0104-2(7)) Life Pubs. International.

The Little Boys' Picnic. Date not set. pap. 5.95 (978-0-87162-985-2(2)) Warner Pr. Pubs.

Little KidsTime: My God & Me. ldr.'s ed. 2004. 464p. 39.99 (978-0-8307-2881-7(3) , Gospel Light) Gospel Light Pubns.

Little KidsTime: My Great Big God. ldr.'s ed. 2004. 464p. 39.99 (978-0-8307-2661-5(6) , Gospel Light) Gospel Light Pubns.

Little KidsTime 1: Bible Story Pictures. 2004. 104p. 19.99 (978-0-8307-2773-5(6) , Gospel Light) Gospel Light Pubns.

Lo Que Creemos (What We Believe) Quarter 2, Level 4. 2000. (Caminando con Jesus (Walking with Jesus) Series B). (SPA.). (J). (gr. 5-6). stu. ed. 3.50 (978-0-570-05165-7(7) , 16-4913) Concordia Publishing Hse.

Lookadoo, Justin & Morgan, Hayley. The Dirt on Breaking Up: A Dateable Book. 2004. (Dirt Ser.). 120p. (YA). (gr. 10-12). reprint ed. pap. 9.99 (978-0-8007-5918-6(4)) Revell.

Lord Teach Me to Love. 2003. 101p. (YA). per. 16.95 (978-0-9716068-1-4(1)) Lamar, Melvin Productions, Inc.

The Lord's Lady Liberty (Children's Book) The Statue of Liberation Through Christ Helping America to Remember God. 2006. (J). pap. 7.00 (978-0-9749019-8-5(9)) Understanding For Life Ministries, Inc.

Ludington, Colleen. What I Like about You. Becker, Paula J., illus. 2003. 32p. (J). 12.99 (978-1-4003-0292-5(7)) Nelson, Thomas Inc.

Lutz, A. Fowler. Stories of the Child Jesus from Many Lands. 2003. (Illus.). viii, 175p. (J). pap. 10.95 (978-1-928832-96-6(2)) Sophia Institute Pr.

MacDonald, Mindy. 7 Days of Creation. 2004. (GodCounts Ser.). 24p. (J). bds. 10.99 (978-1-59052-408-4(X) , Multnomah Kidz) WaterBrook Pr.

Mackenzie, Catherine. God's Little Guidebooks - Creation: God Creates Light. 2004. (Illus.). 16p. (J). pap. (978-1-85792-841-9(5) , Christian Focus) Christian Focus Pubns. GBR. *Dist:* Riverside.

—Mary Slessor, Servant to the Slave. 192p. (J). mass mkt. 5.99 (978-1-85792-348-3(0) , Christian Focus) Christian Focus Pubns. GBR. *Dist:* Riverside.

Main, Judith Lang. A Is for Altar, B Is for Bible. 2003. (Illus.). 65p. (J). 10.00 (978-1-56854-458-8(8) , Catechesis of the Good Shepherd) Liturgy Training Pubns.

Martell, Hazel Mary. Christianity. 2001. (World of Beliefs Ser.). (Illus.). 48p. (J). (gr. 3 up). 16.95 (978-0-87226-683-4(4) , Bedrick, Peter Bks.) School Specialty Publishing.

Marxhausen, Joanne. 3 In 1: A Picture of God. 2nd ed. 2004. (Illus.). 48p. (J). (ps-4). 8.99 (978-0-7586-0680-8(X)) Concordia Publishing Hse.

Matuszak, Pat. Bugs: Bible Critters. 2002. 40p. 9.99 (978-0-310-70067-8(1)) Zondervan.

McDowell, Josh. Is Christ Really God? ldr.'s ed. 2007. 65p. (J). 12.99 (978-1-60098-006-0(6)) Green Key Bks.

—Is Christ Really God? Grades 1-3. 2007. 48p. (J). wbk. ed. 5.99 (978-1-60098-004-6(X)) Green Key Bks.

—Is Christ Really God? Grades 3-6. 2007. 48p. (J). wbk. ed. 5.99 (978-1-60098-005-3(8)) Green Key Bks.

McDowell, Josh & Johnson, Kevin. Children Demand a Verdict: Answering Question about What We Believe & Why We Believe It. 2006. 208p. (J). pap. 10.99 (978-1-60098-012-1(0)) Green Key Bks.

McFarland, Alex. Stand: Core Truths You Must Know for an Unshakable Faith. 2005. 144p. (YA). (gr. 4-7). per. 10.99 (978-1-58997-353-4(4)) Focus on the Family Publishing.

McMullen, Tim. The Gift of a Snowflake. Beyer, William H., illus. 1998. 28p. (J). (ps-3). 12.95 (978-0-9664050-0-2(5)) Prospect Hill Co.

Medina, Sarah. Christian Churches. 2005. (Let's Find Out about Ser.). (Illus.). 32p. (J). (gr. 3-7). lib. bdg. (978-1-4034-7031-7(6)) Steck-Vaughn.

Meloche, Renee. Amy Carmichael: Rescuing the Children. 2002. (Heroes for Young Readers Ser.). (Illus.). 32p. 8.99 (978-1-57658-233-6(7)) YWAM Publishing.

My Story of Jesus. 2006. (J). 16p. pap. 1.99 (978-0-7847-1715-8(X) , 04176); 32p. pap. 2.89 (978-0-7847-1281-8(6) , 22094); (Illus.). 24p. bds. 6.99 (978-0-7847-1397-6(9) , 04057) Standard Publishing.

Nee, Watchman. Christ Is All Spiritual Matters & Things. 2001. 75p. (gr. 6). 6.00 (978-0-7363-0355-2(3) , 06-018-001) Living Stream Ministry.

Newton, Richard. The Safe Compass & How It Points. 2006. pap. 14.99 (***978-1-59925-059-5(4)***) Solid Ground Christian Bks.

Nystrom, Carolyn. Preach, Paul! 2004. (Follow Me Bks.). 10.99 (978-0-8254-3333-7(9)) Kregel Pubns.

—Sing, Mary! 2004. (Follow Me Bks.). 10.99 (978-0-8254-3336-8(3)) Kregel Pubns.

One of a Kind: A Study of Christian Identity. (Crossroads Ser.). (YA). (gr. 6-8). pap., tchr. ed. 14.50 (978-0-930265-73-1(4) , 120035); 2000. (J). (gr. 7-13). pap., stu. ed. 7.95 (978-0-930265-72-4(6) , 120030) CRC Pubns.

O'Neal, Debbie Trafton. The Advent Wreath: A Light in the Darkness. 2004. 16p. 1.99 (978-0-8066-2375-7(6) , 10-23756, Augsburg Bks.) Augsburg Fortress, Pubs.

Orborne, Rick. I Want to Know about the Church. 1998. (I Want to Know Ser.). (Illus.). 32p. (J). (gr. 7-10). 9.99 (978-0-310-22094-7(7)) Zonderkidz.

Pafford, John M. On the Solid Rock: Christianity & Public Policy. 2003. per. 10.99 (978-0-9745948-0-4(6) , 5) Ctr. For Cultural Leadership.

Paterson, Katherine. Who Am I? 2004. 96p. (J). pap. 8.00 (978-0-8028-5270-0(X)) Eerdmans, William B. Publishing Co.

Penney, Sue. Christianity. (World Beliefs & Cultures Ser.). 48p. (J). 2000. (Illus.). (gr. 5-7). lib. bdg. 25.64 (978-1-57572-355-6(7)); 2nd ed. (gr. 6-9). 22.00 (***978-1-4329-0313-8(6)***) Heinemann Library.

Pien, Lark. The Rosary Comic Book. Yang, Gene, illus. 2003. 56p. (J). mass mkt. 5.95 (978-0-8198-6479-6(X) , 332-312) Pauline Bks. & Media.

Plekker, Robert J. Who Is Jesus Christ? & What Is Christianity? 1998. (Illus.). 284p. (Orig.). (YA). (gr. 6 up). pap. 19.95 (978-0-9660565-1-8(5)) Joint Heirs Pubs.

Plum, Joan & Plum, Paul. I Am Special, Kindergarten Child's Activity Book. 5th ed. 2001. 112p. pap. 9.95 (978-0-87973-308-7(X)) Our Sunday Visitor, Publishing Div.

Pockets Learning Staff. Christian Celebrations Book. 1998. (Illus.). 8p. (ps up). 35.00 (978-1-888074-96-3(5)) Pockets of Learning.

Principles of Christian Faith. 2005. (YA). per. 6.50 (978-1-59872-115-7(1)) Instantpublisher.com.

Redden, Vicki. Heroes in Training. 2004. 375p. (J). 13.99 (978-0-8280-1843-2(X) , 84-980) Review & Herald Publishing Assn.

Regina Press Staff. Traditions of Advent for Children. 1999. 32p. (J). (ps-3). pap. 2.50 (978-0-88271-683-1(2)) Regina Pr., Malhame & Co.

Rock, Lois. The Christian Faith. 2003. (Illus.). 128p. (J). pap. 11.99 (978-0-7459-4780-8(8) , Lion) Lion Hudson plc GBR. *Dist:* Independent Pubs. Group.

—Learning about Jesus. 2003. (Illus.). (J). (ps-3). 14.95 (978-0-316-60556-4(5)) Little, Brown Bks. for Young Readers.

—The Path That Runs by the Church: A Year in the Life of a Village School. Comfort, Louise, illus. 2001. 48p. 19.99 (978-0-7459-4188-2(5) , Lion) Lion Hudson plc GBR. *Dist:* Independent Pubs. Group.

Roper, Beryl C. Seekers after Truth. 1998. 90p. (YA). (gr. 9-11). pap. (978-1-885812-04-9(3)) Aquamarine Pubns.

Rue, Nancy N. The Creativity Book: It's a God Thing! 2002. (Ywof Library). 112p. (J). pap. 7.99 (978-0-310-70247-4(X)) Zonderkidz.

Saints & Strangers - Guide. 2003. (YA). pap. 9.99 (978-1-56364-706-2(0)) Vision Video.

Sanna, Ellyn. Folk Religion. 2002. (North American Folklore Ser.). (Illus.). 112p. (J). (gr. 7 up). lib. bdg. (978-1-59084-348-2(7)) Mason Crest Pubs.

Savelle, Jerry. Don't Let Go of Your Dreams. Date not set. mass mkt. 3.99 (978-0-88144-171-0(6)) Victory Graphics & Media.

Sawyer, Kyle. Christianity: Straight to the Point. 2005. (J). per. (978-0-9729498-0-4(1)) K & B First Publishing Co.

Saxon, Terrill. Now I Lay Me down to Sleep. 2006. (Baby Blessings Ser.). (Illus.). 12p. bds. 11.99 (978-0-7847-1241-2(7) , 04053) Standard Publishing.

Science Discovery Works: Concordia Edition. (J). (gr. 1). stu. ed. 21.94 (978-0-570-02500-9(1) , 52-1001) Concordia Publishing Hse.

Scrimshire, Hazel. Tell the Truth. 16p. (J). pap. (978-1-85792-359-9(6) , Christian Focus) Christian Focus Pubns. GBR. *Dist:* Riverside.

Seaman, Alison & Brown, Alan. My Christian Faith. (Illus.). 32p. (978-0-237-51895-0(3) , Evans Brothers, Limited); 2006. (J). (978-1-84234-390-6(4) , Cherrytree Books) Evans Publishing Group.

Self, David. Christianity. 2005. (Illus.). 48p. (J). pap. (978-0-8368-5872-3(7)); lib. bdg. 30.00 (978-0-8368-5866-2(2)) Stevens, Gareth Inc. (World Almanac Library).

Slattery, Kathryn. If I Could Ask God Anything: Awesome Bible Answers for Curious Kids. 2001. (Illus.). 288p. (gr. 4-7). pap. 12.99 (978-1-59145-411-3(5)) Nelson, Thomas Inc.

Smalley, Gary. The Covenant Marriage. 2004. (Focus on the Family Marriage Ser.). 72p. 7.99 (978-0-8307-3119-0(9) , Gospel Light) Gospel Light Pubns.

SPCK. I Can Join in Common Worship: A Children's Communion Book. 2003. (Illus.). 24p. 5.00 (978-0-281-05568-5(8)) SPCK Publishing GBR. *Dist:* Pilgrim Pr., The/United Church Pr.

Spray, Teri A. & Martin, Terry. Blessed to Be a Blessing, 4 vols. Motley, Meredith & Riccle, Jodi, illus. 2001. ring bd. 260.00 (978-0-9714671-4-9(5)) Christian Cottage Schls.

St. Anthony Messenger Press Staff, ed. We Say Thanks: A Young Child's Book for Eucharist. 2000. (Illus.). (J). (ps-3). pap. 2.95 (978-0-86716-362-9(3)) St. Anthony Messenger Pr. & Franciscan Communications.

St. John, Patricia. A Young Person's Guide to Knowing God. 2000. 240p. (J). (gr. 8-13). pap. (978-1-85792-558-6(0) , Christian Focus) Christian Focus Pubns.

Steer, Malcolm. A Christian's Evangelistic Pocket Guide to Islam. 2004. 80p. pap. (978-1-85792-915-7(2) , Christian Focus) Christian Focus Pubns.

Stephens, Andrea. Boyland: A Babe's Guide to Understanding Guys. 2006. (B. A. B. E. Book Ser.). 208p. (J). pap. 12.99 (978-0-8007-5952-0(4)) Revell.

Stinnett, Leia A. Animal Tales: Spiritual Messages from Our Animal Friends. 2000. (Little Angel Bks.). (Illus.). 100p. (J). (gr. k-12). pap. 7.95 (978-1-880737-15-6(9)) Crystal Journeys Publishing.

Tambini, Michael. Christianity. 2006. (DK Eyewitness Bks.). (Illus.). 72p. (J). lib. bdg. 19.99 (978-0-7566-2247-3(6)) Dorling Kindersley Publishing, Inc.

Tangvald, Christine Harder & DeBoer, Rondi. Finish-the-Picture Bible Stories. Lewis, Stephen, illus. 2005. (Finish-the-Picture Ser.). 18p. (J). bds. 6.99 (978-0-310-70897-1(4)) Zonderkidz.

Taylor, Ina, ed. Christianity. 2006. (Illus.). 128p. (YA). pap., stu. ed. 32.50 (978-0-7487-9670-0(3)) Nelson Thornes Ltd. GBR. *Dist:* Trans-Atlantic Pubns., Inc.

Taylor, Jane. God Made Colours. 1998. 16p. (J). (ps-k). 3.99 (978-1-85792-291-2(3) , Christian Focus) Christian Focus Pubns. GBR. *Dist:* Riverside, Spring Arbor Distributors, Inc.

Teece, Geoff. Christianity. 2004. (Religion in Focus Ser.). (J). lib. bdg. (978-1-58340-465-2(1)) Smart Apple Media.

Toward Eternal Commencement. (YA). (gr. 9-12). 20.00 (978-1-931555-44-9(3)) Our Lady of Victory Schl.

Tucker, Beverly. Getting In-Sync with God. 2000. 96p. (J). (gr. 7-12). pap. 4.99 (978-1-57794-300-6(7)) Harrison Hse., Inc.

Understanding Scripture: The Genesis Creation Story. 2004. (Our Catholic Tradition Handbooks Ser.). (978-0-8294-1044-0(9)) Loyola Pr.

Vaisey, Gill & Lewis, Sian. William Booth: Cristion Arbennig Iawn. 2005. (WEL., Illus.). 27p. (978-1-85644-620-4(4)) Univ. of Wales, Aberystwyth, Centre for Educational Studies.

Vander Meer, Lew. What We Believe Pt. 2: Sessions 13-24. 2nd ed. 2000. (Reformed Faith Ser.). 40p. (gr. 8-12). stu. ed. 4.50 (978-1-56212-530-1(3) , 135800, Faith Alive Christian Resources) CRC Pubns.

Video Zoom Box: Heir Force. 1998. 160p. (J). (gr. 1-6). ring bd. 164.99 incl. audio, VHS, sl. (978-1-57405-105-6(9)) CharismaLife Pubs.

Vogel, Jane & Sytsma, Mary. Questions Worth Asking: A Study of the Heidelberg Catechism, Year 2. (Reformed Faith Ser.). (gr. 9-10). stu. ed. 18.50 (978-1-56212-838-8(8) , 130160); 20.95 (978-1-56212-837-1(X) , 130165) CRC Pubns. (Faith Alive Christian Resources).

Washington State Christian Educational Curriculum Book. 2005. (J). 19.95 (978-1-59210-422-2(3)) Whispering Pine Pr., Inc.

Watson-Brugess, Linda. Parade Is Always Good Fun, Isn't It? (J). 2.25 (978-0-687-30067-9(3)) Abingdon Pr.

Watson, Carol. Christian. (Illus.). 32p. (YA). (gr. 3 up). lib. bdg. 27.10 (978-1-932889-11-6(6)) Sea-To-Sea Pubns.

Welborn, Amy. Loyola Kids Book of Saints. 2004. (Loyola Kids Ser.). (Illus.). 336p. (gr. 3-7). 15.95 (978-0-8294-1534-6(3)) Loyola Pr.

Wesemann, Tim. Dr. Devo's New-Fangled Lickety-Split Devotions. Thompson, Dana, illus. 2004. 320p. (J). (gr. 3-6). 9.99 (978-0-310-70697-7(1)) Zonderkidz.

—It's Your Birthday . . . Let's Celebrate! 2003. (J). 5.99 (978-0-9718985-9-2(6)) C T A, Inc.

Wezeman, Phyllis Vos, et al. Wipe the Tears: 30 Children's Sermons on Death. 2005. (New Brown Bag Ser.). (Illus.). 96p. 10.00 (978-0-8298-1520-7(1)) Pilgrim Pr., The/United Church Pr.

Who Am I to God? 2000. (Christian Character Development Ser.). 64p. (YA). (gr. 8-12). pap. 16.99 (978-0-7644-2130-3(1)) Group Publishing, Inc.

Wilkinson, Jessica. The Dream Giver for Teens. 2004. 128p. 12.99 (978-1-59052-459-6(4) , Multnomah) WaterBrook Pr.

Wilkinson, Philip. Christianity. 2006. (DK Eyewitness Bks.). (Illus.). 1p. (J). 15.99 (978-0-7566-2246-6(8)) Dorling Kindersley Publishing, Inc.

Wilson, Nancy. Our Mother Tongue: Answer Key. 2004. 60p. (J). per. 5.00 (***978-1-59128-016-3(8)***) Canon Pr.

Withers, Margaret. Welcome to the Lord's Table Activity Book. Robb, Andy, illus. 1999. 32p. (J). pap., act. bk. ed. (978-1-84101-044-1(8) , Barnabas) Bible Reading Fellowship.

Wood, Angela. Christian Church. 1999. (Places of Worship Ser.). (Illus.). 32p. (J). (gr. 2 up). lib. bdg. 23.33 (978-0-8368-2606-7(X)) Stevens, Gareth Inc.

Zondervan & Yaconelli, Mike. Fundamentos de un Ministerio Juvenil Sano, Los: Nine Biblical Principles That Mark Healthy Youth Ministries. 2007. 144p. pap. 9.99 (978-0-8297-4599-3(8)) Vida Pubs.

CHRISTIANITY—HISTORY

see Church History

CHRISTIANITY AND SCIENCE

see Religion and Science

CHRISTMAS

see also Christmas—Fiction; Christmas Entertainments; Christmas Plays; Christmas Poetry; Jesus Christ—Nativity; Santa Claus

Abingdon. PowerXpress Christmas Around the World. 9.95 incl. audio compact disk (978-0-687-07413-6(4)) Abingdon Pr.

Absolutely Advent! Day by Day to Christmas 2006. 2007. (J). 5.95 (***978-1-933178-69-1(8)***) Pflaum Publishing Group.

Absolutely Advent! Getting Ready for Christmas 2006 for Intermediate Grades. 2006. (J). 5.95 (978-1-933178-43-1(4)) Pflaum Publishing Group.

Absolutely Advent! Getting Ready for Christmas 2006 for Primary Grades. 2006. (J). 5.95 (978-1-933178-42-4(6)) Pflaum Publishing Group.

Adams, Michelle Medlock. What Is Christmas? Wummer, Amy, illus. 2006. 26p. (J). (ps). bds. 6.95 (978-0-8249-6668-3(6) , Candy Cane Pr.) Ideals Pubns.

Alexander, Liza. It's Christmas. 2000. (J). 1.99 (978-0-375-80559-2(1) , Random Hse. Bks. for Young Readers) Random Hse. Children's Bks.

Alvarez, Lourdes. Reyes Magos. 2005. (SPA., Illus.). 29p. (J). bds. 12.95 (978-1-58173-258-0(9)) Sweetwater Pr.

Amery, Heather. Christmas Story. 2002. (gr. k-3). lib. bdg. 12.95 (978-0-613-67533-8(9)) Tandem Library Bks.

—Snowy Christmas Jigsaw Book. Cartwright, Stephen, illus. 2004. (Jigsaw Books Ser.). 14p. (J). 8.95 (978-0-7945-0768-8(9) , Usborne) EDC Publishing.

Amery, Heather, illus. Christmas Treasury. gif. ed. 2004. (Christmas Treasury Ser.). 128p. (J). act. bk. ed. 7.95 incl. audio compact disk (978-0-7945-0224-9(5) , Usborne) EDC Publishing.

Anders, Isabel. Real Night Before Christmas. 1999. (Illus.). 32p. (J). (ps-2). 7.99 (978-0-570-05480-1(X)) Concordia Publishing Hse.

Anderson, Danica. Through the Eyes of a Child: A Christmas Story. 2001. (Illus.). 72p. (J). pap. (978-0-936029-58-0(7) , Batsford, B. T. Ltd.) Anova Bks.

Anglund, Joan Walsh. Little Angels' Book of Christmas. Anglund, Joan Walsh, illus. 2002. (Illus.). 32p. (J). 9.95 (978-0-689-85359-3(9)) Simon & Schuster Children's Publishing.

Atkins, Nancy L. Christmas Through Their Eyes: Letters to Santa. 2001. (Illus.). 48p. (J). (gr. 2-4). pap. 12.95 (978-0-9705747-0-1(3)) EarthSpring Publishing.

Augustine. Celebrate Christmas. 2004. (ps-6). pap. 6.00 (978-0-687-02791-0(8)) Abingdon Pr.

Babyfaith. God Made Christmas: The Story of Baby Jesus. 2006. (Illus.). 12p. (J). (ps-k). bds. 6.99 (978-1-59145-295-9(3)) Nelson, Thomas Inc.

Baker, Robert. What Happened to Merry Christmas? Hill, Dave, illus. 2007. 32p. (J). (gr. k-4). 14.99 (***978-0-7586-1346-2(6)***) Concordia Publishing Hse.

Barnett, Michelle Noble, et al. Theme Pockets - December: December Celebrations; Take It Home; When It's Winter. Evans, Marilyn, ed. Larsen, Jo, illus. 1999. (Making Books with Pockets). 96p. (J). pap., tchr. ed. 12.99 (978-1-55799-709-8(8) , EMC 595) Evan-Moor Educational Pubs.

Barth, Edna. Holly, Reindeer, & Colored Lights: The Story of the Christmas Symbols. Arndt, Ursula, illus. 2000. 96p. (J). (gr. 4-6). tchr. ed. 16.00 (978-0-618-06786-2(8)); pap. 7.95 (978-0-618-06788-6(4)) Houghton Mifflin Co. Trade & Reference Div. (Clarion Bks.).

—Holly, Reindeer, & Colored Lights: The Story of the Christmas Symbols. Arndt, Ursula, illus. 2000. 96p. (J). (ps-7). lib. bdg. 16.40 (978-0-613-31319-3(4)) Tandem Library Bks.

Beall, Pamela Conn & Nipp, Susan Hagen. Wee Sing for Christmas. 2005. (Wee Sing Ser.). 64p. (J). (gr. 1). 9.99 (978-0-8431-1580-2(7) , Price Stern Sloan) Penguin Group (USA) Inc.

Beylon, Cathy. Christmas Family Fun Coloring Book. 2006. 32p. (J). pap. 2.95 (978-0-486-44749-0(9)) Dover Pubns., Inc.

BHB International Staff. Christmas. 1999. 131p. (J). (gr. 1-4). pap. (978-2-215-06262-2(2)) Editions Heritage, Inc.

Bickico Enterprises, concept. BabyKids: Christmas Book. 2005. 16p. (J). pap. 2.95 (978-0-9746508-7-6(0)) Bickico Enterprises, Inc.

Blair, Beth & Ericsson, Jennifer. The Everything Kids' Christmas Puzzle. 2005. (Illus.). 144p. (J). pap., act. bk. ed. 6.95 (978-1-58062-965-2(2)) Adams Media Corp.

Blundell, Trevor & Biblewise Staff. On the Way for 3 - 9's: Christmas & Jesus' Miracles, Vol. 2. 88-104p. (J). pap. 11.99 (978-1-85792-319-3(7) , Christian Focus) Christian Focus Pubns. GBR. *Dist:* Riverside.

Blyton, Enid. El Ninito Jesus. 2nd ed. 1999. (Historias de la Biblia Ser.). (SPA., Illus.). 32p. (ps-3). pap. 4.99 (978-0-8254-1067-3(3) , Editorial Portavoz) Kregel Pubns.

Bodleian Library & F. Warne and Co. Staff. Father Christmas ABC. 2005. (Illus.). 24p. 11.99 (978-1-85124-325-9(9)) Bodleian Library GBR. *Dist:* Chicago Distribution Ctr.

Bonnice, Sherry. Christmas & Santa Claus Folklore. 2003. (North American Folklore Ser.). (Illus.). 112p. (YA). (gr. 7 up). lib. bdg. (978-1-59084-330-7(4)) Mason Crest Pubs.

Box & Sage. My First Christmas Fun Book. 1998. (Illus.). 32p. (J). pap. 7.99 (978-0-7459-3691-8(1) , Lion) Lion Hudson plc GBR. *Dist:* Independent Pubs. Group.

Briggs, Betty. A Tuff-to-Beat Christmas, A New Edition. 2004. (Illus.). 115p. (YA). per. 5.95 (978-0-9656307-4-0(9)) Sunrise Selections.

Broadman, Holman. First Christmas. 1999. 19.95 (978-0-88271-676-3(X)) Regina Pr., Malhame & Co.

Brooks, Felicity. Advent Nativity Bk. 2006. 14p. (J). bds. 14.99 (978-0-7945-1174-6(0) , Usborne) EDC Publishing.

Brooks, Felicity & Allen, Francesca. Baby's Christmas. Wells, Rachel, illus. 2005. 10p. (J). (ps-k). per. 8.95 (978-0-7945-1175-3(9) , Usborne) EDC Publishing.

Browne, Yolanda. Getting Ready for Christmas: A Daily Advent Prayer & Activity Book for the Family. Girouard, Patrick, illus. 2005. (ENG.). 32p. (ps-3). 6.99 (978-0-7586-0860-4(8)) Concordia Publishing Hse.

Bruna, Dick. Christmas. 2004. (Illus.). 24p. pap. 12.99 (978-1-59226-185-7(X)) Big Tent Entertainment, Inc.

Brunner, Sharon. Christmas Came for Easter. 2007. (J). per. 8.99 (****978-1-60247-242-6(4)***) Tate Publishing & Enterprises, L.L.C.

Bryer, Estelle & Nicol, Jenni. Celebrating Christmas Together: Nativity & Three Kings Plays with Stories & Songs. 2001. (Crafts, Festivals & Family Activities Ser.). (Illus.). 96p. pap. 16.95 (978-1-903458-20-4(X)) Hawthorn Pr. GBR. *Dist:* SteinerBooks, Inc.

Buck, Deanna Draper. My First Story of the First Christmas. Harston, Jerry, illus. 2006. 24p. (J). 13.95 (978-1-59038-635-4(3)) Deseret Bk. Co.

Buck, Nola. Santa's Short Suit Shrunk: And Other Christmas Tongue Twisters. 1998. (I Can Read Bks.). (Illus.). 32p. (J). (gr. k-3). pap. 3.75 (978-0-06-444247-3(0)) HarperCollins Pubs.

Bull, Jane. Christmas. 2005. (Sticker activity Bks.). (Illus.). 16p. (J). (ps-ps). pap. 6.99 (978-0-7566-1226-9(8)) Dorling Kindersley Publishing, Inc.

—The Christmas Kit. 2006. 16p. (J). 15.99 (978-0-7566-2031-8(7)) Dorling Kindersley Publishing, Inc.

—The Merry Christmas. 2005. (Jane bull sticker activity Bk Ser.). (Illus.). 48p. (J). (ps-ps). act. bk. ed. 12.99 (978-0-7566-1369-3(8)) Dorling Kindersley Publishing, Inc.

Burke, Tina. It's Christmas. Burke, Tina, illus. 2007. (Illus.). 32p. (J). (ps). 14.95 (****978-1-933605-44-9(8)***) Kane/Miller Bk. Pubs., Inc.

California Classic Christmas Trivia. 2005. 32p. pap. 6.95 (****978-0-635-03357-4(7)***) Gallopade International.

Canfield, Jack L. Chicken Soup for the Soul Christmas Treasury for Kids: A Story a Day from December 1st Through Christmas for Kids & Their Families. 2007. 282p. pap. 14.95 (****978-0-7573-0632-7(2));*** 100p. (J). pap. 14.95 (****978-0-7573-0690-7(X)***) Health Communications, Inc.

Canfield, Jack L., et al. Chicken Soup for the Soul Christmas Treasury for Kids: A Story a Day from December 1st Through Christmas for Kids & Their Families. 2002. (Chicken Soup for the Soul Ser.). (Illus.). 100p. (J). (gr. 1-6). tchr. ed. 14.95 (978-0-7573-0038-7(3)) Health Communications, Inc.

Carlson, Melody. The Wonder of Christmas: A Family Advent Journey. 1999. (Illus.). 110p. (J). (ps-3). 14.99 (978-1-58134-105-8(9) , Crossway Bibles) Crossway Bks.

Carter, Jennifer, illus. Christmas Treasures. 2005. 33p. pap. 3.99 (978-1-904726-00-5(3)) Authentic Media.

Catholic Family Christmas Celebration. 2000. (Illus.). (J). 12.95 (978-0-88271-690 9(5)) Regina Pr., Malhame & Co.

Causely, Charles. Bring in the Holly. Kopper, Lisa, illus. 2000. 32p. (J). (gr. k-5). pap. 10.99 (978-0-7112-1571-9(5)) Lincoln, Frances Ltd. GBR. *Dist:* Antique Collectors' Club.

Celebrate Christmas Kindergart. 2004. 6.95 (978-0-7647-0488-8(5)) School Specialty Publishing.

Celebrate Christmas Preschool. 2004. 6.95 (978-0-7647-0485-7(0)) School Specialty Publishing.

Chambers, Catherine. Christmas. 1998. (World of Holidays Ser.). (Illus.). 32p. (J). (gr. 2-5). pap. 7.95 (978-0-8172-8104-5(5)) Steck-Vaughn.

Chandler, Michael. The Littlest Cowboy's Christmas. Jacobson, Terry, illus. 2006. 32p. (J). 17.95 incl. audio compact disk (978-1-58980-381-7(7)) Pelican Publishing Co., Inc.

Chisholm, Jane. First Christmas. 2004. (First Christmas Ser.). 48p. (J). 13.95 (978-0-7945-0832-6(4) , Usborne) EDC Publishing.

Chocheli, Niko, illus. Prepare O Bethlehem: The Feast of the Nativity. 2000. 32p. (J). 18.00 (978-0-88141-208-6(2)) St. Vladimir's Seminary Pr.

Christmas, Vol. 2. 2005. (One World, Many Cultures Ser.). (YA). (gr. k-3). (978-0-7368-9428-9(4) , Pebble Bks.) Capstone Pr., Inc.

Christmas. (Illus.). (gr. 1-4). 3.00 (978-0-570-05521-1(0) , 54-1031) Concordia Publishing Hse.

Christmas. 2001. (Illus.). 12p. (J). bds. 6.99 (978-0-88271-055-6(9)) Regina Pr., Malhame & Co.

Christmas, 6, Set A, Pack. (Smart Start Ser.). (gr. k-1). 23.00 (978-0-7635-0412-0(2)) Rigby Education.

Christmas 16-Copy Acetate Mini Ed Display. 2004. 79.20 (978-0-7624-2366-8(8)) Running Pr. Bk. Pubs.

Christmas Around the World, 20 vols., Set. 2001. (Illus.). 80p. (YA). (gr. 2 up). 340.00 (978-0-7166-0867-7(7)) World Bk., Inc.

Christmas Around the World, 8 bks. Incl. Christmas in England. Enderlein, Cheryl L. 1998. lib. bdg. 18.60 (978-1-56065-624-1(7)); Christmas in France. Thoennes, Kristin. 1998. 18.60 (978-0-7368-0088-4(3)); Christmas in Germany. Thoennes, Kristin. 1998. lib. bdg. 19.93 (978-0-7368-0089-1(1)); Christmas in Italy. Thoennes, Kristin. 1998. 18.60 (978-0-7368-0090-7(5)); Christmas in Mexico. Enderlein, Cheryl L. 1998. 18.60 (978-1-56065-622-7(0)); Christmas in Norway. Thoennes, Kristin. 1998. 18.60 (978-0-7368-0091-4(3)); Christmas in Sweden. Enderlein, Cheryl L. 1997. 18.60 (978-1-56065-575-6(5)); Christmas in the Philippines. Enderlein, Cheryl L. 1998. 18.60 (978-1-56065-623-4(9)); 24p. (J). (gr. 2-3). (Illus.). Set lib. bdg. 148.80 (978-0-7368-0456-1(0) , Bridgestone Bks.) Capstone Pr., Inc.

Christmas Celebration. 2nd ed. 2001. 19.85 (978-0-06-001317-2(6)) HarperCollins Pubs.

Christmas Coloring Fun Santa Relaxing. 2004. (J). per. 6.95 (978-1-885920-48-5(2)) Pyramid Publishing, Inc.

Christmas Coloring Fun Santa's New Sled. 2004. (J). per. 6.95 (978-1-885920-88-1(1)) Pyramid Publishing, Inc.

Christmas Coloring Fun Snowman. 2004. (J). per. 6.95 (978-1-885920-90-4(3)) Pyramid Publishing, Inc.

Christmas Dot to Dot ¿ Santa¿s Big Dot to Dot. 2004. (J). per. 6.95 (978-1-885920-89-8(X)) Pyramid Publishing, Inc.

Christmas Fun Coloring Book. 2006. 16p. (J). pap. 1.99 (978-0-7847-1745-5(1) , 04371) Standard Publishing.

Christmas Programs for Children. annual 2006. 48p. pap. 5.99 (978-0-7847-1343-3(X) , 08604); 2003rd ed. pap. 5.99 (978-0-7847-1308-2(1) , 08603) Standard Publishing.

Christmas Programs for the Church. annual 2003rd ed. 2006. 48p. pap. 6.99 (978-0-7847-1310-5(3) , 08623) Standard Publishing.

The Christmas Window: Stories of Growing up in the Fifties. 2001. 304p. per. 14.00 (978-1-889406-23-7(6)) Prell Bks. & Multimedia.

Church, Francis P. Yes, Virginia, There Is a Santa Claus. Spector, Joel, illus. 2001. (Courage Children's Ser.). 32p. (gr. 3 up). 9.98 (978-0-7624-1120-7(1) , Courage Bks.) Running Pr. Bk. Pubs.

Church, Jayne, illus. Curious Camel. 1999. (Waggy Tales Ser.). 10p. (ps up). 6.99 (978-0-7847-1116-3(X) , 03524, Bean Sprouts) Standard Publishing.

—Little Donkey. 1999. (Waggy Tales Ser.). 10p. (ps up). 6.99 (978-0-7847-1115-6(1) , 03523, Bean Sprouts) Standard Publishing.

Claybourne, Anna. Christmas around the World. 2006. 48p. (J). 8.99 (978-0-7945-1132-6(5) , Usborne) EDC Publishing.

Color All About: Christmas: A Giant Coloring Book about Christmas. 2004. (SPA & ENG., Illus.). (J). (978-0-9763307-7-6(6)) Food Marketing Consultants, Inc.

Cooner, Donna D. Here Is Christmas. Jenkins, Debra Reid, illus. 2000. 32p. (J). (ps-2). 14.95 (978-1-57856-298-5(8) , WaterBrook Pr.) WaterBrook Pr.

Couri, Kathryn A., illus. Christmas Activity Fun Pack. 2001. 12p. (J). (ps-1). 10.95 (978-0-7641-7493-3(2)) Barron's Educational Series, Inc.

Court, Rob. How to Draw Christmas Things. 2007. (Doodle Bks.). 32p. (J). 21.36 (****978-1-59296-805-3(8)***) Child's World, Inc.

Cowley, Joy. Mrs. Wishy Washy's Christmas. Fuller, Elizabeth, illus. 2005. 40p. (J). (ps-1). 15.99 (978-0-399-24344-8(5) , Philomel) Penguin Group (USA) Inc.

Crossley-Holland, Kevin. How Many Miles to Bethlehem? Malone, Peter, illus. 2004. (J). (978-0-439-67643-4(6)); 32p. 16.95 (978-0-439-67642-7(8)) Scholastic, Inc. (Levine, Arthur A. Bks.).

Crozon, Alain. Adivinanzas de Navidad. Menendez-Ponte, Maria, tr. 1999. Tr. of Christmas Riddles. (SPA., Illus.). 12p. 13.95 (978-84-348-6637-9(4)) SM Ediciones ESP. *Dist:* Distribooks, Inc.

Crozon, Alain & Lanchais, A. What Am I? Christmas! 1999. (What Am I? Ser.). (Illus.). 14p. (J). (ps). 7.95 (978-0-8118-2613-6(9)) Chronicle Bks. LLC.

Cuenta Regresiva de la Navidad.Tr. of Christmas Countdown. (SPA.). (J). 5.99 (978-0-7899-0801-8(8) , 495057) Editorial Unilit.

De Graaf, A. M. La Primera Navidad (The First Christmas) (Divertidas Historias Biblicas para Ninos Ser.). (SPA.). (J). 3.49 (978-0-7899-0526-0(4)) Editorial Unilit.

De Graaf, Anne. The First Christmas. Perez-Montero, Jose, illus. 1998. (Little Children's Bible Bks.). 38p. (J). 5.99 (978-0-8054-1784-5(2)) B&H Publishing Grp.

de Paola, Tomie. Christmas Remembered. 2006. (Illus.). 112p. (J). (ps). 19.99 (978-0-399-24622-7(3) , Putnam Juvenile) Penguin Group (USA) Inc.

de Sturtz, Maria Ester H. & de Perez, Ursula S. Manos a la Obra: La Iglesia Celebra, Bilingual Level 1. (ENG & SPA.). 32p. (J). 6.99 (978-0-7586-0645-7(1)) Concordia Publishing Hse.

—Manos a la Obra: La Iglesia Celebra, Bilingual Level 2. (ENG & SPA.). 32p. (J). 6.99 (978-0-7586-0668-6(0)) Concordia Publishing Hse.

Dent, Jenny. Hoppy's Christmas Book. (Illus.). 16p. (J). (gr. k-3). 1.75 (978-0-85487-061-5(X)) White Eagle Publishing Trust GBR. *Dist:* DeVorss & Co.

Di Silvestro, Frank. A Christmas Visitor. 2001. 77p. pap. (978-0-934591-07-2(5)) Songs & Stories Children Love.

Dickens, Charles & Sims, Lesley. A Christmas Carol. gif. ed. 2004. 64p. (J). (gr. 2 up). 8.95 (978-0-7945-0584-4(8) , Usborne) EDC Publishing.

Dingles, Molly. On Christmas Eve. Wallis, Rebecca, illus. 2005. (Holiday Happenings Ser.). 32p. (J). per. 9.95 (978-1-59646-225-0(6)) Dingles & Co.

Disney Mickey Christmas: Coloring & Activity Book. 2002. (Illus.). 64p. (J). 1.69 (978-1-57759-848-0(2)) Dalmatian Pr.

Disney Pooh Christmas: Coloring & Activity Book. 2002. (Illus.). 64p. (J). 1.69 (978-1-57759-849-7(0)) Dalmatian Pr.

Dittmer, Cherie Pless. Angel! Angel! 2004. (Illus.). 24p. (J). (ps-k). bds. 6.99 (978-0-7586-0687-7(7)) Concordia Publishing Hse.

DK Publishing Staff. Reindeer's First Christmas. 2007. 10p. (J). (ps-1). bds. 8.99 (****978-0-7566-3087-4(8)***) Dorling Kindersley Publishing, Inc.

—Twelve Days of Christmas. 2007. 10p. (J). (ps-1). 4.99 (****978-0-7566-3086-7(X)***) Dorling Kindersley Publishing, Inc.

Dorling Kindersley Publishing Staff. Christmas. 2001. (Scratch & Sniff Ser.). (Illus.). 12p. (J). bds. 6.99 (978-0-7894-7891-7(9)) Dorling Kindersley Publishing, Inc.

—Christmas: Create Your Own Picture Book, over 120 Superb Full-Color Stickers. 2001. (Ultimate Sticker Bks.). (Illus.). 16p. (J). (ps-3). pap. 6.99 (978-0-7894-6501-6(9)) Dorling Kindersley Publishing, Inc.

—Christmas Angel. 2006. 12p. (J). bds. 4.99 (978-0-7566-2030-1(9)) Dorling Kindersley Publishing, Inc.

—Christmas Is Coming. 2006. (Illus.). 20p. (J). (gr. 5). 19.99 (978-0-7566-2216-9(6)) Dorling Kindersley Publishing, Inc.

—Christmas Snow. 2006. 12p. (J). 4.99 (978-0-7566-2036-3(8)) Dorling Kindersley Publishing, Inc.

—Christmas Stocking. 2006. 12p. (J). 4.99 (978-0-7566-2035-6(X)) Dorling Kindersley Publishing, Inc.

—The Christmas Story. 1999. 12p. (J). pap. 7.95 (978-0-7894-4740-1(1)) Dorling Kindersley Publishing, Inc.

—Christmas Tree. 2006. 12p. (J). 4.99 (978-0-7566-2034-9(1)) Dorling Kindersley Publishing, Inc.

—My First Christmas. 2nd rev. ed. 2006. (Illus.). 36p. (J). bds. 5.99 (978-0-7566-0502-5(4)) Dorling Kindersley Publishing, Inc.

—Sparkly Angel. 2005. (Illus.). 12p. (J). bds. 5.99 (978-0-7566-1134-7(2)) Dorling Kindersley Publishing, Inc.

—Toca y Apprende Navidad/Touch & Feel Christmas. 2006. (Touch & Feel Ser.). 12p. (J). bds. 6.99 (978-0-7566-2136-0(4)) Dorling Kindersley Publishing, Inc.

Douglas, Bettye. Safari Oklahoma Presents: The Magic of Christmas Around the World. Douglas, Bettye, ed. Douglas, Punchye, illus. (Multicultural). 16p. (J). (gr. k-6). 5.00 (978-0-9703183-4-3(0)) Douglas, Bettye Forum, Inc., The.

Douglas, Punchye, illus. Safari Oklahoma Presents Operation Safe 2000: Halloween Coloring Book. (Safari Oklahoma Presents). 16p. (J). (gr. k-6). 5.00 (978-0-9703183-2-9(4)) Douglas, Bettye Forum, Inc., The.

Douglas, Vincent. Christmas Stories. 2001. (Keepsake Collection). (Illus.). 96p. (J). 12.98 (978-0-7853-5243-3(0) , 7137000) Publications International, Ltd.

Douglas, Vincent & School Specialty Publishing Staff. Christmas Stories. Schroeder, Warrick, illus. 2003. (Rhythm & Rhyme Ser.). 53p. (J). (ps up). bds. 19.95 (978-1-58845-525-3(4)) School Specialty Publishing.

Doyle, Alfreda C. Christmas Wreath: Story Rhyme Coloring Book. 1998. (Illus.). 24p. (J). (gr. 3-8). pap. 8.95 (978-1-56820-327-0(6)) Story Time Stories That Rhyme.

Elkins, Stephen. The Word & Song Christmas Storybook. O'Connor, Tim, illus. 2000. 32p. (J). (ps-5). 14.99 incl. audio (978-0-8054-2434-8(2)) B&H Publishing Grp.

Ellis, Gwen. La Flor de Pascua. Hansen, Clint, illus. 2005. 32p. (J). (ps-3). 8.99 (978-1-59185-827-0(5) , Charisma Kids) Strang Communications Co.

Elton, Richard & Elton, Candice. My Christmas Album. 2004. (Illus.). 28p. pap. 19.95 (978-1-58685-582-6(4)) Gibbs Smith, Publisher.

Equipo Staff. La Montaña. (Coleccion Mundo Maravilloso). (SPA., Illus.). 32p. (J). (gr. 2-4). (978-84-348-7227-1(7) , SM31364) SM Ediciones ESP. *Dist:* Lectorum Pubns., Inc.

Erickson, Jenny. My Favorite Advent & Christmas Activity Book. 2005. (Illus.). 66p. pap. 14.95 (978-1-58595-516-9(7)) Twenty-Third Pubns./Bayard.

Erlbach, Arlene. Christmas - Celebrating Life, Giving & Kindness. 2001. (Finding Out about Holidays Ser.). (Illus.). 48p. (J). (gr. 1-4). lib. bdg. 23.93 (978-0-7660-1576-0(9)) Enslow Pubs., Inc.

A Family Christmas: Advent Calendar & Storybook. 2000. 32p. (J). 10.99 (978-0-570-07122-8(4)) Concordia Publishing Hse.

First Christmas. 2003. (Illus.). 32p. (J). 4.98 (978-1-4054-0981-0(9)) Parragon, Inc.

The First Christmas. 2003. (Illus.). (J). bds. 6.98 (978-1-4054-0967-4(3)) Parragon, Inc.

The First Christmas. (Illus.). 12p. (J). 4.95 (978-1-58989-102-9(3)) Thurman Hse., LLC.

The First Christmas. 2003. (Illus.). 30p. (J). 14.95 (978-0-8249-5469-7(6)) Ideals Pubns.

First Christmas Wonder Window. 1998. (J). 4.95 (978-0-88271-701-2(4)) Regina Pr., Malhame & Co.

Fite, Bonnie Johnson. The Twelve New Days of Christmas. Bunnell, Gini, illus. 2001. 32p. (J). (ps-6). 16.99 (978-0-9708195-0-5(1)) Profound Promises.

Fittro, Pat, compiled by. Christmas Programs for Children 2002. 2001. 48p. (J). (ps up). pap. 4.99 (978-0-7847-1243-6(3)) Standard Publishing.

Fittro, Pat, ed. Standard Christmas Program Book. 2002nd ed. 2002. 48p. 5.99 (978-0-7847-1295-5(6)) Standard Publishing.

Flanagan, Alice K. Christmas. Woodworth, Viki, illus. 2001. (Holidays & Festivals Ser.). 32p. (J). (gr. 3 up). lib. bdg. 22.60 (978-0-7565-0085-6(0)) Compass Point Bks.

Fletcher, Sarah. My Christmas Prayer Book. Watkins, Bob, illus. 1998. (Arch Bks.). (ENG.). 16p. (J). (gr. k-4). 1.99 (978-0-570-07546-2(7)) Concordia Publishing Hse.

Florida Classic Christmas Trivia. 2005. 32p. pap. 6.95 (****978-0-635-03356-7(9)***) Gallopade International.

Fogle, Robin. Itty-bitty Bible Activity Book, the Legend of the Candy Cane. 2007. (Illus.). 48p. (J). pap. 1.49 (****978-1-59317-212-1(5)***) Warner Pr. Pubs.

Foran, Jill. Christmas. 2003. (Celebrating Cultures Ser.). (Illus.). 24p. (J). lib. bdg. 15.95 (978-1-59036-091-0(5)) Weigl Pubs., Inc.

French, Henry F. It Came upon the Midnight Clear. 2000. (Illus.). 64p. 8.99 (978-0-8066-4050-1(2) , Augsburg Bks.) Augsburg Fortress, Pubs.

Fried, Natasha & Tabori, Lena, eds. The Christmas Almanac. (Illus.). 240p. 24.95 (978-0-941807-27-2(4) , Welcome Bks.) Welcome Enterprises, Inc.

Frisch, Aaron. Christmas. 2005. (My First Look at Holidays Ser.). (Illus.). 24p. (gr. k-3). 15.95 (978-1-58341-366-1(9) , Creative Education) Creative Co., The.

Fujimoto, Makoto. Spot 7: Christmas. 2006. (Illus.). 38p. (J). 12.95 (978-0-8118-5323-1(3)) Chronicle Bks. LLC.

Fyffe, Brian, illus. Christmas Counting: Count & Create with 42 Holiday Stickers. 2003. 10p. (J). (ps up). bds. 4.99 (978-1-57151-722-7(7)) Playhouse Publishing.

Georgia Classic Christmas Trivia. 2005. 32p. pap. 6.95 (****978-0-635-03354-3(2)***) Gallopade International.

Gerth, Melanie. My First Jumbo Book of Christmas. Diaz, Jim, illus. 2003. (My First Jumbo Book Ser.). 10p. (J). pap. 9.95 (978-0-439-52111-6(4) , Cartwheel Bks.) Scholastic, Inc.

Gibson, Ray & Watt, Fiona. Christmas Activities. 1999. (Illus.). 34p. (J). (ps-3). pap. 8.95 (978-0-7460-3707-2(4)) EDC Publishing.

Gill, Nancy Downs. One Christmas Night: For All Who Cherish a Christmas Memory. Shields, Noriko, illus. l.t. ed. 2000. 36p. (J). (ps-6). per. 7.95 (978-0-9675045-0-6(3)) Oak Hill Pr.

Gilleland, Rebecca. A Christmas Carol Study Guide. 2002. (J). stu. ed., ring bd. 14.99 (978-1-58609-185-9(9)) Progeny Pr.

Gillis, Jennifer Blizin. Christmas. 2002. (Candle Time Ser.). (Illus.). 24p. (J). (ps-1). lib. bdg. 18.50 (978-1-58810-529-5(6)) Heinemann Library.

—Las Posadas. 2002. (Candle Time Ser.). (Illus.). 24p. (J). (ps-1). lib. bdg. 18.50 (978-1-58810-531-8(8)) Heinemann Library.

Gillis, Jennifer Blizin & Jordan, Denise M. Christmas. 2002. (Candle Time Ser.). (Illus.). 24p. (J). (ps-1). pap. 5.25 (978-1-58810-738-1(8) , 91384) Heinemann Library.

—Navidad. 2002. (Fiestas Con Velas (Candle Time) Ser.). (SPA.). 24p. (J). (ps-1). lib. bdg. 18.50 (978-1-58810-784-8(1)); (Illus.). pap. 5.25 (978-1-58810-831-9(7) , 9159) Heinemann Library.

—Las Posadas. 2002. (Fiestas Con Velas (Candle Time) Ser.). 24p. (J). (ps-1). (SPA.). lib. bdg. 18.50 (978-1-58810-786-2(8)); (SPA., Illus.). pap. 5.25 (978-1-58810-833-3(3) , 91592); (Illus.). pap. 5.25 (978-1-58810-740-4(X) , 91389) Heinemann Library.

Gittins, Sheri. The Christmas Journey. 2005. (J). pap. 1.79 (****978-1-59317-106-3(4)***) Warner Pr. Pubs.

Golden Books Staff. The First Christmas. deluxe ed. 2005. (Illus.). 32p. (J). (ps-2). pap., pap. 3.99 (978-0-375-83581-0(4) , Golden Inspirational) Random Hse. Children's Bks.

Gordon, Bob. Santa's Christmas. 2005. (Touch & Sparkle Ser.). (Illus.). 12p. (ps-k). per., bds. 5.95 (978-1-905051-79-3(4)) Make Believe Ideas GBR. *Dist:* Ingram Pub. Services.

Graham, Ruth Bell & Watson, Jeffrey. One Wintry Night. 2007. 72p. 12.99 (****978-0-8010-1306-5(2)***) Baker Bks.

Grant, Leigh. Twelve Days of Christmas: A Celebration & History. Grant, Leigh, illus. 1999. (Illus.). 40p. (YA). (gr. 6-8). reprint ed. 21.00 (978-0-7881-6703-4(0)) DIANE Publishing Co.

Greenwood, Barbara. A Pioneer Christmas: Celebrating in the Backwoods in 1841. Collins, Heather, illus. 2004. 48p. (J). (gr. 4-6). (978-1-55074-955-7(2)); (978-1-55074-953-3(6)) Kids Can Pr., Ltd.

Griffin, Mpingo Marilyn. Beings of the Christ Light Share the Meaning of Christmas: The Ultimate Gift for Your Spiritual Growth. 2002. 175p. mass mkt. 12.95 (978-0-9677117-3-7(8) , 110022) Lion's Heart Publishing, LLC.

Guess, Catherine Ritch. The Friendly Beasts. 2006. 256p. pap. 12.95 (****978-1-933341-17-0(3)***) CRM.

Haidle, Helen. The Real Twelve Days of Christmas. 2000. (Illus.). 32p. (J). 14.99 (978-0-310-70118-7(X)) Zondervan.

Hairborne. Baby Praise Christmas. 1998. 24p. (J). 4.95 (978-1-57562-266-8(1) , 30-1207) Copeland, Kenneth Pubns.

Hanegar, Renee. Activites de Noel. (FRE.). 16p. pap. (978-0-590-16904-2(1)) Scholastic Canada, Ltd.

Hansen, Janis. Jesus: The Birthday of the King, 5 vols. Francisco, Wendy, illus. (Bible Adventure Club). 2003. 36p. wbk. ed. 19.99 incl. audio, cd-rom (978-1-58134-331-1(0)); 2001. (J). (978-1-58134-334-2(5)) Crossway Bks.

Harmon, Ruth. The Christmas Story. Date not set. 4.95 (978-0-88271-132-4(6) , 1415) Regina Pr., Malhame & Co.

Haugen, Brenda. Christmas. Ouren, Todd, illus. 2004. (Holidays & Celebrations Ser.). 24p. (gr. k-3). 22.60 (978-1-4048-0192-9(8)) Picture Window Bks.

Heaps, Kelly S. & Dunn, Susan. Miracle: The Story of the First Christmas. Lindgren, Renae, illus. 1999. (Holy Bear's Travel Ser.). 32p. (J). (gr. k-5). pap. 7.95 (978-1-885628-31-2(5)) Buckaroo Bks.

Heiligman, Deborah. Celebrate Christmas: With Carols, Presents, & Peace. 2007. (Holidays Around the World Ser.). (Illus.). 32p. (J). (gr. 1-4). 15.95 (****978-1-4263-0122-3(7));*** lib. bdg. 23.90 (****978-1-4263-0123-0(5)***) National Geographic Society. (National Geographic Children's Bks.).

C D

Henley, Karyn. Jesus Is God's Son: Christmas. (Children's Ministry Folders). (Illus.). 8p. (ps-k). 2.99 (978-0-7847-0670-1(0) , 42220) Standard Publishing.

Henning, Heather. Christmas. Chapman, Gillian, illus. 2007. (ENG.). 16p. (J). pap. 9.99 (*978-0-7586-1383-7(0)*) Concordia Publishing Hse.

Holder, Greg. The Christmas Story. McCallum, Jodie, illus. 1999. (Record Your Own Voice Ser.). 10p. (ps-k). 14.99 (978-0-7847-1111-8(9) , 03537, Bean Sprouts) Standard Publishing.

—The Christmas Story Felt Board Book. Shuttleworth, Cathie, illus. 1999. (Felt Board Bks.). 10p. (J). (ps-k). bds. 14.99 (978-0-7847-1118-7(6) , 03527) Standard Publishing.

Holder, Greg, ed. The Story of Christmas. Garris, Norma, illus. 1998. 24p. (J). (ps-k). pap. 5.99 (978-0-7847-0849-1(5) , 23946, Bean Sprouts) Standard Publishing.

Hooper, Maureen Brett. Silent Night: A Christmas Carol Is Born. Kubiak, Kasi, illus. 2001. 32p. (YA). (gr. k-2). 15.95 (978-1-56397-782-4(6)) Boyds Mills Pr.

Hooper, Meredith. Tom's Rabbit: A Surprise on the Way to Antarctica. Kitchen, Bert, illus. 2002. 27p. reprint ed. 16.00 (978-0-7567-5620-8(0)) DIANE Publishing Co.

Hoyt-Goldsmith, Diane. Las Posadas: An Hispanic Christmas Celebration. 2000. (Illus.). 32p. (J). (ps-7). pap. 6.95 (978-0-8234-1635-6(6)) Holiday Hse., Inc.

Hudson, Cheryl Willis. Hold Christmas in Your Heart: African American Songs, Poems, & Stories for the Holidays. Hudson, Cheryl Willis, illus. 2002. (Illus.). 32p. (J). pap. 5.99 (978-0-590-48025-3(1) , Cartwheel Bks.) Scholastic, Inc.

Hughes, Monica. My Christmas. 2003. (Festivals Ser.). (Illus.). 24p. (J). pap. 5.50 (978-1-4109-0665-6(5)); lib. bdg. 18.56 (978-1-4109-0639-7(6)) Raintree.

Inspirational Press Staff. Three Stories of Christmas. 2000. (Arch Bks.). 56p. (J). 7.99 (978-0-88486-286-4(0) , Arrowood Pr.) BBS Publishing Corp.

Itty-Bitty Bible Activity Book: Christmas Edition. 2005. (J). pap. (978-1-59317-015-8(7)) Warner Pr. Pubs.

Jarrell, Jane & Saathoff, Deborah. Christmas. 2000. (One-Stop Thematic Units Ser.). 64p. (J). (ps-1). 9.50 (978-0-570-05257-9(2)) Concordia Publishing Hse.

Jeffery, Peter. The Truth about Christmas. 2002. (Illus.). 24p. (J). 3.95 (978-0-9710169-5-8(X)) Solid Ground Christian Bks.

Johnson, Cathy Ann, illus. The Christmas Story. 2005. 24p. (J). (ps-k). bds. 6.99 (978-1-4003-0633-6(7)) Nelson, Thomas Inc.

Johnson, Jennifer Hunt & Hansen, Holly T. Christmas Memories, 915 vols. 2003. (Illus.). 26p. 9.95 (978-0-9729610-9-7(7) , CMB09) Tapis & Assocs., Inc.

Jumbo Christmas Coloring & Activity Book. (Illus.). 300p. (J). mass mkt. (978-0-87449-054-1(5)) Unisystems, Inc.

Kaplan, Richard, et al. Santa, NASA y el Hombre en la Luna. Palumbo, Debi, illus. Tr. of Santa, NASA & the Man in the Moon. (SPA.). (Orig.). (J). (ps-5). pap. 14.95 (978-0-9649608-1-7(8)) Batyah Productions, Inc.

Keillor, Garrison. Keillor Christmas. 2000. (Illus.). 32p. (J). (gr. k-3). 15.99 (978-0-7868-0382-8(7)) Disney Pr.

Kelley, Emily. Christmas Around the World. Oeltjenbruns, Joni, illus. rev. ed. 2004. (On My Own Holidays Ser.). 48p. (J). (gr. 2-4). lib. bdg. 25.26 (978-0-87614-915-7(8)) Lerner Publishing Group.

—Christmas Around the World. 2004. (gr. k-3). lib. bdg. 14.10 (978-0-613-65741-9(1)) Tandem Library Bks.

—La Navidad Alrededor del Mundo. Oeltjenbruns, Joni, illus. 2005. (SPA.). 48p. (J). (gr. 2-4). pap. 5.95 (978-0-8225-3117-3(8)) Lerner Publishing Group.

Kelley, Emily & Oeltjenbruns, Joni. La Navidad Alrededor del Mundo. Oeltjenbruns, Joni, illus. 2005. (Yo Solo Festividades (On My Own Holidays) Ser.). (SPA & ENG., Illus.). 48p. (J). (gr. 2-4). lib. bdg. 25.26 (978-0-8225-3116-6(X) , Ediciones Lerner) Lerner Publishing Group.

Kennedy, Marge. Disney's Christmas Crafts for Kids: More Than 75 Festive Ideas for Making Decorations, Wrapping & Gifts. 1998. (Illus.). (J). 18.95 (978-0-7868-3196-8(0)) Disney Pr.

Kim, Magdalena & Jablonski, Patricia E. When Jesus Was Born: The Story of the Very First Christmas. 2001. (Illus.). 40p. (J). pap. 6.95 (978-0-8198-8297-4(6) , 332-407) Pauline Bks. & Media.

King, Martha H. 'Twas the Month Before Christmas: A Coloring & Family Activity Book. 1999. (Illus.). 128p. (ps-5). pap., stu. ed. 10.95 (978-0-8192-1785-1(9) , 5978) Morehouse Publishing.

Kitch. Anglican Kids' Advent Activity Book. 2006. (Illus.). 48p. (J). pap. 7.00 (978-0-8192-2195-7(3)) Morehouse Publishing.

Lang Books(Editors) Staff, ed. Christmas. gif. ed. 2004. 64p. 7.95 (978-0-8249-5866-4(7)) Ideals Pubns.

—Christmas Ideals 2004, 61. 2004. (Illus.). 88p. pap. 5.95 (978-0-8249-1235-2(7)) Ideals Pubns.

Langton, Roger, illus. The Twelve Days of Christmas. (Christmas Titles Ser.: No. S808-15). 28p. (J). 3.95 (978-0-7214-5078-0(4) , Dutton Juvenile) Penguin Group (USA) Inc.

Lankford, Mary D. Christmas Around the World. Dugan, Karen M. & Norman, Irene M., illus. 1998. 48p. (J). (gr. k-3). pap. 6.99 (978-0-688-16323-5(8) , Harper Trophy) HarperCollins Pubs.

—Christmas Around the World. Dugan, Karen M., illus. 1998. 47p. (J). (ps-ps). lib. bdg. 14.15 (978-0-613-11409-7(4)) Tandem Library Bks.

—Christmas USA. Dugan, Karen, illus. 2006. 48p. (J). lib. bdg. 16.89 (978-0-06-000861-1(X)) HarperCollins Pubs.

Larkin, Jean. Absolutely Advent! Getting Ready for Christmas 2007. 2007. (Illus.). 32p. pap. 5.95 (*978-1-933178-68-4(X)*) Pflaum Publishing Group.

Larkin, Jean K. Absolutely Advent! Getting Ready for Christmas 2005. l.t. ed. 2005. (Illus.). (J). 5.95 (978-1-933178-11-0(6) , 3550) Pflaum Publishing Group.

LaRochelle, David. Picture That! Christmas Puzzles. LaRochelle, David, illus. 2002. (Illus.). 48p. (J). 4.99 (978-0-8431-4883-1(7) , Price Stern Sloan) Penguin Group (USA) Inc.

Lawrence, Linda & Hubbard, Donna. Jesse Tree. 3rd ed. 2002. 32p. (J). 7.95 (978-1-930165-02-1(1)) Small Ventures.

Leczkowski, Jennifer, ed. An American Christmas. 2005. (Illus.). 96p. 9.98 (978-0-7624-2477-1(X) , Courage Bks.) Running Pr. Bk. Pubs.

Leigh, Susan. Merry Christmas. 2006. 20p. (J). 4.99 (978-0-7586-1216-8(8)) Concordia Publishing Hse.

Lindecker, Leslie. The First Christmas. Calvert-Weyant, Lynda, tr. Calvert-Weyant, Lynda, illus. 2002. (My First Treasury Ser.). 40p. (J). (978-0-7853-6878-6(7) , 7167800) Publications International, Ltd.

Lingo, Susan L. My Good Night Christmas: With Read & Sing-along CD. Parks, Kathy, illus. 2001. 32p. (J). 17.99 incl. audio compact disk (978-0-7847-1205-4(0)) Standard Publishing.

Litchfield, Jo. Christmas look & Say. Litchfield, Jo, illus. 2005. 10p. (J). 9.95 (978-0-7945-1173-9(2) , Usborne) EDC Publishing.

Lloyd-Jones, Sally. My Merry Christmas: And the Real Reason for Christmas Joy. Clearwater, Linda, illus. 2006. 12p. (J). bds. 10.99 (978-0-7847-1449-2(5) , 04081) Standard Publishing.

Locke, Ian. Cracking Christmas. Rowe, Alan, illus. 21st ed. 2003. 60p. (J). pap. 3.99 (978-0-330-37504-7(0) , Pan) Pan Macmillan GBR. *Dist:* Trafalgar Square Publishing.

Lou Weber Staff, ed. Merry Christmas Stories. 2004. (Illus.). 320p. (J). 15.98 (978-0-7853-6034-6(4)) Publications International, Ltd.

MacKinnon, Debbie, retold by. Away in a Manger. 2000. (Illus.). 24p. (J). (ps-2). 11.99 (978-0-570-07114-3(3)) Concordia Publishing Hse.

Maier, Paul L. The Very First Christmas. 32p. (J). 9.99 (978-0-570-07186-0(0)) Concordia Publishing Hse.

—The Very First Christmas. Ordaz, Francisco, illus. 2004. 20p. (J). (ps-k). bds. 6.99 (978-0-7586-0689-1(3)) Concordia Publishing Hse.

—The Very First Christmas. 1998. (Illus.). 32p. (J). (gr. k-5). 12.99 (978-0-570-05064-3(2)) Concordia Publishing Hse.

M&M's Red Christmas: Coloring & Activity Book. 2002. (Illus.). 64p. (J). 1.69 (978-1-57759-846-6(6)) Dalmatian Pr.

M&M's Yellow Christmas: Coloring & Activity Book. 2002. (Illus.). 64p. (J). 1.69 (978-1-57759-847-3(4)) Dalmatian Pr.

Marsh, Carole. Alabama Classic Christmas Trivia. 2002. (Carole Marsh Alabama Bks.). (Illus.). 32p. pap. 6.95 (978-0-635-01369-9(X) , 1369X); lib. bdg. 21.95 (978-0-635-01370-5(3) , 13703, Marsh, Carole Bks.) Gallopade International.

—Alaska Classic Christmas Trivia. 2002. (Carole Marsh Alaska Bks.). (Illus.). 32p. pap. 6.95 (978-0-635-01371-2(1) , 13711, Marsh, Carole Bks.); lib. bdg. 21.95 (978-0-635-01372-9(X) , 1372X) Gallopade International.

—Arizona Classic Christmas Trivia. 2002. (Carole Marsh Arizona Bks.). (Illus.). 32p. pap. 6.95 (978-0-635-01373-6(8) , 13738, Marsh, Carole Bks.); lib. bdg. 21.95 (978-0-635-01374-3(6) , 13746) Gallopade International.

—Arkansas Classic Christmas Trivia. 2002. (Carole Marsh Arkansas Bks.). (Illus.). 32p. pap. 6.95 (978-0-635-01375-0(4) , 13754); lib. bdg. 21.95 (978-0-635-01376-7(2) , 13762) Gallopade International. (Marsh, Carole Bks.).

—California Classic Christmas Trivia. 2002. (Carole Marsh California Bks.). (Illus.). 32p. pap. 6.95 (978-0-635-01377-4(0) , 13770); lib. bdg. 21.95 (978-0-635-01378-1(9) , 13789) Gallopade International. (Marsh, Carole Bks.).

—A Carolina Christmas. 2002. (Carole Marsh Bks.). 32p. (J). (gr. 4-12). pap. 6.95 (978-0-635-01365-1(7) , 13657); (Illus.). (gr. 3-9). 21.95 (978-0-635-01366-8(5) , 13665, Marsh, Carole Bks.) Gallopade International.

—Christmas Traditions Around the World. 2003. 12p. (J). (gr. k-4). pap. 2.95 (978-0-635-02154-0(4)) Gallopade International.

—Colorado Classic Christmas Trivia. 2002. (Carole Marsh Colorado Bks.). (Illus.). 32p. pap. 6.95 (978-0-635-01379-8(7) , 13797); lib. bdg. 21.95 (978-0-635-01380-4(0) , 13800) Gallopade International. (Marsh, Carole Bks.).

—Connecticut Classic Christmas Trivia. 2002. (Carole Marsh Connecticut Bks.). (Illus.). 32p. pap. 6.95 (978-0-635-01381-1(9) , 13819); lib. bdg. 21.95 (978-0-635-01382-8(7) , 13827) Gallopade International. (Marsh, Carole Bks.).

—Delaware Classic Christmas Trivia. 2002. (Carole Marsh Delaware Bks.). (Illus.). 32p. pap. 6.95 (978-0-635-01383-5(5) , 13835); lib. bdg. 21.95 (978-0-635-01384-2(3) , 13843) Gallopade International. (Marsh, Carole Bks.).

—Florida Classic Christmas Trivia. 2002. (Carole Marsh Florida Bks.). (Illus.). 32p. pap. 6.95 (978-0-635-01385-9(1) , 13851, Marsh, Carole Bks.); lib. bdg. 21.95 (978-0-635-01386-6(X) , 1386X) Gallopade International.

—Georgia Classic Christmas Trivia. 2002. (Carole Marsh Georgia Bks.). (Illus.). 32p. pap. 6.95 (978-0-635-01387-3(8)); lib. bdg. 21.95 (978-0-635-01388-0(6) , 13886) Gallopade International. (Marsh, Carole Bks.).

—Hawaii Classic Christmas Trivia. 2002. (Carole Marsh Hawaii Bks.). (Illus.). 32p. (J). pap. 6.95 (978-0-635-01389-7(4) , 13894); lib. bdg. 21.95 (978-0-635-01390-3(8) , 13908) Gallopade International. (Marsh, Carole Bks.).

—Idaho Classic Christmas Trivia. 2002. (Carole Marsh Idaho Bks.). (Illus.). 32p. pap. 6.95 (978-0-635-01391-0(6) , 13916); lib. bdg. 14.95 (978-0-635-01392-7(4) , 13924) Gallopade International. (Marsh, Carole Bks.).

—Illinois Classic Christmas Trivia. 2002. (Carole Marsh Illinois Bks.). (Illus.). 32p. pap. 6.95 (978-0-635-01393-4(2) , 13932); lib. bdg. 21.95 (978-0-635-01394-1(0) , 13940) Gallopade International.

—Indiana Classic Christmas Trivia. 2002. (Carole Marsh Indiana Bks.). (Illus.). 32p. pap. 6.95 (978-0-635-01395-8(9) , 13959); lib. bdg. 21.95 (978-0-635-01396-5(7) , 13967) Gallopade International. (Marsh, Carole Bks.).

—Iowa Classic Christmas Trivia. 2002. (Carole Marsh Iowa Bks.). (Illus.). 32p. pap. 6.95 (978-0-635-01397-2(5) , 13975, Marsh, Carole Bks.); lib. bdg. 21.95 (978-0-635-01398-9(3)) Gallopade International.

—Kansas Classic Christmas Trivia. 2002. (Carole Marsh Kansas Bks.). (Illus.). 32p. pap. 14.95 (978-0-635-01399-6(1) , 13991, Marsh, Carole Bks.); lib. bdg. 21.95 (978-0-635-01400-9(9) , 14009) Gallopade International.

—Kentucky Classic Christmas Trivia. 2002. (Carole Marsh Kentucky Bks.). (Illus.). 32p. pap. 6.95 (978-0-635-01401-6(7) , 14017); lib. bdg. 21.95 (978-0-635-01402-3(5) , 14025) Gallopade International. (Marsh, Carole Bks.).

—Louisiana Classic Christmas Trivia. 2002. (Carole Marsh Louisiana Bks.). (Illus.). 32p. pap. 6.95 (978-0-635-01403-0(3) , 14033, Marsh, Carole Bks.); lib. bdg. 21.95 (978-0-635-01404-7(1) , 14041) Gallopade International.

—Maine Classic Christmas Trivia. 2002. (Carole Marsh Maine Bks.). (Illus.). 32p. pap. 6.95 (978-0-635-01405-4(X) , 1405X); lib. bdg. 21.95 (978-0-635-01406-1(8) , 14068, Marsh, Carole Bks.) Gallopade International.

—Maryland Classic Christmas Trivia. 2002. (Carole Marsh Maryland Bks.). (Illus.). 32p. pap. 6.95 (978-0-635-01407-8(6) , 14076); lib. bdg. 21.95 (978-0-635-01408-5(4) , 14084) Gallopade International. (Marsh, Carole Bks.).

—Massachusetts Classic Christmas Trivia. 2002. (Carole Marsh Massachusetts Bks.). (Illus.). 32p. pap. 6.95 (978-0-635-01409-2(2) , 14092); lib. bdg. 21.95 (978-0-635-01410-8(6) , 14106) Gallopade International. (Marsh, Carole Bks.).

—Michigan Classic Christmas Trivia. 2002. (Carole Marsh Michigan Bks.). (Illus.). 32p. pap. 6.95 (978-0-635-01411-5(4) , 14114); lib. bdg. 21.95 (978-0-635-01412-2(2) , 14122) Gallopade International. (Marsh, Carole Bks.).

—Minnesota Classic Christmas Trivia. 2002. (Carole Marsh Minnesota Bks.). (Illus.). 32p. pap. 14.95 (978-0-635-01413-9(0) , 14130); lib. bdg. 21.95 (978-0-635-01414-6(9) , 14149) Gallopade International. (Marsh, Carole Bks.).

—Mississippi Classic Christmas Trivia. 2002. (Carole Marsh Mississippi Bks.). (Illus.). 32p. pap. 6.95 (978-0-635-01415-3(7) , 14157); lib. bdg. 21.95 (978-0-635-01416-0(5) , 14165) Gallopade International. (Marsh, Carole Bks.).

—Missouri Classic Christmas Trivia. 2002. (Carole Marsh Missouri Bks.). (Illus.). 32p. pap. 6.95 (978-0-635-01417-7(3) , 14173); lib. bdg. 21.95 (978-0-635-01418-4(1) , 14181) Gallopade International. (Marsh, Carole Bks.).

—Montana Classic Christmas Trivia. 2002. (Carole Marsh Montana Bks.). (Illus.). 32p. pap. 6.95 (978-0-635-01419-1(X) , 1419X); lib. bdg. 21.95 (978-0-635-01420-7(3) , 14203, Marsh, Carole Bks.) Gallopade International.

—Nebraska Classic Christmas Trivia. 2002. (Carole Marsh Nebraska Bks.). (Illus.). 32p. pap. 6.95 (978-0-635-01421-4(1) , 14211, Marsh, Carole Bks.); lib. bdg. 21.95 (978-0-635-01422-1(X) , 1422X) Gallopade International.

—Nevada Classic Christmas Trivia. 2002. (Carole Marsh Nevada Bks.). (Illus.). 32p. pap. 6.95 (978-0-635-01423-8(8) , 14238); lib. bdg. 21.95 (978-0-635-01424-5(6) , 14246) Gallopade International. (Marsh, Carole Bks.).

—New Hampshire Classic Christmas Trivia. 2002. (Carole Marsh New Hampshire Bks.). (Illus.). 32p. pap. 6.95 (978-0-635-01425-2(4) , 14254); lib. bdg. 21.95 (978-0-635-01426-9(2) , 14262, Marsh, Carole Bks.) Gallopade International.

—New Jersey Classic Christmas Trivia. 2002. (Carole Marsh New Jersey Bks.). (Illus.). 32p. pap. 6.95 (978-0-635-01427-6(0) , 14270); lib. bdg. 21.95 (978-0-635-01428-3(9) , 14289) Gallopade International. (Marsh, Carole Bks.).

—New Mexico Classic Christmas Trivia. 2002. (Carole Marsh New Mexico Bks.). (Illus.). 32p. pap. 6.95 (978-0-635-01429-0(7) , 14297); lib. bdg. 21.95 (978-0-635-01430-6(0) , 14300) Gallopade International. (Marsh, Carole Bks.).

—New York Classic Christmas Trivia. 2002. (Carole Marsh New York Bks.). (Illus.). 32p. pap. 6.95 (978-0-635-01431-3(9) , 14319); lib. bdg. 21.95 (978-0-635-01432-0(7) , 14327) Gallopade International. (Marsh, Carole Bks.).

—North Carolina Classic Christmas Trivia. 2002. (Carole Marsh North Carolina Bks.). (Illus.). 32p. pap. 6.95 (978-0-635-01433-7(5) , 14335); lib. bdg. 21.95 (978-0-635-01434-4(3) , 14343) Gallopade International. (Marsh, Carole Bks.).

—North Dakota Classic Christmas Trivia. 2002. (Carole Marsh North Dakota Bks.). (Illus.). 32p. pap. 6.95 (978-0-635-01435-1(1) , 14351, Marsh, Carole Bks.); lib. bdg. 21.95 (978-0-635-01436-8(X) , 01436X) Gallopade International.

—Ohio Classic Christmas Trivia. (Carole Marsh Ohio Bks.). (Illus.). 32p. lib. bdg. 21.95 (978-0-635-01597-6(8) , 15978, Marsh, Carole Bks.); 2004. pap. 6.95 (978-0-635-01596-9(X) , 1596X) Gallopade International.

—Oklahoma Classic Christmas Trivia. 2002. (Carole Marsh Oklahoma Bks.). (Illus.). 32p. (J). pap. 6.95 (978-0-635-01437-5(8) , 14378); lib. bdg. 21.95 (978-0-635-01438-2(6) , 14386) Gallopade International. (Marsh, Carole Bks.).

—Oregon Classic Christmas Trivia. 2002. (Carole Marsh Oregon Bks.). (Illus.). 32p. (J). pap. 14.95 (978-0-635-01439-9(4) , 14394); lib. bdg. 21.95 (978-0-635-01440-5(8) , 14408, Marsh, Carole Bks.) Gallopade International.

—Pennsylvania Classic Christmas Trivia. 2002. (Carole Marsh Pennsylvania Bks.). (Illus.). 32p. pap. 6.95 (978-0-635-01441-2(6) , 14416); lib. bdg. 21.95 (978-0-635-01442-9(4) , 14424) Gallopade International. (Marsh, Carole Bks.).

—Rhode Island Classic Christmas Trivia. 2002. (Carole Marsh Rhode Island Bks.). (Illus.). 32p. pap. 14.95 (978-0-635-01443-6(2) , 14432); lib. bdg. 21.95 (978-0-635-01444-3(0) , 14440) Gallopade International. (Marsh, Carole Bks.).

—South Carolina Classic Christmas Trivia. 2002. (Carole Marsh South Carolina Bks.). (Illus.). 32p. pap. 6.95 (978-0-635-01445-0(9) , 14459); lib. bdg. 21.95 (978-0-635-01446-7(7) , 14467) Gallopade International. (Marsh, Carole Bks.).

—South Dakota Classic Christmas Trivia. 2002. (Carole Marsh South Dakota Bks.). (Illus.). 32p. pap. 14.95 (978-0-635-01447-4(5) , 14475); lib. bdg. 21.95 (978-0-635-01448-1(3) , 14483) Gallopade International. (Marsh, Carole Bks.).

—Tennessee Classic Christmas Trivia. 2002. (Carole Marsh Tennessee Bks.). (Illus.). 32p. pap. 6.95 (978-0-635-01449-8(1) , 14491); lib. bdg. 21.95 (978-0-635-01450-4(5) , 14505) Gallopade International. (Marsh, Carole Bks.).

—Texas Classic Christmas Trivia. 2002. (Carole Marsh Texas Bks.). (Illus.). 32p. pap. 6.95 (978-0-635-01451-1(3) , 14513); lib. bdg. 21.95 (978-0-635-01452-8(1) , 14521) Gallopade International. (Marsh, Carole Bks.).

—Utah Classic Christmas Trivia. 2002. (Carole Marsh Utah Bks.). (Illus.). 32p. pap. 6.95 (978-0-635-01453-5(X) , 1453X); lib. bdg. 21.95 (978-0-635-01454-2(8) , 14548, Marsh, Carole Bks.) Gallopade International.

—Vermont Classic Christmas Trivia. 2002. (Carole Marsh Vermont Bks.). (Illus.). 32p. pap. 14.95 (978-0-635-01455-9(6) , 14556); lib. bdg. 21.95 (978-0-635-01456-6(4) , 14564) Gallopade International. (Marsh, Carole Bks.).

—Virginia Classic Christmas Trivia. 2002. (Carole Marsh Virginia Bks.). (Illus.). 32p. pap. 6.95 (978-0-635-01457-3(2) , 14572); lib. bdg. 21.95 (978-0-635-01458-0(0) , 14580) Gallopade International. (Marsh, Carole Bks.).

—Washington Classic Christmas Trivia. 2002. (Carole Marsh Washington Bks.). (Illus.). 32p. pap. 6.95 (978-0-635-01459-7(9) , 14599); lib. bdg. 21.95 (978-0-635-01460-3(2) , 14602) Gallopade International. (Marsh, Carole Bks.).

—West Virginia Classic Christmas Trivia. 2002. (Carole Marsh West Virginia Bks.). (Illus.). 32p. pap. 6.95 (978-0-635-01461-0(0) , 14610); lib. bdg. 21.95 (978-0-635-01462-7(9) , 14629) Gallopade International. (Marsh, Carole Bks.).

—Why Do We Hang Christmas Stockings. 2003. 12p. (J). (gr. k-4). pap. 2.95 (978-0-635-02152-6(8)) Gallopade International.

—Wyoming Classic Christmas Trivia. 2002. (Carole Marsh Wyoming Bks.). (Illus.). 32p. pap. 6.95 (978-0-635-01465-8(3) , 14653); lib. bdg. 21.95 (978-0-635-01466-5(1) , 14661) Gallopade International. (Marsh, Carole Bks.).

Marx, David F. Christmas. 2000. (Rookie Read-About Holidays Ser.). (Illus.). 32p. (J). (gr. 1-2). 19.50 (978-0-516-22175-5(2)); pap. 5.95 (978-0-516-27153-8(9)) Scholastic Library Publishing. (Children's Pr.).

Marzollo, Jean. I Spy Christmas: A Book of Picture Riddles. Wick, Walter, photos by. 2002. (I Spy Ser.). (Illus.). (J). 21.45 (978-0-7587-4104-2(9)) Book Wholesalers, Inc.

Mattern, Joanne. Celebrate Christmas. 2007. (Celebrate Holidays Ser.). (Illus.). 112p. (J). lib. bdg. 31.93 (978-0-7660-2776-3(7)) Enslow Pubs., Inc.

Matteson, Michael J. Legends of Christmas. Laskey, Robert, illus. l.t. ed. 1998. 144p. (J). (gr. 3-8). pap. 9.50 (978-1-890740-05-4(5)) Remnant Pr., The.

Matthews, Derek. Snappy Sounds Ho, Ho, Ho! 2005. (Snappy Sounds Ser.). (ACE., Illus.). 10p. 12.95 (978-1-59223-453-0(4) , Silver Dolphin Bks.) Advantage Pubs. Group.

May, Darcy. Old-Time Christmas Village Sticker Advent Calendar. 2000. (Illus.). 4p. (J). (ps-5). 5.95 (978-0-486-41053-1(6)) Dover Pubns., Inc.

McNeil, Niki, et al. HOCPP 1130 Christmas Cheer. 2006. spiral bd. 15.50 (*978-1-60308-130-6(5)*) In the Hands of a Child.

—HOCPP1021 Symbols of Christmas. 2004. spiral bd. 15.50 (*978-1-60308-021-7(X)*) In the Hands of a Child.

Medendorp, Donna & Medendorp, Nick. Keeping CHRIST in Christmas for Kids. 2004. (Illus.). 64p. (J). pap. 13.95 (978-0-9764433-0-8(9)) Kids 4 Ever.

Merry Christmas, Dear. 4.95 (978-0-87895-623-4(9)) Modern Curriculum Pr.

Michigan Classic Christmas Trivia. 2005. 32p. pap. 6.95 (*978-0-635-03353-6(4)*) Gallopade International.

Miles, Donna. Twas the Night of Christ's Birth. Walden, Tim, photos by. 2001. 40p. (J). 19.95 (978-0-9671903-0-3(4)) Booksmiles Pr.

Mills, Elise, illus. The Very First Christmas. 2002. (Sticker Stories Ser.). 16p. (J). 4.99 (978-0-448-42867-3(9) , Grosset & Dunlap) Penguin Group (USA) Inc.

Mitman, Freddie. The Magic of Christmas. 2000. (Illus.). 49p. (J). (978-0-7541-1180-1(6)) Minerva Pr. GBR. *Dist:* Unity Distribution.

Mitter, Matt. The Gifts of Christmas. Butcher, Samuel J., illus. 2000. (Precious Moments Ser.). 24p. (J). (gr. k-k). 2.99 (978-0-307-98803-4(1) , 98803, Golden Bks.) Random Hse. Children's Bks.

Moerbeek, Kees. The First Christmas. 2000. (Illus.). (J). (ps-6). 19.99 (978-0-85953-834-3(6)) Child's Play-International.

Montgomery Gibson, Jane. Go Find Christmas. Montgomery Gibson, Jane, illus. 2005. (YA). bds. 8.99 (978-1-4183-0025-8(X)) Christ Inspired, Inc.

Moore, Clement C. The Night Before Christmas. Sabuda, Robert, illus. ltd. ed. 2002. 12p. (J). 250.00 (978-0-689-85020-2(4) , Little Simon) Simon & Schuster Children's Publishing.

Moore, Clement Clarke. Night Before Christmas Storybook. Newsom, Tome, illus. 2004. 32p. 8.99 (978-1-4037-0865-6(7)) Dalmatian Pr.

Murray, Julie. Christmas. 2005. (Holidays Ser.). (Illus.). 24p. (J). (gr. k-4). lib. bdg. 21.35 (978-1-57765-951-8(1)) ABDO Publishing Co.

Nason, Ruth. Gifts at Christmas. 2005. (Start up Religion Ser.). (Illus.). 24p. (J). (gr. 1-4). lib. bdg. (978-1-84234-340-1(8) , Cherrytree Books) Evans Publishing Group.

Navillus, Nell. Verdadero Cuento de Navidad. Alvarez, Lourdes, tr. Eitzen, Allan, illus. 2005. (SPA.). 28p. (J). 12.95 (978-1-58173-250-4(3)) Sweetwater Pr.

Navillus, Nelle. The True Story of Christmas. Eitzen, Allan, illus. 1998. 12.95 (978-1-58173-147-7(7)) Sweetwater Pr.

Nederveld, Patricia L. Jesus Is Born! The Story of Christmas. 1998. (God Loves Me Ser.). (Illus.). 24p. (J). (ps-3). pap. 2.95 (978-1-56212-293-5(2) , 001224, Faith Alive Christian Resources) CRC Pubns.

New York Classic Christmas Trivia. 2005. 32p. pap. 6.95 ***(978-0-635-03355-0(0))*** Gallopade International.

Newman-D'Amico, Fran. Color Your Own Christmas Stickers. 2006. 2p. (J). 2.95 (978-0-486-44896-1(7)) Dover Pubns., Inc.

Nicholaus, Bret & Lowrie, Paul. Christmas Kidchat: Holiday Questions for Kids (and Kids-at-heart) Luken, Scott, illus. 2002. 128p. (J). per. 8.95 (978-0-9634251-7-1(X)) Questmarc Publishing.

Nickelodeon Staff. Nick Jr. I Made It Myself! Christmas: 38 Festive Crafts & Recipes. 2004. (Illus.). 24p. (J). spiral bd. 12.95 (978-0-8118-4420-8(X)) Chronicle Bks. LLC.

Noble, Marty. Santa's Sticker Advent Calendar. 2000. (Dover Little Activity Bks.). (Illus.). 4p. (J). (ps-5). 4.50 (978-0-486-41055-5(2)) Dover Pubns., Inc.

North, Merry. My Christmas: Picture, Play & Tote Book. 2003. (Illus.). 10p. (J). (ps up). bds. 5.99 (978-1-57151-717-3(0)) Playhouse Publishing.

Nutcracker. 2000. (Creative Editions Ser.). (J). (gr. 4-7). 125.00 (978-1-56846-135-9(6)); 35.00 (978-1-56846-136-6(4)) Creative Co., The.

Nye, Penny. My Christmas Memories. 1998. (Illus.). 15p. (J). pap. 12.00 (978-1-890703-13-4(3) , Bookmates) Penny Laine Papers, Inc.

Ohio Classic Christmas Trivia. 2005. 32p. pap. 6.95 ***(978-0-635-03351-2(8))*** Gallopade International.

Olive, Theresa. My Merry Christmas Arch Book: Luke 2:1-20 for Children. Munger, Nancy, illus. 2005. (ENG.). 16p. (J). (ps-ps). 1.99 (978-0-7586-0640-2(0)) Concordia Publishing Hse.

One Starry Night Coloring & Activity. 2005. mass mkt. 2.25 (978-1-59317-006-6(8)) Warner Pr. Pubs.

O'Neal, Debbie Trafton & LaRochelle, David. Before & after Christmas. 2001. (Illus.). 64p. 11.99 (978-0-8066-4156-0(8) , Augsburg Bks.) Augsburg Fortress, Pubs.

Onyefulu, Ifeoma. An African Christmas. 2005. (Illus.). 32p. (J). (ps-3). 15.95 (978-1-84507-387-9(8)) Lincoln, Frances Ltd. GBR. *Dist:* Perseus Distribution.

O'Shea, Denis. The First Christmas. 2002. 160p. 20.00 (978-1-930873-72-8(7)) Neumann Pr., The.

Paris, Pat. The First Noel: A Holiday Pop-Up Book. 1998. (Illus.). 10p. (J). 16.95 (978-0-8054-1793-7(1)) B&H Publishing Grp.

The Perfect Christmas. 2004. (J). mass mkt. 12.95 (978-0-9763223-0-6(7)) Wright, Robert.

Pingry, Patricia A. La Historia de la Navidad. Wells, Lorraine Schreiner, illus. 2000. (SPA.). 24p. (J). (gr. 2-4). reprint ed. 15.00 (978-0-7567-5862-2(9)) DIANE Publishing Co.

—La Historia de la Navidad. Wells, Lorraine Schreiner, illus. 2000. (SPA.). 32p. (J). (ps-k). 6.95 (978-0-8249-4189-5(6)) Ideals Pubns.

Pirotta, Saviour. Christmas. 2007. (J). lib. bdg. ***(978-1-4042-3704-9(6)*** , PowerKids Pr.) Rosen Publishing Group, Inc., The.

Pirotta, Saviour. Joy to the World: Christmas Stories from Around the Globe. Moxley, Sheila, illus. 1998. 48p. (J). (ps-3). 15.95 (978-0-06-027902-8(8)) HarperCollins Pubs.

Poole, Susie. A Christmas Journey. 48p. 11.99 (978-1-86024-273-1(1)) Authentic Media.

—A Christmas Journey. Poole, Susie, illus. 2006. (Illus.). 44p. (J). 14.99 (978-0-7847-1461-4(4) , 04087) Standard Publishing.

Potts, Steve. Christmas. 2001. (Holiday Ser.). (Illus.). 24p. (J). 21.35 (978-1-58340-115-6(6)) Smart Apple Media.

Powell, Jillian. Christmas. 2006. (Illus.). 30p. (J). (978-1-58340-945-9(9)) Smart Apple Media.

Price, Oliva. The 12 Days of Christmas (Vault) 2007. 12p. 19.95 ***(*978-1-58117-624-7(4)*** , Intervisual/Piggy Toes) Dalmatian Pr.

Prokop, Paul. The True Story of Santa Claus. 2000. (Illus.). 32p. (J). pap. 5.95 (978-0-8198-7406-1(X) , 332-393) Pauline Bks. & Media.

Rainbolt, Kelly A. The Savior That God Sent. 2000. (Illus.). 32p. (J). (ps-k). 9.99 (978-0-570-07095-5(3)) Concordia Publishing Hse.

Rau, Dana. Christmas. 2000. (gr. 3-6). lib. bdg. 15.25 (978-0-613-51627-3(3)) Tandem Library Bks.

Rau, Dana Meachen. Christmas. 2000. (True Bks.). (Illus.). 48p. (J). (gr. 3-5). 25.00 (978-0-516-21513-6(2) , Children's Pr.) Scholastic Library Publishing.

Rees, Glyn, et al. Dolig Llawen! 2005. (WEL., Illus.). 46p. (978-0-903131-20-9(X)) Urdd Gobaith Cymru.

Regina Press Staff. First Christmas. 1999. 5.99 (978-0-88271-682-4(4)) Regina Pr., Malhame & Co.

—Who's Coming to Stay? 1999. 3.95 (978-0-88271-680-0(8)) Regina Pr., Malhame & Co.

Remson, Billie. A Mississippi Winter on Bluebird Hill: A True Story about Our Little Farm in the Hills of Southern Mississippi. Garraway, Kym, illus. 2004. (J). per. 12.95 (978-1-59571-044-4(2)) Word Association Pubs.

Richards, V. H. First Christmas Color Act Bk. 24p. pap. 1.25 (978-0-8198-2677-0(4) , 332-096) Pauline Bks. & Media.

Richards, Virginia Helen & Halpin, D. Thomas, illus. My Christmas Picture Book. 2005. 14p. (J). 4.95 (978-0-8198-4829-1(8) , 332-220) Pauline Bks. & Media.

Richmond, Marianne R. Merry Christmas: Celebrating the True Gifts of the Season. 2005. (Illus.). 40p. (YA). 7.95 (978-0-9770000-4-3(4)) Marianne Richmond Studios, Inc.

Richterkessing, Suzanne. The Time of Christmas. 32p. (J). 7.99 (978-0-7586-0149-0(2)) Concordia Publishing Hse.

Rigby, Christopher & Sail, Nicola. Let's Have a Christmas: Flip Quiz. 2003. (Family Flip Quiz Ser.). (Illus.). 152p. (J). spiral bd. 12.95 (978-1-902947-96-9(7)) Miles Kelly Publishing, Ltd. GBR. *Dist:* Independent Pubs. Group.

Ritchey, Kate. We Wish You a Crafty Christmas! 2006. (Pretty Simple Stuff Ser.). 32p. (J). (gr. 2-5). pap. 6.99 (978-0-8431-2087-5(8) , Price Stern Sloan) Penguin Group (USA) Inc.

Roark, Kimberly. Celebrating Christmas: Christmas Decorations. 1999. (ps-2). lib. bdg. 10.65 (978-0-613-34117-2(1)) Tandem Library Bks.

—Celebrating Christmas No. 4533: Christmas Decorations. Kupperstein, Joel, ed. Urbanovic, Jackie, illus. 1999. 16p. (J). (ps-2). pap. 2.99 (978-1-57471-578-1(X)) Creative Teaching Pr., Inc.

Robinson, Helen Lee, compiled by. Guide's Greatest Christmas Stories. 2003. 144p. (J). pap. 10.99 (978-0-8280-1802-9(2)) Review & Herald Publishing Assn.

Rock, Lois. Christmas: Crafts, Stories, Carols. 1999. (Illus.). 48p. (J). (gr. k-3). 16.99 (978-0-7459-3907-0(4) , Lion) Lion Hudson plc GBR. *Dist:* Independent Pubs. Group.

—My Very First Christmas. Ayliffe, Alex, illus. 2006. 128p. (J). 14.99 (978-1-56148-531-4(4)) Good Bks.

Rosinsky, Natalie M. Christmas. 2002. (Let's See Library). (Illus.). 24p. (J). (gr. 1 up). lib. bdg. 19.93 (978-0-7565-0389-5(2)) Compass Point Bks.

Ross, Michael Elsohn. Mexican Christmas. Rigau, Felix, illus. Rigau, Felix, photos by. 2002. (Photo Bks.). 40p. (J). (gr. k-3). lib. bdg. 23.93 (978-0-87614-601-9(9) , Carolrhoda Bks.) Lerner Publishing Group.

Ross, Suzanne. Christmas Fun. 1998. (Illus.). 32p. (J). (ps-5). pap. 1.50 (978-0-486-40250-5(9)) Dover Pubns., Inc.

Running Press Staff. Bear Hugs for You at Christmas. 2003. (Inspirio/Zondervan Miniature Editionstm Ser.). (Illus.). 128p. 4.95 (978-0-7624-1675-2(0) , Running Pr. Minature Editions) Running Pr. Bk. Pubs.

—The Story of Christmas. 2006. (Illus.). 128p. 4.95 (978-0-7624-2816-8(3) , Running Pr.) Running Pr. Bk. Pubs.

Sacks, Janet. The Christmas Story. Rinaldo, Luana, illus. 2005. (Magic Color Bks.). 10p. (J). (ps-ps). 3.95 (978-1-4027-2618-7(X) , Sterling/Pinwheel) Sterling Publishing Co., Inc.

Sacks, Janet & Rinaldo, Luana. Santa's Special Day. ed. 2005. (Magic Color Bks.). (Illus.). 10p. (J). (ps-ps). 3.95 (978-1-4027-2617-0(1) , Sterling/Pinwheel) Sterling Publishing Co., Inc.

Santa at the Crib Make-It-Yourself Book. 2000. 2.98 (978-0-9705482-1-4(4)) JNW Bks.

Scheidies, Carolyn R. The heart of Christmas. 2005. 26p. 12.81 (978-1-4116-5925-4(2)) Lulu.com.

Schlafer, Linda. A Gift for the Christ Child: A Christmas Folktale. Wilson, Anne, illus. 2004. 26p. (ps-3). 15.95 (978-0-8294-1606-0(4)) Loyola Pr.

Scholastic, Inc. Staff. Bulletin Board Sets Happy Birhtday Jesus. 2002. spiral bd. 9.99 ***(*978-0-439-50991-6(2)*** , Teaching Resources) Scholastic, Inc.

School Zone Publishing Company Staff. Christmas ABCs: An Alphabet Book. 1999. (Board Books Ser.). (Illus.). 18p. (J). (ps-3). bds. 4.99 (978-0-88743-601-7(3) , 06602) School Zone Publishing Co.

Schuh, Mari C. Christmas. Saunders-Smith, Gail, ed. 2001. (Holidays & Celebrations Ser.). (Illus.). 24p. (J). (gr. k-1). lib. bdg. 15.93 (978-0-7368-0979-5(1) , Pebble Bks.) Capstone Pr., Inc.

Seeley, Mary Evans. Grandmother Remembers Christmas at the White House. Hunt, Virginia Koenke, ed. Rae, Terri Sopp, illus. 48p. (J). (gr. k-7). 2000. lib. bdg. 16.95 (978-0-9657684-2-9(2)); 2nd rev. l.t. ed. 2002. lib. bdg. 16.95 (978-0-9657684-4-3(9)) Presidential Christmas, A.

Simon, Mary Manz. Una Noche de Paz: La Navidad. 1999. (Hear Me Read Bible Stories Ser.). (SPA.). 32p. (J). 2.75 (978-0-570-09927-7(7)) Concordia Publishing Hse.

Sing A Story, ed. Twelve Days of Christmas. 2007. (Sing-A-Story Ser.). (Illus.). 16p. (J). (ps-k). bds. 10.95 ***(*978-0-7696-5334-1(0))*** School Specialty Publishing.

Snowman's Christmas Sparkly Sticker Fun. 2002. 16p. (J). pap. 2.98 (978-0-7525-6503-3(6)) Parragon, Inc.

Solis, Valerie. Feliz Navidad Barnaby. 2000. Tr. of Merry Christmas Barnaby. (SPA.). 32p. (J). 18.95 (978-84-261-2551-4(4)) Juventud, Editorial ESP. *Dist:* AIMS International Bks., Inc.

Southern Christmas. 2001. 28p. (J). 10.00 (978-0-9713589-0-4(7)) Ubaviel's Gifts.

Spence, Christine, compiled by. Christmas Programs for Children. annual 2005. (Illus.). 48p. (J). pap. 5.99 (978-0-7847-1612-0(9) , 08605) Standard Publishing.

St. Pierre, Stephanie. Bible People Books Nativity Set, 2 vols. Lyon, Tammie Speer, illus. 2002. 14p. 16.99 (978-0-7847-1242-9(5)) Standard Publishing.

Staf, Edie. Christmas Novena: For Home or Classroom. 22p. (J). (gr. 2-8). pap. 1.50 (978-0-8198-1456-2(3) , 332-032) Pauline Bks. & Media.

Standard Publishing Staff. New Baby's Nativity. 1999. (Baby's First Bible Collection). (Illus.). 8p. (J). (ps). 10.99 (978-0-7847-0909-2(2) , 03990, Bean Sprouts) Standard Publishing.

—Standard Christmas Program BK. 2006. 48p. pap. 6.99 (978-0-7847-1647-2(1)) Standard Publishing.

Star Chasers. 2006. (J). pap. 1.79 ***(*978-1-59317-170-4(6))*** Warner Pr. Pubs.

Starr, Debra, compiled by. The Book of Christmas: A Collection of Holiday Verse, Prose, & Carols. 128p. (J). (978-0-681-22004-1(X)) Borders Group, Inc.

Stephens, Chris S. A Christmas Box. 32p. 2003. pap. 20.95 (978-1-84323-306-0(1)); 2002. (Illus.). pap. 13.95 (978-1-84323-037-3(2)) Beekman Bks., Inc.

Stephens, Mattie Freeman. The CHRISTmas Gift. 2006. (J). pap. 15.00 ***(*978-0-8059-7180-4(7))*** Dorrance Publishing Co., Inc.

Stern, Leonard & Price, Roger. Merry Christmas! My First Mad Libs. Daugherty, Heather, illus. 2007. 16p. (J). (ps). pap. 4.99 ***(*978-0-8431-2674-7(4))*** Penguin Group (USA) Inc.

Stewart, Jennifer. What Is Christmas Coloring Book. Garris, Norma, illus. 2000. (Coloring Bks.). 16p. (J). (ps up). pap. 1.99 (978-0-7847-1194-1(1) , 22113) Standard Publishing.

Stewart, Jennifer, ed. Christmas Fun: Sticker Book. Kolding, Richard Max, illus. 1999. 28p. (J). (ps-2). act. bk. ed. 3.29 (978-0-7847-1095-1(3) , 22079, Bean Sprouts) Standard Publishing.

Stiegemeyer, Julie. Things I See at Christmas. Mitter, Kathy, illus. 2005. (ENG.). 16p. (J). (ps-17). bds. 4.99 (978-0-7586-0809-3(8)) Concordia Publishing Hse.

The Story of Christmas. 2003. (J). per. (978-1-57657-806-3(2)) Paradise Pr., Inc.

The Story of Christmas. Date not set. 4.99 (978-0-88271-273-4(X) , 1440) Regina Pr., Malhame & Co.

The Story of Christmas. 2006. 16p. (J). pap. 1.99 (978-0-7847-1548-2(3) , 04364) Standard Publishing.

The Story of Christmas: La Historia de la Navidad. 2001. (SPA & ENG.). 30p. (J). 3.95 (978-0-8249-4134-5(9)) Ideals Pubns.

Taliaferro, Margaret. The Real Reason for Christmas: Letters to Children for the Twelve Nights of Christmas. (Illus.). 118p. (J). (gr. 1-7). reprint ed. pap. 6.95 (978-0-9618730-0-4(0)) FEA Ministries.

Tallarico, Tony. Where Are They? More Than 1,000 Fun Things to Search & Find. 2001. (Illus.). (J). (978-1-56156-916-8(X)) Kidsbooks, Inc.

TerKeurst, Lysa. The Sweetest Story Ever Told Activity Kit. Sparks, Michal, illus. 2003. 14.99 (978-0-8024-7093-5(9)) Moody Pubs.

Texas Classic Christmas Trivia. 2005. 32p. pap. 6.95 ***(*978-0-635-03350-5(X))*** Gallopade International.

Thank You, God, for Christmas Coloring Book. 2006. 16p. (J). pap. 1.99 (978-0-7847-1261-0(1) , 22119) Standard Publishing.

Thoennes, Kristin. Christmas in France. 1998. (Christmas Around the World Ser.). (Illus.). 24p. (J). (gr. 2-3). 18.60 (978-0-7368-0088-1(3) , Bridgestone Bks.) Capstone Pr., Inc.

—Christmas in Germany. 1998. (Christmas Around the World Ser.). (Illus.). 24p. (J). (gr. 2-3). lib. bdg. 19.93 (978-0-7368-0089-1(1) , Bridgestone Bks.) Capstone Pr., Inc.

—Christmas in Italy. 1998. (Christmas Around the World Ser.). (Illus.). 24p. (J). (gr. 2-3). 18.60 (978-0-7368-0090-7(5) , Bridgestone Bks.) Capstone Pr., Inc.

—Christmas in Norway. 1998. (Christmas Around the World Ser.). (Illus.). 24p. (J). (gr. 2-3). 18.60 (978-0-7368-0091-4(3) , Bridgestone Bks.) Capstone Pr., Inc.

Tres Regalos Para el Nino Jesus, 6 vols. 2000. (Arch Bks.). (SPA.). 24p. (J). (ps-3). 2.49 (978-0-570-05171-8(1)) Concordia Publishing Hse.

Trueit, Trudi Strain. Christmas. 2007. (Holidays, Festivals, & Celebrations Ser.). 32p. (J). (gr. k-4). 22.79 ***(*978-1-59296-811-4(2))*** Child's World, Inc.

—Christmas. 2006. (Rookie Read-About Holidays Ser.). (Illus.). 32p. (J). 20.50 (978-0-531-12453-6(3)); (gr. 1-2). pap. 5.95 (978-0-531-11834-4(7)) Scholastic Library Publishing. (Children's Pr.).

The Twelve Days of Christmas. 2003. (Traditional Christmas Stories Ser.). 32p. (J). 4.98 (978-0-7525-8848-3(6)) Parragon, Inc.

Tyrrell, Melissa. Busy Little Angels: A Little Foil Book. 1998. (Merry Little Foil Bks.). (Illus.). 10p. (J). (ps up). 2.95 (978-1-58117-009-2(2) , Intervisual/Piggy Toes) Dalmatian Pr.

Van Leeuwen, Wendy. Itty-bitty Bible Activity Book, God's Big Christmas Plan. 2007. (Illus.). 48p. (J). pap. 1.49 ***(*978-1-59317-211-4(7))*** Warner Pr. Pubs.

Vanus, Lori G. Latter-Day Letters: Christmas. Vanus, Lori G., illus. 1998. (Illus.). 32p. (J). (gr. k-6). pap. 7.95 (978-1-892318-01-5(6)) White Stone Publishing Co.

Virginia Classic Christmas Trivia. 2005. 32p. pap. 6.95 ***(*978-0-635-03352-9(6))*** Gallopade International.

Wade, Lee. The Cheerios Christmas Play Book. Wade, Lee, illus. 2000. (Illus.). 14p. (J). bds. 6.99 (978-0-689-84008-1(X) , Little Simon) Simon & Schuster Children's Publishing.

Walsh, Mary C. Saint Francis Celebrates Christmas. Caswell, Helen Rayburn, illus. 1998. 32p. (ps-3). 15.95 (978-0-8294-1112-6(7)) Loyola Pr.

Walsh, William S. The Story of Santa Klaus: Told for Children of All Ages from Six To. 2007. (ENG.). 216p. per. 24.95 ***(*978-1-4304-4232-5(8))*** Kessinger Publishing, LLC.

Wangerin, Walter, Jr. Angels & All Children: A Nativity Story in Words, Music, & Art. Ladwig, Tim, illus. 2004. 40p. (gr. 2-7). 18.99 incl. audio compact disk (978-0-8066-3712-9(9) , Augsburg Bks.) Augsburg Fortress, Pubs.

—Mary's First Christmas. Ladwig, Tim, illus. 1998. 48p. (J). 19.99 (978-0-310-22216-3(8)) Zonderkidz.

—Mary's First Christmas. 1998. (J). 19.99 (978-0-310-22746-5(1)) Zondervan.

Watt, Fiona. Christmas Baby Jigsaw Book. Wells, Rachel, illus. 2004. (Jigsaw Books Ser.). 14p. (J). 10.95 (978-0-7945-0809-8(X) , Usborne) EDC Publishing.

Watt, Fiona & Wells, Rachel. Christmas. 2004. (Illus.). 10p. (J). 12.95 (978-0-7945-0498-4(1) , Usborne) EDC Publishing.

Wilkinson, Jean & Wilkinson, Ned. Santa at the Crib. 2000. 32p. (J). mass mkt. 4.98 (978-0-9705482-0-7(6)) JNW Bks.

Williams, Colleen Madonna Flood. My Adventure on Christmas. 2006. 44p. (J). 8.99 (978-1-59092-545-4(9) , Orchard Academy Pr.) Windstorm Creative.

Wilner, Isabel. B Is for Bethlehem: A Christmas Alphabet. Kleven, Elisa, illus. 2004. 24p. (J). (ps). bds. 8.99 (978-0-525-47323-7(8) , Dutton Juvenile) Penguin Group (USA) Inc.

Winne, Joanne. Let's Get Ready for Christmas. 2001. (Celebrations Ser.). (Illus.). 24p. (J). (ps-2). 17.00 (978-0-516-23171-6(5)); pap. 4.95 (978-0-516-29567-1(5)) Scholastic Library Publishing. (Children's Pr.).

World Book, Inc. Staff. Christmas in Australia. 1999. (Christmas Around the World Ser.). (Illus.). 80p. (YA). (gr. 2-12). 19.00 (978-0-7166-0850-9(2)) World Bk., Inc.

—Christmas in Finland. 2002. (Christmas Around the World Ser.). 1760p. (gr. 2-8). 24.95 (978-0-7166-0863-9(4) , 20066) World Bk., Inc.

—Christmas in Russia. 2004. (Christmas Around the World Ser.). 1760p. (gr. 2-8). 24.95 (978-0-7166-0862-2(6)) World Bk., Inc.

—Christmas in the Philippines. 2002. (Christmas Around the World Ser.). (Illus.). 1760p. (gr. 2-8). 24.95 (978-0-7166-0853-0(7) , 365) World Bk., Inc.

World Book, Inc Staff, contrib. by. Christmas in America in the 1700's & 1800's. 2006. 80p. (J). (978-0-7166-0808-0(1)) World Bk., Inc.

World Book, Inc. Staff, contrib. by. Christmas in Belgium. 2004. (Christmas Around the World from World Book Ser.). (Illus.). 1760p. (gr. 2-8). 24.95 (978-0-7166-0864-6(2) , 20114) World Bk., Inc.

—Christmas in Puerto Rico. 2002. (Christmas Around the World from World Book Ser.). (Illus.). 80p. (gr. 2-8). 24.95 (978-0-7166-0801-1(4)) World Bk., Inc.

Youd, Pauline. Why Were the Shepherds Excited? A Christmas Story. Sandland, Reg, illus. 2000. 13p. (J). (gr. 1-4). 3.95 (978-0-8198-8298-1(4)) Pauline Bks. & Media.

Zobel-Nolan, Allia. Sigulendo la Estrella (Follow the Star) 2000. (SPA.). (J). (ps-k). bds. (978-0-7899-0817-9(4) , 493785) Editorial Unilit.

Zocchi, Judy. On Christmas Eve. Wallis, Rebecca, illus. 2005. (Holiday Happenings Ser.). 32p. (J). pap. 9.95 (978-1-59646-224-3(8)); lib. bdg. 20.65 (978-1-891997-47-1(5)) Dingles & Co.

—On Christmas Eve/la Nochebuena. Wallis, Rebecca, illus. 2005. (Holiday Happenings Ser.).Tr. of Nochebuena. 32p. (J). pap. 9.95 (978-1-59646-226-7(4)); (ENG & SPA.). lib. bdg. 20.65 (978-1-891997-48-8(3)); (ENG & SPA.). per. 9.95 (978-1-59646-227-4(2)) Dingles & Co.

Zondervan. Bear Hugs for You at Christmas Greeting Book. 2003. 48p. 6.99 (978-0-310-80415-4(9)) Zondervan.

—Beginner's Bible My Christmas Manger. 2006. (Beginner's Bible' Ser.). (Illus.). 14p. (J). 14.99 (978-0-310-71140-7(1)) Zonderkidz.

Zschock, Heather. Merry Christmas Scratch & Sketch. 2006. (Illus.). 64p. (J). 12.99 (978-1-59359-943-0(9)) Peter Pauper Pr. Inc.

CHRISTMAS—DRAMA

see Christmas Plays

CHRISTMAS—FICTION

Aardvark, D. Merry Kissmoose. Aardvark, D., illus. l.t. ed. 2005. (Illus.). 48p. (J). per. 12.95 (978-0-9755567-2-6(X)) Aardvark's Weedpatch Pr.

Abel, Janice. The Little White Christmas Horse. Gallagher, Denyce, illus. 2006. (J). per. 10.95 ***(*978-0-9655739-6-2(6))*** Abel Publishing.

Aboff, Marcie. Hocus Pocus! Style Guide Staff, illus. 2006. (Frosty the Snowman Ser.). 400p. (J). act. bk. ed. 5.99 (978-1-4169-2526-2(0) , Simon Scribbles) Simon & Schuster Children's Publishing.

—Santa's Big Red Helper. Haefele, Steve, illus. 2005. (Clifford Ser.). 80p. (J). (ps-k). pap. 2.99 (978-0-439-79150-2(2)) Scholastic, Inc.

Abrams. Hello Kitty, Hello Christmas! Book & Ornament. 2004. 24p. (gr. 8-17). pap. 9.95 (978-0-8109-5042-9(1)) Abrams, Harry N. , Inc.

Ada, Alma Flor & Campoy, F. Isabel. Celebrate Christmas & Three Kings' Day with Pablo & Carlitos. Torres, Walter, illus. 2006. (J). (978-1-59820-136-9(0)) Santillana USA Publishing Co., Inc.

Adams, Eve. Christmas Eve. 2000. (Illus.). 10p. (J). pap. (978-0-9538369-0-1(8)) E. V. Bks.

Adrienne, Dawn. The Hawaiian Christmas Tree. Brooks, Susan, illus. 1999. 31p. (J). (gr. 2-5). 14.95 (978-0-9667484-1-3(7)) Tamarind.

The Adventures of Molly. 2004. pap. 13.95 ***(*978-1-59526-180-9(X))*** Media Creations, Inc.

Aebersold, Carol V. & Bell, Chanda B. The Elf on the Shelf: A Christmas Tradition. 2005. (J). bds. 21.95 net. (978-0-9769907-0-3(9)) CCA & B, LLC.

Agbodza, Ena and Kwami. The Bad Ices Man & the Girl Who Saved Christmas. 2006. (Illus.). 45p. (J). per. 9.95 (978-1-59453-782-0(8) , Airleaf Publishing) Airleaf Publishing & Bookselling.

Ahlstrom, Leonard. Christmas Shoes for Children. 2004. pap. 7.99 (978-0-9714147-1-6(8)) Point To Point Publishing.

Akmon, Nancy C. Peter Rabbit Celebrates Christmas. Akmon, Roni, ed. 1999. (Illus.). 48p. (J). 8.95 (978-1-884807-45-9(3) , EC745) Blushing Rose Publishing.

Akmon, Nancy C. & Akmon, Roni, eds. Hollyberries of Christmas. 1999. (Illus.). 36p. (J). 8.95 (978-1-884807-44-2(5) , EC744) Blushing Rose Publishing.

Albertson, Bernard. So, You Think There Is No Santa, Bk. 2. 2004. 96p. (J). pap. 7.95 (978-0-87714-744-2(2)) Denlingers Pubs., Ltd.

Albright, Ann. Samuel Sparrow & the Tree of Light. Albright, Ann, illus. 2003. (J). (978-0-9715472-5-4(4)) Ascension Lutheran Church.

Alcott, Louisa May. The Louisa Alcott Reader: A Supplementar. 2006. pap. ***(*978-1-4065-0590-0(0))*** Dodo Pr.

Alcott, Louisa May. Louisa May Alcott's Little Women at Christmas. Flint, Russ, illus. 1999. 48p. (J). (gr. 4-7). 14.95 (978-0-8249-4161-1(6) , Candy Cane Pr.) Ideals Pubns.

Aldous, Kate, illus. The Kingfisher Treasury of Christmas Stories. 2003. (Kingfisher Treasury of Stories Ser.). 160p. (J). (gr. k-3). pap. 5.95 (978-0-7534-5670-5(2) , Kingfisher) Houghton Mifflin Co. Trade & Reference Div.

Alexander, Alec. My Magical Christmas Dream of the Marshmallow Martians. 2000. (Marshmallow Martian Ser.: Vol. 2). (Illus.). 32p. (J). (ps-5). 5.95 (978-0-9670091-1-7(1)) Smart Alec Toys Publishing.

Alexander, Michael. Until Wishes Are Fulfilled. 2007. (ENG.). 160p. per. ***(*978-1-84426-408-7(4))*** Upfront Publishing Ltd.

Alford, Carrie. My Christmas Story. 2003. (J). per. 14.25 (978-1-932301-18-2(6) , 1045) Airleaf Publishing & Bookselling.

All I Want for Christmas. 2003. (J). per. (978-1-57657-707-3(4)) Paradise Pr., Inc.

Allgeier, Steve. Christmas with Norky, the Adventure Begins... 2007. (J). per. 17.99 ***(*978-1-933156-25-5(2)*** , Visikid Bks.) GSVQ Publishing.

Alsenas, Linas. Mrs. Claus Takes a Vacation. 2006. (Illus.). 32p. (J). pap. 16.99 (978-0-439-77978-4(2) , Scholastic Pr.) Scholastic, Inc.

Amedick, Deborah. A Cat Named Wellington: His Lessons for Christmas. 1998. (Animal Ser.). (Illus.). 36p. (J). (ps-1). pap. 4.95 (978-1-891210-79-2(3) , CNWXM1) Bartlett Publishing.

Amery, Heather. Farmyard Tales Christmas. 24p. 14.95 incl. audio (978-0-7945-0218-8(0)) EDC Publishing.

—Farmyard Tales Christmas Flap Bk And. 2006. 24p. 12.99 (978-0-7945-0556-1(2) , Usborne) EDC Publishing.

—Farmyard Tales Christmas Flap Book. 2000. (Farmyard Tales Flap Bks.). (Illus.). 24p. (YA). (ps-3). 9.95 (978-0-7460-4138-3(1)) EDC Publishing.

Anaya, Rudolfo A. The Santero's Miracle: A Bilingual Story. Lamadrid, Enrique E., tr. Cordova, Amy, illus. 2004. (ENG & SPA.). 32p. (J). 16.95 (978-0-8263-2847-2(4)) Univ. of New Mexico Pr.

Anders, C. J. Capeside Christmas. 2000. (gr. 7-12). lib. bdg. 14.15 (978-0-613-73113-3(1)) Tandem Library Bks.

Andersen-Murphy. If You Believe. 2004. 76p. pap. 14.95 (978-0-9743580-8-6(8)) Brzamo Publishing.

Anderson, Derek. How the Easter Bunny Saved Christmas. Anderson, Derek, illus. 2006. (Illus.). 40p. (J). 15.95 (978-0-689-87634-9(3) , Simon & Schuster Children's Publishing) Simon & Schuster Children's Publishing.

Anderson, Rian B. A Christmas Prayer. 2004. pap. 2.95 (978-1-57734-900-6(8)) Covenant Communications, Inc.

Angel, Bruce. I Believe in Santa Claus. 2006. 121p. pap. 17.95 (978-1-4241-1486-3(1)) PublishAmerica, Inc.

Anglund, Joan Walsh. The Cowboy's Christmas. Anglund, Joan Walsh, illus. 2004. (Illus.). 40p. (J). 8.95 (978-0-7407-4675-8(8)) Andrews McMeel Publishing.

Aoki, Hisako. Santa's Favorite Story: Santa Tells the Story of the First Christmas. Gantschev, Ivan, illus. 2007. 28p. (J). (ps-3). 9.99 ***(*978-1-4169-5029-5(X))*** Simon & Schuster Children's Publishing.

Appel, Cindy. The Best Christmas Gift. Collier, Kevin Scott, illus. 2005. (J). E-Book 6.00 incl. cd-rom (978-1-933090-19-1(7)) Guardian Angel Publishing, Inc.

Apperley, Dawn, illus. Santa Claus Will Come Tonight. 2002. 24p. (J). (ps-1). pap. 6.95 (978-0-439-40449-5(5) , Cartwheel Bks.) Scholastic, Inc.

Arnold, Tedd. Huggly's Christmas. Arnold, Tedd, illus. 2001. (Huggly Ser.: No. 7). (Illus.). 32p. (J). (gr. 4-7). pap. 3.25 (978-0-439-13500-9(1) , Cartwheel Bks.) Scholastic, Inc.

Arruda, Suzanne M. A Stocking for Jesus. Ogden, Betina, illus. 2005. (J). pap. 7.95 (978-0-8198-7076-6(5) , 332-372) Pauline Bks. & Media.

Arterburn, Stephen & Hunt, Angela Elwell. Shane. 2004. (Young Believer on Tour Ser.). (J). pap. 3.99 (978-0-8423-8339-4(5)) Tyndale Hse. Pubs.

Artful Doodlers Limited Staff. A LazyTown Christmas. 2006. (LazyTown Ser.). 24p. (J). pap. 3.99 (978-1-4169-1760-1(8) , Simon Spotlight/Nickelodeon) Simon & Schuster Children's Publishing.

Ash, Jo Ann Clark. Yule, the Great Christmas Bear. 2000. (Illus.). 28p. (J). (ps-5). pap. 8.00 (978-0-9715835-0-4(1)) Clark, Jo Ann.

Ashforth, Camilla. Willow at Christmas. Ashforth, Camilla, illus. 2005. (Illus.). 32p. (J). (ps-1). pap. 3.99 (978-0-7636-2927-4(8)) Candlewick Pr.

Athkins, D. Secret Santa. 2001. (gr. 7-12). lib. bdg. 13.00 (978-0-613-58133-2(4)) Tandem Library Bks.

Auch, Mary Jane. The Nutquacker. Auch, Mary Jane, illus. (Illus.). 32p. (J). (gr. k-3). tchr. ed. 17.95 (978-0-8234-1524-3(4)) Holiday Hse., Inc.

Auch, Mary Jane & Auch, Herm, illus. I Was a Third Grade Bodyguard. 2003. 80p. (J). (gr. 4-6). tchr. ed. 15.95 (978-0-8234-1775-9(1)) Holiday Hse., Inc.

Augustine, Peg. One Surprising Night. 2006. 16p. pap. 5.00 ***(*978-0-687-49250-3(5))*** Abingdon Pr.

Augustine, Peggy. It Looks a Lot Like Christmas. 2007. pap. 1.59 ***(*978-0-687-65182-5(4))*** Abingdon Pr.

Autry, Gene & Haldeman, Oakley. Here Comes Santa Claus. Whatley, Bruce, illus. 2002. 32p. (J), (ps up). 18.89 (978-0-06-028269-1(X)) HarperCollins Pubs.

Avi. The Christmas Rat. 2002. 144p. (J). pap. 4.99 (978-0-689-83843-9(3) , Aladdin) Simon & Schuster Children's Publishing.

—The Christmas Rat. 2002. (gr. 3-6). lib. bdg. 13.00 (978-0-613-88162-3(1)) Tandem Library Bks.

Awdry, Christopher. Thomas & the Missing Christmas Tree. Thompson Brothers Studio Staff, illus. 1999. (Jellybean Bks.). 24p. (J). (ps-k). lib. bdg. 7.99 (978-0-375-90078-5(0) , Random Hse. Bks. for Young Readers) Random Hse. Children's Bks.

Awdry, Wilbert V. Christmastime with Thomas. Albrecht, Jeff, illus. 2000. (Painting Time Ser.). 32p. (J). (ps-3). pap. 3.99 (978-0-375-80642-1(3) , Random Hse. Bks. for Young Readers) Random Hse. Children's Bks.

—Thomas's Christmas Delivery. Stubbs, Tommy, illus. 2004. (Thomas & Friends Ser.). 32p. (J). (ps-2). 8.99 (978-0-375-82877-5(X) , Random Hse. Bks. for Young Readers) Random Hse. Children's Bks.

Axelrod, Amy. Pigs on the Move: Fun with Math & Travel. McGinley-Nally, Sharon, illus. 1999. (Pigs Will Be Pigs Ser.). 40p. (J). (ps-4). 15.95 (978-0-689-81070-1(9)) Simon & Schuster Children's Publishing.

—Pigs on the Move: Fun with Math & Travel. 1999. (gr. k-3). lib. bdg. 15.30 (978-0-613-67157-6(0)) Tandem Library Bks.

Axelrod, Amy & McGinley-Nally, Sharon. Pigs on the Move: Fun with Math & Travel. 2002. (Illus.). 40p. (J). pap. 6.99 (978-0-689-85343-2(2) , Aladdin) Simon & Schuster Children's Publishing.

Ayasta, Ayasta. Star. 2007. 117p. 34.95 ***(*978-1-4303-1520-9(2))*** Lulu.com.

Azinger, Marla. The Seaweed Christmas Tree. Azinger, Marla, illus. l.t. ed. 2000. (Illus.). 34p. (J). per. 14.95 (978-1-932373-01-1(2)) Cedar Hill Publishing.

B Small Publishing Staff. Crafty Christmas Stars. 1999. (Illus.). 16p. (J). (gr. 1-4). (978-1-874735-59-5(X)) B Small Publishing.

Babcock, Bruce. Christmas with the Little People. Babcock, Bruce, illus. unabr. ed. 1998. (Illus.). 46p. (J). (ps-6). pap. 7.95 (978-1-892161-04-8(4)) Babcock Publishing Co.

—The Year Santa Got Sick. Babcock, Bruce, illus. unabr. ed. 1998. (Illus.). 32p. (J). (ps-6). pap. 7.95 (978-1-892161-02-4(8)) Babcock Publishing Co.

Baby Strawberry's First Christmas. 2007. (Strawberry Shortcake Baby Ser.). 10p. (J). (ps). bds. 4.99 ***(*978-0-448-44669-1(3)*** , Grosset & Dunlap) Penguin Group (USA) Inc.

Baca, Ana. Benito's Bizcochitos. Castilla, Julia Mercedes, tr. Accardo, Anthony, illus. 1999. Tr. of Bizcochitos de Benito. (ENG & SPA.). 32p. (J). (ps-3). 14.95 (978-1-55885-264-8(6) , Piñata Books) Arte Publico Pr.

Bachand, Stephen. Christmas for Kristi. Bachand, Stephen & Bachand, Del-Marie, illus. 1999. (Booktime Buddies Ser.). (J). (ps-2). pap. 5.00 (978-1-928972-02-0(0)) Critter Pubns.

Baglio, Ben M. Puupy in a Present. 2004. 139p. (J). (978-0-439-68759-1(4)) Scholastic, Inc.

—Terrier in the Tinsel. Baum, Ann & Gregory, Jenny, illus. 2004. (Animal Ark Hauntings Ser.). 160p. (J). (gr. 2-5). pap. 3.99 (978-0-439-44892-5(1) , Scholastic Paperbacks) Scholastic, Inc.

Bak, Jenny. A Very Minty Christmas Reusable Sticker Book. 2005. (My Little Pony Ser.). 12p. (J). pap. 6.99 (978-0-06-084141-6(9) , Harper Festival) HarperCollins Pubs.

Baker, Bonnie Haskins. Twas the Night Before the Christ Came. 2002. (Illus.). 31p. per. 12.99 (978-0-9724680-9-1(9)) Lifevest Publishing, Inc.

Balcerek, Tom. The Cat & the Christmas Tree. 2006. (ENG.). 28p. per. 15.00 ***(*978-1-4259-7334-6(5))*** AuthorHouse.

Balian, Lorna. Bah! Humbug? Balian, Lecia, illus. 2006. 32p. (J). 15.95 (978-1-59572-036-8(7)) Star Bright Bks., Inc.

Ball, Marcia. Christmas Fais Do-Do. 2006. (Illus.). 36p. (J). per. 14.95 ***(*978-1-58939-972-3(2))*** Virtualbookworm.com Publishing, Inc.

Ballard, John. The Girl Who Couldn't Wait for Christmas. 2000. (Illus.). 64p. (J). (ps-5). (978-0-932279-50-7(3)) World Citizens.

Ballesteros, Jose Manuel. La Foto de Navidad.Tr. of Christmas Picture. (SPA.). 63p. 6.00 (978-84-241-7717-1(7)) Everest de Ediciones y Distribucion, S.L. ESP. *Dist:* Lectorum Pubns., Inc.

Bannister, Barbara. The Christmas Train. 2007. (Illus.). 40p. (J). per. 7.95 ***(*978-0-940895-54-6(4))*** Cornerstone Pr. Chicago.

Barkan, Joanne. The Lights of Christmas. 2005. (Twinkle Lights Ser.). (Illus.). 10p. (J). (ps-3). bds. 12.99 (978-0-7944-0774-2(9)) Reader's Digest Assn., Inc., The.

Barker, Cicely Mary. A Flower Fairy Christmas. 2004. (Flower Fairies Ser.). 24p. (J). 4.99 (978-0-7232-4994-8(6) , Warne) Penguin Group (USA) Inc.

Barker, Cicely Mary. Merry Fairy Holidays: Three Enchanted Christmas Stories. 2007. 244p. (J). (gr. 2). 8.99 ***(*978-0-7232-5972-5(0)*** , Warne) Penguin Group (USA) Inc.

Barnes, Laura T. Ernest's Special Christmas. Camburn, Carol A., illus. 2003. (Ernest Ser.). 36p. (J). (gr. k-3). 17.95 (978-0-9674681-3-6(2)) Barnesyard Bks.

Barrett, Anna Pearl. Dreaming of a Neecie Christmas, 4 vols., Vol. 4. Weston, Eunice & Waters, Linda, eds. Peguero, Phillip, illus. 2000. (Neecie Bks.). 60p. (J). (gr. 2-9). pap. 7.95 (978-0-9661330-4-2(8)) Over the Rainbow Productions.

Barrett, Robert, illus. The Other Wise Man. 32p. (J). pap. 6.95 (978-0-8249-5348-5(7) , Ideals Children's Bks.) Ideals Pubns.

Barrick, Sheila. Frazier the Crooked Christmas Tree. Grillo, Donato, illus. 2001. 48p. (J). (ps-7). (978-0-9713414-0-1(0)) Barrick, Sheila.

Barry, Robert. Mr. Willowby's Christmas Tree. Date not set. 32p. (J). 16.95 (978-0-8488-2206-4(4)) Amereon LTD.

—Mr. Willowby's Christmas Tree. Barry, Robert, illus. 2000. (Illus.). 32p. (J). (gr. k-3). 15.95 (978-0-385-32721-3(8) , Doubleday Bks. for Young Readers) Random Hse. Children's Bks.

Basore, Polly M. Santa's Stray in A Piano for Christmas. Williams, Carlene H., illus. 2005. 32p. (J). per. (978-0-9771749-1-1(3)) AngelBooks.

Bateman, Claire Boudreaux. How Christmas Began. Romero, Hannah E., illus. 2002. per. 18.50 (978-0-9706732-1-3(3)) Shell Beach Publishing, LLC.

Bauer, Marion Dane. Christmas in the Forest. Hearn, Diane Dawson, illus. (Holiday House Reader Ser.). 48p. (J). (gr. k-3). tchr. ed. 15.95 (978-0-8234-1371-3(3)) Holiday Hse., Inc.

—Christmas Lights. Mitchell, Susan, illus. 2006. 12p. (J). 12.99 (978-0-689-86942-6(8) , Little Simon) Simon & Schuster Children's Publishing.

Bauer, Robert. Elmer Elf Saves Christmas. 2002. 43p. pap. 9.95 (978-0-7414-1335-2(3)) Infinity Publishing.

Baum, L. Frank. The Life & Adventures of Santa Claus. 2005. (Illus.). 192p. (gr. 12). mass mkt. 4.95 (978-0-451-52997-8(9) , Signet Classics) Penguin Group (USA) Inc.

—Life & Adventures of Santa Claus. 2006. 216p. 24.95 (978-1-55709-180-2(3)) Applewood Bks.

—The Life & Adventures of Santa Claus. Hague, Michael, illus. rev. ed. 2003. 192p. (J). 29.95 (978-0-8050-3822-4(1) , Holt, Henry & Co. Bks. For Young Readers) Holt, Henry & Co.

Baumgart, Klaus. Laura's Christmas Star. 1999. (Illus.). 32p. (J). (ps-2). 16.95 (978-1-888444-59-9(2)) Little Tiger Pr.

—Laura's Christmas Star. Waite, Judy, tr. from GER. 2003. (Illus.). 32p. (J). pap. 8.95 (978-1-58925-382-7(5) , tiger tales) ME Media LLC.

Beach, Don M. Sydney Kangaroo's Christmas. 1999. 22p. (J). 14.95 incl. audio (978-0-9671485-0-2(2)) Dot E. Pubs.

Beck, Andrea, illus. Elliot's Christmas Surprise. 2004. (Elliot Moose Ser.). 32p. (J). (gr. k-3). (978-1-55337-661-3(7)); (978-1-55337-474-9(6)) Kids Can Pr., Ltd.

Beck, Ian. The Christmas Story. 2005. (Illus.). 32p. (J). (gr. 1-2). pap. 9.99 (978-0-552-54937-0(1) , Corgi) Transworld Publishers Ltd. GBR. *Dist:* Independent Pubs. Group.

Bedford, David. I've Seen Santa! Warnes, Tim, illus. 2006. 32p. (J). 15.95 (978-1-58925-058-1(3) , tiger tales) ME Media LLC.

Belardes, Nick. The Blimperwhirls. 2002. 108p. pap. 9.95 (978-0-595-25999-1(5) , Writers Club Pr.) iUniverse, Inc.

Bemelmans, Ludwig. Madeline's Christmas. Bemelmans, Ludwig, illus. 2002. (Madeline Ser.). (Illus.). (J). 14.04 (978-0-7587-5650-3(X)) Book Wholesalers, Inc.

—Madeline's Christmas. Bemelmans, Ludwig, illus. (Puffin Storytime Ser.). 32p. (J). (ps). 2007. 9.99 ***(*978-0-14-240897-1(2)*** , Puffin); 2000. (Illus.). pap. 7.99 (978-0-14-056650-5(3) , Viking Juvenile) Penguin Group (USA) Inc.

—Madeline's Christmas. 1999. (ps-2). lib. bdg. 15.30 (978-0-613-30014-8(9)) Tandem Library Bks.

Bemelsman, Ludwig. La Noel de Madeleine. 2000. (Adventures of Madeleine Ser.).Tr. of Madeline's Christmas. (FRE.). (J). pap. 14.95 (978-2-211-05079-1(4)) Archimede Editions FRA. *Dist:* Distribooks, Inc.

Bender, Esther. Virginia & the Tiny One. Keenan, Joy Dunn, illus. 1998. (Lemon Tree Ser.: Vol. 2). 104p. (J). (gr. 3-7). pap. 6.99 (978-0-8361-9090-8(4)) Herald Pr.

Benjamin, Alan. It's Almost Christmas, Rudolph! 1998. (Shaped Little Nugget Bks.). (Illus.). 16p. (J). (gr. k-ps). bds. 3.99 (978-0-307-13056-3(8) , 13056, Golden Bks.) Random Hse. Children's Bks.

Bennerson, Denise. Daniel & the Christmas Festival. Vega, Edwin, illus. 2001. 12p. (J). 4.00 (978-0-9646279-6-3(5)) Bennerson, Denise.

Bennet, Amy. One Christmas in Lunenburg. Kilby, Don, illus. 2004. 24p. (J). 16.95 (978-1-55028-868-1(7)) Lorimer, James & Co., Ltd., Pubs. CAN. *Dist:* Casemate Pubs. & Bk. Distributors, LLC.

Benoit, Gschwind. My First Little Christmas Book. 2001. 52p. (J). 2.95 (978-1-58595-195-6(1)) Twenty-Third Pubns./Bayard.

Benson, P. Bryn. Josefina the Christmas Cow: A Tale of Hope & Faith. Cinelli, Lisa, illus. 2005. 48p. pap. 9.95 (978-0-929636-47-4(3)) Syren Bk. Co.

Bentley, Dawn. Fuzzy Bear's Christmas. Nagy, Krisztina, illus. 2000. (Fuzzy Bear Ser.). 10p. (J). (ps-3). 11.95 (978-1-58117-105-1(6) , Intervisual/Piggy Toes) Dalmatian Pr.

—Santa's Surprise: A Pop-Up Story Box. Moerbeek, Kees, illus. 1998. 12p. (YA). (gr. 2 up). (978-1-58117-018-4(1) , Intervisual/Piggy Toes) Dalmatian Pr.

Berenstain, Jan & Berenstain, Stan. The Berenstain Bears Trim the Tree. Berenstain, Jan, illus. 2007. (Berenstain Bears Ser.). 16p. (J). (ps-1). 6.99 ***(*978-0-06-057417-8(8)*** , Harper Festival) HarperCollins Pubs.

Berenstain, Jan, et al. The Berenstain Bears Save Christmas. Berenstain, Michael, illus. 2003. (Berenstain Bears Ser.). 48p. (J). (ps-3). 12.99 (978-0-06-052670-2(X)) HarperCollins Pubs.

Berenstain, Stan & Berenstain, Jan. The Berenstain Bears Save Christmas. Berenstain, Michael, illus. 2005. (Berenstain Bears Ser.). 48p. (J). (ps-3). pap. 6.99 (978-0-06-052672-6(6)) HarperCollins Pubs.

Berenstain, Stan, et al. The Berenstain Bears Save Christmas. Berenstain, Stan et al, illus. 2003. (Berenstain Bears Ser.). (J). (gr. k-3). 129.90 (978-0-06-056995-2(6)) HarperCollins Pubs.

Bergeron, Joe. Cosmic Cat. 2005. 50p. pap. 14.99 (978-1-4116-6246-9(6)) Lulu.com.

Bergren, Lisa Tawn. God Gave Us Christmas. Hohn, David, illus. 2006. 40p. (J). 9.99 (978-1-4000-7175-3(5) , WaterBrook Pr.) WaterBrook Pr.

Bernardin, James, illus. The Christmas Story: From the Gospel According to St. Luke. 2002. 32p. (J). lib. bdg. 15.89 (978-0-06-028883-9(3)) HarperCollins Pubs.

Berrios, Frank. Christmas with Pooh. Disney Storybook Artists Staff, illus. 2005. (Disney Winnie the Pooh Ser.). 18p. (J). (gr. k-ps). bds. 3.99 (978-0-7364-2337-3(0) , RH/Disney) Random Hse. Children's Bks.

Beskow, Elsa. Peter & Lotta's Christmas. 2002. (Illus.). 36p. (J). (gr. k-3). 17.95 (978-0-86315-372-3(0)) Floris Bks. GBR. *Dist:* SteinerBooks, Inc.

The Best Christmas. 5th ed. 2001. 96p. 15.95 (978-1-885435-31-6(2)) Twin Lights Pubs., Inc.

The Best Thing about Christmas. 2006. 16p. (J). pap. 1.99 (978-0-7847-1546-8(7) , 04362) Standard Publishing.

Bethers, Linda, retold by. Christmas Oranges. 2004. 13p. pap. 3.95 (978-1-57734-546-6(0) , 01114387) Covenant Communications, Inc.

Bickel, Karla. Surprise Christmas Birthday Party. Bickel, Karla, illus. l.t. ed. 2004. (Illus.). 16p. (J). (ps-6). pap. 5.00 (978-1-891452-12-3(6) , 3) Heart Arbor Bks.

Bieber, Hartmut. Busy Bear Celebrates Christmas. 2003. (Illus.). (J). 5.99 (978-1-59384-006-8(3)) Parklane Publishing.

Birmingham, Christian. Christmas Treasury: Heirloom Edition. 2004. (Illus.). 56p. 16.95 (978-0-7624-2151-0(7) , Running Pr. Kids) Running Pr. Bk. Pubs.

Biro, Val. Gumdrop's Merry Christmas. (Illus.). 26p. (J). (978-0-340-71060-9(8)); pap. (978-0-340-71061-6(6)) Hodder General Publishing Division. (Hodder & Stoughton).

Bjornson, Nancy. Sleds, Skins & Snow. 2007. (J). ***(*978-1-930596-83-2(9))*** Amherst Pr.

Blackburn, C. Edward. The Stories of Christmas: As Told by a Little Lamb. Bishop, Megan, illus. l.t. ed. 2005. 24p. (J). 9.95 (978-0-9727440-3-4(7)) Redline Bks.

Blackmon, D. J. una. Ghetto Waterfront Christmas. 2005. (Illus.). per. 8.99 (978-0-9719943-6-2(6)) Creative Enigma Enterprises.

Blyton, Enid. Family Christmas. (Illus.). 151p. (J). pap. 6.95 (978-0-09-987830-8(5)) Random Hse. GBR. *Dist:* Trafalgar Square Publishing.

Bobby Bright's Greatest Christmas Ever: The Story of the World's First Talking Christmas Tree Light Bulb. ed. 2006. (Illus.). 133p. (J). lib. bdg. 16.95 (978-0-9788227-0-5(6)) Old Farm Pr.

Boegehold, Betty. Hurray for Christmas. Durrell, Julie, illus. 1999. (Jellybean Bks.). 24p. (J). (ps-k). lib. bdg. 7.99 (978-0-375-90148-5(5) , Random Hse. Bks. for Young Readers) Random Hse. Children's Bks.

Boit, Bundy H. Christmas Island. 2004. 24p. (J). per. 6.95 (978-1-930648-95-1(2)) Goose River Pr.

Boling, Ruth. Mouse Tales Vol. 1: Advent-Christmas-Epiphany. Carrier, Tracy, illus. 2005. 80p. (J). 14.95 (978-0-664-22705-0(8)) Westminster John Knox Pr.

Bolliger, Max. The Way to the Stable: A Christmas Story. Lobato, Arcadio, illus. 1999. 32p. (J). (ps-1). 16.95 (978-0-86315-305-1(4)) Floris Bks. GBR. *Dist:* SteinerBooks, Inc.

Bonaddio, T. L. Peek-a-Boo Santa. 2008. (Illus.). 8p. (J). pap. 9.95 ***(*978-0-7624-3011-6(7)*** , Running Pr. Kids) Running Pr. Bk. Pubs.

—Peek-a-Boo Santa (bag Version) 2008. (Illus.). 8p. (J). pap. 9.95 ***(*978-0-7624-3163-2(6)*** , Running Pr. Kids) Running Pr. Bk. Pubs.

Bond, Michael. Paddington Bear & the Christmas Surprise. 1999. (ps-2). lib. bdg. 14.10 (978-0-613-22917-3(7)); (J). (978-0-606-17305-6(6)) Tandem Library Bks.

—Paddington Goes to Town. 2001. (gr. 3-6). lib. bdg. 12.95 (978-0-613-62981-2(7)) Tandem Library Bks.

Boniface, William. Five Little Christmas Angels. Adams, Lynn, illus. 2003. 12p. (J). (ps). 5.99 (978-0-8431-0611-4(5) , Price Stern Sloan) Penguin Group (USA) Inc.

—Five Little Christmas Trees. Adams, Lynn, illus. 2003. 12p. (J). (ps). 5.99 (978-0-8431-0474-5(0) , Price Stern Sloan) Penguin Group (USA) Inc.

—Santa's Sleigh Is Full. Rooney, Ronnie, illus. 2002. (Top This! Ser.). 12p. (J). (ps-2). bds. 9.99 (978-0-8431-4543-4(9) , Price Stern Sloan) Penguin Group (USA) Inc.

—Trim the Tree for Christmas! Palen, Debbie, illus. 2000. 12p. (J). (ps-2). bds. 9.99 (978-0-8431-7558-5(3) , Price Stern Sloan) Penguin Group (USA) Inc.

Borden, Louise. Just in Time for Christmas. 2000. (Illus.). (J). pap. 5.99 (978-0-590-45356-1(4)) Scholastic, Inc.

—Just in Time for Christmas. 2000. (J). 12.79 (978-0-606-19573-7(4)) Tandem Library Bks.

Boshoff, Penny. Come & See Christmas. Gale, Helen, illus. 2003. 24p. (J). 6.90 (978-1-85999-662-1(0)) Scripture Union GBR. *Dist:* Gabriel Resources, STL Distribution North America.

Bosley, Judith A. Sing Christmas. Price, Susan D., illus. l.t. ed. Date not set. (J). (ps-k). pap. 10.95 (978-0-930809-26-3(2)) Grand Bks., Inc.

Bostrom, Kathleen Long. Waiting for Christmas: A Story about the Advent Calendar. Natchev, Alexi, illus. 2006. (Traditions of Faith Ser.). 40p. (J). 15.99 (978-0-310-71015-8(4)) Zonderkidz.

Bostrom, Kathleen Long, et al. Mary's Happy Christmas Day. Banta, Susan, illus. 2003. 26p. (J). bds. 8.99 (978-0-310-70482-9(0)) Zonderkidz.

Bostrom's, Kathleen. Josie's Gift. Ordaz, Frank, illus. 2005. 40p. (J). (ps-3). 16.99 (978-0-8054-3020-2(2)) B&H Publishing Grp.

Bosworth, Evelyn. A Christmas Gift for Michael. 2005. 17.00 (978-0-8059-9013-3(5)) Dorrance Publishing Co., Inc.

Bour, Daniele. Petit ours brun aime Noel. pap. 12.95 (978-2-227-70915-7(4)) Bayard Editions FRA. *Dist:* Distribooks, Inc.

Bouras, Gillian. Saving Christmas. 2000. 96p. (J). pap. 12.75 (978-0-7022-3135-3(5)) Univ. of Queensland Pr. AUS. *Dist:* International Specialized Bk. Services.

Bourgeois, Paulette. Franklin y el Regalo de Navidad. Clark, Brenda, illus. 1999. (Franklin Ser.). (SPA.). (J). (ps-3). pap. 5.95 (978-1-880507-56-8(0) , LC2911) Lectorum Pubns., Inc.

—Franklin's Christmas: A Sticker Activity Book. Clark, Brenda, illus. 2004. (Franklin Sticker & Activity Bks.). 16p. (J). (gr. k-3). (978-1-55337-506-7(8)) Kids Can Pr., Ltd.

—Franklin's Christmas Gift. Clark, Brenda, illus. 1998. (Franklin the Turtle Ser.). (J). (gr. k-3). 32p. (978-1-55074-466-8(6)); 96p. (978-1-55074-468-2(2)) Kids Can Pr., Ltd.

—Franklin's Christmas Gift. Clark, Brenda, illus. 1998. (Franklin Ser.). (J). (ps-3). pap. 54.00 (978-0-590-95169-2(6) , Cartwheel Bks.) Scholastic, Inc.

Bowen, Anne. Christmas Is Coming. Bogacki, Tomasz, illus. 2007. (Carolrhoda Picture Bks.). 32p. (J). (ps-4). 16.95 (***978-1-57505-934-1(7)*** , Carolrhoda Bks.) Lerner Publishing Group.

Bowman, Crystal. Jesus, Me, & My Christmas Tree. Gèvry, Claudine, illus. 2005. 20p. (J). (ps). 6.99 (978-0-310-70874-2(5)) Zonderkidz.

—My Christmas Stocking: Filled with God's Love. Gèvry, Claudine, illus. 2006. 14p. (J). 6.99 (978-0-310-71158-2(4)) Zonderkidz.

—A Star for Jesus. Gèvry, Claudine, illus. 2006. 14p. (J). 6.99 (978-0-310-71216-9(5)) Zonderkidz.

Box. Ready Steady Christmas. 1999. (Illus.). 32p. (J). pap. 6.99 (978-0-7459-4079-3(X) , Lion) Lion Hudson plc GBR. *Dist:* Independent Pubs. Group.

Boynton, Sandra. Bob: And 6 More Christmas Stories. Boynton, Sandra, illus. 1999. (Illus.). 18p. (J). (ps-2). bds. 8.99 (978-0-689-82568-2(4) , Little Simon) Simon & Schuster Children's Publishing.

Bracegirdle, Paul. Comet Can't Wait for Christmas. Mitchell, Susan, illus. 2007. 16p. (J). (ps-1). pap. 5.99 (***978-0-689-87139-9(2)*** , Little Simon) Simon & Schuster Children's Publishing.

Brady, Charles A. The Church Mouse of Saint Nicholas. 2004. (Illus.). 48p. (J). 16.00 (978-1-930873-97-1(2)) Neumann Pr., The.

Brady, Townsend Cyrus. Little Book for Christmas. 2006. 77.99 (***978-1-4280-3886-8(3)***); pap. 70.99 (***978-1-4280-3920-9(1)***) IndyPublish.com.

Brantley, Judi S. & Brantley, Steven. The Perfect Christmas Tree, Vol. 2. Franklin, Pringle, ed. McDaniel-Clark, Carol, illus. 2000. 48p. (J). (ps-7). 16.95 (978-1-892570-05-5(X)) Spring Hse. Bks.

Brantley, Steven & Brantley, Judi. The Legend of Snowflake, the Messenger Deer. McDaniel-Clark, Carol, illus. l.t. ed. 2002. 40p. (J). 16.95 (978-1-892570-04-8(1)) Spring Hse. Bks.

—Molly's Christmas Mystery. McDaniel-Clark, Carol, illus. l.t. ed. 2001. 40p. (J). 16.95 (978-1-892570-06-2(8)) Spring Hse. Bks.

Bratun, Katy. Gingerbread Mouse. Bratun, Katy, illus. 2003. (Illus.). 32p. (J). (ps-2). lib. bdg. 13.89 (978-0-06-009081-4(2)) HarperCollins Pubs.

Bray, Chirs. The Christmas Bike. Hefner, Seyan, illus. 2001. 28p. (J). (gr. k-12). pap. 10.00 (978-0-9712484-0-3(0)) Dunlap, J.A. & Sons Pubs.

Bray, Jeannette D. The Week Before Christmas; The Most Embarrassing Christmas Tree Ever, 2 vols. in 1. Kenyatta, Imani, ed. Mitchell, Denise B., illus. 1998. 96p. (J). (gr. k-6). 16.95 (978-1-886580-43-5(X)) Pinnacle-Syatt Pubns.

Brett, Jan. Christmas Trolls. Brett, Jan, illus. 2002. (Illus.). (J). 23.64 (978-0-7587-2237-9(0)) Book Wholesalers, Inc.

—Christmas Trolls. Brett, Jan, illus. 2000. (Illus.). 32p. (J). (ps-3). pap. 6.99 (978-0-698-11846-1(4) , Putnam Juvenile) Penguin Group (USA) Inc.

—Christmas Trolls. 2000. (ps-2). lib. bdg. 15.30 (978-0-613-29908-4(6)) Tandem Library Bks.

—Gingerbread Baby. ed. 2004. (J). (gr. k-3). spiral bd. (978-0-616-03025-7(8)); spiral bd. (978-0-616-04548-0(4)) Canadian National Institute for the Blind/Institut National Canadien pour les Aveugles.

—Gingerbread Baby. 2001. (J). (gr. k-3). 28.00 incl. audio (978-0-8045-6870-8(7) , 6870) Spoken Arts, Inc.

—Jan Brett's Christmas Treasury. Brett, Jan, illus. 2001. (Illus.). 254p. (J). (ps-3). 39.95 (978-0-399-23741-6(0) , Putnam Juvenile) Penguin Group (USA) Inc.

—The Twelve Days of Christmas. Brett, Jan, illus. 2004. (Illus.). 32p. (J). (ps-1). bds. 6.99 (978-0-399-24329-5(1) , Putnam Juvenile) Penguin Group (USA) Inc.

—Who's That Knocking on Christmas Eve? Brett, Jan, illus. 2002. (Illus.). 32p. (J). (gr. k-3). 16.99 (978-0-399-23873-4(5) , Putnam Juvenile) Penguin Group (USA) Inc.

—The Wild Christmas Reindeer. Brett, Jan, illus. 1998. (Illus.). 32p. (J). (ps-3). reprint ed. pap. 6.99 (978-0-698-11652-8(6) , Putnam Juvenile) Penguin Group (USA) Inc.

—The Wild Christmas Reindeer. 1998. (Illus.). (J). (ps-ps). lib. bdg. 15.30 (978-0-613-10541-5(9)) Tandem Library Bks.

Bridwell, Norman. Clifford's Christmas Treasury. 2005. (Illus.). 96p. (ps-3). pap. 10.99 (978-0-439-79137-3(5)) Scholastic, Inc.

—Clifford's First Christmas. (Clifford, the Big Red Dog Ser.). (FRE., Illus.). (J). (gr. k-2). pap. 5.99 (978-0-590-24374-2(8)) Scholastic, Inc.

—Clifford's First Christmas (Gel Pack Book) 2007. 32p. (J). pap. 7.99 (***978-0-545-02022-0(0)***) Scholastic, Inc.

Bridwell, Norman. La Navidad de Clifford. Bridwell, Norman, illus. 2003. (Clifford Ser.).Tr. of Clifford's Christmas. (SPA., Illus.). 32p. (J). pap. 3.50 (978-0-439-19891-2(7) , Scholastic en Espanol) Scholastic, Inc.

Briggs, Raymond. Father Christmas. (Christmas Ser.). (Illus.). 32p. (J). (ps-3). 4.95 (978-0-241-02260-3(6) , Hamish Hamilton) Penguin Group (USA) Inc.

—The Father Christmas: It's a Blooming Terrible Joke Book. (Illus.). 96p. (J). 5.95 (978-0-14-037354-7(3)) Penguin Bks., Ltd. GBR. *Dist:* Trafalgar Square Publishing.

Brimner, Larry Dane. Merry Christmas, Old Armadillo. Catalano, Dominic, illus. 2003. 32p. (J). (gr. k-2). pap. 7.95 (978-1-56397-678-0(1)) Boyds Mills Pr.

Bronson, Wilfrid S. Pinto's Journey. 2007. (J). pap. (***978-0-86534-557-7(0)***) Sunstone Pr.

Brookes, Derek & Brookes, Michelle. Christmas to Remember. 2001. (Stories to Grow by Ser.). (J). (ps-k). 6.95 (978-3-905332-63-6(9)) Aurora Production AG CHE. *Dist:* Activated Ministries.

Brooks, David, illus. The First Noel. 2005. (Soft Shapes Ser.). 8p. (J). (ps). 8.99 (978-1-58476-363-5(9)) Innovative Kids.

Brown, Elizabeth Ferguson. Coal Country Christmas. Stevenson, Harvey, illus. 2003. 32p. (J). (gr. k-2). 15.95 (978-1-59078-020-6(5)) Boyds Mills Pr.

Brown, Janet Allison. The Little Christmas Tree. Chaffey, Samantha, illus. 2005. (Holidays In 3D Ser.). 8p. (J). bds. 4.95 (978-0-7641-5833-9(3)) Barron's Educational Series, Inc.

Brown, Janet Allison, et al. The First Christmas. Durantz, Summer, illus. 2003. (Inspirational Collection). 24p. (J). pap. 3.99 (978-0-7696-3128-8(2) , Brighter Child) School Specialty Publishing.

Brown, Jeff. Stanley's Christmas Adventure. Nash, Scott, illus. 2003. (Stanley Lambchop Adventure Ser.). 80p. (J). pap. 4.99 (978-0-06-442175-1(9) , Harper Trophy) HarperCollins Pubs.

—Stanley's Christmas Adventure. 2003. (gr. k-3). lib. bdg. 13.00 (978-0-613-68466-8(4)) Tandem Library Bks.

Brown, Marc. Arthur's Christmas. Brown, Marc, illus. 2002. (Arthur Adventure Ser.). (Illus.). (J). 13.15 (978-0-7587-1979-9(5)) Book Wholesalers, Inc.

—Arthur's Christmas. Brown, Marc, illus. 1999. (Arthur Adventure Ser.). 32p. (J). (ps-3). 9.95 (978-0-316-11964-1(4)) Little, Brown Bks. for Young Readers.

—Arthur's Perfect Christmas. 2000. (Illus.). (J). 15.95 (978-0-316-12028-9(6)) Little Brown & Co.

—Arthur's Perfect Christmas. 2004. (Arthur Adventure Ser.). (Illus.). 40p. (J). (ps-1). pap. 6.99 (978-0-316-00130-4(9) , Tingley, Megan Bks.) Little, Brown Bks. for Young Readers.

—Arthur's Perfect Christmas. Brown, Marc, illus. 2000. (Arthur Adventure Ser.). (Illus.). 48p. (J). (ps-3). 15.95 (978-0-316-11968-9(7)) Little, Brown Bks. for Young Readers.

Brown, Marc & Sarfatti, Esther. Arturo y la Navidad. 2004. (SPA.). (J). pap. 6.95 (978-1-930332-48-5(3)) Lectorum Pubns., Inc.

Brown, Margaret Wise. A Child Is Born: Picture Book. Cooper, Floyd, illus. 2000. 32p. (ps-ps). 16.99 (978-0-7868-0673-7(7)) Hyperion Bks. for Children.

—Christmas in the Barn. Goode, Diane, illus. 32p. (J). 2007. pap. 6.99 (***978-0-06-052636-8(X)*** , Harper Trophy); 2004. 16.99 (978-0-06-052634-4(3)) HarperCollins Pubs.

—On Christmas Eve. 2002. (Illus.). (J). 26.13 (978-0-7587-3317-7(8)) Book Wholesalers, Inc.

—On Christmas Eve. 2000. (978-0-606-22060-6(7)); lib. bdg. 14.10 (978-0-613-30074-2(2)) Tandem Library Bks.

—A Pussycat's Christmas. 2002. (Illus.). (J). 14.43 (978-0-7587-3470-9(0)) Book Wholesalers, Inc.

—A Pussycat's Christmas. Mortimer, Anne, illus. 1998. 32p. (J). (ps up). pap. 6.99 (978-0-06-443466-9(4) , Harper Trophy) HarperCollins Pubs.

—A Pussycat's Christmas. 1998. (ps-2). lib. bdg. 14.10 (978-0-613-81428-7(2)) Tandem Library Bks.

Brown, Rachel W. N. Small Camel Follows the Star. Ferri, Giuliano, illus. 2007. 32p. (J). (gr. k-3). 16.95 (***978-0-8075-7453-9(8)***) Whitman, Albert & Co.

Brown, Ruth. The Christmas Mouse. 1998. (Illus.). 40p. (J). pap. (978-0-09-972441-4(3) , Red Fox) Random Hse. Children's Bks.

Bryer, Estelle & Nicol, Janni. Christmas Stories Together: 40 Favourite Stories for Children Aged 3-9 Years. 2002. (Illus.). 128p. (J). (ps-4). pap. 16.95 (978-1-903458-22-8(6)) Hawthorn Pr. GBR. *Dist:* SteinerBooks, Inc.

Buck, Pearl S. Christmas Day in the Morning. Buehner, Mark, illus. 2002. 40p. (J). 16.99 (978-0-688-16267-2(3)) HarperCollins Pubs.

Buckley, Ray. Christmas Moccasins. Buckley, Ray, illus. 2003. (Illus.). 32p. 18.00 (978-0-687-02738-5(1)) Abingdon Pr.

Buehner, Caralyn. Snowmen at Christmas. Buehner, Mark, illus. 2005. 32p. (J). (ps). 16.99 (978-0-8037-2995-7(2) , Dial) Penguin Group (USA) Inc.

Buehner, Caralyn & Buehner, Mark. A Box of Snowmen. 2005. (Illus.). 32p. (J). (ps-7). lthr. 32.99 (978-0-8037-3108-0(6) , Dial) Penguin Group (USA) Inc.

Bujack, Betty. Ikandoo's Blue Ribbon Adventure: A Christmas Adventure Story. Bujack, Betty & Bujack, Lynette, illus. 2000. 32p. (J). (ps-1). 16.95 (978-0-615-11228-2(5)) Bujack Enterprises, Inc.

Bull, Jane. El Libro de la Navidad. Cortes, Eunice, tr. 2003. (SPA.). 48p. (978-970-690-597-0(9)) Planeta Mexicana Editorial S. A. de C. V.

Bullard, Lisa. Not Enough Beds. Oeltjenbruns, Joni, illus. 2004. (Carolrhoda Picture Books Ser.). 32p. (J). (ps-3). pap. 6.95 (978-1-57505-797-2(2)) Lerner Publishing Group.

—Not Enough Beds! A Christmas Alphabet Book. Oeltjenbruns, Joni, illus. 2004. (Picture Bks.). 32p. (J). (ps-3). 15.95 (978-1-57505-356-1(X) , Carolrhoda Bks.) Lerner Publishing Group.

—Not Enough Beds: A Christmas Alphabet Book. Oeltjenbruns, Joni, illus. 2004. 26p. (J). (ps-ps). lib. bdg. 13.75 (978-0-606-30541-9(6)) Tandem Library Bks.

Bunting, Eve. Christmas Cricket. Bush, Timothy, illus. 2002. 32p. (J). (gr. k-3). tchr. ed. 15.00 (978-0-618-06554-7(7) , Clarion Bks.) Houghton Mifflin Co. Trade & Reference Div.

—The Day Before Christmas. 2000. (gr. k-3). lib. bdg. 14.10 (978-0-613-29920-6(5)) Tandem Library Bks.

—Going Home. Diaz, David, illus. 1998. (Trophy Picture Bk.). 32p. (J). (ps-3). pap. 6.99 (978-0-06-443509-3(1) , Harper Trophy) HarperCollins Pubs.

Burgoyne, Tom. Phillie Phanatic's Christmas Wish, Vols. 4. Epstein, Len, illus. 2005. 32p. (J). 5.95 (978-0-9754419-0-9(6)) Middle Atlantic Pr.

Burmingham, John. Harvey Slumfenburger's Christmas Present. 2007. (Illus.). 48p. (J). (ps-3). 8.99 (***978-0-7636-3517-6(0)***) Candlewick Pr.

Burroughs, Scott A. The Christmas Tail of Sampson the Silly-Looking Sock Monkey. 2005. (J). 12.99 (978-0-8254-2300-0(7)) Kregel Pubns.

Burt, Steven E. Snowstorm Christmas. Lindsey, Terry, illus. 2002. (J). pap. 9.95 (978-0-9649283-5-0(3)) Burt Creations.

Burton, Tim. The Nightmare Before Christmas Storybook. Burton, Tim, illus. 2006. (Illus.). 48p. (gr. 1-17). 16.99 (978-0-7868-4908-6(8)) Hyperion Bks. for Children.

Busby, Ailie. Christmas Is Coming. 2001. (Illus.). 16p. (J). bds. 8.95 (978-0-7641-5385-3(4)) Barron's Educational Series, Inc.

Bush, Randall B. Gabriel's Magic Ornament. Schunemann, Ryan, illus. 2003. 120p. (gr. 5-8). pap. 11.95 (978-0-9716633-0-5(0)) Pristine Pubs., Inc.

Bushell, Isobel, illus. Rudolph the Red-Nosed Reindeer: Musical Board Book. 1999. 12p. (YA). (ps up). bds. 5.95 (978-0-694-00564-2(9)) HarperCollins Pubs.

Butler, M. Christina. One Snowy Night. Macnaughton, Tina, illus. 26p. (J). (ps). 2007. bds. 8.95 (***978-1-56148-591-8(8)***); 2005. 16.00 (978-1-56148-452-2(0)) Good Bks.

Buyske, Gail. How the Russian Snow Maiden Helped Santa Claus. Voronina, Natasha, illus. 2005. 32p. (J). 16.95 (978-0-9725027-4-0(2)) Vernissage Pr., LLC.

Byrne, Barbara. The Magic Bell On. 2003. 13p. 12.66 (978-1-4116-1078-1(4)) Lulu.com.

Cabot, Meg. The Princess Present. 2004. (Princess Diaries: Vol. 6 1/2). 96p. (J). (gr. 7 up). 8.99 (978-0-06-075433-4(8)) HarperCollins Pubs.

Cajun Night Before Christmas. (Illus.). (J). 29.95 (978-1-56554-883-1(3)) Pelican Publishing Co., Inc.

Calamari, Barbara. Fright Before Christmas. 2001. (gr. 3-6). lib. bdg. 11.80 (978-0-613-87772-5(1)) Tandem Library Bks.

Caldon, Janet. What Child Is This? Unveiling the Message of the Manger. 2003. 111p. pap. 16.95 (978-1-59286-670-0(0)) PublishAmerica, Inc.

Calhoun, Dia. The Return of Light: A Christmas Tale. Falkenstern, Lisa, illus. 2007. 80p. (J). (gr. 3-7). 12.99 (***978-0-7614-5360-4(1)***) Cavendish, Marshall Corp.

Calhoun, Mary. Henry the Christmas Cat. Ingraham, Erick, illus. 2004. 32p. (J). (ps-3). 15.99 (978-0-688-16560-4(5)); lib. bdg. 16.89 (978-0-688-16561-1(3)) HarperCollins Pubs.

—A Shepherd Boy's Christmas. Colon, Raul, illus. 2001. 32p. (J). (ps-4). 15.95 (978-0-688-15176-8(0)) HarperCollins Pubs.

—A Shepherd's Gift. Colon, Raul, illus. 2001. 32p. (J). (ps-4). 15.89 (978-0-688-15177-5(9)) HarperCollins Pubs.

—A Shepherd's Gift: El Regalo del Pastor. 2001. (SPA., Illus.). 32p. (J). (ps-4). 15.89 (978-0-06-029786-2(7)) HarperCollins Pubs.

Camery-Hoggatt, Jerry. When Mother Was Eleven-Foot-Four: A Christmas Memory. 2007. 32p. (J). (ps-3). 18.99 (978-0-8007-1836-7(4)) Revell.

Campbell, Ellie. The Visiting Elf. 2006. (ENG., Illus.). 32p. per. 25.49 (***978-1-4259-7562-3(3)***) AuthorHouse.

Campbell, Rod. Dear Santa. Campbell, Rod, illus. 2004. (Illus.). 16p. (J). bds. 7.99 (978-0-689-87415-4(4) , Little Simon) Simon & Schuster Children's Publishing.

Canady, Pat. Tippy the Holiday Tree, 1. Bartley, Michael, illus. 2000. 9p. (J). (ps-4). pap. 10.00 (978-1-929889-01-3(1)) Canady SW Publishing.

Capalija, Ann Marie. Rose Blossom's First Christmas. LoRaso, Carlo, illus. 2005. (My Little Pony Ser.). (J). (ps-2). 24p. pap. 4.99 (978-0-06-076182-0(2)); (***978-1-4156-2255-1(8)***) HarperCollins Pubs. (Harper Festival).

Capote, Truman. A Christmas Memory. Peck, Beth, illus. 2006. 48p. (J). (gr. 7). 17.95 incl. audio compact disk (978-0-375-83789-0(2) , Knopf Bks. for Young Readers) Random Hse. Children's Bks.

Capucilli, Alyssa Satin. Biscuit's Christmas. Schories, Pat, illus. 2000. (Biscuit Ser.). 16p. (J). (ps-1). pap. 6.99 (978-0-694-01516-0(4) , Harper Festival) HarperCollins Pubs.

—Biscuit's Christmas. 2003. (gr. k-3). lib. bdg. 15.25 (978-0-613-70855-5(5)) Tandem Library Bks.

—Biscuit's Christmas Eve. Young, Mary O'Keefe, illus. 2007. (Biscuit Ser.). 20p. (J). (ps-1). pap. 6.99 (***978-0-06-112836-3(8)*** , Harper Festival) HarperCollins Pubs.

Capucilli, Alyssa Satin. Biscuit's Pet & Play Christmas. Schories, Pat & Young, Mary O'Keefe, illus. 2006. (Biscuit Ser.). 12p. (J). 6.99 (978-0-06-009470-6(2) , Harper Festival) HarperCollins Pubs.

Carabine, Sue. An Angel's Night Before Christmas. Kawasaki, Shauna Mooney, illus. 2001. 60p. 5.95 (978-1-58685-087-6(3)); 2nd gif. ed. 5.95 (978-1-58685-122-4(5)) Gibbs Smith, Publisher.

—A Cowgirl's Night Before Christmas. Kawasaki, Shauna Mooney, illus. 2001. 60p. 5.95 (978-1-58685-086-9(5)) Gibbs Smith, Publisher.

—A Cowgirl's Night Before Christmas. Kawasaki, Shauna Mooney, photos by. 2nd gif. ed. 2001. (Illus.). 60p. 5.95 (978-1-58685-121-7(7)) Gibbs Smith, Publisher.

—A Dog's Night Before Christmas. Kawasaki, Shauna Mooney, illus. 2001. 60p. 5.95 (978-0-87905-762-6(9)) Gibbs Smith, Publisher.

—A Missionary's Night Before Christmas. Kawasaki, Shauna Mooney, illus. 2002. 60p. 5.95 (978-1-58685-167-5(5)) Gibbs Smith, Publisher.

—Mom's Night Before Christmas. Kawasaki, Shauna Mooney, illus. 2002. 60p. 5.95 (978-1-58685-166-8(7)) Gibbs Smith, Publisher.

—The Night Before Christmas in Arizona. Kawasaki, Shauna Mooney, illus. 2002. 60p. 5.95 (978-1-58685-169-9(1)) Gibbs Smith, Publisher.

—The Night Before Christmas in Nevada. Kawasaki, Shauna Mooney, illus. 2002. 60p. 5.95 (978-1-58685-168-2(3)) Gibbs Smith, Publisher.

—The Night Before Christmas in Oregon. Kawasaki, Shauna Mooney, illus. 2002. 60p. 5.95 (978-1-58685-170-5(5)) Gibbs Smith, Publisher.

—The Night Before Christmas in Utah. Kawasaki, Shauna Mooney, illus. 2000. Vol. 17. 60p. 5.95 (978-0-87905-981-1(8)) Gibbs Smith, Publisher.

—A Teacher's Night Before Christmas. Kawasaki, Shauna Mooney, illus. 2000. 60p. 5.95 (978-0-87905-764-0(5)) Gibbs Smith, Publisher.

Carle, Eric. Dream Snow. Gauch, Patricia Lee, ed. Carle, Eric, illus. 2000. (Illus.). 32p. (J). (ps-1). 21.99 (978-0-399-23579-5(5) , Philomel) Penguin Group (USA) Inc.

Carlson, Melody. King of the Stable. 1998. (Illus.). 32p. (ps-5). 14.99 (978-1-58134-032-7(X) , Crossway Bibles) Crossway Bks.

—'Twas the Night: The Nativity Story. Reagan, Susan Joy, illus. 2005. 32p. (J). (ps-4). 12.99 (978-0-8054-2683-0(3)) B&H Publishing Grp.

Carlson, Nancy. Harriet & George's Christmas Treat. Carlson, Nancy, illus. 2005. (Picture Bks.). (Illus.). 32p. (J). (gr. k-2). 15.95 (978-1-57505-506-0(6)) Lerner Publishing Group.

—Harriet & George's Christmas Treat. 2003. (Illus.). 32p. (J). (gr. k-2). pap. 6.95 (978-1-57505-639-5(9)) Lerner Publishing Group.

—Harriet & George's Christmas Treat. 2001. (gr. k-3). lib. bdg. 15.25 (978-0-613-68088-2(X)) Tandem Library Bks.

—Snowden. 2000. (978-0-606-20371-5(0)); (J). (978-0-606-20255-8(2)) Tandem Library Bks.

Carlstrom, Nancy White. Where Is Christmas, Jesse Bear? 2003. (ps-2). lib. bdg. 15.30 (978-0-613-88993-3(2)) Tandem Library Bks.

Carnehl, Jeff. That Special Starry Night. 2001. 32p. (J). 10.99 (978-0-570-07185-3(2)) Concordia Publishing Hse.

Caro, Joe. Santa's Christmas Train. Shih, Lin, illus. 2005. 32p. pap. (978-0-9628078-2-4(6)) Cowboy Collector Pubns.

—Santa's Christmas Train Coloring Book. Shih, Lin, illus. 2005. 32p. pap. (978-0-9628078-5-5(0)) Cowboy Collector Pubns.

Carr, Jan. Doug's Secret Christmas. 1999. (Doug Ser.). (Illus.). 32p. (J). (gr. k-4). pap. 4.99 (978-0-7868-4351-0(9)) Disney Pr.

Carroll, Pam, illus. S Is for Star: A Christmas Alphabet. 2004. 40p. (J). pap. 6.95 (978-1-58536-247-9(6)) Sleeping Bear Pr.

C
D

Carter, David A. Jingle Bugs: A Merry Pop-up Book with Lights & Music! Carter, David A., illus. 2004. (Illus.). 22p. (J). pap. 10.95 (978-0-689-87416-1(2) , Little Simon) Simon & Schuster Children's Publishing.

—The 12 Bugs of Christmas: A Pop up Christmas Counting Book. Carter, David A., illus. 1999. (Bugs in a Box Books Ser.). (Illus.). 12p. (J). (ps-k). 14.95 (978-0-689-83104-1(8) , Little Simon) Simon & Schuster Children's Publishing.

Carter, David A. & Carter, Noelle. The Nutcracker: A Pop Up Adaptation Of E T A Hoffmanns Original Tale. Carter, David A. & Carter, Noelle, illus. ltd. ed. 2000. (J). 150.00 (978-0-689-84107-1(8) , Little Simon) Simon & Schuster Children's Publishing.

Cazet, Denys. Minnie & Moo: The Night Before Christmas. Cazet, Denys, illus. (Readalongs for Beginning Readers Ser.). (Illus.). 2005. (J). pap. 16.95 incl. audio (978-1-59112-883-0(8)); 2005. (J). pap. 18.95 incl. audio compact disk (978-1-59112-887-8(0)); 2004. 25.95 incl. audio (978-1-59112-884-7(6)); 2004. (J). 28.95 incl. audio compact disk (978-1-59112-888-5(9)); 2004. (J). pap. 31.95 incl. audio compact disk (978-1-59112-889-2(7)); 2004. (J). pap. 29.95 incl. audio (978-1-59112-885-4(4)) Live Oak Media.

—Minnie & Moo: The Night Before Christmas. 2002. (gr. k-3). lib. bdg. 11.80 (978-0-613-68451-4(6)) Tandem Library Bks.

Chaconas, Dori. Christmas Mouseling. Hartung, Susan Kathleen, illus. 2005. 32p. (J). (ps). 15.99 (978-0-670-05984-3(6) , Viking Juvenile) Penguin Group (USA) Inc.

—When Cows Come Home for Christmas. Chapman, Lynne, illus. 2005. 32p. (J). (gr. k-3). 15.95 (978-0-8075-8877-2(6)) Whitman, Albert & Co.

Chapman, Mary Beth & Chapman, Steven Curtis. Shaoey & Dot: A Christmas Miracle. Chapman, Jim, illus. 2005. 32p. (J). (ps-7). pap. 16.99 (978-1-4003-0691-6(4)) Nelson, Thomas Inc.

Charbonnel, Olivier. Santa's Factory. 2000. (Illus.). 12p. (J). pap. 15.95 (978-1-902413-51-8(2)) Van der Meer, a Div. of PHPC GBR. *Dist:* Abbeville Pr., Inc.

Chartrand, Kenneth. A Martian's Dream of Christmas. 2006. 48p. pap. 12.95 (978-1-4241-4123-4(0)) PublishAmerica, Inc.

Chase, Diana. Angel in a Gum Tree. 2006. 32p. pap. 13.50 (978-1-921064-77-7(3)) Fremantle Pr. AUS. *Dist:* International Specialized Bk. Services.

Chen, Chih-Yuan. The Best Christmas Ever. 2006. (Illus.). 48p. (J). 15.95 (978-0-9762056-2-3(9)) Heryin Publishing Corp.

Chen, Pauline. Peiling & the Chicken-Fried Christmas. 2007. 160p. (J). (gr. 3-6). 15.95 (***978-1-59990-122-0(6)***) Bloomsbury Publishing.

Chen's Christmas Tree. 1999. (J). pap. (978-1-58453-038-1(3)) Pioneer Valley Educational Pr., Inc.

Cheshire, Marc. Merry Christmas, Eloise! A Lift-the-Flap Book. Bracken, Carolyn, illus. 2006. 18p. (J). pap. 6.99 (978-0-689-87155-9(4) , Little Simon) Simon & Schuster Children's Publishing.

Chiodo, Stephen & Strain, Jim. Chiodo Bros.' Alien Xmas. Chiodo, Charles, illus. 2006. 40p. (J). 17.95 (978-0-9729388-4-6(2)) Baby Tattoo Bks.

Chivus, Mitch. Fartsy Claus. Reed, Mike, illus. 2007. 32p. (J). lib. bdg. 17.89 (***978-0-06-089467-2(9));*** 16.99 (***978-0-06-089466-5(0))*** HarperCollins Pubs.

Chrismer, Melanie. Phoebe Clappsaddle Has a Tumbleweed Christmas. Roeder, Virginia M., illus. 2004. 32p. (J). 15.95 (978-1-58980-241-4(1)) Pelican Publishing Co., Inc.

Christelow, Eileen. Not until Christmas, Walter! Christelow, Eileen, illus. 2002. (Illus.). 40p. (J). (gr. k-3). pap. 5.95 (978-0-618-24618-2(5) , Clarion Bks.) Houghton Mifflin Co. Trade & Reference Div.

—Not until Christmas, Walter! 2002. (Illus.). 40p. (J). (ps-3). lib. bdg. 14.10 (978-0-613-70984-2(5)) Tandem Library Bks.

Christie, Gerschutz. Samuel the Camel & the Lone Star. 2006. 96p. pap. 7.50 (***978-1-933341-19-4(X)***) CRM.

Christie, Jacky. The Wind Blows North. 2007. (ENG.). 56p. per. 10.99 (***978-1-4141-0835-3(4)***) Pleasant Word.

Christie, Michael G. Olive the Orphan Reindeer. Lucas, Margeaux, illus. 2000. 46p. (gr. 4-7). pap. 7.95 (978-1-889658-16-2(2)) New Canaan Publishing Co. LLC.

—The Story of Olive. 2000. (Illus.). 46p. (gr. 4-7). 14.95 (978-1-889658-18-6(9)) New Canaan Publishing Co. LLC.

Christmas. 2004. (J). mass mkt. 8.99 (978-0-9741215-4-3(1)) Stories of My Life, The.

Christmas - All I Want. 2005. (J). bds. (978-1-4194-0080-3(0)) Paradise Pr., Inc.

Christmas - Candy Canes. 2005. (J). (978-1-4194-0081-0(9)) Paradise Pr., Inc.

Christmas - Cookies. 2005. (J). bds. (978-1-4194-0083-4(5)) Paradise Pr., Inc.

Christmas - Stocking. 2005. (J). bds. (978-1-4194-0082-7(7)) Paradise Pr., Inc.

The Christmas Angel. 1999. (Illus.). 20p. (J). bds. 4.95 (978-0-88271-677-0(8)) Regina Pr., Malhame & Co.

Christmas Book. 2005. (J). bds. (978-1-4194-0071-1(1)) Paradise Pr., Inc.

Christmas Book - Christmas Tree. 2005. (J). bds. (978-1-4194-0073-5(8)) Paradise Pr., Inc.

Christmas Book - Santa Claus. 2005. (J). bds. (978-1-4194-0074-2(6)) Paradise Pr., Inc.

Christmas book s/s - Presents. 2005. (J). bds. (978-1-4194-0072-8(X)) Paradise Pr., Inc.

Christmas Book s/s - Snowman. 2005. (J). bds. (978-1-4194-0075-9(4)) Paradise Pr., Inc.

Christmas Candy Canes. 2003. (J). per. (978-1-57657-706-6(6)) Paradise Pr., Inc.

A Christmas Carol. 2004. (J). cd-rom 7.99 (978-0-9740847-9-4(4)) GiGi Bks.

A Christmas Carol. 2003. (Illus.). 32p. (J). 9.98 (978-1-4054-0997-1(5)); 4.98 (978-1-4054-0980-3(0)) Parragon, Inc.

The Christmas Chair, l.t. ed. 2004. (Illus.). 27p. (J). 12.95 (978-0-9763633-1-6(3)) Williams, Thomas.

The Christmas Eve Caper. 1999. (SmartReader Ser.). (J). pap., tchr. ed. 19.95 incl. audio (978-0-7887-0118-4(5) , 79306T3) Recorded Bks., LLC.

Christmas in Bavaria. 2005. (YA). per. 16.95 (978-0-9763572-7-8(5)) English Garden Talk Pr.

Christmas in Beartown. 2003. (J). bds. 4.99 (978-1-59384-010-5(1)) Book Club of America.

Christmas in the Stable. 2004. pap. 14.95 incl. audio (978-1-56008-083-1(3)) Weston Woods Studios, Inc.

Christmas Is Coming. 2003. (J). 6.99 (978-1-59384-012-9(8)) Parklane Publishing.

Christmas Moon. 2008. (J). (978-0-8118-5034-6(X)) Chronicle Bks. LLC.

A Christmas Prayer. 2003. (J). per. (978-1-57657-805-6(4)) Paradise Pr., Inc.

The Christmas Star. 2005. (Illus.). 28p. (J). (ps-k). bds. 7.95 (978-0-8249-6620-1(1)) Ideals Pubns.

Christmas Stocking. 2003. (J). per. (978-1-57657-705-9(8)) Paradise Pr., Inc.

The Christmas Story. 2002. 12p. (J). 10.99 (978-0-8254-7250-3(4)) Kregel Pubns.

The Christmas Story. 2006. 16p. (J). pap. 1.99 (978-0-7847-1389-1(8) , 22127) Standard Publishing.

A Christmas Story. 2004. (Dick & Jane Ser.). (Illus.). 32p. (J). (ps). 12.99 (978-0-448-43617-3(5) , Grosset & Dunlap) Penguin Group (USA) Inc.

The Christmas Story: From The Gospels of Luke. Date not set. (Illus.). 32p. (J). 5.99 (978-0-06-443661-8(6)) HarperCollins Pubs.

A Christmas Surprise. 2003. (J). (978-1-57657-928-2(X)) Paradise Pr., Inc.

Christmas Surprise for Owl. 2002. (J). bds. 3.98 (978-1-84250-586-1(6) , Bright Sparks) Parragon, Inc.

Christmas Tales: Night Before Christmas; The First Christmas; Christmas Angel; Christmas Kitten. (Lift-A-Flap Ser.). (Illus.). (J). (978-0-7853-2070-8(9)) Publications International, Ltd.

Chronicle Books LLC Staff. Christmas Takealong Bb. 2008. (J). bds. 6.95 (978-0-8118-5171-8(0)) Chronicle Bks. LLC.

—Santa Claus: Finger Puppet Book. 2006. (Illus.). 12p. (J). bds. 6.95 (978-0-8118-5458-0(2)) Chronicle Bks. LLC.

Chronicle Books Staff. Little Reindeer: Finger Puppet Book. 2006. (Illus.). 12p. (J). 6.95 (978-0-8118-5457-3(4)) Chronicle Bks. LLC.

Chronicle Books Staff, contrib. by. Christmas Miniclassics. 2005. (J). 95.40 (978-0-8118-9877-5(6)) Chronicle Bks. LLC.

Chrsitensen, Jo-Anne. Ghost Stories of Christmas. rev. ed. 2001. (Ghost Stories Ser.). (Illus.). 224p. (J). (gr. 4). pap. 10.95 (978-1-55105-334-9(9)) Lone Pine Publishing USA.

Ciletti, Barbara. I Want It All! Morrison, Cathy, illus. 2005. 32p. (J). 14.95 (978-0-7696-4376-2(0) , Gingham Dog Pr.) School Specialty Publishing.

Cimarusti, Marie Torres. Peek-a-Boo Christmas! Peterson, Stephanie, illus. 2006. 12p. (J). (ps). pap. 10.99 (978-0-525-47770-9(5) , Dutton Juvenile) Penguin Group (USA) Inc.

Ciminera, Siobhan. Christmas Is Here! Station Stop 1. S. I. Artists Staff, illus. 2005. (Strawberry Shortcake Ser.). 32p. (J). (ps-2). pap. 3.99 (978-0-448-43955-6(7) , Grosset & Dunlap) Penguin Group (USA) Inc.

Clark, Brenda, illus. Franklin's Christmas Gift. 2002. (Franklin Ser.). (J). 12.40 (978-0-7587-2532-5(9)) Book Wholesalers, Inc.

Clark, Carol. Christmas with Cheii. 2007. pap. 16.95 (***978-0-533-15544-6(4)***) Vantage Pr., Inc.

Clark, Debbie. Amberleigh's Christmas Angel: An Adolescent's Story of Love, Loss, & Renewed Hope for the Future. 2004. 48p. pap. 12.95 (978-1-4137-4528-3(8)) PublishAmerica, Inc.

Clark, Emma Chichester. Melrose & Croc: A Christmas to Remember. Clark, Emma Chichester, illus. 2006. (Illus.). 32p. (J). 16.95 (978-0-8027-9597-7(8)); 17.85 (978-0-8027-9598-4(6)) Walker & Co.

—Merry Christmas to You, Blue Kangaroo! Clark, Emma Chichester, illus. 2004. (Illus.). 32p. (J). (gr. k-k). lib. bdg. 17.99 (978-0-385-90918-1(7) , Doubleday Bks. for Young Readers) Random Hse. Children's Bks.

Claus, Nancy. Santa's Hat. Ferchaud, Steve, illus. 2006. (J). (***978-0-9746747-6-6(1)***) Cypress Bay Publishing.

Claus, Santa. The Santa Legends Present: The Lost Button. 2005. (J). cd-rom 12.00 (978-1-59971-079-2(X)) Aardvark Global Publishing.

Clement, Maria. The Forever Christmas Tree. 2006. (ENG.). 44p. per. 17.99 (***978-1-4259-8639-1(0)***) AuthorHouse.

Clements, Andrew. Bright Christmas: An Angel Remembers. Kiesler, Kate A., illus. 2000. 32p. (J). (gr. k-3). 6.95 (978-0-618-05153-3(8) , Clarion Bks.) Houghton Mifflin Co. Trade & Reference Div.

—Bright Christmas: An Angel Remembers. 2000. (gr. k-3). lib. bdg. 14.10 (978-0-613-31024-6(1)) Tandem Library Bks.

Climo, Shirley. The Cobweb Christmas. Date not set. 32p. (J). (ps-3). pap. 5.99 (978-0-06-443702-8(7)) HarperCollins Pubs.

—Cobweb Christmas: The Tradition of Tinsel. Manning, Jane, illus. rev. ed. 2001. 32p. (J). (gr. k-3). 16.99 (978-0-06-029033-7(1)) HarperCollins Pubs.

Coffey, Tim. Christmas at the Top of the World. Coffey, Tim, illus. 2003. (Albert Whitman Prairie Bks.). (Illus.). 32p. (J). (ps-1). pap. 6.95 (978-0-8075-5763-1(3)) Whitman, Albert & Co.

Coffey, Timothy. Christmas at the Top of the World. Coffey, Timothy, illus. 2003. (Illus.). 32p. (J). (ps-1). 16.95 (978-0-8075-5762-4(5)) Whitman, Albert & Co.

Collington, Peter. A Small Miracle. Collington, Peter, illus. 2002. (Illus.). 32p. (J). (ps-3). reprint ed. 15.95 (978-0-679-88725-6(3) , Knopf Bks. for Young Readers) Random Hse. Children's Bks.

Collins, Chris. Harold Angel Sings. 2004. (ENG.). 36p. (J). per. (978-1-4141-0068-5(X)) Pleasant Word.

—A Mary Little Christmas. Brimer, Molly, illus. l.t. ed. 2002. 32p. (J). lib. bdg. (978-0-9722799-0-1(3)) Words of Grace, Inc.

Collins, Sonny. Mouse Tails. 2006. (ENG.). 52p. per. 12.95 (***978-1-4241-4589-8(9)***) PublishAmerica, Inc.

Collins, Terry. Rancid Little Christmas. 2000. (gr. 3-6). lib. bdg. 11.80 (978-0-613-31628-6(2)) Tandem Library Bks.

Colmont, Marie. Michka. Franquin, Gerard, illus. 2000. (SPA.). (J). (gr. k-2). 12.95 (978-84-241-3345-0(5) , EV5039) Everest de Ediciones y Distribucion, S.L. ESP. *Dist:* Lectorum Pubns., Inc.

Color All About: Christmas: A Giant Coloring Book for Christmas. 2004. (Illus.). (J). (978-0-9763307-0-7(9)) Food Marketing Consultants, Inc.

Conahan, Carolyn. The Twelve Days of Christmas Dogs. Conahan, Carolyn, illus. 2005. (Illus.). 32p. (J). (ps). 15.99 (978-0-525-47486-9(2) , Dutton Juvenile) Penguin Group (USA) Inc.

Concha, Beatriz. Cuatro Milagros de Nochebuena. 1999. (YA). (978-956-240-286-6(X)) Arrayan Editores S.A.

Connelly, Valerie. Arthur, the Christmas Elf: A Christmas Adventure. 2006. (Illus.). 60p. (J). per. 24.95 (978-1-933449-23-4(3)) Nightengale Pr.

Connolly, Brian A. Allegheny River Christmas & Other Stories. 2007. 56p. per. 20.95 (***978-1-58939-992-1(7)***) Virtualbookworm.com Publishing, Inc.

Conrad, Pam. The Tub People's Christmas. Egielski, Richard, illus. 1999. 40p. (J). (ps-3). 15.89 (978-0-06-026029-3(7) , Geringer, Laura Book) HarperCollins Pubs.

Cook, Gary W. Stories for Small Angels. 2007. (J). per. 10.99 (***978-1-59886-977-4(9)***) Tate Publishing & Enterprises, L.L.C.

Cook, Gerri. Christmas in the Badlands. 2003. (Dinosaur Soup Ser.). (Illus.). 120p. (YA). (gr. 3-5). pap. 9.95 (978-1-895836-94-3(8)) River Bks. CAN. *Dist:* Fitzhenry & Whiteside, Ltd.

Cooney, Barbara. The Story of Christmas. Krupinski, Loretta, illus. 1998. (Trophy Picture Bk.). 32p. (J). (gr. k-4). pap. 5.95 (978-0-06-443512-3(1) , Harper Trophy) HarperCollins Pubs.

Cooney, Caroline B. What Child Is This? A Christmas Story. 1999. 160p. (YA). (gr. 7-12). mass mkt. 5.50 (978-0-440-22684-0(8) , Laurel Leaf) Random Hse. Children's Bks.

—What Child Is This? A Christmas Story. 1999. (978-0-606-17218-9(1)); (gr. 7-12). lib. bdg. 13.55 (978-0-613-22959-3(2)) Tandem Library Bks.

Cooper, Ilene. Sam I Am. 256p. (J). 2006. pap. 5.99 (978-0-439-43968-8(X)); 2004. (gr. 4-7). pap. 15.95 (978-0-439-43967-1(1) , Scholastic Pr.) Scholastic, Inc.

Cooper, James Thomas. The First Christmas Teddy Bear. Nardi, Cindy, illus. 1999. 32p. (J). pap. 6.95 (978-0-9675037-0-7(1)) Cooper Publishing Co.

Corey, Shana. Milly & the Macy's Parade. Helquist, Brett, illus. 2006. 38p. (J). (gr. 4-8). reprint ed. 17.00 (978-1-4223-5174-1(2)) DIANE Publishing Co.

—Milly & the Macy's Parade. 2006. 40p. (J). pap. 5.99 (978-0-439-29755-4(9)) Scholastic, Inc.

Corey's Treasure. 2003. (978-0-9726114-1-1(X)) Scottish Christmas.

Cosley, Betty. The Story of Tiny McShane. Shepard, Brian, illus. l.t. ed. 1998. viii, 24p. (J). (ps-3). 14.95 (978-0-9664588-0-0(X)) Cosley Production.

Cotten, Cynthia S. This Is the Stable. Bettoli, Delana, illus. rev. ed. 2006. 32p. (J). (ps-3). 16.95 (978-0-8050-7556-4(9) , Holt, Henry & Co. Bks. For Young Readers) Holt, Henry & Co.

Cousins, Lucy. Maisy's Snowy Christmas Eve. Cousins, Lucy, illus. 2003. (Maisy Ser.). (Illus.). 32p. (J). (gr. k-k). 12.99 incl. audio compact disk (978-0-7636-2196-4(X)) Candlewick Pr.

Craft, Mahlon. Christmas Moon. Craft, K. Y., illus. 2003. 32p. (J). 15.95 (978-1-58717-056-0(6)); lib. bdg. (978-1-58717-057-7(4)) Chronicle Bks. LLC. (SeaStar Bks.).

Creamer, Joan Klatil. The Magic Sceptre - the Legend of Blue Santa Claus. Creamer, Joan Klatil, illus. ed. 2006. (J). 16.95 (978-0-9778476-3-1(2)) Silver Snowflake Publishing.

Crespi, Francesca. The Nativity: Six Glorious Pop-up Scenes. 2005. (Illus.). 12p. (J). 14.95 (978-1-4027-2919-5(7)) Sterling Publishing Co., Inc.

Crew, Linda. Nekomah Creek Christmas. Robinson, Charles, illus. 1999. 147p. (YA). (gr. 6-9). reprint ed. 15.00 (978-0-7881-6628-0(X)) DIANE Publishing Co.

Crissey, Brian. The Loneliest Christmas Tree. Crissey, Noah, illus. 2004. 32p. (J). bds. 25.00 (978-1-893183-35-3(1) , 598) Granite Publishing, LLC.

Crissey, Brian L. The Loneliest Christmas Tree. Crissey, Noah, illus. 2004. (J). (978-1-930724-12-9(8)); (978-1-930724-13-6(6)) Granite Publishing, LLC.

Crocitto, Frank. A Child's Christmas in Brooklyn. Horrigan, Jeremiah, ed. Horrigan, Grady Kane, illus. 2001. 96p. (YA). (gr. 4 up). 10.95 (978-0-9677558-2-3(4) , CHBO1) Candlepower, Inc.

Crompton, Richmal. Just William at Christmas. 2003. (Illus.). 200p. (J). pap. 6.95 (978-0-333-67104-7(X)) Macmillan Publishers Ltd. GBR. *Dist:* Trafalgar Square Publishing.

Cropsey, Sandra J. Tinker's Christmas. Mudd, Barbra, illus. 2002. 64p. (J). 16.99 (978-0-9652368-8-1(9)) Wright Publishing, Inc.

Crowson, Andrew. Flip Flap Christmas. Crowson, Andrew, illus. 2003. (Illus.). 12p. (J). bds. (978-1-85602-476-1(8)) Chrysalis Children's Bks.

Cruikshank, Fran. The Tale of the Not-So-Perfect Christmas Tree. Olson, Tom, illus. 2005. 17p. (J). 9.95 (978-1-59971-055-6(2)) Aardvark Global Publishing.

Culver, Steven. The Magic Christmas Reindeer Bell: A Ho. 2006. pap. 11.00 (***978-1-4259-7114-4(8)***) AuthorHouse.

Cummings, David W. How Biddikins & Buddikins Made Santa Claus Work Fast! 2005. (J). pap. 15.00 (978-0-8059-6814-9(8)) Dorrance Publishing Co., Inc.

Cummings, Priscilla. Santa Claws, the Christmas Crab. Ramsey, Marcy Dunn, illus. 2006. 32p. (J). pap. 10.50 (978-0-87033-576-1(6)) Cornell Maritime Pr., Inc.

Currey, Anna. Truffle's Christmas. 2000. (Illus.). (J). (978-0-531-30289-7(X) , Orchard Bks.) Scholastic, Inc.

Currie, Robin. Baby Bible Christmas Storybook. Adams, Cindy, illus. 2003. (Baby Bible Ser.). 32p. (J). (ps). bds. 10.99 (978-0-7814-3645-8(1) , 0781436451) Cook, David C. Publishing Co.

Currier Brileya, Elizabeth. Grandma B. 's Bedtime Stories. 2006. 68p. (J). pap. 8.39 (978-1-4116-9504-7(6)) Lulu-.com.

Curry, Kenneth. Priscilla & the Reindeer. 2007. (Illus.). 22p. (J). 10.95 (***978-0-9798364-5-9(X)***) Curry Brothers Publishing.

Curti, Anna, illus. Santa Claus. 2000. (Portable Holidays Ser.). 10p. (J). (ps). bds. 7.95 (978-0-8109-5653-7(5)) Abrams, Harry N. , Inc.

Curtiss, A. Phebe. Christmas Stories & Legends. 2006. 41.99 (***978-1-4280-1439-8(X));*** pap. 34.99 (***978-1-4280-1437-4(3)***) IndyPublish.com.

Cushman, Doug. Aunt Eater's Mystery Christmas. Cushman, Doug, illus. 2002. (Aunt Eater Mysteries Ser.). (Illus.). (J). 12.30 (978-0-7587-5991-7(6)) Book Wholesalers, Inc.

Cutlip, Kimbra L. Firefighter's Night Before Christmas. Rice, James, illus. 2002. 32p. (J). (gr. k-3). 15.95 (978-1-58980-054-0(0)) Pelican Publishing Co., Inc.

Cyr, Joe. Two Tales of That Very First Christmas: An Angel Named Etoile & the Straw Girl, Owen, Ramon E., illus. l.t. ed. 2002. 24p. 5.95 (978-0-9713768-1-6(6)) Cyr, Joe.

Dadey, Debbie & Jones, Marcia Thornton. Mrs. Claus Doesn't Climb Telephone Poles. 2002. (Bailey School Kids Holiday Special Ser.). 96p. (J). pap. 3.99 (978-0-439-40832-5(6) , Scholastic Paperbacks) Scholastic, Inc.

Daily, Don. The Gifts of Christmas. 2006. (Illus.). 144p. 14.98 (978-0-7624-2670-6(5) , Running Pr.) Running Pr. Bk. Pubs.

Dale, Jenny. Jingle Belle. Reid, Mick, illus. 2003. 107p. (J). (978-0-439-54366-8(5)) Scholastic, Inc.

—Little Star. Reid, Mick, illus. 2003. 109p. (J). (978-0-439-54363-7(0)) Scholastic, Inc.

—Snowy the Surprise Puppy. Hellard, Susan, illus. 2005. 60p. (J). (***978-0-439-79124-3(3)***) Scholastic, Inc.

Dale, Jenny. Winter's Tale. 2001. (gr. 3-6). lib. bdg. 11.80 (978-0-613-65065-6(4)) Tandem Library Bks.

D'Allance, Mireille. Dejame Decorar el Arbol de Navidad.Tr. of Let Me Decorate the Christmas Tree. (SPA.). 36p. (J). (gr. k-3). 9.20 (978-84-95150-26-4(3)) Corimbo, Editorial S.L. ESP. *Dist:* Lectorum Pubns., Inc.

Dalmatian Press Staff. A Christmas Carol Great Read. 2005. 128p. (J). 5.99 (978-1-4037-1585-2(8)) Dalmatian Pr.

—Christmas Morning Gigantic. 2004. 192p. pap. 2.99 (978-1-4037-0532-7(1)) Dalmatian Pr.

—Elmo Delicious Christmas (Glitter) 2007. 24p. pap. 4.99 (***978-1-4037-3753-3(3)***) Dalmatian Pr.

—The Nutcracker. (Illus.). 13p. (J). (ps-1). 2004. bds. 5.99 (978-1-57759-836-7(9)); 2001. bds. 7.99 (978-1-4037-1583-8(1)) Dalmatian Pr.

—Veggie Tales Star of Christmas BBBTC. 2004. 96p. pap. 2.99 (978-1-4037-1016-1(3)) Dalmatian Pr.

Dalmatian Press Staff, adapted by. Little Women. 2003. (Spot the Classics Ser.). 180p. (J). 4.99 (978-1-57759-560-1(2)) Dalmatian Pr.

Daly, Niki. What's Cooking, Jamela? Daly, Niki, illus. 2001. (Jamela Ser.). (Illus.). 32p. (J). (ps-2). 16.95 (978-0-374-35602-6(5) , Farrar, Straus & Giroux (BYR)) Farrar, Straus & Giroux.

Dann, Penny. The Secret Fairy Christmas. Dann, Penny, illus. 2007. (Secret Fairy Ser.). (Illus.). 20p. (J). (ps-3). 14.99 (***978-1-4169-4905-3(4)*** , Little Simon) Simon & Schuster Children's Publishing.

Danziger, Paula. Thames Doesn't Rhyme with James. 1999. (Illus.). 160p. (J). (gr. 5-9). pap. 3.99 (978-0-698-11788-4(3) , Putnam Juvenile) Penguin Group (USA) Inc.

—Thames Doesn't Rhyme with James. 153p. (J). pap. 3.99 (978-0-8072-1473-2(6) , Listening Library) Random Hse. Audio Publishing Group.

—Thames Doesn't Rhyme with James. 1999. (gr. 3-6). lib. bdg. 13.00 (978-0-613-09469-6(7)) Tandem Library Bks.

Davidson, Alice Joyce. A Christmas Candy Cane. 2006. (Christmas Minis Ser.). 14p. (J). 3.99 (978-0-310-70848-3(6)) Zonderkidz.

—The J Is for Jesus: The Candy Cane Story. Anderson, Nancy Munger, illus. 1998. (Christmas Board Bks.). 14p. (J). (ps). bds. 3.99 (978-0-310-97553-3(0)) Zonderkidz.

Davies, Margo. Do You Believe in Santa Claus? 2003. (J). 6.00 (978-0-9708959-7-4(6)) Accent Pubns.

Davies, Valentine. Miracle on 34th Street. 2002. 80p. pap. 6.25 (978-0-573-62892-4(0)) French, Samuel Inc.

—Miracle on 34th Street. fac. ed. 2001. 136p. (YA). 13.95 (978-0-15-216377-8(8)) Harcourt Children's Bks.

Davis, Caroline, illus. It's Christmas! 2004. (Christmas Wood Tops Ser.). 18p. (J). bds. 4.95 (978-0-7641-5752-3(3)) Barron's Educational Series, Inc.

—Trim the Tree! 2004. (Christmas Wood Tops Ser.). 18p. (J). bds. 4.95 (978-0-7641-5755-4(8)) Barron's Educational Series, Inc.

Davis, Chip, concept. Mannheim Steamroller - the Christmas Angel, Davis, Chip, . 2004. (Illus.). 22p. per. 14.95 (978-0-9754149-1-0(7)) Mannheim Steamroller, LLC.

Davis, Dan. An Orphan's Promise: A Christmas Story. 2006. 96p. 14.95 (978-0-9725977-5-3(1)) Second Star Creations.

Davis, Dan T. The Blacksmith's Gift: A Christmas Story. Davis, Jan, ed. Armstrong, Matthew S., illus. 2004. 64p. 14.95 (978-0-9725977-4-6(3)) Second Star Creations.

Davis, David. Nurse's Night Before Christmas. Rice, James, illus. 2003. 32p. pap. 15.95 (978-1-58980-152-3(0)) Pelican Publishing Co., Inc.

Davis, Donald. Christmas at Grandma's: The Warmth & Humore of Grandma's House at Christmas Time. 2006. (Illus.). 128p. (YA). 14.95 (978-0-87483-746-9(4)) August Hse. Pubs., Inc.

Davis, Holly & Anderson, Nancy Munger. My Birthday, Jesus' Birthday. 1998. 32p. (J). 12.99 (978-0-310-21968-2(X)) Zondervan.

Davis, Holly & Tada, Eareckson J. My Birthday, Jesus' Birthday. Anderson, Nancy Munger, illus. 1998. (J). 5.99 (978-0-310-97420-8(8)) Zonderkidz.

Davoll, Barbara. A Churchmouse Christmas. 1999. (Christopher Churchmouse Classics Ser.). (Illus.). 25p. (J). (ps-3). 9.99 (978-0-8024-5394-5(5)) Moody Pubs.

Day, Nancy Raines. Flamingo's First Christmas. Robinson, Fiona, illus. 2005. 32p. (J). (ps-3). 15.95 (978-0-8109-5765-7(5) , Abrams Bks. for Young Readers) Abrams, Harry N. , Inc.

de Brunhoff, Jean. Babar & Father Christmas. Haas, Merle, tr. from FRE. 2001. Tr. of Babar et le Pere Noel. (Illus.). 48p. (J). (ps-2). 15.95 (978-0-375-81444-0(2) , Random Hse. Bks. for Young Readers) Random Hse. Children's Bks.

de Brunhoff, Laurent. Babar et le Pere Noel. 1999. (Babar Ser.).Tr. of Babar & Father Christmas. (FRE., Illus.). (J). (ps-3). (978-2-01-002549-5(0)) Istra.

de Paola, Tomie. Four Friends at Christmas. de Paola, Tomie, illus. 32p. (J). 2005. pap. 6.99 (978-1-4169-0697-1(5) , Aladdin); 2002. (Illus.). 14.95 (978-0-689-85282-4(7)) Simon & Schuster Children's Publishing.

—Guess Who's Coming to Santa's for Dinner? 2004. (Illus.). 48p. (J). (ps-3). 16.99 (978-0-399-24271-7(6) , Putnam Juvenile) Penguin Group (USA) Inc.

—The Night of las Posadas. de Paola, Tomie, illus. 2001. (Illus.). 32p. (J). pap. 6.99 (978-0-698-11901-7(0) , Putnam Juvenile) Penguin Group (USA) Inc.

—The Night of las Posadas. 2001. (978-0-606-22500-7(5)) Tandem Library Bks.

—The Night of Las Posadas. de Paola, Tomie, illus. 1999. (Illus.). 32p. (J). (ps-3). 16.99 (978-0-399-23400-2(4) , Putnam Juvenile) Penguin Group (USA) Inc.

—Tomie's Little Christmas Pageant. 2002. (Illus.). 32p. (J). bds. 7.99 (978-0-399-23959-5(6) , Putnam Juvenile) Penguin Group (USA) Inc.

Dear Santa- 2005. (Illus.). 24p. (J). (ps-1). bds. 6.95 (978-0-8249-6618-8(X)) Ideals Pubns.

DeBoer, Jesslyn. Countdown to Christmas. 2006. 14p. (J). 3.99 (978-0-310-70845-2(1)) Zondervan.

Dede, Vivian Hughes. Elizabeth's Christmas Story. Morris, Susan, illus. 2004. 16p. (J). 1.99 (978-0-7586-0478-1(5)) Concordia Publishing Hse.

deGroat, Diane. Jingle Bells, Homework Smells. deGroat, Diane, illus. 2003. 32p. (J). (ps-3). pap. 6.99 (978-0-688-17545-0(7)) HarperCollins Pubs.

—Jingle Bells, Homework Smells. 2000. (gr. k-3). lib. bdg. 14.15 (978-0-613-68435-4(4)) Tandem Library Bks.

DeKok, Joy. Room for Bandit. 2006. (ENG.). 36p. (J). per. 16.99 (978-1-4141-0585-7(1)) Pleasant Word.

Demas, Corinne. Two Christmas Mice. Roth, Stephanie, illus. 32p. (J). (ps). 16.95 (978-0-8234-1785-8(9)) Holiday Hse., Inc.

Dempster, Al & Walt Disney Productions Staff. Santa's Toy Shop. 2005. (Illus.). 32p. (J). (gr. k-k). 8.99 (978-0-375-83361-8(7) , Golden/Disney) Random Hse. Children's Bks.

Denis, Erik & LeBlanc, Natalie. The Bubble. 2005. 16p. 10.10 (978-1-4116-6424-1(8)) Lulu.com.

Denson, Sara Ann. Christmas Turtles. McMillen, Tara, illus. 2006. 32p. (J). 16.95 (978-0-9769017-6-1(5)) Purple Sky Publishing.

DePalma, Johnny & Crabapple, Molly. Once upon a Christmas Tree - A Holiday Fairy Tale. 2007. 88p. pap. 10.50 (***978-0-615-15448-0(4)***) Umbrelly Bks.

DePaola, Tomie. Get Dressed, Santa! 2006. (Illus.). 12p. (J). (ps-1). bds. 6.99 (978-0-448-44446-8(1) , Grosset & Dunlap) Penguin Group (USA) Inc.

—Guess Who's Coming to Santa's for Dinner? DePaola, Tomie, illus. 2006. 40p. (J). (ps). pap. 6.99 (978-0-14-240699-1(6) , Puffin) Penguin Group (USA) Inc.

Devine, Monica. Hanna Bear's Christmas. Cassidy, Sean, illus. 2007. 32p. (J). (ps-1). (***978-1-55041-585-8(9)***) Fitzhenry & Whiteside, Ltd.

Dewan, Ted. Crispin: The Pig Who Had It All. 2002. (gr. k-3). lib. bdg. 15.30 (978-0-613-89780-8(3)) Tandem Library Bks.

Dewin, Howie. T' Was the Fight Before Christmas. 2003. (gr. k-3). lib. bdg. 11.80 (978-0-613-72149-3(7)) Tandem Library Bks.

Dharmi, Narinder. Christmas Carol. 2002. (Illus.). 80p. (J). pap. 8.95 (978-0-440-86498-1(4)) Bantam Dell Publishing Group.

Dibene, Anna. Best Dressed Christmas Tree. 2003. (Illus.). 10p. (J). (ps-7). pap. 14.25 (978-1-932301-24-3(0) , 1103) Airleaf Publishing & Bookselling.

DiCamillo, Kate. Great Joy. Ibatoulline, Bagram, illus. 2007. 32p. (J). (ps-3). 16.99 (***978-0-7636-2920-5(0)***) Candlewick Pr.

Dickens, Charles. Charles Dickens/A Christmas Carol. Lo Famia, Jon, illus. 2005. 48p. (gr. 5-8). 25.50 (978-0-7910-9108-1(2)) Facts On File, Inc.

—A Christmas Carol. Blake, Quentin, illus. 2001. 160p. (J). pap. 8.99 (978-1-86205-130-0(5) , Pavilion Bks., Ltd.) Anova Bks. GBR. *Dist:* Trafalgar Square Publishing.

—A Christmas Carol. Date not set. (C). pap. (978-0-7593-9886-3(0) , Thomson Learning) CENGAGE Learning.

—A Christmas Carol. Wheatcroft, Andrew, illus. 2006. (Read & Listen Bks.). 64p. (J). 9.99 (978-0-7566-1831-5(2)) Dorling Kindersley Publishing, Inc.

—A Christmas Carol. Morrissey, Dean, illus. 2001. 80p. (J). (gr. 2-5). 17.89 (978-0-06-028578-4(8)) HarperCollins Pubs.

—A Christmas Carol. Zwerger, Lisbeth, illus. 2001. (ENG & GER.). 72p. (J). (ps up). 19.95 (978-0-7358-1259-8(4)) North-South Bks., Inc.

—A Christmas Carol. 2000. (Illus.). 144p. (J). (gr. 4-7). pap. 5.99 (978-0-439-10133-2(6)) Scholastic, Inc.

—A Christmas Carol. 2004. (Aladdin Classics Ser.). 128p. (J). pap. 3.99 (978-0-689-87180-1(5) , Aladdin) Simon & Schuster Children's Publishing.

—A Christmas Carol. 1999. (Saddleback Classics). (Illus.). (J). 13.75 (978-0-606-21547-3(6)) Tandem Library Bks.

—A Christmas Carol. 1998. (Children's Classics). (ENG., Illus.). 96p. (YA). (ps up). pap. (978-1-85326-121-3(1) , 1211WW) Wordsworth Editions, Ltd.

—A Christmas Carol. Hegarty, Carol, ed. 1998. (Classics Ser.: Set I). (Illus.). 79p. (YA). (gr. 5-12). pap. 6.95 (978-1-56254-256-6(7) , SP2567) Saddleback Educational Publishing.

—A Christmas Carol. 2005. (Great Illustrated Classics Ser.). (Illus.). 238p. (J). (gr. 3-8). 21.35 (978-1-59679-237-1(X) , ABDO & Daughters) ABDO Publishing Co.

—Christmas Carol. 2004. (Fast Track Classics Ser.). (Illus.). 48p. (J). pap. 9.99 (978-0-237-52686-3(7) , Evans Brothers, Limited) Evans Publishing Group GBR. *Dist:* Independent Pubs. Group.

—A Christmas Carol. Lynch, P. J., illus. 2006. 160p. (J). (gr. 5). 19.99 (978-0-7636-3120-8(5)) Candlewick Pr.

—A Christmas Carol. Lo Famia, Jon, illus. 2nd ed. 1998. (Illustrated Classic Book Ser.: Vol. III). 61p. (J). reprint ed. pap. 4.95 (978-1-56767-241-1(8)) Educational Insights, Inc.

—A Christmas Carol. l.t. ed. 1999. (Large Print Heritage Ser.). 140p. (YA). (gr. 7-12). lib. bdg. 24.95 (978-1-58118-041-1(1) , 22510) LRS.

—A Christmas Carol. abr. ed. 2001. (Illus.). 144p. pap. 4.99 (978-0-14-230055-8(1) , Puffin) Penguin Group (USA) Inc.

—A Christmas Carol: Prestwick House Literary Touchstone Edition. 2005. 86p. (YA). per. 3.99 (978-1-58049-579-0(6) , PWH5796) Prestwick Hse., Inc.

—A Christmas Carol - Spotlight Edition. 2004. 102p. (YA). per. 5.95 (978-1-58049-551-6(6) , PWH5516) Prestwick Hse., Inc.

—The Cricket on the Hearth. 2004. reprint ed. pap. 15.95 (978-1-4191-5807-0(4)); pap. 1.99 (978-1-4192-5807-7(9)) Kessinger Publishing, LLC.

—The Cricket on the Hearth. l.t. ed. 2005. 128p. pap. 17.95 (978-1-59688-048-1(1) , 1-59688-048-1) Large Print Bk. Co., The.

—Cuento de Navidad. 2000. (Coleccion "Clasicos Juveniles" Ser.). (SPA.). 148p. (gr. 4-7). pap. 8.95 (978-1-58348-825-6(1)) iUniverse, Inc.

Dickens, Charles & Birmingham, Christian. A Christmas Carol. 2000. (Miniature Editionstm Ser.). (Illus.). 128p. (gr. 4-7). 4.95 (978-0-7624-0831-3(6) , Running Pr. Miniature Editions) Running Pr. Bk. Pubs.

Dickens, Charles & Moore, Clement C. A Christmas Carol & the Night Before Christmas. Rackham, Arthur, illus. deluxe ed. 2006. 192p. 14.99 (978-0-517-22927-9(7) , Gramercy) Random Hse. Value Publishing.

Dickens, Charles & Sims, L. A Christmas Carol. (Young Reading Ser.: Vol. 2). 64p. (J). (gr. 2 up). lib. bdg. 13.95 (978-1-58086-790-0(1) , Usborne) EDC Publishing.

Dickens, Charles & Skarmeas, Nancy J. A Christmas Carol. Flint, Russ, illus. abr. ed. 1998. 48p. (J). (gr. 4-7). 14.00 (978-0-8249-4096-6(2) , Candy Cane Pr.) Ideals Pubns.

Dickens, Charles & Wheatcroft, Andrew. A Christmas Carol. 2000. (Read & Listen Ser.). (Illus.). 64p. (J). pap. incl. cd-rom (978-0-7894-6363-0(6)) Dorling Kindersley Publishing, Inc.

Dickens, Charles, et al. Christmas Books & Stories. 2004. (YA). cd-rom, audio compact disk 25.00 (978-0-917466-15-1(2)) B & R Samizdat Express.

Dickinson, Asa Don & Skinner, Ada M. The Children's Book of Christmas Stories. 2004. reprint ed. pap. 24.95 (978-1-4191-5657-1(8)); pap. 1.99 (978-1-4192-5657-8(2)) Kessinger Publishing, LLC.

Didier, Larry & Didier, Edna. How Christmas Came to the Ghetto. 2000. lib. bdg. 19.95 (978-1-892937-08-7(5)) Special Pubns., Inc.

Dittmer, Cherie. Angel Angel. 2004. 32p. (J). 7.99 (978-0-7586-0062-2(3)) Concordia Publishing Hse.

Dittrick, A. L., as told by. Once upon A Christmas: The 4th Wiseman. 2007. (J). 3.95 net. (***978-0-9767578-0-1(X)*** , Ink Well Publishing) Ink Well.

Dodd, Contance. Santa Meets Mr. Dippleman. 2002. (Illus.). 28p. (J). 10.95 (978-1-886225-76-3(1)) Day of Grace Publishing Services.

Doggett, Sue. Advent Angels: A Host of Stories, Crafts, Puzzles & Things to Do for the Days of Advent. Blake, Francis, illus. 1999. 64p. (J). pap. (978-1-84101-099-1(5) , Barnabas) Bible Reading Fellowship.

Doherty, Berlie. The Nutcracker. 2003. (Illus.). 32p. (J). (gr. k-5). pap. 9.99 (978-0-552-54834-2(0) , Corgi) Transworld Publishers Ltd. GBR. *Dist:* Trafalgar Square Publishing.

Doherty, Berlie & Beck, Ian. The Nutcracker. 2004. (Illus.). 32p. (J). 19.95 (978-0-385-60437-6(8) , Doubleday) Transworld Publishers Ltd. GBR. *Dist:* Trafalgar Square Publishing.

Doles, Sean Patrick. Saving Mr. Bingle: A New Orleans Christmas Fairy Tale. num. ed. 2004. 176p. per. 9.95 (978-0-9758996-0-1(0)) New Orleans Stories.

Dollin, Laura. Christmas Angel. Beardshaw, Rosalind, illus. 2003. 12p. (J). (gr. k-k). bds. 5.99 (978-0-7636-2142-1(0)) Candlewick Pr.

Dooley, Phyllis & Duncan, Alice Faye. Christmas Soup. Gilchrist, Jan Spivey, illus. 2005. 32p. (J). (ps-3). 15.99 (978-0-310-70930-5(X)) Zonderkidz.

Dorling Kindersley Publishing Staff. Christmas Board Book. 2003. (My First Board Books (Bilingual) Ser.). (Illus.). 36p. (J). bds. 6.99 (978-0-7894-9520-4(1)) Dorling Kindersley Publishing, Inc.

—My First Christmas Touch & Feel. 2002. (Illus.). 12p. (J). bds. 9.99 (978-0-7894-8838-1(8)) Dorling Kindersley Publishing, Inc.

Dorling Kindersley Publishing Staff, et al. Christmas. 2001. (Touch & Feel Ser.). (Illus.). 12p. (J). (ps-k). bds. 6.99 (978-0-7894-6512-2(4)) Dorling Kindersley Publishing, Inc.

Douglas, Vincent & School Specialty Publishing Staff. Santa's Workshop, 4 bks., Set. Schroeder, Warren L., illus. 2003. (My Block Book Schoolhouse Collection). 88p. (J). (ps up). bds. 12.95 (978-1-58845-523-9(8)) School Specialty Publishing.

Dower, Laura. From the Files of Madison Finn Bk. 19: Keep It Real. rev. ed. 2005. (From the Files of Madison Finn Ser.: Bk. 19). 176p. (J). (gr. 3-7). pap. 4.99 (978-0-7868-5687-9(4) , Volo) Hyperion Bks. for Children.

—T' Was the Fight Before Christmas. 2003. (gr. k-3). lib. bdg. 11.25 (978-0-613-72148-6(9)) Tandem Library Bks.

Doyle, Roddy. Rover Saves Christmas. Ajhar, Brian, illus. 160p. (J). 2003. pap. 4.99 (978-0-439-30533-4(0)); 2001. (gr. 3-7). pap. 14.95 (978-0-439-30530-3(6)) Scholastic, Inc. (Levine, Arthur A. Bks.).

—Rover Saves Christmas. 2003. (gr. 3-6). lib. bdg. 13.00 (978-0-613-72061-8(X)) Tandem Library Bks.

Draper, Melissa J. Holly the Christmas Collie. Kravanek, J. Elise, illus. 2004. 63p. (J). (978-0-9741081-3-1(8)) Acres Publishing.

Dreyer, Nicole E. Joseph's Christmas Story. Ebert, Len, illus. 2004. (ENG.). 16p. (J). 1.99 (978-0-570-07577-6(7)) Concordia Publishing Hse.

Drvenkar, Zoran. Tell Me What You See. 2005. 304p. (J). pap. 16.99 (978-0-439-72452-4(X) , Chicken Hse., The) Scholastic, Inc.

Duhon, Katherine. The Christmas Angel. 2006. pap. 7.95 (978-0-533-15381-7(6)) Vantage Pr., Inc.

Dukes, LeRoy L. Christmas on Chill Street. 2005. (J). 6.99 (978-0-9664506-2-0(0)) Dukes World, Inc.

Dunham, Terri Hoover. The Legend of Papa Noël: A Cajun Christmas Story. Knorr, Laura, illus. 2006. 32p. (J). (gr. k-5). 17.95 (978-1-58536-256-1(5)) Sleeping Bear Pr.

Dunrea, Olivier. Bear Noel. Dunrea, Olivier, illus. (Illus.). 32p. (J). 2006. pap. 5.95 (978-0-374-40001-9(6)); 2000. 16.00 (978-0-374-39990-0(5)) Farrar, Straus & Giroux. (Farrar, Straus & Giroux (BYR)).

Dunrea, Olivier, illus. Merry Christmas, Ollie! 2005. (J). (978-0-618-53242-1(0)) Houghton Mifflin Co.

Dupuis, Ann. Santa's Secret: A Gatecrasher Adventure with "All the Rules You Need to Know" 2nd ed. 1998. (Illus.). 24p. pap. 4.95 (978-1-887154-05-5(1) , GGG3003) Grey Ghost Pr., Inc.

Durant, Alan. Dear Santa Claus. Cabban, Vanessa, illus. 2005. 32p. (J). (ps-2). 14.99 (978-0-7636-2829-1(8)) Candlewick Pr.

Durant, Alan. Dear Santa Claus: Mini Edition. Cabban, Vanessa, illus. 2007. 32p. (J). (ps-2). 6.99 (***978-0-7636-3465-0(4)***) Candlewick Pr.

Durrant, George D. The Christmas Marble: A Christmas Story. 2004. 70p. (J). 4.95 (978-1-55517-824-6(3) , Bonneville Bks.) Cedar Fort, Inc./CFI Distribution.

Duval, Kathy. The Three Bears' Christmas. Meisel, Paul, illus. 32p. (J). 6.95 (978-0-8234-2039-1(6)); 16.95 (978-0-8234-1871-8(5)) Holiday Hse., Inc.

Earhart, Kristin. Happy's Holiday. 2007. (Big Apple Barn Ser.). 96p. (J). pap. 3.99 (***978-0-545-01774-9(2)*** , Scholastic Paperbacks) Scholastic, Inc.

Easterling, Anne S. Ozzie the Great Christmas Crocodile. 2006. (Illus.). 12p. (J). 3.95 (***978-0-9768890-4-5(8)***) ASE Media.

Edwards, Cory. The Christmas Lizard. Dudash, C. Michael, illus. 2001. 32p. 5.99 (978-1-56292-377-8(3)) Cook, David C. Publishing Co.

—The Christmas Lizard. 2000. (Illus.). 32p. (J). (ps-3). 14.99 (978-1-56292-619-9(5) , 1562926195) Cook, David C. Publishing Co.

Edwards, Gerry. Candy Klaus Trick or Treat. 2004. 56p. per. 10.95 (978-1-59453-394-5(6) , 1074) Airleaf Publishing & Bookselling.

Edwards, Julie Andrews. Dumpy's Happy Holiday. Walton, Tony, illus. 2005. 32p. (J). lib. bdg. 16.89 (978-0-06-052685-6(8) , Julie Andrews Collection) HarperCollins Pubs.

Edwards, Julie Andrews & Hamilton, Emma Walton. Dumpy's Happy Holiday. Walton, Tony, illus. 2005. 32p. (J). 15.99 (978-0-06-052684-9(X) , Julie Andrews Collection) HarperCollins Pubs.

Edwards, Kris. Santa Paws #8 Santa Paws & the Christmas Storm. 2005. 144p. (J). pap. (***978-0-439-78115-2(9)***) Scholastic, Inc.

—Santa Paws on Christmas Island. 2007. (Santa Paws Ser.). 144p. (J). pap. 4.99 (***978-0-439-88812-7(3)*** , Scholastic Paperbacks) Scholastic, Inc.

Edwards, Kris. Santa Paws Saves the Day. 2005. (Santa Paws Ser.: No. 7). 144p. (J). (gr. 3-7). pap. 4.99 (978-0-439-57354-2(8) , Scholastic Paperbacks) Scholastic, Inc.

Edwards, Nicholas. Our Hero. 2002. (gr. k-3). lib. bdg. 12.40 (978-0-613-72041-0(5)) Tandem Library Bks.

—Santa Paws, Our Hero. 2002. (Santa Paws Ser.: No. 5). 176p. (J). pap. 4.99 (978-0-439-37283-1(6)) Scholastic, Inc.

Egan, Kate. A Very Merry Frostmas. 2006. 24p. (ps-2). pap. 3.50 (978-1-4231-0505-3(2)) Disney Pr.

Ehlenbeck, Stan. AllThumbs Mckringle by Stan Ehlenbeck & illustrated by Marilyn Martin. 2007. 29.00 (***978-0-8059-8957-1(9)***) Dorrance Publishing Co., Inc.

Elder, Elizabeth. Christmas with Alice-Ems. Elder, Elizabeth, illus. 2000. (Illus.). 28p. (J). (gr. 2-7). pap. 6.00 (978-0-9678040-2-6(7)) Puddingstone Pubns.

Elliott, Ann. GypsyBridge Friends: The Gift. 2003. 46p. pap. 12.95 (978-0-9721825-1-5(9)) Open Vision Entertainment Corp.

Elmo's Christmas. 2000. (J). 9.99 (978-1-931312-29-5(X)) SoftPlay, Inc.

Elschner, Geraldine. Pashmina the Little Christmas Goat. Kehlenbeck, Angela, illus. 2006. 32p. (J). (ps-3). 16.99 (978-0-698-40046-7(1) , Minedition) Penguin Group (USA) Inc.

Elya, Susan Middleton & Banks, Merry. N Is for Navidad. Cepeda, Joe, illus. 2007. 40p. (J). (ps-3). 14.95 (978-0-8118-5205-0(9)) Chronicle Bks. LLC.

Emerson, Charlotte. Amy's True Prize. 1999. (Little Women Journals Ser.). (J). (978-0-606-16348-4(4)) Tandem Library Bks.

—Beth's Snow Dancer. 1999. (Little Women Journals Ser.). (J). (978-0-606-16347-7(6)) Tandem Library Bks.

Emerson, Charlotte & Alcott, Louisa May. Amy's True Prize. Wasden, Kevin, illus. 1999. (Little Women Journals). 128p. (J). (gr. 3-7). mass mkt. 3.99 (978-0-380-79706-6(2)) HarperCollins Pubs.

—Beth's Snow Dancer. Wasden, Kevin, illus. 1999. (Little Women Journals). 128p. (J). (gr. 3-7). pap. 3.99 (978-0-380-79704-2(6)) HarperCollins Pubs.

—Jo's Troubled Heart. Wasden, Kevin, illus. 1999. (Little Women Journals). 128p. (J). (gr. 3-7). pap. 3.99 (978-0-380-79669-4(4)) HarperCollins Pubs.

Encarnacion, Liz. Santas Christmas Surprise. 2006. (Illus.). 10p. (J). 4.95 (978-0-7624-2814-4(7)) Running Pr. Bk. Pubs.

Encarnacion, Elizabeth. Rudolph, the Red-Nosed Reindeer. 2007. (Illus.). 128p. 4.95 (***978-0-7624-3098-7(2)*** , Running Pr. Minature Editions) Running Pr. Bk. Pubs.

Engelbreit, Mary. Mary Engelbreit's A Merry Little Christmas: Celebrate from A to Z. Engelbreit, Mary, illus. 2006. (Illus.). 40p. (J). lib. bdg. 17.89 (978-0-06-074159-4(7)) HarperCollins Pubs.

—Mary Engelbreit's a Merry Little Christmas: Celebrate from A to Z. Engelbreit, Mary, illus. 2006. (Illus.). 40p. (J). 16.99 (978-0-06-074158-7(9)) HarperCollins Pubs.

—Queen of Christmas. Engelbreit, Mary, illus. 2003. (Ann Estelle Stories Ser.). (J). 32p. 16.99 (978-0-06-058608-9(7)); 159.90 (978-0-06-056902-0(6)); 127.92 (978-0-06-056903-7(4)); (Illus.). 32p. 15.99 (978-0-06-008175-1(9)) HarperCollins Pubs.

—Queen of Christmas. Engelbreit, Mary, illus. 2006. (Ann Estelle Stories Ser.). 32p. (J). pap. 6.99 (978-0-06-008177-5(5) , Harper Trophy) HarperCollins Pubs.

Erickson, John R. The Wounded Buzzard on Christmas Eve. Holmes, Gerald L., illus. 1998. (Hank the Cowdog Ser.: No. 13). 144p. (J). (gr. 2-5). 14.99 (978-0-670-88420-9(0) , Viking Juvenile); pap. 4.99 (978-0-14-130389-5(1) , Puffin) Penguin Group (USA) Inc.

Erlbach, Arlene & Erlbach, Herb. Merry Christmas, Everywhere! Holm, Sharon Lane, illus. 2002. 48p. (gr. k-3). (J). pap. 8.95 (978-0-7613-1699-2(X)); lib. bdg. 23.90 (978-0-7613-1956-6(5)) Lerner Publishing Group. (Millbrook Pr.).

Eubank, Patricia Reeder. Countdown to Christmas. 2003. (Illus.). 14p. (J). (ps-k). 9.95 (978-0-8249-6505-1(1)) Ideals Pubns.

Evans, Clay Bonnyman. The Winter Witch. Bender, Robert, illus. 2005. 32p. (J). (ps-ps). 16.95 (978-0-8234-1615-8(1)) Holiday Hse., Inc.

Evans, Richard Paul. The Christmas Candle. Collins, Jacob, illus. 32p. (J). (ps-3). 2007. 9.99 (***978-1-4169-5047-9(8)***); 2006. 7.99 (978-1-4169-2682-5(8) , Aladdin); 1998. 16.95 (978-0-689-82319-0(3)) Simon & Schuster Children's Publishing.

Evans, Richard Paul & Craig, Daniel. The Light of Christmas. 2002. (Illus.). 32p. (J). (gr. k-3). 16.95 (978-0-689-83468-4(3)) Simon & Schuster Children's Publishing.

Evans, Sandi Gore. Sandi Gore Evans Wishing You Blessings from A to Z. Johnston, Becky, ed. l.t. ed. (Illus.). 32p. 14.95 (978-1-890621-26-1(9)) Landauer Corp.

Falcone, L. M. The Mysterious Mummer. (L.M. Falcone Ser.). 192p. 2005. (978-1-55337-377-3(4)); 2004. (YA). (gr. 13 up). (978-1-55337-376-6(6)) Kids Can Pr., Ltd.

Falconer, Ian. Olivia Helps with Christmas. Falconer, Ian, illus. 2007. (Olivia Ser.). (Illus.). 58p. (J). (ps-2). 18.99 (978-1-4169-0786-2(6) , Atheneum/Anne Schwartz Bks.) Simon & Schuster Children's Publishing.

Falconer, Ian. Olivia Helps with Christmas (W. T.) Mawhinney, Art, illus. 2007. 32p. (J). 5.99 (***978-1-4169-5387-6(6)*** , Simon Scribbles) Simon & Schuster Children's Publishing.

Falwell, Cathryn. Christmas for 10. 2003. (Illus.). 32p. (J). (gr. k-3). 6.95 (978-0-618-37836-4(7) , Clarion Bks.) Houghton Mifflin Co. Trade & Reference Div.

—Christmas for 10. 2003. (gr. k-3). lib. bdg. 15.25 (978-0-613-73019-8(4)) Tandem Library Bks.

C D

Falzon, Adrienne. What Is an Angel? Salzberg, Helen M., illus. 2004. 27p. pap. 14.95 (978-1-4137-4461-3(3)) PublishAmerica, Inc.

Family, Wayans. Miracle on D-Roc's Street. 2006. (Thugaboo Ser.). 64p. (J). pap. 4.99 (978-0-439-90378-3(5), Cartwheel Bks.) Scholastic, Inc.

Fant, Donna. Scotty's Dream. McKeown, David, illus. 2004. 16p. (J). 14.99 (***978-1-931844-17-8(8)***, PP1034) Piano Pr.

Farber, Norma. How the Hibernators Came to Bethlehem. Cooney, Barbara, illus. 2006. 32p. (J). 10.85 (978-0-8027-9611-0(7)); 9.95 (978-0-8027-9610-3(9)) Walker & Co.

Farley, Steven. Wild Spirit. 1999. (Young Black Stallion Ser.: No. 4). (J). (gr. 4-6). (978-0-606-16963-9(6)) Tandem Library Bks.

Farr, Dan. Mr. Finnegan's Giving Chest. 2005. (Illus.). 32p. (J). (ps-3). 19.95 incl. audio compact disk (978-1-59038-555-5(1), Shadow Mountain) Deseret Bk. Co.

Farr, Jamie. Hababy's Christmas Eve. 2003. (ENG.). 36p. per. 13.95 (978-1-59286-486-7(4)) PublishAmerica, Inc.

Faulkner, Keith. Charlie Chimp's Christmas: A Pop-up Extravaganza of Festive Friends. Lambert, Jonathan, illus. 2006. 12p. (J). (ps-3). reprint ed. 10.00 (978-1-4223-5446-9(6)) DIANE Publishing Co.

Fearnley, Jan. Little Robin's Christmas. Fearnley, Jan, illus. 2002. 32p. (J). 5.95 (978-1-58925-371-1(X), tiger tales) ME Media LLC.

Federici, Diane Marie. The Christmas Stocking. 2006. (J). pap. 8.00 (978-0-8059-6874-3(1)) Dorrance Publishing Co., Inc.

Feldman, Thea & Auerbach, Annie. The Snow Family: A Winter's Tale. Alderson, Lisa, illus. 2005. 12p. (J). 13.00 (978-0-7567-9460-6(9)) DIANE Publishing Co.

Feliciano, Jose. Feliz Navidad: Two Stories Celebrating Christmas. Diaz, David, illus. 2005. 23p. (J). reprint ed. 16.00 (978-0-7567-8587-1(1)) DIANE Publishing Co.

—Feliz Navidad: Two Stories Celebrating Christmas. Diaz, David, illus. 2003. 28p. (J). pap. 15.95 (978-0-439-51717-1(6), Cartwheel Bks.) Scholastic, Inc.

Felix: Xmas Around the World Hat. 1998. (J). pap. (978-0-7892-5438-2(7)) Abbeville Pr., Inc.

Ferguson, Jennifer E. The Christmas Miracle. unabr. ed. 1998. (Illus.). 20p. (J). (ps-2). (978-1-892732-01-9(7)) Ferguson, Jennifer E. Pubns.

Ferguson, Sarah. Little Red's Christmas Story. Williams, Sam, illus. 2004. 40p. (J). 15.95 (978-0-689-85561-0(3)) Simon & Schuster Children's Publishing.

Ferguson, Sarah The Duchess of York. Little Red's Christmas Story. Williams, Sam, illus. 2007. 40p. (J). 6.99 (***978-1-4169-5002-8(8)***, Aladdin) Simon & Schuster Children's Publishing.

Fernleigh Books Staff, prod. Santa's Busy Day. 2005. (Illus.). 14p. (J). bds. 14.95 (978-1-4027-2024-6(6)) Sterling Publishing Co., Inc.

Ferrante, Joanne. Where Do the Christmas Trees Go? 2003. (Illus.). 32p. (J). 15.95 (978-0-9721949-0-7(8)) Window Seat Publishing.

Field, Ellen. Merry Ham-Ham Christmas. Haefele, Steve, illus. 2003. (Hamtaro Ser.). 32p. (J). pap. 3.99 (978-0-439-54249-4(9), Scholastic Paperbacks) Scholastic, Inc.

—Merry Ham-Ham Christmas. 2003. (ps-2). lib. bdg. 11.80 (978-0-613-72143-1(8)) Tandem Library Bks.

Field, Eugene. Christmas Tales & Christmas Verse. 2006. pap. 87.99 (***978-1-4280-2196-9(5)***) IndyPublish.com.

Figueredo, D. H. The Road to Santiago. Torrecilla, Pablo, illus. 2003. 32p. (J). 16.95 (978-1-58430-059-5(0)) Lee & Low Bks., Inc.

Fine, Edith Hope. Cricket at the Manger. Pels, Winslow, illus. 2005. 32p. (J). 15.95 (978-1-56397-993-4(4)) Boyds Mills Pr.

Finley, Martha. Christmas with Grandma Elsie, Bk. 14. 2001. mass mkt. 5.99 (978-1-931343-23-7(3)) Hibbard Pubns., Inc.

—Christmas with Grandma Elsie. 2006. 79.99 (***978-1-4280-2610-0(X)***) IndyPublish.com.

Fiona Waters Staff. The Book of Christmas. 2005. (Illus.). 96p. (J). (ps-17). 25.00 (978-1-84365-006-5(1)) Chrysalis Children's Bks. GBR. *Dist:* Trafalgar Square Publishing.

Fiore, Keith M. Leni the Pug: The Comet Christmas Caper. Sacui, Alexandru, illus. 2006. 95p. per. 29.50 (978-0-9785773-0-8(2)) Brownstone Monkey Productions, Inc.

The First Gift of Christmas. 2003. (J). lib. bdg. 16.95 (978-1-931650-21-2(7)) Coastal Publishing Carolina, Inc.

Fischer, Russell. O Tannenbaum: The Story of the Last Christmas Tree. 2003. 108p. pap. 16.95 (978-1-4137-0531-7(6)) PublishAmerica, Inc.

—Open Before Christmas: An Irresistible Treasury of Stories & Poems That Just Wont Wait for December 25th! 2004. 154p. pap. 19.95 (978-1-4137-1072-4(7)) PublishAmerica, Inc.

Fisher, Phyllis Mae Richardson. Twiglet the Little Christmas Tree. Fisher, Phyllis Mae Richardson & Fisher, Douglas W., illus. 2003. (J). 30.00 (978-0-9745615-1-6(7), Twiglet The Little Christmas Tree); 186p. 12.00 (978-0-9745615-4-7(1)) PJs Corner.

Fite, Anna. Ada y Max Viven la Navidad. 2002. (Ada y Max Ser.). (SPA & ENG., Illus.). 10p. 4.95 (978-84-7864-382-0(6)) Combel Editorial, S.A. ESP. *Dist:* Independent Pubs. Group.

Fitzgerald, Linda, creator. Stellar: The Teeniest, Tiniest Star in the WHOLE Universe! 2003. (Illus.). 86p. (J). per. 19.95 (978-0-9745745-0-9(3), 102049562) Turning Point LLC.

Fitzhugh, Louise & Gold, Maya. Harriet the Spy, Double Agent. 2007. 160p. (J). (gr. 4-7). 6.50 (978-0-440-41691-3(4), Yearling) Random Hse. Children's Bks.

Fitzwater, Ivan W. Cappy the Christmas Woodpecker. Paul Hudgins, illus. 2002. pap. 8.95 (978-0-934955-51-5(4)) Watercress Pr.

Flinn, Lias. Unwrapping the Christmas Creche. 18.00 (978-0-687-05441-1(9)) Abingdon Pr.

Flinn, Lisa. Unwrapping the Christmas Creche. 2005. 32p. 15.00 (978-0-687-49783-6(3)) Abingdon Pr.

Flinn, Lisa & Younger, Barbara. The Christmas Garland. Corvino, Lucy, tr. Corvino, Lucy, illus. 2003. 32p. (J). 14.95 (978-0-8249-5460-4(2), Ideals Children's Bks.) Ideals Pubns.

Floss, Laura. Snow Magic! Style Guide Staff, illus. 2006. (Frosty the Snowman Ser.). 96p. (J). act. bk. ed. 2.99 (978-1-4169-1847-9(7), Simon Scribbles) Simon & Schuster Children's Publishing.

Fogelin, Adrian. My Brother's Hero. (Peachtree Junior Publication Ser.). 224p. (J). 2002. (gr. 3-7). 14.95 (978-1-56145-274-3(2)); 2005. reprint ed. pap. 6.95 (978-1-56145-352-8(8)) Peachtree Pubs., Ltd.

Fogle, Robin. The Shepherd Boy's Christmas. 2005. (J). pap. 1.79 (***978-1-59317-105-6(6)***) Warner Pr. Pubs.

Follow the Star 5 Book Set. 2004. 10p. (J). bds. 9.99 (978-0-570-07189-1(5)) Concordia Publishing Hse.

Fontes, Justine. Christmas Club. 2000. (Hello Reader! Ser.). (J). 10.79 (978-0-606-19549-2(1)) Tandem Library Bks.

—Christmas Cub. 1999. (gr. k-3). lib. bdg. 11.80 (978-0-613-32403-8(X)) Tandem Library Bks.

Ford, Linda. Santa Claus, Inc. 1998. pap. 3.99 (978-0-590-11504-9(9)) Scholastic, Inc.

—Santa S. O. S. 2000. 112p. (J). (gr. 3-7). pap. 4.50 (978-0-439-12911-4(7)) Scholastic, Inc.

—Santa S O S. 1999. (gr. 3-6). lib. bdg. 12.40 (978-0-613-33021-3(8)) Tandem Library Bks.

—The Santa Solution. 2000. 112p. (J). (gr. 3-7). pap. 4.50 (978-0-439-21627-2(3)) Scholastic, Inc.

Foreman, Michael. Cat in the Manger. rev. ed. 2001. (Illus.). 32p. (J). (ps-3). 17.95 (978-0-8050-6677-7(2), Holt, Henry & Co. Bks. For Young Readers) Holt, Henry & Co.

Foreman, Michael. The Little Reindeer. 2007. (Illus.). 32p. (J). (ps-3). per. 9.95 (***978-1-84270-582-7(2)***) Andersen GBR. *Dist:* Independent Pubs. Group.

Foreman, Michael, illus. & selected by. Michael Foreman's Christmas Treasury. Foreman, Michael, selected by. 1999. 124p. (J). (gr. 4-7). 22.99 (978-1-86205-197-3(6), Pavilion Bks., Ltd.) Anova Bks. GBR. *Dist:* Independent Pubs. Group.

Foster, Kinsley. Wild Abandon Vol. 3: How to Grow a Snowball. 2000. (YA). pap. 10.95 (978-0-9667634-7-8(5)) What's Inside Pr.

Fox, Mem. Wombat Divine. 2002. (Illus.). (J). 13.19 (978-0-7587-4046-5(8)) Book Wholesalers, Inc.

—Wombat Divine. Argent, Kerry, illus. 1999. 32p. (J). (ps-3). pap. 6.00 (978-0-15-202096-5(9), Harcourt Paperbacks) Harcourt Children's Bks.

—Wombat Divine. 1999. (gr. k-3). lib. bdg. 14.15 (978-0-613-22962-3(2)) Tandem Library Bks.

Frazee, Marla. Santa Claus: The World's Number One Toy Expert. 2005. (Illus.). 40p. (J). (ps-ps). 16.00 (978-0-15-204970-6(3), Harcourt Children's Bks) Harcourt Children's Bks.

Freeman, David. The Nutcracker. Isles, Joanna, illus. 1999. 40p. (J). (gr. 3). pap. 9.99 (978-1-86205-273-4(5), Pavilion Bks., Ltd.) Anova Bks. GBR. *Dist:* Independent Pubs. Group.

Freeman, Don. Christmas Is Here, Corduroy! 2007. 16p. (J). (ps-1). pap. 5.99 (***978-0-448-44650-9(2)***, Grosset & Dunlap) Penguin Group (USA) Inc.

Freeman, Don. Corduroy's Merry Christmas. McCue, Lisa, illus. 2002. 16p. (J). bds. 5.99 (978-0-670-03579-3(3), Viking Juvenile) Penguin Group (USA) Inc.

Freeman, Emily. God Bless Your Way: A Christmas Journey. Burr, Dan, illus. 2007. 32p. (J). (ps-3). 19.95 incl. audio compact disk (***978-1-59038-806-8(2)***) Deseret Bk. Co.

Friedman, Carol. Nicky's Jazz Christmas. 2006. (Illus.). 32p. (J). 16.95 (978-1-57687-341-0(2)) powerHouse Cultural Entertainment, Inc.

Friedrich, Priscilla & Friedrich, Otto. The Easter Bunny That Overslept. Saaf, Donald, illus. 2002. 32p. (J). (ps-3). 16.99 (978-0-06-029645-2(3)); lib. bdg. 17.89 (978-0-06-029646-9(1)) HarperCollins Pubs.

Fry, Sonali. Clifford's Christmas Presents. Kurtz, John, illus. 2002. (Clifford, the Big Red Dog Ser.). 7p. (J). bds. 8.99 (978-0-439-39451-2(1), Cartwheel Bks.) Scholastic, Inc.

Funke, Cornelia. When Santa Fell to Earth. Latsch, Oliver, tr. from GER. Howard, Paul, illus. 2006. 192p. (J). pap. 15.99 (978-0-439-78204-3(X), Chicken Hse., The) Scholastic, Inc.

Furlong Reynolds, Cynthia. S Is for Star: A Christmas Alphabet. Carroll, Pam, illus. rev. ed. 2001. 40p. (J). 18.95 (978-1-58536-064-2(3)) Sleeping Bear Pr.

Gabby & the Christmas Tree. 2000. (J). (978-1-58453-118-0(5)); (978-1-58453-131-9(2)) Pioneer Valley Educational Pr., Inc.

Gaines, Isabel. Pooh's Christmas Gift. 1999. 40p. (J). pap. 3.99 (978-0-7868-4402-9(7)) Disney Pr.

—Pooh's Christmas Sled Ride. Studio Orlando Staff, illus. 2003. 32p. (J). (ps-1). pap. 3.99 (978-0-7364-2165-2(3), RH/Disney) Random Hse. Children's Bks.

Gandolfi, Claudine. The Night Before Christmas dot.com. Barbas, Kerren, illus. 2005. (Charming Petites Ser.). 80p. 4.95 (978-0-88088-844-8(X)) Peter Pauper Pr. Inc.

Gantos, Jack. The Christmas Spirit Strikes Rotten Ralph. 1998. (Illus.). 20p. (J). (ps-3). 6.95 (978-0-694-00986-2(5)) HarperCollins Pubs.

Gantschev, Ivan. The Rabbit & the Bear: A Christmas Tale. Gantschev, Ivan, illus. 2007. (Illus.). 32p. (J). (ps). 16.95 (***978-0-7358-2145-3(3)***) North-South Bks., Inc.

Ganzer, Diane. Patrick the Wayward Setter: A Christmas Miracle. 2005. 60p. pap. 12.95 (978-1-4137-8351-3(1)) PublishAmerica, Inc.

Garcia, Gloria. Navidad. (SPA.). 8p. 9.95 (978-84-272-7278-1(2)) Molino, Editorial ESP. *Dist:* Distribooks, Inc.

Garfield, Valerie. Sergeant Sniff's Christmas Surprise. 2000. (Sergeant Sniff Scratch-and-Sniff Mystery Ser.). (Illus.). 16p. (J). (ps-k). 6.95 (978-0-694-01512-2(1), Harper Festival) HarperCollins Pubs.

Garis, Howard Roger. Johnnie & Billie Bushytail. 2004. reprint ed. pap. 15.95 (978-1-4191-2786-1(1)); pap. 1.99 (978-1-4192-2786-8(6)) Kessinger Publishing, LLC.

Garland, Michael. Christmas Magic. 2003. (Illus.). 32p. (J). (ps-k). pap. 7.99 (978-0-14-250140-5(9), Puffin) Penguin Group (USA) Inc.

—Christmas Magic. Garland, Michael, illus. 2001. (Illus.). 32p. (J). (ps-2). 16.99 (978-0-525-46797-7(1), Dutton Juvenile) Penguin Group (USA) Inc.

—The Mouse Before Christmas. Garland, Michael, illus. 2001. (Illus.). 32p. (J). pap. 6.99 (978-0-14-230005-3(5), Puffin) Penguin Group (USA) Inc.

—Mouse Before Christmas. 2001. (gr. k-3). lib. bdg. 15.30 (978-0-613-71585-0(3)) Tandem Library Bks.

Garvey, Linda K. Doug's Twelve Days of Christmas. 1998. (Doug Ser.). (Illus.). 32p. (J). (ps-2). 8.95 (978-0-7868-3197-5(9)) Disney Pr.

Gates, Josephine Scribner. The Turkey Doll. Flass, E. C., illus. 2007. 62p. (J). lib. bdg. 59.00 (***978-1-60304-016-7(1)***) Dollworks.

Gauvey, D. H. Santa's Socks. Fasolino, Peter, illus. 2003. 35p. (J). (ps-7). per. 13.95 (978-1-59453-454-6(3), 2329) Airleaf Publishing & Bookselling.

Gavrilovskiy, Olga, illus. Elf Night: A Christmas Story. 2006. 52p. (J). 16.95 (***978-0-9788085-0-1(9)***) Tetoca Pr.

Gerlach-Babb nee Maines, Mary & Gerlach, Susan. Best Christmas Gift. 2007. (ENG.). 52p. per. 12.95 (***978-1-4241-6389-2(7)***) PublishAmerica, Inc.

Gershon, Dann. Beez in Toyland. Robinson, David, illus. 1999. (Hangin' with the Hombeez Ser.: Vol. 2). 40p. (J). (gr. k-6). 9.95 (978-0-9656985-4-2(8)) Noware Bks.

Gertie's Christmas Magic. 2000. 28p. pap. 6.00 (978-1-892225-04-7(2)) Winmark Communications.

Getzinger, Donna. Saving Christmas Spirit. Gilbert, Ernie, illus. 1999. 182p. (J). (gr. 3-7). pap. 12.95 (978-0-9668126-1-9(1)) Shadowbox Media.

Gibbs, D. Renee. The Special Little Christmas Tree. 2003. (J). bds. 14.95 (978-0-9741406-0-5(0)) Cranberry Quill Publishing Co.

Gifford, Myrna. When Santa Got Stuck in the Chimney. Cooper, Frances, illus. 2001. 16p. (J). 5.95 (978-0-9720763-0-2(1), PB1) Action Factor, Inc.

Gifford, Peggy Elizabeth. Moxy Maxwell Does Not Love Writing Thank-You Notes. Fisher, Valorie, illus. Fisher, Valorie, photos by. 2008. (J). (***978-0-375-84270-2(5)***); (***978-0-375-94552-6(0)***) Random Hse. Children's Bks. (Schwartz & Wade Bks.).

Gikow, Louise & Attinello, Lauren. Ho Ho Ho, Baby Fozzie. 1998. (Little Golden Bks.). 24p. (J). (ps-k). 2.29 (978-0-307-98817-1(0), Golden Bks.) Random Hse. Children's Bks.

Gilkey, Gail. Miriam's Holiday. Kittell, Kathy, illus. 1998. 32p. (J). (gr. k-5). pap. 5.95 (978-0-9662983-1-4(4)) Windy Hill Pr.

Gillmor, Don. The Christmas Orange. ed. 2004. (Illus.). (J). (gr. k-3). spiral bd. (978-0-616-03035-6(5)) Canadian National Institute for the Blind/Institut National Canadien pour les Aveugles.

—The Christmas Orange. Gay, Marie-Louise, illus. 1999. 15p. (J). (gr. k-4). 16.95 (978-0-7737-3100-4(8)) Stoddart Kids CAN. *Dist:* Fitzhenry & Whiteside, Ltd.

Gillmor, Don & Gay, Marie-Louise. The Christmas Orange. 2003. (Illus.). 32p. pap. (978-1-55005-075-2(3)) Fitzhenry & Whiteside, Ltd.

Ginolfi, Art. The Tiny Snowflake. 2005. 32p. (J). pap. 3.99 (978-1-4003-0684-8(1)) Nelson, Thomas Inc.

Godden, Rumer. Story of Holly & Ivy, the R/I. Cooney, Barbara, illus. 2006. 32p. (J). (gr. k). 17.99 (978-0-670-06219-5(7), Viking Juvenile) Penguin Group (USA) Inc.

Godwin, Laura. Happy Christmas, Honey. 2002. (ps-2). lib. bdg. 11.80 (978-0-613-57505-8(9)) Tandem Library Bks.

Godwin, Laura & Chapman, Jane. Happy Christmas, Honey! 2002. (Ready-to-Read Ser.). (Illus.). 32p. (J). 14.95 (978-0-689-84714-1(9), McElderry, Margaret K.); pap. 3.99 (978-0-689-84764-6(5), Aladdin) Simon & Schuster Children's Publishing.

Gold, Maya & Fitzhugh, Louise. Harriet the Spy, Double Agent. 2005. 160p. (J). (gr. 5 up). 15.95 (978-0-385-32787-9(0), Delacorte Bks. for Young Readers) Random Hse. Children's Bks.

Golden Books Staff. Christmas Book Bag. 2006. (Illus.). 32p. (J). (ps-2). pap. 4.99 (978-0-375-83710-4(8), Golden Bks.) Random Hse. Children's Bks.

—The Christmas Hero. 2007. 16p. (J). pap. 0.38 (***978-0-375-84432-4(5)***, Golden Bks.) Random Hse., Inc.

—Christmas Surprise! 2007. (Deluxe Coloring Book Ser.). (Illus.). 96p. (J). pap. 3.99 (***978-0-375-84101-9(6)***, Golden Bks.) Random Hse. Children's Bks.

—A Colorful Christmas! 2008. (Paint Box Book Ser.). (Illus.). 48p. (J). (ps-2). pap. 3.99 (***978-0-375-84291-7(8)***, Golden Bks.) Random Hse. Children's Bks.

—Holly Jolly Christmas. 2007. 16p. (J). (ps-1). pap. 0.38 (***978-0-375-84433-1(3)***, Golden Bks.) Random Hse., Inc.

—One Magical Night. 1999. (Rudolph Ser.). (Illus.). 16p. (J). (ps-3). pap. 2.99 (978-0-307-28311-5(9), Golden Bks.) Random Hse. Children's Bks.

—The Poky Little Puppy's First Christmas. 2002. (Illus.). 24p. (J). (gr. k-k). 2.99 (978-0-307-96034-4(X), Golden Bks.) Random Hse. Children's Bks.

—Rudolph, the Red-Nosed Reindeer. Karl, Linda, illus. 2004. (Pictureback(R) Ser.). 24p. (J). (gr. k-k). pap. 3.99 (978-0-375-82530-9(4), Golden Bks.) Random Hse. Children's Bks.

Golden Books Staff & Hill, Stuart. Wreck the Halls. 2001. 8p. (J). (ps-3). pap. 3.99 (978-0-307-25300-2(7), Golden Bks.) Random Hse. Children's Bks.

Goldstone, Bruce & Poortvliet, Rien. A Gnome's Christmas. 2004. (Illus.). 48p. 14.95 (978-0-8109-5017-7(0)) Abrams, Harry N., Inc.

Gomez, Rebecca. All I Want for Christmas: Lo Unico Que Quiero para Navidad. Collier-Morales, Roberta, illus. 2003. (ENG & SPA.). (J). (978-0-439-61643-0(3)) Scholastic, Inc.

Gonis, Theofania. An Icon for Christmas: Sophia's Gift: an Icon Christmas Story to Color. Desbarnais, Margo, illus. 2005. 30p. (J). (gr. k-3). pap. 7.95 (978-1-880971-94-9(1)) Light & Life Publishing Co.

Goodrich, Carter & Moore, Clement Clarke. A Creature Was Stirring. Goodrich, Carter, illus. 2006. (Illus.). 40p. (J). 16.95 (978-0-689-86399-8(3), Simon & Schuster Children's Publishing) Simon & Schuster Children's Publishing.

Gordon, Leslie. The Homeless Christmas Tree. Bailey, Court, illus. 2005. 48p. (J). 19.95 (978-1-933285-09-2(5)) Brown Bks. Publishing Group.

Gorgas, Paula Blais. The Perfect Purple Present. l.t. ed. 2007. (Illus.). 24p. (J). 24.99 (***978-0-9794660-4-5(0)***); per. 12.99 (***978-0-9794660-5-2(9)***) Dragonfly Publishing, Inc.

Gramercy Staff. The Tall Book of Christmas. 2006. (Illus.). 96p. (J). 9.99 (978-0-517-22885-2(8), Gramercy) Random Hse. Value Publishing.

Grant, Cindy M. Itty-Bitty Jesus Is Born Christmas Storybook. 2005. (J). pap. 1.29 (978-1-59317-117-9(X)) Warner Pr. Pubs.

Graves, Ann P. Color Me Santa. l.t. ed. 2002. (Illus.). 108p. per. 4.99 (978-0-9721653-0-3(4)) Stylewriter Pubns.

The Great Christmas Tree Adventure. 1998. 40p. (J). per. 14.99 (978-0-689-82607-8(9), Little Simon) Simon & Schuster Children's Publishing.

The Great Mix Up. 2005. (Illus.). 40p. (J). lib. bdg. 15.95 (978-0-9772282-0-1(7)) B. T. Brooks.

Green, Rod. Santa's Reindeer. Wright, Carol et al, illus. 2007. 32p. (J). (ps-5). 16.99 (***978-1-4169-5070-7(2)***, Atheneum) Simon & Schuster Children's Publishing.

Green, Sylvia. The Best Christmas Ever. 2001. 128p. (J). pap. 3.99 (978-0-439-34013-7(6)) Scholastic, Inc.

—The Soft-Hearted Sheepdog. Kavanagh, Peter, illus. 2003. 144p. (J). (978-0-439-62569-2(6)) Scholastic, Inc.

Greenberg, Martin H. & Waugh, Charles, eds. Christmas on the Prairie & Other Selections. l.t. ed. 2001. (Newbery Authors Collection: No. 8). 160p. (J). (gr. 4 up). lib. bdg. 23.33 (978-0-8368-2950-1(6)) Stevens, Gareth Inc.

Greenberg, Martin H. & Waugh, Charles G., eds. A Newbery Christmas: Fourteen Stories of Christmas by Newbery Award - Winning Authors. 2005. 191p. (J). (gr. 4-8). reprint ed. 20.00 (978-0-7567-8943-5(5)) DIANE Publishing Co.

Greenburg, Dan. Young Santa. Miller, Warren, illus. 2005. 96p. (J). (gr. 2-5). pap. 3.99 (978-0-439-61636-2(0)) Scholastic, Inc.

Greene, Rhonda. Santa's Stuck. Cole, Henry, illus. 2006. 32p. (J). (ps). pap. 5.99 (978-0-14-240686-1(4), Puffin) Penguin Group (USA) Inc.

Greene, Rhonda Gowler. Santa's Stuck. Cole, Henry, illus. 2004. 32p. (J). (ps). 16.99 (978-0-525-47292-6(4), Dutton Juvenile) Penguin Group (USA) Inc.

Greene, Stephanie. Christmas at Stony Creek. Sheban, Chris, illus. 2007. 96p. (J). (gr. 2-7). 14.99 (***978-0-06-121486-8(8)***); lib. bdg. 15.89 (***978-0-06-121487-5(6)***) HarperCollins Pubs. (Greenwillow Bks.).

Greenwood, Barbara. Pioneer Christmas: Celebrating in the Backwoods In 1841. 2003. (gr. 3-6). lib. bdg. 16.40 (978-0-613-87159-4(6)) Tandem Library Bks.

Gregory, Larry. A Christmas Surprise. Woolmer, Nancy, illus. 2004. 24p. pap. 14.95 (978-1-4137-3014-2(0)) PublishAmerica, Inc.

Greive, Bradley Trevor. Every Day Is Christmas. 2007. 120p. 9.95 (***978-0-7407-6860-6(3)***) Andrews McMeel Publishing.

Grey, Mini. Traction Man Is Here! 2005. (Illus.). 32p. (J). (ps-3). 15.95 (978-0-375-83191-1(6), Knopf Bks. for Young Readers) Random Hse. Children's Bks.

Grier, Gene & Everson, Lowell. Midnight Miracle: A Musical Christmas Story. 2004. (gr. 2-6). 12.00 incl. audio (978-0-687-01525-2(1)) Abingdon Pr.

Grim, Katie. Gingerbread Land. 2007. 12p. 19.95 (***978-1-58117-635-3(X)***, Intervisual/Piggy Toes) Dalmatian Pr.

Grinarml, Suzan. The Christmas Visitor: On the East Poultrey Farm. Grinarml, Suzan, illus. 1998. (Illus.). 20p. (J). (978-1-878398-15-4(6), Blue Note Bks.) Blue Note Pubns.

Grinch Plush with Book (English) 2000. (J). (978-1-58805-009-0(2)) DS-Max USA, Inc.

Grindley, Sally. Christmas Cheer: A Collection of Holiday Tales. 2008. (Illus.). 96p. (J). 17.95 (***978-1-59990-188-6(9)***, Bloomsbury Children) Bloomsbury Publishing.

Grindley, Sally. Home for Christmas. 2004. (Illus.). 32p. (J). 15.95 (978-1-84507-071-7(2)) Lincoln, Frances Ltd. GBR. *Dist:* Perseus Distribution.

Gutman, Anne. Cadeau de Noel. (FRE.). pap. 17.95 (978-2-01-224134-3(4)) Hachette Groupe Livre FRA. *Dist:* Distribooks, Inc.

—Gaspard & Lisa's Christmas Surprise. Hallensleben, Georg, illus. 2002. 32p. (J). (ps-3). 9.95 (978-0-375-82229-2(1), Knopf Bks. for Young Readers) Random Hse. Children's Bks.

Gwilym, Mari & Thomas, Dylan. Am Ddolig! 2005. (WEL., Illus.). 48p. pap. (978-0-86243-530-1(7)) Y Lolfa.

Hague, Michael. The Nutcracker. ed. 2005. (Illus.). 56p. (J). (ps-7). 7.95 (978-0-8118-5027-8(7)) Chronicle Bks. LLC.

Ioan, Elwyn. Ici'r Ddol A'r Cathod Nadolig. 2005. (WEL., Illus.). 36p. pap. (978-0-86243-361-1(4)) Y Lolfa.

Ipcar, Dahlov. My Wonderful Christmas Tree. 1999. 28p. (J). (ps-3). 9.95 (978-0-89272-475-8(7)) Down East Bks.

It's Time for Christmas. 2003. (J). per. (978-1-57657-807-0(0)); per. (978-1-57657-919-0(0)) Paradise Pr., Inc.

Jackson, Jill L. Fine Feathers Don't Make a Peacock. Kirby, Bertha, illus. 2000. (Lessons for Lucile Ser.). 79p. (J). 24.95 (978-0-9700692-0-7(0)) Noble Endeaver.

Jackson, Kathryn. The Animals' Merry Christmas. Scarry, Richard, illus. 2005. 72p. (J). (gr. k-k). 14.95 (978-0-375-83341-0(2)); lib. bdg. 16.99 (978-0-375-93341-7(7)) Random Hse. Children's Bks. (Golden Bks.).

James, Emma J. A Surprise for Santa. James, Emma J., illus. (Illus.). 32p. (Orig.). (J). (ps-3). pap. (978-1-885935-02-1(1)) Appalachian Log Publishing Co., The.

James, Nathaniel. Debbie Mumm's Mummford Adventures. Mumm, Debbie, illus. 2002. 32p. (gr. k-3). 14.95 (978-1-890621-33-9(1)) Landauer Corp.

James, Sabrina & Scognamiglio, John. Secret Santa. 2007. 368p. (J). (gr. 7 up). pap. 6.99 ***(978-0-439-02695-6(4))*** Scholastic, Inc.

Jane, Pamela. Noelle of the Nutcracker. Brett, Jan, illus. 2003. 64p. (J). (gr. 4-6). tchr. ed. 16.00 (978-0-395-39969-9(6)) Houghton Mifflin Co. Trade & Reference Div.

Janovitz, Marilyn. We Love Christmas! 32p. (J). 9.95 (978-1-59014-126-7(1)); (Illus.). pap. 3.50 (978-1-59014-125-0(3)) Night Sky Bks.

—We Love Christmas! 2007. (Illus.). 32p. (J). (ps). 8.95 (978-0-7358-2089-0(9)) North-South Bks., Inc.

Jareckie, Ellen. A House-Mouse Christmas: House-Mouse Tales. 4th ed. 2004. (Illus.). 22p. (J). (ps-k). bds. 6.99 (978-0-316-73806-4(9)) Little, Brown Bks. for Young Readers.

Jasin, Janie. The Littlest Christmas Tree: A Tale of Growing & Becoming. Kurtz, Pam, illus. 1998. 32p. (J). (ps-3). 19.95 incl. audio compact disk (978-0-916773-82-3(5)) Book Peddlers.

Jasper: A Christmas Caper. 2004. (Illus.). 85p. (J). 24.95 (978-1-928624-20-2(0)) Lucky 3 Ranch, Inc.

Jeffers, Susan. The Nutcracker. Jeffers, Susan, illus. 2007. 40p. (J). (ps-3). lib. bdg. 17.89 ***(978-0-06-074387-1(5));*** (Illus.). 16.99 ***(978-0-06-074386-4(7))*** HarperCollins Pubs.

Jeffs, Stephanie. Christmas Mouse. Thorne, Jenny, illus. 2005. 30p. pap. 11.95 (978-1-59325-054-6(1)) Word Among Us Pr.

—Christopher Bear's First Christmas. Thomas, Jacqui, illus. 2004. (Christopher Bear Ser.). 30p. 5.99 (978-0-8066-4349-6(8) , Augsburg Bks.) Augsburg Fortress, Pubs.

Jeffs, Stephanie, et al. Llygoden y Nadolig. 2005. (WEL., Illus.). 30p. (978-1-85994-497-4(3)) Cyhoeddiadau'r Gair.

Jewett, Sarah Orne. Betty Leicester's Christmas. 2004. reprint ed. pap. 15.95 (978-1-4191-0979-9(0)); pap. 1.99 (978-1-4192-0979-6(5)) Kessinger Publishing, LLC.

Jiménez, Francisco. The Christmas Gift. Cotts, Claire B., illus. 2000. Tr. of Regalo de Navidad. (SPA & ENG.). 32p. (J). (gr. k-3). tchr. ed. 16.00 (978-0-395-92869-1(9)) Houghton Mifflin Co. Trade & Reference Div.

Jocson, Antonio. Monster Christmas. 1998. (Muddy Tom's Wacky Adventure Ser.). (J). 14.95 (978-1-890963-05-7(4)) Liberty Bell Productions.

John, J. Cool Christmas. 2005. (Illus.). 24p. pap. 6.99 (978-1-873824-93-1(9) , Authentic Lifestyle) Authentic Media.

Johns, Barbara L. Christmas at the Candle Factory. Stich, Carolyn R., illus. 2006. 32p. (J). 16.95 (978-0-9762862-1-9(1)) Steeple Ridge Publications.

Johnson, Lisa Sferlazza. Christmas Eve: The Joy of Giving. Johnson, Tucker, illus. 2006. 32p. (J). 15.95 (978-0-9773096-2-7(2)) Positive Spin Pr.

Johnston, Joe. Snag & Me - Christmas Miracle in Blanchard Forks. Johnston, Joe, illus. 2004. (Illus.). (YA). per. 10.00 (978-1-932496-15-4(7)) Penman Publishing, Inc.

Jolin, Dominique. Merry Christmas, Washington! Perkes, Carolyn, tr. from FRE. 2000. (Illus.). 16p. (J). (ps-k). bds. (978-1-894363-63-1(9)) Dominique & Friends.

Jones, Elizabeth Orton. Big Susan. Jones, Elizabeth Orton, illus. anniv. ed. 2001. (Illus.). 88p. (J). (gr. 1-6). 18.95 (978-1-930900-06-6(6)) Purple Hse. Pr.

Jones, James Earl. The Christmas Miracle of Jonathan Toomey. 2000. (J). 24.99 incl. audio compact disk (978-0-8499-7682-7(0)) Nelson, Thomas Inc.

Jones, Monica. 25 Candy Canes for Jesus. 2007. (J). per. 10.99 ***(978-1-59886-859-3(4))*** Tate Publishing & Enterprises, L.L.C.

Jones, T. L. Santa Takes a Holiday! 2005. (Santa Chronicles Ser.: Bk. 1). (Illus.). 100p. (J). per. 12.00 (978-0-9707594-4-3(4) , 00001) Mercury/Hula Babe Productions.

Joy: Tells the Christmas Story with Fresh, New Narrative. on the Opposite Side, Caleb's Family Loses Their Home in a Holiday. 2000. (Lion Cub Upside-Down Bks.). (Illus.). 24p. (J). (ps-3). pap. 5.95 (978-0-87162-848-0(1)) Warner Pr. Pubs.

Joyce, Rita. Gozzy Goose's Christmas Gift. l.t. ed. 2002. (Illus.). 32p. (J). 7.95 (978-1-59094-015-0(6) , 0156) Jawbone Publishing Corp.

Joyce, William. Rolie Polie Olie Christmas Sticker Book! 2002. (Illus.). 10p. (YA). (ps up). pap. 6.99 (978-0-7868-4532-3(5)) Disney Pr.

—Santa Calls. 1998. (Illus.). 36p. (J). (ps-k). bds. 6.95 (978-0-694-01212-1(2) , Harper Festival) HarperCollins Pubs.

Joy's Christmas Dream. 2002. (Illus.). 24p. (J). (gr. k-4). pap. 2.99 (978-1-57759-850-3(4)) Dalmatian Pr.

Judd, Naomi. Gertie the Goldfish & the Christmas Surprise. Bancroft, Tom & Corley, Rob, illus. 2005. 32p. (J). (ps-3). 14.99 (978-1-4003-0780-7(5)) Nelson, Thomas Inc.

Jumbo Christmas Coloring & Activity Book. (Illus.). 300p. (J). mass mkt. (978-0-87449-054-1(5)) Unisystems, Inc.

Kalz, Jill. Boy Who Loved Trains. Erkocak, Sahin, illus. 2007. (Read-It! Readers Ser.). (J). 19.93 (978-1-4048-2401-0(4)) Picture Window Bks.

Kantor, Pamela & Radko, Christopher. Stardust Santa Arrives. Wright, Jane C., illus. 1998. 26p. (J). (gr. 2 up). pap. 5.99 (978-0-9647556-1-1(0)) Starad, Inc.

Karpinski, David. Sarah's Christmas Presence. 2006. 58p. pap. 8.95 (978-0-7414-3411-1(3)) Infinity Publishing.

Kasen, Marty, ed. The Christmas That Almost Wasn't. 1998. (Illus.). 24p. (J). (gr. 1-3). 3.98 (978-1-890095-09-3(5)) Nesak International.

—The Reindeer Who Didn't Like Christmas. 1998. (Illus.). 24p. (J). (gr. 1-3). 3.98 (978-1-890095-08-6(7)) Nesak International.

Kaserman, James & Kaserman, Sarah Jane. How the Pirates Saved Christmas. ed. 2005. (Illus.). 64p. (J). per. 5.99 (978-0-9674081-2-5(1) , (239)939-4845) Pirate Publishing International.

Kastner, Jill. Merry Christmas, Princess Dinosaur! 2002. (Illus.). 32p. (J). 17.89 (978-0-06-000472-9(X)) HarperCollins Pubs.

Katschke, Judy. Case of the Candy Cane Clue. 2002. (gr. 3-6). lib. bdg. 12.40 (978-0-613-64697-0(5)) Tandem Library Bks.

Katz, Karen. Counting Christmas. Katz, Karen, illus. (Classic Board Bks.). (Illus.). (J). (ps-1). 2007. 30p. bds. 7.99 ***(978-1-4169-3624-4(6)*** , Little Simon); 2003. 32p. 14.95 (978-0-689-84925-1(7) , McElderry, Margaret K.) Simon & Schuster Children's Publishing.

Kaye, Bernard. A Coconut for Christmas. 2006. 52p. per. 9.95 (978-1-59886-146-4(8)) Tate Publishing & Enterprises, L.L.C.

Keats, Ezra Jack. The Little Drummer Boy. 2002. (Illus.). (J). 14.04 (978-0-7587-5341-0(1)) Book Wholesalers, Inc.

—The Little Drummer Boy. Keats, Ezra Jack, illus. 2000. (Illus.). 32p. (J). (ps-3). pap. 6.99 (978-0-14-056743-4(7) , Puffin) Penguin Group (USA) Inc.

—The Little Drummer Boy. 2000. (J). (978-0-606-19070-1(8)) Tandem Library Bks.

Kellogg, Steven. The Christmas Witch. Kellogg, Steven, illus. 2002. (Illus.). (J). 25.45 (978-0-7587-2238-6(9)) Book Wholesalers, Inc.

Kelly, Becky. The Night Before Christmas. 2007. 32p. 14.95 ***(978-0-7407-6064-8(5))*** Andrews McMeel Publishing.

Kelman, Marcy. Disney's Little Einsteins: Christmas Wish. rev. ed. 2007. 24p. (J). (ps-1). pap. 4.99 ***(978-1-4231-0210-6(X))*** Disney Pr.

Kenney, Cindy. The Stable That Bob Built. 2004. (Big Idea Books). (Illus.). 32p. 9.99 (978-0-310-70472-0(3)) Zonderkidz.

—The Star of Christmas: A Very Veggie Christmas Story. Bredow, Dennis, illus. 2002. 40p. (gr. k-3). 14.99 (978-0-310-70504-8(5)) Zonderkidz.

Kerr, Judith. Mog's Christmas. Kerr, Judith, illus. 2005. (Illus.). 32p. (J). (ps-3). pap. 9.99 (978-0-00-717135-4(8)) HarperCollins Pubs. Ltd. GBR. *Dist:* Trafalgar Square Publishing.

—Mog's Christmas. (Illus.). 2004. 28p. 7.95 (978-0-00-716705-0(9)); 2005. 32p. 14.00 (978-0-00-719366-0(1)) HarperCollins Pubs. Ltd. GBR. *Dist:* Trafalgar Square Publishing, Independent Pubs. Group.

—Mog's Christmas. l.t. ed. 2001. (Illus.). 32p. (J). (ps-2). 8.99 (978-0-00-664146-9(6)) Headline Bk. Publishing GBR. *Dist:* Trafalgar Square Publishing.

Ketteman, Helen. The Christmas Blizzard. 1999. (J). (978-0-606-17293-6(9)) Tandem Library Bks.

Ketteman, Helen & Warhola, James. Christmas Blizzard. 1999. (Illus.). 32p. (ps-3). pap. 5.99 (978-0-590-13609-9(7)) Scholastic, Inc.

Kimmel, Elizabeth Cody. My Penguin Osbert. Lewis, H. B., illus. 2004. 40p. (J). (ps-3). 16.99 (978-0-7636-1699-1(0)) Candlewick Pr.

King, Dave, photos by. My Christmas Scratch & Sniff Book. 2004. (First Holiday Bks.). (Illus.). 12p. (J). (gr. k-3). bds. 7.95 (978-0-7534-5731-3(8) , Kingfisher) Houghton Mifflin Co. Trade & Reference Div.

King, Emily. Clopper the Christmas Donkey. Olson, Ed, illus. 2004. 32p. 12.99 (978-0-8254-3069-5(0)) Kregel Pubns.

King, Susan. Amy & the Christmas Party/Amy & the New Year's Goals. King, Susan, illus. 2001. (Illus.). 75p. (J). (ps-6). 7.00 (978-0-9714446-1-4(7)) King RIT - ACKS Pubs.

Kingsbury, Karen. We Believe in Christmas. 2008. (J). (978-0-310-71212-1(2)) Zonderkidz.

Kinkade, Thomas, illus. Away in a Manger Board Book. 2007. 28p. (J). bds. 6.99 ***(978-0-06-078735-6(X)*** , Harper Festival) HarperCollins Pubs.

Kinsey-Warnock, Natalie. A Christmas Like Helen's. Azarian, Mary, illus. 2004. 32p. (J). (gr. k-3). tchr. ed. 16.00 (978-0-618-23137-9(4)) Houghton Mifflin Co. Trade & Reference Div.

Kirk, David. Little Miss Spider's Christmas Wish: A Christmas Wish. Kirk, David, illus. 2001. (Miss Spider Ser.). (Illus.). 32p. (J). (ps-2). pap. 12.95 (978-0-439-31463-3(1) , Levine, Arthur A. Bks.) Scholastic, Inc.

—Nova's Christmas Creation. 2006. (Nova the Robot Ser.). 32p. (J). 12.99 (978-0-448-43994-5(8)) Penguin Group (USA) Inc.

Kirkpatrick, June. The Little Church Mouse of the Loretto Chapel. Brokaw, Michele, illus. 2nd ed. 2000. 40p. (J). (gr. k-3). reprint ed. pap. 10.95 (978-0-9708940-5-2(8)) Gently Worded Bks., LLC.

Kirkpatrick, June & Brokaw, Michele. The Little Church Mouse of the Loretto Chapel. l.t. ed. 2000. (Illus.). 40p. (J). (gr. k-5). 16.50 (978-1-929115-02-0(4)) Azro Pr., Inc.

Kleinberg, Naomi. Have Yourself a Furry Little Christmas. Womble, Louis, illus. 2007. 12p. (J). (gr. k-ps). bds. 4.99 ***(978-0-375-84133-0(4)*** , Random Hse. Bks. for Young Readers) Random Hse. Children's Bks.

Kline, Suzy. Horrible Harry & the Christmas Surprise. 1998. (Horrible Harry Ser.: No. 5). (Illus.). 64p. (J). (gr. 2-4). pap. 3.99 (978-0-14-130145-7(7) , Puffin) Penguin Group (USA) Inc.

Klise, Kate. Shall I Knit You A Hat? A Christmas Yarn. Klise, M. Sarah, illus. 2007. 32p. (J). pap. 6.99 ***(978-0-312-37139-5(X))*** Square Fish.

Kneen, Maggie. The Christmas Surprise. Kneen, Maggie, illus. 2006. (Illus.). 18p. (J). (gr. k-4). reprint ed. 16.00 (978-0-7567-9837-6(X)) DIANE Publishing Co.

Knight, Hilary. The Night Before Christmas. 2004. (J). 14.99 (978-0-06-000994-6(2)); 15.89 (978-0-06-000995-3(0)) HarperCollins Pubs.

Knights, Harry B. Angel's Star. 2006. (J). lib. bdg. 20.00 (978-0-9632248-8-0(3)) Synergetic Pubns., Inc.

—The Boy with a Wish. (Nicholas Stories). (Illus.). 48p. (J). 16.95 (978-1-58980-059-5(1)) Pelican Publishing Co., Inc.

—The First Flight of Saint Nicholas. (Nicholas Stories). (Illus.). 48p. (J). 16.95 (978-1-58980-060-1(5)) Pelican Publishing Co., Inc.

—Luigi & The Lost Wish. 2003. (Nicholas Stories : No. 4). (Illus.). 56p. (J). pap. 16.95 (978-1-58980-162-2(8)) Pelican Publishing Co., Inc.

—The Maiden Voyage of Kris Kringle. 2003. (Nicholas Stories : No. 3). (Illus.). 56p. (J). pap. 16.95 (978-1-58980-161-5(X)) Pelican Publishing Co., Inc.

Knott, Joan. Merry Christmas, Marushka! Frohliche Weihnachten, Marie! Knott, Marie, ed. 2006. (J). 7.95 (978-0-9779895-1-5(8)) Knott, Joan.

Knudsen, Michelle & Novak, Matt. Christmas Is Coming. 2004. (Illus.). 14p. 12.95 (978-0-689-85062-2(X) , Little Simon) Simon & Schuster Children's Publishing.

Koller, Jackie French. The Promise. Rogers, Jacqueline, illus. 2001. 80p. (J). (gr. 5-8). 4.99 (978-0-440-41658-6(2) , Yearling) Random Hse. Children's Bks.

—The Promise. 2001. (J). (978-0-606-22036-1(4)); lib. bdg. 13.00 (978-0-613-37034-9(1)) Tandem Library Bks.

Koontz, Dean. Robot Santa: The Further Adventures of Santa's Twin. Parks, Phil, illus. 2004. 72p. (J). 20.89 (978-0-06-050944-6(9)) HarperCollins Pubs.

—Santa's Twin. Parks, Phil, illus. 2004. 64p. pap. 12.95 (978-0-06-057223-5(X)) HarperCollins Pubs.

Korman, Justine. Merry Christmas, Grumpy Bunny. 1999. (gr. k-3). lib. bdg. 11.25 (978-0-613-30602-7(3)) Tandem Library Bks.

Korman, Justine & Grey, Andrew. Tonka the Best Christmas Tree Ever. 1998. (Tonka Ser.). (Illus.). 16p. (J). (ps-2). pap. 9.95 (978-0-590-03283-4(6) , Cartwheel Bks.) Scholastic, Inc.

Kovalski, Maryann. Jingle Bells. Kovalski, Maryann, illus. 1999. (First Flight Ser.). (Illus.). 39p. (J). (978-1-55041-393-9(7)); pap. (978-1-55041-383-0(X)) Fitzhenry & Whiteside, Ltd.

Krenina, Katya, illus. The Spider's Gift: A Ukrainian Christmas Story. 2005. (J). (978-0-8234-1743-8(3)) Holiday Hse., Inc.

Krensky, Stephen. How Santa Lost His Job. Schindler, S. D., illus. 2005. 29p. (J). (gr. k-4). reprint ed. 15.00 (978-0-7567-9405-7(6)) DIANE Publishing Co.

—How Santa Lost His Job. Schindler, S. D., illus. 2004. 32p. (J). pap. 6.99 (978-0-689-87147-4(3) , Aladdin) Simon & Schuster Children's Publishing.

Krenzer, Rolf. The Christmas Bell. Dusikova, Maja, illus. 2003. 32p. (J). 15.95 (978-1-57768-410-7(9) , Gingham Dog Pr.) School Specialty Publishing.

Kroll, Steven. Pooch on the Loose: A Christmas Adventure. Garland, Michael, illus. 2005. 32p. (J). (ps-3). per. 14.95 (978-0-7614-5239-3(7)) Cavendish, Marshall Corp.

Kroll, Virginia. Marta & the Manger Straw: A Christmas Tradition from Poland. Belton, Robyn, illus. 2005. (Traditions of Faith from Around the World Ser.). 40p. (J). (ps-3). 15.99 (978-0-310-70994-7(6)) Zonderkidz.

—Uno, Dos, Tres, Posada! Let's Celebrate Christmas. Lopez, Loretta, illus. 2006. 32p. (J). (ps). 15.99 (978-0-670-05932-4(3) , Viking Adult) Penguin Group (USA) Inc.

Krueger, Diane. Blessly's Carrotnog Christmas Book & Coloring Book. Krueger, Diane & Westenbroek, Ken, illus. 2004. 14.99 (978-0-9763695-1-6(6)) Hope Harvest Publishing.

Krykorka, Ian & Krykorka, Vladyana. Carl, the Christmas Carp. 2006. (Illus.). 32p. (J). 17.95 (978-1-55143-329-5(X)) Orca Bk. Pubs. USA.

Kunhardt Davis, Edith. Pat the Christmas Bunny. 2001. (Touch & Feel Bks.). (Illus.). 8p. (J). (gr. k-ps). bds. 9.99 (978-0-307-12160-8(7) , Golden Bks.) Random Hse. Children's Bks.

Kunhardt, Edith. Pat the Christmas Bunny Gift Set, Set. gif. ed. 2005. (Illus.). 18p. (J). (gr. k-ps). 12.95 (978-0-375-83405-9(2) , Golden Bks.) Random Hse. Children's Bks.

Kvasnosky, Laura McGee. Zelda & Ivy One Christmas. 2001. (J). (gr. k-3). incl. audio Spoken Arts, Inc.

—Zelda & Ivy: One Christmas. Kvasnosky, Laura McGee, illus. 2006. 40p. (J). (gr. 1-4). pap. 4.99 (978-0-7636-3047-8(0)) Candlewick Pr.

—Zelda & Ivy One Christmas: A Story about the Fabulous Fox Sisters. Kvasnosky, Laura McGee, illus. 2002. (Illus.). 48p. (J). (gr. k-4). pap. 6.99 (978-0-7636-1344-0(4)) Candlewick Pr.

Lagerlof, Selma. The Holy Night. Wikland, Ilon, illus. 2004. 40p. (J). 17.00 (978-0-86315-467-6(0)) Floris Bks. GBR. *Dist:* SteinerBooks, Inc.

LaMaster, Melissa. Appaloosa Tales with a Christmas Spirit. 2006. 48p. pap. 12.95 (978-1-4241-3153-2(7)) PublishAmerica, Inc.

Lamut, Sonja. Christmas Rhyme Time. 2000. (My Turn Bks.). (Illus.). 12p. (J). (ps). 4.99 (978-0-448-42026-4(0) , Grosset & Dunlap) Penguin Group (USA) Inc.

Landa, Norbert. The Little Bear's Christmas. Scharff-Kniemeyer, Marlis, illus. 1999. 32p. (J). (ps-3). 14.95 (978-1-888444-60-5(6)) Little Tiger Pr.

Landolf, Diane Wright. Santa Claus Is Coming to Town. Baker, Darrell, illus. 2004. 24p. (J). (gr. k-k). pap. 3.99 (978-0-375-82932-1(6) , Golden Bks.) Random Hse. Children's Bks.

Lane, Queen, illus. & creator. It's Christmas Time (Babytown Storybook) Lane, Queen, creator. 2005. (BABY-TOWN Ser.: Bk. 4). 36p. (J). spiral bd. 15.00 (978-0-9772738-1-2(4)) Quebla.

Langen, Annette. Felix's Christmas Around the World. Droop, Constanza, illus. 2003. 40p. (J). 14.99 (978-1-59384-036-5(5)) Parklane Publishing.

Langley, Karen. Shine! Langley, Jonathan, illus. 2002. 32p. (J). (gr. k-3). 15.95 (978-0-7614-5127-3(7)) Cavendish, Marshall Corp.

Lankford, Mary D. Christmas USA. Dugan, Karen, illus. 2006. 48p. (J). 15.99 (978-0-688-15012-9(8) , Collins) HarperCollins Pubs.

Larousse Staff, ed. Una Navidad Inolvidable. 2003. (SPA., Illus.). 112p. (J). (gr. k-3). tchr. ed. 11.95 (978-970-22-0421-3(6)) Larousse, Ediciones, S. A. de C. V. MEX. *Dist:* Houghton Mifflin Co. Trade & Reference Div.

Lawless, Mary Ann. The Proud Christmas Tree. McCool, Arlene, illus. 2006. (J). 12.95 ***(978-0-9772795-0-0(2))*** Tuesday's Child.

Lawrence, Michael. Baby Christmas. Robins, Arthur, illus. 2006. 32p. (J). 14.99 (978-0-7641-5998-5(4)) Barron's Educational Series, Inc.

Lawson, Polly, tr. from GER. A Child Is Born: A Christmas Story. Capek, Jindra, illus. 2001. 30p. (J). (gr. k-3). 16.95 (978-0-86315-332-7(1)) Floris Bks. GBR. *Dist:* SteinerBooks, Inc.

Lazaro, Georgina. Ya Llegan los Reyes Magos! Fuenmayor, Morella, illus. 2001. (SPA.). 40p. (J). (gr. 1-3). ring bd. 14.95 (978-1-930332-05-8(X)) Lectorum Pubns., Inc.

Lee, Kate. Santa's Suit. Eaves, Edward, illus. 2004. 6p. (J). (gr. k-ps). bds. 10.95 (978-0-439-61499-3(6) , Cartwheel Bks.) Scholastic, Inc.

Lee, Quinlan B. Christmas Angel. 2006. (Clifford's Puppy Days Ser.). (Illus.). 24p. (J). pap. 3.99 (978-0-439-75533-7(6)) Scholastic, Inc.

—Christmas in Care-a-Lot. Johnson, Jay, illus. 2004. (Care Bears Ser.). 16p. (J). (ps-3). pap. 5.99 (978-0-439-66409-7(8)) Scholastic, Inc.

Lee, Stan. Superhero Christmas. Jessell, Tim, illus. 2004. 32p. (J). (ps-2). 16.89 (978-0-06-056560-2(8)) HarperCollins Pubs.

Leeds, Robert X. Christmas Tails. Stetz, Ken, illus. rev. ed. 2005. 56p. 16.95 (978-0-9674025-7-4(3)) EPIC Publishing Co.

Leeson, Christine. The Magic of Christmas. Hansen, Gaby, illus. 2001. 32p. (J). tchr. ed. 14.95 (978-1-58925-011-6(7) , tiger tales) ME Media LLC.

Leeson, Christine. Snow Angel. Chapman, Jane, illus. 2007. 32p. (J). (ps-2). 15.95 ***(978-1-58925-068-0(0)*** , tiger tales) ME Media LLC.

Leigh, Susan K. The Town That Forgot about Christmas. Gordon, David, illus. 2006. (ENG.). 32p. (J). 14.99 (978-0-7586-1107-9(2)) Concordia Publishing Hse.

Leighton, Maxinne R. An Ellis Island Christmas. Nolan, Dennis, illus. 2005. 32p. (J). (gr. k-3). pap. 6.99 (978-0-14-240506-2(X) , Puffin) Penguin Group (USA) Inc.

Leitich Smith, Cynthia & Leitich Smith, Greg. Santa Knows. Bjorkman, Steve, illus. 2006. 32p. (J). (ps). 16.99 (978-0-525-47757-0(8) , Dutton Juvenile) Penguin Group (USA) Inc.

Leppard, Lois Gladys. Mandie & Joe's Christmas Surprise. 2000. (Mandie Bks.). (Illus.). 128p. (J). (gr. 3-9). pap. 4.99 (978-0-7642-2414-0(X)) Bethany Hse. Pubs.

LeSourd, Nancy & Farnsworth, Bill. Christy- Christmastime at Cutter Gap. Farnsworth, Bill, illus. 2003. (Illus.). (J). (gr. k-3). 15.99 (978-0-310-70571-0(1)) Zonderkidz.

Letter to Santa. 2003. (Traditional Christmas Stories Ser.). 32p. (J). 4.98 (978-0-7525-8845-2(1)) Parragon, Inc.

Levack, Joseph, photos by. Picture Me Christmas Cutie. 2001. (Picture Me Ser.). (Illus.). 10p. (J). (ps up). bds. 4.99 (978-1-57151-594-0(1)) Playhouse Publishing.

—Picture Me under the Christmas Tree. 1998. (Illus.). 10p. (J). (ps up). bds. 4.99 (978-1-57151-547-6(X)) Playhouse Publishing.

Lewandowski, Frrich & Riccards, Michael P. It's Christmas Again! 2000. (Illus.). 32p. (J). (gr. 2-3). 13.95 (978-1-929039-04-3(2)) Ambassador Bks., Inc.

Lewis, Anne M. Has Anyone Seen Christmas? Popko, Wendy, illus. 2005. 40p. (J). (ps-3). 18.95 (978-0-9749145-7-2(6)) Mackinac Island Pr., Inc.

Lewis, Beverly. Annika's Secret Wish. Querin, Pamela, illus. 2004. 32p. (J). 16.99 (978-0-7642-2940-4(0)) Bethany Hse. Pubs.

—California Crazy. 2002. (Holly's Heart Ser.: Bk. 5). 160p. (YA). pap. 6.99 (978-0-7642-2504-8(9)) Bethany Hse. Pubs.

Lewis, Beverly & Querin, Pamela. Annika's Secret Wish. 2006. (Illus.). 32p. (J). (gr. k-4). reprint ed. 15.00 (978-0-7567-9876-5(0)) DIANE Publishing Co.

Lewis, Regina N. The Smallest Toy Store, A Christmas Story. Moore, Phyllis M., illus. 2004. 44p. (J). per. 12.95 (978-0-9672585-8-4(8)) CyPress Pubns.

Lewman, David. A Rugrats Night Before Christmas. Cuan, Sergio, illus. 1999. (Rugrats Ser.). 25p. (J). (ps-2). per. 9.99 (978-0-671-03756-7(0) , Simon & Schuster Children's Publishing) Simon & Schuster Children's Publishing.

—A Very Krusty Christmas. Dress, Robert, illus. 2006. (SpongeBob SquarePants Ser.). 24p. (J). pap. 3.99 (978-1-4169-1759-5(4) , Simon Spotlight/Nickelodeon) Simon & Schuster Children's Publishing.

Lin, Grace. Christmas Carols: Let's All Sing!, 3 vols. Lin, Grace, illus. 2nd ed. 2005. (Illus.). 10p. (J). (ps-k). bds. 12.99 (978-0-316-93988-1(9)) Little Brown & Co.

Linko, G. J. Ben's Big Break. 2004. (Seekers Ser.: No. 4). 108p. 5.99 (978-0-8066-4185-0(1) , Augsburg Bks.) Augsburg Fortress, Pubs.

Liput, Andrew L. Evie the Evergreen's Christmas Adventure. 2002. 31p. (J). pap. 9.95 (978-0-7414-1034-4(6)) Infinity Publishing.

The Little Fir Tree. 2003. (Traditional Christmas Stories Ser.). 32p. (J). 4.98 (978-0-7525-8846-9(X)) Parragon, Inc.

Little Fish Christmas Merchandiser. (J). 128.16 (978-0-8307-2909-8(7) , Gospel Light) Gospel Light Pubns.

Little, Jean. Pippin the Christmas Pig. Zimmermann, H. Werner, illus. 2004. 40p. (J). (ps-3). 16.95 (978-0-439-65062-5(3) , Scholastic Pr.) Scholastic, Inc.

Little Miss Muffet: 6 Small Books. (gr. k-2). 23.00 (978-0-7635-8503-7(3)) Rigby Education.

Little Twinkle Toes. 2001. 65p. (J). 14.95 (978-0-9709119-8-8(2)) Limpid Butterfly Productions, The.

The Littlest Angel. 2002. (Illus.). 24p. (J). (gr. k-3). 6.95 (978-0-8249-4224-3(8)) Ideals Pubns.

The Littlest Christmas Tree. 2005. 45.00 (978-0-916773-85-4(X)) Book Peddlers.

Llorente, Pilar Molina. Navidad, el Regreso de Eugenia Mestres. 2000. Tr. of Christmas, the Return of Eugenia Mestre. (SPA.). (gr. 5-8). lib. bdg. 17.60 (978-0-613-83097-3(0)) Tandem Library Bks.

Lloyd, Paul R. Uh-Oh, Mommy Has the Flu. Zuk-Lloyd, Lynn, illus. l.t. ed. 2002. (J). cd-rom 16.95 (978-0-9723773-1-7(X)) PromiseGarden.com.

Lomurno, Inez Regina. Love at Christmas I, II, & III. 2006. 9.00 (978-0-8059-8822-2(X)) Dorrance Publishing Co., Inc.

London, Jonathan. Froggy's Best Christmas. Remkiewicz, Frank, illus. 32p. (J). 2002. pap. 5.99 (978-0-14-056735-9(6) , Puffin); 2000. 15.99 (978-0-670-89220-4(3) , Viking Juvenile) Penguin Group (USA) Inc.

—Froggy's Best Christmas. 2002. (gr. k-3). lib. bdg. 14.15 (978-0-613-83557-2(3)) Tandem Library Bks.

Long, Jamey. A Possum's Christmas Tale. 2007. 28p. (J). per. 12.99 (***978-1-59886-826-5(8)***) Tate Publishing & Enterprises, L.L.C.

Lorbiecki, Marybeth. Sister Anne's Hands. Popp, Wendy, illus. 2000. 32p. (J). (ps-3). pap. 6.99 (978-0-14-056534-8(5) , Puffin) Penguin Group (USA) Inc.

—Sister Anne's Hands. 2000. (J). (978-0-606-20253-4(6)); lib. bdg. 15.30 (978-0-613-33728-1(X)) Tandem Library Bks.

Loter, Darlene. Santa's Promise. 2004. 25p. pap. 9.95 (978-1-4137-1238-4(X)) PublishAmerica, Inc.

Love, Maryann Cusimano. You Are My Miracle. Ichikawa, Satomi, illus. 2005. 32p. (J). (ps-1). 15.99 (978-0-399-24037-9(3) , Philomel) Penguin Group (USA) Inc.

Loyd, Mark. Big Ben: A Little Known Story. Loyd, Mark, illus. ed. 2005. (J). (978-0-9773317-1-0(7)) Too Fun Publshing.

Lucado, Max. Alabaster's Song. Garland, Michael, illus. 2005. 20p. (J). (ps-3). bds., bds. 15.99 (978-1-4003-0697-8(3)) Nelson, Thomas Inc.

—Alabaster's Song: Christmas Through the Eyes of an Angel. 2004. (Max Lucado Ser.). 32p. 19.99 incl. DVD (978-1-4003-0180-5(7)) Nelson, Thomas Inc.

—The Crippled Lamb. Bonham, Liz, illus. 1999. (Max Lucado Ser.). 16p. (J). (ps-2). bds. 6.99 (978-0-8499-7502-8(6)) Nelson, Thomas Inc.

—Jacob's Gift. Hunt, Robert, illus. 2005. 20p. (J). (ps-2). bds., bds. 15.99 (978-1-4003-0696-1(5)) Nelson, Thomas Inc.

—The Twelve Bugs of Christmas. 2004. 20p. (J). bds. 9.99 (978-1-4003-0492-9(X)); (Illus.). bds. 6.99 (978-1-4003-0493-6(8)) Nelson, Thomas Inc.

Lukas, Catherine. Jingle Bell Christmas. 2007. (Backyardigans Ser.). (Illus.). 14p. (J). (ps-k). bds. 6.99 (***978-1-4169-3817-0(6)*** , Simon Spotlight/Nickelodeon) Simon & Schuster Children's Publishing.

Luke, Deanna. Chris Mouse & the Christmas House. Woytek, Joann A., illus. 2001. 40p. (J). (gr. 2-4). 14.95 (978-1-928777-04-5(X) , BOW Bks.) Blessing Our World, Inc.

—Chris Mouse & the Christmas House Audio Story Book. 2001. (J). cd-rom 5.95 (978-1-928777-35-9(X) , BOW Bks.) Blessing Our World, Inc.

Luton, Mildred. Christmas Time in the Mountains. Peattie, Gary, illus. 2003. 44p. (Orig.). (gr. 1-6). pap. 6.95 (978-0-87516-434-2(X)) DeVorss & Co.

Lutz, Nancie Anne. Patsy & Freckles Make Christmas Cookies. Lutz, Nancie Anne, illus. 2005. (Illus.). 25p. (J). (978-0-9760064-1-1(3)) Dollworks.

Maccabe, Catherine. Teddy Bear, Piglet, Kitten & Me. Scruton, Clive, illus. 2004. 28p. 11.99 (978-0-8066-4148-5(7) , Augsburg Bks.) Augsburg Fortress, Pubs.

MacDonald, Marion. Christmas Ice Mystery/San Juan Secret. 2002. (Twin Spins Ser.: 7). 200p. (YA). pap. 10.95 (978-0-7599-1006-5(5)) Hard Shell Word Factory.

MacGregor, Doug. The Incredible Tongue Twister That Swallowed My Sister: Another Santa Story by Doug MacGregor. MacGregor, Doug, illus. ltd. ed. 2006. (J). per. (978-0-9654843-5-0(1)) MacGregor, Doug.

MacKall, Dandi Daley. Gift Horse. 2003. (gr. 3-6). lib. bdg. 14.15 (978-0-613-76879-5(5)) Tandem Library Bks.

Mackall, Dandi Daley. The Legend of Saint Nicholas: A Story of Christmas Giving. Porfirio, Guy, illus. 2007. 32p. (J). (978-0-310-71327-2(7)) Zonderkidz.

—The Legend of the Christmas Cookie: An Inspirational Story of Sharing. Chabrian, Deborah L., illus. 2008. (J). (***978-0-310-71328-9(5)***) Zonderkidz.

—The Light of Christmas. Walker, John, illus. 2007. 32p. (J). (ps-3). 14.99 (***978-0-7586-1270-0(2)***) Concordia Publishing Hse.

—Merry Creature Christmas. 2006. 24p. (J). bds. 9.99 (978-1-4003-0823-1(2)) Nelson, Thomas Inc.

—My Christmas Gift to Jesus. O'Neill, Rachael, illus. 2005. (Carry Me Along Ser.). 24p. (J). (ps). 6.99 (978-0-310-70938-1(5)) Zonderkidz.

—Three Wise Women of Christmas. Magnuson, Diana, illus. 2006. (ENG.). 32p. (J). 14.99 (978-0-7586-1108-6(0)) Concordia Publishing Hse.

MacLennan, David. Santa's Stormy Christmas Eve. Parkinson, Cheryl, tr. Parkinson, Cheryl, illus. 2004. 32p. 7.95 (978-0-9731960-0-9(9)) Full Satchel Pr. CAN. *Dist:* Wilson & Assocs.

Madden, Gloria. Grandmother's Christmas Stories. 2003. (J). per. 12.50 (978-1-59453-017-3(3) , 1594) Airleaf Publishing & Bookselling.

Maggie's Christmas Wish. l.t. ed. 2004. (Illus.). 69p. (J). per. 15.00 (978-0-9764406-0-4(1)) James, JoAnn.

Maguire, Gregory. Five Alien Elves. Clayton, Elaine, illus. 1998. 176p. (J). (gr. 4-6). tchr. ed. 15.00 (978-0-395-83894-5(0) , Clarion Bks.) Houghton Mifflin Co. Trade & Reference Div.

—Five Alien Elves. Clayton, Elaine, illus. 2000. (J). 12.64 (978-0-606-19970-4(5)) Tandem Library Bks.

Maiden, Cecil. The Molliwumps. Price, Christine, illus. 2004. 160p. 12.95 (978-0-9714612-9-1(5)) Green Mansion Pr. LLC.

Major, Kevin. Aunt Olga's Christmas Postcards. Roberts, Bruce, illus. 2005. 40p. (J). 16.95 (978-0-88899-593-3(8)) Groundwood Bks. CAN. *Dist:* Perseus Distribution.

—The House of Wooden Santas. George, Imelda, illus. Pratt, Ned, photos by. 2004. 96p. (J). 24.95 (978-0-88995-166-2(7)) Red Deer Pr. CAN. *Dist:* Fitzhenry & Whiteside, Ltd.

—The House of Wooden Santas. Pratt, Ned, photos by. gif. ed. 2004. (Illus.). 96p. (J). 34.95 (978-0-88995-249-2(3)) Red Deer Pr. CAN. *Dist:* Fitzhenry & Whiteside, Ltd.

Malinow, Wendy Wallin, illus. The Nutcracker. 1998. (BookNotes Ser.). 56p. 14.99 incl. audio compact disk (978-0-88088-406-8(1)) Peter Pauper Pr. Inc.

Malkowski, Paul James. How Penguins Celebrate Christmas. 2007. 20p. pap. 7.95 (***978-0-533-15661-0(0)***) Vantage Pr., Inc.

Mammola-Koravos, Beth. Olivia's Magical Christmas. 2006. (J). pap. 16.95 (***978-1-59526-631-6(3)***) Media Creations, Inc.

Man-Kong, Mary. Rudolph's Bag of Toys. 2006. (Illus.). 10p. (J). (gr. k-ps). bds. 3.99 (978-0-375-84023-4(0) , Golden Bks.) Random Hse. Children's Bks.

Marlow, Herb. Matt's Best Christmas Ever. Head, Pat, illus. l.t. ed. 2000. 44p. (J). (gr. k-7). lib. bdg. 21.95 (978-1-893595-05-7(6) , Matt-1) Four Seasons Bks., Inc.

—Matt's Best Christmas Ever Coloring Book. l.t. ed. 2002. (Illus.). 18p. spiral bd. 5.00 (978-1-893595-27-9(7)) Four Seasons Bks., Inc.

Marr, Andrew. Born in the Darkest Time of Year: Stories for the Season of the Christ Child. 2004. 180p. (J). pap. 13.95 (978-0-595-32633-4(1)) iUniverse, Inc.

Marsden, Carolyn. Mama Had to Work on Christmas. Casilla, Robert, illus. 2003. 80p. (J). (gr. 2-5). 14.99 (978-0-670-03635-6(8) , Viking Juvenile) Penguin Group (USA) Inc.

Marsh, Carole. The Legend of the Candy Cane. 2003. 12p. (J). (gr. k-4). pap. 2.95 (978-0-635-02124-3(2)) Gallopade International.

—The Story of the Christmas Tree. 2003. 12p. (J). (gr. k-4). pap. 2.95 (978-0-635-02150-2(1)) Gallopade International.

—The White House Christmas Mystery. 2003. (Carole Marsh Mysteries Ser.). 160p. (J). (gr. 2-8). 14.95 (978-0-635-01666-9(4)); pap. 5.95 (978-0-635-01664-5(8)) Gallopade International.

—The White House Christmas Mystery. 2003. (gr. 5-8). lib. bdg. 14.10 (978-0-613-73041-9(0)) Tandem Library Bks.

Marshall, James. Merry Christmas, Space Case. 2004. (J). pap. 14.95 incl. audio (978-1-55592-156-9(6)); pap. 14.95 incl. audio (978-1-55592-093-7(4)); pap. 18.95 incl. audio compact disk (978-1-55592-150-7(7)); pap. 32.75 incl. audio (978-1-55592-157-6(4)) Weston Woods Studios, Inc.

Marsoli, Lisa Ann. Christmas Is Coming! Barnard, Lucy, illus. 2007. 10p. (J). (ps-3). 6.99 (***978-0-375-84573-4(9)*** , Robin Corey Bks.) Random Hse. Children's Bks.

Martin, Ann M. On Christmas Eve. 2006. (Illus.). 160p. (J). pap. 15.99 (978-0-439-74588-8(8) , Scholastic) Scholastic, Inc.

Martin, Ann M. 'Tis the Season. 2007. (Main Street Ser.: No. 3). 208p. (J). pap. 6.99 (***978-0-439-86881-5(5)*** , Scholastic Paperbacks) Scholastic, Inc.

Martin, Glenn W. Christmas Stories My Grandpa Wrote for Me. 2000. (Illus.). 128p. (gr. 4-7). pap. 9.95 (978-0-595-14636-9(8)) iUniverse, Inc.

Martin, Hugo. Pablo's Christmas. Chapman, Lee, illus. 2006. 24p. (J). 14.95 (978-1-4027-2560-9(4)) Sterling Publishing Co., Inc.

Martini, T. J. Christmas Lost & Found. Kiejna, Magdalenea, illus. 2007. (J). per. 15.99 (***978-0-9705018-7-5(0)***) Wings, Inc.

Maryon, Laura. Mittens, Mittens & More Mittens! Callahan, Pat, illus. 2003. 32p. (J). (ps-1). pap. 11.99 (978-1-57921-138-7(0)) WinePress Publishing.

Marzollo, Jean. I Spy Little Christmas. Wick, Walter, illus. 1999. (I Spy Bks.). 26p. (J). (ps). bds. 6.99 (978-0-439-08331-7(1) , Cartwheel Bks.) Scholastic, Inc.

Marzollo, Jean. Ten Little Christmas Presents. 2008. (J). (***978-0-545-02791-5(8)***) Scholastic, Inc.

Mason, Richard. The Red Scarf: A Country Boy's Christmas Story. 2007. 160p. 14.95 (***978-0-87483-850-3(9)***) August Hse. Pubs., Inc.

Masurel, Claire. Christmas Is Coming! Henry, Marie H., illus. 2001. 24p. (J). bds. 6.95 (978-0-8118-3322-6(4)) Chronicle Bks. LLC.

—Merry Christmas, Emily! Calitri, Susan, illus. 2002. (Lift-the-Flap Book Ser.). 16p. (J). pap. 6.99 (978-0-14-230198-2(1) , Puffin) Penguin Group (USA) Inc.

Matsuura, Richard & Matsuura, Ruth. Hawaiian Christmas Story. Chao, Linus, illus. (J). 8.95 (978-1-887916-01-1(6)) Orchid Isle Publishing Co.

Mawhinney, Art, illus. Diego Saves Christmas! 2007. (Go, Diego, Go! Ser.). 24p. (J). (ps-2). pap. 5.99 (***978-1-4169-4210-8(6)*** , Simon Spotlight/Nickelodeon) Simon & Schuster Children's Publishing.

Maxwell, Corey. A Paw Island Christmas. Vitale, Steve & Turnbaugh, Paul, illus. 1999. 32p. (J). 12.95 (978-1-890145-02-6(5) , Paw Island Entertainment, Inc.) Pet-Care, Inc.

May, Robert L. Rudolph Shines Again. Papp, Lisa, illus. 2003. 40p. (J). (ps). 9.99 (978-0-448-43198-7(X) , Grosset & Dunlap) Penguin Group (USA) Inc.

—Rudolph the Red-Nosed Reindeer. 2004. 32p. (J). spiral bd. 5.95 incl. audio (978-1-55709-137-6(4)); (Illus.). 9.95 (978-1-55709-139-0(0)) Applewood Bks.

—Rudolph the Red-Nosed Reindeer. Emberley, Michael, illus. 2004. 32p. (J). (ps-3). 9.95 (978-1-55709-294-6(X)) Applewood Bks.

—Rudolph the Red-Nosed Reindeer. Wenzel, David, illus. 2001. 40p. (J). (gr. k-3). 9.99 (978-0-448-42534-4(3) , Grosset & Dunlap) Penguin Group (USA) Inc.

—Rudolph to the Rescue. Papp, Lisa, illus. 2006. 40p. (J). (ps). pap. 6.99 (978-0-448-44142-9(X) , Grosset & Dunlap) Penguin Group (USA) Inc.

—Rudolph's Second Christmas. Emberley, Michael, illus. 2004. 32p. (J). (ps-3). 9.95 (978-1-55709-192-5(7)) Applewood Bks.

Mayer, Mercer. Christmas for Miss Kitty, Vol. 3. 2003. (Little Critter Ser.). (Illus.). 24p. (J). (gr. 1-2). pap. 3.95 (978-1-57768-584-5(9)) School Specialty Publishing.

—Christmas for Miss Kitty. 2003. (gr. k-3). lib. bdg. 11.80 (978-0-613-90232-8(7)) Tandem Library Bks.

—Little Christmas Tree. 2003. (gr. k-3). lib. bdg. 11.80 (978-0-613-84261-7(8)) Tandem Library Bks.

—The Little Christmas Tree, Vol. 2. 2003. (Little Critter Ser.). (Illus.). 24p. (J). (gr. k-1). pap. 3.95 (978-1-57768-583-8(0)) School Specialty Publishing.

—Merry Christmas, Little Critter! Mayer, Mercer, illus. 2004. (Little Critter Ser.). (Illus.). 16p. (J). pap. 6.99 (978-0-06-053972-6(0) , Harper Festival) HarperCollins Pubs.

—Merry Christmas, Mom & Dad. Mayer, Mercer, illus. 1999. (Little Critter Ser.). (Illus.). 24p. (J). (gr. k-k). pap. 3.29 (978-0-307-11886-8(X) , 11886, Random Hse. Bks. for Young Readers) Random Hse. Children's Bks.

McAdam, Claudia Cangilla. The Christmas Tree Cried: The Story of the White House Christmas Tree. Crum, Anna-Maria, illus. 2004. 32p. (J). 16.95 (978-0-9748995-5-8(0)) Two Sons Pr., Inc.

McCain, Steve. A Christmas Tale: The Precious Gift. l.t. ed. 2002. 36p. per. 7.95 (978-0-9719597-1-2(4)) Thornton Publishing.

McCann, Jesse Leon. Scooby-Doo & Santa's Bake Shop. del Sur, Duendes, illus. 2000. (Scooby-Doo Ser.). 24p. (J). (ps-3). pap. 5.99 (978-0-439-20999-1(4)) Scholastic, Inc.

McCann, Thomas P. "Tom". The Tree Nobody Wanted: A Christmas Story. 2007. 14.95 (***978-0-9797407-0-1(3)***) Exeter Pr.

McCardell, Kenneth/W. Bible Rhymes' Christmas Story. Chirco, Antonella, illus. 2007. 32p. (J). 17.95 (***978-0-9790605-2-6(4)*** , BibleRhymes) BibleRhymes Publishing, L.L.C.

McCaughrean, Geraldine. Father & Son: A Nativity Story. Negrin, Fabian, illus. 2006. 40p. (ps-3). 16.99 (978-1-4231-0344-8(0)) Hyperion Pr.

McCaughrean, Geraldine. Wenceslas. Birmingham, Christian, illus. 2007. 32p. (J). (gr. 2-2). 19.95 (***978-0-385-60535-9(8)***) Transworld Publishers Ltd. GBR. *Dist:* Independent Pubs. Group.

McClatchy, Lisa. Eloise Decorates for Christmas. Lyon, Tammie Speer, illus. 2007. (Eloise Ser.). 32p. (J). (ps-1). per. 3.99 (***978-1-4169-4978-7(X)*** , Aladdin) Simon & Schuster Children's Publishing.

McCourt, Frank. Angela & the Baby Jesus. Long, Loren, illus. 2007. 40p. (J). 14.95 (***978-1-4165-7470-5(0)*** , Scribner) Simon & Schuster.

—Angela & the Baby Jesus. Colon, Raul, illus. 2007. 32p. (J). (gr. k-5). 17.99 (***978-1-4169-3789-0(7)***) Simon & Schuster Children's Publishing.

McCourt, Lisa. Merry Christmas, Stinky Face. Moore, Cyd, illus. 2004. 32p. (J). (gr. k). pap. 5.99 (978-0-439-63577-6(2)); pap. 14.95 (978-0-439-63576-9(4)) Scholastic, Inc. (Cartwheel Bks.).

McCray, Ed. Jill Chill & the Baron of Glacier Mountain: Wonder Tales from the Book of Ed. Brewer, Tammy & Harms, Cathy, eds. McCray, Ed, illus. 2003. (Illus.). 150p. (J). mass mkt. 14.95 (978-1-929515-26-4(X) , Solovisions) Comic Library International.

McCutcheon, John. Christmas in the Trenches. Sorensen, Henri, illus. 2006. 32p. (J). 18.95 incl. audio compact disk (978-1-56145-374-0(9) , Peachtree Junior) Peachtree Pubs., Ltd.

McDermott, Michael. Jingle Cats. 2004. (Illus.). 32p. (J). 12.99 (978-1-4003-0469-1(5)); 9.99 (978-1-4003-0471-4(7)) Nelson, Thomas Inc.

McDonald, Megan. Happy New Year, Julie, Bk. 3. McAliley, Susan, illus. 2007. 88p. (YA). (gr. 3 up). 12.95 (***978-1-59369-292-6(7)***) American Girl Publishing, Inc.

—Happy New Year, Julie, Bk. 3. McAliley, Susan & Hunt, Robert, illus. 2007. 88p. (YA). (gr. 3 up). pap. 6.95 (***978-1-59369-291-9(9)***) American Girl Publishing, Inc.

McDonnell, Vincent. The Boy Who Saved Christmas. 2005. (Illus.). 156p. (J). (ps-9). pap. 12.95 (978-1-903464-18-2(8)) Collins Pr., The IRL. *Dist:* Dufour Editions, Inc.

McGauley, Patrick. Santa the King. Wirkklua, Derek, illus. 2004. 40p. (J). 13.95 (978-0-9724209-8-3(3)) McGauley, Patrick.

McGee, Fatty. Santa's Workshop. 2007. 6p. 16.95 (***978-1-58117-599-8(X)*** , Intervisual/Piggy Toes) Dalmatian Pr.

McGrath, Barbara Barbieri & Togel, Peggy. The M & M's' Brand Christmas Gift Book. 2004. (Illus.). 12p. (J). (ps-3). bds. 6.95 (978-1-57091-421-8(4)) Charlesbridge Publishing, Inc.

McGuirk, Leslie. Ho, Ho, Ho, Tucker! McGuirk, Leslie, illus. 2007. (Illus.). 30p. (J). (gr. k-k). pap. 4.99 (***978-0-7636-3663-0(0)***) Candlewick Pr.

McKay, Hilary. Forever Rose. 2008. 304p. (J). 16.99 (***978-1-4169-5486-6(4)*** , McElderry, Margaret K.) Simon & Schuster Children's Publishing.

McKissack, Pat. The All-I'll-Ever-Want Christmas Doll. Pinkney, Jerry, illus. 2007. (J). (***978-0-375-83615-2(2)*** , Schwartz & Wade Bks.) Random Hse. Children's Bks.

McKissack, Patricia. The All-I'll-Ever-Want Christmas Doll. Pinkney, Jerry, illus. 2007. 40p. (J). (ps-3). lib. bdg. 19.99 (***978-0-375-93759-0(5)***); 16.99 (***978-0-375-83759-3(0)***) Random Hse. Children's Bks. (Schwartz & Wade Bks.).

McKissack, Patricia C. Messy Bessey's Holidays. 1999. (gr. k-3). lib. bdg. 12.95 (978-0-613-37457-6(6)) Tandem Library Bks.

McKissack, Patricia C. & McKissack, Fredrick L. Christmas in the Big House: Christmas in the Quarters. Thompson, John, illus. 2002. 80p. (J). pap. 6.99 (978-0-590-43028-9(9)) Scholastic, Inc.

—Messy Bessey's Holidays. Regan, Dana, illus. 1999. (Rookie Readers Ser.). 32p. (J). (gr. 1-2). 19.50 (978-0-516-20829-9(2) , Children's Pr.) Scholastic Library Publishing.

McMahon, Karen. Elmo's Night Before Christmas. 2005. (Sesame Street Ser.). (Illus.). 14p. (J). (ps-3). bds. 10.99 (978-0-7944-0789-6(7)) Reader's Digest Assn., Inc., The.

McMullan, Kate. Fluffy Saves Christmas. Smith, Mavis, illus. 2004. 40p. (J). lib. bdg. 15.00 (978-1-59054-462-4(5)) Fitzgerald Bks.

—Fluffy Saves Christmas, Level 3. Smith, Mavis, illus. 1999. (Hello Reader! Ser.). 40p. (J). (gr. 1-3). pap. 3.99 (978-0-590-52308-0(2) , Cartwheel Bks.) Scholastic, Inc.

—Fluffy, the Secret Santa. Smith, Mavis, illus. 2001. (Hello Reader! Ser.). (J). pap. 3.99 (978-0-439-31942-3(0)) Scholastic, Inc.

McTaggart, William R. A Companion Reader of Ten Christmas Stories, Vol. 1. Hibbard, Eugene J., illus. 1999. (Companion Reader Ser.: Vol. 1). 127p. (J). (ps-5). 16.00 (978-0-9669285-3-2(9)) Gramma Bks. Publishing Co.

—A Companion Reader of Ten Christmas Stories. 1998. (Illus.). 104p. (J). (ps-7). 16.00 (978-1-890394-20-2(3) , Sage Creek Pr.) Rhodes & Easton.

Meadows, Daisy. Holly the Christmas Fairy. 2007. (Rainbow Magic Ser.). 176p. (Orig.). (J). pap. 6.99 (***978-0-439-92880-9(X)*** , Scholastic Paperbacks) Scholastic, Inc.

Mears, Richard Chase. Saint Nick & the Space Nicks. Westerfield, William Stephen, illus. l.t. ed. 2004. 32p. 16.95 (978-0-9754056-0-4(8)) Tuxedo Blue, LLC.

Medearis, Angela Shelf. Too Many Holidays? Papp, Robert, illus. 2003. 149p. (J). (978-0-439-52327-1(3)) Scholastic, Inc.

Medina, Tony. Christmas Makes Me Think. Cox, Chandra, illus. 2001. 32p. (J). (gr. 1-7). (978-1-58430-024-3(8)) Lee & Low Bks., Inc.

Meissner, Susan. A Window to the World. 2005. 320p. pap. 11.99 (978-0-7369-1414-7(5)) Harvest Hse. Pubs.

Melinda, Shoals, illus. The Spriitelees: A Christmas Tale about Kindness. 2006. 32p. (J). 16.00 (978-0-9773460-0-4(5)) Spriitelee Enterprises.

Merry Christmas, 4 bks., Set. 2002. (Illus.). (J). (ps). bds. 7.99 (978-1-57759-994-4(2)) Dalmatian Pr.

Merry Christmas, Amelia Bedelia. 2002. (Amelia Bedelia Ser.). (Illus.). (YA). 12.34 (978-1-4046-1305-8(6)) Book Wholesalers, Inc.

Merry Christmas USA. 2007. (J). bds. 21.95 (***978-0-9745191-3-5(8)***) Lynn Tyner Mitchum & James Rogers.

Metzger, Steve. Dinofours, Our Holiday Show! Wilhelm, Hans, illus. 2002. (J). 3.50 (978-0-439-38218-2(1)) Scholastic, Inc.

Meyer, Brigit. The Christmas Surprise. Mussenbrock, Anne, illus. 2004. 10p. (J). bds. 5.99 (978-1-59384-061-7(6)) Parklane Publishing.

—Merry Christmas, Little Bear. Mussenbrock, Anne, illus. 2004. 10p. (J). bds. 5.99 (978-1-59384-062-4(4)) Parklane Publishing.

Milbourne, Anna. Very First Christmas. 2006. 24p. (J). 9.99 (978-0-7945-1474-7(X) , Usborne) EDC Publishing.

Miller, Edward. Elf Elementary: A Christmas Story. 2004. (Illus.). 32p. (J). (ps-3). 12.95 (978-0-8109-8721-0(X)) Abrams, Harry N. , Inc.

Miller, Sara Swan. Snowden's Magical Christmas. 1999. (Snowden & Friends Ser.). 10p. (J). bds. 4.99 (978-1-57584-419-0(2)) Reader's Digest Children's Publishing, Inc.

C D

Mills, Claudia. Gus & Grandpa & the Christmas Cookies. Stock, Catherine, illus. 2000. (Gus & Grandpa Ser.). 48p. (J). (gr. 1-3). pap. 5.95 (978-0-374-42815-0(8) , Sunburst) Farrar, Straus & Giroux.

—Gus & Grandpa & the Christmas Cookies. Stock, Catherine, illus. 2000. 48p. (J). (gr. 1-3). lib. bdg. 12.95 (978-0-613-30455-9(1)) Tandem Library Bks.

—Gus & Grandpa & the Christmas Cookies. 2000. (J). (978-0-606-20133-9(5)); (Illus.). 11.75 (978-0-606-20396-8(6)) Tandem Library Bks.

Minor, Florence. Christmas Tree! Minor, Wendell & Minor, Florence, illus. 2005. 40p. (J). lib. bdg. 16.89 (978-0-06-056035-5(5) , Tegen, Katherine Bks) HarperCollins Pubs.

Mishica, Clare. Tina Marie's Best Christmas. Ring, Laura, ed. Lucas, Sheila, illus. 1999. (Happy Day Bks.). 24p. (J). (ps-2). pap. 2.49 (978-0-7847-1046-3(5) , 04276, Bean Sprouts) Standard Publishing.

Mitchell, Gloria. The Mouse That Went to Find Christmas. Johnson, Jerome A., illus. (J). pap. (978-0-9706186-0-3(3)) Fourth Generation Pubs.

Mitchell, Susan, illus. The Christmas Pop-up Present. 2005. 24p. (J). 19.95 (978-0-689-86643-2(7) , Little Simon) Simon & Schuster Children's Publishing.

Mitton, Tony. Christmas Wishes. Marlow, Layn, illus. 2007. 32p. (J). (ps-2). 14.99 (*978-0-7641-6086-8(9)) Barron's Educational Series, Inc.

Mobley, Cyn. A Very Airey Christmas. 2004. pap. 16.00 (978-0-9724136-0-2(X)) Greyhound Bks.

Moeri, Louise. Star Mother's Youngest Child. Hyman, Trina Schart, illus. 2005. 48p. (J). (gr. k-3). 5.95 (978-0-618-61509-4(1)); 30th ed. 14.00 (978-0-618-61683-1(7)) Houghton Mifflin Co. Trade & Reference Div.

Mohr, Joseph. Silent Night. Kinkade, Thomas, illus. 2006. 32p. (J). 16.99 (978-0-06-078743-1(0)) HarperCollins Pubs.

Mohr, Joseph. Silent Night, Holy Night. Dusikova, Maja, illus. 2007. 0018p. (J). (ps). bds. 12.95 (*978-0-7358-2162-0(3)) North-South Bks., Inc.

Mole Follows the Christmas Star. 2002. (J). bds. 3.98 (978-1-84250-587-8(4) , Bright Sparks) Parragon, Inc.

Molineaux, Jane. The Twelve Days of Christmas. 2000. (Illus.). 16p. (ps-k). pap. 5.00 (978-0-7548-0703-2(7)) Anness Publishing, Inc.

Momaday, N. Scott. Circle of Wonder: A Native American Christmas Story. Momaday, N. Scott, illus. 2001. (Illus.). 44p. 24.95 incl. audio compact disk (978-0-8263-2796-3(6)) Univ. of New Mexico Pr.

Monroe, Colleen. A Wish to Be a Christmas Tree. Monroe, Michael Glenn, illus. 32p. (J). (ps-3). 2005. bds. 6.99 (978-1-58536-269-1(7)); 2000. 16.95 (978-1-58536-002-4(3)) Sleeping Bear Pr.

Monroe Donovan, Jane. Winter's Gift. Monroe Donovan, Jane, illus. 2004. (Illus.). 32p. (J). 15.95 (978-1-58536-231-8(X)) Sleeping Bear Pr.

Montgomery Gibson, Jane. My Christmas Friend. Montgomery Gibson, Jane, illus. 2005. (YA). bds. 8.99 (978-1-4183-0066-1(7)) Christ Inspired, Inc.

Montgomery, L. M. Christmas with Anne: And Other Holiday Stories. Wilmshurst, Rea, ed. 2002. 224p. pap. 12.95 (978-0-7710-6204-9(4) , McClelland & Stewart) McClelland & Stewart CAN. *Dist:* Random Hse., Inc.

—Christmas with Anne: And Other Holiday Stories. 2001. (gr. 5-8). lib. bdg. 13.00 (978-0-613-90391-2(9)) Tandem Library Bks.

—Christmas with Anne & Other Holiday Stories. Wilmshurst, Rea, ed. 2001. (Illus.). 224p. (YA). (gr. 5 up). pap. 4.99 (978-0-553-57100-4(1) , Starfire) Random Hse. Children's Bks.

Moody, Betty G. Magical Wish. 1998. (Illus.). (J). 15.95 (978-0-9663522-1-4(1)) Character Lines Publishing.

Moore. 'Twas the Night Before Christmas: Or, Account of a Visit from St. Nicholas. Tavares, Matt, illus. 2006. 32p. (J). (gr. k). 8.99 (978-0-7636-3118-5(3)) Candlewick Pr.

Moore, Clement. The Night Before Christmas. Slocum, Bradley, illus. 2007. 8p. (J). (ps-17). 9.99 (*978-1-58476-549-3(6) , IKIDS) Innovative Kids.

Moore, Clement C. Grumpy Santa. Spiridellis, Gregg & Spiridellis, Evan, illus. 2003. (J). pap. (978-0-439-53039-2(3) , Orchard Bks.) Scholastic, Inc.

—Magie de Noel. pap. 16.95 (978-2-07-054886-6(4)) Gallimard, Editions FRA. *Dist:* Distribooks, Inc.

—The Night Before Christmas. Brett, Jan, illus. 1998. 32p. (J). (ps-3). 16.99 (978-0-399-23190-2(0) , Putnam Juvenile) Penguin Group (USA) Inc.

—The Night Before Christmas. ed. 2005. (Illus.). 44p. (J). (ps-7). 7.95 (978-0-8118-5028-5(5)) Chronicle Bks. LLC.

—The Night Before Christmas. Watson, Richard Jesse, illus. 2006. 40p. (J). 16.99 (978-0-06-075741-0(8)); lib. bdg. 17.89 (978-0-06-075742-7(6)) HarperCollins Pubs.

—The Night Before Christmas. Zwerger, Lisbeth, illus. 2005. 40p. (J). (ps-3). 15.99 (978-0-698-40030-6(5) , Minedition) Penguin Group (USA) Inc.

—The Night Before Christmas: A Christmas Treasury. (Illus.). 12p. (J). 4.95 (978-1-58989-101-2(5)) Thurman Hse., LLC.

—La Nochebuena. Alvarez, Lourdes, tr. Eldredge, Larry, illus. 2005. (SPA.). 28p. (J). bds. 12.95 (978-1-58173-257-3(0)) Sweetwater Pr.

—The Teddy Bears' Night Before Christmas. Moore, Clement C., illus. 1999. (Cartwheel Bks.). (Illus.). 32p. (J). (ps-2). pap. 12.95 (978-0-590-03243-8(7) , Cartwheel Bks.) Scholastic, Inc.

—The Teddy Bears' Night Before Christmas. Stevenson, Monica, illus. 1999. (Cartwheel Bks.). (J). pap. (978-0-590-03245-2(3)) Scholastic, Inc.

—A Visit from St. Nicholas. Fernandes, Kim, illus. 1999. 32p. (J). (ps-3). reprint ed. pap. 5.99 (978-1-55209-429-7(4)) Firefly Bks., Ltd.

Moore, Clement C., ed. & illus. The Night Before Christmas. Moore, Clement C., illus. Price, Margaret Evans, illus. 2004. 16p. (J). (ps-3). pap. 9.95 (978-1-59583-009-8(X) , Green Tiger Pr.) Laughing Elephant.

Moore, Clement Clarke. The Night Before Christmas. Newsom, Tom, illus. 2005. 32p. (J). pap. 10.99 (978-1-4037-1604-0(8)) Dalmatian Pr.

Moorman, Margaret. Light the Lights! A Story about Celebrating Hanukkah & Christmas. Moorman, Margaret, illus. 1999. (Illus.). 32p. (J). (gr. k-2). pap. 6.99 (978-0-590-48383-4(8) , Cartwheel Bks.) Scholastic, Inc.

—Light the Lights: A Story about Celebrating Hanukkah & Christmas. 1999. (gr. k-3). lib. bdg. 14.15 (978-0-613-86971-3(0)) Tandem Library Bks.

Moran, Michelle. Nana's Secret Christmas Room. 2006. 80p. per. 8.99 (*978-1-59886-581-3(1)) Tate Publishing & Enterprises, L.L.C.

Morehead, Ruth J. Waiting for Christmas. Morehead, Ruth J., illus. 1999. (Jellybean Bks.). (Illus.). 24p. (J). (ps-k). lib. bdg. 7.99 (978-0-375-90102-7(7) , Random Hse. Bks. for Young Readers) Random Hse. Children's Bks.

Morgan, Ruth & Carpenter, Suzanne. Happy Christmas Sglod. 2003. (WEL & ENG., Illus.). 32p. pap. 12.95 (978-1-84323-261-2(8)) Beekman Bks., Inc.

Morozumi, Atsuko, et al. Santa's Christmas Countdown. Morozumi, Atsuko, illus. 2003. (Illus.). (J). (gr. k-4). 15.95 (978-0-7696-3189-9(4) , Gingham Dog Pr.) School Specialty Publishing.

Morpurgo, Michael. The Best Christmas Present in the World. Foreman, Michael, illus. 2004. 36p. (J). (ps-7). 8.99 (978-1-4052-1518-3(6)) Egmont Bks., Ltd. GBR. *Dist:* Independent Pubs. Group.

Morrissey, Dean. The Christmas Ship. 2000. (Illus.). 40p. (J). (gr. k-4). 16.89 (978-0-06-028576-0(1)) HarperCollins Pubs.

—Christmas Ship. 2000. (gr. k-3). lib. bdg. 14.15 (978-0-613-68414-9(1)) Tandem Library Bks.

Morrissey, Mary E. Sleigh Ride to Christmas. 2003. 17.00 (978-0-8059-6279-6(4)) Dorrance Publishing Co., Inc.

Moulton, Mark. Travelers Gift. Sherwood, Stewart, illus. 2001. 32p. 18.00 (978-0-7412-0867-5(9)) Lang Graphics, Ltd.

Moulton, Mark K. The Visit. Winget, Susan, illus. 2003. 56p. (J). 14.95 (978-0-8249-5475-8(0)) Ideals Pubns.

Moulton, Mark Kimball. A Cricket's Carol. Blowers, Lisa, illus. 2004. 32p. (J). 14.95 (978-0-8249-5488-8(2)) Ideals Pubns.

—A Cricket's Carol. Blowers, Lisa, illus. 2000. 32p. (J). (gr. k-3). 18.00 (978-0-7412-0735-7(4)) Lang Graphics, Ltd.

—Reindeer Moon. Strain, Deb, illus. 2000. 32p. (J). (gr. k-3). 18.00 (978-0-7412-0816-3(4)) Lang Graphics, Ltd.

Mouse Works Staff. Christmas Stocking. 1998. (Standard Characters Ser.). (J). 2.98 (978-1-57082-817-1(2)) Mouse Works.

—Christmas Wreath. 1998. (Pooh Ser.). (J). 2.98 (978-1-57082-819-5(9)) Mouse Works.

—Merry Christmas to You! 1999. (J). 7.98 (978-1-57082-940-6(3)) Mouse Works.

—Merry Xmas from Pooh to You Santa Roo. 1998. 10p. (J). 13.97 (978-0-7364-0054-1(0)) Mouse Works.

—Mickey Mouse's Christmas. 1999. 64p. 6.99 (978-0-7364-0126-5(1)) Mouse Works.

—Mickey's Christmas. 1998. (Disneys Ser.). (Illus.). 10p. (J). (ps). 8.99 (978-1-57082-757-0(5)) Mouse Works.

—Mickey's Christmas Candy Cane. 1998. (Disneys Ser.). (Illus.). 8p. (J). (ps-1). 2.99 (978-1-57082-820-1(2)) Mouse Works.

—Pooh Loves Christmas! A Winnie the Pooh Photo Album & Storybook. 2000. (Keepsake Photo Storybooks Ser.). (Illus.). 10p. (J). (ps-3). 6.99 (978-0-7364-0191-3(1)) Mouse Works.

—Pooh Merry Christmas to You: Hunny Pot Board Book. 1998. (Pooh Ser.). 10p. (J). 7.98 (978-0-7364-0026-8(5)) Mouse Works.

—Santa Mickey Friendly Tales. 1998. (J). 6.99 (978-1-57082-974-1(8)) Mouse Works.

—Winnie the Pooh's Christmas Tree. 1998. (Winnie the Pooh Ser.). (Illus.). 8p. (J). (ps-1). bds. 2.99 (978-1-57082-818-8(0)) Mouse Works.

Mucha Aydlott, Julie A. My Favorite Time of Year. Mucha-Sullivan, Kalie A. & Mucha-Sullivan, Emily V., illus. l.t. ed. 2004. 22p. (J). 5.95 (978-0-9746093-2-4(3)) San Diego Business Accounting Solutions a Non CPA Firm.

Mumaugh, Lene. Touch of Christmas. Skrbic, Melissa, illus. l.t. ed. 2003. 28p. per. 9.95 (978-1-932344-19-6(5)) Thornton Publishing.

Murail, Marie-Aude & Murail, Elvire. Santa's Last Present. Blake, Quentin, illus. 2004. 32p. (J). 12.95 (978-1-56145-319-1(6)) Peachtree Pubs., Ltd.

Murphy, Elspeth Campbell. The Mystery of the Golden Reindeer. 2000. (Three Cousins Detective Club Ser.: No. 30). (Illus.). 64p. (J). (gr. 2-5). pap. 3.99 (978-0-7642-2138-5(8)) Bethany Hse. Pubs.

Murphy, Mary. Christmas Is the Best Bit. 2004. (Illus.). 28p. (Orig.). (J). pap. 6.95 (978-0-7497-4252-2(6)) Egmont Bks., Ltd. GBR. *Dist:* Trafalgar Square Publishing.

—Little Owl & the Star: A Christmas Story. Murphy, Mary, illus. 2003. (Illus.). 32p. (J). (gr. k-k). 12.99 (978-0-7636-2268-8(0)) Candlewick Pr.

Murphy, Michael E. Candy Cane Christmas. 2006. 16p. (J). (978-1-59975-434-5(7)) Independent Pub.

Murray, Brendan. Tev. Rubin, Barry & Veremis, Thanos, eds. 2002. 152p. (YA). pap. 13.95 (978-1-86368-334-0(8)) Fremantle Pr. AUS. *Dist:* International Specialized Bk. Services.

My Crazy Christmas Catastrophe Cat. 2003. (Illus.). 22p. (J). 9.95 (978-0-9744751-1-0(4)) Timothy Lane Pr.

My First Book of Christmas Stories. 2003. (J). 8.99 (978-1-59384-014-3(4)) Parklane Publishing.

My Treasury of Christmas Stories. Date not set. 192p. (J). 12.98 (978-1-4054-1295-7(X)) Parragon, Inc.

Myers, Anna. Captain's Command. 2001. 11.15 (978-0-606-22411-6(4)) Tandem Library Bks.

Myra, Harold. Santa, Are You for Real? Kurisu, Jane, illus. 2005. 18p. (J). (ps-3). bds. 6.99 (978-1-4003-0629-9(9)) Nelson, Thomas Inc.

Nall, Joy & Nall, Thomas, Jr. The Candy Cane Story. Gillette, Amy Floyd, illus. 1998. 32p. (J). (gr. k-5). reprint ed. 11.95 (978-0-9651185-3-8(3)) Gleasner, Bill & Diana Inc.

Napoli, Donna Jo. Happy Holidays. Ben-Ami, Doron, illus. 2000. (Angelwings Ser.: No. 14). 80p. (J). (gr. 2-5). pap. 7.95 (978-0-689-83977-1(4) , Simon Pulse) Simon & Schuster Children's Publishing.

Nash, Mary. Lost Treasures Bk. 2: Mrs. Coverlet's Magician. 2001. 128p. (J). 13.49 (978-0-7868-2597-4(9)) Hyperion Pr.

Natale, Noel. The Adventures of Nicholas: The Boy Who Grew up to Become Santa Claus. 2004. (Illus.). 127p. (YA). per. 17.99 (978-0-9753349-0-4(5)) Open Bk. Publishing Co.

Naylor, Phyllis Reynolds. The Girls' Revenge. 1999. (gr. 3-6). lib. bdg. 13.00 (978-0-613-22858-9(3)) Tandem Library Bks.

—The Girls' Revenge. l.t. ed. 2003. (Thorndike Press Large Print Juvenile Ser.). 172p. (J). 23.95 (978-0-7862-5180-3(8)) Thorndike Pr.

Nazoa, Aquiles. Retablillo de Navidad. Oliver, Maria Fernanda, illus. Tr. of Christmas Nativity. (SPA.). (J). (gr. 3-5). 10.95 (978-980-251-067-6(2)) Ekare, Ediciones VEN. *Dist:* Lectorum Pubns., Inc.

Nelson, S. D. Coyote's Christmas: A Lakota Story. 2007. (Illus.). 40p. (J). (gr. k-4). 15.95 (*978-0-8109-9367-9(8) , Abrams Bks. for Young Readers) Abrams, Harry N. , Inc.

Nettell, Stephanie. The Gramercy Christmas Treasury. Penney, Ian, illus. 2005. 160p. (J). (ps-7). 12.99 (978-0-517-22709-1(6) , Gramercy) Random Hse. Value Publishing.

New Mexico Night Before Christmas. 2006. (YA). per. 19.99 (*978-0-9710675-5-4(4)) 2020 Vision Pr.

Night Before Christmas Paperback Edition Uk Ed. 2003. pap. 1.60 (978-0-7624-1918-0(0)) Running Pr. Bk. Pubs.

Nitzberg, Chuck, illus. Christmas Is Coming! 2007. (I'm Going to Read Ser.). 28p. (J). (ps-1). pap. 3.95 (*978-1-4027-4296-5(7)) Sterling Publishing Co., Inc.

Nivens, Karen. Benjamin P. Blizzard: Welcome to Christmastown. Grisham, Jason, illus. 2007. 48p. (J). per. (*978-0-9798154-1-6(X)) Living Waters Publishing Co.

Noble, Trinka Hakes. Apple Tree Christmas. Noble, Trinka Hakes, illus. 2005. (Illus.). 32p. (J). (ps-3). 16.95 (978-1-58536-270-7(0)) Sleeping Bear Pr.

North Bedford, Annie. Mickey Mouse Flies the Christmas Mail. Walt Disney Company, illus. 2007. (Little Golden Book Ser.). 24p. (J). (gr. k-k). 2.99 (*978-0-7364-2424-0(5) , Golden/Disney) Random Hse. Children's Bks.

Novak, Matt. Rock-A-Bye Christmas. 2007. (Illus.). 16p. (J). (ps-1). 7.95 (*978-1-59643-187-4(3)) Roaring Brook Pr.

NToutome, Jasmine & Freedman, Noriko. Lucille Travels at Christmas. 2001. (Illus.). 28p. 4.99 (978-976-610-167-1(1)) Penguin Group (USA) Inc.

Nuhern, G. A. A Christmas List Learn & Have Fun in School & the Magic of Wisdom. 2002. 124p. pap. 10.95 (978-0-595-25320-3(2) , Writers Club Pr.) iUniverse, Inc.

Nuhern, G. A. Christmas List Learn & Have Fun in School & the Magic of Wisdom. 2002. (ENG.). 124p. 20.95 (*978-0-595-65095-8(3) , Writers Club Pr.) iUniverse, Inc.

Numeroff, Laura. Merry Christmas, Mouse! Bond, Felicia, illus. 2007. (If You Give... Ser.). 24p. (J). (ps). pap. 6.99 (*978-0-06-134499-2(0) , Harper Festival) HarperCollins Pubs.

Numeroff, Laura Joffe. If You Take a Mouse to the Movies. ed. 2004. (Illus.). (J). (gr. k-3). spiral bd. (978-0-616-11128-4(2)); spiral bd. (978-0-616-11129-1(0)) Canadian National Institute for the Blind/Institut National Canadien pour les Aveugles.

—If You Take a Mouse to the Movies. Bond, Felicia, illus. 2000. (If You Give... Ser.). 40p. (J). (ps-2). 15.99 (978-0-06-027867-0(6)); lib. bdg. 16.89 (978-0-06-027868-7(4)) HarperCollins Pubs. (Geringer, Laura Book).

Nunn, Bruce & Jones, Brenda. Buddy the Bluenose Reindeer. 2005. (Illus.). pap. 12.95 (978-1-55109-539-4(4)) Down East Bks.

The Nutcracker. 2003. (Illus.). 32p. (J). 4.98 (978-1-4054-0982-7(7)) Parragon, Inc.

Nyaradi, J. A. Catching Santa. 2006. 140p. pap. 11.95 (978-0-7414-3462-3(8)) Infinity Publishing.

O'Brien, John. Mother Hubbard's Christmas. O'Brien, John, illus. 2003. (Illus.). 32p. (J). (ps-1). 14.95 (978-1-56397-139-6(9)) Boyds Mills Pr.

—The Twelve Days of Christmas. 2003. (gr. k-3). lib. bdg. 17.60 (978-0-613-79888-4(0)) Tandem Library Bks.

O'Fearghail, Charles. The Discovery Bk. 1: The Santa Claus Chronicles. 2003. 216p. (J). per. 18.00 (978-1-58982-009-8(6) , Bedside Bks.) American Bk. Publishing Group.

Offley, Nancy. The Story of Snickers. 2004. (Illus.). 40p. (J). pap. 9.95 (978-0-9748081-0-9(5)) Classroom Enrichment Assocs.

O'Keefe, Susan Heyboer. Christmas Gifts. Emery, Jennifer, illus. 2004. 32p. (J). (ps up). 15.95 (978-1-59078-083-1(3)) Boyds Mills Pr.

Oliver Kringle. 2001. 32p. per. 17.00 (978-1-889191-15-7(9)) Clove Pubns.

Olsen, Mary-Kate & Olsen, Ashley. Two of a Kind No. 32: Santa Girls. 2003. (gr. 3-6). lib. bdg. 13.00 (978-0-613-85153-4(6)) Tandem Library Bks.

Olson, Cynthia. Cherise's Christmas Wish. 2005. 145p. pap. 19.95 (978-1-4137-5664-7(6)) PublishAmerica, Inc.

Ondrias, Rachel. Kolby, the Skating Bear: A Kalamazoo Christmas. Scarborough, Casey, illus. 2007. (J). 16.95 (*978-1-933660-29-5(5) , Tadpole Pr. 4 Kids) Smooth Sailing Pr.

One Christmas Starry Night. 2002. (J). bds. 3.98 (978-1-84250-588-5(2) , Bright Sparks) Parragon, Inc.

One Special Christmas in Duckport. 2001. (Little Suzy's Zoo Ser.). (J). (ps-1). 12.99 (978-1-58668-230-9(X)) Lyrick Studios.

The Ooshes the Night Before Christmas. 2004. (J). mass mkt. (978-1-932233-03-2(2)) Aurora Libris Corp.

Oppel, Kenneth & LaFave, Kim. Follow That Star. (FRE., Illus.). 32p. (J). pap. 7.99 (978-0-590-16022-3(2)) Scholastic, Inc.

Oppenheim, Joanne. El Milagro de la Primera Flora de Nochebuena: Un Cuento Mexicano Sobre la Navidad. Negrin, Fabian, illus. 2003. (SPA.). 32p. (J). 16.99 (978-1-84148-308-5(7)) Barefoot Bks., Inc.

—The Miracle of the First Poinsettia: A Mexican Christmas Story. Negrin, Fabian, illus. 2003. 32p. (J). 16.99 (978-1-84148-245-3(5)) Barefoot Bks., Inc.

Orsini, Marina. The Nutcracker. 2001. 48p. (J). (ps up). pap. 12.95 incl. audio compact disk (978-2-89517-065-5(7)) Coffragants CAN. *Dist:* Penton Overseas, Inc.

O'Ryan, Ellie. Care Bears Christmas Wishes. Moore, Saxton, illus. 2005. (J). (*978-1-4156-8978-3(4)) Scholastic, Inc.

O'ryan, Ellie. Christmas Wishes. 2006. (Care Bears Ser.). (Illus.). 24p. (J). pap. 3.50 (978-0-439-78541-9(3)) Scholastic, Inc.

Osborne, Mary Pope. Christmas in Camelot. Murdocca, Sal, illus. 2001. (Magic Tree House Ser.: No. 29). 128p. (J). (gr. k-3). 11.95 (978-0-375-81373-3(X)); lib. bdg. 13.99 (978-0-375-91373-0(4)) Random Hse. Children's Bks. (Random Hse. Bks. for Young Readers).

—Rocking Horse Christmas. Bittinger, Ned, illus. (Bookshelf Ser.). 32p. (J). 2004. (gr. k-ps). pap. 5.99 (978-0-439-66938-2(3) , Scholastic Paperbacks); 2001. (gr. 4). pap. 5.99 (978-0-439-30520-4(9)) Scholastic, Inc.

Osborne, Rick. The Legend of the Christmas Stocking: An Inspirational Story of a Wish Come True. Griffin, Jim, illus. (J). 2006. 28p. 6.99 (978-0-310-71157-5(6)); 2004. 32p. 15.99 (978-0-310-70898-8(2)) Zonderkidz.

Ostrow, Kim. A Colorful Christmas. Regan, Dana, illus. 2003. (Magical Color Bks.). 10p. (J). 5.95 (978-1-4027-0991-3(9)) Sterling Publishing Co., Inc.

—Spongebob's Christmas Wish. 2003. (gr. k-3). lib. bdg. 14.15 (978-0-613-73410-3(6)) Tandem Library Bks.

Our Shinning Christmas Tree. 2003. (J). per. (978-1-57657-911-4(5)) Paradise Pr., Inc.

Packard, Mary. The Christmas Penguin. Weidner, Teri, illus. 2002. (Hello Reader! Ser.). 32p. (J). pap. 3.99 (978-0-439-32102-0(6) , Cartwheel Bks.) Scholastic, Inc.

Page, Thomas Nelson. Santa Claus's Partner. 2006. 64p. pap. (978-1-84702-187-8(5)) Echo Library.

Paladin, Frank. Hole in My Stocking. Amber, Holly & Lin, Melanie, illus. 2005. 24p. (J). per. 16.95 (978-0-9763635-4-5(2)) Beyond the Stars Pubns.

Palatini, Margie. Mooseltoe. Cole, Henry, illus. 2000. 32p. (ps-3). 15.99 (978-0-7868-0567-9(6)) Hyperion Bks. for Children.

—Three French Hens. Egielski, Richard, illus. 2005. 40p. (ps-3). 15.99 (978-0-7868-5167-6(8)) Hyperion Pr.

Pallotta, Jerry. Who Will Guide My Sleigh Tonight. 2006. (Illus.). 32p. (J). pap. 5.99 (978-0-439-85369-9(9) , Cartwheel Bks.) Scholastic, Inc.

Pallotta, Jerry. Who Will Help Santa This Year? 2007. (Illus.). 32p. (J). (ps-3). pap. 8.99 (*978-0-545-01160-0(4) , Cartwheel Bks.) Scholastic, Inc.

Palmer, Raenette. Santa Quits. Cook, Dylan, illus. 1998. 32p. (J). (gr. k-5). 15.95 (978-1-890394-08-0(4) , Sage Creek Pr.) Rhodes & Easton.

Pape, Gordon & Kerbel, Deborah. Family Quizmas: Christmas Bedtime Stories & Trivia Fun. 2006. (Illus.). 192p. pap. 13.00 (978-0-452-28780-8(4) , Plume) Penguin Group (USA) Inc.

Papineau, Lucie & Dickens, Charles. Christmas Eve Magic. Poulin, Stéphane, illus. 2006. 32p. (J). (978-1-55337-953-9(5)) Kids Can Pr., Ltd.

Parish, Peggy. Merry Christmas, Amelia Bedelia. Sweat, Lynn, illus. 2002. (I Can Read Bks.). 64p. (J). pap. 3.99 (978-0-06-009945-9(3) , Harper Trophy) HarperCollins Pubs.

—Merry Christmas, Amelia Bedelia. 2002. (gr. k-3). lib. bdg. 11.80 (978-0-613-68450-7(8)) Tandem Library Bks.

Parker, Laurie. It Really Said Christmas. Parker, Laurie, illus. 2005. (J). pap. 17.95 (978-0-9772096-0-6(1)) Wild Hare Publishing.

Parker, Toni Trent. Snowflake Kisses & Gingerbread Smiles. Anderson, Earl, illus. 2002. 16p. (J). pap. 6.95 (978-0-439-33872-1(7) , Cartwheel Bks.) Scholastic, Inc.

Parks, Kathy, illus. Christmas with Night-Light. 2006. 18p. (J). bds. 8.99 (978-0-7847-1522-2(X) , 04413) Standard Publishing.

Parry, Alan. Badger's Christmas Day. Parry, Linda, illus. 2004. (ps-3). 15.00 (978-0-687-09703-6(7)) Abingdon Pr.

Parry, Linda & Parry, Alan. Christmastime with Mr Bear. 2006. 12p. (J). bds. 11.99 (978-0-7847-1469-0(X) , 04389) Standard Publishing.

Pass, Erica. Christmas Every Day. Saunders, Zina, illus. 2004. 16p. (J). lib. bdg. 12.00 (*978-1-4242-0970-5(6)) Fitzgerald Bks.

Passey, Marion. My Tiny Book of Christmas. Harston, Jerry, illus. 2006. (J). bds. 5.95 (978-1-886249-33-2(4) , Trumpet Media) WindRiver Publishing.

Paterson, Aileen. Maisie's Merry Christmas. Paterson, Aileen, illus. 2001. (Illus.). 32p. (J). pap. (978-1-871512-46-5(8)) Glowworm Bks., Ltd.

Paterson, Katherine. Angels & Other Strangers: Family Christmas Stories. 2006. 192p. (J). 9.99 (978-0-06-078376-1(1)) HarperCollins Pubs.

—Marvin's Best Christmas Present Ever. Brown, Jane Clark, illus. 2002. (J). 11.91 (978-0-7587-6200-9(3)) Book Wholesalers, Inc.

—Marvin's Best Christmas Present Ever. 1999. (I Can Read Bks.). (J). (978-0-606-17299-8(8)); lib. bdg. 11.80 (978-0-613-22890-9(1)) Tandem Library Bks.

Patterson, James. SantaKid. Garland, Michael, illus. 2004. 48p. (J). (gr. k-3). 14.99 (978-0-316-00061-1(2)) Little, Brown Bks. for Young Readers.

Patterson, Nancy Ruth. The Christmas Cup. Bowman, Leslie, illus. 2001. 108p. (gr. 4-7). pap. 10.95 (978-0-595-19075-1(8)) iUniverse, Inc.

Paulson, Michael W. The Baker Street Bunch No. 1: A Double Mystery Book. l.t. ed. 2004. (Illus.). 154p. (J). per. (978-0-9754241-0-0(6)) MiMar Publishing.

Pearson, Carol Lynn. A Christmas Thief: A Novel. 2003. 67p. 14.95 (978-0-8294-1764-7(8)) Loyola Pr.

PEEF Bears. (J). 7.95 (978-0-931674-38-9(7)); 12.95 (978-0-931674-54-9(9)); 11.95 (978-0-931674-34-1(4)) Waldman Hse. Pr., Inc.

Penn, Preston L. Little Pee-Wee Christmas Tree. Penn, Preston L., illus. 1998. (Illus.). 24p. (J). (ps-6). 14.95 incl. cd-rom (978-0-9667210-0-3(4)) Little Pee-Wee Publishing Co.

Pepper, Randolph E. F. Nicole & the Spirit of Christmas. 2000. 108p. (J). (gr. 4-7). pap. 9.95 (978-0-595-12504-3(2)) iUniverse, Inc.

Perez, Vivian. Stolen Stories for My Nieces. 2007. (ENG.). 68p. per. 12.95 ***(978-1-4241-6679-4(9))*** PublishAmerica, Inc.

A Perfectly Proper Christmas Video & Book Gift Set. 2001. (J). pap. 22.00 incl. VHS (978-0-9714334-1-0(0)) Visual Bk. Co., LLC, The.

Perry, Rex. All Things Bright & Beautiful. Perry, Rex, illus. 2004. (Jump at the Sun Holiday Classics Ser.). (Illus.). 24p. (ps-2). pap. 3.50 (978-0-7868-0925-7(6)) Hyperion Bks. for Children.

Perry, Rex, illus. 'Twas the Night Before Christmas. 2004. 24p. (J). lib. bdg. 8.00 ***(978-1-4242-0641-4(3))*** Fitzgerald Bks.

Peterson, Eugene H. The Christmas Troll. 2004. (Illus.). 40p. 14.99 (978-1-57683-681-1(9)) NavPress Publishing Group.

Peterson, M. Helen. Old Camel's First Christmas. 2004. (ENG.). 44p. (J). per. 17.99 (978-1-4141-0215-3(1)) Pleasant Word.

Pfister, Marcus. Aaron's Secret Message. Martens, Marianne, tr. from GER. 2005. (Illus.). 28p. (J). (ps up). 15.95 (978-0-7358-2020-3(1)) North-South Bks., Inc.

—The Christmas Star. 2004. (Illus.). 12p. (J). bds. 6.95 (978-0-7358-1973-3(4)) North-South Bks., Inc.

—Estrella de Navidad Board Book. 2005. (SPA., Illus.). 14p. (J). (ps up). bds. 6.95 (978-0-7358-2012-8(0)) North-South Bks., Inc.

Phillips, Jean. The Meaning of Christmas: A Children's Story in Picture & Verse. 2005. (ENG., Illus.). 24p. pap. 7.95 (978-0-929292-67-0(7) , 800-747-0738) Hannibal Bks.

Pienkowski, Jan. The First Noel: A Christmas Carousel. Pienkowski, Jan et al, illus. 2004. 10p. (J). 12.99 (978-0-7636-2190-2(0)) Candlewick Pr.

Pierce, Luther C. Taylor & Brittany Discover Christmas. Weber, Owen, illus. 1999. 44p. (J). (gr. 4-6). pap. 5.00 (978-0-9656620-3-1(9)) Birch Hill Pr.

Pilkey, Dav. Dragon's Merry Christmas. 2003. (Dragon's Tales Ser.: Bk. 3). (gr. k-3). lib. bdg. 14.10 (978-0-613-72145-5(4)) Tandem Library Bks.

—'Twas the Night Before Christmas: The Wrath of Mrs. Claus. 1999. (J). (978-0-590-12073-9(5) , Blue Sky Pr., The) Scholastic, Inc.

Pingry, Patricia A. Jolly Old Santa Claus: A Christmas Classic. 2000. (Illus.). 24p. (J). (ps-k). bds. 6.95 (978-0-8249-4182-6(9)) Ideals Pubns.

Pingry, Patricia A. On Christmas Morning. Barretta, Gene, illus. 2007. 26p. (J). (ps-k). bds. 6.99 ***(978-0-8249-6713-0(5)*** , Candy Cane Pr.) Ideals Pubns.

Pinkwater, Daniel M. Wolf Christmas. Pinkwater, Jill, illus. 1998. (Accelerated Reader Bks.). 32p. (J). (ps-3). 15.95 (978-0-7614-5030-6(0) , Cavendish Children's Bks.) Cavendish, Marshall Corp.

Piper, Watty. The Little Engine That Could & the Snowy, Blowy Christmas. Ong, Cristina, illus. (Little Engine That Could Ser.). (J). (ps-1). 2005. 12p. bds. 6.99 (978-0-448-43919-8(0)); 1998. 24p. pap. 3.99 (978-0-448-41850-6(9)) Penguin Group (USA) Inc. (Grosset & Dunlap).

Pittar, Gill. Milly, Molly & the Secret Scarves. 2004. 28p. (978-1-86972-027-8(X)) Milly Molly Bks.

—Milly, Molly & the Secret Scarves (book w/dolls) 2006. 28p. pap. (978-1-877337-42-0(0)) Milly Molly Bks.

Plan Nine Christmas Annual 2000. 2000. (Christmas Annual Ser.). 100p. pap. 14.95 (978-1-929462-21-6(2)) Plan Nine Publishing, Inc.

Plume, Ilse, illus. The Twelve Days of Christmas. 2005. 32p. (J). 17.95 (978-1-56792-300-1(3)) Godine, David R. Pub.

Polacco, Patricia. A Christmas Tapestry. Polacco, Patricia, illus. 2002. (Illus.). 48p. (J). (gr. k-3). 16.99 (978-0-399-23955-7(3) , Philomel) Penguin Group (USA) Inc.

—An Orange for Frankie. Polacco, Patricia, illus. 2004. (Illus.). 48p. (J). (gr. 1-5). 16.99 (978-0-399-24302-8(X) , Philomel) Penguin Group (USA) Inc.

—The Trees of the Dancing Goats. Polacco, Patricia, illus. 2002. (Illus.). (J). 25.11 (978-0-7587-3858-5(7)) Book Wholesalers, Inc.

—The Trees of the Dancing Goats. Polacco, Patricia, illus. 2000. (Illus.). 32p. (J). (gr. k-3). 7.99 (978-0-689-83857-6(3) , Aladdin) Simon & Schuster Children's Publishing.

—The Trees of the Dancing Goats. 2000. (J). (978-0-606-20094-3(0)) Tandem Library Bks.

—Trees of the Dancing Goats. 2000. (gr. k-3). lib. bdg. 15.30 (978-0-613-30164-0(1)) Tandem Library Bks.

—Welcome Comfort. Polacco, Patricia, illus. 2002. 40p. (J). pap. 6.99 (978-0-698-11965-9(7) , Putnam Juvenile) Penguin Group (USA) Inc.

—Welcome Comfort. 1999. (Illus.). 40p. (J). (ps-3). 16.99 (978-0-399-23169-8(2) , Philomel) Penguin Group (USA) Inc.

—Welcome Comfort. 2002. (gr. k-3). lib. bdg. 15.30 (978-0-613-50524-6(7)) Tandem Library Bks.

Pollock, Penny. A Christmas Journey. Watson, Richard Jesse, illus. Date not set. (J). (978-0-316-71356-6(2)) Little Brown & Co.

Ponko, Cindy A. Gary's Forever Christmas Tree. 2006. (J). (978-0-9768230-2-5(0)) Some Kids I Know.

Poole, Jack. Las Primas de Loreto. 2000. (SPA.). 120p. (gr. 4-7). pap. 7.95 (978-1-58348-610-8(0)) iUniverse, Inc.

Poole, Nancy W. Christopher the Christmas Tree. Burghdorf, Christie Stahl, illus. 1999. 28p. (J). (ps-6). pap. 14.95 (978-0-9673359-0-2(6) , 07) Grass Lake Publishing.

Potter, Beatrix. Merry Christmas, Peter Rabbit! 2003. (Illus.). 12p. (J). (ps). bds. 6.99 (978-0-7232-4925-2(3) , Warne) Penguin Group (USA) Inc.

—Peter Rabbit's Christmas Collection, 4 vols. 2003. (Illus.). 272p. (J). pap. 20.00 (978-0-7232-4937-5(7) , Warne) Penguin Group (USA) Inc.

—The Tailor of Gloucester. Jorgensen, David, illus. 2007. (J). 25.65 (978-1-59961-312-3(3)) ABDO Publishing Co.

Poydar, Nancy. Brave Santa. 2004. (Illus.). 32p. (J). (gr. k-3). tchr. ed. 16.95 (978-0-8234-1821-3(9)) Holiday Hse., Inc.

Pratchett, Terry. Hogfather. 2000. (gr. 5-8). lib. bdg. 15.30 (978-0-613-57222-4(X)) Tandem Library Bks.

Prater, John. Is It Christmas? Prater, John, illus. 2003. (Illus.). 32p. (J). 13.95 (978-0-7641-5668-7(3)) Barron's Educational Series, Inc.

Prati, Elisa. Mio Libro di Natale. pap. 24.95 (978-88-09-02754-1(X)) Giunti, Gruppo Editoriale ITA. *Dist:* Distribooks, Inc.

Preller, James. The Case of the Christmas Snowman. Alley, R. W., illus. 1998. (Jigsaw Jones Mystery Ser.: No. 2). 80p. (J). (gr. 1-4). pap. 3.99 (978-0-590-69126-0(0)) Scholastic, Inc.

—A Jigsaw Jones Mystery, Vol. 30. Alley, R. W. & Smith, Jamie, illus. 2006. (Jigsaw Jones Super Special Ser.). 112p. (J). pap. 4.99 (978-0-439-79396-4(3)) Scholastic, Inc.

Presley, Elvis. Elvis Presley's the First Noel. 1999. (Illus.). 32p. (J). (ps-3). 12.95 incl. cd-rom (978-0-06-028126-7(X)) HarperCollins Pubs.

—Elvis Presley's the First Noel. Whatley, Bruce, illus. 1999. 32p. (J). 5.95 (978-0-06-443615-1(2)) HarperCollins Pubs.

Priddy, Roger. Let's Decorate Christmas Stickers. 2007. 24p. (J). 5.95 ***(978-0-312-50020-7(3)*** , Priddy Bks.) St. Martin's Pr.

—Sing-along Christmas Carols. 2007. 24p. (J). bds. 12.95 ***(978-0-312-50019-1(X)*** , Priddy Bks.) St. Martin's Pr.

Primavera, Elise. Auntie Claus. 1999. (Illus.). 40p. (J). (ps-3). 16.00 (978-0-15-201909-9(X) , Silver Whistle) Harcourt Trade Pubs.

—Auntie Claus & the Key to Christmas. Primavera, Elise, illus. 2002. (Illus.). 40p. (J). (gr. k-3). 16.00 (978-0-15-202441-3(7) , Silver Whistle) Harcourt Trade Pubs.

Pritchard, Gretchen Wolff. I Love Christmas. 1999. (Illus.). 76p. (J). (gr. 3-6). pap. 17.95 (978-0-9614022-4-2(5)) Sunday Paper, The.

Pryor, Bonnie. Grandpa Bear's Christmas. 1999. (Illus.). 32p. (J). (ps-3). pap. 4.95 (978-0-688-17066-0(8)) HarperCollins Pubs.

—Grandpa Bear's Christmas. 1999. (J). (978-0-606-17245-5(9)) Tandem Library Bks.

Pulver, Robin. Christmas for a Kitten. Johnson, Layne, illus. (Albert Whitman Prairie Bks.). 32p. (J). (gr. k-3). 2005. pap. 6.95 (978-0-8075-1154-1(4)); 2003. 16.95 (978-0-8075-1151-0(X)) Whitman, Albert & Co.

Purmell, Ann. Christmas Tree Farm. Weber, Jill, illus. 32p. (J). 16.95 (978-0-8234-1886-2(3)) Holiday Hse., Inc.

Quigley's Village Staff. A Christmas Story: Joy of Giving. 1998. (Quigley's Village Ser.: Vol. 5). (J). (ps-2). 12.99 incl. VHS (978-0-310-58249-6(0) , V5155) Zondervan.

Rabe, Tish. Santa's Coming to Town! Sexton, Brenda, illus. 2006. (Nose Knows Ser.). 10p. (J). (ps-17). bds. 9.99 (978-1-58476-484-7(8) , IKIDS) Innovative Kids.

Rader, Laura. Santa's New Suit. Rader, Laura, illus. 2004. (Illus.). 32p. (J). (gr. k-3). reprint ed. 13.00 (978-0-7567-7154-6(4)) DIANE Publishing Co.

—Santa's New Suit. 2000. (Illus.). 40p. (J). (ps-3). 12.95 (978-0-06-028439-8(0)); 12.89 (978-0-06-029284-3(9)) HarperCollins Pubs.

Radzinski, Kandy. What Cats Want for Christmas. rev. ed. 2007. (Holiday Ser.). 32p. (J). 16.95 ***(978-1-58536-340-7(5))*** Sleeping Bear Pr.

Rae, Jaci. Collista's Search for the True Meaning of Christmas. 2007. (Illus.). 59p. per. 14.95 ***(978-0-9746229-1-0(5))*** North Shore Records, Inc.

Rahaman, Vashanti. O Christmas Tree. Lessac, Frane, illus. 2003. 32p. (J). (gr. 2-4). 14.95 (978-1-56397-237-9(9)) Boyds Mills Pr.

Rainsbury, Julie. Outrageous Oomph. Carpenter, Suzanne, illus. 2001. 48p. pap. 11.95 (978-1-84323-034-2(8)) Beekman Bks., Inc.

Ralph, Grampa. How Santa Knows. 2007. 56p. pap. 12.95 ***(978-1-4241-2284-4(8))*** PublishAmerica, Inc.

Randall, MarilynMae. Wishes for Christmas. 2002. (Illus.). (J). 9.99 (978-0-9713589-5-9(8)) Ubaviel's Gifts.

Random House Disney Staff. A Merry Mermaid Christmas. Berry, Bob, illus. 2004. 24p. (J). (ps-2). pap. 3.99 (978-0-7364-2268-0(4) , RH/Disney) Random Hse. Children's Bks.

Random House Disney Staff & Braybrooks, Ann. Funny Hunny Christmas. Williams, Don & Yee, Josie, illus. 2003. 24p. (J). (ps-2). pap. 3.99 (978-0-7364-1328-2(6) , RH/Disney) Random Hse. Children's Bks.

Random House Staff, ed. The Smallest Elf. 1999. lib. bdg. 7.99 (978-0-375-90101-0(9)) Random Hse., Inc.

Rangel, Graciela. Anthony's Christmas Journey. 2006. pap. 9.95 ***(978-1-59526-650-7(X)*** , Llumina Christian Bks.) Llumina Media Creations, Inc.

Ransom, Candice F. The Christmas Dolls. Fain, Moira, illus. 1998. 32p. (J). (gr. k-3). 15.95 (978-0-8027-8659-3(6)); lib. bdg. 16.85 (978-0-8027-8661-6(8)) Walker & Co.

Ransome, James E. Christmas Treasury. Date not set. (J). (978-0-8050-6621-0(7) , Holt, Henry & Co. Bks. For Young Readers) Holt, Henry & Co.

Rasmussen, Liz, illus. Too Fat to Fly. 2007. 32p. (J). 16.95 ***(978-0-9793517-0-9(7))*** Silver Bells Publishing Hse.

Rau, Dana Meachen. Holiday Time. 2004. (Compass Point Early Reader Ser.). (J). 18.60 (978-0-7565-0571-4(2)) Compass Point Bks.

Raudenbush, Brenda. Brilly & the Boot. Meyers, Holly B., illus. 1998. 97p. (J). (gr. 4-6). pap. 9.95 (978-0-9661531-0-1(3)) Panola Publishing Co.

Raum, Elizabeth. The Christmas Star. Johnson, Meredith, illus. 2007. 32p. (J). pap. 3.99 ***(978-0-8249-5567-0(6)*** , Ideals Children's Bks.) Ideals Pubns.

Raum, Elizabeth. Follow That Star: A Christmas Story. Johnson, Meredith, ed. Johnson, Meredith, illus. 2001. 32p. (J). 12.95 (978-0-8249-4136-9(5) , Candy Cane Pr.) Ideals Pubns.

Ray, Mary Lyn. Christmas Farm. Root, Barry, illus. 2008. (J). ***(978-0-15-216290-0(9))*** Harcourt Trade Pubs.

Read, Miss. The Christmas Mouse. Goodall, John S., illus. (J). lib. bdg. 14.95 (978-0-8488-1452-6(5)) Amereon LTD.

Reader's Digest Staff. Shrek the Halls: Lift-the-Flap. 2007. 10p. (J). (ps-k). bds. 9.99 ***(978-0-7944-1365-1(X))*** Reader's Digest Assn., Inc., The.

Reasoner, Charles. Ho! Ho! Ho! Reasoner, Charles, illus. 2003. (Illus.). 14p. (J). (ps). bds. 4.99 (978-0-8431-0281-9(0) , Price Stern Sloan) Penguin Group (USA) Inc.

—A Little Snowflake. Reasoner, Charles, illus. 2003. (Illus.). 14p. (J). (ps). bds. 4.99 (978-0-8431-0268-0(3) , Price Stern Sloan) Penguin Group (USA) Inc.

—No Peeking! Reasoner, Charles, illus. 2003. (Illus.). 14p. (J). bds. 4.99 (978-0-8431-0653-4(0) , Price Stern Sloan) Penguin Group (USA) Inc.

Rebmann, Charles. Christmas Stories from the Jersey Cape. 2003. 94p. pap. 9.95 (978-0-595-29692-7(0)) iUniverse, Inc.

The Recipe for Christmas Snow. 2003. (Illus.). 36p. per. 12.90 (978-0-9743840-3-0(8)) Creek Sound Bks.

Recorvits, Helen. Yoon & the Christmas Mitten. Swiatkowska, Gabi, illus. 2006. 32p. (J). 16.00 (978-0-374-38688-7(9)) Farrar, Straus & Giroux.

Reece, Stephen. Bubblebath & the Christmas Truck. 1998. (Illus.). 12p. (J). (ps-3). pap. 3.65 (978-1-892388-06-3(5)) Little Trucker Bks.

Reese, Michael. Christmas Party on the Farm. 2004. (J). per. 14.95 (978-0-9746213-0-2(7)) Sabre Publishing Hse., Inc.

Reimer, Ramon. The $1.89 Christmas Tree. Schroeder, Maurice, illus. 2002. 32p. (J). (gr. k-6). 14.95 (978-1-931650-17-5(9)) Coastal Publishing Carolina, Inc.

Reindeer. 2003. (Shaped Board Books Ser.). 14p. (J). (ps-k). bds. 9.95 (978-0-7525-8850-6(8)) Parragon, Inc.

Reinheimer, Melinda. A Christmas Tea. 2004. (J). per. 7.95 (978-1-59196-756-9(2)) Instantpublisher.com.

Reiss, Mike. How Murray Saved Christmas. Catrow, David, illus. 2000. 32p. (J). (ps-3). 10.99 (978-0-8431-7610-0(5) , Price Stern Sloan) Penguin Group (USA) Inc.

—How Murray Saved Christmas. Catrow, David, illus. 2004. 32p. (J). (gr. k-3). pap. 5.99 (978-0-14-250145-0(X) , Puffin) Penguin Group (USA) Inc.

—Merry Un-Christmas. Catrow, David, illus. 2006. 32p. (J). 15.99 (978-0-06-059126-7(9)); lib. bdg. 16.89 (978-0-06-059127-4(7)) HarperCollins Pubs.

—Santa Claustrophobia. Catrow, David, illus. 2002. 32p. (J). (gr. 2-5). 10.99 (978-0-8431-7756-5(X) , Price Stern Sloan) Penguin Group (USA) Inc.

—Santa Claustrophobia. Catrow, David, illus. 2006. 32p. (J). (ps). pap. 5.99 (978-0-14-240376-1(8) , Puffin) Penguin Group (USA) Inc.

Reiss, William & Greenblatt, C. H., illus. SpongeBob's Christmas Wish. 2003. (SpongeBob SquarePants Ser.). 32p. (J). 5.99 (978-0-689-85878-9(7) , Simon Spotlight/Nickelodeon) Simon & Schuster Children's Publishing.

Remkiewicz, Frank, illus. Froggy's Best Christmas. 2002. (Froggy Ser.). 13.19 (978-1-4046-1700-1(0)) Book Wholesalers, Inc.

Resnick, Jane Parker. A Christmas Carol: A Young Reader's Edition of the Classic Holiday Tale. Birmingham, Christian, illus. 2000. (Courage Children's Ser.). 56p. (J). (gr. 4-7). 9.98 (978-0-7624-0848-1(0) , Courage Bks.) Running Pr. Bk. Pubs.

Ricci, Christine. Dora's Christmas Adventure. Piluso, Piero, illus. 2006. (Dora the Explorer Ser.). 14p. (J). bds. 6.99 (978-1-4169-1755-7(1) , Simon Spotlight/Nickelodeon) Simon & Schuster Children's Publishing.

Ricci, Christine. Dora's Starry Christmas. Studios, A&J, illus. 2005. 24p. (J). lib. bdg. 9.00 ***(978-1-4242-0980-4(3))*** Fitzgerald Bks.

—Dora's Starry Christmas. Ziegler, Argentina Palacios, tr. A&J Studios Staff, illus. 2005. (Dora the Explorer Ser.). (SPA.). 24p. (J). pap. 3.99 (978-1-4169-1183-8(9) , Libros Para Ninos) Simon & Schuster Children's Publishing.

Ricci, Christine & A&J Studios Staff. Dora's Starry Christmas, Vol. 17. 2005. (Dora the Explorer Ser.). (Illus.). 24p. (J). pap. 3.99 (978-1-4169-0249-2(X) , Simon Spotlight/Nickelodeon) Simon & Schuster Children's Publishing.

Rice, James. Gaston the Green-Nosed Alligator. Rice, James, illus. 2nd ed. 1998. (Illus.). 32p. (ps up). 15.95 (978-1-56554-285-3(1)) Pelican Publishing Co., Inc.

Richards, Kitty. Have Yourself a Thornberry Little Christmas. 2000. (gr. k-3). lib. bdg. 14.15 (978-0-613-31296-7(1)) Tandem Library Bks.

—The Journey Begins: An Early Reader. movie tie-in ed. 2004. (Polar Express Ser.). (Illus.). 32p. (J). (gr. k-3). pap. 3.99 (978-0-618-47795-1(0)) Houghton Mifflin Co. Trade & Reference Div.

—Merry Christmas, Rugrats! Goldberg, Barry, illus. 1999. (Rugrats Ser.). 12p. (J). (ps-2). per. 10.95 (978-0-671-02941-8(X) , Simon & Schuster Children's Publishing) Simon & Schuster Children's Publishing.

Richardson, Faith. Angel Walker. 2003. Orig. Title: The Sea, the Song & the Trumpetfish. (Illus.). 172p. (J). 19.95 (978-0-9744989-2-8(0)); pap. 12.95 (978-0-9744989-3-5(9)) Fox Song Bks.

Richardson, Linda. The Gift. 2003. (J). 6.95 (978-1-59094-021-1(0) , Jawbreakers for Kids) Jawbone Publishing Corp.

Richmond, S. Grace. On Christmas Day in the Evening. 2007. (ENG.). 52p. per. 87.99 ***(978-1-4280-7449-1(X))*** IndyPublish.com.

Richter, Bernd & Richter, Susan. The Twelve Days of Christmas in Alaska. 2002. 14p. bds. 9.95 (978-1-931353-08-3(5)) Saddle Pal Creations, Inc.

Ricks, Kimber Orson. Discovering Santa: A Christmas Story. 2005. (YA). 7.99 (978-1-55517-862-8(6) , Bonneville Bks.) Cedar Fort, Inc./CFI Distribution.

Riley, Kellee, illus. Christmas Wishes. 2006. (Holly Hobbie & Friends Ser.). 24p. (J). pap. 3.99 (978-1-4169-2796-9(4) , Little Simon) Simon & Schuster Children's Publishing.

Rissik, Maureen. Keepsakes Christmas Box: A Holiday Gift to Unlock & Treasure. 2007. 24p. pap. ***(978-0-7624-3039-0(7)*** , Running Pr.); (Illus.). (J). (gr. 1-5). pap. 9.95 ***(978-0-7624-2993-6(3)*** , Running Pr. Kids) Running Pr. Bk. Pubs.

Ritchie, Joseph R. Where's Santa? Halverson, Lydia, illus. 2006. 14p. (J). (ps). bds. 7.95 (978-0-8249-6673-7(2) , Candy Cane Pr.) Ideals Pubns.

Roberts, Bethany. Christmas Mice. Cushman, Doug, illus. 2000. 32p. (J). (gr. k-ps). tchr. ed. 13.00 (978-0-395-91204-1(0) , Clarion Bks.) Houghton Mifflin Co. Trade & Reference Div.

—Christmas Mice. Cushman, Doug, illus. 2004. 32p. (J). (gr. k-ps). 5.95 (978-0-618-48601-4(1) , Clarion Bks.) Houghton Mifflin Co. Trade & Reference Div.

Roberts, Laura Peyton. New Beginnings. 1999. (Clearwater Crossing Ser.: No. 7). (J). (978-0-606-16380-4(8)) Tandem Library Bks.

Robertson, Elysia Hill. Santa the Chimney Sweep / The Candy Cane That Found A Home. Robertson, Elysia Hill, illus. 2005. (Illus.). 37p. (J). per. 6.95 (978-0-9764444-9-7(6)) E. J. Publishing.

Robinson, Angela. Ho Ho Ho: A Jolly Holiday Sticker Book. Cressy, Mike, illus. 2004. 16p. (J). pap. 4.99 (978-0-439-63584-4(5)) Scholastic, Inc.

Robinson, Laura. William & the Christmas Moon: A Shadow Casting Bedtime Story. 2000. (Illus.). 32p. (J). (gr. k up). spiral bd. 32.00 (978-0-87846-596-5(0)) Museum of Fine Arts, Boston.

Roche, Lynne. The Happiest Christmas. 2005. (Illus.). 32p. (J). (978-1-932485-27-1(9)) Reverie Publishing Co.

Rock, John P. Earl & Pearl, the Christmas Squirrels. Cohen, Stephen Z., illus. 1998. 24p. (J). (gr. 1-6). pap. 4.95 (978-0-9665625-3-8(4) , 0024) Habitat Pubns.

Rock, Lois & Ayliffe, Alex. My Very First Christmas Story. 1999. (Illus.). 24p. (J). 9.99 (978-0-7459-4056-4(0) , Lion) Lion Hudson plc GBR. *Dist:* Independent Pubs. Group.

Rockas, Leo. Mice Make War. 2007. 53p. 12.95 ***(978-1-4241-5708-2(0))*** PublishAmerica, Inc.

Rogers, Kenny & Junkerman, Kelly. Kenny Rogers Presents the Toy Shoppe. 2004. (Illus.). 30p. (J). (gr. 4-8). reprint ed. 16.00 (978-0-7567-7758-6(5)) DIANE Publishing Co.

Roll, Renee. A Crooked Christmas Tree. 2006. (J). per. 13.99 ***(978-0-9727995-1-5(6))*** Roll, Renee.

Romance, Trisha. A Star for Christmas. 2007. 40p. (J). 21.95 ***(978-0-88776-836-1(9))*** Tundra Bks. of Northern New York.

Romano, Ralph & Burke, Joe. Elbo Elf: The Package Master of Christmas. l.t. ed. 2000. (Illus.). 29p. (J). (gr. 1-5). 19.95 (978-0-9704125-0-8(9)) Elbo Elf, Inc.

Rosales, Melodye. 'Twas the Night B'Fore Christmas: An African-American Version. Rosales, Melodye, illus. 2002. (Illus.). (J). 22.40 (978-0-7587-3878-3(1)) Book Wholesalers, Inc.

Rosenberg, Liz. On Christmas Eve. Clapp, John, illus. 2000. (J). (978-0-7894-2620-8(X)) Dorling Kindersley Publishing, Inc.

Rouss, Sylvia. Littlest Tree. Binus, Ari, illus. 2005. 32p. (J). pap. 9.95 (978-1-932687-26-2(2) , Devora Publishing) Pitspopany Pr.

Rowlands, Avril. The Animals' Christmas: And Other Stories. 2003. (Illus.). 128p. (J). (gr. 2-5). pap. 7.99 (978-0-7459-3699-4(7) , Lion) Lion Hudson plc GBR. *Dist:* Independent Pubs. Group.

—The Christmas Sheep: And Other Stories. Moran, Rosslyn, illus. 2001. 48p. (J). (ps-3). 16.00 (978-1-56148-336-5(2)) Good Bks.

Rox, John. I Want a Hippopotamus for Christmas. Whatley, Bruce, illus. 2005. 32p. (J). 16.99 (978-0-06-052942-0(3)) HarperCollins Pubs.

Rucker, David. The Valley of the Christmas Trees: A Legend. Laster, Brenda, illus. 2007. 41p. (J). (ps-3). 14.95 (*978-1-931643-94-8(6)) Seven Locks Pr.

Rudolph the Red-Nosed Reindeer. 2004. 4p. (J). 3.95 (978-0-634-09040-0(2)) Leonard, Hal Corp.

Rue, Nancy N. Rough & Rugged Lily. 2002. (Ywof Library). (Illus.). 128p. (J). pap. 5.99 (978-0-310-70260-3(7)) Zonderkidz.

Ruelle, Karen Gray. The Crunchy, Munchy Christmas Tree. Ruelle, Karen Gray, illus. (Holiday House Readers Ser.). (Illus.). 32p. (J). (gr. k-3). tchr. ed. 14.95 (978-0-8234-1787-2(5)) Holiday Hse., Inc.

—Crunchy, Munchy Christmas Tree. (Illus.). 32p. (J). (gr. k-3). pap. 4.95 (978-0-8234-1799-5(9)) Holiday Hse., Inc.

Running Press Staff & Deere, John. Danny Dozer's Perfect Christmas Tree. 2007. (Illus.). 12p. (J). pap. 9.95 (*978-0-7624-3141-0(5)) , Running Pr. Kids) Running Pr. Bk. Pubs.

Running Press Staff & Hoffman, E. T. A. The Nutcracker. 2005. (Magic Windows Ser.). (Illus.). 12p. (J). 12.95 (978-0-7624-2093-3(6) , Running Pr. Kids) Running Pr. Bk. Pubs.

Runyon, Anne Marshall. The Sheltering Cedar. Runyon, Anne Marshall, illus. 2007. (Illus.). 32p. (J). (*978-1-933454-02-3(4)) Portal Pr.

Ruppert, Larry. A Christmas Story. gif. ed. 2007. (Dick & Jane Ser.). 32p. (J). 18.99 (978-0-448-44397-3(X) , Grosset & Dunlap) Penguin Group (USA) Inc.

Ryan, Pam Muñoz. There Was No Snow on Christmas Eve. Nolan, Dennis, illus. 2005. 32p. (ps-1). 15.99 (978-0-7868-5492-9(8)) Hyperion Pr.

Rylant, Cynthia. Christmas in the Country. Goode, Diane, illus. 32p. (J). (ps-3). 2005. pap. 5.99 (978-0-439-76985-3(X) , Scholastic Paperbacks); 2002. pap. 15.95 (978-0-439-07334-9(0) , Blue Sky Pr., The) Scholastic, Inc.

—Henry & Mudge & a Very Merry Christmas. Stevenson, Sucie, illus. (Henry & Mudge Ser.). 40p. (J). 2005. pap. 3.99 (978-0-689-83448-6(9) , Aladdin); 2004. 14.95 (978-0-689-81168-5(3)) Simon & Schuster Children's Publishing.

—Little Whistle's Christmas. Bowers, Tim, illus. 2003. (Little Whistle Ser.). 32p. (J). 16.00 (978-0-15-204590-6(2)) Harcourt Children's Bks.

—Little Whistle's Christmas. Bowers, Tim, illus. 2007. 32p. (J). 24.21 (*978-1-59961-254-6(2)) Spotlight.

Rylant, Cynthia, ed. Children of Christmas & Every Living Thing, Set. unabr. ed. 2000. (Young Adult Cassette Library). 38p. (J). (gr. 4-6). 27.98 incl. audio (978-0-8072-7325-8(2) , YA8185SP, Listening Library) Random Hse. Audio Publishing Group.

Sabuda, Robert. Christmas. 2006. (Illus.). 18p. (J). pap. 12.99 (978-0-439-84568-7(8) , Orchard Bks.) Scholastic, Inc.

—The 12 Days of Christmas: A Pop-up Celebration. Sabuda, Robert, illus. 10th anniv. ed. 2006. (Illus.). 14p. (J). (ps-3). 26.95 (978-1-4169-2792-1(1) , Little Simon) Simon & Schuster Children's Publishing.

Saillens, Ruben & Holder, M. I. G. Papa Panov's Special Day. Downing, Julie, illus. 2002. 32p. (J). (ps-ps). 14.99 (978-0-8423-7741-6(7)) Tyndale Hse. Pubs.

Salazar, Martinez Lydia. Lily, the Lost & Found Lamb. 2004. (Illus.). 32p. (ps-3). pap. 5.00 (978-0-687-09218-5(3)) Abingdon Pr.

Sammy & the White Christmas. 2004. (J). per. 15.99 (978-0-9753533-9-4(X)) Golden Eagle Publishing Hse., Inc.

Sander, Sharolyn. Red Boots for Christmas. 1999. (Illus.). (J). (ps-3). pap. 0.99 (978-0-570-05488-7(5)) Concordia Publishing Hse.

Sander, Sonia. Christmas Cheer. 2007. (Care Bears Ser.). 24p. (J). pap. 3.99 (*978-0-439-89511-8(1)) Scholastic, Inc.

—Twin Gifts. 2006. (Maya & Miguel Ser.: No. 1). 24p. (J). pap. 3.50 (978-0-439-83007-2(9)) Scholastic, Inc.

—Twin Gifts (Maya & Miguel: el Mejor Regalo) 2006. (Maya & Miguel Ser.). 24p. (J). pap. 3.50 (978-0-439-87385-7(1) , Scholastic en Espanol) Scholastic, Inc.

Sandridge, John Solomon. Papa-Cause: The Friend of Santa Claus. Sandridge, John Solomon, illus. 1998. (J). (ps-4). pap. (978-0-9667336-0-0(6)) Museum of Living History.

The Santa Claus Trap: Song-n-Sound Storybook. 2002. (Illus.). 5p. (J). (ps-1). bds. 5.99 (978-1-57759-995-1(0)) Dalmatian Pr.

Santa's Christmas Cookies. 2003. (J). per. (978-1-57657-708-0(2)) Paradise Pr., Inc.

Santa's Workshop. 2004. (J). per. (978-1-57657-450-8(4)) Paradise Pr., Inc.

Santiago, Esmeralda. A Doll for Navidades. Sanchez, Enrique O., illus. 2005. 32p. (J). (ps-3). pap. 16.99 (978-0-439-55398-8(9) , Scholastic Pr.) Scholastic, Inc.

—Una Muneca para el Dia de Reyes. Torres-Vidal, Nina, tr. Sanchez, Enrique O., illus. 2005. (SPA.). 32p. (J). (ps-3). pap. 5.99 (978-0-439-75510-8(7)) Scholastic, Inc.

Sargent, Dave & Sargent, Pat. Reini Reindeer: Special Events, 17, 56. Lenoir, Jane, illus. 2000. (Animal Pride Ser.: 56). (J). 42p. pap. 6.95 (978-1-56763-554-6(7)); 36p. lib. bdg. 19.95 (978-1-56763-553-9(9)) Ozark Publishing.

—Sweetpea: (Purple Corn Welsh) Be Happy, 30, 58. Lenoir, Jane, illus. 2003. (Saddle Up Ser.: Vol. 58). 42p. (J). pap. 6.95 (978-1-56763-816-5(3)); lib. bdg. 22.60 (978-1-56763-815-8(5)) Ozark Publishing.

Sawyer, Ruth. This Way to Christmas. 2004. reprint ed. pap. 22.95 (978-1-4179-3854-4(4)) Kessinger Publishing, LLC.

—The Wee Christmas Cabin of Carn-Na-Ween. Grafe, Max, illus. 2005. 40p. (J). (gr. 3 up). 14.99 (978-0-7636-2553-5(1)) Candlewick Pr.

Say, Allen. Tree of Cranes. Say, Allen, illus. 2002. (Illus.). 25.28 (978-0-7587-3857-8(9)) Book Wholesalers, Inc.

Scallan, Dee. Moby Pincher's Wonderful Christmas Present/ Dee Scallan. 2004. (J). pap. 9.95 (978-1-59453-542-0(6)) Airleaf Publishing & Bookselling.

Scarry, Patricia M. The Sweet Smell of Christmas. Miller, J. P., illus. 2003. 36p. (J). (gr. k-k). 8.99 (978-0-375-82643-6(2) , Golden Bks.) Random Hse. Children's Bks.

Scarry, Richard. The Best Christmas Present Ever. 1999. (J). (978-0-606-17199-1(1)) Tandem Library Bks.

—Christmas Mice. Scarry, Richard, illus. 2004. (Illus.). 26p. (J). (gr. k-k). bds. 4.99 (978-0-375-83004-4(9) , Golden Bks.) Random Hse. Children's Bks.

—Richard Scarry's Christmas Mice. Scarry, Richard, illus. 2004. (Illus.). 23p. (J). (gr. k-4). reprint ed. (978-0-7567-7752-4(6)) DIANE Publishing Co.

—Richard Scarry's Father Cat's Christmas Tree. 2003. (Illus.). 24p. (J). (ps-2). pap. 3.25 (978-0-375-82556-9(8) , Golden Bks.) Random Hse. Children's Bks.

—Richard Scarry's Father Cat's Christmas Tree. 2003. (gr. k-3). lib. bdg. 10.95 (978-0-613-71907-0(7)) Tandem Library Bks.

—Santa Needs Help! 2000. (J). (978-0-606-20036-3(3)) Tandem Library Bks.

Schatzer, Jeffrey L. The Bird in Santa's Beard: How a Christmas Legend Was Forever Changed. Smith, Ty, illus. 2005. 32p. (J). (ps-7). 18.95 (978-1-58726-288-3(6) , Mitten Pr.) Ann Arbor Media Group, LLC.

Schermbrucker, Reviva. An African Christmas Cloth. 2007. 36p. 27.95 (978-1-77009-081-1(9)); (Illus.). 40p. pap. 19.95 (978-1-77009-151-1(3)) Jacana Media ZAF. *Dist:* Independent Pubs. Group.

Schick-Jacobowitz, Jeannie, et al. A Bit of Applause for Mrs. Claus. Malinow, Wendy, illus. rev. ed. 2003. 64p. 9.95 (978-1-4022-0140-0(0)) Sourcebooks, Inc.

Schisgall, Jim. The Sand Witch Saves Christmas. Timmins, John, illus. 1998. 32p. (J). (ps-3). mass mkt. 6.95 (978-1-890997-01-4(3)) Hardy Hill Enterprises, Inc.

Schlafer, Linda. A Gift for the Christ Child: A Christmas Folktale. Wilson, Anne, illus. 2004. 26p. (ps-3). 15.95 (978-0-8294-1606-0(4)) Loyola Pr.

Schmidt, Troy. A Fruitcake Christmas. Glueworks Animation, illus. 2005. (Max Lucado's Hermie & Friends Ser.). (J). (gr. 3-7). 48p. 12.99 (978-1-4003-0545-2(4)); 24p. bds. 6.99 (978-1-4003-0546-9(2)) Nelson, Thomas Inc.

Schneider, Antonie. Advent Storybook: 24 Stories to Share Before Christmas. Dusikova, Maja, illus. 2005. 50p. (J). (ps up). 17.95 (978-0-7358-1963-4(7)) North-South Bks., Inc.

Schneider, Richard H. The Blue Angel Ornament: A Story of Love & Loyalty. Davis, Florence S., illus. 2004. 32p. (ps up). 17.00 (978-0-687-08181-3(5)) Abingdon Pr.

—The Christmas Pea Coat. Bond, Higgins, illus. 2004. 32p. (J). 14.95 (978-0-8249-5474-1(2)) Ideals Pubns.

—Zeek, the Christmas Tree Mouse. Davies, Florence S., illus. 2004. 18.00 (978-0-687-09465-3(8)) Abingdon Pr.

Schoberle, Cecile. Santa Claus & the Christmas Fairies. 1999. (ps-2). lib. bdg. 13.00 (978-0-613-88872-1(3)) Tandem Library Bks.

Scholastic, Inc. Staff. Barney's Christmas Countdown. 2007. (Barney Ser.). 12p. (J). bds. 3.99 (*978-0-545-00061-1(0)) Scholastic, Inc.

—The Christmas Cookie Case. del Sur, Duendes, illus. 2004. (Scooby Doo Ser.). 32p. (J). pap. 3.99 (978-0-439-55714-6(3)) Scholastic, Inc.

—A Christmas Treasury: Twelve Holiday Stories. 2000. (Illus.). 208p. (J). (gr. 4-7). pap. 9.95 (978-0-439-20848-2(3)) Scholastic, Inc.

—Merry Christmas! Neusner, Dena, ed. 2003. (Barney Ser.). 80p. (J). pap. 2.99 (978-0-439-52451-3(2)) Scholastic, Inc.

Scholastic, Inc. Staff. Working at the Christmas Tree Farm. 2007. (Tonka Power Reading Ser.). 32p. (J). pap. 3.99 (*978-0-439-88479-2(9)) Scholastic, Inc.

Scholastic, Inc. Staff & Brooke, Lauren. A Winter's Gift. 3rd rev. ed. 2007. (Heartland Special Edition Ser.). 192p. (J). pap. 5.99 (*978-0-439-92561-7(4) , Scholastic Paperbacks) Scholastic, Inc.

Scholastic, Inc. Staff & Smath, Jerry. Merry Christmas: Keepsake Storybook Collection. 2007. (Merry Christmas Ser.). (Illus.). 96p. (J). pap. 7.99 (*978-0-545-01341-3(0) , Cartwheel Bks.) Scholastic, Inc.

Scholey, Arthur. The Journey of the Christmas Creatures: A Dramatic Cantata. 1999. 57p. (J). (gr. k-8). pap. 25.00 (978-0-87602-370-9(7)) Anchorage Pr.

Schonewill, Lisa. Tell Me Mama, Is Santa Claus Real? 2005. (J). pap. 9.00 (978-0-8059-6373-1(1)) Dorrance Publishing Co., Inc.

Schuler, Karen. The Backyard Bears Present the Story of Christmas: A Nativity Play. Necaise, Jimmy, photos by. 2004. (Illus.). 32p. 14.99 (978-1-58169-148-1(3) , Evergreen Pr.) Genesis Communications, Inc.

Schultz, Charles M. A Charlie Brown Christmas. 2007. (Illus.). 10p. (J). bds. 7.95 (*978-0-7624-3172-4(5)) Running Pr. Bk. Pubs.

—A Charlie Brown Christmas: A Book-and-Tree Kit. 2007. (Illus.). 128p. pap. 8.95 (*978-0-7624-3145-8(8) , Running Pr. Minature Editions) Running Pr. Bk. Pubs.

Schulz, Charles M. A Charlie Brown Christmas. 2003. (Miniature Editionstm Ser.). (Illus.). 128p. 4.95 (978-0-7624-1601-1(7) , Running Pr. Minature Editions) Running Pr. Bk. Pubs.

—Charlie Brown Christmas. 2001. (gr. k-3). lib. bdg. 14.15 (978-0-613-61753-6(3)) Tandem Library Bks.

—A Charlie Brown Christmas. Braddock, Paige, illus. 2004. 28p. (J). (ps-ps). lib. bdg. 12.79 (978-0-606-30053-7(8)) Tandem Library Bks.

—Charlie Brown Christmas, Spec Sales Ed. 2004. 128p. 4.95 (978-0-7624-2289-0(0)) Running Pr. Bk. Pubs.

—Christmas Is Together-Time. 2006. (Peanuts Ser.). (Illus.). 72p. 5.95 (978-1-933662-37-4(9)) Cider Mill Pr. Bk. Pubs. LLC.

Schuyler, Bull. The Nutcracker. Smath, Jerry, illus. 1998. (Jewel Sticker Stories Ser.). 24p. (J). (ps-2). 3.99 (978-0-448-41852-0(5) , Grosset & Dunlap) Penguin Group (USA) Inc.

Schwartz, Betty Ann. The Twelve Days of Christmas. Moffatt, Judith, illus. 2007. 28p. (J). (ps-1). 12.99 (*978-0-06-120911-6(2) , Harper Festival) HarperCollins Pubs.

Scott-Cameron, Nancy. Santa Claus Is on a Diet. Conlan, Craig, illus. 2007. 32p. (J). (ps-k). 19.95 (*978-0-9546576-9-7(1)) Mogzilla GBR. *Dist:* Independent Pubs. Group.

Scott, Christina. All in A Night's Work. 2006. (J). lib. bdg. 19.95 (*978-1-933732-19-0(9) , Bear Hug Bks.) MidAmerica Publishing Co.

—The Chimney. 2006. (J). lib. bdg. 19.95 (*978-1-933732-18-3(0) , Bear Hug Bks.) MidAmerica Publishing Co.

—The North Pole. 2006. (J). lib. bdg. 19.95 (*978-1-933732-17-6(2) , Bear Hug Bks.) MidAmerica Publishing Co.

Scott, Kieran. Jingle Boy. 2003. 240p. (YA). (gr. 7). lib. bdg. 11.99 (978-0-385-90138-3(0) , Delacorte Bks. for Young Readers) Random Hse. Children's Bks.

Scotton, Rob. Russell's Christmas Magic. Scotton, Rob, illus. 2007. 32p. (J). lib. bdg. 17.89 (*978-0-06-059855-6(7)) HarperCollins Pubs.

Scrimger, Richard. Of Mice & Nutcrackers: A Peeler Christmas. 2001. lib. bdg. 16.40 (978-0-613-53630-1(4)) Tandem Library Bks.

—Of Mice & Nutcrackers: A Peeler Christmas. Hendry, Linda, illus. 2001. 232p. (J). (gr. 3-7). pap. 7.95 (978-0-88776-498-1(3)) Tundra Bks., Inc./Livres Toundra, Inc. CAN. *Dist:* Random Hse., Inc.

Scripture Teachers: Solomon & Friends Learn about the Christmas Story. 2003. pap. (*978-0-9712894-4-4(1)) Lighthouse Christian Products Co.

Sedgwick, Patricia Louise. Santa's Key. deluxe ed. 2004. (Illus.). 12.95 incl. audio compact disk (978-0-9688190-1-2(X)) F. D. & D. Corp. CAN. *Dist:* Hushion Hse. Publishing, Ltd.

See, Marcia A. The Candy Cane Rain. 2006. (Illus.). 53p. (J). per. 12.95 (*978-1-60002-218-0(9) , 4315, Airleaf Publishing) Airleaf Publishing & Bookselling.

Seglie, Susan & Schiefelbein, Janis. Sissy's Christmas Program. Zagorski, Astrid, tr. Papish, Adam, illus. 2003. (ENG & SPA.). (J). 4.95 (978-0-9747243-1-7(9)) Seglie, Susan M.

Sehlin, Gunhild. Mary's Little Donkey: And the Flight to Egypt. Latham, Hugh & Maclean, Donald, trs. from SWE. Verheijen, Jan, illus. 2004. 160p. (J). (gr. 3-6). pap. 12.00 (978-0-86315-064-7(0)) Floris Bks. GBR. *Dist:* SteinerBooks, Inc.

Seibold, J. Otto & Walsh, Vivian. Olive, the Other Reindeer. 10th deluxe anniv. ed. 2007. (Illus.). 40p. (J). (ps up). 19.95 (978-0-8118-5719-2(0)) Chronicle Bks. LLC.

Seigerman, Michelle. A Christmastime Book of Rhymes. 2005. 35p. pap. 13.08 (978-1-4116-4960-6(5)) Lulu.com.

A Semi for a Sleigh. 2005. audio compact disk 15.95 (978-1-59433-020-9(4)) Publication Consultants.

Seus. Wie der Grinch Weihnachten. pap. 14.95 (978-3-492-23722-2(3)) Piper Verlag GmbH DEU. *Dist:* Distribooks, Inc.

Seuss, Dr. Como el Grinch Robo la Navidad! 2000. (SPA.). (Illus.). 64p. (J). (ps-1). 15.00 (978-1-880507-73-5(0) , LC1744) Lectorum Pubns., Inc.

—How the Grinch Stole Christmas! 1999. (J). 12.99 (978-0-679-89270-0(2) , Random Hse. Bks. for Young Readers) Random Hse. Children's Bks.

—How the Grinch Stole Christmas! A 50th Anniversary Retrospective. 50th anniv. ed. 2007. (Illus.). 85p. (J). (gr. 1-4). lib. bdg. 32.99 (*978-0-375-93847-4(8)); 24.99 (*978-0-375-83847-7(3)) Random Hse. Children's Bks. (Random Hse. Bks. for Young Readers).

Seuss, Dr. Quomodo Invidiosulus Nomine Grinchus Christi Natalem Abrogaverit: How the Grinch Stole Christmas. Tunberg, Jennifer Morrish & Tunberg, Terence O., trs. from ENG. 1998. (LAT., Illus.). 64p. (ps-3). (J). 25.00 (978-0-86516-419-2(3)); (YA). 19.00 (978-0-86516-420-8(7)) Bolchazy-Carducci Pubs.

Shannon, David. The Amazing Christmas Extravaganza. Shannon, David, illus. 2004. (Bookshelf Ser.). 32p. (J). (gr. k-ps). pap. 5.99 (978-0-439-68347-0(5) , Scholastic Paperbacks) Scholastic, Inc.

Sharkey, Niamh. Santasaurus. Sharkey, Niamh, illus. 2005. (Illus.). 32p. (J). (ps-1). 15.99 (978-0-7636-2671-6(6)) Candlewick Pr.

Shaw, Sandra Anne. The Christmas Lambs. Bott, Mary Lou, illus. 2001. 24p. pap. 12.00 (978-0-9668891-2-3(6)) Teach My Children Pubns.

Shayne, Alan. The Minstrel Tree. Sunshine, Norman, illus. 2001. 100p. (J). 16.95 (978-0-9653431-5-2(4)) Design to Printing.

Shearon, Lillian Nicholson. The Little Mixer. 2005. reprint ed. pap. 15.95 (978-1-4179-1802-7(0)) Kessinger Publishing, LLC.

Shelton, Kathleen. Christmas in the Land of Oro Oro. Shelton, Kathleen, illus. 1999. (Illus.). 50p. (J). (ps-7). spiral bd. 4.95 (978-1-893566-04-0(8)) Kisco Pubns.

Shelton, Rick. Hoggle's Christmas. Gates, Donald, illus. 2007. 80p. (J). pap. 11.95 (*978-1-60306-026-4(X)) NewSouth, Inc.

Shepherd, Jodie. Merry Christmas, Rarity! Fletcher, Lyn, illus. 2006. (My Little Pony Ser.). 32p. (J). pap., act. bk. ed. 3.99 (978-0-06-079472-9(0) , Harper Festival) HarperCollins Pubs.

Sheppard, Dorothy M. & Sheppard, Jack G. Jo Jo the Elf Meets Santa's Enemy. Sheppard, Dorothy M. et al, illus. 65p. (J). (gr. 1-6). pap. 7.95 (978-0-9634300-0-7(9)) D&J Arts Pubs.

Shook Hazen, Barbara. The Christmas Star. 2006. (Nativity Lights Ser.). (Illus.). 10p. (J). bds. 10.99 (978-0-7944-1141-1(X)) Reader's Digest Assn., Inc., The.

Shulman, Mark. Storytime Stickers: Santa's on His Way. Wilburn, Kathy, illus. 2006. (Storytime Stickers Ser.). 16p. (J). pap. 4.95 (978-1-4027-3585-1(5)) Sterling Publishing Co., Inc.

Shulman, Mark & Less, Emma. Christmas Fun. Harpster, Steve, illus. 2005. (Little Scribbles Ser.). 12p. bds. 5.95 (978-1-4027-2254-7(0)) Sterling Publishing Co., Inc.

Silverhardt, Lauryn. Christmas in Blue's Room. Craig, Karen, illus. 2006. (Blue's Room Ser.). 14p. (J). bds. 6.99 (978-1-4169-1569-0(9) , Simon Spotlight/ Nickelodeon) Simon & Schuster Children's Publishing.

Simons, Joseph. Under a Living Sky. 2005. (Orca Young Readers Ser.). (Illus.). 144p. (J). (gr. 3-6). pap. 5.95 (978-1-55143-355-4(9)) Orca Bk. Pubs. USA.

Simont, Marc, illus. Nate the Great & the Crunchy Christmas. 2002. (Nate the Great Ser.). (J). 12.87 (978-0-7587-0704-8(5)) Book Wholesalers, Inc.

Simson, Dana. Countdown to Christmas with Me! 2002. (Sparkle Bks.). (J). bds. 14.95 (978-1-74047-210-4(1)) Book Co. Publishing Pty, Ltd., The AUS. *Dist:* Penton Overseas, Inc.

Skead, Robert. Elves Can't Tackle. 2004. (J). pap. 7.99 (978-1-929478-64-4(X)) Cross Training Publishing.

Skelton, Peter. Mr. Jimmy Chimney Sweep: The Mystery Elf of Christmas. 2000. (Illus.). 29p. (J). (ps-1). per. (978-0-9706099-0-8(6)) Breckenridge Group & Assocs.

—Twinkle Toes: The Magical Elf of Christmas. 2000. 24p. (J). (ps-1). per. (978-0-9706099-1-5(4)) Breckenridge Group & Assocs.

Slangerup, Erik Jon. Santa & Me. Janes, Joshua, illus. 2003. 32p. (J). (gr. k-2). 14.95 (978-1-57768-411-4(7) , Gingham Dog Pr.) School Specialty Publishing.

Slate, Joseph. Little Porcupine's Christmas. Bond, Felicia, illus. 2001. 32p. (J). (ps-1). 9.95 (978-0-06-029533-2(3) , Geringer, Laura Book) HarperCollins Pubs.

—Little Porcupine's Christmas. 2003. (gr. k-3). lib. bdg. 14.15 (978-0-613-68444-6(3)) Tandem Library Bks.

Slater, Teddy & Kindert, Jennifer. The Christmas Puppy. 2005. (Illus.). 24p. (J). (ps-ps). 6.95 (978-1-4027-1980-6(9)) Sterling Publishing Co., Inc.

Smath, Jerry. Once There Was a Christmas Tree. 2005. (Illus.). 40p. (J). (ps-3). pap. 10.99 (978-0-439-72499-9(6) , Cartwheel Bks.) Scholastic, Inc.

Smith, Geof & Hands, Cynthia. A Christmas Coral. 2001. (Little Golden Bks.). 32p. (J). (ps-3). pap. 3.99 (978-0-307-29055-7(7) , Golden Bks.) Random Hse. Children's Bks.

Smith, John A. A Special Christmas for Oscar. 2004. 31p. pap. 17.95 (978-1-4137-2892-7(8)) PublishAmerica, Inc.

Smith, Kathryn. Little Donkey's Christmas Story. Wood, Amanda, illus. 2002. (Snuffleheads Puppet Book Ser.). (J). (ps-3). 14p. 7.99 (978-0-8254-7251-0(2)); 8p. 7.99 (978-1-85985-441-9(9)) Kregel Pubns.

—Little Lamb's Christmas Story. Wood, Amanda, illus. 2002. (Snuffleheads Ser.). 14p. (J). (gr. k-3). 7.99 (978-1-85985-442-6(7)); 7.99 (978-0-8254-7253-4(9)) Kregel Pubns.

Smith, Mavis. 'Twas the Day after Christmas. Smith, Mavis, illus. 2001. (Holiday Lift-the-Flap Ser.). (Illus.). 16p. (J). pap. 5.99 (978-0-689-84162-0(0) , Little Simon) Simon & Schuster Children's Publishing.

Smith, Todd Aaron. Cow & the Christmas Surprise. Smith, Todd Aaron, illus. 2003. (Cows Adventure Ser.). (Illus.). 32p. (gr. k-2). 7.99 (978-0-8010-4517-2(7)) Baker Publishing Group.

Smythe, Theresa. Snowbear's Christmas Countdown, YOU. Ottaviano, Christy, ed. rev. ed. 2004. (Illus.). 40p. (J). 14.95 (978-0-8050-7244-0(6) , Holt, Henry & Co. Bks. For Young Readers) Holt, Henry & Co.

Snell, Gordon. Twas the Day after Christmas. Delonas, Sean, illus. Date not set. 32p. (J). (ps-3). 5.99 (978-0-06-443675-5(6)) HarperCollins Pubs.

—Twelve Days of Christmas. Date not set. (Illus.). 32p. (J). (ps-3). 5.99 (978-0-06-443674-8(8)) HarperCollins Pubs.

Snicket, Lemony, pseud. The Latke that Wouldn't Stop Screaming. Brown, Lisa, illus. 2007. 48p. 9.95 (*978-1-932416-87-9(0)) McSweeney's Publishing.

Snow, Alan. How Santa Really Works. Snow, Alan, illus. 48p. (J). 2007. 7.99 (*978-1-4169-5000-4(1) , Aladdin); 2004. (Illus.). 15.95 (978-0-689-85817-8(5) , Atheneum) Simon & Schuster Children's Publishing.

Snow X-mas. 2004. (J). per. (978-1-57657-384-6(2)) Paradise Pr., Inc.

Snowman. 2003. (Shaped Board Books Ser.). 14p. (J). (ps-k). bds. 9.95 (978-0-7525-8852-0(4)) Parragon, Inc.

Snyder, John. The Golden Ring: A Touching Christmas Story about Giving, Faith, Love & Loss. collector's ed. 1999. 170p. 15.95 (978-0-9675128-0-8(8)) Mountain Breeze Publishing.

Sobel, Gerrie. Jacob & His Magical Flying Bears: A Christmas Story. Torres, Dottie, illus. 2007. 32p. (J). 12.95 (*978-0-9798244-4-9(3)) TRIAD Publishing Group.

Solheim, James. Santa's Secrets Revealed: All Your Questions Answered about Santa's Super Sleigh, His Flying Reindeer, & Other Wonders. Gott, Barry, illus. 2004. (Carolrhoda Picture Books Ser.). 40p. (J). (gr. k-3). 15.95 (978-1-57505-600-5(3)) Lerner Publishing Group.

Sollinger, Emily & Hot Animation Staff, Animation. Arctic Adventure! 2004. (Rubbadubbers Ser.). 12p. (J). bds. 10.95 (978-0-689-87182-5(1) , Simon Spotlight) Simon & Schuster Children's Publishing.

Sommer, A. M. Tucker's Christmas. 2006. pap. 7.95 (978-0-533-15278-0(X)) Vantage Pr., Inc.

Sorenson, Margo. Ambrose & the Princess. Szegedi, Katalin, illus. 2005. 30p. (J). (ps-3). 16.95 (978-0-8146-3043-3(X)) Liturgical Pr.

Sortland, Bjorn. The Dream Factory Starring Anna & Henry. Christianson, Emily V. & Hedin, Robert, trs. from NOR. Elling, Lars, illus. 2003. (Picture Bks.). 40p. (J). (ps-3). 15.95 (978-0-87614-009-3(6) , Carolrhoda Bks.) Lerner Publishing Group.

Sowards, Ben, illus. Christmas Oranges. 2004. 32p. 17.95 (978-1-59156-098-2(5)) Covenant Communications, Inc.

Spangler, Paula Jeanne. Abigail's Christmas ~ Christmas Morn Reveals A Newborn. 2004. 17p. (J). pap. 14.08 (978-1-4116-1045-3(8)) Lulu.com.

Sparkie. Jolly Old Santa Claus: Coloring Book. 1998. (Illus.). 48p. (J). pap. 2.49 (978-0-8249-4098-0(9) , Candy Cane Pr.) Ideals Pubns.

Sparrow, G. Scott & Sparrow, Kathy. Andrews Quest for the Perfect Christmas Gift. 2005. 104p. (YA). pap. 16.95 (978-1-929841-43-1(4)) We Publish Bks.

Speare, Jean. A Candle for Christmas. Blades, Ann, illus. (J). pap. 4.95 (978-0-88899-149-2(5)) Groundwood Bks. CAN. *Dist:* Transition Vendor.

Special X-mas Tree. 2004. (J). per. (978-1-57657-386-0(9)) Paradise Pr., Inc.

Speirs, John. The Best Christmas Hunt Ever. Speirs, John, illus. 1999. (Illus.). 32p. (J). pap. 3.25 (978-0-439-04293-2(3) , Cartwheel Bks.) Scholastic, Inc.

—Little Boys Christmas Gift. 2001. (Illus.). 32p. (J). (ps-3). 16.95 (978-0-8109-4399-5(9)) Abrams, Harry N. , Inc.

Spelvin, Justin. Rainbow Brite Saves Christmas. Oliver, Kora, illus. 2004. (Rainbow Brite Ser.). 48p. (J). (ps-3). pap. 7.99 (978-0-439-65933-8(7)) Scholastic, Inc.

Spiewak, Chet. An Ornaments' Tale. 2006. 32p. pap. 16.95 (978-0-9785827-0-8(5)) CWS Studios, Inc.

Spinelli, Eileen & Parmenter, Wayne. When Christmas Came. Spinelli, Eileen & Parmenter, Wayne, illus. 2006. (Illus.). 32p. (J). (ps). bds. 16.95 (978-0-8249-5507-6(2) , Ideals Pr.) Ideals Pubns.

Spiradellis, Gregg. Jibjab Santa Book. Spiridellis, Evan, illus. 2007. 40p. (ps-17). 15.99 (***978-1-4231-0193-2(6)***) Hyperion Pr.

Spiridellis, Gregg & Spiridellis, Evan. Are You Grumpy, Santa? 2006. 32p. (ps-3). pap. 6.99 (978-0-7868-0997-4(3)) Hyperion Pr.

Spitz, Mary Y. Mint's Christmas Message. Pierce, Joanne Y., illus. 2003. 32p. 14.95 (978-0-9724570-0-2(3)) Mother Moose Pr.

Spohn. Turtle & Snake & the Christmas Tree. 2000. (Easy-to-Read Ser.). (J). (978-0-606-20262-6(5)) Tandem Library Bks.

Spohn, Kate. Turtle & Snake & the Christmas Tree. 2000. (Puffin Easy-to-Read Ser.). (978-0-606-20378-4(8)) Tandem Library Bks.

Spoon, Cynthia. The Ice Angel. 2006. (Illus.). 32p. (J). per. 8.50 (***978-1-60002-280-7(4)*** , 4233, Airleaf Publishing) Airleaf Publishing & Bookselling.

Spowart, Robin. Inside, Outside Christmas. 1998. (Illus.). 24p. (J). (ps-k). tchr. ed. 15.95 (978-0-8234-1370-6(5)) Holiday Hse., Inc.

Springer, David. Patch Quilt Santa. 2005. 16p. 11.95 (978-1-4116-3761-0(5)) Lulu.com.

Stahel, Merry Kesner. Jennifer's Christmas Gift. 2005. 48p. pap. 8.93 (978-1-4116-4029-0(2)) Lulu.com.

Stahl, Deborah Joan. The Man Called Christmas. 2004. (Illus.). 32p. (YA). per. (978-0-9755174-0-6(6)) Stahl Pubns.

Stainton, Sue. Christmas Magic. Melhuish, Eva, illus. 2007. 32p. (J). (ps-1). 15.99 (***978-0-06-078571-0(3)*** , Tegen, Katherine Bks) HarperCollins Pubs.

—Santa's Snow Kitten. Mortimer, Anne, illus. 2008. (J). (***978-0-06-082714-4(9)***); lib. bdg. (***978-0-06-082715-1(7)***) HarperCollins Pubs.

—Snow Cat. 2000. (Illus.). 32p. (J). pap. 15.99 (978-0-7868-0692-8(3)) Hyperion Bks. for Children.

—Snow Cat: Santa's Littlest Cat. Mortimer, Anne, illus. 2000. (J). (978-0-7868-4437-1(X)) Hyperion Bks. for Children.

Steele, Margaret. Wuz Da Nite Befo: A Pidgin Christmas Story in Hawaii. Chang, Roy, illus. 2005. 24p. 10.95 (978-1-56647-750-5(6)) Mutual Publishing LLC.

Steinhofel, Andreas & Jaffa, Alisa. An Elk Dropped In. Meyer, Kerstin, illus. 80p. (J). 16.95 (978-1-932425-80-2(2) , Lemniscaat) Boyds Mills Pr.

Stephens, Ann Marie. Christmas for Bly & Ray. Bolan, Michael P., illus. 2003. 45p. (J). per. 11.95 (978-0-9729285-0-2(2) , 0-9729285-0-2) Kinkachoo Pr., The.

Stephens, Monique. Berry Merry Christmas. Thomas, Laura & Ungrey, Tom, illus. 2003. (Strawberry Shortcake Ser.). 32p. (J). (gr. k-1). 9.99 (978-0-448-43200-7(5) , Grosset & Dunlap) Penguin Group (USA) Inc.

Stephens, Sarah Hines & Mason, Jane B. The Best Christmas. 2005. 128p. (J). (gr. 3-7). pap. 4.99 (978-0-439-68371-5(8) , Scholastic Paperbacks) Scholastic, Inc.

Stephenson, Kristina, illus. The Christmas Story. 2001. 16p. (J). 7.99 (978-0-310-70193-4(7)) Zondervan.

Stevenson, James. Christmas at Mud Flat. 2000. (Illus.). 48p. (J). (gr. 1-3). 15.89 (978-0-688-17302-9(0)) HarperCollins Pubs.

—Night after Christmas. 2003. (J). pap. 2.95 (978-0-590-41600-9(6)) Scholastic, Inc.

Stickland, Henrietta. The Christmas Express: A Pop-Up Village, Toy Train, Light & Sound! Stickland, Paul, illus. 1999. (J). (ps up). 16.95 (978-1-58117-048-1(3) , Intervisual/Piggy Toes) Dalmatian Pr.

Stiegemeyer, Julie. Christmas Night, Fair & Bright. Iwai, Melissa, illus. 2007. 32p. (J). (ps-2). 14.99 (***978-0-7586-1271-7(0)***) Concordia Publishing Hse.

Stiegemeyer, Julie. Merry Christmas, Cheeps! Baicker-McKee, Carol, illus. 2007. 24p. (J). (ps). 9.95 (978-1-59990-064-3(5)) Bloomsbury Publishing.

Stilton, Geronimo. Christmas Catastrophe. ed. 2007. (Geronimo Stilton Ser.). 128p. (J). pap. 6.99 (***978-0-545-00902-7(2)*** , Scholastic Paperbacks) Scholastic, Inc.

—A Christmas Tale. ed. 2005. (Geronimo Stilton Ser.). (Illus.). 64p. (J). (gr. 2-5). pap. 6.99 (978-0-439-79131-1(6) , Scholastic Paperbacks) Scholastic, Inc.

—The Christmas Toy Factory. 2006. (Geronimo Stilton Ser.: No. 27). (Illus.). (J). 128p. pap. 6.99 (978-0-439-84118-4(6) , Scholastic Paperbacks); 95p. (***978-1-4156-8969-1(5)***) Scholastic, Inc.

Stilton, Geronimo. Merry Christmas, Geronimo! Wolf, Matt, illus. 2004. (Geronimo Stilton Ser.: No. 12). 113p. (J). lib. bdg. 10.00 (***978-1-4242-0281-2(7)***) Fitzgerald Bks.

—Merry Christmas, Geronimo! 2004. (Geronimo Stilton Ser.: No. 12). (Illus.). 128p. (J). (gr. 2-5). pap. 6.99 (978-0-439-55974-4(X) , Scholastic Paperbacks) Scholastic, Inc.

Stirnkorb, Patricia. A Place for the King: Christmas from the Angels Point of View. Bock, Suzanne, illus. 2004. 48p. (J). 15.99 (978-0-9758709-6-9(3) , 12420) Journey Stone Creations, LLC.

Stock, Catherine, illus. Gus & Grandpa & the Christmas Cookies. 2002. (Gus & Grandpa Ser.). (J). 22.19 (978-0-7587-1233-2(2)) Book Wholesalers, Inc.

Stoeke, Janet Morgan. A Minerva Louise Christmas. 2007. 24p. (J). (ps). 15.99 (***978-0-525-47857-7(4)*** , Dutton Juvenile) Penguin Group (USA) Inc.

Stohner, Anu. Santa's Littlest Helper Travels the World. Wilson, Henrike, illus. 2007. 32p. (J). (ps-3). 15.95 (***978-1-59990-187-9(0)*** , Bloomsbury Children) Bloomsbury Publishing.

Stone, Carol. Mrs. Claus Invites You. 1999. (J). (gr. k-3). pap. 7.95 (978-0-533-13162-4(6)) Vantage Pr., Inc.

Stoops, Erik, Sr. The Forgotton Ornament , A christmas Story. 2006. (Illus.). 32p. (J). (978-0-9765358-2-9(3)) Strategic Dreamers, LLC.

Story Lady. The Master Toy Maker. 2001. 128p. pap. 10.95 (978-0-595-20708-4(1) , Writers Club Pr.) iUniverse, Inc.

Story of the Christmas Elves. 2001. 26p. (J). 12.95 (978-0-9712332-0-1(9)) G. D. Stewart Publishing.

Stowe, Harriet Beecher. The First Christmas in New England. 2002. (Illus.). 43p. 12.95 (978-1-55709-479-7(9)) Applewood Bks.

Stowell, Gordon. Christmas Trio, 3 vols., Set. Stowell, Gordon, illus. 1999. (Illus.). 18p. (J). (ps-3). bds. 10.00 (978-0-8170-1310-3(5)) Judson Pr.

Stren, Patti. A Real Family Christmas. 1999. (J). (978-0-7868-0187-9(5)) Hyperion Pr.

Strigel, Judy & Edwards, Linda. Stories of Santa & the Elfs: Alexander Reindeer Stories. Erickson, Beverly, ed. Strigel, Judy & Burge, Tom, illus. 1998. (Alexander, Santa's Newest Reindeer Ser.: No. 2). 240p. (J). (gr. 2-4). pap. (978-1-885527-14-1(4)) Feather Fables Publishing Company.

Strockyj, Sonia. The Spider & the Christmas Tree. 2004. 12p. per. 7.95 (978-1-59453-537-6(X) , 2727) Airleaf Publishing & Bookselling.

Stuart, Ruth Mcenery. A Christmas Guest. 2004. reprint ed. pap. 15.95 (978-1-4191-0046-8(7)); pap. 1.99 (978-1-4192-0046-5(1)) Kessinger Publishing, LLC.

Sturges, Philemon. Twelve Days of Christmas. Wolff, Ashley, illus. 2007. 32p. (J). (ps-1). 16.99 (***978-0-316-82323-4(6)***) Little, Brown Bks. for Young Readers.

Sullivan, Ellen. How Santa Got His Elves. Eldredge, Ernie, illus. 1998. (J). (978-1-58173-148-4(5)) Sweetwater Pr.

Sutton, Marvin. Santa & Marvin. 2001. 91p. pap. (978-1-893181-59-5(6) , Lagesse Stevens) Martell Publishing Co.

Swigut, Bernadetta. First Star: Vigilja- First Star. 2006. (J). 16.99 (978-0-9790026-0-1(5)) Steinschneider, Bernadetta.

Sykes, Julie. Bless You, Santa! Warnes, Tim, illus. 2004. 32p. (J). tchr. ed. 15.95 (978-1-58925-041-3(9) , tiger tales) ME Media LLC.

—Careful, Santa! Warnes, Tim, illus. 2002. 32p. (J). (ps-1). tchr. ed. 14.95 (978-1-58925-023-9(0) , tiger tales) ME Media LLC.

—Hurry, Santa! Warnes, Tim, illus. (J). (ps-1). 1999. 14p. bds. 6.95 (978-1-888444-73-5(8)); 1998. 32p. 14.95 (978-1-888444-37-7(1)) Little Tiger Pr.

—Santa's Busy Day: Giant Board Book. Warnes, Tim, illus. 1998. 5p. (J). (ps-1). bds. 11.95 (978-1-888444-48-3(7)) Little Tiger Pr.

—Shhh! Warnes, Tim, illus. 2006. 18p. (J). bds. 6.95 (978-1-58925-796-2(0) , tiger tales) ME Media LLC.

Sypolt, Carl W. Fibber Lygood at Christmas, Easter, & St. Patrick's Day. 2006. 108p. (J). pap. 10.95 (978-0-7414-2982-7(9)) Infinity Publishing.

Tafuri, Nancy. Counting to Christmas. 1998. (J). pap. (978-0-590-27144-8(X)) Scholastic, Inc.

—The Donkey's Christmas Song. Tafuri, Nancy, illus. 2002. (Illus.). 32p. (J). (ps-k). pap. 16.95 (978-0-439-27313-8(7) , Scholastic Pr.) Scholastic, Inc.

—Donkey's Christmas Song. 2006. (Illus.). 32p. (J). bds. 7.99 (978-0-439-74618-2(3) , Scholastic Pr.) Scholastic, Inc.

—The Donkey's Christmas Welcome. 2002. (Illus.). (J). pap. (978-0-439-27314-5(5)) Scholastic, Inc.

Tait, Katie. Catch the Christmas Spirit! 2003. (Care Bears Ser.). (Illus.). 16p. (J). bds. 4.99 (978-0-439-46023-1(9) , Scholastic Paperbacks) Scholastic, Inc.

The Talking Christmas Tree. 2003. (J). per. (978-1-57657-925-1(5)) Paradise Pr., Inc.

Tangvald, Christine. Christmas is...for Me! 2000. (for Me! Bks.). (Illus.). 24p. (J). (ps-2). pap. 3.99 (978-0-7642-2337-2(2)) Bethany Hse. Pubs.

Tangvald, Christine Harder. Let's Remember Jesus' Birth on Christmas. Nobens, Cheryl A., illus. 2006. (Holiday Discovery Ser.). 24p. (J). (ps-3). bds. 6.99 (978-0-7847-1384-6(7) , 04049) Standard Publishing.

Tangvald, Christine Harder & Imhof, Valerie. Twinkle, Twinkle Christmas Star. Imhof, Valerie, illus. 2003. (Illus.). 10p. (J). 7.99 (978-0-310-70570-3(3)) Zonderkidz.

Tanner, Suzy-Jane. The Silly Christmas Card Mix-Up. 1998. (Lift-the-Flap Bk.). (Illus.). 20p. (J). (ps up). 6.95 (978-0-694-01124-7(X)) HarperCollins Pubs.

Tarkington, Booth. Beasley's Christmas Party. 2005. 76p. pap. 10.95 (978-1-4218-0407-1(7) , 1st World Library - Literary Society) 1st World Publishing, Inc.

—Beasley's Christmas Party. Clements, Ruth Sypherd, illus. 2004. reprint ed. pap. 15.95 (978-1-4179-0186-9(1)) Kessinger Publishing, LLC.

—Beasley's Christmas Party. 2004. reprint ed. pap. 1.99 (978-1-4192-0925-3(6)) Kessinger Publishing, LLC.

Taylor, Jeannie St. John. Penguin's Special Christmas Tree. Idle, Molly Schaar, illus. 2007. 24p. (J). (ps-1). 16.95 (***978-1-897073-61-2(5)***); pap. 9.95 (***978-1-897073-64-3(X)***) Lobster Pr. CAN. *Dist:* National Bk. Network.

Tazewell, Charles. The Littlest Angel. lthr. 29.95 (978-0-8249-5333-1(9)) Ideals Pubns.

—The Littlest Angel. Rasmussen, Wendy, illus. 2007. 32p. pap. 3.99 (***978-0-8249-5549-6(8)*** , Ideals Children's Bks.) Ideals Pubns.

—The Littlest Angel. Porfirio, Guy, illus. 2004. 32p. (J). 16.95 (978-0-8249-5473-4(4)) Ideals Pubns.

—The Littlest Angel. Thornburgh, Rebecca McKillip, illus. 2002. (J). (978-0-8249-4232-8(9) , Candy Cane Pr.) Ideals Pubns.

—The Littlest Angel. Lanino, Deborah, illus. 1998. (Modern Rhymes about Ancient Times Ser.). 32p. (YA). (ps up). 29.00 (978-0-516-20433-8(5) , Children's Pr.) Scholastic Library Publishing.

—The Littlest Angel. 1998. pap. 7.95 (978-0-516-26192-8(4) , Children's Pr.) Scholastic Library Publishing.

T'choupi Fete Noel. 2000. (FRE.). (J). (978-2-09-202038-8(2)) Nathan, Fernand FRA. *Dist:* Distribooks, Inc.

Telfeyan, Kate, adapted by. Eloise at Christmas. 2003. 32p. (J). 6.99 (978-0-689-86982-2(7) , Simon Spotlight) Simon & Schuster Children's Publishing.

TerKeurst, Lysa. The Sweetest Story Ever Told: A New Christmas Tradition for Families. Sparks, Michal, illus. 2003. 32p. 9.99 (978-0-8024-7094-2(7)) Moody Pubs.

Tews, Susan. The Gingerbread Doll. 2001. (gr. k-3). lib. bdg. 14.10 (978-0-613-35518-6(0)) Tandem Library Bks.

That's What a Friend Is! 2003. 24p. (J). bds. 6.95 (978-0-8249-5468-0(8)) Ideals Pubns.

Thayer, Jane. The Puppy Who Wanted a Boy. McCue, Lisa, illus. 2005. 32p. (J). pap. 6.99 (978-0-06-052698-6(X) , Harper Trophy) HarperCollins Pubs.

Theriault, Francis Patrick. The Candy Coated Castle's Catastrophe: A Christmas Crisis. 2006. (ENG.). 48p. per. 10.95 (978-1-59800-555-4(3)) Outskirts Press, Inc.

Thomas, Jerry D. The Missing Manger Mystery. Odell, Lad, illus. 2003. (Detective Zack Ser.). 132p. (J). pap., pap. 6.99 (978-0-7814-3789-9(X) , 078143789X) Cook, David C. Publishing Co.

Thomas, Joan M. Mimi's Gift. 2004. (Illus.). 112p. (J). (ps-4). pap. 14.95 (978-1-57921-482-1(7)) WinePress Publishing.

Thomas Nelson Publishing Staff. My Christmas Collection: Three Favorite Stories. 2006. 80p. (J). 14.99 (978-1-4003-0843-9(7)) Nelson, Thomas Inc.

Thompson, Kay. Eloise. Knight, Hilary, illus. 2002. (Eloise Ser.). (SPA.). 64p. (J). (gr. k-3). 17.00 (978-84-264-3735-8(4) , LM30420) Editorial Lumen ESP. *Dist:* Distribooks, Inc., Lectorum Pubns., Inc.

Thompson, Kay. Eloise's Christmas Trinkles. Knight, Hilary, illus. 2007. (Eloise Ser.). 48p. (J). (ps-3). 9.99 (***978-0-689-87425-3(1)***) Simon & Schuster Children's Publishing.

Thompson, Lauren. A Christmas Gift for Mama. Burke, Jim, illus. 2003. (J). 48p. pap. 16.95 (978-0-590-30725-3(8)); pap. 16.95 (978-0-590-30726-0(6)) Scholastic, Inc.

—Mouse's First Christmas. Erdogan, Buket, illus. 2002. (Classic Board Bks.). 34p. (J). (ps-1). 7.99 (978-0-689-85141-4(3) , Little Simon) Simon & Schuster Children's Publishing.

—Mouse's First Christmas. 2003. (ps-2). lib. bdg. 14.15 (978-0-613-91039-2(7)) Tandem Library Bks.

—One Starry Night. 2000. (J). lib. bdg. 16.00 (978-0-689-82851-5(9) , Simon & Schuster Children's Publishing) Simon & Schuster Children's Publishing.

Thompson, Lauren & Erdogan, Buket. Mouse's First Christmas. 2003. (Illus.). 32p. (J). pap. 5.99 (978-0-689-86348-6(9) , Aladdin) Simon & Schuster Children's Publishing.

Thomson. Stocking Full of Christmas Stories. 2000. (Illus.). 165p. (J). pap. 4.95 (978-0-552-52739-2(4) , Corgi Bks. Ltd.) Random Hse. Children's Bks. GBR. *Dist:* Trafalgar Square Publishing.

Thomson, Emma. Dandelion's Christmas. 2007. (Illus.). 32p. 9.95 (***978-0-340-91192-1(1)***) Hodder Children's Division GBR. *Dist:* Independent Pubs. Group.

Thomson, Pat. Cracker Full of Christmas Stories. 2000. (Illus.). 165p. (J). 15.95 (978-0-385-40483-9(2)) Transworld Publishers Ltd. GBR. *Dist:* Trafalgar Square Publishing.

Thorup, Bryce. Doctor Matthews' Family Christmas. Muller, Ruth, illus. 2005. (J). 18.95 (978-0-9765964-1-7(5)) Round Tower Pr.

Thury, Frederick. The Last Straw. van Kampen, Vlasta, illus. 1999. 32p. (J). (ps-3). 15.95 (978-0-88106-152-9(2)) Charlesbridge Publishing, Inc.

Tobiassen, Virginia Hege. The Gift of the Magi Retold in Rhyme. 2002. viii, 40p. pap. 12.95 (978-0-9723095-0-9(0)) Ashe Street Hse., The.

Todd, Ann. Grinchkin Kirkpatrick's First Christmas. 2003. pap. 10.95 (978-0-533-14255-2(5)) Vantage Pr., Inc.

Toews, Rita. Christmas Stars. Macaire, Jennifer, illus. 2002. E-Book 10.95 incl. cd-rom (978-1-59201-005-9(9)) Bks. Unbound E-Publishing Co.

Tolan, Stephanie S. Bartholomew's Blessing. Moore, Margie, illus. 2004. 32p. (J). (ps-3). lib. bdg. 16.89 (978-0-06-001198-7(X)) HarperCollins Pubs.

Tolkien, J. R. R. Father Christmas Letters. 1998. (Illus.). 96p. (ps-3). 5.95 (978-0-395-95919-0(5)) Houghton Mifflin Co. Trade & Reference Div.

—Letters from Father Christmas. Tolkien, Baillie, ed. 2004. (Illus.). 112p. pap. 15.00 (978-0-618-51265-2(9)) Houghton Mifflin Co. Trade & Reference Div.

—Letters from Father Christmas. rev. ed. 1999. (Illus.). 160p. (ps-3). 20.00 (978-0-618-00937-4(X)) Houghton Mifflin Co. Trade & Reference Div.

Tomkinson, Raymond. Bravo the Donkey & Other Stories for Christmas. 2006. 72p. pap. (***978-1-84549-151-2(3)***) arima publishing.

Toner, Gerald. Lipstick Like Lindsay & Other Christmas Stories. 2005. (Illus.). 112p. pap. 12.95 (978-1-58980-357-2(4)) Pelican Publishing Co., Inc.

Too Many Tamales. (Lexile Levels Ser.). 9.09 (978-1-56334-704-7(0)) Hampton-Brown Bks.

Treasury of Christmas Tales. bds. 15.98 (978-0-7853-0820-1(2)) Publications International, Ltd.

Trebi-Ollennu, Flora. A Big Christmas Surprise for Sweetie Awo. Burgesson, Kate & Adu Nyarko, Margaret M., illus. 2000. (Sunbeamy Kids Ser.). 90p. (J). (gr. 4-6). pap. (978-1-894718-00-4(3)) Amerley Treb Bks.

Trent, Ernie. Hoboken's Christmas Surprise. 2003. 28p. pap. 13.99 (978-1-4134-0290-2(9)) Xlibris Corp.

Tripp, Valerie. Kit's Surprise: A Christmas Story, Bk. 3. Rane, Walter & McAliley, Susan, illus. 2000. (American Girls Collection: Bk. 3). 80p. (J). (gr. 2 up). 12.95 (978-1-58485-021-2(3)) American Girl Publishing, Inc.

—Kit's Surprise: A Christmas Story, Bk. 3. Rane, Walter, illus. 2000. (American Girls Collection: Bk. 3). 80p. (YA). (gr. 2 up). pap. 6.95 (978-1-58485-020-5(5)) American Girl Publishing, Inc.

—Kit's Surprise: A Christmas Story. 2000. (gr. 3-6). lib. bdg. 14.10 (978-0-613-28918-4(8)); (American Girls Collection: Bk. 3). (YA). (gr. 2 up). (978-0-606-18944-6(0)) Tandem Library Bks.

Trocme, Andre. Angels & Donkeys: Tales for Christmas & Other Times. Hewett, Nelly Trocme, tr. from FRE. gif. ed. 2002. 170p. 12.95 (978-1-56148-263-4(3)) Good Bks.

Trosclair Staff. Cajun Night Before Christmas Ornament. Jacobs, Howard, ed. Rice, James, illus. 2000. 48p. (J). (ps-3). pap. 8.95 (978-1-56554-849-7(3)) Pelican Publishing Co., Inc.

Tryon, Leslie. Albert's Christmas. 2000. (J). (978-0-606-19247-7(6)) Tandem Library Bks.

Tucker, Author David J. Stickman World Larry & George have a Merry Christmas. 2005. 23p. (J). 11.68 (978-1-4116-5615-4(6)) Lulu.com.

Tudor, Tasha. Corgiville Christmas. 2004. (Corgiville Ser.: Bk. 3). (Illus.). 48p. (J). 15.95 (978-1-932425-00-0(4) , Lemniscaat) Boyds Mills Pr.

—The Dolls' Christmas. unabr. ed. 2000. (YA). (ps). pap. 29.95 incl. audio (978-0-7887-3795-4(3) , 41039X4) Recorded Bks., LLC.

Turk, Ruth. The Doll on the Top Shelf. Volquartz, Per, illus. 1998. 32p. (J). (gr. k-3). 15.95 (978-1-891992-02-5(3)) Owl's Hse. Pr.

Turman, Evelyn. J. B. 's Christmas Presents. Turman, Adam, illus. Lt. ed. 2004. 28p. (J). 15.95 (978-0-9753042-0-4(8)) Turman, E.

Turner, Barbara F. Charles T. Bear & the Christmas Snow. Turner, Barbara F., illus. 1998. (Illus.). (J). (ps-3). pap. 6.00 (978-1-892614-07-0(3) , SC-CTB-2) Briarwood Pubns.

Turner, Christina. Hello Santa! 2007. (Illus.). 16p. (ps). per., bds. 7.95 (***978-0-9790347-0-1(1)***) Mackenzie Smiles.

Turner, Thomas Noel. Hillbilly Night Before Christmas. Rice, James, illus. 1998. 32p. (J). (ps-3). reprint ed. 15.95 (978-0-88289-367-9(X)) Pelican Publishing Co., Inc.

Twas the Night Before Christmas. 2002. (J). bds. 19.95 (978-0-7525-6654-2(7)) Parragon, Inc.

Twelve Days of Christmas with You. gif. ed. 2001. (Illus.). 80p. (978-0-7416-1230-4(5)) Havoc Publishing.

Twyman, Gib. Santa's Wild Goose Chase. Cundiff, Meg, illus. 2002. 30p. (ps-3). 14.95 (978-1-886110-32-8(8)) Addax Publishing Group, Inc.

Tyrrell, Frances. Woodland Christmas: Twelve Days of Christmas in the North Woods. 2000. (J). 5.99 (978-0-590-86368-1(1)) Scholastic, Inc.

Tyrrell, Melissa. Here Comes Santa! A Little Foil Book. 1998. (Merry Little Foil Bks.). (Illus.). 10p. (YA). (ps up). 2.95 (978-1-58117-007-8(6) , Intervisual/Piggy Toes) Dalmatian Pr.

—Hurray for Snow! A Little Foil Book. 1998. (Merry Little Foil Bks.). (Illus.). 10p. (YA). (ps up). 3.95 (978-1-58117-008-5(4) , Intervisual/Piggy Toes) Dalmatian Pr.

—The Little Reindeer: A Little Foil Book. 1998. (Merry Little Foil Bks.). (Illus.). 10p. (YA). (ps up). 2.95 (978-1-58117-010-8(6) , Intervisual/Piggy Toes) Dalmatian Pr.

Ulmer, Louise. The Bible That Wouldn't Burn: How the Tyndale English Version of the Bible Came About. 2nd l.t. ed. 2003. (Illus.). 32p. 4.95 (978-0-941367-01-1(0)) Peach Blossom Pubns.

Uncle Markie. Piglettè & Bobo Christmas in Palm Springs. 2003. (YA). ring bd. 9.95 (978-1-933129-10-5(7)) Studio 403.

C D

Uncle Walt's Christmas Box. 2001. 36p. (J). (gr. k-3). 10.99 (978-0-8254-7243-5(1)) Kregel Pubns.

Ungerer, Tomi. Christmas Eve at the Mellops' Ungerer, Tomi, illus. 1998. (Illus.). 32p. (J). (gr. k-4). pap. 5.95 (978-1-57098-227-9(9)) Rinehart, Roberts Pubs.

Urmy, Deanne, ed. Merry Christmas: Best - Loved Stories & Carols. Green, Donna, illus. 2004. 90p. (J). (gr. 4-8). reprint ed. 20.00 (978-0-7567-7580-3(9)) DIANE Publishing Co.

Valdes, Leslie. Dora's Christmas Parade. Aikins, Dave, illus. 2003. (Dora the Explorer Ser.). 32p. (J). 5.99 (978-0-689-85843-7(4) , Simon Spotlight/Nickelodeon) Simon & Schuster Children's Publishing.

—Dora's Christmas Parade. 2003. (gr. k-3). lib. bdg. 14.15 (978-0-613-73391-5(6)) Tandem Library Bks.

Van Allsburg, Chris. The Polar Express. Van Allsburg, Chris, illus. 2002. (Illus.). (J). 26.23 (978-0-7587-0066-7(0)) Book Wholesalers, Inc.

—The Polar Express. 20th anniv. ed. 2005. (Illus.). 32p. (J). 35.00 (978-0-618-61169-0(X)) Houghton Mifflin Co. Trade & Reference Div.

—The Polar Express Sam's Edition. 2006. (J). (gr. k-3). 35.00 (978-0-618-83659-8(4)) Houghton Mifflin Co. Trade & Reference Div.

Van Dyke, Henry. The Other Wise Man. 2004. pap. 11.95 incl. audio compact disk (978-1-932226-34-8(6)) Wizard Academy Pr.

Van Steenwyk, Elizabeth. Prairie Christmas. Himler, Ronald, illus. 2006. 32p. (J). 17.00 (978-0-8028-5280-9(7) , Eerdmans Bks For Young Readers) Eerdmans, William B. Publishing Co.

Van Syckle, A. & Schwartz, Josh. The OC: 'twas the Night Before Chrismukkah. 2005. 206p. (YA). (978-1-4156-3915-3(9)) Scholastic, Inc.

Vanderklip, Michael. Christmas Star. 2006. (Christmas Minis Ser.). 14p. 3.99 (978-0-310-70847-6(8)) Zondervan.

Vaswani, Navina. A Wonderful Christmas. 2004. (YA). per. (978-0-9754818-5-1(1)) Creative Bk. Pubs.

Ventruella, D. J. First Snow: Jeremiah's Christmas. 1999. 118p. (J). pap. 4.95 (978-1-929804-01-6(6) , Compass Special Editions) Compass Publishing Corp.,The.

Verney, Jeff. The Christmas Book of Hope. 2006. (J). mass mkt. 14.95 (978-0-9771250-0-5(9)) JRV Publishing.

Vivas, Julie. The Nativity. 2005. (Illus.). 36p. (J). (ps-7). 17.00 (978-0-15-205591-2(6) , Gulliver Bks.) Harcourt Children's Bks.

Vlahakis, Andrea. Christmas Eve Blizzard. Emanuel, Schongut, illus. 2005. 32p. (J). (ps-3). 15.95 (978-0-9764943-3-1(7)) Sylvan Dell Pubng.

Voland, Wanda. Ivan Icicle's Wedding. 2007. (J). per. 10.99 (*978-1-60247-064-4(2)) Tate Publishing & Enterprises, L.L.C.

Volk, Kaye Jacobs. The Christmas Cradle. pap. 3.95 (978-1-57734-029-4(9) , 01112503) Covenant Communications, Inc.

Voltz, Ralph, illus. Bible for Me: Christmas. 2005. 48p. (J). (ps-3). 9.99 (978-1-4003-0687-9(6)) Nelson, Thomas Inc.

Von Dornheim, Curt H. The Little Baron's Christmas Angel. Date not set. (Illus.). 64p. 12.95 (978-0-89404-222-5(X)) Aztex Corp.

Waber, Bernard. Lyle at Christmas. Waber, Bernard, illus. 2002. (Lyle the Crocodile Ser.). (Illus.). (J). 23.40 (978-0-7587-3058-9(6)) Book Wholesalers, Inc.

—Lyle at Christmas. 2003. (Lyle the Crocodile Ser.). (Illus.). 48p. (J). (gr. k-3). pap. 5.95 (978-0-618-38002-2(7) , Walter Lorraine) Houghton Mifflin Co. Trade & Reference Div.

—Lyle at Christmas. Waber, Bernard, illus. 1998. (Lyle the Crocodile Ser.). (Illus.). 48p. (J). (gr. k-3). tchr. ed. 16.00 (978-0-395-91304-8(7) , Walter Lorraine) Houghton Mifflin Co. Trade & Reference Div.

Waber, Bernard & Waber, Bernard. Lyle at Christmas. Waber, Bernard, illus. 2003. (Lyle the Crocodile Ser.). (Illus.). 48p. (J). (ps-3). lib. bdg. 14.10 (978-0-613-88087-9(0)) Tandem Library Bks.

Waddell, Martin. Room for a Little One: A Christmas Tale. Cockcroft, Jason, illus. 2004. 32p. (J). 15.95 (978-0-689-86841-2(3) , McElderry, Margaret K.) Simon & Schuster Children's Publishing.

—Room for a Little One: A Christmas Tale. Cockcroft, Jason, illus. 2006. 32p. (J). 9.95 (978-1-4169-2518-7(X) , McElderry, Margaret K.) Simon & Schuster Children's Publishing.

Wahl, Jan. Christmas Present. McCurdy, Michael, illus. 1999. 64p. (gr. 5-9). 18.00 (978-1-56846-165-6(8) , Creative Editions) Creative Co., The.

Walburg, Lori. The Legend of the Candy Cane. Bernardin, James, illus. gif. ed. 2002. (J). (gr. k-3). 19.99 (978-0-310-70328-0(X)) Zondervan.

Waldron, Jan L. Angel Pig & the Hidden Christmas. McPhail, David M., illus. 2002. (J). 23.40 (978-0-7587-1947-8(7)) Book Wholesalers, Inc.

—Angel Pig & the Hidden Christmas. 2000. (Illus.). 32p. (J). (ps-3). 6.99 (978-0-14-056591-1(4) , Puffin) Penguin Group (USA) Inc.

—Angel Pig & the Hidden Christmas. 2000. (gr. k-3). lib. bdg. 15.30 (978-0-613-29873-5(X)) Tandem Library Bks.

Wallace, Bill. The Dog Who Thought He Was Santa. 2007. 224p. (J). (gr. 3-7). 16.95 (*978-0-8234-2114-5(7)) Holiday Hse., Inc.

Wallace, Carol. The Santa Secret. Bjorkman, Steve, illus. 2007. 40p. (J). (gr. k-3). 15.95 (*978-0-8234-2022-3(1)); pap. 4.95 (*978-0-8234-2126-8(0)) Holiday Hse., Inc.

Wallace, Ivy. Pookie Believes in Santa Claus. 2001. (Illus.). 32p. (J). (gr. k-4). 19.99 (978-0-00-198380-9(6)) HarperCollins Pubs. Ltd. GBR. *Dist:* Trafalgar Square Publishing.

Wallace, Patricia H. Cottontale Christmas & the Cottontail Farm. deluxe unabr. ed. 2000. (J). lib. bdg. 12.00 incl. audio (978-0-932079-03-9(2)) TimeFare AudioBooks.

Walsh, Sheila. Gigi & the Perfect Christmas Gift. 2006. (Gigi, God's Little Princess Ser.). (Illus.). 32p. (J). 12.99 (978-1-4003-0801-9(1)) Nelson, Thomas Inc.

Walther, Lou. Three Candle Light Tales for Christmas. Wiesner, Kelly, illus. 2000. 48p. (J). pap. 3.00 (978-0-9612672-4-7(0)) Walther, Lou.

Walton, Rick. Bunny Christmas: A Family Celebration. Miglio, Paige, illus. 2004. 32p. (J). 15.99 (978-0-06-008415-8(4)); lib. bdg. 16.89 (978-0-06-008416-5(2)) HarperCollins Pubs.

Wang, Margaret. Reindeer Waits for Christmas. 2006. 16p. (J). 9.95 (978-1-58117-493-9(4) , Intervisual/Piggy Toes) Dalmatian Pr.

Wangerin, Walter, Jr. Probity Jones & the Fear Not Angel. Ladwig, Tim, illus. 2005. 32p. (J). (gr. 1-4). 16.95 (978-1-55725-457-3(5)) Paraclete Pr., Inc.

Wargin, Kathy-Jo. Once upon a Christmas Eve. Langton, Bruce, illus. 2005. 32p. (J). (gr. 3-7). 17.95 (978-1-58726-290-6(8)) Ann Arbor Media Group, LLC.

Warner, Marty, et al. The Little Girl in the Yellow Dress. 2005. 26p. 14.99 (978-1-4116-3148-9(X)) Lulu.com.

Washington, LaVonne & LaShawn. How the Grinch Hare Became A Christian. 2005. 37p. 11.95 (978-1-4116-2322-4(3)) Lulu.com.

Watkins, Dawn L. Chickadee Winter. Dellosso, Gabriela, illus. 1999. (J). (ps-1). pap. 5.49 (978-1-57924-273-2(1) , 120170) Jones, Bob Univ. Pr.

Watt, Fiona. Christmas Eve Board Book. 2007. (Luxury Touchy-Feely Board Bks). 10p. (J). bds. 11.99 (*978-0-7945-1478-5(2) , Usborne) EDC Publishing.

—Christmas Mice. 2004. (Big Touchy Feely Board Bks.). (Illus.). 10p. (J). 11.95 (978-0-7945-0482-3(5) , Usborne) EDC Publishing.

—Hide-And-Seek Christmas. 2007. (Touchy-Feely Flap Bks). 10p. (J). bds. 16.99 (*978-0-7945-1892-9(3) , Usborne) EDC Publishing.

—Nativity Touchy-feely. 2005. 10p. (J). 15.95 (978-0-7945-1172-2(4) , Usborne) EDC Publishing.

—Santa Claus. 2004. (Sparkly Touchy-Feely Board Bks.). 10p. (J). 15.95 (978-0-7945-0830-2(8) , Usborne) EDC Publishing.

Watt, Fiona. Sparkly Christmas Angel. 2007. (Luxury Touchy-Feely Board Bks). 10p. (J). bds. 15.99 (*978-0-7945-1477-8(4) , Usborne) EDC Publishing.

Wax, Wendy. Animal Family Christmas. 2007. 10p. 14.95 (*978-1-58117-625-4(2) , Intervisual/Piggy Toes) Dalmatian Pr.

Webb, Kimberly. The Christmas Memory Quilt. Gaskin, Jennifer, illus. 2007. 32p. (J). 17.95 (*978-1-934393-00-0(2)) Silverleaf Pr.

Weber, Lou. My First Library Christmas Stories. 2005. 10p. 10.98 (978-1-4127-3914-6(4) , PIL Kids) Publications International, Ltd.

Weber, Lou, ed. Christmas Tales Treasury. rev. ed. 2004. 320p. (J). 15.98 (978-0-7853-7911-9(8) , 3053704) Publications International, Ltd.

—3 Minute Christmas Stories. 2004. (Illus.). 160p. (J). 9.98 (978-1-4127-3245-1(X) , 7235300) Publications International, Ltd.

Webster, Michelle B. The Christmas of Miracles. 2004. 136p. per. 12.95 (978-0-9753117-0-7(0)) Four Sonkist Angels.

Weinberg, Larry. The Forgetful Bears Help Santa. Wolff, Jason, illus. 2001. 40p. (J). (gr. k-2). 9.95 (978-0-307-10684-1(5) , Golden Bks.) Random Hse. Children's Bks.

Weiss, Ellen. Fisher - Price Little People Christmas Is Here! S. I. International Staff, illus. 2002. (Fisher-Price Little People Mini-Flap PlayBooks Ser.). 10p. (J). (ps-k). bds. 9.99 (978-1-57584-997-3(6)) Reader's Digest Children's Publishing, Inc.

Weiss, Ellen, et al. Babar & the Christmas House. 2003. (Illus.). 28p. (J). (ps-1). 9.95 (978-0-8109-4583-8(5) , 53604968) Abrams, Harry N. , Inc.

—Trip to the North Pole: A Junior Novel. movie tie-in ed. 2004. (Polar Express Ser.). (Illus.). 128p. (J). (gr. 5-6). pap. 4.99 (978-0-618-47790-6(X)) Houghton Mifflin Co. Trade & Reference Div.

Wells, Rosemary. Christmas Stocking. 2003. (Max & Ruby Ser.). (Illus.). 16p. (J). (ps-ps). pap. 5.99 (978-0-670-03667-7(6) , Viking Juvenile) Penguin Group (USA) Inc.

—Max & Ruby's Christmas Tree. 2007. (Max & Ruby Ser.). 12p. (J). (ps-k). bds. 7.99 (*978-0-448-44685-1(5) , Grosset & Dunlap) Penguin Group (USA) Inc.

—Max's Christmas. 2000. (Max & Ruby Ser.). (J). (gr. k-2). (978-0-606-20244-2(7)) Tandem Library Bks.

—McDuff's Christmas. Jeffers, Susan, illus. 2005. 32p. (ps-k). 9.99 (978-0-7868-3811-0(6)) Hyperion Pr.

—McDuff's New Friend. 1998. 8.95 (978-0-7868-0493-1(9)) Hyperion Bks. for Children.

—McDuff's New Friend: Includes Stuffed Toy Puppy. 1998. (Illus.). (J). 219.00 (978-0-7868-2825-8(0)) Hyperion Pr.

—McDuff's New Friend with Plush Box Set. 2003. (Illus.). 28p. (J). 14.99 (978-0-7868-1866-2(2) , Disney Editions) Disney Pr.

—Morris's Disappearing Bag. 2001. (ps-ps). (Illus.). (J). lib. bdg. 15.30 (978-0-613-44236-7(9)); (978-0-606-22499-4(8)) Tandem Library Bks.

Wenger, Brahm. Dewey's Magical Sleigh, from the Dewey Doo-it Series. 2005. 32p. 15.95 (978-0-9745143-6-9(5)) RandallFraser Publishing.

Weninger, Brigitte. Davy's Christmas Gift. Tharlet, Eve, illus. 2003. 16p. (J). bds. 6.95 (978-0-7358-1754-8(5)) North-South Bks., Inc.

—Letter to Santa Claus. 2000. (gr. k-3). lib. bdg. 26.35 (978-0-613-81905-3(5)) Tandem Library Bks.

Wensell, Paloma. Christmas Star. Wensell, Ulises, illus. 2006. 16p. (J). 7.95 (978-0-8146-3155-3(X) , Liturgical Pr. Bks.) Liturgical Pr.

Werkema, Mark A. The Flight Before Christmas. 2004. (YA). pap. 13.95 (978-1-58961-306-5(6)) PageFree Publishing, Inc.

West, Jane. The Lonesome Pine. Lujan-Bakerink, Monique, illus. 2000. 64p. (J). (ps). 24.95 (978-0-9701025-7-7(7)) Haylett Publishing.

West, Tracey, et al. The Magic Journey. 2004. (Polar Express Ser.). (Illus.). 32p. (J). (gr. k-3). 9.99 (978-0-618-47788-3(8)) Houghton Mifflin Co.

Westcott, Nadine Bernard. Santa's Christmas Eve. Westcott, Nadine Bernard, illus. 2006. (Illus.). 12p. (J). 6.99 (978-0-689-85656-3(3) , Little Simon) Simon & Schuster Children's Publishing.

Westerlund, Kate. Sharing Christmas. Tharlet, Eve, illus. 2007. 32p. (J). (ps). 16.99 (*978-0-698-40074-0(7) , Minedition) Penguin Group (USA) Inc.

Westerman, Rob. The Legend of Kalikimaka: Alohalani, Kalikimaka Auntie. Tahleh, Eleykaa, illus. 2003. 32p. (J). 12.95 (978-0-9761992-0-5(3)) Gold Boy Music/Pubn.

Whatley, Bruce. The Christmas Watchmaker. Date not set. (J). (978-0-06-026610-3(4)); (978-0-06-026611-0(2)) HarperCollins Pubs.

Wheeler, Joe. The Candle in the Forest: And Other Christmas Stories Children Love. 2007. 96p. 16.99 (*978-1-4165-4219-3(1) , Howard Bks.) Simon & Schuster.

Wheeler, Joe L. The Candle in the Forest: And Other Christmas Stories Children Love. 2007. (J). (*978-1-58229-707-1(X) , Howard Bks.) Simon & Schuster.

Wheeler, Jordan & Jackson, Dennis. Christmas at Wapos Bay. 2006. 176p. (J). pap. (*978-1-55050-324-1(3)) Coteau Bks.

Wheeler, Karla. Timmy's Christmas Surprise. Wheeler, Jenny Lee, illus. l.t. ed. 2001. 24p. 4.95 (978-0-9675532-0-7(2)) Quality of Life Publishing Co.

Wheeler, Lisa. The Christmas Boot. Monroe, Michael Glenn, illus. 2007. 32p. (J). 18.95 (*978-1-58726-327-9(0) , Mitten Pr.) Ann Arbor Media Group, LLC.

White, Ellen Emerson. Santa Paws: Picture Book. Blake, Robert, illus. 2003. (Santa Paws Ser.). 40p. (J). (gr. k-3). pap. 16.95 (978-0-439-32438-0(6)) Scholastic, Inc.

White, Stephen & Scholastic, Inc. Staff. Barney's Night Before Christmas. Davis, Guy, ed. Grayson, Rick, illus. 1999. (Barney Ser.). 24p. (J). (ps-k). pap. 3.50 (978-1-57064-462-7(4)) Scholastic, Inc.

Whitlock, Matt. Punk's Christmas Carol. 2006. 32p. 16.95 (978-0-9769057-1-4(X)) Little Hero.

Whybrow, Ian. Harry & the Dinosaurs Make a Christmas Wish. Reynolds, Adrian, illus. 2004. 32p. (J). (ps-2). 15.95 (978-0-375-83111-9(8) , Random Hse. Bks. for Young Readers) Random Hse. Children's Bks.

Whybrow, Ian. Miss Wire's Christmas Surprise. Clark, E., illus. 2007. 48p. (J). (ps-3). pap. 3.95 (*978-0-7534-6136-5(6) , Kingfisher) Houghton Mifflin Co. Trade & Reference Div.

Whybrow, Ian, compiled by. The Kingfisher Book of Classic Christmas Stories. 2004. (Illus.). 144p. (J). (gr. 3-5). 19.95 (978-0-7534-5732-0(6) , Kingfisher) Houghton Mifflin Co. Trade & Reference Div.

Wigand, Molly. Here Comes Santa! 1999. (gr. k-3). lib. bdg. 11.25 (978-0-613-21698-2(9)) Tandem Library Bks.

Wiggin, Kate Douglas. The Birds' Christmas Carol. reprint ed. (J). lib. bdg. 48.00 (978-0-7426-1056-9(X)); 2001. (Illus.). pap. 28.00 (978-0-7426-6056-4(7)) Classic Bks.

—The Birds' Christmas Carol. Gillespie, Jessie, illus. 1999. 80p. (J). (gr. 4-6). pap. 4.95 (978-0-395-89110-0(8)) Houghton Mifflin Co. Trade & Reference Div.

—The Birds' Christmas Carol. 2004. reprint ed. pap. 15.95 (978-1-4179-9995-8(0)); pap. 1.99 (978-1-4179-9945-3(4)) Kessinger Publishing, LLC.

—The Birds' Christmas Carol. 1999. (gr. 3-6). lib. bdg. 12.95 (978-0-613-22824-4(3)) Tandem Library Bks.

—The Birds' Christmas Carol. 1999. (Illus.). 96p. 16.95 (978-0-941807-52-4(5) , Welcome Bks.) Welcome Enterprises, Inc.

Wiggin, Kate Douglas. The Romance of a Christmas Card. 2006. pap. 33.99 (*978-1-4280-0238-8(3)) IndyPublish.com.

Wilcox. The Great Christmas Tree Adventure. 1998. (J). pap. 1.50 (978-0-689-82608-5(7) , Little Simon) Simon & Schuster Children's Publishing.

Wild, Anne. Christmas Carousel: The Story of the Nativity in Five Scenes to Cut Out & Make. (Illus.). (J). pap. 10.00 (978-0-906212-64-6(2)) Tarquin Pubns. GBR. *Dist:* Parkwest Pubns., Inc.

Wilder, Laura Ingalls. Christmas Stories. Graef, Renee, illus. 1998. (Little House Chapter Bks.: No. 10). 80p. (J). (gr. 2-5). pap. 4.99 (978-0-06-442081-5(7) , Harper Trophy) HarperCollins Pubs.

—Christmas Stories. Graef, Renee, illus. 1998. 72p. (J). (ps-k). lib. bdg. 12.10 (978-0-613-11413-4(2)) Tandem Library Bks.

—A Farmer Boy Christmas. Wheeler, Jody, illus. 1999. (My First Little House Bks.). (J). (ps-1). 12.95 (978-0-06-025940-2(X)); lib. bdg. 12.89 (978-0-06-025941-9(8)) HarperCollins Pubs.

—A Little House Christmas Treasury: Festive Holiday Stories. Williams, Garth, illus. 2005. (Little House Ser.). 144p. (J). 12.99 (978-0-06-076918-5(1)) HarperCollins Pubs.

Wildsmith, Brian. A Christmas Story. Wildsmith, Brian, illus. 1998. (Illus.). 24p. (ps-3). 17.00 (978-0-8028-5173-4(8)) Eerdmans, William B. Publishing Co.

Wilhelm, Hans. Christmas Angel. 2006. (Illus.). 32p. (J). pap. 8.99 (978-0-439-86397-1(X)) Scholastic, Inc.

Wilhelm, Hans. The Christmas Angel. 2007. 32p. (J). (ps-k). pap. 3.99 (*978-0-545-00853-2(0)) Scholastic, Inc.

Wilkes, Irene. Elvie, Santa's Ninth Reindeer. Montgomery, Jason, illus. 2006. 28p. (J). 19.95 (*978-1-59299-227-0(7)) Inkwater Pr.

Wilkin, Eloise. Baby's Christmas. Wilkin, Eloise, illus. 1999. (Jellybean Bks.). (Illus.). 24p. (J). (ps-k). lib. bdg. 7.99 (978-0-375-90146-1(9) , Random Hse. Bks. for Young Readers) Random Hse. Children's Bks.

Willey, Margaret. Clever Beatrice Christmas. Solomon, Heather M., illus. 2006. 40p. (J). 16.95 (978-0-689-87017-0(5) , Atheneum) Simon & Schuster Children's Publishing.

Williams, Jacklyn. Merry Christmas Gus! Cushman, Doug, illus. 2005. (Read-It! Readers Ser.). 32p. (J). (gr. k-3). 18.60 (978-1-4048-0958-1(9)) Picture Window Bks.

Williams, Sam. Angel's Christmas Cookies. Williams, Sam, illus. 2002. (Angel & Elf Ser.). (Illus.). 32p. (J). (ps-3). 9.99 (978-0-06-029651-3(8) , Harper Festival) HarperCollins Pubs.

—Santa's Toys. Gill, Tim, illus. 2003. 14p. bds. (978-1-85602-274-3(9)) Chrysalis Children's Bks.

—Snowy Magic. Williams, Sam, illus. 2002. (Angel & Elf Ser.). (Illus.). 32p. (J). (ps-3). 9.99 (978-0-06-029652-0(6) , Harper Festival) HarperCollins Pubs.

—Teddy Bears Trim the Tree: A Christmas Pull-the-Tab Book. McQuade, Jacqueline, illus. 2000. 12p. (J). (ps-1). bds. 14.95 (978-0-439-19285-9(4)) Scholastic, Inc.

Williams, Thomas. The Christmas Chair. l.t. ed. 2004. (Illus.). 27p. (J). audio compact disk 22.95 (978-0-9763633-0-9(5)) Williams, Thomas.

Williamson, Barbara. Wishbone. 2007. (Illus.). 24p. (J). per. 12.95 (*978-1-60002-197-8(2) , 4216, Airleaf Publishing) Airleaf Publishing & Bookselling.

Williamson, C. N. Rosemary (A Christmas Story) 2006. pap. 87.99 (*978-1-4280-2194-5(9)) IndyPublish.com.

Wilson, Budge & Roscoe, Terry. The Imperfect Perfect Christmas. 2004. (Illus.). 48p. (J). pap. (*978-1-895900-66-8(2)) Pottersfield Pr.

Wilson, F. Paul. The Christmas Thingy. Clark, Alan M., illus. 2000. 32p. (J). 20.00 (978-1-58767-031-2(3)) Cemetery Dance Pubns.

Wilson, Karma. Bear Stays up for Christmas. Chapman, Jane, illus. 2004. 40p. (J). (ps-2). 16.95 (978-0-689-85278-7(9) , McElderry, Margaret K.) Simon & Schuster Children's Publishing.

—Mortimer's Christmas Manger. Chapman, Jane, illus. 2005. 40p. (J). 15.95 (978-0-689-85511-5(7) , McElderry, Margaret K.) Simon & Schuster Children's Publishing.

Winder, Michael K. Christmas Animals. 2002. 19.95 (978-1-890718-09-1(2)) Eborn Bks.

Windham, Kathryn Tucker. It's Christmas! Crump, Buz, illus. 2002. 32p. 15.95 (978-1-57966-031-4(2)) River City Publishing.

Wing, Natasha. The Night Before Summer Vacation. 2002. (gr. k-3). lib. bdg. 11.25 (978-0-613-72501-9(8)) Tandem Library Bks.

—The Night Before Thanksgiving. 2001. (gr. k-3). lib. bdg. 11.25 (978-0-613-72389-3(9)) Tandem Library Bks.

—The Night Before the Night Before Christmas. Lester, Mike, illus. 2002. (Reading Railroad Bks.). 32p. (J). (gr. k-3). pap. 3.99 (978-0-448-42872-7(5) , Grosset & Dunlap) Penguin Group (USA) Inc.

—The Night Before the Night Before Christmas. 2002. (gr. k-3). lib. bdg. 11.25 (978-0-613-72485-2(2)) Tandem Library Bks.

Winthrop, Elizabeth. The First Christmas Stocking. Ibatoulline, Bagram, illus. 2006. 40p. (J). (gr. k-12). 15.95 (978-0-385-32804-3(4) , Delacorte Bks. for Young Readers) Random Hse. Children's Bks.

—The First Christmas Stocking. Tolle, Mitchell D. & Ibatoulline, Bagram, illus. 2006. 40p. (J). (gr. k-12). lib. bdg. 17.99 (978-0-385-90855-9(5) , Delacorte Bks. for Young Readers) Random Hse. Children's Bks.

A Wish for Christmas. 2002. (J). bds. 3.98 (978-1-84250-589-2(0) , Bright Sparks) Parragon, Inc.

Wojciechowski, Susan. The Christmas Miracle of Jonathan Toomey. Lynch, P. J., illus. 1998. 40p. (J). (ps-3). 18.99 incl. cd-rom (978-0-8499-5905-9(5)) Nelson, Thomas Inc.

—Christmas Miracle of Jonathan Toomey. Lynch, P. J., illus. 2004. 40p. (J). (gr. 1-7). reprint ed. 12.99 incl. audio compact disk (978-0-7636-2621-1(X)) Candlewick Pr.

Wojciechowski, Susan. The Christmas Miracle of Jonathan Toomey with CD: Gift Edition. Lynch, P. J., illus. 2007. 40p. (J). (gr. 1-7). 14.99 (*978-0-7636-3629-6(0)) Candlewick Pr.

Wolf, Jackie. My Sparkle Present. 2003. (Sparkle Shape Bks.). (Illus.). 10p. (J). (ps up). bds. 6.99 (978-1-57151-715-9(4)) Playhouse Publishing.

Wolf, Joan. How the Selves Became Elves. Squassoni, Christine, illus. 2001. (J). (ps-2). 19.95 (978-0-9711445-1-4(6)) Cruzane Mountain Publishing.

Wong, Alice, ed. Disney the Little Big Book of Christmas. (Illus.). 352p. 24.95 (978-1-932183-81-8(7) , Welcome Bks.) Welcome Enterprises, Inc.

Wood, Audrey. The Christmas Adventure of Space Elf Sam. Wood, Bruce Robert, illus. 1998. 40p. (J). (ps-4). pap. 15.95 (978-0-590-03143-1(0) , Blue Sky Pr., The) Scholastic, Inc.

—A Cowboy Christmas: The Miracle at Lone Pine Ridge. Florczak, Robert, illus. 2004. 48p. (J). 7.99 (978-0-689-87408-6(1) , Aladdin) Simon & Schuster Children's Publishing.

Wood, Don & Wood, Audrey. Merry Christmas: Big Hungry Bear! Wood, Don, illus. 2002. (Illus.). 48p. (J). (gr. k-2). pap. 15.95 (978-0-439-32092-4(5) , Blue Sky Pr., The) Scholastic, Inc.

Woodruff, Elvira. The Christmas Doll. McClintock, Barbara, illus. 2002. 160p. (J). pap. 4.99 (978-0-590-31879-2(9) , Scholastic Paperbacks) Scholastic, Inc.

Wormell, Christopher. In the Woods. 2004. (Illus.). 32p. (J). (ps). pap., pap. 9.99 (978-0-09-941767-5(7) , Red Fox) Random Hse. Children's Bks. GBR. *Dist:* Trafalgar Square Publishing.

—Through the Animals' Eyes: A Story of the First Christmas. Wormell, Christopher, illus. 2006. (Illus.). 64p. (J). 18.95 (978-0-7624-2669-0(1)) Running Pr. Bk. Pubs.

Wright, Dare. Gift from the Lonely Doll. 2001. (gr. k-3). lib. bdg. 15.25 (978-0-613-35517-9(2)) Tandem Library Bks.

Wright, Lisa. A Christmas Vacation. 2003. (J). per. 11.00 (978-1-4116-0306-6(0)) Lulu.com.

Wright, Sue. The Christmas Path: A Legend of the Luminarias. Wenzel, David, illus. 1998. 32p. (J). (gr. k-3). pap. 15.95 (978-0-590-04709-8(4) , Cartwheel Bks.) Scholastic, Inc.

—Christmas Path: A Legend of the Luminarias. 1998. (J). 191.40 (978-0-590-95977-3(8) , Cartwheel Bks.) Scholastic, Inc.

Wurst, Thomas. Pearl's Christmas Present. Wurst, Thomas, illus. 2004. 40p. 19.99 (*978-0-9790878-7-5(2)) Community Pr.

Wurst, Thomas Scott. Pearl's Christmas Present. Wurst, Thomas Scott, illus. 2006. (Illus.). 40p. (J). 20.00 (*978-0-9772441-1-9(3)) Pearl & Dotty.

X-mas Morning. 2004. (J). per. (978-1-57657-387-7(7)) Paradise Pr., Inc.

X-mas Trees are Special. 2004. (J). per. (978-1-57657-452-2(0)) Paradise Pr., Inc.

Yates, Dan. An Angel's Christmas. 1999. (J). pap. 3.95 (978-1-57734-544-2(4) , 01114379) Covenant Communications, Inc.

Yaun, Ellen R. A Christmas Problem for Samuel James. Murphy, Betsy, illus. 59p. (J). (gr. 2-5). pap. 5.95 (978-0-9673970-1-6(4)) Blue Chip Publishing.

Yee, Wong Herbert. A Small Christmas. 2004. (Illus.). 32p. (J). (gr. k-3). tchr. ed. 12.95 (978-0-618-32612-9(X)) Houghton Mifflin Co. Trade & Reference Div.

Yee, Wong Herbert. Small Christmas. 2007. (Illus.). 32p. (J). (ps-3). 6.95 (*978-0-618-91534-7(6)) Houghton Mifflin Co. Trade & Reference Div.

Yep, Laurence. Dream Soul. (J). (gr. 3-7). 2002. 256p. pap. 6.99 (978-0-06-440788-5(8)); 2000. (Illus.). 224p. 16.89 (978-0-06-028390-2(4)) HarperCollins Pubs.

—Dream Soul. 2002. (gr. 3-6). lib. bdg. 15.30 (978-0-613-85146-6(3)) Tandem Library Bks.

Yin & Soentpiet, Chris K. Dear Santa, Please Come to the 19th Floor. Soentpiet, Chris K., illus. 2002. (Illus.). 32p. (J). (gr. k-3). 17.99 (978-0-399-23636-5(8) , Philomel) Penguin Group (USA) Inc.

Yoon, Salina. Jingle Jungle Jingle Bells. 2007. 10p. (J). (ps-k). bds. 7.99 (*978-0-8431-2497-2(0) , Price Stern Sloan) Penguin Group (USA) Inc.

Yoon, Salina. Santa. 2004. (Illus.). 10p. (J). (ps-1). bds. 5.99 (978-0-8431-1150-7(X) , Price Stern Sloan) Penguin Group (USA) Inc.

Yoon, Salina, illus. My Shimmery Christmas Book. 2005. 10p. (J). bds. 8.95 (978-1-58117-045-0(9) , Intervisual/ Piggy Toes) Dalmatian Pr.

Young, L. H. The Christmas Kitten. 2007. 43p. pap. 7.95 (*978-0-533-15732-7(3)) Vantage Pr., Inc.

Ytreeide, Arnold. Tabitha's Travels: A Family Story for Advent. 2004. 170p. pap. 12.99 (978-0-8307-3501-3(1) , Regal Bks.) Gospel Light Pubns.

Zabrosky, Joseph & Jacobs, Nathaniel. The Christmas Tree, 4 vols., 4bks. l.t. ed. 2005. (Illus.). 32p. (J). per. (978-0-9768831-3-5(9)) Elohim Bks.

Zagwyn, Deborah Turney. The Winter Gift. 2004. (Illus.). 32p. (J). (gr. k-3). 15.95 (978-1-883672-93-5(7) , Tricycle Pr.) Ten Speed Pr.

Zepeda, Monique. Las Pinatas. Graullera, Fabiola, illus. Tr. of Pinatas. (SPA.). 26p. (J). (gr. 3-5). pap. 6.95 (978-968-19-0612-2(8)) Santillana USA Publishing Co., Inc.

Ziefert, Harriet. The Best Smelling Christmas Book Ever: 9 Scents to Scratch & Sniff! Rader, Laura, illus. 2004. 18p. (J). (gr. k-4). reprint ed. 13.00 (978-0-7567-7600-8(7)) DIANE Publishing Co.

—Home for Navidad. Cohen, Santiago, illus. 2003. 32p. (J) (gr. k-3). tchr. ed. 15.00 (978-0-618-34976-0(6) , Walter Lorraine) Houghton Mifflin Co. Trade & Reference Div.

—I Wish Santa Would Come by Helicopter. Haley, Amanda, illus. 2004. 28p. (J). 9.95 (978-1-4027-1708-6(3)) Sterling Publishing Co., Inc.

—Nicky's Christmas Song. Brown, Richard, illus. 2003. 14p. 6.95 (978-1-59354-011-1(6)) Blue Apple Bks.

—Presents for Santa. Rader, Laura, illus. 2000. (Easy-to-Read Ser.). 32p. (J). (gr. k-3). 13.89 (978-0-670-88390-5(5) , Viking Juvenile) Penguin Group (USA) Inc.

—Scooter's Christmas. Brown, Richard, illus. 2005. 16p. (J). pap. 5.95 (978-1-4027-1707-9(5)) Sterling Publishing Co., Inc.

—Twelve Days of Christmas Presents. Bolam, Emily, illus. 2004. 28p. (J). 9.95 (978-1-4027-1700-0(8)) Sterling Publishing Co., Inc.

—What Is Christmas? James, Lillie, illus. 2004. 16p. (J). (ps-ps). pap. 5.95 (978-1-4027-2015-4(7)) Sterling Publishing Co., Inc.

Zobel-Nolan, Allia. The Christmas Star. 2004. (J). bds. 7.99 (978-0-8254-5517-9(0)) Kregel Pubns.

—Flap Nativity. 2001. (Lift-the-Flap Playbook Ser.). (Illus.). 18p. (J). bds. 10.99 (978-1-57584-831-0(7)) Reader's Digest Assn., Inc., The.

—Peek & Find Christmas Story. Cox, Steve, illus. 2004. 14p. (J). bds. 6.99 (978-0-7586-0718-8(0)) Concordia Publishing Hse.

Zoehfeld, Kathleen Weidner. Is It Christmas Yet, Pooh? 2000. 14p. (J). 5.99 (978-0-7364-1058-8(9)) Mouse Works.

—Pooh's Jingle Bells. (Illus.). 32p. (J). (ps-k). 2000. pap. 4.99 (978-0-7868-4419-7(1)); 1998. 11.95 (978-0-7868-3204-0(5)) Disney Pr.

Zolotow, Charlotte. The Beautiful Christmas Tree. Nascimbene, Yan, illus. 2001. 32p. (J). (gr. k-3). pap. 5.95 (978-0-618-15245-2(8)) Houghton Mifflin Co. Trade & Reference Div.

—The Beautiful Christmas Tree. 2001. 12.75 (978-0-606-22252-5(9)); 1999. lib. bdg. 14.10 (978-0-613-37137-7(2)) Tandem Library Bks.

Zschock, Martha Day. Night Before Christmas Shadow Book. 2006. (Illus.). 16p. (J). 12.99 (978-1-59359-942-3(0)) Peter Pauper Pr. Inc.

Zuber, Diane. The Broken Doll. Firtle, Mary, illus. 2006. 32p. (J). 17.95 (978-0-9785551-1-5(2)) Zuber Publishing.

Zuhdi, Darla L. Tale of a Christmas Angel. 2000. (Cat Detectives Present Ser.: Vol. 1). (Illus.). 92p. (J). (gr. 2-7). pap. 5.99 (978-0-9706062-0-4(6)) Aloha Publications.

Zuk-Lloyd, Lynn. Christmas in North Woods: 10 Animated Stories for Children. Zuk-Lloyd, Lynn, illus. l.t. ed. 2002. (Illus.). (J). cd-rom 24.95 (978-0-9723773-0-0(1)) PromiseGarden.com.

Zwerger, Lisbeth. The Gift of the Magi. 2002. 5.95 (978-0-689-85801-7(9) , Simon & Schuster Children's Publishing) Simon & Schuster Children's Publishing.

CHRISTMAS—POETRY

see Christmas Poetry

CHRISTMAS CARDS

see Greeting Cards

CHRISTMAS CAROLS

see Carols

CHRISTMAS COOKERY

Bryant, Ann. Holiday Treats Cookbook. Workman, Lisa, illus. 2006. (Strawberry Shortcake Ser.). 96p. (J). (ps-3). 12.99 (978-0-448-44359-1(7) , Grosset & Dunlap) Penguin Group (USA) Inc.

Cherkerzian, Diane. Merry Things to Make: Christmas Fun & Crafts. 2003. (gr. 3-6). lib. bdg. 16.40 (978-0-613-78902-8(4)) Tandem Library Bks.

Chronicle Books Staff, contrib. by. Homemade Christmas: Fun-to-Make Crafts & Treats. 2003. (Illus.). 32p. (J). pap. 9.95 (978-0-8118-4015-6(8)) Chronicle Bks. LLC.

Devins, Susan. Christmas Cookies! A Holiday Cookbook. Lehman, Barbara, illus. 2007. 40p. (J). (gr. k-7). pap. 4.99 (*978-0-7636-3515-2(4)) Candlewick Pr.

Gilpin, R. & Atkinson, C. Christmas Cooking. 2004. (Activity Bks.). 32p. (J). pap. 6.95 (978-0-7945-0056-6(0) , Usborne) EDC Publishing.

Gilpin, Rebecca & Atkinson, Catherine. Yummy Little Cookbook. rev. ed. 2007. (Children's Cooking Ser.). 96p. (J). 7.99 (*978-0-7945-1655-0(6) , Usborne) EDC Publishing.

Johnson, Kristin & Cummins, Mimi. Christmas Cookies Are for Giving: Recipes, Stories & Tips for Making Heartwarming Gifts. 2003. (Illus.). 208p. 16.95 (978-0-9723473-9-6(9)) Tyr Publishing.

Marsh, Carole. Christmas: Activities, Crafts, Recipes & More! 2003. 32p. (J). (gr. 1-7). pap. 6.95 (978-0-635-02172-4(2)) Gallopade International.

—Christmas Recipes from the Past. 2003. 12p. (J). (gr. k-4). pap. 2.95 (978-0-635-02153-3(6)) Gallopade International.

Pirotta, Saviour. Christian Cookbook. Sloan, Frank, ed. 2001. (Holiday Cookbooks from Around the World). (Illus.). 32p. (J). (gr. 4-7). lib. bdg. 25.69 (978-0-7398-3263-9(8)) Raintree.

Pratt, L. Christmas Fairy Cooking Pb. 2006. 32p. (J). pap. 8.99 (978-0-7945-1118-0(X) , Usborne) EDC Publishing.

Publications International Staff, contrib. by. Christmas Cookies for Kids. 2001. (Illus.). 78p. (J). (978-0-7853-5582-3(0)) Publications International, Ltd.

Raabe, Emily. A Christmas Holiday Cookbook. 2002. (Festive Foods for the Holidays Ser.). (Illus.). 24p. (J). (gr. 2-5). lib. bdg. 19.95 (978-0-8239-5627-2(X) , PowerKids Pr.) Rosen Publishing Group, Inc., The.

Robins, Deri & Downer, Maggie. Christmas Fun: Great Things to Make & Do. 2003. (Holiday Fun Ser.). (Illus.). 32p. (J). (gr. 3-5). 4.95 (978-0-7534-5682-8(6) , Kingfisher) Houghton Mifflin Co. Trade & Reference Div.

Rock, Lois. Easter: Crafts, Stories, Facts. 2003. (Illus.). 48p. (J). pap. 11.99 (978-0-7459-4653-5(4) , Lion) Lion Hudson plc GBR. *Dist:* Independent Pubs. Group.

—First Festivals - Easter: Crafts, Stories, Facts. (Illus.). 48p. (J). 16.95 (978-0-7459-3906-3(6) , Lion) Lion Hudson plc GBR. *Dist:* Trafalgar Square Publishing.

A Traditional German Christmas. 2002. (Illus.). 144p. per. 14.95 (978-0-9717114-0-2(2)) S&V Publishing Co.

Vaughan, Jenny & Beauchamp, Penny. Christmas. 2004. (World of Recipes Ser.). (Illus.). 48p. (J). lib. bdg. (978-1-4034-4697-8(0)) Heinemann Library.

—Christmas Foods. 2004. (World of Recipes Ser.). (Illus.). 48p. (J). pap. 8.50 (978-1-4034-6011-0(6)) Heinemann Library.

Watt, Fiona. Little Bk of Christmas Cooking. gif. ed. 2006. 64p. (J). 6.99 (978-0-7945-1473-0(1) , Usborne) EDC Publishing.

CHRISTMAS DECORATIONS

Aston, Al. A Message for Mary. Hutchinson, Joy, illus. 2005. 16p. 2.00 (978-1-84427-176-4(5)) Scripture Union GBR. *Dist:* STL Distribution North America.

—The Shepherds' Surprise. Hutchinson, Joy, illus. 2005. 16p. pap. 2.00 (978-1-84427-178-8(1)) Scripture Union GBR. *Dist:* STL Distribution North America.

Bicknell, Joanna. Dress Up: The Christmas Story. 2005. (Illus.). 12p. (J). (ps-3). per., bds. 9.95 (978-1-905051-93-9(X)) Make Believe Ideas GBR. *Dist:* Ingram Pub. Services.

Boase, Petra. Fun at Christmas. 2000. (Fun with... Ser.). (Illus.). 96p. (gr. 3-7). 12.95 (978-1-84215-333-8(1) , Southwater) Anness Publishing GBR. *Dist:* National Bk. Network.

Boyds Mills Press, creator. Fun-to-Make Crafts for Christmas. 2005. (Illus.). 63p. (J). (ps-ps). 7.95 (978-1-59078-367-2(0)); per. 15.95 (978-1-59078-342-9(5)) Boyds Mills Pr.

Boyds Mills Press Staff. Merry Things to Make: Christmas Fun & Crafts. 1999. (Illus.). 64p. (YA). (gr. k-7). pap. 7.95 (978-1-56397-838-8(5)) Boyds Mills Pr.

Brighter Vision Publishing Staff. Christmas Crafts to Make. 2000. (Make It Now Crafts Ser.). (Illus.). (J). (ps-3). pap. 3.95 (978-1-55254-179-1(7)) Brighter Vision Pubns.

Bull, Jane. The Christmas Book. Ling, Mary, ed. 2001. (Illus.). 48p. (J). 12.95 (978-0-7894-7873-3(0)) Dorling Kindersley Publishing, Inc.

Cherkerzian, Diane. Merry Things to Make: Christmas Fun & Crafts. 2003. (gr. 3-6). lib. bdg. 16.40 (978-0-613-78902-8(4)) Tandem Library Bks.

Christmas Tree Favorites. 2001. 12.95 (978-0-9719384-3-4(1)) Light in Glass Publishing.

Chronicle Books Staff, contrib. by. Homemade Christmas: Fun-to-Make Crafts & Treats. 2003. (Illus.). 32p. (J). pap. 9.95 (978-0-8118-4015-6(8)) Chronicle Bks. LLC.

D'Allance, Mireille. Dejame Decorar El Arbol De Navidad. (SPA.). 36p. (978-84-95150-36-3(0)) Corimbo, Editorial S.L.

Edgar, Val. How to Be Brilliant at Christmas Time. 2004. (Illus.). 48p. pap. 30.00 (978-1-897675-63-2(1)) Brilliant Pubns. GBR. *Dist:* Parkwest Pubns., Inc.

Gibbons, Gail. Christmas Is... Gibbons, Gail, illus. (Illus.). 32p. (J). (gr. k-3). tchr. ed. 17.95 (978-0-8234-1582-3(1)); pap. 6.95 (978-0-8234-1767-4(0)) Holiday Hse., Inc.

Gibson, R. & Watt, F. Things to Make & Do for Christmas. 2004. (Illus.). 32p. (J). pap., act. bk. ed. 6.95 (978-0-7945-0338-3(1)) EDC Publishing.

Gilpin, Rebecca. Christmas fairy things to make & Do. Fearn, Katrina, illus. 2004. 34p. (J). pap. 6.95 (978-0-7945-0835-7(9) , Usborne) EDC Publishing.

Glow in the Dark Advent Sticker Book. (Illus.). 16p. (J). (ps-5). 6.99 (978-0-8254-7233-6(4)) Kregel Pubns.

Golden Books Staff. A Holly Jolly Christmas! 2004. (Shaped Coloring Book Ser.). (Illus.). 48p. (J). (ps-2). pap. 2.99 (978-0-375-82784-6(6) , Golden Bks.) Random Hse. Children's Bks.

—'Tis the Season. 2004. (Illus.). 32p. (J). (ps-2). pap. 3.99 (978-0-375-82787-7(0) , Golden Bks.) Random Hse. Children's Bks.

Goodings, Christina. Whizzy Bizzy Christmas. 2004. (Illus.). 32p. (J). pap. 5.50 (978-0-7459-4888-1(X)) Lion Hudson plc GBR. *Dist:* Independent Pubs. Group.

Harpine, Elaine C. Christment Tree Pattern: 21 Christian Ornaments on the Meaning of Christmas. 2004. (Illus.). 86p. pap. 12.95 (978-1-56608-102-3(5)) Meriwether Publishing, Ltd.

Imperato, Teresa. Ten Christmas Lights: Count the Lights from One to Ten! Parry, Jo, illus. 2005. 20p. (J). 10.95 (978-1-58117-321-5(0) , Intervisual/Piggy Toes) Dalmatian Pr.

Johnson, Ginger. Make Your Own Christmas Ornaments. Martin Jourdenais, Norma Jean, illus. 2002. (Quick Starts for Kids! Ser.). 64p. (YA). (gr. 3 up). pap. 8.95 (978-1-885593-79-5(1) , Williamson Bks.) Ideals Pubns.

Kaye, Teri, ed. Christmas Crafts on a Budget: Over 100 Project Ideas. 2005. 19.99 (978-0-9759638-2-1(1)) Gizmo Enterprises, Inc.

LaFosse, Michael. Making Origami Christmas Decorations Step by Step. LaFosse, Michael, illus. 2002. (Kid's Guide to Origami Ser.). (Illus.). 24p. (J). (gr. 2-4). lib. bdg. 21.25 (978-0-8239-5874-0(4) , PowerKids Pr.) Rosen Publishing Group, Inc., The.

Lane, Leena & Chapman, Gillian. Step by Step Christmas Creche. 2005. (Illus.). 32p. (ps-1). pap. 6.50 (978-0-687-06257-7(8)) Abingdon Pr.

Lankford, Mary D. Christmas Around the World. Dugan, Karen M., illus. 1998. 47p. (J). (ps-ps). lib. bdg. 14.15 (978-0-613-11409-7(4)) Tandem Library Bks.

Marsh, Carole. Christmas: Activities, Crafts, Recipes & More! 2003. 32p. (J). (gr. 1-7). pap. 6.95 (978-0-635-02172-4(2)) Gallopade International.

May, Darcy. Trim a Victorian Christmas Tree: With 83 Sticker Ornaments. 1998. (Illus.). 4p. (J). (ps-5). pap. 4.50 (978-0-486-40585-8(0)) Dover Pubns., Inc.

McGreggor, Cynthia. Mommy's Little Helper Christmas Crafts. 1999. (gr. k-3). lib. bdg. 16.45 (978-0-613-22030-9(7)) Tandem Library Bks.

Minor, Florence & Minor, Wendell. Christmas Tree! Minor, Wendell, illus. 2005. (Illus.). 40p. (J). (ps-3). 15.99 (978-0-06-056034-8(7) , Tegen, Katherine Bks) HarperCollins Pubs.

Murray, Mary, et al. A Yuletide Ice Cube Fair. Vann, Robert & Eddy, Ron, illus. 2003. 18p. bds. 6.99 (978-0-310-70630-4(0)) Zonderkidz.

Noble, Marty. Fun with Christmas Ornaments Stencils. 2006. (Dover Little Activity Bks.). 6p. (J). pap. 1.50 (978-0-486-44893-0(2)) Dover Pubns., Inc.

Osborne, Rick. The Legend of the Christmas Tree. Dodge, Bill, illus. 2002. 28p. (J). bds. 6.99 (978-0-310-70446-1(4)) Zonderkidz.

Osborne, Rick & Dodge, Bill. The Legend of the Christmas Tree: The Inspirational Story of a Treasured Tradition. Dodge, Bill, illus. 2001. (Illus.). 32p. (J). 15.99 (978-0-310-70043-2(4)) Zonderkidz.

Owen, Cheryl. Gifts for Kids to Make. 2006. (Illus.). 128p. (J). pap. 14.95 (978-0-600-61502-6(2) , Hamlyn) Octopus Publishing Group GBR. *Dist:* Sterling Publishing Co., Inc.

Patchett, Fiona. Rabbits. rev. ed. 2004. (First Pets Ser.). 32p. (J). 12.99 (978-1-58086-588-3(7)) EDC Publishing.

Peter, Val J., creator. Gifts for a Joyous Christmas: From the Kids at Boys Town. 2004. 164p. pap. 5.95 (978-1-889322-39-1(3) , 19-015) Boys Town Pr.

Pomaska, Anna. Shiny Christmas Balls Ornaments. 2006. (Dover Little Activity Bks.). 2p. (J). pap. 1.50 (978-0-486-44943-2(2)) Dover Pubns., Inc.

Press, Judy. Big Fun Christmas Crafts & Activities. 2006. (Illus.). 128p. (J). pap. 12.95 (978-0-8249-6786-4(0) , Williamson Bks.) Ideals Pubns.

Press, Judy. Big Fun Christmas Crafts & Activities. 2006. (Illus.). 128p. (J). 16.95 (978-0-8249-6787-1(9) , Williamson Bks.) Ideals Pubns.

Robins, Deri & Downer, Maggie. Christmas Fun: Great Things to Make & Do. 2003. (Holiday Fun Ser.). (Illus.). 32p. (J). (gr. 3-5). 4.95 (978-0-7534-5682-8(6) , Kingfisher) Houghton Mifflin Co. Trade & Reference Div.

Robinson, Fay. Christmas Crafts. 2004. (Fun Holiday Crafts Kids Can Do Ser.). (Illus.). 32p. (J). lib. bdg. 22.60 (978-0-7660-2257-7(9)) Enslow Pubs., Inc.

Rock, Lois. Christmas: Crafts, Stories, Carols. 1999. (Illus.). 48p. (J). (gr. k-3). 16.99 (978-0-7459-3907-0(4) , Lion) Lion Hudson plc GBR. *Dist:* Independent Pubs. Group.

—Easter: Crafts, Stories, Facts. 2003. (Illus.). 48p. (J). pap. 11.99 (978-0-7459-4653-5(4) , Lion) Lion Hudson plc GBR. *Dist:* Independent Pubs. Group.

—First Festivals - Easter: Crafts, Stories, Facts. (Illus.). 48p. (J). 16.95 (978-0-7459-3906-3(6) , Lion) Lion Hudson plc GBR. *Dist:* Trafalgar Square Publishing.

Rodgers-Mernin, Joy. Christmas Memories. 2005. 30.00 (978-1-892953-25-4(0)) Talus Corp.

Ross, Kathy. Christian Crafts for Christmastime. Holm, Sharon Lane, illus. 2001. 64p. (J). (gr. k-3). pap. 7.95 (978-0-7613-1331-1(1) , First Avenue Editions) Lerner Publishing Group.

—Christian Crafts for Christmastime. 2001. (gr. k-3). lib. bdg. 16.40 (978-0-613-45170-3(8)) Tandem Library Bks.

—Christmas Decorations Kids Can Make. Holm, Sharon Lane, illus. 1999. (Books for the Holidays Ser.). 64p. (J). (gr. k-3). pap. 8.95 (978-0-7613-1275-8(7) , First Avenue Editions) Lerner Publishing Group.

—Christmas Tree Ornaments Kids Can Make. Holm, Sharon Lane, illus. 1998. 64p. (gr. k-3). pap. 9.95 (978-0-7613-0337-4(5) , Millbrook Pr.) Lerner Publishing Group.

Sadler, Judy Ann. Christmas Crafts from Around the World. Bradford, June, illus. 2004. (Kids Can Do It Ser.). 40p. (J). (gr. 4-6). (978-1-55337-428-2(2)); (978-1-55337-427-5(4)) Kids Can Pr., Ltd.

—Christmas Crafts from Around the World. 2003. (gr. 3-6). lib. bdg. 15.25 (978-0-613-84415-4(7)) Tandem Library Bks.

School Zone Publishing Company Staff. Trim the Tree 1, 2, 3: A Numbers Book. 1999. (Board Books Ser.). (Illus.). 16p. (J). (ps-3). bds. 4.99 (978-0-88743-600-0(5) , 06601) School Zone Publishing Co.

Sturgill, Ruthy. Christmas Tree Advent Calendar: A Country Quilted & Appliquéd Project. 2006. 96p. pap. 24.95 (978-1-59800-539-4(1)) Outskirts Press, Inc.

Things to Make & Do for Christmas. 2002. (Activity Books). 32p. (J). pap. (978-0-7945-0055-9(2) , Usborne) EDC Publishing.

Torres, J. Christmas Eve. Harpster, Steve, illus. 2006. (Scribble & Sing Ser.). 80p. (J). 4.99 (978-1-4169-2731-0(X) , Simon Scribbles) Simon & Schuster Children's Publishing.

Umnik, Sharon D. 175 Easy-to-Do Christmas Crafts. 2003. (gr. 3-6). lib. bdg. 15.25 (978-0-613-78846-5(X)) Tandem Library Bks.

Watt, Fiona. Christmas Art Ideas. 2004. (Art Ideas Ser.). 64p. (J). pap. 14.95 (978-0-7945-0833-3(2) , Usborne) EDC Publishing.

—Christmas decorations & Cards. 2005. 34p. (J). pap. 8.95 (978-0-7945-0795-4(6) , Usborne) EDC Publishing.

—50 Christmas Things to Make & Do. 2006. 50p. (J). 9.99 (978-0-7945-1217-0(8) , Usborne) EDC Publishing.

Watt, Fiona & Gilpin, Rebecca. The Usborne Big Book of Christmas Things to Make & Do. Fearn, Katrina, illus. 2005. 99p. (J). (*978-0-439-81506-2(1)) Scholastic, Inc.

Wilson, Martin. The Nativity: A Christmas Pop-Up Decoration. Faulks, Sue, illus. 2001. 12p. (J). 4.95 (978-1-897584-18-7(0)) Electric Paper GBR. *Dist:* CPG Publishing, Inc.

CHRISTMAS ENTERTAINMENTS

see also Christmas Plays

Angel's Christmas Party Activity Fun. 2003. (Christmas Activity Bks.). (Illus.). 128p. (J). 3.98 (978-0-7525-6499-9(4)) Parragon, Inc.

Ball, Liz. Hidden Picture Puzzles Vol. 4: Merry Christmas Hidden Treasures. 2002. (Illus.). 56p. (J). pap. 4.95 (978-0-9678159-3-0(2)) Hidden Pictures.

Birmingham, Christian. A Christmas Treasury: The Children's Classic Edition. rev. ed. 2001. (Courage Children's Ser.). (Illus.). 48p. 9.98 (978-0-7624-1138-2(4) , Courage Bks.) Running Pr. Bk. Pubs.

Brighter Vision Publishing Staff. Wipe Away Christmas. 2000. (Illus.). (J). (ps-3). pap. 2.95 (978-1-55254-184-5(3)) Brighter Vision Pubns.

Charman, Andy. A Christmas Feast with Sticker. Cater, Martin, illus. 2000. 16p. (ps-k). pap. 5.00 (978-0-7548-0706-3(1)) Anness Publishing, Inc.

Christmas Fun. 2002. (Holiday Fun Bks.). 32p. pap. 2.99 (978-0-88724-793-4(8) , CD-0185) Carson-Dellosa Publishing Co., Inc.

Christmas/Advent Fun. 2005. 32p. (J). per. 4.99 (978-1-59441-084-0(4) , CD-204011) Carson-Dellosa Publishing Co., Inc.

Dowling, Iris. Christmas Program Ideas. 2004. 96p. per. 7.95 (978-0-9749836-1-5(6)) Faithful Life Pubs.

Elton, Candice & Elton, Richard. My Christmas Album. Lee, Fran, illus. 2002. 28p. (J). (gr. k-3). spiral bd. 19.95 (978-1-58685-204-7(3)) Gibbs Smith, Publisher.

Frosty the Snowman. 2005. (Illus.). 18p. (J). (ps up). 9.95 (978-0-8249-6595-2(7)) Ideals Pubns.

Golden Books Staff. A Holly Jolly Christmas! 2004. (Shaped Coloring Book Ser.). (Illus.). 48p. (J). (ps-2). pap. 2.99 (978-0-375-82784-6(6) , Golden Bks.) Random Hse. Children's Bks.

Gordon, Lynn. 52 Christmas Activities. Johnson, Karen, illus. 2004. 52p. 6.95 (978-0-8118-4123-8(5)) Chronicle Bks. LLC.

Hill, Grace Livingston. The Best Birthday: A Christmas Entertainment for Children. (J). (gr. 5-6). 15.95 (978-0-89190-404-5(2)) Amereon LTD.

Johnson, Kristin & Cummins, Mimi. Christmas Cookies Are for Giving: Recipes, Stories & Tips for Making Heartwarming Gifts. 2003. (Illus.). 208p. 16.95 (978-0-9723473-9-6(9)) Tyr Publishing.

Kendall, Susanna. Where's the Christmas Party? 2000. (Illus.). 16p. (ps-k). pap. 5.00 (978-0-7548-0705-6(3)) Anness Publishing, Inc.

Life Christmas Sound Book. 1999. 32p. (J). pap. (978-0-7814-0237-8(9)) Cook, David C. Publishing Co.

Marsh, Carole. Christmas: Activities, Crafts, Recipes & More! 2003. 32p. (J). (gr. 1-7). pap. 6.95 (978-0-635-02172-4(2)) Gallopade International.

—Cowboy Christmas Ball. 2002. (Carole Marsh Bks.). (Illus.). 32p. (J). (gr. 2-6). pap. 6.95 (978-0-635-01355-2(X) , 1355X) Gallopade International.

Milbourne, Anna. Christmas Activities. Cartwright, Stephen, illus. 2004. (Activity Books). 32p. (J). pap. 6.95 (978-0-7945-0564-6(3) , Usborne) EDC Publishing.

Nessel, Paula A. It's Christmas Time. Everett, Mimi, illus. 2000. 16p. (ps-k). pap. 5.00 (978-0-7548-0233-4(7)) Anness Publishing, Inc.

Newmarket Press. Junior Su Doku Christmas. 2005. (Illus.). 128p. (YA). pap. 4.95 (978-1-55704-707-6(3)) Newmarket Pr.

Snowman's Winter Coloring Fun. Date not set. (Christmas Activity Bks.). (Illus.). 128p. (J). pap. 3.98 (978-0-7525-6670-2(9)) Parragon, Inc.

Southwater Staff. Christmas Stories. 2000. (Superstickers Ser.). (Illus.). 64p. (ps-2). pap. 7.95 (978-1-84215-262-1(9) , Southwater) Anness Publishing GBR. *Dist:* National Bk. Network.

CHRISTMAS MUSIC

Allen, Dennis. How the Grouch Found Christmas. 1999. 6.95 (978-0-7673-9631-8(6)) LifeWay Christian Resources.

Andrews, Pam, creator. A Christmas Carol: A Chrismas Musical for Children about Giving. 2003. 120p. (J). pap. 7.99 (978-0-8341-7372-9(7)) Lillenas Publishing Co.

—A Shepherd's Story: An Easy to Sing Christmas Musical for Children. 2003. 32p. (J). pap. 5.99 (978-0-8341-7366-8(2)) Lillenas Publishing Co.

Andrews, Pam, creator. Cross Country: A Children's Musical Reminding Us to Race to the Cross. Andrews, Pam, . 2003. 112p. (J). pap. 7.99 (978-0-8341-7235-7(6)) Lillenas Publishing Co.

Berlin, Irving. White Christmas. 2002. 32p. (J). 16.95 (978-0-06-029123-5(0)) HarperCollins Pubs.

Bible Visuals International, compiled by. Christmas Collection. 2004. (Illus.). (J). cd-rom (978-1-933206-39-4(X) , 8001) Bible Visuals International, Inc.

Bower, Bugs. Cartoons & Christmas Tunes. 2004. (Illus.). 68p. (J). 9.95 incl. audio compact disk (978-0-8256-2785-9(0) , NM10097) Music Sales Corp.

Boys Choir of Harlem Staff. O Holy Night: Christmas with the Boys Choir of Harlem. Ringgold, Faith, illus. 2004. 40p. (J). 18.99 (978-0-06-000979-3(9)); 19.89 (978-0-06-051819-6(7)) HarperCollins Pubs.

Bryce, Ellen Woods. Once upon a Holy Night: A Musical Christmas Story Based on Luke 2:1-20 & Matthew 2:1-2. 2004. (gr. 2-5). 40.00 (978-0-687-09890-3(4)) Abingdon Pr.

The Christmas Carol Book. (Illus.). 10p. (J). bds. (978-2-89393-929-2(5)) Phidal Publishing, Inc./Editions Phidal, Inc.

Clancy, Ronald M. Children's Christmas Classics: The Millennia Collection. 2002. (Illus.). 112p. 39.95 incl. audio compact disk (978-0-615-12098-0(9)) Christmas Classics Ltd.

Coates, Dan. My First Book of Christmas. 2000. (J). 6.95 (978-0-7692-8971-7(1) , Warner Bros. Pubns.) Alfred Publishing Co., Inc.

de Paola, Tomie. The Friendly Beasts: An Old English Christmas Carol. 1998. (Illus.). 40p. (J). (ps-3). pap. 6.99 (978-0-698-11661-0(5) , Putnam Juvenile) Penguin Group (USA) Inc.

Feldstein, Sandy & Clark, Larry. Christmas Suprise. 2005. (YA). pap. 40.00 (978-1-932895-97-1(3)) PlayinTime Productions, Inc.

—Christmas Suprise - Conductor Score. 2005. (J). pap. 6.00 (978-1-932895-98-8(1)) PlayinTime Productions, Inc.

—Christmas Toyland. 2004. (YA). pap. 50.00 (978-1-932895-08-7(6)) PlayinTime Productions, Inc.

—Christmas Toyland - conductor's Score. 2004. (YA). pap. 8.00 (978-1-932895-09-4(4)) PlayinTime Productions, Inc.

Flatau, Carole, ed. Porky Pig's Christmas Songs: Level Four for Intermediate Students. 1999. (Looney Tunes Piano Library). (J). 5.95 (978-0-7692-8439-2(6) , Warner Bros. Pubns.) Alfred Publishing Co., Inc.

Gabriel, Andrea, illus. Jolly Old St. Nicholas. 2006. (Read & Sing along Board Books with CDs Ser.). 18p. (J). bds. 7.49 (978-0-7696-4933-7(5)) School Specialty Publishing.

Griffin, Rachel. Twelve Days of Christmas. 2002. (Illus.). 32p. (J). (gr. k-2). 17.99 incl. audio compact disk (978-1-84148-940-7(9)) Barefoot Bks., Inc.

Hal Leonard Corp., creator. Big Idea's VeggieTales - A Very Veggie Christmas: Recorder Fun Pack. 2002. 16p. (J). pap. 9.95 (978-0-634-05398-6(1) , 0634053981) Leonard, Hal Corp.

Hooper, Maureen Brett. Silent Night: A Christmas Carol Is Born. Kubiak, Kasi, illus. 2001. 32p. (YA). (gr. k-2). 15.95 (978-1-56397-782-4(6)) Boyds Mills Pr.

Hopson, Hal H. The World Sings Noel: The Christmas Story in Global Song. unabr. ed. 2002. 40.00 incl. audio (978-0-687-04937-0(7)) Abingdon Pr.

Julian, Alison, illus. The 12 Days of Christmas. 2005. (J). ***(*978-1-74157-281-0(9))*** Hinkler Bks. Pty, Ltd.

Keats, Ezra Jack & Keats, Ezra Jack. The Little Drummer Boy. 2000. (Illus.). (J). (ps-3). lib. bdg. 15.30 (978-0-613-30008-7(4)) Tandem Library Bks.

Kragen, Emma. The Twelve Dogs of Christmas. 2004. 16p. 14.99 (978-1-4003-9404-3(X)) Nelson, Thomas Inc.

The Little Drummer Boy. 2004. pap. 14.95 incl. audio (978-1-56008-156-2(2)) Weston Woods Studios, Inc.

Lou Weber Staff, ed. Merry Christmas Stories. 2004. (Illus.). 320p. (J). 15.98 (978-0-7853-6034-6(4)) Publications International, Ltd.

Mahoney, Anne Marie. Feliz Navidad: Learning Songs & Traditions in Spanish. Bjornson, Barb, illus. 2006. (SPA.). 32p. (J). (gr. k-6). lib. bdg. 19.95 incl. audio compact disk (978-1-59972-060-9(4) , Teach Me...) Teach Me Tapes, Inc.

Mahoney, Judy. Joyeux Noel: Learning Songs & Traditions in French. Bjornson, Barb, illus. 2006. (FRE.). (J). (gr. k-4). lib. bdg. 19.95 incl. audio compact disk (978-1-59972-061-6(2) , Teach Me...) Teach Me Tapes, Inc.

Manson, Christopher, illus. Good King Wenceslas. 2004. 25p. (J). (gr. k-4). reprint ed. 15.00 (978-0-7567-8226-9(0)) DIANE Publishing Co.

Marsh, Don & Marsh, Lorie. Star Journey: A Most Heavenly Children's Christmas Musical. 2000. 88p. 9.99 (978-0-8341-7029-2(9) , MC-522) Lillenas Publishing Co.

—Star Journey, Singer's Edition: A Most Heavenly Children's Christmas Musical. 2000. 44p. (J). pap. 4.99 (978-0-8341-7030-8(2)) Lillenas Publishing Co.

McGinley, Sharon. The Friendly Beasts: A Christmas Carol. McGinley, Sharon, illus. 2000. (Illus.). 24p. (J). (ps-3). 15.95 (978-0-688-17421-7(3)) HarperCollins Pubs.

—The Friendly Beasts: A Christmas Carol. 2000. (Illus.). 24p. (J). (ps-3). 15.89 (978-0-688-17422-4(1)) HarperCollins Pubs.

Moore, Clement C. A Christmas Carol. (Illus.). 12p. (J). 4.95 (978-1-58989-103-6(1)) Thurman Hse., LLC.

National Gallery of Art Staff. Hark! The Herald Angels Sing: The National Gallery, London. (Illus.). 48p. (J). (gr. k up). 19.99 (978-0-7112-0814-8(X)) Lincoln, Frances Ltd. GBR. *Dist:* Antique Collectors' Club.

Neale, J. M. Good King Wenceslas. Ladwig, Tim, illus. 2005. 32p. (J). (ps-17). 16.00 (978-0-8028-5209-0(2) , Eerdmans Bks For Young Readers) Eerdmans, William B. Publishing Co.

Newsom, Tom, illus. The First Noel. 2006. 14p. (J). (gr. k-4). reprint ed. 8.00 (978-1-4223-5413-1(X)) DIANE Publishing Co.

One Baby Jesus/Un Nino Dios. 2003. (ENG & SPA., Illus.). 30p. (J). 3.95 (978-0-8249-5472-7(6)) Ideals Pubns.

O'Neal, Debbie Trafton. Go Tell It on the Mountain. King, Fiona, illus. 2004. 32p. 8.99 (978-0-8066-4559-9(8) , Augsburg Bks.) Augsburg Fortress, Pubs.

—O Christmas Tree. Cook, Ande, illus. 2004. 32p. 8.99 (978-0-8066-4560-5(1) , Augsburg Bks.) Augsburg Fortress, Pubs.

Onorati, Henry, et al. The Little Drummer Boy. Rodanas, Kristina, illus. 2001. 32p. (J). (gr. k-3). tchr. ed. 15.00 (978-0-395-97015-7(6) , Clarion Bks.) Houghton Mifflin Co. Trade & Reference Div.

Rauenhorst, Linda. Frohliche Weihnachten: Learning Songs & Traditions in German. Collier-Morales, Roberta, illus. 2007. (GER & ENG.). 32p. (J). lib. bdg. 19.95 incl. audio compact disk ***(*978-1-59972-063-0(9))*** Teach Me Tapes, Inc.

Ringgold, Faith, illus. O Holy Night: Christmas with the Boys Choir of Harlem. 2006. 30p. (J). (gr. 4-8). 19.00 (978-1-4223-5512-1(8)) DIANE Publishing Co.

Rossi, Sophia. Buon Natale: Learning Songs & Traditions in Italian. Kelleher, Kathie, illus. 2007. (ITA.). (J). lib. bdg. 19.95 ***(*978-1-59972-067-8(1))*** Teach Me Tapes, Inc.

Schiller, David. Christmas Sing-along Car-I-Oke. Robinson, Tim, illus. 2005. 64p. (J). (ps-3). bds. 15.95 (978-0-7611-3984-3(2) , 13984) Workman Publishing Co., Inc.

Sewell, James. Jesus Loves Me! Scriptures & Songs in Sign Language. 2003. 64p. (J). 7.99 (978-0-88724-874-0(8)) Carson-Dellosa Publishing Co., Inc.

Snell, Gordon. Twelve Days: A Christmas Countdown. O'Malley, Kevin, illus. 2005. 30p. (J). (ps-2). reprint ed. 16.00 (978-0-7567-9403-3(X)) DIANE Publishing Co.

Steiger, Terri, et al, illus. Songs of Christmas: 12 Favorite Carols with an Electronic Piano. 2006. 24p. (YA). bds. 16.99 (978-0-7847-1266-5(2) , 04015) Standard Publishing.

Sweet, Melissa. On Christmas Day in the Morning: A Traditional Carol. 2001. (978-0-606-22503-8(X)) Tandem Library Bks.

Sweet, Melissa & Langstaff, John M. On Christmas Day in the Morning: A Traditional Carol. 1999. (J). (978-0-7636-0634-3(0)) Candlewick Pr.

Torme, Mel & Wells, Robert. The Christmas Song: Chestnuts Roasting on an Open Fire. Barrette, Doris, illus. 2007. 32p. (J). lib. bdg. 17.89 ***(*978-0-06-072226-5(6));*** 16.99 ***(*978-0-06-072225-8(8))*** HarperCollins Pubs.

Tormé, Mel & Wells, Robert. The Christmas Song: Chestnuts Roasting on an Open Fire. Barrette, Doris, illus. 2007. (J). lib. bdg. ***(*978-0-06-072227-2(4))*** HarperCollins Pubs.

Tyrell, Frances. Woodland Christmas: Twelve Days of Christmas in the North Woods. 2000. (J). (978-0-606-19624-6(2)) Tandem Library Bks.

Tyrrell, Frances, illus. The Huron Carol. 2004. 32p. 16.00 (978-0-8028-5263-2(7)) Eerdmans, William B. Publishing Co.

Vagin, Vladimir Vasil'evich, illus. The Twelve Days of Christmas. 1999. 32p. (J). (ps-3). 15.95 (978-0-06-027652-2(5)); 15.89 (978-0-06-028399-5(8)) HarperCollins Pubs.

Vasylenko, Veronica, illus. Jingle Bells. 2007. 22p. (J). (ps-k). bds. 7.95 ***(*978-1-58925-821-1(5)*** , tiger tales) ME Media LLC.

Vojtech, Anna, illus. The Friendly Beasts. 2003. (J). 15.95 (978-0-7358-1764-7(2)); lib. bdg. 16.50 (978-0-7358-1765-4(0)) North-South Bks., Inc.

Wood, Don. Joyeux Noel, Ours Affamé! ed. 2004. (FRE., Illus.). (J). (ps up). spiral bd. (978-0-616-14601-9(9)) Canadian National Institute for the Blind/Institut National Canadien pour les Aveugles.

CHRISTMAS PLAYS

Abingdon Press Staff, contrib. by. 5 Christmas Plays for Children. 2004. 32p. pap. 6.00 (978-0-687-01468-2(9)) Abingdon Pr.

Amstutz, Beverly. Tiny Wings: A Christmas Play for Children. Amstutz, Beverly, illus. 2000. (Illus.). (YA). (gr. k-12). pap. 5.00 (978-0-937836-12-5(5)) Precious Resources.

Augustine, Peg. Boys Can Be Angels Too & Three Other Christmas Dramas: Easy Dramas, Speeches & Recitations for Children. 2003. 32p. pap. 6.00 (978-0-687-06517-2(8)) Abingdon Pr.

—Christmas Promise Drama: Easy Dramas, Speeches & Recitations for Children. 2003. 32p. pap. 6.00 (978-0-687-06497-7(X)) Abingdon Pr.

Baker, Steve & Golden, Mark. The Kings of Christmas. 2004. (Illus.). 24p. 15.99 (978-0-9752895-2-5(7)) Shepherd's Workshop, LLC, The.

Cowen, Cynthia E. You Can't Keep Jesus in the Nativity Scene: Sunday School Christmas Program. 2001. 32p. (J). 6.50 (978-0-7880-1839-6(6)) CSS Publishing Co.

Doonan, Gladys & Sorensen, Rebekah M. Crown Him King! A Christmas Program. 2005. (Illus.). 29p. ***(*978-1-59402-299-9(2))*** Regular Baptist Pr.

Fittro, Pat, compiled by. Standard Christmas Program Book. 2001st ed. 2001. 48p. (ps up). 5.99 (978-0-7847-1244-3(1)) Standard Publishing.

Goens, Linda M. The Shepherds: Children's Drama for Christmas Eve. 2001. 12p. (J). 4.50 (978-0-7880-1842-8(6)) CSS Publishing Co.

Hansen, Cindy & Latchaw, Bob. The Mouse's Tale. 2001. (Instant Christmas Pageant Ser.). pap. 24.99 (978-0-7644-2352-9(5)) Group Publishing, Inc.

Hezlep, William. How Come Christmas? 2003. (Theater for Young Audiences Ser.). 18p. (J). pap. 5.00 (978-0-88734-424-4(0)) Players Pr., Inc.

Hibbard, J. Derrick. The Christmas Sweet: A Contemporary Nativity Play. 2001. (Christian Drama Ser.). pap. 3.00 (978-1-57514-369-9(0) , 0066) Encore Performance Publishing.

Howie, Vicki. Story Plays for Christmas: Three Plays Complete with Stories & Interactive Activities. 2005. 96p. pap. (978-1-84101-400-5(1)) Bible Reading Fellowship.

McCaslin, Nellie. Christmas Fiesta. 2003. 55p. (Orig.). (J). (gr. k-6). pap. 5.00 (978-0-88734-400-8(3)) Players Pr., Inc.

—The Christmas Lamb. 2003. (Players Press Nellie McCaslin Ser.). 55p. (Orig.). (J). (gr. k-5). pap. 5.00 (978-0-88734-479-4(8)) Players Pr., Inc.

—A Miracle in the Christmas City: Playscript. 2003. (Players Press Nellie McCaslin Ser.). 16p. (YA). (gr. k-12). pap. 5.00 (978-0-88734-437-4(2)) Players Pr., Inc.

Meacham, Liz. Three Wise Women: A Christmas Story / A Christmas Play. l.t. ed. 2006. (Illus.). 54p. per. 10.99 ***(*978-1-59879-222-5(9))*** Lifevest Publishing, Inc.

Preston, Elizabeth. The Very Best Christmas Plays for Kids. 2007. (J). ***(*978-0-8238-0312-5(0))*** Kalmbach Publishing Co., Bks. Div.

Rabert, Martha S. The Mouse at the Manger: A Children's Christmas Play. 2001. 8p. (J). 3.95 (978-0-7880-1843-5(4)) CSS Publishing Co.

Round, Graham. Bible Masks & Christmas Play Activity Book. 2002. (Illus.). 20p. (J). 7.99 (978-0-8254-7254-1(7)) Kregel Pubns.

Smiley, Kendra. One Rehearsal Christmas Plays: The Easiest Christmas Plays Ever. 2004. (Creative Bible Activities for Children Ser.). 96p. (J). (gr. 4 up). pap., pap. 16.99 (978-0-7814-4120-9(X) , 078144120X) Cook, David C. Publishing Co.

Smith, Charles, Jr. Two Terrific Christmas Plays: Two Plays for Children, Ages 3 to Older Elementary. 2004. pap. 7.25 (978-0-687-07168-5(2)) Abingdon Pr.

Stickler. Praise God! Jesus Is Born! Easy Dramas, Recitations & Speeches for Children. 2006. 48p. pap. 7.25 (978-0-687-49001-1(4)) Abingdon Pr.

Vos Wezeman, Phyllis & Liechty, Anna L. When the Lights Came On: Four Complete Children's Christmas Programs for Churches & Schools. Fittro, Pat, ed. 2002. 48p. 5.99 (978-0-7847-1392-1(8)) Standard Publishing.

Wade, Lee. The Cheerios Christmas Play Book. Wade, Lee, illus. 2000. (Illus.). 14p. (J). bds. 6.99 (978-0-689-84008-1(X) , Little Simon) Simon & Schuster Children's Publishing.

Williams, Guy. A Christmas Carol: 29 Speaking Parts. 2nd ed. 1998. (Dramascripts Classic Texts Ser.). 72p. (J). (gr. 6-9). pap. 17.95 (978-0-17-432547-5(9)) Nelson Thornes Ltd. GBR. *Dist:* Trans-Atlantic Pubns., Inc.

Zonderkidz Staff. My Own Manger: The Read & Play Christmas Story. 2000. (Illus.). (J). 9.99 (978-0-310-97870-1(X)) Zonderkidz.

CHRISTMAS POETRY

see also Carols

Bennett, Jill. Christmas Poems. Sharratt, Nick, illus. 1999. 32p. (J). (gr. k up). (978-0-19-276223-8(0)) Oxford Univ. Pr., Inc.

Birmingham, Christian & Moore, Clement C. Night Before Christmas: The Heirloom Edition. 2004. 48p. 14.99 (978-0-7624-2276-0(9)) Running Pr. Bk. Pubs.

Chaconas, Doris J. That Blessed Christmas Night. Perez-Stable, Deborah, illus. 2004. 32p. 18.00 (978-0-687-00626-7(0)) Abingdon Pr.

Cosley, Betty. The Story of Tiny McShane. Shepard, Brian, illus. l.t. ed. 1998. viii, 24p. (J). (ps-3). 14.95 (978-0-9664588-0-0(X)) Cosley Production.

cummings, e e. The Little Tree. Raschka, Chris, illus. 2001. 32p. (J). 16.49 (978-0-7868-2629-2(0)) Hyperion Bks. for Children.

—Little Tree. Raschka, Chris, illus. 2006. 18p. (ps-1). 6.99 (978-1-4231-0335-6(1)) Hyperion Pr.

Daily, Don. Twelve Days of Christmas. 2007. 32p. 7.98 ***(*978-0-7624-2877-9(5)*** , Courage Bks.) Running Pr. Bk. Pubs.

Dalmatian Press Staff. The Night Before Christmas. 2002. (Illus.). 14p. (J). (ps-1). bds. 5.99 (978-1-57759-612-7(9)) Dalmatian Pr.

—Santa Claus Picture Book. 2005. (Illus.). 32p. (J). pap. 10.99 (978-1-4037-1605-7(6)) Dalmatian Pr.

Davis, David. Librarian's Night Before Christmas. Harris, Jim, illus. 2006. 32p. (J). (gr. k-4). 15.95 (978-1-58980-336-7(1)) Pelican Publishing Co., Inc.

Davis, David R. Trucker's Night Before Christmas. Rice, James, illus. 1999. 32p. (J). (gr. k-3). 15.95 (978-1-56554-656-1(3)) Pelican Publishing Co., Inc.

Dickens, Charles & Moore, Clement C. A Christmas Carol & the Night Before Christmas. Rackham, Arthur, illus. deluxe ed. 2006. 192p. 14.99 (978-0-517-22927-9(7) , Gramercy) Random Hse. Value Publishing.

Dickman, Jean M. Santa in Space. l.t. ed. 2003. (Illus.). 32p. (J). per. 9.95 (978-0-9743718-0-1(7)) Tintagel Publications.

Fiona Waters Staff. The Book of Christmas. 2005. (Illus.). 96p. (J). (ps-17). 25.00 (978-1-84365-006-5(1)) Chrysalis Children's Bks. GBR. *Dist:* Trafalgar Square Publishing.

Fischer, Russell. Open Before Christmas: An Irresistible Treasury of Stories & Poems That Just Wont Wait for December 25th! 2004. 154p. pap. 19.95 (978-1-4137-1072-4(7)) PublishAmerica, Inc.

Foster, John, compiled by. My First Oxford Book of Christmas Poems. 2007. (Illus.). 96p. (YA). 9.95 ***(*978-0-19-276353-2(9))*** Oxford Univ. Pr., Inc.

Geraty, Virginia Mixson. Gullah Night Before Christmas. Rice, James, illus. 1998. (Night Before Christmas Ser.). 32p. (J). (ps-3). 15.95 (978-1-56554-330-0(0)) Pelican Publishing Co., Inc.

Harrison, Michael & Stuart-Clark, Christopher, selected by. Bright Star Shining: Poems for Christmas. 1998. (Illus.). 48p. (J). (ps-3). 15.00 (978-0-8028-5177-2(0) , Eerdmans Bks For Young Readers) Eerdmans, William B. Publishing Co.

Hawkes, Kevin, illus. A Christmas Treasury: Very Merry Stories & Poems. 2001. 48p. (J). 16.89 (978-0-688-12040-5(7)); 16.95 (978-0-688-12039-9(3)) HarperCollins Pubs.

Hopkins, Lee Bennett. Christmas Presents: Holiday Poetry. Hall, Melanie W., illus. (I Can Read Bks.). 32p. (J). 2005. pap. 3.99 (978-0-06-008056-3(6)); 2004. 15.99 (978-0-06-008054-9(X)); 2004. lib. bdg. 16.89 (978-0-06-008055-6(8)) HarperCollins Pubs.

Jakobs, D. Night Before Christmas. 2007. (Littlest Pet Shop Ser.). 32p. (J). pap. 3.99 ***(*978-0-439-91906-7(1))*** Scholastic, Inc.

Johnston, Tony. Noel. Chee, Cheng-Khee, illus. 2005. 32p. (J). (ps-7). lib. bdg. 15.95 (978-1-57505-752-1(2) , Carolrhoda Bks.) Lerner Publishing Group.

Johnstone, Michael. Christmas Hugs. 2003. (Forever Friends Ser.). (Illus.). 64p. pap. 3.95 (978-1-84357-027-1(0)) Contender Entertainment Group GBR. *Dist:* Independent Pubs. Group.

Kaye, Mary Lou. The Meaning of Christmas. Yu, Karl T., illus. 2000. 55p. (Orig.). (J). pap. 9.95 (978-1-58275-023-1(8)) Black Forest Pr.

Layne, Steve. The Principal's Night Before Christmas. Rice, James, illus. 2004. 32p. (J). pap. 15.95 (978-1-58980-252-0(7)) Pelican Publishing Co., Inc.

Lewis, J. Patrick. Under the Kissletoe: Christmastime Poems. Shepperson, Rob, illus. 2007. 32p. (J). (gr. 1-3). 16.95 ***(*978-1-59078-438-9(3)*** , Wordsong) Boyds Mills Pr.

McWilliams, Amanda & Moore, Clement C. Ozark Night Before Christmas. Rice, James, illus. 2004. 32p. pap. 15.95 (978-1-58980-056-4(7)) Pelican Publishing Co., Inc.

Medina, Tony. Just Us. 2004. (Illus.). 48p. (J). (gr. 4 up). pap. 6.95 (978-0-940975-75-0(0) , Sankofa Bks.) Just Us Bks., Inc.

Mills, Donald. The Night Before Christmas. Moore, Clement C., ed. Moore, Clement C., illus. 2000. 32p. (J). (ps-3). 7.95 (978-0-8249-4186-4(1)) Ideals Pubns.

Moore, Clement C. The Night Before Christmas. Brett, Jan, illus. 1998. 32p. (J). (ps-3). 16.99 (978-0-399-23190-2(0) , Putnam Juvenile) Penguin Group (USA) Inc.

—The Night Before Christmas. Fujikawa, Gyo, illus. 2007. 32p. (J). (ps-2). 9.95 ***(*978-1-4027-5065-6(X))*** Sterling Publishing Co., Inc.

—The Night Before Christmas. Whatley, Bruce, illus. (J). (ps up). 2004. 32p. 6.99 (978-0-06-073917-1(7) , Harper Festival); 1999. 40p. 16.99 (978-0-06-026608-0(2)) HarperCollins Pubs.

—The Night Before Christmas. Moore, Clement C., ed. Tudor, Tasha, illus. 1999. 32p. (J). (ps-17). 16.99 (978-0-316-85579-2(0)) Little Brown & Co.

—The Night Before Christmas. Moore, Clement C., ed. Tudor, Tasha & Sanderson, Ruth, illus. 2002. 32p. (J). (ps-17). pap. 6.99 (978-0-316-83271-7(5)) Little, Brown Bks. for Young Readers.

—The Night Before Christmas. Catusanu, Mircea, illus. 2001. (Little Golden Book Ser.). 24p. (J). (gr. k-k). 2.99 (978-0-307-96003-0(X) , Golden Bks.) Random Hse. Children's Bks.

—The Night Before Christmas. Marshall, James, illus. 2004. (Bookshelf Ser.). 32p. (J). pap. 5.99 (978-0-439-66939-9(1) , Scholastic Paperbacks) Scholastic, Inc.

—The Night Before Christmas. Tudor, Tasha, illus. 2000. 64p. (J). (ps up). pap. 7.99 (978-0-689-83932-0(4) , Aladdin) Simon & Schuster Children's Publishing.

—The Night Before Christmas. 2004. (Illus.). 20p. (J). bds. 6.95 (978-0-8118-3933-4(8)) Chronicle Bks. LLC.

—The Night Before Christmas. abr. ed. 2004. (Wee Books for Wee Folks). (Illus.). 64p. (J). (ps-3). 6.95 (978-1-55709-410-0(1)) Applewood Bks.

—The Night Before Christmas. Spirin, Gennady, illus. ltd. ed. 2006. 32p. (J). 16.99 (978-0-7614-5298-0(2)) Cavendish, Marshall Corp.

—The Night Before Christmas. Engelbreit, Mary, illus. rev. ed. 2002. 40p. (J). (gr. k-2). 16.99 (978-0-06-008160-7(0)) HarperCollins Pubs.

—The Night Before Christmas. de Paola, Tomie, illus. abr. ed. 32p. (J). (gr. k-3). 6.95 (978-0-8234-0417-9(X)) Holiday Hse., Inc.

—The Night Before Christmas. abr. ed. 1998. (Miniature Editionstm Ser.). (Illus.). 112p. (ps up). 4.95 (978-0-7624-0352-3(7) , Running Pr. Minature Editions) Running Pr. Bk. Pubs.

—The Night Before Christmas: A Trim-a-Tree Story. l.t. ed. 1999. (Illus.). 16p. (J). (ps-3). 6.99 (978-1-57866-076-6(9) , Galahad Bks.) BBS Publishing Corp.

—The Night Before Christmas: Board Book. Birmingham, Christian, tr. 2007. (Illus.). 26p. (J). pap. 5.95 ***(978-0-7624-3014-7(1)*** , Running Pr. Kids) Running Pr. Bk. Pubs.

—The Night Before Christmas: Pull the Tabs! Change the Pictures! 2003. (Magic Windows Ser.). (Illus.). 10p. (gr. k-3). pap. 12.95 (978-0-7624-1573-1(8) , Running Pr. Kids) Running Pr. Bk. Pubs.

—The Night Before Christmas: The Classic Edition. Birmingham, Christian, illus. abr. ed. 2005. (Children's Illustrated Classics Ser.). 48p. (ps-3). 9.98 (978-1-56138-476-1(3) , Running Pr. Kids) Running Pr. Bk. Pubs.

—A Scratch & Sniff Night Before Christmas. Swanson, Maggie, illus. 2007. 24p. (J). (ps-2). 9.95 ***(978-1-4027-4215-6(0))*** Sterling Publishing Co., Inc.

—The Teddy Bears' Night Before Christmas. 1999. (J). (ps-3). 103.60 (978-0-439-11752-4(6)) Scholastic, Inc.

—A Visit from St. Nicholas. Nast, Thomas, illus. 2006. 24p. (J). (ps-1). 24.95 (978-1-55709-592-3(2)) Applewood Bks.

Moore, Clement C., ed. & illus. The Night Before Christmas. Moore, Clement C., illus. 1999. 40p. (J). (ps-3). 16.89 (978-0-06-028380-3(7)) HarperCollins Pubs.

—The Night Before Christmas. Moore, Clement C., illus. Porfirio, Guy, illus. 2004. 20p. (J). 9.95 (978-0-8249-6553-2(1)) Ideals Pubns.

—The Night Before Christmas. Moore, Clement C., illus. Finster, Howard, illus. 1998. 26p. reprint ed. 14.95 (978-1-56352-533-9(X)) Longstreet Pr., Inc.

—The Night Before Christmas. Moore, Clement C., illus. Rice, James, illus. 2000. 32p. (J). (ps-3). reprint ed. 15.95 (978-0-88289-755-4(1)) Pelican Publishing Co., Inc.

—The Night Before Christmas. Moore, Clement C., illus. Gorsline, Douglas, illus. 32p. (J). Random Hse. Children's Bks.

—The Night Before Christmas. Moore, Clement C., illus. Lobel, Anita, illus. 2003. 32p. (J). 8.95 (978-0-375-82414-2(6) , Knopf Bks. for Young Readers) Random Hse. Children's Bks.

—The Night Before Christmas. Moore, Clement C., illus. Cartwright, Sharon, illus. 1999. (Jellybean Bks.). 24p. (J). (ps-k). lib. bdg. 7.99 (978-0-375-90147-8(7) , Random Hse. Bks. for Young Readers) Random Hse. Children's Bks.

—The Night Before Christmas. Moore, Clement C., illus. Birmingham, Christian, photos by. 1999. 60p. (J). (ps-1). pap. 12.98 (978-1-58048-065-9(9)) Sandvik Publishing.

—The Night Before Christmas. Moore, Clement C., illus. Brett, Jan, illus. 2001. (J). 27.95 incl. audio (978-0-8045-6859-3(6)) Spoken Arts, Inc.

—The Night Before Christmas. Moore, Clement C., illus. Cone, William, illus. 2006. (J). (gr. 2-6). 25.65 (978-1-59197-751-3(7)) Spotlight.

—The Night Before Christmas. Moore, Clement C., illus. 2000. (gr. 3-6). lib. bdg. 15.30 (978-0-613-31526-5(X)); lib. bdg. 15.30 (978-0-613-32892-0(2)) Tandem Library Bks.

—The Night Before Christmas. Moore, Clement C., illus. Lobel, Anita, illus. 2000. (J). (978-0-606-19773-1(7)) Tandem Library Bks.

Moore, Clement C. & Jaramillo, Raquel. The Night Before Christmas. 2001. (Illus.). 40p. (J). (ps up). 18.95 (978-0-689-84053-1(5) , Atheneum/Anne Schwartz Bks.) Simon & Schuster Children's Publishing.

Moore, Clement C., et al. The Night Before Christmas: A Classic Illustrated Edition. 1998. (Illus.). 44p. (J). (ps up). 16.95 (978-0-8118-1712-7(1)) Chronicle Bks. LLC.

Moore, Clement Clarke. Night Before Christmas. Pinkney, Debbie, illus. 2004. (J). ***(978-0-7853-1892-7(5))*** Publications International, Ltd.

—The Night Before Christmas: A Magical Cut-Paper Edition. Puttapipat, Niroot, illus. 2007. 24p. (J). (ps-2). 16.99 ***(978-0-7636-3469-8(7))*** Candlewick Pr.

Moses, Grandma, illus. The Night Before Christmas. 2007. 32p. 17.95 ***(978-0-7893-1568-7(8))*** Universe Publishing.

Mouse, Clement C. A Visit from Saint Nicholas: And Santa Mouse, Too! 1998. 32p. (J). reprint ed. pap. 10.01 (978-0-7868-1176-2(5)) Hyperion Bks. for Children.

The Night Before Christmas. 2003. (Traditional Christmas Stories Ser.). 32p. (J). 4.98 (978-0-7525-8847-6(8)) Parragon, Inc.

O'Brien, John, illus. The Twelve Days of Christmas. 32p. (J). (gr. k-2). pap. 8.95 (978-1-59078-086-2(8)) Boyds Mills Pr.

Roberts, Tom. 'Twas the Night Before Christ. Hoffman, Steve, illus. 2002. per. (978-0-9723868-0-7(7)) T & T Roberts Publishing.

Running Press Staff, et al. The Night Before Christmas. 2001. (Heirloom Editions Ser.). (Illus.). 48p. 16.95 (978-0-7624-1069-9(8) , Running Pr.) Running Pr. Bk. Pubs.

Sabuda, Robert & Moore, Clement C. The Night Before Christmas. 2002. (Illus.). 12p. (J). 26.99 (978-0-689-83899-6(9) , Little Simon) Simon & Schuster Children's Publishing.

Stiegemeyer, Julie. Baby in a Manger. Wong, Nicole, illus. 2004. 32p. (J). (gr. k-4). 9.99 (978-0-7586-0726-3(1)) Concordia Publishing Hse.

Tavares, Matt, illus. 'Twas the Night Before Christmas: Or Account of a Visit from St. Nicholas. 2002. 32p. (J). (gr. k up). 16.00 (978-0-7636-1585-7(4)) Candlewick Pr.

Terrill, Beth. The Barnyard Night Before Christmas. Newbold, Greg, illus. 2007. (Picture Book Ser.). 40p. (J). (ps-1). 14.99 ***(978-0-375-83682-4(9));*** lib. bdg. 17.99 ***(978-0-375-93682-1(3))*** Random Hse. Children's Bks. (Random Hse. Bks. for Young Readers).

Watson, Clyde. Father Fox's Christmas Rhymes. Watson, Wendy, illus. 2003. 40p. (J). 16.00 (978-0-374-37576-8(3) , Farrar, Straus & Giroux (BYR)) Farrar, Straus & Giroux.

—Father Fox's Christmas Rhymes. Watson, Wendy, illus. 2007. 32p. (J). pap. 6.99 ***(978-0-312-37274-3(4))*** Square Fish.

Wick, Walter. Night Before Christmas. Wick, Walter, illus. 2005. (Can You See What I See?). (Illus.). 40p. (J). pap. 13.99 (978-0-439-76927-3(2) , Cartwheel Bks.) Scholastic, Inc.

CHRISTOLOGY

see Jesus Christ

CHRONOLOGY

see Calendars; Time

CHRONOLOGY, HISTORICAL

see also Calendars

also subdivision History—Chronology under names of countries, e.g. United States—History—Chronology

History Makers. 2003. 320p. 5.98 (978-1-4054-0325-2(X)) Parragon, Inc.

Jackson, Ellen B. Turn of the Century: Eleven Centuries of Children & Change. Ellis, Jan Davey, illus. 2003. 32p. pap. 7.95 (978-0-88106-370-7(3)) Charlesbridge Publishing, Inc.

Lorenz Books Staff. Exploring History: A Journey Through Time, from Prehistory to the Modern World. 2001. (Illus.). 512p. (gr. 3-7). 45.00 (978-0-7548-0647-9(2)) Anness Publishing GBR. *Dist:* National Bk. Network.

Mercati, Cynthia. A Trip Through Time. Hatala, Dan, illus. 2000. (Cover-to-Cover Bks.). 64p. (J). 5.60 (978-0-7891-5190-2(1)); (gr. 2-5). lib. bdg. 13.95 (978-0-7807-9510-5(5) , Covercraft) Perfection Learning Corp.

Moskal, Greg. The History of Space Exploration: Sequencing Events Chronologically on a Timeline. 2004. (PowerMath Ser.). (Illus.). 24p. (J). lib. bdg. (978-0-8239-8850-1(3)); lib. bdg. 21.25 (978-0-8239-8962-1(3)) Rosen Publishing Group, Inc., The. (PowerKids Pr.).

CHURCH

see also Christianity

Bagley, Val Chadwick & Beckstrand, Tamara, trs. My Little Book about Prayer. Bagley, Val Chadwick, illus. 2004. (Illus.). (J). bds. 10.95 (978-1-59156-096-8(9)) Covenant Communications, Inc.

Berndt, Clarence & Rathmann, Rodney L. A Bible History: In the Words of Holy Scripture: With Illustrations, Maps, & Notes. 2003. (Illus.). 480p. stu. ed. 18.00 (978-0-7586-0288-6(X)) Concordia Publishing Hse.

Bradley, Erica. I Am Lutheran. 1999. (Religions of the World Ser.). 24p. (J). (gr. k-4). lib. bdg. 18.75 (978-0-8239-5263-2(0)) Rosen Publishing Group, Inc., The.

English, June. Anglican Young People's Dictionary. 2004. (Illus.). 80p. (J). pap. 10.00 (978-0-8192-1985-5(1)) Morehouse Publishing.

Fields, Doug & Eastman, Brett. Connecting Your Heart to Others: 6 Small Group Sessions on Fellowship. 2003. (Life Together Ser.). 144p. pap., stu. ed. 7.99 (978-0-310-25334-1(9)) Zondervan.

—Growing to Be Like Jesus: 6 Small Group Sessions on Discipleship. 2003. (Life Together Ser.). 144p. pap., stu. ed. 7.99 (978-0-310-25335-8(7)) Zondervan.

—Starting to Go Where God Wants You to Be: 6 Small Group Lessons on Beginning Life Together. 2003. (Life Together Ser.). 144p. pap., stu. ed. 7.99 (978-0-310-25333-4(0)) Zondervan.

Gilmore, Ruth. Saving the Ants: And 58 Other Kids Sermons from the Gospel of Matthew. 2001. (Children's Sermons Ser.). (Illus.). 128p. (gr. k-5). 13.99 (978-0-8066-4080-8(4) , Augsburg Bks.) Augsburg Fortress, Pubs.

Hoh, John L., Jr. The Church on the Web: A Hands-On Tutor for the Novice. 2001. (YA). ring bd. 44.95 (978-1-57052-206-2(5)) Church Growth Institute.

Law, Jennifer. I Like to Go to Church. Reeves, Rhonda, ed. 2000. (Missions & Me Ser.). (Illus.). 16p. (J). (gr. 3-5). 7.99 (978-1-56309-313-5(8)) Woman's Missionary Union.

Medina, Sarah. Christian Churches. 2005. (Let's Find Out about Ser.). (Illus.). 32p. (J). (gr. 3-7). lib. bdg. (978-1-4034-7031-7(6)) Steck-Vaughn.

My Church. 2006. 16p. (J). pap. 1.99 (978-0-7847-1453-9(3) , 22132) Standard Publishing.

Nason, Ruth. Visiting a Church. 2005. (Start up Religion Ser.). (Illus.). 24p. (J). (gr. 1-4). lib. bdg. (978-1-84234-342-5(4) , Cherrytree Books) Evans Publishing Group.

Orborne, Rick. I Want to Know about the Church. 1998. (I Want to Know Ser.). (Illus.). 32p. (J). (gr. 7-10). 9.99 (978-0-310-22094-7(7)) Zonderkidz.

Stiegemeyer, Julie & Mitter, Kathy. Things I Do in Church. 2003. (ENG., Illus.). 20p. (J). bds. 4.99 (978-0-7586-0126-1(3)) Concordia Publishing Hse.

Swain. Calling You. 2005. (Illus.). 96p. (J). (978-0-8192-8142-5(5)) Morehouse Publishing.

This Is My Lutheran Church. 2004. (Exploring Luther's Small Catechism Ser.). (ps-k). 2.99 (978-0-8066-6790-4(7)) Augsburg Fortress, Pubs.

Wood, Angela. Christian Church. 1999. (Places of Worship Ser.). (Illus.). 32p. (J). (gr. 2 up). lib. bdg. 23.33 (978-0-8368-2606-7(X)) Stevens, Gareth Inc.

CHURCH AND SOCIAL PROBLEMS

Gatley, Patricia. The Sun Fell Out of the Sky One Day... . 2005. (ENG.). 36p. per. 14.99 (978-1-59781-106-4(8)) Xulon Pr., Inc.

McIntosh, Kenneth & McIntosh, Marsha. When Religion & Politics Mix: How Matters of Faith Influence Political Policies. 2006. (Religion & Modern Culture Ser.). (Illus.). 112p. (J). (gr. 7 up). lib. bdg. 22.95 (978-1-59084-971-2(X)) Mason Crest Pubs.

Woolf, Alex. Fundamentalism. 2003. (Ideas of the Modern World Ser.). (Illus.). 64p. (J). lib. bdg. 28.56 (978-0-7398-6416-6(5)) Raintree.

CHURCH AND STATE

see also Freedom of Religion

Farish, Leah. Lemon vs. Kurtzman: The Religion & Public Funds Case. 2000. (Landmark Supreme Court Cases Ser.). (Illus.). 128p. (YA). (gr. 6-12). lib. bdg. 26.60 (978-0-7660-1339-1(1)) Enslow Pubs., Inc.

Gaustad, Edwin S. Church & State in America. 2nd rev. ed. 2003. (Religion in American Life Ser.). (Illus.). 176p. (YA). 30.00 (978-0-19-516738-2(4)) Oxford Univ. Pr., Inc.

Marzilli, Alan. Religion in Public Schools. 2003. (Point/Counterpoint Ser.). (Illus.). 112p. (gr. 9-13). 32.95 (978-0-7910-7484-8(6) , Chelsea Hse.) Facts On File, Inc.

McIntosh, Kenneth & McIntosh, Marsha. When Religion & Politics Mix: How Matters of Faith Influence Political Policies. 2006. (Religion & Modern Culture Ser.). (Illus.). 112p. (J). (gr. 7 up). lib. bdg. 22.95 (978-1-59084-971-2(X)) Mason Crest Pubs.

Mountjoy, Shane & McNeese, Tim. Engel v. Vitale: School Prayer & the Establishment Clause. 2006. (Great Supreme Court Decisions Ser.). (Illus.). 128p. (YA). (gr. 5-8). 30.00 (978-0-7910-9241-5(0) , Chelsea Hse.) Facts On File, Inc.

New, David W. Religious Freedom in America for Beginners. 2004. (Illus.). 63p. (YA). 4.95 (978-0-9721333-3-3(X)) Pocket Publication, A.

CHURCH ARCHITECTURE

see also Cathedrals; Church Buildings; Temples

Kuhlman, Thomas, et al. The Beauty of Thy House: The History, Art & Architecture of Saint Cecilia Cathedral Omaha. 2005. (Illus.). lib. bdg. 39.95 (978-0-9745410-7-5(9)); per. 14.95 (978-0-9745410-6-8(0)) Omaha Bks.

Michelangelo. Sistine Chapel Coloring Book. 2004. (Dover Coloring Bks.). (Illus.). 32p. (J). pap. 3.95 (978-0-486-43334-9(X)) Dover Pubns., Inc.

CHURCH BELLS

see Bells

CHURCH BIOGRAPHY

see Christian Biography

CHURCH BUILDINGS

see also Cathedrals; Church Architecture

Coniaris, Anthony M. Let's Take a Walk Through Our Orthodox Church. Kizilos, Betty, illus. 1998. 100p. (J). (gr. 3-6). pap. 16.95 (978-1-880971-39-0(9)) Light & Life Publishing Co.

Macaulay, David. Mosque. Macaulay, David, illus. 2003. (Illus.). 96p. (YA). (gr. 5 up). 18.00 (978-0-618-24034-0(9) , Walter Lorraine) Houghton Mifflin Co. Trade & Reference Div.

Medina, Sarah. Christian Churches. 2005. (Let's Find Out about Ser.). (Illus.). 32p. (J). (gr. 3-7). lib. bdg. (978-1-4034-7031-7(6)) Steck-Vaughn.

Nason, Ruth. Visiting a Church. 2005. (Start up Religion Ser.). (Illus.). 24p. (J). (gr. 1-4). lib. bdg. (978-1-84234-342-5(4) , Cherrytree Books) Evans Publishing Group.

Rock, Lois. The Path That Runs by the Church: A Year in the Life of a Village School. Comfort, Louise, illus. 2001. 48p. 19.99 (978-0-7459-4188-2(5) , Lion) Lion Hudson plc GBR. *Dist:* Independent Pubs. Group.

Snyder, Bernadette McCarver. 131 FUN-damental Facts for Catholic Kids. Sharp, Chris, illus. 2006. (Liguori's Fun Facts Ser.). 144p. (J). per. 9.95 (978-0-7648-1502-7(4)) Liguori Pubns.

Wescovich Dill, Pamela. Katrina's Rainbow: The Miracle of the Storm Crosses. 2006. (Illus.). 46p. (J). 17.99 ***(978-1-59879-302-4(0))*** Lifevest Publishing, Inc.

Wilson, Cristi. Just Because. Wilson, Cristi, illus. l.t. ed. 2006. (Illus.). 24p. (J). per. 10.99 ***(978-1-59879-251-5(2))*** Lifevest Publishing, Inc.

CHURCH BUILDINGS—FICTION

Cizmich, Marilyne. Sonia, the Church Cat. 2007. (Illus.). 28p. (J). per. 9.99 ***(978-1-60247-096-5(0))*** Tate Publishing & Enterprises, L.L.C.

Kelly, Veronica & Goody, Wendy. A Peek into My Church. Pruitt, Ginny, illus. 2nd rev. ed. 1998. 44p. (J). (ps-3). 12.95 (978-0-9657218-1-3(7)) WhipperSnapper Bks.

Myers, Bill. Phantom of the Haunted Church. 1998. (Bloodhounds, Inc. Ser.: Vol. 3). (Illus.). 128p. (J). (gr. 3-8). pap. 5.99 (978-1-55661-892-5(1)) Bethany Hse. Pubs.

Rubright, Lynn. Mama's Window. Smith, Duane, illus. 2005. 89p. (J). 16.95 (978-1-57480-160-6(0)) Lee & Low Bks., Inc.

Williams, G. Walton. Of Mice & Bells. Kollock, John, illus. unabr. ed. 1999. 674p. (J). (gr. k-3). pap. 6.95 (978-0-9703570-1-4(X)) Barksdale Hse. Pr.

CHURCH DENOMINATIONS

see Sects

CHURCH FESTIVALS

see Fasts and Feasts

CHURCH HISTORY

see also Church and State; Jews; Missions; Monasticism and Religious Orders; Popes; Protestantism; Reformation; Sects

also names of countries, states, etc. with the subdivision Church History (e.g. United States—Church History; etc.)

Anderson, Dale. Churches & Religion in the Middle Ages. 2005. (World Almanac Library of the Middle Ages). (J). pap. (978-0-8368-5901-0(4)); (Illus.). 48p. (YA). lib. bdg. 30.00 (978-0-8368-5892-1(1)) Stevens, Gareth Inc. (World Almanac Library).

—Monks & Monasteries in the Middle Ages. 2005. (World Almanac Library of the Middle Ages). (J). pap. (978-0-8368-5906-5(5)); (Illus.). 48p. (YA). (gr. 10-12). lib. bdg. 30.00 (978-0-8368-5897-6(2)) Stevens, Gareth Inc. (World Almanac Library).

Appleton, E. R. & Cadman, S. Parkes. An Outline of Religion. 2005. pap. 50.95 (978-1-4179-8460-2(0)) Kessinger Publishing, LLC.

Barter, James. A Medieval Monk. 2003. (Working Life Ser.). (Illus.). 112p. (J). 29.95 (978-1-59018-478-3(5) , Lucent Bks.) Thomson Gale.

Becker, Mary Lee, contrib. by. Living Our Faith Church History: Our Christian Story. 2002. (Living Our Faith Ser.). (Illus.). 112p. pap., stu. ed. 8.95 (978-0-15-900518-7(3)) Harcourt Religion Pubs.

Bible Visuals International, compiled by. The Church Vol. 15: New Testament. 2006. (Illus.). (J). pap. (978-1-932381-45-0(7) , 1015) Bible Visuals International, Inc.

Booth, Edwin P. Martin Luther: The Great Reformer. 1999. (Heroes of the Faith Ser.). 208p. (J). (ps up). 14.95 (978-0-7910-5037-8(8) , Chelsea Hse.) Facts On File, Inc.

DeKock, Paul & Yount, David. The Next Step. 2004. (Illus.). (YA). (gr. 8-12). 40.00 (978-1-57336-406-5(1) , I7130) Interaction Pubs., Inc.

Eastwood, Kay. Places of Worship in the Middle Ages. 2003. (Medieval World Ser.). (Illus.). 32p. (J). (gr. 5). (978-0-7787-1347-0(4)); pap. (978-0-7787-1379-1(2)) Crabtree Publishing Co.

Fudge, Thomas A. & Purtell, April. Honors Church History Syllabus. 1998. 24p. (YA), (gr. 11-12). pap. 4.95 (978-1-57896-032-3(0) , 2533, Hewitt Homeschooling Resources) Hewitt Research Foundation, Inc.

George, Denise & Christian History Institute Staff. History of Christianity. 2000. 48p. (Illus.). (YA). pap., stu. ed., wbk. ed. 9.99 (978-1-56364-368-2(5)); (J). pap. 9.99 (978-1-56364-340-8(5)) Christian History Institute.

George, Timothy. History of Christianity - Program Scripts. 2000. 48p. (YA). pap. 9.99 (978-1-56364-370-5(7)) Christian History Institute.

Hannula, Richard. Trial & Triumph: Stories from Church History. 8th ed. 1999. 304p. (J). (gr. 7-11). per. 21.00 (978-1-885767-54-7(4)) Canon Pr.

Heroes of the Faith. (Illus.). 176-208p. (J). (gr. 5). 179.50 (978-0-7910-4916-7(7) , Chelsea Hse.) Facts On File, Inc.

Hinds, Kathryn. The Church. 2000. (Life in the Middle Ages Ser.). (Illus.). 80p. (J). (gr. 5 up). lib. bdg. 29.93 (978-0-7614-1008-9(2) , Benchmark Bks.) Cavendish, Marshall Corp.

Hodges, George. Saints & Heroes to the End of the Middle Ages (Yesterday's Classics) 2006. (Illus.). 188p. (J). per. 9.95 (978-1-59915-093-2(X)) Yesterday's Classics.

Kingdom Leaders Solving Church Problems. (YA). (978-0-7673-9456-7(9)) LifeWay Christian Resources.

Kuipers, Ken. A. D. A Study of Church History. (Crossroads Ser.). 143p. (gr. 6-8). stu. ed. 9.50 (978-0-930265-44-1(0) , 120010, Faith Alive Christian Resources) CRC Pubns.

Lockman, Vic. Church History for Young Children with Cartoons: The Reformation, 2 vols. 1998. (Illus.). 45p. (J). (ps-4). 1.75 (978-0-936175-36-2(2)) Lockman, Vic.

MacDonald, Fiona. The Reformation. 2002. (Events & Outcomes Ser.). (Illus.). 80p. (J). lib. bdg. (978-0-7398-5800-4(9)) Raintree.

MacDonald, Fiona, intro. Gods, Beliefs & Ceremonies: Through the Ages. 2001. (Through the Ages Ser.). (Illus.). 64p. (gr. 3-7). 12.95 (978-0-7548-0784-1(3)) Anness Publishing GBR. *Dist:* National Bk. Network.

MacLean, Ruth. Snapshots, NT. ed. 1999. (Newsbox Ser.). (Illus.). 40p. (J). (gr. 2-6). pap. 6.99 (978-1-85792-347-6(2) , Christian Focus) Christian Focus Pubns. GBR. *Dist:* Riverside.

C
D

Maier, Paul L. The Very First Christians. Ordaz, Frank, illus. 2001. 32p. (J). 12.99 (978-0-570-07175-4(5)) Concordia Publishing Hse.

Meet Martin Luther. 2004. (Exploring Luther's Small Catechism Ser.). (gr. 3-4). 2.99 (978-0-8066-6784-3(2)) Augsburg Fortress, Pubs.

Melchiore, Susan McCarthy. The Spanish Inquisition. 2001. (Great Disasters, Reforms & Ramifications Ser.). (Illus.). 114p. (YA). (gr. 6-10). 32.00 (978-0-7910-6327-9(5) , Chelsea Hse.) Facts On File, Inc.

Nardo, Don, ed. The Rise of Christianity. 1998. (Turning Points in World History Ser.). (Illus.). 224p. (YA). (gr. 9-12). lib. bdg. 32.45 (978-1-56510-963-6(5) , Greenhaven Pr., Inc.) Thomson Gale.

Phillips, Shannon & Garland, Nick. Celebrating a Century: The Birth & Growth of First Baptist Church Broken Arrow. Schilling, Sarah Phillips, ed. 2005. per. 24.95 (978-0-9764103-3-1(8)) Daylight Pubs.

Ross & Guymon-King. Primary Partners. 2004. cd-rom 11.95 (978-1-57734-691-3(2)) Covenant Communications, Inc.

Rostrom, Laura Lee. My Church History Storybook. 2003. (Illus.). 288p. (J). 19.95 (978-1-55517-698-3(4) , 76984) Cedar Fort, Inc./CFI Distribution.

Shaw, S. B. The Great Revival in Wales. 2002. per. 10.99 (978-1-931393-01-0(X)) Christian Life Bks.

Stoutzenberger, Joseph M. The Church Through History. 2002. 326p. (YA). ring bd. (978-0-15-901100-3(0)) Harcourt Religion Pubs.

Stoutzenberger, Joseph M. & Stoutzenberger, Joseph M. The Church Through History (student) 2002. (Illus.). 340p. (YA). pap., stu. ed. (978-0-15-901094-5(2)) Harcourt Religion Pubs.

Tracy, Kathleen. The Life & Times of Constantine. 2005. (Biography from Ancient Civilizations Ser.). (Illus.). 48p. (J). (gr. 4-8). lib. bdg. 29.95 (978-1-58415-343-6(1)) Mitchell Lane Pubs., Inc.

Van Der Veer, Andrew. Bible Lessons for Juniors, Book 4: The Early Church. 2007. (J). (***978-1-60178-015-7(X)***) Reformation Heritage Bks.

Wellman, Sam. John Wesley: Founder of the Methodist Church. 1999. (Heroes of the Faith Ser.). 208p. (YA). (gr. 4-7). lib. bdg. 17.95 (978-0-7910-5036-1(X) , Chelsea Hse.) Facts On File, Inc.

Yonge, Charlotte M. The Chosen People A Compendium of Sacred & Church History for School Children. 2004. reprint ed. pap. 22.95 (978-1-4191-5664-9(0)); pap. 1.99 (978-1-4192-5664-6(5)) Kessinger Publishing, LLC.

Yonge, Charlotte Mary. The Chosen People: A Compendium of Sacred & Church History for School-Children. 2006. 202p. pap. 12.99 (978-1-4264-2274-4(1)); 214p. pap. 15.99 (978-1-4264-2309-3(8)) BiblioBazaar.

Yonge, Mary Charlott. The Chosen People. 2006. 63.99 (***978-1-4280-3095-4(6)***) IndyPublish.com.

CHURCH HISTORY—FICTION

Polland, Madeleine. City of the Golden House. 2006. (J). per. 12.95 (978-0-9766386-4-3(9)) Hillside Education.

Pope, Amy. Big Church. Meier, Paul, illus. 2004. (J). bds. 9.99 (978-1-4183-0008-1(X)) Christ Inspired, Inc.

Spinelli, Eileen & Parmenter, Wayne. When Christmas Came. Spinelli, Eileen & Parmenter, Wayne, illus. 2006. (Illus.). 32p. (J). (ps). bds. 16.95 (978-0-8249-5507-6(2) , Ideals Pr.) Ideals Pubns.

St. John, Patricia. Twice Freed. 1999. (gr. 7-12). lib. bdg. 14.15 (978-0-613-80123-2(7)) Tandem Library Bks.

Vernon, Louise A. Ink on His Fingers. Eitzen, Allan, illus. 2002. (Louise A. Vernon's Religious Heritage Ser.). 128p. (YA). (gr. 4-9). 7.99 (978-0-8361-1673-1(9)) Herald Pr.

CHURCH HISTORY—REFORMATION

see Reformation

CHURCH MUSIC

see also Carols; Hymns

Advance Cal-Tech Inc. Staff. Let's Praise & Play: Children's Christian Mini-Piano Book. Kung, Edward, ed. McKig, Susan, illus. 36p. (J). (ps-6). (978-0-943759-00-5(5)) Advance Cal Tech, Inc.

Allen, Nan & Allen, Dennis. Living It Up: Contemporary Songs & Sketches for Youth. 1998. 144p. 8.99 (978-0-8341-9841-8(X) , MB-798) Lillenas Publishing Co.

Beall, Pamela Conn & Nipp, Susan Hagen. Wee Sing More Bible Songs. ed. 2002. (Wee Sing Ser.). (Illus.). (J). 11.99 (978-0-8431-4927-2(2)); 64p. pap. 9.99 (978-0-8431-4926-5(4)) Penguin Group (USA) Inc. (Price Stern Sloan).

Bell, M. F. Church Music. 2001. (YA). reprint ed. 150.00 (978-0-7222-5164-5(5)) Library Reprints, Inc.

Belpulsi, Peter A. & Belpulsi, Nathalie B. As the Saying Goes, Vol. 2. 2005. (Illus.). 145p. (gr. 1-7). (978-1-882614-21-9(6)) Globe Pubs.

Bible Visuals International, compiled by. A Christian's Belief. 2005. (Illus.). (J). pap. (978-1-932381-17-7(1) , 6120) Bible Visuals International, Inc.

—God Will Take Care of You. 2005. (Illus.). (J). pap. (978-1-932381-18-4(X) , 6160) Bible Visuals International, Inc.

—Hark! the Herald Angels Sing. 2006. (Illus.). (J). pap. (978-1-932381-95-5(3) , 6200) Bible Visuals International, Inc.

—Who Is He in Yonder Stall? 2005. (Illus.). (J). pap. (978-1-932381-21-4(X) , 6500) Bible Visuals International, Inc.

Bumpus, John Skelton. A History of English Cathedral Music, 1549-1889, 2 vols., set. 2001. (YA). reprint ed. 250.00 (978-0-7222-5165-2(3)) Library Reprints, Inc.

Byrd, William. Church Music. 2001. (YA). reprint ed. 150.00 (978-0-7222-5374-8(5)) Library Reprints, Inc.

Childrens Choir. 2.95 (978-0-7673-6200-9(4)); 4.98 (978-0-7673-6228-3(4)) LifeWay Christian Resources.

Children's Choir. (978-0-7673-8478-0(4)) LifeWay Christian Resources.

Childrens Choir Pak. 44.95 (978-0-7673-6214-6(4)) LifeWay Christian Resources.

Cox, John C. Pulpits, Lecterns, & Organs in English Churches. 2001. 228p. (YA). reprint ed. 98.00 (978-0-7222-5886-6(0)) Library Reprints, Inc.

Cunningham, Edie. Trust & Obey: A Visualized Gospel Song. Anthoine, Leila et al, illus. 2005. 20p. (J). pap. (978-1-932381-20-7(1) , 6480) Bible Visuals International, Inc.

Delman, Elliott. Take-Along Songs: Bible Songs. Pfeiffer, Judith, illus. 2003. (Take-Along Songs Ser.). 16p. (J). bds. 9.98 incl. audio compact disk (978-0-7853-8609-4(2) , 7189100) Publications International, Ltd.

Discovering Music: Bible Story: David, the Music Maker. (Scripture Bites Ser.). (Illus.). (J). 7.99 (978-0-7847-9008-3(6) , 00705) Standard Publishing.

Fettke, Tom, ed. & compiled by. Great Big Praise for a Great Big God Bk. 2: 100 Fun, Exciting, Singable Songs for Older Kids. Fettke, Tom, compiled by. 2001. 184p. 12.99 (978-0-8341-7110-7(4) , MB-854) Lillenas Publishing Co.

Forth, T. F. The Sanctity of Church Music. 2001. (YA). reprint ed. 150.00 (978-0-7222-5169-0(6)) Library Reprints, Inc.

Gardner, George L. H. A Manual of English Church Music. 2001. 232p. (YA). reprint ed. 98.00 (978-0-7222-5171-3(8)) Library Reprints, Inc.

Group Publishing Staff. Sing & Shout Songs for Children's Ministry. 2000. (Illus.). (J). pap. 15.99 (978-0-7644-3071-8(8)); pap. 15.99 (978-0-7644-3072-5(6)); Vol. 1. pap. 15.99 (978-0-7644-3064-0(5)); Vol. 2. pap. 15.99 (978-0-7644-3068-8(8)); Vol. 3. pap. 15.99 (978-0-7644-3073-2(4)); Vol. 3. pap. 15.99 (978-0-7644-3069-5(6)); Vol. 4. pap. 15.99 (978-0-7644-3074-9(2)); Vol. 4. pap. 15.99 (978-0-7644-3070-1(X)) Group Publishing, Inc.

Hopson, Hal H. The World Sings Noel: The Christmas Story in Global Song. 2004. 40.00 incl. audio compact disk (978-0-687-08847-8(X)) Abingdon Pr.

Horman, John. The Angel Band. 2004. (gr. 2-6). 16.00 incl. audio compact disk (978-0-687-04535-8(5)); 12.00 incl. audio compact disk (978-0-687-04565-5(7)) Abingdon Pr.

—The Angel Band Preview Pak: A Christmas Musical Based on Luke 2:1-20. 2002. 24p. (gr. 2-6). 10.00 incl. audio (978-0-687-02881-8(7)) Abingdon Pr.

—The Angel Band Set: A Christmas Musical Based on Luke 2:1-20. 2002. (gr. 2-6). 40.00 incl. audio (978-0-687-04525-9(8)) Abingdon Pr.

Howie, Vicki. Easy to Say, Easy to Play: Three Popular Bible Stories & Sixteen Easy Songs to Sing & Play. 2005. (Illus.). 96p. (J). pap. (978-1-84101-221-6(1) , Barnabas) Bible Reading Fellowship.

Jebb, John. The Choral Service of the United Church of England & Ireland. 2001. 549p. (YA). reprint ed. 98.00 (978-0-7222-6122-4(5)) Library Reprints, Inc.

Just a Closer Walk. 7.50 (978-0-8054-5921-0(9)) B&H Publishing Grp.

Love, James. Scottish Church Music, Its Composers & Sources. 2001. 337p. (YA). reprint ed. 98.00 (978-0-7222-5174-4(2)) Library Reprints, Inc.

Miffleton, Jack. Sing a Song of Joy. (J). (gr. k-6). pap. 15.00 (978-0-937690-87-1(2) , 6111) World Library Pubns.

Mississippi Staff. Best of Mississippi Childrens. 2004. pap. (978-5-550-05701-8(8)) Nairi.

Moss, Donna. How I Praise You! 150 Little Psalms in Song. Moss, Rebecca, illus. 1998. 240p. (J). (ps-8). pap. (978-0-9663809-2-7(4)) Apex Publishing Services.

Music-Children's. 3.50 (978-0-8054-5876-3(X)) B&H Publishing Grp.

O'Brien, John. Great Stories & Songs. 2002. 147p. spiral bd. 24.95 (978-1-57999-137-1(8) , G-5781) GIA Pubns., Inc.

Psalms: Experiencing God. 1999. (Club 56 Ser.). 28p. (J). (gr. 5-6). pap., stu. ed., wbk. ed. 2.79 (978-1-57405-364-7(7)) CharismaLife Pubs.

Richer, Linda S., et al, eds. Chatter with the Angels: An Illustrated Songbook for Children. Hunsberger, Susan Graber, illus. 2000. 100p. (J). 29.95 (978-1-57999-082-4(7) , G-4900) GIA Pubns., Inc.

Robertson, Barny & Robertson, Carter, creators. Son Seekers - Nation Vacation: A 60's Flavored Children's Musical Journey about Knowing & Growing with God! 2002. 112p. (J). pap. 7.99 (978-0-8341-7360-6(3)) Lillenas Publishing Co.

Shaw, Martin. Principles of Church Music Composition. 2001. (YA). reprint ed. 150.00 (978-0-7222-5679-4(5)) Library Reprints, Inc.

Smith, W. Thomas & Batastini, Robert, eds. Hymns for the Gospels. 2001. 175p. per. 6.95 (978-1-57999-158-6(0) , G-5654) GIA Pubns., Inc.

Straw, Eileen Jones. Choir Starters. 2004. (Illus.). 64p. pap. 12.00 (978-0-687-09521-6(2)) Abingdon Pr.

Sunday School Songs. 1999. (Play-a-Song Ser.). (Illus.). 16p. (J). (ps-k). bds. 10.99 (978-0-7847-0968-9(8) , 03630, Bean Sprouts) Standard Publishing.

Terry, Charles S. Bach: The Cantatas & Oratorios, 2 vols., set. 2001. (YA). reprint ed. 250.00 (978-0-7222-6119-4(5)) Library Reprints, Inc.

Woog, Adam. The History of Gospel Music. 2005. (Music Library). (Illus.). 112p. (J). (gr. 4-7). lib. bdg. 32.45 (978-1-59018-735-7(0) , Lucent Bks.) Thomson Gale.

CHURCH OF CHRIST OF LATTER-DAY SAINTS

see Mormons and Mormonism

CHURCH OF CHRIST, SCIENTIST

see Christian Science

CHURCH SETTLEMENTS

see Social Settlements

CHURCHILL, WINSTON, SIR, 1874-1965

Adams, Simon. Winston Churchill. 2003. (20th Century History Makers Ser.). (Illus.). 112p. (J). lib. bdg. 32.85 (978-0-7398-5254-5(X)) Raintree.

Ashworth, Leon. Winston Churchill. 2002. (British History Makers Ser.). (Illus.). 32p. (YA). (gr. 5-8). (978-1-84234-072-1(7) , Cherrytree Books) Evans Publishing Group.

Binns, Tristan Boyer. Winston Churchill: Soldier & Politician. 2004. (Great Life Stories Ser.). (Illus.). 127p. (J). 30.50 (978-0-531-12361-4(8) , Watts, Franklin) Scholastic Library Publishing.

Daynes, Katie. Winston Churchill. Tomlins, Karen, illus. 2006. 64p. (J). 8.99 (978-0-7945-1258-3(5) , Usborne) EDC Publishing.

Hamilton, Janice. Winston Churchill. 2006. (Illus.). 112p. (J). 27.93 (978-0-8225-3419-8(3) , Twenty-First Century Bks.) Lerner Publishing Group.

Haugen, Brenda. Winston Churchill: British Soldier, Writer, Statesman. 2006. (Signature Lives Ser.). (Illus.). 112p. (J). (gr. 5-7). 30.60 (978-0-7565-1582-9(3)) Compass Point Bks.

MacDonald, Fiona. Winston Churchill. 2003. (Trailblazers of the Modern World Ser.). (Illus.). 48p. (J). (gr. 5 up). pap. 14.95 (978-0-8368-5242-4(7)); lib. bdg. 30.00 (978-0-8368-5082-6(3)) Stevens, Gareth Inc. (World Almanac Library).

Reynoldson, Fiona. Winston Churchill. 2001. (Leading Lives Ser.). (Illus.). 64p. (J). (gr. 5 7). lib. bdg. 27.86 (978-1-58810-163-1(0)) Heinemann Library.

Trailblazers of the Modern World: Winston Churchill; Alexander Fleming; Pablo Picasso; Elvis Presley; Venus & Serena Williams; Oprah Winfrey, 6 bks. 2002. (Illus.). (J). (gr. 5 up). pap. 89.70 (978-0-8368-5241-7(9) , World Almanac Library) Stevens, Gareth Inc.

CHURCHYARDS

see Cemeteries

CICERO, MARCUS TULLIUS

Forsyth, Fiona. Cicero: Defender of the Republic. 2003. (Leaders of Ancient Rome Ser.). (Illus.). 112p. (YA). (gr. 5-8). lib. bdg. 31.95 (978-0-8239-3590-1(6) , Rosen Central) Rosen Publishing Group, Inc., The.

Tracy, Kathleen. Cicero. 2006. (Biography from Ancient Civilizations Ser.). (Illus.). 48p. (J). lib. bdg. 20.95 (978-1-58415-510-2(8)) Mitchell Lane Pubs., Inc.

CINCINNATI BENGALS (FOOTBALL TEAM)

Frederick, Sara. The History of the Cincinnati Bengals. 2004. (NFL Today Ser.). (Illus.). 32p. 18.95 (978-1-58341-292-3(1) , Creative Education) Creative Co., The.

CINCINNATI REDS (BASEBALL TEAM)

Goodman, Michael E. The History of the Cincinnati Reds. 1998. (Baseball, the Great American Game Ser.). (Illus.). 32p. (YA). (gr. 3-12). lib. bdg. 21.30 (978-0-88682-905-6(4) , Creative Education) Creative Co., The.

Stewart, Wayne. Cincinnati Reds. 2002. (Baseball Ser.). (Illus.). 32p. (J). (978-1-58341-205-3(0) , Creative Education); pap. 5.95 (978-0-89812-339-5(9) , Creative Paperbacks) Creative Co., The.

CINEMA

see Motion Pictures

CINEMATOGRAPHY

Arruda, Suzanne Middendorf. From Kansas to Cannibals: The Story of Osa Johnson. 2001. (Illus.). 96p. (J). (gr. 6-12). pap. 19.95 (978-1-888105-50-6(X)) Avisson Pr., Inc.

Buckley, Annie. Making Movies. 2006. (Girls Rock! Ser.). (Illus.). 32p. (J). (gr. 1-5). 24.21 (978-1-59296-746-9(9)) Child's World, Inc.

Clee, Paul. Before Hollywood: From Shadow Play to the Silver Screen. 2005. (Illus.). 192p. (YA). (gr. 5-9). 22.00 (978-0-618-44533-2(1) , Clarion Bks.) Houghton Mifflin Co. Trade & Reference Div.

Conley, Robyn. Motion Pictures. (Inventions That Shaped the World Ser.). (J). 2005. (Illus.). 80p. (gr. 5-8). pap. 9.95 (978-0-531-16735-9(6)); 2004. 30.50 (978-0-531-12332-4(4)) Scholastic Library Publishing. (Watts, Franklin).

De Angelis, Gina. Motion Pictures: Making Cinema Magic. 2003. (Innovators Ser.: Vol. 11). (Illus.). 144p. (gr. 5 up). lib. bdg. 21.95 (978-1-881508-78-6(1)) Oliver Pr., Inc.

Fingeroth, Danny. Backstage at an Animated Series. 2003. (High Interest Bks.). (Illus.). 48p. (YA). (gr. 7-12). pap. 6.95 (978-0-516-24385-6(3) , Children's Pr.) Scholastic Library Publishing.

—Backstage at an Animated Series. 2003. (gr. 7-12). lib. bdg. 15.25 (978-0-613-59581-0(5)) Tandem Library Bks.

Gardner, Garth. Gardner's Computer Graphics & Animation Dictionary. 2003. (Gardner's Guide Ser.). (Illus.). 256p. pap. 24.95 (978-1-58965-005-3(0) , 703 793 8604) Gardner, Garth Co., Inc. (GGC).

Garth Gardner Company Staff, ed. Gardner's Film, Video & TV Dictionary. 2002. (Gardner's Guide Ser.). 448p. pap. 24.95 (978-1-58965-006-0(9) , 703 793 8604) Gardner, Garth Co., Inc. (GGC).

Hart, Christopher. Christopher Hart's Animation Studio. 2003. (gr. 3-6). lib. bdg. 16.40 (978-0-613-90862-7(7)) Tandem Library Bks.

High Interest Books: Backstage Pass. 2004. (Illus.). 100.00 (978-0-516-29632-6(9)) Scholastic Library Publishing.

Horn, Geoffrey M. Movie Stunts & Special Effects. 2006. (Making Movies Ser.). (Illus.). 32p. (J). (gr. 4-6). lib. bdg. 23.93 (978-0-8368-6840-1(4)) Stevens, Gareth Inc.

Hyland, Tony. Film & Fiction Robots. 2007. (J). (***978-1-59920-120-7(8)***) Smart Apple Media.

Long, Ben. Making Digital Videos. 2002. (CyberRookies). 320p. pap. 34.95 incl. cd-rom (978-1-58450-099-5(9)) Charles River Media.

Nardo, Don. Computer Animation. 2007. (Eye on Art Ser.). (Illus.). 128p. (J). (gr. 7-10). 31.20 (***978-1-4205-0004-2(X)*** , Lucent Bks.) Thomson Gale.

—Robots. 2007. (Monsters Ser.). (Illus.). 48p. (J). (gr. 4-8). 23.70 (***978-0-7377-3779-0(4)*** , Kidhaven) Thomson Gale.

Segall, Miriam. Career Building Through Digital Moviemaking. 2007. (J). (***978-1-4042-1945-8(5)***) Rosen Publishing Group, Inc., The.

Wellsing, Katherine. Backstage at a Movie Set. 2003. (Backstage Pass Ser.). (Illus.). 48p. (YA). 24.00 (978-0-516-24325-2(X) , Children's Pr.) Scholastic Library Publishing.

Wessling, Katherine. Backstage at a Movie Set. 2003. (High Interest Bks.). (Illus.). 48p. (YA). (gr. 7-12). pap. 6.95 (978-0-516-24387-0(X) , Children's Pr.) Scholastic Library Publishing.

—Backstage at a Movie Set. 2003. (gr. 7-12). lib. bdg. 15.25 (978-0-613-59577-3(7)) Tandem Library Bks.

Wiese, Jim. Movie Science: 40 Mind-Expanding, Reality-Bending, Starstruck Activities for Kids. 2001. (Illus.). 128p. pap. 12.95 (978-0-471-38941-5(2) , Wiley) Wiley, John & Sons, Inc.

CINEMATOGRAPHY, TRICK

Harcourt School Publishers Staff. Do-It-Yourself Monsters Below Level. 3rd ed. 2002. (Trophies Reading Program Ser.). (Illus.). pap. 5.10 (978-0-15-323419-4(9)) Harcourt Schl. Pubs.

Richardson, Christopher. Special Effects. 2005. (X-Zone Ser.). (Illus.). 30p. (gr. 4-8). 23.00 (978-0-7910-8986-6(X)) Facts On File, Inc.

CIPHERS

see also Cryptography; Writing

Adams, Simon. Code Breakers: From Hieroglyphs to Hackers. 2002. (gr. 3-6). lib. bdg. 14.10 (978-0-613-45731-6(5)) Tandem Library Bks.

Brian, Sarah Jane. Brainiac's Secret Agent: Fun Activities for Spies of All Ages. 2005. (Activity Journal Ser.). 128p. act. bk. ed. 12.99 (978-0-88088-446-4(0)) Peter Pauper Pr. Inc.

Dickson, Louise. Lu & Clancy's Secret Languages. Cupples, Pat, illus. unabr. ed. 2001. (Lu & Clancy Ser.). 40p. (J). (gr. k-3). (978-1-55074-695-2(2)); (978-1-55337-025-3(2)) Kids Can Pr., Ltd.

Groves. Knots & Knocks, Bk. 16. Date not set. (Illus.). 32p. (J). pap. 129.15 (978-0-582-18059-8(7)) Addison-Wesley Longman, Ltd. GBR. *Dist:* Trans-Atlantic Pubns., Inc.

Hossell, Karen Price. Ciphers & Codes. 2003. (Communicating Ser.). 48p. (J). (gr. 3-5). pap. 8.50 (978-1-58810-940-8(2) , 91579) Heinemann Library.

James, Elizabeth. How to Keep a Secret. rev. ed. 1998. 64p. (J). (gr. 3-7). pap. 4.95 (978-0-688-16278-8(9)) HarperCollins Pubs.

Janeczko, Paul B. Top Secret: A Handbook of Codes, Ciphers, & Secret Writing. LaReau, Jenna, illus. 2004. 144p. (J). (gr. 4 up). 16.99 (978-0-7636-0971-9(4)) Candlewick Pr.

Lamb, Geoffrey Frederick. Fun with Secret Writing. 2002. (Illus.). 64p. (gr. 4-7). pap. 4.95 (978-0-486-42098-1(1)) Dover Pubns., Inc.

Levy, Janey. Breaking the Code with Cryptography: Analyzing Patterns. 2006. (Math for the Real World Ser.). (Illus.). 32p. pap. (978-1-4042-6089-4(7)); lib. bdg. (978-1-4042-3368-3(7)) Rosen Publishing Group, Inc., The.

Menotti, Andrea. How to Tackle Puzzles, Unravel Riddles, Crack Codes, & Other Ways to Bend Your Brain. 2004. (Illus.). 80p. (J). (978-0-439-57905-6(8)) Scholastic, Inc.

Miller, Marvin. How to Write & Decode Secret Messages. 1998. (Codemaster Ser.: Vol. 1). (Illus.). (J). (gr. 4-7). pap. 4.50 (978-0-590-37386-9(2)); pap. 4.50 (978-0-590-37388-3(9)) Scholastic, Inc.

O'Hare, Jeffrey A. Dragonball Z: Book of Heroes (and Villains) 2005. (Illus.). 48p. (***978-0-439-80172-0(9)***) Scholastic, Inc.

Pincock, Stephen. Codebreaker: The History of Codes & Ciphers, from the Ancient Pharaohs to Quantum Cryptography. 2006. (Illus.). 160p. 19.95 (978-0-8027-1547-0(8)) Walker & Co.

Price Hossell, Karen. Ciphers & Codes. 2003. (Communicating Ser.). (Illus.). 48p. (J). (gr. 3-5). lib. bdg. 27.07 (978-1-58810-484-7(2)) Heinemann Library.

—Morse Code. 2003. (Communicating Ser.). (Illus.). 48p. (J). (gr. 3-5). lib. bdg. 27.07 (978-1-58810-486-1(9)) Heinemann Library.

Raintree Steck-Vaughn Staff. All about Codes. 1999. (Illus.). (J). pap. 35.60 (978-0-7398-0908-2(3)) Steck-Vaughn.

Weller, Janet. Messages in Code. 1998. (Hello Out There! Ser.). (Illus.). 32p. (J). (gr. 2-5). 20.00 (978-0-531-14475-6(5) , Watts, Franklin) Scholastic Library Publishing.

Wiese, Jim & Melton, H. Keith. The Spy's Guide to Secret Codes & Ciphers. 2002. (Illus.). 48p. (J). (978-0-439-33640-6(6)) Scholastic, Inc.

CIPHERS—FICTION

Doyle, Bill. Betrayed! The 1977 Journal of Zeke Moorie. Hoskins, Brian, illus. 2006. 139p. (J). lib. bdg. 18.46 (***978-1-4242-1733-5(4)***) Fitzgerald Bks.

—Betrayed! The 1977 Journal of Zeke Moorie. 4th ed. 2006. (Crime Through Time Ser.: No. 4). 144p. (J). (gr. 3-7). pap. 5.99 (978-0-316-05741-7(X)) Little Brown & Co.

—ICED: The 2007 Journal of Nick Fitzmorgan. 5th ed. 2006. (Crime Through Time Ser.: No. 5). (Illus.). 144p. (J). (gr. 3-7). pap. 5.99 (978-0-316-05753-0(3)) Little Brown & Co.

—Trapped: The 2031 Journal of Otis Fitzmorgan. 6th ed. 2006. (Crime Through Time Ser.: No. 6). 144p. (J). (gr. 3-7). pap. 5.99 (978-0-316-05754-7(1)) Little Brown & Co.

Kilby, Janice Eaton. The Code Chronicles: A Time Traveling, Code-Cracking Adventure. Fields, Robert Edward, illus. 2008. 64p. (J). 12.95 (***978-1-57990-926-0(4)***) Lark Bks.

Powell, Jillian. Code Breakers. Savage, Paul, illus. 2006. 40p. (J). (***978-1-59889-182-9(0)***) Stone Arch Bks.

Richards, Justin. The Chaos Code. 2007. 416p. (YA). (gr. 7 up). 17.95 (***978-1-59990-124-4(2)***) Bloomsbury Publishing.

Robertson, Barbara. Rosemary in Paris: Back to 1889. 2001. (Hourglass Adventures Ser.: Bk. 2). (Illus.). 121p. (J). (gr. 4-7). pap. 4.95 (978-1-890817-56-5(2)) Winslow Pr.

—Rosemary Meets Rosemarie Bk. 1: Berlin in 1870. 2001. (Hourglass Adventures Ser.: Bk. 1). (Illus.). 128p. (J). (gr. 4-6). pap. 5.95 (978-1-890817-55-8(4)) Winslow Pr.

Stilton, Geronimo. The Mona Mousa Code. Wolf, Matt, illus. 2005. (Geronimo Stilton Ser.: No. 15). 113p. (J). lib. bdg. 10.00 (***978-1-4242-0284-3(1)***) Fitzgerald Bks.

—The Mona Mousa Code. Wolf, Matt, illus. 2005. (Geronimo Stilton Ser.: No. 15). 113p. (J). (ps-k). lib. bdg. 13.54 (978-0-606-33278-1(2)) Tandem Library Bks.

Walters, Eric. Death by Exposure. Spreekmeester, Kevin, photos by. 2006. 88p. (J). pap. 9.99 (***978-1-55002-632-0(1)*** , Dundurn Pr.) Dundurn Group, The CAN. *Dist:* Univ. of Toronto Pr.

CIRCULATION OF THE BLOOD

see Blood—Circulation

CIRCUMNAVIGATION

see Voyages around the World

CIRCUS

see also Animals—Training

Alcott, Louisa May. Under the Lilacs. l.t. ed. 2005. 444p. pap. (978-1-84637-059-5(0)) Echo Library.

Beylon, Cathy. At the Circus. 32p. (J). (ps-3). 2006. pap. 3.95 (978-0-486-44635-6(2)); 2003. (Illus.). pap. 2.95 (978-0-486-42645-7(9)) Dover Pubns., Inc.

Bontinck, Helga. At the Circus. 2006. (Illus.). 24p. (J). 22.00 (978-0-8368-6312-3(7)) Stevens, Gareth Inc.

Bryant, Jill. Backyard Circus. MacEachern, Stephen, illus. 2006. 48p. (J). (gr. 2-4). pap. 9.95 (978-1-55451-011-5(2)); lib. bdg. 19.95 (978-1-55451-012-2(0)) Annick Pr., Ltd. CAN. *Dist:* Firefly Bks., Ltd.

Circus: Big Book: Level A. 8p. 20.95 (978-0-322-00340-8(7)) Wright Group, The.

The Circus: Individual Title Six-Packs. (Literatura 2000 Ser.). (ps-1). 28.00 (978-0-7635-0027-6(5)) Rigby Education.

Circus: Level A. 8p. 24.95 (978-0-7802-9105-8(0)) Wright Group, The.

Circus Fun: Step 2, Level C. 2000. (Show & Tell Ser.). (Illus.). 24p. (J). (978-2-922148-90-9(4)) Presses aventure/Adventure Pr.

Color All About: The Circus: A Giant Coloring Book about Going to the Circus. 2004. (Illus.). (J). (978-0-9763307-1-4(7)); (SPA & ENG., (978-0-9763307-9-0(2)) Food Marketing Consultants, Inc.

Dover Staff. Circus Surprise: Silly Sticker Story. 2004. (Dover Little Activity Bks.). 4p. (J). pap. 1.50 (978-0-486-43951-8(8)) Dover Pubns., Inc.

Elya, Susan Middleton. Say Hola to Spanish at the Circus. Lopez, Loretta, illus. 2003. 32p. (J). pap. 6.95 (978-1-58430-042-7(6)) Lee & Low Bks., Inc.

Granfield, Linda. Circus. (Illus.). (J). 19.95 (978-0-88899-292-5(0)) Groundwood Bks. CAN. *Dist:* Transition Vendor.

Granfield, Linda & Groundwood Books Staff. Circus. 2000. (Illus.). (J). (gr. 4-7). pap. 12.95 (978-0-88899-417-2(6)) Groundwood Bks. CAN. *Dist:* Transition Vendor.

Hillert, Margaret. Circus Fun. Raphael, Elaine, illus. rev. ed. 2006. (Beginning to Read Ser.). 30p. (J). lib. bdg. 18.60 (978-1-59953-030-7(9)) Norwood Hse. Pr.

Jordan, Denise M. Artistas de Circo. 2002. Tr. of Circus Performers. 24p. (J). (ps-1). pap. 5.25 (978-1-58810-843-2(0) , 91568); (SPA.). lib. bdg. 17.08 (978-1-58810-796-1(5)) Heinemann Library.

—Bienvenidos al Circo! 2002. Tr. of Welcome to the Circus!. (SPA.). 24p. (J). (ps-1). pap. 5.25 (978-1-58810-842-5(2) , 91572); lib. bdg. 17.08 (978-1-58810-795-4(7)) Heinemann Library.

—Circus 123. (Circus Ser.). 24p. (J). 2003. (Illus.). lib. bdg. (978-1-58810-545-5(8)); 2002. pap. 5.25 (978-1-58810-753-4(1) , 91401) Heinemann Library.

—Circus Animal Acts. 2002. 24p. (J). (ps-1). pap. 5.25 (978-1-58810-751-0(5) , 91398); (Illus.). lib. bdg. 18.50 (978-1-58810-543-1(1)) Heinemann Library.

—Circus Clown ABC. 2002. (Circus Ser.). 24p. (J). (ps-1). pap. 5.25 (978-1-58810-754-1(X)); (Illus.). lib. bdg. 18.50 (978-1-58810-546-2(6)) Heinemann Library.

—Circus Clowns. 2003. (Heinemann Read & Learn Ser.). (Illus.). 24p. (J). (ps-1). lib. bdg. 18.50 (978-1-58810-544-8(X)) Heinemann Library.

—Circus Performers. 2002. (Circus Ser.). (Illus.). 24p. (J). (ps-1). pap. 5.25 (978-1-58810-750-3(7) , 91397); lib. bdg. 18.50 (978-1-58810-542-4(3)) Heinemann Library.

—Welcome to the Circus! 2002. (Heinemann Read & Learn Ser.). (Illus.). 24p. (J). (ps-1). lib. bdg. 18.50 (978-1-58810-541-7(5)) Heinemann Library.

Levy, Barbara Soloff. How to Draw Circus Pictures. 2007. 32p. (J). pap. 2.95 (***978-0-486-45647-8(1)***) Dover Pubns., Inc.

Lobel, Anita. Animal Antics: A to Z. Lobel, Anita, illus. 2005. (Illus.). 32p. (J). 15.99 (978-0-06-051814-1(6)); lib. bdg. 16.89 (978-0-06-051815-8(4)) HarperCollins Pubs.

Marsh, Carole. The Ringling Brothers. 2002. (One Thousand Readers Ser.). (Illus.). 12p. (gr. k-4). 2.95 (978-0-635-01499-3(8) , 14998) Gallopade International.

McFarlane, Sheryl. What's That Sound? at the Circus. LaFave, Kim, illus. 2006. 20p. (J). bds. 7.95 (978-1-55041-959-7(5)) Fitzhenry & Whiteside, Ltd. CAN. *Dist:* F & W Pubns., Inc.

McGuire, Leslie. Circles at the Circus: My First Book of Shapes. Haskamp, Steven, illus. 1999. (Gymboree Book Ser.). 16p. (J). reprint ed. 5.95 (978-1-892374-20-2(X)) Weldon Owen, Inc.

Reader's Clubhouse Staff. Kirby's Circus. 2007. (Reader's Clubhouse Ser.). 24p. (J). (gr. k-2). pap. 3.99 (978-0-7641-3722-8(0)) Barron's Educational Series, Inc.

Rey, H. A. See the Circus. rev. ed. 1998. (Illus.). 22p. (J). (gr. k-ps). pap. 5.95 (978-0-395-90695-8(4)) Houghton Mifflin Co. Trade & Reference Div.

Rinder, Lenore & Moschea, Pat. Star's Circus Parade. 2000. (Illus.). 16p. (J). (ps-4). pap. 5.00 (978-0-9678778-0-8(6) , 001) Child Scope Productions.

Schubert, Leda. Ballet of the Elephants. Parker, Robert Andrew, illus. 2006. 34p. (J). 17.95 (978-1-59643-075-4(3)) Roaring Brook Pr.

Urrea, Lourdes, et al. El Circo. rev. ed. 2006. (Ediciones Castillo Castillo Del Terror Ser.).Tr. of Circus. (SPA.). 132p. (J). (gr. 2-6). pap. 6.95 (978-970-20-0330-4(X)) Castillo, Ediciones, S. A. de C. V. MEX. *Dist:* Macmillan.

Ward, Beck & Hasbro Staff. Circus Fun: Create It All with Play-Doh Modeling Compound & Stencil. 2004. (Illus.). 10p. (J). 9.95 (978-0-7624-1849-7(4) , Running Pr. Kids) Running Pr. Bk. Pubs.

Yoyo Books Staff. At the Circus: Learning Words Series. 2004. 12p. bds. 12.95 (978-90-5843-606-1(3)) YoYo Bks. BEL. *Dist:* National Bk. Network.

3D Circus Puzzle Book. 12p. (J). (978-2-89393-867-7(1)) Phidal Publishing, Inc./Editions Phidal, Inc.

CIRCUS—FICTION

Alger, Horatio. The Young Acrobat of the Great North American Circus. unabr. ed. 2002. (Polyglot Press Alger Ser.). (Illus.). (J). pap. 17.95 (978-1-4115-0070-9(9)) Polyglot Pr., Inc.

Allen, Margaret. Cat & Dog at the Circus. 1999. (ps-2). lib. bdg. 10.65 (978-0-613-34110-3(4)) Tandem Library Bks.

Almond, David. Secret Heart. 2004. 224p. (YA). (gr. 7). pap. 5.99 (978-0-440-41827-6(5) , Laurel Leaf) Random Hse. Children's Bks.

Alsenas, Linas. Peanut. 2007. 32p. (J). (ps-k). pap. 16.99 (***978-0-439-77980-7(4)***) Scholastic, Inc.

Angelo, Alyssa. Sherlock the Circus Dog. 2007. 108p. pap. 11.95 (***978-1-60145-137-8(7)***); pap. 21.95 (***978-1-60145-133-0(4)***) Booklocker.com, Inc.

Avi. Amanda Joins the Circus. 1999. (J). 10.79 (978-0-606-15432-1(9)) Tandem Library Bks.

Banks, Steven. Amazing SpongeBobini. 2007. 24p. (J). 21.35 (***978-1-59961-362-8(X)***) Spotlight.

—Amazing SpongeBobini. 2003. (gr. k-3). lib. bdg. 11.25 (978-0-613-66346-5(2)) Tandem Library Bks.

—The Amazing SpongeBobini. Martinez, Heather, illus. 2003. (SpongeBob SquarePants Ser.). 24p. (J). pap. 3.50 (978-0-689-85602-0(4) , Simon Spotlight/Nickelodeon) Simon & Schuster Children's Publishing.

Banscherus, Jurgen. Trouble under the Big Top. Baron, Daniel C., tr. from GER. Butschkow, Ralf, illus. 2007. 63p. (J). (gr. 3-5). lib. bdg. 22.60 (***978-1-59889-338-0(6)***) Stone Arch Bks.

Banscherus, Jurgen & Baron, Daniel C. Trouble under the Big Top. Butschkow, Ralf, illus. 2007. 63p. (J). pap. (***978-1-59889-433-2(1)***) Stone Arch Bks.

Barnum, P. T. Dick Broadhead: A Story of Perilous Adve. 2006. pap. 30.95 (***978-1-4286-1959-3(3)***) Kessinger Publishing, LLC.

Barnum, Vance. Joe Strong. the Boy Fire-Eater. 2006. pap. (***978-1-4065-0922-9(1)***) Dodo Pr.

—Joe Strong the Boy Fire-Eater or the Mos. 2006. 95.99 (***978-1-4280-0327-9(4)***); pap. 89.99 (***978-1-4280-0329-3(0)***) IndyPublish.com.

Beccia, Carlyn. Who Put the "B" in Ballyhoo? The Most Amazing, Bizarre, & Celebrated Circus Performers. 2007. (Illus.). 32p. (J). (ps-k). 16.00 (978-0-618-71718-7(8)) Houghton Mifflin Co. Trade & Reference Div.

Beccia, Carlyn. Who Put the B in the Ballyhoo? 2007. (Illus.). (J). (***978-1-4287-3570-5(4)***) Houghton Mifflin Co.

Berkeley, Jon. The Palace of Laughter: The Wednesday Tales No. 1. Dorman, Brandon, illus. (J). 2007. 464p. (gr. 3-7). pap. 7.99 (***978-0-06-075509-6(1)*** , Harper Trophy); 2006. 448p. 16.99 (978-0-06-075507-2(5) , Julie Andrews Collection); 2006. 448p. lib. bdg. 17.89 (978-0-06-075508-9(3) , Julie Andrews Collection) HarperCollins Pubs.

—The Tiger's Egg. Dorman, Brandon, illus. 2007. 416p. (J). (gr. 3-7). lib. bdg. 17.89 (***978-0-06-075511-9(3)***); (Wednesday Tales Ser.: No. 2). 16.99 (***978-0-06-075510-2(5)***) HarperCollins Pubs. (Julie Andrews Collection).

Blythe, Enid. Three Boys & a Circus. (Illus.). 80p. (J). (gr. k-6). pap. 5.95 (978-0-09-987870-4(4)) Random Hse. GBR. *Dist:* Trafalgar Square Publishing.

Blyton, Enid. Enid Blyton Circus Stories. (Illus.). (J). 11.95 (978-0-09-914131-0(0)) Random Hse. GBR. *Dist:* Trafalgar Square Publishing.

Bond, Michael. Paddington Bear at the Circus. Alley, R. W., illus. 2000. (Paddington Ser.). 40p. (J). (ps-3). 15.99 (978-0-06-028213-4(4)) HarperCollins Pubs.

Brian Wildsmith's Circus. 2004. (J). pap. 14.95 incl. audio (978-1-56008-165-4(1)) Weston Woods Studios, Inc.

Bridwell, Norman. Clifford at the Circus. Bridwell, Norman, illus. 2002. (Clifford, the Big Red Dog Ser.). (Illus.). (J). 11.45 (978-0-7587-6707-3(2)) Book Wholesalers, Inc.

—Clifford at the Circus. (Clifford, the Big Red Dog Ser.). (Illus.). (J). (gr. k-2). 6.95 (978-0-590-68639-6(9)) Scholastic, Inc.

Brooks, Walter R. Freddy & the Pilot. Wiese, Kurt, illus. 1999. 288p. (J). (gr. 3-7). 23.95 (978-0-87951-941-4(X)) Overlook Pr., The.

—Freddy the Pilot. 2000. (YA). pap. 67.95 incl. audio (978-0-7887-4167-8(5) , 41111) Recorded Bks., LLC.

—Freddy the Pilot. 2001. (978-0-606-22516-8(1)) Tandem Library Bks.

Brown, Marc. Arthur's Chicken Pox. Brown, Marc, illus. 2002. (Arthur Adventure Ser.). (Illus.). (J). 13.15 (978-0-7587-1978-2(7)) Book Wholesalers, Inc.

—Arthur's Chicken Pox. Brown, Marc, illus. 1999. (Arthur Adventure Ser.). (Illus.). 30p. (J). (ps-k). bds. 5.95 (978-0-316-11953-5(9)) Little, Brown Bks. for Young Readers.

—Arthur's Chicken Pox. 1998. (Arthur Adventure Ser.). 32p. (J). (ps-3). 9.95 (978-0-316-11947-4(4)) Little, Brown Bks. for Young Readers.

—Arturo Tiene Varicela. 2001. 13.75 (978-0-606-22646-2(X)) Tandem Library Bks.

Buller, Laura. At the Circus Dot-to-Dot. 2005. (Illus.). 80p. (J). pap. 5.95 (978-1-4027-1186-2(7)) Sterling Publishing Co., Inc.

Callahan, Thera S. Sara Joins the Circus Level B. McLeod, Chum, illus. 2002. (Rookie Readers Ser.). 32p. (J). (gr. 1-2). 19.50 (978-0-516-22273-8(2) , Children's Pr.) Scholastic Library Publishing.

Carlson, Melody. The Day the Circus Came to Town. Butterfield, Ned, illus. 2004. 31p. (ps-3). 14.99 (978-1-58134-158-4(X)) Crossway Bks.

Christie, Jacky. Roger's Big Adventure. 2005. (J). pap. 8.00 (978-0-8059-6889-7(X)) Dorrance Publishing Co., Inc.

Circus Animals. (Puzzle Shapes Ser.). 10p. (J). bds. (978-2-89393-787-8(X)) Phidal Publishing, Inc./Editions Phidal, Inc.

Circus is in Town. 2001. (POL.). (J). (978-1-58805-127-1(7)) DS-Max USA, Inc.

The Circus Mystery, 6 vols., Vol. 2. (Woodland Mysteriestm Ser.). 133p. (gr. 3-7). 42.50 (978-0-7802-7942-1(5)) Wright Group, The.

Clements, Andrew. Circus Family Dog. Truesdell, Sue, illus. 2000. 32p. (J). (gr. k-3). tchr. ed. 16.00 (978-0-395-78648-2(7) , Clarion Bks.) Houghton Mifflin Co. Trade & Reference Div.

Cneut, Carll. The Amazing Love Story of Mr. Morf: An Astonishing Circus Romance. Cneut, Carll, illus. 2003. (Illus.). 32p. (J). (gr. k-3). tchr. ed. 15.00 (978-0-618-33170-3(0) , Clarion Bks.) Houghton Mifflin Co. Trade & Reference Div.

Cook, Vivian E. Danger under the Big Top. Nelson, Grace L, illus. 1999. (Adventures of Spencer, Private Eye & His Psychic Sister, Tiffany Ser.: No. 4). 66p. (J). (gr. 3-5). pap. 8.95 (978-1-928659-03-7(9)) Two Sisters Publishing.

Cooney, Barbara. Lost Treasures Bk. 1: The Kellyhorns. 2001. 256p. (J). 13.49 (978-0-7868-2596-7(0)) Hyperion Pr.

Cooper, Melrose. "Pets!" Heo, Yumi, illus. rev. ed. 1998. 32p. (C). (ps-2). pap. 15.95 (978-0-8050-3893-4(0) , Holt, Henry & Co. Bks. For Young Readers) Holt, Henry & Co.

Copeland, Mark. The Bundle at Blackthorpe Heath. 2006. (Illus.). 208p. (J). (gr. 5). 15.00 (978-0-618-56302-9(4)) Houghton Mifflin Co.

Corder, Zizou. Lionboy. (Lionboy Trilogy : Bk. 1). (Illus.). (gr. 3-6). 2003. 288p. (J). 15.99 (978-0-8037-2982-7(0) , Dial); 2004. 304p. (YA). reprint ed. pap. 7.99 (978-0-14-240226-9(5) , Puffin) Penguin Group (USA) Inc.

Damjan, Mischa. The Clown Said No. ed. 2004. (Illus.). (J). (gr. k-3). spiral bd. (978-0-616-14569-2(1)) Canadian National Institute for the Blind/Institut National Canadien pour les Aveugles.

—The Clown Said No. Casty, Gian, illus. 2007. 32p. (J). 17.99 (***978-0-698-40063-4(1)*** , Minedition) Penguin Group (USA) Inc.

Darlington, Edgar B. P. The Circus Boys Across Continent or Making the Start in the Sawdust Life. 2004. reprint ed. pap. 22.95 (978-1-4191-5679-3(9)); pap. 1.99 (978-1-4192-5679-0(3)) Kessinger Publishing, LLC.

—The Circus Boys in Dixie Land or Winning the Plaudits of the Sunny South. 2004. reprint ed. pap. 22.95 (978-1-4191-5680-9(2)); pap. 1.99 (978-1-4192-5680-6(7)) Kessinger Publishing, LLC.

—The Circus Boys on the Mississippi or Afloat with the Big Show on the Big River. 2004. reprint ed. pap. 22.95 (978-1-4191-5681-6(0)); pap. 1.99 (978-1-4192-5681-3(5)) Kessinger Publishing, LLC.

—The Circus Boys on the Plains or the Young Advance Agents Ahead of the Show. 2004. reprint ed. pap. 22.95 (978-1-4191-5682-3(9)); pap. 1.99 (978-1-4192-5682-0(3)) Kessinger Publishing, LLC.

Das, Christina. Oomph-Pa-Pa at the Circus. l.t. ed. 2005. (Illus.). 32p. (J). 15.95 (978-0-9763082-2-5(3) , A JuneOne Production) JuneOne Publishing Hub.

de Brunhoff, Laurent. Babar & the Circus Star. 2005. (J). (978-0-8109-5774-9(4)) Abrams, Harry N. , Inc.

Dedieu, Thierry. Baby Ringmaster. 2000. (Pull-the-Tab Bks.). (Illus.). 16p. (J). 12.95 (978-0-7868-0110-7(7)) Disney Pr.

Disney Staff. Dumbo. (FRE.). 96p. (J). (gr. k-5). pap. 9.95 (978-0-7859-8849-6(1)) French & European Pubns., Inc.

—Dumbo. 2002. (Illus.). (J). pap. 2.99 (978-0-7364-1287-2(5)) Mouse Works.

Dixon, Franklin W. One False Step. ed. 2005. (Hardy Boys II Ser.: No. 189). 150p. (J). lib. bdg. 15.00 (978-1-59054-846-2(9)) Fitzgerald Bks.

—One False Step. 2005. 150p. (J). (978-1-4155-7722-6(6) , Aladdin) Simon & Schuster Children's Publishing.

Doolin, Jimmy. The Day the Circus Came to My Backyard. l.t. ed. 2003. 39p. lib. bdg. (978-0-9710432-4-4(8)) Children's Literacy Pubns.

Downs, Mike. You See a Circus, I See... McGrory, Anik, illus. (J). 2006. pap. 6.95 (978-1-58089-155-4(1)); 2005. 32p. 14.95 (978-1-58089-097-7(0)) Charlesbridge Publishing, Inc.

Duey, Kathleen & Bale, Karen. Trainwreck: Kansas, 1892. 1999. (Survival! Ser.: No. 8). (J). (gr. 4-7). (978-0-606-16279-1(8)) Tandem Library Bks.

Elwell, Telva & Kelley, Barbara. Ellasense Misses the Train. Elwell, Telva, illus. 2004. (Illus.). 48p. (J). per. 12.95 (978-0-9754591-0-2(4)) Cubby Hole Tales.

Emberley, Rebecca. My Mother's Secret Life. Emberley, Rebecca, illus. 1998. (Illus.). 28p. (J). (ps-3). 15.95 (978-0-316-23496-2(6)) Little Brown & Co.

Esbaum, Jill. To the Big Top. Gordon, David, illus. 2008. 32p. (J). 16.95 (***978-0-374-39934-4(4)***) Farrar, Straus & Giroux.

Falconer, Ian. Olivia Saves the Circus. ed. 2004. (Olivia Ser.). (J). (gr. k-2). spiral bd. (978-0-616-11110-9(X)); spiral bd. (978-0-616-11111-6(8)) Canadian National Institute for the Blind/Institut National Canadien pour les Aveugles.

—Olivia Saves the Circus. Falconer, Ian, illus. (Olivia Ser.). (Illus.). 44p. (J). (ps-2). 2001. 17.95 (978-0-689-82954-3(X) , Atheneum/Anne Schwartz Bks.); 2002. 150.00 (978-0-689-85039-4(5) , Atheneum) Simon & Schuster Children's Publishing.

Fleischman, Paul. Sidewalk Circus. Hawkes, Kevin, illus. 32p. (J). (gr. k-4). 2007. pap. 6.99 (***978-0-7636-2795-9(X)***); 2004. 15.99 (978-0-7636-1107-1(7)) Candlewick Pr.

Fletcher, Ralph J. The Circus Surprise. Vagin, Vladimir Vasil'evich, illus. 2001. 32p. (J). (gr. k-3). tchr. ed. 15.00 (978-0-395-98029-3(1) , Clarion Bks.) Houghton Mifflin Co. Trade & Reference Div.

Foglio, Phil & Foglio, Kaja. Agatha Heterodyne & the Circus of Dreams. 2006. (Girl Genius Ser.: Bk. 4). (Illus.). 128p. pap. 20.95 (978-1-890856-36-6(3)) Studio Foglio, LLC.

A Garden Circus. 2003. (J). 9.99 (978-0-9740847-5-6(1)) GiGi Bks.

Garis, Howard Roger. Tom Cardiff's Circus. King, W. B., illus. 2005. reprint ed. pap. 28.95 (978-1-4179-3393-8(3)) Kessinger Publishing, LLC.

—Umboo, the Elephant. 2005. 132p. pap. 10.95 (978-1-59540-656-9(5) , 1st World Library - Literary Society) 1st World Publishing, Inc.

Garis, Howard Roger. Umboo the Elephant Circus Animal Stories. 2006. 62.99 (***978-1-4280-2342-0(9)***) IndyPublish.com.

Garis, Lilian C. Let's Play Circus. 2005. pap. 24.95 (978-1-4179-9394-9(4)) Kessinger Publishing, LLC.

Gay, Marie-Louise. Fat Charlie's Circus. (Illus.). 32p. 6.95 (978-0-7736-7420-2(9)) Stoddart Kids CAN. *Dist:* Fitzhenry & Whiteside, Ltd.

Gilkey, Gail. Freckles & the Circus. 2004. (J). per. 9.95 (978-0-9662983-3-8(0)) Windy Hill Pr.

Glaze, Dave. The Light-Fingered Gang. 2006. 196p. (YA). (gr. 4-7). pap. 7.95 (978-1-55050-326-5(X)) Coteau Bks. CAN. *Dist:* F & W Pubns., Inc.

Gottfried, Maya. Last Night I Dreamed a Circus. Zakanitch, Robert Rahway, illus. 2003. 32p. (J). (ps-1). 15.95 (978-0-375-82388-6(3) , Knopf Bks. for Young Readers) Random Hse. Children's Bks.

Graham, Bob. Dimity Dumpty: The Story of Humpty's Little Sister. 2007. (Illus.). 40p. (J). (ps). 15.99 (978-0-7636-3078-2(0)) Candlewick Pr.

Halsey, Megan. Circus 1-2-3. Halsey, Megan, illus. 2000. (Illus.). 24p. (J). (ps-k). 14.95 (978-0-688-17104-9(4)) HarperCollins Pubs.

Hamilton, K. R. Caleb, Son of None. 2007. (J). pap. (978-0-7847-1859-9(8)) Standard Publishing.

Hamilton, K. R. A Freaky Kind of Courage. 2007. (J). (***978-0-7847-1909-1(8)***) Standard Publishing.

Hamilton, Kersten. The Battle of Trickum County. 2007. (Caleb Pascal & the Peculiar People Ser.). 141p. (J). per. 6.99 (***978-0-7847-1910-7(1)***) Standard Publishing.

—A Gathering of Brothers. 2007. (Caleb Pascal & the Peculiar People Ser.). 143p. (J). per. 6.99 (***978-0-7847-1911-4(X)***) Standard Publishing.

Harcourt School Publishers Staff. Eliza's Circus: Take-Home Book. 1999. (Signatures Ser.). (Illus.). (J). pap. 1.90 (978-0-15-313906-2(4)) Harcourt Schl. Pubs.

Harlen, Jonathan. Circus Berzerkus. 2004. (Illus.). 156p. (Orig.). (J). pap. 6.95 (978-1-86508-770-2(X)) Allen & Unwin AUS. *Dist:* Independent Pubs. Group.

Harman, Holly. Gumby's Circus. 2000. (Illus.). 22p. (J). (ps). reprint ed. 15.00 (978-0-7567-5737-3(1)) DIANE Publishing Co.

Hayes, Geoffrey, illus. & text. Patrick at the Circus. Hayes, Geoffrey, text. 2002. (J). lib. bdg. (978-0-7868-2595-0(2)) Hyperion Bks. for Children.

Hensley, Sarah M. Caillou Visits the Circus. Storch, Ellen N., illus. l.t. ed. 2005. (Hrl Board Book Ser.). (J). (ps-k). pap. 10.95 (978-1-57332-309-3(8)) HighReach Learning, Inc.

Hill, Clare. Granddad's Circus & Other Stories. 2004. 41p. pap. 19.95 (978-1-4137-3647-2(5)) PublishAmerica, Inc.

Hill, Eric. Spot Goes to the Circus. Hill, Eric, illus. 2006. (Spot Ser.). (Illus.). 24p. (J). pap. 6.99 (978-0-14-240567-3(1) , Puffin) Penguin Group (USA) Inc.

Hillert, Margaret. It's Circus Time, Dear Dragon. Helton, David, illus. rev. exp. ed. 2007. (Beginning to Read Ser.). (J). lib. bdg. (978-1-59953-040-6(6)) Norwood Hse. Pr.

Hoff, Syd. Oliver. Hoff, Syd, illus. 2002. (Illus.). (J). 12.34 (978-0-7587-4575-0(3)) Book Wholesalers, Inc.

C
D

—Oliver. 2000. (I Can Read Bks.). (978-0-606-18709-1(X)); lib. bdg. 11.80 (978-0-613-28307-6(4)) Tandem Library Bks.

—Oliver! Hoff, Syd, illus. 2002. (Illus.). pap. 18.95 incl. audio compact disk (978-1-59112-660-7(6)); pap. 31.95 incl. audio compact disk (978-1-59112-661-4(4)); (J). pap. 16.95 incl. audio (978-0-87499-902-0(2)) Live Oak Media.

—Oliver. Hoff, Syd, illus. rev. ed. 2000. (I Can Read Bks.). (Illus.). 64p. (J). (gr. k-3). pap. 3.99 (978-0-06-444272-5(1), Harper Trophy); lib. bdg. 17.89 (978-0-06-028709-2(8)); 14.95 (978-0-06-028708-5(X)) HarperCollins Pubs.

Horvath, Polly. When the Circus Came to Town. 1999. 144p. (J). (gr. 3-7). pap. 6.95 (978-0-374-48367-8(1), Sunburst) Farrar, Straus & Giroux.

—When the Circus Came to Town. 1999. (978-0-606-16475-7(8)) Tandem Library Bks.

Hyland, Betty. Tressa & the Lost Circus of Ireland. 2004. 85p. (YA). pap. 10.95 (978-0-7414-2268-2(9)) Infinity Publishing.

Jan Baer: And the Mystery of the Silent Circus. 2005. (J). per. 10.00 (978-1-930052-29-1(4)) Cherokee Bks.

Janeczko, Paul B. Worlds Afire: The Hartford Circus Fire of 1944. 2004. 112p. (J). (gr. 7 up). 15.99 (978-0-7636-2235-0(4)) Candlewick Pr.

Johnson, Crockett. Harold's Circus. Johnson, Crockett, illus. 2002. (Illus.). (J). 14.47 (978-0-7587-2697-1(X)) Book Wholesalers, Inc.

Kehret, Peg. Saving Lilly. 160p. (J). 2002. pap. 4.99 (978-0-671-03423-8(5), Aladdin); 2001. (gr. 3-6). 16.95 (978-0-671-03422-1(7)) Simon & Schuster Children's Publishing.

—Saving Lilly. 2002. (gr. 3-6). lib. bdg. 13.00 (978-0-613-64783-0(1)) Tandem Library Bks.

Kenah, Katharine. The Best Teacher in Second Grade. Carter, Abby, illus. 2006. (I Can Read Bks.). 48p. (J). 15.99 (978-0-06-053564-3(4)); lib. bdg. 16.89 (978-0-06-053565-0(2)) HarperCollins Pubs.

Kerrett, Etgar. Dad Runs Away with the Circus. Modan, Rutu, illus. 2004. 40p. (J). 16.99 (978-0-7636-2247-3(8)) Candlewick Pr.

Kidd, Ron. Magical Circus Train. Boyd, Patti, illus. 16p. (J). (ps up). 19.95 (978-0-9627001-5-6(0)) Futech Educational Products, Inc.

Kirby. Ida Lou's Story. 2000. (American Quilts Ser.: Vol. 4). (J). 11.64 (978-0-606-20082-0(7)) Tandem Library Bks.

Knight, Hilary. The Circus Is Coming. Knight, Hilary, illus. 2007. (Golden Classic Ser.). (Illus.). 56p. (J). (ps-4). 15.99 (978-0-375-84066-1(4)); lib. bdg. 18.99 (978-0-375-94066-8(9)) Random Hse. Children's Bks. (Golden Bks.).

Kolb, Diane. My Father Is a Clown. 2003. 115p. pap. 14.95 (978-1-59286-757-8(X)) PublishAmerica, Inc.

Landry, Leo. Eat Your Peas, Ivy Louise. 2005. (J). (ps-k). 12.00 (978-0-618-58112-2(X)); (Illus.). 32p. 12.00 (978-0-618-44886-9(1)) Houghton Mifflin Co. Trade & Reference Div.

Langton, Jane. The Mysterious Circus. 2005. (Hall Family Chronicles). 224p. (J). lib. bdg. 16.89 (978-0-06-009487-4(7)) HarperCollins Pubs.

Leaney, Cindy. The Circus. Whitehouse, Patty, ed. King, Sue & Wilks, Peter, illus. 2004. (Friendly Phonics Ser.). 24p. (J). lib. bdg. 14.95 (978-1-59054-114-2(6)) Fitzgerald Bks.

Lee, Rex. Rann Braden Circus Showman A Circus Adve. 2006. (Illus.). pap. 27.95 (*978-1-4286-5861-5(0)) Kessinger Publishing, LLC.

Liberto, Lorenzo, et al. Practice Makes Perfect / la Practica Hace al Maestro. Torres, Irving, illus. 2004. (ENG & SPA.). 32p. (J). lib. bdg. 20.00 (978-0-9743668-2-1(X)) Harvest Sun Pr., LLC.

Lindgren, Astrid. Pippi Goes to the Circus. Chesworth, Michael, illus. 2000. (Pippi Longstocking Storybooks). 32p. (J). (gr. k-2). pap. 6.99 (978-0-14-130243-0(7), Puffin) Penguin Group (USA) Inc.

—Pippi Goes to the Circus. 2000. (J). (gr. k-3). lib. bdg. 14.15 (978-0-613-28608-4(1)) Tandem Library Bks.

Little Engine-Circus Friends. 2005. (J). (978-1-4194-0005-6(3)) Paradise Pr., Inc.

Lofting, Hugh. The Story of Doctor Dolittle: #2 the Circus Crocodile. 2007. (Easy Reader Classics Ser.). 32p. (J). (ps-3). 21.35 (*978-1-59961-339-0(5)) Spotlight.

Lofting, Hugh. The Story of Doctor Dolittle Bk. 2: The Circus Crocodile. Kanzler, John, illus. 2006. (Easy Reader Classics Ser.). 32p. (J). pap. 3.95 (978-1-4027-3292-8(9)) Sterling Publishing Co., Inc.

Mack, Tracy & Citrin, Michael. The Fall of the Amazing Zalindas. Ruth, Greg, illus. 2006. (Sherlock Holmes & the BSI Ser.). 272p. (J). (gr. 4-7). pap. 16.99 (978-0-439-82836-9(8), Orchard Bks.) Scholastic, Inc.

—The Fall of the Amazing Zalindas. 2006. (Illus.). 259p. (J). (*978-1-4287-0951-5(7), Orchard Bks.) Scholastic, Inc.

Mahy, Margaret. Maddigan's Fantasia. 2007. 512p. (J). (gr. 5 up). 17.99 (978-1-4169-1812-7(4), McElderry, Margaret K.) Simon & Schuster Children's Publishing.

Martin, Bill, Jr. Chicken Chuck. Salerno, Steven, illus. 40p. (J). (ps-3). 2001. pap. 7.95 (978-1-58837-017-4(8)); 2000. 16.95 (978-1-890817-31-2(7)) Winslow Pr.

Martin, Bill. Chicken Chuck. Salerno, Steven, illus. 2005. 32p. (J). pap. 5.95 (978-0-7614-5216-4(8)) Cavendish, Marshall Corp.

Mary, Nanette. Ashby, the Happy Little Elephant. 2007. (Illus.). 40p. (J). per. 12.95 (*978-0-9787112-7-6(0), 01002) New World Publishing.

Marzollo, Dan. Circus. Mills, Liz, ed. Levin, Jimmy, illus. 2003. (I Spy Ser.: No. 2). 24p. (J). pap. 3.50 (978-0-439-44319-7(9), Cartwheel Bks.) Scholastic, Inc.

—I Spy a Circus. 2003. (ps-2). lib. bdg. 11.25 (978-0-613-72196-7(9)) Tandem Library Bks.

Mattaino, J. F. Cotton Candy Circus & Other Performances. 2006. 22.00 (*978-0-8059-8804-8(1)) Dorrance Publishing Co., Inc.

Matthews, Derek. Snappy Sounds Circus. 2006. (Snappy Sounds Ser.). (Illus.). 10p. (J). 12.95 (978-1-59223-564-3(6), Silver Dolphin Bks.) Advantage Pubs. Group.

Maxwell, Katie. Circus of the Darned. 2006. (YA). mass mkt. 5.99 (978-0-8439-5400-5(0), SMOOCH) Dorchester Publishing Co., Inc.

Mayer, Mercer. Good for Me & You. Mayer, Mercer, illus. 2005. (Little Critter Ser.). (Illus.). 24p. (J). (ps-2). pap. 3.99 (978-0-06-053948-1(8), Harper Festival) HarperCollins Pubs.

Mayo, Margaret. Polly of the Circus. 2004. reprint ed. pap. 15.95 (978-1-4191-4251-2(8)); pap. 1.99 (978-1-4192-4251-9(2)) Kessinger Publishing, LLC.

Mazzeo Zocchi, Judy. Paulie & Sasha: Circus or Not. Vannozzi, Don, illus. 2001. (Adventures of Paulie & Sasha Ser.). 32p. (J). (gr. k-4). 15.95 (978-1-891997-00-6(9), Treehouse Court) Dingles & Co.

McCaughrean, Geraldine. The Kite Rider. 2003. (Illus.). 320p. (J). (gr. 7 up). pap. 6.99 (978-0-06-441091-5(9)) HarperCollins Pubs.

—The Kite Rider. 2002. (gr. 7-12). lib. bdg. 15.30 (978-0-613-68440-8(0)) Tandem Library Bks.

McCully, Emily Arnold. Mirette on the High Wire. McCully, Emily Arnold, illus. 2002. (Illus.). (J). 14.04 (978-0-7587-0058-2(X)) Book Wholesalers, Inc.

—Mirette on the High Wire. ed. 2004. (J). (gr. k-3). spiral bd. (978-0-616-01716-6(2)); spiral bd. (978-0-616-01717-3(0)) Canadian National Institute for the Blind/Institut National Canadien pour les Aveugles.

Meredith Books Staff. Cheer Bear's Circus Adventure: Deluxe Sound Storybook. Forlini, Victoria, ed. 2004. (Care Bears Ser.). (ENG., Illus.). 22p. (J). (gr. k-3). 15.95 (978-0-696-22297-9(3)) Meredith Bks.

Miller, Lindsey Michael. The Circus. Griswold, Phillip, illus. 2005. 32p. (J). (ps-ps). 13.95 (978-0-9709104-8-6(7)) Hickory Tales Publishing.

Millman, Isaac. Moses Goes to the Circus. Millman, Isaac, illus. 2003. (Moses Goes To Ser.). (Illus.). 32p. (J). (ps-3). 16.00 (978-0-374-35064-2(7), Farrar, Straus & Giroux (BYR)) Farrar, Straus & Giroux.

Mills, Joyce C. & Crowley, Richard J. Sammy the Elephant & Mr. Camel: A Story to Help Children Overcome Bedwetting. Pillo, Cary, illus. 2nd ed. 2005. 32p. (J). 14.95 (978-1-59147-247-6(4)); pap. 8.95 (978-1-59147-248-3(2)) American Psychological Assn. (Magination Pr.).

Montserrat, Pep. Ms. Rubinstein's Beauty. 2006. (Illus.). 32p. (J). (gr. k-2). 14.95 (978-1-4027-3063-4(2)) Sterling Publishing Co., Inc.

Morgan, Allen. Matthew & the Midnight Hospital. ed. 2004. (Illus.). (J). (gr. k-3). spiral bd. (978-0-616-01529-2(1)) Canadian National Institute for the Blind/Institut National Canadien pour les Aveugles.

Morgan, Allen & Martchenko, Michael. Matthew & the Midnight Hospital. 1999. (Matthew's Midnight Adventures Ser.). (Illus.). 32p. (J). (ps-3). 6.99 (978-0-7737-6014-1(8)) Stoddart Kids CAN. *Dist:* Fitzhenry & Whiteside, Ltd.

Morgan, Jim. The Journey to the Circus. 2003. pap. 7.95 (978-0-533-14472-3(8)) Vantage Pr., Inc.

Morris, Gilbert. Dixie & Stripes. 1998. (Dixie Morris Animal Adventure Ser.: No. 2). 128p. (J). (gr. 4-7). pap. 5.99 (978-0-8024-3364-0(2)) Moody Pubs.

Moulton, Mark. Mr Sparrows Merry Fairy Circus. Good, Karen, illus. 2004. 24p. 18.00 (978-0-7412-1940-4(9)) Lang Graphics, Ltd.

Mr Brown: KinderReaders Individual Title Six-Packs. (Kinderstarters Ser.). 8p. (ps-1). 21.00 (978-0-7635-8653-9(6)) Rigby Education.

Muller, Rachel Dunstan. Ten Thumb Sam. 2007. (Orca Young Readers Ser.). 144p. (J). (gr. 3-6). pap. (*978-1-55143-699-9(X)) Orca Bk. Pubs.

Munro, Roxie. Circus: Over 50 Flaps Plus Seek & Find. 2006. (Illus.). 24p. (J). 15.95 (978-0-8118-5209-8(1)) Chronicle Bks. LLC.

Murphy. Circus Shapes: Recognizing Shapes Big Book. 2002. (Illus.). (J). pap. (978-0-7398-6779-2(2)) Steck-Vaughn.

Murray, Carol. Hurry Up! Garbot, Dave, illus. 2003. (Rookie Reader Ser.). 32p. (J). 19.50 (978-0-516-22585-2(5), Children's Pr.) Scholastic Library Publishing.

My Very Own Circus Play Set. 2004. (J). (978-1-59292-006-8(3)) SoftPlay, Inc.

Nelson, Charlie. The Circus Life. l.t. ed. 2003. (Illus.). 22p. (J). per. 7.95 (978-1-932338-25-6(X)) Lifevest Publishing, Inc.

Nunes, Lygia Bojunga. La Cuerda Floja. (SPA.). 136p. (YA). (gr. 5-8). (978-84-204-3122-2(2), AF1749) Alfaguara, Ediciones, S.A.- Grupo Santillana ESP. *Dist:* Lectorum Pubns., Inc.

Ogden, Charles. High Wire. Carton, Rick, illus. 2006. (Edgar & Ellen Ser.). 208p. (J). 9.95 (978-1-4169-1500-3(1), Aladdin) Simon & Schuster Children's Publishing.

Papineau, Lucie. Gilda the Giraffe & Marvin the Marmoset. Sarrazin, Marisol, illus. 2005. (Gilda the Giraffe Ser.). 32p. (J). (ps-3). lib. bdg. 22.60 (978-1-4048-1516-2(3)) Picture Window Bks.

Papineau, Lucie & Fischman, Sheila. Marvin the Strange Little Marmoset. Sarrazin, Marisol, illus. 2001. 32p. (J). (ps up). pap. (978-1-894363-80-8(9)) Dominique & Friends.

Paul, Ann Whitford & Walker, David. Little Monkey Says Good Night. 2003. (Illus.). 32p. (J). 16.00 (978-0-374-34609-6(7), Farrar, Straus & Giroux (BYR)) Farrar, Straus & Giroux.

Peck, George W. Peck's Bad Boy at the Circus. 2006. 200p. pap. 15.99 (*978-1-4264-4090-8(1)); 178p. pap. 11.99 (*978-1-4264-4031-1(6)) BiblioBazaar.

—Peck's Bad Boy at the Circus. 2004. reprint ed. pap. 1.99 (978-1-4192-4055-3(2)) Kessinger Publishing, LLC.

Peck, W. George. Peck's Bad Boy with the Circus. 2006. 95.99 (*978-1-4219-7363-0(4)); pap. 88.99 (*978-1-4219-7373-9(1)) IndyPublish.com.

Pennell, Kathleen. Circus of Fear. Pennell, Lauren, illus. 2002. (Pony Investigators Ser.: Vol. III). 96p. (J). (gr. 3-6). pap. 5.95 (978-1-930353-47-3(2)) Masthof Pr.

Phillips, Gina & Book Company Staff. Lucas & the Circus. Worthington, Leonie, illus. 2002. (Sparkle Bks.). 16p. (J). bds. 12.95 (978-1-74047-227-2(6)) Book Co. Publishing Pty, Ltd., The AUS. *Dist:* Penton Overseas, Inc.

Picture me in the Circus Mini. 2002. (Baby Costume Minis Ser.). 10p. (J). (ps up). bds. 2.99 (978-1-57151-552-0(6)) Playhouse Publishing.

Pinkwater, Daniel M. Rainy Morning. Pinkwater, Jill, illus. 1999. (Pinkwater Ser.: Vol. 1). 32p. (J). (gr. k-3). 16.00 (978-0-689-81143-2(8), Atheneum) Simon & Schuster Children's Publishing.

Pope, Paul. Escapo: A Life Affirming Romance Set in a Fin-de-Siecle Circus. 1999. (Illus.). 112p. (YA). pap. 9.95 (978-1-882402-14-4(6)) NBM Publishing Co.

Press, Lauren. Circus in the Night Sky. Press, Lauren, illus. 2000. (Illus.). 32p. (J). (ps-3). 12.00 (978-1-56550-087-7(3)) Vision Bks. International.

Price, Reynolds. A Perfect Friend. 2002. 176p. pap. 11.00 (978-0-7432-2521-2(X), Scribner) Simon & Schuster.

—A Perfect Friend. l.t. ed. 2001. 150p. (J). (gr. 4-7). 21.95 (978-0-7862-3589-6(6)) Thorndike Pr.

Priceman, Marjorie. Emeline at the Circus. (J). (gr. k-3). 2000. pap. 6.99 (978-0-375-80351-2(3), Random Hse. Bks. for Young Readers); 1999. (Illus.). 40p. pap. 15.00 (978-0-679-87685-4(5), Knopf Bks. for Young Readers) Random Hse. Children's Bks.

—Emeline at the Circus. 2001. (Illus.). (J). 13.79 (978-0-606-21176-5(4)) Tandem Library Bks.

Puerto, Carlos. Las Alas de la Pantera. (Barco de Vapor). (SPA.). 128p. (YA). (gr. 5-8). (978-84-348-4667-8(5)) SM Ediciones.

Rankin, Robert. The Greatest Show off Earth. 2000. 320p. (J). pap. 10.95 (978-0-552-13924-3(6)) Transworld Publishers Ltd. GBR. *Dist:* Trafalgar Square Publishing.

Rau, Dana Meachen. Clown Around, Level B. Evans, Nate, illus. 2001. (Early Reader Ser.). 32p. (J). (gr. k up). lib. bdg. 18.60 (978-0-7565-0074-0(5)) Compass Point Bks.

Redbank, Tennant. My Name Is Jojo. 2005. (JoJo's Circus Ser.). (Illus.). 24p. (ps-k). pap. 3.50 (978-0-7868-4679-5(8)) Disney Pr.

Rex, Adam. Tree-Ring Circus. 2006. (Illus.). 32p. (J). 16.00 (978-0-15-205363-5(8)) Harcourt Trade Pubs.

Rhoades, Heather. Picture Me in the Circus. 2000. (Picture Me Ser.). (Illus.). 10p. (J). (ps up). bds. 4.99 (978-1-57151-586-5(0)) Playhouse Publishing.

Richards, Jean, reader. Madeline & the Gypsies. 2004. (Illus.). (J). pap. 18.95 incl. audio compact disk (978-1-59112-821-2(8)) Live Oak Media.

Rickenbacker, Edward V. Fighting the Flying Circus. 2001. (Illus.). 371p. (YA). 25.00 (978-0-7567-5194-4(2)) DIANE Publishing Co.

Robertson, Patrisha. Cirque du Soleil: Parade of Colors. Robertson, Patrisha, tr. Cirque du Soleil Group, illus. Seib, Al, photos by. 2003. 40p. (J). (ps-3). 15.95 (978-0-8109-4515-9(0)) Abrams, Harry N., Inc.

Rosensweig, Jay B. & Repka, Janice. The Stupendous Dodgeball Fiasco. Dibley, Glin, illus. 2004. 192p. (J). (gr. 3). 16.99 (978-0-525-47346-6(7), Dutton Juvenile) Penguin Group (USA) Inc.

Ross, Jil M. What's the Matter, Mr. Ticklebritches? Another installment in the Shenanigans Series. 2006. (Illus.). 62p. (J). per. 6.95 (978-1-933324-26-5(0)) Cedar Hill Publishing.

Sally the Great: Individual Title Six-Packs. (gr. k-1). 23.00 (978-0-7635-9026-0(6)) Rigby Education.

Santillo, LuAnn. At the Circus, 6 vols. Santillo, LuAnn, ed. 2003. (Half-Pint Kids Readers Ser.). (Illus.). 42p. (J). (ps-1). pap. 6.99 (978-1-59256-112-4(8)) Half-Pint Kids, Inc.

—The Best Show. Santillo, LuAnn, ed. 2003. (Half-Pint Kids Readers Ser.). (Illus.). 7p. (J). (ps-1). pap. (978-1-59256-117-9(9)) Half-Pint Kids, Inc.

—The Big Top. Santillo, LuAnn, ed. 2003. (Half-Pint Kids Readers Ser.). (Illus.). 7p. (J). (ps-1). pap. (978-1-59256-113-1(6)) Half-Pint Kids, Inc.

—Good Food. Santillo, LuAnn, ed. 2003. (Half-Pint Kids Readers Ser.). (Illus.). 7p. (J). (ps-1). pap. (978-1-59256-118-6(7)) Half-Pint Kids, Inc.

—The Lion Tamer. Santillo, LuAnn, ed. 2003. (Half-Pint Kids Readers Ser.). (Illus.). 7p. (J). (ps-1). pap. (978-1-59256-115-5(2)) Half-Pint Kids, Inc.

—The Tight Rope. Santillo, LuAnn, ed. 2003. (Half-Pint Kids Readers Ser.). (Illus.). 7p. (J). (ps-1). pap. (978-1-59256-114-8(4)) Half-Pint Kids, Inc.

Sargent, Dave & Sargent, Pat. Manny Monkey: Friendship, 56 vols., 52. Lenoir, Jane, illus. 2001. (Animal Pride Ser.: Vol. 52). 36p. (J). lib. bdg. 19.95 (978-1-56763-545-4(8)) Ozark Publishing.

Sargent, Dave, et al. Manny Monkey: Friendship, 17, 52. 2001. (Animal Pride Ser.: 52). (Illus.). 42p. (J). lib. bdg. 19.95 (978-1-56763-546-1(6)) Ozark Publishing.

Scalzo, Linda V. Carazona's Coloring Book. l.t. ed. 2004. (Illus.). 8p. (J). 2.99 (978-0-9753724-3-2(2)) Carazona Creations LLC.

—El circo llega al Pueblo: Version de Lectura Temprana. Torres, Marcela H., tr. Spalinski, Amanda, illus. l.t. ed. 2005. (SPA.). 24p. per. 9.99 (978-0-9753724-2-5(4)) Carazona Creations LLC.

—The Circus is coming to Town: Early Reader Version. Spalinski, Amanda, illus. l.t. ed. 2005. 24p. (J). per. 9.99 (978-0-9753724-1-8(6)) Carazona Creations LLC.

—The Circus Is Coming to Town: Full-Length Version. l.t. ed. 2004. (Illus.). 32p. (J). 9.99 (978-0-9753724-0-1(8)) Carazona Creations LLC.

Scott, Elaine. Secrets of the Cirque Medrano. 2008. (J). (*978-1-57091-712-7(4)) Charlesbridge Publishing, Inc.

Scott, Elaine. The Spanish Web: An Encounter with Picasso. 2004. (Art Encounters Ser.). (J). 15.95 (978-0-8230-0410-2(4)); pap. 6.99 (978-0-8230-0413-3(9)) Watson-Guptill Pubns., Inc.

Sendak, Jack. Circus Girl. 2002. (Sendak Reissues Ser.). (Illus.). 32p. (J). 13.89 (978-0-06-028784-9(5)) HarperCollins Pubs.

—Circus Girl. Sendak, Maurice, illus. 2002. (Sendak Reissues Ser.). 32p. reprint ed. 17.95 (978-0-06-028783-2(7)) HarperCollins Pubs.

Shan, Darren, pseud. A Living Nightmare. (Cirque du Freak: Bk. 1). (J). 2004. (Illus.). 272p. (gr. 3-7). mass mkt. 6.99 (978-0-316-90571-8(2)); 2002. 272p. (gr. 5-17). pap. 7.99 (978-0-316-60510-6(7)); 2001. 272p. (gr. k-3). 15.95 (978-0-316-60340-9(6)); 2001. (Illus.). viii, 279p. (gr. 3-6). pap. (978-0-316-64852-3(3)) Little, Brown Bks. for Young Readers.

—A Living Nightmare. 2002. (Cirque du Freak: Bk. 1). (J). (gr. 3-6). lib. bdg. 14.45 (978-0-613-52592-3(2)) Tandem Library Bks.

—A Living Nightmare. l.t. ed. 2001. (Cirque du Freak: Bk. 1). (Illus.). 280p. (978-0-7089-9544-0(6)) Ulverscroft Large Print Bks.

Shaskan, Trisha. The Ticket. Demski, James, illus. 2006. (Read-It! Readers Ser.). (J). 19.93 (978-1-4048-2423-2(5)) Picture Window Bks.

Shire, Poppy. Sparkle the Circus Pony. Berg, Ron, illus. 2007. (Magic Pony Carousel Ser.: No. 1). 96p. (J). pap. 3.99 (978-0-06-083779-2(9)); 14.99 (978-0-06-083777-8(2)) HarperCollins Pubs. (Harper Trophy).

A Shoe, 6 Packs. (Sails Literacy Ser.). 16p. (gr. k up). 27.00 (978-0-7635-4417-1(5)) Rigby Education.

Sidle, Christian. Murphy Dog at the Circus. Lynn, Dianne, illus. l.t. ed. 2001. 80p. (J). (ps-3). per. 12.50 (978-0-9708053-6-2(5)) Authors & Artists Publishers of New York, Inc.

Slate, Joseph. Miss Bindergarten Plans a Circus with Kindergarten. Wolff, Ashley, illus. 2005. 40p. (J). (gr. k-1). pap. 6.99 (978-0-14-240273-3(7), Puffin) Penguin Group (USA) Inc.

—Miss Bindergarten Plans a Circus with Kindergarten. Wolff, Ashley, illus. 2005. 36p. (J). (ps-ps). lib. bdg. 13.79 (978-0-606-33114-2(X)) Tandem Library Bks.

Slobodkina, Esphyr. Circus Caps for Sale. Slobodkina, Esphyr, illus. 2004. (Illus.). 40p. (J). (ps-2). reprint ed. 17.00 (978-0-7567-8345-7(3)) DIANE Publishing Co.

—Circus Caps for Sale. Slobodkina, Esphyr, illus. (Illus.). 48p. (J). (ps-2). 2002. 16.99 (978-0-06-029655-1(0)); 2004. reprint ed. pap. 6.99 (978-0-06-443793-6(0), Harper Trophy) HarperCollins Pubs.

Spier, Peter. Peter Spier's Circus! Spier, Peter, illus. 2002. (Illus.). (J). 15.26 (978-0-7587-3397-9(6)) Book Wholesalers, Inc.

Stadler, John. Big & Little. 2007. (Illus.). 32p. (J). (ps-1). 9.99 (978-0-375-84175-0(X), Robin Corey Bks.) Random Hse. Children's Bks.

Strong, Beverly Jean. Gypsy the Circus Dog: A Story for Children. Strong, Beverly Jean, illus. 1999. (Illus.). 48p. (J). (ps-3). 24.95 (978-0-86534-300-9(4)) Sunstone Pr.

Taylor, Terry. Tim the Young Magician: Tim & the Circus. 2005. 48p. pap. 12.95 (978-1-4137-6618-9(8)) PublishAmerica, Inc.

Tibo, Gilles. Simon et le Petit Cirque. ed. 2004. Tr. of Simon at the Circus. (FRE.). (J). (ps-2). spiral bd. (978-0-616-01846-0(0)) Canadian National Institute for the Blind/Institut National Canadien pour les Aveugles.

—Le Voyage du Funambule. 2004. (Mon Roman Ser.). (FRE., Illus.). 64p. (J). (gr. 2). pap. (978-2-89021-701-0(9)) Diffusion du livre Mirabel.

Touma, Patricia. Happy Times, the Adventures of Ish & Mish Vol. 1: Ish & Mish Go to the Circus. 2005. per. 7.00 (978-1-58396-873-4(3)) Blue Unicorn Edition, LLC.

Tracey, Diane Eurich. Sensational Sidney the Circus Horse. Kuessner, Pat, ed. Thiel, Caresse C., illus. 2002. 28p. (Orig.). (J). (gr. 2-6). pap. 12.00 (978-0-9701441-5-7(6), 628548) Bokmal Pr.

Tripp, Jenny. Pete & Fremont. Manders, John, illus. 2007. 192p. (J). (gr. 2-4). 16.00 (978-0-15-205629-2(7)) Harcourt Trade Pubs.

Urrea, Lourdes, et al. Te Dije Que No Miraras. rev. ed. 2003. (Ediciones Castillo Castillo Del Terror Ser.).Tr. of I Told You Not to Look. (SPA.). 100p. (J). (gr. 2-6). pap. 6.95 (978-970-20-0308-3(3)) Castillo, Ediciones, S. A. de C. V. MEX. *Dist:* Macmillan.

Valdes, Leslie. At the Carnival. Roper, Robert, illus. 2005. (Dora the Explorer Ser.). 24p. (J). pap. 3.99 (978-0-689-85841-3(8), Simon Spotlight/Nickelodeon) Simon & Schuster Children's Publishing.

Veldkamp, Tjibbe. Little Monkey's Big Peeing Circus. de Boer, Kees, illus. 2006. 32p. (J). (ps-1). 12.95 (978-0-8109-3949-3(5), Abrams Bks. for Young Readers) Abrams, Harry N., Inc.

Villeneuve, Mireille. A Clown in Love. Villeneuve, Anne, illus. 2005. (Read-It! Readers Ser.). 32p. (C). (gr. k-3). 18.60 (978-1-4048-1069-3(2)) Picture Window Bks.

von Konigslow, Andrea Wayne. Bing & Chutney. von Konigslow, Andrea Wayne, illus. 1999. (Bing & Chutney Adventures Ser.). (Illus.). 32p. (J). (gr. k-ps). lib. bdg. 16.95 (978-1-55037-609-8(8)) Annick Pr., Ltd. CAN. *Dist:* Firefly Bks., Ltd.

—Bing & Chutney. 1999. (ps-2). lib. bdg. 14.10 (978-0-613-53145-0(0)) Tandem Library Bks.

Wallace. Morgan the Magnificent. (J). 16.95 (978-0-88899-056-3(1)); 5.95 (978-0-88899-166-9(5)) Groundwood Bks. CAN. (Libros Tigrillo). *Dist:* Transition Vendor.

Wallace, Karen. The Unrivalled Spangles. 2006. 224p. (YA). 16.95 (978-1-4169-1503-4(6)) Simon & Schuster Children's Publishing.

Wiseman, Bernard. Morris & Boris at the Circus. Wiseman, Bernard, illus. 2002. (Illus.). (J). 12.34 (978-0-7587-5557-5(0)) Book Wholesalers, Inc.

The World's Greatest Showman. 2002. (Illus.). (J). pap. (978-0-7398-5072-5(5)) Steck-Vaughn.

Yaccarino, Dan. Deep in the Jungle. Yaccario, Dan, illus. 2002. (J). 25.11 (978-0-7587-2371-0(7)) Book Wholesalers, Inc.

Ziefert, Harriet. Circus Parade. Roitman, Tanya, illus. 2005. 40p. (J). (ps-2). 15.95 (978-1-59354-088-3(4)) Blue Apple Bks.

Zocchi, Judy. Paulie & Sasha: Circus or Not. Vannozzi, Don, illus. 2001. (Paulie & Sasha Ser.). 32p. (J). lib. bdg. 23.00 (978-1-891997-17-4(3)) Dingles & Co.

—Paulie & Sasha: The Rescue. Vannozzi, Don, illus. 2001. (Paulie & Sasha Ser.). 32p. (J). lib. bdg. 23.00 (978-1-891997-15-0(7)) Dingles & Co.

CIRCUS—PICTORIAL WORKS

Circus, 6 bks., Set. 2002. (J). (ps-1). 111.00 (978-1-58810-470-0(2)) Heinemann Library.

Salisbury, Kent. Circus of Shapes: Fun with All Your Exciting Friends at the Big Top. 1998. (Illus.). 13p. (J). (ps-k). 6.99 (978-0-7681-0083-9(6), McClanahan Bk.) Learning Horizons, Inc.

CIRCUS—POETRY

Janeczko, Paul B. Worlds Afire. 2007. (Illus.). 112p. (YA). (gr. 7 up). pap. 6.99 (978-0-7636-3400-1(X)) Candlewick Pr.

CITIES AND TOWNS

Here are entered works on cities and towns. For works on large cities and their surrounding areas use Metropolitan Areas. General works on the government of cities are entered under Municipal Government. General works on local government other than that of cities are entered under Local Government.

see also Markets; Sociology, Urban; Streets

also headings beginning with the word Municipal; and names of individual cities and towns

Ajmera, Maya & Ivanko, John D. Be My Neighbor. 2004. (Illus.). 32p. (J). (gr. k-3). 15.95 (978-1-57091-504-8(0)) Charlesbridge Publishing, Inc.

Anderson, Mercedes Padrino. Cities & Towns in the Middle Ages. 2005. (World Almanac Library of the Middle Ages). (Illus.). 48p. (J). pap. (978-0-8368-5902-7(2), World Almanac Library) Stevens, Gareth Inc.

—Feudalism & Village Life in the Middle Ages. 2005. (World Almanac Library of the Middle Ages). (Illus.). 48p. (J). pap. (978-0-8368-5903-4(0), World Almanac Library) Stevens, Gareth Inc.

Anderson, Mercedes Padrino & Padrino, Mercedes. Cities & Towns in the Middle Ages. 2006. (World Almanac' Library of the Middle Ages). (Illus.). 48p. (J). (gr. 7-10). lib. bdg. 30.00 (978-0-8368-5893-8(X), World Almanac Library) Stevens, Gareth Inc.

Around Town. 2001. (Stick'n Learn Stories Ser.).Tr. of En la ciudad. (Illus.). 96p. (J). (ps-3). pap. 6.95 (978-1-55254-237-8(8)) Brighter Vision Pubns.

Barber, Nicola. City Home. 2007. (Homes Around the World Ser.). 32p. (J). (gr. 2-5). pap. ***(978-0-7787-3554-0(0))*** Crabtree Publishing Co.

Barter, James. Life in a Medieval Village. 2003. (Way People Live Ser.). (Illus.). 96p. (J). 29.95 (978-1-59018-266-6(9), Lucent Bks.) Thomson Gale.

Bevan, Finn. Cities of Splendor. Mayo, Diana, illus. 1999. (Landscapes of Legend Ser.). 32p. (J). (gr. 4-8). pap. 6.95 (978-0-516-26303-8(X), Children's Pr.) Scholastic Library Publishing.

Big City Life. 2002. (Illus.). (J). pap. 5.43 (978-0-7398-5931-5(5)) Steck-Vaughn.

Bodden, Valerie. A City. 2007. (J). (978-1-58341-512-2(2), Creative Education) Creative Co., The.

—A Farming Town. 2007. (J). (978-1-58341-513-9(0), Creative Education) Creative Co., The.

—A Suburb. 2007. (J). (978-1-58341-514-6(9), Creative Education) Creative Co., The.

—A Town. 2007. (J). (978-1-58341-515-3(7), Creative Education) Creative Co., The.

Bowden, Rob. Settlements of the Mississippi River. 2004. (Rivers Through Time Ser.). (Illus.). 48p. (J). pap. (978-1-4034-6250-3(X)) Heinemann Library.

Bowman, Crystal. See the Country, See the City. Thomson, Pam, illus. 2004. 20p. (J). pap. 4.99 (978-0-310-70818-6(4)) Zonderkidz.

—See the Country, See the City. 2000. 24p. (J). 6.99 (978-0-310-23210-0(4)) Zonderkidz.

Burke, Mary McManus. A, My Name Is Andrew. Guevara, Linda L., ed. Ingemanson, Donna, illus. 2003. 40p. (J). (gr. k-5). 16.95 (978-0-9710278-5-5(4)) All About Kids Publishing.

Burton, Margie, et al. Life in the City. Adams, Alison, ed. 1999. (Early Connections Ser.). 16p. (J). (gr. k-2). pap. 4.50 (978-1-58344-069-8(0)) Benchmark Education Co.

Capogna, Vera Vullo. Did You Ever Wonder about Things You Find in Your Backyard? 1999. (Did You Ever Wonder? Ser.). (Illus.). 32p. (J). (gr. k-3). lib. bdg. 22.79 (978-0-7614-0855-0(X), Benchmark Bks.) Cavendish, Marshall Corp.

Chrisp, Peter. Town & Country Life. 2004. (J). (gr. 7-10). 29.95 (978-1-59018-536-0(6), Lucent Bks.) Thomson Gale.

Cities Set 2. 2007. 91.12 (978-1-59679-715-4(0), Checkerboard Library) ABDO Publishing Co.

City Senses: Big Book: Level F. 16p. 31.50 (978-0-322-00374-3(1)) Wright Group, The.

Clare, John D., ed. Fourteenth-Century Towns. 1999. (Illus.). 64p. (J). (gr. 5-7). reprint ed. 17.00 (978-0-7881-6657-0(3)) DIANE Publishing Co.

Collier, Christopher & Collier, James Lincoln. The Rise of the Cities: 1820-1920. 2000. (Drama of American History Ser.). (Illus.). 96p. (J). (gr. 5-9). lib. bdg. 31.36 (978-0-7614-1051-5(1), Benchmark Bks.) Cavendish, Marshall Corp.

Cooper, Ann C. In the City. Emerling, Dorothy, illus. 2000. 49p. (ps-3). pap. 9.95 (978-1-57098-298-9(8)) Rinehart, Roberts Pubs.

Corn, John. Village, Town, City. 1998. (Fact Finders Ser.). (Illus.). 48p. (J). (gr. 3-7). pap. (978-0-563-37506-7(X)) BBC Worldwide.

Coster, Patience. Towns & Cities. Bellwood, Shirley & Turvey, Raymond, illus. 1998. (Step-by-Step Geography Ser.). 32p. (J). (gr. 1-3). 18.50 (978-0-516-20355-3(X), Children's Pr.) Scholastic Library Publishing.

Dewire, Bob. My Guide to Our Habitat. Sullivan, Beth, illus. 2000. 64p. (J). (gr. 2-3). pap. 2.75 (978-1-56762-127-3(9)) Modern Learning Pr.

Doherty, Gillian. 1001 Cosa Que Buscar En Pueblos y Ciudades. 2004. (SPA., Illus.). 32p. (J). (ps up). lib. bdg. 14.95 (978-1-58086-351-3(5), EU31233) EDC Publishing.

Doherty, Gillian & Claybourne, Anna. Los Pueblos Del Mundo - Internet Linked. 2004. (Titles in Spanish Ser.). (SPA.). 96p. (J). pap. 14.95 (978-0-7460-5068-2(2), Usborne) EDC Publishing.

Eastwood, Kay. Medieval Society. 2003. (Medieval World Ser.). (Illus.). 32p. (J). (gr. 5). (978-0-7787-1345-6(8)) Crabtree Publishing Co.

Edwards, Azell. Ghetto Tales Straight from the 'Hood. 1998. 49p. (YA). (gr. 10 up). pap. 7.00 (978-0-8059-4278-1(5)) Dorrance Publishing Co., Inc.

Emberley, Rebecca. My City/ Mi Ciudad. 2005. 10p. (J). (ps-ps). bds. 6.99 (978-0-316-00051-2(5)) Little Brown & Co.

Facts on File, Inc. Staff, ed. Global Cities Set, 6 Vols. 2006. 180.00 (978-0-7910-9457-0(X), Chelsea Hse.) Facts On File, Inc.

Figorito, Christine. In the City. 2002. (PowerPhonics Ser.). (Illus.). 23p. (J). lib. bdg. (978-0-8239-8263-9(7)) Rosen Publishing Group, Inc., The.

—In the City: Learning the Soft C Sound. 2002. (PowerPhonics Ser.). (Illus.). 24p. (J). (gr. 1). lib. bdg. 18.50 (978-0-8239-5918-1(X), PowerKids Pr.) Rosen Publishing Group, Inc., The.

Folch, Sergio & Geis, Patricia. La Gente Que Nos Rodea. 2002. (Our World Ser.). (SPA.). pap. 11.95 (978-84-488-1138-9(0), BS30457) Beascoa, Ediciones S.A. ESP. *Dist:* Lectorum Pubns., Inc.

Geisert, Bonnie. Prairie Town. Geisert, Arthur, illus. 1998. (Small Town U. S. A. Ser.). 32p. (J). (gr. k-3). tchr. ed. 16.00 (978-0-395-85907-0(7), Walter Lorraine) Houghton Mifflin Co. Trade & Reference Div.

Geisert, Bonnie & Geisert, Arthur. River Town. 1999. (Small Town U. S. A. Ser.). (Illus.). 32p. (J). (gr. k-3). tchr. ed. 16.00 (978-0-395-90891-4(4), Walter Lorraine) Houghton Mifflin Co. Trade & Reference Div.

Go to Town. 1998. (High Q Books Ser.). (Illus.). 48p. (J). (gr. k-3). pap. 3.99 (978-0-7681-0018-1(6), McClanahan Bk.) Learning Horizons, Inc.

Gordon, Sharon. At Home in the City. 2005. (Bookworms Ser.). (ENG & SPA., Illus.). 32p. (J). (gr. 3-7). lib. bdg. (978-0-7614-1960-0(8), Benchmark Bks.) Cavendish, Marshall Corp.

—At Home in the City (Mi Casa en la Ciudad) 2006. (Bookworms Ser.). (ENG & SPA., Illus.). 32p. (J). lib. bdg. 22.79 (978-0-7614-2452-9(0)) Cavendish, Marshall Corp.

—Mi Casa en la Ciudad. 2006. (Bookworms Ser.). (SPA.). 32p. (J). lib. bdg. 22.79 (978-0-7614-2372-0(9)) Cavendish, Marshall Corp.

Gralla, Preston. How Cities Work: Open Your Eyes to the Wonders of the Urban Environment. Feasey, Dave & Reimer, Mina, illus. 1999. 130p. (YA). (gr. 8-12). reprint ed. pap. 20.00 (978-0-7881-6090-5(7)) DIANE Publishing Co.

Great Cities of the World: Athens, London, Mexico City, Moscow, New York City, Toronto, 6 bks. 2003. (Illus.). (J). (gr. 5 up). lib. bdg. 175.60 (978-0-8368-5020-8(3), World Almanac Library) Stevens, Gareth Inc.

Great Cities of the World New Releases: Beijing, Los Angeles, Paris, Rio de Janeiro, Sydney, Tokyo, 6 bks. (Illus.). (J). (gr. 5 up). 2004. lib. bdg. 175.60 (978-0-8368-5027-7(0)); 2003. pap. 71.70 (978-0-8368-5187-8(0)) Stevens, Gareth Inc. (World Almanac Library).

Grimes, Nikki. C Is for City. Cummings, Pat, illus. 2003. 40p. (J). (ps up). pap. 10.95 (978-1-59078-013-8(2)) Boyds Mills Pr.

—C Is for City. 2002. (gr. k-3). lib. bdg. 18.75 (978-0-613-56257-7(7)) Tandem Library Bks.

Guin, Valerie. In the City. 2005. (Illus.). 30p. (J). (gr. 3-7). lib. bdg. 27.10 (978-1-58340-696-0(4)) Smart Apple Media.

Harcourt School Publishers Staff. Big Town - Grade 4. 3rd ed. 2002. (Trophies English Language Learners Ser.). pap. 5.10 (978-0-15-327771-9(8)) Harcourt Schl. Pubs.

—Cities of Yesterday, Today, & Tomorrow. 3rd ed. 2002. (Horizons Ser.). (Illus.). (J). pap. 5.50 (978-0-15-333244-9(1)) Harcourt Schl. Pubs.

—City Builders. 3rd ed. 2002. (Trophies English Language Learners Ser.). (Illus.). pap. 5.10 (978-0-15-327826-6(9)) Harcourt Schl. Pubs.

—Our Town: Take-Home Book. 1999. (Collections Ser.). (Illus.). (J). pap. 1.90 (978-0-15-317203-8(7)) Harcourt Schl. Pubs.

—Visit the Capital. 3rd ed. 2002. (Horizons Ser.). (Illus.). (J). pap. 3.70 (978-0-15-333151-0(8)) Harcourt Schl. Pubs.

—Where We Live, Unit 2. 3rd ed. 2003. (Harcourt Brace Social Studies). pap. 76.00 (978-0-15-341067-3(1)) Harcourt Schl. Pubs.

Heo, Yumi. One Afternoon. 1998. (Illus.). 32p. (J). (ps-1). pap. 6.95 (978-0-531-07103-8(0), Orchard Bks.) Scholastic, Inc.

Heywood, Rosie. The Great City Search. 2004. (Great Searches Ser.). 32p. (J). lib. bdg. 16.95 (978-1-58086-626-2(3), Usborne) EDC Publishing.

—Great city Search. rev. ed. 2005. 32p. (J). pap. 7.99 (978-0-7945-1047-3(7), Usborne) EDC Publishing.

Hill, Lee Sullivan. Get Around in the City. 1999. (Get Around Bks.). (Illus.). 32p. (J). (gr. k-3). lib. bdg. 14.60 (978-1-57505-307-3(1), Carolrhoda Bks.) Lerner Publishing Group.

Hinds, Kathryn. The City. (Life in Ancient Egypt Ser.). (Illus.). (J). 2006. 80p. lib. bdg. 32.79 (978-0-7614-2184-9(X)); 2004. 87p. 29.93 (978-0-7614-1655-5(2)); 2000. 80p. (gr. 5 up). lib. bdg. 29.93 (978-0-7614-1005-8(8)) Cavendish, Marshall Corp. (Benchmark Bks.).

Holland, Gini. I Live in a Town. 2004. (Weekly Reader Early Learning Library). (Illus.). 24p. (gr. k up). (J). pap. 5.95 (978-0-8368-4090-2(9)); (YA). lib. bdg. 19.33 (978-0-8368-4083-4(6)) Stevens, Gareth Inc. (Weekly Reader Early Learning Library).

—I Live in a Town/Vivo en un Pueblo. Coffey, Colleen & Carrillo, Consuelo, trs. 2004. (Weekly Reader Early Learning Library). (SPA & ENG., Illus.). 24p. (J). (gr. k up). pap. 5.95 (978-0-8368-4138-1(7)); lib. bdg. 19.33 (978-0-8368-4131-2(X)) Stevens, Gareth Inc. (Weekly Reader Early Learning Library).

—I Live in the City. 2004. (Weekly Reader Early Learning Library). (Illus.). 24p. (gr. k up). (J). pap. (978-0-8368-4085-8(2)); (YA). lib. bdg. 19.33 (978-0-8368-4078-0(X)) Stevens, Gareth Inc. (Weekly Reader Early Learning Library).

—I Live in the City/Vivo en la Ciudad. Coffey, Colleen & Carrillo, Consuelo, trs. 2004. (Weekly Reader Early Learning Library). (SPA & ENG., Illus.). 24p. (J). (gr. k up). pap. 5.95 (978-0-8368-4133-6(6)); lib. bdg. 19.33 (978-0-8368-4126-8(3)) Stevens, Gareth Inc. (Weekly Reader Early Learning Library).

—Where I Live, 6 bks. Incl. I Live in a Town. pap. 5.95 (978-0-8368-4090-2(9)); I Live in the City. pap. (978-0-8368-4085-8(2)); I Live in the Country. pap. (978-0-8368-4086-5(0)); I Live in the Desert. pap. (978-0-8368-4087-2(9)); I Live in the Mountains. pap. (978-0-8368-4088-9(7)); I Live near the Ocean. pap. 5.95 (978-0-8368-4089-6(5)); 24p. (J). (gr. k up). (Illus.). 2004. pap. (978-0-8368-4084-1(4)); Set lib. bdg. 115.98 (978-0-8368-4077-3(1)) Stevens, Gareth Inc. (Weekly Reader Early Learning Library).

—Where I Live/Donde Vivo, 6 bks. Coffey, Colleen & Carrillo, Consuelo, trs. Incl. I Live in a Town/Vivo en un Pueblo. pap. 5.95 (978-0-8368-4138-1(7)); I Live in the City/Vivo en la Ciudad. pap. 5.95 (978-0-8368-4133-6(6)); I Live in the Country/Vivo en el Campo. pap. 5.95 (978-0-8368-4134-3(4)); I Live in the Desert/ Vivo en el Desierto. pap. 5.95 (978-0-8368-4135-0(2)); I Live in the Mountains/Vivo en las Montañas. pap. 5.95 (978-0-8368-4136-7(0)); I Live near the Ocean/ Vivo cerca del Mar. pap. 5.95 (978-0-8368-4137-4(9)); 24p. (J). (gr. k up). (SPA & ENG., Illus.). 2004. Set pap. 35.70 (978-0-8368-4132-9(8)); Set lib. bdg. 115.98 (978-0-8368-4125-1(5)) Stevens, Gareth Inc. (Weekly Reader Early Learning Library).

In the City. (Early Intervention Levels Ser.). 23.10 (978-0-7362-0019-6(3)) Hampton-Brown Bks.

In the City: Individual Title, 6 Packs. (ps-2). 23.00 (978-0-7635-8809-0(1)) Rigby Education.

Ingpen, Robert R. Once upon a Place. Ingpen, Robert R., illus. 2000. (Illus.). 48p. (J). (978-0-85091-909-7(6), Lothian Bks.) Hachette Livre Australia.

Jacobs, Daniel. City Shapes. 2003. (Yellow Umbrella Books for Early Readers). (Illus.). 17p. (J). 15.93 (978-0-7368-2915-1(6)); pap. (978-0-7368-2874-1(5)) Yellow Umbrella Pr.

Jaffe, Charlotte & Doherty, Barbara. Create a City: A Complete Framework for Students to Use in Creating an Original City. Armstrong, Beverly, illus. 1999. 88p. (J). (gr. 5-8). pap., stu. ed. 11.99 (978-0-88160-311-8(2), LW-380, Learning Works, The) Creative Teaching Pr., Inc.

Johnson, Emma. Medieval Town & Country Life. (Illus.). 32p. 18.95 (978-1-932889-28-4(0)) Sea-To-Sea Pubns.

Johnson, Stephen T. Alphabet City. Johnson, Stephen T., illus. 2002. (Illus.). (J). 14.04 (978-0-7587-0088-9(1)) Book Wholesalers, Inc.

—Alphabet City. 1999. (Illus.). 32p. (J). (ps-3). pap. 6.99 (978-0-14-055904-0(3), Puffin) Penguin Group (USA) Inc.

—Alphabet City. 1999. (J). 13.79 (978-0-606-17258-5(0)) Tandem Library Bks.

Kalman, Bobbie. Boomtowns of the West. 1999. (J). (978-0-606-16431-3(6)) Tandem Library Bks.

Kehoe, Stasia Ward. I Live in a City. 2000. (Kids in Their Communities Ser.). (Illus.). 24p. (J). (gr. 3). lib. bdg. 18.75 (978-0-8239-5437-7(4), PowerKids Pr.) Rosen Publishing Group, Inc., The.

Learning Wrap-Ups States & Capitols. 2004. 7.99 (978-0-943343-30-3(5)) Learning Wrap-Ups.

Litchfield, Jo. Town. 2004. (Look & Say Board Books Ser.). (Illus.). 10p. (J). 7.95 (978-0-7945-0701-5(8), Usborne) EDC Publishing.

Llewellyn, Claire. Towns & Cities. 1998. (Illus.). 24p. (J). (gr. 1-6). 19.92 (978-1-57572-197-2(X)) Heinemann Library.

Lomberg, Michelle. Healthy Cities: Imporving Urban Life. 2004. (Understanding Global Issues Ser.). (Illus.). 56p. (J). (gr. 10-12). (978-1-58340-359-4(0)) Smart Apple Media.

Malam, John. Greek Town. 2000. (Metropolis Ser.). (Illus.). 48p. (J). (gr. 5-7). pap. 8.95 (978-0-531-15379-6(7), Watts, Franklin) Scholastic Library Publishing.

McFarlane, Sheryl. In the City. LaFave, Kim, tr. LaFave, Kim, illus. 2004. (What's That Sound? Ser.). 20p. (J). (ps up). bds. (978-1-55041-812-5(2)) Fitzhenry & Whiteside, Ltd.

Milbourne, Anna. 1001 Things to Spot in the Town. 2004. (1001 Things to Spot Ser.). (SPA., Illus.). 32p. (J). (ps-3). lib. bdg. 14.99 (978-1-58086-332-2(9)); pap. 6.99 (978-0-7460-2953-4(5)) EDC Publishing.

—1001 Things to Spot in the Town. 2001. (gr. k-3). lib. bdg. 15.25 (978-0-613-74475-1(6)) Tandem Library Bks.

Milich, Zoran. City 123. 2005. (Illus.). 32p. (J). (gr. k up). (978-1-55337-540-1(8)) Kids Can Pr., Ltd.

Miller, Jake. Who's Who in a Neighborhood. 2005. (Communities at Work Ser.). (Illus.). 24p. (J). 19.95 (978-1-4042-2785-9(7)); pap. (978-1-4042-5024-6(7)) Rosen Publishing Group, Inc., The. (PowerKids Pr.).

—Who's Who in an Urban Community. 2005. (Communities at Work Ser.). 19.95 (978-1-4042-2790-3(3), PowerKids Pr.) Rosen Publishing Group, Inc., The.

Mo, Potato. Fries & Rice: My Treasured Memories. 2002. 157p. (YA). pap. 11.95 (978-0-595-24963-3(9), Writers Club Pr.) iUniverse, Inc.

Morris, Neil. Living in Cities. 2004. (J). lib. bdg. (978-1-58340-483-6(X)) Smart Apple Media.

My Cousin Jake: Individual Title Six-Packs. (ps-2). 27.00 (978-0-7635-9463-3(6)) Rigby Education.

Nathan, Emma. Cities. 2002. (Eyeopeners Ser.). (Illus.). 24p. (J) 22.45 (978-1-56711-596-3(9), Blackbirch Pr., Inc.) Thomson Gale.

Nelson, Robin. Where Is My Town? 2005. (First Step Nonfiction Ser.). (Illus.). 24p. (J). (gr. k-2). lib. bdg. 17.27 (978-0-8225-0190-9(2)) Lerner Publishing Group.

Nichol, Barbara. The City ABC Book. Milich, Zorin, photos by. unabr. ed. 2003. (Illus.). 32p. (J). (ps-k). (978-1-55074-942-7(0)) Kids Can Pr., Ltd.

Nickles, Greg. France - the People. 2000. (gr. 3-6). lib. bdg. 16.40 (978-0-613-27837-9(2)) Tandem Library Bks.

Olson, Nathan. City Patterns. 2007. 32p. (J). (978-0-7368-6730-6(9)) Capstone Pr., Inc.

Padrino, Mercedes. Feudalism & Village Life in the Middle Ages. 2006. (World Almanac' Library of the Middle Ages). (Illus.). 48p. (YA). (gr. 7-10). lib. bdg. 30.00 (978-0-8368-5894-5(8), World Almanac Library) Stevens, Gareth Inc.

Pancella, Peggy. City. 2005. (Illus.). 32p. (J). pap. (978-1-4034-6221-3(6)); lib. bdg. 25.36 (978-1-4034-6215-2(1)) Heinemann Library.

—Ciudades. 2005. (ENG & SPA., Illus.). 32p. (J). (978-1-4034-6232-9(1)); pap. (978-1-4034-6238-1(0)) Heinemann Library.

—Military Base. 2005. (Illus.). 32p. (J). pap. (978-1-4034-6223-7(2)); lib. bdg. 25.36 (978-1-4034-6217-6(8)) Heinemann Library.

—Small Town. 2005. (Illus.). 32p. (J). lib. bdg. 25.36 (978-1-4034-6218-3(6)) Heinemann Library.

—Town. 2005. (Illus.). 32p. (J). pap. (978-1-4034-6224-4(0)) Heinemann Library.

Places of the World Action Sticker Book. 2002. 12p. (J). pap. 3.98 (978-0-7525-8040-1(X)) Parragon, Inc.

Raum, Elizabeth. Fusion: On the Move. 2007. (Illus.). 32p. (J). pap. ***(978-1-4062-0505-3(2))*** Steck-Vaughn.

Riggs, Sandy. Safe Streets. 2006. (Reader's Clubhouse Set B Ser.). (Illus.). 24p. (J). pap. 3.99 (978-0-7641-3300-8(4)) Barron's Educational Series, Inc.

Robson, Pam. My Town. 2004. (Earthwise Ser.). (J). lib. bdg. 27.10 (978-1-932799-49-1(4)) Stargazer Bks.

Roop, Peter & Roop, Connie. A City. 1999. (Walk Around Ser.). (Illus.). 32p. (J). (gr. 1-3). lib. bdg. 21.36 (978-1-57572-129-3(5)) Heinemann Library.

—A City Album. 1999. (Long Ago & Today Ser.). (Illus.). 24p. (J). (gr. 1-3). lib. bdg. 19.92 (978-1-57572-600-7(9)) Heinemann Library.

—Walk Around, 4 bks., Set. Incl. City. 1999. lib. bdg. 21.36 (978-1-57572-129-3(5)); Farming Town. 1998. lib. bdg. 21.36 (978-1-57572-127-9(9)); Suburb. 1999. lib. bdg. 21.36 (978-1-57572-130-9(9)); Town. 1998. lib. bdg. 21.36 (978-1-57572-128-6(7)); 32p. (J). (gr. 1-3). (Illus.). 1999. Set pap. 85.44 (978-1-57572-126-2(0)) Heinemann Library.

Ryan, Pam Muñoz. Our California. Lopez, Rafael, illus. 2008. (J). lib. bdg. ***(978-1-58089-116-5(0))*** Charlesbridge Publishing, Inc.

La Salvaguardia de las Ciudades. (Coleccion Biblioteca Juvenil de Ecología). (SPA., Illus.). (YA). (gr. 5-8). (978-958-04-3262-3(7), NR7196) Norma S.A. COL. *Dist:* Lectorum Pubns., Inc.

Scheunemann, Pam. Cities. Lt. ed. 2001. (Capital Letters Ser.). (Illus.). 24p. (J). (ps-3). lib. bdg. 19.93 (978-1-57765-610-4(5), SandCastle) ABDO Publishing Co.

Schuh, Mari C. In My Town. 2006. (Illus.). 24p. (J). (978-0-7368-4241-9(1)) Capstone Pr., Inc.

Sharp, Jean. Counting in the City. 2007. (J). pap. ***(978-0-8368-8477-7(9))***; (gr. 1-3). lib. bdg. 19.93 ***(978-0-8368-8468-5(X))*** Stevens, Gareth Inc. (Weekly Reader Early Learning Library).

Shuter, Jane. Life in a Roman Town. 2004. (Picture the Past Ser.). (Illus.). 32p. (J). 24.22 (978-1-4034-5828-5(6)); pap. 7.50 (978-1-4034-5836-0(7)) Heinemann Library.

—Life in a Viking Town. 2005. (Picture the Past Ser.). (Illus.). 32p. (J). 25.64 (978-1-4034-6440-8(5)); pap. (978-1-4034-6447-7(2)) Heinemann Library.

—Life in an Egyptian Town. 2004. (Picture the Past Ser.). (Illus.). 32p. (J). 24.22 (978-1-4034-5831-5(6)); pap. (978-1-4034-5839-1(1)) Heinemann Library.

Snedden, Robert. The Growth of Cities. 2004. (Earth's Changing Landscape Ser.). (J). lib. bdg. 28.50 (978-1-58340-474-4(0)) Smart Apple Media.

Spilsbury, Richard. Settlements of the Ganges River. 2005. (Rivers Through Time Ser.). (Illus.). 48p. (J). (gr. 3-7). lib. bdg. 31.43 (978-1-4034-6526-9(6)); pap. (978-1-4034-6527-6(4)) Heinemann.

C
D

Stefoff, Rebecca. Cities & Towns. 2007. (Colonial Life Ser.). (Illus.). 96p. (gr. 6 up). 37.95 (***978-0-7656-8109-6(9)***) Sharpe, M.E. Inc.

Stefoff, Rebecca. The Medieval World. 2003. (Illus.). 48p. (J). 27.07 (978-0-7614-1642-5(0) , Benchmark Bks.) Cavendish, Marshall Corp.

Sterling, Kristin. Urban Communities. 2008. (First Step Nonfiction - Communities Ser.). (J). lib. bdg. 18.60 (***978-0-8225-8597-8(9)*** , Lerner Pubns.) Lerner Publishing Group.

Sweeney, Alyse. Community Helpers, 6 bks., Set. Incl. Let's Visit a Dairy Farm. 2007. 19.00 (978-0-531-16843-1(3) , Watts, Franklin); Pets at the Vet. 2007. 19.00 (978-0-531-16811-0(5) , Watts, Franklin); Police Officers on the Go! 2006. 19.00 (978-0-531-16810-3(7)); 24p. (J). (gr. k-2). (Scholastic News Nonfiction Readers Ser.). (Illus.). 2006. 114.00 (***978-0-531-12474-1(6)*** , Children's Pr.) Scholastic Library Publishing.

Thomas, R. Kayeen. Light: Stories of Urban Resurrection. 2004. 90p. per. 12.00 (978-0-9759582-0-9(8)) MarWel Enterprises, Inc.

Troughton, Lester, illus. Busy City Masterbuilders. 2000. (LEGO Masterbuilders Ser.). 47p. (J). (ps-3). pap. 19.99 (978-1-903276-13-6(6)) Lego Media International, Inc.

Trumbauer, Lisa. Living in a City. 2005. (Communities Ser.). (Illus.). 24p. (J). 15.93 (978-0-7368-3630-2(6) , Pebble Bks.) Capstone Pr., Inc.

Turner, Stephanie. Communities. 1999. (Ecology Alert Ser.). (Illus.). 32p. (J). (gr. 3-7). 25.69 (978-0-8172-5373-8(4)) Raintree.

Vander Meulen, Joe, et al. Building a Sense of Place: A Cooperative Approach to Discovering & Preserving Community Character. 1999. (Illus.). 44p. (YA). (gr. 7 up). 18.00 (978-0-9671861-0-8(2)) Land Information Access Assn.

Weiss, Ellen & Fremont, Elenor. My Little People Busy Town. S. I. International Staff, illus. 2000. (Fisher-Price Little People Mini-Flap PlayBooks Ser.). 10p. (J). (ps-k). bds. 8.99 (978-1-57584-424-4(9) , Reader's Digest Children's Bks.) Reader's Digest Children's Publishing, Inc.

Where I Live - PowerPhonics Skill Set II, 6 bks. Incl. By the Ocean : Learning the Long O Sound. Richter, Abigail. lib. bdg. 18.50 (978-0-8239-5922-8(8)); I Jog Around : Learning the J Sound. Thomas, Maryann. lib. bdg. 18.50 (978-0-8239-5932-7(5)); In the City : Learning the Soft C Sound. Figorito, Christine. lib. bdg. 18.50 (978-0-8239-5918-1(X)); Meet Me on the Farm : Learning the Long E Sound. Braidich, Shelby & Roza, Greg. lib. bdg. 18.50 (978-0-8239-5920-4(1)); On Flat Land : Learning the FL Sound. Roza, Greg. lib. bdg. 18.50 (978-0-8239-5925-9(2)); On My Block : Learning the BL Sound. Fenner, Matthew. lib. bdg. 18.50 (978-0-8239-5924-2(4)); 24p. (J). (gr. 1). 2002. (Illus.). 2001. Set lib. bdg. 108.00 (978-0-8239-7207-4(0) , PowerKids Pr.) Rosen Publishing Group, Inc., The.

CITIES AND TOWNS—FICTION

Aesop. Town Mouse Country Mouse Sha. Hays, Ethel, illus. 2007. 14p. (J). (ps-3). pap. 9.95 (***978-1-59583-192-7(4)*** , Green Tiger Pr.) Laughing Elephant.

Alfonsi, Alice. New Kid in Town: Junior Novel. 2007. 128p. (gr. 3-7). pap. 4.99 (***978-1-4231-1073-6(0)***) Disney Pr.

All Around the Busy Town. l.t. ed. 1999. (Illus.). 20p. (J). pap. 19.00 (978-1-893467-03-3(1)) Spedial Editions Pr.

Alonso, Fernando. Celiana y la Ciudad Sumergida. (Superbks./Superlibros).Tr. of Celiana & the Enchanted City. (J). (gr. k-1). pap. 6.95 (978-0-88272-495-9(9)) Santillana USA Publishing Co., Inc.

Amsden, Janet. Grizzly Pete & the Ghosts. Beder, John, illus. 2002. 32p. (J). (gr. 1-2). pap. 7.95 (978-1-55037-718-7(3)); lib. bdg. 19.95 (978-1-55037-719-4(1)) Annick Pr., Ltd. CAN. *Dist:* Firefly Bks., Ltd.

—Grizzly Pete & the Ghosts. 2002. (gr. k-3). lib. bdg. 16.40 (978-0-613-56404-5(9)) Tandem Library Bks.

Anderson, Sara. Noisy City Day. 2005. (Illus.). 6p. (J). bds. 7.95 (978-1-59354-054-8(X)) Handprint Bks.

—Noisy City Night. 2005. (Illus.). 6p. (J). bds. 7.95 (978-1-59354-055-5(8)) Handprint Bks.

Baker, Jeannie. Home. Baker, Jeannie, illus. 2004. 32p. (J). 16.99 (978-0-06-623935-4(4)) HarperCollins Pubs.

Base, Graeme. Uno's Garden. 2006. (Illus.). 44p. (J). (ps-3). 19.95 (978-0-8109-5473-1(7)) Abrams, Harry N., Inc.

Becker, Bonny. Holbrook, a Lizard's Tale. Carter, Abby, illus. 2006. 128p. (J). (gr. 3-5). 15.00 (978-0-618-71458-2(8) , Clarion Bks.) Houghton Mifflin Co. Trade & Reference Div.

Benson, Edmund F. & Benson, Susan. 31 of Taneka's Urban Life Tales. 1999. (Illus.). 188p. (J). pap., tchr. ed. 12.95 (978-1-58614-099-1(X)) Arise Foundation.

Berry, Eileen M. Looking for Home. 2005. 75p. (J). (978-1-59166-493-2(4)) Jones, Bob Univ. Pr.

Blackstone, Stella. Oso en la ciudad (Bear About Town) Sarfatti, Esther, tr. Harter, Debbie, illus. 2003. (Bear Ser.). (SPA.). 24p. (J). 5.99 (978-1-84148-776-2(7)) Barefoot Bks., Inc.

Blake, Robert J. Fledgling. Blake, Robert J., illus. 2003. (Illus.). 32p. (J). (gr. k-3). pap. 6.99 (978-0-698-11985-7(1) , Putnam Juvenile) Penguin Group (USA) Inc.

—Fledgling. 2003. (gr. k-3). lib. bdg. 15.30 (978-0-613-61622-5(7)) Tandem Library Bks.

Blance, Ellen & Cook. Monster Comes to the City. Date not set. (Illus.). 16p. pap. 129.15 (978-0-582-18588-3(2)) Addison-Wesley Longman, Ltd. GBR. *Dist:* Trans-Atlantic Pubns., Inc.

—Monster Goes Around Town. Date not set. (Illus.). 38p. pap. 129.15 (978-0-582-19309-3(5)) Addison-Wesley Longman, Ltd. GBR. *Dist:* Trans-Atlantic Pubns., Inc.

Brooks, Martha. True Confessions of a Heartless Girl. 2003. 192p. (YA). (gr. 9 up). 16.00 (978-0-374-37806-6(1) , Farrar, Straus & Giroux (BYR)) Farrar, Straus & Giroux.

Brown, Richard, illus. Street Music. 2006. (I'm Going to Read Ser.). 24p. (J). pap. 3.95 (978-1-4027-3073-3(X)) Sterling Publishing Co., Inc.

Buehner, Caralyn. Escape of Marvin the Ape. Buehner, Mark, illus. 1999. 32p. (J). (ps-3). pap. 5.99 (978-0-14-056503-4(5) , Puffin) Penguin Group (USA) Inc.

—Escape of Marvin the Ape. 1999. (gr. k-3). lib. bdg. 14.15 (978-0-613-17791-7(6)) Tandem Library Bks.

Buehner, Caralyn. Escape of Marvin the Ape Board Book. Buehner, Mark, illus. 2007. 24p. (J). (ps). bds. 7.99 (***978-0-8037-3244-5(9)*** , Dial) Penguin Group (USA) Inc.

C D Stampley Enterprises, creator. Billy & Baxter on City Streets, 4 vols. 2005. (Illus.). 24p. (J). (ps-ps). 8.95 (978-1-58087-101-3(1)) Stampley, C.D. Enterprises, Inc.

Chanda, J-P. I Love Big City! Kahata, Etsu, illus. 2003. (Oswald Ser.). 12p. (J). bds. 7.99 (978-0-689-85851-2(5) , Simon Spotlight/Nickelodeon) Simon & Schuster Children's Publishing.

Charlton-Trujillo, E. E. Feels Like Home. 2007. 224p. (YA). (gr. 7 up). 15.99 (978-0-385-73332-8(1)); lib. bdg. 18.99 (978-0-385-90349-3(9)) Random Hse. Children's Bks. (Delacorte Bks. for Young Readers).

The Citiscapes Series, Big bk. (J). pap. 23.00 (978-1-56843-024-9(8)) EMG Networks.

Clark, Sherryl. Take a Hike! 2000. (gr. 7-12). lib. bdg. 12.25 (978-0-613-29088-3(7)) Tandem Library Bks.

Colman, Michelle Sinclair. Urban Babies Wear Black. Dion, Nathalie, illus. 2005. 20p. (J). (ps). 6.95 (978-1-58246-158-8(9) , Tricycle Pr.) Ten Speed Pr.

Cooper, Helen. A Pipkin of Pepper. 2005. (Illus.). 32p. (J). (ps-ps). 16.00 (978-0-374-35953-9(9)) Farrar, Straus & Giroux.

Cormier, Robert. Frenchtown Summer. Krovatin, Dan, illus. 2001. 128p. (YA). (gr. 7 up). mass mkt. 5.99 (978-0-440-22854-7(9) , Laurel Leaf) Random Hse. Children's Bks.

—Frenchtown Summer. 2001. (gr. 7-12). lib. bdg. 14.15 (978-0-613-33808-0(1)) Tandem Library Bks.

Country Mouse & City Mouse. 2002. (Classic Tales Mini Bks.). (Illus.). 32p. (J). (978-1-59069-037-6(0) , T1006); incl. audio compact disk (978-1-59069-104-5(0) , T1106) Studio Mouse LLC.

Cummins, Julie. Country Kid, City Kid. Rand, Ted, illus. rev. ed. 2002. 32p. (J). (ps-1). 17.95 (978-0-8050-6467-4(2) , Holt, Henry & Co. Bks. For Young Readers) Holt, Henry & Co.

Davidson, Susanna. Town Mouse & the Country Mouse. East, Jacqueline, illus. 2007. (First Reading Level 4 Ser.). 48p. (J). 8.99 (***978-0-7945-1613-0(0)*** , Usborne) EDC Publishing.

Dennis-Wyeth, Sharon. Something Beautiful. 2002. 32p. (J). (gr. 2-4). pap. 6.99 (978-0-440-41210-6(2) , Dragonfly Bks.) Random Hse. Children's Bks.

Devlin, Wende. Kiss for a Warthog. Devlin, Harry, illus. 1999. 48p. (J). (gr. 1-3). 14.00 (978-1-892657-01-5(5)) Town Bk. Pr. The.

DiSalvo-Ryan, DyAnne. Spaghettti Park. DiSalvo-Ryan, DyAnne, illus. 2002. (Illus.). 32p. (J). (gr. k-3). tchr. ed. 16.95 (978-0-8234-1682-0(8)) Holiday Hse., Inc.

Doyle, Brian. Easy Avenue. 2004. 122p. (YA). pap. 6.95 (978-0-88899-605-3(5)) Groundwood Bks. CAN. *Dist:* Perseus Distribution.

Dyer, Olive & Scurlock, Val. Gerry's Story. 2002. (Illus.). 36p. pap. 12.95 (978-1-85902-940-4(X)) Beekman Bks., Inc.

Egan, Tim. Metropolitan Cow. ed. 2004. (J). (gr. k-3). spiral bd. (978-0-616-07231-8(7)) Canadian National Institute for the Blind/Institut National Canadien pour les Aveugles.

Fairbairn, John. Highgate Hill Mob. 96p. pap. 10.95 (978-0-7022-2590-1(8)) Univ. of Queensland Pr. AUS. *Dist:* International Specialized Bk. Services.

Fleischman, Paul. Sidewalk Circus. Hawkes, Kevin, illus. 32p. (J). (gr. k-4). 2007. pap. 6.99 (***978-0-7636-2795-9(X)***); 2004. 15.99 (978-0-7636-1107-1(7)) Candlewick Pr.

Graham, Lorenz. North Town. Graham, Lorenz, illus. 2003. (Illus.). 188p. (YA). (gr. 6-9). 16.95 (978-1-59078-162-3(7)) Boyds Mills Pr.

Grahn, Geoffrey. What's Going on in There? A Guessing Book. Grahn, Geoffrey, illus. 2005. (Illus.). 48p. (J). pap. 14.95 (978-0-439-57495-2(1) , Orchard Bks.) Scholastic, Inc.

Grant, Karima. Sofie & the City. Montecalvo, Janet, illus. 2006. 32p. (J). 15.95 (978-1-59078-273-6(9)) Boyds Mills Pr.

Guest, Elissa Haden. Iris & Walter. Davenier, Christine, illus. (Iris & Walter Ser.). 44p. (J). 2006. pap. 5.95 (978-0-15-205644-5(0) , Harcourt Paperbacks); 2000. (gr. 1-3). 14.00 (978-0-15-202122-1(0) , Gulliver Bks.) Harcourt Children's Bks.

—Iris & Walter & Baby Rose. Davenier, Christine, illus. 2006. (Iris & Walter Ser.). 44p. (J). pap. 5.95 (978-0-15-205650-6(5) , Harcourt Paperbacks) Harcourt Children's Bks.

—Iris & Walter & the Substitute Teacher. Davenier, Christine, illus. 2006. (Iris & Walter Ser.). 44p. (J). pap. 5.95 (978-0-15-205376-5(X) , Harcourt Paperbacks) Harcourt Children's Bks.

—Iris & Walter, True Friends. Davenier, Christine, illus. 2006. (Iris & Walter Ser.). 44p. (J). pap. 5.95 (978-0-15-205680-3(7) , Harcourt Paperbacks) Harcourt Children's Bks.

Hamilton, Virginia. Plain City. (Barco de Vapor). (SPA.). 176p. (YA). (gr. 5-8). 6.95 (978-84-348-4686-9(1) , LEC6861) SM Ediciones ESP. *Dist:* Continental Bk. Co., Inc.

—Plain City. 2003. 208p. (J). (gr. 4-7). pap. 5.99 (978-0-590-47365-1(4) , Scholastic Paperbacks) Scholastic, Inc.

Handprint Staff. Traffic Town. 2007. (J). 8.95 (***978-1-59354-186-6(4)***) Handprint Bks.

Hands, Cynthia. Townsville's Super Trio. 2001. 32p. (J). (ps-2). pap. 3.99 (978-0-307-10495-3(8) , Golden Bks.) Random Hse. Children's Bks.

Harcourt School Publishers Staff. A Day in the City. 3rd ed. 2002. (Trophies English Language Learners Ser.). (Illus.). pap. 5.10 (978-0-15-327654-5(1)) Harcourt Schl. Pubs.

—In the City. 3rd ed. 2002. (Trophies English Language Learners Ser.). (Illus.). (J). pap. 3.20 (978-0-15-327575-3(8)) Harcourt Schl. Pubs.

—In the City Park: Below Level. 3rd ed. 2002. (Trophies Reading Program Ser.). (Illus.). (J). pap. 3.20 (978-0-15-322952-7(7)) Harcourt Schl. Pubs.

Harrison, Lisi. The Clique. 2004. (Clique Ser.: No. 1). 24p. (J). (gr. 5-8). pap. 9.99 (978-0-316-70129-7(7) , Poppy) Little, Brown Bks. for Young Readers.

—Invasion of the Boy Snatchers. 2005. (Clique Ser.: No. 4). 256p. (J). (gr. 5-8). pap. 9.99 (978-0-316-70134-1(3) , Poppy) Little, Brown Bks. for Young Readers.

Hassett, Ann & Hassett, John. Cat up a Tree. 2003. (Illus.). 32p. (J). (gr. k-3). pap. 5.95 (978-0-618-33524-4(2) , Walter Lorraine) Houghton Mifflin Co. Trade & Reference Div.

Hassett, John & Hassett, Ann. Cat up a Tree. 1998. (Illus.). 32p. (J). (gr. k-3). tchr. ed. 16.00 (978-0-395-88415-7(2) , Walter Lorraine) Houghton Mifflin Co. Trade & Reference Div.

Hausman, Gerald. Doctor Moledinky's Castle: A Hometown Tale. rev. ed. 1999. 151p. (YA). (gr. 5 up). pap. 10.00 (978-0-9709112-1-6(1)) Irie Bks.

Helldorfer, M. C. Got to Dance. Nakata, Hiroe, illus. 2004. 32p. (J). (gr. k-k). lib. bdg. 17.99 (978-0-385-90865-8(2) , Doubleday Bks. for Young Readers) Random Hse. Children's Bks.

Helprin, Mark. A City in Winter. Van Allsburg, Chris, illus. 2000. 147p. (J). reprint ed. 22.00 (978-0-7881-9103-9(9)) DIANE Publishing Co.

—A City in Winter. unabr. ed. 1998. (J). Class Set. 262.30 incl. audio (978-0-7887-2540-1(8) , 46710); Homework Set. (gr. 6). 58.50 incl. audio (978-0-7887-2235-6(2) , 40719) Recorded Bks., LLC.

Hensley, Sarah M. The Tod Squad Can Go to Town. 2007. (J). bds. (***978-1-57332-444-1(2)***) HighReach Learning, Inc.

Hiley, Vickie. The Sleepy Village. Hiley, Matthew, illus. 2002. 92p. (J). (ps-5). 19.95 (978-0-9717970-0-0(5)) Hiley, Matthew.

Hilton, Nette. In My Backyard. Spudvilas, Anne, illus. 2002. 32p. (YA). (978-0-7344-0185-4(X) , Lothian Bks.) Hachette Livre Australia.

Hipscher, Jerome. White Slavery. 2004. 78p. (YA). pap. 8.95 (978-0-595-31441-6(4)) iUniverse, Inc.

Hirsch, Odo. Hazel Green. 2004. 190p. (J). (gr. 3-7). lib. bdg. 13.60 (978-0-606-30296-8(4)) Tandem Library Bks.

Holt, Kimberly Willis. When Zachary Beaver Came to Town. rev. ed. 1999. 240p. (YA). (gr. 5-9). 17.95 (978-0-8050-6116-1(9) , Holt, Henry & Co. Bks. For Young Readers) Holt, Henry & Co.

—When Zachary Beaver Came to Town. 2000. (J). tchr. ed. 9.95 (978-1-58130-674-3(1)); (YA). stu. ed. 11.95 (978-1-58130-675-0(X)) Novel Units, Inc.

—When Zachary Beaver Came to Town. unabr. ed. 2004. 227p. (J). (gr. 5-9). pap. 36.00 incl. audio (978-0-8072-8394-3(0) , Listening Library) Random Hse. Audio Publishing Group.

—When Zachary Beaver Came to Town. (gr. 5 up). 2003. (Illus.). 256p. (YA). mass mkt. 6.50 (978-0-440-23841-6(2) , Laurel Leaf); 2001. 240p. (J). pap. 6.50 (978-0-440-22904-9(9) , Yearling) Random Hse. Children's Bks.

—When Zachary Beaver Came to Town. 2003. (gr. 5-8). lib. bdg. 14.15 (978-0-613-72251-3(5)); 2000. (J). (978-0-606-20113-1(0)); 2000. (J). (978-0-606-20114-8(9)) Tandem Library Bks.

—When Zachary Beaver Came to Town. l.t. ed. 2000. 224p. (YA). 22.95 (978-0-7862-2515-6(7)) Thorndike Pr.

Hope, Laura Lee. Bobbsey Twins in A Great City. 2006. 77.99 (***978-1-4280-3757-1(8));*** pap. 71.99 (***978-1-4280-3715-1(2)***) IndyPublish.com.

Hopkins, Lee Bennett. Mama. Marchesi, Stephen, illus. 2003. 80p. (YA). (gr. 4-6). pap. 8.95 (978-1-56397-813-5(X)) Boyds Mills Pr.

—Mama. 2000. (gr. 3-6). lib. bdg. 17.60 (978-0-613-78895-3(8)) Tandem Library Bks.

—Mama & Her Boys. Marchesi, Stephen, illus. 2003. 80p. (YA). (gr. 4-6). pap. 8.95 (978-1-56397-814-2(8)) Boyds Mills Pr.

—Mama & Her Boys. 2000. 130p. (J). (gr. 4-7). per. 17.60 (978-0-613-78896-0(6)) Tandem Library Bks.

Howell, Lauren. If I Was the Mayor. Dawson, Sheldon, illus. 2005. 32p. (J). per. (978-0-9735798-1-9(1)) Three Bears Publishing.

Humphrey, Melanie Friedersdorf. The Tiny Town. Biddix, Cheryl L., illus. 1999. 48p. (J). (ps-3). 16.00 (978-0-9658061-7-6(0)) Peaceful Village Publishing.

Hurd, Thacher. Zoom City. 1998. (Growing Tree Ser.). (Illus.). 8p. (J). (ps up). 6.99 (978-0-694-01057-8(X) , Harper Festival) HarperCollins Pubs.

Jam, Teddy. Night Cars. Bellows, Eric, illus. 2000. 32p. (J). (ps-k). 16.95 (978-0-88899-413-4(3)) Groundwood Bks. CAN. *Dist:* Perseus Distribution.

Jarrell, Pamela R. My Town. Linke, Don, Jr. & Carroll, Ken, Jr., illus. l.t. ed. 1998. (Big Bks.). 8p. (J). (ps-k). pap. 10.95 (978-1-57332-125-9(7)) HighReach Learning, Inc.

—My Town. Carroll, Ken, Jr. & Linke, Don, Jr., illus. l.t. ed. 1998. (Cuddle Bks.). 8p. (J). (ps-k). pap. 10.95 (978-1-57332-127-3(3)) HighReach Learning, Inc.

Jenkins, Amanda. City Kids, Country Kids. 2006. 23.00 (***978-1-4108-6184-9(8)***) Benchmark Education Co.

Jennings, Richard W. Mystery in Mt. Mole. 2003. 160p. (J). (gr. 4-6). 15.00 (978-0-618-28478-8(8)) Houghton Mifflin Co. Trade & Reference Div.

Johnston, Tony. Any Small Goodness: A Novel of the Barrio. Colon, Raul, illus. 2001. 128p. (J). (gr. 4 up). 16.95 (978-0-439-18936-1(5) , Blue Sky Pr., The) Scholastic, Inc.

Joosse, Barbara M. Hot City. Gauch, Patricia Lee, ed. Christie, Gregory R., illus. 2004. 32p. (J). (ps-3). 16.99 (978-0-399-23640-2(6) , Philomel) Penguin Group (USA) Inc.

The Journey. 2003. 170p. (YA). per. 10.95 (978-0-9713292-8-7(1)) Aim Higher Bks.

Joyce, Rita. Johnny Peppertoes. 2005. (J). per. 9.95 (978-1-59094-092-1(X)) Jawbone Publishing Corp.

Kauflin, Chris. Smiletown's Big Snow Day. 2006. (J). per. 14.95 (978-0-9785132-0-7(7) , Smiletown Bks.) Smile-a-Lot, LLP.

Keats, Ezra Jack. Goggles. Keats, Ezra Jack, illus. 1998. (Illus.). 40p. (J). 16.99 (978-0-670-88062-1(0) , Viking Juvenile); pap. 6.99 (978-0-14-056440-2(3) , Puffin) Penguin Group (USA) Inc.

Keats, Ezra Jack & Keats, Ezra Jack. Goggles! 1998. (Illus.). (J). (ps-ps). lib. bdg. 15.30 (978-0-8085-2315-4(5)) Tandem Library Bks.

Kerr, M. E. Your Eyes in Stars. 2007. 240p. (J). (gr. 7 up). pap. 6.99 (***978-0-06-075684-0(5)*** , HarperTeen) HarperCollins Pubs.

Kessler, Leonard P. Mr. Pine's Purple House: 40th Anniversary Edition. Kessler, Leonard P., illus. 40th anniv. ed. 2005. (Illus.). 64p. (J). 16.00 (978-1-930900-32-5(5)) Purple Hse. Pr.

Knudsen, Michelle. Carl the Complainer. Cocca-Leffler, Maryann, illus. 2005. 32p. (J). lib. bdg. 20.00 (***978-1-4242-1104-3(2)***) Fitzgerald Bks.

Koertge, Ronald. The Heart of the City. 1998. 128p. (J). (gr. 3-7). 16.99 (978-0-531-33078-4(8) , Orchard Bks.) Scholastic, Inc.

Koldofsky, Eleanor. Clip-Clop. Parkins, David, illus. 2005. 24p. (J). (gr. k-2). 15.95 (978-0-88776-681-7(1)) Tundra Bks., Inc./Livres Toundra, Inc. CAN. *Dist:* Random Hse., Inc.

Kovalski, Maryann. Martha et Edouard. ed. Tr. of Martha et Edouard. (FRE.). (J). pap. 3.99 (978-0-590-74819-3(X)) Scholastic, Inc.

Krakower, Dora B. The Dudley Doohinkle Grocery Store. 2000. 83p. (J). pap. 10.95 (978-0-9643273-4-4(1)) AZURE/BMI.

Krisher, Trudy B. Kinship. 1999. (J). (978-0-606-16170-1(8)) Tandem Library Bks.

Kroll, Virginia K. Faraway Drums. Cooper, Floyd, illus. 1998. 32p. (J). (ps-3). 14.95 (978-0-316-50449-2(1)) Little Brown & Co.

Kurusa. The Streets Are Free. Doppert, Monika, illus. 2000. 50p. (J). (gr. k-5). reprint ed. pap. 7.95 (978-1-55037-370-7(6)) Annick Pr., Ltd. CAN. *Dist:* Firefly Bks., Ltd.

Lambert, Janet. Forever & Ever: A Campbell Story. 2002. (J). per. (978-1-930009-58-5(5) , 800-691-7779) Image Cascade Publishing.

Levithan, David. The Realm of Possibility. 2004. 224p. (gr. 7). (J). lib. bdg. 17.99 (978-0-375-92845-1(6)); (YA). 15.95 (978-0-375-82845-4(1)) Random Hse. Children's Bks. (Knopf Bks. for Young Readers).

Lewis, Elizabeth Foreman. Young Fu of the Upper Yangtze. Low, William, illus. 2007. 320p. (J). pap. (***978-0-8050-8105-3(4));*** (YA). 17.95 (***978-0-8050-8113-8(5)***) Holt, Henry & Co.

Ling, Bettina. The Big City. Ong, Cristina, illus. 1999. (Scholastic At-Home Phonics Reading Program Ser.: Vol. 32). 24p. (J). (978-0-590-68780-5(8)) Scholastic, Inc.

Little People Go to Town. 1998. (Fisher-Price Little People Toddler Skills Workbooks Ser.: Vol. 1). (Illus.). (J). pap. (978-0-7666-0182-6(X) , Honey Bear Bks.) Modern Publishing.

Luna Rising Staff, ed. Elmo's Big Word Book. 2006. (Elmo's World Ser.). (SPA & ENG., Illus.). 12p. (J). 6.95 (978-0-87358-906-2(8) , Luna Rising) Northland Publishing.

Lynch, Chris. Whitechurch. 1999. 256p. (YA). (gr. 12 up). 14.95 (978-0-06-028330-8(0)); (gr. 7 up). 14.89 (978-0-06-028331-5(9)) HarperCollins Pubs.

MacPhail, Catherine. Fighting Back. (Illus.). 128p. (J). 7.95 (978-0-14-038270-9(4)) Penguin Bks., Ltd. GBR. *Dist:* Trafalgar Square Publishing.

Martin, Bill, Jr. Yo Grocer. 2001. (J). 16.95 (978-0-8050-6351-6(X) , Holt, Henry & Co. Bks. For Young Readers) Holt, Henry & Co.

Martin, S. R. Endsville. 2000. (Swampland Trilogy Ser.). 112p. (J). (gr. 7). pap. 4.50 (978-0-439-10568-2(4)) Scholastic, Inc.

Marx, David F. See the City. Revell, Cindy, illus. 2002. (Rookie Reader Skill Set Ser.). 24p. (J). (gr. k-2). pap. 4.95 (978-0-516-25966-6(0) , Children's Pr.) Scholastic Library Publishing.

—See the City. 2001. (gr. k-3). lib. bdg. 12.95 (978-0-613-54445-0(5)) Tandem Library Bks.

Massie. Hushtown: A Peaceful Community. 1999. (Illus.). (J). pap. 5.65 (978-0-7398-0858-0(3)) Steck-Vaughn.

McCloskey, Robert. Centerburg Tales: More Adventures of Homer Price. 1999. (J). (gr. 3-6). lib. bdg. 14.15 (978-0-8085-8462-9(6)) Tandem Library Bks.

McKenzie, Lyn. Betsy, Girl Scout of Woodward Center 1935. 2007. 244p. (YA). pap. 17.95 net. (***978-0-9722839-0-8(0)***) Just Write Bks.

McPhail, David. Sylvie & True. 2007. (Illus.). 32p. (J). (ps). 15.00 (978-0-374-37364-1(7)) Farrar, Straus & Giroux.

Medina, Tony. DeShawn Days. Christie, Gregory R., illus. 2003. 32p. (J). 6.95 (978-1-58430-228-5(3)) Lee & Low Bks., Inc.

Meehl, Brian. Out of Patience. 2006. 304p. (J). (gr. 4-7). 15.95 (978-0-385-73299-4(6) , Delacorte Bks. for Young Readers) Random Hse. Children's Bks.

Merriam, Eve. On My Street. Greenberg, Melanie Hope, illus. 2000. (Growing Tree Ser.). 24p. (J). (ps up). bds. 9.95 (978-0-694-01258-9(0) , Harper Festival) HarperCollins Pubs.

Michels, Dia L. Look What I See! Where Can I Be? in the Neighborhood. Bowles, Michael J. N., illus. 2001. (Look What I See! Where Can I Be? Ser.: Vol. 1). 32p. 16.95 (978-1-930775-00-8(8)) Platypus Media, L.L.C.

Mohr, Nicholasa. Felita. 1999. (J). 12.79 (978-0-606-17413-8(3)); (gr. 3-6). lib. bdg. 13.00 (978-0-8335-4661-6(9)) Tandem Library Bks.

Moncure, Jane Belk. Word Bird Builds a City. 2002. (New Word Bird Library). (Illus.). 32p. (J). (ps-3). 22.79 (978-1-56766-995-4(6)) Child's World, Inc.

Muller, Jorg. The Changing Countryside. 2006. (Illus.). 7p. (J). 17.95 (978-0-9762056-4-7(5)) Heryin Publishing Corp.

My Home Town Has a Hardware Store. 2000. 20p. (J). 7.95 (978-1-931006-52-1(0)) SteppingStones BookCard Pubns., LLC.

My Home Town Has a Hospital. 2000. 20p. (J). 7.95 (978-1-931006-50-7(4)) SteppingStones BookCard Pubns., LLC.

My Home Town Has a School. 2000. 20p. (J). 7.95 (978-1-931006-51-4(2)) SteppingStones BookCard Pubns., LLC.

Myers, Christopher A. Black Cat. Myers, Christopher A., illus. 1999. (Illus.). 40p. (J). (gr. k-3). pap. 16.95 (978-0-590-03375-6(1)) Scholastic, Inc.

Namey, Laura. City Sights. Wise, Noreen, ed. Schneider, Rex, illus. 2000. (Book-a-Day Collection). 32p. (YA). (ps up). pap. 5.95 (978-1-58584-374-9(1)) Huckleberry Pr.

Naylor, Phyllis Reynolds. The Boys Start the War. 2002. 144p. (gr. 4-7). pap. 5.99 (978-0-440-41841-2(0) , Yearling) Random Hse. Children's Bks.

Neubecker, Robert. Wow! City! 2004. (Illus.). 40p. (ps-2). 16.99 (978-0-7868-0951-6(5)) Hyperion Bks. for Children.

Oughton, Jerrie. The War in Georgia. 1999. (978-0-606-16444-3(8)) Tandem Library Bks.

Our Town. 1999. (YA). 9.95 (978-1-56137-625-4(6)) Novel Units, Inc.

Parkinson, Curtis. Mr. Reez's Sneezes. Suomalainen, Sami, illus. 1999. 24p. (J). (ps-2). pap. 5.95 (978-1-55037-556-5(3)) Annick Pr., Ltd. CAN. *Dist:* Firefly Bks., Ltd.

Pascal, Francine. Too Good to Be True. 1999. mass mkt. (978-0-553-24252-2(0)) Random Hse., Inc.

Paulsen, Gary. The Tortilla Factory. 1998. (J). (978-0-606-13857-4(9)) Tandem Library Bks.

—La Tortilleria. Andujar, Gloria de Aragon, tr. Paulsen, Ruth Wright, illus. 1998. (SPA.). 32p. (J). (gr. 3-5). pap. 7.00 (978-0-15-201714-9(3)) Harcourt Children's Bks.

Pearson, Debora. Big City Song! Reed, Lynn Rowe, illus. 2006. 32p. (J). 16.95 (978-0-8234-1988-3(6)) Holiday Hse., Inc.

Pellegrino, Marjorie White. My Grandma's the Mayor. Lund, John, illus. 1999. 32p. (J). (gr. 1-7). (978-1-55798-608-5(8) , 441-6088, Magination Pr.) American Psychological Assn.

Pinkwater, Daniel M. Looking for Bobowicz: A Hoboken Chicken Story. Pinkwater, Jill, illus. 2004. 208p. (J). 15.99 (978-0-06-053554-4(7)) HarperCollins Pubs.

Rappaport, Doreen. The Year of the Paper Menorahs. Alcorn, Stephen, illus. 2000. 32p. (J). 15.99 (978-0-7868-0400-9(9)) Hyperion Bks. for Children.

Raschka, Chris. New York Is English, Chattanooga Is Creek. 2005. (Illus.). 40p. (J). (gr. k-4). 16.95 (978-0-689-84600-7(2) , Atheneum) Simon & Schuster Children's Publishing.

Rey, H. A. Curious George in the Big City. Weston, Martha, illus. 2001. (Curious George Ser.). 24p. (J). (ps-2). 7.95 (978-0-618-15253-7(9)) Houghton Mifflin Co.

Rey, Margret. Curious George in the Big City. Weston, Martha, illus. 2001. (Curious George Ser.). 24p. (J). (gr. k-3). pap. 3.95 (978-0-618-15240-7(7)) Houghton Mifflin Co. Trade & Reference Div.

—Curious George in the Big City. 2001. (gr. k-3). lib. bdg. 11.80 (978-0-613-35500-1(8)) Tandem Library Bks.

Robeson, K. S. Chloe & Bia Bk. 2: Tales from Wind Creek. 2003. 96p. per. 8.95 (978-0-9723530-1-4(1)) Falcor Bks.

Robinson, Sharon. Safe at Home. 2006. 160p. (J). pap. 16.99 (978-0-439-67197-2(3) , Scholastic) Scholastic, Inc.

Ross, Andrea, illus. Chester Goes to the City. 1999. (Chester Earth Ant Ser.). 25p. (J). (gr. k-3). pap. 7.97 (978-1-887683-04-3(6)) Storybook Pr. & Productions.

Ross, Cathy. Tater Town. 2007. (Illus.). 20p. (J). spiral bd. 16.00 (***978-0-9797832-0-3(8)***) Ross, Cathy.

Russo, Marisabina. Mama Talks Too Much. 1999. (Illus.). (J). lib. bdg. (978-0-688-16412-6(9)) HarperCollins Pubs.

—Mama Talks Too Much. Russo, Marisabina, illus. 1999. (Illus.). 288p. (J). (ps-3). 16.00 (978-0-688-16411-9(0)) HarperCollins Pubs.

Rylant, Cynthia. The Case of the Fidgety Fox. Karas, G. Brian, illus. 2004. (High-Rise Private Eyes Ser.: No. 6). 64p. (J). (gr. k-3). pap. 3.99 (978-0-06-009103-3(7) , Harper Trophy) HarperCollins Pubs.

—Old Town in the Green Groves: Laura Ingalls Wilder's Lost Little House Years. LaMarche, Jim, illus. (Little House Ser.). 176p. (J). 2004. pap. 5.99 (978-0-06-440990-2(2) , Harper Trophy); 2002. 15.99 (978-0-06-029561-5(9)) HarperCollins Pubs.

Sarfati, Sonia. La Ville Engloutie. 2003. (Roman Jeunesse Ser.). (FRE.). 96p. (YA). (gr. 4-7). pap. (978-2-89021-179-7(7)) Diffusion du livre Mirabel.

Savoie, Jacques. Une Ville Imaginaire. 2001. (Roman Jeunesse Ser.). (FRE., Illus.). 96p. (YA). (gr. 4-7). pap. (978-2-89021-254-1(8)) Diffusion du livre Mirabel.

Sayre, April Pulley. It's My City! A Singing Map. Roche, Denis, illus. 2001. 32p. (J). (gr. k up). 15.95 (978-0-688-16915-2(5)); 15.89 (978-0-688-16916-9(3)) HarperCollins Pubs.

Scarry, Richard. Busy, Busy Town. Scarry, Richard, illus. 2000. (Golden Bestsellers Ser.). (Illus.). 48p. (J). (ps-2). 14.99 (978-0-307-16803-0(4) , 16803, Golden Bks.) Random Hse. Children's Bks.

Scheving, Magnus & Artful Doodlers Limited Staff. Sleepless in LazyTown. 2006. (LazyTown Ser.). (Illus.). 24p. (J). pap. 3.99 (978-1-4169-0077-1(2) , Simon Spotlight/Nickelodeon) Simon & Schuster Children's Publishing.

Schneider, Peter. Mauerspringer. (GER.). pap. 18.95 (978-3-499-13532-3(9)) Rowohlt Taschenbuch Verlag GmbH DEU. *Dist:* Distribooks, Inc.

Schotz, Leo D. Rooftop. 2005. (Illus.). 32p. (J). 15.95 (978-0-9741319-7-9(0)) 4N Publishing LLC.

Schwartz, Amy. A Teeny Tiny Baby. Schwartz, Amy, illus. 2002. (Illus.). 14.74 (978-1-4046-0277-9(1)) Book Wholesalers, Inc.

Scurlock, Val & Dyer, Olive. Gerry's Story. Evans, Fran, illus. 2002. 31p. pap. 29.95 (978-1-85902-941-1(8)) Beekman Bks., Inc.

Seidler, Tor. The Revenge of Randal Reese-Rat. Helquist, Brett, illus. 2004. 240p. (J). reprint ed. pap. 5.99 (978-0-06-050867-8(1) , Harper Trophy) HarperCollins Pubs.

Shulevitz, Uri. One Monday Morning. 2003. (Illus.). 48p. (J). reprint ed. pap. 6.95 (978-0-374-45648-1(8) , Sunburst) Farrar, Straus & Giroux.

—One Monday Morning. 2003. (ps-2). lib. bdg. 15.25 (978-0-613-71877-6(1)) Tandem Library Bks.

Shusterman, Neal. Red Rider's Hood. 2006. (Dark Fusion Ser.). 192p. (YA). (gr. 7). pap. 6.99 (978-0-14-240678-6(3) , Puffin) Penguin Group (USA) Inc.

Singer, Marilyn. City Lullaby. Cneut, Carll, illus. 2007. 32p. (J). (ps-3). 16.00 (***978-0-618-60703-7(X)*** , Clarion Bks.) Houghton Mifflin Co. Trade & Reference Div.

Sis, Peter. Madlenka's Music. 2005. (J). (978-0-375-82855-3(9)) Random Hse., Inc.

—Madlenka's Soccer Ball. 2005. (J). (978-0-375-82852-2(4)); lib. bdg. (978-0-375-92852-9(9)) Random Hse., Inc.

Smiletown's Little Coloring Book. 2006. (J). 3.99 (978-0-9785132-1-4(5) , Smiletown Bks.) Smile-a-Lot, LLP.

Smiletown's Upside Down. 2007. (J). per. 14.95 (***978-0-9785132-3-8(1)***) Smile-a-Lot, LLP.

Smith, Dana Kessimakis. A Wild Cowboy. Freeman, Laura, illus. 2004. 32p. (ps-1). 14.99 (978-0-7868-1931-7(6)) Hyperion Bks. for Children.

Snicket, Lemony, pseud. The Vile Village. Helquist, Brett, illus. 2001. (Series of Unfortunate Events Ser.: Bk. 7). 272p. (J). (gr. 5 up). 12.99 (978-0-06-440865-3(5)); 7th ed. lib. bdg. 15.89 (978-0-06-028890-7(6)) HarperCollins Pubs.

Spinelli, Eileen. Heat Wave. Lewin, Betsy, illus. 2007. 32p. (J). (gr. k-3). 16.00 (978-0-15-216779-0(X)) Harcourt Trade Pubs.

—Moe McTooth: An Alley Cat's Tale. Bronson, Linda, illus. 2003. 32p. (J). (gr. k-3). tchr. ed. 15.00 (978-0-618-11760-4(1) , Clarion Bks.) Houghton Mifflin Co. Trade & Reference Div.

Stevens, Janet & Stevens, Susan. Shoe Town. 1999. (Green Light Readers Ser.). (978-0-606-16513-6(4)) Tandem Library Bks.

Stewart, Sarah. The Journey. Small, David, illus. 40p. (J). 2001. (gr. 2-6). 16.00 (978-0-374-33905-0(8)); 2006. reprint ed. pap. 6.95 (978-0-374-40010-1(5)) Farrar, Straus & Giroux. (Farrar, Straus & Giroux (BYR)).

—The Journey. Smalls, David, illus. pap. 16.95 incl. audio (978-0-87499-922-8(7)); pap. incl. audio (978-0-87499-924-2(3)); pap. 18.95 incl. audio compact disk (978-1-59112-344-6(5)); pap. incl. audio compact disk (978-1-59112-556-3(1)) Live Oak Media.

—The Journey. 2002. (Illus.). (J). 28.95 incl. audio compact disk (978-1-59112-345-3(3)); 25.95 incl. audio (978-0-87499-923-5(5)) Live Oak Media.

Stewart, Sharon. City of the Dead. 2004. (Illus.). 240p. (YA). pap. 7.95 (978-0-88995-229-4(9)) Red Deer Pr. CAN. *Dist:* Fitzhenry & Whiteside, Ltd.

Summers, Kate. Milly & Tilly: The Story of a Town Mouse & a Country Mouse. 2000. (978-0-606-18433-5(3)) Tandem Library Bks.

Talley, Linda. Toad in Town. Maeno, Itoko, illus. 2001. (Key Concepts in Personal Development Ser.). (gr. k-4). 30p. (J). 89.95 incl. VHS (978-1-55942-165-2(7)); 32p. pap., tchr. ed. 89.95 incl. VHS (978-1-55942-168-3(1) , 9387K3) Marsh Media.

Taylor, Martin D. The Story of Aphid City. Coleman, Catherine N., ed. Taylor, Martin D., illus. 1999. 48p. (YA). (gr. 3-12). pap. 17.95 (978-0-9679114-0-3(0)) Taylor, Kristine.

Thompson, D. R. My New Town: A Flying Naptime Adventure. Thompson, D. R. & Thompson, Dave, illus. 2003. (Naptime Adventure Ser.: Vol. 1). 32p. 14.95 (978-0-9723252-0-2(4)) This New World Publishing, LLC.

Thompson, Kay. Eloise the Ultimate Edition. Knight, Hilary, illus. 2000. 304p. (J). (ps-3). 39.99 (978-0-689-83990-0(1)) Simon & Schuster Children's Publishing.

Tildes, Phyllis Limbacher. The Garden Wall. Tildes, Phyllis Limbacher, illus. 2006. (Illus.). (J). 16.95 (978-1-57091-467-6(2) , 1258423); pap. 7.95 (978-1-57091-468-3(0) , 1258423) Charlesbridge Publishing, Inc.

Il Topo di Citta e il Topo di Campagna. 1999. (ITA., Illus.). 24p. (J). (ps-5). pap. 7.95 (978-88-8148-257-3(6)) European Language Institute ITA. *Dist:* Distribooks, Inc., Midwest European Pubns.

Townsend, Wendy. Lizard Love. 2008. (J). (***978-1-932425-34-5(9)*** , Front Street) Boyds Mills Pr.

Trondheim, Lewis. Harum Scarum: The Spiffy Adventures of McConey, Vol. 1. (Illus.). 48p. (gr. 10 up). pap. 10.95 (978-1-56097-288-4(2)) Fantagraphics Bks.

Tub Tales: The City. 2003. (Illus.). 10p. (J). 6.00 (978-0-9713507-1-7(X) , 842) Panline U.S.A., Inc.

Valgardson, W. D. Garbage Creek: And Other Stories. 1998. (Illus.). 136p. (J). (gr. 3-7). 5.95 (978-0-88899-339-7(0)) Groundwood Bks. CAN. *Dist:* Perseus Distribution.

Van Allsburg, Chris. Bad Day at Riverbend. Van Allsburg, Chris, illus. 2002. (Illus.). (J). 25.28 (978-0-7587-2026-9(2)) Book Wholesalers, Inc.

Walton, Rick. Just Me & 6,000 Rats: A Tale of Conjunctions. Gordon, Mike & Gordon, Carl, illus. 2007. 32p. (J). (ps-3). 15.95 (***978-1-4236-0219-4(6)***) Gibbs Smith, Publisher.

Wegman, William. My Town. Wegman, William, photos by. 1998. (Illus.). 40p. (ps-17). 16.95 (978-0-7868-0410-8(6)) Hyperion Bks. for Children.

Weinstein, Anya. Words Like Weeds Bk. 1: Ring Around the Moon. 2003. (gr. 7-12). lib. bdg. 22.20 (978-0-613-89757-0(9)) Tandem Library Bks.

Weiss, David Cody, et al. It's about Time. 2006. (All Grown Up! Ser.). 64p. (J). pap. 4.99 (978-1-4169-0668-1(1) , Simon Spotlight/Nickelodeon) Simon & Schuster Children's Publishing.

Weston, Martha, illus. Curious George in the Big City. 2001. (Curious George Ser.). 24p. (J). (gr. k-3). tchr. ed. 12.95 (978-0-618-15252-0(0)) Houghton Mifflin Co. Trade & Reference Div.

Whalen, Sharla Scannell. Best Friends under the Sun. 2000. (Faithful Friends Ser.). (Illus.). 64p. (J). (gr. 4). lib. bdg. 21.35 (978-1-57765-228-1(2) , ABDO & Daughters) ABDO Publishing Co.

Whayne, Susanne Santoro. Petropolis. Santoro, Christopher, illus. 2004. 40p. (J). 16.95 (978-1-59354-001-2(9)) Handprint Bks.

Wiggin, Kate Douglas. Rebecca of Sunnybrook Farm. 2003. (Dover Evergreen Classics Ser.). 208p. (J). (gr. 4-7). pap. 3.00 (978-0-486-42845-1(1)) Dover Pubns., Inc.

—Rebecca of Sunnybrook Farm. McClintock, Barbara, illus. 2003. 304p. (J). (gr. 5 up). tchr. ed. 20.00 (978-0-618-34694-3(5)) Houghton Mifflin Co. Trade & Reference Div.

—Rebecca of Sunnybrook Farm. 2005. pap. 30.95 (978-1-4179-1457-9(2)); 2004. reprint ed. pap. 19.95 (978-1-4179-9996-5(9)); 2004. reprint ed. pap. 1.99 (978-1-4179-9946-0(2)) Kessinger Publishing, LLC.

—Rebecca of Sunnybrook Farm. 2003. (Aladdin Classics Ser.). 368p. (J). pap. 4.99 (978-0-689-86001-0(3) , Aladdin) Simon & Schuster Children's Publishing.

—Rebecca of Sunnybrook Farm. Akib, Jamel, illus. 2007. (Classic Starts Ser.). 160p. (J). 4.95 (978-1-4027-3693-3(2)) Sterling Publishing Co., Inc.

—Rebecca of Sunnybrook Farm Book & Charm. 2001. (Charming Classics). (Illus.). 336p. (J). (gr. 3-7). pap. 6.99 (978-0-694-01528-3(8) , Harper Festival) HarperCollins Pubs.

Wild, Margaret. Woolvs in the Sitee. Spudvilas, Anne, illus. 2007. 40p. (YA). (gr. 7 up). 17.95 (***978-1-59078-500-3(2)*** , Front Street) Boyds Mills Pr.

Wilson, Karma. Sakes Alive! A Cattle Drive. Firehammer, Karla, illus. 2005. (J). (***978-1-4156-0890-6(3)***) Little Brown & Co.

Winter, Jonah. Steel Town. Widener, Terry, illus. 2008. 40p. (J). 16.99 (***978-1-4169-4081-4(2)***) Simon & Schuster Children's Publishing.

Woodworth, Viki. Daisy the FireCow. 2003. (Illus.). 32p. (J). (gr. k-2). 15.95 (978-1-56397-934-7(9)) Boyds Mills Pr.

Yaccarino, Dan. Every Friday. 2007. (Illus.). 32p. (J). (ps-2). 16.95 (978-0-8050-7724-7(3)) Holt, Henry & Co.

Yee, Wong Herbert. Did You See Chip? Ovresat, Laura, illus. 2004. (Green Light Readers Level 2 Ser.). 24p. (J). pap. 3.95 (978-0-15-205096-2(5) , Green Light Readers) Harcourt Children's Bks.

—Did You See Chip? 2004. (gr. k-3). lib. bdg. 11.80 (978-0-613-81965-7(9)) Tandem Library Bks.

Younger, Marshal Scott. The Great Kidsboro Takeover. 2000. 126p. (J). (gr. 4-7). pap. 6.99 (978-0-8280-1427-4(2)) Review & Herald Publishing Assn.

Zeitoun, Mary-Lou. 13. 2002. 144p. (YA). 14.95 (978-0-88984-232-8(9)) Porcupine's Quill, Inc. CAN. *Dist:* Univ. of Toronto Pr.

Zimmerman, Andrea Griffing & Clemesha, David. Trashy Town. Yaccarino, Dan, illus. 1999. 32p. (J). (ps-3). 16.99 (978-0-06-027139-8(6)) HarperCollins Pubs.

CITIES AND TOWNS—HISTORY

Bial, Raymond. Cow Towns. 2004. (American Community Ser.). (Illus.). 48p. (J). (gr. 2-5). 29.00 (978-0-516-23706-0(3) , Children's Pr.) Scholastic Library Publishing.

Hinds, Kathryn. The City. 2007. (Life in Elizabethan England Ser.). 80p. (J). lib. bdg. 32.79 (***978-0-7614-2544-1(6)*** , Benchmark Bks.) Cavendish, Marshall Corp.

Jovinelly, Joann & Netelkos, Jason. The Crafts & Culture of a Medieval Town. 2006. (Crafts & Culture of the Middle Ages Ser.). (Illus.). 48p. (J). (gr. 4-8). lib. bdg. 29.25 (978-1-4042-0761-5(9)) Rosen Publishing Group, Inc., The.

Kalman, Bobbie. Boomtowns of the West. 1999. (Life in the Old West Ser.). (Illus.). 32p. (J). (gr. 3-4). lib. bdg. (978-0-7787-0078-4(X)) Crabtree Publishing Co.

—Boomtowns of the West. 1999. (gr. 3-6). lib. bdg. 16.40 (978-0-613-11349-6(7)) Tandem Library Bks.

Steele, Philip. A City Through Time. Dorling Kindersley Publishing Staff, ed. 2004. (Illus.). 32p. (J). 17.99 (978-0-7566-0641-1(1)) Dorling Kindersley Publishing, Inc.

CITIES AND TOWNS—PICTORIAL WORKS

Jakobsen, Kathy. My New York. Jakobsen, Kathy, illus. anniv. rev. ed. 2005. (Illus.). 54p. (J). (gr. k-4). 19.00 (978-0-7567-8588-8(X)) DIANE Publishing Co.

—My New York. Jakobsen, Kathy, illus. anniv. ed. 2003. (Illus.). 48p. (J). (ps-17). 18.95 (978-0-316-92711-6(2)) Little Brown & Co.

CITIES AND TOWNS—PLANNING

see City Planning

CITIES AND TOWNS—POETRY

De Fina, Allan. When a City Leans Against the Sky. Condon, Ken, illus. 2003. 64p. (YA). (gr. 4-6). 9.95 (978-1-56397-137-2(2)) Boyds Mills Pr.

Moore, Lilian. Mural on Second Avenue: And Other City Poems. Karas, Roma, illus. 2005. 32p. (J). (gr. k-2). 16.99 (978-0-7636-1987-9(6)) Candlewick Pr.

CITIES AND TOWNS, RUINED, EXTINCT, ETC.

see also Excavations (Archaeology)

Behr, Alexandra. Lost in Time. 2005. (Real Deal Ser.). (Illus.). 32p. (J). 18.50 (978-0-7910-8771-8(9) , Chelsea Hse.) Facts On File, Inc.

Bial, Raymond. Ghost Towns of the American West. 2001. (Illus.). 48p. (J). (gr. 4-6). tchr. ed. 16.00 (978-0-618-06557-8(1)) Houghton Mifflin Co. Trade & Reference Div.

Church, Alfred John & Gilman, Arthur. The Story of Carthage. 1998. (Illus.). 310p. (YA). (gr. 6-12). reprint ed. pap. 20.00 (978-0-8196-2057-6(2)) Biblo & Tannen Booksellers & Pubs., Inc.

Hook. Lost Cities. 2003. (Mysteries of the Past Ser.). (Illus.). 32p. pap. 7.95 (978-1-4109-0062-3(2)) Raintree.

Hook, Jason. Lost Cities. 2001. (Young Library - Mysteries of the Past). (Illus.). 32p. (J). (gr. 3-5). lib. bdg. 25.69 (978-0-7398-4337-6(0)) Raintree.

—Lost Cities. 2003. (gr. 3-6). lib. bdg. 16.40 (978-0-613-78227-2(5)) Tandem Library Bks.

McEwan, Rebecca. Ciudades perdidas & Lost Cities. 2005. spiral bd. 84.00 (***978-1-4108-5691-3(7)***) Benchmark Education Co.

Morris, Neil. Lost Cities. 2007. (J). (***978-1-59920-108-5(9)***) Smart Apple Media.

Nelson, Julie. Great African Kingdoms. 2001. (Ancient Civilizations Ser.). (Illus.). 48p. (J). lib. bdg. 22.83 (978-0-7398-3581-4(5)) Raintree.

Raum, Elizabeth. Birth & Death of a City. 2006. (Illus.). 32p. (J). (978-1-4109-2597-8(8)); pap. (978-1-4109-2626-5(5)) Steck-Vaughn.

Rinaldo, Denise. Cities of the Dead. 2007. (24/7 - Science Behind the Scenes Ser.). 64p. (J). (gr. 8-12). 26.00 (978-0-531-12079-8(1) , Watts, Franklin) Scholastic Library Publishing.

Rinaldo, Denise. Cities of the Dead: Finding Lost Civilizations. 2008. (24/7: Science Behind the Scenes: Mystery Files Ser.). 64p. (J). pap. 7.95 (***978-0-531-18739-5(X)*** , Watts, Franklin) Scholastic Library Publishing.

CITIES AND TOWNS, RUINED, EXTINCT, ETC.—FICTION

Timothy, Ering. Frog Belly Rat F & G. 2003. (J). bds. 16.99 (978-0-7636-2248-0(6)) Candlewick Pr.

CITIES AND TOWNS—UNITED STATES

Armentrout, David & Armentrout, Patricia. Historic & Famous Cities. 2002. (Guides to State Symbols). (Illus.). 48p. (gr. 3-8). 20.95 (978-1-58952-084-4(X)) Rourke Publishing, LLC.

Bial, Raymond. Cow Towns. 2004. (American Community Ser.). (Illus.). 48p. (J). (gr. 2-5). 29.00 (978-0-516-23706-0(3) , Children's Pr.) Scholastic Library Publishing.

Bowden, Rob. Settlements of the Mississippi River. (Rivers Through Time Ser.). 48p. (J). 2005. pap. 8.50 (978-1-4034-5724-0(7)); 2004. (Illus.). lib. bdg. 29.93 (978-1-4034-5719-6(0)) Heinemann Library.

Brown, Rachel K. Daily Life in a Southern Colonial Town: St. Augustine. 2003. (J). (978-1-58417-014-3(X)); pap. (978-1-58417-077-8(8)) Lake Street Pubs.

Fischer, Laura. Life in a Mississippi River Town. 2003. (Picture the Past Ser.). (Illus.). 32p. (J). lib. bdg. 24.22 (978-1-4034-3797-6(1)); pap. 7.50 (978-1-4034-4283-3(5)) Heinemann Library.

Foster, Mark. Whale Port: A History of Tuckanucket. Foster, Gerald L., illus. 2007. 64p. (J). (gr. 5-9). 18.00 (978-0-618-54722-7(3)) Houghton Mifflin Co.

Geisert, Bonnie. Desert Town. Geisert, Arthur, illus. 2001. (Small Town U. S. A. Ser.). 32p. (J). (gr. k-3). tchr. ed. 16.00 (978-0-395-95387-7(1) , Walter Lorraine) Houghton Mifflin Co. Trade & Reference Div.

Horner, Edith R., ed. California Cities, Towns & Counties 1999. 13th ed. 1999. 608p. pap. 81.00 (978-0-931845-62-8(9)) Morris Publishing.

Kehoe, Stasia Ward. I Live in a Town. 2000. (Kids in Their Communities Ser.). (Illus.). 24p. (J). (gr. 3). lib. bdg. 18.75 (978-0-8239-5440-7(4) , PowerKids Pr.) Rosen Publishing Group, Inc., The.

Liberman, Sherri. A Historical Atlas of the Industrial Age & the Growth of America's Cities. 2005. (United States, Historical Atlases of the Growth of a New Nation Ser.). (Illus.). 64p. (J). (gr. 7-12). lib. bdg. 30.60 (978-1-4042-0205-4(6)) Rosen Publishing Group, Inc., The.

Maurer, Tracy. State Capitals. 1999. (Guide to State Symbols Ser.). (Illus.). 48p. (J). (gr. 3-8). lib. bdg. 29.93 (978-1-57103-296-6(7)) Rourke Publishing, LLC.

Murdico, Suzanne J. Possibilities & Problems in America's New Urban Center: The Rise of Cities. 2003. (America's Industrial Society in the Nineteenth Century Ser.). (Illus.). 32p. (J). pap. (978-0-8239-4277-0(5)) Rosen Publishing Group, Inc., The.

Ryan, Pam Muñoz & Lopez, Rafael. Nuestra California. Lopez, Rafael, illus. 2008. (SPA & ENG.). (***978-1-58089-226-1(4)***) Charlesbridge Publishing, Inc.

C
D

Staeger, Rob. The Boom Towns. 2002. (History of the Old West Ser.). (Illus.). 64p. (YA). (gr. 5 up). lib. bdg. (978-1-59084-068-9(2)) Mason Crest Pubs.

Trumbauer, Lisa. Living in a Small Town. 2005. (Communities Ser.). (Illus.). 24p. (J). 15.93 (978-0-7368-3633-3(0) , Pebble Bks.) Capstone Pr., Inc.

Wirkner, Linda. Learning about Urban Growth in America with Graphic Organizers. 2005. (Graphic Organizers in Social Studies). (J). 19.95 (978-1-4042-2809-2(8) , PowerKids Pr.) Rosen Publishing Group, Inc., The.

CITIES AND TOWNS IN ART

Carroll, Colleen. How Artists See Cities. 1999. (How Artists See Ser.). (Illus.). 48p. (gr. 3-6). 12.95 (978-0-7892-0187-4(9)) Abbeville Pr., Inc.

Pericoli, Matteo. See the City: The Journey of Manhattan Unfurled. 2004. (Illus.). 64p. (J). (gr. 1-5). 15.95 (978-0-375-82469-2(3) , Knopf Bks. for Young Readers) Random Hse. Children's Bks.

Settembrini, Luigi, ed. The Ideal City. 2003. (Illus.). 516p. (YA). (gr. 13 up). pap. 42.95 (978-88-8158-437-6(9)) Charta ITA. *Dist:* D.A.P./Distributed Art Pubs.

CITIZENSHIP

see also Patriotism; Suffrage

Bannatyne-Cugnet, Jo. From Far & Wide: A Canadian Citizenship Scrapbook. Zhang, Song Nan, illus. 2000. 24p. (J). (gr. 2-4). 19.95 (978-0-88776-443-1(6)) Tundra Bks., Inc./Livres Toundra, Inc. CAN. *Dist:* Random Hse., Inc.

Barton, Geoff. Who We Are: A Citizenship Collection. 2007. (Cambridge Collections). (Illus.). 256p. pap. 12.00 ***(*978-0-521-70315-4(8))*** Cambridge Univ. Pr.

Beier, Anne. The Importance of Being an Active Citizen. 2004. (Primary Source Library of American Citizenship). (Illus.). 32p. (J). lib. bdg. (978-1-4042-5089-5(1)) Rosen Publishing Group, Inc., The.

Benchmark Education Staff, compiled by. Eve Bunting's World of Stories & Citizenship. 2005. spiral bd. 225.00 ***(*978-1-4108-5807-8(3))*** Benchmark Education Co.

—GOVT & Citizenship. 2006. spiral bd. 330.00 ***(*978-1-4108-7007-0(3));*** 2006. spiral bd. 109.00 ***(*978-1-4108-7096-4(0));*** 2005. (J). spiral bd. 265.00 ***(*978-1-4108-5767-5(0))*** Benchmark Education Co.

—Social Studies Theme: GOVT & Citizenship. 2005. spiral bd. 115.00 ***(*978-1-4108-5331-8(4))*** Benchmark Education Co.

Bender, Marie. Good Citizenship Counts. 2003. (Character Counts Ser.). (Illus.). 32p. (J). (gr. k-6). lib. bdg. 22.78 (978-1-57765-871-9(X)) ABDO Publishing Co.

Brown, Liz. Civics. 2007. (J). ***(*978-1-59036-766-7(9));*** lib. bdg. ***(*978-1-59036-765-0(0))*** Weigl Pubs., Inc.

Casey & the Growing Spurt: Learning Patriotism, Citizenship, & Character. 2002. (Kamaron Concept Book). 94p. (J). per. 9.99 (978-0-9715713-2-7(5)) Kamaron Institute Pr.

Catalano, Angela. Community Spirit: Symbols of Citizenship in Communities. 2005. (Communities at Work Ser.). (J). 19.95 (978-1-4042-2784-2(9) , PowerKids Pr.) Rosen Publishing Group, Inc., The.

Cherry Lake Publishing, compiled by. Citizens & their Governments. 2008. lib. bdg. ***(*978-1-60279-108-4(2))*** Cherry Lake Publishing.

Citizenship & Character: Understanding America's Civic Values. 2003. 180p. (YA). per. 49.95 incl. cd-rom (978-1-932785-00-5(0)) Bill of Rights Institute, The.

De Capua, Sarah. Becoming a Citizen. 2002. (True Bks.). (Illus.). 48p. (J). (gr. 3-5). pap. 6.95 (978-0-516-27366-2(3)); 25.00 (978-0-516-22331-5(3)) Scholastic Library Publishing. (Children's Pr.).

—Becoming a Citizen. 2002. (gr. 3-6). lib. bdg. 15.25 (978-0-613-53954-8(0)) Tandem Library Bks.

Doak, Robin S. Citizenship. (J). 2003. pap. 7.50 (978-1-4109-0329-7(X)); 2002. (Illus.). 32p. lib. bdg. 24.26 (978-0-7398-5779-3(7)) Raintree.

—Citizenship. 2003. (gr. k-3). lib. bdg. 15.90 (978-0-613-78297-5(6)) Tandem Library Bks.

Esparza, Thomas, Jr. & La Madrid Esparza, Esther. Citizenship, the 100 Questions: Ciudadania, Las Cien Preguntas. 3rd ed. 2002. Tr. of Ciudadania, Las Cien Preguntas. (SPA., Illus.). 64p. (J). per. 9.95 (978-1-879817-26-5(8) , Bilingual) Star Light Pr.

Graves, Ginny. Picture This! An Exercise in Responsible Citizenry. 2001. (Illus.). 125p. (YA). (gr. 5-9). pap. 399.00 (978-0-9632033-4-2(7)) Ctr. for Understanding the Built Environment.

Hamilton, John. Becoming a Citizen. 2005. (Government in Action! Ser.). (J). (gr. k-6). lib. bdg. 22.78 (978-1-59197-642-4(1)) ABDO Publishing Co.

Harcourt School Publishers Staff. Becoming a Citizen. 3rd ed. 2002. (Horizons Ser.). (Illus.). (J). pap. 5.50 (978-0-15-333427-6(4)) Harcourt Schl. Pubs.

—Citizenship Advanced Level. 3rd ed. 2002. (Trophies Reading Program Ser.). (Illus.). pap. 5.10 (978-0-15-323302-9(8)) Harcourt Schl. Pubs.

—Good Citizen, No. 2. 2nd ed. 2003. (Illus.). (gr. 1). pap. 139.70 (978-0-15-337557-6(4)) Harcourt Schl. Pubs.

—Today I Am an American: Independent Reader. 3rd ed. 2002. (Trophies Reading Program Ser.). (Illus.). (J). pap. 2.90 (978-0-15-325471-0(8)) Harcourt Schl. Pubs.

—Today I Am an American Below Level. 3rd ed. 2002. (Trophies Reading Program Ser.). (Illus.). pap. 5.10 (978-0-15-323242-8(0)) Harcourt Schl. Pubs.

Holt, Rinehart and Winston Staff. American Civics: Community Service Handbook. 3rd ed. 2002. pap. 25.80 (978-0-03-067689-5(4)) Holt, Rinehart & Winston.

—American Civics: Simulations & Case Studies. 3rd ed. 2002. pap. 25.80 (978-0-03-067704-5(1)) Holt, Rinehart & Winston.

Keller, Ellen. Kids Are Citizens. 2002. (National Geographic Reading Expeditions Ser.). (Illus.). 32p. (J). pap. (978-0-7922-8683-7(9)) National Geographic Society.

Kishel, Ann-Marie. Citizenship. 2007. (First Step Nonfiction Ser.). 24p. (J). (gr. k-2). 18.60 (978-0-8225-6398-3(3) , Lerner Pubns.) Lerner Publishing Group.

Loewen, Nancy. We Live Here Too! Kids Talk about Good Citizenship. Wesley, Omarr, illus. 2004. (Kids Talk Ser.). 32p. (C). (gr. 2-5). pap. 23.93 (978-1-4048-0035-9(2)) Picture Window Bks.

Luthringer, Chelsea. So What Is Citizenship Anyway? 2000. (Students Guide to American Civics Ser.). 48p. (YA). lib. bdg. 23.95 (978-0-8239-3450-8(0) , Rosen Central) Rosen Publishing Group, Inc., The.

—So What Is Citzenship Anyway? 1999. (Student's Guide to American Civics Ser.). (Illus.). 48p. (YA). (gr. 5-8). lib. bdg. 23.95 (978-0-8239-3097-5(1) , CVCITI, Rosen Central) Rosen Publishing Group, Inc., The.

McGraw-Hill Staff. Civics Today: Citizenship, Economics, & You. 2nd ed. 2004. (C). stu. ed. 82.64 (978-0-07-860970-1(4) , 9780078609701) Glencoe/McGraw-Hill.

—Civics Today: Citizenship, Economics & You. 2nd ed. 2005. cd-rom 106.64 (978-0-07-866528-8(0) , 9780078665288) Glencoe/McGraw-Hill.

—Civics Today: Citizenship, Economics & You, Active Reading Note-Taking Guide. 2nd ed. 2004. (C). stu. ed. 18.00 (978-0-07-865611-8(7) , 9780078656118) Glencoe/McGraw-Hill.

—Civics Today: Citizenship, Economics & You, Spanish Reading Essentials. 2nd ed. 2004. (SPA.). stu. ed., wbk. ed. 18.00 (978-0-07-865613-2(3) , 9780078656132) Glencoe/McGraw-Hill.

—Civics Today: Citizenship, Economy & You, Student Edition. 3rd ed. 2006. 86.64 (978-0-07-874574-4(8) , 9780078745744) Glencoe/McGraw-Hill.

O'Connor, Barbara. Citizenship. 2004. (Illus.). pap. 7.95 (978-0-8225-4743-3(0)) Lerner Publishing Group.

Riehecky, Janet. Citizenship. 2005. (First Facts Ser.). (Illus.). 24p. (J). 21.26 (978-0-7368-3676-0(4)) Capstone Pr., Inc.

—Citizenship. (Everyday Character Education Ser.). 24p. (J). pap. 6.95 (978-0-7368-5144-2(5)) Capstone Pr., Inc.

Roles, Rights & Responsibilities. 2002. (Illus.). (YA). (gr. 6-8). (978-1-4109-0133-0(5)) Raintree.

Salzmann, Mary Elizabeth. I Am a Good Citizen. 2003. (Building Character Ser.). (Illus.). 24p. (J). (ps-3). lib. bdg. 19.93 (978-1-57765-825-2(6)) ABDO Publishing Co.

Schlesinger, Arthur & Israel, Fred, eds. My Fellow Citizens. (I Do Solemnly Swear Ser.). 448p. (gr. 9). pap. 18.95 ***(*978-0-7910-9725-0(0)*** , Checkmark Bks.) Facts On File, Inc.

Small, Mary. Being a Good Citizen: A Book about Citizenship. Previn, Stacey, illus. 2005. (Way to Be! Ser.). 24p. (J). (gr. k-2). lib. bdg. 22.60 (978-1-4048-1050-1(1)) Picture Window Bks.

—Citizenship Is. Ouren, Todd, illus. 2004. (J). lib. bdg. (978-1-4048-0274-2(6)) Picture Window Bks.

Steele, Philip. Citizenship. 2001. (Illus.). 92p. 24.99 (978-0-237-52047-2(8) , Evans Brothers, Limited) Evans Publishing Group GBR. *Dist:* Independent Pubs. Group.

Stout, Carol A. Proud to Be an American, 1. 2004. (Illus.). 168p. pap. 6.95 (978-1-886161-08-5(9)) Millennium Marketing & Publishing.

Taylor, Ina. Directions, Bk. 3. 2002. (Illus.). 128p. (J). (gr. 2-4). pap., stu. ed. 24.00 (978-0-7487-6389-4(9)) Nelson Thornes Ltd. GBR. *Dist:* Trans-Atlantic Pubns., Inc.

Teitelbaum, Michael. The U. S. Constitution. 2004. (Our Government & Citizenship Ser.). (Illus.). 32p. (J). (gr. 2-6). 27.07 (978-1-59296-329-4(3)) Child's World, Inc.

Watson, Susan. Improving the Quality of Life. 2003. 32p. (J). lib. bdg. 24.25 (978-1-58340-403-4(1)) Smart Apple Media.

We Live Here Too! (Kids Talk Ser.). 32p. (J). 8.95 (978-1-4048-0368-8(8)) Picture Window Bks.

CITRUS FRUITS—FICTION

Polacco, Patricia. An Orange for Frankie. Polacco, Patricia, illus. 2004. (Illus.). 48p. (J). (gr. 1-5). 16.99 (978-0-399-24302-8(X) , Philomel) Penguin Group (USA) Inc.

CITY GOVERNMENT

see Municipal Government

CITY LIFE

see Cities and Towns

CITY PLANNING

see also Housing

Houghton, Gillian. Careers in Urban Planning. 2005. (Career Resource Library). (Illus.). 192p. (YA). (gr. 7-12). lib. bdg. 26.50 (978-0-8239-3658-8(9)) Rosen Publishing Group, Inc., The.

Jaffe, Charlotte & Doherty, Barbara. Create a City: A Complete Framework for Students to Use in Creating an Original City. Armstrong, Beverly, illus. 1999. 88p. (J). (gr. 5-8). pap., stu. ed. 11.99 (978-0-88160-311-8(2) , LW-380, Learning Works, The) Creative Teaching Pr., Inc.

Lomberg, Michelle. Avoiding Gridlock. Schwartzenberger, Tina, ed. 2004. (Understanding Global Issues). (Illus.). 56p. (J). (gr. 10-12). lib. bdg. (978-1-58340-357-0(4)) Weigl Pubs., Inc.

Snedden, Robert. The Growth of Cities. 2004. (Earth's Changing Landscape Ser.). (J). lib. bdg. 28.50 (978-1-58340-474-4(0)) Smart Apple Media.

CIVICS

see Citizenship; Political Science; United States—Politics and Government

CIVIL DISOBEDIENCE

see Government, Resistance to

CIVIL DISORDERS

see Riots

CIVIL ENGINEERING

see also Bridges; Canals; Dams; Excavation; Harbors; Hydraulic Engineering; Mechanical Engineering; Mining Engineering; Railroad Engineering; Rivers; Roads; Streets; Subways; Surveying; Tunnels; Water-Supply

Allman, Barbara. Eiffel Tower. 2003. (Building World Landmarks Ser.). (Illus.). 48p. (J). 24.95 (978-1-56711-315-0(X) , Blackbirch Pr., Inc.) Thomson Gale.

Bauer, David. People Change the Land. 2003. (Illus.). 17p. (J). 15.93 (978-0-7368-2929-8(6)); pap. (978-0-7368-2888-8(5)) Yellow Umbrella Pr.

Borchelt, Kelly L. The Longest Tunnel. 2004. (Extreme Places Ser.). (Illus.). 48p. (J). 26.20 (978-0-7377-1882-9(X) , Greenhaven Pr., Inc.) Thomson Gale.

Caney, Steven. Steven Caney's Ultimate Building Book. House, Lauren, illus. 2006. 608p. (J). (gr. 4-8). 29.95 (978-0-7624-0409-4(4) , Running Pr. Kids) Running Pr. Bk. Pubs.

Greene, Meg. The Eiffel Tower. 2000. (Building History Ser.). (Illus.). 96p. (YA). (gr. 6-9). 32.45 (978-1-56006-826-6(4) , Lucent Bks.) Thomson Gale.

Howey, Paul M. Working in Construction. 1998. (Exploring Careers Ser.). (J). 17.95 (978-0-8225-1764-1(7)) Lerner Publishing Group.

Klobuchar, Lisa. How Did They Do That? 2005. (Real Deal Ser.). (Illus.). 32p. (J). pap. (978-0-7608-9633-4(X)) Sundance/Newbridge Educational Publishing.

Levy, Matthys & Panchyk, Richard. Engineering the City: How Infrastructure Works - Projects & Principles for Beginners. 2000. (Illus.). 144p. (J). (gr. 4 up). pap. 14.95 (978-1-55652-419-6(6)) Chicago Review Pr., Inc.

Nicholson, John. Building the Sydney Harbour Bridge. Nicholson, John, illus. 2000. (Illus.). 32p. (J). (978-1-86508-259-2(7)); mass mkt. (978-1-86508-258-5(9)) Allen & Unwin.

Oxlade, Chris. Science Museum Book Construction. (Illus.). 128p. (J). pap. 8.99 (978-0-340-68994-3(3) , Hodder & Stoughton) Hodder General Publishing Division GBR. *Dist:* Trafalgar Square Publishing.

Rogers, Hal. Earthmovers. 1999. (Machines at Work Ser.). (Illus.). 24p. (J). (ps-3). 21.36 (978-1-56766-652-6(3)) Child's World, Inc.

Rooney, Thomas L. Tobey Boland & the Blackstone Canal. Donovan, Patte, illus. 2005. 30p. (J). (978-1-929039-30-2(1)) Ambassador Bks., Inc.

Shepard, Daniel. La Gente cambia la Tierra. 2005. Tr. of People Change the Land. (SPA., Illus.). 16p. (J). (gr. 1 up). lib. bdg. 15.93 (978-0-7368-4179-5(2)) Capstone Pr., Inc.

Sullivan, George. Built to Last: Building America's Amazing Bridges, Dams, Tunnels, & Skyscrapers. 2005. (Illus.). 128p. (J). (gr. 4-7). pap. 18.99 (978-0-439-51737-9(0) , Scholastic Nonfiction) Scholastic, Inc.

Woods, Mary B. & Woods, Michael. Ancient Construction: From Tents to Towers. 2005. (Ancient Technology Ser.). (Illus.). 96p. (gr. 6-12). 25.26 (978-0-8225-2998-9(X)) Lerner Publishing Group.

Zaunders, Bo. The Great Bridge-Building Contest. Munro, Roxie, illus. 2004. 32p. (J). (gr. k-4). 16.95 (978-0-8109-4929-4(6)) Abrams, Harry N. , Inc.

CIVIL ENGINEERING—FICTION

Hancock, H. Irving. The Young Engineers in Arizona or Laying Tracks on the Man Killer Quicksand. 2004. reprint ed. pap. 1.99 (978-1-4192-8913-2(6)) Kessinger Publishing, LLC.

CIVIL GOVERNMENT

see Political Science; United States—Politics and Government

CIVIL LIBERTY

see Liberty

CIVIL RIGHTS

see also Assembly, Right of; Freedom of Religion; Freedom of Speech; Freedom of the Press; Liberty

also subdivision Civil rights under classes of persons and names of ethnic groups

Barbour, Scott. Individual Rights & the Police. 2006. 244p. (gr. 10-12). 36.20 (978-0-7377-2505-6(2) , Greenhaven Pr., Inc.) Thomson Gale.

Bill of Rights Institute, text. Celebrate the Constitution. 2007. 20p. (YA). 4.95 ***(*978-1-932785-30-2(2))*** Bill of Rights Institute, The.

Burns, Kate. Gay Rights Activists. 2005. (History Makers Ser.). (Illus.). 112p. (YA). (gr. 7-10). lib. bdg. 29.95 (978-1-59018-599-5(4) , Lucent Bks.) Thomson Gale.

Civil Rights DBA. 2001. spiral bd. 16.95 (978-1-56004-121-4(8)) Social Studies Schl. Service.

Ditchfield, Christin. Knowing Your Civil Rights. 2004. (True Bks.). (Illus.). 48p. (J). (gr. 3-5). pap. 6.95 (978-0-516-27910-7(6) , Children's Pr.) Scholastic Library Publishing.

Donnelly, Karen J. The Bill of Rights. 2003. (Primary Source Library of American Citizenship). (Illus.). 32p. (J). pap. (978-1-4042-5087-1(5)) Rosen Publishing Group, Inc., The.

Duckworth, Katie. Education. 2004. (Children's Rights Ser.). (J). lib. bdg. 27.10 (978-1-58340-419-5(8)) Smart Apple Media.

Engelbert, Phillis. American Civil Rights: Biographies. 1999. (American Civil Rights Reference Library). (Illus.). xl, 203p. (J). (gr. 4-7). 67.00 (978-0-7876-3173-4(6) , GML00402-112774, UXL) Thomson Gale.

—Understanding American Civil Rights, 2 vols. 1999. (U-X-L American Civil Rights Reference Library). (Illus.). (J). (978-0-7876-3174-1(4) , UXL) Thomson Gale.

Esherick, Joan. Guaranteed Rights: The Legislation that Protects Youth with Special Needs. 2004. (Youth with Special Needs Ser.). (Illus.). 128p. (J). lib. bdg. (978-1-59084-742-8(3)) Mason Crest Pubs.

Faherty, Sara. Victims & Victims' Rights. Sarat, Austin, ed. 1999. (Crime, Justice & Punishment Ser.). (Illus.). 80p. (YA). (gr. 7-12). 30.00 (978-0-7910-4308-0(8) , Chelsea Hse.) Facts On File, Inc.

Fitzgerald, Stephanie. Struggling for Civil Rights. 2004. (On the Front Line Ser.). (Illus.). 48p. (J). pap. 8.95 (978-1-4109-1474-3(7)); (gr. 4-6). 29.93 (978-1-4109-1467-5(4)) Raintree.

Freedman, Russell. In Defense of Liberty: The Story of America's Bill of Rights. 2003. (Illus.). 208p. (J). (gr. 4-6). tchr. ed. 24.95 (978-0-8234-1585-4(6)) Holiday Hse., Inc.

Fridell, Ron. Cruzan V. Missouri & the Right to Die Debate: Debating Supreme Court Decisions. 2005. (Debating Supreme Court Decisions Ser.). (Illus.). 128p. (J). (gr. 8 up). lib. bdg. 26.60 (978-0-7660-2356-7(7)) Enslow Pubs., Inc.

Gogerly, Liz. Nelson Mandela. 2003. (Leading Lives Ser.). (Illus.). 64p. (J). lib. bdg. 28.50 (978-1-4034-0834-1(3)) Heinemann Library.

Gottfried, Ted. Homeland Security vs. Constitutional Rights. 2003. (Single Titles Ser.). (Illus.). 128p. (gr. 7 up). lib. bdg. 24.90 (978-0-7613-2862-9(9) , Twenty-First Century Bks.) Lerner Publishing Group.

Harrison, Jean. Home. 2004. (Children's Rights Ser.). (J). lib. bdg. 27.10 (978-1-58340-418-8(X)) Smart Apple Media.

Haskins, James. Freedom Rides: Journey for Justice. 2005. (Illus.). 88p. (J). (ps-17). pap. 10.95 (978-0-940975-94-1(7) , Sankofa Bks.) Just Us Bks., Inc.

Individual Rights & Civic Responsibility, 8 bks. Incl. Civil Rights. Seidman, David L. lib. bdg. 26.50 (978-0-8239-3231-3(1)); Right to Bear Arms. Sommers, Michael A. lib. bdg. 26.50 (978-0-8239-3232-0(X)); Right to Free Speech. Fontanetta, Karen & Isler, Claudia. lib. bdg. 26.50 (978-0-8239-3234-4(6)); Right to Freedom from Searches. Rocha, Toni L. & Ramen, Fred. lib. bdg. 26.50 (978-0-8239-3237-5(0)); Right to Privacy. Garrett, Brandon. lib. bdg. 26.50 (978-0-8239-3236-8(2)); Right to Vote. Isler, Claudia. lib. bdg. 26.50 (978-0-8239-3235-1(4)); Rights of the Accused. Ramen, Fred. lib. bdg. 26.50 (978-0-8239-3238-2(9)); Women's Rights. Ching, Jacqueline & Ching, Juliet. lib. bdg. 26.50 (978-0-8239-3233-7(8)); 64p. (YA). (gr. 7-12). 2001. (Illus.). Set lib. bdg. 212.00 (978-0-8239-9203-4(9)) Rosen Publishing Group, Inc., The.

Jacobs, Dale W., ed. World Book Focus on Terrorism. 2002. (Illus.). 160p. (J). (978-0-7166-1295-7(X)) World Bk., Inc.

Johnson, Terry. Legal Rights, 6 vols. 2005. (American Rights Ser.). (Illus.). 152p. (YA). (gr. 4-9). per. 35.00 (978-0-8160-5665-1(X)) Facts On File, Inc.

Malloy, Stephanie M. & Martinez, Lorena. It's up to You(th) A Tool for Young Civil Rights Activists. 2000. (Illus.). 32p. (YA). (gr. 6-12). (978-0-89292-258-1(3)) Education Development Ctr., Inc.

McGregor, Tony L., illus. Victory Week. 1998. 40p. (J). lib. bdg. 22.95 (978-0-9634016-9-4(6) , Deaf Life Pr.) MSM Productions, Ltd.

Miller, Debra. The Patriot Act. 2007. (Hot Topics Ser.). (Illus.). 128p. (J). (gr. 7-10). 32.45 ***(*978-1-59018-981-8(7)*** , Lucent Bks.) Thomson Gale.

Murray, Julie. Martin Luther King, Jr. Day. 2005. (Buddy Book Ser.). (Illus.). 24p. (J). (gr. k-4). lib. bdg. 21.35 (978-1-59197-589-2(1)) ABDO Publishing Co.

Pendergast, Tom, et al. Constitutional Amendments Vol. 1: From Freedom of Speech to Flag Burning, 3 vols. Grunow, Elizabeth Shaw, ed. 2001. xlviii, 528p. (J). (978-0-7876-4866-4(3) , UXL) Thomson Gale.

—Constitutional Amendments Vol. 2: From Freedom of Speech to Flag Burning, 3 vols. Grunow, Elizabeth Shaw, ed. 2001. xlviii, 528p. (J). (978-0-7876-4867-1(1) , UXL) Thomson Gale.

—Constitutional Amendments Vol. 3: From Freedom of Speech to Flag Burning, 3 vols. Grunow, Elizabeth Shaw, ed. 2001. xlviii, 528p. (J). (978-0-7876-4868-8(X) , UXL) Thomson Gale.

Reef, Catherine. A. Philip Randolph: Union Leader & Civil Rights Crusader. 2001. (African-American Biographies Ser.). (Illus.). 128p. (J). (gr. 6-12). lib. bdg. 26.60 (978-0-7660-1544-9(0)) Enslow Pubs., Inc.

Rees, Peter. Liberty: Blessing or Burden? 2007. (Shockwave: the Human Experience Ser.). (Illus.). 36p. (J). (gr. 4-6). lib. bdg. 25.00 ***(*978-0-531-17760-0(2)*** , Children's Pr.) Scholastic Library Publishing.

Rivera, Sheila. The Bill of Rights. 2005. (American Moments Ser.). (J). (gr. 4-8). lib. bdg. 25.65 (978-1-59197-279-2(5)) ABDO Publishing Co.

Rondeau, Amanda. Freedom. 2003. (United We Stand Ser.). (Illus.). 24p. (J). (ps-3). lib. bdg. 19.93 (978-1-57765-878-8(7)) ABDO Publishing Co.

Rossi, Anna Maria. The Struggle for Equality: 1955-1975. 2004. (Illus.). 40p. (J). (978-0-7922-4559-9(8)) National Geographic Society.

Shull, Jodie A. Words of Promise: A Story about James Weldon Johnson. Stetz, Ken, illus. 2006. (Creative Minds Biography Ser.). 64p. (J). (gr. 4-7). 22.60 (978-1-57505-755-2(7) , Carolrhoda Bks.) Lerner Publishing Group.

Spangenburg, Ray & Moser, Diane. Civil Liberties. 2005. (Open for Debate Ser.). (Illus.). 143p. (J). (978-0-7614-1886-3(5) , Benchmark Bks.) Cavendish, Marshall Corp.

Stefoff, Rebecca. Security vs. Privacy. 2007. (Open for Debate Ser.). (J). lib. bdg. ***(*978-0-7614-2578-6(0)*** , Benchmark Bks.) Cavendish, Marshall Corp.

Struggling for Civil Rights 6-Pack. 2004. (Illus.). pap. 48.35 (978-1-4109-1481-1(X)) Raintree.

Telgen, Diane. Brown V. Board of Education. 2005. (Defining Moments Ser.). (Illus.). 246p. (YA). (gr. 8 up). lib. bdg. 49.00 (978-0-7808-0775-4(8)) Omnigraphics, Inc.

Wheeler, Jill C. Mary Robinson. 2004. (Women of the World Ser.). (J). (978-1-59197-617-2(0)) ABDO Publishing Co.

Winters, Rob. Freedom of Assembly & Petition. 2006. (Illus.). 128p. (J). (gr. 10-12). 33.70 (978-0-7377-3544-4(9) , Greenhaven Pr., Inc.) Thomson Gale.

CIVIL RIGHTS—UNITED STATES

Adler, David A. Dr. Martin Luther King, Jr. A Historical Perspective. Bootman, Colin, illus. 48p. (J). (gr. k-3). pap. 4.95 (978-0-8234-1803-9(0)) Holiday Hse., Inc.

American Rights Set. 2005. (American Rights Ser.). 128-160p. (gr. 4-9). 210.00 (978-0-8160-6488-5(1)) Facts On File, Inc.

America's Battle Against Terrorism. 2005. (Current Controversies Ser.). 208p. (YA). (gr. 10-13). lib. bdg. 36.20 (978-0-7377-2783-8(7) , Greenhaven Pr., Inc.) Thomson Gale.

Anderson, Dale. The Seneca Falls Women's Rights Convention. 2004. (Landmark Events in American History Ser.). (Illus.). 48p. (J). (gr. 5 up). pap. 11.95 (978-0-8368-5417-6(9)); lib. bdg. 30.00 (978-0-8368-5389-6(X)) Stevens, Gareth Inc. (World Almanac Library).

Armentrout, David & Armentrout, Patricia. The Bill of Rights. (Documents that Shaped the Nation Ser.). 48p. 2005. (Illus.). (gr. 4-6). 20.95 (978-1-59515-234-3(2)); 2004. pap. 7.95 (978-1-59515-329-6(2)) Rourke Publishing, LLC.

—La Carta de Derechos. 2005. (SPA.). (978-1-59515-646-4(1)) Rourke Publishing, LLC.

Brinkman, Patricia. The Bill of Rights. 2006. pap. 42.00 (*978-1-4108-6452-9(9)) Benchmark Education Co.

Burgan, Michael. The Bill of Rights. 2001. (We the People Ser.). (Illus.). 48p. (J). (gr. 4 up). lib. bdg. 21.26 (978-0-7565-0151-8(2)) Compass Point Bks.

—The Reconstruction Amendments. 2006. (Illus.). 48p. (J). (gr. 4-6). 23.93 (978-0-7565-1636-9(6)) Compass Point Bks.

Civil Rights. 2003. 48p. (gr. 4-6). stu. ed. 5.99 (978-0-7424-0083-2(2) , IF2823) School Specialty Publishing.

Civil Rights. 2003. (Illus.). 238p. (YA). (gr. 8-8). lib. bdg. 33.25 (978-0-613-73929-0(9)) Tandem Library Bks.

Crewe, Sabrina & Ingram, Scott. The 1963 Civil Rights March. 2005. (Events That Shaped America Ser.). (Illus.). 32p. (J). lib. bdg. 24.67 (978-0-8368-3411-6(9)) Stevens, Gareth Inc.

Cunningham, Kevin. Power to the People: How We Elect the President & Other Officials. 2004. (Our Government & Citizenship Ser.). (Illus.). 32p. (J). (gr. 2-6). 27.07 (978-1-59296-322-5(6)) Child's World, Inc.

DesChenes, Betz, ed. American Civil Rights: Primary Sources. 1999. (American Civil Rights Reference Library). (Illus.). 240p. (YA). (gr. 6). 67.00 (978-0-7876-3170-3(1) , GML00402-112771, UXL) Thomson Gale.

Ditchfield, Christin. Knowing Your Civil Rights. 2004. (True Bks.). (Illus.). 48p. (J). (gr. 3-5). pap. 6.95 (978-0-516-27910-7(6) , Children's Pr.) Scholastic Library Publishing.

Engelbert, Phillis. American Civil Rights: Almanac, 2 Vols., Vol. 6. 1999. (U-X-L American Civil Rights Reference Library). (Illus.). 400p. (J). 63.00 (978-0-7876-3171-0(X) , GML14099-112773, UXL) Thomson Gale.

Ferris, Jeri Chase. Demanding Justice: A Story about Mary Ann Shadd Cary. Smith, Kimanne, illus. 2003. 64p. (J). 6.95 (978-0-87614-928-7(X) , Carolrhoda Bks.); (gr. 4-8). 22.60 (978-1-57505-177-2(X)) Lerner Publishing Group.

—Demanding Justice: A Story about Mary Ann Shadd Cary. 2003. (gr. 3-6). lib. bdg. 14.10 (978-0-613-58898-0(3)) Tandem Library Bks.

Fireside, Bryna J. Cruzan vs. Missouri: The Right to Die Case. 1999. (Landmark Supreme Court Cases Ser.). (Illus.). 128p. (YA). (gr. 6-12). lib. bdg. 20.95 (978-0-7660-1088-8(0)) Enslow Pubs., Inc.

Freedman, Jeri. America Debates Privacy Versus Security. 2007. lib. bdg. (*978-1-4042-1929-8(3)) Rosen Publishing Group, Inc., The.

Freedom of Speech DBA. 2003. spiral bd. 16.95 (978-1-56004-150-4(1)) Social Studies Schl. Service.

Freedom of the Press DBA. 2003. spiral bd. 16.95 (978-1-56004-149-8(8)) Social Studies Schl. Service.

Gillam, Scott. Civil Liberties. 2007. (Essential Viewpoints Ser.). (ENG., Illus.). 112p. (YA). (gr. 7-9). lib. bdg. 32.79 (*978-1-59928-858-1(3) , Essential Library) ABDO Publishing Co.

Hamilton, John. The Bill of Rights. 2005. (Government in Action! Ser.). (Illus.). 31p. (J). (gr. k-6). lib. bdg. 22.78 (978-1-59197-643-1(X)) ABDO Publishing Co.

Hatt, Christine. Martin Luther King, Jr. 2004. (Judge for Yourself Ser.). (Illus.). 64p. (J). pap. (978-0-8368-5565-4(5)); (gr. 5 up). lib. bdg. 30.00 (978-0-8368-5562-3(0)) Stevens, Gareth Inc. (World Almanac Library).

Horn, Geoffrey M. The Bill of Rights & Other Amendments. 2003. (World Almanac Library of American Government). (Illus.). 48p. (J). (gr. 5 up). pap. 14.95 (978-0-8368-5480-0(2)); lib. bdg. 30.00 (978-0-8368-5475-6(6)) Stevens, Gareth Inc. (World Almanac Library).

Hossell, Karen Price. The Bill of Rights. 2003. (Heinemann Know It Ser.). (Illus.). 48p. (J). 27.07 (978-1-4034-0801-3(7)); pap. 8.50 (978-1-4034-3430-2(1)) Heinemann Library.

Hudson, David L., Jr. The Bill of Rights: The First Ten Amendments of the Constitution. 2002. (Constitution Ser.). (Illus.). 128p. (J). (gr. 6-12). lib. bdg. 26.60 (978-0-7660-1903-4(9)) Enslow Pubs., Inc.

Hunter, Miranda. Story Of Latino Civil Rights: Fighting for Justice. 2005. (Illus.). 112p. (J). lib. bdg. (978-1-59084-934-7(5)) Mason Crest Pubs.

Kowalski, Kathiann M. A Pro/con Look at Homeland Security: Safety vs. Liberty After 9/11. 2008. (Issues in Focus Today Ser.). (Illus.). 104p. (J). (gr. 6 up). lib. bdg. 31.93 (*978-0-7660-2914-9(X)) Enslow Pubs., Inc.

Landau, Elaine. The Civil Rights Movement in America. 2003. (Cornerstones of Freedom, 2ND Ser.). (Illus.). 48p. (J). 26.00 (978-0-516-24219-4(9) , Children's Pr.) Scholastic Library Publishing.

Litwin, Laura Baskes. Fannie Lou Hamer: Fighting for the Right to Vote. 2002. (African-American Biographies Ser.). (Illus.). 128p. (J). (gr. 6-12). lib. bdg. 26.60 (978-0-7660-1772-6(9)) Enslow Pubs., Inc.

Mara, Wil. Thurgood Marshall: Champion for Civil Rights. 2004. (Great Life Stories Ser.). (Illus.). 125p. (J). 30.50 (978-0-531-12058-3(9) , Watts, Franklin) Scholastic Library Publishing.

McGowan, Keith. Sexual Harassment. 1998. (Overview Ser.). (Illus.). 112p. (YA). (gr. 6-9). lib. bdg. 29.95 (978-1-56006-507-4(9) , LML00902-177867, Lucent Bks.) Thomson Gale.

Mirman, Heather Moehn. Issues in Drug Abuse. 2005. (Contemporary Issues Ser.). (Illus.). 112p. (YA). (gr. 7-10). 29.95 (978-1-59018-035-8(6) , Lucent Bks.) Thomson Gale.

Monk, Linda R. The Words We Live By: Your Annotated Guide to the Constitution. annot. ed. 2004. (Illus.). 288p. pap. 14.95 (978-0-7868-8620-3(X)) Hyperion Pr.

Nakaya, Andrea C. America's Battle Against Terrorism. 2005. (Current Controversies Ser.). 208p. (gr. 10-12). pap. 24.95 (978-0-7377-2784-5(5) , Greenhaven Pr., Inc.) Thomson Gale.

Patrick, John J. The Bill of Rights: A History in Documents. 2002. (Pages from History Ser.). (Illus.). 208p. 36.95 (978-0-19-510354-0(8)) Oxford Univ. Pr., Inc.

Polakow, Amy. Daisy Bates: Civil Rights Crusader. 2002. (Illus.). 128p. (J). 25.00 (978-0-208-02513-5(8) , Linnet Bks.) Shoe String Pr., Inc.

Ramen, Fred. The Rights of the Accused. 2001. (Individual Rights & Civic Responsibility Ser.). (Illus.). 64p. (YA). (gr. 7-12). lib. bdg. 26.50 (978-0-8239-3238-2(9)) Rosen Publishing Group, Inc., The.

Robb, Don. This Is America: The American Spirit in Places & People. Pratt, Christine Joy, illus. 2005. 32p. (J). 16.95 (978-1-57091-604-5(7)); pap. 6.95 (978-1-57091-605-2(5)) Charlesbridge Publishing, Inc.

Santella, Andrew. The NAACP: An Organization Working to End Discrimination. 2003. (Journey to Freedom). (Illus.). 40p. (J). (gr. 3-7). 28.50 (978-1-56766-540-6(3)) Child's World, Inc.

Savage, David. The Supreme Court & Individual Rights. 4th ed. 2004. (Illus.). 416p. 40.00 (978-1-56802-887-3(3)) CQ Pr.

Seidman, David L. Civil Rights. 2001. (Individual Rights & Civic Responsibility Ser.). (Illus.). 64p. (YA). (gr. 7-12). lib. bdg. 26.50 (978-0-8239-3231-3(1)) Rosen Publishing Group, Inc., The.

Skog, Jason. The Civil Rights Act of 1964. 2006. 48p. (J). 25.26 (978-0-7565-2459-3(8)) Compass Point Bks.

Smith, Rich. The Bill of Rights: Defining Our Freedoms. 2007. (Bill of Rights Ser.). (ENG., Illus.). 32p. (J). (gr. 4-8). lib. bdg. 25.65 (*978-1-59928-913-7(X) , ABDO & Daughters) ABDO Publishing Co.

Stair, Nancy. The Bill of Rights: A Primary Source Investigation into the First Ten Amendments to the Constitution. 2005. (Great American Political Documents Ser.). (Illus.). 112p. (YA). (gr. 7-12). lib. bdg. 26.50 (978-0-8239-3800-1(X)) Rosen Publishing Group, Inc., The.

Taylor-Butler, Christine. The Bill of Rights. (True Booktrade;: American History Ser.). 48p. (J). 2008. pap. 6.95 (*978-0-531-14777-1(0)); 2007. (Illus.). (gr. 3-5). lib. bdg. 26.00 (*978-0-531-12627-1(7)) Scholastic Library Publishing. (Children's Pr.).

Thomson Gale Staff. Civil Rights Movement. 2002. (gr. 7-12). lib. bdg. 33.25 (978-0-613-73614-5(1)) Tandem Library Bks.

Torr, James D. Civil Liberties in the War on Terrorism. 2004. (Lucent Terrorism Library). (Illus.). 96p. (J). 29.95 (978-1-59018-527-8(7) , Lucent Bks.) Thomson Gale.

Vaughn, Wally G. & Davis, Mattie Campbell, eds. The Selma Campaign, 1963-1965: The Decisive Battle of the Civil Rights Movement. 2006. 261p. pap. 19.95 (978-0-912469-44-7(7)) Majority Pr., Inc., The.

Wright, Susan. The Civil Rights Act Of 1964: Landmark Antidiscrimination Legislation. 2005. (Library of American Laws & Legal Principles). (Illus.). 48p. (J). (ps-ps). lib. bdg. 23.95 (978-1-4042-0455-3(5)) Rosen Publishing Group, Inc., The.

Yero, Judith Lloyd. The Bill of Rights. 2004. (National Geographic Reading Expeditions Ser.). (Illus.). 32p. (J). (978-0-7922-4552-0(0)) National Geographic Society.

CIVIL RIGHTS DEMONSTRATIONS

see also African Americans—Civil Rights

Crewe, Sabrina & Ingram, Scott. The 1963 Civil Rights March. 2005. (Events That Shaped America Ser.). (Illus.). 32p. (J). lib. bdg. 24.67 (978-0-8368-3411-6(9)) Stevens, Gareth Inc.

Doak, Robin S. The March on Washington: Uniting Against Racism. 2007. (J). lib. bdg. (*978-0-7565-3339-7(2)) Compass Point Bks.

March on Washington. 2002. (History in the Headlines Ser.). 32p. (gr. 6-8). 6.99 (978-0-7682-0469-8(0) , GA131694) School Specialty Publishing.

Miller, Jake. Sit-Ins & Freedom Rides: The Power of Nonviolent Resistance. 2004. (Library of the Civil Rights Movement Ser.). (Illus.). 24p. (J). lib. bdg. 19.95 (978-0-8239-6253-2(9) , PowerKids Pr.) Rosen Publishing Group, Inc., The.

—The 1963 March on Washington: Speeches & Songs for Civil Rights. 2004. (Library of the Civil Rights Movement Ser.). (Illus.). 24p. (J). lib. bdg. 19.95 (978-0-8239-6255-6(5) , PowerKids Pr.) Rosen Publishing Group, Inc., The.

CIVIL RIGHTS MOVEMENTS

Adler, David A. Heroes for Civil Rights. Farnsworth, Bill, illus. 2007. 32p. (J). (gr. 1-5). 16.95 (*978-0-8234-2008-7(6)) Holiday Hse., Inc.

Anderson, Dale. Freedom Rides: Campaign for Equality. 2007. (J). lib. bdg. (*978-0-7565-3333-5(3)) Compass Point Bks.

Anderson, Michael. The Civil Rights Movement. 2003. (20th-Century Perspectives Ser.). (Illus.). 48p. (J). pap. (978-1-4034-4179-9(0)); (gr. 5-7). lib. bdg. 27.07 (978-1-4034-3805-8(6)) Heinemann Library.

Aretha, David. Freedom Summer. 2007. (J). (*978-1-59935-059-2(9)) Reynolds, Morgan Inc.

—Selma & the Voting Rights ACT. 2007. (J). (*978-1-59935-056-1(4)) Reynolds, Morgan Inc.

Armentrout, David & Armentrout, Patricia. Coretta Scott King. 2004. (Discover the Life of an American Legend Ser.). (Illus.). 24p. (gr. 2-5). 20.64 (978-1-58952-659-4(7)) Rourke Publishing, LLC.

Bausum, Ann. Freedom Riders: John Lewis & Jim Zwerg on the Front Lines of the Civil Rights Movement. 2005. (Illus.). 80p. (gr. 5 up). (J). 18.95 (978-0-7922-4173-7(8)); (YA). lib. bdg. 28.90 (978-0-7922-4174-4(6)) National Geographic Society. (National Geographic Children's Bks.).

Bjornlund, Lydia. Rosa Parks & the Montgomery Bus Boycott. 2007. (Lucent Library of Black History Ser.). (Illus.). 128p. (J). (gr. 7-10). 28.70 (*978-1-4205-0010-3(4) , Lucent Bks.) Thomson Gale.

Byers, Ann. African-American History from Emancipation to Today: Rising above the Ashes of Slavery. 2004. (Slavery in American History Ser.). (Illus.). 128p. (YA). lib. bdg. 26.60 (978-0-7660-2153-2(X)) Enslow Pubs., Inc.

Cruz, Barbara. Triumphs & Struggles for Latino Civil Rights. 2008. (From Many Cultures, One History Ser.). (Illus.). 128p. (J). (gr. 5 up). lib. bdg. 31.93 (*978-0-7660-2804-3(6)) Enslow Pubs., Inc.

DeGezelle, Terri. Life in the Time of Rosa Parks & the Civil Rights Movement. 2007. (J). (*978-1-4034-9671-3(4)); pap. (*978-1-4034-9679-9(X)) Heinemann Library.

Ditchfield, Christin. Knowing Your Civil Rights. 2004. (True Bks.). (Illus.). 48p. (J). (gr. 3-5). pap. 6.95 (978-0-516-27910-7(6) , Children's Pr.) Scholastic Library Publishing.

Donovan, Sandy. Fannie Lou Hamer. 2003. (Illus.). 64p. (J). pap. 8.95 (978-1-4109-0316-7(8)); lib. bdg. 28.56 (978-0-7398-7030-3(0)) Raintree.

Downing, David. Martin Luther King, Jr. 2002. (Leading Lives Ser.). (Illus.). 64p. (J). (gr. 5-7). lib. bdg. 28.50 (978-1-58810-580-6(6)) Heinemann Library.

Dumas, Bianca. Robert Moses. 2003. (African-American Biographies Ser.). (Illus.). 64p. (J). lib. bdg. 28.56 (978-0-7398-7031-0(9)) Raintree.

—Robert Parris Moses. 2003. (African-American Biographies Ser.). (Illus.). 64p. (J). (ps-7). pap. 9.50 (978-1-4109-0319-8(2)) Raintree.

Fandel, Jennifer. Martin Luther King, Jr. 2005. (Genius Ser.). (Illus.). 48p. (gr. 5-9). 21.95 (978-1-58341-329-6(4) , Creative Education) Creative Co., The.

—Martin Luther King, Jr: Great Civil Rights Leader. 2007. (Graphic Library). (Illus.). 32p. (J). (978-0-7368-6498-5(9)) Capstone Pr., Inc.

Feinstein, Stephen. Read about Martin Luther King, Jr. 2004. (I Like Biographies Ser.!). (Illus.). 24p. (J). lib. bdg. 24.95 (978-0-7660-2300-0(1)) Enslow Pubs., Inc.

Finlayson, Reggie. We Shall Overcome: The History of the American Civil Rights Movement. 2005. (People's History Ser.). (Illus.). 96p. (gr. 6-12). lib. bdg. 26.60 (978-0-8225-0647-8(5)) Lerner Publishing Group.

Fireside, Harvey. The Mississippi Burning Civil Rights Murder Conspiracy Trial. 2002. (Headline Court Cases Ser.). (Illus.). 112p. (YA). (gr. 6-12). lib. bdg. 26.60 (978-0-7660-1762-7(1)) Enslow Pubs., Inc.

Fitzgerald, Stephanie. Struggling for Civil Rights. 2006. (On the Front Line Ser.). (Illus.). 48p. (J). (978-1-4109-2196-3(4)); pap. (978-1-4109-2203 8(0)) Steck-Vaughn.

Fradin, Dennis Brindell & Fradin, Judith Bloom. Ida B. Wells: Mother of the Civil Rights Movement. 2000. (Illus.). 192p. (J). (gr. 5-9). tchr. ed. 19.00 (978-0-395-89898-7(6) , Clarion Bks.) Houghton Mifflin Co. Trade & Reference Div.

Gelfand, Dale Evva & Rhodes, Lisa Renee. Coretta Scott King: Civil Rights Activist. 2nd rev. ed. 2006. (Black Americans of Achievement, Legacy Edition Ser.). (Illus.). 144p. (J). (gr. 6-12). 30.00 (978-0-7910-9522-5(3) , Chelsea Hse.) Facts On File, Inc.

George, Charles. Living Through the Civil Rights Movement. 2006. (Living Through the Cold War Ser.). (Illus.). 192p. (YA). (gr. 7 up). lib. bdg. 33.70 (978-0-7377-2919-1(8) , Greenhaven Pr., Inc.) Thomson Gale.

Green, Richard L., et al, eds. A Salute to Black Civil Rights Leaders. Dobson, S. Gaston, illus. (Empak "Black History" Publication). (J). pap. 1.00 (978-0-9616156-3-5(X)) Empak Publishing Co.

Hardy, P. Stephen & Hardy, Sheila Jackson. Extraordinary People of the Civil Rights Movement. 2006. (Extraordinary People Ser.). (Illus.). 288p. (YA). (gr. 9 up). (978-0-516-25461-6(8)) Children's Pr., Ltd.

Haskins, James. Freedom Rides: Journey for Justice. 2005. (Illus.). 88p. (J). (ps-17). pap. 10.95 (978-0-940975-94-1(7) , Sankofa Bks.) Just Us Bks., Inc.

Haskins, Jim. Delivering Justice: W. W. Law & the Fight for Civil Rights. Andrews, Benny, illus. 2005. 32p. (J). (gr. k-3). 17.99 (978-0-7636-2592-4(2)) Candlewick Pr.

Haskins, Jim & Benson, Kathleen. John Lewis in the Lead: A Story of the Civil Rights Movement. Andrews, Benny, illus. 2006. 40p. (J). 17.95 (978-1-58430-250-6(X)) Lee & Low Bks., Inc.

Hazen, Walter. Everyday Life: Reform Movement. 2005. 112p. pap. (978-1-59647-085-9(2)) Good Year Bks.

Hermann, Spring. The Struggle for Equality: Women & Minorities in America. 2006. (American Saga Ser.). (Illus.). 128p. (J). lib. bdg. 31.93 (978-0-7660-2573-8(X)) Enslow Pubs., Inc.

Howard, Melanie A. Civil Rights Marches. 2005. (American Moments Ser.). (Illus.). (J). (gr. 4-8). lib. bdg. 25.65 (978-1-59197-282-2(5) , ABDO & Daughters) ABDO Publishing Co.

Jones, Joyce Adams. Remembering the Marches in Selma, Alabama. 2006. 8.00 (*978-0-8059-7237-5(4)) Dorrance Publishing Co., Inc.

Kallen, Stuart A. The Civil Rights Movement. 2001. (Black History Ser.). (Illus.). 48p. (J). (gr. 3-8). lib. bdg. 25.65 (978-1-57765-466-7(8) , ABDO & Daughters) ABDO Publishing Co.

—Women of the Civil Rights Movement. 2005. (Women in History Ser.). (Illus.). 112p. (YA). (gr. 7-10). lib. bdg. 32.45 (978-1-59018-569-8(2) , Lucent Bks.) Thomson Gale.

Koestler-Grack, Rachel A. Going to School During the Civil Rights Movement. 2001. (Blue Earth Books). (Illus.). 32p. (J). (gr. 3-4). lib. bdg. 22.60 (978-0-7368-0799-9(3) , Bridgestone Bks.) Capstone Pr., Inc.

Landau, Elaine. The Civil Rights Movement in America. (Cornerstones of Freedomtrade;, Second Ser.). 48p. (J). 2007. pap. 5.95 (*978-0-531-18765-4(9)); 2003. (Illus.). 26.00 (978-0-516-24219-4(9)) Scholastic Library Publishing. (Children's Pr.).

Levine, Ellen. Freedom's Children: Young Civil Rights Activists Tell Their Own Stories. 2000. 14.64 (978-0-606-20359-3(1)); (gr. 7-12). lib. bdg. 15.30 (978-0-613-33699-4(2)) Tandem Library Bks.

Linney, Susan. Martin Luther King, Jr: With a Discussion of Responsibility. 2004. (Values in Action Ser.). (J). (978-1-59203-069-9(6)) Learning Challenge, Inc.

Martin, Oscar, Jr., creator. Civil Rights Leaders. l.t. ed. 2004. (Illus.). 25p. (J). E-Book 19.95 incl. cd-rom (978-0-9748416-9-4(2)) Build Your Story.

Mattern, Joanne. Coretta Scott King: Civil Rights Activist. 2003. (Reading Power Ser.). (Illus.). 24p. (J). lib. bdg. 17.25 (978-0-8239-6504-5(X) , PowerKids Pr.) Rosen Publishing Group, Inc., The.

Matthews, Sherrie Voss, ed. Free at Last: The Struggle for Civil Rights. 2000. (Literature & Thought Ser.). (Illus.). 144p. (J). (978-0-7807-9633-1(0)); (978-0-7891-5213-8(4)); pap. (978-0-7891-5212-1(6)) Perfection Learning Corp.

Mayer, Robert H. When the Children Marched: The Birmingham Civil Rights Movement. 2008. (Prime Ser.). (Illus.). 160p. (J). (gr. 5 up). lib. bdg. 34.60 (*978-0-7660-2930-9(1)) Enslow Pubs., Inc.

McKissack, Fredrick L., Jr. & McGraw-Hill Staff. This Generation of Americans: A Story of the Civil Rights Movement. 2001. (Jamestown Classics Ser.). (Illus.). 144p. (J). (gr. 5-8). pap. 10.00 (978-0-8092-0626-1(9) , 9780809206261) Jamestown.

McNeese, Tim. The Civil Rights Movement: Striving for Justice. 2007. (Reform Movements in American History Ser.). 160p. (J). (gr. 6-12). 30.00 (*978-0-7910-9504-1(5) , Chelsea Hse.) Facts On File, Inc.

McPherson, Stephanie Sammartino. Coretta Scott King. 2007. (J). lib. bdg. (*978-0-8225-7156-8(0)) Twenty First Century Bks.

Mcwhorter, Diane. A Dream of Freedom: The Civil Rights Movement from 1954-1968. 2004. (Illus.). 160p. (J). (gr. 4-7). pap. 19.95 (978-0-439-57678-9(4) , Scholastic Nonfiction) Scholastic, Inc.

Medearis, Angela Shelf. Dare to Dream: Coretta Scott King & the Civil Rights Movement. Rich, Anna, illus. 1999. (Rainbow Biography Ser.). 64p. (J). (gr. 3-7). pap. 4.99 (978-0-14-130202-7(X) , Puffin) Penguin Group (USA) Inc.

—Dare to Dream: Coretta Scott King & the Civil Rights Movement. 1999. (gr. 3-6). lib. bdg. 13.00 (978-0-613-14663-0(8)) Tandem Library Bks.

Michelson, Richard. As Good as Anybody. 2008. 40p. (J). (gr. 1-5). lib. bdg. 19.99 (*978-0-375-93335-6(2) , Knopf Bks. for Young Readers) Random Hse. Children's Bks.

Miller, Calvin Craig. A. Philip Randolph & the African American Labor Movement. 2005. (Civil Rights Leaders Ser.). (Illus.). 160p. (YA). (gr. 6-12). 26.95 (978-1-931798-50-1(8)) Reynolds, Morgan Inc.

—No Easy Answers: Bayard Rustin & the Civil Rights Movement. 2005. (Civil Rights Leaders Ser.). (Illus.). 160p. (J). (gr. 6-12). 26.95 (978-1-931798-43-3(5)) Reynolds, Morgan Inc.

Miller, Jake. The March from Selma to Montgomery: African Americans Demand the Vote. 2004. (Library of the Civil Rights Movement Ser.). (Illus.). 24p. (J). lib. bdg. 19.95 (978-0-8239-6254-9(7) , PowerKids Pr.) Rosen Publishing Group, Inc., The.

—Sit-Ins & Freedom Rides: The Power of Nonviolent Resistance. 2004. (Library of the Civil Rights Movement Ser.). (Illus.). 24p. (J). lib. bdg. 19.95 (978-0-8239-6253-2(9) , PowerKids Pr.) Rosen Publishing Group, Inc., The.

Perrin, Pat, ed. The Civil Rights Movement. 2003. (Researching American History Ser.). (Illus.). 56p. (J). pap. 7.95 (978-1-57960-081-5(6)) History Compass, LLC.

Press, Petra. Coretta Scott King: An Unauthorized Biography. 1999. (Profiles Ser.). (Illus.). 56p. (J). (gr. 4-6). lib. bdg. 24.22 (978-1-57572-496-6(0)) Heinemann Library.

Rappaport, Doreen. Martin's Big Words: The Life of Dr. Martin Luther King Jr. Collier, Bryan, illus. 2001. 40p. (gr. k-4). 15.99 (978-0-7868-0714-7(8)) Hyperion Bks. for Children.

—Nobody Gonna Turn Me 'Round: Stories & Songs of the Civil Rights Movement. Evans, Shane W., illus. 2006. 64p. (J). (gr. 4-7). 19.99 (978-0-7636-1927-5(2)) Candlewick Pr.

Regis, Frankye. A Voice from the Civil Rights Era. 2004. (Voices of Twentieth-Century Conflict Ser.). (Illus.). 184p. 36.95 (978-0-313-32998-2(2) , GR2998, Praeger Pubs.) Greenwood Publishing Group, Inc.

Rhodes, Lisa Renee. Coretta Scott King: Humanitarian. 1999. (Black Americans of Achievement Ser.). (Illus.). 144p. (YA). (gr. 4-7). 30.00 (978-0-7910-4690-6(7)); (gr. 5 up). pap. 6.65 (978-0-7910-4691-3(5)) Facts On File, Inc. (Chelsea Hse.).

Ribeiro, Myra. The Assassination of Medgar Evers. 2003. (Library of Political Assassinations). (Illus.). 64p. (YA). (gr. 7-12). lib. bdg. 26.50 (978-0-8239-3544-4(2)) Rosen Publishing Group, Inc., The.

Roop, Peter & Roop, Connie. Martin Luther King, Jr., Set 1. 2002. (Lives & Times Ser.). (Illus.). 24p. (J). (gr. k-3). pap. 6.50 (978-1-58810-346-8(3) , 91106) Heinemann Library.

Ruffin, Frances E. Martin Luther King & the March on Washington. 2001. (gr. k-3). lib. bdg. 11.80 (978-0-613-31457-2(3)) Tandem Library Bks.

Schuldt, Lori Meek. Martin Luther King, Jr: With Profiles of Mohandas K. Gandhi & Nelson Mandela. 2006. (Biographical Connections Ser.). (Illus.). 112p. (J). (978-0-7166-1822-5(2)) World Bk., Inc.

Sirimarco, Elizabeth. The Civil Rights Movement. 2003. (American Voices From Ser.). (J). 34.21 (978-0-7614-1697-5(8) , Benchmark Bks.) Cavendish, Marshall Corp.

St. Lawrence, Genevieve. Medgar Evers. 2003. (Illus.). 64p. (J). pap. 9.50 (978-1-4109-0318-1(4)); lib. bdg. 28.56 (978-0-7398-7028-0(9)) Raintree.

—Medgar Evers. 2003. (gr. 3-6). lib. bdg. 18.20 (978-0-613-78291-3(7)) Tandem Library Bks.

Supples, Kevin. The Civil Rights Movement. 2003. (People Who Changed America Ser.). (Illus.). 40p. (J). (978-0-7922-8628-8(6)) National Geographic Society.

Tackach, James. The Civil Rights Movement. 2001. (Opposing Viewpoints Digests Ser.). (Illus.). 112p. (J). 21.20 (978-0-7377-0355-9(5) , Greenhaven Pr., Inc.) Thomson Gale.

Tillage, Leon Walter. Leon's Story. 2000. (978-0-606-20397-5(4)); (J). (978-0-606-20134-6(3)) Tandem Library Bks.

Turck, Mary. Civil Rights Movement for Kids: A History with 21 Activities. 2000. (For Kids Ser.). (Illus.). 208p. (J). (gr. 4-8). pap. 14.95 (978-1-55652-370-0(X)) Chicago Review Pr., Inc.

Uschan, Michael V. Martin Luther King, Jr. 2003. (Heroes & Villains Ser.). (Illus.). 112p. (J). 29.95 (978-1-59018-257-4(X) , Lucent Bks.) Thomson Gale.

Uschan, Michael V. Reconstruction. 2007. (Lucent Library of Black History Ser.). (Illus.). 128p. (gr. 7-10). 28.70 (***978-1-4205-0009-7(0)*** , Lucent Bks.) Thomson Gale.

Waxman, Laura Hamilton. Coretta Scott King. 2008. (History Maker Biographies Ser.). (J). lib. bdg. 26.60 (***978-0-8225-7168-1(4)*** , Lerner Pubns.) Lerner Publishing Group.

Welch, Catherine A. Children of the Civil Rights Era. 2005. (Picture the American Past Ser.). (Illus.). 48p. (J). (gr. 2-5). lib. bdg. 22.60 (978-1-57505-481-0(7)) Lerner Publishing Group.

Woog, Adam. The Fight Renewed: the Civil Rights Movement. 2005. (Lucent Library of Black History). (Illus.). 112p. (YA). (gr. 7-10). lib. bdg. 32.45 (978-1-59018-701-2(6) , Lucent Bks.) Thomson Gale.

CIVIL RIGHTS MOVEMENTS—FICTION

Birtha, Becky. Grandmama's Pride. Bootman, Colin, illus. 2005. 32p. (J). (gr. 7-10). 16.95 (978-0-8075-3028-3(X)) Whitman, Albert & Co.

Davis, Ossie. Just Like Martin. (J). 2002. 176p. 15.99 (978-0-7868-0812-0(8)); 2001. pap. (978-0-7868-1642-2(2)) Hyperion Bks. for Children. (Jump at the Sun).

Johnson, Angela. A Sweet Smell of Roses. Velasquez, Eric, illus. 32p. (J). 2007. 6.99 (***978-1-4169-5361-6(2)*** , Aladdin); 2004. 17.99 (978-0-689-83252-9(4)) Simon & Schuster Children's Publishing.

Mazellan, Ron, illus. We Will Walk. 2005. 16p. (J). pap. (***978-0-7367-2919-2(4)***) Zaner-Bloser, Inc.

McKissack, Frederick. This Generation of Americans: A Story of the Civil Rights Movement. 2000. (gr. 5-8). lib. bdg. 14.95 (978-0-613-36884-1(3)) Tandem Library Bks.

McKissack, Fredrick L. This Generation of Americans. 2004. 150p. (J). lib. bdg. 16.92 (***978-1-4242-0769-5(X)***) Fitzgerald Bks.

McKissack, Fredrick L. This Generation of Americans: A Story of the Civil Rights Movement. 2004. (Jamestown's American Portraits Ser.). (Illus.). 152p. (J). (gr. 5-7). pap. 4.95 (978-0-7696-3441-8(9) , Waterbird Bks.) School Specialty Publishing.

McKissack, Patricia C. Abby Takes a Stand. James, Gordon C., illus. 2005. (Scraps of Time Ser.). 112p. (J). (gr. 3). 14.99 (978-0-670-06011-5(9) , Viking Juvenile) Penguin Group (USA) Inc.

Medearis, Angela Shelf. Singing for Dr. King. Wright and Hu, Cornelius Van and Ying-Hwa, illus. 2004. 32p. (J). lib. bdg. 15.00 (***978-1-4242-0237-9(X)***) Fitzgerald Bks.

Nelson, Vaunda Micheaux. Beyond Mayfield. 1999. 1p. (J). (gr. 5-9). 15.99 (978-0-399-23355-5(5) , Putnam Juvenile) Penguin Group (USA) Inc.

Nolan, Han. A Summer of Kings. 2006. (Illus.). 352p. (YA). 17.00 (978-0-15-205108-2(2)) Harcourt Children's Bks.

—A Summer of Kings. 2006. 334p. (J). (978-1-4156-7340-9(3)) Harcourt Trade Pubs.

Owens, Vivian W. I Met a Great Lady: Ivy Meets Mary McLeod Bethune. Maxwell, Carolyn, ed. Watson, Richard J., illus. unabr. ed. 1998. 80p. (J). (gr. 4-11). pap. 8.95 (978-0-9623839-5-3(3)) Eschar Pubns.

Pinkney, Andrea Davis. Boycott Blues. 2008. (J). (***978-0-06-082118-0(3)); (978-0-06-082119-7(1))*** HarperCollins Pubs. (Greenwillow Bks.).

Raven, Margot Theis. Let Them Play. Ellison, Chris, illus. 2005. 40p. (J). 16.95 (978-1-58536-260-8(3)) Sleeping Bear Pr.

Rodman, Mary Ann. Yankee Girl. 2004. (Illus.). 224p. (J). 17.00 (978-0-374-38661-0(7) , Farrar, Straus & Giroux (BYR)) Farrar, Straus & Giroux.

Scholastic, Inc. Staff & Medearis, Angela Shelf. Singing for Dr. King. Van Wright, Cornelius & Hu, Ying-Hwa, illus. 2004. (Just for You! Ser.). 32p. (gr. k-3). pap. 3.99 (978-0-439-56855-5(2) , Teaching Resources) Scholastic, Inc.

Weatherford, Carole Boston. Freedom on the Menu: The Greensboro Sit-Ins. Lagarrigue, Jerome, illus. 2004. 32p. (J). (gr. 1). 16.99 (978-0-8037-2860-8(3) , Dial) Penguin Group (USA) Inc.

CIVIL RIGHTS WORKERS

Adler, David A. Heroes for Civil Rights. Farnsworth, Bill, illus. 2007. 32p. (J). (gr. 1-5). 16.95 (***978-0-8234-2008-7(6)***) Holiday Hse., Inc.

African-American Freedom Fighters. 2000. (My Ancestors—My Heroes Ser.: Vol. 7). (J). (gr. 3-4). (978-1-893091-06-1(6)) Parker Publishing Co.

Alexander, Florence. Dare to Be . . Martin Luther King Jr. Whitmore, Yvette, illus. 2003. (ENG & SPA.). 17p. (J). 3.99 (978-0-915960-65-1(6)) Ebon Research Systems Publishing, LLC.

Ansary, Mir Tamim. Martin Luther King, Jr. Day. 2006. (Illus.). 32p. (J). (***978-1-4034-8889-3(4)***) Heinemann Library.

Aretha, David. Freedom Summer. 2007. (J). (***978-1-59935-059-2(9)***) Reynolds, Morgan Inc.

Armentrout, David & Armentrout, Patricia. Coretta Scott King. 2004. (Discover the Life of an American Legend Ser.). (Illus.). 24p. (gr. 2-5). 20.64 (978-1-58952-659-4(7)) Rourke Publishing, LLC.

Ashby, Ruth. Rosa Parks: Freedom Rider. 2008. (Sterling Biographies Ser.). (Illus.). 128p. (J). pap. 5.95 (***978-1-4027-4865-3(5)***) Sterling Publishing Co., Inc.

Bader, Bonnie. Who Was Martin Luther King Jr. Harrison, Nancy & Wolf, Elizaabeth, illus. 2007. (Who Was... ? Ser.). 112p. (J). (gr. 2-5). 4.99 (***978-0-448-44723-0(1)*** , Grosset & Dunlap) Penguin Group (USA) Inc.

Baker, Courtney. Let's Read About— Rosa Parks. Hunt, Robert, illus. 2004. (Scholastic First Biographies Ser.). 29p. (J). pap. (978-0-439-56413-7(1) , Cartwheel Bks.) Scholastic, Inc.

Banting, Erinn. Rosa Parks. 2005. (Great African American Women for Kids Ser.). (Illus.). 24p. (J). (ps-7). pap. 6.95 (978-1-59036-342-3(6)); lib. bdg. 26.00 (978-1-59036-336-2(1)) Weigl Pubs., Inc.

Bolden, Tonya. M. L. K. The Journey of a King. Adelman, Bob, ed. 2007. 128p. (J). (gr. 5-9). 19.95 (978-0-8109-5476-2(1) , Abrams Bks. for Young Readers) Abrams, Harry N. , Inc.

Brandt, Keith & Mattern, Joanne. Rosa Parks: Freedom Rider. Griffith, Gershom, illus. 2006. 54p. (J). pap. (***978-0-439-66045-7(9)***) Scholastic, Inc.

Brimner, Larry Dane. We Are One: The Story of Bayard Rustin. 2007. 48p. (YA). (gr. 3 up). 17.95 (***978-1-59078-498-3(7)***) Boyds Mills Pr.

Crompton, Samuel Willard. Desmond Tutu: Fighting Apartheid. 2007. (Modern Peacemakers Ser.). (Illus.). 120p. (YA). (gr. 9 up). 30.00 (978-0-7910-9221-7(6) , Chelsea Hse.) Facts On File, Inc.

Donovan, Sandy. Rosa Parks. 2003. (Illus.). 64p. (J). (gr. 4-7). pap. 9.50 (978-1-4109-0320-4(6)); lib. bdg. 28.56 (978-0-7398-7032-7(7)) Raintree.

Downing, David. Martin Luther King, Jr. 2002. (Leading Lives Ser.). 64p. (J). (gr. 5-7). pap. 8.95 (978-1-4034-0123-6(3) , 91614); (Illus.). lib. bdg. 28.50 (978-1-58810-580-6(6)) Heinemann Library.

Dray, Philip. Daughter of Freedom: The Life & Times of Ida B. Wells. Alcorn, Stephen, illus. 2007. (J). (***978-1-56145-417-4(6)***) Peachtree Pubs., Ltd.

Dubois, Muriel L. Rosa Parks. 2003. (Photo-Illustrated Biographies Ser.). (Illus.). 24p. (J). (gr. 2-3). lib. bdg. 18.60 (978-0-7368-1607-6(0) , Bridgestone Bks.) Capstone Pr., Inc.

Dubowski, Cathy East. Rosa Parks: Don't Give In! 2005. (Defining Moments Ser.). (Illus.). 32p. (J). lib. bdg. 25.27 (978-1-59716-078-0(4)) Bearport Publishing Co., Inc.

Dumas, Bianca. Robert Moses. 2003. (African-American Biographies Ser.). (Illus.). 64p. (J). lib. bdg. 28.56 (978-0-7398-7031-0(9)) Raintree.

—Robert Parris Moses. 2003. (African-American Biographies Ser.). (Illus.). 64p. (J). (ps-7). pap. 9.50 (978-1-4109-0319-8(2)) Raintree.

Edwards, Pamela Duncan. The Bus Ride That Changed History: The Story of Rosa Parks. Shanahan, Danny, illus. 2005. 32p. (J). (gr. k-3). 16.00 (978-0-618-44911-8(6)) Houghton Mifflin Co. Trade & Reference Div.

Fandel, Jennifer. Martin Luther King, Jr. 2005. (Genius Ser.). (Illus.). 48p. (gr. 5-9). 21.95 (978-1-58341-329-6(4) , Creative Education) Creative Co., The.

—Martin Luther King, Jr: Great Civil Rights Leader. 2007. (Graphic Library). (Illus.). 32p. (J). (978-0-7368-6498-5(9)) Capstone Pr., Inc.

Ferris, Jeri Chase. Demanding Justice: A Story about Mary Ann Shadd Cary. Smith, Kimanne, illus. 2003. 64p. (J). 6.95 (978-0-87614-928-7(X) , Carolrhoda Bks.); (gr. 4-8). 22.60 (978-1-57505-177-2(X)) Lerner Publishing Group.

—Demanding Justice: A Story about Mary Ann Shadd Cary. 2003. (gr. 3-6). lib. bdg. 14.10 (978-0-613-58898-0(3)) Tandem Library Bks.

Fine, Edith Hope. Rosa Parks: Meet a Civil Rights Hero. 2004. (Meeting Famous People Ser.). (Illus.). 32p. (J). lib. bdg. 22.60 (978-0-7660-2099-3(1)) Enslow Pubs., Inc.

Finlayson, Reggie. Nelson Mandela. (Just the Facts Biographies Ser.). 2006. (Illus.). 112p. (J). (gr. 3-7). 27.93 (978-0-8225-2644-5(1)); 2004. (J). pap. (978-0-8225-5360-1(0)); 1998. (Illus.). 112p. (YA). (gr. 6-12). 27.93 (978-0-8225-4936-9(0)) Lerner Publishing Group. (Lerner Pubns.).

Fleming, Alice Mulcahey. Martin Luther King, Jr. A Dream of Hope. 2008. (Sterling Biographies Ser.). (Illus.). 128p. (J). pap. 5.95 (***978-1-4027-4439-6(0)***) Sterling Publishing Co., Inc.

Fradin, Judith Bloom & Fradin, Dennis Brindell. The Power of One: Daisy Bates & the Little Rock Nine. 2004. (Illus.). 192p. (YA). (gr. 5-9). tchr. ed. 19.00 (978-0-618-31556-7(X) , Clarion Bks.) Houghton Mifflin Co. Trade & Reference Div.

Freedman, Russell. Freedom Walkers: The Story of the Montgomery Bus Boycott. 2006. (Illus.). 112p. (J). (gr. 3-7). 18.95 (978-0-8234-2031-5(0)) Holiday Hse., Inc.

Gelfand, Dale Evva & Rhodes, Lisa Renee. Coretta Scott King: Civil Rights Activist. 2nd rev. ed. 2006. (Black Americans of Achievement, Legacy Edition Ser.). (Illus.). 144p. (J). (gr. 6-12). 30.00 (978-0-7910-9522-5(3) , Chelsea Hse.) Facts On File, Inc.

Gibson, Karen. Jovita Idar. 2002. (Latinos in American History). (Illus.). 56p. (gr. 4-8). lib. bdg. 29.95 (978-1-58415-151-7(X)) Mitchell Lane Pubs., Inc.

Giovanni, Nikki. Rosa. Collier, Bryan, illus. 2007. 40p. (J). pap. 7.99 (***978-0-312-37602-4(2)***) Square Fish.

Gotsch, Patrice. Martin Luther King, Jr: Changing Lives. Arreola, Gil, illus. 2005. 19p. (J). pap. (***978-1-55501-779-8(7)***) Ballard & Tighe Pubs.

Green, Richard L., et al, eds. A Salute to Black Civil Rights Leaders. Dobson, S. Gaston, illus. (Empak "Black History" Publication). (J). pap. 1.00 (978-0-9616156-3-5(X)) Empak Publishing Co.

Hardy, P. Stephen & Hardy, Sheila Jackson. Extraordinary People of the Civil Rights Movement. 2006. (Extraordinary People Ser.). (Illus.). 288p. (YA). (gr. 9 up). (978-0-516-25461-6(8)) Children's Pr., Ltd.

Haskins, Jim. Delivering Justice: W. W. Law & the Fight for Civil Rights. Andrews, Benny, illus. 2005. 32p. (J). (gr. k-3). 17.99 (978-0-7636-2592-4(2)) Candlewick Pr.

Haskins, Jim & Benson, Kathleen. John Lewis in the Lead: A Story of the Civil Rights Movement. Andrews, Benny, illus. 2006. 40p. (J). 17.95 (978-1-58430-250-6(X)) Lee & Low Bks., Inc.

Hatt, Christine. Martin Luther King, Jr. 2004. (Judge for Yourself Ser.). (Illus.). 64p. (J). pap. (978-0-8368-5565-4(5)); (gr. 5 up). lib. bdg. 30.00 (978-0-8368-5562-3(0)) Stevens, Gareth Inc. (World Almanac Library).

Holland, Gini. Nelson Mandela. 2002. (Trailblazers of the Modern World Ser.). (Illus.). 48p. (J). (gr. 5 up). pap. 14.95 (978-0-8368-5238-7(9)); lib. bdg. 30.00 (978-0-8368-5078-9(5)) Stevens, Gareth Inc. (World Almanac Library).

Hughes, Libby. Nelson Mandela: Voice of Freedom. 2000. (Illus.). 152p. (gr. 4-7). pap. 12.95 (978-0-595-00733-2(3) , Backinprint.com) iUniverse, Inc.

Hull, Mary, et al. Rosa Parks: Civil Rights Leader. 2nd rev. ed. 2006. (Black Americans of Achievement: Ser.). 128p. (J). (gr. 6-12). 30.00 (***978-0-7910-9523-2(1)*** , Chelsea Hse.) Facts On File, Inc.

Hull, Mary E. Rosa Parks: Civil Rights Leader. (Black Americans of Achievement Ser.). (Illus.). 112p. (J). (gr. 6-12). 2005. pap. 13.25 (978-0-7910-8338-3(1)); 2004. 30.00 (978-0-7910-8164-8(8)) Facts On File, Inc. (Chelsea Hse.).

Jeffrey, Gary. Martin Luther King, Jr: The Life of a Civil Rights Leader. Riley, Terry, illus. 2006. (Graphic Biographies Ser.). 48p. (J). lib. bdg. 29.95 (978-1-4042-0858-2(5)) Rosen Publishing Group, Inc., The.

—Martin Luther King Jr: The Life of a Civil Rights Leader. Forsey, Christopher, illus. 2006. 48p. (J). (978-1-4042-0920-6(4)); pap. (978-1-4042-0921-3(2)) Rosen Publishing Group, Inc., The.

Jones, Gerald Colman. Mary Robinson: Citizen of the World. 2000. (Contemporary Profiles & Policy Series for the Younger Reader). (Illus.). 72p. (J). (gr. 8 up). 24.00 (978-0-934272-63-6(8)); pap. 15.00 (978-0-934272-64-3(6)) Burke, John Gordon Pub., Inc.

Jones, Rob Lloyd. Martin Luther King, Jr. 2006. (Illus.). 62p. (J). pap. (***978-0-439-02299-6(1)***) Scholastic, Inc.

Kishel, Ann-Marie. Rosa Parks: A Life of Courage. 2006. (Pull Ahead Books). (Illus.). 32p. (J). 22.60 (978-0-8225-3478-5(9) , Lerner Pubns.) Lerner Publishing Group.

—Rosa Parks: Una Vida de Valentía. 2006. (Libros para Avanzar Ser.). (ENG & SPA.). 32p. (J). lib. bdg. 22.60 (978-0-8225-6239-9(1)) Lerner Publishing Group.

MacMillan, Dianne M. Martin Luther King, Jr. Day. 2nd ed. 2008. (Best Holiday Books Ser.). 48p. (J). (gr. 3-4). lib. bdg. 23.93 (***978-0-7660-3043-5(1)***) Enslow Pubs., Inc.

Manolis, Kay. Rosa Parks: A Life of Courage. 2007. (Illus.). 24p. (J). lib. bdg. 19.95 (978-1-60014-088-4(2)) Bellwether Media.

Mara, Wil. Rosa Parks. 2006. (Rookie Biography Ser.). (Illus.). 31p. (J). (978-0-531-12451-2(7)) Children's Pr., Ltd.

—Rosa Parks. (Rookie Biographies Ser.). (Illus.). (J). 2004. 31p. (gr. 1-2). pap. 4.95 (978-0-516-27916-9(5)); 2003. 32p. 19.50 (978-0-516-25876-8(1)) Scholastic Library Publishing. (Children's Pr.).

Mattern, Joanne. Coretta Scott King: Civil Rights Activist. 2003. (Reading Power Ser.). (Illus.). 24p. (J). lib. bdg. 17.25 (978-0-8239-6504-5(X) , PowerKids Pr.) Rosen Publishing Group, Inc., The.

—Coretta Scott King: Civil Rights Activist: Individual Title Six-Packs. (On Deck Ser.: Vol. 2). 24p. (gr. 4-5). 35.00 (978-0-7578-5841-3(4)) Rigby Education.

McKissack, Patricia C. & McKissack, Fredrick L. Mary Church Terrell: Leader for Equality. rev. ed. 2002. (Great African Americans Ser.). (Illus.). 32p. (J). (gr. 1-4). lib. bdg. 18.60 (978-0-7660-1697-2(8)) Enslow Pubs., Inc.

McLeese, Don. Martin Luther King, Jr. 2002. (Illus.). 24p. (J). lib. bdg. 20.64 (978-1-58952-286-2(9)) Rourke Publishing, LLC.

—Rosa Parks. 2002. (Rourke Discovery Library). (Illus.). 24p. (J). lib. bdg. 20.64 (978-1-58952-287-9(7)) Rourke Publishing, LLC.

McPherson, Stephanie Sammartino. Coretta Scott King. 2007. (J). lib. bdg. (***978-0-8225-7156-8(0)***) Twenty First Century Bks.

Michelson, Richard. As Good as Anybody. 2008. 40p. (J). (gr. 1-5). lib. bdg. 19.99 (***978-0-375-93335-6(2)*** , Knopf Bks. for Young Readers) Random Hse. Children's Bks.

Miller, Calvin Craig. A. Philip Randolph & the African American Labor Movement. 2005. (Civil Rights Leaders Ser.). (Illus.). 160p. (YA). (gr. 6-12). 26.95 (978-1-931798-50-1(8)) Reynolds, Morgan Inc.

Miller, Connie Colwell. Rosa Parks & the Montgomery Bus Boycott. 2007. (Graphic Library). (Illus.). 32p. (J). 25.26 (978-0-7368-6495-4(4)) Capstone Pr., Inc.

Mir Tamim Ansary. Martin Luther King Jr. Day. 2nd ed. 2006. (Illus.). 32p. (J). pap. (***978-1-4034-8902-9(5)***) Heinemann Library.

Morris, Roz. Rosa Parks: Mother of the Civil Rights Movement. 2003. (Alabama Roots Biography Ser.). (Illus.). 109p. (J). (978-1-878561-57-2(X)) Seacoast Publishing, Inc.

Myers, Walter Dean. I've Seen the Promised Land: The Life of Dr. Martin Luther King, Jr. Jenkins, Leonard, illus. 2004. 40p. (J). (gr. k-3). lib. bdg. 17.89 (978-0-06-027704-8(1)) HarperCollins Pubs.

Nobleman, Marc Tyler. Rosa Parks. 2002. (Trailblazers of the Modern World Ser.). (Illus.). 48p. (J). (gr. 5 up). pap. 14.95 (978-0-8368-5231-8(1)); lib. bdg. 30.00 (978-0-8368-5071-0(8)) Stevens, Gareth Inc. (World Almanac Library).

—Rosa Parks. 2002. (gr. 3-6). lib. bdg. 19.90 (978-0-613-76804-7(3)) Tandem Library Bks.

Parks, Rosa. I Am Rosa Parks. 2000. (gr. k-3). lib. bdg. 11.80 (978-0-613-22996-8(7)); (Illus.). (J). 10.79 (978-0-606-18410-6(4)) Tandem Library Bks.

—Rosa Parks: My Story. 1999. (Illus.). 200p. (YA). (gr. 5-9). pap. 6.99 (978-0-14-130120-4(1) , Puffin) Penguin Group (USA) Inc.

—Rosa Parks: My Story. 1999. (978-0-606-15995-1(9)); (gr. 5-8). lib. bdg. 15.30 (978-0-613-15120-7(8)) Tandem Library Bks.

Parks, Rosa & Haskins, Jim. I Am Rosa Parks. Clay, Wil, illus. 1999. (Easy-to-Read Ser.). 48p. (J). (gr. 1-3). pap. 3.99 (978-0-14-130710-7(2) , Puffin) Penguin Group (USA) Inc.

Patrick, Denise Lewis. A Lesson for Martin Luther King, Jr. Pate, Rodney S., illus. 2003. (Ready-to-Read Ser.). 32p. (J). pap. 3.99 (978-0-689-85397-5(1) , Aladdin) Simon & Schuster Children's Publishing.

Pingry, Patricia A. The Story of Coretta Scott King. Walker, Steven, illus. 2007. 26p. (J). (ps-k). bds. 6.99 (***978-0-8249-6717-8(8)*** , Candy Cane Pr.) Ideals Pubns.

—The Story of Rosa Parks. Walker, Steven, illus. 2007. 24p. (J). (ps-k). bds. 6.99 (***978-0-8249-6687-4(2)*** , Candy Cane Pr.) Ideals Pubns.

Press, Petra. Coretta Scott King: An Unauthorized Biography. 1999. (Profiles Ser.). (Illus.). 56p. (J). (gr. 4-6). lib. bdg. 24.22 (978-1-57572-496-6(0)) Heinemann Library.

Rappaport, Doreen. Martin's Big Words: The Life of Dr. Martin Luther King Jr. Collier, Bryan, illus. rev. ed. 2007. 40p. (ps-17). pap. 6.99 (***978-1-4231-0635-7(0)*** , Jump at the Sun) Hyperion Bks. for Children.

Rhodes, Lisa Renee. Coretta Scott King: Civil Rights Activist. (Black Americans of Achievement Ser.). (Illus.). 112p. (J). (gr. 6-12). 2005. pap. 13.25 (978-0-7910-8371-0(3)); 2004. 30.00 (978-0-7910-8251-5(2)) Facts On File, Inc. (Chelsea Hse.).

—Coretta Scott King: Humanitarian. 1999. (Black Americans of Achievement Ser.). (Illus.). 144p. (YA). (gr. 4-7). 30.00 (978-0-7910-4690-6(7)); (gr. 5 up). pap. 6.65 (978-0-7910-4691-3(5)) Facts On File, Inc. (Chelsea Hse.).

Rinaldo, Denise. Rosa Parks: With a Discussion of Courage. 2003. (Values in Action Ser.). (J). (978-1-59203-061-3(0)) Learning Challenge, Inc.

Ringgold, Faith. If a Bus Could Talk: The Story of Rosa Parks. Ringgold, Faith, illus. (Illus.). 32p. (J). 2003. (gr. k-4). pap. 7.99 (978-0-689-85676-1(8) , Aladdin); 1999. (gr. 1-4). 16.00 (978-0-689-81892-9(0)) Simon & Schuster Children's Publishing.

—If a Bus Could Talk: The Story of Rosa Parks. 2003. (gr. k-3). lib. bdg. 15.30 (978-0-613-61633-1(2)) Tandem Library Bks.

Riordan, James. The Story of Martin Luther King. 2001. (Illus.). 48p. (J). lib. bdg. 24.25 (978-1-930643-24-6(1)) Chrysalis Education.

Rivera, Sheila. Martin Luther King Jr. Una Vida de Determinacion. 2006. (Libros para Avanzar Ser.). (ENG & SPA.). 32p. (J). lib. bdg. 22.60 (978-0-8225-6237-5(5)) Lerner Publishing Group.

Santella, Andrew. Martin Luther King Jr. Civil Rights Leader & Nobel Prize Winner. 2003. (Journey to Freedom). (Illus.). 40p. (J). (gr. 3-7). 28.50 (978-1-56766-539-0(X)) Child's World, Inc.

Schaefer, Lola M. Rosa Parks. Saunders-Smith, Gail, ed. 2002. (First Biographies Ser.). (Illus.). 24p. (J). (gr. k-1). lib. bdg. 15.93 (978-0-7368-1176-7(1) , Pebble Bks.) Capstone Pr., Inc.

Schraff, Anne E. Ida B. Wells-Barnett: Strike a Blow Against Glaring Evil. 2008. (African-American Biography Library). (Illus.). 128p. (J). (gr. 6 up). lib. bdg. 31.93 (***978-0-7660-2704-6(X)***) Enslow Pubs., Inc.

Schraff, Anne E. Rosa Parks: Tired of Giving In. 2005. (African-American Biography Library). (Illus.). 128p. (J). (gr. 6-12). lib. bdg. 31.93 (978-0-7660-2463-2(6)) Enslow Pubs., Inc.

Schuldt, Lori Meek. Martin Luther King, Jr: With Profiles of Mohandas K. Gandhi & Nelson Mandela. 2006. (Biographical Connections Ser.). (Illus.). 112p. (J). (978-0-7166-1822-5(2)) World Bk., Inc.

Sharpten, Al. African-American Civil Rights Activists: Black Panthers. 2000. (My Ancestors—My Heroes Ser.: Vol. 39). (J). (gr. 3-4). (978-1-893091-38-2(4)) Parker Publishing Co.

Shone, Rob. Rosa Parks: The Life of a Civil Rights Heroine. Spender, Nik, illus. 2006. 48p. (J). (978-1-4042-0926-8(3)); pap. (978-1-4042-0927-5(1)); (gr. 3-8). lib. bdg. 29.95 (978-1-4042-0864-3(X)) Rosen Publishing Group, Inc., The.

Shores, Erika L. Rosa Parks: Civil Rights Poineer. 2005. (Fact Finders Ser.). (Illus.). 32p. (J). (ps-7). lib. bdg. 22.60 (978-0-7368-3746-0(9)) Capstone Pr., Inc.

Stamper, G. C. Nelson Mandela. 2005. (Illus.). 32p. (J). pap. (***978-0-7367-2922-2(4)***) Zaner-Bloser, Inc.

Steele, Phillip. Rosa Parks & Her Protest for Civil Rights. 2002. (Dates with History Ser.). (Illus.). 31p. (J). lib. bdg. 24.25 (978-1-58340-215-3(2)) Smart Apple Media.

The Story of Martin Luther King, Jr. 2001. (Illus.). 24p. (J). (ps-k). 6.95 (978-0-8249-4144-4(6)) Ideals Pubns.

Swain, Gwenyth. Civil Rights Pioneer: A Story about Mary Church Terrell. Beier, Ellen, illus. 64p. (J). pap. 6.95 (978-0-8225-4170-7(X)); 1999. (gr. 4-8). lib. bdg. 22.60 (978-1-57505-355-4(1)) Lerner Publishing Group.

—Civil Rights Pioneer: A Story about Mary Church Terrell. 1999. (gr. 3-6). lib. bdg. 15.25 (978-0-613-68325-8(0)) Tandem Library Bks.

Tieck, Sarah. Rosa Parks. 2007. (Buddy Book Ser.). (Illus.). 32p. (J). 22.78 (978-1-59679-788-8(6)) ABDO Publishing Co.

Time for Kids Editors. Rosa Parks: Civil Rights Pioneer. 2007. (Time for Kids Ser.). (Illus.). 48p. (J). 14.99 (978-0-06-057625-7(1)); pap. 3.99 (978-0-06-057624-0(3)) HarperCollins Pubs.

Waxman, Laura Hamilton. Coretta Scott King. 2008. (History Maker Biographies Ser.). (J). lib. bdg. 26.60 (***978-0-8225-7168-1(4)*** , Lerner Pubns.) Lerner Publishing Group.

Weidt, Maryann N. Rosa Parks. 2003. (History Maker Bios Ser.). (Illus.). 47p. (J). 26.60 (978-0-8225-4673-3(6) , Lerner Pubns.) Lerner Publishing Group.

Wheeler, Jill C. Rosa Parks, Set II. 2003. (Breaking Barriers Ser.). (Illus.). 64p. (J). (gr. 3-8). lib. bdg. 25.65 (978-1-57765-640-1(7)) ABDO Publishing Co.

Wilson, Cammie. Rosa Parks: From the Back of the Bus to the Front of a Movement. 2001. (Scholastic Biography Ser.). (Illus.). 88p. (J). (gr. 3-7). pap. 4.50 (978-0-439-16330-9(7)) Scholastic, Inc.

CIVIL SERVICE

Here are entered general works on the history and development of public service. Works on public personnel administration, including the duties of civil service employees, their salaries, pensions, etc., are entered under the name of the country, state or city with the subdivision Officials and Employees.

see also names of countries, cities, etc. with the subdivision Officials and Employees, e.g. United States—Officials and Employees

Ginyard, John. What Is the Job of a Corrections Officer? 2006. (YA). per. 6.95 (978-1-59094-113-3(6)) Jawbone Publishing Corp.

Horvitz, Leslie Alan. Meg Whitman: President & CEO of EBAY. 2005. (Ferguson Career Biographies Ser.). (Illus.). 128p. (J). (gr. 6-12). 25.00 (978-0-8160-5891-4(1) , Ferguson Publishing Co.) Facts On File, Inc.

J. G. Ferguson Publishing Company Staff, contrib. by. Discovering Careers for Your Future/Government. 2002. (Discovering Careers for Your Future Ser.). (Illus.). 96p. (J). (gr. 4-9). 21.95 (978-0-89434-397-1(1) , Ferguson Publishing Co.) Facts On File, Inc.

Kishel, Ann-Marie. Government Services. 2007. (First Step Nonfiction Ser.). 24p. (J). (gr. k-2). 18.60 (978-0-8225-6397-6(5) , Lerner Pubns.) Lerner Publishing Group.

CIVIL WAR, GREAT BRITAIN, 1642-1649

see Great Britain—History—Puritan Revolution, 1642-1660

CIVIL WAR, U. S., 1861-1865

see United States—History—Civil War, 1861-1865

CIVILIZATION

see also Anthropology; Archaeology; Art; Bronze Age; Culture; Education; Ethics; Ethnology; Industry; Inventions; Learning and Scholarship; Manners and Customs; Primitive Societies; Religions; Science and Civilization; Social Problems; Technology and Civilization

also names of countries, states, etc. with the subdivision Civilization, e.g. United States—Civilization

Ahmad, Iftikhar. World Cultures: A Global Mosaic, 8 vols. l.t. ed. 2004. 2467p. (YA). (gr. 6-9). 1236.00 (978-0-13-036895-9(4) , A-L00012-00) Prentice Hall Pr.

Ali, Daud. Ancient India: What Life Was Like in One of the Earliest Civilizations on Earth. 2003. (Find Out about-...Ser.). (Illus.). 64p. (gr. 3-7). pap. 7.99 (978-1-84215-778-7(7) , Southwater) Anness Publishing GBR. *Dist:* National Bk. Network.

Ashby, Ruth. 1800. 2001. (Around the World Ser.). (Illus.). 96p. (J). 29.93 (978-0-7614-1084-3(8) , Benchmark Bks.) Cavendish, Marshall Corp.

Barter, James. The Ancient Persians. 2005. (Lost Civilizations Ser.). 112p. (YA). (gr. 5-8). lib. bdg. 29.95 (978-1-59018-621-3(4) , Lucent Bks.) Thomson Gale.

Benchmark Education Staff, compiled by. One World, Many Cultures. 2006. spiral bd. 219.00 (***978-1-4108-7066-7(9)***) Benchmark Education Co.

—World Cultures. 2006. spiral bd. 199.00 (***978-1-4108-7129-9(0)***) Benchmark Education Co.

Bumcrot, Curt & Dunlap, Shiree. Testing Targets: For Streams of Civilization. Zyp, Nicole, ed. 2004. 19p. (YA). (gr. 9-12). pap. 5.00 (978-1-888786-43-9(4)) Basic Skills Assessment & Educational Services.

—Testing Targets: For Streams of Civilization, Vol. 2. Zyp, Nikki & Robinson, Heldi, eds. 2004. 20p. (YA). (gr. 9-12). pap. 5.00 (978-1-888786-45-3(0)) Basic Skills Assessment & Educational Services.

Chelsea House Publishing Staff. Journey into Civilization Set. (Illus.). (J). (gr. 3-7). pap. 79.50 (978-0-7910-3773-7(8) , Chelsea Hse.) Facts On File, Inc.

Cultures of the World, 6 vols., Set. Incl. India. Srinivasan, Tadhika & Jermyn, L. lib. bdg. 37.07 (978-0-7614-1354-7(5)); Indonesia. Mirpuri, Gouri & Cooper, R. lib. bdg. 37.07 (978-0-7614-1355-4(3)); Japan. Shelley, Rex. lib. bdg. 37.07 (978-0-7614-1356-1(1)); Malaysia. Munan, Heidi & Foo, Y. lib. bdg. 37.07 (978-0-7614-1351-6(0)); Myanmar. Yin, Saw Myat. lib. bdg. 37.07 (978-0-7614-1353-0(7)); Singapore. Layton, Lesley & Pang, G. K. lib. bdg. 37.07 (978-0-7614-1352-3(9)); 2nd ed. (gr. 5 up). 2001. (Illus.). 144p. 2001. 222.43 (978-0-7614-1350-9(2) , Benchmark Bks.) Cavendish, Marshall Corp.

Cultures of the World - Group 17, 6 vols. Incl. Bangladesh. Whyte, Mariam. (gr. 5-12). 1999. lib. bdg. 37.07 (978-0-7614-0869-7(X)); Czech Republic. Sioras, Efstathia. (gr. 5-12). 1999. lib. bdg. 37.07 (978-0-7614-0870-3(3)); Democratic Republic of the Congo. Heale, Jay. (gr. 5-12). 1999. lib. bdg. 37.07 (978-0-7614-0874-1(6)); Kuwait. O'Shea, Maria. (gr. 5-12). 1999. lib. bdg. 37.07 (978-0-7614-0871-0(1)); Senegal. Berg, Elizabeth. (gr. 5-12). 1999. lib. bdg. 37.07 (978-0-7614-0872-7(X)); Uruguay. Jermyn, Leslie. (J). (gr. k-17). 1998. lib. bdg. 37.07 (978-0-7614-0873-4(8)); 128p. (Illus.). 222.43 (978-0-7614-0868-0(1) , Benchmark Bks.) Cavendish, Marshall Corp.

Cultures of the World - Group 19, 6 vols. Incl. Barbados. Elias, Marie Louise. lib. bdg. 37.07 (978-0-7614-0976-2(9)); Cote d'Ivoire. Sheehan, Patricia. lib. bdg. 37.07 (978-0-7614-0980-9(7)); Cyprus. Spilling, Michael. lib. bdg. 37.07 (978-0-7614-0978-6(5)); Latvia. Barlas, Robert. lib. bdg. 37.07 (978-0-7614-0977-9(7)); Paraguay. Jermyn, Leslie. lib. bdg. 37.07 (978-0-7614-0979-3(3)); Uganda. Barlas, Robert. lib. bdg. 37.07 (978-0-7614-0981-6(5)); 128p. (gr. 5-12). 2000. (Illus.). 222.43 (978-0-7614-0975-5(0) , Benchmark Bks.) Cavendish, Marshall Corp.

Cultures of the World - Group 20, 6 vols. Incl. Bahamas. Barlas, Robert. lib. bdg. 37.07 (978-0-7614-0992-2(0)); Fiji. NgCheong-Lum, Roseline. lib. bdg. 37.07 (978-0-7614-0996-0(3)); Guyana. Jermyn, Leslie. lib. bdg. 37.07 (978-0-7614-0994-6(7)); Malta. Sheehan, Sean. lib. bdg. 37.07 (978-0-7614-0993-9(9)); Moldova. Sheehan, Patricia. lib. bdg. 37.07 (978-0-7614-0997-7(1)); Niger. Seffal, Rabah. lib. bdg. 37.07 (978-0-7614-0995-3(5)); 128p. (gr. 5-12). 2000. (Illus.). 222.43 (978-0-7614-0991-5(2) , Benchmark Bks.) Cavendish, Marshall Corp.

Cultures of the World - Group 21, 6 vols. Incl. Bahrain. Cooper, Robert. 2000. lib. bdg. 37.07 (978-0-7614-1161-1(5)); Cameroon. Sheehan, Sean. (J). 2001. lib. bdg. 37.07 (978-0-7614-1158-1(5)); Croatia. Cooper, Robert. (J). 2000. lib. bdg. 37.07 (978-0-7614-1156-7(9)); Grenada. Cheng, Pang Guek. 2000. lib. bdg. 37.07 (978-0-7614-1160-4(7)); Maldives. NgCheong-Lum, Roseline. 2000. lib. bdg. 37.07 (978-0-7614-1157-4(7)); Scotland. Levy, Patricia. (J). 2000. lib. bdg. 37.07 (978-0-7614-1159-8(3)); 128p. (gr. 5-12). (Illus.). 2000. 222.43 (978-0-7614-1155-0(0) , Benchmark Bks.) Cavendish, Marshall Corp.

Davis, Kevin A. Look What Came from Australia. 1999. (gr. 3-6). lib. bdg. 15.25 (978-0-613-54742-0(X)) Tandem Library Bks.

—Look What Came from Germany. 1999. (gr. 3-6). lib. bdg. 15.25 (978-0-613-29680-9(X)) Tandem Library Bks.

—Look What Came from Greece. 1999. (J). (978-0-606-20145-2(9)) Tandem Library Bks.

Davis, Kevin A. & Harvey, Miles. Look What Came from The Netherlands. 2003. (Look What Came from Ser.). (Illus.). 32p. (J). (gr. 2-4). pap. 6.95 (978-0-531-16631-4(7) , Watts, Franklin) Scholastic Library Publishing.

Excavating the Past, 10 bks. 2005. (J). (gr. 4-6). lib. bdg. 220.00 (978-1-4034-6000-4(0)) Heinemann Library.

Farndon, John. A History of Civilization Illustrated History Encyclopedia: The Great Landmarks in the Development of Mankind. 2006. (Illus.). 256p. (gr. 7-10). reprint ed. pap. 22.00 (978-1-4223-5514-5(4)) DIANE Publishing Co.

Ganeri, Anita. Legacies, 4 vols. 1999. (Illus.). 32p. (J). lib. bdg. 67.80 (978-1-929298-53-2(6)) Chrysalis Education.

Grant, Neil. Everyday Life of the Vikings. 2005. (Uncovering History Ser.). (Illus.). 46p. (J). (gr. 6-9). lib. bdg. 29.95 (978-1-58340-706-6(5)) Smart Apple Media.

Grolier Educational Staff, ed. Lands & Peoples, 6 vols. 1999. (Illus.). 2650p. (J). (gr. 4-12). lib. bdg. 269.00 (978-0-7172-8021-6(7) , Grolier) Scholastic Library Publishing.

Guile, Melanie. Thailand. 2003. (Illus.). 32p. (J). lib. bdg. 25.70 (978-1-4109-0475-1(X)) Raintree.

Harcourt School Publishers Staff. Social Studies, Grade 4: People, Civilizations & World History: Activity Book. 1999. (Harcourt Brace Social Studies). (gr. k-7). pap., tchr. ed. 11.00 (978-0-15-316043-1(8)) Harcourt Schl. Pubs.

Harvey, Miles. Look What Came from India. 1999. (Look What Came from Ser.). 32p. (gr. 2-4). (Illus.). pap. 6.95 (978-0-531-15965-1(5)); (J). 22.00 (978-0-531-11587-9(9)) Scholastic Library Publishing. (Watts, Franklin).

Helgren. People, Places & Change: The Western World. 5th ed. 2004. (Illus.). 58.00 (978-0-03-037643-6(2)) Holt, Rinehart & Winston.

Husain, Shahrukh. The Vikings. 2005. (Stories from Ancient Civilizations Ser.). (Illus.). 32p. (J). (gr. 4 up). lib. bdg. 27.10 (978-1-58340-621-2(2) , 1236428) Smart Apple Media.

Lasseter, Rollin, ed. History: All Ye Lands. (Illus.). 360p. (J). (gr. 6). 55.00 (978-0-89870-944-5(X)) Ignatius Pr.

MacDonald, Fiona. Discovering World Cultures, 4 bks. Incl. Clothing & Jewelry. 2000. lib. bdg. (978-0-7787-0236-8(7)); Food. 2001. lib. bdg. (978-0-7787-0238-2(3)); Homes. 2000. lib. bdg. (978-0-7787-0237-5(5)); Music & Dance. 2000. lib. bdg. (978-0-7787-0239-9(1)); 40p. (J). (gr. 4). (Illus.). 2001. (978-0-7787-0234-4(0)); Set pap. (978-0-7787-0244-3(8)) Crabtree Publishing Co.

—Tribes, Empires & Civilizations. 2001. (Through the Ages Ser.). (Illus.). 64p. (gr. 3-7). 12.95 (978-0-7548-0851-0(3)) Anness Publishing GBR. *Dist:* National Bk. Network.

Manley, Deborah. Gentes y Lugares. 2000. Tr. of People & Places. (SPA.). (J). 4.95 (978-84-01-70184-9(8)) Plaza & Janes Editories, S.A. ESP. *Dist:* AIMS International Bks., Inc.

Millard, Anne. Misterios de las Civilizaciones Perdidas. (Coleccion Misterios De). (SPA., Illus.). 48p. (YA). (gr. 5-8). 19.95 (978-84-348-5638-7(7) , SM5948) SM Ediciones ESP. *Dist:* AIMS International Bks., Inc., Lectorum Pubns., Inc.

Milligan, Jean F. The World Today. 2001. (Illus.). 50p. (YA). (gr. 2-12). lib. bdg. 12.95 (978-0-9637825-3-3(3)) Autumn Hse. Publishing.

Minnis. Ancient Rome. 2004. (Raintree Perspectives Ser.). (Illus.). 32p. (J). 25.70 (978-1-4109-0618-2(3)) Harcourt Schl. Pubs.

O'Donnell, Kerri. The Ancient Civilizations of Greece & Rome: Solving Algebraic Equations. 2005. (PowerMath Ser.). (J). 22.50 (978-1-4042-2930-3(2)); pap. (978-1-4042-5123-6(5)) Rosen Publishing Group, Inc., The. (PowerKids Pr.).

Osborne, Will & Osborne, Mary Pope. Mummies & Pyramids: A Nonfiction Companion to Mummies in the Morning. 2001. (Magic Tree House Research Guide Ser.: No. 3). (Illus.). (J). (gr. k-3). (978-0-606-20781-2(3)) Tandem Library Bks.

Our Own Felicity: We Make or Find. 2002. 140p. (YA). (gr. 10 up). 11.00 (978-0-9644698-8-4(X)) Corey, C. L.

Parker, Victoria. The Ganges. 2003. (Holy Places Ser.). (Illus.). 32p. (J). 24.28 (978-0-7398-6078-6(X)) Raintree.

Peoples of the World Action Sticker Book. 2002. 12p. (J). pap. 3.98 (978-0-7525-8038-8(8)) Parragon, Inc.

Perry, Marvin. Western Civilization: A Brief History. 5th ed. 2004. (Illus.). 524p. (YA). 83.16 (978-0-618-37031-3(5) , 344330) Houghton Mifflin College Div.

Reid, Struan, tr. Cultures & Civilizations. 2002. (World Issues Ser.). (Illus.). 45p. (J). lib. bdg. 28.50 (978-1-931983-34-1(8)) Chrysalis Education.

Richardson, Hazel. Life of the Ancient Celts. 2005. (Peoples of the Ancient World Ser.). (Illus.). 32p. (J). (ps-7). pap. (978-0-7787-2075-1(6)); lib. bdg. (978-0-7787-2045-4(4)) Crabtree Publishing Co.

—Life of the Ancient Vikings. 2005. (Peoples of the Ancient World Ser.). (Illus.). 32p. (J). (ps-9). (978-0-7787-2044-7(6)); pap. (978-0-7787-2074-4(8)) Crabtree Publishing Co.

Romero, Libby. Discover People. 2006. pap. 39.00 (***978-1-4108-6485-7(5)***) Benchmark Education Co.

Rossi, Ann. Two Cultures Meet: Native American & European. 2002. (Reading Expeditions Ser.). (Illus.). 40p. (J). (978-0-7922-8679-0(0)) National Geographic Society.

Southwater Staff. Encyclopedia of Civilizations, Explorers & Conquerers. 2000. (Illus.). 256p. (J). 29.95 (978-1-84215-157-0(6)) Anness Publishing, Inc.

Tanaka, Shelley. Secrets of the Mummies: Uncovering the Bodies of Ancient Egyptians. 2001. (I Was There Bk.). (Illus.). (J). (978-0-606-20900-7(X)) Tandem Library Bks.

Wilson, Amber. Jamaica — the Culture. 2003. (Lands, Peoples, & Cultures Ser.). (Illus.). 32p. (J). pap. (978-0-7787-9700-5(7)) Crabtree Publishing Co.

Wonders of the World Set. 2000. (J). 67.80 (978-0-7910-6051-3(9) , Chelsea Hse.) Facts On File, Inc.

CIVILIZATION, AMERICAN

Benchmark Education Staff, compiled by. Civilizations of the Americas. 2006. spiral bd. 330.00 (***978-1-4108-7008-7(1)***); 2006. spiral bd. 159.00 (***978-1-4108-7110-7(X)***); 2005. (J). spiral bd. 265.00 (***978-1-4108-5768-2(9)***) Benchmark Education Co.

Cooper, Debbie, illus. Ancient Maya: Cultures of the Caribbean & Central America, 2 bks. l.t. ed. 2005. 32p. (J). per. 9.99 (978-0-9760406-1-3(1) , A Kidz World) ABUAA, Inc.

—The Garifuna: Cultures of the Caribbean & Central America, l.t. ed. 2005. 32p. (J). 9.99 (978-0-9760406-0-6(3) , 6-0-3, A Kidz World) ABUAA, Inc.

Green, et al. Encyclopedia of Ancient Americas. 2000. (Illus.). 256p. (J). (gr. 3-7). (978-1-84215-186-0(X) , Southwater) Anness Publishing.

CIVILIZATION, ANCIENT

see also Prehistoric Peoples

Adams, Simon. The Kingfisher Atlas of the Ancient World. Kingfisher Editors, ed. 2006. (Illus.). 48p. (J). (gr. 4-6). 15.95 (978-0-7534-5914-0(0) , Kingfisher) Houghton Mifflin Co. Trade & Reference Div.

Ali, Daud, et al. Great Civilizations of the East: Discover the Remarkable History of Asia & the Far East. 2003. (Illus.). 264p. pap. 19.99 (978-0-7548-1200-5(6)) Anness Publishing GBR. *Dist:* National Bk. Network.

Ancient Civilizations. 2005. (Illus.). 32p. (gr. 4-8). pap. 224.00 (978-0-7910-9089-3(2) , Chelsea Clubhouse) Facts On File, Inc.

Ancient Civilizations. 1999. pap. 29.95 (978-1-930848-68-9(4)) Littleton Coin Co., Inc.

Ancient Civilizations, 10 vols., Set. 2000. (Illus.). (YA). (gr. 5-9). lib. bdg. 319.00 (978-0-7172-9471-8(4) , Grolier) Scholastic Library Publishing.

Ancient Civilizations Classroom Library. (gr. 2-5). lib. bdg. 22.95 (978-0-7368-4552-6(6)) Red Brick Learning.

Ancient Civilizations Collection 2. 2002. (Illus.). pap. (978-0-7398-6028-1(3)) Steck-Vaughn.

Ancient Civilizations Complete Unit. (gr. 2-5). 132.95 (978-0-7368-4551-9(8)) Red Brick Learning.

Ancient Civilizations Series. 2006. (Illus.). (J). (gr. 4-6). 106.40 (978-0-7565-1700-7(1)) Compass Point Bks.

Ancient Civilizations Series. 2001. (J). Set 1. pap. (978-0-7398-4672-8(8)); Set 2. (Illus.). pap. (978-0-7398-4934-7(4)) Steck-Vaughn.

Antram, David, illus. You Wouldn't Want To... Ancient Civilization, 4 bks., Set. Incl. You Wouldn't Want to Be a Sumerian Slave! A Life of Hard Labor You'd Rather Avoid. Morley, Jacqueline. 28.50 (***978-0-531-18728-9(4)***); You Wouldn't Want to Be an Assyrian Soldier! An Ancient Army You'd Rather Not Join. Matthews, Rupert. 28.50 (***978-0-531-18727-2(6)***); You Wouldn't Want to Be Cleopatra! An Egyptian Ruler You'd Rather Not Be. Pipe, Jim. 28.50 (***978-0-531-18726-5(8)***); You Wouldn't Want to Be Tutankhamen! A Mummy Who Really Got Meddled With. Stewart, David. 28.50 (***978-0-531-18725-8(X)***); (Illus.). 32p. (J). (gr. 2-5). 2007. 114.00 (***978-0-531-17738-9(6)*** , Watts, Franklin) Scholastic Library Publishing.

Ardagh, Philip. The Romans. 2001. (History Detectives Ser.). (Illus.). 64p. (J). (gr. 3 up). 16.95 (978-0-87226-631-5(1) , 66311B, Bedrick, Peter Bks.) School Specialty Publishing.

Barron's Educational Editorial Staff. The Pharaohs of Ancient Egypt. 1998. (Megascope Ser.). (Illus.). 64p. (J). (gr. 3-7). 6.95 (978-0-7641-5096-8(0)) Barron's Educational Series, Inc.

The Beginning of Civilization in Sumer: The Advent of Written Communication. (YA). (gr. 6-9). spiral bd., tchr.'s planning gde. ed. 11.50 (978-0-382-40978-3(7)) Cobblestone Publishing Co.

Benchmark Education Staff, compiled by. Ancient Civilization. 2005. (English Explorers Ser.). (J). spiral bd. 265.00 (***978-1-4108-5772-9(7)***) Benchmark Education Co.

—Ancient Civilizations. 2006. spiral bd. 330.00 (***978-1-4108-7012-4(X)***); spiral bd. 169.00 (***978-1-4108-7140-4(1)***) Benchmark Education Co.

—Early River Civilizations. 2006. spiral bd. 330.00 (***978-1-4108-7011-7(1)***); 2006. spiral bd. 169.00 (***978-1-4108-7139-8(8)***); 2005. (J). spiral bd. 265.00 (***978-1-4108-5773-6(5)***) Benchmark Education Co.

—Social Studies Theme: Ancient Civilizations. 2005. spiral bd. 115.00 (***978-1-4108-5327-1(6)***) Benchmark Education Co.

—Social Studies Theme: Early River Civilizations. 2005. spiral bd. 115.00 (***978-1-4108-5325-7(X)***) Benchmark Education Co.

Biography from Ancient Civilizations, 6 Bks, Set. (Illus.). (gr. 4-8). lib. bdg. (978-1-58415-320-7(2)) Mitchell Lane Pubs., Inc.

Boehm, Richard G., et al. Activity Books: Ancient Civilizations. (Harcourt Brace Social Studies). (gr. k-7). 1999. pap., act. bk. ed. 20.00 (978-0-15-310313-1(2)); 1998. pap., act. bk. ed. 10.90 (978-0-15-310309-4(4)) Harcourt Schl. Pubs.

—Assessment Programs: Ancient Civilizations. 1999. (Harcourt Brace Social Studies). (gr. k-7). pap. 95.10 (978-0-15-310302-5(7)) Harcourt Schl. Pubs.

—Daily Geography: Ancient Civilizations. 1999. (Harcourt Brace Social Studies). (gr. k-7). pap. 41.00 (978-0-15-310430-5(9)) Harcourt Schl. Pubs.

—Game Time! Ancient Civilizations. 1998. (Harcourt Brace Social Studies). (gr. k-7). pap. 9.40 (978-0-15-312369-6(9)) Harcourt Schl. Pubs.

—People & Civilizations in World History. 1999. (Harcourt Brace Social Studies). (gr. k-7). pap. 8.60 (978-0-15-314199-7(9)) Harcourt Schl. Pubs.

—Reading Support & Test Preparation: Ancient Civilizations. 1998. (Harcourt Brace Social Studies). (gr. k-7). pap. 32.70 (978-0-15-312395-5(8)) Harcourt Schl. Pubs.

—Social Studies Libraries: Ancient Civilizations. 2003. (Harcourt Brace Social Studies). (gr. k-7). 153.80 (978-0-15-310447-3(3)) Harcourt Schl. Pubs.

Brewer, Paul. Warfare in the Ancient World. 1999. (History of Warfare Ser.). (Illus.). 80p. (YA). (gr. 7-12). lib. bdg. 29.97 (978-0-8172-5442-1(0)) Raintree.

Breyer, Michelle. Ancient Civilizations Brain Teasers. 1998. (Brain Teasers Ser.). (Illus.). 80p. (YA). (gr. 5-8). pap., tchr. ed. 9.99 (978-1-57690-215-8(3) , TCA2215) Teacher Created Materials, Inc.

Brookes, Philip. Great Civilizations: Discover the People & Places of Long Ago. 2003. (History Detectives Ser.). (Illus.). 64p. pap. 7.99 (978-1-84215-695-7(0) , Southwater) Anness Publishing GBR. *Dist:* National Bk. Network.

Brooks, Philip, et al. From the Stone Age to the Space Age. 2003. (Illustrated History Encyclopedia Ser.). (Illus.). 264p. (gr. 3-7). pap. 19.99 (978-0-7548-1202-9(2)) Anness Publishing GBR. *Dist:* National Bk. Network.

Callella, Trisha. Integrating Ancient Civilizations with Reading Instruction. Walter, LaDawn, ed. Campbell, Jenny, illus. 2002. 72p. (J). (gr. 5-7). pap. 10.99 (978-1-57471-907-9(6) , 2832) Creative Teaching Pr., Inc.

Coletti, Sharon. Everything You Need to Teach Ancient Civilizations. 2005. (YA). ring bd. 149.95 (978-1-933558-10-3(5)) InspirEd Educators.

Coupe, Robert. People from the Past. 1999. (Explorers Ser.). (Illus.). 32p. (J). (978-0-7699-0499-3(8)) Shortland Pubns. (U. S. A.) Inc.

Cox, Reg. Seven Wonders of the Ancient World. 2000. (Wonders of the World Ser.). (Illus.). 32p. (J). (gr. 4-7). 21.95 (978-0-7910-6046-9(2) , Chelsea Hse.) Facts On File, Inc.

Cultures of the World: Group 10, 6 vols. 2nd ed. 2006. (Illus.). 144p. (YA). (gr. 6 up). lib. bdg. 222.43 (978-0-7614-2023-1(1) , Benchmark Bks.) Cavendish, Marshall Corp.

Deady, Kathleen W. & Dubois, Muriel L. Ancient China. 2004. (Illus.). 48p. (J). 17.95 (978-0-7368-2466-8(9) , Bridgestone Bks.) Capstone Pr., Inc.

Eagan, Robynne. Medieval Times. Mitchell, Judy, ed. Baird, Philip, photos by. 2002. (Exploring Ancient Civilizations Ser.). (Illus.). 48p. (J). (gr. 3-6). pap., tchr. ed. 7.95 (978-1-57310-308-4(X)) Teaching & Learning Co.

Ellermeyer, Deborah & Rowell, Judy. Ancient Civilizations Reader's Theater Vol. 2246: Develop Reading Fluency & Text Comprehension Skills. Hults, Alaska, ed. Hillam, Corbin & Vangsgard, Amy, illus. 2004. 96p. (J). pap. 12.99 (978-1-59198-041-4(0) , 2246) Creative Teaching Pr., Inc.

Forbes, Claire. Ancient Peoples. 2000. (J). (978-0-606-20291-6(9)) Tandem Library Bks.

Gandiol-Coppin, Brigitte. Ancient Civilizations. Logue, Mary, tr. 2000. (Creative Discoveries Ser.). (Illus.). 80p. (J). (gr. 4 up). lib. bdg. 25.30 (978-0-88682-949-0(6) , Creative Education) Creative Co., The.

Gray, Susan Heinrichs. Scholastic News Nonfiction Readers: Prehistoric World, 6 bks., Set. Incl. Dinosaur Armor. 19.00 (978-0-531-17481-4(6)); Dinosaur Dig! 19.00 (***978-0-531-17482-1(4)***); Dinosaur Eggs. 19.00 (***978-0-531-17483-8(2)***); Dinosaur Teeth. 19.00 (978-0-531-17484-5(0)); Dinosaur Tracks. 19.00 (***978-0-531-17485-2(9)***); Is It a Dinosaur? 19.00 (***978-0-531-17486-9(7)***); (Illus.). 24p. (J). (gr. 1-2). 2007. 2007. 114.00 (***978-0-531-12605-9(6)*** , Children's Pr.) Scholastic Library Publishing.

Greene, Jacqueline Dembar. Slavery in Ancient Greece & Rome. 2000. (History of Slavery Library). (Illus.). 64p. (J). (gr. 5-7). 25.50 (978-0-531-11693-7(X) , Watts, Franklin) Scholastic Library Publishing.

—Slavery in Ancient Greece & Rome. 2000. (gr. 3-6). lib. bdg. 17.60 (978-0-613-34473-9(1)) Tandem Library Bks.

Grolier Educational Staff, contrib. by. Ancient Civilizations. 2000. (J). (978-0-7172-9472-5(2)); (978-0-7172-9473-2(0)) Scholastic Library Publishing. (Grolier).

Handbook to Life Set, 9 vols., Set. 2006. (Handbook to Life Ser.). 400p. (gr. 9). 630.00 (978-0-8160-6811-1(9)) Facts On File, Inc.

Harcourt School Publishers Staff. Ancient Civilization. 2nd ed. 2003. (Horizons Ser.). (Illus.). (gr. k-7). act. bk. ed. 9.80 (978-0-15-335783-1(5)) Harcourt Schl. Pubs.

—Ancient Civilizations. 2nd ed. 2002. (Horizons Ser.). (gr. k-7). pap., tchr. ed., act. bk. ed. 23.30 (978-0-15-335784-8(3)) Harcourt Schl. Pubs.

—Horizons: Ancient Civilizations. 2nd ed. 2002. (Harcourt Horizons Ser.). (gr. 4-7). tchr. ed. 196.90 (978-0-15-335782-4(7)) Harcourt Schl. Pubs.

—Horizons with Ancient Civilizations. 4th ed. 2004. (gr. 3). 53.20 (978-0-15-344221-6(2)) Harcourt Schl. Pubs.

—Horizons with Ancient Civilizations, Grade 3. 4th ed. 2004. Vol. 1. tchr. ed. 104.40 (978-0-15-344222-3(0)); Vol. 2. tchr. ed. 104.40 (978-0-15-344223-0(9)) Harcourt Schl. Pubs.

—Social Studies: Ancient Civilizations. 1998. (Harcourt Brace Social Studies). (gr. k-7). tchr. ed. 196.30 (978-0-15-309799-7(X)) Harcourt Schl. Pubs.

Haywood, John. Art & Entertainment: Art, Culture & Entertainment Through the Ages. 2004. (How We Lived Ser.). (Illus.). 64p. pap. 7.99 (978-1-84215-896-8(1) , Southwater) Anness Publishing GBR. *Dist:* National Bk. Network.

—Everyday Life in the Ancient World. 2003. (Illustrated History Encyclopedia Ser.). (Illus.). 264p. pap. 19.99 (978-0-7548-1224-1(3)) Anness Publishing GBR. *Dist:* National Bk. Network.

—Farming & Trade: Work, Trade & Farming Through the Ages. 2003. (How We Lived Ser.). (Illus.). 64p. (gr. 3-7). pap. 7.99 (978-1-84215-813-5(9) , Southwater) Anness Publishing GBR. *Dist:* National Bk. Network.

—Tribes & Empires. 2004. (Illus.). 64p. pap. 8.99 (978-1-84215-957-6(7) , Southwater) Anness Publishing GBR. *Dist:* National Bk. Network.

History News, 10 bks. Incl. Aztec News. Steele, Philip. 2001. lib. bdg. 24.67 (978-0-8368-2777-4(5)); Egyptian News. Steedman, Scott. 2000. lib. bdg. 24.67 (978-0-8368-2719-4(8)); Explorers. Johnstone, Michael. 2001. lib. bdg. 24.67 (978-0-8368-2875-7(5)); Greek News. Powell, Anton & Steele, Philip. 2000. lib. bdg. 24.67 (978-0-8368-2720-0(1)); In Space. Johnstone, Michael. 2001. lib. bdg. 24.67 (978-0-8368-2876-4(3)); Medicine. Gates, Phil. 2001. lib. bdg. 24.67 (978-0-8368-2877-1(1)); Revolution. Maynard, Christopher. 2001. lib. bdg. 24.67 (978-0-8368-2878-8(X)); Roman News. Langley, Andrew. 2000. lib. bdg. 24.67 (978-0-8368-2721-7(X)); Stone Age News. MacDonald, Fiona. 2001. lib. bdg. 24.67 (978-0-8368-2778-1(3)); Viking News. Wright, Rachel. 2001. lib. bdg. 24.67 (978-0-8368-2779-8(1)); 32p. (J). (gr. 3 up). (Illus.). Set lib. bdg. 246.70 (978-0-8368-2984-6(0)) Stevens, Gareth Inc.

History Pockets: Ancient Civilizations. 2003. (Illus.). 96p. (J). (gr. 1-3). suppl. ed. 12.99 (978-1-55799-900-9(7) , EMC 3701) Evan-Moor Educational Pubs.

Hook, Jason. Lost Cities. 2001. (Young Library - Mysteries of the Past). (Illus.). 32p. (J). (gr. 3-5). lib. bdg. 25.69 (978-0-7398-4337-6(0)) Raintree.

—Lost Cities. 2003. (gr. 3-6). lib. bdg. 16.40 (978-0-613-78227-2(5)) Tandem Library Bks.

Hurdman, Charlotte, et al. Ancient World: How People Lived in the Stone Age, Ancient Egypt, Ancient Greec & the Roman Empire. 2003. (Illustrated History Encyclopedia Ser.). (Illus.). 264p. (gr. 3-7). pap. 19.99 (978-0-7548-1199-2(9) , Lorenz Bks.) Anness Publishing GBR. *Dist:* National Bk. Network.

Hurdman, Main & Steele. Encyclopedia of the Ancient World. 2000. (Illus.). 256p. (J). 29.95 (978-1-84215-072-6(3) , Southwater) Anness Publishing GBR. *Dist:* Hachette Bk. Group.

Hynson, Colin. Ancient Civilizations. 2005. 120.00 (978-0-8368-6188-4(4)) Stevens, Gareth Inc.

Innes, Brian. Mysteries of the Ancients. 1999. (Unsolved Mysteries Ser.). (Illus.). 48p. (YA). (gr. 3 up). lib. bdg. 25.69 (978-0-8172-5481-0(1)) Raintree.

Johnson, Terri, compiled by. What Really Happened in Ancient Times: A Collection of Historical Biographies, 4. 2006. (Illus.). 240p. (J). per. 15.95 (***978-1-932786-21-7(X)***) Knowledge Quest.

Knight, Judson. Ancient Civilizations, 2 vols. McConnell, Stacy A. & Baker, Lawrence W., eds. 1999. (Illus.). (J). (978-0-7876-3984-6(2) , UXL) Thomson Gale.

—Ancient Civilizations: Almanac, 2 vols., Set. McConnell, Stacy A., ed. 2000. (Ancient Civilizations Reference Library). (Illus.). 419p. (J). (gr. 6-9). lib. bdg. 120.00 (978-0-7876-3982-2(6) , GML00502-113788, UXL) Thomson Gale.

—Ancient Civilizations: Biographies. McConnell, Stacy A., ed. 2000. (Ancient Civilizations Reference Library). (Illus.). xlvii, 207p. (J). (gr. 4-7). 67.00 (978-0-7876-3985-3(0) , GML00502-113791, UXL) Thomson Gale.

Knight, Judson & McConnell, Stacy A., eds. Ancient Civilizations, 2 vols. 1999. (Illus.). xlv, 215p. (J). (978-0-7876-3983-9(4)) Thomson Gale.

Larson. The Anasazis. 2000. (Ancient Civilizations Ser.). (Illus.). (J). pap. (978-0-7398-4153-2(X)) Steck-Vaughn.

Let's See Library - Ancient Civilizations, 4 bks. Incl. Ancient Egypt. Klingel, Cynthia Fitterer & Noyed, Robert B. lib. bdg. 19.93 (978-0-7565-0291-1(8)); Ancient Greece. Klingel, Cynthia Fitterer & Noyed, Robert B. lib. bdg. 19.93 (978-0-7565-0293-5(4)); Ancient Mesopotamia. Klingel, Cynthia Fitterer & Noyed, Robert B. lib. bdg. 19.93 (978-0-7565-0294-2(2)); Ancient Rome. Raatma, Lucia. lib. bdg. 19.95 (978-0-7565-0292-8(6)); 24p. (J). (gr. 1 up). 2002. (Illus.). 2003. Set lib. bdg. 79.72 (978-0-7565-0402-1(3)) Compass Point Bks.

Levy, Elizabeth. Awesome Ancient Ancestors. 2001. (America's Horrible Histories Ser.: No. 2). (Illus.). 128p. (J). (gr. 4-6). pap. 4.99 (978-0-590-10795-2(X)) Scholastic, Inc.

MacDonald, Fiona. Women in Ancient Rome. 2000. (Other Half of History Ser.). (Illus.). 48p. (J). (gr. 3 up). 17.95 (978-0-87226-570-7(6) , 65706B, Bedrick, Peter Bks.) School Specialty Publishing.

Madgwick, Wendy. Questions & Answers: Ancient Civilizations. 2000. (978-0-606-20871-0(2)) Tandem Library Bks.

Marks, Anthony & Tingay, Graham. Romans - Internet Linked. 2005. (Illustrated World History Ser.). 96p. (J). pap. 12.95 (978-0-7945-0429-8(9) , Usborne) EDC Publishing.

Mason, Paul. The Mystery of Stone Circles. 2002. (Can Science Solve? Ser.). 32p. (J). (gr. 4-7). (Illus.). lib. bdg. 22.79 (978-1-58810-667-4(5)); pap. 7.50 (978-1-58810-930-9(5)) Heinemann Library.

McGraw-Hill Staff. Journey Across Time: Early Ages, Course 1. 2004. stu. ed. 71.96 (978-0-07-860309-9(9) , 9780078603099) Glencoe/McGraw-Hill.

Merrill, Yvonne Y. Ancient People Vol. 1: Art Activities about Mesopotamia, Egypt, & Islam. Simpson, Mary, illus. 2003. (Hands-on Ser.). 88p. (J). (gr. 2-9). pap. 20.00 (978-0-9643177-8-9(8)) KITS Publishing.

Mitchell Lane Publishers. Biography from Ancient Civilizations. 2007. (Biography from Ancient Civilizations Ser.). (J). lib. bdg. 838.60 (***978-1-58415-546-1(9)***) Mitchell Lane Pubs., Inc.

Morris, Neil. Ancient World. 2003. (Knowledge Masters Ser.). (Illus.). 32p. (YA). pap. incl. cd-rom (978-1-903954-49-2(5)) Chrysalis Children's Bks.

Morris, Neil. Lost Cities. 2007. (J). (***978-1-59920-108-5(9)***) Smart Apple Media.

Nardo, Don. Ancient Greece. 2005. (World History Ser.). (Illus.). 112p. (YA). (gr. 7-10). lib. bdg. 32.45 (978-1-59018-651-0(6) , Lucent Bks.) Thomson Gale.

Panchyk, Richard. Archaeology for Kids: Uncovering the Mysteries of Our Past. 2001. (For Kids Ser.). (Illus.). 160p. (J). pap. 14.95 (978-1-55652-395-3(5)) Chicago Review Pr., Inc.

People from the Past: Level Q, 6 vols., Vol. 3. (Explorers Ser.). 32p. (gr. 3-6). 44.95 (978-0-7699-0623-2(0)) Shortland Pubns. (U. S. A.) Inc.

Pickels, Dwayne E. Ancient Warriors. 1998. (Costume, Tradition & Culture). (Illus.). 64p. (YA). 19.75 (978-0-7910-5166-5(8) , Chelsea Hse.) Facts On File, Inc.

Primary Sources of Ancient Civilizations. (Primary Source Big Bookstm Ser.). 24p. (J). (gr. 4-8). 46.40 (978-0-8239-4590-0(1)) Rosen Publishing Group, Inc., The.

Raintree Steck-Vaughn Staff. Mysteries of the Ancients. 1998. (Unsolved Mysteries Ser.). (Illus.). (J). pap. 8.05 (978-0-8172-4278-7(3)) Steck-Vaughn.

—Mysteries of the Past Series, 5 bks., Set. 2003. (Illus.). pap. 40.30 (978-1-4109-0127-9(0)) Raintree.

Rinaldo, Denise. Cities of the Dead. 2007. (24/7 - Science Behind the Scenes Ser.). 64p. (J). (gr. 8-12). 26.00 (978-0-531-12079-8(1) , Watts, Franklin) Scholastic Library Publishing.

Rinaldo, Denise. Cities of the Dead: Finding Lost Civilizations. 2008. (24/7: Science Behind the Scenes: Mystery Files Ser.). 64p. (J). pap. 7.95 (***978-0-531-18739-5(X)*** , Watts, Franklin) Scholastic Library Publishing.

Schomp, Virginia. Ancient Mesopotamia. 2004. (People of the Ancient World Ser.). (J). 29.50 (978-0-531-11818-4(5) , Watts, Franklin) Scholastic Library Publishing.

Sheehan, Sean & Levy, Patricia M. Rome. 1999. (Ancient World Ser.). (Illus.). 63p. (YA). (gr. 5-10). lib. bdg. 27.12 (978-0-8172-5057-7(3)) Raintree.

Shone, Rob. Ancient Treasures. Spender, Nick, illus. 2007. (Graphic Discoveries Ser.). (J). 48p. (gr. 3-7). lib. bdg. (***978-1-4042-1089-9(X)***); (***978-1-4042-9594-0(1)***); pap. (***978-1-4042-9593-3(3)***) Rosen Publishing Group, Inc., The.

Shukin, Barbara. Ancient History Portfolio: A History of First Civilizations Through the Classical Age. 2004. (J). spiral bd. 24.95 (978-0-9762918-0-0(0)) Homeschool Journey.

Shuter, Jane. The Indus Valley. 2003. (History Opens Windows Ser.). (Illus.). 32p. (J). (gr. 2-4). lib. bdg. 22.79 (978-1-4034-0253-0(1)); pap. 7.50 (978-1-4034-0081-9(4)) Heinemann Library.

Sloan, Frank, ed. Ancient Civilizations, 6 bks., Set. Incl. Anasazis. lib. bdg. 22.83 (978-0-7398-3575-3(0)); China. Deedrick, Tami. lib. bdg. 22.83 (978-0-7398-3580-7(7)); Egypt. Steele, Christy. lib. bdg. 22.83 (978-0-7398-3576-0(9)); Greece. Steele, Christy. lib. bdg. 22.83 (978-0-7398-3577-7(7)); Maya. Deedrick, Tami. lib. bdg. 22.83 (978-0-7398-3585-2(8)); Rome. Steele, Christy. lib. bdg. 22.83 (978-0-7398-3578-4(5)); (J). (gr. 4-7). (Illus.). 48p. 2001. Set lib. bdg. 95.88 (978-0-7398-3587-6(4)) Raintree.

Steck-Vaughn Staff. Ancient Civilizations Series. Set 1. 2000. pap., tchr. ed. (978-0-7398-4156-3(4)); Set 2. 2001. pap., tchr. ed. (978-0-7398-4933-0(6)) Steck-Vaughn.

Steele, Philip. Wonders of the World. 2007. (Kingfisher Knowledge Ser.). (Illus.). 64p. (J). (gr. 3-5). 12.95 (978-0-7534-5979-9(5) , Kingfisher) Houghton Mifflin Co. Trade & Reference Div.

Sylvester, Diane. Ancient Civilization Mysteries. Clark Editorial and Design Staff, ed. Parks, Kathy, illus. 1998. 112p. (J). (gr. 5-8). pap. 13.99 (978-0-88160-307-1(4) , LW-376, Learning Works, The) Creative Teaching Pr., Inc.

Tagholm, Sally, et al. Everyday Life in the Ancient World: A Guide to Travel in Ancient Times. 2002. (Illus.). 128p. (J). (gr. 5-9). tchr. ed. 15.95 (978-0-7534-5464-0(5) , Kingfisher) Houghton Mifflin Co. Trade & Reference Div.

Tames, Richard. Ancient World, the Illus Children. 2007. (Illus.). 512p. pap. 19.99 (***978-1-84476-406-8(0)*** , Southwater) Anness Publishing GBR. *Dist:* National Bk. Network.

Tung, Anthony M. Wonders of Civilization Fandex. 2007. (Illus.). 50p. (J). 9.95 (***978-0-7611-4355-0(6)***) Workman Publishing Co., Inc.

Waring, Diana. Ancient Civilizations & the Bible Elementary Activity Book Bk. A: A Digging Deeper Study Guide Activity Book. Waring, Isaac, photos by. 1999. (Illus.). 91p. (J). pap., stu. ed. 11.95 (978-1-930514-13-3(1)) Diana Waring Presents.

Wilkinson, Philip. Civilizations, Exploration & Conquest: The Illustrated History Encyclopedia. 2001. (gr. 3-6). lib. bdg. 30.35 (978-0-613-82097-4(5)) Tandem Library Bks.

Williams, Brenda & Williams, Brian. Trading Up: Indus Valley Trade. 2007. (J). (***978-1-4109-2892-4(6)***); pap. (***978-1-4109-2899-3(3)***) Steck-Vaughn.

Willis, Laurie J. Early Civilizations Fact Cards. Taylor, Lior, illus. 1998. 84p. (YA). (gr. 5-8). ring bd. 36.00 (978-1-884925-57-3(X)) Toucan Valley Pubns., Inc.

Women in the Ancient Near East: Stories & Primary Sources from the Sumerians through the Early Israelites. l.t. ed. 1999. 94p. (YA). spiral bd. 16.95 net. (978-1-890380-07-6(5)) Women in World History Curriculum.

Wood, A. J. Errata: A Book of Historical Errors. Alles, Hamesh, illus. 1999. 32p. (J). (gr. 5-8). pap. 17.00 (978-0-7881-6206-0(3)) DIANE Publishing Co.

CIVILIZATION—FICTION

Cohat, Yves, et al. Los Vikingos. Gonzalez Batlle, Jorge, tr. 2005. (Tras los pasos de ... Ser.). (SPA., Illus.). 128p. (J). pap. 14.95 (978-84-9801-002-2(0)) Blume ESP. *Dist:* Independent Pubs. Group.

Crew, Gary & Tan, Shaun. The Viewer. 2003. (Illus.). 32p. (gr. 1-6). 16.95 (978-1-894965-02-6(7)) Simply Read Bks. CAN. *Dist:* Perseus Distribution.

Driscoll, Laura. My Brother, the Knight. Smath, Jerry, illus. 2004. 32p. (J). lib. bdg. 20.00 (***978-1-4242-1109-8(3)***) Fitzgerald Bks.

—My Brother, the Knight. Smath, Jerry, illus. 2004. (Social Studies Connects). 32p. (J). (gr. 1-3). pap. 4.99 (978-1-57565-140-8(8)) Kane Pr., The.

Eliet, David F. The Oldest Story Ever Told. 2000. (J). pap. 7.00 (978-0-87602-377-8(4)) Anchorage Pr.

Fleischman, Paul. Weslandia. 2002. (Illus.). (J). 23.40 (978-0-7587-3948-3(6)) Book Wholesalers, Inc.

—Weslandia. braille ed. 2004. (Illus.). (J). (gr. k-3). spiral bd. (978-0-616-01641-1(7)) Canadian National Institute for the Blind/Institut National Canadien pour les Aveugles.

—Weslandia. Hawkes, Kevin, illus. 40p. (J). (ps-3). 2002. pap. 6.99 (978-0-7636-1052-4(6)); 1999. 15.99 (978-0-7636-0006-8(7)) Candlewick Pr.

—Weslandia. Hawkes, Kevin, illus. 2001. (J). (gr. k-4). 26.95 incl. audio (978-0-8045-6869-2(3) , 6869) Spoken Arts, Inc.

—Weslandia. 2002. (gr. k-3). lib. bdg. 14.15 (978-0-613-63531-8(0)) Tandem Library Bks.

Gilligan, Shannon. Struggle down Under. 2007. (Choose Your Own Adventure Ser.: No. 21). (Illus.). 144p. (J). (gr. 3-7). pap. 6.99 (***978-1-933390-21-5(2)***) Chooseco LLC.

Iturralde, Edna. Caminantes del Sol. Gonzalez, Santiago et al, illus. (SPA.). 163p. (J). (gr. 5-8). pap. 14.95 (978-9978-07-431-2(7)) Santillana USA Publishing Co., Inc.

Lavender, William. The Invisible People: A Musical Play. 2000. (J). (gr. 1-8). 7.00 (978-0-87602-400-3(2)) Anchorage Pr.

Mirza, Sandrine. Marco Polo. Gonzalez Batlle, Jorge, tr. 2005. (Tras los pasos de ... Ser.). (SPA., Illus.). 128p. (J). pap. 14.95 (978-84-89396-03-6(5)) Blume ESP. *Dist:* Independent Pubs. Group.

Reformation & Enlightenment. 2004. (Stories in History Ser.). (gr. 6-12). (978-0-618-14223-1(1) , 2-00243) McDougal Littell Inc.

Tomkins, D. Michael. The World Below. 2006. (YA). lib. bdg. 39.95 (978-0-9774451-2-7(7)) DSA Publishing & Design, Inc.

Verdi, Alida. El Nino, el Perro y el Platillo Volador. 2001. (J). (978-956-240-345-0(9)) Arrayan Editores S.A.

Wagner, Edward. The Second People: The Beginning. 2000. (Second People Ser.). 396p. (YA). mass mkt. 14.00 (978-0-9679422-0-9(9)) Wagner Publishing.

CIVILIZATION, GREEK

Adare, Sierra. Greece - The People. 1998. (Lands, Peoples & Cultures Ser.). (Illus.). 32p. (J). (gr. 4-5). (978-0-86505-227-7(1)) Crabtree Publishing Co.

Altman, Susan. Ancient Greece. 2001. (gr. 3-6). lib. bdg. 18.75 (978-0-613-53910-4(9)) Tandem Library Bks.

The Ancient Greeks. 2002. (History Makers Ser.). 32p. (J). 9.95 (978-0-7525-7826-2(X)) Parragon, Inc.

Apel, Melanie Ann. Art & Religion in Ancient Greece. 2004. (Primary Sources of Ancient Civilizations Ser.). (Illus.). 24p. (J). lib. bdg. (978-0-8239-8938-6(0)); lib. bdg. 19.95 (978-0-8239-6770-4(0)) Rosen Publishing Group, Inc., The. (PowerKids Pr.).

—Land & Resources in Ancient Greece. 2004. (Primary Sources of Ancient Civilizations Ser.). (Illus.). 24p. (J). lib. bdg. 19.95 (978-0-8239-6769-8(7) , PowerKids Pr.) Rosen Publishing Group, Inc., The.

—Land & Resources of Ancient Greece. 2004. (Primary Sources of Ancient Civilizations Ser.). (Illus.). 24p. (J). lib. bdg. (978-0-8239-8937-9(2) , PowerKids Pr.) Rosen Publishing Group, Inc., The.

Armentrout, David & Armentrout, Patricia. Greece. 2003. (Timelines of Ancient Civilizations Ser.). (Illus.). 32p. (J). 28.50 (978-1-58952-722-5(4)) Rourke Publishing, LLC.

Bailey, Linda. Adventures in Ancient Greece. Slavin, Bill, illus. 2004. (Good Times Travel Agency Ser.). 48p. (J). (gr. 4-6). (978-1-55074-536-8(0)); (978-1-55074-534-4(4)) Kids Can Pr., Ltd.

—Adventures in Ancient Greece. Slavin, Bill, illus. 2002. 48p. (J). (gr. 4-7). lib. bdg. 16.40 (978-0-613-70945-3(4)) Tandem Library Bks.

Baker, Rosalie F. & Baker, Charles F. Ancient Greece: A Student Companion. 2006. (J). (978-0-19-514286-0(1)) Oxford Univ. Pr., Inc.

Bargallo I Chaves, Eva. Greece. 2005. (Ancient Civilizations Ser.). (Illus.). 32p. (J). (gr. 4-8). lib. bdg. 28.00 (978-0-7910-8605-6(4) , Chelsea Clubhouse) Facts On File, Inc.

Benduhn, Tea. Ancient Greece. 2006. (Illus.). 24p. (J). pap. (***978-0-8368-7787-8(X)***); (gr. 1-3). lib. bdg. 19.93 (***978-0-8368-7782-3(9)***) Stevens, Gareth Inc. (Weekly Reader Early Learning Library).

Broida, Marian. Projects about Ancient Greece. 2006. (Hands-On History Ser.). (Illus.). 48p. (J). (gr. 4-6). lib. bdg. 29.93 (978-0-7614-2259-4(5) , Benchmark Bks.) Cavendish, Marshall Corp.

Califf, David J. Marathon. 2002. (Battles That Changed the World Ser.). (Illus.). 112p. (J). (gr. 7-10). 30.00 (978-0-7910-6679-9(7) , Chelsea Hse.) Facts On File, Inc.

Chrisp, Peter. Ancient Greece. 2000. (My World Ser.). (Illus.). (J). 14.75 (978-0-606-21904-4(8)) Tandem Library Bks.

—Ancient Greece. 1998. (My World Ser.). (Illus.). 32p. (J). (gr. 2-7). (978-0-7166-9406-9(9)) World Bk., Inc.

—Ancient Greece: Come & Discover My World. 2002. (gr. 3-6). lib. bdg. 16.40 (978-0-613-43294-8(0)) Tandem Library Bks.

Chrisp, Peter & Dorling Kindersley Publishing Staff. Ancient Greece. 2003. (Revealed Ser.). (Illus.). 48p. (J). 12.99 (978-0-7894-9271-5(7)) Dorling Kindersley Publishing, Inc.

Clare, John D. Ancient Greece. 2004. (Historic Civilizations Ser.). 32p. (J). lib. bdg. 24.67 (978-0-8368-4198-5(0)) Stevens, Gareth Inc.

Covert, Kim. Ancient Greece. 2004. (Illus.). 48p. (J). 17.95 (978-0-7368-2468-2(5)) Capstone Pr., Inc.

Dargie, Richard. Look Around a Greek Temple. 2007. (J). (***978-1-84193-720-5(7)***) Smart Apple Media.

Davis, Kevin A. Look What Came from Greece. 1999. (J). (978-0-606-20145-2(9)); (gr. 3-6). lib. bdg. 15.25 (978-0-613-29681-6(8)) Tandem Library Bks.

Denti, Mario. Classical Athens. 2001. (Journey to the Past Ser.). (Illus.). 56p. (J). (gr. 6-8). lib. bdg. 27.12 (978-0-7398-1953-1(4)) Raintree.

Ganeri, Anita. Ancient Greeks. 2005. (Ancient Civilizations Ser.). (Illus.). 32p. (J). (gr. 4-6). 26.60 (978-0-7565-1646-8(3)) Compass Point Bks.

Glencoe McGraw-Hill Staff & McGraw-Hill - Jamestown Education Staff. Jamestown's Early Civilizations: Greek Life. 2001. (gr. 5-12). pap. 11.96 (978-0-8092-9599-9(7) , 9780809295999) Jamestown.

Greenblatt, Miriam. Alexander the Great & Ancient Greece. 1999. (Rulers & Their Times Ser.). (Illus.). 80p. (YA). (gr. 6 up). lib. bdg. 29.93 (978-0-7614-0913-7(0) , Benchmark Bks.) Cavendish, Marshall Corp.

Los Griegos: El Nacimiento de la Democracia y de la Cultura Occidental. (Coleccion Bravo). (SPA., Illus.). (YA). (gr. 5-8). pap. 11.16 (978-84-7131-908-1(X), EDI30264) Editex, Editorial S.A. ESP. *Dist:* Lectorum Pubns., Inc.

Hart, Avery. Ancient Greece. 2001. (Illus.). 17.60 (978-0-606-22457-4(2)) Tandem Library Bks.

Hatt, Christine. Ancient Greece. 2004. (Excavating the Past Ser.). (J). pap. 8.50 (978-1-4034-5457-7(4)); lib. bdg. 29.93 (978-1-4034-4837-8(X)) Heinemann Library.

Hewitt, Sally. The Greeks. 2007. (J). (*978-1-59920-045-3(7)) Smart Apple Media.

Hollingsworth, Patricia L., et al. Classical Greece. 1998. (Sails - Students' Active Interdisciplinary Learning Ser.: Vol. 1). (Illus.). (YA). (gr. 3-12). pap. 20.00 (978-1-893413-00-9(4)) Univ. Schl. at the Univ. of Tulsa.

Hull, Robert. Everyday Life. 2006. (World of Ancient Greece Ser.). (Illus.). 32p. (J). (978-1-59771-059-6(8)) Sea-To-Sea Pubns.

—Greece. 1998. (Ancient World Ser.). (Illus.). 63p. (YA). (gr. 5-10). lib. bdg. 27.12 (978-0-8172-5055-3(7)) Raintree.

Hull, Robert E. Religion & the Gods. 2000. (World of Ancient Greece Ser.). (Illus.). 32p. (J). (gr. 4-8). 24.00 (978-0-531-14539-5(5) , Watts, Franklin) Scholastic Library Publishing.

—Trade & Warfare. 2000. (World of Ancient Greece Ser.). (Illus.). 32p. (J). (gr. 4-8). 24.00 (978-0-531-14540-1(9) , Watts, Franklin) Scholastic Library Publishing.

Hynson, Colin. Ancient Greece. 2006. (Illus.). 48p. (J). pap. (978-0-8368-6242-3(2)); lib. bdg. 30.00 (978-0-8368-6190-7(6)) Stevens, Gareth Inc. (World Almanac Library).

Johnson, Sandi. History Pockets: Ancient Greece. Davis, Cindy, illus. 2003. (History Pockets Ser.). 96p. (J). (gr. 4-6). suppl. ed. 12.99 (978-1-55799-903-0(1) , EMC 3705) Evan-Moor Educational Pubs.

Jovinelly, Joann & Netelkos, Jason. The Crafts & Culture of the Ancient Greeks. 2002. (Crafts of the Ancient World Ser.). (Illus.). 48p. (YA). (gr. 5-8). lib. bdg. 29.25 (978-0-8239-3510-9(8) , Rosen Central) Rosen Publishing Group, Inc., The.

Klingel, Cynthia Fitterer & Noyed, Robert B. Ancient Greece. 2002. (Let's See Library). (Illus.). 24p. (J). (gr. 1 up). lib. bdg. 19.93 (978-0-7565-0293-5(4)) Compass Point Bks.

Landau, Elaine. Exploring Ancient Greece with Elaine Landau. 2005. (Exploring Ancient Civilizations with Elaine Landau Ser.). (Illus.). 48p. (J). (gr. 4-7). lib. bdg. 23.93 (978-0-7660-2342-0(7) , Enslow Elementary) Enslow Pubs., Inc.

Lassieur, Allison. The Ancient Greeks. (People of the Ancient World Ser.). (J). 2005. (Illus.). 112p. (gr. 6-8). pap. 9.95 (978-0-531-16739-7(9)); 2004. 30.50 (978-0-531-12339-3(1)) Scholastic Library Publishing. (Watts, Franklin).

MacDonald, Fiona. The Traveler's Guide to Ancient Greece. Foster, Mike S., illus. 1998. (J). (978-0-590-11762-3(9)) Scholastic, Inc.

Malam, John. Ancient Greece. 2004. (Picturing the Past Ser.). (Illus.). 32p. (J). 15.95 (978-1-59270-022-6(5)) Enchanted Lion Bks., LLC.

—The Ancient Greeks. 1999. (History Starts Here Ser.). (Illus.). 32p. (J). (ps-3). lib. bdg. 25.69 (978-0-7398-1350-8(1)) Raintree.

—Exploring Ancient Greece. 1999. (Remains to Be Seen Ser.). (Illus.). 47p. (YA). (gr. 5-8). (978-0-237-51994-0(1) , Evans Brothers, Limited) Evans Publishing Group.

Martell, Hazel Mary. Myths & Civilization of the Ancient Greeks. Stalio, Ivan & D'Ottavi, Francesca, illus. 2000. (Myths & Civilization Ser.). 48p. (J). (gr. 3 up). 16.95 (978-0-87226-283-6(9) , 62839B, Bedrick, Peter Bks.) School Specialty Publishing.

Maynard, Charles W. The Technology of Ancient Greece. 2005. (Technology of the Ancient World Ser.). (Illus.). 48p. (J). (978-1-4042-0555-0(1)) Rosen Publishing Group, Inc., The.

Middleton, Haydn. Ancient Greek Homes. 2002. (People in the Past Ser.). (Illus.). 48p. (J). (gr. 4-6). lib. bdg. 27.07 (978-1-58810-636-0(5)) Heinemann Library.

—Ancient Greek Jobs. 2002. (People in the Past Ser.). (Illus.). 48p. (J). (gr. 4-6). lib. bdg. 27.07 (978-1-58810-638-4(1)) Heinemann Library.

—Ancient Greek Jobs. 2002. (gr. 3-6). lib. bdg. 17.05 (978-0-613-84765-0(2)) Tandem Library Bks.

—Ancient Greek Women. 2002. (People in the Past Ser.). (Illus.). 48p. (J). (gr. 4-6). lib. bdg. 27.07 (978-1-58810-637-7(3)) Heinemann Library.

Middleton, Haydn & Tames, Richard. Ancient Greek Children. 2002. (People in the Past Ser.). 64p. (J). (gr. 4-7). pap. 8.50 (978-1-4034-0131-1(4) , 91636) Heinemann Library.

—Ancient Greek Homes. 2002. (People in the Past Ser.). 64p. (J). (gr. 4-7). pap. 8.50 (978-1-4034-0132-8(2) , 91637) Heinemann Library.

—Ancient Greek Jobs. 2002. (People in the Past Ser.). 64p. (J). (gr. 4-7). pap. 8.50 (978-1-4034-0133-5(0) , 91638) Heinemann Library.

—Ancient Greek Women. 2002. (People in the Past Ser.). 64p. (J). (gr. 4-7). pap. 8.50 (978-1-4034-0135-9(7) , 91640) Heinemann Library.

Minnis, Ivan. Ancient Greece. 2004. (Illus.). 32p. (J). 26.36 (978-1-4109-0617-5(5)) Harcourt Schl. Pubs.

Morris, Ting. Ancient Greece. 2006. (Arts & Crafts of Ser.). (Illus.). 32p. (J). (978-1-58340-912-1(2) , 1262692) Smart Apple Media.

Moulton, Carroll, ed. Ancient Greece & Rome: An Encyclopedia for Students, 4 vols., Set. 1998. (Illus.). 732p. (YA). (gr. 8 up). 460.00 (978-0-684-80507-8(3) , GML00502-165980, Charles Scribner's Sons) Thomson Gale.

Naden, Corinne J. & Blue, Rose. Ancient Greeks & the Parthenon. 2003. (J). (978-1-58417-314-4(9)); pap. (978-1-58417-315-1(7)) Lake Street Pubs.

Nardo, Don. Ancient Athens. 2002. (Traveler's Guide to Ser.). (Illus.). 112p. (J). (gr. 5). 28.70 (978-1-59018-016-7(X) , Lucent Bks.) Thomson Gale.

—Ancient Greece. (World History Ser.). (Illus.). 112p. 2005. (YA). (gr. 7-10). lib. bdg. 32.45 (978-1-59018-651-0(6)); 2002. (J). 27.45 (978-1-59018-004-4(6)) Thomson Gale. (Lucent Bks.).

—Life in Ancient Greece. 2003. (Life During the Great Civilizations Ser.). (Illus.). 48p. (J). (gr. 3-5). 24.95 (978-1-56711-741-7(4) , Blackbirch Pr., Inc.) Thomson Gale.

—The Parthenon of Ancient Greece. 1998. (Building History Ser.). (Illus.). 96p. (YA). (gr. 6-9). 27.45 (978-1-56006-431-2(5) , Lucent Bks.) Thomson Gale.

—Women of Ancient Greece. 2000. (World History Ser.). (Illus.). 112p. (YA). (gr. 8-11). 32.45 (978-1-56006-646-0(6) , LML00902-178000, Lucent Bks.) Thomson Gale.

O'Connell, Kim A. Ancient Greece: A MyReportLinks. com Book. 2004. (Civilizations of the Ancient World Ser.). (Illus.). 48p. (J). lib. bdg. 25.26 (978-0-7660-5250-5(8) , MyReportLinks.com Bks.) Enslow Pubs., Inc.

The Origins of Greek Civilization (NCHS) (J). spiral bd., tchr.'s planning gde. ed. 13.50 (978-0-382-40948-6(5)) Cobblestone Publishing Co.

Peppas, Lynn. Life in Ancient Greece. 2004. (Peoples of the Ancient World Ser.). (Illus.). 32p. (J). (978-0-7787-2035-5(7)); pap. (978-0-7787-2065-2(9)) Crabtree Publishing Co.

Powell, Anton & Sheehan, Sean. Ancient Greece. 2nd rev. ed. 2003. (Cultural Atlas for Young People Ser.). (Illus.). 96p. (J). (gr. 4-9). 35.00 (978-0-8160-5146-5(1)) Facts On File, Inc.

Powell, Anton & Steele, Philip. The Greek New. 1999. lib. bdg. 15.30 (978-0-613-22862-6(6)) Tandem Library Bks.

—The Greek News. 2000. (History News Ser.). (Illus.). 32p. (J). (gr. 3 up). lib. bdg. 24.67 (978-0-8368-2720-0(1)) Stevens, Gareth Inc.

Quennell, Marjorie & Quennell, C. H. Everyday Things in Archaic Greece. 1999. 146p. (YA). pap. 20.00 (978-0-8196-0395-1(3)) Biblo & Tannen Booksellers & Pubs., Inc.

—Everyday Things in Homeric Greece. 1999. 140p. (YA). pap. 20.00 (978-0-8196-0396-8(1)) Biblo & Tannen Booksellers & Pubs., Inc.

Reece, Katherine E. The Greeks: Leaders in Democracy. 2005. (Ancient Civilizations Ser.). (Illus.). 48p. (gr. 4-8). 20.95 (978-1-59515-506-1(6) , 1244351) Rourke Publishing, LLC.

Ross, Stewart. Ancient Greece. 2005. (Rich & Poor in Ser.). (Illus.). 32p. (J). (gr. 4-7). lib. bdg. 27.10 (978-1-58340-721-9(9)) Smart Apple Media.

Schlitz, Laura Amy. The Hero Schliemann: The Dreamer Who Dug up Troy. Byrd, Robert, illus. 2006. 80p. (J). (gr. 4-8). 17.99 (978-0-7636-2283-1(4)) Candlewick Pr.

Schofield, Tracey Ann. Greece. Mitchell, Judy, ed. Baird, Philip, photos by. 2002. (Exploring Ancient Civilizations Ser.). (Illus.). 48p. (J). (gr. 3-6). pap., tchr. ed. 7.95 (978-1-57310-307-7(1)) Teaching & Learning Co.

—Rome. Mitchell, Judy, ed. Baird, Philip, photos by. 2002. (Exploring Ancient Civilizations Ser.). (Illus.). 48p. (J). (gr. 3-6). pap., tchr. ed. 7.95 (978-1-57310-309-1(8)) Teaching & Learning Co.

Shuter, Jane. Ancient Greeks. 1999. (History Opens Windows Ser.). (Illus.). (J). 14.30 (978-0-606-21975-4(7)) Tandem Library Bks.

—Builders, Traders & Craftsmen. 1999. (Ancient Greece Ser.). 32p. (J). (gr. 3-5). lib. bdg. 22.79 (978-1-57572-736-3(6)) Heinemann Library.

—Cities & Citizens. 1999. (Ancient Greece Ser.). 32p. (J). lib. bdg. 22.79 (978-1-57572-738-7(2)) Heinemann Library.

—Discoveries, Inventions & Ideas. 1999. (Ancient Greece Ser.). (Illus.). 32p. (J). lib. bdg. 22.79 (978-1-57572-739-4(0)) Heinemann Library.

—Farmers & Fighters. 1999. (Ancient Greece Ser.). (Illus.). 32p. (J). (gr. 3-5). lib. bdg. 22.79 (978-1-57572-737-0(4)) Heinemann Library.

Steele. Greece. 2000. (Ancient Civilizations Ser.). (Illus.). (J). pap. (978-0-7398-4147-1(5)) Steck-Vaughn.

Steele, Christy. Greece. Sloan, Frank, ed. 2001. (Ancient Civilizations Ser.). (Illus.). 48p. (J). (gr. 4-7). lib. bdg. 22.83 (978-0-7398-3577-7(7)) Raintree.

Steele, Philip. Gods & Gladiators: Everyday Life. 2004. (Illus.). 128p. pap. 17.99 (978-1-84476-032-9(4) , Southwater) Anness Publishing GBR. *Dist:* National Bk. Network.

Tames, Richard. Ancient Greek Children. 2002. (People in the Past Ser.). (Illus.). 48p. (J). (gr. 4-6). lib. bdg. 27.07 (978-1-58810-639-1(X)) Heinemann Library.

Taylor, Pat. The Ancient Greeks. 1999. (History Opens Windows Ser.). 32p. (J). (gr. 2-4). pap. (978-1-57572-589-5(4)) Heinemann Library.

Tracy, Kathleen. The Life & Times of Homer. 2004. (Biography from Ancient Civilizations Ser.). (Illus.). 48p. (J). (gr. 4-8). lib. bdg. 29.95 (978-1-58415-260-6(5)) Mitchell Lane Pubs., Inc.

Waryncia, Lou, et al. If I Were a Kid in Ancient Greece. 2007. (Children of the Ancient World Ser.). (Illus.). 32p. (J). 17.95 (978-0-8126-7929-8(6)) Cricket Bks.

Weber, Belinda & Murrell, Deborah. The Best Book of Ancient Greece. Molan, Chris, illus. 2005. (Best Book of... Ser.). 32p. (J). (gr. k-3). 12.95 (978-0-7534-5871-6(3) , Kingfisher) Houghton Mifflin Co. Trade & Reference Div.

Wheatley, A. Greeks. rev. ed. 2004. (Illustrated World History Ser.). (Illus.). 96p. (J). pap. 12.99 (978-0-7945-0428-1(0)) EDC Publishing.

Williams, Jean Kinney. Empire of Ancient Greece. 2005. (Great Empires of the Past Ser.). (Illus.). 128p. (J). (gr. 6-12). 35.00 (978-0-8160-5561-6(0)) Facts On File, Inc.

Zannos, Susan. The Life & Times of Archimedes. 2004. (Biography from Ancient Civilizations Ser.). (Illus.). 48p. (J). (gr. 4-8). lib. bdg. 29.95 (978-1-58415-242-2(7)) Mitchell Lane Pubs., Inc.

CIVILIZATION—HISTORY

Adams. Religion, Science, Medicine & Warfare. 2000. (Illus.). 256p. (J). (978-1-84215-351-2(X) , Southwater) Anness Publishing GBR. *Dist:* National Bk. Network.

Ash, Russell. Fantastic Millennium Facts. 1999. (Illus.). 128p. (J). (gr. 3-8). lib. bdg. (978-1-55209-441-9(3)) Firefly Bks., Ltd.

Bailey, Linda. Adventures in Ancient China. Slavin, Bill, illus. 2004. (Good Times Travel Agency Ser.). 48p. (J). (gr. 4-6). (978-1-55337-454-1(1)); (978-1-55337-453-4(3)) Kids Can Pr., Ltd.

—Adventures in Ancient China. 2003. (gr. 3-6). lib. bdg. 17.60 (978-0-613-70943-9(8)) Tandem Library Bks.

Baker, Yaba. Just Like Me: The Beginning of Civilization. Oldham, Anne Marie, illus. 1998. 28p. (gr. k-6). pap. 4.95 (978-1-928889-01-4(8)) Just Like Me, Inc.

Buy Sets 1, 2, And 3. 2005. (Primary Sources of World Culturestm Ser.). (Illus.). 128p. (gr. 4-8). lib. bdg. (978-1-4042-2970-9(1)) Rosen Publishing Group, Inc., The.

Cultures of the World, Group 8. 2005. 222.43 (978-0-7614-1844-3(X)) Cavendish, Marshall Corp.

Early Civilizations. (Social Studies Collections). (Illus.). (J). (gr. 3-4). lib. bdg. 95.72 (978-0-7368-2556-6(8)) Capstone Pr., Inc.

Early Civilizations. 2002. (First Book of History Questions & Answers Ser.). 32p. (J). 9.95 (978-0-7525-7577-3(5)) Parragon, Inc.

George, Linda S. 800 A. D. 2001. (Around the World Ser.). (Illus.). 96p. (J). 29.93 (978-0-7614-1085-0(6) , Benchmark Bks.) Cavendish, Marshall Corp.

Gottfried, Ted. Slovenia. 2004. (Cultures of the World Ser.). (Illus.). 144p. (J). 37.07 (978-0-7614-1857-3(1)) Cavendish, Marshall Corp.

Harris, Nicolas. El Libro de Saber: Civilizaciones y Conocimiento. (Coleccion Enciclopedia Ilustrada del Conocimiento).Tr. of Book of Knowledge about Civilizations. (SPA., Illus.). 64p. (J). (gr. 3-5). 7.96 (978-84-7630-750-2(0)) Libsa, Editorial S.A. ESP. *Dist:* Lectorum Pubns., Inc.

Haywood, John. Families at Home: Home Family & Everyday Life Through the Ages. 2003. (How We Lived Ser.). (Illus.). 64p. (gr. 3-7). pap. 7.99 (978-1-84215-812-8(0) , Southwater) Anness Publishing GBR. *Dist:* National Bk. Network.

Helgren. People, Places & Change: The Eastern Hemisphere. 5th ed. 2005. cd-rom 58.00 (978-0-03-037574-3(6)); 2004. (Illus.). 58.00 (978-0-03-037573-6(8)) Holt, Rinehart & Winston.

Historic Civilizations, 6 Vols. 148.02 (978-0-8368-4196-1(4)) Stevens, Gareth Inc.

King, David C. Serbia. 2004. (Cultures of the World Ser.). (Illus.). 144p. (J). 37.07 (978-0-7614-1855-9(5)) Cavendish, Marshall Corp.

Knowlton, MaryLee. Macedonia. 2004. (Cultures of the World Ser.). (Illus.). 144p. (J). 37.07 (978-0-7614-1854-2(7)) Cavendish, Marshall Corp.

Kyi, Tanya Lloyd. Burn: The Life Story of Fire. 2007. (Illus.). 128p. (J). (gr. 5-7). 19.95 (*978-1-55451-082-5(1)); pap. 9.95 (*978-1-55451-081-8(3)) Annick Pr., Ltd. CAN. *Dist:* Firefly Bks., Ltd.

MacDonald, Fiona. History of Culture. 2003. (Culture Encyclopedia Ser.). (Illus.). 40p. (J). (gr. 5 up). lib. bdg. (978-1-59084-477-9(7)) Mason Crest Pubs.

McGraw-Hill Staff. Human Heritage, Activity Workbook, Student Edition. 3rd ed. 2005. pap. 10.00 (978-0-07-869796-8(4) , 9780078697968) Glencoe/McGraw-Hill.

—Human Heritage, Reading Essentials. 2003. (gr. 6-12). pap., stu. ed. 28.37 (978-0-07-860986-7(0) , 9780078609862); 3rd ed. 2005. (C). pap., stu. ed., wbk. ed. 18.00 (978-0-07-869793-7(X) , 9780078697937) Glencoe/McGraw-Hill.

—Human Heritage, Spanish Reading Essentials & Study Guide, Student Edition. 2005. pap. 18.00 (978-0-07-869627-5(5)) Glencoe/McGraw-Hill.

—Human Heritage, StudentWorks Plus. 3rd ed. 2005. cd-rom 88.64 (978-0-07-873136-5(4) , 9780078731365) Glencoe/McGraw-Hill.

Minnis. You Are There Set 1, 4 vols. 2004. (Illus.). 102.80 (978-1-4109-0620-5(5)) Raintree.

Myths & Legends. (Illus.). 40p. (YA). (gr. 5 up). lib. bdg. (978-1-59084-480-9(7)) Mason Crest Pubs.

Primary Sources of World Cultures Set 3. 2005. (Illus.). 128p. (gr. 4-8). lib. bdg. 207.60 (978-1-4042-2969-3(8)) Rosen Publishing Group, Inc., The.

Stanton, Mary & Hyma, Albert. Streams of Civilization Vol. 1: Earliest Times to the Discovery of the New World. 2000. (Illus.). 410p. (YA). (gr. 7-12). 19.95 (978-1-930367-43-2(0) , CLP79555) Christian Liberty Pr.

Wilson, Amber. Jamaica the Culture. 2003. (gr. 3-6). lib. bdg. 16.40 (978-0-613-85048-3(3)) Tandem Library Bks.

Wood, Selina & Bonson, Richard. A Journey Through Time. Parsons, Jayne, ed. Bonson, Richard, illus. 2001. (Illus.). 42p. (J). 17.95 (978-0-7894-7887-0(0)) Dorling Kindersley Publishing, Inc.

CIVILIZATION, MEDIEVAL

see also Art, Medieval; Chivalry; Feudalism; Middle Ages; Monasticism and Religious Orders

Adams, Brian. Medieval Castles. 2006. (Hallmarks of History Ser.). (Illus.). 32p. (J). (978-1-59604-119-6(6)) Stargazer Bks.

Adams, Simon. The Kingfisher Atlas of the Medieval World. Maddison, Kevin, illus. 2007. 48p. (J). (gr. 5-9). 15.95 (978-0-7534-5946-1(9) , Kingfisher) Houghton Mifflin Co. Trade & Reference Div.

Alphin, Elaine Marie. Around the World in 1500. 2001. (Around the World Ser.: Vol. 1). (Illus.). 96p. (J). lib. bdg. 29.93 (978-0-7614-1082-9(1) , Benchmark Bks.) Cavendish, Marshall Corp.

Anderson, Mercedes Padrino. Cities & Towns in the Middle Ages. 2005. (World Almanac Library of the Middle Ages). (Illus.). 48p. (J). pap. (978-0-8368-5902-7(2) , World Almanac Library) Stevens, Gareth Inc.

—Feudalism & Village Life in the Middle Ages. 2005. (World Almanac Library of the Middle Ages). (Illus.). 48p. (J). pap. (978-0-8368-5903-4(0) , World Almanac Library) Stevens, Gareth Inc.

Anderson, Mercedes Padrino & Padrino, Mercedes. Cities & Towns in the Middle Ages. 2006. (World Almanac' Library of the Middle Ages). (Illus.). 48p. (J). (gr. 7-10). lib. bdg. 30.00 (978-0-8368-5893-8(X) , World Almanac Library) Stevens, Gareth Inc.

Barron's Educational Editorial Staff. Life in the Middle Ages. 1998. (Megascope Ser.). (Illus.). 64p. (J). (gr. 3-7). 6.95 (978-0-7641-5094-4(4)) Barron's Educational Series, Inc.

Barter, James. Life in a Medieval Village. 2003. (Way People Live Ser.). (Illus.). 96p. (J). 29.95 (978-1-59018-266-6(9) , Lucent Bks.) Thomson Gale.

—A Medieval Knight. 2005. (Working Life Ser.). (Illus.). 112p. (YA). (gr. 7-10). lib. bdg. 29.95 (978-1-59018-580-3(3) , Lucent Bks.) Thomson Gale.

Bauer, Susan Wise. The Middle Ages Vol. 2: From the Fall of Rome to the Rise of the Renaissance. 2003. (Story of the World: Vol. 2). (Illus.). 21.95 (978-0-9714129-8-9(7)); 336p. (J). pap. 21.95 (978-0-9714129-3-4(6) , SOTW2) Peace Hill Pr.

Benduhn, Tea. Middle Ages. 2006. (Illus.). 24p. (J). pap. (*978-0-8368-7789-2(6)); lib. bdg. (*978-0-8368-7784-7(5)) Stevens, Gareth Inc. (Weekly Reader Early Learning Library).

Bhote, Themina. Charlemagne: Life & Times of an Early Medieval Emperor. 2004. (Medieval Leaders Ser.). (Illus.). 112p. (J). lib. bdg. 31.95 (978-1-4042-0161-3(0)) Rosen Publishing Group, Inc., The.

Bingham, Jane. Medieval world - internet Linked. Firenze, Inklink, illus. rev. ed. 2004. 96p. (J). pap. 14.95 (978-0-7945-0815-9(4) , Usborne) EDC Publishing.

Bodden, Valerie. Medieval Castles. 2008. (J). (*978-1-58341-561-0(0) , Creative Education) Creative Co., The.

Brenner, Barbara. If You Were There in 1492: Everyday Life in the Time of Columbus. 1998. (Illus.). 112p. (J). (gr. 3-7). pap. 6.99 (978-0-689-82241-4(3) , Aladdin) Simon & Schuster Children's Publishing.

Carlson, Laurie M. Days of Knights & Damsels: An Activity Guide. 2003. (Kid's Guide Ser.). (Illus.). 184p. (J). (gr. k-7). pap. 14.95 (978-1-55652-291-8(6)) Chicago Review Pr., Inc.

Chrisp, Peter. The Middle Ages. rev. ed. 2004. (Come & Discover My World Ser.). (Illus.). 32p. (gr. 2-5). (J). pap. 7.95 (978-1-58728-069-6(8)); 14.95 (978-1-58728-063-4(9)) T&N Children's Publishing. (Two Can Publishing).

—The Middle Ages. 2000. (My World Ser.). (Illus.). (J). (978-0-606-21950-1(1)) Tandem Library Bks.

—Town & Country Life. 2004. (J). (gr. 7-10). 29.95 (978-1-59018-536-0(6) , Lucent Bks.) Thomson Gale.

Clare, John D., ed. Fourteenth-Century Towns. 1999. (Illus.). 64p. (J). (gr. 5-7). reprint ed. 17.00 (978-0-7881-6657-0(3)) DIANE Publishing Co.

Coggins, Jack. The Illustrated Book of Knights. 2006. (Illus.). 112p. pap. 14.95 (978-0-486-45134-3(8)) Dover Pubns., Inc.

Cole, Joanna, et al. Ms. Frizzle's Adventures: Medieval Castle. Degen, Bruce, illus. 2003. (Magic School Bus Ser.). 48p. (J). pap. 15.95 (978-0-590-10820-1(4)) Scholastic, Inc.

Coppendale, Jean. Knights & Castles. Hutchinson, Tim, illus. 2005. (Explore Inside Ser.). 10p. (J). (gr. 4-7). 9.98 (978-0-7624-2319-4(6) , Courage Bks.) Running Pr. Bk. Pubs.

Corbishley, Mike. The Middle Ages. 2nd rev. ed. 2003. (Cultural Atlas for Young People Ser.). (Illus.). 96p. (J). (gr. 4-9). 35.00 (978-0-8160-5150-2(X)) Facts On File, Inc.

Dargie, Richard. Knights & Castles. 1998. (Age of Castles Ser.). (Illus.). 48 p. (J). (gr. 3-7). lib. bdg. 25.69 (978-0-8172-5122-2(7)) Raintree.

—Knights & Castles. 1998. (Age of Castles Ser.). (Illus.). 48p. (J). (gr. 4-8). pap. 7.95 (978-0-8172-8122-9(3)) Steck-Vaughn.

Dawson, Imogene. Clothes & Crafts in the Middle Ages. 2000. (Clothes & Crafts in History Ser.). (Illus.). 32p. (J). (gr. 4 up). lib. bdg. 24.67 (978-0-8368-2736-1(8)) Stevens, Gareth Inc.

DK Publishing. Medieval Life. 2008. (DK Eyewitness Bks.). 48p. (J). (gr. 2-8). pap. 9.99 (*978-0-7566-3783-5(X)) Dorling Kindersley Publishing, Inc.

Eastwood, Kay. Life in a Castle. 2003. (Medieval World Ser.). (Illus.). 32p. (J). (gr. 5). pap. (978-0-7787-1343-2(1)); pap. (978-0-7787-1375-3(X)) Crabtree Publishing Co.

—The Life of a Knight. 2003. (Medieval World Ser.). (Illus.). 32p. (J). (gr. 5). (978-0-7787-1342-5(3)); pap. (978-0-7787-1374-6(1)) Crabtree Publishing Co.

—Medieval Society. 2003. (Medieval World Ser.). (Illus.). 32p. (J). (gr. 5). (978-0-7787-1345-6(8)); pap. (978-0-7787-1377-7(6)) Crabtree Publishing Co.

—Women & Girls in the Middle Ages. 2003. (Medieval World Ser.). (Illus.). 32p. (J). (gr. 5). pap. (978-0-7787-1378-4(4)) Crabtree Publishing Co.

Elliott, Lynne. Clothing in the Middle Ages. 2004. (Medieval World Ser.). (Illus.). 32p. pap. (978-0-7787-1383-8(0)); (J). (978-0-7787-1351-7(2)) Crabtree Publishing Co.

C D

Farman, John. The Short & Bloody History of Knights. 2005. (Short & Bloody Histories Ser.). (Illus.). 96p. (gr. 6-12). lib. bdg. 19.93 (978-0-8225-0841-0(9)) Lerner Publishing Group.

—Short & Bloody History of Knights. 2002. (gr. 5-8). lib. bdg. 14.10 (978-0-613-52497-1(7)) Tandem Library Bks.

Galloway, Priscilla. Archers, Alchemists, & 98 Other Medieval Jobs You Might Have Loved or Loathed. Newbigging, Martha, illus. 2003. 96p. (J). (gr. 4-7). 24.95 (978-1-55037-811-5(2)); pap. 14.95 (978-1-55037-810-8(4)) Annick Pr., Ltd. CAN. *Dist:* Firefly Bks., Ltd.

—Archers, Alchemists, & 98 Other Medieval Jobs You Might Have Loved or Loathed. 2003. (gr. 3-6). lib. bdg. 24.55 (978-0-613-78469-6(3)) Tandem Library Bks.

Gelfand, Dale Evva. Charlemagne. 2003. (Ancient World Leaders Ser.). (Illus.). 112p. (gr. 6-12). 30.00 (978-0-7910-7224-0(X) , Chelsea Hse.) Facts On File, Inc.

Gravett, Christopher. Knight. 2007. (DK Eyewitness Bks.). 72p. (J). (gr. 3-8). 15.99 incl. cd-rom (978-0-7566-3003-4(7)) Dorling Kindersley Publishing, Inc.

—Real Knights: Over 20 True Stories of Battle & Adventure. James, John, illus. 2005. 48p. (J). (gr. k-9). 15.95 (978-1-59270-034-9(0)) Enchanted Lion Bks., LLC.

Grolier Educational Staff. Medieval World, 10 vols. 2001. (Illus.). (J). (978-0-7172-5530-6(1) , Grolier) Scholastic Library Publishing.

Grolier Educational Staff, contrib. by. Medieval World, 10 vols. 2001. (Illus.). (J). 800p. 345.00 (978-0-7172-5520-7(4)); (978-0-7172-5521-4(2)); (978-0-7172-5522-1(0)); (978-0-7172-5523-8(9)); (978-0-7172-5524-5(7)); (978-0-7172-5525-2(5)); (978-0-7172-5526-9(3)); (978-0-7172-5527-6(1)); (978-0-7172-5528-3(X)); (978-0-7172-5529-0(8)) Scholastic Library Publishing. (Grolier).

Groves, Marsha. Manners & Customs in the Middle Ages. 2005. (Medieval World Ser.). (Illus.). 32p. (J). (gr. 4-9). (978-0-7787-1357-9(1)) Crabtree Publishing Co.

Guy, John. Medieval Life. 2004. (Illus.). 32p. (J). (gr. 4-7). pap. 6.95 (978-1-86007-002-0(7)) Ticktock Media Ltd. GBR. *Dist:* Consortium Bk. Sales & Distribution.

Hamilton, John. Knights & Heroes. 2005. (Illus.). 32p. (J). (gr. 4-8). lib. bdg. 24.21 (978-1-59679-336-1(8) , ABDO & Daughters) ABDO Publishing Co.

Hanawalt, Barbara. The European World, 400-1450. (Illus.). 2006. 189p. 32.95 (978-0-19-522267-8(9)); 2005. 192p. (YA). 32.95 (978-0-19-517844-9(0)) Oxford Univ. Pr., Inc.

Hanel, Rachael. Knights. 2007. (J). (978-1-58341-536-8(X) , Creative Education) Creative Co., The.

Harcourt School Publishers Staff. Medieval Villages Advanced Level. 3rd ed. 2002. (Trophies Reading Program Ser.). (Illus.). pap. 5.10 (978-0-15-323125-4(4)) Harcourt Schl. Pubs.

Hart, Avery & Mantell, Paul. Knights & Castles: 50 Hands-On Activities to Experience the Middle Ages. 1998. (Kaleidoscope Kids Bks.: Vol. 2). (Illus.). 96p. (J). (gr. 2-8). pap. 12.95 (978-1-885593-17-7(1) , Williamson Bks.) Ideals Pubns.

Hatt, Christine, et al. Clothes of the Medieval World. 2001. (Dress Sense Ser.). (Illus.). 48p. (J). (gr. 5 up). 16.95 (978-0-87226-669-8(9) , Bedrick, Peter Bks.) School Specialty Publishing.

Haywood, John. Medieval Europe. 2007. (J). (***978-1-4109-2909-9(4)**); pap. (***978-1-4109-2915-0(9)***) Steck-Vaughn.

Hinds, Kathryn. The Castle. 2000. (Life in the Middle Ages Ser.). (Illus.). 80p. (J). (gr. 5 up). lib. bdg. 29.93 (978-0-7614-1007-2(4) , Benchmark Bks.) Cavendish, Marshall Corp.

Hodge, Susie. Medieval Europe. 2004. (Historic Civilizations Ser.). (Illus.). 32p. (J). lib. bdg. 24.67 (978-0-8368-4202-9(2)) Stevens, Gareth Inc.

Jane Shuter. The Middle Ages. 2nd ed. 2007. (Illus.). 32p. (J). pap. (***978-1-4034-8820-6(7)***) Heinemann Library.

—The Renaissance. 2nd ed. 2007. (Illus.). 32p. (J). pap. (***978-1-4034-8821-3(5)***) Heinemann Library.

Jarrow, Gail. A Medieval Castle. 2004. (Great Structures in History Ser.). (Illus.). 48p. (J). (gr. 4-7). 26.20 (978-0-7377-2070-9(0)) Thomson Gale.

Jess, Denise & Shepherd-Wundrow, Debra. Travels with a Troubadour: A Journey Through the Middle Ages: An Interactive Curriculum Unit for Social Studies. 2nd ed. 2001. (J). (978-1-885360-25-0(8)) Demco, Inc.

Johnson, Terri, compiled by. What Really Happened During the Middle Ages: A Collection of Historical Biographies, 4. 2005. (Illus.). 224p. (J). per. 15.95 (***978-1-932786-22-4(8)***) Knowledge Quest.

Jordan, William Chester. The Middle Ages: A Watts Guide for Children. 2000. (Reference Ser.). (Illus.). 112p. (J). (gr. 2-6). 37.50 (978-0-531-11715-6(4) , Watts, Franklin) Scholastic Library Publishing.

Kallen, Stuart A. A Medieval Merchant. 2005. (Working Life Ser.). (Illus.). 112p. (YA). (gr. 7-10). lib. bdg. 29.95 (978-1-59018-581-0(1) , Lucent Bks.) Thomson Gale.

Kenney, Karen Latchana. Harsh or Heroic? The Middle Ages. 2007. (Shockwave: History & Politics Ser.). 36p. (J). pap. 6.95 (***978-0-531-18794-4(2)***); (Illus.). (gr. 4-6). lib. bdg. 25.00 (***978-0-531-17754-9(8)***) Scholastic Library Publishing. (Children's Pr.).

Langley, Andrew & Dorling Kindersley Publishing Staff. Medieval Life. 2004. (Dk Eyewitness Books Ser.). (Illus.). 72p. (J). 15.99 (978-0-7566-0705-0(1)); lib. bdg. 19.99 (978-0-7566-0704-3(3)) Dorling Kindersley Publishing, Inc.

Lassieur, Allison. The Celts. 2001. (Lost Civilizations Ser.). (Illus.). 96p. (J). (gr. 6-9). 29.95 (978-1-56006-756-6(X) , LML00902-178104, Lucent Bks.) Thomson Gale.

Leon, Vicki. Outrageous Women of the Middle Ages. 1998. (Outrageous Women Ser.: Vol. 2). (Illus.). 128p. (gr. 4-7). pap. 12.95 (978-0-471-17004-4(6) , Wiley) Wiley, John & Sons, Inc.

Lilly, Melinda. Minstrel. 2002. (Illus.). 32p. (J). lib. bdg. 26.60 (978-1-58952-228-2(1)) Rourke Publishing, LLC.

—Peasant. 2002. (People of the Middle Ages Ser.). (Illus.). 32p. (J). lib. bdg. 26.60 (978-1-58952-229-9(X)) Rourke Publishing, LLC.

—People of the Middle Ages. 2002. 159.60 (978-1-58952-225-1(7)) Rourke Publishing, LLC.

—Pilgrim. 2002. (People of the Middle Ages Ser.). (Illus.). 32p. (J). lib. bdg. 26.60 (978-1-58952-230-5(3)) Rourke Publishing, LLC.

MacDonald, Fiona. Castles. 2001. (Topic Bks.). (Illus.). 32p. (J). (gr. 2-5). 23.50 (978-0-531-14551-7(4) , Watts, Franklin) Scholastic Library Publishing.

—Castles. 2000. (gr. 3-6). lib. bdg. 15.25 (978-0-613-34107-3(4)) Tandem Library Bks.

—Knights & Castles. 2005. (First Look at History Ser.). (Illus.). 24p. (J). lib. bdg. 22.00 (978-0-8368-4526-6(9)) Stevens, Gareth Inc.

—Knights, Castles, & Warfare in the Middle Ages. 2005. (World Almanac Library of the Middle Ages). (Illus.). 48p. (J). pap. (978-0-8368-5904-1(9)); lib. bdg. 30.00 (978-0-8368-5895-2(6)) Stevens, Gareth Inc. (World Almanac Library).

—The Middle Ages. 2005. (History in Art Ser.). (Illus.). 48p. (J). lib. bdg. 29.93 (978-1-4109-0521-5(7)) Steck-Vaughn.

—Women in Medieval Times. 2000. (Other Half of History Ser.). (Illus.). 48p. (J). (gr. 3 up). 17.95 (978-0-87226-569-1(2) , 65692B, Bedrick, Peter Bks.) School Specialty Publishing.

—You Wouldn't Want to Be in a Medieval Dungeon! 2003. (gr. 3-6). lib. bdg. 18.75 (978-0-613-59559-9(9)) Tandem Library Bks.

—You Wouldn't Want to Be in a Medieval Dungeon! Prisoners You'd Rather Not Meet. Antram, David, illus. 2003. (You Wouldn't Want to Ser.). 32p. (J). 28.50 (978-0-531-12312-6(X)); (gr. 2-5). pap. 9.95 (978-0-531-16651-2(1)) Scholastic Library Publishing. (Watts, Franklin).

MacDonald, Fiona & Salariya, David. You Wouldn't Want to Be a Medieval Knight! Armor You'd Rather Not Wear. Antram, David, illus. 2004. (You Wouldn't Want To Ser.). 32p. (J). 28.50 (978-0-531-12353-9(7) , Watts, Franklin) Scholastic Library Publishing.

Marshall, Chris. Warfare in the Medieval World. 1999. (History of Warfare Ser.). (Illus.). 80p. (YA). (gr. 7-12). lib. bdg. 29.97 (978-0-8172-5443-8(9)) Raintree.

Martin, Michael. Knights. 2007. (Edge Books, Warriors of History). (Illus.). 32p. (J). (gr. 3-6). 23.93 (***978-0-7368-6431-2(8)***) Capstone Pr., Inc.

Maynard, Christopher. Days of the Knights: A Tale of Castles & Battles. 1998. (Eyewitness Readers). (Illus.). 48p. (J). (gr. 2-4). pap. 3.99 (978-0-7894-2963-6(2) , 0-7894-4764-9) Dorling Kindersley Publishing, Inc.

McAleavy, Tony. Life in a Medieval Abbey. 2003. (English Heritage (Series)). (Illus.). 64p. (J). (gr. 6-12). 22.00 (978-1-59270-006-6(3)) Enchanted Lion Bks., LLC.

—Life in a Medieval Castle. 2003. (English Heritage (Series)). (Illus.). 64p. (J). (gr. 6-12). 22.00 (978-1-59270-005-9(5)) Enchanted Lion Bks., LLC.

McGovern, Ann. If You Lived in the Days of the Knights. Andreasen, Dan, illus. 2001. (If You Lived Ser.). 80p. (J). (gr. 2-5). pap. 5.99 (978-0-439-10565-1(X)) Scholastic, Inc.

—If You Lived in the Days of the Knights. 2001. (gr. 3-6). lib. bdg. 14.15 (978-0-613-32675-9(X)); 2000. (Illus.). (J). 12.79 (978-0-606-20718-8(X)) Tandem Library Bks.

McNeil, Sarah. The Middle Ages. 1998. (Spotlights Ser.). (Illus.). 46p. (YA). (gr. 4-6). 12.95 (978-0-19-521394-2(7)) Oxford Univ. Pr., Inc.

Medieval Times. 2002. (First Book of History Questions & Answers Ser.). 32p. (J). 9.95 (978-0-7525-7580-3(5)) Parragon, Inc.

Murrell, Deborah. The Best Book of Knights & Castles. 2005. (Best Book of... Ser.). (Illus.). 32p. (J). (gr. k-3). 12.95 (978-0-7534-5935-5(3) , Kingfisher) Houghton Mifflin Co. Trade & Reference Div.

Nardo, Don. Lords, Ladies, Peasants & Knights: Class in the Middle Ages. 2006. (Lucent Library of Historical Eras). 112p. (YA). (gr. 7-10). lib. bdg. 32.45 (978-1-59018-928-3(0) , Lucent Bks.) Thomson Gale.

Osborne, Mary Pope & Osborne, Will. Knights & Castles: A Nonfiction Companion to The Knight at Dawn. 2000. (Magic Tree House Research Guide Ser.: No. 2). (J). (gr. k-3). lib. bdg. 13.00 (978-0-613-26101-2(1)) Tandem Library Bks.

Padrino, Mercedes. Feudalism & Village Life in the Middle Ages. 2006. (World Almanac' Library of the Middle Ages). (Illus.). 48p. (YA). (gr. 7-10). lib. bdg. 30.00 (978-0-8368-5894-5(8) , World Almanac Library) Stevens, Gareth Inc.

Platt, Richard & Biesty, Stephen. Castle. (Illus.). 32p. (J). pap. 21.95 (978-0-590-24346-9(2)) Scholastic, Inc.

Reid, Struan. Lift the Lid on Knights: Explore a Medieval World of Chivalry & Adventure, & Build Your Own Knight! 2001. (Quarto Children's Book Ser.). (Illus.). 32p. (J). 22.95 (978-0-7624-1125-2(2) , Running Pr. Kids) Running Pr. Bk. Pubs.

Sabuda, Robert & Olmon, Kyle. Castle: Medieval Days & Knights. Reinhart, Matthew & Sabin, Tracy, illus. 2006. 6p. (J). 19.99 (978-0-439-54324-8(X) , Orchard Bks.) Scholastic, Inc.

Salley, Victoria. Castles & Knights. Jackson, Rosie, tr. from GER. Ferraro, Andrea, illus. 2001. (Adventures in Architecture Ser.). 30p. (gr. 3-5). 14.95 (978-3-7913-2576-7(0)) Prestel Publishing.

Schlesinger, Arthur M., Jr., intro. Ancient World Leaders. (Illus.). (gr. 6-12). lib. bdg. (978-0-7910-8056-6(0) , Chelsea Hse.) Facts On File, Inc.

Service, Alexandra & Service, Pamela F. Around the World in ...1200. 2001. (Around the World Ser.). (Illus.). 96p. (J). lib. bdg. 29.93 (978-0-7614-1081-2(3) , Benchmark Bks.) Cavendish, Marshall Corp.

Shuter, Jane. Life in a Medieval Castle. 2005. (Picture the Past Ser.). (Illus.). 32p. (J). (gr. 2-4). lib. bdg. 26.79 (978-1-4034-6445-3(6)); pap. (978-1-4034-6452-1(9)) Heinemann Library.

—The Middle Ages. 2007. (Illus.). 32p. (J). (***978-1-4034-8813-8(4)***) Heinemann Library.

—The Renaissance. 2007. (Illus.). 32p. (J). (***978-1-4034-8814-5(2)***) Heinemann Library.

Steele, Philip. Knights. 1998. (Single Subject References Ser.). (Illus.). 64p. (J). (gr. 4-8). tchr. ed. 16.95 (978-0-7534-5154-0(9) , Kingfisher) Houghton Mifflin Co. Trade & Reference Div.

—Medieval World. 2000. (gr. 3-6). lib. bdg. 22.20 (978-0-613-90588-6(1)); (978-0-606-20790-4(2)) Tandem Library Bks.

—The Medieval World. 2006. 96p. (J). (gr. 3-5). pap. 12.95 (978-0-7534-6046-7(7) , Kingfisher) Houghton Mifflin Co. Trade & Reference Div.

—The World of Castles. 2005. (World Of Ser.). (Illus.). 64p. (J). (gr. 4-6). pap. 8.95 (978-0-7534-5834-1(9) , Kingfisher) Houghton Mifflin Co. Trade & Reference Div.

Stefoff, Rebecca. The Medieval World. 2003. (Illus.). 48p. (J). 27.07 (978-0-7614-1642-5(0) , Benchmark Bks.) Cavendish, Marshall Corp.

Streissguth, Thomas. The Middle Ages. 2003. (A to Z Encyclopedias Ser.). (Illus.). 332p. (J). 77.45 (978-0-7377-0793-9(3) , Greenhaven Pr., Inc.) Thomson Gale.

Student Study Guide to the European World, 400-1450. 2005. (Medieval & Early Modern World Ser.). 48p. (YA). 9.95 (978-0-19-522336-1(5)) Oxford Univ. Pr., Inc.

Taylor, Barbara. The Amazing World of Castles: Discover the Fascinating History of Medieval Adventure, Battle & Romance. 2003. (Illus.). 64p. (gr. 3-7). 14.99 (978-0-7548-1206-7(5)) Anness Publishing GBR. *Dist:* National Bk. Network.

Trembinski, Donna. Medieval Myths, Legends, & Songs. 2005. (Medieval World Ser.). (Illus.). 32p. (J). (gr. 4-9). (978-0-7787-1359-3(8)) Crabtree Publishing Co.

Turnbull, Stephanie. Castles - Internet Referenced (Level 1) 2007. 32p. (J). 4.99 (978-0-7945-1335-1(2) , Usborne) EDC Publishing.

Weintraub, Aileen. Knights: Warriors of the Middle Ages. 2005. (Way of the Warrior Ser.). (Illus.). 48p. (J). 24.00 (978-0-516-25117-2(1)); (gr. 7-12). pap. 6.95 (978-0-516-25086-1(8)) Scholastic Library Publishing. (Children's Pr.).

White, Matt. Castles: Towers, Dungeons, Moats, & More. 2002. (High Five Reading Ser.). (Illus.). 48p. (J). (gr. 2-3). lib. bdg. 22.60 (978-0-7368-9549-1(3) , Capstone High-Interest Bks.); pap. (978-0-7368-9527-9(2)) Capstone Pr., Inc.

Whiting, Jim. The Life & Times of Charlemagne. 2005. (Biography from Ancient Civilizations Ser.). (Illus.). 48p. (J). (gr. 4-8). lib. bdg. 29.95 (978-1-58415-346-7(6)) Mitchell Lane Pubs., Inc.

Wilson, Phil, illus. Medieval Castle: A Three Dimensional. 2004. (J). 22.00 (978-1-58117-365-9(2) , Intervisual/Piggy Toes) Dalmatian Pr.

Woog, Adam. A Medieval Knight. 2003. (Daily Life Ser.). (Illus.). 48p. (J). (gr. 4-6). 26.20 (978-0-7377-0992-6(8) , Kidhaven) Thomson Gale.

Zannos, Susan. The Life & Times of Marco Polo. 2004. (Biography from Ancient Civilizations Ser.). (Illus.). 48p. (J). (gr. 4-8). lib. bdg. 29.95 (978-1-58415-264-4(8)) Mitchell Lane Pubs., Inc.

CIVILIZATION, MODERN

see also History, Modern; Renaissance

Adams, Simon. The Kingfisher Atlas of Modern World. 2007. (Kingfisher Atlas Ser.). (Illus.). 48p. (J). (gr. 1-5). 15.95 (***978-0-7534-6034-4(3)*** , Kingfisher) Houghton Mifflin Co. Trade & Reference Div.

Bailey, Viola & Wise, Ella. Victorian Times. Date not set. (Focus on History Ser.). (Illus.). 64p. (J). pap. 129.15 (978-0-582-18240-0(9)) Addison-Wesley Longman, Ltd. GBR. *Dist:* Trans-Atlantic Pubns., Inc.

Baker, Patricia. Fashions of a Decade: The 1940s. 2nd rev. ed. 2006. (Fashions of a Decade Ser.). 64p. (YA). (gr. 6-12). 35.00 (978-0-8160-6720-6(1)) Facts On File, Inc.

—Fashions of A Decade: The 1950s. 2nd rev. ed. 2006. (Fashions of a Decade Ser.). 64p. (J). (gr. 6-12). 35.00 (978-0-8160-6721-3(X)) Facts On File, Inc.

Breaud, Odile, et al. Cultures of the World. 1998. (Creative Discoveries Ser.: Vol. 8). Orig. Title: Living Around the World. (Illus.). 75p. (J). (gr. 2-8). lib. bdg. 23.95 (978-0-88682-957-5(7) , Creative Education) Creative Co., The.

Carnegy, Vicky. Fashions of A Decade: The 1980s. 2nd rev. ed. 2006. (Fashions of a Decade Ser.). 64p. (J). (gr. 6-12). 35.00 (978-0-8160-6724-4(4)) Facts On File, Inc.

Conley, Kate A. Greece's Legacy. 2005. (Life in Ancient Days: Greece Ser.). (J). (978-1-59197-865-7(3)) ABDO Publishing Co.

Connikie, Yvonne. Fashions of A Decade: The 1960s. 2nd rev. ed. 2006. (Fashions of a Decade Ser.). 64p. (J). (gr. 6-12). 35.00 (978-0-8160-6722-0(8)) Facts On File, Inc.

Costantino, Maria. Fashions of a Decade: The 1930s. 2nd rev. ed. 2006. (Fashions of a Decade Ser.). 64p. (YA). (gr. 6-12). 35.00 (978-0-8160-6719-0(8)) Facts On File, Inc.

Cox, Reg. The Seven Wonders of the Modern World. 2000. (Wonders of the World Ser.). (Illus.). 32p. (J). (gr. 4-7). 21.95 (978-0-7910-6048-3(9) , Chelsea Hse.) Facts On File, Inc.

Davis, Kevin A. Look What Came from Austria. 2003. (Look What Came from Ser.). (Illus.). 32p. (J). (gr. 2-4). pap. 6.95 (978-0-531-16627-7(9) , Watts, Franklin) Scholastic Library Publishing.

—Look What Came from England. 1999. (J). (978-0-606-20143-8(2)) Tandem Library Bks.

—Look What Came from Germany. 1999. (J). (978-0-606-20144-5(0)) Tandem Library Bks.

Facts on File, Inc. Staff, ed. Fashions of a Decade, 8 Vols., Set. 2006. (Fashions of a Decade Ser.). 64p. (gr. 6-12). 280.00 (978-0-8160-7059-6(8)) Facts On File, Inc.

Feldman, Elane & McEvoy, Anne. Fashions of A Decade: The 1990s. 2nd rev. ed. 2006. (Fashions of a Decade Ser.). 64p. (gr. 6-12). 35.00 (978-0-8160-6725-1(2)) Facts On File, Inc.

Gold, John C. Environments of the Western Hemisphere. 2000. (Illus.). 96p. (J). (gr. 4-6). 20.00 (978-0-7881-9353-8(8)) DIANE Publishing Co.

Harvey, Miles. Look What Came from Africa. 2003. (Look What Came from Ser.). (Illus.). 32p. (J). (gr. 2-4). pap. 6.95 (978-0-531-16626-0(0) , Watts, Franklin) Scholastic Library Publishing.

—Look What Came from Africa. 2002. (gr. 3-6). lib. bdg. 15.25 (978-0-613-59506-3(8)) Tandem Library Bks.

—Look What Came from Ireland. 2003. (Look What Came from Ser.). (Illus.). 32p. (J). (gr. 2-4). pap. 6.95 (978-0-531-16628-4(7) , Watts, Franklin) Scholastic Library Publishing.

—Look What Came from Ireland. 2002. (gr. 3-6). lib. bdg. 15.25 (978-0-613-59508-7(4)) Tandem Library Bks.

—Look What Came from Switzerland. 2003. (Look What Came from Ser.). (Illus.). 32p. (J). (gr. 2-4). pap. 6.95 (978-0-531-16630-7(9) , Watts, Franklin) Scholastic Library Publishing.

—Look What Came from Switzerland. 2002. (gr. 3-6). lib. bdg. 15.25 (978-0-613-59510-0(6)) Tandem Library Bks.

Herald, Jacqueline. Fashions of a Decade: The 1920s. 2nd rev. ed. 2006. (Fashions of a Decade Ser.). 64p. (YA). (gr. 6-12). 35.00 (978-0-8160-6718-3(X)) Facts On File, Inc.

—Fashions of A Decade: The 1970s. 2nd rev. ed. 2006. (Fashions of a Decade Ser.). 64p. (gr. 6-12). 35.00 (978-0-8160-6723-7(6)) Facts On File, Inc.

Hills, Ken. 1940s. (Take Ten Years Ser.). (Illus.). 47p. (J). pap. (978-0-237-51681-9(0) , Evans Brothers, Limited) Evans Publishing Group.

Hughes, Shirley. A Brush with the Past 1900-1950: The Years That Changed Our Lives. 2005. (Illus.). 112p. 24.99 (***978-0-370-32839-3(6)***) Transworld Publishers Ltd. GBR. *Dist:* Independent Pubs. Group.

Ideas of the Modern World, 4 vols. 2003. (Illus.). (978-0-7398-6418-0(1)); (978-0-7398-6419-7(X)) Raintree.

Jane Shuter. The Renaissance. 2nd ed. 2007. (Illus.). 32p. (J). pap. (***978-1-4034-8821-3(5)***) Heinemann Library.

Levy, Patricia. From Punk Rock to Perestroika: The Mid 1970s to the Mid 1980s. 2005. (Modern Eras Uncovered Ser.). (Illus.). 56p. (J). 32.86 (978-1-4109-1789-8(4)) Raintree.

—From Punk Rock to Perestroika: The Mid 1970s to the Mid 1980s. 2005. (Modern Eras Uncovered Ser.). (Illus.). 56p. (J). pap. (978-1-4109-1798-0(3)) Steck-Vaughn.

—From Speakeasies to Stalinism: The 1920s to the Mid-1930s. 2005. (Modern Eras Uncovered Ser.). (Illus.). 56p. (J). (978-1-4109-1785-0(1)); pap. (978-1-4109-1794-2(0)) Steck-Vaughn.

—Modern Eras Uncovered: From Beatlemania to Watergate. 2005. (Modern Eras Uncovered Ser.). (Illus.). 56p. (J). (978-1-84443-965-2(8)); (978-1-84443-955-3(0)) Steck-Vaughn.

—Modern Eras Uncovered: From Compact Discs to the Gulf War. 2005. (Modern Eras Uncovered Ser.). (Illus.). 56p. (J). (978-1-84443-967-6(4)); (978-1-84443-957-7(7)) Steck-Vaughn.

—Modern Eras Uncovered: From Punk Rock to Perestroika. 2005. (Modern Eras Uncovered Ser.). (Illus.). 56p. (J). (978-1-84443-966-9(6)); (978-1-84443-956-0(9)) Steck-Vaughn.

—Modern Eras Uncovered: From the World Wide Web to September 11. 2005. (Modern Eras Uncovered Ser.). (Illus.). 56p. (J). (978-1-84443-968-3(2)) Steck-Vaughn.

Levy, Patricia & Sheehan, Sean. Modern Eras Uncovered: From the World Wide Web to September 11. 2005. (Modern Eras Uncovered Ser.). (Illus.). 56p. (J). (978-1-84443-958-4(5)) Steck-Vaughn.

Levy, Patricia & Sheehan, Sean. From Compact Discs to the Gulf War: The Mid 1980s to the Early 1990s. 2005. (Modern Eras Uncovered Ser.). (Illus.). 56p. (J). 32.86 (978-1-4109-1790-4(8)) Raintree.

—From Compact Discs to the Gulf War: The Mid 1980s to the Early 1990s. 2005. (Modern Eras Uncovered Ser.). (Illus.). 56p. (J). pap. (978-1-4109-1799-7(1)) Steck-Vaughn.

—From the World Wide Web to September 11: The Early 1990s to 2001. 2005. (Modern Eras Uncovered Ser.). (Illus.). 56p. (J). 32.86 (978-1-4109-1791-1(6)) Raintree.

—From the World Wide Web to September 11: The Early 1990s to 2001. 2005. (Modern Eras Uncovered Ser.). (Illus.). 56p. (J). pap. (978-1-4109-1800-0(9)) Steck-Vaughn.

Modern World Cultures, 10 Vols., Set. 2006. (Modern World Cultures Ser.). 100p. (gr. 6-12). 300.00 (978-0-7910-9323-8(9) , Chelsea Hse.) Facts On File, Inc.

Our Century, 7 bks. Incl. Our Century : 1900-1910. Greene, Janice. lib. bdg. 27.33 (978-0-8368-1032-5(5)); Our Century : 1910-1920. Liberatore, Karen. lib. bdg. 27.33 (978-0-8368-1033-2(3)); Our Century : 1930-1940. Owen, Marna. lib. bdg. 27.33 (978-0-8368-1035-6(X)); Our Century : 1940-1950. Hill, Prescott. lib. bdg. 27.33 (978-0-8368-1036-3(8)); Our Century : 1950-1960.

Jones, S. D. lib. bdg. 27.33 (978-0-8368-1037-0(6)); Our Century : 1970-1980. Hill, Prescott. lib. bdg. 27.33 (978-0-8368-1039-4(2)); Our Century : 1980-1990. Suter, Joanne. lib. bdg. 27.33 (978-0-8368-1040-0(6)); 64p. (J). (gr. 4 up). 1993. (Illus.). Set lib. bdg. 191.31 (978-0-8368-1031-8(7)) Stevens, Gareth Inc.

Sharman, Margaret. Take Ten Years 1900s. (Illus.). 46p. (J). (978-0-237-51257-6(2) , Evans Brothers, Limited) Evans Publishing Group.

Sheehan, Sean. From Beatlemania to Watergate. 2005. (Modern Eras Uncovered Ser.). (Illus.). 56p. (J). (ps-1). lib. bdg. 32.86 (978-1-4109-1788-1(6)) Steck-Vaughn.

—From Beatlemania to Watergate: The Early 1960s to the Mid 1970s. 2005. (Modern Eras Uncovered Ser.). (Illus.). 56p. (J). pap. (978-1-4109-1797-3(5)) Steck-Vaughn.

—From Jessie Owens to Hiroshima: The Mid 1930s to 1945. 2005. (Modern Eras Uncovered Ser.). (Illus.). 56p. (J). (978-1-4109-1786-7(X)); pap. (978-1-4109-1795-9(9)) Steck-Vaughn.

—From Television to the Berlin Wall: The Mid-1940s to the Early 1960s. 2005. (Modern Eras Uncovered Ser.). (Illus.). 56p. (J). (978-1-4109-1787-4(8)); pap. (978-1-4109-1796-6(7)) Steck-Vaughn.

—From the Wright Brothers to the Treaty of Versailles: The 1900s to 1918. 2005. (Modern Eras Uncovered Ser.). (Illus.). 56p. (J). (978-1-4109-1784-3(3)); pap. (978-1-4109-1793-5(2)) Steck-Vaughn.

—Modern Eras Uncovered: From Jesse Owens to Hiroshima. 2005. (Modern Eras Uncovered Ser.). (Illus.). 56p. (J). (978-1-84443-962-1(3)); (978-1-84443-952-2(6)) Steck-Vaughn.

—Modern Eras Uncovered: From Speakeasies to Stalinism. 2005. (Modern Eras Uncovered Ser.). (Illus.). 56p. (J). (978-1-84443-961-4(5)) Steck-Vaughn.

—Modern Eras Uncovered: From Television to the Berlin Wall. 2005. (Modern Eras Uncovered Ser.). (Illus.). 56p. (J). (978-1-84443-963-8(1)) Steck-Vaughn.

—Modern Eras Uncovered: From the Wright Brothers to the Treaty of Versailles. 2005. (Modern Eras Uncovered Ser.). (Illus.). 56p. (J). (978-1-84443-960-7(7)); (978-1-84443-950-8(X)) Steck-Vaughn.

Sheehan, Sean & Levy, Pat. Modern Eras Uncovered: From Speakeasies to Stalinism. 2005. (Modern Eras Uncovered Ser.). (Illus.). 56p. (J). (978-1-84443-951-5(8)) Steck-Vaughn.

—Modern Eras Uncovered: From Television to the Berlin Wall. 2005. (Modern Eras Uncovered Ser.). (Illus.). 56p. (J). pap. (978-1-84443-953-9(4)) Steck-Vaughn.

Shuter, Jane. The Renaissance. 2007. (Illus.). 32p. (J). **(*978-1-4034-8814-5(2)*)** Heinemann Library.

Steele, Philip. Wonders of the World. 2007. (Kingfisher Knowledge Ser.). (Illus.). 64p. (J). (gr. 3-5). 12.95 (978-0-7534-5979-9(5) , Kingfisher) Houghton Mifflin Co. Trade & Reference Div.

Tung, Anthony M. Wonders of Civilization Fandex. 2007. (Illus.). 50p. (J). 9.95 **(*978-0-7611-4355-0(6)*)** Workman Publishing Co., Inc.

Wilson, Janet. Imagine That! Wilson, Janet, illus. 2000. (Illus.). 28p. (J). (ps-5). 14.95 (978-0-7737-3221-6(7)) Stoddart Kids CAN. *Dist:* Fitzhenry & Whiteside, Ltd.

World Book People & Places 2004 Edition, 6 vols. rev. ed. 2004. (Illus.). 1,632p. (gr. 4 up). pap. 299.00 (978-0-7166-3754-7(5)) World Bk., Inc.

CIVILIZATION AND SCIENCE

see Science and Civilization

CIVILIZATION AND TECHNOLOGY

see Technology and Civilization

CLARK, GEORGE ROGERS, 1752-1818

Burgan, Michael. George Rogers Clark. 2001. (Revolutionary War Leaders Ser.). (Illus.). 80p. (J). pap. 27.50 (978-0-7910-6395-8(X)); 27.50 (978-0-7910-6394-1(1)) Facts On File, Inc. (Chelsea Hse.).

Roberts, Russell. George Rogers Clark. 2006. (Profiles in American History Ser.). (Illus.). 48p. (J). (gr. 4-8). lib. bdg. 20.95 (978-1-58415-448-8(9)) Mitchell Lane Pubs., Inc.

CLARK, WILLIAM, 1770-1838

Adler, David A. A Picture Book of Lewis & Clark. Himler, Ronald, illus. 2003. 32p. (J). (gr. k-3). tchr. ed. 16.95 (978-0-8234-1735-3(2)) Holiday Hse., Inc.

Carter, E. J. The Lewis & Clark Journals. 2003. (Heinemann Know It Ser.). (Illus.). 48p. (J). pap. 8.50 (978-1-4034-3433-3(6)); lib. bdg. 27.07 (978-1-4034-0805-1(X)) Heinemann Library.

Devillier, Christy. Lewis & Clark. 2001. (First Biographies Ser.). (Illus.). 32p. (J). (gr. k-4). lib. bdg. 22.78 (978-1-57765-595-4(8) , Buddy Bks.) ABDO Publishing Co.

Ditchfield, Christin. The Lewis & Clark Expedition. 2006. 48p. (gr. 3-5). (YA). pap. 6.95 (978-0-516-25222-3(4)); (Illus.). (J). 25.00 (978-0-516-22835-8(8)) Scholastic Library Publishing. (Children's Pr.).

Espinosa, Rod. Lewis & Clark. 2007. (Bio-Graphics Ser.). (Illus.). 32p. (J). (gr. 3-6). lib. bdg. 27.07 **(*978-1-60270-069-7(9)*** , Graphic Planet) Magic Wagon.

Glaser, Jason. Lewis & Clark. 2004. (Fact Finders Ser.). (Illus.). 32p. (J). lib. bdg. 22.60 (978-0-7368-2665-5(3)) Capstone Pr., Inc.

Gunderson, Jessica Sarah. The Lewis & Clark Expedition. 2007. (Graphic Library). (Illus.). 32p. (J). 25.26 (978-0-7368-6493-0(8)) Capstone Pr., Inc.

Hamilton, John. The Corps of Discovery. 2003. (Lewis & Clark Expedition Ser.). (Illus.). 32p. (J). (gr. 3-8). lib. bdg. 24.21 (978-1-57765-761-3(6)) ABDO Publishing Co.

Kline, Trish. Lewis & Clark. 2002. (Discover the Life of an Explorer Ser.). (Illus.). 24p. (gr. 2-5). 14.95 (978-1-58952-067-7(X)) Rourke Publishing, LLC.

Klingel, Cynthia Fitterer & Noyed, Robert B. Lewis & Clark: Explorers. 2002. (Spirit of America: Our People Ser.). (Illus.). 32p. (J). (gr. 2-6). 27.07 (978-1-56766-164-4(5)) Child's World, Inc.

Kozar, Richard. Lewis & Clark: Explorers of the Louisiana Purchase. 2000. (Explorers of the New World Ser.). (Illus.). 64p. (J). (gr. 4 up). 25.00 (978-0-7910-5513-7(2) , Chelsea Hse.) Facts On File, Inc.

Lilly, Melinda. Sacagawea, Lewis, & Clark. 2003. (Rourke Discovery Library). (Illus.). 24p. (gr. 1-4). 14.95 (978-1-58952-362-3(8)) Rourke Publishing, LLC.

MacGregor, Carol Lynn. Lewis & Clark's Bittersweet Crossing. Hoopes, Gaye, tr. Hoopes, Gaye, illus. 2004. 32p. (J). 16.95 (978-0-87004-437-3(0) , 043700) Caxton Pr.

McCormick, Lisa Wade. Lewis & Clark. 2006. 32p. (gr. 1-2). (YA). pap. 4.95 (978-0-516-21443-6(8)); (Illus.). (J). 20.50 (978-0-516-25039-7(6)) Scholastic Library Publishing. (Children's Pr.).

Molzahn, Arlene Bourgeois. Lewis & Clark: American Explorers. 2003. (Explorers! Ser.). (Illus.). 48p. (J). (gr. 1-4). lib. bdg. 23.93 (978-0-7660-2067-2(3)) Enslow Pubs., Inc.

Petrie, Kristin. Lewis & Clark. 2007. (Illus.). 32p. (J). 22.78 (978-1-59679-743-7(6)) ABDO Publishing Co.

Ransom, Candice F. Lewis & Clark. (History Maker Bios Ser.). (J). 2003. (Illus.). 48p. (gr. 2-4). 26.60 (978-0-8225-0394-1(8) , Lerner Pubns.); 2002. pap. 6.95 (978-0-8225-1562-3(8)) Lerner Publishing Group.

Raum, Elizabeth. Lewis & Clark's Continental Journey. 2007. (J). **(*978-1-4034-9757-4(5)*)** Heinemann Library.

Raum, Elizabeth. William Clark. 2003. (Illus.). 32p. (J). pap. 6.95 (978-1-4034-4202-4(9)); lib. bdg. 24.22 (978-1-4034-4194-2(4)) Heinemann Library.

—William Clark. 2003. (gr. k-3). lib. bdg. 15.25 (978-0-613-87667-4(9)) Tandem Library Bks.

Rodger, Ellen. Lewis & Clark: Opening the American West. 2005. (In the Footsteps of Explorers Ser.). (Illus.). 32p. (J). (ps-9). (978-0-7787-2410-0(7)); pap. (978-0-7787-2446-9(8)) Crabtree Publishing Co.

Santella, Andrew. Lewis & Clark. 2001. (Exploration Library). (Illus.). 64p. (J). (gr. 5-7). 25.50 (978-0-531-20323-1(9) , Watts, Franklin) Scholastic Library Publishing.

Sapp, Richard. Lewis & Clark on Their Journey to the Pacific. 2006. (In the Footsteps of American Heroes Ser.). (Illus.). 64p. (J). pap. (978-0-8368-6434-2(4)); lib. bdg. 32.67 (978-0-8368-6429-8(8)) Stevens, Gareth Inc. (World Almanac Library).

Scheuerman, Richard D., et al. The Expeditions of Lewis & Clark & Zebulon Pike: North American Journeys of Discovery Travelogue. 2nd ed. 2001. (Illus.). (J). (978-1-885360-24-3(X)) Demco, Inc.

Stout, Mary. Lewis & Clark. 2002. (Raintree Biographies Ser.). (Illus.). 32p. (J). lib. bdg. 25.69 (978-0-7398-5677-2(4)) Raintree.

Streissguth, Thomas. Lewis & Clark: Explorers of the Northwest. 1998. (Historical American Biographies Ser.). (Illus.). 128p. (YA). (gr. 6-12). lib. bdg. 26.60 (978-0-7660-1016-1(3)) Enslow Pubs., Inc.

Sullivan, George E. Lewis & Clark. 2000. (In Their Own Words Ser.). (Illus.). 128p. (J). (gr. 4-7). pap. 4.99 (978-0-439-09553-2(0)); pap. 12.95 (978-0-439-14749-1(2)) Scholastic, Inc.

—Lewis & Clark. 2000. (J). 11.64 (978-0-606-19924-7(1)) Tandem Library Bks.

CLASS CONFLICT

see Social Conflict

CLASS DISTINCTION

see Social Classes

CLASS STRUGGLE

see Social Conflict

CLASSES (MATHEMATICS)

see Set Theory

CLASSICAL ANTIQUITIES

see also Archaeology; Art, Greek; Art, Roman; Mythology, Classical

also names of countries, cities, etc. with the subdivision Antiquities, e.g. Greece—Antiquities

Ali, Daud. Ancient India: What Life Was Like in One of the Earliest Civilizations on Earth. 2003. (Find Out about-...Ser.). (Illus.). 64p. (gr. 3-7). pap. 7.99 (978-1-84215-778-7(7) , Southwater) Anness Publishing GBR. *Dist:* National Bk. Network.

Bowkett, L. C. Classical Archaeology in the Field: Approaches. (Illus.). ix, 138p. pap. 18.00 (978-1-85399-617-7(3)) Bristol Classical Pr. GBR. *Dist:* International Publishers Marketing.

Harcourt School Publishers Staff. The Elgin Marbles. 3rd ed. 2002. (Horizons Ser.). (Illus.). (J). pap. 7.30 (978-0-15-333622-5(6)) Harcourt Schl. Pubs.

Panchyk, Richard. Archaeology for Kids: Uncovering the Mysteries of Our Past. 2001. (For Kids Ser.). (Illus.). 160p. (J). pap. 14.95 (978-1-55652-395-3(5)) Chicago Review Pr., Inc.

CLASSICAL ART

see Art, Greek; Art, Roman

CLASSICAL BIOGRAPHY

see Greece—Biography; Rome—Biography

CLASSICAL LANGUAGES

see Latin Language

CLASSICAL MYTHOLOGY

see Mythology, Classical

CLAY, CASSIUS, 1942-

see Ali, Muhammad, 1942-

CLAY, HENRY, 1777-1852

Heinrichs, Ann & Burgan, Michael. Henry Clay: The Great Compromiser. 2004. (Our People Ser.). (Illus.). 32p. (J). (gr. 2-6). 27.07 (978-1-59296-174-0(6)) Child's World, Inc.

Tibbitts, Alison Davis. Henry Clay: From War Hawk to the Great Compromiser. 2003. (Historical American Biographies Ser.). (Illus.). 128p. (J). lib. bdg. 26.60 (978-0-7660-1980-5(2)) Enslow Pubs., Inc.

CLAY

see also Modeling

Browning, Marie. Totally Cool Polymer Clay Projects. (Illus.). 96p. 2005. (J). pap. 12.95 (978-1-4027-2789-4(5)); 2004. 19.95 (978-1-4027-0642-4(1)) Sterling Publishing Co., Inc.

Carlson, Maureen. Clay Characters for Kids. 2003. (Illus.). 64p. (J). pap. 12.99 (978-1-58180-286-3(2) , 32161) F & W Pubns., Inc.

Dean, Irene Semanchuk. Polymer Clay: 30 Terrific Projects to Roll, Mold & Squish. (Illus.). 112p. (ps-7). 2005. (J). pap., pap. 9.95 (978-1-57990-755-6(5)); 2003. 19.95 (978-1-57990-350-3(9)) Lark Bks.

Firestone, Mary. Clay. 2004. (First Facts Ser.). 24p. (J). lib. bdg. 21.26 (978-0-7368-2649-5(1)) Capstone Pr., Inc.

Jennings, Terry. Clay. 2006. (Illus.). 32p. (YA). (gr. 1 up). lib. bdg. 27.10 (978-1-932333-02-2(9)) Chrysalis Education.

Kirby, Huguette. Crafts from Modeling Clay. 2002. (Step by Step Ser.). (Illus.). 32p. (J). (gr. 2-3). lib. bdg. 22.60 (978-0-7368-1477-5(9) , Bridgestone Bks.) Capstone Pr., Inc.

Kohl, MaryAnn F. Mudworks: Creative Clay, Dough, & Modeling Experiences. Kerr, Kathleen, illus. 2003. (Bright Ideas for Learning Ser.: Vol. 2). 152p. (J). (ps-6). pap. 18.95 (978-0-935607-02-4(1)) Bright Ring Publishing, Inc.

—Mudworks: Experiencias Creativas con Arcilla, Masa y Modelado. Viglione, Renata, tr. Kerr, Kathleen, illus. 2001. (Bright Ideas for Learning Ser.: Vol. 7). (SPA & ENG.). 152p. (ps-7). pap. 14.95 (978-0-935607-17-8(X)) Bright Ring Publishing, Inc.

Llimos Plomer, Anna. Clay. 2003. (Let's Create! Ser.). (Illus.). 32p. (J). (gr. 2 up). lib. bdg. 23.33 (978-0-8368-3746-9(0)) Stevens, Gareth Inc.

Storey, Rita. Clay. 2007. (J). **(*978-1-59920-000-2(7)*)** Smart Apple Media.

Taus-Bolstad, Stacy. From Clay to Bricks. 2003. (Start to Finish Ser.). (Illus.). 24p. (J). (gr. k-2). lib. bdg. 18.60 (978-0-8225-4663-4(9)) Lerner Publishing Group.

CLAY MODELING

see Modeling

CLEANING

see also House Cleaning; Soap

Baker, Sue. Wash Day! Stockham, Jess, illus. 2006. (Blanket Babies Ser.). 12p. (J). 6.99 (978-1-904550-89-1(4)) Child's Play-International.

Berry, Joy Wilt. Cleaning Your Room: A Fun & Easy Book About. Bartholomew & Pace, Don, illus. rev. ed. 2000. (Living Skills Ser.: Vol. 2). 48p. (J). (gr. 1-7). pap. 4.95 (978-1-58634-133-6(2)) Goldstar Publishing, Inc.

Budd, E. S. Street Sweepers. 2008. (Machines at Work Ser.). 24p. (J). 22.79 **(*978-1-59296-952-4(6)*)** Child's World, Inc.

DeGezelle, Terri. Street Sweepers. 2006. (Pebble Plus Ser.). (Illus.). 24p. (J). (978-0-7368-5358-3(8)) Capstone Pr., Inc.

Garvel, Linda. The Purple Mop Story. 2000. (Illus.). 24p. (J). (ps-3). pap. (978-0-9679979-0-2(9)) Reader's Writes.

Kishel, Ann-Marie. Custodian. 2007. (First Step Nonfiction Ser.). (J). pap. (978-0-8225-6845-2(4)) Lerner Publishing Group.

Mitchell, Melanie. Killing Germs. 2005. (Illus.). 32p. (J). pap. 5.95 (978-0-8225-2772-5(3) , Lerner Pubns.) Lerner Publishing Group.

Scholastic, Inc. Staff, ed. Play Cleaning. (Illus.). 8p. (J). pap. 19.99 (978-0-590-24957 7(6)) Scholastic, Inc.

CLEANLINESS

see Health

CLEMENS, SAMUEL LANGHORNE, 1835-1910

see Twain, Mark, 1835-1910

CLEMENTE, ROBERTO, 1934-1972

Anderson, Sheila. Roberto Clemente: A Life of Generosity. 2008. (Pull Ahead Books-Biographies Ser.). (J). lib. bdg. 22.60 **(*978-0-8225-8586-2(3)*** , Lerner Pubns.) Lerner Publishing Group.

Benjamin, Lisa. Baseball Dreams: The Story of Roberto Clemente. (Voices Reading Ser.). (Illus.). 32p. (J). (978-0-7367-2912-3(7)) Zaner-Bloser, Inc.

Buckley, James, Jr. Roberto Clemente. 2001. (Eyewitness Readers Ser.). (Illus.). (J). (978-0-606-20888-8(7)); (SPA., (978-0-606-20889-5(5)) Tandem Library Bks.

Buckley, James. Roberto Clemente. 2001. (gr. k-3). lib. bdg. 11.80 (978-0-613-35215-4(7)); (SPA.). lib. bdg. 11.80 (978-0-613-45819-1(2)) Tandem Library Bks.

Buckley, James, Jr. & Dorling Kindersley Publishing Staff. Roberto Clemente. 2001. (Readers Ser.). (Illus.). 48p. (J). (ps-3). pap. 3.99 (978-0-7894-7342-4(9)); (SPA., pap. 3.99 (978-0-7894-7344-8(5)) Dorling Kindersley Publishing, Inc.

Fischer, David. Roberto Clemente. 2004. (Trailblazers of the Modern World Ser.). (J). pap. 11.95 (978-0-8368-5264-6(8)); (Illus.). 48p. (YA). lib. bdg. 30.00 (978-0-8368-5495-4(0)) Stevens, Gareth Inc. (World Almanac Library).

Ford, Carin T. Roberto Clemente: Baseball Legend. 2005. (Latino Biography Library). (Illus.). 128p. (J). (gr. 6-12). lib. bdg. 31.93 (978-0-7660-2485-4(7)) Enslow Pubs., Inc.

Franchino, Vicky. Roberto Clemente. 2008. (J). lib. bdg. 26.00 **(*978-1-60279-073-5(6)*)** Cherry Lake Publishing.

Garcia, Kimberly. Roberto Clemente. l.t. ed. 2002. (Real Life Reader Biography Ser.). (Illus.). 32p. (gr. 3-8). lib. bdg. 24.95 (978-1-58415-127-2(7)) Mitchell Lane Pubs., Inc.

Guzman, Lila & Guzman, Rick. Roberto Clemente: Baseball Hero. 2006. (Famous Latinos Ser.). (Illus.). 32p. (J). lib. bdg. 22.60 (978-0-7660-2640-7(X) , Enslow Elementary) Enslow Pubs., Inc.

Guzman, Lila & Guzman, Rick. Roberto Clemente: Héroe del Béisbol. 2007. (Latinos Famosos Ser.). (SPA., Illus.). 32p. (J). (gr. 3-4). lib. bdg. 22.60 **(*978-0-7660-2675-9(2)*** , Enslow Elementary) Enslow Pubs., Inc.

Harcourt School Publishers Staff. The Pride of Puerto Rico. 3rd ed. 2002. (Horizons Ser.). (Illus.). (J). pap. 7.30 (978-0-15-333591-4(2)) Harcourt Schl. Pubs.

—Roberto's Dream On Level. 3rd ed. 2002. (Trophies Reading Program Ser.). (Illus.). pap. 5.10 (978-0-15-323173-5(4)) Harcourt Schl. Pubs.

Lace, William. Roberto Clemente, Baseball Hall of Famer. 2006. (Twentieth Century's Most Influential: Hispanics Ser.). (Illus.). 112p. (J). (gr. 7-10). 32.45 (978-1-59018-969-6(8) , Lucent Bks.) Thomson Gale.

Mara, Wil. Roberto Clemente. 2005. (Rookie Biographies(R) Ser.). (Illus.). (J). (gr. 1-2). 31p. pap. 4.95 (978-0-516-25824-9(9)); 32p. 20.50 (978-0-516-21845-8(X)) Scholastic Library Publishing. (Children's Pr.).

Marquez, Heron. Roberto Clemente. 2005. (Trailblazer Biography Ser.). (Illus.). 112p. (J). (gr. 5-9). 30.60 (978-1-57505-767-5(0)) Lerner Publishing Group.

Olmstead. Roberto Clemente. 2005. (Hispanic-American Biographies Ser.). pap. 9.50 (978-1-4109-1596-2(4)); Pack. pap. 34.20 (978-1-4109-1601-3(4)) Harcourt Schl. Pubs.

Olmstead, Mary. Roberto Clemente. 2004. (Hispanic-American Biographies Ser.). (Illus.). 64p. (J). pap. 9.50 (978-1-4109-0917-6(4)) Harcourt Schl. Pubs.

—Roberto Clemente. 2004. (Hispanic-American Biographies Ser.). (Illus.). 64p. (J). (gr. 4-6). 32.86 (978-1-4109-0711-0(2)) Raintree.

Roberts, Jerry. Roberto Clemente: Baseball Player. 2005. (Ferguson Career Biographies Ser.). (Illus.). 128p. (J). (gr. 6-12). 25.00 (978-0-8160-6072-6(X) , Ferguson Publishing Co.) Facts On File, Inc.

Thornley, Stew. Roberto Clemente. 2007. (Sports Heroes & Legends Ser.). (Illus.). 106p. (J). 27.93 (978-0-8225-5962-7(5) , Lerner Pubns.) Lerner Publishing Group.

Winter, Jonah. Roberto Clemente: Pride of the Pittsburgh Pirates. Colon, Raul, illus. 2005. 40p. (J). 17.99 (978-0-689-85643-3(1) , Atheneum) Simon & Schuster Children's Publishing.

CLEOPATRA, QUEEN OF EGYPT, D. 30 B.C.

Adams, Michelle Medlock. The Life & Times of Cleopatra. 2005. (Biography from Ancient Civilizations Ser.). (Illus.). 48p. (J). (gr. 4-8). lib. bdg. 29.95 (978-1-58415-335-1(0)) Mitchell Lane Pubs., Inc.

Daynes, Katie. Cleopatra. 2005. (Famous Lives Gift Books Ser.). 64p. (J). 8.95 (978-0-7945-0868-5(5) , Usborne) EDC Publishing.

Geras, Adèle. Cleopatra. 2009. (Illus.). 64p. (J). (gr. 1-5). 16.95 **(*978-0-7534-6025-2(4)*** , Kingfisher) Houghton Mifflin Co. Trade & Reference Div.

Harcourt School Publishers Staff. Cleopatra's Lost City. 3rd ed. 2002. (Horizons Ser.). (Illus.). (J). pap. 7.30 (978-0-15-333628-7(5)) Harcourt Schl. Pubs.

Holub, Joan. Cleopatra & the King's Enemies: Based on a True Story of Cleopatra in Egypt. Aleshina, Nonna, illus. 2007. (Young Princesses Around the World Ser.). 48p. (J). (gr. 1-3). pap. 3.99 (978-0-689-87194-8(5)); lib. bdg. 13.89 (978-0-689-87196-2(1)) Simon & Schuster Children's Publishing. (Aladdin).

Jeffrey, Gary & Ganeri, Anita. Cleopatra: The Life of an Egyptian Queen. 2005. (Graphic Nonfiction Ser.). (Illus.). 48p. (J). lib. bdg. 26.50 (978-1-4042-0242-9(0)) Rosen Publishing Group, Inc., The.

MacDonald, Fiona. Cleopatra. 2006. (DK Discoveries Ser.). 48p. (J). pap. 6.99 (978-0-7566-1964-0(5)) Dorling Kindersley Publishing, Inc.

Naden, Corinne J. & Blue, Rose. Cleopatra. 2001. (Women of Achievement Ser.). (J). 32.00 (978-0-7910-6320-0(8) , Chelsea Hse.) Facts On File, Inc.

Nardo, Don. Cleopatra: Egypt's Last Pharoah. 2005. (Lucent Library of Historical Eras). (Illus.). 112p. (YA). (gr. 7-10). lib. bdg. 32.45 (978-1-59018-660-2(5) , Lucent Bks.) Thomson Gale.

Nardo, Don, ed. Cleopatra. 2000. (People Who Made History Ser.). (Illus.). 173p. (YA). (gr. 9-12). pap. (978-0-7377-0321-4(0) , Greenhaven Pr., Inc.) Thomson Gale.

Pipe, Jim. You Wouldn't Want to Be Cleopatra! An Egyptian Ruler You'd Rather Not Be. Antram, David, illus. 2007. (You Wouldn't Want to... Ser.). 32p. (J). (gr. 2-5). 28.50 **(*978-0-531-18726-5(8)***); pap. 9.95 **(*978-0-531-18923-8(6)*)** Scholastic Library Publishing. (Watts, Franklin).

Reid, Struan. Cleopatra. (Historical Biographies Ser.). 32p. 2003. pap. 7.50 (978-1-58810-998-9(4)); 2002. (Illus.). (J). (gr. 2-4). lib. bdg. 22.79 (978-1-58810-565-3(2)) Heinemann Library.

—Cleopatra. 2002. (gr. 3-6). lib. bdg. 15.25 (978-0-613-45727-9(7)) Tandem Library Bks.

Ross, Stewart. Clever Cleo. Shields, Sue, illus. 32p. pap. 9.99 (978-0-7502-2853-4(9) , Hodder & Stoughton) Hodder General Publishing Division GBR. *Dist:* Trafalgar Square Publishing.

Streissguth, Thomas. Queen Cleopatra. 1999. (Biography Ser.). (Illus.). 112p. (YA). (gr. 6-12). lib. bdg. 27.93 (978-0-8225-4946-8(8) , Lerner Pubns.) Lerner Publishing Group.

Worth, Richard. Cleopatra: Queen of Ancient Egypt. 2006. (Rulers of the Ancient World Ser.). (Illus.). 160p. (J). lib. bdg. 27.93 (978-0-7660-2559-2(4)) Enslow Pubs., Inc.

CLEOPATRA, QUEEN OF EGYPT, D. 30 B.C.—FICTION

Cleopatra the Ambitious: What Made Them Famous? 2006. 156p. (J). per. 15.00 (978-1-931195-97-3(8)) KiwE Publishing, Ltd.

Gregory, Kristiana. Cleopatra VII: Daughter of the Nile, Egypt, 57 B. C. 1999. (Royal Diaries Ser.). (Illus.). 224p. (J). (gr. 4-8). pap. 10.95 (978-0-590-81975-6(5), Scholastic Pr.) Scholastic, Inc.

Lopez, David Mark. Walk Like an Egyptian. 2006. (J). (gr. 3-7). (***978-0-9744097-0-2(7)***) Lopez, David.

Roberts, Katherine. The Cleopatra Curse. 2006. (Seven Fabulous Wonders Ser.). (Illus.). 288p. (J). pap. 11.99 (978-0-00-711284-5(X), HarperCollins Children's Bks.) HarperCollins Pubs. Ltd. GBR. *Dist:* Independent Pubs. Group.

Williams, Maiya. The Hour of the Cobra. 2006. 312p. (YA). (gr. 4-9). 16.95 (978-0-8109-5970-5(4), Amulet Bks.) Abrams, Harry N., Inc.

CLERGY

see also Monasticism and Religious Orders

Ansary, Mir Tamim. Martin Luther King, Jr. Day. 2006. (Illus.). 32p. (J). (***978-1-4034-8889-3(4)***) Heinemann Library.

Aykroyd, Clarissa. Savage Satire: The Story of Jonathan Swift. 2006. (World Writers Ser.). (Illus.). 160p. (J). (gr. 6-12). lib. bdg. 27.95 (978-1-59935-027-1(0)) Reynolds, Morgan Inc.

Bader, Bonnie. Who Was Martin Luther King Jr. Harrison, Nancy & Wolf, Elizaabeth, illus. 2007. (Who Was... ? Ser.). 112p. (J). (gr. 2-5). 4.99 (***978-0-448-44723-0(1)***, Grosset & Dunlap) Penguin Group (USA) Inc.

Benge, Janet & Benge, Geoff. John Wesley: The World, His Parish. 2007. (J). (***978-1-57658-382-1(1)***) YWAM Publishing.

Bozzuti-Jones, Mark Francisco. The Miter Fits Just Fine: A Story about the Rt. Rev. Barbara Clementine Harris, Suffragan Bishop, Diocese of Massachusetts. 2003. 86p. pap. 10.95 (978-1-56101-220-6(3)) Cowley Pubns.

Brown, Terrell. Reverend Run (Run MDC) 2007. (Hip-Hop Ser.). (Illus.). 64p. (J). (gr. 5 up). 22.95 (978-1-4222-0127-5(9)) Mason Crest Pubs.

Davis, Kenneth C. Don't Know Much about Martin Luther King Jr., Vol. 6. Kodaira, Machiyo, illus. 2006. (Don't Know Much About Ser.). 144p. (J). (gr. 2-5). lib. bdg. 16.89 (978-0-06-028822-8(1)) HarperCollins Pubs.

Fandel, Jennifer. Martin Luther King, Jr. 2005. (Genius Ser.). (Illus.). 48p. (J). (gr. 5-9). 21.95 (978-1-58341-329-6(4), Creative Education) Creative Co., The.

Feinstein, Stephen. Read about Martin Luther King, Jr. 2004. (I Like Biographies Ser.!). (Illus.). 24p. (J). lib. bdg. 24.95 (978-0-7660-2300-0(1)) Enslow Pubs., Inc.

Grant, Joseph. ScriptureWalk Junior High: People of Promise. 2003. (ScriptureWalk Ser.). 128p. (YA). per. 22.95 (978-0-88489-644-9(7)) St. Mary's Pr.

Hatt, Christine. Martin Luther King, Jr. 2004. (Judge for Yourself Ser.). (Illus.). 64p. (J). pap. (978-0-8368-5565-4(5)); (gr. 5 up). lib. bdg. 30.00 (978-0-8368-5562-3(0)) Stevens, Gareth Inc. (World Almanac Library).

January, Brendan. Martin Luther King, Jr. Minister & Civil Rights Activist. 2000. (Career Biographies Ser.). (Illus.). 128p. (J). (gr. 6-12). 25.00 (978-0-89434-342-1(4), F405, Ferguson Publishing Co.) Facts On File, Inc.

Jones, Rob Lloyd. Martin Luther King, Jr. 2006. (Illus.). 62p. (J). pap. (***978-0-439-02299-6(1)***) Scholastic, Inc.

Joyce, Mary R. A Priest from the Heart. 1999. (Illus.). 96p. (YA). (gr. 4-12). pap. 9.95 (978-0-9615722-3-5(X)) LifeCom.

Linney, Susan. Martin Luther King, Jr: With a Discussion of Responsibility. 2004. (Values in Action Ser.). (J). (978-1-59203-069-9(6)) Learning Challenge, Inc.

Lowery, Linda. Martin Luther King Jr Day. 2004. (gr. k-3). lib. bdg. 14.10 (978-0-613-79212-7(2)) Tandem Library Bks.

Lutz, Norma Jean. Increase Mather. 2001. (gr. 5-8). lib. bdg. 17.60 (978-0-613-32685-8(7)) Tandem Library Bks.

Mallin, Jay. Al Sharpton: Community Activist. 2007. (Great Life Stories Ser.). (Illus.). 111p. (J). (***978-0-531-13672-0(8)***, Franklin Watts) Hodder Children's Division.

—Al Sharpton: Community Activist. 2006. (Great Life Stories Ser.). (Illus.). 111p. (YA). (gr. 6 up). 30.50 (978-0-531-13872-4(0), Watts, Franklin) Scholastic Library Publishing.

Martin's Big Words. 2004. pap. 38.75 incl. audio compact disk (978-1-55592-637-3(1)); pap. 32.75 incl. audio (978-1-55592-367-9(4)); pap. 14.95 incl. audio (978-1-55592-169-9(8)) Weston Woods Studios, Inc.

Miller, Susan. George Whitefield: Clergyman & Scholar. 2001. (gr. 5-8). lib. bdg. 17.60 (978-0-613-32600-1(8)) Tandem Library Bks.

Mir Tamim Ansary. Martin Luther King Jr. Day. 2nd ed. 2006. (Illus.). 32p. (J). pap. (***978-1-4034-8902-9(5)***) Heinemann Library.

Rappaport, Doreen. Martin's Big Words: The Life of Dr. Martin Luther King Jr. Collier, Bryan, illus. 2001. 40p. (gr. k-4). 15.99 (978-0-7868-0714-7(8)) Hyperion Bks. for Children.

Rappaport, Doreen. Martin's Big Words: The Life of Dr. Martin Luther King Jr. Collier, Bryan, illus. rev. ed. 2007. 40p. (ps-17). pap. 6.99 (***978-1-4231-0635-7(0)***, Jump at the Sun) Hyperion Bks. for Children.

Sidwell, Mark. Free Indeed: Heroes of Black Christian History. exp. ed. 2001. vi, 154p. (J). (gr. 3-6). 10.95 (978-1-57924-734-8(2)) Jones, Bob Univ. Pr.

The Story of Martin Luther King, Jr. 2001. (Illus.). 24p. (J). (ps-k). 6.95 (978-0-8249-4144-4(6)) Ideals Pubns.

Tucker, Margaret E. Biography of Richard Bullard: From Shoe Cobbler in England to Minister for Jesus Christ in America. 2003. pap. 6.75 (978-0-9672363-3-9(9)) Heritage Publishing.

Wagner, Heather Lehr. Benjamin Hooks. 2003. (African American Leaders Ser.). (Illus.). 112p. (gr. 6-12). 30.00 (978-0-7910-7685-9(7), Chelsea Hse.) Facts On File, Inc.

Wellman, Sam. John Wesley: Founder of the Methodist Church. 1999. (Heroes of the Faith Ser.). 208p. (YA). (gr. 4-7). lib. bdg. 17.95 (978-0-7910-5036-1(X), Chelsea Hse.) Facts On File, Inc.

—T. D. Jakes: Religious Leader. (Black Americans of Achievement Ser.). (Illus.). (J). 2000. 112p. (gr. 4-7). 30.00 (978-0-7910-5362-1(8)); 1999. 103p. (gr. 5 up). pap. 30.00 (978-0-7910-5363-8(6)) Facts On File, Inc. (Chelsea Hse.).

Windle, Jeanette & Clements, Jan. Yandicu: Ein Medizinmann Wird Evangelist. Date not set. Tr. of Yandicu - From Witch Doctor to Evangelist. (GER., Illus.). (J). (gr. 2-7). pap. (978-0-9617490-5-7(9)) Gospel Missionary Union.

Winget, Mary. Martin Luther King, Jr. 2003. (History Maker Bios Ser.). (Illus.). 47p. (J). 26.60 (978-0-8225-4674-0(4), Lerner Pubns.) Lerner Publishing Group.

—Martin Luther King, Jr. 2004. (History Maker Bios Ser.). (Illus.). 48p. (J). pap. (978-0-8225-4804-1(6), Lerner Pubns.) Lerner Publishing Group.

Zimmerman, Kate. The Lobster Kids' Guide to Exploring Calgary: 12 Months of Fun. Kirner, Bob, ed. Battuz, Christine, illus. 2000. (Lobster Kids' City Explorers Ser.). 254p. (J). (ps up). pap. 12.95 (978-1-894222-08-2(3)) Lobster Pr. CAN. *Dist:* Univ. of Toronto Pr.

CLERGY—FICTION

Cheripko, Jan. Brother Bartholomew: And the Apple Grove. Kasparavicius, Kestutis, illus. 2004. 32p. (J). (gr. k-2). 15.95 (978-1-59078-096-1(5)) Boyds Mills Pr.

Delibes, Miguel. Los Santos Inocentes Level 5. 1998. (SPA.). (gr. 7-12). lib. bdg. 15.25 (978-0-613-80720-3(0)) Tandem Library Bks.

Erdrich, Louise. The Last Report on the Miracles at Little No Horse: A Novel. 2002. (gr. 7-12). lib. bdg. 22.20 (978-0-613-62146-5(8)) Tandem Library Bks.

Hawthorne, Nathaniel. The Scarlet Letter - Spotlight Edition. Grudzina, Douglas, ed. 2004. (Illus.). 150p. (YA). per. 5.95 (978-1-58049-550-9(8), PWH5508) Prestwick Hse., Inc.

Hernandez, Natalie. Las Aventuras con Padre Serra. Hernandez, Tony Y., tr. Nolan, Claudia, illus. 1999. (ENG & SPA.). 112p. (Orig.). (J). (gr. 3-8). pap. 9.95 (978-0-9644386-1-3(5)) Santa Ines Pubns.

Hunt, Susan & Hunt, Richie. Discovering Jesus in Exodus, Vol. 2. 2005. (Illus.). 176p. pap. 16.99 (978-1-58134-453-0(8), Crossway Bibles) Crossway Bks.

Keeling, Annie E. Andrew Golding A Tale of the Great Plague. 2004. reprint ed. pap. 15.95 (978-1-4191-0694-1(5)); pap. 1.99 (978-1-4192-0694-8(X)) Kessinger Publishing, LLC.

Keeling, E. Annie. Andrew Golding (a Tale of the Great Plag. 2006. 40.99 (***978-1-4280-0516-7(1)***); pap. 34.99 (***978-1-4280-0515-0(3)***) IndyPublish.com.

Ray, Delia. Singing Hands. 2006. (Illus.). 224p. (J). (gr. 5-9). 16.00 (978-0-618-65762-9(2), Clarion Bks.) Houghton Mifflin Co. Trade & Reference Div.

Schmidt, Gary D. Lizzie Bright & the Buckminster Boy. (gr. 5). 2008. 240p. (YA). mass mkt. 6.99 (***978-0-375-84169-9(5)***, Laurel Leaf); 2006. 224p. (J). reprint ed. pap. 6.50 (978-0-553-49495-2(3), Yearling) Random Hse. Children's Bks.

Spinelli, Eileen & Parmenter, Wayne. When Christmas Came. Spinelli, Eileen & Parmenter, Wayne, illus. 2006. (Illus.). 32p. (J). (ps). bds. 16.95 (978-0-8249-5507-6(2), Ideals Pr.) Ideals Pubns.

Tompert, Ann. The Pied Piper of Peru. Kasparavicius, Kestutis, illus. 2003. 32p. (YA). (gr. k-2). 15.95 (978-1-56397-949-1(7)) Boyds Mills Pr.

Van Heerde, Gerrit. The Man with the Red Beard. Van Bergen, Jantien, illus. 2002. (J). (978-0-9579517-0-9(1)) Inheritance Pubns.

Vernon, Louise A. A Heart Strangely Warmed. Eitzen, Allan, illus. 2002. (Louise A. Vernon's Religious Heritage Ser.). 126p. (YA). (gr. 4-9). 7.99 (978-0-8361-1769-1(7)) Herald Pr.

Whelan, Gloria. A Time to Keep Silent. 2004. 144p. (J). pap. 8.00 (978-0-8028-5255-7(6)) Eerdmans, William B. Publishing Co.

—Time to Keep Silent. 2003. (gr. 5-8). lib. bdg. 16.45 (978-0-613-75511-5(1)) Tandem Library Bks.

Wilson, Mike. The Warrior Priest: The Story of Father Roy Bourgeois. (Contemporary Profiles & Policy Series for the Younger Reader). (Illus.). 112p. (YA). (gr. 8 up). 2002. pap. 28.00 (978-0-934272-68-1(9)); 2001. 28.00 (978-0-934272-69-8(7)) Burke, John Gordon Pub., Inc.

CLERGY—POLITICAL ACTIVITY

Jakoubek, Robert E. Martin Luther King, Jr. Civil Rights Leader. (Black Americans of Achievement Ser.). (Illus.). 112p. (gr. 6-12). 2005. pap. 13.25 (978-0-7910-8335-2(7)); 2004. 30.00 (978-0-7910-8161-7(3)) Facts On File, Inc. (Chelsea Hse.).

CLERGY—VOCATIONAL GUIDANCE

McIntosh, Kenneth. Clergy. 2003. (Careers with Character Ser.). (Illus.). 96p. (YA). (gr. 7 up). lib. bdg. 22.95 (978-1-59084-311-6(8)) Mason Crest Pubs.

CLERICAL WORK—TRAINING

see Business Education

CLERKS (SALESMENSHIP)

see Sales Personnel

CLEVELAND, GROVER, 1837-1908

Joseph, Paul. Grover Cleveland. 2001. (United States Presidents Ser.). (Illus.). 32p. (J). (gr. k-6). lib. bdg. 22.78 (978-1-57765-249-6(5), Checkerboard Library) ABDO Publishing Co.

Markel, Rita J. Grover Cleveland. 2007. (Presidential Leaders Ser.). (Illus.). 112p. (J). 29.27 (978-0-8225-1494-7(X), Lerner Pubns.) Lerner Publishing Group.

Ochester, Betsy. Grover Cleveland. 2004. (Encyclopedia of Presidents Ser.). (Illus.). 110p. (J). 34.00 (978-0-516-22962-1(1), Children's Pr.) Scholastic Library Publishing.

Tecco, Betsy Dru. How to Draw the Life & Times of Grover Cleveland. 2006. (Kid's Guide to Drawing the Presidents of the United States of America Ser.). (J). 25.25 (978-1-4042-2999-0(X), PowerKids Pr.) Rosen Publishing Group, Inc., The.

Venezia, Mike. Grover Cleveland. 2006. (Illus.). 32p. (YA). (gr. 3-4). pap. 7.95 (978-0-516-25402-9(2), Children's Pr.) Scholastic Library Publishing.

Venezia, Mike, illus. Grover Cleveland. 2006. (Getting to Know the U. S. Presidents Ser.). 32p. (J). (gr. 3-4). 27.00 (978-0-516-22627-9(4), Children's Pr.) Scholastic Library Publishing.

Williams, Jean Kinney. Grover Cleveland. 2003. (Profiles of the Presidents Ser.). (Illus.). 64p. (J). (gr. 4 up). lib. bdg. 23.93 (978-0-7565-0269-0(1)) Compass Point Bks.

Young, Jeff C. Grover Cleveland: A MyReportLinks. Com Book. 2003. (Presidents Ser.). (Illus.). 48p. (J). lib. bdg. 25.26 (978-0-7660-5128-7(5), MyReportLinks.com Bks.) Enslow Pubs., Inc.

CLEVELAND (OHIO)

Fisher, Antwone Quenton. Finding Fish: A Memoir. 2001. (gr. 7-12). lib. bdg. 23.40 (978-0-613-49314-7(1)) Tandem Library Bks.

Pfingsten, Ralph. From Rockport to West Park. 2004. 45.00 net. (978-0-9759618-0-3(2)) John Marshall High Schl. Alumni Assn.

CLEVELAND (OHIO)—FICTION

Garsee, Jeannine. Before, after, & Somebody in Between. 2007. 352p. (YA). (gr. 9 up). 16.95 (***978-1-59990-022-3(X)***) Bloomsbury Publishing.

Johnson, Angela. Bird. 2006. 144p. (YA). (gr. 5). reprint ed. pap. 5.99 (978-0-14-240544-3(2), Puffin) Penguin Group (USA) Inc.

CLEVELAND BROWNS (FOOTBALL TEAM)

Gilbert, Sara. The History of the Cleveland Browns. 2004. (NFL Today Ser.). (Illus.). 32p. 18.95 (978-1-58341-293-0(X), Creative Education) Creative Co., The.

Stewart, Mark. Cleveland Browns. 2006. (Team Spirit Ser.). (Illus.). 48p. (J). lib. bdg. 25.27 (978-1-59953-064-2(3)) Norwood Hse. Pr.

CLEVELAND INDIANS (BASEBALL TEAM)

Feller, Bob. Hello, Slider! 2007. (J). 14.95 (***978-1-932888-88-1(8)***) Mascot Bks., Inc.

Pietrusza, David. The Cleveland Indians Baseball Team. 2001. (Great Sports Teams Ser.). (Illus.). 48p. (YA). (gr. 4-10). lib. bdg. 23.93 (978-0-7660-1491-6(6)) Enslow Pubs., Inc.

Pueschner, Gordon. The Story of the Cleveland Indians. 2007. (J). (***978-1-58341-485-9(1)***, Creative Education) Creative Co., The.

Rambeck, Richard. The History of the Cleveland Indians. 1998. (Baseball, the Great American Game Ser.). (Illus.). 32p. (J). (gr. 3-12). pap. 21.30 (978-0-88682-906-3(2), Creative Education) Creative Co., The.

Stewart, Wayne. Cleveland Indians. 2002. (Baseball Ser.). (Illus.). 32p. (J). (978-1-58341-206-0(9), Creative Education); pap. 5.95 (978-0-89812-340-1(2), Creative Paperbacks) Creative Co., The.

CLIFF DWELLERS AND CLIFF DWELLINGS

see also Mounds and Mound Builders

Anderson, Dale. The Anasazi Culture at Mesa Verde. 2003. (Landmark Events in American History Ser.). (Illus.). 48p. (J). (gr. 5 up). pap. 14.95 (978-0-8368-5399-5(7)); lib. bdg. 30.00 (978-0-8368-5371-1(7)) Stevens, Gareth Inc. (World Almanac Library).

Arnold, Caroline. The Ancient Cliff Dwellers of Mesa Verde. Hewett, Richard, illus. 2000. 64p. (YA). (gr. 7-7). pap. 7.95 (978-0-618-05149-6(X), Clarion Bks.) Houghton Mifflin Co. Trade & Reference Div.

Crewe, Sabrina & Anderson, Dale. The Anasazi Culture at Mesa Verde. 2003. (Events That Shaped America Ser.). (Illus.). 32p. (J). (gr. 3 up). lib. bdg. 24.67 (978-0-8368-3390-4(2)) Stevens, Gareth Inc.

Shuter, Jane. Mesa Verde. (Visiting the Past Ser.). (Illus.). 32p. (J). (gr. 5-7). 2002. pap. 6.95 (978-1-58810-407-6(9), 91182); 1999. lib. bdg. 24.22 (978-1-57572-858-2(3)) Heinemann Library.

Young, Robert. A Personal Tour of Mesa Verde. 1999. (How It Was Ser.). (Illus.). 64p. (J). (gr. 4-6). lib. bdg. (978-0-8225-3577-5(7), Lerner Pubns.) Lerner Publishing Group.

CLIFFORD, THE BIG RED DOG (FICTITIOUS CHARACTER)—FICTION

Aboff, Marcie. Clifford's Puppy Days: Party Time! Goldberg, Barry, illus. 2005. (Clifford Ser.). 33p. (J). 3.99 (978-0-439-69048-5(X), Cartwheel Bks.) Scholastic, Inc.

—Santa's Big Red Helper. Haefele, Steve, illus. 2005. (Clifford Ser.). 80p. (J). (ps-k). pap. 2.99 (978-0-439-79150-2(2)) Scholastic, Inc.

Barkly, Bob. A Puppy to Love. Kurtz, John, illus. 2001. (Clifford, the Big Red Dog Ser.). (J). (gr. k-2). pap. (978-0-439-22004-0(1)) Scholastic, Inc.

Bridwell, Norman. Bertrand le Chien de Pompiers. (Clifford, the Big Red Dog Ser.). (J). (gr. k-2). (FRE., Illus.). pap. 5.99 (978-0-590-24375-9(6)); 2005. 40p. pap. 3.99 (978-0-439-72524-8(0), Cartwheel Bks.) Scholastic, Inc.

—The Big Leaf Pile. Bridwell, Norman, illus. 2002. (Big Red Readers Ser.). (Illus.). (J). 11.91 (978-0-7587-6773-8(0)) Book Wholesalers, Inc.

—Camping Out. Bracken, Carolyn & Edwards, Ken, illus. 2003. (Big Red Reader Ser.). (J). (978-0-439-45810-8(2)) Scholastic, Inc.

—Clifford. 2006. (Scholastic Reader Collection Level 2 Ser.). 144p. (J). pap. 6.99 (978-0-439-84800-8(8), Cartwheel Bks.) Scholastic, Inc.

—Clifford al Rescate. 2000. (Clifford, the Big Red Dog Ser.). (SPA., Illus.). 32p. (J). (gr. k-2). pap. 3.50 (978-0-439-12956-5(7), SO2943, Scholastic en Espanol) Scholastic, Inc.

—Clifford al Rescate. 2000. (SPA.). (gr. k-3). lib. bdg. 11.25 (978-0-613-24609-5(8)); (Illus.). (J). 10.30 (978-0-606-18534-9(8)) Tandem Library Bks.

—Clifford & the Big Parade. Bridwell, Norman, illus. 2002. (Clifford, the Big Red Dog Ser.). (Illus.). (J). 11.45 (978-0-7587-6372-3(7)) Book Wholesalers, Inc.

—Clifford & the Big Parade. Bridwell, Norman, illus. 1998. (Clifford, the Big Red Dog Ser.). (Illus.). 32p. (J). (gr. k-2). pap. 3.50 (978-0-590-10811-9(5)) Scholastic, Inc.

—Clifford & the Big Parade. 1998. (Clifford, the Big Red Dog Ser.). (J). (gr. k-2). 10.30 (978-0-606-13284-8(8)) Tandem Library Bks.

—Clifford & the Grouchy Neighbors. Bridwell, Norman, illus. 2002. (Clifford, the Big Red Dog Ser.). (Illus.). (J). 11.45 (978-0-7587-7030-1(8)) Book Wholesalers, Inc.

—Clifford & the Halloween Parade. 2004. 32p. (J). lib. bdg. 15.00 (978-1-59054-545-4(1)) Fitzgerald Bks.

—Clifford & the Halloween Parade. (Clifford, the Big Red Dog Ser.). (gr. k-2). 2000. (Illus.). (J). 10.79 (978-0-606-18867-8(3)); 1999. lib. bdg. 11.80 (978-0-613-24610-1(1)) Tandem Library Bks.

—Clifford & the Halloween Parade: Level 1. Bridwell, Norman, illus. 2004. (Clifford, the Big Red Dog Ser.). (Illus.). 32p. (J). (gr. k-3). pap. 3.99 (978-0-439-09834-2(3)) Scholastic, Inc.

—Clifford at the Circus. Bridwell, Norman, illus. 2002. (Clifford, the Big Red Dog Ser.). (Illus.). (J). 11.45 (978-0-7587-6707-3(2)) Book Wholesalers, Inc.

—Clifford at the Circus. (Clifford, the Big Red Dog Ser.). (Illus.). (J). (gr. k-2). 6.95 (978-0-590-68639-6(9)) Scholastic, Inc.

—Clifford Barks! Bridwell, Norman, illus. 2000. (Clifford, the Big Red Dog Ser.). (Illus.). 7p. (J). (ps-k). bds. 3.95 (978-0-439-14999-0(1), Cartwheel Bks.) Scholastic, Inc.

—Clifford Celebrates the Year. 2002. (Clifford Ser.). (Illus.). 256p. (J). pap. 10.99 (978-0-439-46770-4(5)) Scholastic, Inc.

—Clifford Counts 1-2-3. 1998. (Clifford, the Big Red Dog Ser.). (Illus.). 14p. (J). (ps-k). bds. 6.99 (978-0-590-37928-1(3), Cartwheel Bks.) Scholastic, Inc.

—Clifford, el Cachorrito. Suarez, Ana, tr. from ENG. 2003. (Clifford Ser.). (SPA., Illus.). 32p. (J). 3.50 (978-0-439-54566-2(8), Scholastic en Espanol) Scholastic, Inc.

—Clifford Gets a Job. Bridwell, Norman, illus. 2002. (Clifford, the Big Red Dog Ser.). (Illus.). (J). 11.45 (978-0-7587-6390-7(5)) Book Wholesalers, Inc.

—Clifford Goes to Dog School. Bridwell, Norman, illus. 2002. (Clifford, the Big Red Dog Ser.). (Illus.). 32p. (J). (ps-3). pap. 3.50 (978-0-439-32788-6(1)) Scholastic, Inc.

—Clifford Goes to Dog School. 2002. (ps-2). lib. bdg. 11.25 (978-0-613-45580-0(0)) Tandem Library Bks.

—Clifford Goes to Hollywood. Bridwell, Norman, illus. 2002. (Clifford, the Big Red Dog Ser.). (Illus.). (J). 11.45 (978-0-7587-7061-5(8)) Book Wholesalers, Inc.

—Clifford Goes to Washington. Bridwell, Norman, illus. 2005. (Clifford Ser.). (Illus.). 32p. (J). 3.50 (978-0-439-69656-2(9), Cartwheel Bks.) Scholastic, Inc.

—Clifford Grows Up. Bridwell, Norman, illus. 2002. (Clifford, the Big Red Dog Ser.). (Illus.). (J). 11.45 (978-0-7587-1071-0(2)) Book Wholesalers, Inc.

—Clifford Grows Up. 1999. (Clifford, the Big Red Dog Ser.). (J). (gr. k-2). 10.30 (978-0-606-16935-6(0)) Tandem Library Bks.

—Clifford Keeps Cool. Bridwell, Norman, illus. 2002. (Clifford, the Big Red Dog Ser.). (Illus.). (J). 11.45 (978-0-7587-5006-8(4)) Book Wholesalers, Inc.

—Clifford Keeps Cool. 1999. (Clifford, the Big Red Dog Ser.). (gr. k-2). (J). 10.30 (978-0-606-16626-3(2)); lib. bdg. 11.25 (978-0-613-16911-0(5)) Tandem Library Bks.

—Clifford' Keeps Cool. 1999. (Clifford, the Big Red Dog Ser.). (Illus.). 32p. (J). (gr. k-2). pap. 3.99 (978-0-439-04394-6(8)) Scholastic, Inc.

—Clifford Makes a Friend. Bridwell, Norman, illus. 2002. (Clifford, the Big Red Dog Ser.). (Illus.). (J). 11.91 (978-0-7587-5017-4(X)) Book Wholesalers, Inc.

—Clifford Makes a Friend. 2004. 32p. (J). lib. bdg. 15.00 (978-1-59054-547-8(8)) Fitzgerald Bks.

—Clifford Makes a Friend. Bridwell, Norman, illus. 1998. (Clifford, the Big Red Dog Ser.). (Illus.). 32p. (J). (gr. k-2). pap. 3.99 (978-0-590-37930-4(5)) Scholastic, Inc.

—Clifford Makes a Friend. 1998. (Illus.). (J). (ps-ps). lib. bdg. 11.80 (978-0-613-11422-6(1)) Tandem Library Bks.

—Clifford Takes a Trip. Bridwell, Norman, illus. 2002. (Clifford, the Big Red Dog Ser.). (Illus.). (J). 11.45 (978-0-7587-9335-5(9)) Book Wholesalers, Inc.

—Clifford the Big Red Dog Read Along. unabr. ed. 2006. (J). 9.95 (978-0-439-87587-5(0)) Scholastic, Inc.

—Clifford the Big Red Dog Read along Library. 2006. (J). 18.95 (978-0-439-87593-6(5)) Scholastic, Inc.

—Clifford the Small Red Puppy. (J). 2007. 9.95 (978-0-439-92492-4(8)); 2005. 40p. pap. 3.99 (978-0-439-72526-2(7) , Cartwheel Bks.) Scholastic, Inc.

—Clifford the Small Red Puppy - Library Edition. 2007. (J). 18.95 (***978-0-439-02313-9(0)***) Scholastic, Inc.

—Clifford the Small Red Puppy Velour Block with Chime. 2000. (Clifford, the Big Red Dog Ser.). (J). (gr. k-2). 14.99 (978-0-439-09260-9(4)) Scholastic, Inc.

—Clifford to the Rescue. Bridwell, Norman, illus. 2002. (Clifford, the Big Red Dog Ser.). (Illus.). (J). 11.45 (978-0-7587-5005-1(6)) Book Wholesalers, Inc.

—Clifford to the Rescue. Bridwell, Norman, illus. 2000. (Clifford, the Big Red Dog Ser.). (Illus.). 32p. (J). (gr. k-2). pap. 3.99 (978-0-439-14038-6(2) , Cartwheel Bks.) Scholastic, Inc.

—Clifford to the Rescue. 2000. (ps-2). lib. bdg. 11.25 (978-0-613-24611-8(X)); (Illus.). (J). 10.30 (978-0-606-18535-6(6)) Tandem Library Bks.

—Clifford Va A la Escuela. Bridwell, Norman, illus. 2002. (Clifford, the Big Red Dog Ser.). (Illus.). (J). 11.45 (978-0-7587-6587-1(8)) Book Wholesalers, Inc.

—Clifford Va A la Escuela. Bridwell, Norman, illus. 1999. (Clifford, the Big Red Dog Ser.). (Illus.). 32p. (J). (gr. k-2). 3.50 (978-0-439-08284-6(6) , Cartwheel Bks.); (SPA., pap. 3.50 (978-0-439-08729-2(5) , SO4319, Scholastic en Espanol) Scholastic, Inc.

—Clifford Va A la Escuela. 1999. (Cifford the Big Red Dog Ser.). (gr. k-2). (J). lib. bdg. 10.30 (978-0-606-17051-2(0)); lib. bdg. 11.25 (978-0-613-16914-1(X)) Tandem Library Bks.

—Clifford Va a la Escuela. 1999. (Clifford, the Big Red Dog Ser.). (SPA.). (J). (gr. k-2). 10.30 (978-0-606-17052-9(9)) Tandem Library Bks.

—Clifford Va a la Escuela de Perros. 2004. (Clifford Ser.). (SPA., Illus.). 32p. (J). 3.50 (978-0-439-54565-5(X)) Scholastic, Inc.

—Clifford Visita el Hospital. Bridwell, Norman, illus. 2000. (Clifford, the Big Red Dog Ser.). (SPA., Illus.). 32p. (J). (ps-k). pap. 3.50 (978-0-439-18897-5(0) , SO4989, Scholastic en Espanol) Scholastic, Inc.

—Clifford Visita el Hospital. 2000. (SPA., Illus.). (J). 10.05 (978-0-606-18869-2(X)) Tandem Library Bks.

—Clifford Visits the Hospital. Bridwell, Norman, illus. 2002. (Clifford, the Big Red Dog Ser.). (Illus.). (J). 11.45 (978-0-7587-5004-4(8)) Book Wholesalers, Inc.

—Clifford Visits the Hospital. Bridwell, Norman, illus. 2000. (Clifford, the Big Red Dog Ser.). (Illus.). 32p. (J). (ps-k). pap. 3.50 (978-0-439-14096-6(X)) Scholastic, Inc.

—Clifford Visits the Hospital. 2000. (ps-2). lib. bdg. 11.25 (978-0-613-24612-5(8)); (Illus.). (J). 10.30 (978-0-606-18868-5(1)) Tandem Library Bks.

—Clifford y el Dia de Halloween. 2000. (Clifford, the Big Red Dog Ser.). (SPA., Illus.). (J). (gr. k-2). 10.30 (978-0-606-18870-8(3)) Tandem Library Bks.

—Clifford y el Dia de Pascua. 2003. (Clifford, the Big Red Dog Ser.). (SPA., Illus.). 32p. (J). (ps-k). pap. 3.50 (978-0-590-11740-1(8) , SO7533, Scholastic en Espanol) Scholastic, Inc.

—Clifford y el Gran Desfile. Bridwell, Norman, illus. 1998. (Clifford, the Big Red Dog Ser.). (SPA., Illus.). 32p. (J). (ps-k). pap. 3.50 (978-0-590-50663-2(3) , SO7528, Scholastic en Espanol) Scholastic, Inc.

—Clifford y el Gran Desfile. 1998. (Clifford, the Big Red Dog Ser.). (SPA.). (J). (gr. k-2). 10.30 (978-0-606-13285-5(6)) Tandem Library Bks.

—Clifford y el Monton de Hoyas. Salas, Macarena, ed. 2002. (Clifford Big Red Readers Ser.). (SPA., Illus.). 32p. (J). pap. 3.99 (978-0-439-25040-5(4) , SO30514, Scholastic en Espanol) Scholastic, Inc.

—Clifford y la Hora del Bano. 2003. (Clifford Ser.).Tr. of Clifford's Bathtime. (SPA., Illus.). 16p. (J). pap. 3.95 (978-0-439-54567-9(6) , Scholastic en Espanol) Scholastic, Inc.

—Clifford y los Opuestos. 2003. (Clifford Ser.).Tr. of Clifford's Opposites. (SPA., Illus.). 7p. (J). bds. 3.95 (978-0-439-55110-6(2) , Scholastic en Espanol) Scholastic, Inc.

—Clifford y los Sondios de los Animales. 2003. (Clifford Ser.).Tr. of Clifford's Animal Sounds. (SPA.). 7p. (J). bds. 3.95 (978-0-439-55109-0(9) , Scholastic en Espanol) Scholastic, Inc.

—Clifford's.Tr. of Mots Preferes de Bertrand. (FRE., Illus.). (J). pap. 5.99 (978-0-590-74326-6(0)) Scholastic, Inc.

—Clifford's Bedtime. 2003. (Clifford Ser.). (SPA., Illus.). 7p. (J). pap. 3.95 (978-0-439-54568-6(4) , Scholastic en Espanol) Scholastic, Inc.

—Clifford's Best Friend: A Story about Emily Elizabeth. Bridwell, Norman, illus. 2002. (Clifford, the Big Red Dog Ser.). (Illus.). (J). 11.45 (978-0-7587-5007-5(2)) Book Wholesalers, Inc.

—Clifford's Best Friend: A Story about Emily Elizabeth. Bridwell, Norman, illus. 2001. (Clifford, the Big Red Dog Ser.). (Illus.). 32p. (J). (ps-k). pap. 3.50 (978-0-439-21997-6(3)) Scholastic, Inc.

—Clifford's Best Friend: A Story about Emily Elizabeth. 2000. (Clifford, the Big Red Dog Ser.). (gr. k-2). (J). 10.30 (978-0-606-19551-5(3)); lib. bdg. 11.25 (978-0-613-32412-0(9)) Tandem Library Bks.

—Clifford's Big Book of Things to Know: A Book of Fun Facts. Bridwell, Norman, illus. 1999. (Clifford, the Big Red Dog Ser.). (Illus.). 40p. (J). (gr. k-2). pap. 10.95 (978-0-590-00385-8(2) , Cartwheel Bks.) Scholastic, Inc.

—Clifford's Birthday Party. Bridwell, Norman, illus. 2002. (Clifford, the Big Red Dog Ser.). (Illus.). (J). 11.45 (978-0-7587-6391-4(3)) Book Wholesalers, Inc.

—Clifford's Busy Week. Bridwell, Norman, illus. 2002. (Clifford Ser.). 32p. (J). pap. 3.50 (978-0-439-39452-9(X)) Scholastic, Inc.

—Clifford's Busy Week. 2002. (ps-2). lib. bdg. 11.25 (978-0-613-50597-0(2)) Tandem Library Bks.

—Clifford's Christmas Treasury. 2005. (Illus.). 96p. (ps-3). pap. 10.99 (978-0-439-79137-3(5)) Scholastic, Inc.

—Clifford's Day with Dad. Bridwell, Norman, illus. 2003. (Clifford Ser.). 32p. (J). pap. 3.50 (978-0-439-41073-1(8)) Scholastic, Inc.

—Clifford's Day with Dad. 2003. (gr. k-3). lib. bdg. 11.25 (978-0-613-70588-2(2)) Tandem Library Bks.

—Clifford's Family. Bridwell, Norman, illus. 2002. (Clifford, the Big Red Dog Ser.). (Illus.). (J). 11.45 (978-0-7587-6708-0(0)) Book Wholesalers, Inc.

—Clifford's First Christmas. (Clifford, the Big Red Dog Ser.). (FRE., Illus.). (J). (gr. k-2). pap. 5.99 (978-0-590-24374-2(8)) Scholastic, Inc.

—Clifford's First Sleepover. Bridwell, Norman, illus. 2004. (Clifford Ser.). (Illus.). 32p. (J). 3.50 (978-0-439-47285-2(7)) Scholastic, Inc.

—Clifford's First Snow Day. Bridwell, Norman, illus. 2002. (Clifford, the Big Red Dog Ser.). (Illus.). (J). 11.45 (978-0-7587-5008-2(0)) Book Wholesalers, Inc.

—Clifford's' First Snow Day. Bridwell, Norman, illus. 1998. (Clifford, the Big Red Dog Ser.). (Illus.). 32p. (J). (gr. k-2). 3.99 (978-0-590-03480-7(4) , Cartwheel Bks.) Scholastic, Inc.

—Clifford's First Valentine's Day. Bridwell, Norman, illus. 2002. (Clifford, the Big Red Dog Ser.). (Illus.). (J). 11.45 (978-0-7587-6533-8(9)) Book Wholesalers, Inc.

—Clifford's Furry Friends. Bridwell, Norman, illus. rev. ed. 2001. (Clifford, the Big Red Dog Ser.). (Illus.). 14p. (J). (ps-k). bds. 6.99 (978-0-439-24186-1(3)) Scholastic, Inc.

—Clifford's Glow-in-the-Dark Halloween. 2001. (Clifford, the Big Red Dog Ser.). (Illus.). 12p. (J). (ps-k). pap. 6.95 (978-0-439-30566-2(7) , Cartwheel Bks.) Scholastic, Inc.

—Clifford's Good Deeds. 2005. 40p. (J). pap. 3.99 (978-0-439-73561-2(0) , Cartwheel Bks.) Scholastic, Inc.

—Clifford's Happy Easter - Library Edition. 2007. (J). 18.95 (***978-0-439-02329-0(7)***) Scholastic, Inc.

—Clifford's Happy Mother's Day. 2001. (Clifford, the Big Red Dog Ser.). (Illus.). 32p. (J). (gr. k-2). 3.50 (978-0-439-22229-7(X)) Scholastic, Inc.

—Clifford's Manners. 1999. (Clifford, the Big Red Dog Ser.). (J). (ps-2). lib. bdg. 11.25 (978-0-8085-9621-9(7)) Tandem Library Bks.

—Clifford's Opposites. Bridwell, Norman, illus. 2000. (Clifford, the Big Red Dog Ser.). (Illus.). 7p. (J). (ps-k). bds. 3.95 (978-0-439-15000-2(0) , Cartwheel Bks.) Scholastic, Inc.

—Clifford's Pals. 2005. 40p. (J). pap. 3.99 (978-0-439-72523-1(2) , Cartwheel Bks.) Scholastic, Inc.

—Clifford's Riddles. Bridwell, Norman, illus. 2002. (Clifford, the Big Red Dog Ser.). (Illus.). (J). 11.45 (978-0-7587-6709-7(9)) Book Wholesalers, Inc.

—Clifford's Schoolhouse. Bridwell, Norman, illus. 2000. (Clifford, the Big Red Dog Ser.). (Illus.). 10p. (J). (ps-k). bds. 10.95 (978-0-439-16252-4(1)) Scholastic, Inc.

—Clifford's Schoolhouse. 2000. (Clifford, the Big Red Dog Ser.). (Illus.). (J). (gr. k-2). 87.60 (978-0-439-21185-7(9)) Scholastic, Inc.

—Clifford's Sports Day. Bridwell, Norman, illus. 2002. (Clifford, the Big Red Dog Ser.). (Illus.). (J). 11.45 (978-0-7587-6710-3(2)) Book Wholesalers, Inc.

—Clifford's Sports Day. (Clifford, the Big Red Dog Ser.). (Illus.). 32p. (J). (gr. k-2). pap. 5.99 (978-0-590-16002-5(8)) Scholastic, Inc.

—Clifford's Spring Carnival. 2002. (Clifford, the Big Red Dog Ser.). (Illus.). 24p. (J). (gr. k-2). pap. 5.99 (978-0-439-34022-9(5)) Scholastic, Inc.

—Clifford's Spring Clean-Up. Bridwell, Norman, illus. 2002. (Clifford, the Big Red Dog Ser.). (Illus.). (J). 11.45 (978-0-7587-6639-7(4)) Book Wholesalers, Inc.

—Clifford's Thanksgiving Visit. Bridwell, Norman, illus. 2002. (Clifford, the Big Red Dog Ser.). (Illus.). (J). 11.45 (978-0-7587-6640-3(8)) Book Wholesalers, Inc.

—Clifford's Tricks. Bridwell, Norman, illus. 2002. (Clifford, the Big Red Dog Ser.). (Illus.). (J). 11.45 (978-0-7587-7031-8(6)) Book Wholesalers, Inc.

—Clifford's Tricks. (Clifford, the Big Red Dog Ser.). (FRE., Illus.). (J). (gr. k-2). pap. 5.99 (978-0-590-73954-2(9)) Scholastic, Inc.

—Clifford's Valentine. 2001. (ps-2). lib. bdg. 11.80 (978-0-613-50552-9(2)) Tandem Library Bks.

—Clifford's Valentines. 2004. 32p. (J). lib. bdg. 15.00 (978-1-59054-548-5(6)) Fitzgerald Bks.

—Clifford's Valentines. Bridwell, Norman, illus. 2002. (Hello Reader! Ser.). (Illus.). 32p. (J). (ps-3). pap. 3.99 (978-0-439-18300-0(6) , Cartwheel Bks.) Scholastic, Inc.

—Clifford's Valentines. 2001. 10.79 (978-0-606-22241-9(3)) Tandem Library Bks.

—Cooking with Clifford. 1999. (Clifford, the Big Red Dog Ser.). 24p. (J). (gr. k-2). 9.95 (978-0-590-68931-1(2) , Cartwheel Bks.) Scholastic, Inc.

—Cuenta con Clifford. 1999. (Clifford, the Big Red Dog Ser.). (SPA.). (J). (gr. k-2). 10.30 (978-0-606-16907-3(5)) Tandem Library Bks.

—La Familia de Clifford. 1999. (Clifford, the Big Red Dog Ser.). (SPA., Illus.). (J). (gr. k-2). 10.30 (978-0-606-17004-8(9)) Tandem Library Bks.

—Glow-in-the-Dark Christmas. Marderosian, Mark, illus. 2001. (Clifford, the Big Red Dog Ser.). 12p. (J). (ps-k). pap. 6.95 (978-0-439-30567-9(5) , Cartwheel Bks.) Scholastic, Inc.

—My Dog Clifford Plush Book. 2000. (Clifford, the Big Red Dog Ser.). (Illus.). 12p. (J). (ps-k). bds. 7.95 (978-0-439-06046-2(X) , Cartwheel Bks.) Scholastic, Inc.

—La Navidad de Clifford. Bridwell, Norman, illus. 2003. (Clifford Ser.).Tr. of Clifford's Christmas. (SPA., Illus.). 32p. (J). pap. 3.50 (978-0-439-19891-2(7) , Scholastic en Espanol) Scholastic, Inc.

—Oops, Clifford! Bridwell, Norman, illus. 2002. (Clifford, the Big Red Dog Ser.). (Illus.). (J). 11.45 (978-0-7587-5009-9(9)) Book Wholesalers, Inc.

—Oops, Clifford! 1999. (Clifford, the Big Red Dog Ser.). (Illus.). 32p. (J). (gr. k-2). pap. 3.25 (978-0-590-63117-4(9) , Cartwheel Bks.) Scholastic, Inc.

—A Tiny Family. 1999. (Hello Reader! Ser.). 32p. (J). (ps-1). pap. 3.99 (978-0-439-04019-8(1)) Scholastic, Inc.

—What Time Is It, Clifford? Book & Clock Set. 1998. (Clifford, the Big Red Dog Ser.). (Illus.). 32p. (J). (ps-2). 9.95 (978-0-590-76338-7(5)) Scholastic, Inc.

—Where's the Big Red Doggie? Bridwell, Norman, illus. 1998. (Clifford, the Big Red Dog Ser.). (Illus.). 14p. (J). (ps-k). bds. 5.99 (978-0-590-04710-4(8) , Cartwheel Bks.) Scholastic, Inc.

Bridwell, Norman, illus. Clifford the Big Red Dog. 40th anniv. deluxe ed. 2002. (Clifford Ser.). 32p. (J). (ps-1). pap. 14.95 (978-0-439-40396-2(0) , Cartwheel Bks.) Scholastic, Inc.

Bridwell, Norman & Fry, Sonali. Clifford the Weather Dog. Edwards, Ken & Haefele, Steve, illus. 2002. (Clifford, the Big Red Dog Ser.). 5p. (J). bds. 6.99 (978-0-439-39448-2(1)) Scholastic, Inc.

—Clifford's Scary Halloween. Durk, Jim, illus. 2002. (Clifford, the Big Red Dog Ser.). 16p. (J). pap. 4.99 (978-0-439-39453-6(8)) Scholastic, Inc.

—Take Me to School with You! Thompson Brothers Staff, illus. 2002. (Clifford, the Big Red Dog Ser.). 16p. (J). pap. 3.99 (978-0-439-39454-3(6)) Scholastic, Inc.

Bridwell, Norman & Lewison, Wendy Cheyette. Clifford's Loose Tooth. Kurtz, Sandrina & Kurtz, John, illus. 2002. (Clifford Big Red Readers Ser.). 32p. (J). (ps-1). pap. 3.99 (978-0-439-33245-3(1)) Scholastic, Inc.

Bridwell, Norman & Page, Josephine. The Big Leaf Pile. Durk, Jim, illus. 2001. (Clifford Big Red Readers Ser.). 32p. (J). (ps-1). 3.99 (978-0-439-21357-8(6) , Cartwheel Bks.) Scholastic, Inc.

Bridwell, Norman & Scholastic, Inc. Staff. Clifford Plush, Big Red Dog. 1999. (Clifford, the Big Red Dog Ser.). (J). (gr. k-2). 16.99 (978-0-590-27359-6(0) , Sidekicks TM) Scholastic, Inc.

—El Dolor de Barriga. Navarro, Carmen, ed. 2003. (Big Red Reader Ser.). (SPA., Illus.). 32p. (J). (gr. k-2). pap. 3.99 (978-0-439-55113-7(7) , Scholastic en Espanol) Scholastic, Inc.

Bridwell, Norman, et al. T-Bone Tells the Truth. Binder, Eric & Lloyd, Gita, illus. 2002. (Clifford's Big Red Ideas Ser.). 7p. (J). bds. 4.99 (978-0-439-39450-5(3)) Scholastic, Inc.

Bright, J. E. Hide-and-Seek. 2005. (Clifford Ser.). (Illus.). 4p. (J). bds. 6.99 (978-0-439-69042-3(0)) Scholastic, Inc.

Clifford Sticker Activity Books. 2004. (J). act. bk. ed. (978-0-7666-0819-1(0) , 69660); act. bk. ed. (978-0-7666-0820-7(4) , 69660) Modern Publishing.

Clifford the Big Red Dog: Camera Book. 2003. per. (978-0-7853-7980-5(0)) Publications International, Ltd.

Cuddy, Robbin, illus. Amazing Animals! 2004. (Clifford Ser.). 24p. (J). pap. 8.99 (978-0-439-62748-1(6)) Scholastic, Inc.

Davis, Guy. Spring Garden Sticker Storybook. 2005. (Clifford's Puppy Days Ser.). (***978-0-439-69046-1(3)***) Scholastic, Inc.

Feldman, Thea. Clifford Loves Me! Lloyd, Gita & Binder, Eric, illus. 2003. (Clifford, the Big Red Dog Ser.). 24p. (J). (ps-1). pap. 3.50 (978-0-439-45481-0(6)) Scholastic, Inc.

—Don't Wake the Puppies! Goldberg, Barry, illus. 2003. (Clifford Ser.). 24p. (J). pap. 10.95 (978-0-439-44941-0(3)) Scholastic, Inc.

Fisch, Sarah. The Smallest Snowman. Durk, Jim, illus. 2006. (J). (***978-0-439-81616-8(5)***) Scholastic, Inc.

Fry, Sonali. Clifford. Kurtz, John, illus. 2003. (Clifford, the Big Red Dog Ser.). 5p. (J). (ps-1). bds. 6.99 (978-0-439-43427-0(0)) Scholastic, Inc.

—Clifford's Christmas Presents. Kurtz, John, illus. 2002. (Clifford, the Big Red Dog Ser.). 7p. (J). bds. 8.99 (978-0-439-39451-2(1) , Cartwheel Bks.) Scholastic, Inc.

Fry, Sonali, ed. The Missing Beach Ball. 2002. (Clifford, the Big Red Dog Ser.). (Illus.). 24p. (J). (ps-3). pap. 3.95 (978-0-439-33799-1(2) , Cartwheel Bks.) Scholastic, Inc.

Herman, Gail. The Big Red Detective. Cuddy, Robbin, illus. 2003. (Clifford Big Red Chapter Book Ser.: No. 1). 64p. (J). pap. 3.99 (978-0-439-47315-6(2)) Scholastic, Inc.

—Clifford Finds a Clue. Haefele, Steve, illus. 2004. (Clifford Ser.: Bk. 3). 64p. (J). pap. 3.99 (978-0-439-53045-3(8)) Scholastic, Inc.

Jordan, Apple. Clifford Helps Out. Bracken, Carolyn, illus. 2004. (Clifford Ser.). 80p. (J). pap. 2.99 (978-0-439-55670-5(8)) Scholastic, Inc.

Koeppel, Ruth & Sander, Sonia. Let's Spell. 2006. (Clifford Ser.). 8p. (J). bds. 12.99 (978-0-439-73376-2(6) , Scholastic) Scholastic, Inc.

Margulies, Teddy. El Conejo Fugitivo. Bracken, Carolyn et al, illus. 2002. (Clifford Big Red Readers Ser.). (SPA.). 32p. (J). (ps-3). pap. 3.99 (978-0-439-25039-9(0) , SO0080) Scholastic, Inc.

Margulies, Teddy Slater. El Dia de las Sorpresas. Orlando, Studio, illus. 2002. (Clifford Big Red Readers Ser.). (SPA.). 32p. (J). pap. 3.99 (978-0-439-25038-2(2) , SO30537) Scholastic, Inc.

—Show & Tell Surprise. Haefele, Steve, illus. 2001. (J). 10.79 (978-0-606-19913-1(6)) Tandem Library Bks.

Margulies, Teddy Slater & Bridwell, Norman. Clifford & the Runaway Rabbit. Studio Orlando Staff, illus. 2001. (Clifford, the Big Red Dog Ser.). 32p. (J). (gr. k-2). pap. 3.99 (978-0-439-21361-5(4)) Scholastic, Inc.

—Clifford & the Show-and-tell Surprise. Studio Orlando Staff, illus. 2001. (Clifford, the Big Red Dog Ser.). 32p. (J). (gr. k-2). pap. 3.99 (978-0-439-21359-2(2)) Scholastic, Inc.

McVeigh, Mark. Clifford for President. LaPadula, Tom, illus. 2004. (Big Red Reader Ser.). 32p. (J). pap. 3.99 (978-0-439-69391-2(8)) Scholastic, Inc.

Neusner, Dena Wallenstein. Clifford's Touch & Feel Day. Lloyd, Gita & Binder, Eric, illus. 2003. (Clifford Ser.). 5p. (J). bds. 9.99 (978-0-439-44936-6(7)) Scholastic, Inc.

—Follow That School Bus. Yee, Josie, illus. 2003. (Clifford Ser.). 5p. (J). bds. 7.99 (978-0-439-44933-5(2)) Scholastic, Inc.

—The Star of the Snow. Goldberg, Barry, illus. 2004. (Clifford Ser.). 32p. (J). pap. 3.99 (978-0-439-62749-8(4)) Scholastic, Inc.

Nye, Ann Marie, ed. Biggest Easter Egg. 2006. (Clifford the Big Red Dog Ser.). (Illus.). 32p. (J). pap. 3.99 (978-0-439-78954-7(0)) Scholastic, Inc.

Page, Josephine. Tummy Trouble. Edwards, Ken, illus. 2001. (Clifford, the Big Red Dog Ser.). 32p. (J). (gr. k-2). pap. 3.99 (978-0-439-21358-5(4)) Scholastic, Inc.

—Tummy Trouble. Edwards, Ken, illus. 2001. (Clifford, the Big Red Dog Ser.). (J). (gr. k-2). 10.79 (978-0-606-19916-2(0)) Tandem Library Bks.

Parent, Nancy. Clifford's Big Red Easter. Cuddy, Robin, illus. 2003. (Clifford, the Big Red Dog Ser.). 7p. (J). (ps up). bds. 4.99 (978-0-439-43428-7(9)) Scholastic, Inc.

Scholastic, Inc. Staff. Clifford Reduced Floppy. 2001. (Clifford Ser.). (J). 18.99 (978-0-439-30186-2(6) , Sidekicks TM) Scholastic, Inc.

—Clifford the Big Red Dog: The Big Leaf Pile. 2001. (Clifford, the Big Red Dog Ser.). (Illus.). (J). 10.79 (978-0-606-21112-3(8)) Tandem Library Bks.

—Clifford the Big Red Dog: The Dog Who Cried "Woof!" 2001. (Clifford, the Big Red Dog Ser.). (Illus.). (J). 10.79 (978-0-606-21113-0(6)) Tandem Library Bks.

—Clifford the Big Red Dog Art Kit. 1999. (Clifford Ser.). (J). 16.99 (978-0-590-63453-3(4) , Sidekicks TM) Scholastic, Inc.

—Clifford the Big Red Dog Collectible Plush. 2001. (Clifford Ser.). (J). 10.99 (978-0-439-29696-0(X) , Sidekicks TM) Scholastic, Inc.

—Clifford the Big Red Dog Marker Case. 1999. (Clifford Ser.). (J). 12.99 (978-0-590-63456-4(9) , Sidekicks TM) Scholastic, Inc.

—Clifford the Big Red Dog Plush Bookmark. 1999. (Clifford Ser.). (J). 3.99 (978-0-439-21558-9(7) , Sidekicks TM) Scholastic, Inc.

—Clifford the Big Red Dog Rubber Stamp Kit. 1999. (Clifford Ser.). (J). 12.99 (978-0-590-63457-1(7) , Sidekicks TM) Scholastic, Inc.

—Clifford the Small Red Puppy Wooden Puzzle—Daily Activities. 1998. (Clifford Ser.). (J). 13.99 (978-0-590-03433-3(2) , Sidekicks TM) Scholastic, Inc.

—Clifford the Small Red Puppy Wooden Puzzle—Favorite Things. 1998. (Clifford Ser.). (J). 13.99 (978-0-590-03432-6(4) , Sidekicks TM) Scholastic, Inc.

—Clifford Wooden Shape Sorter. 2002. (Clifford Ser.). (J). 24.99 (978-0-439-38816-0(3) , Sidekicks TM) Scholastic, Inc.

—Clifford's Puppy Days Attachable Jiggler. 2004. (Sidekicks Ser.). (J). 11.99 (978-0-439-63683-4(3) , Sidekicks TM) Scholastic, Inc.

—Clifford's Puppy Days (Daffodil Beanbag) 2004. (Sidekicks Ser.). (J). 8.99 (978-0-439-64990-2(0) , Sidekicks TM) Scholastic, Inc.

—Clifford's Puppy Days (Norville Beanbag) 2004. (Sidekicks Ser.). (J). 8.99 (978-0-439-64989-6(7) , Sidekicks TM) Scholastic, Inc.

—Clifford's Puppy Days Wrist Rattle, 12, Pack. 2004. (Sidekicks Ser.). (J). 71.88 (978-0-439-62731-3(1) , Sidekicks TM) Scholastic, Inc.

—Clifford's Scary Halloween. 2002. (ps-2). lib. bdg. 13.00 (978-0-613-72080-9(6)) Tandem Library Bks.

—The Greatest Parade. Hult, Gene, ed. 2004. (Clifford Ser.). 144p. (J). pap. 3.99 (978-0-439-60701-8(9)) Scholastic, Inc.

—The Small Red Puppy Teether Rattle, 12, Pack. 2003. (Clifford Ser.). (J). 83.88 (978-0-439-20131-5(4) , Sidekicks TM) Scholastic, Inc.

—26 Clifford the Big Red Dog. 2002. (Sidekicks Ser.). (J). 124.99 (978-0-439-36229-0(6) , Sidekicks TM) Scholastic, Inc.

Scholastic, Inc. Staff & Bridwell, Norman. Clifford the Small Red Puppy Pull Toy on Wheels. 1998. (Clifford Ser.). (J). 18.99 (978-0-590-46965-4(7) , Sidekicks TM) Scholastic, Inc.

—Finger Puppet. 1999. (Clifford Ser.). (J). 6.99 (978-0-439-09261-6(2) , Sidekicks TM) Scholastic, Inc.

Scholastic, Inc. Staff & Mills, Liz. Go, Clifford, Go! Bracken, Carolyn & Edwards, Ken, illus. 2002. (Clifford, the Big Red Dog Ser.). 10p. (J). bds. 9.99 (978-0-439-39447-5(3)) Scholastic, Inc.

Scholastic, Inc. Staff, et al. 28 Floppy Clifford with Barking Mechanism. 2003. (Clifford Ser.). (J). 49.99 (978-0-439-48643-9(2) , Sidekicks TM) Scholastic, Inc.

Suarez, Ana, tr. from ENG. Le Semana Atareada de Clifford'. Bridwell, Norman, illus. 2002. (Clifford, the Big Red Dog Ser.). (SPA.). 32p. (J). (ps-1). pap. 3.50 (978-0-439-41833-1(X) , Scholastic en Espanol) Scholastic, Inc.

Thompson Brothers Staff, illus. On the Road. movie tie-in ed. 2004. (Clifford Ser.). 24p. (J). pap. 4.99 (978-0-439-62815-0(6)) Scholastic, Inc.

Weinberger, Kimberly. Be-a-Good-Friend Sticker Book. 2001. (Clifford, the Big Red Dog Ser.). (Illus.). 24p. (J). (gr. k-2). 5.99 (978-0-439-22945-6(6)) Scholastic, Inc.

—Clifford el Dia de la Tormenta. 2003. (Big Red Reader Ser.). (SPA., Illus.). 32p. (J). (gr. k-3). pap. 3.99 (978-0-439-55114-4(5) , Scholastic en Espanol) Scholastic, Inc.

—The Stormy Day Rescue. Thompson, Del, illus. 2001. (J). 10.79 (978-0-606-19914-8(4)) Tandem Library Bks.

Weinberger, Kimberly & Bridwell, Norman. The Stormy Day Rescue. 2001. (Clifford, the Big Red Dog Ser.). (Illus.). 32p. (J). (gr. k-2). pap. 3.99 (978-0-439-21360-8(6)) Scholastic, Inc.

CLIMATE

Here are entered works on climate as it relates to man and to plant and animal life, including the effects of changes of climate. Works limited to the climate of a particular region are entered under the name of the place with the subdivision Climate. Works on the state of the atmosphere at a given time and place with respect to heat and cold, wetness or dryness, calm or storm, are entered under Weather. Scientific works on the atmosphere, especially weather factors, are entered under Meteorology.

see also Meteorology; Rain and Rainfall; Seasons; Weather

Alatorre, Antonio. El Apogeo del Castellano. 2000. 11.80 (978-0-606-17642-2(X)) Tandem Library Bks.

Alberti, Theresa Jarosz. Climates. 2005. (Weather Update Ser.). (Illus.). 24p. (J). 21.26 (978-0-7368-3735-4(3)) Capstone Pr., Inc.

Allen, Jean. Blizzards. 2001. (Natural Disasters Ser.). (Illus.). 48p. (J). (gr. 3-4). lib. bdg. 21.26 (978-0-7368-0899-6(X) , Capstone High-Interest Bks.) Capstone Pr., Inc.

Barr, Gary E. Climate Change: Is the World in Danger? 2006. (Behind the News Ser.). (Illus.). 56p. (J). (gr. 5-8). lib. bdg. 32.86 (978-1-4034-8830-5(4)) Heinemann Library.

Benchmark Education Staff. Weather & Climate. 2005. 2.00 (***978-1-4108-4635-8(0)**) Benchmark Education Co.

Benchmark Education Staff, compiled by. Weather & Season. 2006. spiral bd. 249.00 (***978-1-4108-7031-5(6)**) Benchmark Education Co.

Bredeson, Carmen. El Niano & La Niana: Deadly Weather. 2002. (American Disasters Ser.). (Illus.). 48p. (J). (gr. 4-10). lib. bdg. 23.93 (978-0-7660-1551-7(3)) Enslow Pubs., Inc.

Corn, John. Weather & Climates. 2005. (Earth's Changing Landscape Ser.). (Illus.). 46p. (J). lib. bdg. (978-1-58340-478-2(3) , 1236346) Smart Apple Media.

Cullen, Katherine E. Weather & Climate: The People Behind the Science. 2005. (Pioneers in Science Ser.). (Illus.). 176p. (J). (gr. 6-12). 29.95 (978-0-8160-5466-4(5)) Facts On File, Inc.

Desonie, Dana. Climate. 2007. (Our Fragile Planet Ser.). 208p. (gr. 6-12). 35.00 (***978-0-8160-6214-0(5)** , Chelsea Hse.) Facts On File, Inc.

Friedman, Katherine. What If the Polar Ice Caps Melted? 2002. (What If Ser.). (Illus.). 48p. (YA). (gr. 7-12). 24.00 (978-0-516-23914-9(7)); pap. 6.95 (978-0-516-23477-9(3)) Scholastic Library Publishing. (Children's Pr.).

—What If the Polar Ice Caps Melted? 2002. (gr. 7-12). lib. bdg. 15.25 (978-0-613-58817-1(7)) Tandem Library Bks.

Ganeri, Anita. El Sol. 2004. 24p. 19.33 (978-0-8368-4365-1(7)); pap. 5.95 (978-0-8368-4370-5(3)) Stevens, Gareth Inc. (Weekly Reader Early Learning Library).

Gilbert, Miquel Angel. Weather. 2002. (Living Planet Ser.). (Illus.). 32p. (J). 23.70 (978-1-56711-683-0(3) , Blackbirch Pr., Inc.) Thomson Gale.

Green, Jen. Changing Climates. 2006. (Illus.). 32p. (YA). (gr. 4 up). lib. bdg. 27.10 (978-1-59389-118-3(0)) Chrysalis Education.

Holt, Rinehart and Winston Staff. Climate: Chapter Resources: Tennessee Edition. 3rd ed. 2003. (Holt Science & Technology Ser.). pap. 11.40 (978-0-03-069113-3(3)); pap. 11.40 (978-0-03-069149-2(4)) Holt, Rinehart & Winston.

—Environmental Science Chptr. 13: Atmosphere & Climate. 4th ed. Date not set. pap. 11.20 (978-0-03-068073-1(5)) Holt, Rinehart & Winston.

—Holt Science & Technology Chapter 16: Earth Science: Understanding the Weather. 5th ed. 2004. (Illus.). pap. 12.86 (978-0-03-030323-4(0)) Holt, Rinehart & Winston.

—Holt Science & Technology Chapter 17: Earth Science: Climate. 5th ed. 2004. (Illus.). pap. 12.86 (978-0-03-030326-5(5)) Holt, Rinehart & Winston.

Howell, Laura. Introduction to Weather & Climate Change. 2004. (Geography Ser.). (Illus.). 96p. (J). pap. 14.95 (978-0-7945-0629-2(1)) EDC Publishing.

—Weather & Climate Change. 2004. (Geography Ser.). 96p. (J). lib. bdg. 22.95 (978-1-58086-613-2(1) , Usborne) EDC Publishing.

Jennings, Terry. Atmosphere & Weather. 2005. (Illus.). 48p. (J). (gr. 6-9). lib. bdg. 29.95 (978-1-58340-725-7(1)) Smart Apple Media.

—Changing Climates. 2005. (Illus.). 48p. (J). (gr. 6-9). lib. bdg. 29.95 (978-1-58340-728-8(6)) Smart Apple Media.

—Weather Patterns. 2005. (Illus.). 48p. (J). (gr. 6-9). lib. bdg. 29.95 (978-1-58340-726-4(X)) Smart Apple Media.

Law, Norman & Bradley, Raymond. Climate Change & Society. 2001. (Epics Ser.). (Illus.). 104p. (YA). (gr. 11 up). pap. 23.50 (978-0-7487-5823-4(2)) Nelson Thornes Ltd. GBR. *Dist:* Trans-Atlantic Pubns., Inc.

Linde, Barbara M. Climates of the World: Identifying & Comparing Mean, Median, & Mode. 2005. (PowerMath Ser.). (Illus.). 32p. (J). 22.50 (978-1-4042-2932-7(9)); (978-1-4042-5126-7(X)); pap. (978-1-4042-5125-0(1)) Rosen Publishing Group, Inc., The. (PowerKids Pr.).

Linde, Barbara M. Weather & Climate. 2005. 39.00 (***978-1-4108-4587-0(7)**) Benchmark Education Co.

Lindsay, Elizabeth, ed. Investigating Science - Weather & Climate. 2000. 48p. 9.95 (978-1-56234-394-1(7) , Mailbox Bks., The) Education Ctr., Inc.

Mahaney, Ian F. Climate Maps. 2007. 24p. (J). (978-1-4042-2404-9(1)); pap. (978-1-4042-2214-4(6)); (gr. 3-5). lib. bdg. 21.25 (978-1-4042-3058-3(0)) Rosen Publishing Group, Inc., The. (PowerKids Pr.).

Merk, A. The Weather & Us. 2003. (Weather Report Discovery Library). (Illus.). 24p. (gr. 1-4). 14.95 (978-1-58952-574-0(4)) Rourke Publishing, LLC.

Nagle, Garrett. Cold Environments. 2001. (Epics Ser.). (Illus.). 96p. (YA). (gr. 11 up). pap. 23.50 (978-0-7487-5821-0(6)) Nelson Thornes Ltd. GBR. *Dist:* Trans-Atlantic Pubns., Inc.

Parks, Peggy J. Global Warming. (Our Environment Ser.). (Illus.). (J). (ps-7). 2004. 48p. lib. bdg. 26.20 (978-0-7377-1822-5(6) , Greenhaven Pr., Inc.); 2003. 111p. 29.95 (978-1-59018-319-9(3) , Lucent Bks.) Thomson Gale.

—Monsoons. 2006. (Kidhaven Science Library). (Illus.). 48p. (J). (gr. 4-8). 26.20 (978-0-7377-3058-6(7) , 1256753, Kidhaven) Thomson Gale.

Pinna, Lorenzo. El Clima. (SPA.). 326p. (YA). (gr. 5-8). (978-84-7131-928-9(4)) Editex, Editorial S.A. ESP. *Dist:* Lectorum Pubns., Inc.

Pipe, Jim. Weather. 2004. (Earthwise Ser.). (J). lib. bdg. 27.10 (978-1-932799-47-7(8)) Stargazer Bks.

Pringle, Laurence P. Global Warming: Assessing the Greenhouse Threat. 2003. (Illus.). 48p. (J). (gr. 3-7). pap. 6.95 (978-1-58717-228-1(3) , SeaStar Bks.) Chronicle Bks. LLC.

Scheff, Duncan. Blizzards. 2001. (Nature on the Rampage Ser.). (Illus.). 32p. (YA). lib. bdg. 22.83 (978-0-7398-4701-5(5)) Raintree.

—Drought. 2001. (Nature on the Rampage Ser.). (Illus.). 32p. (YA). lib. bdg. 22.83 (978-0-7398-4702-2(3)) Raintree.

Scoones, Simon. Climate Change: Our Impact on the Planet. 2001. (Twenty-First Century Debates Ser.). (Illus.). 64p. (YA). (gr. 6-8). lib. bdg. 27.12 (978-0-7398-3177-9(1)) Raintree.

Spilsbury, Richard & Spilsbury, Louise. Weather. 2006. (Science in Focus Ser.). (Illus.). 48p. (J). 27.00 (978-0-7910-8859-3(6) , Chelsea Hse.) Facts On File, Inc.

Stein, Paul. Biomes of the Future. 2001. (Library of Future Weather & Climate). (Illus.). 64p. (YA). (gr. 4-6). lib. bdg. 26.50 (978-0-8239-3410-2(1)) Rosen Publishing Group, Inc., The.

—Droughts of the Future. 2001. (Library of Future Weather & Climate). (Illus.). 64p. (YA). (gr. 4-6). lib. bdg. 26.50 (978-0-8239-3411-9(X)) Rosen Publishing Group, Inc., The.

—Forecasting the Climate of the Future. 2001. (Library of Future Weather & Climate). (Illus.). 64p. (YA). (gr. 4-6). lib. bdg. 26.50 (978-0-8239-3413-3(6)) Rosen Publishing Group, Inc., The.

Tanaka, Shelley. Climate Change. 2007. (Groundwork Guides). (Illus.). 144p. pap. 9.95 (***978-0-88899-784-5(1)**) Groundwood Bks. CAN. *Dist:* Perseus Distribution.

Taylor, Barbara. Weather & Climate. 2002. (Young Discoverers Ser.). (Illus.). 32p. (J). (gr. k-3). 7.95 (978-0-7534-5509-8(9) , Kingfisher) Houghton Mifflin Co. Trade & Reference Div.

—Weather & Climate. 2002. (gr. k-3). lib. bdg. 16.40 (978-0-613-90903-7(8)) Tandem Library Bks.

Unwin, Mike. Climate Change. 2006. (Planet under Pressure Ser.). (Illus.). 48p. (YA). (gr. 6-8). lib. bdg. 31.43 (***978-1-4034-8216-7(0)**) Heinemann Library.

Varilla, Mary, ed. Scholastic Atlas of Weather. 2004. (Illus.). 80p. (J). pap. 17.95 (978-0-439-41902-4(6) , Scholastic Reference) Scholastic, Inc.

Viegas, Jennifer, ed. Critical Perspectives on Planet Earth. 2006. (Scientific American Critical Anthologies on Environment & Climate Ser.). (Illus.). 278p. (J). (978-1-4042-0687-8(6)) Rosen Publishing Group, Inc., The.

Walsh, Kieran. Weather Math. 2003. (Math & My World Ser.). (Illus.). 48p. (J). 29.93 (978-1-58952-384-5(9)) Rourke Publishing, LLC.

Weather & Climate Assessment Book: Unit 2: Weather & Climate. 2000. (McGraw-Hill Science Ser.). (gr. 5 up). (978-0-02-277764-7(4)) Macmillan/McGraw-Hill Schl. Div.

Weather & Climate Pupil Edition: Unit 2: Weather & Climate. 2000. (McGraw-Hill Science Ser.). (gr. 5 up). (978-0-02-278224-5(9)) Macmillan/McGraw-Hill Schl. Div.

West, Krista. Hands-On Projects about Weather & Climate. 2002. (Great Earth Science Projects Ser.). (Illus.). 24p. (J). lib. bdg. 19.95 (978-0-8239-5845-0(0) , PowerKids Pr.) Rosen Publishing Group, Inc., The.

World Almanac Library Staff, contrib. by. Climate & the Environment. 2002. (Twenty-First Century Science Ser.). (Illus.). 64p. (J). (gr. 5 up). lib. bdg. 32.67 (978-0-8368-5006-2(8) , World Almanac Library) Stevens, Gareth Inc.

World's Climates, 12 vols., Set. 1999. (Illus.). 215.76 (978-0-8114-6442-0(3)) Raintree.

CLIMATOLOGY

see Climate

CLINTON, BILL, 1946-

Aaseng, Nathan. The Impeachment of Bill Clinton. 2000. (Famous Trials Ser.). (Illus.). 112p. (YA). (gr. 7-10). lib. bdg. 29.95 (978-1-56006-651-4(2) , LML00902-178005, Lucent Bks.) Thomson Gale.

Ashby, Ruth. Bill & Hillary Rodham Clinton. 2005. (Illus.). 48p. (J). pap. (978-0-8368-5762-7(3)); lib. bdg. 30.00 (978-0-8368-5756-6(9)) Stevens, Gareth Inc. (World Almanac Library).

Benson, Michael. Bill Clinton. 2004. (Presidential Leaders Ser.). (Illus.). 112p. (J). (gr. 6-12). 29.27 (978-0-8225-0819-9(2)) Lerner Publishing Group.

Cohen, Daniel. The Impeachment of William Jefferson Clinton. 1999. (Single Titles Ser.). (Illus.). 112p. (gr. 7 up). lib. bdg. 23.90 (978-0-7613-1711-1(2) , Twenty-First Century Bks.) Lerner Publishing Group.

Fernandez, Justin. High Crimes & Misdemeanors. 2000. (Crime, Justice & Punishment Ser.). (Illus.). 80p. (J). 30.00 (978-0-7910-5450-5(0) , Chelsea Hse.) Facts On File, Inc.

Gaines, Ann Graham. William J. Clinton: Our Forty-Second President. 2001. (Spirit of America: Our Presidents Ser.). (Illus.). 48p. (J). (gr. 2-6). 28.50 (978-1-56766-876-6(3)) Child's World, Inc.

Greenberg, Keith. Bill & Hillary: Working Together in the White House. (gr. 3-6). lib. bdg. 9.25 (978-0-613-09957-8(5)) Tandem Library Bks.

Gross, Miriam J. How to Draw the Life & Times of William Jefferson Clinton. 2007. (Kid's Guide to Drawing the Presidents of the United States of America Ser.). (Illus.). 32p. (J). 25.25 (978-1-4042-3018-7(1) , PowerKids Pr.) Rosen Publishing Group, Inc., The.

Heinrichs, Ann. William Jefferson Clinton. 2002. (Profiles of the Presidents Ser.). (Illus.). 64p. (J). (gr. 4 up). lib. bdg. 23.93 (978-0-7565-0207-2(1)) Compass Point Bks.

Kelly, Michael. Bill Clinton. 1999. (Overcoming Adversity Ser.). (Illus.). 128p. (YA). (gr. 5 up). pap. 30.00 (978-0-7910-4701-9(6) , Chelsea Hse.) Facts On File, Inc.

—Bill Clinton. 2000. (Illus.). 112p. (J). (ps-7). per. 18.75 (978-0-613-11335-9(7)) Tandem Library Bks.

Marcovitz, Hal. Bill Clinton. 2003. (Childhoods of the Presidents Ser.). (Illus.). 48p. (J). (gr. 4 up). lib. bdg. (978-1-59084-273-7(1)) Mason Crest Pubs.

Mattern, Joanne. Hillary Rodham Clinton. 2007. (First Ladies Ser.). (Illus.). 32p. (J). (gr. k-6). lib. bdg. 24.21 (***978-1-59928-792-8(7)** , Checkerboard Library) ABDO Publishing Co.

McCollum, Sean. Bill Clinton. 2005. (Encyc of Presidents, 2ND Ser.). (Illus.). 112p. (J). (gr. 6-8). 34.00 (978-0-516-22980-5(X) , Watts, Franklin) Scholastic Library Publishing.

O'Shei, Tim. Bill Clinton: A MyReportLinks. Com Book. 2003. (Presidents Ser.). (Illus.). 48p. (J). lib. bdg. 25.26 (978-0-7660-5149-2(8) , MyReportLinks.com Bks.) Enslow Pubs., Inc.

Renehan, Edward. The Clintons. 2005. (J). (978-0-7910-8526-4(0) , Chelsea Hse.) Facts On File, Inc.

Schuman, Michael A. Bill Clinton. rev. ed. 2003. (United States Presidents Ser.). (Illus.). 128p. (J). (gr. 5-12). lib. bdg. 26.60 (978-0-7660-2032-0(0)) Enslow Pubs., Inc.

Venezia, Mike. Bill Clinton. 2008. (Getting to Know the U. S. Presidents Ser.). 32p. (J). pap. 7.95 (***978-0-516-25460-9(X)** , Children's Pr.) Scholastic Library Publishing.

Venezia, Mike, illus. Bill Clinton. 2007. 32p. (J). 28.00 (***978-0-516-22646-0(0)** , Children's Pr.) Scholastic Library Publishing.

CLINTON, HILLARY RODHAM, 1947-

Ashby, Ruth. Bill & Hillary Rodham Clinton. 2005. (Illus.). 48p. (J). pap. (978-0-8368-5762-7(3)); lib. bdg. 30.00 (978-0-8368-5756-6(9)) Stevens, Gareth Inc. (World Almanac Library).

Burgan, Michael. Hillary Rodham Clinton: First Lady & Senator. 2005. (J). (978-0-7565-1588-1(2)) Compass Point Bks.

Driscoll, Laura. Hillary Clinton: An American Journey. Wood, Judith V., illus. 2007. (All Aboard Reading Ser.). 48p. (J). (gr. 1-3). pap. 3.99 (***978-0-448-44787-2(8)** , Grosset & Dunlap) Penguin Group (USA) Inc.

Epstein, Dwayne. Hillary Clinton. 2007. (People in the News Ser.). (Illus.). 128p. (gr. 7-10). 32.45 (***978-1-4205-0031-8(7)** , Lucent Bks.) Thomson Gale.

Freedman, Jeri. Hillary Rodham Clinton: Profile of a Leading Democrat. 2007. (J). (***978-1-4042-1910-6(2)**) Rosen Publishing Group, Inc., The.

Guernsey, JoAnn B. Hillary Rodham Clinton. 2005. (Biography ' Ser.). (Illus.). 112p. (J). 29.27 (978-0-8225-2372-7(8) , Lerner Pubns.); (gr. 6 up). pap. 7.95 (978-0-8225-9613-4(X)) Lerner Publishing Group.

Gullo, James. Hillary Rodham Clinton. 2003. (Importance of Ser.). (Illus.). 112p. (J). 32.45 (978-1-59018-310-6(X) , Lucent Bks.) Thomson Gale.

Horner, Matina S., intro. Hillary Rodham Clinton: First Lady/Attorney. 1999. (Women of Achievement Ser.). (Illus.). 112p. (YA). (gr. 4-7). 32.00 (978-0-7910-4712-5(1)); pap. 30.00 (978-0-7910-4713-2(X)) Facts On File, Inc. (Chelsea Hse.).

LeVert, Suzanne. Hillary Rodham Clinton: First Lady. 1998. (Gateway Biography Ser.: 4). (Illus.). 48p. (gr. 2-4). pap. (978-1-56294-726-2(5) , Millbrook Pr.) Lerner Publishing Group.

Loewen, Nancy. Hillary Rodham Clinton. 1998. (Ovations Ser.: Vol. 8). (Illus.). 32p. (YA). (gr. 4-7). lib. bdg. (978-0-88682-636-9(5) , Creative Education) Creative Co., The.

Mattern, Joanne. Hillary Rodham Clinton. 2007. (First Ladies Ser.). (Illus.). 32p. (J). (gr. k-6). lib. bdg. 24.21 (***978-1-59928-792-8(7)** , Checkerboard Library) ABDO Publishing Co.

Renehan, Edward. The Clintons. 2005. (J). (978-0-7910-8526-4(0) , Chelsea Hse.) Facts On File, Inc.

Ryan, Bernard. Hillary Rodham Clinton: First Lady & Senator. 2004. (Ferguson Career Biographies Ser.). (Illus.). 160p. (J). (gr. 6-12). 25.00 (978-0-8160-5544-9(0) , Ferguson Publishing Co.) Facts On File, Inc.

Wagner, Heather Lehr. Hillary Rodham Clinton. 2004. (Women in Politics Ser.). (Illus.). 120p. 30.00 (978-0-7910-7735-1(7)); 110p. pap. 30.00 (978-0-7910-7999-7(6)) Facts On File, Inc. (Chelsea Hse.).

Wheeler, Jill C. Hillary Rodham Clinton. 2003. (Breaking Barriers Ser.). (Illus.). 64p. (J). (gr. 3-8). lib. bdg. 25.65 (978-1-57765-741-5(1)) ABDO Publishing Co.

CLIPPER SHIPS

Sanford, Candace. Captain Nathaniel Brown Palmer. Scala, Susan, illus. 2007. 96p. (YA). pap. 14.95 (***978-0-9773725-9-1(6)**) Flat Hammock Pr.

CLIPPER SHIPS—FICTION

Kay, Julia. Gulliver Snip & the Clipper Ship. 2008. 32p. (J). 16.95 (***978-0-8050-7992-0(0)**) Holt, Henry & Co.

McKenzie, Lyn. Lavinia's Shoes. 2007. (J). pap. 12.95 (***978-0-9788628-5-5(6)**) Just Write Bks.

CLOCKS AND WATCHES

see also Sundials

Benchmark Education Staff, compiled by. Measuring Time. 2006. spiral bd. 249.00 (***978-1-4108-7074-2(X)**) Benchmark Education Co.

Clever Clock. 2002. (J). pap. 4.95 (978-1-56911-074-4(3)) Learning Resources, Inc.

Clock & Time Workbook. 2002. (J). pap. 8.95 (978-1-56911-043-0(3)) Learning Resources, Inc.

Clockwise Time Workbook. 2001. (J). pap. (978-1-56911-723-1(3)) Learning Resources, Inc.

Fowler, Allan. Seconds, Minutes & Hours. 1999. (Rookie Read-About Science Ser.). (J). (978-0-516-21211-1(7) , Children's Pr.) Scholastic Library Publishing.

Ganeri, Anita. From Candle to Quartz Clock. (Illus.). 30p. (J). (978-0-237-51534-8(2) , Evans Brothers, Limited) Evans Publishing Group.

Gardner, Robert. It's about Time! Science Projects: How Long Does It Take? 2003. (Sensational Science Experiments Ser.). (Illus.). 48p. (J). (gr. 1-4). lib. bdg. 23.93 (978-0-7660-2012-2(6)) Enslow Pubs., Inc.

Klutz Editors. Klutz Design Your Own Charm Watch. 2005. (Illus.). 28p. (J). 21.95 (978-1-57054-212-1(0)) Klutz.

Koscielniak, Bruce. About Time: A First Look at Time & Clocks. 2004. (Illus.). 32p. (J). (gr. 3-5). tchr. ed. 16.00 (978-0-618-39668-9(3)) Houghton Mifflin Co. Trade & Reference Div.

Levy, Janey. Keeping Time Through the Ages: The History of Tools Used to Measure Time. 2004. (PowerMath Ser.). (Illus.). 32p. (J). lib. bdg. (978-0-8239-8917-1(8)); lib. bdg. 22.50 (978-0-8239-8993-5(3)) Rosen Publishing Group, Inc., The. (PowerKids Pr.).

Mara, Wil. The Clock. 2005. (Inventions That Shaped the World Ser.). (Illus.). 80p. (J). 30.50 (978-0-531-12373-7(1) , Watts, Franklin) Scholastic Library Publishing.

—Clock. 2006. 80p. (YA). (gr. 5-8). pap. 9.95 (978-0-531-16743-4(7) , Watts, Franklin) Scholastic Library Publishing.

McEwan, Rebecca. Como medir el tiempo desde la antiguedad hasta nuestros días & Telling Time Through the Ages. 2005. spiral bd. 77.00 (***978-1-4108-5673-9(9)**) Benchmark Education Co.

Older, Jules. Telling Time. 2000. (978-0-606-18030-6(3)) Tandem Library Bks.

—Telling Time: How to Tell Time on Digital & Analog Clocks! Halsey, Megan, illus. 2000. 32p. (J). (gr. k-4). pap. 6.95 (978-0-88106-397-4(5)); 16.95 (978-0-88106-396-7(7)) Charlesbridge Publishing, Inc.

—Telling Time: How to Tell Time on Digital & Analog Clocks! Halsey, Megan, illus. 2000. (J). (ps-ps). lib. bdg. 15.25 (978-0-613-28318-2(X)) Tandem Library Bks.

Osen, Janet E. Mini Maestro Presents the Tic-Toc Clocks. Angermueller, Ivy & Boshart, Martha, illus. 1st. ed. 2000. 30p. (J). (ps-k). 16.95 incl. audio compact disk (978-0-9700489-0-5(4)) Little Fiddle Co., Inc., The.

Patilla, Peter. Time. 2001. (Illus.). 32p. (J). lib. bdg. 24.25 (978-1-930643-17-8(9)) Chrysalis Education.

—Time. 1999. (Math Links Ser.). 32p. (J). (gr. k-2). lib. bdg. 21.36 (978-1-57572-970-1(9)) Heinemann Library.

Randolph, Joanne. All about an Hour. 2007. (J). lib. bdg. (***978-1-4042-3766-7(6)** , PowerKids Pr.) Rosen Publishing Group, Inc., The.

Taylor, Thomas. Tick! Tock! Jungle Clock. 2007. (Illus.). 12p. (J). (ps-2). 9.99 (***978-1-4052-2307-2(3)**) Egmont Bks., Ltd. GBR. *Dist:* Independent Pubs. Group.

Velcro Clock Activity Center. 2001. (Illus.). (J). (gr. k-2). pap. 89.00 (978-0-9673268-2-5(6)) Learning Fasten-Ations, Inc.

CLOCKS AND WATCHES—FICTION

Adams, Clint. My Watch Doesn't Tell Time. 2006. (YA). per. (978-0-9768375-4-1(4)) Adams, Clint.

Anderson, Lena. Tick-Tock. 1998. (J). (978-0-385-32554-7(1) , Doubleday Bks. for Young Readers) Random Hse. Children's Bks.

Archambault, John. Boom Chicka Rock. Chitwood, Suzanne Tanner, illus. 2004. 36p. (J). (ps-2). 15.99 (978-0-399-23587-0(6) , Philomel) Penguin Group (USA) Inc.

Baker, Keith. Hickory Dickory Dock. 2007. (Illus.). 32p. (J). (ps-2). 16.00 (978-0-15-205818-0(4)) Harcourt Trade Pubs.

Bloom, Becky. Mr. Cuckoo. Bloom, Becky, illus. 1998. (Illus.). 32p. (J). (gr. k-4). 15.95 (978-1-57255-626-3(9)) Mondo Publishing.

Brooks, Brian. Oopsy Daisy's Bad Day. Brooks, Brian, illus. 2007. (Illus.). 62p. (J). reprint ed. 13.00 (***978-1-4223-9004-7(7)**) DIANE Publishing Co.

Bruna, Dick. What Time Is It Miffy? Bruna, Dick, illus. 1999. (Miffy Ser.). (Illus.). 20p. (ps-k). bds. 7.95 (978-1-56836-282-3(X)) Kodansha America, Inc.

Bulla, Lynda. The Old Clock on the Wall. Hergenroeder, Ernie, illus. 2002. 20p. (J). lib. bdg. 17.95 (978-0-9724272-0-3(1) , 3000) Katydid Publishing LLC.

Cunliffe, John. Postman Pat Makes a Clock. (Illus.). 20p. (J). pap. 11.99 (978-0-340-73718-7(2) , Hodder & Stoughton) Hodder General Publishing Division GBR. *Dist:* Trafalgar Square Publishing.

Dakin, Glenn & Chapman, Keith. Can We Tell Time? Bob the Builder. 2003. (Illus.). (J). bds. 16.98 (978-0-7853-8809-8(5)) Publications International, Ltd.

Danziger, Paula. It's Justin Time, Amber Brown. Ross, Tony, illus. 9.95 (978-1-59112-294-4(5)) Live Oak Media.

—It's Justin Time, Amber Brown. 2002. (Illus.). (J). pap., tchr.'s planning gde. ed. 29.95 incl. audio (978-0-87499-908-2(1)) Live Oak Media.

—It's Justin Time, Amber Brown. Ross, Tony, illus. 2002. 28.95 incl. audio compact disk (978-1-59112-567-9(7)); pap. 31.95 incl. audio compact disk (978-1-59112-566-2(9)) Live Oak Media.

—It's Justin Time, Amber Brown. abr. ed. 2002. (Illus.). (J). (ps-2). 25.95 incl. audio (978-0-87499-907-5(3)); pap. 16.95 incl. audio (978-0-87499-906-8(5)) Live Oak Media.

—It's Justin Time, Amber Brown. Ross, Tony, illus. 2001. (Amber Brown Ser.: No. 10). lp. (J). (gr. 3-6). 13.99 (978-0-399-23470-5(5) , Putnam Juvenile) Penguin Group (USA) Inc.

—It's Justin Time, Amber Brown. 2001. 10.79 (978-0-606-22522-9(6)); lib. bdg. 11.80 (978-0-613-44396-8(9)) Tandem Library Bks.

Davis, Lee. What Is P. B. Bear Doing? 2001. (P. B. Bear Ser.). (Illus.). 24p. (J). (ps). pap. 4.95 (978-0-7894-2224-8(7) , D K Ink) Dorling Kindersley Publishing, Inc.

Escott, Jamison. The Clockmaker of Mullen. Escott, Esther, illus. 2004. 24p. (J). pap. 8.95 (978-1-57733-127-8(3) , Papillon Publishing) Blue Dolphin Publishing, Inc.

Fraser, Mary Ann. I. Q., It's Time. Fraser, Mary Ann, illus. 2005. (Illus.). 32p. (J). (ps-3). 16.85 (978-0-8027-8980-8(3)); 15.95 (978-0-8027-8978-5(1)) Walker & Co.

Gilmore, Rachna. Grandpa's Clock. Meissner, Amy, illus. 2006. 32p. (ps-2). 17.95 (978-1-55143-333-2(8)) Orca Bk. Pubs. USA.

Gomez, Rebecca. All I Want for Christmas: Lo Unico Que Quiero para Navidad. Collier-Morales, Roberta, illus. 2003. (ENG & SPA.). (J). (978-0-439-61643-0(3)) Scholastic, Inc.

Goodings, Christina. Little Clocks Midnight 2000. Hendra, Sue, illus. 1999. 32p. (J). pap. 2.99 (978-0-7459-3904-9(X) , Lion) Lion Hudson plc GBR. *Dist:* Trafalgar Square Publishing.

Harper, Dan. Telling Time with Big Mama Cat. Moser, Barry & Moser, Cara, illus. 1998. 36p. (J). (ps-3). 16.00 (978-0-15-201738-5(0)) Harcourt Children's Bks.

Heron Books Editors. The Elephant's Clock, 3 vols., Set. 2nd ed. Incl. Elephant's Clock Workbook. 103p. pap., wbk. ed. 15.00 (978-0-89739-007-1(5)); How to Tell Time. 2nd ed. 110p. pap., wbk. ed. 15.00 (978-0-89739-008-8(3)); Story about Learning to Tell Time. 95p. pap. 20.00 (978-0-89739-006-4(7)); (Illus.). (J). (gr. 1-2). 2000. Set pap. 50.00 (978-0-89739-010-1(5)) Heron Bks.

—The Elephant's Clock Workbook. 2000. (Elephant's Clock Ser.: Bk. 2). (Illus.). 103p. (J). (gr. 1-2). pap., wbk. ed. 15.00 (978-0-89739-007-1(5)) Heron Bks.

—How to Tell Time. 2nd ed. 2000. (Elephant's Clock Ser.: Bk. 3). (Illus.). 110p. (J). (gr. 1-2). pap., wbk. ed. 15.00 (978-0-89739-008-8(3)) Heron Bks.

—A Story about Learning to Tell Time. 2000. (Elephant's Clock Ser.: Bk. 1). (Illus.). 95p. (J). (gr. 1-2). pap. 20.00 (978-0-89739-006-4(7)) Heron Bks.

Jaskiewicz, A. E. Hickory & the Big Clock. 2006. (ENG.). 56p. per. 12.95 (***978-1-4241-6024-2(3)***) PublishAmerica, Inc.

Johnson, Sarah. Time to Dance. Lew, Willie, illus. Lew, Willie, photos by. 2003. (J). 16.98 (978-0-7853-8811-1(7)) Publications International, Ltd.

Jones, Carol. What's the Time, Mr. Wolf? 1999. (Illus.). 32p. (J). (gr. k-3). 15.00 (978-0-395-95800-1(8) , Walter Lorraine) Houghton Mifflin Co. Trade & Reference Div.

Keenan, Sheila. What Time Is It? A Book of Math Riddles. Jacobs, Kayne, illus. 2000. (Hello Reader! Math Ser.: Level 2). 32p. (J). (gr. k-2). pap. 3.99 (978-0-590-12008-1(5) , Cartwheel Bks.) Scholastic, Inc.

—What Time Is It? A Book of Math Riddles. 1999. (Hello Reader! Math Ser.). (978-0-606-18614-8(X)) Tandem Library Bks.

—What Time Is It? a Book of Math Riddles. 1999. (gr. k-3). lib. bdg. 11.80 (978-0-613-22609-7(7)) Tandem Library Bks.

Keene, Carolyn. Stop the Clock. ed. 2005. (Nancy Drew Ser.: 12). 160p. (J). lib. bdg. 15.00 (978-1-59054-815-8(9)) Fitzgerald Bks.

Lewis, Paul. Tick Tock. 2004. (Illus.). 36p. pap. 17.95 (978-1-4137-1407-4(2)) PublishAmerica, Inc.

Lou Weber Staff, ed. Exploring Time with Dora Clock. 2004. 10p. (J). bds. 16.98 (978-1-4127-3050-1(3) , 7228800) Publications International, Ltd.

—Winnie the Pooh (Clock) 2004. 10p. (J). bds. 16.98 (978-1-4127-3243-7(3) , 7236300) Publications International, Ltd.

MacCaughrean, Geraldine. El Reloj de Mi Abuela. 2004. (SPA., Illus.). 32p. (J). 14.99 (978-84-241-8643-2(5)) Everest de Ediciones y Distribucion, S.L. ESP. *Dist:* Lectorum Pubns., Inc.

Mamet, David. Bar Mitzvah. Sultan, Donald, illus. 1999. 45p. (YA). reprint ed. 27.00 (978-0-7567-6490-6(4)) DIANE Publishing Co.

—Bar Mitzvah. 1999. (Illus.). 48p. (gr. 8). 26.95 (978-0-8212-2546-2(4)) Little Brown & Co.

Mills, Elizabeth. Tick-Tock Sharks. Bettoli, Delana, illus. 2005. 40p. (J). (ps-ps). 9.99 (978-0-439-72308-4(6) , Cartwheel Bks.) Scholastic, Inc.

Milne, A. A. Pooh's First Clock. Shepard, Ernest H., illus. 1998. 12p. (J). (ps-3). bds. 12.99 (978-0-525-45983-5(9) , Dutton Juvenile) Penguin Group (USA) Inc.

Mirarchi, Anthony J. The King's Challenge. 2007. (Illus.). 220p. (J). (gr. 5-7). per. 9.95 (***978-1-933255-32-3(3)***) DNA Pr.

Molesworth, Mary Louisa. The Cuckoo Clock. 2004. reprint ed. pap. 19.95 (978-1-4191-5839-1(2)); pap. 1.99 (978-1-4192-5839-8(7)) Kessinger Publishing, LLC.

Moon, Nicola. Mouse Tells the Time. Morris, Tony, illus. 2002. 32p. (J). 18.00 (978-1-84365-000-3(2) , Pavilion Bks., Ltd.) Anova Bks. GBR. *Dist:* Independent Pubs. Group.

Murphy, Stuart J. Game Time! Jabar, Cynthia, illus. 2000. (Mathstart Ser.). (J). 11.79 (978-0-606-19984-1(5)) Tandem Library Bks.

Pilegard, Virginia Walton. The Warlord's Alarm. Debon, Nicholas, illus. 2006. 32p. (J). 15.95 (978-1-58980-378-7(7)) Pelican Publishing Co., Inc.

Pinto, Sara. Clockwise. 2006. 32p. (J). 19.95 (978-1-58234-660-1(7)); 16.95 (978-1-58234-669-4(0)) Bloomsbury Publishing.

Poortvliet, Rien. Gnome Clock Book. 1998. (Illus.). 24p. (J). 8.95 (978-1-57909-019-7(2)) Kabouter Products.

Preller, James. The Race Against Time. 2003. (Jigsaw Jones Mystery Ser.: No. 20). (Illus.). 96p. (J). pap. 3.99 (978-0-439-42630-5(8) , Scholastic Paperbacks) Scholastic, Inc.

Pullman, Philip. El Reloj Mecanico. Netzel, Carmen, tr. 2005. (Escritura desatada Ser.). (SPA.). 112p. (J). 15.95 (978-84-406-8065-5(1)) Ediciones B ESP. *Dist:* Independent Pubs. Group.

Pyle, Howard. Pepper & Salt & the Wonder Clock, Set. 2006. (Foundations Ser.). 385p. (J). 45.00 (978-1-933859-14-9(8)) ISI Bks.

—The Wonder Clock: Or Four & Twenty Marvelous Tales, Being One for Each Hour of the Day. Exams Unlimited, Inc. Staff, ed. Pyle, Katharine, illus. 2001. 373p. (J). reprint ed. cd-rom 6.75 (978-1-885343-14-7(0)) Exams Unlimited, Inc.

Resnick, Mike. The World Behind the Door: An Encounter with Salvador Dali. 2007. (Illus.). 144p. (YA). 16.95 (***978-0-8230-0416-4(3)***) Watson-Guptill Pubns., Inc.

Richards, Kitty. It's about Time, Max! Fiammenghi, Gioia, illus. 2000. (Math Matters Ser.). 32p. (J). (gr. 1-3). pap. 4.95 (978-1-57565-088-3(6)) Kane Pr., The.

—It's about Time, Max! 2000. (gr. k-3). lib. bdg. 12.95 (978-0-613-17313-1(9)); (Illus.). (J). 11.75 (978-0-606-18219-5(5)) Tandem Library Bks.

Ring, Susan. Innovative Kids Readers: the Great Barrier Reef - an Undersea Adventure. 2007. 32p. (J). (gr. 1-3). pap. 6.99 (978-1-58476-543-1(7)) Innovative Kids.

Silver Dolphin en Español Editors. Llegs la hora del baile: Time for the Ball, Spanish-Language Edition. 2005. (SPA., Illus.). 22p. (J). 18.95 (978-970-718-287-5(3) , Silver Dolphin en Español) Advanced Marketing, S. de R. L. de C. V. MEX. *Dist:* Perseus Distribution.

Simon & Schuster, eds. Millennium Madness. 2000. (gr. 3-6). lib. bdg. 14.15 (978-0-613-22002-6(1)) Tandem Library Bks.

Stimson, James. Thirteen O'Clock. 2005. (Illus.). 40p. (J). 15.95 (978-0-8118-4839-8(6)) Chronicle Bks. LLC.

Stine, R. L. The Big Blueberry Barf-Off! Park, Trip, illus. 2005. (Rotten School Ser.). 128p. (J). 6.99 (978-0-06-078586-4(1)); lib. bdg. 14.89 (978-0-06-078587-1(X)) HarperCollins Pubs.

Stine, R.L. Rotten School #1: the Big Blueberry Barf-off! Park, Trip, illus. 2008. (Rotten School Ser.). 128p. (J). pap. 4.99 (***978-0-06-078588-8(8)*** , Harper Trophy) HarperCollins Pubs.

Turley, Sandy. The Clock & the Mouse: A Teaching Rhyme about Time. Peterson, Sara & Lindstrom, Brita, illus. 2006. (J). 16.95 (***978-0-9778548-0-6(9)***) Turley, Sandy.

Vischer, Phil. More Veggiecational Fun: A Book about Time & Opposites! 1999. (Veggiecational Ser.). (Illus.). 64p. (J). (ps-2). 10.99 (978-0-8499-7531-8(X)) Nelson, Thomas Inc.

—Time for Tom: A Veggiecational Book about Time! (Veggiecational Ser.). (Illus.). (J). (ps-3). 1999. 12p. 8.99 (978-0-8499-5988-2(8)); 1998. 32p. 8.99 (978-0-8499-1534-5(1)) Nelson, Thomas Inc.

Warner, Gertrude Chandler. Midnight Mystery. 2003. (gr. 3-6). lib. bdg. 11.80 (978-0-613-75712-6(2)) Tandem Library Bks.

Watkins, Dawn L. Nantucket Cats. Bonge, Lynn E., illus. 1998. 32p. (J). (ps-1). pap. 5.49 (978-0-89084-975-0(7)) Jones, Bob Univ. Pr.

Winterson, Jeanette. Tanglewreck. (J). 2007. 416p. (gr. 3-7). pap. 6.95 (***978-1-59990-081-0(5)***); 2006. 250p. 16.95 (978-1-58234-919-0(3)) Bloomsbury Publishing. (Bloomsbury Children).

Young, Steve. 15 Minutes. 2006. 176p. (J). 15.99 (978-0-06-072508-2(7)); lib. bdg. 16.89 (978-0-06-072509-9(5)) HarperCollins Pubs.

CLOCKS AND WATCHES—HISTORY

Dash, Joan. The Longitude Prize: The Race Between the Moon & the Watch-Machine. Petricic, Dusan, illus. 2000. 208p. (J). (gr. 4-7). 17.00 (978-0-374-34636-2(4) , Farrar, Straus & Giroux (BYR)) Farrar, Straus & Giroux.

Martin, W. Eric, et al. Tools of Timekeeping: A Kid's Guide to the History & Science of Telling Time. 2005. (Tools of Discovery Ser.). (Illus.). 144p. (J). pap. 16.95 (978-0-9722026-7-1(6)) Nomad Pr.

Smith, A. G. What Time Is It? (Illus.). 86p. (Orig.). (YA). (gr. 4-9). pap. 13.95 (978-0-7737-6219-0(1)) Stoddart Kids CAN. *Dist:* Fitzhenry & Whiteside, Ltd.

—What Time Is It? 2000. (Orig.). (gr. 3-6). lib. bdg. 23.40 (978-0-613-81886-5(5)) Tandem Library Bks.

Williams, Brian. Measuring Time. 2002. (Illus.). 32p. (J). lib. bdg. 24.25 (978-1-58340-208-5(X)) Smart Apple Media.

CLOG DANCING

see Folk Dancing

CLOISTERS (RELIGIOUS COMMUNITIES)

see Monasteries

CLONING

Balkwill, Fran & Rolph, Mic. Gene Machines. 2002. (Enjoy Your Cells Ser.: Vol. 4). (Illus.). 32p. (J). 13.95 (978-0-87969-616-0(8)); pap. 8.95 (978-0-87969-611-5(7)) Cold Spring Harbor Laboratory Pr.

Cefrey, Holly. Cloning & Genetic Engineering. 2002. (High Interest Bks.). (Illus.). 48p. (YA). (gr. 7-12). pap. 6.95 (978-0-516-24006-0(4) , Children's Pr.) Scholastic Library Publishing.

—Cloning & Genetic Engineering. 2002. (gr. 7-12). lib. bdg. 15.25 (978-0-613-58693-1(X)) Tandem Library Bks.

Cohen, Daniel. Cloning. rev. ed. 2002. (Single Titles Ser.). (Illus.). 160p. (gr. 7 up). lib. bdg. 25.90 (978-0-7613-2802-5(5) , Twenty-First Century Bks.) Lerner Publishing Group.

Fritz, Sandy. Genomics & Cloning. 2003. (Hot Science Ser.). (J). lib. bdg. 28.50 (978-1-58340-365-5(5)) Smart Apple Media.

Goodnough, David. The Debate over Human Cloning. 2003. (Hot Pro/Con Issues Ser.). (Illus.). 64p. (YA). (gr. 6-12). lib. bdg. 27.93 (978-0-7660-1818-1(0)) Enslow Pubs., Inc.

Jefferis, David. Cloning: Frontiers of Genetic Engineering. 1999. (Megatech Ser.). (Illus.). 32p. (J). (gr. 4-5). pap. (978-0-7787-0058-6(5)); lib. bdg. (978-0-7787-0048-7(8)) Crabtree Publishing Co.

—Cloning: Frontiers of Genetic Engineering. 1999. 15.75 (978-0-606-17480-0(X)) Tandem Library Bks.

Kafka, Tina. Cloning. 2007. (Hot Topics Ser.). 128p. (gr. 7-10). 32.45 (***978-1-59018-979-5(5)*** , Lucent Bks.) Thomson Gale.

Morgan, Sally. Body Doubles: Cloning Plants & Animals. 2002. (Science at the Edge Ser.). (Illus.). 64p. (J). (gr. 6-8). lib. bdg. 27.86 (978-1-58810-698-8(5)) Heinemann Library.

—From Sea Urchins to Dolly the Sheep: Discovering Cloning. 2006. (Chain Reactions Ser.). (Illus.). 64p. (YA). (gr. 6-9). lib. bdg. 34.29 (978-1-4034-8838-1(X)) Heinemann Library.

Nardo, Don. Cloning. (Lucent Library of Science & Technology). (Illus.). 2005. 112p. (J). (gr. 7-10). lib. bdg. 29.95 (978-1-59018-773-9(3) , Lucent Bks.); 2003. 48p. (J). 24.95 (978-1-56711-782-0(1) , Blackbirch Pr., Inc.); 2002. 48p. (J). (gr. 3-5). 23.70 (978-0-7377-1403-6(4) , Kidhaven); 2001. 120p. (YA). (gr. 6-9). 29.95 (978-1-56006-927-0(9) , GML12001-178219, Lucent Bks.) Thomson Gale.

Richardson, Hazel. How to Clone a Sheep. Cooke, Andy, illus. 2001. (How to Ser.). 96p. (J). (gr. 5-7). 16.00 (978-0-531-14645-3(6) , Watts, Franklin) Scholastic Library Publishing.

—How to Clone a Sheep. 2001. (gr. 5-8). lib. bdg. 12.95 (978-0-613-54546-4(X)) Tandem Library Bks.

Roleff, Tamara L. Cloning. 2005. (Opposing Viewpoints Ser.). (Illus.). 176p. (YA). (gr. 10-13). lib. bdg. 36.20 (978-0-7377-3311-2(X) , Greenhaven Pr., Inc.) Thomson Gale.

Stanley, Debbie. Genetic Engineering: The Cloning Debate. 2000. (Focus on Science & Society Ser.). (Illus.). 64p. (YA). (gr. 4-6). lib. bdg. 26.50 (978-0-8239-3211-5(7) , FSGEEN) Rosen Publishing Group, Inc., The.

Vanished!, 6 Packs. (Bookweb Ser.). 32p. (gr. 5 up). 34.00 (978-0-7635-3797-5(7)) Rigby Education.

Wimmer, Teresa. Dolly the Sheep. 2008. (J). (***978-1-58341-652-5(8)*** , Creative Education) Creative Co., The.

CLONING—FICTION

Cave, Patrick. Sharp North. 2006. (Illus.). 528p. (J). 16.95 (978-1-4169-1222-4(3) , Atheneum) Simon & Schuster Children's Publishing.

Farmer, Nancy. The House of the Scorpion. (J). 2002. 400p. 17.95 (978-0-689-85222-0(3) , Atheneum/Richard Jackson Bks.); 2004. (Illus.). 416p. reprint ed. pap. 9.99 (978-0-689-85223-7(1) , Simon Pulse) Simon & Schuster Children's Publishing.

—The House of the Scorpion. l.t. ed. 2003. 515p. (J). 24.95 (978-0-7862-5048-6(8)) Thorndike Pr.

Farnell, Chris. Mark II. 2006. (Illus.). 164p. (YA). (gr. 8-10). pap. 14.95 (978-0-9547913-9-1(8)) Tindal Street Pr. GBR. *Dist:* Dufour Editions, Inc.

Haddix, Margaret Peterson. Double Identity. (J). (gr. 5-9). 2007. 192p. pap. 5.99 (978-0-689-87379-9(4) , Aladdin); 2005. 224p. 15.95 (978-0-689-87374-4(3)) Simon & Schuster Children's Publishing.

Halperin, James L. The First Immortal. 1998. 432p. mass mkt. 7.99 (978-0-345-42182-1(5) , Del Rey) Random House Publishing Group.

Homzie, Hillary. Two Heads Are Better Than One. 2002. (gr. k-3). lib. bdg. 11.80 (978-0-613-57587-4(3)) Tandem Library Bks.

Homzie, Hillary & Phillips, Matthew. Two Heads Are Better Than One, Vol. 1. 2002. (Alien Clones from Outer Space Ser.). 80p. (J). pap. 3.99 (978-0-689-82342-8(8) , Aladdin) Simon & Schuster Children's Publishing.

Horowitz, Anthony. Point Blank. (Alex Rider Ser.: Bk. 2). 2006. 304p. (J). (gr. 7). pap. 7.99 (978-0-14-240612-0(0) , Puffin); 2002. 208p. (YA). (gr. 5 up). 17.99 (978-0-399-23621-1(X) , Philomel) Penguin Group (USA) Inc.

It Came from the Lab. 2005. (Thrillogy Ser.). (Illus.). 48p. (gr. 4-8). 17.50 (978-0-7910-8867-8(7)) Facts On File, Inc.

Kaye, Marilyn. Amy, Number Seven. 1999. (Replica Ser.: No. 1). (J). (gr. 4-7). (978-0-606-15933-3(9)) Tandem Library Bks.

—And the Two Shall Meet. 1999. (Replica Ser.: No. 6). (J). (gr. 4-7). (978-0-606-16376-7(X)) Tandem Library Bks.

—Another Amy. 1999. (Replica Ser.: No. 3). (J). (gr. 4-7). (978-0-606-16003-2(5)) Tandem Library Bks.

—The Beginning. 2000. (Replica Ser.: No. 14). (gr. 3-6). lib. bdg. 12.40 (978-0-613-28251-2(5)) Tandem Library Bks.

—The Best of the Best. 1999. (Replica Ser.: No. 7). (978-0-606-16377-4(8)) Tandem Library Bks.

—The Fever. 1999. (Replica Ser.: No. 9). (J). (gr. 4-7). (978-0-606-17482-4(6)) Tandem Library Bks.

—Mystery Mother. 1999. (Replica Ser.: No. 8). (J). (gr. 4-7). (978-0-606-17481-7(8)) Tandem Library Bks.

—Perfect Girls. 1999. (Replica Ser.: No. 4). (J). (gr. 4-7). (978-0-606-16372-9(7)) Tandem Library Bks.

—Pursuing Amy. 1999. (Replica Ser.: No. 2). (J). (gr. 4-7). (978-0-606-15934-0(7)) Tandem Library Bks.

—Secret Clique. 1999. (Replica Ser.: No. 5). (J). (gr. 4-7). (978-0-606-16373-6(5)) Tandem Library Bks.

Kerner, Charlotte. Blueprint. Crawford, Elizabeth D., tr. from GER. 2003. (Young Adult Fiction Ser.). 192p. (YA). (gr. 9-12). 16.95 (978-0-8225-0080-3(9) , Carolrhoda Bks.) Lerner Publishing Group.

Lasky, Kathryn. Star Split. 2001. (YA). (978-0-606-21456-8(9)) Tandem Library Bks.

Marvel Staff. The Clone Trap. 2007. 24p. (J). pap. 3.99 (978-0-696-23477-4(7)) Meredith Bks.

McCaffrey, Tony. Emmanuel McClue & The Mystery of the Shroud. 2002. 155p. (J). (gr. 5-9). pap. 11.95 (978-1-929039-08-1(5)) Ambassador Bks., Inc.

Medina, Rick. Humaliens Vol. 2: The Clone Formula. 1999. 150p. (J). (gr. 4-7). pap. 4.99 (978-1-892587-01-5(7)) Dualstar, Inc.

Merkley, Chad. Too Many Me's. 1999. (Publish-a-Book Ser.). (Illus.). 32p. (J). (gr. 1-6). pap. 8.50 (978-0-7398-0052-2(3)) Steck-Vaughn.

Peel, John. Traitor. 2000. (Twenty Ninety-Nine Ser.: Bk. 3). (Illus.). 160p. (J). (gr. 3-7). pap. 4.99 (978-0-439-06032-5(X) , Scholastic Paperbacks) Scholastic, Inc.

Reynolds, Peter H. So Few of Me. 2006. (Illus.). 32p. (J). (gr. k-12). 14.00 (978-0-7636-2623-5(6)) Candlewick Pr.

Roy, Ron. Kidnapped at the Capital. Woodruff, Liza & Bush, Timothy, illus. 2002. (Road to Reading Ser.: Vol. 2). 80p. (J). (gr. 2-5). pap. 3.99 (978-0-307-26514-2(5) , Random Hse. Bks. for Young Readers) Random Hse. Children's Bks.

—Kidnapped at the Capital. 2002. (gr. 3-6). lib. bdg. 11.80 (978-0-613-50212-2(4)) Tandem Library Bks.

—Who Cloned the President? Woodruff, Liza & Bush, Timothy, illus. 2001. (Road to Reading Ser.: Vol. 1). 80p. (J). (gr. 2-5). pap. 3.99 (978-0-307-26510-4(2) , Random Hse. Bks. for Young Readers) Random Hse. Children's Bks.

—Who Cloned the President? 2001. (gr. k-3). lib. bdg. 11.80 (978-0-613-43141-5(3)) Tandem Library Bks.

Shudo, Takeshi. Art of Pokemon, the Movie: Mewtwo Strikes Back! 1999. (gr. 3-6). lib. bdg. 17.60 (978-0-613-22684-4(4)) Tandem Library Bks.

Singer, Nicky. GemX. 2008. (YA). (***978-0-8234-2108-4(2)***) Holiday Hse., Inc.

Singleton, Linda Joy. Regeneration: The Search. l.t. ed. 2002. 240p. (J). 23.95 (978-0-7862-3868-2(2)) Thorndike Pr.

—Regeneration: The Truth. l.t. ed. 2002. 266p. (YA). 23.95 (978-0-7862-3869-9(0)) Thorndike Pr.

Sleator, William. The Duplicate. 1999. (gr. 5-8). lib. bdg. 14.15 (978-0-8335-5902-9(8)) Tandem Library Bks.

Waddington-Feather, John. Quill's Adventures in Mereful. 2004. 87p. pap. 14.95 (978-1-4137-1632-0(6)) PublishAmerica, Inc.

Werlin, Nancy. Double Helix. 2005. 256p. (YA). (gr. 3-6). pap. 6.99 (978-0-14-240327-3(X) , Puffin) Penguin Group (USA) Inc.

Woolfe, Angela. Avril Crump & Her Amazing Clones. 2005. (Avril Crump Ser.). 224p. (J). 9.95 (978-0-439-65130-1(1) , Orchard Bks.) Scholastic, Inc.

—Avril Crump & the Clone Countdown. 2006. 224p. (J). 9.99 (978-0-439-65132-5(8) , Orchard Bks.) Scholastic, Inc.

CLOTHIERS

see Clothing Trade

CLOTHING AND DRESS

Here are entered works dealing with clothing from a practical standpoint including the art of dress. Descriptive and historical works on the costume of particular countries or periods are entered under Costume.

see also Buttons; Costume; Costume Design; Dressmaking; Fashion; Hats; Shoes

Adamson, Heather. Clothes in Many Cultures. 2008. (J). (***978-1-4296-0018-7(7)***) Capstone Pr., Inc.

All Kinds of Clothes Social Studies, 6 vols. (gr. k-2). 28.95 (978-0-7368-1758-5(1) , Yellow Umbrella Bks.) Capstone Pr., Inc.

Allen, Kit. Galoshes. 2003. (Illus.). 13p. (J). (gr. k-ps). bds. 4.95 (978-0-618-22997-0(3)) Houghton Mifflin Co. Trade & Reference Div.

—Longjohns. 2003. (Illus.). 13p. (J). (gr. k-ps). bds. 4.95 (978-0-618-22996-3(5)) Houghton Mifflin Co. Trade & Reference Div.

—Sweater. 2003. (Illus.). 13p. (J). (gr. k-ps). bds. 4.95 (978-0-618-26370-7(5)) Houghton Mifflin Co. Trade & Reference Div.

Appel, Dee. Let's Play Dress Up. Francour, Kathleen, photos by. Date not set. (Tiny Times Board Book Ser.). (Illus.). 10p. (J). bds. 5.99 (978-0-7369-0563-3(4)) Harvest Hse. Pubs.

Bailey Publishing Staff. A History of Fashion & Costume Set. 2005. (History of Fashion & Costume Ser.). 512p. (gr. 6-12). 280.00 (978-0-8160-5943-0(8)) Facts On File, Inc.

Baker, Patricia. Fashions of a Decade: The 1940s. 2nd rev. ed. 2006. (Fashions of a Decade Ser.). 64p. (YA). (gr. 6-12). 35.00 (978-0-8160-6720-6(1)) Facts On File, Inc.

—Fashions of A Decade: The 1950s. 2nd rev. ed. 2006. (Fashions of a Decade Ser.). 64p. (J). (gr. 6-12). 35.00 (978-0-8160-6721-3(X)) Facts On File, Inc.

Ball, Jacqueline. Clothing Creations: From T-Shirts to Flip-Flops. 2006. (Which Came First? Ser.). (Illus.). 32p. (J). lib. bdg. 25.27 (978-1-59716-128-2(4)) Bearport Publishing Co., Inc.

Barbie Tiara. 2004. (Marketing Support Ser.). (J). (978-1-57584-455-8(9) , Reader's Digest Children's Bks.) Reader's Digest Children's Publishing, Inc.

Barker, Cicely Mary. Flower Fairies Dress-Up for the Ball Boo. 2005. (Illus.). 8p. pap. 7.99 (978-0-7232-5376-1(5) , Warne) Penguin Group (USA) Inc.

Beaton, Clare, illus. Clothes: La Ropa. l.t. ed. 1998. (English-Spanish Bilingual First Bks.). (ENG & SPA.). 24p. (J). (ps up). lib. bdg. 14.45 (978-1-56674-248-1(X)) Forest Hse. Publishing Co., Inc.

Bell, Alison. Fearless Fashion. Mireault, Jerome, illus. 2004. (What's Your Style Ser. ? Ser.). 64p. (J). pap. 14.95 (978-1-894222-86-0(5)) Lobster Pr. CAN. *Dist:* Univ. of Toronto Pr.

Bennett, Tammy. Looking Good from the Inside Out Fashion. 2003. (gr. 7-12). lib. bdg. 26.90 (978-0-613-82398-2(2)) Tandem Library Bks.

Boase, Petra & Beak, Nick Huckleberry. Crafty T-Shirts. Freeman, John, photos by. 1999. (Crafty Kids Ser.). (Illus.). 64p. (J). (gr. 3 up). lib. bdg. 26.00 (978-0-8368-2483-4(0)) Stevens, Gareth Inc.

Bond, Michael. Paddington Dressing Up. 1999. (Paddington Ser.: '). (Illus.). 12p. (J). (ps-3). 4.95 (978-0-694-00425-6(1) , Harper Festival) HarperCollins Pubs.

Bonnice, Sherry. Folk Fashion. 2002. (North American Folklore Ser.). (Illus.). 112p. (J). (gr. 7 up). lib. bdg. (978-1-59084-338-3(X)) Mason Crest Pubs.

Boothroyd, Jennifer. Clothes. 2006. (First Step Nonfiction Ser.). (Illus.). 8p. (J). lib. bdg. (978-0-8225-5732-6(0) , Lerner Pubns.) Lerner Publishing Group.

Brides. Date not set. (Dressing My Dolly Ser.). (Illus.). 16p. (J). 2.98 (978-1-4054-0474-7(4)) Parragon, Inc.

Bull, Jane. The Dress-up Book. 2006. (Illus.). 48p. (J). 12.99 (978-0-7566-1983-1(1)) Dorling Kindersley Publishing, Inc.

Busby, Cylin & Licensing Company Staff. Stylin' Slumber Party. 2003. (Bratz Ser.). (Illus.). 48p. 8.40 (978-0-14-131751-9(5) , Putnam Juvenile) Penguin Group (USA) Inc.

Capstone Press, contrib. by. Warm Clothes, Vol. 3. 2005. (Our Seasons & Weather Ser.). 24p. (YA). (gr. k-3). pap. (978-1-56065-959-4(9) , Pebble Bks.) Capstone Pr., Inc.

Carnegy, Vicky. Fashions of A Decade: The 1980s. 2nd rev. ed. 2006. (Fashions of a Decade Ser.). 64p. (J). (gr. 6-12). 35.00 (978-0-8160-6724-4(4)) Facts On File, Inc.

Casolino, Peter, illus. & photos by. Kid's Clothes: From Start to Finish. Casolino, Peter, photos by. Woods, Samuel G., photos by. 2001. 32p. (J). (gr. 3-6). 23.70 (978-1-56711-483-6(0) , Blackbirch Pr., Inc.) Thomson Gale.

Charlie Needs a Cloak. 2004. 24.95 incl. audio (978-1-56008-023-7(X)); pap. 18.95 incl. audio compact disk (978-1-55592-382-2(8)); pap. 18.95 incl. audio compact disk (978-1-55592-384-6(4)); pap. 38.75 incl. audio compact disk (978-1-55592-383-9(6)); pap. 38.75 incl. audio compact disk (978-1-55592-385-3(2)); pap. 32.75 incl. audio (978-1-55592-200-9(7)); pap. 32.75 incl. audio (978-1-55592-201-6(5)); pap. 14.95 incl. audio (978-1-55592-719-6(X)) Weston Woods Studios, Inc.

Cipriano, Jeri S. All Kinds of Clothes. 2003. (Yellow Umbrella Books). (Illus.). 16p. (J). (gr. 1). lib. bdg. 14.60 (978-0-7368-2025-7(6) , Pebble Bks.) Capstone Pr., Inc.

—All Kinds of Clothes. 2003. (J). (978-0-7368-1722-6(0)) Yellow Umbrella Pr.

Clothes: KinderFacts Individual Title Six-Packs. (Kinderstarters Ser.). 8p. (ps-1). 21.00 (978-0-7635-8743-7(5)) Rigby Education.

Clothes & Crafts in History, 6 bks. Incl. Clothes & Crafts in Ancient Egypt. Balkwill, Richard. lib. bdg. 24.67 (978-0-8368-2733-0(3)); Clothes & Crafts in Ancient Greece. Steele, Philip. lib. bdg. 24.67 (978-0-8368-2734-7(1)); Clothes & Crafts in Aztec Times. Dawson, Imogene. lib. bdg. 24.67 (978-0-8368-2735-4(X)); Clothes & Crafts in Roman Times. Steele, Philip. lib. bdg. 24.67 (978-0-8368-2737-8(6)); Clothes & Crafts in the Middle Ages. Dawson, Imogene. lib. bdg. 24.67 (978-0-8368-2736-1(8)); Clothes & Crafts in Victorian Times. Steele, Philip. lib. bdg. 24.67 (978-0-8368-2738-5(4)); 32p. (J). (gr. 4 up). 2000. (Illus.). 2000. Set lib. bdg. 148.02 (978-0-8368-2732-3(5)) Stevens, Gareth Inc.

Cobb, Vicki. Sneakers. 2006. (Where's the Science Here? Ser.). (Illus.). 48p. (J). (gr. 3-5). 23.93 (978-0-7613-2772-1(X) , Millbrook Pr.) Lerner Publishing Group.

Collins, Elaine Banks. I Like Dressing Up. Floyd, John, Jr., illus. 2005. (J). bds. 5.95 (***978-0-9752860-5-0(6))** Our-Rainbow Pr., LLC.

Connikie, Yvonne. Fashions of A Decade: The 1960s. 2nd rev. ed. 2006. (Fashions of a Decade Ser.). 64p. (gr. 6-12). 35.00 (978-0-8160-6722-0(8)) Facts On File, Inc.

Cooper, Karen. DIY Style. 2002. (Illus.). 160p. (J). (gr. 3). pap. 4.99 (978-0-439-33888-2(3)) Scholastic, Inc.

Corey, Shana. You Forgot Your Skirt, Amelia Bloomer! McLaren, Chesley, illus. 2000. 40p. (J). (gr. k-3). pap. 16.95 (978-0-439-07819-1(9) , Scholastic Reference) Scholastic, Inc.

Costantino, Maria. Fashions of a Decade: The 1930s. 2nd rev. ed. 2006. (Fashions of a Decade Ser.). 64p. (YA). (gr. 6-12). 35.00 (978-0-8160-6719-0(8)) Facts On File, Inc.

Daynes, Katie. Fabulous Story of Fashion. Mistry, Nilesh, illus. 2006. 64p. (J). 8.99 (978-0-7945-1263-7(1) , Usborne) EDC Publishing.

—Revealing Story of Underwear. 2006. 64p. (J). 8.99 (978-0-7945-1352-8(2) , Usborne) EDC Publishing.

de Paola, Tomie. Charlie Needs a Cloak. 2002. (J). (ps-2). lib. bdg. 14.15 (978-0-8335-0342-8(1)) Tandem Library Bks.

Diva Girls. Date not set. (Dressing My Dolly Ser.). (Illus.). 16p. (J). 2.98 (978-1-4054-0475-4(2)) Parragon, Inc.

DK Publishing Staff. Getting Dressed. 2007. 12p. (J). (ps-1). bds. 6.99 (978-0-7566-3020-1(7)) Dorling Kindersley Publishing, Inc.

—My Dress-Up Box. 2007. (Dk Readers Ser.). (Illus.). 32p. (J). 14.99 (978-0-7566-2529-0(7)); pap. 3.99 (978-0-7566-2528-3(9)) Dorling Kindersley Publishing, Inc.

Dorling Kindersley Publishing Staff, ed. Do Gloves Go on Feet? 2005. (Dk See-throughs Ser.). (Illus.). 21p. (J). 6.99 (978-0-7566-0775-3(2)) Dorling Kindersley Publishing, Inc.

Dorling Kindersley Publishing Staff & Spier, Carol. Super Style. 2006. (Illus.). 96p. pap. 8.99 (978-0-7566-1588-8(7)) Dorling Kindersley Publishing, Inc.

Doudna, Kelly. Clothing Around the World. 2004. (Around the World Ser.). (Illus.). 23p. (J). (ps-3). lib. bdg. 19.93 (978-1-59197-565-6(4)) ABDO Publishing Co.

Doudna, Kelly. Look Your Best! 2007. (Illus.). 24p. (J). 19.93 (***978-1-59928-737-9(4))** ABDO Publishing Co.

Draper, Allison Stark. Clothing, Costumes & Uniforms Throughout American History, 6 bks. Incl. What People Wore During the American Revolution. lib. bdg. 19.95 (978-0-8239-5666-1(0) , PKCLRE); What People Wore During the Civil War. lib. bdg. 19.95 (978-0-8239-5669-2(5) , PKCLCI); What People Wore During the Westward Expansion. lib. bdg. 19.95 (978-0-8239-5667-8(9) , PKCLPL); What People Wore in Colonial America. lib. bdg. 19.95 (978-0-8239-5665-4(2) , PKCLCO); What People Wore in Early America. lib. bdg. 19.95 (978-0-8239-5664-7(4) , PKCLEA); What People Wore on Southern Plantations. lib. bdg. 19.95 (978-0-8239-5668-5(7) , PKCLPL); 24p. (J). (gr. 3). 2001. (Illus.). Set lib. bdg. 117.00 (978-0-8239-7060-5(4) ; PKCLAM, PowerKids Pr.) Rosen Publishing Group, Inc., The.

Dress Up. 2007. (J). lib. bdg. 9.95 (***978-0-9768706-4-7(9))** Learning Props.

Dress-Up: A Sticker-Activity Storybook. 2004. (Disney Princess Ser.). (Illus.). 12p. (ps-2). act. bk. ed. 14.99 (978-0-7868-3488-4(9) , Disney Editions) Disney Pr.

Dressing with Pride: Six-Pack. (Greetings Ser.: Vol. 2). (gr. 3-5). 31.00 (978-0-7635-1764-9(X)) Rigby Education.

Easterling, Lisa. Clothing. 2007. (J). (***978-1-4034-9405-4(3)); pap. (*978-1-4034-9414-6(2))** Heinemann Library.

Eck, Kristin. Hide-and-Seek Clothes. 2004. (Hide-And-Seek Books). (Illus.). (J). lib. bdg. 7.95 (978-1-4042-2705-7(9) , PowerKids Pr.) Rosen Publishing Group, Inc., The.

Ehrlich, Fred. Does a Chimp Wear Clothes? Bolam, Emily, illus. 2005. (Early Experiences Ser.). (J). (***978-1-4156-3336-6(3))** Handprint Bks.

Elliott, Lynne. Clothing in the Middle Ages. 2004. (Medieval World Ser.). (Illus.). 32p. pap. (978-0-7787-1383-8(0)); (J). (978-0-7787-1351-7(2)) Crabtree Publishing Co.

Facts on File, Inc. Staff, ed. Fashions of a Decade, 8 Vols., Set. 2006. (Fashions of a Decade Ser.). 64p. (gr. 6-12). 280.00 (978-0-8160-7059-6(8)) Facts On File, Inc.

Feldman, Elane & McEvoy, Anne. Fashions of A Decade: The 1990s. 2nd rev. ed. 2006. (Fashions of a Decade Ser.). 64p. (gr. 6-12). 35.00 (978-0-8160-6725-1(2)) Facts On File, Inc.

Fernandez, Vivian. Body Design. Morrow, Michelle, illus. 1998. 16p. (J). 6.95 (978-1-880592-98-4(3) , Beehive Bk.) Pace Products, Inc.

Florence, Judy. Aprons of the Mid-Twentieth Century: To Serve & Protect. 2001. (Schiffer Book for Collectors Ser.). (Illus.). 160p. (gr. 10-13). pap. 29.95 (978-0-7643-1341-7(X)) Schiffer Publishing, Ltd.

Focus on Fashion! 2004. (Bratz Ser.). (J). 1.49 (978-0-7666-1225-9(2) , 99215) Modern Publishing.

Fung, Karen & Butterfield, Moira. Zipper, Buttons & Bows. Utton, Peter, illus. 2000. 12p. (J). (ps-k). 12.95 (978-0-7641-5289-4(0)) Barron's Educational Series, Inc.

Galford, Ellen. Festivals. 2002. (Twentieth-Century Developments in Fashion & Costume Ser.). (Illus.). 64p. (J). (gr. 7 up). lib. bdg. (978-1-59084-423-6(8)) Mason Crest Pubs.

—Religious Costumes. 2003. (Twentieth-Century Developments in Fashion & Costume Ser.). (Illus.). 64p. (J). (gr. 7 up). lib. bdg. (978-1-59084-429-8(7)) Mason Crest Pubs.

Gilmour, Sarah. The 70s: Punks, Glam Rockers & New Romantics. 1999. (Twentieth Century Fashion Ser.). (Illus.). 32p. (J). (gr. 5 up). lib. bdg. 26.00 (978-0-8368-2602-9(7)) Stevens, Gareth Inc.

Gilpin, Daniel. Food & Clothing. 2004. (History of Invention Ser.). (Illus.). 96p. (YA). (gr. 6-12). 35.00 (978-0-8160-5441-1(X)) Facts On File, Inc.

Gooden, Clare. Customize Your Clothes. 2007. (Illus.). 512p. 24.99 (978-0-7548-1393-4(2) , Lorenz Bks.) Anness Publishing GBR. *Dist:* National Bk. Network.

Greathead, Helen. Clothes & Shoes. 2006. (Illus.). 32p. (978-1-58340-956-5(4)) Smart Apple Media.

Greene, Jacqueline Dembar. The Triangle Shirtwaist Factory Fire. 2007. (Code Red Ser.). (Illus.). 32p. (J). (gr. 3-7). lib. bdg. 25.27 (978-1-59716-359-0(7)) Bearport Publishing Co., Inc.

Gunzi, Christiane. Clothes. (My Very First Look at Ser.). (SPA., Illus.). 24p. (ps-k). 2004. (J). pap. 5.95 (978-1-58728-686-5(6)); 2003. 9.95 (978-1-58728-672-8(6)) T&N Children's Publishing. (Two Can Publishing).

Hall, Margaret. Clothing. (Around the World Ser.). 32p. pap. 6.95 (978-1-4034-4002-0(6)) Heinemann Library.

Hall, Margaret C. Clothing. 2001. (Around the World Ser.). (Illus.). 32p. (J). (gr. k-2). lib. bdg. 21.36 (978-1-58810-101-3(0)) Heinemann Library.

Halstead, Rachel & Reid, Struan, eds. Fashion: Bring the Past Alive with 30 Great Projects. 2003. (Hands-On History Ser.). (Illus.). 64p. (gr. 3-7). pap. 10.99 (978-1-84215-760-2(4) , Southwater) Anness Publishing GBR. *Dist:* National Bk. Network.

Hantman, Clea. I Wanna Make My Own Clothes. Houshyar, Azadeh, illus. 2006. 144p. (J). pap. 9.99 (978-0-689-87462-8(6) , Aladdin) Simon & Schuster Children's Publishing.

Harcourt School Publishers Staff. Going Outside to Play. 3rd ed. 2003. (Trophies English Language Learners Ser.). (Illus.). (J). pap. 3.20 (978-0-15-327569-2(3)) Harcourt Schl. Pubs.

—It's Cold Outside. 3rd ed. 2002. (Trophies English Language Learners Ser.). (Illus.). pap. 5.10 (978-0-15-327696-5(7)) Harcourt Schl. Pubs.

—It's Cold Outside - Grade 3, 5 Packs. 3rd ed. 2002. (Trophies English Language Learners Ser.). pap. 25.60 (978-0-15-327726-9(2)) Harcourt Schl. Pubs.

Harris, Carol & Brown, Mike. Accessories. 2002. (Twentieth-Century Developments in Fashion & Costume Ser.). (Illus.). 64p. (J). (gr. 7 up). lib. bdg. (978-1-59084-419-9(X)) Mason Crest Pubs.

—Children's Costumes. 2002. (Twentieth-Century Developments in Fashion & Costume Ser.). (Illus.). 64p. (J). (gr. 7 up). lib. bdg. (978-1-59084-420-5(3)) Mason Crest Pubs.

—Men's Costumes. 2003. (Twentieth-Century Developments in Fashion & Costume Ser.). (Illus.). 64p. (J). (gr. 7 up). lib. bdg. (978-1-59084-422-9(X)) Mason Crest Pubs.

Hatt, Christine. Clothes of the Early Modern World. Tattersfield, Jane, illus. 2001. (Dress Sense Ser.). 48p. (J). (gr. 5 up). 16.95 (978-0-87226-668-1(0) , Bedrick, Peter Bks.) School Specialty Publishing.

Hazan, Maurice, creator. Clothes & Colors Game in Spanish. 2000. (SPA.). (J). 99.00 (978-1-932770-52-0(6) , SG13) Symtalk, Inc.

Herald, Jacqueline. Fashions of a Decade: The 1920s. 2nd rev. ed. 2006. (Fashions of a Decade Ser.). 64p. (YA). (gr. 6-12). 35.00 (978-0-8160-6718-3(X)) Facts On File, Inc.

—Fashions of A Decade: The 1970s. 2nd rev. ed. 2006. (Fashions of a Decade Ser.). 64p. (gr. 6-12). 35.00 (978-0-8160-6723-7(6)) Facts On File, Inc.

Hewitt, Sally. Happy Dresser. Cameron, Craig, illus. 2003. 14p. (J). pap. 10.95 (978-1-57145-733-2(X) , Silver Dolphin Bks.) Advantage Pubs. Group.

Hinkler Books Staff. Dress up Dolls. Penton Overseas, Inc. Staff, ed. rev. ed. 2006. 64p. (J). (gr. 3-3). pap. 7.95 (978-1-74157-930-7(9)) Hinkler Bks. Pty, Ltd. AUS. *Dist:* Penton Overseas, Inc.

Horne, Jane. Fashion Show. 2007. (Magnetics Ser.). (Illus.). 14p. (J). (ps-k). 12.95 (978-1-84610-471-8(8)) Make Believe Ideas GBR. *Dist:* Ingram Pub. Services.

Hurley, Jo. My Stylebook. Martini, Angela, illus. 2004. 48p. (J). pap. 9.99 (978-0-439-55131-1(5) , Tangerine Pr.) Scholastic, Inc.

Jones, Jen. Fashion. 2008. (J). (***978-1-4296-0129-0(9))** Capstone Pr., Inc.

—Fashion Trends: How Popular Style Is Shaped. 2007. (Illus.). 32p. (J). (978-0-7368-6831-0(3) , 1264962) Capstone Pr., Inc.

Jones, Jen. Fashion Trends: How Popular Style Is Shaped. 2007. (Illus.). 32p. (J). (***978-0-7368-7885-2(8)** , 1264962) Capstone Pr., Inc.

Kalman, Bobbie. Bandannas, Chaps, & Ten-Gallon Hats. 1999. (gr. 3-6). lib. bdg. 16.40 (978-0-613-11305-2(5)) Tandem Library Bks.

Keoke, Emory Dean & Porterfield, Kay Marie. American Indian Contributions to the World: Buildings, Clothing, & Art. 2005. (American Indian Contributions to the World Ser.). (Illus.). 160p. (J). (gr. 4-9). 35.00 (978-0-8160-5394-0(4)) Facts On File, Inc.

Krulik, Nancy E. Prom! The Complete Guide to a Truly Spectacular Night. Johnson, Kim, illus. 2003. 96p. (YA). 8.00 (978-0-7567-9038-7(7)) DIANE Publishing Co.

Krulik, Nancy E. & Ladybird Books Staff. Cloe: Angel with Attitude! 2003. (Bratz Ser.). (Illus.). 32p. pap. 2.99 (978-1-84422-186-8(5) , Putnam Juvenile) Penguin Group (USA) Inc.

Kyi, Tanya Lloyd. The Blue Jean Book: The Story Behind the Seams. 2005. (Illus.). 79p. (J). (gr. 7-12). 24.95 (978-1-55037-917-4(8)); pap. 12.95 (978-1-55037-916-7(X)) Annick Pr., Ltd. CAN. *Dist:* Firefly Bks., Ltd.

Lattimore, Deborah Nourse. I Wonder What's under There? A Brief History of Underwear: A Lift-the-Flap Book. Carter, David A., illus. 2000. 21p. (YA). (gr. 7-9). reprint ed. 16.00 (978-0-7881-9080-3(6)) DIANE Publishing Co.

Learn to Tie Shoelaces. 2003. (Illus.). (J). bds. 4.98 (978-1-4054-1146-2(5)) Parragon, Inc.

Lee, Penny. What Should I Wear? Individual Title Six-Pack Pouch - Level C. (Lighthouse Ser.). 12p. (gr. k-1). 24.00 (978-0-7578-0823-4(9)) Rigby Education.

L'Hommedieu, Arthur John. From Plant to Blue Jeans. 1998. (Changes Ser.). (Illus.). 32p. (J). (gr. 2-3). pap. 6.95 (978-0-516-20366-9(5) , Children's Pr.) Scholastic Library Publishing.

—From Plant to Blue Jeans. 1998. (gr. 3-6). lib. bdg. 15.25 (978-0-613-89022-9(1)) Tandem Library Bks.

Lloyd, Sam. What Color Is Your Underwear? 2004. (Illus.). 16p. (J). pap. 8.99 (978-0-439-57676-5(8) , Cartwheel Bks.) Scholastic, Inc.

Lomas, Clare. The 80s & 90s: Power Dressing to Sportswear. 1999. (Twentieth Century Fashion Ser.). (Illus.). 32p. (J). (gr. 5 up). lib. bdg. 26.00 (978-0-8368-2603-6(5)) Stevens, Gareth Inc.

Look at Me! Individual Title Six-Pack Pouch - Level B. (Lighthouse Ser.). 12p. (gr. k-1). 24.00 (978-0-7578-0811-1(5)) Rigby Education.

Look at Me! KinderWords Individual Title, 6 Packs. (Kinderstarters Ser.). 8p. (ps-1). 21.00 (978-0-7635-8704-8(4)) Rigby Education.

Lorenz Editors. Clothes: With over 50 Reusable Stickers. 2001. (Sticker Fun Ser.). (Illus.). 16p. pap. 2.95 (978-0-7548-0845-9(9) , Lorenz Bks.) Anness Publishing, Inc.

Lundsten, Apryl. The Girls' Life Guide to Being a Style Superstar! Parett, Lisa, illus. 2004. 124p. (J). (978-0-439-44984-7(7)) Scholastic, Inc.

MacDonald, Fiona. Clothing & Jewelry. (Discovering World Cultures Ser.). (Illus.). 40p. (J). (gr. 4). 2001. pap. (978-0-7787-0246-7(4)); 2000. lib. bdg. (978-0-7787-0236-8(7)) Crabtree Publishing Co.

—Clothing & Jewelry. 2001. (gr. 3-6). lib. bdg. 17.60 (978-0-613-32413-7(7)) Tandem Library Bks.

Maggio, Viqui. Baby Tease. 2007. 16p. bds. 10.00 (***978-1-933572-08-6(6))** Centro Bks., LLC.

Mahren, Sue. Make Your Own Teddy Bears & Bear Clothes. Jaskiel, Stan, illus. 2000. (Quick Starts for Kids! Ser.). 64p. (YA). (gr. 3 up). pap. 8.95 (978-1-885593-75-7(9) , Williamson Bks.) Ideals Pubns.

—Make Your Own Teddy Bears & Bear Clothes. 2001. (gr. 3-6). lib. bdg. 16.40 (978-0-613-57610-9(1)) Tandem Library Bks.

Masters, Nancy Robinson. Jeans. 2008. (J). lib. bdg. 25.26 (***978-1-60279-029-2(9))** Cherry Lake Publishing.

Mayer, Cassie. Ropa. 2007. (J). (***978-1-4329-0447-0(7)); pap. (*978-1-4329-0456-2(6))** Heinemann Library.

McDonald, Fiona. Shoes & Boots Through History. 2006. (Illus.). 32p. (J). lib. bdg. (978-0-8368-6857-9(9)) Stevens, Gareth Inc.

—Uniforms Through History. 2006. (Illus.). 32p. (J). lib. bdg. (978-0-8368-6858-6(7)) Stevens, Gareth Inc.

McGraw-Hill Staff & Weber, Jeanette. Clothing: Fashion, Fabrics & Construction, 2 vols. 4th ed. 2002. 630p. (gr. 9-12). stu. ed. 59.96 (978-0-07-829006-0(6) , 9780078290060) Glencoe/McGraw-Hill.

Mee, Sue. 1900-1920: Linen & Lace. 1999. (Twentieth Century Fashion Ser.). (Illus.). 32p. (J). (gr. 5 up). lib. bdg. 26.00 (978-0-8368-2598-5(5)) Stevens, Gareth Inc.

Mitchell, Alycen. The Performing Arts. 2003. (Twentieth-Century Developments in Fashion & Costume Ser.). (Illus.). 64p. (J). (gr. 7 up). lib. bdg. (978-1-59084-426-7(2)) Mason Crest Pubs.

Mitzo Thompson, Kim. What Should I Wear? / ¿Como me Visto? 2006. (Dual Language Readers Ser.). 32p. (J). pap. 4.99 (978-0-7696-4626-8(3)) School Specialty Publishing.

Moore, Willamarie. StarFestival Grades 7-9 Food & Clothing Team: Exploring Cultural Heritage. Miyagawa, Shigeru, ed. 2000. (Illus.). 47p. (YA). (gr. 7-11). pap., stu. ed., wbk. ed. 10.00 (978-1-929724-08-6(X)) StarFestival, Inc.

Morris, Ting. Ancient Greece. 2006. (Arts & Crafts of Ser.). (Illus.). 32p. (J). (978-1-58340-912-1(2) , 1262692) Smart Apple Media.

Muehlenhardt, Amy Bailey. Drawing & Learning about Fashion: Using Shapes & Lines. Muehlenhardt, Amy Bailey, illus. 2005. (Sketch It! Ser.). (Illus.). 24p. (J). (ps-k). lib. bdg. 22.60 (978-1-4048-1191-1(5) , 1243855) Picture Window Bks.

Murphy. A Pair of Socks: Matching Big Book. 2002. (Illus.). pap. (978-0-7398-6776-1(8)) Steck-Vaughn.

Murray, Julie. Sheep to Sweater. 2007. (Illus.). 24p. (J). 21.35 (978-1-59679-914-1(5) , Buddy Bks.) ABDO Publishing Co.

My Clothes: Kindergarten Newcomer Books. (On Our Way to English Ser.). (gr. k up). 23.50 (978-0-7578-7192-4(5)) Rigby Education.

My Dolly Dressing Book of Ballerinas. 2002. 16p. (J). pap. 2.98 (978-0-7525-8042-5(6)) Parragon, Inc.

My Dolly Dressing Book of Fairies. 2002. 16p. (J). pap. 2.98 (978-0-7525-8043-2(4)) Parragon, Inc.

My Dolly Dressing Book of Party Girls. 2002. 16p. (J). pap. 2.98 (978-0-7525-8044-9(2)) Parragon, Inc.

My Dolly Dressing Book of Princesses. 2002. 16p. (J). pap. 2.98 (978-0-7525-8045-6(0)) Parragon, Inc.

Nelson, Angela, creator. Lang-O-Learn: Clothing Cards. 2001. (SPA, FRE, GER, ITA & RUS.). (J). 9.95 (978-0-9668008-5-2(0)) Stages Learning Materials.

Nelson, Robin. Clothing. 2003. (First Step Nonfiction Ser.). (Illus.). 8p. (J). pap. 3.95 (978-0-8225-3927-8(6) , Lerner Pubns.) Lerner Publishing Group.

Novell, Cappi. Barbie Magnetic Fashions: Book & Playset. 2005. (Barbie Magnet Kit Ser.). (Illus.). 16p. (J). bds. 14.99 (978-0-7944-0673-8(4)) Reader's Digest Assn., Inc., The.

O'Brien, Joan. Fashion Accessories Stickers. 2003. (Illus.). 4p. 1.50 (978-0-486-43071-3(5)) Dover Pubns., Inc.

Olson, Nathan. Levi Strauss & Blue Jeans. 2007. (Graphic Library). (Illus.). 32p. (J). (***978-0-7368-9646-7(5))** Capstone Pr., Inc.

—Levi Strauss & Blue Jeans. Miller, Phil & Barnett, Charles, illus. 2007. (Graphic Library). 32p. (J). 25.26 (978-0-7368-6484-8(9)) Capstone Pr., Inc.

Parks, Peggy J. Clothing. 2005. (Yesterday & Today Ser.). (Illus.). 32p. (J). (ps-7). lib. bdg. 23.70 (978-1-56711-828-5(3) , Blackbirch Pr., Inc.) Thomson Gale.

Parr, Todd. Underwear Do's & Don'ts. 2004. (Illus.). 24p. (J). (ps-ps). bds. 6.99 (978-0-316-90806-1(1)) Little, Brown Bks. for Young Readers.

Party Clothes. 2004. (J). (978-1-58453-279-8(3)) Pioneer Valley Educational Pr., Inc.

Patteson, Nelda. Adina de Zavala: "Angel of the Alamo" Her Life Story Presented Through the Clothes She Wore. Patteson, Nelda, illus. 2003. (Women of Texas Ser.: Vol. 3). Orig. Title: Angel of the Alamo. (Illus.). 32p. (J). (gr. 4-8). pap. 14.95 (978-0-9629001-2-9(5)) Smiley Co.

Peacock, John. The Story of Costume. 2006. (Illus.). 48p. 19.95 (978-0-500-51309-5(0)) Thames & Hudson.

Perham, Molly. Customize Your Clothes. Perham, Molly, ed. 2008. (Illus.). 64p. 12.99 (***978-0-7548-1745-1(8)*** , Lorenz Bks.) Anness Publishing GBR. *Dist:* National Bk. Network.

Petelinsek, Kathleen & Primm, E. Russell. Clothes/Ropa. 2006. (Talking Hands Ser.). (ENG & SPA., Illus.). 24p. (J). 21.36 (978-1-59296-680-6(2)) Child's World, Inc.

Powe-Temperley, Kitty. The 60s: Mods & Hippies. 1999. (Twentieth Century Fashion Ser.). (Illus.). 32p. (J). (gr. 5 up). lib. bdg. 26.00 (978-0-8368-2601-2(9)) Stevens, Gareth Inc.

Priddy, Roger. Rattle Cloth Book Words. 2005. (Illus.). 8p. (J). (ps-ps). 6.95 (978-0-312-49451-3(3) , Priddy Bks.) St. Martin's Pr.

Primm III, E. Russell. En el Trabajo. 2006. (Talking Hands Ser.).Tr. of At Work. (ENG & SPA., Illus.). 24p. (J). (ps). 21.36 (978-1-59296-451-2(6)) Child's World, Inc.

Rau, Dana Meachen. Athletic Shoes. 2008. (J). lib. bdg. 25.26 (***978-1-60279-027-8(2)***) Cherry Lake Publishing.

Rau, Dana Meachen. Clothing in American History. 2006. (Illus.). 24p. (J). pap. (978-0-8368-7212-5(6)); lib. bdg. (978-0-8368-7205-7(3)) Stevens, Gareth Inc.

Rayner, Amanda. What We Wear. 2005. (Illus.). 30p. (J). (gr. 3-7). lib. bdg. 27.10 (978-1-58340-694-6(8)) Smart Apple Media.

Ready to Wear. (Totally Girls Ser.). 16p. (J). (978-2-7643-0187-6(1)) Phidal Publishing, Inc./Editions Phidal, Inc.

Reed, Janet. Clases de Ropa. 2005. Tr. of All Kinds of Clothes. (SPA., Illus.). 16p. (J). (gr. 1 up). lib. bdg. 15.93 (978-0-7368-4141-2(5)) Capstone Pr., Inc.

Reynolds, Helen. Coats & Pants. 2003. (Fashionable History of Costume Ser.). (Illus.). 32p. (J). 25.70 (978-1-4109-0032-6(0)) Raintree.

—Dresses & Skirts. 2003. (Fashionable History of Costume Ser.). (Illus.). 32p. (J). lib. bdg. 25.70 (978-1-4109-0031-9(2)) Raintree.

—Jewelry & Accessories. 2003. (Fashionable History of Costume Ser.). (Illus.). 32p. (J). lib. bdg. 25.70 (978-1-4109-0029-6(0)) Raintree.

—The 40s & 50s: Utility to New Look. 1999. (Twentieth Century Fashion Ser.). (Illus.). 32p. (J). (gr. 5 up). lib. bdg. 26.00 (978-0-8368-2600-5(0)) Stevens, Gareth Inc.

Richards, Jon. Clothes. 2005. (Illus.). 32p. (J). (gr. 3 up). lib. bdg. 27.10 (978-1-59389-195-4(4)) Chrysalis Education.

Ridley, Sarah. A Cotton T-Shirt. 2006. (Illus.). 32p. (J). lib. bdg. 23.33 (978-0-8368-6294-2(5)) Stevens, Gareth Inc.

Rinaldo, Luana. Heads & Toes: Let's Dress up & Play! 2003. (Illus.). 6p. (J). 6.95 (978-1-4027-0502-1(6)) Sterling Publishing Co., Inc.

—Heads & Toes: Let's Dress up for a Party! 2003. (Illus.). 6p. (J). 6.95 (978-1-4027-0503-8(4)) Sterling Publishing Co., Inc.

Rooney, Anne. The Eighteenth Century. Woolf, Alex, ed. 2005. (History of Fashion & Costume Ser.). (Illus.). 64p. (J). (gr. 6-12). 35.00 (978-0-8160-5948-5(9)) Facts On File, Inc.

Rosa-Mendoza, Gladys. My Clothes/Mi Ropa. Abello, Patricia & Weber, Amy, eds. Collier, Mary, illus. 2005. (#1 Bilingual Board Book Ser.). (SPA & ENG.). 20p. (J). (ps). bds. 6.95 (978-1-931398-15-2(1)) Me+Mi Publishing.

Royston, Angela. How Is a T-Shirt Made? 2005. (How Are Things Made? Ser.). pap. (978-0-431-46645-3(9)); lib. bdg. (978-0-431-46638-5(6)) Heinemann Library.

—T-Shirt. 2005. (How Are Things Made? Ser.). (Illus.). 32p. (978-0-431-05049-2(X)); pap. (978-0-431-05056-0(2)) Heinemann Library.

Running Press Staff. Dress Up: Pull the Tabs! Change the Pictures! Bottled Lightning Staff, ed. 2004. (Magic Windows Ser.). (Illus.). 8p. (J). pap. 4.95 (978-0-7624-1703-2(X) , Running Pr. Kids) Running Pr. Bk. Pubs.

Running Press Staff & Mann, Holly. Dress Up: Pull the Tabs! Change the Pictures! 2004. (Magic Windows Ser.). (Illus.). 8p. (J). (ps-k). pap. 4.95 (978-0-7624-1702-5(1) , Running Pr. Kids) Running Pr. Bk. Pubs.

Salas, Laura Purdie. Whose Coat Is This? A Look at How Workers Cover Up—Jackets, Smocks, & Robes. Muehlenhardt, Amy Bailey, illus. 2006. (Whose Is It? Ser.). 24p. (J). (ps-2). 22.60 (978-1-4048-1598-8(8)) Picture Window Bks.

—Whose Shoes Are These? A Look at Workers' Footwear—Slippers, Sneakers, & Boots. Muehlenhardt, Amy Bailey, illus. 2006. (Whose Is It? Ser.). 24p. (J). (ps-2). 22.60 (978-1-4048-1601-5(1) , 1253204) Picture Window Bks.

Saunders-Smith, Gail. Warm Clothes. 1998. (J). pap. 13.25 (978-0-516-21249-4(4) , Children's Pr.) Scholastic Library Publishing.

Scott, Janine. Let's Get Dressed: What People Wear. 2002. (Spyglass Books). (Illus.). 24p. (J). (gr. 1 up). lib. bdg. 18.60 (978-0-7565-0366-6(3)) Compass Point Bks.

Sessler, Peter & Sessler, N. Indy Cars. 1999. (Off to the Races Ser.). (Illus.). 24p. (J). (gr. 2-6). lib. bdg. 25.64 (978-1-57103-281-2(9)) Rourke Publishing, LLC.

Shaskin, Kathy. How Underwear Got under There: A Brief History. Dunnick, Regan, illus. 2007. 48p. (J). (gr. 2-5). 16.99 (978-0-525-47178-3(2) , Dutton Juvenile) Penguin Group (USA) Inc.

Sills, Leslie. From Rags to Riches: A History of Girls' Clothing in America. (Illus.). 48p. (J). 16.95 (978-0-8234-1708-7(5)); (YA). (gr. 5 up). pap. 6.95 (***978-0-8234-2048-3(5)***) Holiday Hse., Inc.

Skinner, Tina. Fashionable Clothing from the Sears Catalogs, Mid-1940s. 2003. (Schiffer Book for Collectors Ser.). (Illus.). 160p. (gr. 10-13). pap. 29.95 (978-0-7643-1858-0(6)) Schiffer Publishing, Ltd.

Smith, Alastair. Clothes & Fashion Then & Now. 2004. (Usborne Flip Flaps Ser.). (SPA., Illus.). 16p. (J). (gr. 2 up). pap. 7.95 (978-0-7460-3098-1(3)) EDC Publishing.

Steele, Philip. The Nineteenth Century. 2005. (History of Fashion & Costume Ser.). (Illus.). 64p. (J). (gr. 6-12). 35.00 (978-0-8160-5950-8(0)) Facts On File, Inc.

Sun, Ming-Ju. Japanese Fashions. 1999. (Dover Coloring Bks.). (Illus.). 48p. (J). pap. 3.95 (978-0-486-40569-8(9)) Dover Pubns., Inc.

Tanaka, Rin. Motorcycle Jackets: Ultimate Biker's Fashions. 2003. (Schiffer Book for Collectors Ser.). (Illus.). 304p. (gr. 10-13). 69.95 (978-0-7643-1849-8(7)) Schiffer Publishing, Ltd.

Tejidos. (One Hundred One Things to Do Ser.). (SPA.). (J). (gr. 3-5). pap. 4.76 (978-950-724-207-6(4)) Lumen ARG. *Dist:* Lectorum Pubns., Inc.

Tejidos. (Vamos a Crear Ser.). (SPA., Illus.). (J). 12.00 (978-84-342-2284-7(1)) Parramon Ediciones S.A. ESP. *Dist:* Distribuidora Norma, Inc., Lectorum Pubns., Inc.

Then & Now, 6 Pack. (Discovery World Ser.). 16p. (gr. 1-2). 28.00 (978-0-7635-8463-4(0)) Rigby Education.

Thomson, Ruth. Clothes. 2006. (Illus.). 29p. (978-1-58340-939-8(4)) Smart Apple Media.

Tierney, Tom. Late Victorian & Edwardian Fashions. 2005. (Illus.). 32p. (gr. 3). pap. 3.95 (978-0-486-44458-1(9)) Dover Pubns., Inc.

Top That Publishing Staff, ed. Dressing up Fun. 2006. (Illus.). 16p. (978-1-84666-013-9(0)) Top That! Publishing PLC.

Tuxworth, Nicola. Clothes. 2001. (Very First Picture Bks.). (Illus.). 20p. 5.95 (978-0-7548-0939-5(0)) Anness Publishing GBR. *Dist:* National Bk. Network.

—Learn-a-Word Picture Books: Clothes, 12 vols. 2006. (Learn-A-Word Picture Bks.). (Illus.). 12p. bds. 6.99 (978-0-7548-1458-0(0) , Lorenz Bks.) Anness Publishing GBR. *Dist:* National Bk. Network.

Tuxworth, Nicola & Lorenz Editors. Clothes. 2002. (Let's Look at Board Bks.). (Illus.). 20p. (ps-3). 5.95 (978-0-7548-1029-2(1) , Lorenz Bks.) Anness Publishing GBR. *Dist:* National Bk. Network.

Ventura, Piero. Clothing: Garments, Styles & Uses. Ventura, Piero, illus. 2000. (Illus.). 64p. (YA). reprint ed. 17.00 (978-0-7881-6952-6(1)) DIANE Publishing Co.

Vize, Dania. Look at Me! I Can Be... (Blue) 2006. (Illus.). 12p. (J). (ps-k). bds. 7.95 (978-1-84610-286-8(3)) Make Believe Ideas GBR. *Dist:* Ingram Pub. Services.

—Look at Me! I Can Be... (Pink) 2006. (Illus.). 12p. (J). (ps-k). bds. 7.95 (978-1-84610-287-5(1)) Make Believe Ideas GBR. *Dist:* Ingram Pub. Services.

—My Dress up Book. 2005. (Illus.). 12p. (J). (ps-3). per., bds. 9.95 (978-1-905051-36-6(0)) Make Believe Ideas GBR. *Dist:* Ingram Pub. Services.

Walker, Nicki. The Milliner. Bedell, Barbara, illus. 2001. (Colonial People Ser.). 32p. (J). (gr. 3). (978-0-7787-0745-5(8)); pap. (978-0-7787-0791-2(1)) Crabtree Publishing Co.

Warrick, Leanne. Style Trix for Cool Chix: The One-Stop Guide to Finding Your Perfect Look. 2005. (Illus.). 96p. (J). pap. 9.95 (978-0-8230-4940-0(X)) Watson-Guptill Pubns., Inc.

Watson, Linda. Designers A-F. 2000. (Vogue 20th Century Fashion Ser.). (Illus.). (YA). 24.95 (978-0-7910-6194-7(9) , Chelsea Hse.) Facts On File, Inc.

—Designers G-M. 2000. (Vogue 20th Century Fashion Ser.). (Illus.). (YA). 24.95 (978-0-7910-6195-4(7) , Chelsea Hse.) Facts On File, Inc.

—Designers N-Z. 2000. (Vogue 20th Century Fashion Ser.). (Illus.). (J). 24.95 (978-0-7910-6196-1(5) , Chelsea Hse.) Facts On File, Inc.

—Fashions 1900-1949. 2000. (Vogue 20th Century Fashion Ser.). (Illus.). (J). 24.99 (978-0-7910-6192-3(2) , Chelsea Hse.) Facts On File, Inc.

—Fashions 1950-2000. 2000. (Vogue 20th Century Fashion Ser.). (YA). 24.95 (978-0-7910-6193-0(0) , Chelsea Hse.) Facts On File, Inc.

Weaver, Janice. From Head to Toe: Bound Feet, Bathing Suits, & Other Bizarre & Beautiful Things. Blake, Francis, illus. 2003. 80p. (J). (gr. 5-9). pap. 16.95 (978-0-88776-654-1(4)) Tundra Bks., Inc./Livres Toundra, Inc. CAN. *Dist:* Random Hse., Inc.

Weekly Reader Early Learning Library (Firm) Staff, contrib. by. Things I Wear. 2006. (Things in My World Ser.). (Illus.). 16p. (J). pap. (978-0-8368-6819-7(6)); lib. bdg. (978-0-8368-6812-8(9)) Stevens, Gareth Inc.

—Things I Wear: Las Cosas Que Me Pongo. 2006. (ENG & SPA., Illus.). 16p. (J). pap. (978-0-8368-7231-6(2)); lib. bdg. (978-0-8368-7224-8(X)) Stevens, Gareth Inc. (Weekly Reader Early Learning Library).

What I Like to Wear, 6 Pack. (ps-2). 23.00 (978-0-7635-9016-1(9)) Rigby Education.

Whitty, Helen. Accessories & Adornment. 2001. (Clothing Ser.). (Illus.). 32p. (J). (gr. 4 up). 22.95 (978-0-7910-6573-0(1) , 010401, Chelsea Hse.) Facts On File, Inc.

—Clothing Series, 6 bks. Incl. Accessories & Adornment. 22.95 (978-0-7910-6573-0(1) , 010401); Dressing Up. 22.95 (978-0-7910-6576-1(6) , 010402); Hats, Gloves & Footwear. 22.95 (978-0-7910-6572-3(3) , 010403); Protective Clothing. 22.95 (978-0-7910-6574-7(X) , 010404); Underwear. 22.95 (978-0-7910-6575-4(8) , 010405); You Are What You Wear. 22.95 (978-0-7910-6577-8(4) , 010405); (J). (gr. 4 up). 2001. (Illus.). 32p. 2005. Set pap. 137.70 (978-0-7910-6571-6(5) , 010400S, Chelsea Hse.) Facts On File, Inc.

—Hats, Gloves & Footwear. 2001. (Clothing Ser.). (Illus.). 32p. (J). (gr. 4 up). 22.95 (978-0-7910-6572-3(3) , 010403, Chelsea Hse.) Facts On File, Inc.

—Protective Clothing. 2001. (Clothing Ser.). (Illus.). 32p. (J). (gr. 4 up). 22.95 (978-0-7910-6574-7(X) , 010404, Chelsea Hse.) Facts On File, Inc.

—Underwear. 2001. (Clothing Ser.). (Illus.). 32p. (J). (gr. 4 up). 22.95 (978-0-7910-6575-4(8) , 010405, Chelsea Hse.) Facts On File, Inc.

—You Are What You Wear. 2001. (Clothing Ser.). (Illus.). 32p. (J). (gr. 4 up). 22.95 (978-0-7910-6577-8(4) , 010405, Chelsea Hse.) Facts On File, Inc.

Wilkes, Angela. Dazzling Disguises & Clever Costumes. 2006. (Illus.). 48p. (J). pap. 6.99 (978-0-7566-1935-0(1)) Dorling Kindersley Publishing, Inc.

Williamson, Froser, illus. My Clothes: Individual Title Six-Packs. (Sails Literacy Ser.). 16p. (gr. k up). 27.00 (978-0-7635-4392-1(6)) Rigby Education.

Windsor, Jo. Look at Me! Emergent Level Satellite Individual Title Six-Packs. Gunson, Dave, illus. (Sails Literacy Ser.). (gr. k-1). 27.00 (978-0-7578-7911-1(X)) Rigby Education.

Ziefert, Harriet. Bear Gets Dressed: A Guessing Game Story. Capucilli, Alyssa, illus. 2004. 16p. (J). 9.95 (978-1-4027-1705-5(9)) Sterling Publishing Co., Inc.

Zimmermann, Dottie, creator. Interactive Sing-along Big Books Dress Me Bear. 2007. (J). spiral bd. (***978-1-58650-716-9(8)***) Super Duper Pubns.

20th Century Fashion, 6 bks. Incl. 20s & 30s : Flappers & Vamps. Blackman, Cally. lib. bdg. 26.00 (978-0-8368-2599-2(3)); 40s & 50s : Utility to New Look. Reynolds, Helen. lib. bdg. 26.00 (978-0-8368-2600-5(0)); 60s : Mods & Hippies. Powe-Temperley, Kitty. lib. bdg. 26.00 (978-0-8368-2601-2(9)); 70s : Punks, Glam Rockers & New Romantics. Gilmour, Sarah. lib. bdg. 26.00 (978-0-8368-2602-9(7)); 80s & 90s : Power Dressing to Sportswear. Lomas, Clare. lib. bdg. 26.00 (978-0-8368-2603-6(5)); 1900-1920 : Linen & Lace. Mee, Sue. lib. bdg. 26.00 (978-0-8368-2598-5(5)); 32p. (J). (gr. 5 up). (Illus.). 1999. Set lib. bdg. 104.00 (978-0-8368-2597-8(7)) Stevens, Gareth Inc.

CLOTHING AND DRESS—FICTION

Abdel-Fattah, Randa. Does My Head Look Big in This? 2007. 368p. (J). (gr. 7 up). pap. 16.99 (***978-0-439-91947-0(9)*** , Orchard Bks.) Scholastic, Inc.

Adams-Crymes, Phyllis. Mr. McGinnis's New Shoes. Hardbound, Inc., Staff, ed. Redel, Nicole, illus. 2000. (Children's Diary Ser.: Vol. 1). 27p. (J). 17.00 (978-1-930659-01-8(6)) Adams-Crymes, Phyllis.

Akira, Shouko & Toriyama, Akira. Dr. Slump. 2005. (Dr. Slump Ser.: Vol. 3). 200p. (YA). pap. 7.99 (978-1-59116-991-8(7)) Viz Media.

Alarcon, Pedro Antonio de. The Three-Cornered Hat & Captain Poison: A Dual Language Book. Appelbaum, Stanley, ed. 2002. (Dual-Language Bks.). (SPA & ENG.). 271p. pap. 11.95 (978-0-486-41943-5(6)) Dover Pubns., Inc.

Alford, Douglas J. Cozy Clozy. 2006. (J). 25.00 (978-1-933589-95-4(7)) Scripture Mastery Resources!.

Allan, Nicholas. The Queen's Knickers. 2000. (Illus.). 32p. (J). pap. 9.99 (978-0-09-941314-1(0)) Random Hse. GBR. *Dist:* Independent Pubs. Group.

Andersen, Hans Christian. The Emperor's New Clothes. 2005. 12p. pap. (978-958-30-1782-7(5)) Panamericana Editorial.

—The Emperor's New Clothes. Burton, Virginia Lee, illus. 2004. 48p. (J). (gr. k-3). tchr. ed. 16.00 (978-0-618-34421-5(7)); pap. 6.95 (978-0-618-34420-8(9)) Houghton Mifflin Co. Trade & Reference Div.

—The Emperor's New Clothes. Hall, Francois, illus. 2006. (First Fairy Tales Ser.). 30p. (J). (978-1-59771-071-8(7) , 1262700) Sea-To-Sea Pubns.

—El Traje Nuevo del Emperador. (SPA., Illus.). 48p. (J). (gr. 3-5). (978-84-241-5527-8(0) , EV0621); 4th ed. 2003. 32p. (978-84-241-5520-9(3) , EV0649) Everest de Ediciones y Distribucion, S.L. ESP. *Dist:* Lectorum Pubns., Inc.

—El Traje Nuevo del Emperador. (SPA.). 64p. (J). 9.50 (978-84-207-3349-4(0)) Grupo Anaya, S.A. ESP. *Dist:* AIMS International Bks., Inc.

Anderson, Joseph P., illus. Loop, Swoop, & Pull! 2006. (Read-It! Readers Ser.). 24p. (J). (ps-3). 18.60 (978-1-4048-1611-4(9)) Picture Window Bks.

Anholt, Catherine & Anholt, Laurence. Chimp & Zee's Clothes. 2007. (Chimp & Zee Ser.). (Illus.). 22p. (J). bds. 3.95 (***978-1-84507-729-7(6)***) Lincoln, Frances Ltd. GBR. *Dist:* Perseus Distribution.

Anholt, Laurence. The Emperor's New Underwear. Robins, Arthur, illus. 1999. (J). pap. (978-0-88166-347-1(6)) Meadowbrook Pr.

Arciniegas, Triunfo. La Verdadera Historia del Gato con Botas. (SPA.). (J). 8.95 (978-958-04-7348-0(X)) Norma S.A. COL. *Dist:* Distribuidora Norma, Inc.

Arnold, Tedd. Huggly Gets Dressed. 1998. (Monster under the Bed Ser.). (Illus.). 24p. (J). (gr. k-2). pap. 8.95 (978-0-590-91819-0(2) , Cartwheel Bks.) Scholastic, Inc.

Ashley, Bernard. That's the One! 2007. (J). lib. bdg. 16.95 (***978-1-59566-370-2(3)***) QEB Publishing Inc.

Avery, Kristin. La Colcha de Retazos, Level 3. Ada, Alma Flor, tr. McPhail, David M., illus. 2003. (Dejame Leer Ser.). (SPA.). 16p. (J). (ps-3). 6.50 (978-0-673-36303-9(1) , Good Year Bks.) Celebration Pr.

Bae, Hyun-Joo. New Clothes for New Year's Day. Bae, Hyun-Joo, illus. 2007. (Illus.). 32p. (J). 15.95 (978-1-933605-29-6(4) , 05296) Kane/Miller Bk. Pubs., Inc.

Bartels, Korin. A Secret in My Shoes. l.t. ed. 2005. (Illus.). 20p. (J). per. 10.00 (978-1-59879-031-3(5)) Lifevest Publishing, Inc.

Beardshaw, Rosalind. I am a Spaceman! 2008. (Illus.). 12p. (J). bds. 12.95 (***978-1-4052-2759-1(1)***) Egmont Bks., Ltd. GBR. *Dist:* Independent Pubs. Group.

Beardshaw, Rosalind, illus. I am a Princess! 2008. 12p. (J). bds. 12.95 (***978-1-4052-2758-2(3)***) Egmont Bks., Ltd. GBR. *Dist:* Independent Pubs. Group.

Beaton, Clare, illus. Daisy Gets Dressed. 2005. 24p. (J). 15.99 (978-1-84148-794-6(5)) Barefoot Bks., Inc.

Bechtold, Lisze. Sally & the Purple Socks. Bechtold, Lisze, illus. 2008. 32p. (J). (ps). 15.99 (***978-0-399-24734-7(3)*** , Philomel) Penguin Group (USA) Inc.

Beinstein, Phoebe. All Dressed Up! A Lift-the-Flap Book. Savitsky, Steven, illus. 2005. (Dora the Explorer Ser.). 14p. (J). 6.99 (978-0-689-87718-6(8) , Simon Spotlight/ Nickelodeon) Simon & Schuster Children's Publishing.

Benchmark Education Staff, compiled by. Measuring. 2006. spiral bd. 99.00 (***978-1-4108-7090-2(1)***) Benchmark Education Co.

Bentley, Dawn. Fuzzy Bear: A Getting Dressed Book. Nagy, Krisztina, illus. 1998. (Fuzzy Bear Ser.). 10p. (J). (ps-k). 10.95 (978-1-58117-011-5(4) , Intervisual/Piggy Toes) Dalmatian Pr.

Benton, Jim. My Pants Are Haunted! 2004. (Dear Dumb Diary Ser.: Bk. 2). (Illus.). 144p. (gr. 4 up). mass mkt. 4.99 (978-0-439-62905-8(5) , Scholastic Paperbacks) Scholastic, Inc.

Berenstain, Stan & Berenstain, Jan. The Berenstain Bears & the Dress Code. Berenstain, Stan & Berenstain, Jan, illus. 2002. (Berenstain Bears Big Chapter Bks.). (Illus.). (J). 11.91 (978-0-7587-0444-3(5)) Book Wholesalers, Inc.

Billstrom, Diane. You Can't Go to School Naked! Kilpatrick III, Don, illus. 2008. 32p. (J). (ps-k). 16.99 (***978-0-399-24738-5(6)*** , Putnam Juvenile) Penguin Group (USA) Inc.

Bingham, Deanne Lee. Andrew's Magnificent Mountain of Mittens. La Fave, Kim, illus. (First Flight Ser.). 46p. (J). (gr. 2-4). 1999. pap. (978-1-55041-389-2(9)); 1998. (978-1-55041-397-7(X)) Fitzhenry & Whiteside, Ltd.

Blackaby, Susan. New to Drew. Yi, Hye Won, illus. 2006. (Read-It! Readers Ser.). (J). 19.93 (978-1-4048-2417-1(0)) Picture Window Bks.

—Tricky Twins. Epstein, Len, illus. 2006. (Read-It! Readers Ser.). (J). 19.93 (978-1-4048-2419-5(7)) Picture Window Bks.

—Winter Fun for Kat. Collier-Morales, Roberta, illus. 2005. (Read-It! Readers Ser.). 32p. (J). (gr. k-3). 18.60 (978-1-4048-1007-5(2)) Picture Window Bks.

Blankenship, LeeAnn. Mr. Tuggle's Trouble. Dugan, Karen, illus. 2005. 28p. (J). (ps-3). 15.95 (978-1-59078-196-8(1)) Boyds Mills Pr.

Bobs neue Stiefel. pap. 12.95 (978-3-89748-674-4(1)) Dino Entertainment AG DEU. *Dist:* Distribooks, Inc.

Bockol, Leslie. Tie your shoes rocket Style. 2007. 10p. (J). 9.95 (***978-1-59764-292-7(4)***) New Line Bks.

Boelts, Maribeth. Those Shoes. Jones, Noah Z., illus. 2007. 40p. (J). (gr. k-3). 15.99 (***978-0-7636-2499-6(3)***) Candlewick Pr.

Bonnell, Kris. Dad's Favorite Tie. 2005. (J). 3.75 (978-1-933727-03-5(9)) Reading Reading Bks., LLC.

—Socks. 2005. (J). 3.75 (978-1-933727-15-8(2)) Reading Reading Bks., LLC.

Bos, Maarten. Webster's Wardrobe. 1998. (Illus.). 20p. (J). (ps-k). pap. 8.95 (978-0-531-30097-8(8) , Orchard Bks.) Scholastic, Inc.

Boswall, Nigel. Jerry's Trousers. Melling, David, illus. 2003. 26p. (J). pap. 4.99 (978-0-333-68359-0(5)) Macmillan Publishers Ltd. GBR. *Dist:* Trafalgar Square Publishing.

Boynton, Sandra. Azul el Sombrero, Verde el Sombrero. Boynton, Sandra, illus. 2003. Tr. of Blue Hat, Green Hat. (SPA., Illus.). 14p. (J). bds. 5.99 (978-0-689-86304-2(7) , Libros Para Ninos) Simon & Schuster Children's Publishing.

—Blue Hat, Green Hat. 2001. (Illus.). 8p. (J). bds. 4.99 (978-0-689-83625-1(2) , Simon & Schuster Children's Publishing) Simon & Schuster Children's Publishing.

Brashares, Ann. Forever in Blue: The Fourth Summer of the Sisterhood. 2008. (Sisterhood of Traveling Pants Ser.). 416p. (YA). (gr. 7). pap. 9.99 (***978-0-385-73401-1(8)*** , Delacorte Bks. for Young Readers) Random Hse. Children's Bks.

—Girls in Pants. 2006. (Sisterhood of Traveling Pants Ser.: Bk. 3). 368p. (YA). (gr. 7 up). reprint ed. pap. 8.95 (978-0-553-37593-0(8) , Delacorte Bks. for Young Readers) Random Hse. Children's Bks.

—Girls in Pants: The Third Summer of the Sisterhood. (Sisterhood of Traveling Pants Ser.: Bk. 3). (YA). (gr. 7 up). 2007. 416p. mass mkt. 6.99 (***978-0-553-49504-1(6)*** , Dell Books for Young Readers); 2005. 352p. 16.95 (978-0-385-72935-2(9) , Delacorte Bks. for Young Readers); 2005. 352p. lib. bdg. 18.99 (978-0-385-90919-8(5) , Delacorte Bks. for Young Readers) Random Hse. Children's Bks.

—Girls in Pants: The Third Summer of the Sisterhood. l.t. ed. 2005. (Sisterhood of Traveling Pants Ser. : Bk. 3). 405p. (YA). 23.95 (978-0-7862-7264-8(3) , Large Print Pr.) Thorndike Pr.

—The Second Summer of the Sisterhood. 2003. (Sisterhood of Traveling Pants Ser.: Bk. 2). 400p. (YA). (gr. 7 up). 15.95 (978-0-385-72934-5(0) , Delacorte Bks. for Young Readers) Random Hse. Children's Bks.

—Second Summer of the Sisterhood. 2003. (Sisterhood of Traveling Pants Ser.: Bk. 2). 384p. (YA). (gr. 7 up). lib. bdg. 17.99 (978-0-385-90852-8(0) , Delacorte Bks. for Young Readers) Random Hse. Children's Bks.

—The Sisterhood of the Traveling Pants. (Sisterhood of Traveling Pants Ser.: Bk. 1). (YA). (gr. 7 up). 2004. 352p. mass mkt. 6.99 (978-0-440-22970-4(7) , Dell Books for Young Readers); 2001. 320p. 15.95 (978-0-385-72933-8(2) , Delacorte Bks. for Young Readers) Random Hse. Children's Bks.

—Sisterhood of the Traveling Pants. 2003. (Sisterhood of Traveling Pants Ser.: Bk. 1). 336p. (YA). (gr. 7 up). pap. 8.95 (978-0-385-73058-7(6) , Delacorte Bks. for Young Readers) Random Hse. Children's Bks.

—The Sisterhood of the Traveling Pants. l.t. ed. 2002. (Sisterhood of Traveling Pants Ser. : Bk. 1). 344p. (YA). 24.95 (978-0-7862-3966-5(2)) Thomson Gale.

Brennan, Kevin. Jimmy Jammers/Jaimito Pijama. Raven Tree Press, L.L. C., ed. de la Vega, Eida, tr. Driessen, Elizabeth, illus. 2002. Tr. of Jaimito Pijama. (SPA & ENG.). 32p. (J). (gr. k-3). 16.95 (978-0-9701107-9-4(0) , 626999) Raven Tree Pr.

Brett, Jan. El Sombrero. (Buenas Noches Coleccion).Tr. of Hat. (SPA.). (J). 7.95 (978-958-04-4169-4(3)) Norma S.A. COL. *Dist:* Distribuidora Norma, Inc., Lectorum Pubns., Inc.

CD

Brimner, Larry Dane. The Cool Coats. Tripp, Christine, illus. 2003. (Rookie Choices Ser.). (gr. 1-2). pap. 5.95 (978-0-516-27834-6(7)); 32p. (J). 20.50 (978-0-516-22545-6(6)) Scholastic Library Publishing. (Children's Pr.).

—The Cool Coats. Tripp, Christine, illus. 2003. 31p. (J). (ps-3). lib. bdg. 14.10 (978-0-613-67606-9(8)) Tandem Library Bks.

Brunelle, Lynn. I Go Places: A Fun Sticker Book. Espinosa, Leo, illus. 1999. 20p. (J). reprint ed. 7.95 (978-1-892374-23-3(4)) Weldon Owen, Inc.

Byars, Betsy. Dead Letter. 2006. (Herculeah Jones Mystery Ser.). 160p. (J). (gr. 3). pap. 5.99 (978-0-14-240564-2(7) , Puffin) Penguin Group (USA) Inc.

Callella, Trisha. Patterns All Around Me, Vol. 4471. Kupperstein, Joel, ed. 1998. (Learn to Read Math Ser.). (Illus.). 16p. (J). pap. 2.75 (978-1-57471-378-7(7) , 4471) Creative Teaching Pr., Inc.

Capalija, Ann Marie. Rainbow Dash's Dress-Up Fun. Edwards, Ken, illus. 2004. (My Little Pony Ser.). 12p. (J). (ps-1). 5.99 (978-0-06-055404-0(5) , Harper Festival) HarperCollins Pubs.

Capotosto, Anthony. No Shoes Required. 2005. 49p. pap. 8.00 (978-1-4116-2523-5(4)) Lulu.com.

Carvalho, Paula, et al. The Story of Calvin Cotton. 2001. (Illus.). 20p. (J). (gr. 1-4). 16.95 (978-0-9715636-0-5(8)) Chris Paul USA.

Caudle, Ruth. Yvette, Annette & Renette. 2007. (Illus.). 32p. (J). 16.99 (*978-0-9793039-0-6(7)*) Haiti World.

Chen, Ming & Chen, Wah. Sassparilla's New Shoes. 1999. (Illus.), 40p. (J). (ps-3). 19.95 (978-1-880664-26-1(7)) E. M. Productions.

Cheshire, Marc. Eloise Dresses Up: 50 Reusable Stickers! Hahner, Chris, illus. 2004. (Eloise Ser.). 12p. (J). pap. 6.99 (978-0-689-87455-0(3) , Little Simon) Simon & Schuster Children's Publishing.

Chodos-Irvine, Margaret. Ella Sarah Gets Dressed. 2003. (Illus.). 40p. (J). 16.00 (978-0-15-216413-3(8)) Harcourt Children's Bks.

Chouette Publishing. Caillou: My Clothes. Brignaud, Pierre, illus. rev. ed. 2008. 24p. (J). bds. 7.95 (*978-2-89450-629-5(5)*) Chouette Publishing CAN. *Dist:* Independent Pubs. Group.

Clarke, Jane. I'm Not Wearing That! Mostyn, David, illus. 2005. 24p. (J). lib. bdg. 22.65 (*978-1-59646-716-3(9)*) Dingles & Co.

Clements, Andrew. The Jacket. Gonzalez, Dan & Henderson, McDavid, illus. 2002. 96p. (J). (gr. 3-7). 12.95 (978-0-689-82595-8(1)) Simon & Schuster Children's Publishing.

Cocca-Leffler, Maryann. Mr. Tanen's Ties. 1999. (gr. k-3). lib. bdg. 15.25 (978-0-613-61918-9(8)) Tandem Library Bks.

—Mr. Tanen's Ties. Cocca-Leffler, Maryann, illus. (Illus.). 32p. (J). (gr. k-2). 2004. pap. 6.95 (978-0-8075-5302-2(6)); 1999. 15.95 (978-0-8075-5301-5(8)) Whitman, Albert & Co.

Connelly, Peggy. My Quirky, Oddball, Eccentric, Unpredictable Grandma. 2006. (ENG.). 112p. per. 16.95 (*978-1-4241-4486-0(8)*) PublishAmerica, Inc.

Cortes, Mary. Where on Earth Did My Sock Go? 2006. (J). per. 15.95 (*978-0-9787788-3-5(9)*) LUMEN-US Pubns.

The Costume Party. 2001. (YA). (gr. 6-12). pap. incl. audio (978-0-8224-3288-3(9)) Globe Fearon Educational Publishing.

Cote, M. Theresa. Scooter's New Clothes. Roux, Lynn M., illus. 2001. 48p. (J). (ps-5). pap. 9.95 (978-0-9601302-5-2(X)) Adventures Into Time.

Cottle, Joan. Emily's Shoes. Cottle, Joan, illus. 2000. (Rookie Reader Skill Set Ser.). (Illus.). 32p. (J). (gr. k-2). pap. 4.95 (978-0-516-26544-5(X) , Children's Pr.) Scholastic Library Publishing.

—Emily's Shoes. 1999. (gr. k-3). lib. bdg. 12.95 (978-0-613-54198-5(7)) Tandem Library Bks.

Cousins, Lucy. Maisy Dresses Up. Cousins, Lucy, illus. 1999. (Maisy Bks.). (Illus.). 24p. (J). (gr. k-k). pap. 3.99 (978-0-7636-0909-2(9)) Candlewick Pr.

—Maisy Dresses Up. 1999. (gr. k-3). lib. bdg. 11.00 (978-0-613-21952-5(X)) Tandem Library Bks.

Crunk, Tony. Grandpa's Overall. Nash, Scott, illus. 2001. 32p. (J). (ps). pap. 15.95 (978-0-531-30321-4(7) , Orchard Bks.) Scholastic, Inc.

—Grandpa's Overalls. Nash, Scott, illus. 2001. (J). lib. bdg. (978-0-531-33321-1(3) , Orchard Bks.) Scholastic, Inc.

Cullen, Catherine Ann. The Magical, Mystical, Marvelous Coat. Christiana, David, illus. 2004. 29p. (J). reprint ed. 16.00 (978-0-7567-8234-4(1)) DIANE Publishing Co.

—The Magical, Mystical, Marvelous Coat. Christiana, David, illus. 2001. 32p. (J). (gr. k-3). 15.95 (978-0-316-16334-7(1)) Little, Brown Bks. for Young Readers.

Currey, Anna. Truffle Goes to Town. Currey, Anna, illus. 2003. (Illus.). 32p. (YA). (978-1-85602-429-7(6)) Chrysalis Children's Bks.

Curtis, Matt. Six Empty Pockets. Newell, Mary J., illus. 1998. (Rookie Reader Skill Set Ser.). 32p. (J). (gr. k-2). pap. 4.95 (978-0-516-26253-6(X) , Children's Pr.) Scholastic Library Publishing.

—Six Empty Pockets. DePalma, Mary Newell, illus. 1998. 32p. (J). (gr. k-3). lib. bdg. 12.95 (978-0-613-37539-9(4)) Tandem Library Bks.

Daly, Niki. Jamela's Dress. Daly, Niki, illus. 2004. (Jamela Ser.). (Illus.). 32p. (J). reprint ed. pap. 6.95 (978-0-374-43720-6(3) , Sunburst) Farrar, Straus & Giroux.

—Jamela's Dress. 2001. (J). (ps-2). 26.95 incl. audio (978-0-8045-6878-4(2) , 6878) Spoken Arts, Inc.

Daugharty, Janice. Earl in the Yellow Shirt: A Novel. 1998. 240p. pap. 13.00 (978-0-06-092898-8(0)) HarperCollins Pubs.

David, Ryan. The Magic Raincoat. Shekerdjiska-Benatova, Sybilla, illus. 2007. 40p. (J). (ps-2). 17.95 (978-1-932425-68-0(3) , Front Street) Boyds Mills Pr.

Davidson, Susanna. Emperor's New Clothes. 2006. 24p. (J). 9.99 (978-0-7945-1350-4(6) , Usborne) EDC Publishing.

Davies, Dalene. Sock Monster's Invade Earth: Hold on to Your Socks! 2006. 74p. pap. 12.26 (978-1-4116-8227-6(0)) Lulu.com.

De Angeli, Marguerite. Thee, Hannah! De Angeli, Marguerite, illus. 2nd ed. 2000. (Illus.). 112p. (J). (gr. 3-7). pap. 15.99 (978-0-8361-9106-6(4)) Herald Pr.

Delaney, Michael. The Great Sock-a-Thon. 2004. 192p. (J). (gr. 3-8). 16.99 (978-0-525-46856-1(0) , Dutton Juvenile) Penguin Group (USA) Inc.

Dewan, Ted. Bing: Get Dressed. 2004. (Illus.). 24p. (J). (gr. k-ps). 5.95 (978-0-385-75020-2(X) , Fickling, David Bks.) Random Hse. Children's Bks.

Dischler, Patricia. The Patty Cake Kids & the Lost Imagination Cap. 2007. (Illus.). 24p. (J). per. 9.95 (*978-1-59598-064-9(4)*) Goblin Fern Pr., Inc.

Dixon, Ann. The Blueberry Shoe. Zerbetz, Evon, illus. 1999. 32p. (ps-3). pap. 8.95 (978-0-88240-519-3(5)) Graphic Arts Ctr. Publishing Co.

DK Publishing Staff. Peekaboo Dress Up. 2007. 12p. (J). (ps-2). bds. 6.99 (*978-0-7566-3103-1(3)*) Dorling Kindersley Publishing, Inc.

Dlugolecki, Michele. Mr. Mish Mosh & His Wash. 2007. 17.00 (*978-0-8059-8878-9(5)*) Dorrance Publishing Co., Inc.

Dolan, Penny. Mary & the Fairy. Allwright, Deborah, illus. 2004. (Read-It! Readers Ser.). 32p. (C). (gr. k-3). 18.60 (978-1-4048-0066-3(2)) Picture Window Bks.

Donaldson, Julia. Princess Mirrorbelle & the Magic Shoes. l.t. ed. 2005. pap. 16.95 (978-1-4056-6038-9(4)) BBC Audio GBR. *Dist:* BBC Audiobooks America.

Dornbusch, Erica. Finding Kate's Shoes. 2001. (Illus.). 32p. (J). (gr. k-ps). pap. 6.95 (978-1-55037-670-8(5)); lib. bdg. 17.95 (978-1-55037-671-5(3)) Annick Pr., Ltd. CAN. *Dist:* Firefly Bks., Ltd.

Dougherty, Terri. The Traveling Shoes. Haugen, Ryan, illus. 2006. (Read-It! Readers Ser.). 24p. (J). (ps-3). 18.60 (978-1-4048-1588-9(0)) Picture Window Bks.

Douglas, Vincent & School Specialty Publishing Staff. The Emperors New Clothes. 2004. (Handle Book with CD Ser.). (Illus.). 24p. (J). 3.99 (978-1-58845-719-6(2)) School Specialty Publishing.

Dressing Up: Individual Title Six-Packs. (Literatura 2000 Ser.). (gr. k-1). 28.00 (978-0-7635-0028-3(3)); 23.00 (978-0-7635-0421-2(1)) Rigby Education.

Duke, Shirley Smith. No Bows! Mattheson, Jenny, illus. 2006. 32p. (J). 15.95 (978-1-56145-356-6(0) , Peachtree Junior) Peachtree Pubs., Ltd.

Dunbar, Joyce. Where's My Sock? Rescek, Sanja, illus. 2006. 32p. (J). pap. 15.99 (978-0-439-74831-5(3) , Chicken Hse., The) Scholastic, Inc.

Dunrea, Olivier. Gossie. 2007. (Illus.). 16p. (J). (ps-k). bds. 6.95 (978-0-618-74791-7(5)) Houghton Mifflin Co. Trade & Reference Div.

—Gossie. Dunrea, Olivier, illus. 2002. (Illus.). 32p. (J). (gr. k-ps). tchr. ed. 9.95 (978-0-618-17674-8(8)) Houghton Mifflin Co. Trade & Reference Div.

Dunrea, Olivier. Ollie the Stomper. (Illus.). (J). 2007. 16p. bds. 6.95 (*978-0-618-75504-2(7)*); 2003. 32p. tchr. ed. 9.95 (978-0-618-33930-3(2)) Houghton Mifflin Co. Trade & Reference Div.

Ehrilch, Fred. Does a Chimp Wear Clothes? 2005. (Early Experiences Ser.). (Illus.). 32p. (J). pap. 5.95 (978-1-59354-122-4(8)) Blue Apple Bks.

Ehrlich, Fred. Does a Chimp Wear Clothes? 2005. (Early Experiences Ser.). (Illus.). 32p. (J). 13.50 (978-1-59354-110-1(4)) Blue Apple Bks.

Ellmore, Melba C. U-Shaped Shoes. Roseberry, Susan, illus. 2001. 32p. (J). (ps-3). 14.95 (978-0-8249-5425-3(4) , Ideals Children's Bks.) Ideals Pubns.

Emberley, Rebecca. My Clothes/Mi Ropa. Emberley, Rebecca, illus. 2002. (SPA & ENG., Illus.). 10p. (J). (ps-ps). bds. 6.99 (978-0-316-17454-1(8)) Little, Brown Bks. for Young Readers.

Faye. Jazzy Shoes. l.t. ed. 2006. (ENG., Illus.). 28p. per. 9.95 (*978-1-4327-0176-5(2)*) Outskirts Press, Inc.

Fearnley, Jan. Little Robin's Christmas. Fearnley, Jan, illus. 2002. 32p. (J). 5.95 (978-1-58925-371-1(X) , tiger tales) ME Media LLC.

Feldman, Thea. Princess Party. 2006. 3p. 5.99 (978-1-932915-33-4(8)) Sandvik Publishing.

Fine, Anne. Billy y el Vestido Rosa. 11th ed. 2000. (SPA., Illus.). 104p. (J). (ps-3). (978-84-204-4837-4(0)) Aguilar, S. A. de Ediciones-Grupo Santillana.

—Billy y el Vestido Rosa. Dupasquier, Philippe, illus. 2003. (SPA.). 100p. (J). (gr. 3-5). pap. 8.95 (978-958-24-0175-7(3)) Santillana USA Publishing Co., Inc.

Flam, Chanie. Shoe, Shoe. (Goldie Gold Board Book Ser.: Vol. 4). (Illus.). (J). (ps-1). bds. 4.95 (978-1-58330-028-2(7)) Feldheim Pubs.

Fleming, Candace & Smith, Maggie. This Is the Baby. 2004. (Illus.). 40p. (J). 16.50 (978-0-374-37486-0(4) , Farrar, Straus & Giroux (BYR)) Farrar, Straus & Giroux.

Foxworthy, Jeff. Dirt on My Shirt. Bjorkman, Steve, illus. 2008. 32p. (J). 16.99 (*978-0-06-120846-1(9)*); lib. bdg. 17.89 (*978-0-06-120847-8(7)*) HarperCollins Pubs.

Freedman, Claire. Aliens Love Underpants. Cort, Ben, illus. 2007. 32p. (J). (ps-2). 14.99 (*978-0-7641-6087-5(7)*) Barron's Educational Series, Inc.

Freeman, Don. Corduroy's Buttons. 2008. 12p. (J). (ps-1). bds. 7.99 (*978-0-448-44815-2(7)* , Grosset & Dunlap) Penguin Group (USA) Inc.

Fridman, Sashi. The Last Pair of Shoes. Seva, illus. 2006. 32p. (J). 13.95 (978-0-8266-0031-8(X)) Merkos L'Inyonei Chinuch.

Friedman, Laurie B. A Style All Her Own. Watts, Sharon, illus. 2005. 32p. (J). (ps-3). lib. bdg. 15.95 (978-1-57505-599-2(6)) Lerner Publishing Group.

Fry, Sonali. Make Me a Princess! A Mix-and-Match Dress-Up Book. Stead, Judy, illus. 2007. 12p. (J). (ps-2). 9.99 (*978-1-4169-4769-1(8)* , Little Simon) Simon & Schuster Children's Publishing.

Fuller, Bob. Meet the Kids of Paddywhack Lane. 2007. (Paddywhack Lane Ser.). 24p. (J). pap. 3.99 (978-0-448-44508-3(5) , Grosset & Dunlap) Penguin Group (USA) Inc.

Gardella, Tricia & Coalson, Glo. Blackberry Booties. 2000. (Illus.). 32p. (J). (ps-2). pap. 15.95 (978-0-531-30184-5(2) , Orchard Bks.) Scholastic, Inc.

Garland, Sarah. Ellie's Shoes. 2001. (Illus.). 32p. (J). pap. 9.99 (978-0-09-969251-5(1)) Random Hse. GBR. *Dist:* Independent Pubs. Group.

Garza, Carmen Lomas. Vejigante-Masquerader. (J). (gr. 2-4). (978-0-590-45777-4(2) , SO7640) Scholastic, Inc.

Gates, Susan. Bill's Baggy Pants. Axworthy, Anni, illus. 2004. (Read-It! Readers Ser.). 32p. (C). (gr. k-3). 18.60 (978-1-4048-0050-2(6)) Picture Window Bks.

George, Kristine O'Connell. One Mitten. Smith, Maggie, illus. 2004. 32p. (J). (gr. k-3). tchr. ed. 15.00 (978-0-618-11756-7(3) , Clarion Bks.) Houghton Mifflin Co. Trade & Reference Div.

Get Dressed with Elmo. 2000. (Illus.). 8p. (J). (ps). 19.95 (978-1-56156-883-3(X)) Kidsbooks, Inc.

Get Dressed with Elmo. (J). 2003. (978-1-59292-030-3(6)); 2000. (978-1-931312-09-7(5)); 2000. (978-1-931312-04-2(4)) SoftPlay, Inc.

Ghigna, Charles. One Hundred Shoes. Staake, Bob, illus. 2002. (Road to Reading Ser.: Vol. 2). 32p. (J). (ps-2). pap. 3.99 (978-0-375-82178-3(3) , Random Hse. Bks. for Young Readers) Random Hse. Children's Bks.

—One Hundred Shoes. 2002. (ps-2). lib. bdg. 11.80 (978-0-613-89788-4(9)) Tandem Library Bks.

Gill, Janie S. Lucy's Boot. 2001. (Predictable Readers Ser.). (Illus.). (J). (gr. k-2). lib. bdg. 11.95 (978-0-89868-546-6(X)) ARO Publishing Co.

Gill, Vince. The Emperor's New Clothes: A Country Storybook. Newsom, Carol, illus. 2006. 30p. (J). (gr. 4-8). reprint ed. 17.00 (978-1-4223-5729-3(5)) DIANE Publishing Co.

Gilson, Jamie. Bug in a Rug. deGroat, Diane, illus. 2003. 80p. (J). pap. 4.95 (978-0-618-31670-0(1) , Clarion Bks.) Houghton Mifflin Co. Trade & Reference Div.

—Bug in a Rug. 1998. 80p. (J). (gr. k-3). tchr. ed. 15.00 (978-0-395-86616-0(2) , Clarion Bks.) Houghton Mifflin Co. Trade & Reference Div.

—Bug in a Rug. 2003. (gr. k-3). lib. bdg. 12.95 (978-0-613-64657-4(6)) Tandem Library Bks.

Giovanni, Nikki. The Girls in the Circle. Johnson, Cathy Ann, illus. 2004. 32p. (J). lib. bdg. 15.00 (*978-1-4242-0232-4(9)*) Fitzgerald Bks.

Goethals, Angela. The Sisterhood of the Traveling Pants. 2004. (Sisterhood of Traveling Pants Ser. : Bk. 1). 320p. (YA). (gr. 7 up). pap. 40.00 incl. audio (978-0-8072-2286-7(0) , Listening Library) Random Hse. Audio Publishing Group.

Golden Books Staff. Blue's Dress-up Day. Miller, Victoria, illus. 2005. 48p. (J). (ps-2). pap. 2.99 (978-0-375-83172-0(X) , Golden Bks.) Random Hse. Children's Bks.

—Glamour Girl. Harchy, Atelier Philippe, illus. 2004. 32p. (J). (ps-2). 4.99 (978-0-375-82811-9(7) , Golden Bks.) Random Hse. Children's Bks.

Good, Merle, et al. Dan's Pants: The Adventures of Dan, the Fabric Man. Benner, Cheryl A., illus. 2000. 32p. (J). (ps-3). 16.00 (978-1-56148-307-5(9)) Good Bks.

Goulis, Julie. The Topsy-Turvy Towel. Ferguson, John H., illus. 2006. 32p. (J). 14.95 (978-0-9754621-2-6(1)) Bubblegum Bks.

Grifalconi, Ann. Tiny's Hat. Grifalconi, Ann, illus. 1999. (Illus.). 32p. (J). (gr. k-3). 14.89 (978-0-06-027655-3(X)) HarperCollins Pubs.

Gurney, Stella & Sparklington, Madame. Princess: A Glittering Guide for Young Ladies. Allsop, Sophie et al, illus. 2006. (Genuine & Moste Authentic Gdes Ser.). 32p. (J). (gr. 1-4). 17.99 (978-0-7636-3430-8(1)) Candlewick Pr.

Hall, John. What If I Pulled This Thread. Gilpin, Stephen, illus. 2006. 48p. 12.99 (978-1-59379-067-7(8)) White Stone Bks.

Harcourt School Publishers Staff. Pack Your Pajamas. 3rd ed. 2002. (Trophies English Language Learners Ser.). (Illus.). pap. 5.10 (978-0-15-327646-0(0)) Harcourt Schl. Pubs.

Harley, Bill. Dirty Joe, the Pirate: A True Story. Davis, Jack E., illus. 2008. 32p. (J). 16.99 (*978-0-06-623780-0(7)*); lib. bdg. 17.89 (*978-0-06-623781-7(5)*) HarperCollins Pubs.

Harper, Charise Mericle. Good Night, Leo: A Swashbuckling Bedtime Adventure. 2008. (Illus.). 24p. (J). (gr. k-k). bds. 6.99 (*978-0-375-84234-4(9)* , Robin Corey Bks.) Random Hse. Children's Bks.

Harrison, Lisi. Best Friends for Never. 2004. (Clique Ser.: Bk. 2). 208p. (J). (gr. 5-8). pap. 9.99 (978-0-316-70131-0(9) , Poppy) Little, Brown Bks. for Young Readers.

Harry How Books. Just Luke. l.t. ed. 2006. (ENG., Illus.). 28p. per. 9.95 (*978-1-4327-0178-9(9)*) Outskirts Press, Inc.

Harvey, Damian. Mr. Fox's Socks. Rescek, Sanja, illus. 2004. 16p. (J). lib. bdg. 22.65 (*978-1-59646-678-4(2)*) Dingles & Co.

Hasta Manana Zapatos: See You Tomorrow Shoes. 2006. (J). (978-0-9743359-2-6(4)) Murdock Publishing Co.

Hathon, Elizabeth, photos by. Baby's Dress 'n' Go. 1998. (Photo Board Bks.). (Illus.). 20p. (J). (ps). bds. 2.99 (978-0-7681-0037-2(2) , McClanahan Bk.) Learning Horizons, Inc.

Heape, David. R. That's What Friends Do. l.t. ed. 2006. (ENG., Illus.). 28p. per. 9.95 (*978-1-4327-0177-2(0)*) Outskirts Press, Inc.

Hébert, Marie-Francine & Germain, Philippe. Un Blouson dans la Peau. 2001. (Premier Roman — Special Editions Ser.). (FRE., Illus.). 64p. (J). (gr. 1-4). pap. (978-2-89021-476-7(1)) Diffusion du livre Mirabel.

Hill, Amye Rose. The Amazing Mr. Buddy. 10th ed. 2005. (Illus.). (J). 6.99 (978-0-9769234-0-4(8)) Zany Angel Projects LLC.

Himler, Ronald. Dancing Boy. Himler, Ronald, illus. 2005. (Illus.). 40p. (J). (ps-ps). 15.95 (978-1-59572-020-7(0)) Star Bright Bks., Inc.

Hines-Stephens, Sarah & Mason, Jane. Princess School: If the Shoe Fits. 2004. (Princess School Ser.). 144p. (J). pap. 4.99 (978-0-439-54532-7(3) , Scholastic Paperbacks) Scholastic, Inc.

Hoffman, Kaycee, des. Picture Me Cuddly as a Bunny. 2001. (Picture Me Ser.). 10p. (J). (ps up). bds. 4.99 (978-1-57151-589-6(5)) Playhouse Publishing.

Holabird, Katharine. Dressing Up! Craig, Helen, illus. 2006. (Angelina Ballerina Ser.). 16p. (J). (ps-1). 4.99 (978-0-448-44019-4(9) , Grosset & Dunlap) Penguin Group (USA) Inc.

Hopkins, Cathy. Discount Diva. 2007. (Zodiac Girls Ser.). 184p. (J). (gr. 4-7). pap. 5.95 (*978-0-7534-6131-0(5)* , Kingfisher) Houghton Mifflin Co. Trade & Reference Div.

Houghton Mifflin Company Staff. Curious George Cleans Up. 2007. (Illus.). 24p. (J). (gr. 3-5). 3.99 (*978-0-618-73759-8(6)*) Houghton Mifflin Co. Trade & Reference Div.

Hundred Dresses. 1999. (J). 9.95 (978-1-56137-180-8(7)) Novel Units, Inc.

Huser, Glen. Stitches. 2004. 200p. (J). (gr. 4-7). pap. 6.95 (978-0-88899-578-0(4)) Groundwood Bks. CAN. *Dist:* Perseus Distribution.

Huxtable, Tonja & Huxtable, John, illus. Berry Pretty Princesses. 2008. (Strawberry Shortcake Ser.). 16p. (J). (ps-1). 5.99 (*978-0-448-44715-5(0)* , Grosset & Dunlap) Penguin Group (USA) Inc.

I Love to Dress Up. 2003. (J). per. (978-1-57657-960-2(3)) Paradise Pr., Inc.

Inglee, K. B. Farmer's Daughter, Miller's Son. 2003. 62p. (J). pap. 9.95 (978-0-7414-1667-4(0)) Infinity Publishing.

Irvine, Abby. La increible boda de mi tia Lola. Abbott, Simon, illus. 2005. (SPA.). 16p. (J). bds. 13.95 (978-84-7864-792-7(9)) Combel Editorial, S.A. ESP. *Dist:* Independent Pubs. Group.

Jeanne, Diana. Nathalie's Socks. Rose, Nathalie, illus. 2004. 51p. (J). mass mkt. 7.95 (978-0-9727583-9-0(9)) Taylor-Dth Publishing.

Jenkins, Amanda. Hodja's Fine Coat: A Tale from Turkey. 2006. 42.00 (*978-1-4108-6174-0(0)*) Benchmark Education Co.

Jenkins, Emily. Daffodil. Bogacki, Tomek, illus. 2004. 32p. (J). 16.00 (978-0-374-31676-1(7) , Farrar, Straus & Giroux (BYR)) Farrar, Straus & Giroux.

Jocelyn, Marthe. Hannah & the Seven Dresses. 2006. (Illus.). 23p. (J). (gr. k-4). reprint ed. 15.00 (978-1-4223-5552-7(7)) DIANE Publishing Co.

—Hannah & the Seven Dresses. 2005. 32p. (J). (ps-k). pap. 7.95 (978-0-88776-749-4(4)) Tundra Bks., Inc./Livres Toundra, Inc. CAN. *Dist:* Random Hse., Inc.

Johnson, G. Francis. Has Anybody Lost a Glove? Tokunbo, Dimitrea, illus. 2004. 32p. (J). (gr. k-2). 15.95 (978-1-59078-041-1(8)) Boyds Mills Pr.

Johnson, Marion. Caillou: New Shoes. rev. ed. 2008. (Playtime Ser.). (Illus.). 24p. (J). pap. 4.95 (*978-2-89450-634-9(1)*) Chouette Publishing CAN. *Dist:* Independent Pubs. Group.

Jones, Christianne C. Nate the Dinosaur. Epstein, Len, illus. 2006. (Read-It! Readers Ser.). 24p. (J). (ps-3). 18.60 (978-1-4048-1728-9(X)) Picture Window Bks.

Jones, Dennis. The Life of Socks. 2004. 27p. pap. 14.95 (978-1-4137-2774-6(3)) PublishAmerica, Inc.

Jukes, Mavis. The Green Velvet Dress. 2001. (J). 14.95 (978-0-385-32684-1(X) , Dell Books for Young Readers) Random Hse. Children's Bks.

Kathleen, Jo Ann. NATALIA, O' MIA, WHITE LACES & SHOES. l.t. ed. 2006. (ENG., Illus.). 28p. per. 9.95 (*978-1-4327-0314-1(5)*) Outskirts Press, Inc.

Kay, Verla. Homespun Sarah. Rand, Ted, illus. 2003. 32p. (J). (ps-3). 16.99 (978-0-399-23417-0(9) , Putnam Juvenile) Penguin Group (USA) Inc.

Kellogg, Steven. The Missing Mitten Mystery. Kellogg, Steven, illus. 2002. (Illus.). 14.04 (978-1-4046-1698-1(5)) Book Wholesalers, Inc.

—The Missing Mitten Mystery. Kellogg, Steven, illus. 2000. (Illus.). 40p. (J). (gr. 4-1). 15.99 (978-0-8037-2566-9(3) , Dial) Penguin Group (USA) Inc.

—The Missing Mitten Mystery. 2002. (Illus.). (J). (ps-ps). reprint ed. pap. 6.99 (978-0-14-230192-0(2) , Puffin) Penguin Group (USA) Inc.

Kelman, Marcy. Butterfly Suits. Zaidi, Nadeem, illus. 2006. (Disney's Little Einsteins Ser.). 32p. (ps-1). 6.99 incl. cd-rom (978-0-7868-5538-4(X)) Disney Pr.

Kelman, Marcy. June's New Shoes. Song, Aram, illus. 2007. 24p. (J). (ps-k). pap. 3.99 (*978-1-4231-0213-7(4)*) Disney Pr.

Kinerk, Robert. Timothy Cox Will Not Change His Socks. Gammell, Stephen, illus. 2005. 32p. (J). 16.95 (978-0-689-87181-8(3) , Simon & Schuster Children's Publishing) Simon & Schuster Children's Publishing.

King, Thomas. Coyote's New Suit. Wales, Johnny, illus. rev. ed. 2008. 40p. 15.95 (*978-1-55263-497-4(3)*) Key Porter Bks. CAN. *Dist:* Perseus Distribution.

Klinting, Lars. Beaver the Tailor: A How-to Picture Book. Klinting, Lars, illus. 2004. Orig. Title: Castor Syr.. (Illus.). 32p. (J). (gr. k-3). reprint ed. 17.00 (978-0-7567-7213-0(3)) DIANE Publishing Co.

Kovalski, Maryann. Omar's Halloween. 2007. (Illus.). 32p. (J). (ps-3). per. (***978-1-55455-049-4(1)***) Fitzhenry & Whiteside, Ltd.

Kramer, Alan. The Completely Cool Clothing Company. 2006. 42.00 (***978-1-4108-6180-1(5)***) Benchmark Education Co.

Lasky, Kathryn. The Emperor's Old Clothes. Catrow, David, illus. 2002. 32p. (J). (ps-2). pap. 7.00 (978-0-15-216348-8(4) , Voyager Bks./Libros Viajeros) Harcourt Children's Bks.

—The Emperor's Old Clothes. 2002. (gr. k-3). lib. bdg. 14.15 (978-0-613-53806-0(4)) Tandem Library Bks.

Lawston, Lisa & Sams, B. B. A Pair of Red Sneakers. 1998. (Illus.). 32p. (J). (ps-3). 16.99 (978-0-531-33104-0(0) , Orchard Bks.) Scholastic, Inc.

Le, Ny Jeanine. Once upon A Prom #1 Dream. 2008. 240p. pap. 5.99 (***978-0-545-02815-8(9)*** , Scholastic Paperbacks) Scholastic, Inc.

Leblanc, Louise. Maddie Wants New Clothes. Cummins, Sarah, tr. from FRE. Gay, Marie-Louise, illus. 2000. (First Novels Ser.). 64p. (gr. 1-5). 4.95 (978-0-88780-526-4(4)); (J). (978-0-88780-527-1(2)) Formac Publishing Co., Ltd. CAN. *Dist:* Casemate Pubs. & Bk. Distributors, LLC.

—Maddie Wants New Clothes. 2001. (gr. k-3). lib. bdg. 11.80 (978-0-613-90971-6(2)) Tandem Library Bks.

Lee, Jeanie. Costumes & Bows: A Dress-up Show! Workman, Lisa, illus. 2006. (Holly Hobbie & Friends Ser.). 16p. (J). pap. 5.99 (978-1-4169-2799-0(9) , Little Simon) Simon & Schuster Children's Publishing.

Leonard, Marcia. Dress-up. 1999. (gr. k-3). lib. bdg. 13.00 (978-0-613-16664-5(7)) Tandem Library Bks.

—No New Pants! Handelman, Dorothy, photos by. 1999. (Real Kids Readers Ser.). (Illus.). 32p. (ps-1). lib. bdg. 18.90 (978-0-7613-2063-0(6)); (J). pap. 4.99 (978-0-7613-2088-3(1)) Lerner Publishing Group. (Millbrook Pr.).

—No New Pants! 1999. (J). (978-0-606-19166-1(6)); lib. bdg. 11.80 (978-0-613-18161-7(1)) Tandem Library Bks.

—Pantalones Nuevos, No! Handelman, Dorothy, photos by. 2005. Tr. of No New Pants!. (ENG & SPA., Illus.). 32p. (J). (ps-1). pap. 4.99 (978-0-8225-3297-2(2)) Lerner Publishing Group.

—Pantalones Nuevos, ¡No! Handelman, Dorothy, photos by. 2005. (Lecturas para Niños de Verdad (Real Kids Readers) Ser.). (SPA., Illus.). 32p. (J). (ps-1). pap. 4.99 (978-0-8225-3296-5(4) , Ediciones Lerner) Lerner Publishing Group.

Lester, Helen. The Sheep in Wolf's Clothing. Munsinger, Lynn, illus. 2007. 32p. (J). (gr. k-3). 16.00 (***978-0-618-86844-5(5)***) Houghton Mifflin Co. Trade & Reference Div.

Levy, Michael. The Inspiring Story of Little Goody Two Shoes. 2007. 139p. (YA). per. 12.95 (***978-0-9668069-9-1(9)***) Point of Life, Inc.

Lewis, Rob. Cold Jac. 2002. (Illus.). 32p. pap. 12.95 (978-1-84323-117-2(4)) Beekman Bks., Inc.

Lewison, Wendy Cheyette & Greigo, Tony. So Many Boots. 2000. (My First Hello Reader! Ser.). (J). 3.99 (978-0-439-09865-6(3)) Scholastic, Inc.

Lipp, Frederick. Fatima. Lindmark, Margaret, illus. 2006. 32p. (J). pap. (978-1-59336-302-4(8)) Mondo Publishing.

Litchfield, J. My Clothes. 2004. (Rattle Board Bks.). 16p. (J). 4.95 (978-0-7945-0052-8(8) , Usborne) EDC Publishing.

Lloyd-Jones, Sally. Handbag Friends. Heap, Sue, illus. 2006. 64p. (J). bds. 11.95 (978-0-385-75096-7(X) , Fickling, David Bks.) Random Hse. Children's Bks.

London, Jonathan. Froggy Gets Dressed. 2007. (Puffin Storytime Ser.). 32p. (J). (ps). pap. 9.99 (978-0-14-240870-4(0) , Puffin) Penguin Group (USA) Inc.

Lovett, Darrell. Hi, I'm Alex. l.t. ed. 2006. (ENG., Illus.). 28p. per. 9.95 (***978-1-4327-0195-6(9)***) Outskirts Press, Inc.

—My Dog Tony. l.t. ed. 2006. (ENG., Illus.). 28p. per. 9.95 (***978 1 4327-0187-1(8)***) Outskirts Press, Inc.

Lowell, Susan. Little Red Cowboy Hat. Cecil, Randy, illus. rev. ed. 2000. 32p. (J). (gr. k-3). pap. 7.95 (978-0-8050-6483-4(4) , Holt, Henry & Co. Bks. For Young Readers) Holt, Henry & Co.

—Little Red Cowboy Hat. 2000. (gr. k-3). lib. bdg. 15.25 (978-0-613-28559-9(X)) Tandem Library Bks.

Lucas, David. Halibut Jackson. 2004. (Illus.). 32p. (J). (ps-3). 16.95 (978-0-375-82690-0(4) , Knopf Bks. for Young Readers) Random Hse. Children's Bks.

Lueck, Andrew. Chicabee. 2006. 32p. 16.95 (978-0-9774547-0-9(3)) Lueck Studios.

MacDonald, Maryann. The Costume Copycat. Wilsdorf, Anne, illus. 2006. 32p. (J). (ps). 10.99 (978-0-8037-2929-2(4) , Dial) Penguin Group (USA) Inc.

MacKinnon, Debbie. Find My Boots! Sieveking, Anthea, photos by. 1999. (Illus.). 10p. (J). (978-0-7112-0922-0(7)) Lincoln, Frances Ltd. GBR. *Dist:* Antique Collectors' Club.

Makhijani, Pooja. Mama's Saris. Gomez, Elena, illus. 2007. 32p. (J). (ps-1). 16.99 (978-0-316-01105-1(3)) Little Brown & Co.

Mann, Rachel. The Blue Mittens. Wallner, Alexandra, illus. 2002. 16p. (J). (978-0-439-35072-3(7)) Scholastic, Inc.

Marvin, Isabel R. Beautiful Blue Shirt on Barry Street. 2000. 21p. 3.99 (978-976-610-174-9(4)) Penguin Group (USA) Inc.

Masino, Brian & Family, Wayans. Sneaker Madness. 2006. (Thugaboo Ser.). 64p. (J). pap. 4.99 (978-0-439-74598-7(5) , Cartwheel Bks.) Scholastic, Inc.

Maude, Rachel. Poseur #1. Compani, Jill, illus. 2008. 304p. (J). (gr. 7-17). pap. 9.99 (***978-0-316-06583-2(8)*** , Poppy) Little, Brown Bks. for Young Readers.

McCaughrean, Geraldine. Too Big. 1999. (Corgi Pups Ser.). (Illus.). 61p. (J). pap. 7.99 (978-0-552-54618-8(6)) Transworld Publishers Ltd. GBR. *Dist:* Independent Pubs. Group.

McClintock, Barbara, illus. The Mitten. 2008. (J). (***978-0-439-92544-0(4)*** , Scholastic Pr.) Scholastic, Inc.

McDonald, Megan. Stink & the World's Worst Super-Stinky Sneakers. Reynolds, Peter H., illus. 2007. (Stink Ser.). 144p. (J). (gr. k-3). 12.99 (978-0-7636-2834-5(4)) Candlewick Pr.

McElligott, Matthew. Backbeard & the Birthday Suit: The Hairiest Pirate Who Ever Lived. 2007. (Illus.). 32p. (J). pap. 6.95 (***978-0-8027-9680-6(X)***) Walker & Co.

—Backbeard: Pirate for Hire. McElligott, Matthew, illus. 2007. (Illus.). 32p. (J). 17.85 (***978-0-8027-9633-2(8)***); 16.95 (***978-0-8027-9632-5(X)***) Walker & Co.

McElmurry, Jill. Mad About Plaid. 2000. (Illus.). 40p. (J). (gr. k-5). 14.89 (978-0-688-16952-7(X)) HarperCollins Pubs.

McGuire, Leslie. I Get Dressed: A Fun Sticker Book. Espinosa, Leo, illus. 1999. 20p. (J). reprint ed. 7.95 (978-1-892374-22-6(6)) Weldon Owen, Inc.

McKee, David. King Rollo & the New Stockings. 2001. (Illus.). 32p. (J). 19.99 (978-0-86264-953-1(6)) Andersen GBR. *Dist:* Independent Pubs. Group.

McKenna, Kerin Elaine. I Like Shoes. 2006. 17.00 (978-0-8059-9020-1(8)) Dorrance Publishing Co., Inc.

McKissack, Patricia C. & McKissack, Fredrick L. Bessey, la Desordenada. Regan, Dana, illus. (Rookie Reader Espanol Ser.).Tr. of Messy Bessey. (SPA.). 32p. (J). (gr. k-2). 2003. pap. 4.95 (978-0-516-27794-3(4)); 2002. 19.50 (978-0-516-22685-9(1)) Scholastic Library Publishing. (Children's Pr.).

—El Closet de Bessey, la Desordenada. Regan, Dana, illus. (Rookie Reader Espanol Ser.).Tr. of Messy Bessey's Closet. (SPA.). 32p. (J). (gr. k-2). 2003. pap. 4.95 (978-0-516-27796-7(0)); 2002. 19.50 (978-0-516-22684-2(3)) Scholastic Library Publishing. (Children's Pr.).

—El Jardin de Bessey, la Desordenada. Regan, Dana, illus. rev. ed. 2002. (Rookie Readers Ser.).Tr. of Messy Bessey's Garden. (ENG & SPA.). 32p. (J). (gr. k-2). 19.50 (978-0-516-22688-0(6) , Children's Pr.) Scholastic Library Publishing.

McQuinn, Anna. Wanda's Washing Machine. McCafferty, Jan, illus. 2005. 16p. (J). (ps-ps). 12.95 (978-1-58925-768-9(5) , tiger tales) ME Media LLC.

Meunier, Brian & Edgerton, Perky. Bravo, Tavo! 2007. (Illus.). 32p. (J). (gr. k-3). 16.99 (978-0-525-47478-4(1) , Dutton Juvenile) Penguin Group (USA) Inc.

The Mitten. (Blue-Ribbon Listen-and-Read Ser.). (Orig.). (J). (ps-2). pap. 5.95 incl. audio (978-0-590-63092-4(X)) Scholastic, Inc.

Mom Dresses Up. 2003. (J). (978-1-58453-254-5(8)) Pioneer Valley Educational Pr., Inc.

Morley, Linda. The White Pair with Colorful Dinosaurs. Reyes, Joe, illus. l.t. ed. 2002. 36p. (J). (ps-2). pap. 7.99 (978-0-9662888-3-4(1)) Morley Pr.

Morton, Elizabeth. Anne's New Dress. 2001. (Animated Ser.). (Illus.). (J). (gr. 2-5). pap. 4.99 (978-0-06-442160-7(0)) HarperCollins Pubs.

Moss, Miriam. Bare Bear. McQuillan, Mary, illus. 2005. 32p. (J). 16.95 (978-0-8234-1934-0(7)) Holiday Hse., Inc.

Mould, Wendy. Ants in My Pants. Mould, Wendy, illus. 2001. (Illus.). 32p. (J). (gr. k-3). tchr. ed. 15.00 (978-0-618-09640-4(X) , Clarion Bks.) Houghton Mifflin Co. Trade & Reference Div.

Mulford, Carolyn. The Feedsack Dress. 2007. (YA). per. 7.95 (***978-0-9713497-4-2(6)***) Cave Hollow Pr.

Muller, Birte. I Can Dress Myself! Martens, Marianne, tr. from GER. 2007. (Illus.). 32p. (J). (ps-1). 8.95 (978-0-7358-2128-6(3)) North-South Bks., Inc.

Munsch, Robert. Kiss Me, I'm Perfect! 2008. (Candy Apple Ser.). (SPA.). 32p. (J). pap. 3.99 (***978-0-545-02213-2(4)*** , Scholastic en Espanol) Scholastic, Inc.

Munsch, Robert N. Kiss Me, I'm Perfect. Martchenko, Michael, illus. 2008. 32p. (J). pap. 3.99 (***978-0-545-01827-2(7)***) Scholastic, Inc.

Murphy, Peg. I Can Do Anything. l.t. ed. 2006. (ENG., Illus.). 28p. per. 9.95 (***978-1-4327-0175-8(4)***) Outskirts Press, Inc.

My Holiday Dress. 2003. (J). per. (978-1-57657-929-9(8)) Paradise Pr., Inc.

Nagel, Karen B. Snow? Let's Go! Croll, Carolyn, illus. 2000. (My First Hello Reader! Ser.). 32p. (J). (ps-1). pap. 3.99 (978-0-439-09906-6(4)) Scholastic, Inc.

—Snow? Let's Go! 2000. (Hello Reader! Ser.). (J). (978-0-606-19613-0(7)) Tandem Library Bks.

Nagy, Krisztina. Fuzzy Bear: A Getting Dressed Book. enl. ed. 2000. (Illus.). 10p. (J). 16.95 (978-1-58117-050-4(5) , Intervisual/Piggy Toes) Dalmatian Pr.

Neitzel, Shirley. The Jacket I Wear in the Snow. Parker, Nancy Winslow, illus. 2002. (J). 14.43 (978-0-7587-2882-1(4)) Book Wholesalers, Inc.

Niimi, Nankichi. Buying Mittens. Kuroi, Ken & Huffman, Judith C., illus. 1999. 42p. (ps-3). 14.95 (978-0-8248-2129-6(7) , Kolowalu Bk.) Univ. of Hawaii Pr.

Noland, Charles. The Adventures of Drew & Ellie: The Daring Rescue. Moyer, Tom, illus. 2nd ed. 2006. (J). per. 7.95 (***978-0-9789297-2-5(1)***) TMD Enterprises.

O'Connor, Ilett. Alexandra & the Blue Button. Kahn, Alisha, illus. Wells, Wadell, photos by. 2002. 32p. pap. 10.00 (978-0-9717003-0-7(3)) O'Connor, Ilett K.

O'Connor, Jane. Fancy Nancy & the Posh Puppy. Glasser, Robin Preiss, illus. 2007. (Fancy Nancy Ser.). 32p. (J). lib. bdg. 17.89 (***978-0-06-054215-3(2)***); 16.99 (***978-0-06-054213-9(6)***) HarperCollins Pubs.

—Fancy Nancy Loves! Loves!! Loves!!! Glasser, Robin Preiss, illus. 2007. (Fancy Nancy Ser.). 12p. (J). (ps-3). pap. 6.99 (***978-0-06-123599-3(7)*** , Harper Festival) HarperCollins Pubs.

—Fancy Nancy's Glamorous Gift. Glasser, Robin Preiss, illus. gif. ed. 2007. (Fancy Nancy Ser.). 32p. (J). (ps-2). 24.99 (***978-0-06-137182-0(3)***) HarperCollins Pubs.

Ohi, Ruth. Pants off First! 2001. (Illus.). 22p. (J). (ps-k). bds. (978-1-55041-667-1(7)) Fitzhenry & Whiteside, Ltd.

Oliver, Jasmine. Armani Angels. 2007. (Project Fashion Ser.). 176p. (J). pap. 8.99 (***978-1-4169-3811-8(7)*** , Simon Pulse) Simon & Schuster Children's Publishing.

Olkowski, Mary. The Twirling Dress. Olkowski, Mary, illus. l.t. ed. 2001. (Illus.). 36p. (J). bds. 10.95 (978-0-9709119-0-2(4) , 1011) Limpid Butterfly Productions, The.

Orlev, Uri. A Lion for Michael. Gleich, Jacky, illus. 2000. 32p. (J). (gr. k-4). 15.95 (978-1-58653-172-0(7)) Mondo Publishing.

Panruk, Eva. Aklut Atutuk'ngaput. Panruk, Eva & Brunk, Cara, illus. 1998. Tr. of Clothes We Wear. (ESK.). 16p. (J). (gr. k-3). pap. 6.00 (978-1-58084-027-9(2)) Lower Kuskokwim Schl. District.

Parent, Nancy. Barney's Book of Clothes. Johnson, Jay, illus. 2004. 8p. (J). pap. 5.99 (978-1-58668-309-2(8)) Lyrick Publishing.

—Barney's Book of Clothes. Johnson, Jay, illus. 2004. (Barney Ser.). 8p. (J). bds. 5.99 (978-0-439-63981-1(6)) Scholastic, Inc.

Parker, Jessie, et al. Barbie: A Dress-up Day. S. I. International Staff, illus. 2003. (Step into Reading Ser.: Vol. 1). 32p. (J). (ps-1). pap. 3.99 (978-0-375-82501-9(0) , Random Hse. Bks. for Young Readers) Random Hse. Children's Bks.

Parnell, Robyn. My Closet Threw a Party. Pickering, Jimmy, illus. 2005. 32p. (J). 14.95 (978-1-4027-1298-2(7)) Sterling Publishing Co., Inc.

Parton, Dolly. Coat of Many Colors. Parton, Dolly, . gif. ed. 2006. (Illus.). 24p. (J). bds. 9.99 incl. audio compact disk (978-1-57791-153-1(9) , Little Melody Pr.) Brighter Minds Children's Publishing.

Pascal, Francine. One 2 Many. 1999. (Sweet Valley Jr. High Ser.: No. 27). (gr. 3-6). lib. bdg. 12.40 (978-0-613-16173-2(4)) Tandem Library Bks.

Patches on My Britches. 1998. (Illus.). 293p. (J). (gr. k-12). pap. 14.00 (978-0-9662898-0-0(3)) Selecto Publishing.

Pennypacker, Sara. Stuart Goes to School. Matje, Martin, illus. 64p. (J). 2003. pap. 15.95 (978-0-439-30182-4(3) , Orchard Bks.); 2005. reprint ed. pap. 4.99 (978-0-439-30183-1(1) , Scholastic Paperbacks) Scholastic, Inc.

Pertzig, Faigy. Messes of Dresses. Rosenfeld, Dina, ed. Leff, Tova, illus. 2nd ed. 1999. 32p. (J). (ps-3). reprint ed. 9.95 (978-0-922613-75-5(3)) Hachai Publishing.

Pico Lost His Short Pants. l.t. ed. 2001. 32p. (J). 16.00 (978-0-9711901-0-8(0)) Sur Mar Publishing.

Pilkey, Dav. Big Dog & Little Dog Wearing Sweaters. 1998. (Big Dog & Little Dog Ser.). (Illus.). 14p. (J). (ps-1). bds. 5.95 (978-0-15-200361-6(4) , Red Wagon Bks.) Harcourt Children's Bks.

Pin, Isabel. Bumblebee Blues. James, J. Alison, tr. from GER. 2003. (Illus.). 32p. (J). (gr. k-3). 15.95 (978-0-7358-1813-2(4)); lib. bdg. 16.50 (978-0-7358-1814-9(2)) North-South Bks., Inc. (Michael Neugebauer Bks.).

Pliszka, Jodi. Bella & Gizmo's Adventures: Bella Gets A New Sweater. 2005. (Illus.). 24p. (J). per. 18.95 (978-1-933449-04-3(7)) Nightengale Pr.

—Bella & Gizmo's Adventures — Bella Gets A New Sweater. 2005. 32p. (J). per. 18.95 (978-1-933449-26-5(8)) Nightengale Pr.

Plourde, Lynn. Grandpappy Snippy Snappies. Santoro, Christopher, illus. (J). Date not set. 16.89 (978-0-06-029528-8(7)); 2002. 15.99 (978-0-06-028050-5(6)) HarperCollins Pubs.

—A Mountain of Mittens. Vane, Mitch, illus. 2007. 32p. (J). (gr. k-3). 15.95 (***978-1-57091-585-7(7)***) Charlesbridge Publishing, Inc.

Plourde, Lynn. Pajama Day. Wickstrom, Thor, illus. 2007. 40p. (J). pap. 6.99 (978-0-14-240744-8(5) , Puffin) Penguin Group (USA) Inc.

Pound, Emily. Angel Shoes. 2007. (Illus.). 32p. (J). (ps-k). pap. 9.95 (***978-0-7459-4974-1(6)***) Lion Hudson plc GBR. *Dist:* Independent Pubs. Group.

Prelutsky, Jack. The Frogs Wore Red Suspenders. Mathers, Petra, illus. 2005. 64p. (J). reprint ed. pap. 6.99 (978-0-06-073776-4(X) , Harper Trophy) HarperCollins Pubs.

Pressler, Mirjam. Let Sleeping Dogs Lie. Macki, Erik J., tr. from GER. 2007. 208p. (YA). (gr. 7 up). 16.95 (***978-1-932425-84-0(5)*** , Front Street) Boyds Mills Pr.

Prince, Sarah. Betty Boots. 2001. (gr. k-3). lib. bdg. 11.80 (978-0-613-33335-1(7)) Tandem Library Bks.

Probasco, Teri. Blue Jean Gum. 35p. (J). (ps-4). pap. 5.90 (978-0-932970-95-4(8)) Prinit Pr.

Punnett, Dick. Help Dress Priscilla: A Talk-along Book. Dunnington, Tom, illus. 2nd ed. 2005. (Talk-Along Bks.). 32p. (J). pap. 6.99 (978-0-9657211-3-4(2)) Tomoka Pr.

Rader, Laura. Santa's New Suit. Rader, Laura, illus. 2004. (Illus.). 32p. (J). (gr. k-3). reprint ed. 13.00 (978-0-7567-7154-6(4)) DIANE Publishing Co.

—Santa's New Suit. 2000. (Illus.). 40p. (J). (ps-3). 12.95 (978-0-06-028439-8(0)); 12.89 (978-0-06-029284-3(9)) HarperCollins Pubs.

Rao, Sandhya. My Mother's Sari. Sabnani, Nina, illus. 2006. 28p. (J). (gr. k-2). 14.95 (978-0-7358-2101-9(1)) North-South Bks., Inc.

Reidy, Hannah. All Sorts of Clothes. Dodd, Emma, illus. 2005. (All Sort of Things Ser.). 24p. (C). (gr. k-3). 22.60 (978-1-4048-1063-1(3)) Picture Window Bks.

Reisfeld, Randi, et al. Zoey 101: Pranky Pranky. 2006. (Teenick Ser.: Bk. 3). 120p. (J). pap. 4.99 (978-0-439-83159-8(8)) Scholastic, Inc.

Remkiewicz, Frank, illus. Froggy Gets Dressed. 2002. (Froggy Ser.). (J). 13.19 (978-0-7587-2550-9(7)) Book Wholesalers, Inc.

Ricci, Christine. Dora's Costume Party! Saunders, Zina, illus. 2005. 24p. (J). lib. bdg. 9.00 (***978-1-4242-0978-1(1)***) Fitzgerald Bks.

Richmond, Marianne R. My Shoes Take Me Where I Want to Go! A Journey Through the Imagination. Richmond, Marianne R., illus. 2006. (Illus.). 40p. (J). 15.95 (978-0-9753528-6-1(5)) Marianne Richmond Studios, Inc.

Robert, Naima Bint. The Swirling Hijaab. Mistry, Nilesh, illus. 2004. 24p. (J). (TAM, CZE, VIE, SPA & GUJ.). (978-1-85269-119-6(0)); (TAM, CZE, VIE, SPA & GUJ.). (978-1-85269-143-1(3)); (TAM, CZE, VIE, SPA & GUJ.). (978-1-85269-160-8(3)); (TAM, CZE, VIE, SPA & GUJ.). (978-1-85269-161-5(1)); (TAM, CZE, VIE, SPA & GUJ.). (978-1-85269-163-9(8)); (TAM, CZE, VIE, SPA & GUJ.). (978-1-85269-165-3(4)); (TAM, CZE, VIE, SPA & GUJ.). (978-1-85269-167-7(0)); (TAM, CZE, VIE, SPA & GUJ.). (978-1-85269-178-3(6)); (TAM, CZE, VIE, SPA & GUJ.). (978-1-85269-179-0(4)); (TAM, CZE, VIE, SPA & GUJ.). (978-1-85269-180-6(8)); (TAM, CZE, VIE, SPA & GUJ.). (978-1-85269-181-3(6)); (TAM, CZE, VIE, SPA & GUJ.). (978-1-85269-182-0(4)); (CZE, TAM, VIE, SPA & GUJ.). (978-1-85269-188-2(3)); (TAM, CZE, VIE, SPA & GUJ.). (978-1-85269-189-9(1)); (TAM, CZE, VIE, SPA & GUJ.). (978-1-85269-629-0(X)); (TAM, CZE, VIE, SPA & GUJ.). (978-1-85269-669-6(9)); (TAM, CZE, VIE, SPA & GUJ.). (978-1-85269-910-9(8)) Mantra Publishing, Ltd.

Rollins, Susan. New Shoes, Red Shoes. Rollins, Susan, illus. 2000. (Illus.). 32p. (J). (ps-1). pap. 15.95 (978-0-531-30268-2(7) , Orchard Bks.) Scholastic, Inc.

Rose, Gerald. Millie's Big Surprise. (Illus.). 32p. 2004. (J). pap. 9.99 (978-1-84270-319-9(6)); 2003. (978-1-84270-176-8(2)) Andersen GBR. *Dist:* Independent Pubs. Group, Random Hse. of Canada, Ltd.

Rose, Maddy. Fancy Dress. 2007. (Illus.). 24p. (J). pap. 9.95 (***978-1-86230-341-6(X)***) Transworld Publishers Ltd. GBR. *Dist:* Independent Pubs. Group.

Ross, Tony. Centipede's One Hundred Shoes. rev. ed. 2003. (Illus.). 32p. (J). (ps-2). 16.95 (978-0-8050-7298-3(5) , Holt, Henry & Co. Bks. For Young Readers) Holt, Henry & Co.

Rubin, Cathy. Ellie: The Perfect Dress for Me. Fowler, Christopher, illus. 2005. (Eleanor Ser.). 32p. (J). (gr. k-3). 15.95 (978-0-7696-3299-5(8) , Gingham Dog Pr.) School Specialty Publishing.

Sanders, Lorraine. Where Is Your Jacket! 1999. (Illus.). 20p. (J). (gr. k-6). pap. 5.95 (978-0-9655064-9-6(5)) Amber Bks.

Santa's Suit. 2006. (J). (***978-1-932570-71-7(3)***) Literacy Footprints Inc.

Saunders. The Night Queens Blue Velvet Dress. 1999. pap. (978-0-7398-0870-2(2)) Steck-Vaughn.

Schertle, Alice. The Skeleton in the Closet. Jobling, Curtis, illus. 2003. 32p. (J). (gr. 1 up). 15.99 (978-0-688-17738-6(7)) HarperCollins Pubs.

Schmauss, Judy Kentor. Parade Day. 2006. (Reader's Clubhouse Set B Ser.). (Illus.). 24p. (J). pap. 3.99 (978-0-7641-3293-3(8)) Barron's Educational Series, Inc.

Scholastic, Inc. Staff & Giovanni, Nikki. The Girls in the Circle. Johnson, Cathy Ann, illus. 2004. (Just for You! Ser.). 32p. pap. 3.99 (978-0-439-56861-6(7) , Teaching Resources) Scholastic, Inc.

Schreiber, Anne. Shoe, Shoes, Shoes. Handelman, Dorothy, photos by. 1998. (Real Kids Readers Ser.: 2). (Illus.). 32p. (J). (gr. k-2). pap. 4.99 (978-0-7613-2029-6(6) , Millbrook Pr.) Lerner Publishing Group.

—Shoes, Shoes, Shoes. Handelman, Dorothy, photos by. 1998. (Real Kids Readers Ser.). (Illus.). 32p. (gr. k-2). lib. bdg. 18.90 (978-0-7613-2004-3(0) , Millbrook Pr.) Lerner Publishing Group.

Schwarz, Viviane. Timothy & the Strong Pajamas. 2008. 40p. (J). pap. 16.99 (***978-0-545-03329-9(2)*** , Levine, Arthur A. Bks.) Scholastic, Inc.

Scott, Lori Z. Megan Rose has Ants in Her Pants. 2007. 96p. (J). pap. 4.99 (***978-0-7847-2105-6(X)***) Standard Publishing.

Shahan, Sherry. Un Abrigo Lleno de Burbujas. Romo, Alberto, tr. Becker, Neesa, illus. 1999. (Books for Young Learners).Tr. of Coat Full of Bubbles. (SPA.). 12p. (J). (gr. k-2). pap. 5.00 (978-1-57274-294-9(1)) Owen, Richard C. Pubs., Inc.

Sharmat, Marjorie Weinman. Lost My Shoe. 2000. (J). (978-0-15-202008-8(X)) Harcourt Trade Pubs.

Shea, Bob. New Socks. 2007. (Illus.). 48p. (J). (ps-1). 12.99 (978-0-316-01357-4(9)) Little Brown & Co.

Shuff, Lana Tanaka. Kira Helps A Friend. l.t. ed. 2007. (ENG., Illus.). 28p. (J). per. 9.95 (***978-1-4327-0810-8(4)***) Outskirts Press, Inc.

Sieweke, Susan. Annie Nell & the Sock Gnomes. 2007. (J). per. 9.99 (***978-1-60247-017-0(0)***) Tate Publishing & Enterprises, L.L.C.

Silverhardt, Lauryn. I Can Get Dressed! 2003. (Baby Blue's Clues Ser.). (Illus.). 8p. (J). 17.95 (978-0-689-85977-9(5) , Simon Spotlight/Nickelodeon) Simon & Schuster Children's Publishing.

Slater, David Michael. Jacques & Spock. Tilley, Debbie, illus. 2004. 32p. (J). (gr. k-3). tchr. ed. 15.00 (978-0-618-15980-2(0) , Clarion Bks.) Houghton Mifflin Co. Trade & Reference Div.

Spalding, Andrea. Sarah May & the New Red Dress. 2000. (ps-2). lib. bdg. 15.25 (978-0-613-83716-3(9)) Tandem Library Bks.

Spinelli, Eileen. In My New Yellow Shirt. Takahashi, Hideko, illus. rev. ed. 2001. 32p. (J). (ps-k). 17.95 (978-0-8050-6242-7(4) , Holt, Henry & Co. Bks. For Young Readers) Holt, Henry & Co.

Stine, R.L. Stepsister. 2005. 165p. (J). lib. bdg. 13.00 (***978-1-4242-0998-9(6)***) Fitzgerald Bks.

Stinson, Kathy. One More Clue. 2005. (Streetlights Ser.). 104p. (J). (gr. 2). 7.95 (978-1-55028-888-9(1)) Lorimer, James & Co., Ltd., Pubs. CAN. *Dist:* Casemate Pubs. & Bk. Distributors, LLC.

—Red Is Best. Lewis, Robin Baird, illus. 25th ed. 2006. 32p. (J). (ps-1). lib. bdg. 19.95 (978-1-55451-052-8(X)); pap. 5.95 (978-1-55451-051-1(1)) Annick Pr., Ltd. CAN. *Dist:* Firefly Bks., Ltd.

Strauss, Linda Leopold. The Princess Gown. Laugesen, Malene, illus. 2008. (J). ***(*978-0-618-86259-7(5))*** Houghton Mifflin Co.

Stripling, Ashley. No clothes for Ashley. 2004. 27p. pap. 14.95 (978-1-4137-1826-3(4)) PublishAmerica, Inc.

Su, Lucy. Play Dressing Up. Su, Lucy, illus. 2003. (Kitten & Baby Kitten Ser.). (Illus.). 42p. (J). bds. (978-1-85602-463-1(6)) Chrysalis Children's Bks.

Sydor, Colleen. Fashion Fandango. Pavanel, Jane, ed. Langlois, Suzane & Vernex, Lenka, illus. 2000. (Generation Norah Ser.: Vol. 1). 112p. (J). (gr. 3-7). pap. 6.95 (978-1-894222-17-4(2)) Lobster Pr. CAN. *Dist:* Univ. of Toronto Pr.

Taback, Simms. Joseph Had a Little Overcoat. Taback, Simms, illus. 2002. (Illus.). (J). 22.72 (978-0-7587-0052-0(0)) Book Wholesalers, Inc.

—Joseph Had a Little Overcoat. Taback, Simms, illus. (Illus.). pap. incl. audio compact disk (978-1-59112-608-9(8)); 2001. (J). 28.95 incl. audio compact disk (978-1-59112-412-2(3)) Live Oak Media.

—Joseph Had a Little Overcoat. unabr. ed. 2001. (Live Oak Readalong Ser.). (Illus.). (J). (ps-2). 25.95 incl. audio (978-0-87499-783-5(6)) Live Oak Media.

—Joseph Had a Little Overcoat. Taback, Simms, illus. 1999. (Illus.). 32p. (J). (ps-3). 16.99 (978-0-670-87855-0(3), Viking Juvenile) Penguin Group (USA) Inc.

Tabby, Abigail. Snap! Button! Zip! Moroney, Christopher, illus. 2003. (Sesame Beginnings Ser.). 14p. (J). (gr. k). bds. 7.99 (978-0-375-82369-5(7), Random Hse. Bks. for Young Readers) Random Hse. Children's Bks.

The Tale of Jackie Berry. 2005. (J). per. 12.95 (978-0-9677047-5-3(8)) Marble House Editions.

Thiesing, Lisa. The Scarecrow's New Clothes. Thiesing, Lisa, illus. 2006. (Illus.). 32p. (J). (ps-2). 13.99 (978-0-525-47750-1(0), Dutton Juvenile) Penguin Group (USA) Inc.

Thomassie, Tynia. Mimi's Tutu. Gilchrist, Jan Spivey, illus. 2002. 32p. (J). (gr. k-2). pap. 5.99 (978-0-590-44021-9(7), Scholastic Pr.) Scholastic, Inc.

—Mimi's Tutu. 2001. (978-0-606-22267-9(7)) Tandem Library Bks.

Thomson, Pat. Treasure Sock. (Illus.). 32p. (J). pap. 7.95 (978-0-14-038886-2(9)) Penguin Bks., Ltd. GBR. *Dist:* Trafalgar Square Publishing.

Thorpe, Kiki. New Boots for Bob! 2003. (gr. k-3). lib. bdg. 11.80 (978-0-613-66369-4(1)) Tandem Library Bks.

Tibo, Gilles. Alex & the Team Jersey. Germain, Philippe, illus. 2005. (Read-It! Readers Ser.). 32p. (J). (gr. k-3). 18.60 (978-1-4048-1024-2(2)) Picture Window Bks.

Tinstman, Gretchen. Meet the Silly Sisters. 2006. 28p. (J). per. 12.99 ***(*978-1-59886-683-4(4))*** Tate Publishing & Enterprises, L.L.C.

Tomizawa, Hitoshi. Alien Nine 1, Vol. 1. Pannone, Frank, ed. Jackson, Laura & Kobayashi, Yoko, trs. from JPN. Tomizawa, Hitoshi, illus. 2003. (Illus.). 224p. (gr. 11 up). pap. 15.95 (978-1-58664-891-6(8), CMX 64201G, CPM Manga) Central Park Media Corp.

—Alien Nine 2, Vol. 2. Pannone, Frank, ed. Jackson, Laura & Kobayashi, Yoko, trs. from JPN. Tomizawa, Hitoshi, illus. 2003. (Illus.). 224p. (gr. 11 up). pap. 15.95 (978-1-58664-892-3(6), CMX 64202G, CPM Manga) Central Park Media Corp.

—Alien Nine 3, Vol. 3. Pannone, Frank, ed. Jackson, Laura & Kobayashi, Yoko, trs. from JPN. Tomizawa, Hitoshi, illus. 2003. (Illus.). 224p. pap. 15.95 (978-1-58664-893-0(4), CMX 64203G, CPM Manga) Central Park Media Corp.

Tomos, Angharad. Y Llipryn Llwyd. 2005. (WEL., Illus.). 48p. pap. (978-0-86243-095-5(X)) Y Lolfa.

Too Many Clothes: Individual Title Six-Packs. (Literatura 2000 Ser.). (gr. k-1). 28.00 (978-0-7635-0068-9(2)) Rigby Education.

Toriyama, Akira. Dr. Slump, Vol. 4. Toriyama, Akira, illus. 2005. (Dr. Slump Ser.). 200p. (YA). pap. 7.99 (978-1-4215-0165-9(1)) Viz Media.

Trasler, Janee. Ghost Gets Dressed! 2007. (Little Boo! Bks.). 24p. (J). (ps-1). 5.99 ***(*978-0-316-06530-6(7))*** Little, Brown Bks. for Young Readers.

Valckx, Catharina. Lizette's Green Sock. 2005. (Illus.). 40p. (J). (gr. k-3). 15.00 (978-0-618-45298-9(2), Clarion Bks.) Houghton Mifflin Co. Trade & Reference Div.

Van Kersen, Elizabeth. Who's Riley. 2005. (Illus.). 50p. (J). per. 8.99 (978-1-932338-90-4(X)) Lifevest Publishing, Inc.

Vantrease, Norma. Ants in My Pants. Vantrease, Norma & Cox, Steve, trs. Cox, Steve, illus. 2004. (Rookie Reader Ser.). 31p. (J). 19.50 (978-0-516-23443-4(9), Children's Pr.) Scholastic Library Publishing.

Vestiti Nuovi dell Imperatore. pap. 14.95 (978-88-04-45657-5(4)) Mondadori ITA. *Dist:* Distribooks, Inc.

Vigil-Pion, Evangelina. Marina's Muumuu/ el muumuu de Marina. Torrecilla, Pablo, illus. 2001. Tr. of Muumuu de Marina. (ENG & SPA.). 32p. (J). (ps-3). 14.95 (978-1-55885-350-8(2), Piñata Books) Arte Publico Pr.

Wake, Shelley. Wrinkly Socks Make Me Giggle. Tufts, N. Jo, illus. 2006. (J). pap. 4.95 (978-1-57874-086-4(X)) Kaeden Corp.

Wang, Margaret. The Right Shoes for Me. 2006. (Illus.). 12p. (J). 9.95 (978-1-58117-494-6(2), Intervisual/Piggy Toes) Dalmatian Pr.

Waterton, Betty. A Bumblebee Sweater. LaFave, Kim, illus. 2007. 32p. (J). (ps-3). ***(*978-1-55455-028-9(9))*** Fitzhenry & Whiteside, Ltd.

Watson, J. D. My Socks Don't Match. 2004. 41p. pap. 19.95 (978-1-4137-1935-2(X)) PublishAmerica, Inc.

Webb, Steve. Polly Jean Pyjama Queen. 2006. (Illus.). 32p. (J). pap. 9.99 ***(*978-0-09-946402-0(0)***, Red Fox) Random Hse. Children's Bks. GBR. *Dist:* Independent Pubs. Group.

Wells, Rosemary. Max & Ruby's Snowy Day. 2004. (Max & Ruby Ser.). 10p. (J). (ps). bds. 6.99 (978-0-448-43567-1(5), Grosset & Dunlap) Penguin Group (USA) Inc.

—Max's New Suit. 2003. 12p. (J). pap. 6.99 (978-0-670-88718-7(8), Viking Juvenile) Penguin Group (USA) Inc.

White, Ellen Emerson. White House Autumn. 2008. (YA). pap. 8.99 ***(*978-0-312-37489-1(5))*** Feiwel & Friends.

Willard, Eliza. Totally Crushed. 2008. (Candy Apple Ser.). 160p. (J). pap. 4.99 ***(*978-0-545-02814-1(0)***, Scholastic Paperbacks) Scholastic, Inc.

Williams, Dawn. Centipede looks for New Shoes, 1. 2006. (Illus.). 48p. (J). per. 21.95 (978-0-9770783-0-1(2)) SunriseHouse Pubs.

Williams, Jacklyn. Happy Halloween, Gus! Cushman, Doug, illus. 2005. (Read-It! Readers Ser.). 32p. (J). (gr. k-3). 18.60 (978-1-4048-0960-4(0)) Picture Window Bks.

Williams, Joyce Hall. Can Cousin Kunju Cut a Kanga? 1999. (Illus.). 16p. (J). pap. 8.95 (978-0-7414-0190-8(8)) Infinity Publishing.

Williams, Karen Lynn & Mohammed, Khadra. Four Feet, Two Sandals. Chayka, Doug, illus. 2007. 32p. (J). (gr. 2-5). 17.00 (978-0-8028-5296-0(3), Eerdmans Bks For Young Readers) Eerdmans, William B. Publishing Co.

Williamson, Greg. Why Do I Have to Wear Glasses? Popko, Wendy, illus. 2005. (J). 12.99 (978-0-9666076-5-9(1)) Peerless Publishing, L.L.C.

—Why Do I Have to Wear Glasses? Popkp, Wendy, illus. 2005. (J). pap. 7.99 (978-0-9666076-3-5(5)) Peerless Publishing, L.L.C.

Willson, Sarah. My Dress-up Party. Oxley, Jennifer, illus. ed. 2005. 22p. (J). lib. bdg. 15.00 (978-1-59054-971-1(6)) Fitzgerald Bks.

Wojtowycz, David, illus. What Will You Wear, Claude? 2004. 10p. (J). (ps-3). reprint ed. 8.00 (978-0-7567-8259-7(7)) DIANE Publishing Co.

Zemke, Deborah, illus. I'm Going to Read (Level 2): Green Boots, Blue Hair, Polka-Dot Underwear. 2007. (I'm Going to Read Ser.). 28p. (J). pap. 3.95 (978-1-4027-4245-3(2)) Sterling Publishing Co., Inc.

Ziefert, Harriet. Clara Ann Cookie. Bolam, Emily, illus. 1999. 32p. (J). (gr. k-3). tchr. ed. 15.00 (978-0-395-92324-5(7), Walter Lorraine) Houghton Mifflin Co. Trade & Reference Div.

CLOTHING TRADE

Casolino, Peter, illus. & photos by. Kid's Clothes: From Start to Finish. Casolino, Peter, photos by. Woods, Samuel G., photos by. 2001. 32p. (J). (gr. 3-6). 23.70 (978-1-56711-483-6(0), Blackbirch Pr., Inc.) Thomson Gale.

Giacobello, John. Careers in the Fashion Industry. rev. ed. 1999. (Careers). (Illus.). 122p. (YA). (gr. 7-12). lib. bdg. 18.95 (978-0-8239-2890-3(X), CAFASH) Rosen Publishing Group, Inc., The.

J.G. Ferguson Publishing Company Staff, contrib. by. What Can I Do Now? 2007. (What Can I Do Now Ser.). 168p. (J). (gr. 6-12). 29.95 ***(*978-0-8160-6029-0(0)***, Ferguson Publishing Co.) Facts On File, Inc.

Jones, Jen. Fashion Careers: Finding the Right Fit. 2007. (Illus.). 32p. (J). (978-0-7368-6829-7(1), 1264957, Capstone Bks.) Capstone Pr., Inc.

—Fashion Careers: Finding the Right Fit. 2007. (Illus.). 32p. (J). ***(*978-0-7368-7883-8(1)***, 1264957, Capstone Bks.) Capstone Pr., Inc.

Jones, Jen. Fashion History: Looking Great Through the Ages. 2007. (Illus.). 32p. (J). (978-0-7368-6828-0(3)) Capstone Pr., Inc.

McAlpine, Margaret. Working in the Fashion Industry. 2005. (My Future Career Ser.). (Illus.). 64p. (J). lib. bdg. 26.00 (978-0-8368-4774-1(1)) Stevens, Gareth Inc.

McPherson, Stephanie Sammartino. Levi Strauss. 2007. (History Maker Bios Ser.). (Illus.). 48p. (J). 26.60 (978-0-8225-6581-9(1), Lerner Pubns.) Lerner Publishing Group.

Raatma, Lucia. Levi Strauss. 2004. (Compass Point Early Biographies Ser.). (Illus.). 32p. (J). (gr. 2 up). lib. bdg. 21.26 (978-0-7565-0568-4(2)) Compass Point Bks.

CLOTHING TRADE—FICTION

Carvalho, Paula, et al. The Story of Calvin Cotton. 2001. (Illus.). 20p. (J). (gr. 1-4). 16.95 (978-0-9715636-0-5(8)) Chris Paul USA.

CLOUDS

Aigner-Clark, Julie. Baby Einstein: Baby Galileo, the World Around Me: Sky, Spanish-Language Edition. Zaidi, Nadeem, illus. 2005. (Baby Einstein: Libros de Carton Ser.). (SPA.). 22p. (J). bds. 15.95 (978-970-718-312-4(8), Silver Dolphin en Español) Advanced Marketing, S. de R. L. de C. V. MEX. *Dist:* Perseus Distribution.

Bauer, Marion Dane. Clouds. Wallace, John, illus. ed. 2005. 32p. (J). lib. bdg. 15.00 (978-1-59054-923-0(6)) Fitzgerald Bks.

Bauer, Marion Dane & Wallace, John. Clouds. 2004. (Ready-to-Read Ser.). (Illus.). 32p. (J). pap. 3.99 (978-0-689-85441-5(2), Aladdin) Simon & Schuster Children's Publishing.

Burton, Margie, et al. Clouds. Adams, Alison, ed. 1999. (Early Connections Ser.). 16p. (J). (gr. k-2). pap. 4.50 (978-1-58344-057-5(7)) Benchmark Education Co.

Clouds. 2005. (Our Seasons & Weather Ser.). (YA). (gr. k-3). (978-1-56065-840-5(1), Pebble Bks.) Capstone Pr., Inc.

Clouds: Individual Title Six-Packs. (Literatura 2000 Ser.). (gr. 2-3). 33.00 (978-0-7635-0222-5(7)) Rigby Education.

Clouds Weather. 2006. (Illus.). 24p. (J). (gr. k-2). 18.50 ***(*978-0-531-17876-8(5))*** Scholastic Library Publishing.

Doudna, Kelly. It Is Cloudy. 2003. (Weather Ser.). (Illus.). 23p. (J). (ps-3). lib. bdg. 19.93 (978-1-57765-773-6(X)) ABDO Publishing Co.

Flanagan, Alice K. Clouds. 2003. (Wonder Books Level 1: Weather Ser.). (Illus.). 24p. (J). (ps-2). 22.79 (978-1-56766-450-8(4)) Child's World, Inc.

Galiano, Dean. Clouds, Rain & Snow. rev. ed. 2005. (Weather Watcher's Library). (Illus.). 48p. (gr. 5-8). lib. bdg. 23.95 (978-0-8239-3771-4(2)) Rosen Publishing Group, Inc., The.

Gill, Janie S. Why Clouds Have Shapes. Wing, Lori, illus. 1999. 23p. (J). pap. 3.95 (978-0-89868-447-6(1)) ARO Publishing Co.

Gregoire, Maryellen. Clouds. 2005. (Weather Update Ser.). (Illus.). 25p. (J). 21.26 (978-0-7368-3736-1(1)) Capstone Pr., Inc.

Hannah, Julie & Holub, Joan. The Man Who Named the Clouds. Billin-Frye, Paige, illus. 2006. 40p. (J). 15.95 (978-0-8075-4974-2(6)) Whitman, Albert & Co.

Herriges, Ann. Clouds. 2006. (Blastoff! Readers Ser.). (Illus.). 24p. (J). lib. bdg. 16.95 (978-1-60014-024-2(6)) Bellwether Media.

Jennings, Terry J. The Weather: Clouds. 2004. (J). lib. bdg. 27.10 (978-1-59389-147-3(4)) Chrysalis Education.

Korb, Rena B. Crazy about Clouds. Reibeling, Brandon, illus. 2007. (Science Rocks Ser.). 32p. (J). (ps-4). lib. bdg. 27.07 ***(*978-1-60270-037-6(0)***, Looking Glass Library) Magic Wagon.

Las Nubes: Individual Title Six-Packs. (Literatura 2000 Ser.). (SPA.). (gr. 2-3). 33.00 (978-0-7635-1267-5(2)) Rigby Education.

Learning about Clouds. (Rosen Real Readers Big Bookstm Ser.). 8p. (J). (gr. k-1). 27.95 (978-1-4042-6208-9(3)) Rosen Publishing Group, Inc., The.

MacKall, Dandi Daley. Cloud Counting. Newton, Jill, illus. 2004. (Imagination Ser.). 12p. 6.99 (978-0-8066-4383-0(8), Augsburg Bks.) Augsburg Fortress, Pubs.

Markert, Jenny. Clouds: Faces of the Sky. 2001. (LifeViews Ser.). (Illus.). 32p. (J). lib. bdg. (978-1-58341-243-5(3), Creative Education) Creative Co., The.

Mayer, Cassie. Clouds. 2006. (Illus.). 24p. (J). (978-1-4034-8411-6(2)); pap. 5.99 (978-1-4034-8419-2(8)) Heinemann Library.

—Nubes. 2006. (ENG & SPA., Illus.). 24p. (J). ***(*978-1-4034-8652-3(2))*** Heinemann Library.

—Nubes (Clouds) 2006. (ENG & SPA., Illus.). 24p. (J). pap. ***(*978-1-4034-8660-8(3))*** Heinemann Library.

Merk, A. Clouds. 2003. (Weather Report Discovery Library). (Illus.). 24p. (gr. 1-4). 14.95 (978-1-58952-570-2(1)) Rourke Publishing, LLC.

Miles, Elizabeth. Clouds. 2004. (J). pap. 7.25 (978-1-4034-5673-1(9)); lib. bdg. 24.21 (978-1-4034-5575-8(9)) Heinemann Library.

Nelson, Robin. Cloudy. 2004. (First Step Nonfiction Ser.). (Illus.). 8p. (J). pap. (978-0-8225-5368-7(6), Lerner Pubns.) Lerner Publishing Group.

—A Cloudy Day. (First Step Nonfiction Ser.). (Illus.). 24p. (gr. k-2). 2005. lib. bdg. 17.27 (978-0-8225-0172-5(4)); 2003. (J). pap. 4.25 (978-0-8225-1961-4(5)) Lerner Publishing Group.

Peterson, Roger T., et al. Peterson First Guide to Clouds & Weather. 2nd ed. 1998. (First Guides). (Illus.). 128p. pap. 5.95 (978-0-395-90663-7(6)) Houghton Mifflin Co. Trade & Reference Div.

Picture Window Books, contrib. by. Shapes in the Sky. (Amazing Science Ser.). 24p. (J). pap. 7.95 (978-1-4048-0341-1(6)) Picture Window Bks.

Rau, Dana Meachen. Fluffy, Flat, & Wet: A Book about Clouds. Shea, Denise, illus. 2005. (Amazing Science Ser.). 24p. (J). (ps-k). lib. bdg. 22.60 (978-1-4048-1134-8(6)) Picture Window Bks.

Richards, Julie. It's Cloudy! 2004. (J). lib. bdg. 27.10 (978-1-58340-537-6(2)) Smart Apple Media.

Rockwell, Anne F. Clouds. 40p. (J). (ps-1). Date not set. 15.99 (978-0-06-029101-3(X)); Date not set. pap. 4.99 (978-0-06-445220-5(4)); Date not set. lib. bdg. 16.89 (978-0-06-029102-0(8)) HarperCollins Pubs.

Rodgers, Alan. Cloud Cover. 2003. (gr. 3-6). lib. bdg. 14.75 (978-0-613-45729-3(3)) Tandem Library Bks.

Rodgers, Alan & Streluk, Angella. Cloud Cover. 2002. (Measuring the Weather Ser.). (Illus.). 32p. (J). (gr. 3-5). lib. bdg. 22.79 (978-1-58810-686-5(1)) Heinemann Library.

Rogers, Allen & Streluk, Angella. Cloud Cover. 2002. (Illus.). 32p. (J). (gr. 3-5). pap. (978-1-4034-0126-7(8), 91631) Heinemann Library.

Saunders-Smith, Gail. La Lluvia/Rain. 2003. (Weather Bilingual Ser.). (ENG & SPA., Illus.). 24p. (J). lib. bdg. 15.93 (978-0-7368-2309-8(3)) Capstone Pr., Inc.

Sherman, Joseph. Shapes in the Sky: A Book about Clouds. Wesley, Omarr, illus. 2004. (Amazing Science Ser.). 24p. (C). (gr. k-3). 22.60 (978-1-4048-0097-7(2)) Picture Window Bks.

Staub, Frank. The Kids' Book of Clouds & Sky. 2005. (Illus.). 80p. (J). pap. 9.95 (978-1-4027-2806-8(9)) Sterling Publishing Co., Inc.

Tanner, Susan. Clouds: Learning the CL Sound. (Power-Phonics Ser.). (Illus.). (J). 2002. 24p. (gr. 1). lib. bdg. 18.50 (978-0-8239-5942-6(2)); 2001. 23p. pap. 26.40 (978-0-8239-8287-5(4)) Rosen Publishing Group, Inc., The. (PowerKids Pr.).

Trueit, Trudi Strain. Clouds. 2002. (Watts Library). (Illus.). 64p. (J). (gr. 5-7). 25.50 (978-0-531-11969-3(6), Watts, Franklin) Scholastic Library Publishing.

Webster, Christine. Clouds. 2006. (Science Matters Ser.). (J). (978-1-59036-411-6(2)); pap. (978-1-59036-417-8(1)) Weigl Pubs., Inc.

Wilshire, Florence A. Messages from the Skies. 2005. 82p. pap. 7.42 (978-1-4116-4316-1(X)) Lulu.com.

Winner, Cherie. Clouds, Storms, & Rainbows. Recher, Andrew & Rogge, Rachel, illus. 2008. (J). ***(*978-1-55971-992-6(3))***; pap. ***(*978-1-55971-993-3(1))*** T&N Children's Publishing. (NorthWord Bks. for Young Readers).

The Years of Tears & His Glory, 1. 2003. (Illus.). 240p. per. 10.00 (978-0-9740882-0-4(X), YoT1) C & H Pubns.

CLOWNS

Burgess, Ron. Be a Clown! Techniques from a Real Clown. Barberie, Heather, illus. 2001. (Quick Starts for Kids! Ser.). 64p. (YA). (gr. 3 up). pap. 8.95 (978-1-885593-57-3(0), Williamson Bks.) Ideals Pubns.

The Clown: Individual Title Six-Packs. (Chiquilibros Ser.). (gr. k-1). 23.00 (978-0-7635-0409-0(2)) Rigby Education.

Jordan, Denise M. Circus Clowns. 2003. (Heinemann Read & Learn Ser.). (Illus.). 24p. (J). (ps-1). lib. bdg. 18.50 (978-1-58810-544-8(X)) Heinemann Library.

—Payasos de Circo. 2002. 24p. (J). (ps-1). pap. 5.25 (978-1-58810-845-6(7), 91571); (SPA.). lib. bdg. 17.08 (978-1-58810-798-5(1)) Heinemann Library.

Perkins, Catherine. How to Be a Clown. 2006. (Most Excellent Book Of- Ser.). (Illus.). 32p. (J). (978-1-59604-124-0(2)) Stargazer Bks.

Stolzenberg, Mark. Be a Clown. 2003. (Illus.). 160p. (YA). (gr. 4-12). pap. 10.95 (978-0-8069-5804-0(9)) Sterling Publishing Co., Inc.

Tuxworth, Nicola. Funny Faces. 2005. (Illus.). 12p. (ps). bds. 6.99 (978-0-7548-1332-3(0), Lorenz Bks.) Anness Publishing GBR. *Dist:* National Bk. Network.

—Funny Faces. 1999. (Very First Picture Bks.). (Illus.). 12p. bds. 4.95 (978-0-7548-0066-8(0)) Anness Publishing, Inc.

Wilkerson, J. L. Sad-Face Clown: Emmett Kelly. 2004. (Great Heartlanders Ser.). (Illus.). 118p. (J). per. 9.95 (978-0-9664470-9-5(3), AB7093) Acorn Bks.

CLOWNS—FICTION

Armstrong, Nancy. Bozo: Desktop Bop Bag. 2004. (Illus.). 32p. pap. 8.95 (978-0-7624-1862-6(1), Running Pr. Minature Editions) Running Pr. Bk. Pubs.

Benjamin, Cynthia. What's Going On? Handelman, Dorothy, photos by. 1999. (Real Kids Readers Ser.). (Illus.). 32p. (gr. k-2). lib. bdg. 18.90 (978-0-7613-2070-8(9), Millbrook Pr.) Lerner Publishing Group.

—What's Going On? Handelman, Dorothy, illus. 1999. (Real Kids Readers Ser.). 32p. (J). (gr. k-2). pap. 4.99 (978-0-7613-2095-1(4), Millbrook Pr.) Lerner Publishing Group.

—What's Going On? 1999. (J). (978-0-606-19180-7(1)); lib. bdg. 11.80 (978-0-613-18167-9(0)) Tandem Library Bks.

Blake, Quentin. Clown. 1998. (gr. k-3). lib. bdg. 16.40 (978-0-613-78385-9(9)) Tandem Library Bks.

But You Promised! A Book about Keeping Your Word. 1998. (Big Comfy Couch Ser.). (Illus.). 32p. (J). 5.95 (978-0-7370-1001-5(0)) Time-Life Inc.

Cassidy, Anne. Toby's Trousers. Lewis, Jan, illus. 2005. (Reading Corner Ser.). 24p. (J). (gr. k-3). lib. bdg. 22.80 (978-1-59771-009-1(1)) Sea-To-Sea Pubns.

Clown Is Sick: Individual Title Six-Packs. (Sails Literacy Ser.). (gr. 1-2). 36.00 (978-0-7578-6715-6(4)) Rigby Education.

Clown Paints His House: Early Level Satellite Individual Title Six-Packs. (Sails Literacy Ser.). 16p. (gr. 1-2). 27.00 (978-0-7578-2920-8(1)) Rigby Education.

Clowns. Date not set. 9.95 (978-0-89868-287-8(8)) ARO Publishing Co.

Damjan, Mischa. The Clown Said No. Casty, Gian, illus. 2007. 32p. (J). 17.99 ***(*978-0-698-40063-4(1)***, Minedition) Penguin Group (USA) Inc.

Damschroder, Scott. The Crazy Carnival Clown We Call Croc. 2006. (Illus.). 40p. (J). lib. bdg. 19.95 ***(*978-0-9754728-1-1(X)***, Blue Foot Pr.) MidAmerica Publishing Co.

Fancher, Joseph. Sydney's Travels Through Dreamland Part. 2006. 48p. pap. 12.95 (978-1-4241-3690-2(3)) PublishAmerica, Inc.

Fox, Diane. What Color Is That, Piggywiggy? Fox, Christyan, illus. 2001. 10p. (J). (ps-k). 5.95 (978-1-929766-17-8(3)) Handprint Bks.

Goldberg, Dennis. Double Bubble Trouble. 2007. (J). 14.95 ***(*978-1-933769-19-6(X))*** Level 4 Press, Inc.

Harper, Jo. Ollie Jolly, Rodeo Clown. Meissner, Amy, illus. 2002. 32p. (J). (gr. k-3). 15.95 (978-1-55868-552-9(9)); pap. 8.95 (978-1-55868-553-6(7)) Graphic Arts Ctr. Publishing Co. (West Winds Pr.).

—Ollie Jolly, Rodeo Clown. 2002. (gr. k-3). lib. bdg. 17.60 (978-0-613-89457-9(X)) Tandem Library Bks.

Hayes, Geoffrey, illus. & text. Patrick at the Circus. Hayes, Geoffrey, text. 2002. (J). lib. bdg. (978-0-7868-2595-0(2)) Hyperion Bks. for Children.

Hodes, Loren. How Gumzy the Clown Turned Our Town Upside Down. Hodes, Loren, illus. 2006. (Illus.). 32p. (J). 13.95 (978-1-932443-48-6(7)) Judaica Pr., Inc., The.

Huser, Glen. Touch of the Clown. (YA). (gr. 7-12). 2001. 223p. pap. 5.95 (978-0-88899-357-1(9)); 1999. 176p. 15.95 (978-0-88899-343-4(9)) Groundwood Bks. CAN. *Dist:* Perseus Distribution.

—Touch of the Clown. 2001. (gr. 7-12). lib. bdg. 14.10 (978-0-613-87993-4(7)) Tandem Library Bks.

I Am Jumping, 6 Packs. (Sails Literacy Ser.). 16p. (gr. k up). 27.00 (978-0-7635-4404-1(3)) Rigby Education.

I Can Laugh, 6 Packs. (Sails Literacy Ser.). 16p. (gr. k up). 27.00 (978-0-7635-4397-6(7)) Rigby Education.

I Like Hats: Individual Title, 6 Packs. (Sails Literacy Ser.). 16p. (gr. k up). 27.00 (978-0-7635-4401-0(9)) Rigby Education.

Kline, Trish & Donev, Mary. Don't Frown, Clown! KA Reader 9. 2007. (Illus.). 32p. (J). per. 20.00 ***(*978-1-934307-02-1(5))*** Ghost Hunter Productions.

Krulik, Nancy E. Anyone but Me, No. 1. John and Wendy Staff, illus. 2006. (Katie Kazoo, Switcheroo Ser.: No. 1). 80p. (J). 2.99 (978-0-448-44259-4(0) , Grosset & Dunlap) Penguin Group (USA) Inc.

Lubar, David. Dunk. (YA). (gr. 7-10). 2002. 256p. tchr. ed. 15.00 (978-0-618-19455-1(X) , Clarion Bks.); 2004. 272p. reprint ed. pap. 6.99 (978-0-618-43909-6(9) , Graphia) Houghton Mifflin Co. Trade & Reference Div.

Lyon, Leslie Connell & Lyon, Charles. Surf Clowns. Lyon, Leslie Connell, illus. 2000. (Illus.). 176p. (J). (gr. 3-10). pap. 29.95 (978-0-9675214-4-2(0)) Bad Cat Bks.

MacDonald, Steven. Just Clowning Around: Two Stories. McPhail, David, illus. 2003. 20p. (J). (ps-3). lib. bdg. 11.80 (978-0-613-66362-5(4)) Tandem Library Bks.

—Just Clowning Around: Two Stories. 2000. (Illus.). (J). (978-0-606-18180-8(6)) Tandem Library Bks.

Mackinnon, Debbie & Sieveking, Anthea. What Am I? 2004. (Illus.). 24p. (J). pap. 7.95 (978-1-84507-243-8(X)) Lincoln, Frances Ltd. GBR. *Dist:* Perseus Distribution.

Montgomery Gibson, Jane. Sit down, Clown! Montgomery Gibson, Jane, illus. 2005. (J). bds. 8.99 (978-1-4183-0040-1(3)) Christ Inspired, Inc.

Pennell, Kathleen. Circus of Fear. Pennell, Lauren, illus. 2002. (Pony Investigators Ser.: Vol. III). 96p. (J). (gr. 3-6). pap. 5.95 (978-1-930353-47-3(2)) Masthof Pr.

The Printing Machine: Individual Title Six-Packs. (Literatura 2000 Ser.). (gr. 1-2). 28.00 (978-0-7635-0105-1(0)) Rigby Education.

Randall, Barbara. Baby Clown. Herning, Kathy, ed. 2006. (Mimi's Kids Ser.: vol. 4). (Illus.). 32p. (J). pap. 12.95 (978-0-9712383-8-1(3)) Culture Connection, The.

Rau, Dana Meachen. Clown Around, Level B. Evans, Nate, illus. 2001. (Early Reader Ser.). 32p. (J). (gr. k up). lib. bdg. 18.60 (978-0-7565-0074-0(5)) Compass Point Bks.

Rex, Adam. Tree-Ring Circus. 2006. (Illus.). 32p. (J). 16.00 (978-0-15-205363-5(8)) Harcourt Trade Pubs.

Riddell, Chris & Stewart, Paul. Far-Flung Adventures: Corby Flood. 2006. (Illus.). 256p. (J). (gr. 3-7). 14.95 (978-0-385-75090-5(0)); lib. bdg. 17.99 (978-0-385-75091-2(9)) Random Hse. Children's Bks. (Fickling, David Bks.).

Rigby Education Staff. Clown. (Sails Literacy Ser.). (Illus.). 16p. (gr. 1-2). 27.00 (978-0-7635-9891-4(7) , 698917C99) Rigby Education.

—Clowns Clothes. (Sails Literacy Ser.). (Illus.). 16p. (gr. k-1). 27.00 (978-0-7635-9857-0(7) , 698577C99) Rigby Education.

—A Job for Clown. (Sails Literacy Ser.). (Illus.). 16p. (gr. 1-2). 27.00 (978-0-7635-9907-2(7) , 699077C99) Rigby Education.

—Sailor Sam. (Sails Literacy Ser.). (Illus.). 16p. (gr. 1-2). 27.00 (978-0-7635-9916-4(6) , 699166C99) Rigby Education.

Rodriguez, Lisa M. Bopo Joins the Circus (Bop Se Une al Circo) Rodriguez, David A., ed. Rodriguez, Lisa M., illus. 1998. (Illus.). 34p. (J). (ps-3). 14.95 (978-0-9665575-0-3(6)) BOPO Biligual Bks.

Santillo, LuAnn. Funny Clowns. Santillo, LuAnn, ed. 2003. (Half-Pint Kids Readers Ser.). (Illus.). 7p. (J). (ps-1). pap. (978-1-59256-116-2(0)) Half-Pint Kids, Inc.

Sara & the Crying Clown. 2006. (J). (978-1-933343-15-0(X)) Stabenfeldt Inc.

Scalzo, Linda V. Carazona's Coloring Book. l.t. ed. 2004. (Illus.). 8p. (J). 2.99 (978-0-9753724-3-2(2)) Carazona Creations LLC.

—The Circus Is Coming to Town: Full-Length Version. l.t. ed. 2004. (Illus.). 32p. (J). 9.99 (978-0-9753724-0-1(8)) Carazona Creations LLC.

Shipton, Paul. Clown School. Blake, Beccy, illus. 2005. 24p. (J). lib. bdg. 22.65 (***978-1-59646-752-1(5)***) Dingles & Co.

A Shoe, 6 Packs. (Sails Literacy Ser.). 16p. (gr. k up). 27.00 (978-0-7635-4417-1(5)) Rigby Education.

Stevens, Larry, illus. Clown Games. 2005. (I'm Going to Read Ser.). 32p. (J). (ps-ps). pap. 3.95 (978-1-4027-2723-8(2)) Sterling Publishing Co., Inc.

Tassell, Brad. Billy Fustertag Learns Comedy. Sibrel, Logan, illus. 2000. 32p. (J). pap. 8.00 (978-0-89708-226-6(5)) And Bks.

Time-Life Books Editors. Scaredy Cat: A Book about Being Brave. 1998. (Big Comfy Couch Ser.). (Illus.). 32p. (J). 5.95 (978-0-7370-1000-8(2)) Time-Life Inc.

Los tres Bobos: Individual Title, 6 Packs. (Literatura 2000 Ser.). (SPA.). (gr. 2-3). 33.00 (978-0-7635-1274-3(5)) Rigby Education.

West, Colin. Jenny the Joker. 2006. (Read-It! Chapter Books). (J). 21.26 (978-1-4048-2733-2(1)) Picture Window Bks.

CLUBS

Brian, Sarah Jane. Friendship Bracelets Girls Club Handbook. Barbas, Kerren & Gershman, Jo, illus. 2005. (Activity Journals Ser.). 128p. 12.99 (978-0-88088-365-8(0)) Peter Pauper Pr. Inc.

Whitney, Brooks. Girls Club Kit: Start a Club & Find Friends, Fortune & Fun. 2002. (American Girl Library). (Illus.). 48p. (J). pap. 10.95 (978-1-58485-586-6(X)) American Girl Publishing, Inc.

Winter, Jonah. Paul Revere & the Bell Ringers. Dodson, Bert, illus. 2003. (Ready-to-Read Ser.). 32p. (J). pap. 3.99 (978-0-689-85635-8(0) , Aladdin) Simon & Schuster Children's Publishing.

—Paul Revere & the Bell Ringers. 2003. (gr. k-3). lib. bdg. 11.80 (978-0-613-89003-8(5)) Tandem Library Bks.

CLUBS—FICTION

Anderson, Ho Che. The No-Boys Club. 1998. (J). (gr. 4-7). 160p. 14.95 (978-0-88899-322-9(6)); pap. 5.95 (978-0-88899-321-2(8)) Groundwood Bks. CAN. *Dist:* Perseus Distribution, Transition Vendor.

Arensen, Shel. The Carjackers, Vol. 2. 2003. (Rugendo Rhino Ser.). 128p. pap. 5.99 (978-0-8254-2042-9(3)) Kregel Pubns.

—The Poison Arrow Tree. 2003. (Rugendo Rhino Ser.). (Illus.). 128p. (J). pap. 5.99 (978-0-8254-2041-2(5)) Kregel Pubns.

Bacon, Pamela S. The Beach Club Begins & the Big Dance. 1999. (Beach Club Ser.). 70p. (YA). (gr. 4-10). mass mkt. 3.99 (978-0-9669201-0-9(4)) Pam's Pages.

Barnes, Dawn. Beware of the Haunted Eye. 2007. (Black Belt Club Ser.: No. 3). 128p. (J). pap. 4.99 (978-0-439-85657-7(4) , Blue Sky Pr., The) Scholastic, Inc.

—Night on the Mountain of Fear. Chang, Bernard, illus. 2006. (Black Belt Club Ser.: No. 2). 176p. (J). pap. 4.99 (978-0-439-63939-2(5)); (gr. 2-5). 16.99 (978-0-439-63937-8(9)) Scholastic, Inc. (Blue Sky Pr., The).

Barnes, Dawn. Seven Wheels of Power. 2007. (Black Belt Club Ser.: No. 1). 176p. (J). pap. 2.99 (***978-0-545-01029-0(2)***) Scholastic, Inc.

—Seven Wheels of Power. Chang, Bernard, illus. 2005. (Black Belt Club Ser.: No. 1). 176p. (J). 4.99 (978-0-439-63936-1(0)); pap. 16.95 (978-0-439-63935-4(2)) Scholastic, Inc. (Blue Sky Pr., The).

Bateman, Teresa. The Bully Blockers Club. Urbanovic, Jackie, illus. 32p. (J). (gr. 1-4). 2006. 6.95 (978-0-8075-0919-7(1)); 2004. 15.95 (978-0-8075-0918-0(3)) Whitman, Albert & Co.

Bauer, Marion Dane. The Double-Digit Club. 2004. 126p. (J). (gr. 4-6). tchr. ed. 15.95 (978-0-8234-1805-3(7)) Holiday Hse., Inc.

The Blue Club. 2001. (YA). (gr. 6-12). pap. incl. audio (978-0-8224-3290-6(0)) Globe Fearon Educational Publishing.

Bonsall, Crosby N. The Case of the Scaredy Cats. Bonsall, Crosby N., illus. 2002. (Illus.). 12.30 (978-0-7587-6049-4(3)) Book Wholesalers, Inc.

Borden, Louise. The John Hancock Club. Gustavson, Adam, illus. 2007. 48p. (J). (gr. 2-5). 16.99 (978-1-4169-1813-4(2) , McElderry, Margaret K.) Simon & Schuster Children's Publishing.

Bourgeois, Paulette. Franklin's Secret Club. ed. 2004. (Illus.). (J). (gr. k-3). spiral bd. (978-0-616-01593-3(3)); spiral bd. (978-0-616-01594-0(1)) Canadian National Institute for the Blind/Institut National Canadien pour les Aveugles.

—Franklin's Secret Club. Clark, Brenda, illus. 1998. (Franklin the Turtle Ser.). (J). (gr. k-3). 32p. (978-1-55074-474-3(7)); 96p. (978-1-55074-476-7(3)) Kids Can Pr., Ltd.

—Franklin's Secret Club. Clark, Brenda, illus. 1998. (Franklin Ser.). 32p. (J). (ps-3). pap. 4.99 (978-0-590-13000-4(5) , Scholastic Paperbacks) Scholastic, Inc.

—Franklin's Secret Club. Clark, Brenda, illus. 1998. (Franklin Ser.). (J). (ps-3). 11.30 (978-0-606-13406-4(9)) Tandem Library Bks.

Bourgeois, Paulette & Clark, Brenda. Franklin's Secret Club. 1999. (Franklin Ser.). (Illus.). 194p. (J). (ps-3). (978-1-55074-672-3(3)) Kids Can Pr., Ltd.

Brinley, Bertrand R. The Big Chunk of Ice: The Last Known Adventure of the Mad Scientists' Club. Geer, Charles, illus. 2005. 275p. (J). (gr. 3-7). 18.95 (978-1-930900-29-5(5)) Purple Hse. Pr.

—The Big Kerplop! The Original Adventure of the Mad Scientist's Club. Geer, Charles, illus. 2003. 238p. (J). 17.95 (978-1-930900-22-6(8)) Purple Hse. Pr.

—The Mad Scientists' Club. Geer, Charles, illus. anniv. ed. 2001. 217p. (J). 17.95 (978-1-930900-10-3(4)) Purple Hse. Pr.

Bryant, Bonnie. Carole: The Inside Story. 1999. (J). (978-0-606-19288-0(3)) Tandem Library Bks.

—Horse Crazy. 2007. (Saddle Club Ser.: No. 1). 144p. (J). (gr. 4-7). lib. bdg. 11.99 (978-0-385-90417-9(7) , Yearling) Random Hse. Children's Bks.

—Horse Play. 2007. (Saddle Club Ser.: No. 7). 144p. (J). (gr. 4-6). lib. bdg. 11.99 (***978-0-385-90423-0(1)*** , Yearling) Random Hse. Children's Bks.

—Horse Power. 2007. (Saddle Club Ser.: No. 4). 144p. (J). (gr. 4-6). lib. bdg. 11.99 (978-0-385-90420-9(7) , Yearling) Random Hse. Children's Bks.

—Horse Sense. 2007. (Saddle Club Ser.: No. 3). 144p. (J). (gr. 4-7). lib. bdg. 11.99 (978-0-385-90419-3(3) , Yearling) Random Hse. Children's Bks.

—Horse Show. 2007. (Saddle Club Ser.: No. 8). 160p. (J). (gr. 4-6). lib. bdg. 11.99 (***978-0-385-90424-7(X)*** , Yearling) Random Hse. Children's Bks.

Bryant, Bonnie. Horse Shy. 2007. (Saddle Club Ser.: No. 2). 144p. (J). (gr. 4-6). lib. bdg. 11.99 (978-0-385-90418-6(5) , Yearling) Random Hse. Children's Bks.

Bui-Quang, Phuong-Mai. Tea Club. 2006. (YA). per. 10.95 (978-1-59971-581-0(3)) Aardvark Global Publishing.

Carlson, Melody. Project, Mystery Bus. 2007. (Faithgirlz!#8482; / Girls of 622 Harbor View Ser.). 144p. (J). pap. 6.99 (978-0-310-71187-2(8)) Zonderkidz.

—Project, Rescue Chelsea. 2007. (Faithgirlz!#8482; / Girls of 622 Harbor View Ser.). 144p. (J). pap. 6.99 (978-0-310-71188-9(6)) Zonderkidz.

Clark, Brenda, illus. Franklin's Secret Club. 2002. (Franklin Ser.). (J). 12.40 (978-0-7587-2533-2(7)) Book Wholesalers, Inc.

Cleary, Beverly. Henry & the Clubhouse. 2002. (Illus.). (J). 13.83 (978-0-7587-9142-9(9)) Book Wholesalers, Inc.

Davis, Caitlyn. What's Hot. 2007. (I Heart Bikinis Ser.: No. 3). 208p. (YA). (gr. 7 up). pap. 5.99 (***978-0-439-91852-7(9)***) Scholastic, Inc.

DeLaCroix, Alice. How to Survive a Totally Boring Summer. Fisher, Cynthia, illus. 2007. 96p. (J). (gr. 1-4). 16.95 (***978-0-8234-2024-7(8)***) Holiday Hse., Inc.

Deriso, Christine Hurley. The Right-Under Club. 2007. 208p. (J). (gr. 4-7). lib. bdg. 18.99 (***978-0-385-90351-6(0)*** , Delacorte Bks. for Young Readers) Random Hse. Children's Bks.

Draper, Sharon M. The Battle of Jericho. 2003. (Illus.). 304p. (YA). 17.95 (978-0-689-84232-0(5) , Atheneum) Simon & Schuster Children's Publishing.

—The Buried Bones Mystery. Watson, Jesse Joshua, illus. 2006. (Ziggy & the Black Dinosaurs Ser.: Vol. 1). 112p. (J). pap. 4.99 (978-0-689-87910-4(5)) Simon & Schuster Children's Publishing.

Draper, Sharon M. & Bascoul, Eric. The Battle of Jericho. 2004. 352p. (YA). mass mkt. 6.99 (978-0-689-84233-7(3) , Simon Pulse) Simon & Schuster Children's Publishing.

Enderle, Dotti. Hand of Fate, Vol. 4. Nightingale, Kimberly, ed. 2004. (Fortune Tellers Club Ser.). (Illus.). 144p. (gr. 8-12). pap. 4.99 (978-0-7387-0390-9(7)) Llewellyn Pubns.

—Mirror, Mirror. 2004. (Illus.). 144p. pap. 4.99 (978-0-7387-0436-4(9)) Llewellyn Pubns.

—Playing with Fire. Leuthner, Sandy, ed. 2003. (Fortune Tellers Club Ser.: Bk. 2). (Illus.). 160p. pap. 4.99 (978-0-7387-0340-4(0)) Llewellyn Pubns.

—Playing with Fire: Fortune Tellers Club. 2003. (gr. 3-6). lib. bdg. 13.00 (978-0-613-90789-7(2)) Tandem Library Bks.

English, Karen. Nikki & Deja. Freeman-Hines, Laura, illus. 2007. 80p. (J). (gr. 1-5). 15.00 (***978-0-618-75238-6(2)*** , Clarion Bks.) Houghton Mifflin Co. Trade & Reference Div.

Fontes, Justine. Christmas Club. 2000. (Hello Reader! Ser.). (J). 10.79 (978-0-606-19549-2(1)) Tandem Library Bks.

The Freaky Joe Club. 2005. (J). pap. (***978-1-60015-069-2(1)***) Steps To Literacy, LLC.

Frederick, Heather Vogel. The Mother-Daughter Book Club. 2007. 256p. (J). (gr. 4-7). 15.99 (978-0-689-86412-4(4)) Simon & Schuster Children's Publishing.

Gabriel, Nat. Bubble Trouble. Nez, John, illus. 2004. 32p. (J). lib. bdg. 20.00 (***978-1-4242-1085-5(2)***) Fitzgerald Bks.

—Bubble Trouble. Nez, John, tr. Nez, John, illus. 2004. (Science Solves It! Ser.). (J). pap. 4.99 (978-1-57565-133-0(5)) Kane Pr., The.

Gallagher, Diana G. Whatever! The Complicated Life of Claudia Cristina Cortez. Garvey, Brann, illus. 2008. (J). pap. (***978-1-59889-880-4(9)***); 81p. (gr. 4-8). lib. bdg. 23.93 (***978-1-59889-839-2(6)***) Stone Arch Bks.

Gene, Barbara. Lamar Montgomery & the Freaky Faces Club. 2006. (J). per. 14.95 (978-1-889743-50-9(X)) Robbie Dean Pr.

Givens, Steven J. Stony Point: A Triangle Club Adventure. 2001. 106p. pap. 5.95 (978-1-889658-21-6(9)) New Canaan Publishing Co. LLC.

Gutman, Dan. The Get Rich Quick Club. 128p. (J). 2006. pap. 5.99 (978-0-06-053442-4(7) , Harper Trophy); 2004. 15.99 (978-0-06-053440-0(0)); 2004. lib. bdg. 16.89 (978-0-06-053441-7(9)) HarperCollins Pubs.

Hambrick, Sharon. Tommy's Clubhouse. Manning, Maurie, tr. Manning, Maurie, illus. 2003. (Fig Street Kids Ser.). 78p. (J). (gr. 1-2). pap. 7.49 (978-1-57924-993-9(0)) Jones, Bob Univ. Pr.

—Tommy's Race. Manning, Maurie, illus. 2004. (Fig Street Kids Ser.). 95p. (J). (gr. 1-2). 7.49 (978-1-59166-286-0(9)) Jones, Bob Univ. Pr.

—Tommy's Rocket. Manning, Maurie, illus. 2003. (Fig Street Kids Ser.). 83p. (J). (gr. 1-2). 7.49 (978-1-59166-186-3(2)) Jones, Bob Univ. Pr.

Hamilton, Elizabeth L. Christopher Cat's Character Club. 2003. (Character Critters Ser.: No. 1). (Illus.). 32p. (J). (ps-3). per. 5.95 (978-0-9713749-2-8(9) , Character-in-Action) Quiet Impact, Inc.

Hancock, H. Irving. The High School Boys' Canoe Club. rev. ed. 2006. 220p. 27.95 (978-1-4218-1753-8(5)); pap. 12.95 (978-1-4218-1853-5(1)) 1st World Publishing, Inc. (1st World Library - Literary Society).

Hartinger, Brent. Geography Club. 240p. (J). 2003. 17.99 (978-0-06-001221-2(8)); 2004. reprint ed. pap. 7.99 (978-0-06-001223-6(4) , HarperTeen) HarperCollins Pubs.

—Geography Club. 2004. (gr. 7-12). lib. bdg. 15.30 (978-0-613-71366-5(4)) Tandem Library Bks.

Himmelman, John. The Animal Rescue Club. Himmelman, John, illus. 1999. (Illus.). 46p. (J). (ps-ps). lib. bdg. 11.80 (978-0-613-18234-8(0)) Tandem Library Bks.

Hodgson, Mona Gansberg. Clubhouse Surprises. Sharp, Chris, illus. 1999. (Desert Critter Friends Ser.: Vol. 6). 48p. (J). (ps-2). 4.99 (978-0-570-05082-7(0) , 56-1906GJ) Concordia Publishing Hse.

—Clubhouse Surprises. 1998. (ps-2). lib. bdg. 13.00 (978-0-613-72809-6(2)) Tandem Library Bks.

Howe, James. Horace & Morris, but Mostly Dolores. 1999. (gr. k-3). lib. bdg. 15.30 (978-0-613-61776-5(2)) Tandem Library Bks.

—Horace & Morris, but Mostly Dolores. Waldrod, Amy, illus. 2003. 28.95 incl. audio compact disk (978-1-59112-342-2(9)); pap. 39.95 incl. audio compact disk (978-1-59112-538-9(3)); (J). pap. 18.95 incl. audio compact disk (978-1-59112-341-5(0)); pap. 37.95 incl. audio (978-1-59112-243-2(0)) Live Oak Media.

Hunt, Susan & Hunt, Richie. Discovering Jesus in Exodus, Vol. 2. 2005. (Illus.). 176p. pap. 16.99 (978-1-58134-453-0(8) , Crossway Bibles) Crossway Bks.

In the Clubhouse. 2003. (J). per. (978-1-57657-872-8(0)) Paradise Pr., Inc.

Ismail, Suzy. The BFF Sisters: Jennah's New Friends. 2001. 64p. (J). (978-1-59008-005-4(X)) amana pubns.

Johns, Michael-Anne. Hanging with the Backstreet Boys. 1998. (J). pap. 3.99 (978-0-590-04711-1(6)) Scholastic, Inc.

Johnson, Arden. The Lost Tooth Club. 2004. (Illus.). 32p. (J). (ps-3). 6.95 (978-1-58246-041-3(8) , Tricycle Pr.) Ten Speed Pr.

—The Lost Tooth Club. Johnson, Arden, illus. 2004. (Illus.). 32p. (J). (ps-3). 13.95 (978-1-883672-55-3(4) , Tricycle Pr.) Ten Speed Pr.

Johnson-Crouse, Donna C. The Whispering Kids Club: The Ruby Ring. 2005. 90p. (J). pap. 12.00 (978-1-886098-17-6(4)) Gye Nyame Hse.

Keene, Carolyn. The Crime Lab Case. 2002. (gr. 5-8). lib. bdg. 13.00 (978-0-613-45025-6(6)) Tandem Library Bks.

Kobayashi, Makoto. Club 9, Vol. 1. 2003. (Illus.). 192p. pap. 15.95 (978-1-56971-915-2(2)) Dark Horse Comics.

Krailing, Tessa. The Cat Burglar. Lewis, Jan & Eastwood, John, illus. 1998. (Petsitters Club Ser.: No. 2). 96p. (J). (gr. 2-5). pap. 4.99 (978-0-7641-0570-8(1)) Barron's Educational Series, Inc.

—Jilly the Kid. Lewis, Jan & Eastwood, John, illus. 1998. (Petsitters Club Ser.: No. 1). 96p. (J). (gr. 1-4). pap. 4.50 (978-0-7641-0569-2(8)) Barron's Educational Series, Inc.

—Monkey Puzzle: Vacation Special. Lewis, Jan & Eastwood, John, illus. 1999. (Petsitters Club Ser.). 96p. (J). (gr. 1-4). pap. 3.95 (978-0-7641-0737-5(2)) Barron's Educational Series, Inc.

—Trixie & the Cyber Pet. Lewis, Jan & Eastwood, John, illus. 1998. (Petsitters Club Ser.: No. 6). 96p. (J). (gr. 1-4). pap. 4.50 (978-0-7641-0614-9(7)) Barron's Educational Series, Inc.

—Where's Iggy? Lewis, Jan & Eastwood, John, illus. 1999. (Petsitters Club Ser.: No. 8). 96p. (J). (gr. 1-4). pap. 3.95 (978-0-7641-0693-4(7)) Barron's Educational Series, Inc.

Leedy, Loreen. The Monster Money Book. Leedy, Loreen, illus. 2005. (Illus.). 32p. (J). (gr. k-3). pap. 6.95 (978-0-8234-1558-8(9)) Holiday Hse., Inc.

Levin, Lon, illus. I'm Going to Read (Level 4) The Small Potatoes Club. 2007. (I'm Going to Read Ser.). 48p. (J). pap. 3.95 (978-1-4027-3085-6(3)) Sterling Publishing Co., Inc.

—The Small Potatoes Club. 2007. (I'm Going to Read Ser.). 40p. (J). pap. 3.95 (978-1-4027-3084-9(5)) Sterling Publishing Co., Inc.

Lewis, Beverly. The Midnight Mystery. 2007. (Cul-de-Sac Kids Ser.: Vol. 24). (Illus.). 80p. (J). (gr. 2-5). pap. 3.99 (978-0-7642-2129-3(9)) Bethany Hse. Pubs.

Luke, Deanna. Treetop Clubhouse. Carnehl, Jeff, illus. 2002. 112p. (J). (gr. 2-6). 9.95 (978-1-928777-02-1(3) , BOW Bks.) Blessing Our World, Inc.

Lynch, Chris. Wolf Gang. 1998. (He-Man Women Haters Club Ser.). 128p. (YA). (gr. 3-7). pap. 4.50 (978-0-06-440659-8(8)) HarperCollins Pubs.

Maguire, Gregory. Five Alien Elves. Clayton, Elaine, illus. 1998. 176p. (J). (gr. 4-6). tchr. ed. 15.00 (978-0-395-83894-5(0) , Clarion Bks.) Houghton Mifflin Co. Trade & Reference Div.

—Five Alien Elves. Clayton, Elaine, illus. 2000. (J). 12.64 (978-0-606-19970-4(5)) Tandem Library Bks.

—Six Haunted Hairdos. 1999. (978-0-606-17470-1(2)) Tandem Library Bks.

—Six Haunted Hairdos. l.t. ed. 2002. 178p. (J). 21.95 (978-0-7862-4421-8(6)) Thorndike Pr.

Mahoney, Daniel J. The Perfect Clubhouse. 2004. (Illus.). 32p. (J). (gr. k-3). tchr. ed. 15.00 (978-0-618-34672-1(4) , Clarion Bks.) Houghton Mifflin Co. Trade & Reference Div.

Martin, Ann M. Abby & the Best Kid Ever. 1998. (Baby-Sitters Club Ser.: No. 116). (J). (gr. 3-7). (978-0-606-13160-5(4)) Tandem Library Bks.

—Abby & the Notorious Neighbor. 1998. (Baby-Sitters Club Mystery Ser.: No. 35). (Illus.). (J). (gr. 3-7). pap. 3.99 (978-0-590-05975-6(0) , Scholastic Paperbacks) Scholastic, Inc.

—Abby in Wonderland. 1998. (Baby-Sitters Club Ser.: No. 121). (J). (gr. 3-7). pap. 4.50 (978-0-590-50063-0(5) , Scholastic Paperbacks) Scholastic, Inc.

—Claudia & Crazy Peaches. 1999. (Baby-Sitters Club Ser.: No. 78). 138p. (J). (gr. 3-7). pap. 3.99 (978-0-590-92610-2(1)) Scholastic, Inc.

—Claudia & the Little Liar. 1999. (Baby-Sitters Club Ser.: No. 128). 114p. (J). (gr. 3-7). pap. 4.50 (978-0-590-50351-8(0)) Scholastic, Inc.

—Claudia & the Terrible Truth. 1998. (Baby-Sitters Club Ser.: No. 117). (J). (gr. 3-7). pap. 4.50 (978-0-590-05995-4(5) , Scholastic Paperbacks) Scholastic, Inc.

—Claudia & the Terrible Truth. 1998. (Baby-Sitters Club Ser.: No. 117). (J). (gr. 3-7). (978-0-606-13161-2(2)) Tandem Library Bks.

—Claudia y las Llamadas Fant... 2000. (Baby-Sitters Club Ser.).Tr. of Claudia & the Phantom Phone.... (SPA., Illus.). 168p. (YA). 11.95 (978-84-272-3652-3(2)) Molino, Editorial ESP. *Dist:* AIMS International Bks., Inc.

—Dawn on the Coast. (Baby-Sitters Club Ser.: No. 23). 10p. (J). (gr. 3-7). pap. 3.95 (978-0-590-42007-5(0)) Scholastic, Inc.

—Dawn y los Mensajes Aterradores. Orig. Title: Beware, Dawn!. (SPA.). 136p. (J). 9.95 (978-84-272-2602-9(0)) Molino, Editorial ESP. *Dist:* AIMS International Bks., Inc.

—Gran Idea de Kristy. 2002. (Baby-Sitters Club Ser.).Tr. of Kristy's Great Idea. (SPA.). 168p. (J). 11.95 (978-84-272-3651-6(4)) Molino, Editorial ESP. *Dist:* AIMS International Bks., Inc.

—Karen's Book. 1998. (Baby-Sitters Little Sister Ser.: No. 100). (J). (gr. 3-7). pap. 4.50 (978-0-590-50051-7(1) , Scholastic Paperbacks) Scholastic, Inc.

—Kristy & the Cat Burglar. 1998. (Baby-Sitters Club Mystery Ser.: No. 36). (J). (gr. 3-7). pap. 3.99 (978-0-590-05976-3(9) , Scholastic Paperbacks) Scholastic, Inc.

—Kristy in Charge. 1998. (Baby-Sitters Club Ser.: No. 122). (J). (gr. 3-7). pap. 3.99 (978-0-590-50064-7(3)) Scholastic, Inc.

—Kristy Thomas, Dog Trainer. 1998. (Baby-Sitters Club Ser.: No. 118). (J). (gr. 3-7). (978-0-606-13162-9(0)) Tandem Library Bks.

—Mary Anne & the Playground Fight. 1998. (Baby-Sitters Club Ser.: No. 120). (J). (gr. 3-7). pap. 3.99 (978-0-590-05998-5(X) , Scholastic Paperbacks) Scholastic, Inc.

—Mary Anne & the Playground Fight. 1998. (Baby-Sitters Club Ser.: No. 120). (J). (gr. 3-7). (978-0-606-13164-3(7)) Tandem Library Bks.

—Stacey's Ex-Boyfriend. 1998. (Baby-Sitters Club Ser.: No. 119). (J). (gr. 3-7). pap. 3.99 (978-0-590-05997-8(1)) Scholastic, Inc.

—Stacey's Ex-Boyfriend. 1998. (Baby-Sitters Club Ser.: No. 119). (J). (gr. 3-7). (978-0-606-13163-6(9)) Tandem Library Bks.

McMahon, P. J. The Case of the Psychic Hamster. 2005. (Freaky Joe Club Ser.: No. 4). (Illus.). 153p. (J). (978-1-4155-7725-7(0) , Aladdin) Simon & Schuster Children's Publishing.

—Case of the Psychic Hamster. Manders, John, illus. 2005. 153p. (J). lib. bdg. 15.38 (***978-1-4242-0404-5(6)***) Fitzgerald Bks.

—The Case of the Singing Sea Dragons. 2005. (Freaky Joe Club Ser.: No. 6). (Illus.). 153p. (J). (978-1-4156-4221-4(4) , Aladdin) Simon & Schuster Children's Publishing.

—Case of the Singing Sea Dragons. Manders, John, illus. 2005. 153p. (J). lib. bdg. 15.38 (***978-1-4242-0406-9(2)***) Fitzgerald Bks.

—Case of the Smiling Shark. Manders, John, illus. 2004. 116p. (J). lib. bdg. 15.38 (***978-1-4242-0402-1(X)***) Fitzgerald Bks.

—The Mystery of the Diappearing Dinosaurs. 2005. (Illus.). 120p. (J). (***978-1-4156-0778-7(8)*** , Aladdin) Simon & Schuster Children's Publishing.

Metzger, Steve. No Girls Allowed! Wilhelm, Hans, illus. 2000. (Dinofours Ser.: No. 19). (J). (ps-1). 20.01 (978-0-439-06328-9(0)) Scholastic, Inc.

Mills, Charles. The Bandit of Benson Park. 2003. (Honors Club Story Ser.: Vol. 1). 127p. (J). (978-0-8163-1977-0(4)) Pacific Pr. Pubns.

—The Great Sleepy-Time Stew Rescue. 2004. (Honors Club Story Ser.: Vol. 4). (Illus.). 127p. (J). (978-0-8163-2009-7(8)) Pacific Pr. Publishing Assn.

—The Secret of Scarlett Cove. 2004. (Honors Club Story Ser.: Bk. 3). 127p. (J). (978-0-8163-1999-2(5)) Pacific Pr. Publishing Assn.

Naylor, Phyllis Reynolds. All but Alice. 2002. (Alice Ser.). 160p. (J). (gr. 4-7). pap. 5.99 (978-0-689-85044-8(1) , Aladdin) Simon & Schuster Children's Publishing.

—All but Alice. 2002. (Alice Ser.). (gr. 7-12). lib. bdg. 13.00 (978-0-613-44999-1(1)) Tandem Library Bks.

—Danny's Desert Rats. 1999. 11.15 (978-0-606-17630-9(6)) Tandem Library Bks.

Oryan, Ellie. What Are Friends For. Santanach, Tino, illus. 2005. (Winx Club Ser.). 80p. (J). (ps-k). pap. 2.99 (978-0-439-74420-1(2)) Scholastic, Inc.

—Winx Club Magical Magix. MacKenzie, Kevin, illus. 2005. (Winx Club Ser.). 32p. (J). (ps-k). pap. 4.99 (978-0-439-74421-8(0)) Scholastic, Inc.

Pinkwater, Daniel M. The Artsy Smartsy Club. Pinkwater, Jill, illus. 2005. 176p. (J). 16.89 (978-0-06-053558-2(X)); 15.99 (978-0-06-053557-5(1)) HarperCollins Pubs.

Preble, Laura. The Queen Geek Social Club. 2006. 336p. (YA). (gr. 12). pap. 9.99 (978-0-425-21164-9(9) , Berkley Trade) Penguin Group (USA) Inc.

Preble, Laura. Queen Geeks in Love. 2007. 304p. (gr. 12 up). 9.99 (***978-0-425-21717-7(5)*** , Berkley Trade) Penguin Group (USA) Inc.

Riehecky, Janet. The Red Door Detective Club Mysteries, 4 bks., Set. Halverson, Lydia, illus. (J). (gr. 3-6). lib. bdg. 51.80 (978-1-56674-900-8(X)) Forest Hse. Publishing Co., Inc.

Rogers, Karen M. The Club. Bulet, Getty, illus. 1998. (Think-Kids Book Collection). 16p. (J). (gr. 1-4). pap. 2.95 (978-1-58237-005-7(2)) Creative Thinkers, Inc.

—El Club de Piensa-Tu. Alvarado, Ana María, tr. Bulet, Getty, illus. 2000. (Think-Kids Book Collection).Tr. of Club. (SPA.). 16p. (J). pap. 2.95 (978-1-58237-042-2(7)) Creative Thinkers, Inc.

Rylant, Cynthia. Annie & Snowball & the Tea Cup Club. Stevenson, Sucie, illus. 2008. (Annie & Snowball Ser.). 32p. (J). 15.99 (***978-1-4169-0940-8(0)*** , Simon & Schuster Children's Publishing) Simon & Schuster Children's Publishing.

Rylant, Cynthia. Henry & Mudge & the Sneaky Crackers. Stevenson, Sucie, illus. 2002. (Henry & Mudge Ser.). 28.95 incl. audio compact disk (978-1-59112-639-3(8)); pap. 31.95 incl. audio compact disk (978-1-59112-640-9(1)) Live Oak Media.

—Henry & Mudge & the Sneaky Crackers. Stevenson, Sucie, illus. 1999. (Henry & Mudge Ser.). 48p. (J). (gr. k-3). pap. 3.99 (978-0-689-82525-5(0) , Aladdin) Simon & Schuster Children's Publishing.

San Souci, Daniel. The Dangerous Snake & Reptile Club. 2004. (Illus.). 40p. (J). 15.95 (978-1-58246-131-1(7) , Tricycle Pr.) Ten Speed Pr.

—The Mighty Pigeon Club. 2007. (Illus.). 40p. (J). (ps-2). 15.95 (***978-1-58246-213-4(5)*** , Tricycle Pr.) Ten Speed Pr.

San Souci, Daniel. Space Station Mars. 2005. (Illus.). 40p. (J). (gr. 1-4). 15.95 (978-1-58246-142-7(2) , Tricycle Pr.) Ten Speed Pr.

Sharmat, Marjorie Weinman, et al. The Green Toenails Gang. Brunkus, Denise, illus. 2005. (Oliver Sharp Ser.: Vol. 4). 80p. (J). (gr. 1-4). pap. 4.50 (978-0-440-42063-7(6) , Yearling) Random Hse. Children's Bks.

Shusterman, Neal. The Shadow Club. 2002. 192p. (J). 16.99 (978-0-525-46833-2(1) , Dutton Juvenile); pap. 6.99 (978-0-14-230094-7(2) , Puffin) Penguin Group (USA) Inc.

—Shadow Club. 2002. (gr. 7-12). lib. bdg. 14.15 (978-0-613-50082-1(2)) Tandem Library Bks.

—Shadow Club Rising. 2003. 208p. (YA). (gr. 7). pap. 6.99 (978-0-14-250089-7(5) , Puffin) Penguin Group (USA) Inc.

—Shadow Club Rising. 2003. (gr. 7-12). lib. bdg. 14.15 (978-0-613-67473-7(1)) Tandem Library Bks.

Sorenson, Margo. Clubhouse Threat. 2001. 112p. (J). pap. 5.95 (978-0-7891-5457-6(9)); (gr. 2-5). lib. bdg. 13.95 (978-0-7569-0120-2(0)) Perfection Learning Corp.

Standish, Burt L. Frank Merriwell's Club. Rudman, Jack, ed. 2003. (Frank Merriwell Ser.). 29.95 (978-0-8373-9368-1(X)); pap. 9.95 (978-0-8373-9068-0(0)) Merriwell, Frank Inc.

Suen, Anastasia. Clubhouse. 2003. (gr. k-3). lib. bdg. 11.80 (978-0-613-67447-8(2)) Tandem Library Bks.

Suen, Anastasia, et al. The Clubhouse: Easy to Read—Level 2. 2002. (Peter's Neighborhood Ser.). (Illus.). 32p. (J). (gr. k-2). 13.99 (978-0-670-03537-3(8) , Viking Juvenile) Penguin Group (USA) Inc.

Uhlig, Susan. Lindsey Hits the Club. Wambach, Jennifer, illus. 2001. 96p. (gr. 3-6). pap. 6.75 (978-1-889658-17-9(0)) New Canaan Publishing Co. LLC.

Weber, Lenora Mattingly. Beany Has a Secret Life. 1999. (Beany Malone Ser.). 296p. (J). pap. 12.95 (978-0-9639607-7-1(6)) Image Cascade Publishing.

Williams, Jeff E. The Unknown Priestess. 1998. (Illus.). (J). pap. 8.80 (978-1-56763-343-6(9)); lib. bdg. 25.25 (978-1-56763-342-9(0)) Ozark Publishing.

Wilson, Vickie. Friends Club. Turrentine, Jan, ed. 1999. (Illus.). 24p. (J). (gr. 4-6). pap. 19.99 (978-1-56309-298-5(0)) Woman's Missionary Union.

Young, Kristi. The Secret Club - the Powder Puff Club Book 1. 2007. 140p. (J). per. 12.95 (***978-1-59594-070-4(7)*** , Wingspan Pr.) WingSpan Publishing.

COACHING (ATHLETICS)

Bagley, Katie. Coaches. 2001. (Community Helpers Ser.). (Illus.). 24p. (J). (gr. 1-2). lib. bdg. 18.60 (978-0-7368-0807-1(8) , Bridgestone Bks.) Capstone Pr., Inc.

Facts on File, Inc. Staff, contrib. by. Careers in Focus. 2004. (Careers in Focus Ser.). (Illus.). 192p. (J). (gr. 6-12). 22.95 (978-0-8160-5548-7(3) , Ferguson Publishing Co.) Facts On File, Inc.

Harcourt School Publishers Staff. Coach - Grade 4. 3rd ed. 2002. (Trophies English Language Learners Ser.). pap. 5.10 (978-0-15-327753-5(X)) Harcourt Schl. Pubs.

J. G. Ferguson Publishing Company Staff, contrib. by. Careers in Focus. 2003. (Careers in Focus Ser.). (Illus.). (J). (gr. 6-12). 176p. 22.95 (978-0-8160-5484-8(3)); 3rd ed. 208p. 22.95 (978-0-8160-5486-2(X)) Facts On File, Inc. (Ferguson Publishing Co.).

Nagle, Jeanne M. Careers in Coaching. 2005. (Careers). (Illus.). 192p. (YA). (gr. 7-12). lib. bdg. 26.50 (978-0-8239-2966-5(3) , CACOAC) Rosen Publishing Group, Inc., The.

—Choosing a Career as a Coach. 2005. (World of Work Ser.). (Illus.). 64p. (YA). (gr. 7-12). lib. bdg. 25.25 (978-0-8239-3285-6(0)) Rosen Publishing Group, Inc., The.

COAL MINES AND MINING

see also Mining Engineering

At the Coal Mine. (Rigby Focus Ser.). 24p. (gr. 2 up). 6 Pcks. 28.00 (978-0-7578-5348-7(X)); 6 Pcks. 30.00 (978-0-7578-5578-8(4)) Rigby Education.

Bartoletti, Susan Campbell. Growing up in Coal Country. 1999. (Illus.). 128p. (J). (gr. 4-6). pap. 7.95 (978-0-395-97914-3(5)) Houghton Mifflin Co. Trade & Reference Div.

Ditchfield, Christin. Coal. (True Bks.). (Illus.). 48p. (J). (gr. 3-5). 2003. pap. 6.95 (978-0-516-29366-0(4)); 2002. pap. 25.00 (978-0-516-22342-1(9)) Scholastic Library Publishing. (Children's Pr.).

Goodman, James A. Two Weeks Under: The Sheppton Mine Disaster Miracle. 2004. (Illus.). 144p. per. 12.95 (978-0-9709630-4-8(1)) Coal Hole Productions.

Hyland, Tony. Miners & Drillers. 2006. (Extreme Jobs Ser.). 32p. (J). (gr. 4-6). lib. bdg. 27.10 (978-1-58340-741-7(3)) Smart Apple Media.

Logan, Michale. Coal. 2007. (Opposing Viewpoints Ser.). (Illus.). 240p. (gr. 10-12). 36.20 (***978-0-7377-3908-4(8)***); pap. 24.95 (***978-0-7377-3909-1(6)***) Thomson Gale. (Greenhaven Pr., Inc.).

Malam, John. You wouldn't/be 19th century coal Miner. 2006. (Illus.). 32p. (J). (gr. 2-5). 28.50 (***978-0-531-14971-3(4)***) Scholastic Library Publishing.

Malam, John & Antram, David. You Wouldn't Want to Be a 19th-Century Coal Miner in England! 2006. (Illus.). 32p. (J). (gr. 2-5). pap. 9.95 (978-0-531-16996-4(0) , Watts, Franklin) Scholastic Library Publishing.

Morris, Neil. Coal. 2005. (Illus.). 32p. (J). (gr. 4-7). lib. bdg. 27.10 (978-1-58340-628-1(X)) Smart Apple Media.

Mosier, Dan L. & Williams, Earle E. History of Tesla: A California Coal Mining Town. 2nd rev. ed. 2002. (Illus.). 360p. per. 29.95 (978-1-889064-08-6(4)) Mines Road Bks.

Oxlade, Chris. How We Use Coal. 2004. (Using Materials Ser.). (Illus.). 32p. (J). lib. bdg. 25.70 (978-1-4109-0592-5(6)) Raintree.

Parker, Steve. Coal. 2004. (Science Files Ser.). (Illus.). 32p. (J). (gr. 3 up). lib. bdg. 24.67 (978-0-8368-4029-2(1)) Stevens, Gareth Inc.

COAL MINES AND MINING—FICTION

Almond, David. Kit's Wilderness. l.t. ed. 2000. 263p. (J). pap. 16.95 (978-0-7540-6115-1(9) , Galaxy Children's Large Print) BBC Audiobooks America.

—Kit's Wilderness. unabr. ed. 2004. 240p. (J). (gr. 7 up). pap. 36.00 incl. audio (978-0-8072-8216-8(2) , Listening Library) Random Hse. Audio Publishing Group.

—Kit's Wilderness. (YA). (gr. 7). 2001. (Illus.). 256p. mass mkt. 5.99 (978-0-440-41605-0(1) , Laurel Leaf); 2000. 240p. 15.95 (978-0-385-32665-0(3) , Delacorte Bks. for Young Readers) Random Hse. Children's Bks.

—Kit's Wilderness. 2001. 229p. (YA). (gr. 8-12). lib. bdg. 13.00 (978-0-613-36836-0(3)); (978-0-606-22406-2(8)) Tandem Library Bks.

—Kit's Wilderness. l.t. ed. 2001. (Illus.). 272p. (J). (gr. 4-7). 22.95 (978-0-7862-2772-3(9)) Thorndike Pr.

Armstrong, Jennifer. Theodore Roosevelt: Letters from a Young Coal Miner. 2001. (Dear Mr. President Ser.: Vol. 1). (Illus.). 118p. (J). (gr. 4-7). 8.95 (978-1-890817-27-5(9)) Winslow Pr.

Baker, Julie. Up Molasses Mountain. 2002. 224p. (YA). (gr. 7). lib. bdg. 17.99 (978-0-385-90048-5(1) , Lamb, Wendy) Random Hse. Children's Bks.

Brown, Elizabeth Ferguson. Coal Country Christmas. Stevenson, Harvey, illus. 2003. 32p. (J). (gr. k-2). 15.95 (978-1-59078-020-6(5)) Boyds Mills Pr.

Easton, Richard. A Real American. 2002. 160p. (J). (gr. 4-6). 15.00 (978-0-618-13339-0(9) , Clarion Bks.) Houghton Mifflin Co. Trade & Reference Div.

Haas, Jessie. Chase. 2007. 256p. (J). (gr. 5-9). 16.99 (978-0-06-112850-9(3)); lib. bdg. 17.89 (978-0-06-112851-6(1)) HarperCollins Pubs.

Kehret, Peg. The Ghost's Grave. 224p. 2007. pap. 5.99 (***978-0-14-280819-1(9)*** , Puffin); 2005. (J). (gr. 5). 16.99 (978-0-525-46162-3(0) , Dutton Juvenile) Penguin Group (USA) Inc.

Laskas, Gretchen Moran. The Miner's Daughter. 2007. 256p. (YA). 15.99 (978-1-4169-1262-0(2)) Simon & Schuster Children's Publishing.

Norton, Andre Alice. Ralestone Luck. 2006. pap. (***978-1-4068-3557-1(9)***) Echo Library.

Ramos, Violet M. Pedro & Donkeeta. Wright, Catherine et al, eds. Wilkinson, Gail, illus. 2001. 32p. (J). (ps-4). 15.50 (978-0-9658334-2-4(9)) VR Pubns.

Reilly, Robert T. Rebels in the Shadows. 2000. (Illus.). 192p. (J). (gr. 6-9). pap. 9.95 (978-0-8229-5304-3(8)) Univ. of Pittsburgh Pr.

Seckar, Alvena Vajdak. Misko. Merwin, Decie, illus. 1999. 159p. (J). 19.00 (978-0-86516-465-9(7)) Bolchazy-Carducci Pubs.

—Trapped in the Old Mine. Gotlieb, Jules, illus. 1999. 224p. (J). 19.00 (978-0-86516-466-6(5)) Bolchazy-Carducci Pubs.

—Zuska of the Burning Hills. Voute, Kathleen, illus. 1999. 224p. (J). 18.00 (978-0-86516-467-3(3)) Bolchazy-Carducci Pubs.

Wallace, Bill. The Dog Who Thought He Was Santa. 2007. 224p. (J). (gr. 3-7). 16.95 (***978-0-8234-2114-5(7)***) Holiday Hse., Inc.

Wilson, John. Red Goodwin. 2006. (Illus.). 170p. (J). pap. (***978-1-55380-034-7(6)***) Ronsdale Pr.

Witschen, Kay. Johnny Coalboy. Luckemeyer, Norma, illus. 2003. (J). per. 5.95 (978-0-9741352-0-5(8)) Dwitt Publishing.

Woodson, Marion. Charlotte's Vow. 2006. 144p. (J). pap., tchr. ed. 5.95 (978-0-88878-413-1(9) , Sandcastle Bks.) Dundurn Group, The CAN. *Dist:* Univ. of Toronto Pr.

Yep, Laurence. The Traitor: Golden Mountain Chronicles: 1885. (Golden Mountain Chronicles). 320p. (J). (gr. 5 up). 2004. pap. 6.99 (978-0-06-000831-4(8) , Harper Trophy); 2003. 17.99 (978-0-06-027522-8(7)) HarperCollins Pubs.

COAL OIL

see Petroleum

COASTAL SIGNALS

see Signals and Signaling

COAT COLOR OF ANIMALS

see Animals—Color

COATS OF ARMS

see Heraldry

COBB, TY, 1886-1961

Abrams, Dennis. Ty Cobb. 2007. (Baseball Superstars Ser.). 136p. (J). (gr. 6-12). 30.00 (***978-0-7910-9439-6(1)*** , Chelsea Hse.) Facts On File, Inc.

COCHISE, APACHE CHIEF, D. 1874

Phillips, Larissa. Cochise: Apache Chief. 2003. (Primary Sources of Famous People in American History Ser.). (Illus.). 32p. (J). pap. (978-0-8239-4177-3(9)) Syracuse Univ. Pr.

—Cochise: Jefe Apache. de la Vega, Eida, tr. from ENG. 2003. (Grandes Personajes en la Historia de Los Estados Unidos Ser.). (ENG & SPA., Illus.). 32p. (J). pap. (978-0-8239-4223-7(6)) Rosen Publishing Group, Inc., The.

COCHISE, APACHE CHIEF, D. 1874—FICTION

Sargent, Dave & Sargent, Pat. Charlie: (Appaloosa) Be Brave, 25, 14. Lenoir, Jane, illus. 2001. (Saddle Up Ser.: 14). 36p. (J). pap. 6.95 (978-1-56763-608-6(X)); lib. bdg. 22.60 (978-1-56763-607-9(1)) Ozark Publishing.

COCHRANE, ELIZABETH, 1867-1922

see Bly, Nellie, 1867-1922

COCKROACHES

Allman, Toney. Cricket. 2004. (Bugs Ser.). (J). 24.95 (978-0-7377-1768-6(8) , Greenhaven Pr., Inc.) Thomson Gale.

Birch. Cockroaches up Close, 6, Pack. 2004. (Illus.). pap. 40.50 (978-1-4109-1153-7(5)) Harcourt Schl. Pubs.

Birch, Robin. Cockroaches. 2004. (J). 26.36 (978-1-4109-1139-1(X)); pap. 7.50 (978-1-4109-1146-9(2)) Harcourt Schl. Pubs.

Brimner, Larry Dane. Cockroaches. 2000. (True Bks.). (Illus.). 48p. (J). (gr. 3-5). pap. 6.95 (978-0-516-26758-6(2) , Children's Pr.) Scholastic Library Publishing.

Cockroaches World of Insects. 2006. (Illus.). 24p. (J). (gr. k-2). 18.50 (***978-0-531-17860-7(9)***) Scholastic Library Publishing.

Dickmann, Nancy. Cockroaches. 2005. (Creepy Creatures Ser.). (J). (978-1-4109-1769-0(X)); pap. (978-1-4109-1774-4(6)) Steck-Vaughn.

Green, Emily K. Cockroaches. 2006. (Blastoff! Readers Ser.). (Illus.). 24p. (J). lib. bdg. 16.95 (978-1-60014-010-5(6)) Bellwether Media.

Hartley, Karen. La Cucaracha. 2003. (SPA.). (gr. k-3). lib. bdg. 14.75 (978-0-613-67078-4(7)) Tandem Library Bks.

Hartley, Karen, et al. Cockroach. 2nd ed. 2006. (Bug Books). (Illus.). 32p. (J). (***978-1-4034-8296-9(9)***); pap. (***978-1-4034-8309-6(4)***) Heinemann Library.

Hartley, Karen, et al. La Cucaracha. 2003. (Los Insectos Ser.). (SPA.). 32p. (J). pap. 6.95 (978-1-4034-3032-8(2)) Heinemann Library.

Helget, Nicole Lea. Cockroaches. 2007. (J). (978-1-58341-540-5(8) , Creative Education) Creative Co., The.

Kerby, Mona. Cockroaches & Friendly Bees, Ferocious Bees. 2000. (Illus.). 164p. (gr. 4-7). pap. 11.95 (978-0-595-14664-2(3) , Backinprint.com) iUniverse, Inc.

Kite, L. Patricia. Cockroaches. 2001. (Early Bird Nature Bks.). (Illus.). 48p. (J). (gr. 2-4). lib. bdg. 25.26 (978-0-8225-3046-6(5) , Lerner Pubns.) Lerner Publishing Group.

Kravetz, Jonathan. Cockroaches. 2006. (Illus.). 24p. (J). (978-1-4042-3043-9(2) , PowerKids Pr.) Rosen Publishing Group, Inc., The.

McMonigle, Orin A. & Willis, Richard. Allpet Roaches: Care & Identification Handbook for the Pet & Feeder Cockroaches. 2000. 41p. (C). 15.00 (978-0-9719129-1-5(2) , Allpet Roaches) Elytra & Antenna.

Merrick, Patrick. Cockroaches. 2003. (Naturebooks Ser.). (Illus.). 32p. (J). (gr. 1-5). 25.64 (978-1-56766-206-1(4)) Child's World, Inc.

Prischmann, Deirdre A. Cockroaches. 2005. (World of Insects Ser.). (Illus.). 24p. (J). (ps-7). lib. bdg. 21.26 (978-0-7368-4336-2(1)) Capstone Pr., Inc.

Richardson, Adele D. Cockroaches. 1998. (Bugs Ser.). (Illus.). 32p. (YA). (gr. 3-12). lib. bdg. 16.95 (978-1-887068-31-4(7)) Smart Apple Media.

Rustad, Martha E. H. Cockroaches. 2003. (Insects Ser.). (Illus.). 24p. (J). (gr. k-1). lib. bdg. 15.93 (978-0-7368-1665-6(8) , Pebble Bks.) Capstone Pr., Inc.

—Cockroaches. 2005. (Bugs, Bugs, Bugs Ser.). 24p. (YA). (gr. k-3). pap. (978-0-7368-3387-5(0) , Pebble Bks.) Capstone Pr., Inc.

Twist, Clint. Cockroaches. 2006. (Illus.). 32p. (J). 23.33 (978-0-8368-6373-4(9)) Stevens, Gareth Inc.

Whitehouse, Patricia. La Cucaracha. Abello, Patricia, tr. 2003. (Los Insectos Ser.). (SPA & ENG., Illus.). 32p. (J). lib. bdg. 23.40 (978-1-4034-3009-0(8)) Heinemann Library.

COCKROACHES—FICTION

Alatorcida. 2001. (SPA.). (J). (gr. 1-3). 16.95 (978-84-261-3159-1(X)) Juventud, Editorial ESP. *Dist:* Lectorum Pubns., Inc.

Austin, Michael, illus. Martina the Beautiful Cockroach: A Cuban Folktale. 2007. 32p. (J). (ps-3). 16.95 (***978-1-56145-399-3(4)*** , Peachtree Junior) Peachtree Pubs., Ltd.

Blake-Brekke, Carri. Billy Bully Bug: Learns a Lesson in Hawaii. Melton, Jodi, illus. 2003. (Mrs. B's Story Time... With a Twist! Ser.). 20p. (J). pap. 11.95 incl. audio compact disk (978-0-9720549-2-8(8)) Mom's Pride Enterprises.

Cannon, Janell. Crickwing. 2005. (Illus.). 48p. (J). reprint ed. pap. 7.00 (978-0-15-205061-0(2) , Voyager Bks./Libros Viajeros) Harcourt Children's Bks.

Harlen, Jonathan. The Cockroach War. 2004. 204p. (Orig.). (J). pap. 7.95 (978-1-74114-168-9(0)) Allen & Unwin AUS. *Dist:* Independent Pubs. Group.

Hedrick, Georgia. Share Me a Shadow. l.t. ed. 2002. 48p. (J). cd-rom 12.95 (978-0-9706612-7-2(4)) JetKor.

Lamson, Sharon & Wacky World Staff. Batter up, Squiggz! A Story about Making Big Things Happen. Barry, Bruce, illus. 2006. 28p. (J). 4.99 (978-0-310-71308-1(0)) Zonderkidz.

Lamson, Sharon E. Roach Approach/Squiggz Rides Storm. Barry, Bruce, illus. 2006. 40p. (J). pap. 4.99 (978-0-310-71384-5(6)) Zondervan.

—Roach Ranger Danger at Coaster Cliffs: A Story about Obedience. Barry, Bruce, illus. 2006. (Bug Rangers#8482; Ser.). 28p. (J). 4.99 (978-0-310-71197-1(5)) Zonderkidz.

—Superhero Powers at Muscle Beach: A Story about Giving Credit Where Credit Is Due. Barry, Bruce, illus. 2006. 28p. (J). 4.99 (978-0-310-71198-8(3)) Zonderkidz.

O'Malley, Kevin. Leo Cockroach... Toy Tester. 2001. (Illus.). (J). (978-0-606-20761-4(9)) Tandem Library Bks.

—Leo Cockroach... Toy Tester. O'Malley, Kevin, illus. 1999. (Illus.). 32p. (J). (gr. k-3). lib. bdg. 16.85 (978-0-8027-8690-6(1)) Walker & Co.

—Leo Cockroach, Toy Tester. 2001. (gr. k-3). lib. bdg. 15.25 (978-0-613-35970-2(4)) Tandem Library Bks.

Pochocki, Ethel. The Blessing of the Beasts. Moser, Barry, illus. 2007. 40p. (J). (gr. k up). 18.95 (978-1-55725-502-0(4)) Paraclete Pr., Inc.

Schneider, Howie. Wilky the White House Cockroach. Schneider, Howie, illus. 2006. (Illus.). 32p. (J). (ps-3). 16.99 (978-0-399-24388-2(7)) Penguin Group (USA) Inc.

Speck, Katie. Maybelle in the Soup. Ratz de Tagyos, Paul, illus. 2007. 64p. (J). (gr. 2-5). 15.95 (***978-0-8050-8092-6(9)***) Holt, Henry & Co.

Toney Allman. Cockroach. 2004. 24.95 (978-0-7377-1767-9(X) , Kidhaven) Thomson Gale.

COCOA

see also Chocolate

Grout, Phil. Harvest of Hope. 2003. (Illus.). 96p. per. 13.95 (978-0-9708816-2-5(2)) Publishers@TreeHouse, The.

Harcourt School Publishers Staff. The Chocolate Journey: Take-Home Book. 1999. (Collections Ser.). (Illus.). (J). pap. 1.90 (978-0-15-317312-7(2)) Harcourt Schl. Pubs.

—The Chocolate Journey Below Level. 3rd ed. 2002. (Trophies Reading Program Ser.). (Illus.). pap. 5.10 (978-0-15-323154-4(8)) Harcourt Schl. Pubs.

Murray, Julie. Cocoa Bean to Chocolate. 2007. (Beginning to End Ser.). (Illus.). 24p. (J). (gr. k-3). lib. bdg. 21.35 (978-1-59679-835-9(1) , Buddy Bks.) ABDO Publishing Co.

COCOONS

see Butterflies; Caterpillars; Moths; Silkworms

CODE NAMES

see Ciphers

CODY, WILLIAM FREDERICK, 1846-1917

see Buffalo Bill, 1846-1917

COFFEE

Gilbert, Sara. The Story of Starbucks. 2008. (J). (***978-1-58341-609-9(9)*** , Creative Education) Creative Co., The.

Morganelli, Adrianna. The Biography of Coffee. 2006. (How Did That Get Here? Ser.). (Illus.). 32p. (J). (978-0-7787-2488-9(3) , 1259496) Crabtree Publishing Co.

—The Biography of Coffee. 2006. (How Did That Get Here? Ser.). (Illus.). 32p. (J). (gr. 5). pap. (978-0-7787-2524-4(3) , 1259496) Crabtree Publishing Co.

Sanders, Susan & Sandbeck, Fletcher. Coffee Roasting at Home: The Magic Bean. l.t. ed. 2003. (Magic Bean Coffee Books: Vol. 1). (Illus.). viii, 145p. pap. 17.95 (978-0-9709730-0-9(4) , MB001) Cumuli.

COFFEE—FICTION

Gay, Michel. Zee. Gay, Michel, illus. 2003. (Illus.). 32p. (J). (gr. k-ps). 15.00 (978-0-618-38148-7(1) , Clarion Bks.) Houghton Mifflin Co. Trade & Reference Div.

Mohamed, Sultan, tr. & illus. The Story of Coffee. Mohamed, Sultan, illus. 2003. (ENG & AMH.). 24p. (J). (gr. 4-5). 15.99 (978-0-9605670-9-6(7)) Ananse Pr.

COGNITION

see Knowledge, Theory of

COHAN, GEORGE M. (GEORGE MICHAEL), 1878-1942

Ouren, Todd, illus. You're a Grand Old Flag. 2004. (Patriotic Songs Ser.). 24p. (J). (ps-4). 22.60 (978-1-4048-0173-8(1)) Picture Window Bks.

COIN COLLECTING

see Coins

COINAGE

see also Gold; Mints; Money; Silver

Haydon, Julie. Making Coins & Bills. 2006. (Money Ser.). (Illus.). 32p. (J). (978-1-58340-784-4(7)) Smart Apple Media.

COINS

see also Numismatics

Abeyta, Jennifer. Coins. 2000. (High Interest Bks.). (Illus.). 48p. (YA). (gr. 7-12). 24.00 (978-0-516-23329-1(7) , Children's Pr.) Scholastic Library Publishing.

Attebury, Nancy Garhan. Out & about at the United States Mint. Trover, Zachary, illus. 2005. (Field Trips Ser.). 24p. (J). (ps). lib. bdg. 23.93 (978-1-4048-1151-5(6)) Picture Window Bks.

Brennan-Nelson, Denise. Penny: The Forgotten Coin. Monroe, Michael Glenn, illus. 2003. 32p. (J). (gr. k-5). 15.95 (978-1-58536-128-1(3)) Sleeping Bear Pr.

Coins: First Grade Guided Reading Level A. (On Our Way to English Ser.). (gr. 1 up). 27.75 (978-0-7578-7026-2(0)) Rigby Education.

Fontanille, Jean-Philippe & Gosline, Sheldon Lee. The Coins of Pontius Pilate, Vol. 4. 2001. (Marco Polo Monographs: Vol. 4). (FRE & ENG., Illus.). 176p. (C). 39.95 (978-0-9677201-4-2(1)) Shangri-La Pubns.

Giesecke, Ernestine. From Seashells to Smart Cards: Money & Currency. 2003. (Everyday Economics Ser.). (Illus.). 48p. (J). (gr. 3-5). lib. bdg. 27.07 (978-1-58810-491-5(5)) Heinemann Library.

Hill, Mary. Dimes. 2005. (Welcome Bookstm Ser.). (Illus.). 24p. (J). (ps-2). 18.00 (978-0-516-25056-4(6)); pap. 4.95 (978-0-516-25169-1(4)) Scholastic Library Publishing. (Children's Pr.).

—Dollars. 2005. (Welcome Bookstm Ser.). (Illus.). 24p. (ps-2). 18.00 (978-0-516-25057-1(4) , Children's Pr.) Scholastic Library Publishing.

—Nickels. 2005. (Welcome Bookstm Ser.). (Illus.). 24p. (J). (ps-2). 18.00 (978-0-516-25133-2(3)); pap. 4.95 (978-0-516-25171-4(6)) Scholastic Library Publishing. (Children's Pr.).

—Pennies. 2005. (Welcome Bookstm Ser.). (Illus.). 24p. (J). (ps-2). 18.00 (978-0-516-25132-5(5)); pap. 4.95 (978-0-516-25172-1(4)) Scholastic Library Publishing. (Children's Pr.).

—Quarters. 2005. (Welcome Bks.). (Illus.). 24p. (ps-2). (J). pap. 4.95 (978-0-516-25173-8(2)); 18.00 (978-0-516-25058-8(2)) Scholastic Library Publishing. (Children's Pr.).

How Many Pennies. 2002. (Illus.). (J). pap. (978-0-7398-5939-1(0)) Steck-Vaughn.

Jones, Tammy. We Can Use Coins. 2006. (Early Explorers Ser.). (J). 30.00 (***978-1-4108-6042-2(6)***) Benchmark Education Co.

Kompelien, Tracy. I Know about Money, It Is so Funny! 2007. (Math Made Fun Ser.). (Illus.). 24p. (J). 19.93 (978-1-59928-527-6(4) , SandCastle) ABDO Publishing Co.

—I Know about Money, It Is So Funny! 2006. (Math Made Fun Ser.). (Illus.). 24p. (J). (978-1-59928-528-3(2)) ABDO Publishing Co.

Leap Frog Cool Coins Wipe off Mat. 2006. (J). 3.95 (***978-1-59545-090-6(4)***) Learning Horizons, Inc.

Leedy, Loreen. Follow the Money! 2005. (Illus.). 32p. (Orig.). (J). (gr. k-3). tchr. ed. 17.95 (978-0-8234-1587-8(2)) Holiday Hse., Inc.

Money - Set 1: Coins That Add Up. 2005. (J). spiral bd. 19.90 (978-0-9770248-4-1(9)) Sidedoor Publishing LLC.

Morrison, Taylor. The Buffalo Nickel. 2002. (Illus.). 32p. (J). (gr. 1-5). 16.00 (978-0-618-10855-8(6) , Walter Lorraine) Houghton Mifflin Co. Trade & Reference Div.

Murphy, Stuart J. The Penny Pot. Cravath, Lynne W., illus. 1998. (MathStart Ser.). 40p. (J). (gr. 2 up). 15.95 (978-0-06-027606-5(1)); 15.89 (978-0-06-027607-2(X)); pap. 5.99 (978-0-06-446717-9(1) , Harper Trophy) HarperCollins Pubs.

Otfinoski, Steve. Coin Collecting for Kids. Graham, Jack, illus. ed. 2007. 12p. (J). (gr. 1-7). bds. 15.99 (***978-1-58476-624-7(7)*** , IKIDS) Innovative Kids.

Pistoia, Sara. Money. 2006. (MathBooks Ser.). (Illus.). 24p. (J). 24.21 (978-1-59296-689-9(6)) Child's World, Inc.

Rau, Dana Meachen. Coins. 2005. (Money & Banks Ser.). (Illus.). 24p. (J). pap. (978-0-8368-4875-5(6)); lib. bdg. 19.33 (978-0-8368-4868-7(3)) Stevens, Gareth Inc.

Ring, Susan. Matemuticas y Dinero. Ramos, Gloria, tr. 2005. (SPA., Illus.). 20p. (J). 15.93 (978-0-7368-4156-6(3) , Yellow Umbrella Bks.) Capstone Pr., Inc.

—Money Math. 2003. (J). 15.93 (978-0-7368-2934-2(2)); pap. (978-0-7368-2893-2(1)) Yellow Umbrella Pr.

Savage, Nancy. The True Story of Nickel the Baby Buffalo Who Thought He Was a Dog. Parks, Kathy, illus. 2nd rev. ed. 1999. 32p. (gr. k-3). reprint ed. pap. 9.95 (978-0-9669130-1-9(9)) Savage Parks Pr.

Schaefer, Adam. How Much Is It? A Book about Counting Coins. 2007. (Illus.). 24p. (J). (978-1-59515-978-6(9)); pap. (***978-1-59515-949-6(5)***) Rourke Publishing, LLC.

Seuling, Barbara. Ancient Coins Were Shaped Like Hams: And Other Freaky Facts about Coins, Bills, & Counterfeiting. Skeens, Matthew, illus. 2007. (J). lib. bdg. (***978-1-4048-3750-8(7)***) Picture Window Bks.

Williams, Rozanne Lanczak. The Coin Counting Book. 2001. (Illus.). 32p. (J). (gr. k-4). pap. 6.95 (978-0-88106-326-4(6)) Charlesbridge Publishing, Inc.

—The Coin Counting Book. Williams, Rozanne Lanczak, illus. 2001. (Illus.). 32p. (J). (gr. k-4). 16.95 (978-0-88106-325-7(8)) Charlesbridge Publishing, Inc.

—Coin Counting Book. 2001. (gr. k-3). lib. bdg. 15.25 (978-0-613-51237-4(5)) Tandem Library Bks.

—Learning about Coins. Jarrett, Michael, photos by. 2004. (I Can Do Math Ser.). (Illus.). 24p. (J). (gr. 1 up). lib. bdg. 20.67 (978-0-8368-4110-7(7)) Stevens, Gareth Inc.

COINS—FICTION

The Coin. 2000. 112p. (J). pap. 6.50 (978-0-9658730-1-7(3)) Drew Publishing Co.

Dell, Pamela. The Gold Coin: A Story about New York City's Lower East Side. 2002. (Scrapbooks of America Ser.). (Illus.). 48p. (J). (gr. 2-6). 28.50 (978-1-59187-017-3(8)) Child's World, Inc.

Finney, Patricia & Cavendish, Grace. Deception. 2005. (Lady Grace Mysteries, from the Daybookes of Lady Grace Cavendish Ser.). 224p. (J). (gr. 3-7). 7.95 (978-0-385-73321-2(6)); lib. bdg. 9.99 (978-0-385-90340-0(5)) Random Hse. Children's Bks. (Delacorte Bks. for Young Readers).

Hasquet, DeAnn. The Teeny Tiny Penny. 2000. 10p. (J). pap. 8.99 (978-1-930673-00-7(0)) Childhood Friends, Inc.

Innovative Kids Staff. Coin Count-Y: A Bank in a Book. Talbot, Jim, illus. 1999. 10p. (J). (gr. k-4). spiral bd. 10.99 (978-1-58476-003-0(6)) Innovative Kids.

Lieurance, Suzanne. Pennies. Payne, Tom, illus. (Rookie Reader Skill Set Ser.). (J). 2003. 32p. (gr. k-2). pap. 4.95 (978-0-516-27818 6(5)); 2002. 31p. (gr. 1-2). 19.50 (978-0-516-22286-8(4)) Scholastic Library Publishing. (Children's Pr.).

Maccarone, Grace & Burns, Marilyn. Monster Money. 1998. (Hello Reader! Math Ser.: Level 1). (Illus.). 32p. (J). (ps-3). pap. 3.99 (978-0-590-12007-4(7)) Scholastic, Inc.

Sainsbury, Adam. The Coin. 2005. 84p. (YA). pap. 9.96 (978-1-4116-5358-0(0)) Lulu.com.

Scaglione, Joseph. My Lucky Penny. Szarko, Kathy, illus. deluxe l.t. ed. 1999. 40p. (J). (ps-4). pap. 24.95 incl. cd-rom (978-0-9675011-0-9(5)) New Day Enterprises, Ltd.

Warrington, Dean Grey. Perfiction. 2007. 188p. per. 13.95 (***978-0-595-43758-0(3)***) iUniverse, Inc.

Williams, Suzanne. The Lucky Penny? Carter, Abby, illus. 2004. 56p. (J). lib. bdg. 15.00 (***978-1-4242-0909-5(9)***) Fitzgerald Bks.

COLD WAR

Here are entered works on the post World War II rivalry between western capitalist nations led by the United States and eastern communist nations led by the Soviet Union.

Anderson, Dale. The Cold War Years. 2001. (Making of America Ser.). (Illus.). 96p. (J). (gr. 5-10). lib. bdg. 28.54 (978-0-8172-5711-8(X)) Raintree.

Baker, Lawrence W. Cold War Reference Library Cumulative Index. 2003. (U-X-L Cold War Reference Library). 85p. (J). 5.00 (978-0-7876-7667-4(5) , UXL) Thomson Gale.

—Immigration & Migration Reference. 2003. (U-X-L Cold War Reference Library). (J). 5.00 (978-0-7876-7734-3(5)) Zagat Survey.

Beyer, Mark. Nuclear Weapons & the Cold War. 2005. (Library of Weapons of Mass Destruction). (Illus.). 64p. (J). lib. bdg. 26.50 (978-1-4042-0290-0(0)) Rosen Publishing Group, Inc., The.

Bjornlund, Britta. The Cold War. 2002. (World History Ser.). (Illus.). 112p. (J). (gr. 8-11). 27.45 (978-1-59018-003-7(8) , LML00902-178725, Lucent Bks.) Thomson Gale.

Blohm, Craig E. An Uneasy Peace: 1945 to 1980. 2002. (American War Library). (Illus.). 112p. (J). 29.95 (978-1-59018-201-7(4) , Lucent Bks.) Thomson Gale.

Bodden, Valerie. The Cold War. 2007. (J). (978-1-58341-546-7(7) , Creative Education) Creative Co., The.

Brager, Bruce L. The Iron Curtain: The Cold War in Europe. 2004. (Arbitrary Borders Ser.). (Illus.). 112p. (gr. 9-13). 35.00 (978-0-7910-7832-7(9) , Chelsea Hse.) Facts On File, Inc.

Burgan, Michael. The Berlin Wall: Barrier to Freedom. 2007. (J). lib. bdg. (***978-0-7565-3330-4(9)***) Compass Point Bks.

—Spying & the Cold War. 2006. (On the Front Line Ser.). (Illus.). 48p. (J). (978-1-4109-2195-6(6)); pap. (978-1-4109-2202-1(2)) Steck-Vaughn.

—Spying in the Cold War. 2004. (On the Front Line Ser.). (Illus.). 48p. (J). (gr. 4-6). 29.93 (978-1-4109-1465-1(8)) Raintree.

Campbell, Geoffrey A. The End of the Cold War: 1980 to the Present: The Cold War in the United States. 2002. (American War Library). 112p. (J). 29.95 (978-1-59018-213-0(8) , Lucent Bks.) Thomson Gale.

Chrisp, Peter. The Cuban Missle Crisis. 2002. (Cold War Ser.). (Illus.). 64p. (YA). (gr. 7 up). pap. 14.60 (978-0-8368-5278-3(8) , World Almanac Library) Stevens, Gareth Inc.

The Cold War, 4 bks. Incl. Causes of the Cold War. Ross, Stewart. lib. bdg. 32.67 (978-0-8368-5272-1(9)); Cuban Missile Crisis. Chrisp, Peter. lib. bdg. 32.67 (978-0-8368-5273-8(7)); End of the Cold War. Hatt, Christine. lib. bdg. 32.67 (978-0-8368-5275-2(3)); Vietnam War. Dowswell, Paul. lib. bdg. 32.67 (978-0-8368-5274-5(5)); (YA). (gr. 7 up). (Illus.). 64p. 2002. Set lib. bdg. 130.68 (978-0-8368-5271-4(0) , World Almanac Library) Stevens, Gareth Inc.

The Cold War, 4 bks. Incl. Causes of the Cold War. Ross, Stewart. pap. 14.60 (978-0-8368-5277-6(X)); Cuban Missle Crisis. Chrisp, Peter. pap. 14.60 (978-0-8368-5278-3(8)); End of the Cold War. Hatt, Christine. pap. 14.60 (978-0-8368-5280-6(X)); Vietnam War. Dowswell, Paul. pap. 14.60 (978-0-8368-5279-0(6)); 64p. (YA). (gr. 7 up). (Illus.). 2002. Set pap. 58.40 (978-0-8368-5276-9(1) , World Almanac Library) Stevens, Gareth Inc.

Collier, Christopher & Collier, James Lincoln. The United States in the Cold War. 2001. (Drama of American History Ser.). (Illus.). 96p. (J). (gr. 5-9). lib. bdg. 31.36 (978-0-7614-1317-2(0) , Benchmark Bks.) Cavendish, Marshall Corp.

Corona, Laurel. War Within a War: Vietnam & the Cold War. 2004. (Lucent Library of Historical Eras). (Illus.). 112p. (J). 32.45 (978-1-59018-389-2(4) , Lucent Bks.) Thomson Gale.

Fitzgerald, Brian. McCarthyism: The Red Scare. 2006. 96p. (YA). (gr. 7 up). lib. bdg. (978-0-7565-2007-6(X)) Compass Point Bks.

Gottfried, Ted. The Cold War. 2003. (Rise & Fall of the Soviet Union Ser.). (Illus.). 160p. (gr. 7 up). lib. bdg. 28.90 (978-0-7613-2560-4(3) , Twenty-First Century Bks.) Lerner Publishing Group.

Grant, Reg. The Cold War. 2007. (J). (***978-1-84193-726-7(6)***) Smart Apple Media.

Hanes, Sharon M., et al. Cold War: Almanac, 2 vols. 2003. (Cold War Reference Library). (Illus.). (J). 200p. 55.00 (978-0-7876-7662-9(4)); (978-0-7876-9087-8(2)); lib. bdg. 120.00 (978-0-7876-9089-2(9)) Thomson Gale. (UXL).

—Cold War: Biographies, 2 vols. 2003. (Cold War Reference Library). (Illus.). (J). 400p. 120.00 (978-0-7876-7663-6(2)); xxxv, 473p. (978-0-7876-7664-3(0)); xxxv, 473p. (978-0-7876-7665-0(9)) Thomson Gale. (UXL).

—Cold War Reference Library: Includes Cumulative Index, 4 vols. Incl. Cold War : Almanac. 200p. 55.00 (978-0-7876-7662-9(4)); Cold War : Biographies. 400p. 120.00 (978-0-7876-7663-6(2)); Cold War : Primary Sources. 200p. 67.00 (978-0-7876-7666-7(7)); (J). (Illus.). 800p. 2003. Set lib. bdg. 290.00 (978-0-7876-7609-4(8) , UXL) Thomson Gale.

Harrison, Paul. The Cold War. 2005. (How Did It Happen? Ser.). (Illus.). 48p. (J). (gr. 7-10). 29.95 (978-1-59018-603-9(6) , Lucent Bks.) Thomson Gale.

Hatt, Christine. The End of the Cold War. 2002. (Cold War Ser.). (Illus.). 64p. (YA). (gr. 7 up). pap. 14.60 (978-0-8368-5280-6(X)); lib. bdg. 32.67 (978-0-8368-5275-2(3)) Stevens, Gareth Inc. (World Almanac Library).

Kallen, Stuart A. Primary Sources. 2003. (Illus.). 112p. (J). 29.95 (978-1-59018-243-7(X) , Lucent Bks.) Thomson Gale.

Keeley, Jennifer. Containing the Communists: America's Foreign Entanglements. 2003. (American War Library). (Illus.). 112p. (J). 29.95 (978-1-59018-225-3(1) , Lucent Bks.) Thomson Gale.

—Espionage. 2002. (American War Library). (Illus.). 112p. (J). 29.95 (978-1-59018-210-9(3) , Lucent Bks.) Thomson Gale.

Kelly, Nigel. The Fall of the Berlin Wall: The Cold War Ends. 2006. (Point of Impact Ser.). (Illus.). 32p. (J). (***978-1-4034-9139-8(9)***) Heinemann Library.

Levy, Patricia. The Fall of the Berlin Wall, November 9, 1989. 2002. (Days That Shook the World Ser.). (Illus.). 48p. (J). lib. bdg. 27.12 (978-0-7398-5233-0(7)) Raintree.

McAleavy, Tony. Superpower Rivalry: The Cold War. 1998. (Cambridge History Program Ser.). (Illus.). 79p. pap. 19.00 (978-0-521-59739-5(0)) Cambridge Univ. Pr.

Richard Tames. The Fall of the Berlin Wall. 2nd ed. 2006. (Point of Impact Ser.). (Illus.). 32p. (J). pap. (***978-1-4034-9148-0(8)***) Heinemann Library.

Ross, Stewart. The Causes of the Cold War. 2002. (Cold War Ser.). (Illus.). 64p. (YA). (gr. 7 up). pap. 14.60 (978-0-8368-5277-6(X)); lib. bdg. 32.67 (978-0-8368-5272-1(9)) Stevens, Gareth Inc. (World Almanac Library).

Shaw, George Bernard, intro. CNN: Cold War, 4 bks., Set. 2000. (J). (gr. 4-7). lib. bdg. 399.77 incl. VHS (978-0-7398-3210-3(7)) Raintree.

Sheehan, Sean. The Cold War. 2003. (Questioning History Ser.). (J). lib. bdg. 28.50 (978-1-58340-266-5(7)) Smart Apple Media.

Sherman, Josepha. The Cold War. 2004. (Chronicle of America's Wars Ser.). (Illus.). 96p. (J). (gr. 5-12). 27.93 (978-0-8225-0150-3(3)) Lerner Publishing Group.

Spying in the Cold War, 6 pack. 2004. (Illus.). pap. 48.35 (978-1-4109-1479-8(8)) Raintree.

Stanley, George Edward. America & the Cold War (1949-1969) 2005. (Illus.). 48p. (J). pap. (978-0-8368-5839-6(5)); lib. bdg. 30.00 (978-0-8368-5830-3(1)) Stevens, Gareth Inc. (World Almanac Library).

Stein, R. Conrad. The Cold War: A MyReportLinks.com Book. 2002. (U. S. Wars Ser.). (Illus.). 48p. (J). (gr. 4-10). lib. bdg. 25.26 (978-0-7660-5095-2(5) , MyReportLinks.com Bks.) Enslow Pubs., Inc.

Taylor, David. The Cold War. 2001. (20th Century Perspectives Ser.). (Illus.). 48p. (J). (gr. 5-7). lib. bdg. 25.64 (978-1-57572-434-8(0)) Heinemann Library.

—The Cold War. 2001. (YA). 14.75 (978-0-606-22491-8(2)) Tandem Library Bks.

—Cold War. 2001. (gr. 5-8). lib. bdg. 16.40 (978-0-613-58210-0(1)) Tandem Library Bks.

—The Cold War, Set 1. 2002. (20th Century Perspectives Ser.). (Illus.). 48p. (J). (gr. 5-7). pap. 7.95 (978-1-58810-373-4(0) , 91125) Heinemann Library.

Thomson Gale Staff. Cold War Period: 1945-1992. 2002. (gr. 7-12). lib. bdg. 39.05 (978-0-613-73607-7(9)) Tandem Library Bks.

Tracy, Kathleen. The Fall of the Berlin Wall. 2005. (Illus.). 48p. (J). lib. bdg. 29.95 (978-1-58415-405-1(5)) Mitchell Lane Pubs., Inc.

Uschan, Michael V. Political Leaders. 2002. (American War Library). (Illus.). 112p. (J). 29.95 (978-1-59018-211-6(1) , Lucent Bks.) Thomson Gale.

COLERIDGE, SAMUEL TAYLOR, 1772-1834

Engell, James, ed. Samuel Taylor Coleridge. Chan, Harvey, illus. 2003. (Poetry for Young People Ser.). 48p. (gr. 3 up). 14.95 (978-0-8069-6951-0(2)) Sterling Publishing Co., Inc.

COLLAGE

Balchin, Judy. Collage. 2003. (Step-by-Step Ser.). (Illus.). 32p. (J). (gr. 3-5). lib. bdg. 25.64 (978-1-4034-0697-2(9)) Heinemann Library.

—Collage. 2003. (gr. 3-6). lib. bdg. 16.40 (978-0-613-88509-6(0)) Tandem Library Bks.

—Step-by-Step Collage. 2002. (Step-by-Step Children's Crafts Ser.). (Illus.). 32p. pap. 7.95 (978-1-903975-34-3(4) , 5344) Search Pr., Ltd. GBR. *Dist:* Independent Pubs. Group.

Bohera, Carme. Descubre el Colage. (Coleccion Manualidades Divertidas). (SPA.). 32p. (J). (gr. k-3). 10.00 (978-84-342-1903-8(4)) Parramon Ediciones S.A. ESP. *Dist:* Distribuidora Norma, Inc., Lectorum Pubns., Inc.

Chapman, Gillian & Robson, Pam. Art from Wood. 2007. (J). lib. bdg. (***978-1-4042-3726-1(7)*** , PowerKids Pr.) Rosen Publishing Group, Inc., The.

Collage. (Jump Ser.). (Illus.). 36p. (J). (gr. 2-6). pap. (978-1-882210-34-3(4)) Action Publishing, Inc.

Hodge, Anthony. Collage. 2006. 32p. pap. (978-958-30-1835-0(X)) Panamericana Editorial.

—Collage. 2004. (J). lib. bdg. 27.10 (978-1-932799-03-3(6)) Stargazer Bks.

Johnson, Susan & Johnson, Wil. Making Collages. 2003. (Illus.). 32p. (J). pap. 6.00 (978-1-59034-183-4(X)) Mondo Publishing.

King, Penny & Roundhill, Clare. Amazing Animals. 1998. (Making Pictures Ser.). (J). 21.36 (978-1-57572-192-7(9)) Heinemann Library.

—Secrets of the Sea. 1998. (Making Pictures Ser.). (J). 21.36 (978-1-57572-194-1(5)) Heinemann Library.

—Spooky Things. 1998. (Making Pictures Ser.). (J). 21.36 (978-1-57572-195-8(3)) Rigby Education.

Medina, Sarah. Having Fun with Collage. 2007. (J). lib. bdg. (978-1-4042-3721-6(6) , PowerKids Pr.) Rosen Publishing Group, Inc., The.

QEB Let's Start! Art National Book Stores Edition: Collage. 2006. (J). per. (978-1-59566-301-6(0)) QEB Publishing Inc.

Schecter, Deborah. Creating with Collage. 2002. (Illus.). 32p. (J). (978-0-439-33619-2(8)) Scholastic, Inc.

Thomas, Isabel. Action Art: Making Collage. 2005. (Illus.). 24p. (J). (978-1-4034-6922-9(9)); pap. (978-1-4034-6928-1(8)) Heinemann Library.

COLLECTING

see Collectors and Collecting

COLLECTIONS OF LITERATURE

see Short Stories

also names of literatures and literary forms with the subdivision Collections, e.g. English Literature—Collections; Poetry—Collections

COLLECTIVE SETTLEMENTS

Hunter, David. Teen Life among the Amish & Other Alternative Communities: Choosing a Lifestyle. 2008. (Youth in Rural North America Ser.). (J). (978-1-4222-0017-9(5)) Mason Crest Pubs.

Marx, Paul. Utopia in America. 2002. (To Know the Land Ser.). (Illus.). 109p. (YA). 28.00 (978-0-934272-73-5(5)); pap. 16.00 (978-0-934272-72-8(7)) Burke, John Gordon Pub., Inc.

COLLECTIVE SETTLEMENTS—FICTION

Ryan, Sarah. The Rules for Hearts: A Family Drama. 2007. 224p. (YA). (gr. 9 up). 16.99 (978-0-670-05906-5(4) , Viking Juvenile) Penguin Group (USA) Inc.

COLLECTIVISM

see Communism; Socialism

COLLECTORS AND COLLECTING

see also names of natural specimens with the subdivision Collection and Preservation, e.g. Zoological Specimens—Collection and Preservation

Adams, Yvonne. Meissen Figures 1730-1755: The Kaendler Period. 2001. (Schiffer Book for Collectors Ser.). (Illus.). 208p. (gr. 10-13). 59.95 (978-0-7643-1240-3(5)) Schiffer Publishing, Ltd.

Allen, Tom & Allen, Susan. American Oil Cans Identification & Price Guide. Allen, Tom & Allen, Susan, eds. 2003. (Illus.). 128p. (YA). per. 24.95 (978-0-9728607-0-3(3)) Dean's Bks., Inc.

Baker, H. K. G. Cool Collectibles for Kids: A Kid's & Parent's Guide to the Hobby of Collecting. 2008. (Illus.). 64p. (J). pap. 12.95 (978-1-933317-57-1(4)) Silverleaf Pr.

Blashfield, Jean F. Abraham Lincoln. 2000. (Illus.). 32p. (YA). (gr. 5 up). pap. 5.00 (978-1-890541-23-1(0)) Americana Souvenirs & Gifts.

Bonkers, Izzy. Complete Crazy Bones Collector's Guide. 2000. (Illus.). 96p. (gr. 2-9). pap. 7.99 (978-0-439-15403-1(0)) Scholastic, Inc.

Butler, Steve. Hubley Catalogs: 1946-1965. 2002. (Schiffer Book for Collectors Ser.). (Illus.). 160p. (gr. 10-13). pap. 29.95 (978-0-7643-1563-3(3)) Schiffer Publishing, Ltd.

Cool Collections. 2007. 136.68 (978-1-59679-768-0(1) , Checkerboard Library) ABDO Publishing Co.

Duffey, Betsy. Cody Unplugged. Thompson, Ellen, illus. 2001. (Chapters Ser.). 96p. (J). (gr. 2-5). pap. 4.99 (978-0-14-131240-8(8) , Puffin) Penguin Group (USA) Inc.

—Cody Unplugged. 2001. 11.79 (978-0-606-21116-1(0)); (gr. 3-6). lib. bdg. 13.00 (978-0-613-35917-7(8)) Tandem Library Bks.

Eng, Loman & Eng, Petula. Collecting American Belleek. 2003. (Schiffer Book for Collectors Ser.). (Illus.). 160p. 39.95 (978-0-7643-1860-3(8)) Schiffer Publishing, Ltd.

Ettinger, Roseann. Popular Jewelry, 1840-1940. 3rd rev. ed. 2002. (Illus.). 176p. (gr. 10-13). pap. 29.95 (978-0-7643-1582-4(X)) Schiffer Publishing, Ltd.

Everitt, Robert T. Racket Sports Collectibles. 2002. (Schiffer Book for Collectors Ser.). (Illus.). 288p. (gr. 10-13). 69.95 (978-0-7643-1647-0(8)) Schiffer Publishing, Ltd.

Galaxy, Billy. Collecting Classic Video Games. 2001. (Schiffer Book for Collectors Ser.). (Illus.). 144p. (gr. 10-13). pap. 29.95 (978-0-7643-1456-8(4)) Schiffer Publishing, Ltd.

Greason, Judith Ann & Skinner, Tina. Chenille. collector's ed. 2002. (Schiffer Book for Collectors Ser.). (Illus.). 160p. (gr. 10-13). pap. 29.95 (978-0-7643-1511-4(0)) Schiffer Publishing, Ltd.

Harcourt School Publishers Staff. Kids Collect! On Level. 3rd ed. 2002. (Trophies Reading Program Ser.). (Illus.). pap. 5.10 (978-0-15-323252-7(8)) Harcourt Schl. Pubs.

Hopper, Philip. Anchor Hocking Decorated Pitchers & Glasses: The Depression Years, 3 vols. 2001. (Schiffer Book for Collectors Ser.). (Illus.). 112p. (gr. 10-13). pap. 24.95 (978-0-7643-1486-5(6)) Schiffer Publishing, Ltd.

Hubley, Dan & Hubley, Mary. Kids Collect: Amazing Collections for Fun, Crafts, & Science Fair Projects. Hubley, Mary, illus. 2002. (Illus.). 176p. (J). per. 13.95 (978-0-9707267-1-1(6)) Bluefish Bay Publishing.

Kravitz, Robert J. A Collector's Guide to Fractional Currency: The Pocket Change of the Union Soldier. collector's ed. 2003. (Illus.). 262p. pap. 29.95 (978-0-918501-46-2(6) , RK-2003, Archives Pr.) Media Assocs.

The Liberty Bell. 2001. (Illus.). 32p. (YA). (gr. 5 up). pap. 5.00 (978-1-890541-76-7(1)) Americana Souvenirs & Gifts.

Mack, Charlie. The Encyclopedia of Matchbox Toys. 3rd rev. exp. ed. 2002. (Schiffer Book for Collectors Ser.). (Illus.). 352p. (gr. 10-13). pap. 29.95 (978-0-7643-1571-8(4)) Schiffer Publishing, Ltd.

Martin, Carolyn. Metal Horse Figurines. 2004. (Illus.). 200p. per. 34.95 (978-0-9746808-1-1(8)) Martin, Carolyn.

McMullan, Tigre. Collectible Girlie Glasses. 2003. (Schiffer Book for Collectors Ser.). (Illus.). 128p. pap. 24.95 (978-0-7643-1862-7(4)) Schiffer Publishing, Ltd.

Miller, Judith. Collectibles Price Guide 2005. 2004. (Illus.). 600p. pap. 25.00 (978-0-7566-0523-0(7)) Dorling Kindersley Publishing, Inc.

Miller, Martin. Antiques Source Book: The Definitive Guide to Retail Prices for Antiques & Collectables. (Illus.). 613p. pap. (978-0-681-35573-6(5)) Carlton Bks., Ltd.

Mitchell, James O. Her Black Sparkles! (Illus.). pap. 7.50 (978-0-9646017-1-0(0)) Thirty-Three Hundred Pr.

Newell, Patrick. Military Collectibles. 2000. (High Interest Bks.). (Illus.). 48p. (YA). (gr. 7-12). 24.00 (978-0-516-23331-4(9)); pap. 6.95 (978-0-516-23531-8(1)) Scholastic Library Publishing. (Children's Pr.).

O'Neill, David & Sullivan, Janet O'Neill. Collecting Rose O'Neill's Kewpies. 2003. (Schiffer Book for Collectors Ser.). (Illus.). 160p. (gr. 10-13). pap. 29.95 (978-0-7643-1855-9(1)) Schiffer Publishing, Ltd.

Owens, Thomas S. Collecting Stock Car Racing Memorabilia. 2001. (Illus.). 80p. (gr. 5-8). lib. bdg. 26.90 (978-0-7613-1853-8(4) , Millbrook Pr.) Lerner Publishing Group.

Pascoe, Elaine. Slime, Molds & Fungi. Kuhn, Dwight, photos by. 1998. (Nature Close-Up Ser.). (Illus.). 48p. (J). (gr. 4-8). 23.70 (978-1-56711-182-8(3) , Blackbirch Pr., Inc.) Thomson Gale.

Pina, Leslie, et al. Purple Glass: 20th Century American & European. 2002. (Schiffer Book for Collectors Ser.). (Illus.). 160p. (gr. 10-13). 29.95 (978-0-7643-1515-2(3)) Schiffer Publishing, Ltd.

Pratt, Michael E. Mid-Century Modern Dinnerware: Ak-Sar-Ben to Paden City Pottery: a Pictorial Guide. 2003. (Schiffer Book for Collectors Ser.). (Illus.). 224p. (gr. 10-13). 39.95 (978-0-7643-1736-1(9)) Schiffer Publishing, Ltd.

Provensen, Alice, et al. Caldecott Award Collection, 5 bks., Set. unabr. ed. 1999. (Illus.). (J). pap. 91.95 incl. audio (978-0-87499-489-6(6)) Live Oak Media.

Rendall, Richard & Abrams, Elise. Hand Painted Porcelain Plates: Nineteenth Century to the Present. 2003. (Schiffer Book for Collectors Ser.). (Illus.). 240p. (gr. 10-13). 59.95 (978-0-7643-1692-0(3)) Schiffer Publishing, Ltd.

Resch, Kurt M. The Collector's Guide to Bus Toys & Models. 2002. (Schiffer Book for Collectors Ser.). (Illus.). 176p. (gr. 10-13). pap. 29.95 (978-0-7643-1631-9(1)) Schiffer Publishing, Ltd.

Schiffer, Nancy N. Baskets. 3rd rev. ed. 2001. (Illus.). 176p. (gr. 10-13). pap. 29.95 (978-0-7643-1380-6(0)) Schiffer Publishing, Ltd.

Smith, John, et al. Antique Toothbrush Holders. 2002. (Schiffer Book for Collectors Ser.). (Illus.). 160p. pap. 29.95 (978-0-7643-1654-8(0)) Schiffer Publishing, Ltd.

Snyder, Jeffrey B. Collecting Oyster Plates. 2001. (Schiffer Book for Collectors Ser.). (Illus.). 160p. (gr. 10-13). pap. 29.95 (978-0-7643-1481-0(5)) Schiffer Publishing, Ltd.

Vogt, Gregory L. Space Mission Patches. 2001. (Enthusiastic Astronomy Ser.). (Illus.). 80p. (gr. 5-8). lib. bdg. (978-0-7613-1613-8(2) , Millbrook Pr.) Lerner Publishing Group.

Vourtsis, Phil. The Fabulous Victrola 45. 2002. (Illus.). 176p. (gr. 10-13). pap. 29.95 (978-0-7643-1637-1(0)) Schiffer Publishing, Ltd.

Walk, John. Fenton Special Orders: 1980-Present: QVC; Mary Walrath; Martha Stewart; Cracker Barrel; JC Penney; National Fenton Glass Society; & Fenton Art Glass Club of America. 2003. (Schiffer Book for Collectors Ser.). (Illus.). 240p. 29.95 (978-0-7643-1813-9(6)) Schiffer Publishing, Ltd.

Walt Disney's Feature Animation Department Staff. Disney's Tarzan Postcard Book. 1999. 64p. pap. 9.95 (978-0-7868-8419-3(3)) Disney Pr.

Webb, Spider. Historic Flash. 2002. (Illus.). 80p. (gr. 10-13). pap. 25.00 (978-0-7643-1606-7(0)) Schiffer Publishing, Ltd.

Webber, Hiltrud M. Collecting Butterflies & Moths. l.t. ed. 1999. (Ozarkae Ser.: Vol. 2). (Illus.). 35p. (J). spiral bd. 10.95 (978-0-9652173-2-3(9)) HMW Pubns.

COLLECTORS AND COLLECTING—FICTION

Armstrong-Ellis, Carey. Prudy's Problem & How She Solved It. Armstrong-Ellis, Carey, illus. 2002. (Illus.). 32p. (J). (ps-3). 14.95 (978-0-8109-0569-6(8)) Abrams, Harry N., Inc.

Boniface, William. The Extraordinary Adventures of Ordinary Boy, Book 1: the Hero Revealed. Gilpin, Stephen, illus. 2008. (Extraordinary Adventures of Ordinary Boy Ser.). 320p. (J). pap. 6.99 (***978-0-06-077466-0(5)*** , Harper Trophy) HarperCollins Pubs.

Boniface, William. The Hero Revealed. Gilpin, Stephen, illus. 2006. (Extraordinary Adventures of Ordinary Boy Ser.). 304p. (J). 15.99 (978-0-06-077464-6(9)); lib. bdg. 16.89 (978-0-06-077465-3(7)) HarperCollins Pubs.

Bunting, Eve. Anna's Table. Morley, Taia, illus. 2003. 32p. (gr. k-3). 15.95 (978-1-55971-841-7(2) , NorthWord Bks. for Young Readers) T&N Children's Publishing.

Castle, Kathryn. Todavia Sirven! Alvarado, Ana María, tr. Ahers-Johnson, Patrizia, illus. 2000. (Think-Kids Book Collection).Tr. of Cool Junk. (SPA.). 16p. (J). pap. 2.95 (978-1-58237-057-6(5)) Creative Thinkers, Inc.

Chaconas, Dori. Cork & Fuzz: The Collectors. McCue, Lisa, illus. 2008. 32p. (J). (ps-1). 13.99 (***978-0-670-06286-7(3)*** , Viking Adult) Penguin Group (USA) Inc.

Dahlin, Adam. Junk Collector School. Sandin, Joan, tr. Akerman, Emma, illus. 2007. 32p. (J). (ps-3). 16.00 (***978-91-29-66736-3(4)***) R & S Bks. SWE. *Dist:* Macmillan.

Dell, Pamela. The Gold Coin: A Story about New York City's Lower East Side. 2002. (Scrapbooks of America Ser.). (Illus.). 48p. (J). (gr. 2-6). 28.50 (978-1-59187-017-3(8)) Child's World, Inc.

deRubertis, Barbara. Collection for Kate. 1999. (gr. k-3). lib. bdg. 12.95 (978-0-613-17145-8(4)) Tandem Library Bks.

—A Collection for Kate: Math Concept: Addition. Fiammenghi, Gioia, illus. 1999. (Math Matters Ser.). 32p. (J). (gr. k-2). pap. 4.95 (978-1-57565-089-0(4)) Kane Pr., The.

—A Collection for Kate: Math Concept: Addition. 1999. (Math Matters Ser.). (Illus.). (J). 11.75 (978-0-606-18216-4(0)) Tandem Library Bks.

Donaldson, Julia. The Giants & the Joneses. Swearingen, Greg, illus. 2005. 224p. (J). (gr. 3-5). 14.95 (978-0-8050-7805-3(3)) Holt, Henry & Co.

—The Giants & the Joneses. Swearingen, Greg, illus. 2008. 240p. (J). pap. 6.99 (***978-0-312-37961-2(7)***) Square Fish.

Doudna, Kelly. Pack Rat. Chawla, Neena, illus. 2006. (Fact & Fiction Ser.). 24p. (J). pap. (978-1-59679-956-1(0)) ABDO Publishing Co.

Dussling, Jennifer. Whatcha Got? Wummer, Amy, illus. 2004. 32p. (J). lib. bdg. 20.00 (***978-1-4242-1117-3(4)***) Fitzgerald Bks.

—Whatcha Got? Wummer, Amy, illus. 2004. (Social Studies Connects). 32p. (J). (gr. 1-3). pap. 4.99 (978-1-57565-143-9(2)) Kane Pr., The.

Fletcher, Ralph J. Tommy Trouble & the Magic Marble. Caldwell, Benjamin H., Jr., illus. rev. ed. 2000. 64p. (J). (gr. 2-5). 16.00 (978-0-8050-6387-5(0) , Holt, Henry & Co. Bks. For Young Readers) Holt, Henry & Co.

Gallup, Tracy. Shell Crazy. Gallup, Tracy, illus. 2007. (Crazy Little Ser.). (Illus.). 40p. (J). 9.95 (***978-1-934133-14-9(0)***) Mackinac Island Pr., Inc.

Harcourt School Publishers Staff. An Interview with the Brothers Grim: Take-Home Book. 2001. (Collections Ser.). (Illus.). (J). pap. 1.90 (978-0-15-319501-3(0)) Harcourt Schl. Pubs.

Hillert, Margaret. I Like Things. (J). 4.95 (978-0-87895-683-8(2)) Modern Curriculum Pr.

Jocelyn, Marthe. Hannah's Collections. 2004. (Illus.). 32p. (J). (ps-k). reprint ed. pap. 7.95 (978-0-88776-690-9(0)) Tundra Bks., Inc./Livres Toundra, Inc. CAN. *Dist:* Random Hse., Inc.

Karwoski, Gail Langer. Julie the Rockhound. Downey, Lisa, illus. 2007. 32p. (J). (gr. k-4). 8.95 (***978-1-934359-21-1(1)***) Sylvan Dell Pubng.

Lee, Eun. Antique Gift Shop, Vol. 2. 2005. (Illus.). 180p. (YA). pap. 10.95 (***978-89-527-4475-3(6)***) ICE Kunion KOR. *Dist:* Diamond Bk. Distributors.

Levin, Betty. The Unmaking of Duncan Veerick. 2007. 204p. (YA). (gr. 5 up). 16.95 (***978-1-932425-96-3(9)*** , Front Street) Boyds Mills Pr.

Monroy, Manuel. Rabieta Trebejos. 2000. (Los Especials de A la Orilla Del Viento Ser.). (SPA.). 24p. (J). (ps-ps). per. 13.99 (978-968-16-6080-2(3)) Fondo de Cultura Economica USA.

Rau, Dana Meachen. Stickers, Shells, & Snow Globes. Thivierge, Claude, illus. 2004. (Read-It! Readers Ser.). 32p. (C). (gr. k-3). 18.60 (978-1-4048-0648-1(2)) Picture Window Bks.

—Stickers, Shells, & Snowglobes. 2004. (Compass Point Early Reader Ser.). (J). 18.60 (978-0-7565-0574-5(7)) Compass Point Bks.

Ruzzier, Sergio. The Room of Wonders. 2006. (Illus.). 40p. (J). 16.00 (978-0-374-36343-7(9) , Frances Foster Bks.) Farrar, Straus & Giroux.

Schertle, Alice. Jeremy Bean. Slonim, David, illus. 2008. (J). (978-0-8118-5609-6(7)) Chronicle Bks. LLC.

Shearer, Alex. Canned. 2008. (J). 240p. 16.99 (***978-0-439-90309-7(2) ; *978-0-439-90310-3(6)***) Scholastic, Inc. (Scholastic Pr.).

Slingsby, Janet. Hetty's 100 Hats. Dodd, Emma, illus. 2005. 40p. (J). (ps-ps). 16.00 (978-1-56148-456-0(3)) Good Bks.

West, Tracey. Liz Pone Orden. 1999. (Coleccion Liz). (SPA., Illus.). 24p. (J). (gr. k-3). pap. 3.50 (978-0-439-05869-8(4) , SO3476, Scholastic en Espanol) Scholastic, Inc.

—Liz Sorts It Out. Bracken, Caroline, illus. 1998. (Magic School Bus Ser.). 24p. (J). (gr. 1-4). pap. 3.50 (978-0-590-81838-4(4)) Scholastic, Inc.

COLLECTS

see Prayers

COLLEGE AND SCHOOL JOURNALISM

Manual for Scholastic Newspaper Publishing. 2006. 32.95 net. (978-1-56004-259-4(1)) Social Studies Schl. Service.

COLLEGE ATHLETICS

see Athletics

COLLEGE CHOICE

Greenfeld, Barbara C. The Kids' College Almanac: A First Look at College. 2001. (gr. 7-12). lib. bdg. 26.85 (978-0-613-50078-4(4)) Tandem Library Bks.

Heron, Helen H. College Countdown: A Planning Guide for High School Students. Coleman, William S., illus. 4th rev. ed. 2000. 160p. (YA). pap. 19.95 (978-1-880639-26-9(2)) Heron Publishing.

Lee, Danielle. JumpStart Your Future: A Guide for the College-Bound Christian. 2006. (Illus.). iii, 123p. (YA). per. 12.99 (978-0-9769298-9-5(9)) Olive Pr., The.

Read, Marya & Jana, P. Lynn, contrib. by. An Educated Choice Journal. 2003. 133p. (YA). (978-1-929931-11-8(5)) Intrepid Films, LLC.

Rugg, Frederick E. Thirty Questions & Answers. (gr. 11-12). 5th ed. 1999. 23p. pap. 9.95 (978-1-883062-30-9(6) , 4); 8th rev. ed. 2002. 19p. (YA). pap. 9.95 (978-1-883062-46-0(2)) Rugg's Recommendations.

—Thirty Questions & Answers on the Colleges. (YA). 7th ed. 2001. 20p. (gr. 11-12). pap. 9.95 (978-1-883062-31-6(4)); 9th rev. ed. 2003. 20p. pap. 9.95 (978-1-883062-52-1(7)); 10th rev. ed. 2004. 20p. pap. 9.95 (978-1-883062-56-9(X)); 11th rev. ed. 2005. 21p. pap. 9.95 (978-1-883062-61-3(6)) Rugg's Recommendations.

Zmich, Elizabeth & Adler, Penny. Check Yourself into College: A Quick & Easy Guide for High School Students. 2003. (Illus.). 120p. (YA). pap. 29.99 (978-1-878234-03-2(X) , IBT-100) NETWORK Inc., The.

COLLEGE ENTRANCE REQUIREMENTS

see Universities and Colleges—Entrance Requirements

COLLEGE JOURNALISM

see College and School Journalism

COLLEGE PERIODICALS

see College and School Journalism

COLLEGE STUDENTS

Easley, Michael F. Look Out, College, Here I Come! 2007. (J). (***978-0-8106-2037-7(5)***); pap. (***978-0-8106-2038-4(3)***) National Education Assn.

Isenberg, Marc & Rhoads, Rick. The Real Athletes Guide: How to Succeed in Sports, School & Life. Conley, Sebastian, illus. 1998. 185p. (YA). (gr. 7 up). pap. 19.95 (978-0-9666764-0-2(8)) A-Game, LLC.

Maynigo, Traci. A Girl's Guide to College. (Illus.). 96p. pap. 10.95 (978-1-58786-012-6(0) , Blue Mountain Pr.) Blue Mountain Arts Inc.

Phoenix, Charlotte Y. & Bain-Pew, Gilda. The S. A. F. E. College Planning Guide for Students Grades 9 - 12: What You Need to Know about Selecting, Applyingto, Financing & Excelling in College. 1999. viii, 116p. (YA). (gr. 9-12). pap. 12.95 (978-0-9671869-0-0(0) , 99001) Lenroc Publishing, Inc.

Richmond, Marianne R. Wishes for You Graduate. 2005. (Illus.). 40p. (J). 7.95 (978-0-9763101-3-6(9)) Marianne Richmond Studios, Inc.

COLLEGE TEACHERS

see Educators; Teachers

COLLEGES

see Universities and Colleges

COLLIE

Collard, Sneed B., III. Shep: Our Most Loyal Dog. Yardley, Joanne, illus. 2006. 40p. (J). (gr. k-5). 16.95 (978-1-58536-259-2(X)) Sleeping Bear Pr.

Fitzpatrick, Anne. Collies. 2003. (Dog Breeds Ser.). 24p. (J). lib. bdg. 21.35 (978-1-58340-315-0(9)) Smart Apple Media.

Rake, Jody Sullivan. Collies. 2008. (J). (***978-1-4296-0015-6(2)***) Capstone Pr., Inc.

Wilcox, Charlotte. The Collie. 1998. (Learning about Dogs Ser.). (Illus.). 48p. (J). (gr. 3-4). lib. bdg. 21.26 (978-0-7368-0005-1(0) , Capstone High-Interest Bks.) Capstone Pr., Inc.

COLLIES

see Collie

COLOMBIA

Boraas, Tracey. Colombia. 2002. (Countries & Cultures Ser.). (Illus.). 64p. (J). (gr. 3-4). lib. bdg. 23.93 (978-0-7368-1076-0(5) , Bridgestone Bks.) Capstone Pr., Inc.

Crooker, Richard A. Colombia. 2007. (Modern World Nations Ser.). 120p. (J). (gr. 6-12). 30.00 (***978-0-7910-9509-6(6)*** , Chelsea Hse.) Facts On File, Inc.

DuBois, Jill & Jermyn, L. Colombia. 2nd ed. 2001. (Cultures of the World Ser.). (Illus.). 144p. (gr. 5 up). lib. bdg. 37.07 (978-0-7614-1361-5(8) , Benchmark Bks.) Cavendish, Marshall Corp.

Fox, Mary Virginia. Colombia. 2000. (Visit to Ser.). (Illus.). 32p. (J). (gr. k-2). lib. bdg. 21.36 (978-1-57572-378-5(6)) Heinemann Library.

Fox, Mary Virginia, et al. Vamos a Colombia. 2001. (Vamos a Ser.). (SPA., Illus.). 32p. (J). (gr. k-2). lib. bdg. 21.36 (978-1-57572-382-2(4)) Heinemann Library.

Gelletly, LeeAnne. Colombia. 2003. (Discovering South America Ser.). (Illus.). 64p. (YA). (gr. 5 up). lib. bdg. (978-1-59084-292-8(8)) Mason Crest Pubs.

Grolier Educational Staff, contrib. by. Colombia. 2003. (Illus.). 32p. (J). (978-0-7172-5791-1(6) , Grolier) Scholastic Library Publishing.

Haynes, Tricia. Colombia. 1999. (Major World Nations Ser.). (Illus.). 144p. (YA). (gr. 4-7). 29.95 (978-0-7910-4969-3(8) , Chelsea Hse.) Facts On File, Inc.

Hong, Lim Bee & Jermyn, Leslie. Welcome to Colombia. 2000. (Welcome to My Country Ser.). (Illus.). 48p. (J). (gr. 2 up). lib. bdg. 26.00 (978-0-8368-2508-4(X)) Stevens, Gareth Inc.

Jermyn, Leslie. Colombia. 1999. (Countries of the World Ser.). (Illus.). 96p. (J). (gr. 6 up). lib. bdg. 30.00 (978-0-8368-2308-0(7)) Stevens, Gareth Inc.

Lopata, Peg. Colombia. 2004. (Modern Nations of the World Ser.). 112p. (J). (gr. 7-10). 29.95 (978-1-59018-110-2(7) , Lucent Bks.) Thomson Gale.

Morrison, Marion. Colombia. 2007. 144p. (J). 37.00 (***978-0-516-25947-5(4)*** , Children's Pr.) Scholastic Library Publishing.

Owens, Caleb. Colombia. 2003. (Countries: Faces & Places Ser.). (Illus.). 32p. (J). (gr. 1-5). 25.64 (978-1-56766-905-3(0)) Child's World, Inc.

Spengler, Kremena. Colombia: A Question & Answer Book. 2006. (Fact Finders Ser.). (Illus.). 32p. (J). (978-0-7368-4351-5(5) , Fact Finders) Capstone Pr., Inc.

COLOMBIA—FICTION

Brown, Marc. Buster Climbs the Walls. 9th ed. 2005. (Postcards from Buster Ser.). (Illus.). 48p. (J). (gr. 1-4). pap. 3.99 (978-0-316-00126-7(0)) Little Brown & Co.

Castilla, Julia Mercedes. El Tesoro de la Pordiosera. Diaz, Carlos Manuel, illus. 2002. (SPA.). 118p. pap. 5.30 (978-958-04-6889-9(3)) Norma S.A. COL. *Dist:* Lectorum Pubns., Inc.

Foreman, Michael. Mia's Story: A Sketchbook of Hopes & Dreams. Foreman, Michael, illus. 2006. (Illus.). 32p. (J). (gr. k-3). 15.99 (978-0-7636-3063-8(2)) Candlewick Pr.

Whyman, Matt. Boy Kills Man. 2006. 160p. (J). pap. 6.99 (978-0-06-074665-0(3) , HarperTeen) HarperCollins Pubs.

Windle, Jeanette. Captured in Colombia, Vol. 3. 2002. (Parker Twins Ser.: No. 3). 160p. (gr. 3-8). pap. 5.99 (978-0-8254-4147-9(1)) Kregel Pubns.

COLON, CRISTOBAL, 1451-1506

see Columbus, Christopher, 1451-1506

COLONIAL FURNITURE

see Furniture, American

COLONIAL HISTORY (UNITED STATES)

see United States—History—Colonial Period, ca. 1600-1775

COLONIAL LIFE AND CUSTOMS (UNITED STATES)

see United States—History—Colonial Period, ca. 1600-1775; United States—Social Life and Customs—Colonial Period, ca. 1600-1775

COLOR

see also Dyes and Dyeing

Abbeville Press Staff. Assorted My First Color. 1998. 8.95 (978-0-7892-0581-0(5)) Abbeville Pr., Inc.

Abbink, Emily. Colors of the Navajo. Porter, Janice Lee, illus. 1998. (Colors of the World Ser.). 24p. (J). (gr. 1-4). 5.95 (978-1-57505-269-4(5)); (gr. 3-6). lib. bdg. 19.93 (978-1-57505-207-6(5)) Lerner Publishing Group.

—Colors of the Navajo. Porter, Janice Lee, illus. 1998. 24p. (J). (ps-3). lib. bdg. 14.10 (978-0-613-68208-4(4)) Tandem Library Bks.

Abril, Paco. Colores que se Aman. Decis, Anne, illus. 2004. Tr. of Colors that Love Each Other. (SPA.). (J). 14.99 (978-84-241-7989-2(7)) Everest de Ediciones y Distribucion, S.L. ESP. *Dist:* Lectorum Pubns., Inc.

Accorsi, William. The 10 Color Book. 2007. (Illus.). 14p. bds. 15.95 (***978-0-7611-4739-8(X)***) Workman Publishing Co., Inc.

Aigner-Clark, Julie. Baby Einstein: una ventana al Color: Baby Einstein: Wndows to Color, Spanish-Language Edition. Zaidi, Nadeem, illus. 2006. 10p. (J). bds. 6.95 (***978-970-718-454-1(X)*** , Silver Dolphin en Español) Advanced Marketing, S. de R. L. de C. V. MEX. *Dist:* Perseus Distribution.

—El Mundo de Color de Van Gogh. 2004. (Baby Einstein Ser.). (SPA., Illus.). 12p. (J). bds. 7.95 (978-970-718-158-8(3) , Silver Dolphin en Español) Advanced Marketing, S. de R. L. de C. V. MEX. *Dist:* Perseus Distribution.

—See & Spy Colors. Zaidi, Nadeem, illus. 2006. 16p. (J). (ps-17). 5.99 (978-1-4231-0002-7(6)) Baby Einstein Co., LLC, The.

—Van Gogh's World of Color. Zaidi, Nadeem, illus. 2001. (Baby Einstein Ser.). 12p. (J). (ps-ps). 7.99 (978-0-7868-0805-2(5)) Hyperion Bks. for Children.

Alphabet, Colors, & Numbers. . . 2000. (Kelley Wingate Ser.). 80p. (J). (ps-k). pap. 9.99 (978-0-88724-591-6(9)) Carson-Dellosa Publishing Co., Inc.

Alvarez, Lourdes M. Colores. 2004. (Mi primer libro Ser.). (SPA., Illus.). 9p. (J). bds. 3.95 (978-1-933050-01-0(2)) Sweetwater Pr.

—Colors. Brooks, David, illus. 2005. (My First Book Ser.). 9p. (J). (ps-ps). bds. 3.95 (978-1-933050-07-2(1)) Sweetwater Pr.

American Education Publishing Staff. Colors & Shapes. 2003. (Brighter Child Preschool Flash Cards Ser.). (Illus.). 36p. (J). (ps). 2.99 (978-1-56189-460-4(5) , 31044, American Education Publishing) School Specialty Publishing.

American Heritage Dictionary Editors. What Color Is It? Cote, Pamela & Zagarenski, Pamela, illus. 2001. (Good Beginnings/Un Buen Comienzo Ser.). Orig. Title: Que Color Es Este?. (SPA & ENG.). 4p. (J). (gr. k-ps). bds. 3.95 (978-0-618-16932-0(6)) Houghton Mifflin Co. Trade & Reference Div.

Anastasio, Dina. Colors. 2002. (Clifford, the Big Red Dog Ser.). (Illus.). 32p. (J). (ps). pap., wbk. ed. 2.99 (978-0-439-39850-3(9)) Scholastic, Inc.

Anderson, Moira. Blue. 2005. (Illus.). 24p. (J). pap. (978-1-4034-7449-0(4)); lib. bdg. (978-1-4034-7444-5(3)) Steck-Vaughn.

—Green. 2005. (Illus.). 24p. pap. (978-1-4034-7450-6(8)); lib. bdg. (978-1-4034-7445-2(1)) Steck-Vaughn.

—Red. 2005. (Illus.). 24p. (J). pap. (978-1-4034-7451-3(6)); lib. bdg. (978-1-4034-7446-9(X)) Steck-Vaughn.

—Yellow. 2005. (Illus.). 24p. (J). pap. (978-1-4034-7452-0(4)); lib. bdg. (978-1-4034-7447-6(8)) Steck-Vaughn.

Anderson, Sara. Colors. Anderson, Sara, illus. 2007. 7p. (J). bds. 10.95 (978-1-59354-184-2(8)) Chronicle Bks. LLC.

Arps, Melissa. Colors. 2006. (Illus.). (J). (***978-0-7364-2381-6(8)***) Random Hse., Inc.

Baby's First Colors Book. 2004. 10p. (J). bds. 4.99 (978-1-85854-920-0(5)) Brimax Books Ltd. GBR. *Dist:* Byeway Bks.

Back to the Basics. 2000. (Learning Fun for Little Ones Ser.). (Illus.). 64p. (ps-1). pap. 8.99 (978-0-88724-568-8(4) , CD-6400) Carson-Dellosa Publishing Co., Inc.

Barad, Alexis. World Around Me: Colors, Numbers & More. 2008. (Fisher-Price Ser.). 12p. (J). 7.99 (***978-0-06-145039-6(1)*** , Harper Festival) HarperCollins Pubs.

Barbieri-McGrath, Barbara. Mas Matematicas Con los Chocolates de "M & M's"c. 2001. Tr. of More "M & M's"c Brand Math. (978-0-606-22626-4(5)) Tandem Library Bks.

Base, Graeme. The Water Hole: Coloring Book. 2004. (Illus.). 32p. (J). (ps-4). pap. 9.95 (978-0-8109-8735-7(X)) Abrams, Harry N. , Inc.

Beall, Pamela Conn & Nipp, Susan Hagen. Wee Sing & Learn ABC. Pongmee, Yudthana, illus. 2000. (Wee Sing & Learn Bks.). 32p. (J). (ps-1). pap. 7.99 (978-0-8431-7596-7(6) , Price Stern Sloan) Penguin Group (USA) Inc.

—Wee Sing & Learn Colors. 2005. (Wee Sing & Learn Ser.). 20p. (J). (ps). 9.99 (978-0-8431-1663-2(3) , Price Stern Sloan) Penguin Group (USA) Inc.

—Wee Sing & Learn Colors. Pongmee, Yudthana, illus. 2001. (Reading Railroad Bks.). 32p. (J). (ps-k). pap. 3.49 (978-0-448-42591-7(2) , Grosset & Dunlap) Penguin Group (USA) Inc.

Beaton, Clare, illus. Colors: Los Colores. l.t. ed. 1998. (English-Spanish Bilingual First Bks.). (ENG & SPA.). 24p. (J). (ps up). lib. bdg. 14.45 (978-1-56674-249-8(8)) Forest Hse. Publishing Co., Inc.

Beers, Jack. Bridges - Blue. 2002. (Math Bridges Ser.). (gr. 8). (J). stu. ed., per. 13.95 (978-1-58830-339-4(X)); tchr. ed., per. 19.95 (978-1-58830-340-0(3)) Metropolitan Teaching & Learning Co.

—Bridges - Green. 2002. (Math Bridges Ser.). (J). (gr. 5). stu. ed., per. 13.95 (978-1-58830-298-4(9)) Metropolitan Teaching & Learning Co.

Belle River Readers Staff. Colors. 2002. (Illus.). 12p. (J). (gr. k-1). pap. 2.00 (978-0-9703548-3-9(5) , 4) Belle River Readers, Inc.

Bennett, Madeline. The Silliest Shapes & Colors Book in the Wild West. Bennett, Gary, illus. 2001. 32p. (J). (ps-2). 14.95 (978-1-893860-60-5(4)) Arizona Highways.

Bernthal, Mark. God's Colorful World. McKee, Darren, illus. 2007. (BOZ#8482; Ser.). 14p. (J). 4.99 (978-0-310-71394-4(3)) Zonderkidz.

Binns, Tristan Boyer. What Colour Is an Orange? 2006. (Illus.). 32p. (J). pap. (978-1-4109-2619-7(2)); lib. bdg. (978-1-4109-2590-9(0)) Steck-Vaughn.

Blue 6-Pack. 2004. (Colors in Nature Ser.). (Illus.). pap. 29.70 (978-1-4109-0734-9(1)) Raintree.

Bolchazy, Marie Carducci. Quo Colore Est?/What Color Is It? 2003. (I Am Reading Latin Ser.). (ENG & LAT., Illus.). 64p. (J). (gr. k-3). 12.00 (978-0-86516-539-7(4)) Bolchazy-Carducci Pubs.

Bond, G. T. GT Bond's Absolutely Stupendous Book of Colors. 2007. 60p. pap. 24.95 (***978-0-615-14642-3(2)***) S & S Pr.

Bonwit, Delores. My Little Wipe-off Colors. Adnet, Bernhard, illus. 2000. (My Little Wipe-Off Ser.). 8p. (J). (ps-1). bds. 4.99 (978-0-7681-0224-6(3) , 35015, McClanahan Bk.) Learning Horizons, Inc.

Book Company Staff. Lift & Learn Colors. 2004. (Novelty Bks.). (Illus.). 10p. (J). (gr. 3-5). bds. 7.95 (978-1-74047-556-3(9)) Book Co. Publishing Pty, Ltd., The AUS. *Dist:* Penton Overseas, Inc.

—My Cuddly Book of Colors. 2002. (Novelty Bks.). 6p. (J). 12.95 (978-1-74047-255-5(1)) Book Co. Publishing Pty, Ltd., The AUS. *Dist:* Penton Overseas, Inc.

Boos, Andre, illus. Hi! Read, Stick & Learn about Animals. Little Bears are Brown. 2004. 20p. (J). pap. 6.99 (978-1-59496-003-1(8)) Teora USA LLC.

Borgardt, Marianne. Yellow at Home: A Counting Book of Yellow. Shorten, Chris, photos by. 1999. (Gymboree Book Ser.). (Illus.). 20p. (J). reprint ed. 4.95 (978-1-892374-11-0(0)) Weldon Owen, Inc.

Boye, B. D. The Look Book. Boye, B. D., illus. l.t. ed. 2004. (Illus.). 20p. (J). per. 4.99 (978-0-9768078-1-0(5) , 100001) Innerchild Publishing, Inc.

Bradshaw, Georgine & Wrighton, Charlene. Set of Color Mini-Books (29 Titles) Clark, Irene, illus. 2005. (J). 39.95 (978-1-886441-42-2(1) , CMB4356) Zoo-phonics, Inc.

Brainy Baby Quad Book. 2005. (Brainy Baby Ser.). 40p. (J). bds. 10.39 (978-1-59394-240-3(0)) Bendon Publishing International.

Brighter Vision Publishing Staff. About Colors, Shapes & Sizes. 2000. (My Discovery Bks.). (Illus.). 20p. (J). (ps). pap. 2.95 (978-1-55254-208-8(4)) Brighter Vision Pubns.

—Color & Shapes. 2000. (Illus.). 32p. (J). (ps). pap. 1.39 (978-1-55254-148-7(7)) Brighter Vision Pubns.

Brown. (Colors Ser.). 32p. (J). 7.95 (978-0-7368-5071-1(6)) Capstone Pr., Inc.

Brown, Carron & Montague-Smith, Ann. First Color Book. Stanley, Mandy, illus. 2003. (First Bks.). 48p. (J). (ps-k). 12.95 (978-0-7534-5572-2(2) , Kingfisher) Houghton Mifflin Co. Trade & Reference Div.

Brown, Lisa. Baby Fix My Car. 2006. 12p. 6.95 (978-1-932416-56-5(0)) McSweeney's Publishing.

Brown, Margery W. Book of Colors: Meet the Color Family. Blair, Culverson & Simpson, Howard, illus. 2nd ed. 2004. (Afro-Bets Ser.). 24p. (J). (ps-1). pap. 3.95 (978-0-940975-57-6(2) , Sankofa Bks.) Just Us Bks., Inc.

Bruce. Colors in Nature, 24 Bks, 6 Packs. 2004. (Illus.). pap. 118.80 (978-1-4109-1248-0(5)) Raintree.

Bruce, Lisa. Blue. 2004. (Colors in Nature Ser.). (Illus.). 24p. pap. 5.50 (978-1-4109-0729-5(5)); (J). lib. bdg. 18.56 (978-1-4109-0724-0(4)) Raintree.

—Green. 2004. (Colors in Nature Ser.). (Illus.). 24p. (J). lib. bdg. 18.56 (978-1-4109-0722-6(8)); pap. 5.50 (978-1-4109-0727-1(9)) Raintree.

—Red. 2004. (Colors in Nature Ser.). (Illus.). 24p. (J). lib. bdg. 18.56 (978-1-4109-0723-3(6)); pap. 5.50 (978-1-4109-0728-8(7)) Raintree.

—Yellow. 2004. (Colors in Nature Ser.). (Illus.). 24p. (J). pap. 5.50 (978-1-4109-0730-1(9)); lib. bdg. 18.56 (978-1-4109-0725-7(2)) Raintree.

Bryan, Beth, ed. Yummy Colors: A Pull-and-Pop Book. 2007. (Let's Find Out Ser.). 12p. (J). (ps). 6.99 (978-0-439-85362-0(1) , Cartwheel Bks.) Scholastic, Inc.

Bryant-Mole, Karen, ed. Color. rev. ed. 1999. (First Learning Ser.). (Illus.). 24p. (J). (ps-3). pap., act. bk. ed. 4.95 (978-0-7460-3800-0(3)) EDC Publishing.

Buck, Joanna. My First Shapes & Colors Book. Church, Caroline Jayne, illus. 1999. (My First Bks.). 16p. (J). (ps-1). 16.95 (978-1-57145-361-7(X) , Silver Dolphin Bks.) Advantage Pubs. Group.

Budgell, Gill. Make Colors American English Edition. 2000. (Cambridge Reading Ser.). (Illus.). pap. 5.00 (978-0-521-79890-7(6)) Cambridge Univ. Pr.

—Make Colours. 2000. (Cambridge Reading Ser.). (Illus.). 10p. pap. 5.00 (978-0-521-77464-2(0)) Cambridge Univ. Pr.

Bullard, Lisa. Orange Food Fun. 2006. (A+ Books). (Illus.). 32p. (J). (978-0-7368-5382-8(0)) Capstone Pr., Inc.

—Red Food Fun. 2006. (A+ Books). (Illus.). 32p. (J). (978-0-7368-5383-5(9)) Capstone Pr., Inc.

—White Food Fun. 2006. (A+ Books). (Illus.). 32p. (J). (978-0-7368-5384-2(7)) Capstone Pr., Inc.

—Yellow Food Fun. 2006. (A+ Books). (Illus.). 32p. (J). (978-0-7368-5385-9(5)) Capstone Pr., Inc.

Bulloch, Ivan & James, Diane. Choisis une Couleur. 2000. (My Turn Ser.). (FRE., Illus.). 12p. (J). (ps-k). bds. 6.95 (978-1-58728-169-3(4) , Two Can Publishing) T&N Children's Publishing.

—Elige Tu Color! 2004. (Me Toca a Mi Ser.).Tr. of Pick a Color!. (SPA., Illus.). 12p. (J). (ps-k). bds. 6.95 (978-1-58728-493-9(6) , Two Can Publishing) T&N Children's Publishing.

—Pick a Color! 2004. (My Turn Ser.). (Illus.). 12p. (J). (ps-k). bds. 6.95 (978-1-58728-006-1(X) , Two Can Publishing) T&N Children's Publishing.

Burton, Jane & Taylor, Kim. The Nature & Science of Colour. Bingxin, Wang et al, trs. 2000. (Nature & Science Ser.). (CHI & ENG., Illus.). 32p. (J). 8.95 (978-7-5600-1758-7(4)) Foreign Languages Teaching & Research Pr. CHN. *Dist:* Cheng & Tsui Co.

Byers, Helen. Colors of France. Byers, Helen, illus. (Colors of the World Ser.). (Illus.). 24p. 2005. (gr. 3-6). 5.95 (978-1-57505-565-7(1)); 2001. (J). (gr. 1-4). lib. bdg. (978-1-57505-514-5(7) , Carolrhoda Bks.) Lerner Publishing Group.

—Colors of France. 2001. (gr. k-3). lib. bdg. 14.10 (978-0-613-79240-0(8)) Tandem Library Bks.

Canizares, Susan. The Northern Lights. 1998. (Science Emergent Readers Ser.). (Illus.). (J). lib. bdg. 2.50 (978-0-590-76155-0(2)) Scholastic, Inc.

Carey, Chris. Finding Blue. Howe, Marsha K., illus. 2004. (J). lib. bdg. (978-1-4048-0601-6(6)) Picture Window Bks.

—Finding Green. Howe, Marsha K., illus. 2004. (J). lib. bdg. (978-1-4048-0602-3(4)) Picture Window Bks.

—Finding Orange. Howe, Marsha K., illus. 2004. (J). lib. bdg. (978-1-4048-0603-0(2)) Picture Window Bks.

—Finding Purple. Howe, Marsha K., illus. 2004. (J). lib. bdg. (978-1-4048-0604-7(0)) Picture Window Bks.

—Finding Red. Howe, Marsha K., illus. 2004. (J). lib. bdg. (978-1-4048-0605-4(9)) Picture Window Bks.

—Finding Yellow. Howe, Marsha K., illus. 2004. (J). lib. bdg. (978-1-4048-0606-1(7)) Picture Window Bks.

Carle, Eric. Eric Carle's Colors/Colores. 2008. 12p. (J). (ps-1). bds. 8.99 (***978-0-448-44883-1(1)*** , Grosset & Dunlap) Penguin Group (USA) Inc.

—Let's Paint a Rainbow. Carle, Eric, illus. 1998. (Play-and-Read Book Ser.). (Illus.). 12p. (J). (ps). bds. 6.95 (978-0-590-32844-9(1) , Cartwheel Bks.) Scholastic, Inc.

—My Very First Book of Colors. Carle, Eric, illus. 2005. (Illus.). 20p. (J). (ps-1). bds. 5.99 (978-0-399-24386-8(0) , Philomel) Penguin Group (USA) Inc.

Carolan, Dr. Where Are My Slippers? A Book of Colors. Carolan, Joanna F., illus. 2005. 32p. (J). pap. 16.95 (978-0-9715333-6-3(9)) Banana Patch Pr.

Cheney, Martha C. Colors Workbook: For Preschoolers. 1999. (Gifted & Talented Ser.). (Illus.). 48p. (J). (ps-k). pap., wbk. ed. 5.95 (978-0-7373-0202-8(X)) Lowell Hse.

Cheshire, Gerard. Light & Colors. 2006. (Illus.). 48p. (J). (978-1-58340-996-1(3) , 1262675) Smart Apple Media.

Child's Play Staff. Cyfri'r Plant. 1999. (WEL., Illus.). 14p. (J). (978-0-85953-483-3(9)) Child's Play International Ltd. GBR. *Dist:* Child's Play-International.

Cleland, JoAnn. I Can Make Colors. 2007. (J). (978-1-59515-925-0(8)) Rourke Publishing, LLC.

Color by Numbers Sparkly Sticker Book. Date not set. (Illus.). 16p. (J). 3.98 (978-1-4054-0991-9(6)) Parragon, Inc.

Color, Cut, Paste, & Trace: Colors & Shapes. (ps-k). 2.99 (978-0-7424-0169-3(3) , IF0402) School Specialty Publishing.

Color Mouse Puppet Set. 2006. (J). per. (978-1-57332-431-1(0)) HighReach Learning, Inc.

Color Set 1: Shades of Coolor. 2005. (J). spiral bd. 23.40 (978-0-9770248-8-9(1)) Sidedoor Publishing LLC.

Colores. (Coleccion Mi Primer Libro). (SPA., Illus.). (J). 13.95 (978-84-207-3778-2(X) , ANY875) Grupo Anaya, S.A. ESP. *Dist:* Continental Bk. Co., Inc.

Colores. (Coleccion Libritos Acordeon). (SPA., Illus.). (J). 10p. pap. 5.50 (978-950-11-0792-0(2) , SGM922); 2005. 86p. pap. 7.95 (978-950-11-0904-7(6) , SGM9046) Sigmar ARG. *Dist:* Continental Bk. Co., Inc., AIMS International Bks., Inc., Continental Bk. Co., Inc., Lectorum Pubns., Inc., Iaconi, Mariuccia Bk. Imports.

Colores: Individual Title Six-Packs. (Coleccion Pm Ser.: Vol. 2). Tr. of Colors. (SPA.). 16p. (gr. k-1). 26.00 (978-0-7578-0689-6(9)) Rigby Education.

Los Colores (Colors) (SPA.). (J). 6.95 (978-968-419-049-8(2)) Grijalbo, Editorial MEX. *Dist:* AIMS International Bks., Inc.

Colores en el zoologico/Colors at the Zoo. 2005. (Libros en Espanol Para Ninos Ser.). (SPA.). (YA). (ps-1). 11.97 (978-0-8215-0998-2(5)); 15.75 (978-0-8215-1208-1(0)) Sadlier, William H. Inc.

Colores, Formas y Opuestos. 2007. (Sesame Street Ser.). (SPA & ENG., Illus.). 50p. (J). 2.95 (***978-1-59545-059-3(9)***) Learning Horizons, Inc.

Colors. (Amazing Animals Ser.). 32p. (J). (gr. 1). pap. (978-1-882210-77-0(8)) Action Publishing, Inc.

Colors. 2002. (Home Workbooks Ser.). (Illus.). 64p. (J). 2.49 (978-0-88724-706-4(7) , CD-4508) Carson-Dellosa Publishing Co., Inc.

Colors. 2002. (Puppy Steps Ser.). (Illus.). 10p. (J). (ps-1). bds. 3.99 (978-1-57759-635-6(8)) Dalmatian Pr.

Colors. 2000. (Pajama Bedtime Bear Ser.). (Illus.). 14p. (J). (ps). bds. 3.95 (978-0-7894-1424-3(4) , D K Ink) Dorling Kindersley Publishing, Inc.

Colors. 2003. (J). per. (978-1-57657-914-5(X)); per. (978-1-57657-916-9(6)) Paradise Pr., Inc.

Colors. Date not set. (Illus.). 16p. (J). 2.98 (978-0-7525-9453-8(2)) Parragon, Inc.

Colors. (Rainbow Ryhmes Ser.). 12p. (J). bds. (978-2-7643-0174-6(X)) Phidal Publishing, Inc./Editions Phidal, Inc.

Colors. 2001. (Early Learning Ser.). (J). (gr. k-12). vinyl bd. 4.95 (978-1-58845-048-7(1)) School Specialty Publishing.

Colors. 2002. (Illus.). (J). pap. 3.74 (978-0-7398-5833-2(5)) Steck-Vaughn.

Colors. 2005. (Illus.). (J). (gr. k-1). lib. bdg. 226.00 (978-0-7368-3673-9(X)) Capstone Pr., Inc.

Colors All Around: KinderConcepts Individual Title Six-Packs. (Kinderstarters Ser.). 8p. (ps-1). 21.00 (978-0-7635-8722-2(2)) Rigby Education.

Colors & Shapes Fun Wipe-Off Book. 2001. (Illus.). 16p. (J). (gr. k-2). mass mkt. 3.79 (978-1-889319-99-5(6)) Trend Enterprises, Inc.

Colors at the Zoo. 2005. (Emergent Library: Vol. 2). (YA). (ps-1). 23.94 (978-0-8215-8939-7(3)) Sadlier, William H. Inc.

Colors for Me. 1998. (Fisher-Price Bubble-Bath Bks.). (Illus.). 6p. (J). (ps). vinyl bd. (978-0-7666-0148-2(X) , Honey Bear Bks.) Modern Publishing.

Colors in Nature, 4 vols., Set 1. 2004. (Illus.). 24p. 74.24 (978-1-4109-0726-4(0)); pap. 19.80 (978-1-4109-0731-8(7)) Raintree.

Colours. 2006. (J). bds. (978-1-74021-933-4(3)) Parish, Steve Publishing.

Connelly, Neil O. Colors. Thornburgh, Rebecca, illus. 10p. (J). (ps). bds. 3.95 (978-1-58989-003-9(5)) Thurman Hse., LLC.

Cooper, Cathie Hilterbran. Color & Shape Books for All Ages. 2000. (School Library Media Ser.: No. 18). (Illus.). 176p. pap. 42.00 (978-0-8108-3542-9(8)) Scarecrow Pr., Inc.

Cousins, Lucy. La Gata Katy y Piquito de Oro. 2000. (Illus.). (J). (SPA.). 22p. (gr. 2-4). 16.95 (978-84-88061-38-6(2) , RR7149); (CAT., 16p. (ps). 16.95 (978-84-95040-25-1(5)) Serres, Ediciones, S. L. ESP. *Dist:* Lectorum Pubns., Inc.

Crowther, Robert. Colors. Crowther, Robert, illus. 2001. (Illus.). 16p. (J). (ps-1). 12.99 (978-0-7636-1404-1(1)) Candlewick Pr.

Cummings, Priscilla. Chesapeake Rainbow. Aiken, David, illus. 2004. 32p. (J). 11.95 (978-0-87033-556-3(1) , Tidewater Pubs.) Cornell Maritime Pr., Inc.

Dahl, Michael. Black. 2005. (A+ Colors Ser.). (Illus.). 32p. (J). 22.60 (978-0-7368-3668-5(3)) Capstone Pr., Inc.

—Brown. 2005. (A+ Colors Ser.). (Illus.). 32p. (J). 22.60 (978-0-7368-3669-2(1)) Capstone Pr., Inc.

—Pink. 2005. (A+ Colors Ser.). (Illus.). 32p. (J). 22.60 (978-0-7368-3670-8(5)) Capstone Pr., Inc.

—White. 2005. (A+ Colors Ser.). (Illus.). 32p. (J). 22.60 (978-0-7368-3671-5(3)) Capstone Pr., Inc.

Dalmatian Press Staff. Color Clues. 2002. (Illus.). 24p. (J). (gr. k-5). pap. 2.99 (978-1-57759-364-5(2)) Dalmatian Pr.

—Colors & Shapes. 2003. (Tools Ser.). (Illus.). 32p. (J). (ps up). pap. 2.29 (978-1-57759-191-7(7)) Dalmatian Pr.

—Little Builder: Board Book Set, 4 bks., Set. 2003. (Illus.). 10p. (J). bds. 7.99 (978-1-57759-714-8(1)) Dalmatian Pr.

—My Spanish Book of Colors: Mi libro de los colores en ingles y Espanol. rev. ed. 2007. 12p. 7.99 (***978-1-4037-3052-7(0)***) Dalmatian Pr.

Dalmatian Press Staff. Precious Moments Lowercase Colors & Shapes. 1999. (Precious Moments Ser.). (Illus.). 32p. (J). (ps-3). pap., wbk. ed. 2.99 (978-1-57759-207-5(7)) Dalmatian Pr.

D'Amato-Neff, Adam L. Creative Learning: Letters, Numbers, & Colors. 2002. 122p. (J). pap. 10.95 (978-0-595-23162-1(4) , Writers Club Pr.) iUniverse, Inc.

D'Amelio, Dennis P. Colored Cars. D'Amelio, Dennis P., illus. 1998. (Right Track Bks.: Vol. 4). (Illus.). 24p. (J). (ps-3). pap. (978-1-891528-66-8(1)) Telescopic Pr.

Dandi. Easter Colors Sticker Book: Over 50 stickers Inside! Fyffe, Brian, illus. 2004. 10p. (J). (ps up). bds. 4.99 (978-1-57151-723-4(5)) Playhouse Publishing.

Davies & Ne, Harriet. Teddy Is Yellow. (Illus.). 10p. (J). 9.95 (978-1-85479-258-7(X)) O'Mara, Michael Bks., Ltd. GBR. *Dist:* Trans-Atlantic Pubns., Inc.

Dena, Anael. Colors. Eho, Jerome, illus. 2002. (Rattle Bks.). 12p. (J). 3.95 (978-0-7641-5503-1(2)) Barron's Educational Series, Inc.

DePrisco, Dorothea. Apple. Taxali, Gary, illus. 2005. (Plush Learning Books Ser.). 10p. (J). bds. 6.95 (978-1-58117-191-4(9) , Intervisual/Piggy Toes) Dalmatian Pr.

—Lemon. Taxali, Gary, illus. 2005. (Plush Learning Books Ser.). 10p. (J). bds. 6.95 (978-1-58117-194-5(3) , Intervisual/Piggy Toes) Dalmatian Pr.

Diaz, James. Mi Primer Gran Libro de los Colores. Gerth, Melanie, illus. 2003. (Mi primer gran libro de ... Ser.). (SPA.). 10p. 16.95 (978-84-7864-601-2(9)) Combel Editorial, S.A. ESP. *Dist:* Independent Pubs. Group.

Diaz, James, illus. Blue: A Touchy Feely First Words Color Book. 2000. (Touchy Feely First Words Bks.). 10p. (J). (ps up). 5.95 (978-1-58117-071-9(8) , Intervisual/Piggy Toes) Dalmatian Pr.

—Colors. 1999. (Flip-Pop Ser.). 10p. (J). (ps-k). 9.95 (978-1-58117-067-2(X) , Intervisual/Piggy Toes) Dalmatian Pr.

—Green: A Touchy Feely First Words Book. 2000. (Touchy Feely First Words Bks.). 10p. (J). (ps up). 5.95 (978-1-58117-072-6(6) , Intervisual/Piggy Toes) Dalmatian Pr.

—Red: A Touchy Feely First Words Color Book. 2000. (Touchy Feely First Words Bks.). 10p. (J). (ps up). 5.95 (978-1-58117-070-2(X) , Intervisual/Piggy Toes) Dalmatian Pr.

—Yellow: A Touchy Feely First Words Book. 2000. (Touchy Feely First Words Bks.: Vol. 4). 10p. (J). (ps up). 5.95 (978-1-58117-069-6(6) , Intervisual/Piggy Toes) Dalmatian Pr.

Dingles, Molly. Black as a Bat. Velez, Walter, illus. (Community of Color Ser.). 32p. (J). 2005. pap. 9.95 (978-1-59646-334-9(1)); 2005. per. 9.95 (978-1-59646-335-6(X)); 2003. lib. bdg. 20.65 (978-1-891997-26-6(2)) Dingles & Co.

—Black as a Bat/Negro como un Murcielago. Velez, Walter, illus. (Community of Color Ser.). 32p. (J). 2005. (ENG & SPA.). pap. 9.95 (978-1-59646-100-0(4)); 2005. (ENG & SPA.). per. 9.95 (978-1-59646-106-2(3)); 2003. (SPA.). lib. bdg. 20.65 (978-1-891997-33-4(5)) Dingles & Co.

—Blue as a Blueberry. Velez, Walter, illus. (Community of Color Ser.). 32p. (J). 2005. (ACE.). pap. 9.95 (978-1-59646-328-8(7)); 2005. per. 9.95 (978-1-59646-329-5(5)); 2002. lib. bdg. 20.65 (978-1-891997-20-4(3)) Dingles & Co.

—Blue as a Blueberry/Azul como un Arandano. Velez, Walter, illus. 2005. (Community of Color Ser.). (ENG & SPA.). 32p. (J). pap. 9.95 (978-1-59646-097-3(0)); per. 9.95 (978-1-59646-103-1(9)) Dingles & Co.

—Blue as a Blueberry/Bleu comme un Bleuet. Velez, Walter, illus. 2004. (Community of Color Ser.).Tr. of Bleu comme un Bleuet. (ENG & FRE.). 32p. (J). lib. bdg. 20.65 (978-1-891997-72-3(6)) Dingles & Co.

—Brown as an Acorn. Velez, Walter, illus. (Community of Color Ser.). 32p. (J). 2005. per. 9.95 (978-1-59646-347-9(3)); 2004. 20.65 (978-1-891997-35-8(1)); 2004. pap. 9.95 (978-1-59646-346-2(5)) Dingles & Co.

—Brown as an Acorn/Marron como una Bellota. Velez, Walter, illus. (Community of Color Ser.).Tr. of Marron como una Bellota. (ENG & SPA.). 32p. (J). 2005. per. 9.95 (978-1-59646-109-3(8)); 2004. pap. 9.95 (978-1-59646-093-5(8)); 2004. lib. bdg. 20.65 (978-1-891997-37-2(8)) Dingles & Co.

—Gray as a Dolphin. Velez, Walter, illus. (Community of Color Ser.). 32p. (J). 2005. per. 9.95 (978-1-59646-343-1(0)); 2004. pap. 9.95 (978-1-59646-342-4(2)); 2004. lib. bdg. 20.65 (978-1-891997-57-0(2)) Dingles & Co.

—Gray as a Dolphin/Gris como un Delfin. Velez, Walter, illus. 2004. (Community of Color Ser.).Tr. of Gris como un Delfin. (ENG & SPA.). 32p. (J). pap. 9.95 (978-1-59646-092-8(X)); lib. bdg. 20.65 (978-1-891997-58-7(0)) Dingles & Co.

—Gray as a Dolphin/Gris como un Delfin. Velez, Walter, illus. 2005. (Community of Color Ser.). (ENG & SPA.). 32p. (J). per. 9.95 (978-1-59646-110-9(1)) Dingles & Co.

—Green as a Frog. Velez, Walter, illus. (Community of Color Ser.). 32p. (J). 2005. pap. 9.95 (978-1-59646-330-1(9)); 2005. per. 9.95 (978-1-59646-331-8(7)); 2002. lib. bdg. 20.65 (978-1-891997-21-1(1)) Dingles & Co.

—Green as a Frog/Verde como una Rana. Velez, Walter, illus. 2005. (Community of Color Ser.). (ENG & SPA.). 32p. (J). pap. 9.95 (978-1-59646-098-0(9)); per. 9.95 (978-1-59646-104-8(7)) Dingles & Co.

—Green as a Frog/Vert comme une Grenouille. Velez, Walter, illus. 2004. (Community of Color Ser.).Tr. of Vert comme une Grenouille. (ENG & FRE.). 32p. (J). lib. bdg. 20.65 (978-1-891997-71-6(8)) Dingles & Co.

—Orange as a Pumpkin. Velez, Walter, illus. (Community of Color Ser.). 32p. (J). 2005. pap. 9.95 (978-1-59646-332-5(5)); 2005. per. 9.95 (978-1-59646-333-2(3)); 2003. lib. bdg. 20.65 (978-1-891997-23-5(8)) Dingles & Co.

—Orange as a Pumpkin/Anaranjado como una Calabaza. Velez, Walter, illus. (Community of Color Ser.).Tr. of Anaranjado como una Calabaza. 32p. (J). 2005. (ENG & SPA.). pap. 9.95 (978-1-59646-099-7(7)); 2005. (ENG & SPA.). per. 9.95 (978-1-59646-105-5(5)); 2003. lib. bdg. 20.65 (978-1-891997-31-0(9)) Dingles & Co.

—Orange as a Pumpkin/Orange comme une Citrouille. Velez, Walter, illus. 2004. (Community of Color Ser.).Tr. of Orange comme une Citrouille. (ENG & FRE.). 32p. (J). lib. bdg. 20.65 (978-1-891997-69-3(6)) Dingles & Co.

—Pink as a Piglet. Velez, Walter, illus. (Community of Color Ser.). 32p. (J). 2005. pap. 9.95 (978-1-59646-336-3(8)); 2005. per. 9.95 (978-1-59646-337-0(6)); 2004. lib. bdg. 20.65 (978-1-891997-25-9(4)) Dingles & Co.

—Pink as a Piglet/Rosa como un Cerdito. Velez, Walter, illus. (Community of Color Ser.).Tr. of Rosa como un Cerdito. 32p. (J). 2005. (ENG & SPA.). pap. 9.95 (978-1-59646-348-6(1)); 2005. (ENG & SPA.). per. 9.95 (978-1-59646-349-3(X)); 2004. (SPA & ENG.). lib. bdg. 20.65 (978-1-891997-34-1(3)) Dingles & Co.

—Purple as a Plum. Velez, Walter, illus. (Community of Color Ser.). 32p. (J). 2005. pap. 9.95 (978-1-59646-338-7(4)); 2005. per. 9.95 (978-1-59646-339-4(2)); 2004. lib. bdg. 20.65 (978-1-891997-24-2(6)) Dingles & Co.

—Purple as a Plum/Morado como una Ciruela. Velez, Walter, illus. (Community of Color Ser.). 32p. (J). 2005. (ENG & SPA.). pap. 9.95 (978-1-59646-350-9(3)); 2005. (ENG & SPA.). per. 9.95 (978-1-59646-351-6(1)); 2004. lib. bdg. 20.65 (978-1-891997-32-7(7)) Dingles & Co.

—Purple as a Plum/Violet comme une Prune. Velez, Walter, illus. 2004. (Community of Color Ser.).Tr. of Violet comme une Prune. (ENG & FRE.). 32p. (J). lib. bdg. 20.65 (978-1-891997-68-6(8)) Dingles & Co.

—Red as a Fire Truck. Velez, Walter, illus. (Community of Color Ser.). 32p. (J). 2005. pap. 9.95 (978-1-59646-324-0(4)); 2005. per. 9.95 (978-1-59646-325-7(2)); 2002. lib. bdg. 20.65 (978-1-891997-19-8(X)) Dingles & Co.

—Red as a Fire Truck/Rojo como un camion de Bomberos. Velez, Walter, illus. 2005. (Community of Color Ser.).Tr. of Rojo Como un Camion de Bomberos. (ENG & SPA.). 32p. (J). pap. 9.95 (978-1-59646-095-9(4)); per. 9.95 (978-1-59646-101-7(2)) Dingles & Co.

—Red as a Firetruck/Rouge comme un camion de Pompiers. Velez, Walter, illus. 2004. (Community of Color Ser.).Tr. of Rouge comme un camion de Pompiers. (ENG & FRE.). 32p. (J). lib. bdg. 20.65 (978-1-891997-73-0(4)) Dingles & Co.

—Turquoise as a Parakeet. Velez, Walter, illus. (Community of Color Ser.). (J). 2005. 32p. pap. 9.95 (978-1-59646-344-8(9)); 2005. 2005p. per. 9.95 (978-1-59646-345-5(7)); 2004. 32p. lib. bdg. 20.65 (978-1-891997-59-4(9)) Dingles & Co.

—Turquoise as a Parakeet/Turquesa como un Periquito. Velez, Walter, illus. (Community of Color Ser.).Tr. of Turquesa como un Periquito. (ENG & SPA.). 32p. (J). 2005. per. 9.95 (978-1-59646-107-9(1)); 2004. pap. 9.95 (978-1-59646-094-2(6)); 2004. lib. bdg. 20.65 (978-1-891997-60-0(2)) Dingles & Co.

—White as a Seashell. Velez, Walter, illus. (Community of Color Ser.). 32p. (J). 2005. pap. 9.95 (978-1-59646-340-0(6)); 2005. per. 9.95 (978-1-59646-341-7(4)); 2004. lib. bdg. 20.65 (978-1-891997-36-5(X)) Dingles & Co.

—White as a Seashell/Blanco como una concha Marina. Velez, Walter, illus. (Community of Color Ser.).Tr. of Blanco como una concha Marina. (ENG & SPA.). (J). 2005. 2005p. per. 9.95 (978-1-59646-108-6(X)); 2004. 32p. pap. 9.95 (978-1-59646-091-1(1)); 2004. 32p. lib. bdg. 20.65 (978-1-891997-38-9(6)) Dingles & Co.

—Yellow as a Lemon. Velez, Walter, illus. 2005. (Community of Color Ser.). 32p. (J). pap. 9.95 (978-1-59646-326-4(0)); per. 9.95 (978-1-59646-327-1(9)) Dingles & Co.

—Yellow as a Lemon. 2004. (Community of Color Ser.). (Illus.). 32p. (J). lib. bdg. 20.65 (978-1-891997-22-8(X)) Dingles & Co.

—Yellow as a Lemon/Amarillo como un Limon. Velez, Walter, illus. 2005. (Community of Color Ser.). (ENG & SPA.). 32p. (J). pap. 9.95 (978-1-59646-096-6(2)); per. 9.95 (978-1-59646-102-4(0)) Dingles & Co.

—Yellow as a Lemon/Jaune comme un Citron. Velez, Walter, illus. 2004. (Community of Color Ser.).Tr. of Jaune comme un Citron. (ENG & FRE.). 32p. (J). lib. bdg. 20.65 (978-1-891997-70-9(X)) Dingles & Co.

Disney Publishing Staff. Rainbow Colors, 15 vols. 2003. (It's Fun to Learn Ser.). (Illus.). 32p. (J). (ps-3). 3.99 (978-1-57973-135-9(X)) Advance Pubs. LLC.

Dixon, Malcolm & Smith, Karen. Light & Color. 1998. (Young Scientists Ser.). (Illus.). 32p. (J). (gr. 3-6). lib. bdg. 16.95 (978-1-887068-70-3(8)) Smart Apple Media.

DK Publishing. Colors & Shapes. 2007. 26p. (J). (ps-k). 9.99 (***978-0-7566-3370-7(2)***) Dorling Kindersley Publishing, Inc.

—Rainbow Colors. 2008. 12p. (J). (ps-ps). bds. 6.99 (***978-0-7566-3760-6(0)***) Dorling Kindersley Publishing, Inc.

DK Publishing Staff. Bright, Shiny, Rainbow Colors. 2007. (Touchables Ser.). 10p. (J). (ps-1). bds. 8.99 (978-0-7566-2939-7(X)) Dorling Kindersley Publishing, Inc.

—Color. 2007. (Eye Know Ser.). 24p. (J). (ps-2). 8.99 (***978-0-7566-3084-3(3)***) Dorling Kindersley Publishing, Inc.

—Colors. 2005. 12p. (J). bds. 4.99 (978-0-7566-0989-4(5)) Dorling Kindersley Publishing, Inc.

—Colors & Shapes. 2007. (Let's Look Ser.). (Illus.). 36p. (J). 4.99 (978-0-7566-2594-8(7)) Dorling Kindersley Publishing, Inc.

Dodd, Emma & Macmillan, Fiona. Clever Color! 2006. (Amazing Baby Ser.). (Illus.). 18p. (J). bds. 3.95 (978-1-59223-581-0(6) , Silver Dolphin Bks.) Advantage Pubs. Group.

Doran, Ella, et al. Color. 2006. (Illus.). 56p. (J). (gr. k-3). 19.95 (978-1-85437-697-8(7)) Tate Gallery Publishing, Ltd. GBR. *Dist:* Hachette Bk. Group.

Dorling Kindersley Publishing Staff. Are Lemons Blue? 2003. (DK See Through Ser.). (Illus.). 21p. (J). 6.99 (978-0-7894-9850-2(2)) Dorling Kindersley Publishing, Inc.

—Baby Colors. 1998. (Soft-To-Touch Book Ser.). (Illus.). 16p. (J). (ps-k). bds. 4.99 (978-0-7894-3651-1(5)) Dorling Kindersley Publishing, Inc.

—Los Colores / Colors. 2004. (My 1ST Board Books Ser.). 24p. (J). (ps-3). bds. 3.99 (978-0-7566-0440-0(0)) Dorling Kindersley Publishing, Inc.

—Colorful World. 2006. (Baby Fun Ser.). (Illus.). 20p. (J). (gr. 5). bds. 4.99 (978-0-7566-2007-3(4)) Dorling Kindersley Publishing, Inc.

—Colors. (Baby Genius Ser.). (Illus.). (J). 2003. 16p. bds. 6.99 (978-0-7894-9881-6(2)); 1998. 10p. 6.99 (978-0-7894-2920-9(9)) Dorling Kindersley Publishing, Inc.

—Colors. 2001. (ps-2). lib. bdg. 11.80 (978-0-613-75167-4(1)) Tandem Library Bks.

—Count with Me! 2003. (Baby's World Ser.). (Illus.). 12p. (J). bds. 4.99 (978-0-7894-9214-2(8)) Dorling Kindersley Publishing, Inc.

—My First Touch & Feel Picture Cards: Colors & Shapes. 2005. (Baby Genius Ser.). 16p. (J). pap. 9.99 (978-0-7566-1516-1(X)) Dorling Kindersley Publishing, Inc.

Dorling Kindersley Publishing Staff, contrib. by. Baby Colors. 2003. (Baby's World Ser.). (Illus.). 12p. (J). bds. 4.99 (978-0-7894-9213-5(X)) Dorling Kindersley Publishing, Inc.

—My First Look At: Colors. 2001. (My First Look At... Ser.). (Illus.). 24p. (J). (ps-k). pap. 3.95 (978-0-7894-7658-6(4) , D K Ink) Dorling Kindersley Publishing, Inc.

—Rainbow Colors. 2004. (Baby Love Ser.). (Illus.). 16p. (J). bds. 4.99 (978-0-7566-0212-3(2)) Dorling Kindersley Publishing, Inc.

Dorling Kindersley Publishing Staff & Millard, Anne. Colors. 2002. (Lift-the-Flap Books Ser.). (Illus.). 16p. (J). (ps-k). 6.99 (978-0-7894-8544-1(3)) Dorling Kindersley Publishing, Inc.

Douglas, Vincent & School Specialty Publishing Staff. Alphabet, Colors, & Shapes. 2004. (My Little Heavenly Helpers Ser.). (Illus.). 64p. (J). (ps-k). pap. 3.99 (978-0-7696-3649-8(7) , Brighter Child) School Specialty Publishing.

—Color, Shape, & Size. 2004. (Kindergarten Bound Ser.). (Illus.). 80p. (J). pap. 5.95 (978-0-7696-3520-0(2) , American Education Publishing) School Specialty Publishing.

—Colors & Shapes Touch & Learn Board Book. Touch and Learn Staff, ed. 2003. (Padded Board Books with Textured Letters Ser.). (Illus.). 26p. (J). bds. 19.95 (978-1-58845-575-8(0) , Brighter Child) School Specialty Publishing.

Doyle, Alfreda C. Story Course - Mask: Stories, Poetry & Color Therapy. 1998. (Illus.). 40p. (J). pap., wbk. ed. 29.95 (978-1-56820-377-5(2)) Story Time Stories That Rhyme.

Draze, Dianne. Attribute Block - Sequences: Thinking Activities. 2005. 32p. 9.95 (978-1-59363-053-9(0)) Prufrock Pr.

Eck, Kristin. Colors in My House. 2004. (Look-And-Learn Books). (Illus.). (J). lib. bdg. 7.95 (978-1-4042-2698-2(2) , PowerKids Pr.) Rosen Publishing Group, Inc., The.

Ellering, Joanie. Let's Learn Colors. 1999. (J). (ps-3). (978-1-929343-00-3(0)) Stretching Charts, Inc.

Ellis, Belinda. Colors. 2005. (Baby-See-A Shape Ser.). (Illus.). 12p. (ps-ps). per., bds. 4.95 (978-1-84610-021-5(6)) Make Believe Ideas GBR. *Dist:* Ingram Pub. Services.

Emberley, Rebecca. My Colors/ Mis Colores. Emberley, Rebecca, illus. 2000. (ENG & SPA., Illus.). 10p. (J). (ps-ps). bds. 6.99 (978-0-316-23347-7(1)) Little Brown & Co.

Farndon, John. Color. 2000. (Science Experiments Ser.). (Illus.). 32p. (J). (gr. 3-5). lib. bdg. 25.64 (978-0-7614-1092-8(9) , Benchmark Bks.) Cavendish, Marshall Corp.

Ferarro, Bonita. Color & Shapes: Preschool. 2003. (Brighter Child Workbooks Ser.). (Illus.). 24p. (J). (ps). pap. 2.25 (978-1-56189-058-3(8) , 41210) School Specialty Publishing.

Filipowich, Bob. Splashtime Book of Colors. 2000. (God's Creation Ser.). (Illus.). (J). pap. 4.99 (978-0-310-98095-7(X)) Zonderkidz.

First Steps: Colors & Shapes. 2002. (First Steps Reading Ser.). 32p. (J). pap. 2.95 (978-0-7894-8482-6(X)) Dorling Kindersley Publishing, Inc.

Flores, Cory, illus. Bugs on Parade: A Counting Book. 2006. 8p. (J). (***978-1-58970-400-8(2)***) Lakeshore Learning Materials.

Flux, Paul. Color. (How Artists Use Ser.). (Illus.). 32p. (J). (gr. 1-4). 2002. pap. 6.95 (978-1-58810-436-6(2) , 91164); 2001. lib. bdg. 22.79 (978-1-58810-078-8(2)) Heinemann Library.

Foil Book Colors & Numbers & Shapes, Oh My! (English) 2000. (J). (978-1-58805-033-5(5)) DS-Max USA, Inc.

Forte, Imogene. Ready to Learn Shapes & Colors. 2003. (Illus.). 64p. per. 7.95 (978-0-86530-593-9(5)) Incentive Pubns., Inc.

Fowler, Allan. All the Colors of the Rainbow. 1999. (Rookie Read-About Science Ser.). (Illus.). 32p. (J). (gr. 1-2). pap. 4.95 (978-0-516-26415-8(X) , Children's Pr.) Scholastic Library Publishing.

Freymann, Saxton, illus. Food for Thought: The Complete Book of Concepts for Growing Minds. 2005. 61p. (J). lib. bdg. (978-1-4155-7707-3(2) , Levine, Arthur A. Bks.) Scholastic, Inc.

Freymann, Saxton, et al. Food for Thought: The Complete Book of Concepts for Growing Minds. Freymann, Saxton, illus. 2005. (Illus.). 64p. (J). pap. 14.95 (978-0-439-11018-1(1) , Levine, Arthur A. Bks.) Scholastic, Inc.

Ghione, Yvette & Gurth, Per-Henrik. Canada in Colours. 2008. 24p. (***978-1-55453-240-7(X)***) Kids Can Pr., Ltd.

Gill, Shelley R. Count Alaska's Colors. Cartwright, Shannon, illus. 2002. 32p. (J). (ps-3). pap. (978-0-934007-35-1(7)) Paws IV Publishing.

Gilliland, Lucille. What's All This? Gilliland, Lucille, illus. 2001. (Illus.). 24p. (J). (ps-6). pap. 8.95 (978-0-9716539-0-0(9)) LG Fun Learning Pubns.

Girard, Franck. Mi primer baul de Palabras. Jonniaux, Isabelle, illus. 2005. (Baul de Palabras Ser.). (SPA.). 120p. (J). 18.95 (978-84-7864-788-0(0)) Combel Editorial, S.A. ESP. *Dist:* Independent Pubs. Group.

Glover, David. Color & Light. 2001. (Experiments in Science Ser.). (Illus.). (J). (978-0-7894-7464-3(6)) Dorling Kindersley Publishing, Inc.

Gold-Dworkin, Heidi. Exploring Light & Color. 2000. (gr. 3-6). lib. bdg. 22.20 (978-0-613-27811-9(9)) Tandem Library Bks.

Gold-Dworkin, Heidi, et al. Exploring Light & Color. 1999. (Little Scientists Ser.). (Illus.). 58p. (J). (gr. k-3). pap. 12.95 (978-0-07-134821-8(2) , 9780071348218) McGraw-Hill Cos., The.

Golden Books Staff. Calling All Whos! 2008. (Color Plus Chunky Crayons Ser.). (Illus.). 48p. (J). (ps-2). pap. 3.99 (***978-0-375-83819-4(8)*** , Golden Bks.) Random Hse. Children's Bks.

Gordon, Sharon. El Amarillo. 2007. (Colores Ser.). (SPA.). 24p. (J). lib. bdg. 22.79 (***978-0-7614-2863-3(1)*** , Benchmark Bks.) Cavendish, Marshall Corp.

—El Anaranjado. 2007. (Colores Ser.). (SPA.). 24p. (J). lib. bdg. 22.79 (***978-0-7614-2860-2(7)*** , Benchmark Bks.) Cavendish, Marshall Corp.

—El Azul. 2007. (Colores Ser.). (SPA.). 24p. (J). lib. bdg. 22.79 (***978-0-7614-2858-9(5)*** , Benchmark Bks.) Cavendish, Marshall Corp.

—Blue. 2004. (SPA & ENG., Illus.). 21p. (J). 21.36 (978-0-7614-1774-3(5) , Benchmark Bks.) Cavendish, Marshall Corp.

—Blue/El Azul. 2007. (Colors/Los Colores Ser.). (SPA & ENG.). 24p. (J). lib. bdg. 22.79 (***978-0-7614-2873-2(9)*** , Benchmark Bks.) Cavendish, Marshall Corp.

—Green. 2004. (SPA & ENG., Illus.). 23p. (J). 21.36 (978-0-7614-1773-6(7) , Benchmark Bks.) Cavendish, Marshall Corp.

—Green/El Verde. 2007. (Colors/Los Colores Ser.). (SPA & ENG.). 24p. (J). lib. bdg. 22.79 (***978-0-7614-2874-9(7)*** , Benchmark Bks.) Cavendish, Marshall Corp.

—El Morado. 2007. (Colores Ser.). (SPA.). 24p. (J). lib. bdg. 22.79 (***978-0-7614-2861-9(5)*** , Benchmark Bks.) Cavendish, Marshall Corp.

—Orange. 2004. (Illus.). 23p. (J). 21.36 (978-0-7614-1771-2(0) , Benchmark Bks.) Cavendish, Marshall Corp.

—Orange/El Anaranjado. 2007. (Colors/Los Colores Ser.). (ENG & SPA.). 24p. (J). lib. bdg. 22.79 (***978-0-7614-2875-6(5)*** , Benchmark Bks.) Cavendish, Marshall Corp.

—Purple. 2004. (SPA & ENG., Illus.). 23p. (J). 21.36 (978-0-7614-1775-0(3) , Benchmark Bks.) Cavendish, Marshall Corp.

—Purple/El Morado. 2007. (Colors/Los Colores Ser.). (SPA & ENG.). 24p. (J). lib. bdg. 22.79 (***978-0-7614-2876-3(3)*** , Benchmark Bks.) Cavendish, Marshall Corp.

—Red. 2004. (SPA & ENG., Illus.). 23p. (J). 21.36 (978-0-7614-1770-5(2) , Benchmark Bks.) Cavendish, Marshall Corp.

—Red/El Rojo. 2007. (Colors/Los Colores Ser.). (SPA & ENG.). 24p. (J). lib. bdg. 22.79 (***978-0-7614-2878-7(X)*** , Benchmark Bks.) Cavendish, Marshall Corp.

—El Rojo. 2007. (Colores Ser.). (SPA.). 24p. (J). lib. bdg. 22.79 (***978-0-7614-2862-6(3)*** , Benchmark Bks.) Cavendish, Marshall Corp.

—El Verde. 2007. (Colores Ser.). (SPA.). 24p. (J). lib. bdg. 22.79 (***978-0-7614-2859-6(3)*** , Benchmark Bks.) Cavendish, Marshall Corp.

—Yellow. 2004. (SPA & ENG., Illus.). 23p. (J). 21.36 (978-0-7614-1772-9(9) , Benchmark Bks.) Cavendish, Marshall Corp.

Gordon, Sharon. Yellow/El Amarillo. 2007. (Colors/Los Colores Ser.). (SPA & ENG.). 24p. (J). lib. bdg. 22.79 (***978-0-7614-2879-4(8)*** , Benchmark Bks.) Cavendish, Marshall Corp.

Granowsky, Alvin. Colors. 2001. (ps-2). lib. bdg. 13.00 (978-0-613-45173-4(2)) Tandem Library Bks.

—Colors. 2001. 11.79 (978-0-606-22429-1(7)) Tandem Library Bks.

Green. (Colors Ser.). 32p. (J). 7.95 (978-0-7368-5065-0(1)) Capstone Pr., Inc.

Green 6-Pack. 2004. (Colors in Nature Ser.). (Illus.). pap. 29.70 (978-1-4109-0732-5(5)) Raintree.

Greene, Carol. My Turn Bible Stories about Colors. 1998. (My Turn Bible Stories Ser.). (Illus.). 32p. (J). (ps-1). 6.99 (978-0-570-05061-2(8)) Penguin Group (USA) Inc.

Greenfield Educational Center Staff. Blue-Green (Qing) 2000. (Rainbow Reading Ser.). (CHI., Illus.). (J). pap. 7.99 (978-962-563-035-9(X)); Bk. 2. pap. 7.99 (978-962-563-086-1(4)) Greenfield Enterprises, Ltd. HKG. *Dist:* Cheng & Tsui Co.

—Blue (Lan) 2000. (Rainbow Reading Ser.). (CHI., Illus.). (J). pap. 8.50 (978-962-563-227-8(1)); Bk. 1. pap. 8.50 (978-962-563-036-6(8)); Bk. 2. pap. 8.50 (978-962-563-087-8(2)) Greenfield Enterprises, Ltd. HKG. *Dist:* Cheng & Tsui Co.

Gregorich, Barbara. Shapes & Colors. 2005. 32p. (J). (ps-k). pap. 2.49 (***978-0-88743-728-1(1)***) School Zone Publishing Co.

Grossman, Laurie. Colors of Israel. Byers, Helen, illus. (Colors of the World Ser.). 24p. 2005. (gr. 3-6). lib. bdg. 19.93 (978-1-57505-382-0(9)); 2003. (J). (gr. 1-4). pap. 5.95 (978-1-57505-523-7(6)) Lerner Publishing Group.

—Colors of Israel. 2001. (gr. k-3). lib. bdg. 14.10 (978-0-613-79233-2(5)) Tandem Library Bks.

Gunzi, Christiane. Los Colores. 2004. (Mi Primera Mirada. . . Ser.).Tr. of MVFLA Colores. (SPA., Illus.). 24p. (J). (ps-k). pap. 5.95 (978-1-58728-411-3(1) , Creative Publishing International) Quayside.

—Colors. 2004. (My Very First Look at Ser.). (SPA., Illus.). 24p. (J). (ps-k). pap. 5.95 (978-1-58728-276-8(3) , Two Can Publishing) T&N Children's Publishing.

—My Very First Look at Colors. 2006. (Illus.). 22p. (J). bds. 6.95 (978-1-58728-562-2(2) , Two Can Publishing) T&N Children's Publishing.

Gutierrez, Javiera. El Baul de Mis Fiestas: Un Libro Sobre los Colores. Clocchiatti, Constanza, illus. (Coleccion el Baul Ser.). (SPA.). 10p. (J). (gr. k-1). (978-950-46-1157-8(5)) Santillana USA Publishing Co., Inc.

Hale, Natalie. So Many Colors. 2003. (J). spiral bd. 9.95 (978-0-9702698-5-0(4)) Special Reads for Special Needs.

Hamanaka, Shelia. Colours of the Earth. 2000. (Illus.). 32p. (J). (GUJ & ENG.). 18.95 (978-1-85269-328-2(2)); (SOM & ENG., 18.95 (978-1-85269-329-9(0)) Mantra Publishing, Ltd. GBR. *Dist:* AIMS International Bks., Inc.

Handberg, Irene. The World of Shapes & Colors: Learning Center, Set. rev. ed. 1998. (Illus.). (J). (ps-5). pap. 62.95 (978-1-56831-210-1(5)) Learning Connection, The.

—The World of Shapes & Colors, Grades Preschool-3: Learning Center. 1998. (Illus.). 8p. (J). (gr. k-6). tchr. ed. 24.95 (978-1-56831-212-5(1)) Learning Connection, The.

Harcourt School Publishers Staff. Fall Colors. 3rd ed. 2002. (Trophies English Language Learners Ser.). (Illus.). pap. 5.10 (978-0-15-327632-3(0)) Harcourt Schl. Pubs.

—Moo Moo Brown Cow: Little Book. 2000. (Collections Ser.). (Illus.). (J). pap. 10.20 (978-0-15-314507-0(2)) Harcourt Schl. Pubs.

—What's Your Favorite Color. 3rd ed. 2002. (Trophies English Language Learners Ser.). (Illus.). (J). pap. 4.10 (978-0-15-327588-3(X)) Harcourt Schl. Pubs.

—What's Your Favorite Color? - 5 Pack - Grade 1. 3rd ed. 2002. (Trophies English Language Learners Ser.). 20.10 (978-0-15-327622-4(3)) Harcourt Schl. Pubs.

Harder Tangvald, Christine. God Made Colors...for Me! 1999. (for Me! Bks.). (Illus.). 16p. (J). (ps). pap. 4.99 (978-0-7642-2283-2(X)) Bethany Hse. Pubs.

Haring, Keith. Big. 1998. (Illus.). 14p. (J). pap. 6.95 (978-0-7868-0390-3(8)) Hyperion Bks. for Children.

Harwood, Beth. Twinkle, Twinkle! Dodd, Emily, illus. 2006. (Amazing Baby Ser.). 16p. (J). bds. 5.95 (978-1-59223-586-5(7) , Silver Dolphin Bks.) Advantage Pubs. Group.

Herold, Vickey. Light & Color. 2006. pap. 42.00 (*978-1-4108-6488-8(X)) Benchmark Education Co.

Heurtelou, Maude. Color: Koule. 1999. (Big Book Ser.). (CRP & ENG., Illus.). 12p. (J). (gr. k-2). 19.50 (978-1-58432-069-2(9)) Educa Vision.

Hewitt, Sally. Color. 2007. (J). (*978-1-59604-132-5(3)) Stargazer Bks.

Hicks, Barbara Jean. I Like Colors. Prap, Lila, illus. 2006. 32p. (J). 9.95 (978-1-58925-057-4(5) , tiger tales) ME Media LLC.

Hicks, Diana & Littlejohn, Andrew. American English Primary Colors 1. 2003. (Primary Colours Ser.). 64p. pap., stu. ed. 12.00 (978-0-521-53916-6(1)); pap., act. bk. ed. 8.00 (978-0-521-53917-3(X)) Cambridge Univ. Pr.

—American English Primary Colors 2. 2003. (Primary Colours Ser.). (Illus.). 64p. pap., act. bk. ed. 8.00 (978-0-521-53921-0(8)) Cambridge Univ. Pr.

Hidalgo, Maria. Color. 2002. (Let's Investigate Ser.). (Illus.). 32p. (J). lib. bdg. (978-1-58341-228-2(X) , Creative Education) Creative Co., The.

Hill, Eric. Spot Looks at Colors. Hill, Eric, illus. 2003. (Illus.). 14p. (J). (ps-1). bds. 3.99 (978-0-399-24044-7(6) , Putnam Juvenile) Penguin Group (USA) Inc.

Hofmeyr, Dianne. Mama Mabena's Magic: Ndebele Version. Dube, Grace, tr. 1999. (Cambridge African Language Library Ser.). (NBL & NDE., Illus.). 16p. pap. 3.70 (978-0-521-65828-7(4)) Cambridge Univ. Pr.

Hoglund, Rudy. Roger Tory Peterson's Colors: A Book for Beginner Bird Watchers & Crayon Users. Peterson, Roger Tory, illus. 2002. 48p. (J). 14.95 (978-0-7893-0805-4(3)) Universe Publishing.

Holden, Arianne & Browne, Naima. Colours. 1999. (Fun to Learn Ser.). (Illus.). 32p. (J). (ps-1). 7.95 (978-1-85967-680-6(4) , Lorenz Bks.) Anness Publishing, Inc.

Hood, Karen Jean Matsko. Icelandic Horse Activity & Coloring Book: Second Edition. 2nd ed. 2002. (J). per. 19.95 (978-1-59210-595-3(5)) Whispering Pine Pr., Inc.

Hop, L. L. C. Hooked on Pre-K Super Workbook. 2006. 320p. 12.99 (978-1-931020-72-5(8)) HOP, LLC.

Horacek, Petr. Strawberries Are Red. Horacek, Petr, illus. 2001. (Illus.). 14p. (J). (gr. k-k). bds. 4.99 (978-0-7636-1461-4(0)) Candlewick Pr.

Horne, Jane. Colors. 2007. (Busy Baby Ser.). (Illus.). 12p. (ps-k). per., bds. 6.95 (*978-1-84610-469-5(6)) Make Believe Ideas GBR. Dist: Ingram Pub. Services.

—Hide & Seek in Colors. 2007. (Illus.). 20p. (ps-k). per., bds. 8.99 (*978-1-84610-474-9(2)) Make Believe Ideas GBR. Dist: Ingram Pub. Services.

I Like Red: Individual Title, 6 Packs. (Sails Literacy Ser.). 16p. (gr. k up). 27.00 (978-0-7635-4402-7(7)) Rigby Education.

Imperato, Teresa. Colors All Around: A Turn & Pop Book. Petrone, Valeria, illus. 2005. 10p. (J). bds. 5.95 (978-1-58117-277-5(X) , Intervisual/Piggy Toes) Dalmatian Pr.

In Full Color. 2004. per. (978-1-932948-08-0(2)) Student Pr. Initiative.

Jensen, Karl. Flowers for Grandma. 2002. (Windows on Literacy Ser.). (Illus.). 12p. (J). (978-0-7922-8457-4(7)) National Geographic Society.

Jocelyn, Marthe. One, Some, Many. Slaughter, Tom, illus. 2006. 16p. (J). (gr. k-k). bds. 7.95 (978-0-88776-789-0(3)) Candlewick Pr.

—One, Some, Many. Jocelyn, Marthe, ed. Slaughter, Tom, illus. 2004. 32p. (J). (gr. k-k). 11.95 (978-0-88776-675-6(7)) Tundra Bks., Inc./Livres Toundra, Inc. CAN. Dist: Random Hse., Inc.

Jones, Christianne C. Autumn Orange. 2007. (Know Your Colors Ser.). (Illus.). 24p. (J). (*978-1-4048-3491-0(5) , 1265680) Picture Window Bks.

—Autumn Orange. Ouren, Todd, illus. 2006. (Know Your Colors Ser.). 24p. (J). (978-1-4048-3108-7(8) , 1265680) Picture Window Bks.

—Batty for Black. Ouren, Todd, illus. 2007. (J). lib. bdg. (*978-1-4048-3764-5(7)) Picture Window Bks.

—Big Red Farm. 2007. (Know Your Colors Ser.). (Illus.). 24p (J). (*978-1-4048-3493-4(1) , 1265686) Picture Window Bks.

—Big Red Farm. Ouren, Todd, illus. 2006. (Know Your Colors Ser.). 24p. (J). (978-1-4048-3110-0(X) , 1265686) Picture Window Bks.

—Brown at the Zoo. Ouren, Todd, illus. 2007. (J). lib. bdg. (*978-1-4048-3765-2(5)) Picture Window Bks.

—Camping in Green. 2007. (Know Your Colors Ser.). (Illus.). 24p. (J). (*978-1-4048-3490-3(7) , 1265677) Picture Window Bks.

—Camping in Green. Ouren, Todd, illus. 2006. (Know Your Colors Ser.). 24p. (J). (978-1-4048-3107-0(X) , 1265677) Picture Window Bks.

—Hello, Yellow! 2007. (Know Your Colors Ser.). (Illus.). 24p. (J). (*978-1-4048-3494-1(X) , 1265687) Picture Window Bks.

—Hello, Yellow! Ouren, Todd, illus. 2006. (Know Your Colors Ser.). 24p. (J). (978-1-4048-3111-7(8) , 1265687) Picture Window Bks.

—Pink Takes a Bow. Ouren, Todd, illus. 2007. (J). lib. bdg. (*978-1-4048-3763-8(9)) Picture Window Bks.

—Purple Pride. 2007. (Know Your Colors Ser.). (Illus.). 24p. (J). (*978-1-4048-3492-7(3) , 1265682) Picture Window Bks.

—Purple Pride. Ouren, Todd, illus. 2006. (Know Your Colors Ser.). 24p. (J). (978-1-4048-3109-4(6) , 1265682) Picture Window Bks.

—Splish, Splash, & Blue. 2007. (Know Your Colors Ser.). (Illus.). 24p. (J). (*978-1-4048-3489-7(3) , 1265675) Picture Window Bks.

—Splish, Splash, & Blue. Ouren, Todd, illus. 2006. (Know Your Colors Ser.). 24p. (J). (978-1-4048-3106-3(1) , 1265675) Picture Window Bks.

Jones, Christianne C. Winter White. Ouren, Todd, illus. 2007. (J). lib. bdg. (*978-1-4048-3766-9(3)) Picture Window Bks.

Kalman, Bobbie. What Color Is It? 2007. (Looking at Nature Ser.). (Illus.). 24p. (J). (ps-2). pap. (*978-0-7787-3338-6(6)) Crabtree Publishing Co.

Kamm, Katja. Invisible. 2006. (Illus.). (J). 12.95 (978-0-7358-2052-4(X)) North-South Bks., Inc.

Kassinger, Ruth. Dyes: From Sea Snails to Synthetics. 2003. (Material World Ser.). (Illus.). 80p. (gr. 6-8). lib. bdg. 25.90 (978-0-7613-2112-5(8) , Twenty-First Century Bks.) Lerner Publishing Group.

Keenan, Elaine F. Travelin' Shoes for Infants & Toddlers: Colors. 1998. 14p. (J). (ps-1). 14.95 (978-0-9663273-3-5(0)) Heirloom Memories, Inc.

Keiser, Melissa. My Airplane Book-Colors. 2005. (Board Book Ser.). (Illus.). 12p. bds. 6.95 (978-1-59373-042-0(X)) Bunker Hill Publishing, Inc.

Kelly, Lorraine. Fun To Learn: Colors. 2000. (Fun-to-Learn Ser.). 16p. (J). 4.50 (978-0-233-99906-7(X)) Andre Deutsch GBR. Dist: Independent Pubs. Group.

Kimmelman, Leslie. Colores En Mi Plato. 2007. (Sesame Street Ser.). (SPA & ENG., Illus.). 24p. (J). pap., wbk. ed. 4.99 (*978-1-59545-065-4(3)) Learning Horizons, Inc.

Konigsburg, E. L. Samuel Todd's Book of Great Colors. 1999. (gr. k-3). lib. bdg. 14.15 (978-0-613-22303-4(9)) Tandem Library Bks.

Koski, Mary B. Color, Color, Where Are You, Color? Mason, Janeen, illus. 2004. 28p. (J). bds. 7.95 (978-1-930650-34-3(5)); 32p. 14.95 (978-1-930650-35-0(3)) Trellis Publishing, Inc.

Krulik, Nancy E., et al. Colors That Go. 2004. (Illus.). 20p. (J). pap. 12.95 (978-0-7624-1981-4(4) , Running Pr. Kids) Running Pr. Bk. Pubs.

La Jars, David. One, Two, Red & Blue. rev. ed. 2004. (Talk Together Ser.). (Illus.). 24p. (J). (ps-k). pap. 5.95 (978-1-58728-019-1(1) , Two Can Publishing) T&N Children's Publishing.

Landis, Beth, ed. My First Colors Board Book. 2004. (Illus.). 36p. (J). bds. 5.99 (978-0-7566-0280-2(7)) Dorling Kindersley Publishing, Inc.

Landner, Cobi. Why Is an Orange Called an Orange? Smith, Lisa, illus. 2003. 14.95 (978-1-55278-328-3(6)) McArthur & Co. CAN. Dist: National Bk. Network.

Landoll Inc. Staff. Colors & Shapes Workbook. 2000. (Beginners Bible Ser.). (J). pap. 14.95 (978-1-56189-618-9(7) , American Education Publishing) School Specialty Publishing.

Law, Felicia. Patchwork First Poem Books - Colour. Knight, Paula, illus. (Patchwork First Poem Bks.). 24p. 8.95 (978-1-904668-80-0(1)) Mercury Bks. Ltd. GBR. Dist: International Publishers Marketing.

Layne, Carmela C. I See Many Colors Around My House: Los Colores que Veo Por Mi Casa. Layne, Carmela C., ed. Arevalo, Jose Daniel, illus. l.t. ed. 2005. (SPA.). 24p. (J). (ps-3). pap. 6.95 (978-0-9769538-0-7(3)) Pannycake Pubn.

Layton, Neil. Go Wild with Colors. 2004. (Illus.). 12p. (J). bds. (978-1-84458-044-6(X)) Chrysalis Children's Bks.

LeapFrog Staff, compiled by. Counting on Leap. 2001. (J). (ps-2). spiral bd. 14.99 (978-1-58605-028-3(1)) LeapFrog Enterprises, Inc.

Learn about Colors with Elmo. 2005. (Illus.). 48p. (J). (ps-ps). pap. 3.95 (978-1-58610-909-7(X)) Learning Horizons, Inc.

Learn Colors with Charley. 2001. (Charley & Mimmo Ser.). 24p. pap. 3.50 (978-0-439-32233-1(2)) Scholastic, Inc.

Learning Company Books Staff, ed. Reader Rabbit Fun with Colors. 2004. (Illus.). 32p. (J). pap. 4.99 (978-0-7630-7738-9(0)) Learning Co. Bks.

Lee, Quinlan. Splish! Splash! Splosh! Scholastic, Inc. Staff, ed. Salter, Carlton, illus. 2004. (Rubbadubbers Ser.). 32p. (J). pap. 4.99 (978-0-439-51217-6(4)) Scholastic, Inc.

Leonard, Marcia. Favorite Colors. Handelman, Dorothy, photos by. 2001. (Illus.). 20p. (J). (ps up). 7.95 (978-0-694-01370-8(6) , Harper Festival) HarperCollins Pubs.

El Libro de Contar de los Chocolates M & M's Brand. 2004. 32p. (J). pap. 6.95 (978-1-57091-370-9(6)) Charlesbridge Publishing, Inc.

Lilly, Melinda. Color. Thompson, Scott M., illus. 2003. (J). 20.64 (978-1-58952-646-4(5)) Rourke Publishing, LLC.

Litchfield, Jo. First Colors. Litchfield, Jo, illus. 2006. (Illus.). 18p. (J). bds. 14.99 (978-0-7945-1348-1(4) , Usborne) EDC Publishing.

Littlefield, Holly. Colors of India. Porter, Janice Lee, illus. (Colors of the World Ser.). (Illus.). 24p. 2003. (J). (gr. 1-4). 5.95 (978-1-57505-368-4(3)); 1999. (gr. 3-6). lib. bdg. 19.93 (978-1-57505-344-8(6)) Lerner Publishing Group.

—Colors of India. (Colors of the World Ser.). 2000. (Illus.). (J). 12.75 (978-0-606-21926-6(9)); 1999. (gr. 3-6). lib. bdg. 14.10 (978-0-613-68205-3(X)) Tandem Library Bks.

Lloyd, Sam. What Color Is Your Underwear? 2004. (Illus.). 16p. (J). pap. 8.99 (978-0-439-57676-5(8) , Cartwheel Bks.) Scholastic, Inc.

Lluch, Alex A. I Like to Learn: Alphabet, Numbers, Colors, & Opposites. 2008. 19.95 (*978-1-887169-95-0(4)) Wedding Solutions Publishing, Inc.

Lorenz Books Staff. Colours: With over 50 Reusable Stickers. 1998. (Sticker Fun Ser.). (Illus.). 16p. (ps-k). pap. 4.95 (978-1-85967-770-4(3)) Anness Publishing GBR. Dist: National Bk. Network.

Lorenz Editors. Colours in the Garden, 4 vols., Set 1. 2001. (Illus.). 10p. bds. 12.95 (978-0-7548-0824-4(6) , Lorenz Bks.) Anness Publishing GBR. Dist: National Bk. Network.

Luckiesh, Matthew. The Language of Color. (Illus.). xii, 28p. (gr. 2). reprint ed. lib. bdg. (978-0-7222-3055-8(9)) Library Reprints, Inc.

MacKall, Dandi Daley. Rainbow Party. Halsey, Megan, illus. 2002. (First Things First Ser.). 12p. (ps-k). 6.99 (978-0-8066-4382-3(X) , Augsburg Bks.) Augsburg Fortress, Pubs.

MacKall, Dandi Daley & Kucharik, Elena. Many-Colored Blessings. 2005. (Little Blessings Ser.). (Illus.). 32p. (J). bds. 6.99 (978-1-4143-0289-8(4)) Tyndale Hse. Pubs.

MacKinnon, Debbie. Eye Spy Colors. Sieveking, Anthea, illus. 1998. 24p. (YA). (ps-k). 8.95 (978-0-88106-334-9(7)) Charlesbridge Publishing, Inc.

—What Colour? Sieveking, Anthea, photos by. 2001. (Right Start Ser.). (Illus.). 24p. (J). (ps-3). pap. 7.99 (978-0-7112-1068-4(3)) Lincoln, Frances Ltd. GBR. Dist: Transition Vendor.

Mackinnon, Debbie & Sieveking, Anthea. What Colour? 2004. (Illus.). 24p. (J). pap. 7.95 (978-1-84507-244-5(8)) Lincoln, Frances Ltd. GBR. Dist: Perseus Distribution.

Make Believe Ideas Staff. Baby Fun Colors. 2005. (Illus.). 10p. (ps-ps). per. (978-1-905051-17-5(4)) Make Believe Ideas.

Makeeff, Cyndi Sue. Inky Winky Spider Colors by the Bay. Riley, Kevin, illus. 2006. 32p. (J). pap. 7.99 (978-0-9778310-2-9(7)) New Vision Ent.

Mara, Wil. Why Is the Sky Blue? 2006. (Tell Me Why, Tell Me How Ser.). (Illus.). 32p. (J). lib. bdg. 28.50 (978-0-7614-2108-5(4) , Benchmark Bks.) Cavendish, Marshall Corp.

Marks, Jenny L. Sorting by Color. 2007. (Illus.). 32p. (J). (978-0-7368-6739-9(2)) Capstone Pr., Inc.

Maynard, Christopher & White, Terry. Why Are Zebras Black & White? Questions Children Ask about Colour. (Why Bks.). (Illus.). 24p. (J). pap. 10.99 (978-0-590-24946-1(0)) Scholastic, Inc.

McBratney, Sam. Colors Everywhere. Jeram, Anita, illus. 2007. (Guess How Much I Love You Ser.). 24p. (J). (gr. k-ps). bds. 7.99 (*978-0-7636-3545-9(6)) Candlewick Pr.

McDonald, Jill. Play with Me: Colors. 2007. 10p. pap. 6.95 (*978-1-58117-565-3(5)) Dalmatian Pr.

McGrath, Barbara Barbieri. Kellogg's Froot Loops Color Fun Book. Mazzola, Frank, Jr., illus. 2001. 16p. (J). (ps-k). 5.99 (978-0-694-01577-1(6)) HarperCollins Pubs.

—The M & M's' Brand Color Pattern Book. Glass, Roger, illus. 2004. 32p. (J). 16.95 (978-1-57091-416-4(8)); pap. 6.95 (978-1-57091-417-1(6)) Charlesbridge Publishing, Inc.

—The M & M's' Brand Counting Book. Glass, Roger, illus. rev. ed. 2004. 32p. (J). 16.95 (978-1-57091-367-9(6)); pap. 6.95 (978-1-57091-368-6(4)) Charlesbridge Publishing, Inc.

—Mas Matematicas con los Chocolates de M & M's Brand. Mlawer, Teresa, tr. Glass, Roger, illus. 2004. (SPA.). 32p. (J). pap. 6.95 (978-1-57091-481-2(8) , CH30498) Charlesbridge Publishing, Inc.

—More M & M's' Brand Math. Glass, Roger, illus. 1998. 32p. (J). (gr. 3-7). 16.95 (978-0-88106-993-8(0)); pap. 6.95 (978-0-88106-994-5(9)) Charlesbridge Publishing, Inc.

McGraw-Hill Staff & School Specialty Publishing Staff. Colors. 2001. (Homework Helpers Activity Bks.). (Illus.). 56p. (J). (gr. k-1). pap., act. bk. ed. 2.99 (978-0-7682-0681-4(2) , FS109010, Schaffer, Frank) Schaffer, Frank Pubns.

McMillan, Bruce. Growing Colors. McMillan, Bruce, illus. 2002. (Illus.). (J). 14.43 (978-0-7587-2664-3(3)) Book Wholesalers, Inc.

Merrell, Patrick, illus. Colors & Shapes: Fun Color & Shape Activities! 2001. (My Wipe-Off Book Ser.). (J). (978-0-7853-5861-9(7)) Publications International, Ltd.

Milich, Zoran. City Colors. 2006. (Illus.). 24p. (978-1-55337-981-2(0)) Kids Can Pr., Ltd.

—City colors. 2004. (Illus.). 24p. (J). (ps-k). (978-1-55337-542-5(4)) Kids Can Pr., Ltd.

Miller-Schroeder, Patricia. The Science of Light & Color. 2000. (Living Science Ser.). (Illus.). 32p. (J). (gr. 2 up). lib. bdg. 24.67 (978-0-8368-2679-1(5)) Stevens, Gareth Inc.

Mitchell, Melanie S. Black. 2003. (First Step Nonfiction Ser.). (Illus.). 8p. (J). pap. 3.95 (978-0-8225-3891-2(1) , Lerner Pubns.) Lerner Publishing Group.

—Blue. 2003. (First Step Nonfiction Ser.). (Illus.). 8p. (J). pap. 3.95 (978-0-8225-3892-9(X) , Lerner Pubns.) Lerner Publishing Group.

—Brown. 2003. (First Step Nonfiction Ser.). (Illus.). 8p. (J). pap. 3.95 (978-0-8225-3893-6(8) , Lerner Pubns.) Lerner Publishing Group.

—Green. 2003. (First Step Nonfiction Ser.). (Illus.). 8p. (J). pap. 3.95 (978-0-8225-3894-3(6) , Lerner Pubns.) Lerner Publishing Group.

—Orange. 2003. (First Step Nonfiction Ser.). (Illus.). 8p. (J). pap. 3.95 (978-0-8225-3895-0(4) , Lerner Pubns.) Lerner Publishing Group.

—Purple. 2003. (First Step Nonfiction Ser.). (Illus.). 8p. (J). pap. 3.95 (978-0-8225-3896-7(2) , Lerner Pubns.) Lerner Publishing Group.

—Red. 2003. (First Step Nonfiction Ser.). (Illus.). 8p. (J). pap. 3.95 (978-0-8225-3897-4(0) , Lerner Pubns.) Lerner Publishing Group.

—Yellow. 2003. (First Step Nonfiction Ser.). (Illus.). 8p. (J). pap. 3.95 (978-0-8225-3898-1(9) , Lerner Pubns.) Lerner Publishing Group.

Mixing Colors, 4 vols., Set 1. 2004. (Illus.). 74.24 (978-1-4109-0754-7(6)); pap. 19.80 (978-1-4109-0759-2(7)) Raintree.

Moore, Cassandra. Shape/Color Master. 2007. (Illus.). 75p. (J). spiral bd. 12.95 (*978-1-886297-30-2(4)) Omega Publishing Hse.

Moss, Miriam. Take a Walk on the Rainbow: A First Look at Colour. Woods, Amanda, illus. 2004. (First Look Science Ser.). 32p. (C). (gr. k-3). 22.60 (978-1-4048-0660-3(1)) Picture Window Bks.

Murray, Julie. Color. 2007. (Illus.). 24p. (J). 21.35 (978-1-59679-821-2(1)) ABDO Publishing Co.

My Big Box of Colors, Shapes, & Numbers: Contains Twenty Beautifully Illustrated Board Books. (Illus.). (J). bds. (978-1-904613-80-0(2)) O'Mara, Michael Bks., Ltd.

My First BK Of: Colors. 2007. 12p. pap. 7.99 (*978-1-4037-3057-2(1)) Dalmatian Pr.

Nankivell-Aston, Sally. Science Experiments with Color. 2000. (J). (978-0-606-19789-2(3)) Tandem Library Bks.

Nederveld, Patricia L. Blue & Green & Purple Too! The Story of God's Colorful World. 1998. (God Loves Me Ser.). (Illus.). 24p. (J). (ps-3). pap. 2.95 (978-1-56212-270-6(3) , 001201, Faith Alive Christian Resources) CRC Pubns.

Newbery, Elizabeth. Color in Art. 2001. (Art for All Ser.). (Illus.). 32p. (J). lib. bdg. 24.25 (978-1-930643-30-7(6)) Chrysalis Education.

Nguyen, An Mai. Let's Learn Colors in Vietnamese. 2006. (VIE & ENG., Illus.). (J). bds. 6.95 (978-0-9776482-1-4(4)) Viet Baby, LLC.

Niz, Ellen Sturm. Color. 2005. (First Facts Ser.). (Illus.). 24p. (J). (978-0-7368-5400-9(2)) Capstone Pr., Inc.

Norma Staff, ed. Colores. 2005. 14p. (978-958-04-8068-6(0)) Norma S.A.

Novick, Mary. Colors & Shapes. Harlin, Sybel, illus. 2002. (Double Delight Ser.). 24p. (J). (ps-k). 9.95 (978-1-57145-782-0(8) , Silver Dolphin Bks.) Advantage Pubs. Group.

Novoa, Teresa, illus. Azul. (Cocorolos Ser.). (SPA.). 12p. (J). (ps-k). bds. 7.95 (978-84-294-6923-3(0)) Santillana USA Publishing Co., Inc.

Numbers, Shapes, & Colors. (Puppet & Flannelboard Stories Ser.). (Illus.). 2004. 96p. 11.99 (978-0-7439-3699-6(X)); 2003. 48p. (J). pap. 7.99 (978-0-7439-3230-1(7)) Teacher Created Materials, Inc.

Numeros y Colores. 2007. (Dora The Explorer Ser.). (SPA & ENG., Illus.). 48p. (J). 2.95 (*978-1-59545-057-9(2)) Learning Horizons, Inc.

Olawsky, Lynn Ainsworth. Colors of Mexico. 2000. (Colors of the World Ser.). (Illus.). (J). 13.75 (978-0-606-21929-7(3)) Tandem Library Bks.

Omary, Rachel, illus. Shapes & Colors in Dari. 2004. 5p. (J). spiral bd. 14.95 (978-0-9740535-7-8(0)) Knight Publishing.

—Shapes & Colors in Farsi. l.t. ed. 2004. 5p. (J). spiral bd. 14.95 (978-0-9740535-6-1(2)) Knight Publishing.

—Shapes & Colors in Pashto. l.t. ed. 2004. 5p. (J). spiral bd. 14.95 (978-0-9740535-8-5(9)) Knight Publishing.

Omoto, Garrett, illus. Na Waiho'olu'u - The Colors. 2005. Tr. of (the Colors). (HAW & ENG.). (J). (978-1-933835-00-6(1)) Partners in Development.

O'Neill, Cynthia, ed. My First Colors & Shapes. 2004. (SPA.). 16p. (J). (ps-12). bds. 6.99 (978-0-7566-0449-3(4)) Dorling Kindersley Publishing, Inc.

Onyefulu, Ifeoma. Chidi Only Likes Blue: An African Book of Colours. 2006. (Illus.). 24p. (J). pap. 7.95 (978-1-84507-513-2(7)) Lincoln, Frances Ltd. GBR. Dist: Perseus Distribution.

Orange. (Colors Ser.). 32p. (J). 7.95 (978-0-7368-5066-7(X)) Capstone Pr., Inc.

Orero, Maria Jesus. Nico y los Colores. 2005. (SPA & ESP., Illus.). 12p. (ps-ps). per. 6.99 (978-84-272-6153-2(5)) Molino, Editorial ESP. Dist: Santillana USA Publishing Co., Inc.

Pallotta, Jerry. Icky Bug Colors. Biedryzycki, David, illus. 2004. 32p. (J). pap. 5.99 (978-0-439-38917-4(8) , Cartwheel Bks.) Scholastic, Inc.

Paré, Roger. Colors. Paré, Roger, illus. 2001. (Smart Start Ser.). (Illus.). 24p. (J). (ps up). lib. bdg. 22.00 (978-0-8368-2844-3(5)) Stevens, Gareth Inc.

Parker. Blue with Other Colors, 6 Pack. 2004. (Mixing Colors Ser.). (Illus.). pap. 29.70 (978-1-4109-0761-5(9)) Raintree.

—Mixing Colors, 6-Packs, 24 Bks., Set. 2004. (Illus.). pap. 118.80 (978-1-4109-1265-7(5)) Raintree.

—Red with Other Colors 6-Pack. 2004. (Mixing Colors Ser.). (Illus.). pap. 29.70 (978-1-4109-0760-8(0)) Raintree.

—White with Other Colors 6-Pack. 2004. (Mixing Colors Ser.). (Illus.). pap. 29.70 (978-1-4109-0763-9(5)) Raintree.

—Yellow with Other Colors, 6 Pack. 2004. (Mixing Colors Ser.). (Illus.). pap. 29.70 (978-1-4109-0762-2(7)) Raintree.

Parker, Andy. Mekanimals: Clockwork Safari, Spanish-Language Edition. 2005. (Mekanimals Ser.). (SPA., Illus.). 8p. (J). bds. 12.95 (978-970-718-322-3(5) , Silver Dolphin en Español) Advanced Marketing, S. de R. L. de C. V. MEX. Dist: Perseus Distribution.

—Mekanimals: Robotic Reef, Spanish-Language Edition. 2005. (Mekanimals Ser.). (SPA., Illus.). 8p. (J). bds. 12.95 (978-970-718-321-6(7) , Silver Dolphin en Español) Advanced Marketing, S. de R. L. de C. V. MEX. Dist: Perseus Distribution.

Parker, Ant. Colors. 1999. (Touch & Feel Ser.). (Illus.). 12p. (J). (ps). pap. 4.95 (978-0-7373-0288-2(7) , 02887W, Roxbury Park) Lowell Hse.

Parker, Steve. The Science of Light: Projects & Experiments with Light & Color. 2005. (Illus.). (J). 32p. (gr. 4-6). lib. bdg. 29.29 (978-1-4034-7284-7(X)); 31p. (ps-6). pap. 7.95 (978-1-4034-7291-5(2)) Heinemann Library.

Parker, Victoria. Blue with Other Colors. 2004. (Mixing Colors Ser.). (Illus.). 24p. (J). 18.56 (978-1-4109-0751-6(1)); pap. 5.50 (978-1-4109-0756-1(2)) Raintree.

—Red with Other Colors. 2004. (Mixing Colors Ser.). (Illus.). 24p. (J). 18.56 (978-1-4109-0750-9(3)); pap. 5.50 (978-1-4109-0755-4(4)) Raintree.

—White with Other Colors. 2004. (Mixing Colors Ser.). (Illus.). 24p. (J). 18.56 (978-1-4109-0753-0(8)); pap. 5.50 (978-1-4109-0758-5(9)) Raintree.

—Yellow with Other Colors. 2004. (Mixing Colors Ser.). (Illus.). 24p. (J). 18.56 (978-1-4109-0752-3(X)); pap. 5.50 (978-1-4109-0757-8(0)) Raintree.

Pascoe, Gwen. Deep in a Rainforest. Jefferis, Veronica, illus. 1999. 32p. (J). (gr. k up). lib. bdg. 23.33 (978-0-8368-2149-9(1)) Stevens, Gareth Inc.

Payne, Yadira V. !Viva los Colores! Payne, Yadira V., ed. 2004. (MUL.). (J). pap. 12.50 (978-0-9747350-0-9(0)) Payne, Yadira V. Publishing.

Penton Overseas, Inc. Staff, Colors, Shapes & Sizes. abr. ed. 2003. (J). (ps-3). 12.99 incl. audio, cd-rom (978-1-894677-24-0(2)) Kidzup Productions.

Perrett, Lisa, illus. Princess Colors. 2004. 12p. (J). bds. 4.95 (978-1-4027-1490-0(4)) Sterling Publishing Co., Inc.

Petty, Colin. Colors. 2006. (Concept Sliders Ser.). (Illus.). 10p. (J). 5.99 (978-0-7641-5941-1(0)) Barron's Educational Series, Inc.

Pfister, Marcus. Rainbow Fish: Colors. 2004. (Rainbow Fish Ser.). (Illus.). 24p. (J). (gr. k). bds. 4.99 (978-0-7358-1930-6(0)) North-South Bks., Inc.

Phidal Publishing Staff, ed. Colors. (Turn & Learn Ser.). 12p. (J). (978-2-7643-0077-0(8)) Phidal Publishing, Inc./Editions Phidal, Inc.

Phillips, Sarah. Wipe Clean: Colors. 2007. (Trace, Stick & Learn Ser.). (Illus.). 12p. (J). (ps-3). pap. 4.99 (***978-1-84610-480-0(7)***) Make Believe Ideas GBR. *Dist:* Ingram Pub. Services.

Pilla, Susan. Green. 2000. (gr. k-3). lib. bdg. 11.80 (978-0-613-29635-9(4)) Tandem Library Bks.

Pingry, Patricia A. Colors. Rose, Drew, illus. 2005. 16p. (J). bds. 6.95 (978-0-8249-6580-8(9)) Ideals Pubns.

Pink. (Colors Ser.). 32p. (J). 7.95 (978-0-7368-5072-8(4)) Capstone Pr., Inc.

Piper, Watty. The Little Engine That Could Colors. Ong, Cristina, illus. 1999. (Wee Pudgy Board Bks.). 24p. (J). (ps-k). pap. 1.99 (978-0-448-41971-8(8) , Grosset & Dunlap) Penguin Group (USA) Inc.

Play & Learn Fo, ed. Colors. 2007. (Play & Learn Foam Puzzle Bks.). 10p. (J). bds. 16.95 (***978-0-7696-5369-3(3)*** , Brighter Child) School Specialty Publishing.

Play Bac Publishing Staff, contrib. by. EyelikeColors. 2007. 64p. (J). 9.95 (***978-1-60214-018-9(9)***) Play Bac Publishing, USA.

Poitier, Antonine & School Zone Staff. Colors Spin Wheel Board Books. 2006. (J). (ps-k). bds. 3.99 (***978-0-88743-608-6(0)***) School Zone Publishing Co.

Pooh Colors the World: Paint Box Book. 2000. (J). pap. 3.99 (978-0-307-09202-1(X) , 09202, Golden Bks.) Random Hse. Children's Bks.

Popular Science Editors. Color Me Science. 2007. (Experiment with Science Ser.). 32p. (J). 7.95 (***978-0-531-18758-6(6));*** (Illus.). (gr. 3-6). lib. bdg. 25.00 (***978-0-531-18541-4(9)***) Scholastic Library Publishing. (Children's Pr.).

Potter, Tony & Kolanovic, Dubravka. Colors with Albert & Amy: The Fun Way! Kolanovic, Dubravka, illus. 2005. (Illus.). 10p. (J). (gr. 2-5). bds. 5.95 (978-1-59125-566-6(X)) Penton Overseas, Inc.

Priddy Books Staff. Colors. rev. ed. 2004. (Bright Baby Ser.). (Illus.). 26p. (J). bds. 4.95 (978-0-312-49247-2(2) , Priddy Bks.) St. Martin's Pr.

—First Concepts: Colors. 2003. (Illus.). bds. 8.95 (978-0-312-49233-5(2) , Priddy Bks.) St. Martin's Pr.

Priddy Books Staff & Priddy, Roger. Happy Baby: Colors. 2004. (Illus.). 28p. (J). bds. 8.95 (978-0-312-49194-9(8) , Priddy Bks.) St. Martin's Pr.

—Touch & Feel Colors: Easy Learning Fun, for the Very You. rev. ed. 2004. (Play & Learn Ser.). (Illus.). 12p. (J). bds. 8.95 (978-0-312-49397-4(5) , Priddy Bks.) St. Martin's Pr.

Priddy, Roger. Baby Gund Colors. 2005. (Illus.). 24p. (J). (ps-ps). bds. 5.95 (978-0-312-49515-2(3) , Priddy Bks.) St. Martin's Pr.

—Baby Gund Tales Animal Colors. 2007. (J). 7.95 (***978-0-312-50058-0(0)*** , Priddy Bks.) St. Martin's Pr.

—Baby Gund Tales Animal Noises. 2007. (J). 7.95 (***978-0-312-50059-7(9)*** , Priddy Bks.) St. Martin's Pr.

—Baby Hugs Teether - Colors. 2005. (Illus.). 24p. (J). bds. 5.95 (978-0-312-49633-3(8) , Priddy Bks.) St. Martin's Pr.

—Bright Baby Board Book Colors. 2007. (J). bds. 4.95 (***978-0-312-49778-1(4)*** , Priddy Bks.) St. Martin's Pr.

—Bright Baby Soft-to-Touch Large: Words, Animals, Colors. 2005. (J). 22.95 (978-0-312-49555-8(2) , Priddy Bks.) St. Martin's Pr.

—Colores Colors: Spanish/English Bilingual. 2005. (Happy Baby). (SPA & ENG., Illus.). 28p. (J). bds. 5.95 (978-0-312-49234-2(0) , Priddy Bks.) St. Martin's Pr.

—Counting Colors (large Format) 2007. 20p. (J). 8.95 (***978-0-312-50137-2(4)*** , Priddy Bks.) St. Martin's Pr.

—First Concepts Color: Sticker Activity Colors. rev. ed. 2003. (Illus.). 20p. (J). pap. 5.95 (978-0-312-49142-0(5) , Priddy Bks.) St. Martin's Pr.

—Happy Baby: Colors. rev. ed. 2001. (Baby Soft-to-Touch Ser.). (Illus.). 28p. (J). bds. 5.95 (978-0-312-49047-8(X) , Priddy Bks.) St. Martin's Pr.

—Happy Baby Colors. 2007. (J). bds. 3.95 (***978-0-312-49955-6(8)*** , Priddy Bks.) St. Martin's Pr.

—Lift the Flap - Colors. 2005. (Priddy Books Big Ideas for Little People). (Illus.). 30p. (J). bds. 5.95 (978-0-312-49436-0(X) , Priddy Bks.) St. Martin's Pr.

—Magnetic Learning Book Colors. 2006. 16p. (J). bds. 8.95 (978-0-312-49810-8(1) , Priddy Bks.) St. Martin's Pr.

—Rattle Cloth Animal Colors. 2006. 8p. 7.95 (***978-0-312-49841-2(1)*** , Priddy Bks.) St. Martin's Pr.

Priddy, Roger. Rattle Cloth Book Colors. 2005. (Rattle Cloth Book Ser.). (Illus.). 8p. (J). 6.95 (978-0-312-49452-0(1) , Priddy Bks.) St. Martin's Pr.

Primm & Petelinsek. Colors & Shapes/Colores y Formas. 2004. (Talking Hands, Listening Eyes Ser.). (ENG & SPA., Illus.). 24p. (J). (ps-3). 21.36 (978-1-59296-019-4(7)) Child's World, Inc.

Professor Q's Chinese-English Language Books: Yan Se - Colors. 2006. (J). (978-0-9743359-5-7(9)) Murdock Publishing Co.

Publishing Staff, Carson Dellosa. Shapes & Colors. 2005. 80p. pap. (978-1-59441-277-6(4) , RB-904010) Carson-Dellosa Publishing Co., Inc.

Quadrillion Media Staff. Colors. 1999. (J). pap. 1.99 (978-1-84100-286-6(0)) Quadrillion Media LLC.

—Colors. 1999. (Let's Learn Ser.). (J). pap. 3.99 (978-1-84100-299-6(2)) Quadrillion Publishing.

—Toby Learns Colors. 1999. bds. 3.95 (978-1-58185-211-0(8)) Quadrillion Media LLC.

A Rainbow: Individual Title Six-Packs. (Rigby Focus Ser.). 16p. (gr. k up). 26.00 (978-0-7578-5286-2(6)); 28.00 (978-0-7578-5520-7(2)) Rigby Education.

Rainbow Bridge Publishing Staff. Spanish Colors & Shapes: First Step Spanish, Level 1. 2002. (First Step Spanish Ser.). (SPA., Illus.). 64p. 5.95 (978-1-887923-83-5(7)) Rainbow Bridge Publishing.

Raintree Steck-Vaughn Staff. Colors: Beads in My Pocket. 1998. (Illus.). (J). pap. 12.60 (978-0-8172-8627-9(6)) Steck-Vaughn.

Rea, Thelma. I Wonder Why the Sky Is Blue. 2002. (Reading Room Collection). (Illus.). 24p. (J). lib. bdg. 18.75 (978-0-8239-3724-0(0)) Rosen Publishing Group, Inc., The.

Reader's Clubhouse Staff. Mixing Colors Is Fun. 2007. (Reader's Clubhouse Ser.). 24p. (J). (gr. k-2). pap. 3.99 (978-0-7641-3729-7(8)) Barron's Educational Series, Inc.

Reader's Digest Editors & Zobel-Nolan, Allia. See the Sea! A Book about Colors. Terry, Michael, illus. 2004. (Googly Eyes Ser.). 10p. (J). bds. 7.99 (978-0-7944-0291-4(7) , Reader's Digest Children's Bks.) Reader's Digest Children's Publishing, Inc.

Red 6-Pack. 2004. (Colors in Nature Ser.). (Illus.). pap. 29.70 (978-1-4109-0733-2(3)) Raintree.

Repchuk, Caroline. Fairy Colors. 2007. (J). bds. 5.99 (978-0-439-88704-5(6) , Cartwheel Bks.) Scholastic, Inc.

Richardson, Joy. Using Color in Art. 1999. (How to Look at Art Ser.). (Illus.). 32p. (J). (gr. 1 up). lib. bdg. 23.33 (978-0-8368-2629-6(9)) Stevens, Gareth Inc.

Riley, Peter D. Light & Color. 2005. (Illus.). 32p. (J). (gr. 4-7). lib. bdg. 27.10 (978-1-58340-715-8(4)) Smart Apple Media.

Riley, Peter D. Light & Seeing. 2007. (J). (***978-1-59920-028-6(7)***) Smart Apple Media.

Rinaldo, Luana & Sladen, Louisa. Jungle Animals. 2004. (Magic Color Bks.). (Illus.). 10p. (J). 3.95 (978-1-4027-1208-1(1)) Sterling Publishing Co., Inc.

Rivera, Sheila. What Color Is It? (First Step Nonfiction Ser.). (J). 2005. (Illus.). 32p. (J). (gr. 2-5). pap. 5.95 (978-0-8225-2631-5(X)); 2004. pap. (978-0-8225-5409-7(7) , Lerner Pubns.) Lerner Publishing Group.

Rodrigue, George & Goldstone, Bruce. Why Is Blue Dog Blue? A Tale of Colors. 2002. (Illus.). 40p. (J). (gr. 2-7). 17.95 (978-1-58479-162-1(4)) Stewart, Tabori & Chang.

Rosa-Mendoza, Gladys. Colors & Shapes. Cifuentes, Carolina, ed. Noiset, Michele, illus. 2004. (English-Spanish Foundations Ser.).Tr. of Los Colores y las Figuras. (ENG & SPA.). 20p. (J). bds. 6.95 (978-0-9679748-3-5(6)) Me+Mi Publishing.

Ross, Kathy. Kathy Ross Crafts Colors. Barger, Jan, illus. 2003. (Crafts from Kathy Ross Ser.). 48p. (J). lib. bdg. 23.93 (978-0-7613-2651-9(0) , Millbrook Pr.) Lerner Publishing Group.

Ross, Odette. Colors. 2007. (Illus.). 12p. (J). bds. 5.95 (***978-1-894965-87-3(6)***) Simply Read Bks. CAN. *Dist:* Perseus Distribution.

Rossetti, Christina. What Is Pink? Carr, Holly, illus. 2003. 24p. pap. 9.95 (978-1-894915-13-7(5)) Rubicon Publishing, Inc. CAN. *Dist:* International Publishers Marketing.

Royston, Angela. Color. (My World of Science Ser.). (Illus.). 32p. (J). (gr. k-2). 2002. pap. 6.95 (978-1-4034-0038-3(5) , 91482); 2001. lib. bdg. 22.79 (978-1-58810-238-6(6)) Heinemann Library.

Running Press Staff & Fitashape. Colors. 2000. (Fit-a-Shape Ser.). (Illus.). 10p. (J). (ps-k). pap. 6.95 (978-0-7624-0816-0(2) , Running Pr. Kids) Running Pr. Bk. Pubs.

Running Press Staff & Mann, Holly. Colors. 2003. (Magic Windows Ser.). (Illus.). 8p. (J). pap. 4.95 (978-0-7624-1511-3(8) , Running Pr. Kids) Running Pr. Bk. Pubs.

Sadka, Dewey. Dewey Color Kids: What's Your Favorite Color? 2001. (Illus.). 23p. (J). (ps-3). per. 8.95 (978-0-9671207-2-0(1)) Energia Pr.

Sadler, Wendy. Light: Look Out! 2005. (Raintree Perspectives Ser.). (Illus.). 32p. (J). (978-1-4109-1551-1(4)); pap. (978-1-4109-1559-7(X)) Steck-Vaughn.

Salzmann, Mary Elizabeth. Blue. l.t. ed. 1999. (What Color Is It? Ser.). (Illus.). 24p. (J). (ps-3). lib. bdg. 19.93 (978-1-57765-161-1(8) , SandCastle) ABDO Publishing Co.

—Green. l.t. ed. 1999. (What Color Is It? Ser.). (Illus.). 24p. (J). (ps-3). lib. bdg. 19.93 (978-1-57765-162-8(6) , SandCastle) ABDO Publishing Co.

—Orange. l.t. ed. 1999. (What Color Is It? Ser.). (Illus.). 24p. (J). (ps-3). lib. bdg. 19.93 (978-1-57765-158-1(8) , SandCastle) ABDO Publishing Co.

—Purple. l.t. ed. 1999. (What Color Is It? Ser.). (Illus.). 24p. (J). (ps-3). lib. bdg. 19.93 (978-1-57765-160-4(X) , SandCastle) ABDO Publishing Co.

—Red. l.t. ed. 1999. (What Color Is It? Ser.). (Illus.). 24p. (J). (ps-3). lib. bdg. 19.93 (978-1-57765-159-8(6) , SandCastle) ABDO Publishing Co.

—What Color Is It?, Set. l.t. ed. Incl. Blue. lib. bdg. 19.93 (978-1-57765-161-1(8)); Green. lib. bdg. 19.93 (978-1-57765-162-8(6)); Orange. lib. bdg. 19.93 (978-1-57765-158-1(8)); Purple. lib. bdg. 19.93 (978-1-57765-160-4(X)); Red. lib. bdg. 19.93 (978-1-57765-159-8(6)); Yellow. lib. bdg. 19.93 (978-1-57765-157-4(X)); 24p. (J). (ps-3). 1999. Tr. of ¿de Qué Color Es?. (Illus.). 1999. Set lib. bdg. 119.58 (978-1-57765-264-9(9) , SandCastle) ABDO Publishing Co.

—Yellow. l.t. ed. 1999. (What Color Is It? Ser.). (Illus.). 24p. (J). (ps-3). lib. bdg. 19.93 (978-1-57765-157-4(X) , SandCastle) ABDO Publishing Co.

SAMi. Yellow Red Blue. 2007. (Baby Flip-A Face Ser.). (Illus.). 12p. bds. 8.95 (978-1-59354-587-1(8)) Handprint Bks.

Sammis, Fran. Colors of Kenya. Reeves, Jeni, illus. 1998. (Colors of the World Ser.). (ENG & SWA.). 24p. (gr. 3-6). lib. bdg. 19.93 (978-1-57505-280-9(6)) Lerner Publishing Group.

Sanchez, Richard. Colores (Colors) (SPA.). (J). 4.95 (978-84-243-2191-8(X)) Publicaciones Fher, S.A. ESP. *Dist:* AIMS International Bks., Inc.

Sanders, Nancy I. Adventures with Colors. 1998. (Archy's Activity Bks.). (Illus.). 16p. (J). (ps-2). pap. 3.99 (978-0-570-05079-7(0)) Concordia Publishing Hse.

Santillana & Dorling Kindersley Publishing Staff. Colores. (Show Me Ser.). (SPA., Illus.). 16p. (J). (ps-k). bds. 6.95 (978-1-58986-325-5(9)) Santillana USA Publishing Co., Inc.

Sarfatti, Esther. Colores: Azul/Colors: Blue. 2008. (Conceptos (Bilingual) Ser.). (SPA & ENG., Illus.). 24p. (J). (gr. 3-7). lib. bdg. (***978-1-60044-743-3(0)***) Rourke Publishing, LLC.

—Colores: Rojo/Colors: Red. 2008. (Conceptos (Bilingual) Ser.). (SPA & ENG., Illus.). 24p. (J). (gr. 3-7). lib. bdg. (***978-1-60044-745-7(7)***) Rourke Publishing, LLC.

—Colores: Verde/Colors: Green. 2008. (Conceptos (Bilingual) Ser.). (SPA & ENG., Illus.). 24p. lib. bdg. (***978-1-60044-744-0(9)***) Rourke Publishing, LLC.

—Colors: Blue. 2008. (J). (***978-1-60044-517-0(9)***) Rourke Publishing, LLC.

—Colors: Green. 2008. (J). (***978-1-60044-518-7(7)***) Rourke Publishing, LLC.

—Colors: Red. 2008. (J). (***978-1-60044-519-4(5)***) Rourke Publishing, LLC.

—Colors: Yellow. 2008. (J). (***978-1-60044-520-0(9)***) Rourke Publishing, LLC.

Sargent, Daina. Colors & the Number 1, 11 vols. Lenoir, Jane, illus. (Learn to Read Ser.: 11). 24p. (J). 2005. pap. 9.95 (978-1-59381-031-3(8)); 2004. lib. bdg. 19.95 (978-1-59381-030-6(X)) Ozark Publishing.

—Colors & the Number 10, 11. Lenoir, Jane, illus. l.t. ed. 2004. (Learn to Read Ser.). 24p. (J). lib. bdg. 16.95 (978-1-59381-048-1(2)) Ozark Publishing.

—Colors & the Number 10/Los Colores y el Numero 10, 11 vols. Lenoir, Jane, illus. 2005. (Learn to Read Ser.: 11). (ENG & SPA.). 24p. (J). pap. 9.95 (978-1-59381-147-1(0)); lib. bdg. 19.95 (978-1-59381-146-4(2)) Ozark Publishing.

—Colors & the Number 2, 11. Lenoir, Jane, illus. 2004. (Learn to Read Ser.: 11). 24p. (J). pap. 9.95 (978-1-59381-033-7(4)); lib. bdg. 19.95 (978-1-59381-032-0(6)) Ozark Publishing.

—Colors & the Number 3, 11. Lenoir, Jane, illus. l.t. ed. 2004. (Learn to Read Ser.). 24p. (J). lib. bdg. 19.95 (978-1-59381-034-4(2)) Ozark Publishing.

—Colors & the Number 4, 11 vols. Lenoir, Jane, illus. (Learn to Read Ser.). 24p. (J). 2005. pap. 9.95 (978-1-59381-037-5(7)); 2004. lib. bdg. 19.95 (978-1-59381-036-8(9)) Ozark Publishing.

—Colors & the Number 5, 11. Lenoir, Jane, illus. l.t. ed. 2004. (Learn to Read Ser.). 24p. (J). lib. bdg. 19.95 (978-1-59381-038-2(5)) Ozark Publishing.

—Colors & the Number 6, 11. Lenoir, Jane, illus. l.t. ed. 2004. (Learn to Read Ser.). 24p. (J). lib. bdg. 19.95 (978-1-59381-040-5(7)) Ozark Publishing.

—Colors & the Number 7, 11. Lenoir, Jane, illus. l.t. ed. 2004. (Learn to Read Ser.). 24p. (J). lib. bdg. 19.95 (978-1-59381-042-9(3)) Ozark Publishing.

—Colors & the Number 8, 11. Lenoir, Jane, illus. l.t. ed. 2004. (Learn to Read Ser.). 24p. (J). lib. bdg. 19.95 (978-1-59381-044-3(X)) Ozark Publishing.

—Colors & the Number 9, 11. Lenoir, Jane, illus. l.t. ed. 2004. (Learn to Read Ser.). 24p. (J). lib. bdg. 19.95 (978-1-59381-046-7(6)) Ozark Publishing.

—Introduction to Colors & Numbers, 11 vols. Lenoir, Jane, illus. l.t. ed. 2004. (Learn to Read Ser.: 11). 24p. (J). lib. bdg. 19.95 (978-1-59381-050-4(4)) Ozark Publishing.

—Introduction to Colors & Numbers/Introduccion a los Colores Numeros, 11 vols. Lenoir, Jane, illus. l.t. ed. 2005. (Learn to Read Ser.: 11). (SPA & ENG.). 24p. (J). pap. 9.95 (978-1-59381-149-5(7)) Ozark Publishing.

Saunders, Helen B., creator. Sweet Faces Coloring Book. 2004. (J). 5.95 (978-0-9763143-1-8(2)) Happy Heart Kids Publishing.

Scarry, Richard. Los Colores. 1998. (SPA., Illus.). 122p. (ps-1). (978-84-08-01685-4(7)) GeoPlaneta, Editorial, S. A.

Schneck, Susan J. Shapes & Colors. 1999. (Step Ahead Workbooks Ser.). (Illus.). 32p. (J). (ps). pap., wbk. ed. 2.99 (978-0-307-23556-5(4) , 03556, Golden Bks.) Random Hse. Children's Bks.

Scholastic Editorial Staff. Learn with Lego: Colors. 2007. (Lego Ser.). (J). bds. 5.99 (***978-0-439-89338-1(0)***) Scholastic, Inc.

Scholastic, Inc. Staff. Colors. 2007. (Little Scholastic Ser.). (J). bds. 4.99 (***978-0-439-02145-6(6)***) Scholastic, Inc.

Scholastic, Inc. Staff. My First Colors. 2006. (Leapfrog Ser.). 12p. (J). 9.99 (978-0-439-86587-6(5) , Cartwheel Bks.) Scholastic, Inc.

Scholastic, Inc. Staff, ed. Close-Up Colors. (Changing Picture Bks.). (Illus.). (J). pap. 9.99 (978-0-590-24642-2(9)) Scholastic, Inc.

School Specialty Publishing. Colors. 2003. (Skills for Every Child Ser.). 32p. (J). pap. 5.99 (978-1-57029-454-9(2) , WPH99010, Totline Pubns.) Schaffer, Frank Pubns.

—Colors. 2004. (On-File Ser.). 4p. (J). (gr. k-k). ring bd. 4.99 (978-0-7424-2857-7(5) , Instructional Fair) Schaffer, Frank Pubns.

—Colors & Shapes. 2006. (Brighter Child Flash Cards Ser.). 54p. (J). 2.99 (978-0-7696-4689-3(1) , Brighter Child) School Specialty Publishing.

—Colors & Shapes / Los Colores y las Formas. 2006. (Brighter Child Flash Cards Ser.). 54p. (J). 2.99 (978-0-7696-4769-2(3) , Brighter Child) School Specialty Publishing.

—Colors & Shapes, Preschool. 2006. (Skills for Scholars Ser.). 80p. (C). pap. 4.99 (***978-0-7696-5009-8(0)*** , Schaffer, Frank) Schaffer, Frank Pubns.

—Easy Alphabet, Colors, Numbers & Shapes. 2001. (Phonics Flash Cards Ser.). 104p. (C). 6.99 (978-0-86734-411-0(3) , Schaffer, Frank) Schaffer, Frank Pubns.

—Photo Colors. 2002. (Learning Cards Ser.). 10p. (J). (gr. k-2). 7.99 (978-0-7424-1496-9(5) , Instructional Fair) Schaffer, Frank Pubns.

—Starter sk Wbk-color/shape/sz. 2007. (English-Espanol Starter Skills Ser.). 80p. (J). (gr. k-2). pap. 8.99 (***978-0-7682-3439-8(5)*** , Schaffer, Frank) Schaffer, Frank Pubns.

School Specialty Publishing. 101 Activities: Colors & Shapes. 2004. 80p. (J). pap. 10.99 (978-1-57029-487-7(9) , WPH99029, Totline Pubns.) Schaffer, Frank Pubns.

School Zone Publishing Company Staff. Colors, Shapes & More. rev. ed. 1999. (Flash Cards Ser.). (Illus.). (J). 2.79 (978-0-938256-96-0(3) , 04011) School Zone Publishing Co.

—Guess Who? A Book of Colors & Shapes. 2000. (Illus.). 16p. (J). bds. 4.99 (978-0-88743-606-2(4) , 06607) School Zone Publishing Co.

—Shapes & Colors. 2005. 64p. (J). (ps-k). pap., wbk. ed. 3.79 (978-1-58947-357-7(4)) School Zone Publishing Co.

School Zone Staff. Colors, Shapes & More. 2004. (J). 2.79 (978-1-58947-988-3(2)) School Zone Publishing Co.

Schuette, Sarah L. Amarillo: Mira el Amarillo Que Te Rodea = Yellow: Seeing Yellow All Around Us. 2008. (ENG & SPA.). (J). (***978-1-4296-0011-8(X)***) Capstone Pr., Inc.

—Anaranjado: Mira el Anaranjado Que Te Rodea = Orange: Seeing Orange All Around Us. 2008. (ENG & SPA.). (J). (***978-1-4296-0008-8(X)***) Capstone Pr., Inc.

—Azul: Mira el Azul Que Te Rodea = Blue: Seeing Blue All Around Us. 2008. (ENG & SPA.). (J). (***978-1-4296-0006-4(3)***) Capstone Pr., Inc.

—Blue. 2002. (A+ Color Books). (Illus.). 32p. (J). (gr. k-1). lib. bdg. 22.60 (978-0-7368-1467-6(1) , Aplus Bks.) Capstone Pr., Inc.

—Colors, 6 bks. Incl. Blue. lib. bdg. 22.60 (978-0-7368-1467-6(1)); Green. lib. bdg. 22.60 (978-0-7368-1468-3(X)); Orange. lib. bdg. 22.60 (978-0-7368-1469-0(8)); Purple. lib. bdg. 22.60 (978-0-7368-1470-6(1)); Red. lib. bdg. 22.60 (978-0-7368-1471-3(X)); Yellow. lib. bdg. 22.60 (978-0-7368-1472-0(8)); 32p. (J). (gr. k-1). 2002. (A+ Color Books). (Illus.). 2002. Set lib. bdg. 135.60 (978-0-7368-1473-7(6) , Aplus Bks.) Capstone Pr., Inc.

—Green. 2002. (A+ Color Books). (Illus.). 32p. (J). (gr. k-1). lib. bdg. 22.60 (978-0-7368-1468-3(X) , Aplus Bks.) Capstone Pr., Inc.

—Morado: Mira el Morado Que Te Rodea = Purple: Seeing Purple All Around Us. 2008. (ENG & SPA.). (J). (***978-1-4296-0009-5(8)***) Capstone Pr., Inc.

—Orange. 2002. (A+ Color Books). (Illus.). 32p. (J). (gr. k-1). lib. bdg. 22.60 (978-0-7368-1469-0(8) , Aplus Bks.) Capstone Pr., Inc.

—Purple. 2002. (A+ Color Books). (Illus.). 32p. (J). (gr. k-1). lib. bdg. 22.60 (978-0-7368-1470-6(1) , Aplus Bks.) Capstone Pr., Inc.

—Red. 2002. (A+ Color Books). (Illus.). 32p. (J). (gr. k-1). lib. bdg. 22.60 (978-0-7368-1471-3(X) , Aplus Bks.) Capstone Pr., Inc.

—Rojo: Mira el Rojo Que Te Rodea = Red: Seeing Red All Around Us. 2008. (ENG & SPA.). (J). (***978-1-4296-0010-1(1)***) Capstone Pr., Inc.

—Verde: Mira el Verde Que Te Rodea = Green: Seeing Green All Around Us. 2008. (ENG & SPA.). (J). (***978-1-4296-0007-1(1)***) Capstone Pr., Inc.

Schuette, Sarah L. Yellow. 2002. (A+ Color Books). (Illus.). 32p. (J). (gr. k-1). lib. bdg. 22.60 (978-0-7368-1472-0(8) , Aplus Bks.) Capstone Pr., Inc.

Schumacher, Bev. What Color Is It? 2004. (ENG.). 20p. (J). lib. bdg. 9.95 (978-0-9741549-7-8(0)) Learning Props.

Schwartz, Betty Ann. The Spinning Book of Colors, Shapes, & Numbers. Berg, Michelle, illus. 2007. 16p. (J). (ps-1). 9.99 (978-0-06-079974-8(9) , Harper Festival) HarperCollins Pubs.

Seeger, Laura Vaccaro. Lemons Are Not Red. Seeger, Laura Vaccaro, illus. (Illus.). 32p. (J). 2006. pap. 6.95 (978-1-59643-195-9(4)); 2004. 15.95 (978-1-59643-008-2(7)) Roaring Brook Pr.

Serfozo, Mary. Who Said Red? 1998. (J). pap. 4.95 (978-0-87628-367-7(9)) Ctr. for Applied Research in Education, The.

Sesame Building Blocks: Cube Books. 2002. (J). (978-1-931312-81-3(8)) SoftPlay, Inc.

Sesame Street Colors on My Plate Wipe Off. 2007. (J). 4.99 (***978-1-59545-162-0(5)***) Learning Horizons, Inc.

Sesame Street Rosita's Holiday of Colors & Patterns. 2006. (J). 3.99 ***(978-1-59545-118-7(8))*** Learning Horizons, Inc.

Sevaly, Karen, ed. Hands on Learning: Color & Shape Dominoes. 2006. 12.99 (978-0-439-82402-6(8) , Teaching Resources) Scholastic, Inc.

Shahan, Sherry. Spicy Hot Colors! Colores Picantes! Barragan, Paula, illus. 2004. (ENG & SPA.). 24p. 16.95 (978-0-87483-741-4(3)) August Hse. Pubs., Inc.

Shapes anc colors shaped layer Book. 2006. (J). bds. 4.99 (978-1-934004-08-1(1)) Byeway Bks.

Shopping for Shapes & Colors. 1998. (Fisher-Price Little People Concept Bks.: Vol. 4). (Illus.). 24p. (J). (978-0-7666-0322-6(9) , 19615) Modern Publishing.

Shulman, Mark. There's No Blue on a Bagel. Miline, Bill, photos by. 2006. (Illus.). 12p. (J). (gr. k-4). reprint ed. 6.00 (978-1-4223-5711-8(2)) DIANE Publishing Co.

Siede, George & Press, Donna, photos by. Colors. 1998. (Active Minds Ser.). (Illus.). 10p. (J). bds. 3.99 (978-1-58048-028-4(4)) Sandvik Publishing.

Siede Preis Photography (Firm) Staff & Brian Warling Photography (Firm) Staff, contrib. by. Colors & Shapes. 2004. (Active Minds Ser.). (Illus.). 12p. (J). bds. (978-1-4127-0540-0(1) , 3970905) Publications International, Ltd.

Silver Dolphin en Español Editors. Disney Learning: Colores: Disney Learning: Colors, Spanish-Language Edition. 2006. (Illus.). 20p. (J). 3.99 ***(*978-970-718-430-5(2)*** , Silver Dolphin en Español) Advanced Marketing, S. de R. L. de C. V. MEX. *Dist:* Perseus Distribution.

—Disney Tesoro de libros de Calcomanias: Disney Sticker Book Treasury, Spanish-Language Edition. 2007. (Illus.). 48p. (J). 14.95 ***(*978-970-718-447-3(7)*** , Silver Dolphin en Español) Advanced Marketing, S. de R. L. de C. V. MEX. *Dist:* Perseus Distribution.

Silver Dolphin en Español Staff, ed. Baby Einstein: Libro con ventanas: Colores: Baby Einstein Flip Flap Book: Colors. 2007. (Baby Einstein. Libro con Ventanas Ser.). (Illus.). 5p. (J). 6.95 ***(*978-970-718-469-5(8)*** , Silver Dolphin en Español) Advanced Marketing, S. de R. L. de C. V. MEX. *Dist:* Perseus Distribution.

Silverhardt, Lauryn. Let's Find Colors. Giarrano, Vincent, illus. 2002. (Bob the Builder Super Chubby Ser.). 22p. (J). bds. 4.99 (978-0-689-85065-3(4) , Simon Spotlight) Simon & Schuster Children's Publishing.

Simson, Dana. Colors. 2003. (Dana Simson Chunky Books Ser.). 10p. (J). bds. 2.95 (978-1-74047-261-6(6)) Book Co. Publishing Pty, Ltd., The AUS. *Dist:* Penton Overseas, Inc.

Siomades, Lorianne. My Box of Color. Siomades, Lorianne, illus. 2003. (Illus.). 32p. (J). (ps up). 12.95 (978-1-56397-711-4(7)) Boyds Mills Pr.

Sladen, Louisa. Farm Animals. Rinaldo, Luana, illus. 2004. (Magic Color Bks.). 10p. (J). 3.95 (978-1-4027-1207-4(3)) Sterling Publishing Co., Inc.

Slaughter, Tom. One, Two, Three. 2003. (Illus.). 24p. (J). (gr. k-k). 12.95 (978-0-88776-664-0(1)) Tundra Bks., Inc./ Livres Toundra, Inc. CAN. *Dist:* Random Hse., Inc.

Smart, Parker. CiCi: Color Sampler. Jason, Hall, illus. 2001. 8p. (YA). 3.00 (978-0-9709707-1-8(4)) Spilled Milk.

Snyder, Margaret. Colors. deluxe ed. 1999. (Talking Pages Ser.). (Illus.). 12p. (ps-3). 7.95 (978-1-58224-003-9(5)) Futech Interactive Products, Inc.

Southwater Books Staff. Colors. 2002. (Playschool Ser.). (Illus.). 32p. (ps-2). pap. 5.95 (978-1-84215-607-0(1) , Southwater) Anness Publishing GBR. *Dist:* National Bk. Network.

Southwater Staff. Look & Learn: Colors & Patterns. 2000. (Look & Learn Ser.). (Illus.). 32p. (ps). 7.95 (978-1-84215-041-2(3) , Southwater) Anness Publishing GBR. *Dist:* National Bk. Network.

Steck-Vaughn Staff. Head for Home: Colors & Shapes. 2004. (Illus.). pap. (978-0-7398-8554-3(5)) Steck-Vaughn.

—Red, White & Blue Big Book. 2002. (Illus.). pap. (978-0-7398-5896-7(3)) Steck-Vaughn.

Sterling Publishing Company Staff. Colors & Shapes. 1998. (Balloon Ser.). (Illus.). 16p. (ps-1). pap. 5.95 (978-0-8069-9607-3(2)) Sterling Publishing Co., Inc.

Stewart, Melissa. Why Do We See Rainbows? 2008. (J). ***(978-0-7614-2919-7(0))*** Cavendish, Marshall Bks., Ltd.

Stiegemeyer, Julie. Colors I See in Church. Mitter, Kathy, illus. 2002. (ENG.). 20p. (J). bds. 4.99 (978-0-7586-0029-5(1)) Concordia Publishing Hse.

Stoppard, Miriam. Colors. 2006. (Let's Play Ser.). (Illus.). 14p. (J). bds. 8.99 (978-0-7566-1701-1(4)) Dorling Kindersley Publishing, Inc.

Strelitski, Mies & de Hartog, Arnold. Woobie Paints: A Discovery of Color. 2005. (Illus.). 32p. (J). (ps-3). 16.95 (978-1-59249-472-9(2) , 1F001) Soundprints.

Studio Mouse, ed. Colors & Shapes. rev. ed. 2007. (Illus.). 28p. 16.99 incl. audio compact disk (978-1-59069-505-0(4) , 1C1000) Studio Mouse LLC.

Sueda, Kelly. Aloha Shirt Colors. 2006. 16p. 6.95 ***(*978-1-933067-19-3(5))*** Beachhouse Publishing, LLC.

Swinburne, Stephen R. & Boyds Mills Press Staff. What Color Is Nature? Swinburne, Stephen R., photos by. 2003. (Illus.). 32p. (J). (gr. k-2). 15.95 (978-1-56397-967-5(5)) Boyds Mills Pr.

Taylor, Barbara. Light, Color & Art Activities. 2002. (gr. 3-6). lib. bdg. 17.60 (978-0-613-52871-9(9)) Tandem Library Bks.

Taylor, Barbara, text. Light, Color & Art Activities. 2002. (Arty Facts Ser.). (Illus.). 48p. (J). (gr. 3-4). pap. (978-0-7787-1142-1(0)); lib. bdg. (978-0-7787-1114-8(5)) Crabtree Publishing Co.

Taylor, Terilyn & Milleret, Toni. Basic Cello Scales. 2000. (Color Connection Ser.). (Illus.). 44p. (YA). (gr. 1). pap. 15.95 (978-1-930940-00-0(9)) T&T Publishing.

—Basic Viola Scales. 2000. (Color Connection Ser.). (Illus.). 44p. (YA). (gr. 1 up). pap. 15.95 (978-0-9671719-6-8(2)) T&T Publishing.

Thomas, Isabel. Action Art: Using Color. 2005. (Heinemann Read & Learn Ser.). (Illus.). 24p. (J). (978-1-4034-6920-5(2)); pap. (978-1-4034-6926-7(1)) Heinemann Library.

—Black Foods. (Colors We Eat Ser.). (Illus.). 24p. (J). (ps-1). 2005. lib. bdg. 20.64 (978-1-4034-6315-9(8)); 2004. pap. 5.75 (978-1-4034-6322-7(0)) Heinemann Library.

—Blue & Purple Foods. (Colors We Eat Ser.). (Illus.). 24p. (J). (ps-1). 2005. lib. bdg. 21.36 (978-1-4034-6316-6(6)); 2004. pap. 5.75 (978-1-4034-6323-4(9)) Heinemann Library.

Thompson. Theme Pack: Colors. 2002. (Pair-It Bks.). (J). pap. (978-0-7398-6368-8(1)) Steck-Vaughn.

Thompson, Karen & Mitzo Thompson, Kim. I Like Colors. 2006. (Read & Sing along Board Books with CDs Ser.). (Illus.). 18p. (J). bds. 7.49 (978-0-7696-4585-8(2)) School Specialty Publishing.

Thurmond, Cindy. What If There Were No Colors? 2004. (Illus.). 44p. (J). 16.95 (978-0-9760685-0-1(8)) Overview Publishing.

Timmy Turtle Learns Colors. (Board Bks.). (Illus.). 6p. (J). (ps-k). 4.99 (978-0-7847-1120-0(8) , 03528, Bean Sprouts) Standard Publishing.

Tocci, Salvatore. Experiments with Colors. 2003. (True Book Ser.). (Illus.). 48p. (J). 25.00 (978-0-516-22785-6(8) , Children's Pr.) Scholastic Library Publishing.

Top That Publishing Staff, ed. Colors. 2004. (Magnetic Play & Learn Ser.). (Illus.). 12p. (J). (978-1-84510-047-6(6)) Top That! Publishing PLC.

Trace & Color (Pre-K) 2003. (J). (978-1-58232-043-4(8)) Bryan Hse. Pubs., Inc.

Trapp, Kyrima. Que? Como? Por que?: Los Colores: What? How? Why?: the Colors, Spanish-Language Edition. 2007. (Illus.). 16p. (J). 9.95 ***(*978-970-718-491-6(4)*** , Silver Dolphin en Español) Advanced Marketing, S. de R. L. de C. V. MEX. *Dist:* Perseus Distribution.

Trazos, Ritmo Y Color: Francisco Icaza. 2005. (Coleccion Los Grandes Para Los Mas Pequenos Ser.). (SPA.). (J). pap. 8.95 (978-968-7381-50-3(7)) Tecolote, Ediciones, S.A. de C.V. MEX. *Dist:* Iacòni, Mariuccia Bk. Imports.

Troiano, Joe. Spookley the Square Pumpkin: Colors & Numbers. Brooks, Nan, illus. 2006. 22p. (J). bds. 4.95 (978-1-4027-4109-8(X)) Sterling Publishing Co., Inc.

Tuxworth, Nicola. Colors. 2005. (Illus.). 12p. (gr. 2-13). bds. 6.99 (978-0-7548-1418-4(1) , Lorenz Bks.) Anness Publishing GBR. *Dist:* National Bk. Network.

—A First Book about Colors. 1999. (Look & Learn Ser.). (Illus.). 24p. (J). (gr. 1 up). lib. bdg. 22.00 (978-0-8368-2287-8(0)) Stevens, Gareth Inc.

Tuxworth, Nicola & Lorenz Editors. Colours. 2001. (Let's Look at... Ser.). (Illus.). 20p. 5.95 (978-0-7548-0945-6(5)) Anness Publishing GBR. *Dist:* National Bk. Network.

Tyrrell, Melissa. Colors. 1998. (Pull & Look Sliding Board Bks.). (Illus.). 12p. (J). (ps). bds. 4.95 (978-1-888443-85-1(5) , Intervisual/Piggy Toes) Dalmatian Pr.

Unidad 5 Superlibro: Los colores del Camaleon: Big Books. 2001. (McGraw-Hill. Lectura Ser.). (ENG & SPA.). (gr. 2 up). (978-0-02-186402-7(0)) Macmillan/McGraw-Hill Schl. Div.

Upgrade kit dsm-3 Color&light. (J). 2004. (978-1-59242-527-3(5)); 2003. (978-1-59242-410-8(4)) Delta Education, LLC.

Usilton, Terry. Color Guard Competition. 2003. (Let's Go Team—Cheer, Dance, March Ser.). (Illus.). 64p. (J). (gr. 5 up). lib. bdg. 19.95 (978-1-59084-537-0(4)) Mason Crest Pubs.

Valat, Pierre-Marie. El Color. (SPA., Illus.). 40p. (J). (978-84-348-3471-2(5) , CO9914) SM Ediciones ESP. *Dist:* Lectorum Pubns., Inc.

—Colors. 2001. (Look-Inside Ser.: No. 6). (Illus.). 10p. (J). (ps). bds. 4.95 (978-0-439-29727-1(3) , Cartwheel Bks.) Scholastic, Inc.

Vargo, Julianna. Aprende los Colores Con Elmo. 2007. (Sesame Street Ser.). (SPA & ENG.). 48p. (J), pap., wbk. ed. 3.95 ***(*978-1-59545-070-8(X))*** Learning Horizons, Inc.

Vischer, Phil. Junior's Colors: A Veggiecational Book about Colors! 1999. (Veggiecational Ser.). (Illus.). 12p. (J). (ps-3). 8.99 (978-0-8499-5984-4(5)) Nelson, Thomas Inc.

Votry, Kim & Waller, Curt. A Book of Colors. 2003. (Baby's First Signs Bks.). (Illus.). 16p. (J). pap. 7.95 (978-1-56368-147-9(1)) Gallaudet Univ. Pr.

Walter, Nancy. Bumpsie's Colorful Garden. 2005. 8p. (J). bds. 5.99 (978-0-9770957-1-1(1)) Turtle Time Bks.

Watson, B. S. How to Draw. 2004. (Clifford Ser.). (Illus.). 32p. (J). (ps up). 3.99 (978-0-439-54402-3(5)) Scholastic, Inc.

Watt, Melanie. Colors. 2005. (Learning with Animals Board Bks.). (Illus.). 24p. (J). (gr. k up). (978-1-55337-830-3(X)) Kids Can Pr., Ltd.

—Leon the Chameleon. Watt, Melanie, illus. 2003. (Illus.). 32p. (J). (ps-k). (978-1-55337-527-2(0)) Kids Can Pr., Ltd.

—Leon the Chameleon. 2001. (Illus.). 32p. (J). (ps-k). (978-1-55074-867-3(X)) Kids Can Pr., Ltd.

—Leon the Chameleon. 2001. (gr. k-3). lib. bdg. 14.10 (978-0-613-62429-9(7)) Tandem Library Bks.

Weber, Lou, ed. Shapes & Colors. 2004. 1p. (J). 7.98 (978-1-4127-3300-7(6) , 5542200) Publications International, Ltd.

Webster, Christy. Color Carnival. Moroney, Christopher, illus. 2008. 22p. (J). (gr. k-ps). bds. 7.99 ***(*978-0-375-84132-3(6)*** , Random Hse. Bks. for Young Readers) Random Hse. Children's Bks.

What Are? Colors & Shapes. 1998. (Illus.). 8p. (J). bds. 4.99 (978-1-929174-05-8(5)) Oshkosh B'Gosh, Inc.

What Color Am I? (Peek A Boo Pockets Ser.). (Illus.). 12p. (J). bds. (978-2-89393-975-9(9)) Phidal Publishing, Inc./ Editions Phidal, Inc.

What Color Is It? 2004. Tr. of ¿de Qué Color Es?. (SPA.). lib. bdg. 9.95 net. (978-0-9741549-0-9(3)) Learning Props.

What Color Is It? 2003. (Bear in the Big Blue House Ser.).Tr. of ¿de Qué Color Es?. (Illus.). 16p. (J). (ps-k). pap., act. bk. ed. 4.99 (978-1-57768-701-6(9)) School Specialty Publishing.

What Makes a Rainbow? 14p. (J). 4.95 (978-1-58117-220-1(6) , Intervisual/Piggy Toes) Dalmatian Pr.

White. (Colors Ser.). 32p. (J). 7.95 (978-0-7368-5073-5(2)) Capstone Pr., Inc.

Whitehouse, Patricia. Agrupemos Alimentos. 2002. (Colores Para Comer (The Colors We Eat) Ser.).Tr. of Sorting Foods. 24p. (J). (ps-1). pap. 5.25 (978-1-58810-840-1(6) , 91577); (SPA.). lib. bdg. 18.50 (978-1-58810-793-0(0)) Heinemann Library.

—Alimentos Amarillos. 2002. (SPA.). 24p. (J). (ps-1). pap. 5.25 (978-1-58810-838-8(4) , 91573); lib. bdg. 18.50 (978-1-58810-791-6(4)) Heinemann Library.

—Alimentos Marron. 2003. Tr. of Brown Foods. (SPA.). (ps-2). lib. bdg. 13.30 (978-0-613-82825-3(9)) Tandem Library Bks.

—Alimentos Rojos. 2002. (Colores Para Comer (The Colors We Eat) Ser.).Tr. of Red Foods. (SPA.). 24p. (J). (ps-1). pap. 5.25 (978-1-58810-837-1(6) , 91575); lib. bdg. 18.50 (978-1-58810-790-9(6)) Heinemann Library.

—Alimentos Verdes. 2002. (Colores Para Comer (The Colors We Eat) Ser.). (SPA.). 24p. (J). (ps-1). pap. 5.25 (978-1-58810-836-4(8) , 91576); lib. bdg. 18.50 (978-1-58810-789-3(2)) Heinemann Library.

—Food ABC. 2002. 24p. (J). (ps-1). pap. 5.25 (978-1-58810-748-0(5) , 91416); (Illus.). lib. bdg. 18.50 (978-1-58810-540-0(7)) Heinemann Library.

—Green Foods. 2002. 24p. (J). (ps-1). pap. 5.25 (978-1-58810-743-5(4) , 91417); (Illus.). lib. bdg. 18.50 (978-1-58810-535-6(0)) Heinemann Library.

—Red Foods. 2002. 24p. (J). (ps-1). pap. 5.25 (978-1-58810-744-2(2) , 91418); (Illus.). lib. bdg. 18.50 (978-1-58810-536-3(9)) Heinemann Library.

—Yellow Foods. 2002. (Heinemann Read & Learn Ser.). (Illus.). 24p. (J). (ps-1). pap. 5.25 (978-1-58810-745-9(0) , 91420); lib. bdg. 18.50 (978-1-58810-537-0(7)) Heinemann Library.

Wildsmith, Brian. Los Colores de los Animales. Wildsmith, Brian, illus. 2001. (SPA., Illus.). 16p. (J). (ps-k). bds. 4.95 (978-1-887734-51-6(1)) Star Bright Bks., Inc.

Wildsmith, Brian, illus. Brian Wildsmith's Animal Colors (Korean) 2003. (KOR.). 16p. (J). bds. 4.95 (978-1-932065-28-2(8) , 1-718-784-9112) Star Bright Bks., Inc.

—Brian Wildsmith's Animal Colors (Navajo) 2004. (NAV.). 16p. (J). bds. 4.95 (978-1-932065-34-3(2) , 718-784-9112) Star Bright Bks., Inc.

—Brian Wildsmith's Animal Colors (Portugese) 2003. (POR.). 16p. (J). bds. 4.95 (978-1-932065-27-5(X) , 1-718-784-9112) Star Bright Bks., Inc.

—Brian Wildsmith's Animal Colors (Simplified Chinese) 2004. (CHI.). 16p. (J). bds. 4.95 (978-1-932065-52-7(0) , 7187849112) Star Bright Bks., Inc.

—Brian Wildsmith's Animal Colors (Tagalog) 2003. (TAG.). 16p. (J). bds. 4.95 (978-1-932065-30-5(X) , 1-718-784-9112) Star Bright Bks., Inc.

—Brian Wildsmith's Animal Colors (Traditional Chinese) 2004. (CHI.). 16p. (J). bds. 4.95 (978-1-932065-53-4(9)) Star Bright Bks., Inc.

—Brian Wildsmith's Animal Colors (Vietnamese) 2004. (VIE.). 16p. (J). bds. 4.95 (978-1-932065-51-0(2)) Star Bright Bks., Inc.

Wilkinson, Doris J. Colors of the Rainbow. Wilkinson, Doris J., ed. Chipping, Oliver, illus. 2000. (Jacob's Magic Box Discovery Ser.). 20p. (J). (ps). pap. 4.95 (978-0-9700386-1-6(5)) Magic Box Pubns.

Williams, Sam. Spots & Slots: A Slide the Spot Book of Colors. Stojic, Manya, illus. 2001. 10p. (J). (ps-1). pap. 9.95 (978-0-439-24064-2(6)) Scholastic, Inc.

Winne, Jennifer. Yellow in My World. 2000. (Welcome Bks.). (Illus.). 24p. (J). (ps-2). pap. 4.95 (978-0-516-23053-5(0) , Children's Pr.) Scholastic Library Publishing.

Winne, Joanne. Blue in My World. 2000. (Welcome Bks.). (Illus.). 24p. (J). (ps-2). 17.00 (978-0-516-23123-5(5) , Children's Pr.) Scholastic Library Publishing.

—Blue in My World. 2000. (gr. k-3). lib. bdg. 12.95 (978-0-613-58958-1(0)) Tandem Library Bks.

—Green in My World. 2000. (Welcome Bks.). (Illus.). 24p. (J). (ps-2). 17.00 (978-0-516-23124-2(3) , Children's Pr.) Scholastic Library Publishing.

—Green in My World. 2000. (gr. k-3). lib. bdg. 12.95 (978-0-613-58968-0(8)) Tandem Library Bks.

—Orange in My World. 2000. (Welcome Bks.). (Illus.). 24p. (J). (ps-2). pap. 4.95 (978-0-516-23050-4(6)); 17.00 (978-0-516-23125-9(1)) Scholastic Library Publishing. (Children's Pr.).

—Red in My World. 2000. (World of Color Ser.). (Illus.). 24p. (J). (ps-2). 17.00 (978-0-516-23126-6(X) , Children's Pr.) Scholastic Library Publishing.

—Red in My World. 2000. (gr. k-3). lib. bdg. 12.95 (978-0-613-59013-6(9)) Tandem Library Bks.

—White in My World. 2000. (Welcome Bks.). (Illus.). 24p. (J). (ps-2). 17.00 (978-0-516-23127-3(8) , Children's Pr.) Scholastic Library Publishing.

—White in My World. 2000. (gr. k-3). lib. bdg. 12.95 (978-0-613-59031-0(7)) Tandem Library Bks.

—The World of Color, 6 bks., Set. 2004. (Illus.). 24p. (J). (ps-2). 87.00 (978-0-516-23233-1(9) , Children's Pr.) Scholastic Library Publishing.

—Yellow in My World. 2000. (Welcome Bks.). (Illus.). 24p. (J). (ps-2). 17.00 (978-0-516-23128-0(6) , Children's Pr.) Scholastic Library Publishing.

Wipe-Away Books: Colors & Shapes. 2003. (Illus.). 16p. (J). (ps up). pap. 3.99 (978-0-7682-0069-0(5)) School Specialty Publishing.

Wolf, Gita. Hensparrow Turns Purple. Biswas, Pulak, illus. 2002. 13p. (ps-3). 12.99 (978-81-86211-19-9(5)) Penguin Group (USA) Inc.

Wood, Jakki. Moo Moo, Brown Cow. ed. 2004. (Illus.). (J). (ps up). spiral bd., bds. (978-0-616-14613-2(2)) Canadian National Institute for the Blind/Institut National Canadien pour les Aveugles.

Yates, Irene. Color. 2002. (All about Ser.). (Illus.). 32p. (J). lib. bdg. 24.25 (978-1-930643-99-4(3)) Chrysalis Education.

—Colour. 2004. (Activities for 3-5 Year Olds Ser.). (Illus.). 32p. pap. 11.00 (978-1-897675-26-7(7)) Brilliant Pubns. GBR. *Dist:* Parkwest Pubns., Inc.

Yellow. 2004. (Illus.). 10p. (J). 3.99 (978-1-85997-884-9(3)) Byeway Bks.

Yellow 6-Pack. 2004. (Colors in Nature Ser.). (Illus.). pap. 29.70 (978-1-4109-0735-6(X)) Raintree.

Yenawine, Philip. Colors. 3rd ed. 2006. (Illus.). 32p. (gr. 13 up). 9.95 (978-0-87070-176-4(2)) D.A.P./Distributed Art Pubs.

Yolen, Jane. Animal Train: A Lift-the-Flap Concept Book. Cushman, Doug, illus. 2002. 14p. (J). (ps-1). bds. 8.99 (978-0-689-84838-4(2) , Little Simon) Simon & Schuster Children's Publishing.

Yoon, Salina, creator. Bug Buddies: A Sparkling Little Colors Book. 2005. (Illus.). 12p. (J). 5.95 (978-1-58117-166-2(8) , Intervisual/Piggy Toes) Dalmatian Pr.

Yoon, Salina, illus. Foil Fun Colors. 2000. (Foil Fun Board Bks.). 10p. (J). (ps). bds. 4.95 (978-1-58117-061-0(0) , Intervisual/Piggy Toes) Dalmatian Pr.

—Foil Fun Learning Books: Numbers, Colors, Opposites, Shapes, 4 bks. Incl. Foil Fun Colors. (J). bds. 4.95 (978-1-58117-061-0(0)); Foil Fun Numbers. bds. 4.95 (978-1-58117-062-7(9)); Foil Fun Opposites. (J). bds. 4.95 (978-1-58117-063-4(7)); Foil Fun Shapes. (J). bds. 4.95 (978-1-58117-064-1(5)); 10p. (ps). 2000. (Foil Fun Board Bks.). (Illus.). 2000. Set bds. 14.95 (978-1-58117-065-8(3) , Intervisual/Piggy Toes) Dalmatian Pr.

Your Baby Can Learn! Colors, Vol. 1. 2007. (J). 7.95 ***(*978-1-931026-12-3(2))*** Infant Learning Co., The.

Zambon, Dana. Yo Puedo Cantar los Colores. Hnat, Ana Maria, ed. Hnat, Ana Maria, tr. Lin, Herman, illus. 2002. Tr. of I Can Sing the Colors!. (SPA.). 26p. (J). (ps-3). 39.99 (978-0-9714533-0-2(6)) Yo Puedo Publishing.

Zemlicka, Shannon. Colors of China. Porter, Janice Lee, illus. (Colors of the World Ser.). 24p. 2005. (gr. 3-6). lib. bdg. 19.93 (978-1-57505-478-0(7)); 2003. (J). (gr. 1-4). 5.95 (978-1-57505-563-3(5)) Lerner Publishing Group.

—Colors of China. 2001. (gr. k-3). lib. bdg. 14.10 (978-0-613-79238-7(6)) Tandem Library Bks.

—Colors of Russia. Reeves, Jeni, illus. (Colors of the World Ser.). 24p. (J). 2005. (gr. 3-6). lib. bdg. 19.93 (978-1-57505-513-8(9)); 2003. (gr. 1-4). pap. 5.95 (978-1-57505-564-0(3)) Lerner Publishing Group.

—Colors of Russia. 2001. (gr. k-3). lib. bdg. 14.10 (978-0-613-79239-4(4)) Tandem Library Bks.

Ziefert, Harriet & Bolam, Emily. Buzzy & Friends: Colors. 2007. (Illus.). 16p. (ps-k). bds. 7.95 ***(*978-1-59354-629-8(7))*** Blue Apple Bks.

Zimmerman, Dottie, creator. Interactive Sing-along Big Books Where Are My Crayons? 2007. (J). spiral bd. 12.95 ***(*978-1-58650-712-1(5))*** Super Duper Pubns.

Zoehfeld, Kathleen Weidner. Fall Leaves Change Color. 2001. (Scholastic Science Readers Ser.). 32p. (J). (978-0-439-26986-5(5)) Scholastic, Inc.

Zoller, Arthur David. Fish Colors. 2004. 14p. (J). (ps-k). bds. 6.95 (978-0-88106-073-7(9)) Charlesbridge Publishing, Inc.

Zuckerman, Rory. Colorful Sleepy Sheep. Roos, Maryn, illus. 2004. (J). bds. 12.95 (978-0-9749305-1-0(2)) Castle Pacific Publishing.

COLOR—FICTION

Adlerman, Daniel, et al. The Cool Black Pool. 2001. (Illus.). (J). (978-1-58089-058-8(X)) Charlesbridge Publishing, Inc.

Aigner-Clark, Julie. Baby Einstein: My First Book of Colors. Zaidi, Nadeem, illus. 2007. 24p. (J). (ps-17). bds. 9.99 ***(*978-1-4231-0202-1(9))*** Baby Einstein Co., LLC, The.

—Colors. Zaidi, Nadeem, illus. 2006. (Baby Einstein Ser.). 12p. (J). (ps-17). bds. 6.99 (978-0-7868-4950-5(9)) Baby Einstein Co., LLC, The.

—My Favorite Colors: A Fabric Rattle. 2003. (Baby Einstein Ser.). (Illus.). 6p. (ps-ps). pap. 6.99 (978-0-7868-1904-1(9)) Hyperion Bks. for Children.

Albee, Sarah. Kidoozle Kids & the Great Color Chase! 2004. (Illus.). 12p. bds. 9.95 (978-1-932915-03-7(6)) Sandvik Publishing.

Alexander, Liza & Santomero, Angela C. Blue y Tu, Detective de Colores. Ziegler, Argentina Palacios, tr. Speer-Lyon, Tammie, illus. 2004. (Blue's Clues Ser.).Tr. of Blue & the Color Detectives. (SPA.). 24p. (J). pap. 3.99 (978-0-689-86979-2(7) , Libros Para Ninos) Simon & Schuster Children's Publishing.

Anderson, Dawn. I Am the Artist! Cunningham, Kelley, illus. 2006. (Rookie Reader Skill Set Ser.). 32p. (J). (gr. k-2). 19.50 (978-0-516-24976-6(2) , Children's Pr.) Scholastic Library Publishing.

Anderson, Dawn & Cunningham, Kelley. I Am the Artist! 2006. (Rookie Reader Ser.). (Illus.). 32p. (J). pap. 4.95 (978-0-516-24912-4(6) , Children's Pr.) Scholastic Library Publishing.

Anholt, Laurence. Matisse: The King of Color. 2007. (Anholt's Artists Books for Children Ser.). 32p. (J). (ps-3). 14.99 ***(*978-0-7641-6047-9(8))*** Barron's Educational Series, Inc.

Ardley, Neil & Challoner, Jack. Color. 2000. (J). (gr. 4-6). 11.00 (978-0-8172-9797-8(9)) Steck-Vaughn.

C D

Arma, Tom. Fruity Cutie Colors. 2004. (Illus.). 10p. (J). (ps-ps). bds. 5.95 (978-0-8109-5022-1(7)) Abrams, Harry N., Inc.

Arnosky, Jim. Mouse Colors: A Very First Book. Arnosky, Jim, illus. 2001. (Illus.). 48p. (J). (gr. k-ps). tchr. ed. 5.95 (978-0-618-01521-4(3), Clarion Bks.) Houghton Mifflin Co. Trade & Reference Div.

Aryal, Aimee. Hello Big Red! Craig, Megan, illus. 2004. (J). 19.95 (978-1-932888-24-9(1)) Mascot Bks., Inc.

Atwood, John H. & Atwood, Jenean D. Blue Spots: Yellow Spots! 2000. (Illus.). 32p. (J). (ps-3). pap. 7.99 (978-1-881524-80-9(9)) Milligan Bks., Inc.

Baker, Alan. Los Conejitos Aprenden los Colores. 2003. (Little Rabbit Bks.).Tr. of Little Rabbit's Color Book. (SPA.). 24p. (J). (gr. k-ps). pap. 4.95 (978-0-7534-5598-2(6), Kingfisher) Houghton Mifflin Co. Trade & Reference Div.

—Los Conejitos Aprenden los Colores. 2003. Tr. of Little Rabbit's Color Book. (SPA.). (gr. k-3). lib. bdg. 12.95 (978-0-613-88143-2(5)) Tandem Library Bks.

—White Rabbit's Color Book. 1999. (Little Rabbit Bks.). (Illus.). 24p. (J). (gr. k-ps). pap. 4.95 (978-0-7534-5254-7(5), Kingfisher) Houghton Mifflin Co. Trade & Reference Div.

Baker, Ryan. How I Would Paint the World? 2006. (ENG.). 48p. per. 15.95 (*978-1-59800-969-9(9)) Outskirts Press, Inc.

Bassede, Francine. George Paints His House. 1999. (Illus.). 32p. (J). (ps-1). pap. 14.95 (978-0-531-30150-0(8), Orchard Bks.) Scholastic, Inc.

Beinstein, Phoebe. Dora Explora Los Colores/Dora Explores Colors. Hall, Susan, illus. 2007. (Dora la Exploradora Ser.). (SPA.). 14p. (J). (ps). bds. 4.99 (*978-1-4169-4726-4(4), Libros Para Ninos) Simon & Schuster Children's Publishing.

Benevelli, Alberto. The Colors of the Chameleon. Serofilli, Loretta, illus. 2002. 32p. (J). (gr. k up). lib. bdg. 24.67 (978-0-8368-3042-2(3)) Stevens, Gareth Inc.

Bilgrami, Shaheen. A Magic Color Book: Jungle Art Show. Girouard, Patrick, illus. 2002. (Pinwheel Ser.). 10p. (J). (ps-k). 5.95 (978-1-4027-0206-8(X)) Sterling Publishing Co., Inc.

Blackaby, Susan. Winter Fun for Kat. Collier-Morales, Roberta, illus. 2005. (Read-It! Readers Ser.). 32p. (J). (gr. k-3). 18.60 (978-1-4048-1007-5(2)) Picture Window Bks.

Blackman, Andy. Miles the Crocodile Plays the Colors of Jazz: Baby Loves Jazz. Cunningham, Andrew, illus. 2006. 18p. (J). (ps-1). 7.99 (978-0-8431-2084-4(3), Price Stern Sloan) Penguin Group (USA) Inc.

Blackstone, Stella. Cleo's Color Book. Mockford, Caroline, illus. 2006. 0032p. (J). 15.99 (978-1-905236-30-5(1)) Barefoot Bks., Inc.

Blackstone, Stella & Harter, Debbie. Can You See Red Balloon. 2004. (Illus.). 32p. (J). pap. 6.99 (978-1-84148-788-5(0)) Barefoot Bks., Inc.

Blake, Michel. Colors. Blake, Michel, illus. 2006. (Illus.). 16p. (J). (gr. k-ps). bds. 5.99 (978-0-7636-2746-1(1)) Candlewick Pr.

Bonnell, Kris. Blue? 2005. (J). 3.75 (978-1-933727-01-1(2)) Reading Reading Bks., LLC.

—Dad's Favorite Tie. 2005. (J). 3.75 (978-1-933727-03-5(9)) Reading Reading Bks., LLC.

—Feathers. 2005. (J). 3.75 (978-1-933727-06-6(3)) Reading Reading Bks., LLC.

—Socks. 2005. (J). 3.75 (978-1-933727-15-8(2)) Reading Reading Bks., LLC.

—Soda Pop. 2005. (J). 3.75 (978-1-933727-16-5(0)) Reading Reading Bks., LLC.

Boynton, Sandra. Blue Hat, Green Hat. 2001. (Illus.). 8p. (J). bds. 4.99 (978-0-689-83625-1(2), Simon & Schuster Children's Publishing) Simon & Schuster Children's Publishing.

Bronn, Charles Heil. The Sun, the Moon, & the Gardener's Son. Kami, Y. Z., illus. 2006. 30p. (J). (gr. 4-12). reprint ed. 16.00 (978-1-4223-5222-9(6)) DIANE Publishing Co.

Brown, Margaret Wise. My World of Color. Krupinski, Loretta, illus. 2002. 32p. (ps-k). 15.99 (978-0-7868-0605-8(2)); 16.49 (978-0-7868-2519-6(7)) Hyperion Bks. for Children.

Bruna, Dick. Miffy & Friends: Blue-Green Coloring Book. 2004. (Illus.). 48p. pap. 5.99 (978-1-59226-096-6(9)) Big Tent Entertainment, Inc.

—Miffy & Friends: Yellow-Red Coloring Book. 2004. (Illus.). 48p. pap. 5.99 (978-1-59226-098-0(5)) Big Tent Entertainment, Inc.

Cabrera, Jane. Cat's Colors. Cabrera, Jane, illus. 2000. (Picture Puffin Ser.). (Illus.). 32p. (J). (ps-1). pap. 6.99 (978-0-14-056487-7(X), Puffin) Penguin Group (USA) Inc.

—Cat's Colors. 2000. (gr. k-3). lib. bdg. 15.30 (978-0-613-28438-7(0)); (Illus.). (J). 13.79 (978-0-606-18835-7(5)) Tandem Library Bks.

Campbell, Rod. Colour Bugs. 2003. (Illus.). 10p. (J). bds. 4.95 (978-0-333-73338-7(X)) Macmillan Publishers Ltd. GBR. Dist: Trafalgar Square Publishing.

Campdepadros, Jorgelina & Campdepadros, Eduardo. Coloreando con la Pandilla. 2001. (Pandilla; the Tree House Gang Ser.).Tr. of Coloring with the Tree House Gang. (SPA.). 32p. No. 1. pap. 2.99 (978-0-8254-0875-5(X)); Vol. 2. pap. 2.99 (978-0-8254-0876-2(8)); Vol. 3. pap. 2.99 (978-0-8254-0877-9(6)) Kregel Pubns. (Editorial Portavoz).

Care, Bears. Caring Bears: Caring Colors. 2008. 5p. bds. 5.99 (*978-0-545-00653-8(8), Scholastic) Scholastic, Inc.

Carle, Eric. Hello Red Fox. (J). (gr. k-3). 2000. (Illus.). 26p. per. (978-0-689-83492-9(6)); 1998. per. (978-0-689-00581-7(4)) Simon & Schuster Children's Publishing. (Simon & Schuster Children's Publishing).

—Hello Red Fox. Carle, Eric & Beneduce, Ann, illus. 1998. 32p. (J). (ps-3). 19.95 (978-0-689-81775-5(4)) Simon & Schuster Children's Publishing.

—Hello, Red Fox. Carle, Eric, illus. 2001. (Illus.). 32p. (J). pap. 8.99 (978-0-689-84431-7(X), Aladdin) Simon & Schuster Children's Publishing.

Catalanotto, Peter. Kitten Red, Yellow, Blue. Catalanotto, Peter, illus. 2005. (Illus.). 32p. (J). 15.95 (978-0-689-86562-6(7), Atheneum/Richard Jackson Bks.) Simon & Schuster Children's Publishing.

Chesworth, Michael. Colors. Holmes, Stephen, illus. 1999. (Touch & Feel Surprises Ser.: 5). 12p. (ps-k). pap. 6.95 (978-0-7613-0979-6(9), Millbrook Pr.) Lerner Publishing Group.

Clark, Emma Chichester. The Wild Moon Child. 2008. (Illus.). 32p. (J). 16.95 (*978-1-84270-577-3(6)) Andersen GBR. Dist: Independent Pubs. Group.

Color Board Books 800595, 4. 2005. (J). bds. (978-1-59794-034-4(8)) Environments, Inc.

Color Me Peace, 5 vols., Vol. 1. 2000. 16p. (J). pap. (978-1-931416-00-9(1)) Each One Reach One Child, Inc.

Color zoo - tummy Time. 2007. 8p. (J). 12.95 (*978-1-59764-294-1(0)) New Line Bks.

Coloring Fun: Coloring/Activity Book (English) 2006. (Illus.). (J). (*978-1-933934-20-4(4)) Educational Adventures.

Coloring Fun: Coloring/Activity Book (Spanish) 2006. (Illus.). (J). (*978-1-933934-21-1(2)) Educational Adventures.

Coloring Fun: English/Spanish. 2006. (Illus.). (J). (*978-1-933934-24-2(7)) Educational Adventures.

Colors All Day. (J). 26.20 (978-0-8136-8399-7(8)); 59.50 (978-0-8136-7918-1(4)); 1998. pap. (978-0-8136-8292-1(4)) Modern Curriculum Pr.

Colors, Colors Everywhere. 2000. (Point & Peek Books Ser.). (Illus.). 6p. (J). (ps-1). bds. (978-1-57584-363-6(3)) Reader's Digest Children's Publishing, Inc.

Colors of Rainbow Meadow. 1998. (Fisher-Price Hideaway Hollow Padded Board Bks.). (Illus.). 16p. (J). (gr. 1). bds. (978-0-7666-0115-4(3), Honey Bear Bks.) Modern Publishing.

Cookie's Color Caper. 2005. (J). (978-1-59292-029-7(2)) SoftPlay, Inc.

Coulton, Mia. Danny Likes Red. Coulton, Mia, photos by. 2003. (J). 4.95 (978-0-9720295-2-0(4)) Maryruth Bks., Inc.

Cousineau-Peiffer, Trisha. Have You Ever Heard of a Rainbow Farm. Everett-Hawkes, Bonnie, illus. 2006. 32p. (J). 12.95 (*978-0-9792084-1-6(6)) Dream Ridge Pr.

—Have You Ever Heard of a Rainbow Farm: The Missing Color Kittens. Everett-Hawkes, Bonnie, illus. 2007. 48p. (J). per. 15.95 (*978-0-9792084-2-3(4)) Dream Ridge Pr.

Cousins, Lucy. Los Colores de Maisy. 2001. (Illus.). (J). (ps). (CAT.). 16p. 10.95 (978-84-95040-60-2(3)); (SPA., 24p. 15.95 (978-84-95040-75-6(1), RR7142) Serres, Ediciones, S. L. ESP. Dist: Lectorum Pubns., Inc., Lectorum Pubns., Inc., Libros Sin Fronteras.

—Las Cosas Favoritas de Maisy. 2000. (Maisy Bks.).Tr. of Maisy's Favorite Things. (SPA., Illus.). 16p. (J). (ps). 8.95 (978-84-95040-12-1(3)) Lectorum Pubns., Inc.

—Maisy's Color Collection. Cousins, Lucy, illus. 2005. (Illus.). 14p. (J). (gr. k-k). 6.99 (978-0-7636-2656-3(2)) Candlewick Pr.

—Maisy's Colors. Cousins, Lucy, illus. 2nd ed. 1999. (Maisy Bks.). (Illus.). 24p. (J). (gr. k-ps). bds. 5.99 (978-0-7636-0237-6(X)) Candlewick Pr.

—Maisy's Rainbow Dream. Cousins, Lucy, illus. 2003. (Maisy Ser.). (Illus.). 32p. (J). (ps up). 16.99 (978-0-7636-2195-7(1)) Candlewick Pr.

Cyr, Joe. Magical Trees & Crayons: Great Stories. 2006. (Illus.). pap. 9.95 (*978-0-9778525-6-7(3)) Peppertree Pr., The.

Davis, Caroline, illus. My Toys. 2007. 12p. (J). (ps). bds. 6.95 (*978-1-58925-825-9(8), tiger tales) ME Media LLC.

Davis, Caroline, illus. Swish, Swish, Who's This? 2002. 20p. (J). 5.95 (978-1-58925-686-6(7), tiger tales) ME Media LLC.

Davis, Guy. Witzy's Colors. Spafford, Suzy, illus. 2001. (Little Suzy's Zoo Ser.). 12p. (J). (ps-k). pap. 5.99 (978-1-58668-055-8(2)) Lyrick Studios.

de Brunhoff, Laurent. Babar's Book of Color. 2004. (Illus.). 32p. (J). (ps-1). 17.95 (978-0-8109-4840-2(0)) Abrams, Harry N., Inc.

de Paola, Tomie. Marcus Colors: Red, Yellow & Blue. 2003. (SPA., Illus.). 14p. (J). (ps-1). bds. 5.99 (978-0-399-24010-2(1), Putnam Juvenile) Penguin Group (USA) Inc.

Delval, Marie-Helene. A Gallinita le Gustan los Colores. Courtin, Thierry, illus. 2002. (Palabras Menudas Ser.).Tr. of Little Chicken Likes Colors. (SPA.). 14p. (ps). 5.95 (978-84-7864-514-5(4)) Combel Editorial, S.A. ESP. Dist: Independent Pubs. Group.

Desmazières, Sandra. Emma & Her Friends: A Book about Colors. 2006. (Illus.). 28p. (J). lib. bdg. (978-0-8368-6997-2(4)) Stevens, Gareth Inc.

Dorling Kindersley Publishing Staff. Colorful Day. 2003. (ps-2). lib. bdg. 11.80 (978-0-613-75173-5(6)) Tandem Library Bks.

—Colorful Days. 2003. (Readers Ser.). (Illus.). (J). 32p. 12.99 (978-0-7894-9798-7(0)); 1p. pap. 3.99 (978-0-7894-9799-4(9)) Dorling Kindersley Publishing, Inc.

Dorling Kindersley Publishing Staff, ed. Dias Coloridos. 2004. (Dk Readers Ser.).Tr. of Colorful Days. (SPA.). 32p. (J). 12.99 (978-0-7566-0638-1(1)) Dorling Kindersley Publishing, Inc.

Dowling, Paul. Sally's Amazing Colour Book. 1999. (Illus.). 32p. (J). 17.99 (978-0-86264-801-5(7)) Andersen GBR. Dist: Independent Pubs. Group.

Dumont, Jean-Francois. A Blue So Blue. 2005. (Illus.). 32p. 14.95 (978-1-4027-2139-7(0)) Sterling Publishing Co., Inc.

Dunbar, Polly. Dog Blue. Dunbar, Polly, illus. 2004. (Illus.). 40p. (J). (gr. k-k). 14.99 (978-0-7636-2476-7(4)) Candlewick Pr.

—Flyaway Katie. Dunbar, Polly, illus. 2004. (Illus.). 40p. (J). (gr. k-k). 14.99 (978-0-7636-2366-1(0)) Candlewick Pr.

Dupasquier, Philippe. Blue. 2004. (Illus.). 32p. (J). pap. 8.99 (*978-1-84270-436-3(2)) Andersen GBR. Dist: Independent Pubs. Group.

Edwards, Pamela Duncan. Warthogs Paint: A Messy Color Book. Cole, Henry, illus. 2001. 32p. (ps-4). 15.49 (978-0-7868-2412-0(3)) Hyperion Bks. for Children.

Ehlert, Lois. Planting a Rainbow. Ehlert, Lois, illus. 2003. (Illus.). 32p. (J). bds. 6.95 (978-0-15-204633-0(X), Red Wagon Bks.) Harcourt Children's Bks.

Ehlert, Lois. Planting a Rainbow: Lap-Sized Board Book. 2008. (Illus.). 32p. (J). bds. 10.95 (*978-0-15-206304-7(8), Red Wagon Bks.) Harcourt Children's Bks.

Emberley, Rebecca. My Shapes, My Colors, My Numbers, My Animals. 2005. (J). bds. 24.92 (978-0-316-05781-3(9)) Little Brown & Co.

Ericsson, Jennifer A. A Piece of Chalk. Shapiro, Michelle, illus. rev. ed. 2007. 32p. (J). (ps-3). 16.95 (*978-1-59643-057-0(5)) Roaring Brook Pr.

Feiffer, Kate. Double Pink. Ingman, Bruce, illus. 2005. 32p. (J). 15.95 (978-0-689-87190-0(2), Simon & Schuster Children's Publishing) Simon & Schuster Children's Publishing.

Ficocelli, Elizabeth. Kid Tea. Dibley, Glin, illus. 2007. 40p. (J). (ps-2). 14.99 (978-0-7614-5333-8(4)) Cavendish, Marshall Corp.

Finale, Frank. A Gull's Story, Part 3: Colors at the Shore. Moore, Margie, illus. 2007. (J). 22.00 (*978-0-9777077-2-0(5)) Jersey Shore Pubns.

Fontes, Justine. Black Meets White. Waring, Geoff, illus. 2005. 24p. (J). (gr. k-ps). 12.99 (978-0-7636-1933-6(7)) Candlewick Pr.

Fox, Diane. What Color Is That, Piggywiggy? Fox, Christyan, illus. 2001. 10p. (J). (ps-k). 5.95 (978-1-929766-17-8(3)) Handprint Bks.

Fremont, Eleanor. Colors with Oswald. Schigiel, Gregg, illus. 2004. (Oswald Ser.). 22p. (J). bds. 4.99 (978-0-689-86483-4(3), Simon Spotlight/Nickelodeon) Simon & Schuster Children's Publishing.

Freymann, Saxton & Elffers, Joost. Gus & Button. Freymann, Saxton & Elffers, Joost, illus. 2001. (Illus.). 40p. (J). pap. 15.95 (978-0-439-11015-0(7), Levine, Arthur A. Bks.) Scholastic, Inc.

Furgang, Kathy. A una fiesta de colores & Rainbow Party. 2005. spiral bd. 66.00 (*978-1-4108-5645-6(3)) Benchmark Education Co.

Futterer, Kurt. Emile. Gray, Bronwen et al, trs. from GER. Futterer, Ralf, illus. 2004. (J). 17.95 (978-1-931561-95-2(8)) MacAdam/Cage Publishing, Inc.

Garcia, Marc Khayam, illus. Color Me & My Pals: The Adventures of Billy Butterfly' Coloring Book. 2003. (J). 3.95 (978-0-9747628-3-8(0)) BKB Group, Inc., The.

Genechten, Guido van. Porque Te Quiero Tanto. 2003. (SPA., Illus.). 28p. (J). (gr. k-3). 15.95 (978-970-29-0912-5(0)) Santillana USA Publishing Co., Inc.

Gill, Janie S. The Red Magic Marker. 1999. 23p. (J). 5.95 (978-0-89868-530-5(3)); pap. 3.95 (978-0-89868-529-9(X)); lib. bdg. 10.95 (978-0-89868-528-2(1)) ARO Publishing Co.

Glaser, Byron. Hello Kitty, Hello Color! Higashi, Sandra, photos by. 2006. (Illus.). 23p. (J). (ps-3). reprint ed. 13.00 (978-1-4223-5491-9(1)) DIANE Publishing Co.

Godwin, Laura. Little White Dog. 2000. (ps-2). lib. bdg. 14.15 (978-0-613-31428-2(X)) Tandem Library Bks.

—The Little White Dog. Yaccarino, Dan, illus. 2000. 32p. (ps-k). pap. 5.99 (978-0-7868-1515-9(9)) Disney Pr.

Golden Books Staff. Best Loved Little Golden Books 6 Copy Boxed Set, Set. 2005. (Illus.). 24p. (J). (ps-3). 17.94 (978-0-375-83394-6(3), Golden Bks.) Random Hse. Children's Bks.

—Can We Color It? Yes We Can! 2006. (Illus.). 48p. (J). (ps-2). pap. 3.99 (978-0-375-83480-6(X), Golden Bks.) Random Hse. Children's Bks.

—Fun with Colors & Shapes. 2000. (Disney Ser.). (Illus.). 48p. (J). (ps-k). pap. 2.99 (978-0-307-20132-4(5), 20132, Golden Bks.) Random Hse. Children's Bks.

—Halloween Coloring Book. 2006. (Illus.). 80p. (J). (ps-2). pap. 5.99 (978-0-375-83627-5(6), Golden Bks.) Random Hse. Children's Bks.

—It's a Colorful World. 2000. (Illus.). 48p. (J). (ps-3). pap. 3.99 (978-0-307-25217-3(5), 25217, Golden Bks.) Random Hse. Children's Bks.

—Little Chef. 2007. (Deluxe Coloring Book Ser.). (Illus.). 96p. (J). (ps-2). pap. 3.99 (978-0-7364-2447-9(4), Golden/Disney) Random Hse. Children's Bks.

Gonzalez, Maya Christina. My Colors, My World/Mis Colores, Mi Mundo. 2007. (ENG & SPA., Illus.). 24p. (J). (ps-3). 16.95 (*978-0-89239-221-6(5)) Children's Bk. Pr.

Goobie, Beth. The Colours of Carol Molev. 1998. 198p. (YA). (gr. 9-12). pap. 9.95 (978-1-896184-40-1(5)) Roussan Pubs., Inc./Roussan Editeur, Inc. CAN. Dist: Orca Bk. Pubs. USA.

Gorbachev, Valeri. Red Red Red. Gorbachev, Valeri, illus. 2007. 40p. (J). (ps-3). 16.99 (978-0-399-24628-9(2), Philomel) Penguin Group (USA) Inc.

Gregory, Nan. Pink. Melanson, Luc, illus. 2007. 32p. (J). (ps-2). 17.95 (*978-0-88899-781-4(7)) Groundwood Bks. CAN. Dist: Perseus Distribution.

Grindley, Sally. Silly Goose & Dizzy Duck & the Colorful Day. Reynolds, Adrian, illus. 2001. (Toddlers Ser.). 24p. (J). (ps). pap. 5.95 (978-0-7894-7860-3(9), D K Ink) Dorling Kindersley Publishing, Inc.

Gunzi, Christina. Pretty in Pink: My Day. 2007. (Illus.). 10p. (J). bds. 6.95 (*978-1-59223-755-5(X), Silver Dolphin Bks.) Advantage Pubs. Group.

—Pretty in Pink: My Things. 2007. (Illus.). 10p. (J). bds. 6.95 (*978-1-59223-756-2(8), Silver Dolphin Bks.) Advantage Pubs. Group.

Guy, Ginger Foglesong. Siesta. Moreno, Rene King, illus. 2005. (ENG & SPA.). 32p. (J). (ps-1). 15.99 (978-0-06-056061-4(4)) HarperCollins Pubs.

Halligan, Jim & Newman, John. Seeing Red. 2003. 176p. pap. 6.95 (978-0-86327-903-4(1)) Wolfhound Pr. IRL. Dist: Interlink Publishing Group, Inc.

Hands on Crafts for Kids Staff. Invisible Magic Coloring Book. 2002. (Fun House Paperbacks Ser.). (Illus.). 72p. pap. 2.95 (978-0-8069-8955-6(6)) Sterling Publishing Co., Inc.

Hapka, Catherine. Astro Boy Color, Bk. 1. Merkel, Joe F., illus. 2004. (Astro Boy Ser.). 32p. (J). pap., act. bk. ed. 4.99 (978-0-06-072522-8(2), Harper Festival) HarperCollins Pubs.

—Astro Boy Color & Sticker Book, Bk. 2. Farley, Rick, illus. 2004. (Astro Boy Ser.). 32p. (J). pap. 4.99 (978-0-06-072523-5(0), Harper Festival) HarperCollins Pubs.

Harper, Charise Mericle. Amy & Ivan: What's in That Truck? 2006. (Illus.). 24p. (J). 12.95 (978-1-58246-134-2(1), Tricycle Pr.) Ten Speed Pr.

Harrison, Carlos. Ruben's Rainbow (El Arco Iris de Ruben) Paz, Grizelle, illus. 2001. (ENG & SPA.). 15.95 incl. audio compact disk (978-0-9706953-0-7(6)) Globo Libros.

Harshman, Marc & Ryan, Cheryl. Red Are the Apples. Zahares, Wade, illus. 32p. (J). 2007. pap. 6.00 (*978-0-15-206065-7(0), Voyager Bks./Libros Viajeros); 2001. 17.00 (978-0-15-201917-4(0)) Harcourt Children's Bks.

Hassett, John & Hassett, Ann. Father Sun, Mother Moon. 2001. (Illus.). 32p. (J). (gr. k-3). tchr. ed. 16.00 (978-0-395-97565-7(4), Walter Lorraine) Houghton Mifflin Co. Trade & Reference Div.

Heller, Nicholas. Goblins in Green. Smith, Jos. A., illus. 1999. 32p. (J). (ps-3). pap. 4.95 (978-0-688-17058-5(7), Harper Trophy) HarperCollins Pubs.

Hester, Lyn. Mary Lou Likes Blue. Johnson, Matthew James, illus. 1998. 46p. (J). pap. 10.95 (978-0-9676006-1-1(8)) Marketing Dynamics, Inc.

Hicks, Barbara Jean. I Like Black & White. Prap, Lila, illus. 2006. 32p. (J). 9.95 (978-1-58925-056-7(7), tiger tales) ME Media LLC.

Hill, Eric. Spot's Colors, Shapes, & Numbers. Hill, Eric, illus. 2007. 18p. (J). (ps-k). bds. 12.99 (*978-0-399-24779-8(3), Putnam Juvenile) Penguin Group (USA) Inc.

Hillert, Margaret. I Like Things. (J). 4.95 (978-0-87895-683-8(2)) Modern Curriculum Pr.

Hobbie, Nathaniel. Priscilla & the Pink Planet. Hobbie, Jocelyn, illus. 2008. 32p. (J). (ps-1). pap. 6.99 (978-0-316-11349-6(2)) Little Brown & Co.

—Priscilla & the Pink Planet. Hobbie, Jocelyn, illus. 2004. 32p. (J). (ps-1). 15.99 (978-0-316-73579-7(5)) Little, Brown Bks. for Young Readers.

Hoffman, Eric. Best Colors (Los Mejores Colores) de la Vega, Eida, tr. Henriquez, Celeste, illus. 2004. (Anti-Bias Books for Kids). (ENG & SPA.). 32p. (J). (ps-3). pap. 11.95 (978-1-884834-69-1(8), 709201) Redleaf Pr.

Hopkins, Jane. Diving for Colors in Hawaii: A Color Identification Book for Keiki. Bosgra, Johann, illus. 2003. 18p. (J). bds. 6.95 (978-0-9729905-1-6(8)) Beachhouse Publishing, LLC.

Horacek, Petr. What's Black & White? Horacek, Petr, illus. 2001. (Illus.). 14p. (J). (gr. k-k). bds. 4.99 (978-0-7636-1460-7(2)) Candlewick Pr.

Houghton Mifflin Company Editors. Curious George Discovery Day. 2007. (Illus.). 14p. (J). (gr. k-ps). bds. 13.95 (*978-0-618-73761-1(8)) Houghton Mifflin Co. Trade & Reference Div.

Howard-Parham, Pam. Caillou Finds Colors. Gillen, Lisa P., illus. l.t. ed. 2005. (Hrl Board Book Ser.). (J). (ps-k). bds. 10.95 (978-1-57332-313-0(6)) HighReach Learning, Inc.

Hubbard, Patricia. My Crayons Talk. Karas, G. Brian, illus. rev. ed. 1999. 32p. (J). (ps-2). pap. 7.95 (978-0-8050-6150-5(9), Holt, Henry & Co. Bks. For Young Readers) Holt, Henry & Co.

—My Crayons Talk. 1999. (gr. k-3). lib. bdg. 15.25 (978-0-613-17831-0(9)) Tandem Library Bks.

Humu the Little Fish Who Wished Away His Colors. 2003. (J). 10.99 (978-0-89610-548-5(2)) Island Heritage Publishing.

I Love Birds. 2004. (Illus.). 26p. (J). lib. bdg. 12.95 (978-0-9748165-0-0(7)) Jaylil Publishing Co.

Jones, Miranda. Little Genie: A Puff of Pink. Calver, David, tr. Calver, David, illus. 2004. 128p. (gr. 1-3). lib. bdg. 10.99 (978-0-385-90188-8(7), Delacorte Bks. for Young Readers) Random Hse. Children's Bks.

Joyce, Bill. Little Spot of Color. 2000. (Rolie Polie Olie Ser.). (Illus.). 18p. (ps). 5.99 (978-0-7868-3319-1(X)) Disney Pr.

Kane, Tracy. The Magic of Color. Kane, Tracy, illus. l.t. ed. 2005. (Illus.). 40p. (J). (gr. 1-3). 17.95 (978-0-9766289-0-3(2)) Light-Beams Publishing.

Kann, Elizabeth. Purplicious. Kann, Victoria, illus. 2007. 40p. (J). lib. bdg. 17.89 (*978-0-06-124406-3(6)) HarperCollins Pubs.

Kann, Elizabeth & Kann, Victoria. Pinkalicious. Kann, Victoria, illus. 2006. (Illus.). 40p. (J). 16.99 (978-0-06-077639-8(0)); lib. bdg. 16.89 (978-0-06-077640-4(4)) HarperCollins Pubs.

Kann, Elizabeth & Kann, Victoria. Purplicious. Kann, Victoria, illus. 2007. 40p. (J). (gr. k-3). 16.99 (*978-0-06-124405-6(8)) HarperCollins Pubs.

Kidd, Ron. Bookee Presents Colors, Shapes & Sounds. Nord, Mary, illus. (Talking Book Adventures Ser.). 12p. (J). (ps up). 16.95 (978-0-9627001-1-8(8)) Futech Educational Products, Inc.

Kochalka, James. Squirrelly Gray. 2007. (Picture Book Ser.). (Illus.). 40p. (J). (gr. k-2). 12.99 (***978-0-375-83975-7(5)**); lib. bdg. 15.99 (***978-0-375-93975-4(X)**) Random Hse. Children's Bks. (Random Hse. Bks. for Young Readers).

Koontz, Robin. Creepy Crawly Colors. Koontz, Robin, illus. 2006. (Illus.). 14p. (J). 10.95 (978-1-4169-0707-7(6) , Little Simon) Simon & Schuster Children's Publishing.

Kroll, Virginia L. & Jones, Dawn L. Kingston's Flowering Forest. Maydak, Michael S., illus. 2001. (J). (978-0-9712840-5-0(9)) Boyds Collection Ltd., The.

Learning Colors. 1999. (Illus.). (J). (978-1-56156-835-2(X)) Kidsbooks, Inc.

Lee, Quinlan B. Rainbow Brite: Sparkling Star Sprinkles. Albrecht, Jeff, illus. 2004. (Rainbow Brite Ser.). 25p. (J). (gr. k). 3.99 (978-0-439-66321-2(0)) Scholastic, Inc.

—True Colors. Langer S.L., Jutta, illus. 2005. (Rainbow Brite Ser.). 12p. (J). (ps-ps). pap. 8.99 (978-0-439-74417-1(2)) Scholastic, Inc.

—Twink & the Sprites. Langer, Jutta, illus. 2004. (Rainbow Brite Ser.). 33p. (J). (ps-3). pap. 3.99 (978-0-439-68114-8(6)) Scholastic, Inc.

Lembcke, Marjaleena & Martínez, Eduardo. Tiempo de Secretos. Steffens, Klaus & Martínez, Eduardo, trs. Steffens, Klaus, illus. 2002. (SPA.). 144p. (978-84-89804-58-6(3)) Loguez Ediciones ESP. *Dist:* Lectorum Pubns., Inc.

Lewis, Bisa, as told by. How Flowers Get Their Colors. 2005. (J). (978-0-9745469-9-5(2)) Ashley & Taylor Publishing, Co.

Lionni, Leo. A Color of His Own. Lionni, Leo, illus. 2002. (Illus.). (J). 14.79 (978-0-7587-5604-6(6)) Book Wholesalers, Inc.

—A Color of His Own. Boughton, Simon, ed. Lionni, Leo, illus. 2000. (Illus.). 30p. (J). (gr. k-ps). bds. 6.99 (978-0-375-81091-6(9) , Knopf Bks. for Young Readers) Random Hse. Children's Bks.

—A Color of His Own. 2006. 40p. (J). (gr. k-1). lib. bdg. 14.99 (978-0-375-93697-5(1)); (Illus.). reprint ed. 12.95 (978-0-375-83697-8(7)) Random Hse. Children's Bks. (Knopf Bks. for Young Readers).

—Little Blue & Little Yellow. Lionni, Leo, illus. 2002. (Illus.). (J). 15.49 (978-0-7587-5660-2(7)) Book Wholesalers, Inc.

Lluch, Alex. Do I Look Good in Color? 2006. 30p. bds. 7.95 (978-1-887169-57-8(1)) Wedding Solutions Publishing, Inc.

Lovejoy, Sharon. The Little Green Island with a Little Red House: A Book of Colors & Critters. 2005. (Illus.). 32p. 9.95 (978-0-89272-673-8(3)) Down East Bks.

Lucado, Max. Colors. 2004. (Buginnings Ser.: Vol. 2). (Illus.). 24p. (J). 9.99 (978-1-4003-0422-6(9)) Nelson, Thomas Inc.

Lukas, Catherine & Cosby, Bill. Super Detective Little Bill: A Dial-the-Answer Book. Mastrocinque, Andy, illus. 2002. (Little Bill Ser.). 14p. (J). 8.99 (978-0-689-84200-9(7) , Simon Spotlight/Nickelodeon) Simon & Schuster Children's Publishing.

Lumley, Jemima. The Journey Home from Grandpa's. Fatus, Sophie, illus. 2006. 24p. (J). (978-1-905236-37-4(9)) Barefoot Bks., Inc.

Luna Rising Staff, ed. Elmo's Guessing Game about Colors. 2006. (SPA & ENG., Illus.). 12p. (J). 5.95 (978-0-87358-905-5(X) , Luna Rising) Northland Publishing.

Lunablau, Jani. Little Snowflake. 2006. (Illus.). 32p. (J). 14.95 (978-1-59692-139-9(0)) MacAdam/Cage Publishing, Inc.

Martin, Bill, Jr. A Beasty Story. Kellogg, Steven, illus. 2002. 40p. (J). (gr. k-2). pap. 7.00 (978-0-15-216560-4(6) , Voyager Bks./Libros Viajeros) Harcourt Children's Bks.

—A Beasty Story. Kellogg, Steven, illus. 1999. 40p. (J). (ps-2). 17.00 (978-0-15-201683-8(X) , Silver Whistle) Harcourt Trade Pubs.

Martin, Bill. Beasty Story. 2002. (gr. k-3). lib. bdg. 15.30 (978-0-613-53796-4(3)) Tandem Library Bks.

Martin, Bill, Jr. Brown Bear, Brown Bear, What Do You See? 2002. (Illus.). (J). 26.49 (978-0-7587-2157-0(9)) Book Wholesalers, Inc.

Martin, Bill. Oso Pardo, Oso Pardo, ¿Qué Ves Ahí? Mlawer, Teresa, tr. Carle, Eric, illus. rev. ed. 2002. (SPA.). 28p. (J). (ps-k). bds. 7.95 (978-0-8050-6901-3(1) , Holt, Henry & Co. Bks. For Young Readers) Holt, Henry & Co.

Martinez, Rocio. Matias y el Color del Cielo. 2002. (SPA.). 36p. (J). (978-980-257-262-5(4)) Ekare, Ediciones.

McDunn, Linda L. The Color of Me. Knutson, Barbara, illus. 2005. 32p. (J). 16.95 (978-0-8146-2952-9(0)) Liturgical Pr.

McKay, Sindy. We Both Read-Too Many Cats. Johnson, Meredith, illus. 2003. (We Both Read Ser.). 44p. (J). (gr. k up). 7.99 (978-1-891327-49-0(6)); pap. 3.99 (978-1-891327-50-6(X)) Treasure Bay, Inc.

McKee, David. Elmer's Colours. 2004. (Elmer Ser.). (Illus.). 16p. (J). (ENG & ITA.). bds. 6.95 (978-1-84059-396-9(2)); (ENG & SOM., bds. 6.95 (978-1-84059-397-6(0)); (ARA & ENG., bds. 6.95 (978-1-84059-395-2(4)); (ENG, URD, TUR, VIE & SPA., bds. 6.95 (978-1-84059-055-5(6)); (ENG, URD, TUR, VIE & SPA., bds. 6.95 (978-1-84059-056-2(4)); (ENG, URD, TUR, VIE & SPA., bds. 6.95 (978-1-84059-059-3(9)); (ENG, TUR, URD, VIE & SPA., bds. 6.95 (978-1-84059-060-9(2)); (ENG, URD, TUR, VIE & SPA., bds. 6.95 (978-1-84059-057-9(2)); (VIE, ENG, URD, TUR & SPA., bds. 6.95 (978-1-84059-061-6(0)) Milet Publishing.

—Elmer's Colours. Pullin, Beatriz, tr. 2004. (Elmers Ser.). (ENG, URD, TUR, VIE & CHI., Illus.). 16p. (J). bds. 6.95 (978-1-84059-058-6(0)) Milet Publishing.

Meade, David. Colors & Caring. Byers, Brian, illus. 2005. 14p. (J). (gr. k-5). bds. 6.95 (978-1-59125-520-8(1)) Penton Overseas, Inc.

Meet the Colors Board Book. 2007. (J). bds. 7.99 (***978-0-9770215-5-0(6)**) KRO Publishing.

Meet the Colors Lift the Flap Book. 2007. (J). bds. 9.99 (***978-0-9770215-4-3(8)**) KRO Publishing.

Miller, Margaret. I Love Colors, Vol. 1. Miller, Margaret, illus. 1999. (Look Baby Books Ser.). (Illus.). 14p. (J). (gr. k-3). 6.99 (978-0-689-82356-5(8) , 076714004993, Little Simon) Simon & Schuster Children's Publishing.

Mitter, Matt. Hungry Monsters: A Book about Colors. Brown, Jo, illus. 2008. 10p. (J). 7.99 (***978-0-7944-1305-7(6)**) Reader's Digest Assn., Inc., The.

Mitzo Thompson, Kim. Green, Green Froggy. 2006. (Dual Language Readers Ser.). 32p. (J). pap., pap. 4.99 incl. audio compact disk (978-0-7696-4612-1(3)) School Specialty Publishing.

Moo's Colors. 2002. bds. (978-0-89610-477-8(X)) Island Heritage Publishing.

Munsch, Robert N. Purple, Green & Yellow. Desputeaux, Helene, illus. 2007. (Annikins Ser.). 32p. (J). (ps-2). pap. 1.50 (***978-1-55451-113-6(5)**) Annick Pr., Ltd. CAN. *Dist:* Firefly Bks., Ltd.

My First Gators Book. 2004. (J). bds. 8.95 (978-0-9754317-0-2(6)) JEM Bks., Inc.

My First Hurricanes Book. 2004. (J). bds. 8.95 (978-0-9754317-2-6(2)) JEM Bks., Inc.

Nelson, Sherrie. The Boy of Color. Cantrell, Jaquese, illus. 2006. 32p. (J). 12.99 (978-1-4003-0910-8(7)) Nelson, Thomas Inc.

Nettrour, Nelani. The Dragon Lands Bk. 1: The Ripple. Nettrour, Heather, illus. 2003. 100p. pap. 11.95 (978-1-929381-46-3(8) , Third Millennium Publishing) Sci Fi-Arizona, Inc.

Pan, Hui-Mei. What's in Grandma's Grocery Bag?/¿Qué hay en la bolsa de Abuelita? 2004. (ENG & SPA., Illus.). 16p. (J). bds. 5.95 (978-1-932065-12-1(1)) Star Bright Bks., Inc.

Pan, Hui-Mei, illus. What's in Grandma's Grocery Bag? 2004. 16p. (J). bds. 5.95 (978-1-887734-97-4(X)) Star Bright Bks., Inc.

Park, Linda Sue. What Does Bunny See? A Book of Colors & Flowers. Smith, Maggie, illus. 2005. 32p. (J). (ps-k). 15.00 (978-0-618-23485-1(3) , Clarion Bks.) Houghton Mifflin Co. Trade & Reference Div.

Parr, Todd. ToddWorld: It's a Colorful World! 2006. (Illus.). 10p. (J). (ps-3). bds., bds. 8.99 (978-0-316-05708-0(8)) Little, Brown Bks. for Young Readers.

Paterson, Brian. The Picnic: Board Book. 2006. (Illus.). 16p. (J). (ps). bds. 6.99 (978-0-00-717421-8(7)) HarperCollins Pubs. Ltd. GBR. *Dist:* Trafalgar Square Publishing.

Patterson, Christine. Conversation in the Crayon Box. 2004. 12p. (J). per. 9.33 (978-1-4116-0672-2(8)) Lulu.com.

Paulsen, Gary. Crayons. unabr. ed. 2000. (J). pap. 23.00 incl. audio (978-0-8072-8688-3(5) , YA236SP, Listening Library) Random Hse. Audio Publishing Group.

Pelham, David. Applebee's Colors. 2006. (Illus.). 16p. (J). 12.95 (978-0-7624-2647-8(0) , Running Pr.) Running Pr. Bk. Pubs.

—Applebee's Shapes. 2006. (Illus.). 16p. (J). 12.95 (978-0-7624-2648-5(9) , Running Pr.) Running Pr. Bk. Pubs.

Piggot, Dawn. Gregory & the Magic Line. (Illus.). 32p. (J). pap. 9.99 (978-1-84255-278-0(3)) Dolphin Paperbacks GBR. *Dist:* Trafalgar Square Publishing.

Pinkney, Sandra L. A Rainbow All Around Me. Pinkney, Myles C., illus. 2002. 40p. (J). (ps-1). pap. 15.95 (978-0-439-30928-8(X) , Cartwheel Bks.) Scholastic, Inc.

Powers, Christine. Love Is a Rainbow. 1999. (Leap Frog Lift-A-Flap Ser.). (Illus.). (J). (978-0-7853-3370-8(3)) Publications International, Ltd.

Propaganda, Amanda. People Flavors. 2006. (J). 6.00 (978-1-60149-000-1(3)) Punkin Pr.

Punnett, Dick. Name Lizzy's Colors: A Talk-along Book. Punnett, Yvonne, ed. 2nd ed. 2005. (Talk-Along Bks.). (Illus.). 32p. (J). pap. 6.99 (978-0-9657211-6-5(7)) Tomoka Pr.

Rabe, Tish. I'm a Baby: A Mix & Match Book. Larranaga, Ana, illus. 2006. 14p. (J). (ps-ps). bds. 9.99 (978-1-58476-355-0(8) , IKIDS) Innovative Kids.

Rainbow of Colors. 2003. (J). per. (978-1-57657-952-7(2)) Paradise Pr., Inc.

Rainbow Town: Individual Title Six-Packs. (Sails Literacy Ser.). 16p. (gr. k up). 27.00 (978-0-7635-4441-6(8)) Rigby Education.

Raintree Steck-Vaughn Staff, contrib. by. Planting a Rainbow. 1999. (J). (ps-3). pap. 22.00 (978-0-8172-9787-9(1)) Steck-Vaughn.

Random House Disney Staff. Pooh Colors. Hahn, Rebecca, illus. 2007. (Pooh Thinkables Ser.). 12p. (J). (gr. k-k). bds. 8.99 (978-0-7364-2457-8(1) , RH/Disney) Random Hse. Children's Bks.

Rappa, Desiree & Brian, illus. Big Red. 2003. (J). 4.95 (978-0-9722027-0-1(6)) Covered Bridge Bks.

Rathmell, Donna & Rathmell, Doreen. Octavia Octopus & Her Purple Ink Cloud. McLennan, Connie, illus. 2006. 32p. (J). 15.95 (978-0-9764943-5-5(3)) Sylvan Dell Pubng.

Rau, Dana Meachen. Lots of Balloons, Level A. 2001. (Early Reader Ser.). (Illus.). 24p. (J). (gr. k up), lib. bdg. 18.60 (978-0-7565-0117-4(2)) Compass Point Bks.

—Purple Is Best. Cressy, Mike, illus. (Rookie Reader Skill Set Ser.). 32p. (J). 2000. (gr. k-2). pap. 4.95 (978-0-516-27001-2(X)); 1999. (gr. 1-2). 19.50 (978-0-516-21638-6(4)) Scholastic Library Publishing. (Children's Pr.).

—Purple Is Best. 1999. (gr. k-3). lib. bdg. 12.95 (978-0-613-54849-6(3)) Tandem Library Bks.

Reber, Deborah. Guess Who Loves Blue! 2002. (Blue's Clues Ser.). (Illus.). 14p. (J). bds. 4.99 (978-0-689-84870-4(6) , Simon Spotlight/Nickelodeon) Simon & Schuster Children's Publishing.

Red & Green Choices by Green Irene: Cindy T's Circle Time. 2003. (J). 16.00 (978-0-9742280-2-0(8)) Green Irene.

Rey, H. A., et al. Curious George's Color Fun Board Book. 2007. (Curious George Ser.). (Illus.). 14p. (J). (ps-k). bds. 6.99 (978-0-618-72400-0(1)) Houghton Mifflin Co. Trade & Reference Div.

Rivoli Group Staff, illus. Tarrytown's Rainbow of Colors. 2000. (Jay Jay the Jet Plane's Ready, Set, Let's Learn! Bks.). 10p. (J). (ps-k). 6.95 (978-1-58117-098-6(X) , Intervisual/Piggy Toes) Dalmatian Pr.

Robertson, Patrisha. Cirque du Soleil: Parade of Colors. Robertson, Patrisha, tr. Cirque du Soleil Group, illus. Seib, Al, photos by. 2003. 40p. (J). (ps-3). 15.95 (978-0-8109-4515-9(0)) Abrams, Harry N., Inc.

Rodriguez, Paul. What Color Are You? Rodriguez, Paul, illus. 2003. (Illus.). 32p. (J). lib. bdg. 15.99 (978-0-9744770-2-2(8)) Rodro.

Rogers, Alan. En Forme de Bateau. 2003. (Little Giants Ser.). (FRE., Illus.). 16p. (J). (ps-k). 5.95 (978-1-58728-177-8(5) , Two Can Publishing) T&N Children's Publishing.

—Green Bear. 2004. (Little Giants Ser.). (Illus.). 16p. (ps-k). (J). pap. 3.95 (978-1-58728-159-4(7)); 5.95 (978-1-58728-152-5(X)) T&N Children's Publishing. (Two Can Publishing).

—Ours Vert. 2003. (Little Giants Ser.). (SPA., Illus.). 16p. (J). (ps-k). 5.95 (978-1-58728-180-8(5) , Two Can Publishing) T&N Children's Publishing.

—Rhino Rouge. 2000. (FRE., Illus.). 16p. (J). (ps-k). 5.95 (978-1-58728-174-7(0) , Two Can Publishing) T&N Children's Publishing.

—Ship Shape. 2004. (Little Giants Ser.). (Illus.). 16p. (J). (ps-k). pap. 3.95 (978-1-58728-395-6(6) , Two Can Publishing) T&N Children's Publishing.

Rosell, J. F. & Deleau, J. La Nube. 2004. (SPA.). 32p. 6.95 (978-1-4000-9292-5(2)) Editorial Sudamericana S.A. ARG. *Dist:* Random Hse., Inc.

Rosenwald, Laurie. And to Name but Just a Few: Red, Yellow, Green, Blue. 2007. (Illus.). 40p. (ps-3). 16.95 (978-1-59354-596-3(7)) Blue Apple Bks.

Rossetti, Christina Georgina. What Is Pink? A Poem about Colors. Corwin, Judith Hoffman, illus. 2000. (Growing Tree Ser.). 14p. (J). (ps up). 5.95 (978-0-694-01248-0(3) , Harper Festival) HarperCollins Pubs.

Rowe, Jeannette, illus. YoYo's Colors. 2002. 10p. (J). 3.95 (978-1-58925-682-8(4) , tiger tales) ME Media LLC.

Rowles, Louis. Ida Claire Decorates with Flair. Brownlee, Sunny, illus. 2004. 24p. (J). pap. (978-0-9708748-1-8(2)) Rowles, Louis.

Ruffenach, Jessie, ed. Baby Learns about Colors. Thomas, Peter, tr. from NAV. Blacksheep, Beverly, illus. 2003. (ENG & NAV.). 16p. (J). bds. 7.95 (978-1-893354-48-7(2)) Salina Bookshelf.

Rusch, Elizabeth. A Day with No Crayons. Cameron, Chad, illus. 2007. 32p. (***978-0-87358-910-9(6)** , Rising Moon Bks. for Young Readers) Northland Publishing.

SAMi. Woof-Woof. (J). bds. 8.95 (978-1-59354-137-8(6)); 2006. (Illus.). 24p. bds. 8.95 (978-1-59354-163-7(5)) Blue Apple Bks.

Sander, Sonia. The Color of Veggie. 2006. (VeggieTales Ser.). 32p. (J). 3.99 (978-1-4169-1786-1(1) , Simon Scribbles) Simon & Schuster Children's Publishing.

Sanders, Roy E. Land of Pink: From thesNot So Far Ago Series. 2007. (J). 19.99 (***978-1-59879-327-7(6)**) Lifevest Publishing, Inc.

Sargent, Daina. Colors & the Number 10, 11. Lenoir, Jane, illus. 2004. (Learn to Read Ser.: 11). 24p. (J). pap. 9.95 (978-1-59381-049-8(0)); per. 9.95 (978-1-59381-527-1(1)) Ozark Publishing.

—Colors & the Number 1/Los Colores y el Numero 1, 11. Lenoir, Jane, illus. 2004. (Learn to Read Ser.: 11). (SPA & ENG.). 24p. (J). pap. 9.95 (978-1-59381-129-7(2)) Ozark Publishing.

—Colors & the Number 2, 11. Lenoir, Jane, illus. 2004. (Learn to Read Ser.: 11). 24p. (J). per. 9.95 (978-1-59381-529-5(8)) Ozark Publishing.

—Colors & the Number 2/Los Colores y el Numero 2, 11. Lenoir, Jane, illus. 2004. (Learn to Read Ser.: 11). Tr. of Los colores y el Numero 2. (SPA & ENG.). 24p. (J). pap. 9.95 (978-1-59381-131-0(4)); lib. bdg. 19.95 (978-1-59381-130-3(6)) Ozark Publishing.

—Colors & the Number 3, 11. Lenoir, Jane, illus. 2004. (Learn to Read Ser.: 11). 24p. (J). pap. 9.95 (978-1-59381-035-1(0)); pap. 9.95 (978-1-59381-530-1(1)) Ozark Publishing.

—Colors & the Number 3/Los Colores y el Numero 3, 11. Lenoir, Jane, illus. 2004. (Learn to Read Ser.: 11). Tr. of Los colores y el el Numero 3. (SPA & ENG.). 24p. (J). pap. 9.95 (978-1-59381-133-4(0)); lib. bdg. 19.95 (978-1-59381-132-7(2)) Ozark Publishing.

—Colors & the Number 4, 11. Lenoir, Jane, illus. 2004. (Learn to Read Ser.: 11). 24p. (J). per. 9.95 (978-1-59381-531-8(X)) Ozark Publishing.

—Colors & the Number 4/Los colores y el Numero 4, 11. Lenoir, Jane, illus. 2004. (Learn to Read Ser.: 11). Tr. of Los colores y el Numero 4. (SPA & ENG.). 24p. (J). pap. 9.95 (978-1-59381-135-8(7)); lib. bdg. 19.95 (978-1-59381-134-1(9)) Ozark Publishing.

—Colors & the Number 5, 11. Lenoir, Jane, illus. 2004. (Learn to Read Ser.: 11). 24p. (J). pap. 9.95 (978-1-59381-039-9(3)); per. 9.95 (978-1-59381-532-5(8)) Ozark Publishing.

—Colors & the Number 5/Los colores y el Numero 5, 11. Lenoir, Jane, illus. 2004. (Learn to Read Ser.: 11). Tr. of Los colores y el Numero 5. (SPA & ENG.). 24p. (J). pap. 9.95 (978-1-59381-137-2(3)); lib. bdg. 19.95 (978-1-59381-136-5(5)) Ozark Publishing.

—Colors & the Number 6, 11. Lenoir, Jane, illus. 2004. (Learn to Read Ser.: 11). 24p. (J). pap. 9.95 (978-1-59381-041-2(5)); per. 9.95 (978-1-59381-533-2(6)) Ozark Publishing.

—Colors & the Number 7, 11. Lenoir, Jane, illus. 2004. (Learn to Read Ser.: 11). 24p. (J). pap. 9.95 (978-1-59381-043-6(1)); per. 9.95 (978-1-59381-534-9(4)) Ozark Publishing.

—Colors & the Number 7/Los Colores y el Numero 7, 11. Lenoir, Jane, illus. 2004. (Learn to Read Ser.: 11). Tr. of Los colores y el Numero 7. (SPA & ENG.). 24p. (J). pap. 9.95 (978-1-59381-141-9(1)); lib. bdg. 19.95 (978-1-59381-140-2(3)) Ozark Publishing.

—Colors & the Number 8, 11. Lenoir, Jane, illus. 2004. (Learn to Read Ser.: 11). 24p. (J). pap. 9.95 (978-1-59381-045-0(8)) Ozark Publishing.

—Colors & the Number 8/Los Colores y el Numero 8, 11. Lenoir, Jane, illus. 2004. (Learn to Read Ser.: 11). Tr. of Los colores y el Numero 8. (SPA & ENG.). 24p. (J). pap. 9.95 (978-1-59381-143-3(8)); lib. bdg. 19.95 (978-1-59381-142-6(X)) Ozark Publishing.

—Colors & the Number 9, 11. Lenoir, Jane, illus. 2004. (Learn to Read Ser.: 11). 24p. (J). pap. 9.95 (978-1-59381-047-4(4)) Ozark Publishing.

—Colors & the Number 9/Los Colores y el Numero 9, 11. Lenoir, Jane, illus. 2004. (Learn to Read Ser.: 11). Tr. of Los colores y el Numero 9. (SPA & ENG.). 24p. (J). pap. 9.95 (978-1-59381-145-7(4)); lib. bdg. 19.95 (978-1-59381-144-0(6)) Ozark Publishing.

—Introduction to Colors & Niumbers, 11. Lenoir, Jane, illus. 2005. (Learn to Read Ser.: 11). 24p. (J). pap. 9.95 (978-1-59381-051-1(2)) Ozark Publishing.

—Introduction to Colors & Numbers, 11. Lenoir, Jane, illus. 2005. (Learn to Read Ser.: 11). 24p. (J). per. 9.95 (978-1-59381-528-8(X)) Ozark Publishing.

—Introduction to Colors & Numbers (BL) Introduccion a los colores y a los Numeros, 11. Lenoir, Jane, illus. 2004. (Learn to Read Ser.: 11). (SPA & ENG.). 24p. (J). lib. bdg. 19.95 (978-1-59381-148-8(9)) Ozark Publishing.

Sawyer, Dawn. Meet the Color Kids. Albrecht, Jeff, illus. 2004. (Rainbow Brite Ser.). 32p. (J). (ps-3). pap. 4.99 (978-0-439-65935-2(3)) Scholastic, Inc.

—Rainbow Falls. Albrecht, Jeff, illus. 2004. (Rainbow Brite Ser.). 33p. (J). pap. 3.99 (978-0-439-65936-9(1)) Scholastic, Inc.

Schachner, Judy. Skippyjon Jones: Color Crazy. 2007. 12p. (J). (ps). pap. 6.99 (978-0-525-47782-2(9) , Dutton Juvenile) Penguin Group (USA) Inc.

Schneider, Christine M. Picky Mrs. Pickle. Schneider, Christine M., illus. 1999. (Illus.). 32p. (J). (gr. k-3). lib. bdg. 16.85 (978-0-8027-8703-3(7)); 15.95 (978-0-8027-8702-6(9)) Walker & Co.

Scholastic, Inc. Staff. World of Rainbow Brite. Swendsen, Silje, ed. 2004. (Rainbow Brite Ser.). (Illus.). 17p. (J). (ps-3). pap. 5.99 (978-0-439-65937-6(X)) Scholastic, Inc.

Scholastic, Inc. Staff & Mills, Liz. Go, Clifford, Go! Bracken, Carolyn & Edwards, Ken, illus. 2002. (Clifford, the Big Red Dog Ser.). 10p. (J). bds. 9.99 (978-0-439-39447-5(3)) Scholastic, Inc.

Scholastic, Inc. Staff, et al. Barney's Colorful World. McKee, Darren, illus. 2003. (Barney Ser.). 32p. (J). pap. 3.99 (978-0-439-56881-4(1)) Scholastic, Inc.

Schwartz, Betty Ann. What Makes a Rainbow? A Magic Ribbon Book. Turner, Dona, illus. 2000. (Novelty Book Ser.). (J). (ps-k). 14p. 8.95 (978-1-58117-076-4(9)); 12p. 10.95 (978-1-58117-115-0(3)) Dalmatian Pr. (Intervisual/Piggy Toes).

Schwartz, Betty Ann. Wiggly Worm: A We-Wiggle Book of Colors & Numbers. Sexton, Brenda, illus. 2008. 12p. (J). 9.99 (***978-0-06-113847-8(9)** , Harper Festival) HarperCollins Pubs.

Scott, Susan Carlson. Fip's Magical World of Color, Vol. 14. Scott, Susan Carlson, illus. l.t. ed. 2002. (Illus.). 64p. (J). 15.95 (978-1-887932-94-3(1) , New Concord Pr.) Equine Graphics Publishing Group.

Seuss, Dr. My Many Colored Days. Johnson, Stephen T. & Fancher, Lou, illus. 1998. 16p. (J). (gr. k-ps). bds. 6.99 (978-0-679-89344-8(X) , Knopf Bks. for Young Readers) Random Hse. Children's Bks.

—One Fish, Two Fish, Red Fish, Blue Fish. 2005. (Illus.). 64p. (J). (ps-2). audio compact disk 9.95 (978-0-375-83497-4(4) , Random Hse. Bks. for Young Readers) Random Hse. Children's Bks.

Shannon, George. White Is for Blueberry. Dronzek, Laura, illus. 2005. 40p. (J). (ps). 16.99 (978-0-06-029275-1(X)); lib. bdg. 17.89 (978-0-06-029276-8(8)) HarperCollins Pubs.

Sharpe, Jeannie w. Once There Was an Orange Truck. 2005. 37p. (J). 15.95 (978-0-9763117-0-6(4)) Sharpe, Jeannie W.

Shaw, M. Beatryce. Mr. Browne & the Rose Show: A Child's Perception of "Different" Date not set. 40p. (J). (gr. k-4). pap. 7.95 (978-1-929234-02-8(3)) Schooner Pubns.

—Mr. Browne's Roses: A Story of Early Childhood Color Awareness. 2000. 40p. (J). (gr. k-4). pap. 8.95 (978-1-929234-00-4(7)) Schooner Pubns.

Shukla, Subir. The Boy Who Loved Colour. Sabnani, Nina, illus. 2004. (ENG & HIN.). (J). (978-81-8146-042-4(1)) Tulika Pubs.

Shulman, Mark. Foxy Fox. Chambers, Sally, illus. 2004. 8p. (J). bds. 6.95 (978-1-58925-738-2(3) , tiger tales) ME Media LLC.

Sierra i Fabra, Jordi. Sietecolores. 2001. (J). (978-956-240-303-0(3)) Arrayan Editores S.A.

Slater, Dashka. Baby Shoes. Nakata, Hiroe, illus. 2006. 32p. (J). 15.95 (978-1-58234-684-7(4) , Bloomsbury Children) Bloomsbury Publishing.

Soundar, Chitra. Chasing the Pot of Gold. Amrein, Paul, illus. 2006. 32p. (J). E-Book 5.00 incl. cd-rom (***978-1-933090-36-8(7)**) Guardian Angel Publishing, Inc.

Spelvin, Justin. Rainbow Brite Saves Christmas. Oliver, Kora, illus. 2004. (Rainbow Brite Ser.). 48p. (J). (ps-3). pap. 7.99 (978-0-439-65933-8(7)) Scholastic, Inc.

Stevens, Rita. Glumpkins. 2004. 28p. pap. 10.99 (978-1-4116-1281-5(7)) Lulu.com.

Su Propio Color. 2007. (SPA.). 40p. (J). 12.99 (***978-1-933032-14-6(6)***) Lectorum Pubns., Inc.

Tafuri, Nancy. Blue Goose. Tafuri, Nancy, illus. 2008. 32p. (J). 15.99 (***978-1-4169-2834-8(0)*** , Simon & Schuster Children's Publishing) Simon & Schuster Children's Publishing.

Tashiro, Chisato. Chameleon's Colors. Martens, Marianne, tr. from GER. 2003. (Illus.). 32p. (J). 15.95 (978-0-7358-1887-3(8)) North-South Bks., Inc.

—Chameleon's Colors bilingual L. 2007. (J). 16.50 (978-0-7358-2104-0(6)) North-South Bks., Inc.

—Chameleons Colors bilingual PB. 2007. (SPA.). (J). pap. 6.95 (978-0-7358-2105-7(4)) North-South Bks., Inc.

—Chameleons Colors PB. 2007. (Illus.). (J). pap. 6.95 (978-0-7358-2111-8(9)) North-South Bks., Inc.

Thomas, Valerie. Winnie the Witch. Paul, Korky, illus. 2007. 32p. (J). (ps-3). 14.99 (***978-0-06-117312-7(6)***) HarperCollins Pubs.

Thong, Roseanne. Red Is a Dragon. Lin, Grace, illus. 2001. 40p. (J). 15.95 (978-0-8118-3177-2(9)) Chronicle Bks. LLC.

Thorpe, Kiki. Donde esta Boots? Cuento para levantar la Tapita. Savitsky, Steven, illus. 2005. (Dora the Explorer Ser.).Tr. of Where Is Boots?. (SPA.). 16p. (J). pap. 5.99 (978-1-4169-0621-6(5) , Libros Para Ninos) Simon & Schuster Children's Publishing.

—Where Is Boots? A Lift-the-Flap Story. Savitsky, Steve, illus. 2002. (Dora the Explorer Ser.). 16p. (J). (ps-1). pap. 5.99 (978-0-689-84775-2(0) , Simon Spotlight/Nickelodeon) Simon & Schuster Children's Publishing.

Top That!, ed. Millie the Millipede. Elliot, Rebecca, illus. 2007. 20p. (J). (ps). bds. 10.99 (***978-1-84666-274-4(5)*** , Tide Mill Pr.) Top That! Publishing PLC GBR. *Dist:* Random Hse., Inc.

Tullet, Herve. Pink Lemon. Tullet, Herve, illus. 2002. (Illus.). 100p. (J). 14.50 (978-1-84059-330-3(X)) Milet Publishing.

Twinem, Neecy. Baby Gecko's Colors. (New Board Book Ser.).Tr. of Los colores de Bebe Geco. 2004. (Illus.). 12p. (J). bds. 5.95 (978-0-87358-851-5(7)); (ENG & SPA.). bds. 5.95 (978-0-87358-867-6(3)) Northland Publishing. (Rising Moon Bks. for Young Readers).

Van Fleet, Matthew. Monday the Bullfrog. 2006. (J). (978-978-141-691-0(2) , Simon & Schuster Children's Publishing) Simon & Schuster Children's Publishing.

—Monday the Bullfrog. Van Fleet, Matthew, illus. 2006. (Illus.). 20p. (J). 17.99 (978-1-4169-1231-6(2)) Simon & Schuster Children's Publishing.

—Spotted Yellow Frogs: Fold-Out Fun with Patterns, Colors, 3-D Shapes, Animals. 1998. (Illus.). 24p. (J). (ps-k). 10.99 (978-0-8037-2350-4(4) , Dial) Penguin Group (USA) Inc.

—Tails. 2003. (Illus.). 20p. (J). 13.95 (978-0-15-216773-8(0) , Red Wagon Bks.) Harcourt Children's Bks.

Vilarrubias, Pia. Kiko Sale Del Libro. (SPA.). 36p. 11.95 (978-84-207-1252-9(3)) Grupo Anaya, S.A. ESP. *Dist:* Distribooks, Inc.

Vischer, Phil. The Veggiecational Book: A Book about Numbers, Colors, Shapes & Letters! 1998. (Veggiecational Ser.: Vol. 7). (Illus.). 128p. (J). (ps-2). 19.99 (978-0-8499-5865-6(2)) Nelson, Thomas Inc.

Wallace, Karen. Marvin, the Blue Pig. Williams, Lisa, illus. 2004. (Read-It! Readers Ser.). 32p. (C). (gr. k-3). 18.60 (978-1-4048-0564-4(8)) Picture Window Bks.

Walsh, Ellen Stoll. Mouse Paint. Walsh, Ellen Stoll, illus. 2002. (Illus.). (J). 13.70 (978-0-7587-3180-7(9)) Book Wholesalers, Inc.

—Mouse Paint. 2006. (Illus.). 30p. (J). bds. 10.95 (978-0-15-205533-2(9) , Red Wagon Bks.) Harcourt Children's Bks.

—Pintura de Raton. Campoy, F. Isabel, tr. 2006. (Illus.). 30p. (J). bds. 6.95 (978-0-15-205743-5(9) , Voyager Bks./Libros Viajeros) Harcourt Children's Bks.

Wang, Margaret. Hungry Bunny. 2007. 16p. pap. 9.95 (***978-1-58117-556-1(6)***) Dalmatian Pr.

Warrence, Michelle. Colors, Shapes & Sizes. del Sur, Duendes, illus. 2000. (Jumpstart Workbooks Ser.). 32p. (J). pap., wbk. ed. 3.99 (978-0-439-16421-4(4)) Scholastic, Inc.

Watsuki, Nobuhiro. Busou Renkin Vol. 2: Fade to Black. (Illus.). 203p. (YA). pap. (978-4-08-873587-0(0)) Shuei-Sha.

Watt, Fiona. Hide-and-Seek Dragons. 2007. (Touchy-Feely Flap Bks). 10p. (J). bds. 16.99 (978-0-7945-1590-4(8) , Usborne) EDC Publishing.

Weber, Lou, ed. Pooh Color & Play Stories. 2005. 32p. 7.98 (978-1-4127-3393-9(6)) Publications International, Ltd.

—Spongebob Color Me Sound. 2004. 32p. (J). 7.98 (978-1-4127-3053-2(8) , 7226100) Publications International, Ltd.

Weeks, Sarah. Counting Ovejas. Diaz, David, illus. 2006. (ENG & SPA.). 40p. (J). (ps-1). 17.99 (978-0-689-86750-7(6) , Atheneum) Simon & Schuster Children's Publishing.

—Who's under That Hat? A Lift-the-Flap Pop-up Adventure. Carter, David A., illus. 2006. 14p. (J). (ps-2). 14.00 (978-1-4223-5440-7(7)) DIANE Publishing Co.

Widdowson, Kay, illus. Please, Mr Crocodile... 2006. 24p. (J). (978-1-84643-025-1(9)) Child's Play-International.

Wilcox, Michael. Colors Around Us. Barber, Julia, illus. 2004. 32p. (J). per. 19.95 (978-1-931780-32-2(3)) School of Color Publishing.

—What Is Color. 2004. (Illus.). 32p. (J). per. 19.95 (978-1-931780-31-5(5)) School of Color Publishing.

Wildsmith, Brian, illus. Brian Wildsmith's Animal Colors (Farsi) 2004. (PER.). 16p. (J). bds. 4.95 (978-1-932065-42-8(3)) Star Bright Bks., Inc.

Wilhelm, Hans. I Love Colors! 2000. (gr. k-3). lib. bdg. 11.80 (978-0-613-54811-3(6)) Tandem Library Bks.

Wilhelm, Hans, illus. I Love Colors! 2001. (Hello Reader! Ser.). 32p. (J). (ps-1). pap. 3.99 (978-0-439-19288-0(9) , Cartwheel Bks.) Scholastic, Inc.

Willard, Eliza. Totally Crushed. 2008. (Candy Apple Ser.). 160p. (J). pap. 4.99 (***978-0-545-02814-1(0)*** , Scholastic Paperbacks) Scholastic, Inc.

Williams, Sue. I Went Walking. Vivas, Julie, illus. 2002. (J). 14.79 (978-0-7587-2823-4(9)) Book Wholesalers, Inc.

—I Went Walking. Vivas, Julie, illus. 2005. 30p. (ps-ps). bds. 10.95 (978-0-15-205626-1(2) , Red Wagon Bks.) Harcourt Children's Bks.

—I Went Walking. 2003. (Illus.). (J). pap. 18.95 incl. audio compact disk (978-1-59112-719-2(X)) Live Oak Media.

—I Went Walking. Vivas, Julie, illus. 2003. 28.95 incl. audio compact disk (978-1-59112-720-8(3)); 2003. pap. 39.95 incl. audio compact disk (978-1-59112-721-5(1)); 2000. (J). 25.95 incl. audio (978-0-87499-664-7(3)); 2000. (ENG & SPA.). (J). pap. 33.95 incl. audio (978-0-87499-666-1(X)) Live Oak Media.

—I Went Walking/Sali de Paseo: Lap-Sized Board Book. Ada, Alma Flor, tr. from ENG. Vivas, Julie, illus. 2006. (ENG & SPA.). 30p. (J). bds. 10.95 (978-0-15-205895-1(8) , Voyager Bks./Libros Viajeros) Harcourt Children's Bks.

—Sali de Paseo. Ada, Alma Flor, tr. Vivas, Julie, illus. 2005. (SPA.). 30p. (J). (ps-ps). bds. 6.95 (978-0-15-205614-8(9) , Red Wagon Bks.) Harcourt Children's Bks.

Wilson-Max, Ken. Max Paints the House. 2000. (Illus.). 32p. (ps-k). 14.99 (978-0-7868-0537-2(4)) Disney Pr.

Wolff, Ashley. Oh, the Colors/De Colores: Sing along in English & Spanish!/Vamos a Cantar Junto en Ingles y Espanol! Wolff, Ashley, illus. 2003. (SPA & ENG., Illus.). 22p. (J). (ps-ps). bds. 5.95 (978-0-316-06563-4(3) , Tingley, Megan Bks.) Little, Brown Bks. for Young Readers.

Wood, Audrey. The Deep Blue Sea. Wood, Bruce Robert, illus. 2005. 40p. (J). pap. 15.99 (978-0-439-75382-1(1) , Blue Sky Pr., The) Scholastic, Inc.

Wood, Audrey & Wood, Bruce Robert, illus. The Deep Blue Sea. 2005. (J). (978-0-439-75383-8(X) , Blue Sky Pr., The) Scholastic, Inc.

Yates, Gene, illus. The Chameleon Colors Book. 2006. (J). (***978-1-58865-361-1(7)***) Kidsbooks, Inc.

Yolen, Jane. How Do Dinosaurs Learn Their Colors? Teague, Mark, illus. 2006. 12p. (J). bds. 6.99 (978-0-439-85653-9(1) , Blue Sky Pr., The) Scholastic, Inc.

—How Do Dinosaurs Learn Their Colors (Como Aprenden los Dinosaurios los Colores) 2006. 12p. (J). bds. 6.99 (978-0-439-87192-1(1) , Scholastic en Espanol) Scholastic, Inc.

Yoon, Salina. Jungle Colors. Yoon, Salina, illus. 2005. (Sliding Board Books). (Illus.). 12p. (J). 6.99 (978-0-689-86186-4(9) , Little Simon) Simon & Schuster Children's Publishing.

Yoyo. Toddler's First Puzzle Fun—Blue. 2005. 96p. pap. 5.95 (978-90-5843-615-3(2)) YoYo Bks. BEL. *Dist:* National Bk. Network.

—Toddler's First Puzzle Fun—Green. 2005. 96p. pap. 5.95 (978-90-5843-614-6(4)) YoYo Bks. BEL. *Dist:* National Bk. Network.

—Toddler's First Puzzle Fun—Red. 2005. 96p. pap. 5.95 (978-90-5843-613-9(6)) YoYo Bks. BEL. *Dist:* National Bk. Network.

—Toddler's First Puzzle Fun—Yellow. 2005. 96p. pap. 5.95 (978-90-5843-616-0(0)) YoYo Bks. BEL. *Dist:* National Bk. Network.

Ziraldo. Flicts. Corgatelli, Rosa S., tr. Ziraldo, illus. 2001. Tr. of Flicts. (SPA., Illus.). 48p. pap. 9.95 (978-85-06-50468-0(6)) Companhia Melhoramentos de Sao Paulo Industrias de Papel BRA. *Dist:* Lectorum Pubns., Inc.

Zolotow, Charlotte. El Senor Conejo y el Hermoso Regalo. Sendak, Maurice, illus. 2006. (SPA.). 40p. (J). pap. 6.99 (978-0-06-088704-9(4) , Rayo) HarperCollins Pubs.

COLOR—POETRY

Aigner-Clark, Julie. Baby Van Gogh: A Field Trip for Curious Young Minds into Vivid Colors, Beautiful Art, & Expressive Poems. Van Gogh, Vincent & Ulan, Helen Cerra, illus. 2000. 26p. (J). (978-1-892309-36-5(X)) Baby Einstein Co., LLC, The.

Novoa, Teresa, illus. Rojo. (Cocorolos Ser.). (SPA.). 12p. (J). (ps-k). bds. 7.95 (978-84-294-6921-9(4)) Santillana USA Publishing Co., Inc.

COLOR ETCHINGS

see Prints

COLOR OF ANIMALS

see Animals—Color

COLOR OF MAN

see Human Skin Color

COLORADO

Barker, Jane Valentine. Trappers & Traders. Downing, Sybil, ed. (Colorado Heritage Ser.). (Illus.). 36p. (J). (gr. k-6). reprint ed. pap. 6.95 (978-1-878611-03-1(8)) Silver Rim Pr.

Barker, Jane Valentine & Downing, Sybil. Mountain Treasures. (Colorado Heritage Ser.). (Illus.). 44p. (J). (gr. k-6). reprint ed. pap. 7.95 (978-1-878611-01-7(1)) Silver Rim Pr.

Bledsoe, Sara. Colorado. 2nd exp. rev. ed. (Hello U. S. A. Ser.). (Illus.). 84p. (J). (gr. 3-6). 2002. lib. bdg. 25.26 (978-0-8225-4055-7(X)); 2003. pap. 6.95 (978-0-8225-4153-0(X)) Lerner Publishing Group.

Bograd, Larry. Uniquely Colorado. 2003. (State Studies). (Illus.). 48p. (J). pap. 8.50 (978-1-4034-4502-5(8)); 27.07 (978-1-4034-4487-5(0)) Heinemann Library.

—Uniquely Colorado. 2003. (gr. 3-6). lib. bdg. 38.60 (978-0-613-87968-2(6)) Tandem Library Bks.

Capstone Press, Geography Dept Staff, contrib. by. Colorado. rev. ed. 2002. (One Nation Ser.). (Illus.). 48p. (J). (gr. 3-4). lib. bdg. 22.60 (978-0-7368-1230-6(X) , Bridgestone Bks.) Capstone Pr., Inc.

Christian, Sandra J. Colorado. 2003. (Land of Liberty Ser.). (Illus.). 64p. (J). (gr. 3-4). lib. bdg. 23.93 (978-0-7368-1574-1(0) , Bridgestone Bks.) Capstone Pr., Inc.

Colorado North Sold C 2005. 2004. 404p. (YA). pap. 15.00 (978-1-58553-950-5(3) , 05GC0029) Entertainment Publications, Inc.

Colorado South Sold C 2005. 2004. 420p. (YA). pap. 15.00 (978-1-58553-951-2(1) , 05GC0030) Entertainment Publications, Inc.

Deady, Kathleen W. Colorado. 2006. (Portraits of the States Ser.). (Illus.). 32p. (J). pap. (978-0-8368-4681-2(8)); lib. bdg. 23.33 (978-0-8368-4662-1(1)) Stevens, Gareth Inc.

Denver/Boulder Sold C 2005. 2004. 420p. (YA). pap. 15.00 (978-1-58553-953-6(8) , 05GC0017) Entertainment Publications, Inc.

Elias, Megan. Colorado: The Centennial State. 2002. (World Almanac Library of the States). (Illus.). 48p. (J). (gr. 5 up). lib. bdg. 30.00 (978-0-8368-5130-4(7)); pap. 14.95 (978-0-8368-5300-1(8)) Stevens, Gareth Inc. (World Almanac Library).

Elish, Dan & Ayer, Eleanor H. Colorado. 2nd ed. 2006. (Celebrate the States Ser.). (Illus.). 144p. (J). (978-0-7614-2019-4(3) , Benchmark Bks.) Cavendish, Marshall Corp.

Feinstein, Stephen. Colorado: A MyReportLinks.com Book. 2003. (States Ser.). (Illus.). 48p. (J). (gr. 4-10). lib. bdg. 25.26 (978-0-7660-5029-7(7) , MyReportLinks.com Bks.) Enslow Pubs., Inc.

Gish, Steven. Ethiopia. 2nd ed. 2006. (Cultures of the World Ser.). (Illus.). 144p. (J). lib. bdg. 39.93 (978-0-7614-2025-5(8) , Benchmark Bks.) Cavendish, Marshall Corp.

Heinrichs, Ann. Colorado. 2005. (Welcome to the USA Ser.). 40p. (J). (gr. 1-5). 27.07 (978-1-59296-372-0(2)) Child's World, Inc.

—Colorado. 2002. (This Land Is Your Land Ser.). (Illus.). 48p. (J). (gr. 3 up). lib. bdg. 22.60 (978-0-7565-0331-4(0)) Compass Point Bks.

Justesen, Kim Williams & Falcon Publishing Staff. Hey Ranger! Kids Ask Questions about Rocky Mountain National Park. Newhouse, Judy, illus. 2005. 48p. (J). pap. 9.95 (978-0-7627-3848-9(0) , Falcon) Globe Pequot Pr., The.

Kehoe, Stasia Ward. I Live in the Mountains. 2000. (Kids in Their Communities Ser.). (Illus.). 24p. (J). (gr. 3). lib. bdg. 18.75 (978-0-8239-5442-1(0) , PowerKids Pr.) Rosen Publishing Group, Inc., The.

Krudwig, Vickie Leigh. Hiking Through Colorado History: An Activity Book for Ages 7-12. Krudwig, Vickie Leigh, illus. 1998. (Illus.). 88p. (J). (gr. 2-7). act. bk. ed. 9.95 (978-1-56579-294-4(7) , A185) Westcliffe Pubs.

Mader, Jan. Rocky Mountains. 2004. (Rookie Read-About Geography Ser.). (Illus.). 31p. (J). 20.50 (978-0-516-22759-7(9) , Children's Pr.) Scholastic Library Publishing.

Marsh, Carole. Colorado Classic Christmas Trivia. 2002. (Carole Marsh Colorado Bks.). (Illus.). 32p. pap. 6.95 (978-0-635-01379-8(7) , 13797); lib. bdg. 21.95 (978-0-635-01380-4(0) , 13800) Gallopade International. (Marsh, Carole Bks.).

—Colorado Current Events Projects: 30 Cool, Activities, Crafts, Experiments & More for Kids to Do to Learn about Your State! 2003. (Colorado Experience Ser.). 32p. (gr. k-8). pap. 5.95 (978-0-635-02025-3(4) , Marsh, Carole Bks.) Gallopade International.

—The Colorado Experience Pocket Guide. 2004. (Colorado Experience! Ser.). (Illus.). 96p. (J). (gr. 3-8). pap. 6.95 (978-0-7933-9602-3(6)) Gallopade International.

—Colorado Geography Projects: 30 Cool, Activities, Crafts, Experiments & More for Kids to Do to Learn about Your State! 2003. (Colorado Experience Ser.). 32p. (gr. k-5). pap. 5.95 (978-0-635-01825-0(X) , Marsh, Carole Bks.) Gallopade International.

—Colorado Government Projects: 30 Cool, Activities, Crafts, Experiments & More for Kids to Do to Learn about Your State! 2003. (Colorado Experience Ser.). 32p. (gr. k-5). pap. 5.95 (978-0-635-01925-7(6) , Marsh, Carole Bks.) Gallopade International.

—Colorado Jeopardy! Answers & Questions about Our State! 2004. (Colorado Experience! Ser.). (Illus.). 32p. (J). (gr. 3-8). pap. 7.95 (978-0-7933-9604-7(2)) Gallopade International.

—Colorado "Jography" A Fun Run Thru Our State! 2004. (Colorado Experience! Ser.). 32p. (J). (gr. 3-8). pap. 7.95 (978-0-7933-9605-4(0)) Gallopade International.

—Colorado Millionaire: Game Book. 2001. (Illus.). 32p. (J). (gr. 3-8). pap., act. bk. ed. 9.95 (978-0-635-00028-6(8)) Gallopade International.

—Colorado People Projects: 30 Cool, Activities, Crafts, Experiments & More for Kids to Do to Learn about Your State! 2003. (Colorado Experience Ser.). 32p. (gr. k-5). pap. 5.95 (978-0-635-01975-2(2) , Marsh, Carole Bks.) Gallopade International.

—Colorado Survivor: Game Book. 2001. (Carole Marsh Colorado Bks.). (Illus.). 32p. (J). (gr. 3-8). pap., act. bk. ed. 9.95 (978-0-635-00527-4(1)) Gallopade International.

—Colorado Symbols & Facts Projects: 30 Cool, Activities, Crafts, Experiments & More for Kids to Do to Learn about Your State! 2003. (Colorado Experience Ser.). 32p. (gr. k-5). pap. 5.95 (978-0-635-01874-8(8) , Marsh, Carole Bks.) Gallopade International.

—Colorado's Big Activity Book. 2004. (Colorado Experience! Ser.). (Illus.). 96p. (J). (gr. 2-6). pap. 9.95 (978-0-7933-9606-1(9)) Gallopade International.

—The Cool Colorado Coloring Book. 2004. (Colorado Experience! Ser.). (Illus.). 32p. (J). (gr. k-2). pap. 3.95 (978-0-7933-9607-8(7)) Gallopade International.

—My First Book about Colorado. 2004. (Colorado Experience! Ser.). (Illus.). 32p. (J). (gr. k-4). pap. 7.95 (978-0-7933-9603-0(4)) Gallopade International.

—My First Pocket Guide Colorado. 2000. (Colorado Experience! Ser.). (Illus.). 96p. (J). (gr. 3-8). 12.95 (978-0-635-01296-8(0) , 12960) Gallopade International.

—The Survivor: A Class Challenge. 2001. (Carole Marsh Colorado Bks.). lib. bdg. 29.95 (978-0-635-00652-3(9)) Gallopade International.

—Who Wants to Be a Colorado Millionaire? 2001. (Carole Marsh Colorado Bks.). lib. bdg. 29.95 (978-0-635-00029-3(6)) Gallopade International.

McAuliffe, Emily. Colorado Facts & Symbols. rev. ed. 2003. (States & Their Symbols Ser.). 24p. (J). lib. bdg. 19.93 (978-0-7368-2236-7(4)) Capstone Pr., Inc.

—Colorado Facts & Symbols. 1998. (States & Their Symbols Ser.). 24p. (J). lib. bdg. 14.00 (978-0-531-11549-7(6) , Watts, Franklin) Scholastic Library Publishing.

McCabe, Michael. Colorado: Grassroots. 2000. (Illus.). 48p. (J). (gr. 4-6). pap., stu. ed. 5.95 (978-0-911981-13-1(6)) Cloud Publishing.

—Colorado: Su Origen. 2000. (SPA., Illus.). 64p. (J). (gr. 4-6). pap. 15.95 (978-0-911981-72-8(1)) Cloud Publishing.

McLuskey, Krista. A Guide to Colorado. 2001. (American States Ser.). 32p. (J). (Illus.). (gr. 4-7). lib. bdg. 16.95 (978-1-930954-01-4(8)); per. 7.95 (978-1-930954-41-0(7)) Weigl Pubs., Inc.

Miller, Amy. Colorado. 2002. (From Sea to Shining Sea Ser.: 2). (Illus.). 80p. (J). (gr. 3-5). 30.50 (978-0-516-22379-7(8) , Children's Pr.) Scholastic Library Publishing.

Murray, Julie. Colorado. 2005. (Buddy Book Ser.). (Illus.). 32p. (J). (gr. k-4). lib. bdg. 22.78 (978-1-59197-665-3(0) , Buddy Bks.) ABDO Publishing Co.

Obregon, Jose M. Colorado. 2005. (Bilingual Library of the United States of America: Set 1). (ENG & SPA., Illus.). 32p. (J). (ps-k). lib. bdg. 22.50 (978-1-4042-3070-5(X) , Buenas Letra) Rosen Publishing Group, Inc., The.

Obregon, José María. Colorado. 2006. (Bilingual Library of the United States of America). (SPA.). (J). lib. bdg. (978-1-4042-3145-0(5) , PowerKids Pr.) Rosen Publishing Group, Inc., The.

Oneill, Elizabeth. Alfred Visits Colorado. 2007. (Illus.). 24p. (J). pap. 12.00 (***978-0-9790240-4-7(8)***) Funny Bone Bks.

Payne, Christine N. Kid Places in Colorado Springs. 2003. (J). spiral bd. 8.95 (978-0-9740643-0-7(0)) Payne, Christine.

Perry, Phyllis J. Colorado Fun: Activities for on the Road & at Home. Tarr, Lisa M., illus. 2007. 80p. (J). pap. 12.95 (***978-1-55566-402-2(4)***) Johnson Bks.

Peterson, Sheryl. Colorado. 2008. (J). (***978-1-58341-631-0(5)*** , Creative Education) Creative Co., The.

Schmidt, Cynthia. Colorado: Grassroots. 2000. (Illus.). 64p. (J). (gr. 4-6). reprint ed. 15.95 (978-0-911981-12-4(8)) Cloud Publishing.

Shattil, Wendy & Rozinski, Bob, photos by. On the Trail of Colorado Critters: Wildlife Watching for Kids. 2000. (Illus.). 96p. (J). (gr. 4-7). 14.95 (978-1-56579-350-7(1) , A195) Westcliffe Pubs.

Smith, Duane A. & Shuchter, Kate. Colorado: Our Colorful State. 1999. (Illus.). 415p. (J). (gr. 4). 26.95 (978-0-87081-505-8(9)) Univ. Pr. of Colorado.

Somervill, Barbara A. Colorado. 2007. (America the Beautiful, Third Ser.). 144p. (J). spiral bd. 38.00 (***978-0-531-18570-4(2)*** , Children's Pr.) Scholastic Library Publishing.

Sosco. Colorado. 2000. (Switched on Schoolhouse Ser.). (Illus.). (YA). (gr. 7-12). pap. 24.95 incl. cd-rom (978-0-7403-0258-9(2) , SOSCO) Alpha Omega Pubns., Inc.

Speaker-Yuan, Margaret. Royal Gorge Bridge. 2003. (Building World Landmarks Ser.). (Illus.). 48p. (J). 24.95 (978-1-56711-352-5(4) , Blackbirch Pr., Inc.) Thomson Gale.

Walker, Cynthia. Colorado. (J). (gr. k-2). 2006. (SPA.). 32p. pap. 5.95 (978-0-516-25045-8(0)); 2004. (Illus.). 31p. 20.50 (978-0-516-22735-1(1)) Scholastic Library Publishing. (Children's Pr.).

Whitney, Louise Doak. C Is for Centennial: A Colorado Alphabet. Urban, Helle, illus. 2002. 40p. (J). 17.95 (978-1-58536-058-1(9)) Sleeping Bear Pr.

COLORADO—FICTION

Adams, M.F.T., C.A.C. III, Juanita Beasley, MA. Clancy & the Bear Dance: One Ute Mountain Boy's Journey from Alcoholism & Abuse to Wholeness! 2007. 104p. pap. 11.95 (***978-0-615-14729-1(1)***) Out-of-Body Travel Foundation, The.

Aigner-Clark, Julie. In the Rain with Jane: A Fabric Rattle. 2003. (Baby Einstein Ser.). (Illus.). 6p. (ps-ps). pap. 6.99 (978-0-7868-1903-4(0)) Hyperion Bks. for Children.

Alger, Horatio. Do & Dare. 2006. pap. (***978-1-4250-1766-8(5)***); pap. (***978-1-4250-2027-9(5)***); pap. (***978-1-4250-2300-3(2)***); pap. (***978-1-4250-2118-4(2)***) Assistedreadingbooks.com Inc.

—Do & Dare: Or, A Brave Boy's Fight for Fortune. 2006. 182p. pap. 11.99 (978-1-4264-0880-9(3)); 170p. pap. 14.99 (978-1-4264-0861-8(7)) BiblioBazaar.

—Do & Dare: Or, A Brave Boy's Fight for Fortune. 2006. pap. (***978-1-4065-0701-0(6)***) Dodo Pr.

—Do & Dare: Or, A Brave Boy's Fight for Fortune. unabr. ed. 2002. (Illus.). (J). pap. 17.95 (978-1-931927-90-1(1)) Polyglot Pr., Inc.

Aryal, Aimee. Hello, Wilbur! 2007. (J). 14.95 (***978-1-932888-40-9(3)***) Mascot Bks., Inc.

Atkinson, Elizabeth. Lisa's Totally Unforgettable Winter. 2006. (ENG.). 56p. per. 12.95 (***978-1-4241-6249-9(1)***) PublishAmerica, Inc.

Avi. The Good Dog. 2003. 256p. mass mkt. 5.99 (978-0-689-83825-5(5) , Aladdin) Simon & Schuster Children's Publishing.

—The Good Dog. l.t. ed. 2003. 176p. (J). 23.95 (978-0-7862-5600-6(1)) Thorndike Pr.

—Prairie School. Farnsworth, Bill, illus. 2003. (I Can Read Bks.). 48p. (J). (gr. 3 up). pap. 3.99 (978-0-06-051318-4(7)) HarperCollins Pubs.

—Prairie School. 2001. (gr. 3-6). lib. bdg. 11.80 (978-0-613-66991-7(6)) Tandem Library Bks.

—The Secret School. (gr. 3-6). 2003. (Illus.). 168p. (J). pap. 5.95 (978-0-15-204699-6(2) , 53582853, Harcourt Paperbacks); 2001. 160p. (YA). 16.00 (978-0-15-216375-4(1)) Harcourt Children's Bks.

Ayres, Katherine. Silver Dollar Girl. 2002. (Illus.). 208p. (gr. 3-7). pap. 5.50 (978-0-440-41705-7(8) , Yearling) Random Hse. Children's Bks.

—Silver Dollar Girl. 2002. (gr. 3-6). lib. bdg. 13.00 (978-0-613-64685-7(1)) Tandem Library Bks.

Barbour, Ralph Henry. The Lilac Girl. 2006. (Illus.). pap. (***978-1-4065-0778-2(4)***) Dodo Pr.

Barker, Jane Valentine. Building Up. pap. 7.95 (978-1-878611-07-9(0)) Silver Rim Pr.

Barker, Jane Valentine & Downing, Sybil. Colorado Heritage Series, 10 vols., Set. (Illus.). (J). (ps-8). reprint ed. pap. 9.50 (978-1-878611-00-0(3)) Silver Rim Pr.

Barone, Michelle. Out of the Ordinary. (Adventures in History Ser.). 2004. (Illus.). 120p. (J). pap. (978-1-932663-08-2(8)); 2nd ed. 2005. (YA). pap. (978-1-932663-10-5(X)) History Compass, LLC.

Barron, T. A. High As a Hawk: A Brave Girl's Historic Climb. Lewin, Ted, tr. Lewin, Ted, illus. 2004. 32p. (J). (ps-3). 16.99 (978-0-399-23704-1(6) , Philomel) Penguin Group (USA) Inc.

Bezek, Lyn. Daisy: The Cripple Creek Donkey. 2004. (J). pap. 7.95 (978-1-932738-09-4(6)) Western Reflections Publishing Co.

Bjornson, Nancy. Mustangs, Fires & Snakes. 2007. (J). (***978-1-930596-84-9(7)***) Amherst Pr.

Bograd, Larry & Hubbard, Coleen. Colorado Summer. Rabinowitz, Sandy & Keiffer, Christa, illus. l.t. ed. 1999. (Treasured Horses Collection). 128p. (J). (gr. 4 up). lib. bdg. 23.33 (978-0-8368-2277-9(3)) Stevens, Gareth Inc.

Bollback, Anthony G. Rescue at Cripple Creek, Vol. 4. 1999. (Jack & Jill Mysteries Ser.). 135p. (J). pap. 7.95 (978-1-885729-18-7(9)) Toccoa Falls College Pr.

Braden, Richard. The Archer House Mystery. 2002. 128p. pap. 10.95 (978-0-595-21497-6(5) , Writer's Showcase Pr.) iUniverse, Inc.

Brooke, Lauren. Beyond the Horizon. 2nd rev. ed. 2007. (Heartland Ser.). 208p. (J). pap. 5.99 (978-0-439-91610-3(0) , Scholastic Paperbacks) Scholastic, Inc.

Brown, Marc. Buster Climbs the Walls. 9th ed. 2005. (Postcards from Buster Ser.). (Illus.). 48p. (J). (gr. 1-4). pap. 14.99 (978-0-316-15913-5(1)) Little Brown & Co.

—Buster Hunts for Dinosaurs. 2006. (Postcards from Buster Ser.). 32p. (J). (gr. 1-4). 14.99 (978-0-316-15914-2(X)) Little Brown & Co.

Burkhard, Daryl. Riddle in the Mountain. Riccio, Frank, illus. 2005. 240p. 16.95 (978-0-9668289-5-5(X)) Nomad Pr.

Burnham, Niki. Goddess Games. 2007. 288p. (YA). (gr. 9 up). 15.99 (978-1-4169-2700-6(X)) Simon & Schuster Children's Publishing.

Carbone, Elisa. Last Dance on Holladay Street. 208p. (gr. 7-11). 2006. (YA). mass mkt. 5.99 (978-0-553-49426-6(0) , Laurel Leaf); 2005. (J). 15.95 (978-0-375-82896-6(6) , Knopf Bks. for Young Readers) Random Hse. Children's Bks.

Cather, Willa. The Song of the Lark. 1999. (gr. 7-12). lib. bdg. 21.10 (978-0-613-17521-0(2)) Tandem Library Bks.

Cheek, Roland. Gunnar's Mine. 2003. 288p. per. 14.95 (978-0-918981-11-0(5) , 2) Skyline Publishing.

Cunningham, Albert Benjamin. Animal Tales of the Rockies. 2003. (gr. 3-6). lib. bdg. 26.90 (978-0-613-74801-8(8)) Tandem Library Bks.

Downing, Sybil & Barker, Jane Valentine. Happy Harvest. (Colorado Heritage Ser.). (Illus.). 43p. (J). reprint ed. pap. 7.95 (978-1-878611-02-4(X)) Silver Rim Pr.

—Mesas to Mountains. (Colorado Heritage Ser.). (Illus.). 47p. (J). (ps-8). reprint ed. pap. 7.95 (978-1-878611-04-8(6)) Silver Rim Pr.

Du Jardin, Rosamond. Marcy Catches Up. 2003. (YA). pap. 12.95 (978-1-930009-75-2(5) , 800-691-7779) Image Cascade Publishing.

Duey, Kathleen. HOOFBEATS: Margret & Flynn: 1875: Margret & Flynn: 1875. 2008. 144p. (YA). (gr. 3). 15.99 (***978-0-525-47936-9(8)*** , Dutton Juvenile) Penguin Group (USA) Inc.

—Margret & Flynn 1875. 2008. 160p. (J). (gr. 3). 5.99 (***978-0-14-241019-6(5)*** , Puffin) Penguin Group (USA) Inc.

Duey, Kathleen & Bale, Karen A. Blizzard: Colorado, 1886. 1998. (Survival! Ser.: No. 3). (J). (gr. 4-7). (978-0-606-13827-7(7)) Tandem Library Bks.

Finley, Mary Pearce. Little Fox's Secret: The Mystery of Bent's Fort. Spurlock, Martha J., illus. 1999. 68p. (J). (gr. 3-4). lib. bdg. 15.95 (978-0-86541-049-7(6)) Filter Pr., LLC.

French, Jennifer. Fidgets. 2007. 132p. pap. 9.95 (***978-1-59663-531-9(2)*** , Castle Keep Pr.) Rock, James A. & Co. Pubs.

Gamble, Adam. Good Night Denver. Veno, Joe, illus. 2007. (Good Night Our World Ser.). 20p. (J). bds. 9.95 (***978-1-60219-006-1(2)***) Our World of Books.

Gerwitz, Felice & Gerwitz, Christina. Dinosaur Quest at Diamond Peak, 3, Vol. 2. 2nd rev. ed. 2007. (Truth Seeker's Mystery Ser.). 208p. (YA). per. 8.99 (***978-1-931941-11-2(4)***) Media Angels, Inc.

Griffin, Lydia. Prunes & Rupe. Hunt, Judith, illus. 2007. (J). (***978-0-86541-086-2(0)***); pap. (***978-0-86541-087-9(9)***) Filter Pr., LLC.

Hancock, H. Irving. The Young Engineers in Colorado. rev. ed. 2006. 212p. 27.95 (978-1-4218-1744-6(6)); pap. 12.95 (978-1-4218-1844-3(2)) 1st World Publishing, Inc. (1st World Library - Literary Society).

Hancock, Irving H. The Young Engineers in Colorado or at Ra. 2006. pap. 72.99 (***978-1-4219-9888-6(2)***) IndyPublish.com.

—Young Engineers in Colorado or at Railwo. 2006. 78.99 (***978-1-4219-9872-5(6)***) IndyPublish.com.

Harcourt School Publishers Staff. Bajar el Rio Advanced Level. 3rd ed. 2002. (Trofeos Ser.). (SPA., Illus.). pap. 6.80 (978-0-15-324038-6(5)) Harcourt Schl. Pubs.

—A Trip to the Past On Level. 3rd ed. 2002. (Trophies Reading Program Ser.). (Illus.). pap. 5.10 (978-0-15-323183-4(1)) Harcourt Schl. Pubs.

Harrison, Emma, et al. Slipping Away. 2005. 163p. (YA). (978-1-4155-8181-0(9) , Simon Spotlight) Simon & Schuster Children's Publishing.

Heitzmann, Kristen. Sweet Boundless. 2001. (gr. 5-8). lib. bdg. 22.25 (978-0-613-55670-5(4)) Tandem Library Bks.

Henty, G. A. In the Heart of the Rockies. 2002. 370p. 29.95 (978-1-59087-073-0(5) , GAH073); per. 19.95 (978-1-59087-072-3(7) , GAH072) Althouse Pr.

—In the Heart of the Rockies. l.t. ed. 2006. 322p. pap. 17.99 (978-1-4264-3253-8(4)) BiblioBazaar.

—In the Heart of the Rockies. 2003. (ENG.). pap. 15.99 (***978-1-4142-0081-1(1)***) IndyPublish.com.

—In the Heart of the Rockies. 2004. reprint ed. pap. 27.95 (978-1-4191-2600-0(8)); pap. 1.99 (978-1-4192-2600-7(2)) Kessinger Publishing, LLC.

—In the Heart of the Rockies. Hindley, G. C.., illus. 1998. 388p. (YA). (gr. 8-12). reprint ed. per. 16.95 (978-1-890623-08-1(3)) Lost Classics Bk. Co.

—In the Heart of the Rockies. collector's ed. 2002. (Illus.). im. lthr. 38.85 (978-1-4115-1341-9(X)); pap. 19.95 (978-1-4115-0577-3(8)); 25.95 (978-1-4115-0949-8(8)); pap. 17.95 (978-1-4115-0174-4(8)) Polyglot Pr., Inc.

Hutchens, Paul. The Colorado Kidnapping. rev. ed. 1998. (Sugar Creek Gang Ser.: Vol. 24). 128p. (Orig.). (J). (gr. 4-7). 4.99 (978-0-8024-7028-7(9)) Moody Pubs.

—The Colorado Kidnapping. 1998. (Orig.). (gr. 3-6). lib. bdg. 13.00 (978-0-613-90554-1(7)) Tandem Library Bks.

Jenkins, Jerry B. & Fabry, Chris. Dead End. 2006. (Red Rock Mysteries Ser.). 256p. (J). pap. 5.99 (978-1-4143-0154-9(5) , Tyndale Kids) Tyndale Hse. Pubs.

—Double Fault. 2005. (Tyndale Kids Ser.). 272p. (J). pap. 5.99 (978-1-4143-0146-4(4)) Tyndale Hse. Pubs.

—Hollywood Holdup. 2006. (Red Rock Mysteries Ser.). 224p. (J). pap. 5.99 (978-1-4143-0151-8(0)) Tyndale Hse. Pubs.

—Instant Menace. 2006. (Tyndale Kids Ser.). 256p. (J). pap. 5.99 (978-1-4143-0148-8(0)) Tyndale Hse. Pubs.

—Phantom Writer. 2005. (Red Rock Mysteries Ser.). 256p. (J). pap. 5.99 (978-1-4143-0145-7(6)) Tyndale Hse. Pubs.

—Wind Chill. 2006. (Tyndale Kids Ser.). 240p. (J). pap. 5.99 (978-1-4143-0153-2(7) , Tyndale Kids) Tyndale Hse. Pubs.

Johnson, Kathleen Jeffrie. A Fast & Brutal Wing. 2007. 208p. (YA). pap. 6.99 (***978-0-312-37148-7(9)***) Square Fish.

Kahler, Janet C. 1918 Covered Wagon Adventure. 2006. (Illus.). 94p. (J). per. 10.95 (978-1-57258-444-0(0) , 945-6305) TEACH Services, Inc.

Leather. Birthday Girl. (Illus.). (J). mass mkt. (978-0-671-88667-7(3) , Pocket) Simon & Schuster.

Leather, Sue. Dead Cold Book/Audio CD Pack: Level 2 Elementary/Lower Intermediate. 2007. (Cambridge English Readers Ser.). (Illus.). 48p. pap. 11.00 incl. audio compact disk (978-0-521-69392-9(6)) Cambridge Univ. Pr.

Luxa, Sue. A Cabin in Cripple Creek. 2004. (Illus.). 99p. (J). pap. 8.95 (978-1-932738-04-9(5) , 1234249) Western Reflections Publishing Co.

—Denver Days. 2004. (Illus.). 82p. (J). pap. 8.95 (978-1-890437-98-5(0) , 1234247) Western Reflections Publishing Co.

—One Golden Summer. 2004. (Illus.). 80p. (J). pap. 8.95 (978-1-890437-99-2(9) , 1234248) Western Reflections Publishing Co.

Mac Iver, Kathi. Ghosts of the Mining District. 2003. (Illus.). 60p. 9.95 (978-0-9651272-1-9(4)) Columbine Pr.

MacLean, Kerry Lee, creator. Pigs Ski over Colorado: The Top Ten Reasons Winter Is the Piggies Favorite Season. 2005. (J). per. 15.95 (978-0-9652998-7-9(2)) On the Spot! Bks.

Mandabach, Brian. Or Not. 2007. 408p. (J). (gr. 4-7). 16.95 (***978-0-7387-1100-3(4)*** , Flux) Llewellyn Pubns.

Osorio, Rick. The Great Adventure of Sally Rock & el Lobo. 2007. (ENG.). 96p. per. 14.95 (***978-1-4241-5869-0(9)***) PublishAmerica, Inc.

Paton, Ian, illus. Margaret's Magnificent Colorado Adventure. 1999. 48p. (J). (gr. 4-7). 14.95 (978-1-56579-329-3(3) , A176) Westcliffe Pubs.

Perkins, T. J. The Secret in Phantom Forest: A Kim & Kelly Mystery. 2004. (Illus.). 130p. (YA). 10.99 (978-0-9777538-1-9(6)) GumShoe Press.

Ramthun, Bonnie. The White Gates. 2008. (J). (***978-0-375-84554-3(2)***); pap. (***978-0-375-84555-0(0)***); lib. bdg. (***978-0-375-94554-0(7)***) Random Hse., Inc.

Rottman, S. L. Slalom. 2004. 256p. (YA). (gr. 7). 16.99 (978-0-670-05913-3(7) , Viking Juvenile) Penguin Group (USA) Inc.

Samantha's Colorado Adventure. 1998. (Illus.). 2p. (J). (ps-1). 15.00 (978-1-888074-85-7(X)) Pockets of Learning.

Sargent, Dave & Sargent, Pat. The Colorado Blizzard: Be Determined, 10, 8. Lenoir, Jane, illus. l.t. ed. 2004. (Colorado Cowboys Ser.: 8). 32p. (J). (gr. 3-8). lib. bdg. 22.60 (978-1-59381-026-9(1)) Ozark Publishing.

Savage, Nancy. Nickel, the Baby Buffalo Who Thought He Was a Dog. Parks, Kathy, illus. 1999. 31p. (J). pap. (978-0-9669130-0-2(0)) Savage Parks Pr.

Taylor, Kim. Cissy Funk. 2001. 224p. (J). (gr. 5 up). 15.95 (978-0-06-029041-2(2)); 15.89 (978-0-06-029042-9(0)) HarperCollins Pubs.

Turner, Barbara. Treasure in Ghost Town. 2001. 126p. (J). pap. 11.95 (978-1-55517-540-5(6) , Bonneville Bks.) Cedar Fort, Inc./CFI Distribution.

Wyss, Thelma Hatch. Bear Dancer: The Story of a Ute Girl. 2005. (Illus.). 192p. (J). 15.95 (978-1-4169-0285-0(6) , McElderry, Margaret K.) Simon & Schuster Children's Publishing.

COLORADO—HISTORY

Barker, Jane Valentine & Downing, Sybil. Adventures in the West. (Colorado Heritage Ser.). (Illus.). 40p. (J). reprint ed. pap. 7.95 (978-1-878611-05-5(4)) Silver Rim Pr.

Benchmark Education Staff. The Mesa Verde Communities. 2005. 2.00 (***978-1-4108-4679-2(2)***) Benchmark Education Co.

Hall, Margaret. Rocky Mountain National Park. 2005. (Heinemann First Library). (Illus.). 32p. (J). pap. (978-1-4034-6708-9(0)); lib. bdg. 25.36 (978-1-4034-6701-0(3)) Heinemann Library.

Harcourt School Publishers Staff. Once There Were Anasazi. 3rd ed. 2002. (Horizons Ser.). (Illus.). (J). pap. 7.30 (978-0-15-333553-2(X)) Harcourt Schl. Pubs.

—Trofeos On Level: Viaje Al Pasado. 3rd ed. 2002. (SPA., Illus.). pap. 6.80 (978-0-15-324094-2(6)) Harcourt Schl. Pubs.

Kells, Deanne. The Mesa Verde Communities. 2005. 42.00 (***978-1-4108-4631-0(8)***) Benchmark Education Co.

Kids: Descubre el rio Colorado. 2003. (SPA.). (J). (978-1-888631-42-5(2)) Watercourse, The.

Krudwig, Vickie L. We Are the Noochew - A Brief History of the Ute People & their Colorado Connection. 2004. (Illus.). 76p. (J). spiral bd. (978-0-9700127-1-5(3)) Sweet Success Pr.

Laughlin, Rosemary. The Ludlow Massacre of 1913-14. 2006. (American Workers Ser.). (Illus.). 144p. (J). (gr. 5 up). lib. bdg. 26.95 (978-1-931798-86-0(9)) Reynolds, Morgan Inc.

Lowery, Linda. Aunt Clara Brown: Official Pioneer. Porter, Janice Lee, illus. (On My Own Biographies Ser.). 48p. (J). 2003. (gr. 1-3). 5.95 (978-1-57505-416-2(7)); 1999. (gr. 2-5). lib. bdg. 23.93 (978-1-57505-045-4(5)) Lerner Publishing Group.

—Aunt Clara Brown: Official Pioneer. 1999. (gr. 3-6). lib. bdg. 14.10 (978-0-613-68191-9(6)) Tandem Library Bks.

Marsh, Carole. Colorado History Projects: 30 Cool, Activities, Crafts, Experiments & More for Kids to Do to Learn about Your State! 2003. (Colorado Experience Ser.). 32p. (gr. k-5). pap. 5.95 (978-0-635-01775-8(X) , Marsh, Carole Bks.) Gallopade International.

Orr, Tamra. Colorado. 2003. (Seeds of a Nation Ser.). (Illus.). 48p. (J). (gr. 3-5). 26.20 (978-0-7377-1463-0(8) , Kidhaven) Thomson Gale.

Perry, Phyllis J. A Kid's Look at Colorado. 2005. (Illus.). 204p. (J). (gr. 3-7). pap. 15.95 (978-1-55591-856-9(5)) Fulcrum Publishing.

Sesame Street Learn about Colorado. 1999. (J). 11.99 (978-0-679-89429-2(2) , Random Hse. Bks. for Young Readers) Random Hse. Children's Bks.

Skelton, Renee. A Kid's Guide to Exploring Black Canyon of the Gunnison National Park. 2003. (Illus.). 12p. (J). pap. 4.95 (978-1-58369-035-2(2)) Western National Parks Assn.

Walker, Cynthia. Colorado. (Rookie Español Geografía Ser.). (J). 2005. (ENG & SPA., Illus.). 31p. (ps-ps). 19.50 (978-0-516-25244-5(5)); 2004. 32p. (gr. 1-2). pap. 5.95 (978-0-516-27944-2(0)) Scholastic Library Publishing. (Children's Pr.).

Young, Robert. A Personal Tour of Mesa Verde. 1999. (How It Was Ser.). (Illus.). 64p. (J). (gr. 4-6). lib. bdg. (978-0-8225-3577-5(7) , Lerner Pubns.) Lerner Publishing Group.

COLORADO RIVER AND VALLEY

Barter, James E. The Colorado. 2003. (Rivers of the World Ser.). (Illus.). 112p. (J). 28.70 (978-1-59018-059-4(3) , Lucent Bks.) Thomson Gale.

Bryan, Dale-Marie. The Colorado River. 2006. 32p. (gr. 1-2). (YA). pap. 5.95 (978-0-516-21447-4(0)); (Illus.). (J). 20.50 (978-0-516-25033-5(7)) Scholastic Library Publishing. (Children's Pr.).

Colorado River Map: CR-1. 2nd ed. 2001. pap. 8.00 (978-0-9715563-1-7(8)) Hidden Lakes Pr.

Colorado River Map: CR-2. 2001. pap. 8.00 (978-0-9715563-2-4(6)) Hidden Lakes Pr.

Colorado River Map: CR-3. 2001. pap. 8.00 (978-0-9715563-3-1(4)) Hidden Lakes Pr.

Gilpin, Daniel. The Colorado River. 2003. (Rivers of North America Ser.). (Illus.). 32p. (J). (gr. 3 up). lib. bdg. 24.67 (978-0-8368-3753-7(3)) Stevens, Gareth Inc.

Harcourt School Publishers Staff. A Trip Down a River Advanced Level. 3rd ed. 2002. (Illus.). pap. 5.10 (978-0-15-323127-8(0)) Harcourt Schl. Pubs.

Kids: Discover the Colorado River. 2002. 16p. (YA). pap. (978-1-888631-18-0(X)) Watercourse, The.

McNeese, Tim. The Colorado River. 2004. (Rivers in American Life & Times Ser.). (Illus.). 120p. (gr. 9-13). 30.00 (978-0-7910-7726-9(8)); pap. 13.25 (978-0-7910-8006-1(4)) Facts On File, Inc. (Chelsea Hse.).

Powell, John Wesley. The Diary of John Wesley Powell: Exploring the Grand Canyon. Roop, Connie & Roop, Peter, eds. 2000. (In My Own Words Ser.). (Illus.). 96p. (J). (gr. 5 up). lib. bdg. 24.21 (978-0-7614-1013-3(9) , Benchmark Bks.) Cavendish, Marshall Corp.

Rawlins, Carol B. Colorado River. 1999. (gr. 3-6). lib. bdg. 17.60 (978-0-613-29412-6(2)) Tandem Library Bks.

Ray, Deborah Kogan. Down the Colorado: The Story of John Wesley Powell, the One-Armed Explorer. 2007. (Illus.). 48p. (J). (gr. 3 up). 17.00 (978-0-374-31838-3(7)) Farrar, Straus & Giroux.

Ross, Michael Elsohn. Exploring the Earth with John Wesley Powell. Smith, Wendy, illus. 2006. 48p. (J). (gr. 4-10). reprint ed. 19.00 (978-1-4223-5581-7(0)) DIANE Publishing Co.

Souza, Dorothy M. John Wesley Powell. 2004. (Watts Library). (Illus.). 64p. (J). (gr. 5-7). pap. 8.95 (978-0-531-16653-6(8)); 25.50 (978-0-531-12289-1(1)) Scholastic Library Publishing. (Watts, Franklin).

Waldman, Stuart. The Last River: John Wesley Powell & the Colorado River Exploring Expedition. Manchess, Gregory, illus. 2005. (Great Explorers Ser.). 48p. (J). (gr. 4-12). 19.95 (978-1-931414-09-8(2)) Mikaya Pr.

COLORED PEOPLE (UNITED STATES)

see African Americans

COLORING BOOKS

ABC coloring Book. 2006. (YA). per. 2.99 (978-1-59872-431-8(2)) Instantpublisher.com.

ABC Coloring Book. 2004. 3.00 (978-1-880960-11-0(7)) Scripture Memory Fellowship International.

ABCs. 2002. (Puppy Steps Ser.). (Illus.). 10p. (J). (ps-1). bds. 3.99 (978-1-57759-660-8(9)) Dalmatian Pr.

ABCs of the Bible Coloring Book. (Illus.). 16p. (J). pap. 1.50 (978-0-87162-873-2(2) , E6036) Warner Pr. Pubs.

Aboff, Marcie. The Northern Lights Carry-along Coloring Kit. 2007. (Frosty the Snowman Ser.). (Illus.). 80p. (J). (ps-3). pap. 5.99 (***978-1-4169-3548-3(7)*** , Simon Scribbles) Simon & Schuster Children's Publishing.

Aboff, Marcie, et al. Dream BIG! Cutting, David A. & Riley, Kellee, illus. 2007. (Holly Hobbie & Friends Ser.). 400p. (J). 5.99 (***978-1-4169-3550-6(9)*** , Simon Scribbles) Simon & Schuster Children's Publishing.

Adam, Winky. Around the World Coloring Book. 2005. 32p. (J). pap. 3.95 (978-0-486-43983-9(6)) Dover Pubns., Inc.

—Little Celtic Activity Book. 2000. (Illus.). 64p. (J). pap. 1.00 (978-0-486-41254-2(7)) Dover Pubns., Inc.

—Little Dinosaur ABC Coloring Book. 1998. (Illus.). 64p. (J). pap. 1.50 (978-0-486-40301-4(7)) Dover Pubns., Inc.

Adams, Ann. The Silver Boat Coloring Book. Elbo, Max & Pace, Jeff, illus. 2000. 20p. (J). pap. 9.00 (978-0-9678498-1-2(0)) Silver Boat Productions.

Adams, Pam. Meet Mrs. Honey Doll. 1999. (J). (ps-3). 16.99 (978-0-85953-824-4(9)) Child's Play-International.

Adams, William J. Goin' to the Zoo Coloring Book: Vamos Al Zoologico. Stiglich, Tom, illus. 2007. (ENG & SPA.). (J). pap. 3.95 (***978-0-9772757-3-1(6)***) Mandy & Andy Bks., Inc.

Adly, Muhammad S. Learn & Color (For Children) 24p. (978-1-894264-45-7(2)) Al-Attique Pubs., Inc.

The Advantage Max-4 HD Waterfowl Coloring & Activity Book. 2003. (J). pap. (978-0-9745863-0-4(7)) Cypress Knees Publishing.

Adventures at the Treasure House. 1998. (Captain Kangaroo Coloring Bks.: Vol. 2). (Illus.). 24p. (J). pap. (978-0-7666-0220-5(6) , Honey Bear Bks.) Modern Publishing.

Adventures of My Dentist & the Tooth Fairy Activity & Coloring Book Second Edition. 2nd ed. 2005. (J). per. 19.95 (978-1-59649-535-7(9)) Whispering Pine Pr., Inc.

Aigner-Clark, Julie. Windows to Color. Zaidi, Nadeem, illus. 2004. (Baby Einstein Ser.). 22p. (J). (ps-ps). bds. 5.99 (978-0-7868-5130-0(9)) Hyperion Bks. for Children.

Akaishi, Shinobu & Sarris, Eno, eds. My Book of Coloring. 2006. (Illus.). 80p. (J). per. 6.95 (978-1-933241-28-9(4)) Kumon Publishing North America, Inc.

Akmon, Nancy C. & Akmon, Roni. Roosevelt Bears Coloring Book. 2000. (Illus.). 52p. (J). 7.95 (978-1-884807-49-7(6) , EC 749) Blushing Rose Publishing.

Albee, Sarah. Elmo Loves You! Swanson, Maggie, illus. rev. ed. 2005. 24p. (J). (ps). pap. 3.50 (978-1-4037-1694-1(3)) Dalmatian Pr.

—Hooray for Our Heroes! Brannon, Tom, illus. rev. ed. 2005. 24p. (J). (ps-ps). pap. 3.50 (978-1-4037-1432-9(0)) Dalmatian Pr.

Alexander, Alec. Marshmallow Martian Coloring Book with Fun Activities. 2000. (Marshmallow Martian Ser.). (Illus.). 46p. (J). (ps-5). pap. 3.50 (978-0-9670091-3-1(8)) Smart Alec Toys Publishing.

Ali, Liaquat, text. Color & Learn Allah's 99 Most Beautiful Names: (Asma Al-husna) l.t. ed. 2002. (Illus.). 34p. (J). 4.95 (978-1-56744-714-9(7) , Library of Islam, Ltd.) Kazi Pubns., Inc.

Aliens & Space. Date not set. (Illus.). 64p. (J). 2.98 (978-1-4054-0446-4(9)) Parragon, Inc.

All about God, 6 vols., Set. 1999. (J). pap. 1.50 (978-0-87162-808-4(2)) Warner Pr. Pubs.

Aloka, illus. The Windhorse Colouring Book. 2004. 56p. pap. 17.95 (978-1-899579-42-6(7)) Windhorse Pubns. GBR. *Dist:* Consortium Bk. Sales & Distribution.

Amery, Heather. On the Farm? rev. ed. 2006. 16p. (J). pap. 5.99 (978-0-7945-1288-0(7) , Usborne) EDC Publishing.

Amoss, Berthe. Draw Yourself into a Starlit Journey. 2003. 32p. (J). spiral bd. 12.95 (978-1-59325-004-1(5)) Word Among Us Pr.

C D

—Draw Yourself into the Ark with Noah & His Family. 2003. 32p. (J). spiral bd. 12.95 (978-1-59325-003-4(7)) Word Among Us Pr.

Anderson, Sara. Colors & Numbers. Anderson, Sara, illus. 2007. (J). bds. 19.95 (978-1-59354-183-5(X)) Chronicle Bks. LLC.

Angels: A Coloring Book. 2000. (Illus.). (J). pap. 4.95 (978-0-88388-252-8(3)) Bellerophon Bks.

Animal Faces. 16p. (J). 1.89 (978-0-7847-1020-3(1)) Standard Publishing.

Animals of the Bible. (Illus.). 16p. (J). pap. 1.50 (978-0-87162-874-9(0) , E6035) Warner Pr. Pubs.

Anklam, Londa. Jacob Sheep & More... Not Just a Coloring Book. Anklam, Londa, illus. 2000. (Illus.). 32p. (J). pap. 7.95 (978-0-9701674-0-8(7)) Londa Signs.

Arena Verlag. Kids' Mandalas. 2004. (Illus.). 64p. pap. 4.95 (978-1-4027-1720-8(2)) Sterling Publishing Co., Inc.

Arrigo, Joseph A. Historic Baton Rouge. 1999. (Illus.). 32p. (J). (gr. k-3). 3.25 (978-1-56554-421-5(8)) Pelican Publishing Co., Inc.

—Historic Great Lakes Lighthouses: Coloring Book. 2002. (Illus.). 32p. (J). (gr. 4-7). 3.95 (978-1-55709-537-4(X)) Applewood Bks.

—Historic Pacific Coast Lighthouses: Coloring Book. 2002. (Illus.). 32p. (J). (ps-3). 4.95 (978-1-55709-536-7(1)) Applewood Bks.

—Northern Lighthouses Coloring Book. 2002. (Illus.). 32p. (J). (gr. 4-7). per. 3.95 (978-1-55709-538-1(8)) Applewood Bks.

Artic Circle Coloring & Activity Book. 2001. (J). (978-0-89610-445-7(1)) Island Heritage Publishing.

An Artist's Coloring Book. 2004. (J). 5.95 (978-0-9749672-0-2(3)) JINKS Studio Art & Publishing.

Ashar, Linda. Kerry Bog Pony Sketch & Coloring Book, 2004. (Illus.). (J). 4.00 (978-0-9749728-0-0(0)) Thornapple Farms, LLC.

At the Barbershop, 6 vols. (Multicultural Programs Ser.). 16p. (gr. 1-3). 24.95 (978-0-7802-9209-3(X)) Wright Group, The.

Augen, D. R. Guitar Toons Coloring Book & CD. Kirlin, Jim, ed. Kunkel, Bruce, illus. 1999. 25p. (J). (ps-7). pap. 14.00 incl. audio compact disk (978-0-9669881-3-0(2)) D.R. Auten Music & Assocs.

Augustyn, Brian. One-Way Ticket to Wonderworld. Staton, Joe & DeCarlo, Mike, illus. 2003. (Justice League Ser.). 16p. (J). pap. 2.99 (978-1-4037-0296-8(9)) Dalmatian Pr.

Austen, Jane. Pride & Prejudice. 2004. 400p. (J). 5.99 (978-1-4037-0986-8(6)) Dalmatian Pr.

Auten, D. R. Guitar Toons: Coloring Book. Kirlin, Jim, ed. Kunkel, Bruce, illus. 1999. 25p. (J). (ps-10). pap. 6.00 (978-0-9669881-1-6(6)) D.R. Auten Music & Assocs.

Awaken the Dragon. 1999. (Dragon Ball Z Giant Coloring & Activity Bks.). (Illus.). 96p. (J). (gr. 1-2). pap. (978-0-7666-0539-8(6)) Modern Publishing.

Awesome Activity. 2004. 80p. (J). act. bk. ed. 4.99 (978-1-85997-688-3(3)) Byeway Bks.

Awesome Coloring. 2004. 80p. (J). act. bk. ed. 4.99 (978-1-85997-689-0(1)) Byeway Bks.

Awesome Power. 1999. (Dragon Ball Z Full Color Activity Bks.). (Illus.). 32p. (J). (gr. 2-5). pap. (978-0-7666-0576-3(0)) Modern Publishing.

Axford, Elizabeth C., compiled by. The Music Box & Other Delights. 2003. (Illus.). 72p. (J). spiral bd. 14.95 (978-1-931844-03-1(8) , PP1015) Piano Pr.

Babcock, Jerry. Children's Keepsake Educational Coloring Book, Bk. 1. Babcock, Jerry, illus. l.t. unabr. ed. 1998. (Illus.). 44p. (J). (gr. k-4). pap. 4.99 (978-1-892161-05-5(2)) Babcock Publishing Co.

Baby Looney Tunes Box Set with Coloring Books. 2000. (J). (978-1-58805-130-1(7)) DS-Max USA, Inc.

Bak, Jenny. My Little Pony Color & Poster Book. Middleton, Gayle & Edwards, Ken, illus. 2006. (My Little Pony Ser.). 32p. (J). pap., pap. 3.99 (978-0-06-079470-5(4) , Harper Festival) HarperCollins Pubs.

Baker, Michael. Thinker Doodles: Think, Draw, & Color: Beginning Clues & Choose. 2005. (J). pap. 8.99 (978-0-89455-869-6(2)) Critical Thinking Bks. & Software.

—Thinker Doodles Clues & Choose A1: Think, Draw, & Color. 2005. (J). pap. 8.99 (978-0-89455-870-2(6)) Critical Thinking Bks. & Software.

Baker, Yaba. Just Like Me: A Coloring Book of Careers. Oldham, Anne Marie, illus. 1999. 36p. (J). (gr. 4-7). pap. (978-1-928889-02-1(6)) Just Like Me, Inc.

—Just Like Me: Coloring Book of Careers. Oldham, Anne Marie, illus. 1998. 28p. (gr. k-6). pap. 4.95 (978-1-928889-03-8(4)) Just Like Me, Inc.

Ballerinas. Date not set. (Dot to Dot Ser.). 64p. (J). 2.98 (978-1-4054-0449-5(3)) Parragon, Inc.

Balloon Books. I Can Color: Sticker Workbook. 2003. (Illus.). 18p. (J). pap., wbk. ed. 3.95 (978-1-4027-0493-2(3)) Sterling Publishing Co., Inc.

Balloon Books Staff. I Can Draw. 2003. (Illus.). 18p. (J). pap., wbk. ed. 3.95 (978-1-4027-0494-9(1) , Balloon Bks.) Sterling Publishing Co., Inc.

—Kindergarten Color & Learn. 2003. (Illus.). 64p. (J). pap. 4.95 (978-1-4027-0498-7(4) , Balloon Bks.) Sterling Publishing Co., Inc.

—Pre-School Color & Learn. 2002. (Color & Learn Bks.). (Illus.). 64p. (J). pap. 4.95 (978-1-4027-0497-0(6) , Balloon Bks.) Sterling Publishing Co., Inc.

Balloon Books Staff, ed. Click & Color: 115 Images to Color. 2000. (Balloon Ser.). (Illus.). 16p. (J). pap., pap. 8.95 incl. cd-rom (978-0-8069-2925-5(1) , Balloon Bks.) Sterling Publishing Co., Inc.

—Dot-to-Dots from 1 to 10: Fun House. 2001. (Fun House Paperbacks Ser.). (Illus.). 72p. (J). pap. 2.95 (978-0-8069-2264-5(8) , Balloon Bks.) Sterling Publishing Co., Inc.

—Find the Differences Coloring Book. (Illus.). (J). 2003. 48p. pap. 4.95 (978-0-8069-8957-0(2)); 2001. 72p. pap. 2.95 (978-0-8069-2266-9(4) , Balloon Bks.) Sterling Publishing Co., Inc.

Bambi: Coloring, Paint with Water, Activities. 2000. (Golden Book Ser.). (Illus.). 96p. (J). (ps-3). pap. 3.99 (978-0-307-25403-0(8) , Golden Bks.) Random Hse. Children's Bks.

Baran, Robert J. The Bonsai Coloring Book. Steele, Paul, illus. 2005. 5.95 net. (978-0-9659913-5-3(0)) Pyramid Dancer Pubns.

Barbaresi, Nina. Firefighters Coloring Book. 2003. (Dover Coloring Bks.). (Illus.). 32p. (J). pap. 2.95 (978-0-486-42646-4(7)) Dover Pubns., Inc.

—The Little Animal ABC Coloring Book. 80th ed. 1998. (Stickers Ser.). (Illus.). 64p. (J). (ps-2). pap. 1.50 (978-0-486-25834-8(3)) Dover Pubns., Inc.

—Spanish Alphabet Coloring Book. 1998. (Illus.). 32p. (J). (gr. k-3). pap. 3.95 (978-0-486-27249-8(4)) Dover Pubns., Inc.

Barbaresi, Nina & Beylon, Cathy. Horses & Ponies: Coloring & Sticker Fun (logo) 2006. 32p. (J). pap. 3.95 (978-0-486-45220-3(4)) Dover Pubns., Inc.

Barden, Christine, et al, eds. Coloring Book. 2001. (Music for Little Mozarts Ser.). 48p. (J). Bk. 3. pap. 3.95 (978-0-7390-1741-8(1) , 19671); Bk. 4. pap. 3.95 (978-0-7390-1742-5(X) , 19672) Alfred Publishing Co., Inc.

Barden, Christine, et al. Coloring Book. 2001. (Music for Little Mozarts Ser.). 48p. (J). Bk. 1. pap. 3.95 (978-0-7390-1739-5(X) , 19669); Bk. 2. pap. 3.95 (978-0-7390-1740-1(3)) Alfred Publishing Co., Inc.

Barlow, Dave. Tome of Knowledge; Volcanoes. 2005. (ENG., Illus.). 20p. (YA). per. 4.95 (978-0-9725230-9-7(X)) Wandering Sage Bookstore & More, LLC.

Barlowe, Dot. America the Beautiful to Paint or Color. 2006. 48p. pap. 4.95 (978-0-486-44811-4(8)) Dover Pubns., Inc.

—Country Scenes to Paint or Color. 2005. 48p. (J). (gr. 3). pap. 4.95 (978-0-486-44481-9(3)) Dover Pubns., Inc.

—Nautical Scenes to Paint or Color. 2007. 48p. pap. 4.95 (*978-0-486-45693-5(5)) Dover Pubns., Inc.

—Rocky Mountains Plants & Animals Coloring Book. 2004. (Illus.). 32p. (J). pap. 3.95 (978-0-486-43045-4(6)) Dover Pubns., Inc.

—Seashore Plants & Animals Colouring Book. 2000. (Illus.). 48p. (J). pap. 3.95 (978-0-486-41033-3(1)) Dover Pubns., Inc.

—A Walk in the Woods Coloring Book. 2003. (Dover Coloring Bks.). (Illus.). 32p. (J). pap. 3.95 (978-0-486-42644-0(0)) Dover Pubns., Inc.

Barney Color & Activity Prepack. 2003. (J). 179.40 (978-0-439-47364-4(0)) Scholastic, Inc.

Barrett, Anna Pearl. De Colores: A Spanish/English Neecie Coloring Book. Sells, Kathy & Maddux, Tomas, eds. Pequero, Phillip, illus. 2002. (SPA & ENG.). 32p. (J). (gr. 1-5). pap. 2.95 (978-0-9661330-3-5(X)) Over the Rainbow Productions.

Batchelor, John. Jet Fighters Coloring Book. 1998. (Illus.). 48p. (J). pap. 3.95 (978-0-486-40357-1(2)) Dover Pubns., Inc.

—Old Ship Figureheads Coloring Book. 2002. (Illus.). 32p. (J). pap. 3.95 (978-0-486-42370-8(0)) Dover Pubns., Inc.

Batchlor, Larry G. Juneteenth Story Activity & Coloring Book: From African Slaves to African Americans. Goings, Kenneth & La Rue, Linda, eds. Walker, Felix C., illus. l.t. ed. 2000. 60p. (J). (gr. 4-7). pap. 10.00 (978-0-9701357-0-4(X)) Jubilee Day/Juneteenth Celebration.

Battle Cry. 1999. (Dragon Ball Z Coloring Sticker Activity Bks.). (Illus.). 25p. (J). (gr. 1-2). pap. (978-0-7666-0541-1(8)) Modern Publishing.

Battle Force. 1999. (Dragon Ball Z Coloring & Activity Bks.). (Illus.). 32p. (J). (gr. 1-2). pap. (978-0-7666-0536-7(1)) Modern Publishing.

Bauer, Susan Wise. The Middle Ages. 2003. (Story of the World: Vol. 2). (Illus.). 275p. (J). pap., act. bk. ed. 29.95 (978-0-9714129-4-1(4) , AB2) Peace Hill Pr.

Bausman, Mary, illus. God Loves Me Coloring Pages: For Toddlers And 2's. 2006. (Heartshaper Ser.). 192p. (J). pap. 15.99 (978-0-7847-1796-7(6) , 02446) Standard Publishing.

Bear/Heart: Coloring Activity Book. 2002. (Illus.). 32p. (J). (ps). pap. 2.99 (978-1-57759-639-4(0)) Dalmatian Pr.

Beaulieu, Jeannine. Caillou, 4 vols. 3rd rev. ed. 2006. (Caillou Activity Bks.). (Illus.). 24p. (J). pap. 3.95 (*978-2-89450-573-1(6)) Chouette Publishing CAN. Dist: Independent Pubs. Group.

Beaulieu, Jeannine. Caillou Butterfly. (Illus.). 24p. (J). pap. (978-2-89450-292-1(3)) Chouette Publishing.

Begin, Mary Jane, illus. ABC God Loves Me: Board Book. 2005. 10p. (J). bds. 5.99 (978-1-4037-1416-9(9)) Dalmatian Pr.

Bell, A. L. Jr. Comics Coloring (Fun Time) 2005. 20p. 7.00 (978-1-4116-3758-0(5)) Lulu.com.

Bell-Grey, Mel & Bell-Grey, Jennifer Schwartz. The Adventures of Nani & Koa. 2004. (J). pap. 5.95 (978-0-9729479-8-5(1)) Eyes Wide Open Productions.

Bell, N. Wayne. Childrens' Economics: A Book on Money & Finance. l.t. ed. 2004. (Illus.). 32p. (J). per. (978-0-9729753-5-3(7)) Really Big Coloring Bks., Inc.

—The Really Big Book of Zoo Animals. l.t. ed. 2004. (Illus.). 32p. (J). per. (978-0-9729753-6-0(5)) Really Big Coloring Bks., Inc.

Belovitch, Jeanne. Boston Firsts: A Coloring Book about Boston's History & America's. Parker, Edward, illus. 2002. 28p. (J). (ps-7). pap. 2.50 (978-0-9722969-0-8(5)) CMB Publishing Co.

Benner, Cheryl A. An Amish Christmas Coloring Book. 2002. (Illus.). 10p. (J). (ps-1). 2.95 (978-1-56148-265-8(X)) Good Bks.

Berkowitz, Henry. Birds of Prey: An Educational Coloring Book. Berkowitz, Henry, illus. 2001. (Illus.). 32p. (J). (ps-3). pap. 4.95 (978-0-932855-62-6(8)) Winner Enterprises.

—Extinct Mammals: An Educational Coloring Book. Berkowitz, Henry, illus. 2001. (Illus.). 32p. (J). (ps). pap. 4.95 (978-0-932855-61-9(X)) Winner Enterprises.

—Marine Mammals: An Educational Coloring Book. Berkowitz, Henry, illus. 2001. (Illus.). 32p. (J). (ps-3). pap. 4.95 (978-0-932855-65-7(2)) Winner Enterprises.

—Water Birds: An Educational Coloring Book. Berkowitz, Henry, illus. 2001. (Illus.). 32p. (J). (ps-3). pap. 4.95 (978-0-932855-64-0(4)) Winner Enterprises.

Bernhard, Annika. Freshwater Pond Coloring Book. 2000. (Illus.). 48p. (J). pap. 3.95 (978-0-486-41035-7(8)) Dover Pubns., Inc.

Bernson, Linda. Picture Perfect. 2001. (Seasons: Vol. 1). 124p. pap. 3.95 (978-0-9678285-1-0(1)) Lunchbox Pr.

Berry, Virginia B. Iggie's Big Adventure Coloring Book: A True Story of Faith. Berry, Virginia B., ed. King, Garry W., illus. ed. 2002. 16p. (J). (gr. k-6). pap. 1.00 (978-0-9726091-1-1(3)) Berry Enterprises.

The Best Thing about Easter Coloring Book. 2006. 16p. (J). pap. 1.99 (978-0-7847-1351-8(0) , 22128) Standard Publishing.

Betanzos, Sue, illus. My New Backyard Garden. 2006. Tr. of Mi Nuevo Jardin del Traspatio. (SPA & ENG.). (J). (*978-0-9792253-0-7(2)) Tucson Botanical Gardens.

Beyblade Coloring & Activity Books. 2004. (J). act. bk. ed. (978-0-7666-1253-2(8) , 99225); act. bk. ed. (978-0-7666-1254-9(6) , 99225); act. bk. ed. (978-0-7666-1255-6(4) , 99225); act. bk. ed. (978-0-7666-1256-3(2) , 99225) Modern Publishing.

Beyblade Fun Activity Box Set. 2004. (J). act. bk. ed. (978-0-7666-1360-7(7) , 64033) Modern Publishing.

Beyblade Giant Coloring & Activity Books. 2004. (J). act. bk. ed. (978-0-7666-1257-0(0) , 49285); act. bk. ed. (978-0-7666-1258-7(9) , 49285) Modern Publishing.

Beylon, Cathy. All Aboard! Trains Coloring & Activity Book. 2006. 32p. (J). pap., act. bk. ed. 2.95 (978-0-486-45174-9(7)) Dover Pubns., Inc.

—At the Hospital. 2003. (Dover Coloring Bks.). (Illus.). 32p. (J). pap. 2.95 (978-0-486-43033-1(2)) Dover Pubns., Inc.

—Cats & Kittens Stained Glass Coloring Book. 2005. (Illus.). 16p. (J). (gr. 1-4). pap. 5.95 (978-0-486-44467-3(8)) Dover Pubns., Inc.

—Christmas Family Fun Coloring Book. 2006. 32p. (J). pap. 2.95 (978-0-486-44749-0(9)) Dover Pubns., Inc.

—Firehouse Coloring Book. 2000. (Illus.). 32p. (J). pap. 2.95 (978-0-486-41308-2(X)) Dover Pubns., Inc.

—Going Camping. 2004. 32p. (J). pap. 2.95 (978-0-486-43984-6(4)) Dover Pubns., Inc.

—Halloween Stained Glass Coloring Book. 2007. 16p. (J). pap. 5.95 (*978-0-486-45677-5(3)) Dover Pubns., Inc.

—Hearts Stained Glass Coloring Book. 2004. 8p. (J). pap. 1.50 (978-0-486-43844-3(9)) Dover Pubns., Inc.

—Little Mother Goose Stained Glass Coloring Book. 2002. (Illus.). 8p. (J). pap. 1.50 (978-0-486-42337-1(9)) Dover Pubns., Inc.

—Merry-Go-Round Stained Glass Coloring Book. 2003. (Dover Little Activity Bks.). (Illus.). 8p. (J). pap. 1.50 (978-0-486-43000-3(6)) Dover Pubns., Inc.

—Mother Goose Coloring Book. 2004. (Illus.). 32p. (J). pap. 2.95 (978-0-486-43696-8(9)) Dover Pubns., Inc.

—My Plane Trip. 2005. 32p. (J). pap. 2.95 (978-0-486-43982-2(8)) Dover Pubns., Inc.

—Nature ABC Coloring Book. 2005. 32p. (J). (ps-3). pap. 2.95 (978-0-486-44448-2(1)) Dover Pubns., Inc.

—Noah's Ark Coloring Book. 2003. (Illus.). 32p. (J). pap. 2.95 (978-0-486-42373-9(5)) Dover Pubns., Inc.

—Noah's Ark Stained Glass Coloring Book. 2004. 8p. (J). pap. 1.50 (978-0-486-43843-6(0)) Dover Pubns., Inc.

—Old MacDonald's Farm Coloring Book. 2003. (Illus.). 32p. (J). pap. 2.95 (978-0-486-43034-8(0)) Dover Pubns., Inc.

—Safety First Coloring Book. 2006. 32p. (J). pap. 2.95 (978-0-486-45164-0(X)) Dover Pubns., Inc.

—Teddy Bear Family Stained Glass Coloring Book. 2003. (Illus.). 8p. (J). (gr. k-5). pap. 1.50 (978-0-486-42617-4(3)) Dover Pubns., Inc.

Beylon, Cathy & Barbaresi, Nina. I Love Butterflies. 2007. 32p. (J). pap. 3.95 (*978-0-486-45659-1(5)) Dover Pubns., Inc.

Bible Coloring Book. 1998. (Illus.). (J). (ps-3). pap. 0.99 (978-0-88271-639-8(5)) Regina Pr., Malhame & Co.

Bible Heroes. 2006. 16p. (J). pap. 1.99 (978-0-7847-1354-9(5) , 22123) Standard Publishing.

Bible Story Coloring Pages, Vol. 2. 2004. 248p. 17.99 (978-0-8307-3095-7(8) , Gospel Light) Gospel Light Pubns.

Bickico Enterprises Staff, concept. BabyKids: The Color Book. 2003. 16p. (J). pap. 2.95 (978-0-9746508-2-1(X)) Bickico Enterprises, Inc.

Big Fun! Date not set. (Furby Coloring & Activity Book Ser.). (Illus.). 96p. (J). pap. (978-0-7666-0412-4(8) , Honey Bear Bks.) Modern Publishing.

Big Fun Posters to Color. 2002. 60p. (J). pap. 3.98 (978-0-7525-7601-5(1)) Parragon, Inc.

Big Little Coloring Book. 2004. 192p. (J). act. bk. ed. 4.99 (978-1-85997-234-2(9)) Byeway Bks.

Bike Safe! Life Safety Coloring/Activity Book. 2007. (Illus.). (J). (*978-1-933934-31-0(X)) Educational Adventures.

Bing & Bong's Colouring Book. 2003. (Tiny Planets Ser.). (Illus.). 24p. pap. 4.99 (978-1-84222-876-0(5)) Carlton Bks. Ltd. GBR. Dist: Trafalgar Square Publishing.

Bishop, Beverly. My Friend with Autism. Bishop, Craig, illus. 2002. 30p. (J). (ps-3). pap. 9.95 (978-1-885477-89-7(9)) Future Horizons, Inc.

Bishop, Jennie. Jonah & the Big Fish Coloring Book. 2007. (Illus.). 16p. (J). pap. 1.89 (*978-1-59317-206-0(0)) Warner Pr. Pubs.

—The Squire & the Scroll Coloring Book. 2005. (J). pap. 1.79 (*978-1-59317-085-1(8)) Warner Pr. Pubs.

Bishop, Jennifer Lynn. Geometrix Coloring Book. 2006. (Illus.). 32p. pap. 3.95 (*978-0-486-45672-0(2)) Dover Pubns., Inc.

Black, Harley. Magic Art Class. 2001. (Pinwheel Ser.). (Illus.). 10p. (J). (ps-k). 5.95 (978-0-8069-0600-3(6)) Sterling Publishing Co., Inc.

—Magic Coloring Book. Balloon Books Staff, ed. 2003. (Fun House Paperbacks Ser.). (Illus.). 72p. (J). pap. 2.95 (978-0-8069-2276-8(1) , Balloon Bks.) Sterling Publishing Co., Inc.

blackbird. Mr. HookWorm Coloring Book. 2007. 32p. (J). per. 1.50 (*978-0-9789798-7-4(7)) Blackbird's World Publishing Co.

Blake, William. William Blake Stained Glass Colouring Book. 2005. (Illus.). 32p. (J). (gr. 4). pap. 5.95 (978-0-486-44667-7(0)) Dover Pubns., Inc.

Blazin' Hot: Coloring/Activity Book (English) 2005. (Illus.). (J). (978-0-9770455-0-1(1)) Educational Adventures.

Blazin' Hot: Coloring/Activity Book (English) Incl. Stickers. 2007. (J). (*978-1-933934-51-8(4)) Educational Adventures.

Blendy Pens Activity Book. 2006. (J). spiral bd., act. bk. ed. (978-0-9770652-0-2(0)) Color Loco, LLC.

Bloomfield. Wild Utah Coloring Book. (J). pap. 2.95 (978-0-915749-12-6(2)) Earthwalk Pr.

Bob the Builder. 2003. (J). (ps-2). spiral bd. 14.99 (978-1-59319-000-2(X)) LeapFrog Enterprises, Inc.

Bohn, Kendall. Abstract Adventure II: A Kaleidoscopia Coloring Book. 2006. (Illus.). 58p. per. 8.95 (978-0-929636-66-5(X)) Syren Bk. Co.

Boosel, Brian D. The Saint Vincent Coloring Book, Gabler, Michael, illus. 2005. 36p. (J). 9.99 (978-0-9708216-7-6(0)) St. Vincent Archabbey Pubns.

Bowman, Robert P. & Frank, Kim T. The Magic Coloring Book of Feelings. Daugherty, Tonya & Peterson, Justin, illus. 2001. 120p. (J). (gr. k-8). pap. 19.95 (978-1-889636-41-2(X)) Youthlight, Inc.

Boyer, Melody. Great American Pony Ride. Johnson, Dolores Uselman, illus. 32p. (J). 2.00 (978-0-9704876-3-6(0)) First Mom's Club, The.

Brabham, Barbara. Donkey Tales — Color with Paco! [English/Spanish Versions]. 2006. (J). 2.95 (*978-1-882185-86-3(2)) Cornerstone Publishing, Inc.

Bradley, Barbara. Hawaiian Kids Cook & Color Book. pap. 5.95 (978-0-930492-43-4(9)) Hawaiian Service, Inc.

The Brave Boy. l.t. ed. 2001. 16p. (J). pap. 1.00 (978-81-87570-74-5(1)) Goodword Bks. Pvt. Ltd. IND. Dist: Lodhia Ctr., The.

The Brave Boy: Quran Stories for Little Hearts. l.t. ed. 2001. 24p. (J). pap. 2.25 (978-81-87570-78-3(4)) Goodword Bks. Pvt. Ltd. IND. Dist: Lodhia Ctr., The.

Bros, Warner & Warner Brothers Staff. Harry Potter Color-by-Numbers Bk. 1: The Creatures of Harry Potter & the Sorcerer's Stone. 2001. (Illus.). 32p. (gr. 4-7). 7.99 (978-0-439-28625-1(5)) Scholastic, Inc.

—Harry Potter Stained Glass Art Bk. 1: The Characters of Harry Potter & the Sorcerer's Stone. 2001. (Illus.). 32p. (gr. 4-7). pap. 4.99 (978-0-439-28632-9(8)) Scholastic, Inc.

—Harry Potter Stained Glass Art Bk. 2: Scenes from Harry Potter & the Sorcerer's Stone. 2001. (Illus.). 32p. (gr. 4-7). pap. 4.99 (978-0-439-28633-6(6)) Scholastic, Inc.

Brown, Richard. Blanco's Magic Tails Coloring Book. Brown, Byron, illus. 2001. (Blanco's Magic Tails Coloring Book: Vol. 1). 36p. (J). pap. 5.95 (978-0-9712596-0-7(7)) Magic Tails Pr.

Bruce, Hank. Where Do Snowmen Go When They Melt? Lampert, Erv, ed. Berkowitz, Henry, illus. 1999. (Winner Coloring Bks.). (J). (gr. k-3). pap. 4.95 (978-0-932855-58-9(X)) Winner Enterprises.

Bruna, Dick. Miffy & Friends: Blue-Green Coloring Book. 2004. (Illus.). 48p. pap. 5.99 (978-1-59226-096-6(9)) Big Tent Entertainment, Inc.

—Miffy & Friends: Yellow-Red Coloring Book. 2004. (Illus.). 48p. pap. 5.99 (978-1-59226-098-0(5)) Big Tent Entertainment, Inc.

Brunger, Bruce A & Reimers, Cathy L. Buzz & Pixie Activity Coloring Book: An Entertaining Way to Help Young Children Understand Their Behavior. Brunger, Bruce A, illus. 2003. (Illus.). 105p. (J). (ps up). pap. 9.95 (978-1-886941-33-5(5)) Specialty Pr., Inc.

Bumper Coloring Fun. 2002. 576p. (J). pap. 6.98 (978-0-7525-8925-1(3)) Parragon, Inc.

Bunnell, Deb T. My First French ABC Picture Coloring Book. 2000. (FRE & ENG., Illus.). 32p. (J). pap. 3.50 (978-0-486-41039-5(0)) Dover Pubns., Inc.

—My First Spanish ABC Picture Coloring Book. 1998. (Illus.). 32p. (J). (gr. k-5). pap. 2.95 (978-0-486-40358-8(0)) Dover Pubns., Inc.

Burgess, Thornton W. & Stewart, Pat. Meet Peter Cottontail. 2006. 32p. pap. 2.95 (*978-0-486-45998-1(5)) Dover Pubns., Inc.

Burkhalter, Mary L. Active Children's Literature: Alphabet Story, Colors, Mister Prince. 1998. (Illus.). 50p. (J). (gr. k-4). pap. 20.00 (978-0-934284-09-7(1)) Jolean Publishing Co.

Burnett, Frances Hodgson. The Secret Garden Great Read. 2004. (Great Classics for Children Ser.). 288p. (J). 5.99 (978-1-4037-0989-9(0)) Dalmatian Pr.

Burrows, Roger. Roger Burrows' Images Travel Pack: The Ultimate Portable Coloring Experience. 2005. 100p. (J). (ps-ps). pap. 14.95 (978-0-7624-2288-3(2) , Running Pr.) Running Pr. Bk. Pubs.

The Butterfly. 1998. (Teletubbies Ser.). (Illus.). 24p. (J). (ps). pap. (978-0-7666-0259-5(1) , Honey Bear Bks.) Modern Publishing.

Button, M. A. The Eye Book: A Coloring Book. 2000. (Illus.). 26p. (J). pap. 9.95 (978-0-7414-0424-4(9)) Infinity Publishing.

Caillou: Colors & Shapes. 2003. 32p. pap., wbk. ed. 14.95 incl. cd-rom (978-1-57791-029-9(X)) Brighter Minds Children's Publishing.

Caillou Coloring Book. 2004. (J). act. bk. ed. (978-0-7666-1101-6(9) , 99430); act. bk. ed. (978-0-7666-1102-3(7) , 99430); act. bk. ed. (978-0-7666-1103-0(5) , 99430); act. bk. ed. (978-0-7666-1104-7(3) , 99430) Modern Publishing.

Caillou Fun Activity Box Set. 2004. (J). act. bk. ed. (978-0-7666-1123-8(X) , 64027) Modern Publishing.

Caillou Giant Coloring Book. 2004. (J). act. bk. ed. (978-0-7666-1099-6(3) , 49305); act. bk. ed. (978-0-7666-1100-9(0) , 49305) Modern Publishing.

Caillou Super Coloring Book. 2004. (J). act. bk. ed. (978-0-7666-1158-0(2) , 11853) Modern Publishing.

Caldwell, Lise. Jesus Always Loves Me. Marlin, Kathy, illus. 1999. (Coloring Bks.). 16p. (J). (ps-3). pap. 1.99 (978-0-7847-0878-1(9) , 22070) Standard Publishing.

—Sharing Is Fun! Carter, Nancy, illus. 1999. (Coloring Bks.). 16p. (J). (ps-3). 1.89 (978-0-7847-0876-7(2) , 22068, Bean Sprouts) Standard Publishing.

Caldwell, Lise, ed. Around the World. Burris, Priscilla, illus. 1999. 48p. (J). (ps-2). pap. 2.49 (978-0-7847-0994-8(7) , 22064, Bean Sprouts) Standard Publishing.

Camping Caper: Coloring/Activity Book (English) incl. Stickers. 2007. (Illus.). (J). (***978-1-933934-65-5(4)***) Educational Adventures.

Canine under Cover: Hidden Picture Book to Color. 2004. (Scooby-Doo Ser.). 32p. (J). pap. 3.49 (978-1-4037-0726-0(X)) Dalmatian Pr.

Capalija, Ann Marie. My Little Pony Color & Sticker Book. Middleton, Gayle, illus. 2003. (My Little Pony Ser.). 32p. (J). (ps-1). pap. 3.99 (978-0-06-054945-9(9) , Harper Festival) HarperCollins Pubs.

—Pony Pals Color & Cutie Marks Tattoo Book. Middleton, Gayle, illus. 2003. (My Little Pony Ser.). 32p. (J). (ps-1). pap. 3.99 (978-0-06-054944-2(0)) HarperCollins Pubs.

Care Bears Coloring Books. 2004. (J). act. bk. ed. (978-0-7666-0919-8(7) , 99390); act. bk. ed. (978-0-7666-0920-4(0) , 99390); act. bk. ed. 1.29 (978-0-7666-0921-1(9) , 99390); act. bk. ed. (978-0-7666-0922-8(7) , 99390) Modern Publishing.

Care Bears Fun Activity Box Set. 2004. (J). act. bk. ed. (978-0-7666-0984-6(7) , 64018) Modern Publishing.

Care Bears Giant Coloring Books. 2004. (J). act. bk. ed. (978-0-7666-0923-5(5) , 49590); act. bk. ed. (978-0-7666-0924-2(3) , 49590) Modern Publishing.

Care Bears Sticker Books. 2004. (J). act. bk. ed. (978-0-7666-1154-2(X) , 69570); act. bk. ed. (978-0-7666-1155-9(8) , 69570) Modern Publishing.

Carle, Eric. My Own Very Busy Spider Coloring Book. Carle, Eric, illus. 2004. (Illus.). 32p. (J). (ps-1). pap. 5.99 (978-0-399-24309-7(7) , Philomel) Penguin Group (USA) Inc.

—My Own Very Lonely Firefly Coloring Book. Carle, Eric, illus. 2006. 32p. (J). (ps). pap. 5.99 (978-0-399-24646-3(0) , Philomel) Penguin Group (USA) Inc.

—My Own Very Quiet Cricket Coloring Book. Carle, Eric, illus. 2005. 32p. (J). (ps-1). 5.99 (978-0-399-24475-9(1) , Philomel) Penguin Group (USA) Inc.

—My Very Own Hungry Caterpillar Coloring Book. Carle, Eric, illus. 2003. (Illus.). 32p. (J). 5.99 (978-0-399-24207-6(4) , Philomel) Penguin Group (USA) Inc.

Carlsbad Caverns & Guadalupe Mountains Color Book. 2003. (YA). pap. (978-0-916907-08-2(2)) Carlsbad Caverns Guadalupe Mountains Assn.

Carlson, Faith. Poppins Coloring Book Vol. 1.1: Colors. Carlson, Faith, illus. 2000. (Illus.). 43p. (J). (ps-5). 10.00 (978-1-886498-07-5(5)) Poppin & Co. Communication Materials.

—Poppin's Coloring Book Vol. 1.2: Clothing. Carlson, Faith, illus. 2000. (Illus.). 43p. (J). (ps-5). 10.00 (978-1-886498-08-2(3)) Poppin & Co. Communication Materials.

Carlson, Melody. Jammin' with the Fruit Troop Color Book. 1998. (Stories, Songs, & Riddles Ser.). 64p. (J). pap. 9.99 incl. audio (978-1-57673-305-9(X)) Zonderkidz.

Carney, Karen L. Everything Changes, but Love Endures: Explaining Hospice to Children. Carney, Karen L., illus. 2000. (Barklay & Eve Ser.: Bk. 6). (Illus.). (J). pap. 6.95 (978-0-9667820-5-9(4)) Dragonfly Publishing.

—Honoring Our Loved Ones: Going to a Funeral. Carney, Karen L., illus. 3rd ed. 2001. (Barklay & Eve Ser.: Bk. 2). (Illus.). (J). pap. 6.95 (978-0-9667820-1-1(1)) Dragonfly Publishing.

—Our Special Garden: Understanding Cremation. Carney, Karen L., illus. 1999. (Barklay & Eve Ser.: Bk. 4). (Illus.). (J). pap. 6.95 (978-0-9667820-3-5(8)) Dragonfly Publishing.

—Precious Gifts: The Katie Coolican Story. Carney, Karen L., illus. 2002. (Barklay & Eve Ser.: Bk. 7). (Illus.). (J). pap. 6.95 (978-0-9667820-6-6(2)) Dragonfly Publishing.

—They're Part of the Family: Barklay & Eve Talk to Children about Pet Loss. Carney, Karen L., illus. 2002. (Barklay & Eve Ser.: Bk. 8). (Illus.). (J). pap. 6.95 (978-0-9667820-8-0(9)) Dragonfly Publishing.

—Together, We'll Get Through This! Learning to Cope with Loss & Transition. Carney, Karen L., illus. 1999. (Barklay & Eve Ser.: Bk. 1). (Illus.). (J). pap. 6.95 (978-0-9667820-0-4(3)) Dragonfly Publishing.

—What Is Cancer, Anyway? Explaining Cancer to Children of All Ages. Carney, Karen L., illus. rev. ed. 2001. (Barklay & Eve Ser.: Bk. 5). (Illus.). (J). pap. 6.95 (978-0-9667820-4-2(6)) Dragonfly Publishing.

—What Is the Meaning of Shiva. Carney, Karen L., illus. rev. ed. 2001. (Barklay & Eve Ser.: Bk. 3). Orig. Title: Barklay & Eve. (Illus.). (J). pap. 6.95 (978-0-9667820-2-8(X)) Dragonfly Publishing.

Caro, Joe. Santa's Christmas Train Coloring Book. Shih, Lin, illus. 2005. 32p. pap. (978-0-9628078-5-5(0)) Cowboy Collector Pubns.

Carole Marsh. Los Angeles Coloring & Activity Book. 2004. (City Bks.). 24p. (gr. k-5). pap. 3.95 (978-0-635-02229-5(X)) Gallopade International.

—Chicago Coloring & Activity Book. 2004. (City Bks.). 24p. (gr. k-5). pap. 3.95 (978-0-635-02227-1(3)) Gallopade International.

—Dallas Coloring & Activity Book. 2004. (City Bks.). 24p. (gr. k-5). pap. 3.95 (978-0-635-02231-8(1)) Gallopade International.

—Native American Heritage Coloring Book. 2004. (Native American Heri Ser.). 24p. (gr. k-2). pap. 3.95 (978-0-635-02398-8(9)) Gallopade International.

—New England Coloring. 2004. (City Bks.). 24p. (gr. k-5). pap., act. bk. ed. 3.95 (978-0-635-02233-2(8)) Gallopade International.

—New York City Coloring & Activity Book. 2004. (City Bks.). 24p. (gr. k-5). pap. 3.95 (978-0-635-02226-4(5)) Gallopade International.

—San Francisco Coloring & Activity Book. 2004. (City Bks.). 24p. (J). (gr. k-5). pap., act. bk. ed. 3.95 (978-0-635-02228-8(1)) Gallopade International.

—Washington Dc Coloring & Activity Book. 2004. (City Bks.). 24p. (gr. k-5). pap. 3.95 (978-0-635-02232-5(X)) Gallopade International.

Carpenter, Chad. Tundra Alaska Coloring Book. (J). pap. 3.00 (978-1-878100-32-0(7)) Todd Communications.

Carry-Along Bible Fun. 1999. (Illus.). (J). (ps-1). 9.99 (978-0-310-97866-4(1)) Zonderkidz.

Carson, Carole. Remembering When I Was Young. 2006. (Illus.). 48p. (J). 19.95 (978-0-9766030-8-5(X)) Hound Pr.

—Remembering When I Was Young Coloring Book. 2006. 44p. (J). pap. 6.95 (978-0-9766030-7-8(1)) Hound Pr.

Cartoon Network Staff. Buttercup. 2001. (Powerpuff Girls Ser.). (Illus.). 32p. (J). (ps-3). pap. 3.99 (978-0-307-10802-9(3) , Golden Bks.) Random Hse. Children's Bks.

Casey & Caymus: Sticker Story Book to Color. 2002. (Illus.). 16p. (J). pap. 2.99 (978-1-888567-57-1(0)) Dalmatian Pr.

Cavanagh, Karen, ed. My First Prayer Book: Coloring Book. Luberoff, William, illus. 1999. (Catholic Classics). 32p. (J). pap. 0.99 (978-0-88271-638-1(7)) Regina Pr., Malhame & Co.

CEDCO Publishing Staff. Powerpuff Girls. 2000. (Gel Pen Blank Bks.). (Illus.). 96p. (J). (gr. 4-7). 9.95 (978-0-7683-2229-3(4)) CEDCO Publishing.

Celebrate Jesus! Coloring/Activity Book. 2006. (Illus.). 32p. (J). (ps-2). pap., act. bk. ed. 2.89 (978-0-7847-1125-5(9) , 22090) Standard Publishing.

Chagall, Marc. Chagall Stained Glass Coloring Book. 2000. (Illus.). 16p. (J). pap. 5.95 (978-0-486-41326-6(8)) Dover Pubns., Inc.

Chandler, Lynda E. Fruits & Vegetables Coloring Book. 2001. (Illus.). 48p. (J). pap. 3.95 (978-0-486-41543-7(0)) Dover Pubns., Inc.

Charge of the Goddess. 2007. (Illus.). 20p. (J). 10.00 (***978-0-9795206-4-8(9)***) Unseen Gallery.

Chase, H. Peter. A Book for Coloring & Learning about Diabetes. Reece, Regina, ed. United Artists Corporation Staff, illus. 4th ed. 2000. Orig. Title: A Coloring Book about Diabetes. (SPA.). 102p. (YA). (gr. 9 up). pap. 5.00 (978-0-9675398-1-2(1)) Children's Diabetes Foundation at Denver, The.

Chesterfield, Sadie. Lion, the Witch, & the Wardrobe. Marderosian, Mark, illus. movie tie-in ed. 2005. (Narnia Ser.). 32p. (J). pap., act. bk. ed. 4.99 (978-0-06-076557-6(7)) Zonderkidz.

—Spider-Man 3: Coloring & Activity Book & Crayons. Gordon, Steven E., illus. 2007. (Spider-Man Ser.). 32p. (J). pap. 4.99 (978-0-06-083726-6(8) , Harper Entertainment) HarperCollins Pubs.

Chesterfield, Sadie & S. I. International. Feeling Groovy Art Studio. Cuddy, Robbin, illus. 2007. (Groovy Girls Ser.). 48p. (J). 9.99 (***978-1-4169-3551-3(7)*** , Simon Scribbles) Simon & Schuster Children's Publishing.

Chihak, Sheena, ed. It's a Big Big World Color & Activity with Crayons. 2007. 48p. (J). pap. 3.99 (***978-0-696-23550-4(1)***) Meredith Bks.

Children of the Bible: Dot-to-Dot Coloring Book. (Illus.). 16p. (J). pap. 1.50 (978-0-87162-979-1(8) , E4652) Warner Pr. Pubs.

Chouette & Beaulieu, Jeannine. Caillou, 4 vols. 4th rev. ed. 2006. (Caillou Activity Bks.). (Illus.). 24p. (J). pap. 3.95 (***978-2-89450-574-8(4)***) Chouette Publishing CAN. *Dist:* Independent Pubs. Group.

Christmas Coloring Fun Christmas Carols. 2004. (J). per. 6.95 (978-1-885920-47-8(4)) Pyramid Publishing, Inc.

Christmas Coloring Fun Santa Relaxing. 2004. (J). per. 6.95 (978-1-885920-48-5(2)) Pyramid Publishing, Inc.

Christmas Coloring Fun Santa's New Sled. 2004. (J). per. 6.95 (978-1-885920-88-1(1)) Pyramid Publishing, Inc.

Christmas Coloring Fun Snowman. 2004. (J). per. 6.95 (978-1-885920-90-4(3)) Pyramid Publishing, Inc.

Christmas Fun Coloring Book. 2006. 16p. (J). pap. 1.99 (978-0-7847-1745-5(1) , 04371) Standard Publishing.

Clark, Christian. Mr. Clark's Awesome Designs Coloring Book. 2006. (ENG.). 60p. per. 11.95 (***978-1-59800-883-8(8)***) Outskirts Press, Inc.

Clarkson, Clay. Our 24 Family Ways: Family Devotional Guide. Jarboe, Marvin, illus. 2004. 112p. (J). pap. 14.95 (978-1-888692-07-5(3)) Whole Heart Ministries.

—Our 24 Family Ways: Kids Color-In Book. Jarboe, Marvin, illus. 2004. 64p. (J). pap. 4.95 (978-1-888692-10-5(3)) Whole Heart Ministries.

—Our 24 Family Ways: Kids Color-in Book. 2003. (Illus.). 32p. pap. 4.95 (978-1-888692-16-7(2)) Whole Heart Ministries.

Clements, Andrew. Holiday Fun Coloring Book. 1998. (Illus.). (J). mass mkt. 1.79 (978-0-689-82361-9(4) , Little Simon) Simon & Schuster Children's Publishing.

—Snowden Winter Fun Coloring Book. 1998. (Illus.). 80p. (J). mass mkt. 1.99 (978-0-689-82360-2(6) , Little Simon) Simon & Schuster Children's Publishing.

Clifford Big Coloring. 2004. (J). act. bk. ed. (978-0-7666-0892-4(1) , 49585) Modern Publishing.

Clifford Big Coloring & Activity Books. 2004. (J). act. bk. ed. (978-0-7666-0893-1(X) , 49585) Modern Publishing.

Clifford Big Shape Coloring. 2004. (J). act. bk. ed. (978-0-7666-0869-6(7) , 39595) Modern Publishing.

Clifford Big Shape Coloring & Activity Books. 2004. (J). act. bk. ed. (978-0-7666-0870-2(0) , 39595) Modern Publishing.

Clifford Coloring. 2004. (J). act. bk. ed. (978-0-7666-0890-0(5) , 99510) Modern Publishing.

Clifford Coloring & Activity Books. 2004. (J). act. bk. ed. (978-0-7666-0888-7(3) , 99510); act. bk. ed. (978-0-7666-0889-4(1) , 99510); act. bk. ed. (978-0-7666-0891-7(3) , 99510) Modern Publishing.

Clifford Fun Activity Box Set. 2004. (J). act. bk. ed. (978-0-7666-0989-1(8) , 64026) Modern Publishing.

Clifford Watch Me Color Books. 2004. (J). (978-0-7666-0687-6(2) , 66210); (978-0-7666-0688-3(0) , 66210) Modern Publishing.

Clifton, Dorinda. Everybody Is Somebody. 2006. (J). 6.95 (978-0-9771973-2-3(8)) Bedbug Pr., Inc.

—Take the Cake. 2006. (J). 6.95 (978-0-9771973-3-0(6)) Bedbug Pr., Inc.

Coches. (Coleccion Mundo Maravilloso).Tr. of Drawing Cars. (SPA.). (J). (gr. 3-5). (978-84-348-4429-2(X)) SM Ediciones.

Cole, Heidi & Vogl, Nancy. Am I a Color Too? Purnell, Gerald, illus. 2005. 32p. (J). (ps-3). 15.95 (978-0-9740190-5-5(4)) Illumination Arts Publishing Co., Inc.

Collucci, Jim, concept. Cape Cod for Kids: Coloring Book. 2002. 36p. (J). act. bk. ed. 4.95 (978-0-9722040-0-2(8)) Creative Imagery.

Color All About: A Giant Coloring Book about Dinosaurs: Dinosaurs. 2004. (SPA & ENG., Illus.). 36p. (J). (978-1-59949-001-4(3)) Food Marketing Consultants, Inc.

Color All About: A Giant Coloring Book about Fun Things to do at School: Back to School. 2004. (Illus.). 36p. (J). (978-1-59949-005-2(6)) Food Marketing Consultants, Inc.

Color All About: A Giant Coloring Book about Loving Our Pets: Pets. 2004. (Illus.). 36p. (J). (978-1-59949-002-1(1)) Food Marketing Consultants, Inc.

Color All About: A Giant Coloring Book about Summer Vacation: Summer Vacation. 2004. (Illus.). 36p. (J). (978-1-59949-006-9(4)) Food Marketing Consultants, Inc.

Color All About: A Giant Coloring Book about the Alphabet: the Alphabet. 2004. (SPA & ENG., Illus.). 36p. (J). (978-1-59949-000-7(5)) Food Marketing Consultants, Inc.

Color All About: A Giant Coloring Book about the County Fair: the County Fair. 2004. (SPA & ENG., Illus.). 36p. (J). (978-1-59949-004-5(8)) Food Marketing Consultants, Inc.

Color All About: A Giant Coloring Book about Work & Play on the Farm: the Farm. 2004. (SPA & ENG., Illus.). 36p. (J). (978-1-59949-003-8(X)) Food Marketing Consultants, Inc.

Color All About: America: A Giant Coloring Book about the Birth of a Nation. 2004. (Illus.). (J). (978-0-9763307-3-8(3)) Food Marketing Consultants, Inc.

Color All About: Christmas: A Giant Coloring Book about Christmas. 2004. (SPA & ENG., Illus.). (J). (978-0-9763307-7-6(6)) Food Marketing Consultants, Inc.

Color All About: Christmas: A Giant Coloring Book for Christmas. 2004. (Illus.). (J). (978-0-9763307-0-7(9)) Food Marketing Consultants, Inc.

Color All About: Santa: A Giant Coloring Book about What Santa Does When It's Not Christmas. 2004. (Illus.). (J). (978-0-9763307-4-5(1)); (SPA & ENG., (978-0-9763307-8-3(4)) Food Marketing Consultants, Inc.

Color All About. The Circus: A Giant Coloring Book about Going to the Circus. 2004. (Illus.). (J). (978-0-9763307-1-4(7)); (SPA & ENG., (978-0-9763307-9-0(2)) Food Marketing Consultants, Inc.

Color All About: The County Fair: A Giant Coloring Book about Having Fun When the Fair Comes to Town. 2004. (Illus.). (J). (978-0-9763307-6-9(8)) Food Marketing Consultants, Inc.

Color All About: The Farm: A Giant Coloring Book about Having Fun on a Farm. 2004. (Illus.). (J). (978-0-9763307-5-2(X)) Food Marketing Consultants, Inc.

Color All About: The Zoo: A Coloring Book about Going to the Zoo. 2004. (Illus.). (J). (978-0-9763307-2-1(5)) Food Marketing Consultants, Inc.

Color & Discover Activity Book: The Crabby Lady Gets Historical! 2001. (Suzanne Tate's History Ser.). 32p. (J). pap. 2.95 (978-1-878405-33-3(0)) Nags Head Art, Inc.

Color by Numbers Sticker Activity Books. 2003. (Illus.). 18p. (J). 5.99 (978-0-8254-7264-0(4)); Vol. 2. 5.99 (978-0-8254-7265-7(2)) Kregel Pubns.

Color 'Em Book No. 2: A Coloring Book for All Ages. 2002. (Illus.). 100p. (J). (ps-5). mass mkt. 14.95 (978-0-9672388-1-4(1)) Rosell, Emily.

Color 'Em Book No. 3: A Coloring Book for All Ages. 2002. (Illus.). 100p. (J). (ps-5). mass mkt. 14.95 (978-0-9672388-2-1(X)) Rosell, Emily.

Color Me Monet. 2004. (J). (978-0-9765917-1-9(5)) EDU-KIT, L.L.C.

Color My Mouse - Calendar Mice. 2004. (J). pap. (978-0-9764719-1-2(4)) MiceWorks.

Color My Mouse - Summer Mice. 2005. (J). pap. (978-0-9764719-2-9(2)) MiceWorks.

Color Splitz. 2006. (J). spiral bd. 12.99 (978-0-9770652-1-9(9)) Color Loco, LLC.

Color with Barney. 2000. (Illus.). 448p. (J). (ps-2). 4.99 (978-1-57064-460-3(8) , 97937) Scholastic, Inc.

Colorado Coloring Book. 2003. (J). (978-0-9726022-0-4(8)) Mountain States Specialties.

Coloring Book Assortment. 2003. (J). per. (978-1-932435-22-1(0)) Cardinal Brands, Inc.

Coloring Book Lets Celebrate G. 2006. 16p. (J). pap. 1.99 (978-0-7847-1526-0(2) , 22140) Standard Publishing.

Coloring Book Let's Remember Jesus. 2006. 16p. (J). pap. 1.99 (978-0-7847-1525-3(4) , 22139) Standard Publishing.

Coloring Book Lets Shine Jesus. 2006. 16p. (J). pap. 1.99 (978-0-7847-1523-9(8) , 22137) Standard Publishing.

Coloring Book Let's Show God's Love. 2006. 16p. (J). pap. 1.99 (978-0-7847-1524-6(6) , 22138) Standard Publishing.

Coloring Book Story of David. 2004. pap. (978-1-931471-12-1(6)) United Bible Societies, African Regional Ctr.

Coloring Book/Intermediate/Bible Fun Old Testament. 2006. (J). 14.99 (978-1-59317-146-9(3)) Warner Pr. Pubs.

Coloring Fun: Coloring/Activity Book (English) 2006. (Illus.). (J). (***978-1-933934-20-4(4)***) Educational Adventures.

Coloring Fun: Coloring/Activity Book (Spanish) 2006. (Illus.). (J). (***978-1-933934-21-1(2)***) Educational Adventures.

Coloring Fun: English/Spanish. 2006. (Illus.). (J). (***978-1-933934-24-2(7)***) Educational Adventures.

Coloring Fun Book. 2004. 80p. (J). act. bk. ed. 4.99 (978-1-85997-387-5(6)) Byeway Bks.

Coloring Fun of the U. S. States Images & Facts. 2003. (Illus.). 40p. (J). 3.95 (978-0-9729026-3-2(5)) Midwest Cylinder Management, Inc.

Coloring Fun Presbyterian Children's Hospital: Coloring/Activity Book. 2006. (J). (***978-1-933934-30-3(1)***) Educational Adventures.

Colors, 6 Bks, Set. 2004. (J). 128.14 (978-0-7614-1769-9(9)) Cavendish, Marshall Corp.

Colors & Shapes Booster. 2005. (J). per. 0.00 (978-1-59441-506-7(4) , C04038) Carson-Dellosa Publishing Co., Inc.

Colour the Bible: Ezra-Daniel, Vol. 2. 16p. (J). pap., act. bk. ed. 1.50 (978-1-85792-762-7(1) , Christian Focus) Christian Focus Pubns. GBR. *Dist:* Riverside.

Colour the Bible: Genesis-Chronicles, Bk. 1. 16p. (J). pap., act. bk. ed. 1.50 (978-1-85792-761-0(3) , Christian Focus) Christian Focus Pubns. GBR. *Dist:* Riverside.

Colour the Bible: Hosea-Malachi, Vol. 3. 16p. (J). pap., act. bk. ed. 1.50 (978-1-85792-763-4(X) , Christian Focus) Christian Focus Pubns. GBR. *Dist:* Riverside.

Colour the Bible: Matthew-Acts, Vol. 4. 16p. (J). pap., act. bk. ed. 1.50 (978-1-85792-764-1(8) , Christian Focus) Christian Focus Pubns. GBR. *Dist:* Riverside.

Colour the Bible: Romans-Thessalonians, Vol. 5. 16p. (J). pap., act. bk. ed. 1.50 (978-1-85792-765-8(6) , Christian Focus) Christian Focus Pubns. GBR. *Dist:* Riverside.

Colour the Bible: Timothy-Revelation, Vol. 6. 16p. (J). pap., act. bk. ed. 1.50 (978-1-85792-766-5(4) , Christian Focus) Christian Focus Pubns. GBR. *Dist:* Riverside.

Come Aboard Noah's Ark Coloring Book. abr. ed. (J). pap. 1.99 (978-0-8423-3535-5(8)) Dorling Kindersley Publishing, Inc.

Come & Play. 1998. (Teletubbies Ser.). (Illus.). 96p. (J). (ps). pap. (978-0-7666-0266-3(4) , Honey Bear Bks.) Modern Publishing.

Comickers Coloring Book. 2008. 256p. pap. 18.95 (***978-0-06-124204-5(7)*** , Collins Design) HarperCollins Pubs.

Conant, Susan Sens. Lewis & Clark's Journey of Discovery: A Guide for Young Explorers. Lynn, Rick, illus. 2004. 48p. (J). pap. (***978-0-9725584-1-9(1)***) Little Blue Pr.

Concordia Publishing Staff. My Bible Story Coloring Book. 1998. (ps-2). Vol. 6. (Illus.). 32p. pap. 2.95 (978-0-570-05073-5(1)); Vol. 8. (J). pap. 1.99 (978-0-570-05085-8(5)) Concordia Publishing Hse.

Conley, Nia. Ray's School Daze. l.t. ed. 2003. (Illus.). 30p. (J). (978-0-9743781-2-1(7)) Urban Edge Publishing Co.

Conquering Heroes. 1999. (Digimon Giant Coloring & Activity Bks.). (Illus.). 96p. (J). (ps-2). pap. (978-0-7666-0550-3(7)) Modern Publishing.

Conroy, Don. Colouring & Activity Book. 1999. (J). (gr. 1-4). per. (978-1-902586-53-3(0)) Mentor Bks.

Cookie Jar Editorial Staff, ed. Friends & Favorites! 2007. 96p. (J). pap. 2.99 (978-1-60095-256-2(9)) Cookie Jar.

—Let's Get on the Bus! 2007. 96p. (J). pap. 2.99 (978-1-60095-255-5(0)) Cookie Jar.

Cookie Jar Publishing Staff. Doodlebops: Kids' Favorite Rock Band. 2006. 32p. pap. (978-1-933799-00-1(5)) Carson-Dellosa Publishing Co., Inc.

Cool by the Pool: Coloring / Activity Book incl Snipe. 2007. (Illus.). (J). (***978-0-9770455-8-7(7)***) Educational Adventures.

Cool by the Pool: Coloring/Activity Book. 2005. (Illus.). (J). (978-0-9770455-2-5(8)) Educational Adventures.

Cooper, Diana. Angel Colouring Book. Zoutewelle-Morris, Sarah, illus. 2004. 32p. (J). pap. 5.95 (978-1-84409-042-6(6)) Findhorn Pr. GBR. *Dist:* Independent Pubs. Group, SteinerBooks, Inc.

Copeland, Peter F. American Presidents Coloring Book. 2001. (Illus.). 48p. (J). pap. 3.95 (978-0-486-41324-2(1)) Dover Pubns., Inc.

—The Amistad Coloring Book. 2002. (Illus.). 32p. (J). (gr. 3). pap. 3.95 (978-0-486-42375-3(1)) Dover Pubns., Inc.

—Benjamin Franklin Coloring Book. 2005. 32p. (J). pap. 3.95 (978-0-486-43988-4(7)) Dover Pubns., Inc.

—Blackbeard & Other Notorious Pirates: Coloring Book. 2005. (Illus.). 32p. (J). (ps-ps). pap. 3.95 (978-0-486-44003-3(6)) Dover Pubns., Inc.

—Daniel Boone Coloring Book. 2006. 32p. (J). pap. 3.95 (978-0-486-44738-4(3)) Dover Pubns., Inc.

—Famous Women of the Civil War Coloring Book. 1999. (Illus.). 32p. (J). (gr. 3). pap. 3.95 (978-0-486-40799-9(3)) Dover Pubns., Inc.

—George Washington Coloring Book. 2003. (Dover Coloring Bks.). (Illus.). 48p. (J). (gr. 3). pap. 3.95 (978-0-486-42647-1(5)) Dover Pubns., Inc.
—Naval Battles of the Civil War Coloring Book. 2001. (Illus.). 48p. (J). pap. 3.95 (978-0-486-28815-4(3)) Dover Pubns., Inc.
—Sea Monsters Coloring Book. 1998. (Illus.). 32p. (J). pap. 3.95 (978-0-486-40562-9(1)) Dover Pubns., Inc.
Corbett, Allyson. Spider-Man 3: Coloring & Activity Book & Stickers. Gordon, Steven E., illus. 2007. (Spider-Man Ser.). 32p. (J). pap. 4.99 (978-0-06-083727-3(6) , Harper Entertainment) HarperCollins Pubs.
Count & Color (Pre-K) 2003. (J). (978-1-58232-042-7(X)) Bryan Hse. Pubs., Inc.
Cousins, Lucy. Maisys Easter Paint Book. 2005. (Maisy Ser.). (Illus.). 20p. (J). (gr. k-k). pap. 3.99 (978-0-7636-2622-8(8)) Candlewick Pr.
—Maisy's Favorite Things. Cousins, Lucy, illus. 2001. (Maisy Bks.). (Illus.). 22p. (J). (gr. k-k). bds. 3.99 (978-0-7636-1574-1(9)) Candlewick Pr.
Covington, Jean. Nanny Planted Love: Color Book. 2006. (J). per. 6.99 (***978-1-933732-13-8(X)** , Bear Hug Bks.) MidAmerica Publishing Co.
Crafty Creatures. 2004. (Hidden Pictures Coloring Bks.). (Illus.). 48p. (J). (gr. 1-2). (978-0-7666-0606-7(6) , 99170) Modern Publishing.
Craig, Gary, illus. I Can Be Anything Creative Activity Book. 2006. 44p. (J). 5.99 (978-0-9786813-2-6(0)) Elora Pr.
Craven, Lon Eric, illus. ABC Coloring Book: March of the Teddy Bears Kansas City 2002. l.t. ed. 2002. 32p. per. 5.95 (978-0-9717080-9-9(6)) Kansas City Star Bks.
Creepy Crawlies. (Kid Kits Ser.). (Illus.). 32p. (J). 8.95 (978-1-58086-414-5(7)) EDC Publishing.
Creepy Crawlies. Date not set. (Dot to Dot Ser.). (Illus.). 64p. (J). 2.98 (978-1-4054-0447-1(7)) Parragon, Inc.
Crerand, John J. & Crerand, Teresa. The Adventures of Christopher Otter: Stories for Storytellers, Color Activity Book. Dannerfelter, Bea, illus. 2002. 40p. (J). (gr. k-6). pap. 4.50 (978-0-9719724-1-4(9) , CO-1A) TACCO.
Crisp, Marty. Dogs of the World Dot-to-Dot: Connect the Dots & Color. 2004. (Illus.). 80p. (J). pap. 5.95 (978-1-4027-1048-3(8)) Sterling Publishing Co., Inc.
Crop Circle Coloring Book. 2005. (J). (978-0-9719583-6-4(X)) Onstott, Scott.
Crownover, Amy & Crownover, Dean. My Perfect Man Coloring & Activity Book. 2006. (Illus.). 32p. 12.95 (978-0-9785425-0-4(9)) Retro Recess.
Curry, Don, ed. DC Heroes Ultimate Color & Activity Set. 2005. (J). pap. 9.99 (978-0-696-22892-6(0)) Meredith Bks.
—Fairies Jumbo Color & Activity Book. 2006. 400p. (J). pap. 5.99 (978-0-696-23250-3(2)) Meredith Bks.
—Pirates Jumbo Color & Activity Book. 2006. 400p. (J). pap. 5.99 (978-0-696-23251-0(0)) Meredith Bks.
Dalamatian Press Staff. All Creatures Great & Small. 2005. (Fuzzy Book to Color Ser.). (Illus.). 4p. (J). pap. 3.99 (978-1-4037-1413-8(4)) Dalmatian Pr.
—Creation My Coloring Book. 2005. (Illus.). 32p. (J). pap. 0.99 (978-1-4037-1415-2(0)) Dalmatian Pr.
—Dinosaurs on the Loose. rev. ed. 2005. (Big Best Book to Color Ser.). (Illus.). 48p. (J). pap. 2.99 (978-1-4037-1411-4(8)) Dalmatian Pr.
—Everything I Know about Potty. 2005. (Illus.). 8p. (J). bds. 7.99 (978-1-4037-1278-3(6)) Dalmatian Pr.
—Playhouse Disney Let's Play Every Day. 2005. 80p. (J). pap. 2.99 (978-1-4037-1407-7(X)) Dalmatian Pr.
—Story of Jesus My Coloring Book. 2005. 32p. (J). pap. 0.99 (978-1-4037-1414-5(2)) Dalmatian Pr.
Dalmatian Press, creator. The Lion King Classic Book to Color. 2007. (SPA., Illus.). 48p. (J). (ps-3). 1.99 (978-1-4037-0605-8(0)) Dalmatian Pr.
Dalmatian Press, ed. Mickey Mouse Paint with Water. rev. ed. 2007. 32p. pap. 3.99 (***978-1-4037-3400-6(3)*** Dalmatian Pr.
Dalmatian Press Staff. Alice in Wonderland & the Wind in the Willows. 2004. (Classics to Color with Colored Pencils Ser.). 64p. (J). pap. 2.99 (978-1-4037-0847-2(9)) Dalmatian Pr.
—And a Mummy, Too! Glow Sticker Book to Color. 2002. (Scooby-Doo! Ser.). (Illus.). 16p. (J). pap. 2.99 (978-1-57759-863-3(6)) Dalmatian Pr.
—Animals with Shaped Crayons: Book to Color Play Set. 2003. 64p. (J). pap. 4.99 (978-1-4037-0327-9(2)) Dalmatian Pr.
—Annabelle: Princess Book to Color with Glitter Paints. 2002. (Illus.). 32p. (J). (ps-3). pap. 2.99 (978-1-57759-810-7(5)) Dalmatian Pr.
—Anything but Nice: Sticker Activity Book to Color. 2002. (Powerpuff Girls Ser.). (Illus.). 46p. (J). pap. 1.69 (978-1-57759-873-2(3)) Dalmatian Pr.
—Ariel & Friends: Coloring & Activity Book with Stickers. (Disney Princess Ser.). 64p. (J). pap. (978-1-4037-0977-6(7)) Dalmatian Pr.
—Barney Let's Go to the Park: Sticker Storybook to Color. 2002. (Illus.). 16p. (J). (ps-k). 2.99 (978-1-57759-049-1(X)) Dalmatian Pr.
—Belle & Friends: Coloring & Activity Book with Stickers. 2004. (Disney Princess Ser.). (Illus.). 64p. (J). pap. 1.69 (978-1-4037-0863-2(0)) Dalmatian Pr.
—Berry Fun! Paint with Water Book to Color. 2003. (Strawberry Shortcake Ser.). 32p. (J). pap. 2.99 (978-1-4037-0302-6(7)) Dalmatian Pr.
—Berry Special: Big Best Book to Color. rev. ed. 2003. (Strawberry Shortcake Ser.). 32p. (J). pap. 2.99 (978-1-4037-0343-9(4)) Dalmatian Pr.
—Black Beauty & a Little Princess. 2004. (Classics to Color with Colored Pencils Ser.). 64p. (J). pap. 2.99 (978-1-4037-0845-8(2)) Dalmatian Pr.
—Blossom, Bubbles & Buttercup: Big Best Book to Color. rev. ed. 2002. (Powerpuff Girls Ser.). (Illus.). 96p. (J). pap. 2.99 (978-1-57759-868-8(7)) Dalmatian Pr.
—Bugs Bunny: Looney Games Big Best Book to Color. 2003. (Big Best Book to Color Ser.). 96p. (J). 2.99 (978-1-57759-901-2(2)) Dalmatian Pr.
—Cartoon Cartoons: Stay Tooned... Big Best Book to Color. 2002. (Cartoon Network Ser.). (Illus.). 96p. (J). 2.99 (978-1-57759-882-4(2)) Dalmatian Pr.
—Cartoons Cartoons: 400 Pages of Coloring Fun. 2003. (Cartoon Network Ser.). (Illus.). 400p. (J). pap. 5.99 (978-1-4037-0025-4(7)) Dalmatian Pr.
—Cinderella & Friends: Coloring & Activity Book with Stickers. 2004. (Disney Princess Ser.). (Illus.). 64p. (J). pap. 1.69 (978-1-4037-0864-9(9)) Dalmatian Pr.
—Clued in on Style! Hidden Picture Book to Color. 2004. (Powerpuff Girls Ser.). 32p. (J). pap. 3.49 (978-1-4037-0727-7(8)) Dalmatian Pr.
—Color Trails: Glitter Crayon Book to Color. 2002. (Powerpuff Girls Ser.). (Illus.). 32p. (J). 3.99 (978-1-57759-871-8(7)) Dalmatian Pr.
—Colorful Markie: Bright Idea Book to Color. 2004. (Lisa Frank(R) Ser.). 32p. (J). pap. 4.49 (978-1-57759-806-0(7)) Dalmatian Pr.
—Coloring & Activity Book with Stickers. 68p. (J). pap. 1.69 (978-1-57759-507-6(6)) Dalmatian Pr.
—Coming at You! 3-D Book to Color with 3-D Glasses. 2003. (Scooby-Doo! Ser.). 32p. (J). pap. 4.99 (978-1-4037-0183-1(0)) Dalmatian Pr.
—Count Your Blessings: Board Book. 2005. (Illus.). 10p. (J). bds. 5.99 (978-1-4037-1417-6(7)) Dalmatian Pr.
—Curious George Everybody's Favorite Monkey: Big Best Book to Color. rev. ed. 2005. (Big Best Book to Color Ser.). (Illus.). 80p. (J). pap. 2.99 (978-1-4037-0724-6(3)) Dalmatian Pr.
—Curious George Sticker Book to Color: 75 Stickers +Coloring Fun. rev. ed. 2007. 48p. pap. 3.99 (***978-1-4037-3210-1(8)***) Dalmatian Pr.
—Dexter's Laboratory: Sis-Teria! Book to Color with Slime. 2003. (Cartoon Network Ser.). (Illus.). 32p. (J). pap. 4.49 (978-1-4037-0184-8(9)) Dalmatian Pr.
—Dexter's Laboratory: Sister Wars: Crayons & Paint Box Book. 2002. (Cartoon Network Ser.). (Illus.). 32p. (J). pap. 3.99 (978-1-57759-883-1(0)) Dalmatian Pr.
—Dino World! Velvety Book to Color. 2003. (Fuzzy Book to Color Ser.). (Illus.). 4p. (J). pap. 4.49 (978-1-4037-0712-3(X)) Dalmatian Pr.
—Disney 101 Dalmations: Book to Color with Caryons. 2006. 48p. pap. 2.99 (978-1-4037-1965-2(9)) Dalmatian Pr.
—Disney Animal Friends A Wonderful World of Color. 2006. 12p. bds. 9.99 (978-1-4037-1936-2(5)) Dalmatian Pr.
—Disney Bambi: Sticker Book to Color. 2006. 48p. pap. 2.99 (978-1-4037-1964-5(0)) Dalmatian Pr.
—Disney Best Friends: Valentines Day. 2005. 16p. bds. 5.99 (978-1-4037-1905-8(5)) Dalmatian Pr.
—Disney Bunnies Big Best Book to Color with Stickers. 2007. 96p. pap. 2.99 (***978-1-4037-3009-1(1)***) Dalmatian Pr.
—Disney Bunnies Big Crayon Book to Color. 2007. 48p. pap. 3.99 (***978-1-4037-3010-7(5)***) Dalmatian Pr.
—Disney Bunnies Sticker Book to Color. 2007. 48p. pap. 2.99 (***978-1-4037-3021-3(0)***) Dalmatian Pr.
—Disney Dumbo: Big Best Book to Color. 2006. 96p. pap. 2.99 (978-1-4037-1963-8(2)) Dalmatian Pr.
—Disney Mickey Mouse & Friends: Big Crayon Book to Color. 2006. 48p. pap. 3.99 (978-1-4037-1966-9(7)) Dalmatian Pr.
—Disney the Lion King & Animal Friends: 400 Pages of Coloring Fun. 2006. 400p. 5.99 (978-1-4037-1968-3(3)) Dalmatian Pr.
—Disney's Mickey Mouse Clubhouse Big Crayon Book to Color. 2007. 48p. 3.99 (***978-1-4037-3206-4(X)***) Dalmatian Pr.
—Donald Duck: Coloring Book with Stickers. 2003. 64p. (J). pap. 1.69 (978-1-57759-773-5(7)) Dalmatian Pr.
—Double Vision: Book to Color with Molded Crayons. 2003. (Powerpuff Girls Ser.). (Illus.). 32p. (J). pap. 4.49 (978-1-4037-0334-7(5)) Dalmatian Pr.
—Earthquake! Paint Box Book to Color. 2003. (Power Rangers Ninja Storm Ser.). 32p. (J). pap. 3.99 (978-1-4037-0467-2(8)) Dalmatian Pr.
—Energy Launch: Color-n-Stick Activity Book. 2002. (Power Rangers Time Force Ser.). (Illus.). 64p. (J). pap. 2.99 (978-1-57759-573-1(4)) Dalmatian Pr.
—Everything Nice: Sticker Activity Book to Color. 2002. (Powerpuff Girls Ser.). (Illus.). 64p. (J). pap. 1.69 (978-1-57759-872-5(5)) Dalmatian Pr.
—Extreme Power Coloring Book. 2002. (Power Rangers Time Force Ser.). (Illus.). 32p. (J). (ps-1). pap. 1.15 (978-1-57759-529-8(7)) Dalmatian Pr.
—The Fashion Phantom: Glow Crayon Book to Color. 2003. (Scooby-Doo! Ser.). (Illus.). 32p. (J). pap. 4.49 (978-1-4037-0335-4(3)) Dalmatian Pr.
—Fright Night: Shaped Book to Color with Stickers. 2003. (Scooby-Doo! Ser.). 32p. (J). pap. 2.99 (978-1-4037-0336-1(1)) Dalmatian Pr.
—Gabrielle: Princess Book to Color with Glitter Stickers. 2002. (Illus.). 48p. (J). (ps-3). pap. 2.99 (978-1-57759-808-4(3)) Dalmatian Pr.
—Ghost Fun Glow Crayon Book to Color. 2005. 48p. (J). pap. 2.99 (978-1-4037-1481-7(9)) Dalmatian Pr.
—Gigantosaurus Wrecks: Stamper Marker Book to Color. rev. ed. 2004. (Scooby-Doo Ser.). (Illus.). 32p. (J). pap. 4.49 (978-1-4037-0602-7(6)) Dalmatian Pr.
—God Is Great Big Crayon Book to Color. 2005. (Illus.). 32p. (J). pap. 2.99 (978-1-4037-1184-7(4)) Dalmatian Pr.
—God's Creations: Bright Idea Book to Color. 2003. (Bright Idea Book to Color Ser.). (Illus.). 32p. (J). pap. 3.99 (978-1-57759-892-3(X)) Dalmatian Pr.
—God's Wonderful World: Bright Idea Book to Color. 2003. (Bright Idea Book to Color Ser.). (Illus.). 32p. (J). pap. 3.99 (978-1-57759-893-0(8)) Dalmatian Pr.
—Good Goblin Glow in The. 2004. 48p. pap. 2.99 (978-1-4037-0828-1(2)) Dalmatian Pr.
—Good Goblin Glow Sticker Book to Color. 2005. (Illus.). 48p. (J). pap. 2.99 (978-1-4037-1485-5(1)) Dalmatian Pr.
—Goodness/Apple. 2004. (Fruit of the Spirit Inspirational Ser.). 8p. (J). bds. 5.99 (978-1-4037-0822-9(3)) Dalmatian Pr.
—Goofy: Coloring Book with Stickers. 2003. 64p. (J). 1.69 (978-1-57759-774-2(5)) Dalmatian Pr.
—Groovin'! Velvety Book to Color. 2004. (Scooby-Dootm! Ser.). (Illus.). 8p. (J). pap. 4.99 (978-1-4037-0720-8(0)) Dalmatian Pr.
—Growing Better Every Day! Coloring & Activity Book with Stickers. (Strawberry Shortcake Ser.). 64p. (J). pap. 1.69 (978-1-4037-0789-5(8)) Dalmatian Pr.
—Growing Dinosaurs. 2006. 48p. (J). pap. 3.99 (978-1-4037-1971-3(3)) Dalmatian Pr.
—Growing Sweeter! Coloring & Activity Book with Stickers. (Strawberry Shortcake Ser.). 64p. (J). pap. (978-1-4037-0788-8(X)) Dalmatian Pr.
—Halloween Surprise Paintbox. 2005. (Illus.). 48p. (J). pap. 2.99 (978-1-4037-1487-9(8)) Dalmatian Pr.
—Hanna-Barbera Tom-foolery: 400 Pages of Coloring Fun. 2004. (Illus.). 400p. (J). pap. 5.99 (978-1-4037-0027-8(3)) Dalmatian Pr.
—Happy Treats Gigantic BTC. 2004. 192p. pap. 2.99 (978-1-4037-0832-8(0)) Dalmatian Pr.
—Heroes of the Bible: Big Best Book to Color. (Big Idea's Veggie Tales Ser.). (Illus.). 96p. (J). mass mkt. 2.99 (978-1-4037-0292-0(6)) Dalmatian Pr.
—Hunter: Poster Book to Color. 2002. (Illus.). 32p. (J). pap. 1.35 (978-1-888567-53-3(8)) Dalmatian Pr.
—The Incredibles: Coloring Activity Book with Stickers. 2004. 64p. (J). pap. 1.69 (978-1-4037-0762-8(6)); pap. 1.69 (978-1-4037-0763-5(4)) Dalmatian Pr.
—Isabel: Princess Book to Color with Glitter Crayons. 2002. (Illus.). 32p. (J). (ps-3). pap. 2.99 (978-1-57759-809-1(1)) Dalmatian Pr.
—Jack O Lantern Shaped Photo Real Sticker BTC. 2004. 32p. pap. 2.99 (978-1-4037-0840-3(1)) Dalmatian Pr.
—Kittens Book to Color. 2002. (Illus.). 32p. (J). 1.15 (978-1-888567-52-6(X)) Dalmatian Pr.
—Kooky Critters Glow Critters Book to Color. 2005. (Great Classics for Children Ser.). (Illus.). 48p. (J). pap. 2.99 (978-1-4037-1482-4(7)) Dalmatian Pr.
—A Lesson In... Thankfulness: Book to Color with Stickers. 2003. (Big Idea's Veggie Tales Ser.). (Illus.). 32p. (J). pap. 2.99 (978-1-4037-0293-7(4) , Spirit Pr.) Dalmatian Pr.
—Life Is Sweet! Coloring & Activity Book with Stickers. (Strawberry Shortcaketm Ser.). 64p. (J). pap. (978-1-4037-0893-9(2)) Dalmatian Pr.
—The Life of Jesus: Big Best Book to Color. 2004. (Big Best Book to Color Ser.). (Illus.). 80p. (J). pap. 2.99 (978-1-4037-0758-1(8) , Spirit Pr.) Dalmatian Pr.
—Lights Out! Bright Idea Book to Color. 2004. (Scooby-Doo! Ser.). (Illus.). 32p. (J). reprint ed. pap. (978-1-57759-864-0(4)) Dalmatian Pr.
—Lisa Frank: Coloring Fun. 2005. (Illus.). 400p. (J). pap. 5.99 (978-1-4037-1154-0(2)) Dalmatian Pr.
—Little Chick. 2003. (Jumbo Book to Color Ser.). (Illus.). 160p. (J). pap. 1.99 (978-1-4037-0076-6(1)) Dalmatian Pr.
—Little Guys Can Do Big Things, Too! Coloring & Activity Book with Stickers. 2003. (Big Idea's Veggie Tales Ser.). 64p. (J). pap. 1.69 (978-1-4037-0291-3(8)) Dalmatian Pr.
—Little Ones Bible with Handle. 2005. (Pop-Up & Flap Board Bks.). (Illus.). 10p. (J). bds. 8.99 (978-1-4037-1379-7(0)) Dalmatian Pr.
—Little Women & Anne of Green Gables. 2004. (Classics to Color with Colored Pencils Ser.). 64p. (J). pap. 2.99 (978-1-4037-0846-5(0)) Dalmatian Pr.
—M&M's Brand: Big Best Book to Color. 2002. (Illus.). 112p. (J). (ps-4). pap. 2.99 (978-1-57759-781-0(8)) Dalmatian Pr.
—M&M's Brand: Bright Idea Book to Color. 2002. (Illus.). 32p. (J). (ps-4). 3.99 (978-1-57759-780-3(X)) Dalmatian Pr.
—M&M's Bright Idea Book to Color. 2002. (Illus.). 32p. (J). (ps-4). pap. 2.99 (978-1-57759-783-4(4)) Dalmatian Pr.
—Markie: A Book to Color. 2002. (Illus.). 32p. (J). (ps-4). pap. 1.15 (978-1-57759-245-7(X)) Dalmatian Pr.
—Merry Christmas Scratch n Sniff Sticker. 2004. 48p. pap. 2.99 (978-1-4037-0433-7(3)) Dalmatian Pr.
—Mi Mundo (My World) Spanish/English Book to Color. 2003. (SPA & ENG., Illus.). 192p. (J). pap. 3.99 (978-1-4037-0109-1(1)) Dalmatian Pr.
—Mickey Mouse: Coloring Book with Stickers. 2003. 64p. (J). 1.69 (978-1-57759-771-1(0)) Dalmatian Pr.
—Minnie Mouse: Coloring Book with Stickers. 2003. 64p. (J). pap. 1.69 (978-1-57759-772-8(9)) Dalmatian Pr.
—Monster Fun BBBTC w Stickers. 2004. 96p. pap. 2.99 (978-1-4037-0838-0(X)) Dalmatian Pr.
—My Coloring Book God Loves Me. 2004. 32p. pap. 99.00 (978-1-4037-0305-7(1)) Dalmatian Pr.
—My Coloring Book Two by Two. 2004. 32p. pap. 99.00 (978-1-4037-0304-0(3)) Dalmatian Pr.
—Mystery Mask Mix-Up: Coin Reveal Activity Book to Color. rev. ed. 2002. (Scooby-Doo! Ser.). (Illus.). 32p. (J). pap. 3.99 (978-1-57759-865-7(2)) Dalmatian Pr.
—Ninja Power: Bright Idea Book to Color. 2003. (Power Rangers Ninja Storm Ser.). 32p. (J). pap. 4.49 (978-1-4037-0466-5(X)) Dalmatian Pr.
—Noah's Ark Large Pop Up. rev. ed. 2005. (Pop-Up & Flap Board Bks.). (Illus.). 9p. (J). 10.99 (978-1-4037-1427-5(4)) Dalmatian Pr.
—Nowhere to Hyde! rev. ed. 2002. (Scooby-Doo! Ser.). (Illus.). 32p. (J). pap. 3.99 (978-1-57759-862-6(8)) Dalmatian Pr.
—Olde Tyme Mother Goose. 2004. (Keepsake Treasuries Ser.). 224p. (J). 10.99 (978-1-4037-0881-6(9)) Dalmatian Pr.
—Ooh La Ladybug! 2003. (Jumbo Book to Color Ser.). (Illus.). 160p. (J). pap. 1.99 (978-1-4037-0075-9(3)) Dalmatian Pr.
—Paint Box Book to Color. 2003. (Big Idea's Veggie Tales Ser.). (Illus.). 32p. (J). pap. 3.99 (978-1-4037-0338-5(8) , Spirit Pr.) Dalmatian Pr.
—Peace on Earth Gigantic. 2004. 192p. pap. 2.99 (978-1-4037-0533-4(X)) Dalmatian Pr.
—Pirates: Book to Color Plus 3 Toy Pirates. rev. ed. 2007. 48p. 3.99 (***978-1-4037-3204-0(3)***) Dalmatian Pr.
—Playhouse Disney Big Best Book to Color. 2004. 96p. pap. 2.99 (978-1-4037-0731-4(6)) Dalmatian Pr.
—Ponies & Butterflies: Velvet Bright Book to Color. rev. ed. 2003. (Fuzzy Book to Color Ser.). (Illus.). 4p. (J). pap. 4.49 (978-1-4037-0711-6(1)) Dalmatian Pr.
—Power Rangers Dino Warriors: Activity Book with Action Figure Marker. 2004. (Power Rangers Dino Thunder Ser.). (Illus.). 32p. (J). pap. 4.99 (978-1-4037-0746-8(4)) Dalmatian Pr.
—Power Rangers Go Dino Power: Trivia Sticker Book to Color. 2004. (Power Rangers Dino Thunder Ser.). 16p. (J). pap. 2.99 (978-1-4037-0655-3(7)) Dalmatian Pr.
—Power Rangers S. P. D. All Action Units Go. rev. ed. 2005. (Illus.). 80p. (J). (ps-3). pap. 2.99 (978-1-4037-1181-6(X)) Dalmatian Pr.
—Power Rangers Ultimate Sticker Book: Includes 700 Stickers. rev. ed. 2006. 56p. (J). 12.99 (978-1-4037-1972-0(1)) Dalmatian Pr.
—Princess with Glitter Paints: Book to Color Play Set. rev. ed. 2003. (Illus.). 64p. (J). pap. 4.99 (978-1-4037-0328-6(0)) Dalmatian Pr.
—Pumpkin Party. 2004. (Paint Box Bks.). (Illus.). 32p. (J). (ps-4). pap. 2.99 (978-1-57759-827-5(X)) Dalmatian Pr.
—Pumpkin Party Paintbox. 2005. (Illus.). 48p. (J). pap. 2.99 (978-1-4037-1486-2(X)) Dalmatian Pr.
—Pumpkin Patch Jumbo Book to Color. 2005. (Illus.). 176p. (J). pap. 2.99 (978-1-4037-1484-8(3)) Dalmatian Pr.
—The Pumpkin Patch Scratch & Sniff. 2004. 48p. pap. 2.99 (978-1-4037-0833-5(9)) Dalmatian Pr.
—Rainbow Chaser & Lollipop: A Book to Color. 2002. (Illus.). 32p. (J). pap. 1.15 (978-1-57759-549-6(1)) Dalmatian Pr.
—Rainbow Fish: 400 Pages of Coloring Fun. 2004. (Illus.). 400p. (J). pap. 5.99 (978-1-4037-0810-6(X)) Dalmatian Pr.
—Rainbow Fish: Big Best Activity Book to Color. 2003. 96p. (J). pap. 2.99 (978-1-57759-770-4(2)) Dalmatian Pr.
—Rainbow Fish Big Best Book to Color with Stickers. 2005. 80p. (J). pap. 3.99 (978-1-4037-1406-0(1)) Dalmatian Pr.
—Rainbow Fish Pencil Palette Book to Color. 2004. (Illus.). 64p. (J). pap. 3.99 (978-1-4037-0735-2(9)) Dalmatian Pr.
—Save the World: Best Big Book to Color. 2003. (Power Rangers Ninja Storm Ser.). (Illus.). 96p. (J). (ps-1). pap. 2.99 (978-1-57759-251-8(4)) Dalmatian Pr.
—Scooby Doo: A Dog's Best Friend. 2005. (Big Best Book to Color Ser.). (Illus.). 80p. (J). pap. 2.99 (978-1-4037-1179-3(8)) Dalmatian Pr.
—Scooby-Doo! Dog Napping! Big Best Book to Color. 2002. (Scooby-Doo! Ser.). (Illus.). 96p. (J). pap. 2.99 (978-1-57759-860-2(1)) Dalmatian Pr.
—Scooby-Doo! the Mystery Gang: 400 Pages of Coloring Fun. rev. ed. 2003. (Scooby-Doo! Ser.). (Illus.). 400p. (J). 5.99 (978-1-4037-0024-7(9)) Dalmatian Pr.
—Snow White & Friends: Coloring & Activity Book with Stickers. 2004. (Disney Princess Ser.). (Illus.). 64p. (J). pap. 1.69 (978-1-4037-0862-5(2)) Dalmatian Pr.
—Space Quest: Bright Idea Book to Color with Glow Stickers. 2004. 32p. (J). pap. 4.49 (978-1-4037-0717-8(0)) Dalmatian Pr.
—Spaced Out! Big Best Book to Color. 2002. (Scooby-Doo! Ser.). (Illus.). 96p. (J). pap. 2.99 (978-1-57759-861-9(X)) Dalmatian Pr.
—Spookitty BBBTC w Stickers. 2004. 96p. pap. 2.99 (978-1-4037-0837-3(1)) Dalmatian Pr.
—Squirrelly Business: Shaped Sticker Book to Color. (Powerpuff Girls Ser.). 32p. (J). pap. 2.99 (978-1-4037-0603-4(4)) Dalmatian Pr.
—Sticky Business: Sticker Activity Book to Color. 2002. (Powerpuff Girls Ser.). (Illus.). 16p. (J). 2.99 (978-1-57759-869-5(5)) Dalmatian Pr.
—Storm Strike: Sticker Story Book to Color. 2003. (Power Rangers Ninja Storm Ser.). (Illus.). 16p. (J). pap. 2.99 (978-1-57759-253-2(0)) Dalmatian Pr.
—Strawberry Shortcake: Life Is Good. 2005. (Big Best Book to Color Ser.). (Illus.). 80p. (J). pap. 2.99 (978-1-4037-1180-9(1)) Dalmatian Pr.
—Strawberry Shortcake Berry Best Friends: 400 Pages of Coloring Fun. rev. ed. 2004. (Strawberry Shortcake Ser.). (Illus.). 400p. (J). 5.99 (978-1-4037-0525-9(9)) Dalmatian Pr.
—Strawberry Shortcake Delish! Scratch & Sniff Sticker Book to Color. rev. ed. 2005. (Strawberry Shortcake Ser.). (Illus.). 48p. (J). pap. 3.99 (978-1-4037-1409-1(6)) Dalmatian Pr.
—Strawberry Shortcake Holiday BBBTC. 2004. 96p. pap. 2.99 (978-1-4037-0991-2(2)) Dalmatian Pr.
—Strawberry Shortcake Pretty As a Posy: Velvety Book to Color. 2004. (Strawberry Shortcaketm Ser.). (Illus.). 4p. (J). pap. 4.99 (978-1-4037-0719-2(7)) Dalmatian Pr.

—Strawberry Shortcake Princess: Book to Color with Lip Balm. rev. ed. 2006. 48p. (J). pap. 3.99 (978-1-4037-1942-3(X)) Dalmatian Pr.
—Strawberry Shortcake Sweet As Can Be! Book to Color with Iron-on Stickers. 2003. (Strawberry Shortcake Ser.). (Illus.). 32p. (J). pap. 2.99 (978-1-4037-0303-3(5)) Dalmatian Pr.
—Strawberry Shortcake Sweet As Honey. rev. ed. 2006. 48p. (J). pap. 3.99 (978-1-4037-1941-6(1)) Dalmatian Pr.
—Strawberry Shortcake Sweet Stuff: Book to Color with Stamper Markers. 2003. (Strawberry Shortcake Ser.). (Illus.). 32p. (J). mass mkt. 4.49 (978-1-4037-0341-5(8)) Dalmatian Pr.
—Strawberry Shortcake Sweet Surprises: Amazing Marker. 2004. (Strawberry Shortcake Ser.). (Illus.). 48p. (J). spiral bd. 4.99 (978-1-4037-0764-2(2)) Dalmatian Pr.
—Strawbery Shortcake Glad to be Me: Shaped Sticker Book to Color. 2004. (Strawberry Shortcake Ser.). (Illus.). 32p. (J). pap. 2.99 (978-1-4037-0512-9(7)) Dalmatian Pr.
—Stuart Little 2: Big Best Book to Color. 2002. (Illus.). 96p. (J). (ps-4). pap. 2.99 (978-1-57759-646-2(3)) Dalmatian Pr.
—Stuart Little 2: Sticker Book to Color. 2002. (Illus.). 16p. (J). (ps). pap. 2.99 (978-1-57759-647-9(1)) Dalmatian Pr.
—Sugar & Spice Scratch n Sniff Sticker. 2004. 48p. pap. 2.99 (978-1-4037-0432-0(5)) Dalmatian Pr.
—Sweet & Sassy! Coloring & Activity Book with Stickers. (Strawberry Shortcaketm Ser.). 64p. (J). pap. (978-1-4037-0894-6(0)) Dalmatian Pr.
—Sweet Song. 2003. (Jumbo Book to Color Ser.). (Illus.). 160p. (J). pap. 1.99 (978-1-4037-0074-2(5)) Dalmatian Pr.
—Swing Along: Musical Book to Color. (Looney Tunes Ser.). 32p. (J). pap. 3.99 (978-1-4037-0732-1(4)) Dalmatian Pr.
—Tales from the Crisper: Bright Idea Book to Color. 2003. (Big Idea's Veggie Tales Ser.). (Illus.). 32p. (J). pap. 4.49 (978-1-4037-0339-2(6)) Dalmatian Pr.
—Taz: Razz-Ma-Tazz! Big Best Book to Color. 2003. (Big Best Book to Color Ser.). 96p. (J). pap. 2.99 (978-1-57759-903-6(9)) Dalmatian Pr.
—Time, Money & Fractions. 2003. (Tools Ser.). 32p. (J). (gr. 1-2). pap. 2.29 (978-1-57759-197-9(6)) Dalmatian Pr.
—Trick or Treat. 2002. (Paint Box Bks.). (Illus.). 32p. (J). (ps-4). pap. 2.99 (978-1-57759-828-2(8)) Dalmatian Pr.
—Trick or Treat Scratch & Sniff. 2004. 48p. pap. 2.99 (978-1-4037-0834-2(7)) Dalmatian Pr.
—Truth, Justive & Freedom: Big Best Book to Color. 2003. (Justice League Ser.). 96p. (J). 2.99 (978-1-4037-0295-1(0)) Dalmatian Pr.
—Tweety: How Tweet It Is! Big Best Book to Color. 2003. (Big Best Book to Color Ser.). 96p. (J). pap. 2.99 (978-1-57759-902-9(0)) Dalmatian Pr.
—Veggie Tales the Star of Christmas: Sticker Book to Color. 2005. (Illus.). 48p. (J). pap. 2.99 (978-1-4037-1601-9(3)) Dalmatian Pr.
—Wacky Fun! Coloring & Activity Book with Stickers. 2003. (Big Idea's Veggie Tales Ser.). 64p. (J). pap. 1.69 (978-1-4037-0294-4(2)) Dalmatian Pr.
—Winter Wonderland Gigantic. 2004. 192p. pap. 2.99 (978-1-4037-0473-3(2)) Dalmatian Pr.
—A World of Enchantment. rev. ed. 2005. (Illus.). 400p. (J). 5.99 (978-1-4037-1259-2(X)) Dalmatian Pr.
—World of Justice: Paint Box Book to Color. 2003. (Justice League Ser.). 32p. (J). pap. 3.99 (978-1-4037-0349-1(3)) Dalmatian Pr.
—Xmas Paintbox 1: Wintery Fun. 2004. 32p. pap. 2.99 (978-1-4037-0517-4(8)) Dalmatian Pr.
—Xmas Paintbox 2: Ho, Ho, Ho. 2004. 32p. 2.99 (978-1-4037-0518-1(6)) Dalmatian Pr.
—You Are Special! Coloring Activity Book with Stickers. 2003. (Bigidea's Veggietales(R) Ser.). (Illus.). 64p. (J). pap. 1.89 (978-1-4037-0814-4(2) , Spirit Pr.) Dalmatian Pr.
—Yummy Fun Gigantic BTC. 2004. 192p. pap. 2.99 (978-1-4037-0831-1(2)) Dalmatian Pr.
—Zany Fun! Coloring Activity Book with Stickers. (Bigidea's Veggietales(R) Ser.). 64p. (J). pap. 1.89 (978-1-4037-0813-7(4) , Spirit Pr.) Dalmatian Pr.
—Zoo Fun. rev. ed. 2005. (Illus.). 32p. (J). (ps-ps). pap. 2.99 (978-1-4037-1183-0(6)) Dalmatian Pr.
—400 Pages of Coloring Fun: Looney Tunes. 2003. 400p. (J). pap. 5.99 (978-1-4037-0026-1(5)) Dalmatian Pr.
Dalmatian Press Staff, contrib. by. Barney All Year Long. 1998. (Big Best Book to Color Ser.). (Illus.). 96p. (J). (ps-3). 2.99 (978-1-57759-012-5(0)) Dalmatian Pr.
—Barney Better Than Ever! 1998. (Big Best Book to Color Ser.). (Illus.). 96p. (J). (ps-3). 2.99 (978-1-57759-109-2(7)) Dalmatian Pr.
—Fab Friends: Sticker Story Book to Color. 2003. 16p. (J). pap. 2.99 (978-1-4037-0053-7(2)) Dalmatian Pr.
Dalmatian Press Staff, creator. The Big Box of Coloring Fun. 2003. (J). 5.99 (978-1-4037-0385-9(X)) Dalmatian Pr.
Dalmatian Press Staff, ed. Bambi (Classic Board Book) rev. ed. 2006. 10p. (J). 5.99 (978-1-4037-2376-5(1)) Dalmatian Pr.
—Funshine Bear: Let the Fun Shine In. (Care Bearstm Ser.). 8p. (J). bds. 9.99 (978-1-4037-0558-7(5)) Dalmatian Pr.
—Get a Clue! Sticker Activity Book to Color. 2002. (Scooby-Doo! Ser.). (Illus.). 64p. (J). pap. 1.69 (978-1-57759-866-4(0)) Dalmatian Pr.
—Glamour Girl: Pencil Palette Book to Color. 2004. (Lisa Frank(R) Ser.). 64p. (J). pap. 3.99 (978-1-4037-0721-5(9)) Dalmatian Pr.
—Haunted Hi-Jinks: Sticker Book to Color. 2002. (Scooby-Doo! Ser.). (Illus.). 64p. (J). pap. 1.69 (978-1-57759-867-1(9)) Dalmatian Pr.
—Midnight Snack! Fuzzy Book to Color. 2004. (Scooby-Dootm! Ser.). (Illus.). 32p. (J). pap. 4.49 (978-1-4037-0619-5(0)) Dalmatian Pr.
—Playhouse Disney Twist & Turn: Big Crayon Book to Color. 2004. (Playhouse Disney Ser.). (Illus.). 32p. (J). pap. 3.99 (978-1-4037-0730-7(8)) Dalmatian Pr.
—Powerpuff Girls Glamming It Up: Stamper Marker Book to Color. 2004. (Powerpuff Girlstm Ser.). (Illus.). 32p. (J). pap. 4.49 (978-1-4037-0733-8(2)) Dalmatian Pr.
—Spooky Critters. 2006. 48p. (J). 2.99 (978-1-4037-2462-5(8)) Dalmatian Pr.
—Treat Time Glow Bracelets Book to Color. 2005. (Illus.). 48p. (J). pap. 2.99 (978-1-4037-1483-1(5)) Dalmatian Pr.
—Trick or Scream! Coloring & Activity Book with Stickers. 2005. (Illus.). 64p. (J). pap. 1.89 (978-1-4037-1490-9(8)) Dalmatian Pr.
—Winnie the Pooh Coloring & Activity with Stickers. 2005. (Illus.). 64p. (J). pap. 1.89 (978-1-4037-1491-6(6)) Dalmatian Pr.
Danger Alert: Coloring/Activity Book. 2006. (Illus.). (J). (978-1-933934-05-1(0)) Educational Adventures.
Danger Alert: Coloring/Activity Book (English) Incl. Stickers. 2007. (J). (*978-1-933934-54-9(9)) Educational Adventures.
Danger Ranger Ready! Coloring/Activity Book (English) 2006. (Illus.). (J). (*978-1-933934-22-8(0)) Educational Adventures.
Daniel, (Divertidas Historias Biblicas para Ninos Ser.). (SPA.). (J). 3.49 (978-0-7899-0599-4(X) , 496646) Editorial Unilit.
Daniel. (Illus.). 16p. (J). (ps-3). pap. 1.69 (978-0-7847-0712-8(X) , 22032, Bean Sprouts) Standard Publishing.
Daring Digimons. 1999. (Digimon Coloring & Activity Bks.). (Illus.). 32p. (J). (ps-2). pap. (978-0-7666-0548-0(5)) Modern Publishing.
Dartez, Cecilia Casrill. The Louisiana Plantation Coloring Book. Arrigo, Joseph A., illus. 32p. pap. 3.25 (978-0-88289-473-7(0)) Pelican Publishing Co., Inc.
Daste, Larry. Alphabet Search: Activity & Coloring Book. 2007. 48p. (J). pap. 4.95 (*978-0-486-46196-0(3)) Dover Pubns., Inc.
DC Comics Staff. Batman Big Color & Activity Book: With Stickers. Meredith Books Staff & Forlini, Victoria, eds. 2005. 64p. (J). pap., act. bk. ed. 2.99 (978-0-696-22721-9(5)) Meredith Bks.
—Batman Jumbo Color & Activity Book. Meredith Books Staff et al, eds. 2005. 400p. (J). pap. 5.99 (978-0-696-22722-6(3)) Meredith Bks.
—DC Heroes Jumbo Color & Activity Book. Curry, Don, ed. 2006. 400p. (J). pap. 5.99 (978-0-696-22893-3(9)) Meredith Bks.
—Superman Jumbo Color & Activity Book. Curry, Don, ed. 2006. 400p. (J). pap. 5.99 (978-0-696-22894-0(7)) Meredith Bks.
de Beer, Hans. Jungle Adventure Coloring Storybook. 2004. (Little Polar Bear Story Ser.). (Illus.). 24p. (J). pap. 2.95 (978-1-4027-1286-9(3)) Sterling Publishing Co., Inc.
de Strutz, Maria Ester. From Bethlehem Coloring Book. 2005. (J). 5199.00 (978-0-7586-0962-5(0)) Concordia Publishing Hse.
De Sturtz, Mari. God Gave Me. 2004. (ENG & SPA.). 32p. 1.99 (978-0-7586-0293-0(6)) Concordia Publishing Hse.
—God Is. 2004. (ENG & SPA.). 32p. 1.99 (978-0-7586-0292-3(8)) Concordia Publishing Hse.
Deal, Darlene. Play with Your Food & Learn How to Eat Right: Nutritional Book about Fruits & Vegetables. 2004. (ENG & SPA., Illus.). 22p. (J). (gr. 1-4). pap. 9.95 (978-0-9747299-0-9(6)) Deal, Darlene.
Deam, Peg. Suquamish Coloring Book. 2000. 28p. (ps-3). 4.95 (978-1-57067-060-2(9)) Book Publishing Co., The.
Desplechin, Mar. Verte. pap. 19.95 (978-2-211-04178-2(7)) Archimede Editions FRA. *Dist:* Distribooks, Inc.
Dickens, Charles. A Christmas Carol Coloring Book. Noble, Marty, illus. 1998. 48p. (J). (ps-5). pap. 3.95 (978-0-486-40563-6(X)) Dover Pubns., Inc.
Dickinson, Clive. Dickinson, McGregor, John, illus. 1999. 24p. (J). pap. 6.99 (978-0-233-99584-7(6)) Andre Deutsch GBR. *Dist:* Independent Pubs. Group.
Diddle Doodle - Blue. 2004. (Diddle Doodle Coloring Pads Ser.). 24p. (J). act. bk. ed. 3.99 (978-1-904586-30-2(9)) Byeway Bks.
Diddle Doodle - Red. 2004. (Diddle Doodle Coloring Pads Ser.). 24p. (J). act. bk. ed. 3.99 (978-1-904586-29-6(5)) Byeway Bks.
DiEdwardo, Mary Ann P. & Pasda, Patricia J. Christian Coloring Book for Youth. DiEdwardo, Mary Ann P. & Pasda, Patricia J., illus. 2000. (Illus.). 50p. (J). (gr. k-12). spiral bd. 19.95 (978-0-9641468-7-7(8)) DiEdwardo, Mary Ann P. Publishing.
DigiWorld Defenders. 1999. (Digimon Giant Coloring & Activity Bks.). (Illus.). 96p. (J). (ps-2). pap. (978-0-7666-0549-7(3)) Modern Publishing.
DigiWorld Warriors. 1999. (Digimon Coloring & Activity Bks.). (Illus.). 32p. (J). (ps-2). pap. (978-0-7666-0545-9(0)) Modern Publishing.
Dinosaur Coloring Book. (Illus.). (J). Bk. 1. pap. 1.99 (978-1-59340-008-8(X)); Bk. 2. pap. 1.99 (978-1-59340-009-5(8)) Grandreams Bks., Inc.
Dipsy's Day to Dance. 1998. (Teletubbies Ser.). (Illus.). 32p. (J). (ps). pap. (978-0-7666-0256-4(7) , Honey Bear Bks.) Modern Publishing.
Disney Mickey Christmas: Coloring & Activity Book. 2002. (Illus.). 64p. (J). 1.69 (978-1-57759-848-0(2)) Dalmatian Pr.
Disney Minnie Halloween. 2002. (Illus.). 64p. (J). 1.69 (978-1-57759-844-2(X)) Dalmatian Pr.
Disney Pooh Christmas: Coloring & Activity Book. 2002. (Illus.). 64p. (J). 1.69 (978-1-57759-849-7(0)) Dalmatian Pr.
Disney Pooh Halloween. 2002. (Illus.). 64p. (J). 1.69 (978-1-57759-845-9(8)) Dalmatian Pr.
Disney Staff. Best Buddies. 2001. (Sticker Time Ser.). (Illus.). 16p. (J). (ps-3). pap. 2.99 (978-0-7364-1127-1(5) , Golden/Disney) Random Hse. Children's Bks.
—Bossu Notre Dame. 2002. Tr. of Hunchback Notre Dame. (FRE.). 96p. (J). 11.95 (978-2-89393-546-1(X)) Phidal Publishing, Inc./Editions Phidal, Inc. CAN. *Dist:* AIMS International Bks., Inc.
—Dreams Come True. 2001. (Disney Princess Ser.). (Illus.). 80p. (J). (ps-3). pap. 2.99 (978-0-7364-1117-2(8) , Golden/Disney) Random Hse. Children's Bks.
—Set Sail. 2002. 12p. (J). pap. 3.99 (978-0-7364-2002-0(9) , RH/Disney) Random Hse. Children's Bks.
Disney Staff, creator. Chicken Little: 4x6 sticker Book to Color. 2005. (Illus.). 64p. (J). pap. 1.89 (978-1-4037-1285-1(9)) Dalmatian Pr.
—Chicken Little: Go Acorn. 2005. (Illus.). 64p. (J). pap. 1.89 (978-1-4037-1286-8(7)) Dalmatian Pr.
—Cinderella: 4x6 Sticker Book: A Lovely Dream. 2005. (Illus.). 64p. (J). pap. 1.89 (978-1-4037-1507-4(6)) Dalmatian Pr.
—Cinderella: 4x6 Sticker Book to Color: Once upon A Time. 2005. (Illus.). 64p. (J). pap. 1.89 (978-1-4037-1508-1(4)) Dalmatian Pr.
Dobson, Shirley. God Answers Prayer: Coloring Book. 2004. 16p. 1.49 (978-0-8307-2750-6(7) , Gospel Light) Gospel Light Pubns.
—God Cares for Me Coloring Book. 2003. 16p. pap. 1.49 (978-0-8307-3270-8(5) , Gospel Light) Gospel Light Pubns.
—God Helps Me Share: Coloring Book about Abigail & David. 2004. (Illus.). 12p. pap. 1.49 (978-0-8307-2894-7(5) , Gospel Light) Gospel Light Pubns.
—God Loves You! Coloring Book: A Read-Aloud Coloring Book about God's Plan for Salvation. 1998. 16p. (ps-3). pap. 1.49 (978-0-8307-2329-4(3) , Gospel Light) Gospel Light Pubns.
—God Made the World Coloring Book. 2004. (Illus.). 16p. 1.49 (978-0-8307-2487-1(7) , Gospel Light) Gospel Light Pubns.
—God Made the World Coloring Book: 100-Unit Counter Merchandiser. 2004. 16p. 99.00 (978-0-8307-2488-8(5) , Gospel Light) Gospel Light Pubns.
—God's Little Helper Coloring Book. 2004. (Illus.). 16p. pap. 1.49 (978-0-8307-2188-7(6) , Gospel Light) Gospel Light Pubns.
—Growing as God's Child Coloring Book. 2004. (Illus.). 16p. pap. 1.49 (978-0-8307-2622-6(5) , Gospel Light) Gospel Light Pubns.
Dobson, Shirley, contrib. by. God Gives Me Joy Coloring Book. 2004. 16p. 1.49 (978-0-8307-3054-4(0) , Gospel Light) Gospel Light Pubns.
Dodd, Emma. Dog's Colorful Day: A Messy Story about Colors & Counting. 2003. (gr. k-3). lib. bdg. 14.15 (978-0-613-57720-5(5)) Tandem Library Bks.
Doell, Glenn, illus. & concept. Creative Coloring Books: The What If. . . series. Doell, Glenn, concept. 2003. (What If. . . ser.). 41p. (J). spiral bd. 8.95 (978-0-9742438-0-1(9)) Curtis Elliott Designs, Ltd.
Dorling Kindersley Publishing Staff. Colores de Bebe/Baby Colors. 2005. (Soft-to-touch Bks.). (SPA & ENG., Illus.). 16p. (J). bds. 4.99 (978-0-7566-1203-0(9)) Dorling Kindersley Publishing, Inc.
Dot-to-Dot Bible Pictures. 2004. 32p. (J). pap. 3.99 (978-0-88724-220-5(0) , CD-2041); pap. 3.99 (978-0-88724-219-9(7) , CD-2040) Carson-Dellosa Publishing Co., Inc.
Douglas, Bettye. Safari Oklahoma Presents: The Magic of Christmas Around the World. Douglas, Bettye, ed. Douglas, Punchye, illus. (Multicultural). 16p. (J). (gr. k-6). 5.00 (978-0-9703183-4-3(0)) Douglas, Bettye Forum, Inc., The.
Douglas, Punchye. Safari Oklahoma Presents: Thanksgiving History Coloring Book. (Illus.). 16p. (J). (gr. k-6). 5.00 (978-0-9703183-3-6(2)) Douglas, Bettye Forum, Inc., The.
Douglas, Punchye, illus. Safari Oklahoma Presents Operation Safe 2000: Halloween Coloring Book. (Safari Oklahoma Presents). 16p. (J). (gr. k-6). 5.00 (978-0-9703183-2-9(4)) Douglas, Bettye Forum, Inc., The.
Dover Publications Staff. Full Color Pets Illustrations. 2002. (Illus.). 48p. pap. 19.95 incl. cd-rom (978-0-486-99526-7(7)) Dover Pubns., Inc.
Dover Staff. Art Masterpieces to Color: 60 Great Paintings from Botticelli to Picasso. 2004. (Dover Super Value Editions Ser.). (Illus.). 128p. pap. 8.95 (978-0-486-43381-3(1)) Dover Pubns., Inc.
—Big Book of Geometric Designs & Illusions to Color. 2002. (Dover Super Value Editions Ser.). (Illus.). 144p. (J). pap. 7.95 (978-0-486-42791-1(9)) Dover Pubns., Inc.
—Color & Learn Birds, Butterflies & Wild Flowers. 2002. (Dover Super Value Editions Ser.). (Illus.). 144p. (J). pap. 8.95 (978-0-486-42788-1(9)) Dover Pubns., Inc.
—Color & Learn Dinosaurs & Prehistoric Creatures. 2002. (Illus.). 144p. (J). pap. 7.95 (978-0-486-42789-8(7)) Dover Pubns., Inc.
—Impressionist Art Masterpieces to Color. 2007. (Illus.). 128p. pap. 8.95 (978-0-486-45135-0(6)) Dover Pubns., Inc.
—Listen & Color: Favorite Poems for Children. Kliros, Thea, illus. 2004. 48p. (J). pap. 6.95 (978-0-486-43891-7(0)) Dover Pubns., Inc.
—Listen & Color: Hans Christian Andersen Fairy Tales. O'Brien, Joan, illus. 2004. 48p. (J). pap. 6.95 (978-0-486-43773-6(6)) Dover Pubns., Inc.
—Listen & Color: Native American Legends. Green, John, illus. 2004. 48p. (J). pap. 6.95 incl. audio compact disk (978-0-486-43892-4(9)) Dover Pubns., Inc.
Down on the Farm Coloring Book. 2004. (J). mass mkt. (978-0-9745863-9-7(0)) Cypress Knees Publishing.
Doyle, Alfreda C. Alfreda's Coloring Books: A Directory to Reproduce. Doyle, Alfreda C., illus. 1998. (Illus.). 62p. (J). (gr. 4). ring bd. 39.95 (978-1-56820-247-1(4)) Story Time Stories That Rhyme.
—Animals & Their Life Spans: Story Rhyme Coloring Book. 1998. (Illus.). 24p. (J). (gr. 3-8). pap. 8.95 (978-1-56820-325-6(X)) Story Time Stories That Rhyme.
—Christmas Wreath: Story Rhyme Coloring Book. 1998. (Illus.). 24p. (J). (gr. 3-8). pap. 8.95 (978-1-56820-327-0(6)) Story Time Stories That Rhyme.
—News Crew: Story Rhyme Coloring Book. 1998. (Illus.). 24p. (J). (gr. 3-8). pap. 8.95 (978-1-56820-326-3(8)) Story Time Stories That Rhyme.
—ZueToo Masqke Go to the Gallery: Story Rhyme Coloring Book. 1998. (Illus.). 24p. (J). (gr. 3-8). pap. 8.95 (978-1-56820-328-7(4)) Story Time Stories That Rhyme.
Doyle, Arthur Conan. The Lost World. rev. ed. 2004. 224p. (J). 5.99 (978-1-4037-0985-1(8)) Dalmatian Pr.
Doyle, Peter Reese. Drums of War A Captive in Williamsburg. 2005. 160p. (J). pap. 7.99 (978-1-4037-1458-9(4)) Dalmatian Pr.
—Drums of War at Bunker Hill. 2005. 160p. (J). pap. 7.99 (978-1-4037-1459-6(2)) Dalmatian Pr.
—Drums of War Independence. 2005. (Illus.). 160p. (J). pap. 7.99 (978-1-4037-1457-2(6)) Dalmatian Pr.
Doyle, Richard. Fairyland Stained Glass Coloring Book. 2003. (Illus.). 16p. (J). (gr. 3). pap. 5.95 (978-0-486-43049-2(9)) Dover Pubns., Inc.
—Richard Doyle's Fairyland Coloring Book. 2002. (Glitter Stickers Ser.). (Illus.). 32p. (J). (gr. k-5). pap. 3.95 (978-0-486-42384-5(0)) Dover Pubns., Inc.
Dragons: Coloring Book. 2007. (Illus.). 20p. (J). 10.00 (*978-0-9795206-5-5(7)) Unseen Gallery.
Driggs, Scout. Dress-up Day. Middleton, Gayle, illus. 2005. (My Little Pony Ser.). 96p. (J). pap. 2.99 (978-0-06-074448-9(0) , Harper Festival) HarperCollins Pubs.
Duhgam, P. Island Hopping with Anancy. 24p. (978-976-8184-11-5(6)) LMH Publishing, Ltd.
Duhon, Keith V. Cajun Country Fun Coloring & Activity Book. Bertrand, Neal, ed. Guidry, Richard, tr. 2001. (Illus.). 32p. (J). (ps-6). 4.95 (978-0-9705868-0-3(9)) Cypress Cove Publishing.
Duling, Jean Saunders. Marco Island A-Z: A Coloring Book for You. Duling, Jean Saunders, ed. 2003. (Illus.). 36p. (J). (ps-6). pap. 5.95 (978-0-9743445-0-8(8)) Duling Designs.
Dunfey, Beth, ed. Codename: Kids Next Door Operations. 2006. 48p. (J). act. bk. ed. 3.99 (978-0-439-75547-4(6) , Scholastic Paperbacks) Scholastic, Inc.
Dwyer, Kerry, illus. Rhett's Colorful Campus Tour- Boston University A-Z. 2004. (J). 9.99 (978-1-933069-03-6(1)) Odd Duck Ink, Inc.
E. Mason Design Inc. Staff, illus. Angels on Earth: Color Me Cards, 2001. (J). pap. (978-1-933075-05-1(8)) Mason, E. Design, Inc.
—Friend's in the Sun: Color Me Cards, 2001. Orig. Title: Color Me Cards. (J). pap. (978-1-933075-04-4(X)) Mason, E. Design, Inc.
—Heart & Soul: Color Me Cards, 2001. Orig. Title: Color Me Cards. (J). pap. (978-1-933075-03-7(1)) Mason, E. Design, Inc.
—Meet Jazzy & Kitty: Color Me Cards, , No. 5. 2001. Orig. Title: Color Me Cards. (J). pap. 5.95 (978-1-933075-02-0(3)) Mason, E. Design, Inc.
—Violet-Berry: Color Me Cards. 2004th ed. 2001. 3p. (J). pap. 5.95 (978-1-933075-00-6(7)) Mason, E. Design, Inc.
Easter. (Illus.). (gr. 1-4). 3.00 (978-0-570-05524-2(5) , 54-1034) Concordia Publishing Hse.
Easter Fun. 2003. (Holiday Fun Bks.). 32p. (J). 2.99 (978-0-88724-926-6(4)) Carson-Dellosa Publishing Co., Inc.
Eckhardt, Eleanor June. Elmer the Hero Coloring Book. 2nd ed. 2001. 1.50 (978-0-9709986-3-7(5)) His Majesty's Pubns.
Educational Adventures, creator. Charlotte Mecklenburg Police Department Coloring Book. 2007. (Illus.). 24p. (J). (*978-1-933934-71-6(9)) Educational Adventures.
—Cool by the Pool: Coloring/Activity Book (Spanish) w/ Snipe. 2007. (Illus.). (J). per. (*978-1-933934-73-0(5)) Educational Adventures.
—Danger Alert: Coloring/Activity Book (Spanish) w/ Snipe. 2006. (Illus.). (J). (*978-1-933934-06-8(9)) Educational Adventures.
—Danger Ranger Ready: Coloring/Activity Book (Spanish) w/ Snipe. 2007. (Illus.). (J). (*978-1-933934-74-7(3)) Educational Adventures.
—Free Wheelin' Coloring/Activity Book (English) w/ Snipe. 2007. (J). (*978-1-933934-52-5(2)) Educational Adventures.
—It's Smart to be Safe! Coloring/Activity Book (Spanish) w/ Snipe. 2007. (Illus.). (J). (*978-1-933934-76-1(X)) Educational Adventures.
—Poison Patrol: Coloring/Activity Book (Spanish) w/ Snipe. 2006. (Illus.). (J). (*978-1-933934-02-0(6)) Educational Adventures.
—Street Smarts: Coloring/Activity Book (Spanish) w/ Snipe. 2006. (Illus.). (J). (*978-1-933934-19-8(0)) Educational Adventures.
—That's a Danger Proof Plan! Coloring/Activity Book (Spanish) w/ Snipe. 2007. (Illus.). (J). (*978-1-933934-75-4(1)) Educational Adventures.
—Think Safe! Play Safe! Be Safe! Coloring/Activity Book (Spanish) w/ Snipe. 2006. (Illus.). (J). (*978-1-933934-32-7(8)) Educational Adventures.
Ehreth, Linda, et al. Where History Happens. Austin, Brian, illus. 1999. 35p. (Orig.). (J). (gr. k-7). pap. 2.95 (978-1-891419-17-1(X)) State Historical Society of North Dakota.

C D

Ellison, Renee. Character Traits Coloring Book pages PDF Files. 2003. (J). cd-rom 8.00 (978-0-9749455-5-2(2)) Cross-Over.

Elson, Lawrence M. The Physics Coloring Book. 2001. (HarperCollins Coloring Books). (Illus.). 256p. (J). (gr. k-5). pap. 20.00 (978-0-06-273719-9(8)) HarperCollins Pubs.

Emerick, Yahiya. Color & Learn Salah. Meehan, Patricia, illus. l.t. ed. 1999. 100p. (J). (gr. k-2). mass mkt. 6.00 (978-1-889720-31-9(3)) Amirah Publishing.

—Color & Learn Salah Textbook & Coloring Book, Meehan, Patricia, illus. l.t. ed. 2000. 91p. (J). pap. 5.95 (978-1-933269-06-1(5)) Noorart, Inc.

—My First Book about Islam, l.t. ed. 2001. 292p. pap. 12.99 (978-1-933269-04-7(9)) Noorart, Inc.

Endangered Mammals - Africa: An Educational Coloring Book. (J). (gr. 3 up). pap. 1.99 (978-0-86545-213-8(X)) Spizzirri Pr., Inc.

Endangered Mammals - Asia & China: An Educational Coloring Book. (J). (gr. 3 up). pap. 1.99 (978-0-86545-214-5(8)) Spizzirri Pr., Inc.

Endangered Mammals - South America: An Educational Coloring Book. (J). pap. 1.99 (978-0-86545-215-2(6)) Spizzirri Pr., Inc.

Equipo Staff. Cabezas. (Coleccion Mundo Maravilloso).Tr. of Drawing Heads. (SPA.). 20p. (J). (gr. 3-5). (978-84-348-4430-8(3)) SM Ediciones.

—El Libro de la Mariposa: Colores. 2000. Tr. of Colors. (SPA., Illus.). 36p. (J). (ps-k). 8.95 (978-84-488-0858-7(4)) Beascoa, Ediciones S.A. ESP. *Dist:* Distribooks, Inc.

Erte. Erte Fashions Coloring Book. Noble, Marty, ed. 2003. (Illus.). 32p. (J). pap. 3.95 (978-0-486-43041-6(3)) Dover Pubns., Inc.

Erte. Erte Stained Glass Coloring Book. 2007. 16p. pap. 5.95 (***978-0-486-45794-9(X)***) Dover Pubns., Inc.

Evans, Brad. Bishop Museum Color & Activity Book. 2004. (Illus.). 24p. (J). pap. 4.95 (978-1-58178-034-5(6)) Bishop Museum Pr.

Extreme Furby Fun. 1999. (Furby Coloring & Activity Book Ser.). (Illus.). (J). pap. (978-0-7666-0409-4(8) , Honey Bear Bks.) Modern Publishing.

Extreme Sports Coloring Book. 2004. (J). mass mkt. 5.99 (978-0-9763757-0-8(2)) Cypress Knees Publishing.

Eyre, Jane. Creatures of the New Jersey Pine Barrens Coloring Book, 1 vol. Eyre, Jane, illus. 2004. (Illus.). 36p. spiral bd. 6.00 (978-0-9762483-0-9(1)) Pyxie Moss Pr.

Falconer, Ian. Olivia Helps with Christmas (W. T.) Mawhinney, Art, illus. 2007. 32p. (J). 5.99 (***978-1-4169-5387-6(6)*** , Simon Scribbles) Simon & Schuster Children's Publishing.

—Olivia's Carry-along Coloring Kit. 2007. 64p. (J). 6.99 (***978-1-4169-5427-9(9)*** , Simon Scribbles) Simon & Schuster Children's Publishing.

Falini, Nancy Patin. Gluten-Free Friends: An Activity Book for Kids. 2003. (Illus.). 64p. (J). 18.95 (978-1-889374-09-3(1)) Savory Palate, Inc.

Fantastic Antics. 1999. (Furby Coloring & Activity Book Ser.). (Illus.). 32p. (J). pap. (978-0-7666-0417-9(9) , Honey Bear Bks.) Modern Publishing.

Farmer Fred's Activity Book: Coloring. 2002. 64p. pap. 2.98 (978-0-7525-8339-6(5)) Parragon, Inc.

Favorite Couples with Other & Paint Brush. 2000. (Color Plus Fun Bks.). (Illus.). 56p. (J). (ps-3). pap. 3.99 (978-0-307-27601-8(5) , Golden Bks.) Random Hse. Children's Bks.

Feelings Garden Coloring & Activity Book. 2005. (J). (978-0-9768827-2-5(8)) Prevention Through Puppetry, Inc.

Felix the Cat/el Gato Felix: The Professor's Mix-Up/El Lio Del Profesor. 2005. (J). 64p. pap. 3.99 (978-0-9762071-2-2(5)); 32p. pap. (978-0-9762071-8-4(4)); 64p. pap. (978-0-9762071-5-3(X)) Big City Publishing.

Felix the Cat/el Gato Felix: World of Fun. 2005. 32p. (J). pap. (978-0-9762071-6-0(8)) Big City Publishing.

Ferguson, Suzanie P. Ferris, Color & Activity Book: Libro de Colorear & Actividad. Date not set. (ENG & SPA., Illus.). 28p. (Orig.). (J). (gr. k-6). pap. (978-0-9658745-1-9(6)) Ferguson, Suzanie Pamela.

Fire Safe! Life Safety Coloring/Activity Book. 2007. (Illus.). (J). (***978-1-933934-23-5(9)***) Educational Adventures.

The First Man on the Earth. l.t. ed. 2001. 16p. (J). pap. 1.00 (978-81-87570-89-9(X)) Goodword Bks. Pvt. Ltd. IND. *Dist:* Lodhia Ctr., The.

Fisher, Phyllis Mae Richardson. Twiglet's Coloring Book. 2004. (J). 14.00 (978-0-9745615-2-3(5)) PJs Corner.

Fisher, Phyllis Mae Richardson, illus. Rueben & Rachel's Paper Doll Coloring Book. Fisher, Phyllis Mae Richardson, . 2003. (J). 8.00 (978-0-9745615-0-9(9)) PJs Corner.

Fisher-Price Rescue Heroes Coloring & Activity Books. 2004. (J). act. bk. ed. (978-0-7666-0514-5(0) , 99570); act. bk. ed. (978-0-7666-0515-2(9) , 99570); act. bk. ed. (978-0-7666-0516-9(7) , 99570); act. bk. ed. (978-0-7666-0517-6(5) , 99570) Modern Publishing.

Fisher-Price Rescue Heroes Fun Activity Box Set. 2004. (J). act. bk. ed. (978-0-7666-0949-5(9) , 64045) Modern Publishing.

Fisher-Price Rescue Heroes Giant Coloring & Activity Books. 2004. (J). act. bk. ed. (978-0-7666-0914-3(6) , 49440); act. bk. ed. (978-0-7666-0915-0(4) , 49440) Modern Publishing.

Flags over Corydon Coloring Book. 2005. (J). 4.95 (978-0-9769829-1-3(9)) Dorcas Pubns., LLC.

Flanagan, Anne. Family Saints Col/Act Bk. 24p. pap. 1.25 (978-0-8198-2678-7(2) , 332-097) Pauline Bks. & Media.

—Miracles of Jesus Act/Col Bk. 24p. pap. 1.25 (978-0-8198-4836-9(0) , 332-225) Pauline Bks. & Media.

Flanagan, Anne Joan. Miracles of Jesus: Coloring Book. Keating, Elizabeth A., illus. 2001. (J). 1.95 (978-0-8198-4812-3(3)) Pauline Bks. & Media.

Flintstones Color Quarry Box Set with Coloring Books. 2000. (J). (978-1-58805-131-8(5)) DS-Max USA, Inc.

Flip along Fun. (Illus.). 22p. (J). (ps-k). spiral bd. (978-1-56021-374-1(4) , #221) W.J. Fantasy, Inc.

Florida Activity & Coloring Book. 2001. (978-0-9715160-0-7(6)) Coloring Bks. 'N Stuff.

Florida's Colorful Critters. 2002. (Illus.). (J). pap. 2.95 (978-0-8200-1102-8(9)) Great Outdoors Publishing Co.

Floss, Laura. Doin' My Thing Carry-Along Coloring Kit. Riley, Kellee, illus. 2008. (Holly Hobbie & Friends Ser.). 80p. (J). (ps-3). 5.99 (***978-1-4169-4786-8(8)*** , Simon Scribbles) Simon & Schuster Children's Publishing.

Fogle, Robin. Baby Moses Coloring Book. 2007. (Illus.). 16p. (J). pap. 1.89 (***978-1-59317-189-6(7)***) Warner Pr. Pubs.

—Daniel & the Lions' Den Coloring Book. 2007. (Illus.). 16p. (J). pap. 1.89 (***978-1-59317-191-9(9)***) Warner Pr. Pubs.

—David & Golaith Coloring Book. 2007. (Illus.). 16p. (J). pap. 1.89 (***978-1-59317-205-3(2)***) Warner Pr. Pubs.

—The Easter Story Coloring Book. 2007. (Illus.). 16p. (J). pap. 1.89 (***978-1-59317-190-2(0)***) Warner Pr. Pubs.

—My Favorite Bible Stories Color-by-number. 2007. (Illus.). 16p. (J). pap. 1.89 (***978-1-59317-208-4(7)***) Warner Pr. Pubs.

Forlini, Victoria, ed. Batman Begins Color & Activity Book with Stickers: Trained & Ready. 2005. (ENG.). 32p. (J). pap., act. bk. ed. 2.99 (978-0-696-22392-1(9)) Meredith Bks.

Formas y Colores. (Coleccion Picaros Peluchines). (SPA.). (J). 5.50 (978-950-11-0400-4(1) , SGM400) Sigmar ARG. *Dist:* Continental Bk. Co., Inc.

Forte, Lauren & S. I. International. Sugar Sweet Carry-along Coloring Kit. 2008. (Peeps Ser.). 80p. (J). 5.99 (***978-1-4169-4796-7(5)*** , Simon Scribbles) Simon & Schuster Children's Publishing.

Fox, Blanche, illus. The Saints Are My Friends: Coloring Book. 2002. 24p. (J). reprint ed. pap. 6.00 (978-1-930873-67-4(0)) Neumann Pr., The.

Frances, Dee. Pink Milk Sea Coloring Book. Patrick, Scot, illus. Date not set. 32p. (J). pap. 3.00 (978-1-885519-26-9(5)) DDDD Pubns.

—The Pink Milk Sea Coloring Book. Date not set. (J). 3.00 (978-1-885519-58-0(3)) DDDD Pubns.

Francis. More Saints of the Eucharist. 2006. (J). 2.50 (***978-0-9778570-1-2(8)***) MOS, Inc.

Francis of Assisi: Activities & Coloring Fun for Children. 2001. (Illus.). 72p. (J). (gr. 4-7). pap. 9.95 (978-0-86716-458-9(1)) St. Anthony Messenger Pr. & Franciscan Communications.

Frank, Lisa. Posh Velvet Book to Color. 2004. (Lisa Frank(R) Ser.). 8p. (J). pap. 4.99 (978-1-4037-0718-5(9)) Dalmatian Pr.

Frank, Lisa, creator. Violet & Velvet: Big Best Book to Color. 2002. (Illus.). 96p. (J). pap. 2.99 (978-1-57759-390-4(1)) Dalmatian Pr.

Frantz, Jennifer. My Little Pony Color & Iron-Ons Book. Middleton, Gayle, illus. 2005. (My Little Pony Ser.). 32p. (J). (ps-1). pap. 3.99 (978-0-06-074441-0(3) , Harper Festival) HarperCollins Pubs.

Free Wheelin' Coloring/Activity Book (English) 2005. (Illus.). (J). (978-0-9770455-7-0(9)) Educational Adventures.

Freeborn, Andrew J., illus. Colorways: For Days. abr. ed. 2005. 32p. pap. (978-0-9769575-0-8(7)) N8TIVE.

Freed, Shirley Ann & Morelan, Bill. I Can Draw. Evans, Cassie & Harrell, Rob, illus. l.t. ed. 2002. 16p. (J). (gr. 5). pap. 3.99 (978-1-58938-014-1(2)) Concerned Communications.

Frey, Daniel J., illus. Jacy's Coloring & Activity Book. 2006. 32p. (J). 3.00 (978-0-9755314-2-6(5)) Majestic Publishing, LLC.

Frey, Lisa A. The Story of Monet & Renoir. Frey, Lisa A. & Darroch, Jane, eds. Darroch, Jane & Riley, Scott, illus. 2004. (Color & Learn Book Ser.). 32p. (gr. k-4). pap. 12.99 (978-0-9707110-1-4(8)) Starshell Pr., Ltd.

—The Story of van Gogh & Gauguin: A Color & Learn Book. 2002. (Color & Learn Book Ser.). (Illus.). 32p. pap. 12.99 (978-0-9707110-0-7(X)) Starshell Pr., Ltd.

Fried, Miriam. My Jelly Bean Book. 2005. (Illus.). (J). (978-1-57400-049-8(7)) Data Trace Publishing, Co.

Frieza's Frenzy. 1999. (Dragon Ball Z Giant Coloring & Activity Bks.). (Illus.). 96p. (J). (gr. 1-2). pap. (978-0-7666-0540-4(X)) Modern Publishing.

Frog. 2004. (Peek-A-Boo Coloring Pads Ser.). 48p. (J). act. bk. ed. 3.99 (978-1-85997-394-3(9)) Byeway Bks.

Frost, Bruno, illus. The Story of Our Lady: Coloring Book. 2002. 24p. (J). reprint ed. pap. 6.00 (978-1-930873-64-3(6)) Neumann Pr., The.

Fun with Bobbin. 2001. (Illus.). 16p. (J). (ps-3). 1.89 (978-0-7847-1257-3(3)) Standard Publishing.

Fun with Foster Kids Activity & Coloring Book. 2005. (J). spiral bd. 17.95 (978-1-59649-173-1(6)); per. 17.95 (978-1-59649-466-4(2)) Whispering Pine Pr., Inc.

Fun with Foster Kids Activity & Coloring Book - English / Spanish Bilingual Translation. 2005. (J). 19.95 (978-1-59649-475-6(1)); per. 19.95 (978-1-59649-474-9(3)); cd-rom 19.95 (978-1-59649-477-0(8)) Whispering Pine Pr., Inc.

Fun with Foster Kids Activity & Coloring Book English/ French Bilingual Translation. 2005. (FRE.). (J). 19.95 (978-1-59808-749-5(5)) Whispering Pine Pr., Inc.

Fun with Foster Kids Activity & Coloring Book English/ French Bilingual Translation. 2005. (FRE.). (J). spiral bd. 19.95 (978-1-59808-748-2(7)); per., act. bk. ed. 19.95 (978-1-59808-747-5(9)); cd-rom 13.95 (978-1-59808-750-5(9)) Whispering Pine Pr., Inc.

Fun with Foster Kids Activity & Coloring Books - English / Spanish Bilingual Translation. 2005. (J). spiral bd. 19.95 (978-1-59649-476-3(X)) Whispering Pine Pr., Inc.

Fun with Foster Kids Adventure in Learning Book - English / Spanish Bilingual Translation. 2005. (J). 19.95 (978-1-59649-480-0(8)); spiral bd. 19.95 (978-1-59649-481-7(6)); per. 19.95 (978-1-59649-479-4(4)); cd-rom 19.95 (978-1-59649-482-4(4)) Whispering Pine Pr., Inc.

Fun with Foster Kids Adventures in Learning Book. 2005. (J). per. 19.95 (978-1-59649-467-1(0)); cd-rom 13.95 (978-1-59649-170-0(1)) Whispering Pine Pr., Inc.

Fun with Kids Activity & Coloring Book. 2005. (J). cd-rom 13.95 (978-1-59649-174-8(4)) Whispering Pine Pr., Inc.

Fun with Lacey. 2001. (Illus.). 16p. (J). (ps-3). 1.89 (978-0-7847-1256-6(5)) Standard Publishing.

Fun with Patches. 2001. (Illus.). 16p. (J). (ps-3). 1.89 (978-0-7847-1258-0(1)) Standard Publishing.

A Funny Day. 1998. (Teletubbies Ser.). (Illus.). 32p. (J). (ps). pap. (978-0-7666-0264-9(8) , Honey Bear Bks.) Modern Publishing.

Funny Faces: Big Best Book to Color. 2002. (Mr. Potato Head Ser.). (Illus.). 96p. (J). (ps-1). pap. 2.99 (978-1-57759-267-9(0)) Dalmatian Pr.

Funtime at the Treasure House. 1998. (Captain Kangaroo Coloring Bks.: Vol. 3). (Illus.). 24p. (J). pap. (978-0-7666-0221-2(4) , Honey Bear Bks.) Modern Publishing.

Funtime Posters to Color. 2002. 60p. (J). pap. 3.98 (978-0-7525-7599-5(6)) Parragon, Inc.

Furby Frenzy. 1999. (Furby Coloring & Activity Book Ser.). (Illus.). 240p. (J). pap. (978-0-7666-0456-8(X) , Honey Bear Bks.) Modern Publishing.

Gaited Horse Activity & Coloring Book-English/German/ Spanish Edition. 2006. (ENG, GER & SPA.). (J). per. 17.95 (978-1-59649-522-7(7)) Whispering Pine Pr., Inc.

Galaxy Defenders. 1999. (Dragon Ball Z Coloring & Activity Bks.). (Illus.). 32p. (J). (gr. 1-2). pap. (978-0-7666-0537-4(X)) Modern Publishing.

Garaway, Margaret K. Old Hogan Coloring Book. (J). pap. 2.50 (978-0-9638851-1-1(1)) Old Hogan Publishing Co.

Garlington, William R. The Great Divide: Coloring & Activity Book. 2004. (Illus.). (J). 5.95 (978-0-9708395-4-1(5)) Legacy Publishing Services, Inc.

Gaspas, Dianne. African Animals Stained Glass Coloring Book. 2000. (Illus.). 16p. (J). pap. 4.95 (978-0-486-41327-3(6)) Dover Pubns., Inc.

—Chinese Designs. 2002. (Illus.). 32p. (J). pap. 3.95 (978-0-486-42083-7(3)) Dover Pubns., Inc.

—Forest Animals Coloring Book. 2001. (Illus.). 48p. (J). (gr. 3-7). pap. 3.95 (978-0-486-41316-7(0)) Dover Pubns., Inc.

—Native American Masks Coloring Book. 2002. (Illus.). 32p. (J). pap. 3.95 (978-0-486-42054-7(X)) Dover Pubns., Inc.

—Southwest Indian Designs Coloring Book. 2003. (Illus.). 32p. (J). pap. 3.95 (978-0-486-43042-3(1)) Dover Pubns., Inc.

Gaudet, Mary Kate. Peppa Pig: Coloring & Activity Book & Crayons. 2007. (Peppa Pig Ser.). 32p. (J). pap. 4.99 (***978-0-06-117374-5(6)*** , Harper Entertainment) HarperCollins Pubs.

Gauguin, Paul & Noble, Marty. Color Your Own Gaugin Paintings. 2001. (Illus.). 32p. (J). pap. 3.95 (978-0-486-41325-9(X)) Dover Pubns., Inc.

Geddes, Anne. Colors. Geddes, Anne, photos by. 2005. (Illus.). 14p. (J). (ps-k). 6.95 (978-0-7407-5581-1(1)) Andrews McMeel Publishing.

—Colors. 2005. (Illus.). 24p. (J). (ps-k). 12.95 (978-0-7407-5583-5(8)) Andrews McMeel Publishing.

Giant Posters to Color. 2002. 60p. (J). pap. 3.98 (978-0-7525-7600-8(3)) Parragon, Inc.

Gibson, Ray & Watt, Fiona. Summer Activities. 2001. (Sticker Book Ser.). (Illus.). 34p. (J). (ps-3). pap. 8.95 (978-0-7460-4095-9(4)) EDC Publishing.

Giddy Up Staff. Backyardigans Color Blast. 2006. 72p. 7.99 (978-1-59524-216-7(3)); 24p. 7.99 (978-1-59524-187-0(6)) Giddy Up, LLC.

Ginyard, John. What Is the Job of a Corrections Officer? 2006. (YA). per. 6.95 (978-1-59094-113-3(6)) Jawbone Publishing Corp.

Girard, Connie Smith. Lake Erie Coloring Book: Fun for Kids at Ohio's North Coast. Girard, Connie Smith, illus. 2002. (Illus.). 24p. (J). (ps-3). pap. 6.00 (978-1-887018-56-2(5)) March 4th Publishing Co.

Gittins, Sheri. The Christmas Journey. 2005. (J). pap. 1.79 (***978-1-59317-106-3(4)***) Warner Pr. Pubs.

Gladly's Bible Lands Coloring Book. 2003. (J). spiral bd. (978-0-9706684-7-9(3)) Cortright Fellowship Pr.

Glintenkamp, Pamela. Sarah McSleuth's Coloring Casebook: Mystery in the Museum. Stern, Steven, ed. Glintenkamp, Pamela, illus. 1999. (Illus.). 32p. (J). (gr. 2-7). pap. 4.95 (978-1-892572-01-1(X)) Zen Comics, Inc.

Godfrey, Jan. Mira! (SPA., Illus.). 24p. (J). 2.95 (978-958-607-886-3(8)) Sociedad de San Pablo ESP. *Dist:* Alba Hse.

God's Fruit Basket Coloring Book. 1998. (Illus.). 32p. (J). pap. 1.99 (978-0-9664750-1-2(1)) Fountain of Youth.

God's Girls: Groovy Coloring Book with Crayons. 2003. (Groovy Coloring Bks.). (Illus.). 32p. (J). 3.99 (978-1-57759-887-9(3)) Dalmatian Pr.

God's World of Animals. 2006. 16p. (J). pap. 1.99 (978-0-7847-1019-7(8) , 22120) Standard Publishing.

Golden Books Staff. Aang's Challenges. 2008. (Spiral Activity Book Ser.). (Illus.). 56p. (J). (ps-3). pap. 4.99 (***978-0-375-84579-6(8)*** , Golden Bks.) Random Hse., Inc.

—Always in Fashion/Travel in Style. Duarte, Pamela, illus. 2005. 64p. (J). (ps-2). pap. 2.99 (978-0-375-83067-9(7) , Golden Bks.) Random Hse. Children's Bks.

—Animal Amigos. 2007. (Color Plus Gatefold Sticker Ser.). (Illus.). 16p. (J). (ps-2). pap. 3.99 (978-0-375-84147-7(4) , Golden Bks.) Random Hse. Children's Bks.

—Backyard Explorers! 2007. (Color Plus Gatefold Sticker Ser.). (Illus.). 16p. (J). (ps-2). pap. 3.99 (978-0-375-84122-4(9) , Golden Bks.) Random Hse. Children's Bks.

—Best Friends: Super Coloring Book. 1999. (Disney Ser.). (Illus.). 24p. (ps-3). pap. 2.29 (978-0-307-28021-3(7) , Golden Bks.) Random Hse. Children's Bks.

—Blueberry Adventure. 2002. (Paint Box Book Ser.). (Illus.). 32p. (J). (ps-2). pap. 4.99 (978-0-307-29962-8(7) , Golden Bks.) Random Hse. Children's Bks.

—Bug Hunt. 2002. (Color Plus Chunky Crayons Ser.). (Illus.). 48p. (J). (ps-3). pap. 4.99 (978-0-307-28213-2(9) , Golden Bks.) Random Hse. Children's Bks.

—Built to Be Wild. 2006. (Illus.). 48p. (J). (ps-2). pap. 2.99 (978-0-375-83647-3(0) , Golden Bks.) Random Hse. Children's Bks.

—Bunny Coloring Book. 2006. (Illus.). 48p. (J). (ps-2). pap. 4.99 (978-0-375-83576-6(8) , Golden Bks.) Random Hse. Children's Bks.

—Christmas Cheer! 2005. (Jumbo Coloring Bk.). (Illus.). 320p. (J). (ps-2). 4.99 (978-0-375-83457-8(5) , Golden Bks.) Random Hse. Children's Bks.

—The Christmas Hero. ed. 2000. (Rudolph Ser.). (Illus.). 80p. (J). (ps-2). pap. 2.99 (978-0-307-25727-7(4) , Golden Bks.) Random Hse. Children's Bks.

—Don't Worry, Be Hoppy! 2005. (Stickerific Ser.). (Illus.). 32p. (J). (ps-3). pap. 2.99 (978-0-375-83101-0(0) , Golden Bks.) Random Hse. Children's Bks.

—Dora the Explorer - Dora Place Mats. 2001. (Illus.). 64p. (J). (ps-2). pap. 4.99 (978-0-307-23420-9(7) , Golden Bks.) Random Hse. Children's Bks.

—Dora's Super Silly Coloring Book. 2005. (Jumbo Coloring Book Ser.). (Illus.). 224p. (J). (ps-2). pap. 4.99 (978-0-375-83659-6(4) , Golden Bks.) Random Hse. Children's Bks.

—Easter Eggstravaganza. 2000. (Disney Ser.). (Illus.). 16p. (J). (ps-3). pap. 2.99 (978-0-307-28318-4(6) , Golden Bks.) Random Hse. Children's Bks.

—An Egg-straordinary Adventure! 2008. (Deluxe Coloring Book Ser.). (Illus.). 96p. (J). (ps-2). pap. 3.99 (***978-0-375-84736-3(7)*** , Golden Bks.) Random Hse., Inc.

—Fairy Dance. 2007. (Deluxe Coloring Book Ser.). (Illus.). 96p. (J). (ps-2). 3.99 (978-0-375-83973-3(9) , Golden Bks.) Random Hse. Children's Bks.

—Fairy Tale Princesses. 2000. (Barbie Ser.). (Illus.). 144p. (J). (ps-2). pap. 3.99 (978-0-307-25254-8(X) , Golden Bks.) Random Hse. Children's Bks.

—The Fire Engine Book & Other Stories to Color. Gergely, Tibor, illus. 2007. (Super Coloring Book Ser.). 96p. (J). (ps-2). pap. 2.99 (***978-0-375-83929-0(1)*** , Golden Bks.) Random Hse. Children's Bks.

—Friends from Sodor. 2008. (Deluxe Paint Box Book Ser.). (Illus.). 128p. (J). (ps-2). pap. 7.99 (***978-0-375-84292-4(6)*** , Golden Bks.) Random Hse., Inc.

—Giant Steps! 2007. (Giant Coloring Book Ser.). (Illus.). 40p. (J). (ps-2). pap. 9.99 (***978-0-375-84727-1(8)*** , Golden Bks.) Random Hse. Children's Bks.

—Helping Hands/Things to Do with the Crew. Baker, Darrell, illus. 2005. 64p. (J). (ps-2). pap. 2.99 (978-0-375-83060-0(X) , Golden Bks.) Random Hse. Children's Bks.

—Hooray for Best Friends! 2006. (Deluxe Coloring Book Ser.). (Illus.). 96p. (J). (ps-2). 3.99 (978-0-375-83981-8(X) , Golden Bks.) Random Hse. Children's Bks.

—I Spot, You Spot. 2007. (Illus.). 48p. (J). (ps-2). pap. 3.99 (978-0-375-83986-3(0) , Golden Bks.) Random Hse. Children's Bks.

—Intergalactic Gonzos: Special Edition Coloring Book. 1999. (Muppets Ser.). (Illus.). 84p. (J). (ps-3). pap. 2.99 (978-0-307-25724-6(X) , Golden Bks.) Random Hse. Children's Bks.

—It's Hug Day! Miller, Victoria, illus. 2005. 64p. (J). (ps-2). pap. 2.99 (978-0-375-83484-4(2) , Golden Bks.) Random Hse. Children's Bks.

—Joseph & the Coat of Many Colors. deluxe ed. 2006. (Illus.). 32p. (J). (ps-2). pap. 3.99 (978-0-375-83574-2(1) , Golden Inspirational) Random Hse. Children's Bks.

—Jumbo Bible Coloring Book, Bk. C&A. 2006. (Illus.). 320p. (J). (ps-2). pap. 4.99 (978-0-375-83625-1(X) , Golden Inspirational) Random Hse. Children's Bks.

—Little Lost Wolf Pup. Fruchter, Jason, illus. 2006. 64p. (J). (ps-2). pap. 3.99 (978-0-375-83590-2(3) , Golden Bks.) Random Hse. Children's Bks.

—Meet the Wonder Pets! 2008. (Paint Box Book Ser.). (Illus.). 48p. (J). (ps-2). pap. 3.99 (***978-0-375-84211-5(X)*** , Golden Bks.) Random Hse., Inc.

—Move to the Beat! 2006. (Illus.). 32p. (J). (ps-2). pap. 3.99 (978-0-375-83623-7(3) , Golden Bks.) Random Hse. Children's Bks.

—New Friends for Thomas. Santanach, Tino, illus. 2005. 32p. (J). (ps-2). pap. 3.99 (978-0-375-83086-0(3) , Golden Bks.) Random Hse. Children's Bks.

—Noah's Ark / Angels. Butcher, Samuel J., illus. 2000. (Precious Moments Ser.). 96p. (J). (ps-2). pap. 2.99 (978-0-307-25228-9(0) , Golden Bks.) Random Hse. Children's Bks.

—Painting Pals. Baker, Darrell, illus. 2005. 32p. (J). (ps-2). pap. 3.99 (978-0-375-82789-1(7) , Golden Bks.) Random Hse. Children's Bks.

—Powerpuff Girls: Coloring Book. ed. 2000. (Illus.). 70p. (J). (ps-3). pap. 2.99 (978-0-307-25736-9(3) , Golden Bks.) Random Hse. Children's Bks.

—Rudolph: Santa's Little Helper. 1999. (Rudolph Ser.). (Illus.). 32p. (J). (ps-2). pap. 3.99 (978-0-307-09234-2(8) , Golden Bks.) Random Hse. Children's Bks.

—Safari Grande. 2007. (Giant Coloring Book Ser.). (Illus.). 40p. (J). (ps-2). pap. 9.99 (***978-0-375-84728-8(6)*** , Golden Bks.) Random Hse. Children's Bks.

—Santa's Big Big Book to Color. 2006. (Illus.). 80p. (J). (ps-2). pap. 4.99 (978-0-375-83651-0(9) , Golden Bks.) Random Hse. Children's Bks.

—Snowy Holidays. Saunders, Zina, illus. 2003. 32p. (J). (ps-2). pap. 2.99 (978-0-307-10481-6(8) , Golden Bks.) Random Hse. Children's Bks.

—SpongeBob's Best Days!, 6 bks. in 1. 2006. (Jumbo Coloring Book Ser.). (Illus.). 224p. (J). (ps-2). pap. 4.99 (978-0-375-84100-2(8) , Golden Bks.) Random Hse. Children's Bks.

—Spy Race! 2008. (Color Plus Chunky Crayons Ser.). (Illus.). 48p. (J). (ps-2). pap. 3.99 ***(978-0-375-84008-1(7)*** , Golden Bks.) Random Hse., Inc.

—Super Big Coloring Book. 2006. (Jumbo Coloring Book Ser.). (Illus.). 224p. (J). (ps-2). pap. 4.99 (978-0-375-83846-0(5) , Golden Bks.) Random Hse. Children's Bks.

—Super Coloring Fiesta! 2006. (Super Stickerific Ser.). 64p. (J). (ps-2). pap. 12.99 (978-0-375-84134-7(2) , Golden Bks.) Random Hse. Children's Bks.

—Thankful Thoughts. Emslie, Peter, illus. 2006. 32p. (J). (ps-2). pap. 2.99 (978-0-375-83546-9(6) , Golden Inspirational) Random Hse. Children's Bks.

—Thomas' Giant Coloring Book. 2007. (Giant Coloring Book Ser.). (Illus.). 40p. (J). (ps-2). pap. 9.99 ***(978-0-375-84725-7(1)*** , Golden Bks.) Random Hse. Children's Bks.

—Thomas Trainloads of Fun. 2005. (Illus.). 224p. (J). (ps-2). pap. 4.99 (978-0-375-83660-2(8) , Golden Bks.) Random Hse. Children's Bks.

—Tigger Movie: Movie Edition Coloring Book. 2000. (Illus.). 70p. (J). (ps-3). pap. 2.99 (978-0-307-33761-0(8) , Golden Bks.) Random Hse. Children's Bks.

—To the North Pole! Hall, Susan, illus. 2003. 32p. (J). (ps-2). pap. 3.99 (978-0-307-10491-5(5) , Golden Bks.) Random Hse. Children's Bks.

—Top Dog. 2007. (Deluxe Coloring Book Ser.). (Illus.). 64p. (J). (ps-3). pap. 3.99 (978-0-375-83708-1(6) , Golden Bks.) Random Hse. Children's Bks.

—Travel with Thomas. 2007. (Deluxe Coloring Book Ser.). (Illus.). 96p. (J). (ps-2). pap. 3.99 (978-0-375-83953-5(4) , Golden Bks.) Random Hse. Children's Bks.

—Ultimate Bible Coloring Book. 1999. (Religious Ser.). 288p. (J). (ps-3). pap. 3.99 (978-0-307-44500-1(3) , Golden Bks.) Random Hse. Children's Bks.

—Welcome to Colorland! 2006. (Illus.). 32p. (J). (ps-2). pap. 3.99 (978-0-375-83481-3(8) , Golden Bks.) Random Hse. Children's Bks.

—Wonderful Princess World. 2007. (Super Stickerific Ser.). (Illus.). 64p. (J). (ps-2). pap. 12.99 (978-0-375-84171-2(7) , Golden/Disney) Random Hse. Children's Bks.

Golden Books Staff. World of Colors. 2008. (Deluxe Paint Box Book Ser.). (Illus.). 128p. (J). (ps-2). pap. 7.99 ***(978-0-375-84293-1(4)*** , Golden Bks.) Random Hse., Inc.

Golden Books Staff, ed. Best Buddies: Special Edition Coloring Book. 1999. (Disney Ser.). (Illus.). 84p. (J). (ps-3). pap. 2.99 (978-0-307-25728-4(2) , Golden Bks.) Random Hse. Children's Bks.

—Princesses: Coloring, Paint with Water, Activities. 2000. (Golden Book Ser.). (Illus.). 96p. (J). (ps-3). pap. 3.99 (978-0-307-25402-3(X) , Golden Bks.) Random Hse. Children's Bks.

Gomi, Taro. Doodles: A Really Giant Coloring & Doodling Book. 2006. (Illus.). 368p. (J). pap. 18.95 (978-0-8118-5250-0(4)) Chronicle Bks. LLC.

Gomi, Taro. Squiggles. 2007. 204p. (J). 18.95 ***(978-0-8118-6151-9(1))*** Chronicle Bks. LLC.

Good, Phyllis Pellman. Plain Pig's ABC Coloring Book. Benner, Cheryl A., illus. 2000. 20p. (J). (ps-1). 2.95 (978-1-56148-266-5(8)) Good Bks.

Got, Yves. Sam's Pop-up Schoolhouse. Got, Yves, illus. 2004. (Illus.). 6p. (J). (gr. k-4). reprint ed. 17.00 (978-0-7567-8065-4(9)) DIANE Publishing Co.

Gottesman, Eric. Classic Tattoo Designs Coloring Book. 2006. 32p. pap. 3.95 (978-0-486-44759-9(6)) Dover Pubns., Inc.

—Color Your Own Patriotic Posters. 2003. (Dover Coloring Bks.). (Illus.). 32p. (J). pap. 3.95 (978-0-486-42650-1(5)) Dover Pubns., Inc.

—Hooray for the USA! Stained Glass Coloring Book. 2005. (Illus.). 8p. (J). (gr. k-5). pap. 1.50 (978-0-486-44480-2(5)) Dover Pubns., Inc.

—I Love America Stained Glass Coloring Book. 2003. (Tattoos Ser.). (Illus.). 16p. (J). (gr. 3). pap. 5.95 (978-0-486-43050-8(2)) Dover Pubns., Inc.

—Wizards & Dragons Stained Glass Coloring Book. 2003. (Dover Coloring Bks.). (Illus.). 16p. (J). (gr. 3). pap. 5.95 (978-0-486-42770-6(6)) Dover Pubns., Inc.

Grace, Will. Red Train. Vere, Ed, illus. 2006. 18p. (J). bds. 3.99 (978-0-439-81439-3(1) , Cartwheel Bks.) Scholastic, Inc.

Grack, David. Birds of the Northwoods Activity Book: A Coloring & Learning Guide. 2007. 64p. pap. 7.95 ***(978-1-59193-166-9(5))*** Adventure Pubns., Inc.

Gran Libro de Actividades: Blue Cover. 2004. (SPA., Illus.). (J). (gr. 1-2). (978-0-7666-0591-6(4) , 79540) Modern Publishing.

Gran Libro de Actividades: Red Cover. 2004. (SPA., Illus.). (J). (gr. 1-2). (978-0-7666-0590-9(6) , 79540) Modern Publishing.

Gran Libro de Oro. 2003. (SPA., Illus.). 9.95 (978-84-7971-268-6(6)) Servilibro Ediciones, S.A. ESP. *Dist:* Giron Bks.

Grant, Gaia. Journey to Bali Coloring Book. 2005. (Illus.). 16p. pap. 6.95 (978-0-7946-0333-5(5)) Tuttle Publishing.

Gray, Susan. Colorful Ohio! A Bird's Eye View with Worthington Cardinal, 7 bks. Gray, Susan & Messer, Celia, illus. 2003. 28p. (J). 4.95 (978-0-9742862-5-9(7)) Two's Company.

Great Feasts of the Church Colouring Book. (Illus.). 32p. pap. 5.00 (978-1-879038-97-4(8)) St. Vladimir's Seminary Pr.

Greek Goddesses: A Coloring Book. 2000. (Illus.). (J). pap. 4.95 (978-0-88388-253-5(1)) Bellerophon Bks.

Green, J. Space Explorer Stained Glass Coloring Book. 2005. (Illus.). (J). 1.00 (978-0-486-28533-7(2)) Dover Pubns., Inc.

Green, John. Arabian Nights Coloring Book. 2004. 32p. (J). pap. 3.95 (978-0-486-43635-7(7)) Dover Pubns., Inc.

—Bugs Stained Glass Coloring Book. 2000. (Shiny Stickers Ser.). (Illus.). 8p. (J). pap. 1.50 (978-0-486-41257-3(1)) Dover Pubns., Inc.

—Fairy World Stained Glass Coloring Book. 2004. (Illus.). 8p. (J). (gr. k-5). pap. 1.50 (978-0-486-43846-7(5)) Dover Pubns., Inc.

—Favorite Horses: Coloring Book. 2005. (Illus.). 32p. (J). (ps-ps). pap. 3.95 (978-0-486-44010-1(9)) Dover Pubns., Inc.

—Frogs Stained Glass Coloring Book. 2000. (Illus.). 8p. (J). pap. 1.50 (978-0-486-41258-0(X)) Dover Pubns., Inc.

—Great Race Horses. 2006. 32p. (J). pap. 3.95 (978-0-486-45162-6(3)) Dover Pubns., Inc.

—Great Whales Stained Glass Coloring Book. 2006. 16p. (J). pap. 5.95 (978-0-486-45022-3(8)) Dover Pubns., Inc.

—Heavenly Snowflakes Stained Glass Coloring Book. 2006. (Dover Little Activity Bks.). 8p. (J). pap. 1.50 (978-0-486-44923-4(8)) Dover Pubns., Inc.

—Horse Anatomy: Coloring Book. 2006. 32p. pap. 3.95 (978-0-486-44813-8(4)) Dover Pubns., Inc.

—Horses of the Old West. 2007. 32p. (J). pap. 3.95 ***(978-0-486-45675-1(7))*** Dover Pubns., Inc.

—Horses Stained Glass Coloring Book. 2004. (Pictorial Archive Ser.). (Illus.), 16p. (J). (gr. 3). pap. 5.95 (978-0-486-43341-7(2)) Dover Pubns., Inc.

—King Arthur Stained Glass Coloring Book. 1999. 8p. (J). (gr. k-5). pap. 1.50 (978-0-486-40496-7(X)) Dover Pubns., Inc.

—The Language of Flowers Coloring Book. 2004. (Dover Coloring Bks.). (Illus.). 32p. (J). pap. 3.95 (978-0-486-43035-5(9)) Dover Pubns., Inc.

—A Midsummer Night's Dream Stained Glass Coloring Book. 2004. 16p. (J). pap. 5.95 (978-0-486-43986-0(0)) Dover Pubns., Inc.

—The Miracles of Jesus Stained Glass Coloring Book. 2007. 16p. (J). pap. 5.95 ***(978-0-486-46226-4(9))*** Dover Pubns., Inc.

—Musical Instruments Stained Glass Coloring Book. 2006. (Dover Little Activity Bks.). 8p. (J). pap. 1.50 (978-0-486-44936-4(X)) Dover Pubns., Inc.

—Pirates Ahoy! Stained Glass Coloring Book. 2006. (Illus.). 8p. (J). (gr. k-5). pap. 1.50 (978-0-486-44488-8(0)) Dover Pubns., Inc.

—Pirates Stained Glass Coloring Book. 2004. (Illus.). 32p. (J). pap. 5.95 (978-0-486-43731-6(0)) Dover Pubns., Inc.

—Ponies of the World Coloring Book. 1999. (Pictorial Archive Ser.). (Illus.). 48p. (J). pap. 3.95 (978-0-486-40564-3(8)) Dover Pubns., Inc.

—Ponies Stained Glass Coloring Book. 2000. (Stencils Ser.). (Illus.). 8p. (J). (gr. k-5). pap. 1.50 (978-0-486-41032-6(3)) Dover Pubns., Inc.

—The War of the Worlds. 2005. (Illus.). 32p. (gr. 3). pap. 3.95 (978-0-486-44455-0(4)) Dover Pubns., Inc.

—Women of the Bible. 2006. 32p. (J). pap. 3.95 (978-0-486-45193-0(3)) Dover Pubns., Inc.

—Wonderful World of Horses Coloring Book. 2005. 32p. (J). (gr. 2). pap. 3.95 (978-0-486-44465-9(1)) Dover Pubns., Inc.

Green, John. World of Cats to Paint or Color. 2007. 48p. pap. 4.95 ***(978-0-486-46233-2(1))*** Dover Pubns., Inc.

Green, Yuko. Story of Hawaii Coloring Book. 1998. (Illus.). 48p. (J). pap. 3.95 (978-0-486-40565-0(6)) Dover Pubns., Inc.

Gregory, Charles Matthew. Ski Tales Coloring Book. 2006. (J). 24.00 (978-0-9766442-4-8(X)) Gregory, Charles Matthew.

Gregory, Jeannette. Once upon A Time. 2004. (J). 6.99 (978-0-9754779-8-4(6)) Chosen Word Publishing.

Grey, Rochelle, text. My RiverPlace on the Schuylkill Coloring Book. 2006. (Illus.). 12p. (J). (978-0-9785538-0-7(2)) RiverPlace Development Corp.

Grimsley-Fambro, Sonja. Santa Spent the Night with Me - Coloring Book. Garfinkel, Dana, illus. l.t. ed. 2002. 16p. (J). 4.99 (978-1-893108-89-9(9)) Neighborhood Pr. Publishing.

Groovy: Coloring Book. 2002. (Far Out Girls Ser.). (Illus.). 32p. (J). (ps-4). pap. 3.99 (978-1-57759-443-7(6)) Dalmatian Pr.

Grosset and Dunlap Staff & Heller, Ruth. Prisms. 2000. (Designs for Coloring Ser.). (Illus.). 64p. (J). (ps-3). pap. 5.99 (978-0-448-42251-0(4) , Grosset & Dunlap) Penguin Group (USA) Inc.

Gruetzke, Mary, ed. Real Mother Goose. 2006. (Scholastic Hands-on Learning Ser.). (J). 9.99 (978-0-439-81223-8(2) , Cartwheel Bks.) Scholastic, Inc.

Hal Leonard Corp., creator. Holy Christmas Carols Coloring Book. 2000. 24p. pap. 6.95 (978-1-57560-368-1(3) , 1575603683) Cherry Lane Music Co.

—Popular Christmas Carols Coloring Book. 2000. 24p. pap. 6.95 (978-1-57560-367-4(5) , 1575603675) Cherry Lane Music Co.

Haley, Amanda. Un Mundo de Peques. 2004. (SPA., Illus.). 34p. (J). 17.99 (978-84-95620-97-2(9)) Brosquil Ediciones, S.L. ESP. *Dist:* Lectorum Pubns., Inc.

Halfmann, Janet. Best Friends. Mada Design Staff, illus. 2005. (Davey & Goliath Color & Activity Ser.: No. 1). 32p. (J). pap. 3.99 (978-0-439-69833-7(2) , Scholastic Paperbacks) Scholastic, Inc.

—Davey & Goliath: Finders Keepers. Mada Design Staff, illus. 2005. (Davey & Goliath Color & Activity Ser.: No. 2). 32p. (J). pap. 3.99 (978-0-439-69834-4(0) , Scholastic Paperbacks) Scholastic, Inc.

Hallmark, Darla, illus. More Dragons: Coloring Book by Darla Hallmark. 2007. 20p. (YA). 10.00 ***(978-0-9795206-8-6(1))*** Unseen Gallery.

Halpin, D. I Learn about Jesus Col/Act Bk. 32p. pap. 1.25 (978-0-8198-3686-1(9) , 332-139) Pauline Bks. & Media.

—My Guardian Angel Col/Act Bk. 24p. pap. 1.25 (978-0-8198-4825-3(5) , 332-216) Pauline Bks. & Media.

Halpin, D. Thomas. The Beatitudes Coloring & Activity Book. Richards, Virginia Helen, illus. 2006. (J). 1.95 (978-0-8198-2359-5(7)) Pauline Bks. & Media.

Hamilton, Tisha. Picnic in the Park. Style Guide Staff, illus. 2006. (Raggedy Ann Ser.). 96p. (J). 2.99 (978-1-4169-1749-6(7) , Simon Scribbles) Simon & Schuster Children's Publishing.

Han, Yu-Mei. Animal Family Fun Coloring Book. 2005. (Illus.). 32p. (J). pap. 2.95 (978-0-486-43980-8(1)) Dover Pubns., Inc.

Hands, Cynthia. Marked for Crime. 2001. (Powerpuff Girls Ser.). (Illus.). 32p. (J). pap. 4.99 (978-0-307-10375-8(7) , Golden Bks.) Random Hse. Children's Bks.

Hanna Barbera. Hanna Barbera Classic Cartoon Collection Treasury. 2005. (Illus.). 160p. (J). 10.99 (978-1-4037-1428-2(2)) Dalmatian Pr.

—Tom & Jerry Bilingual Play & Count. 2005. (SPA & ENG., Illus.). 11p. (J). bds. 4.99 (978-1-4037-1422-0(3)) Dalmatian Pr.

—Tom & Jerry Play & Count. 2005. (Illus.). 11p. (J). bds. 4.99 (978-1-4037-1461-9(4)) Dalmatian Pr.

Happy Halloween, 4 bks., Set. 2002. (Illus.). (J). (ps). bds. 7.99 (978-1-57759-876-3(8)) Dalmatian Pr.

Happy Thanksgiving Coloring Book. 2006. 16p. (J). pap. 1.99 (978-0-7847-1744-8(3) , 04370) Standard Publishing.

Harcourt School Publishers Staff. Paint Me: Take-Home Book. 1999. (Signatures Ser.). (Illus.). (J). pap. 1.70 (978-0-15-313827-0(0)) Harcourt Schl. Pubs.

Hargreaves, Roger. Mr. Happy: Coloring & Activity. 2006. (Mr. Men & Little Miss Ser.). 16p. (J). (ps-1). 2.99 (978-0-8431-2040-0(1) , Price Stern Sloan) Penguin Group (USA) Inc.

—Mr. Messy: Coloring & Activity. 2006. (Mr. Men & Little Miss Ser.). 24p. (J). (ps-1). 2.99 (978-0-8431-2041-7(X) , Price Stern Sloan) Penguin Group (USA) Inc.

Harper, Betty. Color My World Vol. 1: Early Elvis (Coloring Book) Harper, Betty, illus. 2004. (Illus.). 32p. (J). 4.95 (978-0-932117-42-7(2)) Osborne Enterprises Publishing.

Harper, Marrisa and Normita. ABC Book. 2005. 58p. 8.19 (978-1-4116-2660-7(5)) Lulu.com.

Harris, Jerald D. Dinosaur Discovery Dot-to-Dot: Connect the Dots & Color. 2004. (Illus.). 80p. (J). pap. 5.95 (978-1-4027-0815-2(7)) Sterling Publishing Co., Inc.

Harry Potter Color-by-Numbers Bk. 2: The Magic of Harry Potter & the Sorcerer's Stone, No. 2. 2001. (Illus.). 32p. (gr. 4-7). 7.99 (978-0-439-28977-1(7)) Scholastic, Inc.

Harston, David, illus. Michigan Coloring Book. 2005. 24p. (J). pap. (978-1-893624-32-0(3)) Penrod/Hiawatha Co.

Hartz, Wilson H., Jr., et al. Kids Rock: A Geologic Coloring Guide from Cody to Yellowstone. 2002. (Illus.). 32p. (YA). (gr. 6-9). pap. 6.95 (978-0-9652942-7-0(7)) WordsWorth.

Harville, Shawn T. Tell a Story Stock Car Coloring Book. Harville, Shawn T., illus. 1999. (Illus.). 64p. (J). (gr. k-4). mass mkt. 3.95 (978-1-893691-00-1(4) , 20001) Sundown Publishing Co.

Hashanah, Rosh & Kippur, Yom. Rosh Hashanah & Yom Kippur Coloring Book. 2.99 (978-1-58330-168-5(2)) Feldheim Pubs.

Hawaiian Kids Coloring Book. No. 1. pap. 4.95 (978-0-930492-41-0(2)); No. 2. pap. 4.95 (978-0-930492-42-7(0)) Hawaiian Service, Inc.

Hawkes, Spencer, illus. Beagles in My Bed Coloring Book. 2005. 50p. (J). 5.95 (978-0-9774563-1-4(5)) David Ladd Press.

Hay DeSimone, Corkey. Air & Space Activity & Coloring Book: An Early Introduction to the History of Flight. Hay DeSimone, Corkey, illus. 2006. (J). 7.95 (978-0-9747921-4-9(4)) Gentle Giraffe Pr.

—Dinosaur Explore Activity & Coloring Book: Dinosaurs designed for their littlest Fans. Hay DeSimone, Corkey, illus. 2006. (J). 4.95 (978-0-9777394-0-0(6)) Gentle Giraffe Pr.

—Mammal Animal Coloring & Activity Book: What Is a mammal? You are a mammal Too! 2005. (J). 4.95 (978-0-9747921-2-5(8)) Gentle Giraffe Pr.

—Panda Promise Activity & Coloring Book. Hay DeSimone, Corkey, illus. 2006. (J). 4.95 (978-0-9747921-9-4(5)) Gentle Giraffe Pr.

Hayes, Alan. Dad's Golf Story: Coloring Book. Hayes, Alan, illus. 2000. (Illus.). 24p. (J). (ps-2). pap. 4.95 (978-0-615-11424-8(5)) A R T L U Publishing.

Hays, Susan. Nature Friends Creativity Book. 2003. (Illus.). 52p. (J). 11.95 (978-0-9729192-0-3(1)) Art & Soul Expressions.

Heidi & Pollyanna. 2004. (Classics to Color with Stickers Ser.). 80p. (J). pap. 2.49 (978-1-4037-0728-4(6)) Dalmatian Pr.

Hein, Connie L. Toliver in Time: For a Fourth of July Celebration. Theobald, Denise, illus. 2003. 40p. (J). lib. bdg. 19.95 (978-0-9740855-8-6(8)); per. 12.95 (978-0-9740855-9-3(6)) Still Water Publishing.

Heller, Elaine. Thinker Doodles Half 'n Half Animals A1: Think, Draw, & Color. 2005. (J). pap. 7.99 (978-0-89455-867-2(6)) Critical Thinking Bks. & Software.

—Thinker Doodles Half 'n Half Animals B1: Think, Draw, & Color. 2005. (J). pap. 7.99 (978-0-89455-868-9(4)) Critical Thinking Bks. & Software.

Heller, Ruth. Geometrics. 1998. (Ruth Heller's Stained Glass Designs for Coloring Ser.). (Illus.). 32p. (J). (ps-3). pap. 6.99 (978-0-448-41853-7(3) , Grosset & Dunlap) Penguin Group (USA) Inc.

—More Geometrics. 2000. (Designs for Coloring Ser.). Orig. Title: Designs for Coloring. (Illus.). 1p. (J). (ps-3). pap. 6.99 (978-0-448-42199-5(2) , Grosset & Dunlap) Penguin Group (USA) Inc.

Hendler, Muncie. Infinite Designs Coloring Book. 2006. 32p. (J). pap. 3.95 (978-0-486-44892-3(4)) Dover Pubns., Inc.

Herr, Jansen. Denali National Park Coloring Book for Kids. Brannon, Amanda, illus. 1999. 32p. (J). (ps-5). pap. (978-0-936425-62-7(8)) Greatland Graphics.

Herrero, M. N. Mi Libro de Seguridad Infantil. (SPA.). 95p. (J). pap. 7.95 (978-968-416-831-2(4) , FN8314) Fernandez USA Publishing.

Hicks, Diana & Littlejohn, Andrew. Primary Colours Level 4 Activity Book. 2007. (Primary Colours Ser.). pap. 10.00 ***(978-0-521-69983-9(5))*** Cambridge Univ. Pr.

—Primary Colours Level 4 Pupil's Book. 2007. (Primary Colours Ser.). pap. 15.00 ***(978-0-521-69982-2(7))*** Cambridge Univ. Pr.

The Hiking & Camping Coloring Book. 2004. (J). mass mkt. (978-0-9745863-8-0(2)) Cypress Knees Publishing.

Hill, Eric. Spot Aprende Los Colores. (SPA.). pap. 4.95 (978-950-07-1965-0(7)) Editorial Sudamericana S.A. ARG. *Dist:* Distribooks, Inc.

Hilltree, Angela. ABC Coloring Book: Creation Science & Geology. 2004. (Illus.). 26p. (J). 6.50 ***(978-1-931941-10-5(6))*** Media Angels, Inc.

Hirsch, Ancilla. Holy Mass Col & Act Bk. 32p. pap. 1.25 (978-0-8198-3380-8(0) , 332-118) Pauline Bks. & Media.

La Historias de Jeremias Coloring Book. (SPA.). 32p. pap. 1.95 (978-1-931471-94-7(0)) United Bible Societies/ Americas Service Ctr.

Holabird, Katharine. Dance of the Sunbeams. Craig, Helen, illus. 2006. (Angelina Ballerina Ser.). 24p. (J). (ps-1). 4.99 (978-0-448-44020-0(2) , Grosset & Dunlap) Penguin Group (USA) Inc.

Holokai, Ben W., Jr. Myths & Legends of Hawai'i Coloring Book. 2004. (Illus.). 32p. 5.95 (978-1-57306-212-1(X)) Bess Pr., Inc.

Holy Eucharist. 2005. (Illus.). 32p. (J). (ps-7). pap. 1.95 (978-0-8198-3387-7(8) , 332-425) Pauline Bks. & Media.

Honue'a & Honu: Color & Activity Book. 2002. 4.99 (978-0-89610-408-2(7)) Island Heritage Publishing.

Hood, Karen Jean Matsko. Adventure Travel Activity & Coloring Book: Activity & Coloring Book. 2006. (Educational Activity & Coloring Book Ser.). (J). spiral bd. 17.95 (978-1-59649-334-6(8)); cd-rom 13.95 (978-1-59649-921-8(4)); (ENG.). per. 17.95 (978-1-59210-590-8(4)) Whispering Pine Pr., Inc.

—Adventure Travel Activity & Coloring Book: Activity & Coloring Book Series. 2006. (Educational Activity & Coloring Book Ser.). (Illus.). (J). 17.95 (978-1-930948-58-7(1)) Whispering Pine Pr., Inc.

—Adventure Travel Activity & Coloring Book First Edition: Activity & Coloring Book Series. braille ed. 2006. (J). spiral bd. 22.95 (978-1-59808-637-9(5)) Whispering Pine Pr., Inc.

—Adventures of My Dentist & the Tooth Fairy Activity & Coloring Book Second Edition. 2nd ed. 2005. (Educational Activity & Coloring Book Ser.).Tr. of Japanese. (J). spiral bd. 15.95 (978-1-59649-233-2(3)) Whispering Pine Pr., Inc.

—Adventures of My Dentist & the Tooth Fairy Christian Educationl Curriculum Book. 2005. (J). spiral bd. 15.95 (978-1-59210-357-7(X)) Whispering Pine Pr., Inc.

—Adventures of My Dentist & the Tooth Fairy Christian Educational Curriculum Book. 2005. (J). 15.95 (978-1-59210-356-0(1)); cd-rom 13.95 (978-1-59649-333-9(X)) Whispering Pine Pr., Inc.

—Adventures of My Dentist & the Tooth Fairy Educational Curriculum Book. 2005. (J). cd-rom 13.95 (978-1-59649-332-2(1)) Whispering Pine Pr., Inc.

—Adventures of My Dentist & the Tooth Fairy Educational Curriculum Book: Educational Curriculum Series. 2005. (J). 15.95 (978-1-59210-294-5(8)); spiral bd. 15.95 (978-1-59210-307-2(3)) Whispering Pine Pr., Inc.

—Adventures of My Dentist & Tooth Fairy Activity & Coloring Book. Keyama, Hiroshi Hata, tr. Keyama, Hiroshi Hata, illus. 160p. pap. 9.95 (978-1-930948-76-1(X)) Whispering Pine Pr., Inc.

—Fun with Angels: Educational Activity & Coloring Book Series. 2003. 15.95 (978-1-930948-62-4(X)) Whispering Pine Pr., Inc.

—Fun with Foster Kids Activity & Coloring Book. (J). 2008. (Illus.). 128p. 22.95 ***(978-1-59808-542-6(5));*** 2008. (Illus.). 128p. cd-rom 13.95 ***(978-1-59808-541-9(7));*** 2005. 17.95 (978-1-930948-99-0(9)) Whispering Pine Pr., Inc.

—Gaited Horse Activity & Coloring Book. 2006. (J). 17.95 (978-1-59649-626-2(6)); per. 17.95 (978-1-59210-591-5(2)); cd-rom 13.95 (978-1-59649-625-5(8)) Whispering Pine Pr., Inc.

—Gaited Horse Activity & Coloring Book-English/French/ Italian Edition. 2006. (J). 19.95 (978-1-59649-714-6(9)); spiral bd. 19.95 (978-1-59649-716-0(5)); per. 17.95 (978-1-59649-521-0(9)); cd-rom 13.95 (978-1-59649-717-7(3)) Whispering Pine Pr., Inc.

—Gaited Horse Activity & Coloring Book-English/French/ Italian Edition: Braille. 2006. (J). spiral bd. 22.95 (978-1-59649-983-6(4)) Whispering Pine Pr., Inc.

—Gaited Horse Activity & Coloring Book-English/German/ Spanish Edition: Braille. 2006. (J). spiral bd. 17.95 (978-1-59649-961-4(3)) Whispering Pine Pr., Inc.

—Girls Can Do Activity & Coloring Book. (Educational Activity & Coloring Book Ser.).Tr. of Japanese. (J). 2005. spiral bd. 15.95 (978-1-59649-361-2(5)); 2005. cd-rom 13.95 (978-1-59649-363-6(1)); 2005. (Illus.). 160p. 15.95 (978-1-930948-54-9(9)); 2002. per. 13.95 (978-1-59210-593-9(9)) Whispering Pine Pr., Inc.

C D

—Icelandic Horse Activity & Coloring Book: Educational Activity & Coloring Book Series. Smith, Mary S., illus. 2005. (Icelandic Horse Activity & Coloring Book: 1). 160p. (J). (gr. k-1). 19.95 (978-0-9679368-0-2(2)) Whispering Pine Pr., Inc.

—Kids' Kindness Activity & Coloring Book: Educational Book Series. braille ed. 2006. (J). spiral bd. 22.95 (978-1-59210-076-7(7)) Whispering Pine Pr., Inc.

—Montana State: Educational Activity & Coloring Book Series. 2003. 15.95 (978-1-930948-66-2(2)) Whispering Pine Pr., Inc.

—My Dentist & the Tooth Fairy Activity & Coloring Book. Scripture-Smith, Mary, illus. 2005. (Educational Activity & Coloring Book Ser.). (J). spiral bd. 15.95 (978-1-59649-315-5(1)); cd-rom (978-1-59649-316-2(X)); 15.95 (978-0-9679368-1-9(0)) Whispering Pine Pr., Inc.

—My Dentist & the Tooth Fairy Activity & Coloring Book. 2002. (J). per. 17.95 (978-1-59210-596-0(3)) Whispering Pine Pr., Inc.

—Oregan State Activity & Coloring Book: Geographical Educational Book Series. 2006. (J). per. 19.95 (978-1-59434-988-1(6)) Whispering Pine Pr., Inc.

—Oregon State: Activity & Coloring Book, State Educational Book Series. 2006. (J). 19.95 (978-1-59434-990-4(8)); spiral bd. 19.95 (978-1-59434-989-8(4)); per. 24.95 (978-1-59434-991-1(6)); cd-rom 13.95 (978-1-59434-992-8(4)) Whispering Pine Pr., Inc.

—Oregon State: Adventures in Learning Book, State Educational Book Series. braille ed. 2006. (Educational Activity & Coloring Book Ser.). (J). spiral bd. 22.95 (978-1-59434-814-3(6)) Whispering Pine Pr., Inc.

—Oregon State Activity & Coloring Book. 2007. (Educational Activity & Coloring Book Ser.). (J). 22.95 ***978-1-59210-015-6(5));** ring bd. 24.95 (***978-1-59210-014-9(7))** Whispering Pine Pr., Inc.

Hood, Karen Jean Matsko. Washington State: Activity & Coloring Book. Parker, Michael, illus. l.t. ed. 2001. (Educational Activity & Coloring Book Ser.). 160p. (J). 9.95 (978-1-930948-56-3(5)) Whispering Pine Pr., Inc.

Hood, Karen Jean Matsko, told to. Adventures of My Dentist & the Tooth Fairy Activity & Coloring Book Second Edition. 2nd ed. 2005. (Educational Activity & Coloring Book Ser.).Tr. of Japanese. (J). cd-rom 13.95 (978-1-59649-234-9(1)) Whispering Pine Pr., Inc.

Hooray for Barney: Sticker Activity Book. 2002. (Illus.). 32p. (J). pap. 2.29 (978-1-57759-268-6(9)) Dalmatian Pr.

HOP, LLC. Hooked on Learning Coloring. 2006. 64p. 3.79 (978-1-933863-92-4(7)) HOP, LLC.

Horemis, Spyros. Geometrical Design Coloring Book. 1998. (Illus.). 48p. (J). pap. 3.95 (978-0-486-20180-1(5)) Dover Pubns., Inc.

Hot Wheels Coloring. 2004. (J). act. bk. ed. (978-0-7666-0677-7(5) , 99120) Modern Publishing.

Hot Wheels Coloring & Activity Books. 2004. (J). act. bk. ed. (978-0-7666-0678-4(3) , 99120); act. bk. ed. (978-0-7666-0679-1(1) , 99120); act. bk. ed. (978-0-7666-0680-7(5) , 99120) Modern Publishing.

Hot Wheels Fun Activity Box Set. 2004. (J). act. bk. ed. (978-0-7666-1244-0(9) , 64009) Modern Publishing.

Hot Wheels Giant Coloring. 2004. (J). act. bk. ed. (978-0-7666-0675-3(9) , 49540) Modern Publishing.

Hot Wheels Giant Coloring & Activity Books. 2004. (J). act. bk. ed. (978-0-7666-0676-0(7) , 49540) Modern Publishing.

Howdeshell, Gary. Genesis to Revelation: A Bible Coloring Book. 1999. (Illus.). 48p. (J). pap. 5.95 (978-0-934426-92-3(9)) NAPSAC Reproductions.

Hughes, Bill. Texas History Coloring Book & Punch Out Playset. 2004. (Illus.). 16p. (J). 4.95 (978-0-9746784-0-5(6)) Hughes, Bill.

Hummingbird, Jesse & Hummingbird, Sandy. Cherokee Clothing. 2006. 32p. (J). act. bk. ed. 4.95 (978-1-57067-180-7(X) , Native Voices) Book Publishing Co., The.

—Native American Ledger Art Coloring Book. 2001. 28p. 4.95 (978-1-57067-119-7(2)) Book Publishing Co., The.

Hurricane Harbor: Coloring/Activity Book incl Stickers. 2007. (Illus.). (J). (***978-1-933934-69-3(7))** Educational Adventures.

Hutchinson, Alberta. Mystical Mandala Coloring Book. 2007. (Illus.). 32p. (J). pap. 3.95 (***978-0-486-45694-2(3))** Dover Pubns., Inc.

I Am Coloring Book. 2004. 3.00 (978-1-880960-27-1(3)) Scripture Memory Fellowship International.

I Like Church, 6 vols., Set. 1999. (Illus.). (J). pap. 1.50 (978-0-87162-810-7(4)) Warner Pr. Pubs.

I Love You Daddy Color. 2006. 96p. pap. 2.99 (978-0-7666-2226-5(6)) Modern Publishing.

I Love You Grandma Color. 2006. 96p. pap. 2.99 (978-0-7666-2228-9(2)) Modern Publishing.

I Love You Grandpa Color. 2006. 96p. pap. 2.99 (978-0-7666-2227-2(4)) Modern Publishing.

I Love You Mommy Color. 2006. 96p. pap. 2.99 (978-0-7666-2225-8(8)) Modern Publishing.

Ice Age Coloring Book. 1998. (Illus.). 16p. (J). pap. 1.95 (978-1-884549-11-3(X)) Virginia Museum of Natural History.

Icelandic Sheepdog Activity & Coloring Book. 2005. (J). 15.95 (978-1-59210-342-3(1)) Whispering Pine Pr., Inc.

Intermediate/Bible Fun New Testament: Coloring Book. 2006. (J). 14.99 (978-1-59317-147-6(1)) Warner Pr. Pubs.

Ioan, Elwyn & Gruffudd, Lefi. Llyfr Lliwio Guto Nyth Bran. 2005. (WEL., Illus.). 16p. (978-0-86243-707-7(5)) Y Lolfa.

iQue Gran Vida! No? Jumbo Book to Color. (SPA.). 160p. (J). 1.99 (978-1-4037-0604-1(2)) Dalmatian Pr.

Island Style Alphabets: Color & Activity Book. 2000. (J). 5.99 (978-0-89610-453-2(2)) Island Heritage Publishing.

Jackie Chan Adventures: Activity Book. 2002. (Illus.). 32p. (J). (ps). pap. 1.15 (978-1-57759-645-5(5)) Dalmatian Pr.

Jackie Chan Adventures: Big Best Book to Color. 2002. (Illus.). 96p. (J). (ps-3). pap. 2.99 (978-1-57759-644-8(7)) Dalmatian Pr.

Jackie Chan Adventures: Poster Book to Color. 2002. (Illus.). 32p. (J). (ps). pap. 1.35 (978-1-57759-618-9(8)) Dalmatian Pr.

Jackie Chan Adventures: Sticker Book to Color. 2002. (Illus.). 16p. (J). (ps). pap. 2.99 (978-1-57759-619-6(6)) Dalmatian Pr.

Jackson, Ellen B. Extreme Animals Dot-to-Dot. Salvucci, Richard, illus. 2001. (Connect the Dots & Color Ser.). 80p. (J). (gr. 1-4). pap. 5.95 (978-0-8069-5783-8(2)) Sterling Publishing Co., Inc.

Jackson, Marianne Bell. The Swan Twins, No. 1. 1999. (Illus.). 22p. (YA). (gr. k up). pap. 5.00 (978-0-9669554-0-8(4)) ColorAnDraw.

Jacobs, Lana. Land Before Time: Coloring & Activity Book & Stickers. 2008. (Land Before Time Ser.). 32p. (J). pap. 3.99 (***978-0-06-135302-4(7)** , Harper Entertainment) HarperCollins Pubs.

—Land Before Time Coloring & Activity Book with Crayons. 2007. (Land Before Time Ser.). 32p. (J). pap. 4.99 (***978-0-06-134772-6(8)** , Harper Entertainment) HarperCollins Pubs.

—Paint Book. Merkel, Joe F., illus. 2007. (Surf's Up Ser.). 32p. (J). pap. 4.99 (***978-0-06-115334-1(6)** , Harper Entertainment) HarperCollins Pubs.

—Spider-Man 3: Coloring & Activity Book & Sticky Spider. 2007. (Spider-Man Ser.). 32p. (J). pap. 4.99 (978-0-06-083728-0(4) , Harper Entertainment) HarperCollins Pubs.

—Surf's Up: Coloring & Activity Book & Tattoos. Merkel, Joe F., illus. 2007. (Surf's Up Ser.). 32p. (J). pap. 3.99 (***978-0-06-115336-5(2)** , Harper Entertainment) HarperCollins Pubs.

—Transformers Coloring & Activity Book & Stickers. 2007. (Transformers Ser.). 32p. (J). pap. 3.99 (***978-0-06-088826-8(1)** , Harper Entertainment) HarperCollins Pubs.

Jacobs, Lana & Raymond, N. T. Surf's up: Coloring & Activity Book 3-in-1. Morgan, Tom & Sazaklis, John, illus. 2007. (Surf's Up Ser.). 96p. (J). pap. 2.99 (***978-0-06-115338-9(9)** , Harper Entertainment) HarperCollins Pubs.

James, Margaret. The Living Land. James, Margaret, illus. 2002. (978-0-9720825-4-9(9)) Toy Box Pr., The.

Jay Jay the Jet Plane Coloring & Activity Books. 2004. (J). act. bk. ed. (978-0-7666-0877-1(8) , 99680); act. bk. ed. (978-0-7666-0878-8(6) , 99680); act. bk. ed. (978-0-7666-0879-5(4) , 99680); act. bk. ed. (978-0-7666-0880-1(8) , 99680) Modern Publishing.

Jay Jay the Jet Plane Fun Activity Box Set. 2004. (J). act. bk. ed. (978-0-7666-0900-6(6) , 64050) Modern Publishing.

Jay Jay the Jet Plane Giant Coloring & Activity Books. 2004. (J). act. bk. ed. (978-0-7666-0875-7(1) , 49580); act. bk. ed. (978-0-7666-0876-4(X) , 49580) Modern Publishing.

Jesus: Very Easy Coloring Fun. 1998. (Coloring Bks.). (Illus.). 16p. (J). (ps-3). pap. 1.69 (978-0-7847-0751-7(0) , 22041, Bean Sprouts) Standard Publishing.

Jesus & His Disciples: Coloring Book. (Illus.). 16p. (J). pap. 1.50 (978-0-87162-856-5(2) , E6040) Warner Pr. Pubs.

Jesus Is Alive! Coloring Book. 2006. 16p. (J). pap. 1.99 (978-0-7847-1353-2(7) , 22122) Standard Publishing.

Jesus Is Born. 2004. (978-0-8294-9909-4(1)) Loyola Pr.

Jesus Miracles. 2004. (gr. 3-4). pap. 6.95 (978-0-382-30784-3(4)) Cobblestone Publishing Co.

Johnson, Charisse, et al. Charisse & Leah's—Misunderstood: Coloring/Sticker Book (with Positive Messages) Chambers-Benjamin, Carol, ed. Johnson, Loren G., illus. l.t. ed. 1999. (Dreamers Ser.: No. 2C). 24p. (J). (ps-8). pap. 1.99 (978-1-889151-09-0(2)) Licensing by Loren, Inc.

Johnson, Loren G., et al. Charisse & Leah's—Jesus & Me: Coloring/Sticker Book (with Positive Messages) Chambers-Benjamin, Carol, ed. l.t. ed. 1999. (Dreamers Ser.: No. 1C). (Illus.). 24p. (J). (ps-8). pap. 1.99 (978-1-889151-08-3(4)) Licensing by Loren, Inc.

Jones, Kirk. Lisa the Ministering Mole: Meet the Mole. Jones, Kirk, illus. 2004. (Illus.). 24p. (J). bds. 5.00 net. (978-0-9759688-0-2(7)) Jones, Kirk.

Jones, Victoria. Forest Animals Dot-to-Dot: Connect the Dots & Color. 2005. (Illus.). 80p. (J). pap. 5.95 (978-1-4027-1093-3(3)) Sterling Publishing Co., Inc.

Jordan, Apple. The Bungle in the Jungle. 2005. (Madagascar Ser.). 32p. (J). 3.99 (978-0-439-69629-6(1)) Scholastic, Inc.

—Clifford Helps Out. Bracken, Carolyn, illus. 2004. (Clifford Ser.). 80p. (J). pap. 2.99 (978-0-439-55670-5(8)) Scholastic, Inc.

—Madagascar: Fearless Foursome. 2005. (Madagascar Ser.). 64p. (J). 3.99 (978-0-439-69628-9(3)) Scholastic, Inc.

Jordan, Apple & S. I. International Staff. Get into the Groove. Cardona, Jose, illus. 2006. (Groovy Girls Ser.). 48p. (J). 3.99 (978-1-4169-2826-3(X) , Simon Scribbles) Simon & Schuster Children's Publishing.

Jordan, Carol. San Diego Coloring Book. VillaNueva, Julie, illus. 2000. 32p. (J). (ps-6). pap. 5.95 (978-0-9678482-0-4(2)) Here & There Publishing.

Jorgenson, Karen. Making Room in Your Family & Coloring Books, 11. ldr.'s ed. 2002. (Illus.). (J). 40.00 (978-1-892194-28-2(7)) Northwest Media, Inc.

Joseph: A Bible Story to Color. (Illus.). 16p. (J). pap. 1.50 (978-0-87162-812-1(0) , E6020) Warner Pr. Pubs.

Joseph: Very Easy Coloring Fun. (Coloring Bks.). (Illus.). 16p. (J). (ps-k). pap. 1.69 (978-0-7847-0711-1(1) , 22031, Bean Sprouts) Standard Publishing.

Joseph & the Colorful Coat: A Little Story in Color. (Illus.). 16p. (J). pap. 1.50 (978-0-87162-733-9(7) , E4313) Warner Pr. Pubs.

Jumbo Christmas Coloring & Activity Book. (Illus.). 300p. (J). mass mkt. (978-0-87449-054-1(5)) Unisystems, Inc.

Jumbo Coloring. Date not set. (Illus.). 256p. (J). 5.98 (978-1-4054-0699-4(2)) Parragon, Inc.

Kachmann, Rudy. Kid Scripts: Just What the Doctor Ordered. Lynch, Dan, illus. 2005. (ENG.). 48p. (J). spiral bd. 12.95 (978-1-893270-38-1(6)) Evangel Author Services.

Kalin, Julia. Nighttime Nonsense: A Picture-It Storybook - A Reader Illustrated Storybook. 1999. (Illus.). 12p. (J). (ps-6). pap. 12.95 (978-0-9672430-7-8(6)) Stay, Play & Learn.

—Pickles the Frog: A Picture-It Storybook - A Reader Illustrated Storybook. 1999. (Illus.). 12p. (J). (ps-6). pap. 12.95 (978-0-9672430-6-1(8)) Stay, Play & Learn.

Karmel, Annabel. Mom & Me Cookbook: Have Fun in the Kitchen! 2005. 48p. (J). (gr. 5-ps). 10.99 (978-0-7566-1006-7(0)) Dorling Kindersley Publishing, Inc.

Keene, Gail. Color My Country. Larsen, Dana, illus. 2005. 28p. (gr. k-3). pap. 8.95 (978-1-889658-29-2(4)) New Canaan Publishing Co. LLC.

Keiki Calabash Coloring & Activity. 2002. (J). 4.99 (978-0-89610-332-0(3)) Island Heritage Publishing.

Keiki Discovery Hawaii: Color & Activity Book. 2001. (J). 4.99 (978-0-89610-458-7(3)); 5.99 (978-0-89610-345-0(5)) Island Heritage Publishing.

Keiki Discovery Kauai: Color & Activity Book. 2001. (J). 4.99 (978-0-89610-455-6(9)) Island Heritage Publishing.

Keiki Discovery Kauai Color & Activity w/ Crayons. 2001. (J). 5.99 (978-0-89610-329-0(3)) Island Heritage Publishing.

Keiki Discovery Maui: Color & Activity Book. 2001. (J). 4.99 (978-0-89610-457-0(5)) Island Heritage Publishing.

Keiki Discovery Maui Color & Activity with Crayons. 2001. (Illus.). (J). 5.99 (978-0-89610-335-1(8)) Island Heritage Publishing.

Keiki Discovery Oahu: Color & Activity Book. 2001. (J). 4.99 (978-0-89610-456-3(7)); 5.99 (978-0-89610-338-2(2)) Island Heritage Publishing.

Kellogg's Coloring & Activity Books. 2004. (J). act. bk. ed. (978-0-7666-1004-0(7) , 99350); act. bk. ed. (978-0-7666-1005-7(5) , 99350); act. bk. ed. (978-0-7666-1006-4(3) , 99350); act. bk. ed. (978-0-7666-1007-1(1) , 99350) Modern Publishing.

Kellogg's Fun Activity Box Set. 2004. (J). act. bk. ed. (978-0-7666-1120-7(5) , 64019) Modern Publishing.

Kellogg's Giant Coloring & Activity Books. 2004. (J). act. bk. ed. (978-0-7666-1008-8(X) , 49435); act. bk. ed. (978-0-7666-1009-5(8) , 49435) Modern Publishing.

Kelly, Amy. Albany, the Coolest Small Town in Texas: Historic Coloring Book. 2004. (Illus.). 32p. 5.95 (978-1-931721-35-6(1)) Bright Sky Pr.

Kenny, Cindy. Draw with Jonah & Friends. 2002. (Big Idea Books Ser.). (Illus.). 18p. (J). 6.99 (978-0-310-70463-8(4)) Zonderkidz.

Kershner, Gerry. Lancaster Landmarks Coloring Book. Kershner, Gerry, illus. 2006. (Illus.). 248p. (J). 4.50 (***978-1-60126-010-9(5))** Masthof Pr.

Khan, Saniyasnain. The Ark of Nuh & the Animals Colouring Book: Quran Stories of Little Hearts. 2001. (Colour A Story Ser.). 24p. (J). pap. 2.25 (978-81-87570-84-4(9)) Goodword Bks. Pvt. Ltd. IND. *Dist:* Lodhia Ctr., The.

—Origin of Life (Colouring Book) l.t. ed. 2001. 16p. (J). pap. 1.00 (978-81-87570-81-3(4)) Goodword Bks. Pvt. Ltd. IND. *Dist:* Lodhia Ctr., The.

Kids' Kindness Activity & Coloring Book. 2005. (J). 19.95 (978-1-59808-045-2(8)) Whispering Pine Pr., Inc.

Kid's Kindness Activity & Coloring Book. 2005. (J). 19.95 (978-1-59808-754-3(1)); spiral bd. 19.95 (978-1-59808-753-6(3)); per. 19.95 (978-1-59808-752-9(5)); cd-rom 13.95 (978-1-59808-755-0(X)) Whispering Pine Pr., Inc.

Kindergarten Coloring & Activity. 2006. (J). per. 4.99 (***978-1-59545-032-6(7))** Learning Horizons, Inc.

Kindness Counts: Sticker & Activity Book. 2001. (Illus.). 28p. (J). (ps-2). 3.29 (978-0-7847-1250-4(6)) Standard Publishing.

Kinsella, Sheralyn Mary. A Coloring Adventure with the Coralville Kids: The Coralville Kids in a Coloring Adventure True Colors, an Odyssey in the Sea Coloring & Activity Book. Davis, Bob, illus. 2002. 38p. (J). spiral bd., act. bk. ed. (978-0-9666841-2-4(5)) Odyssey Tales, LLC.

—Ven a Colorear Con Los Amigos de Villa Coral: Los Amigos de Villa Coral en Una Adventura de Colores Los Colores Veraderos, Una Odisea en el Mar Libro Para Iluminar Con Actividades. Davis, Bob, illus. 2002. (SPA.). 38p. (J). spiral bd. (978-0-9666841-3-1(3)) Odyssey Tales, LLC.

Kipling, Rudyard, ed. The Jungle Book Great Read. 2004. (Great Classics for Children Ser.). 146p. (J). 5.99 (978-1-4037-0984-4(X)) Dalmatian Pr.

Klutz Shrinky Dinks Refill Pack. 40p. 8.95 (978-1-57054-585-6(5)) Klutz.

Knipe, Floyd P. Forest Goes Snow Skiing Coloring Book. Jackson, James K., illus. 2000. (Forest the Huggable Dog Ser.: Vol. 4). 23p. (J). (ps-3). pap. 2.00 (978-1-930130-11-1(2)) Nature's Nest Bks.

—Forest Visits the Daycare Coloring Book. Jackson, James K., illus. 1999. (Forest the Huggable Dog Ser.: Vol. 3). 23p. (J). (ps-3). pap. 2.00 (978-1-930130-03-6(1)) Nature's Nest Bks.

Knowles, Rebecca. Disney. 2002. (Ultimate Sticker Bks.). (Illus.). 16p. (J). pap. 6.99 (978-0-7894-8863-3(9)) Dorling Kindersley Publishing, Inc.

koenigsberg, Phyllis & Winkler, Ziporah, creators. Color My Alef Bet. 2004. (J). (978-965-90462-5-6(1)) Mazo Pubs.

Koski, Mary B. Color, Color, Where Are You, Color? Mason, Janeen, illus. 2004. 28p. (J). bds. 7.95 (978-1-930650-34-3(5)); 32p. 14.95 (978-1-930650-35-0(3)) Trellis Publishing, Inc.

Kryttre, Krystine. The Coloring Book. 2001. (Illus.). 24p. (J). pap. 5.95 (978-0-86719-524-8(X)) Last Gasp of San Francisco.

Kubistal, Lester. Kaleidoscopic Design Coloring Book. 1999. 32p. (J). pap. 3.95 (978-0-486-40566-7(4)) Dover Pubns., Inc.

Kuhn, Walter N., Jr. Freddy's Folk Tales Coloring. Kuhn, Walter N., Sr., illus. 2000. 20p. (J). (ps-5). No. 1. spiral bd. 2.99 (978-1-891547-30-0(5)); No. 2. spiral bd. 2.99 (978-1-891547-31-7(3)); No. 3. spiral bd. 2.99 (978-1-891547-32-4(1)) Hoppa Productions, Inc.

Kumon Publishing Staff. More Let's Color. 2006. (Illus.). 40p. 5.95 (978-1-933241-32-6(2)) Kumon U.S.A., Inc.

Kumon Publishing Staff, creator. Let's Color! A Kumon First Steps. 2005. (Illus.). 40p. (J). (ps). per., wbk. ed. 5.95 (978-1-933241-11-1(X)) Kumon Publishing North America, Inc.

Kumon Publishing Staff, ed. My Book of Coloring at Zoo. 2007. 80p. pap. 6.95 (***978-1-933241-39-5(X))** Kumon Publishing North America, Inc.

Laa Laa Gets a Guitar. 1998. (Teletubbies Ser.). (Illus.). 32p. (J). (ps). pap. (978-0-7666-0257-1(5) , Honey Bear Bks.) Modern Publishing.

LaFontaine, Bruce. The Adventures of Ulysses. 2004. (Dover Coloring Bks.). (Illus.). 32p. (J). pap. 3.95 (978-0-486-43328-8(5)) Dover Pubns., Inc.

—All about the Weather. 2004. (Illus.). 48p. (J). (gr. 3). pap. 3.95 (978-0-486-43036-2(7)) Dover Pubns., Inc.

LaFontaine, Bruce. Classic Cars Coloring Book. 2007. 112p. pap. 7.95 (***978-0-486-46067-3(3))** Dover Pubns., Inc.

Lafontaine, Bruce. Construction Trucks Stained Glass Coloring Book. 2004. 8p. (J). pap. 1.50 (978-0-486-44106-1(7)) Dover Pubns., Inc.

LaFontaine, Bruce. Famous Trains. 2005. (Illus.). 32p. (J). (ps-ps). pap. 3.95 (978-0-486-44009-5(5)) Dover Pubns., Inc.

—Gods of Ancient Egypt. 2002. (Illus.). 32p. (J). pap. 3.95 (978-0-486-42088-2(4)) Dover Pubns., Inc.

—Homes of the American Presidents Coloring Book. 1999. (Illus.). 48p. (J). pap. 3.95 (978-0-486-40801-9(9)) Dover Pubns., Inc.

—Luxury Cars Coloring Book. 2005. (Illus.). 32p. (gr. 3). pap. 3.95 (978-0-486-44436-9(8)) Dover Pubns., Inc.

—Paul Bunyan Coloring Book. 2003. (Dover Coloring Bks.). (Illus.). 32p. (J). pap. 3.95 (978-0-486-43043-0(X)) Dover Pubns., Inc.

—Police Cars Coloring Book: From Paddy Wagons to Patrol Cars. 2003. (Dover Coloring Bks.). (Illus.). 48p. (J). pap. 3.95 (978-0-486-42649-5(1)) Dover Pubns., Inc.

—Railroad Engines from Around the World Coloring Book. 2003. (Illus.). 48p. (J). pap. 3.95 (978-0-486-42378-4(6)) Dover Pubns., Inc.

—Spacecraft Stained Glass Coloring Book. 2002. (Illus.). 8p. (J). pap. 1.50 (978-0-486-42099-8(X)) Dover Pubns., Inc.

—The Story of the Wright Brothers. 2000. (Illus.). 32p. (J). pap. 3.95 (978-0-486-41321-1(7)) Dover Pubns., Inc.

—Trains Stained Glass Colouring Book. 2000. (Illus.). 8p. (J). pap. 1.50 (978-0-486-40972-6(4)) Dover Pubns., Inc.

—Warriors Through the Ages. 2002. (Illus.). 48p. (J). pap. 3.95 (978-0-486-42071-4(X)) Dover Pubns., Inc.

Langer, Jutta, illus. Barney: My 1st Color by Number! 2005. (Barney Ser.). 32p. (J). 3.99 (978-0-439-69157-4(5)) Scholastic, Inc.

Lantos, Jeff, et al. Read-Draw-Remember American History Activities. 2003. 48p. pap. 10.95 (978-0-439-38519-0(9) , Teaching Resources) Scholastic, Inc.

Larousse Color ABC y 123 (Amarillo), Vol. 1. 2003. (SPA., Illus.). 6p. (J). 2.98 (978-970-22-0163-2(2)) Larousse, Ediciones, S. A. de C. V. MEX. *Dist:* Giron Bks.

Larsen, Jill. There's a Moose on the Loose Coloring Book. 2004. (J). pap. 4.99 (978-0-9755200-0-0(8)) Kids, Critters & Country Publishing.

The Laughing Lavender Field. 2005. (J). 5.00 (978-0-9765731-0-4(5)) DTJ, LLC.

Le Jars, David. 1, 2, 3, Couleurs. 2000. (Talk Together Ser.). (Illus.). 24p. (J). (ps-k). pap. 5.95 (978-1-58728-182-2(1) , Two Can Publishing) T&N Children's Publishing.

Learning Fun at the Treasure House. 1998. (Captain Kangaroo Coloring & Activity Bks.: Vol. 1). (Illus.). 32p. (J). pap. (978-0-7666-0223-6(0) , Honey Bear Bks.) Modern Publishing.

Learning My Prayers: Coloring & Activity Book. 2005. (Illus.). (J). (ps-3). pap. 1.95 (978-0-8198-4518-4(3) , 332-426) Pauline Bks. & Media.

Lee, Betsy B. A Purple Cow. Varnedoe, Catharine E., illus. 2000. 28p. (J). (ps-4). pap. 5.95 (978-0-9658853-4-8(8)) Learning Abilities Bks.

Lee, Quinlan B. Going Places. Harris, Annmarie, ed. 2006. (Barney Ser.). (Illus.). 96p. (J). pap. 2.99 (978-0-439-82953-3(4)) Scholastic, Inc.

—Rainbow Brite: Rainbow Surprises. Langer S.L., Jutta, illus. 2005. (Rainbow Brite Ser.). 16p. (J). 5.99 (978-0-439-69163-5(X)) Scholastic, Inc.

Leonard, Barry, ed. NASCAR Jumbo Coloring & Activity Book, 2 vols. 2004. (Illus.). 150p. (J). (gr. k-4). reprint ed. pap. 12.00 (978-0-7567-7715-9(1)) DIANE Publishing Co.

Leonhard, Herb, illus. The Faerie Garden Coloring Book. 2004. 24p. (J). 3.50 (978-0-9763555-0-2(7)) Prancing Pony, The.

Less, Emma. Little Scribbles: Horse Fun. Harpster, Steve, illus. 2007. (Little Scribbles Ser.). 12p. (J). bds. 5.95 (***978-1-4027-4665-9(2))** Sterling Publishing Co., Inc.

Penn, John I., Sr. About Caring & Healing: A Coloring & Activities Book about a Loving & Healing God. Rains, Wanda, illus. rev. l.t. ed. 2002. 36p. (J). 5.95 (978-0-9720785-0-4(9) , 821448) Penn, John.

Penrod. Indiana Coloring Book. 2005. pap. (978-1-893624-40-5(4)) Penrod/Hiawatha Co.

—Ohio Coloring Book. 2005. pap. (978-1-893624-41-2(2)) Penrod/Hiawatha Co.

People for the Ethical Treatment of Animals Staff. We're All Animals Coloring Book. 2001. (Illus.). 16p. (J). pap. 3.95 (978-0-9622101-0-5(2)) Peta Pubns.

Perkins, Charles D. The African-American Coloring Book of Inventions, No. 1. 1998. (Illus.). 23p. (J). (ps-4). 5.00 (978-1-892088-00-0(2)) Man For All Seasons, A.

Perry, Robert. The Ferry Boat Ride Colouring Book. Guzek, Greta, illus. unabr. ed. 32p. (Orig.). (J). (978-0-88971-159-4(3)) Harbour Publishing Co., Ltd.

Petach, Heidi. Sea Life Dot-to-Dot. 2001. (Illus.). 32p. (J). (ps-2). pap. 3.95 (978-0-486-41541-3(4)) Dover Pubns., Inc.

Peter & Paul: Very Easy Coloring Book. 1998. (Coloring Bks.). (Illus.). 16p. (J). (ps up). 1.89 (978-0-7847-0752-4(9) , 22042, Bean Sprouts) Standard Publishing.

Peter Pauper Press Staff & Zschock, Heather. Princess Bella: An Art Activity Story Book for Princesses of All Ages. Barbas, Kerren, illus. 2005. (Activity Journal Ser.). 64p. (J). (ps-7). 14.99 (978-1-59359-972-0(2)) Peter Pauper Pr. Inc.

Petruccio, Steven James. Little Cars Stained Glass Coloring Book. 2003. (Dover Little Activity Bks.). (Illus.). 8p. (J). (gr. k-5). pap. 1.50 (978-0-486-43002-7(2)) Dover Pubns., Inc.

—Rodeo Coloring Book. 2004. (Dover Coloring Bks.). (Illus.). 32p. (J). pap. 3.95 (978-0-486-43330-1(7)) Dover Pubns., Inc.

Petty Power. 1998. (Hot Wheels Ser.). (Illus.). (J). (ps-1). pap. (978-0-7666-0098-0(X) , Honey Bear Bks.) Modern Publishing.

Pfeil, Susan. Professor Kiwi, Explorer of the Seven Seas: The Eye of Easter Island. 2005. (J). per. 6.95 (978-1-59094-062-4(8)) Jawbone Publishing Corp.

Pfister, Marcus. Rainbow Fish Coloring Book. 2002. (Illus.). 32p. (J). (ps-4). pap. 3.99 (978-1-57759-585-4(8)) Dalmatian Pr.

—The Rainbow Fish Coloring Storybook. 2001. (Rainbow Fish & Friends Ser.). (Illus.). 32p. (J). (ps-3). pap. 4.99 (978-1-59014-004-8(4)) North-South Bks., Inc.

—Rainbow Fish Colors/Colores. Pfister, Marcus, illus. 2005. (ENG & SPA., Illus.). 24p. (J). bds. 4.99 (978-0-7358-1978-8(5)) North-South Bks., Inc.

—Rainbow Fish Watercolor Paint Book. 2002. (Illus.). 32p. (J). pap. 3.99 (978-1-57759-620-2(X)) Dalmatian Pr.

Philadelphia from A to Z Coloring Book. 2001. (Illus.). (J). 10.00 (978-0-9714438-0-8(7)) Marmardesign.

Phillips, Lavearne. Consonant Blends & Digraphs Coloring Book. Phillips, Lavearne, illus. 1999. 16p. (J). (gr. 1-3). pap. 4.00 (978-1-930058-03-3(9)) Phillips, Lavearne Products.

—Easy to Read Short Poems Coloring Book. Phillips, Lavearne & Phillips, Angela, illus. 1998. 23p. (J). (gr. k-2). pap. 4.00 (978-1-930058-00-2(4)) Phillips, Lavearne Products.

—Learning to Count 1 2 3 Coloring Book. Phillips, Lavearne, illus. 1999. 12p. (J). (ps-1). pap. 3.00 (978-1-930058-02-6(0)) Phillips, Lavearne Products.

—Now Let's Say Alphabet Coloring Book. Phillips, Lavearne & Phillips, Angela, illus. 1998. 15p. (J). (ps-1). pap. 3.00 (978-1-930058-01-9(2)) Phillips, Lavearne Products.

A Picture & A Promise: Coloring Book. 2003. (J). spiral bd. (978-0-9706684-6-2(5)) Cortright Fellowship Pr.

Pierce, Terry. Coral Reefs A to Z Coloring Book. Kofsky, Kristen, illus. 2003. 32p. 4.95 (978-1-57306-122-3(0)) Bess Pr., Inc.

—Surfing A to Z Coloring Book. Kofsky, Kristen, illus. 2004. 24p. pap. 4.95 (978-1-57306-178-0(6)) Bess Pr., Inc.

—Volcanoes A to Z Coloring Book. Villalobos, Ethel M., illus. 2003. 24p. pap. 4.95 (978-1-57306-123-0(9)) Bess Pr., Inc.

Pierce, Terry & Kofsky, Kristen. Dangerous Sea Creatures A to Z Coloring Book. 2004. (Illus.). 24p. pap. 4.95 (978-1-57306-177-3(8)) Bess Pr., Inc.

Pingry, Patricia. America the Beautiful: A Patriotic Coloring Book. 2005. 46p. (J). pap. 3.95 (978-0-8249-5504-5(8)) Ideals Pubns.

Pinkham, Julia. The Rainforest Encyclopedia Coloring Book. Pinkham, Julia, illus. 1998. (Naturencyclopedia Ser.). (Illus.). 48p. (J). (gr. 3-6). pap. 6.95 (978-0-88045-142-0(6)) Stemmer Hse. Pubs., Inc.

PLayhouse Disney Let's Get Moving: Sticker Book to Color. 2004. (Playhouse Disney Ser.). (Illus.). 16p. (J). 2.99 (978-1-4037-0709-3(X)) Dalmatian Pr.

Playtime Posters to Color. 2002. 60p. (J). pap. 3.98 (978-0-7525-7598-8(8)) Parragon, Inc.

Playtime with Captain Kangaroo & Friends. 1998. (Captain Kangaroo Coloring Bks.: Vol. 4). (Illus.). 24p. (J). pap. (978-0-7666-0222-9(2) , Honey Bear Bks.) Modern Publishing.

Po Follows a Path. 1998. (Teletubbies Ser.). (Illus.). 32p. (J). (ps). pap. (978-0-7666-0258-8(3) , Honey Bear Bks.) Modern Publishing.

Poison Patrol: Coloring/Activity Book (English) 2005. (Illus.). (J). (978-1-933934-01-3(8)) Educational Adventures.

Poison Patrol: Coloring/Activity (English) Incl. Posters, Stickers. 2007. (J). (*978-1-933934-53-2(0)) Educational Adventures.

Poison Safe! Life Safety Coloring/Activity Book. 2007. (Illus.). (J). (*978-1-933934-33-4(6)) Educational Adventures.

Pomaska, Anna. Flowers. 2000. (Illus.). 32p. (J). pap. 1.00 (978-0-486-41028-9(5)) Dover Pubns., Inc.

—Little ABC Coloring Book. 1998. (Illus.). 64p. (J). (ps-2). pap. 1.50 (978-0-486-25156-1(X)) Dover Pubns., Inc.

Pomaska, Anna. Same & Different. 2007. pap. 2.95 (*978-0-486-46107-6(6)) Dover Pubns., Inc.

A Pond Full of Pigs: Coloring & Activity Book. 2001. (Illus.). 32p. (J). (ps-2). 2.69 (978-0-7847-1126-2(7)) Standard Publishing.

Potter, Marian. The Little Red Hen & Other Stories to Color. Miller, J. P. & Gergely, Tibor, illus. 2007. (Super Coloring Book Ser.). 96p. (J). (ps-2). 2.99 (978-0-375-83535-3(0) , Golden Bks.) Random Hse. Children's Bks.

Power Attack. 1999. (Dragon Ball Z Coloring & Activity Bks.). (Illus.). 32p. (J). (gr. 1-2). pap. (978-0-7666-0535-0(3)) Modern Publishing.

Power Block Kids/Cabritos Del Bloque De Energia. 2005. 64p. (J). pap. (978-0-9762071-4-6(1) , 371-008) Big City Publishing.

Powerpuff Girls Blossom. 2001. (Powerpuff Girls Ser.). (Illus.). 32p. (J). (ps-3). pap. 3.99 (978-0-307-10804-3(X) , Golden Bks.) Random Hse. Children's Bks.

Powerpuff Girls Bubbles. 2001. (Powerpuff Girls Ser.). (Illus.). 32p. (J). (ps-3). pap. 3.99 (978-0-307-10803-6(1) , Golden Bks.) Random Hse. Children's Bks.

Prather, Eric & Prather, Joy. Color the Black Hills: A Nature Coloring & Activity Book. 1998. (Illus.). 32p. (J). (ps-3). pap. 3.95 (978-0-87108-300-5(0)) Pruett Publishing Co.

Preschool Coloring & Activity. 2006. (J). per. 4.99 (*978-1-59545-031-9(9)) Learning Horizons, Inc.

Prestel. Coloring Book Claude Monet. 2006. (Illus.). 32p. 8.95 (978-3-7913-3713-5(0)) Prestel Publishing.

—Coloring Book Kandinsky. 2006. (Illus.). 32p. 8.95 (978-3-7913-3712-8(2)) Prestel Publishing.

Prestel, ed. Coloring Book Klimt. 2007. 32p. pap. 8.95 (*978-3-7913-3790-6(4)) Prestel Publishing.

Prestofillipo, Mary Nazarene, tr. The Story of Creation. Flamini, Lorella, illus. 2005. Orig. Title: Piccola storia della Creazione. (ITA.). 36p. (J). pap. 12.95 (978-0-8198-7093-3(5)) Pauline Bks. & Media.

Price, Marjorie Baker. Merinda & the Magic Mirror: Children's Self Help Coloring Book. Price, David & Price, David, illus. 2002. 30p. (J). spiral bd. 4.95 (978-0-9713013-9-9(5)) Centering Pubns.

Priddy, Roger. Soft-to-Touch Slipcase 2: Colors,123,Abc. 2004. 84p. (J). bds. 22.95 (978-0-312-49423-0(8) , Priddy Bks.) St. Martin's Pr.

Puppy/Bunny: Coloring Activity Book. 2002. (Illus.). 32p. (J). (ps-2). pap. 2.99 (978-1-57759-638-7(2)) Dalmatian Pr.

Puzzling Pictures. 2004. (Hidden Pictures Coloring Bks.). (Illus.). 48p. (J). (gr. 1-2). (978-0-7666-0609-8(0) , 99170) Modern Publishing.

Quantum Control: Poster Book to Color. 2002. (Power Rangers Time Force Ser.). (Illus.). 16p. (J). pap. 1.35 (978-1-57759-530-4(0)) Dalmatian Pr.

Rackham, Arthur. Rackham Fairy Tale Stained Glass Coloring Book. 2005. (Illus.). 32p. (J). (gr. 3-3). pap. 5.95 (978-0-486-44435-2(X)) Dover Pubns., Inc.

Radtke, Becky. At the State Fair Coloring Book. 2004. (Dover Coloring Bks.). (Illus.). 32p. (J). pap. 2.95 (978-0-486-43339-4(0)) Dover Pubns., Inc.

—Neighborhood Helpers Coloring Book. 2004. (Illus.). 32p. (J). pap. 2.95 (978-0-486-43688-3(8)) Dover Pubns., Inc.

Rain Forest Color & Discover Pack. 1998. (Color & Discover Packs Ser.). (Illus.). 28p. (J). reprint ed. pap. (978-1-881469-34-6(4)) Safari, Ltd.

Rains, Larry C., Jr., illus. & creator. Animal Palooza. Rains, Larry C., Jr., creator. 2002. 48p. (J). act. bk. ed. 2.00 (978-0-9714445-0-8(1)) Spitwad Studios.

Raintree Steck-Vaughn Staff. Cambian los Colores. 1999. (Coleccion en Parejas). (SPA.). (J). pap., stu. ed. 21.50 (978-0-7398-0819-1(2)) Steck-Vaughn.

Random House Disney Staff. Around the Bend. Disney Storybook Artists Staff, illus. 2006. (Color Plus Tattoos Ser.). 32p. (J). (ps-2). pap. 3.99 (978-0-375-83376-2(5) , Golden/Disney) Random Hse. Children's Bks.

—Beauty & the Beast Shaped Coloring Book. 2006. (Illus.). 48p. (J). (ps-2). pap. 2.99 (978-0-7364-2359-5(1) , Golden/Disney) Random Hse. Children's Bks.

—The Big Book of Princesses. 2007. (Giant Coloring Book Ser.). (Illus.). 40p. (J). (ps-2). pap. 9.99 (*978-0-375-84726-4(X) , Golden/Disney) Random Hse. Children's Bks.

—Colors Galore: Winnie the Pooh. 2005. (Illus.). 32p. (J). (ps-2). pap. 3.99 (978-0-375-83070-9(7) , Golden/Disney) Random Hse. Children's Bks.

—Dreams Come True Forever. 2006. (Disney Princess Ser.). (Illus.). 224p. (J). (ps-2). pap. 4.99 (978-0-7364-2399-1(0) , Golden/Disney) Random Hse. Children's Bks.

—The Fast Lane. Disney Storybook Artists Staff, illus. 2006. (Deluxe Coloring Book Ser.). 64p. (J). (ps-2). pap. 3.99 (978-0-375-83377-9(3) , Golden/Disney) Random Hse. Children's Bks.

—Fin-tastic Fun. 2005. (Illus.). 48p. (J). (ps-2). pap. 2.99 (978-0-375-83059-4(6) , Golden/Disney) Random Hse. Children's Bks.

—Happy Hugs. Yee, Josie, illus. 2001. (Disney's Winnie the Pooh Ser.). 32p. (J). (gr. k-1). pap. 3.99 (978-0-7364-1136-3(4) , Golden/Disney) Random Hse. Children's Bks.

—Honest & True. 2007. (Paint Box Book Ser.). (Illus.). 48p. (J). (ps-2). pap. 3.99 (*978-0-7364-2500-1(4) , Golden/Disney) Random Hse. Children's Bks.

—Like Father, Like Son. Disney Storybook Artists Staff & Artful Doodlers Limited Staff, illus. 2006. 64p. (J). (ps-2). pap. 2.99 (978-0-7364-2358-8(3) , Golden/Disney) Random Hse. Children's Bks.

—Love at First Sight. 2003. (Disney Princess Ser.). (Illus.). 32p. (J). (ps-3). pap. 3.99 (978-0-7364-2119-5(X) , Golden/Disney) Random Hse. Children's Bks.

—Love at First Sight. 2003. (Disney Princess Ser.). (gr. k-3). lib. bdg. 11.80 (978-0-613-73762-3(8)) Tandem Library Bks.

—Pooh Draws. Hahn, Rebecca, illus. 2007. (Pooh Adorables Ser.). 12p. (J). (ps-k). 7.99 (978-0-7364-2444-8(X) , RH/Disney) Random Hse. Children's Bks.

—Pooh's Heffalump Movie: Little Adventurers. 2005. (Illus.). 64p. (J). (ps-2). pap. 3.99 (978-0-7364-2286-4(2) , Golden/Disney) Random Hse. Children's Bks.

—Together Time. Yee, Josie & De la Paz, Orlando, illus. 2001. (Super Coloring Time Ser.). 80p. (J). (ps-3). pap. 2.99 (978-0-7364-1095-3(3) , Golden/Disney) Random Hse. Children's Bks.

—Ultimate Movie Mix. 2006. (Jumbo Coloring Book Ser.). 224p. (J). (ps-2). pap. 4.99 (978-0-7364-2415-8(6) , Golden/Disney) Random Hse. Children's Bks.

—Untamed World. 2007. (Deluxe Coloring Book Ser.). (Illus.). 96p. (J). (ps-2). pap. 3.99 (*978-0-7364-2452-3(0) , RH/Disney) Random Hse. Children's Bks.

Random House Disney Staff. Weather Watcher. 2006. 96p. (J). (ps-2). pap. 2.99 (978-0-7364-2407-3(5) , Golden/Disney) Random Hse. Children's Bks.

Random House Staff. Wingdings & Dragon Things Super Coloring Time. 2002. (J). pap. 2.99 (978-0-375-81583-6(X)) Random Hse. Children's Bks.

Rao, Lisa. Surf's Up: Coloring & Activity Book & Crayons. Merkel, Joe F., illus. 2007. (Surf's Up Ser.). 32p. (J). pap. 4.99 (*978-0-06-115335-8(4) , Harper Entertainment) HarperCollins Pubs.

Raptors - Birds of Prey Coloring Book. 2005. (Illus.). 24p. (J). pap. 4.95 (978-0-88839-600-6(7)) Hancock Hse. Pubs., Ltd. CAN. *Dist:* Hancock Hse. Pubs.

Rea, Monique F. Toulouse the Moose Coloring Book. 2007. (J). (*978-0-9788926-3-0(1)) Trails of Discovery.

Read-Aloud Story & Activity Book. 128p. act. bk. ed. 16.99 (978-0-8307-2770-4(1)); Vol. 2. 112p. act. bk. ed. 16.99 (978-0-8307-2885-5(6)) Gospel Light Pubns. (Gospel Light).

Read & Color Book Series. Date not set. (Illus.). (J). (ps-5). pap. (978-0-86545-223-7(7)) Spizzirri Pr., Inc.

Ready Set Learn Staff. Chirps Colors. 2005. (Illus.). 24p. (J). (ps-2). bds. 15.99 (978-1-59249-518-4(4) , 1C300) Soundprints.

Reagan, Dawn. Bear Toons Coloring Book. Toon Takes Staff, ed. Reagan, Dawn, illus. 1999. (Illus.). 32p. (J). (ps-5). pap. 3.00 (978-1-929456-08-6(5)) Myrtle-Seal Publishing.

—Duck Toons Coloring Book. Toon Takes Staff, ed. Reagan, Dawn, illus. 1999. (Illus.). 32p. (J). (ps-5). pap. 3.00 (978-1-929456-07-9(7)) Myrtle-Seal Publishing.

—Toon Takes Turtles: Coloring Book of Turtle Toons. Toon Takes Staff, ed. Reagan, Dawn, illus. 1999. (Illus.). 32p. (J). (ps-2). pap. 3.00 (978-1-929456-06-2(9)) Myrtle-Seal Publishing.

—Toon Toys Trio: Coloring Book & Toy Kit. Toon Takes Staff, ed. deluxe ed. 1999. (Illus.). 15p. (J). (ps-7). pap. 15.95 (978-1-929456-09-3(3)) Myrtle-Seal Publishing.

The Really Big Butterfly Coloring Book ' A Teaching & Learning Tool. 2004. Orig. Title: Same. (J). per. 7.95 (978-0-9729753-2-2(2)) Really Big Coloring Bks., Inc.

Realtime Associates and Mazer Corporation Staff & LeapFrog Staff, compiled by. Compare & Contrast. 2002. (J). (gr. 2). 66.75 (978-1-58605-296-6(9)); (gr. 3). 66.75 (978-1-58605-358-1(2)); (gr. 4). 66.75 (978-1-58605-414-4(7)); (gr. 5). 66.75 (978-1-58605-473-1(2)) LeapFrog Enterprises, Inc. (LeapFrog Schl. Hse.).

The Realtree Deer Hunting Activity & Coloring Book. 2003. (J). pap. (978-0-9745863-1-1(5)) Cypress Knees Publishing.

The Realtree Hunting Coloring Book. 2003. (J). pap. (978-0-9745863-3-5(1)) Cypress Knees Publishing.

Reidy, Hannah. Crazy Creature Colors. Mackie, Clare, illus. 2003. (Crazy Creatures Ser.). 20p. (J). pap. (978-1-84089-221-5(8) , Zero to Ten, Limited) Evans Publishing Group.

Renoir, Pierre Auguste. Color Your Own Renoir Paintings. Noble, Marty, illus. 2001. 32p. (J). pap. 3.95 (978-0-486-41546-8(5)) Dover Pubns., Inc.

Rentfro, Jeanne. Cowboy Country Coloring Book. 2007. (J). per. 5.00 (*978-0-9761128-9-1(2)) Hafabanana Pr.

Rey, Margret, creator. Curious George Big Treats! rev. ed. 2005. (Illus.). 16p. (J). (ps-ps). 3.99 (978-1-4037-0725-3(1)) Dalmatian Pr.

Rhodes, Karen. God's Word Then & Now Activity Book. 2007. (Illus.). 16p. (J). pap. 1.89 (*978-1-59317-207-7(9)) Warner Pr. Pubs.

Rich, J. Milton. Heavenly Fathers Plan of Salvation Coloring Book. Knaupp, Andrew & Koford, Adam, illus. 2003. 108p. (J). per. 7.95 (978-0-9726670-2-9(4)) Rich Publishing.

Richards, V. H. First Christmas Color Act Bk. 24p. pap. 1.25 (978-0-8198-2677-0(4) , 332-096) Pauline Bks. & Media.

—My Rosary Color & Act Bk. 32p. pap. 1.25 (978-0-8198-4823-9(9) , 332-214) Pauline Bks. & Media.

Richer, William. What Do You Wanna-Bee? An Encyclopedia Activity Coloring Book of Professional Busy Bee's. 2nd ed. 2000. Orig. Title: To Be or not to Be, What Do You Wanna-Be?. (Illus.). 68p. (J). (gr. 1). pap. 6.95 (978-0-9703609-0-8(8)) I Wanna Bee.

Riders in the Sky: Cartoon Cowboy Coloring Book. 2004. (J). (978-0-9746784-1-2(4)) Hughes, Bill.

Rigol, Francesc, illus. Los Colores. 2002. (Aprendo con Dan y Din Ser.).Tr. of Colors. (SPA.). 10p. (ps). 5.95 (978-84-7864-522-0(5)) Combel Editorial, S.A. ESP. *Dist:* Independent Pubs. Group.

Rivard, Bill. The simplest zoo to Do: An Alphabetical Coloring Book. 2006. pap. 7.95 (978-0-533-15436-4(7)) Vantage Pr., Inc.

Rizzon, Roberto. Grandmother's Footsteps: A Journey in Search of Penelope Betjeman. 1999. (Let's Play Series 2 Ser.). (Illus.). 24p. (J). (ps-3). pap. 3.99 (978-0-85953-711-7(0)) Child's Play-International.

—Moving Home. 1999. (Let's Play Series 2 Ser.). (Illus.). 24p. (J). (ps-3). pap. 3.99 (978-0-85953-712-4(9)) Child's Play-International.

Robert, Cerny. My Kingdom Pal Adventure Color Activity Book. 2004. (Illus.). 32p. (J). (978-0-9748251-1-3(5) , 10000) Zoe Life Publishing.

Robert, Jeffrey. Start America Coloring Workbook. 2001. 16p. pap. 14.95 (978-0-9715441-0-9(7)) Crayon Artist, LLC, The.

Roberts, Cindy. Cindy Roberts: Lunar New Year for Kids. Glasner, Beth & Roberts, Tom, eds. 2000. (Illus.). 45p. (J). pap., wbk. ed. 12.00 (978-0-9706660-0-0(4)) Roberts, Cindy.

Roberts, Shelly. Sissy & the Old Crow (Coloring Book) 2006. (Illus.). 36p. (J). per. 6.50 (978-0-9789798-3-6(4) , 978-0-9789798-3-6) Blackbird's World Publishing Co.

Robinson, Alice. Shining Stars: A Colors Book. 2005. (Illus.). 16p. (J). (ps-k). per. 6.95 (978-1-58117-392-5(X) , Intervisual/Piggy Toes) Dalmatian Pr.

Rodriguez, Orlando & Sabio Y Prudente Ministries Staff. The Garden of Eden. 2000. (Sabio Y Prudente Ser.). (SPA.). 32p. (J). (ps-2). pap. 4.99 (978-0-8254-0979-0(9) , Editorial Portavoz) Kregel Pubns.

—The Garden of Eden, Grades Preschool-2. 2000. (Sabio Y Prudente Ser.). (SPA.). 32p. (J). pap., tchr. ed. 4.99 (978-0-8254-0977-6(2) , Editorial Portavoz) Kregel Pubns.

Rogers, Judy. Go to the Ant Coloring Book: Learning from Proverbs. Lockman, Vic, illus. 2001. 16p. (J). pap. 1.99 (978-0-87552-566-2(0)) P & R Publishing.

—Isabelle Is a Pig Coloring Book: Learning from Proverbs. Lockman, Vic, illus. 2002. 16p. (J). pap. 2.99 (978-0-87552-567-9(9)) P & R Publishing.

Rogers, Kathy. Color & Learn - Africa. Adams, Elizabeth, illus. 1999. 32p. (J). (gr. 2-6). pap., wbk. ed. 3.99 (978-1-56472-208-9(2) , EP208) Edupress, Inc.

—Color & Learn - Ancient Egypt. Adams, Elizabeth, illus. 1999. 32p. (J). (gr. 2-6). pap., wbk. ed. 3.99 (978-1-56472-200-3(7) , EP200) Edupress, Inc.

—Color & Learn - Ancient Greece. Adams, Elizabeth, illus. 1999. 32p. (J). (gr. 2-6). pap., wbk. ed. 3.99 (978-1-56472-209-6(0) , EP209) Edupress, Inc.

—Color & Learn - Australia. Adams, Elizabeth, illus. 1999. 32p. (J). (gr. 2-6). pap., wbk. ed. 3.99 (978-1-56472-203-4(1) , EP203) Edupress, Inc.

—Color & Learn - China. Adams, Elizabeth, illus. 1999. 32p. (J). (gr. 2-6). pap., wbk. ed. 3.99 (978-1-56472-207-2(4) , EP207) Edupress, Inc.

—Color & Learn - Colonial America. Adams, Elizabeth, illus. 1999. 32p. (J). (gr. 2-6). pap., wbk. ed. 3.99 (978-1-56472-204-1(X) , EP204) Edupress, Inc.

—Color & Learn - Inca, Aztec, Maya. Adams, Elizabeth, illus. 1999. 32p. (J). (gr. 2-6). pap., wbk. ed. 3.99 (978-1-56472-211-9(2) , EP211) Edupress, Inc.

—Color & Learn - Japan. Adams, Elizabeth, illus. 1999. 32p. (J). (gr. 2-6). pap., wbk. ed. 3.99 (978-1-56472-206-5(6) , EP206) Edupress, Inc.

—Color & Learn - Medieval Times. Adams, Elizabeth, illus. 1999. 32p. (J). (gr. 2-6). pap., wbk. ed. 3.99 (978-1-56472-201-0(5) , EP201) Edupress, Inc.

—Color & Learn - Mexico. Adams, Elizabeth, illus. 1999. 32p. (J). (gr. 2-6). pap., wbk. ed. 3.99 (978-1-56472-205-8(8) , EP205) Edupress, Inc.

—Color & Learn - Native America. Adams, Elizabeth, illus. 1999. 32p. (J). (gr. 2-6). pap., wbk. ed. 3.99 (978-1-56472-202-7(3) , EP202) Edupress, Inc.

Romano, Elaine. The Magic Potato - la Papa Magica: Story & coloring book in English & Spanish. I. Nielsen, Emily, tr. Winchel, Heidi, illus. 2nd ed. 2004. (SPA.). 20p. (J). 3.00 (978-0-9728225-3-4(4)) Mill Park Publishing.

Rose, Drew, illus. God's Heroes. 2005. (Bible Activity Bks.). 96p. (J). (ps-3). 2.99 (978-0-7814-4313-5(X) , 078144313X) Cook, David C. Publishing Co.

—God's Son, Jesus. 2005. (Bible Activity Bks.). 96p. (J). (ps-3). 2.99 (978-0-7814-4314-2(8) , 0781443148) Cook, David C. Publishing Co.

—God's World. 2005. (Bible Activity Bks.). 96p. (J). (ps-3). 2.99 (978-0-7814-4312-8(1) , 0781443121) Cook, David C. Publishing Co.

Rose, J. R. Christmas Fun with Pup. 2000. (Illus.). 64p. (J). (gr. k-3). pap. 5.95 (978-1-56554-713-1(6)) Pelican Publishing Co., Inc.

Rudolph's Sleigh Ride Coloring Fun. Date not set. (Christmas Activity Bks.). (Illus.). 128p. (J). pap. 3.98 (978-0-7525-6671-9(7)) Parragon, Inc.

Rugg, Michael. Bigfoot Discovery Book. 2005. (Illus.). 32p. (J). pap., act. bk. ed. 5.95 (978-0-88839-592-4(2)) Hancock Hse. Pubs., Ltd. CAN. *Dist:* Hancock Hse. Pubs.

Rugg, Michael & Kieffer, Steve. Dinosaur Coloring Book. 2005. (Illus.). 24p. (J). pap. 4.95 (978-0-88839-593-1(0)) Hancock Hse. Pubs., Ltd. CAN. *Dist:* Hancock Hse. Pubs.

Rundstrom, Teressa. A Herd of Cows Came by My House. Waldron, Drue, illus. 2002. 50p. (J). per. (978-1-932062-39-7(4)) Hability Solution Services, Inc.

Running Press Staff. Angels. 2001. 44p. pap. 5.95 (978-0-933470-16-3(9)) International Evangelism Crusades, Inc.

—Lighthouses. 2006. (Illus.). 96p. 9.98 (978-0-7624-2640-9(3) , Courage Bks.) Running Pr. Bk. Pubs.

C D

Ruth, Annie. Little Angels Coloring & Activity Book: The Special Gift. Ruth, Annie, illus. l.t. ed. 1999. (Illus.). 24p. (J). (gr. k-3). 3.50 (978-0-9656306-2-7(5)) Ruth, A. Creations.

Sabio, et al. Libro de Califgrafia, Vol. 3. 2000. (Sabio Y Prudente Ser.). (SPA.). 64p. (J). (ps-3). 4.99 (978-0-8254-0994-3(2) , Editorial Portavoz) Kregel Pubns.

Saborea & Huele!Tr. of Taste & Small!. (SPA.). (J). 2.95 (978-958-607-887-0(6)) Sociedad de San Pablo ESP. *Dist:* Alba Hse.

Sacks, Janet. Mini Magic Color Book: Bunny's Spring Day. Rinaldo, Luana, illus. 2007. 10p. (J). 3.95 (978-1-4027-4591-1(5) , Sterling/Pinwheel) Sterling Publishing Co., Inc.

—Mini Magic Color Book: Cars. Rinaldo, Luana, illus. 2007. 10p. (J). 3.95 (978-1-4027-4592-8(3) , Sterling/Pinwheel) Sterling Publishing Co., Inc.

Salisbury, Kent. Color Fun: What Colors Are Your Favorite Things? 1998. (Illus.). 24p. (J). (ps-k). 6.99 (978-0-7681-0084-6(4) , McClanahan Bk.) Learning Horizons, Inc.

The Saltwater Game Fish Coloring Book. 2005. (J). mass mkt. (978-0-9763757-1-5(0)) Cypress Knees Publishing.

Sam & Sarge. 2004. (J). 5.00 (978-0-9767215-1-2(1)) Family Guidance & Outreach Ctr. of Lubbock.

Sander, Sonia. The Kooky Carry-along Coloring Kit. 2008. (Wow! Wow! Wubbzy! Ser.). 80p. (J). 5.99 (***978-1-4169-4794-3(9)*** , Simon Scribbles) Simon & Schuster Children's Publishing.

The Pirates Who Don't Color Anything! Funnypages Productions, illus. 2006. (VeggieTales Ser.). 48p. (J). 3.99 (978-1-4169-1784-7(5) , Simon Scribbles) Simon & Schuster Children's Publishing.

—Sagwa: Festival of Lanterns. Thompson Brothers Staff, illus. 2003. (Sagwa, the Chinese Siamese Cat Ser.). 32p. (J). (ps-3). pap. 3.99 (978-0-439-45179-6(5)) Scholastic, Inc.

—Sagwa: Sagwa's Lucky Bat. George, Chris, illus. 2003. (Sagwa, the Chinese Siamese Cat Ser.). 64p. (J). (ps-3). 2.99 (978-0-439-45181-9(7)) Scholastic, Inc.

Sargent, Daina. Colors & the Number 6/Los Colores y el Numero 6, 11 vols. Lenoir, Jane, illus. 2005. (Learn to Read Ser.: 11). (ENG & SPA.). 24p. (J). pap. 9.95 (978-1-59381-139-6(X)) Ozark Publishing.

Sargent, Daina & Lenoir, Jane. Colors & the Number 6/Los colores y el Numero 6, 11 vols. 2005. (Learn to Read Ser.).Tr. of Los colores y el Numero 6. (ENG & SPA., Illus.). 24p. (J). lib. bdg. 19.95 (978-1-59381-138-9(1)) Ozark Publishing.

Sawyers, William. What Am I? Bugs. 2005. 65p. (J). pap. 16.01 (978-1-4116-3402-2(0)) Lulu.com.

Scalzo, Linda V. Carazona's Coloring Book. l.t. ed. 2004. (Illus.). 8p. (J). 2.99 (978-0-9753724-3-2(2)) Carazona Creations LLC.

Schilling, Mickey. Colorado Rockies Coloring & Activity Book. 1998. (Illus.). 48p. (J). (ps-6). pap. (978-0-9663885-0-3(X)) Schilling, Mickey.

Schmidt, Nathan, illus. Zoey & the Zones: Coloring Book. 2002. 0.99 (978-0-9718120-3-1(9)); 2. 2003. 0.99 (978-0-9718120-7-9(1)) HealthSprings, LLC.

Scholastic Editorial Staff. Learn with Lego: In the City. 2007. (Lego Ser.). 24p. (J). 4.99 (978-0-439-90399-8(8)) Scholastic, Inc.

—Lego Learn with Lego at the Zoo. 2007. (Lego Ser.). 24p. (J). 4.99 (978-0-439-90398-1(X)) Scholastic, Inc.

Scholastic, Inc. Staff. Harry Potter: Deluxe Coloring Book. movie tie-in ed. 2007. (Harry Potter Movie V Ser.). 288p. (J). pap. 4.99 (***978-0-439-02488-4(9)***) Scholastic, Inc.

—Harry Potter & the Chamber of Secrets Scene for Scene. Enik, Ted, illus. 2002. (Harry Potter Art Coloring Bks.: No. 4). 32p. (J). 5.99 (978-0-439-41898-0(4)) Scholastic, Inc.

—Harry Potter & the Chamber of Secrets Stencil Art. Ruiz, Aristides, illus. movie tie-in ed. 2002. (Harry Potter Art Coloring Bks.: No. 3). 32p. (J). 5.99 (978-0-439-41897-3(6)) Scholastic, Inc.

—Harry Potter & the Chamber of Secrets Sticker Scenes. Miralles, Joseph, illus. movie tie-in ed. 2002. (Harry Potter Art Coloring Bks.: No. 2). 32p. (J). 5.99 (978-0-439-42526-1(3)) Scholastic, Inc.

—King-Sized Color & Activity Book. Hult, Gene, ed. 2005. (Clifford Ser.). 400p. (J). pap., act. bk. ed. 5.99 (978-0-439-78955-4(9) , Scholastic) Scholastic, Inc.

Scholastic, Inc. Staff, ed. Adventures with Hagrid. movie tie-in ed. 2001. (Harry Potter Coloring Adventures Ser.). 32p. (J). 4.99 (978-0-439-28620-6(4)) Scholastic, Inc.

—Friendship. movie tie-in ed. 2001. (Harry Potter Coloring Adventures Ser.). 32p. (J). 4.99 (978-0-439-28621-3(2)) Scholastic, Inc.

—Harry Potter & the Chamber of Secrets Trace a Scene. Miralles, Joseph, illus. movie tie-in ed. 2002. (Harry Potter Art Coloring Bks.: No. 1). 32p. (J). 5.99 (978-0-439-42525-4(5)) Scholastic, Inc.

—Harry Potter & the Sorcerer's Stone: Invisible Image Coloring Book. movie tie-in ed. 2001. (Illus.). 48p. (J). 4.99 (978-0-439-28615-2(8)) Scholastic, Inc.

—Hogwart's School. movie tie-in ed. 2001. (Harry Potter Coloring Adventures Ser.). 32p. (J). 4.99 (978-0-439-28619-0(0)) Scholastic, Inc.

—Sorting Hat Ceremony. movie tie-in ed. 2001. (Harry Potter Coloring Adventures Ser.). 32p. (J). 4.99 (978-0-439-28617-6(4)) Scholastic, Inc.

Scholastic, Inc. Staff & Salas, Macarena, eds. Dive Right In!/-LyNzate Al Agua! 2004. (Rubbadubbers Ser.). (ENG & SPA.). 80p. (J). 2.99 (978-0-439-63204-1(8) , Scholastic en Espanol) Scholastic, Inc.

School Specialty Publishing. Learn about Dinosaurs. 2005. (Learn about Coloring Bks.). 32p. (J). (ps-3). pap. 1.99 (978-0-7696-4157-7(1) , Brighter Child) School Specialty Publishing.

—Learn about Going to School. 2005. (Learn about Coloring Bks.). 32p. (J). (ps-3). pap. 1.99 (978-0-7696-4160-7(1) , Brighter Child) School Specialty Publishing.

—Learn about Home. 2005. (Learn about Coloring Bks.). 32p. (J). (ps-3). pap. 1.99 (978-0-7696-4161-4(X) , Brighter Child) School Specialty Publishing.

—Learn about the Alphabet. 2005. (Learn about Coloring Bks.). 32p. (J). (ps-3). pap. 1.99 (978-0-7696-4156-0(3) , Brighter Child) School Specialty Publishing.

—Learn about the Farm. 2005. (Learn about Coloring Bks.). 32p. (J). (ps-3). pap. 1.99 (978-0-7696-4158-4(X) , Brighter Child) School Specialty Publishing.

—Learn about the Forest. 2005. (Learn about Coloring Bks.). 32p. (J). pap. 1.99 (978-0-7696-4159-1(8) , Brighter Child) School Specialty Publishing.

—Learn about the Ocean. 2005. (Learn about Coloring Bks.). 32p. (J). (ps-3). pap. 1.99 (978-0-7696-4162-1(8) , Brighter Child) School Specialty Publishing.

—Learn about the Zoo. 2005. (Learn about Coloring Bks.). 32p. (J). (ps-3). pap. 1.99 (978-0-7696-4163-8(6) , Brighter Child) School Specialty Publishing.

—My Very Best Coloring & Activity Book: Catepillar. 2002. 120p. (J). (gr. k-3). pap. 1.99 (978-0-7696-2788-5(9) , American Education Publishing) School Specialty Publishing.

—My Very Best Coloring & Activity Book: Hippo Dance. 2002. 120p. (J). (gr. k-3). pap. 1.99 (978-0-7696-2789-2(7) , American Education Publishing) School Specialty Publishing.

—My Very Best Coloring & Activity Book: Ladybug Picnic. 2002. 120p. (J). (gr. k-3). pap. 1.99 (978-0-7696-2786-1(2) , American Education Publishing) School Specialty Publishing.

—My Very Best Coloring & Activity Book: Zebra Birthday. 2002. 120p. (J). (gr. k-3). pap. 1.99 (978-0-7696-2787-8(0) , American Education Publishing) School Specialty Publishing.

—1-2-3 Sorting & Classifying. 2003. (1-2-3 Ser.). 80p. (J). pap. 10.99 (978-1-57029-471-6(2) , WPH99022, Totline Pubns.) Schaffer, Frank Pubns.

School Specialty Publishing Staff. All about God's Love. 2001. (All about Coloring Book Ser.). 32p. (J). (gr. k-3). pap. 3.99 (978-0-7647-0583-0(0) , In Celebration) Schaffer, Frank Pubns.

School Specialty Publishing Staff & Mears, Henrietta C. All about the New Testament. 2001. (All about Coloring Book Ser.). 32p. (J). (gr. k-3). pap. 3.99 (978-0-7647-0581-6(4) , In Celebration) Schaffer, Frank Pubns.

School Zone Publishing Company Staff. Kindergarten Big Get Ready! 1999. (Big Get Ready Ser.). (Illus.). 320p. (J). pap., wbk. ed. 9.99 (978-0-88743-146-3(1) , 06316) School Zone Publishing Co.

Schwartz, Suzanne & Schwartz, Robert. The Christmas Palm Tree: A Storybook to Color. Schwartz, Suzanne & Schwartz, Robert, illus. l.t. ed. 2005. (Illus.). 22p. (J). spiral bd. 3.99 (978-0-9764152-3-7(2)) Seascay Productions.

—My Friend Hibby Picture & Coloring Book Set, 2 vols. 2005. (Illus.). 46p. (J). spiral bd. 8.00 (978-0-9764152-2-0(4)) Seascay Productions.

Schwartz, Suzanne & Schwartz, Robert, illus. Hibby's Coloring Book. 2005. 24p. (J). spiral bd. 3.95 (978-0-9764152-1-3(6)) Seascay Productions.

Schweitzer Mountain Activity & Coloring Book. 2005. (J). 19.95 (978-1-59649-240-0(6)); spiral bd. 19.95 (978-1-59649-239-4(2)); cd-rom 13.95 (978-1-59649-241-7(4)) Whispering Pine Pr., Inc.

Schwietzer Mountain Activity & Coloring Book. 2005. (J). per. 19.95 (978-1-59649-230-1(9)) Whispering Pine Pr., Inc.

Scott, Kathleen. We are All Special... Babies are Very Special! l.t. ed. 2002. (Illus.). 40p. (J). 5.00 (978-0-9749177-4-0(5)) A New Day...A New Way!.

The Seasons of Mount Rushmore Coloring Book. 2006. (J). (978-0-9752617-7-4(0)) Mount Rushmore History Assn.

Sebring Lowrey, Janette & Crampton, Gertrude. The Poky Little Puppy & Other Stories to Color. Tenggren, Gustaf & Gergely, Tibor, illus. 2007. 96p. (J). (ps-2). 2.99 (978-0-375-83536-0(9) , Golden Bks.) Random Hse. Children's Bks.

Serensits, Jaime F. M. Alphabet Train Coloring Book. Serensits, Jaime F. M., illus. 2001. 32p. (J). pap. 5.00 (978-1-931477-01-7(9)) Railroad Pr., The.

Sesame Street, creator. Sesame Street Elmo's ABC Book. rev. ed. 2005. (Illus.). 24p. (J). pap. 3.50 (978-1-4037-1043-7(0)) Dalmatian Pr.

—Sesame Street Red or Blue, I Like You. rev. ed. 2005. (Illus.). 24p. (J). pap. 3.50 (978-1-4037-1045-1(7)) Dalmatian Pr.

—Sesame Street Zoe Just the Way You Are. rev. ed. 2005. (Illus.). 24p. (J). pap. 3.50 (978-1-4037-1431-2(2)) Dalmatian Pr.

Sesame's: A Giant Coloring Book about Fun Things to do at School. 2006. (J). 6.99 (978-1-59949-495-1(7)) Food Marketing Consultants, Inc.

Sesame's: A Giant Coloring Book about Fun Things to do over the Summer. 2006. (J). 6.99 (978-1-59949-496-8(5)) Food Marketing Consultants, Inc.

Sesame's: A Giant Coloring Book that Introduces Kids to the Alphabet: the ABCs of Sesame Street. 2006. (J). 6.99 (978-1-59949-498-2(1)) Food Marketing Consultants, Inc.

Sesame's: A Giant Coloring Book that Teaches about Opposites. 2006. (J). 6.99 (978-1-59949-497-5(3)) Food Marketing Consultants, Inc.

Sesame's: A Giant Coloring Book that teaches Healthy Eating Habits. 2006. (J). 6.99 (978-1-59949-499-9(X)) Food Marketing Consultants, Inc.

Sforza, Daniella, ed. Savannah Blue's Activity Book/Libro de Actividades de Savannah Azul. Spagnoli, Maria Eugenia, tr. Rakusin, Sudie, illus. 2005. Tr. of Libro de Actividades de Savannah Azul. (SPA & ENG.). 48p. (J). 10.95 (978-0-9664805-4-2(6)) Winged Willow Pr.

Shaffer, Christy. Carousel Animals Coloring Book. 1999. 32p. (J). pap. 3.95 (978-0-486-40804-0(3)) Dover Pubns., Inc.

—Carousel Horses Stained Glass Coloring Book. 2002. (Pictorial Archive Ser.). (Illus.). 16p. (J). pap. 5.95 (978-0-486-42188-9(0)) Dover Pubns., Inc.

—Dragons Coloring Book. 2002. (Pictorial Archive Ser.). (Illus.). 32p. (J). pap. 3.95 (978-0-486-42057-8(4)) Dover Pubns., Inc.

—Legendary Dragons Stained Glass Coloring Book. 2007. 16p. (J). pap. 5.95 (***978-0-486-46224-0(2)***) Dover Pubns., Inc.

—Magical Horses Stained Glass Coloring Book. 2004. (Pictorial Archive Ser.). (Illus.). 16p. (J). (gr. 3). pap. 5.95 (978-0-486-43342-4(0)) Dover Pubns., Inc.

—Magical Unicorns Stained Glass Coloring Book. 2004. (Illus.). 16p. pap. 5.95 (978-0-486-43705-7(1)) Dover Pubns., Inc.

—Nature's Backyard Scenes Stained Glass Coloring Book. 2006. 16p. (J). pap. 5.95 (978-0-486-44708-7(1)) Dover Pubns., Inc.

—Unicorns Coloring Book. 2000. (Pictorial Archive Ser.). (Illus.). 32p. (J). pap. 3.95 (978-0-486-41319-8(5)) Dover Pubns., Inc.

Shank, Charles C. The 911 Coloring Book. 2002. 103p. pap. 14.95 (978-0-7414-1077-1(X)) Infinity Publishing.

Sheely, Tiffany, illus. Captain William Clark's Great Montana Adventure. 2003. 32p. (J). mass mkt. 3.95 (978-0-9711667-0-7(6)) Outlook Publishing, Inc.

Shepherd Mountain Press Staff. What Can You See on the Coast? A Shepherd Mountain Press Coloring Book. 2003. (Illus.). 36p. (J). pap. 4.50 (978-0-9749282-0-3(8)) Shepherd Mountain Pr.

Sherman, Janice. Colorful Critters Color Match Coloring Book. 2007. (ENG., Illus.). 10p. (J). pap. 1.99 (***978-0-9797139-3-4(5)***) Jan's Looks & Bks.

Shirley Dobson Bible Story Coloring Book Sampler Merchandiser. 129.00 (978-0-8307-2753-7(1) , Gospel Light) Gospel Light Pubns.

Shirley Dobson Bible Story Coloring Book Sampler Merchandiser: 55 Unit Mini-Merch. 70.95 (978-0-8307-3024-7(9) , Gospel Light) Gospel Light Pubns.

Shoup, Andrew J. Andy & Elmer's Apple Dumpling Adventure. 2nd ed. 2007. (J). 16.95 (***978-0-9720436-3-2(2)***) TokoBooks.

—Andy & Elmer's Apple Dumpling Adventure Coloring & Activity Book. Shoup, Andrew J., illus. 2007. (Illus.). 36p. (J). 3.95 (***978-0-9720436-2-5(4)***) TokoBooks.

Shumate, A. M. The True-Color Book. 2003. (Illus.). 120p. pap. 44.95 (978-1-894921-14-5(3)) Briston Hse. CAN. *Dist:* Independent Pubs. Group.

Siede, George & Press, Donna, photos by. Collections. 1998. (Active Minds Ser.). (Illus.). 40p. (J). bds. 12.98 (978-1-58048-032-1(2)) Sandvik Publishing.

Sim, David. Matt's Hat: A Find the Hat Color Book, 2 bks. Sim, David, illus. 2003. (Illus.). 10p. (J). 7.95 (978-1-58117-197-6(8) , Intervisual/Piggy Toes) Dalmatian Pr.

Simard, Remy, illus. Busy Day Coloring Storybook. 2003. (Rainbow Fish & Friends Ser.). 24p. (J). mass mkt. 2.99 (978-1-59014-132-8(6)) Night Sky Bks.

—Favorite Places Coloring Storybook. 2003. (Rainbow Fish & Friends Ser.). 24p. (J). mass mkt. 2.99 (978-1-59014-133-5(4)) Night Sky Bks.

Simon-Kerr, Julia. Coloring & Activity Book & Tattoos. Merkel, Joe F., illus. 2006. (Open Season Ser.). 32p. (J). pap. 3.99 (978-0-06-084615-2(1)) HarperCollins Pubs.

—The Lion, the Witch, & the Wardrobe. Coloring & Activity Book & Magnets. Redondo, Jesus, illus. movie tie-in ed. 2005. (Narnia Ser.). 32p. (J). pap., act. bk. ed. 4.99 (978-0-06-076558-3(5)) Zonderkidz.

—Princess Party Paint Book. Edwards, Ken, illus. 2005. (My Little Pony Ser.). 32p. (J). pap. 3.99 (978-0-06-074699-5(8) , Harper Festival) HarperCollins Pubs.

Skiles, Janet, illus. Thru-the-Bible Coloring Pages: Ages 3-6. 2005. 240p. (J). (ps-3). pap. 15.99 (978-0-7847-1783-7(4) , 02272) Standard Publishing.

—Thru-the-Bible Coloring Pages: Ages 6-8. 2005. 240p. (J). (ps-3). pap. 15.99 (978-0-7847-1785-1(0) , 02274) Standard Publishing.

Skillicorn, Mark, tr. & illus. Scooby Doo Wipe off Book. Skillicorn, Mark, illus. 2001. (My Wipe-Off Book Ser.). 16p. (J). spiral bd., bds. 10.98 (978-0-7853-4803-0(4) , 7129400) Publications International, Ltd.

Sladen, Louisa. Baby Animals. Rinaldo, Luana, illus. 2005. (Magic Color Bks.). 10p. (J). 3.95 (978-1-4027-2054-3(8) , Sterling/Pinwheel) Sterling Publishing Co., Inc.

—Dinosaurs. Rinaldo, Luana, illus. 2005. (Magic Color Bks.). 10p. (J). 3.95 (978-1-4027-2055-0(6) , Sterling/Pinwheel) Sterling Publishing Co., Inc.

—My Pets. Rinaldo, Luana, illus. 2005. (Magic Color Bks.). 10p. (J). 3.95 (978-1-4027-2053-6(X) , Sterling/Pinwheel) Sterling Publishing Co., Inc.

—Sea Creatures. Rinaldo, Luana, illus. 2005. (Magic Color Bks.). 10p. (J). 3.95 (978-1-4027-2056-7(4) , Sterling/Pinwheel) Sterling Publishing Co., Inc.

Smith, A. G. Beautiful Butterflies Stained Glass Coloring Book. 2003. (Illus.). 16p. (J). (gr. 3). pap. 5.95 (978-0-486-43061-4(8)) Dover Pubns., Inc.

—British Castles. 2004. (Dover Coloring Bks.). (Illus.). 32p. (J). pap. 3.95 (978-0-486-43572-5(5)) Dover Pubns., Inc.

—Castles Stained Glass Coloring Book. 2003. (Illus.). 16p. (J). pap. 5.95 (978-0-486-43048-5(0)) Dover Pubns., Inc.

—Classic Posters Stained Glass Coloring Book. 2004. (Pictorial Archive Ser.). (Illus.). 16p. (J). (gr. 3). pap. 5.95 (978-0-486-43343-1(9)) Dover Pubns., Inc.

—Create Your Own Tiffany Windows Stained Glass Coloring Book. 2003. (Dover Coloring Bks.). (Illus.). 16p. (J). pap. 5.95 (978-0-486-42751-5(X)) Dover Pubns., Inc.

—Easy Kaleidoscope Stained Glass Coloring Book. 2005. (Illus.). 8p. (J). pap. 1.50 (978-0-486-44182-5(2)) Dover Pubns., Inc.

—Fun to Color Stained Glass Coloring Book. 2004. (Illus.). 8p. (J). (gr. k-5). pap. 1.50 (978-0-486-43452-0(4)) Dover Pubns., Inc.

—Geometric Designs Stained Glass Coloring Book. 1999. (Illus.). 16p. (J). (gr. 3). pap. 5.95 (978-0-486-40808-8(6)) Dover Pubns., Inc.

—Geometric Star Designs Coloring Book. 2005. (Illus.). 32p. (J). pap. 3.95 (978-0-486-44102-3(4)) Dover Pubns., Inc.

—Heraldic Designs Stained Glass Coloring Book. 2000. (Illus.). 16p. (J). pap. 4.95 (978-0-486-41043-2(9)) Dover Pubns., Inc.

—Knights in Armor Stained Glass Coloring Book. 2001. (Dover Little Activity Bks.). (Illus.). 8p. (J). (gr. k-5). pap. 1.50 (978-0-486-41615-1(1)) Dover Pubns., Inc.

—Little Geometric Stained Glass Coloring Book. 2000. (Illus.). 8p. (J). (gr. k-5). pap. 1.50 (978-0-486-41256-6(3)) Dover Pubns., Inc.

—Little Mandalas Stained Glass Coloring Book. 2006. (Dover Little Activity Bks.). 8p. (J). pap. 1.50 (978-0-486-44937-1(8)) Dover Pubns., Inc.

—Masks of the World Coloring Book. 2003. (Illus.). 32p. (J). pap. 3.95 (978-0-486-43039-3(1)) Dover Pubns., Inc.

—Medieval Castle. 2002. (Dover Coloring Bks.). (Illus.). 32p. (J). pap. 3.95 (978-0-486-42080-6(9)) Dover Pubns., Inc.

—Northwest Coast Indian Designs Coloring Book. 2002. (Illus.). 16p. (J). pap. 5.95 (978-0-486-42081-3(7)) Dover Pubns., Inc.

—Snowflake Designs Coloring Book. 2007. 32p. pap. 3.95 (***978-0-486-45686-7(2)***) Dover Pubns., Inc.

—Snowflake Designs Stained Glass Coloring Book. 2007. 16p. (J). pap. 5.95 (***978-0-486-45769-7(9)***) Dover Pubns., Inc.

—Starbursts Stained Glass Coloring Book. 2005. (Illus.). 8p. (J). (gr. k-5). pap. 1.50 (978-0-486-44460-4(0)) Dover Pubns., Inc.

—Traditional Houses from Around the World. 2000. (Illus.). 48p. (J). pap. 3.95 (978-0-486-41322-8(5)) Dover Pubns., Inc.

—Viking Designs Stained Glass Coloring Book. 2004. (Illus.). 32p. pap. 5.95 (978-0-486-44070-5(2)) Dover Pubns., Inc.

—Wonders of the World Coloring Book. 2003. (Illus.). 32p. (J). pap. 3.95 (978-0-486-43044-7(8)) Dover Pubns., Inc.

Smith, Dororthy. Noah's Ark Coloring Book. 2007. (Illus.). 16p. (J). pap. 1.89 (***978-1-59317-188-9(9)***) Warner Pr. Pubs.

Smith Novelty Company Staff. Monterey & Carmel Coloring Book. 2006. (J). pap. 5.99 (978-1-932387-23-0(4)) Smith Novelty Co., Inc.

Smith, Susan Carlton. 3 Famous Artist-Naturalists of the Colonial Period: John Abbot, Insects; William Bartram, Flowers; Mark Catesby, Birds: A Coloring Book for All Ages. 2002. (Illus.). (J). pap. 7.00 (978-0-9718587-0-1(5)) Gazebo Pr., The.

Smokey's Coloring Book. (J). 29.50 (978-1-56230-055-5(5)); (SPA.). 29.50 (978-1-56230-212-2(4)) Syndistar, Inc.

Snowman's Winter Coloring Fun. Date not set. (Christmas Activity Bks.). (Illus.). 128p. (J). pap. 3.98 (978-0-7525-6670-2(9)) Parragon, Inc.

Snozek, Lee Anne. Nature Kaleidoscope Coloring Book. 2006. 32p. pap. 3.95 (978-0-486-45173-2(9)) Dover Pubns., Inc.

—Simply Circular Designs Coloring Book. 2005. (Illus.). 32p. (gr. 3). pap. 3.95 (978-0-486-44461-1(9)) Dover Pubns., Inc.

Soffer, Ruth. Amazing Animals Coloring Book. 2002. (Illus.). 48p. (J). pap. 3.95 (978-0-486-42061-5(2)) Dover Pubns., Inc.

—Australian Wildlife Coloring Book. 2006. 32p. (J). pap. 3.95 (978-0-486-45167-1(4)) Dover Pubns., Inc.

—Baby Animals Coloring Book. 2004. (Illus.). 32p. (J). pap. 2.95 (978-0-486-43331-8(5)) Dover Pubns., Inc.

—Birds Alphabet: Coloring Book. 2005. (Illus.). 32p. (J). (ps-ps). pap. 3.95 (978-0-486-44035-4(4)) Dover Pubns., Inc.

—Butterflies & Flowers to Paint or Color. 2005. 48p. (J). (gr. 3). pap. 4.95 (978-0-486-44496-3(1)) Dover Pubns., Inc.

—The Cat Lovers' Coloring Book. 2007. (Illus.). 32p. pap. 3.95 (***978-0-486-46200-4(5)***) Dover Pubns., Inc.

—Favorite Birds Stained Glass Coloring Book. 2004. (Illus.). 16p. (J). pap. 5.95 (978-0-486-43690-6(X)) Dover Pubns., Inc.

—The Flower Garden Coloring Book. 2005. (Illus.). 32p. (J). (gr. 3-3). pap. 3.95 (978-0-486-44497-0(X)) Dover Pubns., Inc.

—Garden Flowers Alphabet Coloring Book. 2004. (Dover Coloring Bks.). (Illus.). 32p. (J). pap. 3.95 (978-0-486-43595-4(4)) Dover Pubns., Inc.

—Great Barrier Reef Coloring Book. 2007. 32p. pap. 3.95 (***978-0-486-45689-8(7)***) Dover Pubns., Inc.

—Nature Alphabet Coloring Book. 2006. 96p. pap. 7.95 (***978-0-486-45921-9(7)***) Dover Pubns., Inc.

—Sea & Shore Birds Coloring Book. 1999. (Illus.). 48p. (J). pap. 3.95 (978-0-486-40805-7(1)) Dover Pubns., Inc.

—Sea Life Alphabet Coloring Book. 2003. (Dover Coloring Bks.). (Illus.). 32p. (J). pap. 3.95 (978-0-486-42653-2(X)) Dover Pubns., Inc.

Sovak, Jan. Alaskan Wildlife Coloring Book. 2006. 32p. (J). pap. 3.95 (978-0-486-45221-0(2)) Dover Pubns., Inc.

—Before the Dinosaurs. 1999. (Illus.). 48p. (J). pap. 3.95 (978-0-486-40568-1(0)) Dover Pubns., Inc.

—Dinosaurs Stained Glass Coloring Book. 2005. (Illus.). 16p. (J). (gr. 1). pap. 5.95 (978-0-486-44668-4(9)) Dover Pubns., Inc.

—Galapagos Islands Coloring Book. 2006. 32p. (J). pap. 3.95 (978-0-486-44886-2(X)) Dover Pubns., Inc.

—Giants & Ogres Coloring Book. 2004. (Illus.). 32p. (J). pap. 3.95 (978-0-486-43680-7(2)) Dover Pubns., Inc.

—Insects Stained Glass Coloring Book. 2003. (Illus.). 16p. (J). (gr. 3). pap. 5.95 (978-0-486-43047-8(2)) Dover Pubns., Inc.

—Lizards Coloring Book. 2006. 32p. (J). pap. 3.95 (978-0-486-44820-6(7)) Dover Pubns., Inc.

—Lizards Stained Glass Coloring Book. 2006. 16p. (J). pap. 5.95 (978-0-486-44817-6(7)) Dover Pubns., Inc.

—Prehistoric Man Coloring Book. 2005. (Illus.). 32p. (J). (gr. 3-3). pap. 3.95 (978-0-486-44432-1(5)) Dover Pubns., Inc.

Sowash, Rick. Heroes of Ohio Coloring Book. 2003. (J). 5.95 (978-0-9762412-6-3(9)) Sowash, Rick Publishing Co.

Spear, Kevin. David & the Giant. 2005. (J). pap. 1.79 ***(978-1-59317-087-5(4))*** Warner Pr. Pubs.

Spenceley, Angela. Virgin Islands Coloring Book. 2006. (Illus.). 24p. (J). 2.00 net. (978-0-9778913-9-9(9)) Coconut Pr., LLC.

Spenceley, Angela, compiled by. Pirate Coloring & Sticker Book: Your Complete Guide to Famous Pirates. l.t. ed. 2006. (Illus.). 24p. (J). pap. 8.95 (978-0-9702168-6-1(6)) Coconut Pr., LLC.

Spengler, Kenneth. The Wild Desert Coloring Book. (Illus.). (J). act. bk. ed. 3.95 (978-0-87358-804-1(5) , Rising Moon Bks. for Young Readers) Northland Publishing.

Sphere Search. 1999. (Dragon Ball Z Coloring & Activity Bks.). (Illus.). 32p. (J). (gr. 1-2). pap. (978-0-7666-0538-1(8)) Modern Publishing.

Spider-Man Coloring. 2003. (J). per. (978-1-57657-904-6(2)) Paradise Pr., Inc.

Spiderman Coloring. 2003. (J). per. (978-1-57657-905-3(0)) Paradise Pr., Inc.

Spieler, Cathy. My More-Than-Coloring Book about Christmas, Vol. 1. 1999. (My More-Than-Coloring Bks.). (Illus.). 63p. (J). (ps-2). pap. 5.00 (978-0-570-05555-6(5)) Concordia Publishing Hse.

—My More-Than-Coloring Book about God's Creation, Vol. 1. 1999. (My More-Than-Coloring Bks.). 64p. (J). (ps-2). pap. 5.00 (978-0-570-05556-3(3)) Concordia Publishing Hse.

—My More-Than-Coloring Book about Me. 2000. (Illus.). 64p. (J). (gr. k-2). 4.99 (978-0-570-07027-6(9)) Concordia Publishing Hse.

Spieler, Cathy M. My More-Than-Coloring Book about Easter. 2000. (My More-Than-Coloring Bks.). (Illus.). 64p. (J). (ps-2). pap. 4.99 (978-0-570-07028-3(7)) Concordia Publishing Hse.

Spizzirri, Linda, ed. Counting & Coloring Dinosaurs. (Illus.). 32p. (J). (gr. 1-8). pap. 4.98 incl. audio (978-0-86545-044-8(7)) Spizzirri Pr., Inc.

—Northeast Indians. (Illus.). 32p. (J). (gr. 1-8). pap. 4.98 incl. audio (978-0-86545-040-0(4)) Spizzirri Pr., Inc.

—Northwest Indians. (Illus.). 32p. (J). (gr. 1-8). pap. 4.98 incl. audio (978-0-86545-047-9(1)) Spizzirri Pr., Inc.

Splash Zone: Rock & Reef Homes: Coloring & Sticker Book. 2000. (Illus.). 16p. (J). (ps-2). pap. 5.95 (978-1-878244-33-8(7)) Monterey Bay Aquarium.

St. Paul, Mary. I Believe in God: Coloring Book. 2002. (Illus.). 24p. (J). reprint ed. pap. 6.00 (978-1-930873-66-7(2)) Neumann Pr., The.

—Meet Your Angel: A Book for Little Catholics to Color & Keep. 2005. (J). pap. 6.00 (978-0-911845-06-8(2)) Neumann Pr., The.

—Talking to God: A Book for Little Catholics to Color & Keep. 2005. (J). pap. 6.00 (978-0-911845-07-5(0)) Neumann Pr., The.

Standard Publishing Staff, contrib. by. Favorite Bible Stories to Color: For Ages 6 - 10, Old & New Testament Stories. 2006. (Heartshaper Ser.). 192p. (J). pap. 15.99 (978-0-7847-1797-4(4) , 02447) Standard Publishing.

Stanley's Adventure: Sticker Book to Color. (Playhouse Disney Ser.). 16p. (J). 2.99 (978-1-4037-0710-9(3)) Dalmatian Pr.

Stark, Fred. Gray's Anatomy: A Fact-Filled Coloring Book. rev. ed. 2000. (Start Exploring Ser.). (Illus.). 128p. (J). (gr. 2 up). pap. 9.95 (978-0-7624-0944-0(4) , Running Pr. Kids) Running Pr. Bk. Pubs.

StarKidz. I Am Who I Am. l.t. ed. 2003. (Illus.). 28p. (J). 16.95 (978-0-9743964-1-5(9)) World of Angels, A.

Stein, Erin K. Peppa Pig: Paint Book. 2007. (Peppa Pig Ser.). 32p. (J). pap. 4.99 ***(978-0-06-117376-9(2)*** , Harper Entertainment) HarperCollins Pubs.

Sterling Publishing Company Staff. First Words Coloring Book: 2-3 Years. 2003. (Balloon Ser.). (Illus.). 160p. (J). pap. 2.95 (978-0-8069-2661-2(9) , Balloon Bks.) Sterling Publishing Co., Inc.

Sterling/Balloon. First Words Coloring Book: 3-4 Years. 2000. (Balloon Ser.). (Illus.). 160p. (J). pap. 2.95 (978-0-8069-2663-6(5) , Balloon Bks.) Sterling Publishing Co., Inc.

Stern, Shirley. Let's Get Moving: Carry-along Coloring Kit. 2008. (Franny's Feet Ser.). 80p. (J). (ps-1). 5.99 ***(978-1-4169-4918-3(6)*** , Simon Scribbles) Simon & Schuster Children's Publishing.

Stewart, Jennifer. Noah's Ark Animals. Garris, Norma, illus. 2000. (Coloring Bks.). 16p. (J). (ps up). pap. 1.99 (978-0-7847-1192-7(5) , 22111) Standard Publishing.

—What Is Christmas Coloring Book. Garris, Norma, illus. 2000. (Coloring Bks.). 16p. (J). (ps up). pap. 1.99 (978-0-7847-1194-1(1) , 22113) Standard Publishing.

Stewart, Pat. Hans Christian Andersen Fairy Tales Stained Glass Coloring Book. 2004. (Illus.). 16p. (J). pap. 5.95 (978-0-486-43770-5(1)) Dover Pubns., Inc.

—Little Circus Stained Glass Coloring Book. 2004. (Illus.). 8p. (J). pap. 1.50 (978-0-486-43303-5(X)) Dover Pubns., Inc.

—Little Wizard of Oz Stained Glass Coloring Book. 1999. (Illus.). 8p. (J). pap. 1.50 (978-0-486-40499-8(4)) Dover Pubns., Inc.

—Tropical Butterflies Stained Glass Coloring Book. 2002. (Illus.). 8p. (J). (gr. k-5). pap. 1.50 (978-0-486-42152-0(X)) Dover Pubns., Inc.

Stewart, Pat L. Nutcracker Stained Glass Coloring Book. 1998. (Illus.). 8p. (J). (ps-5). pap. 1.50 (978-0-486-40260-4(6)) Dover Pubns., Inc.

—Zoo Animals Coloring Fun. 2005. 32p. (J). pap. 2.95 (978-0-486-44498-1(0)) Dover Pubns., Inc.

Stillerman, Robbie. The Little Wizards Stained Glass Coloring Book. 2001. (Dover Little Activity Bks.). 8p. (J). pap. 1.50 (978-0-486-41828-5(6)) Dover Pubns., Inc.

Stone, Slade. Frank Junior's 1st Pumpkin: 6x6 Board Book. Dalby, Danny, illus. 2005. 12p. (J). bds. 4.99 (978-1-4037-1496-1(7)) Dalmatian Pr.

Storad, Conrad J. Head over Heels about Arizona: A Color & Learning Book. Rumphorst, John, illus. 1999. 32p. (J). (gr. 1-4). pap. 2.95 (978-1-891795-10-7(4)) RGU Group, The.

Street Safe! Life Safety Coloring/Activity Book. 2007. (Illus.). (J). ***(978-1-933934-34-1(4))*** Educational Adventures.

Street Smarts: Coloring/Activity Book (English) Incl. Stickers. 2006. (Illus.). (J). ***(978-1-933934-18-1(2))*** Educational Adventures.

Striker, Susan & Kimmel, Edward. The First Anti-Coloring Book: Creative Activities for Ages 6 & Up. 2001. (Illus.). 96p. (J). pap. 11.95 (978-0-8050-6842-9(2) , Owl Bks.) Holt, Henry & Co.

Stuart Little 2. 2002. (Illus.). 32p. (J). (ps). pap. 1.15 (978-1-57759-648-6(X)) Dalmatian Pr.

Sturtz, Maria. God Gave Me. 2004. 32p. (J). 1.79 (978-0-7586-0105-6(0)) Concordia Publishing Hse.

—God Gave Me Spanish. 2004. (SPA.). 32p. 1.99 (978-0-7586-0059-2(3)) Concordia Publishing Hse.

—God Is. 2004. 32p. (J). 1.79 (978-0-7586-0104-9(2)) Concordia Publishing Hse.

—God Is Spanish. 2004. (SPA.). 32p. 1.99 (978-0-7586-0058-5(5)) Concordia Publishing Hse.

—Spanish Coloring in the Bible. 2004. (SPA.). 32p. 1.99 (978-0-7586-0060-8(7)) Concordia Publishing Hse.

—Spanish Coloring Living for Je. 2004. (SPA.). 32p. 1.99 (978-0-7586-0061-5(5)) Concordia Publishing Hse.

Summers, Sue L. Eye Spy Program: Early Youth Education Program. (J). (gr. k-3). pap. 15.00 (978-0-9676616-1-2(7)) Media Alert!.

—Programa Espio Con los Ojos: Programa de Educacion para Jovenes. (SPA.). (J). (gr. k-3). pap. 15.00 (978-0-9676616-2-9(5)) Media Alert!.

Sun, Ming-Ju. Chinese Fashions. 2002. (Illus.). 48p. (J). pap. 3.95 (978-0-486-42053-0(1)) Dover Pubns., Inc.

—Godey's Fashions. 2005. (Illus.). 32p. pap. 3.95 (978-0-486-43998-3(4)) Dover Pubns., Inc.

—Japanese Kimono Designs Coloring Book. 2007. 32p. pap. 3.95 ***(978-0-486-46223-3(4))*** Dover Pubns., Inc.

—Old Time Children's Fashions Coloring Book. 2005. 32p. (J). (gr. 3). pap. 3.95 (978-0-486-44484-0(8)) Dover Pubns., Inc.

—Women of the Ukiyo-E. 2004. (Dover Coloring Bks.). (Illus.). 32p. (J). pap. 3.95 (978-0-486-43332-5(3)) Dover Pubns., Inc.

Super Coloring Pad. Date not set. (Illus.). 384p. (J). 7.98 (978-0-7525-9574-0(1)) Parragon, Inc.

Super Furby Fun. 1999. (Furby Coloring & Activity Book Ser.). (Illus.). 48p. (J). pap. (978-0-7666-0410-0(1) , Honey Bear Bks.) Modern Publishing.

T. M. K. Dewey Does Coloring. 2001. (Dewey Does Ser.). (Illus.). (J). (ps-3). pap., wbk. ed. (978-0-9711474-8-5(5)) A B C-123 Publishing.

Tag Art Studio Editors. Chagrin Falls Coloring Book. 2000. (Illus.). 24p. (J). (ps-7). pap. 4.95 (978-0-9700846-2-0(5)) Fireside Book Shop, Inc.

Tagel, Peggy, illus. Color My World Blue. 2005. (J). (978-1-58987-101-4(4)) Kindermusik International.

Tallarico, Tony. Find & Color Activity Book. 2007. 48p. (J). pap. 4.95 ***(978-0-486-45679-9(X))*** Dover Pubns., Inc.

Tandy, Rachel, ed. Highlight This Book: Wild Coloring & Crazy Activities. 2005. (Chicken Socks). (Illus.). 44p. (J). 9.95 (978-1-59174-353-8(2)) Klutz.

Tarbox, Charlene. Color Your Own Great Flower Prints. 2001. (Dover Coloring Bks.). (Illus.). 32p. (J). pap. 3.95 (978-0-486-41553-6(8)) Dover Pubns., Inc.

Tarbox, Charlene. Floral Beauty Coloring Book. 2006. 96p. (J). pap. 7.95 ***(978-0-486-45922-6(5))*** Dover Pubns., Inc.

Tate, Suzanne. Color with the Wright Brothers: See How They Made History. Melvin, James, illus. 2003. (Suzanne Tate's History Ser.). 32p. (J). pap. 2.95 (978-1-878405-41-8(1)) Nags Head Art, Inc.

Taz Marker Mania Box Set with Coloring Books. 2000. (J). (978-1-58805-132-5(3)) DS-Max USA, Inc.

Tebo, Mary Elizabeth & Hermes, Kathryn J. Feast Days & Holy Days Color-by-Number Book. Mossi, Teresa, illus. 1999. 32p. (J). (gr. k-4). pap. 1.95 (978-0-8198-2670-1(7) , 332-091) Pauline Bks. & Media.

Teenage Mutant Ninja Turtles Fun Activity Box Set. 2004. (J). act. bk. ed. (978-0-7666-1362-1(3) , 64024) Modern Publishing.

Teis, Kyra. Look! Teis, Kyra, illus. 2005. (Illus.). 20p. (J). (ps-ps). per. 6.95 (978-1-59572-022-1(7)) Star Bright Bks., Inc.

Teletubbies' Favorite Things. 1998. (Teletubbies Ser.). (Illus.). 24p. (J). (ps). pap. (978-0-7666-0262-5(1) , Honey Bear Bks.) Modern Publishing.

Temko, Florence. Cut & Color Things That Go. 2006. 32p. (J). pap. 3.95 (978-0-486-45294-4(8)) Dover Pubns., Inc.

Ten Commandments/Beatitudes. 1998. (Illus.). (J). pap. 0.99 (978-0-88271-641-1(7)) Regina Pr., Malhame & Co.

Tennyson, Patrick & Bickford, Nicole. Tarantula Tracks: Rosie's Wild Adventure. l.t. ed. 2004. (Illus.). 32p. (J). 2.95 (978-0-9729000-1-0(2)) Butterfly Pavilion.

Thank You, God, for Christmas Coloring Book. 2006. 16p. (J). pap. 1.99 (978-0-7847-1261-0(1) , 22119) Standard Publishing.

Thank You Jesus for Special People in My World. 2005. (J). pap. 1.79 ***(978-1-59317-086-8(6))*** Warner Pr. Pubs.

That's a Danger Proof Plan! Coloring/Activity Book (English) 2006. (Illus.). (J). ***(978-1-933934-28-0(X))*** Educational Adventures.

Things I See in God's World. (Illus.). 16p. (J). pap. 1.50 (978-0-87162-957-9(7) , E4997) Warner Pr. Pubs.

Think Safe! Play Safe! Be Safe! Coloring/Activity Book (English) 2006. (Illus.). (J). ***(978-1-933934-26-6(3))*** Educational Adventures.

Thiruvalluvar. Tirukkural Manthiram Coloring Book with Meditation. 2006. Tr. of Tirukkural. (ENG, FRE & ZUL., Illus.). (J). 5.00 incl. audio (978-0-9676212-3-4(2)) International Tamil Language Foundation.

Thomas, Keith A. Cross-Lengua Coloring Book for Kids. Thomas, Keith A., illus. l.t. ed. 2004. (ENG & SPA., Illus.). 22p. (J). (gr. 3 up). pap. (978-0-9617451-2-7(6)) KALEXT Productions, LLC.

Thomas Nelson Publishing Staff. Coloring Art Book: Prince of Egypt. 1998. (Prince of Egypt Ser.). (Illus.). 64p. (J). (gr. 1-4). pap. 5.99 (978-0-8499-5899-1(7)) Nelson, Thomas Inc.

Thorpe, Erick E. The Chozen-4: Coloring Book. Thorpe, Erick E., illus. 2001. (Illus.). 48p. (J). (ps-3). pap. 5.50 (978-0-9713096-0-9(4) , Fresch Fruitz) Got2Bfunki Artworks.

Thumbs up Johnnie, Little Digit & the Special Delivery: Reading Heart to Heart, Coloring & Activity Book. 2006. (J). pap. (978-0-9761421-5-7(5)) Pixie Stuff LLC.

Tierney, Tom. Fashions of the Old South Coloring Book. 2004. (Illus.). 32p. (J). pap. 3.95 (978-0-486-43876-4(7)) Dover Pubns., Inc.

—Spanish & Moorish Fashions. 2003. (Dover Coloring Bks.). (Illus.). 48p. (J). pap. 3.95 (978-0-486-42652-5(1)) Dover Pubns., Inc.

Time for a Walk. 1998. (Teletubbies Ser.). (Illus.). 32p. (J). (ps). pap. (978-0-7666-0263-2(X) , Honey Bear Bks.) Modern Publishing.

Tinky-Winky's Tubby Toast. 1998. (Teletubbies Ser.). (Illus.). 32p. (J). (ps). pap. (978-0-7666-0255-7(9) , Honey Bear Bks.) Modern Publishing.

Toca! (J). 2.95 (978-958-607-885-6(X)) Sociedad de San Pablo COL. *Dist:* Alba Hse.

Tolliver, Gabrielle. The Holiday Cookie Coloring Kit. Cook, Corinda, illus. 2005. 32p. pap. 6.95 (978-0-7624-2238-8(6) , Running Pr. Minature Editions) Running Pr. Bk. Pubs.

Tolliver, Kathleen. Learning While I Color: Children's Coloring Sheets for Cycle A. 2001. 64p. (J). 7.95 (978-0-7880-1849-7(3)) CSS Publishing Co.

Tom & Jerry Box Set with Coloring Books. 2000. (J). (978-1-58805-133-2(1)) DS-Max USA, Inc.

Tonka Coloring & Activity Books. 2004. (J). act. bk. ed. (978-0-7666-0813-9(1) , 99520); act. bk. ed. (978-0-7666-0814-6(X) , 99520); act. bk. ed. (978-0-7666-0815-3(8) , 99520); act. bk. ed. (978-0-7666-0816-0(6) , 99520) Modern Publishing.

Tonka Fun Activity Box Set. 2004. (J). act. bk. ed. (978-0-7666-0985-3(5) , 64028) Modern Publishing.

Tonka Giant Coloring & Activity Books. 2004. (J). act. bk. ed. (978-0-7666-0951-8(0) , 49260); act. bk. ed. (978-0-7666-0952-5(9) , 49260) Modern Publishing.

Tonka Paint with Water Books. 2004. (J). (978-0-7666-1140-5(X) , 15320); (978-0-7666-1141-2(8) , 15320) Modern Publishing.

Torto, Adam D. Chiro-Kids Coloring Book. McCloy, John, illus. 2nd rev. ed. 1999. 18p. (J). (ps-12). pap. (978-0-9672222-0-2(6)) DC Products.

Touched by Him: Bible Story Coloring Book. ed. 2006. (ENG, CHI & RUS.). (J). 1.99 (978-0-9777446-0-2(4)) Childrens Bible Society.

Toulouse-Lautrec, Henri de. Color Your Own Toulouse-Lautrec Masterpieces. 2006. 32p. (J). pap. 3.95 (978-0-486-44714-8(6)) Dover Pubns., Inc.

Toutz-Hager, Tanya. Goddesses of Legend & Myth: A Coloring Book Celebrating the Heroines of Ancient Europe. Stockton, Greta & Philbrick, Katie, illus. Date not set. 40p. (YA). (gr. 4-12). pap. 8.95 (978-0-9672107-0-4(4)) MoonStar Pr.

Trago Publishing Staff. The Dinosaur Coloring Pad. 1999. (My Art Ser.). 35p. (J). (ps-3). pap. 3.95 (978-0-9683883-4-1(5)) Sterling Publishing Co., Inc.

The Travels of Prophet Ibrahim: Colouring Book. 2001. (Quran Stories for Tiny Tots). 16p. (J). pap. 1.00 (978-81-7898-007-2(X)) Goodword Bks. Pvt. Ltd. IND. *Dist:* Lodhia Ctr., The.

Treasure House Funtime Friends. 1998. (Captain Kangaroo Coloring & Activity Bks.: Vol. 2). (Illus.). 32p. (J). pap. (978-0-7666-0224-3(9) , Honey Bear Bks.) Modern Publishing.

A Treasure House Learning Adventure. 1998. (Captain Kangaroo Coloring & Activity Bks.: Vol. 3). (Illus.). 32p. (J). pap. (978-0-7666-0225-0(7) , Honey Bear Bks.) Modern Publishing.

Treasures in Heaven. 2004. (In Celebration Coloring & Activity Book Ser.). 32p. (J). pap. 1.99 (978-0-7647-1017-9(6) , In Celebration) Schaffer, Frank Pubns.

Tronick, Ed, contrib. by. Grade 1 Learning Tools Workbook. 2005. (Home Learning Tools Ser.). (Illus.). 320p. (J). (gr. 1 up). pap. 5.99 (978-1-4037-0388-0(4)) Dalmatian Pr.

—Grade 2 Learning Tools Workbook. 2005. (Illus.). 320p. (J). (gr. 2 up). pap. 5.99 (978-1-4037-0389-7(2)) Dalmatian Pr.

—Kindergarten Learning Tools Workbook. 2005. (Home Learning Tools Ser.). (Illus.). 320p. (J). (gr. k up). pap. 5.99 (978-1-4037-0387-3(6)) Dalmatian Pr.

—Preschool Learning Tools Workbook. 2005. (Home Learning Tools Ser.). (Illus.). 320p. (J). (ps up). pap. 5.99 (978-1-4037-0386-6(8)) Dalmatian Pr.

Trucks. 2004. (Illus.). 18p. (J). bds. 5.99 (978-1-85854-431-1(9)) Brimax Books Ltd. GBR. *Dist:* Byeway Bks.

Tubb, Kristin O'Donnell. Craft Corner Art Studio. Riley, Kellee, illus. 2007. (Holly Hobbie & Friends Ser.). 48p. (J). 9.99 ***(978-1-4169-3423-3(5)*** , Simon Scribbles) Simon & Schuster Children's Publishing.

Tubb, Kristin O'Donnell. Scooby Doo: A Girl's Best Friend Spiral Activity. rev. ed. 2005. (Illus.). 64p. (J). spiral bd. 8.99 (978-1-4037-1401-5(0)) Dalmatian Pr.

Tubby Custard Mess. 1998. (Teletubbies Ser.). (Illus.). 24p. (J). (ps). pap. (978-0-7666-0261-8(3) , Honey Bear Bks.) Modern Publishing.

Tulip, Jenny. Old MacDonald's Farm. 2001. (Illus.). 16p. (ps-3). pap. 5.00 (978-0-7548-0112-2(8)) Anness Publishing, Inc.

Turnbull, Elizabeth. Bel Peyi Mwen: My Beautiful Country - A Children's Coloring Book of Haiti. Battles, Kristopher, illus. 4th ed. 2000. 32p. (J). 5.95 (978-0-9679937-4-4(1)) Light Messages.

Turnbull, S. Trains. 2004. (Discovery Program Ser.). (SPA., Illus.). 48p. (J). (gr. 3 up). lib. bdg. 16.95 (978-1-58086-410-7(4)) EDC Publishing.

Turner, Gary. Progressive's Young Beginner Guitar Giant Coloring Book. 2003. (Illus.). 36p. (J). pap. 23.95 incl. audio compact disk (978-1-86469-096-5(8)) Learntoplaymusic.com AUS. *Dist:* Bookworld Trade, Inc.

—Progressive's Young Beginner Keyboard Giant Coloring Book. 2003. (Illus.). 36p. (J). pap. 23.95 incl. audio compact disk (978-1-86469-097-2(6)) Learntoplaymusic.com AUS. *Dist:* Bookworld Trade, Inc.

—Progressive's Young Beginner Piano Giant Coloring Book. 2003. (Illus.). 36p. (J). pap. 23.95 incl. audio compact disk (978-1-86469-098-9(4)) Learntoplaymusic.com AUS. *Dist:* Bookworld Trade, Inc.

—Progressive's Young Beginner Recorder Giant Coloring Book. 2003. (Illus.). 36p. (J). pap. 23.95 incl. audio compact disk (978-1-86469-099-6(2)) Learntoplaymusic.com AUS. *Dist:* Bookworld Trade, Inc.

Turner, Harry. The Triad Optical Illusions Coloring Book. 2006. 32p. pap. 3.95 (978-0-486-44861-9(4)) Dover Pubns., Inc.

Turton, Karalynn Teresa. The Passion for Children: Bilingual (English & Spanish) Guide to the Passion of Christ, 1 bk. Ruiz, Jeanette, tr. Burnett, Anne, illus. 2005. (J). 3.00 (978-0-9765180-0-6(7)) Catholic World Mission.

Twain, Mark. Tom Sawyer Coloring Book. Blaisdell, Bob, ed. Wright, Jane, illus. 2001. 48p. (J). pap. 3.50 (978-0-486-41672-4(0)) Dover Pubns., Inc.

Tweety Box Set with Coloring Books. 2000. (J). (978-1-58805-134-9(X)) DS-Max USA, Inc.

The Two Sons of Adam: Colouring Book. l.t. ed. 2001. 16p. pap. 1.00 (978-81-87570-92-9(X)) Goodword Bks. Pvt. Ltd. IND. *Dist:* Lodhia Ctr., The.

Ultimate Challenge. 1999. (Dragon Ball Z Full Color Activity Bks.). (Illus.). 32p. (J). (gr. 2-5). pap. (978-0-7666-0577-0(9)) Modern Publishing.

An Unbeatable Team. 1999. (Digimon Coloring & Activity Bks.). (Illus.). 32p. (J). (ps-2). pap. (978-0-7666-0547-3(7)) Modern Publishing.

United We Stand. 2001. (Illus.). 16p. 6.95 (978-0-9727833-5-4(0)) Really Big Coloring Bks., Inc.

Unstoppable Champions. 1999. (Digimon Coloring & Activity Bks.). (Illus.). 32p. (J). (ps-2). pap. (978-0-7666-0546-6(9)) Modern Publishing.

Urban, Erin & Romano, Alexis, eds. Sailors' Snug Harbor Coloring Book. 2005. (Illus.). (J). spiral bd. (978-0-9623017-1-1(X)) Noble Maritime Collection, The.

Vamos a Divertirnos, 4 bks., Set. (SPA & ENG.). 120p. (J). pap. 9.95 (978-970-607-688-5(3) , LA6883) Larousse, Ediciones, S. A. de C. V. MEX. *Dist:* Continental Bk. Co., Inc.

Van Gogh, Vincent. Van Gogh Stained Glass Coloring Book. 2007. 16p. pap. 5.95 ***(978-0-486-45671-3(4))*** Dover Pubns., Inc.

Van Leeuwed, Wendy. Agents of God Activity Book. 2007. (Illus.). 16p. (J). pap. 1.89 ***(978-1-59317-193-3(5))*** Warner Pr. Pubs.

Van Leeuwen, Wendy. Miracle Man Activity Book. 2007. (Illus.). 16p. (J). pap. 1.89 ***(978-1-59317-209-1(5))*** Warner Pr. Pubs.

—The Ten Commandments Activity Book. 2007. (Illus.). 16p. (J). pap. 1.89 ***(978-1-59317-210-7(9))*** Warner Pr. Pubs.

Vanus, Lori G. Latter-Day Letters: Christmas. Vanus, Lori G., illus. 1998. (Illus.). 32p. (J). (gr. k-6). pap. 7.95 (978-1-892318-01-5(6)) White Stone Publishing Co.

—Latter-Day Letters: The New Testament. Vanus, Lori G., illus. 1998. (Illus.). 56p. (J). (gr. k-6). pap. 9.95 (978-1-892318-00-8(8)) White Stone Publishing Co.

Veggie Tales: Champs of the Bible. 2005. pap. ***(978-1-4037-0544-0(5))*** Dalmatian Pr.

Veggie Tales Cast. Esther, the Girl Who Became Queen. 2004. 24p. pap. 1.99 (978-1-4037-0491-7(0)) Dalmatian Pr.

C
D

—King George & the Ducky. rev. ed. 2004. 24p. pap. 1.99 (978-1-4037-0490-0(2)) Dalmatian Pr.

—Veggietales Lots of Fun Color. rev. ed. 2004. (Illus.). 400p. (J). pap. 5.99 (978-1-4037-0538-9(0) , Spirit Pr.) Dalmatian Pr.

Vernon, Tannis & Longmore, Rich, illus. Glacier National Park Wildlife. 2004. (Postcard Book Ser.). 40p. 9.95 (978-0-7627-2903-6(1) , Falcon) Globe Pequot Pr., The.

Vic Visits Ground Zero. 2004. (J). (978-0-9761102-0-0(2)) Adams, Evelyn.

Vida Publishers Staff, contrib. by. Los Guarda Historias, Bk. 2. 1998. (SPA., Illus.). 64p. (J). (ps-3). pap. 2.49 (978-0-8297-2228-4(9)) Vida Pubs.

Vintage Little Ones. 2002. (978-0-9720825-3-2(0)) Toy Box Pr., The.

Virginia Activity & Coloring Book. 2001. (978-0-9715160-1-4(0)) Coloring Bks. 'N Stuff.

Volke, Gordon. Big World Activity Sticker Book, Vol. 2. 2004. (Illus.). 16p. 7.25 (978-1-84161-130-3(1)) Ravette Publishing, Ltd. GBR. *Dist:* Parkwest Pubns., Inc.

Vrato, Elizabeth & Mann, Holly. Trucks. 2003. (Magic Window Bks.). (Illus.). 8p. (J). pap. 4.95 (978-0-7624-1575-5(4) , Running Pr. Kids) Running Pr. Bk. Pubs.

Wade, Lee. The Crayon Coloring Play Book. Wade, Lee, illus. 2002. (Illus.). 14p. (J). (ps-k). 5.99 (978-0-689-84812-4(9) , Little Simon) Simon & Schuster Children's Publishing.

Waldrep, Mary Carolyn. Traditional Patchwork Designs Stained Glass Coloring Book. 2006. (Illus.). 16p. (J). pap. 5.95 (978-0-486-44842-8(8)) Dover Pubns., Inc.

Walker, Gary C. Confederate Coloring & Learning Book. Breaux, Joe Ann, illus. 2004. 41p. (J). (gr. 1-7). pap. 4.95 (978-0-9617898-5-5(9)) A&W Enterprises.

Wallace, Bruce, et al. Lift & Learn Colors. Snaith, Andy, photos by. 2006. (Illus.). 24p. (ps-ps). per., bds. 5.95 (978-1-84610-028-4(3)) Make Believe Ideas GBR. *Dist:* Ingram Pub. Services.

Walter Foster Publishing Staff & Swenson, Brenda. Keeping a Watercolor Sketchbook. 2005. (Artist's Library). (Illus.). 64p. pap. 8.95 (978-1-56010-899-3(1)) Foster, Walter Publishing, Inc.

War Zone. 1999. (Dragon Ball Z Coloring Sticker Activity Bks.). (Illus.). 25p. (J). (gr. 1-2). pap. (978-0-7666-0542-8(6)) Modern Publishing.

Warner, Anna & Bradbury, William B. Jesus Loves Me. Marlin, Kathy, illus. 2000. (Coloring Bks.). 16p. (J). (ps up). pap. 1.99 (978-0-7847-1193-4(3) , 22112) Standard Publishing.

Warner Press Staff. Jesus in My Heart Coloring Books Intermediate. 2005. 2.69 (978-0-87162-939-5(9)) Warner Pr. Pubs.

—Jesus Loves Me Coloring Book Pre-K. 2005. (J). pap. 2.69 (978-1-59317-017-2(3)) Warner Pr. Pubs.

—Preschool: Bible Coloring & Crafts Pages. 1999. (Illus.). (J). pap. 3.95 (978-0-87162-863-3(5)) Warner Pr. Pubs.

Warner Press Staff & Bishop, Jennie. The Crayon Kingdom: Coloring & Activity Book. 1999. (Illus.). 48p. (J). pap. 3.95 (978-0-87162-860-2(0) , E6029) Warner Pr. Pubs.

Washington State: Activity & Coloring Book. 2005. (J). spiral bd. 15.95 (978-1-59649-434-3(4)) Whispering Pine Pr., Inc.

Water Safe! Life Safety Coloring/Activity Book. 2007. (Illus.). (J). (***978-1-933934-25-9(5)***) Educational Adventures.

Waves of Glory: Big Best Book to Color. 2002. (Armed Forces Ser.). (Illus.). 96p. (J). (ps-3). pap. 2.99 (978-1-57759-484-0(3)) Dalmatian Pr.

We Adopted a Greyhound: A Coloring Book. 2001. 36p. (J). pap. 8.95 (978-0-9713838-1-4(2)) Hawaiian Publishing.

Weber, Lou, ed. Tonka Trucks Are Everywhere Color Sound. 2004. 32p. (J). 7.98 (978-1-4127-3056-3(2) , 7226400) Publications International, Ltd.

—Tummy Time Color Zoo. 2004. 8p. 6.98 (978-1-4127-3065-5(1)) Publications International, Ltd.

Weiss, Ellen. Mickey's Color Game. 2001. 12p. (J). 5.99 (978-0-7364-1038-0(4)) Mouse Works.

Wells, H. G. The Time Machine Great Read. rev. ed. 2004. (Great Classics for Children Ser.). 128p. (J). 5.99 (978-1-4037-0990-5(4)) Dalmatian Pr.

Welsh Books Staff. Llyfr Lliwio Sali Mali. 2nd ed. 2005. (WEL., Illus.). 22p. (978-1-902416-88-5(0)) Cymdeithas Lyfrau Ceredigion.

Wengerd, Marvin, ed. Color & Discover: Color the Marked Areas, Out Jumps a Surprise Animal. Conner, Carol & Fabian, Melinda, illus. l.t. ed. 2000. (Nature Friend Fun Ser.: Vol. 2). 24p. (J). (gr. k-5). pap. 4.00 (978-1-890050-43-6(1)) Carlisle Pr.- Walnut Creek.

Werden's class. Nunamiut ABC: A Child's View of Life in an Alaska Village. Written & Illustrated by the 4th & 5th Graders of Anaktuvuk Pass, Alaska. Werden's class, illus. 2003. (Illus.). 28p. (J). 3.95 (978-0-930931-54-4(8)) Alaska Natural History Assn.

What's So Funny? Book to Color. 2002. (Mr. Potato Head Ser.). (Illus.). 32p. (J). (ps). pap. 1.15 (978-1-57759-266-2(2)) Dalmatian Pr.

Wheeler, Kathryn. All Together Now! 2007. 32p. (J). pap. 3.99 (978-1-60095-247-0(X)) Cookie Jar.

—Count on Me! 2007. 32p. (J). pap. 3.99 (978-1-60095-248-7(8)) Cookie Jar.

—Growing Moe! 2007. 32p. (J). pap. 3.99 (978-1-60095-249-4(6)) Cookie Jar.

White, Kimberly. Music & Me. 2001. (Musical Colors Rhyming Story Coloring Book Ser.). 16p. (J). spiral bd. 10.95 (978-0-9673325-5-0(9) , PP1006) Piano Pr.

Whited, Linda Robinson. The Promised Land: An Old Testament Activity Book. 1999. 48p. (J). (gr. 4-7). act. bk. ed. 4.00 (978-0-687-08191-2(2)) Abingdon Pr.

Who Lives in the Coral Reef. 2004. (J). 4.99 (978-0-931548-12-3(8)) Island Heritage Publishing.

Why I Believe in Jesus: A Finish-the-Picture Coloring Book. (Illus.). 16p. (J). pap. 1.50 (978-0-87162-814-5(7) , E6027) Warner Pr. Pubs.

Widder, Edith. The Bioluminescence Coloring Book. Baker, Charissa, illus. 2nd rev. l.t. ed. 2002. 25p. (J). 19.95 (978-0-9659686-6-9(9)) Harbor Branch Oceanographic Institution, Inc.

The Wiggles Coloring & Activity Books. 2004. (J). act. bk. ed. (978-0-7666-1046-0(2) , 99530); act. bk. ed. 0.99 (978-0-7666-1047-7(0) , 99530); act. bk. ed. 0.99 (978-0-7666-1048-4(9) , 99530); act. bk. ed. 0.99 (978-0-7666-1049-1(7) , 99530) Modern Publishing.

The Wiggles Giant Coloring & Activity Books. 2004. (J). act. bk. ed. 1.99 (978-0-7666-1050-7(0) , 49220); act. bk. ed. 1.99 (978-0-7666-1051-4(9) , 49220) Modern Publishing.

Wild, Wonderful West Virginia Activity & Coloring Book. 2001. (978-0-87012-654-3(7)) Coloring Bks. 'N Stuff.

Wildlife Coloring Book. 2004. (Illus.). 24p. (J). pap. 4.95 (978-0-88839-599-3(X)) Hancock Hse. Pubs., Ltd. CAN. *Dist:* Hancock Hse. Pubs.

Williams, John R. Daddy & Me: Children's Story & Coloring Book. 2006. (ENG.). 48p. per. 11.95 (978-1-59800-799-2(8)) Outskirts Press, Inc.

Wilson. Southwest Desert Animal Coloring Book. (J). pap. 2.00 (978-0-918080-86-8(X) , Rio Nuevo Pubs.) Treasure Chest Bks.

Wingfield, Albert B. Come & See: And Other Things. 2001. (J). (ps-3). pap. 2.95 (978-1-930260-08-5(3)) CTS Family Pr.

Winston, Pat. Earl the Emu Series Coloring & Activity Book. Allen, Cathy H., illus. 2001. 8p. (J). (ps-3). pap. 3.50 (978-0-9702821-2-5(5)) Light Way Pubns., The.

Witty One Funny Family Fotos Coloring Book. 2003. (J). (978-1-932435-17-4(4)) Cardinal Brands, Inc.

Witty One Restickable Coloring Book - Animal Morphs. 2003. (Illus.). (J). per. (978-1-932435-05-4(0)) Cardinal Brands, Inc.

Witty One Restickable Coloring Book - Invisible. 2003. per. (978-1-932435-15-3(8)) Cardinal Brands, Inc.

Witty One Restickable Coloring Book - Noah's Ark. 2003. per. (978-1-932435-06-1(9)) Cardinal Brands, Inc.

Witty One Restickable Coloring Book - under the Sea. 2003. per. (978-1-932435-10-8(7)); per. (978-1-932435-00-9(X)) Cardinal Brands, Inc.

Witty One Restickable Sticker Search Coloring Book. 2003. (J). spiral bd. (978-1-932435-08-5(5)) Cardinal Brands, Inc.

Witzy's Very First Color & Activity Book. 2001. (Little Suzy's Zoo Ser.). 112p. (J). pap. 2.99 (978-1-58668-084-8(6)) Lyrick Studios.

Womersley, S. Dios es Bueno: Libro de Colorear. 2000. Tr. of God is Good: Coloring Book. pap. 1.69 (978-0-7899-0256-6(7)) Editorial Unilit.

—Dios nos Cuida: Libro de Colorear. 2000. Tr. of God Cares: Coloring Book. pap. 1.69 (978-0-7899-0257-3(5)) Editorial Unilit.

Wonderland Unicorns: Coloring book by Darla Hallmark. 2007. (Illus.). 20p. (YA). 10.00 (***978-0-9795206-1-7(4)***) Unseen Gallery.

Wooding, Sharon. Mark Twain in Nevada, a History Coloring Book for Children. l.t. ed. 2003. (Illus.). 25p. (J). (SPA.). pap. 5.95 (978-0-9727757-1-7(4)); pap. 5.95 (978-0-9727757-0-0(6)) Susy & Livy Pubns.

Woodworth, Viki. Insects A-B-C Coloring Book. 2004. (Illus.). 32p. (J). pap. 2.95 (978-0-486-43689-0(6)) Dover Pubns., Inc.

Workman. 365 Birds Color Page-a-Day. 2001. (Illus.). 320p. (J). cd-rom 11.95 (978-1-57965-180-0(1)) Artisan.

The World of Eric Carle My Color Wheel Activity Kit. 2007. (J). 16.99 (***978-0-9794445-2-4(7)***) Loew-Cornell, Inc.

The World of Eric Carle My Warm & Cool Color Activity Kit. 2007. (J). 16.99 (***978-0-9794445-5-5(1)***) Loew-Cornell, Inc.

Wynne, Patricia J. King Tut Coloring Book. 2005. (Illus.). 32p. (J). (gr. 3). pap. 3.95 (978-0-486-44444-4(9)) Dover Pubns., Inc.

Yacoubou, Jeanne. I Am a Rainbow Child Coloring-Story Book. Stebakova, Elena, illus. 2005. 16p. (J). (978-0-9788737-4-5(2)) Alaafia Kids Co.

—Wanna Play? Coloring-Story Book. Stebakova, Elena, illus. 2005. 16p. (J). (978-0-9788737-5-2(0)) Alaafia Kids Co.

—What's My Heritage? Coloring-Story Book. Stebakova, Elena, illus. 2006. 24p. (J). (978-0-9788737-2-1(6)) Alaafia Kids Co.

Yee, T. Keiki Discovery Land of Aloha: Color & Activity Book. 2001. (J). pap. 5.99 (978-0-89610-433-4(8)) Island Heritage Publishing.

—Keiki Discovery Land of Aloha Color & Activity Book. 2002. (J). pap. 5.99 (978-0-89610-430-3(3)) Island Heritage Publishing.

Yogi Bear Box Set with Coloring Books. 2000. (J). (978-1-58805-135-6(8)) DS-Max USA, Inc.

Yoon, Salina, creator. Country Pals: A Sparkling Little Colors Book. 2005. (Illus.). 12p. (J). 5.95 (978-1-58117-167-9(6) , Intervisual/Piggy Toes) Dalmatian Pr.

—Little Friends: A Sparkling Little Colors Book, 4 vols. 2005. (Illus.). 12p. (J). 5.95 (978-1-58117-168-6(4) , Intervisual/Piggy Toes) Dalmatian Pr.

Zambarano, Richard, illus. Wilbur & Wilma's Colorful Campus Tour - University of Arizona A-Z. 2004. (J). 9.99 (978-1-933069-02-9(3)) Odd Duck Ink, Inc.

Zappler, Georg. Learn about... Texas Dinosaurs. Ivy, Elena T., illus. rev. ed. 2001. (Learn about Texas Ser.). 48p. (J). pap. 9.95 (978-1-885696-37-3(X)) Texas Parks & Wildlife Pr.

—Learn about... Texas Freshwater Fishes. Ivy, Elena T., illus. 2001. (Learn about Texas Ser.). 96p. (J). pap. 9.95 (978-1-885696-36-6(1)) Texas Parks & Wildlife Pr.

Zarrika's Horse Show Coloring & Activity Book. 2006. (J). (***978-0-9758663-3-7(8)***) Zarrika, Ltd.

Zimmerman, Erik. Booga-Boo - Coloring Book. 2005. (Illus.). 32p. (J). per. 7.99 (978-1-59879-009-2(9)) Lifevest Publishing, Inc.

Zoey Coloring Book Pack. 2002. 9.90 (978-0-9718120-4-8(7)) HealthSprings, LLC.

Zorn, Steven & Martin, Mary. Masterpieces with Poster Vol. 12: A Fact-Filled Coloring Book. rev. ed. 2000. (Start Exploring Ser.). (Illus.). 128p. (J). (gr. 4-7). pap. 9.95 (978-0-7624-0945-7(2) , Running Pr. Kids) Running Pr. Bk. Pubs.

Zschock, Heather. Wild Safari: An Art Activity Book for Imaginative Artists of All Ages. Barbas, Kerren, illus. 2005. (Activity Journal Ser.). 64p. (J). (ps-7). 12.99 (978-1-59359-971-3(4)) Peter Pauper Pr. Inc.

2006-2007 Tongue River Elementary 3rd Graders, text. Sheridan County History ABC Coloring & Activity Book - 2007. 2006-2007 Tongue River Elementary 3rd Graders, . 2007. (Illus.). 32p. (J). 3.95 (***978-0-9792871-1-4(1)***) Sherian County Historical Society Pr.

COLORS

see Color

COLUMBIA RIVER AND VALLEY

Jackson, Tom. The Columbia River. 2003. (Rivers of North America Ser.). (Illus.). 32p. (J). (gr. 3 up). lib. bdg. 24.67 (978-0-8368-3754-4(1)) Stevens, Gareth Inc.

Lashnits, Tom. Columbia River. 2004. (Rivers in American Life & Times Ser.). (Illus.). 120p. (gr. 9-13). 30.00 (978-0-7910-7728-3(4)); pap. 13.25 (978-0-7910-8003-0(X)) Facts On File, Inc. (Chelsea Hse.).

Rubin, Rick. Naked Against the Rain: The People of the Lower Columbia River, 1770-1830. 1999. (Illus.). 431p. (YA). (gr. 10 up). 29.95 (978-1-883287-00-9(6)) Far Shore Pr.

COLUMBUS, CHRISTOPHER, 1451-1506

Abnett, Dan. Christopher Columbus & the Voyage of 1492. Q2A, illus. 2007. (Jr. Graphic Biographies Ser.). 24p. (J). (978-1-4042-2333-2(9)); pap. (978-1-4042-2143-7(3)); (gr. 2-6). lib. bdg. 21.25 (978-1-4042-3390-4(3)) Rosen Publishing Group, Inc., The. (PowerKids Pr.).

Aller, Susan Biven. Christopher Columbus. 2002. (History Maker Bios Ser.). (Illus.). (J). pap. 6.95 (978-0-8225-1560-9(1)) Lerner Publishing Group.

Aller, Susan Bivin. Christopher Columbus. 2003. (History Maker Bios Ser.). (Illus.). 48p. (J). (gr. 3-5). lib. bdg. 26.60 (978-0-8225-0398-9(0)) Lerner Publishing Group.

Alter, Judy. Christopher Columbus: Explorer. 2002. (Spirit of America: Our People Ser.). (Illus.). 32p. (J). (gr. 2-6). 27.07 (978-1-56766-161-3(0)) Child's World, Inc.

Ansary, Mir Tamim. Columbus Day. (J). 2006. (Illus.). 32p. (***978-1-4034-8883-1(5)***); 2002. (Illus.). 32p. pap. 6.95 (978-1-58810-430-4(3) , 91158); 1999. (Illus.). 32p. lib. bdg. 21.36 (978-1-57572-702-8(1)); 1998. lib. bdg. 19.92 (978-0-01-575702-1(1)) Heinemann Library.

Benge, Janet & Benge, Geoff. Christopher Columbus: Across the Ocean Sea. 2005. 190p. (J). (978-1-932096-23-1(X)) Emerald Bks.

Brenner, Barbara. If You Were There In 1492: Everyday Life in the Time of Columbus. 1998. (gr. 3-6). 17.60 (978-0-613-09952-3(4)) Tandem Library Bks.

Burgan, Michael. Christopher Columbus: Opening the Americas to European Exploration. 2004. (Proud Heritage: the Hispanic Library Ser.). 40p. (J). (gr. 3-7). 28.50 (978-1-59296-142-9(8)) Child's World, Inc.

Capstone Press. Christopher Columbus: Famous Explorer. 2007. (Graphic Library). (Illus.). 32p. (J). (***978-0-7368-6853-2(4)*** , 1264941) Capstone Pr., Inc.

Carrero, Luis Maria. El Secreto de Cristobal Colon. 1998. (SPA.). (gr. 7-12). lib. bdg. 14.10 (978-0-613-80707-4(3)) Tandem Library Bks.

Chrisp, Peter. Christopher Columbus. 2006. (DK Discoveries Ser.). 48p. (J). pap. 6.99 (978-0-7566-1965-7(3)) Dorling Kindersley Publishing, Inc.

—Christopher Columbus: Admiral of the Ocean Sea. Parsons, Jayne, ed. Dennis, Peter, illus. 2001. (DK Discoveries Ser.). 48p. (J). 14.95 (978-0-7894-7936-5(2)) Dorling Kindersley Publishing, Inc.

Christopher Columbus, 6 vols. (gr. k-2). 28.95 (978-0-7368-9369-5(5)) Red Brick Learning.

Collier, James Lincoln. Christopher Columbus: To the New World. 2006. (Great Explorations Ser.). (Illus.). 80p. (J). lib. bdg. 32.79 (978-0-7614-2221-1(8) , Benchmark Bks.) Cavendish, Marshall Corp.

Craats, Rennay. Columbus Day. 2004. (American Holidays Ser.). (Illus.). 24p. (J). pap. 6.95 (978-1-59036-164-1(4)); lib. bdg. 15.95 (978-1-59036-106-1(7)) Weigl Pubs., Inc.

de Kay, James T. Meet Christopher Columbus. Edens, John, illus. 2001. 80p. (J). (gr. 1-5). pap. 4.99 (978-0-375-81210-1(5) , Random Hse. Bks. for Young Readers) Random Hse. Children's Bks.

Devillier, Christy. Christopher Columbus. 2001. (First Biographies Ser.). (Illus.). 32p. (J). (gr. k-4). lib. bdg. 22.78 (978-1-57765-594-7(X) , Buddy Bks.) ABDO Publishing Co.

Doak, Robin S. Christopher Columbus: Explorer of the New World. 2004. (Signature Lives Ser.). (Illus.). 112p. (J). 30.60 (978-0-7565-0811-1(8) , 1240120) Compass Point Bks.

Dodson Wade, Mary. Christopher Columbus: Famous Explorer. 2007. (Graphic Library). (Illus.). 32p. (J). (***978-0-7368-7905-7(6)*** , 1264941) Capstone Pr., Inc.

Duviols, Jean-Paul. Cristobal Colon. Gonzalez Batlle, Jorge, tr. 2005. (Tras los pasos de ... Ser.). (SPA., Illus.). 128p. (J). pap. 14.95 (978-84-9801-000-8(4)) Blume ESP. *Dist:* Independent Pubs. Group.

Foster, Genevieve. The World of Columbus & Sons. 1998. (Illus.). 406p. (YA). (gr. 5 up). reprint ed. pap. 15.95 (978-0-9643803-8-7(2)) Beautiful Feet Bks.

Ganeri, Anita. Story of Christopher Columbus. 2001. (gr. k-3). lib. bdg. 11.80 (978-0-613-50371-6(6)) Tandem Library Bks.

—The Story of Columbus, Vol. 2. Ling, Mary, ed. 2001. (Readers Ser.). (Illus.). 32p. (J). (gr. 5-3). pap. 3.99 (978-0-7894-7878-8(1)) Dorling Kindersley Publishing, Inc.

Ganeri, Anita & Dorling Kindersley Publishing Staff. The Story of Columbus. 2001. (Readers Ser.). (Illus.). 32p. (J). (gr. 1-3). 14.99 (978-0-7894-7877-1(3)) Dorling Kindersley Publishing, Inc.

Great Explorers: Captain James Cook; Christopher Columbus; Ferdinand Magellan; John Cabot, 4 bks. 2002. (Illus.). (J). (gr. 5 up). pap. (978-0-8368-5179-3(X)); lib. bdg. 117.06 (978-0-8368-5019-2(X)) Stevens, Gareth Inc. (World Almanac Library).

Green, Tamara. Christopher Columbus. 2001. (Great Explorers Ser.). (Illus.). 48p. (J). (gr. 5 up). lib. bdg. 30.00 (978-0-8368-5013-0(0) , World Almanac Library) Stevens, Gareth Inc.

Healy, Nick. Christopher Columbus. 2003. (Explorers of the Unknown Ser.). (J). (978-1-58417-034-1(4)); pap. (978-1-58417-097-6(2)) Lake Street Pubs.

Higgins, Nadia. Columbus & the Age of Explorers. 2007. (Illus.). 48p. (J). (978-1-60044-119-6(X)) Rourke Publishing, LLC.

Hoogenboom, Lynn. Christopher Columbus: A Primary Source Biography. 2006. (Illus.). 24p. (J). lib. bdg. (978-1-4042-3036-1(X) , PowerKids Pr.) Rosen Publishing Group, Inc., The.

HSP. First-Place Reading for Title I: Christopher Columbus. 2nd ed. 2002. (Harcourt Title I Reading Programs Ser.). (gr. 5 up). pap. 44.00 (978-0-15-338163-8(9)) Harcourt Schl. Pubs.

Isaacs, Sally Senzell. America in the Time of Columbus: Earliest Times to 1590. 1999. (America in the Time of... Ser.). (Illus.). 48p. (J). (gr. 4-7). pap. 8.50 (978-1-57572-933-6(4)) Heinemann Library.

Kaufman, Mervyn D. Christopher Columbus. 2004. (Fact Finders Ser.). (Illus.). 32p. (J). 16.95 (978-0-7368-2486-6(3)) Capstone Pr., Inc.

King, Thomas. A Coyote Columbus Story. Monkman, William K., illus. 2002. (J). (978-0-88899-155-3(X)) Groundwood Bks.

Kline, Trish. Christopher Columbus. 2001. (Discover the Life of an Explorer Ser.). (Illus.). 24p. (J). (gr. 1-4). lib. bdg. 20.64 (978-1-58952-066-0(1)) Rourke Publishing, LLC.

Kudlinski, Kathleen. Christopher Columbus: Young Explorer. 2005. 199p. (J). lib. bdg. 18.46 (***978-1-4242-1727-4(X)***) Fitzgerald Bks.

—Christopher Columbus: Young Explorer. 2005. (Childhood of World Figures Ser.). 208p. (J). pap. 4.99 (978-0-689-87648-6(3) , Aladdin) Simon & Schuster Children's Publishing.

Kurtz, Jane. What Columbus Found: It Was Orange, It Was Round. Billin-Frye, Paige, illus. 2007. (Ready-to-Reads Ser.). 32p. (J). lib. bdg. 13.89 (***978-0-689-86763-7(8)*** , Aladdin Library) Simon & Schuster Children's Publishing.

Lacey, Minna. Christopher Columbus. 2005. (Famous Lives Gift Books Ser.). 64p. (J). 8.95 (978-0-7945-0871-5(5) , Usborne) EDC Publishing.

Landau, Elaine. Columbus Day: Celebrating a Famous Explorer. 2001. (Finding Out about Holidays Ser.). (Illus.). 48p. (J). (gr. 1-4). lib. bdg. 23.93 (978-0-7660-1573-9(4)) Enslow Pubs., Inc.

Larkin, Tanya. Christopher Columbus. 2001. (Famous Explorers Ser.). (Illus.). 24p. (J). (gr. 3). lib. bdg. 18.75 (978-0-8239-5554-1(0) , PowerKids Pr.) Rosen Publishing Group, Inc., The.

Leavitt, Amie. Christopher Columbus. 2007. (What's So Great About... ? Ser.). (J). lib. bdg. 25.70 (***978-1-58415-578-2(7)***) Mitchell Lane Pubs., Inc.

Lilly, Melinda. The Journey of Columbus. 2002. (Rourke Discovery Library). (Illus.). 24p. (J). lib. bdg. 20.64 (978-1-58952-358-6(X)) Rourke Publishing, LLC.

MacDonald, Fiona, et al. You Wouldn't Want to Sail with Christopher Columbus! Uncharted Waters You'd Rather Not Cross. 2004. (You Wouldn't Want To Ser.). (J). 28.50 (978-0-531-12355-3(3) , Watts, Franklin) Scholastic Library Publishing.

Malam, John. Columbus Reaches the Americas. 2003. (Dates with History Ser.). 45p. (J). lib. bdg. 28.50 (978-1-58340-411-9(2)) Smart Apple Media.

Marsh, Carole. Christopher Columbus. 2002. (One Thousand Readers Ser.). (Illus.). 12p. (J). (gr. k-4). 2.95 (978-0-635-01495-5(5) , 14955) Gallopade International.

—Christopher Columbus: An Ohio Experience Reader. 2001. (J). (gr. k-5). pap. 1.95 (978-0-635-00437-6(2)) Gallopade International.

Marzollo, Jean. En 1492. 2002. (SPA., Illus.). 32p. (J). (ps-3). pap. 4.99 (978-0-590-49442-7(2) , SO5713, Scholastic en Espanol) Scholastic, Inc.

—In 1492. (J). (gr. 1-3). pap. (978-0-590-44414-9(X) , SO3017) Scholastic, Inc.

Mattern, Joanne. Celebrate Columbus Day. 2006. (Celebrate Holidays Ser.). (Illus.). 104p. (J). lib. bdg. 31.93 (978-0-7660-2580-6(2)) Enslow Pubs., Inc.

McCormick, Lisa Wade. Christopher Columbus. 2005. (Scholastic News Nonfiction Readers Ser.). (Illus.). 24p. (J). (gr. 1-2). 19.00 (978-0-516-24938-4(X) , Children's Pr.) Scholastic Library Publishing.

McNeese, Tim. Christopher Columbus & the Discovery of the Americas. Goetzmann, William H., ed. 2005. (Explorers of New Lands Ser.). (Illus.). 166p. (J). (gr. 4-8). lib. bdg. 30.00 (978-0-7910-8613-1(5) , Chelsea Hse.) Facts On File, Inc.

Mir Tamim Ansary. Columbus Day. 2nd ed. 2006. (Illus.). 32p. (J). pap. (***978-1-4034-8896-1(7)***) Heinemann Library.

Molzahn, Arlene Bourgeois. Christopher Columbus: Famous Explorer. 2003. (Explorers! Ser.). (Illus.). 48p. (J). (gr. 1-4). lib. bdg. 23.93 (978-0-7660-2066-5(5)) Enslow Pubs., Inc.

Morganelli, Adrianna. Christopher Columbus: Sailing to a New World. 2005. (In the Footsteps of Explorers Ser.). (Illus.). 32p. (J). (ps-9). (978-0-7787-2409-4(3)); pap. (978-0-7787-2445-2(X)) Crabtree Publishing Co.

Murray, Julie. Columbus Day. 2005. (Holidays Ser.). (Illus.). 24p. (J). (gr. k-4). lib. bdg. 21.35 (978-1-59197-587-8(5)) ABDO Publishing Co.

Nathan, Melissa. Christopher Columbus. 2003. (Great Explorers Ser.). (Illus.). 48p. (J). (gr. 5 up). pap. 14.60 (978-0-8368-5173-1(0) , World Almanac Library) Stevens, Gareth Inc.

Otfinoski, Steven. The Voyages of Christopher Columbus. 2005. (Navigators Ser.). (J). pap. 42.00 (***978-1-4108-5105-5(2)***) Benchmark Education Co.

Pancella, Peggy. Christopher Columbus. 2003. (Historical Biographies Ser.). (Illus.). 32p. (J). pap. 6.95 (978-1-4034-3708-2(4)); lib. bdg. 22.79 (978-1-4034-3700-6(9)) Heinemann Library.

Parin D'Aulaire, Ingri & Parin D'Aulaire, Edgar. Christopher Columbus. unabr. ed. 2001. (J). (gr. 3-5). pap. 20.00 incl. audio (978-0-8045-6716-9(6)) Spoken Arts, Inc.

Petrie, Kristin. Christopher Columbus. 2004. (Explorers Set I Ser.). (Illus.). 32p. (J). (gr. k-6). lib. bdg. 22.78 (978-1-59197-595-3(6)) ABDO Publishing Co.

Pollard, Josephine. A Child's History of the Life of Christopher Columbus, No. 6. unabr. ed. 2000. (Illus.). 240p. (YA). reprint ed. 17.95 (978-1-889128-66-5(X)) Mantle Ministries.

Reid, Struan. Christopher Columbus. 2002. (Groundbreakers Ser.). 48p. (J). (gr. 5-7). (Illus.). lib. bdg. 27.07 (978-1-58810-593-6(8)); pap. 8.50 (978-1-58810-986-6(0) , 91601) Heinemann Library.

Roop, Connie & Roop, Peter. Christopher Columbus. 2001. (In Their Own Words Ser.). (Illus.). 128p. (J). pap. 4.99 (978-0-439-15807-7(9)) Scholastic, Inc.

Roop, Peter. Christoper Columbus. 2000. (gr. 3-6). lib. bdg. 12.40 (978-0-613-36264-1(0)) Tandem Library Bks.

Saunders, Nicholas. The Life of Christopher Columbus. 2006. (Stories from History Ser.). 48p. (J). 14.95 (***978-0-7696-4716-6(2));*** pap. 6.95 (***978-0-7696-4696-1(4)***) School Specialty Publishing.

Schaefer, Lola M. Christopher Columbus. Saunders-Smith, Gail, ed. 2002. (First Biographies Ser.). (Illus.). 24p. (J). (gr. k-1). lib. bdg. 15.93 (978-0-7368-1173-6(7) , Pebble Bks.) Capstone Pr., Inc.

—Christopher Columbus. 2005. (First Biographies Ser.). 24p. (YA). (gr. k-3). pap. (978-0-7368-9368-8(7) , Pebble Bks.) Capstone Pr., Inc.

Sis, Peter. Follow the Dream: The Story of Christopher Columbus. Sis, Peter, illus. 2003. (Illus.). 40p. (J). (ps-3). 15.95 (978-0-679-80628-8(8)); lib. bdg. 17.99 (978-0-679-90628-5(2)) Random Hse. Children's Bks. (Knopf Bks. for Young Readers).

Sundel, Al. Christopher Columbus & the Age of Exploration in World History. 2002. (In World History Ser.). (Illus.). 128p. (YA). (gr. 5-12). lib. bdg. 26.60 (978-0-7660-1820-4(2)) Enslow Pubs., Inc.

Tucker, Mary. Christopher Columbus. Mitchell, Judy, ed. Hierstein, Judith, illus. 2002. (History - Hands On! Ser.). 32p. (J). (gr. 1-4). pap., tchr. ed. 6.95 (978-1-57310-328-2(4)) Teaching & Learning Co.

Wade, Mary Dodson. Christopher Columbus. 2003. (Rookie Biographies Ser.). (Illus.). (J). (gr. 1-2). 31p. pap. 4.95 (978-0-516-27769-1(3)); 32p. 20.50 (978-0-516-22851-8(X)) Scholastic Library Publishing. (Children's Pr.).

—Christopher Columbus. 2003. (gr. k-3). lib. bdg. 12.95 (978-0-613-67602-1(5)) Tandem Library Bks.

Weinberger, Kimberly. Let's Read about Christopher Columbus. Van Wright, Cornelius & Hu, Ying-Hwa, illus. 2001. (Scholastic First Biographies Ser.). (J). (978-0-439-29546-8(7)) Scholastic, Inc.

West, David & Gaff, Jackie. Christopher Columbus: The Life of a Master Navigator & Explorer. 2005. (Illus.). 48p. (J). (gr. 4-6). lib. bdg. 26.50 (978-1-4042-0243-6(9)) Rosen Publishing Group, Inc., The.

COLUMBUS, CHRISTOPHER, 1451-1506—FICTION

Dorris, Michael. Morning Girl. rev. ed. 1999. 80p. (gr. 4-17). pap. 4.99 (978-0-7868-1358-2(X)) Hyperion Pr.

Hi-stories Presents Christopher Cowlumbus. 2004. (Illus.). 58p. (J). (978-0-9763233-0-3(3)) Little Germ That Could...Creations, Inc., The.

Histories presents Christopher Cowlumbus. 2006. (J). bds. 14.99 (978-0-9763233-3-4(8)) Little Germ That Could-...Creations, Inc., The.

King, Thomas. A Coyote Columbus Story. Monkman, William Kent, illus. 2007. 32p. (J). pap. 6.95 (***978-0-88899-830-9(9)***) Groundwood Bks. CAN. *Dist:* Perseus Distribution.

Lewin, Waldtraut. Freedom Beyond the Sea. 2003. (gr. 7-12). lib. bdg. 13.55 (978-0-613-72276-6(0)) Tandem Library Bks.

Lewin, Waldtraut & Crawford, Elizabeth. Freedom Beyond the Sea. 2003. 272p. (YA). (gr. 9-12). pap. 5.50 (978-0-440-22868-4(9) , Laurel Leaf) Random Hse. Children's Bks.

Losada, Basilio. Cristobal Colon. (SPA., Illus.). 160p. (YA). 11.95 (978-84-7281-053-2(4) , AF1053) Auriga, Ediciones S.A. ESP. *Dist:* Continental Bk. Co., Inc.

McAndrews, Anita. Blessed Be the Light of Day. Kabak, Carrie, illus. 2001. 48p. (J). (gr. 2-5). 14.95 (978-1-930093-02-7(0)) Brookfield Reader, Inc., The.

Rocca, Al. Explorer Courage: The First Voyage of Christopher Columbus. l.t. ed. 2006. (Illus.). 72p. (J). per. 4.95 (***978-0-9643378-1-7(9)***) Renown Publishing Co.

Whittier, Mary Ann. Tales from 1492. (YA). (gr. 7 up). lib. bdg. 19.99 (978-0-89824-981-1(3)) Royal Fireworks Publishing Co.

COLUMBUS DAY

Ansary, Mir Tamim. Columbus Day. (J). 2006. (Illus.). 32p. (***978-1-4034-8883-1(5)***); 2002. (Illus.). 32p. pap. 6.95 (978-1-58810-430-4(3) , 91158); 1999. (Illus.). 32p. lib. bdg. 21.36 (978-1-57572-702-8(1)); 1998. lib. bdg. 19.92 (978-0-01-575702-1(1)) Heinemann Library.

Craats, Rennay. Columbus Day. 2004. (American Holidays Ser.). (Illus.). 24p. (J). pap. 6.95 (978-1-59036-164-1(4)); lib. bdg. 15.95 (978-1-59036-106-1(7)) Weigl Pubs., Inc.

Gardeski, Christina Mia. Columbus Day. 2001. (Rookie Read-About Holidays Ser.). (Illus.). 32p. (J). (gr. 1-2). pap. 5.95 (978-0-516-26310-6(2) , Children's Pr.) Scholastic Library Publishing.

—Columbus Day. 2001. (gr. k-3). lib. bdg. 14.10 (978-0-613-54141-1(3)) Tandem Library Bks.

Landau, Elaine. Columbus Day: Celebrating a Famous Explorer. 2001. (Finding Out about Holidays Ser.). (Illus.). 48p. (J). (gr. 1-4). lib. bdg. 23.93 (978-0-7660-1573-9(4)) Enslow Pubs., Inc.

Mattern, Joanne. Celebrate Columbus Day. 2006. (Celebrate Holidays Ser.). (Illus.). 104p. (J). lib. bdg. 31.93 (978-0-7660-2580-6(2)) Enslow Pubs., Inc.

Murray, Julie. Columbus Day. 2005. (Holidays Ser.). (Illus.). 24p. (J). (gr. k-4). lib. bdg. 21.35 (978-1-59197-587-8(5)) ABDO Publishing Co.

COLUMBUS DAY—FICTION

Park, Barbara. Junie B. , First Grader: Shipwrecked. Brunkus, Denise, illus. 2004. 88p. (J). lib. bdg. 18.46 (***978-1-4242-0360-4(0)***) Fitzgerald Bks.

—Junie B., 1st Grader: Shipwrecked. Brunkus, Denise, illus. 2004. (Junie B. Jones Ser.: No. 23). 96p. (J). (gr. 1-4). 11.95 (978-0-375-82804-1(4) , Random Hse. Bks. for Young Readers) Random Hse. Children's Bks.

—Junie B., First Grader: Shipwrecked. Brunkus, Denise, illus. (Junie B. Jones Ser.: No. 23). 96p. (J). (gr. k-3). 2005. mass mkt. 3.99 (978-0-375-82805-8(2)); 2004. lib. bdg. 13.99 (978-0-375-92804-8(9)) Random Hse. Children's Bks. (Random Hse. Bks. for Young Readers).

COLUMNISTS

see Journalists

COMEDY

Doyle, Alfreda C. Alfreda's Reader's Theatre: Comedy Club. Date not set. (Illus.). (J). spiral bd. 8.95 (978-1-56820-362-1(4)) Story Time Stories That Rhyme.

Swisher, Clarice. Readings on "The Merchant of Venice" 2000. (Literary Companion to American Literature Ser.). (Illus.). 224p. (YA). (gr. 9-12). pap. (978-0-7377-0178-4(1) , Greenhaven Pr., Inc.) Thomson Gale.

COMETS

Asimov, Isaac & Hantula, Richard. Comets & Meteors. 2005. (Isaac Asimov's 21st Century Library of the Universe). (Illus.). 32p. (J). lib. bdg. 24.67 (978-0-8368-3966-1(8)) Stevens, Gareth Inc.

Birch, Robin. Comets, Asteroids, & Meteors. 2002. (Space Ser.). (Illus.). 32p. (gr. k-2). 23.00 (978-0-7910-6973-8(7) , 104051, Chelsea Hse.) Facts On File, Inc.

Bonar, Samantha. Comets. 1998. (First Bks.). (Illus.). 63p. (J). (gr. 3-5). 23.00 (978-0-531-20301-9(8) , Watts, Franklin) Scholastic Library Publishing.

Bortz, Alfred B. Collision Course! Cosmic Impacts & Life on Earth. 2001. (Enthusiastic Astronomy Ser.). (Illus.). 72p. (gr. 5-8). lib. bdg. 25.90 (978-0-7613-1403-5(2) , Twenty-First Century Bks.) Lerner Publishing Group.

Chrismer, Melanie. Comets. (Scholastic News Nonfiction Readers: Space Science Ser.). 24p. (J). 2008. pap. 6.95 (***978-0-531-14759-7(2));*** 2007. (Illus.). (gr. 1-2). lib. bdg. 20.00 (***978-0-531-14694-1(4)***) Scholastic Library Publishing. (Children's Pr.).

Cole, Michael D. Comets & Asteroids: Ice & Rocks in Space. 2003. (Countdown to Space Ser.). (Illus.). 48p. (J). (gr. 4-10). lib. bdg. 23.93 (978-0-7660-1954-6(3)) Enslow Pubs., Inc.

Graham, Ian. Comets & Asteroids. 2007. (J). (***978-1-59920-074-3(0)***) Smart Apple Media.

Han, E. M. Comets & Asteroids. 2001. (Spinning Through Space Ser.). (Illus.). 32p. (J). (gr. 3-4). lib. bdg. 25.69 (978-0-7398-2742-0(1)) Raintree.

Miller, Ron. Asteroids, Comets, & Meteors. 2006. (Worlds Beyond Ser.). (Illus.). 80p. (J). (gr. 5-9). 27.93 (978-0-7613-2363-1(5) , Twenty-First Century Bks.) Lerner Publishing Group.

—Worlds Beyond, 10 vols. 2004. (Illus.). (YA). (gr. 7 up). (978-0-7613-3174-2(3) , Twenty-First Century Bks.) Lerner Publishing Group.

Mist, Rosalind. Could an Asteroid Hit the Earth? Asteroids, Comets, Meteors, & More. 2006. (Stargazers Guides Ser.). (Illus.). 48p. (J). pap. (978-1-4034-7716-3(7)); lib. bdg. 31.43 (978-1-4034-7709-5(4)) Heinemann Library.

Nardo, Don. Comets & Asteroids. 2003. (Lucent Science & Technology Library). (Illus.). 112p. (J). 29.95 (978-1-59018-286-4(3) , Lucent Bks.) Thomson Gale.

Nicolson, Cynthia. Discover Space Rocks. Slavin, Bill, illus. 2006. 32p. (J). lib. bdg. 15.38 (***978-1-4242-1195-1(6)***) Fitzgerald Bks.

Nicolson, Cynthia Pratt. Comets, Asteroids & Meteorites. Slavin, Bill, illus. 1999. (Starting with Space Ser.). 40p. (J). (gr. 4-6). (978-1-55074-580-1(8)) Kids Can Pr., Ltd.

—Comets, Asteroids & Meteorites. 1999. (gr. 3-6). lib. bdg. 15.25 (978-0-613-21370-7(X)) Tandem Library Bks.

—Discover Space Rocks. Slavin, Bill, illus. 2006. (Kids Can Read Ser.). 32p. (J). (gr. 2-4). (978-1-55337-900-3(4)) Kids Can Pr., Ltd.

—Discover Space Rocks. Slavin, Bill, illus. 2006. 32p. 3.95 (978-1-55337-901-0(2)) Kids Can Pr., Ltd. CAN. *Dist:* Wybel Marketing Group.

Orme, David. Comets. 2007. (Trailblazers Ser.). (Illus.). 36p. pap. 7.95 (***978-1-84167-424-7(9)***) Ransom Publishing Ltd. GBR. *Dist:* International Publishers Marketing.

Orme, Helen & Orme, David. Let's Explore Comets & Asteroids. 2006. (J). pap. (***978-0-8368-8132-5(X));*** lib. bdg. (***978-0-8368-7947-6(3)***) Stevens, Gareth Inc.

Parker, Steve. Comets, Asteroids, & Meteors. 2007. (J). lib. bdg. (***978-1-4042-3738-4(0)***) Rosen Publishing Group, Inc., The.

Pobst, Sandy. Life of a Comet. 2006. (Navigators Ser.). (J). pap. 44.00 (***978-1-4108-6242-6(9)***) Benchmark Education Co.

Prinja, Raman. Comets, Asteroids, & Meteors. (Universe Ser.). (J). 2003. (Illus.). 32p. (gr. 3-5). lib. bdg. 22.79 (978-1-58810-909-5(7)); 2002. pap. (978-1-4034-0610-1(3)) Heinemann Library.

Rau, Dana Meachen. Comets, Asteroids, & Meteoroids. 2003. (Our Solar System Ser.). (Illus.). 32p. (J). (gr. 3 up). lib. bdg. 21.26 (978-0-7565-0437-3(6)) Compass Point Bks.

—Space Leftovers: A Book about Comets, Asteroids, & Meteoroids. Shea, Denise, illus. 2005. (Amazing Science Ser.). 24p. (J). (ps-k). lib. bdg. 22.60 (978-1-4048-1137-9(0)) Picture Window Bks.

Rau, Dana Meachen & Shea, Denise. Sobras Del Espacio: Un Libro Sobre Cometas, Asteroides y Meteoroides. Shea, Denise, illus. 2006. (SPA.). (J). lib. bdg. (***978-1-4048-3230-5(0)***) Picture Window Bks.

Romero, Libby. Comets. 2006. pap. 39.00 (***978-1-4108-6505-2(3)***) Benchmark Education Co.

—Discover Comets. 2006. pap. 39.00 (***978-1-4108-6508-3(8)***) Benchmark Education Co.

Simon, Seymour. Comets, Meteors & Asteroids. 1998. (J). 13.79 (978-0-606-13288-6(0)) Tandem Library Bks.

—Comets, Meteors, & Asteroids. 1998. (Illus.). 32p. (J). (ps-3). pap. 6.99 (978-0-688-15843-9(9) , Harper Trophy) HarperCollins Pubs.

Sparrow, Giles. Asteroids, Comets & Meteors. 2001. (Exploring the Solar System Ser.). (Illus.). 39p. (J). (gr. 4-6). lib. bdg. 24.22 (978-1-58810-037-5(5)) Heinemann Library.

—Asteroids, Comets, & Meteors. 2002. (Exploring the Solar System Ser.). (Illus.). 40p. (J). (gr. 4-6). pap. 7.95 (978-1-58810-959-0(3) , 91442) Heinemann Library.

Spinning Through Space: Includes: Comets & Asteroids; Constellations; Space Mysteries; Space Travel, 4 bks., Set. 2001. (Illus.). (J). (gr. 2-4). 71.92 (978-0-7398-2746-8(4)) Raintree.

Vogt, Gregory L. Asteroids, Comets, & Meteors. 2000. (Our Universe Ser.). (Illus.). 48p. (YA). (gr. 5-12). lib. bdg. 22.83 (978-0-7398-3112-0(7)) Raintree.

—Asteroids, Comets, & Meteors. 2000. (Our Universe Ser.). (Illus.). (J). pap. (978-0-7398-3351-3(0)) Steck-Vaughn.

—Comets. 2002. (Galaxy Ser.). (Illus.). 24p. (J). (gr. 2-3). lib. bdg. 18.60 (978-0-7368-1119-4(2) , Bridgestone Bks.) Capstone Pr., Inc.

Waldeck, Aaron. Space Rocks: A Look at Asteroids & Comets. 2002. (Reading Room Collection). 24p. (J). lib. bdg. 18.75 (978-0-8239-3737-0(2)) Rosen Publishing Group, Inc., The.

Way, Jennifer. Exploring Comets. 2007. (Objects in the Sky Ser.). 24p. (J). pap. (978-1-4042-2177-2(8)); (Illus.). (gr. 4-6). lib. bdg. 21.25 (978-1-4042-3469-7(1)) Rosen Publishing Group, Inc., The. (PowerKids Pr.).

COMIC BOOKS, STRIPS, ETC.

see also Cartoons and Comics

Abnett, Dan, et al. The Lords of Misrule. 1999. 200p. (gr. 11 up). pap. 17.95 (978-1-56971-352-5(9)) Dark Horse Comics.

Akahori, Satoru. Abenobashi: Magical Shopping Arcade, 2 vols., Vol. 1. Deguchi, Ryusei, illus. 2004. pap. 9.99 (978-1-59182-790-0(6) , Tokyopop Adult) TOKYOPOP, Inc.

Aki, Katsu. Psychic Academy, Vol. 11. 11th rev. ed. 2006. (Illus.). pap. 9.99 (978-1-59532-430-6(5) , Tokyopop Adult) TOKYOPOP, Inc.

Akimoto, Nami. Miracle Girls, 9 vols., Vol. 2. 2nd rev. ed. 2001. (Illus.). 194p. (gr. 7-12). pap. 9.99 (978-1-892213-69-3(9)) TOKYOPOP, Inc.

Akira, Shouko & Toriyama, Akira. Dr. Slump. 2005. (Dr. Slump Ser.: Vol. 3). 200p. (YA). pap. 7.99 (978-1-59116-991-8(7)) Viz Media.

Akiyama, Tamayo. Mouryo-Kiden: Legend of the Nymphs, 3 vols., Vol. 1. 2004. (Illus.). 208p. pap. 9.99 (978-1-59532-245-6(0) , Tokyopop Adult) TOKYOPOP, Inc.

Allred, Mike & Allred, Laura. Red Rocket 7. 1998. (Illus.). 208p. (YA). (gr. 7 up). pap. 29.95 (978-1-56971-347-1(2)) Dark Horse Comics.

Allred, Mike, et al. Madman Boogaloo! 1999. 80p. (YA). (gr. 7 up). pap. 8.95 (978-1-56971-404-1(5)) Dark Horse Comics.

Amakawa, Sumiko. Cross, 5 vols., Vol. 1. 2004. (Graphic Novel-Manga Ser.). (Illus.). 192p. pap. 9.99 (978-1-59532-227-2(2) , Tokyopop Adult) TOKYOPOP, Inc.

—Cross, Vol. 2. Amakawa, Sumiko, illus. rev. ed. 2005. (Illus.). 192p. pap. 9.99 (978-1-59532-228-9(0) , Tokyopop Adult) TOKYOPOP, Inc.

Amakawa, Sumiko, illus. & creator. Cross, Vol. 3. Amakawa, Sumiko, creator. rev. ed. 2005. 200p. pap. 9.99 (978-1-59532-229-6(9) , Tokyopop Adult) TOKYOPOP, Inc.

Amano, Shiro. Kingdom Hearts, 4 vols., Vol. 2. 2nd rev. ed. 2006. (Disney Squaresoft Ser.). (Illus.). (J). pap. 5.99 (978-1-59816-218-9(7) , Tokyopop Kids) TOKYOPOP, Inc.

Amend, Bill. Am I a Mutant, or What ! A FoxTrot Collection. 2004. (Illus.). 128p. pap. 8.95 (978-0-7407-4132-6(2)) Andrews McMeel Publishing.

—Who's up for Some Bonding? a FoxTrot Collection. 2003. (gr. 7-12). lib. bdg. 17.60 (978-0-613-67590-1(8)) Tandem Library Bks.

—Your Momma Thinks Square Roots Are Vegetables: A FoxTrot Collection. 2003. (gr. 7-12). lib. bdg. 17.60 (978-0-613-67592-5(4)) Tandem Library Bks.

Anzai, Nobuyuki. Flame of Recca. 2006. (Flame of Recca Ser.). 208p. (YA). Vol. 16. pap. 9.99 (978-1-4215-0250-2(X)); Vol. 17. pap. 9.99 (978-1-4215-0381-3(6)) Viz Media.

Aoki, Takao. Beyblade. 2006. (Beyblade Ser.). 208p. (YA). Vol. 9. pap. 7.99 (978-1-4215-0249-6(6)); Vol. 10. pap. 7.99 (978-1-4215-0380-6(8)) Viz Media.

Aragones, Sergio. The Groo Kingdom. 2001. (Groo Ser.). 96p. (YA). (gr. 5 up). pap. 9.95 (978-1-56971-478-2(9)) Dark Horse Comics.

—Louder Than Words. 1998. (Illus.). 160p. (YA). (gr. 7 up). pap. 12.95 (978-1-56971-343-3(X)) Dark Horse Comics.

Ashihara, Hinako. Sos. Ashihara, Hinako, illus. 2005. (Sos Ser.). (Illus.). 192p. (YA). pap. 9.99 (978-1-59116-735-8(3)) Viz Media.

Avi. City of Light, City of Dark. Floca, Brian, illus. 2004. (Comic-Book Ser.). 192p. (J). (ps up). pap. 8.99 (978-0-531-07058-1(1) , Orchard Bks.) Scholastic, Inc.

Azzarello, Brian. A Forgone Tomorrow. Risso, Eduardo, illus. rev. ed. 2002. 264p. pap. 17.99 (978-1-56389-827-3(6)) DC Comics.

Baltazar, Art & Aureliani, Franco, creators. Patrick the Wolf Boy Vols. 3 & 4: Giant Size Collection. 2004. (J). pap. 15.00 (978-0-9749941-1-6(1)) Blind Wolf Studios.

Barks, Carl, et al. Uncle Scrooge #369. 2007. 64p. pap. 7.99 (***978-1-888472-99-8(5)***) Gemstone Publishing, Inc.

Barnes, Bill & Ambaum, Gene. Unshelved, Vol. 1. 2004. (Illus.). 128p. (YA). pap. 14.95 (978-0-9740353-0-7(0)) Overdue Media LLC.

—What Would Dewey Do? An Unshelved Collection. 2004. (Illus.). 128p. (YA). pap. 14.95 (978-0-9740353-1-4(9)) Overdue Media LLC.

Beatty, Scott & Dougall, Alastair. The Ultimate Guide to the Amazon Princess. 2003. (Illus.). 144p. (J). 24.99 (978-0-7894-9616-4(X)) Dorling Kindersley Publishing, Inc.

Beck, C. C. The Shazam!, Vol. 3. rev. ed. 2002. (Illus.). 216p. 49.95 (978-1-56389-832-7(2)) DC Comics.

Beck, William F. Bible Stories in Pictures. Rogers, Ruth W. et al, illus. 2nd ed. 2003. (ALB, SPA & SWE.). 376p. pap. 6.50 (978-1-931891-08-0(7)) Multi-Language Pubns.

Bedard, Tony, et al. Exiles Vol. 8: Earn Your Wings TPB. 2004. (X-Men Ser.). (Illus.). 144p. 14.99 (978-0-7851-1459-8(9)) Marvel Enterprises, Inc.

Benintendi, Stephen F. PowerMark Issue 21: Ultimatum. 2004. (YA). 2.95 (978-0-9717876-0-5(3)) PowerMark Productions.

—PowerMark Seeker Series Issue 1: Quest for Truth. 2003. (SPA.). (J). 0.25 (978-0-9729135-1-5(3)) PowerMark Productions.

—PowerMark Seeker Series Issue 2: Let there Be... Light. 2003. (J). 1.75 (978-0-9729135-2-2(1)) PowerMark Productions.

—PowerMark Seeker Series Issue 3: Sabotage. 2003. (ENG & SPA.). (J). 1.75 (978-0-9729135-3-9(X)) PowerMark Productions.

Benintendi, Steve. PowerMark Issue 6 5-PK. 2003. 32p. (J). pap. 14.75 (978-0-9725121-0-7(1)) PowerMark Productions.

Beranek, Adam, et al. Silent Forest, 1. Burke, Chris et al, illus. 2004. 136p. per. 11.95 (978-0-9752582-0-0(6)) Silent Devil Productions.

Bleatham, Graham & Denham, Sam, eds. Thunderbirds Classic Comics. 2002. (Illus.). 160p. (J). 27.50 (978-1-84222-731-2(9)) Carlton Bks., Ltd. GBR. *Dist:* Independent Pubs. Group.

Bruzzone, Catherine. Lucy the Cat at the Farm: La Gatita Lucia en la Granja. Martin, Rosa Maria, tr. from ENG. Beaton, Clare, illus. 2005. (Bilingual Picture Strip Bks.). (SPA & ENG.). 24p. (J). pap. 4.95 (978-0-7641-3150-9(8)) Barron's Educational Series, Inc.

—Lucy the Cat in Town: La Gatita Lucia en la Cuidad. Martin, Rosa Maria, tr. Beaton, Clare, illus. 2005. (Bilingual Picture Strip Bks.). (SPA & ENG.). 24p. (J). pap. 4.95 (978-0-7641-3149-3(4)) Barron's Educational Series, Inc.

Buckley, James, Jr. The Incredible Hulk's Book of Strength. 2003. (DK Readers Ser.). (Illus.). 48p. pap. 3.99 (978-0-7894-9263-0(6)) Dorling Kindersley Publishing, Inc.

Buckley, James & Dorling Kindersley Publishing Staff. The Incredible Hulk's Book of Strength. 2003. (DK Readers Ser.). 48p. (J). 12.99 (978-0-7894-9543-3(0)) Dorling Kindersley Publishing, Inc.

Bulloch, Ivan, et al. Cartoons & Animation. 2005. (Illus.). 32p. (J). (gr. 3-7). lib. bdg. 27.10 (978-1-932889-81-9(7) , 1247651) Sea-To-Sea Pubns.

Burgan, Michael. Benedict Arnold: American Hero & Traitor. 2007. (Graphic Library). (Illus.). 32p. (J). (gr. 3-5). pap. 7.95 (***978-0-7368-7906-4(4)***) Capstone Pr., Inc.

Byers, Reggie, illus. & creator. Kidz of the KING Bk. 1: There's No Egg Scuse for Doing Violence! Byers, Reggie, creator. 2002. 32p. (J). 4.95 (978-0-9721164-0-4(0)) Sheepdog Publishing.

Byrne, John A. Generations: An Imaginary Tale. Crain, Dale, ed. Byrne, John, illus. rev. ed. 2000. (Superman/Batman Ser.). 208p. pap. 17.95 (978-1-56389-605-7(2)) DC Comics.

Cabiya, Pedro, creator. Anima Sola: Hambre. 2003. (SPA.). 40p. (YA). pap. 8.95 (978-0-9745825-0-4(6)) Zemi Comics.

Carroll, Lewis, pseud. Alice. 2004. 112p. (J). pap. 8.95 (978-0-9716338-3-4(5)) About Comics.

Chan, Mari. Dark Horse Deluxe Stationery Exotique: Mari-Chan Super Fun Kids. 2003. 4.99 (978-1-56971-922-0(5)) Dark Horse Comics.

Clamp. CardCaptor Sakura, Vol. 3. 3rd rev. ed. 2004. (Juvenile Favorite Ser.). (Illus.). (J). pap. 9.99 (978-1-59182-880-8(5) , Tokyopop Kids) TOKYOPOP, Inc.

—CardCaptor Sakura, Vol. 4. Clamp, illus. rev. ed. 2005. (Illus.). 200p. pap. 9.99 (978-1-59182-881-5(3) , Tokyopop Kids) TOKYOPOP, Inc.

—Cardcaptor Sakura: Anime, 10 bks. 2002. Bk. 4. 148p. pap. 14.99 (978-1-59182-043-7(X)); Bk. 5. 148p. pap. 14.99 (978-1-59182-044-4(8)); Bk. 6. 148p. pap. 14.99 (978-1-59182-045-1(6)); Bk. 7. 148p. pap. 14.99 (978-1-59182-046-8(4)); Bk. 8. 148p. pap. 14.99 (978-1-59182-047-5(2)); Vol. 6. 184p. (gr. 2-6). pap. 9.99 (978-1-892213-74-7(5)) TOKYOPOP, Inc.

—Magic Knight Rayearth II, 3 vols., Vol. 3. rev. ed. 2004. (Illus.). 192p. pap. 9.99 (978-1-59182-268-4(8) , Tokyopop Kids) TOKYOPOP, Inc.

—Waltz, Vol. 15. Clamp, illus. 2004. (X/1999 Ser.). (Illus.). 200p. (YA). pap. 9.95 (978-1-59116-349-7(8)) Viz Media.

Clamp, ed. Magic Knight Rayearth II, 3 vols., Vol. 1. 2004. (Illus.). 192p. pap. 9.99 (978-1-59182-266-0(1) , Tokyopop Kids) TOKYOPOP, Inc.

Claremont, Chris & Lopresti, Aaron. Excalibur: Forging the Sword. 2004. (X-Men Ser.). (Illus.). 96p. 9.99 (978-0-7851-1527-4(7)) Marvel Enterprises, Inc.

Claremont, Chris, et al. Essential Iron Fist, Vol. 1. 2004. (Marvel Heroes Ser.). (Illus.). 584p. 16.99 (978-0-7851-1546-5(3)) Marvel Enterprises, Inc.

The Comic Adventures of Felix the Cat. 2004. (Illus.). 128p. (YA). per. 12.95 (978-0-615-12660-9(X)) Felix Comics, Inc.

Comic Book Facts. 2003. (Illus.). pap. 5.60 (978-0-7398-7514-8(0)) Steck-Vaughn.

Conway, Gerry, et al. Super-Villain Team-Up. 2004. (Marvel Heroes Ser.). (Illus.). 552p. (YA). 16.99 (978-0-7851-1545-8(5)) Marvel Enterprises, Inc.

Crilley, Mark. Akiko Pocket-Size. 2004. (Illus.). 128p. Vol. 2. pap. 9.95 (978-1-57989-068-1(7)); Vol. 3. pap. 9.95 (978-1-57989-069-8(5)) Sirius Entertainment, Inc.

Dalrymple, Farel. Pop Gun War. 2003. (Illus.). 136p. (gr. 11 up). pap. 13.95 (978-1-56971-934-3(9)) Dark Horse Comics.

Dark Horse Comics Staff & Sakai, Stan. Grasscutter. 1999. (Usagi Yojimbo Ser.). (Illus.). 256p. (YA). (gr. 5 up). pap. 16.95 (978-1-56971-413-3(4)) Dark Horse Comics.

—Grey Shadows. 2000. (Usagi Yojimbo Ser.). (Illus.). 208p. (YA). (gr. 5 up). pap. 14.95 (978-1-56971-459-1(2)) Dark Horse Comics.

Dark Horse Comics Staff & Schultz, Mark. Apocalypse - The Destroying Angels. 1999. (Aliens Ser.). (Illus.). 96p. (gr. 11 up). pap. 10.95 (978-1-56971-399-0(5)) Dark Horse Comics.

David, Peter, et al. The Deadly Gourmet Affair, Vol. 1. 2001. (SpyBoy Ser.). (Illus.). 80p. (YA). (gr. 5 up). pap. 8.95 (978-1-56971-463-8(0)) Dark Horse Comics.

—Trial & Terror, Vol. 2. 2001. (SpyBoy Ser.: Bk. 2). 80p. (YA). (gr. 5 up). pap. 8.95 (978-1-56971-501-7(7)) Dark Horse Comics.

DC Comics Staff. They Saved Luthor's Brain. rev. ed. 2000. (Superman Ser.). (Illus.). 160p. pap. 14.95 (978-1-56389-601-9(X)) DC Comics.

DC Comics Staff & Simonson, Louise. Superman Returns: The Junior Novel. novel ed. 2006. (Illus.). 176p. (J). (ps-17). pap. 4.99 (978-0-316-17805-1(5)) Little, Brown Bks. for Young Readers.

—Superman Returns: Strange Visitor. 2nd novel rev. ed. 2006. 144p. (J). (ps-17). pap. 4.99 (978-0-316-17799-3(7)) Little, Brown Bks. for Young Readers.

Denton, Shannon. Zapt! Villavert, Armand, Jr., illus. 2006. pap. 5.99 (978-1-59816-588-3(7) , Tokyopop Kids) TOKYOPOP, Inc.

Denton, Shannon, et al. Komikwerks Presents Nuts & Bolts, 2004. (Illus.). 144p. (YA). per. 9.95 (978-0-9742803-2-5(1)) Komikwerks, LLC.

Disney Staff. Monkey Fist Strikes & Attack of the Killer Be. 2003. (gr. 3-6). lib. bdg. 16.45 (978-0-613-79932-4(1)) Tandem Library Bks.

—Pirates of the Caribbean: Dead Man's Chest. 2006. pap. 5.99 (978-1-59816-482-4(1) , Tokyopop Adult) TOKYOPOP, Inc.

Disney Staff, prod. Cine-Manga Vol. 9: Magic Train & Grubby Longjohn's Olde Tyme Revue, 12 vols. 2004. (Illus.). 96p. pap. 7.99 (978-1-59532-280-7(9) , Tokyopop Kids) TOKYOPOP, Inc.

—Gordo & the Girl & You're a Good Man. 2004. (Lizzie McGuire Ser.: Vol. 8). (Illus.). 96p. pap. 7.99 (978-1-59532-279-1(5) , Tokyopop Kids) TOKYOPOP, Inc.

—Sparring & Charring. 2004. (Lilo & Stitch: Vol. 2). (Illus.). 96p. pap. 7.99 (978-1-59532-068-1(7) , Tokyopop Kids) TOKYOPOP, Inc.

Distribooks Inc. Staff. Asterix Bind-Ups: Asterix & Friends. 1998. (Asterix Ser.). (Illus.). 240p. (J). (978-0-340-72755-3(1) , Hodder & Stoughton) Hodder General Publishing Division.

Doran, Colleen. Girl to Grrrl Manga. 2006. (Illus.). 128p. pap. 19.99 (978-1-58180-809-4(7) , North Light Bks.) F & W Pubns., Inc.

Dorling Kindersley Publishing Staff. Catwoman. 2004. (Ultimate Sticker Bks.). 16p. (J). pap. 6.99 (978-0-7566-0773-9(6)) Dorling Kindersley Publishing, Inc.

Dorling Kindersley Publishing Staff, ed. The Incredibles. 2004. (Ultimate Sticker Bks.). (Illus.). 16p. (J). pap. 6.99 (978-0-7566-0588-9(1)) Dorling Kindersley Publishing, Inc.

Dorsey, Angela. Horse Angel Comic. 2008. (J). pap. (***978-1-933343-82-2(6)**) Stabenfeldt Inc.

—Horse Angel Comic: Rough Diamond 0711. 2007. (YA). pap. (***978-1-933343-66-2(4)**) Stabenfeldt Inc.

Dougall, Alastair. Justice League of America Sticker Book. 2002. (Ultimate Sticker Bks.). (Illus.). 16p. (J). pap. 6.99 (978-0-7894-8892-3(2)) Dorling Kindersley Publishing, Inc.

Driggs, Scout. Power Up! 2004. (Astro Boy Ser.). (Illus.). 24p. (J). pap. 3.50 (978-0-06-072525-9(7) , Harper Festival) HarperCollins Pubs.

Dufaux, Jean. Rapaces. Marini, Enrico, illus. 2004. (SPA.). Vol. 1. 56p. pap. 17.95 (978-1-59497-003-0(3)); Vol. 2. 56p. pap. 17.95 (978-1-59497-004-7(1)); Vol. 3. 64p. pap. 17.95 (978-1-59497-005-4(X)) Public Square Bks.

Dunn, Ben. How to Draw Manga. 2004. (Illus.). 344p. (YA). pap. 3.25 (978-1-59412-063-3(3)) Mud Puddle, Inc.

Dyer, Sarah, tr. Snow Drop, 12 vols., Vol. 6. rev. ed. 2004. (Teen Ser.). (Illus.). 192p. (gr. 11 up). pap. 9.99 (978-1-59182-689-7(6) , Tokyopop Adult) TOKYOPOP, Inc.

Eliot, Jan. Stone Soup the Comic Strip: The Third Collection of the Syndicated Cartoon, No. 3. 2004. (Illus.). 192p. pap. 13.95 (978-0-9674102-1-0(5)) Four Panel Pr.

—You Can't Say Boobs on Sunday: The Second Collection of the Syndicated Cartoon Stone Soup, No. 2. 2004. (Illus.). 192p. pap. 13.95 (978-0-9674102-0-3(7)) Four Panel Pr.

Elliott, Craig. Racer Buddies-Opening Day at Daytona. William, Harper, illus. 2004. 40p. (J). per. 12.95 (978-0-9746445-0-9(1) , 1234022) Powerband, LLC.

Endoh, Minari. Dazzle, Vol. 1. 2006. (Illus.). (YA). (gr. 8 up). pap. 9.99 (978-1-59816-092-5(3) , Tokyopop Kids) TOKYOPOP, Inc.

Estep, Joanna, illus. Roadsong, Vol. 1. 2006. 200p. pap. 9.99 (978-1-59816-398-8(1) , Tokyopop Adult) TOKYOPOP, Inc.

Figueroa, Acton. I Am Astro. 2004. (Festival Reader Ser.). (Illus.). 32p. (J). pap. 3.99 (978-0-06-072526-6(5) , Harper Festival) HarperCollins Pubs.

—Invisible Robot. 2004. (Festival Reader Ser.). (Illus.). 32p. (J). pap. 3.99 (978-0-06-072527-3(3) , Harper Festival) HarperCollins Pubs.

—Rocket Ball. 2004. (Astro Boy Ser.). (Illus.). 24p. (J). pap. 3.50 (978-0-06-072524-2(9) , Harper Festival) HarperCollins Pubs.

Finger, Bill. The Golden Age. Nodell, Martin, illus. rev. ed. 1999. (Green Lantern - Archives Ser.: Vol. 1). 224p. 49.95 (978-1-56389-507-4(2)) DC Comics.

Fontes, Ron & Fontes, Justine, creators. Ron & Justine Fontes Present Tales of the Terminal Diner. 2004. (Illus.). 96p. (YA). per. 9.95 (978-0-9754615-0-1(8) , 001) Critter Publishing.

Fox, Gardner. All Star Comics. Kubert, Joe et al, illus. rev. ed. 2001. (Archives Ser.: Vol. 7). 216p. 49.95 (978-1-56389-720-7(2)) DC Comics.

—All Star Comics. rev. ed. (Illus.). 2000. (Archives Ser.: Vol. 6). 240p. 49.95 (978-1-56389-636-1(2)); Vol. 5. 1999. 224p. 49.95 (978-1-56389-497-8(1)) DC Comics.

Fox, Gardner, et al. All Star Comics, Vol. 8. Infantino, Carmine & Irwin, H., illus. rev. ed. 2002. 228p. 49.95 (978-1-56389-812-9(8)) DC Comics.

Friends of Lulu Presents: Broad Appeal. 2003. (YA). per. 9.95 (978-0-9740960-1-8(6)) Friends of Lulu.

Fujima, Takuya, creator. Deus Vitae, 3 vols., Vol. 3. 3rd rev. ed. 2004. (Illus.). 264p. pap. 9.99 (978-1-59182-771-9(X) , Tokyopop Adult) TOKYOPOP, Inc.

Fujishima, Kosuke. Oh My Goddess!, Vol. 2. 2006. 192p. (J). pap. 10.95 (978-1-59307-457-9(3)) Dark Horse Comics.

Fukushima, Haruka, creator. Instant Teen: Just Add Nuts, 4 vols., Vol. 2. rev. ed. 2004. (Illus.). 192p. pap. 9.99 (978-1-59532-147-3(0) , Tokyopop Kids) TOKYOPOP, Inc.

Fukushima, Haruka, illus. & creator. Instant Teen, Vol. 3. Fukushima, Haruka, creator. rev. ed. 2005. 208p. pap. 9.99 (978-1-59532-148-0(9) , Tokyopop Kids) TOKYOPOP, Inc.

Furuyama, Kan & Taniguchi, Jiro. Samurai Legend. Pannone, Frank, ed. Kobayashi, Mayumi, tr. from JPN. 2003. Orig. Title: Kaze No Sho. (Illus.). 240p. pap. 15.95 (978-1-58664-856-5(X) , CMX 63801G, CPM Manga) Central Park Media Corp.

Gainax. FLCL, Vol. 1. Ueda, Hajime, illus. 2003. 192p. (YA). pap. 9.99 (978-1-59182-396-4(X) , Tokyopop Adult) TOKYOPOP, Inc.

—FLCL, Vol. 2. Yoshimoto, Ray, tr. from JPN. Ueda, Hajime, illus. rev. ed. 2003. (ENG.). 204p. (YA). pap. 9.99 (978-1-59182-397-1(8) , Tokyopop Adult) TOKYOPOP, Inc.

Gallagher, Michael. X-Men, Magneto's Master Plan. Severin, Marie, illus. 24p. (YA). (gr. k up). 12.95 (978-0-9627001-6-3(9)) Futech Educational Products, Inc.

Gentile, Joe. Werewolf the Apocalypse Fang & Claw Vol. 1: Raging Fury. 2003. (Illus.). 168p. (gr. 11 up). pap. 15.95 (978-0-9721668-7-4(4)) Moonstone.

Gibbons, Dave & Milligan, Peter. Aliens: Salvation & Sacrifice. Mignola, Mike et al, illus. 2001. 112p. (YA). (gr. 11 up). pap. 12.95 (978-1-56971-561-1(0)) Dark Horse Comics.

Gilroy, Henry, et al. Joker/Mask. 2001. 96p. (YA). (gr. 7 up). pap. 11.95 (978-1-56971-518-5(1)) Dark Horse Comics.

Glick, Shifra. Shikufitzky. Glick, Shifra, illus. 2002. (Illus.). 100p. (J). 19.99 (978-1-58330-569-0(6)) Feldheim Pubs.

Go Office Staff. How to Draw Manga: Official More How to Draw Manga Illustration Kit, 1. 2004. (Illus.). 126p. 29.99 (978-1-59396-121-3(9)) Diamond Bk. Distributors.

Goscinny, René. Absolutely Asterix. 1998. (Illus.). 204p. (J). 24.95 (978-0-340-72756-0(X) , Hodder & Stoughton) Hodder General Publishing Division GBR. *Dist:* Trafalgar Square Publishing.

—Asterix & Caesar's Gift. Uderzo, Albert, illus. 2005. 48p. 12.95 (978-0-7528-6645-1(1)) Orion Bks. Ltd. GBR. *Dist:* Sterling Publishing Co., Inc.

—Asterix & Cleopatra. Uderzo, Albert, illus. 2004. 48p. 12.95 (978-0-7528-6606-2(0)) Orion Bks. Ltd. GBR. *Dist:* Sterling Publishing Co., Inc.

—Asterix & Obelix All at Sea. Uderzo, Albert, illus. 2002. 48p. (978-0-7528-4717-7(1)) Orion Media.

—Asterix & the Banquet. Uderzo, Albert, illus. 2004. 48p. 12.95 (978-0-7528-6608-6(7)) Orion Bks. Ltd. GBR. *Dist:* Sterling Publishing Co., Inc.

—Asterix & the Big Fight. Uderzo, Albert, illus. 2004. 48p. 12.95 (978-0-7528-6616-1(8)) Orion Bks. Ltd. GBR. *Dist:* Sterling Publishing Co., Inc.

—Asterix & the Cauldron. Uderzo, Albert, illus. 2004. 48p. 12.95 (978-0-7528-6628-4(1)) Orion Bks. Ltd. GBR. *Dist:* Sterling Publishing Co., Inc.

—Asterix & the Great Crossing. Uderzo, Albert, illus. 2005. 48p. 12.95 (978-0-7528-6647-5(8)) Orion Bks. Ltd. GBR. *Dist:* Sterling Publishing Co., Inc.

—Asterix & the Normans. (Illus.). (J). pap. 9.95 (978-0-02-497290-3(8)) International Language Centre.

—Asterix & the Normans. Uderzo, Albert, illus. 2004. 48p. 12.95 (978-0-7528-6622-2(2)) Orion Bks. Ltd. GBR. *Dist:* Sterling Publishing Co., Inc.

—Asterix at the Olympic Games. Uderzo, Albert, illus. 2004. 48p. 12.95 (978-0-7528-6626-0(5)) Orion Bks. Ltd. GBR. *Dist:* Sterling Publishing Co., Inc.

—Asterix aux Jeux Olympiques. (FRE.). (J). pap. 21.95 (***978-2-01-210144-9(5)**) Hachette Groupe Livre FRA. *Dist:* Distribooks, Inc.

—Asterix et Cleopatre. (FRE.). (J). pap. 21.95 (***978-2-01-210138-8(0)**); (Illus.). 21.95 (978-2-01-210111-1(9)) Hachette Groupe Livre FRA. *Dist:* Distribooks, Inc.

—Asterix et les Normaands. (FRE.). (J). pap. 21.95 (***978-2-01-210141-8(0)**) Hachette Groupe Livre FRA. *Dist:* Distribooks, Inc.

—Asterix in Britain. Uderzo, Albert, illus. 2004. 48p. 12.95 (978-0-7528-6618-5(4)) Orion Bks. Ltd. GBR. *Dist:* Sterling Publishing Co., Inc.

—Asterix in Spain. Uderzo, Albert, illus. 2004. 48p. 12.95 (978-0-7528-6630-7(3)) Orion Bks. Ltd. GBR. *Dist:* Sterling Publishing Co., Inc.

—Asterix in Switzerland. Uderzo, Albert, illus. 2004. 48p. 12.95 (978-0-7528-6634-5(6)) Orion Bks. Ltd. GBR. *Dist:* Sterling Publishing Co., Inc.

—Asterix the Gaul. Uderzo, Albert, illus. 2004. 48p. 12.95 (978-0-7528-6604-8(4)) Orion Bks. Ltd. GBR. *Dist:* Sterling Publishing Co., Inc.

—Asterix the Gladiator. Uderzo, Albert, illus. 2004. 48p. 12.95 (978-0-7528-6610-9(9)) Orion Bks. Ltd. GBR. *Dist:* Sterling Publishing Co., Inc.

Goscinny, René & Uderzo, Albert. Asterix & Cleopatra. Uderzo, Albert, illus. 2004. (Illus.). 48p. pap. 9.95 (978-0-7528-6607-9(9)) Orion Bks. Ltd. GBR. *Dist:* Sterling Publishing Co., Inc.

—Asterix & the Big Fight. Uderzo, Albert, illus. 2004. (Illus.). 48p. pap. 9.95 (978-0-7528-6617-8(6)) Orion Bks. Ltd. GBR. *Dist:* Sterling Publishing Co., Inc.

—Asterix & the Class Act. 2005. (Illus.). 56p. pap. 9.95 (978-0-7528-6640-6(0)) Orion Bks. Ltd. GBR. *Dist:* Sterling Publishing Co., Inc.

—Asterix & the Class Act. Bell, Anthea & Hockridge, Derek, trs. from FRE. Uderzo, Albert, illus. 2004. (Illus.). 56p. 12.95 (978-0-7528-6068-8(2)) Orion Bks. Ltd. GBR. *Dist:* Sterling Publishing Co., Inc.

—Asterix & the Golden Sickle. 2004. (Illus.). 48p. 12.95 (978-0-7528-6612-3(5)) Orion Bks. Ltd. GBR. *Dist:* Sterling Publishing Co., Inc.

—Asterix & the Laurel Wreath. Uderzo, Albert, illus. 2005. (Illus.). 48p. 12.95 (978-0-7528-6636-9(2)) Orion Bks. Ltd. GBR. *Dist:* Sterling Publishing Co., Inc.

—Asterix & the Soothsayer. Uderzo, Albert, illus. 2005. (Illus.). 48p. 12.95 (978-0-7528-6641-3(9)) Orion Bks. Ltd. GBR. *Dist:* Sterling Publishing Co., Inc.

—Asterix in Britain. Uderzo, Albert, illus. 2004. (Illus.). 48p. pap. 9.95 (978-0-7528-6619-2(2)) Orion Bks. Ltd. GBR. *Dist:* Sterling Publishing Co., Inc.

—Los Laureles del Cesar. (SPA.). 48p. 9.95 (978-84-7510-031-9(7)) Grijalbo-Dargaud, S.A. Editores ESP. *Dist:* Distribooks, Inc.

Goscinny, René & Uderzo, M. Asterix el Galo. (SPA., Illus.). (J). (gr. 7-10). 24.95 (978-0-8288-4933-3(1)) French & European Pubns., Inc.

—Streit um Asterix. (GER., Illus.). (J). 24.95 (978-0-8288-4906-7(4)) French & European Pubns., Inc.

Gray, Peter C. How to Draw Manga Animals. 2006. (Kid's Guide to Drawing Ser.). (Illus.). 32p. (J). (978-1-4042-3329-4(6) , PowerKids Pr.) Rosen Publishing Group, Inc., The.

—How to Draw Manga Female Action Figures. 2006. (Kid's Guide to Drawing Ser.). (Illus.). 32p. (J). lib. bdg. 25.25 (978-1-4042-3327-0(X) , PowerKids Pr.) Rosen Publishing Group, Inc., The.

—How to Draw Manga Heroes & Villains. 2006. (Kid's Guide to Drawing Ser.). (Illus.). 32p. (J). 25.25 (978-1-4042-3330-0(X) , PowerKids Pr.) Rosen Publishing Group, Inc., The.

—How to Draw Manga Male Action Figures. 2006. (Kid's Guide to Drawing Ser.). (Illus.). 32p. (J). lib. bdg. (978-1-4042-3328-7(8) , PowerKids Pr.) Rosen Publishing Group, Inc., The.

—How to Draw Manga Monsters. 2006. (Kid's Guide to Drawing Ser.). (Illus.). 32p. (J). lib. bdg. 25.25 (978-1-4042-3331-7(8) , PowerKids Pr.) Rosen Publishing Group, Inc., The.

—How to Draw Manga Robots. 2006. (Kid's Guide to Drawing Ser.). (Illus.). 32p. (J). lib. bdg. (978-1-4042-3332-4(6) , PowerKids Pr.) Rosen Publishing Group, Inc., The.

Groening, Matt. Big Bad Book of Bart Simpson. 2003. (Bart Simpson Comic Collection). (gr. 5-8). lib. bdg. 22.20 (978-0-613-67067-8(1)) Tandem Library Bks.

—Simpsons Comics Royale. 2001. (Simpsons Comics Ser.). (Illus.). 160p. pap. 14.95 (978-0-00-711854-0(6)) HarperCollins Pubs.

Hajikete BB. 2005. (J). pap. 9.99 (978-1-59182-598-2(9)); Vol. 2. pap. 9.99 (978-1-59182-599-9(7)); Vol. 3. pap. 9.99 (978-1-59182-600-2(4)); Vol. 4. pap. 9.99 (978-1-59182-601-9(2)); Vol. 5. pap. 9.99 (978-1-59182-602-6(0)) TOKYOPOP, Inc.

Hakase, Mizuki. The Demon Ororon, 4 vols. 2004. (Illus.). Vol. 1. 232p. pap. 9.99 (978-1-59182-725-2(6)); Vol. 3. 200p. pap. 9.99 (978-1-59182-727-6(2)) TOKYOPOP, Inc. (Tokyopop Adult).

Hakase, Mizuki, creator. Demon Ororon, 4 vols., Vol. 4. 4th rev. ed. 2004. (Illus.). 192p. (YA). pap. 9.99 (978-1-59182-728-3(0) , Tokyopop Adult) TOKYOPOP, Inc.

Harris, Joe. Narda. 2005. (J). (978-0-9772259-0-3(9)) Character Arts.

Hart, Christopher. Kids Draw Anime. 2003. (gr. 3-6). lib. bdg. 19.90 (978-0-613-88815-8(4)) Tandem Library Bks.

—Kids Draw Anime. 2002. (Kids Draw Ser.). (Illus.). 64p. (J). (gr. 3-6). pap. 11.95 (978-0-8230-2690-6(6)) Watson-Guptill Pubns., Inc.

—Kids Draw Manga. 2004. (Kids Draw Ser.). (Illus.). 64p. (J). pap. 11.95 (978-0-8230-2623-4(X)) Watson-Guptill Pubns., Inc.

—Kids Draw Manga Monsters! 2007. (Illus.). 64p. (J). pap. 11.95 (***978-0-8230-9840-8(0)**) Watson-Guptill Pubns., Inc.

Hart, Christopher. Xtreme Art: Draw Manga Villains! 2004. (Xtreme Art Ser.). (Illus.). 64p. (J). pap. 7.95 (978-0-8230-0370-9(1)) Watson-Guptill Pubns., Inc.

Hartman, Rachel. Amy Unbounded: Belondweg Blossoming. 2002. 208p. (J). pap. 16.95 (978-0-9717900-0-1(0)) Pug House Pr.

Hergé. Tintin in America. 2004. (Adventures of Tintin Ser.). Orig. Title: Tintin en Amerique. (Illus.). 124p. 24.95 (978-0-86719-904-8(0)) Last Gasp of San Francisco.

Hikawa, Kyoko. From Far Away. Hikawa, Kyoko, illus. 2005. (From Far Away Ser.). (YA). Vol. 6. 184p. pap. 9.99 (978-1-59116-972-7(0)); Vol. 7. (Illus.). 177p. (gr. 8-12). pap. 9.99 (978-1-4215-0088-1(4)) Viz Media.

Hinds, Gareth. The Merchant of Venice. Hinds, Gareth, illus. 2008. (Illus.). 80p. (J). (gr. 7). 19.99 (***978-0-7636-3024-9(1)**); pap. 11.99 (***978-0-7636-3025-6(X)**) Candlewick Pr.

Hiwatari, Saki. Please Save My Earth, Vol. 12. Hiwatari, Saki, illus. 2005. (Please Save My Earth Ser.). 184p. (YA). pap. 9.99 (978-1-59116-987-1(9)) Viz Media.

Ho-Kyung, Yeo. Honey Mustard, 2 vols. 2005. (Illus.). 176p. pap. 9.99 (978-1-59532-239-5(6) , Tokyopop Adult) TOKYOPOP, Inc.

Holbrook, Bill. Accepting Domestication. 1999. (Kevin & Kell Ser.: Vol. 3). (Illus.). 147p. (YA). pap. 12.95 (978-0-9660676-6-8(5)) Plan Nine Publishing, Inc.

Holkins, Jerry. Penny Arcade Vol 1: Attack of the Bacon Robots! 2006. (Illus.). 120p. (YA). pap. 12.95 (978-1-59307-444-9(1)) Dark Horse Comics.

Hongo, Akiyoshi. Digimon Zero Two, 2 vols., Vol. 1. 2003. (Illus.). 192p. pap. 9.99 (978-1-59182-667-5(5)) TOKYOPOP, Inc.

Horn, Maurice. Women in the Comics, 3 vols. rev. ed. 2001. (Illus.). 288p. (YA). (gr. 9 up). 125.00 (978-0-7910-5910-4(3) , Chelsea Hse.) Facts On File, Inc.

Horowitz, Anthony. Stormbreaker: The Graphic Novel. Kanako & Yuzuru, illus. 2006. (Alex Rider Ser.). 144p. (J). (gr. 4). pap. 14.99 (978-0-399-24633-3(9) , Philomel) Penguin Group (USA) Inc.

Hotta, Yumi. Hikaru No Go. Obata, Takeshi, illus. (Hikaru No Go Ser.). 208p. (YA). Vol. 5. 2005. pap. 7.95 (978-1-59116-689-4(6)); Vol. 6. 2006. pap. 7.95 (978-1-4215-0275-5(5)) Viz Media.

In-Soo, Ra. King of Hell, 8 vols., Vol. 8. Jae-Hwan, Kim, illus. rev. ed. 2005. Tr. of Ma-Je. 200p. pap. 9.99 (978-1-59182-914-0(3) , Tokyopop Adult) TOKYOPOP, Inc.

Inada, Koji. Beet the Vandel Buster, Vol. 3. Inada, Koji, illus. 2005. (Beet the Vandel Buster Ser.). (Illus.). 216p. (YA). pap. 7.99 (978-1-59116-693-1(4)) Viz Media.

—Beet the Vandel Buster, Vol. 9. Sanjo, Riku, illus. 2006. (Beet the Vandel Buster Ser.). 208p. (YA). pap. 7.99 (978-1-4215-0270-0(4)) Viz Media.

Inagaki, Riichiro. Eyeshield 21. Murata, Yusuke, illus. (Eyeshield 21 Ser.). (YA). Vol. 4. 2005. 200p. pap. 7.99 (978-1-4215-0074-4(4)); Vol. 6. 2006. 208p. pap. 7.99 (978-1-4215-0274-8(7)); Vol. 7. 2006. 208p. pap. 7.99 (978-1-4215-0405-6(7)) Viz Media.

Inui, Sekihiko. Comic Party, 3 vols., Vol. 1. 2004. (Illus.). 192p. pap. 9.99 (978-1-59182-854-9(6) , Tokyopop Adult) TOKYOPOP, Inc.

—Comic PartyTM, 3 vols., Vol. 2. Kiefl, Mike, tr. from JPN. rev. ed. 2004. (Illus.). 192p. pap. 9.99 (978-1-59182-855-6(4) , Tokyopop Adult) TOKYOPOP, Inc.

Inui, Sekihiko, creator. Comic Party, 3 vols., Vol. 3. rev. ed. 2004. (Illus.). 192p. pap. 9.99 (978-1-59182-856-3(2) , Tokyopop Adult) TOKYOPOP, Inc.

Inui, Sekihiko, illus. & creator. Comic Party, Vol. 4. Inui, Sekihiko, creator. rev. ed. 2004. 192p. pap. 9.99 (978-1-59532-584-6(0) , Tokyopop Adult) TOKYOPOP, Inc.

The Invincible Ed. 2002. 24p. (J). 3.50 (978-0-9716357-0-8(6)) Summertime Bks. & Comics.

Jacques, Brian. Redwall: The Graphic Novel. Blevins, Bret, illus. 2007. (Redwall Ser.). 148p. (YA). (gr. 3 up). 12.99 (***978-0-399-24481-0(6)** , Philomel) Penguin Group (USA) Inc.

Jae-Hwan, Kim. King of Hell, 6 vols., Vol. 6. Na, Lauren, tr. from KOR. In-Soo, Ra, illus. rev. ed. 2004. 216p. pap. 9.99 (978-1-59182-484-8(2) , Tokyopop Adult) TOKYOPOP, Inc.

Jeffery, Gary & Petty, Kate. Abraham Lincoln: The Life of America's Sixteenth President. Lacey, Mike, illus. 2005. 48p. (YA). pap. 9.95 (978-1-4042-5164-9(2)) Rosen Publishing Group, Inc., The.

Johns, Geoff. A Kid's Game. rev. ed. 2004. (Teen Titans Go! Ser.). (Illus.). 192p. pap. 9.99 (978-1-4012-0308-5(6)) DC Comics.

Johnson, Yuki N., tr. from JPN. Tramps Like Us, 7 vols., Vol. 2. rev. ed. 2004. (Teen Ser.). (Illus.). 200p. pap. 9.99 (978-1-59532-140-4(3) , Tokyopop Adult) TOKYOPOP, Inc.

Johnston, Antony. Julius. 2004. (Illus.). 168p. pap. 14.95 (978-1-929998-80-7(5)) Oni Pr., Inc.

Jones, Gerard. Pikachu Meets the Press: A Pokemon Newspaper Strip Collection. 2001. (Illus.). (J). (978-0-606-22061-3(5)) Tandem Library Bks.

Ju-Yeon, Rhim. President Dad, Vol. 1. 2004. (Illus.). 192p. pap. 9.99 (978-1-59532-234-0(5) , Tokyopop Kids) TOKYOPOP, Inc.

Kaneko, Shinya. Culdcept, Vol. 3. 3rd rev. ed. 2004. (Illus.). pap. 9.99 (978-1-59182-954-6(2) , Tokyopop Adult) TOKYOPOP, Inc.

—Culdcept, Vol. 4. Kaneko, Shinya, illus. rev. ed. 2005. (Illus.). 234p. pap. 9.99 (978-1-59532-447-4(X) , Tokyopop Adult) TOKYOPOP, Inc.

Kaneko, Shinya, creator. Culdcept, Vol. 2. rev. ed. 2004. (Illus.). 210p. pap. 9.99 (978-1-59182-783-2(3) , Tokyopop Adult) TOKYOPOP, Inc.

Kanietzko, Bryan. Avatar, Vol. 2. 2006. (Illus.). pap. 7.99 (978-1-59532-892-2(0) , Tokyopop Kids) TOKYOPOP, Inc.

Kanietzko, Bryan & Dante DiMartino, Michael. Avatar, Vol. 3. 2006. pap. 7.99 (978-1-59816-757-3(X) , Tokyopop Kids) TOKYOPOP, Inc.

Kanzaka, Hajime & Yoshinaka, Shoko. Slayers Super-Explosive Demon Story 4: Return, Vol. 4. 2004. Orig. Title: Slayers: Super Explosive Magic Story Book 4. (Illus.). 136p. pap. 9.99 (978-1-58664-914-2(0) , CMX 64604G, CPM Manga) Central Park Media Corp.

Kasane, Katsumoto, illus. Hands Off!, Vol. 3. 3rd rev. ed. 2005. pap. 9.99 (978-1-59532-155-8(1) , Tokyopop Adult) TOKYOPOP, Inc.

Katsumoto, Kasane. Hands Off!, 8 vols. (Teen Ser.). (Illus.). Vol. 1. 2004. 192p. pap. 9.99 (978-1-59532-153-4(5)); Vol. 2. 2005. 184p. pap. 9.99 (978-1-59532-154-1(3)) TOKYOPOP, Inc. (Tokyopop Adult).

Katsura, Masakazu. Off-Line. Katsura, Masakazu, illus. 2nd ed. 2004. (Video Girl Ai Ser.). 200p. (YA). pap. 9.99 (978-1-59116-104-2(5)) Viz Media.

—Recall Vol. 3. Katsura, Masakazu, illus. 2nd ed. 2004. (Video Girl Ai Ser.). 184p. (YA). pap. 9.99 (978-1-59116-103-5(7)) Viz Media.

—Spinoff, Vol. 5. Katsura, Masakazu, illus. 2004. (Video Girl Ai Ser.). (Illus.). 200p. (YA). pap. 9.99 (978-1-59116-146-2(0)) Viz Media.

Kazumi, Yuana. Flower of the Deep Sleep, 2 vols., Vol. 1. 2000. (Teen Ser.). (Illus.). pap. 9.99 (978-1-59532-271-5(X)) TOKYOPOP, Inc.

Kazuo, Umezu. Reflections. 2006. (Scary Book Ser.: Vol. 1). 232p. (YA). pap. 13.95 (978-1-59307-476-0(X)) Dark Horse Comics.

Kellaher, Karen. Comic-Strip Writing Prompts: 50 Favorite Comic Strips with Terrific Writing Prompts That Get Kids Revved up for Writing. 2001. 64p. (gr. 3). pap. 10.95 (978-0-439-15977-7(6)) Scholastic, Inc.

Kennedy, Mike. Batgirl: The Resurrection Engine. 2001. (Ghost Ser.). (Illus.). 96p. (YA). (gr. 9 up). pap. 11.95 (978-1-56971-570-3(X)) Dark Horse Comics.

—The Language of Chaos. 2003. (Lone Wolf 2100 Ser.: Vol. 2). (Illus.). 120p. (gr. 11 up). pap. 12.95 (978-1-56971-997-8(7)) Dark Horse Comics.

Kesel, Barbara, ed. CrossGen Illustrated, Vol. 1. 2001. (Illus.). 192p. (YA). (gr. 7 up). 24.95 (978-1-931484-05-3(8)) CrossGeneration Comics, Inc.

Kill Me, Kiss Me, Vol. 5. 2005. (YA). pap. 9.99 (978-1-59182-597-5(0)) TOKYOPOP, Inc.

Kim, Kang Won. The Queen's Knight, 14 vols. 2004. (Illus.). pap. 9.99 (978-1-59532-257-9(4) , Tokyopop Kids) TOKYOPOP, Inc.

Kishimoto, Masashi. Naruto. Kishimoto, Masashi, illus. 2004. (Naruto Ser.). (Illus.). 200p. (YA). Vol. 4. pap. 7.95 (978-1-59116-358-9(7)); Vol. 5. pap. 7.95 (978-1-59116-359-6(5)) Viz Media.

Kishiro, Yukito. Battle Angel Alita: Last Order. Kishiro, Yukito, illus. 2005. (Battle Angel Alita Last Order Ser.). 192p. (YA). pap. 9.99 (978-1-4215-0057-7(4)) Viz Media.

Knudtsen, Ken. My Monkey's Name Is Jennifer. 2003. (Illus.). 152p. (gr. 11 up). pap. 15.95 (978-0-943151-71-7(6)) Slave Labor Bks.

Kobayashi, Makoto. Club 9, Vol. 1. 2003. (Illus.). 192p. pap. 15.95 (978-1-56971-915-2(2)) Dark Horse Comics.

Koike, Kazuo. Day of the Demons. 2001. (Lone Wolf & Cub Ser.: Vol. 14). (Illus.). 320p. (gr. 11 up). pap. 9.95 (978-1-56971-586-4(6)) Dark Horse Comics.

Koshi, Rikdo. Excel Saga, Vol. 14. 2006. (Excel Saga Ser.). 208p. (YA). pap. 9.99 (978-1-4215-0481-0(2)) Viz Media.

Kowitt, Holly. 2 Grrrls Locker Talk: Cool School Comics. 2002. (gr. 3-6). lib. bdg. 13.00 (978-0-613-72026-7(1)) Tandem Library Bks.

Krefta, Ben. Step-by-Step Manga. 2005. (Step-by-step Manga Ser.). (Illus.). 64p. (J). pap. 6.99 (978-0-439-67706-6(8)) Scholastic, Inc.

Kubert, Joe. Fax from Sarajevo: A Story of Survival. Kubert, Joe, illus. 1998. (Illus.). 224p. (YA). (gr. 9 up). pap. 16.95 (978-1-56971-346-4(4)) Dark Horse Comics.

Kunkel, Mike & Heuser, Randy. The Land of Sokmunster. 2004. 60p. 14.95 (978-0-9721259-2-5(2)) Astonish Comics.

Kuroda, Yosuke & Hayashiya, Shizuru. Onegai Teacher, 2 vols., Vol. 1. 2003. (Illus.). 200p. (YA). 9.95 (978-1-58899-196-6(2)) ComicsOne Corp./Dr. Masters.

Kurumada, Masami. B'tX, 16 vols. 2004. (Illus.). 192p. Vol. 2. 2nd rev. ed. pap. 9.99 (978-1-59182-640-8(3)); Vol. 3. 3rd rev. ed. pap. 9.99 (978-1-59182-641-5(1)); Vol. 4. 4th rev. ed. pap. 9.99 (978-1-59182-642-2(X)) TOKYOPOP, Inc. (Tokyopop Adult).

—Knights of the Zodiac. Kurumada, Masami, illus. (Knights of the Zodiac (Saint Seiya) Ser.). (YA). 2004. (Illus.). 200p. pap. 7.95 (978-1-59116-525-5(3)); Vol. 5. 2004. 200p. pap. 7.95 (978-1-59116-470-8(2)); Vol. 7. 2005. (Illus.). 200p. pap. 7.95 (978-1-59116-616-0(0)); Vol. 11. 2005. (Illus.). 184p. pap. 7.95 (978-1-59116-993-2(3)) Viz Media.

—Knights of the Zodiac, Vol. 15. 2006. (Knights of the Zodiac Ser.). 208p. (YA). pap. 7.95 (978-1-4215-0656-2(4)) Viz Media.

—Knights of the Zodiac (Saint Seiya), Vol. 12. Kurumada, Masami, illus. 2005. (Knights of the Zodiac (Saint Seiya) Ser.). 184p. (YA). pap. 7.95 (978-1-4215-0117-8(1)) Viz Media.

Kusunoki, Kei & Ohashi, Kaoru. Diabolo. 2004. (Graphic Novel-Manga Ser.). (Illus.). 208p. pap. 9.99 (978-1-59532-232-6(9)); Vol. 2. 192p. pap. 9.99 (978-1-59532-233-3(7)) TOKYOPOP, Inc. (Tokyopop Adult).

Lambil, Willy & Raoul, Cauvin. The Blues in Black & White. 2004. (Blue Tunics Ser.: Vol. 1). (Illus.). (J). 12.45 (978-0-9752688-0-3(5)) Reney Editions, Inc.

Lee, Jong-Kyu. Evil's Return, 4 vols., Vol. 2. Shin, Hwan, illus. 2nd rev. ed. 2004. 184p. pap. 9.99 (978-1-59182-785-6(X) , Tokyopop Adult) TOKYOPOP, Inc.

Lee, Sang-Eun. Love or Money, 5 vols., Vol. 1. 2004. (Illus.). 192p. pap. 9.99 (978-1-59532-248-7(5) , Tokyopop Kids) TOKYOPOP, Inc.

Lee, Sang-Eun, illus. & creator. Love or Money, Vol. 2. Lee, Sang-Eun, creator. rev. ed. 2005. 192p. pap. 9.99 (978-1-59532-249-4(3) , Tokyopop Kids) TOKYOPOP, Inc.

Lee, Stan & Kirby, Jack. Essential Fantastic Four, Vol. 4. 2005. (Fantastic Four Ser.: Vol. 4). (Illus.). 536p. (YA). pap. 16.99 (978-0-7851-1484-0(X)) Marvel Enterprises, Inc.

Lee, Stan, et al. Essential Defenders, Vol. 1. 2005. (Marvel Heroes Ser.). (Illus.). 544p. pap. 16.99 (978-0-7851-1547-2(1)) Marvel Enterprises, Inc.

Lee, Sun-Hee. Neck & Neck, 3 vols., Vol. 1. 2004. (Illus.). 192p. (YA). pap. 9.99 (978-1-59532-253-1(1) , Tokyopop Kids) TOKYOPOP, Inc.

Lee, Vin, creator. Crazy Love Story, 5 vols. (Teen Ser.). (Illus.). Vol. 1. 2004. 192p. pap. 9.99 (978-1-59182-772-6(8)); Vol. 2. 2005. 208p. pap. 9.99 (978-1-59182-773-3(6)) TOKYOPOP, Inc. (Tokyopop Kids).

—One, Vol. 4. 5th rev. ed. 2004. (Teen Ser.). (Illus.). 200p. pap. 9.99 (978-1-59182-755-9(8) , Tokyopop Kids) TOKYOPOP, Inc.

Lenhard, Elizabeth, et al. The Power of Five. 2004. (W. I. T. C. H. Ser.: Bk. 1). (Illus.). 158p. (J). (gr. 3-7). pap. 4.99 (978-0-7868-5257-4(7) , Volo) Hyperion Bks. for Children.

Lenkov, Peter. R. I. P. D. 2003. (Illus.). 96p. (J). (gr. 7 up). pap. 12.95 (978-1-56971-928-2(4)) Dark Horse Comics.

Lobdell, Scott. Note from the Underground. 2003. (Angel/Buffy the Vampire Slayer Ser.). (Illus.). 104p. (YA). (gr. 7 up). pap. 12.95 (978-1-56971-888-9(1)) Dark Horse Comics.

Luke, Eric, et al. Black October. 1999. (Ghost Ser.). 144p. (YA). (gr. 9 up). pap. 14.95 (978-1-56971-377-8(4)) Dark Horse Comics.

Lynde, Stan. Rick O'Shay, Hipshot & Me: A Memoir. Gold, Mike, ed. 2nd ed. (Illus.). 264p. reprint ed. pap. 18.95 (978-0-9626999-0-0(X) , 1402) Cottonwood Publishing, Inc.

Ma, Wing Shing. A Tale of No Name, Vol. 1. 2005. (Storm Riders Ser.). (Illus.). 300p. (YA). pap. 7.95 (978-1-58899-375-5(2)) ComicsOne Corp./Dr. Masters.

The Man in the Iron Mask. 2002. (Illus.). 80p. (YA). per. 6.95 (978-1-56254-527-7(2) , SP5272) Saddleback Educational Publishing.

The Man in the Iron Mask Study Guide. 2002. (Illus.). 48p. (YA). per. 17.95 (978-1-56254-528-4(0) , SP5280) Saddleback Educational Publishing.

Martin, Bev. War Comes to Madeline. 2001. 185p. (YA). (gr. 7-17). pap. 9.99 (978-0-88092-463-4(2) , 4632) Royal Fireworks Publishing Co.

Marz, Ron. Fear Itself. Parker, Brad, illus. 1999. (Green Lantern Ser.). 80p. (YA). 24.95 (978-1-56389-310-0(X)) DC Comics.

Masami, Kurumada. B'tx, Vol. 10. 10th rev. ed. 2006. (Illus.). 192p. pap. 9.99 (978-1-59532-380-4(5) , Tokyopop Adult) TOKYOPOP, Inc.

Mashima, Hiro. Rave Master. 2006. (Illus.). Vol. 19. 19th rev. ed. pap. 9.99 (978-1-59532-024-7(5)); Vol. 20. 20th rev. ed. pap. 9.99 (978-1-59532-025-4(3)) TOKYOPOP, Inc. (Tokyopop Kids).

Mays, Rick. Kabuki: Masks of the Noh. Mack, David, illus. 2001. 128p. (J). (gr. 4-7). pap. (978-1-58727-999-7(1)) Unapix Entertainment, Inc.

McBride, Earvin, Jr. The American Blonds. McBride, Earvin, Jr., illus. unabr. ed. 2002. (Earvin MacBride's Fun Fun Lovable Cartoons Ser.). (Illus.). 123p. (J). (gr. 7-12). pap. 4.95 (978-1-892511-01-0(0)) MacBride, E. J. Pubn., Inc.

—The Bowdery Rodeo Cowboys of Texas. McBride, Earvin, Jr., illus. 2nd unabr. ed. 2003. (Earvin MacBride's Amazing Sci-Fi & Adventure Heroes Ser.). (Illus.). 329p. (J). (gr. 7-12). pap. 4.95 (978-1-892511-07-2(X)) MacBride, E. J. Pubn., Inc.

—Earvin MacBride's Amazing Sci-Fi & Adventure Heroes, 7 vols. McBride, Earvin, Jr., illus. 2nd unabr. ed. 2003. (Illus.). (J). (gr. 7-12). pap. 25.95 (978-1-892511-05-8(3)) MacBride, E. J. Pubn., Inc.

—The Eerie Adventures of Detective Omar Mendez. McBride, Earvin, Jr., illus. 2nd unabr. ed. 2003. (Earvin MacBride's Amazing Sci-Fi & Adventure Heroes Ser.). (Illus.). 329p. (J). (gr. 7-12). pap. 5.95 (978-1-892511-08-9(8)) MacBride, E. J. Pubn., Inc.

—The Joyous Adventures of Sam & Pam. McBride, Earvin, Jr., illus. unabr. ed. 2002. (Earvin MacBride's Fun Fun Lovable Cartoons Ser.). (Illus.). 123p. (J). (gr. 7-12). pap. 3.95 (978-1-892511-03-4(7)) MacBride, E. J. Pubn., Inc.

—The Mice. McBride, Earvin, Jr., illus. unabr. ed. 2002. (Earvin MacBride's Fun Fun Lovable Cartoons Ser.). (Illus.). 123p. (J). (gr. 7-12). pap. 3.95 (978-1-892511-04-1(5)) MacBride, E. J. Pubn., Inc.

—Space - M. D. 3001. McBride, Earvin, Jr., illus. 2nd unabr. ed. 2003. (Earvin MacBride's Amazing Sci-Fi & Adventure Heroes Ser.). (Illus.). 329p. (J). (gr. 7-12). pap. 4.95 (978-1-892511-09-6(6)) MacBride, E. J. Pubn., Inc.

Mignola, Mike. Batman/Hellboy/Starman (En Español). Riera, Ernest, tr. from ENG. 2004. (SPA., Illus.). 64p. (YA). pap. 12.95 (978-1-59497-025-2(4)) Public Square Bks.

—Hellboy: Baba Yaga y Otros Relatos, 1. Abuli, Enrique Sanchez, tr. from ENG. 2004. Orig. Title: Hellboy: the Chained Coffin & Others. (SPA., Illus.). 72p. pap. 12.95 (978-1-59497-028-3(9)) Public Square Bks.

—Hellboy: Despierta al Demonio, Abuli, Enrique Sanchez, tr. from ENG. Sinclair, James, illus. 2004. Orig. Title: Hellboy: Wake the Devil. (SPA.). 144p. pap. 22.95 (978-1-59497-027-6(0)) Public Square Bks.

—Hellboy: El gusano Vencedor, Abuli, Enrique Sanchez, tr. from ENG. 2004. Orig. Title: Hellboy: the Conqueror Worm. (SPA., Illus.). 144p. pap. 25.95 (978-1-59497-029-0(7)) Public Square Bks.

—Hellboy: La Caja del Mal, Abuli, Enrique Sanchez, tr. from ENG. 2004. Orig. Title: Hellboy: Box Full of Evil. (SPA., Illus.). 64p. pap. 12.95 (978-1-59497-031-3(9)) Public Square Bks.

Mihara, Mitsukazu, creator. Doll, 6 vols., Vol. 3. rev. ed. 2005. (Illus.). 192p. pap. 9.99 (978-1-59182-888-4(0) , Tokyopop Adult) TOKYOPOP, Inc.

Milky, D. J. Treasure Chess. 2004. (Illus.). 200p. (YA). pap. 9.99 (978-1-59182-658-3(6)) TOKYOPOP, Inc.

Miller, Frank. Sin City: Alcohol, Chicas y Balas. 2005. Orig. Title: Sin City: Booze, Broads & Bullets. (SPA., Illus.). 160p. pap. 15.00 (978-1-59497-021-4(1)) Public Square Bks.

—Sin City: Valores Familiares, 2005. Orig. Title: Sin City: Family Values. (SPA., Illus.). 128p. pap. 15.00 (978-1-59497-017-7(3)) Public Square Bks.

Minsky, Terri. Mom's Best Friend & Movin' on Up, 7 vols. (Lizzie McGuire Ser.). (Illus.). 96p. Vol. 6. 2004. pap. 7.99 (978-1-59182-572-2(5)); Vol. 7. 2004. pap. 7.99 (978-1-59182-573-9(3)); Vol. 10. 2005. pap. 7.99 (978-1-59532-281-4(7)) TOKYOPOP, Inc. (Tokyopop Kids).

Minsky, Terri, creator. Lizzie McGuire: Pool Party; Picture Day, 7 vols., Vol 1. 2003. (Lizzie McGuire Ser.: Vol. 1). (Illus.). 96p. (gr. 2 up). pap. 7.99 (978-1-59182-147-2(9) , Tokyopop Kids) TOKYOPOP, Inc.

—Rumors & I've Got Rhythmic, 7 vols. , Vol. 2. 2003. (Lizzie McGuire Ser.: Vol. 2). (Illus.). 96p. (gr. 2 up). pap. 7.99 (978-1-59182-148-9(7) , Tokyopop Kids) TOKYOPOP, Inc.

Miyasaka, Kaho. Kare First Love. Watanabe, Akira, tr. Miyasaka, Kaho, illus. 2004. (Kare First Love Ser.: Vol. 1). (Illus.). 200p. (YA). pap. 9.95 (978-1-59116-394-7(3)) Viz Media.

—Kare First Love, Vol. 2. Miyasaka, Kaho, illus. 2004. (Kare First Love Ser.). (Illus.). 200p. (YA). pap. 9.95 (978-1-59116-395-4(1)) Viz Media.

—Kare First Love. (Kare First Love Ser.). (YA). Vol. 5. 2005. 200p. pap. 9.99 (978-1-59116-986-4(0)); Vol. 7. 2006. 208p. pap. 9.99 (978-1-4215-0325-7(5)) Viz Media.

Miyazaki, Hayao. Film Comic. Miyazaki, Hayao, illus. 2005. (My Neighbor Totoro Ser.: Vol. 3). 152p. (YA). pap. 9.99 (978-1-59116-699-3(3)); Vol. 4. pap. 9.99 (978-1-59116-700-6(0)) Viz Media.

—Howl's Moving Castle Film Comic, Vol. 4. 2005. (Howl's Moving Castle Film Comics Ser.). 176p. (YA). pap. 9.99 (978-1-4215-0094-2(9)) Viz Media.

—Kiki's Delivery Service Film Comics. 2006. (Kiki's Delivery Service Film Comics Ser.). (YA). Vol. 1. 144p. pap. 9.99 (978-1-59116-724-2(8)); Vol. 2. 208p. pap. 9.99 (978-1-59116-749-5(3)) Viz Media.

—My Neighbor Totoro: Film Comic. Miyazaki, Hayao, illus. 2004. (My Neighbor Totoro Ser.: Vol. 1). 152p. (YA). pap. 9.99 (978-1-59116-647-4(0)); Vol. 2. (Illus.). pap. 9.99 (978-1-59116-684-9(5)) Viz Media.

—Nausicaa of the Valley of the Wind. Miyazaki, Hayao, illus. 2nd ed. 2004. (Nausicaa of the Valley of the Wind Ser.). (YA). Vol. 6. 168p. pap. 9.95 (978-1-59116-354-1(4)); Vol. 7. 232p. pap. 9.95 (978-1-59116-355-8(2)) Viz Media.

Mizuki, Hakase. The Demon Ororon, 4 vols., Vol. 2. rev. ed. 2004. (Illus.). 208p. pap. 9.99 (978-1-59182-726-9(4) , Tokyopop Adult) TOKYOPOP, Inc.

Moore, Alan & Gray, Mick. Promethea Book 2, Vol. 2. Williams, J. H., illus. 2nd rev. ed. 2003. 176p. pap. 14.99 (978-1-56389-957-7(4)) DC Comics.

Moore, Alan & Veitch, Rick. Greyshirt: Indigo Sunset. 2003. (Illus.). 224p. pap. 19.95 (978-1-56389-909-6(4)) DC Comics.

Moore, Terry. Terry Moore's Paradise Too Bk. 2: Checking for Weirdos. 2003. 136p. pap. 14.95 (978-1-892597-21-2(7)) Abstract Studio, Inc.

Morioka, Hiroyuki. Seikai Trilogy Vol. 3: Banner of the Stars II, 3 vols. Miyakoshi, Wasoh, illus. rev. ed. 2004. 240p. pap. 9.99 (978-1-59182-859-4(7) , Tokyopop Adult) TOKYOPOP, Inc.

Mortier, R. Shamms. 3D Comic Design. 2001. (CyberRookies Ser.). (Illus.). xxi, 297p. pap. 34.95 incl. cd-rom (978-1-58450-011-7(5)) Charles River Media.

Nakazaki, Tow. Et Cetera, Vol. 4. Nakazaki, Tow, illus. rev. ed. 2005. (Illus.). 200p. pap. 9.99 (978-1-59532-133-6(0) , Tokyopop Kids) TOKYOPOP, Inc.

Nakazaki, Tow, creator. Et Cetera, 9 vols. rev. ed. 2004. (Illus.). 192p. Vol. 2. pap. 9.99 (978-1-59532-131-2(4)); Vol. 3. pap. 9.99 (978-1-59532-132-9(2)) TOKYOPOP, Inc. (Tokyopop Kids).

Nakazaki, Tow, illus. & creator. Et Cetera, Vol. 5. Nakazaki, Tow, creator. 5th rev. ed. 2005. 208p. pap. 9.99 (978-1-59532-134-3(9) , Tokyopop Kids) TOKYOPOP, Inc.

Nishiyama, Yukio. Dragon Voice, Vol. 3. Nishiyama, Yukio, illus. rev. ed. 2005. (Illus.). 208p. pap. 9.99 (978-1-59532-121-3(7) , Tokyopop Adult) TOKYOPOP, Inc.

Nishiyama, Yukio, creator. Dragon Voice. 2004. (Teen Ser.). (Illus.). Vol. 1. 208p. pap. 9.99 (978-1-59532-119-0(5)); Vol. 2. 192p. pap. 9.99 (978-1-59532-120-6(9)) TOKYOPOP, Inc. (Tokyopop Adult).

O'Brien, Anne Sibley. The Legend of Hong Kil Dong, the Robin Hood of Korea. O'Brien, Anne Sibley, illus. 2006. (Illus.). 48p. (J). 14.95 (978-1-58089-302-2(3)) Charlesbridge Publishing, Inc.

Ogawa, Yayoi, creator. Tramps Like Us, 7 vols., Vol. 3. rev. ed. 2004. (Illus.). 192p. pap. 9.99 (978-1-59532-141-1(1) , Tokyopop Adult) TOKYOPOP, Inc.

Okum, David. Draw super Manga. 2005. (Illus.). 64p. pap. 6.99 (978-1-58180-732-5(5) , 1245828, Impact) F & W Pubns., Inc.

—Draw super manga Monsters. 2005. (Illus.). 64p. pap. 6.99 (978-1-58180-733-2(3) , 1245829, Impact) F & W Pubns., Inc.

Ozaki, Kaori. Immortal Rain, 3 vols., Vol. 1. Wert, Michael, tr. from JPN. 2004. (Graphic Novel-Manga Ser.). (Illus.). 192p. pap. 9.99 (978-1-59182-722-1(1) , Tokyopop Adult) TOKYOPOP, Inc.

—Immortal Rain, 3 vols., Vol. 2. rev. ed. 2004. (Graphic Novel-Manga Ser.). (Illus.). 192p. pap. 9.99 (978-1-59182-723-8(X) , Tokyopop Adult) TOKYOPOP, Inc.

Ozaki, Kaori, creator. Immortal Rain. rev. ed. (Graphic Novel-Manga Ser.). (Illus.). Vol. 3. 2004. 208p. pap. 9.99 (978-1-59182-724-5(8)); Vol. 4. 2005. 200p. pap. 9.99 (978-1-59182-990-4(9)) TOKYOPOP, Inc. (Tokyopop Adult).

Ozaki, Kaori, illus. & creator. Immortal Rain, Vol. 5. Ozaki, Kaori, creator. rev. ed. 2005. 216p. pap. 9.99 (978-1-59182-991-1(7) , Tokyopop Adult) TOKYOPOP, Inc.

Parker, Jeff. Interman. 2003. (gr. 7-12). lib. bdg. 30.35 (978-0-613-66783-8(2)) Tandem Library Bks.

Perry, Fred. Gold Digger Pocket Manga, No. 9. 2003. 128p. (YA). pap. 12.95 (978-0-9663588-2-7(1)) Antarctic Pr., Inc.

Peyo. Los Pitufos Vol. 1: La Flauta de los Pitufos. Díaz, Lorenzo, tr. from FRE. 2004. Orig. Title: Johan et Pirlouit: la Flute a Six Schtroumpfs. (SPA., Illus.). 66p. 14.95 (978-1-59497-050-4(5)) Public Square Bks.

Pfarrer, Chuck, et al. Virus. 2nd ed. 1998. 144p. (YA). (gr. 9 up). pap. 16.95 (978-1-56971-317-4(0)) Dark Horse Comics.

Phillips, Gary. Midnight Mover. 2004. (Illus.). 120p. pap. 11.95 (978-1-929998-77-7(5)) Oni Pr., Inc.

Pilkey, Dav. The All New Captain Underpants Extra-Crunchy Book O' Fun 2. 2002. (Captain Underpants Ser.). (gr. 3-6). lib. bdg. 11.80 (978-0-613-49472-4(5)) Tandem Library Bks.

—The Captain Underpants Set: The Adventures of Captain Underpants; Captain Underpants & the Attack of the Talking Toilets; Captain Underpants & the Invasion of the Incredibly Naughty Cafeteria Ladies from Outer Space; Captain Underpants & the Perilous Plot of Professor Poopypants, 4 vols. 2000. (Captain Underpants Ser.: Nos. 1-4). (J). (gr. 2-5). pap. 19.95 (978-0-439-22700-1(3) , Blue Sky Pr., The) Scholastic, Inc.

Price, Pamela S. Cool Comics. 2007. (Illus.). 32p. 22.78 (978-1-59679-769-7(X)) ABDO Publishing Co.

Quinn, David, et al. Mindhunter. 2001. (Aliens vs Predator Ser.). (Illus.). 96p. pap. 12.95 (978-1-56971-615-1(3)) Dark Horse Comics.

Quino. Mafalda & Friends. 2004. (SPA., Illus.). 96p. (978-950-515-759-4(2)); (978-950-515-760-0(6)) De La Flor.

Ra, In-Soo. King of Hell, 8 vols., Vol. 7. Jae-Hwan, Kim, illus. 7th rev. ed. 2004. pap. 9.99 (978-1-59182-867-9(8) , Tokyopop Adult) TOKYOPOP, Inc.

Raicht, Mike. Incredible Digest, Vol. 1. 2005. (Incredible Hulk Ser.: Vol. 1). (Illus.). 96p. pap. 5.99 (978-0-7851-1616-5(8)) Marvel Enterprises, Inc.

Raiku, Makoto. Zatch Bell! 2006. (Zatch Bell Ser.). (YA). Vol. 5. 200p. pap. 9.99 (978-1-4215-0283-0(6)); Vol. 6. 184p. pap. 9.99 (978-1-4215-0387-5(5)) Viz Media.

Raiku, Makoto, creator. Zatch Bell! 2005. 24.98 (978-1-4215-0215-1(1)) Viz Media.

Raymond, N. T. Spider-Man's New Suit. 2007. (Spider-Man Ser.: No. 3). 24p. (J). pap. 3.99 (978-0-06-083718-1(7) , Harper Entertainment) HarperCollins Pubs.

Raymond, N. T., et al, illus. I Am Venom. 2007. (Spider-Man Ser.: No. 3). 24p. (J). pap. 3.99 (978-0-06-083719-8(5) , Harper Entertainment) HarperCollins Pubs.

Resnikoff, Irene, et al. OG Returns: OG's Further Adventures in Prayerbook Hebrew. Goldstien, Jessica, ed. Jokelson, Paul, illus. 1998. (OG the Terrible Ser.: Vol. 2). (HEB.). 24p. (J). (gr. 1-6). pap. 4.50 (978-0-939144-27-3(1)) EKS Publishing Co.

Ribeiro, Nelson & Gorelick, Victor. Archie in Jet Ski Scandal. 2007. (Illus.). 80p. (J). 24.21 (978-1-59961-259-1(3)) Spotlight.

—Archie in Snooze Button. 2007. (Illus.). 80p. (J). 24.21 (978-1-59961-261-4(5)) Spotlight.

—Betty & Veronica in Color Blind. 2007. (Illus.). 80p. (J). 24.21 (978-1-59961-265-2(8)) Spotlight.

C D

—Jughead with Archie in a Day to Remember. 2007. (Illus.). 80p. (J). 24.21 (978-1-59961-272-0(0)) Spotlight.

—Jughead with Archie in Family Photos. 2007. (Illus.). 80p. (J). 24.21 (978-1-59961-273-7(9)) Spotlight.

—Jughead with Archie in Fool Proof. 2007. (Illus.). 80p. (J). 24.21 (978-1-59961-274-4(7)) Spotlight.

—Jughead with Archie in Pup-Ularity Contest. 2007. (Illus.). 80p. (J). 24.21 (978-1-59961-276-8(3)) Spotlight.

—Jughead with Archie in Wish Fulfillment. 2007. (Illus.). 80p. (J). 24.21 (978-1-59961-277-5(1)) Spotlight.

—Laugh with Fore! 2007. (Illus.). 80p. (J). 24.21 (978-1-59961-279-9(8)) Spotlight.

Rimmer, Ian. Catch of the Day. Hansen, Jimmy, illus. 2003. 48p. pap. 8.95 (978-1-84023-496-1(2)) Titan Bks. Ltd. GBR. *Dist:* Perseus Distribution.

Robinson, James, et al. The Terminator: The Endgame. 1999. (Illus.). 80p. (YA). (gr. 9 up). pap. 9.95 (978-1-56971-373-0(1)) Dark Horse Comics.

Rock, Brian. Don't Play with Your Food!, Moerner, John, illus. 2005. 32p. (J). 14.99 (978-0-9754411-0-7(8)) First Light Publishing.

Royston, Angela. Paper: Let's Look at a Comic Book. 2005. (Heinemann Read & Learn Ser.). (Illus.). 24p. (J). (978-1-4034-7671-5(3)); pap. (978-1-4034-7680-7(2)) Heinemann Library.

—Paper: Let's Look at a Comic Book. 2005. (J). (978-1-4109-1818-5(1)); pap. (978-1-4109-1827-7(0)) Steck-Vaughn.

Rucka, Greg. Introspect. Austen, Chuck, illus. 2002. (Elektra Ser.: Vol. 1). 160p. 16.99 (978-0-7851-0973-0(0)) Marvel Enterprises, Inc.

Saito, Takao. Golgo 13. 2006. (Golgo 13 Ser.). 208p. (YA). pap. 9.99 (978-1-4215-0382-0(4)) Viz Media.

Satrapi, Marjane. Persépolis (En Español), Agut, Albert, tr. from FRE. 2004. (SPA., Illus.). 160p. Vol. 1. pap. 22.95 (978-1-59497-035-1(1)); Vol. 2. pap. 22.95 (978-1-59497-036-8(X)); Vol. 3. pap. 22.95 (978-1-59497-037-5(8)) Public Square Bks.

Saudelli, Franco. Otto Porfiri: Drama on the Cliff. 2001. 88p. (gr. 11 up). pap. 9.95 (978-1-56971-626-7(9)) Dark Horse Comics.

Schneider, Maxwell. Do You Hear Me? Laughs for the Hard of Hearing by the Hard of Hearing, 1. 2003. (Illus.). 138p. per. 8.95 (978-0-9727520-0-8(5) , B555) Harris Communications, Inc.

Schulz, Charles M. Caps Are for Losers, Marcie! 1999. (Illus.). 32p. (J). pap. 3.50 (978-0-694-01053-0(7)) HarperCollins Pubs.

—It's Back to School, Charlie Brown! 2003. (Illus.). 160p. pap. 11.95 (978-0-345-45283-2(6) , Ballantine Bks.) Random House Publishing Group.

—Peppermint Patty Dog School Studt. Schulz, Charles M., illus. 2000. (Peanuts Ser.). (Illus.). 20p. (J). (ps-3). pap. 3.75 (978-0-694-00975-6(X) , Harper Festival) HarperCollins Pubs.

Sengupta, Anita, tr. from JPN. Magic Knight Rayearth II, 3 vols., Vol. 2. rev. ed. 2004. (Illus.). 221p. pap. 9.99 (978-1-59182-267-7(X) , Tokyopop Kids) TOKYOPOP, Inc.

Shigeno, Shuichi. Initial-D, Vol. 3. rev. ed. 2002. (Illus.). 224p. pap. 9.99 (978-1-59182-036-9(7) , Tokyopop Adult) TOKYOPOP, Inc.

Shimizu, Aki. Suikoden III, Vol. 8. 8th rev. ed. 2005. (Illus.). (YA). pap. 9.99 (978-1-59182-433-6(8) , Tokyopop Adult) TOKYOPOP, Inc.

—Suikoden III: Successor of Fate, 4 vols., Vol. 2. rev. ed. 2004. (Illus.). 200p. (YA). pap. 9.99 (978-1-59182-766-5(3) , Tokyopop Adult) TOKYOPOP, Inc.

—Suikoden III: Successor of Fate, 4 vols., Vol. 4. Coffman, Patrick, tr. from JPN. rev. ed. 2004. (Illus.). 192p. (YA). pap. 9.99 (978-1-59182 768 9(X) , Tokyopop Adult) TOKYOPOP, Inc.

—Suikoden III: The Successor of Fate, 4 vols., Vol. 1. 2004. (Illus.). 200p. (YA). pap. 9.99 (978-1-59182-765-8(5) , Tokyopop Adult) TOKYOPOP, Inc.

Shimizu, Aki, creator. Suikoden III: The Successor of Fate, 4 vols., Vol. 3. rev. ed. 2004. (Illus.). 180p. (YA). pap. 9.99 (978-1-59182-767-2(1) , Tokyopop Adult) TOKYOPOP, Inc.

Shimizu, Aki, ed. Suikoden III: The Successor of Fate, Vol. 5. rev. ed. 2005. (Illus.). 176p. (YA). pap. 9.99 (978-1-59532-435-1(6) , Tokyopop Adult) TOKYOPOP, Inc.

Shin, Chi Sup. The Three Little Turtles & the Big Bad Pelican. 2003. (J). pap. 15.99 (978-1-4134-3760-7(5)) Borders Personal Publishing.

Shinohara, Chie. Red River, Vol. 11. 2006. (Red River Ser.). 208p. (YA). pap. 9.99 (978-1-4215-0327-1(1)) Viz Media.

—Red River, Vol. 12. Shinohara, Chie, illus. 2006. (Red River Ser.). 208p. (YA). pap. 9.99 (978-1-4215-0554-1(1)) Viz Media.

Shiozu, Shuri. Eerie Queerie!, 4 vols., Vol. 1. 2004. (Illus.). 192p. pap. 9.99 (978-1-59182-719-1(1) , Tokyopop Adult) TOKYOPOP, Inc.

—Eerie Queerie!, 3, Vol. 2. Yamaguchi, Heidi, tr. from JPN. rev. ed. 2004. (Illus.). 192p. pap. 9.99 (978-1-59182-720-7(5) , Tokyopop Adult) TOKYOPOP, Inc.

—Eerie Queerie!, 3 , Vol. 3. rev. ed. 2004. (Illus.). 192p. pap. 9.99 (978-1-59182-721-4(3) , Tokyopop Adult) TOKYOPOP, Inc.

Shipman, Gary, illus. Pakkins' Land: Tavitah, 4. 2003. (Pakkins' Land: 4). 128p. pap. 16.95 (978-0-9700241-4-5(2)) Pakkins Presents.

Siegel, Jerry. Archives. Shuster, Joe, illus. rev. ed. 2000. (Superman Archives Ser.: Vol. 5). 224p. 49.95 (978-1-56389-602-6(8)) DC Comics.

Silke, Jim. Bettie Page: Queen of the Nile. 2000. (Illus.). 96p. (gr. 11 up). pap. 12.95 (978-1-56971-473-7(8)) Dark Horse Comics.

Soda, Masahito. Firefighter, Vol. 12. Soda, Masahito, illus. 2005. (Firefighter Ser.). 200p. (YA). pap. 9.95 (978-1-59116-980-2(1)) Viz Media.

Spilsbury, Richard. Comics & Graphic Novels. 2006. (Art off the Wall Ser.). (Illus.). 56p. (978-1-4034-8286-0(1)) Heinemann Library.

Stabenfeldt, prod. Starshine Legacy 2: Comic Book 0706. 2007. (YA). pap. ***978-1-933343-56-3(7)*** Stabenfeldt Inc.

Stephens, Jay. Atomic City Tales Vol. 2: Doc Phantom. 2003. (Illus.). 80p. (gr. 12 up). pap. 12.95 (978-1-929998-27-2(9)) Oni Pr., Inc.

Steven, Hillenburg. Who's Hungry?, Vol. 11. 2006. (Cine-Manga Ser.). (Illus.). pap. 7.99 (978-1-59532-889-2(0) , Tokyopop Kids) TOKYOPOP, Inc.

Straczynski, J. Michael. Until the Stars Turn Cold, Vol. 3. Romita, John, Jr., illus. 2002. 144p. (YA). (gr. 7). 12.99 (978-0-7851-1075-0(5)) Marvel Enterprises, Inc.

Sugisaki, Yukiru. The Candidate for Goddess, 5 vols. 2004. (Illus.). 192p. Vol. 1. pap. 9.99 (978-1-59182-747-4(7)); Vol. 2. pap. 9.99 (978-1-59182-748-1(5)); Vol. 3. pap. 9.99 (978-1-59182-749-8(3)) TOKYOPOP, Inc. (Tokyopop Adult).

Sugisaki, Yukiru, creator. The Candidate for Goddess, 5 vols., Vol. 4. rev. ed. 2004. (Illus.). 192p. pap. 9.99 (978-1-59182-750-4(7) , Tokyopop Adult) TOKYOPOP, Inc.

—Candidate for Goddess, 5 vols., Vol. 5. rev. ed. 2004. (Illus.). 192p. pap. 9.99 (978-1-59182-751-1(5) , Tokyopop Adult) TOKYOPOP, Inc.

Takada, Yuzo. Curse of the Gesu. 2nd ed. 2003. (3 X 3 Eyes Ser.). (Illus.). 152p. (YA). (gr. 12 up). pap. 14.95 (978-1-56971-931-2(4)) Dark Horse Comics.

Takahashi, Kazuki. Yu-Gi-Oh! Duelist!, Vol. 1. Takahashi, Kazuki, illus. 2005. (Yu-Gi-Oh! Ser.). (Illus.). 200p. (YA). pap. 7.95 (978-1-59116-614-6(4)) Viz Media.

—Yu-Gi-Oh! Duelist. 2006. (Yu-Gi-Oh! Duelist Ser.). 208p. (YA). Vol. 13. pap. 7.95 (978-1-4215-0277-9(1)); Vol. 14. pap. 7.95 (978-1-4215-0339-4(5)) Viz Media.

Takahashi, Rumiko. Inu-Yasha, Vol. 23. Takahashi, Rumiko, illus. 2005. (Inuyasha Ser.). 192p. (YA). pap. 8.95 (978-1-4215-0024-9(8)) Viz Media.

—Inu Yasha, Vol. 25. 2006. (Inuyasha Ser.). 208p. (YA). pap. 8.95 (978-1-4215-0383-7(2)) Viz Media.

—Inu-Yasha: Anime/Manga Box Set. Takahashi, Rumiko, illus. 2003. (Inuyasha Ser.). 200p. (YA). pap. 39.98 (978-1-59116-235-3(1) , Viz Comics) Viz Media.

—Inu Yasha Animanga, Vol. 14. 2006. (Inuyasha Ani-Manga Ser.). 208p. (YA). pap. 11.99 (978-1-4215-0384-4(0)) Viz Media.

—Mermaid Saga. Takahashi, Rumiko, illus. 2004. (Mermaid Saga Ser.). (Illus.). (YA). 3. 176p. pap. 9.99 (978-1-59116-483-8(4)); Vol. 2. 2nd ed. 208p. pap. 9.99 (978-1-59116-484-5(2)); Vol. 4. 2nd ed. 192p. pap. 9.99 (978-1-59116-482-1(6)) Viz Media.

Takanashi, Mitsuba. Crimson Hero, Vol. 2. 2006. (Crimson Hero Ser.). 208p. (YA). pap. 8.99 (978-1-4215-0396-7(4)) Viz Media.

Takashima, Kazusa, illus. & creator. Wild Rock: Yaoi, 1. Takashima, Kazusa, creator. 2006. 184p. (YA). pap. 9.99 (978-1-59816-101-4(6) , Tokyopop Adult) TOKYOPOP, Inc.

Takemoto, Novala. Kamikaze Girls Novel, Vol. 1. 2006. (Kamikaza Girls Novel Ser.). 208p. (YA). 17.99 (978-1-4215-0269-4(0)) Viz Media.

Takeuchi, Naoko. Sailor Moon Stars, Vol. 2. 2nd rev. ed. 2001. (Sailor Moon Stars Ser.: Vol. 2). (Illus.). 176p. (gr. 7-12). pap. 9.99 (978-1-892213-70-9(2)) TOKYOPOP, Inc.

Tamura, Yumi. Basara, Vol. 14. Tamura, Yumi, illus. 2005. (Basara Ser.). 200p. (YA). pap. 9.99 (978-1-4215-0017-1(5)) Viz Media.

—Basara. 2006. (Basara Ser.). 208p. (YA). Vol. 16. pap. 9.99 (978-1-4215-0261-8(5)); Vol. 17. pap. 9.99 (978-1-4215-0391-2(3)) Viz Media.

Tanabe, Yellow. Kekkaishi. 2006. (Kekkaishi Ser.). (Illus.). 208p. (YA). Vol. 4. pap. 9.99 (978-1-4215-0253-3(4)); Vol. 5. pap. 9.99 (978-1-4215-0486-5(3)) Viz Media.

Taniguchi, Tomoko. Just a Girl, 2 bks., Bk. 1. Pannone, Frank, ed. Hiroe, Ikoi, tr. from JPN. Taniguchi, Tomoko, illus. 2004. (Illus.). 184p. (YA). pap. 9.99 (978-1-58664-911-1(6) , CMX 64801G, CPM Manga) Central Park Media Corp.

—Just a Girl 2, 2 vols., Vol. 2. Pannone, Frank, ed. Hiroe, Ikoi, tr. from JPN. Taniguchi, Tomoko, illus. 2004. (Illus.). 168p. pap. 9.99 (978-1-58664-912-8(4) , CMX 64802G, CPM Manga) Central Park Media Corp.

Teenage Mutant Ninja Turtles: Art-O-Bibliography. 2002. (Illus.). 296p. 39.95 (978-1-882931-85-9(8)) Heavy Metal Magazine.

Teitelbaum, Michael. Speed Trap. 2003. (gr. 3-6). lib. bdg. 13.00 (978-0-613-72713-6(4)) Tandem Library Bks.

Teitelbaum, Michael & Bender, Howard. Making Comic Books. 2006. (Boys Rock! Ser.). (Illus.). 32p. (J). (gr. 1-5). 24.21 (978-1-59296-733-9(7)) Child's World, Inc.

Teitelbaum, Michael & Dorling Kindersley Publishing Staff. The Story of the Incredible Hulk. 2003. (DK Readers Ser.). (Illus.). 48p. (J). 12.99 (978-0-7894-9544-0(9)); Vol. 4. pap. 3.99 (978-0-7894-9262-3(8)) Dorling Kindersley Publishing, Inc.

Tezuka, Osamu. Metropolis. 2003. (Illus.). 169p. (YA). (gr. 8 up). pap. 13.95 (978-1-56971-864-3(4)) Dark Horse Comics.

—A Tale of the Future. Tezuka, Osamu, illus. 2nd ed. 2004. (Phoenix Ser.). 200p. (YA). pap. 15.95 (978-1-59116-608-5(X)) Viz Media.

Thomas, Roy, et al. Essential Avengers, Vol. 4. 2004. (Avengers Ser.). (Illus.). 640p. 16.99 (978-0-7851-1485-7(8)) Marvel Enterprises, Inc.

Thompson, Jill. Scary Godmother: Ghoul's Out for Summer. 2002. (Illus.). 128p. pap. 14.95 (978-1-57989-052-0(0)) Sirius Entertainment, Inc.

Thorsland, Dan, et al. The Kalarba Adventures. Hughes, Bill et al, illus. (Star Wars Ser.). 200p. (J). (gr. 3 up). pap. 17.95 (978-1-56971-064-7(3)) Dark Horse Comics.

Tokyopop Staff. Passion Fruit: Sweat & Honey, 3 vols., Vol. 1. Tokyopop Staff, illus. ltd. ed. 2005. (Illus.). 208p. pap. 19.99 (978-1-59182-796-2(5)) TOKYOPOP, Inc.

Tokyopop Staff, creator. Contents under Pressure, Vol. 3. 2005. (Lilo & Stitch Ser.). (Illus.). 89p. (gr. 3-7). pap., pap. 7.99 (978-1-59532-069-8(5) , Tokyopop Kids) TOKYOPOP, Inc.

—Pop Displays - 2004. 2004. (Illus.). Vol. 10. pap. 319.68 (978-1-59532-273-9(6)); Vol. 16. pap. 255.68 (978-1-59532-477-1(1)) TOKYOPOP, Inc. (Tokyopop Adult).

Tokyopop Staff, ed. Pop Displays - 2004, Vol. 19. 2004. (Illus.). pap. 319.68 (978-1-59532-593-8(X) , Tokyopop Adult) TOKYOPOP, Inc.

Tomita, Sukehiro. Young Love, Vol. 7. Yazawa, Nao, illus. 2004. (Wedding Peach Ser.). 200p. (YA). pap. 9.95 (978-1-59116-450-0(8)) Viz Media.

Toriyama, Akira. Dr. Slump, Vol. 4. Toriyama, Akira, illus. 2005. (Dr. Slump Ser.). 200p. (YA). pap. 7.99 (978-1-4215-0165-9(1)) Viz Media.

—Dragon Ball 10. 2003. (gr. 3-6). lib. bdg. 16.40 (978-0-613-67401-0(4)) Tandem Library Bks.

—Dragon Ball 11. 2003. (gr. 3-6). lib. bdg. 16.40 (978-0-613-67400-3(6)) Tandem Library Bks.

—Dragon Ball Z, Vol. 22. Toriyama, Akira, illus. 2005. (Dragon Ball Z Ser.). 192p. (YA). pap. 7.95 (978-1-4215-0051-5(5)) Viz Media.

—Dragon Ball Z. 2006. (Dragon Ball Z Ser.). 208p. (YA). Vol. 24. pap. 7.95 (978-1-4215-0273-1(9)); Vol. 25. pap. 7.95 (978-1-4215-0404-9(9)) Viz Media.

Torres, J. Alison Dare, Little Miss Adventures Vol. 1: Is That a Dare? 2002. (Illus.). 96p. pap. 8.95 (978-1-929998-20-3(1)) Oni Pr., Inc.

Trillo, Carlos. The Big Hoax. 2001. 128p. (gr. 11 up). pap. 10.95 (978-1-56971-629-8(3)) Dark Horse Comics.

Tsukirino, Yumi. Almond's Adventure Club, Vol. 1, Pt. 2. Tsukirino, Yumi, illus. 2000. (Magical Pokemon Journey Ser.: No. 1, pt. 2). (Illus.). 40p. (YA). (ps up). pap. 4.95 (978-1-56931-481-4(0)) Viz Media.

—Eevee the Genius. Tsukirino, Yumi, illus. 2000. (Magical Pokemon Journey Ser.: No. 2, pt. 2). (Illus.). 40p. (YA). (ps up). pap. 4.95 (978-1-56931-482-1(9)) Viz Media.

—Gold & Silver, Vol. 1. Tsukirino, Yumi, illus. 2001. (Magical Pokemon Journey Ser.: Nos. 1-4). (Illus.). 168p. (YA). (gr. k-3). pap. 13.95 (978-1-56931-506-4(X)) Viz Media.

—Pikachu's Hot Springs, Pt. 2. Tsukirino, Yumi, illus. 2000. (Magical Pokemon Journey : No. 4, pt. 2). (Illus.). 40p. (YA). (ps up). pap. 4.95 (978-1-56931-484-5(5)) Viz Media.

Turner, Ginger & Shimpi, Shekhar. Gold Mine! The California Gold Rush Story. 2004. (Illus.). 44p. (J). pap. 15.95 (978-0-9742502-3-6(6)) Gossamer Bks., LLC.

Uderzo, Albert. Asterix & Son. Bell, Anthea & Hockbridge, Derek, trs. from FRE. 2002. (Asterix Ser.). (Illus.). 48p. pap. 9.95 (978-0-7528-4775-7(9)) Orion Bks. Ltd. GBR. *Dist:* Sterling Publishing Co., Inc.

Uderzo, Albert & Goscinny, René. Asterix & Obelix All at Sea. 2002. (Asterix Ser.). (Illus.). 48p. pap. 9.95 (978-0-7528-4778-8(3)) Orion Bks. Ltd. GBR. *Dist:* Sterling Publishing Co., Inc.

—Asterix & Son. 2007. (Illus.). 48p. ***978-0-7528-4714-6(7)*** Orion Media.

Uderzo, Albert & Goscinny, René. Asterix & the Secret Weapon. 2002. (Asterix Ser.). (Illus.). 48p. pap. 9.95 (978-0-7528-4777-1(5)) Orion Bks. Ltd. GBR. *Dist:* Sterling Publishing Co., Inc.

Asterix & the Secret Weapon. 2002. (Illus.). 48p. (978-0-7528-4716-0(3)) Orion Media.

Ueda, Miwa. Peach Girl, Vol. 1. 2004. (Teen Ser.). (Illus.). pap. 9.99 (978-1-59532-171-8(3) , Tokyopop Kids) TOKYOPOP, Inc.

—Peach Girl, Vol. 2. Papia, Dan, tr. Ueda, Miwa, illus. rev. ed. 2004. (Illus.). 192p. pap. 9.99 (978-1-59532-172-5(1) , Tokyopop Kids) TOKYOPOP, Inc.

—Peach Girl, Vol. 3. Ueda, Miwa, illus. rev. ed. 2005. (Illus.). 192p. pap. 9.99 (978-1-59532-173-2(X) , Tokyopop Kids) TOKYOPOP, Inc.

—Peach Girl Vol. 11: Change of Heart. Ueda, Miwa, illus. 2004. (YA). pap. 9.99 (978-1-59182-500-5(8)) TOKYOPOP, Inc.

Ueda, Miwa, creator. Peach Vol. 1: Miwa Ueda Illustrations. 2004. (Illus.). 92p. pap. 29.99 (978-1-59182-042-0(1) , Tokyopop Adult) TOKYOPOP, Inc.

Urasawa, Naoki. Naoki Urasawa's Monster. 2006. (Naoki Urasawa's Monster Ser.). 208p. (YA). pap. 9.99 (978-1-4215-0255-7(0)); Vol. 4. pap. 9.99 (978-1-4215-0385-1(9)) Viz Media.

Usual Gang of Idiots Staff & Hahn, Phil. The Mad Monster Book of Horrifying Cliches. Coker, Paul, illus. 2002. 96p. 9.95 (978-1-56389-884-6(5)) DC Comics.

Valverde, Mikel. El Botin de los Gangsters (The Gangsters' Loot) Valverde, Mikel, illus. 2001. (Comics Ser.: No. 7). (SPA., Illus.). 30p. (J). 10.95 (978-84-348-8055-9(5)) SM Ediciones ESP. *Dist:* AIMS International Bks., Inc.

Van Hamme, Jean. Thorgal Vol. 4: La Galera Negra. Rosinski, Grzegorz, illus. 2004. Orig. Title: Thorgal : la Galere Negra. (SPA.). 48p. pap. 16.95 (978-1-59497-009-2(2)) Public Square Bks.

Vin, Lee, creator. One, 11 vols., Vol. 5. rev. ed. 2004. (Teen Ser.). (Illus.). 192p. pap. 9.99 (978-1-59182-756-6(6) , Tokyopop Kids) TOKYOPOP, Inc.

Waid, Mark. Fantastic Four, Vol. 1. Wieringo, Mike, illus. 2004. (Fantastic Four Ser.). 368p. (YA). 29.99 (978-0-7851-1486-4(6)) Marvel Enterprises, Inc.

Watase, Yu. Imadoki: Nowadays. Watase, Yu, illus. 2004. (Imadoki Ser.). (Illus.). 200p. (YA). Vol. 2. pap. 9.95 (978-1-59116-469-2(9)); Vol. 4. pap. 9.95 (978-1-59116-618-4(7)) Viz Media.

—Nowadays, Vol. 3. Watase, Yu, illus. 2004. (Imadoki Ser.). 200p. (YA). pap. 9.95 (978-1-59116-504-0(0)) Viz Media.

Watase, Yuu. Ceres, Vol. 14. 2006. (Ceres, Celestial Legend Ser.). 208p. (YA). pap. 9.95 (978-1-4215-0263-2(1)) Viz Media.

—Friend, Vol. 8. Watase, Yuu, illus. 2nd ed. 2005. (Fushigi Yugi Ser.). (Illus.). 200p. (YA). pap. 9.95 (978-1-59116-087-8(1)) Viz Media.

—Nowadays. Watase, Yuu, illus. 2005. (Imadoki Ser.: No. 5). 200p. (YA). pap. 9.95 (978-1-59116-619-1(5)) Viz Media.

Watsuki, Nobuhiro. Rurouni Kenshin. Watsuki, Nobuhiro, illus. (Rurouni Kenshin Ser.). (Illus.). (YA). 9. 2004. 200p. pap. 7.95 (978-1-59116-669-6(1)); Vol. 6. 2004. 200p. pap. 7.95 (978-1-59116-356-5(0)); Vol. 7. 2004. 200p. pap. 7.95 (978-1-59116-357-2(9)); Vol. 10. 2005. 192p. pap. 7.95 (978-1-59116-703-7(5)) Viz Media.

—Rurouni Kenshin: A Beautiful Night, Vol. 13. Watsuki, Nobuhiro, illus. 2005. (Rurouni Kenshin Ser.). (Illus.). 192p. (YA). pap. 7.95 (978-1-59116-713-6(2)) Viz Media.

Watts, Claire & Nicholson, Robert. Spine-Tingling Tales. 2000. (Info Adventure Ser.). (Illus.). 32p. (J). (gr. 3-6). pap. 3.95 (978-1-58728-102-0(3) , Two Can Publishing) T&N Children's Publishing.

Weinstein, Lauren R. Girl Stories. 2006. (Illus.). 240p. (YA). pap. 16.95 (978-0-8050-7863-3(0)) Holt, Henry & Co.

Weissman, Steven. The Kid Firechief. 2004. (Illus.). 96p. pap. 12.95 (978-1-56097-596-0(2)) Fantagraphics Bks.

—White Flower Day. 2003. (Illus.). 112p. pap. 14.95 (978-1-56097-514-4(8)) Fantagraphics Bks.

Which Pet Measures Up? 2003. (J). per. (978-1-932524-02-4(9)) Region IV Education Service Ctr.

Wilson, Bob. Stanley Bagshaw & the Short-Sighted Football Trainer. 2006. (Stanley Bagshaw Ser.). (Illus.). 32p. (J). pap. 6.95 (978-1-903015-26-1(X)) Barn Owl Bks, London GBR. *Dist:* Independent Pubs. Group.

Wizards of the Coast Staff. Duel Masters, Vol. 4. 2005. (Illus.). 96p. (J). pap. 7.99 (978-1-59532-674-4(X) , Tokyopop Kids) TOKYOPOP, Inc.

Wolfman, Marv & McKenzie, Roger. Tomb of Dracula. 2004. (Marvel Heroes Ser.: Vol. 2). (Illus.). 592p. pap. 16.99 (978-0-7851-1461-1(0)) Marvel Enterprises, Inc.

Wong, Tony. Weapons of the Gods, Vol. 6. 2003. (Illus.). 120p. (YA). (gr. 8 up). pap. 13.95 (978-1-58899-206-2(3)) ComicsOne Corp./Dr. Masters.

Wookie World. 2003. (Star Wars Ser.: Vol. 6). (Illus.). 360p. pap. 29.95 (978-1-56971-907-7(1)) Dark Horse Comics.

Yagi, Norihiro. Claymore, Vol. 1. 2006. (Claymore Ser.). (Illus.). 208p. (YA). pap. 7.99 (978-1-4215-0618-0(1)) Viz Media.

Yamada, Shutaro. Read or Die, Vol. 2. Kurata, Hideyuki, illus. 2006. (Read or Die Ser.). 208p. (YA). pap. 9.99 (978-1-4215-0257-1(7)) Viz Media.

—Read or Die Vol. 1: R.O.D. Kurata, Hideyuki, illus. 2006. (Ranma 1/2 Ser.). 208p. (YA). pap. 9.99 (978-1-4215-0248-9(8)) Viz Media.

Yang, Gene Luen. American Born Chinese. Pien, Lark, illus. rev. ed. 2006. 240p. (J). pap. 17.95 (978-1-59643-152-2(0) , First Second Bks.) Roaring Brook Pr.

—American Born Chinese, Collector's Edition. rev. ed. 2006. 240p. (J). 29.95 (978-1-59643-208-6(X) , First Second Bks.) Roaring Brook Pr.

Yoshida, Akimi. Banana Fish, Vol. 10. Yoshida, Akimi, illus. 2005. (Banana Fish Ser.). (Illus.). 192p. (YA). pap. 9.99 (978-1-4215-0048-5(5)) Viz Media.

—Banana Fish. (Banana Fish Ser.). Vol. 11. 2005. 186p. pap. 9.99 (978-1-4215-0134-5(1)); Vol. 12. 2006. 208p. (YA). pap. 9.99 (978-1-4215-0260-1(7)); Vol. 13. 2006. 208p. (YA). pap. 9.99 (978-1-4215-0390-5(5)) Viz Media.

Yoshimoto, Ray, tr. from JPN. The One I Love: Watashi No Sukinahito. 2004. (Teen Ser.). (Illus.). 128p. pap. 9.99 (978-1-59182-764-1(7) , Tokyopop Adult) TOKYOPOP, Inc.

Yoshimoto, Roy Kenichi, tr. from JPN. Change of Heart, 10 vols., Vol. 10. rev. ed. 2004. (Illus.). 192p. pap. 9.99 (978-1-59182-499-2(0) , Tokyopop Adult) TOKYOPOP, Inc.

Yoshizumi, Wataru. Ultra Maniac, Vol. 2. Yoshizumi, Wataru, illus. 2005. (Ultra Maniac Ser.). 184p. (YA). pap. 8.99 (978-1-59116-974-1(7)) Viz Media.

Yudetamago. The Kinnikuman Legancy, Vol. 8. 2005. (Ultimate Muscle Ser.). 224p. (YA). pap. 7.95 (978-1-59116-997-0(6)) Viz Media.

Yukimura, Makoto. Planetes, 3 vols., Vol. 2. Nakamara, Yuki, tr. from JPN. Yukimura, Makoto, illus. rev. ed. 2004. (Illus.). 192p. pap. 9.99 (978-1-59182-509-8(1) , Tokyopop Adult) TOKYOPOP, Inc.

COMIC BOOKS, STRIPS, ETC.—HISTORY AND CRITICISM

Beatty, Scott. Catwoman: The Visual Guide to the Feline Fatale. 2004. (Illus.). 64p. (J). 19.99 (978-0-7566-0383-0(8)) Dorling Kindersley Publishing, Inc.

Buckley, James. Creating the X-Men: How Comic Books Came to Life. 2000. (gr. k-3). lib. bdg. 11.80 (978-0-613-32428-1(5)) Tandem Library Bks.

Buckley, James & Dorling Kindersley Publishing Staff. Creating the X-Men: How Comic Books Come to Life. 2000. (Dorling Kindersley Readers Ser.). (Illus.). 32p. (J). (gr. 4-7). 12.95 (978-0-7894-6694-5(5)) Dorling Kindersley Publishing, Inc.

—Creating the X-Men: How Comic Books Come to Life. O'Neill, Cynthia, ed. 2000. (Dorling Kindersley Readers Ser.). (Illus.). 32p. (J). (gr. 4-7). pap. 3.99 (978-0-7894-6695-2(3)) Dorling Kindersley Publishing, Inc.

Defalco, Tom. Avengers: The Ultimate Guide. 2005. (Illus.). 128p. (J). 24.99 (978-0-7566-1461-4(9)) Dorling Kindersley Publishing, Inc.

Evanier, Mark. Wertham Was Right! Another Collection of POV Columns. 2003. (Illus.). 200p. (gr. 11 up). pap. 12.95 (978-1-893905-26-9(8)) TwoMorrows Publishing.

Teitelbaum, Michael. Creating the X-Men: How It All Began. 2000. (gr. k-3). lib. bdg. 11.80 (978-0-613-33109-8(5)) Tandem Library Bks.

Weaver, Robyn M. Cartoonists. 2000. (History Makers Ser.). (Illus.). 112p. (YA). (gr. 7-10). 27.45 (978-1-56006-668-2(7) , Lucent Bks.) Thomson Gale.

COMIC LITERATURE

see Comedy

COMIC OPERA

see Opera; Operetta

COMMANDMENTS, TEN

see Ten Commandments

COMMENTARIES, BIBLICAL

see Bible—Commentaries

COMMERCE

see also Banks and Banking; Business; Commercial Geography; Markets; Merchants; Retail Trade; Statistics; Stock Exchanges; Stocks; Trade Routes; Transportation

Adil, Janeen R. Goods & Services. 2006. (First Facts. Learning about Money Ser.). (Illus.). 24p. (J). (978-0-7368-5395-8(2)) Capstone Pr., Inc.

Bailey, Gerry & Law, Felicia. Save, Spend, Share: Using Your Money. Phillips, Mike et al, illus. 2006. (My Money Ser.). 24p. (J). (gr. 4-6). 27.93 (978-0-7565-1672-7(2)) Compass Point Bks.

Basel, Roberta. The History of Money. 2006. (First Facts Ser.). (Illus.). 24p. (J). (978-0-7368-5396-5(0)) Capstone Pr., Inc.

Canizares, Susan & Chanko, Pamela. Store. 2000. (Scholastic Placebook Ser.). (Illus.). 16p. (J). pap. (978-0-439-15369-0(7)) Scholastic, Inc.

Cefrey, Holly. The Interstate Commerce ACT: The Government Takes Control of Trade Between the States. 2003. (America's Industrial Society in the Nineteenth Century Ser.). (Illus.). 32p. (J). pap. (978-0-8239-4282-4(1)) Rosen Publishing Group, Inc., The.

Cherry Lake Publishing, compiled by. Global Products. 2008. lib. bdg. (***978-1-60279-104-6(X)***) Cherry Lake Publishing.

Cooper, Adrian. Fair Trade? (J). 2007. (***978-1-59604-145-5(5));*** 2005. (Illus.). 48p. (J). (gr. 6-9). lib. bdg. 29.95 (978-1-59604-072-4(6) , 1247745) Stargazer Bks.

Coupe, Robert. Travelers & Traders. 1999. (J). (978-0-7699-0487-0(4)) Shortland Pubns. (U. S. A.) Inc.

Craig, Tom. Internet: Technology, People, Process. 2003. (Media Wise Ser.). 64p. (J). lib. bdg. 28.50 (978-1-58340-257-3(8)) Smart Apple Media.

Davis, Lucile. Trade & Commerce. 2004. (Yesterday & Today Ser.). (Illus.). 32p. (J). 23.70 (978-1-56711-829-2(1) , Blackbirch Pr., Inc.) Thomson Gale.

Frost, Randall. The Globalization of Trade. 2004. (Understanding Global Issues Ser.). (Illus.). 56p. (J). (gr. 10-12). lib. bdg. (978-1-58340-363-1(9)) Smart Apple Media.

Haywood, John. Farming & Trade: Work, Trade & Farming Through the Ages. 2003. (How We Lived Ser.). (Illus.). 64p. (gr. 3-7). pap. 7.99 (978-1-84215-813-5(9) , Southwater) Anness Publishing GBR. *Dist:* National Bk. Network.

Kallen, Stuart A. A Medieval Merchant. 2005. (Working Life Ser.). (Illus.). 112p. (YA). (gr. 7-10). lib. bdg. 29.95 (978-1-59018-581-0(1) , Lucent Bks.) Thomson Gale.

Keoke, Emory Dean & Porterfield, Kay Marie. American Indian Contributions to the World. 2005. (American Indian Contributions to the World Ser.). (Illus.). 160p. (gr. 4-9). (J). 35.00 (978-0-8160-5395-7(2)); (YA). 35.00 (978-0-8160-5397-1(9)) Facts On File, Inc.

Loewen, Nancy. Let's Trade: A Book about Bartering. Fitzpatrick, Brad, illus. 2004. (J). (978-1-4048-0949-9(X)) Picture Window Bks.

MacDonald, Fiona. Travel & Trade in the Middle Ages. 2005. (World Almanac Library of the Middle Ages). (Illus.). 48p. (J). pap. (978-0-8368-5908-9(1)); (gr. 10-12). lib. bdg. 30.00 (978-0-8368-5899-0(9)) Stevens, Gareth Inc. (World Almanac Library).

Smith, Wendy. A Journey Through the Commercial World: Commerce for Years 9 & 10. 2003. 252p. pap. 16.55 (978-0-521-53965-4(X)) Cambridge Univ. Pr.

Teichmann, Iris. Globalization. 2003. (In the News Ser.). (J). lib. bdg. 24.25 (978-1-58340-397-6(3)) Smart Apple Media.

Zodl, Joseph A. Export Import: Everything You & Your Company Need to Know to Compete in World Markets. 4th ed. 2005. (Illus.). 173p. (J). per. (978-0-9773098-0-1(0)) IIEI Pr.

COMMERCIAL AVIATION

see Aeronautics, Commercial

COMMERCIAL EDUCATION

see Business Education

COMMERCIAL GEOGRAPHY

Here are entered works on the branch of geography that deals with commodities according to their places of origin and their paths of transportation. Works on the commercial geography of particular countries, cities, etc., are entered under the name of the place subdivided by Commerce.

see also Economic Geography

Carnibucci, Patricia. Geography & Society: Over 15 Complete Printable Unit Studies with Interactive Links. 2002. 160p. (gr. k-12). cd-rom 15.95 (978-1-891400-98-8(3)) Champion Pr., Ltd.

COMMERCIAL PRODUCTS

see also Commercial Geography; Forest Products; Manufactures; Marine Resources

Biggs, Andy, et al. Product Design for Key Stage 3. 2000. (Design & Make It Ser.). (Illus.). 144p. (J). (gr. 6-9). pap. 22.50 (978-0-7487-4429-9(0)) Nelson Thornes Ltd. GBR. *Dist:* Trans-Atlantic Pubns., Inc.

Cherry Lake Publishing, compiled by. Global Products. 2008. lib. bdg. (***978-1-60279-104-6(X)***) Cherry Lake Publishing.

Harcourt School Publishers Staff. Goods Around the World. 3rd ed. 2002. (Horizons Ser.). (Illus.). (J). pap. 3.70 (978-0-15-333235-7(2)) Harcourt Schl. Pubs.

Kramer, Barbara. The Founders of Famous Food Companies. 2002. (Collective Biographies Ser.). (Illus.). 112p. (YA). (gr. 6-12). lib. bdg. 26.60 (978-0-7660-1537-1(8)) Enslow Pubs., Inc.

COMMERCIAL SCHOOLS

see Business Education

COMMERCIAL TRAVELERS

see Sales Personnel

COMMON MARKET

see European Economic Community

COMMON SCHOOLS

see Public Schools

COMMONWEALTH, THE

see Political Science

COMMONWEALTH OF INDEPENDENT STATES

Loy, Lily. Kazakhstan. 2004. (J). lib. bdg. 30.00 (978-0-8368-3116-0(0)) Stevens, Gareth Inc.

COMMUNAL LIVING

see Collective Settlements

COMMUNES

see Collective Settlements

COMMUNICABLE DISEASES

see also Bacteriology; Immunity; Insects As Carriers of Disease; Sexually Transmitted Diseases; Vaccination

Altman, Linda Jacobs. Plague & Pestilence: A History of Infectious Disease. 1998. (Issues in Focus Ser.). (Illus.). 128p. (YA). (gr. 6-12). lib. bdg. 26.60 (978-0-89490-957-3(6)) Enslow Pubs., Inc.

Ballard, Carol. Fighting Infectious Diseases. 2006. (Illus.). 64p. (J). lib. bdg. (***978-0-8368-7864-6(7)*** , World Almanac Library) Stevens, Gareth Inc.

Barnard, Bryn. Outbreak! Plagues That Changed History. 2005. (Illus.). 48p. (J). (gr. 3-7). 17.95 (978-0-375-82986-4(5)); lib. bdg. 19.99 (978-0-375-92986-1(X)) Random Hse. Children's Bks. (Crown Books For Young Readers).

Brownlee, Christen. Cute, Furry, & Deadly: Diseases You Can Catch from Your Pet! 2007. (24/7: Science Behind the Scenes: Medical Files Ser.). 64p. (J). pap. 7.95 (***978-0-531-18737-1(3));*** (YA). (gr. 8-12). 26.00 (978-0-531-12072-9(4)) Scholastic Library Publishing. (Watts, Franklin).

Burles, Kenneth T. & Hundley, David H. Fever. 1998. (Learning about Your Health Ser.). (Illus.). 32p. (J). (gr. 2-5). lib. bdg. 26.60 (978-1-57103-256-0(8)) Rourke Publishing, LLC.

Claybourne, Anna. World's Worst Germs. 2005. (Illus.). 32p. (J). (978-1-4109-1972-4(2)) Steck-Vaughn.

—World's Worst Germs: Microorganisms & Disease. 2005. (Illus.). 32p. (J). (gr. 3-5). lib. bdg. 28.21 (978-1-4109-1941-0(2)) Steck-Vaughn.

Cole, Joanna. The Magic School Bus Inside Ralphie: A Book about Germs. 2002. (Magic School Bus Ser.). (Illus.). (J). 11.45 (978-0-7587-6980-0(6)) Book Wholesalers, Inc.

Davidson, Tish. Influenza. 2006. 112p. (J). (gr. 7-10). 32.45 (978-1-59018-675-6(3) , Lucent Bks.) Thomson Gale.

DiConsiglio, John. There's a Fungus among Us! True Stories of Killer Molds. 2007. (24/7 - Science Behind the Scenes Ser.). 64p. (YA). (gr. 8-12). 26.00 (978-0-531-12071-2(6) , Watts, Franklin) Scholastic Library Publishing.

—There's a Fungus among Us! True Stories of Killer Molds. 2007. (24/7: Science Behind the Scenes: Medical Files Ser.). 64p. (J). pap. 7.95 (***978-0-531-17530-9(8)*** , Watts, Franklin) Scholastic Library Publishing.

—When Birds Get Flu & Cows Go Mad! How Safe Are We? 2007. (24/7: Science Behind the Scenes: Medical Files Ser.). 64p. (YA). (gr. 5 up). pap. 7.95 (***978-0-531-17528-6(6)*** , Watts, Franklin) Scholastic Library Publishing.

Farrell, Jeanette. Invisible Enemies: Stories of Infectious Disease. 2nd rev. ed. 2005. (Illus.). 272p. (YA). 18.00 (978-0-374-33607-3(5) , Farrar, Straus & Giroux (BYR)) Farrar, Straus & Giroux.

Finer, Kim Renee. Smallpox. 2004. (Deadly Diseases & Epidemics Ser.). (Illus.). 112p. (J). (gr. 9-13). 31.95 (978-0-7910-7594-4(X) , Chelsea Hse.) Facts On File, Inc.

Gallagher, Aileen. Hepatitis. 2004. (Epidemics Ser.). (Illus.). 64p. (YA). lib. bdg. 26.50 (978-1-4042-0255-9(2)) Rosen Publishing Group, Inc., The.

Gordon, Melanie Apel. Let's Talk about Head Lice. 1999. (Let's Talk Library). (Illus.). 24p. (J). (gr. 3). lib. bdg. 18.75 (978-0-8239-5200-7(2) , PowerKids Pr.) Rosen Publishing Group, Inc., The.

Grabowski, John F. Meningitis. 2006. 112p. (J). (gr. 7-10). 32.45 (978-1-59018-411-0(4) , Lucent Bks.) Thomson Gale.

Grady, Denise. Deadly Invaders: Virus Outbreaks Around the World, from Marburg Fever to Avian Flu. 2006. (New York Times Ser.). (Illus.). 128p. (J). (gr. 7). 16.95 (978-0-7534-5995-9(7)) Houghton Mifflin Co.

Hoffmann, Gretchen. The Flu. 2006. (Health Alert Ser.). (Illus.). 64p. (J). lib. bdg. 31.36 (978-0-7614-2208-2(0) , Benchmark Bks.) Cavendish, Marshall Corp.

Holt, Rinehart and Winston Staff. Decisions for Health Blue, Chptr. 17: Infectious Diseases. 4th ed. 2004. pap. 11.20 (978-0-03-068052-6(2)) Holt, Rinehart & Winston.

—Decisions for Health Red Chptr. 14: Infectious Diseases. 4th ed. 2004. pap. 11.20 (978-0-03-068041-0(7)) Holt, Rinehart & Winston.

Hugen, David & Musser, Susan. Pandemics. 2007. (At Issue Ser.). 128p. (J). (gr. 10-12). 29.95 (***978-0-7377-3603-8(8));*** pap. 21.20 (***978-0-7377-3604-5(6))*** Thomson Gale. (Greenhaven Pr., Inc.).

Infectious Disease Workshop. 2003. cd-rom (978-1-929524-02-0(1)) P K I Ds.

Karner, Julie. Plague & Pandemic Alert! Disaster Alert! 2004. (Disaster Alert! Ser.). (Illus.). 32p. (J). pap. (978-0-7787-1612-9(0)) Crabtree Publishing Co.

King, David C. Learning about AIDS & Other Diseases. Maccarone, Sandra F., illus. Jerome, Karen & Haeger, Leigh, photos by. 3rd rev. ed. 1999. (AIDS Awareness Ser.). 25p. (J). (gr. 2-4). pap. (978-0-8374-3237-3(5)) Weekly Reader Corp.

Klosterman, Lorrie. Meningitis. 2006. (Health Alert Ser.). (Illus.). 64p. (J). lib. bdg. 31.36 (978-0-7614-2211-2(0) , Benchmark Bks.) Cavendish, Marshall Corp.

Kneib, Martha. Meningitis. 2004. (Epidemics Ser.). (Illus.). 64p. (YA). lib. bdg. 26.50 (978-1-4042-0257-3(9)) Rosen Publishing Group, Inc., The.

Krohn, Katherine E. The 1918 Flu Pandemic. Hall, Bob et al, illus. 2008. (J). (***978-1-4296-0158-0(2))*** Capstone Pr., Inc.

Lewis Tilden, Thomasine E. Help! What's Eating My Flesh? Runaway Staph & Strep Infections! 2007. (24/7: Science Behind the Scenes: Medical Files Ser.). 64p. (J). pap. 7.95 (***978-0-531-18738-8(1));*** (YA). (gr. 8-12). 26.00 (978-0-531-12073-6(2)) Scholastic Library Publishing. (Watts, Franklin).

Miller, Debra A. Pandemics. 2006. (Hot Topics Ser.). 112p. (YA). (gr. 8 up). lib. bdg. 32.45 (978-1-59018-965-8(5) , Lucent Bks.) Thomson Gale.

Morgan, Sally. Germ Killers: Fighting Disease. (Science at the Edge Ser.). 64p. 8.95 (978-1-4034-4121-8(9)); 2002. (Illus.). (J). (gr. 6-8). lib. bdg. 27.86 (978-1-58810-699-5(3)) Heinemann Library.

O'Neal, Claire. The Influenza Pandemic Of 1918. 2007. (Natural Disasters Ser.). (J). lib. bdg. 25.70 (***978-1-58415-569-0(8))*** Mitchell Lane Pubs., Inc.

Orr, Tamra. Avian Flu. 2006. (Coping in a Changing World Ser.). 112p. (YA). (gr. 7-12). lib. bdg. 31.95 (***978-1-4042-0950-3(6))*** Rosen Publishing Group, Inc., The.

O'Shei, Tim. The World's Deadliest Diseases. 2006. (Edge Books, the World's Top Ten). (Illus.). 32p. (J). (978-0-7368-5452-8(5)) Capstone Pr., Inc.

Robert Green. Diseases & Disorders - SARS. 2004. (Illus.). 112p. 32.45 (978-1-59018-529-2(3)) Thomson Gale.

Routh, Kristina. Meningitis. 2004. (Just the Facts Ser.). (J). lib. bdg. 27.07 (978-1-4034-5146-0(X)) Heinemann Library.

—Tuberculosis. 2004. (Just the Facts Ser.). (Illus.). 56p. (J). lib. bdg. 27.07 (978-1-4034-5147-7(8)) Heinemann Library.

Segall, Miriam. Pandemics: Epidemics in a Shrinking World. 2006. (In the News Ser.). (Illus.). 64p. (J). (gr. 7-12). lib. bdg. 27.95 (***978-1-4042-0975-6(1))*** Rosen Publishing Group, Inc., The.

Senior, Kathryn & Salariya, David. You Wouldn't Want to Be Sick in the 16th Century! Diseases You'd Rather Not Catch. Antram, David, illus. 2002. (You Wouldn't Want to Ser.). 32p. (J). (gr. 2-5). 28.50 (978-0-531-14605-7(7) , Watts, Franklin) Scholastic Library Publishing.

Sfakianos, Jeffrey N. & Organization, World Health. Avian Flu. (Deadly Diseases & Epidemics Ser.). (Illus.). 88p. pap. 12.95 (***978-0-7910-9547-8(9)*** , Checkmark Bks.) Facts On File, Inc.

Shader, Laurel & Zonderman, John. Mononucleosis & Other Infectious Diseases. 1999. (Twenty-First Century Health & Wellness Ser.). (Illus.). 112p. (YA). (gr. 9 up). 24.95 (978-0-7910-5520-5(5) , Chelsea Hse.) Facts On File, Inc.

Siderovski, Susan. Tularemia. 2006. (Deadly Diseases & Epidemics Ser.). (Illus.). 120p. (J). (gr. 9-12). 31.95 (978-0-7910-8679-7(8) , Chelsea Hse.) Facts On File, Inc.

Silverstein, Alvin. What Are Germs? 2002. (gr. 3-6). lib. bdg. 15.25 (978-0-613-59556-8(4)) Tandem Library Bks.

Silverstein, Alvin, et al. What Are Germs? 2003. (My Health Ser.). 48p. (J). (gr. 3-5). pap. 6.95 (978-0-531-16640-6(6) , Watts, Franklin) Scholastic Library Publishing.

Snedden, Robert. Fighting Infectious Diseases. 2000. (Microlife Ser.). (Illus.). 48p. (YA). (gr. 6-8). lib. bdg. 22.79 (978-1-57572-243-6(7)) Heinemann Library.

Somervill, Barbara A. Lice: Head Hunters. 2008. (J). lib. bdg. (***978-1-4042-3803-9(4)*** , PowerKids Pr.) Rosen Publishing Group, Inc., The.

Sommers, Michael A. Yeast Infections, Trichomoniasis, & Toxic Shock Syndrome. 2007. (J). lib. bdg. (***978-1-4042-1951-9(X)*** , Rosen Central) Rosen Publishing Group, Inc., The.

Walker, Richard. Epidemics & Plagues. Kingfisher Publications, Inc. Staff, ed. 2006. (Kingfisher Knowledge Ser.). 64p. (J). (gr. 5-9). 12.95 (978-0-7534-6035-1(1) , Kingfisher) Houghton Mifflin Co. Trade & Reference Div.

—Epidemics & Plagues. 2006. (Kingfisher Knowledge Ser.). (Illus.). 64p. (J). (***978-0-7534-1376-0(0)*** , Kingfisher) Houghton Mifflin Co. Trade & Reference Div.

West, Krista. Urinary Tract Infections. 2006. (Library of Sexual Health). (Illus.). 64p. (J). lib. bdg. (978-1-4042-0905-3(0)) Rosen Publishing Group, Inc., The.

World Book, Inc Staff, contrib. by. Forces of Nature. 2007. (J). (***978-0-7166-9806-7(4))*** World Bk., Inc.

—Pandemics. 2007. (J). (***978-0-7166-9811-1(0))*** World Bk., Inc.

COMMUNICATION

see also Books and Reading; Cybernetics; Language and Languages; Mass Media; Newspapers; Postal Service; Writing

Allen, Joy. Baby Signs: A Baby-Sized Guide to Speaking with Sign Language. 2008. 16p. (J). (ps). bds. 6.99 (***978-0-8037-3193-6(0)*** , Dial) Penguin Group (USA) Inc.

Babler, Susan. Communication Station. Bittinger, Gayle, ed. Mohrman, Gary, illus. 1998. (Kinderstation Ser.). 160p. (J). (ps). pap. 15.95 (978-1-57029-159-3(4) , WPH 4502, Totline Pubns.) Schaffer, Frank Pubns.

Berry, Joy Wilt. A Book about Gossiping. 2005. (Illus.). (J). (978-0-7172-8590-7(1)) Scholastic, Inc.

—A Book about Whining. 2005. (Illus.). (J). (978-0-7172-7898-5(0)) Scholastic, Inc.

Bowers, Linda, et al. No Glamour Language & Reasoning. 2003. (J). per. 41.95 (978-0-7606-0500-4(9)) LinguiSystems, Inc.

Braunius, Marlene, et al. Exploring Language Arts Through Literature. 2nd rev. ed. 2004. 332p. (ps-8). 44.05 (978-0-7575-0794-6(8) , 0757507948) Kendall/Hunt Publishing Co.

Brinkerhoff, Shirley. Folk Speech. 2003. (North American Folklore Ser.). (Illus.). 112p. (YA). (gr. 7 up). lib. bdg. (978-1-59084-345-1(2)) Mason Crest Pubs.

Broekhuizen, Richard J. Graphic Communications. 4th ed. 1999. (Illus.). 160p. (YA). (gr. 6-12). stu. ed., wbk. ed. 7.92 (978-0-02-676307-3(9)) Glencoe/McGraw-Hill.

Burke, Sandra & Flebotte, Morrigan. The Crusading Communicator. Flebotte, Morrigan, ed. 2004. (Illus.). 2p. (J). per. (978-0-9735303-8-4(3)) Black Castle Industries, Inc.

Catala, Ellen. Ways We Communicate. 2003. (J). (978-0-7368-1726-4(3)); (Illus.). 16p. (gr. 1). lib. bdg. 14.60 (978-0-7368-2029-5(9) , Pebble Bks.) Capstone Pr., Inc.

Chambers, Catherine. Speaking Through Pictures. Cockcroft, David, illus. 1998. (Hello Out There! Ser.). 32p. (J). (gr. 2-5). 20.00 (978-0-531-14469-5(0) , Watts, Franklin) Scholastic Library Publishing.

Communication Then & Now, 6 vols., Set D. (Phonics Readers Ser.). (gr. k-2). 28.95 (978-0-7368-4063-7(X)) Red Brick Learning.

Communications. 2nd rev. ed. 2004. 73p. stu. ed., wbk. ed. (978-0-86657-510-2(3)) Lab-Volt Systems, Inc.

Communications TCG. 2nd rev. ed. 2004. 72p. pap. (978-0-86657-511-9(1)) Lab-Volt Systems, Inc.

CommunicationsAdvAddOn CELL Guide. 2nd rev. ed. 2004. 124p. pap. (978-0-86657-495-2(6)) Lab-Volt Systems, Inc.

Cooper, Scott. Speak up & Get Along! Learn the Mighty Might, Thought Chop, & More Tools to Make Friends, Stop Teasing, & Feel Good about Yourself! 2005. (Illus.). 128p. (J). (gr. 3-7). pap. 12.95 (978-1-57542-182-7(8)) Free Spirit Publishing, Inc.

Damm, Antje. Ask Me. rev. ed. 2003. (Illus.). 224p. (J). 14.95 (978-0-7613-1845-3(3)) Roaring Brook Pr.

David C. Cook. Substance Abuse, Communicating with Others, Who Is Jesus? 2003. (Domain 456 Ser.). 128p. (J). (gr. 4-6). pap., pap. 15.99 (978-0-7814-5519-0(7) ; 0781455197) Cook, David C. Publishing Co.

Dickerson, Karle. Girl Chat: The Fine Art of Talk, Talk, Talk. 2001. (Illus.). 105p. (J). (978-0-439-18745-9(1)) Scholastic, Inc.

Doudna, Kelly. It's Not Too Late, Let's Communicate! (Illus.). 24p. (J). 2007. 19.93 (978-1-59928-606-8(8)); 2006. pap. (978-1-59928-607-5(6)) ABDO Publishing Co.

Doudna, Kelly. Speak Up! 2007. (Illus.). 24p. (J). 19.93 (***978-1-59928-741-6(2))*** ABDO Publishing Co.

Epstein, Charlotte. Getting along with Others, Respect. 2000. (Illus.). 92p. (J). (978-1-57279-184-8(5)) Young People's Pr., Inc.

Everly, Nita. Early Social Behavior Books Can Your Talk to Your Friends. 2007. (J). spiral bd. 11.95 (***978-0-7606-0739-8(7))*** LinguiSystems, Inc.

Feely, Jenny. Sending Messages. 2001. (gr. k-3). lib. bdg. 11.65 (978-0-613-33427-3(2)) Tandem Library Bks.

Galvin, Kathleen M., et al. The Basics of Speech: Learning to Be a Competent Communicator. 3rd ed. 1999. 606p. (C). 78.64 (978-0-8442-0382-9(3) , 9780844203829) Glencoe/McGraw-Hill.

Gifford, Clive & Dorling Kindersley Publishing Staff. Media & Communication. 2000. (Eyewitness Bks.). (Illus.). 64p. (J). (gr. 4-7). 15.99 (978-0-7894-6294-7(X)) Dorling Kindersley Publishing, Inc.

—Media & Communications. 2000. (Eyewitness Bks.). (Illus.). 64p. (J). (gr. 4-7). lib. bdg. 19.99 (978-0-7894-6629-7(5)) Dorling Kindersley Publishing, Inc.

Gilmore, Susan K. & Fraleigh, Patrick W. Communication Style Profile for Students. 3rd ed. 1999. (Illus.). 40p. (Orig.). (YA). (gr. 8 up). pap. 10.00 (978-0-938070-04-7(5)) Friendly Pr.

Glencoe McGraw-Hill Staff. Communication Works! 2001. stu. ed. 82.64 (978-0-658-00299-1(6) , 9780658002991) Glencoe/McGraw-Hill.

Grimshaw, Caroline. Communication: Follow the Journey of a Message. 2000. (Invisible Journeys Ser.). (Illus.). 32p. (J). (gr. 3-6). 10.95 (978-1-58728-333-8(6)); pap. 5.95 (978-1-58728-326-0(3)) T&N Children's Publishing. (Two Can Publishing).

Harte, Lawrence. Wireless Technology Basics. 2004. (Illus.). 50p. per. 12.99 (978-1-932813-03-6(9)) Althos.

Harte, Lawrence, ed. Wireless Dictionary. 2005. (Illus.). per. 39.95 (978-0-9746943-1-3(2)) Althos.

Hazen, Walter A. Communication. 2004. (Everyday Life Ser.). (Illus.). 96p. pap. (978-0-673-58664-3(2)) Good Year Bks.

Holt, Rinehart and Winston Staff. Allez Viens! Level 1: Activities for Communication. 1998. pap. 21.86 (978-0-03-052643-5(4)) Holt, Rinehart & Winston.

—Allez Viens! Level 1: Video Guide. 1998. pap. 21.26 (978-0-03-052647-3(7)) Holt, Rinehart & Winston.

—Elements of Language: Communications - Grade 10. 2000. pap. 109.00 (978-0-03-056408-6(5)) Holt, Rinehart & Winston.

—Elements of Language: Communications - Grade 11. 2000. pap. 109.00 (978-0-03-056409-3(3)) Holt, Rinehart & Winston.

—Elements of Language: Communications - Grade 12. 2000. pap. 109.00 (978-0-03-056411-6(5)) Holt, Rinehart & Winston.

—Elements of Language: Communications - Grade 6. 2003. (Elements of Language Ser.). 109.00 (978-0-03-056403-1(4)) Holt, Rinehart & Winston.

—Elements of Language: Communications - Grade 7. 2000. pap. 109.00 (978-0-03-056404-8(2)) Holt, Rinehart & Winston.

—Elements of Language: Communications - Grade 8. 2000. pap. 109.00 (978-0-03-056406-2(9)) Holt, Rinehart & Winston.

—Elements of Language: Communications - Grade 9. 2000. pap. 109.00 (978-0-03-056407-9(7)) Holt, Rinehart & Winston.

—Elements of Language: Literature & Communication Skills: Media - Grade 6. 2003. (Elements of Language Ser.). 148.73 (978-0-03-057398-9(X)) Holt, Rinehart & Winston.

—Elements of Language, Grade 11. annot. ed. (Elements of Language Ser.). 2003. tchr. ed. 108.20 (978-0-03-054793-5(8)); 2000. tchr. ed. 119.33 (978-0-03-052103-4(3)); Vol. 1. 2000. 65.53 (978-0-03-064923-3(4)) Holt, Rinehart & Winston.

—Komm Mit! Level 1: Activities for Communication. 1998. pap. 21.86 (978-0-03-052899-6(2)) Holt, Rinehart & Winston.

Hossell, Karen Price. Body Language. 2002. (Communicating Ser.). 48p. (J). (gr. 3-5). pap. 8.50 (978-1-58810-939-2(9) , 91578) Heinemann Library.

—Body Language. 2003. (gr. 3-6). lib. bdg. 16.40 (978-0-613-45717-0(X)) Tandem Library Bks.

—Communicating, 6 bks., Set. 2003. (Illus.). (J). (gr. 3-5). lib. bdg. 153.84 (978-1-58810-475-5(3)) Heinemann Library.

Isbell, Rebecca & Raines, Shirley C. Tell It Again! Easy to Tell Stories with Activities for Young Children. 2004. (Tell It Again Ser.). (Illus.). 192p. (ps-3). pap. 14.95 (978-0-87659-200-7(0) , 19628) Gryphon Hse., Inc.

Janssen-Mathes, Mieke. The Secret of Otherland. Kwakkenbos, Frans, illus. 2007. 96p. pap. 34.95 (978-90-6832-587-4(6)) KIT (Koninklijk Instituut voor de Tropen) NLD. *Dist:* Stylus Publishing, LLC.

Jareaux, Marlena. 26 Things to Teach Your Parents. 2007. (Illus.). 76p. (YA). per. 10.95 (***978-0-9790415-1-8(1)***) Inspired By the Beach Publishing.

Jeffrey, R. Stephen. Rules of the Game. 1999. 145p. (J). pap. 11.95 (978-1-893455-01-6(7)) Aloha Publishing & Marketing.

Jones, Myoushi. Communication Skills Vol. 2: Let's Get to Know One Another. Reams, Damaris, illus. 2000. 35p. (J). (gr. 2-6). pap. 6.95 (978-0-9703537-4-0(X)) Myoushi Enterprises.

Kronenwetter, Michael. Media Impact. 1998. 128p. (YA). (gr. 7 up). 22.40 (978-0-7613-3018-9(6) , Twenty-First Century Bks.) Lerner Publishing Group.

La Raja, Taryn & Pruger, Elizabeth. Smart Start! A Preparatory Guide. 1999. (Smart Start Ser.). (Illus.). 64p. (YA). (gr. 8). pap. 5.95 (978-1-893110-05-2(2)) Silver Moon Pr.

Lakeshore Learning Materials Staff, contrib. by. Skills for Living No. 4: Everyday Communications. 2000. (J). pap. 29.95 (978-1-929255-97-9(7)) Lakeshore Learning Materials.

The Language of Literature: Grammar, Usage, & Mechanics Book. 2004. (gr. 10 up). (978-0-618-30393-9(6) , 2-04298); 2001. (gr. 7 up). (978-0-618-15376-3(4) , 2-04131) McDougal Littell Inc.

The Language of Literature: Grammar, Usage, & Mechanics Book Answer Key. 2004. (gr. 10 up). (978-0-618-30799-9(0) , 2-04414); 2001. (gr. 7 up). (978-0-618-15377-0(2) , 2-04132) McDougal Littell Inc.

Laraja, Taryn & Kaplan, Farida. Smart Start! Grade 3. 2000. (Illus.). 68p. (J). pap. 5.95 (978-1-893110-14-4(1)) Silver Moon Pr.

Layton, Meredith. Baby's First Words: A Sign & Say Interactive Language Book. Anderson, Brad & Goodwin, Sharon, illus. David Nester Photography Staff, photos by. 1999. (Sign & Say Interactive Language Ser.). 32p. (J). 16.95 (978-0-9670821-0-3(2)) Peek-A-Boo Publishing.

Lieberman, Lillian. Starting Points for Language Arts. Barr, Marilynn G., illus. 1999. 128p. (J). (gr. 1-3). pap. 14.95 (978-1-57612-069-9(4) , MM2082) Monday Morning Bks., Inc.

McGraw-Hill Staff. Communication Applications. 2000. stu. ed. 80.00 (978-0-02-817244-6(2) , 9780028172446) Glencoe/McGraw-Hill.

Nelson, Carol Ann. Red & Red. Costain, illus. unabr. ed. 1998. (Sing along Bks.). 32p. (J). (ps-1). 16.95 (978-1-893886-00-1(X)) How I Learn & Grow.

O'Dell. Elements of Language. (Elements of Language Ser.). 2003. (gr. 6 up). pupil's gde. ed. 64.73 (978-0-03-052662-6(0)); 2000. (gr. 11). 73.33 (978-0-03-052668-8(X)); 2000. (gr. 12). 73.33 (978-0-03-052669-5(8)); 2000. (gr. 7). 67.46 (978-0-03-052663-3(9)); 2000. (gr. 8). 67.46 (978-0-03-052664-0(7)) Holt, Rinehart & Winston.

Parker, Janice. Messengers, Morse Code & Modems: The Science of Communication. 2000. (Science @ Work Ser.). (Illus.). 48p. (J). (gr. 4-6). lib. bdg. 27.12 (978-0-7398-0138-3(4)) Raintree.

Parker, Steve. Communications. 2002. (Tomorrow's Technology Ser.). (Illus.). 32p. (J). lib. bdg. 24.25 (978-1-931983-22-8(4)) Chrysalis Education.

Perry, Robert. Personal Computer Communications. 2000. (Watts Library). (Illus.). 64p. (YA). (gr. 5-7). pap. 8.95 (978-0-531-16483-9(7) , Watts, Franklin) Scholastic Library Publishing.

Perry, Robert L. Personal Computer Communications. 2000. (Illus.). 64p. (J). (gr. 5-7). lib. bdg. 17.60 (978-0-613-37497-2(5)) Tandem Library Bks.

Platt, Richard. Communication. 2007. (Kingfisher Knowledge Ser.). (Illus.). 64p. (J). pap. 8.95 (***978-0-7534-6159-4(5)*** , Kingfisher) Houghton Mifflin Co. Trade & Reference Div.

Platt, Richard. Communication: From Hieroglyphs to Hyperlinks. 2004. (Kingfisher Knowledge Ser.). (Illus.). 64p. (J). (gr. 4-8). 12.95 (978-0-7534-5769-6(5) , Kingfisher) Houghton Mifflin Co. Trade & Reference Div.

Pleau-Murissi, Marilyn. Caillou: The Phone Call. 2003. (Clubhouse Ser.). (Illus.). 24p. (J). pap. 2.50 (978-2-89450-446-8(2)) Chouette Publishing CAN. *Dist:* Independent Pubs. Group.

Powell, Jillian. Me & My Family. 2007. (J). (***978-1-59771-088-6(1)***) Sea-To-Sea Pubns.

Price Hossell, Karen. Body Language. 2003. (Communicating Ser.). (Illus.). 48p. (J). (gr. 3-5). lib. bdg. 27.07 (978-1-58810-483-0(4)) Heinemann Library.

Pruger, Elizabeth & Zernone, Michelle. Smart Start! A Preparatory Guide. 1999. (Smart Start Ser.). (Illus.). 64p. (YA). (gr. 4). pap. 5.95 (978-1-893110-06-9(0)) Silver Moon Pr.

Pruger, Liz & Zernone, Michelle. Listen, Take Note!, Level A. 2000. (Illus.). 48p. (J). pap. 5.95 (978-1-893110-18-2(4)) Silver Moon Pr.

—Smart Start! Grade 7. 2000. (Illus.). 60p. (YA). (gr. 7). pap. 5.95 (978-1-893110-21-2(4)) Silver Moon Pr.

Reilly, Mary A. ESPA Companion: Achieving Language Art Literacy. 1998. (Illus.). 184p. (J). pap. 39.95 (978-1-886292-25-3(6)) CEO Software Solutions.

—GEPA Companion: Achieving Language Arts Literacy. 1999. (Illus.). 208p. (YA). (gr. 7-8). 39.95 (978-1-886292-33-8(7)) CEO Software Solutions.

Ring, Susan. Maneras de Comunicar. 2005. Tr. of Ways We Communicate. (SPA., Illus.). 16p. (J). (gr. 1 up). lib. bdg. 15.93 (978-0-7368-4145-0(8)) Capstone Pr., Inc.

Schwartz, Stuart B. & Conley, Craig. Communicating with Others. (Job Skills Ser.). pap. 6.95 (978-0-7368-8025-1(9) , LifeMatters Bks.) Capstone Pr., Inc.

Seymour, Richard D., et al. Exploring Communication. 2000. (Illus.). 380p. (J). 44.80 (978-1-56637-678-5(5)) Goodheart-Willcox Pub.

Shea, Ann T. All about Me: Inside & Out: Ready-to-Go Activities, Games, Literature Links & Hands-On Reproductions. Oh, Paul, illus. 2000. 48p. (J). pap. 9.95 (978-0-439-05009-8(X)) Scholastic, Inc.

Sherman, Joanne. Because It's My Body! Keep 'Em Safe Series: Anxiety-Free Learning for Children. Gurney, John Steven, illus. 2006. 40p. (J). 18.95 (978-0-9711735-9-0(1)) S.A.F.E. for Children Publishing, LLC.

Shiotsu, Vicky. Second Grade Language Arts: Boosting Your Way to Success in School. Guianan, Eve, illus. 1998. (Grade Boosters Ser.). 64p. (J). (gr. 2-3). pap. 4.95 (978-1-56565-676-5(8) , 06768W) Lowell Hse. Juvenile.

Smith, J. L. How to Use Parts of Speech. Arquilevich, Gabriel, ed. Chaney, Howard, illus. 1999. (How to Ser.). 48p. (gr. k-3). pap., tchr. ed. 7.99 (978-1-57690-355-1(9) , TCA2355) Teacher Created Materials, Inc.

Sommers, Annie Leah. Everything You Need to Know about Effective Communication at School & at Work. 2005. (Need to Know Library). (Illus.). 64p. (YA). (gr. 7-12). lib. bdg. 25.25 (978-0-8239-3227-6(3) , NTEFCO) Rosen Publishing Group, Inc., The.

Steck-Vaughn Staff. Communication Skills-Start Smart. 2002. (J). pap. (978-0-7398-6014-4(3)) Steck-Vaughn.

Stringer, John. Communication & Art Activities. 2002. (Arty Facts Ser.). (Illus.). 48p. (J). (gr. 3-4). pap. (978-0-7787-1147-6(1)); lib. bdg. (978-0-7787-1119-3(6)) Crabtree Publishing Co.

—Communication & Art Activities. 2002. (gr. 3-6). lib. bdg. 17.60 (978-0-613-52824-5(7)) Tandem Library Bks.

Talking Points, 4 vols. 1999. (Illus.). (J). 108.48 (978-0-7398-1508-3(3)); Set. 64p. (gr. 6-8). pap. 162.66 (978-0-8172-5316-5(5)) Raintree.

Transportation & Communication. (J). (gr. k-1). (978-84-342-2418-6(6) , PR30572) Parramon Ediciones S.A. ESP. *Dist:* Lectorum Pubns., Inc.

Tubbs, Janet. Talking about Problems. 2000. (Spud Packs Ser.). (Illus.). 16p. (J). (ps-4). pap. 19.95 (978-1-881185-25-3(7)) Arcadia Pr.

Velcro Interactive Phonic Lab. (Illus.). (J). (gr. 2-4). (978-0-9673268-0-1(X)) Learning Fasten-Ations, Inc.

Wandberg, Robert. Communication: Creating Understanding. (Life Skills-Contemporary Issues Ser.). (Illus.). (J). 2001. 48p. pap. 8.95 (978-0-7368-8834-9(9)); 2000. 64p. (gr. 4-6). lib. bdg. 23.93 (978-0-7368-0693-0(8)) Capstone Pr., Inc. (LifeMatters Bks.).

Waters, Jennifer. Let's Talk: How We Communicate. 2002. (Spyglass Books). (Illus.). 24p. (J). (gr. 1 up). lib. bdg. 18.60 (978-0-7565-0381-9(7)) Compass Point Bks.

Weber, Rebecca. Body Language. 2004. (Spyglass Books). 24p. (J). (gr. 1 up). lib. bdg. 19.93 (978-0-7565-0650-6(6)) Compass Point Bks.

Wells, James. Stuffy, the Short-Neck Giraffe Who Liked Peanut Butter. 2006. 9.00 (978-0-8059-9174-1(3)) Dorrance Publishing Co., Inc.

Williams, Brian. Communications. 2001. (Great Inventions Ser.). (Illus.). 48p. (J). (gr. 6-8). lib. bdg. 25.64 (978-1-58810-209-6(2)) Heinemann Library.

Wilson, Anthony. Communications. 1999. (How the Future Began Ser.). (Illus.). 64p. (J). (gr. 5). tchr. ed. 15.95 (978-0-7534-5179-3(4) , Kingfisher) Houghton Mifflin Co. Trade & Reference Div.

Woods, Mary B. & Woods, Michael. Ancient Communication: From Grunts to Graffiti. 2005. (Ancient Technology Ser.). (Illus.). 96p. (gr. 6-12). 25.26 (978-0-8225-2996-5(3)) Lerner Publishing Group.

Zimmermann, Dottie. Interactive BigBooks (Set 1), 5 vols. 2001. (J). ring bd. 44.00 (978-1-888222-77-7(8)) Super Duper Pubns.

—Interactive BigBooks (Set 2), 5 vols. 2002. (J). ring bd. 44.00 (978-1-888222-87-6(5)) Super Duper Pubns.

COMMUNICATION—FICTION

Austin, Margot & McPhail, David M. A Friend for Growl Bear Board Book. 1999. (Illus.). 32p. (J). (ps-k). 6.95 (978-0-694-01257-2(2) , Harper Festival) HarperCollins Pubs.

Baer, Edith. Words are like Faces. Teis, Kyra, illus. 2007. 32p. (J). 15.95 (***978-1-59572-108-2(8)***) Star Bright Bks., Inc.

Brooke, William J. A Is for AARRGH! 1999. 256p. (J). (gr. 5 up). 14.89 (978-0-06-023394-5(X)) HarperCollins Pubs.

Cheng, Andrea. Grandfather Counts. Zhang, Ange, illus. 32p. (J). 2003. (978-1-58430-158-5(9)); 2000. 15.95 (978-1-58430-010-6(8)) Lee & Low Bks., Inc.

—Grandfather Counts. 2000. (gr. k-3). lib. bdg. 15.25 (978-0-613-65692-4(X)) Tandem Library Bks.

Clements, Andrew. No Talking. Elliott, Mark, illus. 2007. 160p. (J). (gr. 3-7). 15.99 (***978-1-4169-0983-5(4)***) Simon & Schuster Children's Publishing.

Cutler, Jane. Common Sense & Fowls. Barasch, Lynne, illus. 2005. 144p. (J). 16.00 (978-0-374-32262-5(7) , Farrar, Straus & Giroux (BYR)) Farrar, Straus & Giroux.

Donaldson, Julia. Follow the Swallow. Ursell, Martin, illus. 2001. (Blue Bananas Ser.). 48p. (J). (gr. 1-2). (978-0-7787-0842-1(X)); pap. (978-0-7787-0888-9(8)) Crabtree Publishing Co.

—Follow the Swallow. 2002. (gr. k-3). lib. bdg. 12.95 (978-0-613-52844-3(1)) Tandem Library Bks.

Edwards, Pamela. Oliver Has Something to Say! Pilon, Louis, illus. 2007. 24p. (J). (ps-1). (978-1-897073-52-0(6)) Lobster Pr.

Emigh, Karen. Bookworm. 2007. (Illus.). 21p. (J). (ps-3). pap. 9.95 (***978-1-932565-42-3(6)***) Future Horizons, Inc.

Fair, Sylvia. Big Talk. 1998. (J). (gr. 5-7). pap. 13.95 (978-0-8464-4597-5(2)) Beekman Bks., Inc.

Gaberman, Judith. Bigmouth. 2001. 124p. (gr. 4-7). pap. 9.95 (978-0-595-15798-3(X) , Backinprint.com) iUniverse, Inc.

Grossman, Linda Sky. It's No Joke, My Telephone Broke. Bockus, Petra, illus. (I'm a Great Little Kid Ser.). 24p. (ps-3). 2002. 12.95 (978-1-896764-51-1(7)); 2001. pap. 4.95 (978-1-896764-45-0(2)) Second Story Pr. CAN. *Dist:* Orca Bk. Pubs. USA, Univ. of Toronto Pr.

—Sam Speaks Out. Bockus, Petra, illus. 24p. pap. 4.95 (978-1-896764-57-3(6)); 2002. 11.95 (978-1-896764-59-7(2)) Second Story Pr. CAN. *Dist:* Orca Bk. Pubs. USA.

Heller, Ruth. Up, up & Away: A Book about Adverbs. Heller, Ruth, illus. 1998. (World of Language Ser.). (Illus.). 48p. (J). (gr. k-3). pap. 7.99 (978-0-698-11663-4(1) , Putnam Juvenile) Penguin Group (USA) Inc.

Lofting, Hugh. The Story of Doctor Dolittle: #1 Animal Talk. 2007. (Easy Reader Classics Ser.). 32p. (J). (ps-3). 21.35 (***978-1-59961-338-3(7)***) Spotlight.

MacDonald, Alan. Snarlyhissopus. Voce, Louise, illus. 2002. 32p. (J). pap. 5.95 (978-1-58925-370-4(1)); tchr. ed. 14.95 (978-1-58925-021-5(4)) ME Media LLC. (tiger tales).

—Snarlyhissopus. 2002. (ps-2). lib. bdg. 14.10 (978-0-613-53314-0(3)) Tandem Library Bks.

Mason, Prue. Camel Rider. 2007. 204p. (J). (gr. 5-9). 15.95 (***978-1-58089-314-5(7)***) Charlesbridge Publishing, Inc.

Murray, Marjorie Dennis. Hippo Goes Bananas! O'Malley, Kevin, illus. 2006. 32p. (J). 14.95 (978-0-7614-5224-9(9)) Cavendish, Marshall Corp.

Owens, Greg. Rupert the Wrong-Word Pirate. Beaky, Suzanne, illus. 2006. (J). (978-1-58987-143-4(X)) Kindermusik International.

Parsons, Garry. Krong! Parsons, Garry, illus. 2006. (Illus.). 36p. (J). 15.95 (978-1-58925-061-1(3) , tiger tales) ME Media LLC.

Rand, Ann & Rand, Paul. Sparkle & Spin: A Book about Words. 2006. (Illus.). 40p. (J). 15.95 (978-0-8118-5003-2(X)) Chronicle Bks. LLC.

Rigby Education Staff. Mickey Maloney's Mail. (Sails Literacy Ser.). (Illus.). 16p. (gr. 2-3). 27.00 (978-0-7635-9939-3(5) , 699395C99) Rigby Education.

Seuss, Dr. Gerald McBoing Boing. Seuss, Dr., illus. 2004. (Little Golden Book Ser.). (Illus.). 24p. (J). (gr. k-k). 2.99 (978-0-375-82721-1(8) , Golden Bks.) Random Hse. Children's Bks.

—Gerald McBoing Boing. Crawford, Mel, illus. 2000. 32p. (J). (gr. k-3). 12.95 (978-0-679-89140-6(4) , Random Hse. Bks. for Young Readers) Random Hse. Children's Bks.

Shapiro, Arnold. Mice Squeak, We Speak. de Paola, Tomie, illus. 2000. 32p. (J). (ps-1). pap. 5.99 (978-0-698-11873-7(1) , Putnam Juvenile) Penguin Group (USA) Inc.

—Mice Squeak, We Speak. 2000. (ps-2). lib. bdg. 14.15 (978-0-613-30029-2(7)) Tandem Library Bks.

—Mice Squeak, We Speak. de Paola, Tomie, illus. 2000. (978-0-606-20364-7(8)) Tandem Library Bks.

Simon, Charnan. Come! Sit! Speak! Weissman, Bari, illus. 1998. (Rookie Reader Skill Set Ser.). 32p. (J). (gr. k-2). pap. 4.95 (978-0-516-26250-5(5) , Children's Pr.) Scholastic Library Publishing.

Sweetland, Nancy Rose. Yelly Kelly/Kelly, el Griton. de la Vega, Eida, tr. Sweetland, Robert, illus. rev. ed. 2004. Tr. of Kelly, el Griton. (SPA & ENG.). 32p. (J). (gr. k-3). 16.95 (978-0-9720192-0-0(0) , 626999) Raven Tree Pr.

Thiesing, Lisa. The Aliens Are Coming. 2004. (Illus.). 32p. (J). (ps). 13.99 (978-0-525-47277-3(0) , Dutton Juvenile) Penguin Group (USA) Inc.

Tidd, Louise Vitellaro. Did You Hear about Jake? Handelman, Dorothy, photos by. 1999. (Real Kids Readers Ser.). (Illus.). 32p. (gr. k-2). lib. bdg. 18.90 (978-0-7613-2058-6(X)); (J). pap. 4.99 (978-0-7613-2083-8(0)) Lerner Publishing Group. (Millbrook Pr.).

—Did You Hear about Jake? 1999. (J). 10.79 (978-0-606-19153-1(4)); lib. bdg. 11.80 (978-0-613-16658-4(2)) Tandem Library Bks.

Tidd Louise Vitellaro. ¿Ya te enteraste? (Did You Hear about Jake?) 2007. (Lecturas para niños de verdad - Nivel 2 (Real Kids Readers - Level 2) Ser.). (J). pap. 5.95 (***978-0-8225-7802-4(6)*** , Ediciones Lerner) Lerner Publishing Group.

Wallace, Nancy Elizabeth. Tell-a-Bunny. 2007. 32p. (J). pap. 5.99 (***978-0-7614-5369-7(5)***) Cavendish, Marshall Corp.

Yamanaka, Lois-Ann. The Heart's Language. Jasinski, Aaron, illus. 2005. 32p. (ps-3). 15.99 (978-0-7868-1848-8(4)) Hyperion Bks. for Children.

COMMUNICATION—HISTORY

Cannarella, Deborah & Fournier, Jane. Communication. 1999. (Into the Next Millennium Ser.). (Illus.). 32p. (J). (gr. 4-8). lib. bdg. 27.93 (978-1-57103-271-3(1)) Rourke Publishing, LLC.

Hamilton, Sue L. Communication: A Pictorial History of the Past One Thousand Years. 2000. (Millennium Ser.). (Illus.). 48p. (J). (gr. 3-8). lib. bdg. 25.65 (978-1-57765-359-2(9) , ABDO & Daughters) ABDO Publishing Co.

Hossell, Karen Price. Ciphers & Codes. 2003. (Communicating Ser.). 48p. (J). (gr. 3-5). pap. 8.50 (978-1-58810-940-8(2) , 91579) Heinemann Library.

Jarnow, Jesse. Telegraph & Telephone Networks: Ground Breaking Developments in American Communications. 2003. (America's Industrial Society in the 19th Century Ser.). (Illus.). 32p. (J). pap. (978-0-8239-4279-4(1)) Rosen Publishing Group, Inc., The.

Mary J. Scarbrough. Long-Distance Communication. 2004. (Yesterday & Today Ser.). (Illus.). 32p. (J). 23.70 (978-1-56711-832-2(1) , Blackbirch Pr., Inc.) Thomson Gale.

McCormick, Anita Louise. The Invention of the Telegraph & Telephone in American History. 2004. (In American History Ser.). (Illus.). 128p. (J). lib. bdg. 26.60 (978-0-7660-1841-9(5)) Enslow Pubs., Inc.

Nelson, Robin. Communication. 2003. (First Step Nonfiction Ser.). (Illus.). 24p. (J). (gr. k-2). lib. bdg. 18.60 (978-0-8225-4638-2(8)) Lerner Publishing Group.

Platt, Richard. Technology & Communications. 2001. (Datafiles Ser.). (Illus.). 84p. (J). (gr. 3-7). 15.95 (978-1-57145-479-9(9) , Silver Dolphin Bks.) Advantage Pubs. Group.

Somervill, Barbara A. The History of the Telephone. 2004. (Timeline Library Ser.). 32p. (J). (gr. 2-6). 27.07 (978-1-59296-346-1(3)) Child's World, Inc.

Woods, Mary B. & Woods, Michael. Ancient Communication: From Grunts to Graffiti. 2005. (Ancient Technology Ser.). (Illus.). 96p. (gr. 6-12). 25.26 (978-0-8225-2996-5(3)) Lerner Publishing Group.

Woods, Michael & Woods, Mary B. The History of Communication. 2006. (Major Inventions Through History Ser.). (Illus.). 56p. (J). (gr. 4-7). 26.60 (978-0-8225-3807-3(5) , Twenty-First Century Bks.) Lerner Publishing Group.

Yates, Vicki. Communication. 2007. (***978-1-4034-9829-8(6)***); pap. (***978-1-4034-9837-3(7)***) Heinemann Library.

COMMUNICATION AMONG ANIMALS

see Animal Communication

COMMUNICATIONS RELAY SATELLITES

see Artificial Satellites in Telecommunication

COMMUNISM

see also Anti-Communist Movements; Social Conflict; Socialism

Allan, Tony. The Long March: The Making of Communist China. 2001. (Point of Impact Ser.). (Illus.). 32p. (J). (gr. 5-7). lib. bdg. 24.22 (978-1-58810-073-3(1)) Heinemann Library.

Downing, David & Tames, Richard. Communism. 2003. (Political & Economic Systems Ser.). (Illus.). 64p. (YA). (gr. 5-8). lib. bdg. 28.50 (978-1-4034-0316-2(3)) Heinemann Library.

Grant, R. G. Communism. 2005. (Systems of Government Ser.). (Illus.). 48p. (J). (978-0-8368-5887-7(5)); lib. bdg. 30.00 (978-0-8368-5882-2(4)) Stevens, Gareth Inc. (World Almanac Library).

Jarnow, Jesse. Socialism: A Primary Source Analysis. 2003. (Primary Sources of Political Systems Ser.). (Illus.). 64p. (J). lib. bdg. 29.25 (978-0-8239-4521-4(9)) Rosen Publishing Group, Inc., The.

Keeley, Jennifer. Containing the Communists: America's Foreign Entanglements. 2003. (American War Library). (Illus.). 112p. (J). 29.95 (978-1-59018-225-3(1) , Lucent Bks.) Thomson Gale.

Lansford, Tom. Communism. 2007. (Political Systems of the World Ser.). 160p. (YA). (gr. 9 up). lib. bdg. 39.93 (978-0-7614-2628-8(0) , Benchmark Bks.) Cavendish, Marshall Corp.

Malaspina, Ann. The Chinese Revolution & Mao Zedong in World History. 2004. (In World History Ser.). (Illus.). 128p. (J). lib. bdg. 26.60 (978-0-7660-1935-5(7)) Enslow Pubs., Inc.

Miller, Debra A. North Korea. 2004. (Modern Nations of the World Ser.). (Illus.). 112p. (J). 29.95 (978-1-59018-118-8(2) , Lucent Bks.) Thomson Gale.

Porterfield, Jason. Communism: A Primary Source Analysis. 2003. (Primary Sources of Political Systems Ser.). (Illus.). 64p. (J). 29.25 (978-0-8239-4517-7(0)) Rosen Publishing Group, Inc., The.

Rise & Fall of Communism. 2003. spiral bd. 16.95 (978-1-56004-172-6(2)) Social Studies Schl. Service.

Ritchie, Nigel. Communism. 2001. (Ideas of the Modern World Ser.). (Illus.). 64p. (YA). (gr. 7-9). lib. bdg. 25.69 (978-0-7398-3158-8(5)) Raintree.

Ross, Stewart. The Collapse of Communism. 2004. (Illus.). 56p. (J). pap. 8.95 (978-1-4034-5525-3(2)); lib. bdg. 27.07 (978-1-4034-4865-1(5)) Heinemann Library.

COMMUNISM—FICTION

Compestine, Ying Chang. Revolution Is Not a Dinner Party. 2007. 256p. (YA). (gr. 5 up). 16.95 (***978-0-8050-8207-4(7)*** , Holt, Henry & Co. Bks. For Young Readers) Holt, Henry & Co.

Durbin, William. Darkest Evening. 2004. 240p. (J). (gr. 7 up). pap. 15.95 (978-0-439-37307-4(7) , Orchard Bks.) Scholastic, Inc.

Fine, Anne. The Road of Bones. 2008. 224p. (YA). 16.95 (***978-0-374-36316-1(1)***) Farrar, Straus & Giroux.

Heuston, Kimberley Burton. Book of Jude. 2008. (J). (***978-1-932425-26-0(8)*** , Front Street) Boyds Mills Pr.

Szablya, Helen M. & Anderson, Peggy King. The Fall of the Red Star. 2003. 168p. (YA). (gr. 4-6). pap. 9.95 (978-1-56397-977-4(2)) Boyds Mills Pr.

COMMUNISM—SOVIET UNION

Downing, David. Vladimir Ilyich Lenin. 2002. (Leading Lives Ser.). 64p. (J). (gr. 5-7). (Illus.). lib. bdg. 28.50 (978-1-58810-582-0(2)); pap. 8.95 (978-1-4034-0137-3(3) , 91616) Heinemann Library.

Naden, Corinne J. & Blue, Rose. Lenin. 2003. (Importance of Ser.). (Illus.). 112p. (J). 32.45 (978-1-59018-233-8(2) , Lucent Bks.) Thomson Gale.

Ross, Stewart. The Collapse of Communism. 2004. (Illus.). 56p. (J). pap. 8.95 (978-1-4034-5525-3(2)); lib. bdg. 27.07 (978-1-4034-4865-1(5)) Heinemann Library.

COMMUNIST COUNTRIES

Keeley, Jennifer. Containing the Communists: America's Foreign Entanglements. 2003. (American War Library). (Illus.). 112p. (J). 29.95 (978-1-59018-225-3(1) , Lucent Bks.) Thomson Gale.

COMMUNITY CHESTS

see Fund Raising

COMMUNITY LIFE

see also Cities and Towns

Ajmera, Maya & Ivanko, John D. Be My Neighbor. 2004. (Illus.). 32p. (J). (gr. k-3). 15.95 (978-1-57091-504-8(0)) Charlesbridge Publishing, Inc.

—Be My Neighbor: With Words of Wisdom from Fred Rogers. 2006. 32p. (J). pap. 6.95 (978-1-57091-685-4(3)) Charlesbridge Publishing, Inc.

—Ser Vecinos. 2007. (SPA.). (J). 16.95 (978-1-57091-703-5(5)); pap. 7.95 (***978-1-57091-704-2(3)***) Charlesbridge Publishing, Inc.

Around the Neighborhood: Take-Home Book. 2005. (Lee Bennett Hopkins Worlds of Poetry Classroom Library). (YA). (gr. k-3). 13.50 (978-0-8215-0567-0(X)) Sadlier, William H. Inc.

Beckman, Paula J. My Community, My Family. 2001. (Me, Too! Ser.). (Illus.). 20p. pap. 19.95 (978-1-55766-511-9(7) , 5117) Brookes, Paul H. Publishing Co.

Benchmark Education Staff. Living in a Community. 2005. 2.00 (***978-1-4108-4665-5(2)***) Benchmark Education Co.

Benchmark Education Staff, compiled by. Living in Communities. 2006. spiral bd. 279.00 (***978-1-4108-7067-4(7)***) Benchmark Education Co.

—Social Studies Theme: Communities. 2005. spiral bd. 115.00 (***978-1-4108-5329-5(2)***) Benchmark Education Co.

—19th Century Communities. 2006. spiral bd. 109.00 (***978-1-4108-7099-5(5)***) Benchmark Education Co.

Bergstrom, Joan M. Community Unity. 1999. (Illus.). 197p. (J). (gr. k-6). 29.95 (978-1-931042-00-0(4)) Activities Club, Inc., The.

Bial, Raymond. Early American Villages. 2004. (American Community Ser.). (Illus.). 48p. (J). 29.00 (978-0-516-23704-6(7) , Children's Pr.) Scholastic Library Publishing.

Boehm, Richard G., et al. Activity Books: Communities. 2003. (Harcourt Brace Social Studies). (gr. k-7). act. bk. ed. 13.80 (978-0-15-310310-0(8)) Harcourt Schl. Pubs.

—Assessment Programs: Communities. 2003. (Harcourt Brace Social Studies). (gr. k-7). 50.60 (978-0-15-310299-8(3)) Harcourt Schl. Pubs.

—Game Time! Communities. 2003. (Harcourt Brace Social Studies). (gr. k-7). 7.30 (978-0-15-312355-9(9)) Harcourt Schl. Pubs.

Brighter Vision Publishing Staff. About the Neighborhood. (My Discovery Bks.). (ps). 2000. (Illus.). 20p. (J). pap. 2.95 (978-1-55254-203-3(3)); 1998. pap. 7.95 (978-1-55254-034-3(0)); 1998. 32p. (J). pap. 3.99 (978-1-55254-002-2(2)) Brighter Vision Pubns.

Catalano, Angela. Community Plans: Economic Decision Making in Communities. 2005. (Communities at Work Ser.). (Illus.). 24p. (J). 19.95 (978-1-4042-2779-8(2) , PowerKids Pr.) Rosen Publishing Group, Inc., The.

—Community Plans: Making Choices about Money in Communities. 2005. (Communities at Work Ser.). (Illus.). 24p. (J). pap. (978-1-4042-5014-7(X) , PowerKids Pr.) Rosen Publishing Group, Inc., The.

—Community Resources: Human, Capital, & Natural Resources in Communities. 2005. (Communities at Work Ser.). (Illus.). 24p. (J). 19.95 (978-1-4042-2781-1(4) , PowerKids Pr.) Rosen Publishing Group, Inc., The.

—Community Resources: The Land & the People in Communities. 2005. (Communities at Work Ser.). (Illus.). 24p. (J). pap. (978-1-4042-5016-1(6) , PowerKids Pr.) Rosen Publishing Group, Inc., The.

—Community Spirit: Symbols of Citizenship in Communities. 2005. (Communities at Work Ser.). (J). 19.95 (978-1-4042-2784-2(9) , PowerKids Pr.) Rosen Publishing Group, Inc., The.

Claycomb, Patty. Community Places: Ages 3-5. 2002. (Early Learner Photo Fun Activities Ser.). 8p. 6.95 (978-1-56472-383-3(6)) Edupress, Inc.

Community Helpers Puppet Set, Series 2. 2006. (J). per. (978-1-57332-430-4(2)) HighReach Learning, Inc.

Cowen-Fletcher, Jane. Se Necesita Todo un Pueblo. 2003. (SPA., Illus.). (J). pap. 4.76 net. (978-0-590-29394-5(X) , SO30915) Scholastic, Inc.

Donnelly, Karen. Biomes of the Past & Future. 2003. (Earths Changing Weather & Climate Ser.). (Illus.). 24p. (J). lib. bdg. 18.75 (978-0-8239-6215-0(6) , PowerKids Pr.) Rosen Publishing Group, Inc., The.

Emmer, Rae. Community Service. 2002. (Reading Power Ser.). (Illus.). 24p. (J). (gr. 1). lib. bdg. 17.25 (978-0-8239-5967-9(8) , PowerKids Pr.) Rosen Publishing Group, Inc., The.

Fenner, Matthew. On My Block: Learning the BL Sound. (PowerPhonics Ser.). (Illus.). (J). 2002. 24p. (gr. 1). lib. bdg. 18.50 (978-0-8239-5924-2(4)); 2001. 23p. pap. 26.40 (978-0-8239-8269-1(6)) Rosen Publishing Group, Inc., The. (PowerKids Pr.).

Gillis, Jennifer Blizin. Ayudantes Del Vecindario/Jennifer B. Gillis. 2007. (SPA & ENG., Illus.). 24p. (J). (***978-1-60044-292-6(7)***) Rourke Publishing, LLC.

—Neighborhood Helpers. 2007. (Illus.). 24p. (J). (978-1-60044-203-2(X)) Rourke Publishing, LLC.

—Puedes Ayudar/Jennifer Gillis. 2007. (SPA & ENG., Illus.). 24p. (J). (***978-1-60044-295-7(1)***) Rourke Publishing, LLC.

Gillis, Jennifer Blizin. You Can Help! 2007. (Illus.). 24p. (J). (978-1-60044-206-3(4)) Rourke Publishing, LLC.

Gresko, Marcia S. A World of Communities. 1998. (Illus.). (J). (gr. 3-5). 80p. pap. 17.45 (978-1-56711-297-9(8)); 32p. pap., act. bk. ed. 11.20 (978-1-56711-298-6(6)) Thomson Gale. (Blackbirch Pr., Inc.).

Harcourt School Publishers Staff. Building a Better Community. 3rd ed. 2002. (Horizons Ser.). (Illus.). (J). pap. 3.70 (978-0-15-333189-3(5)) Harcourt Schl. Pubs.

—Horizons Unit 1: Living in the Community. 3rd ed. 2001. (Illus.). (gr. 2). pap. 169.80 (978-0-15-322576-5(9)) Harcourt Schl. Pubs.

—Living in Our World. 97th ed. 1998. (Stories in Time Ser.). (gr. 3). tchr. ed. 148.00 (978-0-15-302046-9(6)); (Illus.). 58.10 (978-0-15-302039-1(3)) Harcourt Schl. Pubs.

—Living in the Community, Bk. 1. 2nd ed. 2003. (Illus.). pap. 139.70 (978-0-15-337563-7(9)) Harcourt Schl. Pubs.

Johnston, Marianne. Our Community, 6 bks. Incl. Let's Visit the Bank. lib. bdg. 18.75 (978-0-8239-5432-2(3)); Let's Visit the Fire Station. lib. bdg. 18.75 (978-0-8239-5435-3(8)); Let's Visit the Library. lib. bdg. 18.75 (978-0-8239-5431-5(5)); Let's Visit the Police Station. lib. bdg. 18.75 (978-0-8239-5434-6(X)); Let's Visit the Post Office. lib. bdg. 18.75 (978-0-8239-5433-9(1)); Let's Visit the Supermarket. lib. bdg. 18.75 (978-0-8239-5436-0(6)); 24p. (J). (gr. 3). (Illus.). 2000. Set lib. bdg. 103.50 (978-0-8239-7011-7(6) , PowerKids Pr.) Rosen Publishing Group, Inc., The.

Kalman, Bobbie. What Is a Community? From A to Z. 2000. (978-0-606-18070-2(2)) Tandem Library Bks.

—What Is a Community? from A to Z. 1999. (AlphaBasiCs Ser.). (Illus.). 32p. (J). (gr. 2-3). pap. (978-0-86505-414-1(2)); lib. bdg. (978-0-86505-384-7(7)) Crabtree Publishing Co.

—What Is a Community? from A to Z. 2000. (gr. 3-6). lib. bdg. 16.40 (978-0-613-22603-5(8)) Tandem Library Bks.

Katz, Welwyn W. Come Like Shadows. Springett, Martin, illus. 2005. 318p. (gr. 7-12). 7.95 (978-1-55050-170-4(4)) Coteau Bks. CAN. *Dist:* Fitzhenry & Whiteside, Ltd.

LeapFrog Staff, compiled by. Neighborhood: (Blue Book) 2002. (J). (ps-2). 19.95 (978-1-58605-692-6(1)) LeapFrog Enterprises, Inc.

—Neighborhood: (Green Book) 2002. (J). (ps-2). 19.95 (978-1-58605-690-2(5)) LeapFrog Enterprises, Inc.

—Neighborhood: (Orange Book) 2002. (J). (ps-2). 19.95 (978-1-58605-691-9(3)) LeapFrog Enterprises, Inc.

—Neighborhood: (Purple Book) 2002. (J). (ps-2). 19.95 (978-1-58605-689-6(1)) LeapFrog Enterprises, Inc.

Lesko, Wendy Schaetzel. Youth: The 26% Solution, 1. 1998. (YA). pap. 14.95 (978-1-878346-47-6(4)) Information U.S.A., Inc.

Linde, Barbara M. Living in a Community. 2005. 39.00 (***978-1-4108-4617-4(2)***) Benchmark Education Co.

Low, Robert S., ed. My Guide to Our Community. 2001. 32p. (J). (gr. 2-3). pap., wbk. ed. 3.25 (978-1-56762-142-6(2)) Modern Learning Pr.

Michels, Dia L. Look What I See! Where Can I Be?, 3 vols. 2001. (Look What I See! Where Can I Be? Ser.). (Illus.). (J). 39.95 (978-1-930775-37-4(7)) Platypus Media, L.L.C.

Miller, Jake. Community Needs: Meeting Needs & Wants in Communities. 2005. (Communities at Work Ser.). (Illus.). 24p. (J). 19.95 (978-1-4042-2780-4(6)); pap. (978-1-4042-5012-3(3)) Rosen Publishing Group, Inc., The. (PowerKids Pr.).

—Who's Who in a Neighborhood. 2005. (Communities at Work Ser.). (Illus.). 24p. (J). 19.95 (978-1-4042-2785-9(7)); pap. (978-1-4042-5024-6(7)) Rosen Publishing Group, Inc., The. (PowerKids Pr.).

—Who's Who in a Public Housing Community. 2005. (Communities at Work Ser.). (Illus.). 24p. (J). 19.95 (978-1-4042-2786-6(5)); pap. (978-1-4042-5026-0(3)) Rosen Publishing Group, Inc., The. (PowerKids Pr.).

—Who's Who in a Rural Community. 2005. (Communities at Work Ser.). (Illus.). 24p. (J). (gr. 2-4). lib. bdg. 19.95 (978-1-4042-2787-3(3) , PowerKids Pr.) Rosen Publishing Group, Inc., The.

—Who's Who in a Suburban Community. 2005. (Communities at Work Ser.). (Illus.). 24p. (J). (gr. 2-4). lib. bdg. 19.95 (978-1-4042-2789-7(X) , PowerKids Pr.) Rosen Publishing Group, Inc., The.

—Who's Who in an Urban Community. 2005. (Communities at Work Ser.). 19.95 (978-1-4042-2790-3(3) , PowerKids Pr.) Rosen Publishing Group, Inc., The.

Miller, Michelle. Aggie & Rowdy Say No Way to Cigarettes: Dog Tales, Cancer Stories for Kids. 2007. 53p. pap. 12.99 (***978-1-58752-258-1(6)***) Timberwolf Pr., Inc.

North, Merry. My Neighborhood. Adams, Lynn, illus. 1999. (Giant Flap Bks.). 10p. (J). (ps-k). bds. (978-1-57584-346-9(3) , Reader's Digest Children's Bks.) Reader's Digest Children's Publishing, Inc.

Press, Judy. All Around Town! Exploring Your Community Through Craft Fun. 2002. (Williamson's Little Hands Book Ser.). (Illus.). 128p. (J). (ps-3). pap. 12.95 (978-1-885593-68-9(6) , Williamson Bks.) Ideals Pubns.

Ready, Dee. Servidores Comunitarios (Community Helpers), 10 bks. Ferrer, Martín Luis Guzman, tr. Incl. Bibliotecarios y Bibliotecarias. Schon, Isabel, ed. (gr. 1-2). lib. bdg. 18.60 (978-1-56065-799-6(5)); Bomberos y Bomberas. Schon, Isabel, ed. (gr. 2-4). lib. bdg. 18.60 (978-1-56065-797-2(9)); Carteros y Carteras. Schon, Isabel, ed. (gr. 1-2). lib. bdg. 18.60 (978-1-56065-800-9(2)); Choferes de Autobuses Escolares. Schon, Isabel, ed. (gr. 1-2). lib. bdg. 18.60 (978-1-56065-803-0(7)); Dentistas. (gr. 1-2). lib. bdg. 18.60 (978-1-56065-795-8(2)); Doctores y Doctoras. Schon, Isabel, ed. (gr. 1-2). lib. bdg. 18.60 (978-1-56065-796-5(0)); Enfermeras y Enfermeros. Schon, Isabel, ed. (gr. 1-2). lib. bdg. 18.60 (978-1-56065-801-6(0)); Granjeros y Granjeras. Schon, Isabel, ed. (gr. 1-2). lib. bdg. 18.60 (978-1-56065-798-9(7)); Policias. Schon, Isabel, ed. (gr. 1-2). lib. bdg. 18.60 (978-1-56065-802-3(9)); Veterinarios y Veterinarias. Schon, Isabel, ed. (gr. 1-2). lib. bdg. 18.60 (978-1-56065-804-7(5)); 24p. (J). 1998. (SPA., Illus.). Set lib. bdg. 186.00 (978-0-7368-0147-8(2) , Bridgestone Bks.) Capstone Pr., Inc.

Riehecky, Janet. Citizenship. 2005. (First Facts Ser.). (Illus.). 24p. (J). 21.26 (978-0-7368-3676-0(4)) Capstone Pr., Inc.

Robson, Pam. My Town. 2004. (Earthwise Ser.). (J). lib. bdg. 27.10 (978-1-932799-49-1(4)) Stargazer Bks.

Scholastic, Inc. Staff. Scholastic Word Wall Bulletin Boardsets: Neighborhood Prepack. 2002. (Scholastic Word Wall Bulletin Boards Ser.). pap. 8.95 (978-0-439-35410-3(2) , Teaching Resources) Scholastic, Inc.

Schuh, Mari C. In My Neighborhood. 2006. (Illus.). 24p. (J). (978-0-7368-4239-6(X)) Capstone Pr., Inc.

Steck-Vaughn Staff. Social Studies Level J-M: Communities Around the World. 2003. (Illus.). pap. (978-0-7398-7688-6(0)) Steck-Vaughn.

Sterling, Kristin. Suburban Communities. 2008. (First Step Nonfiction - Communities Ser.). (J). lib. bdg. 18.60 (***978-0-8225-8598-5(7)*** , Lerner Pubns.) Lerner Publishing Group.

Thomas, Maryann. I Jog Around: Learning the J Sound. (PowerPhonics Ser.). (Illus.). (J). 2002. 24p. (gr. 1). lib. bdg. 18.50 (978-0-8239-5932-7(5)); 2001. 23p. pap. 26.40 (978-0-8239-8277-6(7)) Rosen Publishing Group, Inc., The. (PowerKids Pr.).

Treays, Rebecca. My Street. Wells, R., illus. 1999. (Young Geography Ser.). (SPA.). 24p. (J). (gr. 1 up). pap. 8.95 (978-0-7460-3077-6(0) , EDC0770) EDC Publishing.

Trumbauer, Lisa. Communities. Saunders-Smith, Gail, ed. 2005. (Pebble Ser.). (Illus.). (J). (gr. k-1). lib. bdg. 63.72 (978-0-7368-3798-9(1)) Capstone Pr., Inc.

—Communities. 2000. (Yellow Umbrella Books). (Illus.). 16p. (J). (gr. 1). lib. bdg. 14.60 (978-0-7368-0744-9(6) , Pebble Bks.) Capstone Pr., Inc.

Weiss, Ellen. Math in the Neighborhood. 2007. (Scholastic News Nonfiction Readers: Everyday Math—NEW SUBSET Ser.). 24p. (J). pap. 6.95 (***978-0-531-18785-2(3)***); (Illus.). (gr. 1-2). lib. bdg. 20.00 (***978-0-531-18532-2(X)***) Scholastic Library Publishing. (Children's Pr.).

Willis, Tammy A., ed. Community Helpers Puppet Set, Series 1. 2006. (J). per. (978-1-57332-400-7(0)) HighReach Learning, Inc.

Yoon, Salina. My Little Shimmery Neighborhood, 4 vols. Yoon, Salina, illus. 2002. (Illus.). 12p. (J). bds. 5.95 (978-1-58117-164-8(1) , Intervisual/Piggy Toes) Dalmatian Pr.

COMMUNITY LIFE—FICTION

Baggette, Susan K. Jonathan Goes to the Grocery Store. Moriarty, William J., photos by. 1998. (Jonathan Adventures Ser.). (Illus.). 16p. (J). (ps-k). bds. 5.95 (978-0-9660172-2-9(6)) Brookfield Reader, Inc., The.

—Jonathan Goes to the Library. Moriarty, William J., photos by. 1998. (Jonathan Adventures Ser.). (Illus.). 16p. (J). (ps-k). bds. 5.95 (978-0-9660172-3-6(4)) Brookfield Reader, Inc., The.

Barboza, Steven. Sugar Hill. 1998. 96p. (J). (978-0-7868-0130-5(1)) Hyperion Pr.

Bourgeois, Paulette. Franklin's Neighborhood. Clark, Brenda, illus. 1999. (Franklin Ser.). (J). (ps-3). 32p. (978-1-55074-704-1(5)); 270p. (978-1-55074-702-7(9)) Kids Can Pr., Ltd.

Bridwell, Norman. Clifford's Neighborhood: Lots to Learn Around Town. Bracken, Carolyn & Edwards, Ken, illus. 2002. (Clifford, the Big Red Dog Ser.). 10p. (J). (ps-k). pap. 10.99 (978-0-439-33242-2(7) , Cartwheel Bks.) Scholastic, Inc.

Bullard, Lisa. My Neighborhood: Places & Faces. Wesley, Omarr, illus. 2004. (All about Me Ser.). 24p. (C). (gr. k-1). 21.26 (978-1-4048-0047-2(6)) Picture Window Bks.

Burton, Margie, et al. Community Jobs. Adams, Alison, ed. 1999. (Early Connections Ser.). 16p. (J). (gr. k-2). pap. 4.50 (978-1-58344-058-2(5)) Benchmark Education Co.

Caseley, Judith. On the Town: A Community Adventure. Caseley, Judith, illus. 2002. (Illus.). 32p. (J). (gr. k-2). 16.99 (978-0-06-029584-4(8)); lib. bdg. 17.89 (978-0-06-029585-1(6)) HarperCollins Pubs.

Choyce, Lesley. Thunderbowl. 2004. (Orca Soundings Ser.). 112p. (J). (gr. 7-12). pap. 7.95 (978-1-55143-277-9(3)) Orca Bk. Pubs. USA.

Clover, Peter. Hercules: New Pup on the Block. l.t. ed. 2005. (Illus.). 200p. (J). pap. (978-0-7540-6162-5(0) , CLP 353) BBC Audio.

Cushman, Doug. Inspector Hopper. Cushman, Doug, illus. 2001. (I Can Read Bks.). (Illus.). 64p. (J). (ps-3). pap. 3.99 (978-0-06-444260-2(8) , Harper Trophy) HarperCollins Pubs.

—Inspector Hopper. 2001. (gr. k-3). lib. bdg. 11.80 (978-0-613-31359-9(3)); (Illus.). (J). 10.79 (978-0-606-20477-4(6)) Tandem Library Bks.

—Inspector Hopper's Mystery Year, No. 2. Cushman, Doug, illus. 2003. (I Can Read Bks.). (Illus.). 64p. (J). (gr. k-3). 15.99 (978-0-06-008962-7(8)); 16.89 (978-0-06-008963-4(6)) HarperCollins Pubs.

Davis, Guy. Barney's Neighborhood. Davis, Guy, illus. Dipold, Jane, photos by. 1999. (Barney Ser.). (Illus.). 18p. (J). (ps-k). 6.95 (978-1-57064-463-4(2)) Scholastic, Inc.

DeLaCroix, Alice. How to Survive a Totally Boring Summer. Fisher, Cynthia, illus. 2007. 96p. (J). (gr. 1-4). 16.95 (***978-0-8234-2024-7(8)***) Holiday Hse., Inc.

DiSalvo-Ryan, DyAnne. Grandpa's Corner Store. DiSalvo-Ryan, DyAnne, illus. 2000. (Illus.). 40p. (J). (gr. k-3). 16.99 (978-0-688-16716-5(0)) HarperCollins Pubs.

—Grandpa's Corner Store. 2000. (Illus.). 40p. (J). (gr. k-3). 15.89 (978-0-688-16717-2(9)) HarperCollins Pubs.

Dunkling, Leslie. Battle of Newton Road. 2002. (Illus.). 16p. pap. (978-0-582-42770-9(3) , Putnam Juvenile) Penguin Group (USA) Inc.

Elliott, David. The Transmogrification of Roscoe Wizzle. 2004. (Illus.). 128p. (J). (gr. 2-5). reprint ed. pap. 5.99 (978-0-7636-1880-3(2)) Candlewick Pr.

Firmin, Josie. My Week. Firmin, Josie, illus. 2001. (Illus.). 12p. (J). (gr. k-k). 6.99 (978-0-7636-1548-2(X)) Candlewick Pr.

Forest, Heather. Stone Soup. 2000. (gr. 3-6). lib. bdg. 15.25 (978-0-613-54363-7(7)) Tandem Library Bks.

Grahame, Kenneth. The Wind in the Willows. 1999. (978-0-606-17323-0(4)) Tandem Library Bks.

Group/McGraw-Hill, Wright. The Bazaar, 6 vols. (D-Man Beans Ser.). 47p. (gr. 4-6). 42.50 (978-0-322-06260-3(8)) Wright Group, The.

—Who Is Tuffy 2000?, 6 vols. (D-Man Beans Ser.). 47p. (gr. 4-6). 42.50 (978-0-322-06261-0(6)) Wright Group, The.

Hall, Kirsten. My New Town. Suzan, Gerardo, illus. (J). (gr. k-1). 2006. 32p. pap. 3.95 (978-0-516-24972-8(X)); 2005. 31p. 18.50 (978-0-516-24877-6(4)) Scholastic Library Publishing. (Children's Pr.).

Hambrick, Sharon. Tommy's Clubhouse. Manning, Maurie, tr. Manning, Maurie, illus. 2003. (Fig Street Kids Ser.). 78p. (J). (gr. 1-2). pap. 7.49 (978-1-57924-993-9(0)) Jones, Bob Univ. Pr.

Harris, Erin. Elephant on My Roof. Harris, Erin, illus. 2006. (Illus.). 32p. (J). 15.95 (978-1-60108-002-8(6)) Red Cygnet Pr.

Herman, Gail. New Dog in Town. Nez, John, illus. 2006. 32p. (J). lib. bdg. 20.00 (***978-1-4242-1110-4(7)***) Fitzgerald Bks.

Herrera, Juan Felipe. Grandma & Me at the Flea / Los Meros Meros Remateros. Rohmer, Harriet & Cumpiano, Ina, eds. Lucio-Brock, Anita de, illus. 2002. Tr. of Los Meros Meros Remateros. (ENG & SPA.). 32p. (J). (gr. 1 up). 16.95 (978-0-89239-171-4(5)) Children's Bk. Pr.

hooks, bell. Skin Again. Raschka, Chris, illus. 2004. 32p. (ps-3). 16.99 (978-0-7868-0825-0(X)) Hyperion Bks. for Children.

Hutton, Linda & Murley, Karen. Every Monday Morning. 2005. (J). 10.99 (978-0-8254-2895-1(5)) Kregel Pubns.

Johnson, James Weldon. Lift Every Voice & Sing. Gilchrist, Jan Spivey, illus. 2002. 32p. (J). pap. 5.99 (978-0-439-35106-5(5) , Scholastic Pr.) Scholastic, Inc.

Jones, Shelley. My Street. 2000. (gr. k-3). lib. bdg. 11.80 (978-0-613-29706-6(7)) Tandem Library Bks.

Lawlor, Laurie. The Worst Kid Who Ever Lived on Eighth Avenue: A Holiday House Reader. Fisher, Cynthia, illus. 48p. (J). (gr. k-3). tchr. ed. 14.95 (978-0-8234-1350-8(0)) Holiday Hse., Inc.

Leblanc, Louise. Leo's Poster Challenge. Prud'homme, Jules & Cummins, Sarah, trs. from FRE. Prud'homme, Jules, illus. 2003. (First Novel Ser.). 64p. (J). (gr. 2-5). 4.95 (978-0-88780-608-7(2)) Formac Publishing Co., Ltd. CAN. *Dist:* Casemate Pubs. & Bk. Distributors, LLC.

—Leo's Poster Challenge. Prud'homme, Jules & Cummins, Sarah, trs. from FRE. Prud'homme, Jules & Jules, Prud'homme, illus. 2003. (First Novel Ser.). 64p. (J). (gr. 2-5). (***978-0-88780-609-4(0)***) Formac Publishing Co., Ltd. CAN. *Dist:* Casemate Pubs. & Bk. Distributors, LLC.

Leon, Ulalume Gonzales de. Las Tres Manzanas de Naranja. 2001. (SPA.). (J). (gr. 3-5). pap. 8.40 (978-968-494-003-1(3)) Centro de Informacion y la Literatura MEX. *Dist:* Lectorum Pubns., Inc.

Lowry, Lois. Messenger. 2004. 176p. (YA). (gr. 7 up). tchr. ed. 16.00 (978-0-618-40441-4(4) , Walter Lorraine) Houghton Mifflin Co. Trade & Reference Div.

—Messenger. 2006. 192p. (YA). (gr. 7). pap. 8.95 (978-0-385-73253-6(8) , Delacorte Bks. for Young Readers) Random Hse. Children's Bks.

—Messenger. l.t. ed. 2004. 184p. 23.95 (978-0-7862-6686-9(4) , Large Print Pr.) Thorndike Pr.

Martin, Bill, Jr. Yo Grocer. 2001. (J). 16.95 (978-0-8050-6351-6(X) , Holt, Henry & Co. Bks. For Young Readers) Holt, Henry & Co.

McGovern, Ann. The Lady in the Box. Backer, Marni, illus. 1999. 40p. (J). (ps up). pap. 9.95 (978-1-890515-15-7(9)) Turtle Bks.

Mills, David. Mei Ling's Hiccups. Brazell, Derek, illus. 2004. (J). (TAM, CZE, VIE, SPA & GUJ.). 24p. (978-1-85269-552-1(8)); (TAM, CZE, VIE, SPA & GUJ.). 24p. (978-1-85269-554-5(4)); (TAM, CZE, VIE, SPA & GUJ.). 24p. (978-1-85269-556-9(0)); (TAM, CZE, VIE, SPA & GUJ.). 24p. (978-1-85269-557-6(9)); (TAM, CZE, VIE, SPA & GUJ.). 24p. (978-1-85269-559-0(5)); (CZE, TAM, VIE, SPA & GUJ.). 24p. (978-1-85269-566-8(8)); (TAM, CZE, VIE, SPA & GUJ.). 24p. (978-1-85269-567-5(6)); (TAM, CZE, SPA, VIE & GUJ.). 24p. (978-1-85269-569-9(2)); (TAM, CZE, VIE, SPA & GUJ.). 24p. (978-1-85269-704-4(0)); (TAM, CZE, VIE, SPA & GUJ.). 23p. (978-1-85269-558-3(7)); (TAM, CZE, VIE, SPA & GUJ.). 23p. (978-1-85269-561-3(7)); (TAM, CZE, VIE, SPA & GUJ.). 23p. (978-1-85269-568-2(4)); (TAM, CZE, VIE, SPA & GUJ.). 24p. (978-1-85269-560-6(9)); (TAM, CZE, VIE, SPA & GUJ.). 24p. (978-1-85269-553-8(6)); (TAM, CZE, VIE, SPA & GUJ.). 24p. (978-1-85269-555-2(2)) Mantra Publishing, Ltd.

Mills, David & Brazell, Derek, illus. Mei Ling's Hiccups. 2004. (TAM, CZE, VIE, SPA & GUJ.). (J). 23p. (978-1-85269-563-7(3)); 24p. (978-1-85269-562-0(5)); 24p. (978-1-85269-565-1(X)); 24p. (978-1-85269-626-9(5)); 24p. (978-1-85269-682-5(6)) Mantra Publishing, Ltd.

Orion the Skateboard Kid. 2001. 63p. (YA). per. 9.95 (978-0-9672585-0-8(2)) CyPress Pubns.

Our Town. 1999. (YA). 9.95 (978-1-56137-625-4(6)) Novel Units, Inc.

Perkyns, Dorothy. Last Days in Africville. 2005. (Illus.). 144p. (YA). pap., tchr. ed. (978-0-88878-446-9(5) , Sandcastle Bks.) Dundurn Group, The.

—Last Days in Africville. 2006. 120p. (J). pap. 10.99 (*978-1-55002-630-6(5) , Dundurn Pr.) Dundurn Group, The CAN. *Dist:* Univ. of Toronto Pr.

Rey, H. A. & Rey, Margret. Curious George's Neighborhood: A Lift-the-Flap Adventure. Weston, Martha, illus. 2004. 10p. (J). (gr. k-3). bds. 7.99 (978-0-618-41203-7(4)) Houghton Mifflin Co. Trade & Reference Div.

Ross, Tony. Stone Soup: Grades K-3. 2001. (Literature Units Ser.). (Illus.). 48p. pap., tchr. ed. 7.99 (978-0-7439-3005-5(3) , TCA3005) Teacher Created Materials, Inc.

Santillo, LuAnn. Community Helpers, 6 vols. Santillo, LuAnn, ed. 2003. (Half-Pint Kids Readers Ser.). 42p. (J). (ps-1). pap. 6.99 (978-1-59256-119-3(5)) Half-Pint Kids, Inc.

Sasso, Sandy Eisenberg. God in Between. Sweetland, Sally, illus. 1998. 32p. (J). (ps-3). 16.95 (978-1-879045-86-6(9)) Jewish Lights Publishing.

Slyder, Ingrid. Fabulous Flying Fandinis. Slyder, Ingrid, illus. 1999. 32p. (J). pap. 4.99 (978-0-14-056266-8(4) , Puffin) Penguin Group (USA) Inc.

Starke, Ruth. Stella by the Sea: Stella's Not Just an Ordinary Girl in an Ordinary World! 2006. (Chomps Ser.) (Illus.). 96p. (J). (gr. 3-7). pap. 3.95 (978-0-7624-2625-6(X) , Running Pr. Kids) Running Pr. Bk. Pubs.

Tarpley, Natasha Anastasia. Destiny's Gift. Burrowes, Adjoa J., tr. Burrowes, Adjoa J., illus. 2004. 32p. (J). 16.95 (978-1-58430-156-1(2)) Lee & Low Bks., Inc.

Taulbert, Clifton L. Little Cliff & the Porch People. Kane, Cindy, ed. Lewis, Earl, illus. 1999. 32p. (J). (ps-3). 16.99 (978-0-8037-2174-6(9) , Dial) Penguin Group (USA) Inc.

Thomas, Joyce Carol. Marked by Fire. rev. ed. 2007. 192p. (YA). (gr. 8-17). 15.99 (*978-1-4231-0143-7(X)); pap. 7.99 (*978-1-4231-0144-4(8)) Hyperion Bks. for Children. (Jump at the Sun).

Velasquez, Crystal. Neighborhood Friends. 2005. (Maya & Miguel Ser.: No. 1). 96p. (J). (ps-ps). pap. 3.99 (978-0-439-73384-7(7)) Scholastic, Inc.

Waber, Bernard. Betty's Day Off. Date not set. (J). (978-0-618-46875-1(7)) Houghton Mifflin Co.

Warbelow, Willy Lou & Warbelow-Tack, Cyndie, illus. The Guffinys Too. 1999. 104p. (J). (gr. 2-6). 19.95 (978-0-9618314-4-8(8)) Warbelow, Willy Lou.

White, Ruth. Way down Deep. 2007. (Illus.). 208p. (J). (gr. 5 up). 16.00 (978-0-374-38251-3(4) , Farrar, Straus & Giroux (BYR)) Farrar, Straus & Giroux.

COMMUNITY SCHOOLS

see Schools

COMMUNITY SONGBOOKS

see Songbooks

COMPACT DISC READ-ONLY MEMORY

see CD-ROMs

COMPACT DISCS

Here are entered works on small optical disks in general as well as audio compact discs.

see also CD-ROMs

Bernard, Yves & Fredette, Nathalie. Le Guide de la Musique du Monde. 2004. (FRE., Illus.). 230p. (J). pap. (978-2-89021-662-4(4)) Diffusion du livre Mirabel.

COMPANY UNIONS

see Management—Employee Participation

COMPARATIVE ANATOMY

see Anatomy, Comparative

COMPARATIVE PHYSIOLOGY

see Physiology, Comparative

COMPARATIVE RELIGION

see Religions

COMPETITION (PSYCHOLOGY)

Aboff, Marcie. The Lemonade Standoff. Olin, Troy, illus. 2007. (J). lib. bdg. (*978-1-4048-3668-6(3)) Picture Window Bks.

Cooper, Adrian. Fair Trade? 2005. (Issues of the World Ser.). (Illus.). 48p. (J). (gr. 6-9). lib. bdg. 29.95 (978-1-59604-072-4(6) , 1247745) Stargazer Bks.

Davidson, Tish. Facing Competition: Can You Play by the Rules & Stay in the Game? 2005. (Scholastic Choices Ser.). (Illus.). 112p. (J). (gr. 7-12). 22.50 (978-0-531-16754-0(2) , Watts, Franklin) Scholastic Library Publishing.

Karnes, Frances A. & Riley, Tracy L. Competitions for Talented Kids: Win Scholarships, Big Prize Money, & Recognition. 2005. 295p. (J). (gr. 4-7). pap. 17.95 (978-1-59363-156-7(1) , 1247810) Prufrock Pr.

Messier, Mireille. Competition: From Start to Finish. Murray, Steven, illus. 2004. (Deal with It Ser.). 32p. (J). (gr. 4-8). 12.95 (978-1-55028-832-2(6)) Lorimer, James & Co., Ltd., Pubs. CAN. *Dist:* Casemate Pubs. & Bk. Distributors, LLC.

Middleton, Don. Dealing with Competitiveness. 1999. (Conflict Resolution Library). 24p. (J). lib. bdg. 18.75 (978-0-8239-5267-0(3) , PowerKids Pr.) Rosen Publishing Group, Inc., The.

COMPETITION (PSYCHOLOGY)—FICTION

Arena, Felice & Kettle, Phil. Battle of the Games. Gordon, Gus, illus. 2004. (J). pap. (978-1-59336-372-7(9)) Mondo Publishing.

Baldacci, David & Baldacci, Rudy. Fries Alive! 2006. (Freddy & the French Fries Ser.). (Illus.). 192p. (J). (gr. 3-7). pap. 4.99 (978-0-316-05901-5(3)) Little Brown & Co.

Christopher, Matt. The Captain Contest. 2001. 11.79 (978-0-606-22565-6(X)) Tandem Library Bks.

Crawford, K. Michael, illus. The Munched-Up Flower Garden. 2006. 32p. (J). pap. 10.95 (978-1-933176-06-2(7) , Red Pebble Bks.); (978-1-933176-04-8(0)) Red Rock Pr., Inc.

Diersch, Sandra. False Start. 2005. (Sports Stories Ser.). 104p. (J). (gr. 3-8). (*978-1-55028-873-5(3)); 7.95 (978-1-55028-872-8(5)) Lorimer, James & Co., Ltd., Pubs. CAN. *Dist:* Casemate Pubs. & Bk. Distributors, LLC.

Dorros, Arthur & Dorros, Alex. Numero Uno. Guevara, Susan, illus. 2007. 32p. (J). (ps-3). 16.95 (*978-0-8109-5764-0(7)) Abrams, Harry N. , Inc.

Duffey, Betsy. The Gadget War. Wilson, Janet, illus. 2000. 80p. (J). (gr. 2-5). pap. 4.99 (978-0-14-130708-4(0) , Puffin) Penguin Group (USA) Inc.

—Gadget War. 2000. (gr. 3-6). lib. bdg. 13.00 (978-0-7857-9891-0(9)) Tandem Library Bks.

Duke, Kate. The Tale of Pip & Squeak. 2007. 32p. (J). (ps). 16.99 (978-0-525-47777-8(2) , Dutton Juvenile) Penguin Group (USA) Inc.

Elliott, Laura. Hunter & Stripe & the Soccer Showdown. Munsinger, Lynn, illus. 2005. 32p. (J). (ps-2). lib. bdg. 16.89 (978-0-06-052760-0(9)) HarperCollins Pubs.

Elliott, Laura Malone. Hunter & Stripe & the Soccer Showdown. Munsinger, Lynn, illus. 2005. 32p. (J). (ps-2). 15.99 (978-0-06-052759-4(5)) HarperCollins Pubs.

Gammell, Stephen. The Art Contest. 2001. (J). (978-0-15-202048-4(9)) Harcourt Trade Pubs.

Hutchins, Hazel J. Robyn's Best Idea. Cathcart, Yvonne, illus. 2001. (First Novels Ser.: Vol. 20). 62p. (gr. 1-5). (J). (978-0-88780-531-8(0)); 4.95 (978-0-88780-530-1(2)) Formac Publishing Co., Ltd. CAN. *Dist:* Casemate Pubs. & Bk. Distributors, LLC.

Jackson, Ellen B. Jean Henry. 1999. (J). 15.00 (978-0-15-202225-9(2)) Assessment Systems, Inc.

Kent, Renee Holmes. Cassie, You're a Winner! 2004. (Adventures in Misty Falls Ser.: Vol. 1). (Illus.). 100p. (gr. 4-7). pap. 2.99 (978-1-56309-735-5(4) , N007116) New Hope Pubs.

Lee, Milly. Nim & the War Effort. Choi, Yangsook, illus. 2002. 40p. (J). pap. 6.95 (978-0-374-45506-4(6) , Sunburst) Farrar, Straus & Giroux.

—Nim & the War Effort. 2002. (gr. 3-6). lib. bdg. 14.10 (978-0-613-53846-6(3)) Tandem Library Bks.

Lewis, Beverly. Better Than Best. 2000. (Girls Only (Go!) Ser.: Vol. 6). (Illus.). 128p. (J). (gr. 3-8). pap. 6.99 (978-1-55661-641-9(4)) Bethany Hse. Pubs.

Lucado, Max. Punchinello & the Most Marvelous Gift. Martinez, Sergio, illus. 2005. (Tales of Wemmicksville Ser.: Bk. 5). 32p. (J). 15.99 (978-1-58134-546-9(1) , Crossway Bibles); 2003. 28p. bds. 6.99 (978-1-58134-562-9(3)) Crossway Bks.

Lucado, Max. Punchinello & the Most Marvelous Gift: And, Your Special Gift. Martinez, Sergio, illus. 2007. (J). (*978-1-58134-877-4(0)) Crossway Bks.

Maddox, Jake. Motorcross Double-Cross. Tiffany, Sean, illus. 2008. (J). pap. (*978-1-59889-897-2(3)); lib. bdg. (*978-1-59889-845-3(0)) Univ. of Minnesota Pr.

—Snowboard Duel. Tiffany, Sean, illus. 2008. (J). pap. (*978-1-59889-895-8(7)); lib. bdg. (*978-1-59889-843-9(4)) Stone Arch Bks.

Madonna. The New Girl. Fulvimari, Jeffrey, illus. 2007. (English Roses Ser.). 123p. (J). (gr. 2). 9.99 (*978-0-14-240884-1(0) , Puffin) Penguin Group (USA) Inc.

Martino, Alfred C. Pinned. (YA). 2005. 320p. 17.00 (978-0-15-205355-0(7)); 2006. (Illus.). 324p. reprint ed. pap. 6.95 (978-0-15-205631-5(9) , Harcourt Paperbacks) Harcourt Children's Bks.

Naylor, Phyllis Reynolds. The Girls Take Over. 2004. 160p. (gr. 4-7). pap. 5.99 (978-0-440-41678-4(7) , Yearling) Random Hse. Children's Bks.

—The Girls Take Over. 2004. (gr. 3-6). lib. bdg. 13.00 (978-0-613-81402-7(9)) Tandem Library Bks.

—The Girls Take Over. l.t. ed. 2004. (Boys Girl Battle Ser.). 170p. (J). 22.95 (978-0-7862-5823-9(3)) Thorndike Pr.

O'Connell, Matthew J. The Adventures of Rick Cliff: The Almost Great Penguin Race. 2004. 80p. (J). pap. 6.95 (*978-1-932560-66-4(1) , Llumina Pr.) Media Creations, Inc.

Paratore, Coleen. Mack McGinn's Big Win. 2007. 192p. (J). (gr. 4-7). 15.99 (*978-1-4169-1613-0(X) , Simon & Schuster Children's Publishing) Simon & Schuster Children's Publishing.

Patterson, Nancy Ruth. The Winner's Walk. Yezerski, Thomas, illus. 2006. 128p. (J). 16.00 (978-0-374-38445-6(2)) Farrar, Straus & Giroux.

Polak, Monique. Flip Turn. 2004. (Sports Stories Ser.). 104p. (J). (gr. 3-13). (*978-1-55028-819-3(9)); 7.95 (978-1-55028-818-6(0)) Lorimer, James & Co., Ltd., Pubs. CAN. *Dist:* Casemate Pubs. & Bk. Distributors, LLC.

Rallison, Janette. Life, Love, & the Pursuit of Free Throws. 2006. 192p. (J). pap. 6.95 (978-0-8027-8898-6(X)) Walker & Co.

Rayner, Robert. Just for Kicks. 2004. (Sports Stories Ser.). 120p. (J). (gr. 3-8). 7.95 (978-1-55028-824-7(5)); (*978-1-55028-825-4(3)) Lorimer, James & Co., Ltd., Pubs. CAN. *Dist:* Casemate Pubs. & Bk. Distributors, LLC.

Recheis, Kathe. Little Raccoon Always Knows Best. Kunstreich, Pieter, illus. 2002. Tr. of Kleiner Waschbar Weiss Alles Besser. 24p. (J). 14.95 (978-0-7940-0009-7(6)); lib. bdg. 15.95 (978-0-7940-0010-3(X)) Munchweiler Pr.

RH Disney. The Fairy Berry Bake-off. 2008. (Step into Reading Ser.). 48p. (J). (gr. k-3). pap. 3.99 (*978-0-7364-2525-4(X)); lib. bdg. 11.99 (*978-0-7364-8061-1(7)) Random Hse. Children's Bks. (RH/Disney).

Roberts, Laura Peyton. The Queen of Second Place. 336p. (gr. 7). 2006. (YA). pap. 5.99 (978-0-440-23871-3(4) , Laurel Leaf); 2005. (J). lib. bdg. 17.99 (978-0-385-90200-7(X) , Delacorte Bks. for Young Readers); 2005. (YA). 15.95 (978-0-385-73162-1(0) , Delacorte Bks. for Young Readers) Random Hse. Children's Bks.

Roth, Roger. Fishing for Methuselah. 1998. (Illus.). 32p. (J). (ps-3). 14.95 (978-0-06-027592-1(8)) HarperCollins Pubs.

Rue, Nancy N. Totally Unfair. 2005. (Invert / 'Nama Beach High Ser.). 160p. (YA). pap. 6.99 (978-0-310-25183-5(4)) Zondervan.

Silverman, Erica. Don't Fidget a Feather. Schindler, S. D., illus. 1998. 32p. (J). (ps-2). 6.99 (978-0-689-81967-4(6) , Aladdin) Simon & Schuster Children's Publishing.

—Don't Fidget a Feather. 1998. 12.79 (978-0-606-13340-1(2)) Tandem Library Bks.

Singletary, Mabel Elizabeth. Something to Jump About! 2008. 150p. pap. 5.99 (*978-0-8024-2252-1(7)) Moody Pubs.

Smith, Stephen & Caldwell, Lise. Strike Three. 2006. (Game on for Girls Ser.). 128p. (J). pap. 5.99 (978-0-7847-1729-5(X) , 42146) Standard Publishing.

Smith, Stephen D. & Caldwell, Lise. Rivals on the Waves. 2006. 128p. (J). pap. 5.99 (978-0-7847-1470-6(3) , 42141) Standard Publishing.

Stadler, John. Ready, Set, Go! Stadler, John, illus. 1998. (Trophy I Can Read Bks.). (Illus.). 32p. (J). (ps-2). pap. 3.99 (978-0-06-444238-1(1) , Harper Trophy) HarperCollins Pubs.

—Ready, Set, Go! 1998. (I Can Read Bks.). (J). (ps-1). (978-0-606-13022-6(5)) Tandem Library Bks.

Stanley, George Edward. The Battle of the Bakers. Graves, Linda Dockey, illus. 2000. (Katie Lynn Cookie Company Ser. : Vol. 3). (J). (978-0-606-19900-1(4)) Tandem Library Bks.

Stone Fox. 1998. (J). (gr. 5). pap. 3.95 (978-0-439-04473-8(1)) Scholastic, Inc.

Turner, Sandy. Cool Cat, Hot Dog. Turner, Sandy, illus. 2005. (Illus.). 48p. (J). (ps-ps). 16.95 (978-0-689-84946-6(X) , Atheneum) Simon & Schuster Children's Publishing.

Wallace, Rich. Fast Company. 2005. (Winning Season Ser.: Vol. 3). 128p. (J). (gr. 3-6). pap. 4.99 (978-0-14-240468-3(3) , Puffin) Penguin Group (USA) Inc.

—Fast Company No. 3. 2005. 128p. (J). (gr. 3-7). 14.99 (978-0-670-05942-3(0) , Viking Juvenile) Penguin Group (USA) Inc.

Wallington, Aury & Schwartz, Josh. The OC: Bait & Switch. 2005. 163p. (YA). (978-1-4156-2363-3(5)) Scholastic, Inc.

Walters, Celeste. The Last Race. 2000. (UQP Young Adult Fiction Ser.). 224p. (J). pap. 16.95 (978-0-7022-3172-8(X)) Univ. of Queensland Pr. AUS. *Dist:* International Specialized Bk. Services.

Weaver, Will. Hard Ball. (gr. 6 up). 1999. 256p. (J). pap. 5.99 (978-0-06-447208-1(6) , Harper Trophy); 1998. 240p. (YA). 15.89 (978-0-06-027122-0(1)); 1998. 240p. (YA). 15.95 (978-0-06-027121-3(3)) HarperCollins Pubs.

—Hard Ball. 1999. (J). 12.64 (978-0-606-16706-2(4)); (gr. 7-12). lib. bdg. 14.15 (978-0-613-18254-6(5)) Tandem Library Bks.

—Hard Ball: A Billy Baggs Novel. l.t. ed. 2000. (Illus.). 270p. (YA). (gr. 8-12). 20.95 (978-0-7862-2752-5(4)) Thorndike Pr.

Wedekind, Annie. A Horse of Her Own. 2008. 288p. (J). 16.95 (*978-0-312-36927-9(1)) Feiwel & Friends.

Welton, Jude. Adam's Alternative Sports Day. 2005. (Illus.). 112p. (J). pap. (978-1-84310-300-4(1)) Kingsley, Jessica Ltd.

West, J. A. C. Wipeout. Lawrie, Robin, illus. 2008. (J). pap. (*978-1-59889-905-4(8)); 33p. (YA). (gr. 5-9). lib. bdg. 21.26 (*978-1-59889-853-8(1)) Stone Arch Bks.

West, Tracey. Me & My Robot No.2: The Show-and-Tell Show-off. Revell, Cindy, illus. 2003. (All Aboard Reading Ser.). 48p. (J). 13.89 (978-0-448-43282-3(X) , Grosset & Dunlap) Penguin Group (USA) Inc.

Winston, Sherri. Kayla Chronicles. 2008. 208p. (YA). (gr. 7-17). 16.99 (*978-0-316-11430-1(8)) Little, Brown Bks. for Young Readers.

Wishinsky, Frieda. A Bee in Your Ear. Laliberte, Louise-Andree, illus. 2004. 64p. (J). lib. bdg. 20.00 (*978-1-4242-1255-2(3)) Fitzgerald Bks.

COMPLEXION

see Beauty, Personal; Cosmetics

COMPOSERS

Allman, Barbara. Her Piano Sang: A Story about Clara Schumann. 2003. (Creative Minds Biographies Ser.). (Illus.). 64p. (J). (gr. 3-6). pap. 22.60 (978-1-57505-151-2(6)) Lerner Publishing Group.

—Musical Genius: A Story about Wolfgang Amadeus Mozart. Hamlin, Janet, illus. 2004. (Creative Minds Biographies Ser.). 64p. (J). pap. 6.95 (978-1-57505-637-1(2)); 22.60 (978-1-57505-604-3(6)) Lerner Publishing Group.

Anderson, M. T. Strange Mr. Satie. Mathers, Petra, illus. 2003. 32p. (J). (gr. k-3). 16.99 (978-0-670-03637-0(4) , Viking Juvenile) Penguin Group (USA) Inc.

Banister, Henry C. George Alexander Macfarren: His Life, Works & Influence. 2001. 419p. (YA). reprint ed. 98.00 (978-0-7222-5458-5(X)) Library Reprints, Inc.

Bankston, John. The Life & Times of Duke Ellington. 2004. (Masters of Music Ser.). (Illus.). 48p. (gr. 4-8). lib. bdg. 20.95 (978-1-58415-248-4(6)) Mitchell Lane Pubs., Inc.

—The Life & Times of Scott Joplin. 2004. (Masters of Music Ser.). (Illus.). 48p. (gr. 4-8). lib. bdg. 20.95 (978-1-58415-270-5(2)) Mitchell Lane Pubs., Inc.

Baptie, David. Sketches of the English Glee Composers: Historical, Biographical & Critical. 2001. 235p. (YA). reprint ed. 98.00 (978-0-7222-6134-7(9)) Library Reprints, Inc.

Barrett, William A. Balfe: His Life & Work. 2nd ed. 2001. 313p. (YA). reprint ed. 98.00 (978-0-7222-5321-2(4)) Library Reprints, Inc.

Beier, Jean. Pyotr Ilich Tchaikovsky. 2006. (Lives & Times of Famous Composers Ser.). (J). lib. bdg. (978-1-4042-0725-7(2)) Rosen Publishing Group, Inc., The.

Bellasis, Edward. Cherubini: Memorials Illustrative of His Life. 2nd ed. 2001. 239p. (YA). reprint ed. 98.00 (978-0-7222-5377-9(X)) Library Reprints, Inc.

Benedict, Julius. Weber. 2001. 176p. (YA). reprint ed. 88.00 (978-0-7222-5189-8(0)) Library Reprints, Inc.

Blashfield, Jean F. Leonard Bernstein: Conductor & Composer. 2000. (Career Biographies Ser.). (Illus.). 128p. (YA). (gr. 6-12). 25.00 (978-0-89434-337-7(8) , F404, Ferguson Publishing Co.) Facts On File, Inc.

Bowdish, Lynea. Francis Scott Key & the "Star Spangled Banner" Burman, Harry, illus. 2002. 32p. (J). (gr. 1-5). 15.95 (978-1-59034-038-7(8)) Mondo Publishing.

Boyes, Kate. Paul McCartney. 2003. (Importance of Ser.). (J). 32.45 (978-1-59018-283-3(9) , Lucent Bks.) Thomson Gale.

Bredeson, Carmen & Thibodeau, Ralph. Ten Great American Composers. 2002. (Collective Biographies Ser.). (Illus.). 104p. (YA). (gr. 6-12). lib. bdg. 26.60 (978-0-7660-1832-7(6)) Enslow Pubs., Inc.

Brighton, Catherine. Mozart: Scenes from the Childhood of the Great Composer. 2000. (Illus.). 30p. (J). (gr. 1 up). pap. 9.99 (978-0-7112-1604-4(5)) Lincoln, Frances Ltd. GBR. *Dist:* Transition Vendor

Brown, Gene. Duke Ellington: Jazz Master. 2001. (Giants of Art & Culture Ser.). (Illus.). 128p. (J). (gr. 5-8). 28.70 (978-1-56711-505-5(5) , Blackbirch Pr.) Thomson Gale.

Bryant, Jen. Music for the End of Time. Peck, Beth, illus. 2005. 32p. (J). (gr. 3-5). 17.00 (978-0-8028-5229-8(7)) Eerdmans, William B. Publishing Co.

Cencetti, Greta. Bach. 2002. (Classic Composers Ser.). (Illus.). 40p. (J). incl. audio compact disk (978-1-59069-092-5(3) , T2102) Studio Mouse LLC.

—Beethoven. 2002. (Classic Composers Ser.). (Illus.). 40p. (J). incl. audio compact disk (978-1-59069-091-8(5) , T2101) Studio Mouse LLC.

—Chopin. 2002. (Classic Composers Ser.). (Illus.). 40p. (J). incl. audio compact disk (978-1-59069-093-2(1) , T2103) Studio Mouse LLC.

—Handel. 2002. (Classic Composers Ser.). (Illus.). 40p. (J). incl. audio compact disk (978-1-59069-096-3(6) , T2106) Studio Mouse LLC.

—Handel: Getting to Know Your Classical Composers. 2002. (Classic Composers Ser.). (Illus.). 32p. (978-1-59069-029-1(X) , T2006) Studio Mouse LLC.

—Mozart. 2002. (World of Composers Ser.). (Illus.). 40p. (J). (gr. 1-5). 18.95 (978-1-58845-471-3(1) , Bedrick, Peter Bks.) School Specialty Publishing.

—Mozart. 2002. (Classic Composers Ser.). (Illus.). 40p. (J). incl. audio compact disk (978-1-59069-097-0(4) , T2107) Studio Mouse LLC.

—Tchaikovsky. 2002. (Classic Composers Ser.). (Illus.). 40p. (J). incl. audio compact disk (978-1-59069-095-6(8) , T2105) Studio Mouse LLC.

—Verdi. 2002. (Classic Composers Ser.). (Illus.). 40p. (J). incl. audio compact disk (978-1-59069-094-9(X) , T2104) Studio Mouse LLC.

—Wagner. 2002. (World of Composers Ser.). (Illus.). 40p. (J). (gr. 1-5). 18.95 (978-1-58845-474-4(6) , Bedrick, Peter Bks.) School Specialty Publishing.

—The World of Composers Carrying Case, 8 bks., Set. 2002. (Classic Composers Ser.). (Illus.). (J). incl. audio compact disk (978-1-59069-108-3(3) , TD2102) Studio Mouse LLC.

—The World of Composers Set, 8 bks., Set. 2002. (Classic Composers Ser.). (Illus.). (J). incl. audio compact disk (978-1-59069-107-6(5) , TD2101) Studio Mouse LLC.

Chadwick, George W. Horatio Parker. 2001. 26p. (YA). reprint ed. 88.00 (978-0-7222-5493-6(8)) Library Reprints, Inc.

Chapin, Anna A. Makers of Song. 2001. 339p. (YA). reprint ed. 98.00 (978-0-7222-6071-5(7)) Library Reprints, Inc.

Crowest, Frederick J. The Great Tone Poets: Being Short Memoirs of the Greater Musical Composers. 2001. 373p. (YA). reprint ed. 98.00 (978-0-7222-5234-5(X)) Library Reprints, Inc.

Cummings, William H. Henry Purcell, 1658-1695. 2001. 124p. (YA). reprint ed. 88.00 (978-0-7222-5191-1(2)) Library Reprints, Inc.

Dent, Edward J. Alessandro Scarlatti: His Life & Works. 2001. 236p. (YA). reprint ed. 88.00 (978-0-7222-5507-0(1)) Library Reprints, Inc.

du Bouchet, Paule. Johann Sebastian Bach. 2007. (Descubrimos a los Musicos Ser.). (Illus.). 24p. (J). 14.95 ***978-84-9825-162-3(1))*** Combel Editorial, S.A. ESP. *Dist:* Independent Pubs. Group.

Elson, Arthur. Modern Composers of Europe: An Account of the Most Recent Musical Progress in the Various European Nations. 2001. 291p. (YA). reprint ed. 98.00 (978-0-7222-5241-3(2)) Library Reprints, Inc.

Fellowes, Edmund Horace. The English Madrigal Composers. 2001. 364p. (YA). reprint ed. 98.00 (978-0-7222-5298-7(6)) Library Reprints, Inc.

—Orlando Gibbons: A Short Account of His Life & Work. 2001. 117p. (YA). reprint ed. 88.00 (978-0-7222-5412-7(1)) Library Reprints, Inc.

Finck, Henry Theophilus. Massenet & His Operas. 2001. 245p. (YA). reprint ed. 98.00 (978-0-7222-5462-2(8)) Library Reprints, Inc.

Fowler, Joseph T. The Life & Letters of John Bacchus Dykes. 2001. 344p. (YA). reprint ed. 98.00 (978-0-7222-5404-2(0)) Library Reprints, Inc.

Franck, Cesar. D'Indy. 2001. (YA). reprint ed. 150.00 (978-0-7222-5409-7(1)) Library Reprints, Inc.

Gagelmann, Hartmut. Nicolae Bretan, His Life & His Music. 2000. (Lives in Music Ser.: No. 2). (Illus.). vii, 309p. (J). pap. 60.00 (978-1-57647-021-3(0)) Pendragon Pr.

Gerstein, Mordicai. What Charlie Heard. Gerstein, Mordicai, illus. (Illus.). pap. 18.95 incl. audio compact disk (978-1-59112-277-7(5)); pap. incl. audio (978-1-59112-279-1(1)); pap. 16.95 incl. audio (978-1-59112-484-9(0)); pap. incl. audio compact disk (978-1-59112-525-9(1)); 2003. (J). 28.95 incl. audio compact disk (978-1-59112-486-3(7)); 2003. (J). 25.95 incl. audio (978-1-59112-278-4(3)) Live Oak Media.

Getzinger, Donna & Felsenfeld, Daniel. Antonio Vivaldi & the Baroque Tradition. 2004. (Classical Composers Ser.). (Illus.). 144p. (YA). (gr. 6-12). 26.95 (978-1-931798-20-4(6)) Reynolds, Morgan Inc.

—George Frideric Handel & Music for Voices. 2004. (Classical Composers Ser.). (Illus.). 144p. (YA). (gr. 6-12). 26.95 (978-1-931798-23-5(0)) Reynolds, Morgan Inc.

—Johann Sebastian Bach & the Art of Baroque Music. 2004. (Classical Composers Ser.). (Illus.). 144p. (YA). (gr. 6-12). 26.95 (978-1-931798-22-8(2)) Reynolds, Morgan Inc.

—Johannes Brahms & the Twilight of Romanticism. 2004. (Classical Composers Ser.). (Illus.). 144p. (YA). (gr. 6-12). 26.95 (978-1-931798-21-1(4)) Reynolds, Morgan Inc.

—Richard Wagner & German Opera. 2004. (Classical Composers Ser.). (Illus.). 144p. (YA). (gr. 6-12). 26.95 (978-1-931798-24-2(9)) Reynolds, Morgan Inc.

Gillis, Jennifer Blizin. Irving Berlin: America's Songwriter. 2005. (J). pap. (978-1-4034-6758-4(7)); (Illus.). 32p. (978-1-4034-6750-8(1)) Heinemann Library.

—John Philip Sousa: The King of March Music. 2005. (J). pap. (978-1-4034-6759-1(5)); (Illus.). 32p. 24.21 (978-1-4034-6751-5(X)) Heinemann Library.

—Scott Joplin: Ragtime Legend. 2005. (J). pap. (978-1-4034-6757-7(9)); (Illus.). 32p. 24.21 (978-1-4034-6749-2(8)) Heinemann Library.

Gounod, Charles. Memoirs of an Artist: An Autobiography. 2001. 223p. (YA). reprint ed. 98.00 (978-0-7222-5420-2(2)) Library Reprints, Inc.

Graves, Charles L. Hubert Parry: His Life & Works, 2 vols., set. 2001. (YA). reprint ed. 250.00 (978-0-7222-5494-3(6)) Library Reprints, Inc.

Green, John. Great Composers. 2008. 32p. (J). pap. 3.95 ***(978-0-486-46214-1(5))*** Dover Pubns., Inc.

Hadden, James C. Composers in Love & Marriage. 2001. (YA). reprint ed. 150.00 (978-0-7222-5250-5(1)) Library Reprints, Inc.

Hadow, William H. A Croatian Composer. 2001. 96p. (YA). reprint ed. 88.00 (978-0-7222-5437-0(7)) Library Reprints, Inc.

—William Byrd, 1623-1923. 2001. (YA). reprint ed. 150.00 (978-0-7222-5376-2(1)) Library Reprints, Inc.

Halliwell, Sarah. The Romantics: Artists, Writers & Composers. 1998. (Who & When Ser.: Vol. 4). (Illus.). 96p. (J). (gr. 7-12). lib. bdg. 29.97 (978-0-8172-4729-4(7)) Raintree.

—The 19th Century: Artists, Writers & Composers. 1998. (Who & When Ser.). (Illus.). 96p. (J). (gr. 7-12). lib. bdg. 29.97 (978-0-8172-4728-7(9)) Raintree.

—The 20th Century: Post-1945 - Artists, Writers & Composers. 1998. (Who & When Ser.). (Illus.). 96p. (J). (gr. 7-12). lib. bdg. 29.97 (978-0-8172-4732-4(7)) Raintree.

Hauptmann, Moritz. The Letters of a Leipzig Cantor: The Letters of Moritz Hauptmann to Franz Hauser, Ludwig Spohr, & Other Musicians, 2 vols., set. 2001. (YA). reprint ed. 250.00 (978-0-7222-5436-3(9)) Library Reprints, Inc.

Hensel, Sebastian. The Mendelssohn Family, 1729-1847, 2 vols., set. 2nd ed. 2001. (YA). reprint ed. 250.00 (978-0-7222-5469-1(5)) Library Reprints, Inc.

Hervey, Arthur. Alfred Bruneau. 2001. 86p. (YA). reprint ed. 88.00 (978-0-7222-6308-2(2)) Library Reprints, Inc.

—Masters of French Music. 2001. 289p. (YA). reprint ed. 98.00 (978-0-7222-5306-9(0)) Library Reprints, Inc.

Horowitz, Joseph. Dvoerak in America. 2003. (Illus.). x, 158p. (J). pap. 8.95 (978-0-8126-2692-6(3)) Cricket Bks.

—Dvorak in America: In Search of the New World. 2003. (Marcato Book Ser.). (Illus.). 160p. (YA). 17.95 (978-0-8126-2681-0(8)) Cricket Bks.

Hubbard-Brown, Janet. Scott Joplin. 2006. (Black Americans of Achievement Ser.). (Illus.). 112p. (J). (gr. 6-12). 30.00 (978-0-7910-9211-8(9) , Chelsea Hse.) Facts On File, Inc.

Hull, Arthur E. Cyril Scott: Composer, Poet & Philosopher. 2001. 195p. (YA). reprint ed. 88.00 (978-0-7222-5520-9(9)) Library Reprints, Inc.

Hullah, Annette. Theodor Leschetizky. 2001. 85p. (YA). reprint ed. 88.00 (978-0-7222-5442-4(3)) Library Reprints, Inc.

Introducing Composers. 2005. 32p. pap. 153.65 (978-0-7910-8754-1(9) , Chelsea Hse.) Facts On File, Inc.

Introducing Composers Set. Date not set. (Illus.). (YA). (gr. 8 up). 135.60 (978-0-7910-6045-2(4) , Chelsea Hse.) Facts On File, Inc.

Josephson, Judith Pinkerton. Ludwig Van Beethoven. Kiwak, Barbara, illus. 2007. (Creative Minds Biography Ser.). 64p. (J). spiral bd. 22.60 (978-0-8225-5987-0(0)) Lerner Publishing Group.

Kalischer, A. C. The Life of Strauss. 2001. (YA). reprint ed. 150.00 (978-0-7222-5531-5(4)) Library Reprints, Inc.

Kallen, Stuart A. Great Composers. 2000. (History Makers Ser.). (Illus.). 128p. (YA). (gr. 7-10). 27.45 (978-1-56006-669-9(5) , Lucent Bks.) Thomson Gale.

Kinghorn, Harriet, et al. Let's Meet Famous Composers. 1999. 96p. (J). (gr. 1-6). pap. 10.99 (978-0-513-02101-3(9) , TSD21019, Instructional Fair) Schaffer, Frank Pubns.

Kobbe, Gustav. The Loves of Great Composers. 2001. 175p. (YA). reprint ed. 88.00 (978-0-7222-5266-6(8)) Library Reprints, Inc.

LeapFrog Staff, compiled by. Hit It Maestro. 2001. (J). (ps-1). spiral bd. 14.99 (978-1-58605-077-1(X)) LeapFrog Enterprises, Inc.

Levin, Judy. Wolfgang Amadeus Mozart: Virtuoso of the Classical Form. 2006. (Lives & Times of the Great Composers of the World Ser.). (J). lib. bdg. (978-1-4042-0722-6(8)) Rosen Publishing Group, Inc., The.

Levine, Robert T. & Hamilton, Meredith. The Story of the Orchestra: Listen While You Learn about the Instruments, the Music & the Composers Who Wrote the Music! 2000. (Illus.). 96p. (J). (gr. 4-7). tchr. ed. 19.95 (978-1-57912-148-8(9) , 81148) Black Dog & Leventhal Pubs., Inc.

Lowe, George. Josef Holbrooke & His Work. 2001. 314p. (YA). reprint ed. 98.00 (978-0-7222-5440-0(7)) Library Reprints, Inc.

Malaspina, Ann. Frédéric Chopin: Expressive Poet of the Piano. 2006. (Lives & Times of the Great Composers of the World Ser.). (J). lib. bdg. (978-1-4042-0723-3(6)) Rosen Publishing Group, Inc., The.

Massenet, Jules E. My Recollections. 2001. 304p. (YA). reprint ed. 98.00 (978-0-7222-5461-5(X)) Library Reprints, Inc.

Mayer-Skumanz, Lene. Ludwig von Beethoven. Opgenoorth, Winfried, illus. 2007. 40p. (J). (gr. 1). 20.00 ***(978-0-7358-2123-1(2))*** North-South Bks., Inc.

McDonough, Yona Zeldis. Who Was Wolfgang Amadeus Mozart? Robbins, Carrie, illus. 2003. (Who Was...? Ser.). 112p. (J). (gr. 3-7). pap. 4.99 (978-0-448-43104-8(1) , Grosset & Dunlap) Penguin Group (USA) Inc.

—Who Was Wolfgang Amadeus Mozart? 2003. (gr. 3-6). lib. bdg. 13.00 (978-0-613-61669-0(3)) Tandem Library Bks.

Montagu-Nathan, Montagu. Glinka. 2001. 85p. (YA). reprint ed. 88.00 (978-0-7222-5413-4(X)) Library Reprints, Inc.

—Rimsky-Korsakof. 2001. 124p. (YA). reprint ed. 88.00 (978-0-7222-6319-8(8)) Library Reprints, Inc.

Myers, Carrie Mieko. What If You'd Met Beethoven? 2004. (Illus.). 16p. (J). (978-0-439-69713-2(1)) Scholastic, Inc.

Newman, Ernest. Richard Strauss. 2001. 144p. (YA). reprint ed. 88.00 (978-0-7222-5533-9(0)) Library Reprints, Inc.

Norton, James R. Haydn's World. 2007. (J). ***(978-1-4042-0727-1(9))*** Rosen Publishing Group, Inc., The.

Pancella, Peggy. Johann Sebastian Bach. 2005. (J). pap. (978-1-4034-6753-9(6)); (Illus.). 32p. (978-1-4034-6745-4(5)) Heinemann Library.

—Ludwig Van Beethoven. 2005. (J). pap. (978-1-4034-6754-6(4)); (Illus.). 32p. (978-1-4034-6746-1(3)) Heinemann Library.

—Stephen Foster. 2005. (J). pap. (978-1-4034-6756-0(0)); (Illus.). 32p. 24.21 (978-1-4034-6748-5(X)) Heinemann Library.

—Wolfgang Amadeus Mozart. 2005. (J). pap. (978-1-4034-6755-3(2)); (Illus.). 32p. (978-1-4034-6747-8(1)) Heinemann Library.

Parry, Charles H. H. Studies of Great Composers. 8th ed. 2001. 376p. (YA). reprint ed. 98.00 (978-0-7222-5278-9(1)) Library Reprints, Inc.

Pearce, Charles W. The Life & Works of Hopkins. 2001. (YA). reprint ed. 150.00 (978-0-7222-5930-6(1)) Library Reprints, Inc.

The Primary Source Library of Famous Composers. (Illus.). (J). (gr. 3-5). 127.50 (978-1-4042-3303-4(2)) Rosen Publishing Group, Inc., The.

Pyne, Zoe Kendrick. Giovanni Pierluigi da Palestrina: His Life & Times. 2001. 232p. (YA). reprint ed. 98.00 (978-0-7222-5492-9(X)) Library Reprints, Inc.

Reef, Catherine. William Grant Still: African-American Composer. 2004. (Modern Music Masters Ser.). (Illus.). 112p. (YA). (gr. 6-12). 23.95 (978-1-931798-11-2(7)) Reynolds, Morgan Inc.

Riggs, Kate. Wolfgang Amadeus Mozart. 2008. (J). ***(978-1-58341-664-8(1)*** , Creative Education) Creative Co., The.

Rosenfeld, Paul. Musical Portraits: Interpretations of Twenty Modern Composers. 2001. 314p. (YA). reprint ed. 98.00 (978-0-7222-5283-3(8)) Library Reprints, Inc.

Ross, Stewart. The Story of Ludwig von Beethoven. 2002. (Lifetimes Ser.). (Illus.). 48p. (J). lib. bdg. 28.50 (978-1-931983-15-0(1)) Chrysalis Education.

—Wolfgang Amadeus Mozart: Musical Genius. 2004. (Famous Lives Ser.). (Illus.). 48p. (J). (gr. 3). lib. bdg. 29.93 (978-0-7398-6627-6(3)) Raintree.

Schoell, William. Giuseppe Verdi & Italian Opera. 2007. (Illus.). 128p. (J). (gr. 9 up). lib. bdg. 27.95 (978-1-59935-041-7(6)) Reynolds, Morgan Inc.

Scott, Cyril. My Years of Indiscretion. 2001. 282p. (YA). reprint ed. 98.00 (978-0-7222-5519-3(5)) Library Reprints, Inc.

Sharp, Robert F. Makers of Music: Biographical Sketches of Great Composers. 4th ed. 2001. 245p. (YA). reprint ed. 98.00 (978-0-7222-5290-1(0)) Library Reprints, Inc.

Shefelman, Janice Jordan & Shefelman, Tom. I, Vivaldi. Shefelman, Janice Jordan & Shefelman, Tom, illus. 2007. (J). (978-0-8028-5318-9(8)) Eerdmans, William B. Publishing Co.

Sis, Peter. Play, Mozart, Play! Sis, Peter, illus. 2006. (Illus.). 32p. (J). 16.99 (978-0-06-112181-4(9)); lib. bdg. 17.89 (978-0-06-112182-1(7)) HarperCollins Pubs. (Greenwillow Bks.).

Sombart, Elisabeth & Lafaye, Jean-Jacques. Doce Vidas para la Musica.Tr. of Twelve Composers. (SPA.). 118p. (J). 17.95 (978-84-261-3115-7(8) , JV11155) Juventud, Editorial ESP. *Dist:* Lectorum Pubns., Inc.

Summerer, Eric Michael. Franz Joseph Haydn. 2006. (Primary Source Library of Famous Composers). (Illus.). 32p. (J). 21.95 (978-1-4042-2767-5(9) , PowerKids Pr.) Rosen Publishing Group, Inc., The.

—Franz Peter Schubert. 2006. (Primary Source Library of Famous Composers). (Illus.). 32p. (J). 21.95 (978-1-4042-2768-2(7) , PowerKids Pr.) Rosen Publishing Group, Inc., The.

—Frederic Chopin. 2006. (Primary Source Library of Famous Composers). (Illus.). 32p. (J). 21.95 (978-1-4042-2769-9(5) , PowerKids Pr.) Rosen Publishing Group, Inc., The.

—Johann Sebastian Bach. 2006. (Primary Source Library of Famous Composers). (Illus.). 32p. (J). 21.95 (978-1-4042-2770-5(9) , PowerKids Pr.) Rosen Publishing Group, Inc., The.

—Ludwig Van Beethoven. 2006. (Primary Source Library of Famous Composers). (Illus.). 32p. (J). 21.95 (978-1-4042-2771-2(7) , PowerKids Pr.) Rosen Publishing Group, Inc., The.

—Wolfgang Amadeus Mozart. 2006. (Primary Source Library of Famous Composers). (Illus.). 32p. (J). 21.95 (978-1-4042-2772-9(5) , PowerKids Pr.) Rosen Publishing Group, Inc., The.

Swan, Alfred J. Scriabin. 2001. 119p. (YA). reprint ed. 88.00 (978-0-7222-5522-3(5)) Library Reprints, Inc.

Terrill, Richard. Duke Ellington. 2003. (African-American Biographies Ser.). (Illus.). 64p. (J). lib. bdg. 28.56 (978-0-7398-6869-0(1)) Raintree.

Thomas, Theodore. A Musical Autobiography, 2 vols., set. 2001. (YA). reprint ed. 250.00 (978-0-7222-5551-3(9)) Library Reprints, Inc.

Turner, Barrie Carson. Beethoven. 2003. (Famous Childhoods Ser.). (Illus.). (J). lib. bdg. 24.25 (978-1-59389-112-1(1)) Chrysalis Education.

—Mozart. 2003. (Famous Childhoods Ser.). (Illus.). (J). lib. bdg. 24.25 (978-1-59389-115-2(6)) Chrysalis Education.

Venezia, Mike. Frederic Chopin. (Getting to Know the World's Greatest Composers Ser.). (Illus.). 32p. (J). (gr. 3-4). 2000. pap. 6.95 (978-0-516-26534-6(2)); 1999. 27.00 (978-0-516-21588-4(4)) Scholastic Library Publishing. (Children's Pr.).

—Frederic Chopin. 1999. (gr. k-3). lib. bdg. 15.25 (978-0-613-37351-7(0)) Tandem Library Bks.

—Johann Sebastian Bach. 1998. (Getting to Know the World's Greatest Composers Ser.). (Illus.). 32p. (J). (gr. 3-4). 27.00 (978-0-516-20760-5(1) , Children's Pr.) Scholastic Library Publishing.

—Johannes Brahms. 1999. (Getting to Know the World's Greatest Composers Ser.). (Illus.). 32p. (J). (gr. 3-4). 27.00 (978-0-516-21056-8(4) , Children's Pr.) Scholastic Library Publishing.

—John Philip Sousa. Venezia, Mike, illus. 1998. (Getting to Know the World's Greatest Composers Ser.). (Illus.). 32p. (J). (gr. 3-4). 27.00 (978-0-516-20761-2(X) , Children's Pr.) Scholastic Library Publishing.

Walcker, Yann. Ludwig Van Beethoven. 2007. (Descubrimos a los Musicos Ser.). (Illus.). 24p. (J). 14.95 ***(978-84-7864-959-4(X))*** Combel Editorial, S.A. ESP. *Dist:* Independent Pubs. Group.

—Wolfgang Amadeus Mozart. 2007. (Descubrimos a los Musicos Ser.). (Illus.). 24p. (J). 14.95 ***(978-84-7864-958-7(1))*** Combel Editorial, S.A. ESP. *Dist:* Independent Pubs. Group.

Wellesz, Egon. Arnold Schonberg. 2001. 159p. (YA). reprint ed. 88.00 (978-0-7222-5506-3(3)) Library Reprints, Inc.

Whiting, Jim. The Life & Times of Antonio Lucio Vivaldi. 2004. (Masters of Music Ser.). (Illus.). 48p. (gr. 4-8). lib. bdg. 20.95 (978-1-58415-241-5(9)) Mitchell Lane Pubs., Inc.

—The Life & Times of Franz Liszt. 2004. (Masters of Music Ser.). (Illus.). 48p. (gr. 4-8). lib. bdg. 20.95 (978-1-58415-280-4(X)) Mitchell Lane Pubs., Inc.

—The Life & Times of Frederic Chopin. 2004. (Masters of Music Ser.). (Illus.). 48p. (gr. 4-8). lib. bdg. 20.95 (978-1-58415-245-3(1)) Mitchell Lane Pubs., Inc.

—The Life & Times of Guiseppe Verdi. 2004. (Masters of Music Ser.). (Illus.). 48p. (gr. 4-8). lib. bdg. 20.95 (978-1-58415-281-1(8)) Mitchell Lane Pubs., Inc.

—The Life & Times of Hector Berlioz. 2004. (Masters of Music Ser.). (Illus.). 48p. (gr. 4-8). lib. bdg. 20.95 (978-1-58415-259-0(1)) Mitchell Lane Pubs., Inc.

—The Life & Times of Richard Wagner. 2004. (Masters of Music Ser.). (Illus.). 48p. (gr. 4-8). lib. bdg. 20.95 (978-1-58415-278-1(8)) Mitchell Lane Pubs., Inc.

COMPOSERS—DICTIONARIES

Elson, Louis C. Great Composers & Their Work. 2001. 302p. (YA). reprint ed. 98.00 (978-0-7222-5243-7(9)) Library Reprints, Inc.

Masters of Russian Music. 2001. (YA). reprint ed. 264.00 (978-0-7222-6371-6(6)) Library Reprints, Inc.

Montagu-Nathan, Montagu. Contemporary Russian Composers. 2001. 329p. (YA). reprint ed. 98.00 (978-0-7222-5309-0(5)) Library Reprints, Inc.

Streatfeild, R. A. Masters of Italian Music. 2001. 269p. (YA). reprint ed. 98.00 (978-0-7222-5308-3(7)) Library Reprints, Inc.

COMPOSERS—FICTION

Anderson, M. T. Handel, Who Knew What He Liked. Hawkes, Kevin, illus. 2001. 48p. (J). (gr. 3-7). 16.99 (978-0-7636-1046-3(1)) Candlewick Pr.

Celenza, Anna Harwell. The Farewell Symphony. Kitchel, JoAnn E., illus. 2005. 32p. (J). pap. 7.95 (978-1-57091-407-2(9)) Charlesbridge Publishing, Inc.

—The Farewell Symphony. 2000. (Illus.). 32p. (J). (ps-3). 19.95 (978-1-57091-406-5(0)) Charlesbridge Publishing, Inc.

—Gershwin's Rhapsody in Blue. Kitchel, JoAnn E., illus. 2006. 32p. (J). 19.95 incl. audio compact disk (978-1-57091-556-7(3)) Charlesbridge Publishing, Inc.

—The Heroic Symphony. Kitchel, JoAnn E., illus. 2004. 32p. (J). 19.95 incl. audio compact disk (978-1-57091-509-3(1)) Charlesbridge Publishing, Inc.

—Pictures at an Exhibition. Kitchel, JoAnn E., illus. 2003. 32p. (J). (gr. 3-6). 19.95 (978-1-57091-492-8(3)) Charlesbridge Publishing, Inc.

Leroux, Gaston. The Phantom of the Opera. l.t. ed. 1999. (Large Print Heritage Ser.). 420p. (J). (gr. 7-12). lib. bdg. 35.95 (978-1-58118-043-5(8) , 22512) LRS.

Swain, Gwenyth. I Wonder As I Wander. Himler, Ronald, illus. 2004. 32p. (gr. 2-5). 16.00 (978-0-8028-5214-4(9)) Eerdmans, William B. Publishing Co.

Winter, Jonah. The 39 Apartments of Ludwig Van Beethoven. Blitt, Barry, illus. 2006. 40p. (J). (ps-4). 15.95 (978-0-375-83602-2(0) , Schwartz & Wade Bks.) Random Hse. Children's Bks.

COMPOSITION (RHETORIC)

see Rhetoric

also names of languages with the subdivision Composition and exercises, e.g. English Language—Composition and exercises

COMPULSORY SCHOOL ATTENDANCE

see School Attendance

COMPUTER ART

Brilliant, Ken. Digital Dinosaurs. 2002. (Charles River Media Graphics Ser.). (Illus.). 375p. 49.95 (978-1-58450-209-8(6)) Charles River Media.

Gardner, Garth. Careers in Computer Graphics & Animation: Gardner's Guide Series. Ford, Bonney, ed. 2006. (Gardner's Guide Ser.). (Illus.). 256p. pap. 29.95 (978-0-9661075-2-4(7)) Gardner, Garth Co., Inc. (GGC).

Knapp-Grosz, Tamara & Loyd, Elizabeth. Some Things Are Made to Smoke. McCue, Patrick, illus. 2004. 20p. (J). pap. (978-1-893974-23-4(5) , Design Pr. Bks.) Savannah College of Art & Design.

Rooney, Anne. Picture This. 2004. (QEB Learn Computing Ser.). (Illus.). 32p. (J). lib. bdg. 18.95 (978-1-59566-039-8(9)) QEB Publishing Inc.

Sabbeth, Carol. Kids' Computer Creations: Using Your Computer for Art & Craft Fun. 1999. (Kids Can Bks.: No. 14). (Illus.). 160p. (J). (ps-5). pap. 12.95 (978-0-913589-92-2(6) , Williamson Bks.) Ideals Pubns.

Top That! Team Staff, contrib. by. I [Love] Dogs & Puppies. 2002. (Art Rom Ser.). (Illus.). 48p. (J). (978-0-439-53072-9(5)) Scholastic, Inc.

COMPUTER BULLETIN BOARDS

Wolinsky, Art. Communicating on the Internet. 1999. (Internet Library). (Illus.). 64p. (YA). (gr. 4-12). lib. bdg. 22.60 (978-0-7660-1260-8(3)) Enslow Pubs., Inc.

—Locating & Evaluating Information on the Internet. 1999. (Internet Library). (Illus.). 64p. (YA). (gr. 4-12). lib. bdg. 22.60 (978-0-7660-1259-2(X)) Enslow Pubs., Inc.

COMPUTER CONTROL

see Automation

COMPUTER CRIMES

Bauchner, Elizabeth. Computer Investigation. 2006. (Forensics, the Science of Crime-Solving Ser.). (Illus.). 112p. (J). (gr. 7 up). 22.95 (978-1-4222-0035-3(3)) Mason Crest Pubs.

Chappell, Laura A. Laura Chappell Presents Vol. 103: Introduction to Cyber Crime. 2000. (Illus.). 150p. (YA). wbk. ed. 150.00 (978-1-893939-31-8(6)) podbooks.com, LLC.

Dahl, Michael. Computer Evidence. 2004. (Edge Books, Forensic Crime Solvers). (Illus.). 32p. (J). lib. bdg. 22.60 (978-0-7368-2698-3(X)) Capstone Pr., Inc.

DeAngelis, Gina & Marvis, B. Cyber Crimes. Sarat, Austin, ed. 1999. (Crime, Justice & Punishment Ser.). (Illus.). 80p. (YA). (gr. 7-12). 30.00 (978-0-7910-4252-6(9), Chelsea Hse.) Facts On File, Inc.

Goranson, Christopher D. Everything You Need to Know about Misinformation on the Internet. 2005. (Need to Know Library). (Illus.). 64p. (YA). (gr. 4-6). lib. bdg. 25.25 (978-0-8239-3521-5(3)) Rosen Publishing Group, Inc., The.

Grant-Adamson, Andrew. Cyber Crime. 2003. (Crime & Detection Ser.). (Illus.). 96p. (J). (gr. 7 up). lib. bdg. (978-1-59084-369-7(X)) Mason Crest Pubs.

Hynes, Patricia Freeland. Cyber Cop. 2007. (J). lib. bdg. (***978-1-60279-056-8(6)***) Cherry Lake Publishing.

Judson, Karen. Computer Crime: Phreaks, Spies & Salami Slicers. rev. ed. 2000. (Issues in Focus Ser.). (Illus.). 128p. (YA). (gr. 6-12). lib. bdg. 26.60 (978-0-7660-1243-1(3)) Enslow Pubs., Inc.

Marzilli, Alan. Policing the Internet. 2004. (Point/Counterpoint Ser.). (Illus.). 112p. (gr. 9-13). 32.95 (978-0-7910-8088-7(9), Chelsea Hse.) Facts On File, Inc.

McIntosh, Neil. Cyber Crime. 2003. (Face the Facts Ser.). (Illus.). 56p. (J). lib. bdg. 28.56 (978-0-7398-6432-6(7)) Raintree.

Wolinsky, Art. Safe Surfing on the Internet. 2003. (Internet Library). (Illus.). 64p. (YA). (gr. 4-12). lib. bdg. 22.60 (978-0-7660-2030-6(4)) Enslow Pubs., Inc.

COMPUTER ENGINEERING

Donelly, Karen. Hardware Engineer. 2000. (CoolCareers.com Ser.). (Illus.). 48p. (YA). (gr. 5-8). lib. bdg. 23.95 (978-0-8239-3118-7(8), CCHAEN, Rosen Central) Rosen Publishing Group, Inc., The.

Mattern, Joanne. Grace Hopper: Computer Pioneer. 2003. (Reading Power Ser.). (Illus.). 24p. (J). lib. bdg. 17.25 (978-0-8239-6505-2(8), PowerKids Pr.) Rosen Publishing Group, Inc., The.

Maupin, Melissa. Computer Engineer. 2000. (Career Exploration Ser.). (Illus.). 48p. (J). (gr. 3-4). lib. bdg. 21.26 (978-0-7368-0591-9(5), LifeMatters Bks.) Capstone Pr., Inc.

Zannos, Susan. Edward Roberts & the Story of the Personal Computer. l.t. ed. 2002. (Unlocking the Secrets of Science Ser.). (Illus.). 56p. (gr. 4-10). lib. bdg. 25.70 (978-1-58415-118-0(8)) Mitchell Lane Pubs., Inc.

COMPUTER GAMES

Allison, David. Custom Ultimate Code Book 2000. 2000. (Prima's Official Strategy Guide Ser.). (Illus.). (YA). pap. 14.99 (978-0-7615-2738-1(9), Prima Lifestyles) Crown Publishing Group.

Andersen, Neil. At the Controls: Questioning Video & Computer Games. 2007. (Fact Finders Ser.). (Illus.). 32p. (J). (978-0-7368-6768-9(6), 1264909, Fact Finders) Capstone Pr., Inc.

Andersen, Neil. At the Controls: Questioning Video & Computer Games. 2007. (Fact Finders Ser.). (Illus.). 32p. (J). (***978-0-7368-7864-7(5)***, 1264909) Capstone Pr., Inc.

Anderson, Pamela. My New School. 2004. (J). cd-rom 12.95 (978-1-932555-08-0(0)) Watch Me Grow Kids.

At the Edge of Dreams. 2002. per. 18.95 (978-0-9717729-5-3(9)) MonkeyGod Enterprises.

Birlew, Dan. Metal Gear Solid 3(R) Snake Eater(TM) Strategy Guide. ltd. ed. 2004. 96p. pap. 29.99 (978-0-7440-0476-2(4)) Brady GAMES.

Birlew, Dan & BradyGames Staff. Lemony Snicket's: A Series of Unfortunate Events Official Strategy Guide. 2004. (Illus.). 128p. pap. 14.99 (978-0-7440-0462-5(4)) Brady GAMES.

BradyGames Staff & Deats, Adam. Baten Kaitos(TM) Official Strategy Guide. 2004. (Illus.). 176p. pap. 14.99 (978-0-7440-0487-8(X)) Brady GAMES.

Burns, Jan. Shigeru Miyamoto. 2006. (Inventors & Creators Ser.). 48p. (J). (gr. 4-8). 27.45 (978-0-7377-3534-5(1), Greenhaven Pr., Inc.) Thomson Gale.

Christian Founders 3D Adventure. 2004. (YA). cd-rom 19.95 (978-1-931203-12-8(1)) Inspired Idea.

Click a Pic Photo Cube Creator. 2002. (J). cd-rom 49.00 net. (978-1-890265-10-6(1)) Janelle Pubns., Inc.

Cohen, Judith Love. You Can Be A Woman Video Game Producer. l.t. ed. 2005. (Illus.). 72p. (J). 17.95 (978-1-880599-74-7(0)); pap. 12.95 (978-1-880599-73-0(2)) Cascade Pass, Inc.

Facts on File, Inc. Staff, ed. Aviation. 2005. (Careers in Focus Ser.). (Illus.). 192p. (YA). (gr. 6-12). 22.95 (978-0-8160-5850-1(4)) Facts On File, Inc.

Farkas, Bart G. BloodRayne 2 Official Strategy Guide. 2004. (Illus.). 128p. pap. 14.99 (978-0-7440-0426-7(8)) Brady GAMES.

Fields, Doug. Screen Play 2: Another 16 Ready-to-Use Interactive Visual Games to Get Your Students Laughing & Talking. unabr. ed. 2003. cd-rom 19.99 (978-0-310-25190-3(7)) Zondervan.

Das Geheimnis der Burg. 1998. (Meyer Multimedia Ser.). (J). (gr. 5 up). cd-rom 45.00 (978-3-411-06291-1(6)) Langenscheidt Pubs Inc.

Kuehl, William Aksel. Aksel's Field Guide to Monsters. 2004. cd-rom 9.99 (978-0-9752528-0-2(1)) William Askel Art.

Odom, Mel. Barbie: Software for Girls: Official Guide. 1999. 96p. (gr. 2-4). pap. 14.99 (978-0-7615-2405-2(3), Prima Lifestyles) Crown Publishing Group.

Olesky, Walter. Video Game Designer. 2000. (CoolCareers.com Ser.). (Illus.). 48p. (YA). (gr. 5-8). lib. bdg. 23.95 (978-0-8239-3117-0(X), CCVIGA, Rosen Central) Rosen Publishing Group, Inc., The.

Penner, Cornelia. Games That Byte: Helping Youth Evaluate Computer Games. 1998. 41p. (YA). (gr. 6-12). pap. 8.95 (978-0-87303-331-2(0)) Faith & Life Pr.

Pondsmith, Mike. DragonBall Z: The Anime Adventure Game. 1999. (J). pap. 20.00 (978-1-891933-00-4(0)) Talsorian Games, Inc.

Pratt, Gary Thomas. Code of Unaris: Chat Roleplaying. LePorte, Christine, ed. 2004. (Illus.). 314p. per. 15.95 (978-0-9748757-0-5(8), GDL 1001) Goldleaf Games, LLC.

Prima Publishing Staff. Big Nintendo Book. 2000. (Prima's Official Strategy Guide Ser.). (Illus.). 192p. (YA). pap. 14.99 (978-0-7615-2799-2(0), Prima Lifestyles) Crown Publishing Group.

—Planet of the Apes: Prima's Official Strategy Guide. 2001. (Prima's Official Strategy Guide Ser.). (Illus.). 96p. (J). pap. (978-0-7615-2596-7(3), Prima Lifestyles) Crown Publishing Group.

Prima Temp Authors Staff & Chin, Elliott. Drakengard 2: Prima Official Game Guide. 2006. 192p. pap. 16.99 (978-0-7615-5297-0(9), Prima Games) Random Hse. Information Group.

Schlesinger, Hank. Digimon Power. 2000. (J). 71.88 (978-0-312-97652-1(6), St. Martin's Paperbacks) St. Martin's Pr.

Splat! Spelling Software. 2000. (gr. 1 up). 20.76 (978-0-673-28917-9(6)); (gr. 1 up). 20.76 (978-0-673-28923-0(0)); (gr. 2 up). 20.76 (978-0-673-62853-4(1)); (gr. 2 up). 20.76 (978-0-673-61828-3(5)); (gr. 3 up). 20.76 (978-0-673-28919-3(2)); (gr. 3 up). 20.76 (978-0-673-28925-4(7)); (gr. 4 up). 20.76 (978-0-673-28920-9(6)); (gr. 4 up). 20.76 (978-0-673-28926-1(5)); (gr. 5 up). 20.76 (978-0-673-28921-6(4)); (gr. 5 up). 20.76 (978-0-673-28927-8(3)); (gr. 6 up). 20.76 (978-0-673-28922-3(2)) Addison-Wesley Educational Pubs., Inc.

Truthware. 2003. cd-rom 34.95 (978-1-931203-09-8(1)) Inspired Idea.

Vinopol, Corinne. Con-SIGN-tration 3: Computer Software Game in American Sign Language. 2003. (J). cd-rom 19.95 (978-0-9752933-6-2(2)) Institute for Disabilities Research & Training, Inc.

—Con-SIGN-tration 4: Computer Software Game in American Sign Language. 2003. (J). cd-rom (978-0-9752933-7-9(0)) Institute for Disabilities Research & Training, Inc.

Vinopol, Corinne & Bednarczyk, Angela. ASL Tales & Games for Kids - Woof Woof Way: Computer Software in American Sign Language. 2002. (J). cd-rom 34.95 (978-0-9667589-6-2(X)) Institute for Disabilities Research & Training, Inc.

West, Tracey. Official Handbook & Strategy Guide. 2007. 96p. pap. 6.99 (978-0-439-87772-5(5)) Scholastic, Inc.

COMPUTER GAMES—FICTION

Brown, Marc. Arthur's Computer Disaster. 1999. (Arthur Adventure Ser.). (J). (gr. k-3). pap. 5.95 (978-0-316-12373-0(0)) Little, Brown Bks. for Young Readers.

—Arthur's Computer Disaster. Brown, Marc, illus. 1999. (Arthur Adventure Ser.). (Illus.). 32p. (J). (ps-3). pap. 6.99 (978-0-316-10534-7(1)) Little, Brown Bks. for Young Readers.

—Arturo y el Desastre de la Computadora. Sarfatti, Esther, tr. (SPA.). (J). (gr. k-2). pap. 6.95 (978-1-930332-01-0(7), LC30180) Lectorum Pubns., Inc.

—Arturo y el Desastre de la Computadora. 2001. (SPA.). (gr. k-3). lib. bdg. 15.25 (978-0-613-35900-9(3)) Tandem Library Bks.

Carmi, Daniella. Samir & Yonatan. Lotan, Yael, tr. from HEB. 2002. 192p. (J). (gr. 3-7). pap. 4.99 (978-0-439-13523-8(0), Scholastic Paperbacks) Scholastic, Inc.

—Samir & Yonatan. 2000. (gr. 3-6). lib. bdg. 13.00 (978-0-613-45824-5(9)) Tandem Library Bks.

—Samir & Yonatan. 2000. (Illus.). 192p. (J). (gr. 3-7). pap. 15.95 (978-0-439-13504-7(4), Levine, Arthur A. Bks.) Scholastic, Inc.

Collins, Paul. Knockout. 2000. (gr. 7-12). lib. bdg. 12.25 (978-0-613-28920-7(X)) Tandem Library Bks.

Collins, Suzanne. When Charlie McButton Lost Power. Lester, Mike, illus. 2005. 32p. (J). (ps-3). 15.99 (978-0-399-24000-3(4), Putnam Juvenile) Penguin Group (USA) Inc.

Collins, Suzanne. When Charlie Mcbutton Lost Power. Lester, Mike, illus. 2007. 32p. (J). (ps). pap. 5.99 (***978-0-14-240857-5(3)***, Puffin) Penguin Group (USA) Inc.

Graves, Damien. End Game. 2006. (Midnight Library: No. 3). 192p. (J). pap. 5.99 (978-0-439-87188-4(3), Scholastic Paperbacks) Scholastic, Inc.

Hale, Jane. Heartland. 1999. (Illus.). 288p. (J). (gr. 8-12). pap. 12.95 (978-0-934426-91-6(0)) NAPSAC Reproductions.

Kostick, Conor. Epic. 2008. 384p. (J). (gr. 4-6). pap. 9.99 (***978-0-14-241159-9(0)***, Puffin) Penguin Group (USA) Inc.

Lawrence, Michael. The Toilet of Doom. 2004. 256p. (J). pap. 16.95 (978-0-7540-7913-2(9), Galaxy Children's Large Print) BBC Audiobooks America.

Lorimer, Janet. Scavenger Hunt. 2001. (PageTurner Spy Ser.). 80p. (YA). per. 3.95 (978-1-56254-139-2(0), SP 1390) Saddleback Educational Publishing.

Mielcarek, David. Time for your Mind. Mielcarek, David, ed. 2006. (Illus.). 38p. (J). (978-0-9785480-1-0(0)) Mielcarek, David.

O'Malley, Kevin. Lucky Leaf. O'Malley, Kevin, illus. 2004. (Illus.). 32p. (J). 15.95 (978-0-8027-8924-2(2)) Walker & Co.

Osterweil, Adam. The Amulet of Komondor. Thorpe, Peter, illus. 2004. 112p. (J). (gr. 3-7). 15.95 (978-1-886910-81-2(2), Lemniscaat) Boyds Mills Pr.

Paulsen, Gary. The Time Hackers. 2005. 96p. (J). (gr. 4-7). lib. bdg. 17.99 (978-0-385-90896-2(2)); (gr. 5). 13.95 (978-0-385-74659-5(8)) Random Hse. Children's Bks. (Lamb, Wendy).

Pratchett, Terry. Only You Can Save Mankind. 224p. (J). 2006. pap. 5.99 (978-0-06-054187-3(3), Harper Trophy); 2005. (gr. 3 up). 15.99 (978-0-06-054185-9(7)); 2005. (gr. 3 up). lib. bdg. 16.89 (978-0-06-054186-6(5)) HarperCollins Pubs.

Ralles, H. J. Keeper of the Colony. 2006. (YA). pap. 10.95 (978-1-929976-35-5(6)) Top Pubns., Ltd.

Stem, Jacqueline. Dangerous Games, Vol. 4. Eckhardt, Jason C., illus. 2002. (Hollow Tree Mystery Ser.). 160p. 16.95 (978-1-57168-701-2(7)); 12.95 (978-1-57168-702-9(5)) Eakin Pr.

Swallow, Donald. Secret Game. 2000. (gr. 7-12). lib. bdg. 21.60 (978-0-613-74554-3(X)) Tandem Library Bks.

Thompson, Lisa. Tokyo Techno. Chan, Jimmy, illus. 2006. (Read-It! Chapter Books). 80p. (J). (gr. 2-4). 19.95 (978-1-4048-1673-2(9)) Picture Window Bks.

Time for Your Mind. l.t. ed. 2006. (Illus.). 35p. (J). (978-0-9785480-1-8(9)) Mielcarek, David.

Vande Velde, Vivian. User Unfriendly. 2001. 244p. (YA). (gr. 8-12). lib. bdg. 14.15 (978-0-613-57486-0(9)); (978-0-606-22618-9(4)) Tandem Library Bks.

Warner, Gertrude Chandler. The Mystery in the Computer Game. 2000. (Boxcar Children Ser.: No. 78). (J). (gr. 2-5). (978-0-606-20298-5(6)) Tandem Library Bks.

Warner, Gertrude Chandler, creator. The Mystery in the Computer Game. (Boxcar Children Ser.: No. 78). (Illus.). 115p. (J). (gr. 2-5). 2000. lib. bdg. 13.95 (978-0-8075-5468-5(5)); Vol. 78. 2004. pap. 4.50 (978-0-8075-5469-2(3)) Whitman, Albert & Co.

Zucker, Jonny. Inside the Game. Smith, Pete, illus. 2007. 33p. (J). pap. (***978-1-59889-426-4(9)***); 40p. (YA). (gr. 5-9). lib. bdg. 21.26 (***978-1-59889-330-4(0)***) Stone Arch Bks.

COMPUTER GRAPHICS

Computer Graphic Design Module Guide. 4th rev. ed. 2004. 52p. pap. (978-0-86657-531-7(6)) Lab-Volt Systems, Inc.

Estudio Multimedia. 2000. (SPA.). (gr. k-5). cd-rom 69.96 (978-0-673-64020-8(5)) Addison-Wesley Educational Pubs., Inc.

Gardner, Garth. Careers in Computer Graphics & Animation: Gardner's Guide Series. Ford, Bonney, ed. 2006. (Gardner's Guide Ser.). (Illus.). 256p. pap. 29.95 (978-0-9661075-2-4(7)) Gardner, Garth Co., Inc. (GGC).

—Gardner's Computer Graphics & Animation Dictionary. 2003. (Gardner's Guide Ser.). (Illus.). 256p. pap. 24.95 (978-1-58965-005-3(0), 703 793 8604) Gardner, Garth Co., Inc. (GGC).

Kalbag, Asha. Computer Graphics & Animation. 1999. (gr. 5-8). lib. bdg. 19.90 (978-0-613-74413-3(6)) Tandem Library Bks.

Lockman, Darcy. Computer Animation. 2000. (Kaleidoscope Ser.). (Illus.). 48p. (J). (gr. 3 up). lib. bdg. 25.64 (978-0-7614-1048-5(1), Benchmark Bks.) Cavendish, Marshall Corp.

Miyazaki, Hayao. The Art of Miyazaki's Spirited Away. Miyazaki, Hayao, illus. 2002. (Anime Art Gallery Ser.). (Illus.). 240p. (YA). 34.95 (978-1-56931-777-8(1)) Viz Media.

Multimedia. 1998. 192p. (YA). pap. 19.95 (978-0-7894-3536-1(5)) Dorling Kindersley Publishing, Inc.

Nardo, Don. Computer Animation. 2007. (Eye on Art Ser.). (Illus.). 128p. (J). (gr. 7-10). 31.20 (***978-1-4205-0004-2(X)***, Lucent Bks.) Thomson Gale.

QEB Let's Start! Computing National Book Stores Edition: Making Charts. 2006. (J). per. (978-1-59566-297-2(9)) QEB Publishing Inc.

Red Bird Press Staff. Amazing 3D Magic. 2004. (Amazing Stereoscopic 3D Ser.). 24p. (J). pap. 5.95 (978-1-902626-64-2(8)) Red Bird Publishing GBR. *Dist:* Weatherhill, Inc.

Rose, John N. Direct Approach: Maya 5. l.t. ed. 2003. (Illus.). 302p. per. 49.95 (978-0-9742948-0-3(2), DA-Ma5) Platinum Rose Publishing.

Shires, Jeremy. Careers in Computer Animation. 2005. (Career Resource Library). (Illus.). 192p. (YA). (gr. 7-12). lib. bdg. 26.50 (978-0-8239-3190-3(0)) Rosen Publishing Group, Inc., The.

Shumaker, Terence M. & Madsen, David A. AutoCAD & Its Applications: Advanced 2000/2000i Edition, Student Work Disk. 2001. (gr. 9-13). stu. ed. 50.00 (978-1-56637-806-2(0)) Goodheart-Willcox Pub.

Steinhauser, Peggy L. Mousetracks: A Kid's Computer Idea Book. Steinhauser, Peggy L., illus. 2004. (Illus.). 104p. (gr. k-5). pap. 12.95 (978-1-883672-48-5(1), Tricycle Pr.) Ten Speed Pr.

Totter, Donald. Architectural Presentation with DataCad 10. 2004. (YA). spiral bd. (978-0-9740796-3-9(4)) Technology Education Concepts Inc.

COMPUTER LITERACY

Here are entered works on the ability to use and understand computers, including their capabilities, applications, and social implications, in order to function in a computer-based society.

Computer Science Pure & Simple Book 1, 2. 2003. (Illus.). 126p. (gr. 5 up). spiral bd. 24.99 (978-0-9749653-0-7(8), 001) Motherboard Bks.

COMPUTER PROGRAMMING

Bitetto, Marco A. V. Theme Stream Vol. 7: Helicopters. l.t. ed. 2002. (Illus.). 120p. (YA). (gr. 9-12). pap. 22.00 (978-1-58578-481-3(8)) Institute of Cybernetics Research, Inc.

—Theme Stream Vol. 10: Helicopters. l.t. ed. 2003. (Illus.). 128p. (YA). (gr. 9-12). pap. 22.00 (978-1-58578-483-7(4)) Institute of Cybernetics Research, Inc.

Bonnice, Sherry. Computer Programmer. 2003. (Careers with Character Ser.). (Illus.). 96p. (YA). (gr. 7 up). lib. bdg. 22.95 (978-1-59084-312-3(6)) Mason Crest Pubs.

Brashares, Ann. Linus Torvalds: Software Rebel. 2001. (Techies Ser.: up). (Illus.). 80p. (J). (gr. 5 up). lib. bdg. 23.90 (978-0-7613-1960-3(3), Twenty-First Century Bks.) Lerner Publishing Group.

Easttom, William. C++ Programming Fundamentals: CyberRookies. 2003. (CyberRookies). (Illus.). 416p. pap. 34.95 incl. cd-rom (978-1-58450-237-1(1)) Charles River Media.

Facts on File, Inc. Staff, ed. Aviation. 2005. (Careers in Focus Ser.). (Illus.). 192p. (YA). (gr. 6-12). 22.95 (978-0-8160-5850-1(4)) Facts On File, Inc.

Fain, Yakov. Java Programming for Kids. 2004. (Illus.). 216p. per. (978-0-9718439-5-0(3)) Smart Data Processing, Inc.

Levin, Judith. Careers Creating Search Engines. 2006. (Cutting Edge Careers Ser.). (Illus.). 64p. (J). (gr. 7-12). lib. bdg. 27.95 (978-1-4042-0957-2(3)) Rosen Publishing Group, Inc., The.

McGinty, Alice B. Software Designer. (CoolCareers.com Ser.). 48p. (YA). 2004. lib. bdg. 23.95 (978-0-8239-4086-8(1)); 2000. (Illus.). (gr. 5-8). lib. bdg. 23.95 (978-0-8239-3149-1(8), CCSODE, Rosen Central) Rosen Publishing Group, Inc., The.

Parks, Peggy J. Computer Animator. 2005. (Exploring Careers Ser.). (Illus.). 48p. (J). (gr. 4-8). lib. bdg. 26.20 (978-0-7377-2065-5(4), Kidhaven) Thomson Gale.

—Computer Programming. 2003. (Exploring Careers Ser.). (Illus.). 48p. (J). (gr. 3-5). 26.20 (978-0-7377-1483-8(2), Kidhaven) Thomson Gale.

QEB Let's Start! Computing National Book Stores Edition: Using Instructions. 2006. (J). per. (978-1-59566-298-9(7)) QEB Publishing Inc.

Roff, Jason T. & Roff, Kimberly A. Careers in E-Commerce Software Development. 2005. (Library of E-Commerce & Internet Careers). (Illus.). 64p. (YA). (gr. 7-12). lib. bdg. 26.50 (978-0-8239-3421-8(7)) Rosen Publishing Group, Inc., The.

Starno, Nancy. HTML Two Student Activities Book. Matthews, Douglas L., ed. 2003. (Illus.). stu. ed., per., wbk. ed. (978-1-931680-47-9(7), Expert Systems for Teachers) Teaching Point, Inc.

Stewart, Gail B. Larry Page & Sergey Brin: The Google Guys. 2007. (Innovators Ser.). (Illus.). 64p. (J). (gr. 4-8). 24.95 (***978-0-7377-3863-6(4)***, Kidhaven) Thomson Gale.

Tracy, Kathleen. Marc Andreessen & the Development of the Web Browser. 2002. (Unlocking the Secrets of Science Ser.). (Illus.). 56p. (gr. 4-10). lib. bdg. 25.70 (978-1-58415-092-3(0)) Mitchell Lane Pubs., Inc.

Wallner, Rosemary. Computer Programmer. 2000. (Career Exploration Ser.). (Illus.). 48p. (J). (gr. 3-4). lib. bdg. 21.26 (978-0-7368-0488-2(9), LifeMatters Bks.) Capstone Pr., Inc.

COMPUTER SOFTWARE

see also names of specific computer software, e.g. Lotus 1-2-3 (Computer Program)

Ashdown, David. Hyperstudio Made Very Easy! Easy Step-by-Step Lessons & Projects That Help Every Kid-and Every Teacher-Master the Essentials of HyperStudio. 2000. (Illus.). 64p. pap. 10.95 (978-0-439-13897-0(3)) Scholastic, Inc.

Because You're NOT a Dummy! for Windows 95 - Xp. 5th ed. 2003. Orig. Title: Because You're NOT a Dummy!. per. 29.95 (978-0-9719613-1-9(X)) Wood, Char, The Computer Granny.

Brocklehurst, R. An Introduction to Powerpoint. 2004. (Computer Guides). 24p. (J). pap. 7.95 (978-0-7945-0345-1(4)) EDC Publishing.

Brown, Jonatha A. Bill Gates. 2004. (Gente Que Hay Que Conocer Ser.). (SPA & ENG., Illus.). 24p. (J). pap. (978-0-8368-4359-0(2)) Stevens, Gareth Inc.

—Bill Gates. Acosta, Tatiana & Gutierrez, Guillermo, trs. 2004. (Gente Que Hay Que Conocer Ser.). (SPA., Illus.). 24p. (J). lib. bdg. 19.33 (978-0-8368-4352-1(5)) Stevens, Gareth Inc.

Core HLE Tools for Pocket PC. 2004. (YA). cd-rom (978-0-9762083-4-1(2)) GoKnow Learning.

Diction 2004. 2004. (J). cd-rom (978-0-9764218-0-1(1)) Dawasoft.

Ganeri, Anita, et al. Larry Ellison: Sheer Nerve. 2001. (Techies Ser.: up). (Illus.). 80p. (gr. 5 up). lib. bdg. 23.90 (978-0-7613-1962-7(X), Twenty-First Century Bks.) Lerner Publishing Group.

Howell, Dusti D. & Howell, Deanne K. Powerful Presentations in Powerpoint: The Quick, Easy & Fun Way to Learn Powerpoint. 2nd rev. ed. 2002. 90p. spiral bd. 19.95 incl. cd-rom (978-0-9677328-2-4(4)) SolidA, Inc.

Image Pasters. 2004. (J). cd-rom (978-0-9764218-1-8(X)) Dawasoft.

Kuhn, Gerald. Cadkey V21 Cookbook. 2003. (Illus.). 197p. spiral bd. (978-0-9740796-2-2(6)) Technology Education Concepts Inc.

Lee, Lauren. Bill Gates. 2002. (Trailblazers of the Modern World Ser.). (Illus.). 48p. (J). (gr. 5 up). pap. 14.95 (978-0-8368-5237-0(0)); lib. bdg. 30.00 (978-0-8368-5077-2(7)) Stevens, Gareth Inc. (World Almanac Library).

Patchett, Fiona. Introduction to Word Processing Word 2000. 2001. (gr. 5-8). lib. bdg. 19.90 (978-0-613-74466-9(7)) Tandem Library Bks.

Snap! PSAT/SAT, 2002. cd-rom 4.99 (978-1-59150-162-6(8)) TOPICS Entertainment.

Stagecast Creator 2.0 German Education Edition. 2004. (GER.). (YA). cd-rom 99.95 (978-1-929721-15-3(3)) Stagecast Software, Inc.

Stagecast Creator 2.0 German Standard Edition. 2004. (GER.). (YA). cd-rom 49.95 (978-1-929721-14-6(5)) Stagecast Software, Inc.

StudioLine Web Edition - English. 2004. cd-rom 279.00 (978-1-885936-80-6(X)) H&M Systems Software, Inc.

StudioLine Web Edition - French. 2004. cd-rom 279.00 (978-1-885936-82-0(6)) H&M Systems Software, Inc.

StudioLine Web Edition - German. 2004. cd-rom 279.00 (978-1-885936-81-3(8)) H&M Systems Software, Inc.

StudioLine Web Edition - Italian. 2004. cd-rom 279.00 (978-1-885936-83-7(4)) H&M Systems Software, Inc.

Trailblazers of the Modern World: Neil Armstrong; Bob Dylan; Bill Gates; Nelson Mandela; Eleanor Roosevelt; Steven Spielberg, 6 bks. 2002. (Illus.). (J). (gr. 5 up). pap. 87.60 (978-0-8368-5234-9(6) , World Almanac Library) Stevens, Gareth Inc.

Vargas, Daraciela. HyperStudio: Para Maestros y Estudiantes: 20 Ejercicios de Practica. 2003. ring bd. 14.99 (978-0-9702021-8-5(0)) Conexion Educativa.

Wilson, Carole. Exploring Information & Software Technology Teacher CD-ROM. 4th rev. ed. 2007. tchr. ed. 74.00 incl. cd-rom (*978-0-521-69264-9(4)) Cambridge Univ. Pr.

Worldmanac 2004. 2004. (J). cd-rom (978-0-9764218-2-5(8)) Dawasoft.

Zocchi, Judy. Curtain Up: Application Software. 2006. (Click & Squeak Ser.). (Illus.). 32p. (J). 20.65 (978-1-891997-63-1(7)) Dingles & Co.

COMPUTERS

see also Calculators; Cyberspace; Electronic Data Processing; Information Storage and Retrieval Systems

Aaseng, Nathan. Business Builders in Computers. 2000. (Business Builders Ser.: Vol. 2). (Illus.). 160p. (gr. 5 up). lib. bdg. 22.95 (978-1-881508-57-1(9)) Oliver Pr., Inc.

Ambrose, Ann & Wells, Dolores J. Computer Concepts BASICS. 3rd rev. ed. 2006. 480p. (C). spiral bd. 59.95 (978-1-4188-6503-0(6)) Thomson Course Technology, Inc.

Andelora, Sharon & McGraw-Hill Staff. Horizons! Computing Across the Curriculum, ClarisWorks 5.0 (Mac) 1998. (Horizons, Computing Across the Curriculum Ser.). 351p. stu. ed. 51.41 (978-0-02-804225-1(5) , 9780028042251) Glencoe/McGraw-Hill.

Ani's Early Literacy Kit. 2002. (SPA.). (J). pap. 149.95 incl. cd-rom (978-1-931872-31-7(7)) APTE, Inc.

Ashley, Susan. I Can Use a Computer. 2004. (Illus.). 24p. (J). pap. (978-0-8368-4332-3(0)); (YA). lib. bdg. 19.33 (978-0-8368-4325-5(8)) Stevens, Gareth Inc.

Bailey. Computer Science Tea Man. (J). (gr. 10-12). 42.00 (978-0-669-95256-8(7)) Houghton Mifflin Co. (Schl. Div.).

Bailey, Edward R. Computer Science: A Structure. (J). (gr. 10-12). 37.75 (978-0-669-95104-2(8)) Houghton Mifflin Co. (Schl. Div.).

Baker, Christopher W. A New World of Simulators: Training with Technology. 2001. (New Century Technology Ser.: 8). (Illus.). 48p. (gr. 5-8). lib. bdg. 23.90 (978-0-7613-1352-6(4) , Millbrook Pr.) Lerner Publishing Group.

Ballweg, Judy K. KI Pix Digital Gallery: Cameras, Scanners & Computers. 2000. (Illus.). 120p. (J). (gr. k-2). spiral bd. 26.95 (978-1-56484-156-8(1)) International Society for Technology in Education.

—Kid Pix ABC: Art, Books & Computers. 2000. (Illus.). 150p. (J). (gr. k-2). spiral bd. 25.95 (978-1-56484-155-1(3)) International Society for Technology in Education.

Baum, L. Frank. Frank Baum: Oz Books. 2003. (J). cd-rom 19.00 (978-0-931968-41-9(0)) B & R Samizdat Express.

Baxter, Roberta. Computers. 2005. (Kidhaven Science Library). (Illus.). 48p. (J). (gr. 4-8). 26.20 (978-0-7377-3053-1(6) , Greenhaven Pr., Inc.) Thomson Gale.

Behr, Ashley F. Camp ICMI. Karn, George, illus. 1998. (21st Century Kids Ser.). 32p. (J). (ps-3). per. 5.95 (978-0-9660533-0-2(3)) Behr, D. J. Co.

Bennington, Stephen. Computers. 2001. (Investigations Ser.). (Illus.). 64p. (gr. 3 up). 14.95 (978-0-7548-0653-0(7)) Anness Publishing GBR. *Dist:* National Bk. Network.

Billings, Charlene W. & Grady, Sean M. Supercomputers: Charting the Future of Cybernetics. 2nd ed. 2004. (Science & Technology in Focus Ser.). (Illus.). 240p. (J). (gr. 6-12). 35.00 (978-0-8160-4730-7(8)) Facts On File, Inc.

Bitetto, Marco A. V. Journal of Amateur Computing: Spring/Summer 2003 Issue. Bitetto, Marco A. V., ed. l.t. ed. 2003. (Illus.). 120p. (YA). (gr. 9-12). pap. 22.00 (978-1-58578-482-0(6)) Institute of Cybernetics Research, Inc.

Bodden, Valerie. Computers. 2008. (J). (*978-1-58341-556-6(4) , Creative Education) Creative Co., The.

Brashares, Ann. Linus Torvalds: Software Rebel. 2001. (Techies Ser.: up). (Illus.). 80p. (J). (gr. 5 up). lib. bdg. 23.90 (978-0-7613-1960-3(3) , Twenty-First Century Bks.) Lerner Publishing Group.

—Steve Jobs: Thinks Different. 2001. (Techies Ser.: up). (Illus.). 80p. (gr. 5 up). lib. bdg. 23.90 (978-0-7613-1959-7(X) , Twenty-First Century Bks.) Lerner Publishing Group.

Bud's Easy Research Paper Manual. 4th exp. ed. 2001. 225p. (YA). stu. ed., per. 11.50 (978-1-891707-05-6(1)) Lawrence Hse. Pubs.

Burstein, John. Usar Computadoras: Una Maquina con Raton: Basado en la Serie de Television Publica Math Monsters(Tm), Desarrollada en Colaboracion con el Consejo Nacional de Maestros de Matematicas (NCTM) 2006. (ENG & SPA., Illus.). 24p. (J). pap. (978-0-8368-6694-0(0)); lib. bdg. 19.33 (978-0-8368-6679-7(7)) Stevens, Gareth Inc.

—Using Computers: Machine with a Mouse. Destiny Images Staff, illus. 2003. (Math Monsters Ser.). 24p. (YA). (gr. 1 up). lib. bdg. 19.33 (978-0-8368-3817-6(3) , Weekly Reader Early Learning Library) Stevens, Gareth Inc.

Chambers, Catherine. Look Inside a Computer. 2002. (Illus.). 24p. (J). (gr. k-3). pap. (978-1-57572-470-6(7) , 90459) Heinemann Library.

Champion, Neil & Babbage, Charles. Charles Babbage. 2000. (Groundbreakers Ser.). (Illus.). 48p. (J). (gr. 5-7). lib. bdg. 25.64 (978-1-57572-367-9(0)) Heinemann Library.

Chan, David. Meeting the Computer - One Byte at a Time (Chinese Edition) 2004. (CHI.). 296p. per. 25.00 (978-0-9754302-1-7(1)) Chan, David.

Chandler, Fiona, et al. The Usborne First Encyclopedia of History. Hancock, David, illus. 2005. 64p. (J). (978-0-439-78717-8(3)) Scholastic, Inc.

Chappell, Laura A. Laura Chappell Presents: Packet-Level Protocols: DHCP Workbook. 2000. (Illus.). 100p. (YA). wbk. ed. 150.00 (978-1-893939-34-9(0)) podbooks.com, LLC.

—Laura Chappell Presents Vol. 104: Introduction to Network Design & Data Flows. 2000. 100p. (YA). wbk. ed. 150.00 (978-1-893939-32-5(4)) podbooks.com, LLC.

Chen, Chin-Sheng & Lin, Hui-Chung. Computer Numerical Control. 2002. 700p. (C). per. 95.00 incl. cd-rom (978-1-59022-100-6(1)) Glory Educational Resource, Inc.

Childrens Press Staff. The World Wide Web. 1999. (True Bks.). (Illus.). 48p. (J). (gr. 2-4). pap. 6.95 (978-0-516-26181-2(9) , Children's Pr.) Scholastic Library Publishing.

Cipriano, Jeri. Lo que hacen las Computadoras. 2005. Tr. of What Computers Do. (SPA., Illus.). 16p. (J). (gr. 1 up). lib. bdg. 15.93 (978-0-7368-4169-6(5)) Capstone Pr., Inc.

Claybourne, Anna. Computer Dictionary for Beginners. 2001. (gr. 5-8). lib. bdg. 19.90 (978-0-613-74412-6(8)) Tandem Library Bks.

—World Wide Web for Beginners. 1999. (Usborne Computer Guides Ser.). (Illus.). 48p. (YA). (gr. 5 up). lib. bdg. 18.95 (978-0-88110-788-3(3)) EDC Publishing.

Collier, Bruce & MacLachlan, James. Charles Babbage: And the Engines of Perfection. Gingerich, Owen, ed. 1998. (Oxford Portraits in Science Ser.). (Illus.). 128p. (YA). (gr. 7 up). 30.00 (978-0-19-508997-4(9)) Oxford Univ. Pr., Inc.

Collier, Bruce & Maclachlan, James. Charles Babbage & the Engines of Perfection. 2006. (Illus.). 123p. reprint ed. pap. 12.00 (978-1-4223-5040-9(1)) DIANE Publishing Co.

The Computer: KinderFacts Individual Title Six-Packs. (Kinderstarters Ser.). 8p. (ps-1). 21.00 (978-0-7635-8744-4(3)) Rigby Education.

Computer & You: Level Q, 6 vols. (Wonder Worldtm Ser.). 48p. 39.95 (978-0-7802-3179-5(1)) Wright Group, The.

The Computer: Passport to the Digital Age: Individual Title Six-Packs. (On Deck Ser.: Vol. 2). 24p. (gr. 4-5). 35.00 (978-0-7578-5859-8(7)) Rigby Education.

Computers at Work, High School, 6 vols., Vol. 6. 2001. (At Work High School Ser.: Vol. 6). (YA). cd-rom 69.95 (978-1-929879-22-9(9)) Career Kids.

Computers Can Help. 2002. (Illus.). (J). pap. (978-0-7398-5936-0(6)) Steck-Vaughn.

Cook, Peter. Why Doesn't My Floppy Disk Flop? 1999. (gr. 3-6). lib. bdg. 22.20 (978-0-613-16574-7(8)) Tandem Library Bks.

Cook, Peter & Manning, Scott. Why Doesn't My Floppy Disk Flop? And Other Kids' Computer Questions Answered by the CompuDudes. Morrow, Ed, illus. 1999. 90p. (gr. 3-7). pap. 12.95 (978-0-471-18429-4(2) , Wiley) Wiley, John & Sons, Inc.

Coolcareers.com, 8 bks. Incl. Computer Animator. O'Donnell, Annie. lib. bdg. 23.95 (978-0-8239-3101-9(3) , CCCOAN); Hardware Engineer. Donelly, Karen. lib. bdg. 23.95 (978-0-8239-3118-7(8) , CCHAEN); Multimedia & New Media Developer. Mazor, Barry. lib. bdg. 23.95 (978-0-8239-3102-6(1) , CCMEDE); Software Designer. McGinty, Alice B. lib. bdg. 23.95 (978-0-8239-3149-1(8) , CCSODE); Video Game Designer. Olesky, Walter. lib. bdg. 23.95 (978-0-8239-3117-0(X) , CCVIGA); Web Entrepreneur. Oleksy, Walter. lib. bdg. 23.95 (978-0-8239-3103-3(X) , CCWEEN); Web Page Designer. Oleksy, Walter. lib. bdg. 23.95 (978-0-8239-3112-5(9) , CCWEPA); Webmaster. Brown, Marty. lib. bdg. 23.95 (978-0-8239-3111-8(0) , CCWEMA); 48p. (YA). (gr. 5-8). 2000. (Illus.). Set lib. bdg. 191.60 o.p. (978-0-8239-9089-4(3) , CCCOCA, Rosen Central) Rosen Publishing Group, Inc., The.

Cowan, Carla Romaine. E-Commerce Careers in Multimedia. 2005. (Library of E-Commerce & Internet Careers). (Illus.). 64p. (YA). (gr. 7-12). lib. bdg. 26.50 (978-0-8239-3427-0(6)) Rosen Publishing Group, Inc., The.

Dalton, James. The Computer Classroom. (Illus.). (J). (gr. 5-6). pap. (978-1-876973-00-1(5)) Wizard Bks.

De Angelis, Gina & Bianco, David J. Computers: Processing the Data. 2005. (Innovators Ser.: Vol. 13). (Illus.). 144p. (J). (gr. 5 up). lib. bdg. 24.95 (978-1-881508-87-8(0)) Oliver Pr., Inc.

De la Bédoyère, Guy. The First Computers. 2005. (Milestones in Modern Science Ser.). (J). pap. (978-0-8368-5861-7(1)); (Illus.). 48p. (YA). lib. bdg. 30.00 (978-0-8368-5854-9(9)) Stevens, Gareth Inc. (World Almanac Library).

Dietz, Kevin C., ed. A+ Network + Certification. 1999. (Illus.). (YA). pap. (978-0-7423-0365-2(9) , ACD36ANETKIT) ComputerPREP, Inc.

Doherty, Gillian. 101 Cosas Que Hacer Con Tu Ordenador. 2000. Tr. of One Hundred & One Things to Do with Your Computer. (SPA.). (gr. 5-8). lib. bdg. 19.90 (978-0-613-90022-5(7)) Tandem Library Bks.

—101 Things to Do with Your Computer. 1998. (Computer Guides Ser.). (Illus.). 64p. (J). (gr. 5 up). lib. bdg. 18.95 (978-1-58086-123-6(7)) EDC Publishing.

—101 Things to Do with Your Computer. 1998. (gr. 5-8). lib. bdg. 19.90 (978-0-613-74473-7(X)) Tandem Library Bks.

Dubois, Muriel L. I Like Computers: What Can I Be? 2000. (What Can I Be? Ser.). (Illus.). 24p. (J). (gr. 1-2). lib. bdg. 18.60 (978-0-7368-0631-2(8) , Bridgestone Bks.) Capstone Pr., Inc.

Dymond, Kenneth. A Guide to the CMMI: Interpreting the Capability Maturity Model Integration. Dymond, Detta, ed. Faassen, Louis, illus. 2004. spiral bd. 20.00 (978-0-9646008-4-3(6)) Process Transition International, Inc.

Edwards, Susan Denise. Computer Science. 2003. (Illus.). stu. ed., per., wbk. ed. (978-1-931680-28-8(0) , Expert Systems for Teachers) Teaching Point, Inc.

Endres, Hollie J. What Computers Do. (Science Ser.). (Illus.). (J). 2004. 16p. lib. bdg. 15.93 (978-0-7368-2941-0(5) , Yellow Umbrella Bks.); 2003. 17p. pap. (978-0-7368-2900-7(8)) Capstone Pr., Inc.

Faust, Roberta. The Children's Computer Handbook: Just Follow the Bug. Scott, Cheyne R., tr. Brown, Erin, illus. 2002. (SPA.). 37p. (J). (gr. 1-6). pap. 14.95 (978-1-889743-20-2(8)) Robbie Dean Pr.

Festante, Dom. Computer Applications. Matthews, Douglas L., ed. 2004. (Illus.). stu. ed., per., act. bk. ed. (978-1-931680-98-1(1) , Expert Systems for Teachers) Teaching Point, Inc.

First Grade Technology: 32 lessons every First Grader can accomplish on a Computer. 2006. 18.99 net. (978-0-9787800-1-2(9)) Structured Learning.

Fitzpatrick, Anne. The Computer. 2003. 24p. (J). lib. bdg. 21.35 (978-1-58340-318-1(3)) Smart Apple Media.

Flynn, Roger, ed. Computer Sciences Vol. 1: Foundations: Ideas & People, 4 vols. 2000. (Science Library for Students). (Illus.). 192p. (J). 85.00 (978-0-02-865567-3(2) , Macmillan Reference USA) Thomson Gale.

Freedman, Jeri. Intellectual Property. 2008. (J). lib. bdg. (*978-1-4042-1348-7(1)) Rosen Publishing Group, Inc., The.

Futurekids Staff, creator. Real Journeys in Technology 1. 1 PC Version: Grade 1 - Pink Level. 2002. mass mkt., stu. ed. (978-1-58739-421-8(9)) Futurekids, Inc.

—Real Journeys in Technology 1. 1 PC Version: Grade 2 - White Level. 2002. mass mkt., stu. ed. (978-1-58739-422-5(7)) Futurekids, Inc.

—Real Journeys in Technology 1. 1 PC Version: Grade 3 - Red Level. 2002. mass mkt., stu. ed. (978-1-58739-423-2(5)) Futurekids, Inc.

—Real Journeys in Technology 1. 1 PC Version: Grade 4 - Orange Level. 2002. mass mkt., stu. ed. (978-1-58739-424-9(3)) Futurekids, Inc.

—Real Journeys in Technology 1. 1 PC Version: Grade 5 - Yellow Level. 2002. mass mkt., stu. ed. (978-1-58739-425-6(1)) Futurekids, Inc.

—Real Journeys in Technology 1. 1 PC Version: Grade 6 - Green Level. 2002. stu. ed., per (978-1-58739-426-3(X)) Futurekids, Inc.

—Real Journeys in Technology 1. 1 PC Version: Grade 7 - Blue Level. 2002. mass mkt., stu. ed. (978-1-58739-427-0(8)) Futurekids, Inc.

—Real Journeys in Technology 1. 1 PC Version: Grade 8 - Purple Level. 2002. mass mkt., stu. ed. (978-1-58739-428-7(6)) Futurekids, Inc.

—Real Journeys in Technology 1. 1 PC Version: Grade K - Gray Level. 2002. mass mkt., stu. ed. (978-1-58739-420-1(0)) Futurekids, Inc.

Gibson, Diane. Computers. 1999. (Making Contact Ser.). (Illus.). 32p. (J). (gr. 4 up). lib. bdg. 16.95 (978-1-887068-60-4(0)) Smart Apple Media.

Goldberg, Jan & Rowh, Mark. Great Jobs for Computer Science Majors. 2nd ed. 2002. (Great Jobs Ser.). (Illus.). 224p. pap. 14.95 (978-0-07-139039-2(1) , 9780071390392) McGraw-Hill Cos., The.

Goranson, Christopher D. Everything You Need to Know about Misinformation on the Internet. 2005. (Need to Know Library). (Illus.). 64p. (YA). (gr. 4-6). lib. bdg. 25.25 (978-0-8239-3521-5(3)) Rosen Publishing Group, Inc., The.

Graham, Ian. Computers. 2001. (Technoworld Ser.). (Illus.). 32p. (J). lib. bdg. 25.69 (978-0-7398-3252-3(2)) Raintree.

—The World of Computers & Communication. 2000. (Inside Look Ser.). (Illus.). 48p. (J). (gr. 4 up). lib. bdg. 26.00 (978-0-8368-2727-9(9)) Stevens, Gareth Inc.

Gralla, Preston. Online Activities for Kids: Projects for School, Extra Credit, or Just Plain Fun! 2001. (Illus.). 256p. pap. 16.95 (978-0-471-39073-2(9) , Wiley) Wiley, John & Sons, Inc.

—Online Kids: A Young Surfer's Guide to Cyberspace. 2nd rev. ed. 1999. (Illus.). 288p. 29.95 (978-0-471-33329-6(8) , Wiley) Wiley, John & Sons, Inc.

Greenhaven Staff. Technological Revolution. 2002. (gr. 7-12). lib. bdg. 33.25 (978-0-613-73854-5(3)) Tandem Library Bks.

Greenia, Mark W. History of Computing: An Encyclopedia of the People & Machines That Made Computer History. exp. ed. 2001. (Professional Reference Ser.). 2000p. cd-rom 19.95 (978-0-944601-78-5(2)) Lexikon Services.

Haddon, Jean. Words: A Computer Lesson. Vargo, Sharon Hawkins, illus. 2003. (Silly Millies Ser.). 32p. (ps-1). (J). pap. 4.99 (978-0-7613-1797-5(X)); lib. bdg. 17.90 (978-0-7613-2870-4(X)) Lerner Publishing Group. (Millbrook Pr.).

Handheld Learning Environment (HLE) for Pocket PC. 2004. (YA). cd-rom (978-0-9762083-1-0(8)) GoKnow Learning.

Heese, VaReane. Net Venture. 2002. (Illus.). (J). (gr. 3-6). 2081.00 (978-1-57336-376-1(6) , 2081) Interaction Pubs., Inc.

Henderson, Harry. Computer Viruses. 2005. (Lucent Library of Science & Technology Ser.). (Illus.). 128p. (YA). (gr. 7-10). lib. bdg. 29.95 (978-1-59018-102-7(6) , Lucent Bks.) Thomson Gale.

Henderson, Harry. Encyclopedia of Computer Science & Technology. 2nd rev. ed. 2008. (Science Encyclopedia Ser.). 544p. (gr. 9). 87.50 (*978-0-8160-6382-6(6)) Facts On File, Inc.

Henderson, Lyndsey. Chip (Computer Facts) 2001. (Teacher's Pet Ser.). 48p. (J). 4.95 (978-0-439-17343-8(4)) Scholastic, Inc.

Herz, Joe. Exploring Computers: Challenging. 2001. (Computers in Middle Schools Ser.). (Illus.). 176p. pap. 16.99 (978-1-57690-462-6(8)) Teacher Created Materials, Inc.

Hoare, Stephen. Computer World. (J). (978-0-528-87857-2(3)) Checkerboard Pr., Inc.

Hoggatt, Jack, et al. Century 21 Computer Applications & Keyboarding. 7th rev. ed. 2001. (Illus.). 608p. (C). 76.95 (978-0-538-69152-9(2)) Thomson South-Western.

How Do I... 2005. (YA). per. 24.95 (978-0-9770372-0-9(7)) Brown, Samuel E.

Hughes, L. Activators Computers Unlimited. (Illus.). 126p. (J). pap. 8.99 (978-0-340-71520-8(0) , Hodder & Stoughton) Hodder General Publishing Division GBR. *Dist:* Trafalgar Square Publishing.

Informatik: Grundbegriffe der Informatik. (Duden-Schuelerduden Ser.). (GER., Illus.). 560p. (YA). (978-3-411-04483-2(7)) Bibliographisches Institut & F. A. Brockhaus AG DEU. *Dist:* International Bk. Import Service, Inc.

Inventing the Computer. 2007. (Illus.). 32p. (J). (gr. 3-9). (*978-0-7787-2816-0(1)); pap. (*978-0-7787-2838-2(2)) Crabtree Publishing Co.

J. G. Ferguson Publishing Company Staff. Discovering Careers for Your Future/Computers. 2001. (Discovering Careers for Your Future Ser.). (Illus.). 96p. (J). (gr. 4-9). 21.95 (978-0-89434-389-6(0) , Ferguson Publishing Co.) Facts On File, Inc.

Jefferis, David. Cyberspace: Virtual Reality & the World Wide Web. 1999. (Megatech Ser.). (Illus.). 32p. (J). (gr. 4-5). pap. (978-0-7787-0057-9(7)); lib. bdg. (978-0-7787-0047-0(X)) Crabtree Publishing Co.

Jortberg, Charles A. The Big Machines: Kids & Computers. 2004. (Illus.). 39p. (J). (gr. k-4). reprint ed. 14.00 (978-0-7567-8456-0(5)) DIANE Publishing Co.

Judd, Philip, et al. Learning with Computers: Level 6 Blue. 2005. 400p. (C). pap. 49.95 (978-0-538-43968-8(8)) Thomson South-Western.

Kahn, Jetty. Women in Computer Science Careers. 1999. (Short Biographies Ser.). (Illus.). 48p. (J). (gr. 3-4). lib. bdg. 22.60 (978-0-7368-0316-8(5) , Bridgestone Bks.) Capstone Pr., Inc.

—Women in Computer Science Careers. 1999. (Illus.). 48p. (J). (gr. 3-7). pap. 19.93 (978-0-516-21883-0(2) , Children's Pr.) Scholastic Library Publishing.

Kalbag, Asha. Homework on Your Computer. Sheikh Miller, Jonathan, ed. 2000. (Illus.). (J). (978-0-606-18129-7(6)) Tandem Library Bks.

Kalman, Bobbie. The Computer from A to Z. 1998. (AlphaBasiCs Ser.). (Illus.). 32p. (J). (gr. 2-3). pap. (978-0-86505-409-7(6)); lib. bdg. (978-0-86505-379-3(0)) Crabtree Publishing Co.

—The Computer from A to Z. 1999. (gr. 3-6). lib. bdg. 16.40 (978-0-613-07521-3(8)) Tandem Library Bks.

Kauffman, Dorothy. The Computer Age. 2005. (Content Area Readers Ser.). 4.95 (978-0-19-430960-8(6)) Oxford Univ. Pr., Inc.

Kazunas, Charnan & Kazunas, Thomas. The Internet for Kids. 2nd rev. ed. 2000. (True Bks.). (Illus.). 48p. (J). (gr. 3-5). 25.00 (978-0-516-21936-3(7) , Children's Pr.) Scholastic Library Publishing.

Komando, Kim. The 50 Biggest Computer Mistakes (and How You Can Avoid Them!) 2002. cd-rom 19.95 (978-0-9725247-0-4(3)) WestStar TalkRadio Network.

Lesinski, Jeanne M. Bill Gates. (Biography Ser.). (Illus.). 112p. (gr. 6-12). 2005. lib. bdg. 27.93 (978-0-8225-4949-9(2)); 2003. (J). pap. 7.95 (978-0-8225-9689-9(X)) Lerner Publishing Group.

—Bill Gates. 2000. (Illus.). (J). 15.50 (978-0-606-18814-2(2)) Tandem Library Bks.

Levy, Elizabeth. El Misterio de la Computadora Siniestra. 2001. (978-0-606-22663-9(X)) Tandem Library Bks.

Lockman, Darcy. Computers. 2000. (Kaleidoscope Ser.). (Illus.). 48p. (J). (gr. 3 up). lib. bdg. 25.64 (978-0-7614-1045-4(7) , Benchmark Bks.) Cavendish, Marshall Corp.

Luehrmann, Arthur & Peckham, Herbert. Hands-On Microsoft Office. 1999. (Illus.). 512p. (YA). (gr. 7 up). spiral bd. 46.60 (978-1-57426-145-5(2)) Computer Literacy Pr.

Mandel, Mimi. Teen Resources on the Web: A Guide for Librarians, Parents & Teachers. 2000. 120p. (YA). (gr. 6-12). pap. 17.95 (978-1-57950-042-9(0) , Upstart Bks.) Highsmith Inc.

Marsh, Carole. Let's Discover Georgia! 2004. (Georgia Experience! Ser.). (J). (gr. 2-8). cd-rom 14.95 (978-0-7933-9488-3(0)) Gallopade International.

—Let's Discover Ohio! 2004. (Ohio Experience! Ser.). (J). (gr. 2-8). cd-rom 14.95 (978-0-7933-9493-7(7)) Gallopade International.

Mattern, Joanne. The Computer: Passport to the Digital Age. 2003. (Reading Power Ser.). (Illus.). 24p. (J). lib. bdg. 17.25 (978-0-8239-6492-5(2) , PowerKids Pr.) Rosen Publishing Group, Inc., The.

McAlpine, Margaret. Working with Computers. 2004. (My Future Career Ser.). (Illus.). 64p. (J). lib. bdg. 26.00 (978-0-8368-4242-5(1)) Stevens, Gareth Inc.

McDonagh, Sorcha, et al. Computers & Technology. 2006. (Science News for Kids Ser.). (Illus.). 64p. (J). 30.00 (978-0-7910-9120-3(1) , Chelsea Clubhouse) Facts On File, Inc.

McGraw-Hill Staff. Glencoe Keyboarding with Computer Applications, Lessons 1-80. 2003. (gr. 6-12). stu. ed. 63.96 (978-0-07-860242-9(4) , 9780078602429) Glencoe/McGraw-Hill.

—Glencoe Keyboarding with Computer Applications, Short Course, Lessons 1-80. 2000. (C). stu. ed. 66.00 (978-0-07-830154-4(8) , 9780078301544) Glencoe/McGraw-Hill.

McGraw-Hill Staff, et al. Glencoe Computer Connections: Projects & Applications. 2nd ed. 2003. 386p. (C). (gr. 6-12). stu. ed. 55.32 (978-0-07-861399-9(X) , 9780078613999) Glencoe/McGraw-Hill.

McNutt, Todd A. Other People's Secrets: A Techno-Expose' on the Legal Invasion of Privacy by Computers. 2nd ed. 1999. 60p. (YA). (gr. 11 up). pap. 9.95 (978-1-885037-06-0(6)) SEEBIC Publishing Co.

Meredith, Susan. Starting Computers. 2000. (gr. k-3). lib. bdg. 18.75 (978-0-613-90027-0(8)) Tandem Library Bks.

Miller, Deborah J. Careers with an Internet Service Provider. 2005. (Library of E-Commerce & Internet Careers). (Illus.). 64p. (YA). (gr. 7-12). lib. bdg. 26.50 (978-0-8239-3425-6(X)) Rosen Publishing Group, Inc., The.

Morfeld, Rebecca, et al. My Computer Story Book - for Early Readers: Charming Stories & Illustrations. 2001. (J). cd-rom 10.00 (978-1-931457-12-5(3)) Stargate Electronic Library, Inc.

Morrison, Toni & Morrison, Slade. The Big Box. Potter, Giselle, illus. 2004. 40p. (J). (gr. k-4). reprint ed. 20.00 (978-0-7567-8167-5(1)) DIANE Publishing Co.

A Mouse Sized Mystery: Navigating the Computer. 2004. (Click & Squeak Ser.). (978-1-891997-62-4(9)) Dingles & Co.

NETS Project Staff. National Educational Technology Standards for Students: Connecting Curriculum & Technology. 2000. (National Educational Technology Standards for Students Ser.). (Illus.). 373p. (J). (gr. k-12). spiral bd. 29.95 (978-1-56484-150-6(2)) International Society for Technology in Education.

Northrup, Mary. American Computer Pioneers. 1998. (Collective Biographies Ser.). (Illus.). 112p. (YA). (gr. 6-12). lib. bdg. 26.60 (978-0-7660-1053-6(8)) Enslow Pubs., Inc.

O'Donnell, Annie. Computer Animator. 2000. (CoolCareers.com Ser.). (Illus.). 48p. (YA). (gr. 5-8). lib. bdg. 23.95 (978-0-8239-3101-9(3) , CCCOAN, Rosen Central) Rosen Publishing Group, Inc., The.

Otfinoski, Steven. Computers. 2007. (Great Inventions Ser.). (Illus.). 144p. (YA). (gr. 9 up). lib. bdg. 39.93 ***978-0-7614-2597-7(7)** , Benchmark Bks.) Cavendish, Marshall Corp.

Oxlade, Chris. My First Computer Guide: Chris Oxlade. 2007. (J). (***978-1-4329-0018-2(8)**); pap. (***978-1-4329-0022-9(6)***) Heinemann Library.

Packard, Mary. High-Tech Inventions: A Chapter Book. 2004. (True Tales Ser.). (J). 22.50 (978-0-516-23728-2(4) , Children's Pr.) Scholastic Library Publishing.

Parker, Steve. Computers. 2002. (Tomorrow's Technology Ser.). (Illus.). 32p. (J). lib. bdg. 24.25 (978-1-931983-23-5(2)) Chrysalis Education.

Pasternak, Ceel & Thornburg, Linda. Cool Careers for Girls in Computers. 1999. (Cool Careers for Girls Ser.). (Illus.). (gr. 5). 125p. pap. 12.95 (978-1-57023-103-2(6)); 124p. (YA). 19.95 (978-1-57023-106-3(0)) Impact Pubns.

Patrice Cassedy. Computer Technology. 2004. (Careers for the Twenty-First Century Ser.). (Illus.). 112p. (J). 29.95 (978-1-56006-896-9(5)) Thomson Gale.

Pelton, Stephen, et al. Basic Computers for Beginners. 2003. per. 29.95 (978-0-9748237-0-6(8)) Web Wise Services, Inc.

Perry, Robert. Multimedia Magic. 2000. (Computer Science Library). (Illus.). 64p. (J). (gr. 5-7). 25.50 (978-0-531-11755-2(3) , Watts, Franklin) Scholastic Library Publishing.

—Personal Computer Communications. 2000. (Watts Library). (Illus.). 64p. (YA). (gr. 5-7). pap. 8.95 (978-0-531-16483-9(7) , Watts, Franklin) Scholastic Library Publishing.

Perry, Robert L. Personal Computer Communications. 2000. (Illus.). 64p. (J). (gr. 5-7). lib. bdg. 17.60 (978-0-613-37497-2(5)) Tandem Library Bks.

QEB Let's Start! Computing National Book Stores Edition: Finding Facts. 2006. (J). per. (978-1-59566-295-8(2)) QEB Publishing Inc.

QEB Let's Start! Computing National Book Stores Edition: Making Pictures. 2006. (J). per. (978-1-59566-293-4(6)) QEB Publishing Inc.

QEB Let's Start! Computing National Book Stores Edition: Starting with Words. 2006. (J). per. (978-1-59566-294-1(4)) QEB Publishing Inc.

QEB Let's Start! Computing National Book Stores Edition: Using Instructions. 2006. (J). per. (978-1-59566-298-9(7)) QEB Publishing Inc.

QEB Let's Start! Computing National Book Stores Edition: World Art. 2006. (J). per. (978-1-59566-300-9(2)) QEB Publishing Inc.

Quadrillion Media Staff. Internet (Das Internet) Surfin' the Web. 1998. (Start Me Up Ser.). 64p. (J). (gr. 3-8). pap. 15.95 (978-1-58185-023-9(9) , Tessloff Publishing) Quadrillion Media LLC.

Rau, Dana Meachen. Bill & Melinda Gates. 2008. (J). lib. bdg. 26.00 (***978-1-60279-068-1(X)***) Cherry Lake Publishing.

Raum, Elizabeth. The History of the Computer. 2007. (J). (***978-1-4034-9649-2(8)***); pap. (***978-1-4034-9655-3(2)***) Heinemann Library.

Real Journeys in Technology: Grade 1. 2001. (J). stu. ed., spiral bd., wbk. ed. (978-1-58739-231-3(3)) Futurekids, Inc.

Real Journeys in Technology: Grade 2. 2001. (J). spiral bd. (978-1-58739-212-2(7)) Futurekids, Inc.

Real Journeys in Technology: Kindergarten. 2001. (J). stu. ed., spiral bd., wbk. ed. (978-1-58739-230-6(5)) Futurekids, Inc.

Real Journeys in Technology: Mac Grade 1. 2001. stu. ed., spiral bd. (978-1-58739-251-1(8)) Futurekids, Inc.

Real Journeys in Technology: Mac Grade 2. 2001. stu. ed., spiral bd. (978-1-58739-262-7(3)) Futurekids, Inc.

Real Journeys in Technology: Mac Grade 3. 2001. stu. ed., spiral bd. (978-1-58739-273-3(9)) Futurekids, Inc.

Real Journeys in Technology: Mac Grade 5. 2001. stu. ed., spiral bd. (978-1-58739-265-8(8)) Futurekids, Inc.

Real Journeys in Technology: Mac Grade 6. 2001. stu. ed., spiral bd. (978-1-58739-266-5(6)) Futurekids, Inc.

Real Journeys in Technology: Mac Grade 7. 2001. stu. ed., spiral bd. (978-1-58739-257-3(7)) Futurekids, Inc.

Real Journeys in Technology: Mac Grade 8. 2001. stu. ed., spiral bd. (978-1-58739-268-9(2)) Futurekids, Inc.

Real Journeys in Technology: PC Grade 3. 2001. stu. ed., spiral bd. (978-1-58739-243-6(7)) Futurekids, Inc.

Real Journeys in Technology: PC Grade 4. 2001. stu. ed., spiral bd., wbk. ed. (978-1-58739-274-0(7)) Futurekids, Inc.

Real Journeys in Technology: PC Grade 8. 2001. stu. ed., spiral bd. (978-1-58739-248-1(8)) Futurekids, Inc.

Reeves, Diane Lindsey. Career Ideas for Kids Who Like Computers. 2nd rev. ed. (Career Ideas for Kids Ser.). 208p. (J). (gr. 4-9). pap. 16.95 (***978-0-8160-6544-8(6)*** , Checkmark Bks.); 2007. 32.95 (***978-0-8160-6543-1(8)*** , Ferguson Publishing Co.) Facts On File, Inc.

Renaissance Learning, Inc. Staff. STAR Early Literacy Made EZ (v 2. 1) RP: Quick Guide to Software. 2004. 23p. spiral bd. 21.95 (978-1-931819-41-1(6)) Renaissance Learning, Inc.

Rooney, Anne. Computers. 2006. (Illus.). 56p. (J). pap. (978-1-4034-7432-2(X)) Heinemann.

—Computers. 2005. (Technology All Around Us Ser.). (Illus.). 32p. (J). (gr. 4-7). lib. bdg. 27.10 (978-1-58340-750-9(2)) Smart Apple Media.

—Finding Facts, 6 vols. 2005. (QEB Computer Tutors Ser.). (Illus.). 32p. (J). (gr. 1-4). lib. bdg. 18.95 (978-1-59566-109-8(3)) QEB Publishing Inc.

—Starting with Words, 6 vols. 2005. (QEB Computer Tutors Ser.). (Illus.). 32p. (J). (gr. 1-4). lib. bdg. 18.95 (978-1-59566-108-1(5)) QEB Publishing Inc.

—Take Control. 2004. (QEB Learn Computing Ser.). (Illus.). 32p. (J). lib. bdg. 18.95 (978-1-59566-040-4(2)) QEB Publishing Inc.

—Using Instructions, 6 vols. 2005. (QEB Learn Computing Ser.). (Illus.). 32p. (J). (gr. 1-4). lib. bdg. 18.95 (978-1-59566-112-8(3)) QEB Publishing Inc.

—What If? 2004. (QEB Learn Computing Ser.). (Illus.). 32p. (J). lib. bdg. 18.95 (978-1-59566-041-1(0)) QEB Publishing Inc.

Ross & Guymon-King, Jennette. Primary Partners: Ages 4 to 7 (CTR A): A-Z Activities to Make Learning Fun! 2004. (ps-2). cd-rom 11.95 (978-1-57734-569-5(X) , 3522377) Covenant Communications, Inc.

—Primary Partners: Nursery-Age 3, Vol. 2. 2004. cd-rom 11.95 (978-1-57734-568-8(1) , 3522369) Covenant Communications, Inc.

—Primary Partners: Nursery-Age 3: A-Z Activities to Make Learning Fun. 2004. (ps up). cd-rom 11.95 (978-1-57734-567-1(3) , 3522350) Covenant Communications, Inc.

Savage, Jeff. Y2K: What Every Youngster Should Know about the Millennium Bug! 1999. (J). 22.83 (978-0-7398-1377-5(3)) Raintree.

—Y2K: What Every Youngster Should Know about the Millennium Bug! 1999. pap. 6.95 (978-0-7398-1478-9(8)) Steck-Vaughn.

Shimp, Emily. ABC Play Book. Dorn, Dave, ed. 1998. (Illus.). 28p. (Orig.). (J). (ps-1). pap., wbk. ed. (978-0-9658251-0-8(8)) KidBoard, Inc.

SIRS Discoverer. 2005. (J). mass mkt. (978-0-89777-566-3(X)) SIRS Publishing, Inc.

SIRS Discoverer: Getting Started Manual Spring 2004. 2003. (YA). cd-rom 1425.00 (978-0-89777-542-7(2)) SIRS Publishing, Inc.

Sloan, Peter. Computers. 1999. (gr. k-3). lib. bdg. 11.80 (978-0-613-30330-9(X)) Tandem Library Bks.

Stazzer, James. My TV's Alive! Real Life Robots, Future Computers & Clones. 1999. (Illus.). 128p. (gr. 4-7). pap. 4.95 (978-1-902618-35-7(1)) Element Children's Bks.

Steadman, Ralph. Little.com. 2002. (Illus.). 40p. 17.99 (978-0-86264-994-4(3)) Andersen GBR. *Dist:* Trafalgar Square Publishing.

Stearns, Peggy Healy. Stationery Studio - Single: Single Computer License. Reynolds, Peter H., illus. 2003. 112p. (J). 69.95 incl. cd-rom (978-1-891405-07-5(1)) FableVision Pr.

Steck-Vaughn Staff. Calling All Problem Solvers. 1998. pap. 665.20 (978-0-8172-8551-7(2)) Steck-Vaughn.

—Calling All Problem Solvers: Windows & Macintosh Version. 1998. pap. 83.10 incl. cd-rom (978-0-8172-8546-3(6)) Steck-Vaughn.

—Calling All Problem Solvers: Windows/Macintosh Labs. 1998. pap. 249.40 incl. cd-rom (978-0-8172-8547-0(4)) Steck-Vaughn.

—Calling All Problem Solvers 10-Pack. 1998. pap. 748.30 (978-0-8172-8550-0(4)) Steck-Vaughn.

—Calling All Problem Solvers 3-Pack. 1998. pap. 415.70 (978-0-8172-8548-7(2)) Steck-Vaughn.

—Calling All Problem Solvers 5-Pack. 1998. pap. 582.00 (978-0-8172-8549-4(0)) Steck-Vaughn.

—Power up Multimedia Workout Book Set, Level 3. 2002. (Illus.). pap. (978-0-7398-6478-4(5)); pap. (978-0-7398-6479-1(3)) Steck-Vaughn.

—Power Up Multimedia Workout Book Set Level 2. 2002. (Illus.). pap. (978-0-7398-6477-7(7)) Steck-Vaughn.

Stevens, M. & Treays, R. Computers for Beginners. 1998. (Computer Guides Ser.). (Illus.). 48p. (YA). (gr. 5 up). lib. bdg. 17.95 (978-1-58086-156-4(3)) EDC Publishing.

Strother, Ruth. Bill Gates. 2007. (Essential Lives Ser.). (ENG., Illus.). 112p. (J). (gr. 6-8). lib. bdg. 32.79 (***978-1-59928-841-3(9)*** , Essential Library) ABDO Publishing Co.

Super Cyber Box: Cyber Tours, Quarter 3. 1999. 160p. (J). (gr. 1-6). 164.99 (978-1-57405-441-5(4)) CharismaLife Pubs.

TBC Staff. Cutting Edge Computers: Faster, Smaller & Smarter. 2006. (Illus.). 56p. (J). (978-0-431-13269-3(0)) Heinemann.

Thompson, Gary. Digital Photography & Your PC: A Guide to Using Your PC to Create Your Own Personalized Photo Albums. 2003. (Illus.). 166p. (YA). spiral bd. 29.95 (978-0-9749763-0-3(X)) Guiding Horizons.

TNT Stone and Associates Staff & Petertil Design Partners Staff, illus. Computers. 1998. (Powertools for Kids Ser.: No. 16). 4p. (J). (gr. 2-5). pap., wbk. ed. 4.95 (978-1-58220-015-6(7) , 32506, PowerTools for Kids) Navigator Systems, Inc.

Toby, Edna & Stevens, Robert. What's a Computer? Stevens, Robert, illus. 1998. (Illus.). 32p. (J). (gr. k-3). 19.95 (978-0-9662813-0-9(6)) New Traditions Pr., Inc.

—What's a Computer Program? Stevens, Robert, illus. 1998. (Illus.). 32p. (J). (ps-3). 19.95 (978-0-9662813-2-3(2)) New Traditions Pr., Inc.

Trebnik, Brittanney. Windows 3.1 for Teens. 1999. (Illus.). 248p. (gr. 7-12). reprint ed. pap. 10.00 (978-0-7881-6506-1(2)) DIANE Publishing Co.

Trumbauer, Lisa. Computer Fun Christmas. 1999. (J). (978-0-606-19149-4(6)) Tandem Library Bks.

—Computer Fun Halloween. 1999. (J). (978-0-606-19150-0(X)) Tandem Library Bks.

Vande Velde, Vivian. User Unfriendly. 2001. (Illus.). 256p. (YA). (gr. 7). pap. 6.95 (978-0-15-216353-2(0) , Magic Carpet Bks.) Harcourt Children's Bks.

Vargas, Daraciela, des. Internet en la Escuela y el Hogar. 2003. (SPA.). ring bd. 14.99 (978-0-9702021-7-8(2)) Conexion Educativa.

Ward-Johnson, Chris. Computers: A Magic Mouse Guide. Laughing Gravy Design Staff, illus. 2003. (Magic Mouse Guides). 32p. (J). lib. bdg. 22.60 (978-0-7660-2263-8(3)) Enslow Pubs., Inc.

—E-Mail: A Magic Mouse Guide. Laughing Gravy Design Staff, illus. 2003. (Magic Mouse Guides). 32p. (J). lib. bdg. 22.60 (978-0-7660-2261-4(7)) Enslow Pubs., Inc.

Ward-Johnson, Chris & Gould, William. The Magic Mouse Dictionary of Computers & Information Technology. Laughing Gravy Design Staff, illus. 2003. (Magic Mouse Guides). 64p. (J). lib. bdg. 27.93 (978-0-7660-2264-5(1)) Enslow Pubs., Inc.

Weber, Rebecca. Computers Then & Now. 2004. (Spyglass Books). 24p. (J). (gr. 1 up). lib. bdg. 19.93 (978-0-7565-0654-4(9)) Compass Point Bks.

Weber, Sandra. Personal Computer. 2003. (Transforming Power of Technology Ser.). (Illus.). 112p. (J). (gr. 9-13). 30.00 (978-0-7910-7450-3(1) , Chelsea Hse.) Facts On File, Inc.

White, Nancy. The Magic School Bus Gets Programmed: A Book about Computers. 1999. (gr. k-3). lib. bdg. 11.25 (978-0-613-21948-8(1)) Tandem Library Bks.

Willard, Nancy E. Computer Ethics, Etiquette, & Safety for the 21st-Century Student. Novotny, Michael, illus. 2002. 85p. spiral bd. 17.50 (978-1-56484-184-1(7)) International Society for Technology in Education.

Williams, Brian. Computers. 2002. (Great Inventions Ser.). (Illus.). 48p. (YA). (gr. 5-8). lib. bdg. 25.64 (978-1-58810-210-2(6)) Heinemann Library.

Wilson, Anthony. Communications. 1999. (How the Future Began Ser.). (Illus.). 64p. (J). (gr. 5). tchr. ed. 15.95 (978-0-7534-5179-3(4) , Kingfisher) Houghton Mifflin Co. Trade & Reference Div.

Wilson, Carole. Exploring Computing Studies. 2nd rev. ed. 2001. (Cambridge Secondary It Ser.). (Illus.). 332p. pap. 23.00 (978-0-521-78714-7(9)) Cambridge Univ. Pr.

Wilson, Suzan. Steve Jobs: Wizard of Apple Computer. 2001. (People to Know Ser.). (Illus.). 128p. (YA). (gr. 6-12). lib. bdg. 26.60 (978-0-7660-1536-4(X)) Enslow Pubs., Inc.

Wolinsky, Art. Internet Power Research Using the Big Approach. rev. ed. 2005. (Internet Library). (Illus.). 64p. (J). lib. bdg. 22.60 (978-0-7660-1563-0(7)) Enslow Pubs., Inc.

—Internet Power Research Using the Big6 Approach. 2005. (Internet Library). (Illus.). 64p. pap. (978-0-7660-1564-7(5)) Enslow Pubs., Inc.

Woodford, Chris. Communication & Computers. 2004. (History of Invention Ser.). (Illus.). 96p. (J). (gr. 6-12). 35.00 (978-0-8160-5443-5(6)) Facts On File, Inc.

WordPerfect 9.0 Introduction. (Illus.). (YA). pap. (978-0-7423-0397-3(7) , WRDPF9001LG) ComputerPREP, Inc.

Words & Images. (Illus.). (J). (gr. 4-6). pap. (978-1-876367-98-5(9)) Wizard Bks.

Worland, Gayle. The Computer. 2003. (Fact Finders Ser.). (Illus.). 32p. (J). lib. bdg. 22.60 (978-0-7368-2215-2(1)) Capstone Pr., Inc.

—The Computer, 6 vols. (gr. 2-5). 36.95 (978-0-7368-4614-1(X)) Red Brick Learning.

Zocchi, Judy. Meet Click & Squeak: How Computers Work. 2006. (Click & Squeak Ser.). (Illus.). 32p. (J). lib. bdg. 20.65 (978-1-891997-61-7(0)) Dingles & Co.

—The Secret Diary: Saving Files. 2006. (Click & Squeak Ser.). (Illus.). 32p. (J). lib. bdg. 20.65 (978-1-891997-65-5(3)) Dingles & Co.

—Squeak for President: Printing Documents. 2006. (Click & Squeak Ser.). (Illus.). 32p. (J). lib. bdg. 20.65 (978-1-891997-66-2(1)) Dingles & Co.

COMPUTERS, ELECTRONIC

see Computers

COMPUTERS—FICTION

Adams, W. Royce. The Computer's Nerd. (J). 2004. 136p. pap. 9.95 (978-0-9712206-4-5(6)); 2002. 128p. (gr. 4 up). 17.95 (978-0-9712206-2-1(X)) Rairarubia Bks.

Alexander, Alma. Spellspam. 2008. (Worldweavers Ser.). 448p. (J). 17.99 (***978-0-06-083958-1(9)***); lib. bdg. 18.89 (***978-0-06-083959-8(7)***) HarperCollins Pubs. (Eos).

Balan, Bruce. In Pursuit of Picasso. 1998. (Cyber Kdz Ser.). 176p. pap. 3.99 (978-0-380-79499-7(3)) HarperCollins Pubs.

Barba, Rick. The Quantum Quandary. 2006. (Spy Gear Adventures Ser.). 208p. (J). pap. 4.99 (978-1-4169-0889-0(7) , Aladdin) Simon & Schuster Children's Publishing.

Barlow, Steve & Skidmore, Steve. The Doomsday Virus. Buckley, Harriet, illus. 2008. (J). pap. (***978-1-59889-907-8(4)***); lib. bdg. (***978-1-59889-871-2(X)***) Stone Arch Bks.

Baxter, Stephen. Web Webcrash. 1998. 128p. (J). pap. 7.99 (978-1-85881-632-6(7)) Orion Children's Bks. GBR. *Dist:* Trafalgar Square Publishing.

Behr, Ashley F. Camp ICMI. Karn, George, illus. 1998. (21st Century Kids Ser.). 32p. (J). (ps-3). per. 5.95 (978-0-9660533-0-2(3)) Behr, D. J. Co.

—Nailah's Surprise. O'Neill, Terry, ed. Karn, George, illus. 1998. 32p. (J). (ps-3). per. 5.95 (978-0-9660533-1-9(1)) Behr, D. J. Co.

Berenstain, Stan & Berenstain, Jan. The Berenstain Bears Lost in Cyberspace. 1999. (Berenstain Bears Big Chapter Bks.). (J). (gr. 2-6). (978-0-606-16839-7(7)) Tandem Library Bks.

Blackfield, Neil. New Computer & Other Stories. 1999. (gr. 7-12). lib. bdg. 11.60 (978-0-613-30623-2(6)) Tandem Library Bks.

Boyd, David. Bottom Drawer. 2002. 126p. pap. 4.95 (978-0-921156-58-1(8)) Rubicon Publishing, Inc. CAN. *Dist:* International Publishers Marketing.

—Bottom Drawer. 2002. (gr. 7-12). lib. bdg. 12.95 (978-0-613-77607-3(0)) Tandem Library Bks.

Brooks, Hindi. Computer Pals: A Short Comedy. 1998. (Illus.). 8p. pap. 3.50 (978-0-88680-452-7(3) , C4523) Clark, I. E. Pubns.

Brown, Marc. Arthur's Computer Disaster. ed. 2004. (Arthur Adventure Ser.). (J). (gr. k-3). spiral bd. (978-0-616-07220-2(1)); spiral bd. (978-0-616-07221-9(X)) Canadian National Institute for the Blind/Institut National Canadien pour les Aveugles.

Burkhart, Christina. Surf Sammy's New Computer: A Surf Sammy & Friends Computer Adventure. 1999. (Surf Sammy & Friends Computer Adventure Ser.). (Illus.). 32p. (J). (ps-k). 14.95 (978-0-9662025-0-2(3)) Roof Publishing Co.

Carrick, Carol. Patrick's Dinosaurs on the Internet. Milgrim, David, illus. 1999. 32p. (J). (gr. k-3). tchr. ed. 16.00 (978-0-395-50949-4(1) , Clarion Bks.) Houghton Mifflin Co. Trade & Reference Div.

Clancy, Tom. The Ultimate Escape. 1999. (Tom Clancy's Net Force Ser.). (978-0-606-20429-3(6)) Tandem Library Bks.

—Virtual Vandals. 1999. (Tom Clancy's Net Force Ser.). (978-0-606-20430-9(X)) Tandem Library Bks.

Cole, Joanna. The Magic School Bus Gets Programmed: A Book about Computers. 2002. (Magic School Bus Ser.). (J). 11.45 (978-0-7587-6702-8(1)) Book Wholesalers, Inc.

Colfer, Eoin. The Eternity Code. 2003. (Artemis Fowl Ser.: Bk. 3). 320p. (ps-17). 16.95 (978-0-7868-1914-0(6)) Hyperion Bks. for Children.

Delaney, Mark. The Vanishing Chip. 1998. (Misfits, Inc. Ser.: No. 1). 240p. (J). (gr. 7-11). pap. 5.95 (978-1-56145-176-0(2) , Q21568) Peachtree Pubs., Ltd.

D'Lacey, Chris. Break in the Chain. 2002. (gr. 3-6). lib. bdg. 12.95 (978-0-613-52812-2(3)) Tandem Library Bks.

Dower, Laura. From the Files of Madison Finn: Double Dare. 2003. (gr. 3-6). lib. bdg. 13.00 (978-0-613-68230-5(0)) Tandem Library Bks.

—From the Files of Madison Finn: Give & Take. 2002. (gr. 3-6). lib. bdg. 13.00 (978-0-613-75024-0(1)) Tandem Library Bks.

—Three's a Crowd, Bk. 16. rev. ed. 2004. (From the Files of Madison Finn Ser.: Vol. 16). 192p. (J). (gr. 3-7). pap. 4.99 (978-0-7868-0986-8(8)) Hyperion Bks. for Children.

Duane, Diane. High Wizardry. (Young Wizards Ser.: Bk. 3). (YA). 2003. 372p. (ps-7). pap. 6.95 (978-0-15-204941-6(X)); 2001. 368p. (gr. 5 up). pap. 6.95 (978-0-15-216244-3(5)) Harcourt Children's Bks. (Magic Carpet Bks.).

—High Wizardry. 2003. (gr. 3-6). lib. bdg. 15.25 (978-0-613-71634-5(5)); 2001. (gr. 5-8). lib. bdg. 15.25 (978-0-613-36065-4(6)) Tandem Library Bks.

DuPrau, Jeanne. Car Trouble. 288p. (J). 2006. pap. 6.99 (978-0-06-073675-0(5) , HarperTeen); 2005. 15.99 (978-0-06-073672-9(0)); 2005. lib. bdg. 16.89 (978-0-06-073674-3(7)) HarperCollins Pubs.

Duval, Kristy. Pete & Re-Pete the Computer Worms: A Story about Two Worms Surfing the Net. Gillen, Michael, illus. 2005. (ENG.). 32p. (J). (ps-7). per. 18.00 (978-1-4208-1959-5(3)) AuthorHouse.

Esmaili, Roza. Zagros & Nature Force: Coloring Book. Sun Rise Illustration and Computer Animation Staff, illus. Date not set. 74p. (J). (gr. k-8). pap. 2.49 (978-0-9656185-1-9(X)) Esmaili, Inc.

Fiore, Michael. The Mouse, the Computer, & the Mouse. 1999. (Illus.). 32p. (J). (gr. k-3). pap. 6.75 (978-0-8059-4604-8(7)) Dorrance Publishing Co., Inc.

Garcia, Belinda. Alyson's Adventures in Computer Land. 2005. 184p. (J). pap. 15.95 (978-1-58736-484-6(0) , Hats Off Bks.) Wheatmark.

Geissen, Steve. Willie & the World Wide Web. Kuon, Vuthy, illus. 1998. 40p. (J). (gr. 1-7). lib. bdg. 15.95 (978-0-9661974-0-2(2)) Three Leaves Publishing.

Gerson, Corinne. Cyberdog. 1999. 62p. (J). (gr. 3-5). pap. 9.99 (978-0-88092-447-4(0) , 4470) Royal Fireworks Publishing Co.

Gioseffi, Anthony P. Mainframe. 2007. 144p. per. 11.95 (***978-0-595-44953-8(0)***) iUniverse, Inc.

Gutman, Dan. The Homework Machine. 2007. 176p. (J). pap. 4.99 (*978-0-689-87679-0(3) , Aladdin) Simon & Schuster Children's Publishing.

Gutman, Dan. Virtually Perfect. 128p. (gr. 3-7). 1999. pap. 4.99 (978-0-7868-1316-2(4)); 2003. pap. 5.99 (978-0-7868-1745-0(3)) Hyperion Bks. for Children.

—Virtually Perfect. 2003. (gr. 3-6). lib. bdg. 14.15 (978-0-613-75029-5(2)); 1999. (978-0-606-16673-7(4)) Tandem Library Bks.

Gutsche, Brigitte. The Intruder. 2006. (J). pap. (*978-0-88092-743-7(7)) Royal Fireworks Publishing Co.

Haddix, Margaret Peterson. Escape from Memory. (YA). 2005. 288p. (gr. 7-12). mass mkt. 6.99 (978-1-4169-0338-3(0) , Simon Pulse); 2003. (Illus.). 224p. 16.95 (978-0-689-85421-7(8)) Simon & Schuster Children's Publishing.

Harcourt School Publishers Staff. A Message in Cybertime On Level. 3rd ed. 2002. (Trophies Reading Program Ser.). (Illus.). pap. 5.10 (978-0-15-323459-0(8)) Harcourt Schl. Pubs.

Harrison, Cora. Milleniumdrumshee. 1999. (Drumshee Timeline Ser.). (Illus.). 143p. (J). (978-0-86327-715-3(2)) Wolfhound Pr.

Hart, James W. Grandpa & the Computer. Kingsley, Steven, ed. Glasbergen, Randy, illus. l.t. ed. 2001. 84p. per. 12.95 (978-1-893798-18-2(6)) AIL Newmedia Publishing.

Henry. Biode. 2008. (J). (*978-0-374-30802-5(0)) Farrar, Straus & Giroux.

Hoffman, Keely. Visit from Grandfather Abacus. 1999. (Publish-a-Book Ser.). (Illus.). 32p. (J). (gr. 1-6). pap. 8.50 (978-0-7398-0051-5(5)) Steck-Vaughn.

—Visit from Grandfather Abacus. 1999. (J). (978-0-606-19513-3(0)) Tandem Library Bks.

Holbrook, Bill. Surviving Y2K. 2001. (On the Fastrack Ser.: Vol. 3). 160p. pap. 12.95 (978-1-929462-31-5(X)) Plan Nine Publishing, Inc.

Holl, Kristi. Chat Freak. 2004. 128p. (J). pap. 5.99 (978-1-4003-0326-7(5)) Nelson, Thomas Inc.

Holl, Kristi D. Chat Freak. 2005. (TodaysGirls.com Ser.: Vol. 6). 144p. (J). (gr. 4-7). pap. 5.99 (978-1-4003-0760-9(0)) Nelson, Thomas Inc.

Hoobler, Dorothy & Hoobler, Thomas. The 1990s: Families. Hoffman, Robin, illus. 2002. (Century Kids Ser.). 160p. (gr. 5-8). lib. bdg. 22.90 (978-0-7613-1609-1(4) , Twenty-First Century Bks.) Lerner Publishing Group.

Hope, Chip, the Little Computer. Anders, Tim, ed. Hamilton, Dan, illus. 1999. (Life Lessons Ser.). (ENG & SPA.). 36p. (J). (ps-3). 16.95 (978-1-885624-55-0(7)) Alpine Publishing.

Jennings, Sharon, et al. Franklin & the Computer. Southern, Shelley et al, illus. 2003. (Franklin TV Storybook Ser.). 32p. (J). (ps-3). (978-1-55337-362-9(6)) Kids Can Pr., Ltd.

Johansen, K. V. The Cassandra Virus. 2006. 176p. (gr. 3-7). pap. 7.95 (978-1-55143-497-1(0)) Orca Bk. Pubs. USA.

Johansen, K. V. The Drone War: A Cassandra Virus Novel. 2007. (Cassandra Virus Ser.). 150p. (YA). pap. 9.95 (*978-0-9739505-2-6(8)) Sybertooth Inc. CAN. *Dist:* Lightning Source, Inc.

Kahn, Michele. Un Ordenador Nada Ordinario. LaPointe, Claude, illus. 2003. (SPA.). 104p. (J). (gr. 3-5). 13.95 (978-84-204-4817-6(6)) Alfaguara, Ediciones, S.A.-Grupo Santillana ESP. *Dist:* Santillana USA Publishing Co., Inc.

Kindig, Tess. Luv @ First Site. 2004. 128p. (J). pap. 5.99 (978-1-4003-0325-0(7)) Nelson, Thomas Inc.

Lavette, Lavaille. The Adventures of Roopster Roux: Surfing the Net. Mitchell, Louis H., illus. 1998. (Adventures of Roopster Roux Ser.). 32p. (J). (ps-3). pap. 5.95 (978-1-56554-361-4(0)) Pelican Publishing Co., Inc.

Laybourn, Emma. Megamouse. 2001. 92p. (J). pap. 8.99 (978-1-84270-013-6(8)) Andersen GBR. *Dist:* Independent Pubs. Group.

Levy, Elizabeth. The Creepy Computer Mystery. Brunkus, Denise, illus. 2004. 48p. (J). lib. bdg. 15.00 (978-1-59054-534-8(6)) Fitzgerald Bks.

Lorimer, Janet. Deadly Game. 2001. (gr. 7-12). lib. bdg. 11.80 (978-0-613-34174-5(0)) Tandem Library Bks.

Lovegrove, James. Web Computopia. 1998. 115p. (J). pap. 7.99 (978-1-85881-642-5(4)) Orion Children's Bks. GBR. *Dist:* Trafalgar Square Publishing.

Manley, Craig. The Rammarg Files. 2006. (J). lib. bdg. (*978-0-88092-742-0(9)) Royal Fireworks Publishing Co.

Maselli, Christopher P. N. Choke Hold Bk. 7: They Must Not Surrender to Fear's Grip. 2004. 128p. (J). pap. 4.99 (978-0-310-70666-3(1)) Zonderkidz.

—Double-Take: Things Are Not What They Seem. 2002. (2:52 Soul Gear Ser.). (Illus.). 128p. (J). pap. 4.99 (978-0-310-70339-6(5)) Zonderkidz.

—In Pursuit of the Enemy. 1998. (Commander Kellie & the Superkids' Early Adventures Ser.). (J). pap. (978-1-57562-218-7(1)) Copeland, Kenneth Pubns.

—Shut Down! Bk. 8: True Courage Reveals the Laptop's Truth. 2004. 128p. (J). pap. 4.99 (978-0-310-70667-0(X)) Zonderkidz.

Maselli, Christopher P. N. & Zondervan. Reality Shift: They Changed the Future. 2002. (Illus.). 144p. (J). pap. 4.99 (978-0-310-70338-9(7)) Zonderkidz.

Meade, Marie. Are We Allowed to Spam Them Back? Featuring Computious - the Impish Sage of The. 2003. (gr. 3-6). lib. bdg. 21.05 (978-0-613-78069-8(8)) Tandem Library Bks.

Mills, Charles. The Truth Trackers. 2001. 144p. (YA). pap. 7.99 (978-0-8280-1462-5(0)) Review & Herald Publishing Assn.

Myers, Bill. My Life as a Computer Cockroach, Vol. 17. 1999. (Incredible Worlds of Wally McDoogle Ser.: No. 17). 128p. (J). (gr. 3-7). pap. 6.99 (978-0-8499-4026-2(5)) Nelson, Thomas Inc.

Pohlig, Thomas. Tweeker the Speaker. 2006. 22p. 17.01 (978-1-4116-8140-8(1)) Lulu.com.

Pollack, Pam. Web Sight. 2000. (So Weird Ser.: No. 5). (Illus.). 144p. (gr. 3-7). pap. 4.99 (978-0-7868-4441-8(8)) Disney Pr.

Pratchett, Terry. The Bromeliad: Truckers, Diggers, & Wings. 2003. 512p. (J). (gr. 5 up). 18.99 (978-0-06-009493-5(1)); 18.89 (978-0-06-054855-1(X)) HarperCollins Pubs.

—Diggers. 2004. (Bromeliad Trilogy Ser.). 224p. (J). (gr. 5 up). reprint ed. pap. 5.99 (978-0-06-009494-2(X) , Harper Trophy) HarperCollins Pubs.

Prowse, Philip. Help! Level 1. 1999. (Cambridge English Readers Ser.). (Illus.). 32p. pap. 6.00 (978-0-521-65615-3(X)) Cambridge Univ. Pr.

Ralles, H. J. Keeper of the Kingdom. 2001. 200p. (gr. 3-11). pap. 9.95 (978-1-929976-03-4(8)) Top Pubns., Ltd.

Regan, Dian Curtis. Cyberpals According to Kaley. 2006. 128p. (J). (gr. 3-5). 15.95 (978-1-58196-051-8(4)) Darby Creek Publishing.

Richards, Barbara. Barbie Com: Ballet Buddies. 2000. (gr. 3-6). lib. bdg. 11.80 (978-0-613-27723-5(6)) Tandem Library Bks.

Rocklin, Joanne & Burns, Marilyn. The Incredibly Awesome Box. Pillo, Cary, illus. 2000. (Hello Reader! Math Ser.). (J). pap. 3.99 (978-0-439-09955-4(2)) Scholastic, Inc.

Rue, Nancy. Sophie Loves Jimmy, Vol. 10. 2006. (Faithgirlz Ser.). 144p. (J). pap. 6.99 (978-0-310-71025-7(1)) Zonderkidz.

Seuling, Barbara. Robert Finds a Way. Brewer, Paul, illus. 2005. (Robert Bks.). 150p. (J). 15.95 (978-0-8126-2734-3(2)) Cricket Bks.

Shearer, Alex. Computer Wizard. (Illus.). 112p. (J). 7.95 (978-0-14-130011-5(6)) Penguin Group (USA) Inc.

Sherman, Deborah. Triple Chocolate Brownie Genius. 2007. 120p. (J). (gr. 4-6). pap. (*978-1-55455-035-7(1)) Fitzhenry & Whiteside, Ltd.

Somerville, Scott. Olympus: It's Not Just a Game. 2000. (J). per. 12.95 (978-1-56857-083-9(X)) Noble Publishing Assocs.

Sommer, Carl. Time Remote! Read-along, 1 bk. 2003. (Another Sommer-Time Story Ser.). (Illus.). 48p. (J). lib. bdg. 23.95 incl. audio compact disk (978-1-57537-712-4(8)); lib. bdg. 23.95 incl. audio (978-1-57537-762-9(4)) Advance Publishing, Inc.

Stannard, Russell. WWW Here-I-Am. 2002. (gr. 7-12). lib. bdg. 18.75 (978-0-613-84233-4(2)) Tandem Library Bks.

—www.Here-I-Am. Pugh, Jonathan, illus. 2002. 160p. (gr. 5-8). 9.95 (978-1-890151-85-0(8)) Templeton Foundation Pr.

Steadman, Ralph. Punto.com. (Illus.). (J). 2002. (SPA.). 166p. (gr. 1-3). 14.95 (978-84-8488-009-7(5) , RR7727); 2001. (CAT., 40p. 14.95 (978-84-8488-013-4(3)) Serres, Ediciones, S. L. ESP. *Dist:* Lectorum Pubns., Inc.

Summers, Kim. Senor Mundo & Me: A Happy Birthday Story. Mariscal, Javier, illus. 2004. 31p. (J). (gr. k-4). 20.00 (978-0-7567-7759-3(3)) DIANE Publishing Co.

Supercomputer Pizzas: Individual Title Six-Packs. (Bookweb Ser.). 32p. (gr. 3 up). 34.00 (978-0-7635-3938-2(4)) Rigby Education.

Taiz, Lincoln & Taiz, Lee. Libra: The Cat Who Saved Silicon Valley. 2001. (Illus.). 326p. pap. 15.95 (978-0-9723044-1-2(X) , AGP-1) Amsea Group, Inc.

Tashjian, Janet. Tru Confessions. 1999. (Illus.). 176p. (J). pap. 4.99 (978-0-590-96047-2(4)) Scholastic, Inc.

—Tru Confessions. 2007. 176p. (J). pap. 6.99 (*978-0-312-37273-6(6)) Square Fish.

—Tru Confessions. 1999. (978-0-606-16611-9(4)) Tandem Library Bks.

Techno Terror. 2005. (Thrillogy Ser.). (Illus.). 48p. (gr. 4-8). 17.50 (978-0-7910-8869-2(3)) Facts On File, Inc.

Tinsley, P. S. A House with No Mouse. Deans, Nora L., ed. Castro, Luis F., illus. 2003. 28p. 14.95 (978-0-9723213-1-0(4) , Mousetime Bks.) Mousetime Media LLC.

Townley, Roderick. Into the Labyrinth. (Illus.). 272p. (gr. 5-9). 2006. (YA). pap. 5.99 (978-1-4169-1392-4(0) , Aladdin); 2002. (J). 16.95 (978-0-689-84615-1(0) , Atheneum/Richard Jackson Bks.) Simon & Schuster Children's Publishing.

Vega, Denise. Click Here: To Find Out How I Survived Seventh Grade. 2006. 224p. (J). (gr. 5-8). reprint ed. pap. 7.99 (978-0-316-98559-8(7)) Little Brown & Co.

Wallace, Barbara Brooks. Miss Switch Online. 2002. 192p. (J). (gr. 4-6). 16.00 (978-0-689-84376-1(3) , Atheneum) Simon & Schuster Children's Publishing.

—Miss Switch Online. 2003. (gr. 3-6). lib. bdg. 13.00 (978-0-613-91040-8(0)) Tandem Library Bks.

Watkins, Shelagh. Mr. Planemaker's Flying Machine. 2005. 197p. pap. 19.95 (978-1-4137-7136-7(X)) PublishAmerica, Inc.

Zondervan. 2:52 Laptop 1 Reality Shift/Laptop 2 Double Take - Focus on the Family: 52 Laptop 1 Reality Shift/ Laptop 2 Double Take - Focus on the Family. 2004. (J). pap. 9.98 (978-0-310-70934-3(2)) Zonderkidz.

COMPUTERS—PROGRAMMING

see Computer Programming

COMPUTERS—STUDY AND TEACHING (ELEMENTARY)

Jesson, Jill & Peacock, Graham. Cambridge ICT Starters Part 1: Next Steps Microsoft. 2006. (Illus.). 64p. pap. 11.00 (978-0-521-61773-4(1)) Cambridge Univ. Pr.

—Cambridge ICT Starters Part 2: Next Steps Microsoft. 2006. (Illus.). 52p. pap. 11.00 (978-0-521-61774-1(X)) Cambridge Univ. Pr.

—Starter Award in ICT Pt. 2: On Track Microsoft. 2007. pap. 9.95 (978-0-521-61776-5(6)) Cambridge Univ. Pr.

Ringer, Robert J. Wordasaurus Quick-Answer Guide: The System for Mastering Microsoft Word. 1998. (Illus.). 640p. (J). (gr. 6-12). spiral bd. 34.95 (978-0-9665991-0-7(1)) North Pine, Ltd.

Weller, Alyssa. Computer Activities A-Z. 1999. (Illus.). 144p. (J). pap., tchr. ed. 19.99 incl. cd-rom (978-1-57690-461-9(X) , TCA2461) Teacher Created Materials, Inc.

COMPUTERS—VOCATIONAL GUIDANCE

Hayhurst, Chris. Careers in E-Commerce Security & Encryption. 2005. (Library of E-Commerce & Internet Careers). (Illus.). 64p. (YA). (gr. 7-12). lib. bdg. 26.50 (978-0-8239-3420-1(9)) Rosen Publishing Group, Inc., The.

J. G. Ferguson Publishing Company Staff, ed. Careers in Focus. 3rd ed. 2006. (Careers in Focus Ser.). (Illus.). 192p. (J). (gr. 6-12). 29.95 (978-0-8160-6564-6(0) , Ferguson Publishing Co.) Facts On File, Inc.

J.G. Ferguson Publishing Company Staff, contrib. by. What Can I Do Now? 2007. (What Can I Do Now Ser.). 208p. (J). (gr. 6-12). 29.95 (*978-0-8160-6027-6(4) , Ferguson Publishing Co.) Facts On File, Inc.

Miller, Deborah J. Careers with an Internet Service Provider. 2005. (Library of E-Commerce & Internet Careers). (Illus.). 64p. (YA). (gr. 7-12). lib. bdg. 26.50 (978-0-8239-3425-6(X)) Rosen Publishing Group, Inc., The.

Penna, Christina & Shook, Rachael. Careers in Network Engineering. 2005. (Library of E-Commerce & Internet Careers). (Illus.). 64p. (YA). (gr. 7-12). lib. bdg. 26.50 (978-0-8239-3422-5(5)) Rosen Publishing Group, Inc., The.

Reeves, Diane Lindsey, et al. Career Ideas for Teens in Information Technology. (Career Ideas for Teens Ser.). (gr. 6-12). 192p. pap. 16.95 (978-0-8160-6921-7(2) , Checkmark Bks.); 2005. (Illus.). 184p. (J). per. 40.00 (978-0-8160-5293-6(X) , Ferguson Publishing Co.) Facts On File, Inc.

Weigant, Chris. Choosing a Career in Computers. rev. ed. 2005. (World of Work Ser.). (Illus.). 64p. (YA). (gr. 7-12). lib. bdg. 25.25 (978-0-8239-3044-9(0) , WW-COMP) Rosen Publishing Group, Inc., The.

COMPUTING MACHINES (ELECTRONIC)

see Computers

COMSTOCK LODE (NEV.)

Hopkins, Ellen H. Tarnished Legacy: The Story of the Comstock Lode. 2001. (Cover-to-Cover Bks.). (Illus.). 64p. (J). pap. (978-0-7891-1003-9(2)) Perfection Learning Corp.

Kraft, Eric. ¡la fiebre del oro! & Gold Rush! 2005. spiral bd. 84.00 (*978-1-4108-5699-9(2)) Benchmark Education Co.

CONCENTRATION CAMPS

Bitton-Jackson, Livia. I Have Lived a Thousand Years: Growing up in the Holocaust. 1999. 224p. (YA). (gr. 7-12). pap. 5.99 (978-0-689-82395-4(9) , Simon Pulse) Simon & Schuster Children's Publishing.

—I Have Lived a Thousand Years: Growing up in the Holocaust. 1999. (J). 11.64 (978-0-606-15948-7(7)); (gr. 7-12). lib. bdg. 13.00 (978-0-613-17811-2(4)) Tandem Library Bks.

Colson, Mary. The Story Behind Anne Holm's I Am David. 2006. (History in Literature Ser.). (Illus.). 56p. (YA). (gr. 7 up). lib. bdg. 32.86 (978-1-4034-8204-4(7)) Heinemann Library.

Cooper, Michael L. Remembering Manzanar: Life in a Japanese Relocation Camp. 2002. (Illus.). 80p. (J). (gr. 4-6). tchr. ed. 15.00 (978-0-618-06778-7(7) , Clarion Bks.) Houghton Mifflin Co. Trade & Reference Div.

Currie, Stephen. Escapes from Nazi Persecution. 2003. (Great Escapes Ser.). (Illus.). 112p. (J). 29.95 (978-1-59018-279-6(0) , Lucent Bks.) Thomson Gale.

Donlan, Leni. How Did This Happen Here? Japanese Internment Camps. 2007. (*978-1-4109-2701-9(6)); pap. (*978-1-4109-2712-5(1)) Steck Vaughn.

Japanese-American Internment. 2004. (Historical Reader Ser.). (Illus.). 240p. (gr. 6-12). 13.32 (978-0-618-00365-5(7) , 2-00102) McDougal Littell Inc.

Lehman-Wilzig, Tami. Keeping the Promise: A Torah's Journey. Orback, Craig, illus. 2004. 32p. (J). (gr. 1-5). 16.95 (978-1-58013-117-9(4)); pap. 6.95 (978-1-58013-118-6(2)) Kar-Ben Publishing.

Perl, Lila. Barbed Wire & Guard Towers: The Internment of Japanese Americans During World War II. 2002. (Great Journeys Ser.). (Illus.). 112p. (J). 32.79 (978-0-7614-1321-9(9) , Benchmark Bks.) Cavendish, Marshall Corp.

—Four Perfect Pebbles: A Holocaust Story. 1999. (Illus.). 144p. (J). (gr. 3 up). pap. 5.99 (978-0-380-73188-6(6) , Harper Trophy) HarperCollins Pubs.

—Four Perfect Pebbles: A Holocaust Story. 1999. (Illus.). (J). 12.64 (978-0-606-17971-3(2)) Tandem Library Bks.

Rubin, Susan Goldman. Fireflies in the Dark: The Story of Freidl Dicker-Brandeis & the Children of Terezin. (Illus.). 48p. (J). (gr. 4-6). 2005. pap. 8.95 (978-0-8234-1681-3(X)); 2000. tchr. ed. 18.95 (978-0-8234-1461-1(2)) Holiday Hse., Inc.

Sheehan, Sean. The Death Camps. 2001. (Holocaust Ser.). (Illus.). 64p. (J). (gr. 5-8). lib. bdg. 28.54 (978-0-7398-3258-5(1)) Raintree.

Shuter, Jane. Auschwitz. (Visiting the Past Ser.). 32p. (J). (gr. 5-7). 2002. (Illus.). pap. 6.95 (978-1-58810-408-3(7) , 91179); 1999. lib. bdg. 24.22 (978-1-57572-856-8(7)) Heinemann Library.

—Auschwitz. 2001. (978-0-606-22578-6(1)) Tandem Library Bks.

—The Camp System. 2003. (Holocaust Ser.). 56p. (Illus.). (YA). lib. bdg. 28.50 (978-1-4034-0809-9(2)); pap. 8.95 (978-1-4034-3201-8(5)) Heinemann Library.

—Life & Death in the Camps. 2003. (Holocaust Ser.). (Illus.). 56p. (J). lib. bdg. 28.50 (978-1-4034-0812-9(2)); pap. 8.95 (978-1-4034-3204-9(X)) Heinemann Library.

Tito, E. Tina. Liberation: Teens in the Concentration Camps & the Teen Soldiers Who Liberated Them. 1999. (Teen Witnesses to the Holocaust Ser.). (Illus.). 64p. (YA). (gr. 7-12). lib. bdg. 26.50 (978-0-8239-2846-0(2) , TWLIBE) Rosen Publishing Group, Inc., The.

CONCENTRATION CAMPS—FICTION

Boyne, John. The Boy in the Striped Pajamas. 2007. 240p. (YA). (gr. 7). pap. 8.99 (*978-0-385-75153-7(2) , Fickling, David Bks.) Random Hse. Children's Bks.

Bunting, Eve. One Candle. Popp, K. Wendy, illus. (J). (ps-3). 2004. 40p. pap. 6.99 (978-0-06-008560-5(6) , Harper Trophy); 2002. 32p. 15.99 (978-0-06-028115-1(4) , Cotler, Joanna Books); 2002. 32p. lib. bdg. 17.89 (978-0-06-028116-8(2) , Cotler, Joanna Books) HarperCollins Pubs.

Evans, Marion, Anna Baraitser. Home Number One. 2006. (Illus.). 63p. (YA). pap. (978-0-9529426-7-2(4)) Loki Books Ltd.

Greif, Jean-Jacques. The Fighter. 2006. 288p. (YA). (gr. 9 up). 16.95 (978-1-58234-891-9(X) , Bloomsbury Children) Bloomsbury Publishing.

Hesse, Karen. Aleutian Sparrow. Zerbetz, Evon, illus. 2003. 160p. (J). (gr. 5-9). 16.95 (978-0-689-86189-5(3) , McElderry, Margaret K.) Simon & Schuster Children's Publishing.

—Aleutian Sparrow. McGillivray, Kim & Zerbetz, Evon, illus. 2005. 160p. (J). reprint ed. pap. 5.99 (978-1-4169-0327-7(5) , Aladdin) Simon & Schuster Children's Publishing.

Innocenti, Roberto. Rose Blanche. Innocenti, Roberto, illus. 2003. (Illus.). 32p. (YA). (gr. 4 up). 17.95 (978-1-56846-189-2(5)) Creative Co., The.

Kacer, Kathy. Clara's War. 2005. (Holocaust Remembrance Ser.). (Illus.). 196p. (YA). (gr. 5 up). pap. 5.95 (978-1-896764-42-9(8)) Second Story Pr. CAN. *Dist:* Orca Bk. Pubs. USA, Univ. of Toronto Pr., Univ. of Toronto Pr.

—Clara's War. 2001. (gr. 5-8). lib. bdg. 14.10 (978-0-613-51538-2(2)) Tandem Library Bks.

Moskin, Marietta D. I Am Rosemarie. 1999. 258p. (J). pap. 12.95 (978-0-7351-0226-2(0)); lib. bdg. 24.95 (978-0-7351-0225-5(2)) Replica Bks.

—I Am Rosemarie. 2000. (J). pap. 1.95 (978-0-590-04278-9(5)) Scholastic, Inc.

Pausewang, Gudrun. Final Journey. Crampton, Patricia, tr. 1998. 160p. (J). (gr. 7-12). pap. 6.99 (978-0-14-130104-4(X) , Puffin) Penguin Group (USA) Inc.

Schmidt, Gary. Mara's Stories: Glimmers in the Darkness. 2008. 128p. (J). pap. 6.99 (*978-0-312-37388-7(0)) Square Fish.

Uchida, Yoshiko. Journey to Topaz. 2005. 160p. pap. 9.95 (978-1-890771-91-1(0)) Heyday Bks.

Walters, Eric. Caged Eagles. 2001. 256p. (J). (gr. 7-12). pap. 7.95 (978-1-55143-139-0(4)) Orca Bk. Pubs. USA.

—Caged Eagles. 2001. (gr. 7-12). lib. bdg. 16.40 (978-0-613-86415-2(8)) Tandem Library Bks.

Wiseman, Eva. Kanada. 2006. (Illus.). 264p. (J). (gr. 5). pap. 9.95 (978-0-88776-729-6(X)) Tundra Bks., Inc./Livres Toundra, Inc. CAN. *Dist:* Random Hse., Inc.

Yolen, Jane. The Devil's Arithmetic. 2002. (J). 13.19 (978-0-7587-9594-6(7)) Book Wholesalers, Inc.

—The Devil's Arithmetic. 2004. (Puffin Modern Classics Ser.). 176p. (gr. 3). pap. 6.99 (978-0-14-240109-5(9) , Puffin) Penguin Group (USA) Inc.

CONCEPTION—PREVENTION

see Birth Control

CONCERTS

Dunn, Mary. My Adventure at a Concert Hall. 2006. 44p. (J). 8.99 (978-1-59092-288-0(3) , Orchard Academy Pr.) Windstorm Creative.

Guy, Suzanne & Lacy, Donna. The Orchestra, the Orchestra! Lacy, Donna, illus. 2002. (Illus.). (J). (978-0-9672885-6-7(8)) Live Wire Pr.

Hopkinson, Deborah. Sweet Land of Liberty. Jenkins, Leonard, illus. 2007. 32p. (J). (gr. 1-5). 16.95 (978-1-56145-395-5(1) , Peachtree Junior) Peachtree Pubs., Ltd.

Radabaugh, Melinda Beth. Going to a Concert. 2004. (Heinemann Read & Learn Ser.). (Illus.). 24p. (J). pap. 5.75 (978-1-4034-3882-9(X)); lib. bdg. 18.50 (978-1-4034-3867-6(6)) Heinemann Library.

CONCHOLOGY

see Mollusks; Shells

CONCORD, BATTLE OF, 1775

Anderson, Dale. Lexington & Concord: April 19, 1775. 2004. (American Battlefields Ser.). (Illus.). 32p. (J). 14.95 (978-1-59270-027-1(6)) Enchanted Lion Bks., LLC.

Battles of Lexington & Concord. (American Revolution Ser.). 32p. (YA). 7.95 (978-0-7368-4491-8(0)) Capstone Pr., Inc.

Crewe, Sabrina & Uschan, Michael V. Lexington & Concord. 2004. (Events That Shaped America Ser.). (Illus.). 32p. (J). (gr. 3 up). lib. bdg. 24.67 (978-0-8368-3398-0(8)) Stevens, Gareth Inc.

Fradin, Dennis Brindell. Let It Begin Here! Lexington & Concord: First Battles of the American Revolution. Day, Larry, illus. 2005. 32p. (J). 17.85 (978-0-8027-8946-4(3)); 16.95 (978-0-8027-8945-7(5)) Walker & Co.

Kent, Deborah. Lexington & Concord. 1998. (Cornerstones of Freedom Ser.). (Illus.). 32p. (J). (gr. 4-6). pap. 5.95 (978-0-516-26229-1(7) , Children's Pr.) Scholastic Library Publishing.

Kimmel, Heidi. Battles of Lexington & Concord. 2006. (Cornerstones of Freedom Ser.). (Illus.). 48p. (J). (978-0-516-23627-8(X)) Children's Pr., Ltd.

Kimmel, Heidi. The Battles of Lexington & Concord. 2007. (Cornerstones of Freedomtrade;, Second Ser.). 48p. (J). pap. 5.95 ***(*978-0-531-18763-0(2)***, Children's Pr.) Scholastic Library Publishing.

Niz, Xavier. Paul Revere's Ride. Bascle, Brian, illus. 2005. (Graphic Library). 32p. (J). (gr. 3-7). lib. bdg. 25.26 (978-0-7368-4965-4(3)) Capstone Pr., Inc.

Peacock, Judith. The Battles of Lexington & Concord. 2002. (Let Freedom Ring Ser.). (Illus.). 48p. (J). (gr. 3-4). lib. bdg. 22.60 (978-0-7368-1096-8(X), Bridgestone Bks.) Capstone Pr., Inc.

Raatma, Lucia. The Battles of Lexington & Concord. 2003. (We the People Ser.). (Illus.). 48p. (J). (gr. 4 up). lib. bdg. 22.60 (978-0-7565-0490-8(2)) Compass Point Bks.

Waldman, Scott P. The Battle of Lexington & Concord. 2003. (Atlas of Famous Battles of the American Revolution Ser.). (Illus.). 24p. (J). lib. bdg. 21.25 (978-0-8239-6328-7(4), PowerKids Pr.) Rosen Publishing Group, Inc., The.

Whitelaw, Nancy. The Shot Heard Round the World: The Battles of Lexington & Concord. 2004. (First Battles Ser.). (Illus.). 112p. (J). (gr. 6-12). 23.95 (978-1-883846-75-6(7), First Biographies) Reynolds, Morgan Inc.

CONDOMINIUMS

see Apartment Houses

CONDORS

Becker, John E. The California Condor. 2004. (Returning Wildlife Ser.). (Illus.). 48p. (J). 26.20 (978-0-7377-2292-5(4), Kidhaven) Thomson Gale.

Eckart, Edana. California Condor. 2003. (Welcome Book Ser.). (Illus.). 24p. (J). 17.00 (978-0-516-24296-5(2), Children's Pr.) Scholastic Library Publishing.

—California Condor. 2003. (gr. k-3). lib. bdg. 12.95 (978-0-613-67700-4(5)) Tandem Library Bks.

Houston, David. Condors & Vultures. rev. ed. 2001. (World-Life Library). (Illus.). 72p. (gr. 5 up). pap. 17.95 (978-0-89658-523-2(9)) Voyageur Pr., Inc.

Macken, JoAnn Early. Condors. 2006. (Illus.). 24p. (J). pap. 5.95 (978-0-8368-6323-9(2)); lib. bdg. 19.33 (978-0-8368-6316-1(X)) Stevens, Gareth Inc.

—Condors: Condor. 2006. (ENG & SPA., Illus.). 24p. (J). pap. (978-0-8368-6454-0(9)); lib. bdg. 19.33 (978-0-8368-6447-2(6)) Stevens, Gareth Inc.

Martin, Patricia. California Condors. 2002. (gr. 3-6). lib. bdg. 15.25 (978-0-613-59455-4(X)) Tandem Library Bks.

Martin, Patricia A. Fink. California Condors. (True Bks.). (Illus.). 48p. (J). (gr. 3-5). 2003. pap. 6.95 (978-0-516-27470-6(8)); 2002. pap. 25.00 (978-0-516-22161-8(2)) Scholastic Library Publishing. (Children's Pr.).

Ring, Susan & Miller-Schroeder, Patricia, trs. California Condors. 2003. (Untamed World Ser.). (Illus.). 64p. (J). lib. bdg. 28.56 (978-0-7398-6843-0(8)) Raintree.

CONDUCT OF LIFE

see also Behavior; Obedience

Abadie, M. J. The Goddess in Every Girl: Develop Your Teen Feminine Power. 2002. (Illus.). 272p. 14.95 (978-0-89281-909-6(X), Bindu Bks.) Inner Traditions International, Ltd.

Adams, Christine. Learning to Be a Good Friend: A Guidebook for Kids. Alley, R. W., illus. 2004. 32p. (J). per. 7.95 (978-0-87029-388-7(5)) Abbey Pr.

Adams, M.H. Small Means & Great Ends (Illustrated. 2006. pap. ***(*978-1-4065-0478-1(5))*** Dodo Pr.

AG Publishers Editors. The Best That I Can Be: Inspiring Words for American Girls. 2002. (American Girls Collection Ser.). (Illus.). 80p. (J). (gr. 2). 9.95 (978-1-58485-516-3(9)) American Girl Publishing, Inc.

—I Can Do Anything! Smart Cards for Strong Girls. 2002. (American Girl Library). (Illus.). 64p. (J). (gr. 3). pap. 6.95 (978-1-58485-622-1(X)) American Girl Publishing, Inc.

Aikins, Anne Marie. Misconduct: Without Bending the Rules. Murray, Steven, illus. 2005. (Deal with It Ser.). 32p. (J). (gr. 4-8). 12.95 (978-1-55028-871-1(7)) Lorimer, James & Co., Ltd., Pubs. CAN. *Dist:* Casemate Pubs. & Bk. Distributors, LLC.

Aimwell, Walter. Oscar or the Boy Who Had His Own Way. 2006. pap. 89.99 ***(*978-1-4280-2158-7(2))*** IndyPublish-.com.

Allen, Laura. The Quiz Book: Clues to You & Your Friends, Too! Tilley, Debbie, illus. 1999. (American Girl Library). 80p. (J). (gr. 3 up). spiral bd. 7.95 (978-1-56247-750-9(1)) American Girl Publishing, Inc.

Allenbaugh, Kay. Chocolate for a Teen's Spirit: Inspiring Stories for Young Women about Hope, Strength, & Wisdom. 2002. (Illus.). 256p. pap. 12.00 (978-0-7432-2289-1(X), Fireside) Simon & Schuster.

Alonzo, Ray. Simple Acts of Kindness for Kids: Little Ways to Make a Big Difference. 2000. (Illus.). 160p. (J). (ps-3). pap. 6.99 (978-1-57757-765-2(5), 1577577655) Cook, David C. Publishing Co.

Amos, Janine. Admitting Mistakes. Spenceley, Annabel, illus. 2002. (Courteous Kids Ser.). 32p. (J). (ps up). lib. bdg. 23.33 (978-0-8368-3168-9(3)) Stevens, Gareth Inc.

—After You! Spenceley, Annabel, illus. 2001. (Courteous Kids Ser.). 32p. (J). (ps up). lib. bdg. 23.33 (978-0-8368-2802-3(X)) Stevens, Gareth Inc.

—Being Helpful. Spenceley, Annabel, illus. 2002. (Courteous Kids Ser.). 32p. (J). (ps up). lib. bdg. 23.33 (978-0-8368-3169-6(1)) Stevens, Gareth Inc.

—Being Kind. Spenceley, Annabel, illus. 2002. (Courteous Kids Ser.). 32p. (J). (ps up). lib. bdg. 23.33 (978-0-8368-3170-2(5)) Stevens, Gareth Inc.

—Courteous Kids: Don't Do That!; Don't Say That!; Go Away!; It Won't Work!; It's Mine!; Move Over!, 6 bks. Spenceley, Annabel, illus. 2002. (J). (ps up). lib. bdg. 127.60 (978-0-8368-3604-2(9)) Stevens, Gareth Inc.

—Don't Do That! Spenceley, Annabel, illus. 2002. (Courteous Kids Ser.). 32p. (J). (ps up). lib. bdg. 23.33 (978-0-8368-3605-9(7)) Stevens, Gareth Inc.

—Don't Say That! Spenceley, Annabel, illus. 2002. (Courteous Kids Ser.). 32p. (J). (ps up). lib. bdg. 23.33 (978-0-8368-3606-6(5)) Stevens, Gareth Inc.

—Hello! Spenceley, Annabel, illus. 2001. (Courteous Kids Ser.). 32p. (J). (ps up). lib. bdg. 23.33 (978-0-8368-2803-0(8)) Stevens, Gareth Inc.

—I'm Sorry! Spenceley, Annabel, illus. 2001. (Courteous Kids Ser.). 32p. (J). (ps up). lib. bdg. 23.33 (978-0-8368-2804-7(6)) Stevens, Gareth Inc.

—It Won't Work! Spenceley, Annabel, illus. 2002. (Courteous Kids Ser.). 32p. (J). (ps up). lib. bdg. 23.33 (978-0-8368-3608-0(1)) Stevens, Gareth Inc.

—It's Mine! Spenceley, Annabel, illus. 2002. (Courteous Kids Ser.). 32p. (J). (ps up). lib. bdg. 23.33 (978-0-8368-3609-7(X)) Stevens, Gareth Inc.

—Making Friends. Spenceley, Annabel, illus. 2002. (Courteous Kids Ser.). 32p. (J). (ps up). lib. bdg. 23.33 (978-0-8368-3171-9(3)) Stevens, Gareth Inc.

—Move Over! Spenceley, Annabel, illus. 2002. (Courteous Kids Ser.). 32p. (J). (ps up). lib. bdg. 23.33 (978-0-8368-3610-3(3)) Stevens, Gareth Inc.

—Ninos Educados, 12 bks. Carrillo, Consuelo, tr. Incl. Admitir Nuestros Errores. Coffey, Colleen, tr. 2002. lib. bdg. 23.33 (978-0-8368-3203-7(5)); Ayudar a los Demas. Coffey, Colleen, tr. 2002. lib. bdg. 23.33 (978-0-8368-3204-4(3)); Compartir. Coffey, Colleen, tr. 2002. lib. bdg. 23.33 (978-0-8368-3205-1(1)); ¡Es Mio! Coffee, Carol, tr. Spenceley, Annabel, illus. 2002. lib. bdg. 23.33 (978-0-8368-3678-3(2)); Esperar Nuestro Turno. Coffey, Colleen, tr. 2002. lib. bdg. 23.33 (978-0-8368-3206-8(X)); Hacer Amigos. Coffey, Colleen, tr. 2002. lib. bdg. 23.33 (978-0-8368-3207-5(8)); ¡No Digas Eso! Coffee, Carol, tr. Spenceley, Annabel, illus. 2002. lib. bdg. 23.33 (978-0-8368-3679-0(0)); ¡No Funciona! Coffee, Carol, tr. Spenceley, Annabel, illus. 2002. lib. bdg. 23.33 (978-0-8368-3680-6(4)); ¡No Hagas Eso! Coffee, Carol, tr. Spenceley, Annabel, illus. 2002. lib. bdg. 23.33 (978-0-8368-3681-3(2)); ¡Quitate de Aqui! Coffee, Carol, tr. Spenceley, Annabel, illus. 2002. lib. bdg. 23.33 (978-0-8368-3682-0(0)); Ser Amables. Coffey, Colleen, tr. 2002. lib. bdg. 23.33 (978-0-8368-3208-2(6)); ¡Vete! Coffee, Carol, tr. Spenceley, Annabel, illus. lib. bdg. 23.33 (978-0-8368-3683-7(9)); 32p. (J). (ps up). (SPA.). Set lib. bdg. 279.96 (978-0-8368-3645-5(6)) Stevens, Gareth Inc.

—No, Thank You! Spenceley, Annabel, illus. 2001. (Courteous Kids Ser.). 32p. (J). (ps up). lib. bdg. 23.33 (978-0-8368-2805-4(4)) Stevens, Gareth Inc.

—Sharing. Spenceley, Annabel, illus. 2002. (Courteous Kids Ser.). 32p. (J). (ps up). lib. bdg. 23.33 (978-0-8368-3172-6(1)) Stevens, Gareth Inc.

—Taking Turns. Spenceley, Annabel, illus. 2002. (Courteous Kids Ser.). 32p. (J). (ps up). lib. bdg. 23.33 (978-0-8368-3173-3(X)) Stevens, Gareth Inc.

—Thank You! Spenceley, Annabel, illus. 2001. (Courteous Kids Ser.). 32p. (J). (ps up). lib. bdg. 23.33 (978-0-8368-2807-8(0)) Stevens, Gareth Inc.

Anderson, Judith. Me & My Friends. 2007. (J). ***(*978-1-59771-089-3(X))*** Sea-To-Sea Pubns.

Andries, Kathryn. Soul Choices: Six Paths to Find Your Life Purpose. Brill, Darlene, ed. 2003. (Illus.). 206p. (YA). pap. 19.95 (978-0-9741334-0-9(X)) Intuitive Arts Pr.

Appreciation of Diversity. 2005. (Promoting Peace with the Friends from Sunshine Center Ser.). (Illus.). 32p. (J). 14.95 (978-0-9768827-1-8(X)) Prevention Through Puppetry, Inc.

Artson, Bradley Shavit & Gevirtz, Gila. Making a Difference: Putting Jewish Spirituality into Action, One Mitzvah at a Time. 2001. (Illus.). 144p. (J). (gr. 7-9). pap. 8.95 (978-0-87441-712-8(0)) Behrman Hse., Inc.

Asquith, Ros. I Was a Teenage Worrier. 2000. (Illus.). 294p. pap. 11.99 (978-0-552-14027-0(9)) Transworld Publishers Ltd. GBR. *Dist:* Independent Pubs. Group.

—The Teenage Worrier's Guide to Life. 2000. (Teenage Worrier Ser.). (Illus.). 336p. mass mkt. 9.99 (978-0-552-14534-3(3), Corgi) Transworld Publishers Ltd. GBR. *Dist:* Trafalgar Square Publishing.

Barrington Jones, Barbara & Thomas, Janet. Dear Barbara: Answers to the Most-Asked Questions from Teenage Girls. 1998. (YA). pap. 13.95 (978-1-57345-369-1(2)) Deseret Bk. Co.

Barron, T. A. The Hero's Trail: A Guide for a Heroic Life. 2007. 144p. (J). (gr. 3 up). pap. 6.99 (978-0-14-240760-8(7), Puffin) Penguin Group (USA) Inc.

Bazin, Fritz. Youth Age Crisis. 2004. 93p. (YA). per. 13.98 (978-1-59453-149-1(8), 2020) Airleaf Publishing & Bookselling.

Be a Perfect Person in Just Three Days. 2000. (J). 9.95 (978-1-56137-281-2(1)) Novel Units, Inc.

Beck, Randy. Teen Quest. l.t. ed. 2004. 80p. (YA). per. 12.95 (978-1-59196-535-0(7)) Instantpublisher.com.

Beckerman, Menucha. The Real Hero. (Illus.). 24p. (J). (gr. k-5). 4.95 (978-1-931681-08-7(2)) Israel Bk. Shop.

—Where Is Michael? 2003. (My Middos World Ser.: Vol. 8). (Illus.). 24p. (J). 11.95 (978-1-931681-16-2(3)) Israel Bk. Shop.

—Who Dropped the Chick. 2003. (My Little World Ser.: Vol. 4). (Illus.). 32p. (J). (gr. k-5). 5.95 (978-1-931681-09-4(0)) Israel Bk. Shop.

—Why Did Dina-dee's Face Shine. Gaash, Elisheva, illus. 2003. (My Middos World Ser.: Vol. 6). 24p. (J). (gr. k-5). 11.95 (978-1-931681-05-6(8)) Israel Bk. Shop.

Bennett, William. Our Country's Founders: Words of Advice from the Founders in Stories, Lteers, Po. 2001. (gr. 7-12). lib. bdg. 18.80 (978-0-613-37163-6(1)) Tandem Library Bks.

Berg, Yehuda. The Mystery Teacher: The Power of Kabbalah Kid Series. 2005. (Illus.). 45p. 19.95 (978-1-57189-300-0(8)) Research Centre of Kabbalah.

Bernson, Janet. Un-Masking the Soul: A Creative Approach to Working with the Masks in the Mirror. 2001. 125p. spiral bd. 25.00 (978-0-9720509-3-7(0), UM1); 3rd ed. 2003. (Illus.). 134p. per. 17.95 (978-0-9720509-4-4(9)) Bernson Pr.

Berry, Joy. Achieve Goals. 3rd ed. 2005. (Winning skills series, work it! Ser.). (Illus.). 48p. (J). pap. 3.95 (978-1-57687-285-7(8), PowerHouse Kids) powerHouse Cultural Entertainment, Inc.

—Be a Star. 2005. (Winning skills series, go for It! Ser.). (Illus.). 48p. (J). pap. 3.95 (978-1-57687-289-5(0), PowerHouse Kids) powerHouse Cultural Entertainment, Inc.

—Be a Winner. 2005. (Winning skills series, go for It! Ser.). (Illus.). 48p. (J). pap. 3.95 (978-1-57687-290-1(4), PowerHouse Kids) powerHouse Cultural Entertainment, Inc.

—Be Assertive. 2005. (Winning skills series, work It! Ser.). (Illus.). 48p. (J). pap. 3.95 (978-1-57687-295-6(5), PowerHouse Kids) powerHouse Cultural Entertainment, Inc.

—Be Beautiful. 2005. (Winning skills series, go for It! Ser.). (Illus.). 48p. (J). pap. 3.95 (978-1-57687-286-4(6), PowerHouse Kids) powerHouse Cultural Entertainment, Inc.

—Be Happy. 2005. (Winning skills series, go for It! Ser.). (Illus.). 48p. (J). pap. 3.95 (978-1-57687-288-8(2), PowerHouse Kids) powerHouse Cultural Entertainment, Inc.

—Be in Control. 2005. (Winning skills series, work It! Ser.). (Illus.). 48p. (J). pap. 3.95 (978-1-57687-283-3(1), PowerHouse Kids) powerHouse Cultural Entertainment, Inc.

—Be Liked. 2005. (Winning skills series, go for It! Ser.). (Illus.). 48p. (J). pap. 3.95 (978-1-57687-287-1(4), PowerHouse Kids) powerHouse Cultural Entertainment, Inc.

—Be Organized. 2005. (Winning skills series, work It! Ser.). (Illus.). 48p. (J). pap. 3.95 (978-1-57687-284-0(X), PowerHouse Kids) powerHouse Cultural Entertainment, Inc.

—Be Smart. 2005. (Winning skills series, work It! Ser.). (Illus.). 48p. (J). pap. 3.95 (978-1-57687-281-9(5), PowerHouse Kids) powerHouse Cultural Entertainment, Inc.

—Criticism & Rejection. 2005. (Winning skills series, get over It! Ser.). (Illus.). 48p. (J). 3.95 (978-1-57687-277-2(7)) powerHouse Cultural Entertainment, Inc.

—Have a Great Future. 3rd ed. 2005. (Winning skills series, go for It! Ser.). (Illus.). 48p. (J). pap. 3.95 (978-1-57687-291-8(2), PowerHouse Kids) powerHouse Cultural Entertainment, Inc.

—Rude People. 2005. (Winning skills series, get over It! Ser.). (Illus.). 48p. (J). 3.95 (978-1-57687-278-9(5), PowerHouse Kids) powerHouse Cultural Entertainment, Inc.

—Stress. 2005. (Winning skills series, get over It! Ser.). (Illus.). 48p. (J). 3.95 (978-1-57687-276-5(9), PowerHouse Kids) powerHouse Cultural Entertainment, Inc.

—Work it! Set, 6 vols. 2005. (Winning skills series, work It! Ser.). (Illus.). 288p. (J). pap. 19.95 (978-1-57687-293-2(9)) powerHouse Cultural Entertainment, Inc.

Berry, Joy Wilt. A Book about Being a Bad Sport. 2005. (Illus.). (J). (978-0-7172-8588-4(X)) Scholastic, Inc.

—A Book about Being Bullied. 2005. (Illus.). (J). (978-0-7172-8578-5(2)) Scholastic, Inc.

—A Book about Being Forgetful. 2005. (Illus.). (J). (978-0-7172-8589-1(8)) Scholastic, Inc.

—A Book about Being Greedy. 2005. (Illus.). (J). (978-0-7172-8598-3(7)) Scholastic, Inc.

—A Book about Being Lazy. 2005. (Illus.). (J). (978-0-7172-7899-2(9)) Scholastic, Inc.

—A Book about Being Mean. 2005. (Illus.). (J). (978-0-7172-8591-4(X)) Scholastic, Inc.

—A Book about Being Messy. 2005. (Illus.). (J). (978-0-7172-8577-8(4)) Scholastic, Inc.

—A Book about Being Rude. 2005. (Illus.). (J). (978-0-7172-8592-1(8)) Scholastic, Inc.

—A Book about Being Selfish. 2005. (Illus.). (J). (978-0-7172-8579-2(0)) Scholastic, Inc.

—A Book about Breaking Promise. 2005. (Illus.). (J). (978-0-7172-8600-3(2)) Scholastic, Inc.

—A Book about Cheating. 2005. (Illus.). (J). (978-0-7172-8583-9(9)) Scholastic, Inc.

—A Book about Lying. 2005. (Illus.). (J). (978-0-7172-8576-1(6)) Scholastic, Inc.

—A Book about Overdoing It. 2005. (Illus.). (J). (978-0-7172-8575-4(8)) Scholastic, Inc.

—A Book about Stealing. 2005. (Illus.). (J). (978-0-7172-8585-3(5)) Scholastic, Inc.

—A Book about Tattling. 2005. (Illus.). (J). (978-0-7172-7897-8(2)) Scholastic, Inc.

—A Book about Teasing. 2005. (Illus.). (J). (978-0-7172-8580-8(4)) Scholastic, Inc.

—A Children's Book about Being Destructive. 2005. (Illus.). (J). (978-0-7172-8596-9(0)) Scholastic, Inc.

Blumenthal, Scott. A Kid's Mensch Handbook: Step by Step to a Lifetime of Jewish Values. 2004. (J). (978-0-87441-700-5(7)) Behrman Hse., Inc.

Bohensky, Anita. Self Esteem Workbook for Teens. 2002. (Illus.). 101p. 54.00 (978-1-893505-07-0(3)) Growth Publishing.

Bolton, April. Seven Lonely Places, Seven Warm Places: The Vices & Virtues for Children. Beck, Brent, illus. 2002. 39p. (J). 15.95 (978-0-86716-482-4(4)) St. Anthony Messenger Pr. & Franciscan Communications.

Born to Win. 2004. (J). 7.99 net. (978-0-9763141-0-3(X)) G.S. Enterprises of America Inc.

Bottoms, James "Bud". Kid Ethics: From A to Z. 2006. (J). per. 12.95 ***(*978-0-9794863-0-2(0))*** Summerland Publishing.

—Kid Ethics 2: From A to Z. 2007. (J). per. 12.95 ***(*978-0-9794863-1-9(9))*** Summerland Publishing.

Bowman, Susan. The Adventures of Dakota: A Friendly Wolf Who Teaches Children (Grades K-4) Lessons about Life. 2004. (Illus.). 56p. (J). (978-1-889636-60-3(6)) Youthlight, Inc.

Boyd, Ervin D., Sr. Help for the Hurting: Getting Beyond This Veil of Tears! 2003. (Illus.). 200p. (YA). spiral bd. 22.00 (978-0-9744024-0-6(0)) Anointed Word Pubns.

Boys to Men: A Christian Teen Survival Guide by Young Men Who Are Survivors. 2007. 165p. (J). ***(*978-0-929540-59-7(X))*** Publishing Designs, Inc.

Bremner, Shawn, compiled by. Aspire to Something Higher: A Pocket Book of Inspired Thoughts. 2003. 129p. per. (978-0-9682738-0-7(7)) Happy Publishing.

Buddhist Text Translation Society Staff, et al. Spider Thread. 2000. (ENG & CHI., Illus.). 100p. (J). 8.00 (978-0-88139-856-4(X)) Buddhist Text Translation Society.

Bullock, Reginald L. Father to Son: A Guide to Growing up in a Difficult World. 2002. (gr. 7-12). lib. bdg. 26.85 (978-0-613-87274-4(6)) Tandem Library Bks.

Burns, Marilyn. Brown Paper School Book: I Am Not a Short Adult. 2007. 128p. (J). pap. 12.99 (978-0-316-05979-4(X)) Little Brown & Co.

Buxton, Toni. The Secret to Your College Success: 101 Ways to Make the Most of Your College Experience. 2002. 243p. pap. 18.95 (978-0-595-21759-5(1), Writers Club Pr.) iUniverse, Inc.

Byrd, Sandra. Girl Talk: 61 Questions from Girls Like You. 2001. (Girls Like You Ser.). 128p. (J). (gr. 3-7). pap. 7.99 (978-0-7642-2492-8(1)) Bethany Hse. Pubs.

—A Growing up Guide: What Girls Like You Want to Know. 2003. (Girls Like You Ser.). (Illus.). 126p. (J). pap. 8.99 (978-0-7642-2752-3(1)) Bethany Hse. Pubs.

Cambridge Educational, prod. Personal Development Hybr Lb. (YA). cd-rom 245.95 (978-0-7365-4352-1(X)) Films Media Group.

Candell, Arianna. Mind Your Manners: At Parties. Curto, Rosa M., illus. 2005. (Mind Your Manners Ser.). (ENG & SPA.). 36p. (J). pap. 6.95 (978-0-7641-3167-7(2)) Barron's Educational Series, Inc.

—Mind Your Manners: In School. Curto, Rosa M., illus. 2005. (Mind Your Manners Ser.). 36p. (J). pap. 6.95 (978-0-7641-3166-0(4)) Barron's Educational Series, Inc.

Canfield, Jack L. Chicken Soup for the Kid's Soul: 101 Stories of Courage, Hope & Laughter. 2000. (Illus.). (J). 19.60 (978-0-606-18203-4(9)) Tandem Library Bks.

—Chicken Soup for the Preteen Soul. 2000. (gr. 5-8). lib. bdg. 22.20 (978-0-613-30313-2(X)) Tandem Library Bks.

—Chicken Soup for the Preteen Soul: 101 Stories of Changes, Choices & Growing Up. 2001. (Illus.). (J). 19.60 (978-0-606-20599-3(3)) Tandem Library Bks.

—Chicken Soup for the Teenage Soul III. 2000. (gr. 7-12). lib. bdg. 22.20 (978-0-613-24541-8(5)) Tandem Library Bks.

—Chicken Soup for the Teenage Soul Letters. 2001. (gr. 7-12). lib. bdg. 22.20 (978-0-613-30314-9(8)) Tandem Library Bks.

Canfield, Jack L. & Hansen, Mark Victor. Bouillon de Poulet pour l'Ame des Ados. 2002. Tr. of Chicken Soup for the Teenage Soul. (FRE., Illus.). 48p. (J). pap. 18.95 incl. audio compact disk (978-2-89558-045-4(6)) Coffragants CAN. *Dist:* Penton Overseas, Inc.

—A Little Spoonful of Chicken Soup for the Kids Soul Desktop Inspiration. 1999. (Illus.). 96p. (J). (gr. k-8). pap. 6.99 (978-1-58375-548-8(9), 5489) Garborg's, Inc.

Canfield, Jack L. & Hansen, Mark Victor, creators. Chicken Soup for the Teen Soul: Life Stripped to the Core. 2007. 288p. (YA). pap. 14.95 ***(*978-0-7573-0682-2(9))*** Health Communications, Inc.

Canfield, Jack L., et al. Chicken Soup for the Child's Soul Character-Building Stories to Read with Kids. 2007. 288p. (J). pap. 14.95 ***(*978-0-7573-0589-4(X))*** Health Communications, Inc.

—Chicken Soup for the Kid's Soul: 101 Stories of Courage, Hope & Laughter. 1998. (Chicken Soup for the Soul Ser.). (Illus.). 352p. (J). (gr. 4-7). tchr. ed. 24.00 (978-1-55874-608-4(0)) Health Communications, Inc.

—Chicken Soup for the Kid's Soul: 101 Stories of Courage, Hope & Laughter. Hansen, Patty, illus. 1998. (Chicken Soup for the Soul Ser.). 352p. (gr. 4-7). pap. 14.95 (978-1-55874-609-1(9)) Health Communications, Inc.

—Chicken Soup for the Preteen Soul: 101 Stories of Changes, Choices & Growing up for Kids, Ages 9-13. 2000. (Chicken Soup for the Soul Ser.). (Illus.). 380p. (gr. 5-7). (J). tchr. ed. 24.00 (978-1-55874-801-9(6)); pap. 14.95 (978-1-55874-800-2(8)) Health Communications, Inc.

—Chicken Soup for the Preteen Soul II: Stories about Taking Charge, Making a Difference & Moving Through the Preteen Years for Kids Ages 9-13. 2004. 384p. (YA). pap. 14.95 (978-0-7573-0150-6(9)) Health Communications, Inc.

—Chicken Soup for the Teenage Soul: Stories about Disses, Losses, Messes, Stresses & More. 2006. 280p. (YA). pap. 14.95 (978-0-7573-0407-1(9)) Health Communications, Inc.

—Chicken Soup for the Teenage Soul IV: More Stories of Life, Love & Learning, Vol. IV. Claspy, Mitch, ed. 2004. 400p. pap. 14.95 (978-0-7573-0233-6(5)) Health Communications, Inc.

—Una 2nd Racion de Sopa de Pollo para el Alma del Adolescente: Mas Relatos Sobre la Vida el Amour y el Aprendizaje. 2nd ed. 2003. Tr. of Chicken Soup for the Teenage Soul. (SPA., Illus.). 350p. (YA). pap. 12.95 (978-0-7573-0134-6(7)) Health Communications, Inc.

Canizares, Susan & Betsey, Chessen. Two Can Do It! 1999. (ps-2). lib. bdg. 10.10 (978-0-613-22540-3(6)) Tandem Library Bks.

Canizares, Susan & Chessen, Betsey. Two Can Do It! 1999. (Social Studies Emergent Readers). (J). 2.50 (978-0-439-04559-9(2)) Scholastic, Inc.

Cap Compass Staff. Life after School, Explained. 2002. 182p. (YA). per. 13.95 (978-0-9717366-0-3(X)) Cap & Compass, LLC.

Caponigro, Jeffrey R. On Your Own: Advice for Young Adults Leaving Home for the First Time. 2002. 160p. (YA). per. 9.95 (978-0-9659606-3-2(3)) Barker Business Bks., Inc.

Carlson, Dale. Who Said What? Philosophy Quotes for Teens. Nicklaus, Carol, illus. 2003. 256p. (gr. 7-12). 14.95 (978-1-884158-28-5(5)) Bick Publishing Hse.

Carr, Dan. God I Need to Talk Hurting Oth. 2004. 16p. (J). 99.00 (978-0-7586-0517-7(X)) Concordia Publishing Hse.

Carriero, John P. Staying on Top of Things Before It's Too Late, Vol. 1. 2nd unabr. rev. ed. 2000. (Illus.). 54p. (YA). (gr. 8-10). 15.00 (978-0-9703109-0-3(0)) McQuaid Jesuit High Schl.

Carry the Sunshine in Your Heart. 2004. (J). pap. 7.99 net. (978-0-9763141-1-0(8)) G.S. Enterprises of America Inc.

Carter, Carol S., creator. Appreciation of Diversity. 2005. (Promoting Peace with the Friends from Sunshine Center Ser.). (J). pap. 12.95 (978-0-9768827-0-1(1)) Prevention Through Puppetry, Inc.

Chicken Soup for the Preteen Soul Personal Organizer. 2001. (YA). (gr. 5-7). spiral bd. 9.00 (978-1-58794-018-7(3)) Day-Timers, Inc.

Chicken Soup for the Teenage Soul Personal Organizer. 2000. 272p. (YA). (gr. 7-12). spiral bd. 12.95 (978-1-58794-002-6(7)) Day-Timers, Inc.

Child of the Moon. 2001. 48p. lib. bdg. 24.95 (978-0-9672982-2-1(9)) Mythic Rain Publishing, Inc.

Chobanian, Elizabeth, ed. Coconut's Guide to Life: Life Lessons from a Girl's Best Friend. Lukatz, Casey, illus. 2003. (Coconut Ser.). 32p. (J). 5.95 (978-1-58485-771-6(4)); 21.95 (978-1-58485-772-3(2)) American Girl Publishing, Inc.

Choron, Harry. Book of Lists for Teens. 2002. (gr. 7-12). lib. bdg. 21.10 (978-0-613-90477-3(X)) Tandem Library Bks.

Clark, Sondra. Snap 2 It! A Real Girl's Guide to Keeping a Positive Outlook (even when you're having a bad hair day, just got a pimple on your nose & you & your best friend are fighting) 2007. 128p. pap. 7.95 (***978-1-4022-0954-3(1)***) Sourcebooks, Inc.

Claussen, Janet. Biblical Women: Exploring Their Stories with Girls. 2003. 120p. (YA). pap. 24.95 (978-0-88489-699-9(4)) St. Mary's Pr.

Clyde, Addie M. Sophie the Sofa. l.t. ed. 2004. 40p. (J). per. (978-1-59196-744-6(9)) Instantpublisher.com.

Coca-Cola Valued Youth Programme: Tutor Workbook. 1998. (Illus.). 87p. (J). (gr. k-12). wbk. ed. (978-1-878550-65-1(9)) Intercultural Development Research Assn.

Coil, Carolyn. Becoming an Achiever. exp. rev. ed. 2004. (J). pap. 16.95 (978-1-931334-57-0(9)) Pieces of Learning.

Colclasure, Dale & Jensen, David. Gift of the Soul: A Spiritual Journey. 2002. 300p. (YA). (gr. 8 up). pap. 17.95 (978-0-9703988-1-9(6)) Rainbow Pride Pr.

Concordia Publishing House, compiled by. Stand Your Ground: Devotions by Teens for Teens. 2001. (ENG.). 128p. (YA). pap. 8.99 (978-0-570-05291-3(2)) Concordia Publishing Hse.

Cook, Billie Montgomery. The Real Deal: A Spiritual Guide for Black Teen Girls. 2004. 144p. 13.00 (978-0-8170-1458-2(6)) Judson Pr.

Cooper, Scott. Speak up & Get Along! Learn the Mighty Might, Thought Chop, & More Tools to Make Friends, Stop Teasing, & Feel Good about Yourself! 2005. (Illus.). 128p. (J). (gr. 3-7). pap. 12.95 (978-1-57542-182-7(8)) Free Spirit Publishing, Inc.

Cooperation. (Character Education Classroom Helpers Ser.). 24p. (gr. k up). 3.99 (978-0-7682-2620-1(1) , FS99060); (gr. 2 up). 3.99 (978-0-7682-2622-5(8) , FS99062); (gr. 4 up). 3.99 (978-0-7682-2624-9(4) , FS99064); (gr. 5 up). 3.99 (978-0-7682-2625-6(2) , FS99065) Schaffer, Frank Pubns.

Coping: Problems Facing Today's Teens, 6 bks. Incl. Coping with Aggression. Emanuele, Patricia. lib. bdg. 26.50 (978-0-8239-3360-0(1)); Coping with an Abusive Relationship. Cobb, Carlene. lib. bdg. 26.50 (978-0-8239-2822-4(5)); Coping with Bipolar Disorder & Manic-Depressive Illness. Jovinelly, Joann. lib. bdg. 26.50 (978-0-8239-3193-4(5)); Coping with Media Violence. Cefrey, Holly. lib. bdg. 26.50 (978-0-8239-2893-4(4)); Coping with Rejection. Moe, Barbara. lib. bdg. 26.50 (978-0-8239-3362-4(8)); Coping with Social Anxiety. Moehn, Heather. lib. bdg. 26.50 (978-0-8239-3363-1(6)); 192p. (YA). (gr. 7-12). 2005. (Illus.). 2000. Set lib. bdg. 151.50 (978-0-8239-9414-4(7)) Rosen Publishing Group, Inc., The.

Corriveau, Danielle. Trail Mix: Stories of Youth Overcoming Adversity. 2001. 128p. (YA). (gr. 9 up). per. 14.95 (978-0-9702366-0-9(3)) Corvo Communications.

Costanzo, Charlene A. The Twelve Gifts of Birth. Ackison, Wendy Wassink, illus. Reger, Jill, photos by. 1998. 64p. (J). (ps-3). 19.95 (978-1-891836-12-1(9)) Featherfew.

—The Twelve Gifts of Birth. Ackison, Wendy Wassink, illus. Reger, Jill, photos by. 2001. 64p. 19.95 (978-0-06-621104-6(2) , Rayo) HarperCollins Pubs.

Cotner, June. Teen Sunshine Reflections: Words for the Heart & Soul. 2002. (J). (gr. 8 up). (Illus.). 208p. pap. 9.95 (978-0-06-000527-6(0) , Harper Trophy); 160p. 15.89 (978-0-06-000526-9(2)); (Illus.). 208p. 15.95 (978-0-06-000525-2(4)) HarperCollins Pubs.

Courtesy Counts. 1999. (Health & Human Development Resource Library). (J). (gr. k-3). 69.95 (978-1-55942-123-2(1) , 9222V9) Marsh Media.

Covey, Sean. Daily Reflections for Highly Effective Teens. 1999. (Illus.). 384p. pap. 12.00 (978-0-684-87060-1(6) , Fireside) Simon & Schuster.

—Daily Reflections for Highly Effective Teens. 1999. (gr. 5-8). lib. bdg. 19.95 (978-0-613-29218-4(9)) Tandem Library Bks.

—The 7 Habits Journal for Teens. 2002. (Illus.). 208p. reprint ed. pap. 11.95 (978-0-7432-3707-9(2) , Fireside) Simon & Schuster.

Crist, James J. What to Do When You're Scared & Worried: A Guide for Kids. 2004. (Illus.). 128p. (YA). (gr. 4-8). pap. 9.95 (978-1-57542-153-7(4)) Free Spirit Publishing, Inc.

Crouch, Amie. Feng Shui Workbook for Teens. 2003. (ENG.). 19.95 (***978-0-595-65513-7(0));*** 128p. (YA). pap. 9.95 (978-0-595-26061-4(6)) iUniverse, Inc. (Writer's Showcase Pr.).

Cullen, Murray & O'Neill, Susan. Try: Treatment Readiness for Youth at Risk. 2005. (J). pap. 15.00 net. (978-1-56991-178-5(9)) American Correctional Assn.

Culp, Bruce & Culp, Melody. The Value of the Gift: A Spiritual Guide to Love & Intimacy, for Young Adults. l.t. ed. 2000. 96p. (YA). (gr. 7 up). pap. 8.95 (978-0-9672616-1-4(9)) Oak Hammock Publishing.

Daniel, Thesina C. How to Succeed Through Your Teenage Years: And Avoid Yielding to Drugs, Teen Pregnancy, Suicide & Serving Time in Jail. Bookmasters, Inc. Staff, ed. 2000. 130p. (YA). (gr. 8 up). per. 9.95 (978-0-9678621-1-8(6)) Gardenia Publishing.

Dawson, George. Life Is So Good. 2001. (gr. 7-12). lib. bdg. 23.45 (978-0-613-36465-2(1)) Tandem Library Bks.

Dayton, Tian. It's My Life! A Workout for Your Mind. 2000. (Illus.). 220p. (YA). (gr. 8 up). pap. 11.95 (978-1-55874-833-0(4)) Health Communications, Inc.

De Anda, Diane. Stress Management for Adolescents: A Cognitive-Behavioral Program. 2004. 66p. stu. ed., spiral bd. 13.95 (978-0-87822-436-4(X) , 5163) Research Pr.

Dee, Catherine. The Girls' Book of Wisdom: Empowering, Inspirational Quotes from over 400 Fabulous Females. Douglass, Ali, ed. Pollack, Lou M., illus. 1999. 208p. (J). (gr. 7-17). pap. 9.99 (978-0-316-17956-0(6)) Little, Brown Bks. for Young Readers.

—The Girls' Guide to Life: Take Charge of Your Personal Life, Your School Time, Your Social Scene, & Much More! 2nd ed. 2005. (Illus.). 160p. (J). (gr. 5-17). pap. 15.99 (978-0-316-73628-2(7) , Tingley, Megan Bks.) Little, Brown Bks. for Young Readers.

DeGezelle, Terri. Manners at a Friend's Home. 2004. (First Facts Ser.). (Illus.). 24p. (J). (gr. k-2). lib. bdg. 21.26 (978-0-7368-2643-3(2) , First Facts) Capstone Pr., Inc.

DePino, Catherine S. Hi God, It's Me! E-Prayers for Teenage Boys. 2002. (gr. 7-12). lib. bdg. 22.20 (978-0-613-79632-3(2)) Tandem Library Bks.

—Hi God, It's Me! E-Prayers for Teenage Girls. 2002. (gr. 7-12). lib. bdg. 22.20 (978-0-613-79634-7(9)) Tandem Library Bks.

Desetta, Al. Struggle to Be Strong: True Stories by Teens about Overcoming Tough Times. 2000. (gr. 7-12). lib. bdg. 24.55 (978-0-613-89621-4(1)) Tandem Library Bks.

Desrosiers, James P. Young People's Guide to Goal Setting: Life-Long Skills Needed to Achieve Any Goal on the Planet! 2001. 40p. (YA). per. 14.95 (978-0-9715507-0-4(0)) GROWTHco.

Dial Books, creator. Making It Home: Real-Life Stories from Children Forced to Flee. 2005. (Illus.). 128p. (J). (gr. 5). 17.99 (978-0-8037-3083-0(7) , Dial) Penguin Group (USA) Inc.

Dieffenbach, Tim. Why Me? When Life's Not Fair. 2002. (Life Wise Ser.). 64p. tchr. ed. 19.95 (978-1-56212-787-9(X) , 131326, Faith Alive Christian Resources) CRC Pubns.

Discovering Your Own... Teen Esteem. 2003. (Illus.). 345p. (YA). 24.95 (978-0-9753482-0-8(5)) Identity Pr.

Do You Have What It Takes. 2007. (YA). per. 35.00 (***978-0-9661256-9-6(X)***) Youth Communication - New York Center.

Doudna, Kelly. Right on Time! 2007. (Character Concepts Ser.). (Illus.). 24p. (J). (gr. k-3). lib. bdg. 19.93 (***978-1-59928-740-9(4)***) ABDO Publishing Co.

Drill, Esther, et al. Deal with It! A Whole New Approach to Your Body, Brain & Life as a GURL. 1999. (Illus.). 320p. (YA). (gr. 7-12). pap. 19.95 (978-0-671-04157-1(6) , Pocket) Simon & Schuster.

Dromgoole, Glenn. What Puppies Teach Us: Life's Lessons Learned from Our Little Friends. 2003. (Illus.). 32p. tchr. ed. 12.95 (978-1-57223-684-4(1) , 6841) Willow Creek Pr., Inc.

Dunham, Kelli S. The Boy's Body Book: Everything You Need to Know for Growing up You. Bjorkman, Steven, illus. 2007. 112p. (YA). (gr. 5 up). pap. 9.95 (***978-1-933662-74-9(3)***) Cider Mill Pr. Bk. Pubs. LLC.

Dyer, Wayne W. Unstoppable Me: 10 Ways to Soar Through Life. Heller Budnick, Stacy, illus. 2006. 32p. 14.95 (978-1-4019-1186-7(2)) Hay Hse., Inc.

Edelman, Marian Wright. Lanterns: A Memoir of Mentors. 2000. (gr. 7-12). lib. bdg. 23.45 (978-0-613-31403-9(4)) Tandem Library Bks.

Edwards, Josephine Cunnington. Children Can Be Taught. 2004. (Illus.). 84p. per. 9.95 (978-1-57258-293-4(6) , 945-6145) TEACH Services, Inc.

Ellis, Mike. Work Ethic Mini Series. Reichard, Don, ed. Tucker, Keith, illus. 2001. (Teen Pressure Points Ser.). (YA). (gr. 7-12). pap. 8.95 (978-1-931235-17-4(1)) Word of Life Fellowship, Inc.

En las Buenas y Para Siempre. 2001. Tr. of For Better & for Ever. (SPA.). 200p. (YA). pap. 12.50 (978-0-9677223-2-0(2)) Redemptorists Marriage Preparation Resources.

The Encyclopedia of Danger. (Illus.). 112-128p. (gr. 5). pap. 19.90 (978-0-7910-3759-1(2) , Chelsea Hse.) Facts On File, Inc.

Espeland, Pamela. Knowing Me, Knowing You: The I-Sight Way to Understand Yourself & Others. 2004. (Illus.). 128p. (YA). (gr. 8-12). pap. 13.95 (978-1-57542-090-5(2)) Free Spirit Publishing, Inc.

—A Leader's Guide to Knowing Me, Knowing You. 2004. 112p. (gr. 6-12). tchr. ed. 21.95 (978-1-57542-091-2(0)) Free Spirit Publishing, Inc.

—Life Lists for Teens: Tips, Steps, Hints, & How-tos for Growing up, Getting Al. 2003. (gr. 7-12). lib. bdg. 21.05 (978-0-613-63048-1(3)) Tandem Library Bks.

—Life Lists for Teens: Tips, Steps, Hints, & How-Tos for Growing up, Getting along, Learning, & Having Fun. 2004. 272p. (YA). (gr. 5 up). pap. 11.95 (978-1-57542-125-4(9) , 785) Free Spirit Publishing, Inc.

Espeland, Pamela & Verdick, Elizabeth. Doing & Being Your Best: The Boundaries & Expectations Assets. 2005. (Adding Assets Series for Kids). (Illus.). 80p. (J). (gr. 3-7). pap. 9.95 (978-1-57542-171-1(2) , 909) Free Spirit Publishing, Inc.

—Knowing & Doing Whats Right. 2005. (Adding Assets Series for Kids). (Illus.). 80p. (J). (gr. 3-7). pap. 9.95 (978-1-57542-184-1(4)) Free Spirit Publishing, Inc.

Espeland, Pamela & Verdick, Elizabeth. See You Later, Procrastinator! (Get It Done) Mark, Steve, illus. 2008. 112p. (J). pap. (***978-1-57542-278-7(6)***) Free Spirit Publishing, Inc.

Evans, Kristina. Cherish Today: A Celebration of Life's Moments. Collier, Bryan, illus. 2007. (J). (***978-1-4287-3968-0(8)*** , Jump at the Sun) Hyperion Bks. for Children.

FAQ: Teen Life, Set 2. Incl. Frequently Asked Questions about ADD & ADHD. Pomere, Jonas. (YA). lib. bdg. 27.95 (***978-1-4042-1970-0(6));*** Frequently Asked Questions about Date Rape. Orr, Tamra. (YA). lib. bdg. 27.95 (***978-1-4042-1972-4(2));*** Frequently Asked Questions about Dating : Teen Life. Baish, Vanessa. (J). lib. bdg. 27.95 (***978-1-4042-1969-4(2));*** Frequently Asked Questions about Drug Testing. Pomere, Jonas. (J). lib. bdg. 27.95 (***978-1-4042-1973-1(0)*** , 1267045); Frequently Asked Questions about My Pyramid : Eating Right. Williams, Kara. (J). lib. bdg. 27.95 (***978-1-4042-1974-8(9));*** Frequently Asked Questions about Online Romance. Boger, Ann. (YA). lib. bdg. 27.95 (***978-1-4042-1971-7(4));*** (Illus.). 64p. (gr. 7-12). 2006. 2007. Set lib. bdg. 167.70 (***978-1-4042-1062-2(8))*** Rosen Publishing Group, Inc., The.

Farrell, Juliana. High School: The Real Deal. 2001. (gr. 7-12). lib. bdg. 16.40 (978-0-613-81954-1(3)) Tandem Library Bks.

Farrell, Juliana & Mayall, Beth. Middle School: The Real Deal: From Cafeteria Food to Combination Locks. 2007. 176p. (J). (gr. 4-7). pap. 7.99 (***978-0-06-122742-4(0))*** HarperCollins Pubs.

Ferebee, Janice. Got It Goin' On: Power Tools for Girls. Fentress, Tara, ed. DeFreitas, Peter, illus. 2000. 150p. (YA). (gr. 7-12). pap. 19.95 (978-0-9651166-1-9(1)) Got It Goin' On.

Fighting the Monster. 2004. (YA). ring bd. 59.95 (***978-0-9661256-2-7(2))*** Youth Communication - New York Center.

Finding Your Way: A Guidebook. 2004. pap. 12.00 (978-0-9744877-0-0(8)) Noller, Gail.

Fishel, Danielle & Rizzo, Monica. A Teenager's Guide to Life. 1999. (Girls Get Real Ser.). (Illus.). 144p. (J). (gr. 3-9). pap. 5.99 (978-0-439-08788-9(0)) Scholastic, Inc.

Flutie, Doug. Never Say Never. 2000. (Positively for Kids Ser.). (Illus.). 40p. 14.95 (978-0-87833-165-9(4)) Taylor Trade Publishing.

Fone, Ann. Elf-help for Giving the Gift of You. 2005. per. 4.95 (978-0-87029-392-4(3)) Abbey Pr.

Foote, Tracy. My Potty Reward Stickers for Boys: 126 Boy Stickers & Chart to Motivate Toilet Training. 2003. (J). 7.95 (978-0-9708226-6-6(9)) TracyTrends.

—My Potty Reward Stickers for Girls: 126 Girl Stickers & Chart to Motivate Toilet Training. 3rd rev. ed. 2003. (J). 7.95 (978-0-9708226-5-9(0)) TracyTrends.

Fox, Annie & Kirschner, Ruth. Too Stressed to Think? A Teen Guide to Staying Sane When Life Makes You Crazy. Verdick, Elizabeth, ed. 2005. (Illus.). 176p. (YA). (gr. 7 up). pap. 14.95 (978-1-57542-173-5(9) , 908) Free Spirit Publishing, Inc.

Francis, Snip & Gilbert, Melanie. Happy Stories (Camping Cover) Bk. 1: 12 True Stories for Happy Living. Fisher, Brian, ed. Howrani, Ameen, photos by. 2002. (Illus.). 112p. (J). (gr. 1-6). 14.95 (978-1-890616-23-6(0)) Salamander Group, Inc., The.

Frankel Hauser, Jill. The Kids Guide to Becoming the Best You Can Be! Developing 5 Traits You Need to Achieve Your Personal Best. 2006. (Illus.). 128p. (J). pap. 12.95 (978-0-8249-6788-8(7) , Williamson Bks.) Ideals Pubns.

Friel, John C. Seven Best Things Smart Teens Do. 2000. (gr. 7-12). lib. bdg. 22.20 (978-0-613-30721-5(6)) Tandem Library Bks.

Fry, Eva. Be a Winner in Life: How to Overcome the Trials & Tempatations of Life to Find. 2002. (gr. 7-12). lib. bdg. 24.00 (978-0-613-78039-1(6)) Tandem Library Bks.

Garborg's Inc. Staff, compiled by. The Pocket Treasury of Inspirational Verse Gift Book. 1999. 352p. (J). pap. 3.99 (978-1-58375-477-1(6)) Garborg's, Inc.

—Royal Doulton: Naples - To Love & to Cherish Day-Brightener. 1999. (Illus.). 366p. (J). pap. 9.99 (978-1-58375-496-2(2)) Garborg's, Inc.

Gareth Stevens Publishing Staff. No Funciona! 2003. (SPA.). (gr. k-3). lib. bdg. 14.10 (978-0-613-76726-2(8)) Tandem Library Bks.

Garrett, Byron. The ABC's of Life. 2004. (YA). pap. 16.95 (978-0-9755938-0-6(3)) TRI LIFE Pr.

Geisler, Norman L. & Holden, Joseph. Living Loud: Defending Your Faith. 2004. (TruthQuest Ser.). (Illus.). 176p. (gr. 7-12). pap. 9.99 (978-0-8054-2482-9(2)) B&H Publishing Grp.

Gellman, Marc. And God Cried, Too: A Kid's Book of Healing & Hope. Bliss, Harry, illus. 2002. 128p. (J). (gr. 2 up). pap. 5.99 (978-0-06-009886-5(4)); 17.89 (978-0-06-009887-2(2)) HarperCollins Pubs.

Gerard, Franck J. Time Waits for No One! Prioritize to Change Your Life! 2005. (Illus.). 90p. per., training bk. ed. 14.99 net. (978-0-9772685-0-4(0)) ABC Pubs.

Gerety, Ed. Combinations: Opening the Door to Student Leadership. 2003. 160p. (YA). per. 14.95 (978-0-9725938-3-0(7)) Whaleback Publishing.

Get a Grip on Life: What Every Teen Must Know to Have a Great Life. 2004. 240p. (YA). per. 14.00 (978-0-9748994-0-4(2)) Youth Quest Institute.

Getting Through College. 2004. (YA). per. 13.95 (978-1-56870-507-1(7)) RonJon Publishing, Inc.

Gibb, Fiona & Shaw, Tucker. Any Advice? Schwartz, Sara, illus. 2000. 172p. (YA). (gr. 7-12). lib. bdg. 14.15 (978-0-613-33871-4(5)) Tandem Library Bks.

Gibbons, Casey Hartley. A Girl's Life with God. 2006. 160p. pap. 8.99 (978-1-56309-757-7(5) , N034115) New Hope Pubs.

Gillis, Jennifer Blizin. You & Me ABC. 2003. (You & Me Ser.). (Illus.). 24p. (J). lib. bdg. 18.50 (978-1-4034-2510-2(8)) Heinemann Library.

Girls Can Do Christian Adventures in Learning Book. 2005. (J). 19.95 (978-1-59649-223-3(6)) Whispering Pine Pr., Inc.

Girls Know Best, 7 bks. l.t. ed. Incl. Boys Know It All : Wise Thoughts & Wacky Ideas from Guys Like You. Roehm, Michelle, compiled by. 167p. 1999. lib. bdg. 23.33 (978-0-8368-2455-1(5)); Girls Know Best Vol. 2 : Tips on Life & Fun Stuff to Do. Monson-Burton, Marianne, compiled by. 1999. lib. bdg. 23.33 (978-0-8368-2453-7(9)); Girls Know Best Vol. 3 : Your Words, Your World. Monson-Burton, Marianne, compiled by. 153p. 2000. lib. bdg. 23.33 (978-0-8368-2672-2(8)); Girls Knows Best : Advice for Girls from Girls on Just about Everything. Roehm, Michelle, compiled by. 160p. 1999. lib. bdg. 23.33 (978-0-8368-2452-0(0)); Girls Who Rocked the World : Heroines from Sacagawea to Sheryl Swoopes. Welden, Amelie. McCann, Jerry, illus. 117p. 1999. lib. bdg. 23.33 (978-0-8368-2454-4(7)); Girls Who Rocked the World Vol. 2 : Heroines from Harriet Tubman to Mia Hamm. Roehm, Michelle, compiled by. 152p. 2000. lib. bdg. 23.33 (978-0-8368-2673-9(6)); Throw Like a Girl : Discovering the Body, Mind & Spirit of the Athlete in You! Frost, Shelley & Troussieux, Ann. 128p. 2000. lib. bdg. 23.33 (978-0-8368-2674-6(4)); (J). (gr. 3 up). (Illus.). Set lib. bdg. 163.31 (978-0-8368-2741-5(4)) Stevens, Gareth Inc.

Glendinning, Margaret. Every Day a Victory. 2001. 40p. 5.00 (978-0-9714649-5-7(2)) MPG Pr.

Gomez Seitz, M. Stella. The Master Cookie-Maker: A True Life Story for Children. 2003. 133p. (J). pap. 13.95 (978-0-595-26314-1(3) , Writers Club Pr.) iUniverse, Inc.

Good Character Adventure Pack: Adventures in Empathy. 2006. (J). wbk. ed. 4.95 (978-1-55548-002-8(0) , 4202) Human Relations Media.

Good Character Adventure Pack: Adventures in Perseverance. 2006. (J). 4.95 (978-1-55548-004-2(7) , 4204) Human Relations Media.

Good Character Adventure Pack: Adventures in Responsibility Workbook. 2006. (J). 4.95 (978-1-55548-003-5(9) , 4203) Human Relations Media.

Goodier, Steve. Lessons of the Turtle: Living Right Side Up. 2002. 136p. pap. 14.95 (978-1-929664-15-3(X)) Life Support System Publishing, Inc.

Gordon, Sharon. Compartimos. 2006. (Bookworms Ser.). (SPA & ENG., Illus.). 24p. (J). lib. bdg. 22.79 (978-0-7614-2360-7(5) , Benchmark Bks.) Cavendish, Marshall Corp.

—Decimos la Verdad. 2006. (Bookworms Ser.). (SPA & ENG., Illus.). 24p. (J). lib. bdg. 22.79 (978-0-7614-2362 1(1) , Benchmark Bks.) Cavendish, Marshall Corp.

—Respetamos las Reglas. 2006. (Bookworms Ser.). (SPA & ENG., Illus.). 24p. (J). lib. bdg. 22.79 (978-0-7614-2358-4(3) , Benchmark Bks.) Cavendish, Marshall Corp.

—Somos Amables. 2006. (Bookworms Ser.). (SPA & ENG., Illus.). 24p. (J). lib. bdg. 22.79 (978-0-7614-2356-0(7) , Benchmark Bks.) Cavendish, Marshall Corp.

—We Are Kind (Somos Amables) 2006. (Bookworms Ser.). (ENG & SPA., Illus.). 24p. (J). lib. bdg. 22.79 (978-0-7614-2435-2(0)) Cavendish, Marshall Corp.

—We Follow the Rules. 2005. (Bookworms Ser.). (ENG & SPA., Illus.). 24p. (J). (gr. 3-7). lib. bdg. (978-0-7614-1995-2(0) , Benchmark Bks.) Cavendish, Marshall Corp.

—We Follow the Rules (Respetamos las Reglas) 2006. (Bookworms Ser.). (ENG & SPA., Illus.). 24p. (J). lib. bdg. 22.79 (978-0-7614-2438-3(5)) Cavendish, Marshall Corp.

—We Share. 2005. (Bookworms Ser.). (ENG & SPA., Illus.). 24p. (J). (gr. 3-7). lib. bdg. (978-0-7614-1993-8(4) , Benchmark Bks.) Cavendish, Marshall Corp.

—We Share (Compartimos) 2006. (Bookworms Ser.). (ENG & SPA., Illus.). 24p. (J). lib. bdg. 22.79 (978-0-7614-2441-3(5)) Cavendish, Marshall Corp.

—We Tell the Truth (Decimos la Verdad) 2006. (Bookworms Ser.). (ENG & SPA., Illus.). 24p. (J). lib. bdg. 22.79 (978-0-7614-2442-0(3)) Cavendish, Marshall Corp.

Graham, Stedman. Teens Can Make It Happen. 2001. (Illus.). 176p. pap., wbk. ed. 12.00 (978-0-7432-2558-8(9) , Fireside) Simon & Schuster.

Greenberg, Judith. Girl's Guide to Growing Up: Making the Right Choices. 2000. (gr. 7-12). lib. bdg. 18.75 (978-0-613-34230-8(5)) Tandem Library Bks.

Greenberg, Judith E. A Girl's Guide to Growing Up: Making the Right Choices. 2001. (Single Titles Social Studies Ser.). (Illus.). 144p. (YA). (gr. 9-12). pap. 9.95 (978-0-531-16542-3(6) , Watts, Franklin) Scholastic Library Publishing.

Greive, Bradley Trevor. The Blue Day Book for Kids: A Lesson in Cheering Yourself Up. 2005. (Illus.). 48p. 9.95 (978-0-7407-5023-6(2)) Andrews McMeel Publishing.

Grippo, Daniel. Playing Fair, Having Fun: A Kid's Guide to Sports & Games. Alley, R. W., illus. 2004. 32p. (J). per. 7.95 (978-0-87029-384-9(2)) Abbey Pr.

Hale, Mable. Beautiful Girlhood. 2001. (Inspirational Library). 224p. pap. 4.99 (978-1-58660-260-4(8)) Barbour Publishing, Inc.

Haley, Dennis & Brown, Marci. We Both Read-When I Grow Up. 2005. (We Both Read Ser.). (Illus.). 44p. (J). (gr. 1 up). 7.99 (978-1-891327-57-5(7)); pap. 3.99 (978-1-891327-58-2(5)) Treasure Bay, Inc.

Halman, Jacqueline. The Karma Queen's Little Book of Big Tips on Living a Lucky Life. 2003. 144p. (YA). 10.95 (978-1-931722-27-8(7) , Sixth Avenue Bks.) Grand Central Publishing.

Halper, Sharon. To Learn Is to Do: A Tikkun Olam Road Map. Koffsky, Ann D., illus. 2004. vi, 56p. (gr. 4-6). pap. 8.95 (978-0-8074-0729-5(1) , 123935) URJ Pr.

Haltom, Cris. Stranger of the Table. 2004. (YA). per. 5.68 (978-1-56870-517-0(4)) RonJon Publishing, Inc.

Hamm, Mia. WUSA Girl's Guide to Soccer Life. 2003. (Illus.). 192p. (J). (gr. 3-11). per. 19.99 (978-1-59186-040-2(7)) Cool Springs Pr.

Handford, Elizabeth Rice. Those Kids in Proverbsville. 2000. 93p. (J). (gr. 4-7). pap. 3.95 (978-0-87398-823-0(X)) Sword of the Lord Pubs.

Harcourt School Publishers Staff. Trofeos Advanced Level: Antes y Ahora. 3rd ed. 2002. (SPA., Illus.). pap. 6.80 (978-0-15-323939-7(5)) Harcourt Schl. Pubs.

Harris-Johnson, Debrah. African-American Teenagers Guide to Personal Growth, Health, Saftey, Sex An. 2001. (gr. 7-12). lib. bdg. 30.35 (978-0-613-90283-0(1)) Tandem Library Bks.

Harvey, Roger. Caillou & the Rain. rev. ed. 2006. (Abracadabra Ser.). (Illus.). 24p. (J). pap. 4.95 (***978-2-89450-595-3(7)***) Chouette Publishing CAN. *Dist:* Independent Pubs. Group.

Hatch, Ines Arnsberger. Marsha's Song: A Celebration of Life. 2004. 300p. (YA). per. 18.00 (978-1-932496-19-2(X)) Penman Publishing, Inc.

Hauser, Jill Frankel. The Kids Guide to Becoming the Best You Can Be. 2006. 128p. (J). 16.95 (978-0-8249-6789-5(5) , Williamson Bks.) Ideals Pubns.

Hawkins, Chad S. Youth & the Temple. 2002. (Illus.). vii, 136p. (J). pap. 12.95 (978-1-57008-846-9(2)) Scribbulations LLC.

Hayhurst, Chris. Stay Cool: A Guy's Guide to Handling Conflict. 2005. (Guys' Guides Ser.). (Illus.). 48p. (YA). (gr. 5-8). lib. bdg. 23.95 (978-0-8239-3159-0(5) , GUSTCO) Rosen Publishing Group, Inc., The.

Heffernan, Eileen & Jablonski, Patricia E., eds. Jesus Is Good! Five Gospel-Based Stories for Little People. 2001. (J). pap. (978-0-8198-3973-2(6)) Daughters of St. Paul.

Hest, Amy. Tu Puedes Hacerlo, Sam. Jeram, Anita, illus. 2004. Tr. of You Can Do It, Sam. (SPA.). (J). 16.00 (978-1-930332-53-9(X)) Lectorum Pubns., Inc.

Hillery, Susie Moore. Count Your Blessings. 2003. pap. 20.00 (978-0-8059-6194-2(1)) Dorrance Publishing Co., Inc.

Hirschhorn, Vera. America's Young Heroes Journal: A Celebration. 2002. pap. 19.95 (978-0-9718197-1-9(8)) America's Young Heroes Pubns.

Hodge, Aleta S. The Value Book. 2002. 230p. 13.95 (978-0-9648316-3-6(5)) Money Counsel, Inc.

Hollis, Randy. Meet Sneazle, 1. Rahn, Jess, illus. 2004. 20p. (J). 6.95 (978-0-9758815-0-7(7)) SNZ Publishing.

Holofcener, Mark. Evan's Earthly Adventure. l.t. ed. 2003. (Illus.). 202p. (YA). mass mkt. 11.00 (978-0-9718626-1-6(3)) Holofcener, Mark.

Holyoke, Nancy. A Smart Girl's Guide to Manners: The Secrets to Grace, Confidence, & Being Your Best. Watkins, Michelle, ed. Mingus, Cathi, illus. 2005. (American Girl Library). 120p. (J). (gr. 3). pap. 9.95 (978-1-58485-983-3(0) , American Girl) American Girl Publishing, Inc.

Hong, K. L. Life Freaks Me Out: And Then I Deal with It. Gemelke, Tenessa & Griffin-Wiesner, Jennifer, eds. 2005. (Illus.). 160p. (YA). pap. 9.95 (978-1-57482-856-6(8)) Search Institute.

Hoolihan, Patricia. Teen Girls Only! Daily Thoughts for Teenage Girls. 2000. (Illus.). 388p. (gr. 7-12). pap. 12.00 (978-0-930100-31-5(X)) Holy Cow! Pr.

Hopkins, Cathy. The Mates, Dates Guide to Life, Love, & Looking Luscious. 2005. (Mates, Dates Ser.). (Illus.). 160p. (YA). pap. 6.99 (978-1-4169-0279-9(1) , Simon Pulse) Simon & Schuster Children's Publishing.

Hot Issues, 19 bks., Set. Incl. Cult Awareness. Goodnough, David. (YA). 2000. lib. bdg. 27.93 (978-0-7660-1196-0(8)); Cyberdanger & Internet Safety. Lawler, Jennifer. (YA). 2000. lib. bdg. 27.93 (978-0-7660-1368-1(5)); Date Rape. Winkler, Kathleen. (YA). 1999. lib. bdg. 27.93 (978-0-7660-1198-4(4)); Drug Abuse & Teens. Masline, Shelagh Ryan. (YA). 2000. lib. bdg. 27.93 (978-0-7660-1372-8(3)); Eating Disorders. Goodnough, David. (YA). 1999. lib. bdg. 27.93 (978-0-7660-1336-0(7)); Endangered Animals of North America. Goodnough, David. (YA). 2001. lib. bdg. 27.93 (978-0-7660-1373-5(1)); Hate & Racist Groups. Altman, Linda Jacobs. (J). 2001. lib. bdg. 27.93 (978-0-7660-1371-1(5)); Multiethnic Teens & Cultural Identity. Cruz, Barbara C. (YA). 2001. lib. bdg. 27.93 (978-0-7660-1201-1(8)); Runaway Teens. Rebman, Renee C. (YA). 2001. lib. bdg. 27.93 (978-0-7660-1640-8(4)); Sexually Transmitted Diseases. Byers, Ann. (YA). 1999. lib. bdg. 27.93 (978-0-7660-1192-2(5)); Stalking. Goodnough, David. (YA). 2000. lib. bdg. 27.93 (978-0-7660-1364-3(2)); Teen Privacy Rights. Durrett, Deanne. (YA). 2001. lib. bdg. 27.93 (978-0-7660-1374-2(X)); Teen Smoking & Tobacco Use. Moe, Barbara. (YA). 2000. lib. bdg. 27.93 (978-0-7660-1359-9(6)); Teens & Pregnancy. Byers, Ann. (YA). 2000. lib. bdg. 27.93 (978-0-7660-1365-0(0)); Teens, Depression & the Blues. Winkler, Kathleen. (YA). 2000. lib. bdg. 27.93 (978-0-7660-1369-8(3)); Vegetarianism & Teens. Winkler, Kathleen. (YA). 2001. lib. bdg. 27.93 (978-0-7660-1375-9(8)); Women's Movement & Young Women Today. Berg, Barbara J. (YA). 2000. lib. bdg. 27.93 (978-0-7660-1200-4(X)); 64p. (gr. 6-12). (Illus.). 2000. Set lib. bdg. 379.05 (978-0-7660-1403-9(7)) Enslow Pubs., Inc.

Hot Pro/Con Issues, 12 bks., Set. Incl. Abortion Conflict : A Pro/Con Issue. Durrett, Deanne. (J). 2000. lib. bdg. 27.93 (978-0-7660-1193-9(3)); Animal Experimentation & Testing : A Pro/Con Issue. Woods, Geraldine. (YA). 1999. lib. bdg. 27.93 (978-0-7660-1191-5(7)); Death Penalty for Teens : A Pro/Con Issue. Day, Nancy. (YA). 2000. lib. bdg. 27.93 (978-0-7660-1370-4(7)); Drug Legalization. Lawler, Jennifer. (YA). 1999. lib. bdg. 27.93 (978-0-7660-1197-7(6)); Drug Testing in Schools : A Pro/Con Issue. Lawler, Jennifer. (YA). 2000. lib. bdg. 27.93 (978-0-7660-1367-4(7)); Rain Forests : A Pro/Con Issue. Johnson, Linda Carlson. (YA). 1999. lib. bdg. 21.95 (978-0-7660-1202-8(6)); School Dress Codes : A Pro/Con Issue. Cruz, Barbara C. (J). 2001. lib. bdg. 27.93 (978-0-7660-1465-7(7)); Separate Sexes, Separate Schools : A Pro/Con Issue. Cruz, Barbara C. (YA). 2000. lib. bdg. 27.93 (978-0-7660-1366-7(9)); Space Exploration : A Pro/Con Issue. Flowers, Sarah. (YA). 2000. lib. bdg. 27.93 (978-0-7660-1199-1(2)); 64p. (gr. 6-12). (Illus.). 1999. Set lib. bdg. 239.40 (978-0-7660-1404-6(5)) Enslow Pubs., Inc.

Hsuan Hua. Dew Drops: Pearls of Wisdom by the Venerable Master Hua = [Zhao Lu: Xuanhuashangren Yi Li Ming Zhu]. 2003. (ENG & CHI., Illus.). 91p. (J). 5.00 (978-0-88139-862-5(4)) Buddhist Text Translation Society.

Hughes. My First..., 4 vols., Set 1. 2003. (Illus.). (J). 74.24 (978-1-4109-0642-7(6)) Raintree.

Humphrey, Sandra McLeod & Barker, Dan. More-If You Had to Choose, What Would You Do? Strassburg, Brian, illus. 2004. 110p. pap. 13.00 (978-1-59102-077-6(8) , Pyr Bks.) Prometheus Bks., Pubs.

I Am Responsible. 2003. (Illus.). 48p. per. 9.00 (978-0-9726451-1-9(X)) Sheets, Judy.

I Can Do It Club. 2003. (J). mass mkt. (978-0-9747331-9-7(9)) Illusion Factory, The.

Jaffe, Betsy. Altered Ambitions: What's Next in Your Life? 2000. (Illus.). 260p. pap. 18.95 (978-0-595-08950-5(X)) iUniverse, Inc.

Jefferson, Anita. Climb Every Obstacle: Eliminate Your Limits!. 2004. (Illus.). 216p. per. 19.95 (978-0-9743088-0-7(3)) RealWord Pubns.

John Paul II, pseud. For the Children: Words of Love & Inspiration from His Holiness Pope John Paul II. 2000. (Illus.). 32p. (J). (gr. 4-7). pap. 16.95 (978-0-439-14902-0(9) , Scholastic Reference) Scholastic, Inc.

Johnson, Kevin. Total Devotion: 365 Days to Hang Tight with Jesus. 2004. 384p. (J). reprint ed. pap. 13.99 (978-0-7642-2884-1(6)) Bethany Hse. Pubs.

Johnson, Spencer. ¿Quién Se Ha Llevado Mi Queso? Para Jovenes: ¡Una Forma Sorprendente de Cambiar y Ganar! 2004. (SPA., Illus.). 98p. 12.95 (978-84-7953-528-5(8) , UO32376) Ediciones Urano S. A. ESP. *Dist:* Bilingual Pubns. Co., The, Lectorum Pubns., Inc.

—Who Moved My Cheese? for Teens: An A-Mazing Way to Change & Win! 2002. (Illus.). 96p. (YA). (gr. 4). 19.95 (978-0-399-24007-2(1) , Putnam Juvenile) Penguin Group (USA) Inc.

Jones, Brenn. A Character Building Book: Set 4: Inspirational Role Models, 6 bks. Incl. Learning about Achievement from the Life of Maya Angelou. lib. bdg. 18.75 (978-0-8239-5780-4(2)); Learning about Equal Rights from the Life of Ruth Bader Ginsburg. lib. bdg. 18.75 (978-0-8239-5781-1(0)); Learning about Love from the Life of Mother Teresa. lib. bdg. 18.75 (978-0-8239-5777-4(2)); Learning about Public Service from the Life of John F. Kennedy, Jr. lib. bdg. 18.75 (978-0-8239-5776-7(4)); Learning about Resilience from the Life of Lance Armstrong. lib. bdg. 18.75 (978-0-8239-5779-8(9)); Learning about Teamwork from the Lives of Sir Edmund Hillary & Tenzig Norgay. lib. bdg. 18.75 (978-0-8239-5778-1(0)); 24p. (J). (gr. 3). 2002. (Illus.). Set lib. bdg. 103.50 (978-0-8239-7136-7(8) , PowerKids Pr.) Rosen Publishing Group, Inc., The.

Jones, Kirby K. & Carr, Terrance A. Soul Ties: Redeemed from Destruction. 2000. viii, 141p. (YA). (gr. 7 up). per. 10.99 (978-0-9703968-0-8(5)) Jones, Kirby K.

Jordan, Denise. You & Me ABC. 2003. (Heinemann Read & Learn Ser.). (Illus.). 24p. (J). pap. 5.25 (978-1-4034-2512-6(4)) Heinemann Library.

Joy, Donald M. Becoming a Man: A Celebration of Sexuality, Responsibility & the Christian Young Man. 2nd ed. 2001. (ENG.). 125p. pap. 12.99 (978-1-928915-18-8(3)) Evangel Publishing Hse.

Karnes, Frances A., et al. Empowered Girls: A Girl's Guide to Positive Activism, Volunteering, & Philanthropy. 2005. 192p. (J). (gr. 4-7). pap. 14.95 (978-1-59363-163-5(4)) Prufrock Pr.

Keller, Helen. To Love This Life: Quotations by Helen Keller. 2002. (Time to Love Ser.). 144p. (J). reprint ed. pap. 4.50 (978-0-439-31913-3(7)) Scholastic, Inc.

Keller, Irene. Thingamajig Book of Do's & Don'ts. Keller, Dick, illus. 2005. 30p. (J). bds. 7.95 (978-0-8249-6591-4(4)) Ideals Pubns.

Kent, Susan. Learning How to Say You Are Sorry. 2001. (Violence Prevention Library). (Illus.). 24p. (J). (gr. 3). lib. bdg. 18.75 (978-0-8239-5614-2(8) , PowerKids Pr.) Rosen Publishing Group, Inc., The.

Kerr, Harold. Pout or Purpose? A Simple Approach for Understanding Your Purpose Pie & Improving Your Life. 2005. (Illus.). 120p. 19.95 (978-0-9767078-0-6(2)) K.C. Fox Publishing.

Keuss, Jeff & Sloth, Lia. Rachel's Challenge: A Columbine Legacy. 2006. (YA). per. 10.95 (978-0-9765722-5-1(7)) Positively for Kids, Inc.

Kick, Fran. Kick It In: Developing the Self-Motivation to Take the Lead (Participant Book) 2002. 36p. 10.00 (978-1-59199-010-9(6)) Instruction & Design Concepts.

King, Bart. The Big Book of Girl Stuff. Kalis, Jennifer, illus. 2006. 320p. (J). (gr. 3-9). reprint ed. 19.95 (978-1-58685-819-3(X)) Gibbs Smith, Publisher.

Kirberger, Kimberly. Teen Love, on Relationships: A Book for Teenagers. 1999. (Teen Love Ser.). (Illus.). 300p. (YA). (gr. 8-12). pap. 14.95 (978-1-55874-734-0(6)) Health Communications, Inc.

Knight 6 Personal Growth Planbook: Extreme Quest. 2003. (Illus.). 48p. (J). pap. 4.95 (978-1-59312-047-4(8)) North American Mission Board, SBC.

Knowles, Jon. The Facts of Life: A Guide for Teens & Their Families. 2004. (YA). 2.00 (978-1-930996-72-4(1)) Planned Parenthood Federation of America, Inc.

Kristofer Says: Know Your Rules. 2006. (J). 5.95 (978-0-9777022-1-3(9)) Mother's Love Publishing, A.

Krulik, Nancy E. Don't Stress! How to Keep Life's Problems Little. 1998. (J). pap. 39.92 (978-0-439-04192-8(9)); 80p. (gr. 3-7). pap. 4.99 (978-0-590-63271-3(X)) Scholastic, Inc.

Kubiak, Shannon. God Called a Girl: How Mary Changed Her World — And You Can Too. 2005. 176p. (J). reprint ed. pap. 11.99 (978-0-7642-0029-8(1)) Bethany Hse. Pubs.

Kuchler, B. L. That's Life. 2003. (Illus.). 112p. (J). tchr. ed. 14.95 (978-1-57223-709-4(0) , 7090) Willow Creek Pr., Inc.

Kuchler, Bonnie Louise, compiled by. Just Kids: Pictures, Poems & Other Silly Animal Stuff Just for Kids! 2003. (Illus.). 32p. tchr. ed. 12.95 (978-1-57223-598-4(5) , 5985) Willow Creek Pr., Inc.

Kushner, Lawrence & Kushner, Karen. How Does God Make Things Happen? Majewski, Dawn W., illus. 2001. (Early Childhood Spirituality Ser.). 24p. (J). (ps-k). bds. 7.99 (978-1-893361-24-9(1)) SkyLight Paths Publishing.

Lad 1 Personal Growth Planbook: Clue Chasers. 2003. (Illus.). 48p. (J). pap. 4.95 (978-1-59312-042-9(7)) North American Mission Board, SBC.

Lad 2 Personal Growth Planbook: Everglade Explorers. 2003. (Illus.). 48p. (J). pap. 4.95 (978-1-59312-043-6(5)) North American Mission Board, SBC.

Lad 3 Personal Growth Planbook: Rawhide Wranglers. 2003. (Illus.). 48p. (J). pap. 4.95 (978-1-59312-044-3(3)) North American Mission Board, SBC.

Larson, Alan & Nunley, Jay. The Debate over the Nature of Reality. 1999. 56p. (YA). (gr. 12 up). pap. (978-0-89739-020-0(2)) Heron Bks.

Learner Resources: Blue Semester. 2004. (978-0-8066-4752-4(3)); (gr. 1-2). (978-0-8066-4758-6(2)); (gr. 3-4). (978-0-8066-4761-6(2)); (gr. 5-6). (978-0-8066-4765-4(5)); (gr. 7-8). (978-0-8066-4768-5(X)); (ps-k). (978-0-8066-4755-5(8)); Vol. 2. (978-0-8066-4773-9(6)); Vol. 2. (gr. 1-2). (978-0-8066-4779-1(5)); Vol. 2. (gr. 3-4). (978-0-8066-4782-1(5)); Vol. 2. (gr. 5-6). (978-0-8066-4786-9(8)); Vol. 2. (gr. 7-8). (978-0-8066-4789-0(2)); Vol. 2. (ps-k). (978-0-8066-4776-0(0)) Augsburg Fortress, Pubs.

Leigh, Susan K. God, I Need to Talk to You about Disrespect. 2005. (J). 5.99 (978-0-7586-0810-9(1)) Concordia Publishing Hse.

—God, I Need to Talk to You about Greed. Clark, Bill, illus. 2005. (ENG.). 16p. (J). pap. 0.99 (978-0-7586-0795-9(4)) Concordia Publishing Hse.

—God, I Need to Talk to You about Laziness. 2005. (J). 5.99 (978-0-7586-0812-3(8)) Concordia Publishing Hse.

—God, I Need to Talk to You about Whining. Clark, Bill, illus. 2005. pap. 5.94 (978-0-7586-0794-2(6)) Concordia Publishing Hse.

Lifeways - Group 5, 4 bks., Set. 136.86 (978-0-7614-1412-4(6) , Benchmark Bks.) Cavendish, Marshall Corp.

Lishinski, Ann King. Let Your Light Shine. Morello, Charles, ed. Lishinski, Jamie, illus. 2003. (J). pap. 9.95 (978-0-9709575-0-4(5)) Singing River Pubns.

Llewellyn, Claire. Why Should I Help? Gordon, Mike, illus. 2005. (Why Should I? Bks.). 32p. (J). pap. 5.99 (978-0-7641-3218-6(0)) Barron's Educational Series, Inc.

—Why Should I Listen? Gordon, Mike, illus. 2005. (Why Should I? Bks.). 32p. (J). pap. 6.99 (978-0-7641-3219-3(9)) Barron's Educational Series, Inc.

—Why Should I Share? Gordon, Mike, illus. 2005. (Why Should I? Bks.). 32p. (J). pap. 6.99 (978-0-7641-3220-9(2)) Barron's Educational Series, Inc.

Lookadoo, Justin & DiMarco, Hayley. The Dateable Rules: A Guide to the Sexes. 2004. (Illus.). 176p. (YA). reprint ed. pap. 11.99 (978-0-8007-5915-5(X)) Revell.

Lorig, Steffanie & Jacobs, Jeanean. Chill & Spill: A Place to Put it down & Work it Out. 2005. (Illus.). 112p. (YA). (gr. 6 up). 18.95 (978-0-9715240-4-0(1)) Art With Heart Press.

Lucado, Max. Plunge! Come Thirsty. 2004. 128p. (YA). pap., stu. ed. 7.99 (978-1-4185-0028-3(3)) Nelson, Thomas Inc.

Lundsten, Apryl. Why Me? Humiliation Hotsheet. 2001. (Teen Magazine Ser.). (Illus.). 128p. (J). (gr. 7-12). pap. 4.99 (978-0-439-11469-1(1)) Scholastic, Inc.

MacAdam, Lea. You & the Rules in Your Family. 2005. (Family Matters Ser.). (Illus.). 48p. (YA). (gr. 5-8). lib. bdg. 23.95 (978-0-8239-3350-1(4)) Rosen Publishing Group, Inc., The.

MacGregor, Cynthia. Think for Yourself: A Kid's Guide to Solving Life's Dilemmas & Other Sticky Problems. Farias, Susan Norberg, illus. 2004. 96p. (J). (gr. 4-7). pap. 7.95 (978-1-894222-73-0(3)) Lobster Pr. CAN. *Dist:* Univ. of Toronto Pr.

MacKall, Dandi Daley. Kids' Rules for Life: A Guide to Life's Journey from Those Just Starting Out. 2003. (Illus.). 176p. pap. 8.95 (978-1-57071-909-7(8)) Sourcebooks, Inc.

Marcovitz, Hal. Teens & Cheating on Tests. 2005. (Gallup Youth Survey, Major Issues & Trends Ser.). (Illus.). 112,128p. (J). (gr. 7-9). lib. bdg. 22.95 (978-1-59084-871-5(3)) Mason Crest Pubs.

Marshall, Mark. God Knows What It's Like to Be a Teenager. 2001. 308p. pap. 14.95 (978-0-9647552-5-3(4)) Westminster Literature Resources, Inc.

Marston, Ralph S., Jr. Living the Wonder of It All: Positive, Empowering Messages from the Daily Motivator. 2003. 200p. (YA). pap. 14.50 (978-0-9664634-1-5(2)) Image Express, Inc.

Martin, LaJoyce. Dear Grandma, I Like Cookies That Don't Crumble. Love, Ashton: Character Building Stories for Youth. 2000. 140p. (J). pap. (978-0-7392-0501-3(3) , PO3945) Morris Publishing.

Mastromarino, Diane. Girl's Guide to Loving Yourself: A Book about Falling in Love with the One. 2003. (gr. 7-12). lib. bdg. 17.60 (978-0-613-84748-3(2)) Tandem Library Bks.

Mastromarino, Diane, ed. For an Extra-Special Teen: Words to Help You Strive, Thrive, & Make This World Yours! (Illus.). 64p. (J). (gr. 3-6). pap. 9.95 (978-0-88396-750-8(2) , Blue Mountain Pr.) Blue Mountain Arts Inc.

Mather, Anne. Character Building Day by Day. 2006. 240p. (J). (gr. 3-6). pap. 15.95 (978-1-57542-178-0(X)) Free Spirit Productions.

Maurer, Tracy. A to Z of Ps & Qs. 2002. (A to Z Ser.). (Illus.). 48p. (gr. k-2). 20.95 (978-1-58952-062-2(9)) Rourke Publishing, LLC.

Mayer, Cassie. Being Fair. 2007. (J). (***978-1-4034-9483-2(5)***); pap. (***978-1-4034-9499-3(1)***) Heinemann Library.

McCarnes, Kayla, et al. Bully-Proofing in Early Childhood: Building a Caring Community. 2004. (Illus.). 197p. per. (978-1-59318-240-3(6)) Sopris West Educational Services.

McCormick, Kimberly A. The Way I See It: 50 Values-Oriented Monologs for Teens. 2001. 128p. pap. 14.95 (978-1-56608-072-9(X) , N-B245) Meriwether Publishing, Ltd.

McCourt, Lisa. Chicken Soup for the Soul Family Storybook Collection. 1998. (gr. k-3). lib. bdg. 22.20 (978-0-613-78768-0(4)) Tandem Library Bks.

McFarlane, Evelyn & Saywell, James. If... Questions for Teens. 2001. (Illus.). 144p. 10.95 (978-0-375-50555-3(5) , Villard Bks.) Random House Publishing Group.

McGraw, Jay. Daily Life Strategies for Teens. 2001. 408p. (YA). pap. 11.00 (978-0-7432-2471-0(X) , Fireside) Simon & Schuster.

—Daily Life Strategies for Teens. 2002. (gr. 7-12). lib. bdg. 19.95 (978-0-613-87263-8(0)) Tandem Library Bks.

—Life Strategies for Teens. 2001. (Illus.). 240p. (YA). 19.99 (978-0-7432-3288-3(7) , Fireside) Simon & Schuster.

—Life Strategies for Teens. 2000. (gr. 7-12). lib. bdg. 23.45 (978-0-613-58485-2(6)) Tandem Library Bks.

—Life Strategies for Teens: Exercises & Self-Tests to Help You Change Your Life. 2001. (Illus.). 176p. (YA). pap., wbk. ed. 15.00 (978-0-7432-2470-3(1) , Fireside) Simon & Schuster.

—Life Strategies for Teens Cards. 2002. 15.95 (978-1-4019-9999-5(9)) Hay Hse., Inc.

McIntosh, Kenneth & Livingston, Phyllis. Youth with Conduct Disorder: In Trouble with the World. 2008. (J). (***978-1-4222-0140-4(6)***) Mason Crest Pubs.

McIntyre, Thomas. The Behavior Survival Guide for Kids: How to Make Good Choices & Stay Out of Trouble. 2004. (Illus.). 176p. (YA). (gr. 4-9). pap. 14.95 (978-1-57542-132-2(1)) Free Spirit Publishing, Inc.

McKelvey, Brian. I Can Man: Characters with Concepts. 2005. (J). 14.95 (978-1-57921-791-4(5)); 7.95 (978-1-57921-785-3(0)) WinePress Publishing.

—Oath of I Can Man: Characters with Concepts. 2005. (J). 7.95 (978-1-57921-786-0(9)) WinePress Publishing.

Mead, David. Little Ben Franklin Learns a Lesson in Generosity: Generosity. Sharp, Chris, illus. 2003. (American Virtues for Kids Ser.). (J). bds. 6.95 (978-0-9746440-2-8(1)) Ideals Pubns.

Mefford, David. How to Make A Friend in Three Days or Less. 2004. (YA). (978-0-9762143-0-4(X)) Mefford, David.

Meier, Katie. A Girl's Guide to Life: The Real Dish on Growing up, Being True, & Making Your Teen Years Fabulous! 2004. (Illus.). 208p. (YA). pap. 13.99 (978-0-8499-4443-7(0)) Nelson, Thomas Inc.

Meiners, Cheri J. Know & Follow Rules. Johnson, Meredith, illus. 2005. (Learning to Get Along Ser.). 40p. (J). (ps-3). pap. 10.95 (978-1-57542-130-8(5)) Free Spirit Publishing, Inc.

—Share & Take Turns. 2004. (Learning to Get Along Ser.). (Illus.). 40p. (J). (ps-3). pap. 10.95 (978-1-57542-124-7(0) , 786) Free Spirit Publishing, Inc.

—Understand & Care. 2003. (Learning to Get Along Ser.). (Illus.). 40p. (J). (ps-3). pap. 10.95 (978-1-57542-131-5(3)) Free Spirit Publishing, Inc.

—When I Feel Afraid. 2004. (Learning to Get along Ser.). (Illus.). 40p. (J). (ps-3). pap. 10.95 (978-1-57542-138-4(0)) Free Spirit Publishing, Inc.

Mercadante, Frank. Positively Dangerous: Live Loud, Be Real, Change the World. 2003. 117p. (YA). 9.95 (978-0-88489-790-3(7)) St. Mary's Pr.

Meredith Books Staff, ed. Life Is Good. 2007. 132p. 20.00 (***978-0-696-23625-9(7)***) Meredith Bks.

Meyer, Joyce. The Advice to Teenagers Book. 2000. 160p. (J). pap. 8.99 (978-1-57794-374-7(0)) Harrison Hse., Inc.

Millennium Male: Separating the Men from the Boys. 2003. 88p. pap. 7.50 (978-0-9712585-6-3(2)) JuDe Publishing.

Mitchell, Janet Lynn. Principles to Live By. 2006. 80p. (J). per. 6.99 (978-1-59441-289-9(8) , CD-204021) Carson-Dellosa Publishing Co., Inc.

Mitchell, Jason. Class Is in Session: And So Is Life. 2001. (gr. 7-12). lib. bdg. 22.20 (978-0-613-85095-7(5)) Tandem Library Bks.

Monckeberg, Paulina. Pascoalina 2005 Portuguese. 2004. (Pascualina Family of Products Ser.). 272p. (J). spiral bd. 16.99 (978-956-8222-18-5(9)) Pascualina Producciones S.A.

Monson-Burton, Marianne. Girls Know Best Vol. 3: Your Words, Your World. 1999. (gr. 3-6). lib. bdg. 17.60 (978-0-613-33368-9(3)) Tandem Library Bks.

Monson-Burton, Marianne, compiled by. Girls Know Best Vol. 2: Tips on Life & Fun Stuff to Do. l.t. ed. 1999. (Girls Know Best Ser.). (Illus.). (J). (gr. 3 up). lib. bdg. 23.33 (978-0-8368-2453-7(9)) Stevens, Gareth Inc.

—Girls Know Best Vol. 3: Your Words, Your World. l.t. ed. 2000. (Girls Know Best Ser.). (Illus.). 153p. (J). (gr. 3 up). lib. bdg. 23.33 (978-0-8368-2672-2(8)) Stevens, Gareth Inc.

Moore-Mallinos, Jennifer. Los Colores del Arco Iris: The Colors of the Rainbow (Spanish Edition) Fabrega, Marta, illus. 2005. (Let's Talk about It! Bks.). (SPA.). 32p. (J). (ps-2). pap. 6.99 (978-0-7641-3278-0(4)) Barron's Educational Series, Inc.

—I Remember. Fabrega, Marta, illus. 2005. (Let's Talk about It! Bks.). 32p. (J). (ps-2). pap. 6.99 (978-0-7641-3274-2(1)) Barron's Educational Series, Inc.

Morgenstern, Mindy. Real Rules for Real Girls. 2002. (gr. 3-6). lib. bdg. 24.60 (978-0-613-62540-1(4)) Tandem Library Bks.

Morgenstern, Susie. A Book of Coupons. 2003. (gr. 3-6). lib. bdg. 14.15 (978-0-613-67446-1(4)) Tandem Library Bks.

Morrill, Del Hunter. Great Escapes Vol. IV: Additional Scripts for Children & Pre-Teens, 1 of a series of 4. 2002. 95p. ring bd. (978-0-9705862-7-8(2) , Transitions, Inc.) New Beginnings Publishing.

—Great Escapes, Volume I: Transforming Children's Lives Through the Means of Visualization, Hypnosis, & Other Imaginative Methods, 4 vols., Vol. 1. 2000. 86p. ring bd. 29.95 (978-0-9705862-2-3(1) , Transitions, Inc.) New Beginnings Publishing.

Moses, Brian. Excuse Me. 2000. (gr. k-3). lib. bdg. 14.45 (978-0-613-30388-0(1)) Tandem Library Bks.

—I Don't Care. 2000. (gr. k-3). lib. bdg. 14.45 (978-0-613-30488-7(8)) Tandem Library Bks.

—It Wasn't Me. 2000. (gr. k-3). lib. bdg. 14.45 (978-0-613-30524-2(8)) Tandem Library Bks.

—Perdon: Aprender a Ser Amable. Gordon, Mike, illus. 2000. (SPA.). 32p. (J). (ps-k). 7.95 (978-950-24-0806-4(3)) Lectorum Pubns., Inc.

Moss, Samantha. Where's My Stuff? The Ultimate Teen Organizing Guide. Wertz, Michael, illus. 2007. 96p. (J). spiral bd. 16.95 (***978-0-9772660-5-0(2)** , Zest Bks.) Orange Avenue Publishing.

Muhaiyaddeen, M. R. Bawa. Why Can't I See the Angels? Children's Questions to a Sufi Saint. 2002. (Illus.). 220p. (J). 27.00 (978-0-914390-62-6(7)); pap. 22.00 (978-0-914390-63-3(5)) Fellowship Pr.

Muharrar, Aisha. More Than a Label: Why What You Wear & Who You're with Doesn't Define Who You Are. 2004. (Illus.). 152p. (YA). (gr. 8 up). pap. 13.95 (978-1-57542-110-0(0)) Free Spirit Publishing, Inc.

My Journey. 2005. (YA). spiral bd. 12.95 (978-0-9747181-1-8(4)) Jodan Collections.

Navarra, Tova. The Kids' Guidebook: Great Advice to Help Kids Cope. Kerr, Tom, illus. 2nd ed. 2002. 128p. (J). (gr. 2-7). pap. 10.95 (978-0-7641-2066-4(2)) Barron's Educational Series, Inc.

—Young People. 2002. Tr. of Tough Problems. (gr. 5-8). lib. bdg. 15.25 (978-0-613-83481-0(X)) Tandem Library Bks.

Naybor, Deborah. Making a Difference: 182 1/2 Ways to Change the World. 2002. 54p. per. 10.00 (978-0-9744540-0-9(1) , 061857) Dragonladies, Ltd.

The Need to Know Library: Creative Solutions to Everyday Problems, 8 bks. Incl. Everything You Need to Know about Chicken Pox & Shingles. Plumb, Jennifer. lib. bdg. 25.25 (978-0-8239-3323-5(7)); Everything You Need to Know about Compulsive Sexual Behavior. Gilbert, Laura. lib. bdg. 25.25 (978-0-8239-3290-0(7)); Everything You Need to Know about Credit Cards & Fiscal Responsibilty. Green, Meg. lib. bdg. 25.25 (978-0-8239-3327-3(X)); Everything You Need to Know about Cystic Fibrosis. Lee, Justin. lib. bdg. 25.25 (978-0-8239-3321-1(0)); Everything You Need to Know about the Dangers of Binge Drinking. Ruiz, Ruth Anne. lib. bdg. 25.25 (978-0-8239-3289-4(3) , NTBIDR); Everything You Need to Know about the Dangers of Tattooing & Body Piercing. Reybold, Laura. lib. bdg. 25.25 (978-0-8239-3469-0(1)); Everything You Need to Know about the Riot Grrrl Movement : The Feminism of a New Generation. Turner, Cherie. lib. bdg. 25.25 (978-0-8239-3400-3(4)); Everything You Need to Know about Wicca : Ancient Beliefs for a Modern World. Giordano, Geraldine. lib. bdg. 25.25 (978-0-8239-3401-0(2)); 64p. (YA). (gr. 4-6). 2001. (Illus.). Set lib. bdg. 202.00 (978-0-8239-9434-2(1)) Rosen Publishing Group, Inc., The.

The Need to Know Library: Important Information for Teens, 9 bks. Incl. Everything You Need to Know about Anemia. Ross, Allison J. (YA). 25.25 (978-0-8239-3218-4(4) , NTANEM); Everything You Need to Know about Cliques. Moehn, Heather. (J). 25.25 (978-0-8239-3326-6(1)); Everything You Need to Know about Custody. Manley, Claudia B. (YA). 25.25 (978-0-8239-3328-0(8)); Everything You Need to Know about Measles & Rubella. Hawkins, Trisha. (YA). 25.25 (978-0-8239-3322-8(9)); Everything You Need to Know about Multiple Sclerosis. Goldstein, Margaret J. (YA). 25.25 (978-0-8239-3292-4(3) , NTMUSC); Everything You Need to Know about Social Anxiety. Ross, Allison J. (YA). 25.25 (978-0-8239-3324-2(5)); Everything You Need to Know about Staying in the Hospital. Murphy, Patricia. (YA). 25.25 (978-0-8239-3325-9(3)); Everything You Need to Know about Vision Disorders. Stanley, Debbie. (YA). 25.25 (978-0-8239-3225-2(7)); Everything You Need to Know about Volunteering. Weeldreyer, Laura. (J). 25.25 (978-0-8239-3220-7(6) , NTVOLU); 64p. (gr. 7-12). (Illus.). 2005. 227.25 (978-0-8239-9435-9(X)) Rosen Publishing Group, Inc., The.

The Need to Know Library: Important Issues Affecting Every Teen, 8 bks. Incl. Everything You Need to Know about Peer Mediation. Rue, Nancy N. (gr. 4-6). lib. bdg. 25.25 (978-0-8239-3464-5(0)); Everything You Need to Know about Peer Pressure. Feller, Robyn M. (gr. 4-6). lib. bdg. 25.25 (978-0-8239-3440-9(3)); Everything You Need to Know about Placing Your Baby for Adoption. Sherman, Aliza. (gr. 9 up). lib. bdg. 25.25 (978-0-8239-3465-2(9)); Everything You Need to Know about Relationship Violence. White, Katherine. (gr. 4-6). lib. bdg. 25.25 (978-0-8239-3398-3(9)); Everything You Need to Know about Romance & the Internet : How to Stay Safe. Brooks, Sheldon. (gr. 4-6). lib. bdg. 25.25 (978-0-8239-3399-0(7)); Everything You Need to Know about Sexual Harassment. Bouchard, Elizabeth. (gr. 4-6). lib. bdg. 25.25 (978-0-8239-3466-9(7)); Everything You Need to Know about Stress. Ayer, Eleanor H. (gr. 4-6). lib. bdg. 25.25 (978-0-8239-3467-6(5)); Everything You Need to Know about Teen Motherhood. Hammerslough, Jane. (gr. 4-6). lib. bdg. 25.25 (978-0-8239-3441-6(1)); 64p. (YA). 2001. (Illus.). Set lib. bdg. 202.00 (978-0-8239-9433-5(3)) Rosen Publishing Group, Inc., The.

The Need to Know Library: Important Resources for Today's Teens at Risk, 7 bks. Incl. Everything You Need to Know about Food Additives. Hayhurst, Chris. lib. bdg. 25.25 (978-0-8239-3548-2(5)); Everything You Need to Know about Growth Spurts & Delayed Growth. Favor, Lesli J. lib. bdg. 25.25 (978-0-8239-3549-9(3)); Everything You Need to Know about Meditation. Croix, Judith Sainte. lib. bdg. 25.25 (978-0-8239-3550-5(7)); Everything You Need to Know about Misinformation on the Internet. Goranson, Christopher D. lib. bdg. 25.25 (978-0-8239-3521-5(3)); Everything You Need to Know about Organic Foods. Dunn-Georgiou, Elisha. lib. bdg. 25.25 (978-0-8239-3551-2(5)); Everything You Need to Know about the Dangers of Cosmetic Surgery. Alagna, Magdalena. lib. bdg. 25.25 (978-0-8239-3552-9(3)); Everything You Need to Know If You & Your Parents Are New Americans. Santos, Edward J. lib. bdg. 25.25 (978-0-8239-3547-5(7)); 64p. (YA). (gr. 4-6). (Illus.). 2005. Set lib. bdg. 176.75 (978-0-8239-9715-2(4)) Rosen Publishing Group, Inc., The.

The Need to Know Library: Making All the Right Choices, 9 bks. Incl. Everything You Need to Know about Being a Teen Driver. Winters, Adam. (gr. 7-12). 2005. 25.25 (978-0-8239-3287-0(7) , NTTEDR); Everything You Need to Know about Birth Order. Krohn, Katherine E. (gr. 7-12). 2005. 25.25 (978-0-8239-3228-3(1) , NTBIOR); Everything You Need to Know about Cults. Dolan, Sean. (gr. 7-12). 2005. 25.25 (978-0-8239-3230-6(3) , NTCLT); Everything You Need to Know about Epilepsy. Emanuele, Patricia. (gr. 7-12). 2005. 25.25 (978-0-8239-3161-3(7) , NTEPIL); Everything You Need to Know about Family Violence. Stark, Evan. (gr. 7-12). 2005. 25.25 (978-0-8239-3278-8(8) , NTFAVI); Everything You Need to Know about Healing from Rape Trauma. Coppin, Cheryl Branch. (gr. 7-12). 2005. 25.25 (978-0-8239-3122-4(6) , NTHERT); Everything You Need to Know about Lyme Disease. Donnelly, Karen J. (gr. 7-12). 2005. 25.25 (978-0-8239-3216-0(8) , NTLYDI); Everything You Need to Know about School Violence. Kreiner, Anna. (gr. 4-6). 2000. lib. bdg. 25.25 (978-0-8239-3304-4(0) , NTSCVI); Everything You Need to Know about Street Gangs. Stark, Evan. (gr. 4-6). 2000. lib. bdg. 25.25 (978-0-8239-3305-1(9) , NTSTGA); 64p. (YA). (Illus.). 2005. 252.50 (978-0-8239-9436-6(8)) Rosen Publishing Group, Inc., The.

The Need to Know Library: Straight Talk for Reluctant Readers, 8 bks. Incl. Everything You Need to Know about Being HIV-Positive. Shire, Amy. (YA). (gr. 7-12). 1999. lib. bdg. 25.25 (978-0-8239-3077-7(7) , NTHIPO); Everything You Need to Know about Dating & Relationships. Hovanec, Erin M. (YA). (gr. 7-12). 2005. lib. bdg. 25.25 (978-0-8239-3081-4(5) , NTDARE); Everything You Need to Know about Dealing with Sexual Assault. Kaminker, Laura. (YA). (gr. 7-12). 2005. lib. bdg. 25.25 (978-0-8239-3303-7(2)); Everything You Need to Know about Eating Disorders. Kubersky, Rachel. (YA). (gr. 7-12). 1999. lib. bdg. 25.25 (978-0-8239-3078-4(5) , NTEADI); Everything You Need to Know about Self-Confidence. Ignoffo, Matthew. (YA). (gr. 7-12). 1999. lib. bdg. 25.25 (978-0-8239-3037-1(8) , NTSECO); Everything You Need to Know about Smoking. Keyishan, Elizabeth. (J). (gr. 4-6). 2000. lib. bdg. 25.25 (978-0-8239-3221-4(4) , NTSMOK); Everything You Need to Know about Yoga : An Introduction for Teens. Weiss, Stefanie Iris. (YA). (gr. 7-12). 1999. lib. bdg. 25.25 (978-0-8239-2959-7(0) , NTYOGA); 64p. (Illus.). Set lib. bdg. 202.00 (978-0-8239-9284-3(5)) Rosen Publishing Group, Inc., The.

The Need to Know Library: The Importance of Responsibility, 8 bks. Incl. Everything You Need to Know about Alcohol. Taylor, Barbara. (YA). lib. bdg. 25.25 (978-0-8239-2952-8(3) , NTALCO); Everything You Need to Know about Being a Vegan. Weiss, Stefanie Iris. (J). lib. bdg. 25.25 (978-0-8239-2958-0(2) , NTVEGA); Everything You Need to Know about Being Adopted. Kaminker, Laura. (YA). lib. bdg. 25.25 (978-0-8239-2834-7(9) , NTADOP); Everything You Need to Know about Conflict Resolution. Nathan, Amy. (YA). lib. bdg. 25.25 (978-0-8239-2955-9(8) , NTCORE); Everything You Need to Know about Learning Disabilities. Bowman-Kruhm, Mary & Wirths, Claudine G. (YA). lib. bdg. 25.25 (978-0-8239-2956-6(6) , NTLEDI); Everything You Need to Know about Living with a Single Parent. Mancini, Richard E. (YA). lib. bdg. 25.25 (978-0-8239-3039-5(4) , NTSIPA); Everything You Need to Know about Teen Pregnancy. Hughes, Tracy. (YA). lib. bdg. 25.25 (978-0-8239-3041-8(6) , NTTEPR); Everything You Need to Know about Teens Who Kill. Margolis, Jeffrey A. (YA). lib. bdg. 25.25 (978-0-8239-2883-5(7) , NTTEKI); 64p. (gr. 7-12). 1999. (Illus.). 2005. Set lib. bdg. 202.00 (978-0-8239-9285-0(3)) Rosen Publishing Group, Inc., The.

The Need to Know Library: Unique Topics Covering Unique Issues, 8 bks. Incl. Everything You Need to Know about Down Syndrome. Bowman-Kruhm, Mary, ed. (gr. 4-6). 1999. lib. bdg. 25.25 (978-0-8239-2949-8(3) , NTDOSY); Everything You Need to Know about Guns in Your Home. Croft, Jennifer. (gr. 7-12). 2005. lib. bdg. 25.25 (978-0-8239-3162-0(5) , NTGUHO); Everything You Need to Know about Migraines & Other Headaches. Moe, Barbara. (gr. 7-12). 2005. lib. bdg. 25.25 (978-0-8239-3291-7(5) , NTMIHE); Everything You Need to Know about Sexual Identity. Forbes, Jeff Donaldson. (gr. 7-12). 2005. lib. bdg. 25.25 (978-0-8239-3089-0(0) , NTSEID); Everything You Need to Know about Sports Gambling. Willker, Joshua D. G. (gr. 7-12). 2005. lib. bdg. 25.25 (978-0-8239-3229-0(X) , NTSPGA); Everything You Need to Know about Student-on-Student Sexual Harassment. Stanley, Debbie. (gr. 7-12). 2005. lib. bdg. 25.25 (978-0-8239-3281-8(8) , NTSTHA); Everything You Need to Know about the Dangers of Computer Hacking. Knittel, John & Soto, Michael. (gr. 4-6). 2000. lib. bdg. 25.25 (978-0-8239-3034-0(3) , NTHACK); Everything You Need to Know about the Goth Scene. Acker, Kerry. (gr. 7-12). 2005. lib. bdg. 25.25 (978-0-8239-3223-8(0) , NTGOSC); 64p. (YA). (Illus.). Set lib. bdg. 202.00 (978-0-8239-9280-5(2)) Rosen Publishing Group, Inc., The.

Nelson, Robin. Being Fair. 2003. (First Step Nonfiction Ser.). (Illus.). (J). 23p. pap. 5.95 (978-0-8225-1322-3(6)); 24p. lib. bdg. 18.60 (978-0-8225-1285-1(8)) Lerner Publishing Group.

—Being Responsible. (First Step Nonfiction Ser.). (Illus.). (J). (gr. k-2). 2003. 24p. lib. bdg. 18.60 (978-0-8225-1288-2(2)); 2002. 23p. pap. 3.95 (978-0-8225-1343-8(9) , Lerner Pubns.) Lerner Publishing Group.

—Following Rules. 2003. (First Step Nonfiction Ser.). (Illus.). (J). 23p. pap. 5.95 (978-0-8225-1321-6(8)); 24p. lib. bdg. 18.60 (978-0-8225-1284-4(X)) Lerner Publishing Group.

—Respecting Others. 2003. (First Step Nonfiction Ser.). (Illus.). (J). 23p. pap. 5.95 (978-0-8225-1323-0(4)); 24p. lib. bdg. 18.60 (978-0-8225-1286-8(6)) Lerner Publishing Group.

Norris, Teresa Rae. Beauty, Brains & Talent: A Workbook for Girls on Self Esteem, Well Being & Safety. Norris, Tresseca M., photos by. 2001. (Illus.). 160p. pap. 24.95 (978-0-9713685-0-7(3)) Morning Star.

Olien, Rebecca. Peacefulness. 2005. (First Facts Ser.). (Illus.). 24p. (J). (ps-7). lib. bdg. 21.26 (978-0-7368-4280-8(2)) Capstone Pr., Inc.

Orero, Maria Jesus. Nico y Sus Cosas. 2005. (SPA & ESP., Illus.). 12p. (ps-ps). per. 6.99 (978-84-272-6151-8(9)) Molino, Editorial ESP. *Dist:* Santillana USA Publishing Co., Inc.

Osborne, Rick, et al. Creepy Creatures & Bizarre Beasts from the Bible. Carpenter, Anthony, illus. 2004. (2:52 Ser.). 128p. (J). pap. 7.99 (978-0-310-70654-0(8)) Zonderkidz.

Paarmann, Al. Please Let Me Help: I Need Validation. Paarmann, Lesley, photos by. unabr. ed. 2003. 150p. (YA). pap. 12.95 (978-0-9715963-1-3(X)) Paarmann, Al International.

Page, Brenda. In the Hands of the Potter: Shaped for Purpose. Elum, Deborah, ed. 2004. (YA). per. 9.98 net. (978-0-9679441-6-6(3)) All That Productions, Inc.

Pagratis, Maggie & Pagratis, Illustrator Liliane, MaggieGrenier. With Their Tiny Hands. 2005. 19p. (J). 9.87 (978-1-4116-3763-4(1)) Lulu.com.

Parkman, Tina. Show Me Some Love: Recipes of Survival for at Risk Teens & Young Adults. 2003. 96p. (YA). pap. 9.99 (978-1-56229-009-2(6) , Christian Living Bks.) Pneuma Life Publishing, Inc.

Patnaik, Gayatri. Secret Life of Teens: Young People Speak Out about Their Lives. 2000. (gr. 7-12). lib. bdg. 22.20 (978-0-613-33961-2(4)) Tandem Library Bks.

Pendharkar, Sumant S. Raising Yourself: Making the Right Choices. 2001. (Illus.). 112p. (YA). (gr. 5-12). pap. 11.95 (978-0-9708131-3-8(9)) Hillview Bks.

Perfection Learning Staff, contrib. by. And Justice for All. 2000. (Literature & Thought Ser.). (Illus.). 144p. (J). (978-0-7807-9665-2(9)); pap. (978-0-7891-5228-2(2)) Perfection Learning Corp.

Perry, Janice Kapp. I'm Trying to Be Like Jesus. Abts, Stacey, illus. 2003. (J). (978-1-57008-843-8(8)) Scribbulations LLC.

Perry, Jason & Keels, Steve. You Are Not Your Own: Living Loud for God. 2004. (TruthQuest Ser.). 144p. (gr. 7 up). pap. 12.99 (978-0-8054-2591-8(8)) B&H Publishing Grp.

Perry, M. Daily Pages to Create the Life You Want: A Companion Workbook to Pictures of My Days. 2005. pap. 13.00 (978-0-9759251-4-0(8) , PlayGround) Forest Hill Publishing, LLC.

—Pictures of My Days: An Art & Writing Workbook for Creating the Life You Want. 2005. pap. 13.00 (978-0-9759251-3-3(X) , PlayGround) Forest Hill Publishing, LLC.

Perspectives on Mental Health, 10 bks. Incl. ADD & ADHD. Peacock, Judith. lib. bdg. 23.93 (978-0-7368-1029-6(3)); Anger Management. Peacock, Judith & Stutman, Suzanne. lib. bdg. 23.93 (978-0-7368-0433-2(1)); Anorexia. Graves, Bonnie. lib. bdg. 23.93 (978-0-7368-0431-8(5)); Bipolar Disorder. Peacock, Judith. lib. bdg. 23.93 (978-0-7368-0434-9(X)); Bulimia. Graves, Bonnie. lib. bdg. 23.93 (978-0-7368-0430-1(7)); Compulsive Overeating. Peacock, Judith. lib. bdg. 23.93 (978-0-7368-0437-0(4)); Depression. Peacock, Judith & Casey, Jackie. lib. bdg. 23.93 (978-0-7368-0435-6(8)); Panic Disorder. Campbell, Nancy M. lib. bdg. 23.93 (978-0-7368-1030-2(7)); Stress Management. Gregson, Susan R. lib. bdg. 23.93 (978-0-7368-0432-5(3)); Teen Suicide. Peacock, Judith. lib. bdg. 23.93 (978-0-7368-0436-3(6)); 64p. (J). (gr. 4-6). 2000. (Illus.). 1999. Set lib. bdg. 239.90 (978-0-7368-1039-5(0) , LifeMatters Bks.) Capstone Pr., Inc.

Pitts, Lee. These Things I Wish. 2006. 64p. 14.95 (978-0-06-089018-6(5) , ReganBooks) HarperCollins Pubs.

Porter, Daniel. Taming Monster Moments: Turning on Soul Lights to Help Children Handle Fear Anda. 1999. (ps-2). lib. bdg. 14.10 (978-0-613-75754-6(8)) Tandem Library Bks.

PowerXpress Living God's Word Forgiveness. 2005. 115.00 (978-0-687-06281-2(0)) Abingdon Pr.

PowerXpress Living God's Word Respect. 2005. 115.00 (978-0-687-06351-2(5)) Abingdon Pr.

PowerXpress LIving God's Word Sharing & Kindness. 2005. 115.00 (978-0-687-06321-5(3)) Abingdon Pr.

PowerXpress Living God's Word Time & Money. 2005. 115.00 (978-0-687-00730-1(5)) Abingdon Pr.

Puerto, Carlos. La Mirada. 3rd ed. (Punto de Encuentro Ser.).Tr. of Glance. (SPA., Illus.). 144p. (YA). (gr. 5 up). 9.95 (978-84-241-5962-7(4)) Everest de Ediciones y Distribucion, S.L. ESP. *Dist:* Lectorum Pubns., Inc.

Quaglia, Russell & Fox, Kristine M. Raising Student Aspirations Grades K-5: Classroom Activities. 2004. 122p. (gr. k-5). pap. 25.95 (978-0-87822-480-7(7) , 5197) Research Pr.

Raatma, Lucia. Character Education, 18 bks. Incl. Caring. 2000. lib. bdg. 18.60 (978-0-7368-0366-3(1)); Consideration. 2000. lib. bdg. 18.60 (978-0-7368-0367-0(X)); Cooperation. 2000. lib. bdg. 18.60 (978-0-7368-0506-3(0)); Courage. 2000. lib. bdg. 18.60 (978-0-7368-0507-0(9)); Determination. 2002. lib. bdg. 18.60 (978-0-7368-1387-7(X)); Forgiveness. 2002. lib. bdg. 18.60 (978-0-7368-1132-3(X)); Friendliness. 2000. lib. bdg. 18.60 (978-0-7368-0368-7(8)); Generosity. 2002. lib. bdg. 18.60 (978-0-7368-1388-4(8)); Honesty. 2000. lib. bdg. 18.60 (978-0-7368-0369-4(6)); Leadership. 2002. lib. bdg. 18.60 (978-0-7368-1389-1(6)); Loyalty. 2002. lib. bdg. 18.60 (978-0-7368-1390-7(X)); Patience. 2000. lib. bdg. 18.60 (978-0-7368-0508-7(7)); Patriotism. 2000. lib. bdg. 18.60 (978-0-7368-0509-4(5)); Peacefulness. 1999. lib. bdg. 18.60 (978-0-7368-0370-0(X)); Politeness. 2002. lib. bdg. 18.60 (978-0-7368-1134-7(6)); Prudence. 2000. lib. bdg. 18.60 (978-0-7368-0510-0(9)); Respect. 2000. lib. bdg. 18.60 (978-0-7368-0371-7(8)); Responsibility. 2000. lib. bdg. 18.60 (978-0-7368-0372-4(6)); Self-Discipline. 2000. lib. bdg. 18.60 (978-0-7368-0511-7(7)); Self-Respect. 2002. lib. bdg. 18.60 (978-0-7368-1133-0(8)); Sportsmanship. 2002. lib. bdg. 18.60 (978-0-7368-1135-4(4)); Tolerance. 2000. lib. bdg. 18.60 (978-0-7368-0373-1(4)); 24p. (J). (gr. 1-2). (Illus.). Set lib. bdg. 409.20 (978-0-7368-1391-4(8) , Bridgestone Bks.) Capstone Pr., Inc.

Rainey, Dennis, et al. So You're about to Be a Teenager: Godly Advice for Preteens on Friends, Love, Sex, Faith, & Other Life Issues. 2003. (Illus.). 176p. pap. 13.99 (978-0-7852-6279-4(2)) Nelson, Thomas Inc.

Raintree Steck-Vaughn Staff. Real World Situations. 1999. (J). (gr. 1). pap. (978-0-8172-5188-8(X)) Steck-Vaughn.

Ratoff, Michael, comment. Of Dreams, Life, & Stories, Vol. 3. gif. ed. 2001. (YA). per. 15.00 (978-0-9627986-8-9(1)) Rebel Butterfly Pr.

Ratto, Linda Lee & Copes, Arthur. COPES-ing with Change. 2005. (J). (978-0-9748508-6-3(1)) Power Pr.

Rice, Ashley. Girls Rule: A Very Special Book Created Especially for Girls. Rice, Ashley, illus. (Illus.). 64p. (J). pap. 9.95 (978-0-88396-627-3(1) , Blue Mountain Pr.) Blue Mountain Arts Inc.

Rice, Wayne & Zondervan. Read This Book or You're Grounded! A Secret Guide to Surviving Home. 2003. (Studentware Ser.). (Illus.). 160p. (J). pap. 9.99 (978-0-310-25049-4(8)) Zondervan.

Richmond, Marianne. Hooray for You! A Celebration of You-ness. Richmond, Marianne, illus. 2001. (Illus.). 40p. (J). (gr. 3 up). per. 15.95 (978-0-931674-44-0(1)) Marianne Richmond Studios, Inc.

Rickard, Cathy. That's Mine! A Lesson in Sharing. 2004. (Illus.). 16p. (YA). 16.95 (978-1-932373-55-4(1) , Cedar Hill Pr.) Cedar Hill Publishing.

Riehecky, Janet. Cooperation. 2005. (Illus.). 24p. (J). 21.26 (978-0-7368-3678-4(0)) Capstone Pr., Inc.

Riley, Jim. Spiritual Grit: Pass It on to Kids, 2004. (Illus.). 125p. per. 8.95 (978-1-57166-315-3(0)) Quixote Pr.

Roberts, Anita. Safe Teen: Powerful Alternatives to Violence. 2002. (Illus.). 312p. (gr. 10 up). pap. 14.95 (978-1-896095-99-8(2)) Raincoast Bk. Distribution CAN. *Dist:* Perseus Distribution.

Robinson, Sharon. Jackie Robinson's Values to Live By: Becoming Your Best Self. 2002. (Jackie's 9 Ser.). 192p. (J). (gr. 4-9). pap. 4.99 (978-0-439-38550-3(4)) Scholastic, Inc.

—Jackie's Nine: Jackie Robinson's Values to Live By. 2002. (gr. 5-8). lib. bdg. 13.00 (978-0-613-50333-4(3)) Tandem Library Bks.

—Promises to Keep: How Jackie Robinson Changed America. 2004. (Illus.). 64p. (YA). pap. 16.95 (978-0-439-42592-6(1)) Scholastic, Inc.

Robus, Debbie. What to Say & Do... When You Don't Know What to Say & Do. 2004. 7.95 (978-0-9762034-0-7(5)) Robus, Debbie.

Roehm, Michelle, compiled by. Girls Knows Best: Advice for Girls from Girls on Just about Everything. 1999. (Girls Know Best Ser.). (Illus.). 160p. (J). (gr. 3 up). lib. bdg. 23.33 (978-0-8368-2452-0(0)) Stevens, Gareth Inc.

—Girls Who Rocked the World Vol. 2: Heroines from Harriet Tubman to Mia Hamm. 2000. (Girls Know Best Ser.). (Illus.). 152p. (J). (gr. 3 up). lib. bdg. 23.33 (978-0-8368-2673-9(6)) Stevens, Gareth Inc.

Roehm, Michelle, ed. Girls Know Best: Advice for Girls on Just about Everything. Roth, Marci Doane, illus. 1999. 160p. (J). (gr. 4-7). 6.98 (978-1-56731-313-0(2) , MJF Bks.) Fine Communications.

Roets, Lois F. Understanding Success & Failure: Life's Two Biggest Challenges. 3rd rev. ed. 2001. 36p. (J). (gr. k-12). pap. 10.00 (978-0-911943-81-8(1)) Leadership Pub., Inc.

Rondina, Catherine. Rudeness: If You Please. Workman, Dan, illus. 2005. (Deal with It Ser.). 32p. (J). (gr. 4-8). 12.95 (978-1-55028-870-4(9)) Lorimer, James & Co., Ltd., Pubs. CAN. *Dist:* Casemate Pubs. & Bk. Distributors, LLC.

Roots, Robert. Prepare for the Wolf: Success Secrets from the Three Little Pigs. 2002. 96p. (YA). pap. 12.95 (978-0-9715336-0-8(1)) Roots, Robert.

Rosen Publishing Group Staff. FAQ: Teen Life, 6 bks., Set 1. 2007. (YA). lib. bdg. 167.70 ***(978-1-4042-1050-9(4))*** Rosen Publishing Group, Inc., The.

Rosenberg, Ellen. Growing up Feeling Good: A Growing up Handbook Especially for Kids. 3rd ed. 2002. (Illus.). 544p. (J). pap. 18.00 (978-0-9711349-0-4(1)) Lima Bean Pr., Inc.

Ross, Margaret. Casey & the Amazing Good Finder: Teaching Adults & Children How to Succeed in School, Work, Life & Relationships. l.t. ed. 2005. (Illus.). 32p. (J). 9.99 (978-0-9715713-5-8(X)) Kamaron Institute Pr.

Ross, Michael. Bloom: A Girl's Guide to Growing Up. 2003. (gr. 7-12). lib. bdg. 28.05 (978-0-613-79771-9(X)) Tandem Library Bks.

Rue, Nancy N. The Values & Virtues Book: It's a God Thing! 2002. (Ywof Library). (Illus.). 112p. (J). pap. 7.99 (978-0-310-70257-3(7)) Zondervan.

Running Press Staff & Ruditis, Paul. The Hardy Boys Guide to Life. 2007. (Illus.). 128p. 4.95 (978-0-7624-2987-5(9) , Running Pr. Minature Editions) Running Pr. Bk. Pubs.

Sabin, Ellen. The Hero Book: Learning Lessons from the People You Admire. Barbas, Keren, illus. 2005. 64p. bds. 19.95 (978-0-9759868-1-3(3)) Watering Can.

Salas, Laura Purdie. Taking the Plunge. 2004. (Illus.). 250p. (J). pap. 12.95 (978-1-58760-012-8(9) , 10129, Child & Family Pr.) Child Welfare League of America, Inc.

Salzmann, Mary Elizabeth. I Am a Good Citizen. 2003. (Building Character Ser.). (Illus.). 24p. (J). (ps-3). lib. bdg. 19.93 (978-1-57765-825-2(6)) ABDO Publishing Co.

—I Am Responsible. 2003. (Building Character Ser.). (Illus.). 24p. (J). (ps-3). lib. bdg. 19.93 (978-1-57765-830-6(2)) ABDO Publishing Co.

—Responsibility Counts. 2003. (Character Counts Ser.). 32p. (J). (gr. k-6). lib. bdg. 22.78 (978-1-57765-874-0(4)) ABDO Publishing Co.

Santorum, Karen. Everyday Graces: A Child's Book of Good Manners. Torode, Sam, illus. 2003. (Foundations Ser.). 407p. (J). 25.00 (978-1-932236-09-5(0)) ISI Bks.

Schab, Lisa M. The Stop, Relax & Think Workbook. 2002. (J). (gr. 1-6). per. 17.95 (978-1-58815-053-0(4) , 61503) Childswork/Childsplay.

Scheunemann, Pam. Acting with Kindness. 2004. (Keeping the Peace Ser.). (Illus.). 23p. (J). (ps-3). lib. bdg. 19.93 (978-1-59197-557-1(3)) ABDO Publishing Co.

—Being a Peacekeeper. 2004. (Keeping the Peace Ser.). (Illus.). 23p. (J). (ps-3). lib. bdg. 19.93 (978-1-59197-558-8(1)) ABDO Publishing Co.

—Coping with Anger. 2004. (Keeping the Peace Ser.). (Illus.). 23p. (J). (ps-3). lib. bdg. 19.93 (978-1-59197-559-5(X)) ABDO Publishing Co.

—Dealing with Bullies. 2004. (Keeping the Peace Ser.). (Illus.). 23p. (J). (ps-3). lib. bdg. 19.93 (978-1-59197-560-1(3)) ABDO Publishing Co.

—Keeping the Peace. 2004. (Illus.). (J). (ps-3). lib. bdg. 119.58 (978-1-59197-556-4(5) , SandCastle) ABDO Publishing Co.

—Learning about Differences. 2004. (Keeping the Peace Ser.). (Illus.). 23p. (J). (ps-3). lib. bdg. 19.93 (978-1-59197-561-8(1)) ABDO Publishing Co.

School Specialty Publishing. Cooperation. 2003. (Character Education Classroom Helpers Ser.). 24p. (J). (gr. 1 up). pap. 3.99 (978-0-7682-2621-8(X) , FS99061); (gr. 3 up). pap. 3.99 (978-0-7682-2623-2(6) , FS99063) Schaffer, Frank Pubns.

Schuette, Sarah L. I Am Responsible. Saunders-Smith, Gail, ed. 2002. (Character Values Ser.). (Illus.). 24p. (J). (gr. k-1). lib. bdg. 15.95 (978-0-7368-1443-0(4) , Pebble Bks.) Capstone Pr., Inc.

—I Am Tolerant. 2004. (Character Values Ser.). (Illus.). 24p. (J). lib. bdg. 15.93 (978-0-7368-2573-3(8) , Pebble Bks.) Capstone Pr., Inc.

Schwartz, Linda & Clark, Kimberley, eds. A Book about You Written by Me. Armstrong, Beverly, illus. 1999. 32p. (J). (gr. 1). pap. 5.99 (978-0-88160-320-0(1) , LW383) Creative Teaching Pr., Inc.

Scrapbook of Virtues Vol. 1: Building Character Through Virtues. l.t. ed. 2001. (Illus.). 82p. (J). 21.95 (978-0-9740504-0-9(7)) Virtuous Conquerors.

Secret Life of Guys. 2001. (gr. 3-6). lib. bdg. 13.00 (978-0-613-54649-2(0)) Tandem Library Bks.

Seder, Isaac. Justice & Fairness. (J). 2003. pap. 7.50 (978-1-4109-0330-3(3)); 2002. (Illus.). 32p. lib. bdg. 24.26 (978-0-7398-5805-9(X)) Raintree.

—Responsibility. (J). 2003. pap. 7.50 (978-1-4109-0332-7(X)); 2002. (Illus.). 32p. lib. bdg. 24.26 (978-0-7398-5781-6(9)) Raintree.

—Responsibility. 2003. (gr. k-3). lib. bdg. 15.90 (978-0-613-78299-9(2)) Tandem Library Bks.

Sennery, Isabelle. Discovery Set: A Young Person's Guide to Growing up Today. gif. ed. 2000. (Illus.). 171p. (J). (gr. 2-9). pap. 39.95 incl. audio (978-0-9577945-2-8(5)) Odyssey Mind Institute AUS. *Dist:* Kerr, Dana.

Sheindlin, Judy. Win or Lose by How You Choose! Tore, Bob, illus. 2000. 80p. (J). (gr. 2-7). 14.89 (978-0-06-028474-9(9)) HarperCollins Pubs.

—You Can't Judge a Book by Its Cover: Cool Rules for School. Tore, Bob, illus. 2001. 96p. (J). (gr. 2-7). 14.89 (978-0-06-029484-7(1)) HarperCollins Pubs.

Simon, Mary Manz & Lee, Jeanie. My Harvest of Blessings. Nakata, Hiroe, illus. 2009. 18p. (J). bds. 8.99 ***(978-1-4169-3609-1(2)*** , Little Simon Inspirations) Simon & Schuster Children's Publishing.

Skills for Better Living. (Skills for Better Living Ser.). (YA). cd-rom 279.95 (978-0-7365-9935-1(5)) Films Media Group.

Small, Mary. Being Responsible: A Book about Responsibility. Previn, Stacey, illus. 2005. (Way to Be! Ser.). 24p. (J). (gr. k-2). lib. bdg. 22.60 (978-1-4048-1052-5(8)) Picture Window Bks.

—Being Trustworthy: A Book about Trustworthiness. Previn, Stacey, illus. 2005. (Way to Be! Ser.). 24p. (J). (gr. k-2). lib. bdg. 22.60 (978-1-4048-1054-9(4)) Picture Window Bks.

Smith, Brenda J. Where Did Mommy Go? A Spiritual Tool to Help Children Grow from Grief to Peace. Smith, Brenda J. & Cloud, Olivia, eds. Smith, Brock R. & Smith, Raissa B., illus. 2004. Orig. Title: Listed Above. 52p. (gr. 3-12). pap. 16.95 (978-0-9744549-0-0(7)) Tall Through Bks.

Smith, Tim. Buck Wilder's Animal Wisdom. Herrick, Mark, illus. 2006. 32p. (J). (978-1-934133-02-6(7)) Mackinac Island Pr., Inc.

Snicket, Lemony, pseud. Horseradish: Bitter Truths You Can't Avoid. Tucker, Mark, illus. 2007. 176p. (J). (gr. 5 up). 12.99 ***(978-0-06-124006-5(0))*** HarperCollins Pubs.

Sprick, Randall S. The Solution Book. (Solution Book Ser.). (gr. k-8). 99.90 (978-0-07-568978-2(2)) SRA/McGraw-Hill.

Squire 5 Personal Growth Planbook: Daring Depths. 2003. (Illus.). 48p. (J). pap. 4.95 (978-1-59312-046-7(X)) North American Mission Board, SBC.

St. John, Patricia. A Young Person's Guide to Knowing God. 2000. 240p. (J). (gr. 8-13). pap. (978-1-85792-558-6(0) , Christian Focus) Christian Focus Pubns.

Standing Tall & Respecting All. 2004. (J). pap. 7.99 net. (978-0-9763141-2-7(6)) G.S. Enterprises of America Inc.

Stanley, Robin. I Can Be a Good Sport. Harpster, Steve & Julien, Terry, illus. 2006. (Happy Day Summer Titles Ser.). 16p. (J). pap. 1.99 (978-0-7847-1808-7(3) , 04190) Standard Publishing.

Stewart, Jan. Stars: Respecting Others. 2004. (Illus.). 32p. (J). pap. 9.95 (978-0-89793-313-1(3)) Hunter Hse., Inc.

Stillman, Sarah. Soul Searching: A Girl's Guide to Finding Herself. Gross, Susan, illus. 2000. 140p. (YA). (gr. 7). pap. 10.95 (978-1-58270-035-9(4)) Beyond Words Publishing, Inc.

—Soul Searching: A Girl's Guide to Finding Herself. 2000. (gr. 5-8). lib. bdg. 19.90 (978-0-613-65115-8(4)) Tandem Library Bks.

—Soul Searching Journal: A Guide to Self Discovery for Girls. Gross, Susan, illus. 2001. 88p. (YA). (gr. 7-12). 11.95 (978-1-58270-056-4(7)) Beyond Words Publishing, Inc.

Stoppard, Miriam. Every Girl's Life Guide. 1999. (J). (978-0-606-16987-5(3)) Tandem Library Bks.

Stormer, Kate. A Stranger in Casey's World. Lowes, Tom, illus. l.t. ed. 2004. 32p. (J). 16.95 (978-0-9647663-1-0(0)) Caseys World Bks.

Strazzabosco, Jeanne M. Learning about Responsibility. 2004. (Character Building Book Ser.). 24p. (J). lib. bdg. 18.75 (978-0-8239-6927-2(4) , PowerKids Pr.) Rosen Publishing Group, Inc., The.

Sullivan, James Kevin, illus. What Went RIght Today? Journal: WWRT Journal. 2007. 72p. (J). spiral bd. 12.95 ***(978-0-9766990-1-9(X))*** Buz-Land Presentations, Inc.

Swain, Claudia. What's a Girl to Do? 2004. 128p. pap. 6.99 (978-1-56309-440-8(1)) New Hope Pubs.

Swainston, Jeani. Grandma Stuff: ... it's what love Is made Of. 2006. (J). ***(978-0-9791384-0-9(X))*** Rock Cliff Media.

Tadder, Karen Mc. Donald. Picture Your Invisible Self: A Universal Lesson Plan for Learning Intrapersonal Skills. 2005. 20p. per. 8.00 (978-1-59196-911-2(5)) Instantpublisher.com.

Taking Godly Care of My Money. 2005. 80p. (J). per. 9.99 (978-1-59441-082-6(8) , CD-204009) Carson-Dellosa Publishing Co., Inc.

Tang, Greg. Math Fables. Cahoon, Heather, illus. 2004. 40p. (J). pap. 16.95 (978-0-439-45399-8(2)) Scholastic, Inc.

—Math Fables. 2003. (Illus.). (J). pap. (978-0-439-45400-1(X)) Scholastic, Inc.

Teal, Joyce. Hang in There Kid. 2005. 128p. pap. 8.95 (978-1-58501-090-5(1) , CeShore) SterlingHouse Pubs., Inc.

Teal, Joyce Willard. Don't Sweat It, Kid. 2002. 152p. (J). 7.95 (978-1-56315-292-4(4)) SterlingHouse Pubs., Inc.

Team Dawg It's All about Respect, 1. 2004. (Illus.). 30p. (J). bds. 14.99 (978-0-9749378-0-9(0)) Team Dawg Productions, Inc.

There's Beauty in the Rainbow. 2006. (J). per. 12.00 (978-0-9786154-0-6(9)) Milestones Publishing.

Thoennes Keller, Kristin & Keller, Kristin Thoennes. Responsibility. 2005. (Illus.). 24p. (J). (ps-ps). lib. bdg. 21.26 (978-0-7368-3683-8(7)) Capstone Pr., Inc.

Thompson, Carol & Thompson, Carol. America the Good: Stories of Goodwill by Good Americans. 2003. (Illus.). 95p. bds. 15.95 (978-0-9744111-0-1(8)) Wren's Nest Publishing, Inc.

Thorn, Catherine O'Neill, ed. Why Keep Tryin'? Voices from the Street. 2000. (Illus.). vi, 74p. (YA). (gr. 9 up). pap. 12.95 (978-0-9678874-0-1(2)) O'Neill Publishing.

Titcomb, Timothy. Lessons in Life: a Series of Familiar Essays. 2007. pap. 31.95 ***(978-1-4304-7511-8(0))*** Kessinger Publishing, LLC.

Todo lo Que Necesitas Saber Series, Set. 2003. (Todo lo Que Necesitas Saber Ser.). (SPA & ENG., Illus.). (J). lib. bdg. 238.50 (978-0-8239-9719-0(7) , Buenas Letra) Rosen Publishing Group, Inc., The.

Tousey, Ben. Acting Your Dreams: Using Acting Techniques to Interpret Your Dreams, 1. 2003. (C). per. 14.95 (978-0-9724292-0-7(4)) Yhabbut Publishing.

Turk, Cynthia. My Daddy Stays at Home with Me. 2004. 27p. pap. 14.95 (978-1-4137-3363-1(8)) PublishAmerica, Inc.

Tyndale House Publishers Staff. Boom: A Guy's Guide to Growing Up. 2003. (gr. 7-12). lib. bdg. 28.05 (978-0-613-79770-2(1)) Tandem Library Bks.

Vereb, Jerome M. & John Paul II. Every Child a Light: The Pope's Message to Young People. 2003. (Illus.). 48p. (YA). (gr. 2-4). 16.95 (978-1-56397-090-0(2)) Boyds Mills Pr.

Vickery, A. Lou. How to Be a Winner: The Young Athlete's Notebook. 1998. 176p. (YA). (gr. 5 up). pap. 12.95 (978-0-9654140-2-9(7)) Upword Pr.

Vogel, Elizabeth. Dealing with Rules at Home. 2000. (Conflict Resolution Library). (Illus.). 24p. (J). (gr. 3). lib. bdg. 18.75 (978-0-8239-5411-7(0) , PowerKids Pr.) Rosen Publishing Group, Inc., The.

Wandberg, Robert. Ethics: Doing the Right Thing. 2000. (Life Skills-Contemporary Issues Ser.). (Illus.). (J). 64p. (gr. 4-6). lib. bdg. 23.93 (978-0-7368-0699-2(7)) ; 48p. pap. 8.95 (978-0-7368-8840-0(3)) Capstone Pr., Inc. (LifeMatters Bks.).

—Resilience: Bouncing off, Bouncing Back. 2000. (Life Skills-Contemporary Issues Ser.). (Illus.). 64p. (J). (gr. 4-6). lib. bdg. 23.93 (978-0-7368-0698-5(9) , LifeMatters Bks.) Capstone Pr., Inc.

—Self-Direction: Taking Positive Risks, Following Your Dreams. 2000. (Contemporary Issues Ser.). (Illus.). 64p. (J). (gr. 4-6). lib. bdg. 23.93 (978-0-7368-0696-1(2) , LifeMatters Bks.) Capstone Pr., Inc.

Watkins, James N. Is There Really Life after Death? 2000. (5 Minute Bible Studies). (Illus.). 160p. (YA). (gr. 7-11). 9.99 (978-0-570-05247-0(5)) Concordia Publishing Hse.

Way We Live. 2000. 40p. (YA). 8.33 (978-0-7525-4525-7(6)) Parragon, Inc.

Webb, Douglas. Motivation Levitation. 2002. 149p. per. 12.95 (978-1-930908-16-1(4) , 1) AGB Publishing.

Weedn, Lisa. Getting Real: Listen to My Heart & Finding Peace with Who I Am. Weedn, Flavia M., illus. 2001. 144p. (YA). (gr. 7-12). pap. 9.95 (978-0-7683-2236-1(7)) CEDCO Publishing.

Welden, Amelie. Girls Who Rocked the World: Heroines from Sacagawea to Sheryl Swoopes. McCann, Jerry, illus. l.t. ed. 1999. (Girls Know Best Ser.). 117p. (J). (gr. 3 up). lib. bdg. 23.33 (978-0-8368-2454-4(7)) Stevens, Gareth Inc.

Wesbrooks, Linda. The New You: Lessons for Teenage Girls. (YA). pap. 7.99 (978-0-89098-406-2(9)) Twentieth Century Christian Bks.

Wesemann, Tim. The Book of Cool: Cool Questions, Cooler Answers. 2004. (2:52 / Soul Gear#8482; Ser.). (Illus.). 112p. (J). (gr. 3-6). 7.99 (978-0-310-70696-0(3)) Zonderkidz.

Weston, Carol. For Teens Only: Quotes, Notes, & Advice You Can Use. 2002. (gr. 7-12). lib. bdg. 17.60 (978-0-613-82532-0(2)) Tandem Library Bks.

What Color Is Death, Daddy? A Story about Love & Loss for Very Young Children. 2002. (J). 4.95 (978-0-9717266-2-8(0)) MISS Foundation Publishing.

White, Ellen G. The Ministry of Healing. 2005. reprint ed. pap. 42.95 (978-1-4191-4425-7(1)) Kessinger Publishing, LLC.

Wiggin, Kate Douglas. The Story of Patsy. 2004. reprint ed. pap. 15.95 (978-1-4179-2620-6(1)) Kessinger Publishing, LLC.

Wilbur, Regina, ed. Keys to Success. 2003. (YA). stu. ed. 6.95 (978-0-9710925-2-5(4)) EniCare Consulting, Inc.

—Keys to Success: Getting Control of Mr. & Mrs. Attitude & Temper (A. T.) 2003. tchr. ed., spiral bd. 8.95 (978-0-9710925-1-8(6) , 0-9710925-1-6) EniCare Consulting, Inc.

Wilkinson, Bruce & Thomas, Mack. A Life God Rewards: Guys Only. ltd. ed. 2006. 96p. bds. 9.99 (978-1-60142-002-2(1) , Multnomah Kidz) WaterBrook Pr.

Williams, Shery L. Let's Be Frank, Pt. 2. 1999. (YA). pap. 6.95 (978-1-56794-192-0(3)) Star Bible & Tract Corp.

Williams, Terrie. Stay Strong: Simple Life Lessons for Teens. 2002. (Stay Strong Ser.). (Illus.). 240p. (J). (gr. 7 up). pap. 4.99 (978-0-439-12972-5(9)) Scholastic, Inc.

—Stay Strong: Simple Life Lessons for Teens. 2002. (gr. 7-12). lib. bdg. 13.00 (978-0-613-89055-7(8)) Tandem Library Bks.

Winfree, Woody. We Are More Than Beautiful: 46 Real Teen Girls Speak Out about Beauty, Happiness, Love & Life. 2007. 112p. pap. 7.95 ***(978-1-4022-0953-6(3))*** Sourcebooks, Inc.

Woods, Earl & Tiger Woods Foundation Staff. Start Something: You Can Make a Difference. 2006. 144p. pap. 14.00 (978-1-4165-3704-5(X)) Simon & Schuster.

Words Inc., prod. Skills for Better Living -Volume. (Skills for Better Living Ser.). (YA). cd-rom 99.95 (978-0-7365-9936-8(3)); cd-rom 99.95 (978-0-7365-9937-5(1)); cd-rom 99.95 (978-0-7365-9938-2(X)) Films Media Group.

Wounded Voices Unwise Choices: The Truth from Our Youth. 2004. (YA). per. 12.00 (978-0-9754191-0-6(2)) Morals & Values Pr.

Wynn, Robbin. The Final Showdown under the Sun: You vs. Adversary. 2005. (YA). per. 13.00 incl. audio (978-0-9770682-0-3(X)) Inner Circle Publishing.

Xingyun, et al. Prescription for the Heart: Between Ignorance & Enlightenment 2. 2003. (Between Ignorance & Enlightenment Ser.: Vol. 2). 131p. 13.00 (978-1-932293-02-9(7)) Buddha's Light Publishing.

Yaconelli, Mike. A Gift for My Daughter. 2nd ed. 2002. (Illus.). 64p. (J). pap. 6.99 (978-0-7459-4786-0(7) , Lion) Lion Hudson plc GBR. *Dist:* Independent Pubs. Group.

—A Gift for My Grandchild. 2nd ed. 2002. (Illus.). 64p. (J). pap. 6.99 (978-0-7459-4788-4(3) , Lion) Lion Hudson plc GBR. *Dist:* Independent Pubs. Group.

Yonikus, Sandi. Dominga's Wonderful Year/El Año Maravilloso del Domingo. Nelson, Annika, illus. 2005. (SPA & ENG.). 32p. 16.95 (978-0-8146-2876-8(1)) Liturgical Pr.

The Young Woman's Empowerment Journal: From Dreaming to Reaching Your Full Potential. 2004. (YA). per. 14.99 (978-0-9748017-0-4(4)) Adelante Productions, Inc.

Youngs, Bettie. Taste Berries for Teens: Inspirational Short Stories & Encouragement on Life, 1999. (gr. 7-12). lib. bdg. 22.20 (978-0-613-17746-7(0)) Tandem Library Bks.

Youngs, Bettie B., et al. Taste BerriesTM for Teens: Inspirational Short Stories & Encouragement on Life, Love, Friendship & Tough Issues. 1999. (Illus.). 400p. (YA). (gr. 7-12). pap. 12.95 (978-1-55874-669-5(2)) Health Communications, Inc.

Zimmerman, Bill. 100 Things Guys Need to Know. 2005. (Illus.). 128p. (J). (gr. 4-8). pap. 13.95 (978-1-57542-167-4(4)) Free Spirit Publishing, Inc.

CONDUCT OF LIFE—FICTION

Abbott, Jacob. Rollo at Work & Rollo at Play. 2006. (Illus.). pap. 34.95 ***(978-1-4286-4095-5(9))*** Kessinger Publishing, LLC.

Abdul-Rauf, Muhammad. The Story of Tawaddud: A Brilliant & Beautiful Girl & a Model of Good Moral Conduct. 2005. xx, 185p. (978-983-9184-66-2(0)) Institut Perkembangan Minda.

Adventures at Walnut Grove A Lesson about Teasing. l.t. ed. 2007. (Illus.). 32p. (J). 15.95 ***(978-0-9792686-0-1(5)*** , 5,000) Lehman Publishing.

Ain, Beth Levine. The Portrait. 2008. (J). ***(978-0-7636-3396-7(8))*** Candlewick Pr.

Alexander, Alma. Gift of the Unmage. 2007. (Worldweavers Ser.: Bk. 1). 400p. (YA). (gr. 7 up). 16.99 (978-0-06-083955-0(4)); lib. bdg. 17.89 (978-0-06-083956-7(2)) HarperCollins Pubs.

Alexander, Geoff. Toothbugs!, Carole, Isaacs, illus. l.t. ed. 2005. 12p. (J). bds. 12.95 (978-0-9760944-0-1(1)) Alexander-Marcus Publishing.

Alexander, Mary Helen. Please & Thank You. 2005. 23p. pap. 14.95 (978-1-4137-6240-2(9)) PublishAmerica, Inc.

Alford, Doug. Ogs, Zogs & Useful Cogs. 2007. (J). pap. 5.99 net. ***(978-1-933589-96-1(5))*** Scripture Mastery Resources!.

Alger, Horatio. Andy Grant's Pluck. 2006. 190p. pap. 13.99 (978-1-4264-0879-3(X)); 188p. pap. 16.99 (978-1-4264-0860-1(9)) BiblioBazaar.

—Andy Grant's Pluck. 2006. 79.99 ***(978-1-4280-3135-7(9))*** IndyPublish.com.

—A Boy's Fortune: Or, The Strange Adventures of Ben Baker. unabr. ed. 2002. (Polyglot Press Alger Ser.). (Illus.). (J). pap. 17.95 (978-1-931927-79-6(0)) Polyglot Pr., Inc.

—Cast upon the Breakers. unabr. ed. 2002. (Polyglot Press Alger Ser.). (Illus.). (J). pap. 17.95 (978-1-931927-81-9(2)) Polyglot Pr., Inc.

—Do & Dare. 2006. pap. ***(978-1-4250-1766-8(5))***; pap. ***(978-1-4250-2027-9(5))***; pap. ***(978-1-4250-2300-3(2))***; pap. ***(978-1-4250-2118-4(2))*** Assistedreadingbooks.com Inc.

—Do & Dare: Or, A Brave Boy's Fight for Fortune. 2006. 182p. pap. 11.99 (978-1-4264-0880-9(3)); 170p. pap. 14.99 (978-1-4264-0861-8(7)) BiblioBazaar.

—Do & Dare: Or, A Brave Boy's Fight for Fortune. 2006. pap. ***(978-1-4065-0701-0(6))*** Dodo Pr.

—Do & Dare: Or, A Brave Boy's Fight for Fortune. unabr. ed. 2002. (Illus.). (J). pap. 17.95 (978-1-931927-90-1(1)) Polyglot Pr., Inc.

—Facing the World. 2006. pap. ***(978-1-4250-2212-9(X))*** Assistedreadingbooks.com Inc.

—Facing the World. 2006. pap. ***(978-1-4065-0704-1(0))*** Dodo Pr.

—Finding a Fortune. unabr. ed. 2002. (Polyglot Press Alger Ser.). (Illus.). (J). pap. 17.95 (978-1-4115-0089-1(X)) Polyglot Pr., Inc.

—Frank's Campaign: Or, The Farm & the Camp. 2006. 196p. pap. 11.99 (978-1-4264-0484-9(0)); 188p. pap. 14.99 (978-1-4264-0527-3(8)) BiblioBazaar.

—Frank's Campaign: Or, The Farm & the Camp. 2006. pap. ***(978-1-4065-0705-8(9))*** Dodo Pr.

—Frank's Campaign: Or, What Boys Can Do on the Farm for the Camp. unabr. ed. 2002. (Polyglot Press Alger Ser.). (Illus.). (J). pap. 17.95 (978-1-4115-0000-6(8)) Polyglot Pr., Inc.

—Hector's Inheritance: Or, The Boys of Smith Institute. 2006. pap. ***(978-1-4065-0708-9(3))*** Dodo Pr.

—Hector's Inheritance: Or, The Boys of Smith Institute. unabr. ed. 2002. (Polyglot Press Alger Ser.). (Illus.). (J). pap. 17.95 (978-1-4115-0004-4(0)) Polyglot Pr., Inc.

—Helping Himself. 2006. 180p. pap. 13.99 (978-1-4264-0881-6(1)); 168p. pap. 16.99 (978-1-4264-0862-5(5)) BiblioBazaar.

—Helping Himself. 2006. pap. (***978-1-4065-0709-6(1)***) Dodo Pr.

—Helping Himself: Or, Grant Thornton's Ambition. unabr. ed. 2002. (Polyglot Press Alger Ser.). (Illus.). (J). pap. 17.95 (978-1-4115-0006-8(7)) Polyglot Pr., Inc.

—Herbert Carter's Legacy. 2006. pap. (***978-1-4065-0710-2(5)***) Dodo Pr.

—Jack's Ward. 2006. pap. (***978-1-4065-0711-9(3)***) Dodo Pr.

—Jack's Ward: Or, The Boy Guardian. 2006. 176p. pap. 13.99 (978-1-4264-0882-3(X)); 168p. pap. 16.99 (978-1-4264-0863-2(3)) BiblioBazaar.

—Joe the Hotel Boy. 2006. pap. (***978-1-4065-0712-6(1)***) Dodo Pr.

—Joe's Luck: Or, Always Wide Awake. 2007. 172p. pap. 11.99 (***978-1-4264-6426-3(6)***); 2006. 176p. pap. 13.99 (978-1-4264-0883-0(8)); 2007. 186p. pap. 14.99 (***978-1-4264-6500-0(9)***); 2006. 170p. pap. 16.99 (978-1-4264-0864-9(1)) BiblioBazaar.

—Joe's Luck: Or, Always Wide Awake. 2006. pap. (***978-1-4065-0713-3(X)***) Dodo Pr.

—Luck & Pluck: Or, John Oakley's Inheritance. unabr. ed. 2002. (Polyglot Press Alger Ser.). (Illus.). (J). pap. 17.95 (978-1-4115-0019-8(9)) Polyglot Pr., Inc.

—Making His Way: Or, Frank Courtneys Struggle. 2006. 96.99 (***978-1-4280-2109-9(4)***); pap. 89.99 (***978-1-4280-2133-4(7)***) IndyPublish.com.

—Mark Manning's Mission: The Story of a Shoe Factory Boy. unabr. ed. 2002. (Polyglot Press Alger Ser.). (Illus.). (J). pap. 17.95 (978-1-4115-0022-8(9)) Polyglot Pr., Inc.

—Only an Irish Boy: Or, Andy Burke's Fortunes & Misfortunes. 2006. pap. (***978-1-4065-0716-4(4)***) Dodo Pr.

—Paul Prescott's Charge: A Story for Boys. 2006. pap. (***978-1-4250-2995-1(7)***) Assistedreadingbooks.com Inc.

—Paul Prescott's Charge: A Story for Boys. unabr. ed. 2002. (Polyglot Press Alger Ser.). (Illus.). (J). pap. 17.95 (978-1-4115-0034-1(2)) Polyglot Pr., Inc.

—Risen from the Ranks: Or, Harry Walton's Success. 2007. 194p. pap. 11.99 (***978-1-4264-6391-4(X)***); 216p. pap. 15.99 (***978-1-4264-6465-2(7)***) BiblioBazaar.

—Risen from the Ranks: Or, Harry Walton's Success. 2006. pap. (***978-1-4065-0721-8(0)***) Dodo Pr.

—Risen from the Ranks: Or, Harry Walton's Success. 2006. 79.99 (***978-1-4219-9893-0(9)***); pap. 72.99 (***978-1-4219-9877-0(7)***) IndyPublish.com.

—The Store Boy. 2006. 170p. pap. 11.99 (***978-1-4264-4359-6(5)***); 182p. pap. 14.99 (***978-1-4264-4397-8(8)***) BiblioBazaar.

—The Store Boy. 2006. pap. (***978-1-4065-0722-5(9)***) Dodo Pr.

—Struggling Upward: Or, Luke Larkin's Luck. 2006. pap. (***978-1-4065-0723-2(7)***) Dodo Pr.

—Struggling Upward: Or, Luke Larkin's Luck. unabr. ed. 2002. (Polyglot Press Alger Ser.). (Illus.). (J). pap. 17.95 (978-1-4115-0053-2(9)) Polyglot Pr., Inc.

—Timothy Crump's Ward: A Story of American Life. 2006. pap. (***978-1-4250-3339-2(3)***) Assistedreadingbooks.com Inc.

—Tom Temple's Career. reprint ed. pap. 79.00 (978-1-4047-3611-5(5)) Classic Textbooks.

—Tom Temple's Career. l.t. ed. 2002. (Illus.). pap. 19.95 (978-1-4115-0422-6(4)); (J). pap. 17.95 (978-1-4115-0057-0(1)) Polyglot Pr., Inc.

—The Young Acrobat of the Great North American Circus. unabr. ed. 2002. (Polyglot Press Alger Ser.). (Illus.). (J). pap. 17.95 (978-1-4115-0070-9(9)) Polyglot Pr., Inc.

—The Young Book Agent: Or, Frank Hardy's Road to Success. unabr. ed. 2002. (Polyglot Press Alger Ser.). (Illus.). (J). pap. 17.95 (978-1-4115-0074-7(1)) Polyglot Pr., Inc.

—The Young Musician. reprint ed. pap. 79.00 (978-1-4047-3629-0(8)) Classic Textbooks.

—The Young Musician. 2006. pap. (***978-1-4068-0673-1(0)***) Echo Library.

Alger, Horatio. $500: Or, Jacob Marlowe's Secret. unabr. ed. 2002. (Polyglot Press Alger Ser.). (Illus.). (J). pap. 17.95 (978-1-931927-97-0(9)) Polyglot Pr., Inc.

Alger Jr. Horatio Staff. Hector's Inheritance. rev. ed. 2006. 276p. 28.95 (978-1-4218-1758-3(6)); pap. 13.95 (978-1-4218-1858-0(2)) 1st World Publishing, Inc. (1st World Library - Literary Society).

—Herbert Carter's Legacy. rev. ed. 2006. 264p. 28.95 (978-1-4218-1756-9(X)); pap. 13.95 (978-1-4218-1856-6(6)) 1st World Publishing, Inc. (1st World Library - Literary Society).

—Only an Irish Boy. rev. ed. 2006. 284p. 28.95 (978-1-4218-1759-0(4)); pap. 13.95 (978-1-4218-1859-7(0)) 1st World Publishing, Inc. (1st World Library - Literary Society).

Almond, David. The Fire-Eaters. l.t. ed. 2005. 239p. (J). (ps-7). per. 22.95 (978-0-7862-7695-0(9) , Large Print Pr.) Thorndike Pr.

Amerel. The Summer Holidays: A Story for Childre. 2006. pap. (***978-1-4065-0808-6(X)***) Dodo Pr.

Amos, Janine. Selfish. 2007. (Good & Bad Ser.). (Illus.). 32p. (J). (ps-2). pap. 9.95 (***978-1-84234-397-5(1)*** , Evans Brothers, Limited) Evans Publishing Group GBR. *Dist:* Independent Pubs. Group.

An Angry Day: Social/Emotional Lap Book. (Pebble Soup Explorations Ser.). (ps up). 16.00 (978-0-7635-7572-4(0)) Rigby Education.

Anonymous. Confessions of a Backup Dancer. l.t. ed. 2005. 360p. (YA). (gr. 8-12). per. 20.95 (978-0-7862-7881-7(1) , Large Print Pr.) Thorndike Pr.

Archie in Quiet Please. 2007. (Illus.). 80p. (J). 24.21 (***978-1-59961-260-7(7)***) Spotlight.

Arraras, Maria Celeste. El Baston Magico (The Magic Cane) 2008. (I Love My Mommy Ser.). 32p. (J). pap. 5.99 (***978-0-545-00532-6(9)*** , Scholastic en Espanol) Scholastic, Inc.

Arraras, María Celeste. The Magic Cane. Raimondi, Pablo, illus. 2007. 32p. (J). (ps-3). pap. 16.99 (***978-0-439-57419-8(6)*** , Orchard Bks.) Scholastic, Inc.

Arrington, H. J. Friends Again? Kitchel, JoAnn E., illus. 2001. 32p. (J). 15.95 (978-1-56554-834-3(5)) Pelican Publishing Co., Inc.

Aryal, Aimee. Hello Big Al! Moore, Danny, illus. 2004. (J). 19.95 (978-1-932888-03-4(9)) Mascot Bks., Inc.

Atkinson, Juliette. I'm Sorry. Atkinson, John, illus. 2008. 32p. (J). (ps-k). 16.99 (***978-0-698-40079-5(8)*** , Minedition) Penguin Group (USA) Inc.

Auer, Chris. Molly & the Good Shepherd. Wummer, Amy, illus. 2005. 40p. (J). 12.99 (978-0-310-70826-1(5)) Zonderkidz.

Badger, Pearstina. Jessica's Journeys: Stories about Life's Lessons. 2006. 56p. pap. 12.95 (978-1-4241-1576-1(0)) PublishAmerica, Inc.

Baker, Ginger. Walking Home Alone. Levy, Pamela R., illus. 2003. (Books for Young Learners). 16p. (J). pap. 5.00 net. (978-1-57274-604-6(1) , 2534) Owen, Richard C. Pubs., Inc.

Ballantyne, Michael. Blown to Bits or the Lonely Man of Rakat. 2006. 36.99 (***978-1-4280-4221-6(0)***); pap. 30.99 (***978-1-4280-4226-1(1)***) IndyPublish.com.

Ballantyne, R. M. Blown to Bits; or, the Lonely Man of Rak. 2006. pap. (***978-1-4065-0515-3(3)***) Dodo Pr.

Ballart, Elisabet. Aprendamos a Convivir. Capdevila, Roser, illus. Tr. of Let's Learn to Get Along. (SPA.). 48p. (J). (gr. 3-5). 13.56 (978-84-233-3109-3(1)) Ediciones Destino ESP. *Dist:* Lectorum Pubns., Inc.

Banks, Celia. God Loves Me. 2007. (J). per. (978-0-9764460-8-8(1)) BMCFerrell.

Baras, Renee. Be Special, Be Yourself for Teenagers. 2005. 171p. (YA). per. (***978-0-9757976-0-0(3)***) Be Happy in LIFE.

Barnum, P. T. Dick Broadhead: A Story of Perilous Adve. 2006. pap. 30.95 (***978-1-4286-1959-3(3)***) Kessinger Publishing, LLC.

Bartlett, Susan. Opening Day. Wrenn, Luanne, illus. 2007. 32p. (J). 16.95 (***978-0-88448-288-8(X)***) Tilbury Hse. Pubs.

Bateson, Catherine. Rain May & Captain Daniel. 2002. 144p. (YA). pap. 15.50 (978-0-7022-3337-1(4)) Univ. of Queensland Pr. AUS. *Dist:* International Specialized Bk. Services.

Bateson, Catherine. Stranded in Boringsville. 144p. (gr. 5-9). (J). 16.95 (978-0-8234-1969-2(X)); 2007. (YA). pap. 6.95 (***978-0-8234-2113-8(9)***) Holiday Hse., Inc.

Baum, L. Frank. Wonderful Wizard of Oz: A Classic Story about Cooperation. 2003. (Illus.). 32p. per. 3.95 (978-0-9747133-5-9(X) , Values to Live By Classic Stories) Thomas, Frederic Inc.

Be Kind, Be Friendly, Be Thankful: The Adventures of Brisky Bear & Trooper Dog. 2007. Orig. Title: Friends for Always. (J). pap. 7.95 incl. audio compact disk (***978-0-9795127-0-4(0)***) Glory Be Collectibles.

Bea, Holly. Thank You, God. Howard, Kim, illus. 2003. 32p. 15.00 (978-1-932073-04-1(3)) Kramer, H.J. Inc.

Bee, Clair. Dugout Jinx. (J). 17.95 (978-0-8488-1247-8(6)) Amereon LTD.

—Dugout Jinx, Vol. 8. 1999. (Chip Hilton Sports Ser.: Vol. 8). x, 207p. (J). reprint ed. pap. 5.99 (978-0-8054-1990-0(X)) B&H Publishing Grp.

Behrens, Andy. All the Way. 2006. 256p. (YA). (gr. 9). 16.99 (978-0-525-47761-7(6) , Dutton Juvenile) Penguin Group (USA) Inc.

Bell, Hilari. Shield of Stars. 2007. (Shield, Sword, & Crown Ser.). (Illus.). 272p. (J). 16.99 (978-1-4169-0594-3(4) , Simon & Schuster Children's Publishing) Simon & Schuster Children's Publishing.

Bennett, Elizabeth. The New Bug. Scherer, Jeffrey, illus. 2003. 32p. (J). (978-0-439-46641-7(5)) Scholastic, Inc.

Between the Lions - Early Literacy Kit - Help!, 1 cass., 1 bk. 2005. (Between the Lions Ser.). 24p. (J). VHS 29.95 (978-1-59375-284-2(9) , WG38623) WGBH Boston Video.

Bildner, Phil. Busted. 2007. 256p. (YA). (gr. 9 up). 15.99 (***978-1-4169-2424-1(8)***) Simon & Schuster Children's Publishing.

Bishop, Jennie. The Squire & the Scroll Coloring Book. 2005. (J). pap. 1.79 (***978-1-59317-085-1(8)***) Warner Pr. Pubs.

Black Beauty: A Classic Story about Respect. 2003. (Illus.). 32p. per. 3.95 (978-0-9747133-0-4(9) , Values to Live By Classic Stories) Thomas, Frederic Inc.

Blackaby, Susan. The Missing Tooth. Haugen, Ryan, illus. 2006. (Read-It! Readers Ser.). 32p. (J). (ps-3). 18.60 (978-1-4048-1592-6(9)) Picture Window Bks.

—Syd's Room. Moore, Frances, illus. 2006. (Read-It! Readers Ser.). 24p. (J). (ps-3). 18.60 (978-1-4048-1585-8(6)) Picture Window Bks.

Blackford. The Eskdale Herd Boy A Scottish Tale for the Instruction & Amusement of Young Persons. 2004. reprint ed. pap. 15.95 (978-1-4191-6125-4(3)) Kessinger Publishing, LLC.

Blackman, Malorie. Black & White. 2007. 512p. (YA). (gr. 9 up). pap. 7.99 (978-1-4169-0017-7(9) , Simon Pulse) Simon & Schuster Children's Publishing.

Blume, Judy. Are You There God? It's Me, Margaret. 149p. (J). (gr. 4-6). pap. 3.50 (978-0-8072-1421-3(3)); (YA). (gr. 5 up). pap. 4.99 (978-0-8072-1508-1(2)) Random Hse. Audio Publishing Group. (Listening Library).

—Are You There God Its Me Margaret. 2001. 160p. (J). (gr. 4-6). 17.95 (978-0-689-84158-3(2) , Atheneum/Richard Jackson Bks.) Simon & Schuster Children's Publishing.

—Otherwise Known As Sheila the Great. (Fudge Ser.). (J). 2007. 144p. 5.99 (978-0-14-240879-7(4) , Puffin); 2002. (Illus.). 128p. 15.99 (978-0-525-46928-5(1) , Dutton Juvenile) Penguin Group (USA) Inc.

Bohlken, Robert L. Listening to the Mukies: And Their Character Building Adventures. Veasey, Michele, illus. 2003. (J). pap. 14.95 (978-0-930643-15-7(1)) Images Unlimited.

—Listening to the Mukies & Their Character Building Adventures. Veasey, Michele, illus. 2003. (J). 24.95 (978-0-930643-17-1(8)) Images Unlimited.

Bonin, Liane. Pretty on the Outside: Fame Unlimited. 2007. 288p. (YA). pap. 9.99 (***978-0-451-22122-3(2)*** , N A L Trade) Penguin Group (USA) Inc.

Booth, Bradley. Shepherd Warrior. 2007. 127p. (J). (***978-0-8163-2161-2(2)***) Pacific Pr. Pubns.

Borchard, Therese Johnson. Whitney Coaches David on Fighting Goliath: And Learns to Stand up for Herself. 2000. (Emerald Bible Collection). (Illus.). 80p. (gr. 3-7). 5.95 (978-0-8091-6669-5(0) , 6669-0) Paulist Pr.

—Whitney Rides the Whale with Jonah: And Learns She Can't Run Away. 1999. (Emerald Bible Collection). (Illus.). 80p. (gr. 3-7). 5.95 (978-0-8091-6663-3(1) , 6663-1) Paulist Pr.

—Whitney Sews Joseph's Many-Colored Coat: And Learns a Lesson about Jealousy. 1999. (Emerald Bible Collection). (Illus.). 80p. (gr. 3-7). 5.95 (978-0-8091-6664-0(X) , 6664-x) Paulist Pr.

Boritzer, Etan. What Is Right? l.t. ed. 2004. (What Is? Ser.: No. 6). (Illus.). 32p. 14.95 (978-0-9762743-1-5(0)) Lane, Veronica Bks.

Bosak, Susan V. Dream: A Tale of Wonder, Wisdom & Wishes. Dillon, Leo and Diane et al, illus. 2004. 40p. (J). (978-1-896232-04-1(3) , TCP Pr.) Communication Project, The.

Boulden, James. Buddy Gets Angry: Student Involvement Pack. 2003. (Illus.). 21p. (J). 24.95 (978-1-892421-73-9(9)) Boulden Publishing.

—Buddy Learns about Bullying Video Kit. 2003. (J). pap. 39.95 incl. VHS (978-1-892421-89-0(5)) Boulden Publishing.

—Buddy Learns about Tattling: Student Involvement Pack. 2003. (Illus.). 21p. (J). 24.95 (978-1-892421-80-7(1)) Boulden Publishing.

—Buddy learns about Teasing: Student Involvement Pack. 2003. (Illus.). 21p. (J). 24.95 (978-1-892421-72-2(0) , 720) Boulden Publishing.

Boulden, Jim. One step at a Time: Student Involvement Pack. 2002. (Illus.). 17p. (J). 24.95 (978-1-892421-43-2(7) , 437SET) Boulden Publishing.

Bowman, Crystal. My Happy Pumpkin. 2007. (Illus.). 14p. (J). 6.99 (***978-0-310-71160-5(6)***) Zonderkidz.

Brande, Robin. Evolution, Me & Other Freaks of Nature. 2007. 272p. (gr. 7). (J). lib. bdg. 18.99 (***978-0-375-94349-2(8)***); (YA). 15.99 (***978-0-375-84349-5(3)***) Random Hse. Children's Bks. (Knopf Bks. for Young Readers).

Brashares, Ann. Forever in Blue: The Fourth Summer of the Sisterhood. (Sisterhood of Traveling Pants Ser.). (YA). (gr. 7). 2008. 416p. pap. 9.99 (***978-0-385-73401-1(8)***); 2007. 400p. 18.99 (978-0-385-72936-9(7)) Random Hse. Children's Bks. (Delacorte Bks. for Young Readers).

—Girls in Pants. 2006. (Sisterhood of Traveling Pants Ser.: Bk. 3). 368p. (YA). (gr. 7 up). reprint ed. pap. 8.95 (978-0-553-37593-0(8) , Delacorte Bks. for Young Readers) Random Hse. Children's Bks.

—Girls in Pants: The Third Summer of the Sisterhood. (Sisterhood of Traveling Pants Ser.: Bk. 3). (YA). (gr. 7 up). 2007. 416p. mass mkt. 6.99 (***978-0-553-49504-1(6)*** , Dell Books for Young Readers); 2005. 352p. 16.95 (978-0-385-72935-2(9) , Delacorte Bks. for Young Readers); 2005. 352p. lib. bdg. 18.99 (978-0-385-90919-8(5) , Delacorte Bks. for Young Readers) Random Hse. Children's Bks.

—Girls in Pants: The Third Summer of the Sisterhood. l.t. ed. 2005. (Sisterhood of Traveling Pants Ser. : Bk. 3). 405p. (YA). 23.95 (978-0-7862-7264-8(3) , Large Print Pr.) Thorndike Pr.

—The Sisterhood of the Traveling Pants. movie tie-in ed. 2005. (Sisterhood of Traveling Pants Ser.: Bk. 1). (Illus.). 352p. (YA). (gr. 7 up). mass mkt. 6.99 (978-0-553-49479-2(1) , Dell Books for Young Readers) Random Hse. Children's Bks.

—The Sisterhood of the Traveling Pants. 2003. (Sisterhood of Traveling Pants Ser. : Bk. 1). (YA). (gr. 7 up). lib. bdg. 17.60 (978-0-613-60397-3(4)) Tandem Library Bks.

Bredsdorff, Bodil. The Crow-Girl: The Children of Crow Cove. Ingwersen, Faith, tr. 2006. 160p. (J). reprint ed. pap. 5.95 (978-0-374-40003-3(2) , Farrar, Straus & Giroux (BYR)) Farrar, Straus & Giroux.

Brewer, Gary. Journey to the Spring at Crystal Mountain. 2000. (Illus.). 151p. (J). pap. 9.95 (978-1-57895-043-0(0)) Bridge Resources.

Brian, Kate. Sweet 16. 2007. 288p. (YA). pap. 8.99 (***978-1-4169-0033-7(0)*** , Simon Pulse) Simon & Schuster Children's Publishing.

Brightwood, Laura, illus. Ka-ulu the Strong. Brightwood, Laura, . 2006. (J). (***978-0-9789871-3-8(6)***) 3-C Institute for Social Development.

Brimner, Larry Dane. The Birthday Flowers. Tripp, Christine, illus. 2002. (Rookie Choices Ser.). 32p. (J). (gr. 1-2). 20.50 (978-0-516-22540-1(5) , Children's Pr.) Scholastic Library Publishing.

—The Birthday Flowers. 2002. (gr. k-3). lib. bdg. 14.10 (978-0-613-50185-9(3)) Tandem Library Bks.

Brisson, Pat. Melissa Parkington's Beautiful, Beautiful Hair. Bloom, Suzanne, illus. 2006. (J). 15.95 (978-1-59078-409-9(X)) Boyds Mills Pr.

Brooks, George W. The Spirit of 1906. 2004. reprint ed. pap. 15.95 (978-1-4191-8328-7(1)) Kessinger Publishing, LLC.

—The Spirit Of 1906. 2004. reprint ed. pap. 1.99 (978-1-4192-8328-4(6)) Kessinger Publishing, LLC.

Brouwer, Sigmund. Bug's Eye View: Annie Ant, Don't Cry! 2004. (Bug's-Eye View Bks.). (Illus.). 18p. (J). bds. 4.99 (978-0-8499-7757-2(6)) Nelson, Thomas Inc.

—Daddy Ant, You Never Listen. 2004. (Bug's-Eye View Bks.). (Illus.). 18p. (J). bds. 4.99 (978-0-8499-7755-8(X)) Nelson, Thomas Inc.

—Mystery Pennies. 2003. (Watch Out for Joel Ser.). (Illus.). 32p. (J). pap. 3.99 (978-0-7642-2584-0(7)) Bethany Hse. Pubs.

Brown, Tryla. Pink Shirt - Blue Shirt. l.t. ed. 2005. (Illus.). 17p. (J). per. 13.99 (978-1-59879-056-6(0)) Lifevest Publishing, Inc.

Brumbeau, Jeff. The Quiltmaker's Journey. De Marcken, Gail, illus. ed. 2005. 56p. (J). pap. 17.95 (978-0-439-51219-0(0) , Orchard Bks.) Scholastic, Inc.

Building a Winner. 2005. (Book Treks Ser.). (J). (gr. 3 up). stu. ed. 34.95 (978-0-673-62848-0(5)) Celebration Pr.

Bundschuh, Rick & Hamilton, Bethany. Storm. 2007. (Soul Surfer#8482; Ser.). 144p. (J). pap. 6.99 (978-0-310-71224-4(6)) Zonderkidz.

Burnett, Frances Hodgson. Editha's Burglar: A Story for Children. Sandham, Henry, illus. 2005. reprint ed. pap. 15.95 (978-1-4179-0135-7(7)) Kessinger Publishing, LLC.

Butler, Dori Hillestad. Tank Talbott's Guide to Girls. 2006. (Illus.). 135p. (J). 15.95 (978-0-8075-7761-5(8)) Whitman, Albert & Co.

Cabot, Meg. Pants on Fire. 2007. 272p. (gr. 7-10). (J). lib. bdg. 17.89 (978-0-06-088016-3(3)); (YA). 16.99 (978-0-06-088015-6(5)) HarperCollins Pubs. (HarperTeen).

—Teen Idol. l.t. ed. 2006. 366p. (YA). 23.95 (978-0-7862-7760-5(2)) Thorndike Pr.

Caldwell, V. M. Runt: Story of a Boy. 2006. 208p. (J). 16.95 (978-1-57131-662-2(0)); pap. 6.95 (978-1-57131-661-5(2)) Milkweed Editions.

Cameron, Peter. Someday This Pain Will Be Useful to You. 2007. 240p. (YA). (gr. 9 up). 16.00 (978-0-374-30989-3(2)) Farrar, Straus & Giroux.

Canfield, Jack L., et al. Chicken Soup for Little Souls Reader: The Greatest Gift of All. Ladwig, Tim, illus. 2005. 48p. (J). pap. 3.95 (978-0-7573-0280-0(7)) Health Communications, Inc.

Canterbury, Chloe. Tobee & the Amazing Bird Choir. 2000. (Illus.). xi, 97p. (J). (978-1-57895-037-9(6)) Bridge Resources.

Capucilli, Alyssa Satin. Biscuit Is Thankful. Schories, Pat, illus. 2003. (Biscuit Ser.). 16p. (J). (ps-1). 4.99 (978-0-694-01519-1(9)) HarperCollins Pubs.

Carlson, Melody. Diary of a Teenage Girl - It's My Life: Diary Number 2. 2002. (gr. 7-12). lib. bdg. 22.25 (978-0-613-88463-1(9)) Tandem Library Bks.

—Just Ask. 2005. (Diary of a Teenage Girl Ser.). 256p. (J). pap. 12.99 (978-1-59052-321-6(0) , Multnomah) WaterBrook Pr.

—Love Your Neighbor. Reagan, Susan Joy, illus. 2004. (Just Like Jesus Said Ser.). 32p. (J). (ps-5). 12.99 (978-0-8054-2383-9(4)) B&H Publishing Grp.

—My Name Is Chloe. 2005. 288p. (YA). mass mkt. 7.99 (978-1-59052-736-8(4) , Multnomah) WaterBrook Pr.

—My Name Is Chloe: Diary of a Teenage Girl. 2003. (gr. 7-12). lib. bdg. 22.25 (978-0-613-87416-8(1)) Tandem Library Bks.

—On My Own. 2002. (gr. 7-12). lib. bdg. 22.25 (978-0-613-85855-7(7)) Tandem Library Bks.

—On My Own: Diary Number 4. 2002. (Diary of a Teenage Girl Ser.: Bk. 4). 300p. (J). pap. 12.99 (978-1-59052-017-8(3) , Multnomah) WaterBrook Pr.

Carlson, Nancy. Get up & Go! Carlson, Nancy, illus. 2006. (Illus.). 32p. (J). (gr. k-3). 15.99 (978-0-670-05981-2(1) , Viking Juvenile) Penguin Group (USA) Inc.

—Smile a Lot! Carlson, Nancy, illus. 2003. (Words Are Categorical Ser.). (Illus.). 32p. (J). (gr. k-2). 15.95 (978-0-87614-869-3(0) , Carolrhoda Bks.) Lerner Publishing Group.

Carlson, Nancy. ¡Sonríe! (Smile a Lot!) Carlson, Nancy, illus. 2007. (Ediciones Lerner Single Titles Ser.). (SPA., Illus.). 32p. (J). (gr. k-2). 15.95 (***978-0-8225-7817-8(4)*** , Ediciones Lerner) Lerner Publishing Group.

Carlson, Nathan, et al. The Great Train Set Robbery. 2001. (Little Dogs on the Prairie Ser.). (Illus.). 64p. (J). (gr. 1-4). 4.99 (978-0-8499-7649-0(9)) Nelson, Thomas Inc.

Carman, Debby. Chewdalootie, Doing My Duty. 2006. (J). (978-0-9777340-3-0(X)) Faux Paw Media Group.

Carr, Dennis & Carr, Elise. Welcome to Wahoo. 2006. 250p. (YA). 16.95 (978-1-58234-696-0(8) , Bloomsbury Children) Bloomsbury Publishing.

Carr, Elise & Carr, Dennis. Welcome to Wahoo. 2007. 240p. (YA). pap. 6.95 (***978-1-59990-096-4(3)*** , Bloomsbury Children) Bloomsbury Publishing.

Carty, Jay, et al. O. Whillikers in the Hall of Champions. 2000. (Illus.). 112p. (J). pap. 13.00 (978-0-8307-2634-9(9) , Gospel Light) Gospel Light Pubns.

Casey & the See Through Head: Secrets for a Successful Life. 3rd ed. 2003. (Kamaron Concept Book:). (J). per. 9.99 (978-0-9715713-3-4(3)) Kamaron Institute Pr.

Castellucci, Cecil. The Queen of Cool. 2006. 176p. (YA). (gr. 9). 15.99 (978-0-7636-2720-1(8)) Candlewick Pr.

—The Queen of Cool. l.t. rev. ed. 2007. 172p. (YA). 22.95 (***978-0-7862-9551-7(1)***) Thorndike Pr.

Cather, Willa. Willa Cather. Balkovek, James, illus. 2004. (Great American Short Stories Ser.). 80p. (J). lib. bdg. 23.33 (978-0-8368-4251-7(0)) Stevens, Gareth Inc.

Cesena, Denise. Orderliness. Cesena, Denise & Perez, Maureen T., illus. l.t. ed. 2003. 28p. (J). 10.00 (978-0-9740418-2-7(3)) Night LIght Pubns., LLC.

—Orderliness - Companion Book. Cesena, Denise & Perez, Maureen T., illus. l.t. ed. 2003. 12p. (J). 2.00 (978-0-9740418-3-4(1)) Night LIght Pubns., LLC.

—Respect. Cesena, Denise & Perez, Maureen T., illus. l.t. ed. 2003. 28p. (J). (978-0-9740418-4-1(X)) Night LIght Pubns., LLC.

Charlton-Trujillo, E. E. Feels Like Home. 2007. 224p. (YA). (gr. 7 up). 15.99 (978-0-385-73332-8(1)); lib. bdg. 18.99 (978-0-385-90349-3(9)) Random Hse. Children's Bks. (Delacorte Bks. for Young Readers).

Child, Lauren. Clarice Bean Spells Trouble. Child, Lauren, illus. 2006. (Clarice Bean Ser.). 192p. (J). (gr. 3-6). pap. 5.99 (978-0-7636-2903-8(0)) Candlewick Pr.

Chin, Oliver Clyde. Julie Black Belt: The Kung Fu Chronicles. Chua, Charlene, illus. 2007. 36p. (J). (ps-3). 15.95 (***978-1-59702-009-1(5)***) Immedium.

Christophe, Le Masne. Tom en el Hospital. Bawin, Marie-Aline, illus. 2002. (Tom Ser.). (SPA & ENG.). 24p. (ps-k). 9.95 (978-84-7864-318-9(4)) Combel Editorial, S.A. ESP. *Dist:* Independent Pubs. Group.

Cindrich, Lisa. In the Shadow of the Pali: A Story of the Hawaiian Leper Colony. 2002. 240p. (YA). 18.99 (978-0-399-23855-0(7) , Putnam Juvenile) Penguin Group (USA) Inc.

Cirrone, Dorian. Prom Kings & Drama Queens. 2008. 208p. (J). 16.99 (***978-0-06-114372-4(3)***); lib. bdg. 17.89 (***978-0-06-114373-1(1)***) HarperCollins Pubs. (HarperTeen).

Clark, Clara Gillow. Hattie on Her Way. Thompson, John, illus. 2005. 208p. (J). (gr. 5 up). 15.99 (978-0-7636-2286-2(9)) Candlewick Pr.

Clark, Emma Chichester. No More Teasing! 2005. (Illus.). 32p. (J). pap. 8.99 (978-1-84270-470-7(2)) Trafalgar Square Publishing.

Clark, Sherryl. Prove It! 2000. (gr. 7-12). lib. bdg. 12.25 (978-0-613-29023-4(2)) Tandem Library Bks.

Clarke, Lyndia A. Tidy up Tommy. Clarke, Lyndia A., illus. 2006. (Illus.). 28p. (J). per. 19.95 (978-1-59453-971-8(5) , 3513, Airleaf Publishing) Airleaf Publishing & Bookselling.

—Tidy up Tommy. Clarke, Lyndia A., illus. 2005. (J). 1700.00 (978-0-9762898-6-9(5)) LightHouse Pr.

Cloci, Gabriella. Minda's Happily Ever After. 2003. (J). pap. 9.95 (978-0-7414-1501-1(0)) Infinity Publishing.

Cole, Sheila. The Canyon. 2002. 160p. (J). (gr. 3-7). 15.89 (978-0-06-029496-0(5)) HarperCollins Pubs.

Collins, Arda. Another Way of Life. l.t. ed. 2005. (Illus.). 30p. (J). per. 9.99 (978-1-59879-023-8(4)) Lifevest Publishing, Inc.

Collins-Varni, H. Elizabeth. The Doll Lady. Kuusisto, Judy, illus. 2001. 32p. (J). (ps-3). 15.95 (978-0-935699-24-1(4) , 0935699244) Illumination Arts Publishing Co., Inc.

Colon, Suzan. Smallville No.9: Temptation Book. 2004. (gr. 7-12). lib. bdg. 14.15 (978-0-613-71778-6(3)) Tandem Library Bks.

Colson-Becker, Mary. Flavor of Life. 2004. 67p. pap. 14.95 (978-1-4137-5617-3(4)) PublishAmerica, Inc.

Comor-Jacobs, Annie. Reesy: A Little Girl Learning Life's Lessons: Reesy Learning about Divorce; Reesy Learning about the Deep South; Reesy Learning about Deafness; Reesy Learning about Death, 4 vols. Price, Chris, illus. 2000. 40p. (J). (gr. 2-5). pap. 30.00 (978-1-889743-18-9(6)) Robbie Dean Pr.

Conner, Wendy Simpson. Stuff, Stuff, I Want More Stuff. (Illus.). (J). 16.95 (978-1-889599-22-9(0)) Interstellar Publishing Co.

Coolidge, Susan. What Katy Did. 2006. 62.99 (***978-1-4280-3108-1(1)***) IndyPublish.com.

Cooper, Ilene. The Golden Rule. Swiatowska, Gabi, illus. 2007. 32p. (J). (ps-3). 16.95 (978-0-8109-0960-1(5)) , Abrams Bks. for Young Readers) Abrams, Harry N. , Inc.

Cooper, John. First Day. Roscetti, John, illus. l.t. ed. 2002. (Heroes Start As Kids!: Vol. 1). 97p. (J). (gr. 2-7). per. 5.95 (978-0-9711474-9-2(3)) A B C-123 Publishing.

Cosby, Bill. The Day I Saw My Father Cry. 2000. (Little Bill Books for Beginning Readers Ser.). (Illus.). (J). 10.79 (978-0-606-20470-5(9)) Tandem Library Bks.

—The Day I Saw My Father Cry. Honeywood, Varnette P., illus. 2000. (J). (ps-k). lib. bdg. 11.80 (978-0-613-21412-4(9)) Tandem Library Bks.

Cosby, Bill & Honeywood, Varnette P. The Day I Saw My Father Cry. 2000. (Little Bill Books for Beginning Readers Ser.). (Illus.). 40p. (J). (gr. k-3). pap. 15.95 (978-0-590-52197-0(7)) Scholastic, Inc.

Cosgrove, Stephen. The Bigg Family: Getting along with Others. Arroyo, Fian, illus. 2004. (J). (978-1-58804-354-2(1)) PCI Educational Publishing.

—Hickory B. Hopp: Paying Attention. Arroyo, Fian, illus. 2004. (J). (978-1-58804-379-5(7)) PCI Educational Publishing.

—Zippity Zoom. 2001. (gr. k-3). lib. bdg. 13.00 (978-0-613-81846-9(6)) Tandem Library Bks.

Coulter, Laura Heidser. The Least. 2002. 109p. pap. 16.95 (978-1-59129-674-4(9)) PublishAmerica, Inc.

Courtenay, Bryce. The Power of One. 2005. 304p. (J). (gr. 5-12). lib. bdg. 17.99 (978-0-385-90274-8(3)) , Delacorte Bks. for Young Readers) Random Hse. Children's Bks.

Cox, Judy. Cool Cat, School Cat. Sims, Blanche, illus. 2002. 96p. (J). (gr. 4-6). tchr. ed. 15.95 (978-0-8234-1714-8(X)) Holiday Hse., Inc.

Crawford, Neil. The Journeyers. 2006. (J). pap. (***978-0-9778205-4-2(8)***) Helm Publishing.

Creech, Sharon. Replay. 240p. (J). (gr. 3-7). 2007. pap. 5.99 (978-0-06-054021-0(4) , Harper Trophy); 2005. 15.99 (978-0-06-054019-7(2) , Cotler, Joanna Books); 2005. lib. bdg. 16.89 (978-0-06-054020-3(6) , Cotler, Joanna Books) HarperCollins Pubs.

Cummings, Priscilla. Red Kayak. (gr. 5). 2006. 224p. (YA). pap. 6.99 (978-0-14-240573-4(6) , Puffin); 2004. 192p. (J). 15.99 (978-0-525-47317-6(3) , Dutton Juvenile) Penguin Group (USA) Inc.

Curry, Kenneth. Chuka & the Drum. 2007. (Illus.). 22p. (J). 10.95 (***978-0-9798364-4-2(1)***) Curry Brothers Publishing.

Curtis, Jamie Lee. I'm Gonna Like Me: Letting off a Little Self-Esteem. Cornell, Laura, illus. 2002. (J). (ps-3). 32p. 16.99 (978-0-06-028761-0(6)); 40p. lib. bdg. 17.89 (978-0-06-028762-7(4)) HarperCollins Pubs. (Cotler, Joanna Books).

—Is There Really a Human Race? Cornell, Laura, illus. 2006. 40p. 16.99 (978-0-06-075346-7(3)); lib. bdg. 17.89 (978-0-06-075348-1(X)) HarperCollins Pubs. (Cotler, Joanna Books).

Cyanne Bandanna Kindergartner always Tell the Truth. 2005. (YA). per. (978-1-59872-133-1(X)) Instantpublisher-.com.

Dale, Fanny. Golden Rule or Second Series of Househol. 2006. pap. 26.95 (***978-1-4286-5592-8(1)***) Kessinger Publishing, LLC.

Dalecki, Linden. Kid B. 2006. 178p. (J). (gr. 8). pap. 7.99 (978-0-618-60566-8(5)) Houghton Mifflin Co.

Davoll, Barbara. Christopher & His Family. Hockerman, Dennis, illus. 2003. (Christopher Churchmouse Ser.). 128p. (J). 14.99 (978-0-8423-5735-7(1)) Tyndale Hse. Pubs.

—Christopher & His Friends. Hockerman, Dennis, illus. 2003. (Christopher Churchmouse Ser.). 128p. (J). 14.99 (978-0-8423-5734-0(3)) Tyndale Hse. Pubs.

De Lint, Charles. The Blue Girl. 2006. 384p. (YA). (gr. 7). reprint ed. pap. 7.99 (978-0-14-240545-1(0) , Puffin) Penguin Group (USA) Inc.

Deckers, Amber. Ella Mental: And the Good Sense Guide. 2006. (Illus.). 240p. (YA). mass mkt. 6.99 (978-1-4169-1322-1(X) , Simon Pulse) Simon & Schuster Children's Publishing.

Del Amo, Montserrat. La Piedra y el Agua. (SPA.). 119p. (J). (978-84-279-3127-5(1) , NG1011) Noguer y Caralt Editores, S. A. ESP. *Dist:* Lectorum Pubns., Inc.

DeLoach, Kathleen. Daniel's World. Best, Cathy, illus. 2004. (J). pap. 15.95 (978-0-9747440-5-6(0)) Three Moons Media.

Deriso, Christine Hurley. Do-Over. 2006. 192p. (J). (gr. 4-7). 15.95 (978-0-385-73333-5(X)); lib. bdg. 17.99 (978-0-385-90350-9(2)) Random Hse. Children's Bks. (Delacorte Bks. for Young Readers).

Deriso, Christine Hurley. Do-Over. 2007. 160p. (J). (gr. 4-7). 5.99 (***978-0-440-42119-1(5)*** , Yearling) Random Hse. Children's Bks.

DeRosa, Nancy. Lazy Robert. Verona Publishing, illus. 2006. (J). 5.95 (978-0-9769031-0-9(5)) Verona (Bk.) Publishing, Inc.

Deseret Book Company Staff, contrib. by. A Story to Tell: The Classic Book of Virtues for Children. 2nd ed. 2004. 508p. (J). 16.95 (978-1-59038-359-9(1)) Deseret Bk. Co.

Dietz, Irene Andrighetti. Clariss, Did You Do This? 2006. (J). pap. 8.00 (978-0-8059-6968-9(3)) Dorrance Publishing Co., Inc.

Dobrin, Arthur. Love Your Neighbor: Stories of Values & Virtues. Rogers, Jacqueline, illus. 1999. 64p. (J). (ps-3). pap. 16.95 (978-0-590-04410-3(9)) Scholastic, Inc.

Dockter, Toni. Percy & the Plod. (Illus.). 200p. (J). pap. 14.95 (978-0-9712201-0-2(7)) Dockter, Toni.

Dougherty, Mary. Life Adventures with Fossy. 2004. 7p. (J). pap. 10.58 (978-1-4116-1497-0(6)) Lulu.com.

Doughty, Rebecca. Some Helpful Tips for a Better World & a Happier Life. 2008. (J). (***978-0-375-84272-6(1)***); (***978-0-375-94555-7(5)***) Random Hse. Children's Bks. (Schwartz & Wade Bks.).

Downs Webb, Michelle. What Color Is Love? 2005. 24p. 10.95 (978-1-4116-2783-3(0)) Lulu.com.

Doyle, Brian. Dam Lies. 1999. 128p. (J). (gr. 4 up). 15.95 (978-0-88899-349-6(8)); pap. (978-0-88899-350-2(1)) Groundwood Bks. CAN. *Dist:* Transition Vendor.

Duble, Kathleen Benner. Hearts of Iron. 2006. 256p. (J). 15.95 (978-1-4169-0850-0(1) , McElderry, Margaret K.) Simon & Schuster Children's Publishing.

DuPrau, Jeanne. The Prophet of Yonwood. 2006. 304p. (J). (gr. 4-8). lib. bdg. 17.99 (978-0-375-97526-4(8)); (Books of Ember Ser.: Bk. 3). 15.95 (978-0-375-87526-7(3)) Random Hse. Children's Bks. (Random Hse. Bks. for Young Readers).

—Prophet of Yonwood. 2007. (Books of Ember Ser.: Bk. 3). 304p. (J). (gr. 4-7). 6.50 (978-0-440-42124-5(1) , Yearling) Random Hse. Children's Bks.

Duran, Patricia. A Surprise for Nora. Sorrento, Lisha, illus. 2005. 32p. (J). pap. 18.00 (978-1-4208-2717-0(0)) AuthorHouse.

Easton, Patricia Harrison. Davey's Blue-Eyed Frog. Wohnoutka, Mike, illus. 2003. 112p. (J). (gr. 3-5). tchr. ed. 14.00 (978-0-618-18185-8(7) , Clarion Bks.) Houghton Mifflin Co. Trade & Reference Div.

Egan, Tim. The Pink Refrigerator. 2007. (Illus.). (J). (***978-1-4287-3954-3(8)***) Houghton Mifflin Co.

Elster, Jean Alicia. I Have a Dream, Too! Tadgell, Nicole, illus. 2002. (Joe Joe in the City Ser.: No. 2). 32p. (gr. 1-5). 12.00 (978-0-8170-1397-4(0)) Judson Pr.

—I'll Do the Right Thing. Tadgell, Nicole, illus. 2003. (Joe Joe in the City Ser.). 32p. (gr. 1-5). 12.00 (978-0-8170-1408-7(X)) Judson Pr.

—I'll Fly My Own Plane. Tadgell, Nicole, illus. 2002. (Joe Joe in the City Ser.: 3). 32p. 12.00 (978-0-8170-1407-0(1)) Judson Pr.

Emesse, Tea. Yumi Talks the Talk. 2006. (Star Sisterztm Ser.: Bk. 6). 144p. (YA). pap. 4.99 (978-0-7869-3992-3(3) , Mirrorstone) Wizards of the Coast.

Enright, Robert D. Rising above the Storm Clouds: What It's Like to Forgive. Finney, Kathryn Kunz, illus. 2004. 32p. (J). 14.95 (978-1-59147-075-5(7)); pap. 8.95 (978-1-59147-076-2(5)) American Psychological Assn. (Magination Pr.).

Ethier, Vicki. I Know My Nana Rosa Is an Alien. Ethier, Vicki, illus. 2003. (Illus.). 20p. (J). 6.00 (978-1-928972-10-5(1)) Critter Pubns.

Evans, Michael Robert. 68 Knots: A Novel. 2007. 350p. (gr. 9 up). 15.95 (***978-1-933718-14-9(5)***) Tanglewood Pr.

Evans, Richard Paul. The Christmas Candle. Collins, Jacob, illus. 2006. 32p. (J). 7.99 (978-1-4169-2682-5(8) , Aladdin) Simon & Schuster Children's Publishing.

Evans, Richard Paul & Craig, Daniel. The Light of Christmas. 2002. (Illus.). 32p. (J). (gr. k-3). 16.95 (978-0-689-83468-4(3)) Simon & Schuster Children's Publishing.

Everett Hale, Edward. Last of the Peterkins with Others of the. 2006. pap. (***978-1-4068-1087-5(8)***) Echo Library.

Ewing, Lynne. The Sacrifice. Scalora, Suza, illus. 5th rev. ed. 2001. (Daughters of the Moon Ser.: Bk. 5). 288p. (gr. 7-17). 9.99 (978-0-7868-0706-2(7) , Volo) Hyperion Bks. for Children.

Farrar, F. W. Eric or Little by Little (a Tale of Rosl. 2006. 35.99 (***978-1-4219-8395-0(8)***) IndyPublish.com.

Feely, Jenny. Big Pig's Wig. 2001. (gr. k-3). lib. bdg. 11.65 (978-0-613-33336-8(5)) Tandem Library Bks.

Feldman, Jody. The Gollywhopper Games. Jamieson, Victoria, illus. 2008. 336p. (J). 16.99 (***978-0-06-121450-9(7)***); lib. bdg. 17.89 (***978-0-06-121451-6(5)***) HarperCollins Pubs. (Greenwillow Bks.).

Ferrin, Wendy Wakefield. Germs on Their Fingers! Tono, Lucia, tr. Broyles, Beverly Ashley, illus. 2003. Tr. of Germenes en Tus Manos!. (SPA & ENG.). 64p. (J). (gr. 1-7). 17.95 (978-0-9703632-1-3(4)); pap. 12.95 (978-0-9703632-0-6(6)) Wakefield Connection, The.

Fielding, Sarah. The Governess or the Little Female Academy. 2004. reprint ed. pap. 19.95 (978-1-4191-6442-2(2)); pap. 1.99 (978-1-4192-6442-9(7)) Kessinger Publishing, LLC.

Fields, Terri. Holdup. 2007. 176p. (YA). (gr. 10 up). 16.95 (978-1-59643-219-2(5)) Roaring Brook Pr.

Finding Our Way: True Stories of Dilemmas, Difficulties & Discoveries. 2004. (J). pap. 15.00 net. (978-0-9710606-3-0(0)) Streetside Stories, Inc.

Finley, Martha. Elsie's Impossible Choice. Bk. 2. Williams, Scott, illus. 1999. (Elsie Dinsmore: Bk. 2). 238p. (YA). (gr. 5-9). 12.99 (978-1-928749-02-8(X)) Zonderkidz.

—Elsie's Impossible Choice, Vol. 2. 2006. (Life of Faith': Elsie Dinsmore Ser.). 224p. (J). pap. 7.99 (978-1-928749-81-3(X)) Zonderkidz.

—Elsie's Stolen Heart. 224p. Bk. 4. 1999. (Elsie Dinsmore: Bk. 4). (Illus.). (YA). (gr. 5-9). 12.99 (978-1-928749-04-2(6)); Vol. 4. 2006. (Life of Faith': Elsie Dinsmore Ser.). (J). pap. 7.99 (978-1-928749-83-7(6)) Zonderkidz.

Flake, Sharon G. The Broken Bike Boy & the Queen of 33rd Street. Bootman, Colin, illus. 2007. 144p. (gr. 3-7). 15.99 (***978-1-4231-0032-4(8)*** , Jump at the Sun) Hyperion Bks. for Children.

Fontaine, Catherine Silliman. Have a Not for Christmas ... & Always. 2006. (Illus.). 44p. (J). 11.95 (978-0-9776958-0-5(8)) CyPress Pubns.

Forbush, Kyle. The Sourdoughs' Five Children. Forbush, Lisa, illus. 2004. (J). bds. 6.95 (978-1-57833-258-8(3)) Todd Communications.

Fox, Diane & Fox, Christyan. Tyson the Terrible. Fox, Diane, illus. 2006. (Illus.). 24p. (J). (ps-2). 12.95 (978-1-58234-734-9(4)) Bloomsbury Publishing.

Fox, Mem. Fairy, Fairy Quite Contrary. Swearingen, Greg, illus. 2005. (J). (978-0-15-202260-0(0)) Holt, Rinehart & Winston.

—Que Crees. Goodman, Vivienne, illus. 2000. (Los Especiales de A la Orilla Del Viento Ser.). (SPA.). 29p. (J). (ps-7). per. 13.99 (978-968-16-6023-9(4) , FC6177) Fondo de Cultura Economica USA.

Frank, Christian M. Catholic (Reluctantly) 2007. (YA). pap. 11.95 (***978-1-928832-99-7(7)***) Sophia Institute Pr.

Freedman, Phylllis. Wrapping Paper. 2006. pap. 7.95 (978-0-533-15350-3(6)) Vantage Pr., Inc.

Friedman, Laurie B. Campfire Mallory. Kalis, Jennifer, illus. 2008. (Mallory Ser.). (J). lib. bdg. 15.95 (***978-0-8225-7657-0(0)*** , Carolrhoda Bks.) Lerner Publishing Group.

Fullerton, Alma. Walking on Glass. 2007. 144p. (J). (gr. 9 up). 15.99 (978-0-06-077851-4(2)); lib. bdg. 16.89 (978-0-06-077852-1(0)) HarperCollins Pubs. (HarperTeen).

Fuqua, Jonathon Scott. King of the Pygmies. 2007. (Illus.). 256p. (YA). (gr. 9). pap. 7.99 (***978-0-7636-3412-4(3)***) Candlewick Pr.

Gaberman, Judith. Bigmouth. 2001. 124p. (gr. 4-7). pap. 9.95 (978-0-595-15798-3(X) , Backinprint.com) iUniverse, Inc.

Gallego Garcia, Laura. The Legend of the Wandering King. 2005. (Illus.). 224p. (J). (gr. 7-17). pap. 16.95 (978-0-439-58556-9(2) , Levine, Arthur A. Bks.) Scholastic, Inc.

Gallego Garcia, Laura & Bellm, Dan. The Legend of the Wandering King. 2005. (J). (978-0-439-58557-6(0) , Levine, Arthur A. Bks.) Scholastic, Inc.

Gallo, Donald R. No Easy Answers. 1999. (978-0-606-15903-6(7)) Tandem Library Bks.

—No Easy Answers: Short Stories about Teenagers Making Tough Choices. 1999. 336p. (YA). (gr. 7-12). pap. 6.50 (978-0-440-41305-9(2) , Laurel Leaf) Random Hse. Children's Bks. .

—No Easy Answers: Short Stories about Teenagers Making Tough Choices. 1999. (gr. 7-12). lib. bdg. 13.55 (978-0-613-13200-8(9)) Tandem Library Bks.

Garcia, Joan. Footsteps of Angels. 2003. 52p. (J). pap. 11.95 (978-0-7414-1602-5(6)) Infinity Publishing.

Geldart, Thomas. Emilie the Peacemaker. 2004. reprint ed. pap. 15.95 (978-1-4191-1769-5(6)); pap. 1.99 (978-1-4192-1769-2(0)) Kessinger Publishing, LLC.

Gemmen, Heather. Quit Looking at Me! Lagares, Luciano, illus. 2003. (Tough Stuff for Kids Ser.). 32p. (J). pap., pap. 5.99 (978-0-7814-3852-0(7) , 0781438527) Cook, David C. Publishing Co.

Give, Save, Spend. 2006. 16p. (J). pap. 1.99 (978-0-7847-1691-5(9) , 02993) Standard Publishing.

Gloria Whelan. The Turning. l.t. ed. 2006. 190p. (YA). 21.95 (978-0-7862-9035-2(8)) Thorndike Pr.

Godwin, Jane. Falling from Grace. 2007. 204p. (YA). (gr. 6 up). 16.95 (***978-0-8234-2105-3(8)***) Holiday Hse., Inc.

Going, K. L. Saint Iggy. 2006. (Illus.). 272p. (YA). 17.00 (978-0-15-205795-4(1)) Harcourt Children's Bks.

Golding, Jacqueline. Healing Stories: Picture Books for the Big & Small Changes in a Child's Life. 2006. 336p. pap. 17.95 (978-1-59077-097-9(8)); 26.95 (978-1-59077-104-4(4)) Evans, M. & Co., Inc.

Goldolphin, Mary. Sandford & Merton. 2005. reprint ed. pap. 15.95 (978-1-4191-0539-5(6)) Kessinger Publishing, LLC.

Goldsboro, Bobby. Jonah & the Whale/Daniel & the Lion's Den, Vol. 2. Stewart, Toni D., illus. 2003. (Adventures of Cheze & Kwackers Ser.: Bk. 2). 48p. (J). (gr. k-3). pap. 8.95 (978-1-889658-28-5(6)) New Canaan Publishing Co. LLC.

—Noah & the Ark/David & Goliath. Stewart, Toni D., illus. 2003. (Adventures of Cheze & Kwackers Ser.: Bk. 1). 48p. (J). (gr. k-3). pap. 8.95 (978-1-889658-27-8(8)) New Canaan Publishing Co. LLC.

Gonzalez, Rigoberto & Alvarez, Cecilia Concepcion. Antonio's Card. 2005. (ENG & SPA., Illus.). 32p. (J). 16.95 (978-0-89239-204-9(5)) Children's Bk. Pr.

Got, Yves. Chambre de Didou. pap. 12.95 (978-2-226-12991-8(X)) Albin-Michel, Editions FRA. *Dist:* Distribooks, Inc.

Goto, Scott. The Perfect Sword. 2008. (J). (***978-1-57091-697-7(7)***) Charlesbridge Publishing, Inc.

Grandpa & Little Guy. 2004. (J). 15.95 (978-0-9764012-0-9(7)) Rockmill Publishing Co.

Green, David. Tonya Baldwin. 2005. 78p. pap. 14.95 (978-1-4137-6135-1(6)) PublishAmerica, Inc.

Greene, Bette. Summer of My German Soldier. 2006. (Puffin Modern Classics Ser.). 240p. (J). (gr. 5). pap. 6.99 (978-0-14-240651-9(1) , Puffin) Penguin Group (USA) Inc.

Greene, Thomas. Whacked Out Wrestling: Memorial - A tale of Headlocks, Hurricanranas, & High School. 2007. 228p. pap. 14.95 (***978-1-60145-175-0(X)***) Booklocker-.com, Inc.

Gregory, Nan. I'll Sing You One-O. 2006. 224p. (J). (gr. 4-6). 16.00 (978-0-618-60708-2(0) , Clarion Bks.) Houghton Mifflin Co. Trade & Reference Div.

Griffin, Adele. My Almost Epic Summer. 2008. 176p. (YA). (gr. 7). pap. 6.99 (***978-0-14-240805-6(0)*** , Puffin); 2006. 192p. (J). (gr. 4). 15.99 (978-0-399-23784-3(4) , Putnam Juvenile) Penguin Group (USA) Inc.

Griffin, Adele. My Almost Epic Summer (Splashproof Ed.) 2007. 1p. (YA). (gr. 7). pap. 6.99 (978-0-14-240860-5(3) , Puffin) Penguin Group (USA) Inc.

Griffin, Peni R. The Music Thief. rev. ed. 2002. 160p. (YA). (gr. 5-8). 16.95 (978-0-8050-7055-2(9) , Holt, Henry & Co. Bks. For Young Readers) Holt, Henry & Co.

—The Music Thief. l.t. ed. 2003. 190p. (J). 21.95 (978-0-7862-5606-8(0)) Thorndike Pr.

Gross, Philip. The Lastling. 2006. 256p. (YA). (gr. 7). 16.00 (978-0-618-65998-2(6) , Clarion Bks.) Houghton Mifflin Co. Trade & Reference Div.

Grossman, Linda Sky. Respect Is Correct. Bockus, Petra, illus. 24p. pap. 4.95 (978-1-896764-56-6(8)); 2002. 11.95 (978-1-896764-58-0(4)) Second Story Pr. CAN. *Dist:* Orca Bk. Pubs. USA.

Gummelt, Donna & Melchiorre, Dondino. Your Name Is Mud. Wall, Randy Hugh, ed. Varela, Carmen, tr. Varela, Juan D., illus. l.t. ed. 2006. Tr. of Tu nombre es Mud. 34p. (J). 14.95 (978-0-9764798-3-3(4)) Story Store Collection Publishing.

Gunn, Robin Jones. Sierra Jensen Collection: Close Your Eyes; Without a Doubt; With This Ring, Vol. 2. 2006. (Sierra Jensen Ser.: Bks. 4-6). 496p. (J). 14.99 (978-1-59052-589-0(2) , Multnomah Fiction) WaterBrook Pr.

—Sierra Jensen Collection: Hold on Tight; Closer Than Ever; Take My Hand, Vol. 4. 2006. (Sierra Jensen Ser.: Bks. 10-12). 464p. (J). 14.99 (978-1-59052-591-3(4) , Multnomah Fiction) WaterBrook Pr.

—Sierra Jensen Collection: Only You; Sierra, In Your Dreams; Don't You Wish, Vol. 1. 2006. (Sierra Jensen Ser.: Bks. 1-3). 432p. (J). 14.99 (978-1-59052-588-3(4) , Multnomah Fiction) WaterBrook Pr.

—Sierra Jensen Collection: Open Your Heart; Time Will Tell; Now Picture This, Vol. 3. 2006. (Sierra Jensen Ser.: Bks. 7-9). 480p. (J). 14.99 (978-1-59052-590-6(6) , Multnomah Fiction) WaterBrook Pr.

Haddix, Margaret Peterson. Among the Betrayed. (Shadow Children Ser.). (gr. 4-9). 2003. 176p. (YA). pap. 5.99 (978-0-689-83909-2(X) , Aladdin); 2002. 160p. (J). 16.95 (978-0-689-83905-4(7)) Simon & Schuster Children's Publishing.

—Among the Betrayed. 2003. (Shadow Children Ser.). (gr. 5-8). lib. bdg. 13.00 (978-0-613-90190-1(8)) Tandem Library Bks.

—Among the Betrayed. l.t. ed. 2006. (Shadow Children Ser.). 205p. (YA). 22.95 (978-0-7862-8279-1(7)) Thorndike Pr.

—Among the Enemy. (Shadow Children Ser.). (J). 2006. 240p. pap. 5.99 (978-0-689-85797-3(7) , Aladdin); 2005. 224p. (gr. 3-7). 16.95 (978-0-689-85796-6(9) , Simon & Schuster Children's Publishing) Simon & Schuster Children's Publishing.

—Among the Free. (Shadow Children Ser.). 208p. (J). 2007. pap. 5.99 (*978-0-689-85799-7(3)* , Aladdin); 2006. (gr. 3-7). 16.95 (978-0-689-85798-0(5) , Simon & Schuster Children's Publishing) Simon & Schuster Children's Publishing.

Haines, J. D. Flight of the Eagle. 2002. (Illus.). 88p. 15.95 (978-1-57168-744-9(0)) Eakin Pr.

Hallem, J. The Super Electrics. Dale, Rae, illus. 2006. (Read-It! Chapter Books). 64p. (J). (gr. 2-4). 19.95 (978-1-4048-1663-3(1)) Picture Window Bks.

Hallinan, P. K. Heartprints. 2004. (Illus.). 26p. (J). bds. 6.95 (978-0-8249-6564-8(7)) Ideals Pubns.

—Let's Be Happy. 2005. (Illus.). 26p. (J). (ps-k). bds. 7.95 (978-0-8249-6588-4(4)) Ideals Pubns.

—Let's Be Helpful. 2004. (Illus.). 26p. (J). bds. 7.95 (978-0-8249-6563-1(9)) Ideals Pubns.

Harcourt School Publishers Staff. Changes Advanced Level. 3rd ed. 2002. (Trophies Reading Program Ser.). (Illus.). pap. 5.10 (978-0-15-323204-6(8)) Harcourt Schl. Pubs.

Harper, Charise Mericle. The Invisible Mistakecase. 2005. (Illus.). 32p. (J). (gr. k-3). 16.00 (978-0-618-44885-2(3)) Houghton Mifflin Co. Trade & Reference Div.

Hartnett, Sonya. The Silver Donkey. Powers, Don, illus. 272p. (J). (gr. 5). 2007. pap. 7.99 (*978-0-7636-3681-4(9));* 2006. 15.99 (978-0-7636-2937-3(5)) Candlewick Pr.

—The Silver Donkey. Spudvilas, Anne, illus. 2004. viii, 193p. (J). (978-0-670-04240-1(4) , Viking Adult) Penguin Group (USA) Inc.

Havel, Geoff. The Facts of Life. Tholen, Shane, illus. 2001. 120p. (J). (gr. 3-5). pap. 13.95 (978-1-86368-321-0(6)) Fremantle Pr. AUS. *Dist:* International Specialized Bk. Services.

Hawthorne, Nathaniel. The Scarlet Letter - Literary Touchstone Edition. 2005. 216p. (YA). per. 4.99 (978-1-58049-595-0(8) , PWH5958) Prestwick Hse., Inc.

Hayes, Sonia. Ms. Thang. 2006. (ENG.). 192p. (YA). per. 9.95 (978-0-9777573-0-5(7)) NUA Multimedia.

Hayes, Sonia. Urban Goddess. 2007. 224p. (YA). per. 9.95 (*978-0-9777573-1-2(5)*) NUA Multimedia.

Hays, Helen Ashe. The Adventures of Prince Lazybones: And Other Stories. 2007. 152p. pap. 11.99 (*978-1-4264-8474-2(7));* 168p. pap. 14.99 (*978-1-4264-8532-9(8)*) BiblioBazaar.

Hedji, Charles. Fields of Discovery. 2006. 220p. pap. 19.95 (978-1-4241-0605-9(2)) PublishAmerica, Inc.

Hege, Evelyn. A Letter for Titus. 2004. (Illus.). 24p. (ps-5). 2.70 (978-0-7399-2345-0(5) , 2791) Rod & Staff Pubs., Inc.

Helping Hands. 2004. (J). per. 15.99 (978-0-9753533-8-7(1)) Golden Eagle Publishing Hse., Inc.

Hennessy, B. G. Because of You: A Book of Kindness. Nakata, Hiroe, illus. 2005. 24p. (J). (gr. k-2). 15.99 (978-0-7636-1926-8(4)) Candlewick Pr.

Hennessy, Claire. Afterwards. 2005. 188p. (YA). pap. (*978-1-84223-207-1(X)*) Poolbeg Pr.

Hennessy, James. Shane's Game. 2003. 184p. 23.95 (978-0-595-74739-9(6)); pap. 13.95 (978-0-595-28112-1(5)) iUniverse, Inc.

Henty, G. A. With Wolfe in Canada: The Winning of a Continent. 2001. (Illus.). 353p. (J). (978-0-921100-86-7(8)); pap. (978-0-921100-87-4(6)) Inheritance Pubns.

—With Wolfe in Canada: The Winning of a Continent. (Illus.). 353p. (J). 2000. (gr. 8-12). pap. 14.99 (978-1-887159-30-2(4)); 1998. lib. bdg. 20.99 (978-1-887159-18-0(5)) Preston-Speed Pubns.

—With Wolfe in Canada: The Winning of a Continent. 2006. per. 8.95 (978-1-57646-980-4(8)) Quiet Vision Publishing.

Hetzer, Michael. The Get Well Picture. Clayton, Kim, illus. 2005. (J). 2nd collector's ed. 32p. 18.95 (978-0-9728222-5-1(9)); 3rd ed. 18.95 (978-0-9728222-6-8(7)) Webster Henrietta Publishing.

Hill, Karen. Finding the Golden Ruler. Hoshino, Felicia, illus. 2005. 24p. (J). 9.99 (978-1-4169-0513-4(8) , Little Simon) Simon & Schuster Children's Publishing.

—Finding the Golden Ruler. Hoshino, Felicia, illus. 2005. 24p. (J). pap. 3.99 (978-1-4169-0317-8(8)) Simon & Schuster, Inc.

Hockerman, Dennis, illus. The Little Seed: A Tale about Integrity. 2006. (J). (*978-1-59939-094-9(9)* , Reader's Digest Young Families, Inc.) Reader's Digest Children's Publishing, Inc.

Holm, H. R. Against an Amber Sky. 2007. viii, 214p. (J). (*978-1-55517-991-5(6)*) Cedar Fort, Inc./CFI Distribution.

Honeywood, Varnette P., illus. The Day I Saw My Father Cry. 2002. (Little Bill Ser.). (J). 11.91 (978-0-7587-1093-2(3)) Book Wholesalers, Inc.

Hostetter, Joyce. Healing Water. 2008. (YA). (*978-1-59078-514-0(2)* , Calkins Creek) Boyds Mills Pr.

Howe, James. The Misfits. 2003. (gr. 7-12). lib. bdg. 14.15 (978-0-613-66423-3(X)) Tandem Library Bks.

Howe, Norma. The Adventures of Blue Avenger. unabr. ed. 2004. (Blue Avenger Ser.). 240p. (J). (gr. 6 up). pap. 36.00 incl. audio (978-0-8072-8423-0(8) , YA167SP, Listening Library) Random Hse. Audio Publishing Group.

—The Adventures of Blue Avenger. 2000. 229p. (YA). (gr. 7-12). lib. bdg. 15.30 (978-0-613-29862-9(4)); 1999. (J). 13.64 (978-0-606-20028-8(2)) Tandem Library Bks.

Hubery, Julia. A Christmas Wish. Williams, Sophy, illus. 2007. 28p. (J). (ps-2). 16.95 (*978-1-56148-589-5(6)*) Good Bks.

Hughes, Dean. Soldier Boys. (YA). 2003. 240p. (gr. 7-12). mass mkt. 5.99 (978-0-689-86021-8(8) , Simon Pulse); 2001. 176p. (gr. 4-6). 16.95 (978-0-689-81748-9(7) , Atheneum) Simon & Schuster Children's Publishing.

—Soldier Boys. 2003. (gr. 3-6). lib. bdg. 13.00 (978-0-613-66437-0(X)) Tandem Library Bks.

Jackson, Bobby L. Boon the Raccoon & Easel the Weasel. Rodriguez, Christina, illus. 2004. 32p. (J). pap. 11.95 (978-1-884242-03-8(0) , BREW2NED); 19.95 (978-1-884242-02-1(2) , BREW2NED) Multicultural Pubns.

Jarvis, Robin. The Crystal Prison. (Deptford Mice Ser.: Bk. 2). (Illus.). 256p. (YA). 2002. pap. 6.95 (978-1-58717-161-1(9)); 2001. (gr. 5 up). 17.95 (978-1-58717-107-9(4)) Chronicle Bks. LLC. (SeaStar Bks.).

—Crystal Prison. 2002. (gr. 5-8). lib. bdg. 15.25 (978-0-613-56295-9(X)) Tandem Library Bks.

Jenkins, Jerry B. & Fabry, Chris. The Book of the King. 2007. (Wormling Ser.). 288p. (J). (gr. 5-9). pap. 7.99 (*978-1-4143-0155-6(3)*) Tyndale Hse. Pubs.

—The Changeling. 2007. (Wormling Ser.). 336p. (J). (gr. 5-9). pap. 7.99 (*978-1-4143-0157-0(X)*) Tyndale Hse. Pubs.

Jesse, Mary. Abbey & Friends M Is for Manners. Cherif, Jennifer, illus. 2003. 48p. (J). 15.95 (978-0-9729958-0-1(3)) Hexagon Blue.

Johnson-Choong, Shelly. The Jewelry Box. 2nd ed. 2004. (YA). reprint ed. pap. 10.95 (978-1-932280-40-1(5) , 80405) Granite Publishing & Distribution.

Johnson, Kathleen Jeffrie. Gone. 2007. 176p. (YA). (gr. 9 up). 16.95 (978-1-59643-138-6(5)) Roaring Brook Pr.

Johnson, Kimberly P. The Adventures of the Itty Bitty Spider & the Itty Bitty Mouse. 2004. (Illus.). 31p. (gr. k-2). 14.95 (978-1-57197-236-1(6)) Pentland Pr., Inc.

Johnson, Lissa Halls & Hanscome, Jeanette. Dragonfly on My Shoulder, Vol. 9. 2005. (Brio Girls Ser.: Bk. 9). (Illus.). 192p. (YA). pap. 7.99 (978-1-58997-088-5(8)) Focus on the Family Publishing.

Johnson, Regan. Little Bunny Kung Fu. Johnson, Regan, illus. 2005. (Illus.). 32p. (J). 16.95 (978-0-9769417-8-1(3)) Blooming Tree Pr.

Johnston, Annie Fellows. The Little Colonel. 2004. reprint ed. pap. 1.99 (978-1-4192-7020-8(6)) Kessinger Publishing, LLC.

The Jonah & the Big Fish, Beginner's Biblereg; 2007. (Biblia para Principiantes Ser.). 24p. (J). 5.99 (978-0-8297-5009-6(6)) Vida Pubs.

Jones, Christianne C. Room to Share. Trover, Zachary, illus. 2005. (Read-It! Readers Ser.). 24p. (J). (ps). lib. bdg. 18.60 (978-1-4048-1185-0(0)) Picture Window Bks.

Jones, Juanita. Mr. Nice Guy. 2003. (YA). per. (978-0-9740833-7-7(2)) Port Town Publishing.

Jones, Lara. Me Gusta Mi Orinal. (SPA.). 10p. 17.95 (978-84-272-7865-3(9)) Molino, Editorial ESP. *Dist:* Distribooks, Inc.

Jones, Shelley Lynn. The Story of Corey & Alice. 2005. (J). pap. 8.00 (978-0-8059-6846-0(6)) Dorrance Publishing Co., Inc.

Jones, Traci L. Standing Against the Wind. 2006. 192p. (J). 16.00 (978-0-374-37174-6(1)) Farrar, Straus & Giroux.

June, Calvin. Daphne's Daisies. 2001. (gr. 7-12). lib. bdg. 30.35 (978-0-613-84245-7(6)) Tandem Library Bks.

Kalz, Jill. I Hate to Read: Belle Pepper. 2004. (Illus.). 32p. (J). pap. 9.95 (978-0-89812-521-4(9) , Creative Paperbacks) Creative Co., The.

Karon, Jan. Miss Fannie's Hat. Goffe, Toni, illus. 2003. 32p. (ps-2). cd-rom 17.99 (978-0-8066-4585-8(7) , Augsburg Bks.) Augsburg Fortress, Pubs.

—Miss Fannie's Hat. Goffe, Toni, illus. 2001. (Picture Puffin Ser.). 32p. (J). (ps-3). pap. 6.99 (978-0-14-056812-7(3) , Puffin) Penguin Group (USA) Inc.

—Miss Fannie's Hat. 2001. (gr. 3-6). lib. bdg. 15.30 (978-0-613-31483-1(2)) Tandem Library Bks.

Kavasch, E. Barrie. Dream Catcher. Holland, Gay W., illus. 2003. (Books for Young Learners). 16p. (J). 5.00 net. (978-1-57274-257-4(7) , 2733) Owen, Richard C. Pubs., Inc.

Keeling, Annie E. Andrew Golding A Tale of the Great Plague. 2004. reprint ed. pap. 15.95 (978-1-4191-0694-1(5)); pap. 1.99 (978-1-4192-0694-8(X)) Kessinger Publishing, LLC.

Keeling, E. Annie. Andrew Golding (a Tale of the Great Plag 2006. 40.99 (*978 1 4280-0516-7(1)),* pap. 34.99 (*978-1-4280-0515-0(3)*) IndyPublish.com.

Keller, Holly. That's Mine, Horace. Keller, Holly, illus. 2000. (Illus.). 24p. (J). (ps up). 16.99 (978-0-688-17159-9(1)) HarperCollins Pubs.

Kemp, Cecil O., Jr. & Smeby, Mark. The Secret Meeting Place. 2002. 110p. (gr. 9 up). pap. 12.95 (978-1-893668-22-5(3)) STL Distribution North America.

Kenney, Cindy. Cool Hand Cuke: A Lesson in Giving. Big Idea Design Staff, illus. 2006. (VeggieTown Values Ser.: Bk. 5). 32p. (J). pap. 3.99 (978-0-310-70738-7(2)) Zonderkidz.

—God Is Bigger Than the Boogie Man: And Other Bedtime Stories. Hardin, Greg & Vann, Robert, illus. 2002. 40p. 12.99 (978-0-310-70465-2(0)) Zonderkidz.

—Madame Blueberry Learns to Be Thankful. 2004. (Illus.). 22p. bds. 4.99 (978-0-310-70782-0(X)) Zonderkidz.

Kenney, Cindy & Big Idea, Inc. Staff. A Knight to Remember. 2005. (Big Idea Bks.). (Illus.). 40p. (gr. k-3). 9.99 (978-0-310-70730-1(7)) Zonderkidz.

Kenney, Cindy, et al. Frog Wars: A Lesson in Perseverance. 2005. (VeggieTown Values Ser.: Bk. 2). (Illus.). 32p. pap. 3.99 (978-0-310-70627-4(0)) Zonderkidz.

Kenney, Peterson, et al. The Snooze Brothers: A Lesson in Responsibility. Big Idea Design Staff, illus. 2006. (VeggieTown Values Ser.: Bk. 6). 32p. (J). pap. 3.99 (978-0-310-70739-4(0)) Zonderkidz.

Kerr, M. E. Your Eyes in Stars. 240p. 2007. (J). (gr. 7 up). pap. 6.99 (*978-0-06-075684-0(5)* , HarperTeen); 2006. (J). lib. bdg. 16.89 (978-0-06-075683-3(7)); 2006. (YA). 15.99 (978-0-06-075682-6(9)) HarperCollins Pubs.

Ketchum, Liza. Where the Great Hawk Flies. 2005. 272p. (J). (gr. 5-9). 16.00 (978-0-618-40085-0(0) , Clarion Bks.) Houghton Mifflin Co. Trade & Reference Div.

Kijinski, Paul. Camp Limestone. 2006. (Illus.). 104p. (YA). per. 7.99 (978-1-59958-016-6(0)) Journey Stone Creations, LLC.

King, Lisa. Austin has a Conscience: Book II: Angie's Ponytail. 2006. pap. 7.95 (978-0-533-15228-5(3)) Vantage Pr., Inc.

Kipling, Rudyard. The Jungle Book: A Classic Story about Uniqueness. 2003. (Illus.). 32p. per. 3.95 (978-0-9747133-1-1(7) , Values to Live By Classic Stories) Thomas, Frederic Inc.

Koja, Kathe. Buddha Boy. 2003. 128p. (YA). (gr. 7 up). 16.00 (978-0-374-30998-5(1) , Farrar, Straus & Giroux (BYR)) Farrar, Straus & Giroux.

—Buddha Boy. 2004. 128p. (YA). (gr. 6-11). reprint ed. pap. 5.99 (978-0-14-240209-2(5) , Puffin) Penguin Group (USA) Inc.

—Buddha Boy. l.t. ed. 2003. 113p. (J). 24.95 (978-0-7862-6012-6(2)) Thomson Gale.

Korman, Gordon. Jake, Reinvented. 2005. 224p. (gr. 7-17). pap. 5.99 (978-0-7868-5697-8(1)) Hyperion Bks. for Children.

Kranz, Linda. Only One You. 2006. (Illus.). 32p. (J). 12.95 (978-0-87358-901-7(7) , Rising Moon Bks. for Young Readers) Northland Publishing.

Kroll, Steven. Sweet America. 2004. 172p. (J). lib. bdg. 16.92 (*978-1-4242-0773-2(8)*) Fitzgerald Bks.

—When I Dream of Heaven. 2004. 156p. (J). lib. bdg. 16.92 (*978-1-4242-0770-1(3)*) Fitzgerald Bks.

Kroll, Virginia L. Boy, You're Amazing! Yoshikawa, Sachiko, illus. 2004. 32p. (J). (ps-2). 15.95 (978-0-8075-0868-8(3)) Whitman, Albert & Co.

—Cristina Keeps a Promise. Sanchez, Enrique O., illus. 2006. (Way I ACT Books: Vol. 6). 24p. (J). (gr. 1-3). 15.95 (978-0-8075-1350-7(4)) Whitman, Albert & Co.

—Forgiving a Friend. Billin-Frye, Paige, illus. 2005. (Way I ACT Ser.). 24p. (J). (gr. k-3). lib. bdg. 15.95 (978-0-8075-0618-9(4)) Whitman, Albert & Co.

—Good Citizen Sarah. Cote, Nancy, illus. 2007. (Way I ACT Books). 24p. (J). (gr. 1-4). 15.95 (*978-0-8075-2992-8(3)*) Whitman, Albert & Co.

—Jason Takes Responsibility. Cote, Nancy, illus. 2005. (Way I ACT Ser.). 24p. (J). (gr. k-3). lib. bdg. 15.95 (978-0-8075-2537-1(5)) Whitman, Albert & Co.

—Ryan Respects. Billin-Frye, Paige, illus. 2006. (Way I ACT Ser.). 24p. (J). 15.95 (978-0-8075-6946-7(1)) Whitman, Albert & Co.

Lagerlof, Selma. The Wonderful Adventures of Nils. 2004. reprint ed. pap. 34.95 (978-1-4191-8845-9(3)); pap. 1.99 (978-1-4192-8845-6(8)) Kessinger Publishing, LLC.

Lamplighter Staff. Stick to the Raft. 2004. 14.00 (978-1-58474-029-2(9)) Cornerstone Family Ministries/ Lamplighter Publishing.

Lampshire Hayden, Gwendolen. Really Truly Stories #1/9. 2006. 128p. per. 11.95 (978-1-57258-433-4(5) , 945-6294) TEACH Services, Inc.

—Really Truly Stories #2/9. 2006. (Illus.). 128p. per. 11.95 (978-1-57258-434-1(3) , 945-6295) TEACH Services, Inc.

—Really Truly Stories #3/9. 2006. (Illus.). 128p. (J). per. 11.95 (978-1-57258-435-8(1) , 945-6296) TEACH Services, Inc.

—Really Truly Stories #4/9. 2006. (Illus.). 128p. (YA). per. 11.95 (978-1-57258-436-5(X) , 945-6297) TEACH Services, Inc.

Lanagan, Margo. Black Juice. 2005. 208p. (J). (gr. 7 up). 15.99 (978-0-06-074390-1(5)); lib. bdg. 16.89 (978-0-06-074391-8(3)) HarperCollins Pubs.

—White Time. 2006. 224p. (J). (gr. 7 up). 15.99 (978-0-06-074393-2(X) , Eos); lib. bdg. 16.89 (978-0-06-074394-9(8)) HarperCollins Pubs.

Laser, Michael. Cheater. 2008. 224p. (YA). (gr. 7). 16.99 (*978-0-525-47826-3(4)* , Dutton Juvenile) Penguin Group (USA) Inc.

Lavender, William. Aftershocks. 2006. (Illus.). 352p. (YA). 17.00 (978-0-15-205882-1(6)) Harcourt Children's Bks.

Lawrence, Sara. Those Girls. 2007. 320p. (YA). (gr. 9). pap. 9.99 (*978-1-59514-169-9(3)* , Razorbill) Penguin Group (USA) Inc.

Lawton, Wendy. Changing Faces: Real TV, Take 1. 2004. (Real Tv - Real Transformations Series (Take 1) Ser.). 224p. (J). pap. 10.99 (978-0-8024-5413-3(5)) Moody Pubs.

Leaney, Cindy. Everyone Makes a Difference: A Story about Community. Wilks, Peter, illus. 2004. 32p. (J). 28.50 (978-1-58952-733-1(X)) Rourke Publishing, LLC.

—It's Your Turn Now: Politeness. Wilks, Peter, tr. Wilks, Peter, illus. 2003. 31p. (J). 28.50 (978-1-58952-735-5(6)) Rourke Publishing, LLC.

—Lost & Found: Honesty. Wilks, Peter, tr. Wilks, Peter, illus. 2003. 32p. (J). 28.50 (978-1-58952-736-2(4)) Rourke Publishing, LLC.

—Summer Vacation: Patience. Wilks, Peter, tr. Wilks, Peter, illus. 2003. 32p. (J). 28.50 (978-1-58952-737-9(2)) Rourke Publishing, LLC.

—Taking Care of Mango: Responsibility. 2003. (Illus.). 31p. (J). 28.50 (978-1-58952-738-6(0)) Rourke Publishing, LLC.

Legge, James. The Hsiao King or Classic of Filial Piet. 2004. reprint ed. pap. 15.95 (978-1-4191-6687-7(5)) Kessinger Publishing, LLC.

—The Hsiao King or Classic of Filial Piety. 2004. reprint ed. pap. 1.99 (978-1-4192-6687-4(X)) Kessinger Publishing, LLC.

Lenam, Salva. El aseo de Kiko. 2005. (Kiko Ser.). (SPA., Illus.). 10p. (J). 3.95 (978-84-95761-73-6(4)) Ediciones Norte, Inc.

—Hoy Empieza la Escuela, Kiko! Roman, Santi, illus. 2005. (Kiko Ser.). (SPA.). 10p. (J). 3.95 (978-84-95761-76-7(9)) Ediciones Norte, Inc.

—A Kiko le Gusta la Playa. Roman, Santi, illus. 2005. (Kiko Ser.). (SPA.). 10p. (J). 3.95 (978-84-95761-75-0(0)) Ediciones Norte, Inc.

—A Kiko le Pican los Ojitos. Roman, Santi, illus. 2005. (Kiko Ser.). (SPA.). 10p. (J). 3.95 (978-84-95761-82-8(3)) Ediciones Norte, Inc.

Leverich, Kathleen. Hilary & the Troublemakers. 1999. (Beech Tree Chapter Bks.). (Illus.). 144p. (J). (gr. 1-4). pap. 4.95 (978-0-688-16453-9(6) , Harper Trophy) HarperCollins Pubs.

Levithan, David. Realm of Possibility. 2006. 224p. (YA). (gr. 7). reprint ed. pap. 8.95 (978-0-375-83657-2(8) , Knopf Bks. for Young Readers) Random Hse. Children's Bks.

Lewis, Regina N. The Smallest Schoolhouse. Moore, P. M., illus. 2007. 56p. (J). pap. 12.95 (*978-0-9776958-3-6(2)*) CyPress Pubns.

Licciardi, Paula. Wasting Calvin's Time. 2006. 9.00 (978-0-8059-8138-4(1)) Dorrance Publishing Co., Inc.

Liebenthal, Jean Z. Curiosity. 1999. 133p. (J). (978-1-57008-707-3(5)) Scribbulations LLC.

Lieshout, Elle van & Os, Erik van. The Nothing King. Gerritsen, Paula, illus. 2004. 32p. (J). (gr. k-3). 15.95 (978-1-932425-14-7(4) , Lemniscaat) Boyds Mills Pr.

Littman, Sarah. Confessions of a Closet Catholic. 2006. 208p. (J). (gr. 5). reprint ed. pap. 5.99 (978-0-14-240597-0(3) , Puffin) Penguin Group (USA) Inc.

Long, Adam, told to. What if You See What I C? 2005. 71p. per. 19.95 (978-1-59453-439-3(X) , 2504) Airleaf Publishing & Bookselling.

Long, John Arthur & Meyer, Chet. The Tooth Fairy Legend: The Touch of Kindness. Zenobi, Nadine, illus. 2002. 56p. (J). 14.95 (978-0-9710749-1-0(7)) L & M Creations.

—The Tooth Fairy Legend: The Touch of Kindness. 2002. (Illus.). 56p. (J). audio compact disk 24.95 (978-0-9710749-0-3(9)) L & M Creations.

Lorenzen, Margaret. Slinky Slithertail. Habalou, Matthew, illus. 2001. 112p. (J). (gr. 2-6). per. 15.00 (978-0-9708053-4-8(9)) Authors & Artists Publishers of New York, Inc.

Lorimer, Janet. No Place Like Home, Set 3. 2002. 32p. (YA). 2.95 (978-1-56254-430-0(6) , SP 4306) Saddleback Educational Publishing.

Losier, Dave. Fred's Prayer Machine. 2002. (Illus.). 152p. (J). pap. 11.95 (978-1-929039-07-4(7)) Ambassador Bks., Inc.

Louise, Cynthia. Through a Child's Eyes. 2005. 56p. pap. 12.95 (978-1-4137-6142-9(9)) PublishAmerica, Inc.

Loving, W. The Flibbertigibbet - A Mess-O-Fish. Loving, W., illus. 2000. (Illus.). 47p. (J). (ps-6). pap. 12.95 (978-0-9708193-0-7(7)) Loving, William M.

Lowry, Brigid. Follow the Blue. 2006. 208p. (YA). pap. 8.95 (978-0-312-34297-5(7) , St. Martin's Griffin) St. Martin's Pr.

Lubar, David. Sleeping Freshmen Never Lie. (YA). 2007. 288p. pap. 6.99 (978-0-14-240780-6(1) , Puffin); 2005. 160p. (gr. 6-10). 16.99 (978-0-525-47311-4(4) , Dutton Juvenile) Penguin Group (USA) Inc.

Lucado, Max. Best of All. Martinez, Sergio, illus. 2005. (Wemmicks Ser.). 32p. 15.99 (978-1-58134-501-8(1) , Crossway Bibles) Crossway Bks.

—Buzby, the Misbehaving Bee. 2005. (Hermie & Friends Ser.: No. 4). (Illus.). 48p. (J). 12.99 (978-1-4003-0510-0(1)) Nelson, Thomas Inc.

—If Only I Had a Green Nose. Martinez, Sergio, illus. 2005. (Wemmicks Ser.). 28p. 6.99 (978-1-58134-533-9(X)); 31p. 15.99 (978-1-58134-397-7(3)) Crossway Bks. (Crossway Bibles).

—You Are Mine. Martinez, Sergio, illus. 2005. (Wemmicks Ser.). 28p. bds. 6.99 (978-1-58134-429-5(5) , Crossway Bibles) Crossway Bks.

—You Are Mine: Read & Sing Along. Martinez, Sergio, illus. 2005. (Wemmicks Ser.). 32p. (ps-3). 15.99 (978-1-58134-276-5(4) , Crossway Bibles) Crossway Bks.

—You Are Mine & Best of All, 2 vols. 2006. (Illus.). 64p. (J). 19.99 (978-1-58134-804-0(5)) Crossway Bks.

—You Are Mine & If Only I Had A Green Nose, vol. 2. 2006. (Illus.). 64p. (J). 19.99 (978-1-58134-805-7(3)) Crossway Bks.

Lucia, Ruth. The Sad Little Cloud. 2004. (Illus.). 25p. (J). pap. 9.95 (978-1-932373-14-1(4)) Cedar Hill Publishing.

Luke, Deanna. Marky & the Mouse. Chambers, Lynne, illus. 2000. (Marky Ser.: Vol. No. 1). 32p. (J). (gr. 2-6). 8.95 (978-1-928777-05-2(8) , BOW Bks.) Blessing Our World, Inc.

Lundy, Charlotte. Thank You, God. Waldrep, Evelyn L., ed. James, Margaret Ray, illus. 2004. 32p. (J). (gr. k-3). 15.95 (978-0-9670280-9-5(4)) Bay Light Publishing.

Lynch, Chris. Me, Dead Dad, & Alcatraz. 3rd ed. 2005. 240p. (J). 15.99 (978-0-06-059709-2(7)) HarperCollins Pubs.

Lyon, Justice. Little Monkey Smarty. 2002. 16p. (J). 4.95 (978-0-9716596-1-2(3) , GWS-02) 7 Heads Publishing.

Mac, Carrie. The Beckoners. 2007. 224p. (YA). (gr. 7 up). pap. (*978-1-55143-729-3(5)*) Orca Bk. Pubs.

—The Beckoners. 2004. 224p. (J). (gr. 7-12). lib. bdg. 16.95 (978-1-55143-309-7(5) , 1234128) Orca Bk. Pubs. USA.

MacDonald, George. Gutta Percha Willie a Duplex. Hughes, Arthur, illus. unabr. ed. 1998. (George MacDonald Original Works Ser.: Series III). 384p. reprint ed. lib. bdg. 24.00 (978-1-881084-62-4(0)) Johannesen Printing & Publishing.

MacKall, Dandi Daley. Kyra's Story. 2003. (Degrees of Guilt Ser.). (YA). pap. 9.99 (978-0-8423-8284-7(4)) Tyndale Hse. Pubs.

Mackall, Dandi Daley. The Legend of Saint Nicholas: A Story of Christmas Giving. Porfirio, Guy, illus. 2007. 32p. (J). (978-0-310-71327-2(7)) Zonderkidz.

C
D

MacKall, Dandi Daley. Sierra's Story. 2004. (Degrees of Betrayal Ser.). 336p. (YA). pap. 9.99 (978-0-8423-8726-2(9)) Tyndale Hse. Pubs.

Marshall, Gloria. Little Ones Volume Two. 2006. pap. 21.99 (*978-1-4259-5752-0(8)) AuthorHouse.

Marston, Elsa. Figs & Fate: Stories about Growing up in the Arab World Today. 2005. 146p. (J). 22.50 (978-0-8076-1551-5(X)); pap. 15.95 (978-0-8076-1554-6(4)) Braziller, George Inc.

Martenz, Arden. Ocho: A Character-Education Story. 2002. 32p. (J). 6.95 (978-1-57543-112-3(2)) MAR*CO Products, Inc.

Martin, Ann M. Error de Stacey. (SPA.). 144p. (J). 11.95 (978-84-272-3668-4(9)) Molino, Editorial ESP. *Dist:* AIMS International Bks., Inc.

Martin, Cory. The Summer of Summer. novel ed. 2005. (O. C. Ser.). 140p. (J). pap. 6.99 (978-0-439-69633-3(X)) Scholastic, Inc.

Mary Mccowski Was Not a Pretty Girl: About a Girl Who Isn't Pretty, & Never Will Be Pretty but Finds Success Anyway. 2005. (J). 3.99 (978-0-9754420-0-5(7)) www.underdogpublishing.com.

Mass, Wendy. Jeremy Fink & the Meaning of Life. 2006. 304p. (J). (gr. 4-7). 15.99 (978-0-316-05829-2(7)) Little Brown & Co.

—Jeremy Fink & the Meaning of Life. 2008. 304p. (J). (gr. 3-7). pap. 6.99 (*978-0-316-05849-0(1)) Little, Brown Bks. for Young Readers.

Matheson, Dawn. Ruby Lee the Bumble Bee: A Bee's Bit of Wisdom. Cindy, Huffman, ed. Barcita, Pamela, illus. 2004. 40p. (J). 17.95 (978-0-9754342-0-8(9)) Bumble Bee Publishing.

Mazer, Anne. That's the Way the Cookie Crumbles. 2005. (Amazing Days of Abby Hayes Ser.: No. 16). 119p. (J). lib. bdg. 16.92 (*978-1-4242-0748-0(7)) Fitzgerald Bks.

McCarnes, Kayla, et al. Making a Happy Heart: A Storeybook to Accompany Bully-Proofing in Early Childhood: Building a Caring Community. 2004. (Illus.). 28p. (978-1-59318-242-7(2)) Sopris West Educational Services.

McCourt, Lisa, et al. Chicken Soup for the Little Souls: 3 Colorful Stories to Warm the Hearts of Children. Dodson, Bert et al, illus. 2000. 96p. (J). (ps-3). pap. 12.95 (978-1-55874-812-5(1)) Health Communications, Inc.

McCusker, Paul. Point of No Return. 2006. (Adventures in Odyssey Bks.). 336p. (J). pap. 13.99 (978-1-58997-332-9(1)) Focus on the Family Publishing.

—Strange Journey Back. 2006. (Adventures in Odyssey Ser.: No. 1). 304p. (J). pap. 13.99 (978-1-58997-325-1(9)) Focus on the Family Publishing.

McDonald, Ann-Eve. The Bad Day. 2004. (J). (978-0-9770158-1-8(5)) BeachWalk Bks. Inc.

McDowell, Josh & Hostetler, Bob. The Truth Twisters. 2006. 170p. (YA). pap. 11.99 (978-1-932587-84-5(5)) Green Key Bks.

McGowan, Anthony. Hellbent. 2006. 272p. (YA). pap. 8.99 (978-1-4169-0814-2(5) , Simon & Schuster Children's Publishing) Simon & Schuster Children's Publishing.

McKissack, Patricia C. The Honest-to-Goodness Truth. 2002. (Illus.). (J). 25.11 (978-0-7587-2741-1(0)) Book Wholesalers, Inc.

—The Honest-to-Goodness Truth. Potter, Giselle, illus. 2000. 40p. (J). (ps-3). 16.00 (978-0-689-82668-9(0) , Atheneum/Anne Schwartz Bks.) Simon & Schuster Children's Publishing.

—The Honest-to-Goodness Truth. 2003. (gr. k-3). lib. bdg. 15.30 (978-0-613-61627-0(8)) Tandem Library Bks.

McKissack, Patricia C. & Potter, Giselle. The Honest-to-Goodness Truth. 2003. (Illus.). 40p. (J). (ps-3). pap. 7.99 (978-0-689-85395-1(5) , Aladdin) Simon & Schuster Children's Publishing.

McNamara, Margaret. Martin Luther King Jr. Day. Gordon, Mike, illus. 2007. (Robin Hill School Ser.). 32p. (J). pap. 3.99 (*978-1-4169-3494-3(4)); lib. bdg. 13.89 (*978-1-4169-3495-0(2)) Simon & Schuster Children's Publishing. (Aladdin).

McNutt, William Slavens. Poor Little Eddie. 2004. reprint ed. pap. 15.95 (978-1-4191-4260-4(7)); pap. 1.99 (978-1-4192-4260-1(1)) Kessinger Publishing, LLC.

Medearis, Angela Shelf. Seven Spools of Thread: A Kwanzaa Story. Minter, Daniel, illus. 2000. 40p. (J). (gr. 2-5). 15.95 (978-0-8075-7315-0(9)); pap. 6.95 (978-0-8075-7316-7(7)) Whitman, Albert & Co.

Messer, Celeste M. The Boy Who Cried Wolf. Hoeffner, Deb, illus. 2004. 82-92p. 4.95 (978-0-9702171-9-6(6)) AshleyAlan Enterprises.

—When Eagles Fly. Hoeffner, Deb, illus. 2004. 82-92p. 4.95 (978-0-9702171-8-9(8)) AshleyAlan Enterprises.

Mills, Claudia. Being Teddy Roosevelt. Alley, R. W., illus. 2007. 96p. (J). (gr. 2-5). 16.00 (978-0-374-30657-1(5) , Farrar, Straus & Giroux (BYR)) Farrar, Straus & Giroux.

—Perfectly Chelsea. Rogers, Jacqueline, illus. 2004. 128p. (J). 16.00 (978-0-374-31244-2(3) , Farrar, Straus & Giroux (BYR)) Farrar, Straus & Giroux.

Mills, Joyce C. Little Tree: A Story for Children with Serious Medical Illness. Sebern, Brian, illus. 2nd ed. 2003. 32p. (J). pap. 8.95 (978-1-59147-042-7(0)); 14.95 (978-1-59147-041-0(2)) American Psychological Assn. (Magination Pr.).

Mills, Sam. The Viper Within. 2008. 304p. (J). (gr. 7). 16.99 (*978-0-375-84465-2(1)); lib. bdg. 19.99 (*978-0-375-94465-9(6)) Random Hse. Children's Bks. (Knopf Bks. for Young Readers).

Minou: Evaluation Guide. 2006. (J). (978-1-55942-416-5(8)) Marsh Media.

Montgomery, L. M. Midnight Madness & Mayhem. Griffin, Jim, illus. 2005. (Story Girl Ser.). 112p. (J). (gr. 3-7). pap. 4.99 (978-0-310-70861-2(3)) Zonderkidz.

—Wedding Wishes & Woes. Griffin, Jim, illus. 2005. (Story Girl#8482; Ser.). 112p. (J). (gr. 3-7). pap. 4.99 (978-0-310-70860-5(5)) Zonderkidz.

—The Winds of Change. 2005. (Story Girl#8482; Ser.). (Illus.). 112p. (J). (gr. 3-7). pap. 4.99 (978-0-310-70862-9(1)) Zonderkidz.

—Winter on the Island. Griffin, Jim, illus. 2005. (Story Girl Ser.). 112p. (J). (gr. 3-7). pap. 4.99 (978-0-310-70859-9(1)) Zonderkidz.

Moore, Eva. Good Children Get Rewards: A Story of Colonial Times. 2001. (Hello Reader! Ser.). (J). 10.79 (978-0-606-19563-8(7)) Tandem Library Bks.

Moost, Nele. It's All Mine! Or the Little Raven's Mischief. Rudolph, Annet, illus. 1999. 28p. (J). (ps-3). 14.95 (978-0-7892-0529-2(7)) Abbeville Pr., Inc.

Morales, Maximino. Lucky Me! (Que Suerte!) 2002. (ENG & SPA., Illus.). 32p. (J). (gr. k-3). pap. 6.95 (978-0-9740308-2-1(1)) Maximum Publishing Co.

—The Wooden Go-Cart (El Carrito de Madera) 2002. (ENG & SPA., Illus.). 24p. (J). (gr. k-3). pap. 6.95 (978-0-9740308-0-7(5)) Maximum Publishing Co.

More, Hannah. Stories for the Young or Cheap Repositor. 2006. 32.99 (*978-1-4280-3380-1(7)) IndyPublish.com.

Morneau, Robert F. A Tale from Paleface Creek. Mau, Marjorie M., illus. 2001. 32p. (J). (ps-3). 9.95 (978-0-8091-6678-7(X) , 6678-x) Paulist Pr.

Morty, Ducktor. Can Do & the Mall: A Story for Us All. 2005. (Illus.). 34p. (J). pap. (978-0-9768384-0-1(0)) Can Do Duck Publishing.

Moses, Shelia P. Sallie Gal & the Wall-a-Kee Man. Daly, Niki, illus. 2007. 160p. (J). (gr. 2-5). pap. 15.99 (*978-0-439-90890-0(6)) Scholastic, Inc.

Muldrow, Diane. Truth Without the Trimmings. Pollak, Barbara, illus. 2007. (Dish Ser.). 160p. (J). pap. 4.99 (978-0-448-44530-4(1) , Grosset & Dunlap) Penguin Group (USA) Inc.

Murphy, Jim. Fergus & the Night-Demon: An Irish Ghost Story. Manders, John, illus. 2006. 32p. (J). (gr. 3-5). 16.00 (978-0-618-33955-6(8) , Clarion Bks.) Houghton Mifflin Co. Trade & Reference Div.

Muth, Jon J. The Three Questions. Muth, Jon J., illus. 2002. (Illus.). 32p. (J). (gr. 1-4). pap. 16.99 (978-0-439-19996-4(4) , Scholastic Pr.) Scholastic, Inc.

Myers, Bill. My Life As a Tarantula Toe Tickler, Vol. 22. 2003. (Incredible Worlds of Wally McDoogle Ser.: Vol. 22). (Illus.). 128p. (J). pap. 6.99 (978-0-8499-5993-6(4)) Nelson, Thomas Inc.

Myers, Laurie. Surviving Brick Johnson. Yaccarino, Dan, illus. 2000. 80p. (J). (gr. 4-6). tchr. ed. 15.00 (978-0-395-98031-6(3) , Clarion Bks.) Houghton Mifflin Co. Trade & Reference Div.

Myers, Walter Dean. Handbook for Boys: A Novel. (Amistad Ser.). (J). (gr. 5 up). 2003. 224p. pap. 6.99 (978-0-06-440930-8(9)); 2002. (Illus.). 192p. 16.99 (978-0-06-029146-4(X)) HarperCollins Pubs.

—Handbook for Boys: A Novel. 2003. (gr. 5-8). lib. bdg. 14.15 (978-0-613-65786-0(1)) Tandem Library Bks.

Myracle, Lauren. Rhymes with Witches. (YA). (gr. 8-17). 2006. 272p. pap. 6.95 (978-0-8109-9215-3(9)); 2005. 224p. 16.95 (978-0-8109-5859-3(7) , Amulet Bks.) Abrams, Harry N. , Inc.

Napoli, Donna Jo. Hush: An Irish Princess' Tale. 2007. 320p. (YA). (gr. 7 up). 16.99 (*978-0-689-86176-5(1)) Simon & Schuster Children's Publishing.

Naylor, Phyllis Reynolds. All but Alice. 2002. (Alice Ser.). 160p. (J). (gr. 4-7). pap. 5.99 (978-0-689-85044-8(1) , Aladdin) Simon & Schuster Children's Publishing.

—All but Alice. 2002. (Alice Ser.). (gr. 7-12). lib. bdg. 13.00 (978-0-613-44999-1(1)) Tandem Library Bks.

—Dangerously Alice. 2007. (Alice Ser.). 304p. (YA). (gr. 9 up). 15.99 (978-0-689-87094-1(9) , Atheneum) Simon & Schuster Children's Publishing.

Nelsen, Michael & Nelsen, Wendy. My CTR Ring. Jensen, Jodi, illus. 2000. 32p. (J). (978-1-57345-467-4(2)) Scribbulations LLC.

Nelson, Blake. The New Rules of High School. 2004. 240p. (YA). reprint ed. pap. 6.99 (978-0-14-240242-9(7) , Puffin) Penguin Group (USA) Inc.

—Paranoid Park. 2006. 176p. (YA). (gr. 7). 15.99 (978-0-670-06118-1(2) , Viking Juvenile) Penguin Group (USA) Inc.

Newman, Leslea. The Boy Who Cried Fabulous. Ferguson, Peter, illus. 32p. (J). (ps-2). 2007. pap. 7.95 (*978-1-58246-224-0(0)); 2004. 15.95 (978-1-58246-101-4(5)) Ten Speed Pr. (Tricycle Pr.).

Nicholson, William. Jango. 2007. (YA). (Noble Warriors Trilogy: Bk. 2). (Illus.). 432p. (gr. 7 up). 17.00 (978-0-15-206011-4(1)); 409p. (*978-1-4287-4812-5(1)) Harcourt Trade Pubs.

—Jango: Book Two of the Noble Warriors. 2008. (Noble Warriors Ser.). (Illus.). 448p. (YA). pap. 7.95 (*978-0-15-206160-9(6) , Harcourt Paperbacks) Harcourt Children's Bks.

—Noman. 2008. (YA). (*978-0-15-206005-3(7)) Harcourt Trade Pubs.

Nicholson, William. Seeker. 2007. (Noble Warriors Trilogy Ser.: Bk. 1). (Illus.). 448p. (YA). (gr. 7 up). pap. 7.95 (978-0-15-205866-1(4) , Harcourt Paperbacks) Harcourt Children's Bks.

—Seeker. 2006. (Noble Warriors Trilogy Ser.: Bk. 1). (Illus.). 432p. (YA). 17.00 (978-0-15-205768-8(4)) Harcourt Trade Pubs.

Nigro, D. M. The Wolfman, the Shrink & the Eighth-Grade Election. 2006. 116p. (J). pap. 13.50 (978-1-931201-66-7(8)) Twilight Times Bks.

Nikola-Lisa, W. Bein' with You This Way - La Alegria de Ser Tu y Yo, 2 bks., Set. Ganetti, Yanitzia, tr. Bryant, Michael, illus. unabr. ed. 1999. (SPA & ENG.). (J). (gr. k-3). pap. 33.95 incl. audio (978-0-87499-561-9(2)) Live Oak Media.

Nixon-Weaver, Elizabeth. Rooster. 2001. (Illus.). 320p. (J). (gr. 7 up). 16.95 (978-1-58837-001-3(1)) Winslow Pr.

Nunes, Rachel & Lindsley, David. Daughter of a King Board Book. 2004. bds. 10.95 (978-1-59156-054-8(3)) Covenant Communications, Inc.

Nunes, Rachel Ann. Daughter of a King. 2004. (Illus.). 17.95 (978-1-57734-935-8(0)) Covenant Communications, Inc.

O'Connor, Barbara. How to Steal a Dog. 2007. 176p. (J). (gr. 3-7). 16.00 (978-0-374-33497-0(8)) Farrar, Straus & Giroux.

O'Dell, Kathleen. Agnes Parker... Girl in Progress. Harper, Charise Mericle, illus. 2003. 160p. (J). (gr. 5). 16.99 (978-0-8037-2648-2(1) , Dial) Penguin Group (USA) Inc.

—Agnes Parker... Girl in Progress. 2004. 176p. (J). (gr. 3-6). reprint ed. pap. 5.99 (978-0-14-240228-3(1) , Puffin) Penguin Group (USA) Inc.

—Bad Tickets. 2007. 240p. (YA). (gr. 7). 15.99 (978-0-375-83801-9(5)); lib. bdg. 18.99 (978-0-375-93801-6(X)) Random Hse. Children's Bks. (Knopf Bks. for Young Readers).

Oke, Janette. Prairie Dog Town. Munger, Nancy, illus. rev. ed. 2001. (Janette Oke's Animal Friends Ser.). 80p. (J). (gr. 1-5). pap. 6.99 (978-0-7642-2455-3(7)) Bethany Hse. Pubs.

Olaizola, José Luis. La Montana de los Hongos Dorados. 2000. (SPA., Illus.). 130p. 9.95 (978-84-239-7092-6(2)) Espasa Calpe, S.A. ESP. *Dist:* Libros Sin Fronteras.

Olasky, Susan. Will Northaway & the Gathering Storm. 2005. (Young American Patriots Ser.: No. 4). 96p. (J). (ps-7). pap. 5.99 (978-1-58134-478-3(3) , Crossway Bibles) Crossway Bks.

—Will Northaway & the Price of Loyalty. 2005. (Young American Patriots Ser.: #3). 93p. (J). (ps-7). pap. 5.99 (978-1-58134-477-6(5) , Crossway Bibles) Crossway Bks.

Oliver the Clownfish: The Invitation Slip-up. 2006. (J). 5.95 (978-1-59664-000-9(6)); 14.95 (978-1-59664-001-6(4)) Not So Plain Jane Publishing.

Olmstead, Kathleen & Porter, Eleanor H. Pollyanna. Akib, Jamel, illus. 2007. (Classic Starts Ser.). 154p. (J). (*978-1-4287-4209-3(3)) Sterling Publishing Co., Inc.

On Thin Ice. 2005. per. (978-0-9772505-2-3(0)) Adibooks.com.

Optic, Oliver. Poor & Proud, or the Fortunes of Katy. 2006. 51.99 (*978-1-4219-7997-7(7)); pap. 45.99 (*978-1-4219-7992-2(6)) IndyPublish.com.

Osborne, Rick. The Legend of the Christmas Stocking: An Inspirational Story of a Wish Come True. Griffin, Jim, illus. (J). 2006. 28p. 6.99 (978-0-310-71157-5(6)); 2004. 32p. 15.99 (978-0-310-70898-8(2)) Zonderkidz.

Osborne, Susan Titus. Dog Paws & Sandy Claws. Durrell, Julie, illus. 2001. (Parables in Action Ser.: Vol. 8). 48p. (J). (ps-2). 4.99 (978-0-570-07140-2(2)) Concordia Publishing Hse.

O'Brien, Kathryn. I¿d Be Your Princess. Garland, Michael, illus. 2007. (J). 6.99 (*978-0-7847-1964-0(0)) Standard Publishing.

Paine, Penelope C. Time for Horatio. Maeno, Itoko, illus. 2001. 48p. (J). per. 17.95 (978-0-9707944-7-5(9)) Paper Posie.

Paladin, Frank. Hole in My Stocking. Amber, Holly & Lin, Melanie, illus. 2005. 24p. (J). per. 16.95 (978-0-9763635-4-5(2)) Beyond the Stars Pubns.

Pansy (Isabella M. Alden). Tip Lewis & His Lamp. 2006. 112p. pap. (978-1-84702-198-4(0)) Echo Library.

Parker, David. I Am a Leader! Walker, Sylvia, illus. 2005. (J). (978-0-439-73585-8(8)) Scholastic, Inc.

Parker, David. I Will Keep Trying! Ramsey, Marcy Dunn, illus. 2005. (J). pap. (*978-0-439-73588-9(2)) Scholastic, Inc.

Pascal, Francine. Lucha por la Fama. Orig. Title: Claim to Fame. (SPA.). 128p. (J). 6.95 (978-84-272-3793-3(6)) Molino, Editorial ESP. *Dist:* AIMS International Bks., Inc.

A Pat on the Back. 2003. (J). per. (978-1-57657-879-7(8)) Paradise Pr., Inc.

Patience - Companion Book. 2003. (J). 2.00 (978-0-9740418-9-6(0)) Night LIght Pubns., LLC.

Patterson, Nancy Ruth. A Simple Gift. 2003. 128p. (J). 16.00 (978-0-374-36924-8(0) , Farrar, Straus & Giroux (BYR)) Farrar, Straus & Giroux.

Paulsen, Gary. The Tent. 2006. (Illus.). 96p. (J). pap. 5.95 (978-0-15-205833-3(8) , Harcourt Paperbacks) Harcourt Children's Bks.

Peach Laminated Book. 2005. (J). per. 15.95 (978-1-59649-307-0(0)) Whispering Pine Pr., Inc.

Pear Laminated Book. 2005. (J). per. 15.95 (978-1-59649-308-7(9)) Whispering Pine Pr., Inc.

Peck, Lisa J. Brittany to the Rescue: CTR Club - Book Two, 4 bks. 2005. (J). pap. 6.95 (*978-0-9749241-6-8(4)) Golden Wings Enterprises.

—Meagan's Secret: CTR Club - Book Three, 4 bks. 2005. (J). pap. 6.95 (*978-0-9749241-7-5(2)) Golden Wings Enterprises.

—Skating with Spencer: CTR Club - Book Four, 4 bks. 2005. (J). pap. 6.95 (*978-0-9749241-8-2(0)) Golden Wings Enterprises.

Petersen, P. J. Rising Water. 2003. (Illus.). 128p. (J). pap. 4.99 (978-0-689-86356-1(X) , Aladdin) Simon & Schuster Children's Publishing.

Peterson, Doug. Ben Hurry: Lesson in Patience. Big Idea Design Staff, illus. 2006. (VeggieTown Values Ser.: Bk. 8). 32p. (J). pap. 3.99 (978-0-310-70743-1(9)) Zonderkidz.

—Field of Beans: A Lesson in Faith. 2005. (VeggieTown Values Ser.: Bk. 3). (Illus.). 32p. pap. 3.99 (978-0-310-70628-1(9)) Zonderkidz.

—The Trouble with Larry. Big Idea Design Staff, illus. 2006. (Mess Detectives Ser.). 40p. 6.99 (978-0-310-70741-7(2)) Zonderkidz.

—West Slide Story: A Lesson in Making Peace. Big Idea Design Staff, illus. 2006. (VeggieTown Values Ser.: Bk. 7). 32p. (J). pap. 3.99 (978-0-310-70742-4(0)) Zonderkidz.

Peterson, Doug & Kenney, Cindy. Lost in Place: A Lesson in Overcoming Fear. Big Idea Productions Staff, illus. 2005. (VeggieTown Values Ser.: Bk. 4). 32p. pap. 3.99 (978-0-310-70629-8(7)) Zonderkidz.

—The Spoon in the Stone: A Lesson in Serving Others. 2005. (VeggieTown Values Ser.: Bk. 1). (Illus.). 32p. pap. 3.99 (978-0-310-70626-7(2)) Zonderkidz.

Pierce, Chonda & Pierce, David. Tales from the Manger. LeBarre, Matt, illus. 2004. 96p. (J). pap. 9.99 (978-0-310-70849-0(4)) Zonderkidz.

Pinkett-Smith, Jada. Girls Hold up This World. Kennedy-McCullough, Donyelle, photos by. 2005. (Illus.). 40p. (J). 16.95 (978-0-439-08793-3(7) , Cartwheel Bks.) Scholastic, Inc.

—Girls Hold up This World. 2003. (Illus.). (J). pap. (978-0-439-11332-8(6)) Scholastic, Inc.

Pinkney, Andrea Davis. Raven in a Dove House. 1999. (978-0-606-17789-4(2)) Tandem Library Bks.

Pinkwater, Daniel M. The Picture of Morty & Ray. Davis, Jack E., illus. 2003. 32p. (J). (gr. 1-5). 15.99 (978-0-06-623785-5(8)) HarperCollins Pubs.

Pittar, Gill. Basura No, Gracias! Rioja, Alberto Jiménez, tr. Morrell, Cris, illus. 2003. (Milly Molly Ser.). (SPA.). 24p. (J). pap. (978-84-241-8695-1(8)) Everest de Ediciones y Distribucion, S.L. ESP. *Dist:* Lectorum Pubns., Inc.

—Milly, Molly & Beaky. Morrell, Cris, illus. 2005. 28p. (ps). pap. (978-1-86972-048-3(2)) Milly Molly Bks.

—Milly, Molly & I Love You. 2005. 28p. pap. (978-1-86972-047-6(4)) Milly Molly Bks.

—Milly, Molly & the Bike Ride. 2005. 28p. pap. (978-1-86972-046-9(6)) Milly Molly Bks.

—Milly, Molly & the Picnic. Morrell, Cris, illus. 2005. 28p. (ps-ps). pap. (978-1-86972-045-2(8)) Milly Molly Bks.

Pitts, Constance. Chulita the Blind Cat. 2007. (Illus.). 48p. (J). (*978-0-9652902-2-7(0)) Beevinwood, Inc.

Please & Thank You. 2003. (J). per. (978-1-57657-820-9(8)) Paradise Pr., Inc.

Polston, Deborah Ehler. Eagle Child Series 1-3. 2006. 182p. per. 12.95 (978-1-933290-26-3(9)) Tate Publishing & Enterprises, L.L.C.

Porter, Eleanor H. Classic Starts: Pollyanna. Akib, Jamel, illus. 2007. (Classic Starts Ser.). 160p. (J). 4.95 (978-1-4027-3692-6(4)) Sterling Publishing Co., Inc.

—Pollyanna. Gual, illus. 2002. (Great Illustrated Classics Ser.). 240p. (J). (gr. 3-8). 21.35 (978-1-57765-822-1(1) , ABDO & Daughters) ABDO Publishing Co.

—Pollyanna. 2000. (Historias de Siempre Ser.). (SPA., Illus.). 198p. (YA). (gr. 4-7). 15.95 (978-84-204-5730-7(2)) Alfaguara, Ediciones, S.A.- Grupo Santillana ESP. *Dist:* Santillana USA Publishing Co., Inc.

—Pollyanna. (J). 21.95 (978-0-8488-1445-8(2)) Amereon LTD.

—Pollyanna. 2003. (Dover Evergreen Classics Ser.). 208p. (J). (gr. 4-7). pap. 3.00 (978-0-486-43206-9(8)) Dover Pubns., Inc.

—Pollyanna. Date not set. (J). 14.99 (978-0-06-028226-4(6)); 32p. pap. 4.99 (978-0-06-443536-9(9)) HarperCollins Pubs.

—Pollyanna. l.t. ed. 2000. (Large Print Heritage Ser.). 310p. (J). (gr. 7-12). lib. bdg. 29.95 (978-1-58118-069-5(1) , 23663) LRS.

—Pollyanna. 2002. (Classics Ser.). (Illus.). 304p. (J). pap. 4.99 (978-0-689-84910-7(9) , Aladdin) Simon & Schuster Children's Publishing.

—Pollyanna. l.t. ed. 2001. 267p. (J). 27.95 (978-0-7838-9602-1(6) , Hall, G. K. & Co.) Thomson Gale.

—Pollyanna Grows Up. Date not set. 216p. (J). 21.95 (978-0-8488-1447-2(9)) Amereon LTD.

—Pollyanna 'n Hollywood. (J). 17.95 (978-0-8488-1448-9(7)) Amereon LTD.

—Pollyanna's Debt of Honor. (J). 15.95 (978-0-8488-1446-5(0)) Amereon LTD.

Poth, Karen. Tale of Two Sumos. 2004. (Big Idea Books). (Illus.). 32p. 9.99 (978-0-310-70933-6(4)) Zonderkidz.

Powling, Chris. Treasure at the Flea Market. Reid, Michael, illus. 2006. 48p. (J). (gr. 2-4). 19.95 (978-1-4048-1661-9(5)) Picture Window Bks.

Pratchett, Terry. Only You Can Save Mankind. 224p. (J). 2006. pap. 5.99 (978-0-06-054187-3(3) , Harper Trophy); 2005. (gr. 3 up). 15.99 (978-0-06-054185-9(7)); 2005. (gr. 3 up). lib. bdg. 16.89 (978-0-06-054186-6(5)) HarperCollins Pubs.

Price, Leo. The Grumpy Tree. rev. ed. 1999. Orig. Title: The Tree That Always Said No!. (Illus.). 40p. (J). (gr. k-2). pap. 6.95 (978-0-8198-3097-5(6)) Pauline Bks. & Media.

R. Friend Swallows Her Pride. 2003. (Down on Friendly Acres Ser.: No. 1). (J). per. 5.95 (978-0-9743627-0-0(0) , 1179809) Sunflower Seeds Pr.

Raintree Steck-Vaughn Staff. Los Modales de Manolo. 1999. (Coleccion en Parejas). (SPA.). (J). pap., stu. ed. 21.50 (978-0-7398-0836-8(2)) Steck-Vaughn.

Ramon, Elisa. Aquello Que Tanto Queria Susana. Lavarello, Jose Maria, illus. 2004. Tr. of What Susana Loved Dearly. (SPA.). (J). pap. 7.99 (978-84-236-6702-4(2)) Edebé ESP. *Dist:* Lectorum Pubns., Inc.

Ramos, Peregrina. The Little Clay Jar = la Vasijita de Barro. Graham, Dennis, illus. 2006. Tr. of vasijita de Barro. (SPA & ENG.). (J). per. 15.95 (978-0-9788381-0-2(6)) Word Gift Pubns.

Rand, Edward A. The Knights of the White Shield: Up-the-Ladder Club Series Round One Play. 2007. 166p. pap. 11.99 (*978-1-4264-8273-1(6)); 184p. pap. 14.99 (*978-1-4264-8310-3(4)) BiblioBazaar.

Random House Staff. The Sisterhood of the Traveling Pants: The Official Scrapbook. movie tie-in ed. 2005. (Illus.). 160p. (YA). (gr. 7). pap. 9.95 (978-0-553-37607-4(1) , Delacorte Bks. for Young Readers) Random Hse. Children's Bks.

Ray, Delia. Singing Hands. 2006. (Illus.). 224p. (J). (gr. 5-9). 16.00 (978-0-618-65762-9(2) , Clarion Bks.) Houghton Mifflin Co. Trade & Reference Div.

Redfield, James & Lillegard, Dee. The Song of Celestine. Morrissey, Dean, illus. 2004. 46p. (J). (gr. 4-8). reprint ed. 15.00 (978-0-7567-8115-6(9)) DIANE Publishing Co.

Rees, Douglas. Smoking Mirror. 2005. (Art Encounters Ser.). (Illus.). 176p. (YA). 15.95 (978-0-8230-4863-2(2)) Watson-Guptill Pubns., Inc.

Reynolds, Aaron. Breaking Out of the Bungle Bird: Based on Proverbs 13:10. Whitehead, Peter, illus. 2005. (Insect-Inside Ser.). 40p. (J). 9.99 (978-0-310-70956-5(3)) Zonderkidz.

Reynolds, Peter. The Best Kid in the World. 2006. (Illus.). (J). (***978-1-4156-9188-5(6)***) Simon & Schuster Children's Publishing.

Reynolds, Peter H. So Few of Me. 2006. (Illus.). 32p. (J). (gr. k-12). 14.00 (978-0-7636-2623-5(6)) Candlewick Pr.

Rice, Alice Caldwell Hegan. Lovey Mary. 2006. 62.99 (***978-1-4280-1869-3(7)***) IndyPublish.com.

Rice, David L. Because Brian Hugged His Mother. Thompson, K. Dyble, illus. 1999. (J). (ps-ps). lib. bdg. 16.40 (978-0-613-23140-4(6)) Tandem Library Bks.

Rich, K. L. From Roaches to Riches. 2003. 107p. (YA). per. 15.95 (978-0-9728219-0-2(2)) Riches Publishing Co.

Richardson, Beverly J. Timbs. Where do Angels Come From? 2006. (Illus.). 44p. pap. 14.95 (978-1-59800-650-6(9)) Outskirts Press, Inc.

Richter, Jutta. The Cat, or, How I Lost Eternity. Brailovsky, Anna, tr. from GER. 2007. (Illus.). 80p. (J). (gr. 3 up). 14.00 (***978-1-57131-676-9(0)***) Milkweed Editions.

Robbins, Sandra. Ring Around a Rainbow: A Healthy & Safety Story. 2001. (See-More's Stories Ser.). 32p. (J). pap. 16.95 incl. audio compact disk (978-1-882601-42-4(4)) See-More's Workshop.

Roberts, Emma. Mrs. Murphy's Marvelous Mansion. Rogalski, Robert, illus. 2006. 32p. (J). 15.95 (978-0-9740190-4-8(6) , 888-210-8216) Illumination Arts Publishing Co., Inc.

Robertson, Elysia Hill. We Make the World A Special Place. Robertson, Elysia Hill & Bruce, Cindy, illus. 2005. 100p. (J). per. 12.95 (978-0-9764444-0-4(2) , EJWV-001) E. J. Publishing.

Robins, Eleanor. Just Be Yourself. 2004. 48p. (YA). 3.95 (978-1-56254-772-1(0) , SP7720) Saddleback Educational Publishing.

—One More Chance. 2004. (Illus.). 48p. (YA). per. 3.95 (978-1-56254-774-5(7) , SP7747) Saddleback Educational Publishing.

—Too Late. 2003. (Illus.). 48p. (YA). per. 3.95 (978-1-56254-693-9(7) , SP6937) Saddleback Educational Publishing.

Rockwell, Anne F. Chip & the Karate Kick. Meisel, Paul, illus. 2004. (Good Sports Ser.). 40p. (J). (ps-1). lib. bdg. 15.89 (978-0-06-028446-6(3)) HarperCollins Pubs.

Rouss, Sylvia A. No Rules for Michael. Simon, Susan, illus. 2003. 24p. (J). (ps-1). pap. 6.95 (978-1-58013-044-8(5)) Kar-Ben Publishing.

Ruby, Laura. Good Girls. 2008. 304p. (J). pap. 8.99 (***978-0-06-088225-9(5)***); 2006. 288p. (J). lib. bdg. 17.89 (978-0-06-088224-2(7)); 2006. 288p. (YA). 16.99 (978-0-06-088223-5(9)) HarperCollins Pubs. (HarperTeen).

Rue, Nancy. Sophie Loses the Lead, Vol. 11. 2006. (Faithgirlz! Ser.). 144p. (J). pap. 6.99 (978-0-310-71026-4(X)) Zonderkidz.

Rue, Nancy N. Sophie Breaks the Code, Vol. 7. 2005. (Faithgirlz Ser.). (Illus.). 144p. (J). pap. 6.99 (978-0-310-71022-6(7)) Zonderkidz.

—Sophie Flakes Out, Vol. 9. 2006. (Faithgirlz Ser.). (Illus.). 128p. (J). pap. 6.99 (978-0-310-71024-0(3)) Zonderkidz.

Rushton, Rosie. Olivia. 2000. 224p. (gr. 5-9). pap. 4.99 (978-0-7868-1392-6(X)) Disney Pr.

Russell, Cheryl & Brouch, Dan. The Story of the Starhearts. l.t. ed. 1999. 30p. (J). (ps-3). 15.95 (978-0-9713181-0-6(7)) StarHeart Productions.

Russon, Penni. Breathe. 2007. (Illus.). 368p. (J). (gr. 9 up). 16.99 (978-0-06-079393-7(7)); lib. bdg. 17.89 (978-0-06-079394-4(5)) HarperCollins Pubs.

—Undine. 2006. (Illus.). 336p. (J). 16.99 (978-0-06-079389-0(9)); lib. bdg. 17.89 (978-0-06-079390-6(2)) HarperCollins Pubs.

Ryan, Patrick. Saints of Augustine. 2007. 320p. (J). lib. bdg. 17.89 (***978-0-06-085811-7(7)***); (gr. 7 up). 16.99 (***978-0-06-085810-0(9)***) HarperCollins Pubs. (HarperTeen).

Rylant, Cynthia. A Fine White Dust. 2006. 112p. (J). pap. 4.99 (978-1-4169-2769-3(7) , Aladdin); 2000. (Illus.). (YA). (gr. 5-9). 25.00 (978-0-689-84087-6(X) , Atheneum/Richard Jackson Bks.) Simon & Schuster Children's Publishing.

—A Fine White Dust. l.t. ed. 2005. 148p. 21.95 (978-0-7862-7306-5(2) , Large Print Pr.) Thorndike Pr.

Salerno, Tony. Where's Beeper? A Learning Adventure in Helpfulness, 4 vols. 2005. 56p. (J). 14.99 (978-0-89221-603-1(4)) New Leaf Pr., Inc.

Samuels, Barbara. Happy Valentine's Day, Dolores. 2005. (Dolores Ser.). (Illus.). 32p. (J). 16.00 (978-0-374-32844-3(7) , Nelanie Kroupa Bks.) Farrar, Straus & Giroux.

Sanchez, Juanvi. El Cuento del Senor Pato. 2001. (Mi Primera Sopa de Libros Coleccion). (SPA., Illus.). 16p. (J). 11.95 (978-84-207-8963-7(1)) Grupo Anaya, S.A. ESP. *Dist:* Distribooks, Inc., Lectorum Pubns., Inc.

—La Noche. 2001. (Mi Primera Sopa de Libros Coleccion). (SPA., Illus.). (J). pap. 11.95 (978-84-207-8964-4(X)) Grupo Anaya, S.A. ESP. *Dist:* Distribooks, Inc., Lectorum Pubns., Inc.

Sargent, Dave. Baldy. Lenoir, Jane, illus. 2000. (J). pap. 6.95 (978-1-56763-445-7(1)) Ozark Publishing.

—Bogart Blue Jay. Lenoir, Jane, illus. 2000. (J). lib. bdg. 19.95 (978-1-56763-477-8(X)) Ozark Publishing.

—Buzz. Lenoir, Jane, illus. 2000. (J). lib. bdg. 19.95 (978-1-56763-459-4(1)) Ozark Publishing.

—Storky Stork: Be Trustworthy, 19, 18. Lenoir, Jane, illus. 2003. (Feather Tales Ser.: 18). 42p. (J). pap. 6.95 (978-1-56763-754-0(X)) Ozark Publishing.

Sargent, Dave & Lenoir, Jane. Baldy. 2000. (Illus.). (J). lib. bdg. 19.95 (978-1-56763-446-4(X)) Ozark Publishing.

—Bogart Blue Jay. 2000. (Illus.). (J). pap. 6.95 (978-1-56763-478-5(8)) Ozark Publishing.

Sargent, Dave & Lenoir, Jane, illus. Buzz. 2000. (J). pap. 6.95 (978-1-56763-460-0(5)) Ozark Publishing.

Sargent, Dave & Sargent, David, Jr. Kitty Hawk: Stealing, 20, 11. Lenoir, Jane, illus. 2003. (Feather Tales Ser.: 11). 42p. (J). pap. 6.95 (978-1-56763-740-3(X)) Ozark Publishing.

—Pinkie Flamingo: Leaving Home, 19, 15. Lenoir, Jane, illus. 2003. (Feather Tales Ser.: 15). 42p. (J). pap. 6.95 (978-1-56763-748-9(5)) Ozark Publishing.

Sargent, Dave & Sargent, Pat. Bandit: I Help Others, 38 bks., 14. Huff, Jeane, illus. 2nd rev. ed. 2003. (Animal Pride Ser.: No. 14). 42p. (J). pap. 6.95 (978-1-56763-786-1(8)) Ozark Publishing.

—Wally Wolverine: Eager, 56 vols., 59. Lenoir, Jane, illus. 2001. (Animal Pride Ser.: Vol. 59). 36p. (J). lib. bdg. 19.95 (978-1-56763-559-1(8)) Ozark Publishing.

—Willy Wildebeest: Thoughtfulness, 56 vols., 60. Lenoir, Jane, illus. 2001. (Animal Pride Ser.: Vol. 60). 36p. (J). lib. bdg. 19.95 (978-1-56763-561-4(X)); pap. 6.95 (978-1-56763-562-1(8)) Ozark Publishing.

Sargent, Dave, et al. Berry Picking Time Vol. 3: (Apache) Be Brave, 20. Lenoir, Jane, illus. l.t. ed. 2003. (Story Keeper Ser.: 3). 42p. (J). Vol. 3. lib. bdg. 22.60 (978-1-56763-907-0(0)); vol. 3. pap. 6.95 (978-1-56763-908-7(9)) Ozark Publishing.

—Fields of Golden Corn Vol. 6: (Navajo) Be Energetic, 20 bks. Lenoir, Jane, illus. l.t. ed. 2003. (Story Keeper Ser.: 6). 42p. (J). pap. 6.95 (978-1-56763-914-8(3)); lib. bdg. 22.60 (978-1-56763-913-1(5)) Ozark Publishing.

—A Hole in the Sun: (Choctaw) Be Independent, 20, Vol. 1. Lenoir, Jane, illus. l.t. ed. 2003. (Story Keeper Ser.: 1). 42p. (J). pap. 6.95 (978-1-56763-904-9(6)); lib. bdg. 22.60 (978-1-56763-903-2(8)) Ozark Publishing.

—Knocking the Rice Vol. 9: (Chippewa) Be Powerful, 20. Lenoir, Jane, illus. l.t. ed. 2003. (Story Keeper Ser.: 9). 42p. (J). lib. bdg. 22.60 (978-1-56763-919-3(4)) Ozark Publishing.

—Ladder at the Door Vol. 10: (Hopi) Be Curious, 20. Lenoir, Jane, illus. l.t. ed. 2004. (Story Keeper Ser.: 10). 48p. (J). pap. 6.95 (978-1-56763-922-3(4)); lib. bdg. 22.60 (978-1-56763-921-6(6)) Ozark Publishing.

—Land of the Sun Vol. 11: (Ute) Respect Elders, 20. Lenoir, Jane, illus. l.t. ed. 2004. (Story Keeper Ser.: Bk. 11). 48p. (J). 11. pap. 6.95 (978-1-56763-924-7(0)); Vol. 11. lib. bdg. 22.60 (978-1-56763-923-0(2)) Ozark Publishing.

—Little One Vol. 12: (Cherokee) Be Inventive, 20. Lenoir, Jane, illus. l.t. ed. 2003. (Story Keeper Ser.: Vol. 12). 42p. (J). pap. 6.95 (978-1-56763-926-1(7)); 12. lib. bdg. 22.60 (978-1-56763-925-4(9)) Ozark Publishing.

—On the Banks of the Wallowa River: (Nez Perce) Use Your Talent, 20, 13. Lenoir, Jane, illus. l.t. ed. 2004. (Story Keeper Ser.: 13). 48p. (J). lib. bdg. 22.60 (978-1-56763-927-8(5)) Ozark Publishing.

—Wally Wolverine: Eager, 56, 59. 2000. (Animal Pride Ser.: 59). (Illus.). 36p. (J). pap. 6.95 (978-1-56763-560-7(1)) Ozark Publishing.

Satz, Aaron. Unspoken Comprehension: Stuff You Already Know, but Never Realized. 2000. (gr. 7-12). lib. bdg. 31.55 (978-0-613-73910-8(8)) Tandem Library Bks.

Schatzer, Jeffery. The Runaway Garden. Ebbeler, Jeffrey, illus. 2007. 32p. (J). 17.95 (***978-1-58726-436-8(6)*** , Mitten Pr.) Ann Arbor Media Group, LLC.

Sebasco, Salvador. The Boy, the King, & the Chihuahua. 2005. (ENG.). 84p. per. 17.25 (978-1-4208-6315-4(0)) AuthorHouse.

Seidler, Tor. Terpin. 2002. (Illus.). 112p. (J). 14.89 (978-0-06-623608-7(8) , Geringer, Laura Book) HarperCollins Pubs.

—Terpin. 2004. (gr. 3-6). lib. bdg. 14.15 (978-0-613-81688-5(9)) Tandem Library Bks.

Seskin Steve & Shamblin Allen. Chance to Shine. 2006. (Illus.). 32p. 16.95 incl. audio compact disk (978-1-58246-167-0(8) , Tricycle Pr.) Ten Speed Pr.

Shams, K. The Pigle. Spears, Ashley E., illus. l.t. ed. 2004. 20p. (J). 9.99 (978-0-9728872-9-8(6)) Trent's Prints.

Shan, Darren, pseud. A Living Nightmare. 2001. (Cirque du Freak: Bk. 1). (J). 272p. (gr. k-3). 15.95 (978-0-316-60340-9(6)); (Illus.). viii, 279p. (gr. 3-6). pap. (978-0-316-64852-3(3)) Little, Brown Bks. for Young Readers.

Shaw, Janet Beeler. Kaya's Hero. 2002. (gr. 3-6). lib. bdg. 14.10 (978-0-613-46224-2(6)) Tandem Library Bks.

—Kaya's Hero Bk. 3: A Story of Giving. Farnsworth, Bill & McAliley, Susan, illus. 2002. (American Girls Collection: Bk. 3). 88p. (gr. 2-7). (J). 12.95 (978-1-58485-428-9(6)); 6.95 (978-1-58485-427-2(8)) American Girl Publishing, Inc.

—Meet Kaya. 2002. (gr. 3-6). lib. bdg. 14.10 (978-0-613-46227-3(0)) Tandem Library Bks.

Shea, Pegi Deitz, et al. The Boy & the Spell. Riglietti, Serena, illus. 2007. (Musical Stories Ser.). 36p. (J). (ps-3). 16.95 (978-0-9646010-4-8(4)) Pumpkin Hse., Ltd.

Sheldon, Dyan. Sophie Pitt-Turnbull Discovers America. 2005. 192p. (YA). (gr. 7 up). 15.99 (978-0-7636-2740-9(2)) Candlewick Pr.

Shepard, Sara. Flawless. 2008. (Pretty Little Liars Ser.: Bk. 2). 352p. (J). pap. 8.99 (***978-0-06-088735-3(4)*** , HarperTeen) HarperCollins Pubs.

—Perfect. 2007. (Pretty Little Liars Ser.: Bk. 3). 320p. (YA). (gr. 9 up). 16.99 (***978-0-06-088736-0(2)*** , HarperTeen) HarperCollins Pubs.

—Pretty Little Liars. 2007. (Pretty Little Liars Ser.: Bk. 1). 304p. (J). pap. 8.99 (***978-0-06-088732-2(X)*** , HarperTeen) HarperCollins Pubs.

—Unbelievable. 2008. (Pretty Little Liars Ser.: Bk. 4). 352p. (J). 16.99 (***978-0-06-088739-1(7)*** , HarperTeen) HarperCollins Pubs.

Sheppard, Caroline. Bart, el Valentino. Oehlberg, Marie, tr. 2001. (Illus.). (J). pap. 19.00 net. (978-1-931310-15-4(7)) National Institute for Trauma & Loss in Children, The/TLC.

Shinn, Sharon. Truth-Teller's Tale. 2005. 256p. (J). (gr. 7). 16.99 (978-0-670-06000-9(3) , Viking Juvenile) Penguin Group (USA) Inc.

Shipman, Todd. Morse the Horse Gets His Chance. 2007. 24p. (J). per. 17.99 (***978-1-59886-819-7(5)***) Tate Publishing & Enterprises, L.L.C.

The Short & the Tall of It, the Black & the White of It: A Very Important Experiment at Daylily Elementary. 2006. (J). mass mkt. 16.95 (978-0-9740410-4-9(1)) WordMaster Publishing.

Showstack, Richard. The Gift of the Magic: And Other Enchanting Character-Building Stories for Smart Teenage Girls Who Want to Grow up to Be Strong Women. Eric, Whitfield, illus. 2004. 156p. (YA). per. 14.95 (978-1-888725-64-3(8) , BeachHouse Bks.) Science & Humanities Pr.

—The Gift of the Magic: And Other Enchanting Character-Building Stories for Smart Teenage Girls Who Want to Grow up to Be Strong Women. Whitfield, Eric, illus. l.t. ed. 2004. 156p. (YA). per. 24.95 (978-1-888725-65-0(6) , MacroPrintBooks) Science & Humanities Pr.

—Peggy: And Other Enchanting Character-Building Stories for Smar Boys Who Want to Grow up to Be Strong Men. Whitfild, Eric, illus. 2004. 200p. (YA). per. 14.95 (978-1-888725-66-7(4) , BeachHouse Bks.) Science & Humanities Pr.

—Peggy: And Other Enchanting Character-Building Stories for Smar Boys Who Want to Grow up to Be Strong Men. Whitfield, Eric, illus. l.t. ed. 2004. 200p. (YA). per. 24.95 (978-1-888725-67-4(2) , MacroPrintBooks) Science & Humanities Pr.

Shragg, Karen. A Solstice Tree for Jenny. Schwabacher, Heidi, illus. 2004. (Young Readers Ser.). 50p. (gr. k up). 12.00 (978-1-57392-930-1(1) , Pyr Bks.) Prometheus Bks., Pubs.

Simon, Charnan. Messy Molly. Gallagher-Cole, Mernie, illus. 2006. (Magic Door to Learning Ser.). 24p. (J). (gr. 1-3). 21.36 (978-1-59296-625-7(X)) Child's World, Inc.

Smelcer, John. The Trap. 2006. 176p. (YA). (gr. 4-7). 15.95 (978-0-8050-7939-5(4)) Holt, Henry & Co.

—The Trap. 2007. 192p. (YA). pap. 7.99 (***978-0-312-37755-7(X)***) Square Fish.

The Smile of A Golden Child. 2004. (J). per. 16.99 (978-0-9753533-6-3(5)) Golden Eagle Publishing Hse., Inc.

Smith, Alexander McCall. The Perfect Hamburger & Other Delicious Stories. Rankin, Laura, illus. 2007. 288p. (J). (gr. 2-4). 15.95 (***978-1-59990-134-3(X)***); pap. 7.95 (***978-1-59990-157-2(9)***) Bloomsbury Publishing. (Bloomsbury Children).

Smith, Anya. Respect - Companion Book. Cesena, Denise, illus. l.t. ed. 2003. 12p. (J). 2.00 (978-0-9740418-5-8(8)) Night LIght Pubns., LLC.

Smith, Harriet. Pollyanna's Debt of Honor. (J). 17.95 (978-1-56723-091-8(1)) Yestermorrow, Inc.

Smith, Todd Aaron. Riley O'Smiley. 2006. (Illus.). 32p. (J). 12.99 (978-1-4003-0818-7(6)) Nelson, Thomas Inc.

Snedeker, Caroline. Downright Dencey. Barney, Maginel Wright, illus. 2003. (Young Adult Library). 274p. (YA). pap. 11.95 (978-1-883937-79-9(5)) Bethlehem Bks.

Snyder, Jackie. Secret Pal Surprises. 1999. (978-0-606-17743-6(4)) Tandem Library Bks.

Something Wise, 15 vols. 2004. (Illus.). 39p. (J). (gr. 1-2). per. 6.00 (978-0-9714844-2-9(2)) Zion Publishing.

Sommer, Carl. Dare to Dream. Martinez, Jorge et al, illus. 2007. (J). (***978-1-57537-024-8(7)***); lib. bdg. (***978-1-57537-073-6(5)***) Advance Publishing, Inc.

—Miserable Millie. Vignolo, Enrique, illus. (J). 2006. (***978-1-57537-022-4(0)***); 2005. (978-1-57537-071-2(9)) Advance Publishing, Inc.

—Spike the Rebel. Vignolo, Enrique, illus. 2007. (J). (***978-1-57537-023-1(9)***); lib. bdg. (***978-1-57537-072-9(7)***) Advance Publishing, Inc.

Sommer, Carl. Time Remote! 2003. (Another Sommer-Time Story Ser.). (Illus.). 48p. (J). (gr. 1-4). 16.95 incl. audio compact disk (978-1-57537-512-0(5)); 16.95 incl. audio (978-1-57537-561-8(3)) Advance Publishing, Inc.

—Time Remote! Budwine, Greg, illus. 2000. (Another Summer-Time Story Ser.). 48p. (J). (gr. 1-4). 9.95 (978-1-57537-012-5(3)); lib. bdg. 16.95 (978-1-57537-064-4(6)) Advance Publishing, Inc.

Southern, Randy. Ruled Out. 2000. (Kidwitness Tales Ser.). (Illus.). 128p. (J). (gr. 3-7). pap. 5.99 (978-1-56179-884-1(3)) Bethany Hse. Pubs.

Spain, Susan Rosson. The Deep Cut. 2006. (Illus.). 224p. (J). 16.99 (978-0-7614-5316-1(4)) Cavendish, Marshall Corp.

Spaulding, Norma. The Little Blue Parcel. King, Stephen Michael, illus. 1999. 64p. (J). (978-1-86388-854-7(3)) Scholastic, Inc.

Spinelli, Jerry. Zinkoff, el Inutil. (SPA.). (YA). 8.95 (978-958-04-7446-3(X)) Norma S.A. COL. *Dist:* Distribuidora Norma, Inc.

Squires, Mary L. Margaret Who Dared to Dream. l.t. ed. 2003. (Illus.). 45p. 12.95 (978-0-9631547-3-6(7)) Popular Truth, Inc.

Stahler, David, Jr. Doppelganger. 2006. 272p. (J). 16.99 (978-0-06-087232-8(2)); lib. bdg. 17.89 (978-0-06-087233-5(0)) HarperCollins Pubs.

StarKidz: I Am Who I Am. l.t. ed. 2003. (Illus.). 28p. (J). 16.95 (978-0-9743964-1-5(9)) World of Angels, A.

Stellinga, Mark. Buster Boogernose & the Liar. 2007. (J). per. 9.95 (***978-0-9796421-7-3(5)***) Stellinga, Mark.

Stevenson, Robert Louis. Treasure Island: A Classic Story about Responsibility. 2003. (Illus.). 32p. per. 3.95 (978-0-9747133-4-2(1) , Values to Live By Classic Stories) Thomas, Frederic Inc.

Stickle, Beverly Graham. Slow down & Simplify: Busy People Share Tips for Rediscovering Peace in Your Life. Wade, Kenneth R., ed. 1998. 158p. pap. 10.99 (978-0-8163-1688-5(0)) Pacific Pr. Publishing Assn.

Stoutland, Allison. Put Your Best Foot Forward: More Little Lessons for a Happier World. Hofher, Cathy, illus. 2000. 32p. (J). 14.95 (978-0-9670941-1-3(9)) Inch By Inch Pubns., LLC.

Stuart, Tara. Trees: A Tara's Tale about Being Yourself. 2006. (Illus.). (J). bds. 15.00 (978-0-9765060-3-4(3)) TouchSmart Publishing, LLC.

Susan, Sister. The Sun in My Belly. Nghiem, Sister Tin, illus. 2007. 32p. pap. 11.95 (***978-1-888375-64-0(7)*** , Plum Blossom Bks.) Parallax Pr.

Swallow, Pamela Curtis. It Only Looks Easy. rev. ed. 2003. 176p. (J). (gr. 3-7). 15.95 (978-0-7613-1790-6(2)) Roaring Brook Pr.

Swan, S. Annie. Thankful Rest (a Tale) 2006. 77.99 (***978-1-4219-9988-3(9)***); pap. 70.99 (***978-1-4142-5872-0(0)***) IndyPublish.com.

Sweet, Melissa. Carmine: A Little More Red. 2005. (Illus.). 40p. (J). (gr. k-3). 16.00 (978-0-618-38794-6(3)) Houghton Mifflin Co. Trade & Reference Div.

Taylor-Gaines, Lonnetta. Fia & the Butterfly: 7 Stories for Character Education. 2005. 13.00 (978-0-8059-9848-1(9)) Dorrance Publishing Co., Inc.

Taylor, Jeannie St. John. Out at Home: A Novel. 2004. 144p. (J). pap. 6.99 (978-0-8254-3724-3(5)) Kregel Pubns.

Thank You, Meiling: Evaluation Guide. 2006. (J). (978-1-55942-423-3(0)) Marsh Media.

Thomas, Jerry D. My Friend Fang & Other Great Stories for Kids: Learning How to Be Someone Who Has Good Friends. 2001. (Illus.). 95p. (J). (978-0-8163-1822-3(0)) Pacific Pr. Publishing Assn.

Thomas, Marlo. Free to Be You & Me No. 5: A Different Kind of Book for Children & Adults to Enjoy Together. 2002. (Illus.). 144p. pap. 12.95 (978-0-7624-1306-5(9) , Running Pr.) Running Pr. Bk. Pubs.

Thompson, Joel. Critter Sitters: And Other Stories That Teach Christian Values. 2003. (ClubZone Kids Ser.). (Illus.). 80p. (J). pap. 5.99 (978-0-8010-4511-0(8)) Baker Bks.

—Shortcuts: And Other Stories That Teach Christian Values. 2003. (Clubzone Kids Ser.). (Illus.). 80p. (J). pap. 5.99 (978-0-8010-4510-3(X)) Baker Bks.

Thunder Brook: Escape from the Land of Huffra, Adam & the Valley of the Weedgrass. 2005. (Illus.). 136p. (J). 14.95 (978-0-9768152-0-4(6)) Buttercup Media.

Tichenor, Richard. Tales from the Woods of Wisdom, Bk. 1. (J). 2000. 185p. pap. 16.95 (978-1-888725-37-7(0) , BeachHouse Bks.); 2001. 275p. per. 24.95 (978-1-888725-50-6(8) , MacroPrintBooks) Science & Humanities Pr.

Tidd, Louise Vitellaro. I'll Do It Later. 1999. (gr. k-3). lib. bdg. 11.80 (978-0-613-18158-7(1)) Tandem Library Bks.

Tompert, Ann. The Errant Knight. Keith, Doug, illus. 2003. 32p. 15.95 (978-0-9701907-6-5(X)) Illumination Arts Publishing Co., Inc.

Tripp, Valerie. Changes for Kit: A Winter Story. Rane, Walter & McAliley, Susan, illus. 2001. (American Girls Collection: Bk. 6). 86p. (J). (gr. 2 up). 12.95 (978-1-58485-027-4(2)); 6.95 (978-1-58485-026-7(4)) American Girl Publishing, Inc.

—Changes for Kit: A Winter Story. 2001. (American Girls Collection). (Illus.). (J). 12.75 (978-0-606-21107-9(1)) Tandem Library Bks.

—Changes for Kit: A Winter Story 1934. Rane, Walter & McAliley, Susan, illus. 2001. 64p. (J). (gr. 3-6). lib. bdg. 14.10 (978-0-613-44636-5(4)) Tandem Library Bks.

Troeger, Virginia B. Secret along the St. Mary's. Swisher, Michael-Che, tr. Swisher, Michael-Che, illus. 2003. (Mysteries in Time Ser.). 92p. (J). 14.95 (978-1-893110-35-9(4)) Silver Moon Pr.

Troulis, Jennifer. Penelope & Prisilla & the Enchanted House of Whispers. 2004. 240p. (YA). per. 13.95 (978-0-9741805-5-7(6)) American LaserTechnic.

Trujillo Stephens, Kristina. I Can Follow the Rules. ed. 2006. (J). pap. (978-1-57332-428-1(0)) HighReach Learning, Inc.

Trupin/Nascimbeni, Nick/Barbara. Sorry Sam. 2006. (Illus.). 32p. (J). lib. bdg. 9.00 (***978-1-4242-0884-5(X)***) Fitzgerald Bks.

Tytler, Sarah. Girlhood & Womanhood the Story of Some. 2007. 43.99 (***978-1-4280-5160-7(0)***); pap. 36.99 (***978-1-4280-5161-4(9)***) IndyPublish.com.

Valgardson, W. D. Divorced Kids Club: And Other Stories. 2000. (gr. 5-8). lib. bdg. 15.25 (978-0-613-33888-2(X)) Tandem Library Bks.

Van Draanen, Wendelin. Flipped. 224p. (gr. 5-9). 2003. (J). pap. 8.95 (978-0-375-82544-6(4)); 2001. (J). 14.95 (978-0-375-81174-6(5)); 2001. lib. bdg. 16.99 (978-0-375-91174-3(X)) Random Hse. Children's Bks. (Knopf Bks. for Young Readers).

Velthuijs, Max. Sapo y Cerdito. 2001. (Mi Primera Sopa de Libros Coleccion). (SPA., Illus.). 12p. (J). 11.95 (978-84-207-9275-0(6)) Grupo Anaya, S.A. ESP. *Dist:* Distribooks, Inc., Lectorum Pubns., Inc.

—Sapo y Pata. 2001. (Mi Primera Sopa de Libros Coleccion). (SPA., Illus.). 12p. (J). 11.95 (978-84-207-9276-7(4)) Grupo Anaya, S.A. ESP. *Dist:* Distribooks, Inc., Lectorum Pubns., Inc.

Vision, David & Vision, Mutiya Sahar. Missing You. Alcantara, Ignacio, illus. 2005. 40p. (J). mass mkt. 17.00 (978-0-9659538-6-3(6)) Soul Vision Works Publishing.

Volponi, Paul. Rucker Park Setup. 2007. 208p. (J). 15.99 (978-0-670-06130-3(1) , Viking Juvenile) Penguin Group (USA) Inc.

von Ziegesar, Cecily. Lucky. 2007. (It Girl Ser.: No. 5). 256p. (YA). (gr. 10-17). pap. 9.99 (***978-0-316-11347-2(6)*** , Poppy) Little, Brown Bks. for Young Readers.

Wade, Rebecca. The Theft & the Miracle. 2007. 368p. (J). (gr. 5-9). 16.99 (978-0-06-077493-6(2)); lib. bdg. 17.89 (978-0-06-077495-0(9)) HarperCollins Pubs.

Walker, Raynn. Toadina: The Story of a Lady Toad. 2005. (J). pap. 15.00 (978-0-8059-6726-5(5)) Dorrance Publishing Co., Inc.

Wallace, Bill. Pick of the Litter. 2005. 160p. (J). (ps-7). 16.95 (978-0-8234-1921-0(5)) Holiday Hse., Inc.

—Pick of the Litter. 2006. 176p. (J). pap. 4.99 (978-1-4169-2511-8(2) , Aladdin) Simon & Schuster Children's Publishing.

Wallace, Nancy Elizabeth. The Kindness Quilt. 2006. (Illus.). 48p. (J). (gr. k-2). 16.99 (978-0-7614-5313-0(X)) Cavendish, Marshall Corp.

Wallace, Rich. One Good Punch. 2007. 128p. (YA). (gr. 7). 15.99 (***978-0-375-81352-8(7));*** lib. bdg. 18.99 (***978-0-375-91352-5(1))*** Random Hse. Children's Bks. (Knopf Bks. for Young Readers).

Wallington, Aury, adapted by. The O. C. Novelization: The Misfit, No. 2. novel ed. 2004. (O. C. Novelization Ser.). (Illus.). 256p. (J). (gr. 7 up). 6.99 (978-0-439-67700-4(9)) Scholastic, Inc.

Walsh, Sheila. Einstein's Enormous Error: A Story about Forgiving Others. Sullivan, Don, illus. 2002. (Gnoo Zoo Ser.: Bk. 3). 40p. (J). 9.95 (978-1-57856-335-7(6) , WaterBrook Pr.) WaterBrook Pr.

Waltman, Kevin. Learning the Game. 2005. 224p. (J). (gr. 7 up). pap. 16.95 (978-0-439-73109-6(7) , Scholastic Pr.) Scholastic, Inc.

Ward, Helen. The Boat. Andrew, Ian, illus. 2005. 32p. (J). (ps-17). 16.95 (978-1-894965-18-7(3)) Simply Read Bks. CAN. *Dist:* Perseus Distribution.

Wasserman, Robin. Wrath. 2006. (Seven Deadly Sins Ser.). (Illus.). 256p. (YA). pap. 8.99 (978-0-689-87785-8(4) , Simon Pulse) Simon & Schuster Children's Publishing.

Watkins, Dawn L., et al. Pollyanna. 2006. (J). (978-1-59166-669-1(4)) Jones, Bob Univ. Pr.

Weaver, Elizabeth Nixon. Rooster. 2005. 208p. (J). reprint ed. pap. 5.95 (978-0-7614-5218-8(4)) Cavendish, Marshall Corp.

Weil, Zoe. Claude & Medea: The Hellburn Dogs. 2007. 112p. (J). (gr. 4-7). pap. 30.00 (***978-1-59056-105-8(8))*** Lantern Bks.

Wells, Rosemary. Lassie. Jeffers, Susan, illus. 2000. (SPA.). 48p. (J). (gr. 3-5). 12.95 (978-84-241-3362-7(5) , EV8276) Everest de Ediciones y Distribucion, S.L. ESP. *Dist:* Lectorum Pubns., Inc.

Whelan, Gloria. The Turning. 2006. 224p. (J). 15.99 (978-0-06-075593-5(8)) HarperCollins Pubs.

Whidbee, Evelyn, told to. It's Called Blame. 2004. (J). pap. 8.00 (978-0-8059-6361-8(8)) Dorrance Publishing Co., Inc.

Whitfield, Mary. Mrs. Adams Teaches a Lesson for a Lifetime. 2003. 14p. (J). 7.00 (978-0-9720445-1-6(5)) Cathier Pr.

Whitney, Kim Ablon. The Perfect Distance. 2007. 256p. (YA). (gr. 7). pap. 5.99 (978-0-553-49467-9(8) , Laurel Leaf) Random Hse. Children's Bks.

—See You down the Road: A Novel. 2004. 192p. (J). (gr. 7). lib. bdg. 17.99 (978-0-375-92467-5(1) , Knopf Bks. for Young Readers) Random Hse. Children's Bks.

Why Am I Special? (Peek A Boo Pockets Ser.). 12p. (J). bds. (978-2-7643-0105-0(7)) Phidal Publishing, Inc./Editions Phidal, Inc.

Wilde, Oscar. The Picture of Dorian Gray. Marcos, Pablo, illus. 2002. (Great Illustrated Classics Ser.). 240p. (J). (gr. 3-8). 21.35 (978-1-57765-821-4(3) , ABDO & Daughters) ABDO Publishing Co.

—The Picture of Dorian Gray, 2 vols. l.t. ed. (YA). (gr. 10 up). reprint ed. 10.00 (978-0-89064-049-4(1)) National Assn. for Visually Handicapped.

—The Picture of Dorian Gray, Level 3. abr. ed. 2000. (Bookworms Ser.). (Illus.). 77p. 6.50 (978-0-19-423011-7(2)) Oxford Univ. Pr., Inc.

—The Picture of Dorian Gray. Ross, Tony, illus. 2001. (Whole Story Ser.). 272p. (YA). (gr. 10 up). 25.99 (978-0-670-89494-9(X) , Viking Juvenile) Penguin Group (USA) Inc.

—The Picture of Dorian Gray. 2003. (gr. 7-12). lib. bdg. 16.45 (978-0-613-64313-9(5)); 1999. 240p. (YA). (gr. 8-12). per. 11.80 (978-0-613-17434-3(8)) Tandem Library Bks.

Williams, Suzanne. Hilary's Super Secret. 2003. (Illus.). 133p. (J). (978-0-439-32990-3(6)) Scholastic, Inc.

Williams, Tamara L. Truth & Lies. 2002. (SideStreets Ser.). 128p. (***978-1-55028-753-0(2));*** (gr. 7-12). 7.95 (978-1-55028-756-1(7)) Lorimer, James & Co., Ltd., Pubs. CAN. *Dist:* Casemate Pubs. & Bk. Distributors, LLC.

—Truth & Lies. 2002. (gr. 7-12). lib. bdg. 13.00 (978-0-613-78319-4(0)) Tandem Library Bks.

Winston, Pat. Earl the EMU: God Has a Purpose for Those Who Are Different. Allen, Cathy H., photos by. 2000. (Illus.). 24p. (J). (ps-5). 12.95 (978-0-9702821-0-1(9)) Light Way Pubns., The.

Wojciechowski, Susan. The Christmas Miracle of Jonathan Toomey with CD: Gift Edition. Lynch, P. J., illus. 2007. 40p. (J). (gr. 1-7). 14.99 (***978-0-7636-3629-6(0))*** Candlewick Pr.

Wolff, Ferida. Is a Worry Worrying You? 32p. 2007. pap. 7.95 (***978-1-933718-05-7(6));*** 2005. (Illus.). (J). 15.95 (978-0-9749303-2-9(6)) Tanglewood Pr.

Wolff, Virginia Euwer. Make Lemonade. 2006. 208p. (YA). pap. 6.95 (978-0-8050-8070-4(8) , Holt, Henry & Co. Bks. For Young Readers) Holt, Henry & Co.

—Make Lemonade. l.t. ed. 2004. 257p. pap. 10.95 (978-0-7862-6358-5(X)) Thorndike Pr.

—True Believer. 2004. (Make Lemonade Trilogy Ser.). 272p. (J). (gr. 7 up). pap. 38.00 incl. audio (978-0-8072-2283-6(6) , Listening Library) Random Hse. Audio Publishing Group.

—True Believer. Gordon, Russell, illus. 2002. 272p. (YA). pap. 8.99 (978-0-689-85288-6(6) , Simon Pulse) Simon & Schuster Children's Publishing.

—True Believer. 2001. (Make Lemonade Trilogy Ser.). 272p. (J). (gr. 7 up). 17.00 (978-0-689-82827-0(6) , Atheneum) Simon & Schuster Children's Publishing.

—True Believer. 2002. (gr. 7-12). lib. bdg. 16.45 (978-0-613-60942-5(5)) Tandem Library Bks.

Wolfson, Jill. What I Call Life. rev. ed. 2005. (Illus.). 272p. (J). (ps-7). 16.95 (978-0-8050-7669-1(7)) Holt, Henry & Co.

—What I Call Life. 2008. 288p. (J). pap. 6.99 (***978-0-312-37752-6(5))*** Square Fish.

Wood, Douglas. The Secret of Saying Thanks. Shed, Greg, illus. 2005. 32p. (J). 16.95 (978-0-689-85410-1(2)) Simon & Schuster Children's Publishing.

Woods, Ron. The Hero. 2003. 224p. (J). (gr. 4-7). pap. 5.50 (978-0-440-22978-0(2) , Yearling) Random Hse. Children's Bks.

Woods, Shirley. The Planet of Success. 2006. (Illus.). 41p. (J). per. 9.95 (978-1-60002-183-1(2) , 4207) Airleaf Publishing & Bookselling.

Wright, Caleb E. Marcus Blair A Story of Provincial Times. 2006. pap. 22.95 (***978-1-4286-6303-9(7))*** Kessinger Publishing, LLC.

Wullschleger Daldini, Elena. Ma tu, che Babbo Natale Sei? Caccia, Christiane, illus. 2004. (ITA.). 48p. (J). 19.00 (978-88-87469-33-2(4) , gce) Gabriele Capelli Editore Sagl CHE. *Dist:* SPD-Small Pr. Distribution.

Yeahpau, Thomas M. X-Indian Chronicles: The Book of Mausape. 2006. 240p. (YA). (gr. 9). 16.99 (978-0-7636-2706-5(2)) Candlewick Pr.

Young, Jan. The Orange Slipknot. Lehmkuhl, Pat, illus. 2007. 178p. (J). per. 10.00 (***978-0-9772525-5-8(8))*** Raven Publishing Inc. of Montana.

Yumel, Demain. Little Yellow Pear Tomatoes. Tamarin, Nicole, illus. 2005. 32p. (J). 15.95 (978-0-9740190-2-4(X)) Illumination Arts Publishing Co., Inc.

Zeises, Lara M. Anyone but You. 256p. (YA). (gr. 9). 2007. mass mkt. 6.50 (***978-0-440-23858-4(7)*** , Laurel Leaf); 2005. 15.95 (978-0-385-73145-4(0) , Delacorte Bks. for Young Readers) Random Hse. Children's Bks.

Ziefert, Harriet. Messy Bessie: Where's My Homework. De Muth, Roger, illus. 2007. 36p. 12.95 (978-1-59354-181-1(3)) Handprint Bks.

—Thank You, Nicky! Brown, Richard, illus. 2002. 7p. (ps). bds. 6.95 (978-1-929766-73-4(4)) Blue Apple Bks.

Zindel, Lizabeth. Girl of the Moment. 288p. (YA). (gr. 7). 2008. pap. 8.99 (***978-0-14-241104-9(3)*** , Puffin); 2007. 16.99 (978-0-670-06210-2(3) , Viking Juvenile) Penguin Group (USA) Inc.

CONDUCTING

Here are entered works on orchestral conducting or a combination of orchestral and choral conducting.

see also Bands (Music); Orchestra

Gehrkens, Karl W. Essentials in Conducting. 2001. 184p. (YA). reprint ed. 88.00 (978-0-7222-5683-1(3)) Library Reprints, Inc.

CONDUCTORS (MUSIC)

see also Conducting

Anderton, H. Orsmond. Granville Bantock. 2001. 155p. (YA). reprint ed. 88.00 (978-0-7222-5323-6(0)) Library Reprints, Inc.

Arditi, Luigi. My Reminiscences. 2001. 314p. (YA). reprint ed. 98.00 (978-0-7222-6277-1(9)) Library Reprints, Inc.

Bulow, Hans Guido von. The Early Correspondence of Hans Von Bulow. 2001. 266p. (YA). reprint ed. 98.00 (978-0-7222-5372-4(9)) Library Reprints, Inc.

Croger, Thomas R. Notes on Conductors & Conducting: The Organizing & Conducting of Amateur Orchestras. 2nd ed. 2001. 63p. (YA). reprint ed. 88.00 (978-0-7222-5682-4(5)) Library Reprints, Inc.

Damrosch, Walter. My Musical Life. 2001. 376p. (YA). reprint ed. 98.00 (978-0-7222-5398-4(2)) Library Reprints, Inc.

Glover, Jimmy. Jimmy Glover: Master of Music at Drury Lane Theatre. 2001. 299p. (YA). reprint ed. 98.00 (978-0-7222-5414-1(8)) Library Reprints, Inc.

Godfrey, Dan. Memories & Music: Thirty-Five Years of Conducting. 2001. 327p. (YA). reprint ed. 98.00 (978-0-7222-5418-9(0)) Library Reprints, Inc.

Hallett, Charles. The Life & Letters of Sir Charles Halle. 2001. 432p. (YA). reprint ed. 98.00 (978-0-7222-5426-4(1)) Library Reprints, Inc.

Rodgers, J. A. Dr. Henry Coward, the Pioneer Chorus-Master. 2001. 101p. (YA). reprint ed. 88.00 (978-0-7222-5395-3(8)) Library Reprints, Inc.

CONFECTIONERY

Anderson, Jenna. How It Happens at the Candy Company. Wolfe, Bob & Wolfe, Diane, photos by. 2002. (How It Happens Ser.). (Illus.). 32p. (J). (gr. 2-5). lib. bdg. 19.95 (978-1-881508-91-5(9)) Oliver Pr., Inc.

Cacciatore, Stacy. Candy Around the World. 2008. 90p. pap. 7.95 (978-0-9717119-4-5(1)) Consumer Pr., The.

Dalmatian Press Staff. M&M's Brand: Bright Idea Book to Color. 2002. (Illus.). 32p. (J). (ps-4). 3.99 (978-1-57759-780-3(X)) Dalmatian Pr.

—M&M's Brand I'm Outta Here! Sticker Book. 2002. (Illus.). 48p. (J). (ps-4). 2.99 (978-1-57759-782-7(6)) Dalmatian Pr.

Dawson, Susan H. & Norton, Susan R. Pyramid Pal - Sweets: Eating Should Always Be Fun for a Kid. O'Hare, Mark, illus. 2000. (Adventures in Eating with the Nutrition Champion of Kids Ser.). 16p. (J). pap. 3.00 (978-1-58000-069-7(X)) Griffin Publishing Group.

Gilpin, Rebecca. Chocolates & Candies to Make. rev. ed. 2004. 32p. (J). pap. 6.95 (978-0-7945-0823-4(5) , Usborne) EDC Publishing.

Gilpin, Rebecca & Atkinson, Catherine. Yummy Little Cookbook. rev. ed. 2007. (Children's Cooking Ser.). 96p. (J). 7.99 (***978-0-7945-1655-0(6)*** , Usborne) EDC Publishing.

Kihm, Steve. The Lost Candy Bar. 2004. (J). mass mkt. 6.95 (978-0-9786794-0-8(7)) Lost Candy Bar Pr., LLC.

Klingel, Cynthia Fitterer & Noyed, Robert B. Fats & Sweets. Andersen, Gregg, photos by. 2002. (Weekly Reader Early Learning Library). (Illus.). 24p. (J). (ps up). pap. 7.93 (978-0-8368-3145-0(4)); lib. bdg. 19.33 (978-0-8368-3056-9(3)) Stevens, Gareth Inc. (Weekly Reader Early Learning Library).

Kreger, Claire. Jelly Beans: From Start to Finish. Carney, Patrick, illus. Carney, Patrick, photos by. 2002. (Made in the USA Ser.). 32p. (J). 23.70 (978-1-56711-477-5(6) , Blackbirch Pr., Inc.) Thomson Gale.

Landau, Elaine. Chewing Gum: A Sticky Treat. 2000. (Tasty Treats Ser.). (Illus.). 24p. (J). (gr. 1-4). lib. bdg. 23.93 (978-1-57103-335-2(1)) Rourke Publishing, LLC.

Love, Ann & Drake, Jane. Sweet! The Delicious Story of Candy. Davila, Claudia, illus. 2007. 64p. (J). (gr. 4-7). 19.95 (978-0-88776-752-4(4)) Tundra Bks., Inc./Livres Toundra, Inc. CAN. *Dist:* Random Hse., Inc.

Mother Estelle's Easy Homemade Candy Cookbook. 2001. 108p. per. 9.95 (978-0-9701466-8-7(X)) Athenean Pr., Inc.

Nelson, Robin. Fats, Oils, & Sweets. 2003. (First Step Nonfiction Ser.). (Illus.). 24p. (J). (gr. k-2). lib. bdg. 18.60 (978-0-8225-4634-4(5)) Lerner Publishing Group.

—From Cocoa Bean to Chocolate. 2003. (Start to Finish Ser.). (Illus.). 24p. (J). (gr. k-2). lib. bdg. 18.60 (978-0-8225-4665-8(5)) Lerner Publishing Group.

Ridley, Sarah. A Chocolate Bar. 2006. (Illus.). 32p. (J). lib. bdg. 23.33 (978-0-8368-6293-5(5)) Stevens, Gareth Inc.

Royston, Angela. Chocolate. 2005. (How Are Things Made? Ser.). (Illus.). 32p. (J). tchr. ed. (978-0-431-05046-1(5)); pap. (978-0-431-05053-9(8)) Heinemann Library.

—How Is Chocolate Made? 2005. (How Are Things Made? Ser.). (Illus.). 32p. (J). (gr. k-2). lib. bdg. 24.21 (978-1-4034-6641-9(6)) Heinemann Library.

Smalley, Carol Parenzan. Fats, Oils, & Sweets. 2005. (Rookie Read-About Health Ser.). (Illus.). 31p. (J). (ps-3). 20.50 (978-0-516-25289-6(5) , Children's Pr.) Scholastic Library Publishing.

—Fats, Oils & Sweets. 2006. 32p. (J). (gr. k-2). pap. 5.95 (978-0-516-24759-5(X) , Children's Pr.) Scholastic Library Publishing.

Thomas, Ann. Fats, Oils, & Sweets. 2002. (Food Ser.). (Illus.). 32p. (gr. k-2). 23.00 (978-0-7910-6979-0(6) , Chelsea Hse.) Facts On File, Inc.

CONFEDERATE STATES OF AMERICA

Anderson, Dale. A Soldier's Life in the Civil War. 2004. (World Almanac Library of the Civil War). (Illus.). 48p. (J). (gr. 5 up). pap. 11.95 (978-0-8368-5595-1(7)); lib. bdg. 30.00 (978-0-8368-5586-9(8)) Stevens, Gareth Inc. (World Almanac Library).

Anderson, Paul Christopher. Robert E. Lee: Legendary Commander of the Confederacy. 2005. (Library of American Lives & Times). (Illus.). 112p. (YA). (gr. 4-8). lib. bdg. 31.95 (978-0-8239-5748-4(9)) Rosen Publishing Group, Inc., The.

Beller, Susan Provost. Billy Yank & Johnny Reb: Soldiering in the Civil War. 2007. (Soldiers on the Battlefront Ser.). (Illus.). 112p. (YA). (gr. 6-8). lib. bdg. 33.26 (978-0-8225-6803-2(9)) Lerner Publishing Group.

Blashfield, Jean F. Horse Soldiers: Cavalry in the Civil War. 1998. (First Bks.). (Illus.). 64p. (J). (gr. 5-7). 22.00 (978-0-531-20300-2(X) , Watts, Franklin) Scholastic Library Publishing.

Brager, Bruce L. There He Stands: The Story of Stonewall Jackson. 2005. (Civil War Leaders Ser.). (Illus.). 176p. (J). (gr. 6-12). 26.95 (978-1-931798-44-0(3)) Reynolds, Morgan Inc.

Brownell, Richard. The Civil War: The Fall of the Confederacy & the End of Slavery. 2005. (History's Great Defeats Ser.). (Illus.). 109p. (YA). (gr. 7-10). lib. bdg. 29.95 (978-1-59018-429-5(7) , Lucent Bks.) Thomson Gale.

Carter, E. J. Jefferson Davis. 2004. (American War Biographies Ser.). (Illus.). 48p. (J). pap. 8.50 (978-1-4034-5089-0(7)); lib. bdg. 27.07 (978-1-4034-5082-1(X)) Heinemann Library.

—Robert E. Lee. 2004. (American War Biographies Ser.). (Illus.). 48p. (J). pap. 8.50 (978-1-4034-5088-3(9)); lib. bdg. 27.07 (978-1-4034-5081-4(1)) Heinemann Library.

Connell, Kate. Yankee Blue or Rebel Grey? The Civil War Adventures of Sam Shaw. 2003. (gr. 3-6). lib. bdg. 15.30 (978-0-613-67133-0(3)) Tandem Library Bks.

Ditchfield, Christin. Joseph E. Johnston: Confederate General. 2001. (Famous Figures of the Civil War Era Ser.). (Illus.). (J). 79p. pap. (978-0-7910-6413-9(1)); 80p. (gr. 5 up). 25.00 (978-0-7910-6412-2(3)) Facts On File, Inc. (Chelsea Hse.).

Doak, Robin S. Thomas "Stonewall" Jackson: Confederate General. 2005. (Signature Lives Ser.). (Illus.). 112p. (J). (gr. 5-7). (978-0-7565-0987-3(4)) Compass Point Bks.

Gaines, Ann Graham. The Confederacy & the Civil War in American History. 2000. (In American History Ser.). (Illus.). 128p. (YA). (gr. 5-12). lib. bdg. 26.60 (978-0-7660-1417-6(7)) Enslow Pubs., Inc.

Gillis, Jennifer Blizin. The Confederate Soldier. 2006. 48p. (J). (gr. 4-6). lib. bdg. (978-0-7565-2025-0(8)) Compass Point Bks.

—Robert E. Lee: Confederate Commander. 2004. (Signature Lives Ser.). (Illus.). 112p. (J). 30.60 (978-0-7565-0821-0(5) , 1240144) Compass Point Bks.

Green, Carl R. & Sanford, William R. Confederate Generals of the Civil War. 1998. (Collective Biographies Ser.). (Illus.). 112p. (YA). (gr. 6-12). lib. bdg. 26.60 (978-0-7660-1029-1(5)) Enslow Pubs., Inc.

Greene, Meg. Jeb Stuart: Confederate General. 2001. (Famous Figures of the Civil War Era Ser.). (Illus.). 80p. (J). (gr. 5 up). pap. 25.00 (978-0-7910-6415-3(8)); 25.00 (978-0-7910-6414-6(X)) Facts On File, Inc. (Chelsea Hse.).

Hale, Sarah Elder, ed. Stonewall Jackson: Spirit of the South. 2005. (Cobblestone the Civil War Ser.). (Illus.). 48p. (J). 17.95 (978-0-8126-7907-6(5)) Cobblestone Publishing Co.

Jefferson Davis. (Civil War Biographies Ser.). 48p. (YA). 7.95 (978-0-7368-4524-3(0)) Capstone Pr., Inc.

Jensen, Leslie D. Johnny Reb Vol. 5: The Uniform of the Confederate Army, 1861-1865. 1999. (G. I. Ser.). (Illus.). 80p. (YA). (gr. 5 up). 27.50 (978-0-7910-5369-0(5) , Chelsea Hse.) Facts On File, Inc.

Jerome, Kate Boehm. Civil War Sub Vol. 3: The Mystery of the Hunley. Sofo, Frank & Farnsworth, Bill, illus. 2002. (All Aboard Reading Ser.). 48p. (J). pap. 3.99 (978-0-448-42597-9(1) , Grosset & Dunlap) Penguin Group (USA) Inc.

—Civil War Sub Vol. 3: The Mystery of the Hunley. 2002. (gr. k-3). lib. bdg. 11.80 (978-0-613-64032-9(2)) Tandem Library Bks.

Katcher, Philip R. N. Civil War Confederate Troops. 2003. (Battle Ready Ser.). 48p. (J). 28.56 (978-1-4109-0120-0(3)) Raintree.

—Civil War State Troops. 2003. (Battle Ready Ser.). (Illus.). 48p. (YA). 28.56 (978-1-4109-0121-7(1)) Raintree.

—Confederate Flags of the Civil War. 2003. (Battle Ready Ser.). (Illus.). 48p. (J). 28.56 (978-1-4109-0122-4(X)) Raintree.

Landers, Eli P. Weep Not for Me, Dear Mother. Roberson, Elizabeth Whitley, ed. 1998. 168p. (J). (gr. 3-7). pap. 14.95 (978-1-56554-390-4(4)) Pelican Publishing Co., Inc.

Lieurance, Suzanne. Weapons & Strategies of the Civil War: A MyReportLinks. com Book. 2004. (American Civil War Ser.). (Illus.). 48p. (J). lib. bdg. 25.26 (978-0-7660-5185-0(4) , MyReportLinks.com Bks.) Enslow Pubs., Inc.

Marcovitz, Hal. The Confederate Flag. 2002. (American Symbols & Their Meanings Ser.). (Illus.). 48p. (YA). (gr. 4 up). lib. bdg. (978-1-59084-035-1(6)) Mason Crest Pubs.

McCarthy, Pat. Famous Confederate Generals & Leaders of the South: A Myreportlinks. com Book. 2004. (American Civil War Ser.). (Illus.). 48p. (J). lib. bdg. 25.26 (978-0-7660-5189-8(7) , MyReportLinks.com Bks.) Enslow Pubs., Inc.

McLeese, Don. Jeb Stuart. 2006. (Civil War Military Leaders Ser.). (Illus.). 32p. (gr. 3-6). 19.95 (978-1-59515-479-8(5)) Rourke Publishing, LLC.

—Robert E. Lee. 2006. (Civil War Military Leaders Ser.). (Illus.). 32p. (gr. 3-6). 19.95 (978-1-59515-476-7(0)) Rourke Publishing, LLC.

—Stonewall Jackson. 2006. (Civil War Military Leaders Ser.). (Illus.). 32p. (gr. 3-6). 19.95 (978-1-59515-477-4(9)) Rourke Publishing, LLC.

Monroe, Judy. Robert E. Lee. 2002. (Let Freedom Ring Ser.). (Illus.). 48p. (J). (gr. 3-4). lib. bdg. 22.60 (978-0-7368-1089-0(7) , Bridgestone Bks.) Capstone Pr., Inc.

Pingry, Patricia A. Meet Robert E. Lee. Johnson, Meredith, illus. 2004. (J). 9.95 (978-0-8249-5465-9(3) , Ideals Pr.) Ideals Pubns.

—The Story of Robert E. Lee. Johnson, Meredith, illus. 2004. 26p. (J). (ps-k). bds. 6.95 (978-0-8249-6501-3(9)) Ideals Pubns.

Reger, James P. Civil War Generals of the Confederacy. 1998. (History Makers Ser.). (Illus.). 144p. (YA). (gr. 7-10). 27.45 (978-1-56006-359-9(9) , Lucent Bks.) Thomson Gale.

Robertson, James I., Jr. Robert E. Lee: Virginian Soldier, American Citizen. 2005. (Illus.). 176p. (YA). (gr. 7 up). 21.95 (978-0-689-85731-7(4) , Atheneum) Simon & Schuster Children's Publishing.

Smolinski, Diane. The Home Front in the South. (Americans at War Ser.). (Illus.). 32p. (J). (gr. 4-7). 2002. pap. 6.95 (978-1-58810-394-9(3) , 91134); 2001. lib. bdg. (978-1-58810-100-6(2)) Heinemann Library.

—Soldiers of the Civil War. 2002. (Americans at War Ser.). (Illus.). 32p. (J). (gr. 4-6). lib. bdg. (978-1-58810-098-6(7)); pap. 6.95 (978-1-58810-392-5(7) , 91132) Heinemann Library.

Waryncia, Lou. Robert E. Lee: Duty & Honor. Hale, Sarah Elder, ed. 2005. (Civil War Ser.). (Illus.). 48p. (J). 17.95 (978-0-8126-7905-2(9)) Cobblestone Publishing Co.

CONFEDERATE STATES OF AMERICA—FICTION

Connell, Kate. Yankee Blue or Rebel Grey: A Family Divided by the Civil War. 2003. (I Am American Ser.). (Illus.). 40p. (J). (gr. 3-7). pap. 6.99 (978-0-7922-5179-8(2) , National Geographic Children's Bks.) National Geographic Society.

Gibboney, Douglas Lee. Stonewall Jackson at Gettysburg. 2002. (Illus.). 132p. pap. 12.95 (978-1-57249-317-9(8) , Burd Street Pr.) White Mane Publishing Co., Inc.

Hahn, Stephen. Pike McCallister. 1998. 253p. (YA). (gr. 6 up). per. 14.95 (978-1-888125-29-0(2)) Publication Consultants.

Page, Thomas Nelson. Two Little Confederates. 1999. (Illus.). 180p. (J). (gr. 4-7). pap. 14.95 (978-1-56554-574-8(5)) Pelican Publishing Co., Inc.

—Two Little Confederates. 1999. (Notable American Authors Ser.). reprint ed. lib. bdg. 125.00 (978-0-7812-4689-7(X)) Reprint Services Co.

Sappey, Maureen S. Dreams of Ships, Dreams of Julia: At Sea with the Monitor & the Merrimack-Virginia, 1862. 1998. (Young American Ser.: Vol. 2). (Illus.). 140p. (YA). (gr. 4-7). 5.99 (978-1-57249-134-2(5)) White Mane Publishing Co., Inc.

Smiley, Brad & Smiley, Barbara. The Stone Wall: The Story of a Confederate Soldier. Hartman, Frank, photos by. 1998. (Illus.). 355p. (J). 23.00 (978-0-9664424-1-0(5)) Kennesaw Publishing.

CONFEDERATION OF AMERICAN COLONIES

see United States—History—1783-1809

CONFLICT, SOCIAL

see Social Conflict

CONFUCIUS AND CONFUCIANISM

Buddhist Text Translation Society Staff, contrib. by. Standards for Students: Instructions in Virtue from the Chinese Heritage = [Di Zi Gui]. 2003. (ENG & CHI., Illus.). 41p. (J). (978-0-88139-489-4(0)) Buddhist Text Translation Society.

Carew-Miller, Anna. Confucius: Great Chinese Philosopher. 2002. (Great Names Ser.). (Illus.). 32p. (J). (gr. 3 up). lib. bdg. (978-1-59084-149-5(2)) Mason Crest Pubs.

Freedman, Russell. Confucius: The Golden Rule. Clement, Frederic, illus. 2002. (Confucius Ser.). 48p. (J). (gr. 3-7). pap. 17.99 (978-0-439-13957-1(0)); pap. (978-0-439-13958-8(9)) Scholastic, Inc. (Levine, Arthur A. Bks.).

Hoobler, Thomas & Hoobler, Dorothy. Confucianism. 2nd rev. ed. 2004. (World Religions Ser.). Orig. Title: Confucianism. (Illus.). 128p. (YA). (gr. 6-12). 30.00 (978-0-8160-5728-3(1)) Facts On File, Inc.

Taylor, Rodney L. & Choy, Howard. The Illustrated Encyclopedia of Confucianism, 2 vols. 2003. (Illus.). xxxvii, 869p. (J). 106.47 (978-0-8239-4080-6(2)); (978-0-8239-4081-3(0)) Rosen Publishing Group, Inc., The.

Tracy, Kathleen. The Life & Times of Confucius. 2004. (Biography from Ancient Civilizations Ser.). (Illus.). 48p. (J). (gr. 4-8). lib. bdg. 29.95 (978-1-58415-246-0(X)) Mitchell Lane Pubs., Inc.

CONGO, BELGIAN

see Congo (Democratic Republic)

CONGO (BRAZZAVILLE)—FICTION

Hergé. The Adventures of Tintin in the Congo: Reporter for Le Petit Vingtieme. 2004. (Adventures of Tintin Ser.). (Illus.). 120p. (J). 24.95 (978-0-86719-902-4(4)) Last Gasp of San Francisco.

CONGO (DEMOCRATIC REPUBLIC)

DiPiazza, Francesca. Democratic Republic of Congo in Pictures. 2008. (J). lib. bdg. ***(978-0-8225-8572-5(3))*** Twenty First Century Bks.

Fish, Bruce & Fish, Becky Durost. The Congo. 2001. (Exploration of Africa Ser.). (Illus.). 112p. (J). 35.00 (978-0-7910-6198-5(1) , Chelsea Hse.) Facts On File, Inc.

Heale, Jay. Democratic Republic of the Congo. 1999. (Cultures of the World Ser.). (Illus.). 128p. (gr. 5-12). lib. bdg. 37.07 (978-0-7614-0874-1(6) , Benchmark Bks.) Cavendish, Marshall Corp.

Kushner, Nina. Democratic Republic of the Congo. 2001. (Countries of the World Ser.). (Illus.). 96p. (J). (gr. 6 up). lib. bdg. 30.00 (978-0-8368-2330-1(3)) Stevens, Gareth Inc.

Lerner Publications, Department of Geography Staff. Congo in Pictures. 1998. (Visual Geography Ser.). (Illus.). 64p. (YA). (gr. 6-12). lib. bdg. (978-0-8225-1900-3(3) , Lerner Pubns.) Lerner Publishing Group.

Milios, Rita. Democratic Republic of the Congo. 2004. (Africa Ser.). (Illus.). 79p. (J). lib. bdg. (978-1-59084-815-9(2)) Mason Crest Pubs.

Oppong, Joseph R. & Woodruff, Tania. Democratic Republic of the Congo. 2007. (Modern World Nations Ser.). (Illus.). 104p. (J). (gr. 6-12). 30.00 ***(*978-0-7910-9249-1(6)*** , Chelsea Hse.) Facts On File, Inc.

Owhonda, John. Congo. 2003. (Modern Nations of the World Ser.). (Illus.). 112p. (J). 29.95 (978-1-59018-111-9(5) , Lucent Bks.) Thomson Gale.

Quinlan, Jane. Karibu Means Welcome. Bland, Linda, ed. Manganz, Kibanza, illus. Wright, Barbara & White, Sara, photos by. 1999. 36p. (J). (gr. 3-6). pap. 10.00 (978-0-9678688-0-6(7)) Ursuline Sisters of Tildonk.

Roberts, Mary Nooter & Roberts, Allen F. Luba. 2005. (Visions of Africa Ser.). (Illus.). 145p. ring bd. 34.95 (978-88-7439-297-1(4)) 5 Continents Editions ITA. *Dist:* Antique Collectors' Club.

Willis, Terri. Democratic Republic of the Congo. 2004. (Enchantment of the World, Second Ser.). (Illus.). 144p. (YA). (gr. 5-9). 36.00 (978-0-516-24250-7(4) , Children's Pr.) Scholastic Library Publishing.

Wynaden, Jo & Kushner, Nina. Welcome to the Democratic Republic of the Congo. 2002. (Welcome to My Country Ser.). (Illus.). 48p. (J). (gr. 2 up). lib. bdg. 26.00 (978-0-8368-2530-5(6)) Stevens, Gareth Inc.

CONGO (DEMOCRATIC REPUBLIC)—FICTION

Goodall, Jane. Rickie & Henri: A True Story. Marks, Alan, illus. 2004. 32p. (J). (ps). 15.99 (978-0-698-40002-3(X) , Minedition) Penguin Group (USA) Inc.

Hergé. Tintin au Congo. 1999. (Tintin Ser.). (FRE., Illus.). 62p. (J). (gr. 4-7). 21.95 (978-2-203-00101-5(1)) Casterman, Editions FRA. *Dist:* Distribooks, Inc.

—Tintin au Congo. (FRE., Illus.). (J). (gr. 7-9). 24.95 (978-0-8288-5090-2(9)) French & European Pubns., Inc.

—Tintin en el Congo. (SPA., Illus.). 62p. (J). 24.95 (978-0-8288-5095-7(X)) French & European Pubns., Inc.

—Tintin en el Congo. (Tintin Ser.). (SPA.). 64p. (J). 14.95 (978-84-261-1401-3(6)) Juventud, Editorial ESP. *Dist:* Distribooks, Inc.

—Tintin im Kongo. (GER., Illus.). 62p. (J). pap. 24.95 (978-0-8288-4998-2(6)) French & European Pubns., Inc.

Luba Folk Tales. 2005. (YA). 10.00 (978-1-59872-207-9(7)) Instantpublisher.com.

Shepard, Aaron. The Magic Flyswatter: A Superhero Tale of Africa, Retold from the Mwindo Epic. 2008. (Ancient Fantasy Ser.: 3). 44p. (J). pap. 6.00 ***(*978-0-938497-39-4(1));*** lib. bdg. 15.00 ***(*978-0-938497-38-7(3))*** Shepard Pubns. (Skyhook Pr.).

CONGO RIVER

Fish, Bruce & Fish, Becky Durost. The Congo. 2001. (Exploration of Africa Ser.). (Illus.). 112p. (J). 35.00 (978-0-7910-6198-5(1) , Chelsea Hse.) Facts On File, Inc.

CONGRESS—UNITED STATES

see United States—Congress

CONGRESSMEN

see Legislators—United States; United States—Congress

CONJURING

see Magic Tricks

CONNECTICUT

Brown, Vanessa. Connecticut. (Bilingual Library of the United States of America). (J). 2006. (SPA.). lib. bdg. (978-1-4042-3146-7(3) , PowerKids Pr.); 2005. (ENG & SPA., Illus.). 32p. lib. bdg. 22.50 (978-1-4042-3071-2(8) , Buenas Letra) Rosen Publishing Group, Inc., The.

Burgan, Michael. Connecticut. 2003. (It's My State! Ser.). (Illus.). 80p. (J). 27.07 (978-0-7614-1523-7(8) , Benchmark Bks.) Cavendish, Marshall Corp.

Capstone Press Staff, contrib. by. Connecticut. rev. ed. 2002. (One Nation Ser.). (Illus.). 48p. (J). (gr. 3-4). lib. bdg. 22.60 (978-0-7368-1231-3(8) , Bridgestone Bks.) Capstone Pr., Inc.

Connecticut. 2000. (Switched on Schoolhouse Ser.). (Illus.). (YA). (gr. 7-12). pap. 24.95 incl. cd-rom (978-0-7403-0259-6(0) , SOSCT) Alpha Omega Pubns., Inc.

Connecticut Department of Transportation Staff & Connecticut Department of Environmental Protection Staff, CT Dept.of, compiled by. Pathways Through Connecticut: A Guide to Multi Use Trails in Connecticut. 2001. (DEP Bulletin Ser.). 132p. per. 9.95 (978-0-942085-09-9(4)) Connecticut Dept. of Environmental Protection, Environmenal & Geographic Information Ctr.

de Paola, Tomie. Here We All Are. de Paola, Tomie, illus. 2002. 13.19 (978-1-4046-0935-8(0)) Book Wholesalers, Inc.

—Here We All Are. de Paola, Tomie, illus. 2001. (Illus.). 80p. (J). pap. 5.99 (978-0-698-11909-3(6) , Putnam Juvenile) Penguin Group (USA) Inc.

—Here We All Are. unabr. ed. 2004. (Fairmount Avenue Ser.: Vol. 2). 80p. (J). (gr. 2-5). pap. 17.00 incl. audio (978-0-8072-0655-3(5) , LDTR 246 SP, Listening Library) Random Hse. Audio Publishing Group.

—Here We All Are. 2001. 12.79 (978-0-606-22515-1(3)); (gr. 3-6). lib. bdg. 14.15 (978-0-613-44390-6(X)) Tandem Library Bks.

—Here We All Are: A 26 Fairmount Avenue Book. 2000. (26 Fairmount Avenue Bks.). (Illus.). 80p. (J). (gr. 2-6). 13.99 (978-0-399-23496-5(9) , Putnam Juvenile) Penguin Group (USA) Inc.

—I'm Still Scared: A 26 Fairmount Avenue Book. 2006. (Illus.). 96p. (J). (gr. 1-4). 13.99 (978-0-399-24502-2(2) , Putnam Juvenile) Penguin Group (USA) Inc.

—Things Will Never Be the Same: A 26 Fairmount Avenue Book. 2003. (Illus.). 96p. (J). (ps-5). 13.99 (978-0-399-23982-3(0) , Putnam Juvenile) Penguin Group (USA) Inc.

—Why? The War Years. 2007. (26 Fairmount Avenue Book Ser.). (Illus.). 96p. (J). (gr. 2-4). 14.99 (978-0-399-24692-0(4) , Putnam Juvenile) Penguin Group (USA) Inc.

Elissa, Grodin. N Is for Nutmeg: A Connecticut Alphabet. Brookfield, Maureen, illus. 2003. 40p. (J). 17.95 (978-1-58536-124-3(0)) Sleeping Bear Pr.

Evento, Susan. Connecticut. (Rookie Español Geografía Ser.). (Illus.). (J). 2006. (SPA & ENG.). 32p. (gr. k-2). pap. 5.95 (978-0-516-25046-5(9)); 2005. (ENG & SPA., 31p. (ps-ps). 19.50 (978-0-516-25245-2(3)); 2005. 32p. (gr. 1-2). pap. 5.95 (978-0-516-25927-7(X)) Scholastic Library Publishing. (Children's Pr.).

Evento, Susan & Vargus, Nanci Reginelli. Connecticut. 2004. (Rookie Read-About Geography Ser.). (J). 20.50 (978-0-516-22751-1(3) , Children's Pr.) Scholastic Library Publishing.

Furstinger, Nancy. Connecticut. 2002. (From Sea to Shining Sea Ser.: 2). (Illus.). 80p. (J). (gr. 3-5). pap. 30.50 (978-0-516-22324-7(0) , Children's Pr.) Scholastic Library Publishing.

Gelman, Amy. Connecticut. 2nd rev. exp. ed. 2002. (Hello U. S. A. Ser.). (Illus.). 84p. (J). (gr. 3-6). lib. bdg. 25.26 (978-0-8225-4077-9(0)) Lerner Publishing Group.

—Connecticut. rev. ed. 2002. (gr. 3-6). lib. bdg. 15.25 (978-0-613-46055-2(3)) Tandem Library Bks.

George, Jean Craighead. Autumn Moon. 2003. (J). (gr. 3-7). 20.75 (978-0-8446-7241-0(6)) Smith, Peter Pub., Inc.

Goldstein, Phyllis. Uniquely Connecticut. 2003. (State Studies). (Illus.). 48p. (J). pap. 8.50 (978-1-4034-4503-2(6)); lib. bdg. 27.07 (978-1-4034-4488-2(9)) Heinemann Library.

Grodin, Elissa. Yankee Doodle Numbers: A Connecticut Number Book. Brookfield, Maureen K., illus. rev. ed. 2007. 40p. (J). 17.95 (978-1-58536-175-5(5)) Sleeping Bear Pr.

Heinrichs, Ann. Connecticut. 2005. (Welcome to the USA Ser.). 40p. (J). (gr. 1-5). 27.07 (978-1-59296-442-0(7)) Child's World, Inc.

—Connecticut. 2003. (This Land Is Your Land Ser.). (Illus.). 48p. (J). (gr. 3 up). lib. bdg. 22.60 (978-0-7565-0340-6(X)) Compass Point Bks.

Jacobs, Robert P. & O'Connell, Eileen B. Fisheries Guide to Lakes & Ponds of Connecticut: Including the Connecticut River & Its Coves. 2002. (DEP Bulletin Ser.: 35). 368p. lib. bdg. 29.95 (978-0-942085-12-9(4)); (Illus.). pap. 19.95 (978-0-942085-11-2(6)) Connecticut Dept. of Environmental Protection, Environmenal & Geographic Information Ctr.

Kent, Zachary. Connecticut. 2007. (America the Beautiful, Third Ser.). 144p. (J). spiral bd. 38.00 ***(*978-0-531-18571-1(0)*** , Children's Pr.) Scholastic Library Publishing.

Khanna, Rachel. Oh the Places to Know: A Guide to Greenwich for Kids. 2006. per. 18.95 (978-0-9779568-0-7(6)) Khanna, Rachel.

Knapp, Ron. Connecticut: A MyReportLinks. Com Book. 2003. (States Ser.). (Illus.). 48p. (J). lib. bdg. 25.26 (978-0-7660-5121-8(8) , MyReportLinks.com Bks.) Enslow Pubs., Inc.

Labairon, Cassandra Sharri. Connecticut. 2008. (J). ***(*978-1-58341-632-7(3)*** , Creative Education) Creative Co., The.

Marsh, Carole. Connecticut Classic Christmas Trivia. 2002. (Carole Marsh Connecticut Bks.). (Illus.). 32p. pap. 6.95 (978-0-635-01381-1(9) , 13819); lib. bdg. 21.95 (978-0-635-01382-8(7) , 13827) Gallopade International. (Marsh, Carole Bks.).

—Connecticut Current Events Projects: 30 Cool, Activities, Crafts, Experiments & More for Kids to Do to Learn about Your State! 2003. (Connecticut Experience Ser.). 32p. (gr. k-8). pap. 5.95 (978-0-635-02026-0(2) , Marsh, Carole Bks.) Gallopade International.

—The Connecticut Experience Pocket Guide. 2004. (Connecticut Experience! Ser.). (Illus.). 96p. (J). (gr. 3-8). pap. 6.95 (978-0-7933-9578-1(X)) Gallopade International.

—Connecticut Geography Projects: 30 Cool, Activities, Crafts, Experiments & More for Kids to Do to Learn about Your State! 2003. (Connecticut Experience Ser.). 32p. (gr. k-5). pap. 5.95 (978-0-635-01826-7(8) , Marsh, Carole Bks.) Gallopade International.

—Connecticut Government Projects: 30 Cool, Activities, Crafts, Experiments & More for Kids to Do to Learn about Your State! 2003. (Connecticut Experience Ser.). 32p. (gr. k-5). pap. 5.95 (978-0-635-01926-4(4) , Marsh, Carole Bks.) Gallopade International.

—Connecticut Jeopardy! Answers & Questions about Our State! 2004. (Connecticut Experience! Ser.). (Illus.). 32p. (J). (gr. 3-8). pap. 7.95 (978-0-7933-9580-4(1)) Gallopade International.

—Connecticut "Jography" A Fun Run Thru Our State! 2004. (Connecticut Experience! Ser.). (Illus.). 32p. (J). (gr. 3-8). pap. 7.95 (978-0-7933-9581-1(X)) Gallopade International.

—Connecticut People Projects: 30 Cool, Activities, Crafts, Experiments & More for Kids to Do to Learn about Your State! 2003. (Connecticut Experience Ser.). 32p. (gr. k-5). pap. 5.95 (978-0-635-01976-9(0) , Marsh, Carole Bks.) Gallopade International.

—Connecticut Symbols & Facts Projects: 30 Cool, Activities, Crafts, Experiments & More for Kids to Do to Learn about Your State! 2003. (Connecticut Experience Ser.). 32p. (gr. k-5). pap. 5.95 (978-0-635-01876-2(4) , Marsh, Carole Bks.) Gallopade International.

—Connecticut's Big Activity Book. 2004. (Connecticut Experience! Ser.). (Illus.). 96p. (J). (gr. 2-6). pap. 9.95 (978-0-7933-9582-8(8)) Gallopade International.

—The Cool Connecticut Coloring Book. 2004. (Connecticut Experience! Ser.). (Illus.). 32p. (J). (gr. k-2). pap. 3.95 (978-0-7933-9583-5(6)) Gallopade International.

—My First Book about Connecticut. 2004. (Connecticut Experience! Ser.). (Illus.). 32p. (J). (gr. k-4). pap. 7.95 (978-0-7933-9579-8(8)) Gallopade International.

—My First Pocket Guide Connecticut. 2000. (Connecticut Experience! Ser.). (Illus.). 96p. (J). (gr. 3-8). 12.95 (978-0-635-01297-5(9) , 12979) Gallopade International.

—The Survivor: A Class Challenge. 2001. (Carole Marsh Connecticut Bks.). lib. bdg. 29.95 (978-0-635-00653-0(7)) Gallopade International.

—Who Wants to Be a Connecticut Millionaire? 2001. (Carole Marsh Connecticut Bks.). lib. bdg. 29.95 (978-0-635-00031-6(8)) Gallopade International.

McAuliffe, Emily. Connecticut Facts & Symbols. 1999. lib. bdg. 14.00 (978-0-531-11800-9(2)); 1999. (Illus.). 24p. (J). (gr. 2-3). lib. bdg. 18.60 (978-0-7368-0214-7(2) , Bridgestone Bks.); 2003. 24p. (J). lib. bdg. 19.93 (978-0-7368-2237-4(2)) Capstone Pr., Inc.

McClellan, Dina & Lauren, Emily. Connecticut. 2004. (Life in the Thirteen Colonies Ser.). (Illus.). 124p. (J). 36.00 (978-0-516-24568-3(6) , Children's Pr.) Scholastic Library Publishing.

McNeil, Niki, et al. HOCPP 1141 Connecticut. 2007. spiral bd. 24.00 ***(*978-1-60308-141-2(0))*** In the Hands of a Child.

Mezzanotte, Jim. Connecticut. 2006. (Portraits of the States Ser.). (Illus.). 32p. (J). pap. 8.95 (978-0-8368-4682-9(6)); lib. bdg. 23.33 (978-0-8368-4663-8(X)) Stevens, Gareth Inc.

Murray, Julie. Connecticut. 2005. (Buddy Book Ser.). (Illus.). 32p. (J). (gr. k-4). lib. bdg. 22.78 (978-1-59197-666-0(9) , Buddy Bks.) ABDO Publishing Co.

Mysling, Donald & Murphy, Brian. Small Ponds in Connecticut: A Guide for Fish Management. 2nd ed. 2000. (DEP Bulletin Ser.: Vol. 30). 78p. pap. 9.95 (978-0-942085-07-5(8)) Connecticut Dept. of Environmental Protection, Environmenal & Geographic Information Ctr.

Pell, Ed. Connecticut. 2003. (Land of Liberty Ser.). (Illus.). 64p. (J). (gr. 3-4). lib. bdg. 23.93 (978-0-7368-1575-8(9) , Bridgestone Bks.) Capstone Pr., Inc.

Sherrow, Victoria. Connecticut. 2nd ed. 2006. (Celebrate the States Ser.). (J). lib. bdg. 39.93 (978-0-7614-2155-9(6) , Benchmark Bks.) Cavendish, Marshall Corp.

Webster, Christine. Connecticut. 2001. (American States Ser.). (Illus.). 32p. (J). lib. bdg. 16.95 (978-1-930954-89-2(1)) Weigl Pubs., Inc.

Wiener. The 13 Colonies Pack: Connecticut, 6. 2004. (Illus.). 48.30 (978-1-4109-0364-8(8)) Harcourt Schl. Pubs.

CONNECTICUT—FICTION

At Aunt Hattie's House. 2005. (YA). 12.00 net. (978-0-9763793-1-7(7)) Mitchell, Karan.

Baskin, Nora Raleigh. Basketball (or Something Like It) 176p. (J). 2007. (gr. 4-7). pap. 5.99 (978-0-06-059612-5(0) , Harper Trophy); 2005. 15.99 (978-0-06-059610-1(4)); 2005. lib. bdg. 16.89 (978-0-06-059611-8(2)) HarperCollins Pubs.

Biagiotti, Aldo. Escape from Death Valley: A Tale of Two Burros. Biagiotti, Aldo, photos by. 2003. (Books for Young Learners). (Illus.). 16p. (J). pap. 5.00 net. (978-1-57274-661-9(0) , 2737) Owen, Richard C. Pubs., Inc.

Bradbury, Bianca. Flight into Spring. 2005. 184p. (YA). pap. ***(*978-1-932350-01-2(2))*** Bethlehem Bks.

Cooney, Caroline B. Diamonds in the Shadow. 2007. (YA). (gr. 7). 240p. lib. bdg. 18.99 ***(*978-0-385-90278-6(6));*** 228p. 15.99 ***(*978-0-385-73261-1(9))*** Random Hse. Children's Bks. (Delacorte Bks. for Young Readers).

Curtis, Alice Turner. A Little Maid of Old Connecticut. Smith, Wuanita, illus. 2004. (Little Maid Ser.). 192p. (J). (gr. 4-7). reprint ed. per. 9.95 (978-1-55709-328-8(8)) Applewood Bks.

Daniels, Sara. Pieces of the Sky. 2005. 135p. pap. 15.99 (978-1-4116-4291-1(0)) Lulu.com.

Eager, Edward. Magic or Not? Bodecker, N. M., illus. 1999. (Odyssey Classics). 208p. (J). (gr. 3-7). pap. 7.00 (978-0-15-202080-4(2) , Odyssey Classics) Harcourt Children's Bks.

—Magic or Not? 1999. (J). (978-0-606-19001-5(5)) Tandem Library Bks.

Estes, Eleanor. The Middle Moffat. Slobodkin, Louis, illus. 2001. (Odyssey Classics). 256p. (YA). (gr. 3 up). pap. 6.00 (978-0-15-202529-8(4) , Odyssey Classics) Harcourt Children's Bks.

—The Moffat Museum. 2001. (Odyssey Classics). (Illus.). 256p. (gr. 3 up). pap. 6.00 (978-0-15-202553-3(7) , Odyssey Classics) Harcourt Children's Bks.

—The Moffat Museum. 2001. (J). (978-0-606-20805-5(4)); (gr. 3-6). lib. bdg. 14.15 (978-0-613-35463-9(X)) Tandem Library Bks.

—The Moffats. Tusa, Tricia & Slobodkin, Louis, illus. 2001. (Young Classics). 224p. (YA). (gr. 3 up). 17.00 (978-0-15-202535-9(9) , Odyssey Classics) Harcourt Children's Bks.

—The Moffats. Slobodkin, Louis, illus. 2001. (Odyssey Classics). 224p. (YA). (gr. 3 up). pap. 6.00 (978-0-15-202541-0(3) , Odyssey Classics) Harcourt Children's Bks.

—Rufus M. 2001. (gr. 3-6). lib. bdg. 14.15 (978-0-613-35468-4(0)) Tandem Library Bks.

—Rufus M. Slobodkin, Louis, illus. 2001. (Odyssey Classics). 256p. (YA). (gr. 3 up). pap. 6.00 (978-0-15-202577-9(4) , Odyssey Classics) Harcourt Children's Bks.

Franklin, Emily. The Other Half of Me. 2007. 256p. (YA). (gr. 9). 15.99 ***(*978-0-385-73445-5(X));*** lib. bdg. 18.99 ***(*978-0-385-90449-0(5))*** Random Hse. Children's Bks. (Delacorte Bks. for Young Readers).

Fuller, Harvey. Tommy & the Island. Fuller, Harvey, illus. 2007. (J). pap. 18.95 ***(*978-0-9773725-7-7(X))*** Flat Hammock Pr.

Grabenstein, Chris. The Crossroads. 2008. 368p. (J). (gr. 4-7). 16.99 ***(*978-0-375-84697-7(2)*** , Random Hse. Bks. for Young Readers) Random Hse. Children's Bks.

Hominick, Judy & Spreier, Jeanne. Ride for Freedom: The Story of Sybil Ludington. 2001. (Heroes to Remember Ser.). (Illus.). 52p. (J). 14.95 (978-1-893110-24-3(9)) Silver Moon Pr.

Hughes, Pat. Open Ice. 288p. (YA). (gr. 9). 2007. mass mkt. 6.50 ***(*978-0-553-49444-0(9)*** , Laurel Leaf); 2005. 15.95 (978-0-385-74675-5(X) , Lamb, Wendy) Random Hse. Children's Bks.

Hurst, Carol Otis. Through the Lock. 2001. 176p. (J). (gr. 5-9). tchr. ed. 15.00 (978-0-618-03036-1(0) , Walter Lorraine) Houghton Mifflin Co. Trade & Reference Div.

Janeczko, Paul B. Worlds Afire: The Hartford Circus Fire of 1944. 2004. 112p. (J). (gr. 7 up). 15.99 (978-0-7636-2235-0(4)) Candlewick Pr.

Kuehnel, Judy Lyons. The Autumn of Aunt Charlotte. 2006. (ENG.). 132p. per. 9.95 ***(*978-1-59800-688-9(6))*** Outskirts Press, Inc.

Leigh, Tina. Groundhog Day for Essex Ed. Leigh, Tina, illus. 2001. (Illus.). 32p. (J). pap. 14.95 (978-0-9715673-0-6(1)) Leigh, Tina Illustrator.

Lenski, Lois. Bound Girl of Cobble Hill. (J). 23.95 (978-0-89190-632-2(0)) Amereon LTD.

Literature Connections English: Homecoming. 2004. (gr. 6-12). (978-0-395-85802-8(X) , 2-70802) McDougal Littell Inc.

Louthain, J. A. Tagger: Alone along the Mystic River. 2002. (Illus.). 215p. (YA). per. 14.95 (978-0-9679416-0-8(1) , 0-1) Alexie Bks.

Rinaldi, Ann. The Education of Mary: A Little Miss of Color, 1832. 2000. 256p. (gr. 5-9). 15.99 (978-0-7868-0532-7(3) , Jump at the Sun) Hyperion Bks. for Children.

—The Education of Mary: A Little Miss of Color, 1832. 2005. 176p. (J). pap. (978-0-7868-1377-3(6)) Hyperion Pr.

Schuck, Philip. A Ricochet from Circumstance. 2005. (YA). 19.95 (978-0-9764670-0-7(3)) Smithfield Capital Corp.

Seidler, Tor. The Silent Spillbills. 1998. 224p. (J). (gr. 3-7). 14.95 (978-0-06-205180-6(6)); 14.89 (978-0-06-205181-3(4)) HarperCollins Pubs.

Wollman, Jessica. Switched. 2007. 256p. (gr. 7). (J). lib. bdg. 18.99 (978-0-385-90410-0(X)); (YA). 15.99 (978-0-385-73396-0(8)) Random Hse. Children's Bks. (Delacorte Bks. for Young Readers).

Wright, Bil. When the Black Girl Sings. 2008. 272p. (YA). (gr. 7 up). 16.99 (***978-1-4169-3995-5(4)*** , Simon & Schuster Children's Publishing) Simon & Schuster Children's Publishing.

Wright, Bill. Sunday You Learn to Box. 2000. (gr. 7-12). lib. bdg. 21.10 (978-0-613-33972-8(X)) Tandem Library Bks.

CONNECTICUT—HISTORY

Boyd, John. Annals of Winchester, CT. 2004. Orig. Title: Annals & Family Records of Winchester, Conn. with Exercises of the Centennial Celebration on the 16th & 17th Days of August 1871. cd-rom 20.00 (978-0-9727403-5-7(X) , EJ04-01) Between the Lakes Group, LLC.

Burgan, Michael. Connecticut, 1614-1776. 2007. (Voices from Colonial America Ser.). (Illus.). 112p. (YA). (gr. 5-9). 21.95 (***978-1-4263-0068-4(9)***); lib. bdg. 32.90 (***978-1-4263-0069-1(7)***) National Geographic Society. (National Geographic Children's Bks.).

Burgan, Michael. The Connecticut Colony. 2003. (Spirit of America). (Illus.). 40p. (J). (gr. 2-6). 28.50 (978-1-56766-609-0(4)) Child's World, Inc.

de Paola, Tomie. 26 Fairmount Avenue. de Paola, Tomie, illus. 2005. (Illus.). 58p. (J). (gr. k-4). reprint ed. 14.00 (978-0-7567-8722-6(X)) DIANE Publishing Co.

DePaola, Tomie. I'm Still Scared: A 26 Fairmount Avenue Book. 2007. 96p. (J). (gr. 2-6). pap. 5.99 (978-0-14-240826-1(3) , Puffin) Penguin Group (USA) Inc.

Dodd, Marion. Mystic by the A,B, Sea. Dodd, Marion, illus. 2006. (J). 17.95 (978-0-9773725-2-2(9)) Flat Hammock Pr.

Doherty, Craig A. & Doherty, Katherine M. Connecticut. 2005. (Thirteen Colonies Ser.). (Illus.). 144p. (J). (gr. 4-9). 35.00 (978-0-8160-5417-6(7)) Facts On File, Inc.

Dubois, Muriel L. The Connecticut Colony. 2005. (Fact Finders Ser.). (Illus.). 32p. (J). (978-0-7368-2672-3(6)) Capstone Pr., Inc.

Girod, Christina M. Connecticut. 2001. (Thirteen Colonies Ser.). (Illus.). 104p. (YA). (gr. 4-12). lib. bdg. 29.95 (978-1-56006-892-1(2) , LML00902-178213, Lucent Bks.) Thomson Gale.

Italia, Bob. The Connecticut Colony. 2001. (Colonies Ser.). (Illus.). 32p. (J). (gr. k-6). lib. bdg. 22.78 (978-1-57765-586-2(9) , Checkerboard Library) ABDO Publishing Co.

Krebs, Laurie. A Day in the Life of a Colonial Miller. 2004. (Library of Living & Working in Colonial Times). (Illus.). 24p. (J). lib. bdg. 18.75 (978-0-8239-6230-3(X) , PowerKids Pr.) Rosen Publishing Group, Inc., The.

Loeper, John J. Meet the Dudleys in Colonial Times. 1998. (Early American Family Ser.). (Illus.). 64p. (J). (gr. 3 up). lib. bdg. 25.64 (978-0-7614-0841-3(X)) Cavendish, Marshall Corp.

Lucas, Eileen. Prudence Crandall. Smith, Kimanne, illus. 2001. (On My Own Biographies Ser.). 48p. (J). (gr. 1-3). lib. bdg. (978-1-57505-480-3(9) , Carolrhoda Bks.) Lerner Publishing Group.

Malaspina, Ann. A Primary Source History of the Colony of Connecticut. 2005. (Primary Sources of the Thirteen Colonies & the Lost Colony Ser.). (Illus.). 64p. (J). (gr. 3-7). pap. 14.60 (978-1-4042-0665-6(5)); (YA). (gr. 5-8). lib. bdg. 29.25 (978-1-4042-0424-9(5)) Rosen Publishing Group, Inc., The.

Marsh, Carole. Connecticut History Projects: 30 Cool, Activities, Crafts, Experiments & More for Kids to Do to Learn about Your State! 2003. (Connecticut Experience Ser.). 32p. (gr. k-5). pap. 5.95 (978-0-635-01776-5(8) , Marsh, Carole Bks.) Gallopade International.

Miller, Jake. The Colony of Connecticut: A Primary Source History. 2006. (Primary Source Library of the Thirteen Colonies & the Lost Colony). (Illus.). 24p. (J). lib. bdg. (978-1-4042-3030-9(0) , PowerKids Pr.) Rosen Publishing Group, Inc., The.

Whitehurst, Susan. The Colony of Connecticut. 2000. (Library of the Thirteen Colonies & the Lost Colony). (Illus.). 24p. (J). (gr. 3). lib. bdg. 19.95 (978-0-8239-5479-7(X) , PowerKids Pr.) Rosen Publishing Group, Inc., The.

Wiener, Roberta & Arnold, James R. Connecticut. 2004. (Illus.). 64p. (J). 31.36 (978-0-7398-6877-5(2)) Harcourt Schl. Pubs.

—The 13 Colonies: Connecticut. 2004. (Illus.). 64p. (J). 8.95 (978-1-4109-0301-3(X)) Harcourt Schl. Pubs.

Wyborny, Sheila. Connecticut. 2003. (Seeds of a Nation Ser.). (Illus.). 48p. (J). (gr. 3-5). 23.70 (978-0-7377-1445-6(X) , Kidhaven) Thomson Gale.

CONNECTICUT—HISTORY—FICTION

Bond, Douglas. Guns of Thunder. 2007. (J). 11.99 (978-1-59638-013-4(6)) P & R Publishing.

Duble, Kathleen Benner. Hearts of Iron. 2006. 256p. (J). 15.95 (978-1-4169-0850-0(1) , McElderry, Margaret K.) Simon & Schuster Children's Publishing.

Evan, Frances Y. The Forgotten Flag: Revolutionary Struggle in Connecticut. 2003. (Illus.). 92p. (J). 5.95 (978-1-57249-338-4(0) , White Mane Kids) White Mane Publishing Co., Inc.

CONQUISTADORES

see America—Discovery and Exploration

CONSCIENTIOUS OBJECTORS—FICTION

Reeder, Carolyn. Shade of Gray. 1999. (978-0-606-16311-8(5)) Tandem Library Bks.

—Shades of Gray. O'Brien, Tim, illus. 1999. 160p. (J). (gr. 3-7). pap. 4.99 (978-0-689-82696-2(6) , 076714004993, Aladdin) Simon & Schuster Children's Publishing.

CONSERVATION OF ENERGY

see Force and Energy

CONSERVATION OF FORESTS

see Forests and Forestry; Natural Resources

CONSERVATION OF NATURAL RESOURCES

see also Natural Resources

Ball, Jackie. Conservation & Natural Resources. 2004. (Discovery Channel School Science Ser.). (Illus.). 32p. (J). (gr. 5 up). lib. bdg. 24.67 (978-0-8368-3377-5(5)) Stevens, Gareth Inc.

Bishop, Keith. Environment. 1998. (Fact Finders Ser.). (Illus.). 48p. (J). (gr. 3-7). pap. (978-0-563-37352-0(0)) BBC Worldwide.

Braun, Eric & Donovan, Sandy. River, Lakes, & Ponds. 2001. (Illus.). 32p. (J). lib. bdg. 22.83 (978-0-7398-4757-2(0)) Raintree.

—Scientists of Rivers, Lakes, & Ponds. 2001. (Scientists of the Biomes Ser.). (Illus.). 48p. (J). lib. bdg. 24.26 (978-0-7398-4755-8(4)) Raintree.

Buffett, Howard G. Cuidando Nuestro Mundo. Buffett, Devon G., ed. 2001. Tr. of Taking Care of Our World. (SPA., Illus.). 48p. (J). (gr. 2-5). (978-0-9707385-2-3(8)) BioImages.

Burton, Margie, et al. Are We Hurting the Earth. Adams, Alison, ed. 1999. (Early Connections Ser.). 16p. (J). (gr. k-2). pap. 4.50 (978-1-58344-053-7(4)) Benchmark Education Co.

Camp, William G. & Daugherty, Thomas B. Managing Our Natural Resources. 4th rev. ed. 2000. (Illus.). 416p. (C). 108.95 (978-0-7668-1554-4(4)) Thomson Delmar Learning.

Fitzgerald, Dawn. Julia Butterfly Hill: Saving the Redwoods. 2002. (Gateway Greens Ser.). (Illus.). 48p. (J). (gr. 2-4). lib. bdg. 23.90 (978-0-7613-2654-0(5) , Millbrook Pr.) Lerner Publishing Group.

Green Alert Set 1, 7 vols., Set. 2004. (Illus.). (J). 171.36 (978-0-7398-7017-4(3)) Raintree.

Green, Jen. Feeding the People. 2004. (J). lib. bdg. (978-1-59389-138-1(5)) Chrysalis Education.

—Saving Oceans & Wetlands. 2004. (J). lib. bdg. 27.10 (978-1-59389-139-8(3)) Chrysalis Education.

Haddock, Patricia. Environmental Time Bomb: Our Threatened Planet. 2000. (Issues in Focus Ser.). (Illus.). 112p. (YA). (gr. 6-12). lib. bdg. 26.60 (978-0-7660-1229-5(8)) Enslow Pubs., Inc.

Hall, Godfrey. Environment. 1998. (Find Out about Ser.). (Illus.). 24p. (J). (ps-3). (978-0-563-39620-8(2)) BBC Worldwide.

Hunter, Rebecca M. Pollution & Conservation. 2001. (Discovering Science Ser.). (Illus.). 32p. (J). (gr. 3-7). lib. bdg. 25.69 (978-0-7398-3246-2(8)) Raintree.

Jakab, Cheryl. Natural Resources. 2007. (J). (***978-1-59920-125-2(9)***) Smart Apple Media.

Kishel, Ann-Marie. Reuse. 2006. (First Step Nonfiction Ser.). (Illus.). 8p. (J). pap. (978-0-8225-5675-6(8) , Lerner Pubns.) Lerner Publishing Group.

Lalley, Pat & Kittmans-Lalley, Janet. Ocean Scientists. 2001. (Scientists of the Biomes Ser.). (Illus.). 48p. (J). lib. bdg. 24.26 (978-0-7398-4750-3(3)) Raintree.

Lalley, Pat & Lalley, Janet. Grasslands Scientists. 2001. (Scientists of the Biomes Ser.). (Illus.). 48p. (J). (gr. 4-7). lib. bdg. 24.26 (978-0-7398-4753-4(8)) Raintree.

Mason, Cherie & Kellogg Markowsky, Judy. Everybody's Somebody's Lunch: The Role of Predator & Prey in Nature. Giebfried, Rosemary, illus. 1998. 70p. (gr. 3-6). pap., tchr. ed., tchr.'s training gde. ed. 9.95 (978-0-88448-199-7(9)) Tilbury Hse. Pubs.

Mazur, Ivan & Mazur, Elena. Neptune's Kingdom. Freedman, Stella, ed. Piatikop, Alexander, illus. 1998. (Ecology for Children Ser.: Vol. 1). 48p. (J). (gr. 2-6). 11.95 (978-1-892316-03-5(X)) Rama Pr., Inc.

Morrison, Yvonne. Earth Matters. 2007. (Shockwave: People & Communities Ser.). (Illus.). 36p. (J). (gr. 4-6). lib. bdg. 25.00 (***978-0-531-17747-1(5)*** , Children's Pr.) Scholastic Library Publishing.

Nelson, Sara Elizabeth. Let's Reuse! 2007. (Illus.). 24p. (J). 15.93 (978-0-7368-6325-4(7)) Capstone Pr., Inc.

Parks, Peggy J. Global Resources (Overview) 2004. (Overview Ser.). (Illus.). 112p. (J). (gr. 7-10). 29.95 (978-1-56006-979-9(1) , Lucent Bks.) Thomson Gale.

Petersen, Christine. Land Preservation. 2004. (True Book Ser.). (Illus.). 48p. (J). 25.00 (978-0-516-22806-8(4) , Children's Pr.) Scholastic Library Publishing.

Philip, Neil, ed. In a Sacred Manner I Live: Native American Wisdom. 2005. (Illus.). 93p. (J). (gr. 5-7). pap., pap. 8.95 (978-0-618-60483-8(9) , Clarion Bks.) Houghton Mifflin Co. Trade & Reference Div.

Raintree Steck-Vaughn Staff. Environment Starts Here, 4 bks. 1998. (Illus.). (gr. 1-4). 71.92 (978-0-8172-5354-7(8)) Raintree.

Spilsbury, Louise. Saving Resources. 2004. (Illus.). 48p. (J). 28.56 (978-1-4109-1117-9(9)) Raintree.

Spilsbury, Louise & Spilsbury, Richard. The Future—Bleak or Bright? Earth's Resources. 2005. (Illus.). 32p. lib. bdg. (978-1-4109-1928-1(5)) Steck-Vaughn.

Spilsbury, Richard & Spilsbury, Louise. The Earth's Resources. 2006. (Science in Focus Ser.). 48p. (J). 27.00 (978-0-7910-8863-0(4) , Chelsea Hse.) Facts On File, Inc.

—The Future - Bleak or Bright? Earth's Resources. 2005. (Illus.). 32p. (J). (gr. 6-9). 7.85 (978-1-4109-1959-5(5)) Steck-Vaughn.

Thomas, Jeff. Simply Greener... for Kids! 101 Simple Things You Can Do TODAY to Save the Planet. 2007. 150p. pap. 12.95 (***978-1-56625-314-7(4)*** , Volt Pr.) Bonus Bks., Inc.

Watson, Susan. Living Sustainably. 2003. 32p. (J). lib. bdg. 24.25 (978-1-58340-404-1(X)) Smart Apple Media.

West, Krista. Hands-On Projects about Saving the Earth's Resources. 2002. (Great Earth Science Projects Ser.). (Illus.). 24p. (J). lib. bdg. 19.95 (978-0-8239-5847-4(7) , PowerKids Pr.) Rosen Publishing Group, Inc., The.

Winters, Adam. Sustainable Development. 2006. (Extreme Environmental Threats Ser.). (Illus.). 64p. (YA). lib. bdg. (978-1-4042-0746-2(5)) Rosen Publishing Group, Inc., The.

CONSERVATION OF NATURAL RESOURCES—FICTION

Adams, Pam. Mrs. Honey's Tree. 2000. (Illus.). 32p. (J). (ps-3). 3.99 (978-0-85953-852-7(4)) Child's Play-International.

Barron, T. A. The Ancient One. 2003. 320p. (gr. 12). mass mkt. 6.99 (978-0-441-01032-5(6) , Ace Bks.) Penguin Group (USA) Inc.

Berenstain, Stan & Berenstain, Jan. The Berenstain Bears Don't Pollute (Anymore) 1999. (Berenstain Bears First Time Bks.). (Illus.). (J). (ps-2). lib. bdg. 10.95 (978-0-8335-6545-7(1)) Tandem Library Bks.

Cherry, Lynne. The Dragon & the Unicorn. 1998. 13.80 (978-0-606-13347-0(X)) Tandem Library Bks.

—Great Kapok Tree. 2000. (gr. k-3). lib. bdg. 15.30 (978-0-613-28507-0(7)) Tandem Library Bks.

—Great Kapok Tree: A Tale of the Amazon Rain Forest. 2000. (Illus.). 33p. lib. bdg. 13.80 (978-0-606-17843-3(0)) Tandem Library Bks.

Cole, Sheila. The Canyon. 2002. 160p. (J). (gr. 3-7). 15.89 (978-0-06-029496-0(5)) HarperCollins Pubs.

Doolittle, Bev & Maclay, Elise. The Earth Is My Mother. Doolittle, Bev, illus. 2000. (Illus.). 176p. (J). (gr. 4-7). tchr. ed. 17.95 (978-0-86713-044-7(X) , 85163) Greenwich Workshop Pr.

Francis, Margaret Thornton. Bucky Roo. Springer, Becky Francis, illus. 1998. (J). (978-1-882194-43-8(8)) Tennessee Valley Publishing.

Ingold, Jeanette. Hitch. 2005. 288p. (YA). (gr. 7-12). 17.00 (978-0-15-204747-4(6)) Harcourt Children's Bks.

Kposowa, Tibbie S. The Forests Are No Longer Green. 1999. 320p. (Orig.). (gr. 7 up). pap. 14.00 (978-1-887935-25-8(8)) Tabay Pubns.

Kylie's Concert: Evaluation Guide. 2006. (J). (978-1-55942-413-4(3)) Marsh Media.

Mark of the Stone. 2000. 45p. (J). (gr. 3-6). per. 9.99 (978-0-9707770-0-3(0)) Blue Horse Mukwa Publishing.

Thomas, Lowell P. The Panther & the Windigo. 2002. (Illus.). 264p. (YA). (gr. 5-9). per. 10.99 (978-0-9668559-3-7(0)) East of the Sun Publishing.

CONSERVATION OF WATER

see Water Conservation

CONSERVATION OF WILDLIFE

see Wildlife Conservation

CONSERVATISM

see also Right and Left (Political Science)

Armentrout, David. John Muir. 2002. (SPA.). (gr. k-3). lib. bdg. 14.10 (978-0-613-79836-5(8)) Tandem Library Bks.

Armentrout, David & Armentrout, Patricia. John Muir. 2002. (Discover Someone Who Made a Difference Discovery Library Ser.). (Illus.). 24p. (gr. 2-5). 14.95 (978-1-58952-055-4(6)) Rourke Publishing, LLC.

—John Muir. Sarfatti, Esther & de la Vega, Eida, trs. 2001. (Personas que Cambiaron la Historia Ser.). (SPA., Illus.). 24p. (J). (gr. 1-4). lib. bdg. 19.27 (978-1-58952-168-1(4) , RK7725) Rourke Publishing, LLC.

Doherty, Kieran. Marjory Stoneman Douglas: Guardian of the 'Glades. 2002. (Techies Ser.). (Illus.). 160p. (gr. 7 up). lib. bdg. 24.90 (978-0-7613-2371-6(6) , Twenty-First Century Bks.) Lerner Publishing Group.

CONSPIRACIES—FICTION

Brooke, Lauren. Chestnut Hill. 2006. 192p. (J). pap. 4.99 (978-0-439-85998-1(0)) Scholastic, Inc.

Margolin, Phillip. El Asociado. 2002. (SPA.). 412p. 34.95 (978-84-666-0658-5(0) , EB13952) Ediciones B ESP. *Dist:* Lectorum Pubns., Inc.

Mitchell, Jack. The Roman Conspiracy. 2005. 172p. (J). (gr. 5-8). pap. 8.95 (978-0-88776-713-5(3)) Tundra Bks., Inc./Livres Toundra, Inc. CAN. *Dist:* Random Hse., Inc.

Prose, Francine. After. 336p. (J). 2003. (gr. 5 up). lib. bdg. 17.89 (978-0-06-008082-2(5) , Cotler, Joanna Books); 2003. (gr. 5 up). 16.99 (978-0-06-008081-5(7) , Cotler, Joanna Books); 2004. reprint ed. pap. 8.99 (978-0-06-008083-9(3) , HarperTeen) HarperCollins Pubs.

Wick. Elfish Fantasy: The Great Chocolate Caper. 2003. 128p. (YA). pap. 11.95 (978-0-595-29038-3(8)) iUniverse, Inc.

Zerfing, Robert A. The Silencer: A U. N. Conspiracy Novel. 2nd ed. 2003. 326p. (YA). per. 14.95 (978-0-9747881-0-4(4)) Clawfoot Publishing.

CONSTANTINE I, EMPEROR OF ROME, D. 337

Briere, Euphemia. Victor Constantinus, Maximus Augustus: The Life of Saint Constantine, the First Christian Emperor & His Mother, Saint Helena. 2003. (Illus.). (J). 4.00 (978-0-913026-90-8(5) , VC) St. Nectarios Pr.

Morgan, Julian. Constantine: Ruler of Christian Rome. 2003. (Leaders of Ancient Rome Ser.). (Illus.). 112p. (YA). (gr. 5-8). lib. bdg. 31.95 (978-0-8239-3592-5(2) , Rosen Central) Rosen Publishing Group, Inc., The.

Tracy, Kathleen. The Life & Times of Constantine. 2005. (Biography from Ancient Civilizations Ser.). (Illus.). 48p. (J). (gr. 4-8). lib. bdg. 29.95 (978-1-58415-343-6(1)) Mitchell Lane Pubs., Inc.

CONSTELLATIONS

see Astronomy; Stars

CONSTITUTION (FRIGATE)

Cooper, Jason. U. S. S. Constitution. 2000. (Historic Landmarks Ser.). (Illus.). 24p. (J). (gr. 1-4). lib. bdg. 20.64 (978-1-55916-329-3(1)) Rourke Publishing, LLC.

Wachtel, Roger. Old Ironsides. 2003. (Cornerstones of Freedom). (Illus.). 48p. (J). (gr. 4-6). 26.00 (978-0-516-24207-1(5) , Children's Pr.) Scholastic Library Publishing.

Young, Robert. A Personal Tour of Old Ironsides. 2001. (How It Was Ser.). (Illus.). 64p. (J). (gr. 4-6). lib. bdg. (978-0-8225-3580-5(7) , Lerner Pubns.) Lerner Publishing Group.

CONSTITUTIONAL AMENDMENTS

Oatman, Eric. Amending the Constitution. 2006. (Navigators Ser.). (J). pap. 42.00 (***978-1-4108-6257-0(7)***) Benchmark Education Co.

CONSTITUTIONAL AMENDMENTS—UNITED STATES

Armentrout, David & Armentrout, Patricia. The Bill of Rights. (Documents that Shaped the Nation Ser.). 48p. 2005. (Illus.). (gr. 4-6). 20.95 (978-1-59515-234-3(2)); 2004. pap. 7.95 (978-1-59515-329-6(2)) Rourke Publishing, LLC.

—La Carta de Derechos. 2005. (SPA.). (978-1-59515-646-4(1)) Rourke Publishing, LLC.

Banfield, Susan. The Fifteenth Amendment: African-American Men's Right to Vote. 1998. (Constitution Ser.). (Illus.). 128p. (YA). (gr. 6-12). lib. bdg. 26.60 (978-0-7660-1033-8(3)) Enslow Pubs., Inc.

Bozonelis, Helen Koutras. A Look at the Nineteenth Amendment: Women Win the Right to Vote. 2008. (J). (***978-1-59845-067-5(0)***) Enslow Pubs., Inc.

Brinkman, Patricia. Discover the Bill of Rights. 2006. pap. 39.00 (***978-1-4108-6455-0(3)***) Benchmark Education Co.

Burgan, Michael. The Bill of Rights. 2001. (We the People Ser.). (Illus.). 48p. (J). (gr. 4 up). lib. bdg. 21.26 (978-0-7565-0151-8(2)) Compass Point Bks.

—The Reconstruction Amendments. 2006. (Illus.). 48p. (J). (gr. 4-6). 23.93 (978-0-7565-1636-9(6)) Compass Point Bks.

Conway, John Richard. A Look at the First Amendment: Freedom of Speech & Religion. 2008. (J). (***978-1-59845-069-9(7)*** , MyReportLinks.com Bks.) Enslow Pubs., Inc.

Cooper, Terry, ed. Bill of Rights. 2001. 6p. 3.95 (978-0-439-30948-6(4)) Scholastic, Inc.

Donnelly, Karen J. The Bill of Rights. 2003. (Primary Source Library of American Citizenship). (Illus.). 32p. (J). pap. (978-1-4042-5087-1(5)) Rosen Publishing Group, Inc., The.

Due Process DBA. 2003. spiral bd. 16.95 (978-1-56004-148-1(X)) Social Studies Schl. Service.

Fernandez, Justin. Guns, Crime & the 2nd Amendment. 2001. (Crime, Justice & Punishment Ser.). (Illus.). 80p. (J). 30.00 (978-0-7910-5765-0(8) , Chelsea Hse.) Facts On File, Inc.

Fireside, Harvey. The Fifth Amendment: The Right to Remain Silent. 1998. (Constitution Ser.). (Illus.). 128p. (YA). (gr. 6-12). lib. bdg. 26.60 (978-0-89490-894-1(4)) Enslow Pubs., Inc.

The First Amendment & the Bill of Rights for Beginners. 2002. 50p. (YA). 4.95 (978-0-9721333-2-6(1)) Pocket Publication, A.

Freedman, Russell. In Defense of Liberty: The Story of America's Bill of Rights. 2003. (Illus.). 208p. (J). (gr. 4-6). tchr. ed. 24.95 (978-0-8234-1585-4(6)) Holiday Hse., Inc.

Hamilton, John. The Bill of Rights. 2005. (Government in Action! Ser.). (Illus.). 31p. (J). (gr. k-6). lib. bdg. 22.78 (978-1-59197-643-1(X)) ABDO Publishing Co.

Hanson, Freya Ottem. The Second Amendment: The Right to Own Guns. 1998. (Constitution Ser.). (Illus.). 128p. (YA). (gr. 6-12). lib. bdg. 26.60 (978-0-89490-925-2(8)) Enslow Pubs., Inc.

Horn, Geoffrey M. The Bill of Rights & Other Amendments. 2003. (World Almanac Library of American Government). (Illus.). 48p. (J). (gr. 5 up). pap. 14.95 (978-0-8368-5480-0(2)); lib. bdg. 30.00 (978-0-8368-5475-6(6)) Stevens, Gareth Inc. (World Almanac Library).

—World Almanac Library of American Government: The Bill of Rights & Other Amendments; The Cabinet & Federal Agencies; The Constitution; Political Parties, Interest Groups & the Media, 4 bks. 2003. (Illus.). (J). (gr. 5 up). lib. bdg. 117.06 (978-0-8368-5474-9(8) , World Almanac Library) Stevens, Gareth Inc.

Hossell, Karen Price. The Bill of Rights. 2003. (Heinemann Know It Ser.). (Illus.). 48p. (J). 27.07 (978-1-4034-0801-3(7)); pap. 8.50 (978-1-4034-3430-2(1)) Heinemann Library.

Hudson, David L., Jr. The Bill of Rights: The First Ten Amendments of the Constitution. 2002. (Constitution Ser.). (Illus.). 128p. (J). (gr. 6-12). lib. bdg. 26.60 (978-0-7660-1903-4(9)) Enslow Pubs., Inc.

—The Fourteenth Amendment: Equal Protection under the Law. 2002. (Constitution Ser.). (Illus.). 128p. (J). (gr. 6-12). lib. bdg. 26.60 (978-0-7660-1904-1(7)) Enslow Pubs., Inc.

Krull, Kathleen. A Kids' Guide to America's Bill of Rights: Curfews, Censorship, & the 100-Pound Giant. DiVito, Anna, illus. 1999. (Avon Camelot Bks.). 240p. (J). (gr. 5-9). 16.99 (978-0-380-97497-9(5)) HarperCollins Pubs.

Lucas, Eileen. The Eighteenth & Twenty-First Amendments: Alcohol - Prohibition & Repeal. 1998. (Constitution Ser.). (Illus.). 128p. (YA). (gr. 6-12). lib. bdg. 26.60 (978-0-89490-926-9(6)) Enslow Pubs., Inc.

Marren, Joe. A Look at the Fifth Amendment Against Self-Incrimination. 2008. (J). (***978-1-59845-068-2(9)***) Enslow Pubs., Inc.

Morin, Isobel V. Our Changing Constitution: How & Why We Have Amended It. 1998. (Single Titles Ser.: up). (Illus.). 176p. (gr. 7-12). lib. bdg. 23.90 (978-0-7613-0222-3(0) , Millbrook Pr.) Lerner Publishing Group.

Patrick, John J. The Bill of Rights: A History in Documents. 2002. (Pages from History Ser.). (Illus.). 208p. 36.95 (978-0-19-510354-0(8)) Oxford Univ. Pr., Inc.

Pearl, Norman. The Bill of Rights. 2006. (Illus.). 24p. lib. bdg. (978-1-4048-2213-9(5)) Picture Window Bks.

Pendergast, Tom, et al. Constitutional Amendments Vol. 1: From Freedom of Speech to Flag Burning, 3 vols. Grunow, Elizabeth Shaw, ed. 2001. xlviii, 528p. (J). (978-0-7876-4866-4(3) , UXL) Thomson Gale.

—Constitutional Amendments Vol. 2: From Freedom of Speech to Flag Burning, 3 vols. Grunow, Elizabeth Shaw, ed. 2001. xlviii, 528p. (J). (978-0-7876-4867-1(1) , UXL) Thomson Gale.

—Constitutional Amendments Vol. 3: From Freedom of Speech to Flag Burning, 3 vols. Grunow, Elizabeth Shaw, ed. 2001. xlviii, 528p. (J). (978-0-7876-4868-8(X) , UXL) Thomson Gale.

Rife, Douglas M. Emancipation Proclamation. Mitchell, Judy, ed. Smith, Bron, illus. 2002. 32p. (J). (gr. 4-8). pap. 5.95 (978-1-57310-349-7(7)) Teaching & Learning Co.

Rivera, Sheila. The Bill of Rights. 2005. (American Moments Ser.). (J). (gr. 4-8). lib. bdg. 25.65 (978-1-59197-279-2(5)) ABDO Publishing Co.

Schleichert, Elizabeth. The Thirteenth Amendment: Ending Slavery. 1998. (Constitution Ser.). (Illus.). 128p. (YA). (gr. 6-12). lib. bdg. 26.60 (978-0-89490-923-8(1)) Enslow Pubs., Inc.

Smith, Rich. The Bill of Rights: Defining Our Freedoms. 2007. (Bill of Rights Ser.). (ENG., Illus.). 32p. (J). (gr. 4-8). lib. bdg. 25.65 ***978-1-59928-913-7(X)*** , ABDO & Daughters) ABDO Publishing Co.

—Eighth Amendment: The Right to Mercy. 2007. (Bill of Rights Ser.). (ENG., Illus.). 32p. (J). (gr. 4-8). lib. bdg. 25.65 (***978-1-59928-920-5(2)*** , ABDO & Daughters) ABDO Publishing Co.

—Fifth Amendment: The Right to Fairness. 2007. (Bill of Rights Ser.). (ENG., Illus.). 32p. (J). (gr. 4-8). lib. bdg. 25.65 (***978-1-59928-917-5(2)*** , ABDO & Daughters) ABDO Publishing Co.

—First Amendment: The Right of Expression. 2007. (Bill of Rights Ser.). (ENG., Illus.). 32p. (J). (gr. 4-8). lib. bdg. 25.65 (***978-1-59928-914-4(8)*** , ABDO & Daughters) ABDO Publishing Co.

—Fourth Amendment: The Right to Privacy. 2007. (Bill of Rights Ser.). (ENG., Illus.). 32p. (J). (gr. 4-8). lib. bdg. 25.65 (***978-1-59928-916-8(4)*** , ABDO & Daughters) ABDO Publishing Co.

—How Amendments Are Adopted. 2007. (Bill of Rights Ser.). (ENG., Illus.). 32p. (J). (gr. 4-8). lib. bdg. 25.65 (***978-1-59928-922-9(9)*** , ABDO & Daughters) ABDO Publishing Co.

—Ninth & Tenth Amendments: The Right to More Rights. 2007. (Bill of Rights Ser.). (ENG., Illus.). 32p. (J). (gr. 4-8). lib. bdg. 25.65 (***978-1-59928-921-2(0)*** , ABDO & Daughters) ABDO Publishing Co.

—Second & Third Amendments: The Right to Security. 2007. (Bill of Rights Ser.). (ENG., Illus.). 32p. (J). (gr. 4-8). lib. bdg. 25.65 (***978-1-59928-915-1(6)*** , ABDO & Daughters) ABDO Publishing Co.

—Seventh Amendment: The Right to a Trial by Jury. 2007. (Bill of Rights Ser.). (ENG., Illus.). 32p. (J). (gr. 4-8). lib. bdg. 25.65 (***978-1-59928-919-9(9)*** , ABDO & Daughters) ABDO Publishing Co.

—Sixth Amendment: The Right to a Fair Trial. 2007. (Bill of Rights Ser.). (ENG., Illus.). 32p. (J). (gr. 4-8). lib. bdg. 25.65 (***978-1-59928-918-2(0)*** , ABDO & Daughters) ABDO Publishing Co.

Stair, Nancy. The Bill of Rights: A Primary Source Investigation into the First Ten Amendments to the Constitution. 2005. (Great American Political Documents Ser.). (Illus.). 112p. (YA). (gr. 7-12). lib. bdg. 26.50 (978-0-8239-3800-1(X)) Rosen Publishing Group, Inc., The.

Taylor-Butler, Christine. The Bill of Rights. (True Booktrade;: American History Ser.). 48p. (J). 2008. pap. 6.95 (***978-0-531-14777-1(0));*** 2007. (Illus.). (gr. 3-5). lib. bdg. 26.00 (***978-0-531-12627-1(7))*** Scholastic Library Publishing. (Children's Pr.).

Yero, Judith Lloyd. The Bill of Rights. 2004. (National Geographic Reading Expeditions Ser.). (Illus.). 32p. (J). (978-0-7922-4552-0(0)) National Geographic Society.

Zacharias, Gary. Bill of Rights. 2003. (gr. 7-12). lib. bdg. 28.90 (978-0-613-57345-0(5)) Tandem Library Bks.

CONSTITUTIONAL HISTORY

Benchmark Education Staff, compiled by. The Constitution. 2006. spiral bd. 159.00 (***978-1-4108-7126-8(6))*** Benchmark Education Co.

Brinkman, Patricia. The Constitution. 2006. pap. 39.00 (***978-1-4108-6451-2(0))*** Benchmark Education Co.

—Discover the Constitution. 2006. pap. 39.00 (***978-1-4108-6454-3(5))*** Benchmark Education Co.

Finkelman, Paul. The Constitution. 2005. (American Documents Ser.). (Illus.). 48p. (gr. k-3). (J). 15.95 (978-0-7922-7937-2(9)); 23.90 (978-0-7922-7975-4(1)) National Geographic Society. (National Geographic Children's Bks.).

Good Apple. Our Living Constitution - Then & Now. 2nd ed. 2002. (J). (gr. 5-8). pap. 16.99 (978-0-7682-2456-6(X) , GA15015) School Specialty Publishing.

McComb, Marianne. Emancipation Proclamation. 2005. (American Documents (Washington, D.C.) Ser.). (Illus.). 48p. (gr. k-3). (J). 15.95 (978-0-7922-7916-7(6)); 23.90 (978-0-7922-7936-5(0)) National Geographic Society. (National Geographic Children's Bks.).

Staunton, Ted. Confederation. Pilsworth, Graham, illus. 2004. (Dreadful Truth Ser.). 80p. (J). (gr. 3-8). (***978-0-88780-630-8(9))*** Formac Publishing Co., Ltd. CAN. *Dist:* Casemate Pubs. & Bk. Distributors, LLC.

Thompson, Gare. Shaping the Constitution. 2006. (Navigators Ser.). (J). pap. 42.00 (***978-1-4108-6256-3(9))*** Benchmark Education Co.

CONSTITUTIONAL HISTORY—UNITED STATES

Allen, Kathy. The U.S. Constitution. 2007. (Illus.). 24p. (J). 19.93 (978-0-7368-9594-1(9)) Capstone Pr., Inc.

Armentrout, David & Armentrout, Patricia. La Constitucion. 2005. (SPA.). (J). (978-1-59515-643-3(7)) Rourke Publishing, LLC.

—The Constitution. (Documents that Shaped the Nation Ser.). 48p. 2005. (Illus.). (gr. 4-6). 20.95 (978-1-59515-231-2(8)); 2004. pap. 7.95 (978-1-59515-330-2(6)) Rourke Publishing, LLC.

Banks, Joan. The U. S. Constitution. 2001. (Your Government Ser.). (Illus.). 64p. (J). (gr. 4-7). 25.00 (978-0-7910-5991-3(X) , Chelsea Hse.) Facts On File, Inc.

Burgan, Michael. The Creation of the U.S. Constitution. Purcell, Gordon & Beatty, Terry, illus. 2007. (Graphic Library). 32p. (J). 25.26 (978-0-7368-6491-6(1)) Capstone Pr., Inc.

Collier, Christopher & Collier, James Lincoln. Creating the Constitution: 1787. 1998. (Drama of American History Ser.). (Illus.). 96p. (J). (gr. 5-9). lib. bdg. 31.36 (978-0-7614-0776-8(6) , Benchmark Bks.) Cavendish, Marshall Corp.

Conway, John Richard. A Look at the Constitution: Creating a More Perfect Union. 2008. (J). (***978-1-59845-072-9(7)*** , MyReportLinks.com Bks.) Enslow Pubs., Inc.

Debnam, Betty. The Mini Page Guide to the Constitution. 2006. 32p. pap. 9.95 (***978-0-7407-6511-7(6))*** Andrews McMeel Publishing.

Dunn, John M. The Constitution & the Founding of America. 2007. (American History Ser.). 128p. (J). (gr. 7-10). 31.20 (***978-1-59018-956-6(6)*** , Lucent Bks.) Thomson Gale.

Eck, Kristin. Drafting the Constitution: Weighing Evidence to Draw Sound Conclusions. 2005. (Critical Thinking in American History Ser.). (Illus.). 48p. (YA). (gr. 5-8). lib. bdg. 25.25 (978-1-4042-0412-6(1)) Rosen Publishing Group, Inc., The.

Elish, Dan. The U. S. Supreme Court. 2007. (Cornerstones of Freedom). (Illus.). 48p. (J). (gr. 4-6). 26.00 (978-0-516-23637-7(7) , Children's Pr.) Scholastic Library Publishing.

Feinberg, Barbara Silberdick. The Articles of Confederation: The First Constitution of the United States. 2002. (Single Titles Ser.). (Illus.). 112p. (gr. 7 up). lib. bdg. 24.90 (978-0-7613-2114-9(4) , Twenty-First Century Bks.) Lerner Publishing Group.

Feinstein, Steve. Rising of a New Nation. 2000. (978-0-606-20383-8(4)) Tandem Library Bks.

Fradin, Dennis Brindell. The Founders: The 39 Stories Behind the U. S. Constitution. McCurdy, Michael, illus. 2005. 144p. (J). (gr. 5-9). 23.85 (978-0-8027-8973-0(0)); 22.95 (978-0-8027-8972-3(2)) Walker & Co.

—The U. S. Constitution. 2007. (Turning Points in U. S. History Ser.). (Illus.). 47p. (J). (gr. 4-7). lib. bdg. (978-0-7614-2036-1(3) , Benchmark Bks.) Cavendish, Marshall Corp.

Graves, Kerry A. The Constitution: The Story Behind America's Governing Document. 2004. (America in Words & Song Ser.). (Illus.). 32p. (gr. 3-5). 23.00 (978-0-7910-7333-9(5) , Chelsea Hse.) Facts On File, Inc.

Hamilton, John. The Constitution. 2005. (Government in Action! Ser.). (J). (gr. k-6). lib. bdg. 22.78 (978-1-59197-645-5(6)) ABDO Publishing Co.

Horn, Geoffrey M. The Constitution. 2003. (World Almanac Library of American Government). (Illus.). 48p. (J). (gr. 5 up). pap. 14.95 (978-0-8368-5482-4(9)); lib. bdg. 30.00 (978-0-8368-5477-0(2)) Stevens, Gareth Inc. (World Almanac Library).

Hossell, Karen Price. The Articles of Confederation. 2003. (Heinemann Know It Ser.). 48p. (J). pap. 8.50 (978-1-4034-3429-6(8)); lib. bdg. 27.07 (978-1-4034-0800-6(9)) Heinemann Library.

—The United States Constitution. 2003. (Heinemann Know It Ser.). (Illus.). 48p. (J). 27.07 (978-1-4034-0804-4(1)); pap. 8.50 (978-1-4034-3434-0(4)) Heinemann Library.

Hubbard-Brown, Janet. How the Constitution Was Created. 2007. (U. S. Government: How It Works). 104p. (J). (gr. 5-8). 30.00 (***978-0-7910-9420-4(0)*** , Chelsea Hse.) Facts On File, Inc.

Hughes, Chris. The Constitutional Convention. 2005. (People at the Center of Ser.). (Illus.). 48p. (J). (ps-7). lib. bdg. 24.95 (978-1-56711-918-3(2) , Blackbirch Pr., Inc.) Thomson Gale.

Hull, Mary E. Shays' Rebellion & the Constitution in American History. 2000. (In American History Ser.). (Illus.). 112p. (YA). (gr. 5-12). lib. bdg. 26.60 (978-0-7660-1418-3(5)) Enslow Pubs., Inc.

Leebrick, Kristal. The United States Constitution. 2002. (Let Freedom Ring Ser.). (Illus.). 48p. (J). (gr. 3-4). lib. bdg. 22.60 (978-0-7368-1094-4(3) , Bridgestone Bks.) Capstone Pr., Inc.

Micklos, John. From Thirteen Colonies to One Nation. 2008. (Revolutionary War Library). (Illus.). 48p. (J). (gr. 3-4). lib. bdg. 23.93 (***978-0-7660-3015-2(6))*** Enslow Pubs., Inc.

Mountjoy, Shane & McNeese, Tim. Marbury V. Madison. 2006. (Great Supreme Court Decisions Ser.). (Illus.). 144p. (J). (gr. 5-8). 30.00 (978-0-7910-9240-8(2) , Chelsea Hse.) Facts On File, Inc.

New, David W. The Constitution for Beginners. 2003. 50p. (J). 4.95 (978-0-9721333-1-9(3)) Pocket Publication, A.

Pearl, Norman. The U. S. Constitution. Skeens, Matthew, illus. 2006. 24p. (J). (ps-2). lib. bdg. 23.93 (978-1-4048-2643-4(2)) Picture Window Bks.

Perrin, Pat & Coleman, Wim, eds. The Constitution & the Bill of Rights. 2000. (Researching American History Ser.). (Illus.). 56p. (J). 7.95 (978-1-57960-069-3(7)) History Compass, LLC.

Peterson, Christine. The U.S. Constitution. 2007. (First Facts Ser.). (Illus.). 24p. (J). 21.26 (978-0-7368-9595-8(7)) Capstone Pr., Inc.

Plair, James B., Sr. Three Score & Thirteen: A Study of the United States Constitution & the Federalist Papers. 2002. 251p. (YA). (gr. 4 up). pap. 14.95 (978-0-9718770-0-9(9)) Plair, James B.

Price, Sean. Designing America: The Constitutional Convention. 2007. (J). (***978-1-4109-2693-7(1));*** pap. (***978-1-4109-2704-0(0))*** Steck-Vaughn.

Randolph, Joanne. What Is the U. S. Constitution? 2003. (Reading Room Collection). (Illus.). 24p. (J). lib. bdg. 18.75 (978-0-8239-3704-2(6)) Rosen Publishing Group, Inc., The.

Rebman, Renée C. The Articles of Confederation. 2006. (We the People Ser.). (Illus.). 48p. (J). (gr. 4-6). 23.93 (978-0-7565-1627-7(7)) Compass Point Bks.

Rosenberg, John M. First in Peace: George Washington, the Constitution & the Presidency. 1998. (Single Titles Ser.: up). (Illus.). 256p. (gr. 7-12). lib. bdg. 25.90 (978-0-7613-0422-7(3) , Millbrook Pr.) Lerner Publishing Group.

Shh! We're Writing the Constitution. 2004. 24.95 incl. audio (978-1-56008-220-0(8)); 29.95 incl. cd-rom (978-1-55592-682-3(7)); 24.95 incl. audio (978-1-55592-680-9(0)); pap. 18.95 incl. audio compact disk (978-1-55592-681-6(9)); pap. 32.75 incl. audio (978-1-55592-353-2(4)); pap. 14.95 incl. audio (978-1-55592-679-3(7)) Weston Woods Studios, Inc.

Smith, Robert W. Spotlight on America: The Constitution. 2004. 64p. pap. 9.99 (978-0-7439-3211-0(0)) Teacher Created Materials, Inc.

Taylor-Butler, Christine. The Constitution. (True Booktrade;: American History Ser.). 48p. (J). 2008. pap. 6.95 (***978-0-531-14779-5(7));*** 2007. (Illus.). (gr. 3-5). lib. bdg. 26.00 (***978-0-531-12629-5(3))*** Scholastic Library Publishing. (Children's Pr.).

United States Constitution. (American Revolution Ser.). 32p. (YA). 7.95 (978-0-7368-4495-6(3)) Capstone Pr., Inc.

Weidner, Daniel. The Constitution: The Preamble & the Articles. 2002. (Constitution Ser.). (Illus.). 160p. (YA). (gr. 6-12). lib. bdg. 26.60 (978-0-7660-1906-5(3)) Enslow Pubs., Inc.

CONSTITUTIONAL LAW

see also Citizenship; Civil Rights; Constitutional Amendments; Democracy; Political Science; Suffrage

Brinkman, Patricia. Writing the Constitution. 2006. pap. 39.00 (***978-1-4108-6450-5(2))*** Benchmark Education Co.

Callahan, Kerry P. The Articles of Confederation: A Primary Source Investigation into the Document That Preceded the U.S. Constitution. 2005. (Great American Political Documents Ser.). (Illus.). 112p. (YA). (gr. 7-12). lib. bdg. 26.50 (978-0-8239-3799-8(2)) Rosen Publishing Group, Inc., The.

Catrow, David. We the Kids: The Preamble to the Constitution of the United States. 2002. (Illus.). 32p. (J). (gr. k-5). 16.99 (978-0-8037-2553-9(1) , Dial) Penguin Group (USA) Inc.

Harris, Nancy. What's the State Legislative Branch? 2007. (J). (***978-1-4034-9510-5(6)***); pap. (***978-1-4034-9516-7(5))*** Heinemann Library.

Hirsch, E. D., ed. Making the Constitution. 2003. tchr. ed. 9.95 (978-0-7690-5048-5(4)); stu. ed. 49.95 (978-0-7690-2953-5(1)) Pearson Learning.

Horn, Geoffrey M. The Constitution. 2003. (World Almanac Library of American Government). (Illus.). 48p. (J). (gr. 5 up). pap. 14.95 (978-0-8368-5482-4(9) , World Almanac Library) Stevens, Gareth Inc.

Moehn, Heather. The U. S. Constitution: A Primary Source Investigation into the Fundamental Law of the United States. 2005. (Great American Political Documents Ser.). (Illus.). 112p. (YA). (gr. 7-12). lib. bdg. 26.50 (978-0-8239-3804-9(2)) Rosen Publishing Group, Inc., The.

Sobel, Syl. The U. S. Constitution & You. 2001. (Illus.). 48p. (J). (gr. 3-5). pap. 6.95 (978-0-7641-1707-7(6)) Barron's Educational Series, Inc.

Weidner, Daniel. The Constitution: The Preamble & the Articles. 2002. (Constitution Ser.). (Illus.). 160p. (YA). (gr. 6-12). lib. bdg. 26.60 (978-0-7660-1906-5(3)) Enslow Pubs., Inc.

CONSTITUTIONAL LAW—UNITED STATES

Banks, Joan. The U. S. Constitution. 2001. (Your Government Ser.). (Illus.). 64p. (J). (gr. 4-7). 25.00 (978-0-7910-5991-3(X) , Chelsea Hse.) Facts On File, Inc.

Catrow, David. We the Kids: The Preamble to the Constitution of the United States. Catrow, David, illus. 2005. (Illus.). 32p. (J). (ps-ps). pap. 6.99 (978-0-14-240276-4(1) , Puffin) Penguin Group (USA) Inc.

Conway, John Richard. A Look at the Constitution: Creating a More Perfect Union. 2008. (J). (***978-1-59845-072-9(7)*** , MyReportLinks.com Bks.) Enslow Pubs., Inc.

CQ Press Editors. Understanding Constitutional Issues: Selections from the CQ Researcher. 2004. (Illus.). 400p. 40.00 (978-1-56802-885-9(7)) CQ Pr.

Friedman, Mark. Government: How Local, State, & Federal Government Works. 2004. (Our Government & Citizenship Ser.). 32p. (J). (gr. 2-6). 27.07 (978-1-59296-323-2(4)) Child's World, Inc.

Graves, Kerry A. The Constitution: The Story Behind America's Governing Document. 2004. (America in Words & Song Ser.). (Illus.). 32p. (gr. 3-5). 23.00 (978-0-7910-7333-9(5) , Chelsea Hse.) Facts On File, Inc.

Hamilton, John. The Constitution. 2005. (Government in Action! Ser.). (J). (gr. k-6). lib. bdg. 22.78 (978-1-59197-645-5(6)) ABDO Publishing Co.

Hirsch, E. D., ed. The United States Constitution, Level 4. 2003. tchr. ed. 9.95 (978-0-7690-5069-0(7)); stu. ed. 49.95 (978-0-7690-2846-0(2)) Pearson Learning.

Horn, Geoffrey M. The Constitution. 2003. (World Almanac Library of American Government). (Illus.). 48p. (J). (gr. 5 up). pap. 14.95 (978-0-8368-5482-4(9) , World Almanac Library) Stevens, Gareth Inc.

Maddex, Robert L. State Constitutions of the United States. 2nd ed. 2005. 529p. (gr. 9 up). 125.00 (978-1-933116-25-9(0)) CQ Pr.

New, David W. The Constitution for Beginners. 2003. 50p. (J). 4.95 (978-0-9721333-1-9(3)) Pocket Publication, A.

Our Supreme Court: A History with 14 Activities. 2006. (For Kids Ser.). (Illus.). 196p. (YA). (gr. 7 up). pap. 16.95 (978-1-55652-607-7(5)) Chicago Review Pr., Inc.

Pearl, Norman. The U. S. Constitution. Skeens, Matthew, illus. 2006. 24p. (J). (ps-2). lib. bdg. 23.93 (978-1-4048-2643-4(2)) Picture Window Bks.

Pendergast, Tom, et al. Constitutional Amendments Vol. 1: From Freedom of Speech to Flag Burning, 3 vols. Grunow, Elizabeth Shaw, ed. 2001. xlviii, 528p. (J). (978-0-7876-4866-4(3) , UXL) Thomson Gale.

—Constitutional Amendments Vol. 2: From Freedom of Speech to Flag Burning, 3 vols. Grunow, Elizabeth Shaw, ed. 2001. xlviii, 528p. (J). (978-0-7876-4867-1(1) , UXL) Thomson Gale.

—Constitutional Amendments Vol. 3: From Freedom of Speech to Flag Burning, 3 vols. Grunow, Elizabeth Shaw, ed. 2001. xlviii, 528p. (J). (978-0-7876-4868-8(X) , UXL) Thomson Gale.

Randolph, Joanne. What Is the U. S. Constitution? 2003. (Reading Room Collection). (Illus.). 24p. (J). lib. bdg. 18.75 (978-0-8239-3704-2(6)) Rosen Publishing Group, Inc., The.

Sobel, Syl. The U. S. Constitution & You. Gilgannon, Denise, illus. 2001. (gr. 3-6). lib. bdg. 15.25 (978-0-613-83479-7(8)) Tandem Library Bks.

—The U. S. Constitution & You. 2001. (978-0-606-22468-0(8)) Tandem Library Bks.

United States. Constitucion de los Estados Unidos American. 2002. (SPA.). 30p. 9.95 (978-1-55709-459-9(4)) Applewood Bks.

CONSTRUCTION

see Architecture; Building; Engineering

CONSTRUCTION EQUIPMENT

Abramson, Andra Serlin. Heavy Equipment up Close. 2008. (Illus.). 28p. (J). 9.95 (***978-1-4027-4799-1(3))*** Sterling Publishing Co., Inc.

Adair, Amy. Tonka Trucks. Kleven, Dean, illus. 2002. (J). (978-0-7853-7015-4(3)) Publications International, Ltd.

Butterfield, Moira. Bulldozers & Other Construction Machines. Lyon, Chris & Biggin, Gary, illus. (J). mass mkt. 8.99 (978-0-590-24556-2(2)) Scholastic, Inc.

Caterpillar Inc. Staff, contrib. by. Big Trucks & Diggers: Touch & Feel. 2004. (Illus.). 12p. (J). 9.95 (978-0-8118-4302-7(5)) Chronicle Bks. LLC.

Dussling, Jennifer. Construction Trucks. Courtney, illus. 1998. (All Aboard Bks.). 32p. (J). (ps-3). pap. 3.99 (978-0-448-41885-8(1) , Grosset & Dunlap) Penguin Group (USA) Inc.

—Construction Trucks. 1998. (gr. k-3). lib. bdg. 11.25 (978-0-613-72421-0(6)) Tandem Library Bks.

Hoban, Tana. Construction Zone. Hoban, Tana, illus. 1999. (Illus.). 15p. (J). (ps-2). 6.99 (978-0-688-16918-3(X)) HarperCollins Pubs.

Kilby, Don. At a Construction Site. 2003. (Wheels at Work Ser.). (Illus.). 24p. (J). (ps-k). (978-1-55337-378-0(2)); (978-1-55337-044-4(9)) Kids Can Pr., Ltd.

—At A Construction Site. Kilby, Don, illus. 2006. 24p. (978-1-55337-987-4(X)) Kids Can Pr., Ltd.

Korman, Justine. Tonka Building the Skyscraper. 1999. (ps-2). lib. bdg. 11.25 (978-0-613-72020-5(2)) Tandem Library Bks.

Lorenz Books Staff & Tuxworth, Nicola. Diggers & Dumpers. 2000. (Illus.). 12p. (ps). bds. 4.95 (978-0-7548-0063-7(6)) Anness Publishing, Inc.

MacAulay, Kelley & Kalman, Bobbie. Cool Construction Vehicles. 2007. (Vehicles on the Move Ser.). (Illus.). 32p. (J). (gr. 1-5). (***978-0-7787-3042-2(5)***); pap. (***978-0-7787-3056-9(5))*** Crabtree Publishing Co.

Moore, Elaine. See You Later, Excavator. 2001. (Planet Reader Ser.). (Illus.). (J). (978-0-606-20901-4(8)) Tandem Library Bks.

Pallotta, Jerry. The Construction Alphabet Book. Bolster, Rob, illus. 2006. (Jerry Pallotta's Alphabet Bks.). 32p. (J). (gr. 4). 16.95 (978-1-57091-437-9(0)); (ps-4). pap. 7.95 (978-1-57091-438-6(9)) Charlesbridge Publishing, Inc.

Randolph, Joanne. Backhoes. 2002. (PowerKids Readers Ser.). (Illus.). 24p. (J). (gr. 1). lib. bdg. 16.00 (978-0-8239-6029-3(3) , PowerKids Pr.) Rosen Publishing Group, Inc., The.

—Wheel Loaders. 2002. (PowerKids Readers Ser.). (Illus.). 24p. (J). (gr. 1). lib. bdg. 16.00 (978-0-8239-6026-2(9) , PowerKids Pr.) Rosen Publishing Group, Inc., The.

Sloan, Peter. Front Loader. 1999. (gr. k-3). lib. bdg. 11.55 (978-0-613-30419-1(5)) Tandem Library Bks.

Wallace, Karen. Big Machines. 2000. (Readers Ser.). (Illus.). 32p. (J). (ps-1). pap. 3.99 (978-0-7894-5411-9(4)) Dorling Kindersley Publishing, Inc.

—Big Machines. 2000. (gr. k-3). lib. bdg. 11.80 (978-0-613-24358-2(7)); (Illus.). (J). 10.79 (978-0-606-18114-3(8)) Tandem Library Bks.

—Gigantes de Hierro. 2003. (SPA.). (gr. k-3). lib. bdg. 11.80 (978-0-613-75200-8(7)) Tandem Library Bks.

Wallace, Karen & Dorling Kindersley Publishing Staff. Big Machines. 2000. (Eyewitness Readers). (Illus.). 32p. (J). (ps-1). 12.99 (978-0-7894-5412-6(2)) Dorling Kindersley Publishing, Inc.

C
D

Zemlicka, Shannon. From Rock to Road. 2004. (Start to Finish Ser.). (J). pap. 4.95 (978-0-8225-2146-4(6)); 18.60 (978-0-8225-1391-9(9) , Lerner Pubns.) Lerner Publishing Group.

CONSTRUCTION EQUIPMENT—FICTION

Carter, Don. Get to Work, Trucks! Carter, Don, illus. rev. ed. 2002. (Illus.). 24p. (J). (ps-1). 14.95 (978-0-7613-1543-8(8)) Roaring Brook Pr.

Copeland, Cynthia L. What Are You Waiting For? Gordon, Mike, illus. 2003. (Silly Millies Ser.: 1). 32p. lib. bdg. 17.90 (978-0-7613-2804-9(1) , Millbrook Pr.) Lerner Publishing Group.

Copeland, Cynthia L. & Gordon, Mike. What Are You Waiting For? 2003. (Silly Millies Ser.: Vol.1). (Illus.). 32p. (J). (ps-1). pap. 4.99 (978-0-7613-1828-6(3) , Millbrook Pr.) Lerner Publishing Group.

Fontes, Justine & Grey, Andrew. Working Hard with the Mighty Crane. Petruccio, Steven James, illus. 1998. (Tonka Ser.). 32p. (J). (ps-2). pap. 3.50 (978-0-590-13094-3(3)) Scholastic, Inc.

Leman, Nora. The Alpha Building Crew. Hartmann, April, illus. 2005. (J). (978-1-58987-110-6(3)) Kindermusik International.

Lewis, Kevin. Lot at the End of My Block. Cartwright, Reg, illus. 2001. 32p. (ps-1). 15.49 (978-0-7868-2512-7(X)) Hyperion Bks. for Children.

Lund, Deb. Monsters on Machines. Neubecker, Robert, illus. 2008. (J). (*978-0-15-205365-9(4)) Harcourt Trade Pubs.

My Day at a Construction Site. 2004. (J). ring bd. 4.50 (978-0-9762740-8-7(6)) Smart Smiles Co., The.

Nevius, Carol. Building with Dad. Thomson, Bill, illus. 2006. 32p. (J). (ps-3). 16.99 (978-0-7614-5312-3(1)) Cavendish, Marshall Corp.

Packard, Mary. Rob's Shiny Dump Truck. SGA Graphics Staff, illus. 1999. (Fisher-Price All Around Town Playbooks Ser.). 18p. (J). (ps-k). bds. 5.99 Reader's Digest Children's Publishing, Inc.

Rockwell, Anne. Good Morning, Digger. Greenberg, Melanie Hope, illus. 2007. 32p. (J). (ps). pap. 5.99 (978-0-14-240823-0(9) , Puffin) Penguin Group (USA) Inc.

Rockwell, Anne F. Good Morning, Digger. Greenberg, Melanie Hope, illus. 2005. 32p. (J). (ps-1). 15.99 (978-0-670-05959-1(5) , Viking Juvenile) Penguin Group (USA) Inc.

Sobel, June. B Is for Bulldozer: A Construction ABC. Iwai, Melissa, illus. 2006. 32p. (J). pap. 6.00 (978-0-15-205774-9(9) , Voyager Bks./Libros Viajeros) Harcourt Children's Bks.

Spence, Ann & Halifax, Guy. Bob's Busy Building Day. 2003. (Illus.). (J). (978-0-7853-8421-2(9)) Publications International, Ltd.

Todd, Mark. Monster Trucks! Todd, Mark, illus. 2003. (Illus.). 32p. (J). (gr. k-ps). tchr. ed. 15.00 (978-0-618-18208-4(X)) Houghton Mifflin Co. Trade & Reference Div.

—Monster Trucks. 2005. 13p. (J). (gr. k-ps). bds. 8.95 (978-0-618-58119-1(7)) Houghton Mifflin Co. Trade & Reference Div.

Whiting, Sue. Machine Mates. Townsend, Peter, illus. 2003. 12p. (J). (gr. k-3). 22.00 (978-0-7567-6650-4(8)) DIANE Publishing Co.

Whiting, Sue & Book Company Staff. Machine Mates. Townsend, Peter, illus. 2002. (Novelty Bks.). 12p. (J). 12.95 (978-1-74047-183-1(0)) Book Co. Publishing Pty, Ltd., The AUS. *Dist:* Penton Overseas, Inc.

Zimmerman, Andrea Griffing & Clemesha, David. Dig! Rosenthal, Marc, tr. Rosenthal, Marc, illus. 2004. 32p. (J). 16.00 (978-0-15-216785-1(4) , Silver Whistle) Harcourt Trade Pubs.

CONSTRUCTION OF ROADS

see Roads

CONSULS

see Diplomats

CONSUMER EDUCATION

Here are entered works on the selection and most efficient use of consumer goods and services, including methods of educating the consumer. Works on the economic theory of consumption are entered under Consumption (Economics).

see also Shopping

Berry, Joy Wilt. A Book about Being Wasteful. 2005. (Illus.). (J). (978-0-7172-8587-7(1)) Scholastic, Inc.

—A Children's Book about Being Destructive. 2005. (Illus.). (J). (978-0-7172-8596-9(0)) Scholastic, Inc.

Bowen, Nancy. Ralph Nader: Man with a Mission. 2002. (Single Titles Ser.). (Illus.). 144p. (gr. 7 up). lib. bdg. 24.90 (978-0-7613-2365-5(1) , Twenty-First Century Bks.) Lerner Publishing Group.

Garey, Marita. Kids Are Consumers. 2002. (Illus.). 32p. (J). (978-0-7922-8700-1(2)) National Geographic Society.

McGraw-Hill Staff, et al. Consumer Education & Economics. 5th ed. 2002. (C). (gr. 6-12). stu. ed. 60.64 (978-0-07-825155-9(9) , 9780078251559) Glencoe/McGraw-Hill.

Menhard, Francha Roffe. Teen Consumer Smarts: Shop, Save & Steer Clear of Scams. 2002. (Teen Issues Ser.). (Illus.). 64p. (J). (gr. 6-12). lib. bdg. 22.60 (978-0-7660-1667-5(6)) Enslow Pubs., Inc.

Money Matters: How to Become a Smart Consumer. 2000. (J). per. 10.95 (978-1-883055-36-3(9)) Dandy Lion Pubns.

Moran, Katherine J. Diabetes: The Ultimate Teen Guide. Merriman, Lisa P., illus. 2004. (It Happened to Me Ser.: No. 7). 208p. 39.50 (978-0-8108-4806-1(6)) Scarecrow Pr., Inc.

Schwartz, Stuart B. & Conley, Craig. Finding an Apartment. (Life Skills-Career Bks.). 48p. pap. 6.95 (978-0-7368-8508-9(0) , LifeMatters Bks.) Capstone Pr., Inc.

CONSUMER GOODS

see Manufactures

CONSUMERS' GUIDES

see Consumer Education

CONSUMPTION (ECONOMICS)

Bailey, Gerry & Law, Felicia. Save, Spend, Share: Using Your Money. Phillips, Mike et al, illus. 2006. (My Money Ser.). 24p. (J). (gr. 4-6). 27.93 (978-0-7565-1672-7(2)) Compass Point Bks.

Love, Ann & Drake, Jane. Trash Action: A Fresh Look at Garbage. Thurman, Mark, illus. 2006. 80p. (J). (gr. 3). pap. 14.95 (978-0-88776-721-0(4)) Tundra Bks., Inc./Livres Toundra, Inc. CAN. *Dist:* Random Hse., Inc.

Rau, Dana Meachen. Spending Money. 2005. (Money & Banks Ser.). (Illus.). 24p. (J). pap. (978-0-8368-4879-3(9)); lib. bdg. 19.33 (978-0-8368-4872-4(1)) Stevens, Gareth Inc.

Rosinsky, Natalie M. Spending Money. 2003. (Let's See Library). (Illus.). 24p. (J). (gr. 1 up). 19.93 (978-0-7565-0485-4(6)) Compass Point Bks.

Royston, Angela. Consumerism of the Future. 2007. (J). (*978-1-4329-0128-8(1)); pap. (*978-1-4329-0133-2(8)) Heinemann Library.

Thayer, Tanya. Spending Money. 2005. (First Step Nonfiction Ser.). (Illus.). 24p. (gr. k-2). lib. bdg. 17.27 (978-0-8225-1261-5(0)) Lerner Publishing Group.

CONTACT LENSES

see Eyeglasses

CONTAGION AND CONTAGIOUS DISEASES

see Communicable Diseases

CONTAGIOUS DISEASES

see Communicable Diseases

CONTESTS—FICTION

Allison, Jennifer. Gilda Joyce: The Ghost Sonata. 2007. 288p. (J). (gr. 5-8). 15.99 (*978-0-525-47808-9(6) , Dutton Juvenile) Penguin Group (USA) Inc.

Anderson, Scoular, illus. Stan the Dog Becomes Superdog. 2006. 52p. (J). lib. bdg. (*978-1-4048-3131-5(2)) Picture Window Bks.

Auerbach, Annie. Most World Records. 2000. (gr. 3-6). lib. bdg. 11.80 (978-0-613-26278-1(6)) Tandem Library Bks.

Baker, Keith. Lucky Days with Mr. & Mrs. Green. (Mr. & Mrs. Green Ser.). (Illus.). 72p. (J). 2006. pap. 5.95 (978-0-15-205604-9(1) , Harcourt Paperbacks); 2005. 16.00 (978-0-15-216500-0(2) , Gulliver Bks.) Harcourt Children's Bks.

Belgue, Nancy. Casey Little: Yo-Yo Queen. 2005. (Orca Young Readers Ser.). (Illus.). 144p. (J). (gr. 3-6). pap. 5.95 (978-1-55143-357-8(5)) Orca Bk. Pubs. USA.

Beller, Jasmine. Raise the Roof, No. 4. 2007. 160p. (J). pap. 4.99 (978-0-448-44445-1(3) , Grosset & Dunlap) Penguin Group (USA) Inc.

Braver, Vanita. Madison & the Two-Wheeler. DiRocco, Carl, illus. 2007. 32p. (J). 14.95 (*978-1-59572-109-9(6)) Star Bright Bks., Inc.

Bricker, Chris. The Leaping Frogs of Calameris County. 2006. 48p. pap. 12.95 (978-1-4241-2408-4(5)) PublishAmerica, Inc.

Brimner, Larry Dane. Noodle Game. 2001. (gr. k-3). lib. bdg. 14.10 (978-0-613-54442-9(0)) Tandem Library Bks.

Brown, Marc. Arturo Visita la Casa Blanca. 2001. (SPA.). lib. bdg. 15.25 (978-0-613-64341-2(0)) Tandem Library Bks.

The Bubble Gum Contest. 2007. (J). per. (*978-1-932570-62-5(4)) Literacy Footprints Inc.

Buchanan, Paul. Lock-in. 2001. (gr. 3-6). lib. bdg. 14.15 (978-0-613-72847-8(5)) Tandem Library Bks.

Bunting, Eve. Some Frog! Medlock, Scott, illus. 2002. 48p. (J). (gr. 1-4). pap. 6.00 (978-0-15-216384-6(0) , Voyager Bks./Libros Viajeros) Harcourt Children's Bks.

—Some Frog! 2002. (gr. 3-6). lib. bdg. 14.15 (978-0-613-53865-7(X)) Tandem Library Bks.

Burgard, Anna Marlis. Flying Feet: A Story of Irish Dance. Dees, Leighanne, illus. 2006. 31p. (J). (gr. 4-8). 16.00 (978-1-4223-5255-7(2)) DIANE Publishing Co.

Caple, Kathy. Worm Gets a Job. Caple, Kathy, illus. 2004. (Illus.). 40p. (J). (gr. k-3). 15.99 (978-0-7636-1694-6(X)) Candlewick Pr.

Cappo, Nan Willard. Cheating Lessons. 2003. 272p. (YA). mass mkt. 5.99 (978-0-689-86018-8(8) , Simon Pulse) Simon & Schuster Children's Publishing.

—Cheating Lessons. 2003. (gr. 7-12). lib. bdg. 13.00 (978-0-613-64795-3(5)) Tandem Library Bks.

—Cheating Lessons. l.t. ed. 2003. 274p. (J). 24.95 (978-0-7862-5325-8(8)) Thorndike Pr.

Carter, Aubrey Smith. The Enchanted Lizard: La Lagartijita Magica. Nelson, Esther Whitt, ed. Branton, Molly, illus. 2006. (ENG & SPA.). 96p. (J). 18.95 (978-1-893271-38-8(2)) Maverick Publishing Co.

Catalanotto, Peter. Emily's Art. Catalanotto, Peter, illus. 2006. (Illus.). 32p. (J). pap. 6.99 (978-1-4169-2688-7(7) , Aladdin) Simon & Schuster Children's Publishing.

Child, Lauren. Utterly Me, Clarice Bean. Child, Lauren, illus. 2003. (Illus.). 192p. (J). (gr. 3-7). 15.99 (978-0-7636-2186-5(2)) Candlewick Pr.

—Utterly Me, Clarice Bean. 2002. (Illus.). 160p. (J). 5.99 (978-1-84121-918-9(5) , Orchard Bks.) Scholastic, Inc.

Child, Lauren, et al. Fi'n Hollol, Carys Blodyn. 2005. (WEL., Illus.). 192p. pap. (978-1-85596-675-8(1)) Dref Wen.

Chrismer, Melanie. Phoebe Clappsaddle & The Tumbleweed Gang. Roeder, Virginia M., illus. 2002. 32p. (J). 14.95 (978-1-56554-966-1(X)) Pelican Publishing Co., Inc.

Clements, Andrew. No Talking. Elliott, Mark, illus. 2007. 160p. (J). (gr. 3-7). 15.99 (*978-1-4169-0983-5(4)) Simon & Schuster Children's Publishing.

Collins, Paul. Final Countdown. 2000. (gr. 7-12). lib. bdg. 12.25 (978-0-613-28841-5(6)) Tandem Library Bks.

Coombs, Kate. The Runaway Princess. 2006. 288p. (J). 17.00 (978-0-374-35546-3(0)) Farrar, Straus & Giroux.

Cosgrove, Stephen. Mizz Buggly: Doing Your Best. Arroyo, Fian, illus. 2004. (J). (978-1-58804-380-1(0)) PCI Educational Publishing.

Cutler, Jane. Leap, Frog. Pearson, Tracey Campbell, illus. 2005. 208p. (J). (gr. 3-7). pap. 6.95 (978-0-374-44320-7(3) , Farrar, Straus & Giroux (BYR)) Farrar, Straus & Giroux.

D'Amico, Carmela & D'Amico, Steven. Ella Sets the Stage. 2006. (Illus.). 48p. (J). pap. 16.99 (978-0-439-83152-9(0) , Levine, Arthur A. Bks.) Scholastic, Inc.

Davis, Joyce. Can't Stop the Shine. 2007. 256p. pap. 9.99 (*978-0-373-83078-7(5)) Harlequin Enterprises, Ltd. CAN. *Dist:* Simon & Schuster, Inc.

de Witt, Peter. Toaster Pond. 2006. 248p. (YA). pap. 14.95 (978-1-933255-21-7(8)) DNA Pr.

deGroat, Diane. Annie Pitts, Burger Kid. 2001. (gr. 3-6). lib. bdg. 11.80 (978-0-613-43671-7(7)) Tandem Library Bks.

DePaola, Tomie. Mr. Satie & the Great Art Contest. 2007. 32p. (J). (ps). pap. 5.99 (978-0-14-240771-4(2) , Puffin) Penguin Group (USA) Inc.

Disney Press, ed. Disney High School Musical: Wildcats Box Set. rev. ed. 2007. (gr. 3-7). pap. 15.99 (*978-1-4231-1082-8(X)) Disney Pr.

Donaldson, Julia. Bricks for Breakfast. Dupasquier, Philippe, illus. 2005. (Read-It! Chapter Bks.). 52p. (J). (ps-k). lib. bdg. 19.95 (978-1-4048-1275-8(X)) Picture Window Bks.

Dorros, Arthur. Julio's Magic. Date not set. 32p. (ps-1). mass mkt. 5.99 (978-0-06-443686-1(1)) HarperCollins Pubs.

—Julio's Magic. Grifalconi, Ann, illus. 2005. 32p. (J). (ps-4). 15.99 (978-0-06-029004-7(8)); lib. bdg. 17.89 (978-0-06-029005-4(6)) HarperCollins Pubs.

Doudna, Kelly. Doggie Pants. Haberstroh, Anne, illus. 2006. (Fact & Fiction Ser.). 24p. (J). 21.35 (978-1-59679-931-8(5) , SandCastle); pap. (978-1-59679-932-5(3)) ABDO Publishing Co.

Dower, Laura. From the Files of Madison Finn: Double Dare. 2003. (gr. 3-6). lib. bdg. 13.00 (978-0-613-68230-5(0)) Tandem Library Bks.

Driscoll, Laura. The Blast off Kid! Thornburgh, Rebecca McKillip, illus. 2003. (Math Matters Ser.). 32p. (J). 4.99 (978-1-57565-130-9(0)) Kane Pr., The.

Duble, Kathleen Benner. Bravo Zulu, Samantha! 2007. 144p. (J). (gr. 4-7). 14.95 (*978-1-56145-401-3(X) , Peachtree Junior) Peachtree Pubs., Ltd.

Dunmore, Helen. Going to Egypt. 2003. 144p. (Orig.). (J). pap. 9.99 (978-0-09-941195-6(4) , Red Fox) Random Hse. Children's Bks. GBR. *Dist:* Trafalgar Square Publishing.

Ellis, Kathryn. Joey Jeremiah. 2006. (Degrassi Junior High Ser.). 184p. (YA). (gr. 5-10). 7.95 (978-1-55028-924-4(1)) Lorimer, James & Co., Ltd., Pubs. CAN. *Dist:* Casemate Pubs. & Bk. Distributors, LLC.

Enriquez, Jose. Saving the Mango Farm. 2006. 23p. (J). 10.98 (978-1-4116-5917-9(1)) Lulu.com.

Esparza-Harris, Mech. Sage. 2006. 69p. pap. 14.95 (978-1-4241-3035-1(2)) PublishAmerica, Inc.

Evans, Douglas. MVP: Magellan Voyage Project. Shelley, John, illus. 2004. 232p. (J). 16.95 (978-1-932425-13-0(6) , Lemniscaat) Boyds Mills Pr.

Feldman, Jody. The Gollywhopper Games. Jamieson, Victoria, illus. 2008. 336p. (J). 16.99 (*978-0-06-121450-9(7)); lib. bdg. 17.89 (*978-0-06-121451-6(5)) HarperCollins Pubs. (Greenwillow Bks.).

Fisch, Sarah. The Smallest Snowman. Durk, Jim, illus. 2006. (J). (*978-0-439-81616-8(5)) Scholastic, Inc.

Furgang, Kathy. The Cooking Contest. ed. 2003. (Early Connections Ser.). (J). pap. 35.00 (978-1-4108-1560-6(9)) Benchmark Education Co.

Gallagher, Diana G. Guilty! The Complicated Life of Claudia Cristina Cortez. Garvey, Brann, illus. 2008. (J). pap. (*978-1-59889-881-1(7)); 77p. (gr. 4-8). lib. bdg. 23.93 (*978-1-59889-838-5(8)) Stone Arch Bks.

Gantos, Jack. Best in Show for Rotten Ralph: A Rotten Ralph Rotten Reader. Rubel, Nicole, illus. 2005. (Rotten Ralph Reader Ser.: No. 4). 48p. (J). 15.00 (978-0-374-36358-1(7) , Farrar, Straus & Giroux (BYR)) Farrar, Straus & Giroux.

Grace, N. B. Broadway Dreams. rev. ed. 2007. (High School Musical Ser.: No. 5). 128p. (gr. 3-7). pap. 4.99 (*978-1-4231-0623-4(7)) Disney Pr.

Gutman, Dan. The Million Dollar Kick. 2nd ed. 2006. (Illus.). 208p. (gr. 3-7). pap. 5.99 (978-1-4231-0082-9(4)) Hyperion Pr.

—The Million Dollar Putt. 2006. 176p. (gr. 3-7). 15.99 (978-0-7868-3641-3(5)) Hyperion Bks. for Children.

—Million Dollar Putt. 2007. 176p. (gr. 3-7). pap. 5.99 (*978-0-7868-3642-0(3)) Hyperion Pr.

Gutman, Dan. The Million Dollar Shot. 2nd ed. 2006. 128p. (gr. 3-7). pap. 5.99 (978-1-4231-0084-3(0)) Hyperion Pr.

Hapka, Cathy. Showdown at the Okey Dokey Corral. 2000. (gr. 3-6). lib. bdg. 13.00 (978-0-613-31699-6(1)) Tandem Library Bks.

High School Musical: All-Access. rev. ed. 2007. 32p. (J). (gr. 2-7). 19.99 (*978-1-4231-1066-8(8)) Disney Pr.

Hirshfield, Lynn & Fishbein, Dena. Sassafras Goes to Hollywood. 2007. 32p. (J). 15.99 (978-0-8431-2191-9(2) , Price Stern Sloan) Penguin Group (USA) Inc.

Hobbs, William. Down the Yukon. 2002. (gr. 5-8). lib. bdg. 14.10 (978-0-613-60801-5(1)) Tandem Library Bks.

Hockerman, Dennis, illus. The Little Seed: A Tale about Integrity. 2006. (J). (*978-1-59939-094-9(9) , Reader's Digest Young Families, Inc.) Reader's Digest Children's Publishing, Inc.

Howe, James. Pinky & Rex & the Spelling Bee. 1999. (gr. k-3). lib. bdg. 11.80 (978-0-613-22921-0(5)) Tandem Library Bks.

—Pinky & Rex & the Spelling Bee. 2006. (J). (gr. 1-4). 24.21 (978-1-59961-079-5(5)) Spotlight.

Howe, Norma. Blue Avenger & the Theory of Everything. 2002. (Illus.). 240p. (J). (gr. 7-10). 17.95 (978-0-8126-2654-4(0)) Cricket Bks.

Huber, Robert C. Chew City's Troubles with Too Many Bubbles. Maguire, Kerry, illus. 2006. 32p. (J). pap. 12.00 (978-1-931945-60-8(8)) Expert Publishing, Inc.

Jane, Pamela. Winky Blue Goes Wild! Tilley, Debbie, illus. 2003. 64p. (J). 13.95 (978-1-59034-588-7(6)); pap. (978-1-59034-589-4(4)) Mondo Publishing.

Jennings, Sharon. Franklin & the Contest. Jeffrey, Sean et al, illus. 2004. 32p. (J). lib. bdg. 15.38 (*978-1-4242-1166-1(2)) Fitzgerald Bks.

Jennings, Sharon, et al. Franklin & the Contest. Jeffrey, Sean et al, trs. Jeffrey, Sean et al, illus. 2004. (Kids Can Read Ser.). 32p. (J). (gr. k-3). (978-1-55337-492-3(4)); (978-1-55337-491-6(6)) Kids Can Pr., Ltd.

Jones, Melanie Davis. Field Day. 2004. (Rookie Reader Skill Set Ser.). (Illus.). 31p. (J). (gr. k-2). pap. 4.95 (978-0-516-27772-1(3) , Children's Pr.) Scholastic Library Publishing.

—Field Day. Molnar, Albert, illus. 2003. (Rookie Reader - Level B Ser.). 32p. (J). 19.50 (978-0-516-22880-8(3) , Children's Pr.) Scholastic Library Publishing.

Keats, Ezra Jack. Pet Show. 2001. (ps-2). lib. bdg. 15.30 (978-0-613-44246-6(6)) Tandem Library Bks.

Keene, Carolyn. Riding Club Crime. 2003. (gr. 5-8). lib. bdg. 13.00 (978-0-613-65082-3(4)) Tandem Library Bks.

Ketteman, Helen. The Great Cake Bake. Collins, Matt, illus. 2005. 32p. (J). 16.95 (978-0-8027-8950-1(1)) Walker & Co.

Klein, Abby. The Pumpkin Elf Mystery. McKinley, John, illus. 2007. (Ready, Freddy! Ser.: No. 11). 96p. (J). pap. 3.99 (*978-0-439-89591-0(X) , Blue Sky Pr., The) Scholastic, Inc.

Kompelien, Tracy. Leap Frog. Haberstroh, Anne, illus. (Fact & Fiction Ser.). 24p. (J). 2007. 21.35 (978-1-59928-448-4(0)); 2006. (978-1-59928-449-1(9)) ABDO Publishing Co.

Konigsburg, E. L. Retrato del Sabado. 2002. (SPA.). (gr. 3-6). lib. bdg. 18.75 (978-0-613-64589-8(8)) Tandem Library Bks.

Korelitz, Jean Hanff. Interference Powder. 144p. (J). 2006. pap. 5.95 (978-0-7614-5275-1(3)); 2003. 15.95 (978-0-7614-5139-6(0)) Cavendish, Marshall Corp.

Korman, Gordon. The Contest. 2002. (Everest Ser.: Bk. 1). 146p. (gr. 3-8). pap. 4.99 (978-0-439-40139-5(9)) Scholastic, Inc.

—Maxx Comedy: The Funniest Kid in America. 2006. 160p. (gr. 3-7). pap. 5.99 (978-0-7868-3895-0(7)) Hyperion Pr.

Kroll, Steven. The Biggest Snowman Ever. Bassett, Jeni, illus. 2005. 32p. (J). (ps-3). pap. 3.99 (978-0-439-62768-9(0) , Cartwheel Bks.) Scholastic, Inc.

Krulik, Nancy E. Any Way You Slice It, No. 9. John and Wendy Staff, illus. 2003. (Katie Kazoo, Switcheroo Ser.: No. 9). 80p. (J). (gr. 2-6). pap. 3.99 (978-0-448-43204-5(8) , Grosset & Dunlap) Penguin Group (USA) Inc.

—No Messin' with My Lesson, No. 11. 2004. (Katie Kazoo, Switcheroo Ser.: No. 11). (gr. 3-6). lib. bdg. 11.80 (978-0-613-72569-9(7)) Tandem Library Bks.

Leedy, Loreen. The Great Graph Contest. Leedy, Loreen, illus. 2006. (Illus.). 32p. (J). 6.95 (978-0-8234-2029-2(9)) Holiday Hse., Inc.

Lin, Grace. The Year of the Dog. (Illus.). (J). (gr. 3-7). 2007. 162p. pap. 5.99 (978-0-316-06002-8(X)); 2005. 144p. 14.99 (978-0-316-06000-4(3)) Little Brown & Co.

MacDonald, Alan. Contest Crazy. Brown, Judy, illus. 2006. (Read-It! Chapter Books). 48p. (J). lib. bdg. (*978-1-4048-3134-6(7) , 1265803) Picture Window Bks.

Mahoney, Daniel J. A Really Good Snowman. 2005. (Illus.). 32p. (J). (gr. k-3). 15.00 (978-0-618-47554-4(0) , Clarion Bks.) Houghton Mifflin Co. Trade & Reference Div.

Mahony, Mary. Harry Scores A Hat Trick, Pawns, Pucks, & Scoliosis: The Sequel to Stand Tall, Harry. Pasternack, Susan, ed. Larkin, Catherine, illus. 2003. 130p. (YA). (gr. 5-8). per. 14.95 (978-0-9658879-4-6(4)) Redding Pr.

Mann, Seymour. The Purple Automobile & the Newspaper Girl. 2003. 112p. 20.95 (978-0-595-66076-6(2)); pap. 10.95 (978-0-595-29907-2(5)) iUniverse, Inc.

May, Eleanor. The Real Me. Gott, Barry, illus. 2006. (Social Studies Connects). 32p. (J). (gr. k-3). pap. 4.99 (978-1-57565-186-6(6)) Kane Pr., The.

McDonald, Megan. Judy Moody Saves the World! Reynolds, Peter H., illus. (Judy Moody Ser.: No. 3). 160p. (J). (gr. 1-5). 2004. pap. 5.99 (978-0-7636-2087-5(4)); 2002. 15.99 (978-0-7636-1446-1(7)) Candlewick Pr.

McMahon, P. J. The Case of the Singing Sea Dragons. 2005. (Freaky Joe Club Ser.: No. 6). (Illus.). 153p. (J). (978-1-4156-4221-4(4) , Aladdin) Simon & Schuster Children's Publishing.

—Case of the Singing Sea Dragons. Manders, John, illus. 2005. 153p. (J). lib. bdg. 15.38 (*978-1-4242-0406-9(2)) Fitzgerald Bks.

—The Mystery of the Diappearing Dinosaurs. 2005. (Illus.). 120p. (J). (*978-1-4156-0778-7(8) , Aladdin) Simon & Schuster Children's Publishing.

McMullan, Kate. Wheel of Misfortune. Basso, Bill, illus. 2003. (Dragon Slayers' Academy Ser.: No. 7). 112p. (J). pap. 4.99 (978-0-448-43507-7(1) , Grosset & Dunlap) Penguin Group (USA) Inc.

—Wheel of Misfortune. 2007. (Dragon Slayers' Academy Ser.: No. 7). 112p. (J). (gr. 1-6). 24.21 (*978-1-59961-381-9(6)) Spotlight.

McNamara, Margaret. The Counting Race. Gordon, Mike, illus. 2003. (Ready-to-Read Ser.). 32p. (J). pap. 3.99 (978-0-689-85539-9(7) , Aladdin) Simon & Schuster Children's Publishing.

—Counting Race. 2003. (gr. k-3). lib. bdg. 11.80 (978-0-613-66490-5(6)) Tandem Library Bks.

Medearis, Angela Shelf. The Art Riddle Contest. 1999. (Illus.). (J). pap. 5.65 (978-0-7398-0866-5(4)) Steck-Vaughn.

Merola, Caroline. Toni Biscotti's Magic Trick. Cummins, Sarah, tr. from FRE. Merola, Caroline, illus. 2006. (First Novel Ser.). (Illus.). 64p. (J). (gr. 2-5). ***(978-0-88780-719-0(4));*** 4.95 ***(978-0-88780-715-2(1))*** Formac Publishing Co., Ltd. CAN. *Dist:* Casemate Pubs. & Bk. Distributors, LLC.

Miller, Jennifer. Run, Rasputin, Run! Trials & Friendships (Book 2) 2006. (ENG., Illus.). 172p. per. ***(978-1-4120-8494-9(6))*** Trafford Publishing.

Mills, Claudia. Ziggy's Blue-Ribbon Day. Alley, R. W. & Alley, Robert W., illus. 2005. 32p. (J). (ps-ps). 16.00 (978-0-374-32352-3(6) , Farrar, Straus & Giroux (BYR)) Farrar, Straus & Giroux.

Most, Bernard. Very Boastful Kangaroo. 1999. (Green Light Readers Ser.). (978-0-606-18193-8(8)); lib. bdg. 11.80 (978-0-613-63362-8(8)) Tandem Library Bks.

Muldrow, Diane. Ice Skating Dreams. 2000. (gr. k-3). lib. bdg. 11.00 (978-0-613-83883-2(1)) Tandem Library Bks.

Munsch, Robert. More Pies! 2003. (ps-2). lib. bdg. 11.80 (978-0-613-72214-8(0)) Tandem Library Bks.

—More Pies. Martchenko, Michael, illus. ed. 2004. (J). (gr. k-3). spiral bd. (978-0-616-14590-6(X)) Canadian National Institute for the Blind/Institut National Canadien pour les Aveugles.

Munsch, Robert N. The Sand Castle Contest. Martchenko, Michael, illus. 2005. 28p. (J). (ps). lib. bdg. 11.19 (978-0-606-33821-9(7)) Tandem Library Bks.

O'Connor, Barbara. Fame & Glory in Freedom, Georgia. 2003. 112p. (J). 16.00 (978-0-374-32258-8(9) , Farrar, Straus & Giroux (BYR)) Farrar, Straus & Giroux.

Ostrow, Kim. Dil in a Pickle. 2000. (Rugrats Chapter Bks.). (Illus.). (J). 10.79 (978-0-606-20628-0(0)) Tandem Library Bks.

Parent, Nancy. Care Bears: Caring Contest. Stein, David, illus. 2003. (Care Bears 8x8 Ser.). 24p. (J). (ps-1). pap. 3.50 (978-0-439-45158-1(2)) Scholastic, Inc.

Park, Frances. Royal Bee. 2000. (gr. 3-6). lib. bdg. 17.60 (978-0-613-29043-2(7)) Tandem Library Bks.

Park, Linda Sue. The Kite Fighters. 2002. (gr. 5-8). lib. bdg. 13.00 (978-0-613-57908-7(9)) Tandem Library Bks.

Per, Sharon Mills. Double Dutch. 2004. (gr. 5-8). lib. bdg. 13.00 (978-0-613-88160-9(5)) Tandem Library Bks.

Perelman-Bernstein, Helen. Heart to Heart. 6th rev. ed. 2007. (High School Musical Ser.: No. 6). 128p. (gr. 3-7). pap. 4.99 ***(978-1-4231-0624-1(5))*** Disney Pr.

Polacco, Patricia. Rotten Richie & the Ultimate Dare. Polacco, Patricia, illus. 2006. (Illus.). 48p. (J). (gr. k). 16.99 (978-0-399-24531-2(6) , Philomel) Penguin Group (USA) Inc.

Poryes, Michael & Sherman, Susan. Dueling Divas. 2005. (That's So Raven Ser.: Vol. 8). (Illus.). 137p. (J). ***(978-1-4156-0366-6(9))*** Disney Pr.

—Showtime! 2005. (That's So Raven Ser.: Vol. 9). (Illus.). 134p. (J). ***(978-1-4156-1643-7(4))*** Disney Pr.

Pulver, Robin. Nouns & Verbs Have a Field Day. Reed, Lynn Rowe, illus. 32p. (J). (ps-3). 16.95 (978-0-8234-1982-1(7)); 2007. 6.95 ***(978-0-8234-2097-1(3))*** Holiday Hse., Inc.

Quattlebaum, Mary. Sparks Fly High: The Legend of Dancing Point. Gore, Leonid, illus. 2006. 40p. (J). 16.00 (978-0-374-34452-8(3)) Farrar, Straus & Giroux.

Rika, Tanaka. Kilala Princess. 20th rev. ed. 2007. (Illus.). pap. 5.99 ***(978-1-59816-768-9(5)*** , Tokyopop Kids) TOKYOPOP, Inc.

Robinson, Sharon. Slam Dunk! 2007. 160p. (J). (gr. 4-7). pap. 16.99 ***(978-0-439-67199-6(X)*** , Scholastic Pr.) Scholastic, Inc.

Rucker, Mike. Terry & the Elephant. pap. (978-1-56002-746-1(0)) Univ. Editions.

Rudisill, J. J., et al, illus. The Boys Against the Girls. 1999. (Wimzie's House Bks.). 24p. (J). pap. 3.99 (978-0-88724-515-2(3) , CD-4840) Carson-Dellosa Publishing Co., Inc.

Rylant, Cynthia. Henry & Mudge & the Snowman Plan. Stevenson, Sucie, illus. 2002. (Henry & Mudge Ser.). (J). 11.91 (978-0-7587-4471-5(4)) Book Wholesalers, Inc.

—Henry & Mudge & the Snowman Plan. Stevenson, Sucie, illus. 2002. (Henry & Mudge Ser.). 28.95 incl. audio compact disk (978-1-59112-651-5(7)); pap. 31.95 incl. audio compact disk (978-1-59112-652-2(5)) Live Oak Media.

Salzmann, Mary Elizabeth. Goldfish Bowl. Chawla, Neena, illus. 2006. (Fact & Fiction Ser.). 24p. (J). 21.35 (978-1-59679-939-4(0) , SandCastle); pap. (978-1-59679-940-0(4)) ABDO Publishing Co.

—Presidential Seal. Nobens, C. A., illus. 2007. (Fact & Fiction Ser.). 24p. (J). pap. (978-1-59928-465-1(0)); 21.35 (978-1-59928-464-4(2)) ABDO Publishing Co.

Scheunemann, Pam. Pig Pens. Nobens, C. A., illus. 2006. (Fact & Fiction Ser.). 24p. (J). 21.35 (978-1-59679-959-2(5) , SandCastle); pap. (978-1-59679-960-8(9)) ABDO Publishing Co.

Seuling, Barbara. Robert & the Weird & Wacky Facts. Brewer, Paul, illus. 2002. (Robert Bks.). 112p. (J). (gr. 1-4). 15.95 (978-0-8126-2653-7(2)) Cricket Bks.

Shan, Darren, pseud. Trials of Death. (Cirque du Freak: Bk. 5). 224p. (J). (gr. 5-17). 2005. mass mkt. 6.99 (978-0-316-00095-6(7)); 2004. pap. 7.99 (978-0-316-60395-9(3)); 2003. (Illus.). 16.99 (978-0-316-60367-6(8)) Little, Brown Bks. for Young Readers.

Skolsky, Mindy Warshaw. You're the Best Hannah! 2000. (978-0-606-18733-6(2)) Tandem Library Bks.

Smath, Jerry. The Best Easter Egg Ever! Smath, Jerry, illus. 2003. (Illus.). 32p. (J). (ps-3). 3.50 (978-0-439-44321-0(0) , Cartwheel Bks.) Scholastic, Inc.

—Best Easter Egg Ever! 2003. (gr. k-3). lib. bdg. 11.25 (978-0-613-66616-9(X)) Tandem Library Bks.

Spinelli, Eileen. Callie Cat, Ice Skater. Kennedy, Anne, illus. 2007. 32p. (J). (gr. 1-4). 16.95 ***(978-0-8075-1042-1(4))*** Whitman, Albert & Co.

Spohn, Kate. Turtle & Snake's Day at the Beach. Spohn, Kate, illus. 2004. (Easy-to-Read, Puffin Ser.). (Illus.). 32p. (J). (ps up). pap. 3.99 (978-0-14-240157-6(9) , Puffin) Penguin Group (USA) Inc.

Stern, Ricki & Worcester, Heidi P. Adventure: Lonely Leader. Bates, Amy June, illus. 2003. (Beryl E. Bean Ser.: No. 3). 64p. (J). lib. bdg. 16.89 (978-0-06-028774-0(8)) HarperCollins Pubs.

Stewart, Paul. Hot Dog & the Talent Competition. Ward, Nick, illus. 2006. (Read-It! Chapter Books). 48p. (J). ***(978-1-4048-3129-2(0)*** , 1265809) Picture Window Bks.

Stine, R. L. The Big Blueberry Barf-Off! Park, Trip, illus. 2005. (Rotten School Ser.). 128p. (J). 6.99 (978-0-06-078586-4(1)); lib. bdg. 14.89 (978-0-06-078587-1(X)) HarperCollins Pubs.

—The Great Smelling Bee. Park, Trip, illus. 2005. (Rotten School Ser.). 128p. (J). lib. bdg. 14.89 (978-0-06-078590-1(X)); 6.99 (978-0-06-078589-5(6)) HarperCollins Pubs.

Stine, R.L. Night of the Creepy Things. Park, Trip, illus. 2007. (Rotten School Ser.: No. 14). 128p. (J). lib. bdg. 14.89 ***(978-0-06-123273-2(4));*** (gr. 3-7). 6.99 ***(978-0-06-123272-5(6))*** HarperCollins Pubs.

—Punk'd & Skunked. Park, Trip, illus. 2007. 108p. (J). pap. ***(978-0-06-078832-2(1))*** HarperCollins Pubs.

—Rotten School #1: the Big Blueberry Barf-off! Park, Trip, illus. 2008. (Rotten School Ser.). 128p. (J). pap. 4.99 ***(978-0-06-078588-8(8)*** , Harper Trophy) HarperCollins Pubs.

Thaler, Mike. The Field Day from the Black Lagoon. Lee, Jared D., illus. 2008. (Little Apple Ser.). 64p. (J). 3.99 ***(978-0-439-68076-9(X))*** Scholastic, Inc.

—Field Day from the Black Lagoon. Lee, Jared D., illus. 2005. 64p. (J). lib. bdg. 15.00 ***(978-1-4242-2261-2(3))*** Fitzgerald Bks.

Thompson, Lisa, illus. New York City. 2006. (Read-It! Chapter Books). 80p. (J). (gr. 2-4). 19.95 (978-1-4048-1670-1(4)) Picture Window Bks.

TJ & the Mysterious Stranger. 2004. (J). bds. 16.95 (978-0-9710487-2-0(X)) Highlights of Chicago Pr.

Trailblazers! Individual Title Six-Packs. (Action Packs Ser.). 104p. (gr. 3-5). 44.00 (978-0-7635-2992-5(3)) Rigby Education.

Trembath, Don. The Big Show. 2003. (Black Belt Ser.). (Illus.). 144p. (J). (gr. 3-7). pap. 6.95 (978-1-55143-266-3(8)) Orca Bk. Pubs. USA.

Tremblay, Carole. The Old Man & the C. 2006. (Illus.). 27p. (J). 15.95 (978-1-56164-354-7(8)) Pineapple Pr., Inc.

Turnowski, Lauren. The Great Halloween Costume Contest. Pierce, Mindy, illus. 2003. (Sticker Stories Ser.). 24p. (J). (ps-2). pap. 4.99 (978-0-448-43115-4(7) , Grosset & Dunlap) Penguin Group (USA) Inc.

Walters, Eric. Three on Three. 1999. (Young Reader Ser.). (J). (978-0-606-19479-2(7)) Tandem Library Bks.

Wax, Wendy. Practice Makes Perfect. Date not set. (Rocket Power Ready-to-Read Ser.: Vol. 6). (J). 3.99 (978-0-689-86591-6(0) , Simon Spotlight/Nickelodeon) Simon & Schuster Children's Publishing.

Weaver, Tess. Frederick Finch, Loudmouth. 2008. (J). ***(978-0-618-45239-2(7)*** , Clarion Bks.) Houghton Mifflin Co. Trade & Reference Div.

Wells, Rosemary. The Halloween Parade. 2001. (ps-2). lib. bdg. 11.80 (978-0-613-53195-5(7)) Tandem Library Bks.

West, Tracey. Great Coaster Contest. 2003. (gr. 3-6). lib. bdg. 13.00 (978-0-613-72547-7(6)) Tandem Library Bks.

White, Andrea. Surviving Antarctica: Reality TV 2083. (J). 2006. 448p. pap. 6.99 (978-0-06-055456-9(8)); 2005. 336p. (gr. 7 up). 16.99 (978-0-06-055454-5(1) , HarperCollins); 2005. 336p. (gr. 7 up). lib. bdg. 16.89 (978-0-06-055455-2(X)) HarperCollins Pubs.

Whybrow, Ian & Ross, Tony. Young Robin's Hood. 2002. (Illus.). 32p. (J). (gr. 1-4). pap. 4.95 (978-1-59034-476-7(6)) Mondo Publishing.

Williams, Carol Lynch. My Angelica. 2001. (978-0-606-21340-0(6)) Tandem Library Bks.

Williams, Jacklyn. Happy Halloween, Gus! Cushman, Doug, illus. 2005. (Read-It! Readers Ser.). 32p. (J). (gr. k-3). 18.60 (978-1-4048-0960-4(0)) Picture Window Bks.

Winerip, Michael. Adam Canfield Watch Your Back! 2007. (Adam Canfield of the Slash Ser.). (Illus.). 256p. (J). (gr. 3-7). 15.99 ***(978-0-7636-2341-8(5))*** Candlewick Pr.

Winters, Kay. Teeny Tiny Ghost & the Monster. Munsinger, Lynn, illus. 2006. 32p. (J). pap. 6.99 (978-0-06-443662-5(4) , Harper Trophy) HarperCollins Pubs.

Ziefert, Harriet. Scare the Moon. Karas, G. Brian, illus. 2004. 16p. (J). 9.95 (978-1-4027-1702-4(4)) Sterling Publishing Co., Inc.

Zucker, Jonny. Basketball War. Savage, Paul, illus. 2006. 40p. (J). (gr. 2-3). lib. bdg. (978-1-59889-009-9(3)) Stone Arch Bks.

—Skateboard Power. Savage, Paul, illus. 2006. 40p. (J). (gr. 2-3). lib. bdg. (978-1-59889-007-5(7)) Stone Arch Bks.

Zucker, Jonny. Spin Off. Troiano, Enzo, illus. 2007. 33p. (J). pap. ***(978-1-59889-429-5(3));*** 40p. (YA). (gr. 5-9). lib. bdg. 21.26 ***(978-1-59889-333-5(5))*** Stone Arch Bks.

CONTRACEPTION

see Birth Control

CONTRACTIONS

see Ciphers

CONUNDRUMS

see Riddles

CONVICTS

see Crime and Criminals; Prisons

COOK, JAMES, 1728-1779

Beales, R. A. James Cook: The Pacific Coast & Beyond. 2005. (In the Footsteps of Explorers Ser.). (Illus.). 32p. (J). (gr. 3-9). (978-0-7787-2415-5(8)); pap. (978-0-7787-2451-3(4)) Crabtree Publishing Co.

Bergin, Mark. You Wouldn't Want to Travel with Captain Cook. Antram, David, illus. 2006. 32p. (J). (gr. 2-5). pap. 9.95 (978-0-531-12446-8(0) , Watts, Franklin) Scholastic Library Publishing.

—You Wouldn't Want to Travel with Captain Cook! A Voyage You'd Rather Not Make. Antram, David, illus. 2006. (You Wouldn't Want To Ser.). 32p. (J). (gr. 2-5). 28.50 (978-0-531-12421-5(5) , Watts, Franklin) Scholastic Library Publishing.

Bingham, Jane. Captain Cook's Pacific Explorations. 2007. (J). ***(978-1-4034-9756-7(7))*** Heinemann Library.

Bowen, Richard. Captain James Cook: British Explorer. 2002. (Great Names Ser.). (Illus.). 32p. (J). (gr. 3 up). lib. bdg. (978-1-59084-147-1(6)) Mason Crest Pubs.

Broderick, Enid. Capt. James Cook. 2003. (Great Explorers Ser.). (Illus.). 48p. (J). (gr. 5 up). pap. 14.60 (978-0-8368-5174-8(9) , World Almanac Library) Stevens, Gareth Inc.

—Captain James Cook. 2001. (Great Explorers Ser.). (Illus.). 48p. (J). (gr. 5 up). lib. bdg. 30.00 (978-0-8368-5014-7(9) , World Almanac Library) Stevens, Gareth Inc.

Cook. (Exploring the World Ser.). 48p. (YA). 8.95 (978-0-7565-1140-1(2)) Compass Point Bks.

Gaines, Ann Graham. Captain Cook Explores the Pacific in World History. 2002. (In World History Ser.). (Illus.). 128p. (J). (gr. 5-12). lib. bdg. 26.60 (978-0-7660-1823-5(7)) Enslow Pubs., Inc.

Great Explorers: Captain James Cook; Christopher Columbus; Ferdinand Magellan; John Cabot, 4 bks. 2002. (Illus.). (J). (gr. 5 up). pap. (978-0-8368-5179-3(X)); lib. bdg. 117.06 (978-0-8368-5019-2(X)) Stevens, Gareth Inc. (World Almanac Library).

Kline, Trish. James Cook. (Rourke Discovery Library). 2003. (Illus.). 24p. (gr. 2-5). 14.95 (978-1-58952-292-3(3)); 2002. lib. bdg. 19.27 (978-1-58952-426-2(8)) Rourke Publishing, LLC.

McCarthy, Shaun & Cook, James. James Cook. 2002. (Groundbreakers Ser.). (Illus.). 48p. (J). (gr. 5-7). lib. bdg. 27.07 (978-1-58810-595-0(4)) Heinemann Library.

Meltzer, Milton, et al. Captain James Cook: Three Times Around the World. 2001. (Great Explorations Ser.). (Illus.). 80p. (J). (gr. 4 up). lib. bdg. 28.50 (978-0-7614-1240-3(9) , Benchmark Bks.) Cavendish, Marshall Corp.

Petrie, Kristin. James Cook. 2004. (Explorers Set I Ser.). (Illus.). 32p. (J). (gr. k-6). lib. bdg. 22.78 (978-1-59197-596-0(4)) ABDO Publishing Co.

Shields, Charles J. James Cook & the Exploration of the Pacific. 2001. (Explorers of New Worlds Ser.). (Illus.). (J). 63p. pap. 25.00 (978-0-7910-6423-8(9)); 64p. 25.00 (978-0-7910-6422-1(0)) Facts On File, Inc. (Chelsea Hse.).

Williams, Jean Kinney. Cook: Captain James Cook Charts the Pacific Ocean. 2003. (Exploring the World Ser.). (Illus.). 48p. (J). (gr. 4 up). lib. bdg. 22.60 (978-0-7565-0421-2(X)) Compass Point Bks.

COOK, JAMES, 1728-1779—FICTION

Hesse, Karen. Stowaway. unabr. ed. 2004. 328p. (J). (gr. 5-9). pap. 48.00 incl. audio (978-0-8072-8760-6(1) , LYA 259 SP, Listening Library) Random Hse. Audio Publishing Group.

—Stowaway. Parker, Robert Andrew, illus. 2002. 320p. (J). (gr. 5-9). pap. 6.99 (978-0-689-83989-4(8) , Aladdin) Simon & Schuster Children's Publishing.

—Stowaway. Parker, Robert Andrew & Prato, Rodica, illus. 2000. 328p. (J). (gr. 5-9). 17.95 (978-0-689-83987-0(1) , McElderry, Margaret K.) Simon & Schuster Children's Publishing.

—Stowaway. 2002. (gr. 5-8). lib. bdg. 15.30 (978-0-613-45110-9(4)) Tandem Library Bks.

COOK BOOKS

see Cookery

COOKBOOKS

see Cookery

COOKERY

see also Baking; Bread; Coffee; Confectionery; Cookery for the Sick; Desserts; Diet; Food; Menus; Outdoor Cookery; Pastry; Salads; Sandwiches; Soups

Abrams, Pam. Gadgetology: Kid-Friendly Recipes, Playtime Activities, & Simple Experiments Using 35 Fun Kitchen Gadgets. 2007. 96p. 14.95 (978-1-55832-346-9(5)) Harvard Common Pr.

Adsit, Kimberly S. & Gilstrap, Wendy R. Hooks, Books & Cooks. 1999. pap. 19.95 (978-0-9671864-0-5(4)) HB&C Pr.

After-School Snacks. 2000. (Kids Cook Ser.). (Illus.). 80p. (J). (gr. 4-7). pap. 7.99 (978-1-896891-45-3(4)) Recipe Factory, Inc. CAN. *Dist:* Picasso Distribution Services.

Allred, Erin. 5-Alarm Cookbook: For Those Who Just Can't Get It Hot Enough. 2003. (YA). spiral bd. 9.95 (978-1-885027-22-1(2)) Apricot Pr.

Amari, Suad. Cooking the Lebanese Way. 2nd rev. ed. 2003. (Easy Menu Ethnic Cookbooks). (Illus.). 72p. (J). 25.26 (978-0-8225-4116-5(5) , Lerner Pubns.) Lerner Publishing Group.

Amato, William. Math in the Kitchen. 2002. (gr. k-3). lib. bdg. 12.95 (978-0-613-58790-7(1)) Tandem Library Bks.

American Cancer Society Staff. Kids' First Cookbook: Delicious - Nutritious Treats to Make Yourself! 2005. (Illus.). 96p. (ps-7). 13.95 (978-0-944235-19-5(0) , 9780944235195) McGraw-Hill Cos., The.

American Girl Editorial Staff. Coconut Cookbook: Fun & Fluffy Treats to Eat. 2004. (Illus.). 56p. (J). 7.95 (978-1-58485-892-8(3)) American Girl Publishing, Inc.

Ancona, George. Mis Comidas. 2006. Tr. of My Food. (SPA.). 32p. (J). (gr. 1-3). pap. 8.95 (978-0-516-25496-8(0) , Children's Pr.) Scholastic Library Publishing.

—Mis Comidas/My Foods. 2005. (Somos Latinos (We Are Latinos) Ser.). (ENG & SPA., Illus.). 32p. (J). 21.00 (978-0-516-25292-6(5) , Children's Pr.) Scholastic Library Publishing.

Bag Lunches. 2000. (Kids Cook Ser.). (Illus.). 80p. (J). pap. 7.99 (978-1-896891-43-9(8)) Recipe Factory, Inc. CAN. *Dist:* Picasso Distribution Services.

Baking Day: Individual Title Six-Packs. (gr. 1-2). 22.00 (978-0-7635-9168-7(8)) Rigby Education.

Barasch, Lynne. Hiromi's Hands. Barasch, Lynne, illus. 2007. (Illus.). 40p. (J). (gr. k-6). 17.95 (978-1-58430-275-9(5)) Lee & Low Bks., Inc.

Barlow, Kathleen & Schetselaar, Britney, eds. Gross-Out Cakes: The Kitty Litter Cake & Other Classics. 2006. (Illus.). 64p. (J). pap. 12.95 (978-1-933317-48-9(5)) Leatherwood Pr.

Barnes, Peter W., et al. Capital Cooking with Woodrow & Friends. Barnes, Cheryl Shaw, illus. 1998. 32p. (J). (gr. 1-6). pap. 9.95 (978-0-9637688-7-2(5)) Vacation Spot Publishing.

Bass, Jules. Cooking with Herb, the Vegetarian Dragon: A Cookbook for Kids. Harter, Debbie, illus. 1999. 40p. (J). (ps-3). 16.95 (978-1-84148-041-1(X)) Barefoot Bks., Inc.

Bates, Dorothy R. Kids Can Cook: Vegetarian Recipes. 7th ed. 1999. (Illus.). 176p. (gr. 3-7). reprint ed. pap. 12.95 (978-1-57067-086-2(2)) Book Publishing Co., The.

Bates, Dorothy R., et al. Munchie Madness: Vegetarian Meals for Teens. 2001. (Illus.). 160p. pap. 9.95 (978-1-57067-115-9(X)) Book Publishing Co., The.

Bauld, Jane Scoggins & Hefner, Kim. 101 Things to Cook. l.t. ed. 2000. 125p. (J). (ps-3). pap. 8.95 (978-1-929701-01-8(2)) Under the Green Umbrella.

Beach, Mark. Simply in Season for Kids. 2006. (Illus.). 78p. (J). pap. 21.99 (978-0-8361-9336-7(9)) Herald Pr.

Beatty, Theresa M. Food & Recipes of Africa. 1999. (Kids in the Kitchen). (Illus.). 24p. (J). (gr. k-4). lib. bdg. 19.95 (978-0-8239-5220-5(7) , PowerKids Pr.) Rosen Publishing Group, Inc., The.

—Food & Recipes of Japan. 1999. (Kids in the Kitchen). (Illus.). 24p. (J). (gr. k-4). lib. bdg. 19.95 (978-0-8239-5319-6(X)) Rosen Publishing Group, Inc., The.

—Food & Recipes of the Caribbean. 1999. (Kids in the Kitchen). 24p. (J). (gr. k-4). lib. bdg. 19.95 (978-0-8239-5221-2(5) , PowerKids Pr.) Rosen Publishing Group, Inc., The.

Beery, Barbara. Batter up Kids Sensational Snacks: Healthy Eats from the Premier Children's Cooking School. Snortum, Marty, photos by. 2005. (Illus.). 64p. (J). (gr. 1-7). spiral bd. 19.95 (978-1-58685-798-1(3)) Gibbs Smith, Publisher.

Beery, Barbara. Fairies Cookbook. 2007. (Illus.). 64p. (J). (gr. 1 up). 14.95 ***(978-1-4236-0290-3(0))*** Gibbs Smith, Publisher.

Behnke, Alison. Cooking the Middle Eastern Way: Culturally Authentic Foods Including Low-Fat & Vegetarian Recipes. 2nd rev. ed. 2005. (Easy Menu Ethnic Cookbooks). (Illus.). 72p. (J). (ps-7). 25.26 (978-0-8225-1238-7(6) , Lerner Pubns.) Lerner Publishing Group.

Behnke, Alison & Duro, Karin L. Cooking the Brazilian Way. 2nd rev. ed. 2004. (Easy Menu Ethnic Cookbooks). (Illus.). 72p. (J). (gr. 5-12). lib. bdg. 25.26 (978-0-8225-4111-0(4)) Lerner Publishing Group.

Behnke, Alison, et al. Cooking the Mediterranean Way. 2nd rev. ed. 2005. (Easy Menu Ethnic Cookbooks). (Illus.). 72p. (J). 25.26 (978-0-8225-1237-0(8) , Lerner Pubns.) Lerner Publishing Group.

Bergna, Monica, compiled by. Recetas para Compartir: Galletas y Dulces. 2002. (Recipes to Share Collection). (SPA.). 36p. (gr. 3-5). 15.95 (978-980-6437-30-2(6) , PLE31960) Playco Editores, C.A.

Better Homes and Gardens Editors. Snack Attack! 2006. (Illus.). 96p. (J). spiral bd. 16.95 (978-0-696-23387-6(8) , Better Homes & Gardens Bks.) Meredith Bks.

Better Homes and Gardens Editors & Miller, Jan, eds. Junior Cook Book: For the Hostess & Host of Tomorrow. 2005. (Illus.). 204p. (ps-17). ring bd. 16.95 (978-0-696-22833-9(5) , Better Homes & Gardens Bks.) Meredith Bks.

—New Junior Cook Book. 7th rev. ed. 2004. (ENG., Illus.). 128p. (J). spiral bd. 16.95 (978-0-696-22000-5(8) , Better Homes & Gardens Bks.) Meredith Bks.

Betty Crocker Editors. Betty Crocker's Cookbook for Boys & Girls. fac. ed. 2003. (Illus.). 192p. 16.95 (978-0-7645-2634-3(0) , Betty Crocker) Wiley, John & Sons, Inc.

Black, Rosemary. Sweet Celebrations: A Holiday Dessert Book for Kids. (Illus.). (J). pap. (978-0-312-31023-3(4)); mass mkt. (978-0-312-98759-6(5)) St. Martin's Pr. (St. Martin's Paperbacks).

Blackstone, Stella. Making Minestrone. Brooks, Nan, illus. 2000. 32p. (J). (ps-3). 15.99 (978-1-84148-211-8(0)) Barefoot Bks., Inc.

—Making Minestrone. Brooks, Nan, illus. 2006. 32p. (J). (gr. k-4). reprint ed. 16.00 (978-0-7567-9926-7(0)) DIANE Publishing Co.

Blakey, Nancy. Lotions, Potions, & Slime: Mudpies & More! Watts, Melissah, illus. 2004. 120p. (J). (ps-7). 9.95 (978-1-883672-21-8(X) , Tricycle Pr.) Ten Speed Pr.

Bledsoe, Michele. The Birdie Treats Cookbook. Rupert, Chris & Schaefer, Kelly, illus. 2000. 13p. (gr. 1 up). pap. 9.95 (978-0-9653042-5-2(6)) Come & Get It Publishing.

Blue Lantern Studio Staff, ed. Fun in the Kitchen. Roetter, Sonia, illus. 2007. (J). (gr. 3-7). 15.95 (***978-1-59583-189-7(4)***, Green Tiger Pr.) Laughing Elephant.

Blues, Mary. The Blues Lover's Cookbook for Kids. 1999. (Illus.). 72p. (J). 15.00 (978-0-9676216-0-9(7)) N.R. Etc.

Boyce, Claire & Hains, Harriet. First Cook Book. 2003. (J). bds. 5.98 (978-0-7525-8921-3(0)) Parragon, Inc.

Brami, Elisabeth. Sweet Treats, Nasty Eats. McGowan, Siobhan, tr. from FRE. Bertrand, Philippe, illus. 1999. 32p. (J). (ps-3). 14.95 (978-1-55670-946-3(3)) Stewart, Tabori & Chang.

Brennan, Georgeanne. Green Eggs & Ham Cookbook. Seuss, Dr., illus. Frankeny, Frankie, photos by. 2006. 64p. (J). (gr. 3-5). 16.95 (978-0-679-88440-8(8), Random Hse. Bks. for Young Readers) Random Hse. Children's Bks.

Brooks, Felicity. Sam the Chef. 2005. (Jobs People Do Ser.). 24p. (J). pap. 6.95 (978-0-7945-0894-4(4), Usborne) EDC Publishing.

Brown, Debbie. Favorite Character Cakes. 1999. (Illus.). 96p. pap. 9.95 (978-3-8290-1480-9(5), 520918) Konemann.

Brown, Karen. Mommy's Little Helper Cookbook. 2000. viii, 133p. (J). pap. (978-0-88166-346-4(8)) Meadowbrook Pr.

Brownlie, Alison. West Africa. 1999. (Food & Festivals Ser.). (Illus.). 32p. (J). (gr. 1-4). lib. bdg. 25.69 (978-0-8172-5552-7(4)) Raintree.

Buck-Murray, Marion. Kids Make Pizza: 40 Fun & Easy Recipes. 1998. (Illus.). 89p. (J). pap. 12.00 (978-0-7881-5297-9(1)) DIANE Publishing Co.

Buck, Patricia R. Mommy & Me in the Kitchen: Mixes, Recipes, Gifts & Ideas for Each Month of the Year! Johnson, Sheryl Lynn, illus. 1999. 70p. (J). pap. 9.95 (978-0-615-11330-2(3)) Sheryl Lynn's.

Bugni, Alice. Moose Racks, Bear Tracks & Other Alaska Kidsnacks: Cooking with Kids Has Never. 1999. (gr. k-3). lib. bdg. 17.60 (978-0-613-51288-6(X)) Tandem Library Bks.

—Moose Racks, Bear Tracks & Other Alaska Kidsnacks: Cooking with Kids Has Never Been So Easy! Cartwright, Shannon, illus. 2002. 32p. (gr. k up). pap. 9.95 (978-1-57061-214-5(5)) Sasquatch Bks.

Bull, Jane. The Cooking Book. 2002. (Illus.). 48p. (J). 12.99 (978-0-7894-8834-3(5)) Dorling Kindersley Publishing, Inc.

Bulloch, Ivan. Cook. James, Diane, illus. rev. ed. 2000. (Let's Ser.). 24p. (J). (ps-1). 9.95 (978-1-58728-025-2(6)); pap. 5.95 (978-1-58728-029-0(9)) T&N Children's Publishing. (Two Can Publishing).

—Watch It Cook. James, Diane, illus. 2004. (I Can Do It Ser.). 32p. (J). (gr. 2-5). 12.95 (978-1-58728-510-3(X)); pap. 5.95 (978-1-58728-511-0(8)) T&N Children's Publishing. (Two Can Publishing).

Bulloch, Ivan & James, Diane. La Cuisine. 2000. (Let's Ser.). (FRE., Illus.). 24p. (J). (ps-1). pap. 5.95 (978-1-58728-208-9(9), Two Can Publishing) T&N Children's Publishing.

—Qui Monge Quoi. 2000. (My Turn Ser.). (Illus.). 12p. (J). (ps-k). bds. 6.95 (978-1-58728-173-0(2), Two Can Publishing) T&N Children's Publishing.

Burby, Liza N. A Day in the Life of a Chef. 1999. (Kids' Career Library). (Illus.). 24p. (J). (gr. 3). lib. bdg. 18.75 (978-0-8239-5298-4(3), PowerKids Pr.) Rosen Publishing Group, Inc., The.

Burckhardt, Ann L. Multicultural Cookbooks, 4 bks. Incl. People of Africa & Their Food. lib. bdg. 22.60 (978-1-56065-434-6(1)); People of China & Their Food. lib. bdg. 22.60 (978-1-56065-433-9(3)); People of Mexico & Their Food. lib. bdg. 22.60 (978-1-56065-432-2(5)); People of Russia & Their Food. lib. bdg. 22.60 (978-1-56065-435-3(X)); 24p. (J). (gr. 3-4). 1996. (Illus.). Set lib. bdg. 90.40 (978-1-56065-639-5(5), Bridgestone Bks.) Capstone Pr., Inc.

Burleigh, Robert. Chocolate: Riches from the Rainforest. 2002. (Illus.). 40p. (J). (gr. 1-5). 16.95 (978-0-8109-5734-3(5)) Abrams, Harry N., Inc.

Busby, Barbara Sheen. Foods of Ethiopia. 2007. (Taste of Culture Ser.). (Illus.). 64p. (J). (gr. 3-6). 24.95 (***978-0-7377-3775-2(1)***, Kidhaven) Thomson Gale.

—Foods of the Caribbean. 2007. (Taste of Culture Ser.). (Illus.). 64p. (J). (gr. 3-6). 24.95 (***978-0-7377-3774-5(3)***, Kidhaven) Thomson Gale.

Busby, Cylin & Licensing Company Staff. Stylin' Slumber Party. 2003. (Bratz Ser.). (Illus.). 48p. 8.40 (978-0-14-131751-9(5), Putnam Juvenile) Penguin Group (USA) Inc.

Butler, Daphne. What Happens When Food Cooks? 2004. (Illus.). 31p. (J). (gr. k-4). reprint ed. 10.00 (978-0-7567-7561-2(2)) DIANE Publishing Co.

Canas-Jovel, Lourdes E. & Acock, Anthony W. Little Vegan Monsters' Cookbook. Schiller, Caitlin, ed. 2006. (J). per. 19.95 (***978-0-9787590-3-2(6)***) Little Vegan Monsters Publishing.

Carew-Miller, Anna. Native American Cooking. 2002. (Native American Life Ser.). (Illus.). 64p. (YA). (gr. 5 up). lib. bdg. (978-1-59084-131-0(X)) Mason Crest Pubs.

Carle, Meghan, et al. Teens Cook: How to Cook What You Want to Eat. 2004. (Illus.). 176p. 19.95 (978-1-58008-584-7(9)) Ten Speed Pr.

Carlota's Cooking Class: Fourth Grade Guided Comprehension Level K. (On Our Way to English Ser.). (gr. 4 up). 34.50 (978-0-7578-7147-4(X)) Rigby Education.

Carlson, Laurie M. Green Thumbs: A Kid's Activity Guide to Indoor & Outdoor Gardening. 2003. (Kid's Guide Ser.). (Illus.). 144p. (J). (gr. k-7). pap. 12.95 (978-1-55652-238-3(X)) Chicago Review Pr., Inc.

Carroll, Jennifer Y. The Pre-K Gourmet: Children's Recipes & Related Activities to Encourage Learning. Young, Dianne, ed. Hanlon, Leslie, illus. 1998. 140p. (J). pap. 14.95 (978-0-9645202-1-9(4)) Communication Counts.

Chambers, Brent, illus. Cooking: First Wave Satellite Individual Title Six-Packs. (Sails Literacy Ser.). 16p. (gr. k up). 27.00 (978-0-7578-6863-4(0)) Rigby Education.

Choy, Sam. Sam Choy's Cooking with Kids. 2001. 168p. pap. 13.95 (978-1-56647-493-1(0)) Mutual Publishing LLC.

Chung, Okwha & Monroe, Judy. Cooking the Korean Way: Includes New Low-Fat & Vegetarian Recipes. 2nd exp. rev. ed. 2003. (Easy Menu Ethnic Cookbooks). (Illus.). 72p. (J). 25.26 (978-0-8225-4115-8(7), Lerner Pubns.) Lerner Publishing Group.

Chung, Okwha & Monroe, Judy M. Cooking the Korean Way. 1998. (Easy Menu Ethnic Cookbooks). (Illus.). 48p. (J). (gr. 5-9). lib. bdg. 19.93 (978-0-8225-0921-9(0), Lerner Pubns.) Lerner Publishing Group.

Clegg, Holly. Holly Clegg's Trim & Terrific Freezer Friendly Meals. 2006. (Illus.). 304p. spiral bd. 19.95 (978-0-7624-2597-6(0)) Running Pr. Bk. Pubs.

Cocineros: Individual Title Six-Packs. (On Deck en Espanol Ser.).Tr. of Chefs. (SPA.). 24p. (gr. 4-5). 35.00 (978-0-7578-6410-0(4)) Rigby Education.

Collison, Cathy, et al, eds. Heart Smart Kids Cookbook. 2000. 152p. spiral bd. 14.95 (978-0-937247-33-4(2)) Detroit Free Pr., Inc.

Collister, Linda. Cooking with Kids. Davies, Vanessa, photos by. 2003. (Illus.). 128p. (gr. 6-11). tchr. ed. (978-1-84172-498-0(X)) Ryland Peters & Small.

Compass Point Books, contrib. by. Chefs. (Community Workers Ser.). 24p. (J). pap. 7.95 (978-0-7565-1187-6(9)) Compass Point Bks.

Conger, Holli, intro. Little Chef. 2007. 5p. bds. 8.95 (***978-1-58117-597-4(3)***, Intervisual/Piggy Toes) Dalmatian Pr.

Contini, Mary. Easy Peasy Sweetie Pie: Truly Scrumptious Treats for Kids Who Love to Bake. 2000. (Illus.). 128p. 24.99 (978-0-09-187787-3(3), Ebury Pr.) Ebury Publishing GBR. *Dist:* Independent Pubs. Group.

Contini, Mary & Irvine, Pru. Easy Peasy: Real Food for Kids Who Want to Cook. 1999. (Illus.). 128p. 29.99 (978-0-09-186840-6(8)) Random Hse. GBR. *Dist:* Independent Pubs. Group.

Cook, Deanna. FamilyFun Cooking with Kids. Ganssle, Grace, ed. 2006. (Illus.). 224p. (ps-4). 24.95 (978-1-4231-0086-7(7), Disney Editions) Disney Pr.

Cook, Deanna F. Family Fun Super Snacks: 125 Quick Snacks That Are Fun to Make & to Eat. 2004. (Illus.). 96p. (ps-17). 14.95 (978-0-7868-5424-0(3), Disney Editions) Disney Pr.

Cooking. 2004. (Illus.). (J). lib. bdg. 27.10 (978-1-932889-22-2(1)) Sea-To-Sea Pubns.

Cooking Books for Children, 6 bks. (J). lib. bdg. 104.70 (978-1-56674-903-9(4)) Forest Hse. Publishing Co., Inc.

Cooking with Christian Kids. 2004. pap. 10.95 (978-0-7647-0542-7(3)) School Specialty Publishing.

Cooking with Kids: Recipes for Year-Round Fun. 48p. (ps-3). 8.99 (978-0-7682-0288-5(4), FE211008, Totline Pubns.) Schaffer, Frank Pubns.

Cooking with Mickey & Friends Cookbook. 2005. (Illus.). 32p. 9.99 (978-0-7868-4425-8(6)) Disney Pr.

Cool Cooking. 2007. (J). 136.68 (***978-1-59928-720-1(X)***, Checkerboard Library) ABDO Publishing Co.

Cooper, Hilda. Family Secrets: A Southern Heritage Cookbook Of Closely Guarded Family Recipes. 2001. 550p. per. 24.95 (978-0-9701466-5-6(5)) Athenean Pr., Inc.

—Holiday Traditions: A Southern Heritage Cookbook. 2001. 500p. per. 21.95 (978-0-9701466-4-9(7)) Athenean Pr., Inc.

Cornell, Kari & Thomas, Peter. Cooking the Southern African Way. 2nd rev. ed. 2005. (Easy Menu Ethnic Cookbooks). (Illus.). 72p. (J). 25.26 (978-0-8225-1239-4(4), Lerner Pubns.) Lerner Publishing Group.

Cosgrove, Stephen & Higgins, Kitty, told to. The Tasty Tort Trial. ed. 2004. (Reader's Theater Ser.). (J). pap. 22.00 (978-1-4108-1144-8(1)) Benchmark Education Co.

Coxson, Lorraine, et al. Cooking to Learn. 1999. 290p. (J). ring bd. (978-1-884074-86-8(3)) PCI Educational Publishing.

Cramer, Lisa. My Kids Can't Cook Book. 2005. spiral bd. 24.95 (978-1-932252-47-7(9)) Creative Continuum, Inc.

Crocker, Betty. Betty Crocker Kids Cook! 2nd rev. ed. 2007. (Illus.). 159p. 19.95 (978-0-471-75309-4(2)) Wiley, John & Sons, Inc.

Cruz, Abel. Juguitos para Ninos.Tr. of Juices for Kids. (SPA.). 9.98 (978-970-643-350-3(3)) Selector, S.A. de C.V. MEX. *Dist:* AIMS International Bks., Inc., Giron Bks.

Curry, Ella I. Ella's Little Cookbook. 2003. 71p. (YA). pap. 9.95 (978-0-7414-1536-3(4)) Infinity Publishing.

Dahl, Felicity & Dahl, Roald. Roald Dahl's Even More Revolting Recipes. Blake, Quentin, illus. Baldwin, Jan, photos by. 2003. 64p. (J). pap. 7.99 (978-0-14-250165-8(4), Puffin) Penguin Group (USA) Inc.

Dahl, Roald. Roald Dahl's Even More Revolting Recipes. 2003. (gr. k-3). lib. bdg. 16.45 (978-0-613-86702-3(5)) Tandem Library Bks.

Dalgleish, Sharon. Fast Food. 2006. (Illus.). 32p. (J). (978-1-58340-747-9(2)) Smart Apple Media.

—Lunch Box Food/By Sharon Dalgleish. 2006. (Illus.). 32p. (J). (978-1-58340-749-3(9)) Smart Apple Media.

—Party Food. 2006. (Illus.). 32p. (J). (978-1-58340-746-2(4)) Smart Apple Media.

—Snack Food. 2006. (Illus.). 32p. (J). (978-1-58340-748-6(0)) Smart Apple Media.

D'Amico, Joan & Drummond, Karen Eich. The Healthy Body Cookbook: Over 50 Fun Activities & Delicious Recipes for Kids. Cash-Walsh, Tina, illus. 1998. 192p. (gr. 4-7). pap. 12.95 (978-0-471-18888-9(3), Wiley) Wiley, John & Sons, Inc.

Dann, Penny. My Big Rainy Day Activity Book. Smee, Nicola, illus. 2004. 96p. (J). act. bk. ed. 7.99 (978-1-85854-554-7(4)) Brimax Books Ltd. GBR. *Dist:* Byeway Bks.

Darling, Abigail. The Teddy Bear's Picnic Cookbook. Day, Alexandra, illus. rev. ed. 2003. 32p. (J). (gr. 3-7). 14.50 (978-1-883211-60-8(3), Green Tiger Pr.) Laughing Elephant.

Davis, Tina. Look & Cook: A Cookbook for Children. 2004. (Illus.). 160p. 19.95 (978-1-58479-358-8(9)) Stewart, Tabori & Chang.

Dear SOS: Favorite Restaurant Recipes. 2001. 272p. kivar 18.95 (978-1-883792-60-2(6)) Los Angeles Times.

Denning, Timmy. The Kids' No Cook Cookbook. 2001. (Illus.). 142p. spiral bd. 9.95 (978-1-57166-204-0(9)) Hearts 'N Tummies Cookbook Co.

Denny, Roz. Cooking for Beginners. 1998. (gr. 3-6). lib. bdg. 16.40 (978-0-613-88987-2(8)) Tandem Library Bks.

—Rice. 1998. (Food in Focus Ser.). (Illus.). 32p. (J). (978-1-57572-658-8(0)) Heinemann.

Denzer, Barbara & Denzer, Missy. The Crazy Kids Guide to Cooking for Your Pet: Recipes, Jokes, Pet Care Tips & Fun Things to Do with Your Pet Featuring the Back Bones of Character. Rodriguez, Manny, illus. 2004. 64p. (J). (gr. k-7). 12.95 (978-0-9744749-0-8(8)) Crazy Pet Pr., The.

DerKazarian, Susan E. BFF Cookbook: More Than 30 Yummy Recipes for Friendship Fun! 2000. 88p. (J). (978-0-439-20348-7(1)) Scholastic, Inc.

DK Publishing. Grow It, Cook It. 2008. 80p. (J). (gr. 2-5). 16.99 (***978-0-7566-3367-7(2)***) Dorling Kindersley Publishing, Inc.

DK Publishing Staff. The Pirate Cookbook. 2007. 24p. (J). (gr. 1-4). pap. 6.99 (978-0-7566-3000-3(2)) Dorling Kindersley Publishing, Inc.

—Shrek Cookbook. 2007. 80p. (J). (gr. 1-4). ring bd. 17.99 (978-0-7566-2989-2(6)) Dorling Kindersley Publishing, Inc.

DK Publishing Staff & Graimes, Nichola. Kids' Fun & Healthy Cookbook. 2007. 128p. (J). (gr. 2-5). 17.99 (978-0-7566-2916-8(0)) Dorling Kindersley Publishing, Inc.

Dodge, Abigail Johnson. Around the World Cookbook. 2008. 128p. (J). (gr. 2-5). ring bd. 19.99 (***978-0-7566-3744-6(9)***) Dorling Kindersley Publishing, Inc.

Dodge, Abigail Johnson. The Kid's Cookbook: A Great Book for Kids Who Love to Cook! Williams, Chuck, ed. Beisch, Leigh, photos by. 2002. (Williams-Sonoma). (Illus.). 128p. (gr. 4 up). 22.95 (978-0-8487-2607-2(3), 130029) Oxmoor Hse., Inc.

Domnauer, Teresa. Incredible Edibles: Level 3. 2006. (Extreme Readers Ser.). (Illus.). 32p. (J). (gr. 1-2). pap. 3.95 (978-0-7696-4339-7(6)) School Specialty Publishing.

Dorling Kindersley Publishing Staff. DK Children's Cookbook. 2004. (Illus.). 128p. (J). 17.99 (978-0-7566-0597-1(0), 1235962) Dorling Kindersley Publishing, Inc.

Douglas, Vincent & School Specialty Publishing Staff. Experiments You Can Do in Your Kitchen. Pearce, Q. L., tr. 2003. (Science Experiments Ser.). (Illus.). 96p. (J). (gr. 5-8). 16.95 (978-1-57768-623-1(3), Waterbird Bks.) School Specialty Publishing.

Duden, Jane. Vegetarianism for Teens. 2000. (Nutrition & Fitness Ser.). (Illus.). 64p. (J). (gr. 4-6). lib. bdg. 23.93 (978-0-7368-0712-8(8), LifeMatters Bks.) Capstone Pr., Inc.

Duffy, Kate. Fit Kids in the Kitchen with Pete & Rosa. 2002. (Illus.). 96p. (J). pap. 19.95 (978-0-9709301-6-3(X)) Fit Kids.

Dunnewind, Stephanie. Come to Tea: Fun Tea Party Themes, Recipes, Crafts, Games, Etiquette & More. Mazille, Capucine, illus. 2003. 80p. (J). pap. 7.95 (978-1-4027-0854-1(8)) Sterling Publishing Co., Inc.

—Come to Tea: Fun Tea Party Themes, Recipes, Crafts, Games, Etiquette & More. 2003. (gr. 3-6). lib. bdg. 16.40 (978-0-613-78021-6(3)) Tandem Library Bks.

Dunnington, Rose. Big Snacks, Little Meals: After School, Dinnertime, Anytime. 2006. (Illus.). 112p. (J). (gr. 6 up). 9.95 (978-1-57990-780-8(6), 1252010) Lark Bks.

—Delicious Drinks to Sip, Slurp, Gulp & Guzzle. 2006. (Illus.). 112p. (J). 9.95 (978-1-57990-779-2(2), 1252097) Lark Bks.

Elffers, Joost & Freymann, Saxton. Play with Your Food. 2002. (Illus.). 112p. (J). 9.98 (978-1-58663-230-4(2), MetroBooks) Friedman, Michael Publishing Group, Inc.

Elliott, Lynne. Food & Feasts in the Middle Ages. 2004. (Medieval World Ser.). (Illus.). 32p. pap. (978-0-7787-1380-7(6)); (J). (978-0-7787-1348-7(2)) Crabtree Publishing Co.

Enviornment Canada Staff. Oil, Water & Chocolate Mousse. (Illus.). 28p. (J). pap. 5.95 (978-0-660-15503-6(6)) Canadian Government Publishing CAN. *Dist:* International Specialized Bk. Services.

Erdosh, George. The African American Kitchen: Food for Body & Soul. 1999. (Library of African American Arts & Culture). (Illus.). 64p. (YA). (gr. 7-12). lib. bdg. 26.50 (978-0-8239-1850-8(5), AAKITC) Rosen Publishing Group, Inc., The.

Ericsson, Jennifer A. Gingerbread Houses for Kids. Blair, Beth L., illus. 1998. 64p. (J). (gr. 4 up). pap. 14.95 (978-0-9661204-0-0(X)) White Birch Pr.

Eriksson, Christina Wyss & Collins, Carolyn Strom. Inside the Secret Garden: A Treasury of Crafts, Recipes, & Activities. Collier, Mary & Tudor, Tasha, illus. 2002. 136p. (J). (gr. 3 up). 24.99 (978-0-06-027922-6(2)) HarperCollins Pubs.

Erwin, Vicki B. Scooby-Doo! Groovy Guide to Party Fun. 2002. (Illus.). 32p. (J). (978-0-439-37462-0(6)) Scholastic, Inc.

Evangelista, Gloria. In Search of the Perfect Pumpkin. Shea, Shawn, illus. 2004. 32p. (gr. 4-6). 17.95 (978-1-55591-994-8(4)) Fulcrum Publishing.

Evans, Lynn. Peas & Honey: A Young Persons Guide to Gracious Dining. 1999. (Illus.). (J). (gr. k-5). 10.00 (978-0-9669658-6-5(8)) Poole & Smith Publishing.

Fajardo, Renee & Ruby, Carl. Pinch a Lotta Enchiladas & Other Tummy Tales. Fajardo, Renee & Ruby, Carl, eds. 2002. (Illus.). 104p. (YA). (gr. 4-8). pap. 14.00 (978-0-9724472-0-1(2)) Just Enjoyable Memorable Story Bks.

Falstein, Mark. Welcoming the Sabbath: Creative Projects, Rituals, & Recipes for Kids. Clark Editorial and Design Staff, ed. Parks, Kathy, illus. 1999. 72p. (J). (gr. 1-7). pap. 9.95 (978-0-88160-323-1(6), LW386) Creative Teaching Pr., Inc.

Family Fixin's. 2001. (FAMILY FIXIN'S). vi, 164p. spiral bd. 12.95 (978-0-9714111-0-4(7)) Demerest, Cheryl Carlisle.

Familyfun Magazine, Experts At. What's Cooking? A Cookbook for Kids. Disney Storybook Artists Staff, illus. 2007. 64p. (ps-2). 12.99 (***978-1-4231-0540-4(0)***) Disney Pr.

Farmer, Jacqueline. Bananas! 1999. (gr. k-3). lib. bdg. 15.25 (978-0-613-24034-5(0)) Tandem Library Bks.

Favorite Recipes Press Staff. Big Top Recipes for Little People: The Big Apple Circus Official Cookbook for Kids & Would-Be Kids. 1999. (Illus.). 64p. (ps up). spiral bd. 13.95 (978-0-87197-469-3(X)) Favorite Recipes Pr.

Feely, Jenny. Making Lunch. 1999. (ps-2). lib. bdg. 11.80 (978-0-613-30592-1(2)) Tandem Library Bks.

Fishbein, Susie. Kosher by Design Kids in the Kitchen. Uher, John, photos by. 2005. (Illus.). 192p. (YA). (gr. 4-12). 22.99 (978-1-57819-071-3(1)) Mesorah Pubns., Ltd.

Food Around the World, 10 vols. 1999. 159.80 (978-0-8172-4981-6(8)) Raintree.

Ford, Jean. Latino Cuisine & Its Influence on American Foods: The Taste of Celebration. 2005. (Illus.). 112p. (J). (ps-7). lib. bdg. (978-1-59084-935-4(3), 1234497) Mason Crest Pubs.

Ford, Jean & Libal, Autumn. The Truth about Diets: The Pros & Cons. 2005. (Obesity Ser.). (Illus.). 104p. (J). (ps-7). lib. bdg. 23.95 (978-1-59084-946-0(9)) Mason Crest Pubs.

Foster Children's Favorite Recipes. 2005. spiral bd. 19.95 (978-1-59808-239-5(6)); per. 19.95 (978-1-59808-238-8(8)); cd-rom 13.95 (978-1-59808-240-1(X)) Whispering Pine Pr., Inc.

Francis, Suzanne. How to Make an Egg Swim, Grow Mold, Eat "Ants," & Other Ways to Play with Your Food. 2004. (How to Survive Anything Club Ser.). (Illus.). 80p. (J). (978-0-439-57909-4(0)) Scholastic, Inc.

Frankeny, Frankie & Martin, Wesley. The Star Wars Cook Book 2: Darth Malt & More Galactic Recipes. 2005. (Illus.). 62p. reprint ed. 16.00 (978-0-7567-9543-6(5)) DIANE Publishing Co.

Frankeny, Frankie, et al. The Star Wars Cookbook II Vol. II: Darth Malt & More Galactic Recipes. 2000. (Illus.). 60p. (J). (gr. 3-5). pap. 16.95 (978-0-8118-2803-1(4)) Chronicle Bks. LLC.

Freymann, Saxton. How Are You Peeling? 1999. (J). 159.50 (978-0-439-11733-3(X)) Scholastic, Inc.

Freymann, Saxton & Elffers, Joost. How Are You Peeling? Foods with Moods. 1999. (Illus.). 48p. (J). (ps-3). pap. 16.95 (978-0-439-10431-9(9), Levine, Arthur A. Bks.) Scholastic, Inc.

Galvin, Laura Gates. My First Cookbook: Family Fun in the Kitchen. 2005. (Family Fun Ser.). (Illus.). 40p. (J). (ps-3). 12.99 incl. audio compact disk (978-1-59069-451-0(1), 1A702) Studio Mouse LLC.

Germaine, Elizabeth & Burckhardt, Ann. Cooking the Australian Way. 2nd rev. ed. 2004. (Easy Menu Ethnic Cookbooks). (Illus.). 72p. (J). (gr. 5-12). 25.26 (978-0-8225-4101-1(7)) Lerner Publishing Group.

Gibson, Ray. Easter Activities. (Activity Bks.). (Illus.). 32p. (J). pap. 6.95 (978-0-7460-4234-2(5)) EDC Publishing.

—What Shall I Cook? Barlow, Amanda, illus. rev. ed. 2002. 32p. (J). pap. 7.95 (978-0-7945-0374-1(8), Usborne) EDC Publishing.

Gillies, Judi & Glossop, Jennifer. The Jumbo Vegetarian Cookbook. Phillips, Louise, illus. unabr. ed. 2002. (Jumbo Bks.). 256p. (J). (gr. 4-6). (978-1-55074-977-9(3)) Kids Can Pr., Ltd.

—Kids Can Press Jumbo Cookbook. Phillips, Louise, illus. 2000. 256p. (J). (gr. 4-7). lib. bdg. 24.55 (978-0-613-83963-1(3)) Tandem Library Bks.

—The Kids Can Press Jumbo Cookbook. Phillips, Louise, illus. unabr. ed. 2000. (Jumbo Bks.). 256p. (J). (gr. 4-6). (978-1-55074-621-1(9)) Kids Can Pr., Ltd.

Gilpin, Rebecca. Little Children's Cookbook. 2005. 96p. (J). 7.95 (978-0-7945-1113-5(9), Usborne) EDC Publishing.

Gilpin, Rebecca & Atkinson, Catherine. Easter Cooking. 2003. 32p. (J). pap. 6.95 (978-0-7945-0412-0(4), Usborne) EDC Publishing.

—Fairy Cooking. 2004. (Children's Cooking Ser.). (Illus.). 32p. (Orig.). (J). pap. 6.95 (978-0-7945-0633-9(X), Usborne) EDC Publishing.

—Yummy Little Cookbook. 2004. (Children's Cooking Ser.). 96p. (J). 7.95 (978-0-7945-0676-6(3), Usborne) EDC Publishing.

Gioffre, Rosalba. The Young Chef's Italian Cookbook: Step-by-Step Fun Recipes for Young Chefs. 2001. (I'm the Chef! Ser.). (Illus.). 32p. (J). (gr. 3). pap. (978-0-7787-0293-1(6)) Crabtree Publishing Co.

Gold, Rozanne. Kids Cook 1-2-3: Recipes for Young Chefs Using Only 3 Ingredients. Pinto, Sara, illus. 2006. 144p. (J). (gr. 3-6). 17.95 (978-1-58234-735-6(2)) Bloomsbury Publishing.

Golosi, Rosanne. Best Friends Forever! Martini, Angela, illus. 2005. 64p. (J). (***978-0-439-80072-3(2)***) Scholastic, Inc.

The Good Book Cookbook. 2004. 64p. (J). pap. 9.99 (978-0-88724-216-8(2) , CD-2037) Carson-Dellosa Publishing Co., Inc.

Good Cookin' Runs in the Family: Favorite Recipes from the Race King & Mary Pauline Wilson Family. 2000. (978-0-9727291-0-9(0)) Swonke, Cheryl.

Gooseberry Patch Staff. M878 Kids in the Kitchen: Recipes for Fun. 2007. (ENG., Illus.). 80p. spiral bd. 16.95 (***978-1-933494-04-3(2)***) Gooseberry Patch.

Gourmet in a Pinch: A Cook Book for Busy People Who Are Passionate about Food. 2002. per. 16.95 (978-0-9723016-0-2(7)) Huffman, Wendie.

Gourmet with Google. 2004. (YA). per. (978-0-9754307-2-9(6)) Avant Garde Publishing.

Gow, Emma-Lee. The Giant Kid's Cookbook. 2002. (Illus.). 32p. (YA). pap. 13.99 (978-0-09-188790-2(9) , Ebury Pr.) Ebury Publishing GBR. *Dist:* Trafalgar Square Publishing.

Graimes, Nicola. Healthy Cooking for Kids!: 50 Fun Recipe Cards: 50 Fun Recipe Cards. 2008. 50p. (J). (gr. 2-5). 15.99 (***978-0-7566-3743-9(0)***) Dorling Kindersley Publishing, Inc.

Grant, Amanda. Kids' Kitchen: Good Food Made Easy. Yorke, Francesca, photos by. 2007. (Illus.). 176p. (gr. 5-9). pap. 14.95 (978-1-84533-316-4(0) , Mitchell Beazley) Octopus Publishing Group GBR. *Dist:* Sterling Publishing Co., Inc.

Green, Bessie. How to Make Fish Strips. Nevak, Caroline, illus. l.t. ed. 1999. 12p. (J). (gr. k-3). pap. 17.00 (978-1-58084-072-9(8)) Lower Kuskokwim Schl. District.

—Neqliller Pinwaneg Iqallugneg (How to Make Fish Strips) Nevak, Caroline, illus. l.t. ed. 1999. (ESK.). 12p. (J). (gr. k-3). pap. 17.00 (978-1-58084-107-8(4)) Lower Kuskokwim Schl. District.

Greenfield, Tonya. Nonnie's Kitchen: Fun & Food in the Kitchen with Kids. 2nd ed. 2005. (Illus.). 132p. (J). reprint ed. per. 16.95 (978-0-9768884-1-3(6)) M2M Partners.

Greenfield, Tonya G. Nonnies Kitchen Fun & Food in the Kitchen with Kids. 2005. 132p. (YA). spiral bd. 16.95 (978-0-9768884-0-6(8) , 65,000) M2M Partners.

Gregg, Sue & Barnes, Emilie. Lunches & Snacks: With Lessons for Children. 2nd rev. ed. 2000. (Eating Better Cookbooks: Basic Set: Vol. 4). (Illus.). 193p. (J). (gr. 2-12). spiral bd. 14.00 (978-1-878272-03-4(9)) Gregg, Sue Cookbooks.

Griffin, Vicki & Griffin, Gina. Guilt-Free Gourmet: A Vegan Cookbook & Lifestyle Resource Manual. Griffin, Dane, ed. 1999. (Illus.). 400p. (YA). spiral bd. 19.95 (978-1-891041-25-9(8)) LifeLine Bks.

Grolier Educational Staff, contrib. by. Crafts for Kids, 16 vols. 2003. (Illus.). (J). (978-0-7172-5760-7(6) , Grolier) Scholastic Library Publishing.

Guhin, Paula. Can We Eat the Art? Incredible Edibles & Art You Can't Eat. Schimmell, David, illus. 2001. 80p. (J). (gr. k-8). pap. 9.95 (978-0-86530-471-0(8) , IP #280-0) Incentive Pubns., Inc.

Hale, Bruce. Chet Gecko's Detective Handbook (and Cookbook) Tips for Private Eyes & Snack Food Lovers. 2005. (Chet Gecko Mystery Ser.). (Illus.). 272p. (J). (ps-7). spiral bd. 9.95 (978-0-15-205288-1(7)) Harcourt Children's Bks.

Hall, Margaret. El Cacahuate. 2003. (Alimentos Ser.).Tr. of Peanuts. (Illus.). 32p. (J). lib. bdg. 22.79 (978-1-4034-3737-2(8)) Heinemann Library.

—El Maiz. 2003. (Alimentos Ser.).Tr. of Corn. (SPA & ENG., Illus.). 32p. (J). lib. bdg. 22.79 (978-1-4034-3735-8(1)) Heinemann Library.

Hall, Margaret C. Corn. 2003. (Food Ser.). (Illus.). 32p. (J). (gr. k-2). lib. bdg. 22.79 (978-1-58810-617-9(9)) Heinemann Library.

—Peanuts. 2003. (Food Ser.). (Illus.). 32p. (J). (gr. k-2). lib. bdg. 22.79 (978-1-58810-619-3(5)) Heinemann Library.

Hansen, Mark Victor, et al. Chicken Soup for the Soul Kids in the Kitchen: Tasty Recipes & Fun Activities for Budding Chefs. 2007. (Chicken Soup for the Soul (Paperback Health Communications) Ser.). (Illus.). 248p. per. 19.95 (***978-0-7573-0579-5(2)***) Health Communications, Inc.

Harcourt School Publishers Staff. Hold the Anchovies: Library Book. 3rd ed. 2002. (Trophies Reading Program Ser.). (Illus.). pap. 13.50 (978-0-15-326526-6(4)) Harcourt Schl. Pubs.

—What's Cooking. 3rd ed. 2002. (Trophies English Language Learners Ser.). (Illus.). pap. 5.10 (978-0-15-327638-5(X)) Harcourt Schl. Pubs.

—What's Cooking, Khufu? On Level. 3rd ed. 2002. (Trophies Reading Program Ser.). (Illus.). pap. 5.10 (978-0-15-323443-9(1)) Harcourt Schl. Pubs.

Hardesty, Constance. Grow Your Own Pizza: Gardening Plans & Recipes for Kids. McClung, Jeff, illus. 2004. 128p. (gr. 4-7). pap. 16.95 (978-1-55591-398-4(9)) Fulcrum Publishing.

Harvey, Gill. Starting Cooking - Internet Linked. 2005. 32p. (J). pap. 4.95 (978-0-7945-0666-7(6) , Usborne) EDC Publishing.

—Starting Cooking Kid Kit. 2005. 32p. (J). 14.99 (978-1-58086-744-3(8) , Usborne) EDC Publishing.

Hawkins, Linda J. Catering to Children: With Recipes for Memorable Tea Parties. Yonts, Barbara, photos by. 2003. (Illus.). 56p. (J). (gr. k-5). 19.99 (978-0-9742806-0-8(7)) Heart to Heart Publishing.

Hazelton, Jack W. Grandma Claus' Rolling Pin. Hazelton, Jack W., illus. l.t. ed. 2002. (Illus.). 48p. (J). 14.95 (978-1-928907-53-4(9)) Jack's Bookshelf, Inc.

Head, Honor. Dairy. 2006. (QEB What's for Lunch? Ser.). (Illus.). 32p. (J). lib. bdg. 19.95 (978-1-59566-197-5(2)) QEB Publishing Inc.

Heap, Will & Dunne, Kevin, photos by. The Kids' Cookbook. 2006. (Illus.). 128p. 9.95 (***978-1-85626-626-0(5)***) Cathie, Kyle Ltd. GBR. *Dist:* Independent Pubs. Group.

Hershberger, Fannie. Kinder Kookin' Amish Children Share Their Own Recipes. 216p. spiral bd. 7.95 (978-0-9725806-0-1(3)) Hershberger, Ivan & Fannie.

Hickson, Christine. Macaroni & Cheese, Hot Dogs & Peas. Koehler, Ed, illus. 2000. (ENG.). 34p. (J). (ps-k). bds. 7.99 (978-0-570-07044-3(9)) Concordia Publishing Hse.

Hill, Mary. In the Kitchen, 6 vols., Set. 2004. (Illus.). 24p. (J). (ps-2). 87.00 (978-0-516-29310-3(9)) Scholastic Library Publishing.

—Let's Make a Sandwich. 2002. (Welcome Bks.). (Illus.). 24p. (J). (ps-2). pap. 4.95 (978-0-516-24017-6(X) , Children's Pr.) Scholastic Library Publishing.

—Let's Make Pizza. 2002. (Welcome Bks.). (Illus.). 24p. (J). (ps-2). pap. 4.95 (978-0-516-24020-6(X) , Children's Pr.) Scholastic Library Publishing.

—Let's Make Pizza. 2002. (gr. k-3). lib. bdg. 12.95 (978-0-613-58785-3(5)) Tandem Library Bks.

Holiday Cookbooks from Around the World, 4 bks., Set. Incl. Chinese Cookbook. Thompson, Stuart. lib. bdg. 25.69 (978-0-7398-3262-2(X)); Christian Cookbook. Pirotta, Saviour. Sloan, Frank, ed. (gr. 4-7). lib. bdg. 25.69 (978-0-7398-3263-9(8)); Hindu Cookbook. Marchant, Kerena. Mukhida, Zul, illus. (gr. 4-7). lib. bdg. 25.69 (978-0-7398-3264-6(6)); Jewish Cookbook. Randall, Ronne. Mukhida, Zul, illus. (gr. 4-7). lib. bdg. 25.69 (978-0-7398-3265-3(4)); 32p. (J). 2001. Set lib. bdg. 102.76 (978-0-7398-3266-0(2)) Raintree.

Hood, Karen Jean Matsko. Holiday Cookbook for Foster Families. 2002. 15.95 (978-1-59210-460-4(6)); cd-rom 13.95 (978-1-59210-484-0(3)) Whispering Pine Pr., Inc.

—Holiday Gifts-in-a-Jar Cookbook. 2005. cd-rom 13.95 (978-1-59210-655-4(2)) Whispering Pine Pr., Inc.

—Hood & Matsko Family Cookbook Vol. 1: Aka O'Hood & Macko Family, Our Favorite Recipes-Vol. I, 2006. cd-rom 13.95 (978-1-59210-673-8(0)) Whispering Pine Pr., Inc.

—Hood & Matsko Family Cookbook Vol. 2: Aka O'Hood & Macko Family, Our Favorite Recipes-Vol. I. 2006. 19.95 (978-1-59210-669-1(2)) Whispering Pine Pr., Inc.

—Hood & Matsko Family Cookbook Our Favorite Recipes Vol. 2: Aka O'Hood & Macko Family Cookbook. 2005. 24.95 (978-1-59210-672-1(2)) Whispering Pine Pr., Inc.

—Hood & Matsko Family Cookbook Volume II Vol. 2: Aka O'Hood & Macko Family Cookbook. 2005. cd-rom 13.95 (978-1-59210-671-4(4)) Whispering Pine Pr., Inc.

—Hood & Matsko Family Favorite Christmas Sweets: Annual Edition 2002. 2002. 15.95 (978-1-59210-538-0(6)); cd-rom 13.95 (978-1-59210-539-7(4)) Whispering Pine Pr., Inc.

—Hood & Matsko Family Holiday & Birthday Menu Cookbook: 2002. annual 2002. 19.95 (978-1-59210-659-2(5)) Whispering Pine Pr., Inc.

—Hood & Matsko Family Holiday & Birthday Menu Cookbook: Annual Edition 2002. 2002. (Illus.). cd-rom 13.95 (978-1-59210-660-8(9)) Whispering Pine Pr., Inc.

—Hood & Matsko Family Sunday Menu Cookbook: Annual Edition 2002. 2002. 15.95 (978-1-59210-662-2(5)); cd-rom 13.95 (978-1-59210-664-6(1)) Whispering Pine Pr., Inc.

—Hood Family Dessert Cookbook. 2003. ring bd. 24.95 (978-1-930948-68-6(9)) Whispering Pine Pr., Inc.

—Hood Family Ethnic Cookbook. 2003. ring bd. 24.95 (978-1-930948-69-3(7)) Whispering Pine Pr., Inc.

—Hood Family Favorite Restaurants Menu Cookbook: Annual Edition 2002. 2002. 15.95 (978-1-59210-502-1(5)); cd-rom 13.95 (978-1-59210-503-8(3)) Whispering Pine Pr., Inc.

—Hood Family Heritage Cookbook. 2003. ring bd. 24.95 (978-1-930948-70-9(0)) Whispering Pine Pr., Inc.

—Hood Family Kids Cookbook. 2003. ring bd. 24.95 (978-1-930948-72-3(7)) Whispering Pine Pr., Inc.

—Hood Family Vegetarian Cookbook. 2003. ring bd. 24.95 (978-1-930948-73-0(5)) Whispering Pine Pr., Inc.

Hopkinson, Deborah. Fannie in the Kitchen: The Whole Story from Soup to Nuts of How Fannie Farmer Invented Recipes with Precise Measurements. Carpenter, Nancy, illus. 40p. (J). (ps-4). 2001. 16.00 (978-0-689-81965-0(X) , Atheneum/Anne Schwartz Bks.); 2004. reprint ed. 7.99 (978-0-689-86997-6(5) , Aladdin) Simon & Schuster Children's Publishing.

Houts, Amy. Cooking Around the Calendar with Kids: Holiday & Seasonal Food & Fun. Willson, Terri, illus. 2002. 128p. 24.95 (978-0-930643-14-0(3)); 2nd ed. 2001. 125p. (J). otabind 12.95 (978-0-930643-12-6(7)) Images Unlimited.

Hubbard, L. P. A Little Book for a Little Cook. 2004. (Illus.). 32p. reprint ed. 8.95 (978-1-55709-171-0(4)) Applewood Bks.

Hughes, Helga. Cooking the Austrian Way. 2nd rev. ed. 2004. (Easy Menu Ethnic Cookbooks). (Illus.). 72p. (J). (gr. 5-12). 25.26 (978-0-8225-4102-8(5)) Lerner Publishing Group.

Hughes, Meredith Sayles. Green Power: Leaf & Flower Vegetables. 2005. (Plants We Eat Ser.). (Illus.). 104p. (gr. 6-9). 26.60 (978-0-8225-2839-5(8)) Lerner Publishing Group.

—Hard to Crack: Nut Trees. 2005. (Plants We Eat Ser.). (Illus.). 104p. (gr. 6-9). 26.60 (978-0-8225-2838-8(X)) Lerner Publishing Group.

—Spill the Beans & Pass the Peanuts: Legumes. 1999. (Plants We Eat Ser.). (Illus.). 104p. (gr. 6-9). 26.60 (978-0-8225-2834-0(7)) Lerner Publishing Group.

Hunter, Dette. 38 Ways to Entertain Your Babysitter. MacEachern, Stephen, illus. 2003. 48p. (J). (ps-4). pap., act. bk. ed. 9.95 (978-1-55037-794-1(9)); lib. bdg., act. bk. ed. 19.95 (978-1-55037-795-8(7)) Annick Pr., Ltd. CAN. *Dist:* Firefly Bks., Ltd.

—38 Ways to Entertain Your Grandparents. Betteridge, Deirdre, illus. 2002. 48p. (J). (ps-4). pap., act. bk. ed. 9.95 (978-1-55037-748-4(5)); lib. bdg., act. bk. ed. 19.95 (978-1-55037-749-1(3)) Annick Pr., Ltd. CAN. *Dist:* Firefly Bks., Ltd.

Hupp, Abby. A Wizard in the Kitchen: Magical recipes for Kids of All Ages. 2006. (YA). spiral bd. 13.99 (978-0-9785798-0-7(1)) Plan B Bks.

Ibbs, Katharine. I Can Cook! Recipe Card Set. 2007. 50p. (J). (gr. 2-4). 15.99 (978-0-7566-2990-8(X)) Dorling Kindersley Publishing, Inc.

I'm a Chef, 6 Packs. (Literatura 2000 Ser.). (gr. 2-3). 33.00 (978-0-7635-0263-8(4)) Rigby Education.

I'm the Chef!, 4 bks. Incl. Young Chef's Chinese Cookbook : Step-by-Step Fun Recipes for Young Chefs. Lee, Frances. (978-0-7787-0280-1(4)); Young Chef's French Cookbook : Step-by-Step Fun Recipes for Young Chefs. Gioffre, Rosalba. (978-0-7787-0282-5(0)); Young Chef's Italian Cookbook : Step-by-Step Fun Recipes for Young Chefs. Gioffre, Rosalba. (978-0-7787-0279-5(0)); Young Chef's Mexican Cookbook : Step-by-Step Fun Recipes for Young Chefs. Ward, Karen. (978-0-7787-0281-8(2)); 32p. (J). (gr. 3). 2001. (Illus.). 2001. (978-0-7787-0278-8(2)); Set pap. (978-0-7787-0292-4(8)) Crabtree Publishing Co.

In Nonna's Kitchen: Individual Title Six-Packs. (ps-2). 23.00 (978-0-7635-8996-7(9)) Rigby Education.

Irvine, Pru. Easy Peasy All the Time: More Real Food for Kids Who Want to Cook. 2001. (Illus.). 128p. (J). 24.99 (978-0-09-187782-8(2) , Ebury Pr.) Ebury Publishing GBR. *Dist:* Independent Pubs. Group.

Iselin, Tom. The Bread of Life: For the Table ... for Eternity, 2004. 300p. pap. 25.00 (978-0-9649139-7-4(6) , 964913976) Pelican Lake Pr.

Jacques, Brian. The Redwall Cookbook. Denise, Christopher, illus. 2005. 104p. (J). (gr. 1-5). pap. 24.99 (978-0-399-23791-1(7) , Philomel) Penguin Group (USA) Inc.

Johnson Foote, Barbara. Cup Cooking: Individual Child-Portion Picture Recipes. Plemons, Betty, illus. exp. rev. ed. 1998. (J). (ps up). pap. 6.50 (978-0-9604390-3-4(X)) Early Educators Pr.

Jones, Carol. Honey. 2002. (From Farm to You Ser.). (Illus.). 32p. (gr. 4-8). 28.00 (978-0-7910-7009-3(3) , Chelsea Hse.) Facts On File, Inc.

—Pasta & Noodles. 2002. (From Farm to You Ser.). (Illus.). 32p. (gr. 4-8). 28.00 (978-0-7910-7004-8(2) , Chelsea Hse.) Facts On File, Inc.

—Sausage. 2002. (From Farm to You Ser.). (Illus.). 32p. (gr. 4-8). 28.00 (978-0-7910-7006-2(9) , Chelsea Hse.) Facts On File, Inc.

Joyal, Kristen. Baking with Mommy Cookbook: Recipes for Kid-Size Ovens. 2002. (Illus.). 96p. spiral bd. 11.95 (978-0-9718515-2-8(2)) Straight Forward Technologies.

Julius, Jennifer. I Like Pasta. 2001. (gr. k-3). lib. bdg. 12.95 (978-0-613-52090-4(4)) Tandem Library Bks.

Junior League of Tyler, Texas Staff, contrib. by. Ring Around the Rosie: A Collection of Children's Recipes. 2007. (Illus.). 176p. (J). (***978-0-9607122-2-9(4)***) Junior League of Tyler, Inc., The.

Just for Kids: Favorite All Time Recipes. 2003. (Illus.). 96p. spiral bd. (978-0-7853-9489-1(3)) Publications International, Ltd.

Kalman, Bobbie. Breakfast Blast. 2003. (gr. 3-6). lib. bdg. 17.60 (978-0-613-59123-2(2)) Tandem Library Bks.

—Delicious Desserts. 2003. (Kid Power Ser.). (Illus.). 32p. (J). pap. (978-0-7787-1276-3(1)); (gr. 3). (978-0-7787-1254-1(0)) Crabtree Publishing Co.

—Delicious Desserts. 2003. (gr. 3-6). lib. bdg. 17.60 (978-0-613-70815-9(6)) Tandem Library Bks.

—Lunch Munch. 2003. (Illus.). 32p. (J). (gr. 4-7). lib. bdg. 17.60 (978-0-613-59132-4(1)) Tandem Library Bks.

—Lunch Munch: Step-by-Step Recipes. 2003. (Kid Power Ser.). (Illus.). 32p. (J). (gr. 3). (978-0-7787-1251-0(6)); pap. (978-0-7787-1273-2(7)) Crabtree Publishing Co.

—Super Snacks. 2003. (gr. 3-6). lib. bdg. 17.60 (978-0-613-59139-3(9)) Tandem Library Bks.

—Super Snacks: Step-by-Step Recipes. 2003. (Kid Power Ser.). (Illus.). 32p. (J). (gr. 3). (978-0-7787-1252-7(4)); pap. (978-0-7787-1274-9(5)) Crabtree Publishing Co.

Kalman, Bobbie & Brown, Ellen. The Colonial Cook. 2001. (Colonial People Ser.). (Illus.). 32p. (J). (gr. 3). (978-0-7787-0748-6(2)); pap. (978-0-7787-0794-3(6)) Crabtree Publishing Co.

Kann, Bob. A Recipe for Success: Lizzie Kander & Her Cookbook. 2006. (Badger Biographies Ser.). (Illus.). 144p. (J). pap. 12.95 (978-0-87020-373-2(8)) Wisconsin Historical Society.

Katzen, Mollie. Honest Pretzels: And 64 Other Amazing Recipes for Kids. 2004. (Illus.). 192p. (J). (gr. 3-7). 19.95 (978-1-883672-88-1(0) , Tricycle Pr.) Ten Speed Pr.

—Salad People & More Real Recipes: A New Cookbook for Preschoolers & Up. 2005. (Illus.). 93p. (J). (ps-7). 17.95 (978-1-58246-141-0(4) , Tricycle Pr.) Ten Speed Pr.

Katzen, Mollie & Henderson, Ann. Pretend Soup & Other Real Recipes: A Cookbook for Preschoolers & Up. Katzen, Mollie, illus. 2004. (Illus.). 96p. (J). (ps-3). tchr. ed. 17.95 (978-1-883672-06-5(6) , Tricycle Pr.) Ten Speed Pr.

Kaufman, Cheryl Davidson. Cooking the Caribbean Way. (Easy Menu Ethnic Cookbooks). (Illus.). (J). (gr. 5-9). 1998. 48p. 19.93 (978-0-8225-0920-2(2) , Lerner Pubns.); 2nd rev. expurg. ed. 2002. 72p. 25.26 (978-0-8225-4103-5(3)) Lerner Publishing Group.

Kaur, Sharon. Food in India. 2000. (International Food Library). (Illus.). 24p. (J). (gr. 3-6). lib. bdg. 26.60 (978-0-86625-339-0(4)) Rourke Publishing, LLC.

Keene, Carolyn. The Nancy Drew Cookbook. 2000. (YA). 19.95 (978-0-8488-2860-8(7)) Amereon LTD.

—The Nancy Drew Cookbook: Clues to Good Cooking. 2005. (Nancy Drew Mystery Stories). (Illus.). 144p. (J). (gr. 3-8). 9.99 (978-0-448-43984-6(0) , Grosset & Dunlap) Penguin Group (USA) Inc.

Key Ingredients: Opening Doors to Hours of Happiness. 2002. 310p. 23.95 (978-0-9722730-0-8(X)) Le Bonheur Club, Inc.

Kids' Cooking: Great Recipes Kids Will Love to Cook. 2002. 64p. (J). pap. 14.98 (978-0-7525-8871-1(0)) Parragon, Inc.

Kids' Favorite Classroom Treats. 2004. (Illus.). 192p. (J). (978-1-4127-2016-8(8)) Publications International, Ltd.

Kids in the Kitchen: A Cookbook of Yummy Foods That Kids Can Easily Prepare. 2001. 128p. per. 10.95 (978-0-9701466-9-4(8)) Athenean Pr., Inc.

Kim, Jeannie. Body & Mind: A Guide to Life. 2003. (gr. 3-6). lib. bdg. 12.40 (978-0-613-72134-9(9)) Tandem Library Bks.

Kindersley, Dorling. 1St Cooking Act Bk. 2008. 48p. (J). (gr. 3). ring bd. 9.99 (***978-0-7566-3503-9(9)***) Dorling Kindersley Publishing, Inc.

Kingham, Jennifer L. Cooking Kids! 2002. (gr. 3-6). lib. bdg. 19.90 (978-0-613-86664-4(9)) Tandem Library Bks.

—Cooking Kids! 2002. (ENG.). 20.95 (***978-0-595-65355-3(3));*** 130p. pap. 10.95 (978-0-595-25815-4(8)) iUniverse, Inc. (Writers Club Pr.).

Kishel, Ann-Marie. Cook. 2007. (First Step Nonfiction Ser.). (J). pap. (978-0-8225-6844-5(6)) Lerner Publishing Group.

Konemann Staff. Fast Food for Kids. 2000. (Illus.). (J). pap. 1.95 (978-3-8290-2365-8(0) , 771110) Konemann.

—New Kids' Cookbook. 1999. (Mini Cook Bks.). (Illus.). 64p. (gr. 3-7). pap. 1.95 (978-3-8290-1613-1(1) , 770115) Konemann.

Krizmanic, Judy. Teen's Vegetarian Cookbook. 1999. (978-0-606-18454-0(6)); (gr. 7-12). lib. bdg. 18.80 (978-0-613-15216-7(6)) Tandem Library Bks.

Kushner, Malcolm. California Squisine: Healthy Food That's Fast, Fun & Squeezable for Kids. 2006. (Illus.). 112p. (J). pap. 11.95 (978-1-931741-67-5(0)) Reed, Robert D. Pubs.

Labat, Yancey C., illus. S'mores, Shakes & Chocolate Cakes: Chocolate, Chocolate All Day Long. 2006. 56p. (J). (***978-0-439-83226-7(8)***) Scholastic, Inc.

Lagasse, Emeril. Emeril's There's a Chef in My Family! Recipes to Get Everybody Cooking. Yuen, Charles, illus. Bacon, Quentin, photos by. 2004. 224p. (YA). (gr. 3-6). 22.99 (978-0-06-000439-2(8)) HarperCollins Pubs.

—Emeril's There's a Chef in My Soup! Recipes for the Kid in Everyone. Yuen, Charles, illus. 2002. 256p. (J). 22.99 (978-0-688-17706-5(9)) HarperCollins Pubs.

Landau, Elaine. Popcorn. Lies, Brian, illus. 2003. 32p. (J). 16.95 (978-1-57091-442-3(7)); pap. 6.95 (978-1-57091-443-0(5)) Charlesbridge Publishing, Inc.

Langston, Laura. Abuelita, te Acuerdas? Gardiner, Lindsey, illus. 2004. Tr. of Mile High Apple Pie. (SPA.). (J). 18.99 (978-84-488-1911-8(X)) Beascoa, Ediciones S.A. ESP. *Dist:* Lectorum Pubns., Inc.

Lee, Sandra. Semi-Homemade Cool Kids' Cooking. 2006. (Illus.). 144p. spiral bd. 16.95 (978-0-696-23265-7(0)) Meredith Bks.

Legacy Press Staff. Gobble up the Bible: Cookbook for Kids. 1998. (Illus.). 192p. (J). (gr. k-7). pap. 14.99 (978-1-885358-59-2(8) , LP46811, Legacy Pr.) Rainbow Pubs. & Legacy Pr.

Lehman-Wilzig, Tami. Tasty Bible Stories: A Menu of Tales & Matching Recipes. Kahn, Katherine Janus, illus. 2003. 64p. (J). (gr. 2 up). pap. 10.95 (978-1-58013-080-6(1)) Kar-Ben Publishing.

Levy, Janey. Recipes for a Medieval Feast: Working Flexibly with Fractions. 2006. (Math for the Real World Ser.). (Illus.). 32p. (J). pap. (978-1-4042-6061-0(7)); lib. bdg. (978-1-4042-3354-6(7)) Rosen Publishing Group, Inc., The.

Lewis, Carole. New First Place Favorites. 2004. 19.99 (978-0-8307-3231-9(4) , Gospel Light) Gospel Light Pubns.

Lewis, Sara. Kids' Baking: Over 60 Delicious Recipes for Children to Make. 2006. (Illus.). 144p. (J). pap. 12.95 (978-0-600-61501-9(4) , Hamlyn) Octopus Publishing Group GBR. *Dist:* Sterling Publishing Co., Inc.

Libal, Joyce, compiled by. Midwest. 2005. (American Regional Cooking Library). (Illus.). 72p. (J). lib. bdg. (978-1-59084-616-2(8)) Mason Crest Pubs.

Liddy, Michael. Kid's Cooking in the Kitchen. 2006. 80p. 6.95 (978-1-58581-019-2(3)) Golden West Pubs.

Lilly, Melinda. Olives. 2001. (Around the World with Food & Spices Ser.). (Illus.). 32p. (J). (gr. 3-5). lib. bdg. 26.60 (978-1-58952-044-8(0)) Rourke Publishing, LLC.

—Oranges. 2001. (Around the World with Food & Spices Ser.). (Illus.). 32p. (J). (gr. 3-5). lib. bdg. 26.60 (978-1-58952-045-5(9)) Rourke Publishing, LLC.

—Peanuts. 2001. (Around the World with Food & Spices Ser.). (Illus.). 32p. (J). (gr. 3-5). lib. bdg. 26.60 (978-1-58952-046-2(7)) Rourke Publishing, LLC.

—Rice. 2001. (Around the World with Food & Spices Ser.). (Illus.). 32p. (J). (gr. 3-5). lib. bdg. 26.60 (978-1-58952-047-9(5)) Rourke Publishing, LLC.

Linder, Dorothy Perillo. A Vegetable Collection: Recipes & Rhymes to Conquer Kids of All Ages. 2007. 35.00 (***978-0-9753334-2-6(9)***) Sanctuary Bks.

Linton, Marilyn. Just Desserts: And Other Treats for Kids to Make. Reid, Barbara, illus. 1998. 64p. (J). (ps-ps). lib. bdg. 12.95 (978-0-613-16368-2(0)) Tandem Library Bks.

Locricchio, Matthew. The Cooking of India. 2003. (Superchef Ser.). (Illus.). 80p. (J). 29.93 (978-0-7614-1730-9(3) , Benchmark Bks.) Cavendish, Marshall Corp.

CD

Low, Jennifer A. Kitchen for Kids: 100 Amazing Recipes Your Children Can Really Make. 2004. (Illus.). 144p. pap. 19.95 (978-1-55285-455-6(8)) Whitecap Bks., Ltd. CAN. *Dist:* Firefly Bks., Ltd.

MacLeod, Elizabeth. Bake It & Build It. Walker, Tracy, illus. (Kids Can Do It Ser.). (J). (gr. 4-6). 2004. 40p. (978-1-55337-754-2(0)); 1998. 134p. (978-1-55074-427-9(5)) Kids Can Pr., Ltd.

—Chock Full of Chocolate. Bradford, June, illus. 2005. 40p. (J). (gr. 3). (978-1-55337-763-4(X)); (978-1-55337-762-7(1)) Kids Can Pr., Ltd.

—Gifts to Make & Eat. Bradford, June, illus. 2001. (Kids Can Do It Ser.). 40p. (J). (gr. 4-6). (978-1-55074-958-8(7)) Kids Can Pr., Ltd.

—Gifts to Make & Eat. Bradford, June et al, illus. 2001. (Kids Can Do It Ser.). 40p. (J). (gr. 4-6). (978-1-55074-956-4(0)) Kids Can Pr., Ltd.

—Gifts to Make & Eat. 2001. (gr. 3-6). lib. bdg. 14.10 (978-0-613-50798-1(3)) Tandem Library Bks.

Madavan, Vijay. Cooking the Indian Way. 2nd ed. (Easy Menu Ethnic Cookbooks). (Illus.). 72p. (J). (gr. 5-12). 2003. pap. 7.95 (978-0-8225-0534-1(7)); 2002. 25.26 (978-0-8225-4110-3(6) , Lerner Pubns.) Lerner Publishing Group.

Make your own Cakes & Cookies. 2004. (How 2 Kits Ser.). (Illus.). 48p. (J). (978-1-84229-936-4(0)) Top That! Publishing PLC.

Making Pizza with Math: Second Grade Guided Reading Level I. (On Our Way to English Ser.). (gr. 2 up). 34.50 (978-0-7578-7087-3(2)) Rigby Education.

Marchant, Kerena. Hindu Cookbook. Mukhida, Zul, illus. 2001. (Holiday Cookbooks from Around the World). 32p. (J). (gr. 4-7). lib. bdg. 25.69 (978-0-7398-3264-6(6)) Raintree.

Markle, Sandra. Smart about Chocolate. Harper, Charise Mericle, illus. 2004. (Smart about History Ser.). 32p. (J). (gr. k-5). pap. 5.99 (978-0-448-43480-3(6) , Grosset & Dunlap) Penguin Group (USA) Inc.

Marsh, Carole. Classroom Cooking! E-Z, Fun, Healthy, Education, Historical Things to Cook up Right in the Classroom. 2001. (Here & Now Series!). (Illus.). 48p. (J). (gr. 1-6). pap. 7.95 (978-0-635-00266-2(3)) Gallopade International.

—Kitchen House. 2002. 36p. (gr. 3-8). pap. 7.95 (978-0-635-01581-5(1)) Gallopade International.

Martineau, Susan. Gruesome Grub & Disgusting Dishes: Deliciously Edible Recipes! Ursell, Martin, illus. 2000. 32p. (J). (gr. 2-7). pap. 6.95 (978-0-7373-0428-2(6) , 04286W, Roxbury Park Juvenile) Lowell Hse. Juvenile.

Matt, F. Cooking, Vegetarian Cooking, Pizza & Pasta, Cakes & Cookies. 2004. (Cooking School Ser.). (Illus.), 195p. (J). pap. 19.95 (978-0-7945-0353-6(5)) EDC Publishing.

—Pasta & Pizza for Beginners. rev. ed. 2004. (Cooking School Ser.). (Illus.). 48p. (J). pap. 7.95 (978-0-7945-0555-4(4)) EDC Publishing.

Mattern, Joanne. Chefs. 2002. (Reading Power Ser.). (Illus.). 24p. (J). (gr. 1). lib. bdg. 17.25 (978-0-8239-5982-2(1) , PowerKids Pr.) Rosen Publishing Group, Inc., The.

—Cocineros. 2004. (Trabajo en Grupo Ser.). (SPA & ENG., Illus.). 24p. (J). (gr. 3-6). lib. bdg. 17.25 (978-0-8239-6841-1(3) , Buenas Letra) Rosen Publishing Group, Inc., The.

—I Use Math in the Kitchen. 2005. (Illus.). 24p. (J). pap. (978-0-8368-4864-9(0)); lib. bdg. 19.33 (978-0-8368-4857-1(8)) Stevens, Gareth Inc.

—I Use Math in the Kitchen: Uso Las Matematicas en la Cocina. 2005. (Illus.). 24p. (SPA.). (978-0-8368-6009-2(8)); (ENG & SPA., lib. bdg. 19.33 (978-0-8368-6002-3(0)) Stevens, Gareth Inc.

Matthews, Rupert. Cooking a Meal. 2000. (Everyday History Ser.). (Illus.). (J). (978-0-606-20615-0(9)) Tandem Library Bks.

Maxwell, Sarah. I Can Cook: How to Cook Activity Projects for the Very Young. 2000. (Show Me How Ser.). (Illus.). 48p. (ps-2). pap. 7.95 (978-0-7548-0096-5(2)) Anness Publishing, Inc.

Mayer, Marianna. The Mother Goose Cookbook: Rhymes & Recipes for the Very Young. Schwartz, Carol, illus. 1998. 37p. (J). (ps-3). 11.95 (978-0-688-15242-0(2)) HarperCollins Pubs.

Mayo Clinic Staff, contrib. by. 20 Tasty Recipes for People with Diabetes. 2002. (Mayo Clinic on Health Ser.). (Illus.). 36,52p. (YA). (gr. 8 up). lib. bdg. (978-1-59084-247-8(2)) Mason Crest Pubs.

Mayo, Gretchen Will. Applesauce. 2004. (Weekly Reader Early Learning Library). (Illus.). 24p. (gr. 2 up). (J). pap. 5.95 (978-0-8368-4071-1(2)); (YA). lib. bdg. 19.33 (978-0-8368-4064-3(X)) Stevens, Gareth Inc. (Weekly Reader Early Learning Library).

Maze, Stephanie. I Want to Be a Chef. 1999. (I Want to Be Ser.). (Illus.). 48p. (YA). (gr. 2-7). pap. 10.00 (978-0-15-201936-5(7)) Harcourt Children's Bks.

—I Want to Be a Chef. 1999. (I Want to Be Ser.). (Illus.). 48p. (YA). (gr. 4-9). pap. 18.98 (978-0-8172-6373-7(X)) Raintree.

—I Want to Be a Chef. 1999. (J). (ps-7). (Illus.). 47p. lib. bdg. 17.65 (978-0-613-15841-1(5)); 15.80 (978-0-606-16519-8(3)) Tandem Library Bks.

McConnell, Sharon. Let's Bring Mom Breakfast: Learning the BR Sound. 2002. (PowerPhonics Ser.). (Illus.). 24p. (J). (gr. 1). lib. bdg. 18.50 (978-0-8239-5936-5(8) , PowerKids Pr.) Rosen Publishing Group, Inc., The.

McCord, Marianne. Gilbert! Front & Center! Maginn, Traci, illus. 2003. 24p. (J). per. 5.95 (978-0-9743352-0-9(7)) Jades Publishing.

McCulloch, Julie. Caribbean. 48p. (J). 2002. (Illus.). (gr. 4-6). pap. (978-1-58810-385-7(4) , 91135); 2001. (gr. 3-5). lib. bdg. 25.64 (978-1-58810-153-2(3)) Heinemann Library.

—India. 2002. (Illus.). 48p. (J). (gr. 4-6). pap. (978-1-58810-387-1(0) , 91137) Heinemann Library.

—Italy. (Illus.). 48p. (J). 2002. (gr. 4-6). pap. (978-1-58810-388-8(9) , 91137); 2001. (gr. 3-5). lib. bdg. 25.64 (978-1-58810-086-3(3)) Heinemann Library.

—Italy. 2001. (Illus.). 48p. (J). (gr. 3-3). lib. bdg. 17.05 (978-0-613-89892-8(3)) Tandem Library Bks.

—Japan. 2002. (Illus.). 48p. (J). (gr. 4-6). pap. (978-1-58810-389-5(7) , 91139) Heinemann Library.

—Japan. Davies, Nicholas Beresford, illus. 2001. (World of Recipes Ser.). 48p. (J). (gr. 3-5). lib. bdg. 25.64 (978-1-58810-087-0(1)) Heinemann Library.

—A World of Recipes, 6 bks., Set 1. 2001. (Illus.). (J). (gr. 3-5). lib. bdg. 153.84 (978-1-58810-017-7(0)) Heinemann Library.

McLeese, Tex. Rodeo Steer Wrestling. 2001. (Illus.). 24p. (J). (gr. 1-4). lib. bdg. (978-1-57103-349-9(1)) Rourke Publishing, LLC.

McQuillan, Susan & Sesame Workshop Staff. Sesame Street C Is for Cooking: Recipes from the Street. 2007. 128p. 16.95 (978-0-471-79101-0(6) , Wiley) Wiley, John & Sons, Inc.

Medved, Denise Sullivan. The Tiny Kitchen: Cooking & Entertaining. Healy, Todd, illus. Wellens, Jeri Pinson, photos by. 2002. 152p. 16.95 (978-0-9716028-0-9(8)) Tiny Kitchen Publishing.

Meredith Books Staff, ed. Cooking for Kids. 2004. (Illus.). 200p. 19.95 (978-0-696-22227-6(2) , Food Network Kitchens) Meredith Bks.

Meredith Books Staff & Karpinske, Stephanie, eds. The Magic Kitchen Cookbook. 2007. 128p. (J). spiral bd. 16.95 (*978-0-696-23732-4(6)) Meredith Bks.

Metz, Kate. Kids in the Kitchen: A Cookbook of Yummy Foods That Kids Can Easily Prepare. 2001. (gr. k-3). lib. bdg. 19.90 (978-0-613-77897-8(9)) Tandem Library Bks.

Miller, Heather. Chef. 2003. (This Is What I Want to Be Ser.). (Illus.). 24p. (J). lib. bdg. 18.50 (978-1-4034-0912-6(9)); pap. 5.25 (978-1-4034-3607-8(X)) Heinemann Library.

—Chef. 2003. (ps-2). lib. bdg. 13.30 (978-0-613-60958-6(1)) Tandem Library Bks.

—Cocinero. 2003. (Esto es lo Que Quiero Ser (This Is What I Want to Be) Ser.). (SPA.). 24p. (J). pap. 5.25 (978-1-4034-3395-4(X)) Heinemann Library.

—Cocinero (Chef) 2003. (Illus.). 24p. (J). lib. bdg. 18.50 (978-1-4034-0947-8(1)) Heinemann Library.

Minden, Cecilia. Cooking by the Numbers. 2008. (J). lib. bdg. 25.26 (*978-1-60279-007-0(8)) Cherry Lake Publishing.

—Family Dinnertime by the Numbers. 2008. (J). lib. bdg. 25.26 (*978-1-60279-013-1(2)) Cherry Lake Publishing.

Miss O, Harlie, Justine, and Isabella, with Devra Newberger Speregen, Juliette. Miss O & Friends Book of Fabulous Fun: Cool Stuff to make, recipes, quizzes, & More! 2006. (Miss O & Friends Ser.). (Illus.). 96p. (J). pap. 9.95 (978-0-8230-2943-3(3)) Watson-Guptill Pubns., Inc.

Mix, Make & Munch: Individual Title Six-Packs. (gr. k-1). 23.00 (978-0-7635-8833-5(4)) Rigby Education.

Mohan, et al. Parties with Pizzazz: A Complete Resource for Holiday Classroom Parties. 2004. (Illus.). 128p. pap. 19.95 (978-0-9744936-0-2(0)) Pizzazz Publishing.

Monroe, Julia A. Tiny Treats: Fun foods to make & Eat. 2006. (Illus.). 56p. (YA). spiral bd. 9.95 (978-1-58485-979-6(2) , American Girl) American Girl Publishing, Inc.

Montgomery, Bertha Vining & Nabwire, Constance R. Cooking the East African Way. 2nd rev. exp. ed. 2002. (Easy Menu Ethnic Cookbooks). (Illus.). 72p. (J). (gr. 5-12). 25.26 (978-0-8225-4164-6(5)) Lerner Publishing Group.

Montgomery, Bertha Vining, et al. Cooking the West African Way. 2nd rev. exp. ed. 2002. (Easy Menu Ethnic Cookbooks). (Illus.). 72p. (J). (gr. 5-12). 25.26 (978-0-8225-4163-9(7) , Lerner Pubns.) Lerner Publishing Group.

Montgomery, L. M. Anne of Green Gables Cookbook. 22.95 (978-0-8488-2657-4(4)) Amereon LTD.

Moore, Kelly D. The Lil' Montessori Gourmet: A Collection of Recipes & Ideas for the Prepared Environment. 2002. (Illus.). 104p. (J). spiral bd. 25.00 (978-0-9755613-0-8(8)) Moore, Kelly D.

Moore, Sharon. Native American Foods & Recipes. 2002. (Reading Room Collection). (Illus.). 24p. (J). pap. (978-0-8239-8164-9(9)); lib. bdg. 18.75 (978-0-8239-3727-1(5)) Rosen Publishing Group, Inc., The.

Morina, Barbara. Recipes a Cooking Journal. Morina, Barbara, ed. 2002. (Write It down Ser.). (Illus.). 202p. 19.95 (978-1-892033-32-1(1)) Journals Unlimited, Inc.

Muldrow, Diane. Lights! Camera! Cook! 2003. (gr. 3-6). lib. bdg. 13.00 (978-0-613-72473-9(9)) Tandem Library Bks.

Mullican, Judy. What Can Li Zhang Cook? Coates, Jennifer, illus. l.t. ed. 2000. (BB Ser.). 8p. (J). (ps-1). pap. 10.95 (978-1-57332-160-0(5)); pap. 10.95 (978-1-57332-161-7(3)) HighReach Learning, Inc.

Munton, Gill. Make a Banana Treat. 2000. (Cambridge Reading Ser.). (Illus.). 10p. pap. 5.00 (978-0-521-77463-5(2)) Cambridge Univ. Pr.

My Tea Party: Incl. 9 Piece Tea Set, Cookie Cutter & Carrying Case. (J). (gr. 3 up). pap. (978-1-56021-299-7(3) , 200) W.J. Fantasy, Inc.

Nania, Max & Nania, Sienna, photos by. Cooking with Max: 45 Really Fun & Kind of Messy Recipes Kids Can Make. 2007. (J). (*978-1-58985-059-0(9)) Five Star Pubns., Inc.

Nelson, Robin. Los Productos Lacteos. 2003. (First Step Nonfiction Ser.). (SPA., Illus.). 24p. (J). (gr. k-2). lib. bdg. 18.60 (978-0-8225-5060-0(1)) Lerner Publishing Group.

Nguyen, Chi & Monroe, Judy. Cooking the Vietnamese Way: Includes New Low-Fat & Vegetarian Recipes. 2nd rev. expurg. ed. 2002. (Easy Menu Ethnic Cookbooks). (Illus.). 72p. (J). (gr. 5-12). 25.26 (978-0-8225-4125-7(4) , Lerner Pubns.) Lerner Publishing Group.

Nickelodeon Staff, contrib. by. Stir, Squirt, Sizzle: A Nick Cookbook. 2004. (Nick Jr Ser.). (Illus.). 56p. (J). spiral bd. 12.95 (978-0-8118-4419-2(6)) Chronicle Bks. LLC.

Nilsen, Beth A. Burning down the House, Cooking with Kids. Downer, David, illus. 2000. 96p. pap. 9.95 (978-0-9701019-0-7(2)) T. C. Publishing.

Nissenberg, Sandra K. The Everything' Kids' Cookbook: From Mac 'n Cheese to Double Chocolate Chip Cookies - All You Need to Have Some Finger Lickin' Fun. 2002. (Everything Ser.). (Illus.). 144p. (J). 6.95 (978-1-58062-658-3(0)) Adams Media Corp.

—Everything Kid's Cookbook: From Mac'n Cheese to Double Chocolate Chip Cooki. 2002. (gr. 3-6). lib. bdg. 15.25 (978-0-613-79321-6(8)) Tandem Library Bks.

Nissenberg, Sandra K. & Nissenberg, Heather. I Made It Myself! Mud Cups, Pizza Puffs, & over 100 Other Fun & Healthy Recipes for Kids to Make. 1998. (Illus.). 144p. (gr. 4-7). (J). pap. 13.95 (978-1-56561-151-1(9)); pap. 13.95 (978-0-471-34740-8(X) , Wiley) Wiley, John & Sons, Inc.

The No Wheat, No What? Cookbook. 2001. (Illus.). 314p. 20.00 (978-0-9715432-0-1(8)) Fink, Andie.

Norton, Frances Maree. The Victorian Tea Spirit: A Girl's Guide to Her Secret Self, 1. 100th ed. 2003. (Illus.). 230p. (YA). per. 19.95 (978-0-9632938-1-7(8)) Norton, Frances M.

Numeroff, Laura Joffe. If You Give a Bear a Brownie Recipes. Bond, Felicia, illus. Date not set. 32p. (J). (ps-2). 12.99 (978-0-06-028559-3(1)) HarperCollins Pubs.

—If You Give a Cat a Cupcake Recipes. Bond, Felicia, illus. Date not set. 32p. (J). (ps-2). 12.99 (978-0-06-028560-9(5)) HarperCollins Pubs.

—If You Give a Moose a Muffin Recipe Book. Bond, Felicia, illus. Date not set. 32p. (J). (ps-2). 12.99 (978-0-06-028562-3(1)) HarperCollins Pubs.

—Pig Pancakes. Bond, Felicia, illus. Date not set. 32p. (J). (ps-2). 1.00 (978-0-06-028563-0(X)) HarperCollins Pubs.

An Old Family Recipe. (Early Intervention Levels Ser.). 4.73 (978-0-7362-1757-6(6)); 28.38 (978-0-7362-2165-8(4)) Hampton-Brown Bks.

Oppenlander, Meredith. How to Make Snack Mix: Math B. Harston, Jerry, illus. l.t. ed. 1998. 16p. (J). (gr. k-2). pap. 4.95 (978-1-57874-004-8(5)) Kaeden Corp.

Pare, Jean. Company's Coming for Kids: Lunches. 1998. 142p. (J). (gr. 5-12). pap. (978-1-896891-36-1(5)) Company's Coming Publishing, Ltd.

Parnell, Helga. Cooking the South American Way. 2nd rev. ed. 2003. (Easy Menu Ethnic Cookbooks). (Illus.). 72p. (J). 25.26 (978-0-8225-4121-9(1) , Lerner Pubns.) Lerner Publishing Group.

Paul, Aileen. Kids Cooking Without a Stove: A Cookbook for Young Children. Inouye, Carol, illus. rev. ed. 2005. 64p. (J). pap. 10.95 (978-0-86534-060-2(9)) Sunstone Pr.

Paulsen, Gary. The Tortilla Factory. Paulsen, Ruth Wright, illus. 1998. (J). (ps-ps). lib. bdg. 15.30 (978-0-613-08930-2(8)) Tandem Library Bks.

Paulson, M. W. Cooking with the Baker Street Bunch. 2006. 139p. spiral bd. 12.31 (978-1-4116-8005-0(7)) Lulu-.com.

Pentland, Peter & Stoyles, Pennie. Kitchen Science. 2003. (Science & Scientists Ser.). (Illus.). 32p. (gr. 4-8). lib. bdg. 27.00 (978-0-7910-7014-7(X) , Chelsea Hse.) Facts On File, Inc.

Peterseil, Tamar. Zap It! A Microwave Cookbook Just for Kids. 2003. (Illus.). 32p. (YA). (gr. 4-7). 12.95 (978-0-943706-13-9(0)) Pitspopany Pr.

Pillsbury Editors. Pillsbury Kids Cookbook: Food Fun for Boys & Girls. 2005. (Illus.). 160p. (ps-7). 19.95 (978-0-7645-7861-8(8) , Wiley) Wiley, John & Sons, Inc.

The Popcorn Book. 1998. (J). (gr. 2). pap. 3.95 (978-0-439-04441-7(3)) Scholastic, Inc.

PopPopPopcorn! Individual Title Six-Packs. (ps-2). 23.00 (978-0-7635-8992-9(6)) Rigby Education.

Pratt, Dianne. Let's Stir It Up! Kids' Cookbook & Earth Friendly Fun. Eldridge, Sherri, ed. Winter, Janet, illus. 1998. 40p. (J). (gr. k-8). pap. 4.95 (978-1-886862-29-6(X) , MN KIDS) Harvest Hill Pr.

Quiri, Patricia Ryon. Chefs. 2000. (Community Workers Ser.). (Illus.). 32p. (J). (gr. 1 up). lib. bdg. 21.26 (978-0-7565-0007-8(9)) Compass Point Bks.

Raab, Evelyn. Clueless in the Kitchen: A Cookbook for Teens. 1998. (Illus.). 216p. (YA). (gr. 7-12). per. 22.20 (978-0-613-23697-3(1)) Tandem Library Bks.

—Clueless in the Kitchen: A Cookbook for Teens & Other Beginners. Walker, George, illus. 2006. (Clueless Ser.). 216p. (gr. 7-12). pap. 12.95 (978-1-55209-224-8(0)) Firefly Bks., Ltd.

Raintree Steck-Vaughn Staff. Sunflower Cheese & Other Recipes. 2000. (Read All about It Ser.). (Illus.). (J). (gr. k-3). pap. 4.95 (978-0-8114-3775-2(2)) Steck-Vaughn.

Rao, Nikhil & Wolf, Gita. All about Indian Food. 2005. (Illus.). 146p. 10.99 (978-81-86211-79-3(9)) Penguin Group (USA) Inc.

Rau, Dana Meachen. Applesauce. 2008. (J). (*978-0-7614-2894-7(1)) Cavendish, Marshall Bks., Ltd.

—Chefs. 2007. (Tools We Use Ser.). 32p. (J). lib. bdg. 22.79 (*978-0-7614-2657-8(4) , Benchmark Bks.) Cavendish, Marshall Corp.

—Los Chefs. 2007. (Instrumentos de Trabajo Ser.). (SPA.). 32p. (J). lib. bdg. 22.79 (*978-0-7614-2798-8(8) , Benchmark Bks.) Cavendish, Marshall Corp.

—Chefs/Los Chefs. 2007. (Tools We Use/Instrumentos de Trabajo Ser.). (SPA & ENG.). 32p. (J). lib. bdg. 22.79 (*978-0-7614-2822-0(4) , Benchmark Bks.) Cavendish, Marshall Corp.

Ray, Rachael. Rachael Ray's 30-Minute Meals for Kids: Cooking Rocks! Kalb, Chris, illus. 2004. 192p. spiral bd. 16.95 (978-1-891105-15-9(9)) Lake Isle Pr., Inc.

A Really Cool Cookbook for Kids. 2nd ed. 2000. 48p. spiral bd. 7.00 (978-0-9705997-0-4(6)) Touch Your Heart Collections.

Romero, Libby. Discover Kitchen Chemistry. 2006. pap. 39.00 (*978-1-4108-6501-4(0)) Benchmark Education Co.

—Kitchen Chemistry. 2006. pap. 39.00 (*978-1-4108-6498-7(7)) Benchmark Education Co.

Rosenbaum, Stephanie. Fun Food. 2006. (Illus.). 128p. 19.95 (978-0-7432-7856-0(9) , Free Pr.) Simon & Schuster.

Royston, Angela. How Is Chocolate Made? 2005. (Illus.). 32p. (J). pap. 7.60 (978-1-4034-6648-8(3)) Heinemann Library.

Sanger, Amy Wilson. Mangia! Mangia! 2005. (Illus.). 18p. (J). (ps-7). per. 6.95 (978-1-58246-144-1(9) , Tricycle Pr.) Ten Speed Pr.

Sanner, Catie. Cooking with Catie: The 3ABN Kids Time Cookbook. Walsh, Brenda, ed. 2004. 86p. (J). ring bd. (978-0-9720888-4-8(9)) Three Angels Broadcasting Network.

Saunders-Smith, Gail. Eating Apples. 1998. (J). pap. 13.25 (978-0-516-21242-5(7) , Children's Pr.) Scholastic Library Publishing.

Schloss, Andrew & Joachim, David. Mastering the Grill: The Owner's Manual for Outdoor Cooking. Miksch, Alison, photos by. 2007. (Illus.). 416p. pap. 24.95 (978-0-8118-4964-7(3)) Chronicle Bks. LLC.

Scholastic, Inc. Staff & Gerasole, Isabella. Spatulatta Cookbook. 2007. 128p. (J). (gr. 4-7). 16.99 (*978-0-439-02250-7(9) , Scholastic Reference) Scholastic, Inc.

Scobey, Joan. Fannie Farmer Junior Cookbook. rev. ed. 2000. (Illus.). (J). (978-0-606-18258-4(6)) Tandem Library Bks.

Seideman, Rob. Real Cooking for Kids. 2002. (Illus.). 96p. 14.95 (978-0-7624-1323-2(9) , Running Pr. Kids) Running Pr. Bk. Pubs.

Sell, Colleen & Frank, Melinda. Everything Kids' Gross Cookbook: Get your hands dirty in the kitchen with these yucky Meals! 2007. (Illus.). 144p. pap. 7.95 (978-1-59869-324-9(7)) Adams Media Corp.

Seltzer, Donna Lee & Thorne, Lawrence R., creators. The Carnival Cookbook: From the Kitchen of the Hurricane Grille. 2nd ed. 2004. spiral bd. 15.00 (978-0-9747072-3-5(6)) Bon Tiki Bks.

Sheen, Barbara. Foods of Iran. 2006. (Taste of Culture Ser.). (Illus.). 64p. (J). (gr. 3-6). 27.45 (978-0-7377-3453-9(1) , Greenhaven Pr., Inc.) Thomson Gale.

—Foods of the Philippines. 2006. (Taste of Culture Ser.). (Illus.). 64p. (J). (gr. 3-6). 27.45 (978-0-7377-3454-6(X) , Greenhaven Pr., Inc.) Thomson Gale.

Shouting in the Hush Arbor Recipe Guide. 2.00 (978-0-687-32722-5(9)) Abingdon Pr.

Silate, Jennifer. Planning & Preparing Healthy Meals & Snacks: A Day-to-Day Guide to a Healthier Diet. 2004. (Library of Nutrition). (Illus.). 48p. (J). lib. bdg. 25.25 (978-1-4042-0302-0(8)) Rosen Publishing Group, Inc., The.

Sindeldecker, Erica & Sindeldecker, Brittany. Just for Kids Cookbook. 2007. (Christmas at Home Ser.). 160p. pap. 3.97 (*978-1-59789-802-7(3)) Barbour Publishing, Inc.

Skaug, Joshua. Kooking for Kids. Skaug, Terry, ed. 2004. (Illus.). 82p. (J). 11.50 (978-0-9764323-0-2(7)) Prickly Pear Pr.

Sloan, Peter. Making Pancakes. 2000. (gr. k-3). lib. bdg. 11.80 (978-0-613-31446-6(8)) Tandem Library Bks.

—My Milk Shake. 2000. (gr. k-3). lib. bdg. 11.65 (978-0-613-30619-5(8)) Tandem Library Bks.

Smith, Sarah. Pizza Shop. 2001. (gr. k-3). lib. bdg. 11.95 (978-0-613-33413-6(2)) Tandem Library Bks.

Smithyman, Kathryn & Kalman, Bobbie. Native North American Foods & Recipes. 2005. (Native Nations of North America Ser.). (Illus.). 32p. (J). (gr. 3-9). lib. bdg. (978-0-7787-0383-9(5)); pap. (978-0-7787-0475-1(0)) Crabtree Publishing Co.

Smoothies & Juices. Date not set. 96p. spiral bd. 6.98 (978-1-4054-0630-7(5)) Parragon, Inc.

Snow, Panky. Chefs & Cooks. 2001. (Community Helpers Ser.). (Illus.). 24p. (J). (gr. 1-2). lib. bdg. 18.60 (978-0-7368-0955-9(4) , Bridgestone Bks.) Capstone Pr., Inc.

Snyder, Inez. Apples to Applesauce. 2005. (How Things Are Made Ser.). (Illus.). 24p. (J). pap. 4.95 (978-0-516-25525-5(8)); 18.00 (978-0-516-25195-0(3)) Scholastic Library Publishing. (Children's Pr.).

—Beans to Chocolate. 2003. (Welcome Bks.). (Illus.). 24p. (J). (ps-2). pap. 4.95 (978-0-516-24361-0(6) , Watts, Franklin) Scholastic Library Publishing.

—Beans to Chocolate. 2003. (gr. k-3). lib. bdg. 12.95 (978-0-613-59582-7(3)) Tandem Library Bks.

—Berries to Jelly. 2005. (How Things Are Made Ser.). (Illus.). 24p. (J). (ps-2). pap. 4.95 (978-0-516-25526-2(6)); 18.00 (978-0-516-25196-7(1)) Scholastic Library Publishing. (Children's Pr.).

—Cooking Tools. 2002. (Welcome Bks.). (Illus.). 24p. (J). (ps-2). pap. 4.95 (978-0-516-24035-0(8) , Children's Pr.) Scholastic Library Publishing.

—Cooking Tools. 2002. (gr. k-3). lib. bdg. 12.95 (978-0-613-58829-4(0)) Tandem Library Bks.

—Tomatoes to Ketchup. 2003. (Welcome Bks.). (Illus.). 24p. (J). (ps-2). pap. 4.95 (978-0-516-24358-0(6) , Watts, Franklin) Scholastic Library Publishing.

—Tomatoes to Ketchup. 2003. (gr. k-3). lib. bdg. 12.95 (978-0-613-59742-5(7)) Tandem Library Bks.

Solis, Lisa. Classroom Cupboard: Lessons, Activities & Culinary Concoctions for Kids. 2003. (Illus.). 160p. pap. 27.00 (978-1-56308-957-2(2) , LU9572) Libraries Unlimited, Inc.

Southwater Staff. Fun with Cooking. 2000. (Illus.). 96p. 12.95 (978-1-84215-137-2(1)) Anness Publishing, Inc.

—Party Food for Kids. 2001. (Cook's Essentials Ser.). (Illus.). 64p. 4.95 (978-1-84215-353-6(6) , Southwater) Anness Publishing GBR. *Dist:* National Bk. Network.

Spano, Andrea. NOT Just Desserts: Stories, Desserts, & Food Recipes. 2004. (Illus.). 187p. spiral bd. 42.95 (978-1-932373-33-2(0) , Cedar Hill Pr.) Cedar Hill Publishing.

Spencer, Gwynne. What's Cooking in Children's Literature. 2001. (Professional Growth Ser.). (Illus.). 160p. 36.95 (978-1-58683-005-2(8)) Linworth Publishing, Inc.

Spilsbury, Louise. El Arroz (Rice) 2003. (Alimentos Ser.). (Illus.). 32p. (J). lib. bdg. 22.79 (978-1-4034-3738-9(6)) Heinemann Library.

—Bananas. (Food Ser.). 32p. pap. 6.95 (978-1-4034-4046-4(8)); 2003. (Illus.). (J). lib. bdg. 22.79 (978-1-58810-615-5(2)) Heinemann Library.

—Oranges. (Food Ser.). 32p. pap. 6.95 (978-1-4034-4048-8(4)); 2003. (Illus.). (J). lib. bdg. 22.79 (978-1-58810-618-6(7)) Heinemann Library.

—Pasta. 2001. (Food in Focus Ser.). (Illus.). 32p. (J). (gr. k-2). lib. bdg. 21.36 (978-1-58810-148-8(7)) Heinemann Library.

—El Platano. 2003. (Alimentos Ser.).Tr. of Bananas. (SPA & ENG., Illus.). 32p. (J). lib. bdg. 22.79 (978-1-4034-3734-1(3)) Heinemann Library.

—El Platano. 2003. (Alimentos Ser.). (ENG & SPA.). 32p. (J). pap. 6.50 (978-1-4034-3740-2(8)) Heinemann Library.

Spilsbury, Louise & Hall, Margaret. La Naranja. 2003. (Alimentos Ser.).Tr. of Oranges. (SPA & ENG., Illus.). 32p. (J). lib. bdg. 22.79 (978-1-4034-3736-5(X)) Heinemann Library.

The Sport Fishermen's Cookbook. (Illus.). 64p. (YA). (gr. 7 up). lib. bdg. (978-1-59084-498-4(X)) Mason Crest Pubs.

Springer, David. Samhain in the Kitchen. 2005. 52p. (J). spiral bd. 9.00 (978-1-4116-3670-5(8)) Lulu.com.

Steck-Vaughn Staff. Measure & Cook. 2002. (Illus.). (J). pap. (978-0-7398-5979-7(X)) Steck-Vaughn.

—Nana's Kitchen - You Can Cook. 1999. (Take Me Home Ser.). (Illus.). (J). pap. (978-0-7398-2592-1(5)) Steck-Vaughn.

Stern, Sam & Stern, Susan. Cooking up a Storm: The Teen Survival Cookbook. 2006. (Illus.). 128p. (J). (gr. 5). pap. 16.99 (978-0-7636-2988-5(X)) Candlewick Pr.

Stern, Sam & Stern, Susan. Real Food, Real Fast. 2007. (Illus.). 128p. (J). (gr. 5). pap. 16.99 (***978-0-7636-3533-6(2)***) Candlewick Pr.

Storey Publishing Staff. Dinner from Dirt: Ten Meals Kids Can Grow & Cook. 1998. pap. 10.00 (978-0-676-57342-8(8)) Random Hse., Inc.

Story Time Staff. Alfreda Presents a Story Rhyme Cookbook. 2001. 50p. (J). spiral bd. 8.95 (978-1-56820-397-3(7)) Story Time Stories That Rhyme.

Superchef: Group 2, 4 Bks, Set. 2004. (J). 119.71 (978-0-7614-1728-6(1)) Cavendish, Marshall Corp.

Superchef Series, 4 bks., Set. 119.71 (978-0-7614-1213-7(1) , Benchmark Bks.) Cavendish, Marshall Corp.

Therrien, Patricia. Amish & Mennonite Cooking. 2005. (American Regional Cooking Library). (Illus.). 72p. (J). lib. bdg. (978-1-59084-612-4(5)); lib. bdg. 299.25 (978-1-59084-609-4(5)) Mason Crest Pubs.

—Hawaiian. 2005. (American Regional Cooking Library). (Illus.). 72p. (J). lib. bdg. (978-1-59084-614-8(1)) Mason Crest Pubs.

Thomas, John. The Ultimate Book of Kid Concoctions 2. 2006. (Illus.). 80p. (J). pap. 14.99 (978-0-8054-4444-5(0)) B&H Publishing Grp.

Thomas, John & Thomas, Danita. The Ultimate Book of All Occasion Kid Concoctions: More Than 50 Wacky, Wild & Crazy Concoctions for All Occasions. 2006. (Illus.). 80p. (J). pap. 14.99 (978-0-8054-4445-2(9)) B&H Publishing Grp.

—The Ultimate Book of Kid Concoctions. 2006. (Illus.). 80p. (J). pap. 14.99 (978-0-8054-4443-8(2)) B&H Publishing Grp.

Thomas, John E. & Pagel, Danita. The Ultimate Book of Kid Concoctions Vol. 1: More Than 65 Wacky, Wild & Crazy Concoctions, 4 vols. Durr, Robb, illus. Dragga, Bill, photos by. 1998. 80p. (J). (ps-9). per. 14.95 (978-0-9661088-0-4(9)) Kid Concoctions Co.

Thomas, John E. & Thomas, Danita. The Ultimate Book of Kid Concoctions Vol. 2: More Than 65 New Wacky, Wild & Crazy Concoctions, 4 vols. Briller, Margaret, ed. Durr, Robb, illus. 2000. 80p. (J). (ps-9). per. 14.95 (978-0-9661088-1-1(7)) Kid Concoctions Co.

Tocci, Salvatore. Experiments with Foods. 2003. (True Book Ser.). (Illus.). 48p. (J). 25.00 (978-0-516-22787-0(4) , Children's Pr.) Scholastic Library Publishing.

Top That Publishing Editors, ed. Ghastly Grub. Dahl, Roald, illus. 2005. 24p. (J). pap. (978-1-905359-54-7(3)) Top That! Publishing PLC.

Top That Publishing Staff, ed. Favorite Recipes. 2005. 120p. (978-1-84510-560-0(5)) Top That! Publishing PLC.

Townsend, Sue. A World of Recipes, 4 bks., Set 2. 2002. (J). (gr. 3-5). lib. bdg. 108.28 (978-1-58810-480-9(X)) Heinemann Library.

Townsend, Sue & McCulloch, Julie. A World of Recipes, 10 bks., Set. 2003. (J). (gr. 3-5). lib. bdg. 270.70 (978-1-4034-0146-5(2)) Heinemann Library.

Townsend, Sue & Young, Caroline. Egypt. 2003. (Illus.). 48p. (J). lib. bdg. (978-1-4034-0979-9(X)) Heinemann Library.

—Indonesia. 2003. (World of Recipes Ser.). (Illus.). 48p. (J). lib. bdg. (978-1-4034-0976-8(5)) Heinemann Library.

—Vegetarian Recipes from Around the World. 2003. (World of Recipes Ser.). (Illus.). 48p. (J). pap. 7.95 (978-1-4034-3653-5(3)); lib. bdg. 27.07 (978-1-4034-0977-5(3)) Heinemann Library.

Turck, Mary. Healthy Snack & Fast-Food Choices. 2000. (Nutrition & Fitness Ser.). (Illus.). 64p. (J). (gr. 4-6). lib. bdg. 23.93 (978-0-7368-0710-4(1) , LifeMatters Bks.) Capstone Pr., Inc.

The Ultimate Brownie, Bar & Cookie Cookbook: Over 200 Recipes for Fudgy Brownies, Chewy Bars & Buttery Cookies. 2001. 156p. per. 11.95 (978-0-9701466-7-0(1)) Athenean Pr., Inc.

Usborne Books, creator. Starting Cooking Kid Kit. 2005. (Illus.). 32p. (J). 14.99 (978-1-58086-873-0(8) , Usborne) EDC Publishing.

Van der Linde, Polly & Van der Linde, Tasha. Around the World in Eighty Dishes. Lemke, Horst, illus. 88p. (J). (gr. k-7). 12.95 (978-0-87592-007-8(1)) Scroll Pr., Inc.

Van Loon, Joan & Gate, Gabriel. The Chocolate Lovers: A Children's Story & Cookbook. Stewart, Chantal, illus. 2001. 32p. 14.95 (978-1-55285-233-0(4)) Whitecap Bks., Ltd. CAN. *Dist:* Graphic Arts Ctr. Publishing Co.

Vaughan, Jenny & Beauchamp, Penny. Festival Foods. 2004. (World of Recipes Ser.). (Illus.). 48p. (J). pap. 8.50 (978-1-4034-6012-7(4)) Heinemann Library.

—Festivals. 2004. (World of Recipes Ser.). (Illus.). 48p. (J). lib. bdg. (978-1-4034-4699-2(7)) Heinemann Library.

Vilicich-Solomon, Tina. Grosser Goodies: Sickening Snacks That Look Scummy but Taste Scrumptious. Yamamoto, Neal, illus. 1998. 80p. (J). (gr. 3-7). pap. 6.95 (978-1-56565-736-6(5) , 07365W) Lowell Hse. Juvenile.

Vize, Dania. High Chair Buddy Silly Snacks. 2006. (High Chair Buddy Ser.). (Illus.). 10p. (ps-ps). per., bds. 6.95 (978-1-84610-016-1(X)) Make Believe Ideas GBR. *Dist:* Ingram Pub. Services.

Wagner, Lisa. Cool Cuisine for Super Sleepovers: Easy Recipes for Kids to Cook. 2007. (Cool Cooking Ser.). (Illus.). 32p. (J). (gr. 4-6). lib. bdg. 22.78 (***978-1-59928-721-8(8)*** , Checkerboard Library) ABDO Publishing Co.

—Cool Foods for Fun Fiestas: Easy Recipes for Kids to Cook. 2007. (Cool Cooking Ser.). (Illus.). 32p. (J). (gr. 4-6). lib. bdg. 22.78 (***978-1-59928-722-5(6)*** , Checkerboard Library) ABDO Publishing Co.

—Cool Lunches to Make & Take: Easy Recipes for Kids to Cook. 2007. (Cool Cooking Ser.). (Illus.). 32p. (J). (gr. 4-6). lib. bdg. 22.78 (***978-1-59928-723-2(4)*** , Checkerboard Library) ABDO Publishing Co.

—Cool Meals to Start Your Wheels: Easy Recipes for Kids to Cook. 2007. (Cool Cooking Ser.). (Illus.). 32p. (J). (gr. 3-6). lib. bdg. 22.78 (***978-1-59928-724-9(2)*** , Checkerboard Library) ABDO Publishing Co.

—Cool Pizza to Make & Bake: Easy Recipes for Kids to Cook. 2007. (Cool Cooking Ser.). (Illus.). 32p. (J). (gr. 3-6). lib. bdg. 22.78 (***978-1-59928-725-6(0)*** , Checkerboard Library) ABDO Publishing Co.

Walkup, Betsy. Creative Kids: Kids in the Kitchen. 2005. (Creative Kids Ser.). 160p. pap. 15.99 (978-1-4206-3193-7(4)) Teacher Created Materials, Inc.

Walsh, Kieran. Kitchen Math. 2003. (Math & My World Ser.). (Illus.). 48p. (J). 29.93 (978-1-58952-382-1(2)) Rourke Publishing, LLC.

Walton. Nana's Kitchen. 1999. (Illus.). (J). pap. 5.18 (978-0-7398-2410-8(4)) Steck-Vaughn.

Watt, Fiona. Children's Cookbook. Cartwright, Stephen, illus. 2004. (Children's Cooking Ser.). 48p. (J). 12.95 (978-0-7945-0361-1(6) , Usborne) EDC Publishing.

—Internet-Linked Children's World Cookbook. 2000. (Illus.). 96p. (J). 39.95 (978-0-7460-4218-2(3)) EDC Publishing.

—Pasta for Beginners. Lane, Kim, illus. Allman, Howard, photos by. 1998. (Cooking for Beginners Ser.). 48p. (YA). (gr. 5 up). lib. bdg. 15.95 (978-0-88110-969-6(X)) EDC Publishing.

—Vegetarian Cooking. rev. ed. 2004. (Cooking School Ser.). (Illus.). 48p. (J). pap. 7.95 (978-0-7945-0524-0(4)) EDC Publishing.

—Vegetarian Cooking for Beginners. 2001. (Cooking School Ser.). (Illus.). 48p. (YA). (gr. 5 up). lib. bdg. 15.95 (978-1-58086-203-5(9)) EDC Publishing.

—30 Easy Things to Cook & Eat. 2007. 30p. (J). 9.99 (978-0-7945-1586-7(X) , Usborne) EDC Publishing.

—30 Healthy Things to Cook & Eat. 2007. 30p. (J). 9.99 (978-0-7945-1587-4(8) , Usborne) EDC Publishing.

—30 Yummy Things to Cook & Eat. 2007. 30p. (J). 9.99 (978-0-7945-1588-1(6) , Usborne) EDC Publishing.

Webb, Sarah & Myler, Terry. Kids Can Cook. 1998. (Illus.). 112p. (J). pap. 9.95 (978-1-901737-03-5(9)) Anvil Bks., Ltd. IRL. *Dist:* Dufour Editions, Inc.

Weber, Lenora Mattingly. The Beany Malone Cookbook. Levering, Robert, illus. 1999. (Beany Malone Ser.). 300p. (J). reprint ed. pap. 12.95 (978-1-930009-07-3(0)) Image Cascade Publishing.

Weber, Lou. Kids Cooking Shaped Bk. 2006. (Illus.). 48p. (J). 9.98 (978-1-4127-2469-2(4) , PIL Kids) Publications International, Ltd.

Webster, Penny. Allergy Free for All Ages: Milk-Free, Egg-Free, Nut-Free Recipes. 2005. 124p. pap. 17.95 (978-1-4137-9852-4(7)) PublishAmerica, Inc.

Weekend Treats. 2000. (Kids Cook Ser.). (Illus.). 80p. (J). pap. 7.99 (978-1-896891-46-0(2)) Recipe Factory, Inc. CAN. *Dist:* Picasso Distribution Services.

Weil, Carolyn Beth. Williams-Sonoma Kids in the Kitchen: Sweet Treats. 2006. (Illus.). 128p. 19.95 (978-0-7432-7857-7(7) , Free Pr.) Simon & Schuster.

Weiss, Ellen. Math in the Kitchen. 2007. (Scholastic News Nonfiction Readers: Everyday Math—NEW SUBSET Ser.). 24p. (J). pap. 6.95 (***978-0-531-18784-5(5) ;*** (Illus.). (gr. 1-2). lib. bdg. 20.00 (***978-0-531-18531-5(1))*** Scholastic Library Publishing. (Children's Pr.).

Westin, Margaret E. & Westin, Norman W. You Can Make a Dinosaur... & Eat It Too! Westin, Margaret E., illus. 1998. (Illus.). 40p. (J). (ps-4). spiral bd. 14.95 (978-0-9664453-0-5(9)) Icorn/F3K Productions, Ltd.

Wheeler, Susan & Kortepeter, Paul. Let's Have Tea Together: Recipes & Celebrations for Every Season. 2nd gif. ed. 2002. Orig. Title: Tea with Victoria Rose. (Illus.). 80p. 15.99 (978-0-7369-1043-9(3)) Harvest Hse. Pubs.

Whitehouse, Patricia. Alimentos Blancos. 2002. (Colores Para Comer (The Colors We Eat) Ser.). (SPA.). 24p. (J). (ps-1). pap. 5.25 (978-1-58810-839-5(2) , 91574) Heinemann Library.

—Alimentos Marron. 2003. Tr. of Brown Foods. (SPA.). (ps-2). lib. bdg. 13.30 (978-0-613-82825-3(9)) Tandem Library Bks.

—The Colors We Eat, 7 bks., Set. 2002. (J). (ps-1). lib. bdg. 102.48 (978-1-58810-471-7(0)) Heinemann Library.

Wilkes, Angela. The Children's Quick & Easy Cookbook. 2006. (Illus.). 96p. (J). (gr. 5). pap. 9.99 (978-0-7566-1814-8(2)) Dorling Kindersley Publishing, Inc.

—The Children's Step-by-Step Cook Book. 2000. (Illus.). 128p. (J). (gr. 1-7). 17.99 (978-1-56458-474-8(7)) Dorling Kindersley Publishing, Inc.

—First Cookbook. Cartwright, Stephen, illus. 2007. 72p. (J). 18.99 (978-0-7945-1479-2(0) , Usborne) EDC Publishing.

—Mi Primer Libro de Cocina. (SPA.). 48p. (J). (gr. 3-5). (978-84-272-1700-3(5) , ML4524) Molino, Editorial ESP. *Dist:* Lectorum Pubns., Inc.

Williams, Judy. Kids Can Cook: Over 130 Recipes for Young Children. 2003. (Flipcook Ser.). (Illus.). 160p. 17.99 (978-1-84215-802-9(3) , Southwater) Anness Publishing GBR. *Dist:* National Bk. Network.

Wilson, Lia. Class Treats: Take-To-School Goodies for Every Occasion: All Nut-Free Recipes. 2003. (Illus.). 125p. (J). (978-1-931294-58-4(5)) Cookbook Resources, LLC.

Winget, Mary. Cooking the North African Way. 2nd rev. ed. 2004. (Easy Menu Ethnic Cookbooks). (Illus.). 72p. (J). 25.26 (978-0-8225-4169-1(6) , Lerner Pubns.) Lerner Publishing Group.

Woo. You Can Cook. 1999. (Illus.). (J). pap. 4.93 (978-0-7398-2411-5(2)) Steck-Vaughn.

(Your Child's Name Here) Cookbook: 100 Fun to Cook Recipes. 2007. (J). 10.00 (***978-0-9766756-6-2(8))*** Shively, Lisa Cookbooks.

Zanzarella, Marianne & Good Housekeeping Editors. The Good Housekeeping Illustrated Children's Cookbook. 2006. (Illus.). 176p. 12.95 (978-1-58816-424-7(1)) Sterling Publishing Co., Inc.

Zerlin, Elizabeth. Little Treasures for Little People. 1999. (Illus.). 72p. (J). (gr. k-6). pap. 8.00 (978-0-8059-4621-5(7)) Dorrance Publishing Co., Inc.

COOKERY (DAIRY PRODUCTS)

Jones, Carol. Cheese. 2002. (From Farm to You Ser.). (Illus.). 32p. (J). (gr. 4-8). 28.00 (978-0-7910-7005-5(0) , Chelsea Hse.) Facts On File, Inc.

COOKERY—FICTION

Andrew, Alice, et al. Castun Neqliyarer. McCarr, Edith, illus. l.t. ed. 1999. Tr. of How to Prepare Fish. (ESK.). 8p. (J). (gr. k-3). pap. 6.00 (978-1-58084-115-3(5)) Lower Kuskokwim Schl. District.

—Hannairniaqtaa Iqaluum. McCarr, Edith, illus. l.t. ed. 1999. Tr. of How to Prepare Fish. (ESK.). 8p. (J). (gr. k-3). pap. 6.00 (978-1-58084-131-3(7)) Lower Kuskokwim Schl. District.

—How to Prepare Fish. McCarr, Edith, illus. l.t. ed. 1999. 8p. (J). (gr. k-3). pap. 6.00 (978-1-58084-052-1(3)) Lower Kuskokwim Schl. District.

—Iqaluum Sannaiyautaa. McCarr, Edith, illus. l.t. ed. 1999. Tr. of How to Prepare Fish. (ESK.). 8p. (J). (gr. k-3). pap. 6.00 (978-1-58084-124-5(4)) Lower Kuskokwim Schl. District.

—Neqliuryaraq. McCarr, Edith, illus. l.t. ed. 1999. Tr. of How to Prepare Fish. (ESK.). 8p. (J). (gr. k-3). pap. 6.00 (978-1-58084-053-8(1)) Lower Kuskokwim Schl. District.

—Qanuq Itqanaiyarnagpat Qalut. McCarr, Edith, illus. l.t. ed. 1999. Tr. of How to Prepare Fishs. (ESK.). 8p. (J). (gr. k-3). pap. 6.00 (978-1-58084-139-9(2)) Lower Kuskokwim Schl. District.

Animal Cookies: Individual Title Six-Pack. (Story Steps Ser.). (gr. k-2). 23.00 (978-0-7635-9822-8(4)) Rigby Education.

Argueta, Jorge & Alvarez, María Jesus. La Fiesta de Las Tortillas. Alvarez, María Jesus, illus. 2005. (ENG & SPA., Illus.). 32p. (J). 14.95 (978-1-59820-094-2(1) , Alfaguara) Santillana USA Publishing Co., Inc.

Auch, Mary Jane & Auch, Herm. The Princess & the Pizza. 2002. (Illus.). 32p. (J). (gr. k-3). 6.95 (978-0-8234-1798-8(0)) Holiday Hse., Inc.

Axelrod, Amy. Pigs in the Pantry: Fun with Math & Cooking. McGinley-Nally, Sharon, illus. 1999. 40p. (J). (ps-3). 6.99 (978-0-689-82555-2(2) , 076714005990, Aladdin) Simon & Schuster Children's Publishing.

—Pigs in the Pantry: Fun with Math & Cooking. 1999. (978-0-606-16329-3(8)) Tandem Library Bks.

Baisa, Marie. Mirabelle Mouse Bakes Cookies. 2005. (ENG.). 36p. per. 21.75 (978-1-4208-2043-0(5)) AuthorHouse.

Barlow, Steve & Skidmore, Steve. Tales of Dark Forest Trilogy. 3rd ed. 2003. (Tales of the Dark Forest Ser.). (Illus.). 192p. (J). pap. 10.99 (978-0-00-710865-7(6)) HarperCollins Pubs. Ltd. GBR. *Dist:* Independent Pubs. Group.

Béha, Philippe, illus. Fairy Tale Feasts: A Literary Cookbook for Young Readers & Eaters. 2006. 200p. (J). 24.95 (978-1-56656-643-8(6)) Interlink Publishing Group, Inc.

Bridwell, Norman. Cooking with Clifford. 1999. (Clifford, the Big Red Dog Ser.). 24p. (J). (gr. k-2). 9.95 (978-0-590-68931-1(2) , Cartwheel Bks.) Scholastic, Inc.

Brooks, F. Sam the Chef. 24p. (J). lib. bdg. 14.95 (978-1-58086-763-4(4) , Usborne) EDC Publishing.

Buckless, Andrea. Too Many Cooks! Jacobs, Kayne & Burns, Marilyn, illus. 2002. (Hello Reader! Science Ser.). 32p. (J). (gr. 1-3). pap. 3.99 (978-0-439-16966-0(6) , Cartwheel Bks.) Scholastic, Inc.

—Too Many Cooks! 2000. (gr. k-3). lib. bdg. 11.80 (978-0-613-63571-4(X)) Tandem Library Bks.

Carle, Eric. Pancakes, Pancakes! Carle, Eric, illus. 2005. (Stories to Go! Ser.). (Illus.). 36p. (J). reprint ed. pap. 4.99 (978-0-689-87833-6(8) , Aladdin) Simon & Schuster Children's Publishing.

Chaos in the Kitchen: Individual Title Six-Packs. (gr. k-1). 23.00 (978-0-7635-9076-5(2)) Rigby Education.

Chavarria-Chairez, Becky. Magda's Tortillas (Las Tortillas de Magda) Castilla, Julia Mercedes, tr. Vega, Anne, illus. 2000. (SPA & ENG.). 32p. (J). (ps-2). 14.95 (978-1-55885-286-0(7) , Piñata Books) Arte Publico Pr.

Compestine, Ying Chang. Boy Dumplings. Yamasaki, James, illus. 2007. (J). (978-0-8234-1955-5(X)) Holiday Hse., Inc.

—The Story of Noodles. Xuan, Yong-Sheng, illus. 2002. 32p. (J). (gr. k-3). tchr. ed. 16.95 (978-0-8234-1600-4(3)) Holiday Hse., Inc.

Conford, Ellen. What's Cooking, Jenny Archer? Palmisciano, Diane, illus. 2006. 80p. (J). (gr. 1-4). pap. 3.99 (978-0-316-01488-5(5)) Little Brown & Co.

Cooper, Helen. Pumpkin Soup. Cooper, Helen, illus. 2002. (Illus.). (J). 24.36 (978-0-7587-3463-1(8)) Book Wholesalers, Inc.

—Pumpkin Soup. braille ed. 2004. (J). (gr. k-3). spiral bd. (978-0-616-07224-0(4)) Canadian National Institute for the Blind/Institut National Canadien pour les Aveugles.

—Pumpkin Soup. Cooper, Helen, illus. 1999. (Illus.). 32p. (J). (ps-3). 16.00 (978-0-374-36164-8(9) , Farrar, Straus & Giroux (BYR)) Farrar, Straus & Giroux.

Costella, Deborah. Cooking with Granddad. Morisson, Connie, ed. 2002. 42p. pap. 14.95 (978-0-9718155-5-1(0) , 14) Inkwell Productions, LLC.

Creech, Sharon. Granny Torrelli Makes Soup. Raschka, Chris, illus. 160p. (J). 2003. (gr. 3-6). 15.99 (978-0-06-029290-4(3) , HarperChildren's Audio); 2003. (gr. 4-7). lib. bdg. 16.89 (978-0-06-029291-1(1) , Cotler, Joanna Books); 2005. reprint ed. pap. 5.99 (978-0-06-440960-5(0) , Harper Trophy) HarperCollins Pubs.

Crowther, Robert. Let's Cook! A Press-Out-and-Play Book. Crowther, Robert, illus. 2004. (Illus.). 10p. (J). (gr. k-k). 10.99 (978-0-7636-2266-4(4)) Candlewick Pr.

Cunningham, Bradley S. Tucket Teddy's Day at Work. 7.95 (978-0-9653674-0-0(1)) Nantucket Cobblestones, Ltd.

Dad cooks Breakfast: Individual Title Six-Packs. (gr. 1-2). 25.00 (978-0-7635-9135-9(1)) Rigby Education.

Dalmatian Press Staff. Let's Eat. 2007. 24p. pap. 3.50 (***978-1-4037-3428-0(3))*** Dalmatian Pr.

de Paola, Tomie. Pascual & the Kitchen Angels. de Paola, Tomie, illus. 2006. (Illus.). 32p. (J). pap. 5.99 (978-0-14-240536-9(1) , Puffin) Penguin Group (USA) Inc.

Demar, Regier. Good Food. Clar, David Austin, illus. 2005. (My First Reader Ser.). 31p. (J). (ps-ps). 18.50 (978-0-516-24879-0(0) , Children's Pr.) Scholastic Library Publishing.

Denise, Anika. Pigs Love Potatoes. Denise, Christopher, illus. 2007. 40p. (J). (ps-1). 15.99 (978-0-399-24036-2(5) , Philomel) Penguin Group (USA) Inc.

deRubertis, Barbara. Lulu's Lemonade. Billin-Frye, Paige, illus. 2000. (Math Matters Ser.). 32p. (J). (ps-3). pap. 4.95 (978-1-57565-093-7(2)) Kane Pr., The.

—Lulu's Lemonade. 2000. (gr. k-3). lib. bdg. 12.95 (978-0-613-27957-4(3)); (Illus.). (J). (978-0-606-18222-5(5)) Tandem Library Bks.

Dickinson, Rebecca. Monster Cake. Dickinson, Rebecca, illus. 2000. (Illus.). 32p. (J). (ps-2). pap. 4.99 (978-0-439-06752-2(9)) Scholastic, Inc.

—Monster Cake. 2000. (J). (978-0-606-19579-9(3)) Tandem Library Bks.

Donohue, Dorothy. Veggie Soup. 40p. (J). (ps-1). 2002. pap. 6.95 (978-1-58837-020-4(8)); 2000. (Illus.). 16.95 (978-1-890817-21-3(X)) Winslow Pr.

Dooley, Norah. Everybody Brings Noodles. Thornton, Peter J., illus. (J). (gr. k-2). 2005. 32p. pap. 6.95 (978-1-57505-916-7(9)); 2003. 40p. 15.95 (978-0-87614-455-8(5) , Carolrhoda Bks.) Lerner Publishing Group.

Downing, Johnette. Today Is Monday in Louisiana. Kadair, Deborah Ousley, illus. 2006. 32p. (J). 15.95 (978-1-58980-406-7(6)) Pelican Publishing Co., Inc.

Dumas, Bianca. Tia Luisa, the Magical Cook: A Tale in English & Spanish. Dumas, Bianca, illus. 2000. (SPA & ENG., Illus.). 32p. (J). (gr. k-4). per. 7.95 (978-0-9669645-4-7(3) , AlterLingo Bks.) O'Hollow Publishing.

Edwards, Frank B. & Bianchi, John. New at the Zoo. 2001. (New Reader Ser.). (Illus.). 24p. (J). (ps-k). lib. bdg. 14.95 (978-1-894323-29-1(7)); pap. 4.95 (978-1-894323-26-0(2)) Pokeweed Pr. CAN. *Dist:* Fitzhenry & Whiteside, Ltd.

Emmett, Jonathan. The Conjuror's Cookbook Vol. I: Goblin Stew. (Illus.). 64p. (J). pap. 7.99 (978-0-7475-4403-6(4)) Bloomsbury Publishing Plc GBR. *Dist:* Trafalgar Square Publishing.

—The Conjuror's Cookbook Vol. II: Serpent Soup. (Illus.). 64p. (J). pap. 7.99 (978-0-7475-4408-1(5)) Bloomsbury Publishing Plc GBR. *Dist:* Trafalgar Square Publishing.

—The Conjuror's Cookbook Vol. III: Ghostly Goulash. (Illus.). 64p. (J). pap. 7.99 (978-0-7475-4413-5(1)) Bloomsbury Publishing Plc GBR. *Dist:* Trafalgar Square Publishing.

English, Karen. Just Right Stew. Rich, Anna, illus. 32p. (J). (gr. k-2). pap. 8.95 (978-1-59078-168-5(6)) Boyds Mills Pr.

—Just Right Stew. 2003. (Illus.). 32p. (J). (gr. k-4). 15.95 (978-1-56397-487-8(8)) Boyds Mills Pr.

Fajardo, Renee & Ruby, Carl. Chili Today, Hot Tamale & Other Tummy Tales. Fajardo, Renee & Ruby, Carl, eds. 2004. (Illus.). 110p. (YA). (gr. 4-8). pap. 14.00 (978-0-9724472-2-5(9)) Just Enjoyable Memorable Story Bks.

Falwell, Cathryn. Feast for 10. Falwell, Cathryn, illus. 2002. (Illus.). (J). 14.74 (978-0-7587-2485-4(3)) Book Wholesalers, Inc.

—Feast for 10. Falwell, Cathryn, illus. 2003. (Illus.). 28p. (J). (gr. k-ps). bds. 4.95 (978-0-618-38226-2(7) , Clarion Bks.) Houghton Mifflin Co. Trade & Reference Div.

Fearnley, Jan. Mr. Wolf & the Three Bears. 2002. (Illus.). 32p. (J). (ps-2). 16.00 (978-0-15-216423-2(5)) Harcourt Children's Bks.

Ferber, Brenda A. Julia's Kitchen. 2006. (Illus.). 160p. (J). 16.00 (978-0-374-39932-0(8)) Farrar, Straus & Giroux.

Fleming, Maria. Chicken Soup with Rice & Mice. Sasaki, Ellen Joy, illus. 2002. (Word Family Tales Ser.). 16p. (ps-2). pap. 2.95 (978-0-439-26259-0(3)) Scholastic, Inc.

Forde, Catherine. Fat Boy Swim. 2004. 240p. (J). (gr. 7). lib. bdg. 17.99 (978-0-385-90237-3(9) , Delacorte Bks. for Young Readers) Random Hse. Children's Bks.

Fuchs, Menucha. The Little Helpers. 2004. (Illus.). 20p. (J). 6.95 (978-1-932443-14-1(2) , TLHH) Judaica Pr., Inc., The.

Furgang, Kathy. The Cooking Contest. ed. 2003. (Early Connections Ser.). (J). pap. 35.00 (978-1-4108-1560-6(9)) Benchmark Education Co.

Gabriel, Michelle. Rucheleh's Challah. Kaltman, I. Lawrence, illus. 2001. 28p. (J). (gr. k-3). pap. 12.00 (978-0-9643475-1-9(2)) Gabriel Pr.

Gershenson, Harold P. Noodles from Scratch. Mills, Christopher, illus. 2006. (J). (978-1-58987-007-9(7)) Kindermusik International.

Glaser, Linda. Mrs. Greenberg's Messy Hanukkah. Cote, Nancy, illus. 32p. (J). (gr. 1-3). 2006. 6.95 (978-0-8075-5298-8(4)); 2004. 15.95 (978-0-8075-5297-1(6)) Whitman, Albert & Co.

Gomes, Filomena. My Mom Loves Me More Than Sushi. Spires, Ashley, illus. 2006. 24p. (J). pap. (****978-1-897187-13-5(0)***) Second Story Pr.

—My Mom Loves Me More Than Sushi. Spires, Ashley, illus. 2006. 32p. (J). 12.95 (978-1-897187-09-8(2)) Second Story Pr. CAN. *Dist:* Orca Bk. Pubs. USA.

Grim, Katie. Gingerbread Land. 2007. 12p. 19.95 (****978-1-58117-635-3(X)*** , Intervisual/Piggy Toes) Dalmatian Pr.

Harcourt School Publishers Staff. Let's Make Lunch: Take-Home Book. 1999. (Collections Ser.). (Illus.). (J). pap. 1.90 (978-0-15-317200-7(2)) Harcourt Schl. Pubs.

Harris, Joanne. Five Quarters of the Orange. 2002. (gr. 7-12). lib. bdg. 23.40 (978-0-613-62140-3(9)) Tandem Library Bks.

Hartley, Pamela. Dough for It. Wise, Noreen, ed. Wethington, Liz, illus. 2001. (Gold Mixed Collection). 128p. (J). (gr. k-12). pap. 9.95 (978-1-58584-480-7(2)) Huckleberry Pr.

Hechtman, Betty Jacobson, Jr. & Brown Barn Books Staff. Blue Schwartz & Nefertiti's Necklace: A Mystery with Recipes. 2006. 152p. (J). (gr. 5-9). pap. 8.95 (978-0-9768126-3-0(0)) Brown Barn Bks.

Herman, Gail. Scooby-Doo! Snack Snatcher. 2001. (gr. k-3). lib. bdg. 11.80 (978-0-613-36675-5(1)) Tandem Library Bks.

Hester, Denia Lewis. Grandma Lena's Big Ol' Turnip. Urbanovic, Jackie, illus. 2005. 32p. (J). (ps-3). 16.95 (978-0-8075-3027-6(1)) Whitman, Albert & Co.

Holub, Joan. The Pizza That We Made. Cravath, Lynne W., illus. 2001. (Puffin-Easy-to-Read Ser.). 32p. (J). pap. 3.99 (978-0-14-230019-0(5) , Puffin) Penguin Group (USA) Inc.

—Pizza That We Made. 2001. (gr. k-3). lib. bdg. 11.80 (978-0-613-64422-8(0)) Tandem Library Bks.

I Love to Cook. 2003. (Illus.). (J). per. (978-1-57657-959-6(X)) Paradise Pr., Inc.

Jackson, Ellen B. Scatterbrain Sam. Faulkner, Matt, illus. 2001. (J). (gr. k-4). 6.95 (978-0-88106-395-0(9)); 32p. (gr. 3-6). 15.95 (978-0-88106-394-3(0)) Charlesbridge Publishing, Inc.

Jan, Romero Stevens. Carlos Digs to China Carlos Excava Hasta la China. Jeanne, Arnold, illus. 2004. (SPA.). 0032p. pap. 7.95 (978-0-87358-870-6(3) , Rising Moon Bks. for Young Readers) Northland Publishing.

Jarman, Julia. The Magic Backpack. Gon, Adriano, illus. 2004. (Flying Foxes Ser.). 48p. (J). (978-0-7787-1487-3(X)); pap. (978-0-7787-1533-7(7)) Crabtree Publishing Co.

"Johnson, Vincent L. ". Daddy's Good Cookin' 2007. 32p. (J). 16.95 (978-0-9657033-3-8(9)) Marzetta Bks.

Jorden, Edwin W. Cookie Paws. Waywell, Valerie B., illus. 2007. (J). 9.95 (****978-0-9793483-0-3(7)***) Gilded Dog Enterprises LLC.

Kalz, Jill. Tuckerbean in the Kitchen. Mahan, Ben, illus. 2007. (Read-It! Readers Ser.). (J). 19.93 (978-1-4048-2402-7(2)) Picture Window Bks.

Keenan, Penny. Cooking with Ginger: Ginger Gets Lost Book I. Murray, Carol, illus. 2005. (J). per. 19.95 (****978-1-932604-23-8(5)***) Tennessee Valley Publishing.

Keene, Carolyn. Scream for Ice Cream. 2007. (Nancy Drew & the Clue Crew Ser.). 96p. (J). (gr. 2-4). 24.21 (****978-1-59961-347-5(6)***) Spotlight.

Kenah, Katharine. The Best Chef in Second Grade. Carter, Abby, illus. 2007. (I Can Read Bks.). 48p. (J). lib. bdg. 16.89 (****978-0-06-053562-9(8));*** 15.99 (****978-0-06-053561-2(X)***) HarperCollins Pubs.

Kids in the Kitchen Adventures in Learning Book. 2005. (J). 15.95 (978-1-59210-318-8(9)) Whispering Pine Pr., Inc.

Kids in the Kitchen Christian Adventures in Learning Book. 2005. (J). 15.95 (978-1-59210-413-0(4)) Whispering Pine Pr., Inc.

Laird, Donivee Martin. The Magic Shark Learns to Cook. Johnson, Carol Ann, illus. 2004. 48p. (J). 9.95 (978-1-57306-233-6(2)) Bess Pr., Inc.

Law, Felicia. Rumble Meets Chester the Chef. Pak, Yoon Mi, illus. 2006. (Read-It! Readers Ser.). 32p. (J). (gr. 2-4). 18.60 (978-1-4048-1335-9(7)) Picture Window Bks.

—Rumble Meets Wally Warthog. 2005. (Read-It! Readers Ser.). (Illus.). 32p. (J). (ps-k). lib. bdg. 18.60 (978-1-4048-1289-5(X)) Picture Window Bks.

Lawrence, Mike. The Macaroni Disaster! 2006. 44p. pap. 12.00 (978-1-4116-8613-7(6)) Lulu.com.

Leaney, Cindy. Oodles of Noodles. Whitehouse, Patty, ed. King, Sue & Wilks, Peter, illus. 2004. (Friendly Phonics Ser.). 24p. (J). lib. bdg. 14.95 (978-1-59054-030-5(1)) Fitzgerald Bks.

Lee, Quinlan B. What's in Your Lunchbox? Scrumptious Scratch & Sniff Smorgasbord. Raymond, Victoria, illus. 2001. 12p. (J). (ps-k). 6.95 (978-0-694-01585-6(7) , Harper Festival) HarperCollins Pubs.

Leno, Jay & Whitehead, S. B. If Roast Beef Could Fly. 2004. (Illus.). 32p. (J). 17.95 (978-0-689-86767-5(0)) Simon & Schuster Children's Publishing.

Let's Bake Cookies. 1999. (Tami & Moishy Ser.: Vol. 2). (J). bds. 6.95 (978-0-87306-963-2(3)) Feldheim Pubs.

Lin, Grace. Dim Sum for Everyone! Lin, Grace, illus. 2001. (Illus.). 32p. (J). (gr. k-3). 14.95 (978-0-375-81082-4(X) , Knopf Bks. for Young Readers) Random Hse. Children's Bks.

Loehr, Patrick. Mucumber Mcgee & the Half-Eaten Hot Dog. Loehr, Patrick, illus. 2007. (Illus.). 32p. (J). (ps-3). 15.99 (****978-0-06-082327-6(5));*** lib. bdg. 16.89 (****978-0-06-082328-3(3)***) HarperCollins Pubs. (Tegen, Katherine Bks).

Lowell, Jax Peters. No More Cupcakes & Tummy Aches. Kirkwood, Jane, illus. 2004. (ENG.). 44p. (J). (ps-7). per. 26.99 (978-1-4134-6254-8(5)) Xlibris Corp.

Macaroni & Baloney. 2001. 32p. (J). spiral bd. 14.95 (978-0-9702698-1-2(1)) Special Reads for Special Needs.

Markowitz, Susan Meredith. Maggie hace macarrones & Maggie Makes Macaroni. 2005. spiral bd. 66.00 (****978-1-4108-5649-4(6)***) Benchmark Education Co.

Martchenko, Michael. Mmm, Cookies! 2002. (ps-2). lib. bdg. 11.80 (978-0-613-53839-8(0)) Tandem Library Bks.

McAlister, Caroline. Holy Molé! A Folktale from Mexico. Czernecki, Stefan, illus. 2007. 32p. (gr. k-3). 16.95 (978-0-87483-775-9(8)) August Hse. Pubs., Inc.

McNamara, Margaret. Eloise Breaks Some Eggs. Lyon, Tammie, illus. ed. 2005. 30p. (J). lib. bdg. 15.00 (978-1-59054-978-0(3)) Fitzgerald Bks.

—Eloise Breaks Some Eggs. Lyon, Tammie, illus. 2004. (Ready-to-Read Ser.). 32p. (J). pap. 3.99 (978-0-689-87368-3(9) , Aladdin) Simon & Schuster Children's Publishing.

—Eloise Breaks Some Eggs. Lyon, Tammie, illus. 2005. 24p. (J). (ps-1). lib. bdg. 11.19 (978-0-606-33475-4(0)) Tandem Library Bks.

Meredith-Markowitz, Susan. Maggie Makes Macaroni. ed. 2003. (Early Connections Ser.). (J). pap. 33.00 (978-1-4108-1369-5(X)) Benchmark Education Co.

Mills, Charles. The Great Sleepy-Time Stew Rescue. 2004. (Honors Club Story Ser.: Vol. 4). (Illus.). 127p. (J). (978-0-8163-2009-7(8)) Pacific Pr. Publishing Assn.

Mitsui Brown, Janet, illus. Oshogatsu with Obaachan. 2005. (J). (978-1-879965-24-9(0)) Polychrome Publishing Corp.

Monkeys Can't Cook! 2004. (J). 10.95 (978-0-9761350-3-6(5)) Blue Zebra Entertainment, INc.

Mothershead, Martha Fulford. Petoskey Stone Soup. Clarkson, Janet M., illus. 2006. 32p. (J). 18.95 (978-0-9785465-0-2(4)) Whaleback Pr.

Muldrow, Diane. Boiling Point, No. 3. Pollak, Barbara, illus. 2007. (Dish Ser.). 160p. (J). (gr. 4-7). pap. 4.99 (978 0-448-44528-1(X) , Grosset & Dunlap) Penguin Group (USA) Inc.

—Lights! Camera! Cook! Pollak, Barbara, illus. 2007. (Dish Ser.: No. 8). 160p. (J). pap. 4.99 (978-0-448-44533-5(6) , Grosset & Dunlap) Penguin Group (USA) Inc.

—On the Back Burner, No. 6. Pollak, Barbara, illus. 2007. (Dish Ser.). 160p. (J). pap. 4.99 (978-0-448-44531-1(X) , Grosset & Dunlap) Penguin Group (USA) Inc.

—Stirring It Up, No. 1. Pollak, Barbara, illus. 2007. (Dish Ser.). 160p. (J). pap. 4.99 (978-0-448-44526-7(3) , Grosset & Dunlap) Penguin Group (USA) Inc.

—Sweet-and-Sour Summer, No. 9. Pollack, Barbara, illus. 2007. (Dish Ser.). 160p. (J). (gr. 4-7). pap. 4.99 (****978-0-448-44661-5(8)*** , Grosset & Dunlap) Penguin Group (USA) Inc.

—Truth Without the Trimmings. Pollak, Barbara, illus. 2007. (Dish Ser.). 160p. (J). pap. 4.99 (978-0-448-44530-4(1) , Grosset & Dunlap) Penguin Group (USA) Inc.

—Turning up the Heat. Pollak, Barbara, illus. 2007. (Dish! Ser.: Vol. 3). 160p. (J). (gr. 4-7). pap. 4.99 (978-0-448-44527-4(1) , Grosset & Dunlap) Penguin Group (USA) Inc.

Muldrow, Diane. Winner Takes the Cake. Pollack, Barbara, illus. 2007. (Dish Ser.: No. 11). 160p. (J). (gr. 4-7). pap. 4.99 (****978-0-448-44666-0(9)*** , Grosset & Dunlap) Penguin Group (USA) Inc.

Munsch, Robert. Mmmm, Cookies! Martchenko, Michael, illus. 2002. 32p. (J). pap. 3.99 (978-0-590-89604-7(0)) Scholastic, Inc.

Nozick, Betsy. Grandma & Me & Her Secret Recipe. Morgan, Polsky, illus. 2000. 32p. (J). 16.95 (978-1-57168-473-8(5)) Eakin Pr.

Numeroff, Laura Joffe. Mouse Cookies & More: A Treasury. Bond, Felicia, illus. 2006. (If You Give... Ser.). 224p. 24.99 (978-0-06-113763-1(4) , Geringer, Laura Book) HarperCollins Pubs.

O'Keefe, Susan. Death by Eggplant. rev. ed. 2004. 144p. (J). 15.95 (978-1-59643-011-2(7)) Roaring Brook Pr.

Oppenheim, Shulamith Levey. Ali & the Magic Stew. Pels, Winslow, illus. 2003. 32p. (YA). (gr. k-2). 15.95 (978-1-56397-869-2(5)) Boyds Mills Pr.

Oxenbury, Helen. It's My Birthday. Oxenbury, Helen, illus. 2002. (Illus.). (J). 11.91 (978-0-7587-5178-2(8)) Book Wholesalers, Inc.

Park, Frances & Park, Ginger. Where on Earth Is My Bagel? Lin, Grace, illus. 2001. 32p. (J). (ps-4). 16.00 (978-1-58430-033-5(7)) Lee & Low Bks., Inc.

Park, Linda Sue. Bee-Bim Bop! Lee, Ho Baek, illus. 2005. 32p. (J). (gr. k-3). 15.00 (978-0-618-26511-4(2) , Clarion Bks.) Houghton Mifflin Co. Trade & Reference Div.

Paulsen, Gary. The Cookcamp. 2003. 128p. (J). pap. 4.99 (978-0-439-52357-8(5) , Scholastic Paperbacks) Scholastic, Inc.

Pitt, Roosevelt, Jr. A Day at the Four Seasons: "Finding the Ingredients" Kuumba, Mshindo, illus. 2005. (Food Adventures with Charles the Chef Ser.). (J). per. 12.95 (978-0-9760745-0-2(8)) AMARA Entertainment.

Quinn, Lin. Best Mud Pie. 2001. (gr. k-3). lib. bdg. 12.95 (978-0-613-62268-4(5)) Tandem Library Bks.

Random House Disney Staff. Bon Appetit! 2007. (Illus.). 12p. (J). (ps-3). pap. 6.99 (978-0-7364-2437-0(7) , RH/Disney) Random Hse. Children's Bks.

—Ratatouille. 2007. (Read-Aloud Storybook Ser.). (J). 72p. (ps-3). 8.99 (978-0-7364-2440-0(7)); (Illus.). 24p. (gr. k-k). 2.99 (978-0-7364-2423-3(7)); (Illus.). 128p. (gr. 3-7). pap. 4.99 (978-0-7364-2439-4(3)) Random Hse. Children's Bks. (RH/Disney).

—Recipe for Disaster. 2007. (Illus.). 80p. (J). (gr. 2-5). pap. 3.99 (978-0-7364-2449-3(0) , RH/Disney) Random Hse. Children's Bks.

—Run, Remy, Run! 2007. (Step into Reading Ser.). (Illus.). 32p. (J). (ps-1). pap. 3.99 (978-0-7364-2476-9(8)); lib. bdg. 11.99 (978-0-7364-8054-3(4)) Random Hse. Children's Bks. (RH/Disney).

Rau, Dana Meachen. Uncle's Bakery, Level B. Baskin, Janie, illus. 2001. (Compass Point Early Reader Ser.). 32p. (J). (gr. k up). lib. bdg. 18.60 (978-0-7565-0119-8(9)) Compass Point Bks.

Reggier, DeMar & Jensen, Patricia. Good Food. Clar, David Austin, illus. 2006. 32p. (J). (gr. k-1). pap. 3.95 (978-0-516-24969-8(X) , Children's Pr.) Scholastic Library Publishing.

Rex, Michael. The Pie Is Cherry. 2001. (J). 15.95 (978-0-8050-6308-0(0) , Holt, Henry & Co. Bks. For Young Readers) Holt, Henry & Co.

Rey, Margret & Rey, H. A. Curious George Makes Pancakes. 1998. (Curious George Ser.). (Illus.). 24p. (J). (gr. k-3). tchr. ed. 12.95 (978-0-395-91903-3(7)) Houghton Mifflin Co. Trade & Reference Div.

—Curious George Makes Pancakes. Interactive, Vipah, illus. 1998. (Curious George Ser.). 24p. (J). (gr. k-3). pap. 3.95 (978-0-395-91908-8(8)) Houghton Mifflin Co. Trade & Reference Div.

Reynolds, Aaron. Chicks & Salsa. Bogan, Paulette, illus. 32p. (J). (ps-3). 2007. pap. 6.95 (****978-1-59990-099-5(8)*** , Bloomsbury Children); 2005. 16.95 (978-1-58234-972-5(X)) Bloomsbury Publishing.

Rigby Education Staff. Dad's Pasta. (Sails Literacy Ser.). (Illus.). 16p. (gr. 2-3). 27.00 (978-0-7635-9951-5(4) , 699514C99) Rigby Education.

—Pancakes. (Sails Literacy Ser.). (Illus.). 16p. (gr. 1-2). 27.00 (978-0-7635-9911-9(5) , 699115C99) Rigby Education.

Roche, Hannah. My Sister Is Super. 1998. (Science Made Simple Ser.). (Illus.). 24p. (J). (ps-k). pap. (978-1-84089-015-0(0) , 868238Q, Zero to Ten, Limited) Evans Publishing Group.

Rumbley, Rose-Mary. What? No Chili? Rowden, Susan, illus. rev. ed. 2000. 144p. (J). (gr. 6-8). pap. 16.95 (978-0-89015-992-7(0)) Eakin Pr.

Sandman, Rochel. Perfect Porridge: A Story about Kindness. Zakashansky-Zverev, Chana, illus. 2000. 32p. (J). (ps-2). 9.95 (978-0-922613-92-2(3)) Hachai Publishing.

Sanger, Amy Wilson. Hola! Jalapeno. 2004. (Illus.). 20p. (J). bds. 6.95 (978-1-58246-072-7(8) , Tricycle Pr.) Ten Speed Pr.

—A Little Bit of Soul Food. 2004. (World Snacks Ser.). (Illus.). 20p. (J). bds. 6.95 (978-1-58246-109-0(0) , Tricycle Pr.) Ten Speed Pr.

—Yum Yum Dim Sum. 2004. (Illus.). 20p. (J). bds. 6.95 (978-1-58246-108-3(2) , Tricycle Pr.) Ten Speed Pr.

Sargent, Dave, et al. Rays of the Sun Vol. 15: (shoshone) Learn Lessons, 20 vols. Lenoir, Jane, illus. l.t. ed. 2004. (Story Keeper Ser.: 15). 48p. (J). pap. 6.95 (978-1-56763-932-2(1)) Ozark Publishing.

—Rays of the Sun Vol. 15: (Shoshone) Learn Lessons, 20 vols. Lenoir, Jane, illus. l.t. ed. 2004. (Story Keeper Ser.: 15). 48p. (J). lib. bdg. 22.60 (978-1-56763-931-5(3)) Ozark Publishing.

Schachner, Judith B. Mr. Emerson's Cook. 2002. (J). per. 7.95 (978-1-930654-27-3(8)) Reading Matters, Inc.

Secret Soup: Individual Title Six-Packs. (Literatura 2000 Ser.). (gr. 1-2). 28.00 (978-0-7635-0111-2(5)) Rigby Education.

Smith, Sherri L. Hot, Sour, Salty, Sweet. 2008. 176p. (J). (****978-0-385-73417-2(4));*** lib. bdg. (****978-0-385-90431-5(2)***) Dell Publishing. (Delacorte Pr.).

Soto, Gary. Chato's Kitchen. 2002. (Illus.). (J). 14.04 (978-0-7587-2216-4(8)) Book Wholesalers, Inc.

Stanley, George Edward. Frogs' Legs for Dinner? 2000. (Katie Lynn Cookie Company Ser.). (Illus.). (J). (978-0-606-18501-1(1)) Tandem Library Bks.

—Wedding Cookies, No. 4. 2001. (Katie Lynn Cookie Company Ser.). (Illus.). (J). (978-0-606-21278-6(7)) Tandem Library Bks.

Steadman, Ralph. The Jelly Book. Steadman, Ralph, illus. (Illus.). 32p. (J). (ps-3). 14.95 (978-0-87592-026-9(8)) Scroll Pr., Inc.

Stewart, Pauline. What's in the Pan, Man? Ayliffe, Alex, illus. 2002. 32p. (J). 19.99 (978-0-370-32583-5(4)) Random Hse. GBR. *Dist:* Independent Pubs. Group.

Talley, Rebecca C. Grasshopper Pie. Talley, Angela, illus. 2003. 25p. (J). 14.95 (978-1-886249-09-7(1)) WindRiver Publishing.

Thompson, Lisa. Taste of Thailand. Cantell, Brenda, illus. 2006. (Read-It! Chapter Books). 80p. (J). (gr. 2-4). 19.95 (978-1-4048-1677-0(1)) Picture Window Bks.

Too Many Tamales. 2004. (J). (ps-3). 24.95 incl. audio (978-1-55592-098-2(5)); 29.95 incl. cd-rom (978-1-55592-137-8(X)) Weston Woods Studios, Inc.

Torres, Leyla. Sancocho del Sabado. 1999. Tr. of Saturday Sancocho. (978-0-606-16478-8(2)) Tandem Library Bks.

—Sancocho Del Sabado. 1999. (SPA.). (gr. k-3). lib. bdg. 14.10 (978-0-613-17852-5(1)) Tandem Library Bks.

Torrisi, Cathy. Who Will Help Ms. A? Moehl, Crista K., illus. 2002. (Read-To-Me Ser.). 24p. (J). (978-0-7665-1201-6(0)) Abrams, Harry N. , Inc.

Travers, P. L. Mary Poppins in the Kitchen: A Cookery Book with a Story. Shepard, Mary, illus. 2006. 88p. (J). 14.00 (978-0-15-206080-0(4)) Harcourt Children's Bks.

Two Smart Cookies. 2005. 44p. (J). 3.99 (978-0-9763213-5-4(1)) OHC Group LLC.

Urbanovic, Jackie. Duck Soup. 2008. 32p. (J). 17.89 (****978-0-06-121442-4(6)***) HarperCollins Pubs.

—Duck Soup. Urbanovic, Jackie, illus. 2008. 32p. (J). 16.99 (****978-0-06-121441-7(8)***) HarperCollins Pubs.

Wax, Wendy. Picnic Day! Artful Doodlers, illus. 2006. 24p. (J). lib. bdg. 15.00 (****978-1-4242-0952-1(8)***) Fitzgerald Bks.

Weinstock, Robert. Giant Meatball. 2008. (J). (****978-0-15-205595-0(9)***) Harcourt Trade Pubs.

Wellington, Monica. Pizza at Sally's. Wellington, Monica, illus. 2006. (Illus.). 32p. (J). (ps-2). 14.99 (978-0-525-47715-0(2) , Dutton Juvenile) Penguin Group (USA) Inc.

Whaley, Barbara P. Rutabagas for Dinner. Acey-Hendrick, Betty, illus. 1998. 32p. (Orig.). (J). (gr. 3-5). pap. 7.95 (978-1-884242-87-8(1)) Multicultural Pubns.

Whytock, Cherry. My Scrumptious Scottish Dumplings: The Life of Angelica Cookson Potts. Whytock, Cherry, illus. 2006. 192p. (YA). mass mkt. 5.99 (978-0-689-86552-7(X) , Simon Pulse) Simon & Schuster Children's Publishing.

Whytock, Cherry, illus. My Scrumptious Scottish Dumplings: The Life of Angelica Cookson Potts. 2004. 176p. (YA). 14.95 (978-0-689-86549-7(X)) Simon & Schuster Children's Publishing.

Winkler, Henry & Oliver, Lin. Holy Enchilada! Heyer, Carol & Watson, Jesse Joshua, illus. 2004. (Hank Zipzer Ser.: No. 6). 160p. (J). (gr. 3-8). pap. 4.99 (978-0-448-43353-0(2) , Grosset & Dunlap) Penguin Group (USA) Inc.

—Holy Enchilada!, No. 6. Watson, Jesse Joshua, illus. 2004. (Hank Zipzer Ser.: No. 6). 160p. (J). (gr. 3-7). 13.99 (978-0-448-43554-1(3) , Grosset & Dunlap) Penguin Group (USA) Inc.

—Holy Enchilada! 2006. (Hank Zipzer Ser.: No. 6). (J). (gr. 3-8). 24.21 (978-1-59961-105-1(8)) Spotlight.

—Holy Enchilada! 2003. (Hank Zipzer Ser.: No. 6). (gr. 3-6). lib. bdg. 13.00 (978-0-613-72546-0(8)) Tandem Library Bks.

—The Zippity Zinger. 2003. (Hank Zipzer Ser.: No. 4). (Illus.). 160p. (J). (gr. 3-8). mass mkt. 4.99 (978-0-448-43193-2(9) , Grosset & Dunlap) Penguin Group (USA) Inc.

—The Zippity Zinger. Heyer, Carol, illus. 2003. (Hank Zipzer Ser.: No. 4). 160p. (J). 13.99 (978-0-448-43287-8(0) , Grosset & Dunlap) Penguin Group (USA) Inc.

Winner, Ramana Moreno. Freaky Foods from Around the World: Platillos Sorprendentes de todo el Mundo. Haake, Susana, tr. Borsan, Luis, illus. 2004. (ENG & SPA.). (J). (gr. 1-5). pap. 15.95 (978-0-9651174-2-5(1)) BrainStorm 3000.

Winslow, Marjorie. Mud Pies & Other Recipes: A Cookbook for Dolls. Blegvad, Erik, illus. 2001. 48p. (J). (ps-3). 12.95 (978-0-8027-8767-5(3)) Walker & Co.

Wolff, Nancy. Tallulah in the Kitchen. 2005. (Illus.). 40p. (J). 16.95 (978-0-8050-7463-5(5) , Holt, Henry & Co. Bks. For Young Readers) Holt, Henry & Co.

Wong, Janet S. Apple Pie Fourth of July. Chodos-Irvine, Margaret, illus. 2006. 40p. (J). pap. 7.00 (978-0-15-205708-4(0) , Voyager Bks./Libros Viajeros) Harcourt Children's Bks.

Wood, Nancy. Mr. & Mrs. God in the Creation Kitchen. Ering, Timothy Basil, illus. 2006. 32p. (J). (gr. k). 16.99 (978-0-7636-1258-0(8)) Candlewick Pr.

Worth, Bonnie. The Cat in the Hat: Cooking with the Cat. Moroney, Christopher, illus. 2003. (Step into Reading Ser.). 32p. (J). (ps-1). lib. bdg. 11.99 (978-0-375-92494-1(9) , Random Hse. Bks. for Young Readers) Random Hse. Children's Bks.

—Cooking with the Cat. Moroney, Christopher, illus. 2003. (Step into Reading Ser.). 32p. (J). (ps-1). pap. 3.99 (978-0-375-82494-4(4) , 53560581, Random Hse. Bks. for Young Readers) Random Hse. Children's Bks.

Zolkower, Edie Stoltz. Too Many Cooks: A Passover Parable. 2000. (gr. k-3). lib. bdg. 14.10 (978-0-613-81767-7(2)) Tandem Library Bks.

COOKERY (FISH)

Green, Bessie. How to Make Fish Strips. Nevak, Caroline, illus. l.t. ed. 1999. 12p. (J). (gr. k-3). pap. 17.00 (978-1-58084-072-9(8)) Lower Kuskokwim Schl. District.

—KiarneruaIiyaraq. Nevak, Caroline, illus. l.t. ed. 1999. Tr. of How to Make Fish Strips. (ESK.). 12p. (J). (gr. k-3). pap. 17.00 (978-1-58084-073-6(6)) Lower Kuskokwim Schl. District.

Ono, Kaoru. Sushi for Kids: A Children's Introduction to Japan's Favorite Food. Howlett, Peter et al, trs. from JPN. 2003. (Illus.). 32p. 10.95 (978-0-8048-3346-2(X)) Tuttle Publishing.

COOKERY (NATURAL FOODS)

Karmel, Annabel. Toddler Cookbook. 2008. 48p. (J). (gr. 5). 10.99 (*978-0-7566-3505-3(5)) Dorling Kindersley Publishing, Inc.

COOKERY (SEAFOOD)

Draper, Charla L. Cooking on Nineteenth-Century Whaling Ships. 2000. (Blue Earth Books). (Illus.). 32p. (J). (gr. 3-4). lib. bdg. 22.60 (978-0-7368-0602-2(4) , Bridgestone Bks.) Capstone Pr., Inc.

Green, Bessie. How to Make Fish Strips. Nevak, Caroline, illus. l.t. ed. 1999. 12p. (J). (gr. k-3). pap. 17.00 (978-1-58084-072-9(8)) Lower Kuskokwim Schl. District.

COOKERY (VEGETABLES)

Cornell, Kari & Turkoglu, Nurcay. Cooking the Turkish Way. 2nd rev. ed. 2004. (Easy Menu Ethnic Cookbooks). (Illus.). 72p. (J). 25.26 (978-0-8225-4123-3(8) , Carolrhoda Bks.) Lerner Publishing Group.

Dasa, Kurma. Quick Vegetarian Dishes: Recipes You Can Prepare in a Hurry. 2002. (Illus.). 220p. (J). 24.95 (978-0-9578345-0-7(0)) Mandala Publishing.

Gillies, Judi. Jumbo Vegetarian Cookbook. 2002. (gr. 3-6). lib. bdg. 24.55 (978-0-613-56468-7(5)) Tandem Library Bks.

Hughes, Meredith Sayles. Stinky & Stringy: Stem & Bulb Vegetables. 1998. (Plants We Eat Ser.). (Illus.). 104p. (gr. 6-9). 26.60 (978-0-8225-2833-3(9)) Lerner Publishing Group.

Hughes, Meredith Sayles & Hughes, E. Thomas. Cool as a Cucumber, Hot as a Pepper: Fruit Vegetables. 1998. (Plants We Eat Ser.). (Illus.). 80p. (J). (gr. 5-7). 26.60 (978-0-8225-2832-6(0) , Lerner Pubns.) Lerner Publishing Group.

Spilsbury, Louise. Carrots. 2003. (Food Ser.). (Illus.). 32p. (J). (gr. k-2). lib. bdg. 22.79 (978-1-58810-616-2(0)) Heinemann Library.

—Peas. 2003. (Food Ser.). (Illus.). 32p. (J). (gr. k-2). lib. bdg. 22.79 (978-1-58810-620-9(9)) Heinemann Library.

Watt, Fiona. Vegetarian Cooking. rev. ed. 2004. (Cooking School Ser.). (Illus.). 48p. (J). lib. bdg. 15.95 (978-1-58086-566-1(6)) EDC Publishing.

COOKERY (WINE)

Braker, Festive Baker. 2008. 35.00 (978-0-8118-4547-2(8)) Chronicle Bks. LLC.

Harris, Jessica B. Martha's Vineyard Table. Cushner, Susie, photos by. 2007. (Illus.). 204p. 35.00 (978-0-8118-4999-9(6)) Chronicle Bks. LLC.

Viestad, Andreas. Where Flavor Was Born. 2007. (Illus.). 288p. 40.00 (978-0-8118-4965-4(1)) Chronicle Bks. LLC.

COOKERY, AFRICAN AMERICAN

see African American Cookery

COOKERY, AMERICAN

Behnke, Alison, et al. Cooking the Central American Way. 2nd rev. ed. 2005. (Easy Menu Ethnic Cookbooks). (Illus.). 72p. (J). 25.26 (978-0-8225-1236-3(X) , Lerner Pubns.) Lerner Publishing Group.

Blue Earth Books: Exploring History Through Simple Recipes, 12 bks. Incl. American Indian Cooking Before 1500. Gunderson, Mary. lib. bdg. 22.60 (978-0-7368-0605-3(9)); California Gold Rush Cooking. Schroeder, Lisa Golden. lib. bdg. 22.60 (978-0-7368-0603-9(2)); Civil War Cooking : The Confederacy. Dosier, Susan. lib. bdg. 22.60 (978-0-7368-0350-2(5)); Civil War Cooking : The Union. Dosier, Susan. lib. bdg. (978-0-7368-0351-9(3)); Colonial Cooking. Dosier, Susan. lib. bdg. 22.60 (978-0-7368-0352-6(1)); Cooking on Nineteenth-Century Whaling Ships. Draper, Charla L. lib. bdg. 22.60 (978-0-7368-0602-2(4)); Cooking on the Lewis & Clark Expedition. Gunderson, Mary. lib. bdg. 22.60 (978-0-7368-0354-0(8)); Cowboy Cooking. Gunderson, Mary. lib. bdg. 22.60 (978-0-7368-0353-3(X)); Nineteenth-Century Lumber Camp Cooking. Fischer, Maureen M. lib. bdg. 22.60 (978-0-7368-0604-6(0)); Oregon Trail Cooking. Gunderson, Mary. lib. bdg. 22.60 (978-0-7368-0355-7(6)); Pioneer Farm Cooking. Gunderson, Mary. lib. bdg. 22.60 (978-0-7368-0356-4(4)); Southern Plantation Cooking. Gunderson, Mary. lib. bdg. 22.60 (978-0-7368-0357-1(2)); 32p. (J). (gr. 3-4). 2000. (Illus.). Set lib. bdg. 271.20 (978-0-7368-0680-0(6) , Bridgestone Bks.) Capstone Pr., Inc.

Bradley, Barbara. Hawaiian Kids Cook & Color Book. pap. 5.95 (978-0-930492-43-4(9)) Hawaiian Service, Inc.

Cobb, L. B., compiled by. Old-Fashioned Recipes for Modern Cooks: Foods with All the Flavor You Remember in Grandmother's Cooking. 2001. 112p. pap. 12.00 (978-0-9706224-0-2(6) , Advance Bks. Co.) Advance Bks. Co.

Culinary Institute of America Staff, contrib. by. Mexican American. 2005. (American Regional Cooking Library). (Illus.). 72p. (J). lib. bdg. (978-1-59084-622-3(2)) Mason Crest Pubs.

D'Amico, Joan & Drummond, Karen Eich. The U. S. History Cookbook: Delicious Recipes & Exciting Events from the Past. Cline, Jeff & Cash-Walsh, Tina, illus. 2003. 192p. pap. 14.95 (978-0-471-13602-6(6) , Howell Bk. Hse.) Wiley, John & Sons, Inc.

D'Amico, Joan & Drumond, Karen Eich. The US History Cook Book: Delicious Recipes & Exciting Events from the Past. 2006. (Illus.). 180p. (J). (gr. 4-8). reprint ed. pap. 15.00 (*978-1-4223-5809-2(7)) DIANE Publishing Co.

Dosier, Susan. Civil War Cooking: The Confederacy. 2000. (Blue Earth Books). (Illus.). 32p. (J). (gr. 3-4). lib. bdg. 22.60 (978-0-7368-0350-2(5) , Bridgestone Bks.) Capstone Pr., Inc.

—Civil War Cooking: The Confederacy. 1999. (Exploring History Through Simple Recipes Ser.). (Illus.). 32p. (J). (gr. 2-7). pap. 14.60 (978-0-516-21933-2(2) , Children's Pr.) Scholastic Library Publishing.

—Civil War Cooking: The Union. 2000. (Blue Earth Books). (Illus.). 32p. (J). (gr. 3-4). lib. bdg. (978-0-7368-0351-9(3) , Bridgestone Bks.) Capstone Pr., Inc.

—Civil War Cooking: The Union. 1999. (Exploring History Through Simple Recipes Ser.). (Illus.). 32p. (J). (gr. 2-7). pap. 14.60 (978-0-516-21862-5(X) , Children's Pr.) Scholastic Library Publishing.

—Colonial Cooking. 2000. (Blue Earth Books). (Illus.). 32p. (J). (gr. 3-4). lib. bdg. 22.60 (978-0-7368-0352-6(1) , Bridgestone Bks.) Capstone Pr., Inc.

—Colonial Cooking. 1999. (Exploring History Through Simple Recipes Ser.). (Illus.). 32p. (J). (gr. 2-7). pap. 14.60 (978-0-516-21863-2(8) , Children's Pr.) Scholastic Library Publishing.

Drummond, Karen Eich. United States Cookbook: Fabulous Foods & Fascinating Facts from All 50 States. Cline, Jeff & Cash-Walsh, Tina, illus. 2000. 186p. (J). (ps-7). per. 22.20 (978-0-613-27385-5(0)) Tandem Library Bks.

Drummond, Karen Eich & D'Amico, Joan. The Coming to America Cookbook: Delicious Recipes & Fascinating Stories from America's Many Cultures. 2005. (Illus.). 192p. (ps-7). pap. 14.95 (978-0-471-48335-9(4) , Wiley) Wiley, John & Sons, Inc.

Farmer, Fannie. Original 1896 Boston Cooking-School Cook Book. 2000. (YA). 37.95 (978-0-8488-2929-2(8)) Amereon LTD.

Fischer, Maureen M. Nineteenth-Century Lumber Camp Cooking. 2000. (Blue Earth Books). (Illus.). 32p. (J). (gr. 3-4). lib. bdg. 22.60 (978-0-7368-0604-6(0) , Bridgestone Bks.) Capstone Pr., Inc.

Florence, Sarah. Pilgrim Food & Recipes. 2002. (Reading Room Collection). (J). pap. (978-0-8239-8165-6(7)); (Illus.). 24p. lib. bdg. 18.75 (978-0-8239-3728-8(3)) Rosen Publishing Group, Inc., The.

Gammon, Shana B. The Great State Cookbook: Recipes from Around the Country-for Kids. 2003. (Illus.). 62p. (J). spiral bd., act. bk. ed. 8.95 (978-0-9743795-0-0(6)) Willow Tree Pr.

George, Lynn. Civil War Recipes: Adding & Subtracting Simple Fractions. 2004. (PowerMath Ser.). (Illus.). 24p. (J). lib. bdg. (978-0-8239-8896-9(1)); lib. bdg. 21.25 (978-0-8239-8973-7(9)) Rosen Publishing Group, Inc., The. (PowerKids Pr.).

Gooseberry Patch Staff, ed. M423 Country Friends Kids in the Kitchen: Kid-size adventures at the kitchen Counter. 2002. (Country Friends Collection: 36). (ENG.). 32p. pap. 4.95 (978-1-931890-25-0(0)) Gooseberry Patch.

Gunderson, Mary. American Indian Cooking Before 1500. 2000. (Blue Earth Books). (Illus.). 32p. (J). (gr. 3-4). lib. bdg. 22.60 (978-0-7368-0605-3(9) , Bridgestone Bks.) Capstone Pr., Inc.

—Cooking on the Lewis & Clark Expedition. 2000. (Blue Earth Books). (Illus.). 32p. (J). (gr. 3-4). lib. bdg. 22.60 (978-0-7368-0354-0(8) , Bridgestone Bks.) Capstone Pr., Inc.

—Cooking on the Lewis & Clark Expedition. 1999. (Exploring History Through Simple Recipes Ser.). (Illus.). 32p. (J). (gr. 2-7). pap. 14.60 (978-0-516-21865-6(4) , Children's Pr.) Scholastic Library Publishing.

—Oregon Trail Cooking. 2000. (Blue Earth Books). (Illus.). 32p. (J). (gr. 3-4). lib. bdg. 22.60 (978-0-7368-0355-7(6) , Bridgestone Bks.) Capstone Pr., Inc.

—Oregon Trail Cooking. 1999. (Exploring History Through Simple Recipes Ser.). (Illus.). 32p. (J). (gr. 2-7). pap. 14.60 (978-0-516-21866-3(2) , Children's Pr.) Scholastic Library Publishing.

Hale, Sarah J. Early American Cookery. 2000. (YA). 20.95 (978-0-8488-2932-2(8)) Amereon LTD.

Hunt, Sharon. African-American Georgia Kids Cookbook: Kid's Cookin' 1999. pap. (978-0-9654517-1-0(2)) African American Queen Hunt Production, Inc.

—Dinner Cookbook for Men at Work: Menus, Recipes & Market Orders. 1999. pap. (978-0-9654517-2-7(0)) African American Queen Hunt Production, Inc.

Ichord, Loretta Frances. Hasty Pudding, Johnnycakes, & Other Good Stuff: Cooking in Colonial America. 2000. (Illus.). (J). 15.75 (978-0-606-18291-1(8)) Tandem Library Bks.

Ichord, Loretta Frances & Millbrook Press. Skillet Bread, Sourdough, & Vinegar Days: Cooking in Pioneer Days. Ellis, Jan Davey, illus. 2005. 64p. (J). (gr. 4-8). pap. 8.95 (978-0-7613-9521-8(0) , First Avenue Editions) Lerner Publishing Group.

Kalman, Bobbie. Breakfast Blast: Step-by-Step Recipes. 2003. (Kid Power Ser.). (Illus.). 32p. (J). (gr. 3). (978-0-7787-1250-3(8)); pap. (978-0-7787-1272-5(9)) Crabtree Publishing Co.

—Colonial Cook. 2002. (gr. k-3). lib. bdg. 16.40 (978-0-613-87234-8(7)) Tandem Library Bks.

—Pioneer Recipes. 2001. (gr. 3-6). lib. bdg. 16.40 (978-0-613-32950-7(3)); 2000. (J). (978-0-606-20111-7(4)) Tandem Library Bks.

Kalman, Bobbie, et al. Pioneer Recipes. 2000. (Historic Communities Ser.). (Illus.). 32p. (J). (gr. 3). pap. (978-0-86505-468-4(1)); lib. bdg. (978-0-86505-438-7(X)) Crabtree Publishing Co.

Kuntz, Lynn & Fleming, Jan. American Grub: Eats for Kids from All Fifty States. Hicks, Mark A., illus. 2003. 80p. (YA). pap. 7.95 (978-1-58685-260-3(4)) Gibbs Smith, Publisher.

Larkin, Tanya. Cooking Throughout American History Set 2, 6 bks. Incl. What Was Cooking in Abigail Adam's White House? lib. bdg. 19.95 (978-0-8239-5607-4(5)); What Was Cooking in Dolly Madison's White House? lib. bdg. 19.95 (978-0-8239-5608-1(3)); What Was Cooking in Edith Roosevelt's White House? lib. bdg. 19.95 (978-0-8239-5610-4(5)); What Was Cooking in Julia Grant's White House? lib. bdg. 19.95 (978-0-8239-5611-1(3)); What Was Cooking in Martha Washington's Presidential Mansions? lib. bdg. 19.95 (978-0-8239-5606-7(7)); What Was Cooking in Mary Todd Lincoln's White House? lib. bdg. 19.95 (978-0-8239-5609-8(1)); 24p. (J). (gr. 3). 2001. (Illus.). Set lib. bdg. 117.00 (978-0-8239-7062-9(0) , PowerKids Pr.) Rosen Publishing Group, Inc., The.

—What Was Cooking in Abigail Adam's White House? 2001. (Cooking Throughout American History Ser.). (Illus.). 24p. (J). (gr. 3). lib. bdg. 19.95 (978-0-8239-5607-4(5) , PowerKids Pr.) Rosen Publishing Group, Inc., The.

—What Was Cooking in Dolly Madison's White House? 2001. (Cooking Throughout American History Ser.). (Illus.). 24p. (J). (gr. 3). lib. bdg. 19.95 (978-0-8239-5608-1(3) , PowerKids Pr.) Rosen Publishing Group, Inc., The.

—What Was Cooking in Edith Roosevelt's White House? 2001. (Cooking Throughout American History Ser.). (Illus.). 24p. (J). (gr. 3). lib. bdg. 19.95 (978-0-8239-5610-4(5) , PowerKids Pr.) Rosen Publishing Group, Inc., The.

—What Was Cooking in Julia Grant's White House? 2001. (Cooking Throughout American History Ser.). (Illus.). 24p. (J). (gr. 3). lib. bdg. 19.95 (978-0-8239-5611-1(3) , PowerKids Pr.) Rosen Publishing Group, Inc., The.

—What Was Cooking in Martha Washington's Presidential Mansions? 2001. (Cooking Throughout American History Ser.). (Illus.). 24p. (J). (gr. 3). lib. bdg. 19.95 (978-0-8239-5606-7(7) , PowerKids Pr.) Rosen Publishing Group, Inc., The.

—What Was Cooking in Mary Todd Lincoln's White House? 2001. (Cooking Throughout American History Ser.). (Illus.). 24p. (J). (gr. 3). lib. bdg. 19.95 (978-0-8239-5609-8(1) , PowerKids Pr.) Rosen Publishing Group, Inc., The.

Libal, Autumn. Cuban Americans: Exiles from an Island Home, 16 vols. 2006. (Illus.). 112p. (J). lib. bdg. (978-1-59084-924-8(8) , 1234497) Mason Crest Pubs.

Libal, Joyce. California. 2005. (American Regional Cooking Library). (Illus.). 72p. (J). lib. bdg. (978-1-59084-613-1(3)) Mason Crest Pubs.

—Southern. 2005. (American Regional Cooking Library). (Illus.). 72p. (J). lib. bdg. (978-1-59084-621-6(4)) Mason Crest Pubs.

—Texas. 2005. (American Regional Cooking Library). (Illus.). 72p. (J). lib. bdg. (978-1-59084-623-0(0)) Mason Crest Pubs.

Libal, Joyce, compiled by. Mid-Atlantic Cooking. 2005. (American Regional Cooking Library). (Illus.). 72p. (J). lib. bdg. (978-1-59084-618-6(4)) Mason Crest Pubs.

Picone, Linda. Food & Drink in Colonial America. 2004. (Everyday Life Long Ago Ser.). (J). (978-0-7368-2161-2(9) , Blue Earth Bks.) Capstone Pr., Inc.

Publications International, Ltd Staff, contrib. by. Kids Love It. 2005. (Illus.). 192p. (J). (978-1-4127-2116-5(4)) Publications International, Ltd.

Rau, Dana Meachen. Food & Cooking in American History. 2006. (Illus.). 24p. (J). pap. (978-0-8368-7213-2(4)); lib. bdg. (978-0-8368-7206-4(1)) Stevens, Gareth Inc.

Sagan, Miriam. The Middle Atlantic States. Date not set. (American Food Library). 48p. (J). (gr. 3-6). lib. bdg. 22.60 (978-0-86625-508-0(7)) Rourke Publishing, LLC.

Sanna, Ellyn, compiled by. American Indian. 2005. (American Regional Cooking Library). (Illus.). 72p. (J). lib. bdg. (978-1-59084-611-7(7)) Mason Crest Pubs.

Schroeder, Lisa Golden. California Gold Rush Cooking. 2000. (Blue Earth Books). (Illus.). 32p. (J). (gr. 3-4). lib. bdg. 22.60 (978-0-7368-0603-9(2) , Bridgestone Bks.) Capstone Pr., Inc.

Therrien, Patricia. Southern Appalachian Cooking. 2005. (American Regional Cooking Library). (Illus.). 72p. (J). lib. bdg. (978-1-59084-620-9(6)) Mason Crest Pubs.

Thomas, Mark. Food in Colonial America. 2002. (Wel-Colonial America Ser.). (Illus.). 24p. (J). (ps-2). 18.00 (978-0-516-23936-1(8)); pap. 4.95 (978-0-516-23491-5(9)) Scholastic Library Publishing. (Children's Pr.).

—Food in Colonial America. 2002. (gr. k-3). lib. bdg. 12.95 (978-0-613-58772-3(3)) Tandem Library Bks.

Vazquez, Itos, contrib. by. La Cocina Argentina.Tr. of Argentine Cooking. (SPA., Illus.). 160p. 15.95 (978-958-30-0592-3(4) , PV12640) Panamericana Editorial COL. *Dist:* Lectorum Pubns., Inc.

—La Cocina Colombiana.Tr. of Colombian Cooking. (SPA., Illus.). 160p. 15.95 (978-958-30-0596-1(7) , PV1193) Panamericana Editorial COL. *Dist:* Lectorum Pubns., Inc.

—La Cocina Peruana.Tr. of Peruvian Cooking. (SPA., Illus.). 160p. 15.95 (978-958-30-0594-7(0) , PV11200) Panamericana Editorial COL. *Dist:* Lectorum Pubns., Inc.

—La Cocina Venezolana.Tr. of Venezuelan Cooking. (SPA., Illus.). 160p. 15.95 (978-958-30-0597-8(5) , PV12642) Panamericana Editorial COL. *Dist:* Lectorum Pubns., Inc.

Williams, Thelma. Our Family Table: Recipes & Food Memories from African-American Life Models. 2004. (Illus.). 94p. (YA). reprint ed. 15.00 (978-0-7567-8093-7(4)) DIANE Publishing Co.

Williamson, Sarah A. & Williamson, Zachary. Kids Cook! Fabulous Food for the Whole Family. Williamson, Susan, ed. Trezzo, Loretta, illus. 1999. (Kids Can Bks.: No. 6). 160p. (J). (gr. 2 up). pap. 12.95 (978-0-913589-61-8(6) , Williamson Bks.) Ideals Pubns.

COOKERY, AMERICAN—NEW ENGLAND STYLE

Libal, Joyce. New England. 2005. (American Regional Cooking Library). (Illus.). 72p. (J). lib. bdg. (978-1-59084-617-9(6)) Mason Crest Pubs.

COOKERY, ASIAN

Nguyen, Chi & Monroe, Judy. Cooking the Vietnamese Way: Includes New Low-Fat & Vegetarian Recipes. rev. expurg. ed. 2003. (Easy Menu Ethnic Cookbooks). (Illus.). 72p. pap. 7.95 (978-0-8225-0513-6(4)) Lerner Publishing Group.

Sanmugam, Devagi. Fun with Asian Food: A Kids' Cookbook. 2005. (Illus.). 32p. (J). 15.95 (978-0-7946-0339-7(4)) Tuttle Publishing.

Sanna, Ellyn, compiled by. American Indian. 2005. (American Regional Cooking Library). (Illus.). 72p. (J). lib. bdg. (978-1-59084-611-7(7)) Mason Crest Pubs.

Sheen, Barbara. Foods of India. 2006. (Illus.). 64p. (J). (gr. 3-6). 27.45 (978-0-7377-3553-6(8) , Kidhaven) Thomson Gale.

Townsend, Sue & Young, Caroline. Vietnam. 2003. 48p. (J). pap. 7.95 (978-1-4034-3654-2(1)); (Illus.). lib. bdg. 27.07 (978-1-4034-0980-5(3)) Heinemann.

Weston, Reiko. Cooking the Japanese Way. 2nd rev. exp. ed. 2002. (Easy Menu Ethnic Cookbooks). (Illus.). 72p. (J). (gr. 5-12). 25.26 (978-0-8225-4114-1(9) , Lerner Pubns.) Lerner Publishing Group.

COOKERY, CHINESE

Beatty, Theresa M. Food & Recipes of China. 1999. (Kids in the Kitchen). (Illus.). 24p. (J). (gr. k-4). lib. bdg. 19.95 (978-0-8239-5222-9(3) , PowerKids Pr.) Rosen Publishing Group, Inc., The.

Hoyt-Goldsmith, Diane. Celebrating Chinese New Year. Migdale, Lawrence, photos by. (Illus.). 32p. (YA). (gr. 4-6). tchr. ed. 17.95 (978-0-8234-1393-5(4)) Holiday Hse., Inc.

Lee, Frances. The Young Chef's Chinese Cookbook: Step-by-Step Fun Recipes for Young Chefs. 2001. (I'm the Chef! Ser.). (Illus.). 32p. (J). (gr. 3). (978-0-7787-0280-1(4)); pap. (978-0-7787-0294-8(4)) Crabtree Publishing Co.

Maher, Erin. Chinese Foods & Recipes. 2002. (Reading Room Collection). (Illus.). 24p. (J). lib. bdg. 18.75 (978-0-8239-3748-6(8)) Rosen Publishing Group, Inc., The.

McCulloch, Julie. China. (Illus.). 48p. (J). 2002. (gr. 4-6). (978-1-58810-386-4(2) , 91136); 2001. (gr. 3-5). lib. bdg. 25.64 (978-1-58810-152-5(5)) Heinemann Library.

Sheen, Barbara. Foods of China. 2006. (Taste of Culture Ser.). 64p. (J). (gr. 3-6). 27.45 (978-0-7377-3031-9(5) , Greenhaven Pr., Inc.) Thomson Gale.

Thompson, Stuart, et al. Chinese Cookbook. 2001. (Holiday Cookbooks from Around the World). (Illus.). 32p. (J). lib. bdg. 25.69 (978-0-7398-3262-2(X)) Raintree.

Yu, Ling. Cooking the Chinese Way. 2nd exp. rev. ed. (Easy Menu Ethnic Cookbooks). (Illus.). 72p. (J). (gr. 5-12). 2002. lib. bdg. 25.26 (978-0-8225-4104-2(1)); 2003. pap. 7.95 (978-0-8225-4160-8(2)) Lerner Publishing Group.

—Cooking the Chinese Way. 2001. (Illus.). 72p. (J). (gr. 4-7). lib. bdg. 16.40 (978-0-613-59145-4(3)) Tandem Library Bks.

COOKERY, ENGLISH

Hill, Barbara W. Cooking the English Way. 2nd rev. ed. 2003. (Easy Menu Ethnic Cookbooks). (Illus.). 72p. (J). (gr. 5-12). 25.26 (978-0-8225-4105-9(X)) Lerner Publishing Group.

COOKERY, FRENCH

Crump, A. K., ed. Chocolate French: Recipes, Language, & Directions to Francais Au Chocolat. 2004. (Illus.). 192p. (gr. 10). pap. 19.95 (978-0-9674898-4-1(9)) TCB-Cafe Publishing.

Fisher, Teresa. A Flavor of France. 1999. (Food & Festivals Ser.). (Illus.). 32p. (J). (gr. 1-4). lib. bdg. 25.69 (978-0-8172-5550-3(8)) Raintree.

Gioffre, Rosalba. The Young Chef's French Cookbook: Step-by-Step Fun Recipes for Young Chefs. 2001. (I'm the Chef! Ser.). (Illus.). 32p. (J). (gr. 3). (978-0-7787-0282-5(0)); pap. (978-0-7787-0296-2(0)) Crabtree Publishing Co.

Locricchio, Matthew. The Cooking of France. 2002. (Superchef Ser.). (Illus.). 79p. (J). 29.93 (978-0-7614-1216-8(6) , Benchmark Bks.) Cavendish, Marshall Corp.

Murphy, Frank. Thomas Jefferson's Feast. Walz, Richard, illus. 2003. 48p. (J). (gr. 2-4). pap. 3.99 (978-0-375-82289-6(5) , Random Hse. Bks. for Young Readers) Random Hse. Children's Bks.

—Thomas Jefferson's Feast. 2003. (gr. k-3). lib. bdg. 11.80 (978-0-613-86238-7(4)) Tandem Library Bks.

Parks, Peggy J. Foods of France. 2005. (Taste of Culture Ser.). (Illus.). 64p. (J). (gr. 4-8). lib. bdg. 27.45 (978-0-7377-3032-6(3) , Greenhaven Pr., Inc.) Thomson Gale.

Townsend, Sue. France. 2002. (World of Recipes Ser.). (Illus.). 48p. (J). (gr. 3-5). lib. bdg. 27.07 (978-1-58810-609-4(8)) Heinemann Library.

Waldee, Lynne Marie. Cooking the French Way. 2nd rev. exp. ed. 2002. (Easy Menu Ethnic Cookbooks). (Illus.). 72p. (J). (gr. 5-12). 25.26 (978-0-8225-4106-6(8)) Lerner Publishing Group.

COOKERY, GERMAN

Parnell, Helga. Cooking the German Way. 2nd rev. ed. 2003. (Easy Menu Ethnic Cookbooks). (Illus.). 72p. (J). (gr. 5-12). 25.26 (978-0-8225-4107-3(6)) Lerner Publishing Group.

Sheen, Barbara. Foods of Germany. 2006. 64p. (J). (gr. 3-6). 27.45 (978-0-7377-3554-3(6) , Kidhaven) Thomson Gale.

Townsend, Sue. Germany. 2002. (World of Recipes Ser.). (Illus.). 48p. (J). (gr. 3-5). lib. bdg. 27.07 (978-1-58810-610-0(1)) Heinemann Library.

A Traditional German Christmas. 2002. (Illus.). 144p. per. 14.95 (978-0-9717114-0-2(2)) S&V Publishing Co.

COOKERY, GREEK

Beatty, Theresa M. Food & Recipes of Greece. 1999. (Kids in the Kitchen). (Illus.). 24p. (J). (gr. k-4). lib. bdg. 19.95 (978-0-8239-5223-6(1) , PowerKids Pr.) Rosen Publishing Group, Inc., The.

McLeese, Tex. Rodeo Roping. 2001. (Illus.). 24p. (J). (gr. 1-4). lib. bdg. 19.27 (978-1-57103-348-2(3)) Rourke Publishing, LLC.

Townsend, Sue. Greece. 2002. (World of Recipes Ser.). (Illus.). 48p. (J). (gr. 3-5). lib. bdg. 27.07 (978-1-58810-611-7(X)) Heinemann Library.

Villios, Lynne W. Cooking the Greek Way. 2003. (Easy Menu Ethnic Cookbooks). (Illus.). 72p. pap. 7.95 (978-0-8225-0533-4(9)) Lerner Publishing Group.

—Cooking the Greek Way. Wolfe, Robert L. & Wolfe, Diane, illus. Wolfe, Robert L. & Wolfe, Diane, photos by. 2nd rev. expurg. ed. 2002. (Easy Menu Ethnic Cookbooks). 72p. (J). (gr. 5-12). lib. bdg. 25.26 (978-0-8225-4131-8(9)) Lerner Publishing Group.

—Cooking the Greek Way. 2002. (gr. 5-8). lib. bdg. 16.40 (978-0-613-76567-1(2)) Tandem Library Bks.

COOKERY, HUNGARIAN

Hargittai, Magdolna. Cooking the Hungarian Way. 2nd rev. ed. 2003. (Easy Menu Ethnic Cookbooks). (Illus.). 72p. (J). 25.26 (978-0-8225-4132-5(7) , Lerner Pubns.) Lerner Publishing Group.

COOKERY, INTERNATIONAL

Ashworth, Sue. Desserts. 2004. (World of Recipes Ser.). (Illus.). 48p. (J). lib. bdg. (978-1-4034-4698-5(9)) Heinemann Library.

—Snacks. 2004. (World of Recipes Ser.). (Illus.). 48p. (J). lib. bdg. (978-1-4034-4700-5(4)) Heinemann Library.

Behnke, Alison, compiled by. Vegetarian Cooking Around the World. 2nd rev. expurg. ed. 2002. (Easy Menu Ethnic Cookbooks). (Illus.). 72p. (J). 25.26 (978-0-8225-4130-1(0) , Lerner Pubns.) Lerner Publishing Group.

Braman, Arlette. Kids Around the World Cook! the Best Foods & Recipes from Many Lands. 2000. (gr. 3-6). lib. bdg. 22.20 (978-0-613-25879-1(7)) Tandem Library Bks.

Braman, Arlette N. Kids Around the World Cook! The Best Foods & Recipes from Many Lands. 2000. (J). (978-0-606-19689-5(7)) Tandem Library Bks.

—Kids Around the World Cook! The Best Foods & Recipes from Many Lands. Bosson, Jo-Ellen, illus. 2000. (Kids Around the World Ser.: Vol. 1). 128p. (gr. 4-7). pap. 12.95 (978-0-471-35251-8(9) , Wiley-Interscience) Wiley, John & Sons, Inc.

Cornell, Kari A., ed. Holiday Cooking Around the World. Wolfe, Robert L. & Wolfe, Diane, illus. Wolfe, Robert L. & Wolfe, Diane, photos by. 2nd rev. exp. ed. 2003. (Easy Menu Ethnic Cookbooks). 72p. (J). (gr. 5-12). pap. 7.95 (978-0-8225-4159-2(9)) Lerner Publishing Group.

Dorling Kindersley Publishing Staff & Fedele, Frank. The Artist's Palate: Cooking with the World's Great Artists. 2003. (Illus.). 192p. 30.00 (978-0-7894-7768-2(8)) Dorling Kindersley Publishing, Inc.

Drummond, Karen Eich & D'Amico, Joan. The Coming to America Cookbook: Delicious Recipes & Fascinating Stories from America's Many Cultures. 2005. (Illus.). 192p. (ps-7). pap. 14.95 (978-0-471-48335-9(4) , Wiley) Wiley, John & Sons, Inc.

Engfer, Lee, ed. Desserts Around the World. 2nd rev. ed. 2004. (Easy Menu Ethnic Cookbooks). (Illus.). 72p. (J). 25.26 (978-0-8225-4126-4(2)) Lerner Publishing Group.

Gregoire, Maryellen. Morning Meals Around the World. Yesh, Jeff, illus. 2004. (Meals Around the World Ser.). 24p. (J). (gr. k-4). 22.60 (978-1-4048-0280-3(0) , 1229527) Picture Window Bks.

Kalman, Bobbie. Multicultural Meals. 2003. (gr. 3-6). lib. bdg. 17.60 (978-0-613-87232-4(0)) Tandem Library Bks.

—Multicultural Meals: Step-by-Step Healthy Recipes for Kids. 2003. (Kid Power Ser.). (Illus.). 32p. (J). (gr. 3). (978-0-7787-1255-8(9)); pap. (978-0-7787-1277-0(X)) Crabtree Publishing Co.

Kelly, Denis. World Grilling: With More Than 100 International Recipes. 2007. (Illus.). 176p. pap. 19.95 (978-1-57061-519-1(5)) Sasquatch Bks.

Lagasse, Emeril. Emeril's There's a Chef in My World! Recipes That Take You Places. Yuen, Charles, illus. Bacon, Quentin, photos by. 2006. 224p. (gr. 4 up). 22.99 (978-0-06-073926-3(6) , HarperCollins) HarperCollins Pubs.

Locricchio, Matthew. The International Cookbook for Kids. McConnell, Jack, photos by. 2004. (Illus.). 176p. (J). 18.95 (978-0-7614-5185-3(4)) Cavendish, Marshall Corp.

McCulloch, Julie. India. 2001. (World of Recipes Ser.). (Illus.). 48p. (J). (gr. 3-5). lib. bdg. 25.64 (978-1-58810-085-6(5)) Heinemann Library.

Midday Meals around the World. (Meals Around the World Ser.). 24p. (J). 7.95 (978-1-4048-1131-7(1)) Picture Window Bks.

Morning Meals around the World. (Meals Around the World Ser.). 24p. (J). 7.95 (978-1-4048-1130-0(3)); 7.95 (978-1-4048-1133-1(8)) Picture Window Bks.

Pirotta, Saviour. Christian Cookbook. Sloan, Frank, ed. 2001. (Holiday Cookbooks from Around the World). (Illus.). 32p. (J). (gr. 4-7). lib. bdg. 25.69 (978-0-7398-3263-9(8)) Raintree.

Robins, Deri. Kids' Around the World Cookbook. 2000. (J). (978-0-606-19435-8(5)) Tandem Library Bks.

Townsend, Sue & Young, Caroline. Vegetarian Recipes from Around the World. 2003. (World of Recipes Ser.). (Illus.). 48p. (J). pap. 7.95 (978-1-4034-3653-5(3)); lib. bdg. 27.07 (978-1-4034-0977-5(3)) Heinemann Library.

Vaughan, Jenny & Beauchamp, Penny. Christmas. 2004. (World of Recipes Ser.). (Illus.). 48p. (J). lib. bdg. (978-1-4034-4697-8(0)) Heinemann Library.

—Christmas Foods. 2004. (World of Recipes Ser.). (Illus.). 48p. (J). pap. 8.50 (978-1-4034-6011-0(6)) Heinemann Library.

—Festival Foods. 2004. (World of Recipes Ser.). (Illus.). 48p. (J). pap. 8.50 (978-1-4034-6012-7(4)) Heinemann Library.

—Festivals. 2004. (World of Recipes Ser.). (Illus.). 48p. (J). lib. bdg. (978-1-4034-4699-2(7)) Heinemann Library.

Vaughan, Jenny, et al. A World of Recipes. 2004. (J). (gr. 3-5). lib. bdg. 114.00 (978-1-4034-4701-2(2)) Heinemann Library.

Wallace, Paula S. The World of Food. 2003. (Life Around the World Ser.). (Illus.). 48p. (J). (gr. 2 up). lib. bdg. 24.67 (978-0-8368-3660-8(X)) Stevens, Gareth Inc.

Watt, Fiona. Children's World Cookbook. 2004. (Children's Cooking Ser.). (Illus.). 96p. (J). pap. 13.95 (978-0-7945-0098-6(6) , Usborne); lib. bdg. 21.95 (978-1-58086-365-0(5)) EDC Publishing.

Wolfe, Robert L. & Wolfe, Diane, illus. Holiday Cooking Around the World. Wolfe, Robert L. & Wolfe, Diane, photos by. 2nd rev. exp. ed. 2002. (Easy Menu Ethnic Cookbooks). 72p. (J). (gr. 5-12). 25.26 (978-0-8225-4128-8(9) , Lerner Pubns.) Lerner Publishing Group.

Yesh, Jeff, illus. Meals Around the World, 4 bks. Incl. Evening Meals Around the World. Zurakowski, Michele. 22.60 (978-1-4048-0282-7(7)); Midday Meals Around the World. Zurakowski, Michele. 22.60 (978-1-4048-0281-0(9) , 1229526); Morning Meals Around the World. Gregoire, Maryellen. 22.60 (978-1-4048-0280-3(0) , 1229527); Snack Time Around the World. Zurakowski, Michele. 22.60 (978-1-4048-0283-4(5) , 1229528); 24p. (J). (gr. k-4). 2004. (Illus.). 2004. 85.04 (978-1-4048-0279-7(7)) Picture Window Bks.

Zurakowski, Michele. Evening Meals Around the World. Yesh, Jeff, illus. 2004. (Meals Around the World Ser.). 24p. (J). (gr. k-4). 22.60 (978-1-4048-0282-7(7)) Picture Window Bks.

—Midday Meals Around the World. Yesh, Jeff, illus. 2004. (Meals Around the World Ser.). 24p. (J). (gr. k-4). 22.60 (978-1-4048-0281-0(9) , 1229526) Picture Window Bks.

—Snack Time Around the World. Yesh, Jeff, illus. 2004. (Meals Around the World Ser.). 24p. (J). (gr. k-4). 22.60 (978-1-4048-0283-4(5) , 1229528) Picture Window Bks.

COOKERY, ITALIAN

Bisignano, Alphonse. Cooking the Italian Way. 2nd rev. exp. ed. 2003. (Easy Menu Ethnic Cookbooks). (Illus.). 72p. (J). (gr. 5-12). pap. 7.95 (978-0-8225-4161-5(0)) Lerner Publishing Group.

—Cooking the Italian Way. Wolfe, Robert L., illus. 2nd rev. exp. ed. 2002. (Easy Menu Ethnic Cookbooks). 72p. (J). (gr. 5-12). 25.26 (978-0-8225-4113-4(0) , Lerner Pubns.) Lerner Publishing Group.

Gioffre, Rosalba. The Young Chef's Italian Cookbook: Step-by-Step Fun Recipes for Young Chefs. 2001. (I'm the Chef! Ser.). (Illus.). 32p. (J). (gr. 3). (978-0-7787-0279-5(0)) Crabtree Publishing Co.

Locricchio, Matthew. The Cooking of Italy. 2002. (Superchef Ser.). (Illus.). 72p. (J). 29.93 (978-0-7614-1215-1(8) , Benchmark Bks.) Cavendish, Marshall Corp.

Matt, F. Pasta & Pizza for Beginners. rev. ed. 2004. (Cooking School Ser.). (Illus.). 48p. (J). lib. bdg. 15.95 (978-1-58086-567-8(4)) EDC Publishing.

Pirotta, Saviour. Italy. 1999. (Food & Festivals Ser.). (Illus.). 32p. (J). (gr. 1-4). lib. bdg. 25.69 (978-0-8172-5760-6(8)) Raintree.

Sheen, Barbara. Foods of Italy. 2005. (Taste of Culture Ser.). (Illus.). 64p. (J). (gr. 4-8). lib. bdg. 27.45 (978-0-7377-3034-0(X) , Greenhaven Pr., Inc.) Thomson Gale.

COOKERY, JEWISH

Bacon, Josephine. Cooking the Israeli Way. 2nd rev. exp. ed. 2002. (Easy Menu Ethnic Cookbooks). (Illus.). 72p. (J). (gr. 5-12). 25.26 (978-0-8225-4112-7(2) , Lerner Pubns.) Lerner Publishing Group.

Cooper, Ilene. Jewish Holidays All Year Round: A Family Treasury. Savadier, Elivia, illus. 2002. 80p. (J). 19.95 (978-0-8109-0550-4(7)) Abrams, Harry N., Inc.

Juicing. 2000. 112p. (YA). pap. 12.95 (978-0-7894-5521-5(8)) Dorling Kindersley Publishing, Inc.

Kropf, Latifa Berry. It's Challah Time! Cohen, Tod, illus. 2002. 24p. (J). (ps-1). 12.95 (978-1-58013-036-3(4)) Kar-Ben Publishing.

Nathan, Joan. The Children's Jewish Holiday Kitchen: 70 Fun Recipes for You & Your Kids, from the Author of Jewish Cooking in America. 2000. (Illus.). 176p. pap. 14.95 (978-0-8052-1056-9(3) , Schocken) Knopf Publishing Group.

Raabe, Emily. A Hanukkah Holiday Cookbook. 2002. (Festive Foods for the Holidays Ser.). (Illus.). 24p. (J). (gr. 2-5). lib. bdg. 19.95 (978-0-8239-5626-5(1) , PowerKids Pr.) Rosen Publishing Group, Inc., The.

Randall, Ronne. Jewish Cookbook. Mukhida, Zul, illus. 2001. (Holiday Cookbooks from Around the World). 32p. (J). (gr. 4-7). lib. bdg. 25.69 (978-0-7398-3265-3(4)) Raintree.

Rauchwerger, Lisa. Chocolate Chip Challah: And Other Twists on the Jewish Holiday Table. Rauchwerger, Lisa, illus. 2004. (Illus.). 127p. (gr. k-3). pap. 17.95 (978-0-8074-0700-4(3) , 510606) URJ Pr.

Tabs, Judy & Steinberg, Barbara. Matzah Meals: A Passover Cookbook for Kids. Hauser, Bill, illus. 2004. (Passover Ser.). 64p. (J). (gr. k up). pap. 7.95 (978-1-58013-086-8(0)) Kar-Ben Publishing.

COOKERY, MEXICAN

Ancona, George. The Foods: Viva Mexico. 2001. (Viva Mexico! Ser.). (Illus.). 48p. (J). (gr. 3 up). lib. bdg. 24.21 (978-0-7614-1328-8(6) , Benchmark Bks.) Cavendish, Marshall Corp.

Beatty, Theresa M. Food & Recipes of Mexico. 1999. (Kids in the Kitchen). 24p. (J). (gr. k-4). lib. bdg. 19.95 (978-0-8239-5224-3(X) , PowerKids Pr.) Rosen Publishing Group, Inc., The.

Coronado, Rosa. Cooking the Mexican Way. 2nd rev. exp. ed. (Easy Menu Ethnic Cookbooks). (Illus.). 72p. (J). (gr. 5-12). 2003. pap. 7.95 (978-0-8225-4162-2(9)); 2002. 25.26 (978-0-8225-4117-2(3) , Lerner Pubns.) Lerner Publishing Group.

—Cooking the Mexican Way. 2002. (gr. 5-8). lib. bdg. 16.40 (978-0-613-59146-1(1)) Tandem Library Bks.

Culinary Institute of America Staff, contrib. by. Mexican American. 2005. (American Regional Cooking Library). (Illus.). 72p. (J). lib. bdg. (978-1-59084-622-3(2)) Mason Crest Pubs.

Dawson, Imogen. Food & Feasts with the Aztecs. 2004. (Illus.). 32p. (J). (gr. 4-8). reprint ed. 14.00 (978-0-7567-7143-0(9)) DIANE Publishing Co.

Equipo Staff. La Cocina Mexicana Paso a Paso. 1999. Tr. of Mexican Cooking. (SPA., Illus.). 160p. 29.95 (978-958-30-0593-0(2) , PV12641) Panamericana Editorial COL. *Dist:* Lectorum Pubns., Inc., Libros Sin Fronteras.

Hill, Mary. Let's Make Tacos. 2002. (Welcome Bks.). (Illus.). 24p. (J). (ps-2). pap. 4.95 (978-0-516-24021-3(8) , Children's Pr.) Scholastic Library Publishing.

—Let's Make Tacos. 2002. (gr. k-3). lib. bdg. 12.95 (978-0-613-58786-0(3)) Tandem Library Bks.

Illsley, Linda. Mexico. 1999. (Food & Festivals Ser.). (Illus.). 32p. (J). (gr. 1-4). lib. bdg. 25.69 (978-0-8172-5553-4(2)) Raintree.

Locricchio, Matthew. The Cooking of Mexico. 2002. (Superchef Ser.). (J). 29.93 (978-0-7614-1217-5(4) , Benchmark Bks.) Cavendish, Marshall Corp.

McCulloch, Julie. Mexico. (Illus.). 48p. (J). 2002. (gr. 4-6). pap. (978-1-58810-390-1(0) , 91140); 2001. (gr. 3-5). lib. bdg. 25.64 (978-1-58810-088-7(X)) Heinemann Library.

McDaniel, Jan. The Food of Mexico. 2002. (Encyclopedia of Mexico Ser.). (Illus.). 64,80p. (YA). (gr. 5 up). lib. bdg. (978-1-59084-085-6(2)) Mason Crest Pubs.

Ward, Karen. The Young Chef's Mexican Cookbook: Step-by-Step Fun Recipes for Young Chefs. 2001. (I'm the Chef! Ser.). (Illus.). 32p. (J). (gr. 3). (978-0-7787-0281-8(2)); pap. (978-0-7787-0295-5(2)) Crabtree Publishing Co.

Wood, Ira. A Mexican Feast: The Food & Recipes of Mexico. 2002. (Reading Room Collection). (Illus.). 24p. (J). lib. bdg. 18.75 (978-0-8239-3736-3(4)) Rosen Publishing Group, Inc., The.

COOKERY, MIDDLE EASTERN

Cornell, Kari & Turkoglu, Nurcay. Cooking the Turkish Way. 2nd rev. ed. 2004. (Easy Menu Ethnic Cookbooks). (Illus.). 72p. (J). 25.26 (978-0-8225-4123-3(8) , Carolrhoda Bks.) Lerner Publishing Group.

COOKERY, OUTDOOR

Kerl, Mary Ann. Camp Cookin' 1999. 164p. spiral bd. 9.95 (978-1-57166-187-6(5)) Hearts 'N Tummies Cookbook Co.

COOKERY, POLISH

Zamojska-Hutchins, Danuta. Cooking the Polish Way. 2nd rev. expurg. ed. 2002. (Easy Menu Ethnic Cookbooks). (Illus.). 72p. (J). (gr. 5-12). 25.26 (978-0-8225-4119-6(X) , Lerner Pubns.) Lerner Publishing Group.

COOKERY, RUSSIAN

Plotkin, Gregory & Plotkin, Rita. Cooking the Russian Way: Revised & Expanded to Include New Low-Fat & Vegetarian Recipes. 2nd rev. ed. 2003. (Easy Menu Ethnic Cookbooks). (Illus.). 72p. (J). 25.26 (978-0-8225-4120-2(3) , Lerner Pubns.) Lerner Publishing Group.

Sheen, Barbara. Foods of Russia. 2006. (Taste of Culture Ser.). 64p. (J). (gr. 3-6). 27.45 (978-0-7377-3538-3(4) , Greenhaven Pr., Inc.) Thomson Gale.

Townsend, Sue & Young, Caroline. Russia. 2003. 48p. (J). 7.95 (978-1-4034-3651-1(7)); (Illus.). lib. bdg. 27.07 (978-1-4034-0981-2(1)) Heinemann Library.

COOKERY, SCANDINAVIAN

Munsen, Sylvia. Cooking the Norwegian Way. 2nd rev. expurg. ed. 2002. (Easy Menu Ethnic Cookbooks). (Illus.). 72p. (J). (gr. 5-12). 25.26 (978-0-8225-4118-9(1) , Lerner Pubns.) Lerner Publishing Group.

COOKERY, SPANISH

Christian, Rebecca. Cooking the Spanish Way. 2nd rev. exp. ed. 2002. (Easy Menu Ethnic Cookbooks). (Illus.). 72p. (J). (gr. 5-12). 25.26 (978-0-8225-4122-6(X) , Lerner Pubns.) Lerner Publishing Group.

Goodwin, Bob. Taste of Spain. 2000. (Food Around the World Ser.). (J). (gr. 4-7). 7.14 (978-0-8172-4857-4(9)) Raintree.

McLeese, Tex. Joining the Rodeo. 2000. (Illus.). 24p. (J). (gr. 1-4). lib. bdg. 19.27 (978-1-57103-346-8(7)) Rourke Publishing, LLC.

Townsend, Sue & Young, Caroline. Spain. 2003. (World of Recipes Ser.). (Illus.). 48p. (J). lib. bdg. 27.07 (978-1-4034-0978-2(1)) Heinemann Library.

COOKERY, THAI

Harrison, Supenn. Cooking the Thai Way: Revised & Expanded to Include New Low-Fat & Vegetarian. 2003. (gr. 5-8). lib. bdg. 16.40 (978-0-613-67075-3(2)) Tandem Library Bks.

Harrison, Supenn & Monroe, Judy. Cooking the Thai Way. 2003. (Easy Menu Ethnic Cookbooks). (Illus.). 72p. (J). (gr. 5-12). pap. 7.95 (978-0-8225-0608-9(4)); 2nd rev. ed. 25.26 (978-0-8225-4124-0(6) , Lerner Pubns.) Lerner Publishing Group.

Locricchio, Matthew. The Cooking of Thailand. 2004. (Superchef Ser.). (Illus.). 80p. (J). 29.93 (978-0-7614-1731-6(1) , Benchmark Bks.) Cavendish, Marshall Corp.

Sheen, Barbara. Foods of Thailand. 2006. (Taste of Culture Ser.). 64p. (J). (gr. 3-6). 27.45 (978-0-7377-3037-1(4) , Greenhaven Pr., Inc.) Thomson Gale.

Townsend, Sue. Thailand. 2002. (World of Recipes Ser.). (Illus.). 48p. (J). (gr. 3-5). lib. bdg. 27.07 (978-1-58810-612-4(8)) Heinemann Library.

COOKERY FOR THE SICK

Geil, Patricia Bazel & Ross, Tami A. Cooking up Fun for Kids with Diabetes. 2003. (Illus.). 128p. pap. 14.95 (978-1-58040-134-0(1) , 9781580401340) McGraw-Hill/ Contemporary.

COOKIES

Bush, Timothy, illus. All in Just One Cookie. 2006. 32p. (J). lib. bdg. 17.89 (978-0-06-009093-7(6)) HarperCollins Pubs.

Devins, Susan. Christmas Cookies! A Holiday Cookbook. Lehman, Barbara, illus. 2007. 40p. (J). (gr. k-7). pap. 4.99 (*978-0-7636-3515-2(4)) Candlewick Pr.

Farrow, Joanna & Lewis, Sara. Cookies for Kids: Fabulous, Fun Recipes to Cook with Your Family. 2003. (Illus.). 96p. 17.99 (978-0-7548-1208-1(1)) Anness Publishing GBR. *Dist:* National Bk. Network.

Goodman, Susan E. All in Just One Cookie. Bush, Timothy, illus. 2006. 32p. (J). 16.99 (978-0-06-009092-0(8)) HarperCollins Pubs.

Hill, Mary. Let's Make Cookies. 2002. (Welcome Bks.). (Illus.). 24p. (J). (ps-2). pap. 4.95 (978-0-516-24019-0(6) , Children's Pr.) Scholastic Library Publishing.

—Let's Make Cookies. 2002. (gr. k-3). lib. bdg. 12.95 (978-0-613-58784-6(7)) Tandem Library Bks.

Landau, Elaine. Pretzels: One of the World's Oldest Snacks. 2001. (Tasty Treats Ser.). (Illus.). 24p. (J). (gr. 1-4). lib. bdg. 23.93 (978-1-57103-340-6(8)) Rourke Publishing, LLC.

MacLeod, Elizabeth. Bake & Make Amazing Cookies. Bradford, June, illus. 2005. (Kids Can Do It Ser.). 40p. (YA). (gr. 3 up). (978-1-55337-632-3(3)); (978-1-55337-631-6(5)) Kids Can Pr., Ltd.

—Bake It & Build It. Walker, Tracy, illus. (Kids Can Do It Ser.). (J). (gr. 4-6). 2004. 40p. (978-1-55337-754-2(0)); 1998. 134p. (978-1-55074-427-9(5)) Kids Can Pr., Ltd.

Panik, Alison Saeger. Ginger Snap's Cookie Book: A Sugar & Spice Adventure. 2005. (Illus.). 39p. (J). (978-0-439-70467-0(7)) Scholastic, Inc.

Pearson, Debora. Cookie Animals: A Cookbook & Cookie Cutter Set. van Kampen, Vlasta, illus. 2007. 24p. (J). (gr. 3 up). 15.95 (*978-1-932403-28-2(0)) Handprint Bks.

Publications International Staff, contrib. by. Christmas Cookies for Kids. 2001. (Illus.). 78p. (J). (978-0-7853-5582-3(0)) Publications International, Ltd.

Rau, Dana Meachen. Cookies. 2008. (J). (*978-0-7614-2890-9(9)) Cavendish, Marshall Bks., Ltd.

Stanley, George Edward. The Secret Ingredient. 1999. (Katie Lynn Cookie Company Ser.). (Illus.). (J). (978-0-606-18500-4(3)) Tandem Library Bks.

—Wedding Cookies: Katie Lynn Cookie Company. Graves, Linda, illus. 2001. (Stepping Stone Book Ser.: Vol. 4). 54p. (J). (gr. k-3). lib. bdg. 11.99 (978-0-679-99223-3(5) , Random Hse. Bks. for Young Readers) Random Hse. Children's Bks.

Williamson, Sarah A. Bake the Best-Ever Cookies! Ernst, Tom, illus. 2001. (Quick Starts for Kids! Ser.). 64p. (J). (gr. 4 up). pap. 8.95 (978-1-885593-56-6(2) , Williamson Bks.) Ideals Pubns.

Young, Bev. Presidential Cookies. 2nd ed. 2005. Orig. Title: Presidential Cookies the Lure & the Lore. (ENG., Illus.). 168p. (YA). 23.95 (978-0-9729095-3-2(2) , SAN 255-1077) Presidential Publishing.

COOKING

see Cookery

COOKING, OUTDOOR

see Outdoor Cookery

COOKING UTENSILS

see Household Equipment and Supplies

COOLIDGE, CALVIN, 1872-1933

Allen, Michael Geoffrey. Calvin Coolidge. 2002. (United States Presidents Ser.). (Illus.). 112p. (YA). (gr. 5-12). lib. bdg. 26.60 (978-0-7660-1703-0(6)) Enslow Pubs., Inc.

Doak, Robin S. Calvin Coolidge. 2003. (Profiles of the Presidents Ser.). (Illus.). 64p. (J). (gr. 4 up). lib. bdg. 23.93 (978-0-7565-0276-8(4)) Compass Point Bks.

Feldman, Ruth Tenzer. Calvin Coolidge. 2007. (Presidential Leaders Ser.). (Illus.). 112p. (J). 29.27 (978-0-8225-1496-1(6)) Lerner Publishing Group.

Graham, Amy. Calvin Coolidge: A MyReportLinks.com Book. 2002. (Presidents Ser.). (Illus.). 48p. (J). (gr. 4-10). lib. bdg. 25.26 (978-0-7660-5015-0(7) , MyReportLinks.com Bks.) Enslow Pubs., Inc.

Johansen, Heidi Leigh. How to Draw the Life & Times of Calvin Coolidge. 2007. (Kid's Guide to Drawing the Presidents of the United States of America Ser.). (Illus.). 32p. (J). 25.25 (978-1-4042-3006-4(8) , PowerKids Pr.) Rosen Publishing Group, Inc., The.

Joseph, Paul. Calvin Coolidge. 1999. (United States Presidents Ser.). (Illus.). 32p. (J). (gr. k-6). lib. bdg. 22.78 (978-1-57765-237-3(1) , Checkerboard Library) ABDO Publishing Co.

Maupin, Melissa. Calvin Coolidge: Our Thirtieth President. 2001. (Spirit of America: Our Presidents Ser.). (Illus.). 48p. (J). (gr. 2-6). 28.50 (978-1-56766-864-3(X)) Child's World, Inc.

Otfinoski, Steven. Calvin Coolidge. 2008. (J). (*978-0-7614-2836-7(4)) Cavendish, Marshall Bks., Ltd.

Stein, R. Conrad. Calvin Coolidge. 2004. (Encyclopedia of Presidents Ser.). (Illus.). 110p. (J). 34.00 (978-0-516-22960-7(5) , Children's Pr.) Scholastic Library Publishing.

Venezia Mike. Calvin Coolidge. 2006. (J). (978-0-516-22634-7(7)) Children's Pr., Ltd.

Venezia, Mike, illus. Herbert Hoover. 2006. 32p. (J). (978-0-516-22635-4(5)) Children's Pr., Ltd.

COOLING APPLIANCES

see Refrigeration and Refrigerating Machinery

COOPERATION, INTERNATIONAL

see International Cooperation

COPE, E. D. (EDWARD DRINKER), 1840-1897

Goldish, Meish. The Fossil Feud: Marsh & Cope's Bone Wars. 2007. (Fossil Hunters Ser.). 32p. (J). (gr. 3-7). lib. bdg. 25.27 (978-1-59716-256-2(6)) Bearport Publishing Co., Inc.

Hartzog, Brooke. The Dinosaur Bone Battle Between O. C. Marsh & Edward Drinker Cope. 1999. (Dinosaurs & Their Discoverers Ser.). 24p. (J). (gr. k-4). lib. bdg. 18.75 (978-0-8239-5327-1(0) , PowerKids Pr.) Rosen Publishing Group, Inc., The.

COPERNICUS, NICOLAUS, 1473-1543

Andronik, Catherine M. Copernicus: Founder of Modern Astronomy. 2002. (Great Minds of Science Ser.). (Illus.). 112p. (J). (gr. 4-10). lib. bdg. 26.60 (978-0-7660-1755-9(9)) Enslow Pubs., Inc.

Boerst, William J. Nicholas Copernicus & the Founding of Modern Astronomy. 2004. (Profiles in Science Ser.). (Illus.). 144p. (YA). (gr. 6-12). lib. bdg. 26.95 (978-1-883846-99-2(4) , First Biographies) Reynolds, Morgan Inc.

Fradin, Dennis Brindell. Nicolaus Copernicus: The Earth Is a Planet. Buhler, Cynthia von, tr. Buhler, Cynthia von, illus. 2003. 32p. (J). (gr. 2-6). 15.95 (978-1-59336-006-1(1)); pap. (978-1-59336-007-8(X)) Mondo Publishing.

Gingerich, Owen & MacLachlan, James H. Nicolaus Copernicus: Making the Earth a Planet. 2005. (Oxford Portraits in Science Ser.). (Illus.). 128p. (YA). 30.00 (978-0-19-516173-1(4)) Oxford Univ. Pr., Inc.

Ingram, Scott. Nicolaus Copernicus: Father of Modern Astronomy. 2004. (Illus.). 64p. (J). 26.20 (978-1-56711-489-8(X) , Blackbirch Pr., Inc.) Thomson Gale.

Sakolsky, Josh. Copernicus & Modern Astronomy. 2004. (Primary Sources of Revolutionary Scientific Discoveries & Theories Ser.). (Illus.). 64p. (J). lib. bdg. 29.25 (978-1-4042-0305-1(2)) Rosen Publishing Group, Inc., The.

Somervill, Barbara A. Nicolaus Copernicus: Father of Modern Astronomy. 2004. (Signature Lives Ser.). (Illus.). 112p. (J). 30.60 (978-0-7565-0812-8(6)) Compass Point Bks.

COPPER

Beatty, Richard. Copper. 2000. (Elements Ser.). (Illus.). 32p. (J). (gr. 3-5). lib. bdg. 25.64 (978-0-7614-0945-8(9) , Benchmark Bks.) Cavendish, Marshall Corp.

Murray, Peter. Copper. 2001. (From the Earth Ser.). (Illus.). 24p. (J). 21.35 (978-1-58340-112-5(1)) Smart Apple Media.

Tocci, Salvatore. Copper. 2005. (True Bks.). (Illus.). (J). (gr. 3-5). 47p. pap. 6.95 (978-0-516-25569-9(X)); 48p. 25.00 (978-0-516-23693-3(8)) Scholastic Library Publishing. (Children's Pr.).

CORAL REEFS AND ISLANDS

Albert, Toni. The Incredible Coral Reef: Another Active-Learning Book for Kids. Hanlon, Ada, illus. 1998. 64p. (Orig.). (J). (gr. 3-8). pap. 10.95 (978-0-9640742-1-7(4)) Trickle Creek Bks.

Banting, Erinn. The Great Barrier Reef. 2004. (Illus.). 32p. (J). lib. bdg. 18.20 (978-1-59036-272-3(1)) Weigl Pubs., Inc.

Benchmark Education Staff. Coral Reefs. 2005. 2.00 ***(978-1-4108-4656-3(3))*** Benchmark Education Co.

Bingham, Caroline & Dorling Kindersley Publishing Staff. Coral Reef. 2005. (24 Hours Ser.). (Illus.). 48p. (J). 12.99 (978-0-7566-1125-5(3)) Dorling Kindersley Publishing, Inc.

Boyle, Doe. Coral Reef Hideaway: The Story of a Clown Anemonefish. (Illus.). 32p. (J). (ps-2). pap. 6.95 (978-1-59249-480-4(3) , S4008) Soundprints.

Brannon, Barbara. Discover Coral Reefs. 2005. 39.00 ***(978-1-4108-5131-4(1))*** Benchmark Education Co.

Brinkworth, Brian. Life in a Coral Reef. 2006. (Illus.). 16p. (J). lib. bdg. (978-1-4042-3342-3(3) , PowerKids Pr.) Rosen Publishing Group, Inc., The.

Brooke, Samantha. Coral Reefs: in Danger: In Danger. Bull, Peter, illus. 2008. (All Aboard Science Reader Ser.). 48p. (J). (gr. 1-3). pap. 3.99 ***(978-0-448-44872-5(6)*** , Grosset & Dunlap) Penguin Group (USA) Inc.

Carole Telford and Rod Theodorou. Inside a Coral Reef. 2nd ed. 2006. (Illus.). 32p. (J). pap. ***(978-1-4034-8797-1(9))*** Heinemann Library.

Cole, Melissa S. Coral Reefs. 2004. (Illus.). 24p. (J). 22.45 (978-1-56711-908-4(5) , Blackbirch Pr., Inc.) Thomson Gale.

Collard, Sneed B., III. Lizard Island: Science & Scientists on Australia's Great Barrier Reef. (Single Title Science Pb Ser.). (Illus.). 144p. (YA). (gr. 9-12). 2001. pap. 12.95 (978-0-531-16519-5(1)); 2000. 26.00 (978-0-531-11719-4(7)) Scholastic Library Publishing. (Watts, Franklin).

Collard, Sneed B. On the Coral Reef. 2005. (Science Adventures Ser.). (Illus.). 43p. (J). 25.64 (978-0-7614-1953-2(5) , Benchmark Bks.) Cavendish, Marshall Corp.

A Coral Reef, 6 Pack. (Rigby Focus Ser.). 16p. (gr. 1 up). 28.00 (978-0-7578-5315-9(3)) Rigby Education.

A Coral Reef: Individual Title Six-Packs. (Rigby Focus Ser.). 16p. (gr. 1 up). 30.00 (978-0-7578-5547-4(4)) Rigby Education.

Creature Color & Discover Coral Reef. (Illus.). 28p. (J). (gr. 1-8). reprint ed. (978-1-881469-42-1(5)) Safari, Ltd.

Dorling Kindersley Publishing Staff. Coral Reef. 2000. (978-0-606-17803-7(1)) Tandem Library Bks.

—Fishy Tales. 2003. (Dorling Kindersley Readers Ser.). (Illus.). 32p. (J). (gr. 5). pap. 3.99 (978-0-7894-9797-0(2)) Dorling Kindersley Publishing, Inc.

Dorling Kindersley Publishing Staff, ed. El Mundo Marino. 2004. (Dk Readers Ser.). (SPA.). 32p. (J). 12.99 (978-0-7566-0637-4(3)) Dorling Kindersley Publishing, Inc.

Douglas, Lloyd G. Coral Reef: Early Intervenion Level 9. 2005. (Welcome Bookstm Ser.). (Illus.). 24p. (J). (ps-ps). 18.00 (978-0-516-25026-7(4) , Children's Pr.) Scholastic Library Publishing.

Dunphy, Madeleine. Here Is the Coral Reef. Leonard, Tom, illus. 2006. (Web of Life Ser.). 32p. (J). 16.95 (978-0-9773795-5-2(8)); pap. 9.95 (978-0-9773795-4-5(X)) Web of Life Children's Bks.

Dunphy, Madeline. Here Is the Coral Reef. Leonard, Tom, illus. 1998. 32p. (J). (ps-3). 14.95 (978-0-7868-0163-3(8)) Hyperion Bks. for Children.

—Here Is the Coral Reef. Leonard, Tom, illus. 1998. 32p. (J). (ps-3). 15.49 (978-0-7868-2135-8(3)) Hyperion Bks. for Children.

Earle, Sylvia A. Coral Reefs; Jump into Science. Matthews, Bonnie, illus. 2003. (Jump into Science Ser.). 32p. (J). (ps-3). 16.95 (978-0-7922-6953-3(5) , National Geographic Children's Bks.) National Geographic Society.

—Hello, Fish! Visiting the Coral Reef. Henry, Wolcott, illus. 32p. (J). (ps-3). 2001. pap. 6.95 (978-0-7922-6697-6(8)); 1999. 15.95 (978-0-7922-7103-1(3)) National Geographic Society. (National Geographic Children's Bks.).

Eldin, Peter. Born Free Coral Reef Sticker Facts. Q2A Solutions, illus. 2005. 18p. (J). (978-1-84510-752-9(7)) Top That! Publishing PLC.

Fishy Tales. 12p. (J). (978-2-7643-0193-7(6)) Phidal Publishing, Inc./Editions Phidal, Inc.

Frisch, Aaron. Coral Reefs. 2008. (J). ***(978-1-58341-570-2(X)*** , Creative Education) Creative Co., The.

Furgang, Kathy. Let's Take a Field Trip to a Coral Reef. 2000. (Neighborhoods in Nature Ser.). (Illus.). 24p. (J). (gr. 3-5). lib. bdg. 18.75 (978-0-8239-5445-2(5) , PowerKids Pr.) Rosen Publishing Group, Inc., The.

Galko, Francine. Coral Reef Animals. 2003. (Animals in Their Habitats Ser.). (Illus.). 32p. (J). (gr. k-2). lib. bdg. 21.36 (978-1-4034-0177-9(2)); pap. 6.95 (978-1-4034-0434-3(8)) Heinemann Library.

Gambrell, Linda B. DK Readers Level 1: Pre - Level 1. 2003. (ps-2). lib. bdg. 11.80 (978-0-613-75170-4(1)) Tandem Library Bks.

Gambrell, Linda B. & Dorling Kindersley Publishing Staff. Fishy Tales. 2003. (Readers Ser.). (Illus.). 32p. (J). 12.99 (978-0-7894-9796-3(4)) Dorling Kindersley Publishing, Inc.

George, Michael. Coral Reefs: Cities of the Sea. 2003. (LifeViews Ser.). (Illus.). 32p. (J). lib. bdg. (978-1-58341-254-1(9) , Creative Education) Creative Co., The.

Gibbons, Gail. Coral Reefs. Gibbons, Gail, illus. 2007. (Illus.). 32p. (J). (ps-3). 16.95 ***(978-0-8234-2080-3(9))*** Holiday Hse., Inc.

Gray, Susan Heinrichs. Coral Reefs. 2000. (First Reports). (Illus.). 48p. (J). (gr. 3 up). lib. bdg. 21.26 (978-0-7565-0018-4(4)) Compass Point Bks.

Green, Jen. A Coral Reef. 2002. (Small Worlds Ser.). (Illus.). 32p. (J). (gr. 3-4). (978-0-7787-0138-5(7)); pap. (978-0-7787-0152-1(2)) Crabtree Publishing Co.

—Coral Reef. 2002. (gr. 3-6). lib. bdg. 17.60 (978-0-613-52946-4(4)) Tandem Library Bks.

Gunzi, Christiane. Coral Reefs. (Collectafact Ser.). (J). 2002. 14.95 (978-1-58728-674-2(2)); 2002. pap. 7.95 (978-1-58728-774-9(9)); 2001. (Illus.). 48p. (gr. 1-5). 4.95 (978-1-58728-758-9(7)) T&N Children's Publishing. (Two Can Publishing).

Habitat Explorer, 9 bks., Set 1. 2004. (Illus.). 102.80 (978-1-4109-0516-1(0)) Raintree.

Hall, David, photos by & text. Life on a Coral Reef. Hall, David, text. 2006. (Undersea Encounters Ser.). (Illus.). 48p. (J). (gr. 3-5). 27.00 (978-0-516-24395-5(0) , Children's Pr.) Scholastic Library Publishing.

Hanson, Krista Finstad. Great Barrier Reef. 2004. (Natural Wonders of the World Ser.). (Illus.). 32p. (J). lib. bdg. 18.95 (978-1-58341-324-1(3) , Creative Education) Creative Co., The.

Harcourt School Publishers Staff. The Great Barrier Reef: Take-Home Book. 2001. (Collections Ser.). (Illus.). (J). pap. 1.90 (978-0-15-319527-3(4)) Harcourt Schl. Pubs.

—The Great Barrier Reef Below Level. 3rd ed. 2002. (Trophies Reading Program Ser.). (Illus.). pap. 5.10 (978-0-15-323324-1(0)) Harcourt Schl. Pubs.

Hartman, Jeff. The Red Coral House. Horton, Kate, illus. l.t. ed. 2002. 32p. 8.95 (978-0-9703490-1-9(7)) Hartman Publishing.

Haugen, Hayley Mitchell. Life in a Coral Reef. 2003. (Ecosystems Library). (Illus.). 48p. (J). 23.70 (978-0-7377-1370-1(4) , Greenhaven Pr., Inc.) Thomson Gale.

Hook, Cheryl. Coral Reefs. 2001. (Water Worlds Ser.). (Illus.). 32p. (J). (gr. 4 up). 28.00 (978-0-7910-6567-9(7) , 010352, Chelsea Hse.) Facts On File, Inc.

Jarrell, Pamela R. Diving at the Reef. Ruminski, Jeff, illus. 2002. (Big Bks.). 8p. (J). (ps-1). pap. 10.95 (978-1-57332-200-3(8)); pap. 10.95 (978-1-57332-201-0(6)) HighReach Learning, Inc.

Kids: Discover Coral Reefs. 2005. (J). 1.00 (978-1-888631-32-6(5)) Watercourse, The.

Levy, Janey. Discovering Coral Reefs. 2008. (J). lib. bdg. ***(978-1-4042-3786-5(0)*** , PowerKids Pr.) Rosen Publishing Group, Inc., The.

Llewellyn, Claire. Coral Reefs. 2000. (Heinemann First Library). (Illus.). 32p. (J). (gr. k-2). lib. bdg. 21.36 (978-1-57572-203-0(8)) Heinemann Library.

—Coral Reefs. 2000. (gr. k-3). lib. bdg. 14.75 (978-0-613-45734-7(X)) Tandem Library Bks.

Llewellyn, Claire, et al. Coral Reefs. 2002. (Geography Starts Ser.). (Illus.). 32p. (J). (gr. k-2). pap. 6.95 (978-1-58810-969-9(0) , 91452) Heinemann Library.

Macken, JoAnn Early. Coral Reefs: Arrecifes de Coral. 2005. (SPA., Illus.). 24p. (J). pap. (978-0-8368-6035-1(7)) Stevens, Gareth Inc.

—Coral Reefs/Arrecifes de Coral. 2005. (SPA., Illus.). 24p. (J). (ps-17). lib. bdg. 19.33 (978-0-8368-6028-3(4)) Stevens, Gareth Inc.

Moss, Miriam. This Is the Coral Reef. Kennaway, Adrienne, illus. 2007. 32p. (J). (gr. k-4). 16.95 ***(978-1-84507-573-6(0))*** Lincoln, Frances Ltd. GBR. *Dist:* Perseus Distribution.

Phillips, Dee. Find It on a Coral Reef. 2006. (Illus.). 24p. (J). lib. bdg. 22.00 (978-0-8368-6302-4(X)) Stevens, Gareth Inc.

Pike, Katy & Turner, Garda. Coral Reefs. 2003. (Ocean Facts Ser.). (Illus.). 24p. (gr. 2-4). 23.00 (978-0-7910-7285-1(1) , Chelsea Hse.) Facts On File, Inc.

Pitkin, Linda M. Journey under the Sea. 2003. (Illus.). 48p. (YA). 22.95 (978-0-19-521971-5(6)) Oxford Univ. Pr., Inc.

Pyers. Coral Reef Explorer. 2004. (Habitat Explorer Ser.). (Illus.). pap. 7.50 (978-1-4109-0909-1(3)); pap. 40.50 (978-1-4109-0914-5(X)) Raintree.

Pyers, Greg. Coral Reef Explorer. 2004. (Habitat Explorer Ser.). (Illus.). 32p. (J). lib. bdg. 25.70 (978-1-4109-0515-4(2)) Raintree.

Rau, Dana Meachen. Los Arrecifes de Coral. 2007. (Maravillas de la Naturaleza Ser.). (SPA.). 32p. (J). lib. bdg. 22.79 ***(978-0-7614-2805-3(4)*** , Benchmark Bks.) Cavendish, Marshall Corp.

—Coral Reefs. 2007. (Wonders of Nature Ser.). 32p. (J). lib. bdg. 22.79 ***(978-0-7614-2666-0(3)*** , Benchmark Bks.) Cavendish, Marshall Corp.

—Coral Reefs/Los Arrecifes de Coral. 2007. (Wonders of Nature/Maravillas de la Naturaleza Ser.). (SPA & ENG.). 32p. (J). lib. bdg. 22.79 ***(978-0-7614-2829-9(1)*** , Benchmark Bks.) Cavendish, Marshall Corp.

Romero, Libby. Coral Reefs. 2005. 42.00 ***(978-1-4108-4608-2(3))*** Benchmark Education Co.

Schick, Joel, illus. El Autobus Magico se Zambulle: Un Libro sobre los Arrecifes de Coral. 1998. (Coleccion El Autobus Magico). (SPA.). 100p. (J). (gr. k-4). pap. 3.50 (978-0-590-51040-0(1) , SO8943) Scholastic, Inc.

Sheppard, Charles. Coral Reefs: Ecology, Threats, & Conservation. 2002. (World Life Library). (Illus.). 72p. pap. 17.95 (978-0-89658-220-0(5)) Voyageur Pr., Inc.

Sommers, Joan. The Coral Reef Tunnel Book: Take a Peek under the Sea! 2007. (Take a Peek Ser.). (Illus.). 16p. (J). 14.95 (978-0-9754150-2-3(6)) Tunnel Vision.

Stewart, Melissa. Extreme Coral Reef! Q & A. 2008. 48p. (J). 16.99 ***(978-0-06-111577-6(0))*** ; pap. 6.99 ***(978-0-06-111575-2(4))*** Smithsonian Institution Pr.

Stone, Lynn M. Corals. 2003. (Rourke Discovery Library). (Illus.). 24p. (gr. 2-5). 14.95 (978-1-58952-318-0(0)) Rourke Publishing, LLC.

Taylor-Butler, Christine. A Home in the Coral Reef. 2006. (Scholastic News Nonfiction Readers Ser.). (Illus.). 24p. (J). (gr. 1-3). 19.00 (978-0-516-25344-2(1) , Children's Pr.) Scholastic Library Publishing.

Telford, Carole & Theodorou, Rod. Inside a Coral Reef. (Illus.). 32p. (J). 2006. ***(978-1-4034-8790-2(1));*** 1998. (gr. 2-4). lib. bdg. 22.79 (978-1-57572-154-5(6)) Heinemann Library.

Tocci, Salvatore. Coral Reefs: Life below the Sea. (Watts Library). (J). 2005. (Illus.). 64p. (gr. 5-7). pap. 8.95 (978-0-531-16669-7(4)); 2004. 25.50 (978-0-531-12304-1(9)) Scholastic Library Publishing. (Watts, Franklin).

Walker, Pam & Wood, Elaine. The Coral Reef. 2005. (Life in the Sea Ser.). (Illus.). 140p. (J). (gr. 4-9). 35.00 (978-0-8160-5703-0(6)) Facts On File, Inc.

Walker, Sally M. Reefs. 2007. (Early Bird Earth Science Ser.). (J). 26.60 ***(978-0-8225-6738-7(5)*** , Lerner Pubns.) Lerner Publishing Group.

Whitehouse, Patricia. Hiding in a Coral Reef. 2003. (Illus.). 32p. pap. 6.50 (978-1-4034-3185-1(X)); (J). lib. bdg. 22.79 (978-1-4034-0795-5(9)) Heinemann Library.

Wood, Jennifer. Coral Reefs. 2004. (Interfact Ser.). (SPA., Illus.). 48p. (J). (gr. 3-6). pap. 14.95 incl. cd-rom (978-1-58728-456-4(1) , Two Can Publishing) T&N Children's Publishing.

CORALS

Collard, Sneed B., III. One Night in the Coral Sea. Brickman, Robin, illus. 32p. (J). 2006. pap. 6.95 (978-1-57091-390-7(0)); 2005. 15.95 (978-1-57091-389-1(7)) Charlesbridge Publishing, Inc.

Corals. (Under the Sea Ser.). 24p. (J). 6.95 (978-0-7368-5116-9(X)) Capstone Pr., Inc.

Corals Oceans Alive. 2006. (Illus.). 24p. (J). (gr. k-2). 18.50 ***(978-0-531-17866-9(8))*** Scholastic Library Publishing.

Douglas, Lloyd G. Coral Reef. 2005. (Ocean Life Ser.). (Illus.). 24p. (J). (ps-2). pap. 4.95 (978-0-516-23739-8(X) , Children's Pr.) Scholastic Library Publishing.

—Coral Reef: Early Intervenion Level 9. 2005. (Welcome Bookstm Ser.). (Illus.). 24p. (J). (ps-ps). 18.00 (978-0-516-25026-7(4) , Children's Pr.) Scholastic Library Publishing.

Herriges, Ann. Corals. 2006. (Blastoff! Readers Ser.). (Illus.). 24p. (J). lib. bdg. 16.95 (978-1-60014-049-5(1)) Bellwether Media.

Hirschmann, Kris. Coral. 2005. (Creatures of the Sea Ser.). (Illus.). 48p. (J). (gr. 4-8). 26.20 (978-0-7377-3007-4(2) , Greenhaven Pr., Inc.) Thomson Gale.

Houston, Rob. Corals. 2004. (Nature's Children Ser.). (Illus.). 48p. (J). (978-0-7172-5961-8(7) , Grolier) Scholastic Library Publishing.

Lindeen, Carol. Corales: Corals. 2007. (SPA.). (J). ***(978-0-7368-7651-3(0))*** Capstone Pr., Inc.

Lindeen, Carol K. Corals. 2005. (Under the Sea Ser.). (Illus.). 24p. (J). 19.93 (978-0-7368-3660-9(8)) Capstone Pr., Inc.

Llewellyn, Claire. Coral Reefs. 2000. (Heinemann First Library). (Illus.). 32p. (J). (gr. k-2). lib. bdg. 21.36 (978-1-57572-203-0(8)) Heinemann Library.

—Coral Reefs. 2000. (gr. k-3). lib. bdg. 14.75 (978-0-613-45734-7(X)) Tandem Library Bks.

Llewellyn, Claire, et al. Coral Reefs. 2002. (Geography Starts Ser.). (Illus.). 32p. (J). (gr. k-2). pap. 6.95 (978-1-58810-969-9(0) , 91452) Heinemann Library.

Patent, Dorothy Hinshaw. Colorful, Captivating Coral Reefs. Jubb, Kendahl Jan, tr. Jubb, Kendahl Jan, illus. 2003. 40p. (J). 17.95 (978-0-8027-8862-7(9)) Walker & Co.

Schaefer, Lola M. Corals. Saunders-Smith, Gail, ed. 1999. (Ocean Life Ser.). (Illus.). 24p. (J). (gr. k-1). lib. bdg. 15.93 (978-0-7368-0244-4(4) , Pebble Bks.) Capstone Pr., Inc.

—Corals. 1999. 13.25 (978-0-516-21832-8(8) , Children's Pr.) Scholastic Library Publishing.

—Corals. 2005. (Ocean Life Ser.). 24p. (YA). (gr. k-3). pap. (978-0-7368-8215-6(4) , Pebble Bks.) Capstone Pr., Inc.

Stone, Lynn M. Corals. 2003. (Rourke Discovery Library). (Illus.). 24p. (gr. 2-5). 14.95 (978-1-58952-318-0(0)) Rourke Publishing, LLC.

CORDUROY (FICTITIOUS CHARACTER)—FICTION

Freeman, Don. Un Bolsillo para Corduroy & A Pocket for Corduroy, 2 bks. Freeman, Don, illus. unabr. ed. 1999. (Corduroy Ser.). (SPA & ENG., Illus.). (J). (gr. k-3). pap. 33.95 incl. audio (978-0-87499-565-7(5)) Live Oak Media.

—Corduroy. Freeman, Don, illus. 2002. (Corduroy Ser.). (Illus.). (J). 13.19 (978-0-7587-2275-1(3)) Book Wholesalers, Inc.

—Corduroy. 2000. (Corduroy Ser.). (J). (gr. k-1). pap. 19.97 incl. audio (978-0-7366-9201-4(0)) Books on Tape, Inc.

—Corduroy. Freeman, Don, illus. (Illus.). (J). 2004. pap. 18.95 incl. audio compact disk (978-1-59112-789-5(0)); Set. 1999. (SPA & ENG., pap. 33.95 incl. audio (978-0-87499-566-4(3)) Live Oak Media.

—Corduroy. 2003. (Illus.). (J). bds. (978-0-670-03690-5(0) , Viking Adult) Penguin Group (USA) Inc.

—Corduroy 40th Anniversary Edition. Freeman, Don, illus. 2008. 40p. (J). (ps). 19.99 ***(978-0-670-06336-9(3)*** , Viking Juvenile) Penguin Group (USA) Inc.

—Corduroy & Company: A Don Freeman Treasury. 2001. (Corduroy Ser.). (Illus.). 128p. (J). (gr. k-1). 25.00 (978-0-670-03510-6(6) , Viking Juvenile) Penguin Group (USA) Inc.

—Corduroy's Best Halloween Ever. McCue, Lisa, illus. 2001. (Reading Railroad Bks.). 32p. (J). (gr. k-1). 3.99 (978-0-448-42499-6(1) , Grosset & Dunlap) Penguin Group (USA) Inc.

—Corduroy's Best Halloween Ever. 2001. (gr. k-3). lib. bdg. 11.25 (978-0-613-72457-9(7)); (Illus.). (J). 10.29 (978-0-606-21123-9(3)) Tandem Library Bks.

—Corduroy's Busy Street. 2005. 14p. (J). (ps-ps). pap. 5.99 (978-0-670-05994-2(3) , Viking Juvenile) Penguin Group (USA) Inc.

—Corduroy's Buttons. 2008. 12p. (J). (ps-1). bds. 7.99 ***(978-0-448-44815-2(7)*** , Grosset & Dunlap) Penguin Group (USA) Inc.

—Corduroy's Christmas Surprise. McCue, Lisa, illus. 2000. (Corduroy Ser.). 32p. (J). (gr. k-1). pap. 3.99 (978-0-448-42191-9(7) , Grosset & Dunlap) Penguin Group (USA) Inc.

—Corduroy's Christmas Surprise. 2000. (gr. k-3). lib. bdg. 11.25 (978-0-613-31090-1(X)) Tandem Library Bks.

—Corduroy's Easter. McCue, Lisa, illus. 1999. (Corduroy Ser.). 8p. (J). (gr. k-1). 11.99 (978-0-670-88101-7(5) , Viking Juvenile) Penguin Group (USA) Inc.

—Corduroy's Easter Party. McCue, Lisa, illus. 2000. (Corduroy Ser.). 32p. (J). (gr. k-1). pap. 3.49 (978-0-448-42154-4(2) , Grosset & Dunlap) Penguin Group (USA) Inc.

—Corduroy's Easter Party. 2000. (ps-2). lib. bdg. 11.25 (978-0-613-24691-0(8)) Tandem Library Bks.

—Corduroy's Sweet Surprise. 2008. 12p. (J). (ps-k). bds. 7.99 ***(978-0-448-44821-3(1)*** , Grosset & Dunlap) Penguin Group (USA) Inc.

—Corduroy's Trick-or-Treat. McCue, Lisa, illus. 2002. 12p. (J). bds. 5.99 (978-0-670-03562-5(9) , Viking Juvenile) Penguin Group (USA) Inc.

—Happy Easter, Corduroy. McCue, Lisa, illus. 2004. 16p. (J). (ps-ps). bds. 5.99 (978-0-670-03677-6(3) , Viking Juvenile) Penguin Group (USA) Inc.

A Pocket for Corduroy. Freeman, Don, illus. 2002. (Corduroy Ser.). (Illus.). (J). 13.19 (978-0-7587-3431-0(X)) Book Wholesalers, Inc.

—A Pocket for Corduroy. Freeman, Don, illus. 2000. (Corduroy Ser.). (J). (gr. k-1). pap. 19.97 incl. audio (978-0-7366-9202-1(9)) Books on Tape, Inc.

—A Pocket for Corduroy. Freeman, Don, illus. 2004. (Illus.). (J). pap. 18.95 incl. audio compact disk (978-1-59112-793-2(9)) Live Oak Media.

Freeman, Don & Hennessy, B. G. Corduroy at the Zoo. McCue, Lisa, illus. 2001. (Corduroy Ser.). 20p. (J). (gr. k-1). 11.99 (978-0-670-89288-4(2) , Viking Juvenile) Penguin Group (USA) Inc.

Freeman, Don & Inches, Alison. Corduroy Makes a Cake. Eitzen, Allan, illus. 2003. 32p. (J). (gr. k-3). pap. 3.99 (978-0-14-250163-4(8) , Puffin) Penguin Group (USA) Inc.

—Corduroy Writes a Letter. Eitzen, Allan, illus. 2004. (Easy-to-Read, Puffin Ser.). 32p. (J). (gr. k-3). pap. 3.99 (978-0-14-240130-9(7) , Puffin) Penguin Group (USA) Inc.

—Corduroy's Garden. Freeman, Don & Eitzen, Allan, illus. 2004. (Easy-to-Read, Puffin Ser.). 32p. (J). (gr. k-3). pap. 3.99 (978-0-14-240131-6(5) , Puffin) Penguin Group (USA) Inc.

Hennessy, B. G. & Freeman, Don. Corduroy Goes to the Library. 2005. 20p. (J). (gr. 1). 11.99 (978-0-670-05991-1(9) , Viking Juvenile) Penguin Group (USA) Inc.

Inches, Alison. Corduroy Makes a Cake. 2003. (gr. k-3). lib. bdg. 11.80 (978-0-613-87824-1(8)) Tandem Library Bks.

—Corduroy's Hike. Eitzen, Allan, illus. 2003. 32p. (J). (gr. k-2). pap. 3.99 (978-0-14-250164-1(6) , Puffin) Penguin Group (USA) Inc.

—Corduroy's Hike. 2003. (gr. k-3). lib. bdg. 11.80 (978-0-613-87823-4(X)) Tandem Library Bks.

Inches, Alison & Freeman, Don. Corduroy's Garden. Eitzen, Allan, illus. 2002. (Viking Easy-to-Read Ser.). 32p. (J). (gr. k-3). 13.99 (978-0-670-03547-2(5) , Viking Juvenile) Penguin Group (USA) Inc.

—Corduroy's Hike. Eitzen, Allan, illus. 2001. (Corduroy Ser.). 32p. (J). (gr. k-1). 13.99 (978-0-670-88945-7(8) , Viking Juvenile) Penguin Group (USA) Inc.

Unknown. Corduroy Visits the Farm! 2008. 16p. (J). (ps-1). pap. 5.99 (*978-0-448-44786-5(X)* , Grosset & Dunlap) Penguin Group (USA) Inc.

—Corduroy's Alphabet Hunt. 2008. 12p. (J). (ps-1). 9.99 (*978-0-448-44882-4(3)* , Grosset & Dunlap) Penguin Group (USA) Inc.

CORN

Basel, Roberta. From Corn to Cereal. 2005. (First Facts Ser.). (Illus.). 24p. (J). (ps-7). lib. bdg. 21.26 (978-0-7368-4284-6(5)) Capstone Pr., Inc.

Cooper, Jason. Corn. 1999. (Farm to Market Discovery Library). (Illus.). 24p. (J). (gr. k-4). lib. bdg. 18.60 (978-1-57103-620-9(2)) Rourke Publishing, LLC.

Corn. 2001. (Botany Ser.). (J). (gr. k-12). vinyl bd. 4.95 (978-1-58845-137-8(2)) School Specialty Publishing.

Fine, Edith Hope. Barbara McClintock: Nobel Prize Geneticist. 1998. (People to Know Ser.). (Illus.). 128p. (YA). (gr. 6-12). lib. bdg. 26.60 (978-0-89490-983-2(5)) Enslow Pubs., Inc.

Franks, Katie. Corn up Close. 2008. (J). lib. bdg. (*978-1-4042-4142-8(6)* , PowerKids Pr.) Rosen Publishing Group, Inc., The.

Hall, Margaret. Corn. (Food Ser.). 32p. pap. 6.95 (978-1-4034-4047-1(6)) Heinemann Library.

—El Maiz. 2003. (Alimentos Ser.).Tr. of Corn. 32p. (J). (SPA & ENG., Illus.). lib. bdg. 22.79 (978-1-4034-3735-8(1)); (ENG & SPA.). pap. 6.50 (978-1-4034-3741-9(6)) Heinemann Library.

—El Maiz. 2003. Tr. of Corn. (SPA.). (gr. k-3). lib. bdg. 14.75 (978-0-613-67103-3(1)) Tandem Library Bks.

Hall, Margaret C. Corn. 2003. (Food Ser.). (Illus.). 32p. (J). (gr. k-2). lib. bdg. 22.79 (978-1-58810-617-9(9)) Heinemann Library.

Heurtelou, Maude. Mwen Pito Mayi. Hippolyte, Johanne & Corbett, Kecia, illus. 2001. (Big Book Ser.).Tr. of I Prefer Corn. (CRP.). (J). (gr. k-2). 14p. 19.50 (978-1-58432-082-1(6)); 13p. pap. 6.50 (978-1-58432-077-7(X)) Educa Vision.

Hipp, Andrew. Corn. 2004. (Getting into Nature Ser.). (Illus.). 32p. (J). lib. bdg. 21.25 (978-0-8239-4205-3(8)) Rosen Publishing Group, Inc., The.

Landau, Elaine. Corn. 1999. (True Bks.). (Illus.). 48p. (J). (gr. 3-5). 25.00 (978-0-516-21026-1(2) , Children's Pr.) Scholastic Library Publishing.

—Corn. 1999. (gr. 3-6). lib. bdg. 15.25 (978-0-613-37317-3(0)) Tandem Library Bks.

—Popcorn. Lies, Brian, illus. 2003. 32p. (J). 16.95 (978-1-57091-442-3(7)); pap. 6.95 (978-1-57091-443-0(5)) Charlesbridge Publishing, Inc.

—Popcorn! 2003. (gr. 3-6). lib. bdg. 15.25 (978-0-613-84269-3(3)) Tandem Library Bks.

El Maiz: Por Dentro y Por Fuera. 2004. (SPA., Illus.). 32p. lib. bdg. 21.25 (978-1-4042-2863-4(2)) Rosen Publishing Group, Inc., The.

Mattern, Joanne. How Corn Grows: Como Crece el Maíz. 2006. (ENG & SPA., Illus.). 24p. (J). pap. (978-0-8368-6468-7(9) , Weekly Reader Early Learning Library) Stevens, Gareth Inc.

—How Corn Grows/ Como crece el maiz. 2006. (ENG & SPA., Illus.). 24p. (J). 19.33 (978-0-8368-6461-8(1)) Stevens, Gareth Inc.

Mexico's Marvelous Corn: Six-Pack. (Greetings Ser.: Vol. 2). (gr. 3-5). 31.00 (978-0-7635-1809-7(3)) Rigby Education.

Murray, Julie. Corn. 2007. (Life Cycles Ser.). 24p. (J). (gr. k-4). lib. bdg. 21.35 (*978-1-59928-705-8(6)* , Buddy Bks.) ABDO Publishing Co.

Nelson, Robin. From Kernel to Corn. (First Step Nonfiction Ser.). (J). 2003. (Illus.). 24p. 18.60 (978-0-8225-4659-7(0)); 2002. pap. 4.95 (978-0-8225-4735-8(X)) Lerner Publishing Group. (Lerner Pubns.).

Nielsen, L. Michelle. The Biography of Corn. 2007. (How Did That Get Here? Ser.). (Illus.). 32p. (J). (gr. 2-9). (*978-0-7787-2491-9(3));* pap. (*978-0-7787-2527-5(8))* Crabtree Publishing Co.

Powell, Patricia Hruby. Zinnia: How the Corn Was Saved. Ruffenach, Jessie, ed. Thomas, Peter, tr. Benally, Kendrick, illus. 2004. (ENG & NAV.). 32p. 17.95 (978-1-893354-38-8(5)) Salina Bookshelf.

Robson, Pam. Corn. 1998. (What's for Lunch? Ser.). (Illus.). 32p. (J). (gr. k-2). pap., stu. ed. 6.95 (978-0-516-26219-2(X) , Children's Pr.) Scholastic Library Publishing.

Trumbauer, Lisa. Corn. 2005. (Yellow Umbrella Ser.). (J). (978-0-7368-5312-5(X)); (Illus.). 16p. (978-0-7368-5276-0(X)) Capstone Pr., Inc.

Weiss, Ellen. From Kernel to Corncob. 2007. (Scholastic News Nonfiction Readers: How Things Grow—NEW SUBSET Ser.). 24p. (J). pap. 6.95 (*978-0-531-18789-0(6));* (Illus.). (gr. 1-2). lib. bdg. 20.00 (*978-0-531-18536-0(2))* Scholastic Library Publishing. (Children's Pr.).

CORN—FICTION

Anaya, Rudolfo. The First Tortilla: A Bilingual Story. Lamadrid, Enrique R., tr. Cordova, Amy, illus. 2007. (SPA & ENG.). 32p. (J). (gr. 2-4). 16.95 (*978-0-8263-4214-0(0))* Univ. of New Mexico Pr.

Cotes, Gilles. OGM et Chant de Mais. Begin, Jean-Guy, illus. 2004. (FRE.). 112p. (J). (978-2-89599-002-4(6)) Editions de la Paix CAN. *Dist:* World of Reading, Ltd.

Pugliano-Martin, Carol. Quetzacoatl Brings Corn to His People: A Legend from Mexico. 2006. spiral bd. 42.00 (*978-1-4108-7168-8(1))* Benchmark Education Co.

Robey, Stephanie. My Favorite Food. Loeffelholz, Sarah, illus. 2006. (J). 14.95 (978-0-9786850-0-3(8)) Overdue Bks.

Santucci, Barbara. Anna's Corn. Bloom, Lloyd, illus. 2004. 32p. (J). (gr. 1 up). 16.00 (978-0-8028-5119-2(3)) Eerdmans, William B. Publishing Co.

Tadjo, Veronique. The Lucky Grain of Corn. 2000. (Veronique Tadjo Ser.). (Illus.). 24p. (J). (BEN, ENG, VIE, CHI & ARA.). pap. 9.95 (978-1-84059-276-4(1)); (CHI, ENG, VIE, ARA & BEN., pap. 9.95 (978-1-84059-277-1(X)); (GER, ENG, VIE, CHI & ARA., pap. 9.95 (978-1-84059-279-5(6)); (GUJ, ENG, VIE, CHI & ARA., pap. 9.95 (978-1-84059-280-1(X)); (SOM, ENG, VIE, CHI & ARA., pap. 9.95 (978-1-84059-281-8(8)); (TUR, ENG, VIE, CHI & ARA., pap. 9.95 (978-1-84059-282-5(6)); (URD, ENG, VIE, CHI & ARA., pap. 9.95 (978-1-84059-283-2(4)); (VIE, ENG, CHI, ARA & BEN., pap. 9.95 (978-1-84059-284-9(2)); pap. 7.95 (978-1-84059-274-0(5)) Milet Publishing.

Watson, Gayle. Catie Corn & the Corn Cops. Fautsch, Jackie, illus. l.t. ed. 22p. (J). 2006. 15.99 (978-1-59879-098-6(6)); 2005. per. 9.99 (978-1-59879-079-5(X)) Lifevest Publishing, Inc.

CORNWALL (ENGLAND : COUNTY)

French, Allen. The Lost Baron. Wyeth, Andrew, illus. 2001. 320p. (J). (gr. 5-12). reprint ed. pap. 14.95 (978-1-883937-53-9(1) , 53-1) Bethlehem Bks.

CORNWALL (ENGLAND : COUNTY)—FICTION

Cooper, Susan. The Dark Is Rising. (Dark Is Rising Sequence Ser.). 244p. (YA). (gr. 5 up). pap. 4.99 (978-0-8072-1533-3(3) , Listening Library) Random Hse. Audio Publishing Group.

—The Dark Is Rising. (Dark Is Rising Sequence Ser.). 2007. 272p. (YA). pap. 8.99 (*978-1-4169-4965-7(8)* , Simon Pulse); 2005. 232p. pap. 2.99 (978-1-4169-0528-8(6) , Aladdin); 1999. 232p. (J). (gr. 7 up). pap. 5.99 (978-0-689-82983-3(3) , Aladdin); 2007. 256p. (J). (gr. 4-8). pap. 6.99 (*978-1-4169-4995-4(X)* , Aladdin); 2007. 272p. (YA). (gr. 7). pap. 8.99 (*978-1-4169-4969-5(0)* , Simon Pulse) Simon & Schuster Children's Publishing.

—The Dark Is Rising. 1999. (Dark Is Rising Sequence Ser.). (gr. 5-8). lib. bdg. 13.00 (978-0-613-90606-7(3)) Tandem Library Bks.

—The Dark Is Rising. l.t. ed. 2001. (Dark Is Rising Sequence Ser.). 395p. (J). (gr. 4-7). 21.95 (978-0-7862-2920-8(9)) Thorndike Pr.

—The Dark Is Rising Boxed Set: The Dark Is Rising, Greenwitch, over Sea, under Stone, Silver on the Tree, the Grey King. 2007. (Dark Is Rising Sequence Ser.). 1088p. (J). pap., pap. 29.99 (*978-1-4169-4996-1(8)* , Aladdin) Simon & Schuster Children's Publishing.

—Greenwitch. (Dark Is Rising Sequence Ser.). 2007. 176p. (YA). pap. 8.99 (*978-1-4169-4966-4(6)* , Simon Pulse); 2000. 144p. (J). (gr. 4-7). pap. 5.99 (978-0-689-84034-0(9) , Aladdin) Simon & Schuster Children's Publishing.

—Greenwitch. 2000. (Dark Is Rising Sequence Ser.). (J). 11.64 (978-0-606-19710-6(9)); (gr. 3-6). lib. bdg. 13.00 (978-0-613-29971-8(X)) Tandem Library Bks.

—Greenwitch. l.t. ed. 2001. (Dark Is Rising Sequence Ser.). 131p. (J). 21.95 (978-0-7862-2923-9(3)) Thorndike Pr.

Cooper, Susan. Over Sea, under Stone. 2002. (Dark Is Rising Sequence Ser.). (Illus.). (J). 13.40 (978-0-7587-5635-0(6)) Book Wholesalers, Inc.

—Over Sea, under Stone. 2007. (Dark Is Rising Sequence Ser.). 224p. (YA). pap. 8.99 (*978-1-4169-4964-0(X)* , Simon Pulse) Simon & Schuster Children's Publishing.

—Over Sea, under Stone. Wiesner, David, illus. 2000. (Dark Is Rising Sequence Ser.). 208p. (J). (gr. 4-7). pap. 5.99 (978-0-689-84035-7(7) , Aladdin) Simon & Schuster Children's Publishing.

—Over Sea, under Stone. 2000. (Dark Is Rising Sequence Ser.). (gr. 7-12). lib. bdg. 13.00 (978-0-613-30082-7(3)) Tandem Library Bks.

—Over Sea, under Stone. l.t. ed. 2000. (Dark Is Rising Sequence Ser.). 332p. (J). (gr. 4-7). 22.95 (978-0-7862-2918-5(7)) Thorndike Pr.

Dunmore, Helen. Ingo. 2008. 336p. (J). pap. 6.99 (*978-0-06-081854-8(9)* , Harper Trophy) HarperCollins Pubs.

—The Tide Knot. 2008. (J). (*978-0-06-081857-9(3));* 336p. 16.99 (*978-0-06-081855-5(7));* 336p. lib. bdg. 17.89 (*978-0-06-081856-2(5))* HarperCollins Pubs.

Foreman, Michael. Cat on the Hill. 2005. (Illus.). 32p. (J). pap. 8.99 (*978-1-84270-471-4(0))* Andersen GBR. *Dist:* Independent Pubs. Group.

Green, Julia. Hunter's Heart. 2007. 264p. (YA). (gr. 7-12). 16.95 (*978-0-7613-9493-8(1)* , Carolrhoda Bks.) Lerner Publishing Group.

Grow, Mary L. Chester Meets the Walker House Ghost, No. 1. Richel, Jean - Marc, illus. 2000. 72p. (Orig.). (J). (gr. 8-12). pap. 12.00 (978-0-9700777-0-7(X)) Studio 17.

Hopkins, Cathy. All Mates Together. 2007. (Truth or Dare Ser.: No. 8). 240p. (YA). (gr. 7 up). mass mkt. 5.99 (978-1-4169-2722-8(0) , Simon Pulse) Simon & Schuster Children's Publishing.

Hussey, Charmian. The Valley of Secrets. Crump, Christopher, illus. 400p. 2006. (J). pap. 9.99 (978-1-4169-0015-3(2) , Simon Pulse); 2005. (YA). 17.95 (978-0-689-87862-6(1)) Simon & Schuster Children's Publishing.

Jones, Allan Frewin. The Wreckers. 2003. 163p. (J). mass mkt. (978-0-330-36810-0(9) , Pan) Pan Macmillan.

Mendes, Valerie. The Drowning. 2006. 256p. (J). pap. 8.99 (978-1-4169-0127-3(2)) Simon & Schuster, Ltd. GBR. *Dist:* Trafalgar Square Publishing.

Quiller-Couch, Mabel. Kitty Trenire. 2007. 210p. pap. 12.99 (*978-1-4264-7475-0(X));* 230p. pap. 16.99 (*978-1-4264-7552-8(7))* BiblioBazaar.

—Kitty Trenire. 2006. 78.99 (*978-1-4280-1957-7(X))* IndyPublish.com.

CORONADO, FRANCISCO VASQUEZ DE, 1510-1554

Cantor, Carrie Nichols. Francisco Vasquez de Coronado: The Search for Cities of Gold. 2003. (Proud Heritage-The Hispanic Library). (Illus.). 40p. (J). (gr. 3-7). 28.50 (978-1-56766-210-8(2)) Child's World, Inc.

Capstone Press, contrib. by. Coronado. (Exploring the World Ser.). 48p. (YA). pap. 8.95 (978-0-7565-1141-8(0)) Compass Point Bks.

Crisfield. Earth's Explorers: Francisco de Coronado. 2000. (SPA., Illus.). pap. (978-0-7398-3338-4(3)) Steck-Vaughn.

Crisfield, Deborah. The Travels of Francisco de Coronado. 1999. (Explorers & Exploration Ser.). (Illus.). 48p. (J). (gr. 4-7). lib. bdg. 22.83 (978-0-7398-1493-2(1)) Raintree.

Doak, Robin S. Coronado: Francisco Vazquez de Coronado Explores the Southwest. 2001. (Exploring the World Ser.). (Illus.). 48p. (J). (gr. 4 up). lib. bdg. 22.60 (978-0-7565-0123-5(7)) Compass Point Bks.

Hossell, Karen Price. Francisco Coronado. 2003. (gr. 5-8). lib. bdg. 16.40 (978-0-613-45758-3(7)) Tandem Library Bks.

Hurwicz, Claude. Francisco Vasquez de Coronado. 2001. (Famous Explorers Ser.). (Illus.). 24p. (J). (gr. 3). lib. bdg. 18.75 (978-0-8239-5564-0(8) , PowerKids Pr.) Rosen Publishing Group, Inc., The.

Kline, Trish. Francisco Coronado. 2002. (ENG & SPA.). (J). lib. bdg. 19.27 (978-1-58952-428-6(4)) Rourke Publishing, LLC.

—Francisco Vazquez de Coronado. 2003. (Rourke Discovery Library). (Illus.). 24p. (gr. 2-5). 14.95 (978-1-58952-294-7(X)) Rourke Publishing, LLC.

Marcovitz, Hal. Coronado to Escalate: Francisco Coronado & the Exploration of the American Southwest. 1999. (Explorers of the New World Ser.). (Illus.). 64p. (J). (gr. 4 up). 31.00 (978-0-7910-5515-1(9) , Chelsea Hse.) Facts On File, Inc.

Mountjoy, Shane. Francisco Coronado & the Seven Cities of Gold. Goetzmann, William H., ed. 2005. (Explorers of New Lands Ser.). (Illus.). 142p. (J). (gr. 4-8). lib. bdg. 30.00 (978-0-7910-8631-5(3) , Chelsea Hse.) Facts On File, Inc.

Nardo, Don. Francisco Coronado. 2001. (Exploration Library). (Illus.). 64p. (J). (gr. 5-7). 25.50 (978-0-531-11974-7(2) , Watts, Franklin) Scholastic Library Publishing.

Otfinoski, Steven. Francisco Coronado: In Search of the Seven Cities of Gold. 2002. (Great Explorations Ser.). (Illus.). 76p. (J). 29.93 (978-0-7614-1484-1(3) , Benchmark Bks.) Cavendish, Marshall Corp.

Petrie, Kristin. Francisco Vasquez de Coronado. 2004. (Explorers Set I Ser.). (J). (gr. k-6). lib. bdg. 22.78 (978-1-59197-597-7(2)) ABDO Publishing Co.

Price Hossell, Karen. Francisco Coronado. (Groundbreakers Ser.). (Illus.). 48p. (J). 2003. (gr. 5-7). lib. bdg. 27.07 (978-1-4034-0242-4(6)); 2002. pap. 8.50 (978-1-4034-0478-7(X)) Heinemann Library.

Two Worlds Meet: the Travels of Francisco de Coronado: Fourth Grade Guided Comprehension Level R. (On Our Way to English Ser.). (gr. 4 up). 34.50 (978-0-7578-7184-9(4)) Rigby Education.

Whiting, Jim. Francisco Vasquez de Coronado. 2002. (Latinos in American History). (Illus.). 56p. (gr. 4-8). lib. bdg. 29.95 (978-1-58415-146-3(3)) Mitchell Lane Pubs., Inc.

CORONARY HEART DISEASES

see Heart—Diseases

CORPULENCE

see Weight Control

CORRECTIONAL INSTITUTIONS

see Prisons

CORRESPONDENCE

see Business Letters; Letter Writing; Letters

CORRUPTION (IN POLITICS)

see Political Corruption

CORSAIRS

see Pirates

CORTES, HERNANDO, 1485-1547

Abnett, Dan. Hernan Cortes & the Fall of the Aztec Empire. 2007. (Jr. Graphic Biographies Ser.). (J). (978-1-4042-2334-9(7)); (Illus.). 24p. pap. (978-1-4042-2144-4(1)); (Illus.). 24p. (gr. 2-6). lib. bdg. 21.25 (978-1-4042-3391-1(1)) Rosen Publishing Group, Inc., The. (PowerKids Pr.).

Angelis, Gina De. Hernando Cortes & the Conquest of Mexico. 2007. (Illus.). 63p. (J). 25.00 (*978-1-4223-6717-9(7))* DIANE Publishing Co.

Calvert, Patricia. Hernando Cortes: Fortune Favored the Bold. 2002. (Great Explorations Ser.). (Illus.). 80p. (J). 29.93 (978-0-7614-1482-7(7) , Benchmark Bks.) Cavendish, Marshall Corp.

Crisfield, Deborah. The Travels of Hernan Cortes. 2000. (Explorers & Exploration Ser.). (Illus.). 48p. (J). (gr. 4-7). lib. bdg. 22.83 (978-0-7398-1488-8(5)) Raintree.

Donaldson-Forbes, Jeff. Hernan Cortes. 2002. (Famous Explorers Ser.). (Illus.). 24p. (J). (gr. 3). lib. bdg. 18.75 (978-0-8239-5832-0(9) , PowerKids Pr.) Rosen Publishing Group, Inc., The.

Flowers, Charles. Cortes & the Conquest of the Aztec Empire in World History. 2001. (In World History Ser.). (Illus.). 128p. (J). (gr. 5-12). lib. bdg. 26.60 (978-0-7660-1395-7(2)) Enslow Pubs., Inc.

Gaff, Jackie. Hernan Cortes: The Life of a Spanish Conquistador. 2005. (Graphic Nonfiction Ser.). (Illus.). 48p. (J). (gr. 4-6). lib. bdg. 26.50 (978-1-4042-0244-3(7)) Rosen Publishing Group, Inc., The.

Henty, G. A. By Right of Conquest: Or with Cortez in Mexico. 2000. 348p. (YA). (gr. 3 up). mass mkt. 7.99 (978-1-887159-67-8(3)) Preston-Speed Pubns.

January, Brendan. Hernan Cortes. (Groundbreakers Ser.). (Illus.). 48p. 2003. (J). (gr. 5-7). lib. bdg. 27.07 (978-1-4034-0243-1(4)); 2002. pap. (978-1-4034-0479-4(8)) Heinemann Library.

Kline, Trish. Hernan Cortes. (Rourke Discovery Library). 2003. (Illus.). 24p. (gr. 2-5). 14.95 (978-1-58952-293-0(1)); 2002. 19.27 (978-1-58952-427-9(6)) Rourke Publishing, LLC.

Koestler-Grack, Rachel A. Hernando Cortes: And the Fall of the Aztecs. Goetzmann, William H., ed. 2005. (Explorers of New Lands Ser.). (Illus.). 158p. (J). (ps-8). lib. bdg. 30.00 (978-0-7910-8609-4(7) , Chelsea Hse.) Facts On File, Inc.

Petrie, Kristin. Hernan Cortes. 2004. (Explorers Set I Ser.). (Illus.). 32p. (J). (gr. k-6). lib. bdg. 22.78 (978-1-59197-598-4(0)) ABDO Publishing Co.

Streissguth, Thomas, tr. Hernan Cortes. 2004. (Fact Finders Ser.). (Illus.). 32p. (J). 16.95 (978-0-7368-2489-7(8)) Capstone Pr., Inc.

Zronik, John Paul. Hernando Cortés: Spanish Invader of Mexico. 2006. (In the Footsteps of Explorers Ser.). (Illus.). 32p. (J). (gr. 3-9). pap. (978-0-7787-2470-4(0)) Crabtree Publishing Co.

CORTES, HERNANDO, 1485-1547—FICTION

Henty, A. G. By Right of Conquest or with Cortez in Mexico. 2007. (ENG.). 356p. 45.99 (*978-1-4280-7223-7(3));* per. 39.99 (*978-1-4280-7201-5(2))* IndyPublish.com.

COSMETICS

see also Perfumes

African-American Makeup Manufacturers. 2000. (My Ancestors—My Heroes Ser.: Vol. 41). (J). (gr. 3-4). (978-1-893091-40-5(6)) Parker Publishing Co.

Bennett, Tammy. Looking Good from the Inside Out Fashion. 2003. (gr. 7-12). lib. bdg. 26.90 (978-0-613-82398-2(2)) Tandem Library Bks.

Carpenter, Deb. Nature's Beauty Kit: Cosmetic Recipes You Can Make at Home. 2004. (Illus.). 144p. (gr. 4). reprint ed. pap. 10.95 (978-1-55591-221-5(4)) Fulcrum Publishing.

Everett, Felicity. Makeup. rev. ed. 1998. (Usborne Fashion Guides Ser.). (Illus.). 32p. (gr. 6-12). (J). lib. bdg. 14.95 (978-1-58086-035-2(4)); (YA). pap. 6.95 (978-0-7460-3111-7(4)) EDC Publishing.

Hall, Margaret. Madam C. J. Walker. 2003. (Illus.). 32p. (J). lib. bdg. 22.79 (978-1-4034-3252-0(X)) Heinemann Library.

Katschke, Judy. Beautiful Makeup Book. Chapmanworks Staff, illus. 2000. (Barbie Ser.). (J). (gr. k-3). bds. 12.99 (978-1-57584-650-7(0) , Reader's Digest Children's Bks.) Reader's Digest Children's Publishing, Inc.

Kent, Jacqueline C. Business Builders in Cosmetics. 2003. (Business Builders Ser.: Vol. 7). (Illus.). 160p. (gr. 5 up). lib. bdg. 22.95 (978-1-881508-82-3(X)) Oliver Pr., Inc.

Krohn, Katherine E. Madam C.J. Walker & New Cosmetics. Dominguez, Richard & Barnett, Charles, illus. 2007. (Graphic Library). 32p. 25.26 (978-0-7368-6485-5(7)) Capstone Pr., Inc.

Mayall, Beth. Galaxy Girl. 2002. (Get the Look Ser.). (Illus.). 32p. (J). (978-0-439-32894-4(2)) Scholastic, Inc.

—Glamour Girl. 2002. (Get the Look Ser.). (Illus.). 31p. (J). (978-0-439-32896-8(9)) Scholastic, Inc.

McDonald, Fiona. Jewelry & Makeup Through History. 2006. (J). lib. bdg. (978-0-8368-6856-2(0)) Stevens, Gareth Inc.

Nichols, Catherine. Madam C.J. Walker. 2005. (Scholastic News Nonfiction Readers Ser.). (Illus.). 24p. (J). pap. (978-0-516-24784-7(0)) Children's Pr., Ltd.

Reynolds, Helen. Makeup & Body Decorations. 2003. (Fashionable History of Costume Ser.). (Illus.). 32p. (J). lib. bdg. 25.70 (978-1-4109-0028-9(2)) Raintree.

Strazzabosco, Jeanne M. Choosing a Career in Cosmetology. 2005. (World of Work Ser.). (Illus.). 64p. (YA). (gr. 7-12). lib. bdg. 25.25 (978-0-8239-2279-6(0) , WW-COSM) Rosen Publishing Group, Inc., The.

COSMETICS—FICTION

Fowler, Susi Gregg. Beautiful. Fowler, Jim, illus. 1998. 32p. (J). (ps-3). 15.00 (978-0-688-15111-9(6)) HarperCollins Pubs.

Munsch, Robert. Makeup Mess. ed. 2004. (Illus.). (J). (gr. k-3). spiral bd. (978-0-616-11125-3(8)) Canadian National Institute for the Blind/Institut National Canadien pour les Aveugles.

—Makeup Mess. Martchenko, Michael, illus. ed. 2004. (J). (gr. k-3). spiral bd. (978-0-616-11124-6(X)) Canadian National Institute for the Blind/Institut National Canadien pour les Aveugles.

Ostrow, Kim. Makeup Mayhem. Durk, Jim, illus. 2006. (Ready-To-Read Ser.: Vol. 2). 32p. (J). pap. 3.99 (978-0-689-87724-7(2) , Simon Spotlight) Simon & Schuster Children's Publishing.

Pietri, Annie. The Orange Trees of Versailles. 2005. 144p. (J). (gr. 3-7). pap. 5.99 (978-0-440-41948-8(4) , Yearling) Random Hse. Children's Bks.

Wells, Rosemary. Ruby's Beauty Shop. Wells, Rosemary, illus. (Max & Ruby Ser.). 32p. (J). (gr. k-3). 2004. pap. 6.99 (978-0-14-240194-1(3) , Puffin); 2002. (Illus.). 15.99 (978-0-670-03553-3(X) , Viking Juvenile) Penguin Group (USA) Inc.

COSMOGONY

see Universe

COSMOGONY, BIBLICAL

see Creation

COSMOGRAPHY

see Universe

COSMOLOGY

see Universe

COSMOLOGY, BIBLICAL

see Creation

COSMONAUTS

see Astronauts

COSTA RICA

Cooper, Sharon Katz. Costa Rica ABCs: A Book about the People & Places of Costa Rica. Eitzen, Allan, illus. 2006. (Country ABCs Ser.). 32p. (J). (gr. k-5). lib. bdg. 25.26 (***978-1-4048-2249-8(6)***) Picture Window Bks.

Corwin, Jeff. Into Wild Costa Rica. 2004. (Animal Planet Ser.). (Illus.). 48p. (J). 24.95 (978-1-4103-0226-7(1)); 11.20 (978-1-4103-0227-4(X)) Thomson Gale. (Blackbirch Pr., Inc.).

Cox, Vicki. Oscar Arias Sanchez: Bringing Peace to Central America. 2007. (Modern Peacemakers Ser.). (Illus.). 128p. (YA). (gr. 9 up). 30.00 (***978-0-7910-8999-6(1)*** , Chelsea Hse.) Facts On File, Inc.

Cunningham, Patrick. Costa Rica. 2004. (Letters from Around the World Ser.). (J). lib. bdg. (978-1-84234-246-6(0) , Cherrytree Books) Evans Publishing Group.

Deady, Kathleen W. Costa Rica. (True Bks.). (J). 2005. (Illus.). 48p. (gr. 3-5). pap. 6.95 (978-0-516-25831-7(1)); 2004. 25.00 (978-0-516-22810-5(2)) Scholastic Library Publishing. (Children's Pr.).

Dendinger, Roger. Costa Rica. 2003. (Modern World Nations Ser.). (Illus.). 150p. (gr. 6-12). 30.00 (978-0-7910-7242-4(8) , Chelsea Hse.) Facts On File, Inc.

Englar, Mary. Costa Rica: A Question & Answer Book. 2006. (Fact Finders Ser.). (Illus.). 32p. (J). (978-0-7368-4352-2(3)) Capstone Pr., Inc.

Exploring Costa Rica 2001. 9th ed. 2000. 288p. per. 13.95 (978-0-01-409207-9(7)) Tico Times, The.

Foley, Erin & Cooke, Barbara. Costa Rica. 2nd ed. 2007. (Cultures of the World Ser.). 144p. (J). lib. bdg. 39.93 (***978-0-7614-2079-8(7)*** , Benchmark Bks.) Cavendish, Marshall Corp.

Fox, Mary Virginia. Costa Rica. (Visit to Ser.). 32p. pap. 6.50 (978-1-4034-4146-1(4)); 2000. (Illus.). (J). lib. bdg. 21.36 (978-1-57572-379-2(4)) Heinemann Library.

Frank, Nicole. Costa Rica. 2000. (Countries of the World Ser.). (Illus.). 94p. (J). (gr. 6 up). lib. bdg. 30.00 (978-0-8368-2323-3(0)) Stevens, Gareth Inc.

Frerer, Fredrick. Costa Rica. 1999. (Festivals of the World Ser.). (Illus.). 32p. (J). (gr. 3 up). lib. bdg. 24.67 (978-0-8368-2022-5(3)) Stevens, Gareth Inc.

Frisch, Joy. Costa Rica. 2000. (Let's Investigate Ser.). (Illus.). 32p. (J). (gr. 4-7). lib. bdg. (978-1-58341-083-7(X) , Creative Education) Creative Co., The.

Garrett, Rosalie & Frank, Nicole. Welcome to Costa Rica. 2001. (Welcome to My Country Ser.). (Illus.). 48p. (J). (gr. 2 up). lib. bdg. 26.00 (978-0-8368-2523-7(3)) Stevens, Gareth Inc.

Haynes, Tricia. Costa Rica. 1999. (Major World Nations Ser.). (Illus.). 144p. (YA). (ps up). lib. bdg. 19.95 (978-0-7910-4973-0(6) , Chelsea Hse.) Facts On File, Inc.

Marcus, Amy. Exploring Costa Rica with the Five Themes of Geography/By Amy Marcus. 2005. (Library of the Western Hemisphere). (J). (Illus.). 24p. 19.95 (978-1-4042-2672-2(9) , PowerKids Pr.); (978-0-8239-4644-0(4)); (Illus.). 24p. pap. (978-0-8239-4632-7(0)) Rosen Publishing Group, Inc., The.

Miller, Debra A. Costa Rica. 2005. (Modern Nations of the World Ser.). (Illus.). 112p. (YA). (gr. 7-10). lib. bdg. 29.95 (978-1-59018-623-7(0) , Lucent Bks.) Thomson Gale.

Morris, Noelle. Costa Rica. 2003. (World Tour Ser.). (Illus.). 48p. (J). lib. bdg. 25.70 (978-0-7398-6809-6(8)) Raintree.

Morrison, Marion. Costa Rica. (Enchantment of the World, Second Ser.). (Illus.). 144p. (J). (gr. 5-9). rev. ed. 2007. 36.00 (978-0-516-24884-4(7)); 2nd ed. 1998. 36.00 (978-0-516-20469-7(6)) Scholastic Library Publishing. (Children's Pr.).

Scimone, Diana. Adventures with Pawpaw: Costa Rica. Wiedemer, Leah, illus. 2003. 32p. (J). 8.95 (978-0-9729507-2-5(9)) Peapod Publishing, Inc.

Shields, Charles J. Costa Rica. 2002. (Let's Discover Central America Ser.). (Illus.). 64p. (YA). (gr. 5 up). lib. bdg. (978-1-59084-093-1(3)) Mason Crest Pubs.

West, Tracey. Costa Rica. 1999. (Ticket to Ser.). (Illus.). 48p. (gr. 2-4). lib. bdg. 22.60 (978-1-57505-134-5(6)); (J). (gr. 3-5). lib. bdg. 22.60 (978-1-57505-109-3(5) , Carolrhoda Bks.) Lerner Publishing Group.

COSTA RICA—FICTION

Banks, Joan. Song of La Selva: A Story of a Costa Rican Rain Forest. Bond, Higgins, illus. 1998. (Habitat Ser.: No. 9). 36p. (J). (gr. 1-4). 15.95 (978-1-56899-586-1(5) , B7009); 19.95 incl. audio (978-1-56899-588-5(1) , BC7009); pap. 6.95 (978-1-56899-587-8(3)); pap. 10.95 incl. audio (978-1-56899-589-2(X)) Soundprints.

—Song of La Selva: A Story of a Costa Rican Rain Forest, Incl. toy. Higgins-Bond, illus. 1998. (Habitat Ser.: Vol. 9). 36p. (J). (gr. 1-4). 26.95 (978-1-56899-590-8(3)) Soundprints.

—Song of La Selva: A Story of a Costa Rican Rain Forest, Incl. toy. Bond, Higgins, illus. 1998. (Habitat Ser.: Vol. 9). 36p. (J). (gr. 1-4). 31.95 incl. audio (978-1-56899-592-2(X)) Soundprints.

—Song of La Selva: A Story of a Costa Rican Rain Forest, Incl. toy. Bond, Higgins & Kaye, Randye, illus. 1998. (Habitat Ser.: Vol. 9). 36p. (J). (gr. 1-4). pap. 19.95 incl. audio (978-1-56899-593-9(8)) Soundprints.

Cronin, Susan L. Gidget Goes Away. 2006. 54p. pap. 12.95 (978-1-4137-9878-4(0)) PublishAmerica, Inc.

Harcourt School Publishers Staff. My Great Adventure. 3rd ed. 2002. (Trophies English Language Learners Ser.). (Illus.). pap. 51.00 (978-0-15-327895-2(1)) Harcourt Schl. Pubs.

Keister, Douglas. Fernando's Gift/el Regalo de Fernando. Keister, Douglas, photos by. 2001. (SPA., Illus.). 32p. (J). (ps-3). pap. 7.95 (978-0-87156-927-1(2)) Sierra Club Bks. for Children.

—El Regalo de Fernando. 1998. (Sierra Club Bks.).Tr. of Fernando's Gift. (J). 13.75 (978-0-606-13382-1(8)) Tandem Library Bks.

Russell, Barbara Timberlake. The Remembering Stone. Peck, Beth, illus. 1999. (J). (978-0-7894-2583-6(1)) Dorling Kindersley Publishing, Inc.

—The Remembering Stone. Cotts, Claire B., illus. 2004. 32p. (J). 16.00 (978-0-374-36242-3(4) , Farrar, Straus & Giroux (BYR)) Farrar, Straus & Giroux.

Tennyson, Michael. Morpha: A Rain Forest Story. Yoswa, Jennifer H., illus. 2002. (CMC Wilderness Kids Ser.). 40p. 14.95 (978-0-9671466-8-3(2)) Colorado Mountain Club Pr., The.

Uncle Markie. Piglette & Bobo Go to Costa Rica. 2002. 34p. (YA). ring bd. 9.95 (978-1-933129-03-7(4)) Studio 403.

COSTUME

Here are entered descriptive and historical works on the costume of particular countries or periods and for works on fancy costume. Works dealing with clothing from a practical standpoint, including the art of dress, are entered under Clothing and Dress. Works describing the prevailing mode or style in dress are entered under Fashion.

see also Arms and Armor; Clothing and Dress; Cosmetics; Dressmaking; Fashion; Hats; Indians of North America—Costume and Adornment; Jewelry; Make-Up, Theatrical; Uniforms, Military

Aikman, Louise. North American Dress. 2002. (Twentieth-Century Developments in Fashion & Costume Ser.). (Illus.). 64p. (J). (gr. 7 up). lib. bdg. (978-1-59084-425-0(4)) Mason Crest Pubs.

Beak, Nick Huckleberry. Crafty Masks. Freeman, John, photos by. 1999. (Crafty Kids Ser.). (Illus.). 64p. (J). (gr. 3 up). lib. bdg. 26.00 (978-0-8368-2482-7(2)) Stevens, Gareth Inc.

Bonnice, Sherry. Folk Fashion. 2002. (North American Folklore Ser.). (Illus.). 112p. (J). (gr. 7 up). lib. bdg. (978-1-59084-338-3(X)) Mason Crest Pubs.

Bracken, Thomas. Children of the World. 1999. (Looking Into the Past Ser.). (Illus.). 64p. (YA). (gr. 5 up). 14.00 (978-0-7910-4685-2(0) , Chelsea Hse.) Facts On File, Inc.

Brend, Dawn & Craig, Rebecca. Jazzy Jewelry: Recycle Materials to Make Cool Stuff. 2007. (EcoCrafts Ser.). 48p. (J). pap. 7.95 (***978-0-7534-5968-3(X)*** , Kingfisher) Houghton Mifflin Co. Trade & Reference Div.

Brown, Mike. Rescue Services. 2003. (Twentieth-Century Developments in Fashion & Costume Ser.). (Illus.). 64p. (J). (gr. 7 up). lib. bdg. (978-1-59084-428-1(9)) Mason Crest Pubs.

Costume, Tradition & Culture: Reflecting on the Past, 12 bks. 1999. (Illus.). 64p. (J). (gr. 5). 215.40 (978-0-7910-5161-0(7) , Chelsea Hse.) Facts On File, Inc.

Doudna, Kelly. Clothing Around the World. 2004. (Around the World Ser.). (Illus.). 23p. (J). (ps-3). lib. bdg. 19.93 (978-1-59197-565-6(4)) ABDO Publishing Co.

Draper, Allison Stark. What People Wore During the Civil War. 2001. (Clothing, Costumes & Uniforms Thoughout American History Ser.). (Illus.). 24p. (J). (gr. 3). lib. bdg. 19.95 (978-0-8239-5669-2(5) , PKCLCI, PowerKids Pr.) Rosen Publishing Group, Inc., The.

—What People Wore During the Westward Expansion. 2001. (Clothing, Costumes & Uniforms Thoughout American History Ser.). (Illus.). 24p. (J). (gr. 3). lib. bdg. 19.95 (978-0-8239-5667-8(9) , PKCLPL, PowerKids Pr.) Rosen Publishing Group, Inc., The.

—What People Wore in Colonial America. 2001. (Clothing, Costumes & Uniforms Thoughout American History Ser.). (Illus.). 24p. (J). (gr. 3). lib. bdg. 19.95 (978-0-8239-5665-4(2) , PKCLCO, PowerKids Pr.) Rosen Publishing Group, Inc., The.

Fancy Dress Princess. 2004. (Fun Kits Ser.). (Illus.). 48p. (J). (978-1-84229-733-9(3)) Top That! Publishing PLC.

Franck, Irene M. & Brownstone, David M. Dress Through the Ages, 16 vols. 2001. (Illus.). (J). (978-0-7172-9550-0(8)); (978-0-7172-9554-8(0)); (978-0-7172-9546-3(X)); (978-0-7172-9551-7(6)); (978-0-7172-9543-2(5)); (978-0-7172-9544-9(3)); (978-0-7172-9541-8(9)); (978-0-7172-9553-1(2)); (978-0-7172-9547-0(8)); (978-0-7172-9556-2(7)); (978-0-7172-9548-7(6)); (978-0-7172-9542-5(7)); (978-0-7172-9555-5(9)); (978-0-7172-9545-6(1)); (978-0-7172-9552-4(4)); Set. (978-0-7172-9549-4(4)) Scholastic Library Publishing. (Grolier).

—Dress Through the Ages: Cowboy, 16 vols. 2001. (Illus.). (J). (gr. 5-7). 265.00 (978-0-7172-9558-6(3) , Grolier) Scholastic Library Publishing.

Fremont, Eleanor. Picture Me As a Dinosaur. 2003. (Baby Costume Minis Ser.). (Illus.). 10p. (J). (ps up). bds. 4.99 (978-1-57151-568-1(2)) Playhouse Publishing.

Galford, Ellen. Festivals. 2002. (Twentieth-Century Developments in Fashion & Costume Ser.). (Illus.). 64p. (J). (gr. 7 up). lib. bdg. (978-1-59084-423-6(8)) Mason Crest Pubs.

—Religious Costumes. 2003. (Twentieth-Century Developments in Fashion & Costume Ser.). (Illus.). 64p. (J). (gr. 7 up). lib. bdg. (978-1-59084-429-8(7)) Mason Crest Pubs.

Golden Books Staff. Surprise Disguise! Baker, Darrell, illus. 2004. 32p. (J). (ps-2). pap. 2.99 (978-0-375-82792-1(7) , Golden Bks.) Random Hse. Children's Bks.

Grosset and Dunlap Staff & Noble, Marty. Costume Ball. Jarnow, Jill, ed. 2001. (Sticker Styles Ser.). (Illus.). 1p. (J). (ps-3). pap. 4.99 (978-0-448-42466-8(5) , Grosset & Dunlap) Penguin Group (USA) Inc.

Harris, Carol & Brown, Mike. Accessories. 2002. (Twentieth-Century Developments in Fashion & Costume Ser.). (Illus.). 64p. (J). (gr. 7 up). lib. bdg. (978-1-59084-419-9(X)) Mason Crest Pubs.

—Ceremonial Costumes. 2002. (Twentieth-Century Developments in Fashion & Costume Ser.). (Illus.). 64p. (J). (gr. 7 up). lib. bdg. (978-1-59084-424-3(6)) Mason Crest Pubs.

—Children's Costumes. 2002. (Twentieth-Century Developments in Fashion & Costume Ser.). (Illus.). 64p. (J). (gr. 7 up). lib. bdg. (978-1-59084-420-5(3)) Mason Crest Pubs.

—Women's Costumes. 2002. (Twentieth-Century Developments in Fashion & Costume Ser.). (Illus.). 64p. (J). (gr. 7 up). lib. bdg. (978-1-59084-421-2(1)) Mason Crest Pubs.

House, Deborah. Quick Costumes for Kids: 30 Great Fancy Dress Ideas. 2007. (Illus.). 144p. pap. 17.95 (***978-0-600-61484-5(0)*** , Hamlyn) Octopus Publishing Group GBR. *Dist:* Sterling Publishing Co., Inc.

Kohl, MaryAnn F. Making Make-Believe: Fun Props, Costumes & Creative Play Ideas. 2004. (Illus.). 192p. (gr. 1-3). pap. 16.95 (978-0-87659-198-7(5) , 19674) Gryphon Hse., Inc.

Lee Humphrey, Robert, ed. Culture & Costumes: Symbols of Their Period, 13 vols., Set. (Illus.). 64p. (YA). (gr. 7 up). lib. bdg. (978-1-59084-430-4(0)) Mason Crest Pubs.

McArthur, Alex & Shepard, Tristram. Textiles Technology for Key Stage 3. 2000. (Design & Make It Ser.). (Illus.). 144p. (J). (gr. 6-9). pap., stu. ed. 22.50 (978-0-7487-4431-2(2)) Nelson Thornes Ltd. GBR. *Dist:* Trans-Atlantic Pubns., Inc.

McNab, Chris. Everyday Dress. 2002. (Twentieth-Century Developments in Fashion & Costume Ser.). (Illus.). 64p. (J). (gr. 7 up). lib. bdg. (978-1-59084-427-4(0)) Mason Crest Pubs.

Miller, Brandon Marie. Dressed for the Occasion: What Americans Wore, 1620-1970. 1999. (People's History Ser.). (Illus.). 96p. (gr. 6-12). lib. bdg. 26.60 (978-0-8225-1738-2(8)) Lerner Publishing Group.

Mitchell, Alycen. The Performing Arts. 2003. (Twentieth-Century Developments in Fashion & Costume Ser.). (Illus.). 64p. (J). (gr. 7 up). lib. bdg. (978-1-59084-426-7(2)) Mason Crest Pubs.

Nelson, Robin. Clothing. 2003. (First Step Nonfiction Ser.). (Illus.). 8p. (J). pap. 3.95 (978-0-8225-3927-8(6) , Lerner Pubns.) Lerner Publishing Group.

Noble, Marty. Playtime Princesses. 2002. (Sticker Styles Ser.). (Illus.). (J). mass mkt. 12.95 (978-0-448-42840-6(7) , Planet Dexter) Penguin Group (USA) Inc.

Norris, Herbert. Ancient European Costume & Fashion. 1999. (Illus.). 336p. pap. 16.95 (978-0-486-40723-4(3)) Dover Pubns., Inc.

Rowland-Warne, L. Costume. 2000. (Eyewitness Bks.). (Illus.). 64p. (J). (gr. 4-7). 15.99 (978-0-7894-5586-4(2)) Dorling Kindersley Publishing, Inc.

—Trajes. (Coleccion Biblioteca Visual).Tr. of Costumes. (SPA.). 64p. (YA). (gr. 5-8). (978-84-372-3768-8(8)) Altea, Ediciones, S.A. - Grupo Santillana.

Schaefer, Lola M. Costumes. Saunders-Smith, Gail, ed. 1998. (Fall Fun Ser.). (Illus.). 24p. (J). (gr. k-1). lib. bdg. 15.93 (978-0-7368-0104-1(9) , Pebble Bks.) Capstone Pr., Inc.

Steele, Philip. Clothes & Crafts in Ancient Greece. 2000. (Clothes & Crafts in History Ser.). (Illus.). 32p. (J). (gr. 4 up). lib. bdg. 24.67 (978-0-8368-2734-7(1)) Stevens, Gareth Inc.

—Clothes & Crafts in Victorian Times. 2000. (Clothes & Crafts in History Ser.). (Illus.). 32p. (J). (gr. 4 up). lib. bdg. 24.67 (978-0-8368-2738-5(4)) Stevens, Gareth Inc.

Stillerman, Robbie. Blair the Beauty Queen. 2002. (Sticker Paper Dolls Ser.). (Illus.). 4p. (J). pap. 1.50 (978-0-486-42349-4(2)) Dover Pubns., Inc.

Stuart, Keith. Spain & Portugal. 2002. (Cultures & Costumes Ser.). (Illus.). 64p. (J). (gr. 7 up). lib. bdg. (978-1-59084-440-3(8)) Mason Crest Pubs.

Sun, Ming-Ju. Japanese Warrior Costumes Paper Dolls. 2000. (J). pap. 6.95 (978-0-486-41046-3(3)) Dover Pubns., Inc.

—Russian Folk Costumes Paper Dolls. 2003. 32p. (J). pap. 5.95 (978-0-486-42390-6(5)) Dover Pubns., Inc.

Svitil, Torene & Dunkleberger, Amy. So You Want to Work in Set Design, Costuming, or Make-up? 2008. (Careers in Film & Television Ser.). (Illus.). 128p. (J). (gr. 6 up). lib. bdg. 31.93 (***978-0-7660-2740-4(6)***) Enslow Pubs., Inc.

Tadano, Kazuko. Girls' Life Illustration File. Ozawa, Tadashi, illus. 2003. (How to Draw Manga Ser.: Vol. 15). 132p. (YA). pap. 21.99 (978-4-7661-1338-9(1)) Graphic-Sha JPN. *Dist:* Diamond Bk. Distributors.

Taliadoros, Jenny, ed. Greer Garson Paper Dolls. Madan, Fredric & Ernst, Clara, illus. 2007. 8p. pap. 12.00 (***978-0-9790668-6-3(7)***) Paper Studio Pr.

—Judy Garland Cut-Out Dolls. 2007. (Illus.). 8p. pap. 12.00 (***978-0-9790668-9-4(1)***) Paper Studio Pr.

—Lana Turner Paper Dolls. Valliant, Regina & Meixner, Jo Hedwig, illus. 2007. 8p. (J). pap. 12.00 (***978-0-9790668-1-8(6)***) Paper Studio Pr.

—The Lollypop Crowd Stand-up Paper Dolls. 2007. (Illus.). 8p. pap. 12.00 (***978-0-9795053-1-7(3)***) Paper Studio Pr.

—Rita Hayworth Paper Doll: Dancing Star Dolls & Clothes. Mingo, Norman & Ernst, Clara, illus. 2007. 8p. (J). pap. 12.00 (***978-0-9790668-0-1(8)***) Paper Studio Pr.

Taymor, Julie. Costumes of the Lion King on Broadway. 2000. 128p. (J). pap. 24.95 (978-0-7868-8380-6(4)) Disney Pr.

Thomas, Mark. Clothes in Colonial America. 2002. (Welcome Books). (Illus.). 24p. (J). (ps-2). 18.00 (978-0-516-23932-3(5)); pap. 4.95 (978-0-516-23490-8(0)) Scholastic Library Publishing. (Children's Pr.).

—Clothes in Colonial America. 2002. (gr. k-3). lib. bdg. 12.95 (978-0-613-58754-9(5)) Tandem Library Bks.

Tierney, Tom. Edwardian Costumes Paper Dolls. 2001. (Illus.). 16p. (J). pap. 3.95 (978-0-486-41556-7(2)) Dover Pubns., Inc.

—Fashion Parade Paper Dolls: 4 Decades of Great Designs, from 1960 To 2000. 2002. (Illus.). 136p. (J). pap. 12.95 (978-0-486-42738-6(2)) Dover Pubns., Inc.

Walker, Sylvia. Dream Dresses. 2002. (Sticker Styles Ser.). (Illus.). (J). mass mkt. 12.95 (978-0-448-42841-3(5) , Planet Dexter) Penguin Group (USA) Inc.

Whitty, Helen. Dressing Up. 2001. (Clothing Ser.). (Illus.). 32p. (J). (gr. 4 up). 22.95 (978-0-7910-6576-1(6) , 010402, Chelsea Hse.) Facts On File, Inc.

—You Are What You Wear. 2001. (Clothing Ser.). (Illus.). 32p. (J). (gr. 4 up). 22.95 (978-0-7910-6577-8(4) , 010405, Chelsea Hse.) Facts On File, Inc.

Wilhelm, Hans. I'm Not Scared! 2005. (Illus.). 30p. (J). (ps-3). lib. bdg. 11.19 (978-0-606-33830-1(6)) Tandem Library Bks.

Wilkes, Angela. Dazzling Disguises & Clever Costumes. 2006. (Illus.). 48p. (J). pap. 6.99 (978-0-7566-1935-0(1)) Dorling Kindersley Publishing, Inc.

Wolf, Jackie. Picture Me Easter Baby (mini Bunny) 2003. (Baby Costume Minis Ser.). (Illus.). 10p. (J). (ps up). bds. 2.99 (978-1-57151-566-7(6)) Playhouse Publishing.

—Picture Me Easter Baby (mini Chick) 2003. (Illus.). 10p. (J). (ps up). bds. 2.99 (978-1-57151-565-0(8)) Playhouse Publishing.

COSTUME—HISTORY

Brent, Lynnette R. Clothing. 2003. (Times Change Ser.). (Illus.). 32p. (J). (978-1-4034-4540-7(0)) Heinemann Library.

—Getting Dressed: Long Ago & Today. 2003. (Times Change Ser.). (Illus.). 32p. (J). lib. bdg. 24.22 (978-1-4034-4534-6(6)) Heinemann Library.

Brooke, Iris. English Costume of the Early Middle Ages. Landes, William-Alan, ed. 3rd rev. exp. ed. 2003. (Illus.). 96p. (gr. 4-12). pap. 23.00 (978-0-88734-945-4(5)) Players Pr., Inc.

Cheshire, Gerard & Hammond, Paula. The Middle East. 2002. (Cultures & Costumes Ser.). (Illus.). 64p. (J). (gr. 7 up). lib. bdg. (978-1-59084-434-2(3)) Mason Crest Pubs.

Dawson, Imogene. Clothes & Crafts in the Middle Ages. 2000. (Clothes & Crafts in History Ser.). (Illus.). 32p. (J). (gr. 4 up). lib. bdg. 24.67 (978-0-8368-2736-1(8)) Stevens, Gareth Inc.

Draper, Allison Stark. What People Wore During the American Revolution. 2001. (Clothing, Costumes & Uniforms Thoughout American History Ser.). 24p. (J). (gr. 3). lib. bdg. 19.95 (978-0-8239-5666-1(0) , PKCLRE, PowerKids Pr.) Rosen Publishing Group, Inc., The.

—What People Wore in Early America. 2001. (Clothing, Costumes & Uniforms Thoughout American History Ser.). (Illus.). 24p. (J). (gr. 3). lib. bdg. 19.95 (978-0-8239-5664-7(4) , PKCLEA, PowerKids Pr.) Rosen Publishing Group, Inc., The.

—What People Wore on Southern Plantations. 2001. (Clothing, Costumes & Uniforms Thoughout American History Ser.). (Illus.). 24p. (J). (gr. 3). lib. bdg. 19.95 (978-0-8239-5668-5(7) , PKCLPL, PowerKids Pr.) Rosen Publishing Group, Inc., The.

Fischell, Emma. Northern Europe. 2002. (Cultures & Costumes Ser.). (Illus.). 64p. (J). (gr. 7 up). lib. bdg. (978-1-59084-439-7(4)) Mason Crest Pubs.

Greig, Charlotte. The British Isles. 2002. (Cultures & Costumes Ser.). (Illus.). 64p. (J). (gr. 7-12). lib. bdg. (978-1-59084-431-1(9)) Mason Crest Pubs.

—Oceania. 2002. (Cultures & Costumes Ser.). (Illus.). 64p (J). (gr. 7 up). lib. bdg. (978-1-59084-432-8(7)) Mason Crest Pubs.

Grieg, Charlotte. Africa. 2002. (Cultures & Costumes Ser.). (Illus.). 64p. (J). (gr. 7 up). lib. bdg. (978-1-59084-433-5(5)) Mason Crest Pubs.

Hammond, Paula. China & Japan. 2002. (Cultures & Costumes Ser.). (Illus.). 64p. (J). (gr. 7 up). lib. bdg. (978-1-59084-436-6(X)) Mason Crest Pubs.

—Greece & Turkey. 2002. (Cultures & Costumes Ser.). (Illus.). 64p. (J). (gr. 7 up). lib. bdg. (978-1-59084-437-3(8)) Mason Crest Pubs.

—Italy & Switzerland. 2002. (Cultures & Costumes Ser.). (Illus.). 64p. (J). (gr. 7 up). lib. bdg. (978-1-59084-438-0(6)) Mason Crest Pubs.

Harris, Carol & Brown, Mike. Men's Costumes. 2003. (Twentieth-Century Developments in Fashion & Costume Ser.). (Illus.). 64p. (J). (gr. 7 up). lib. bdg. (978-1-59084-422-9(X)) Mason Crest Pubs.

Hatt, Christine. Clothes of the Ancient World. 2001. (Dress Sense Ser.). (Illus.). 48p. (J). (gr. 5 up). 16.95 (978-0-87226-670-4(2) , Bedrick, Peter Bks.) School Specialty Publishing.

—Clothes of the Early Modern World. Tattersfield, Jane, illus. 2001. (Dress Sense Ser.). 48p. (J). (gr. 5 up). 16.95 (978-0-87226-668-1(0) , Bedrick, Peter Bks.) School Specialty Publishing.

Hatt, Christine, et al. Clothes of the Medieval World. 2001. (Dress Sense Ser.). (Illus.). 48p. (J). (gr. 5 up). 16.95 (978-0-87226-669-8(9) , Bedrick, Peter Bks.) School Specialty Publishing.

Hoobler, Dorothy & Hoobler, Thomas. Vanity Rules: A History of American Fashion & Beauty. 2000. (Single Titles Ser.). (Illus.). 160p. (gr. 7 up). lib. bdg. 28.90 (978-0-7613-1258-1(7) , Millbrook Pr.) Lerner Publishing Group.

Israel, Fred L., intro. National Costumes of the Old World. 1999. (Looking into the Past). (Illus.). 64p. (YA). lib. bdg. 19.75 (978-0-7910-4684-5(2) , Chelsea Hse.) Facts On File, Inc.

Kilgallon, Conor. India & Sri Lanka. 2002. (Cultures & Costumes Ser.). (Illus.). 64p. (J). (gr. 7 up). lib. bdg. (978-1-59084-443-4(2)) Mason Crest Pubs.

McNab, Chris. Eastern Europe. 2002. (Cultures & Costumes Ser.). (Illus.). 64p. (J). (gr. 7 up). lib. bdg. (978-1-59084-441-0(6)) Mason Crest Pubs.

Mitchell, Alycen. France. 2002. (Cultures & Costumes Ser.). (Illus.). 64p. (J). (gr. 7 up). lib. bdg. (978-1-59084-442-7(4) , 1247999) Mason Crest Pubs.

Nunn, Joan. Fashion in Costume 1200-1980. 1999. (gr. 7-12). lib. bdg. 29.20 (978-0-8335-6240-1(1)) Tandem Library Bks.

Peacock, John. The Story of Costume. 2006. (Illus.). 48p. 19.95 (978-0-500-51309-5(0)) Thames & Hudson.

Rowland-Warne, L. & Dorling Kindersley Publishing Staff. Costume. 2000. (Eyewitness Bks.). (Illus.). 64p. (J). (gr. 4-7). lib. bdg. 19.99 (978-0-7894-6584-9(1)) Dorling Kindersley Publishing, Inc.

Scott, Janine. Let's Get Dressed: What People Wear. 2002. (Spyglass Books). (Illus.). 24p. (J). (gr. 1 up). lib. bdg. 18.60 (978-0-7565-0366-6(3)) Compass Point Bks.

Skinner, Tina. Fashionable Clothing from the Sears Catalogs, Mid-1940s. 2003. (Schiffer Book for Collectors Ser.). (Illus.). 160p. (gr. 10-13). pap. 29.95 (978-0-7643-1858-0(6)) Schiffer Publishing, Ltd.

Steele, Philip. Clothes & Crafts in Roman Times. 2000. (Clothes & Crafts in History Ser.). (Illus.). 32p. (J). (gr. 4 up). lib. bdg. 24.67 (978-0-8368-2737-8(6)) Stevens, Gareth Inc.

Sturm, Ellen. Clothing & Accessories in Colonial America. 2004. (Everyday Life Long Ago Ser.). (J). (978-0-7368-2160-5(0) , Blue Earth Bks.) Capstone Pr., Inc.

Tierney, Tom. Empire Fashions. 2001. (Pictorial Archive Ser.). (Illus.). 48p. (J). pap. 3.95 (978-0-486-41869-8(3)) Dover Pubns., Inc.

Twentieth-Century Developments in Fashion & Costume, 12 vols., Set. (Illus.). 64p. (YA). (gr. 7 up). lib. bdg. (978-1-59084-417-5(3)) Mason Crest Pubs.

COSTUME DESIGN

Constanza, Orozco Vargas. Coco Chanel. 2005. 156p. pap. (978-958-30-1765-0(5)) Panamericana Editorial.

Gaines, Ann Graham. Coco Chanel. (Women in the Arts Ser.). 2004. 116p. pap. 30.00 (978-0-7910-7950-8(3)); 2003. (Illus.). 112p. (gr. 6-12). 30.00 (978-0-7910-7455-8(2)) Facts On File, Inc. (Chelsea Hse.).

Haley, Gail E., illus. Costumes for Plays & Playing. 2002. 134p. (J). 19.95 (978-1-887905-62-6(6)) Parkway Pubs., Inc.

Jones, Jen. Fashion Design: The Art of Style. 2007. (Illus.). 32p. (J). (978-0-7368-6827-3(5) , 1264959) Capstone Pr., Inc.

—Fashion Design School: Learning the Skills to Succeed. 2007. (Illus.). 32p. (J). (978-0-7368-6832-7(1) , 1264958) Capstone Pr., Inc.

Matthews, Elizabeth. Different Like Coco. 2007. (Illus.). (J). (gr. k-4). 40p. 16.99 (978-0-7636-2548-1(5)); (***978-1-4287-3582-8(8)***) Candlewick Pr.

Maze, Stephanie. I Want to Be a Fashion Designer. Maze, Stephanie, photos by. 2000. (I Want to Be Ser.). (Illus.). 48p. (J). (gr. 3-7). pap. 10.00 (978-0-15-201938-9(3)) Harcourt Children's Bks.

—I Want to Be a Fashion Designer. 2000. (I Want to Be Ser.). (Illus.). 48p. (YA). (gr. 4-9). lib. bdg. 27.12 (978-0-7398-1970-8(4)) Raintree.

—I Want to Be a Fashion Designer. (I Want to Be Ser.). 2000. (Illus.). (J). (978-0-606-18177-8(6)); 1999. (gr. 3-6). lib. bdg. 17.65 (978-0-613-25642-1(5)) Tandem Library Bks.

Noble, Marty. Color Your Own Basket Ballet Designs. 2005. (Illus.). 32p. pap. 3.95 (978-0-486-43995-2(X)) Dover Pubns., Inc.

—Victorian Fashions Stained Glass Coloring Book. 2001. (Illus.). 32p. (J). pap. 5.95 (978-0-486-41555-0(4)) Dover Pubns., Inc.

Salmansohn, Karen. Fashion. Stauffer, Brian, illus. 2005. (Petit Connoisseur Ser.). 16p. bds. 6.95 (978-1-58246-105-2(8) , Tricycle Pr.) Ten Speed Pr.

Stephens, Monique Z. Pob Novelty Scrapbook with Pack-trollz: Fashion & Design Sketchbook. 2006. (Trollz Ser.). 48p. (J). pap. 9.99 (978-0-439-82957-1(7)) Scholastic, Inc.

Tierney, Tom. Famous Movie Wedding Gowns Paper Dolls. 2007. 32p. pap. 6.95 (***978-0-486-45800-7(8)***) Dover Pubns., Inc.

Tierney, Tom. Jacobean & Early Bourbon Fashions. 2004. (Dover Coloring Bks.). (Illus.). 48p. (J). pap. 3.95 (978-0-486-43333-2(1)) Dover Pubns., Inc.

Wallis, Jeremy. Coco Chanel. 2001. (Creative Lives Ser.). (Illus.). 64p. (J). (gr. 6-8). lib. bdg. 27.07 (978-1-58810-202-7(5)) Heinemann Library.

Wallner, Rosemary. Fashion Designer. 2000. (Career Exploration Ser.). (Illus.). 48p. (J). (gr. 3-4). lib. bdg. 21.26 (978-0-7368-0595-7(8) , LifeMatters Bks.) Capstone Pr., Inc.

COSTUME DESIGN—FICTION

Child, Lauren. But I Am an Alligator. 2008. (Charlie & Lola Ser.). 24p. (J). (ps-1). 3.99 (***978-0-448-44697-4(9)*** , Grosset & Dunlap) Penguin Group (USA) Inc.

Maxwell, Miranda. Princess Lola's Wobbly Week. 2005. (Illus.). (J). 20.00 (978-0-340-87848-4(7)); pap. 10.99 (978-0-340-87849-1(5)) Hodder General Publishing Division GBR. (Hodder & Stoughton). *Dist:* Trafalgar Square Publishing.

Ricci, Christine. Dora's Costume Party! Saunders, Zina, illus. 2005. (Dora the Explorer Ser.). 24p. (J). (ps-ps). pap. 3.99 (978-1-4169-0010-8(1) , Simon Spotlight/ Nickelodeon) Simon & Schuster Children's Publishing.

—Dora's Costume Party. 2006. (J). (ps-2). 21.35 (978-1-59961-071-9(X)) Spotlight.

Schaefer, Carole Lexa. The Bora-Bora Dress. Stock, Catherine, illus. 2005. 32p. (J). (ps-1). 16.99 (978-0-7636-1234-4(0)) Candlewick Pr.

Stonebraker Wright, Susan. Enchanted Costume Shop. 2004. 73p. pap. 14.95 (978-1-4137-3862-9(1)) PublishAmerica, Inc.

Tibo, Gilles. Simon et les Deguisements. 2001. Tr. of Simon's Disguise. (FRE & SPA.). 24p. (J). (ps-1). pap. 4.95 (978-0-88776-546-9(7) , Livres Toundra) Tundra Bks., Inc./Livres Toundra, Inc. CAN. *Dist:* Random Hse., Inc.

Willson, Sarah. My Dress-up Party. 2003. (gr. k-3). lib. bdg. 11.80 (978-0-613-58160-8(1)) Tandem Library Bks.

Wilson, Jacqueline. My Brother Bernadette. Roberts, David, illus. 2002. (Yellow Bananas Ser.). 48p. (J). (gr. 3-4). pap. (978-0-7787-0986-2(8)); lib. bdg. (978-0-7787-0940-4(X)) Crabtree Publishing Co.

—My Brother Bernadette. 2002. (gr. 3-6). lib. bdg. 12.95 (978-0-613-52884-9(0)) Tandem Library Bks.

Wojciechowski, Susan. The Best Halloween of All. Meddaugh, Susan, illus. 2000. (J). (ps-ps). lib. bdg. 13.00 (978-0-613-31973-7(7)) Tandem Library Bks.

COSTUMES, MILITARY

see Uniforms, Military

COTE D'IVOIRE

Habeeb, William Mark. Ivory Coast. 2004. (Africa Ser.). (Illus.). 79p. (J). lib. bdg. (978-1-59084-808-1(X)) Mason Crest Pubs.

Hamilton, Janice. Ivory Coast in Pictures. 2nd rev. expurg. ed. 2004. (Visual Geography Ser.). (Illus.). 80p. (J). (gr. 5-12). 27.93 (978-0-8225-1992-8(5)) Lerner Publishing Group.

Sheehan, Patricia. Cote d'Ivoire. 2000. (Cultures of the World Ser.). (Illus.). 128p. (gr. 5-12). lib. bdg. 37.07 (978-0-7614-0980-9(7) , Benchmark Bks.) Cavendish, Marshall Corp.

Weber, Valerie. I Come from Ivory Coast. 2006. (Illus.). 24p. (J). pap. (978-0-8368-7243-9(6)); lib. bdg. (978-0-8368-7236-1(3)) Stevens, Gareth Inc. (Weekly Reader Early Learning Library).

COTTAGES

see Houses

COTTON

see also Fibers

Alonso, Manuel L. Algodon.Tr. of Cotton. (SPA.). 56p. (J). (gr. 2-3). 7.96 (978-84-321-2743-4(4)) Rialp, Ediciones, S.A. ESP. *Dist:* Lectorum Pubns., Inc.

Franck, Irene M. & Brownstone, David M. Cotton. 2003. (Illus.). 32p. (J). (978-0-7172-5714-0(2) , Grolier) Scholastic Library Publishing.

Gleason, Carrie. The Biography of Cotton. 2005. (How Did That Get There?). (Illus.). 32p. (J). (gr. 3-9). pap. (978-0-7787-2516-9(2)) Crabtree Publishing Co.

Johnson, Guinevere. Cotton. 1999. (Let's Investigate Ser.). (Illus.). 32p. (J). (gr. 1-4). lib. bdg. (978-0-88682-959-9(3) , Creative Education) Creative Co., The.

Kras, Sara Louise. Cotton. 2006. (First Facts Ser.). (J). (978-0-7368-4297-6(7)) Capstone Pr., Inc.

L'Hommedieu, Arthur John. From Plant to Blue Jeans. 1998. (Changes Ser.). (Illus.). 32p. (J). (gr. 2-3). pap. 6.95 (978-0-516-20366-9(5) , Children's Pr.) Scholastic Library Publishing.

—From Plant to Blue Jeans. 1998. (gr. 3-6). lib. bdg. 15.25 (978-0-613-89022-9(1)) Tandem Library Bks.

Mercier, Sheryl & Hoover, Evalyn. Crazy about Cotton. Cordel, Betty & Youngs, Michelle, eds. Mercier, Sheryl, illus. 2001. 166p. (J). pap. 18.95 (978-1-881431-88-6(6) , 1216) AIMS Education Foundation.

Nelson, Robin. From Cotton to T-Shirt. 2003. (Start to Finish Ser.). (Illus.). 24p. (J). (gr. k-2). lib. bdg. 18.60 (978-0-8225-4661-0(2)) Lerner Publishing Group.

Oxlade, Chris. Cotton. 2002. (Materials, Materials, Materials Ser.). (Illus.). 32p. (J). (gr. k-2). lib. bdg. 22.79 (978-1-58810-584-4(9)); pap. 6.95 (978-1-4034-0085-7(7) , 91526) Heinemann Library.

—Cotton. 2002. (gr. k-3). lib. bdg. 14.75 (978-0-613-45735-4(8)) Tandem Library Bks.

—How We Use Cotton. 2004. (Illus.). 32p. (J). (ps-ps). pap. 7.50 (978-1-4109-0992-3(1)); lib. bdg. 25.70 (978-1-4109-0593-2(4)) Raintree.

Ridley, Sarah. A Cotton T-Shirt. 2006. (Illus.). 32p. (J). lib. bdg. 23.33 (978-0-8368-6294-2(5)) Stevens, Gareth Inc.

Walker, Niki & Gleason, Carrie. The Biography of Cotton. 2005. (How Did That Get Here? Ser.). (Illus.). 32p. (J). (978-0-7787-2480-3(8)) Crabtree Publishing Co.

COTTON—FICTION

Carvalho, Paula, et al. The Story of Calvin Cotton. 2001. (Illus.). 20p. (J). (gr. 1-4). 16.95 (978-0-9715636-0-5(8)) Chris Paul USA.

COTTON MANUFACTURE

Huff, Regan A. Eli Whitney: The Cotton Gin & American Manufacturing. 2005. (Library of American Lives & Times). (Illus.). 112p. (J). (gr. 4-8). lib. bdg. 31.95 (978-0-8239-6628-8(3)) Rosen Publishing Group, Inc., The.

Oxlade, Chris. Cotton. 2002. (Materials, Materials, Materials Ser.). (Illus.). 32p. (J). (gr. k-2). lib. bdg. 22.79 (978-1-58810-584-4(9)); pap. 6.95 (978-1-4034-0085-7(7) , 91526) Heinemann Library.

—Cotton. 2002. (gr. k-3). lib. bdg. 14.75 (978-0-613-45735-4(8)) Tandem Library Bks.

—How We Use Cotton. 2004. (Using Materials Ser.). (Illus.). 32p. (J). lib. bdg. 25.70 (978-1-4109-0593-2(4)) Raintree.

COUGARS

see Pumas

COUNSELING

see also Educational Counseling; Vocational Guidance

Coping: Essential Educational Resources, 6 bks. Incl. Coping in an Interfaith Family. Packard, Gwen K. 1993. lib. bdg. 26.50 (978-0-8239-1452-4(6) , COINFA); Coping When a Parent Goes Back to Work. Packard, Gwen K. 1995. lib. bdg. 26.50 (978-0-8239-1698-6(7) , COPABA); Coping When a Parent Has AIDS. Draimin, Barbara Hermie. 1994. lib. bdg. 26.50 (978-0-8239-1664-1(2) , COPAAI); Coping with Choosing a Therapist : A Young Person's Guide to Counseling & Psychotherapy. Backman, Margaret E. 1994. lib. bdg. 26.50 (978-0-8239-1699-3(5) , COCHTH); Coping with Codependency. Porterfield, Kay Marie. 1994. lib. bdg. 26.50 (978-0-8239-1813-3(0) , COCODE); 192p. (YA). (gr. 7-12). (Illus.). 2005. Set lib. bdg. 1132.50 (978-0-8239-8043-7(X)) Rosen Publishing Group, Inc., The.

Coping: Help & Guidance for Teens in Need, 4 bks. Incl. Coping in a Single-Parent Home. Wagonseller, Bill R. 192p. 1997. lib. bdg. 26.50 (978-0-8239-2625-1(7) , COSIPA); Coping When a Grandparent Has Alzheimer's Disease. Wilkinson, Beth. Rosen, Ruth C., ed. 146p. 1995. lib. bdg. 25.25 (978-0-8239-1947-5(1) , COALDI); Coping with Homelessness. Hurwitz, Sue & Hurwitz, Eugene. 192p. 1997. lib. bdg. 26.50 (978-0-8239-2072-3(0) , COHOME); Coping with Sleep Disorders. Simpson, Carolyn. 192p. 1996. lib. bdg. 26.50 (978-0-8239-2068-6(2) , COSLDI); (YA). (gr. 7-12). (Illus.). Set lib. bdg. 101.00 (978-0-8239-8042-0(1)) Rosen Publishing Group, Inc., The.

Discovery Cove. 1998. (K. I. D. S. Church Ser.: Vol. 4). Tr. of La cueva del descubrimiento. 160p. (J). (gr. 1-6). ring bd. 119.99 incl. audio, trans. (978-1-57405-038-7(9)) CharismaLife Pubs.

Group/McGraw-Hill, Wright. The Magic Shoes: Level N, 6 vols. 128p. (gr. 3-6). 36.95 (978-0-322-05884-2(8)) Wright Group, The.

Landau, Elaine. Family Therapy. 2004. (Life Balance Ser.). 80p. (J). 20.50 (978-0-531-12216-7(6) , Watts, Franklin) Scholastic Library Publishing.

Marshall, Peter, et al. Sounding Forth the Trumpet for Children. 1999. (Illus.). 208p. (J). (gr. 4-7). pap. 14.99 (978-0-8007-5692-5(4)) Revell.

McCarty, Robert J. Teen to Teen: Responding to Peers in Crisis. Shuck, Vicki, illus. 2003. 104p. (YA). spiral bd. 22.95 (978-0-88489-353-0(7)) St. Mary's Pr.

Mills, Roger C. & Spittle, Elsie. The Health Realization Primer Vol. 1: Empowering Individuals & Communities. rev. ed. 2003. (Illus.). 72p. (gr. 4). pap. 14.95 (978-1-55105-020-1(X)) Lone Pine Publishing USA.

Painter, Carol. Friends Helping Friends: A Manual for Peer Counselors. Sorenson, Don L., ed. 1998. 275p. (YA). (gr. 9-12). pap. 9.95 (978-0-932796-28-8(1)) Educational Media Corp.

Porter, Daniel. Taming Monster Moments: Tips for Turning on Soul Lights to Help Children Handle Fear & Danger. Nathan, Cheryl, illus. 1999. (Creative Meditations for Children Ser.). 32p. (ps-2). 5.95 (978-0-8091-6655-8(0) , 6655-0) Paulist Pr.

Stewart, Jan. Stars Getting along with Others. 2004. (Illus.). 32p. (J). pap. 9.95 (978-0-89793-312-4(5)) Hunter Hse., Inc.

COUNSELING—VOCATIONAL GUIDANCE

Smead, Rosemarie. Skills for Young Vol. 2: Group Counseling Activities for Young Adolescents. 2004. (Illus.). 298p. pap. 31.95 (978-0-87822-420-3(3) , 3185) Research Pr.

Vandawalker, Marianne. Career Fun. 1999. 40p. (J). (gr. k-5). pap. 24.95 (978-1-57543-061-4(4)) MAR*CO Products, Inc.

COUNTER-REFORMATION

see Reformation

COUNTERFEITS AND COUNTERFEITING—FICTION

Alger, Horatio. Jack's Ward. 2006. pap. (***978-1-4065-0711-9(3)***) Dodo Pr.

—Jack's Ward: Or, The Boy Guardian. 2006. 176p. pap. 13.99 (978-1-4264-0882-3(X)); 168p. pap. 16.99 (978-1-4264-0863-2(3)) BiblioBazaar.

Alger, Horatio. Timothy Crump's Ward: A Story of American Life. 2006. pap. (***978-1-4250-3339-2(3)***) Assistedreadingbooks.com Inc.

Bossley, Michele Martin. Cracked. 2007. (Orca Currents Ser.). 112p. (YA). (gr. 5 up). pap. (***978-1-55143-700-2(7)***); lib. bdg. (***978-1-55143-702-6(3)***) Orca Bk. Pubs.

Doyle, Bill. Nabbed! The 1925 Journal of G. Codd Fitzmorgan. 2nd ed. 2006. (Crime Through Time Ser.: No. 2). (Illus.). 128p. (J). (gr. 3-7). pap. 5.99 (978-0-316-05737-0(1)) Little Brown & Co.

—Silenced! The 1969 Journal of Malcolm Moorie. 3rd ed. 2006. (Crime Through Time Ser.: No. 3). (Illus.). 144p. (J). (gr. 3-7). pap. 5.99 (978-0-316-05738-7(X)) Little Brown & Co.

—Swindled! The 1906 Journal of Fitz Morgan. Dow, Brian, illus. 2006. 138p. (J). lib. bdg. 18.46 (***978-1-4242-1737-3(7)***) Fitzgerald Bks.

—Swindled! The 1906 Journal of Fitz Morgan. 2006. (Crime Through Time Ser.: No. 1). (Illus.). 144p. (J). (gr. 3-7). pap. 5.99 (978-0-316-05736-3(3)) Little Brown & Co.

Finney, Patricia & Cavendish, Grace. Deception. 2005. (Lady Grace Mysteries, from the Daybookes of Lady Grace Cavendish Ser.). 224p. (J). (gr. 3-7). 7.95 (978-0-385-73321-2(6)); lib. bdg. 9.99 (978-0-385-90340-0(5)) Random Hse. Children's Bks. (Delacorte Bks. for Young Readers).

Roberts, Willo Davis. Rebel. 160p. (J). 2005. pap. 5.99 (978-0-689-85081-3(6) , Aladdin); 2003. (Illus.). 16.95 (978-0-689-85073-8(5) , Atheneum) Simon & Schuster Children's Publishing.

Roy, Ron. The Invisible Island. Gurney, John Steven, illus. 1999. (A to Z Mysteries Ser.: No. 9). 96p. (J). (gr. k-3). lib. bdg. 11.99 (978-0-679-99457-2(2)); pap. 3.99 (978-0-679-89457-5(8)) Random Hse. Children's Bks. (Random Hse. Bks. for Young Readers).

—The Invisible Island. Gurney, John Steven, illus. 1999. (A to Z Mysteries Ser.: No. 9). (gr. k-3). 90p. lib. bdg. 10.79 (978-0-606-17265-3(3)); (J). lib. bdg. 11.80 (978-0-613-21768-2(3)) Tandem Library Bks.

Van Dyne, Edith. Mary Louise. 2006. 148p. pap. 10.99 (978-1-4264-1952-2(X)); 144p. pap. 13.99 (978-1-4264-2063-4(3)) BiblioBazaar.

COUNTERPOINT

Gladstone, Francis E. A Treatise on Strict Counterpoint. 2001. (YA). reprint ed. 150.00 (978-0-7222-5691-6(4)) Library Reprints, Inc.

MacPherson, Stewart. Practical Counterpoint: A Concise Treatise Illustrative of Both the Strict & Free Styles. 2001. 170p. (YA). reprint ed. 88.00 (978-0-7222-5697-8(3)) Library Reprints, Inc.

Prout, Ebenezer. Double Counterpoint & Canon. 2001. 283p. (YA). reprint ed. 98.00 (978-0-7222-5703-6(1)) Library Reprints, Inc.

COUNTING BOOKS

Aber, Linda Williams. Who's Got Spots? Fiammenghi, Gioia, illus. 2000. (Math Matters Ser.). 32p. (J). (ps-3). pap. 4.95 (978-1-57565-099-9(1)) Kane Pr., The.

—Who's Got Spots? Fiammenghi, Gioia, illus. 2000. 32p. (J). (ps-3). lib. bdg. 12.95 (978-0-613-39375-1(9)) Tandem Library Bks.

—Who's Got Spots? 2000. (Math Matters Ser.). (J). (978-0-606-20184-1(X)) Tandem Library Bks.

Ada, Alma Flor & Campoy, F. Isabel, contrib. by. One, Two, Three. Who Can it Be! (Gateways to the Sun). (SPA.). 32p. (J). (gr. k-6). pap. 13.95 (978-1-58105-959-5(0)) Santillana USA Publishing Co., Inc.

Adams, Gloria. Five Little Skunks. Collier-Morales, Roberta, illus. 2006. (Sing-A-Story Ser.). 16p. (J). bds. 10.95 (978-0-7696-4916-0(5)) School Specialty Publishing.

Adams, Pam. Ten Beads Tall. 2002. (Illus.). 16p. (J). bds. 9.99 (978-0-85953-903-6(2)) Child's Play-International.

Adding Up. 2004. (Wall Charts Ser.). (J). 4.99 (978-1-85997-319-6(1)) Byeway Bks.

Adly, Muhammad S. Let's Count in Arabic, Bk. 1. 24p. (978-1-894264-46-4(0)) Al-Attique Pubs., Inc.

Aigner-Clark, Julie. Asomate Y Ve Los Numeros. Zaidi, Nadeem, illus. 2004. (Baby Einstein Ser.). (SPA.). 16p. (J). bds. 5.95 (978-970-718-150-2(8) , Silver Dolphin en Español) Advanced Marketing, S. de R. L. de C. V. MEX. *Dist:* Perseus Distribution.

—See & Spy Counting. Zaidi, Nadeem, illus. 2001. (Baby Einstein Ser.). 16p. (J). (ps-ps). 5.99 (978-0-7868-0808-3(X)) Hyperion Bks. for Children.

Albrecht, Jeff, illus. NASCAR Counting. 2003. (Active Minds Ser.). 16p. (J). spiral bd., bds. (978-0-7853-9003-9(0) , 7196600) Publications International, Ltd.

Alda, Arlene. Arlene Alda's 1 2 3: What Do You See? (Illus.). 24p. (ps-k). 2003. (YA). 12.95 (978-1-883672-71-3(6)); 2004. (J). reprint ed. 6.95 (978-1-58246-119-9(8)) Ten Speed Pr. (Tricycle Pr.).

Allan, Nicholas. More & More Rabbits. 2007. (Illus.). 32p. (J). pap. 9.95 (***978-0-09-947758-7(0)*** , Red Fox) Random Hse. Children's Bks. GBR. *Dist:* Independent Pubs. Group.

Aloha Bear's Counting 1-2-3 Workbook. 2000. (J). 4.99 (978-0-89610-431-0(1)) Island Heritage Publishing.

Alphabet, Colors, & Numbers. . . 2000. (Kelley Wingate Ser.). 80p. (J). (ps-k). pap. 9.99 (978-0-88724-591-6(9)) Carson-Dellosa Publishing Co., Inc.

Amazing ABCs And 123s. 2005. 128p. (J). per. 19.99 (978-1-59441-189-2(1) , DJ-604009) Carson-Dellosa Publishing Co., Inc.

American Education Publishing Staff & Douglas, Vincent. Numbers & Counting: Kindergarten. 2001. (Illus.). 32p. (C). pap. 2.99 (978-1-56189-625-7(X) , American Education Publishing) School Specialty Publishing.

Amery, Heather. On the Farm? rev. ed. 2006. 16p. (J). pap. 5.99 (978-0-7945-1288-0(7) , Usborne) EDC Publishing.

Amery, Heather, ed. Starting to Count. 1998. (Sticker Learning Bks.). (Illus.). 18p. (J). (ps-3). pap. 6.95 (978-0-7460-3406-4(7)) EDC Publishing.

Anastasio, Dina. Getting Ready for Math. 2002. (Clifford, the Big Red Dog Ser.). 32p. (J). pap. 2.99 (978-0-439-39854-1(1)) Scholastic, Inc.

Anderson, Debby, illus. Kindness Counts! 2007. (J). (***978-1-58134-861-3(4)***) Crossway Bks.

Anderson, Sara. Numbers. Anderson, Sara, illus. 2007. 11p. (J). bds. 10.95 (978-1-59354-185-9(6)) Chronicle Bks. LLC.

Andreasen, Dan. The Baker's Dozen: A Counting Book. 2007. (Illus.). 32p. (J). (ps-1). 16.95 (***978-0-8050-7809-1(6)***) Holt, Henry & Co.

Anno, Mitsumasa. Anno's Counting Book. Anno, Mitsumasa, illus. 2002. (Illus.). 15.49 (978-0-7587-4223-0(1)) Book Wholesalers, Inc.

Ant, Exupery. Imparo a Contare con il Picco. pap. 13.95 (978-88-451-2268-2(9)) Fabbri - RCS Libri ITA. *Dist:* Distribooks, Inc.

Apperley, Dawn. Crash Bang, Thud! 2002. (Illus.). 25p. (J). (978-0-340-78800-4(3) , Hodder & Stoughton) Hodder General Publishing Division.

—Crash Bang, Thud! 2002. (Illus.). 32p. (J). pap. 9.99 (978-0-340-78801-1(1) , Hodder & Stoughton) Hodder General Publishing Division GBR. *Dist:* Trafalgar Square Publishing.

Arciero, Susan. Nantucket 1, 2, 3. Arciero, Susan, illus. l.t. ed. 2000. (Illus.). (J). (ps). 7.95 (978-0-9677548-2-6(8)) Pigtail Publishing.

Arenson, Roberta. One, Two, Skip a Few! First Number Rhymes. 1998. (Illus.). 32p. (J). (ps-2). 15.95 (978-1-901223-99-6(X)) Barefoot Bks., Inc.

—One, Two, Skip a Few! First Number Rhymes. Arenson, Roberta, illus. 2000. (Illus.). (ps-2). lib. bdg. 15.30 (978-0-613-31555-5(3)) Tandem Library Bks.

Arnold, Caroline. Who Has More? Who Has Fewer? Arnold, Caroline, illus. 2004. (Illus.). 18p. (J). bds. 5.95 (978-1-57091-493-5(1)) Charlesbridge Publishing, Inc.

Arps, Melissa. Numbers. 2006. (Illus.). (J). (***978-0-7364-2380-9(X))*** Random Hse., Inc.

Atkinson, Sue, et al. Seven Dizzy Dragons & Other Maths Rhymes Big Book. 1998. (New Cambridge Mathematics Ser.). (Illus.). 32p. (ps-1). pap. 50.00 (978-0-521-63421-2(0)) Cambridge Univ. Pr.

Atlas, Ron. Ten Pigs Fiddling. Flint, Stacie, illus. 2nd rev. ed. 2006. 32p. (J). 17.95 (978-0-9630243-3-6(7)) Amberwood Pr.

Auerbach, Annie. Where's the Chick? Counting Book. Whitehead, Paul, illus. 2005. (J). bds. 14.99 (978-0-9767325-5-6(6)) Toy Quest.

Augarde, Steve. One Paper Hat. 2004. (Silly Monsters Ser.). (Illus.). 8p. (J). 5.95 (978-0-7696-3339-8(0) , Gingham Dog Pr.) School Specialty Publishing.

Ayers, Amy. Using Math at the Class Party. 2007. (J). pap. (***978-0-8368-8484-5(1));*** 24p. (gr. 1-3). lib. bdg. 19.93 (***978-0-8368-8475-3(2))*** Stevens, Gareth Inc. (Weekly Reader Early Learning Library).

—Using Money at the Lemonade Stand. 2007. pap. (***978-0-8368-8481-4(7));*** 24p. (J). (gr. 1-3). lib. bdg. 19.93 (***978-0-8368-8472-2(8))*** Stevens, Gareth Inc. (Weekly Reader Early Learning Library).

Baby's First Counting Book. 2004. 10p. (J). bds. 4.99 (978-1-85854-924-8(8)) Brimax Books Ltd. GBR. *Dist:* Byeway Bks.

Back to the Basics. 2000. (Learning Fun for Little Ones Ser.). (Illus.). 64p. (ps-1). pap. 8.99 (978-0-88724-568-8(4) , CD-6400) Carson-Dellosa Publishing Co., Inc.

Bader, Bonnie. 100 Monsters in My School, Vol. 2. Hendrix, Bryan, illus. 2002. (All Aboard Math Reader Ser.). 48p. (J). pap. 3.99 (978-0-448-42859-8(8) , Grosset & Dunlap) Penguin Group (USA) Inc.

—100 Monsters in My School. 2002. (gr. k-3). lib. bdg. 11.80 (978-0-613-64089-3(6)) Tandem Library Bks.

Bailey, Linda. Goodnight, Sweet Pig. Masse, Josée, illus. 2007. 32p. (J). (ps-k). (***978-1-55337-844-0(X))*** Kids Can Pr., Ltd.

Bajaj, Varsha. How Many Kisses Do You Want Tonight? Bates, Ivan, illus. 2004. 28p. (J). (ps-3). 15.99 (978-0-316-82381-4(3)) Little, Brown Bks. for Young Readers.

Baker, Alan. Gray Rabbit's 1, 2, 3. 1999. (Little Rabbit Bks.). (Illus.). 24p. (J). (gr. k-ps). 4.95 (978-0-7534-5252-3(9) , Kingfisher) Houghton Mifflin Co. Trade & Reference Div.

—Gray Rabbit's 1, 2, 3. 1999. (ps-2). lib. bdg. 11.80 (978-0-613-88047-3(1)) Tandem Library Bks.

—Little Rabbits' First Number Book. 1998. (Little Rabbit Bks.). (Illus.). 32p. (J). (gr. k-ps). tchr. ed. 11.95 (978-0-7534-5167-0(0) , Kingfisher) Houghton Mifflin Co. Trade & Reference Div.

—Little Rabbits' First Number Book. 2001. (ps-2). lib. bdg. 14.10 (978-0-613-90587-9(3)) Tandem Library Bks.

Baker, Keith. Mama Clo-clo! Ada, Alma Flor & Campoy, F. Isabel, trs. 2007. (Illus.). 30p. (J). bds. 6.95 (978-0-15-205890-6(7) , Voyager Bks./Libros Viajeros) Harcourt Children's Bks.

—Quack & Count! 1999. (Illus.). 24p. (J). (ps-2). 15.00 (978-0-15-292858-2(8)) Harcourt Children's Bks.

—Quack & Count. 2002. (Illus.). (J). 20.00 (978-0-7587-4193-6(6)) Book Wholesalers, Inc.

—Quack & Count. (Illus.). (J). 2004. 24p. pap. 6.00 (978-0-15-205025-2(6) , Voyager Bks./Libros Viajeros); 2003. 22p. bds. 6.95 (978-0-15-204751-1(4) , Red Wagon Bks.) Harcourt Children's Bks.

Balloon Books Staff. Dot to Dot Count to 25. 2007. (Illus.). 64p. (J). pap. 4.95 (978-1-4027-4626-0(1)) Sterling Publishing Co., Inc.

—Dot to Dot Count to 50. 2003. 64p. (J). pap. 4.95 (978-1-4027-0631-8(6) , Balloon Bks.) Sterling Publishing Co., Inc.

Balloon Books Staff, ed. 1-20 Dot to Dot. 2002. (Fun House Paperbacks Ser.). (Illus.). 72p. (J). pap. 4.95 (978-0-8069-8953-2(X)) Sterling Publishing Co., Inc.

Banek, Yvette Santiago, illus. Counting Farm. 2003. (J). (978-0-7853-7824-2(3)) Publications International, Ltd.

Bang, Molly Garrett. Ten, Nine, Eight. Bang, Molly Garrett, illus. 2002. (Illus.). (J). 14.43 (978-0-7587-4590-3(7)) Book Wholesalers, Inc.

Barber, Patti. First Number Book. Stanley, Mandy, illus. 2001. (First Bks.). 48p. (J). (gr. k-ps). tchr. ed. 12.95 (978-0-7534-5338-4(X) , Kingfisher) Houghton Mifflin Co. Trade & Reference Div.

—First Number Fun. Stanley, Mandy, illus. 2003. 48p. (J). (gr. k-ps). 7.95 (978-0-7534-5627-9(3) , Kingfisher) Houghton Mifflin Co. Trade & Reference Div.

Barbieri-McGrath, Barbara. Mas Matematicas Con los Chocolates de "M & M's"c. 2001. Tr. of More "M & M's"c Brand Math. (978-0-606-22626-4(5)) Tandem Library Bks.

Bardwell, Yvett. My Little Black Book of Numbers. 2007. (ENG & SPA.). (J). 19.95 (***978-0-9790826-7-2(6))*** Acacia Publishing, Inc.

—My Little Green Book of Numbers. 2007. (ENG & SPA.). (J). 19.95 (***978-0-9792531-1-9(X))*** Acacia Publishing, Inc.

—My Little Red Book of Numbers. 2007. (ENG & SPA.). (J). 19.95 (***978-0-9790826-9-6(2))*** Acacia Publishing, Inc.

—My Little White Book of Numbers. 2007. (ENG & SPA.). (J). 19.95 (***978-0-9790826-8-9(4))*** Acacia Publishing, Inc.

—My Little Yellow Book of Numbers. 2007. (ENG & SPA.). (J). 19.95 (***978-0-9792531-0-2(1))*** Acacia Publishing, Inc.

Barlow, Amanda. 1 2 3. 2004. (Baby Board Bks.). (Illus.). 10p. (J). (ps up). 4.95 (978-0-7460-4099-7(7)) EDC Publishing.

Barrett, Judi. I Knew Two Who Said Moo: A Counting & Rhyming Book. Moreton, Daniel, illus. 2000. 32p. (J). (ps-k). 16.00 (978-0-689-82104-2(2) , Atheneum) Simon & Schuster Children's Publishing.

Barry, Frances. Duckie's Ducklings: A One-to-Ten Counting Book. Barry, Frances, illus. 2005. (Illus.). 32p. (J). (gr. k-ps). 7.99 (978-0-7636-2514-6(0)) Candlewick Pr.

Base, Graeme. Uno's Garden. 2006. (Illus.). 44p. (J). (ps-3). 19.95 (978-0-8109-5473-1(7)) Abrams, Harry N. , Inc.

—The Water Hole. Base, Graeme, illus. 2001. (Illus.). 32p. (J). (gr. 2-7). 18.95 (978-0-8109-4568-5(1)) Abrams, Harry N. , Inc.

—The Water Hole. Base, Graeme, illus. 2004. 32p. (J). reprint ed. pap. 8.99 (978-0-14-240197-2(8) , Puffin) Penguin Group (USA) Inc.

Bassede, Francine. George's Store at the Shore. Barth, Dominic, tr. 1998. (Illus.). 32p. (J). (ps-1). 15.99 (978-0-531-33083-8(4) , Orchard Bks.) Scholastic, Inc.

Bateman, Donna M. Deep in the Swamp. Lies, Brian, illus. 2007. 32p. (J). (ps-1). 15.95 (978-1-57091-596-3(2)); pap. 6.95 (***978-1-57091-597-0(0))*** Charlesbridge Publishing, Inc.

Beall, Pamela Conn & Nipp, Susan Hagen. Wee Sing & Learn 1-2-3. Pongmee, Yudthana, illus. 2001. (Reading Railroad Bks.). 32p. (J). (ps-k). pap. 3.49 (978-0-448-42589-4(0) , Grosset & Dunlap) Penguin Group (USA) Inc.

—Wee Sing & Learn 123. 2005. (Wee Sing & Learn Ser.). 20p. (J). (ps). 9.99 (978-0-8431-1662-5(5) , Price Stern Sloan) Penguin Group (USA) Inc.

Bearman, Jane. Eight Nights: A Chanukah Counting Book. 1999. (Illus.). (J). (ps-3). pap. 6.00 (978-0-8074-0025-8(4)) URJ Pr.

Beaton, Clare. Un Alce, Veinte Ratones. Beaton, Clare, illus. 2002. (SPA., Illus.). 32p. (J). (gr. k-2). 5.99 (978-1-84148-911-7(5)) Barefoot Bks., Inc.

—Un Alce, Viente Ratones. 2002. (SPA.). (ps-2). lib. bdg. 14.15 (978-0-613-53790-2(4)) Tandem Library Bks.

—One Moose, Twenty Mice. 1999. (Barefoot Beginner Ser.). (Illus.). 32p. (J). (ps-k). 14.95 (978-1-902283-37-1(6)) Barefoot Bks., Inc.

Beaumont, Karen. Doggone Dogs! Catrow, David, illus. 2008. (J). (***978-0-8037-3157-8(4)*** , Dial) Penguin Group (USA) Inc.

Becker, John E. Seven Little Rabbits. Cooney, Barbara, illus. 2007. 32p. (J). 8.85 (978-0-8027-9635-6(4)); 7.95 (978-0-8027-9634-9(6)) Walker & Co.

Bedford, David & Worthington, Leonie. One-O-Saur, Two-O-Saur. 2007. (Illus.). 22p. (J). (ps-k). 9.95 (***978-1-877003-84-4(0))*** Little Hare Bks. AUS. *Dist:* Independent Pubs. Group.

Beeler, Selby B. How Many Elephants? A Lift-the-Flap Counting Book. Saltzberg, Barney, illus. 2004. 20p. (J). (gr. k-k). 9.99 (978-0-7636-1583-3(8)) Candlewick Pr.

Beers, Jack. Bears, Ten by Ten. 2000. (Metro Math Readers Yellow Level Ser.). (J). (gr. 1-2). 3.75 (978-1-58120-407-0(8)) Metropolitan Teaching & Learning Co.

—Los Numeros 6 - 2000. (Metro Math Readers Red Level Ser.). (J). (gr. k-1). 46.95 (978-1-58830-522-0(8)) Metropolitan Teaching & Learning Co.

—The Numbers 6 -9. 2000. (Metro Math Readers Red Level Ser.). (J). (gr. k-1). 49.77 (978-1-58120-552-7(X)) Metropolitan Teaching & Learning Co.

Beil, Karen Magnuson. Mooove Over! A Book about Counting by Twos. Meisel, Paul, tr. Meisel, Paul, illus. 2004. 32p. (J). (gr. k-3). tchr. ed. 16.95 (978-0-8234-1736-0(0)) Holiday Hse., Inc.

Beinstein, Phoebe. Count with Dora! A Counting Book in Both English & Spanish. Thompson Brothers Staff, illus. 2002. (Dora the Explorer Ser.). 14p. (J). bds. 4.99 (978-0-689-84818-6(8) , Simon Spotlight/Nickelodeon) Simon & Schuster Children's Publishing.

—Counting with Oswald. Kahata, Etsu, illus. 2003. (Oswald Ser.). 22p. (J). bds. 4.99 (978-0-689-85434-7(X) , Simon Spotlight/Nickelodeon) Simon & Schuster Children's Publishing.

Benchmark Education Staff, compiled by. Counting. 2006. spiral bd. 315.00 (***978-1-4108-7048-3(0))*** Benchmark Education Co.

—Estimation. 2006. spiral bd. 95.00 (***978-1-4108-7054-4(5))*** Benchmark Education Co.

Bennett, Gary & Bennett, Madeline. The Best Counting Book in the Wild West. 2000. (Illus.). 32p. (J). (ps-2). 14.95 (978-1-893860-13-1(2)) Arizona Highways.

Bentley, Dawn. Cat Nap: A Counting Book. Nagy, Krisztina, illus. 1999. 10p. (J). (ps-3). 9.95 (978-1-58117-033-7(5) , Intervisual/Piggy Toes) Dalmatian Pr.

Berger, Samantha & Chessen, Betsey. Apples. 1999. (J). 2.50 (978-0-439-04592-6(4)) Scholastic, Inc.

Berkes, Marianne. Over in the Jungle: A Rainforest Rhyme. Canyon, Jeanette, illus. 2007. 32p. (J). (ps-2). 16.95 (***978-1-58469-091-7(7));*** pap. 8.95 (***978-1-58469-092-4(5))*** Dawn Pubns.

Berkes, Marianne. Over in the Ocean: In a Coral Reef. Canyon, Jeanette, illus. (J). 2006. 26p. bds. 7.95 (978-1-58469-082-5(8)); 2004. 32p. 16.95 (978-1-58469-063-4(1)); 2004. 36p. pap. 8.95 (978-1-58469-062-7(3)) Dawn Pubns.

Berkes, Marianne Collins. Seashells by the Seashore. Noreika, Robert, illus. 2004. (Sharing Nature with Children Book Ser.). 32p. (J). (ps-5). 16.95 (978-1-58469-035-1(6)); pap. 8.95 (978-1-58469-034-4(8)) Dawn Pubns.

—Seashells by the Seashore. 2002. (gr. k-3). lib. bdg. 17.60 (978-0-613-62835-8(7)) Tandem Library Bks.

Berry, Lynne. Duck Dunks. Nakata, Hiroe, illus. 2008. 32p. (J). 16.95 (***978-0-8050-8128-2(3))*** Holt, Henry & Co.

Bestselling Counting Books: Ten Little Ladybugs; Eight Silly Monkeys; This Little Piggy. (J). 29.99 (978-1-58117-380-2(6) , Intervisual/Piggy Toes) Dalmatian Pr.

Bianchi, Mike & Novak, Marisol. Swampmeet: A Gator Counting Book. Marlette, Andy, illus. 2004. 32p. (J). (ps-k). 6.95 (978-1-58261-780-0(5)) Sports Publishing, LLC.

Bickico Enterprises Staff, concept. BabyKids Bk. 2: The Counting Book. 2003. 16p. (J). pap. 2.95 (978-0-9746508-1-4(1)) Bickico Enterprises, Inc.

Blackstone, Stella. Bear in a Square. 2000. (J). 12.79 (978-0-606-19702-1(8)) Tandem Library Bks.

—Cleo's Counting Book. Mockford, Caroline, illus. 24p. (J). 2004. pap. 5.99 (978-1-84148-174-6(2)); 2003. 15.99 (978-1-84148-207-1(2)) Barefoot Bks., Inc.

—Counting Cockatoos. Bauer, Stephanie, illus. 2006. 32p. (J). 16.99 (978-1-905236-31-2(X)) Barefoot Bks., Inc.

Blake, Michel. Numbers: Easy Open. Blake, Michel, illus. 2006. (Illus.). 16p. (J). (gr. k-ps). bds. 5.99 (978-0-7636-2747-8(X)) Candlewick Pr.

Blathwayt, Benedict. One Farm. (Illus.). 32p. (J). 2001. pap. 9.99 (978-0-09-940759-1(0)); 2000. 17.99 (978-0-09-176966-6(3)) Random Hse. GBR. *Dist:* Trafalgar Square Publishing, Independent Pubs. Group.

Boegehold, Lindley. Contando Ositos de Goma. 2001. (SPA., Illus.). 22p. (J). (978-84-89675-89-6(9)) Zendrera Zariquiey, Editorial ESP. *Dist:* Lectorum Pubns., Inc.

Bolchazy, Marie Carducci. How Many Animals? Quot Animalia? Stock, Kristie, illus. 2002. (I Am Reading Latin Ser.). (LAT & ENG.). 64p. (J). 12.00 (978-0-86516-540-3(8)) Bolchazy-Carducci Pubs.

Boniface, William. Five Little Christmas Angels. Adams, Lynn, illus. 2003. 12p. (J). (ps). 5.99 (978-0-8431-0611-4(5) , Price Stern Sloan) Penguin Group (USA) Inc.

—Five Little Turkeys. Adams, Lynn, illus. 2003. 12p. (J). (ps). 5.99 (978-0-8431-0464-6(3) , Price Stern Sloan) Penguin Group (USA) Inc.

Book Company Staff. Counting. 2003. (Bug Chunkie Board Bks.). (Illus.). (J). bds. 2.95 (978-1-74047-346-0(9)) Book Co. Publishing Pty, Ltd., The AUS. *Dist:* Penton Overseas, Inc.

—Lift & Learn 123. 2005. (Novelty Ser.). (Illus.). 8p. (J). (gr. 3-5). bds. 10.95 (978-1-74047-459-7(7)) Book Co. Publishing Pty, Ltd., The AUS. *Dist:* Penton Overseas, Inc.

Boothroyd, Jennifer. Counting. 2007. (First Step Nonfiction Ser.). (J). pap. (978-0-8225-6827-8(6)) Lerner Publishing Group.

—Skip Counting. 2007. (First Step Nonfiction Ser.). (J). pap. (978-0-8225-6828-5(4)) Lerner Publishing Group.

Borgardt, Marianne. Yellow at Home: A Counting Book of Yellow. Shorten, Chris, photos by. 1999. (Gymboree Book Ser.). (Illus.). 20p. (J). reprint ed. 4.95 (978-1-892374-11-0(0)) Weldon Owen, Inc.

Boueri, Marijean. Lebanon 1-2-3: A Counting Book in Three Languages. Badaji, Mona Trade, illus. 2005. (ENG, ARA & FRE.). 32p. (J). 16.95 (978-1-933002-03-3(4)) PublishingWorks.

Bowdish, Lynea. One Glad Man. Sorra, Kristin, illus. 1999. (Rookie Readers Ser.). 32p. (J). (gr. 1-2). 19.50 (978-0-516-21595-2(7) , Children's Pr.) Scholastic Library Publishing.

—One Glad Man. Sorra, Kristin, illus. 2000. 31p. (J). (ps-3). lib. bdg. 12.95 (978-0-613-54628-7(8)) Tandem Library Bks.

Bowen, Betsy. Gathering: A Northwoods Counting Book. Bowen, Betsy, illus. 1999. (Illus.). 32p. (J). (gr. k-3). tchr. ed. 16.00 (978-0-395-98133-7(6)); pap. 6.95 (978-0-395-98134-4(4)) Houghton Mifflin Co. Trade & Reference Div.

—Gathering: A Northwoods Counting Book. 1999. (J). (978-0-606-17369-8(2)) Tandem Library Bks.

Boynton, Sandra. Hippos Go Berserk! 2000. (Illus.). 32p. (J). per. 7.99 (978-0-689-83499-8(3) , Simon & Schuster Children's Publishing) Simon & Schuster Children's Publishing.

Bracken, Carolyn. 1 2 3 Fun. Garcia, Segundo, illus. 2001. (Fisher-Price Little People Ser.). 16p. (J). spiral bd., bds. (978-0-7853-5190-0(6) , 7134600) Publications International, Ltd.

Brainy Baby Quad Book. 2005. (Brainy Baby Ser.). 40p. (J). bds. 10.39 (978-1-59394-240-3(0)) Bendon Publishing International.

Bratton, Heidi, photos by. Count Your Blessings. 2000. (Walking with God Board Bks.). (Illus.). 16p. (J). (ps-k). bds. 5.95 (978-0-8091-6659-6(3) , 6659-3) Paulist Pr.

Briggs, Harry, illus. Come una y Cuenta Veinte. 2004. Tr. of Grapes of Math. (SPA.). (J). 14.99 (978-84-241-8075-1(5)) Everest de Ediciones y Distribucion, S.L. ESP. *Dist:* Lectorum Pubns., Inc.

Brighter Vision Publishing Staff. About Numbers. 1998. (My Discovery Bks.). (ps). 32p. (J). pap. 3.99 (978-1-55254-004-6(9)); (Illus.). pap. 7.95 (978-1-55254-036-7(7)) Brighter Vision Pubns.

Brimner, Larry Dane. Monkey Math. Kulka, Joe, illus. 2006. (Rookie Reader Skill Set Ser.). 32p. (J). (gr. k-2). 19.50 (978-0-531-12463-5(0) , Children's Pr.) Scholastic Library Publishing.

Brocklehurst, Ruth. 1001 Animals to Spot. 2004. (1001 Things to Spot Ser.). (SPA., Illus.). 32p. (J). (ps up). pap. 6.95 (978-0-7945-0149-5(4) , Usborne) EDC Publishing.

Broekstra, Lorette. Baby Bbear Goes to the Farm. 2004. (Baby-Bear Ser.). (Illus.). 32p. (J). 5.99 (978-1-85854-488-5(2)) Brimax Books Ltd. GBR. *Dist:* Byeway Bks.

Brooks, Alan. Frogs Jump: A Counting Book. Kellogg, Steven, illus. 1999. 48p. (J). (ps-1). pap. 6.99 (978-0-590-45529-9(X)) Scholastic, Inc.

—Frogs Jump: A Counting Book. 1999. (J). lib. bdg. (978-0-606-17058-1(8)) Tandem Library Bks.

Brooks, David. You Can Count in the Jungle. 2005. (Illus.). 24p. (J). bds. (978-1-55971-931-5(1) , NorthWord Bks. for Young Readers) T&N Children's Publishing.

Brooks, Felicity & Litchfield, Jo. First Numbers. 2004. (First Numbers Ser.). (SPA., Illus.). 28p. (J). pap. 7.95 (978-0-7945-0092-4(7) , Usborne) EDC Publishing.

Brooks, Felicity & Tyler, Jenny. The Usborne 1, 2, 3 Jigsaw Book. Cartwright, Stephen, illus. 2005. 12p. (J). bds. 15.95 (978-0-7945-1168-5(6) , Usborne) EDC Publishing.

Brown, Margaret Wise. Goodnight Moon 123: A Counting Book. Hurd, Clement, illus. 2007. 32p. (J). lib. bdg. 17.89 (978-0-06-112594-2(6)); 16.99 (978-0-06-112593-5(8)) HarperCollins Pubs.

—Goodnight Moon 123 Board Book: A Counting Book. Hurd, Clement, illus. 2008. 30p. (J). 8.99 (***978-0-06-112597-3(0)*** , Harper Festival) HarperCollins Pubs.

—Goodnight Moon 123/Buenas Noches, Luna 123: A Counting Book/Un Libro para Contar. Hurd, Clement, illus. 2007. (ENG & SPA.). 32p. (J). (ps-k). 16.99 (***978-0-06-117325-7(8)*** , Rayo) HarperCollins Pubs.

—Goodnight Moon Big Book. Hurd, Clement, illus. 2007. 32p. (J). pap. 24.99 (***978-0-06-111977-4(6)*** , Harper Festival) HarperCollins Pubs.

Browne, Eileen. Handa's Hen. 2004. (J). (ALB & ENG.). (978-1-84444-188-4(1)); (ARA & ENG.). (978-1-84444-184-6(9)); (BEN & ENG.). (978-1-84444-189-1(X)); (CHI & ENG.). (978-1-84444-185-3(7)); (CRO & ENG.). (978-1-84444-190-7(3)); (ENG & FRE.). (978-1-84444-191-4(1)); (ENG & GUJ.). (978-1-84444-192-1(X)); (ENG & HIN.). (978-1-84444-193-8(8)); (ENG & PAN.). (978-1-84444-194-5(6)); (ENG & RUS.). (978-1-84444-195-2(4)); (ENG & SOM.). (978-1-84444-187-7(3)); (ENG & URD.). (978-1-84444-196-9(2)); (ENG & VIE.). (978-1-84444-197-6(0)) Mantra Publishing, Ltd.

Bruna, Dick. Miffy's Counting Book. 2004. (Illus.). 20p. bds. 7.99 (978-1-59226-034-8(9)) Big Tent Entertainment, Inc.

—Miffy's Counting Book. Bruna, Dick, illus. 1999. (Miffy Ser.). (Illus.). 20p. (ps-k). bds. 7.95 (978-1-56836-281-6(1)) Kodansha America, Inc.

Brunelle, Lynn. My Blue Zoo. Shorten, Chris, photos by. 1999. (Gymboree Book Ser.). (Illus.). 20p. (J). reprint ed. 4.95 (978-1-892374-13-4(7)) Weldon Owen, Inc.

—Red on the Go: A Counting Book of Red. Shorten, Chris, photos by. 1999. (Gymboree Book Ser.). (Illus.). 20p. (J). reprint ed. 4.95 (978-1-892374-12-7(9)) Weldon Owen, Inc.

Bryant-Mole, Karen. Counting. Mukhida, Zul, photos by. 1999. (Mortimer's Math Ser.). (Illus.). 24p. (J). (ps up). lib. bdg. 22.00 (978-0-8368-2617-3(5)) Stevens, Gareth Inc.

—Dot-to-Dot on Seashore. Round, Graham, illus. 2003. 24p. (J). pap. 3.99 (978-0-7945-0494-6(9) , Usborne) EDC Publishing.

Bucerra, Patricia & Holloway, Zena. Counting, No. 2. 1999. (Water Babies Ser.). 12p. (J). (ps). bds. 6.99 (978-0-439-04775-3(7)) Scholastic, Inc.

Buckley, James, Jr. & Dorling Kindersley Publishing Staff. Baseball 1-2-3. 2001. (Illus.). 24p. (J). (gr. 4-7). bds. 6.99 (978-0-7894-7339-4(9)) Dorling Kindersley Publishing, Inc.

Bulloch, Ivan & James, Diane. Learn with Me 123. Pangbourne, Daniel, illus. Pangbourne, Daniel, photos by. 2007. (J). pap. (***978-1-58728-622-3(X)*** , Two Can Publishing) T&N Children's Publishing.

Bumpy Slide Books Staff. Count & Save with Blue. Nickelodeon/Viacom International Staff, ed. 2000. (Blue's Clues: No. 17). (Illus.). 32p. (J). (ps-1). 3.49 (978-1-57973-083-3(3)) Advance Pubs. LLC.

Burg, Ann E. Times Square: A New York State Number Book. Brookfield, Maureen K., illus. 2005. (Count Your Way Across the USA Ser.). 40p. (J). (gr. k-5). 16.95 (978-1-58536 195 3(X)) Sleeping Bear Pr.

Burningham, John. Numbers. Burningham, John, illus. 2003. (First Steps Board Books Ser.). (Illus.). 24p. (J). (gr. k-k). bds. 5.99 (978-0-7636-2043-1(2)) Candlewick Pr.

Burstein, John. Counting: Follow That Fish! Destiny Images Staff, illus. 2003. (Math Monsters Ser.). 24p. (YA). (gr. 1 up). lib. bdg. 19.33 (978-0-8368-3806-0(8) , Weekly Reader Early Learning Library) Stevens, Gareth Inc.

—Counting: Follow That Fish! 2003. (Weekly Reader Early Learning Library). (Illus.). 24p. (J). (gr. 1 up). pap. 7.93 (978-0-8368-3821-3(1) , Weekly Reader Early Learning Library) Stevens, Gareth Inc.

—Making Tens: Groups of Gollywomples. Destiny Images Staff, illus. 2003. (Math Monsters Ser.). 24p. (YA). (gr. 1 up). lib. bdg. 19.33 (978-0-8368-3812-1(2) , Weekly Reader Early Learning Library) Stevens, Gareth Inc.

—Making Tens: Groups of Gollywomples. 2003. (Weekly Reader Early Learning Library). (Illus.). 24p. (J). (gr. 1 up). pap. 7.93 (978-0-8368-3827-5(0) , Weekly Reader Early Learning Library) Stevens, Gareth Inc.

Burton, Margie, et al. Counting 1-5. Evento, Susan, ed. 1998. (Early Connections Ser.). 16p. (J). (gr. k-2). pap. 4.25 (978-1-892393-28-9(X)) Benchmark Education Co.

—Counting Insects. Adams, Alison, ed. 1999. (Early Connections Ser.). 16p. (J). (gr. k-2). pap. 4.50 (978-1-58344-059-9(3)) Benchmark Education Co.

—Counting Seeds. Evento, Susan, ed. 1998. (Early Connections Ser.). 16p. (J). (gr. k-2). pap. 4.25 (978-1-892393-34-0(4)) Benchmark Education Co.

—How Many? Evento, Susan, ed. 1998. (Early Connections Ser.). 16p. (J). (gr. k-2). pap. 4.25 (978-1-892393-40-1(9)) Benchmark Education Co.

—How Many Are Left? Adams, Alison, ed. 1999. (Early Connections Ser.). 16p. (J). (gr. k-2). pap. 4.50 (978-1-58344-066-7(6)) Benchmark Education Co.

C D

—Numbers Are Everywhere. Evento, Susan, ed. 1998. (Early Connections Ser.). 16p. (J). (gr. k-2). pap. 4.25 (978-1-892393-39-5(5)) Benchmark Education Co.

—We Use Numbers. Adams, Alison, ed. 1999. (Early Connections Ser.). 16p. (J). (gr. k-2). pap. 4.50 (978-1-58344-086-5(0)) Benchmark Education Co.

—What Comes in Twos? Evento, Susan, ed. 1998. (Early Connections Ser.). 16p. (J). (gr. k-2). pap. 4.25 (978-1-892393-36-4(0)) Benchmark Education Co.

Buster Books Staff. Counting 1-10. 2003. (Flip Me! Ser.). 10p. (J). (ps-3). per. 5.95 (978-1-904613-03-9(9)) O'Mara, Michael Bks., Ltd. GBR. *Dist:* Ingram Pub. Services.

Byeway Wall Charts Staff. Numbers 1-20 Wall Chart. 2004. (Wall Charts Ser.). (J). 4.99 (978-1-85997-282-3(9)) Byeway Bks.

Campbell Books. Numbers. 2001. (Illus.). 12p. (J). 8.99 (978-0-333-71273-3(0)) Macmillan Publishers Ltd. GBR. *Dist:* Trafalgar Square Publishing.

Campbell, Mel. Grupos Desfilando. 2007. (J). ***(978-1-60044-286-5(2))** Rourke Publishing, LLC.

Campbell, Mel. Parades of Arrays. 2007. (Illus.). 24p. (J). (978-1-59515-980-9(0)) Rourke Publishing, LLC.

Campbell, Rod. Counting Bugs. 1999. (Illus.). 12p. (J). 6.99 (978-0-333-73337-0(1)) Macmillan Publishers Ltd. GBR. *Dist:* Independent Pubs. Group.

Canizares, Susan & Chessen, Betsey. Numbers All Around. 1999. (Learning Center Emergent Readers Ser.). (J). 2.50 (978-0-439-04598-8(3)) Scholastic, Inc.

Capucilli, Alyssa Satin. Mrs. McTats & Her Houseful of Cats. Rankin, Joan, illus. 32p. (J). 2004. 6.99 (978-0-689-86991-4(6) , Aladdin); 2001. 17.99 (978-0-689-83185-0(4) , McElderry, Margaret K.) Simon & Schuster Children's Publishing.

Carder, Ken & Laroy, Sue. Songs That Teach Alphabet & Counting. 2006. (Songs That Teach Ser.). 72p. (J). pap. 14.95 (978-0-7696-6459-0(8) , American Education Publishing) School Specialty Publishing.

Carle, Eric. Count with the Very Hungry Caterpillar. 2006. (World of Eric Carle Ser.). 16p. (J). (ps-1). pap. 4.99 (978-0-448-44420-8(8) , Grosset & Dunlap) Penguin Group (USA) Inc.

—Let's Paint a Rainbow. Carle, Eric, illus. 1998. (Play-and-Read Book Ser.). (Illus.). 12p. (J). (ps). bds. 6.95 (978-0-590-32844-9(1) , Cartwheel Bks.) Scholastic, Inc.

—My Very First Book of Numbers. Carle, Eric, illus. 2006. 10p. (J). (ps-1). bds. 5.99 (978-0-399-24509-1(X) , Philomel) Penguin Group (USA) Inc.

—1, 2, 3 to the Zoo: A Counting Book. Carle, Eric, illus. 1998. (Illus.). 32p. (J). (ps-k). pap. 6.99 (978-0-698-11645-0(3) , Putnam Juvenile) Penguin Group (USA) Inc.

—1,2,3 to the Zoo. 2007. (World of Eric Carle Ser.). 24p. (J). (ps-1). pap. 4.99 (978-0-448-44493-2(3) , Grosset & Dunlap) Penguin Group (USA) Inc.

Caroll, Danielle. What Is a Hundred? 2006. 16p. (J). (gr. k-2). 15.93 (978-0-7368-5860-1(1) , Yellow Umbrella Bks.) Capstone Pr., Inc.

Carroll, Danielle. Is It Odd or Even? 2005. (Yellow Umbrella Books for Early Readers). (Illus.). 17p. (J). (978-0-7368-5285-2(9)); (978-0-7368-5321-7(9)) Capstone Pr., Inc.

—What Is a Hundred? 2005. (Illus.). 16p. (J). (978-0-7368-5290-6(5)); (978-0-7368-5326-2(X)) Capstone Pr., Inc.

Carter, David A. How Many Bugs in a Box? Carter, David A., illus. ed. 2006. 20p. (J). 10.95 (978-1-4169-0804-3(8) , Little Simon) Simon & Schuster Children's Publishing.

—The 12 Bugs of Christmas: A Pop up Christmas Counting Book. Carter, David A., illus. 1999. (Bugs in a Box Books Ser.). (Illus.). 12p. (J). (ps-k). 14.95 (978-0-689-83104-1(8) , Little Simon) Simon & Schuster Children's Publishing.

Carter, Noelle. Birthday Fun 1, 2, 3! A Counting Flap Book. Carter, Noelle, illus. 2005. (Illus.). 14p. (J). bds. 6.99 (978-0-689-86027-0(7) , Little Simon) Simon & Schuster Children's Publishing.

Cassels, Jean. The Twelve Days of Christmas in Louisiana. Cravath, Lynne Avril, illus. 2007. 32p. (J). (gr. k up). 9.95 ***(978-1-4027-3814-2(5))** Sterling Publishing Co., Inc.

Catala, Ellen. I Love a Parade. 2006. (Illus.). (J). 16p. (978-0-7368-5981-3(0)); (SPA & ENG., 18p. (978-0-7368-6017-8(7)) Yellow Umbrella Pr.

Catalanotto, Peter. Daisy 1, 2, 3. Catalanotto, Peter, illus. 2003. (Illus.). 32p. (J). 15.95 (978-0-689-85457-6(9) , Atheneum/Richard Jackson Bks.) Simon & Schuster Children's Publishing.

Caterpillar Inc. Staff, contrib. by. Trucks & Diggers from One to Ten. 2003. (Illus.). 20p. (J). bds. 6.95 (978-0-8118-4029-3(8)) Chronicle Bks. LLC.

Cato, Sheila. Counting & Numbers. Sweeten, Sami, illus. 1999. (Question of Math Ser.). 32p. (J). (gr. k-3). lib. bdg. 25.26 (978-1-57505-322-6(5) , Carolrhoda Bks.) Lerner Publishing Group.

Cave, Kathryn. One Child, One Seed: A South African Counting Book. Wulfsohn, Gisele, photos by. 2003. (Illus.). 32p. (J). (ps-2). 17.95 (978-0-8050-7204-4(7) , Holt, Henry & Co. Bks. For Young Readers) Holt, Henry & Co.

—Out for the Count: A Counting Adventure. Riddell, Chris, illus. 2006. 32p. pap. 7.95 (978-1-84507-539-2(0)) Lincoln, Frances Ltd. GBR. *Dist:* Perseus Distribution.

Celebrations Grade Level Libraries: Anno's Counting Book. 2005. (Little Celebrations Ser.). (J). (gr. k-3). 82.95 (978-0-673-75780-7(3)) Celebration Pr.

Chaconas, Doris J. One Little Mouse. Pham, Le Uyen, illus. 2002. 32p. (J). 15.99 (978-0-670-88947-1(4) , Viking Juvenile) Penguin Group (USA) Inc.

Chamberlin-Calamar, Pat. Alaska's 12 Days of Summer. Cartwright, Shannon, illus. 2003. (PAWS IV Ser.). 32p. (J). pap. 9.95 (978-1-57061-341-8(9)); 16.95 (978-1-57061-340-1(0)) Sasquatch Bks.

—Alaska's 12 Days of Summer. 2003. (gr. k-3). lib. bdg. 18.75 (978-0-613-79151-9(7)) Tandem Library Bks.

Chang, Maria, ed. Counting 1-20. 2005. lthr. 9.99 (978-0-439-73293-2(X)) Scholastic, Inc.

Cheney, Martha C. Counting Workbook. Runnells, Treesha, illus. 1998. (Gifted & Talented Ser.). 48p. (J). (ps-k). pap., wbk. ed. 5.95 (978-1-56565-841-7(8) , 08418W) Lowell Hse. Juvenile.

Cheng, Andrea. Grandfather Counts. ed. 2004. (Illus.). (J). (gr. k-3). spiral bd. (978-0-616-07253-0(8)) Canadian National Institute for the Blind/Institut National Canadien pour les Aveugles.

Chester, Jonathan. Splash! A Penguin Counting Book. 2000. (978-0-606-20317-3(6)) Tandem Library Bks.

Chester, Jonathan & Melville, Kirsty. Splash! A Penguin Counting Book. 2004. (Illus.). 24p. (J). (ps-k). 6.95 (978-1-58246-042-0(6) , Tricycle Pr.) Ten Speed Pr.

Chester, Jonathon. Splash! A Penguin Counting Book. 2000. (J). (978-0-606-20279-4(X)) Tandem Library Bks.

Chichester-Clark, Emma. Mimi's Book of Counting. Chichester-Clark, Emma, illus. 2004. (Illus.). 24p. (J). 9.95 (978-1-57091-573-4(3)) Charlesbridge Publishing, Inc.

Child, Lauren. Charlie & Lola's Numbers. Child, Lauren, illus. 2007. (Charlie & Lola Ser.). (Illus.). 12p. (J). (ps). bds. 6.99 ***(978-0-7636-3534-3(0))** Candlewick Pr.

Chouette, ed. Caillou Count with Me! rev. ed. 2006. (Caillou Board Bks.). (ENG & FRE., Illus.). 24p. (J). pap. 7.95 ***(978-2-89450-591-5(4))** Chouette Publishing CAN. *Dist:* Independent Pubs. Group.

Christelow, Eileen. En un Arbol Estan los Cinco Monitos / Five Little Monkeys Sitting in a Tree. 2007. Tr. of Five Little Monkeys Sitting in a Tree. (ENG & SPA., Illus.). 28p. (J). (gr. k-ps). bds. 5.95 (978-0-618-75248-5(X) , Clarion Bks.) Houghton Mifflin Co. Trade & Reference Div.

—Five Little Monkeys Jumping on the Bed. Christelow, Eileen, illus. 2002. (Illus.). (J). 14.66 (978-0-7587-2511-0(6)) Book Wholesalers, Inc.

—Five Little Monkeys Jumping on the Bed. 1998. (Five Little Monkeys Ser.). (Illus.). 14p. (J). (gr. k-ps). bds. 5.95 (978-0-395-90023-9(9) , Clarion Bks.) Houghton Mifflin Co. Trade & Reference Div.

—Five Little Monkeys Jumping on the Bed. 2000. (Illus.). (J). 12.75 (978-0-606-18041-2(9)) Tandem Library Bks.

—Five Little Monkeys Wash the Car. (Illus.). 40p. (J). (ps-1). 2004. 5.95 (978-0-618-48602-1(X)); 2000. tchr. ed. 15.00 (978-0-395-92566-9(5)) Houghton Mifflin Co. Trade & Reference Div. (Clarion Bks.).

Christian, Cheryl. Cuantos Hay? 2001. (Photoflaps Ser.). Orig. Title: How Many?. (SPA., Illus.). 12p. (J). (ps-k). bds. 5.50 (978-1-887734-25-7(2)) Star Bright Bks., Inc.

—Dondé Va? 2001. (Photoflaps Ser.). Orig. Title: Where Does it Go?. (SPA., Illus.). 12p. (J). (ps-k). bds. 5.50 (978-1-887734-49-3(X)) Star Bright Bks., Inc.

—How Many? (English/Haitian Creole) 2005. (Illus.). 12p. (J). bds. 5.50 (978-1-59572-024-5(3)) Star Bright Bks., Inc.

—How Many? (Korean) 2004. (KOR., Illus.). 12p. (J). bds. 5.50 (978-1-932065-82-4(2)) Star Bright Bks., Inc.

—How Many? (Simplified Chinese) 2004. (CHI., Illus.). 12p. (J). bds. 5.50 (978-1-932065-70-1(9)) Star Bright Bks., Inc.

—How Many? (Traditional Chinese) 2004. (CHI., Illus.). 12p. (J). bds. 5.50 (978-1-932065-64-0(4)) Star Bright Bks., Inc.

Christmas Numbers. 2001. (Illus.). 13p. (J). pap. 2.95 (978-1-55254-274-3(2) , BV24017) Brighter Vision Pubns.

Churchill, Jill. Five Little Ducks. Yaccarino, Dan, illus. 2005. 26p. (J). (ps up). pap. 5.99 (978-0-06-073465-7(5) , Harper Festival) HarperCollins Pubs.

Cisner, Naftali. Count with Mendel. Cisner, Naftali, illus. 2003. (Illus.). 10p. (J). bds. 5.95 (978-1-880582-84-8(8) , CWMH) Judaica Pr., Inc., The.

Clare, James. The Zoo Rap. Vagnozzi, Barbara, illus. 2005. (Reading Corner Ser.). 24p. (J). (gr. k-3). lib. bdg. 22.80 (978-1-59771-003-9(2)) Sea-To-Sea Pubns.

Clark, Emma Chichester. Little Miss Muffet's Count-Along Surprise. 2000. (Illus.). (J). (978-0-606-18000-9(1)) Tandem Library Bks.

Clark, Kimberly. Three Is the Perfect Number. Hummel, Victoria, illus. 1998. 16p. (J). (ps-k). pap. 5.95 (978-1-891846-01-4(9)) Business Word, The.

Cleland, JoAnn. ¿Cuantos Son? 2007. (ENG & SPA.). (J). ***(978-1-60044-283-4(8))** Rourke Publishing, LLC.

Cleland, JoAnn. How Many Are There? 2007. (Illus.). 24p. (J). (978-1-59515-973-1(8)); pap. ***(978-1-59515-943-4(6))** Rourke Publishing, LLC.

Coats, Lucy. Down in the Daisies. Bolam, Emily, illus. 2004. 32p. pap. 8.95 (978-1-84255-210-0(4)) Dolphin Paperbacks GBR. *Dist:* Trafalgar Square Publishing.

—Down in the Daisies: A Baby Animal Counting Book. Bolam, Emily, illus. 2002. 32p. (YA). 19.95 (978-1-85881-513-8(4)) Orion Bks. Ltd. GBR. *Dist:* Trafalgar Square Publishing.

Cohen, Caron Lee. How Many Fish? Schindler, S. D., illus. (My First I Can Read Bks.). 32p. (J). (ps up). 2000. pap. 3.99 (978-0-06-444273-2(X)); 1998. 14.89 (978-0-06-027714-7(9)); 1998. pap. 12.95 (978-0-06-027713-0(0)) HarperCollins Pubs.

—How Many Fish? 2000. (gr. k-3). lib. bdg. 11.80 (978-0-613-22995-1(9)); (Illus.). (J). 10.79 (978-0-606-18695-7(6)) Tandem Library Bks.

Coleman, Michael. One, Two, Three, Oops! Williamson, Gwyneth, illus. 1999. 32p. (J). (ps-2). 14.95 (978-1-888444-45-2(2)) Little Tiger Pr.

Colonial Williamsburg Foundation Staff & Watson, Amy Z. The Folk Art Counting Book: From the Abby Aldrich Rockefeller Folk Art Center. 1999. (Illus.). 40p. (J). (ps). 9.95 (978-0-87935-084-0(9)) Colonial Williamsburg Foundation.

Conlon, Mara. One Hungry Bunny. Wittwer, Hala, illus. 2003. (Reading Railroad Bks.). 14p. (J). (ps-1). bds. 5.99 (978-0-448-43121-5(1) , Grosset & Dunlap) Penguin Group (USA) Inc.

Connelly, Neil O. Numbers. Thornburgh, Rebecca, illus. (Cuddly Beasties Ser.). 10p. (J). (ps). bds. 3.95 (978-1-58989-001-5(9)) Thurman Hse., LLC.

Contar. (Coleccion Mundo Maravilloso). (SPA., Illus.). (J). (gr. 2-7). (978-84-348-4320-2(X) , SM0098) SM Ediciones ESP. *Dist:* Lectorum Pubns., Inc.

Coplans, Peta. Cat & Dog. 2000. (Illus.). (J). pap. (978-0-14-056140-1(4) , Puffin) Penguin Group (USA) Inc.

Count & Color (Pre-K) 2003. (J). (978-1-58232-042-7(X)) Bryan Hse. Pubs., Inc.

Count to 100 with the NBA. 2001. (NBA Ser.). 32p. pap. 3.50 (978-0-439-34308-4(9)) Scholastic, Inc.

Count to Ten. (J). 26.20 (978-0-8136-8410-9(2)); 26.20 (978-0-8136-8411-6(0)); 59.50 (978-0-8136-7942-6(7)) Modern Curriculum Pr.

Count with Me. 2002. (Puppy Tales Ser.). (Illus.). 24p. (J). (gr. k-3). 1.49 (978-1-57759-271-6(9)) Dalmatian Pr.

Count with Me. 1998. (Fisher-Price Bubble-Bath Bks.). (Illus.). 6p. (J). (ps-k). vinyl bd. 5.99 (978-0-7666-0147-5(1) , Honey Bear Bks.) Modern Publishing.

Count Your Blessings 123: My Wipe-off Book. 2003. spiral bd. (978-0-7853-8570-7(3)) Publications International, Ltd.

Count Your Chickens. 2000. 20p. (J). (ps-3). pap. (978-0-7696-1679-7(8) , American Education Publishing) School Specialty Publishing.

Counting, Bk. 2. 2005. (J). per. 8.95 (978-1-59566-157-9(3)) QEB Publishing Inc.

Counting 1 2 3. 2004. (Active Minds Ser.). (Illus.). 12p. (J). bds. (978-1-4127-0539-4(8) , 3998604) Publications International, Ltd.

Counting 123. 2003. (Active Minds Ser.). (Illus.). (J). (978-0-7853-7827-3(8)) Publications International, Ltd.

Counting 123: How Many Monsters Can You See? 2002. (J). 7.98 (978-0-7525-7935-1(5)) Parragon, Inc.

Counting & Numbers with Mr Wiggle. 32p. (gr. 2 up). 4.99 (978-1-56451-992-4(9) , ID99008) School Specialty Publishing.

Counting Animals. (Illus.). 12p. (J). (978-2-7643-0149-4(9)) Phidal Publishing, Inc./Editions Phidal, Inc.

Counting Book 1. 2005. (J). per. 8.95 (978-1-59566-153-1(0)) QEB Publishing Inc.

Counting Books, 3 bks. Incl. Baby Animals 1, 2, 3 : A Counting Book of Animal Offspring. Knox, Barbara. 32p. 2003. lib. bdg. 22.60 (978-0-7368-1675-5(5)); Eating Pairs : Counting Fruits & Vegetables by Twos. Schuette, Sarah L. 16p. 2003. 22.60 (978-0-7368-1676-2(3)); How Many Birds? Curry, Don L. 16p. 2000. 22.60 (978-0-7368-7039-9(3)); More Bugs? Less Bugs? Curry, Don L. 32p. 2000. lib. bdg. 22.60 (978-0-7368-7037-5(7)); My Counting Book. Curry, Don L. 16p. 2000. 22.60 (978-0-7368-7041-2(5)); Under the Sea 1, 2, 3 : An Ocean Life Counting Book. Knox, Barbara. 32p. 2003. lib. bdg. 22.60 (978-0-7368-1677-9(1)); 3, 2, 1 Go! A Transportation Countdown. Schuette, Sarah L. 32p. 2003. lib. bdg. 22.60 (978-0-7368-1678-6(X)); (J). (gr. k-1). (Illus.). 2000. Set lib. bdg. 158.20 (978-0-7368-1681-6(X) , Aplus Bks.) Capstone Pr., Inc.

Counting Coins & Bills. (Modified Basic Skills Ser.). 48p. (gr. k-4). 5.99 (978-0-7424-1926-1(6) , LL90003) School Specialty Publishing.

Counting Fun. 2002. 192p. (J). pap. 3.98 (978-0-7525-7920-7(7)) Parragon, Inc.

Counting Fun Wipe-Off Book. 2001. (Illus.). 16p. (J). (gr. k-2). mass mkt. 3.79 (978-1-889319-98-8(8)) Trend Enterprises, Inc.

Counting in the Garden Dog (Magalina) 2006. (J). 11.99 (978-0-439-84307-2(3) , Scholastic) Scholastic, Inc.

Counting Is Fun with Food. 1998. (Illus.). 7p. (J). 8.99 (978-1-929174-11-9(X)) Oshkosh B'Gosh, Inc.

Counting, Numbers, & Shapes. 2004. (Beastieville Ser.). 198.80 (978-0-516-25145-5(7) , Children's Pr.) Scholastic Library Publishing.

Counting Puzzles. Date not set. (Illus.). 96p. (J). 2.98 (978-0-7525-7519-3(8)) Parragon, Inc.

Counting with Animals. 2007. (Illus.). 10p. bds. 14.95 ***(978-1-59125-794-3(8)** , Penton Kids) Penton Overseas, Inc.

Counting with Fish. 2006. (J). bds. (978-0-9771117-4-9(1)) JMG Studio.

Cousins, Lucy. Count with Maisy. Cousins, Lucy, illus. 2nd ed. 1999. (Maisy Bks.). (Illus.). 24p. (J). (gr. k-ps). bds. 5.99 (978-0-7636-0234-5(5)) Candlewick Pr.

—La Gata Katy y Piquito de Oro. 2000. (Illus.). (J). (SPA.). 22p. (gr. 2-4). 16.95 (978-84-88061-38-6(2) , RR7149); (CAT., 16p. (ps). 16.95 (978-84-95040-25-1(5)) Serres, Ediciones, S. L. ESP. *Dist:* Lectorum Pubns., Inc.

—1 2 3, Maisy. Cousins, Lucy, illus. 2005. (Maisy Ser.). (Illus.). 14p. (J). (gr. k-k). 6.99 (978-0-7636-2655-6(4)) Candlewick Pr.

Cowder, Pansy. Decenas y unidades juntas: Metro Math Readers Yellow Level. 2000. (Metro Math Readers Yellow Level Ser.). (J). (gr. 1-2). 3.75 (978-1-58120-471-1(X)) Metropolitan Teaching & Learning Co.

—How Many Groups? 2000. (Metro Math Readers Yellow Level Ser.). (J). (gr. 1-2). 46.95 (978-1-58830-106-2(0)) Metropolitan Teaching & Learning Co.

Coyle, Carmela LaVigna. Do Princesses Count? Gordon, Mike & Gordon, Carl, illus. 2007. 26p. (J). bds. (978-0-87358-916-1(5) , Rising Moon Bks. for Young Readers) Northland Publishing.

Crabtree, Sally & Wallace, John. One Spinning Spider. 2000. (Finger Puppet Bks.). (Illus.). 24p. (J). (ps-k). 10.95 (978-1-86233-167-9(7)) Sterling Publishing Co., Inc.

Crane, Carol. Discover Florida, 2 bks. Monroe, Michael Glenn & Monroe Donovan, Jane, illus. 2003. 40p. (J). 27.95 (978-1-58536-226-4(3)) Sleeping Bear Pr.

—Discover Texas, 2 bks. Stacy, Alan, illus. 2003. 40p. (J). 27.95 (978-1-58536-227-1(1)) Sleeping Bear Pr.

—Georgia Number. Braught, Mark, illus. rev. ed. 2007. (State Counting Ser.). 40p. (J). 17.95 ***(978-1-58536-177-9(1))** Sleeping Bear Pr.

—Round Up: A Texas Counting Book. Stacey, Alan, illus. 2003. 40p. (J). 16.95 (978-1-58536-133-5(X)) Sleeping Bear Pr.

—Sunny Numbers: A Florida Counting Book. Monroe Donovan, Jane, illus. 2004. 40p. (J). pap. 6.95 (978-1-58536-246-2(8)) Sleeping Bear Pr.

—Sunny Numbers: A Florida Counting Book. Donovan, Jane Monroe, illus. 2001. 40p. (J). 16.95 (978-1-58536-050-5(3)) Sleeping Bear Pr.

—Wright Numbers: A North Carolina Number Book. Palmer, Gary, illus. 2005. (Count Your Way Across the USA Ser.). 40p. (J). (gr. k-5). 16.95 (978-1-58536-196-0(8)) Sleeping Bear Pr.

Crazy Elephants' First Number Fun. 2002. (J). bds. 4.98 (978-0-7525-8862-9(1)) Parragon, Inc.

Cronin, Doreen. Click, Clack, Splish, Splash. 2006. (J). (ps-3). 22.78 (978-1-59961-090-0(6)) Spotlight.

Crossley, David, illus. Baby's First Learning Book: 123. 2004. 10p. (J). bds. 2.99 (978-0-681-03556-0(0)) Autumn Publishing Group, LLC.

—123. 2004. (Baby's First Learning Ser.). 12p. (J). bds. 4.99 (978-1-85854-891-3(8)) Brimax Books Ltd. GBR. *Dist:* Byeway Bks.

Crum, Shutta. The House in the Meadow. Billin-Frye, Paige, illus. 2003. 32p. (J). (ps-2). 16.95 (978-0-8075-3393-2(9)) Whitman, Albert & Co.

Cuddly Kittens First Number Fun. 2002. (J). bds. 4.98 (978-0-7525-8864-3(8)) Parragon, Inc.

Cummings, Priscilla. Chesapeake 1-2-3. Aiken, David, illus. 2002. 32p. (J). (ps-2). 11.95 (978-0-87033-542-6(4) , Tidewater Pubs.) Cornell Maritime Pr., Inc.

Curry, Don L. A+ Books - Counting: How Many Birds?; More Bugs? Less Bugs?; My Counting Book, 3 bks. 2000. (A+ Counting Books). (Illus.). (J). (ps-2). lib. bdg. 63.78 (978-0-7368-7047-4(4) , Pebble Bks.) Capstone Pr., Inc.

—How Many Birds? 2000. (A+ Counting Books). (Illus.). 16p. (J). (gr. k-1). 22.60 (978-0-7368-7039-9(3) , Aplus Bks.) Capstone Pr., Inc.

—More Bugs? Less Bugs? 2000. (A+ Counting Books). (Illus.). 32p. (J). (gr. k-1). lib. bdg. 22.60 (978-0-7368-7037-5(7) , Aplus Bks.) Capstone Pr., Inc.

—My Counting Book. 2000. (A+ Counting Books). (Illus.). 16p. (J). (gr. k-1). 22.60 (978-0-7368-7041-2(5) , Aplus Bks.) Capstone Pr., Inc.

Curry, Don L. & Kaufman, Johanna. Counting with Birds. 1999. (Illus.). (J). 13.25 (978-0-7368-7052-8(0)) Capstone Pr., Inc.

Dahl, Michael. Ants at the Picnic: Counting by 10s. Trover, Zachary, illus. 2006. 24p. (J). (ps-2). 22.60 (978-1-4048-1318-2(7)) Picture Window Bks.

—Bunches of Buttons: Counting by 10s. Trover, Zachary, illus. 2006. 24p. (J). (ps-2). 22.60 (978-1-4048-1315-1(2)) Picture Window Bks.

—Downhill Fun: A Counting Book about Winter. Ouren, Todd, illus. 2004. (Know Your Numbers Ser.). 24p. (C). (gr. k-3). 22.60 (978-1-4048-0579-8(6)) Picture Window Bks.

—Eggs & Legs: Counting by Twos. Ouren, Todd, illus. 2004. (Know Your Numbers Ser.). 24p. (C). (gr. k-3). 22.60 (978-1-4048-0945-1(7)) Picture Window Bks.

—From the Garden: A Counting Book about Growing Food. Ouren, Todd, illus. 2004. (Know Your Numbers Ser.). 24p. (C). (gr. k-3). 22.60 (978-1-4048-0578-1(8) , 1229520) Picture Window Bks.

—Know Your Numbers, 6 bks. Incl. Downhill Fun : A Counting Book about Winter. Ouren, Todd, illus. (C). 22.60 (978-1-4048-0579-8(6)); From the Garden : A Counting Book about Growing Food. Ouren, Todd, illus. (C). 22.60 (978-1-4048-0578-1(8) , 1229520); On the Launch Pad : A Counting Book about Rockets. Aldermand, Derrick & Shea, Denise, illus. (J). 22.60 (978-1-4048-0581-1(8)); One Big Building : A Counting Book about Construction. Ouren, Todd, illus. (C). 22.60 (978-1-4048-0580-4(X) , 1229521); One Checkered Flag : A Counting Book about Racing. Aldermand, Derrick & Shea, Denise, illus. (J). 22.60 (978-1-4048-0576-7(1) , 1229522); One Giant Splash : A Counting Book about the Ocean. Ouren, Todd, illus. (C). 22.60 (978-1-4048-0577-4(X) , 1229523); 24p. (gr. k-3). 2004. 2004. Set lib. bdg. 135.60 (978-1-4048-0582-8(6)) Picture Window Bks.

—Lots of Ladybugs! Counting by Fives. Ouren, Todd, illus. 2004. (Know Your Numbers Ser.). 24p. (C). (gr. k-3). 22.60 (978-1-4048-0944-4(9)) Picture Window Bks.

—On the Launch Pad: A Counting Book about Rockets. Aldermand, Derrick & Shea, Denise, illus. 2004. (Know Your Numbers Ser.). 24p. (J). (gr. k-3). 22.60 (978-1-4048-0581-1(8)) Picture Window Bks.

—One Big Building: A Counting Book about Construction. Ouren, Todd, illus. 2004. (Know Your Numbers Ser.). 24p. (C). (gr. k-3). 22.60 (978-1-4048-0580-4(X) , 1229521) Picture Window Bks.

—One Checkered Flag: A Counting Book about Racing. Aldermand, Derrick & Shea, Denise, illus. 2004. (Know Your Numbers Ser.). 24p. (J). (gr. k-3). 22.60 (978-1-4048-0576-7(1) , 1229522) Picture Window Bks.

—One Giant Splash: A Counting Book about the Ocean. Ouren, Todd, illus. 2004. (Know Your Numbers Ser.). 24p. (C). (gr. k-3). 22.60 (978-1-4048-0577-4(X) , 1229523) Picture Window Bks.

—Plenty of Petals: Counting by 10s. Trover, Zachary, illus. 2006. 24p. (J). (ps-2). 22.60 (978-1-4048-1317-5(9)) Picture Window Bks.

—Speed, Speed Centipede! Counting by 10s. Trover, Zachary, illus. 2006. 24p. (J). (ps-2). 22.60 (978-1-4048-1316-8(0)) Picture Window Bks.

—Tail Feather Fun: Counting by 10s. Trover, Zachary, illus. 2006. 24p. (J). (ps-2). 22.60 (978-1-4048-1319-9(5)) Picture Window Bks.

—Toasty Toes: Counting by 10s. Trover, Zachary, illus. 2006. 24p. (J). (ps-2). 22.60 (978-1-4048-1320-5(9)) Picture Window Bks.

Dale, Penny. Ten in the Bed. Dale, Penny, illus. 2007. (Illus.). 24p. (J). (gr. k-ps). bds. 5.99 (*978-0-7636-3514-5(6)) Candlewick Pr.

Dale, Penny, illus. Ten in the Bed. 2001. 12p. (J). (gr. k-ps). bds. 6.99 (978-0-7636-1575-8(7)) Candlewick Pr.

Dalmatian Press Staff. Count with Me. 2002. (Illus.). 24p. (J). (gr. k-5). pap. 2.99 (978-1-57759-475-8(4)) Dalmatian Pr.

—Counting 1-10. rev. ed. 1999. (Tools Ser.). (Illus.). 32p. (J). (ps up). pap. 2.29 (978-1-57759-144-3(5)) Dalmatian Pr.

—Numbers 1-12. 2002. (Tools Ser.). (Illus.). 32p. (J). (gr. k-1). pap. 2.29 (978-1-57759-193-1(3)) Dalmatian Pr.

—Ten Little Monkeys. 2002. (Illus.). 24p. (J). (gr. k-5). pap. 2.99 (978-1-57759-368-3(5)) Dalmatian Pr.

Dalton, Julie. Counting Money. (J). 2006. 32p. (gr. 1-2). pap. 5.95 (978-0-516-25361-9(1)); 2005. (Illus.). 31p. (ps-ps). 20.50 (978-0-516-25260-5(7)) Scholastic Library Publishing. (Children's Pr.).

—Look & Count. 2006. 32p. (gr. 1-2). (YA). pap. 5.95 (978-0-516-21446-7(2)); (Illus.). (J). 20.50 (978-0-516-24958-2(4)) Scholastic Library Publishing. (Children's Pr.).

—Making Change at the Fair. 2006. 32p. (gr. 1-2). (YA). pap. 5.95 (978-0-516-21224-1(9)); (Illus.). (J). 20.50 (978-0-516-24960-5(6)) Scholastic Library Publishing. (Children's Pr.).

D'Amelio, Dennis P. Counting Cars. D'Amelio, Dennis P., illus. 1998. (Right Track Bks.: Vol. 1). (Illus.). (J). (ps). pap. (978-1-891528-50-7(5)) Telescopic Pr.

D'Andrea, Deborah. Picture Me Counting 1,2,3. Ayers, Michael B., illus. rev. ed. 2000. (Picture Me Ser.). 10p. (J). (ps-1). bds. 4.99 (978-1-57151-581-0(X)) Playhouse Publishing.

—Picture Me Numbers 1,2,3. 2002. (Learning Basics Ser.). (Illus.). 10p. (J). (ps up). bds. 4.99 (978-1-57151-557-5(7)) Playhouse Publishing.

Dann, Lucy & Riches, Francine Ngardarb. Bardi Counting Book. 2000. (Illus.). 24p. (J). pap. 4.95 (978-1-875641-54-3(8)) Magabala Bks. AUS. *Dist:* International Specialized Bk. Services.

David C. Cook. Learning to Count. 2004. (My Jesus Pocket Bks.). (Illus.). 32p. (J). (gr. 5-3). pap., pap. 8.90 (978-1-55513-097-8(6) , 1555130976) Cook, David C. Publishing Co.

Davidson, Alice Joyce. How Many Sheep? A Bible Counting Book. Cony, Frances, illus. 2000. (Baby Blessings Ser.). 10p. (ps-k). bds. 10.99 (978-0-7847-1138-5(0) , 04318) Standard Publishing.

Davidson, Rosemary. Fishy Numbers, Pack of 6. 2001. (Cambridge Storybooks Ser.). (Illus.). 8p. pap. 16.00 (978-0-521-00741-2(0)) Cambridge Univ. Pr.

—Fishy Numbers ELT Edition. Hellard, Susan, illus. 2001. (Cambridge Storybooks Ser.). 8p. pap. 3.00 (978-0-521-00667-5(8)) Cambridge Univ. Pr.

—One Teddy Bear All Alone ELT Edition. Rosato, Amelia, illus. 2001. (Cambridge Storybooks Ser.). 8p. pap. 3.00 (978-0-521-00662-0(7)) Cambridge Univ. Pr.

Davies. Fun Holidays. 2002. (Illus.). 10p. (J). 9.95 (978-1-85479-246-4(6)) O'Mara, Michael Bks., Ltd. GBR. *Dist:* Trans-Atlantic Pubns., Inc.

Davies, Gill. Ten in a Bed: A Pop-up Counting Book. Guile, Gill, illus. 20p. (J). (978-1-59394-120-8(X)) Bendon Publishing International.

Davis, Caroline, illus. My Babies. 2007. 12p. (J). (ps). bds. 6.95 (*978-1-58925-822-8(3) , tiger tales) ME Media LLC.

Davis, Caroline, illus. One, Two, Who's Who? 2002. 20p. (J). 5.95 (978-1-58925-685-9(9) , tiger tales) ME Media LLC.

Davis, David. Ten Redneck Babies: A Southern Counting Book. Ward, Sue Marshall, illus. 2004. 32p. (J). (gr. k-3). pap. 15.95 (978-1-58980-232-2(2)) Pelican Publishing Co., Inc.

Davis, Katie. Party Animals. 2002. (Illus.). 40p. (J). (gr. k-k). 15.00 (978-0-15-216675-5(0)) Harcourt Children's Bks.

Davis, Rebecca Fjelland. Beaches & Bicycles: A Summer Counting Book. 2006. (J). (978-0-7368-6891-4(7)); (Illus.). 32p. (978-0-7368-5378-1(2)) Capstone Pr., Inc.

—Counting down with Polar Animals. 2007. (Illus.). 32p. (J). 23.93 (978-0-7368-6374-2(5)) Capstone Pr., Inc.

—Counting Pets by Twos. 2007. (A+ Books. Counting Books). (Illus.). 32p. (J). 23.93 (978-0-7368-6375-9(3)) Capstone Pr., Inc.

—Falling Leaves & Footballs: A Fall Counting Book. 2006. (A+ Books). (Illus.). 32p. (J). (978-0-7368-5376-7(6)) Capstone Pr., Inc.

—Flowers & Showers: A Spring Counting Book. 2006. (J). (978-0-7368-6890-7(9)); (Illus.). 32p. (978-0-7368-5377-4(4)) Capstone Pr., Inc.

—Footballs & Falling Leaves: A Fall Counting Book. 2006. (J). (978-0-7368-6889-1(5)) Capstone Pr., Inc.

—More or Less: A Rain Forest Counting Book. 2007. (Illus.). 32p. (J). 23.93 (978-0-7368-6376-6(1)) Capstone Pr., Inc.

—Snowflakes & Ice Skates: A Winter Counting Book. 2006. (A+ Books). (Illus.). 32p. (J). (978-0-7368-5379-8(0)) Capstone Pr., Inc.

—Zoo Animals 1, 2, 3. 2007. (Illus.). 32p. (J). 23.93 (978-0-7368-6377-3(X)) Capstone Pr., Inc.

de Brunhoff, Laurent. Babar's Counting Book. 2003. (Illus.). 32p. (J). (ps-k). 16.95 (978-0-8109-4243-1(7)) Abrams, Harry N. , Inc.

de Paola, Tomie. Marcus Counts: One, Two, Three. 2003. (SPA., Illus.). 14p. (J). (ps-1). bds. 5.99 (978-0-399-24011-9(X) , Putnam Juvenile) Penguin Group (USA) Inc.

DeBoer, Jesslyn. Countdown to Christmas. 2006. 14p. (J). 3.99 (978-0-310-70845-2(1)) Zondervan.

Deegan, Kim. My First Book of Numbers. Deegan, Kim, illus. 2002. (Illus.). 24p. (J). (ps-1). 7.95 (978-1-58234-755-4(7) , Bloomsbury Children) Bloomsbury Publishing.

Del 'Homme, Melissa. Number Recognition & Counting & Quantity. McMahon, Kelly, illus. 2nd ed. 2000. (Tutor Bks.). 160p. (YA). (gr. k up). pap., wbk. ed. 12.95 (978-0-7373-0454-1(5) , 04545W, Roxbury Park Juvenile) Lowell Hse. Juvenile.

Delessert, Etienne. Hungry for Numbers. 2006. (Illus.). 32p. (J). 18.95 (978-1-56846-198-4(4)) Creative Co., The.

Del'Homme, Melissa. Counting & Quantity Workbook. McMahon, Kelly, illus. 1999. (Tutor Bks.). 80p. (YA). (gr. k up). pap., wbk. ed. 8.95 (978-1-56565-847-9(7) , 08477W) Lowell Hse. Juvenile.

Delval, Marie-Helene. Mama Pata Cuenta a Sus Pequeqos. Courtin, Thierry, illus. 2002. (Palabras Menudas Ser.).Tr. of Mother Duck Counts to Her Young. (SPA.). 14p. (ps). 4.95 (978-84-7864-516-9(0)) Combel Editorial, S.A. ESP. *Dist:* Independent Pubs. Group.

Dena, Anael. Los Numbers. (SPA.). 46p. (J). (978-84-263-3289-9(7)) Vives, Luis Editorial (Edelvives) ESP. *Dist:* Lectorum Pubns., Inc.

Denise, Anika. Pigs Love Potatoes. Denise, Christopher, illus. 2007. 40p. (J). (ps-1). 15.99 (978-0-399-24036-2(5) , Philomel) Penguin Group (USA) Inc.

Derke, Connie Butterfield. Mommy Has 1 Foot: Learning about Numbers - Learning about People. Smith, Tracy, illus. 2003. (Kayla's Learning Books). 24p. (J). (gr. 1-6). pap. 5.95 (978-0-9747063-0-6(2)) Derke, Connie.

deRubertis, Barbara. Count on Pablo. Thornburgh, Rebecca McKillip, illus. 1999. (Math Matters Ser.). 32p. (gr. k-2). pap. 4.95 (978-1-57565-090-6(8)) Kane Pr., The.

—Count on Pablo. 1999. (Math Matters Ser.). (Illus.). (J). 11.75 (978-0-606-18217-1(9)) Tandem Library Bks.

Diaz, James & Gerth, Melanie, illus. My First Jumbo Book of Numbers. 2002. (My First Jumbo Book Ser.). 10p. (J). pap. 9.95 (978-0-439-40353-5(7) , Cartwheel Bks.) Scholastic, Inc.

Díaz, James, et al. Mi Primer Gran Libro de los Numeros: Divertido Aprendizaje para los Mas Pequenos. 2003. (Mi primer gran libro de ... Ser.). (ENG & SPA., Illus.). 10p. 16.95 (978-84-7864-687-6(6)) Combel Editorial, S.A. ESP. *Dist:* Independent Pubs. Group.

Diehl, David. 1 Baby, 2 Cats, 3 Trucks: My Counting Book. 2007. (Illus.). 22p. (J). (ps). bds. 4.95 (*978-1-60059-115-0(9)) Lark Bks.

Dillon, Leo & Dillon, Diane. Mother Goose Numbers on the Loose. 2007. (Illus.). 56p. (J). (ps-2). 17.00 (978-0-15-205676-6(9)) Harcourt Trade Pubs.

Dingles, Molly. Number 10 Where Is the Hen? Wallis, Rebecca, illus. 2005. (Community of Counting Ser.). (ENG.). 32p. (J). lib. bdg. 20.65 (978-1-891997-90-7(4)) Dingles & Co.

—Number 2 Let's Go to the Zoo! Wallis, Rebecca, illus. 2005. (Community of Counting Ser.). 32p. (J). pap. 9.95 (978-1-59646-276-2(0)) Dingles & Co.

—Number 2 Let's Go to the Zoo!/Numero 2 ¡Vamos al Zoologico! Wallis, Rebecca, illus. 2005. (Community of Counting Ser.).Tr. of Numero 2 ¡Vamos al Zoologico!. (ENG & SPA.). 32p. (J). pap. 9.95 (978-1-59646-278-6(7)); lib. bdg. 20.65 (978-1-891997-88-4(2)) Dingles & Co.

—Number 3 What's in the Sea? 2005. (Community of Counting Ser.). (ENG., Illus.). 32p. (J). lib. bdg. 20.65 (978-1-891997-97-6(1)) Dingles & Co.

—Number 3 What's in the Sea? Wallis, Rebecca, illus. 2005. (Community of Counting Ser.). 32p. (J). pap. 9.95 (978-1-59646-280-9(9)) Dingles & Co.

—Number 3 What's in the Sea?/Numero 3 ¿Qué hay en el Mar? Wallis, Rebecca, illus. 2005. (Community of Counting Ser.).Tr. of Numero 3 ¿Qué hay en el Mar?. (ENG & SPA.). 32p. (J). pap. 9.95 (978-1-59646-282-3(5)); lib. bdg. 20.65 (978-1-891997-87-7(4)) Dingles & Co.

—Number 4 Shop at the Store! Wallis, Rebecca, illus. (Community of Counting Ser.). 32p. (J). 2005. pap. 9.95 (978-1-59646-284-7(1)); 2004. (ENG.). lib. bdg. 20.65 (978-1-891997-96-9(3)) Dingles & Co.

—Number 4 Shop at the Store!/Numero 4 ¡Vamos de compras a la Tienda! Wallis, Rebecca, illus. 2005. (Community of Counting Ser.).Tr. of Numero 4 ¡Vamos de compras a la Tienda!. (ENG & SPA.). 32p. (J). pap. 9.95 (978-1-59646-286-1(8)); lib. bdg. 20.65 (978-1-891997-86-0(6)) Dingles & Co.

—Number 5 Let's Go for a Drive! Wallis, Rebecca, illus. 2005. (Community of Counting Ser.). 32p. (J). pap. 9.95 (978-1-59646-288-5(4)); (ENG.). lib. bdg. 20.65 (978-1-891997-95-2(5)) Dingles & Co.

—Number 5 Let's Go for a Drive!/Numero 5 ¡Vamos a viajar en Coche! Wallis, Rebecca, illus. 2005. (Community of Counting Ser.).Tr. of Numero 5 ¡Vamos a viajar en Coche!. (ENG & SPA.). 32p. (J). pap. 9.95 (978-1-59646-290-8(6)); lib. bdg. 20.65 (978-1-891997-85-3(8)) Dingles & Co.

—Number 6 What Can We Mix? Wallis, Rebecca, illus. 2005. (Community of Counting Ser.). 32p. (J). pap. 9.95 (978-1-59646-292-2(2)) Dingles & Co.

—Number 6 What Can We Mix ? Wallis, Rebecca, illus. 2005. (Community of Counting Ser.). 32p. (J). lib. bdg. 20.65 (978-1-891997-94-5(7)) Dingles & Co.

—Number 6 What Can We Mix?/Numero 6 ¿Qué podemos Mezclar? Wallis, Rebecca, illus. 2005. (Community of Counting Ser.).Tr. of Numero 6 ¿Que podemos Mezclar?. (ENG & SPA.). 32p. (J). pap. 9.95 (978-1-59646-294-6(9)); lib. bdg. 20.65 (978-1-891997-84-6(X)) Dingles & Co.

—Number 7 Stars in the Heaven. Wallis, Rebecca, illus. (Community of Counting Ser.). 32p. (J). 2005. pap. 9.95 (978-1-59646-296-0(5)); 2004. lib. bdg. 20.65 (978-1-891997-93-8(9)) Dingles & Co.

—Number 7 Stars in the Heaven/Numero 7 Estrellas en el Cielo. Wallis, Rebecca, illus. (Community of Counting Ser.).Tr. of Numero 7 Estrellas en el Cielo. (ENG & SPA.). 32p. (J). 2005. pap. 9.95 (978-1-59646-298-4(1)); 2004. lib. bdg. 20.65 (978-1-891997-83-9(1)) Dingles & Co.

—Number 8 Let's Stay up Late! Wallis, Rebecca, illus. 2005. (Community of Counting Ser.). 32p. (J). pap. 9.95 (978-1-59646-300-4(7)) Dingles & Co.

—Number 8 Let's Stay up Late!/Numero 8 ¡Vamos a quedarnos en vela hasta muy Noche! Wallis, Rebecca, illus. (Community of Counting Ser.).Tr. of Numero 8 ¡Vamos a quedarnos en vela hasta muy Noche!. (ENG & SPA.). 32p. (J). 2005. pap. 9.95 (978-1-59646-302-8(3)); 2004. lib. bdg. 20.65 (978-1-891997-82-2(3)) Dingles & Co.

—Number 9 Dress up to Dine! Wallis, Rebecca, illus. (Community of Counting Ser.). 32p. (J). 2005. pap. 9.95 (978-1-59646-304-2(X)); 2004. lib. bdg. 20.65 (978-1-891997-91-4(2)) Dingles & Co.

—Number 9 Dress up to Dine!/Numero 9 ¡Vestirse con elegancia para Cenar! Wallis, Rebecca, illus. 2005. (Community of Counting Ser.).Tr. of Numero 9 ¡Vestirse con elegancia para Cenar!. (ENG & SPA.). 32p. (J). pap. 9.95 (978-1-59646-306-6(6)); lib. bdg. 20.65 (978-1-891997-81-5(5)) Dingles & Co.

Disney Staff. Pooh Counts to Five. Disney Staff, illus. 1999. (Pooh's Learn & Grow Ser.: Vol. 4). (Illus.). 12p. (J). 3.49 (978-1-57973-038-3(8)) Advance Pubs. LLC.

DiTerlizzi, Tony. G Is for One Gzonk! An Alpha-Number-Bet Book. DiTerlizzi, Tony, illus. 2006. (Illus.). 80p. (J). (ps-2). 16.95 (978-0-689-85290-9(8)) Simon & Schuster Children's Publishing.

Diyan Leake. Adding & Counting On. 2006. (Illus.). 24p. (J). pap. (*978-1-4034-8160-3(1)) Heinemann Library.

DK Publishing. Counting 1 To 10. 2008. 16p. (J). (ps-k). bds. 9.99 (*978-0-7566-3846-7(1)) Dorling Kindersley Publishing, Inc.

—Numbers: Let's Get Counting. 2008. 28p. (J). (gr. 12). 9.99 (*978-0-7566-3604-3(3)) Dorling Kindersley Publishing, Inc.

—Water Magic Baby Animals 123. 2007. 16p. (J). bds. 7.99 (*978-0-7566-3449-0(0)) Dorling Kindersley Publishing, Inc.

DK Publishing Staff. Count & Spell. 2006. 10p. (J). 3.99 (978-0-7566-2710-2(9)) Dorling Kindersley Publishing, Inc.

—Counting with Animals. 2007. 12p. (J). (ps-1). 3.99 (978-0-7566-2924-3(1)) Dorling Kindersley Publishing, Inc.

—Magic Count & Spell. 2007. 24p. (J). (ps-1). ring bd. 12.99 (978-0-7566-2932-8(2)) Dorling Kindersley Publishing, Inc.

—My First Word Lift-the-Flap Board Book. 1999. (My First Bks.). (Illus.). 12p. (J). (ps-k). bds. 9.99 (978-0-7894-4736-4(3)) Dorling Kindersley Publishing, Inc.

—Numbers. 2007. 26p. (J). (ps-1). bds. 9.99 (978-0-7566-3026-3(6)) Dorling Kindersley Publishing, Inc.

—Pop-Up Dinosaur 123. 2007. (DK Toys & Games Ser.). (Illus.). (J). (ps-2). 12.99 (978-0-7566-2728-7(1)) Dorling Kindersley Publishing, Inc.

Dobson, Christina. Pizza Counting. 2003. (gr. k-3). lib. bdg. 15.25 (978-0-613-70600-1(5)) Tandem Library Bks.

—The Pizza Counting Book. Holmes, Matthew, illus. 2004. 32p. (J). 16.95 (978-0-88106-338-7(X)); pap. 6.95 (978-0-88106-339-4(8)) Charlesbridge Publishing, Inc.

Dodd, Emma. Dog's Colorful Day: A Messy Story about Colors & Counting. Dodd, Emma, illus. 2003. (Illus.). 32p. (J). (gr. k-3). pap. 5.99 (978-0-14-250019-4(4) , Puffin) Penguin Group (USA) Inc.

—Dog's Colorful Day: A Messy Story about Colors & Counting. 2003. (gr. k-3). lib. bdg. 14.15 (978-0-613-57720-5(5)) Tandem Library Bks.

Dodd, Lynley. Sniff-Snuff-Snap! Dodd, Lynley, illus. 2000. (Gold Star First Readers Ser.). (Illus.). 32p. (J). (gr. 1 up). lib. bdg. 22.00 (978-0-8368-2677-7(9)) Stevens, Gareth Inc.

Doherty, Gillian. 1001 Cosas Que Buscar en el Mundo de las Hadas. 2007. 32p. (J). 9.99 (*978-0-7460-8346-8(7) , Usborne) EDC Publishing.

Donaldson, Julia. One Ted Falls Out of Bed. Currey, Anna, illus. 2006. 32p. (J). 15.95 (978-0-8050-7787-2(1)) Holt, Henry & Co.

Donkersloot, Sara Feriante. Down by the River: An Alaska Counting Rhyme. Pratt, Dale, illus. 1999. 32p. (gr. 3-6). 14.95 (978-1-888125-60-3(8)) Publication Consultants.

Donoghue, Stella. Lift & Learn 123. Snaith, Andy, photos by. 2006. (Illus.). 24p. (ps). per., bds. 5.95 (978-1-84610-030-7(5)) Make Believe Ideas GBR. *Dist:* Ingram Pub. Services.

Doris, Fisher & Dani, Sneed. One Odd Day. Karen, Lee, illus. 2006. 32p. (J). 15.95 (978-0-9768823-3-6(7)) Sylvan Dell Pubng.

Dorling Kindersley Publishing Staff. Baby 1 2 3. 1998. (Soft-To-Touch Book Ser.). (Illus.). 16p. (J). (ps-k). bds. 4.99 (978-0-7894-3649-8(3)) Dorling Kindersley Publishing, Inc.

—Barbie Numbers Book. 2006. (Illus.). 48p. (J). 12.99 (978-0-7566-1857-5(6)) Dorling Kindersley Publishing, Inc.

—Bath Books: 1 2 3. 1998. (Bath Bks.). (Illus.). 10p. (J). (ps-k). 6.99 (978-0-7894-2922-3(5)) Dorling Kindersley Publishing, Inc.

—Count with Me! 2003. (Baby's World Ser.). (Illus.). 12p. (J). bds. 4.99 (978-0-7894-9214-2(8)) Dorling Kindersley Publishing, Inc.

—Counting. 2003. (Baby Genius Ser.). (Illus.). 16p. (J). bds. 6.99 (978-0-7894-9883-0(9)) Dorling Kindersley Publishing, Inc.

—Farm Counting Fun. 2006. (DK Toys & Games Ser.). (J). 9.99 (978-0-7566-2233-6(6)) Dorling Kindersley Publishing, Inc.

—My First Number Bath Book. 2000. (Bath Bks.). (Illus.). 10p. (J). (ps-k). 6.99 (978-0-7894-6517-7(5)) Dorling Kindersley Publishing, Inc.

—My First Number Sticker Book. 2003. (My First Sticker Board Bks.). (Illus.). 12p. (J). pap. 6.99 (978-0-7894-9551-8(1)) Dorling Kindersley Publishing, Inc.

—My First Touch & Feel Picture Cards: Numbers & Counting. 2005. (Baby Genius Ser.). 16p. (J). pap. 9.99 (978-0-7566-1517-8(8)) Dorling Kindersley Publishing, Inc.

—Los Numeros/numbers. 2004. (My 1ST Board Books Ser.). 24p. (J). bds. 3.99 (978-0-7566-0439-4(7)) Dorling Kindersley Publishing, Inc.

—Words in My World. 2006. (Fun Flaps Ser.). (Illus.). 14p. (J). bds. 4.99 (978-0-7566-1764-6(2)) Dorling Kindersley Publishing, Inc.

—1, 2, 3. 2000. (Touch & Feel Ser.). (Illus.). 12p. (J). (ps). bds. 6.99 (978-0-7894-5220-7(0)) Dorling Kindersley Publishing, Inc.

Dorling Kindersley Publishing Staff, contrib. by. Baby Colors. 2003. (Baby's World Ser.). (Illus.). 12p. (J). bds. 4.99 (978-0-7894-9213-5(X)) Dorling Kindersley Publishing, Inc.

—Counting Toes. 2004. (DK Baby Ser.). (Illus.). 14p. (J). pap. (978-1-4053-0585-3(1)) Dorling Kindersley Publishing, Inc.

Dorling Kindersley Publishing Staff, ed. Barbie 1, 2, 3. 2004. (SPA & ENG., Illus.). 36p. (J). bds. 6.99 (978-0-7566-0452-3(4)) Dorling Kindersley Publishing, Inc.

—Counting Toes. 2004. (Baby Love Ser.). (Illus.). 16p. (J). bds. 4.99 (978-0-7566-0548-3(2)) Dorling Kindersley Publishing, Inc.

—My First Counting. 2005. (Touch & Feel Ser.). (Illus.). 12p. (J). bds. 9.99 (978-0-7566-0584-1(9)) Dorling Kindersley Publishing, Inc.

Dorling Kindersley Publishing Staff & King, Dave. Counting Book. 1998. (Illus.). 32p. (J). (ps-2). 12.99 (978-0-7894-3448-7(2)) Dorling Kindersley Publishing, Inc.

Douglas, Kathy M. Simple Centers. 1999. 240p. (J). (gr. k up). pap. 16.99 (978-1-56822-305-6(6) , IF8666) School Specialty Publishing.

Douglas, Vincent & School Specialty Publishing Staff. Counting. 2003. (Rhythm & Rhyme Ser.). (Illus.). 53p. (J). (ps up). bds. 19.95 (978-1-58845-519-2(X)) School Specialty Publishing.

—Counting Critters. 2004. (Kindergarten Bound Ser.). (Illus.). 80p. (J). (ps up). pap. 5.95 (978-0-7696-3437-1(0) , American Education Publishing) School Specialty Publishing.

—How Many? 2004. (Kindergarten Bound Ser.). (Illus.). 80p. (J). pap. 5.95 (978-0-7696-3530-9(X) , American Education Publishing) School Specialty Publishing.

—Numbers Dot-to-Dot. 2003. (Homework Helpers Ser.). (Illus.). 32p. (J). (gr. k-1). pap. 2.99 (978-0-7696-2924-7(5) , American Education Publishing) School Specialty Publishing.

—Numbers Hidden Pictures. 2003. (Homework Helpers Ser.). (Illus.). 32p. (J). (gr. k-1). pap. 2.99 (978-0-7696-2925-4(3) , American Education Publishing) School Specialty Publishing.

—Numbers Touch & Learn. Touch and Learn Staff, ed. 2003. (Padded Board Books with Textured Letters Ser.). (Illus.). 26p. (J). bds. 19.95 (978-1-58845-574-1(2) , Brighter Child) School Specialty Publishing.

Dowling, Paul. Sally's Fantastic Counting Book. 2000. (Illus.). 8p. (J). (ps). 15.95 (978-0-86264-802-2(5)) Andersen GBR. *Dist:* Trafalgar Square Publishing.

Downhill Fun. (Know Your Numbers Ser.). 24p. (J). 7.95 (978-1-4048-1092-1(7)) Picture Window Bks.

Drake, Aaron & Drake, Jennifer. A-B-C & 1-2-3 Travel Coloring Book. 2007. (Illus.). 80p. (J). 4.99 (978-1-56251-799-1(6)) AAA.

Dugan, Joanne. 123 Nyc: A Counting Book of New York City. 2007. (Illus.). 48p. (J). (ps-1). 15.95 (*978-0-8109-1381-3(X) , Abrams Bks. for Young Readers) Abrams, Harry N. , Inc.

Duke, Kate. One Guinea Pig Is Not Enough. 2001. (Illus.). (J). (978-0-606-20842-0(9)) Tandem Library Bks.

Dunn, Opal. Number Rhymes to Say & Play! Gon, Adriano, illus. 2005. 32p. (J). (ps). pap. 7.95 (978-1-84507-441-8(6)) Lincoln, Frances Ltd. GBR. *Dist:* Perseus Distribution.

Dunrea, Olivier. Gossie's Busy Day. 2007. (Illus.). 10p. (J). (ps-k). 11.99 (*978-0-618-82148-8(1)) Houghton Mifflin Co. Trade & Reference Div.

Dupasquier, Philippe. 1 2 3 Follow Me. 2002. (Illus.). 20p. (J). (gr. k-k). bds. 6.99 (978-0-7636-1797-4(0)) Candlewick Pr.

DuTemple, Lesley A. One Little Balsam Fir: A Northwoods Counting Book. Robinson, Susan, illus. 2006. (J). (*978-1-892384-37-9(X)) Avery Color Studios, Inc.

Eason, Cassandra & Sterling Publishing Company Staff. Benjamin's First Counting Book. 1998. (Balloon Ser.). (Illus.). 10p. (J). (ps-k). bds. 8.95 (978-0-8069-9445-1(2)) Sterling Publishing Co., Inc.

Edwards, Frank B. Nightgown Countdown. 1999. (New Reader Ser.). (Illus.). (J). (978-0-606-22035-4(6)) Tandem Library Bks.

Edwards, Frank B. & Bianchi, John. Nightgown Countdown. 1999. (New Reader Ser.). (Illus.). 24p. (J). (ps-1). pap. 4.95 (978-1-894323-04-8(1)); lib. bdg. 14.95 (978-1-894323-05-5(X)) Pokeweed Pr. CAN. *Dist:* Fitzhenry & Whiteside, Ltd.

Edwards, Pamela Duncan. Roar! Cole, Henry, illus. Date not set. 32p. (J). (ps-2). pap. 5.99 (978-0-06-443572-7(5)) HarperCollins Pubs.

—Roar! A Noisy Counting Book. Cole, Henry, illus. 2000. 32p. (J). (ps-2). 16.99 (978-0-06-028384-1(X)); 15.89 (978-0-06-028385-8(8)) HarperCollins Pubs.

Ehlert, Lois. Fish Eyes: A Book You Can Count On. Ehlert, Lois, illus. 2001. (Illus.). 40p. (J). bds. 6.95 (978-0-15-216281-8(X) , Red Wagon Bks.) Harcourt Children's Bks.

Ekblad, Linda. From Twenty to Fifty. 2000. (Metro Math Readers Yellow Level Ser.). (J). (gr. 1-2). 46.95 (978-1-58830-102-4(8)) Metropolitan Teaching & Learning Co.

—Una Mitad es lo Justo: Metro Math Readers Yellow Level. 2000. (Metro Math Readers Yellow Level Ser.). (J). (gr. 1-2). 3.75 (978-1-58120-486-5(8)) Metropolitan Teaching & Learning Co.

—Money. 2000. (Metro Math Readers Yellow Level Ser.). (J). (gr. 1-2). 49.95 (978-1-58830-101-7(X)) Metropolitan Teaching & Learning Co.

—Twenty, More or Less: Metro Math Readers Yellow Level. 2000. (Metro Math Readers Yellow Level Ser.). (J). (gr. 1-2). 3.75 (978-1-58120-402-5(7)) Metropolitan Teaching & Learning Co.

—Veinte, Mas o Menos: Metro Math Readers Yellow Level. 2000. (Metro Math Readers Yellow Level Ser.). (J). (gr. 1-2). 3.75 (978-1-58120-465-0(5)) Metropolitan Teaching & Learning Co.

Elliott, David. One Little Chicken: A Counting Book. Long, Ethan, illus. 2007. 24p. (J). (ps-k). 16.95 (*978-0-8234-1983-8(5)) Holiday Hse., Inc.

Elya, Susan Middleton. Eight Animals on the Town. Chapman, Lee, illus. (SPA.). (J). 2002. 32p. pap. 6.99 (978-0-698-11961-1(4)); 2000. 1p. 15.99 (978-0-399-23437-8(3)) Penguin Group (USA) Inc. (Putnam Juvenile).

—Eight Animals on the Town. 2002. (gr. k-3). lib. bdg. 15.30 (978-0-613-73480-6(7)) Tandem Library Bks.

Emberley, Ed, et al. Three: An Emberley Family Scrapbook. Emberley, Ed et al, illus. 1998. 64p. (J). (gr. 2-5). 17.95 (978-0-316-23506-8(7)) Little Brown & Co.

Emberley, Rebecca. My Numbers/ Mis Numeros. Emberley, Rebecca, illus. 2000. (ENG & SPA., Illus.). 10p. (J). (ps-ps). bds. 6.99 (978-0-316-23350-7(1)) Little Brown & Co.

—My Numbers (Mis Numeros) braille ed. 2004. (ENG & SPA.). (J). (gr. 1). spiral bd., bds. (978-0-616-07272-1(4)) Canadian National Institute for the Blind/Institut National Canadien pour les Aveugles.

Eng, Cindy. Spring Peeps! Yoon, Salina, illus. 2006. (Peeps Ser.). 12p. (J). 5.99 (978-1-4169-0649-0(5) , Little Simon) Simon & Schuster Children's Publishing.

Epstein, Brad M. Auburn Tigers 123: My first counting Book. l.t. ed. 2006. (Illus.). 22p. (J). bds. 14.95 (*978-1-932530-44-5(4) , 123 Bk.) Michaelson Entertainment.

—LSU Tigers 123: My first counting Book. l.t. ed. 2006. (Illus.). 22p. (J). bds. 14.95 (*978-1-932530-49-0(5) , 123 Bk.) Michaelson Entertainment.

—Michigan State University Spartans 123: My first counting Book. l.t. ed. 2006. (Illus.). 22p. (J). bds. 14.95 (*978-1-932530-50-6(9) , 123 Bk.) Michaelson Entertainment.

—The Ohio State University Buckeyes 123: My first counting Book. l.t. ed. 2006. (Illus.). 22p. (J). bds. 15.95 (*978-1-932530-55-1(X) , 123 Bk.) Michaelson Entertainment.

—Texas A&M Aggies 123: My first counting Book. l.t. ed. 2006. (Illus.). 22p. (J). bds. 14.95 (*978-1-932530-53-7(3) , 123 Bk.) Michaelson Entertainment.

—UCLA Bruins 123: My first counting Book. l.t. ed. 2006. (Illus.). 22p. (J). bds. 14.95 (*978-1-932530-45-2(2) , 123 Bk.) Michaelson Entertainment.

—University of Alabama Crimson Tide 123: My first counting Book. l.t. ed. 2006. (Illus.). 22p. (J). bds. 14.95 (*978-1-932530-43-8(6) , 123 Bk.) Michaelson Entertainment.

—University of Georgia Bulldogs 123: My first counting Book. l.t. ed. 2006. (Illus.). 22p. (J). bds. 14.95 (*978-1-932530-46-9(0) , 123 Bk.) Michaelson Entertainment.

—University of Illinois Fighting Illini 123: My first counting Book. l.t. ed. 2006. (Illus.). 22p. (J). bds. 14.95 (*978-1-932530-47-6(9) , 123 Bk.) Michaelson Entertainment.

—University of Iowa Hawkeyes 123: My first counting Book. l.t. ed. 2006. (Illus.). 22p. (J). bds. 14.95 (*978-1-932530-48-3(7) , 123 Bk.) Michaelson Entertainment.

—University of Michigan 123: My First Counting Book. l.t. ed. 2005. (Illus.). 30p. (J). 14.95 (978-1-932530-36-0(3)) Michaelson Entertainment.

—University of Notre Dame Fighting Irish 123: My first counting Book. l.t. ed. 2006. (Illus.). 22p. (J). bds. 15.95 (*978-1-932530-52-0(5) , 123 Bk.) Michaelson Entertainment.

—University of South Carolina 101: My First Text-Board-Book. l.t. ed. 2007. (101—My First Text-Board Books). (Illus.). 20p. (J). bds. 10.95 (*978-1-932530-41-4(X) , 101 Bk.) Michaelson Entertainment.

—University of Texas Longhorns 123: My first counting Book. l.t. ed. 2006. (Illus.). 22p. (J). bds. 14.95 (*978-1-932530-54-4(1) , 123 Bk.) Michaelson Entertainment.

Epstein, Brad M. Usc 123: My First Counting Book. l.t. ed. 2005. (Illus.). 30p. (J). bds. 14.95 (978-1-932530-35-3(5)) Michaelson Entertainment.

Eubank, Patricia Reeder. Countdown to Christmas. 2003. (Illus.). 14p. (J). (ps-k). 9.95 (978-0-8249-6505-1(1)) Ideals Pubns.

Evans, Lezlie. Can You Count Ten Toes? Count to 10 in 10 Different Languages. Roche, Denis, illus. 1999. (MUL & ENG.). 32p. (J). (gr. k-3). tchr. ed. 16.00 (978-0-395-90499-2(4)) Houghton Mifflin Co. Trade & Reference Div.

—Can You Count Ten Toes? Count to 10 in 10 Different Languages. Roche, Denis, illus. 2004. 32p. (J). (gr. k-3). pap. 5.95 (978-0-618-49487-3(1)) Houghton Mifflin Co. Trade & Reference Div.

Ewing, Susan. Ten Rowdy Ravens. Zerbetz, Evon, illus. 2005. 32p. (J). (ps-1). 15.95 (978-0-88240-606-0(X) , Alaska Northwest Bks.) Graphic Arts Ctr. Publishing Co.

Exclaim Entertainment & Bernthal, Mark. BOZtrade;-Count Your Blessings! McKee, Darren, illus. 2007. (BOZ#8482; Ser.). 14p. (J). 4.99 (978-0-310-71395-1(1)) Zonderkidz.

Falconer, Ian. Olivia Counts. 2002. (Olivia Ser.). bds. 6.99 (978-0-689-85447-7(1) , Atheneum) Simon & Schuster Children's Publishing.

—Olivia Counts. Falconer, Ian, illus. 2002. (Olivia Ser.). (Illus.). 12p. (J). (ps-1). bds. 6.99 (978-0-689-85087-5(5) , Atheneum) Simon & Schuster Children's Publishing.

Falwell, Cathryn. Christmas for 10. 2003. (Illus.). 32p. (J). (gr. k-3). 6.95 (978-0-618-37836-4(7) , Clarion Bks.) Houghton Mifflin Co. Trade & Reference Div.

—Feast for 10. Falwell, Cathryn, illus. 2002. (Illus.). (J). 14.74 (978-0-7587-2485-4(3)) Book Wholesalers, Inc.

—Feast for 10. Falwell, Cathryn, illus. 2003. (Illus.). 28p. (J). (gr. k-ps). bds. 4.95 (978-0-618-38226-2(7) , Clarion Bks.) Houghton Mifflin Co. Trade & Reference Div.

—Nicky, 1-2-3. 1998. (Illus.). 26p. (J). (gr. k-ps). bds. 5.95 (978-0-395-92952-0(0) , Clarion Bks.) Houghton Mifflin Co. Trade & Reference Div.

Falwell, Cathryn. Turtle Splash! Countdown at the Pond. Falwell, Cathryn, illus. 2002. (Illus.). (J). 25.04 (978-0-7587-8827-6(4)) Book Wholesalers, Inc.

—Turtle Splash! Countdown at the Pond. Falwell, Cathryn, illus. 32p. (J). 2008. pap. 6.99 (*978-0-06-142927-9(9) , Harper Trophy); 2001. (Illus.). (gr. 7 up). 16.99 (978-0-06-029462-5(0)); 2001. (Illus.). (gr. 7 up). lib. bdg. 17.89 (978-0-06-029463-2(9)) HarperCollins Pubs.

Faulkner, Keith. Ten Little Monkeys. Lambert, Jonathan, illus. 2001. 16p. (J). (ps-1). pap. 9.95 (978-0-439-26240-8(2)) Scholastic, Inc.

—Ten Little Monkeys: A Counting Story Book. Lambert, Jonathan, illus. 2004. 12p. (J). reprint ed. 20.00 (978-0-7567-8203-0(1)) DIANE Publishing Co.

Feelings, Muriel L. Moja Means One: Swahili Counting Book. Feelings, Tom, illus. 2004. 20p. (J). (gr. k-4). reprint ed. pap. 5.00 (978-0-7567-7108-9(0)) DIANE Publishing Co.

Feely, Jenny. One, Two, Three... Harradine, Dona, tr. 1999. (Hello! Lote Ser.). (IND., Illus.). 23p. (J). pap. 29.99 (978-0-7339-1305-1(9)) Pearson Education Australia AUS. *Dist:* Cheng & Tsui Co.

—One, Two, Three... Batt, Deleece, tr. 1999. (Hello! Lote Ser.). (JPN., Illus.). 23p. (J). pap. 29.99 (978-0-7339-1322-8(9)) Pearson Education Australia AUS. *Dist:* Cheng & Tsui Co.

Ferrante, Joanne. R. G.'s on Vacation! 2003. (Illus.). 32p. (J). 15.95 (978-0-9721949-1-4(6)) Window Seat Publishing.

Figuerola & Alonso. Cinco Lobitos. 2002. (SPA.). 8p. 5.99 (978-84-263-4737-4(1)) Vives, Luis Editorial (Edelvives) ESP. *Dist:* Lectorum Pubns., Inc.

—Cuando Da la Luna. 2002. (SPA.). 8p. 5.99 (978-84-263-4742-8(8)) Vives, Luis Editorial (Edelvives) ESP. *Dist:* Lectorum Pubns., Inc.

First Second Third. 2002. (Illus.). (J). pap. 3.74 (978-0-7398-5860-8(2)) Steck-Vaughn.

First Steps: 123. 2002. (First Steps Reading Ser.). 32p. (J). pap. 2.95 (978-0-7894-8480-2(3)) Dorling Kindersley Publishing, Inc.

Fisher, Valorie. How High Can a Dinosaur Count? ...and Other Math Mysteries. Fisher, Valorie, illus. 2006. (Illus.). 40p. (J). (gr. k-4). 16.95 (978-0-375-83608-4(X) , Schwartz & Wade Bks.) Random Hse. Children's Bks.

Five Funny Monsters. 2003. (Illus.). (J). pap. 14.99 (978-0-7424-1564-5(3)) School Specialty Publishing.

Five Little Frogs. 2003. (Illus.). (J). pap. 14.99 (978-0-7424-1565-2(1)) School Specialty Publishing.

Five Snuggly Bears. 2003. (Illus.). (J). pap. 14.99 (978-0-7424-1563-8(5)) School Specialty Publishing.

Flather, Lisa, contrib. by. Ten Silly Dogs: A Countdown Story. 1999. (J). (ps-2). lib. bdg. (978-0-531-33192-7(X) , Watts, Franklin) Scholastic Library Publishing.

Fleming, Denise. Count! Fleming, Denise, illus. 2002. (Illus.). (J). 15.49 (978-0-7587-2282-9(6)) Book Wholesalers, Inc.

Flip along Fun. (Illus.). 22p. (J). (ps-k). spiral bd. (978-1-56021-374-1(4) , #221) W.J. Fantasy, Inc.

Flores, Cory, illus. Bugs on Parade: A Counting Book. 2006. 8p. (J). (*978-1-58970-400-8(2)) Lakeshore Learning Materials.

Fontes, Justine. Cheerios Count to 100. Croll, Carolyn, illus. 2005. (*978-0-439-70341-3(7)) Scholastic, Inc.

Fontes, Justine. Count to 100. 2006. (Cheerios Ser.). (Illus.). 32p. (J). pap. 5.99 (978-0-439-77359-1(8) , Cartwheel Bks.) Scholastic, Inc.

Food - Set 3: Foods That Count. 2004. (J). spiral bd. 23.40 (978-0-9770248-3-4(0)) Sidedoor Publishing LLC.

Forsythe, Demming. The Ten Little Menehunes: A Hawaiian Counting Book. l.t. ed. 2005. (Illus.). 40p. (J). (ps-ps). per. 18.95 (978-0-932529-75-6(5) , Earth Rider) Oldcastle Publishing.

Foucht, Dawna. 1,2,3 Count Beanies with Me. 1998. (J). (978-1-885628-15-2(3)) Buckaroo Bks.

Franco, Betsy. Birdsongs: A Backwards Counting Book. Jenkins, Steve, illus. 2007. 40p. (J). (ps-2). 16.99 (978-0-689-87777-3(3) , McElderry, Margaret K.) Simon & Schuster Children's Publishing.

—Many Ways to 100. 2002. (Yellow Umbrella Books). (Illus.). 16p. (J). (gr. 1). lib. bdg. 14.60 (978-0-7368-1285-6(7) , Pebble Bks.) Capstone Pr., Inc.

Freeman, Marcia S. A Dozen Cousins: Exploring the Number 12. 2008. (J). (*978-1-60044-637-5(X)) Rourke Publishing, LLC.

—More Ice Cream: Words for Math Comparisons. 2008. (J). (*978-1-60044-641-2(8)) Rourke Publishing, LLC.

—What Makes Ten? Number Facts. 2008. (J). (*978-1-60044-642-9(6)) Rourke Publishing, LLC.

—1, 2, 3 ... Go! A Book about Counting. 2008. (J). (*978-1-60044-634-4(5)) Rourke Publishing, LLC.

Freeman, Tina. Ten Little Monkeys: Jumping on the Bed. 2001. (gr. k-3). lib. bdg. 15.30 (978-0-613-77001-9(3)) Tandem Library Bks.

Freymann, Saxton, illus. Food for Thought: The Complete Book of Concepts for Growing Minds. 2005. 61p. (J). lib. bdg. (978-1-4155-7707-3(2) , Levine, Arthur A. Bks.) Scholastic, Inc.

Freymann, Saxton, et al. Food for Thought: The Complete Book of Concepts for Growing Minds. Freymann, Saxton, illus. 2005. (Illus.). 64p. (J). pap. 14.95 (978-0-439-11018-1(1) , Levine, Arthur A. Bks.) Scholastic, Inc.

Fried, Miriam. My Jelly Bean Book. 2005. (Illus.). (J). (978-1-57400-049-8(7)) Data Trace Publishing, Co.

Friedman, Carol. Baby Cat Nicky 123. 2005. (Illus.). 24p. (J). (ps-k). per. 7.95 (978-1-57687-273-4(4) , PowerHouse Kids) powerHouse Cultural Entertainment, Inc.

Froeb, Lori & Brown, Jo. Zoo! A Big Fold-Out Counting Book. 2007. 10p. (J). (ps-k). bds. 12.99 (*978-0-7944-1361-3(7)) Reader's Digest Assn., Inc., The.

Fun with Numbers. 2005. (Active Minds Ser.). (J). (*978-1-4127-6029-4(1)) Publications International, Ltd.

Funny Friends, LLC Staff. Counting with Funny Friends. 1999. (Illus.). 18p. (J). bds. (978-1-929758-02-9(2)) Funny Friends, LLC.

—Counting with Funny Friends Value Pack: With Plush Toy. 1999. (Illus.). (J). bds. (978-1-929758-05-0(7)) Funny Friends, LLC.

Fyffe, Brian, illus. Christmas Counting: Count & Create with 42 Holiday Stickers. 2003. 10p. (J). (ps up). bds. 4.99 (978-1-57151-722-7(7)) Playhouse Publishing.

Galvin, Laura Gates. Counting Rhymes Travel Pack. rev. ed. 2006. 80p. 14.99 (978-1-59069-485-5(6)) Studio Mouse LLC.

—Disney Princess Take-with-Me Counting. 2006. 34p. 12.99 (978-1-59069-481-7(3)) Studio Mouse LLC.

Gant, Robert, illus. My Big Box of Numbers. gif. ed. 2005. 64p. (J). cd-rom 24.95 (978-1-57791-194-4(6)) Brighter Minds Children's Publishing.

Garland, Michael. How Many Mice? 2007. (Illus.). 32p. (J). (gr. k-2). 15.99 (978-0-525-47833-1(7) , Dutton Juvenile) Penguin Group (USA) Inc.

Gateman, Ryan, creator. Spelling the Number Words: From a Child¿s View. 2004. (Illus.). 24p. (J). 8.95 (978-1-932226-23-2(0)) Wizard Academy Pr.

Gayzagian, Doris. One White Wishing Stone: A Beach Day Counting Book. 2006. (Illus.). 32p. (J). (ps-1). 16.95 (978-0-7922-5110-1(5)); 25.90 (978-0-7922-5573-4(9)) National Geographic Society. (National Geographic Children's Bks.).

Geddes, Anne. 123. 2005. (Illus.). 24p. (J). (ps-k). 12.95 (978-0-7407-5580-4(3)) Andrews McMeel Publishing.

—123. Geddes, Anne, photos by. 2005. (Illus.). 24p. (J). (ps-k). bds. 6.95 (978-0-7407-5578-1(1)) Andrews McMeel Publishing.

Geisert, Arthur. Pigs from 1 to 10. 2002. (Illus.). 32p. (J). (gr. k-3). pap. 6.95 (978-0-618-21611-6(1) , Walter Lorraine) Houghton Mifflin Co. Trade & Reference Div.

Gerth, Melanie. Ten Little Ladybugs. Huliska-Beith, Laura, illus. 22p. (ps-k). 2005. (J). 10.95 (978-1-58117-091-7(2)); 2000. (YA). lp 12.95 (978-1-58117-122-8(6)) Dalmatian Pr. (Intervisual/Piggy Toes).

Gerver, Jane E. Grow a Pumpkin Pie! 2001. (My First Hello Reader! Ser.). (Illus.). (J). (978-0-606-21220-5(5)) Tandem Library Bks.

Getty, J. Paul, Museum Staff. 1 to 10 & Back Again: A Getty Museum Counting Book. 1999. (Books for Young Readers Ser.). (Illus.). 52p. (ps-1). 16.95 (978-0-89236-525-8(0)) Oxford Univ. Pr., Inc.

Gibson, R. Contar y Estampar. 2004. Tr. of I Can Count. (SPA., Illus.). 32p. (J). lib. bdg. 12.95 (978-1-58086-395-7(7)) EDC Publishing.

Gibson, Ray. Number Activities. Watt, Fiona & Tyler, Jenny, eds. Barlow, Amanda, illus. (Playtime Ser.). 96p. (J). 16.95 (978-0-7460-3679-2(5)) EDC Publishing.

Giganti, Paul, Jr. Counting Many Ways. 2002. (Yellow Umbrella Books). (Illus.). 16p. (J). (gr. 1). lib. bdg. 14.60 (978-0-7368-1280-1(6) , Pebble Bks.) Capstone Pr., Inc.

—Each Orange Had 8 Slices. Crews, Donald, illus. 1999. 32p. (J). (ps-3). pap. 6.99 (978-0-688-13985-8(X) , Harper Trophy) HarperCollins Pubs.

—Each Orange Had 8 Slices. 1999. (J). 12.79 (978-0-606-16756-7(0)) Tandem Library Bks.

Giganti, Paul. Each Orange Had Eight Slices: A Counting Book. 1999. (ps-2). lib. bdg. 14.15 (978-0-613-16665-2(5)) Tandem Library Bks.

Gill, Shelley R. Count Alaska's Colors. Cartwright, Shannon, illus. 2002. 32p. (J). (ps-3). pap. (978-0-934007-35-1(7)) Paws IV Publishing.

Gillham, Bill. How Many Sharks in the Bath? Fox, Christyan, illus. 32p. (J). 2006. pap. 7.95 (978-1-84507-564-4(1)); 2005. 14.95 (978-1-84507-288-9(X)) Lincoln, Frances Ltd. GBR. *Dist:* Perseus Distribution.

Gillieron, Rebecca. Spooky Sums & Counting Horrors. Cobb, Rebecca, illus. 2006. 32p. (J). 14.95 (978-0-7145-3307-0(6)) Boyars, Marion Pubs., Inc.

Gilliland, Lucille. What's All This? Gilliland, Lucille, illus. 2001. (Illus.). 24p. (J). (ps-6). pap. 8.95 (978-0-9716539-0-0(9)) LG Fun Learning Pubns.

Gillis, Jennifer Blizin. Candle Time 123. 2002. (Candle Time Ser.). (Illus.). 24p. (J). (ps-1). pap. 5.25 (978-1-58810-742-8(6) , 91382); lib. bdg. 18.50 (978-1-58810-533-2(4)) Heinemann Library.

Gillis, Jennifer Blizin & Jordan, Denise M. Fiestas con Velas 123. 2002. (Fiestas Con Velas (Candle Time) Ser.). (SPA.). 24p. (J). (ps-1). lib. bdg. 18.50 (978-1-58810-787-9(6)); (Illus.). pap. 5.25 (978-1-58810-834-0(1) , 91589) Heinemann Library.

Ginkel, Anne. I've Got an Elephant. Bynum, Janie, illus. 2006. 32p. (J). 16.95 (978-1-56145-373-3(0) , Peachtree Junior) Peachtree Pubs., Ltd.

Giogas, Valarie. In My Backyard. Zecca, Katherine, illus. 2007. 32p. (J). (ps-3). 8.95 (*978-1-934359-17-4(3)) Sylvan Dell Pubng.

Giogas, Valerie. In My Backyard. Zecca, Katherine, illus. 2007. 32p. (J). (ps-3). 15.95 (*978-0-9777423-1-8(8)) Sylvan Dell Pubng.

Girnis, Meg. 1, 2, 3 for You & Me. Green, Shirley Leamon, photos by. 2001. (Concept Book Ser.). (Illus.). 32p. (J). (ps-4). 15.95 (978-0-8075-6107-2(X)) Whitman, Albert & Co.

Gisler, David. Addition Annie. Beise, Sarah A., illus. rev. ed. 2002. (Rookie Reader Skill Set Ser.). 32p. (J). (gr. k-2). pap. 4.95 (978-0-516-27378-5(7) , Children's Pr.) Scholastic Library Publishing.

—Addition Annie. 2002. (gr. k-3). lib. bdg. 12.95 (978-0-613-53789-6(0)) Tandem Library Bks.

—Addition Annie Level C. Beise, Sarah A., illus. rev. ed. 2002. (Rookie Readers Ser.). 32p. (J). (gr. 1-2). 19.50 (978-0-516-22560-9(X) , Children's Pr.) Scholastic Library Publishing.

Gobo Books Staff. My Magnetic Counting Book. 2006. 20p. 9.95 (978-1-932915-16-7(8)) National Bk. Network.

—Ready for Numbers: Little Learners. 2007. (Magnix Little Learners Ser.). 42p. (J). (ps-1). bds., act. bk. ed. 14.95 (*978-1-932915-45-7(1)) Sandvik Innovations, LLC.

—Ready to Read & Write: Little Learners. 2007. (Magnix Little Learners Ser.). 40p. (J). (ps-1). bds. 14.95 (*978-1-932915-44-0(3)) Sandvik Innovations, LLC.

Gold, Kari Jenson. Skip-Counting by Twos, Threes, Fives & Tens. Date not set. (Early Math Big Bks.). (Illus.). 16p. (J). (ps-2). pap. 16.95 (978-1-58273-144-5(6)) Sundance/Newbridge Educational Publishing.

Golden Books Staff. Count along with Thomas. 2000. (Thomas the Tank Engine Ser.). (J). (ps-3). bds. 12.99 (978-0-307-71308-7(3) , Golden Bks.) Random Hse., Inc.

—Fun with Numbers. 2000. (Disney Ser.). (Illus.). 48p. (J). (ps-k). pap. 2.99 (978-0-307-20131-7(7) , 20131, Golden Bks.) Random Hse. Children's Bks.

—I Know Numbers. 1999. (Step Ahead Workbooks Ser.). (Illus.). 64p. (J). (ps). pap. 3.99 (978-0-307-03671-1(5) , 03671, Golden Bks.) Random Hse. Children's Bks.

—Numbers. 2001. 54p. (J). (ps-3). 2.99 (978-0-307-05040-3(8) , Golden Bks.) Random Hse. Children's Bks.

Gollub, Matthew. Ten Oni Drummers. Stone, Kazuko G., illus. 2000. (JPN & ENG.). 32p. (J). (ps-3). 15.95 (978-1-58430-011-3(6)) Lee & Low Bks., Inc.

Gonzalez, Xose Manuel & Thomassen, Hellen. Eleven Adventurous Ladies. 2002. (Illus.). 32p. (J). 14.95 (978-84-95730-21-3(9)) Kalandraka Catalunya, Edicions, S.L. ESP. *Dist:* Independent Pubs. Group.

Goodings, Christina. Around the Year: A Calendar & Counting Rhyme. Lewis, Jan, illus. 2001. 32p. (J). pap. 13.99 (978-0-7459-4451-7(5) , Lion) Lion Hudson plc GBR. *Dist:* Independent Pubs. Group.

Gordon, Bob. Giant See-a-Shape My Giant 123 Book. 2005. (Giant See a Shape Ser.). (Illus.). 44p. (ps-k). 9.95 (978-1-84610-023-9(2)) Make Believe Ideas GBR. *Dist:* Ingram Pub. Services.

Gordon, Maria & Gordon, Mike, illus. Cats Can't Count, 4 vols. 2000. (Kids Corner Literacy Stories: Vol. 4). (J). (978-0-7608-4270-6(1)) Sundance/Newbridge Educational Publishing.

—Dogs Can't Read, 4 vols. 2000. (Kids Corner Literacy Stories: Vol. 1). (J). (978-0-7608-4271-3(X)) Sundance/Newbridge Educational Publishing.

—Mice Can't Write, 4 vols. 2000. (Kids Corner Literacy Stories: Vol. 2). (J). (978-0-7608-4272-0(8)) Sundance/Newbridge Educational Publishing.

—Spiders Can't Spell, 4 vols. 2000. (Kids Corner Literacy Stories: Vol. 3). (J). (978-0-7608-4273-7(6)) Sundance/Newbridge Educational Publishing.

Gould, Ellen. The Blue Number Counting Book. Kelly, Cathy, illus. 13p. (J). (ps-2). pap. 6.00 (978-0-938017-01-1(2)) Learning Tools Co.

Gowan, Barbara. Desert Digits: An Arizona Number Book. Toddy, Irving, illus. 2006. 40p. (J). 17.95 (978-1-58536-162-5(3)) Sleeping Bear Pr.

Granstrom, Brita, illus. Many Hands Counting Book. 1999. (Reading Together Ser.). 24p. (J). (ps). pap. 3.99 (978-0-7636-0853-8(X)) Candlewick Pr.

Gravelle, Karen. Eight Little Legs. Davis, Nelle, illus. 2004. 20p. (J). (gr. k-2). pap. 4.95 (978-1-57874-042-0(8)) Kaeden Corp.

Greenstein, Elaine. One Child Dreaming. 2000. (Illus.). (J). (978-0-439-06303-6(5)) Itsy Bitsy Entertainment Co.

Gregoire, Caroline. Counting with Apollo. Gregoire, Caroline, illus. 2004. (Illus.). 32p. (J). 13.95 (978-1-929132-58-4(1)) Kane/Miller Bk. Pubs., Inc.

Grégoire, Caroline. Counting with Apollo. Grégoire, Caroline, illus. 2007. (Illus.). 32p. (J). pap. 7.95 (978-1-933605-42-5(1)) Kane/Miller Bk. Pubs., Inc.

Grodin, Elissa. Everyone Counts: A Citizen's Number Book. Juhasz, Victor, illus. rev. ed. 2006. 40p. (J). 17.95 (978-1-58536-295-0(6)) Sleeping Bear Pr.

—Yankee Doodle Numbers: A Connecticut Number Book. Brookfield, Maureen K., illus. rev. ed. 2007. 40p. (J). 17.95 (978-1-58536-175-5(5)) Sleeping Bear Pr.

Grosset and Dunlap Staff & Lamut, Sonja. At the Bakery. Commander, Bob, illus. 1999. (Sticker Stories Ser.). 16p. (J). (ps-1). pap. 4.99 (978-0-448-42080-6(5) , Grosset & Dunlap) Penguin Group (USA) Inc.

Group/McGraw-Hill, Wright. And the Winner Is: Level N, 6 vols. 128p. (gr. 3-6). 36.95 (978-0-322-05885-9(6)) Wright Group, The.

—How not to Catch the Moon: Level L, 6 vols. 128p. (gr. 3-6). 36.95 (978-0-322-05886-6(4)) Wright Group, The.

Grundon, Holly & Novelli, Joan. Smartpads Numbers & Counting: 40 Fun Games to Help Kids Master Numbers & Counting. 2005. 48p. pap. 7.99 (978-0-439-72081-6(8) , Teaching Resources) Scholastic, Inc.

Gunzi, Christiane. My Very First Look at Numbers. 2006. (My Very First Look at Ser.). (Illus.). 22p. (J). bds. 6.95 (978-1-58728-563-9(0) , Two Can Publishing) T&N Children's Publishing.

—Los Numeros. 2004. (Mi Primera Mirada. . . Ser.).Tr. of MVFLA Numbers. (SPA., Illus.). 24p. (ps-k). (J). pap. 5.95 (978-1-58728-414-4(6)); 9.95 (978-1-58728-423-6(5)) Quayside. (Creative Publishing International).

Gurth, Per-Henrik & Bellefontaine, Kim. Canada 123. 2008. 24p. (***978-1-55453-235-3(3)***) Kids Can Pr., Ltd.

Gurule, Jennifer. Look at Aunt Clare's Hair. Gurule, Jennifer, illus. ed. 2005. (Daddy's Collection). (J). pap. 11.50 (978-1-59134-033-1(0)) Maval Publishing, Inc.

Gustafson, Scott. Animal Orchestra: A Counting Book. Gustafson, Scott, illus. 2003. (Illus.). 32p. (J). (ps-k). 14.95 (978-0-86713-030-0(X) , 88070) Greenwich Workshop Pr.

Gutman, Anne & Hallensleben, Georg. Mommy Loves. 2005. (Illus.). 14p. (J). bds. 5.95 (978-0-8118-4616-5(4)) Chronicle Bks. LLC.

Guy, Ginger Foglesong. Fiesta. Moreno, Rene King, illus. 2007. 32p. (J). pap. 6.99 (***978-0-06-088226-6(3)*** , Rayo) HarperCollins Pubs.

Hague, Kathleen. Alphabears: An ABC Book. Hague, Michael, illus. rev. ed. 1999. 28p. (J). (ps-k). bds. 6.95 (978-0-8050-6208-3(4) , Holt, Henry & Co. Bks. For Young Readers) Holt, Henry & Co.

—Numbears: A Counting Book. Hague, Michael, illus. rev. ed. 1999. 28p. (J). (ps-k). bds. 6.95 (978-0-8050-6207-6(6) , Holt, Henry & Co. Bks. For Young Readers) Holt, Henry & Co.

—Ten Little Bears. Hague, Michael, illus. 1999. 24p. (J). (ps-k). 16.00 (978-0-688-16383-9(1)) HarperCollins Pubs.

Hale, Natalie. How Many Pizzas? 2002. (J). spiral bd. 9.95 (978-0-9702698-4-3(6)) Special Reads for Special Needs.

Hall, Kirsten. Birthday Beastie: All about Counting. Luedecke, Bev, illus. 2003. (Beastieville Ser.). 32p. (J). 19.50 (978-0-516-22891-4(9) , Children's Pr.) Scholastic Library Publishing.

Hall, Pam. The Odds Get Even. Chapman, Lynne, illus. 2005. 16p. (J). 12.95 (978-1-58117-216-4(8) , Intervisual/Piggy Toes) Dalmatian Pr.

Hammer, JoAnne. Find & Count with Molly Mouse. Simpson, D. J., illus. 1999. (J). 7.95 (978-1-56451-224-6(X) , Ideal School Supply) Schaffer, Frank Pubns.

Hammond, Franklin. Dix Petits Canards. (FRE., Illus.). (J). pap. 5.99 (978-0-590-74161-3(6)) Scholastic, Inc.

Handa's Hen. 2004. (PER & ENG.). (J). (978-1-84444-186-0(5)) Mantra Publishing, Ltd.

Hands-On Crafts for Kids. Count the Animals on the Farm. 2002. (Balloon Ser.). (Illus.). 10p. (J). bds. 4.95 (978-1-4027-0174-0(8) , Balloon Bks.) Sterling Publishing Co., Inc.

Harcourt School Publishers Staff. Counting My Friends. 3rd ed. 2002. (Trophies English Language Learners Ser.). (Illus.). (J). pap. 4.10 (978-0-15-327586-9(3)) Harcourt Schl. Pubs.

—Counting My Friends - Grade 1, 5 pack. 3rd ed. 2002. (Trophies English Language Learners Ser.). 20.10 (978-0-15-327620-0(7)) Harcourt Schl. Pubs.

Harder Tangvald, Christine. Ribbit! Roar! Quack, Quack, Quack! Conteh-Morgan, Jane, illus. 2000. (God's Noisy 1, 2, 3s Ser.). 24p. (J). (ps-k). bds. 7.99 (978-0-570-07097-9(X)) Concordia Publishing Hse.

Hargreaves, Roger. Mr. Bounce. Hargreaves, Roger, illus. rev. ed. 2000. (Mr. Men & Little Miss Ser.). (Illus.). 32p. (J). (gr. k-3). pap. 3.99 (978-0-8431-7562-2(1) , Price Stern Sloan) Penguin Group (USA) Inc.

Haring, Keith. Ten. 1998. (Illus.). 14p. (J). 6.95 (978-0-7868-0391-0(6)) Hyperion Bks. for Children.

Harley, Bill. Sitting down to Eat. 2000. (ps-2). lib. bdg. 15.25 (978-0-613-86915-7(X)) Tandem Library Bks.

Harper, Charise Mericle. Amy & Ivan: What's in That Truck? 2006. (Illus.). 24p. (J). 12.95 (978-1-58246-134-2(1) , Tricycle Pr.) Ten Speed Pr.

Harrast, Tracy. My Bible 1-2-3s. Munger, Nancy, illus. 1998. 32p. (J). (ps). 4.99 (978-0-310-91781-6(6)) Zondervan.

Harris, Marie. Primary Numbers: A New Hampshire Numbers Book. Holman, Karen, illus. 2004. 40p. (J). 16.95 (978-1-58536-192-2(5)) Sleeping Bear Pr.

Harris, Nancy. Sticky Fingers: Exploring the Number 5. 2008. (J). (***978-1-60044-639-9(6)***) Rourke Publishing, LLC.

Harris, Trudy. 100 Days of School. Johnson, Beth, illus. 1999. (Fun Early Math Concepts Ser.). 32p. (gr. k-3). lib. bdg. 22.90 (978-0-7613-1271-0(4) , Millbrook Pr.) Lerner Publishing Group.

—100 Days of School. 1999. (Math Is Fun! Ser.: 3). (Illus.). 32p. (J). (ps-3). pap. 7.95 (978-0-7613-1431-8(8) , Millbrook Pr.) Lerner Publishing Group.

—100 Days of School. 2000. (J). (978-0-606-20193-3(9)); 1999. lib. bdg. 15.25 (978-0-613-26480-8(0)) Tandem Library Bks.

Harte, May. 1, 2, 3 in My House. 2004. (Look-And-Learn Books). (Illus.). (J). lib. bdg. 7.95 (978-1-4042-2823-8(3) , PowerKids Pr.) Rosen Publishing Group, Inc., The.

Haskins, James & Benson, Kathleen. Count Your Way Through Afghanistan. Moore, Megan, illus. 2007. (Count Your Way Ser.). 24p. (J). 19.93 (978-1-57505-880-1(4) , Millbrook Pr.) Lerner Publishing Group.

—Count Your Way Through Egypt. Rama, Sue, illus. 2007. (Count Your Way Ser.). 24p. (J). 19.93 (978-1-57505-882-5(0) , Millbrook Pr.) Lerner Publishing Group.

—Count Your Way Through Kenya. Lévêque, Lyne, illus. 2007. (Count Your Way Ser.). 24p. (J). 19.93 (978-1-57505-884-9(7) , Millbrook Pr.) Lerner Publishing Group.

—Count Your Way Through South Africa. Neibert, Alissa, illus. 2007. (Count Your Way Ser.). 24p. (J). 19.93 (978-1-57505-883-2(9) , Millbrook Pr.) Lerner Publishing Group.

—Count Your Way Through Zimbabwe. Park, Janie Jaehyun, illus. 2007. (Count Your Way Ser.). 24p. (J). 19.93 (978-1-57505-885-6(5) , Millbrook Pr.) Lerner Publishing Group.

Haskins, James, et al. Count Your Way Through Iran. 2007. (Count Your Way Ser.). (Illus.). 24p. (J). 19.93 (978-1-57505-881-8(2) , Millbrook Pr.) Lerner Publishing Group.

Haugen, Janie. Coin-u-lator Worksheet Program. Von Dohlen, Happy, ed. 1998. (Illus.). 100p. (J). ring bd., wbk. ed. 29.95 (978-1-884074-61-5(8) , PCI 713) PCI Educational Publishing.

Hayes, Larry E. My Name Starts with S (Library Version) Anderson, Airlie, illus. 2004. (My Name Starts With Ser.). 32p. (J). lib. bdg. 12.95 (978-0-9725292-8-0(4)) Inspire Pubns.

Hays, Anna Jane. Kindergarten Countdown. Davick, Linda, illus. 2007. 24p. (J). (ps-1). lib. bdg. 11.99 (978-0-375-94252-5(1)); 8.99 (978-0-375-84252-8(7)) Random Hse. Children's Bks. (Knopf Bks. for Young Readers).

Head, Debby & Pollett, Libby. BBY Practice Pages: Choosing Coins. 2004. (Illus.). 93p. spiral bd. 29.00 (978-1-885775-18-4(0)) BBY Pubns.

Heath, Beverly C. Counting with Colors. Floyd, John, Jr., illus. 2005. (J). bds. 5.95 (***978-0-9752860-0-5(5)***) Our-Rainbow Pr., LLC.

Heck, Cathy. Zoophabet 123: Board Book with Plush Toy. rev. ed. 2007. 10p. bds. 12.99 (***978-1-4037-2553-0(5)***) Dalmatian Pr.

Helman, Andrea. 1, 2, 3 Moose: A Counting Book. Wolfe, Art, photos by. 2003. (Illus.). 32p. (J). pap., pap. 9.95 (978-1-57061-393-7(1)) Sasquatch Bks.

Henderson, Kathy. Counting Farm. Henderson, Kathy, illus. 1998. (Illus.). 16p. (J). (gr. k-ps). bds. 4.99 (978-0-7636-0460-8(7)) Candlewick Pr.

Hennessy, B. G. One Little, Two Little, Three Little Pilgrims. 2001. (gr. k-3). lib. bdg. 15.30 (978-0-613-85724-6(0)) Tandem Library Bks.

Henson, Laura J. & Grooms, Duffy. Ten Little Elvi. Gorissen, Dean, illus. 2004. 30p. (J). 12.95 (978-1-58246-124-3(4) , Tricycle Pr.) Ten Speed Pr.

Hiebert, Elfrieda H. & Juel, Connie. I Like to Count. (Little Book Practice Reader). (J). (978-0-8136-1952-1(1)) Modern Curriculum Pr.

Hierlmaier Nelson, Christine M. Green Yellow Go! Nat Knows Bananas. Hierlmaier, Joy, illus. 2004. 26p. (J). spiral bd. 14.95 (978-0-9759362-0-7(4)) Expressive Ink.

Highlights for Children Editorial Staff. The Timbertoes 123 Counting Book. Hunt, Judith, illus. 2003. 32p. (J). (ps up). 7.95 (978-1-56397-627-8(7)) Boyds Mills Pr.

Hill, Eric. Spot Can Count. Hill, Eric, illus. 2003. (Illus.). 24p. (J). pap. 6.99 (978-0-14-250121-4(2) , Puffin) Penguin Group (USA) Inc.

—Spot Can Count. 1999. (Spot Ser.). (Illus.). 32p. (J). (ps). 12.99 (978-0-399-23454-5(3) , Putnam Juvenile) Penguin Group (USA) Inc.

Hill, Eric. Spot's Colors, Shapes, & Numbers. Hill, Eric, illus. 2007. 18p. (J). (ps-k). bds. 12.99 (***978-0-399-24779-8(3)*** , Putnam Juvenile) Penguin Group (USA) Inc.

Hindley, Judy. Ten Bright Eyes. Bartlett, Alison, illus. 1998. 32p. (J). (ps-3). 14.95 (978-1-56145-173-9(8)) Peachtree Pubs., Ltd.

Hirsch, Esther. Counting on Friends. 2005. 13p. (J). 10.00 (978-1-4116-3620-0(1)) Lulu.com.

Hoban, Tana. Let's Count. 1999. (Illus.). 48p. (J). (ps-k). 16.89 (978-0-688-16009-8(3)) HarperCollins Pubs.

—Let's Count. Hoban, Tana, illus. 1999. (Illus.). 48p. (J). (ps-3). 16.99 (978-0-688-16008-1(5)) HarperCollins Pubs.

Hodgekiss, Jo. Libro de los Numeros (Book of Numbers) (SPA.). (J). 12.95 (978-84-243-2795-8(0)) Publicaciones Fher, S.A. ESP. *Dist:* AIMS International Bks., Inc.

Holliday, Patricia. A Is for Anjelina: an Introduction to ABC's And 123's. 2005. 29p. (J). 12.26 (978-1-4116-4471-7(9)) Lulu.com.

Holmes, Stephen. Number Farm. 2003. (J). bds. 5.98 (978-0-7525-8920-6(2)) Parragon, Inc.

Hop, L. L. C. Hooked on Pre-K: Numbers 0-20. 2006. 64p. 3.79 (978-1-931020-64-0(7)) HOP, LLC.

—Hooked on Pre-K Super Workbook. 2006. 320p. 12.99 (978-1-931020-72-5(8)) HOP, LLC.

Horacek, Petr. When the Moon Smiled. 2004. (Illus.). 32p. (J). (ps-k). 14.99 (978-0-7636-2209-1(5)) Candlewick Pr.

Horowitz, Dave. Five Little Gefiltes. Horowitz, Dave, illus. 2007. (Illus.). 32p. (J). (ps-2). 12.99 (978-0-399-24608-1(8) , Putnam Juvenile) Penguin Group (USA) Inc.

Houghton Mifflin Company Editors. Curious George Discovery Day. 2007. (Illus.). 14p. (J). (gr. k-ps). bds. 13.95 (***978-0-618-73761-1(8)***) Houghton Mifflin Co. Trade & Reference Div.

How Many? (English/Russian) 2005. (Photo Flap Bks.). (RUS., Illus.). 12p. (J). bds. 5.50 (978-1-932065-88-6(1)) Star Bright Bks., Inc.

How Many Are There? (Peek A Boo Pockets Ser.). 12p. (J). bds. (978-2-89393-979-7(1)) Phidal Publishing, Inc./ Editions Phidal, Inc.

How Many Are There? 2003. (Bear in the Big Blue House Ser.). (Illus.). 16p. (J). (ps-k). pap., act. bk. ed. 4.99 (978-1-57768-702-3(7)) School Specialty Publishing.

Hubbard, Patricia. Trick or Treat Countdown. Letzig, Michael, illus. 1999. 32p. (J). (gr. k-3). tchr. ed. 16.95 (978-0-8234-1367-6(5)) Holiday Hse., Inc.

Huck, Charlotte S. A Creepy Countdown. Smith, Jos. A., illus. 2002. (J). 14.43 (978-0-7587-4599-6(0)) Book Wholesalers, Inc.

—A Creepy Countdown. Smith, Jos. A., illus. 2000. 24p. (J). (ps-2). pap. 5.95 (978-0-688-17717-1(4) , Harper Trophy) HarperCollins Pubs.

Hudson, Cheryl Willis. Afro-Bets 1 2 3 Book. rev. ed. 2000. (Afro-Bets Ser.). (Illus.). 24p. (J). (ps-3). pap. 3.95 (978-0-940975-98-9(X)) Just Us Bks., Inc.

—1, 2, 3 Book. 2002. (ps-2). lib. bdg. 11.25 (978-0-613-84573-1(0)) Tandem Library Bks.

Huelin, Jodi. Countdown to Thanksgiving. Motoyama, Keiko, illus. 2002. 24p. (J). pap. 3.99 (978-0-8431-4880-0(2) , Price Stern Sloan) Penguin Group (USA) Inc.

—Countdown to Valentine's Day. Haskamp, Steve, illus. 2002. 24p. (J). pap. 3.99 (978-0-8431-4882-4(9) , Price Stern Sloan) Penguin Group (USA) Inc.

Hughes, Shirley. Alfie's 123. 2000. (Illus.). 32p. (J). (ps-k). 15.95 (978-0-688-17705-8(0)) HarperCollins Pubs.

—Alfie's Numbers. 2007. (Illus.). 32p. (J). pap. 8.95 (***978-0-09-940792-8(2)*** , Red Fox) Random Hse. Children's Bks. GBR. *Dist:* Independent Pubs. Group.

—Alfie's Numbers Board Bk. 2007. (Illus.). 12p. (J). bds. 7.95 (***978-0-370-32600-9(8)***) Transworld Publishers Ltd. GBR. *Dist:* Independent Pubs. Group.

Hunt, Angela Elwell. Pretzels by the Dozen: A Story with a Twist. 2002. (Illus.). 32p. (J). 14.99 (978-0-310-70173-6(2)) Zonderkidz.

Hunt, Darleen L. Ellen Elizabeth's Peanut Butter Jar: Counting. Komarck, Michael, illus. 2003. (Sherman's Math Corner Ser.). (J). (ps-3). (978-1-929591-11-4(X)) Reading Rock, Inc.

—Lyle & Mildred Are a Pair: Counting by 2's. Komarck, Michael, illus. 2003. (Sherman's Math Corner Ser.). (J). (ps-3). (978-1-929591-00-8(4)) Reading Rock, Inc.

—Spider Inventories: Count & Record. Komarck, Michael, illus. 2003. (Sherman's Math Corner Ser.). (J). (ps-3). (978-1-929591-05-3(5)) Reading Rock, Inc.

I Can Count. (First Bks.: No. S808-2). (Illus.). (J). (ps). pap. 3.95 (978-0-7214-5053-7(9) , Dutton Juvenile) Penguin Group (USA) Inc.

I Love a Parade. 2006. (Yellow Umbrella Math Ser.). 8,16p. (J). 6.50 (978-0-7368-1693-9(3)) Red Brick Learning.

Ideal Instructional Fair Staff. Find & Add with Billy Bug. 1999. (J). pap. 7.95 (978-1-56451-225-3(8) , Ideal School Supply) Schaffer, Frank Pubns.

Ideals Editors Staff. Baby Looney Tunes Count to 10. 2005. (Illus.). (J). bds. 7.95 (978-0-8249-6575-4(2)) Ideals Pubns.

Ikids. My Giant 123 Bath Book. Delice, Shelly Meredith, illus. 2005. (Soft Shapes Numbers Ser.). 2p. (J). (ps-17). 14.99 (978-1-58476-357-4(4)) Innovative Kids.

Imperato, Teresa. How Many Ducks in a Row? A Turn & Pop Book. Petrone, Valeria, illus. 2005. 10p. (J). bds. 5.95 (978-1-58117-278-2(8) , Intervisual/Piggy Toes) Dalmatian Pr.

—Ten Christmas Lights: Count the Lights from One to Ten! Parry, Jo, illus. 2005. 20p. (J). 10.95 (978-1-58117-321-5(0) , Intervisual/Piggy Toes) Dalmatian Pr.

Inkpen, Mick. Kipper's Book of Numbers. Inkpen, Mick, illus. 2002. (Kipper Ser.). (Illus.). (J). 13.19 (978-0-7587-6465-2(0)) Book Wholesalers, Inc.

Ipcar, Dahlov. Brown Cow Farm: A Counting Book. 2003. (gr. k-3). lib. bdg. 18.75 (978-0-613-77417-8(5)) Tandem Library Bks.

Irwin-Ayotte, Tracy. Bilingual Songs: English-French. 2003. 48p. (J). pap. 14.95 incl. audio (978-1-894262-77-4(8) , JMP F24K) Jordan Music Productions, Inc.

—Bilingual Songs Vol. 1: English-French. 2003. 48p. (J). pap. 14.95 incl. audio (978-1-894262-72-9(7) , JMP F23K) Jordan Music Productions, Inc.

Isaacson, Marlys J. Picture Me Learning the Numbers from 0 - 20: With Pictures & Rhymes to Make It Fun. 2001. 10.00 (978-0-9742951-9-0(1) , Picture Me...! Pubns.) Picture Me Reading!.

Isadora, Rachel. 123 Pop! Isadora, Rachel, illus. 2002. (Illus.). (J). 22.72 (978-0-7587-1887-7(X)) Book Wholesalers, Inc.

Itonya & Kaarn. Good Day Tamale, Good Day! A Ghanian Counting Book. 2001. (Illus.). 32p. (J). (ps-3). pap. 24.95 (978-1-891657-17-7(8) , MLS1000) Lift Every Voice.

Jackson, Woody. Counting Cows. 1999. (Illus.). 24p. (J). (ps). bds. 5.95 (978-0-15-202174-0(4) , Red Wagon Bks.) Harcourt Children's Bks.

Jacobs, Daniel. Count Your Chickens. 2003. (Yellow Umbrella Books for Early Readers). (Illus.). 17p. (J). 15.93 (978-0-7368-2918-2(0)); pap. (978-0-7368-2877-2(X)) Yellow Umbrella Pr.

Jane, Pamela. Fall Is Here! Counting 1 to 10. Haskamp, Steve, illus. 2005. 20p. (J). 8.99 (978-0-689-87470-3(7) , Little Simon) Simon & Schuster Children's Publishing.

—Monster Countdown: A Spooky Counting Book. Zarin-Ackerman, Nick, illus. 2001. (J). (ps-2). 14.95 (978-1-58653-857-6(8)) Mondo Publishing.

Jay, Alison. 1-2-3: A Child's First Counting Book. 2007. 40p. (J). (ps-3). 15.99 (***978-0-525-47836-2(1)*** , Dutton Juvenile) Penguin Group (USA) Inc.

Jocelyn, Marthe. One, Some, Many. Slaughter, Tom, illus. 2006. 16p. (J). (gr. k-k). bds. 7.95 (978-0-88776-789-0(3)) Candlewick Pr.

—One, Some, Many. Jocelyn, Marthe, ed. Slaughter, Tom, illus. 2004. 32p. (J). (gr. k-k). 11.95 (978-0-88776-675-6(7)) Tundra Bks., Inc./Livres Toundra, Inc. CAN. *Dist:* Random Hse., Inc.

Johnson, Cynthia. Twenty Wiggly Toes. Kaleda, Valri Blasi, illus. 1998. 16p. (J). (ps). pap. 5.95 (978-0-9655442-4-5(9)) Business Word, The.

Johnson, Julia. One Humpy Grumpy Camel. Styles, Emily, illus. 2003. 32p. (J). (gr. 3-6). 15.95 (978-1-900988-75-9(5)) Stacey International Pubs. GBR. *Dist:* Interlink Publishing Group, Inc.

Johnson, Stephen. City by Numbers. 2003. (Illus.). 32p. (J). (gr. k-3). pap. 6.99 (978-0-14-056636-9(8) , Puffin) Penguin Group (USA) Inc.

Johnson, Stephen T. City by Numbers. 2003. (gr. k-3). lib. bdg. 15.30 (978-0-613-67534-5(7)) Tandem Library Bks.

Johnson, Steve & Fancher, Lou. A Bug's Life: The Quest for the One Big Thing. 1998. (Illus.). 32p. (J). 11.49 (978-0-7868-5091-4(4)) Hyperion Pr.

—The Quest for the One Big Thing: A Counting Book. 1998. (Illus.). 32p. (J). (gr. k-4). 10.95 (978-0-7868-3198-2(7)) Disney Pr.

Jolin, Dominique. Deecee in Color. Perkes, Carolyn, tr. from FRE. Jolin, Dominique, illus. 2001. (Deecee Ser.). (Illus.). 14p. (J). bds. (978-1-894363-66-2(3)) Dominique & Friends.

Jones, Colleen. Counting on Friends. 2000. (Metro Math Readers Yellow Level Ser.). (Illus.). (J). (gr. 1-2). 3.75 (978-1-58120-403-2(5)) Metropolitan Teaching & Learning Co.

—How Many Now? 2000. (Metro Math Readers Yellow Level Ser.). (J). (gr. 12-2). 52.95 (978-1-58120-557-2(0)) Metropolitan Teaching & Learning Co.

—Vamos a Compartir Yellow Level: Metro Math Reader. 2000. (Metro Math Readers Yellow Level Ser.). (SPA., Illus.). (J). (gr. 1-2). 3.75 (978-1-58120-479-7(5)) Metropolitan Teaching & Learning Co.

Jordan, Denise M. Circus 123. (Circus Ser.). 24p. (J). 2003. (Illus.). lib. bdg. (978-1-58810-545-5(8)); 2002. pap. 5.25 (978-1-58810-753-4(1) , 91401) Heinemann Library.

Julian, Alison, illus. The 12 Days of Christmas. 2005. (J). (***978-1-74157-281-0(9)***) Hinkler Bks. Pty, Ltd.

Kaminski, Linda. Aprende a Contar Con el Conde. 2006. (Sesame Street Ser.). (SPA & ENG.). 48p. (J). pap., wbk. ed. 3.95 (***978-1-59545-069-2(6)***) Learning Horizons, Inc.

Katz, Karen. Counting Christmas. Katz, Karen, illus. 2003. (Illus.). 32p. (J). 14.95 (978-0-689-84925-1(7) , McElderry, Margaret K.) Simon & Schuster Children's Publishing.

—Counting Kisses. Katz, Karen, illus. 2001. (Kiss & Read Ser.). (Illus.). 32p. (J). (ps-k). 14.95 (978-0-689-83470-7(5) , McElderry, Margaret K.) Simon & Schuster Children's Publishing.

—Counting Kisses: A Kiss & Read Book. Katz, Karen, illus. 2003. (Kiss & Read Ser.). (Illus.). 32p. (J). bds. 7.99 (978-0-689-85658-7(X) , Little Simon) Simon & Schuster Children's Publishing.

—Daddy Hugs 1 2 3. Katz, Karen, illus. 2005. (Illus.). 32p. (J). 14.99 (978-0-689-87771-1(4) , McElderry, Margaret K.) Simon & Schuster Children's Publishing.

—Ten Tiny Tickles. 2005. (Illus.). 32p. (J). 14.95 (978-0-689-85976-2(7) , McElderry, Margaret K.) Simon & Schuster Children's Publishing.

Keats, Ezra Jack. One Red Sun: A Counting Book. Keats, Ezra Jack, illus. 1999. (Illus.). 14p. (J). (ps-2). bds. 5.99 (978-0-670-88478-0(2) , Viking Juvenile) Penguin Group (USA) Inc.

Keiki Counting. 2000. (J). bds. 3.99 (978-0-89610-438-9(9)) Island Heritage Publishing.

Keiser, Melissa. My Airplane Book-Counting. 2005. (Board Book Ser.). (Illus.). 12p. bds. 6.95 (978-1-59373-041-3(1)) Bunker Hill Publishing, Inc.

Keller, Laurie S. Grandpa Gazillion's Number Yard. 2005. (Illus.). 32p. (J). (ps-ps). 16.95 (978-0-8050-6282-3(3) , Holt, Henry & Co. Bks. For Young Readers) Holt, Henry & Co.

Kellogg, Steven. Give the Dog a Bone. 2000. (Illus.). 33p. (J). (gr. k-3). 16.50 (978-1-58717-002-7(7) , SeaStar Bks.) Chronicle Bks. LLC.

Kelly, Lorraine. Mary Ellen & Cameron Play Hopscotch. 2000. pap. 8.99 (978-0-233-99921-0(3)) Andre Deutsch GBR. *Dist:* Trafalgar Square Publishing.

Kelly, Mij. One More Sheep. Ayto, Russell, illus. 2006. 30p. (J). 16.95 (978-1-56145-378-8(1) , Peachtree Junior) Peachtree Pubs., Ltd.

Kennedy, Anne Vittur. One Shining Star: A Christmas Counting Book. 2006. (Illus.). 22p. (J). 6.99 (978-0-310-71029-5(4)) Zonderkidz.

Kent, Lorna, illus. Baby's First Counting Book. 2004. 12p. (J). bds. 7.99 (978-1-85854-616-2(8)) Brimax Books Ltd. GBR. *Dist:* Byeway Bks.

Kido, Yukiko, illus. I'm Going to Read (Level 3): A Dozen Dozens. 2007. (I'm Going to Read Ser.). 32p. (J). pap. 3.95 (978-1-4027-4246-0(0)) Sterling Publishing Co., Inc.

Kids Can Press Staff, Press Can. Numbers. 2004. (Kids Can Learn with Franklin Ser.). (Illus.). 32p. (J). (gr. k-3). (978-1-55337-591-3(2)) Kids Can Pr., Ltd.

Kilgras, Heidi. Cinderella's Countdown to the Ball. Harchy, Atelier Philippe, illus. 2002. 32p. (J). (ps-1). pap. 3.99 (978-0-7364-1225-4(5) , RH/Disney) Random Hse. Children's Bks.

—Cinderella's Countdown to the Ball. 2002. (gr. k-3). lib. bdg. 11.80 (978-0-613-73603-9(6)) Tandem Library Bks.

C
D

Kittler, Robert. Can't Sleep, Count Sheep. Jackson, Nick, illus. 1998. 123p. (gr. 4-7). pap. 9.95 (978-0-9668622-0-1(1)) Count Sheep Publishing.

Klein, Adria. Counting Down. 2000. (Metro Math Readers Yellow Level Ser.). (J). (gr. 1-2). 49.95 (978-1-58830-108-6(7)) Metropolitan Teaching & Learning Co.

—Dentro y fuera de la caja: Metro Math Readers Yellow Level. 2000. (Metro Math Readers Yellow Level Ser.). (J). (gr. 1-2). 3.75 (978-1-58120-480-3(9)) Metropolitan Teaching & Learning Co.

—Los Numeros 1 - 2000. (Metro Math Readers Red Level Ser.). (J). (gr. k-1). 49.95 (978-1-58830-521-3(X)) Metropolitan Teaching & Learning Co.

—The Numbers 1 - 2000. (Metro Math Readers Red Level Ser.). (J). (gr. k-1). 52.95 (978-1-58120-551-0(1)) Metropolitan Teaching & Learning Co.

—Skip Counting. 2000. (Metro Math Readers Yellow Level Ser.). (J). (gr. 1-2). 49.95 (978-1-58830-103-1(6)) Metropolitan Teaching & Learning Co.

Knight, Kathryn. Zoophabet 123. Heck, Cathy, illus. 2006. 20p. bds. 5.99 (978-1-4037-1988-1(8)) Dalmatian Pr.

Knight, Paula, illus. A Little Box of Learning. 2007. 40p. (J). (ps). bds. 6.99 (978-0-7641-9303-3(1)) Barron's Educational Series, Inc.

Know your Numbers. (Illus.). (C). (gr. k-2). 271.20 (978-1-4048-0993-2(7)) Picture Window Bks.

Knox, Barbara. Baby Animals 1, 2, 3: A Counting Book of Animal Offspring. 2003. (A+ Counting Books). (Illus.). 32p. (J). (gr. k-1). lib. bdg. 22.60 (978-0-7368-1675-5(5) , Aplus Bks.) Capstone Pr., Inc.

—Bajo Las Olas 1, 2, 3: Vamos a Contar la Vida Marina. 2008. (SPA & ENG.). (J). ***(978-1-4296-1199-2(5))*** Capstone Pr., Inc.

Knox, Barbara. Under the Sea 1, 2, 3: An Ocean Life Counting Book. 2003. (A+ Counting Books). (Illus.). 32p. (J). (gr. k-1). lib. bdg. 22.60 (978-0-7368-1677-9(1) , Aplus Bks.) Capstone Pr., Inc.

Koffsky, Ann D. My Jewish Counting Book. 1998. (HEB & ENG., Illus.). 10p. (J). (ps-k). spiral bd. 5.99 (978-0-914080-12-1(1)) Shulsinger Sales, Inc.

Koller, Jackie French. Seven Spunky Monkeys. Munsinger, Lynn M., illus. 2005. 32p. (J). (ps-ps). 16.00 (978-0-15-202519-9(7)) Harcourt Trade Pubs.

Kompelien, Tracy. Can You Count More Than Before? (Math Made Fun Ser.). (Illus.). 24p. (J). 2007. 19.93 (978-1-59928-511-5(8)); 2006. pap. (978-1-59928-512-2(6)) ABDO Publishing Co.

—I Know about Money, It Is So Funny! 2006. (Math Made Fun Ser.). (Illus.). 24p. (J). (978-1-59928-528-3(2)) ABDO Publishing Co.

—Skip Count by 10, Let's Do It Again. 2007. (Math Made Fun Ser.). (Illus.). 24p. (J). 19.93 (978-1-59928-541-2(X) , SandCastle) ABDO Publishing Co.

—Skip Count by 10, Let's Do It Again! 2006. (Math Made Fun Ser.). (Illus.). 24p. (J). pap. (978-1-59928-542-9(8)) ABDO Publishing Co.

—Skip Count by 2, Now Can You? (Math Made Fun Ser.). (Illus.). 24p. (J). 2007. 19.93 (978-1-59928-545-0(2) , SandCastle); 2006. pap. (978-1-59928-546-7(0)) ABDO Publishing Co.

—Skip Count by 5, It's No Jive. 2007. (Math Made Fun Ser.). (Illus.). 24p. (J). 19.93 (978-1-59928-543-6(6) , SandCastle) ABDO Publishing Co.

—Skip Count by 5, It's No Jive! 2006. (Math Made Fun Ser.). (Illus.). 24p. (J). pap. (978-1-59928-544-3(4)) ABDO Publishing Co.

—1, 2, 3— It's Easy for Me! (Math Made Fun Ser.). (Illus.). 24p. (J). 2007. 19.93 (978-1-59928-505-4(3)); 2006. pap. (978-1-59928-506-1(1)) ABDO Publishing Co.

Kono, Erin Eitter, illus. The Twelve Days of Christmas in Wisconsin. 2007. 32p. (J). (gr. k up). 9.95 ***(978-1-4027-3815-9(3))*** Sterling Publishing Co., Inc.

Koomen, Michele. Numbers: Counting It Up. 2001. (Exploring Math Ser.). (Illus.). 24p. (J). (gr. 1-2). lib. bdg. 18.60 (978-0-7368-0818-7(3) , Bridgestone Bks.) Capstone Pr., Inc.

Koontz, Robin. Up All Night Counting. Koontz, Robin, illus. 2006. (Illus.). 14p. (J). 10.95 (978-1-4169-0706-0(8) , Little Simon) Simon & Schuster Children's Publishing.

Kramer, Alan. Counting at the Zoo. 2004. (Reader's Theater Ser.). (J). pap. 22.00 (978-1-4108-0692-5(8)) Benchmark Education Co.

Krebs, Laurie. We All Went on Safari: A Counting Journey Through Tanzania. Cairns, Julia, illus. 2003. (ENG & SWA.). 32p. (J). (gr. k-3). 15.99 (978-1-84148-478-5(4)) Barefoot Bks., Inc.

Krishnaswami, Uma. Hooray! 100 Days. 2006. (Early Explorers Ser.). (J). 34.00 ***(978-1-4108-6114-6(7))*** Benchmark Education Co.

Kroll, Virginia. Uno, Dos, Tres, Posada! Let's Celebrate Christmas. Lopez, Loretta, illus. 2006. 32p. (J). (ps). 15.99 (978-0-670-05932-4(3) , Viking Adult) Penguin Group (USA) Inc.

Krulik, Nancy E. Playing with Numbers: A Learning-to-Write Book. Baroux, illus. 2004. (My Little Chalkboard Ser.). 16p. (J). pap. 12.95 (978-0-7624-1436-9(7) , Running Pr. Kids) Running Pr. Bk. Pubs.

Kumon Publishing, creator. Numbers 1-30 Write & Wipe! 2006. 32p. (J). 9.95 (978-1-933241-08-1(X)) Kumon Publishing North America, Inc.

Kunhardt, Katharine. Let's Count the Puppies. 2004. (Illus.). 32p. (J). (ps-1). 13.89 (978-0-06-054337-2(X)) HarperCollins Pubs.

Kusugak, Michael Arvaarluk. My Arctic 1, 2, 3. Krykorka, Vladyana Langer, illus. 2005. 24p. (J). (ps-1). pap. 7.95 (978-1-55037-504-6(0)) Annick Pr., Ltd. CAN. *Dist:* Firefly Bks., Ltd.

Ladybird Books Staff. My Counting Book. (Early Readers Ser.: No. S8711-6). (Illus.). 24p. (J). (ps-2). 3.95 (978-0-7214-5146-6(2) , Dutton Juvenile) Penguin Group (USA) Inc.

—1,2,3. 1998. (First Steps Ser.). (Illus.). 32p. (J). 2.50 (978-0-7214-1875-9(9) , Dutton Juvenile) Penguin Group (USA) Inc.

Lakeshore Learning Materials Staff, contrib. by. Counting Mice Activity Kit. 2000. (J). pap. 29.95 (978-1-929255-53-5(5)) Lakeshore Learning Materials.

—Counting Pairs Activity Kit. 2000. (J). pap. 29.95 (978-1-929255-55-9(1)) Lakeshore Learning Materials.

Lalley, Kristine. How Many Legs? 2006. (Rosen Publishing Group's Reading Room Collection). (Illus.). 16p. (J). lib. bdg. (978-1-4042-3336-2(9) , PowerKids Pr.) Rosen Publishing Group, Inc., The.

Langham, Tony. Creepy Crawly Calypso. Harter, Debbie, illus. 2004. 32p. (J). 16.99 incl. audio compact disk (978-1-84148-699-4(X)) Barefoot Bks., Inc.

Langham, Tony & Harter, Debbie. Creepy Crawly Calypso. 2006. 32p. pap. 9.99 incl. cd-rom (978-1-902283-46-3(5)) Barefoot Bks., Inc.

Langstaff, John. Over in the Meadow. Rojankovsky, Feodor, illus. 2002. (J). 14.04 (978-0-7587-3352-8(6)) Book Wholesalers, Inc.

LaPenta, Marilyn. 1 2 3 in the Sea: Including Abacus. Canals, Sonia, illus. 1999. 12p. (J). (ps-1). 9.95 (978-0-7641-7256-4(5)) Barron's Educational Series, Inc.

Larousse Mexico Staff, ed. Contar Preescolar Nivel A. 2005. (Yo quiero Saber Ser.). (SPA.). 23p. (ps-k). pap. 3.95 (978-970-22-0910-2(2)) Larousse, Ediciones, S. A. de C. V. MEX. *Dist:* Houghton Mifflin Co. Trade & Reference Div.

—Contar Preescolar Nivel B. 2005. (Yo quiero Saber Ser.). (SPA.). 32p. (ps-k). pap. 3.95 (978-970-22-0913-3(7)) Larousse, Ediciones, S. A. de C. V. MEX. *Dist:* Houghton Mifflin Co. Trade & Reference Div.

—Contar Preescolar Nivel C. 2005. (Yo quiero Saber Ser.). (SPA.). 32p. (ps-k). pap. 3.95 (978-970-22-0916-4(1)) Larousse, Ediciones, S. A. de C. V. MEX. *Dist:* Houghton Mifflin Co. Trade & Reference Div.

Lavie, A. Apprender a Contar. 2000. Tr. of Learn to Count. (SPA.). (J). 5.95 (978-980-6053-27-4(3)) Litexsa Venezolana S.A. VEN. *Dist:* AIMS International Bks., Inc.

Leacock, Elspeth. Antes Habia Doce: Metro Math Readers Yellow Level. 2000. (Metro Math Readers Yellow Level Ser.). (J). (gr. 1-2). 3.75 (978-1-58120-469-8(8)) Metropolitan Teaching & Learning Co.

LeapFrog Counting Wipe Off. 2007. (J). 4.99 ***(978-1-59545-139-2(0))*** Learning Horizons, Inc.

LeapFrog Staff. Imagination Desk Counting Day at the Beach. 2003. (Illus.). 9.99 (978-1-59319-025-5(5)) LeapFrog Enterprises, Inc.

—Lots & Lots of Honeypots. 2003. (Illus.). (J). spiral bd. 14.99 (978-1-59319-002-6(6)) LeapFrog Enterprises, Inc.

LeapFrog Staff, compiled by. My First LeapPad: Richard Scarry ABC. 2001. (J). (ps-2). spiral bd. 12.99 (978-1-58605-217-1(9)) LeapFrog Enterprises, Inc.

Learn about Counting with the Count. 2005. (Illus.). 48p. (J). (ps-ps). pap. 3.95 (978-1-58610-908-0(1)) Learning Horizons, Inc.

Learn to Count. 2004. (Alphabet & Counting Ser.). 12p. (J). bds. 5.99 (978-1-85997-810-8(X)) Byeway Bks.

Learn to Count. 1999. (Illus.). (J). (978-1-56156-834-5(1)) Kidsbooks, Inc.

Learning Company Books Staff, ed. Reader Rabbit Fun with Crayons: 1-2-3. 2004. (Illus.). 32p. (J). pap. 4.99 (978-0-7630-7736-5(4)) Learning Co. Bks.

Learning Numbers. (Learning Ser.). 22p. (J). bds. (978-2-7643-0110-4(3)) Phidal Publishing, Inc./Editions Phidal, Inc.

Learning Numbers. 2003. (Kermit the Frog & Friends Ser.). (Illus.). 16p. (J). (ps-k). pap., act. bk. ed. 4.99 (978-1-57768-705-4(1)) School Specialty Publishing.

Learning Wrap Staff. Skip Counting Video & Cassette. 2004. 24.95 (978-0-943343-32-7(1)) Learning Wrap-Ups.

Lebron, Karen. My Big Book of Numbers. Lonsdale, Mary, illus. 2004. 48p. (J). 5.99 (978-1-85854-317-8(7)) Brimax Books Ltd. GBR. *Dist:* Byeway Bks.

Lee, Huy Voun. 1, 2, 3, Go! rev. ed. 2001. (ENG & CHI., Illus.). 32p. (J). (ps-4). 17.95 (978-0-8050-6205-2(X) , Holt, Henry & Co. Bks. For Young Readers) Holt, Henry & Co.

Leffingwell, Richard. Adding & Counting On. 2006. (J). pap. (978-1-4034-8165-8(2)); (Illus.). 24p. 21.36 (978-1-4034-8155-9(5)) Steck-Vaughn.

Leffingwell, Richard. Sumar y Contar Hacia Adelante. 2006. (ENG & SPA.). (J). ***(978-1-4034-9186-2(0));*** pap. ***(978-1-4034-9191-6(7))*** Heinemann Library.

Leroe, Ellen. Princess Fun: Count 10 to 1. Takahashi, Hideko, illus. 2005. 12p. (J). 5.99 (978-0-689-86895-5(2) , Little Simon) Simon & Schuster Children's Publishing.

Lessac, Frane. Island Counting 1 2 3. Lessac, Frane, illus. 2007. (Illus.). 24p. (J). (gr. k-ps). bds. 6.99 ***(978-0-7636-3518-3(9))*** Candlewick Pr.

Lesser, Carolyn. Spots: Counting Creatures from Sky to Sea. Regan, Laura, illus. 1999. 32p. (YA). (ps-3). 16.00 (978-0-15-200666-2(4)) Harcourt Children's Bks.

Lets Skip-Count. 2002. (J). pap. (978-0-7398-5945-2(5)) Steck-Vaughn.

Letters & Numbers. (Early Learning Ser.). (J). incl. audio NewSound, LLC.

Letters & Numbers. 2004. 12.99 incl. audio compact disk (978-1-57583-300-2(X)) Twin Sisters Productions, LLC.

Letters/Numbers, 4 bks., Set. Incl. Let's Add to Ten, Again & Again! Miller, Amanda. Michael, Joan J., illus. Levin, James, photos by. lib. bdg. 18.00 (978-0-531-14869-3(6)); Let's Count Critters, 1-20. Madden, Caolan. Vangsgard, Amy, illus. lib. bdg. 18.00 (978-0-531-14870-9(X)); Let's Have Fun with Alphabet Riddles. Madden, Caolan. 18.00 ***(978-0-531-14868-6(8));*** Let's Make Letters : ABC Kids. Behrens, Janice. 18.00 ***(978-0-531-14867-9(X));*** (Illus.). 32p. (J). (ps-k). (Let's Find Out Early Learning Bks.). 2007. 72.00 ***(978-0-531-17599-6(5)*** , Children's Pr.) Scholastic Library Publishing.

Lewis, Paul Owen. P Bear's New Year's Party: A Counting Book. 1999. (ps-2). lib. bdg. 15.25 (978-0-613-86794-8(7)) Tandem Library Bks.

Lieurance, Suzanne. Pennies. Payne, Tom, illus. (Rookie Reader Skill Set Ser.). (J). 2003. 32p. (gr. k-2). pap. 4.95 (978-0-516-27818-6(5)); 2002. 31p. (gr. 1-2). 19.50 (978-0-516-22286-8(4)) Scholastic Library Publishing. (Children's Pr.).

Lisi, Branden. Count on the Farm. Lisi, Margaret, illus. 2006. (J). lib. bdg. 15.95 (978-0-9771472-0-5(7)) Count On Learning.

Litchfield, J. Very First Numbers. 2004. (First Words Board Bks.). 10p. (J). 4.95 (978-0-7945-0095-5(1) , Usborne) EDC Publishing.

Litchfield, Jo. 123 (Dime Lo Que Ves) 2007. 22p. (J). bds. 14.99 ***(978-0-7460-8354-3(8)*** , Usborne) EDC Publishing.

Litchfield, Jo & Jones, Stephanie, illus. First 123 Look & Say. 2006. 22p. (J). bds. 14.95 (978-0-7945-1219-4(4) , Usborne) EDC Publishing.

Little Golden Books Staff & Moore, Lilian. My First Counting Book. 2001. (Little Golden Bks.). (Illus.). 24p. (J). (gr. k-k). 2.99 (978-0-307-02067-3(3) , 98771, Golden Bks.) Random Hse. Children's Bks.

Lluch, Alex A. I Like to Learn: Alphabet, Numbers, Colors, & Opposites. 2008. 19.95 ***(978-1-887169-95-0(4))*** Wedding Solutions Publishing, Inc.

Lobel, Anita. One Lighthouse, One Moon. Lobel, Anita, illus. (Illus.). 48p. (J). 2002. pap. 6.99 (978-0-06-000537-5(8) , Harper Trophy); 2000. 16.99 (978-0-688-15539-1(1)) HarperCollins Pubs.

—One Lighthouse, One Moon. 2002. (gr. k-3). lib. bdg. 15.25 (978-0-613-84613-4(3)) Tandem Library Bks.

Lodge, Bernard. How Scary! Who Scares Who from One to Ten. 2001. (Illus.). 32p. (J). (gr. k-ps). tchr. ed. 15.00 (978-0-618-11547-1(1) , Walter Lorraine) Houghton Mifflin Co. Trade & Reference Div.

Lombardi, Kristine. A Day at the Zoo: Learning Numbers. 2006. (Show & Tell Ser.). 12p. (J). pap. 12.99 (978-0-7944-0906-7(7)) Reader's Digest Assn., Inc., The.

London, Jonathan. Count the Ways, Little Bear. 2003. (gr. k-3). lib. bdg. 15.30 (978-0-613-82997-7(2)) Tandem Library Bks.

—Count the Ways, Little Brown Bear. Moore, Margie, illus. 2004. 32p. (J). (ps-3). lib. bdg. 14.19 (978-0-606-30362-0(6)) Tandem Library Bks.

Long, Lynette. One Dollar: My First Book about Money. 1998. (Illus.). 32p. (J). (ps-2). bds. 8.95 (978-0-7641-0319-3(9)); bds. 13.95 (978-0-7641-7132-1(1)) Barron's Educational Series, Inc.

Look & Count. 2005. (J). pap. 3.99 (978-1-933200-19-4(7)) Family Bks. at Home.

Lorenz Books Staff. Sums. 2000. (Sticker Fun Ser.). (Illus.). 16p. (ps-k). pap. 4.95 (978-0-7548-0436-9(4)) Anness Publishing GBR. *Dist:* National Bk. Network.

Lorenz Editors. Count to 100: With over 50 Reusable Stickers. 2001. (Sticker Fun Ser.). (Illus.). 16p. (gr. k up). pap. 2.95 (978-0-7548-0795-7(9) , Lorenz Bks.) Anness Publishing, Inc.

Love, Maryann Cusimano. HOLIducks. 2007. 16p. (J). (ps-k). bds. 6.99 ***(978-0-8431-2683-9(3)*** , Price Stern Sloan) Penguin Group (USA) Inc.

Lucado, Max. Numbers. 2004. (Buginnings Ser.). (Illus.). 24p. (J). 9.99 (978-1-4003-0418-9(0)) Nelson, Thomas Inc.

Lyon, George Ella & Dorling Kindersley Publishing Staff. Counting on the Woods. Olson, Ann W., illus. 1998. 32p. (J). (ps-3). 15.99 (978-0-7894-2480-8(0)) Dorling Kindersley Publishing, Inc.

Maccarone, Grace. Monster Math. Hartelius, Margaret A., illus. 2002. (J). 11.91 (978-0-7587-1457-2(2)) Book Wholesalers, Inc.

Maccarone, Grace, ed. Numbers & Counting. 2006. (Carry Wipe Clean Wheel Bks.). (Illus.). 26p. (J). 7.99 (978-0-439-85365-1(6) , Cartwheel Bks.) Scholastic, Inc.

Maccarone, Grace & Burns, Marilyn. Monster Money. 1998. (Hello Reader! Math Ser.: Level 1). (Illus.). 32p. (J). (ps-3). pap. 3.99 (978-0-590-12007-4(7)) Scholastic, Inc.

Maccarone, Grace, et al. Monster Math Picnic. Hartelius, Margaret A., illus. 1998. (Hello Reader! Math Ser.). 32p. (J). (ps-4). pap. 3.99 (978-0-590-37127-8(4)) Scholastic, Inc.

MacCarthy, Patricia. Ocean Parade: A Counting Book. MacCarthy, Patricia, illus. 2005. (Illus.). 24p. (J). (ps-3). reprint ed. 12.00 (978-0-7567-8983-1(4)) DIANE Publishing Co.

MacDonald, Suse. Fish, Swish! Splash, Dash! Counting Round & Round. MacDonald, Suse, illus. 2007. 30p. (J). (ps-2). 8.99 ***(978-1-4169-3605-3(X)*** , Little Simon) Simon & Schuster Children's Publishing.

MacKall, Dandi Daley. Cloud Counting. Newton, Jill, illus. 2004. (Imagination Ser.). 12p. 6.99 (978-0-8066-4383-0(8) , Augsburg Bks.) Augsburg Fortress, Pubs.

—One Lost Sheep. Halsey, Megan, illus. 2002. (First Things First Ser.). 12p. (ps-k). 6.99 (978-0-8066-4381-6(1) , Augsburg Bks.) Augsburg Fortress, Pubs.

Madden, Caolan. Let's Count Critters, 1-20. Vangsgard, Amy, illus. 2007. (Let's Find Out Early Learning Bks.). 32p. (J). (ps-k). lib. bdg. 18.00 (978-0-531-14870-9(X) , Children's Pr.) Scholastic Library Publishing.

Mahan, Ben. God's World Letters & Numbers. 1999. (Illus.). 48p. (J). (ps-2). 2.99 (978-0-7847-0757-9(X) , Bean Sprouts) Standard Publishing.

Make Believe Ideas Staff. Baby Fun 123. 2005. (Illus.). 10p. (ps-ps). per. (978-1-905051-18-2(2)) Make Believe Ideas.

Mallat, Kathy. Seven Stars More! Mallat, Kathy, illus. 1998. (Illus.). 24p. (J). (ps-1). 14.95 (978-0-8027-8675-3(8)); lib. bdg. 15.85 (978-0-8027-8676-0(6)) Walker & Co.

Marks, Jenny L. Sorting Money. 2007. (Sorting Ser.). (Illus.). 32p. (J). (gr. k-3). lib. bdg. 23.93 (978-0-7368-6738-2(4)) Capstone Pr., Inc.

Marsh, T. J. & Ward, Jennifer. Way Out in the Desert. Spengler, Kenneth J., illus. 2002. 20p. (J). bds. 6.95 (978-0-87358-802-7(9)); 1999. 32p. 15.95 (978-0-87358-687-0(5)) Northland Publishing. (Rising Moon Bks. for Young Readers).

Marsh, Valerie. Storytelling with Shapes & Numbers. 1999. (Illus.). 86p. (J). (ps-1). pap. 15.95 (978-1-57950-024-5(2) , Upstart Bks.) Highsmith Inc.

Martin, Bill, Jr. & Sampson, Michael. Chicka Chicka 1, 2, 3. Ehlert, Lois, illus. 2005. (J). (ps-3). 24.95 incl. audio (978-0-439-76675-3(3) , WHRA669); 29.95 incl. audio compact disk (978-0-439-76677-7(X) , WHCD669) Weston Woods Studios, Inc.

Martin, Bill, Jr. & Sampson, Michael R. Chicka Chicka 1, 2, 3. Ehlert, Lois, illus. 2004. 40p. (J). 16.99 (978-0-689-85881-9(7)) Simon & Schuster Children's Publishing.

Marzollo, Jean. Ten Little Christmas Presents. 2008. (J). ***(978-0-545-02791-5(8))*** Scholastic, Inc.

Masaurel, Claire. Ten Dogs in the Window. 2000. (978-0-606-18323-9(X)) Tandem Library Bks.

Masurel, Claire. Ten Dogs in the Window: A Countdown Book. Paparone, Pamela, illus. 2000. 32p. (J). (ps-1). pap. 6.95 (978-0-7358-1301-4(9)) North-South Bks., Inc.

Matching & Counting, Set A. 2002. (J). (gr. k-2). act. bk. ed. 6.99 (978-1-56451-413-4(7)) School Specialty Publishing.

Matthews/Worsley, Bill/Belinda. Ben's Counting Walk. 2005. (Illus.). 32p. (J). lib. bdg. 9.00 ***(978-1-4242-0877-7(7))*** Fitzgerald Bks.

McCue, Dick. Bunny's Numbers. McCue, Lisa, illus. 2000. 14p. (J). (ps-3). bds. 4.99 (978-0-689-83086-0(6) , Little Simon) Simon & Schuster Children's Publishing.

McCully, Emily Arnold & Schertle, Alice. 1, 2, I Love You. 2004. (Illus.). 32p. (J). (ps-k). 16.95 (978-0-8118-3518-3(9)) Chronicle Bks. LLC.

McDonald, Jill. Hand Puppet Board Book (Vamos A Contar) Un Libro de Carton con Titeres. 2006. (Let's Count Ser.). 6p. (J). bds. 12.99 (978-0-439-85118-3(1) , Scholastic en Espanol) Scholastic, Inc.

—Let's Count! A Hand-Puppet Board Book. Schutz, Samantha, ed. McDonald, Jill, illus. 2006. 6p. (J). bds. 12.99 (978-0-439-80283-3(0)) Scholastic, Inc.

McDonald, Ronald L. Over in the Meadow: A Counting Rhyme. Voce, Louise, ed. Voce, Louise, illus. 1999. (Reading Together Ser.). 32p. (J). (ps). pap. 3.99 (978-0-7636-0852-1(1)) Candlewick Pr.

McFarlane, Sheryl. A Pod of Orcas: A Seaside Counting Book. Wakelin, Kirsti, illus. 2006. 28p. (J). pap. 7.95 (978-1-55041-722-7(3)) Fitzhenry & Whiteside, Ltd. CAN. *Dist:* F & W Pubns., Inc.

McFarlane, Sheryl & Hartmann, Barbara. A Pod of Orcas: A Seaside Counting Book. Wakelin, Kirsti Anne, illus. 2002. 24p. (J). (978-1-55041-681-7(2)) Fitzhenry & Whiteside, Ltd.

McGehee, Claudia. A Woodland Counting Book. 2006. (Bur Oak Book Ser.). (Illus.). 32p. (J). 17.95 (978-0-87745-989-7(4)) Univ. of Iowa Pr.

McGrath, Barbara Barbieri. The Baseball Counting Book. Shaw, Brian, illus. 1999. 32p. (J). (ps-3). 15.95 (978-0-88106-332-5(0)); pap. 6.95 (978-0-88106-333-2(9)) Charlesbridge Publishing, Inc.

—The Baseball Counting Book. Shaw, Brian, illus. 1999. (J). (ps-ps). lib. bdg. 15.25 (978-0-613-16324-8(9)) Tandem Library Bks.

—The Cheerios Counting Book. Bolster, Rob & Mazzola, Frank, Jr., illus. 1998. 32p. (J). (gr. k-1). pap. 10.95 (978-0-590-00321-6(6) , Cartwheel Bks.) Scholastic, Inc.

—Hershey's Kisses: Counting Board Book, 1. 1998. (978-0-9662445-0-2(8)) Corporate Board Bks.

—M & M's' Brand Count Around the Circle. 2004. (Illus.). 24p. (J). bds. 7.95 (978-1-57091-436-2(2)) Charlesbridge Publishing, Inc.

—The M & M's' Brand Count to One Hundred Book. 2004. (Illus.). 32p. (J). 16.95 (978-1-57091-570-3(9)); pap. 6.95 (978-1-57091-571-0(7)) Charlesbridge Publishing, Inc.

—The M & M's' Brand Counting Book. Glass, Roger, illus. rev. ed. 2004. 32p. (J). 16.95 (978-1-57091-367-9(6)); pap. 6.95 (978-1-57091-368-6(4)) Charlesbridge Publishing, Inc.

—Mas Matematicas con los Chocolates de M & M's Brand. Mlawer, Teresa, tr. Glass, Roger, illus. 2004. (SPA.). 32p. (J). pap. 6.95 (978-1-57091-481-2(8) , CH30498) Charlesbridge Publishing, Inc.

—More M & M's' Brand Math. Glass, Roger, illus. 1998. 32p. (J). (gr. 3-7). 16.95 (978-0-88106-993-8(0)); pap. 6.95 (978-0-88106-994-5(9)) Charlesbridge Publishing, Inc.

—Pepperidge Farm Goldfish Counting Board Book. Bolster, Rob & Mazzola, Frank, Jr., illus. 1998. 12p. (J). (ps-k). bds. 4.95 (978-1-893017-50-4(8)) Jennings Pond, LLC.

—The Pepperidge Farm Goldfish Fun Book. Bolster, Rob & Mazzola, Frank, Jr., illus. 1999. 16p. (J). (ps up). 5.99 (978-0-694-01450-7(8) , Harper Festival) HarperCollins Pubs.

McGrath, Barbara Barbieri & Alderman, Peter. Soccer Counts! Estrada, Pau, illus. 2004. 32p. (J). 16.95 (978-1-57091-553-6(9)); pap. 6.95 (978-1-57091-554-3(7)) Charlesbridge Publishing, Inc.

McGrath, Barbara Barbieri & Shaw, Brian. Cuenta con el Beisbol. Canetti, Yanitzia, tr. from SPA. Shaw, Brian, illus. 2005. (Illus.). 32p. (J). pap. 7.95 (978-1-57091-608-3(X)) Charlesbridge Publishing, Inc.

C D

McKissack, Fredrick, Jr. & McKissack, Lisa Beringer. Counting in the Desert. 2008. (Counting in the Biomes Ser.). 32p. (J). (gr. 1-3). lib. bdg. 22.60 (*978-0-7660-2988-0(3)) Enslow Pubs., Inc.

—Counting in the Grasslands. 2008. (J). (*978-0-7660-2991-0(3)) Enslow Pubs., Inc.

—Counting in the Oceans. 2008. (J). (*978-0-7660-2994-1(8)) Enslow Pubs., Inc.

—Counting in the Rain Forest. 2008. (J). (*978-0-7660-2992-7(1)) Enslow Pubs., Inc.

—Counting in the Temperate Forest. 2008. (J). (*978-0-7660-2990-3(5)) Enslow Pubs., Inc.

—Counting in the Tiaga. 2008. (J). (*978-0-7660-2995-8(6)) Enslow Pubs., Inc.

—Counting in the Tundra. 2008. (Counting in the Biomes Ser.). 32p. (J). (gr. 1-3). lib. bdg. 22.60 (*978-0-7660-2989-7(1)) Enslow Pubs., Inc.

—Counting in the Wetlands. 2008. (J). (*978-0-7660-2993-4(X)) Enslow Pubs., Inc.

McLaughlin, Julie. Hungry Mr. Gator. McKay, Ann Marie, illus. 2002. 32p. (J). (gr. k-2). pap. (978-0-615-12335-6(X)) JAM Publishers.

—Hungry Mr. Gator. McKay, Ann Marie, illus. 2005. (J). 15.99 (978-0-933101-24-1(4)) Legacy Pubns.

McNamara, Margaret. The Counting Race. Gordon, Mike, illus. ed. 2005. 32p. (J). lib. bdg. 15.00 (978-1-59054-967-4(8)) Fitzgerald Bks.

—The Counting Race. Gordon, Mike, illus. 2003. (Ready-to-Read Ser.). 32p. (J). pap. 3.99 (978-0-689-85539-9(7), Aladdin) Simon & Schuster Children's Publishing.

—How Many Seeds in a Pumpkin? Karas, G. Brian, illus. 2007. 40p. (J). (ps-2). 14.99 (978-0-375-84014-2(1)); lib. bdg. 17.99 (*978-0-375-94014-9(6)) Random Hse. Children's Bks. (Schwartz & Wade Bks.).

—One Hundred Days. 2003. (ps-2). lib. bdg. 11.80 (978-0-613-58162-2(8)) Tandem Library Bks.

—One Hundred Days (Plus One) Gordon, Mike, illus. 2003. (Ready-to-Reads Ser.). 32p. (J). pap. 3.99 (978-0-689-85535-1(4), Aladdin) Simon & Schuster Children's Publishing.

McNamara, Margaret. Too Many Cooks: A Counting Book. Wragg, Nate, illus. 2007. 48p. (ps-2). 14.99 (*978-1-4231-0539-8(7)) Disney Pr.

McNaught, Harry, illus. ABC & 1,2,3: A Sesame Street Treasury of Words & Numbers. 1998. (Sesame Street Ser.). 80p. (J). (gr. k-ps). 9.99 (978-0-375-80042-9(5), Random Hse. Bks. for Young Readers) Random Hse. Children's Bks.

McOmber, Rachel B., ed. McOmber Phonics Storybooks: Number Fun. rev. ed. (Illus.). (J). (978-0-944991-58-9(0)) Swift Learning Resources.

MCP Staff. Eight Friends in All, Level 4, Bk. 44. 2003. (J). (ps-3). 24.50 (978-0-8136-0772-6(8)) Modern Curriculum Pr.

—I Like to Count, Level 3, Bk. 23. (J). (ps-3). 24.50 (978-0-8136-1953-8(X)) Modern Curriculum Pr.

McTaggart, Stephen & McTaggart, Debra. Bookee Presents 1, 2, 3 Count with Me. Nord, Mary, illus. (Talking Book Adventures Ser.). 14p. (J). (ps up). 16.95 (978-0-9627001-3-2(4)) Futech Educational Products, Inc.

Melmed, Laura. This First Thanksgiving Day: A Counting Story. Buehner, Mark, illus. 2003. 32p. (J). (ps-3). pap. 6.99 (978-0-06-054184-2(9)) HarperCollins Pubs.

Melmed, Laura Krauss. This First Thanksgiving Day: A Counting Story. 2003. (gr. k-3). lib. bdg. 14.15 (978-0-613-68468-2(0)) Tandem Library Bks.

Merberg, Julie & Bober, Suzanne. Quiet Time with Cassatt. 2006. (Illus.). 22p. (J). bds. 6.95 (978-0-8118-5504-4(X)) Chronicle Bks. LLC.

Merriam, Eve. Ten Rosy Roses. Horton, Julia, illus. 1999. 32p. (J). (ps-1). 14.95 (978-0-06-027887-8(0)) HarperCollins Pubs.

—12 Ways to Get 11. 1998. (J). pap. 5.99 (978-0-87628-369-1(5)) Ctr. for Applied Research in Education, The.

Merry Monkeys' First Number Fun. 2002. (J). bds. 4.98 (978-0-7525-8865-0(6)) Parragon, Inc.

Metropolitan Museum of Art Staff. Museum 123. 2004. (Illus.). 48p. (J). (ps-1). 16.99 (978-0-316-16044-5(X)) Little, Brown Bks. for Young Readers.

Metzger, Steve. Five Spooky Ghosts Playing Tricks at School. Harrald-Pilz, Marilee, illus. 2005. (J). (*978-0-439-80381-6(0)) Scholastic, Inc.

Michaels, Julie. 102 Dalmatians: Numbers. 2000. (Illus.). 12p. (J). (ps-k). bds. 4.99 (978-0-7364-0192-0(X), RH/Disney) Random Hse. Children's Bks.

Micklethwait, Lucy. I Spy Two Eyes: Numbers in Art. 1999. (Illus.). (J). 17.79 (978-0-606-15581-6(3)) Tandem Library Bks.

Miles, L. Empiezo a Contar. 2005. (Computer Guide Ser.). Orig. Title: Starting to Count Sticker Book. (SPA.). 18p. (J). pap. 6.95 (978-0-7460-4530-5(1)) EDC Publishing.

Milich, Zoran. City 123. 2005. (Illus.). 32p. (J). (gr. k up). (978-1-55337-540-1(8)) Kids Can Pr., Ltd.

Milios, Rita. Bears, Bears, Everywhere. Motoyama, Keiko, illus. rev. ed. 2003. (Rookie Reader Ser.). 32p. (J). 19.50 (978-0-516-22847-1(1), Children's Pr.) Scholastic Library Publishing.

Millard, Anne. Baby's Little Library. 2001. (Illus.). 1p. (J). 9.99 (978-0-7894-6798-0(4)) Dorling Kindersley Publishing, Inc.

—My First Number. Boursnell, Clive, illus. 2001. (My First Word Books). 12p. (J). (ps-3). 9.99 (978-0-7894-7930-3(3)) Dorling Kindersley Publishing, Inc.

Miller Molengraft, Lisa. Simple Centers. 1999. 240p. (J). (gr. 1 up). pap. 16.99 (978-1-56822-306-3(4), IF8667); (gr. 2 up). pap. 16.99 (978-1-56822-307-0(2), IF8668) School Specialty Publishing.

Miller, Virginia. Ten Red Apples: A Bartholomew Bear Counting Book. 2002. (Illus.). 32p. (J). (ps-k). 13.99 (978-0-7445-9280-1(1)) Candlewick Pr.

Milne, A. A. Slide & Seek Numbers: A Sliding Window Book. 1999. (Illus.). 8p. (J). 10.99 (978-0-7868-3241-5(X)) Disney Pr.

Mishica, Clare. Here Comes the Parade. Richard, Ilene, illus. 24p. (J). (gr. k-2). 2006. pap. 4.95 (978-0-516-25016-8(7)); 2005. 19.50 (978-0-516-24857-8(X)) Scholastic Library Publishing. (Children's Pr.).

Mishica, Clare & Richard, Ilene. Vamos Al Desfile. Richard, Ilene, illus. 2006. (Rookie Reader Español Ser.). (ENG & SPA., Illus.). 22p. (J). (978-0-516-25309-1(3)) Children's Pr., Ltd.

Mitchell, Judy, ed. Things to Count: Food 11-15. Mohrman, Gary, illus. 2000. 32p. (J). (ps-1). pap. 4.95 (978-1-57310-225-4(3)) Teaching & Learning Co.

Mitter, Matt. 1 2 3. Cushman, Doug, illus. 2000. (Talking Pages Deluxe Ser.). 14p. (J). 12.95 (978-1-58224-134-0(1)) Futech Interactive Products, Inc.

Mitzo Thompson, Kim. Alphabet & Counting, 2 Packs. 2006. (Read & Sing along Board Books with CDs Ser.). 36p. (J). bds. 14.98 (978-0-7696-4592-6(5)) School Specialty Publishing.

—At the Zoo. 2006. (Dual Language Readers Ser.). 32p. (J). pap., pap. 4.99 incl. audio compact disk (978-0-7696-4616-9(6)) School Specialty Publishing.

Modesitt, Jeanne. 1, 2, 3 Valentine's Day: A Counting Book. Spowart, Robin, illus. 2003. 32p. (J). (ps up). 15.95 (978-1-56397-868-5(7)) Boyds Mills Pr.

Moncure, Jane Belk. My Eight Book. 2006. (My First Steps to Mathtrade; Ser.). (Illus.). 32p. (J). 21.36 (978-1-59296-663-9(2)) Child's World, Inc.

—My Five Book. 2006. (My First Steps to Mathtrade; Ser.). (Illus.). 32p. (J). 21.36 (978-1-59296-660-8(8)) Child's World, Inc.

—My Four Book. 2006. (My First Steps to Mathtrade; Ser.). (Illus.). 32p. (J). 21.36 (978-1-59296-659-2(4)) Child's World, Inc.

—My Nine Book. 2006. (My First Steps to Mathtrade; Ser.). (Illus.). 32p. (J). 21.36 (978-1-59296-664-6(0)) Child's World, Inc.

—My One Book. 2006. (My First Steps to Mathtrade; Ser.). (Illus.). 32p. (J). 21.36 (978-1-59296-656-1(X)) Child's World, Inc.

—My Seven Book. 2006. (My First Steps to Mathtrade; Ser.). (Illus.). 32p. (J). 21.36 (978-1-59296-662-2(4)) Child's World, Inc.

—My Six Book. 2006. (My First Steps to Mathtrade; Ser.). (Illus.). 32p. (J). 21.36 (978-1-59296-661-5(6)) Child's World, Inc.

—My Ten Book. 2006. (My First Steps to Mathtrade; Ser.). (Illus.). 32p. (J). 21.36 (978-1-59296-665-3(9)) Child's World, Inc.

—My Three Book. 2006. (My First Steps to Mathtrade; Ser.). (Illus.). 32p. (J). 21.36 (978-1-59296-658-5(6)) Child's World, Inc.

—My Two Book. 2006. (My First Steps to Mathtrade; Ser.). (Illus.). 32p. (J). 21.36 (978-1-59296-657-8(8)) Child's World, Inc.

Monica, Carol. Elmo's Easy As 1 2 3. 2006. (Sesame Street Ser.). 10p. (J). 15.99 (978-0-7944-1018-6(9)) Reader's Digest Assn., Inc., The.

Monreal, Violeta. Sos Se Necesita Sonrisa. 2004. (Coleccion Pictogramas Pictograms Ser.). (SPA.). 36p. (J). 8.50 (978-84-241-8101-7(8)) Everest de Ediciones y Distribucion, S.L. ESP. *Dist:* Continental Bk. Co., Inc., Lectorum Pubns., Inc.

Montague-Smith, Ann. Counting Book 1. 2004. (QEB Start Math Ser.). (Illus.). 24p. (J). Vol. 1. lib. bdg. 15.95 (978-1-59566-024-4(0)); Vol. 2. lib. bdg. 15.95 (978-1-59566-028-2(3)) QEB Publishing Inc.

Moody, Camilla & Priddy, Roger. Touch & Feel: Millie Moo. rev. ed. 2005. (Illus.). 20p. (J). (ps). bds. 12.95 (978-0-312-49537-4(4), Priddy Bks.) St. Martin's Pr.

Mora, Pat. Uno, Dos, Tres. Lavallee, Barbara, illus. 2002. Tr. of One, Two, Three. (SPA.). (J). 14.74 (978-0-7587-3892-9(7)) Book Wholesalers, Inc.

—Uno, Dos, Tres: Lavallee, Barbara, illus. 2000. Tr. of One, Two, Three. (SPA & ENG.). 48p. (J). (gr. k-3). pap. 6.95 (978-0-618 05468-8(5), Clarion Bks.) Houghton Mifflin Co. Trade & Reference Div.

Morales, Yuyi. Just a Minute: A Trickster Tale & Counting Book. 2003. (SPA & ENG., Illus.). 36p. (J). 15.95 (978-0-8118-3758-3(0)) Chronicle Bks. LLC.

More Numbers. 2004. (Kids Can Learn with Franklin Ser.). (Illus.). 32p. (J). (gr. k-3). pap. (978-1-55337-598-2(X)) Kids Can Pr., Ltd.

Moreton, Daniel. Animal Babies: A Counting Book. 1998. (Science Emergent Readers Ser.). 32p. (J). pap. 2.50 (978-0-590-76164-2(1)) Scholastic, Inc.

—Animal Babies: A Counting Book. 1998. lib. bdg. 10.10 (978-0-613-89009-0(4)) Tandem Library Bks.

Moshel, Eluzer. My Number Book, Vol. 1. 2004. pap. 8.50 (978-0-9728849-6-9(3)) Cong Bais Tziporah.

Moss, Lloyd. Zin! Zin! Zin! A Violin. Priceman, Marjorie, illus. 2002. (J). 15.53 (978-0-7587-0170-1(5)) Book Wholesalers, Inc.

—Zin! Zin! Zin! A Violin. Priceman, Marjorie, illus. (Stories to Go! Ser.). 32p. (J). 2005. 4.99 (978-1-4169-0838-8(2)); 2000. pap. 6.99 (978-0-689-83524-7(8)) Simon & Schuster Children's Publishing. (Aladdin).

Mouse Works Staff. Learn & Grow Carry Along. 1999. (J). 9.99 (978-0-7364-0181-4(4)) Mouse Works.

Muench-Williams, Heather, ed. Color, Shape, & Number Fun for Little Ones: Activities for Preschoolers. 2005. (J). pap. (978-1-57332-380-2(2)) HighReach Learning, Inc.

Murphy. Every Buddy Counts: Counting Big Book. 2002. (Illus.). pap. (978-0-7398-6777-8(6)) Steck-Vaughn.

Murphy, Chuck. Colors. Murphy, Chuck, illus. 2001. (Slide 'n' Seek Ser.). (Illus.). 12p. (J). (ps-k). bds. 5.99 (978-0-689-84010-4(1), Little Simon) Simon & Schuster Children's Publishing.

—How Many Hearts. 1999. (Razzle Dazzle Book Ser.). (Illus.). 12p. (J). (ps-k). pap. 5.99 (978-0-689-82257-5(X), Little Simon) Simon & Schuster Children's Publishing.

Murphy, Patricia J. Counting Puppies & Kittens. 2007. (Puppy & Kitten Math Ser.). (Illus.). 32p. (J). lib. bdg. 22.60 (978-0-7660-2724-4(4), Enslow Elementary) Enslow Pubs., Inc.

Murphy, Stuart J. Coyotes All Around. Bjorkman, Steve, illus. 2003. (MathStart Ser.). 40p. (J). (gr. 1 up). 15.99 (978-0-06-051529-4(5)); pap. 5.99 (978-0-06-051531-7(7)) HarperCollins Pubs.

—Coyotes All Around. 2003. (gr. k-3). lib. bdg. 13.00 (978-0-613-68415-6(X)) Tandem Library Bks.

—Henry the Fourth. Nash, Scott, illus. 1999. (MathStart Ser.). 40p. (YA). (ps-3). 15.89 (978-0-06-027611-9(8)); 15.95 (978-0-06-027610-2(X)) HarperCollins Pubs.

—Jack the Builder. Rex, Michael, illus. 2006. (MathStart Ser.). 40p. (J). 15.99 (978-0-06-055774-4(5)); pap. 5.99 (978-0-06-055775-1(3)) HarperCollins Pubs.

—Leaping Lizards. Adinolfi, JoAnn, illus. 2005. (MathStart Ser.). 40p. (J). 15.99 (978-0-06-000130-8(5)); pap. 5.99 (978-0-06-000131-5(3)) HarperCollins Pubs.

—Mall Mania. Andriani, Renee, illus. 2006. (MathStart Ser.). 40p. (J). 15.99 (978-0-06-055776-8(1)); pap. 5.99 (978-0-06-055777-5(X)) HarperCollins Pubs.

—Missing Mittens. Karas, G. Brian, illus. 2001. (MathStart Ser.). 40p. (J). (gr. 2-4). pap. 5.99 (978-0-06-446733-9(3), Harper Trophy) HarperCollins Pubs.

—Missing Mittens. 2001. (ps-2). lib. bdg. 13.00 (978-0-613-31485-5(9)); (Illus.). (J). (978-0-606-20803-1(8)) Tandem Library Bks.

—Missing Mittens: Big Book. 2002. (Illus.). pap. (978-0-7398-6784-6(9)) Steck-Vaughn.

—The Penny Pot. Cravath, Lynne W., illus. 1998. (MathStart Ser.). 40p. (J). (gr. 2 up). 15.95 (978-0-06-027606-5(1)); 15.89 (978-0-06-027607-2(X)); pap. 5.99 (978-0-06-446717-9(1), Harper Trophy) HarperCollins Pubs.

—Spunky Monkeys on Parade. 1999. (MathStart Ser.). (Illus.). 40p. (YA). (gr. 1 up). 15.95 (978-0-06-028014-7(X)) HarperCollins Pubs.

—Spunky Monkeys on Parade. 1999. (Math Start Ser.). (978-0-606-17496-1(6)); lib. bdg. 13.00 (978-0-613-22430-7(2)) Tandem Library Bks.

—100 Days of Cool. Bendall-Brunello, John, illus. 2004. (MathStart 2 Ser.). 40p. (J). (gr. 1 up). pap. 5.99 (978-0-06-000123-0(2)) HarperCollins Pubs.

My Book of Numbers 1-120. 2004. (Illus.). 80p. (J). per. 6.95 (978-4-7743-0704-6(1)) Kumon Publishing North America, Inc.

My Book of Numbers 1-30. 2004. (Illus.). 80p. (J). per. 6.95 (978-4-7743-0703-9(3)) Kumon Publishing North America, Inc.

My First 1 2 3. Date not set. (Illus.). (J). bds. 5.98 (978-0-7525-7983-2(5)) Parragon, Inc.

My TakeAlong Li, ed. Counting. 2007. (My Take-along Library). 120p. (J). (ps-k). bds. 14.95 (*978-0-7696-5539-0(4)) School Specialty Publishing.

Myers, Samantha Ann. ABC's & 123's of the Great Outdoors. 2006. (ENG.). 28p. per. 13.99 (*978-1-4259-6659-1(4)) AuthorHouse.

Nadja. Cinco Deditos. (SPA.). 12p. (978-84-8470-019-7(4)) Corimbo, Editorial S.L.

Napier, Matt. Hat Tricks Count. rev. ed. 2007. (Board Ser.). 32p. bds. 7.99 (*978-1-58536-346-9(4)) Sleeping Bear Pr.

Nayer, Judy. Adding It up at the Zoo. 2002. (Yellow Umbrella Books). (Illus.). 16p. (J). (gr. 1). lib. bdg. 14.60 (978-0-7368-1278-8(4), Pebble Bks.) Capstone Pr., Inc.

Neubauer, Julie. Ten Little Freckles. 2006. 30p. (J). per. 13.99 (*978-1-59886-702-2(4)) Tate Publishing & Enterprises, L.L.C.

Newman, Leslea & Oller, Erika. Dogs, Dogs, Dogs! 2002. (Illus.). 32p. (J). (ps-3). 16.00 (978-0-689-84492-8(1)) Simon & Schuster Children's Publishing.

Nguyen, An Mai. Let's Learn How to Count in Vietnamese. 2006. (VIE & ENG., Illus.). (J). bds. 6.95 (978-0-9776482-2-1(2)) Viet Baby, LLC.

Nikola-Lisa, W. Can You Top That? Lee, Hector Viveros, illus. 2000. 32p. (J). (ps-2). 15.95 (978-1-880000-99-1(7)) Lee & Low Bks., Inc.

Nobisso, Josephine. The Numbers Dance: A Counting Comedy. Ziborova, Dasha, illus. 2005. 32p. (J). (ps-4). 16.95 (978-0-940112-11-7(6)); pap. 8.95 (978-0-940112-12-4(4)) Gingerbread Hse.

Noble, Trinka Hakes. One for All: A Pennsylvania Number Book. Papp, L. W., illus. 2005. (Count Your Way Across the USA Ser.). 40p. (J). (gr. k-5). 22.95 (978-1-58536-200-4(X)) Sleeping Bear Pr.

Nolan, Kathy. Let's Learn Numbers. 1999. (J). (ps-3). (978-1-929343-02-7(7)) Stretching Charts, Inc.

Norma Staff, ed. Numeros. 2005. 14p. (978-958-04-8069-3(9)) Norma S.A.

Norton, George. Ten Buttermilk Pancakes. Hutcherson, Darren, illus. Date not set. (J). 9.95 (978-1-889506-10-4(9)) Kendar Publishing, Inc.

Novit, Renee Z. Counting by Tens & Fives. (Kidz & Katz Educational Learning Book Ser.). (Illus.). 16p. (J). (ps). pap. 7.95 (978-1-883371-02-9(3)) Kidz & Katz Publishing Co.

—Counting One to Twenty. (Kidz & Katz Educational Learning Book Ser.). (Illus.). 16p. (J). (ps). pap. 7.95 (978-1-883371-01-2(5)) Kidz & Katz Publishing Co.

Number Circus. 1998. (Fisher-Price Little People Concept Bks.: Vol. 3). (Illus.). 24p. (J). (978-0-7666-0321-9(0), 19615) Modern Publishing.

Number Farm. 2002. 32p. (J). 4.98 (978-0-7525-7880-4(4)) Parragon, Inc.

Number Hunt. 2000. (Pooh Learning Ser.). (J). (ps-3). pap. 6.98 incl. audio (978-0-7634-0473-4(X)) Walt Disney Records.

Number Search: Travel Games with Press & Peel Clings. 1999. (J). (ps-3). pap. 4.29 (978-0-88743-732-8(X)) School Zone Publishing Co.

Numbers. 2002. (Puppy Steps Ser.). (Illus.). 10p. (J). (ps). bds. 3.99 (978-1-57759-634-9(X)) Dalmatian Pr.

Numbers. 2000. (Pajama Bedtime Bear Ser.). (Illus.). 14p. (J). (ps). bds. 3.95 (978-0-7894-1423-6(6), D K Ink) Dorling Kindersley Publishing, Inc.

Numbers. (Butterfly Bks.). (ARA., Illus.). 15p. (J). 11.95 (978-0-86685-614-0(5), LDL6164) International Bk. Ctr., Inc.

Numbers. (Illus.). (J). pap. 2.79 (978-0-88743-712-0(5)) School Zone Publishing Co.

Numbers 1-100. 2004. (Wall Charts Ser.). (J). 4.99 (978-1-85997-285-4(3)) Byeway Bks.

Numbers 1 to 10. 2001. (Early Learning Ser.). (J). (gr. k-12). vinyl bd. 4.95 (978-1-58845-050-0(3)) School Specialty Publishing.

Numeroff, Laura Joffe. When Sheep Sleep. McPhail, David, illus. 2006. 24p. (J). (ps-3). 15.95 (978-0-8109-5469-4(9)) Abrams, Harry N., Inc.

O'Brady, Terry. Count the Animals. 2002. (Windows on Literacy Ser.). (Illus.). 10p. (J). (978-0-7922-8484-0(4)) National Geographic Society.

Ochiltree, Dianne. Cats Add Up! Dunn-Ramsey, Marcy, illus. 1998. (Hello Reader! Math Ser.). 48p. (J). (gr. 1-3). pap. 3.99 (978-0-590-12005-0(0)) Scholastic, Inc.

Ochiltree, Dianne. It's a Firefly Night. Snyder, Betsy, illus. 2008. (J). (*978-1-55971-991-9(5), NorthWord Bks. for Young Readers) T&N Children's Publishing.

O'Connell, Jennifer. Ten Timid Ghosts. O'Connell, Jennifer, illus. 2000. (Read with Me Paperbacks Ser.). (Illus.). 32p. (J). (ps-3). 3.99 (978-0-439-15804-6(4)) Scholastic, Inc.

O'Keefe, Susan Heyboer. Un Esperpento Hambriento: Un Libro Rimado Para Contar. (SPA., Illus.). (J). pap. (978-0-590-50705-9(2), SO7981) Scholastic Canada, Ltd. CAN. *Dist:* Lectorum Pubns., Inc.

Olson-Brown, Ellen. Ten Stinky Babies. 2005. (Illus.). 28p. (J). (ps-ps). 12.95 (978-1-58246-137-3(6), Tricycle Pr.) Ten Speed Pr.

Olson, K. C. & Gordon, David. Construction Countdown. rev. ed. 2004. (Illus.). 24p. (J). 14.95 (978-0-8050-6920-4(8), Holt, Henry & Co. Bks. For Young Readers) Holt, Henry & Co.

Omoto, Garrett, illus. Tutu Books- A set of three Books w/ CD. 2006. (ENG & HAW.). (YA). (978-1-933835-04-4(3)) Partners in Development.

On the Launch Pad. (Know Your Numbers Ser.). 24p. (J). 7.95 (978-1-4048-1119-5(2)) Picture Window Bks.

One, Two, Three, Four: KinderWords Individual Title Six-Packs. (Kinderstarters Ser.). 8p. (ps-1). 21.00 (978-0-7635-8705-5(2)) Rigby Education.

One, Two, Three, Picnic. 1998. (Fisher-Price Hideaway Hollow Padded Board Bks.). (Illus.). 16p. (J). (gr. 1). bds. (978-0-7666-0120-8(X), Honey Bear Bks.) Modern Publishing.

Ong, Cristina & Piper, Watty. The Little Engine That Could Numbers. 1999. (Wee Pudgy Board Bks.). (Illus.). 20p. (J). (ps-k). 1.99 (978-0-448-41972-5(6), Grosset & Dunlap) Penguin Group (USA) Inc.

Onyefulu, Ifeoma. Emeka's Gift: An African Counting Book. 1999. (Illus.). 24p. (J). (ps-3). pap. 6.99 (978-0-14-056500-3(0), Puffin) Penguin Group (USA) Inc.

—Emeka's Gift: An African Counting Story. 1999. (Illus.). (J). (978-0-606-22074-3(7)) Tandem Library Bks.

Orozco, Jose-Luis. Rin, Rin, Rin / Do, Re, Mi. Diaz, David, illus. 2005. 32p. (J). pap. 16.95 (978-0-439-64941-4(2), Orchard Bks.) Scholastic, Inc.

—Rin, Rin, Rin/Do, Re, Mi. Diaz, David, illus. 2005. 32p. (J). (ps-k). pap. 3.50 (978-0-439-75531-3(X), Orchard Bks.) Scholastic, Inc.

Over in the Meadow. 2004. 29.95 incl. cd-rom (978-1-55592-852-0(8)); 24.95 incl. audio (978-1-56008-213-2(5)); pap. 18.95 incl. audio compact disk (978-1-55592-809-4(9)); pap. 38.75 incl. audio compact disk (978-1-55592-759-2(9)); pap. 32.75 incl. audio (978-1-55592-290-0(2)); pap. 14.95 incl. audio (978-1-56008-088-6(4)) Weston Woods Studios, Inc.

Packard, Mary & Mitter, Matt. 1, 2, 3: Counting Rymes. Cushman, Doug & Banta, Susan, illus. 2004. (Rhyme Time Learning Ser.). 16p. (J). (gr. 1 up). lib. bdg. 20.67 (978-0-8368-4094-0(1)) Stevens, Gareth Inc.

Pallotta, Jerry. Count to a Million: 1,000,000. Bolster, Rob, tr. Bolster, Rob, illus. 2003. (J). (978-0-439-38915-0(1)) Scholastic, Inc.

—Hershey's Kisses Addition Book. 2001. (gr. k-3). lib. bdg. 14.10 (978-0-613-35724-1(8)); (Illus.). (J). 12.79 (978-0-606-21232-8(9)) Tandem Library Bks.

—The Icky Bug Counting Board Book. Masiello, Ralph, illus. 2004. (J). bds. 6.95 (978-1-57091-624-3(1)) Charlesbridge Publishing, Inc.

—Icky Bug Numbers. Biedrzycki, David & Bolster, Rob, illus. 2004. 32p. (J). (ps-3). pap. 5.99 (978-0-439-56010-8(1)) Scholastic, Inc.

—Ocean Counting: Odd Numbers. Bersani, Shennen, illus. 2005. 32p. (J). 16.95 (978-0-88106-151-2(4)); pap. 6.95 (978-0-88106-150-5(6)) Charlesbridge Publishing, Inc.

—Reese's Pieces Count by Fives. 2000. (978-0-606-18886-9(X)) Tandem Library Bks.

—Reese's Pieces Peanut Butter: Counting Board Book. 1998. 4.95 (978-0-9662445-1-9(6)) Corporate Board Bks.

—Underwater Counting: Even Numbers. 2001. (Illus.). (J). (978-0-606-20964-9(6)) Tandem Library Bks.

Palotta, Jerry. Underwater Counting: Even Numbers. 2001. (gr. 3-6). lib. bdg. 15.25 (978-0-613-51270-1(7)) Tandem Library Bks.

C
D

—Underwater Counting Even Numbers. Biedrzycki, David, illus. 2001. 32p. (J). (gr. 1-4). 16.95 (978-0-88106-952-5(3)); pap. 6.95 (978-0-88106-800-9(4)) Charlesbridge Publishing, Inc.

Pantuso, Mike. 1, 2, 3 by Elmo. 2004. (Illus.). 32p. (J). (gr. k-ps). bds. 6.99 (978-0-375-82948-2(2) , Random Hse. Bks. for Young Readers) Random Hse. Children's Bks.

Pantuso, Mike & Henson, Jim. 1,2,3 by Elmo. 2001. (Illus.). (J). lib. bdg. (978-0-375-91390-7(4) , Random Hse. Bks. for Young Readers) Random Hse. Children's Bks.

Paparone, Pamela. Five Little Ducks. Paparone, Pamela, illus. 2004. (Illus.). 26p. (J). bds. 5.95 (978-0-7358-1857-6(6)) North-South Bks., Inc.

Paré, Roger. Les Chiffres. 2004. (Livres-jeux Ser.). (FRE.). 12p. (J). (ps). pap. (978-2-89021-654-9(3)) Diffusion du livre Mirabel.

—Numbers. Lantier, Patricia, tr. from FRE. Paré, Roger, illus. 2001. (Smart Start Ser.). (Illus.). 24p. (J). (ps up). lib. bdg. 22.00 (978-0-8368-2845-0(3)) Stevens, Gareth Inc.

Parenteau, Shirley. One Frog Sang. Jabar, Cynthia, illus. 2007. (Read & Wonder Ser.). 32p. (J). (gr. k). pap. 6.99 (978-0-7636-3285-4(6)); 15.99 (978-0-7636-2394-4(6)) Candlewick Pr.

Park, Margaret. Now for My Next Number! Songs for Multiplying Fun. Esterman, Sophia, illus. 2007. 48p. (J). (gr. 3-6). 16.95 (***978-0-915556-38-0(3)**) Great River Bks.

Parker, Ant. Counting. 1999. (Touch & Feel Ser.). (Illus.). 12p. (J). (ps). pap. 4.95 (978-0-7373-0292-9(5) , 02925W, Roxbury Park) Lowell Hse.

Parker, Kim. Counting in the Garden. 2005. (Illus.). 32p. (J). pap. 16.95 (978-0-439-69452-0(3) , Orchard Bks.) Scholastic, Inc.

Parker, Sandy. What Month Is It? Hofher, Cathy, illus. l.t. ed. 2004. 32p. 15.95 (978-0-9643462-5-3(7) , Just Think Bks.) Canary Connect Pubns.

Partis, Joanne. Try Counting Sheep. 2007. (Illus.). (J). (ps-k). bds. 12.95 (***978-0-7696-5342-6(1)** , Gingham Dog Pr.) School Specialty Publishing.

Paterson, Brian. Dives In. 2004. (Illus.). 14p. (J). (ps). 6.99 (978-0-00-717420-1(9)) HarperCollins Pubs. Ltd. GBR. *Dist:* Independent Pubs. Group.

Patilla, Peter. Starting off with Counting. 2001. (Starting Off Ser.). (J). (978-0-606-21461-2(5)) Tandem Library Bks.

Patnaude, Jeffrey. Penny. 2003. (Illus.). 32p. (J). (ps-3). 19.95 (978-0-9704122-2-5(3)) White Rhino Pr.

Paul, Ann Whitford. Count on Culebra. Long, Ethan, illus. 2008. (J). (***978-0-8234-2124-4(4)**) Holiday Hse., Inc.

Peek, Merle. ¡Dénse Vuelta!/Roll Over! 2008. (ENG & SPA., Illus.). 24p. (J). (gr. k-ps). bds. 5.95 (***978-0-618-89420-8(9)** , Clarion Bks.) Houghton Mifflin Co. Trade & Reference Div.

Pelham, David. Applebee's Numbers: A Cat & Mouse. 2005. (Illus.). 16p. (J). (ps). 12.95 (978-0-7624-2551-8(2) , Running Pr. Kids) Running Pr. Bk. Pubs.

Perl, Erica S. Ninety-Three in My Family. Lester, Mike, illus. 2006. 32p. (J). (ps-3). 15.95 (978-0-8109-5760-2(4)) Abrams, Harry N. , Inc.

Petty, Colin. Numbers. 2006. (Concept Sliders Ser.). (Illus.). 10p. (J). 5.99 (978-0-7641-5942-8(9)) Barron's Educational Series, Inc.

Petty, Kate. Little Rabbits' First Number Book. Baker, Alan, illus. 1998. 30p. (J). pap. 12.98 (978-1-58048-054-3(3)) Sandvik Publishing.

Pfister, Marcus. Rainbow Fish: Counting. 2004. (Rainbow Fish Ser.). (Illus.). 24p. (J). (gr. k). bds. 4.99 (978-0-7358-1653-4(0)) North-South Bks., Inc.

—Rainbow Fish 1, 2, 3. 2002. (Rainbow Fish Ser.). (Illus.). 20p. (J). 9.95 (978-0-7358-1716-6(2)) North-South Bks., Inc.

—Rainbow Fish: Counting: El Pez Arco Iris: Numeros. Pfister, Marcus, illus. 2005. (ENG & SPA., Illus.). 24p. (J). bds. 4.99 (978-0-7358-1979-5(3)) North-South Bks., Inc.

Phillips, Laverne. Learning to Count 1 2 3 Coloring Book. Phillips, Laverne, illus. 1999. 12p. (J). (ps-1). pap. 3.00 (978-1-930058-02-6(0)) Phillips, Laverne Products.

Phillips, Sarah. Touch & Learn: 123. 2007. (Touch & Learn (Make Believe Ideas) Ser.). (Illus.). 12p. (ps). per., bds. 6.95 (978-1-84610-462-6(9)) Make Believe Ideas GBR. *Dist:* Ingram Pub. Services.

—Touch & Learn 123. 2005. (Illus.). 12p. (J). (ps-1). per., bds. 12.95 (978-1-905051-76-2(X)) Make Believe Ideas GBR. *Dist:* Ingram Pub. Services.

Phillips, Sarah & Wallace, Bruce. Flip Flaps Counting. 2005. (Flip Flaps (Make Believe Ideas) Ser.). (Illus.). 12p. (ps-k). per., bds. 5.95 (978-1-905051-94-6(8)) Make Believe Ideas GBR. *Dist:* Ingram Pub. Services.

Pichette, Marise & Rousseau, Serge. Show & Tell at Home. 2000. (Illus.). 12p. (J). (ps-1). bds. (978-2-922148-82-4(3)) Presses aventure/Adventure Pr.

Pierce, Patricia A. Numbers in a Row: An Iowa Number Book. Rohner, Dorothia, illus. 2006. 40p. (J). 17.95 (978-1-58536-164-9(X)) Sleeping Bear Pr.

Piggy Toes Press Staff. Fun with Numbers, One to Ten: A Baby Jungle Animals Board Book Set, 10 bks., Set. 2000. (Illus.). (J). (ps-k). bds., act. bk. ed. 16.95 (978-1-58117-080-1(7) , Intervisual/Piggy Toes) Dalmatian Pr.

Pinwheel, ed. Numbers. Chambers, Sally, illus. 2001. (Bounce-Along Bks.). 12p. (J). bds. 4.95 (978-0-8069-8089-8(3)) Sterling Publishing Co., Inc.

Pistoia, Sara. Counting. 2006. (MathBooks Ser.). (Illus.). 24p. (J). 24.21 (978-1-59296-685-1(3)) Child's World, Inc.

—Money. 2006. (MathBooks Ser.). (Illus.). 24p. (J). 24.21 (978-1-59296-689-9(6)) Child's World, Inc.

Play & Learn Fo, ed. Counting. 2007. (Play & Learn Foam Puzzle Bks.). 10p. (J). bds. 16.95 (***978-0-7696-5379-2(0)** , Brighter Child) School Specialty Publishing.

Play Bac Edu-Team, creator. EyeLike Numbers. 2007. (Illus.). 64p. (J). 9.95 (***978-1-60214-019-6(7)**) Play Bac Publishing, USA.

Pluckrose, Henry. Numbers & Counting. 2001. (Let's Explore Ser.). (Illus.). 32p. (J). (gr. 1 up). lib. bdg. 23.33 (978-0-8368-2964-8(6)) Stevens, Gareth Inc.

Pluckrose, Henry Arthur. How Many Are There? 2007. (Illus.). 32p. (J). (***978-1-59771-037-4(7)**) Sea-To-Sea Pubns.

Pocket Chart Math: Counting & Sorting. 2002. (J). pap. 9.95 (978-1-56911-079-9(4)) Learning Resources, Inc.

Poitier, Antonine & School Zone Staff. Counting Spin Wheel Board Books. 2006. (J). (ps-k). bds. 3.99 (***978-0-88743-609-3(9)**) School Zone Publishing Co.

Pomeroy, Diana. One Potato: A Counting Book of Potato Prints. 2000. (Illus.). 28p. (J). (ps-3). pap. 6.00 (978-0-15-202330-0(5) , Harcourt Paperbacks) Harcourt Children's Bks.

—One Potato: A Counting Book of Potato Prints. 2000. (978-0-606-18807-4(X)) Tandem Library Bks.

Porter, Matthew. Count the Birdies. 2007. (Illus.). 22p. (J). bds. 8.95 (978-1-894965-73-6(6)) Simply Read Bks. CAN. *Dist:* Perseus Distribution.

Potter, Beatrix. Count with Peter Rabbit. 2003. (Peter Rabbit Seedlings Ser.). (Illus.). 12p. (J). (ps). pap. 5.99 (978-0-7232-4913-9(X) , Warne) Penguin Group (USA) Inc.

Potter, Tony & Kolanovic, Dubravka. Counting with Albert & Amy: The Fun Way! Kolanovic, Dubravka, illus. 2005. (Illus.). 10p. (J). (gr. 2-5). bds. 5.95 (978-1-59125-567-3(8)) Penton Overseas, Inc.

Pountney, Beth. Farmyard Friends. 2007. (Lift & Count Ser.). (Illus.). 12p. (ps). per., bds. 5.95 (978-1-84610-458-9(0)) Make Believe Ideas GBR. *Dist:* Ingram Pub. Services.

—Playful Pets. 2007. (Lift & Count Ser.). (Illus.). 12p. (ps). per., bds. 5.95 (978-1-84610-459-6(9)) Make Believe Ideas GBR. *Dist:* Ingram Pub. Services.

Practice Pals Bilingual Practice Book: Counting. 2006. (ENG & FRE., Illus.). 16p. (J). (ps-1). spiral bd. (978-1-930355-53-8(X)) Greenbrier/Scentex.

Practice Power Bilingual Practice Pals: Counting. 2003. (Illus.). 16p. (J). (ps-1). spiral bd. (978-1-930355-49-1(1)) Greenbrier/Scentex.

Practice Power Practice Book Counting. 2001. (Illus.). 18p. (J). (ps-1). spiral bd. (978-1-930355-35-4(1)) Greenbrier/Scentex.

Prelutsky, Jack. Halloween Countdown. Yaccarino, Dan, illus. 2002. 24p. (J). (ps-1). 6.99 (978-0-06-000512-2(2)) HarperCollins Pubs.

Priddy Books Staff. First Concepts: Numbers. 2003. (Illus.). (J). bds. (978-0-312-49232-8(4) , Priddy Bks.) St. Martin's Pr.

Priddy, Roger. Baby Gund Numbers. 2005. (Illus.). 24p. (J). (ps-ps). bds. 5.95 (978-0-312-49516-9(1) , Priddy Bks.) St. Martin's Pr.

—Baby Gund Rattle Cloth Book Counting Bugs. 2006. 8p. (J). 7.95 (***978-0-312-49842-9(X)** , Priddy Bks.) St. Martin's Pr.

—Bright Baby 1 2 3. 2004. (Illus.). (J). bds. 4.95 (978-0-312-49266-3(9) , Priddy Bks.) St. Martin's Pr.

—Counting Colors (large Format) 2007. 20p. (J). 8.95 (***978-0-312-50137-2(4)** , Priddy Bks.) St. Martin's Pr.

—Counting Colors Padded Board Book. 2005. (Illus.). 22p. (J). bds. 10.95 (978-0-312-49458-2(0)) St. Martin's Pr.

—Early Learning Activity Pack - Numbers. 2007. 53p. (J). 14.95 (***978-0-312-49967-9(1)** , Priddy Bks.) St. Martin's Pr.

—First Learning Animals: Sticker Activity Animals. rev. ed. 2003. (Sticker Activity Ser.). (Illus.). 20p. (J). pap. 5.95 (978-0-312-49188-8(3) , Priddy Bks.) St. Martin's Pr.

—First Learning Numbers: Sticker Activity Numbers. 2003. (Illus.). 20p. (J). 5.95 (978-0-312-49160-4(3) , Priddy Bks.) St. Martin's Pr.

—First Learning Trucks. rev. ed. 2003. (Sticker Activity Ser.). (Illus.). 20p. (J). pap. 5.95 (978-0-312-49187-1(5) , Priddy Bks.) St. Martin's Pr.

—Happy Baby: 123. rev. ed. 2001. (Baby Soft-to-Touch Ser.). (Illus.). 28p. (J). bds. 5.95 (978-0-312-49023-2(2) , Priddy Bks.) St. Martin's Pr.

—My Little Counting Book. 2005. (Illus.). 28p. (J). bds. 9.95 (978-0-312-49435-3(1) , Priddy Bks.) St. Martin's Pr.

—Smart Baby Let's Count. 2007. 22p. (J). bds. 12.95 (***978-0-312-50036-8(X)** , Priddy Bks.) St. Martin's Pr.

—Wipe Clean Numbers. rev. ed. 2004. (Wipe Clean Ser.). (Illus.). 28p. (J). 8.95 (978-0-312-49264-9(2) , Priddy Bks.) St. Martin's Pr.

—123: Spanish/English Bilingual. 2004. (Happy Baby). (SPA & ENG., Illus.). 28p. (J). bds. 5.95 (978-0-312-49235-9(9) , Priddy Bks.) St. Martin's Pr.

Priddy, Roger, et al. Counting Colors. Brown, Richard, photos by. rev. ed. 2004. (Illus.). 22p. (J). 9.95 (978-0-312-49258-8(8) , Priddy Bks.) St. Martin's Pr.

Prodan, John. Count with Me. 2000. (Illus.). 24p. (J). (ps-k). pap. 8.00 (978-0-8059-4910-0(0)) Dorrance Publishing Co., Inc.

Pruett, Scott & Pruett, Judy. Twelve Little Race Cars. Eytchison, Glen, ed. Dietz, Mike & Toft, Kevin, illus. 1999. 32p. (J). (ps-3). 12.95 (978-0-9670600-0-2(1)) Word Weaver Bks., Inc.

Publications International Staff, contrib. by. Count Your Blessings 123. 2001. (My Wipe-Off Book Ser.). (Illus.). (J). (978-0-7853-5103-0(5)) Publications International, Ltd.

QEB Start Math Book Stores Edition: Counting - Book 2. 2006. (J). per. (978-1-59566-275-0(8)) QEB Publishing Inc.

QEB Start Maths National Book Stores Edition: Counting - Book 1. 2006. (J). per. (978-1-59566-271-2(5)) QEB Publishing Inc.

Quack! Quack! 2002. (Tab Board Books Ser.). 12p. (J). bds. 4.95 (978-0-7894-8474-1(9)) Dorling Kindersley Publishing, Inc.

Quadrillion Media Staff. Let's Learn 123. 1999. (J). pap. 1.99 (978-1-84100-284-2(4)) Quadrillion Media LLC.

—Let's Learn 123: Sticker Books. 1999. (J). pap. 3.99 (978-1-84100-297-2(6)) Quadrillion Media LLC.

—Peek-a-Boo Counting Animals Boardbook. 1999. (Peek-A-Boo Bks.). (Illus.). 12p. (ps). 5.95 (978-1-58185-216-5(9)) Quadrillion Media LLC.

—Toby Learns How to Count. 1999. bds. 3.95 (978-1-58185-208-0(8)) Quadrillion Media LLC.

Radabaugh, Melinda Beth. First Time 1 2 3. 2003. (First Time Ser.). (Illus.). 24p. (J). pap. 5.75 (978-1-4034-3884-3(6)) Heinemann Library.

—First Time 123. 2003. (First Time Ser.). (Illus.). 24p. (J). lib. bdg. 18.50 (978-1-4034-3869-0(2)) Heinemann Library.

—Me Corto el Cabello. (La Primera Vez (First Time) Ser.).Tr. of Getting a Haircut. 24p. pap. 5.25 (978-1-4034-0471-8(2)) Heinemann Library.

—Voy a la biblioteca. (La Primera Vez (First Time) Ser.). 24p. pap. 5.25 (978-1-4034-0476-3(3)) Heinemann Library.

Raintree Steck-Vaughn Staff. Cuantas Semillas Hay? 2000. (Coleccion en Parejas). (SPA.). (J). pap., stu. ed. 20.45 (978-0-7398-0831-3(1)) Steck-Vaughn.

—Cuantos Monos Hay? 1999. (Coleccion en Parejas). (SPA.). (J). pap., stu. ed. 21.50 (978-0-7398-0816-0(8)) Steck-Vaughn.

Rainy Day Counting: Big Book: Level C. 8p. 20.95 (978-0-322-00368-2(7)) Wright Group, The.

Ramos, Mario. Mama! 2005. Tr. of Mom!. (SPA., Illus.). 24p. (J). (ps-1). 14.50 (978-84-8470-145-3(X)) Corimbo, Editorial S.L. ESP. *Dist:* Lectorum Pubns., Inc.

Rand, Ann & Rand, Paul. Little 1. 2006. (Illus.). 40p. (J). 15.95 (978-0-8118-5004-9(8)) Chronicle Bks. LLC.

Raschka, Chris. Five for a Little One. Raschka, Chris, illus. 2006. (Illus.). 48p. (J). (ps-k). 16.95 (978-0-689-84599-4(5) , Atheneum/Richard Jackson Bks.) Simon & Schuster Children's Publishing.

Rathmann, Peggy. 10 Minutos Antes de Dormir. 2004. (SPA.). 46p. (J). (gr. k up). pap. 6.99 (978-980-257-276-2(4)) Ekare, Ediciones VEN. *Dist:* Lectorum Pubns., Inc., Iaconi, Mariuccia Bk. Imports.

Rauen, Amy. Counting at the Market. 2008. (J). pap. (***978-0-8368-8986-4(X)**); lib. bdg. (***978-0-8368-8981-9(9)**) Stevens, Gareth Inc.

—Counting at the Zoo. 2007. (J). pap. (***978-0-8368-8478-4(7)**); 24p. (gr. 1-3). lib. bdg. 19.93 (***978-0-8368-8469-2(8)**) Stevens, Gareth Inc. (Weekly Reader Early Learning Library).

—Usamos Matematicas en la Fiesta Del Salon. 2007. (SPA & ENG.). (J). pap. (***978-0-8368-8502-6(3)** , Weekly Reader Early Learning Library) Stevens, Gareth Inc.

—Usamos Matematicas en la Fiesta del Salon (Using Math at the Class Party) 2007. (Matematicas en Nuestro Mundo (Math in Our World) Ser.). (SPA.). 24p. (J). (gr. 1-3). lib. bdg. 19.93 (***978-0-8368-8493-7(0)** , Weekly Reader Early Learning Library) Stevens, Gareth Inc.

—Using Math Outdoors. 2008. (J). pap. (***978-0-8368-8989-5(4)**); lib. bdg. (***978-0-8368-8984-0(3)**) Stevens, Gareth Inc.

Read-Think-Do Math: Counting Book 1. 2006. pap. 4.49 (978-1-4206-8164-2(8)) Teacher Created Materials, Inc.

Read-Think-Do Math: Counting Book 2. 2006. pap. 4.49 (978-1-4206-8168-0(0)) Teacher Created Materials, Inc.

Really Big Coloring Books Staff. ABC 123 Learn My Letters & Numbers. l.t. ed. 2003. Orig. Title: 123-ABC Learn My Letters & Numbers. (Illus.). 321p. (J). (978-0-9729753-1-5(4)) Really Big Coloring Bks., Inc.

Realtime Associates and Mazer Corporation Staff & Leap-Frog Staff, compiled by. Skip Count to 100 by Two, Five, & Ten. 2002. (J). (gr. 2). 66.75 (978-1-58605-330-7(2) , LeapFrog Schl. Hse.) LeapFrog Enterprises, Inc.

Reece, Stephen. The Little Trucker Counting Book. 1998. 16p. (J). (ps-3). pap. 3.65 (978-1-892388-01-8(4)) Little Trucker Bks.

Reidy, Hannah. Crazy Creatures Counting. Mackie, Clare, illus. 2003. (Crazy Creatures Ser.). 26p. (J). pap. (978-1-84089-220-8(X) , Zero to Ten, Limited) Evans Publishing Group.

Reiser, Lynn. Hardworking Puppies. 2006. (Illus.). 40p. (J). 16.00 (978-0-15-205404-5(9)) Harcourt Trade Pubs.

Reiser, Lynn W. Two Dogs Swimming. Reiser, Lynn W., illus. 2005. (Illus.). 32p. (J). 15.99 (978-0-06-008647-3(5)) HarperCollins Pubs.

Reiter, Cheryl & Braddock, Paige, eds. Peanut's Counting Book. Hogan, Jayne, illus. 2000. 10p. (J). mass mkt. 9.99 (978-1-887327-68-8(1)) Ertl Co., Inc.

Rey, H. A. Curious George Learns to Count from 1 to 100: Counting , Grouping, Mapping, & More! Hines, Anna Grossnickle, illus. 2005. 64p. (J). (ps-k). bds. 16.00 (978-0-618-47602-2(4)) Houghton Mifflin Co. Trade & Reference Div.

Reynolds, Cynthia Furlong. Fishing for Numbers: A Maine Number Book. Brett, Jeannie, illus. 2005. (Count Your Way Across the USA Ser.). 40p. (J). (gr. k-5). 16.95 (978-1-58536-035-2(X)) Sleeping Bear Pr.

Rhodes, Karen. Numeros en la Biblia. 2004. (SPA., Illus.). 16p. (J). pap. 1.89 (***978-1-59317-062-2(9)**) Warner Pr. Pubs.

Rice, Judy. Counting Fair. 2007. 20p. (J). per. 10.95 (***978-1-59594-173-2(8)** , Wingspan Pr.) WingSpan Publishing.

Rigol, Francesc, illus. Los Numeros. 2002. (Aprendo con Dan y Din Ser.).Tr. of Numbers. (SPA.). 10p. (ps). 4.95 (978-84-7864-523-7(3)) Combel Editorial, S.A. ESP. *Dist:* Independent Pubs. Group.

Ring! Ring! 2002. (Tab Board Books Ser.). 12p. (J). bds. 4.95 (978-0-7894-8475-8(7)) Dorling Kindersley Publishing, Inc.

Ring, Susan. Cuantos Peces? 2005. Tr. of How Many Fish?. (SPA., Illus.). 16p. (J). (gr. k-1). lib. bdg. 15.93 (978-0-7368-4130-6(X)) Capstone Pr., Inc.

—Cuenta tus Gallinas. 2005. Tr. of Count Your Chickens. (SPA., Illus.). 16p. (J). (gr. k-1). lib. bdg. 15.93 (978-0-7368-4151-1(2)) Capstone Pr., Inc.

—Matemuticas y Dinero. Ramos, Gloria, tr. 2005. (SPA., Illus.). 20p. (J). 15.93 (978-0-7368-4156-6(3) , Yellow Umbrella Bks.) Capstone Pr., Inc.

—Money Math. 2003. (J). 15.93 (978-0-7368-2934-2(2)); pap. (978-0-7368-2893-2(1)) Yellow Umbrella Pr.

—One Green Frog. 2003. (Illus.). 17p. (J). 15.93 (978-0-7368-2917-5(2)); pap. (978-0-7368-2876-5(1)) Yellow Umbrella Pr.

Ringler, Matt. One Little, Two Little, Three Little Apples. Kennedy, Anne, illus. 2005. (J). pap. (***978-0-439-77500-7(0)**) Scholastic, Inc.

Riordan, James. Little Bunny Bobkin. Warnes, Tim, illus. 1999. 32p. (J). (ps-2). 14.95 (978-1-888444-38-4(X)) Little Tiger Pr.

Rivoli Group Staff, illus. Number Fun in Tarrytown. 2000. (Jay Jay the Jet Plane's Ready, Set, Let's Learn! Bks.). 10p. (J). (ps-k). 6.95 (978-1-58117-099-3(8) , Intervisual/Piggy Toes) Dalmatian Pr.

Robert, Christi. One Baby, Two Baby, Three Baby, Four! Bischel, Mark, illus. 1998. 16p. (J). (ps). pap. 5.95 (978-1-891846-00-7(0)) Business Word, The.

Robinson, Alise. Blast Off! A Numbers Books. 2005. (Illus.). 16p. (J). (ps-k). per. 6.95 (978-1-58117-394-9(6) , Intervisual/Piggy Toes) Dalmatian Pr.

Rogers, Jacqueline. Kindergarten Count to 100. Rogers, Jacqueline, illus. 2004. (Illus.). 40p. (J). pap. 10.95 (978-0-439-60741-4(8) , Cartwheel Bks.) Scholastic, Inc.

Roll Over: Individual Title Six-Packs. (Literatura 2000 Ser.). (gr. 1-2). 28.00 (978-0-7635-0150-1(6)) Rigby Education.

Romeo Rabbit Counting in the Garden. 2006. (J). 11.99 (978-0-439-84309-6(X) , Scholastic) Scholastic, Inc.

Root, Phyllis. One Duck Stuck. Chapman, Jane, illus. 2001. 32p. (J). (gr. k-ps). bds. 6.99 (978-0-7636-1104-0(2)) Candlewick Pr.

—One Duck Stuck. 2003. (gr. k-3). lib. bdg. 14.15 (978-0-613-60361-4(3)) Tandem Library Bks.

—One Duck Stuck: A Mucky Ducky Counting Book. Chapman, Jane, illus. (J). (gr. k-k). 2003. 40p. pap. 5.99 (978-0-7636-1566-6(8)); 1998. 32p. 15.99 (978-0-7636-0334-2(1)) Candlewick Pr.

Rose, Deborah Lee. One Nighttime Sea. Jenkins, Steve, illus. 2003. 40p. (J). pap. 16.95 (978-0-439-33906-3(5)) Scholastic, Inc.

—The Twelve Days of Kindergarten: A Counting Book. Armstrong-Ellis, Carey, illus. 2003. 30p. (J). (ps-1). 14.95 (978-0-8109-4512-8(6)) Abrams, Harry N. , Inc.

—The Twelve Days of Winter: A School Counting Book. Armstrong-Ellis, Carey, illus. 2006. 32p. (J). (ps-3). 14.95 (978-0-8109-5472-4(9) , Abrams Bks. for Young Readers) Abrams, Harry N. , Inc.

Rosen, Michael J. Chanukah Lights Everywhere. Iwai, Melissa, illus. 2000. (J). (978-0-15-201810-8(7)) Harcourt Trade Pubs.

Ross, Odette. Counting. 2007. (Wordless Board Bks.). (Illus.). 12p. (J). (ps). bds. 5.95 (***978-1-894965-91-0(4)**) Simply Read Bks. CAN. *Dist:* Perseus Distribution.

Roth, Carol. Ten Dirty Pigs, Ten Clean Pigs. Paparone, Paula, illus. 2002. 32p. (J). pap. 6.95 (978-0-7358-1569-8(0)) North-South Bks., Inc.

—Ten Dirty Pigs, Ten Clean Pigs. 1999. (gr. k-3). lib. bdg. 15.25 (978-0-613-51415-6(7)) Tandem Library Bks.

Roth, Susan L. Night-Time Numbers: A Scary Counting Book. 1999. (Barefoot Beginners Ser.). (Illus.). 32p. (J). (ps-k). 15.95 (978-1-84148-001-5(0)) Barefoot Bks., Inc.

Rothstein, Gloria L. Sheep Asleep. Date not set. 224p. (J). (ps-1). pap. 4.99 (978-0-06-443717-2(5)) HarperCollins Pubs.

Rovetch, Lissa. 1,2,3 Octopus & Me. Gévry, Claudine, illus. 2006. (J). (978-1-58987-011-6(5)) Kindermusik International.

Rowe, Jeannette, illus. YoYo's Numbers. 2002. 10p. (J). 3.95 (978-1-58925-683-5(2) , tiger tales) ME Media LLC.

Roy, Jennifer Rozines & Roy, Gregory. Money at the Store. 2006. (Math All Around Ser.). (Illus.). 32p. (J). lib. bdg. 28.50 (978-0-7614-2264-8(1) , Benchmark Bks.) Cavendish, Marshall Corp.

—Numbers on the Street. 2005. (Math All Around Ser.). (Illus.). 31p. (J). (978-0-7614-2002-6(9) , Benchmark Bks.) Cavendish, Marshall Corp.

Rubin, Alan. How Many Fish? 2003. (Yellow Umbrella Books). (Illus.). 16p. (J). (gr. 1). lib. bdg. 14.60 (978-0-7368-2013-4(2) , Pebble Bks.) Capstone Pr., Inc.

—How Many Fish? 2003. (Math Ser.). (J). (978-0-7368-1699-1(2)) Yellow Umbrella Pr.

Rubin, Susan Goldman & Thiebaud, Wayne. Counting with Wayne Thiebaud. 2007. (Illus.). 26p. (J). bds. 6.95 (978-0-8118-5720-8(4)) Chronicle Bks. LLC.

Rudy Cat Counting in the Garden. 2006. (J). 11.99 (978-0-439-84308-9(1) , Scholastic) Scholastic, Inc.

Ruffenach, Jessie, ed. Baby Learns to Count. Thomas, Peter, tr. Blacksheep, Beverly, illus. l.t. ed. 2003. (NAV & ENG.). 16p. (J). bds. 7.95 (978-1-893354-47-0(4)) Salina Bookshelf.

Rundstrom, Teressa. A Herd of Cows Came by My House. Waldron, Drue, illus. 2002. 50p. (J). per. (978-1-932062-39-7(4)) Hability Solution Services, Inc.

Running Press Staff. Numbers. 2003. (Illus.). 8p. (J). pap. 4.95 (978-0-7624-1525-0(8)) Running Pr. Bk. Pubs.

Running Press Staff & Mann, Holly. Numbers. 2003. (Magic Windows Ser.). (Illus.). 8p. (J). pap. 4.95 (978-0-7624-1510-6(X) , Running Pr. Kids) Running Pr. Bk. Pubs.

Salisbury, Kent. Route 1-2-3: Follow the Road Through the World of Numbers. 1998. (Illus.). 13p. (J). (ps-k). 6.99 (978-0-7681-0085-3(2) , McClanahan Bk.) Learning Horizons, Inc.

SAMi. Seven Little Teddy Bears. 2007. (Illus.). 18p. (J). bds. 14.95 (978-1-59354-597-0(5)) Blue Apple Bks.

Samuel, Stuart. One, Two, Three! This Book 's for Me! 2002. (Illus.). 26p. (J). 11.95 (978-0-9655176-5-2(9)) Jupiter Scientific Publishing Co.

San Diego Zoo Staff. Count to 10 & Back Again: San Diego Zoo. 2004. (Illus.). 24p. (J). 7.95 (978-0-8249-6552-5(3)) Ideals Pubns.

Sanchez, Juanvi. Seis. (SPA.). (J). bds. (978-84-348-7184-7(X)) SM Ediciones ESP. *Dist:* Lectorum Pubns., Inc.

Sanchez, Richard. Numeros (Numbers) (SPA.). (J). 4.95 (978-84-243-2190-1(1)) Publicaciones Fher, S.A. ESP. *Dist:* AIMS International Bks., Inc.

Sander, Sonia. Care Bears. Johnson, Jay, illus. 2004. (Care Bears Ser.). 8p. (J). bds. 5.99 (978-0-439-54961-5(2)) Scholastic, Inc.

Sanders, Nancy I. Adventures with Numbers. 1998. (Archy's Activity Bks.). (Illus.). 16p. (J). (ps-2). pap. 3.99 (978-0-570-05078-0(2)) Concordia Publishing Hse.

Santillo, LuAnn. Liz. Santillo, LuAnn, ed. 2003. (Half-Pint Kids Readers Ser.). (Illus.). 7p. (J). (ps-1). pap. (978-1-59256-037-7(0)) Half-Pint Kids, Inc.

Sarfatti, Esther. Contar: de Cinco en Cinco/Counting by: Fives. 2008. (Conceptos (Bilingual) Ser.). (SPA & ENG., Illus.). 24p. (J). (gr. 3-7). lib. bdg. (*978-1-60044-747-1(3)) Rourke Publishing, LLC.

—Contar: de DOS en DOS/Counting by: Twos. 2008. (Conceptos (Bilingual) Ser.). (SPA & ENG., Illus.). 24p. (J). lib. bdg. (*978-1-60044-750-1(3)) Rourke Publishing, LLC.

—Contar: de Tres en Tres/Counting by: Threes. 2008. (Conceptos (Bilingual) Ser.). (SPA & ENG., Illus.). 24p. (J). lib. bdg. (*978-1-60044-749-5(X)) Rourke Publishing, LLC.

—Counting By: Fives. 2008. (J). (*978-1-60044-521-7(7)) Rourke Publishing, LLC.

—Counting By: Tens. 2008. (J). (*978-1-60044-522-4(5)) Rourke Publishing, LLC.

—Counting By: Threes. 2008. (J). (*978-1-60044-523-1(3)) Rourke Publishing, LLC.

—Counting By: Twos. 2008. (J). (*978-1-60044-524-8(1)) Rourke Publishing, LLC.

Sargent, Brian. Guess the Order. 2006. 32p. (gr. 1-2). (YA). pap. 5.95 (978-0-516-29809-2(7)); (Illus.). (J). 20.50 (978-0-516-24963-6(0)) Scholastic Library Publishing. (Children's Pr.).

—Pen Pals Compare. (J). 2006. 32p. (gr. 1-2). pap. 5.95 (978-0-516-25363-3(8)); 2005. (Illus.). 31p. (ps-ps). 20.50 (978-0-516-25262-9(3)) Scholastic Library Publishing. (Children's Pr.).

Saul, Carol P. Barn Cat: A Counting Book. Azarian, Mary, illus. 2000. (J). 12.75 (978-0-606-19836-3(9)) Tandem Library Bks.

Sayre, April Pulley & Sayre, Jeff. One Is a Snail, Ten Is a Crab: A Counting by Feet Book. Cecil, Randy, illus. 40p. (J). (gr. k-3). 2006. pap. 6.99 (978-0-7636-2631-0(7)); 2003. 15.99 (978-0-7636-1406-5(8)) Candlewick Pr.

Scagliotti, Loti. Silly Number Nonsense. 2006. (Silly Word & Number Stories Ser.). (Illus.). 28p. (J). 12.95 (978-9974-7960-1-0(6)) Hardenville SA URY. *Dist:* Independent Pubs. Group.

Scarry, Richard. Richard Scarry's Best Counting Book Ever. Scarry, Richard, illus. 2004. (SPA & ENG., Illus.). 40p. 14.95 (978-0-87358-875-1(4) , Rising Moon Bks. for Young Readers); (J). pap. 8.95 (978-0-87358-876-8(2) , Luna Rising) Northland Publishing.

Scarry, Richard, illus. Counting to Ten Jigsaw Book: With Six 24-Piece Jigsaws Inside. 2004. 12p. (J). bds. (978-1-74124-406-9(4)) Five Mile Pr. Pty Ltd. The.

Schachner, Judy. Skippyjon Jones 1-2-3. 2008. 12p. (J). (ps). pap. 6.99 (*978-0-525-47956-7(2) , Dutton Juvenile) Penguin Group (USA) Inc.

—Skippyjon Jones Shapes Up. 2008. 12p. (J). (ps). pap. 6.99 (*978-0-525-47957-4(0) , Dutton Juvenile) Penguin Group (USA) Inc.

Schaefer, Adam. How Much Is It? A Book about Counting Coins. 2007. (Illus.). 24p. (J). (978-1-59515-978-6(9)); pap. (*978-1-59515-949-6(5)) Rourke Publishing, LLC.

Schaefer, Carole Lexa. One Wheel Wobbles. Morgan, Pierr, illus. 2003. 32p. (J). (ps-3). 15.99 (978-0-7636-0472-1(0)) Candlewick Pr.

Schaefer, Lola M. Animales Acorazados 123. 2002. (Animales Acorazados (Musty-Crusty Animals) Ser.). (SPA.). 24p. (J). (ps-1). lib. bdg. 18.50 (978-1-58810-859-3(7)); (Illus.). pap. 5.25 (978-1-58810-821-0(X) , 91556) Heinemann Library.

—Animales Resbalosos 123. 2002. (Animales Resbalosos (Ooey-Gooey Animals) Ser.). (SPA.). 24p. (J). (ps-1). lib. bdg. 18.50 (978-1-58810-769-5(8)); (Illus.). pap. 5.25 (978-1-58810-813-5(9)) Heinemann Library.

—Body Pairs. 2003. (It's My Body Ser.). (Illus.). 24p. (J). (ps-1). lib. bdg. 18.50 (978-1-4034-0895-2(5)); pap. (978-1-4034-3479-1(4)) Heinemann Library.

—Homes 1 2 3. 2003. (Heinemann Read & Learn Ser.). (Illus.). 24p. (J). pap. 5.25 (978-1-4034-0482-4(8)) Heinemann Library.

—Homes 123. 2003. (Home for Me Ser.). (Illus.). 24p. (J). (ps-1). lib. bdg. 18.50 (978-1-4034-0259-2(0)) Heinemann Library.

—Musty-Crusty Animals 123. 2002. (Musty-Crusty Animals Ser.). (Illus.). 24p. (J). (ps-1). pap. 5.25 (978-1-58810-728-2(0) , 91379); lib. bdg. 17.08 (978-1-58810-519-6(9)) Heinemann Library.

—Ooey-Gooey Animals 123. 2002. (Ooey-Gooey Animals Ser.). (Illus.). 24p. (J). (ps-1). pap. 5.25 (978-1-58810-720-6(5) , 91370); lib. bdg. 17.08 (978-1-58810-511-0(3)) Heinemann Library.

—Pares del Cuerpo. (Es Mi Cuerpo (It's My Body) Ser.).Tr. of Body Pairs. 24p. pap. 5.25 (978-1-4034-3384-8(4)) Heinemann Library.

—Piernas, Rodillas, Pies y Dedos. (Es Mi Cuerpo (It's My Body) Ser.).Tr. of Legs, Knees, Feet, & Toes. 24p. pap. 5.25 (978-1-4034-3385-5(2)) Heinemann Library.

—Tiny-Spiny Animals 123. 2003. (Heinemann Read & Learn Ser.). (Illus.). 24p. (J). pap. 5.25 (978-1-4034-3514-9(6)); lib. bdg. 18.50 (978-1-4034-3322-0(4)) Heinemann Library.

Schaefer, Ted. ¿Cuanto Es un Par? 2007. (J). (*978-1-60044-284-1(6)) Rourke Publishing, LLC.

—Harvest Time. 2007. (Illus.). 24p. (J). (978-1-59515-975-5(4)); pap. (*978-1-59515-946-5(0)) Rourke Publishing, LLC.

—How Many Is a Pair? 2007. (Illus.). 24p. (J). (978-1-59515-976-2(2)); pap. (*978-1-59515-947-2(9)) Rourke Publishing, LLC.

Schaefer, Ted. Tiempo de Cosecha. 2007. (J). (*978-1-60044-282-7(X)) Rourke Publishing, LLC.

Schafer, Kevin. Penguins 123. (Penguins Ser.). (Illus.). (ps up). 2004. 28p. (J). bds. 6.95 (978-1-55971-906-3(0)); 2002. 32p. 14.95 (978-1-55971-830-1(7)) T&N Children's Publishing. (NorthWord Bks. for Young Readers).

Schieber, Jennifer. Counting at the Olympics. ed. 2004. (Shared Connections Ser.). (J). pap. 27.00 (978-1-4108-1632-0(X)); pap., instr.'s gde. ed. 27.00 (978-1-4108-1608-5(7)) Benchmark Education Co.

Schmandt-Besserat, Denise. The History of Counting. Hays, Michael, illus. 1999. 48p. (J). (gr. 3 up). 18.99 (978-0-688-14118-9(8)); (ps-7). lib. bdg. 18.89 (978-0-688-14119-6(6)) HarperCollins Pubs.

Schnetzler, Pattie L. Ten Little Dinosaurs. Harris, Jim, illus. gif. ed. 2002. 28p. (J). bds. 24.99 (978-1-57939-115-7(X)) Accord Publishing, Ltd.

Scholastic Editorial Staff. Learn with Lego: Numbers. 2007. (Lego Ser.). (J). bds. 5.99 (*978-0-439-89337-4(2)) Scholastic, Inc.

Scholastic, Inc. Staff. Barney's Christmas Countdown. 2007. (Barney Ser.). 12p. (J). bds. 3.99 (*978-0-545-00061-1(0)) Scholastic, Inc.

—Classic Counting Rhymes. Wright, Blanche Fisher & Yee, Josie, illus. 2002. (Real Mother Goose Library Ser.). 8p. (J). bds. 5.99 (978-0-439-39535-9(6)) Scholastic, Inc.

—Count to 100 with the NBA. 2001. (J). (978-0-606-22222-8(7)) Tandem Library Bks.

—Counting Penguins. 2000. (Illus.). (J). (ps-3). 4.95 (978-0-439-15516-8(9)) Scholastic, Inc.

—Counting to 100. 2005. 5.99 (*978-0-439-73282-6(4) , Teaching Resources) Scholastic, Inc.

—Five Little Stars. 2007. (Little Scholastic Ser.). (Illus.). 12p. (J). bds. 7.99 (*978-0-439-02148-7(0)) Scholastic, Inc.

Scholastic, Inc. Staff, ed. Comptons les Animaux Grandeur Nature.Tr. of Lifesize Animal Counting Book. (FRE., Illus.). (J). 16.99 (978-0-590-24358-2(6)) Scholastic, Inc.

—Lifesize Animal Counting Book. (Illus.). (J). (ps). pap. 16.95 (978-0-590-24270-7(9)) Scholastic, Inc.

Scholastic, Inc. Staff & Schreiber, Anne. Jumpstart Pre-k: Counting 1-20. del Sur, Duendes, illus. 2000. (Jumpstart Ser.). 32p. (J). (ps). pap., wbk. ed. 3.99 (978-0-439-16422-1(2)) Scholastic, Inc.

Scholastic, Inc. Staff & White Heat Ltd. Staff. My School Box. Tong, Willabel, illus. 2004. (J). bds. 9.99 (978-0-439-61092-6(3) , Cartwheel Bks.) Scholastic, Inc.

Schonberg, Marcia. Cardinal Numbers: An Ohio Counting Book. Langton, Bruce, illus. 2002. 40p. (J). 16.95 (978-1-58536-084-0(8)) Sleeping Bear Pr.

—Discover Ohio, 2 bks. Langton, Bruce, illus. 2003. 40p. (J). 27.95 (978-1-58536-225-7(5)) Sleeping Bear Pr.

School Specialty Publishing. Counting & Numbers with Mr Wiggle. 2003. 32p. (J). (gr. k up). pap. 5.99 (978-1-56451-990-0(2) , ID99006); (gr. 1 up). pap. 5.99 (978-1-56451-991-7(0) , ID99007) School Specialty Publishing.

—Matching & Counting. 2000. (Funtastic Frogs Activity Cards Ser.). 18p. (J). (gr. k-2). 8.99 (978-1-56451-344-1(0)) School Specialty Publishing.

—Mathematics: A Step-by-Step Approach. 1999. (Practice Drills Ser.). 86p. (J). (gr. 1-1). pap. 2.99 (978-0-88012-452-2(0) , IF0110, Instructional Fair) Schaffer, Frank Pubns.

—Numbers 1 - 10, Preschool. 2006. (Skills for Scholars Ser.). 80p. (C). pap. 4.99 (*978-0-7696-5039-5(2) , Schaffer, Frank) Schaffer, Frank Pubns.

—Numbers 1-10. 2004. (On-File Ser.). 4p. (J). (gr. k-k). ring bd. 4.99 (978-0-7424-2876-8(1) , Instructional Fair) Schaffer, Frank Pubns.

—Numbers 1 to 26. 2006. (Brighter Child Flash Cards Ser.). 54p. (J). 2.99 (978-0-7696-4739-5(1) , Brighter Child) School Specialty Publishing.

—Numbers 1 to 26 / Numeros del 1 Al 26. 2006. (Brighter Child Flash Cards Ser.). 54p. (J). 2.99 (978-0-7696-4789-0(8) , Brighter Child) School Specialty Publishing.

School Specialty Publishing. Total Numbers & Counting Learn. 2007. (Total Learning Kits Ser.). 1028p. (J). pap. 49.95 (*978-0-7696-5499-7(1)) School Specialty Publishing.

School Specialty Publishing Staff & Douglas, Vincent. My Little Library of Counting. 2005. (My Little Library with CD Ser.). (Illus.). 120p. (J). (ps-ps). bds. 12.95 (978-1-58845-762-2(1)) School Specialty Publishing.

School Zone Interactive Staff. Flash Action Software Go Fish / Old Maid. 2005. (J). cd-rom 12.99 (978-1-58947-830-5(4)) School Zone Publishing Co.

School Zone Publishing Company Staff. Counting 1-10. (Illus.). (J). 19.99 incl. audio compact disk (978-0-88743-925-4(X)) School Zone Publishing Co.

—Counting 1-10 Bilingual: Get Ready! 2004. 64p. (J). pap. 3.79 (978-1-58947-973-9(4)) School Zone Publishing Co.

—Numbers 1-100. rev. ed. 1999. (Flash Cards Ser.). 56p. (J). 2.79 (978-0-938256-90-8(4) , 04005) School Zone Publishing Co.

—Trim the Tree 1, 2, 3: A Numbers Book. 1999. (Board Books Ser.). (Illus.). 16p. (J). (ps-3). bds. 4.99 (978-0-88743-600-0(5) , 06601) School Zone Publishing Co.

—You Can't Scare Me: A Book of Numbers. 2000. (Illus.). 18p. (J). bds. 4.99 (978-0-88743-604-8(8) , 06605) School Zone Publishing Co.

School Zone Staff. Old Maid. 2004. (J). 2.79 (978-1-58947-992-0(0)) School Zone Publishing Co.

School Zone Staff, ed. Preschool Counting Farm. 2006. 8p. (J). (gr. k). 5.99 (*978-1-58947-846-6(0)) School Zone Publishing Co.

Schroeder, Lisa. Baby Can't Sleep. Garofoli, Viviana, illus. 2005. 32p. (J). (ps). 12.95 (978-1-4027-2171-7(4)) Sterling Publishing Co., Inc.

Schuepbach, Lynnette. Froggy Hollow. Schuepbach, Lynnette, illus. l.t. ed. 2004. (Illus.). 32p. (J). 7.00 net. (978-0-9759613-0-8(6)) Creative Sources.

Schuette, Sarah L. Eating Pairs: Counting Fruits & Vegetables by Twos. 2003. (A+ Counting Books). (Illus.). 16p. (J). (gr. k-1). 22.60 (978-0-7368-1676-2(3) , Aplus Bks.) Capstone Pr., Inc.

—3, 2, 1 Go! A Transportation Countdown. 2003. (A+ Counting Books). (Illus.). 32p. (J). (gr. k-1). lib. bdg. 22.60 (978-0-7368-1678-6(X) , Aplus Bks.) Capstone Pr., Inc.

Schulman, Janet. Countdown to Spring! An Animal Counting Book. So, Meilo, illus. 2004. 24p. (J). (gr. k-ps). bds. 6.99 (978-0-375-82695-5(5) , Knopf Bks. for Young Readers) Random Hse. Children's Bks.

—10 Trick-Or-Treaters: A Halloween Counting Book. Davick, Linda, illus. 2005. 32p. (J). (ps-3). 8.95 (978-0-375-83225-3(4) , Knopf Bks. for Young Readers) Random Hse. Children's Bks.

Schumacher, Bev. Count on Me! 2004. 20p. (J). lib. bdg. 9.95 (978-0-9741549-6-1(2)) Learning Props.

Schwartz, Betty Ann. The Spinning Book of Colors, Shapes, & Numbers. Berg, Michelle, illus. 2007. 16p. (J). (ps-1). 9.99 (978-0-06-079974-8(9) , Harper Festival) HarperCollins Pubs.

Schwartz, Betty Ann. Wiggly Worm: A We-Wiggle Book of Colors & Numbers. Sexton, Brenda, illus. 2008. 12p. (J). 9.99 (*978-0-06-113847-8(9) , Harper Festival) HarperCollins Pubs.

Schwartz, David M. Cuanto Es un Millon? Kellogg, Steven, illus. 2003. (SPA.). (J). (gr. k-3). pap. 3.96 net. (978-0-590-47393-4(X) , SO30942) Scholastic, Inc.

—How Much Is a Million? Kellogg, Steven, illus. 2000. (J). (gr. 1-4). pap. 12.95 incl. audio Weston Woods Studios, Inc.

Scillian, Devin. One Nation: America by the Numbers. Carroll, Pam, illus. 40p. (J). 2004. pap. 7.95 (978-1-58536-249-3(2)); 2002. 19.95 (978-1-58536-063-5(5)) Sleeping Bear Pr.

Sehmi, Amritpal Kaur. Punjabi Numbers & Stickers. Sehmi, Amritpal Kaur & Sarch, Oren, eds. Sarch, Gagan Kaur, illus. 2002. (PAN.). 18p. bds. 8.95 (978-0-9709736-0-3(8)) Small People Publishing.

Selway, Martina. So Many Babies: A Fun to Count Book. 2001. (Illus.). 32p. (J). 17.99 (978-0-09-176986-4(8)) Random Hse. GBR. *Dist:* Independent Pubs. Group.

Sempere, Vicky. 1-2-3 Vamos a Contar. Sempere, Vicky, illus. 1999. (Jardin de los Ninos Ser.). (SPA., Illus.). 24p. (J). (ps-1). pap. 6.99 (978-980-257-199-4(7)) Ekare, Ediciones VEN. *Dist:* Kane/Miller Bk. Pubs., Inc., Lectorum Pubns., Inc.

Seuss, Dr. Ten Apples up on Top! 1998. (Bright & Early Bks.). (Illus.). (J). bds. 4.99 (978-0-679-89343-1(1) , Random Hse. Bks. for Young Readers) Random Hse. Children's Bks.

Sevaly, Karen, ed. Hands on Learning: Numbers & Counting Dominoes. 2006. 12.99 (978-0-439-82401-9(X) , Teaching Resources) Scholastic, Inc.

Shahan, Sherry. Cool Cats Counting. Barragan, Paula, illus. 2005. (ENG & SPA.). 24p. (gr. k-2). 16.95 (978-0-87483-757-5(X)) August Hse. Pubs., Inc.

Sharp, Jean. Counting in the City. 2007. (J). pap. (*978-0-8368-8477-7(9)); 24p. (gr. 1-3). lib. bdg. 19.93 (*978-0-8368-8468-5(X)) Stevens, Gareth Inc. (Weekly Reader Early Learning Library).

Shaw, Cathy Conway. Fear No More the Missing Floor. Gajewski, Patty, illus. 2003. 48p. (J). lib. bdg. 19.95 (978-1-59098-821-3(3)) Wooster Bk. Co., The.

Shea, Pegi Deitz & Weill, Cynthia. Ten Mice for Tet. Trang, Ngoc, illus. 2003. 36p. (J). 15.95 (978-0-8118-3496-4(4)) Chronicle Bks. LLC.

Sheather, Allan. One Less Fish. Toft, Kim Michelle, illus. 1998. 32p. (J). (ps-3). 15.95 (978-0-88106-322-6(3)); pap. 6.95 (978-0-88106-323-3(1)) Charlesbridge Publishing, Inc.

Shepherd, Rajean Luebs. Nebraska Number. Appleoff, Sandy, illus. rev. ed. 2007. (State Counting Ser.). 40p. (J). 17.95 (*978-1-58536-190-8(9)) Sleeping Bear Pr.

Sherman, Janice. Colorful Critters. 2007. (ENG., Illus.). 10p. (J). pap. 4.99 (*978-0-9797139-2-7(7)) Jan's Looks & Bks.

—Colorful Critters Color Match Coloring Book. 2007. (ENG., Illus.). 10p. (J). pap. 1.99 (*978-0-9797139-3-4(5)) Jan's Looks & Bks.

—Counting Critters. 2007. (ENG., Illus.). 10p. (J). pap. 4.99 (*978-0-9797139-1-0(9)) Jan's Looks & Bks.

—Critters A-Z. 2007. (ENG., Illus.). 26p. (J). pap. 5.99 (*978-0-9797139-0-3(0)) Jan's Looks & Bks.

Shorten, Chris, photos by. One, Two, Three! My First Counting Book. 1999. (Illus.). 16p. (J). reprint ed. 5.95 (978-1-892374-19-6(6)) Weldon Owen, Inc.

Shostak, Myra. Rainbow Candles: A Hanukkah Counting Book. Springer, Sally, illus. 2003. 12p. (J). (ps up). bds. (978-1-58013-031-8(3)) Kar-Ben Publishing.

Shoulders, Michael. Count on Us: A Tennessee Number Book. Langton, Bruce, illus. 2003. 40p. (J). 16.95 (978-1-58536-131-1(3)) Sleeping Bear Pr.

—Discover Tennessee: Count on Us; V is for Volunteer, 2 bks. Langton, Bruce, illus. 2003. 40p. (J). 27.95 (978-1-58536-228-8(X)) Sleeping Bear Pr.

—1 Mississippi 2 Mississippi: A Mississippi Number Book. Anderson, Rick, illus. 2004. 40p. (J). 16.95 (978-1-58536-188-5(7)) Sleeping Bear Pr.

Shulman, Mark. I'll Take a Dozen! Miline, Bill, photos by. 2006. (Illus.). 12p. (J). (gr. k-4). reprint ed. 6.00 (978-1-4223-5725-5(2)) DIANE Publishing Co.

Siede, George & Press, Donna, photos by. Collections. 1998. (Active Minds Ser.). (Illus.). 40p. (J). bds. 12.98 (978-1-58048-032-1(2)) Sandvik Publishing.

—Counting. 1998. (Active Minds Ser.). (Illus.). 10p. (J). bds. 3.99 (978-1-58048-030-7(6)) Sandvik Publishing.

Sierra, Judy. Counting Crocodiles. Hillenbrand, Will, illus. 2001. 40p. (J). (gr. k-2). pap. 7.00 (978-0-15-216356-3(5) , Voyager Bks./Libros Viajeros) Harcourt Children's Bks.

—Counting Crocodiles. 2001. (ps-2). lib. bdg. 15.30 (978-0-613-82223-7(4)); 13.80 (978-0-606-22596-0(X)) Tandem Library Bks.

Silvano, Wendi. Counting Coconuts/Contando Cocos: A Counting Story in English & Spanish. Raven Tree Press Staff, ed. Granius, Marty, illus. 2004. Tr. of Contando Cocos. (SPA & ENG.). 32p. (J). (ps-3). 16.95 (978-0-9720192-6-2(X) , 626999) Raven Tree Pr.

Silverhardt, Lauryn. A contar con Blue (Counting with Blue) Style Guide Staff, illus. 2005. (Blue's Clues Ser.). (SPA.). 14p. (J). bds. 4.99 (978-0-689-87748-3(X) , Libros Para Ninos) Simon & Schuster Children's Publishing.

Silverman, Erica. Halloween House. 1999. (J). (978-0-606-17220-2(3)) Tandem Library Bks.

Sim, David. Matt's Mat: A Touch & Feel Counting Book, 2 vols. Sim, David, illus. 2003. (Illus.). 10p. (J). 7.95 (978-1-58117-198-3(6) , Intervisual/Piggy Toes) Dalmatian Pr.

Simmons, Al. Counting Feathers. Floca, Brian, illus. 2001. 32p. (J). (ps). pap. 4.95 (978-1-55285-275-0(X)) Whitecap Bks., Ltd. CAN. *Dist:* Firefly Bks., Ltd.

Simpson. Gretchen's 1-2-3. 1998. 32p. (J). 16.00 (978-0-06-024305-0(8)) HarperCollins Pubs.

Simson, Dana. Numbers. 2003. (Dana Simson Chunky Books Ser.). 10p. (J). bds. 2.95 (978-1-74047-259-3(4)) Book Co. Publishing Pty, Ltd., The AUS. *Dist:* Penton Overseas, Inc.

Sing & Learn, ed. Numbers & Counting. 2007. (Sing & Learn Padded Board Bks.). 53p. (J). bds. 16.95 (*978-0-7696-5459-1(2)) School Specialty Publishing.

Singer, Marilyn. City Lullaby. Cneut, Carll, illus. 2007. 32p. (J). (ps-3). 16.00 (*978-0-618-60703-7(X) , Clarion Bks.) Houghton Mifflin Co. Trade & Reference Div.

Singer, Marilyn. Quiet Night. Manders, John, illus. 2002. 32p. (J). (gr. k-ps). 15.00 (978-0-618-12044-4(0) , Clarion Bks.) Houghton Mifflin Co. Trade & Reference Div.

Sirett, Dawn & Dorling Kindersley Publishing Staff. My First 1 2 3 Play Book. 2004. (Illus.). 80p. (J). 12.99 (978-0-7566-0214-7(9)) Dorling Kindersley Publishing, Inc.

Siwak, Brenda S. Counting on the Bay. Dodge, Barbara A., illus. 2006. (J). per. 14.95 (*978-0-9790906-0-8(1)) Pleasant Plains Pr.

Siy, Alexandra. Old Macdonald had a Farm. Rogers, Jacqueline, illus. 2008. (J). (*978-0-8234-1923-4(1)) Holiday Hse., Inc.

Skinner, Daphne. Henry Keeps Score. 2001. (gr. k-3). lib. bdg. 12.95 (978-0-613-39326-3(0)); (Illus.). (J). 11.75 (978-0-606-20702-7(3)) Tandem Library Bks.

Slate, Joseph. Miss Bindergarten Celebrates the 100th Day of Kindergarten. 2002. (Miss Bindergarten Ser.). (Illus.). (YA). 15.53 (978-1-4046-2578-5(X)) Book Wholesalers, Inc.

Slater, Teddy. 98, 99, 100! Ready or Not Here I Come! Fiammenghi, Gioia, illus. 1999. (Hello Reader! Math Ser.: Level 2). 32p. (J). (gr. k-2). pap. 3.99 (978-0-590-12009-8(3) , Cartwheel Bks.) Scholastic, Inc.

—98, 99, 100! Ready or Not Here I Come! 1999. (Hello Reader! Ser.). (978-0-606-17538-8(5)) Tandem Library Bks.

Slaughter, Tom. One, Two, Three. Jocelyn, Marthe, illus. 2006. 16p. (J). (gr. k-k). bds. 7.95 (978-0-88776-788-3(5)) Tundra Bks., Inc./Livres Toundra, Inc. CAN. *Dist:* Random Hse., Inc.

—One, Two, Three. 2003. (Illus.). 24p. (J). (gr. k-k). 12.95 (978-0-88776-664-0(1)) Tundra Bks., Inc./Livres Toundra, Inc. CAN. *Dist:* Random Hse., Inc.

—Un, deux, Trois. Slaughter, Tom, illus. 2006. (FRE., Illus.). 24p. (J). (gr. k-k). pap. 7.95 (978-0-88776-802-6(4) , Livres Toundra) Tundra Bks., Inc./Livres Toundra, Inc. CAN. *Dist:* Random Hse., Inc.

Smith, Maggie. Counting Our Way to Maine. 1999. (ps-2). lib. bdg. 15.30 (978-0-613-72619-1(7)); (J). (978-0-606-16918-9(0)) Tandem Library Bks.

—One Naked Baby. 2007. (Illus.). 40p. (J). (ps-k). 15.99 (978-0-375-83329-8(3)); lib. bdg. 17.99 (978-0-375-93329-5(8)) Random Hse. Children's Bks. (Knopf Bks. for Young Readers).

Sollinger, Emily. Find the Sheep, Piggley! A Jakers! Counting Book. Entara Ltd. Staff, photos by. 2006. (Jakers! Ser.). 14p. (J). 7.99 (978-1-4169-0613-1(4) , Simon Spotlight) Simon & Schuster Children's Publishing.

Soper, Sandra. Counting Practice. 2003. (Illus.). 32p. pap. 6.99 (978-0-330-32079-5(3) , Pan) Pan Macmillan GBR. *Dist:* Trafalgar Square Publishing.

Soundprints. Pooh's First Concepts Pack. rev. ed. (First Concepts Ser.). (Illus.). 36p. (J). 12.99 incl. cd-rom (978-1-59069-363-6(9) , 1A502) Studio Mouse LLC.

Southwater Books Staff. Counting. 2002. (Playschool Ser.). (Illus.). 32p. (ps-2). pap. 5.95 (978-1-84215-608-7(X) , Southwater) Anness Publishing GBR. *Dist:* National Bk. Network.

Southwater Staff. Look & Learn Counting. 2001. (Look & Learn Ser.). (Illus.). 32p. (ps). 7.95 (978-1-84215-287-4(4)) Anness Publishing, Inc.

—Numbers: Look & Learn. 2000. (Look & Learn Ser.). (Illus.). 32p. (ps). 7.95 (978-1-84215-170-9(3) , Southwater) Anness Publishing GBR. *Dist:* National Bk. Network.

—Read, Count, Sort & Stick: Activity Play with over 200 Reusable Stickers. 2002. (Superstickers Ser.). (Illus.). 64p. (ps-k). pap. 7.95 (978-1-84215-426-7(5) , Southwater) Anness Publishing GBR. *Dist:* National Bk. Network.

Spelvin, Justin. Deep-Sea Countdown. McGee, Warner, illus. 2006. (Backyardigans Ser.). 26p. (J). bds. 5.99 (978-1-4169-1484-6(6) , Simon Spotlight/Nickelodeon) Simon & Schuster Children's Publishing.

Sper, Emily. Hanukkah: A Counting Book. 2001. (978-0-606-22155-9(7)) Tandem Library Bks.

—Hanukkah: A Counting Book in English - Hebrew - Yiddish. Sper, Emily, illus. 2003. (Hanukkah Ser.). (ENG, HEB & YID.). 28p. (J). pap. 5.99 (978-0-439-56704-6(1) , Cartwheel Bks.) Scholastic, Inc.

—Hanukkah: A Counting Book in English, Hebrew, & Yiddish. 2001. (HEB, YID & ENG., Illus.). 32p. (J). (ps-1). pap. 6.95 (978-0-439-28291-8(8) , Cartwheel Bks.) Scholastic, Inc.

Spotty e I Numeri. 1999. (ITA.). (J). pap. 8.95 (978-88-450-2774-1(0)) Fabbri - RCS Libri ITA. *Dist:* Distribooks, Inc.

Spowart, Robin. Ten Little Bunnies. Spowart, Robin, illus. 2001. (Illus.). 24p. (J). (ps). pap. 7.95 (978-0-439-20863-5(7)) Scholastic, Inc.

Spurr, Elizabeth. Two Bears Beneath the Stairs. Westcott, Nadine Bernard, illus. 2002. 16p. (J). (ps-1). 8.99 (978-0-689-84759-2(9) , Little Simon) Simon & Schuster Children's Publishing.

Stagno, Laura, illus. Yo Tenia 10 Perritos. 2004. (SPA.). 24p. (J). (gr. k up). pap. 6.50 (978-980-257-277-9(2)) Ekare, Ediciones VEN. *Dist:* Lectorum Pubns., Inc., Iaconi, Mariuccia Bk. Imports.

Steck-Vaughn Staff. Counting Baby Animals Big Book. 2002. (Illus.). (J). pap. (978-0-7398-5897-4(1)) Steck-Vaughn.

—Counting Rhymes: One Potato. 1998. (Illus.). (J). pap. (978-0-8172-8631-6(4)) Steck-Vaughn.

—Skip-Count by Threes. 2003. pap. 4.10 (978-0-7398-7660-2(0)) Steck-Vaughn.

Stemple, Heidi E. Y. One if by Land: A Massachusetts Number Book. Brett, Jeannie, illus. 2006. 40p. (J). 17.95 (978-1-58536-186-1(0)) Sleeping Bear Pr.

Sterling, Kristin. Money. 2008. (J). pap. (***978-0-8225-8848-1(X)***) Lerner Publishing Group.

Sterling Publishing Co., Inc., ed. Dot-to-Dot Count to 100. 2002. (Illus.). 64p. (J). pap. 4.95 (978-0-8069-8469-8(4)) Sterling Publishing Co., Inc.

—Dot-to-Dot Count to 20. 2002. (Illus.). 64p. (J). pap. 4.95 (978-0-8069-8463-6(5)) Sterling Publishing Co., Inc.

Sterling Publishing Company Staff. Bamboo's Sticker Book Counting Games. 1998. (Balloon Ser.). (Illus.). 16p. (J). (ps-k). pap. 5.95 (978-0-8069-9605-9(6)) Sterling Publishing Co., Inc.

—Benjamin Counts 1 to 10. 1999. (Adventures with Benjamin Bear Ser.). (Illus.). 10p. (ps-k). 5.95 (978-0-8069-1929-4(9)) Sterling Publishing Co., Inc.

—Learning to Count with Benjamin the Bear: Wipe & Clean Book. 1998. (Illus.). 14p. (J). (ps-1). pap. 5.95 (978-0-8069-9603-5(X)) Sterling Publishing Co., Inc.

Sterling Publishing Company Staff, ed. First Counting Games. 2000. (Billy the Bear Activity Bks.). (Illus.). 16p. (J). (ps-k). pap. 3.95 (978-0-8069-5591-9(0)) Sterling Publishing Co., Inc.

Stott, Dorothy, illus. Six Little Ducks. 2006. (Sing-A-Story Ser.). 16p. (J). bds. 10.95 (978-0-7696-5057-9(0)) School Specialty Publishing.

Studio Mouse. Disney Bunnies: Take-with-Me Counting: Zip & Carry Book & CD. rev. ed. 2007. 36p. 12.99 (***978-1-59069-568-5(2)***) Studio Mouse LLC.

—Princess ABC's & 123's. rev. ed. 2007. (Disney Princess Ser.). 24p. 4.99 (***978-1-59069-560-9(7)***) Studio Mouse LLC.

—Sesame Street: Counting All Around: Zip & Carry Book & CD. rev. ed. 2007. 36p. 12.99 (***978-1-59069-571-5(2)***) Studio Mouse LLC.

Sugita, Yutaka. Goodnight, One, Two, Three. Sugita, Yutaka, illus. (Illus.). 32p. (J). (ps-2). 14.95 (978-0-87592-022-1(5)) Scroll Pr., Inc.

Sullivan, Erin. Counting Clues. 2003. (Early Connections Ser.). (J). pap. 33.00 (978-1-4108-1094-6(1)) Benchmark Education Co.

Summers, Ginger. Cuantos Son Cincuenta: Metro Math Readers Yellow Level. 2000. (Metro Math Readers Yellow Level Ser.). (J). (gr. 1-2). 3.75 (978-1-58120-472-8(8)) Metropolitan Teaching & Learning Co.

—From Ten to One Hundred. 2000. (Metro Math Readers Yellow Level Ser.). (J). (gr. 1-2). 49.95 (978-1-58830-107-9(9)) Metropolitan Teaching & Learning Co.

—We Celebrate 100: Metro Math Readers Yellow Level. 2000. (Metro Math Readers Yellow Level Ser.). (J). (gr. 1-2). 3.75 (978-1-58120-410-0(8)) Metropolitan Teaching & Learning Co.

Swinburne, Stephen R. Water for One, Water for Everyone: A Counting Book of African Animals. Levine, Melinda, illus. 1998. (Fun Early Math Concepts Ser.). 32p. (ps-1). lib. bdg. 22.90 (978-0-7613-0269-8(7) , Millbrook Pr.) Lerner Publishing Group.

—What's a Pair? What's a Dozen? Swinburne, Stephen R., illus. 2003. (Illus.). 32p. (YA). (gr. k-2). 15.95 (978-1-56397-827-2(X)) Boyds Mills Pr.

Szekeres, Cyndy. I Can Count 100 Bunnies: And So Can You! 1999. (Illus.). 48p. (J). (ps-2). pap. 12.95 (978-0-590-38361-5(2)) Scholastic, Inc.

Szekeres, Cyndy & Cynthia, Cyndy, illus. Learn to Count Funny Bunnies. 2000. 12p. (J). (ps). bds. 6.99 (978-0-439-14994-5(0) , Cartwheel Bks.) Scholastic, Inc.

Tabletop Pocket Chart Counting & Numbers Card Set. 2004. (J). pap. 8.95 (978-1-56911-169-7(3)) Learning Resources, Inc.

Tafuri, Nancy. Counting to Christmas. 1998. (J). pap. (978-0-590-27144-8(X)) Scholastic, Inc.

Tang, Greg. Math Fables. Cahoon, Heather, illus. 2004. 40p. (J). pap. 16.95 (978-0-439-45399-8(2)) Scholastic, Inc.

—Math Fables. 2003. (Illus.). (J). pap. (978-0-439-45400-1(X)) Scholastic, Inc.

—Math Fables Too: Making Science Count. Morley, Taia, illus. 2007. 40p. (J). (ps-k). pap. 16.99 (***978-0-439-78351-4(8)*** , Scholastic Pr.) Scholastic, Inc.

—Math for All Seasons: Mind-Stretching Math Riddles. Briggs, Harry, illus. 2002. 40p. (J). pap. 16.95 (978-0-439-21042-3(9) , Scholastic Pr.) Scholastic, Inc.

—Math-Terpieces. 2003. (J). pap. (978-0-439-44389-0(X)) Scholastic, Inc.

—Math-Terpieces: The Art of Problem-Solving. Paprocki, Greg, illus. 2003. 32p. (J). pap. 16.95 (978-0-439-44388-3(1)) Scholastic, Inc.

Taragan, Barbara. Los Numeros 10 - 2000. (Metro Math Readers Red Level Ser.). (J). (gr. k-1). 41.95 (978-1-58830-523-7(6)) Metropolitan Teaching & Learning Co.

—The Numbers 10 - 2000. (Metro Math Readers Red Level Ser.). (J). (gr. k-1). 44.47 (978-1-58120-553-4(8)) Metropolitan Teaching & Learning Co.

Tarbett, Debbie. Five Little Ducks. Penton Overseas, Inc. Staff, ed. Tarbett, Debbie, illus. 2006. (Illus.). 16p. (J). (gr. 3-5). bds. 10.95 (978-1-59125-747-9(6) , Penton Kids) Penton Overseas, Inc.

Taylor-Butler, Christine. Ah-Choo. Koeller, Carol, illus. 2005. (My First Reader Ser.). (J). (gr. k-1). 31p. pap. 3.95 (978-0-516-25275-9(5)); 32p. 18.50 (978-0-516-25175-2(9)) Scholastic Library Publishing. (Children's Pr.).

Taylor, Geraldine & Harker, Jillian. Twinkle, Twinkle, Little Star. Sharratt, Nick, illus. 1999. (Baby Touch & Count Ser.). 12p. (J). 7.99 (978-0-7214-2737-9(5) , Dutton Juvenile) Penguin Group (USA) Inc.

Teddy Bear Counters. (Illus.). 24p. (J). (gr. k-2). pap. 6.95 (978-1-55254-043-5(X) , BV25001) Brighter Vision Pubns.

Ten Little Monkeys. 2002. (Puppy Tales Ser.). (Illus.). 24p. (J). (gr. k-3). 1.49 (978-1-57759-218-1(2)) Dalmatian Pr.

Ten Toads, Eleven Lizards: Consonants l, t. 2003. (J). 38.50 (978-0-8136-9129-9(X)) Modern Curriculum Pr.

Tenorio-Coscarelli, Jane. The Ants. Coscarelli, Nicole, tr. l.t. ed. 1998. Tr. of Hormigas. (SPA & ENG.). 32p. (J). (gr. k-4). pap. 11.95 (978-0-9653422-2-3(0)) Quarter-Inch Publishing.

Tetro, Marc. One, Two, Three. 2005. (Illus.). (J). (978-1-55278-434-1(7)) McArthur & Co.

Thayer, Tanya. Counting Money. 2005. (First Step Nonfiction Ser.). (Illus.). 24p. (gr. k-2). lib. bdg. 17.27 (978-0-8225-1258-5(0)) Lerner Publishing Group.

The White Stone Co., illus. Birds on a Wire. The White Stone Co., . 1998. (ENG.). 24p. (J). (ps-1). 7.95 (978-1-880122-06-8(5) , Little Shepherd Bks.) White Stone Co., The.

Thompson, Kim Mitzo & Mitzo Hilderbrand, Karen. Ten in the Bed. Ortner, Tammy, illus. 2005. (Read & Sing along Board Books with CDs Ser.). 18p. (J). (ps-k). bds., bds. 7.49 incl. audio compact disk (978-0-7696-4457-8(0)) School Specialty Publishing.

Thompson, Lauren. Little Quack's Hide & Seek. Anderson, Derek, illus. 2007. (Classic Board Bks.). 34p. (J). 7.99 (978-1-4169-0325-3(9) , Little Simon) Simon & Schuster Children's Publishing.

—Sat on the Go. Anderson, Derek, illus. 2006. 12p. (J). 7.99 (978-1-4169-0932-3(X) , Little Simon) Simon & Schuster Children's Publishing.

Thompson, Richard & Thompson, Ofa. Ko'eku Tohi Lau Fika. Lee, Bill, illus. 2003. (TOG.). 24p. (J). (ps up). pap. 5.00 (978-0-9678979-1-2(2)) Friendly Isles Pr.

Thong, Roseanne. One Is a Drummer: A Book of Numbers. Lin, Grace, illus. 2004. 40p. (J). 14.95 (978-0-8118-3772-9(6)) Chronicle Bks. LLC.

Thong, Roseanne. Ten Friendly Fireflies. 2007. 20p. 11.95 (***978-1-58117-561-5(2)***) Dalmatian Pr.

Thorne-Thomsen, Kathleen. A Shaker's Dozen: Counting Book. Thorne-Thomsen, Kathleen, illus. Rocheleau, Paul, photos by. 2003. (Illus.). 27p. (J). (gr. k-13). reprint ed. 16.00 (978-0-7567-9041-7(7)) DIANE Publishing Co.

Thornhill, Jan. The Wildlife ABC & 123: A Nature Alphabet & Counting Book. 2004. (Illus.). 64p. (J). 16.95 (978-1-897066-09-6(0)) Maple Tree Pr. CAN. *Dist:* Perseus Distribution.

Three Bear Family: Counting & Numbers Activity Book. 2003. (J). pap. 4.95 (978-1-56911-102-4(2)) Learning Resources, Inc.

Tofts, Hannah. One Cool Watermelon. 2006. (Things I Eat Ser.). (Illus.). 24p. (J). 12.95 (978-1-84089-450-9(4) , Zero to Ten, Limited) Evans Publishing Group GBR. *Dist:* Independent Pubs. Group.

—One Cool Watermelon. Horrox, Rupert, illus. Horrox, Rupert, photos by. 2006. (J). (***978-0-8368-7488-4(9)***); pap. (***978-0-8368-8143-1(5)***) Stevens, Gareth Inc.

Top That Publishing Staff. How Many. 2006. 10p. (978-1-84666-099-3(8)) Top That! Publishing PLC.

Top That Publishing Staff, ed. Counting. 2004. (Magnetic Play & Learn Ser.). (Illus.). 12p. (J). (978-1-84510-050-6(6)) Top That! Publishing PLC.

Top That!, ed. Counting on the Farm. Sapp, Karen, illus. 2007. 16p. (J). (ps). 14.99 (***978-1-84666-270-6(2)*** , Tide Mill Pr.) Top That! Publishing PLC GBR. *Dist:* Random Hse., Inc.

—In My Little Blue Bed. Henley, Claire, illus. 2007. 11p. (J). (ps). bds. 9.99 (***978-1-84666-280-5(X)*** , Tide Mill Pr.) Top That! Publishing PLC GBR. *Dist:* Random Hse., Inc.

—In My Little Pink Bed. Henley, Claire, illus. 2007. 11p. (J). (ps). bds. 9.99 (***978-1-84666-285-0(0)*** , Tide Mill Pr.) Top That! Publishing PLC GBR. *Dist:* Random Hse., Inc.

Topek, Susan Remick. Ten Good Rules: A Counting Book. Cohen, Tod, illus. 2007. 24p. (J). (ps-1). 15.95 (***978-0-8225-7293-0(1)***) Kar-Ben Publishing.

Touchable Counting Books Tote. 2005. (J). 14.95 (978-1-58117-284-3(2) , Intervisual/Piggy Toes) Dalmatian Pr.

Trease, Christine K. Count to Ten with Your Indian Friends. 2000. 18p. (J). (ps-4). cd-rom 14.95 (978-1-929450-11-4(7)) Lexico.

Tronick, Ed, contrib. by. Learn, Practice & Play Set: Beginning Counting. (Home Learning Tools(R) Ser.). 32p. (J). pap. 3.99 (978-1-4037-0776-5(6)) Dalmatian Pr.

Trottier, Maxine. One Is Canada. ed. 2004. (Illus.). (J). (gr. 1-5). spiral bd. (978-0-616-01797-5(9)) Canadian National Institute for the Blind/Institut National Canadien pour les Aveugles.

—One Is Canada. Slavin, Bill, illus. 2000. 32p. (J). pap. (978-0-00-638663-6(6)) HarperCollins Canada, Ltd.

—One Is Canada. Slavin, Bill, illus. 2000. 24p. (J). (ps-5). 17.95 (978-0-00-224556-2(6)) HarperCollins Pubs.

Tucker, Sian. My Book of First Numbers. Tucker, Sian, illus. 2003. (My Book of. . . Ser.). (Illus.). 48p. (YA). (978-1-85602-482-2(2)) Chrysalis Children's Bks.

Tulip, Jenny. On the Farm. 2000. (Illus.). 16p. (ps-k). pap. 5.00 (978-0-7548-0133-7(0)) Anness Publishing, Inc.

—Playtime. 2000. (Illus.). 16p. (ps-k). pap. 5.00 (978-0-7548-0134-4(9)) Anness Publishing, Inc.

Tuxworth, Nicola. Numbers. 2005. (Illus.). 12p. (gr. 2-13). bds. 6.99 (978-0-7548-1419-1(X) , Lorenz Bks.) Anness Publishing GBR. *Dist:* National Bk. Network.

Tuxworth, Nicola & Lorenz Books Staff. Numbers. 1999. (Let's Look at Board Bks.). (Illus.). 12p. 4.95 (978-0-7548-0059-0(8)) Anness Publishing, Inc.

Tuxworth, Nicola & Lorenz Editors. Numbers. 2001. (Let's Look at...Ser.). (Illus.). 20p. 5.95 (978-0-7548-0948-7(X) , Lorenz Bks.) Anness Publishing GBR. *Dist:* National Bk. Network.

Twin Sisters Productions Staff, prod. Alphabet & Counting: Songs That Teach. 2005. (J). per. 12.99 (978-1-57583-819-9(2)) Twin Sisters Productions, LLC.

Twinem, Neecy. Baby Coyote Counts. 2004. (New Board Book Ser.).Tr. of Bebe Coyote cuenta. (Illus.). 12p. (J). bds. 5.95 (978-0-87358-852-2(5) , Rising Moon Bks. for Young Readers) Northland Publishing.

Twinkle, Twinkle, Little Star. 2002. (DK Ladybird Ser.). 12p. (J). bds. 6.95 (978-0-7894-8473-4(0)) Dorling Kindersley Publishing, Inc.

Two Piece Fun Flip Over Books - 123's. 2000. (Illus.). (J). (978-1-58805-113-4(7)) DS-Max USA, Inc.

Tyler, Jenny & Gee, R. Counting up To 10. 2004. (First Learning Ser.). 24p. (J). pap., act. bk. ed. 4.95 (978-0-7945-0499-1(X)) EDC Publishing.

Ulmer, Mike. Loonies & Toonies: A Canadian Number Book. Rose, Melanie, illus. rev. ed. 2006. 40p. (J). 18.95 (978-1-58536-239-4(5)) Sleeping Bear Pr.

Ultimate Counting 1-10. 2002. (Illus.). 158p. (J). (ps-k). wbk. ed. 4.97 (978-1-57759-126-9(7)) Dalmatian Pr.

'Umi Keiki Li'i Li'i - Ten Little Children. 2005. Orig. Title: 'Umi Keiki Li'i Li'i. (HAW.). (J). (978-1-933835-01-3(X)) Partners in Development.

Usborne Publishing Staff, ed. Juegos con Numeros. 2000. Tr. of Fun with Numbers. (SPA., Illus.). 32p. (J). (ps-3). lib. bdg. 10.36 (978-1-58086-284-4(5)) EDC Publishing.

Valer, Frantisek, illus. The Buffalo & the Boat: Thathanka na Wata. 2004. (DAK, ENG & SIO.). 18p. (J). 9.95 (978-0-9761082-3-8(2)) Lakota Language Consortium, Inc.

—Prairie Dog Goes to School: Pispíza wan Wayawa Iyaye. 2004. (DAK, ENG & SIO.). 24p. (J). 9.95 (978-0-9761082-4-5(0)) Lakota Language Consortium, Inc.

Van der Meer, Mara. How Many Monsters? A Monster Counting Book. (Illus.). (J). (ps-3). 2001. 24p. pap. 8.99 (978-0-7112-1500-9(6)); 2000. 35p. 19.99 (978-0-7112-1499-6(9)) Lincoln, Frances Ltd. GBR. *Dist:* Transition Vendor, Antique Collectors' Club.

—How Many Monsters: A Monster Counting Book. 2004. (Illus.). 24p. (J). pap. 7.95 (978-1-84507-196-7(4)) Lincoln, Frances Ltd. GBR. *Dist:* Perseus Distribution.

Van Der Meer, Ron. How Many? ltd. ed. 2007. (Illus.). 12p. (J). (gr. 2). 250.00 (***978-0-375-84239-9(X)*** , Robin Corey Bks.) Random Hse. Children's Bks.

—How Many? Spectacular Paper Sculptures. 2007. (Illus.). 12p. (J). (gr. 2-7). 24.99 (***978-0-375-84226-9(8)*** , Robin Corey Bks.) Random Hse. Children's Bks.

Very First Numbers Kid Kit. 2004. 10p. (J). (ps up). 11.95 (978-1-58086-448-0(1)) EDC Publishing.

Vischer, Phil. How Many Veggies? A Veggiecational Book about Numbers! 1999. (Veggiecational Ser.: Vol. 1). (Illus.). 12p. (J). (ps). 8.99 (978-0-8499-5985-1(3)) Nelson, Thomas Inc.

—The Veggiecational Book: A Book about Numbers, Colors, Shapes & Letters! 1998. (Veggiecational Ser.: Vol. 7). (Illus.). 128p. (J). (ps-2). 19.99 (978-0-8499-5865-6(2)) Nelson, Thomas Inc.

Visscher, Jenny. I Can Have My Picnic in a Patch of Roses. 2000. 28p. (J). pap. (978-1-896239-67-5(6)) Shillingford, J. Gordon Publishing.

Volke, Gordon & Book Company Staff. Disco Fish. 2004. (Novelty Bks.). 10p. (J). (gr. 3-5). bds. (978-1-74047-496-2(1)) Book Co. Publishing Pty, Ltd., The.

Wadsworth, Ginger. One Tiger Growls: A Counting Book of Animal Sounds. 1999. (978-0-606-16407-8(3)) Tandem Library Bks.

Wadsworth, Ginger & Needham, James M. One Tiger Growls: A Counting Book of Animal Sounds. 1999. (Illus.). 32p. (J). (ps-3). pap. 6.95 (978-0-88106-274-8(X)) Charlesbridge Publishing, Inc.

Wadsworth, Olive A. Over in the Meadow. 2003. (ps-2). lib. bdg. 15.25 (978-0-613-73548-3(X)) Tandem Library Bks.

—Over in the Meadow: A Counting Rhyme. Vojtech, Anna, illus. 2003. 32p. (J). pap. 6.95 (978-0-7358-1871-2(1)) North-South Bks., Inc.

Wallace, Nancy Elizabeth. Count down to Clean Up! 2001. (Illus.). 32p. (J). (gr. k-3). tchr. ed. 14.00 (978-0-618-10130-6(6)) Houghton Mifflin Co. Trade & Reference Div.

Walling, Sandy Seeley. A Day at the Beach. A Seaside Counting Book from One to Ten. Walling, Sandy Seeley, illus. l.t. ed. 2003. (Illus.). 28p. (J). 6.95 (978-0-9741940-0-4(X)) Abernathy Hse. Publishing.

Wallis, Rebecca, illus. Number 1 What Grows in the Sun? 2005. (Community of Counting Ser.). 32p. (J). pap. 9.95 (978-1-59646-272-4(8)) Dingles & Co.

—Number 1 What Grows in the Sun?/Numero 1 ¿Qué crece en el Sol? 2005. (Community of Counting Ser.).Tr. of Numero 1 Qué crece en el Sol?. (ENG & SPA.). 32p. (J). pap. 9.95 (978-1-59646-274-8(4)); lib. bdg. 20.65 (978-1-891997-89-1(0)) Dingles & Co.

—Number 10 Where Is the Hen? 2005. (Community of Counting Ser.). 32p. (J). pap. 9.95 (978-1-59646-308-0(2)) Dingles & Co.

—Number 10 Where Is the Hen?/Numero 10 ¿en donde esta la Gallina? 2005. (Community of Counting Ser.).Tr. of Numero 10 ¿en donde esta la Gallina?. (ENG & SPA.). 32p. (J). pap. 9.95 (978-1-59646-310-3(4)); lib. bdg. 20.65 (978-1-891997-80-8(7)) Dingles & Co.

Wallis, Rebecca, intro. Number 1 What Grows in the Sun? 2005. (Community of Counting Ser.). (ENG., Illus.). 32p. (J). lib. bdg. 20.65 (978-1-891997-99-0(8)) Dingles & Co.

—Number 2 Let's Go to the Zoo! 2005. (Community of Counting Ser.). (Illus.). 32p. (J). lib. bdg. 20.65 (978-1-891997-98-3(X)) Dingles & Co.

Walton, Rick. One More Bunny: Adding from One to Ten. 2000. (Illus.). 24p. (J). (ps-3). 15.89 (978-0-688-16848-3(5)) HarperCollins Pubs.

—So Many Bunnies: A Bedtime ABC & Counting Book. Miglio, Paige, illus. 32p. (J). (ps-3). 2002. pap. 5.95 (978-0-06-443751-6(5) , Harper Trophy); 2000. 6.99 (978-0-688-17364-7(0) , Harper Festival) HarperCollins Pubs.

—So Many Bunnies: A Bedtime ABC & Counting Book. 1998. (Illus.). 32p. (J). (ps-1). 15.89 (978-0-688-13657-4(5)) HarperCollins Pubs.

—So Many Bunnies: A Bedtime ABC & Counting Book. Miglio, Paige, illus. 1998. 32p. (J). (ps-3). 17.99 (978-0-688-13656-7(7)) HarperCollins Pubs.

Wang, Margaret. Five Little Puppies. 2006. (Illus.). 12p. (J). 9.95 (978-1-58117-487-8(X) , Intervisual/Piggy Toes) Dalmatian Pr.

—Hungry Bunny. 2007. 16p. pap. 9.95 (***978-1-58117-556-1(6)***) Dalmatian Pr.

Wang, Margaret. Mini Eency Weency Spider. 2006. 12p. (J). 5.95 (978-1-58117-505-9(1) , Intervisual/Piggy Toes) Dalmatian Pr.

Wanhala, Dwight, illus. Scooby-Doo! Look & Find Number Mystery. 2002. (My Wipe-Off Book Ser.). 16p. (J). spiral bd. (978-0-7853-7823-5(5) , 7176800) Publications International, Ltd.

Ward, Jennifer. Over in the Garden. Spengler, Kenneth J., illus. 2002. 32p. (ps-2). 15.95 (978-0-87358-793-8(6) , Rising Moon Bks. for Young Readers) Northland Publishing.

—Somewhere in the Ocean. 2000. (J). (978-0-606-19468-6(1)) Tandem Library Bks.

Ward, Jennifer. Way up in the Arctic. Spengler, Kenneth J., illus. 2007. (SPA & ENG.). 32p. 15.95 (***978-0-87358-928-4(9)*** , Rising Moon Bks. for Young Readers) Northland Publishing.

Ward, Jennifer, et al. Somewhere in the Ocean. Spengler, Kenneth J., illus. 2000. 32p. (ps-2). 15.95 (978-0-87358-748-8(0) , Rising Moon Bks. for Young Readers) Northland Publishing.

Wargin, Kathy-Jo. Prairie Numbers: An Illinois Number Book. O'Malley, Kathy, illus. 2006. 40p. (J). 17.95 (978-1-58536-180-9(1)) Sleeping Bear Pr.

Warnes, Tim. Little Tiger's Funtime 123. 2001. (J). bds. 8.95 (978-1-58925-660-6(3) , tiger tales) ME Media LLC.

Watt, Melanie. Numbers. 2005. (Learning with Animals Board Bks.). (Illus.). 24p. (J). (gr. k up). (978-1-55337-831-0(8)) Kids Can Pr., Ltd.

Wayne, D. 1-2-3 Chubby Little Elephants. 2001. 32p. (J). 17.00 (978-0-8059-5414-2(7)) Dorrance Publishing Co., Inc.

Weatherill, Steve. Count on Goz. (Illus.). 21p. (J). (ps). pap. (978-0-7112-0691-5(0)) Lincoln, Frances Ltd. GBR. *Dist:* Transition Vendor.

Weber, Lou. Barneys Counting Party Active Point. 2006. 24p. (J). 19.98 (978-1-4127-3176-8(3) , 7233300) Publications International, Ltd.

Weber, Lou, ed. Counting Bilingual. 2005. 12p. 7.98 (978-1-4127-3475-2(4)) Publications International, Ltd.

—Fisher Price 123 Stencil Fun. 2005. 22p. (J). spiral bd., bds. 10.98 (978-1-4127-3447-9(9) , 7247800) Publications International, Ltd.

—Numbers. (J). 2005. 46p. 4.98 (978-1-4127-3462-2(2) , 7261900); 2004. 1p. 7.98 (978-1-4127-3299-4(9) , 5542100) Publications International, Ltd.

Weekly Reader Early Learning Library (Firm) Staff, contrib. by. I Know Numbers. 2006. (I'm Ready for Math Ser.). (Illus.). 16p. (J). pap. (978-0-8368-6480-9(8)); lib. bdg. 16.67 (978-0-8368-6475-5(1)) Stevens, Gareth Inc.

—I Know Numbers: Los Numeros. 2006. (ENG & SPA., Illus.). 16p. (J). pap. 4.50 (978-0-8368-6490-8(5)); lib. bdg. 16.67 (978-0-8368-6485-4(9)) Stevens, Gareth Inc.

Weeks, Stephanie. I Like Numbers! Weeks, Stephanie, illus. 2001. (Chalk It up to Learning Ser.). (Illus.). 10p. (J). (ps-3). bds. 8.95 (978-1-57091-365-5(X)) Charlesbridge Publishing, Inc.

Weisenfluh, C. C. In the Garden with the LittleWeeds: A Counting Book for Little Ones. Freeman, Julie, illus. 2004. 26p. (J). 11.95 (978-0-9746782-0-7(1)) B'Squeak Productions.

Wells, Robert E. Can You Count to Googol? 2000. (gr. 3-6). lib. bdg. 15.25 (978-0-613-27758-7(9)) Tandem Library Bks.

Wells, Rosemary. Adding It Up: Based on Timothy Goes to School & Other Stories. 2001. (ps-2). lib. bdg. 14.15 (978-0-613-43914-5(7)) Tandem Library Bks.

—Emily's First 100 Days of School. 2000. (Illus.). 64p. (J). (ps-1). 16.99 (978-0-7868-0507-5(2)) Hyperion Bks. for Children.

—Emily's First 100 Days of School. 2000. (Illus.). 64p. (ps-1). pap. 5.99 (978-0-7868-1354-4(7)) Hyperion Paperbacks for Children.

—Emily's First 100 Days of School. 2006. (Illus.). (J). (ps-4). 29.95 incl. audio compact disk (978-0-439-84900-5(4) , WHCD654); 24.95 incl. audio (978-0-439-84898-5(9) , WHRA654); pap. 14.95 incl. audio (978-0-439-84902-9(0) , WPRA654); pap. 18.95 incl. audio compact disk (978-0-439-84903-6(9) , WPCD654) Weston Woods Studios, Inc.

—How Many? How Much? 2001. (Get Set for Kindergarten Ser.). (Illus.). (J). 12.79 (978-0-606-20712-6(0)) Tandem Library Bks.

—Max Counts His Chickens. Wells, Rosemary, illus. 2007. (Illus.). 32p. (J). (ps). 15.99 (978-0-670-06222-5(7) , Viking Juvenile) Penguin Group (USA) Inc.

—Max's Toys: A Counting Book. 2004. 12p. (J). pap. 5.99 (978-0-670-88720-0(X) , Viking Juvenile) Penguin Group (USA) Inc.

Wen, Dref. Fy Llyfr Rhifau Cyntaf. 2005. Tr. of My First Numbers. (WEL., Illus.). 32p. bds. (978-1-85596-672-7(7)) Dref Wen.

Wenger, Shaunda. How Many Muffins? 2006. (Early Explorers Ser.). (J). 34.00 (***978-1-4108-6120-7(1)*** Benchmark Education Co.

Western Publishing Co., Inc. Staff & Golden Books Staff. Counting to Ten. 1999. (Step Ahead Workbooks Ser.). (Illus.). 32p. (J). (ps). pap. 2.99 (978-0-307-23562-6(9) , 03562, Golden Bks.) Random Hse. Children's Bks.

Wheldon, Nicole. The 1, 2, 3 Bees: A Counting Book. Zourelias-Noro, Diana, illus. 2005. 24p. (J). 17.95 (978-0-9744792-1-7(7)) Acmon Blue Publishing.

Whitehead, Pete, illus. Ink, Wink, & Blink Work Out! 2007. (I'm Going to Read Ser.). 32p. (J). pap. 3.95 (978-1-4027-4242-2(8)) Sterling Publishing Co., Inc.

Whitehouse, Patricia. Las Estaciones 1 2 3. (Las Estaciones (Seasons) Ser.). 24p. pap. 5.25 (978-1-4034-0548-7(4)) Heinemann Library.

—Matematicas con Plantas. (Plantas (Plants) Ser.). (SPA.). 24p. (J). (ps-1). 2003. lib. bdg. 17.08 (978-1-58810-780-0(9)); 2002. (Illus.). pap. 5.25 (978-1-58810-827-2(9) , 91648) Heinemann Library.

—Plant Math. 2002. (Plants Ser.). 24p. (J). (ps-1). pap. 5.25 (978-1-58810-734-3(5) , 91406); (Illus.). lib. bdg. 17.08 (978-1-58810-523-3(7)) Heinemann Library.

—Primavera. (Las Estaciones (Seasons) Ser.). 24p. pap. 5.25 (978 1 4034-0550-0(6)) Heinemann Library.

—Que Esta Despierto? 1 2 3. 2002. (Que Esta Despierto? (What's Awake?) Ser.).Tr. of What's Awake? 1 2 3. (SPA.). 24p. (J). (ps-1). pap. 5.25 (978-1-4034-0640-8(5)) Heinemann Library.

—Quien Esta Despierto? 1 2 3. 2003. (Que Esta Despierto? (What's Awake?) Ser.). (SPA.). 24p. (J). (ps-1). lib. bdg. 17.08 (978-1-4034-0399-5(6)) Heinemann.

—Verano. (Las Estaciones (Seasons) Ser.). 24p. pap. 5.25 (978-1-4034-0552-4(2)) Heinemann Library.

—What's Awake 1 2 3. 2003. (What's Awake? Ser.). (Illus.). 24p. (J). (ps-1). lib. bdg. 17.08 (978-1-58810-885-2(6)) Heinemann Library.

—What's Awake 123. 2003. (What's Awake? Ser.). (Illus.). 24p. pap. 5.25 (978-1-4034-0631-6(6)) Heinemann Library.

—Zoo Pairs. 2002. 24p. (J). (ps-1). pap. (978-1-58810-757-2(4) , 91411); (Illus.). lib. bdg. 18.50 (978-1-58810-549-3(0)) Heinemann Library.

Whiting, Sue & Book Company Staff. Bugs at Play. Mosley, Dudley, illus. 2002. (Button Bks.). 12p. (J). bds. 12.95 (978-1-74047-219-7(5)) Book Co. Publishing Pty, Ltd., The AUS. *Dist:* Penton Overseas, Inc.

—Flippity Frog's Number Adventure. Texidor, Dee, illus. 2002. (Novelty Bks.). 14p. (J). bds. 9.95 (978-1-74047-197-8(0)) Book Co. Publishing Pty, Ltd., The AUS. *Dist:* Penton Overseas, Inc.

—Flying High. Mosley, Dudley, illus. 2002. (Button Bks.). 12p. (J). bds. (978-1-74047-184-8(9)) Book Co. Publishing Pty, Ltd., The.

—The Great Race. Mosley, Dudley, illus. 2002. (Button Bks.). 12p. (J). bds. (978-1-74047-163-3(6)) Book Co. Publishing Pty, Ltd., The.

Whittington, Melanie & Holtz, Lara Tankel, eds. Counting Book. King, Dave, photos by. 2003. (Illus.). 32p. (J). (978-0-681-62667-6(4)) Dorling Kindersley.

Wickings, Ruth. Number Box. 2007. (Illus.). 14p. 19.95 (***978-1-84560-037-2(1)***) Mercury Bks. Ltd. GBR. *Dist:* International Publishers Marketing.

Wildsmith, Brian. Brian Wildsmith ABC. Fiol, Maria A., tr. Wildsmith, Brian, illus. 1998. (SPA., Illus.). 32p. (J). (ps). bds. 6.95 (978-1-887734-16-5(3)) Star Bright Bks., Inc.

—Brian Wildsmith's Animals to Count (Portugese) Wildsmith, Brian, illus. 2003. (POR., Illus.). 16p. (J). bds. 4.95 (978-1-932065-15-2(6) , 17187849112) Star Bright Bks., Inc.

—Cuantos Animales Hay? Fiol, María A., tr. Wildsmith, Brian, illus. 1998. (SPA., Illus.). 16p. (J). (ps). bds. 4.95 (978-1-887734-17-2(1)) Star Bright Bks., Inc.

Wildsmith, Brian, illus. Brian Wildsmith's Animal Colors (Arabic) 2004. (ARA.). 16p. (J). bds. 4.95 (978-1-932065-44-2(X) , 718-784-9112) Star Bright Bks., Inc.

—Brian Wildsmith's Animals to Count (Arabic) 2004. (ARA.). 16p. (J). bds. 4.95 (978-1-932065-45-9(8) , 718-784-9112) Star Bright Bks., Inc.

—Brian Wildsmith's Animals to Count (Farsi) 2004. (PER.). 16p. (J). bds. 4.95 (978-1-932065-43-5(1)) Star Bright Bks., Inc.

—Brian Wildsmith's Animals to Count (Korean) 2003. (KOR.). 16p. (J). bds. 4.95 (978-1-932065-13-8(X) , 1718-784-9112) Star Bright Bks., Inc.

—Brian Wildsmith's Animals to Count (Simplified Chinese) 2003. (CHI.). 16p. (J). bds. 4.95 (978-1-932065-17-6(2) , 1718-784-9112) Star Bright Bks., Inc.

—Brian Wildsmith's Animals to Count (Tagalog) 2003. (TAG.). 16p. (J). bds. 4.95 (978-1-932065-31-2(8) , 1-718-784-9112) Star Bright Bks., Inc.

—Brian Wildsmith's Animals to Count (Traditional Chinese) 2003. (CHI.). 16p. (J). bds. 4.95 (978-1-932065-18-3(0) , 1-718-784-9112) Star Bright Bks., Inc.

—Brian Wildsmith's Animals to Count (Vietnamese) 2003. (VIE.). 16p. (J). bds. 4.95 (978-1-932065-16-9(4) , 17187849112) Star Bright Bks., Inc.

Wildsmith, Brian & Ayiilaa, Naaltsoos. Brian Wildsmith's Animals to Count (Navajo) 2004. Tr. of Animals to Count. (NAV., Illus.). 16p. (J). bds. 4.95 (978-1-932065-25-1(3)) Star Bright Bks., Inc.

Wiles, Deborah. One Wide Sky: A Bedtime Lullaby. Bowers, Tim, illus. 2003. 32p. (J). 16.00 (978-0-15-202334-8(8)) Harcourt Children's Bks.

Wilkinson, Doris J. Numbers 1-10. Wilkinson, Doris J., ed. Chipping, Oliver, illus. 2000. (Jacob's Magic Box Discovery Ser.). 20p. (J). (ps). pap. 4.95 (978-0-9700386-0-9(7)) Magic Box Pubns.

Williams, Jean & Eason, Sarah. Coming Top: Counting Sticker Books. 2007. (Illus.). 32p. pap. 4.99 (978-0-7548-1640-9(0)); pap. 4.99 (978-0-7548-1639-3(7)); pap. 4.99 (978-0-7548-1638-6(9)); pap. 4.99 (978-0-7548-1637-9(0)) Anness Publishing GBR. (Lorenz Bks.). *Dist:* National Bk. Network.

Williams, Rozanne Lanczak. The Coin Counting Book. 2001. (Illus.). 32p. (J). (gr. k-4). pap. 6.95 (978-0-88106-326-4(6)) Charlesbridge Publishing, Inc.

—The Coin Counting Book. Williams, Rozanne Lanczak, illus. 2001. (Illus.). 32p. (J). (gr. k-4). 16.95 (978-0-88106-325-7(8)) Charlesbridge Publishing, Inc.

—The Coin Counting Book. 2001. (Illus.). (J). 13.75 (978-0-606-20612-9(4)) Tandem Library Bks.

—Coin Counting Book. 2001. (gr. k-3). lib. bdg. 15.25 (978-0-613-51237-4(5)) Tandem Library Bks.

—Crayola Counting. Jarrett, Michael, illus. Jarrett, Michael, photos by. 2004. (I Can Do Math Ser.). 24p. (J). (gr. 1 up). 20.67 (978-0-8368-4109-1(3)) Stevens, Gareth Inc.

—Learning about Coins. Jarrett, Michael, photos by. 2004. (I Can Do Math Ser.). (Illus.). 24p. (J). (gr. 1 up). lib. bdg. 20.67 (978-0-8368-4110-7(7)) Stevens, Gareth Inc.

Williams, Sue. Let's Go Visiting. Vivas, Julie, illus. 32p. (J). 2003. bds. 6.95 (978-0-15-204638-5(0) , Red Wagon Bks.); 2000. pap. 7.00 (978-0-15-202410-9(7) , Voyager Bks./Libros Viajeros) Harcourt Children's Bks.

—Let's Go Visiting. 1998. 90.00 (978-0-15-202036-1(5) , Gulliver Bks.) Harcourt Children's Bks.

—Let's Go Visiting. Vivas, Julie, illus. 1998. 32p. (J). (ps). 16.00 (978-0-15-201823-8(9) , Gulliver Bks.) Harcourt Children's Bks.

—Let's Go Visiting. 2000. (978-0-606-20330-2(3)); (J). (978-0-606-20167-4(X)) Tandem Library Bks.

Williams, Suzanne. Ten Naughty Little Monkeys. Watts, Suzanne, illus. 2007. 32p. (J). (ps-k). 16.99 (978-0-06-059904-1(9)); lib. bdg. 17.89 (978-0-06-059905-8(7)) HarperCollins Pubs.

Wilson, Zachary. Number One Puppy. Pertile, Paula, illus. 2006. (Rookie Reader Skill Set Ser.). 32p. (J). (gr. k-2). 19.50 (978-0-531-15475-5(0) , Children's Pr.) Scholastic Library Publishing.

Winburn, William B., photos by. 10 Rubber Duckies. 2005. (Illus.). 24p. (J). (ps). 9.95 (978-1-4027-1943-1(4)) Sterling Publishing Co., Inc.

Wipe-Away Books: Counting 1-20. 2003. (Illus.). 16p. (J). (ps up). pap. 3.99 (978-0-7682-0071-3(7)) School Specialty Publishing.

Wipe-Away Books: Numbers to 100. 2003. (Illus.). 16p. (J). (ps up). pap. 3.99 (978-0-7682-0447-6(X)) School Specialty Publishing.

Wipe-Away Books: Skip Counting by 5's & 10's. 2003. (Illus.). 16p. (J). (gr. 1 up). pap. 3.99 (978-0-7682-0448-3(8)) School Specialty Publishing.

Wipe Clean 123 Workbook. 2000. (J). 5.99 (978-0-89610-410-5(9)) Island Heritage Publishing.

Wise, William. Ten Sly Piranhas: A Counting Story in Reverse (A Tale of Wickedness - And Worse!) 2004. (Illus.). 32p. (J). pap. 5.99 (978-0-14-240074-6(2) , Puffin) Penguin Group (USA) Inc.

Witty One Creature Count Number Book. 2003. (J). per. (978-1-932435-21-4(2)) Cardinal Brands, Inc.

Wojtowycz, David. Eat up Dudley! Counting. 2002. (Dudley! Ser.). (Illus.). (J). 3.95 (978-1-58925-669-9(7) , tiger tales) ME Media LLC.

Wolf, Jackie. Sparkle Basket. 2003. (Illus.). 10p. (J). (ps up). bds. 6.99 (978-1-57151-713-5(8)) Playhouse Publishing.

Wolfe, Art. 1, 2, 3 Moose: A Counting Book. 2003. (ps-2). lib. bdg. 18.75 (978-0-613-79150-2(9)) Tandem Library Bks.

Wong, Janet S. Hide & Seek. Chodos-Irvine, Margaret, illus. 2005. 40p. (J). 16.00 (978-0-15-204934-8(7)) Harcourt Trade Pubs.

Wood, Audrey. Ten Little Fish. Wood, Bruce, illus. 2004. 40p. (J). (ps up). pap. 15.95 (978-0-439-63569-1(1) , Blue Sky Pr., The) Scholastic, Inc.

Wood, Jakki. March of the Dinosaurs: A Dinosaur Counting Book. (Illus.). 30p. (J). (ps-1). pap. 10.99 (978-0-7112-1456-9(5)) Lincoln, Frances Ltd. GBR. *Dist:* Transition Vendor.

—Moo Moo, Brown Cow. ed. 2004. (Illus.). (J). (ps up). spiral bd., bds. (978-0-616-14613-2(2)) Canadian National Institute for the Blind/Institut National Canadien pour les Aveugles.

—Number Parade. (Illus.). 30p. (J). pap. (978-0-7112-0905-3(7)) Lincoln, Frances Ltd. GBR. *Dist:* Transition Vendor.

—Number Parade: A Wildlife Counting Book. 1999. (Illus.). 32p. (J). (ps-1). (978-0-7112-0863-6(8)) Lincoln, Frances Ltd.

Woodward, Kay. La Cuenta Regresiva Level P. AMIT, Ofra, illus. 2006. (Lightning Readers Ser.). 32p. (J). pap. 3.95 (978-0-7696-4205-5(5) , Gingham Dog Pr.) School Specialty Publishing.

World Book, Inc. Staff. The Adventures of Poldy, 5 vols., Set. 2001. 48p. (J). (gr. k-2). 28.00 (978-0-7166-6129-0(2) , 6069) World Bk., Inc.

Wormell, Christopher. A Number of Animals. 2003. (Illus.). 24p. (J). (ps-3). pap. 7.95 (978-0-89812-384-5(4) , Creative Paperbacks) Creative Co., The.

—Number of Animals. 2003. (gr. k-3). lib. bdg. 16.40 (978-0-613-77491-8(4)) Tandem Library Bks.

—Teeth, Tails & Tentacles. 2006. (Illus.). 22p. (J). pap. 6.95 (978-0-7624-2728-4(0) , Running Pr. Kids) Running Pr. Bk. Pubs.

—Teeth, Tails & Tentacles: An Animal Counting Book. 2004. (Illus.). 64p. 18.95 (978-0-7624-2100-8(2) , Running Pr. Kids); 18.95 (978-0-7624-2085-8(5)) Running Pr. Bk. Pubs.

Yates, Gene, illus. The Giraffe Numbers Book. 2006. (J). (***978-1-58865-364-2(1)***) Kidsbooks, Inc.

Yektai, Niki. Bears at the Beach: Counting 10 to 20. 2001. (Illus.). (J). 14.75 (978-0-606-21053-9(9)) Tandem Library Bks.

Yolen, Jane. An Invitation to the Butterfly Ball: A Counting Rhyme. Zalben, Jane Breskin, illus. 2003. 32p. (J). (gr. k-2). pap. 9.95 (978-1-56397-692-6(7)) Boyds Mills Pr.

Yoon, Salina. Animal Count. Yoon, Salina, illus. 2004. (Illus.). 12p. (J). 6.99 (978-0-689-86185-7(0) , Little Simon) Simon & Schuster Children's Publishing.

—Count My Blessings, One Through Ten. Yoon, Salina, illus. 2006. (Illus.). 32p. (J). (ps-k). 9.99 (978-0-399-24660-9(6) , Putnam Juvenile) Penguin Group (USA) Inc.

—Maggie Can Count: A Counting Tweeter Book. 1999. 10p. (J). 7.95 (978-1-58117-056-6(4) , Intervisual/Piggy Toes) Dalmatian Pr.

Yoon, Salina, illus. Foil Fun Numbers. 2000. (Foil Fun Board Bks.). 10p. (ps). bds. 4.95 (978-1-58117-062-7(9) , Intervisual/Piggy Toes) Dalmatian Pr.

Young, Judy & Young, Ross B. Missouri Number. rev. ed. 2007. (State Counting Ser.). 40p. (J). 17.95 (***978-1-58536-156-4(9)***) Sleeping Bear Pr.

Your Baby Can Learn! Numbers, Vol. 1. 2007. (J). 7.95 (***978-1-931026-14-7(9)***) Infant Learning Co., The.

Yoyo Books, creator. Maxi Peekaboo Learning to Count 2005. (Illus.). 40p. (ps-7). bds. 6.95 (978-90-5843-889-8(9)) YoYo Bks. BEL. *Dist:* National Bk. Network.

Ziefert, Harriet. Knick-Knack Paddywhack. Bolam, Emily, illus. 2005. 16p. (ps-k). bds. 5.95 (978-1-4027-2292-9(3)) Sterling Publishing Co., Inc.

—Two Little Witches 8x8 Stkr Bk. Taback, Simms, illus. 2007. 20p. (J). (gr. k-k). pap. 3.99 (***978-0-7636-3309-7(7)***) Candlewick Pr.

Ziefert, Harriet. 10 Little Sock Monkeys. Winburn, William B., illus. 2005. 24p. (J). 9.95 (978-1-4027-1944-8(2)) Sterling Publishing Co., Inc.

Ziefert, Harriet, text. A Dozen Dozens. 2007. (I'm Going to Read Ser.). (Illus.). (J). (***978-1-4287-2803-5(1)***) Sterling Publishing Co., Inc.

Zimmerman, Dottie, creator. Interactive Sing-along Big Books Five Little Ducks. 2007. (J). spiral bd. 12.95 (***978-1-58650-713-8(3)***) Super Duper Pubns.

—Interactive Sing-along Big Books Here Come the Bugs! 2007. (J). spiral bd. 12.95 (***978-1-58650-714-5(1)***) Super Duper Pubns.

Zimmermann, Dottie, creator. Interactive Sing-along Big Books This Old Man. 2007. (J). spiral bd. 12.95 (***978-1-58650-720-6(6)***) Super Duper Pubns.

Zoller, Arthur David. Fish Counting. 2004. (Illus.). 14p. (J). (ps-k). bds. 6.95 (978-0-88106-074-4(7)) Charlesbridge Publishing, Inc.

Zuckerman, Rory. Counting Sleepy Sheep. Roos, Maryn, illus. 2004. (J). bds. 12.95 (978-0-9749305-0-3(4)) Castle Pacific Publishing.

1 2 3. 2003. (First Concepts Book Ser.). 32p. (J). 3.98 (978-0-7525-8891-9(5)) Parragon, Inc.

123. 2002. (First Steps Reading Ser.). 24p. (J). pap. 3.95 (978-0-7894-8486-4(2)) Dorling Kindersley Publishing, Inc.

COUNTRY HOUSES

see Architecture, Domestic

COUNTRY LIFE

Here are entered descriptive, popular and literary works on living in the country. Works dealing with social organization and conditions in rural communities are entered under Sociology, Rural.

see also Farm Life; Outdoor Life; Sociology, Rural

Barber, Nicola. Village Home. 2007. 32p. (gr. 7-10). pap. (***978-0-7787-3558-8(3)***) Crabtree Publishing Co.

Barbour, Karen. Mr. Williams. rev. ed. 2005. (Illus.). 32p. (J). 16.95 (978-0-8050-6773-6(6) , Holt, Henry & Co. Bks. For Young Readers) Holt, Henry & Co.

Bigmama's. 1998. (J). pap. 3.95 (978-0-439-04436-3(7)) Scholastic, Inc.

Bowman, Crystal. See the Country, See the City. Thomson, Pam, illus. 2004. 20p. (J). pap. 4.99 (978-0-310-70818-6(4)) Zonderkidz.

—See the Country, See the City. 2000. 24p. (J). 6.99 (978-0-310-23210-0(4)) Zonderkidz.

Chapman, Cindy. Where Is Your Home? 2003. (Compass Point Phonics Readers Ser.). (Illus.). 16p. (J). (gr. 1 up). 13.26 (978-0-7565-0532-5(1)) Compass Point Bks.

Crews, Donald. Bigmama's. 2001. (J). (gr. k-3). pap. 16.90 incl. audio (978-0-8045-6840-1(5) , 6840) Spoken Arts, Inc.

Dendrites, Waymore. Branton's Blossoms. 2006. per. 5.95 (***978-0-9769715-3-5(4)***) Pangus Publishing.

Flanagan, Alice K. The Zieglers & Their Apple Orchard. 1999. (Our Neighborhood Ser.). (Illus.). 32p. (gr. 1-2). pap. 6.95 (978-0-516-26471-4(0) , Children's Pr.) Scholastic Library Publishing.

Geisert, Bonnie. Prairie Town. Geisert, Arthur, illus. 1998. (Small Town U. S. A. Ser.). 32p. (J). (gr. k-3). tchr. ed. 16.00 (978-0-395-85907-0(7) , Walter Lorraine) Houghton Mifflin Co. Trade & Reference Div.

Golden Books Staff. Ride along the Countryside. Santanach, Tino, illus. 2004. 32p. (J). (ps-2). pap. 3.99 (978-0-375-82820-1(6) , Golden Bks.) Random Hse. Children's Bks.

Guin, Valerie. In the Country. 2005. (Illus.). 30p. (J). (gr. 3-7). lib. bdg. 27.10 (978-1-58340-695-3(6)) Smart Apple Media.

Hinds, Kathryn. The Countryside. (Life in Elizabethan England Ser.). (J). 2007. 80p. lib. bdg. 32.79 (***978-0-7614-2543-4(8)***); 2006. (Illus.). 80p. lib. bdg. 32.79 (978-0-7614-2185-6(8)); 2004. (Illus.). 72p. 29.93 (978-0-7614-1656-2(0)); 2000. (Illus.). 80p. (gr. 5 up). lib. bdg. 29.93 (978-0-7614-1006-5(6)) Cavendish, Marshall Corp. (Benchmark Bks.).

Holland, Gini. I Live in the Country. 2004. (Weekly Reader Early Learning Library). (Illus.). 24p. (gr. k up). (J). pap. (978-0-8368-4086-5(0)); (YA). lib. bdg. 19.33 (978-0-8368-4079-7(8)) Stevens, Gareth Inc. (Weekly Reader Early Learning Library).

—I Live in the Country/Vivo en el Campo. Coffey, Colleen & Carrillo, Consuelo, trs. 2004. (Weekly Reader Early Learning Library). (Illus.). 24p. (J). (gr. k up). (ENG & SPA.). pap. 5.95 (978-0-8368-4134-3(4)); (SPA & ENG., lib. bdg. 19.33 (978-0-8368-4127-5(1)) Stevens, Gareth Inc. (Weekly Reader Early Learning Library).

Hubbell, Sue. Country Year: Living the Questions. 1999. (gr. 7-12). lib. bdg. 22.25 (978-0-613-63700-8(3)) Tandem Library Bks.

Johnson, Emma. Medieval Town & Country Life. (Illus.). 32p. 18.95 (978-1-932889-28-4(0)) Sea-To-Sea Pubns.

My Cousin Jake: Individual Title Six-Packs. (ps-2). 27.00 (978-0-7635-9463-3(6)) Rigby Education.

Nickles, Greg. France - the People. 2000. (gr. 3-6). lib. bdg. 16.40 (978-0-613-27837-9(2)) Tandem Library Bks.

Nicodemus, Laura Konger. Grandma's House Had No Electricity, 4 vols. Nicodemus, Laura Konger, illus. 2002. (Illus.). 16p. (J). 3.99 (978-0-9722216-2-7(X)) Grandma's Stories, Inc.

—Grandma's House Had No Water, 4 vols. Nicodemus, Laura Konger, illus. 2002. (Illus.). 16p. (J). (gr. 1-4). 3.99 (978-0-9722216-1-0(1)) Grandma's Stories, Inc.

—Grandma's Onion Patch, 4 vols. Nicodemus, Laura Konger, illus. 2002. (Illus.). 16p. (J). (gr. 1-4). 3.99 (978-0-9722216-3-4(8)) Grandma's Stories, Inc.

North, Sterling. Rascal. 2004. (Illus.). 240p. (J). pap. 5.99 (978-0-14-240252-8(4) , Puffin) Penguin Group (USA) Inc.

—Rascal. unabr. ed. 1998. 189p. (J). (gr. 4-7). pap. 36.00 incl. audio (978-0-8072-7897-0(1) , 1124-AB, Listening Library) Random Hse. Audio Publishing Group.

—Rascal. unabr. ed. 1998. (YA). Class Set. 100.70 incl. audio (978-0-7887-2541-8(6) , 46711); Homework Set. (gr. 7). 43.24 incl. audio (978-0-7887-2236-3(0) , 40720) Recorded Bks., LLC.

—Rascal. 2001. (SPA.). (J). (978-0-606-20879-6(8)) Tandem Library Bks.

Onyefulu, Ifeoma. One Big Family: Sharing Life in an African Village. Onyefulu, Ifeoma, illus. 2006. (Illus.). 32p. pap. 7.95 (978-1-84507-686-3(9)) Lincoln, Frances Ltd. GBR. *Dist:* Perseus Distribution.

Pringle, Laurence P. One Room School. 2003. (Illus.). 32p. (J). (gr. 2-4). 16.95 (978-1-56397-583-7(1)) Boyds Mills Pr.

Sterling, Kristin. Rural Communities. 2008. (First Step Nonfiction - Communities Ser.). (J). lib. bdg. 18.60 (***978-0-8225-8599-2(5)*** , Lerner Pubns.) Lerner Publishing Group.

Stevens, B. C. Tales from Hinman Hollow. rev. ed. 2002. (Illus.). 112p. per. 7.95 (978-0-9677938-3-2(1)) Country Bumpkin Pubns.

COUNTRY LIFE—FICTION

Abbott, Jacob. Rollo at Play. 2004. reprint ed. pap. 15.95 (978-1-4191-4527-8(4)); pap. 1.99 (978-1-4192-4527-5(9)) Kessinger Publishing, LLC.

Agell, Charlotte. Welcome Home or Someplace Like It. rev. ed. 2003. (Illus.). 240p. (J). 16.95 (978-0-8050-7083-5(4) , Holt, Henry & Co. Bks. For Young Readers) Holt, Henry & Co.

Alexander, Pamela & Kight, Rhonda Frost. The Onion Ambassador. Alexander, Pamela, illus. 2001. (Illus.). 24p. (J). (gr. 1-4). 12.95 (978-0-9709105-0-9(9)) Be Sweet Pubns., Inc.

Alger, Horatio. Herbert Carter's Legacy. 2006. pap. (*978-1-4065-0710-2(5)) Dodo Pr.

Ashforth, Camilla. Willow on the River. Ashforth, Camilla, illus. 2002. (Illus.). 32p. (J). (ps-2). 12.00 (978-0-7636-1088-3(7)) Candlewick Pr.

Atwell, Debby. Barn. Atwell, Debby, illus. 2001. (Illus.). 32p. (J). (gr. k-3). pap. 5.95 (978-0-618-15316-9(0) , Walter Lorraine) Houghton Mifflin Co. Trade & Reference Div.

Bailey, Linda. When Addie Was Scared. ed. 2004. (Illus.). (J). (gr. k-3). spiral bd. (978-0-616-01535-3(6)); spiral bd. (978-0-616-01537-7(2)) Canadian National Institute for the Blind/Institut National Canadien pour les Aveugles.

—When Addie Was Scared. Bailey, Wendy, illus. unabr. ed. 2002. 32p. (J). (gr. k-3). (978-1-55337-163-2(1)) Kids Can Pr., Ltd.

Baker, Barrie. The Village of a Hundred Smiles. Jorisch, Stephane, illus. 1998. 48p. (J). (gr. k-3). pap. 7.95 (978-1-55037-535-0(0)) Annick Pr., Ltd. CAN. *Dist:* Firefly Bks., Ltd.

—The Village of a Hundred Smiles. Jorisch, Stephane, illus. 1998. 48p. (J). (gr. k-3). lib. bdg. 18.95 (978-1-55037-522-0(9)) Firefly Bks., Ltd.

Bauer, Joan. Squashed. 2005. 208p. (YA). (gr. 7). pap. 7.99 (978-0-14-240426-3(8) , Puffin) Penguin Group (USA) Inc.

—Squashed. 2001. (978-0-606-22520-5(X)) Tandem Library Bks.

—Squashed! 2001. 208p. (YA). 16.99 (978-0-399-23750-8(X) , Putnam Juvenile) Penguin Group (USA) Inc.

Bawden, Nina. Off the Road. 2001. (J). (978-0-606-21364-6(3)); (gr. 5-8). lib. bdg. 14.15 (978-0-613-35993-1(3)) Tandem Library Bks.

The Bean Trees. 1998. 44p. (YA). 11.95 (978-1-56137-891-3(7) , NU8917SP) Novel Units, Inc.

Belton, Sandra. From Miss Ida's Porch. 1998. (J). pap. 5.99 (978-0-87628-329-5(6)) Ctr. for Applied Research in Education, The.

Birney, Betty G. The Seven Wonders of Sassafras Springs. Phelan, Matt, illus. 2005. 224p. (J). (ps-7). 16.95 (978-0-689-87136-8(8) , Atheneum) Simon & Schuster Children's Publishing.

—The Seven Wonders of Sassafras Springs. Phelan, Matt, illus. 2007. 224p. (J). pap. 5.99 (978-1-4169-3489-9(8) , Aladdin) Simon & Schuster Children's Publishing.

—The Seven Wonders of Sassafras Springs. l.t. ed. 2006. 206p. (J). 22.95 (978-0-7862-8287-6(8)) Thorndike Pr.

Blume, Lesley M. M. The Rising Star of Rusty Nail. 2007. 288p. (J). (gr. 3-7). 15.99 (978-0-375-83524-7(5) , Knopf Bks. for Young Readers) Random Hse. Children's Bks.

—The Rising Star of the Rusty Nail. 2007. 288p. (J). (gr. 3-7). lib. bdg. 18.99 (978-0-375-93524-4(X) , Knopf Bks. for Young Readers) Random Hse. Children's Bks.

Borden, Louise. Just in Time for Christmas. 2000. (Illus.). (J). pap. 5.99 (978-0-590-45356-1(4)) Scholastic, Inc.

—Just in Time for Christmas. 2000. (J). 12.79 (978-0-606-19573-7(4)) Tandem Library Bks.

Bowman, Eddie. Gravy on a Bucket Lid. Prater, Howard, illus. 1998. (Silly Songs Ser.). (J). pap. 6.95 (978-1-56763-430-3(3)); lib. bdg. 19.95 (978-1-56763-429-7(X)) Ozark Publishing.

Braun, Lilian Jackson. The Cat Who Saw Stars. 2000. lib. bdg. 15.30 (978-0-613-21306-6(8)) Tandem Library Bks.

—The Cat Who Smelled a Rat. 2002. (gr. 5-8). lib. bdg. 15.30 (978-0-613-51533-7(1)) Tandem Library Bks.

Broach, Elise. Wet Dog! Catrow, David, illus. 32p. (J). (gr. k). 2007. pap. 5.99 (978-0-14-240855-1(7) , Puffin); 2005. 16.99 (978-0-8037-2809-7(3) , Dial) Penguin Group (USA) Inc.

Brooke, Lauren. Thicker Than Water. 2002. (Heartland Ser.: No. 8). 192p. (J). (gr. 3-7). 4.99 (978-0-439-31715-3(0)) Scholastic, Inc.

—Thicker Than Water. 2002. (gr. 3-6). lib. bdg. 12.40 (978-0-613-62921-8(3)) Tandem Library Bks.

Brooks, Nigel & Horner, Abigail. Country Mouse Cottage: How We Lived One Hundred Years Ago. Brooks, Nigel & Horner, Abigail, illus. 2000. (Illus.). 32p. (J). (ps-3). 15.95 (978-0-8027-8752-1(5)) Walker & Co.

Burch, Robert. Ida Early Comes over the Mountain. 2001. (J). (gr. 3-6). 20.75 (978-0-8446-7171-0(1)) Smith, Peter Pub., Inc.

—Queenie Peavy. abr. ed. 1999. (J). (gr. 4-7). pap. 15.95 incl. audio (978-0-670-58427-7(4)) Live Oak Media.

Burns, Laura. A Fine State of Affairs, No. 3. 2006. (Darcy's Wild Life Ser.: Bk. 3). 176p. (J). (gr. 4-7). pap. 4.99 (978-0-448-44260-0(4) , Grosset & Dunlap) Penguin Group (USA) Inc.

Burns, Laura J. Go West, Darcy! 2006. (Darcy's Wild Life Ser.: Bk. 6). 160p. (J). (*978-1-4156-8867-0(2) , Grosset & Dunlap) Penguin Group (USA) Inc.

Carter, Alden R. Up Country. 2004. 256p. (J). (gr. 5). pap. 6.99 (978-0-14-240243-6(5) , Puffin) Penguin Group (USA) Inc.

Cassidy, Cathy. Scarlett. 2006. 272p. (YA). 16.99 (978-0-670-06068-9(2) , Viking Juvenile) Penguin Group (USA) Inc.

Caudill, Rebecca. A Pocketful of Cricket. Ness, Evaline, illus. rev. ed. 2004. 48p. (J). 18.95 (978-0-8050-7524-3(0) , Holt, Henry & Co. Bks. For Young Readers) Holt, Henry & Co.

Center for Learning Network Staff. A Long Way from Chicago/A Year down Yonder: Curriculum Unit. 2002. (Novel Ser.). 84p. (J). tchr. ed., spiral bd. 19.95 (978-1-56077-723-6(0)) Ctr. for Learning, The.

Chronicles of Avonlea. 2004. 142p. (YA). pap. 7.95 (978-1-57646-893-7(3)) Quiet Vision Publishing.

Cohen, Caron Lee. Everything Is Different at Nonna's House. Nakata, Hiroe, illus. 2003. 40p. (J). (gr. k-3). tchr. ed. 16.00 (978-0-618-07335-1(3) , Clarion Bks.) Houghton Mifflin Co. Trade & Reference Div.

Coles Notes Staff. Canterbury Tales. 1999. (YA). 9.95 (978-1-56137-919-4(0)); (J). 11.95 (978-1-56137-920-0(4)) Novel Units, Inc.

Colman, Michelle Sinclair. Country Babies Wear Plaid. Dion, Nathalie, illus. 2006. 20p. (J). (ps). bds. 6.95 (978-1-58246-172-4(4) , Tricycle Pr.) Ten Speed Pr.

Conly, Jane Leslie. What Happened on Planet Kid. rev. ed. 2000. (Illus.). 160p. (YA). (gr. 5-9). 16.95 (978-0-8050-6065-2(0) , Holt, Henry & Co. Bks. For Young Readers) Holt, Henry & Co.

Country Mouse & City Mouse. 2002. (Classic Tales Mini Bks.). (Illus.). 32p. (J). (978-1-59069-037-6(0) , T1006); incl. audio compact disk (978-1-59069-104-5(0) , T1106) Studio Mouse LLC.

Couvillon, Jacques. The Chicken Dance. 2007. 336p. (YA). (gr. 5 up). 16.95 (*978-1-59990-043-8(2) , Bloomsbury Children) Bloomsbury Publishing.

Crawford, Ann Fears. Vangie: The Ghost of the Pines. 2002. 142p. (J). 17.95 (978-1-57168-710-4(6) , Eakin Pr.) Eakin Pr.

Creech, Sharon. Ruby Holler. (J). 2004. 336p. pap. 6.99 (978-0-06-056015-7(0) , Harper Trophy); 2002. 320p. (gr. 3-7). lib. bdg. 17.89 (978-0-06-027733-8(5) , Cotler, Joanna Books); 2002. 320p. (gr. 4-7). 16.99 (978-0-06-027732-1(7) , Cotler, Joanna Books) HarperCollins Pubs.

—Ruby Holler. 2004. (gr. 3-6). lib. bdg. 14.15 (978-0-613-86272-1(4)) Tandem Library Bks.

—Ruby Holler. l.t. ed. 2003. (Juvenile Ser.). 250p. (J). 22.95 (978-0-7862-5429-3(7)) Thorndike Pr.

Crumly, Billie Lang. The Best of Country Living. 2004. (Illus.). 171p. per. (978-0-9760577-0-3(0)) Crumly, Billie.

Dalmatian Press Staff, adapted by. Anne of Green Gables. 2002. (Spot the Classics Ser.). (Illus.). 176p. (J). (gr. k-5). 4.99 (978-1-57759-543-4(2)) Dalmatian Pr.

Darrow, Sharon. Painters of Lexieville. 2003. (Illus.). 192p. (YA). (gr. 9). 16.99 (978-0-7636-1437-9(8)) Candlewick Pr.

Day, Alexandra. Carl's Summer Vacation. Day, Alexandra, illus. 2008. (Carl Ser.). (Illus.). 32p. (J). 12.95 (*978-0-374-31085-1(8) , Farrar, Straus & Giroux (BYR)) Farrar, Straus & Giroux.

DeFelice, Cynthia C. Old Granny & the Bean Thief. Smith, Cat Bowman, illus. 2003. 32p. (J). 16.00 (978-0-374-35614-9(9) , Farrar, Straus & Giroux (BYR)) Farrar, Straus & Giroux.

Dennard, Deborah. Hedgehog Haven: A Story of a British Hedgerow Community. 2005. (Soundprints' Wild Habitats Ser.). (Illus.). 32p. (J). (gr. 1-4). 8.95 incl. audio (978-1-59249-108-7(1) , SC7020) Soundprints.

—Hedgehog Haven: The Story of an English Hedgerow Community. Hynes, Robert, illus. (Wild Habitats Ser.). (J). (gr. 1-4). 2005. 32p. 15.95 (978-1-56899-987-6(9) , B7020); 2005. 32p. 19.95 incl. audio (978-1-56899-989-0(5) , BC7020); 2005. 32p. pap. 6.95 (978-1-56899-988-3(7) , S7020); 2001. 36p. 26.95 (978-1-56899-991-3(7)) Soundprints.

Dudley, David L. The Bicycle Man. 2005. 256p. (J). (gr. 5-9). 16.00 (978-0-618-54233-8(7) , Clarion Bks.) Houghton Mifflin Co. Trade & Reference Div.

Dunmore, Helen. Tara's Tree House. Littlewood, Karin, illus. 2005. (Yellow Go Bananas Ser.). 48p. (J). lib. bdg. (978-0-7787-2721-7(1)) Crabtree Publishing Co.

Dussling, Jennifer. L. M. Montgomery's Anne of Green Gables. 2001. (gr. k-3). lib. bdg. 11.80 (978-0-613-35608-4(X)) Tandem Library Bks.

Edwards, Frank B. A Crowded Ride in the Countryside. Bianchi, John, illus. 1999. (New Reader Ser.). 24p. (J). (ps-1). lib. bdg. 14.95 (978-1-894323-03-1(3)) Pokeweed Pr. CAN. *Dist:* Fitzhenry & Whiteside, Ltd.

Edwards, Frank B. & Bianchi, John. A Crowded Ride in the Countryside. 1999. (New Reader Ser.). (Illus.). 24p. (J). (ps-1). pap. 4.95 (978-1-894323-02-4(5)) Pokeweed Pr. CAN. *Dist:* Fitzhenry & Whiteside, Ltd.

Enright, Elizabeth. The Four-Story Mistake. Enright, Elizabeth, illus. rev. ed. 2002. (Melendy Quartet Ser.: Bk. 2). (Illus.). 208p. (J). (gr. 3-7). 16.95 (978-0-8050-7061-3(3) , Holt, Henry & Co. Bks. For Young Readers) Holt, Henry & Co.

—Then There Were Five. Enright, Elizabeth, illus. rev. ed. 2002. (Melendy Quartet Ser.: Bk. 3). (Illus.). 176p. (J). (gr. 3-7). 16.95 (978-0-8050-7062-0(1) , Holt, Henry & Co. Bks. For Young Readers) Holt, Henry & Co.

Feneziani, Serena. In My Basket. 1998. 10p. (J). (ps-1). pap. 15.95 (978-0-7894-2451-8(7)) Dorling Kindersley Publishing, Inc.

Fisher, Dorothy Canfield. Understood Betsy. Root, Kimberly B., illus. rev. ed. 1999. 240p. (J). (gr. 4-6). 17.95 (978-0-8050-6073-7(1) , Holt, Henry & Co. Bks. For Young Readers) Holt, Henry & Co.

—Understood Betsy. 2004. reprint ed. pap. 1.99 (978-1-4192-9201-9(3)); pap. 24.95 (978-1-4179-0955-1(2)) Kessinger Publishing, LLC.

—Understood Betsy. 1999. (Hardscrabble Bks.). 182p. (J). reprint ed. pap. 9.95 (978-0-87451-920-4(9)) Univ. Pr. of New England.

Foreman, Wilmoth & Boyds Mills Press Staff. Summer of the Skunks. 2004. 152p. (J). 15.95 (978-1-886910-80-5(4) , Lemniscaat) Boyds Mills Pr.

Frazier, Craig. Stanley Goes for a Drive. 2004. (Illus.). 40p. (J). 15.95 (978-0-8118-4429-1(3)) Chronicle Bks. LLC.

Friedman, Aimee. Year My Sister Got Lucky. 2008. 384p. (J). pap. 16.99 (*978-0-439-92227-2(5)) Scholastic, Inc.

Garis, Howard Roger. Uncle Wiggily in the Country. Date not set. 192p. (J). 20.95 (978-0-8488-2282-8(X)) Amereon LTD.

Garland, Michael. King Puck. Garland, Michael, illus. 2007. (Illus.). 32p. (J). (gr. k-3). 16.99 (978-0-06-084809-5(X)); lib. bdg. 17.89 (978-0-06-084810-1(3)) HarperCollins Pubs.

Gershator, Phillis. Old House, New House. Potter, Katherine, illus. 2008. (J). (*978-0-7614-5386-4(5)) Cavendish, Marshall Corp.

Gibbons, Faye. Full Steam Ahead. Meidell, Sherry, illus. 2003. 32p. (J). (gr. k-2). 15.95 (978-1-56397-858-6(X)) Boyds Mills Pr.

Gilge-Barnes, Jeanette. City-Kid Farmer. 2000. 128p. (J). (gr. 5-7). pap. 4.95 (978-0-9679371-6-8(7)) WinePress Publishing.

—Growing-Up Summer. Hauge, Carl, illus. 2000. (J). (gr. 5-7). pap. 9.99 (978-0-9679371-8-2(3)) WinePress Publishing.

Gingerbread Farm. 2001. (Gingerbread Farm). 40p. (J). per. 8.95 (978-1-892003-02-7(3)) Clever Hands Publishing.

Good, Millie B. The Prairie Kingdom of the West. 2000. 176p. (J). (ps up). pap. 16.95 (978-1-56167-566-1(0) , Five Star Special Edition) American Literary Pr.

Grab, Daphne. Alive & Well in Prague, NY. 2008. 256p. (J). 16.99 (*978-0-06-125670-7(6)); lib. bdg. 17.89 (*978-0-06-125671-4(4)) HarperCollins Pubs. (Geringer, Laura Book).

Grahame, Kenneth. Dream Days. Shepard, Ernest H., illus. 2001. (Company of Books Ser.). 163p. (YA). 22.95 (978-1-58579-018-0(4) , Common Reader Editions) Akadine Pr., The.

—El Viento en los Sauces. 2001. (SPA.). 229p. (YA). 12.95 (978-84-261-5577-1(4)) Juventud, Editorial ESP. *Dist:* AIMS International Bks., Inc.

—El Viento en los Sauces. 2002. (Clover Ser.). (SPA., Illus.). 208p. (YA). 11.50 (978-84-392-8012-5(2) , EV2974) Lectorum Pubns., Inc.

Griese, Arnold A. The Way of Our People. Coalson, Glo, illus. 2003. 96p. (J). (gr. 4-6). pap. 10.95 (978-1-56397-648-3(X)) Boyds Mills Pr.

Guest, Elissa Haden. Iris & Walter. Davenier, Christine, illus. (Iris & Walter Ser.). 44p. (J). 2006. pap. 5.95 (978-0-15-205644-5(0) , Harcourt Paperbacks); 2000. (gr. 1-3). 14.00 (978-0-15-202122-1(1) , Gulliver Bks.) Harcourt Children's Bks.

—Iris & Walter & Baby Rose. Davenier, Christine, illus. 2006. (Iris & Walter Ser.). 44p. (J). pap. 5.95 (978-0-15-205650-6(5) , Harcourt Paperbacks) Harcourt Children's Bks.

—Iris & Walter & the Substitute Teacher. Davenier, Christine, illus. 2006. (Iris & Walter Ser.). 44p. (J). pap. 5.95 (978-0-15-205376-5(X) , Harcourt Paperbacks) Harcourt Children's Bks.

—Iris & Walter, True Friends. Davenier, Christine, illus. 2006. (Iris & Walter Ser.). 44p. (J). pap. 5.95 (978-0-15-205680-3(7) , Harcourt Paperbacks) Harcourt Children's Bks.

Hadley, Caroline. Woodside or Look Listen & Learn. 2007. pap. 87.99 (*978-1-4280-5242-0(9)) IndyPublish.com.

—Woodside; or, Look, Listen & Learn. 2007. (ENG., Illus.). 80p. per. (*978-1-4065-1557-2(4)) Dodo Pr.

Hardy, Lorién Trover. Firefly Summer. Yilmaz, Necdet, illus. 2007. (Read-It! Readers Ser.). (J). 19.93 (978-1-4048-2397-6(2)) Picture Window Bks.

Harrar, George. The Trouble with Jeremy Chance. 2007. (Historical Fiction for Young Readers Ser.). 168p. (J). pap. 6.95 (978-1-57131-669-1(8)) Milkweed Editions.

Harshman, Marc. A Little Excitement. Rand, Ted, illus. 2002. 32p. (J). per. 6.95 (978-1-891852-21-3(3)) Quarrier Pr.

Haywood, Carolyn. Two & Two Are Four. 2005. (Illus.). 160p. (J). 16.00 (978-0-15-205230-0(5) , Harcourt Young Classics) ; pap. 5.95 (978-0-15-205231-7(3) , Odyssey Classics) Harcourt Children's Bks.

Helldorfer, Mary-Claire. Anne of Green Gables. Beier, Ellen, illus. 2003. 40p. (J). (gr. k-3). pap. 6.99 (978-0-440-41614-2(0) , Dragonfly Bks.) Random Hse. Children's Bks.

Hill, Elizabeth Starr. Wildfire! Shepperson, Rob, illus. 2004. 80p. (J). 16.00 (978-0-374-31712-6(7) , Farrar, Straus & Giroux (BYR)) Farrar, Straus & Giroux.

Hobbs, Valerie. Defiance. 2005. 128p. (J). 16.00 (978-0-374-30847-6(0)) Farrar, Straus & Giroux.

—Defiance. l.t. ed. 2006. 147p. 22.95 (978-0-7862-8667-6(9)) Thorndike Pr.

Hundal, Nancy. Prairie Summer. Deines, Brian, illus. 1999. 34p. (J). (gr. k-3). (978-1-55041-403-5(8)) Fitzhenry & Whiteside, Ltd.

Inches, Alison. In the Mushroom Meadow. 2002. (gr. k-3). lib. bdg. 10.95 (978-0-613-86241-7(4)) Tandem Library Bks.

Jacobs, Jimmy. Moonlight Through the Pines: Tales of the Georgia Evenings. Ward, Calvin H., illus. 2000. x, 116p. (J). (gr. 7-12). pap. 11.95 (978-0-9637477-3-0(8)) Franklin-Sarrett Pubs.

Jewett, Sarah Orne. The Country of the Pointed Firs & Other Stories. 2000. (gr. 7-12). lib. bdg. 11.80 (978-0-613-27778-5(3)) Tandem Library Bks.

Johnson, Sandi. Cowgirls Dream. Perritt, Jordona, illus. Date not set. (Kooky Kountry Ser.). (J). (ps-6). 8.99 (978-1-929063-56-7(3)) Moons & Stars Publishing For Children.

Karon, Jan & Cecka, Melanie. Violet Goes to the Country. McCully, Emily Arnold, illus. 2007. 36p. (J). (ps). 16.99 (*978-0-670-06181-5(6) , Viking Juvenile) Penguin Group (USA) Inc.

Kennedy, Joe. Lucy Goes to the Country. Canemaker, John, illus. 2004. (Alyson Wonderland Ser.). 32p. (ps-k). 15.95 (978-1-55583-428-9(0) , Alyson Wonderland) Alyson Pubns.

Klingel, Cynthia Fitterer & Noyed, Robert B. Carmen & the Letter C. 2003. (Alphaphonics Ser.). (Illus.). 24p. (J). (ps-2). 21.36 (978-1-59296-093-4(6)) Child's World, Inc.

Kuhn, Betsy. Not Exactly Nashville. 1999. (978-0-606-16708-6(0)) Tandem Library Bks.

Lachtman, Ofelia Dumas. A Good Place for Maggie. 2002. 160p. (YA). pap. 9.95 (978-1-55885-372-0(3) , Piñata Books) Arte Publico Pr.

—A Good Place for Maggie. 2002. (gr. 3-6). lib. bdg. 18.75 (978-0-613-85296-8(6)) Tandem Library Bks.

Lankester-Brisley, Joyce. Milly-Molly-Mandy Stories. 2002. (Kingfisher Modern Classics Ser.). (Illus.). 240p. (J). (gr. k-3). tchr. ed. 15.95 (978-0-7534-5559-3(5) , Kingfisher) Houghton Mifflin Co. Trade & Reference Div.

Lawrence, Mary. What's That Sound? Adams, Lynn, illus. 2002. (Science Solves It! Ser.). 32p. (J). (gr. 1-3). 4.99 (978-1-57565-118-7(1)) Kane Pr., The.

—What's That Sound? 2002. (gr. k-3). lib. bdg. 13.00 (978-0-613-53786-5(6)) Tandem Library Bks.

The Legend of the Bluebonnet. 1999. (J). 9.95 (978-1-56137-328-4(1)) Novel Units, Inc.

Les Becquets, Diane. The Stones of Mourning Creek. 2005. 306p. (YA). (gr. 7). reprint ed. pap. 6.95 (978-0-7614-5238-6(9)) Cavendish, Marshall Corp.

—The Stones of Mourning Creek. 2001. (Illus.). 320p. (J). (gr. 7 up). 16.95 (978-1-58837-004-4(6)) Winslow Pr.

MacDonald, George. Ranald Bannerman's Boyhood. 2006. 63.99 (*978-1-4280-3039-8(5)) IndyPublish.com.

Malokas, Ann. Military Dads. 2002. (Illus.). 20p. 6.95 (978-0-9708415-5-1(8)) Guilty Mom Pr.

—Military Moms. 2002. (Illus.). 20p. (J). 6.95 (978-0-9708415-4-4(X)) Guilty Mom Pr.

Mason, Jane B. & Stephens, Sarah Hines. Bella Baxter & the Itchy Disaster. Shelley, John, illus. 2005. (Bella Baxter Ser.). 80p. (J). pap. 3.99 (978-0-689-86281-6(4) , Aladdin) Simon & Schuster Children's Publishing.

McCormick, Wendy. Daniel & His Walking Stick. Bergum, Constance Rummel, illus. 2005. 32p. (J). 15.95 (978-1-56145-330-6(7)) Peachtree Pubs., Ltd.

McHugh, Fiona, adapted by. Anne of Green Gables Storybook. 2007. (Illus.). 80p. (J). (gr. 2-7). pap. 9.95 (978-0-920668-42-9(9)) Firefly Bks., Ltd.

McKay, Sindy. We Both Read-My Car Trip. Johnson, Meredith, illus. 2005. (J). (*978-1-4156-3785-2(7)) Book Wholesalers, Inc.

Meyer, Carolyn. Loving Will Shakespeare. 2006. 272p. (YA). 17.00 (978-0-15-205451-9(0)) Harcourt Children's Bks.

Montgomery, L. M. Anne of Avonlea. 2000. (Anne of Green Gables Ser.: Vol. No. 2). 194p. (gr. 5-8). pap. 12.99 (978-1-57646-304-8(4)); (YA). 24.95 (978-1-57646-305-5(2)) Quiet Vision Publishing.

—Anne of Avonlea Book & Charm. 2002. (Charming Classics). 256p. (ps-1). pap. 6.99 (978-0-694-01584-9(9) , Harper Festival) HarperCollins Pubs.

—Anne of Green Gables. 2004. 400p. per. 16.95 (978-1-59540-110-6(5)) 1st World Publishing, Inc.

—Anne of Green Gables. Miralles, Joseph, illus. 2002. (Great Illustrated Classics Ser.). 240p. (J). (gr. 3-8). 21.35 (978-1-57765-816-0(7) , ABDO & Daughters) ABDO Publishing Co.

—Anne of Green Gables. 349p. (978-1-58726-053-7(0)) Ann Arbor Media Group, LLC.

—Anne of Green Gables. 2000. (Avonlea Ser.: No. 1). 280p. (YA). (gr. 5-8). pap. 15.00 (978-0-7881-9155-8(1)) DIANE Publishing Co.

—Anne of Green Gables. 2004. (Great Classics for Children Ser.). 288p. (J). 5.99 (978-1-4037-0980-6(7)) Dalmatian Pr.

—Anne of Green Gables. 2007. per. 6.99 (*978-1-4209-2922-5(4)) Digireads.com.

—Anne of Green Gables. 2000. (Avonlea Ser.: No. 1). 320p. (J). (gr. 4-7). pap. 3.50 (978-0-486-41025-8(0)) Dover Pubns., Inc.

—Anne of Green Gables. 2000. (Avonlea Ser.: No. 1). (YA). (gr. 5-8). (978-0-06-028227-1(4)); 1999. (Charming Classics). 400p. (J). (ps up). pap. 6.99 (978-0-694-01251-0(3) , Harper Festival) HarperCollins Pubs.

—Anne of Green Gables. 2003. 276p. pap. 15.99 (*978-1-4043-6066-2(2)) IndyPublish.com.

—Anne of Green Gables. Stemach, Jerry, ed. Ham, Jeff, illus. 2000. 65.00 incl. audio, cd-rom (978-1-58702-311-8(3)) Johnston, Don Inc.

—Anne of Green Gables. 1998. 352p. (J). pap. (978-1-55109-249-2(2)) Nimbus Publishing, Ltd.

—Anne of Green Gables. Rubio, Mary & Waterson, Elizabeth, eds. 2006. (Norton Critical Edition Ser.). (Illus.). 400p. (C). pap. 9.00 (978-0-393-92695-8(8)) Norton, W. W. & Co., Inc.

—Anne of Green Gables. (Oxford Children's Classics). 2007. 400p. (YA). 9.95 (*978-0-19-272000-9(7)); 2004. 8.50 (978-0-19-423273-9(5)) Oxford Univ. Pr., Inc.

—Anne of Green Gables. 2003. 320p. (gr. 12). 4.95 (978-0-451-52882-7(4) , Signet Classics); 2002. (Illus.). (J). pap. 9.99 (978-0-14-250102-3(6) , Puffin) Penguin Group (USA) Inc.

—Anne of Green Gables. 2000. (Anne of Green Gables Ser.: Vol. No. 1). 220p. (gr. 5-8). pap. 12.99 (978-1-57646-300-0(1)); 24.95 (978-1-57646-301-7(X)) Quiet Vision Publishing.

—Anne of Green Gables. Howell, Troy, illus. 2002. 256p. (J). 12.99 (978-0-517-22111-2(X) , Gramercy) Random Hse. Value Publishing.

—Anne of Green Gables. 1998. (Children's Classics Ser.: No. 1). (Illus.). 256p. (J). (gr. 4-7). 6.99 (978-0-517-18968-9(2) , Children's Classics) Random Hse. Value Publishing.

—Anne of Green Gables. 2006. (Scholastic Classics Ser.). (Illus.). viii, 272p. (J). (gr. 9-12). 25.00 (978-0-531-16980-3(4) , Watts, Franklin) Scholastic Library Publishing.

—Anne of Green Gables. 2001. (Aladdin Classics Ser.). (Illus.). 480p. (J). pap. 5.99 (978-0-689-84622-9(3) , Aladdin) Simon & Schuster Children's Publishing.

—Anne of Green Gables. McKowen, Scott, illus. 2004. (Unabridged Classics Ser.). 304p. 9.95 (978-1-4027-1451-1(3)) Sterling Publishing Co., Inc.

—Anne of Green Gables. 1999. (Avonlea Ser.: No. 1). (YA). (gr. 5-8). 23.95 (978-0-8057-8090-1(4) , Macmillan Reference USA) Thomson Gale.

—Anne of Green Gables. Fernandez, Laura & Jacobson, Rick, illus. 2000. (Avonlea Ser.: No. 1). 328p. (J). (gr. 5-8). 24.95 (978-0-88776-515-5(7)) Tundra Bks., Inc./Livres Toundra, Inc. CAN. *Dist:* Random Hse., Inc.

—Anne of Green Gables. MQ Publications Staff, ed. 1998. (Little Brown Notebooks Ser.). (Illus.). 256p. (978-1-84072-063-1(8)) Watson-Guptill Pubns., Inc.

—Anne of Green Gables. 2001. (Children's Classics). (ENG.). 288p. (J). pap. (978-1-85326-139-8(4)) Wordsworth Editions, Ltd.

—Anne of Green Gables. Corvino, Lucy, illus. 2005. (Classic Starts Ser.). 160p. 4.95 (978-1-4027-1130-5(1)) Sterling Publishing Co., Inc.

—Anne of Green Gables. l.t. ed. 2006. (ENG.). pap. (***978-1-4068-3174-0(3)*** Echo Library.

—Anne of Green Gables. Stemach, Jerry, ed. Ham, Jeff, illus. l.t. ed. 2000. 50.00 (978-1-58702-502-0(7)) Johnston, Don Inc.

—Anne of Green Gables. 1998. (Avonlea Ser.). 252p. (YA). (gr. 5-8). reprint ed. (978-1-55109-013-9(9)) Nimbus Publishing, Ltd.

—Anne of Green Gables. 1998. 310p. (YA). (gr. 5-8). reprint ed. lib. bdg. 25.00 (978-1-58287-014-4(4)) North Bks.

—Anne of Green Gables. l.t. ed. 2000. (Anne of Green Gables Ser.: Vol. 1). 294p. (gr. 5-8). pap. 17.95 (978-1-57646-302-4(8)) Quiet Vision Publishing.

—Anne of Green Gables. rev. ed. 2002. (Scholastic Classic Ser.). 400p. (J). pap. 4.99 (978-0-439-29577-2(7)) Scholastic, Inc.

—Anne of Green Gables, 100th Anniversary Edition. 2008. 19.95 (***978-0-399-15478-2(7)*** , Putnam Adult) Penguin Group (USA) Inc.

—Anne of Ingleside. 2000. (Avonlea Ser.: No. 10). (YA). (gr. 5-8). 23.95 (978-0-8488-0890-7(8)) Amereon LTD.

—Anne of Ingleside, Vol. 6. 1999. 384p. (J). pap. 3.99 (978-0-14-036801-7(9) , Putnam Juvenile) Penguin Group (USA) Inc.

—Anne's House of Dreams. l.t. ed. 1999. (Avonlea Ser.: No. 5). 364p. (YA). (gr. 5-8). lib. bdg. 34.95 (978-1-58118-048-0(9) , 22517) LRS.

—Anne's House of Dreams, Vol. 5. 1999. 320p. (J). 3.99 (978-0-14-036799-7(3) , Putnam Juvenile) Penguin Group (USA) Inc.

—Anne's House of Dreams. 2000. (Anne of Green Gables Ser.: Vol. No. 5). (gr. 5-8). 182p. 24.95 (978-1-57646-313-0(3)); 182p. pap. 14.99 (978-1-57646-312-3(5)); 336p. pap. 19.99 (978-1-57646-314-7(1)) Quiet Vision Publishing.

—The Golden Road. 2000. (Sara Stanley of Avonlea Ser.: Vol. 2). 180p. 24.99 (978-1-57646-317-8(6)); 198p. pap. 12.99 (978-1-57646-316-1(8)); 328p. 31.95 (978-1-57646-319-2(2)); 328p. pap. 19.99 (978-1-57646-318-5(4)) Quiet Vision Publishing.

Montgomery, L. M. Mary Engelbreit's Classic Library: Anne of Green Gables. Engelbreit, Mary, illus. 2008. (Mary Engelbreit's Classic Library). 464p. (J). 9.99 (***978-0-06-008138-6(4)*** , Harper Festival) HarperCollins Pubs.

Montgomery, L. M. & Greenwood, Barbara. Anne of Green Gables. Wood, Muriel, illus. rev. ed. 2001. (Avonlea Ser.: No. 1). 94p. (J). (gr. 5-8). pap. 9.95 (978-1-55013-431-5(0)) Key Porter Bks. CAN. *Dist:* Firefly Bks., Ltd.

Montgomery, L. M. & Hedge, Tricia. Anne of Green Gables, Level 2. 2nd abr. ed. 2000. (Bookworms Ser.). (Illus.). 64p. 6.50 (978-0-19-422965-4(3)) Oxford Univ. Pr., Inc.

Moore, Brenda M. Together on the Mountain. Varnedoe, Catharine E., illus. 1998. 32p. (J). (ps-3). 14.95 (978-1-890326-14-2(3)) First Story Pr.

Moore, Lilian. Don't Be Afraid, Amanda. 2001. (Ready-for-Chapters Ser.). (Illus.). (J). (978-0-606-21154-3(3)) Tandem Library Bks.

—I'll Meet You at the Cucumbers. Wooding, Sharon, illus. 2001. (Ready-for-Chapters (Library) Ser.). 63p. (J). (gr. 2-6). lib. bdg. 11.80 (978-0-613-90800-9(7)) Tandem Library Bks.

—I'll Meet You at the Cucumbers. 2001. (Ready-for-Chapters Ser.). (Illus.). (J). 10.79 (978-0-606-21326-4(0)) Tandem Library Bks.

Morgan, Nicola. Chicken Friend. 2005. 160p. (J). (gr. 4-7). 15.99 (978-0-7636-2735-5(6)) Candlewick Pr.

Morpurgo, Michael, ed. More Muck & Magic. Blake, Quentin, illus. 2001. 148p. (J). pap. 8.99 (978-0-7497-4094-8(9)) Egmont Bks., Ltd. GBR. *Dist:* Independent Pubs. Group.

Moverley, Richard. The Reluctant Rajput. Dean, David, illus. 2005. (Yellow Go Bananas Ser.). 48p. (J). lib. bdg. (978-0-7787-2723-1(8)) Crabtree Publishing Co.

Nesbit, E. The Railway Children. Dryhurst, Dinah, illus. 2000. 224p. (J). pap. 8.99 (978-1-86205-235-2(2) , Pavilion Bks., Ltd.) Anova Bks. GBR. *Dist:* Trafalgar Square Publishing.

—The Railway Children. Dryhurst, Dinah, tr. Dryhurst, Dinah, illus. 2004. 184p. 18.95 (978-1-56792-261-5(9)) Godine, David R. Pub.

—The Railway Children. 2002. (gr. 3-6). lib. bdg. 23.40 (978-0-613-86551-7(0)) Tandem Library Bks.

—The Railway Children. 1998. (Children's Classics). (ENG., Illus.). 208p. (J). (gr. 4-7). pap. (978-1-85326-107-7(6) , 1076WW) Wordsworth Editions, Ltd.

—Railway Children. Brock, C. E., illus. (YA). 14.95 (978-0-8118-4933-3(3)) Chronicle Bks. LLC.

—Railway Children. 2000. (Dover Juvenile Classics Ser.). (Illus.). 208p. (J). (gr. 4-7). pap. 2.50 (978-0-486-41022-7(6)) Dover Pubns., Inc.

—Railway Children. 2006. pap. (***978-1-4068-3505-2(6)***) Echo Library.

—Railway Children. (J). (978-0-340-71497-3(2) , Hodder & Stoughton) Hodder General Publishing Division.

—Railway Children. 2004. (ENG.). 580p. (***978-0-9548401-2-9(7)***) Shoes & Ships & Sealing Wax Ltd.

—The Railway Children. Brock, C. E., illus. 100th ed. 2005. 240p. (J). (ps-7). 14.95 (978-1-58717-279-3(8)); pap. 9.95 (978-1-58717-280-9(1)) Chronicle Bks. LLC. (SeaStar Bks.).

—The Railway Children. unabr. ed. 2004. (Chrysalis Children's Classics Ser.). (Illus.). 190p. (YA). pap. (978-1-84365-050-8(9)) Chrysalis Children's Bks.

—The Railway Children. 2004. reprint ed. pap. 22.95 (978-1-4191-7972-3(1)); pap. 1.99 (978-1-4192-7972-0(6)) Kessinger Publishing, LLC.

—The Railway Children. l.t. ed. 2006. (Large Print Ser.). lib. bdg. 26.00 (***978-1-58287-890-4(0)***) North Bks.

—The Railway Children, Level 3. 2nd ed. 2000. (Bookworms Ser.). (Illus.). 74p. 6.50 (978-0-19-423013-1(9)) Oxford Univ. Pr., Inc.

—The Railway Children, Level 2. 2000. (Illus.). 48p. (C). pap. 9.00 (978-0-582-41790-8(2)) Pearson ESL.

Nolan, Lucy. The Lizard Man of Crabtree County. Kastner, Jill, illus. 32p. (J). 2005. pap. 5.95 (978-0-7614-5144-0(7)); 1999. 15.95 (978-0-7614-5049-8(1) , Cavendish Children's Bks.) Cavendish, Marshall Corp.

O'Connor, Barbara. Moonpie & Ivy. 160p. (J). 2001. (gr. 5 up). 16.00 (978-0-374-35059-8(0) , Farrar, Straus & Giroux (BYR)); 2004. (Illus.). reprint ed. pap. 7.95 (978-0-374-45320-6(9) , Sunburst) Farrar, Straus & Giroux.

Pavlicin, Karen. Perch, Mrs. Sackets, & Crow's Nest. 2007. (J). 160p. 16.95 (***978-1-934617-00-7(8)***); pap. (***978-1-934617-01-4(6)***) Elva Resa Publishing, LLC. (Alma Little).

Peck, Richard. Here Lies the Librarian. 160p. (J). (gr. 5 up). 2007. 6.99 (***978-0-14-240908-4(1)*** , Puffin); 2006. 16.99 (978-0-8037-3080-9(2) , Dial) Penguin Group (USA) Inc.

—Here Lies the Librarian. rev. ed. 175p. 23.95 (***978-0-7862-9183-0(4)***) Thorndike Pr.

—A Long Way from Chicago. 2002. (Illus.). (J). 13.19 (978-0-7587-6520-8(7)) Book Wholesalers, Inc.

—A Long Way from Chicago. (Puffin Modern Classics Ser.). 2004. 160p. (gr. 3-6). pap. 6.99 (978-0-14-240110-1(2) , Puffin); 2000. (Illus.). 176p. (J). (gr. 5-9). pap. 6.99 (978-0-14-130352-9(2) , Puffin); 1998. 192p. (J). (gr. 4-7). 16.99 (978-0-8037-2290-3(7) , Dial) Penguin Group (USA) Inc.

—A Long Way from Chicago. 2000. (J). (978-0-606-19769-4(9)) Tandem Library Bks.

—The Teacher's Funeral: A Comedy in Three Parts. 2004. 208p. (J). (gr. 5). 16.99 (978-0-8037-2736-6(4) , Dial); 2006. 224p. (YA). (gr. 3). reprint ed. pap. 6.99 (978-0-14-240507-9(8) , Puffin) Penguin Group (USA) Inc.

—The Teacher's Funeral: A Comedy in Three Parts. l.t. ed. 2005. 226p. 22.95 (978-0-7862-7750-6(5) , Large Print Pr.) Thorndike Pr.

—A Year down Yonder. 2002. (Illus.). (YA). 13.19 (978-1-4046-1795-7(7)) Book Wholesalers, Inc.

—A Year down Yonder. 2002. 144p. (gr. 5-8). pap. 6.99 (978-0-14-230070-1(5) , Puffin) Penguin Group (USA) Inc.

—A Year down Yonder. Cieslawski, Steve, illus. 2000. 144p. (J). (gr. 5-9). 16.99 (978-0-8037-2518-8(3) , Dial) Penguin Group (USA) Inc.

—A Year down Yonder. unabr. ed. 2004. (Middle Grade Cassette Librariestm Ser.). 144p. (J). (gr. 5-9). pap. 29.00 incl. audio (978-0-8072-0991-2(0) , S YA 256 SP, Listening Library) Random Hse. Audio Publishing Group.

—A Year down Yonder. 2002. (gr. 5-8). lib. bdg. 14.15 (978-0-613-57934-6(8)) Tandem Library Bks.

—A Year down Yonder. l.t. ed. 2001. 160p. (J). 24.95 (978-0-7862-3282-6(X)) Thorndike Pr.

Peterson. Anne of Green Gables. 1999. (Avonlea Ser.: No. 1). 32p. (YA). (gr. 5-8). pap. 4.95 (978-0-06-443535-2(0)) HarperCollins Pubs.

Ransom, Candice. Seeing Sky-Blue Pink. 2007. (Exceptional Reading & Language Arts Titles for Intermediate Grades Ser.). 128p. (J). (gr. 3-6). 16.95 (***978-0-8225-7142-1(0)*** , Carolrhoda Bks.) Lerner Publishing Group.

Ransom, Candice F. Finding Day's Bottom. 2006. 168p. (J). (gr. 4-6). 15.95 (978-1-57505-933-4(9) , Carolrhoda Bks.) Lerner Publishing Group.

Resau, Laura. What the Moon Saw. l.t. rev. ed. 2007. 300p. (YA). 22.95 (***978-0-7862-9278-3(4)***) Thorndike Pr.

Rideout, Steve. Don't Go Up a Windmill. 1999. (Illus.). 96p. (gr. 4-10). lib. bdg. (978-3-09-670157-0(1)) Blue Windmill Bks.

—Don't Go up a Windmill. 1999. (Illus.). 96p. (YA). (gr. 4-8). pap. 9.95 (978-0-9670157-0-5(7)) Blue Windmill Bks.

Rosen, Michael J. A Drive in the Country. Burckhardt, Marc, illus. 2007. 32p. (J). (gr. k-5). 16.99 (***978-0-7636-2140-7(4)***) Candlewick Pr.

Rylant, Cynthia. The Blue Hill Meadows. 2001. (gr. 3-6). lib. bdg. 14.15 (978-0-613-35490-5(7)); (Illus.). (J). 12.80 (978-0-606-21075-1(X)) Tandem Library Bks.

—Scarecrow. Stringer, Lauren, illus. 1998. 40p. (J). (gr. 1-7). 16.00 (978-0-15-201084-3(X)) Harcourt Children's Bks.

—This Year's Garden. Szilagyi, Mary, illus. 1998. (J). pap. 4.95 (978-0-87628-397-4(0)) Ctr. for Applied Research in Education, The.

—This Year's Garden. 1999. (Illus.). (J). (ps-2). lib. bdg. 12.95 (978-0-8085-9240-2(8)) Tandem Library Bks.

Sam, Bangs & Moonshine. 1999. (J). 9.95 (978-1-56137-040-5(1)) Novel Units, Inc.

Samton, Sheila W. Rosa Digs a Hole. 2000. (Brand New Readers Ser.). (Illus.). (J). (978-0-7636-1122-4(0)) Candlewick Pr.

Schertle, Alice. Down the Road. Lewis, Earl, illus. 2000. 40p. (J). (gr. k-3). pap. 7.00 (978-0-15-202471-0(9) , Harcourt Paperbacks) Harcourt Children's Bks.

—Down the Road. Lewis, E. B., illus. 2000. (J). (ps-17). lib. bdg. 14.15 (978-0-613-29935-0(3)) Tandem Library Bks.

—Down the Road. 2000. 12.80 (978-0-606-20324-1(9)) Tandem Library Bks.

Seymour, Tres. Auction! Smith, Cat Bowman, illus. 2005. 32p. (J). (gr. 1-4). 16.99 (978-0-7636-1242-9(1)) Candlewick Pr.

Sherrill, Ronda Scott. The Year of the New Barn. 2002. 132p. (J). pap. 19.95 (978-1-59129-140-4(2)) PublishAmerica, Inc.

Smith, Lanc. The Happy Hocky Family Moves to the Country! 2003. (Illus.). 64p. (J). 16.99 (978-0-670-03594-6(7) , Viking Juvenile) Penguin Group (USA) Inc.

Spinelli, Eileen. The Best Time of Day. Langdo, Bryan, illus. 2007. 32p. (J). pap. 6.00 (978-0-15-205862-3(1) , Voyager Bks./Libros Viajeros) Harcourt Children's Bks.

—The Best Time of Day. Langdo, Bryan, illus. 2005. 32p. (J). (ps-ps). 16.00 (978-0-15-205051-1(5)) Harcourt Trade Pubs.

Stone, Phoebe. Deep down Popular. 2008. (J). 288p. pap. 16.99 (***978-0-439-80245-1(8)***); (***978-0-439-80244-4(X)***) Scholastic, Inc. (Levine, Arthur A. Bks.).

Talley, Linda. Toad in Town. Maeno, Itoko, illus. 2001. (Key Concepts in Personal Development Ser.). (gr. k-4). 30p. (J). 89.95 incl. VHS (978-1-55942-165-2(7)); 32p. pap., tchr. ed. 89.95 incl. VHS (978-1-55942-168-3(1) , 9387K3) Marsh Media.

Taste of Blackberries. 1999. (J). 11.95 (978-1-56137-826-5(7)); 9.95 (978-1-56137-334-5(6)) Novel Units, Inc.

Taylor, Mildred D. Lloro por la Tierra. 1999. (SPA.). 299p. (YA). (gr. 7 up). pap. 9.95 (978-958-04-4388-9(2) , NR8277) Norma S.A. COL. *Dist:* Lectorum Pubns., Inc., Libros Sin Fronteras.

Toad in Town - Teaching Guide. 2000. 17.95 (978-1-55942-167-6(3)) Marsh Media.

Il Topo di Citta e il Topo di Campagna. 1999. (ITA., Illus.). 24p. (J). (ps-5). pap. 7.95 (978-88-8148-257-3(6)) European Language Institute ITA. *Dist:* Distribooks, Inc., Midwest European Pubns.

Townsend, Wendy. Lizard Love. 2008. (J). (***978-1-932425-34-5(9)*** , Front Street) Boyds Mills Pr.

Trease, Christine K. Mike E. Meanderer Moves to the Country. Trease, Christine K., illus. 1999. (Illus.). 22p. (J). (ps-7). 14.95 (978-1-929450-00-8(1)); (Adventure Ser.: Vol. No. 1). cd-rom 14.95 (978-1-929450-01-5(X)) Lexico.

Tubb, Kristin. Sunny Days. Style Guide Staff & Riley, Kellee, illus. 2006. (Holly Hobbie & Friends Ser.). 32p. (J). act. bk. ed. 4.99 (978-1-4169-1850-9(7) , Simon Scribbles) Simon & Schuster Children's Publishing.

Unknown. Strawberry Shortcake's Country Fair Fun. 2008. (Strawberry Shortcake Ser.). 32p. (J). (ps-1). pap. 5.99 (***978-0-448-44861-9(0)*** , Grosset & Dunlap) Penguin Group (USA) Inc.

Van Dyne, Edith. Mary Louise. 2006. 148p. pap. 10.99 (978-1-4264-1952-2(X)); 144p. pap. 13.99 (978-1-4264-2063-4(3)) BiblioBazaar.

van Stockum, Hilda. A Day on Skates: 2007 Commemorative Edition. van Stockum, Hilda, illus. 2007. (Illus.). 44p. (J). 19.95 (***978-1-932350-18-0(7)***) Bethlehem Bks.

Verlander, Susan. Goodnight Country. 2004. (Illus.). 28p. (J). 13.95 (978-0-8118-4172-6(3)) Chronicle Bks. LLC.

Waddell, Martin. Tiny's Big Adventure. Lawrence, John, illus. 2004. 32p. (J). (ps-1). 15.99 (978-0-7636-2170-4(6)) Candlewick Pr.

Weeks, Jan. The Marathon Runner. Harrison, Paul, illus. 2006. (Read-It! Chapter Books). 64p. (J). (gr. 2-4). 19.95 (978-1-4048-1669-5(0)) Picture Window Bks.

Whelan, Gloria. The Pathless Woods: Ernest Hemingway's Sixteenth Summer in Northern Michigan. Wolff, Glenn, illus. 2nd rev. ed. 1998. (J). (gr. 6-10). 16.95 (978-1-882376-63-6(3)); 176p. (gr. 7-12). pap. 11.95 (978-1-882376-44-5(7)) Thunder Bay Pr.

Where the Red Fern Grows. 8.97 (978-0-673-58326-0(0)) Addison-Wesley Longman, Inc.

Where the Red Fern Grows. 1998. (J). 9.95 (978-1-56137-244-7(7)) Novel Units, Inc.

Wiley, Melissa. Down to the Bonny Glen: Martha Years. 2001. (Martha Years Ser.). (Illus.). (J). 12.64 (978-0-606-21160-4(8)) Tandem Library Bks.

Woodruff, Elvira. Dear Austin: Letters from the Underground Railroad. 2000. (gr. 5-8). lib. bdg. 13.00 (978-0-613-28463-9(1)) Tandem Library Bks.

Woodworth, Chris. Busted.com. 2008. 176p. (YA). 16.00 (***978-0-374-30987-9(6)***) Farrar, Straus & Giroux.

Zagwyn, Deborah Turney. Turtle Spring. 2004. (Illus.). 32p. (J). (gr. k-2). 6.95 (978-1-58246-052-9(3) , Tricycle Pr.) Ten Speed Pr.

COUNTY PLANNING

see Regional Planning

COUPS D'ETAT

see Revolutions

COURAGE

see also Fear; Heroes

Burch, Regina G. Dare to Have Courage: Learning about Standing Strong. Hamaguchi, Carla, ed. Adnet, Bernard, illus. 2002. (Character Education Readers). 16p. (J). (gr. k-4). pap. 2.99 (978-1-57471-824-9(X) , CTP 3123) Creative Teaching Pr., Inc.

Character Ed Says Courtesy Is Contagious. 2006. (J). 4.95 (978-1-55548-055-4(1) , 676) Human Relations Media.

Donahue, Jill L. Being Brave. Previn, Stacey, illus. 2007. (J). lib. bdg. (***978-1-4048-3780-5(9)***) Picture Window Bks.

—Being Courageous. Previn, Stacey, illus. 2007. (J). lib. bdg. (***978-1-4048-3778-2(7)***) Picture Window Bks.

Doudna, Kelly. I Feel Brave. l.t. ed. 1999. (How Do You Feel? Ser.). (Illus.). 24p. (J). (ps-3). lib. bdg. 19.93 (978-1-57765-190-1(1) , SandCastle) ABDO Publishing Co.

Dowswell, Paul. True Stories of Heroes. rev. ed. 2004. (True Adventure Stories Ser.). 144p. (J). pap. 4.99 (978-0-7945-0094-8(3)) EDC Publishing.

Edgar, Kathleen J., et al. Courage. 2003. (J). (978-1-59203-056-9(4)) Learning Challenge, Inc.

Finn, Carrie. Kids Talk about Bravery. Muehlenhardt, Amy Bailey, illus. 2006. (Kids Talk Junior Ser.). 32p. (J). (gr. k-2). lib. bdg. 23.93 (978-1-4048-2314-3(X)) Picture Window Bks.

Good Character Adventure Pack: Adventures in Courage. 2006. (J). 4.95 (978-1-55548-005-9(5) , 4205) Human Relations Media.

Greive, Bradley Trevor. A Teaspoon of Courage for Kids: A Little Book of Encouragement for Whenever You Need It. 2007. 48p. 9.95 (***978-0-7407-6949-8(9)***) Andrews McMeel Publishing.

Hamilton, Elizabeth L. & Hamilton, David E. Courage. 2003. (Character Builder Ser.: No. 2). 64p. per. 5.95 (978-0-9713749-8-0(8) , Character-in-Action) Quiet Impact, Inc.

Harcourt School Publishers Staff. A Certain Courage. 3rd ed. 2002. (Horizons Ser.). (Illus.). (J). pap. 7.30 (978-0-15-333589-1(0)) Harcourt Schl. Pubs.

Hearne, Betsy. Seven Brave Women. Andersen, Bethanne, illus. 2006. 24p. (J). reprint ed. pap. 6.99 (978-0-06-079921-2(8) , Harper Trophy) HarperCollins Pubs.

Hirschmann, Kris. Courage. 2003. (Illus.). 32p. (J). pap. 7.50 (978-1-4109-0323-5(0)); lib. bdg. 24.28 (978-0-7398-7003-7(3)) Raintree.

I Can Do It! (Kids Talk Ser.). 32p. (J). 8.95 (978-1-4048-0365-7(3)) Picture Window Bks.

Jensen, Hay R. Home with Honor Vol. 1: A Vietnam P.O.W. Tells How to Conquer Adversity Through Courage, Honor & Faith. (Illus.). 171p. (Orig.). (YA). pap. 14.95 (978-1-877898-15-0(5)) P.O.W. (Pubns. of Worth).

Kipling, Rudyard. Land & Sea Tales. 2001. 194p. 8.95 (978-1-84232-946-7(4)) House of Stratus, Inc. GBR. *Dist:* Midpoint Trade Bks., Inc.

Klingel, Cynthia Fitterer. Courage. 2007. (Learn about Values Ser.). 24p. (J). 21.36 (978-1-59296-667-7(5)) Child's World, Inc.

Kosek, Jane Kelly. Learning about Courage from the Life of Christopher Reeve. 1999. (Character Building Book Ser.). (Illus.). 24p. (J). (gr. 3). lib. bdg. 18.75 (978-0-8239-5346-2(7) , PowerKids Pr.) Rosen Publishing Group, Inc., The.

Loewen, Nancy. I Can Do It! Kids Talk about Courage. Wesley, Omarr, illus. 2004. (Kids Talk Ser.). 32p. (C). (gr. 2-5). 23.93 (978-1-4048-0032-8(8)) Picture Window Bks.

Mead, David. Little Teddy Roosevelt Learns a Lesson in Courage: Courage. Sharp, Chris, illus. 2003. (American Virtues for Kids Ser.). (J). bds. 6.95 (978-0-9746440-3-5(X)) Ideals Pubns.

Medina, Sarah. Brave. Brooker, Jo, illus. 2007. (J). (***978-1-4034-9791-8(5)***); pap. (***978-1-4034-9798-7(2)***) Heinemann Library.

Molan, Chris, illus. Heroic Stories. 2004. (Red Hot Reads Ser.). 256p. (J). (gr. 4-8). pap. 6.95 (978-0-7534-5720-7(2) , Kingfisher) Houghton Mifflin Co. Trade & Reference Div.

O'Shei, Tim. The World's Most Amazing Survival Stories. 2007. (Edge Books, the World's Top Ten). (Illus.). 32p. (J). 23.93 (978-0-7368-6437-4(7) , 1258961) Capstone Pr., Inc.

Rinaldo, Denise. Amelia Earhart: With a Discussion of Courage. 2004. (Values in Action Ser.). (J). (978-1-59203-068-2(8)) Learning Challenge, Inc.

—Rosa Parks: With a Discussion of Courage. 2003. (Values in Action Ser.). (J). (978-1-59203-061-3(0)) Learning Challenge, Inc.

Scheunemann, Pam. Courage. 2003. (United We Stand Ser.). (Illus.). 24p. (J). (ps-3). lib. bdg. 19.93 (978-1-57765-877-1(9)) ABDO Publishing Co.

Schuette, Sarah L. I Am Courageous. 2007. (Character Values Ser.). 24p. (J). 15.93 (978-0-7368-6335-3(4)) Capstone Pr., Inc.

Thoennes Keller, Kristin. Courage. 2005. (Illus.). 24p. (J). 21.26 (978-0-7368-3679-1(9)) Capstone Pr., Inc.

Waber, Bernard. Courage. Waber, Bernard, illus. 2002. (Illus.). 40p. (J). (gr. k-3). lib. bdg. 12.00 (978-0-618-23855-2(7) , Walter Lorraine) Houghton Mifflin Co. Trade & Reference Div.

Waite, Elsie, et al. Following Rules. Sparck, Carole C., illus. l.t. ed. 2001. 8p. (J). pap. 6.00 (978-1-58084-169-6(4)) Lower Kuskokwim Schl. District.

Waldman, Jackie. Teens with the Courage to Give: Young People Who Triumphed over Tragedy & Volunteered to Make a Difference. 2000. (Call to Action Ser.). (Illus.). 192p. (gr. 9-12). pap. 15.95 (978-1-57324-504-3(6) , Red Wheel) Red Wheel/Weiser.

—Teens with the Courage to Give: Young People Who Triumphed over Tragedy & Volunteered to Make a Difference. 2000. (gr. 7-12). lib. bdg. 25.70 (978-0-613-79193-9(2)) Tandem Library Bks.

C D

Warner Press Staff. Courage. 2000. (Lion Cub Upside-Down Books Ser.). (J). (ps-3). pap. 5.95 (978-0-87162-822-0(8)) Warner Pr. Pubs.

Weil, Ann. Great Heroes. 2006. (Atomic Ser.). (Illus.). 32p. (J). (gr. 4-6). lib. bdg. 28.21 (978-1-4109-2483-4(1)) Raintree.

—Great Heroes. 2006. (Illus.). 32p. (J). pap. (978-1-4109-2488-9(2)) Steck-Vaughn.

COURAGE—FICTION

Alger, Horatio. Forging Ahead. unabr. ed. 2002. (Polyglot Press Alger Ser.). (Illus.). (J). pap. 17.95 (978-1-931927-69-7(3)) Polyglot Pr., Inc.

Allred, Chris Ross. Sir E. Bobbo! 2004. 21p. pap. 14.95 (978-1-4137-2785-2(9)) PublishAmerica, Inc.

Anaya, Rudolfo. The First Tortilla: A Bilingual Story. Lamadrid, Enrique R., tr. Cordova, Amy, illus. 2007. (SPA & ENG.). 32p. (J). (gr. 2-4). 16.95 (***978-0-8263-4214-0(0)***) Univ. of New Mexico Pr.

Araki, Mie. Kitten's Big Adventure. 2005. (Illus.). 40p. (J). 15.00 (978-0-15-216738-7(2)) Harcourt Trade Pubs.

Arnold, Marsha D. The Bravest of Us All. Sneed, Brad, illus. 2000. 32p. (J). (ps-3). 16.99 (978-0-8037-2409-9(8) , Dial) Penguin Group (USA) Inc.

Asare, Meshack. Sosu's Call. Asare, Meshack, illus. 2002. (Illus.). 40p. (J). (gr. k-4). 15.95 (978-1-929132-21-8(2)) Kane/Miller Bk. Pubs., Inc.

Averill, Esther. Jenny's Moonlight Adventure. 32p. (J). pap. 12.95 (978-0-553-15145-9(2)) Bantam Bks.

—Jenny's Moonlight Adventure. Averill, Esther, illus. 2005. (New York Review Children's Collection). (Illus.). 32p. (J). (ps-ps). pap. 12.95 (978-1-59017-160-8(8) , NYR Children's Collection) New York Review of Bks., Inc., The.

Bartoletti, Susan Campbell. The Boy Who Dared. 2008. 192p. (J). pap. 16.99 (***978-0-439-68013-4(1)*** , Scholastic Pr.) Scholastic, Inc.

Belinsky, Ruth. I Dream Before I Sleep. 2002. (Illus.). 32p. pap. 9.95 (978-0-9740012-0-3(1)) Idee, LLC.

Bell, William. Death Wind. 2006. 112p. (YA). lib. bdg. 14.95 (978-1-55143-543-5(8)) Orca Bk. Pubs. USA.

Bendro Bach. 2005. (WEL., Illus.). 30p. (978-1-902416-84-7(8)) Cymdeithas Lyfrau Ceredigion.

Bloor, Edward. Crusader. 2007. (Illus.). 496p. (YA). pap. 6.95 (***978-0-15-206314-6(5)*** , Harcourt Paperbacks) Harcourt Children's Bks.

Booth, Bradley. Shepherd Warrior. 2007. 127p. (J). (***978-0-8163-2161-2(2)***) Pacific Pr. Pubns.

Borchard, Therese Johnson. Whitney Coaches David on Fighting Goliath: And Learns to Stand up for Herself. 2000. (Emerald Bible Collection). (Illus.). 80p. (gr. 3-7). 5.95 (978-0-8091-6669-5(0) , 6669-0) Paulist Pr.

Brightwood, Laura, illus. King's New Suit. Brightwood, Laura, . 2007. (J). DVD (***978-1-934409-05-3(7)***) 3-C Institute for Social Development.

Broadley, Leo. Pedro the Brave. Swain, Holly, illus. 2002. (J). 5.95 (978-1-58925-375-9(2)); 32p. tchr. ed. 14.95 (978-1-58925-024-6(9)) ME Media LLC. (tiger tales).

—Pedro the Brave. 2002. (gr. k-3). lib. bdg. 14.10 (978-0-613-56567-7(3)) Tandem Library Bks.

Carlson, Nancy. Harriet & the Roller Coaster. 20th anniv. ed. (Nancy Carlson's Neighborhood Ser.). (Illus.). 32p. (gr. k-2). 2005. 15.95 (978-1-57505-053-9(6)); 2003. (J). (978-1-57505-202-1(4)) Lerner Publishing Group.

—Harriet & the Roller Coaster. 2003. (gr. k-3). lib. bdg. 15.25 (978-0-613-68089-9(8)) Tandem Library Bks.

Catchpool, Michael. Where There's a Bear, There's Trouble! Cabban, Vanessa, illus. 2002. 28p. (J). (ps-k). tchr. ed. 14.95 (978-1-58925-022-2(2) , tiger tales) ME Media LLC.

Clark, Eleanor. Victoria Grace: Courageous Patriot. 2007. (Eleanor Jo Ser.). (J). 14.99 (978-0-9753036-8-9(6)) HonorNet.

Clark, Sherryl. Nibbles: the Littlest Pirate & the Hammerheads: Time to Track down Treasure! rev. ed. 2008. (Nibbles, Bites, & Chomps: Ser.). (Illus.). 72p. (J). pap. 3.95 (***978-0-7624-3064-2(8)*** , Running Pr. Kids) Running Pr. Bk. Pubs.

Conley, Deane W. Angelino Courage to Fly. 2007. (J). lib. bdg. 19.95 (***978-1-933732-27-5(X)*** , Bear Hug Bks.) MidAmerica Publishing Co.

Coughlin, Denise. Dragon in My Pocket. Kastan, Bill, illus. 2005. (J). (***978-0-9765905-0-7(6)***) Rose Valley Publishing.

Courage of Sarah Noble. 1999. (J). 9.95 (978-1-56137-239-3(0)) Novel Units, Inc.

Crews, Dana-Susan. Our Daddy's Cancer: How We Helped Him Fight. 2007. (J). per. 10.99 (***978-1-60247-409-3(5)***) Tate Publishing & Enterprises, L.L.C.

Cutler, Jane. The Cello of Mr. O. Couch, Greg, illus. 1999. 32p. (J). (gr. k-4). 15.99 (978-0-525-46119-7(1) , Dutton Juvenile) Penguin Group (USA) Inc.

Dalgliesh, Alice. The Courage of Sarah Noble. Weisgard, Leonard, illus. 2002. (J). 13.40 (978-0-7587-0249-4(3)) Book Wholesalers, Inc.

Davie, Jan. Stairway to the Stars. 2005. 76p. pap. (***978-1-84401-569-6(6)***) Athena Pr.

de Beer, Hans. Little Polar Bear & the Brave Little Hare. de Beer, Hans, illus. 1998. (Illus.). 32p. (J). (gr. k-3). 15.95 (978-0-7358-1011-2(7)) North-South Bks., Inc.

—Little Polar Bear & the Brave Little Hare. 2000. (gr. k-3). lib. bdg. 15.25 (978-0-613-30007-0(6)) Tandem Library Bks.

Dell, Patricia. Zander. Dell, Patricia, illus. 2000. (Illus.). 12p. (J). (gr. k-6). pap. 10.00 (978-0-9702221-0-7(6)) Zanderbooks.

Demi. The Boy Who Painted Dragons. Demi, illus. 2007. 52p. (J). (gr. 2-5). 21.99 (978-1-4169-2469-2(8) , McElderry, Margaret K.) Simon & Schuster Children's Publishing.

Dodd, Lynley. Scarface Claw. Dodd, Lynley, illus. 2002. (Gold Star First Readers Ser.). (Illus.). 32p. (J). (gr. 1 up). lib. bdg. 22.00 (978-0-8368-3161-0(6)) Stevens, Gareth Inc.

Dunkle, Clare B. By These Ten Bones. rev. ed. 2005. 240p. (YA). (gr. 6-9). 16.95 (978-0-8050-7496-3(1) , Holt, Henry & Co. Bks. For Young Readers) Holt, Henry & Co.

Egan, Kate, adapted by. The Courage to Choose, Bk.15. rev. ed. 2005. (W. I. T. C. H. Ser.: Bk. 15). (Illus.). 144p. (J). (gr. 3-7). pap. 4.99 (978-0-7868-5193-5(7) , Volo) Hyperion Bks. for Children.

Emmett, Jonathan. Terry Takes Off. Rutherford, Peter, illus. 2006. 32p. (J). (***978-1-4048-3132-2(0)***) Picture Window Bks.

Engelbreit, Mary. Queen of Halloween. 2008. 32p. (J). 16.99 (***978-0-06-008190-4(2))***; lib. bdg. 17.89 (***978-0-06-008191-1(0)***) HarperCollins Pubs.

Forte, Joyce. The Brave Little Girl. 2004. 37p. pap. 17.95 (978-1-4137-1833-1(7)) PublishAmerica, Inc.

Fox, Paula. How Many Miles to Babylon? 2005. 104p. (J). pap. (978-1-932425-39-0(X) , Lemniscaat) Boyds Mills Pr.

Frantz, Jennifer. Saro Tells a Story. Grosvenor, Charles, illus. 2007. (Land Before Time Ser.). 24p. (J). (ps-2). pap. 3.99 (***978-0-06-134766-5(3)*** , Harper Entertainment) HarperCollins Pubs.

French, Vivian. Te Presento al Mamut!, Level P. Williams, Lisa, illus. 2006. (Lightning Readers Ser.). (SPA.). 32p. (J). pap. 3.95 (978-0-7696-4217-8(9) , Gingham Dog Pr.) School Specialty Publishing.

French/Williams, Vivian/Lisa. Meet the Mammoth! 2005. (Illus.). 32p. (J). lib. bdg. 9.00 (***978-1-4242-0881-4(5)***) Fitzgerald Bks.

Froeber, Sarah & Mosher, Kim. Pelican & Pelicant. 2003. (Illus.). 36p. (J). 17.99 (978-0-9744926-0-5(4)) Toucan Pr., Inc.

Gantos, Jack. Desire Lines. 2006. 144p. (YA). reprint ed. pap. 7.95 (978-0-374-41703-1(2)) Macmillan.

Gawade, Akansha A. This Is Who I Am. 2006. (J). pap. 8.00 (978-0-8059-6886-6(5)) Dorrance Publishing Co., Inc.

Geter, Maurice. My Friend Buddy. Geter, Maurice, illus. 2006. (Illus.). 24p. (J). (978-1-4120-9646-1(4)) Trafford Publishing.

Giff, Patricia Reilly. Willow Run. 160p. (J). (gr. 4-7). 2007. pap. 5.99 (978-0-440-23801-0(3) , Yearling); 2005. 15.95 (978-0-385-73067-9(5) , Lamb, Wendy); 2005. lib. bdg. 17.99 (978-0-385-90096-6(1) , Lamb, Wendy) Random Hse. Children's Bks.

Goodman, Joan Elizabeth. Hope's Crossing. 1998. (Illus.). 224p. (J). (gr. 4-6). tchr. ed. 16.00 (978-0-395-86195-0(0)) Houghton Mifflin Co. Trade & Reference Div.

—Hope's Crossing. 1999. (Illus.). 224p. (J). (gr. 3-7). pap. 6.99 (978-0-698-11807-2(3) , Putnam Juvenile) Penguin Group (USA) Inc.

—Hope's Crossing. 1999. (J). 12.64 (978-0-606-19068-8(6)); (gr. 3-6). lib. bdg. 14.15 (978-0-613-21719-4(5)) Tandem Library Bks.

Graff, Nancy Price. A Long Way Home. 2001. 208p. (J). (gr. 5-9). tchr. ed. 15.00 (978-0-618-12042-0(4) , Clarion Bks.) Houghton Mifflin Co. Trade & Reference Div.

Gray, Luli. Falcon & the Charles Street Witch. 2002. 144p. (J). (gr. 5-9). 16.00 (978-0-618-16410-3(3)) Houghton Mifflin Co. Trade & Reference Div.

Gummelt, Donna & Melchiorre, Dondino. My Sunshine Friend. Wall, Randy Hugh, ed. Varela, Juan D., tr. Varela, Juan D., illus. ed. 2006. (SPA.). 32p. (J). 14.95 (978-0-9764798-2-6(6)) Story Store Collection Publishing.

Hall, Kirsten. I'm Not Scared. Holub, Joan, illus. 2003. (My First Reader Ser.). 32p. (J). 18.50 (978-0-516-22929-4(X) , Children's Pr.) Scholastic Library Publishing.

Hallagin, Janet. The Way of Courage. 2006. 30.99 (***978-1-4257-1249-5(5))***; pap. 20.99 (***978-1-4257-1248-8(7)***) Xlibris Corp.

Hamilton, Elizabeth L. Passport to Courage. 2002. (Character-in-Action Ser.: No. 1). (Illus.). 384p. (YA). per. 19.95 (978-0-9713749-3-5(7) , Character-in-Action) Quiet Impact, Inc.

Heffernan, Colleen. A Kind of Courage. 2005. 160p. (J). (gr. 7-12). pap. 12.00 (978-1-55143-358-5(3)) Orca Bk. Pubs. USA.

Henkes, Kevin. Sheila Rae, the Brave. Henkes, Kevin, illus. (Illus.). 9.95 (978-1-59112-865-6(X)); 2002. 28.95 incl. audio compact disk (978-1-59112-550-1(2)); 2002. pap. 35.95 incl. audio compact disk (978-1-59112-549-5(9)) Live Oak Media.

—Sheila Rae, the Brave. 2002. (Illus.). (J). pap., tchr.'s planning gde. ed. 33.95 incl. audio (978-0-87499-954-9(5)); 25.95 incl. audio (978-0-87499-953-2(7)) Live Oak Media.

Holabird, Katharine. Angelina & Henry. Craig, Helen, illus. 2006. 32p. (J). pap. 5.99 (978-0-14-240590-1(6) , Puffin) Penguin Group (USA) Inc.

—The Rose Fairy Princess. Craig, Helen, illus. 2006. (Angelina Ballerina Ser.). 24p. (J). (ps-1). 3.99 (978-0-448-44465-9(8) , Grosset & Dunlap) Penguin Group (USA) Inc.

Jacobsen, Annie. Ivar, the Short, but Brave Viking. Hanson, Susan Jo, illus. 2007. (J). lib. bdg. 16.95 (***978-0-9778276-1-9(5)***) Pickled Herring Pr.

James, Brian. The Shark Who Was Afraid of Everything. 2006. (Illus.). 32p. (J). pap. 5.99 (978-0-439-78672-0(X) , Cartwheel Bks.) Scholastic, Inc.

—The Shark Who Was Afraid of Everything. McNally, Bruce J., illus. 2002. (J). (978-0-439-36865-0(0)) Scholastic, Inc.

Jenkins, Amanda. Tornado! 2005. 22.00 (***978-1-4108-4212-1(6)***) Benchmark Education Co.

Jonell, Lynne. Bravemole. ed. 2004. (Illus.). (J). (gr. k-3). spiral bd. (978-0-616-14579-1(9)) Canadian National Institute for the Blind/Institut National Canadien pour les Aveugles.

Jordan, Christopher & Boey, Stephanie. The Little Beaver. 2008. (Illus.). 24p. 15.95 (***978-1-55168-249-5(4)***) Key Porter Bks. CAN. *Dist:* Perseus Distribution.

Jordan, Mark. Courage the Monkey. 2006. (Illus.). 40p. (J). 13.95 (978-0-9717013-7-3(7)) Decere Publishing.

Julian, Alison. Brave as a Bunny Can Be. Julian, Alison, illus. 2001. (Illus.). 40p. (J). (gr. 2 up). 15.95 (978-0-931674-46-4(8)) Waldman Hse. Pr., Inc.

Keller, Holly. Brave Horace. 1998. (Illus.). 32p. (J). (ps-3). 14.89 (978-0-688-15408-0(5)) HarperCollins Pubs.

Lamson, Sharon. The Roach Rangers Cross Panic Pier: A Story about Courage. Barry, Bruce, illus. 2006. (Bug Rangers Ser.). 24p. (J). pap. 6.99 (978-0-310-71006-6(5)) Zonderkidz.

Lears, Laurie. Becky the Brave: A Story about Epilepsy. Piazza, Gail, illus. 2002. 32p. (J). (gr. 1-4). 15.95 (978-0-8075-0601-1(X)) Whitman, Albert & Co.

Leblanc, Louise. Leo's Midnight Rescue. Prud'homme, Jules, illus. 2004. 62p. (J). lib. bdg. 12.00 (***978-1-4242-1217-0(0)***) Fitzgerald Bks.

—Leo's Midnight Rescue. Cummins, Sarah, tr. from FRE. Prud'homme, Jules, illus. 2004. (First Novel Ser.). 64p. (J). (gr. 2-5). 4.95 (978-0-88780-640-7(6)); (***978-0-88780-641-4(4)***) Formac Publishing Co., Ltd. CAN. *Dist:* Casemate Pubs. & Bk. Distributors, LLC.

Lindquist, Susan Hart. Summer Soldiers. 2000. (J). (978-0-606-19132-6(1)) Tandem Library Bks.

Malone, Patricia. Lady Ilena: Way of the Warrior. 2007. 176p. (YA). (gr. 7-11). mass mkt. 5.99 (***978-0-440-23901-7(X)*** , Laurel Leaf) Random Hse. Children's Bks.

Marcum, Lance. The Cottonmouth Club. 2005. 336p. (J). 18.00 (978-0-374-31562-7(0) , Farrar, Straus & Giroux (BYR)) Farrar, Straus & Giroux.

Marien, Donna. Waiting at the Bay: A Young Woman's Reflections on Journeys in the Sea of Life. 2003. 108p. (YA). pap. 10.95 (978-0-595-26304-2(6) , Writers Club Pr.) iUniverse, Inc.

Marlow, Layn. The Witch with a Twitch. Dreidemy, Joelle, illus. 2005. 32p. (J). (ps-ps). 15.95 (978-1-58925-052-9(4) , tiger tales) ME Media LLC.

—Witch with a Twitch. Dreidemy, Joelle, illus. 2006. 32p. (J). pap. 6.95 (978-1-58925-400-8(7) , tiger tales) ME Media LLC.

Marsh, T. F. Quest for Courage. Marsh, T. F., illus. 2006. (Amazing Travels of Wannabeb Ser.). (Illus.). 32p. (J). 8.99 (978-0-7847-1801-8(6) , 04127) Standard Publishing.

Martin, Rafe. The Brave Little Parrot. Gaber, Susan, illus. 1998. 1p. (J). (ps-3). 16.99 (978-0-399-22825-4(X) , Putnam Juvenile) Penguin Group (USA) Inc.

McDonald, Megan. Beetle McGrady Eats Bugs! Manning, Jane K., illus. 2005. 32p. (J). 15.99 (978-0-06-001354-7(0)); lib. bdg. 17.89 (978-0-06-001355-4(9)) HarperCollins Pubs.

McGahan, Mary. Raid at Red Mill. Butterfield, Ned, illus. 2001. (Adventures in America Ser.). 96p. (J). (gr. 3-7). lib. bdg. 14.95 (978-1-893110-11-3(7)) Silver Moon Pr.

McKissack, Patricia C. & Moss, Onawumi Jean. Precious & the Boo Hag. Brooker, Kyrsten, illus. 2005. 40p. (J). (ps-3). 17.99 (978-0-689-85194-0(4) , Atheneum/Anne Schwartz Bks.) Simon & Schuster Children's Publishing.

McQuerry, Maureen Doyle. Wolfproof. Murphy, John, illus. 2006. (J). 183p. 24.95 (978-1-59597-006-0(1)); 176p. per. 14.95 (978-1-59597-009-1(6)) Idylls Pr.

McSwigan, Marie. Snow Treasure. Mary, Reardon, illus. 2006. 208p. (J). (gr. 3). pap. 5.99 (978-0-14-240224-5(9) , Puffin) Penguin Group (USA) Inc.

Merialdo, Lee K. Kidnapped. 2006. 112p. pap. 10.95 (978-0-7414-3407-4(5)) Infinity Publishing.

Miller, S. K., illus. & creator. Jesse's Color Field. Miller, S. K., creator. l.t. ed. 2002. 68p. (J). (gr. k-5). pap. 16.95 (978-0-9714636-0-8(3)) Treehouse Treasures Corp.

Morgan, Michaela. Brave, Brave Mouse. Cartlidge, Michelle, illus. 2004. 32p. (J). (ps-2). 15.95 (978-0-8075-0869-5(1)) Whitman, Albert & Co.

Morris, Deborah. Teens 911: Snowbound. 2002. (Illus.). 250p. (YA). pap. 12.95 (978-0-7573-0039-4(1) , HCI Teens) Health Communications, Inc.

Morrison, P. R. The Wind Tamer. 2006. 336p. (YA). 16.95 (978-1-58234-781-3(6)) Bloomsbury Publishing.

Morrison, P. R. Wind Tamer. 2007. 336p. (YA). pap. 7.95 (***978-1-59990-147-3(1)*** , Bloomsbury Children) Bloomsbury Publishing.

Nanette. Sunny the Orange Puppy. 2004. (Life on Granny's Farm Ser.). (J). 12.95 (978-0-9741269-6-8(9)) St. Bernard Publishing, LLC.

Napoli, Donna Jo. One Leap Forward. 1999. (Angelwings Ser.: No. 4). (Illus.). 96p. (J). (gr. 2-5). pap. 7.95 (978-0-689-82986-4(8) , Aladdin) Simon & Schuster Children's Publishing.

—One Leap Forward. 1999. (Angelwings Ser.: No. 4). (Illus.). (J). (978-0-606-17907-2(0)) Tandem Library Bks.

Narsimhan, Mahtab. The Third Eye. 2007. 240p. (YA). pap. 11.99 (***978-1-55002-750-1(6)*** , Boardwalk Bks.) Dundurn Group, The CAN. *Dist:* Univ. of Toronto Pr.

Nash, Ogden. Custard the Dragon & the Wicked Knight. Munsinger, Lynn, illus. 1999. 32p. (J). (ps-3). pap. 6.99 (978-0-316-59905-4(0)) Little Brown & Co.

—Custard the Dragon & the Wicked Knight. 1999. (J). (gr. k up). pap., stu. ed. 25.20 incl. audio (978-0-7887-2986-7(1) , 40868); Class set. pap. 91.30 incl. audio (978-0-7887-3016-0(9) , 46833) Recorded Bks., LLC.

—The Tale of Custard the Dragon. Munsinger, Lynn, illus. 1998. 32p. (J). (ps-3). pap. 6.99 (978-0-316-59031-0(2)) Little Brown & Co.

—The Tale of Custard the Dragon. 1998. (J). (978-0-606-13833-8(1)) Tandem Library Bks.

Opperman, Jennifer N. Silent Cry: Katy's Story. 2004. 124p. (YA). pap. 12.95 (978-1-58736-264-4(3) , Starbound Bks.) Wheatmark.

Orr, Wendy. Peeling the Onion. 1999. (Laurel-Leaf Bks.). 176p. (YA). (gr. 7-12). mass mkt. 5.50 (978-0-440-22773-1(9) , Laurel Leaf) Random Hse. Children's Bks.

—Peeling the Onion: A Gripping Story, Told with Honesty & Biting Humour. 1999. (978-0-606-15918-0(5)); (gr. 7-12). lib. bdg. 13.00 (978-0-613-15339-3(1)) Tandem Library Bks.

Park, Linda Sue. When My Name Was Keoko. 2002. 208p. (YA). (gr. 5-9). 16.00 (978-0-618-13335-2(6) , Clarion Bks.) Houghton Mifflin Co. Trade & Reference Div.

—When My Name Was Keoko. 2004. (Illus.). 208p. (J). (gr. 5). pap. 6.50 (978-0-440-41944-0(1) , Yearling) Random Hse. Children's Bks.

Patten, William. The Junior Classics, Volume 7: Stories O. 2006. 29.99 (***978-1-4280-0585-3(4))***; pap. 22.99 (***978-1-4280-0561-7(7)***) IndyPublish.com.

Peck, Lisa J. Skating with Spencer: CTR Club - Book Four, 4 bks. 2005. (J). pap. 6.95 (***978-0-9749241-8-2(0)***) Golden Wings Enterprises.

Peters, Andrew Fusek. Ant & the Big Bad Bully Goat. Wadham, Anna, illus. 2007. 32p. pap. 7.99 (***978-1-84643-079-4(8)***) Child's Play International Ltd. GBR. *Dist:* Child's Play-International.

Pinkney, Brian. Jojo's Flying Sidekick. Pinkney, Brian, illus. 1998. (Illus.). 32p. (J). (gr. k-3). pap. 6.99 (978-0-689-82192-9(1) , Aladdin) Simon & Schuster Children's Publishing.

Prater. Really Brave Tim. 2001. (Illus.). 26p. (J). 19.99 (978-0-370-32389-3(0)) Random Hse. GBR. *Dist:* Independent Pubs. Group.

Prater, John. Really Brave Tim. 1999. (Illus.). 26p. (J). pap. 9.99 (978-0-09-940838-3(4)) Random Hse. GBR. *Dist:* Independent Pubs. Group.

Preiss, Thomas. The Other Side of the Window. 2005. pap. 7.95 (978-0-533-15028-1(0)) Vantage Pr., Inc.

Prince, Sarah. I'm Brave. 1999. (ps-2). lib. bdg. 11.55 (978-0-613-30510-5(8)) Tandem Library Bks.

Quigley's Village Staff. The Wonder Kids' Colossal Caper: Courage. 1998. (Quigley's Village Ser.: Vol. 7). (J). (ps-2). 12.99 incl. VHS (978-0-310-58309-7(8)) Zondervan.

Reit, Seymour, et al. Great Stories of Courage/[adapted by Seymour Reit ; Art by Ernie Colon]. 2006. pap. (***978-0-8368-7933-9(3))***; lib. bdg. (***978-0-8368-7926-1(0)***) Stevens, Gareth Inc. (World Almanac Library).

Ridley, R. W. Dèlon City: Book Two of the Oz Chronicles. 2006. (YA). per. 14.99 (***978-0-9792067-0-2(7)***) Middleburry Hse. Publishing.

Riggio, Anita. Secret Signs: An Escape Through the Underground Railroad. Riggio, Anita, illus. 2003. (Illus.). 32p. (J). (gr. k-3). 15.95 (978-1-56397-555-4(6)) Boyds Mills Pr.

Rinaldi, Ann. Keep Smiling Through. 2005. 208p. (J). pap. 6.95 (978-0-15-205399-4(9) , Gulliver Bks.) Harcourt Children's Bks.

Robinson, Hilary. Pippin's Big Jump. Warburton, Sarah, illus. 2004. (Read-It! Readers Ser.). 32p. (C). (gr. k-3). 18.60 (978-1-4048-0555-2(9)) Picture Window Bks.

Rodowsky, Colby. The Next-Door Dogs. Bates, Amy June, illus. 2005. 112p. (J). 15.00 (978-0-374-36410-6(9) , Farrar, Straus & Giroux (BYR)) Farrar, Straus & Giroux.

Scott, Rosanna. Peter & Friends at Camp. Fargo, Todd, illus. l.t. ed. 2006. (Turtle Books). 32p. (J). (gr. k-4). pap. 9.95 (978-0-944727-51-5(4)); lib. bdg. 15.95 (978-0-944727-52-2(2)) Jason & Nordic Pubs. (Turtle Bks.).

Shannon, George. Tippy-Toe Chick, Go! Dronzek, Laura, illus. 2003. 32p. (J). lib. bdg. 16.89 (978-0-06-029824-1(3)); 16.99 (978-0-06-029823-4(5)) HarperCollins Pubs.

Sheila Rae, the Brave. 2003. (Illus.). (J). (ps-2). 18.95 (978-1-59112-326-2(7)) Live Oak Media.

Shipton, Paul. The Pig Scrolls. 2007. (Illus.). 304p. (J). (gr. 5-9). 6.99 (***978-0-7636-3302-8(X)***) Candlewick Pr.

Shlasko, Robert. Molly & the Sword. Diamond, Donna, illus. 2004. 32p. (J). 15.95 (978-0-9745077-4-3(1)) Jane & Street Pubs. Ltd.

Simon, Charnan. Big Bad Buzz. Epstein, Len, illus. 2006. (Magic Door to Learning Ser.). 24p. (J). (gr. 1-3). 21.36 (978-1-59296-617-2(9)) Child's World, Inc.

Sinke, Janet Mary. Priscilla McdoodleNutMcDoodleMcMae Asks Why. Pennington, Craig, illus. 2007. 40p. (J). 17.95 (978-0-9742732-8-0(7)) My Grandma & Me Pubs.

Sivulich, Sandra Stroner. Principle Woods Celebrates Courage. 2002. 64p. (J). mass mkt. 12.95 (978-0-9700601-9-8(X)) Principle Woods, Inc.

Slepian, Jan. The Alfred Summer. 2001. (978-0-606-22507-6(2)) Tandem Library Bks.

Smucker, Anna Egan. To Keep the South Manitou Light. 2004. (J). pap. 19.95 (978-0-8143-3236-8(6)); (Illus.). 144p. 23.95 (978-0-8143-3235-1(8) , Painted Turtle) Wayne State Univ. Pr.

Sperry, Armstrong. Call It Courage. 2008. Tr. of Newbery Summer. 128p. (YA). mass mkt. 5.99 (***978-1-4169-5368-5(X)*** , Simon Pulse) Simon & Schuster Children's Publishing.

Spinelli, Jerry. Wringer. 1998. (HarperClassics Ser.). 240p. (J). (gr. 3-6). pap. 6.99 (978-0-06-440578-2(8) , Harper Trophy) HarperCollins Pubs.

—Wringer. 2000. (J). tchr. ed. 9.95 (978-1-58130-676-7(8)) Novel Units, Inc.

—Wringer. 1999. 15p. (J). pap., tchr.'s training gde. ed. 15.95 (978-1-58303-099-8(9)) Pathways Publishing.

—Wringer. 1998. (J). (978-0-606-13930-4(3)) Tandem Library Bks.

—Wringer. l.t. ed. 2000. (Juvenile Ser.). 223p. (J). (gr. 4-7). 21.95 (978-0-7862-2774-7(5)) Thorndike Pr.

COURTESY

COURTING

COURTS

COURTS AND COURTIERS

COURTS AND COURTIERS—FICTION

COURTSHIP

COUSTEAU, JACQUES-YVES, 1910-1997

COVERLETS

COW

COWBOYS

C
D

Hominick, Judy & Spreier, Jeanne. Best Cowboy in the West: The Story of Nat Love. 2001. (Heroes to Remember Ser.). (Illus.). 60p. (J). 14.95 (978-1-893110-25-0(7)) Silver Moon Pr.

Isaacs, Sally Senzell. Cattle Trails & Cowboys. 2004. (Illus.). 32p. (J). (978-1-4034-2502-7(7)); pap. 7.50 (978-1-4034-4773-9(X)) Heinemann Library.

James, Will. The Will James Cowboy Book, Vol. 1. rev. ed. (Illus.). 128p. (J). (gr. 4). 18.00 (978-0-87842-469-6(5) , 816) Mountain Pr. Publishing Co., Inc.

Kalman, Bobbie. Bandanas, Chaps & Ten-Gallon Hats. 1998. (Life in the Old West Ser.). (Illus.). 32p. (J). (gr. 3-4). lib. bdg. (978-0-7787-0073-9(9)) Crabtree Publishing Co.

—Bandannas, Chaps, & Ten-Gallon Hats. 1999. (gr. 3-6). lib. bdg. 16.40 (978-0-613-11305-2(5)) Tandem Library Bks.

—Life on the Trail. 1998. (Life in the Old West Ser.). (Illus.). 32p. (J). (gr. 3-4). pap. (978-0-7787-0104-0(2)) Crabtree Publishing Co.

Kubke, Jane & Kubke, Jessica. Bull Riding. 2005. (World of Rodeo Ser.). (Illus.). 48p. (J). lib. bdg. 26.50 (978-1-4042-0544-4(6)) Rosen Publishing Group, Inc., The.

Landau, Elaine. Bill Pickett: Wild West Cowboy. 2004. (Best of the West Biographies Ser.). (Illus.). 48p. (J). lib. bdg. 23.93 (978-0-7660-2215-7(3)) Enslow Pubs., Inc.

Liebeman, Dan. Cowboy. 1999. (I Want to Be Ser.). (Illus.). 24p. (J). (ps-2). lib. bdg. 14.95 (978-1-55209-447-1(2)) Firefly Bks., Ltd.

Liebman, Dan. I Want to Be a Cowboy. 1999. (I Want to Be Ser.). (Illus.). 24p. (J). (ps-2). pap. 3.99 (978-1-55209-432-7(4)) Firefly Bks., Ltd.

Marsh, Carole. Cowboy Christmas Ball. 2002. (Carole Marsh Bks.). (Illus.). 32p. (J). (gr. 3-9). lib. bdg. 21.95 (978-0-635-01356-9(8) , 13568, Marsh, Carole Bks.) Gallopade International.

McCall, Edith. Adventures of Cowboys on Cattle Drivers, Vol. 5. 2001. (Adventures on the American Frontiers Ser.). (Illus.). 127p. (J). (gr. 3-7). pap. 9.99 (978-0-89824-306-2(8) , 306-8) Royal Fireworks Publishing Co.

McPherson, James M. Into the West: From Reconstruction to the Final Days of the American Frontier. 2006. 96p. (J). (gr. 4-9). 22.95 (978-0-689-86543-5(0) , Atheneum) Simon & Schuster Children's Publishing.

Merchant, Peter. Cowboys. 2002. (Illus.). 16p. (J). pap. (978-0-439-35103-4(0)) Scholastic, Inc.

Miller, Heather. Cowboy. 2003. (This Is What I Want to Be Ser.). (Illus.). 24p. (ps-1). (J). lib. bdg. 18.50 (978-1-4034-0366-7(X)); pap. 5.25 (978-1-4034-0588-3(3)) Heinemann Library.

Moran, Margaret. Los vaqueros y el arreo de ganado & Cowhands & Cattle Trails. 2005. spiral bd. 84.00 (***978-1-4108-5700-2(X)***) Benchmark Education Co.

Munro, Roxie. The Wild West Trail Ride Maze. 2006. (Illus.). 40p. (J). 16.95 (978-1-931721-67-7(X)) Bright Sky Pr.

Murdoch, David H. & Dorling Kindersley Publishing Staff. Cowboy. 2000. (Eyewitness Bks.). (Illus.). 64p. (J). (gr. 4-7). lib. bdg. 19.99 (978-0-7894-6594-8(9)) Dorling Kindersley Publishing, Inc.

Murdoch, David S. Cowboy. 2000. (Eyewitness Bks.). (Illus.). 64p. (J). (gr. 4-7). 15.99 (978-0-7894-5854-4(3)) Dorling Kindersley Publishing, Inc.

Nobleman, Marc Tyler. Cowboy. 2007. (J). (***978-1-4109-2961-7(2)***); pap. (***978-1-4109-2982-2(5)***) Steck-Vaughn.

Oatman, Eric. Cowboys on the Western Trail: The Cattle Drive Adventures of Joshua McNabb & Davy Bartlett. 2004. (I Am American Ser.). (Illus.). 40p. (J). (gr. 3-7). pap. 6.99 (978-0-7922-6553-5(X) , National Geographic Children's Bks.) National Geographic Society.

Penn, Sarah. Nat Love: African American Cowboy. 2003. (Famous People in American History Ser.). (Illus.). 32p. (J). pap. (978-0-8239-4188-9(4)) Rosen Publishing Group, Inc., The.

Petruccio, Steven James. Cowboy Tattoos. 2003. (Dover Little Activity Bks.). (Illus.). 2p. (J). (gr. k-5). pap. 1.50 (978-0-486-43028-7(6)) Dover Pubns., Inc.

Pinkney, Andrea Davis. Bill Pickett: Rodeo-Ridin' Cowboy. Pinkney, Brian, illus. 1999. (J). (gr. 5-8). lib. bdg. 14.15 (978-0-613-22822-0(7)) Tandem Library Bks.

—Bill Pickett: Rodeo-Ridin' Cowboy. 1999. (J). 12.80 (978-0-606-17356-8(0)) Tandem Library Bks.

Price, Sean. Crooks, Cowboys, & Characters: The Wild West. 2007. (J). (***978-1-4109-2695-1(8)***); pap. (***978-1-4109-2706-4(7)***) Steck-Vaughn.

Randolph, Ryan P. Black Cowboys. 2003. (Library of the Westward Expansion). (Illus.). 24p. (J). lib. bdg. 19.95 (978-0-8239-6294-5(6)) Rosen Publishing Group, Inc., The.

Raum, Elizabeth. Wild West Legends. 2007. (J). (***978-1-4109-2968-6(X)***); pap. (***978-1-4109-2989-1(2)***) Steck-Vaughn.

Sandler, Martin W. Cowboys. 2000. (Library of Congress Classics). (Illus.). 96p. (J). (gr. 3 up). pap. 10.95 (978-0-06-446745-2(7) , Harper Trophy) HarperCollins Pubs.

—Cowboys. 1999. (Illus.). (J). (978-0-606-18685-8(9)) Tandem Library Bks.

Sanford, William R. The Chisholm Trail in American History. 2000. (Illus.). 112p. (YA). (gr. 5-12). lib. bdg. 26.60 (978-0-7660-1345-2(6)) Enslow Pubs., Inc.

Schlissel, Lillian. Black Frontiers. 2000. (Illus.). 80p. (J). (gr. 3-7). pap. 7.99 (978-0-689-83315-1(6) , Aladdin) Simon & Schuster Children's Publishing.

—Black Frontiers: A History of African American Heroes in the Old West. 2000. (gr. 3-6). lib. bdg. 16.45 (978-0-613-21229-8(0)); (Illus.). (J). 14.79 (978-0-606-17914-0(3)) Tandem Library Bks.

Seidman, Laurence I. Once in the Saddle: The Cowboy's Frontier 1866-1896. 1999. 158p. (J). lib. bdg. 21.95 (978-0-7351-0221-7(X)) Replica Bks.

Sundling, Charles W. Cowboys of the Frontier. 2000. (Frontier Land Ser.). (Illus.). 32p. (J). (gr. 3-8). lib. bdg. 24.21 (978-1-57765-045-4(X) , ABDO & Daughters) ABDO Publishing Co.

Underwood, Deborah. Nat Love. 2008. (History Maker Biographies Ser.). (J). lib. bdg. 26.60 (***978-0-8225-7171-1(4)*** , Lerner Pubns.) Lerner Publishing Group.

Whitney, Gleaves & Whitney, Louise. B Is for Buckaroo: A Cowboy Alphabet. Guy, Sue, illus. rev. ed. 2003. 40p. (J). 17.95 (978-1-58536-139-7(9)) Sleeping Bear Pr.

Whitney, Gleaves & Whitney, Louise. A Cowboy Alphabet. 2007. 40p. pap. 7.95 (***978-1-58536-336-0(7)***) Sleeping Bear Pr.

Woog, Adam. A Cowboy in the Old West. 2002. (Daily Life Ser.). (Illus.). 48p. (J). (gr. 3-5). 23.70 (978-0-7377-0990-2(1) , LML00902-178599, Kidhaven) Thomson Gale.

COWBOYS—FICTION

Ames, Joseph B. Pete Cow Puncher a Story of the Texas Plains. Perard, Victor, illus. 2005. reprint ed. pap. 31.95 (978-0-7661-9421-2(3)) Kessinger Publishing, LLC.

Anglund, Joan Walsh. The Brave Cowboy. 2000. (Illus.). 40p. (J). (ps-3). 6.99 (978-0-7407-0649-3(7)) Andrews McMeel Publishing.

—Cowboy & His Friend. 2002. (Illus.). 40p. 6.95 (978-0-7407-2211-0(5)) Andrews McMeel Publishing.

—The Cowboy's Christmas. Anglund, Joan Walsh, illus. 2004. (Illus.). 40p. (J). 8.95 (978-0-7407-4675-8(8)) Andrews McMeel Publishing.

—Cowboy's Secret Life. Anglund, Joan Walsh, illus. anniv. ed. 2002. (Illus.). 40p. (gr. k-3). 6.95 (978-0-7407-2680-4(3)) Andrews McMeel Publishing.

Arena, Felice & Kettle, Phil. Bull Riding. Cox, David, illus. 2004. (J). pap. (978-1-59336-370-3(2)) Mondo Publishing.

Bailey, Len. Clabbernappers. 2005. (Illus.). 224p. (J). 17.95 (978-0-7653-0981-5(5) , Tor Bks.) Doherty, Tom Assocs., LLC.

Bain, Michelle. The Adventures of Thumbs up Johnnie: Johnnie Finds A Buddy Color Version 2. Lizana, Lorenzo, illus. 2007. (J). 14.95 (***978-0-9761421-6-4(3)***) Pixie Stuff LLC.

—Las aventuras de Juanito el Pulgarcito: Juanito encuentra un Compañerito. Lizana, Lorenzo, illus. 2006. Tr. of Johnnie Finds a Buddy. (SPA.). (J). 16.95 (978-0-9761421-4-0(7)) Pixie Stuff LLC.

Bain, Michelle. Las aventuras de Juanito el Pulgarcito: Liborio el Microbio y el apreton de Manos. Lizana, Lorenzo, illus. 2007. Tr. of Jimmy Jam Germ & the Happy Handshake!. (SPA.). (J). 16.95 (***978-0-9795832-1-6(7)***) Pixie Stuff LLC.

Barnett, Rogers Cheryl, et al. The All-American Cowboy Grill: Sizzlin' Recipes from the World's Greatest Cowboys. 2005. (Illus.). 240p. spiral bd. 16.99 (978-1-4016-0200-0(2)) Nelson, Thomas Inc.

Bell, Cece. Sock Monkey Rides Again. Bell, Cece, illus. 2006. (Illus.). 32p. (J). (ps-2). 13.99 (978-0-7636-3089-8(6)) Candlewick Pr.

Bowman, James Cloyd. Pecos Bill: The Greatest Cowboy of All Time. Bannon, Laura, illus. 2007. 296p. (J). (gr. 5-9). 18.95 (978-1-59017-224-7(8) , NYR Children's Collection) New York Review of Bks., Inc., The.

Brian, Kate. Untouchable. 2006. (Private Ser.). 240p. (YA). pap. 8.99 (978-1-4169-1875-2(2) , Simon Pulse) Simon & Schuster Children's Publishing.

Brimner, Larry Dane. Cowboy Up! Miller, Susan, illus. 1999. (Rookie Reader Skill Set Ser.). 32p. (J). (gr. k-2). pap. 4.95 (978-0-516-26475-2(3) , Children's Pr.) Scholastic Library Publishing.

—Cowboy Up! 1999. (gr. k-3). lib. bdg. 12.95 (978-0-613-37319-7(7)) Tandem Library Bks.

Brooks, Walter R. Freddy the Cowboy. Wiese, Kurt, illus. 2002. (Freddy the Pig Ser.). 233p. (J). (gr. 3). 23.95 (978-1-58567-225-7(4)) Overlook Pr., The.

Charlip, Remy. Little Old Beard & Big Young Little Beard. Rettenmund, Tamara, illus. 2006. 32p. (J). 5.95 (978-0-7614-5288-1(5)) Cavendish, Marshall Corp.

—Little Old Big Beard & Big Young Little Beard: A Short & Tall Tale. Charlip, Remy & Rettenmund, Tamara, illus. 2003. 32p. (J). 16.95 (978-0-7614-5142-6(0)) Cavendish, Marshall Corp.

Charlip, Remy & Rettenmund, Tamara, illus. Little Old Big Beard & Big Young Little Beard: A Short & Tall Tale. 2002. (J). (978-1-58837-000-6(3)) Winslow Pr.

Chrismer, Melanie. Phoebe Clappsaddle & The Tumbleweed Gang. Roeder, Virginia M., illus. 2002. 32p. (J). 14.95 (978-1-56554-966-1(X)) Pelican Publishing Co., Inc.

Clifford, Rowan. Rodeo Ron & His Milkshake Cows. 2005. (Illus.). 32p. (J). (gr. k-3). 15.95 (978-0-375-83195-9(9) , Knopf Bks. for Young Readers) Random Hse. Children's Bks.

Cowboys on a Ranch: Second Grade Guided Reading Level G. (On Our Way to English Ser.). (gr. 2 up). 34.50 (978-0-7578-7079-8(1)) Rigby Education.

Cunningham, Kay. Bucky, the Adventures of the Dinosaur Cowboy. Wilson, Mary Ann, illus. 2004. 32p. (J). 18.99 (978-1-57860-173-8(8) , Guild Pr. of Indiana); pap. 12.99 (978-1-57860-174-5(6)) Emmis Bks.

Czernecki, Stefan. Ride 'Em, Cowboy. 2004. (Illus.). 48p. (J). 16.95 (978-1-894965-06-4(X)) Simply Read Bks. CAN. *Dist:* Perseus Distribution.

Danneberg, Julie. Cowboy Slim. Apple, Margot, illus. 2006. (J). 15.95 (978-1-58089-045-8(8)) Charlesbridge Publishing, Inc.

Davis, David. Texas Zeke & the Longhorn. Stacey, Alan, illus. 2006. 32p. (J). 15.95 (978-1-58980-348-0(5)) Pelican Publishing Co., Inc.

Dearen, Patrick. On the Pecos Trail. 2001. (gr. 3-6). lib. bdg. 17.60 (978-0-613-83166-6(7)) Tandem Library Bks.

—On the Pecos Trail. 2001. (Lone Star Heroes Ser.). 128p. (gr. 4-7). pap. 8.95 (978-1-55622-830-8(9) , Republic of Texas Pr.) Wordware Publishing, Inc.

Dubowski, Cathy East. Cowboy Roy. 2000. (gr. k-3). lib. bdg. 11.80 (978-0-613-28282-6(5)) Tandem Library Bks.

Dubowski, Cathy East & Dubowski, Mark. Cowboy Roy. Dubowski, Cathy East & Dubowski, Mark, illus. 2000. (All Aboard Reading Ser.). (Illus.). 32p. (J). (ps-1). pap. 3.99 (978-0-448-41568-0(2) , Grosset & Dunlap) Penguin Group (USA) Inc.

Elya, Susan Middleton. Cowboy Jose. Raglin, Tim, illus. 2005. 32p. (J). 15.99 (978-0-399-23570-2(1) , Putnam Juvenile) Penguin Group (USA) Inc.

Erickson, John R. The Case of the Vanishing Fishhook. Holmes, Gerald L., illus. 1999. (Hank the Cowdog Ser.: No. 31). (J). (gr. 2-5). 11.64 (978-0-606-16826-7(5)) Tandem Library Bks.

—Slim's Good-Bye. Holmes, Gerald L., illus. 2000. (Hank the Cowdog Ser.: No. 34). 144p. (J). (gr. 2-5). 15.99 (978-0-670-88889-4(3) , Viking Juvenile); Vol. 34. pap. 4.99 (978-0-14-130677-3(7) , Puffin) Penguin Group (USA) Inc.

—Slim's Good-Bye. 2000. (Hank the Cowdog Ser.: No. 34). (Illus.). (J). (gr. 2-5). (978-0-606-18408-3(2)) Tandem Library Bks.

Failing, Barbara Larmon. Lasso Lou & Cowboy Mccoy. Arnold, Tedd, illus. 2003. 40p. (J). (gr. k-3). 16.99 (978-0-8037-2578-2(7) , Dial) Penguin Group (USA) Inc.

Ferris, James Cody. The X Bar X Boys on Big Bison Trail. Rogers, Walter S., illus. 2004. reprint ed. pap. 24.95 (978-1-4179-3953-4(2)) Kessinger Publishing, LLC.

Frank, John. The Toughest Cowboy: Or How the Wild West Was Tamed. 2006. 48p. (J). (gr. 4-6). 6.99 (978-0-689-83462-2(4) , Aladdin) Simon & Schuster Children's Publishing.

—The Toughest Cowboy: Or How the Wild West Was Tamed. Pullen, Zachary, illus. 2004. 48p. (J). (gr. k-3). 17.95 (978-0-689-83461-5(6)) Simon & Schuster Children's Publishing.

Fraser, Jess, illus. The Legend of the Cosmic Cowboy. 2007. (J). cd-rom 12.99 (***978-0-9795190-7-9(1)***) Color & Learn.

Frederick, Heather Vogel. Calamity Wayne at the O.K. Corral. Brown, Kathryn, illus. 2007. (J). (978-0-15-205789-3(7)) Harcourt Trade Pubs.

Garland, Sherry. Goodnight, Cowboy. Kanzler, John, illus. 1998. (J). 15.95 (978-0-590-98831-5(X)) Scholastic, Inc.

Goodman, Larry. The Cowboy. unabr. ed. 2000. (Illus.). (J). pap. 18.00 incl. audio (978-1-58807-038-8(7)) Americana Publishing, Inc.

Goscinny. Billy the Kid. Morris, illus. 2007. 48p. pap. 11.95 (***978-1-905460-11-3(2)***) CineBook GBR. *Dist:* Biblio Distribution.

Goscinny, R. A Lucky Luke Adventure: Barbed Wire on the Prairie. Spear, Luke, tr. from FRE. Morris, illus. 2007. 48p. pap. 9.99 (***978-1-905460-24-3(4)***) CineBook GBR. *Dist:* Biblio Distribution.

Goscinny, R. A Lucky Luke Adventure Dalton City. Morris, illus. 2007. 48p. pap. 9.99 (***978-1-905460-13-7(9)***) CineBook GBR. *Dist:* Biblio Distribution.

—A Lucky Luke Adventure in the Shadow of the Derricks. Morris, illus. 2007. 48p. pap. 9.99 (***978-1-905460-17-5(1)***) CineBook GBR. *Dist:* Biblio Distribution.

—A Lucky Luke Adventure Jesse James. Morris, illus. 2007. 48p. pap. 9.99 (***978-1-905460-14-4(7)***) CineBook GBR. *Dist:* Biblio Distribution.

Goscinny, René. Ma Dalton. 2007. (Illus.). 48p. pap. 9.99 (***978-1-905460-18-2(X)***) CineBook GBR. *Dist:* Biblio Distribution.

Harcourt School Publishers Staff. Sitting around the Campfire: Take-Home Book. 1999. (Collections Ser.). (Illus.). (J). pap. 1.90 (978-0-15-317234-2(7)) Harcourt Schl. Pubs.

—Vaquero, the Cowboy Advanced level. 3rd ed. 2002. (Trophies Reading Program Ser.). (Illus.). pap. 5.10 (978-0-15-323375-3(3)) Harcourt Schl. Pubs.

Harper, Jo. Jalapeno Hal. Harris, Jennifer Beck, illus. Date not set. 40p. (gr. 4). 8.95 (978-1-57168-206-2(6)) Eakin Pr.

—Mayor Jalapeno Hal from Presidio, Texas. 2003. (Illus.). (J). (978-1-57168-767-8(X) , Eakin Pr.) Eakin Pr.

—Ollie Jolly, Rodeo Clown. Meissner, Amy, illus. 2002. 32p. (J). (gr. k-3). 15.95 (978-1-55868-552-9(9)); pap. 8.95 (978-1-55868-553-6(7)) Graphic Arts Ctr. Publishing Co. (West Winds Pr.).

—Ollie Jolly, Rodeo Clown. 2002. (gr. k-3). lib. bdg. 17.60 (978-0-613-89457-9(X)) Tandem Library Bks.

Heath, Lorraine. Avon True Romance: Samantha & the Cowboy. 2002. (gr. 7-12). lib. bdg. 13.00 (978-0-613-71505-8(5)) Tandem Library Bks.

Heaton, Layce D. The Many Tracks of Lap'n Tap, 1. Heaton, Layce D., illus. 2006. (Illus.). 32p. (J). lib. bdg. 18.95 (978-0-9761128-3-9(3)) Hafabanana Pr.

Henty, G. A. A Tale of the Western Plains. 2006. (Dover Value Editions Ser.). (Illus.). 352p. pap. 8.95 (978-0-486-45261-6(1)) Dover Pubns., Inc.

Hiebert, Elfrieda H. & Juel, Connie. The Three Silly Cowboys. (Little Book Practice Reader Ser.). (J). (978-0-8136-0889-1(9)) Modern Curriculum Pr.

Holub, Joan. Cinderdog & the Wicked Stepcat. 2001. (Illus.). 32p. (J). (ps-3). 15.95 (978-0-8075-1178-7(1)) Whitman, Albert & Co.

Hurt-Newton, Tania. Yee-Ha Harvey. Hurt-Newton, Tania, illus. 2007. (Illus.). 14p. (J). 14.95 (***978-0-00-724414-0(2)***) HarperCollins Pubs. Ltd. GBR. *Dist:* Independent Pubs. Group.

Hutchens, Paul. The Battle of the Bees. 1999. (gr. 3-6). lib. bdg. 13.00 (978-0-613-90330-1(7)) Tandem Library Bks.

James, Will. Cowboy in the Making. rev. ed. (Illus.). 104p. (gr. 4-6). pap. 15.00 (978-0-87842-439-9(3) , 811) Mountain Pr. Publishing Co., Inc.

—Look-See with Uncle Bill. (Illus.). 190p. 26.00 (978-0-87842-459-7(8) , 815); (J). (gr. 4). pap. 14.00 (978-0-87842-458-0(X) , 814) Mountain Pr. Publishing Co., Inc.

—My First Horse, Vol. 1. rev. ed. (Illus.). 48p. (J). (gr. 4). 16.00 (978-0-87842-488-7(1) , 819) Mountain Pr. Publishing Co., Inc.

—Scorpion: A Good Bad Horse. 2001. (Illus.). 254p. (YA). 30.00 (978-0-87842-436-8(9) , 810); (gr. 4). pap. 15.00 (978-0-87842-435-1(0) , 809) Mountain Pr. Publishing Co., Inc.

—Smoky, the Cow Horse. 2003. (J). (gr. 3-8). 20.50 (978-0-8446-7247-2(5)) Smith, Peter Pub., Inc.

—Uncle Bill. Carey, Jennifer, ed. (Tumbleweed Ser.). (Illus.). 185p. (gr. 4 up). reprint ed. 26.00 (978-0-87842-379-6(6) , 695) Mountain Pr. Publishing Co., Inc.

—Uncle Bill: A Tale of Two Kids & a Cowboy. rev. ed. (Tumbleweed Ser.). (Illus.). 185p. (gr. 4-12). pap. 14.00 (978-0-87842-380-4(X) , 694) Mountain Pr. Publishing Co., Inc.

—Young Cowboy. (Tumbleweed Ser.). (Illus.). (J). 2000. 72p. (978-0-87842-444-3(X)); 2004. 88p. (gr. 4-7). 15.00 (978-0-87842-419-1(9) , 806) Mountain Pr. Publishing Co., Inc.

Keith, Harold. Chico & Dan. Arbuckle, Scott, illus. 1998. 120p. (gr. 4-7). 16.95 (978-1-57168-216-1(3)) Eakin Pr.

Ketteman, Helen. Waynetta & the Cornstalk: A Texas Fairy Tale. Greenseid, Diane, illus. 2007. 32p. (J). 16.95 (978-0-8075-8687-7(0)) Whitman, Albert & Co.

Kinerk, Robert. Slim & Miss Prim. Harris, Jim, illus. (J). pap. 7.95 (978-0-87358-819-5(3) , Rising Moon Bks. for Young Readers) Northland Publishing.

Knight, Barbara. The Cowboys with penny the mustang Pony. 2006. (Illus.). 16p. (J). 14.95 net. (***978-0-9766270-1-2(9)***) Mustang BKS.

Knowlton, Laurie Lazzaro. Why Cowgirls Are Such Sweet Talkers. Rice, James, illus. 2000. 31p. (ps-3). 15.95 (978-1-56554-698-1(9)) Pelican Publishing Co., Inc.

Krensky Stephen. Pecos Bill. Tong, Paul, illus. 2007. (On My Own Folklore Ser.). (J). pap. 6.95 (***978-0-8225-6475-1(0)*** , First Avenue Editions) Lerner Publishing Group.

Kyne, Peter B. The Three Godfathers. 2005. reprint ed. pap. 15.95 (978-1-4179-0351-1(1)) Kessinger Publishing, LLC.

Lenski, Lois. Cowboy Small. 2006. (Illus.). 32p. (J). (gr. k-ps). bds. 6.99 (978-0-375-83570-4(9) , Random Hse. Bks. for Young Readers) Random Hse. Children's Bks.

—Cowboy Small. Lenski, Lois, illus. 2001. (Illus.). 56p. (J). (ps-1). 11.95 (978-0-375-81075-6(7)); lib. bdg. 13.99 (978-0-375-91075-3(1)) Random Hse. Children's Bks. (Random Hse. Bks. for Young Readers).

Lester, Julius. Black Cowboy, Wild Horses. Pinkney, Jerry, illus. 1998. 32p. (J). (gr. k-3). 18.99 (978-0-8037-1787-9(5) , Dial) Penguin Group (USA) Inc.

Loomis, Christine. Cowboy Bunnies. Eitan, Ora, illus. 2000. (J). (978-0-606-18397-0(3)) Tandem Library Bks.

Lowe, Pat. Desert Cowboy. Pike, Jimmy, illus. 2000. (Yinti Ser.: Bk. 3). 128p. pap. 16.45 (978-1-875641-57-4(2)) Magabala Bks. AUS. *Dist:* International Specialized Bk. Services.

Lukas, Catherine & Artifact Group. Trouble on the Train. 2007. (Backyardigans Ser.). (Illus.). 24p. (J). pap. 3.99 (978-1-4169-2818-8(9) , Simon Spotlight/Nickelodeon) Simon & Schuster Children's Publishing.

The Many Tracks of Lap'n Tap. 2007. (J). per. 10.95 (***978-0-9761128-4-6(1)***) Hafabanana Pr.

Margetson, Donald. The Unhappy Cow. 2004. 21p. pap. 14.95 (978-1-4137-1004-5(2)) PublishAmerica, Inc.

Marsh, Carole. The Case of the Crybaby Cowboy. 2006. 64p. (gr. 1-3). pap. 3.99 (978-0-635-06166-9(X) , Marsh, Carole Bks.); 14.95 (***978-0-635-06199-7(6)***) Gallopade International.

McAllister, Angela. The Clever Cowboy. 2000. (978-0-606-17801-3(5)) Tandem Library Bks.

McBride, Earvin, Jr. The Bowdery Rodeo Cowboys of Texas. McBride, Earvin, Jr., illus. 2nd unabr. ed. 2003. (Earvin MacBride's Amazing Sci-Fi & Adventure Heroes Ser.). (Illus.). 329p. (J). (gr. 7-12). pap. 4.95 (978-1-892511-07-2(X)) MacBride, E. J. Pubn., Inc.

McCann, Jesse Leon. Scooby-Doo & the Phantom Cowboy. 2002. (gr. k-3). lib. bdg. 11.25 (978-0-613-50736-3(3)) Tandem Library Bks.

McClements, George. Ridin' Dinos with Buck Bronco. 2007. (Illus.). 40p. (J). (ps-2). 16.00 (978-0-15-205989-7(X)) Harcourt Trade Pubs.

McKenzie, Tim. Baxter Barret Brown's Cowboy Band. Atkinson, Elaine, illus. 2006. 24p. (J). 19.95 (978-1-931721-77-6(7)) Bright Sky Pr.

Medearis, Angela Shelf. The Worst Cowboy in the West. 1999. (Illus.). (J). 15.99 (978-0-525-67555-6(8) , Dutton Juvenile) Penguin Group (USA) Inc.

Miles, Ellen. Taylor-Made Tales. 2006. 144p. (J). pap. 4.99 (978-0-439-59710-4(2) , Scholastic Paperbacks) Scholastic, Inc.

Minor, Wendell. Pumpkin Heads! 2007. 32p. (J). (ps-3). pap. 6.99 (***978-0-590-52138-3(1)***) Scholastic, Inc.

Mitchell, Marianne. Joe Cinders. Langdo, Bryan, illus. rev. ed. 2002. 48p. (J). (ps-3). 17.95 (978-0-8050-6529-9(6) , Holt, Henry & Co. Bks. For Young Readers) Holt, Henry & Co.

Mora, Jo. Budgee Budgee Cottontail. Mora, Jo, illus. 2004. (Jo Mora Titles Ser.). (Illus.). 60p. (gr. 2 up). 15.00 (978-0-922029-23-5(7) , BK-30004) Stoecklein Publishing.

Morgan, Michaela. Buffalo Bert: The Cowboy Grandad. Newsham, Ian, illus. 2006. (Read-It! Chapter Books). 48p. (J). (gr. 2-4). 19.95 (978-1-4048-1660-2(7)) Picture Window Bks.

Moser, Barry, illus. Cowboy Stories. 2007. 184p. (YA). (gr. 7 up). 16.95 (978-0-8118-5418-4(3) , SeaStar Bks.) Chronicle Bks. LLC.

Muldrow, Diane. Woody's Round-Up. 1999. (Disney Ser.). (Illus.). 24p. (J). (ps-k). pap. 3.29 (978-0-307-13326-7(5) , Golden Bks.) Random Hse. Children's Bks.

Myers, Walter Dean. The Journal of Joshua Loper: A Black Cowboy: The Chisholm Trail, 1871. 1999. (My Name Is America Ser.). (Illus.). 160p. (J). (gr. 4-8). pap. 10.95 (978-0-590-02691-8(7)) Scholastic, Inc.

Naylor, Phyllis Reynolds. Walker's Crossing. 2001. 240p. (J). (gr. 5-9). pap. 4.99 (978-0-689-84261-0(9) , Aladdin) Simon & Schuster Children's Publishing.

Nislick, June Levitt. Zayda Was a Cowboy. 2005. 128p. (J). pap. 9.95 (978-0-8276-0817-7(9)) Jewish Pubn. Society.

Northland Publishing Staff, ed. Jack & the Giant/Cowboy Billy. 1998. (J). pap. 15.95 (978-0-87358-696-2(4) , Rising Moon Bks. for Young Readers) Northland Publishing.

Nusz, Janean. The Littlest Cowboy. 2005. 26p. 12.30 (978-1-4116-4019-1(5)) Lulu.com.

Patchin, Gee Frank. The Pony Rider Boys in Montana. 2006. 63.99 ***(978-1-4280-1132-8(3));*** pap. 57.99 ***(978-1-4280-1126-7(9))*** IndyPublish.com.

—The Pony Rider Boys in the Grand Canyon. 2006. 33.99 ***(978-1-4219-7869-7(5));*** pap. 27.99 ***(978-1-4219-7871-0(7))*** IndyPublish.com.

—The Pony Rider Boys in the Rockies. 2006. 63.99 ***(978-1-4280-0930-1(2));*** pap. 57.99 ***(978-1-4280-0940-0(X))*** IndyPublish.com.

—The Pony Rider Boys with the Texas Range. 2006. 78.99 ***(978-1-4280-0012-4(7));*** pap. 72.99 ***(978-1-4280-0014-8(3))*** IndyPublish.com.

Peck, Robert Newton. Cowboy Ghost. 1999. 208p. (YA). (gr. 7 up). 15.95 (978-0-06-028168-7(5) , Harper Trophy) HarperCollins Pubs.

—Cowboy Ghost. 1999. (YA). pap., stu. ed. 52.95 incl. audio (978-0-7887-3189-1(0) , 40924) Recorded Bks., LLC.

—Cowboy Ghost. 2000. (Illus.). (J). 11.60 (978-0-606-18684-1(0)) Tandem Library Bks.

Poulsen, David A. Cowboy Cool. 2002. (Lawrence High Yearbook Ser.). 106p. (YA). pap. 3.99 (978-1-55305-028-5(2)) Cygnet Publishing Group, Inc./Coolreading.com CAN. *Dist:* Orca Bk. Pubs. USA.

Proimos, James. Cowboy Boy. 2003. 96p. (J). 14.95 (978-0-439-41681-8(7) , Scholastic Pr.) Scholastic, Inc.

Puttock, Simon. Cowboy Coyote. (Illus.). 32p. (978-0-19-272545-5(9)) Oxford Univ. Pr., Inc.

Reed, Sharon. Tara: Prairie Horse Series. 2006. pap. 14.00 ***(978-0-8059-7091-3(6))*** Dorrance Publishing Co., Inc.

Rice, James. Too Tall Thomas Rides the Grub Line. Rice, James, illus. 2004. (Illus.). 32p. 15.95 (978-1-58980-177-6(6)) Pelican Publishing Co., Inc.

Rice, James, tr. & illus. Trail Boss: J. M. Daugherty. Rice, James, illus. 2003. (J). (978-1-57168-769-2(6) , Eakin Pr.) Eakin Pr.

Roach, Joyce Gibson. Horned Toad Canyon. 2004. (Illus.). 48p. 17.95 (978-1-931721-01-1(7)) Bright Sky Pr.

Robinson, David. The Australian Cowboy & the Big Storm. Plante, Alyson, illus. 2002. 20p. (J). pap. 7.95 (978-0-9718091-0-9(0)) Robinson Pubs.

Robles, Eric. Billy Was Born to Be a Cowboy! 2007. (J). (978-0-375-83422-6(2)); lib. bdg. (978-0-375-93422-3(7)) Random Hse., Inc.

Rogers, Lisa Waller. Get along Little Dogies: The Chisholm Trail Diary of Hallie Lou Wells. 2001. (Lone Star Journals: Vol. 1). (Illus.). 174p. (J). (gr. 4-7). 14.50 (978-0-89672-446-4(8)) Texas Tech Univ. Pr.

—Get along, Little Dogies: The Chisholm Trail Diary of Hallie Lou Wells, South Texas 1878. 2001. (Lone Star Journals). (Illus.). 174p. (J). (gr. 4-7). 8.95 (978-0-89672-448-8(4)) Texas Tech Univ. Pr.

Rossi. El Chaparron Torrencial. 2000. Tr. of Gullywasher. (SPA.). (J). 14.75 (978-0-606-19852-3(0)) Tandem Library Bks.

Rossi, Joyce. The Gullywasher (El Chaparron Torrencial) 1998. (ENG & SPA., Illus.). 32p. (J). (gr. k-3). 7.95 (978-0-87358-728-0(6) , Rising Moon Bks. for Young Readers) Northland Publishing.

Santillo, LuAnn. The Ball. Santillo, LuAnn, ed. 2003. (Half-Pint Kids Readers Ser.). (Illus.). 7p. (J). (ps-1). pap. (978-1-59256-081-3(4)) Half-Pint Kids, Inc.

—The Best Tricks. Santillo, LuAnn, ed. 2003. (Half-Pint Kids Readers Ser.). (Illus.). 7p. (J). (ps-1). pap. (978-1-59256-082-0(2)) Half-Pint Kids, Inc.

Sargent, Dave & Denton, Ivan. Blizzard: Don't Give Up #5, 6, Vol. 5. Denton, Ivan, illus. 2004. (Real Cowboy Ser.: 5). (Illus.). 36p. (YA). lib. bdg. 22.60 (978-1-59381-008-5(3)) Ozark Publishing.

—Blizzard No. 5: Don't Give Up. Denton, Ivan, illus. 2004. (Illus.). 36p. (J). pap. 9.95 (978-1-59381-009-2(1)) Ozark Publishing.

—My Grandpa Is a Cowboy: Learning Is Fun #1, 6. Denton, Ivan, illus. 2004. (Illus.). 36p. (J). pap. 9.95 (978-1-59381-001-6(6)); (Real Cowboy Ser.: 1). lib. bdg. 22.60 (978-1-59381-000-9(8)) Ozark Publishing.

—Saddle for Sally No. 2: Loyalty Rewarded, 6 vols. Denton, Ivan, illus. 2004. (Real Cowboy Ser.: 2). (Illus.). 36p. (YA). lib. bdg. 22.60 (978-1-59381-002-3(4)) Ozark Publishing.

—Secret of the Lost Herd: Be Persistent #3, 6. Denton, Ivan, illus. 2004. (Real Cowboy Ser.: 3). (Illus.). 36p. (YA). lib. bdg. 22.60 ***(978-1-59381-006-1(7))*** Ozark Publishing.

—Will Learns to Rope: Skill Pays #6, 6. Denton, Ivan, illus. 2004. (Real Cowboy Ser.: 6). (Illus.). 36p. (YA). lib. bdg. 22.60 ***(978-1-59381-010-8(5))*** Ozark Publishing.

Sargent, Dave & Sargent, Pat. The Chuck Wagon: Don't Be Stubborn, 10. Lenoir, Jane, illus. 2005. (Colorado Cowboys Ser.: 7). 32p. (J). 7. lib. bdg. 22.60 (978-1-59381-098-6(9)); Vol. 7. pap. 9.95 (978-1-59381-099-3(7)) Ozark Publishing.

—The Colorado Blizzard: Be Determined, 10. Lenoir, Jane, illus. l.t. ed. (Colorado Cowboys Ser.: 8). 32p. (J). 8. 2004. (gr. 3-8). lib. bdg. 22.60 (978-1-59381-026-9(1)); Vol. 8. 2005. pap. 9.95 (978-1-59381-027-6(X)) Ozark Publishing.

—The Drought: Have Faith, 10. Lenoir, Jane, illus. 2005. (Colorado Cowboys Ser.: 9). 32p. (J). 9. lib. bdg. 22.60 (978-1-59381-102-0(0)); Vol. 9. pap. 9.95 (978-1-59381-103-7(9)) Ozark Publishing.

—The Fire: A Second Chance, 10 vols., Vol. 10. Lenoir, Jane, illus. 2005. (Colorado Cowboys Ser.: 10). 32p. (J). pap. 9.95 (978-1-59381-105-1(5)) Ozark Publishing.

—The Fire Vol. 10: Second Chance, 10 vols. Lenoir, Jane, illus. l.t. ed. 2005. (Colorado Cowboys Ser.: Vol. 10). 32p. (J). (gr. 3-8). lib. bdg. 22.60 (978-1-59381-104-4(7)) Ozark Publishing.

—Rusty: (Red Roan) Be Strong & Brave, 30, 52. Lenoir, Jane, illus. 2003. (Saddle Up Ser.: Vol. 52). 42p. (J). pap. 6.95 (978-1-56763-804-2(X)); lib. bdg. 22.60 (978-1-56763-803-5(1)) Ozark Publishing.

Sauer, Tammi. Cowboy Camp. Reed, Mike, illus. 2005. 32p. (J). (ps-2). 14.95 (978-1-4027-2224-0(9)) Sterling Publishing Co., Inc.

Schaefer, Jack. Shane. Minor, Wendell, illus. 2001. (Illustrated American Classics Ser.). 144p. (YA). (gr. 7-9). tchr. ed. 22.00 (978-0-395-94116-4(4)) Houghton Mifflin Co. Trade & Reference Div.

Schertle, Alice. How Now, Brown Cow. 1998. (978-0-606-13496-5(4)) Tandem Library Bks.

Schnetzler, Pattie L. Widdermaker. Sealock, Rick, illus. 2005. 32p. (gr. k-2). 15.95 (978-0-87614-647-7(7)) Lerner Publishing Group.

Scieszka, Jon. Cowboy & Octopus. Smith, Lane, illus. 2007. 40p. (J). (ps-5). 16.99 ***(978-0-670-91058-8(9)*** , Viking Juvenile) Penguin Group (USA) Inc.

—The Good, the Bad, & the Goofy, Vol. 3. 2004. (Time Warp Trio Ser.: No. 3). (Illus.). 80p. (J). (gr. 2-6). pap. 4.99 (978-0-14-240046-3(7) , Puffin) Penguin Group (USA) Inc.

—You Can't, but Genghis Khan. 2006. (Time Warp Trio). 80p. (J). (gr. 2-5). pap. 4.99 (978-0-06-111636-0(X) , Harper Trophy) HarperCollins Pubs.

Smith, Dana Kessimakis. A Wild Cowboy. Freeman, Laura, illus. 2004. 32p. (ps-1). 14.99 (978-0-7868-1931-7(6)) Hyperion Bks. for Children.

Smith, Janice Lee. Jess & the Stinky Cowboys. Thiesing, Lisa, illus. 2004. (Dial Easy-to-Read Ser.). 48p. (J). (gr. k-3). 14.99 (978-0-8037-2641-3(4) , Dial) Penguin Group (USA) Inc.

Stanley, George Edward. The Spy Who Barked. Francis, Guy, illus. 2002. (Adam Sharp Ser.: No. 1). 48p. (J). (gr. 2-4). pap. 3.99 (978-0-307-26412-1(2) , Random Hse. Bks. for Young Readers) Random Hse. Children's Bks.

Steig, Jeanne. Tales from Gizzard's Grill. Turner, Sandy, illus. 2004. 80p. (J). 17.89 (978-0-06-000960-1(8)); 16.99 (978-0-06-000959-5(4)) HarperCollins Pubs. (Cotler, Joanna Books).

Stein, David Ezra. Cowboy Ned & Andy. Stein, David Ezra, illus. 2006. (Illus.). 32p. (J). (ps-1). 14.95 (978-1-4169-0041-2(1) , Simon & Schuster Children's Publishing) Simon & Schuster Children's Publishing.

—Ned's New Friend. Stein, David Ezra, illus. 2007. (Cowboy Ned & Andy Ser.). 32p. (J). (ps-1). 14.99 (978-1-4169-2490-6(6) , Simon & Schuster Children's Publishing) Simon & Schuster Children's Publishing.

Stillerman, Robbie. Jake the Cowboy. 2001. (Illus.). 4p. (J). pap. 1.50 (978-0-486-41633-5(X)) Dover Pubns., Inc.

Stilton, Geronimo. The Wild, Wild West. 2005. (Geronimo Stilton Ser.: No. 21). (Illus.). 128p. (J). 5.99 (978-0-439-69144-4(3) , Scholastic Paperbacks) Scholastic, Inc.

Stoddard, Jack. Cowboy Dreams. 2006. 144p. pap. 15.95 (978-1-60047-002-8(5)) Wasteland Pr.

Stuart, Kelly. Cowgirls Can Do! Amazing Things, Too! Clarke, Cynthia & Clarke, Bradley, illus. 2002. (Can Do! Bks.). 32p. 14.95 (978-0-9709987-4-3(0)) Bright Sky Pr.

Stutson, Caroline. CowPokes. Hawkes, Kevin, illus. 1999. 24p. (J). (ps-1). 14.89 (978-0-688-13974-2(4)) HarperCollins Pubs.

Taylor, Bonnie Highsmith. To Be a Cowboy. McCabe, Kay, illus. 1999. (Cover-to-Cover Bks.). (J). 54p. pap. (978-0-7891-2901-7(9)); 56p. (gr. 1-4). lib. bdg. 16.95 (978-0-7807-8155-9(4)) Perfection Learning Corp.

Thumbs up Johnnie, Little Digit & the Special Delivery: Reading Heart to Heart, Coloring & Activity Book. 2006. (J). pap. (978-0-9761421-5-7(5)) Pixie Stuff LLC.

Tibo, Gilles. L' Enfant Cowboy. Kapas, Tom, illus. 2000. (FRE & SPA.). 32p. (J). (gr. k-2). 16.95 (978-0-88776-511-7(4) , Livres Toundra) Tundra Bks., Inc./Livres Toundra, Inc. CAN. *Dist:* Random Hse., Inc.

Timberlake, Amy. The Dirty Cowboy. Rex, Adam, illus. 2003. 32p. (J). 16.00 (978-0-374-31791-1(7) , Farrar, Straus & Giroux (BYR)) Farrar, Straus & Giroux.

Townsend, Tom. The Ballad of Ol' Hook. 2006. (YA). pap. 9.95 ***(978-1-932196-91-7(9))*** WordWright.biz, Inc.

Toy Box Innovations, creator. Disney/Pixar 2: Volume 2. abr. ed. 2006. (Disney's Read along Collection Ser.). (J). (ps-3). pap. 14.99 incl. audio compact disk (978-0-7634-2181-6(2)) Walt Disney Records.

Vens, William D. Alias Pecos Bill. 2003. per. 13.95 (978-1-891929-92-2(5)) Four Seasons Pubs.

Waites, Joan C., illus. How-to Cowboy: 22 Secret, Magic How-to Fun Tricks. 2003. 96p. (J). pap. 5.95 (978-0-9716911-1-7(8)) IM Pr.

Watanabe, Shinichiro. Cowboy Bebop Film Comic, Vol 1. 2006. (Illus.). 164p. (YA). pap. 10.99 (978-1-59409-532-0(9)) Bandai Entertainment.

Webster, Frank V. Comrades of the Saddle. 2007. (ENG.). 176p. per. 11.95 ***(978-1-4218-3329-3(8))*** 1st World Publishing, Inc.

—Comrades of the Saddle or the Young Rough Riders of the Plains. 2004. reprint ed. pap. 1.99 (978-1-4192-1372-4(5)) Kessinger Publishing, LLC.

Webster, Frank V. Cowboy Dave. 2007. (ENG.). 176p. per. 11.95 ***(978-1-4218-3330-9(1))*** 1st World Publishing, Inc.

West, Jill Marie. Smokey. 2002. (Illus.). 32p. (J). per. (978-0-9719283-2-9(0)) Mishe-Mokwa Design Prepress & Publishing.

Whatley, Bruce. Cowboy Pirate. 2002. (Illus.). 32p. 14.95 (978-0-207-19891-5(8)) HarperCollins Pubs.

Wheeler, Lisa. Avalanche Annie: A Not-So-Tall Tale. Cyrus, Kurt, illus. 2005. 30p. (J). (gr. k-4). reprint ed. 16.00 (978-0-7567-8536-9(7)) DIANE Publishing Co.

—Avalanche Annie: A Not-So-Tall Tale. Cyrus, Kurt, illus. 2003. 32p. (J). 16.00 (978-0-15-216735-6(8)) Harcourt Children's Bks.

—Sixteen Cows. Cyrus, Kurt, illus. 2002. 32p. (J). (ps-2). 16.00 (978-0-15-202676-9(2)) Harcourt Children's Bks.

Wood, Audrey. A Cowboy Christmas: The Miracle at Lone Pine Ridge. Florczak, Robert, illus. 2004. 48p. (J). 7.99 (978-0-689-87408-6(1) , Aladdin) Simon & Schuster Children's Publishing.

Worcester, Donald E. Cowboy with a Camera: Erwin E. Smith, Cowboy Photograph. Smith, Erwin E., photos by. 1999. (Illus.). 48p. (J). (gr. 4-7). 18.95 (978-0-88360-091-7(9)) Amon Carter Museum.

Young, Jan. The Orange Slipknot. Lehmkuhl, Pat, illus. 2007. 178p. (J). per. 10.00 ***(978-0-9772525-5-8(8))*** Raven Publishing Inc. of Montana.

COWBOYS—SONGS AND MUSIC

Moon, Dolly M. My Very First Piano Book of Cowboy Songs: 22 Favorite Songs Easy in Piano Arrangement. 1998. (Illus.). 46p. (J). (gr. 2 up). pap. 4.95 (978-0-486-24311-5(7)) Dover Pubns., Inc.

COWS

see also Dairying; Milk

Blackstone, Stella. There's a Cow in the Cabbage Patch. Beaton, Clare, illus. 2002. 24p. (J). (gr. k-2). bds. 6.99 (978-1-84148-961-2(1)) Barefoot Bks., Inc.

Brady, Peter. Vacas. Schon, Isabel, ed. Ferrer, Martín Luis Guzman, tr. from ENG. Munoz, William, illus. 1998. (Coleccion Primeros Lectores). (SPA.). 24p. (J). (gr. k-3). lib. bdg. 18.60 (978-1-56065-788-0(X) , Bridgestone Bks.) Capstone Pr., Inc.

Butterfield, Moira. Cow. 2000. (Who Am I? Ser.). (Illus.). 32p. (J). (ps-1). lib. bdg. 16.95 (978-1-929298-89-1(7)) Chrysalis Education.

Cooper, Jason. Calf to Cow. 2003. (Rourke Discovery Library). (Illus.). 24p. (J). 20.64 (978-1-58952-690-7(2)) Rourke Publishing, LLC.

Cows. Date not set. (Old MacDonald Stickers Ser.). (Illus.). 16p. (J). 2.98 (978-0-7525-7057-0(9)); 5.98 (978-0-7525-9966-3(6)) Parragon, Inc.

Cows (for Doubleday Entertainment USA) Down on the Farm. 2006. (J). per. 6.95 (978-1-59566-225-5(1)) QEB Publishing Inc.

Cows Have Calves. (Animals & Their Young Ser.). 24p. (J). 7.95 (978-0-7565-1238-5(7)) Compass Point Bks.

Cows on the Farm, 6 vols. (gr. k-2). 28.95 (978-0-7368-9229-2(X)) Red Brick Learning.

Do Cows Eat Cake? (Animals All Around Ser.). 24p. (J). 7.95 (978-1-4048-0371-8(8)) Picture Window Bks.

Flanagan, Alice K. Raising Cows on the Koebels' Farm. Flanagan, Romie, illus. 1999. (Our Neighborhood Ser.). 32p. (J). (gr. 1-2). 20.00 (978-0-516-21133-6(1) , Children's Pr.) Scholastic Library Publishing.

Gish, Melissa. A Dairy Farm. 2003. (Field Trips Ser.). 24p. (J). lib. bdg. 14.95 (978-1-58340-325-9(6)) Smart Apple Media.

Green, Emily. Cows. 2007. (Blastoff! Readers Ser.). 24p. (J). (gr. k-2). 18.50 ***(978-0-531-17551-4(0)*** , Children's Pr.) Scholastic Library Publishing.

Green, Emily K. Cows. 2007. (Illus.). 24p. (J). lib. bdg. 16.95 (978-1-60014-065-5(3)) Bellwether Media.

Group/McGraw-Hill, Wright. Fibonacci's Cows: Level O, 6 vols. 128p. (gr. 6 up). 36.95 (978-0-322-06737-0(5)) Wright Group, The.

Hall, Margaret. Cows & Their Calves. 2003. (Animal Offspring Ser.). (Illus.). 24p. (J). lib. bdg. 17.26 (978-0-7368-2105-6(8) , Pebble Bks.) Capstone Pr., Inc.

Hunter, Sara. Kirsty's Surprise. Maguire, Kerry, illus. 1998. 32p. (J). (gr. k-3). 12.95 (978-1-58021-009-6(0)); (gr. k-3). pap. 5.95 (978-1-58021-010-2(4)); (gr. k-3). pap. 19.95 incl. audio (978-1-58021-011-9(2)); (gr. 1-5). pap. 9.95 incl. audio (978-1-58021-013-3(9)) Benefactory, Inc., The.

—Kirsty's Surprise: Includes Plush Toy Animal. Maguire, Kerry, illus. 1998. 32p. (J). (gr. 1-5). 29.95 (978-1-58021-018-8(X)); pap. 14.95 (978-1-58021-012-6(0)) Benefactory, Inc., The.

—Kirsty's Surprise: Includes Tape & Plush Toy Animal. Maguire, Kerry, illus. 1998. 32p. (J). (gr. 1-5). 34.95 incl. audio (978-1-58021-017-1(1)) Benefactory, Inc., The.

Jackson, Ellen B. December. 2004. (It Happens in the Month of... Ser.). (Illus.). 32p. (YA). (ps-4). 8.95 (978-0-88106-958-7(2)) Charlesbridge Publishing, Inc.

Jackson, Woody. Counting Cows. 1999. (Illus.). 24p. (J). (ps). bds. 5.95 (978-0-15-202174-0(4) , Red Wagon Bks.) Harcourt Children's Bks.

Kishel, Ann-Marie. Cows & Calves. 2006. (First Step Nonfiction Ser.). (Illus.). 8p. (J). lib. bdg. (978-0-8225-5649-7(9) , Lerner Pubns.) Lerner Publishing Group.

The Life Cycle of a Cow, Vol. 2. 2005. (Animals, Animals, Animals Ser.). (YA). (gr. k-3). (978-0-7368-3393-6(5) , Pebble Bks.) Capstone Pr., Inc.

Macken, JoAnn Early. Cows. 2004. (Animals That Live on the Farm Ser.). (Illus.). 24p. (J). pap. (978-0-8368-4279-1(0)); (YA). lib. bdg. 19.33 (978-0-8368-4272-2(3)) Stevens, Gareth Inc.

—Cows: Las Vacas. 2004. (ENG & SPA., Illus.). 24p. (J). pap. (978-0-8368-4293-7(6)); lib. bdg. 19.33 (978-0-8368-4286-9(3)) Stevens, Gareth Inc.

Miller, Heather. My Cows. 2000. (Welcome Bks.). (Illus.). 24p. (J). (ps-2). 17.00 (978-0-516-23106-8(5) , Children's Pr.) Scholastic Library Publishing.

—My Cows. 2000. (gr. k-3). lib. bdg. 12.95 (978-0-613-58859-1(2)) Tandem Library Bks.

Miller, Sara Swan. Cows. (True Bks.). (Illus.). 48p. (J). (gr. 3-5). 2001. pap. 6.95 (978-0-516-27181-1(4)); 2000. 25.00 (978-0-516-21577-8(9)) Scholastic Library Publishing. (Children's Pr.).

Murphy, Andy. Out & About at the Dairy Farm. McMullen, Anne, illus. 2004. (Field Trips Ser.). 24p. (C). (gr. k-3). 23.93 (978-1-4048-0038-0(7)) Picture Window Bks.

Murray, Julie. Cows. 2005. (Animal Kingdom Set Ii Ser.). (Illus.). 24p. (J). (gr. k-4). lib. bdg. 21.35 (978-1-59197-310-2(4)) ABDO Publishing Co.

—Grass to Milk. 2007. (Beginning to End Ser.). (Illus.). 24p. (J). (gr. k-3). lib. bdg. 21.35 (978-1-59679-837-3(8) , Buddy Bks.) ABDO Publishing Co.

Peterson, Cris. Clarabelle: Making Milk & So Much More. Lundquist, David, illus. 2007. 32p. (J). (gr. 1 up). 16.95 ***(978-1-59078-310-8(7))*** Boyds Mills Pr.

Pohl, Kathleen. What Happens at a Dairy Farm? 2006. (Illus.). 24p. (J). pap. (978-0-8368-6893-7(5)); lib. bdg. (978-0-8368-6886-9(2)) Stevens, Gareth Inc.

—What Happens at a Dairy Farm? Qué Pasa en una Granja Lechera? 2006. (ENG & SPA., Illus.). 24p. (J). pap. (978-0-8368-7394-8(7)); lib. bdg. (978-0-8368-7387-0(4)) Stevens, Gareth Inc. (Weekly Reader Early Learning Library).

Powell, Jillian. From Calf to Cow. 2001. (How Do They Grow? Ser.). (Illus.). 32p. (J). lib. bdg. 25.69 (978-0-7398-4426-7(1)) Raintree.

Ray, Hannah. Cows. Davidson, Chris, illus. 2006. (Down on the Farm Ser.). 24p. (J). (gr. k-2). lib. bdg. 15.95 (978-1-59566-180-7(8)) QEB Publishing Inc.

Schuh, Mari C. Cows on the Farm. 2001. (On the Farm Ser.). (Illus.). 24p. (J). (gr. k-1). lib. bdg. 15.93 (978-0-7368-0992-4(9) , Pebble Bks.) Capstone Pr., Inc.

—Cows on the Farm. (On the Farm Ser.). 24p. (J). pap. 5.95 (978-0-7368-9143-1(9)) Capstone Pr., Inc.

Sloan, Peter. From Grass to Milk. 1999. (gr. k-3). lib. bdg. 11.80 (978-0-613-30418-4(7)) Tandem Library Bks.

Stone, Lynn M. Cows Have Calves. 2000. (Animals & Their Young Ser.). (Illus.). 24p. (J). (gr. 1 up). lib. bdg. 18.60 (978-0-7565-0001-6(X)) Compass Point Bks.

Taus-Bolstad, Stacy. From Grass to Milk. 2004. (Start to Finish Ser.). (Illus.). 24p. (J). 18.60 (978-0-8225-4664-1(7) , Lerner Pubns.) Lerner Publishing Group.

Top That Publishing Staff, ed. Wacky Cow. 2004. (Wacky Animals Ser.). (Illus.). 10p. (J). pap. (978-1-84510-088-9(3)) Top That! Publishing PLC.

Trumbauer, Lisa. The Life Cycle of a Cow. 2002. (Life Cycles Ser.). (Illus.). 24p. (J). (gr. k-1). lib. bdg. 15.93 (978-0-7368-1451-5(5) , Pebble Bks.) Capstone Pr., Inc.

Van Laan, Nancy. Tiny, Tiny Boy & the Big, Big Cow. 2000. (978-0-606-18092-4(3)) Tandem Library Bks.

Wolfman, Judy. Life on a Cattle Farm. Winston, David Lorenz, photos by. 2005. (Life on a Farm Ser.). (Illus.). 48p. (gr. 2-5). lib. bdg. 23.93 (978-1-57505-516-9(3)) Lerner Publishing Group.

—Life on a Dairy Farm. Winston, David Lorenz, illus. Winston, David Lorenz, photos by. 2004. (Life on a Farm Ser.). 48p. (J). (gr. 2-5). lib. bdg. 23.93 (978-1-57505-190-1(7)) Lerner Publishing Group.

COWS—FICTION

Ada, Alma Flor. In the Cow's Backyard. (Stories the Year 'Round Ser.). (Illus.). 18p. (J). (gr. k-3). pap. 8.95 (978-1-58105-212-1(X)) Santillana USA Publishing Co., Inc.

—In the Cow's Backyard. 1999. (gr. k-3). lib. bdg. 17.60 (978-0-613-51367-8(3)) Tandem Library Bks.

—La Sorpresa de Mama Coneja. (Cuentos para Todo el Ano Ser.). (SPA., Illus.). 28p. (J). (gr. k-3). pap. 8.95 (978-1-58105-174-2(3)) Santillana USA Publishing Co., Inc.

Alonso de Santiago, Belén. El Muu Sterio de la Vaca Descoyuntada. (SPA., Illus.). 134p. 6.00 (978-968-16-6022-2(6) , FC33679) Fondo de Cultura Economica MEX. *Dist:* Lectorum Pubns., Inc.

Antillano, Laura. Una Vaca Querida. Ochoa, Ana, illus. (Literary Encounters Ser.). (SPA.). (J). (gr. 3-5). pap. (978-968-494-077-2(7) , CI7709) Centro de Informacion y Desarrollo de la Comunicacion y la Literatura MEX. *Dist:* Lectorum Pubns., Inc.

Applegate, Katherine. Home of the Brave. 2007. 256p. (J). (gr. 5-9). 16.95 ***(978-0-312-36765-7(1))*** Feiwel & Friends.

Arena, Felice & Kettle, Phil. On the Farm/By Felice Arena & Phil Kettle ; Illustrated by Susy Boyer. Boyer, Susy, illus. 2004. (J). pap. (978-1-59336-363-5(X)) Mondo Publishing.

Arkin, Alan. Cassie Loves Beethoven. l.t. ed. 2003. (Children's Large Print Ser.). 28.95 (978-1-58118-108-1(6)) LRS.

Arnold, Marsha Diane. Prancing, Dancing Lily. Manders, John, illus. 2004. 32p. (J). (gr. k-3). 16.99 (978-0-8037-2823-3(9) , Dial) Penguin Group (USA) Inc.

Bachand, Stephen. Velma the Lost Calf. 1999. (Booktime Buddies Ser.: Vol. 4). (Illus.). (J). (ps-2). pap. 5.00 (978-1-928972-03-7(9)) Critter Pubns.

C D

Bailey, Arthur. The Tale of Old Mr Crow. 2002. 132p. pap. 19.95 (978-1-932080-51-3(1)) Ross & Perry, Inc.

Balan, Bruce. Cows Going Past. Nash, Scott, illus. 2005. 32p. (J). (ps-ps). 9.99 (978-0-8037-2902-5(2)) Penguin Group (USA) Inc.

Balmer, Fred. Festus & His New Job. Newcomb, Kristene, illus. 2004. 26p. (J). per. 7.00 (***978-0-9760790-1-9(1))*** Folsom Fallies Pr.

—Festus & the Hole in the Fence Gang. Newcomb, Kristene, illus. 2005. 33p. (J). per. 7.00 (***978-0-9760790-3-3(8))*** Folsom Fallies Pr.

—Festus & the Missing Bag of Feed. Newcomb, Kristene, illus. 2004. 26p. (J). per. 7.00 (***978-0-9760790-0-2(3))*** Folsom Fallies Pr.

—Festus & the Stranger. Miller, Callie, ed. Newcomb, Kristene, illus. 2007. 30p. (J). per. 7.00 (***978-0-9760790-4-0(6))*** Folsom Fallies Pr.

Banicki, Patsy & Staige, Pat. Farmer Carpenter's Barn & the Cow's Saturday Night Dance. Staige, Pat & Stanton, Janet, illus. Date not set. (Orig.). (J). (gr. k-4). pap. (978-0-9641375-1-6(8)) Staige Productions.

Banscherus, Jurgen & Baron, Daniel C. The Secret of the Flying Cows. Butschkow, Ralf, illus. 2008. (J). pap. (***978-1-59889-913-9(9));*** lib. bdg. (***978-1-59889-877-4(9))*** Stone Arch Bks.

Baurys, Florence. The Coyote Calf. Holmes, Gerald L., illus. 2000. 32p. (J). (ps-3). 16.95 (978-0-88415-236-1(7)) Lone Star Bks.

Becker, Suzy. Manny's Cows: The Niagara Falls Tale. Becker, Suzy, illus. 2006. (Illus.). 40p. (J). 15.99 (978-0-06-054152-1(0)); lib. bdg. 16.89 (978-0-06-054153-8(9)) HarperCollins Pubs.

Beckerman, Menucha. Avi & Chavi Meet Cocoa the Cow. Peleg, Tirza, illus. 2002. (My Middos World Ser.: 11). (J). 11.95 (978-1-931681-28-5(7)) Israel Bk. Shop.

Beil, Karen Magnuson. Mooove Over! A Book about Counting by Twos. Meisel, Paul, tr. Meisel, Paul, illus. 2004. 32p. (J). (gr. k-3). tchr. ed. 16.95 (978-0-8234-1736-0(0)) Holiday Hse., Inc.

Benson, P. Bryn. Josefina the Christmas Cow: A Tale of Hope & Faith. Cinelli, Lisa, illus. 2005. 48p. pap. 9.95 (978-0-929636-47-4(3)) Syren Bk. Co.

Bentley, Dawn. Take a Bow, Cow: Hand Puppet & Story Book. 1998. (Read-Along Pals Ser.). (Illus.). 10p. (YA). (gr. 2 up). bds. 9.95 (978-1-888443-63-9(4) , Intervisual/Piggy Toes) Dalmatian Pr.

—Who Says Moo? Tom-Nellis, Susan, illus. 1998. (Baby Buddy Bks.). 12p. (J). (ps-3). bds. 4.95 (978-1-888443-73-8(1) , Intervisual/Piggy Toes) Dalmatian Pr.

Blair, Eric. El Ninito de Jengibre. Peterson, Ben, illus. 2006. (Read-It! Readers en Espanol Ser.).Tr. of Gingerbread Man. (SPA.). 32p. (J). (ps-3). 19.95 (978-1-4048-1647-3(X)) Picture Window Bks.

Boynton, Sandra. Moo Cow Book. Boynton, Sandra, illus. 2004. (Illus.). 10p. (J). 16.95 (978-0-689-87683-7(1) , Little Simon) Simon & Schuster Children's Publishing.

Bradman, Tony. Has Anyone Seen Jack. rev. ed. 2007. (Illus.). 24p. (J). 7.95 (***978-1-84507-706-8(7))*** Lincoln, Frances Ltd. GBR. *Dist:* Perseus Distribution.

Bunting, Eve. The Baby Shower. Love, Judy, illus. 2007. 28p. (J). (ps-1). 15.95 (978-1-58089-139-4(X)) Charlesbridge Publishing, Inc.

—The Wedding. Trapani, Iza, illus. 32p. (J). (ps). 2005. pap. 6.95 (978-1-58089-118-9(7)); 2004. 15.95 (978-1-58089-040-3(7)) Charlesbridge Publishing, Inc.

Cazet, Denys. Minnie & Moo: Minnie & Moo & the Musk of Zorro. Cazet, Denys, illus. 2002. (Live Oak Readalong Ser.). (Illus.). (J). pap. 18.95 incl. audio compact disk (978-1-59112-388-0(7)) Live Oak Media.

—Minnie & Moo: Minnie & Moo & the Thanksgiving Tree. Cazet, Denys, illus. 2002. (Live Oak Readalong Ser.). (Illus.). (J). pap. 18.95 incl. audio compact disk (978-1-59112-386-6(0)) Live Oak Media.

—Minnie & Moo: Minnie & Moo Go Dancing. Cazet, Denys, illus. 2001. (Live Oak Readalong Ser.). (Illus.). (J). pap. 18.95 incl. audio compact disk (978-1-59112-390-3(9)) Live Oak Media.

—Minnie & Moo: Minnie & Moo Go to Paris. Cazet, Denys, illus. 2001. (Live Oak Readalong Ser.). (Illus.). (J). pap. 18.95 incl. audio compact disk (978-1-59112-394-1(1)) Live Oak Media.

—Minnie & Moo: Minnie & Moo Go to the Moon. Cazet, Denys, illus. (Live Oak Readalong Ser.). (Illus.). (J). 18.95 incl. audio compact disk (978-1-59112-392-7(5)) Live Oak Media.

—Minnie & Moo: Minnie & Moo Save the Earth. Cazet, Denys, illus. 2001. (Live Oak Readalong Ser.). (Illus.). (J). pap. 18.95 incl. audio compact disk (978-1-59112-396-5(8)) Live Oak Media.

—Minnie & Moo: Minnie & Moo: Will You Be My Valentine? Cazet, Denys, illus. 2005. (Live Oak Readalong Ser.). (Illus.). (J). pap. 16.95 incl. audio (978-1-59112-891-5(9)) Live Oak Media.

—Minnie & Moo: The Attack of the Easter Bunnies. Cazet, Denys, illus. 2004. (I Can Read Bks.). (Illus.). 48p. (J). (gr. k-3). 15.99 (978-0-06-000506-1(8)); lib. bdg. 17.89 (978-0-06-000507-8(6)) HarperCollins Pubs.

—Minnie & Moo: The Case of the Missing Jelly Donut. Cazet, Denys, illus. (I Can Read Bks.). 48p. (J). 2006. pap. 3.99 (978-0-06-073009-3(9) , Harper Trophy); 2005. (Illus.). 15.99 (978-0-06-073007-9(2)) HarperCollins Pubs.

—Minnie & Moo: The Night Before Christmas. Cazet, Denys, illus. (Readalongs for Beginning Readers Ser.). (Illus.). 2005. (J). pap. 16.95 incl. audio (978-1-59112-883-0(8)); 2004. 25.95 incl. audio (978-1-59112-884-7(6)) Live Oak Media.

—Minnie & Moo: The Night of the Living Bed. Cazet, Denys, illus. (I Can Read Bks.). 48p. (J). (gr. k-3). 2004. pap. 3.99 (978-0-06-000505-4(X) , Harper Trophy); 2003. (Illus.). 16.99 (978-0-06-000503-0(3)); 2003. (Illus.). lib. bdg. 16.89 (978-0-06-000504-7(1)) HarperCollins Pubs.

—Minnie & Moo: Wanted Dead or Alive. Cazet, Denys, illus. (I Can Read Bks.). 48p. (J). 2007. pap. 3.99 (***978-0-06-073012-3(9)*** , Harper Trophy); 2006. (Illus.). 15.99 (978-0-06-073010-9(2)); 2006. (Illus.). lib. bdg. 16.89 (978-0-06-073011-6(0)) HarperCollins Pubs.

—Minnie & Moo: Will You Be My Valentine? Cazet, Denys, illus. 2002. (I Can Read Bks.). (Illus.). 48p. (J). (gr. k-3). 15.99 (978-0-06-623754-1(8)); lib. bdg. 16.89 (978-0-06-623755-8(6)) HarperCollins Pubs.

—Minnie & Moo & the Haunted Sweater. Cazet, Denys, illus. 2007. (I Can Read Bks.). 48p. (J). (ps-3). 15.99 (***978-0-06-073016-1(1));*** lib. bdg. 16.89 (***978-0-06-073017-8(X))*** HarperCollins Pubs.

—Minnie & Moo & the Musk of Zorro. Cazet, Denys, illus. 2002. (Minnie & Moo Ser.). (Illus.). (J). 11.49 (978-0-7587-6205-4(4)) Book Wholesalers, Inc.

—Minnie & Moo & the Musk of Zorro. Cazet, Denys, illus. 2002. (Live Oak Readalong Ser.). (Illus.). (ps-3). (J). pap. 16.95 incl. audio (978-0-87499-918-1(9)); (J). pap., tchr.'s planning gde. ed. 29.95 incl. audio (978-0-87499-920-4(0)); (J). 25.95 incl. audio (978-0-87499-919-8(7)); 28.95 incl. audio compact disk (978-1-59112-589-1(8)); pap. 31.95 incl. audio compact disk (978-1-59112-588-4(X)) Live Oak Media.

—Minnie & Moo & the Musk of Zorro. 2000. (ps-2). lib. bdg. 11.80 (978-0-613-32838-8(8)); (Illus.). (J). (978-0-606-22032-3(1)) Tandem Library Bks.

—Minnie & Moo & the Seven Wonders of the World. Cazet, Denys, illus. 2003. (Illus.). 144p. (J). 16.95 (978-0-689-85330-2(0) , Atheneum/Richard Jackson Bks.) Simon & Schuster Children's Publishing.

—Minnie & Moo & the Thanksgiving Tree. Cazet, Denys, illus. 2002. (Minnie & Moo Ser.). (Illus.). (J). 11.45 (978-0-7587-6206-1(2)) Book Wholesalers, Inc.

—Minnie & Moo & the Thanksgiving Tree. Cazet, Denys, illus. 2002. (Live Oak Readalong Ser.). (Illus.). (J). pap. 16.95 incl. audio (978-0-87499-914-3(6)); (J). pap., tchr.'s planning gde. ed. 29.95 incl. audio (978-0-87499-916-7(2)); (J). 25.95 incl. audio (978-0-87499-915-0(4)); 28.95 incl. audio compact disk (978-1-59112-587-7(1)) Live Oak Media.

—Minnie & Moo & the Thanksgiving Tree. 2000. (ps-2). lib. bdg. 11.80 (978-0-613-32839-5(6)) Tandem Library Bks.

—Minnie & Moo Go Dancing. Cazet, Denys, illus. 2002. (Minnie & Moo Ser.). (Illus.). (J). 11.49 (978-0-7587-1443-5(2)) Book Wholesalers, Inc.

—Minnie & Moo Go Dancing. Cazet, Denys, illus. 2001. (Illus.). 25.95 incl. audio (978-0-87499-722-4(4)); 28.95 incl. audio compact disk (978-1-59112-591-4(X)); pap. 29.95 incl. audio (978-0-87499-723-1(2)); pap. 31.95 incl. audio compact disk (978-1-59112-590-7(1)) Live Oak Media.

—Minnie & Moo Go Dancing. 2001. (Live Oak Readalong Ser.). (Illus.). (J). (ps-4). pap. 16.95 incl. audio (978-0-87499-721-7(6)) Live Oak Media.

—Minnie & Moo Go to Paris. Cazet, Denys, illus. 2002. (Minnie & Moo Ser.). (Illus.). (J). 11.45 (978-0-7587-1442-8(4)) Book Wholesalers, Inc.

—Minnie & Moo Go to Paris. Cazet, Denys, illus. 2001. (Illus.). 28.95 incl. audio compact disk (978-1-59112-595-2(2)); pap. 29.95 incl. audio (978-0-87499-768-2(2)); pap. 31.95 incl. audio compact disk (978-1-59112-594-5(4)) Live Oak Media.

—Minnie & Moo Go to Paris. 2001. (Illus.). (J). (gr. 1-3). 25.95 incl. audio (978-0-87499-767-5(4)); pap. 16.95 incl. audio (978-0-87499-766-8(6)) Live Oak Media.

—Minnie & Moo Go to Paris. 1999. (gr. k-3). lib. bdg. 11.80 (978-0-613-22012-5(9)) Tandem Library Bks.

—Minnie & Moo Go to the Moon. Cazet, Denys, illus. 2002. (Minnie & Moo Ser.). (Illus.). (J). 11.32 (978-0-7587-1444-2(0)) Book Wholesalers, Inc.

—Minnie & Moo Go to the Moon. Cazet, Denys, illus. 2001. (Illus.). 25.95 incl. audio (978-0-87499-718-7(6)); pap. 29.95 incl. audio (978-0-87499-719-4(4)); pap. 31.95 incl. audio compact disk (978-1-59112-592-1(8)); pap. 18.95 incl. audio compact disk (978-1-59112-593-8(6)) Live Oak Media.

—Minnie & Moo Go to the Moon. 2001. (Live Oak Readalong Ser.). (Illus.). (J). (ps-4). pap. 16.95 incl. audio (978-0-87499-717-0(8)) Live Oak Media.

—Minnie & Moo Holiday Series. Cazet, Denys, illus. 2004. (Illus.). pap. 45.95 incl. audio (978-1-59112-851-9(X)); pap. 51.95 incl. audio compact disk (978-1-59112-852-6(8)) Live Oak Media.

—Minnie & Moo Meet Frankenswine. Cazet, Denys, illus. 2002. (Minnie & Moo Ser.). (Illus.). 12.34 (978-1-4046-1308-9(0)) Book Wholesalers, Inc.

—Minnie & Moo Meet Frankenswine. Cazet, Denys, illus. (I Can Read Bks.: Bk. 3). (Illus.). 48p. (J). 2002. pap. 3.99 (978-0-06-444311-1(6)); 2001. 15.89 (978-0-06-623749-7(1)); 2001. 14.95 (978-0-06-623748-0(3)) HarperCollins Pubs.

—Minnie & Moo Meet Frankenswine. Cazet, Denys, illus. (Readalongs for Beginning Readers Ser.). (Illus.). 2005. (J). pap. 16.95 incl. audio (978-1-59112-261-6(9)); 2005. (J). pap. 18.95 incl. audio compact disk (978-1-59112-875-5(7)); 2004. 28.95 incl. audio compact disk (978-1-59112-876-2(5)); 2004. (J). 25.95 incl. audio (978-1-59112-262-3(7)); 2004. (J). pap. 29.95 incl. audio (978-1-59112-263-0(5)); 2004. (J). pap. 31.95 incl. audio compact disk (978-1-59112-877-9(3)) Live Oak Media.

—Minnie & Moo Meet Frankenswine. 2002. (gr. k-3). lib. bdg. 11.80 (978-0-613-62183-0(2)) Tandem Library Bks.

—Minnie & Moo on the Go Series. Cazet, Denys, illus. 2001. (Illus.). pap. 61.95 incl. audio (978-0-87499-996-9(0)); pap. 68.95 incl. audio compact disk (978-1-59112-848-9(X)) Live Oak Media.

—Minnie & Moo Save the Earth. Cazet, Denys, illus. 2002. (Minnie & Moo Ser.). (Illus.). (J). 11.45 (978-0-7587-1445-9(9)) Book Wholesalers, Inc.

—Minnie & Moo Save the Earth. Cazet, Denys, illus. 2001. (Illus.). 25.95 incl. audio (978-0-87499-771-2(2)); 28.95 incl. audio compact disk (978-1-59112-597-6(9)); pap. 29.95 incl. audio (978-0-87499-772-9(0)); pap. 31.95 incl. audio compact disk (978-1-59112-596-9(0)) Live Oak Media.

—Minnie & Moo Save the Earth. 2001. (Live Oak Readalong Ser.). (Illus.). (J). (ps-4). pap. 16.95 incl. audio (978-0-87499-770-5(4)) Live Oak Media.

—Minnie & Moo Save the Earth. 1999. (gr. k-3). lib. bdg. 11.80 (978-0-613-62800-6(4)) Tandem Library Bks.

—The Night of the Living Bed. Cazet, Denys, illus. unabr. ed. 2005. (Minnie & Moo Ser.). (J). (gr. k-4). (Illus.). 25.95 incl. audio (978-1-59519-389-6(8)); (Illus.). 28.95 incl. audio compact disk (978-1-59519-393-3(6)); (Illus.). pap. 16.95 incl. audio (978-1-59519-388-9(X)); (Illus.). pap. 18.95 incl. audio compact disk (978-1-59519-392-6(8)); Set. pap. 31.95 incl. audio compact disk (978-1-59519-394-0(4)); Set. (Illus.). pap. 29.95 incl. audio (978-1-59519-390-2(1)) Live Oak Media.

Cazet, Denys, reader. Minnie & Moo: Will You Be My Valentine? (Read-Alongs for Beginning Readers Ser.). (Illus.). (J). (ps-3). 2005. pap. 18.95 incl. audio compact disk (978-1-59112-895-3(1)); 2004. 25.95 incl. audio (978-1-59112-892-2(7)); 2004. pap. 31.95 incl. audio compact disk (978-1-59112-897-7(8)); 2004. pap. 29.95 incl. audio (978-1-59112-893-9(5)) Live Oak Media.

Cazet, Denys & Dorling Kindersley Publishing Staff. Minnie & Moo & the Musk of Zorro. 2000. (Illus.). 48p. (J). (gr. 1-3). pap. 3.99 (978-0-7894-2653-6(6)); (gr. 5-3). 12.99 (978-0-7894-2652-9(8)) Dorling Kindersley Publishing, Inc.

—Minnie & Moo & the Thanksgiving Tree. Cazet, Denys, illus. 2000. (Illus.). 48p. (J). (gr. 1-3). 12.99 (978-0-7894-2654-3(4)); pap. 3.99 (978-0-7894-2655-0(2)) Dorling Kindersley Publishing, Inc.

—Minnie & Moo Go Dancing. 1998. (Minnie & Moo Ser.: Vol. 2). (Illus.). 48p. (J). (gr. 1-3). 12.99 (978-0-7894-2515-7(7)); pap. 3.99 (978-0-7894-2536-2(X)) Dorling Kindersley Publishing, Inc.

—Minnie & Moo Go to the Moon. 1998. (Minnie & Moo Ser.: Vol. 1). (Illus.). 48p. (J). (gr. 1-3). 12.99 (978-0-7894-2516-4(5)); pap. 3.99 (978-0-7894-2537-9(8)) Dorling Kindersley Publishing, Inc.

—Minnie & Moo Save the Earth, Vol. 3. 1999. (Minnie & Moo Ser.: Vol. 3). (Illus.). 48p. (J). (gr. 1-3). 12.99 (978-0-7894-2594-2(7)); pap. 3.99 (978-0-7894-3929-1(8)) Dorling Kindersley Publishing, Inc.

Chaconas, Dori. When Cows Come Home for Christmas. Chapman, Lynne, illus. 2005. 32p. (J). (gr. k-3). 15.95 (978-0-8075-8877-2(6)) Whitman, Albert & Co.

Chambers, Angela. How Now, Cow? Abel, Simone, illus. 2001. (Pinwheel Ser.). 10p. (J). bds. 3.95 (978-0-8069-0275-3(2)) Sterling Publishing Co., Inc.

Charlip, Remy. Little Old Beard & Big Young Little Beard. Rettenmund, Tamara, illus. 2006. 32p. (J). 5.95 (978-0-7614-5288-1(5)) Cavendish, Marshall Corp.

Chloe Cow & the Party. 2004. (Play Pals Ser.). (Illus.). 12p. (J). bds. (978-1-84229-644-8(2)) Top That! Publishing PLC.

Choldenko, Gennifer. Moonstruck: The True Story of the Cow Who Jumped over the Moon. 1999. (978-0-606-17169-4(X)) Tandem Library Bks.

Chung, Chi & Lewis, Beverley. Cows in the House. 1998. (Bethany Backyard Ser.). (Illus.). 32p. (J). (ps-3). 14.99 (978-0-7642-2096-8(9)) Bethany Hse. Pubs.

Clara Cow Wraps up Warm. 2002. (J). 5.98 (978-0-7525-8905-3(9)) Parragon, Inc.

Clarissa - Evaluation Guide: Evaluation Guide. 2006. (J). (978-1-55942-402-8(8)) Marsh Media.

Click Clack Moo Cows That Type Spanish. 2004. (J). pap. 32.75 incl. audio (978-1-55592-652-6(5)); (SPA.). pap. 14.95 incl. audio (978-1-55592-653-3(3)) Weston Woods Studios, Inc.

Clifford, Rowan. Rodeo Ron & His Milkshake Cows. 2005. (Illus.). 32p. (J). (gr. k-3). 15.95 (978-0-375-83195-9(9) ; Knopf Bks. for Young Readers) Random Hse. Children's Bks.

Coulman, Valerie. Rafi et les Cochons Volants. Duchesne, Christiane, tr. from ENG. Girard, Roge, illus. (FRE.). 32p. (J). pap. 6.95 (***978-2-922435-02-3(4))*** Editions Homard CAN. *Dist:* Univ. of Toronto Pr.

—Sink or Swim. Roge, tr. Roge & Girard, Roge, illus. 2004. 32p. (J). 15.95 (978-1-894222-54-9(7)) Lobster Pr. CAN. *Dist:* Univ. of Toronto Pr.

—When Pigs Fly. Roge, illus. 2004. 32p. (J). pap. 6.95 (978-1-894222-79-2(2)) Lobster Pr. CAN. *Dist:* Univ. of Toronto Pr.

A Cow Had a Wish. l.t. ed. Date not set. (Illus.). 32p. (J). (gr. 1-6). (978-0-9653327-1-2(3)) BF Publishing.

Cow up a Tree, 6 vols., Pack. (Story Steps Ser.). (gr. k-2). 23.00 (978-0-7635-9807-5(0)) Rigby Education.

Cow Wants to Sing. 2002. (J). 4.98 (978-0-7525-7220-8(2)) Parragon, Inc.

Cowley, Joy. Mrs. Wishy-Washy's Farm. Fuller, Elizabeth, illus. 32p. (J). (ps). 2006. pap. 5.99 (978-0-14-240299-3(0) , Puffin); 2003. 15.99 (978-0-399-23872-7(7) , Philomel) Penguin Group (USA) Inc.

Crockett, Johns. Click Clack Meuuh. 29.95 (978-2-87142-345-4(8)) Mijade Editions BEL. *Dist:* Distribooks, Inc.

Cronin, Doreen. Clic, Clac, Muu: Vacas Escritoras. Rioja, Alberto Jiménez, tr. Lewin, Betsy, illus. Tr. of CLICK, CLACK, MOO: COWS THAT TYPE. (SPA.). (J). (gr. k-2). 15.00 (978-1-930332-28-7(9) , LC4357) Lectorum Pubns., Inc.

—Clic, Clac, Muu: Vacas Escritoras. 2004. Tr. of CLICK, CLACK, MOO: COWS THAT TYPE. (SPA.). (J). (ps-4). 24.95 incl. audio (978-1-55592-155-2(8)) Weston Woods Studios, Inc.

—Click, Clack, Moo: Cows That Type. Lewin, Betsy, illus. 2000. 32p. (J). (ps-3). 15.95 (978-0-689-83213-0(3)) Simon & Schuster Children's Publishing.

—Click, Clack, Moo: Cows That Type. 2004. 29.95 incl. cd-rom (978-1-55592-104-0(3)); (J). pap. 18.95 incl. audio compact disk (978-1-55592-139-2(6)); (J). pap. 38.75 incl. audio compact disk (978-1-55592-630-4(4)); (J). pap. 32.75 incl. audio (978-1-55592-183-5(3)); (J). pap. 32.75 incl. audio (978-1-55592-347-1(X)); (J). pap. 14.95 incl. audio (978-1-55592-171-2(X)) Weston Woods Studios, Inc.

—Click, Clack, Moo: Cows That Type. Lewin, Betsy, illus. 2004. (J). 24.95 incl. audio (978-1-55592-077-7(2)) Weston Woods Studios, Inc.

—Click, Clack, Moo: Cows that Type. 2006. (Illus.). (J). (ps-3). 22.78 (978-1-59961-088-7(4)) Spotlight.

—Click, Clack, Moo: Cows That Type. braille ed. 2004. (Illus.). (J). (gr. k-3). spiral bd. (978-0-616-07227-1(9)); spiral bd. (978-0-616-07228-8(7)) Canadian National Institute for the Blind/Institut National Canadien pour les Aveugles.

—Teque, Teque, Muu: Vacas que Escrevem a Maquina. pap. 26.95 (978-85-325-1566-7(5)) Rocco, Editora, Ltda BRA. *Dist:* Distribooks, Inc.

Cutbill, Andy. The Cow That Laid an Egg. Ayto, Russell, illus. 2008. 32p. (J). 16.99 (***978-0-06-137295-7(1))*** HarperCollins Pubs.

D'Allance, Mireille. No, No Y No! 2005. (SPA., Illus.). (J). 15.99 (978-84-8470-114-9(X)) Corimbo, Editorial S.L. ESP. *Dist:* Iaconi, Mariuccia Bk. Imports.

Dawson, Joy. Maggie, the Color-Blind Cow: A loving heart—that didn't see Color. 2006. (ENG., Illus.). 36p. (J). per. 12.95 (***978-1-59800-892-0(7))*** Outskirts Press, Inc.

Day, Jan. Kissimmee Pete, Cracker Cow Hunter: A Tall Tale. Mason, Janeen I., illus. 2005. 32p. (J). (gr. 2-4). 15.95 (978-1-58980-325-1(6)) Pelican Publishing Co., Inc.

DeGrazia, Leah. My Mother Is a Moo Cow. DeGrazia, Leah, illus. 2000. 32p. (J). spiral bd. 9.95 (978-1-883477-47-9(6)) Lone Oak Pr., Ltd.

Dickinson, Donald J. A Bird's Eye View of the Civil War in Loudon County & Campbell's Station, TN: A Book for Children. 2003. (Illus.). 251p. (J). per. (978-0-9637951-3-7(9)) Hart-Whitlow Pubs.

Disney Storybook Artists Staff, illus. Disney's Home on the Range: A Hero of a Horse. 2004. (Step into Reading Ser.). 32p. (J). (ps-1). pap. 3.99 (978-0-7364-2210-9(2) , RH/Disney) Random Hse. Children's Bks.

Dockweiler, Sharon. No Buttons for Suzy Cow. Silbert, Barbara Briggs, illus. 1999. (J). (978-1-929453-00-9(0)) Sharon's Small Pr.

Dolan, Penny. Moo! Sharp, Melanie, illus. 2004. (Read-It! Readers Ser.). 32p. (C). (gr. k-3). 18.60 (978-1-4048-0643-6(1)) Picture Window Bks.

Don't Eat the Bluebonnets. 2006. (J). lib. bdg. 17.95 (978-0-9645493-3-3(6)) Bluebonnets, Boots & Bks.

Dow, Jill. Moonbeam's Big Splash. Dow, Jill, illus. 1999. (Windy Edge Farm Ser.). (Illus.). 32p. (J). (ps-2). pap. 7.99 (978-0-7112-1028-8(4)) Lincoln, Frances Ltd. GBR. *Dist:* Transition Vendor.

Duffield, Katy. Farmer McPeepers' Milk Cows. Gray, Steve, illus. 2003. 32p. (gr. k-4). 15.95 (978-0-87358-825-6(8) , Rising Moon Bks. for Young Readers) Northland Publishing.

Dunsmuir, Tom. You Can't Milk a Dancing Cow. Jones, Brian T., illus. 2005. 24p. (ps). 14.95 (978-0-9749303-3-6(4)) Tanglewood Pr.

Dwire, Joyann. What Kind of Cow Are You? Being Content with How God Made You. Dickson, Bill, illus. 2006. 24p. (J). per. 2.99 (978-1-59958-006-7(3)) Journey Stone Creations, LLC.

Edens, Cooper. Santa Cow Island. 1999. (J). (978-0-606-18952-1(1)) Tandem Library Bks.

Edmond, Wally. Cuddles the Chocolate Cow & Friends. Melinda, Sheffler, illus. 2006. 39p. (J). 14.95 (978-1-59879-108-2(7)); per. 9.99 (978-1-59879-125-9(7)) Lifevest Publishing, Inc.

Egan, Tim. Metropolitan Cow. ed. 2004. (J). (gr. k-3). spiral bd. (978-0-616-07231-8(7)) Canadian National Institute for the Blind/Institut National Canadien pour les Aveugles.

—Metropolitan Cow. Egan, Tim, illus. 1999. (Illus.). 32p. (J). (gr. k-3). pap. 6.95 (978-0-395-96059-2(2)) Houghton Mifflin Co. Trade & Reference Div.

Erickson, John R. The Case of the Tricky Trap. 2005. (Hank the Cowdog Ser.: No. 46). (Illus.). 160p. (J). (gr. 3-7). 15.99 (978-0-670-05993-5(5) , Viking Juvenile) Penguin Group (USA) Inc.

Esoldi, Vin. May Maisey Moo's Cowllection of Moo Tales Vol. I: The Convention. Bourdeaux, Robert, illus. 1999. (J). 48p. 17.95 (978-1-929745-00-5(1) , MMM 001); 99p. 29.95 (978-1-929745-01-2(X) , MM 001) Paula Pr. Pubs. (May Maisey Moo).

Fajerman, Deborah. How to Speak Moo! 2002. (Illus.). 32p. (J). (ps-1). pap. 5.99 (978-0-7641-2285-9(1)) Barron's Educational Series, Inc.

Fisher, Susan. Clarence the Carnival Cow. 1998. (Illus.). 14p. (J). (ps-6). pap. 6.50 (978-0-9663228-0-4(0)) A to Z Kinder Pr.

Fleming, Denise. The Cow Who Clucked. 2006. (Illus.). (J). (***978-1-4156-9208-0(4))*** Holt, Henry & Co.

—The Cow Who Clucked. Fleming, Denise, illus. rev. ed. 2006. (Illus.). 40p. (J). 16.95 (978-0-8050-7265-5(9) , Holt, Henry & Co. Bks. For Young Readers) Holt, Henry & Co.

Forsythe, Ryan. The Little Veal Cutlet That Couldn't. 2005. 32p. (YA). pap. 14.98 (978-1-4116-6370-1(5)) Lulu-.com.

Fox, George. My First Cow: Ranch Stories. 2001. (Illus.). 160p. pap. 11.95 (978-1-894454-13-1(8)) Balmur Entertainment, Ltd. CAN. *Dist:* General Distribution Services, Inc.

Fox, Mem. A Particular Cow. Denton, Terry, illus. 2000. 40p. (J). 16.00 (978-0-15-200250-3(2)) Harcourt Trade Pubs.

Franke, Gary F. Cinci Freedom - A Cow's Story. Franke, Eric L., illus. 2006. (J). 24.95 (978-0-9772720-0-6(1)) Jarndyce & Jarndyce Pr.

Freeman, Martha. Mrs. Wow Never Wanted a Cow. Salerno, Steven, illus. 2006. 48p. (J). (gr. k-3). 8.99 (978-0-375-83418-9(4)); lib. bdg. 11.99 (978-0-375-93418-6(9)) Random Hse. Children's Bks. (Random Hse. Bks. for Young Readers).

—Mrs. Wow Never Wanted a Cow. Salerno, Steven, illus. 2006. (J). (978-0-375-83419-6(2)) Random Hse., Inc.

French, Jackie. Demasiadas Peras!/Too Many Pears! Whatley, Bruce, illus. 2005. Tr. of Too Many Pears!. (ENG & SPA.). 40p. (J). 16.95 (978-1-59572-012-2(X)) Star Bright Bks., Inc.

—Demasiadas Peras!/Too Many Pears! (bilingual) Whatley, Bruce, illus. 2005. Tr. of Too Many Pears!. (ENG & SPA.). 40p. (J). pap. 5.95 (978-1-59572-013-9(8)) Star Bright Bks., Inc.

—Too Many Pear (Japanese/English Bilingual) Whatley, Bruce, illus. 2007. (JPN.). 32p. (J). pap. 5.95 ***(978-1-59572-112-9(6))*** Star Bright Bks., Inc.

French, Jackie. Too Many Pears! Whatley, Bruce, illus. 2003. 40p. (J). 16.95 (978-1-932065-47-3(4) , 718-784-9112) Star Bright Bks., Inc.

Gitomer, Helaine D. & Weinstock, Harriett. The Magic Cow: A Gift. Gitomer, Helaine D. & Weinstock, Harriett, illus. 2000. (Illus.). (J). (978-0-9676205-0-3(3)) Orbin Publishing, Ltd.

The Goose Who Acted Like a Cow. (Early Intervention Levels Ser.). 31.86 (978-0-7362-0627-3(2)) Hampton-Brown Bks.

Greenleaf, E. Who Wants to Nap? (Illus.). 32p. (J). (gr. 2-3). lib. bdg. 9.95 (978-0-87783-050-4(9)) Oddo Publishing, Inc.

Hamilton, Arlene. Only a Cow. Griffiths, Dean, illus. 2006. 32p. (J). (ps-2). ***(978-1-55041-871-2(8))*** Fitzhenry & Whiteside, Ltd.

Harcourt School Publishers Staff. Bess & Tess: On Level. 3rd ed. 2002. (Trophies Reading Program Ser.). (Illus.). (J). pap. 4.10 (978-0-15-322986-2(1)) Harcourt Schl. Pubs.

—Boots for Red: Below Level. 3rd ed. 2002. (Trophies Reading Program Ser.). (Illus.). (J). (gr. 1). pap. 3.20 (978-0-15-322946-6(2)) Harcourt Schl. Pubs.

Harrison, David L. When Cows Come Home. 2003. (Illus.). 32p. (J). (ps up). pap. 8.95 (978-1-56397-946-0(2)) Boyds Mills Pr.

—When Cows Come Home. 2001. (ps-2). lib. bdg. 16.40 (978-0-613-78920-2(2)) Tandem Library Bks.

The Healthy Way with Wow the Cow. 2006. (Illus.). 32p. (J). 4.95 (978-0-9668611-4-3(0)) Kimberly Pr., LLC.

Heller, Maryellen. My Favorite Place. Friar, Joanne, illus. 2005. 16p. (J). pap. 5.00 (978-1-57274-535-3(5) , 2771, Bks. for Young Learners) Owen, Richard C. Pubs., Inc.

Herman, John. One Winter's Night. Dillon, Leo & Dillon, Diane, illus. 2003. 40p. (J). (ps-3). 16.99 (978-0-399-23418-7(7) , Philomel) Penguin Group (USA) Inc.

—One Winter's Night. Dillon, Leo & Dillon, Diane, illus. 2005. 32p. (J). pap. 5.99 (978-0-14-240458-4(6) , Puffin) Penguin Group (USA) Inc.

Hill, Ros. Shamoo: A Whale of a Cow. 2005. (Illus.). 32p. (ps-3). 15.95 (978-1-59687-188-5(1) , Milk & Cookies) ibooks, Inc.

—Shamooo: A Whale of a Cow. Hill, Ros, illus. 2005. (Illus.). 32p. (J). 15.95 (978-0-689-04634-6(0) , Milk & Cookies) ibooks, Inc.

Hillert, Margaret. The Cow That Got Her Wish. (J). 4.95 (978-0-87895-694-4(8)) Modern Curriculum Pr.

Hobbs, Valerie. Defiance. 2005. 128p. (J). 16.00 (978-0-374-30847-6(0)) Farrar, Straus & Giroux.

—Defiance. l.t. ed. 2006. 147p. 22.95 (978-0-7862-8667-6(9)) Thorndike Pr.

Hoberman, Mary Ann. Mrs. O'Learys Cow. Mattheson, Jenny, illus. 2007. 32p. (J). (ps-1). 16.99 (978-0-316-14840-5(7)) Little Brown & Co.

Hogan, Jayne. Callie Cow. Reiter, Cheryl, ed. Solheim, Kermit, illus. (J). (ps). mass mkt. 12.99 (978-1-887327-55-8(X)) Ertl Co., Inc.

Horvath, Polly. An Occasional Cow. Fiammenghi, Gioia, illus. 2003. 144p. (YA). (gr. 3-7). pap. 5.95 (978-0-374-45573-6(2) , Sunburst) Farrar, Straus & Giroux.

Hume, Lachie. Clancy the Courageous Cow. Hume, Lachie, illus. 2007. (Illus.). 32p. (gr. k-1). 16.99 (978-0-06-117249-6(9)) HarperCollins Pubs.

Hunter, S.C. The Little Cow in Valle Grande: El Becerrito en Valle Grande. Ritthaler, Sarah Pilcher, tr. from ENG. Sundstrom, Mary, illus. 2006. (SPA & ENG.). 32p. (J). (978-0-8263-4044-3(X)) Univ. of New Mexico Pr.

Hurd, Thacher. Moo Cow Kaboom! Hurd, Thacher, illus. 2003. (Illus.). 32p. (J). (ps-3). 16.99 (978-0-06-050501-1(X)) HarperCollins Pubs.

—Moo Cow Kaboom. Hurd, Thacher, illus. unabr. ed. 2006. (Picture Book Readalong Ser.). (J). 25.95 incl. audio (978-1-59519-498-5(3)); 28.95 incl. audio compact disk (978-1-59519-502-9(5)) Live Oak Media.

Hutchens, Paul. The Blue Cow. rev. ed. 1998. (Sugar Creek Gang Ser.: No. 30). 144p. (J). (gr. 4-7). 4.99 (978-0-8024-7034-8(3)) Moody Pubs.

—The Case of the Missing Calf. rev. ed. 1999. (Sugar Creek Gang Ser.: No. 36). 96p. (J). (gr. 4-7). 4.99 (978-0-8024-7040-9(8)) Moody Pubs.

Jack & the Magic Harp: Individual Title, 6 Packs. 32p. (gr. 2 up). 37.00 (978-0-7635-9403-9(2)) Rigby Education.

Jay, Larsen. What If Cows Could... ? 2005. (J). lib. bdg. 19.95 ***(978-1-933732-01-5(6)*** , Bear Hug Bks.) MidAmerica Publishing Co.

Johnson, Paul Brett. The Cow Who Wouldn't Come Down. Johnson, Paul Brett, illus. 2002. (Illus.). (J). 13.83 (978-1-4046-2066-7(4)) Book Wholesalers, Inc.

Jumbo & the Mean Tenant. 2004. (J). per. 15.99 (978-0-9744205-9-2(X)) Golden Eagle Publishing Hse., Inc.

Kaminsky, Jeff & Atwater, Martha. Cow. Kaminsky, Jeff, illus. 2002. (Stickamajigs Ser.: Vol. 3). (Illus.). 8p. (ps-1). 5.99 (978-0-7868-0712-3(1)) Hyperion Bks. for Children.

Kelly, Ellen A. Buckamoo Girls. Curry, Tom, illus. 2006. 32p. (J). (ps-3). 15.95 (978-0-8109-5471-7(0) , Abrams Bks. for Young Readers) Abrams, Harry N. , Inc.

Keylocke, Andrew, illus. Dashing Daisy. 2004. (Crazy Racers Ser.). 12p. (J). bds. 4.95 (978-0-7641-5745-5(0)) Barron's Educational Series, Inc.

Kinerk, Robert. Clorinda. Kellogg, Steven, illus. 2007. 40p. (J). (ps-3). pap. 6.99 ***(978-1-4169-3964-1(4)*** , Aladdin) Simon & Schuster Children's Publishing.

Kinerk, Robert. Clorinda Takes Flight. Kellogg, Steven, illus. 2007. 40p. (J). (ps-3). 16.99 (978-0-689-86864-1(2) , Simon & Schuster/Paula Wiseman Bks.) Simon & Schuster Children's Publishing.

Kinerk, Robert & Kellogg, Steven. Clorinda. 2003. (Illus.). 40p. (J). (gr. k-3). 15.95 (978-0-689-86449-0(3) , Simon & Schuster/Paula Wiseman Bks.) Simon & Schuster Children's Publishing.

Kovalski, Maryann. Queen Nadine. Kovalski, Maryann, illus. 2000. (Illus.). 32p. (J). (ps-2). 14.95 (978-1-55143-093-5(2)); 6.95 (978-1-55143-095-9(9)) Orca Bk. Pubs. USA.

—Queen Nadine. 2000. lib. bdg. 15.25 (978-0-613-54850-2(7)) Tandem Library Bks.

Krauskopf, Sharma. Moonbeam Cow. Howland, Naomi, illus. 1999. (Books for Young Learners). 16p. (J). (gr. k-2). pap. 5.00 (978-1-57274-271-0(2) , A2756) Owen, Richard C. Pubs., Inc.

Lamerton, Todd, illus. Wow! What a Cow- A Tale from Funky Farm. 2003. (J). (978-0-7575-0005-3(6)) Kendall/Hunt Publishing Co.

Landry, Leo. Fat Bat & Swoop. rev. ed. 2005. (Illus.). 64p. (J). (gr. 1-3). 15.95 (978-0-8050-7003-3(6) , Holt, Henry & Co. Bks. For Young Readers) Holt, Henry & Co.

Lane, Nickel. Maggy, the Cow that Jumped over the Moon. 2004. 15p. (J). pap. 7.47 (978-1-4116-1728-5(2)) Lulu.com.

Leaf, Munro. The Story of Ferdinand. Lawson, Robert, illus. 2002. (J). 14.04 (978-0-7587-3711-3(4)) Book Wholesalers, Inc.

—The Story of Ferdinand. Lawson, Robert, illus. 2007. (Puffin Storytime Ser.). 72p. (J). (ps). 9.99 ***(978-0-14-240952-7(9)*** , Puffin) Penguin Group (USA) Inc.

Leaf, Munro, ed. The Story of Ferdinand: El Cuento de Ferdinando, 2 bks., Set. Belpré, Pura, tr. Lawson, Robert, illus. unabr. ed. 1999. (ENG & SPA.). (J). (gr. 1-3). pap. 33.95 incl. audio (978-0-87499-567-1(1)) Live Oak Media.

Leavy, Una. Tomas No Quiere Zapatos. 2005. (SPA., Illus.). 64p. (J). (gr. k-1). 6.95 (978-84-348-6355-2(3)) SM Ediciones ESP. *Dist:* Iaconi, Mariuccia Bk. Imports.

LeLeu, Lisa. Miss Moo-Moo the Cow Story Starter: Puppet Book Story Starter. 2004. (Puppet Show Bks.). (Illus.). 14p. 1.50 (978-0-9710537-1-7(5)) LeLeu, Lisa Studios! Inc.

Little Softy Cow. 2002. (J). (978-1-931312-90-5(7)) Soft-Play, Inc.

Lodge, Jo. Cow. 2006. (Cosy Cuddlers Ser.). (Illus.). 8p. (J). (ps). 7.99 (978-0-333-98751-3(9)) Macmillan Publishers Ltd. GBR. *Dist:* Trafalgar Square Publishing.

Losordo, Stephen. Cow Moo Me. Conteh-Morgan, Jane, illus. 1998. (Growing Tree Ser.). 16p. (J). (ps up). 5.95 (978-0-694-01108-7(8) , Harper Festival) HarperCollins Pubs.

Lovelace, Kelley. Ready Set Go Organic. 2006. 7.99 ***(978-0-9791029-0-5(1))*** KelleyGreenworks Publishing.

Lyon, Irving W. & O'Connor, Sandra Day. Chico: A True Story from the Childhood of the First Woman Supreme Court Justice. 2005. (Illus.). 32p. (J). (gr. k). 16.99 (978-0-525-47452-4(8) , Dutton Adult) Penguin Group (USA) Inc.

Maar, Paul & Schulte, T. Gloria the Cow. 2006. (Illus.). 32p. (J). 16.95 (978-0-7358-2096-8(1)) North-South Bks., Inc.

Maddern, Eric. The Cow on the Roof. Hess, Paul, illus. 2006. 32p. (J). 15.95 (978-1-84507-374-9(6)) Lincoln, Frances Ltd. GBR. *Dist:* Perseus Distribution.

Mallet, C. Claire. Disparition Chez les Lutins. Begin, Jean-Guy, illus. 2003. (Collection des 6 Ans : Vol. 21). (FRE.). 64p. (J). 7.95 (978-2-922565-64-5(5)) Editions de la Paix CAN. *Dist:* World of Reading, Ltd.

Mayfield, Mary. Snowbank, the Great Texas Cow. 2005. (Illus.). 18p. (J). per. 7.99 (978-1-932338-98-0(5)) Lifevest Publishing, Inc.

McNaughton, Colin. Cushie Butterfield: She's a Little Cow. 2005. (Illus.). 24p. (Orig.). (J). pap. 8.99 (978-0-00-715466-1(6) , HarperSport) HarperCollins Pubs. Ltd. GBR. *Dist:* Trafalgar Square Publishing.

—What Now, Cushie Butterfield? 2005. (Illus.). 24p. (J). (ps-ps). pap. 8.99 (978-0-00-715468-5(2) , HarperSport); 18.00 (978-0-00-715467-8(4)) HarperCollins Pubs. Ltd. GBR. *Dist:* Trafalgar Square Publishing, Independent Pubs. Group.

Mercer, Peggy. Ten Cows to Texas. 2005. (Illus.). 40p. (J). 17.50 (978-1-59354-129-3(5)) Handprint Bks.

—Ten Cows to Texas. Crews, Bill, illus. 2005. 40p. (J). 16.95 (978-1-59354-116-3(3)) Handprint Bks.

Milgrim, David. Cows Can't Fly. Milgrim, David, illus. 2000. (Picture Puffin Ser.). (Illus.). 32p. (J). (ps-3). pap. 5.99 (978-0-14-056721-2(6) , Puffin) Penguin Group (USA) Inc.

—Cows Can't Fly. 2000. 12.79 (978-0-606-17859-4(7)); lib. bdg. 14.15 (978-0-613-28455-4(0)) Tandem Library Bks.

Moffatt, Julia. Buttercup, the Clumsy Cow. Williams, Lisa, illus. 2005. (Lightning Readers Ser.). 32p. (J). (gr. k-k). pap. 3.95 (978-0-7696-4039-6(7) , Gingham Dog Pr.) School Specialty Publishing.

—Buttercup, the Clumsy Cow. Williams, Lisa, illus. 2005. 32p. (J). (ps-k). lib. bdg. 11.15 (978-0-606-33581-2(1)) Tandem Library Bks.

—Manchita, la vaquita Torpe. Williams, Lisa, illus. 2005. (Lightning Readers Ser.). 32p. (J). (gr. k-k). pap. 3.95 (978-0-7696-4079-2(6) , Gingham Dog Pr.) School Specialty Publishing.

Moo & Chew. 2002. 10p. (J). 9.95 (978-0-7525-5579-9(0)) Parragon, Inc.

Moody-Luther, Jacqui. Word World Cow. 2005. NAp. 11.95 (978-0-7624-2461-0(3)) Running Pr. Bk. Pubs.

Morton, Jane & Dreier, Ted. Moozie's Cow Wisdom for Loving to the "Uddermost" Royse, Jane, illus. 2003. (J). pap. 4.95 (978-0-9662268-3-6(6)) Best Friends Bks.

Most, Bernard. Cow That Went Oink. 2003. (ps-2). lib. bdg. 14.15 (978-0-613-70495-3(9)) Tandem Library Bks.

—La Vaca Que Decia Oink. Mlawer, Teresa, tr. (SPA., Illus.). (J). (gr. k-2). pap. 6.99 (978-1-880507-66-7(8) , LC4889) Lectorum Pubns., Inc.

—La Vaca Que Decia Oink. 2000. (Illus.). (J). (978-0-606-20757-7(0)) Tandem Library Bks.

Mullican, Judy. Connie Cow's Friends. Metzger, Jeanne, illus. l.t. ed. 1999. (Cuddle Bks.). 6p. (J). (ps-k). pap. 10.95 (978-1-57332-137-2(0)) HighReach Learning, Inc.

Mustaine Hettinger, Cynthia. Casey the Confused Cow. Ramsey, Jayne, illus. 2003. (Electra's Acres Ser.). 32p. (J). per. 14.95 (978-0-9746330-1-5(1)) Anton Berkshire Publishing.

Newman, Marlene. Myron's Magic Cow. Jago, illus. 2005. 40p. (J). (ps-3). 16.99 (978-1-84148-496-9(2)) Barefoot Bks., Inc.

Palatini, Margie. Moo Who? Graves, Keith, illus. 40p. (J). (ps-2). 2007. pap. 6.99 ***(978-0-06-000107-0(0)*** , Harper Trophy); 2004. 15.99 (978-0-06-000105-6(4) , Tegen, Katherine Bks); 2004. lib. bdg. 16.89 (978-0-06-000106-3(2)) HarperCollins Pubs.

Parfitt, Tim. Spanish Vogue Book. 2006. 254p. pap. 22.00 ***(978-1-4050-4619-0(8))*** Macmillan Publishers Ltd. GBR. *Dist:* Independent Pubs. Group.

Parkinson, Siobhan. Cows Are Vegetarians. 2002. (Red Flag Ser.: Vol. 3). (Illus.). 80p. (J). pap. 8.95 (978-0-86278-694-6(0)) O'Brien Pr., Ltd., The IRL. *Dist:* Independent Pubs. Group.

Paterson, Katherine. The Smallest Cow in the World. Brown, Jane Clark, illus. 2002. (J). 12.34 (978-0-7587-1673-6(7)) Book Wholesalers, Inc.

Pedersen, Janet. Millie in the Meadow. Pedersen, Janet, illus. 2003. (Illus.). 32p. (J). (ps-1). 14.99 (978-0-7636-1725-7(3)) Candlewick Pr.

—Millie Wants to Play! Pedersen, Janet, illus. 2004. (Illus.). 32p. (J). (ps-1). 15.99 (978-0-7636-1993-0(0)) Candlewick Pr.

Pereira, William. The Adventures of LC, the Lucky Calf. Bowlsby, Tina Marie, illus. 2005. (J). 18.95 (978-0-9773133-0-3(1)) Little Tule Bks.

Pietrapiana. Tomasa the Cow. Pietrapiana, illus. 1999. Tr. of Vaca Tomasa. (SPA & ENG., Illus.). 32p. (J). (ps-3). 14.95 (978-1-55885-284-6(0) , Piñata Books) Arte Publico Pr.

Popp, Monika. Farm Year. Popp, Monika & Schmuck, Regine Frick-von, illus. 2002. 48p. (J). (gr. k-3). 18.95 (978-0-88899-452-3(4)) Groundwood Bks. CAN. *Dist:* Perseus Distribution.

Portratz, Wendy. Agnes Plays Soccer: A Young Cow's Lesson in Sportsmanship. 2006. 90p. (J). per. 9.95 (978-1-59886-326-0(6)) Tate Publishing & Enterprises, L.L.C.

Powell, Richard. I See a Cow. Davis, Caroline, illus. 2003. (Plastic Shapes Ser.). 12p. (J). bds. 5.95 (978-0-7641-5647-2(0)) Barron's Educational Series, Inc.

Priddy, Roger. Funny Faces Millie Cow. 2007. (J). bds. 14.95 ***(978-0-312-50112-9(9)*** , Priddy Bks.) St. Martin's Pr.

Purkapile, Susan. Nosy Noodles, the Curious Cow. Ducommun, Barbara, illus. 2005. 16p. (J). (978-1-930596-34-4(0)) Amherst Pr.

Puttock, Simon. Horsey. Julian, Russell, illus. 2004. 32p. (J). 17.99 (978-1-4052-1058-4(3)) Egmont Bks., Ltd. GBR. *Dist:* Independent Pubs. Group.

Random House Disney Staff. Hero of a Horse. 2004. (ps-2). lib. bdg. 11.80 (978-0-613-73715-9(6)) Tandem Library Bks.

Rassmus, Jens. Farmer Enno & His Cow. 1998. (Illus.). 32p. (J). (gr. k-4). pap. 14.95 (978-0-531-30081-7(1) , Orchard Bks.) Scholastic, Inc.

Reid, Barbara, illus. El Ternero Recien Nacido. (SPA.). 32p. (J). (ps-1). pap. 4.99 (978-0-590-46106-1(0) , SO30492) Scholastic, Inc.

Rettore, Kenny E. & Rettore, A. S. Cow & Pig. Lyly, Olivia, illus. 2004. (Stroller Softies Ser.). 12p. (J). 11.95 (978-0-7641-7768-2(0)) Barron's Educational Series, Inc.

Rizzati, Lorella. Cow. 2001. (Portable Pets Ser.). (Illus.). 12p. (J). (ps-ps). bds. 6.95 (978-0-8109-5688-9(8)) Abrams, Harry N. , Inc.

Root, Phyllis. Kiss the Cow. Hillenbrand, Will, illus. 2003. 32p. (J). (ps-3). pap. 5.99 (978-0-7636-2003-5(3)) Candlewick Pr.

—Kiss the Cow. 2003. (gr. k-3). lib. bdg. 14.15 (978-0-613-60357-7(5)) Tandem Library Bks.

Rundstrom, T. S. A Herd of Cows Came by My House. Waldron, Drue K. & Stevens, Amber, illus. 2002. 59p. (J). per. 16.00 (978-1-932062-18-2(1)) Hability Solution Services, Inc.

Rundstrom, Teressa. A Herd of Cows Came by My House. Waldron, Drue, illus. 2002. 50p. (J). per. (978-1-932062-39-7(4)) Hability Solution Services, Inc.

Russell, Natalie. Hamish the Highland Cow. 2003. (J). 7.99 (978-1-58234-818-6(9)) Bloomsbury Publishing.

Salan, Felipe Lopez, illus. Jack & the Beanstalk. 2006. 32p. (J). 16.50 (978-1-933327-12-9(X)) Purple Bear Bks., Inc.

Sargent, Dave & Sargent, Pat. Ding Bat: Accuracy, 56 vols., 44. Lenoir, Jane, illus. 2001. (Cherokee Indian Legend Ser.: Vol. 44). 36p. (J). lib. bdg. 19.95 (978-1-56763-529-4(6)) Ozark Publishing.

—Ding Bat: Accuracy, 17 bks, 44. Huff, Jean Lirley, illus. 2000. (Animal Pride Ser.: 44). 42p. (J). pap. 6.95 (978-1-56763-530-0(X)) Ozark Publishing.

—Fancy Fannie: Show Off!, 56 vols., 28. Huff, Jeane, illus. 2001. (Animal Pride Ser.: Vol. 28). 36p. (J). pap. 19.95 (978-1-56763-373-3(0)) Ozark Publishing.

Sastrias, Martha. Queta la Vaca Coqueta. Martinez, Enrique, illus. 2001. (SPA.). 36p. (J). (gr. k-2). (978-968-16-5757-4(8) , FC6144) Fondo de Cultura Economica MEX. *Dist:* Lectorum Pubns., Inc.

Scheunemann, Pam. Cow Licks. Haberstroh, Anne, illus. 2006. (Fact & Fiction Ser.). 24p. (J). 21.35 (978-1-59679-929-5(3) , SandCastle); pap. (978-1-59679-930-1(7)) ABDO Publishing Co.

Schuyer, Silvia. Vaca de Esta Hist. Bernalene, Poly, illus. 2002. Tr. of This Cow's Story. (SPA.). 24p. (J). 12.50 (978-950-08-2569-6(4)) Atlantida ARG. *Dist:* LD Bks., Inc.

Shulman, Mark. Some Cows. Nguyen, Vincent, illus. 2003. (Some Animals Ser.). 24p. (J). 5.95 (978-0-7641-5650-2(0)) Barron's Educational Series, Inc.

Silverman, Erica. Partners. Lewin, Betsy, illus. 2007. (Cowgirl Kate & Cocoa Ser.). 44p. (J). pap. 5.95 (978-0-15-206010-7(3) , Harcourt Paperbacks) Harcourt Children's Bks.

Simmons, Lynn Sheffield. Sugar Lump, the Orphan Calf. 2004. (Illus.). 50p. (YA). pap. 8.95 (978-1-58980-216-2(0)) Pelican Publishing Co., Inc.

Sleepy Brown Cow. (J). (gr. 2-3). 75.00 (978-0-669-13450-6(3)) Houghton Mifflin Co. (Schl. Div.).

Smith. When the Moon Fell Down. Date not set. 32p. (J). (ps up). pap. 4.99 (978-0-06-443550-5(4)) HarperCollins Pubs.

Smith, Mary Ann & Milway, Katie Smith. Cappuccina Goes to Town. Fernandes, Eugenie, illus. 2004. 32p. (J). (gr. k-3). (978-1-55337-686-6(2)) Kids Can Pr., Ltd.

Smith, Mary Ann, et al. Cappuccina Goes to Town. Fernandes, Eugenie, illus. unabr. ed. 2002. 32p. (J). (gr. k-3). (978-1-55074-807-9(6)) Kids Can Pr., Ltd.

Smith, Nicole. Cody the Allergic Cow: A Children's Story of Milk Allergies. 2004. 26p. (J). 15.00 (978-1-58628-051-2(1)) Allergic Child Publishing Group.

Smith, Todd Aaron. Cow & the Christmas Surprise. Smith, Todd Aaron, illus. 2003. (Cows Adventure Ser.). (Illus.). 32p. (J). (gr. k-2). 7.99 (978-0-8010-4517-2(7)) Baker Publishing Group.

—Cow Finds a Friend. 2003. (Cows Adventure Ser.). (Illus.). 32p. (J). (gr. k-2). 7.99 (978-0-8010-4516-5(9)) Baker Publishing Group.

—Cow Goes for a Ride. 2002. (Cows Adventure Ser.). (Illus.). 32p. (ps-2). 7.99 (978-0-8010-4504-2(5) , New Kids Media) Baker Bks.

—Cow in the Rain. 2002. (Cows Adventure Ser.). (Illus.). 32p. (J). (ps-2). 7.99 (978-0-8010-4503-5(7) , New Kids Media) Baker Bks.

—Cow Makes a Difference. Smith, Todd Aaron, illus. 2001. (Cows Adventure Ser.). (Illus.). 32p. (ps-2). 7.99 (978-0-8010-4475-5(8)) Baker Bks.

Spinelli Eileen. Something to Tell the Grandcows. Slavin Bill, illus. 2006. 32p. (J). pap. 8.00 (978-0-8028-5304-2(8) , Eerdmans Bks For Young Readers) Eerdmans, William B. Publishing Co.

Steffensmeier, Alexander. Millie Waits for the Mail. Steffensmeier, Alexander, illus. 2007. (Illus.). 32p. (J). (gr. k-2). 16.95 ***(978-0-8027-9662-2(1));*** 17.85 ***(978-0-8027-9663-9(X))*** Walker & Co.

Taylor, Marshall, illus. & photos by. Adventures of Cow. Taylor, Marshall, photos by. 2005. 32p. (J). 12.95 (978-1-58246-139-7(2) , Tricycle Pr.) Ten Speed Pr.

—Adventures of Cow, Too. Taylor, Marshall, photos by. 2007. 32p. (J). (ps-1). 12.95 (978-1-58246-189-2(9) , Tricycle Pr.) Ten Speed Pr.

Toms, Kate. I Udderly Love You. 2007. (Illus.). 25p. (ps). per., bds. 7.95 (978-1-84610-460-2(2)) Make Believe Ideas GBR. *Dist:* Ingram Pub. Services.

Townsend, Una Belle. Grady's in the Silo. Artley, Bob, illus. 2003. 32p. (J). 15.95 (978-1-58980-098-4(2)) Pelican Publishing Co., Inc.

Vail, Rachel. Over the Moon. Nash, Scott, illus. 32p. (J). (ps-2). 2001. pap. 5.95 (978-0-531-07184-7(7)); 1998. 16.99 (978-0-531-33068-5(0)); 1998. pap. 15.95 (978-0-531-30068-8(4)) Scholastic, Inc. (Orchard Bks.).

Vanderwerff, Corrine. Lucy, the Curiously Comical Cow. 1998. (Julius & Friends Ser.: Vol. 5). (J). 6.99 (978-0-8163-1582-6(5)) Pacific Pr. Publishing Assn.

Weidt, Maryann N. Daddy Played Music for the Cows. Sorensen, Henri, illus. 2nd ed. 2004. 32p. (J). pap. 7.95 (978-0-89317-060-8(7) , WW-0607, Windward Publishing) Finney Co., Inc.

Weis, Carol. When the Cows Got Loose. Hoyt, Ard, illus. 2006. 40p. (J). (ps-1). 16.95 (978-0-689-85166-7(9)) Simon & Schuster Children's Publishing.

Wheeler, Lisa. Sixteen Cows. Cyrus, Kurt, illus. 32p. (J). (ps-2). 2002. 16.00 (978-0-15-202676-9(2)); 2006. reprint ed. pap. 6.00 (978-0-15-205592-9(4) , Voyager Bks./Libros Viajeros) Harcourt Children's Bks.

Whishaw, Iona. Henry & the Cow Problem. McLeod, Chum, illus. 2003. (Annikins Ser.: Vol. 12). 24p. (J). (ps-1). pap. 0.99 (978-1-55037-254-0(8)) Annick Pr., Ltd. CAN. *Dist:* Firefly Bks., Ltd.

Willever, Lisa Funari. Everybody Moos at Cows: Even Matthew McFarland. Poller, Elaine & Byrne, Glenn, illus. 2001. (Tales of Matthew McFarland Ser.). 32p. (ps-3). 11.95 (978-0-9679227-0-6(4) , 329-004) Franklin Mason Pr.

Willis, Jeanne. Misery Moo. Ross, Tony, illus. rev. ed. 2005. 32p. (J). 16.95 (978-0-8050-7672-1(7)) Holt, Henry & Co.

Wilson, Karma. Sakes Alive! A Cattle Drive. Firehammer, Karla, illus. 2005. (J). (ps-3). 32p. 15.99 (978-0-316-98841-4(3)); (**978-1-4156-0890-6(3)*) Little Brown & Co.

Woodworth, Viki. Daisy the Dancing Cow. Woodworth, Viki, illus. 2003. (Illus.). 32p. (J). (gr. k-2). 15.95 (978-1-59078-059-6(0)) Boyds Mills Pr.

—Daisy the FireCow. 2003. (Illus.). 32p. (J). (gr. k-2). 15.95 (978-1-56397-934-7(9)) Boyds Mills Pr.

Yorinks, Arthur. The Floating Cow & Other Stories. 2000. (J). (978-0-439-09255-5(8)) Scholastic, Inc.

Young, James. The Cows Are in the Corn. 2001. (Hello Reader! Ser.). (Illus.). (J). 10.79 (978-0-606-21125-3(X)) Tandem Library Bks.

Ziefert, Harriet & Taback, Simms. Who Said Moo? 2002. (Lift-the-Flap Bks.). (Illus.). 8p. bds. 7.95 (978-1-929766-47-5(5)) Blue Apple Bks.

Zullo, Germano. Marta & the Bicycle. Albertine, illus. 2002. 28p. (J). (gr. k-3). 14.95 (978-1-929132-35-5(2)) Kane/Miller Bk. Pubs., Inc.

COYOTES

Barret & Allen. El Coyote. 2002. (Perros Salvajes Serie).Tr. of Wild Dogs: The Coyote. (SPA.). 24p. (J). (gr. 3-5). 22.45 (978-1-4103-0013-3(7) , Blackbirch Pr., Inc.) Thomson Gale.

Bradley, James V. The Coyote. 2006. (Nature Walk Ser.). (Illus.). 64p. (J). 28.00 (978-0-7910-9114-2(7) , Chelsea Hse.) Facts On File, Inc.

The Coyote. (Wildlife of North America Ser.). 48p. (YA). 7.95 (978-0-7368-8485-3(8)) Capstone Pr., Inc.

The Coyote, 6 vols. (gr. 4 up). 39.95 (978-0-7368-8497-6(1)) Red Brick Learning.

Coyotes: Level J. Group 2. (Story Box(R) Ser.). 16p. 31.50 (978-0-322-02461-8(7)) Wright Group, The.

Dennard, Deborah. Coyote at Pinon Place. Genzo, John Paul, illus. 1999. (Smithsonian's Backyard Ser.: No. 18). 32p. (J). (ps-2). 15.95 (978-1-56899-767-4(1) , B5018) Soundprints.

Dunlap, Julie. Coyotes. Recher, Andrew, illus. 2007. 48p. (**978-1-55971-982-7(6)* , NorthWord Bks. for Young Readers) T&N Children's Publishing.

Dunlap, Julie & Vogel, Julia. Coyotes. Recher, Andrew, illus. 2007. 48p. (J). pap. (**978-1-55971-983-4(4)* , NorthWord Bks. for Young Readers) T&N Children's Publishing.

Gentle, Victor & Perry, Janet. Coyotes. 2002. (Imagination Library). (Illus.). 24p. (J). (gr. 2 up). lib. bdg. 22.00 (978-0-8368-3095-8(4)) Stevens, Gareth Inc.

Hodge, Deborah. Wild dogs: Wolves, coyotes & foxes. Stephens, Pat, illus. unabr. ed. 2004. (Kids Can Press Wildlife Ser.). 32p. (J). (gr. k-3). (978-1-55074-420-0(8)) Kids Can Pr., Ltd.

Hyman, Teresa L. Coyotes. 2003. (Nature's Predators Ser.). (Illus.). 48p. (J). 26.20 (978-0-7377-1886-7(2) , Greenhaven Pr., Inc.) Thomson Gale.

Lee, Sandra. Coyotes. 2006. (New Naturebooks). (Illus.). 32p. (J). (gr. 1-5). 27.07 (978-1-59296-634-9(9)) Child's World, Inc.

Macken, JoAnn Early. Coyotes. 2005. (Illus.). 24p. (J). pap. (978-0-8368-4833-5(0)); lib. bdg. 19.33 (978-0-8368-4826-7(8)) Stevens, Gareth Inc.

—Coyotes: Coyotes. 2005. (ENG & SPA., Illus.). 24p. (J). pap. (978-0-8368-4847-2(0)) Stevens, Gareth Inc.

—Coyotes/ Coyotes. 2005. (ENG & SPA., Illus.). 24p. (J). (ps-17). lib. bdg. 19.33 (978-0-8368-4840-3(3)) Stevens, Gareth Inc.

Mara, Wil. Coyotes. 2008. (J). (**978-0-7614-2928-9(X)*) Cavendish, Marshall Bks., Ltd.

Mattern, Joanne. The Coyote. 1998. (Wildlife of North America Ser.). (Illus.). 48p. (J). (gr. 3-4). lib. bdg. 21.26 (978-0-7368-0029-7(8) , Capstone High-Interest Bks.) Capstone Pr., Inc.

—Coyotes Are Night Animals. 2006. (Illus.). 24p. (J). pap. (**978-0-8368-7854-7(X)*); lib. bdg. (**978-0-8368-7847-9(7)*) Stevens, Gareth Inc. (Weekly Reader Early Learning Library).

—Coyotes Are Night Animals: Los Coyotes Son Animales Nocturnos. 2006. (ENG & SPA., Illus.). 24p. (J). pap. (**978-0-8368-8051-9(X)*); lib. bdg. (**978-0-8368-8044-1(7)*) Stevens, Gareth Inc. (Weekly Reader Early Learning Library).

McDermott, Gerald. Coyote: A Trickster Tale from the American Southwest. 1999. (Illus.). 32p. (J). pap. 7.00 (978-0-15-201958-7(8) , Harcourt Paperbacks) Harcourt Children's Bks.

—Coyote: A Trickster Tale from the American Southwest. 1999. (gr. k-3). lib. bdg. 15.30 (978-0-613-18244-7(8)) Tandem Library Bks.

Murdico, Suzanne J. Coyote Attacks. 2000. (High Interest Bks.). (Illus.). 48p. (YA). (gr. 7-12). pap. 6.95 (978-0-516-23513-4(3) , Children's Pr.) Scholastic Library Publishing.

—Coyote Attacks. 2000. (gr. 7-12). lib. bdg. 15.25 (978-0-613-52015-7(7)) Tandem Library Bks.

Murphy, Patricia J. Coyotes. Saunders-Smith, Gail, ed. 2004. (Grassland Animals Ser.). (Illus.). 24p. (J). (gr. k-1). lib. bdg. 15.93 (978-0-7368-2072-1(8) , Pebble Bks.) Capstone Pr., Inc.

Murphy, Stuart J. Coyotes All Around. Bjorkman, Steve, illus. 2003. (MathStart Ser.). 40p. (J). (gr. 1 up). 15.99 (978-0-06-051529-4(5)); pap. 5.99 (978-0-06-051531-7(7)) HarperCollins Pubs.

—Coyotes All Around. 2003. (gr. k-3). lib. bdg. 13.00 (978-0-613-68415-6(X)) Tandem Library Bks.

Perry, Phyllis J. Crafty Canines: Coyotes, Foxes & Wolves. 1999. (Watts Library). (Illus.). 64p. (J). (gr. 5-7). 25.50 (978-0-531-11680-7(8) ; Watts, Franklin) Scholastic Library Publishing.

—Crafty Canines: Coyotes, Foxes, & Wolves. 1999. (gr. 3-6). lib. bdg. 17.60 (978-0-613-29416-4(5)) Tandem Library Bks.

Swanson, Diane. Coyotes. 2002. (Welcome to the World of Animals Ser.). (Illus.). 32p. (J). (gr. 3 up). lib. bdg. 23.33 (978-0-8368-3313-3(9)) Stevens, Gareth Inc.

—Coyotes. 2003. (gr. k-3). lib. bdg. 14.10 (978-0-613-78511-2(8)) Tandem Library Bks.

—Welcome to the World of Coyotes. 2001. (Welcome to the World Ser.). (Illus.). 32p. (J). (ps-2). 9.95 (978-1-55285-308-5(X)); pap. 5.95 (978-1-55285-258-3(X)) Whitecap Bks., Ltd. CAN. *Dist:* Firefly Bks., Ltd.

Swinburne, Stephen R. Coyote: North America's Dog. 2003. (Illus.). 32p. (YA). (gr. 4-6). 15.95 (978-1-56397-765-7(6)) Boyds Mills Pr.

Webster, Christine. Coyotes. 2007. (J). (**978-1-59036-673-8(5)*); (**978-1-59036-674-5(3)*) Weigl Pubs., Inc.

Whitehouse, Patricia. El Coyote. 2003. (Que Esta Despierto? (What's Awake? Ser.).Tr. of Coyotes. (SPA.). 24p. (J). (ps-1). lib. bdg. 17.08 (978-1-4034-0394-0(5)) Heinemann Library.

—El coyote. 2003. (¿Qué esta despierto? Ser.). (SPA., Illus.). 24p. pap. 5.25 (978-1-4034-0635-4(9)) Heinemann Library.

—Coyotes. 2003. (What's Awake? Ser.). (Illus.). 24p. (ps-1). (J). lib. bdg. 17.08 (978-1-58810-879-1(1)); pap. 5.25 (978-1-4034-0626-2(X)) Heinemann Library.

Wolves & Coyotes. (Eyes on Nature Ser.). 32p. (J). (gr. 1). pap. (978-1-882210-57-2(3)) Action Publishing, Inc.

Wolves & Coyotes. (Eyes on Nature Ser.). (Illus.). 32p. (J). (gr. 1 up). 7.95 (978-1-56156-424-8(9)) Kidsbooks, Inc.

COYOTES—FICTION

Beaumont, Karen. Duck, Duck, Goose! (A Coyote's on the Loose!) Aruego, Jose, illus. 2004. 32p. (J). (ps-2). 16.99 (978-0-06-050802-9(7)); lib. bdg. 17.89 (978-0-06-050804-3(3)) HarperCollins Pubs.

Bierhorst, John. Doctor Coyote: A Native American Aesop's Fables. 1998. (J). pap. 5.99 (978-0-87628-341-7(5)) Ctr. for Applied Research in Education, The.

Czernecki, Stefan. Huevos Rancheros. 2001. (SPA., Illus.). 32p. (J). (ps-3). 15.95 (978-1-56656-429-8(8)) Interlink Publishing Group, Inc.

Czernecki, Stefan, illus. Huevos Rancheros. 2002. (SPA.). 32p. (J). (ps-3). 15.95 (978-1-56656-428-1(X)) Interlink Publishing Group, Inc.

De Montano, Marty K. Coyote in Love with a Star. Coffin, Tom, illus. 1998. (Tales of the People Ser.). 30p. (ps up). 14.95 (978-0-7892-0162-1(3)) Abbeville Pr., Inc.

Dennard, Deborah. Coyote at Pinon Place. Genzo, John Paul, illus. 1999. (Smithsonian's Backyard Ser.: No. 18). 32p. (J). (ps-2). 19.95 incl. reel tape (978-1-56899-766-7(3) , BC5018); Includes toy. 9.95 (978-1-56899-765-0(5) , PB5068); Includes toy. 32.95 (978-1-56899-764-3(7)) Soundprints.

—Coyote at Pinon Place: Micro Edition. Genzo, John Paul, illus. 1999. (Smithsonian's Backyard Ser.: Vol. 18). 32p. (J). (ps-2). 4.95 (978-1-56899-763-6(9) , B5068) Soundprints.

Erickson, John R. The Case of the Deadly Ha-Ha Game. 2001. (Hank the Cowdog Ser.: No. 37). (gr. 3-6). lib. bdg. 13.00 (978-0-613-33649-9(6)) Tandem Library Bks.

Garrido, Felipe. El Coyote Tonto. Gonzalez, Francisco, illus. 2003. (Infantil Alfaguara Ser.). (SPA.). 60p. (J). (gr. 3-5). pap. 10.95 (978-968-19-0277-3(7)) Santillana USA Publishing Co., Inc.

Harcourt School Publishers Staff. Coyote: Library Edition. 1999. (Collections Ser.). (Illus.). (J). 4.70 (978-0-15-314331-1(2)) Harcourt Schl. Pubs.

—Coyote & the Butterflies: Library Edition. 1999. (Collections Ser.). (Illus.). (J). 4.70 (978-0-15-314343-4(6)) Harcourt Schl. Pubs.

Hiscock, Bruce. Coyote & Badger: Desert Hunters of the Southwest. 2003. (Illus.). 32p. (J). (gr. 2-4). 15.95 (978-1-56397-848-7(2)) Boyds Mills Pr.

Jenkins, Amanda. Leaf Monster: A Spanish AMER Tale. 2006. 23.00 (**978-1-4108-6176-4(7)*) Benchmark Education Co.

Johnston, Tony. The Tale of Rabbit & Coyote. DePaola, Tomie, illus. 1998. 32p. (J). (ps-ps). pap. 6.99 (978-0-698-11630-6(5) , Putnam Juvenile) Penguin Group (USA) Inc.

—The Tale of Rabbit & Coyote. de Paola, Tomie, illus. 1998. (978-0-606-13834-5(X)) Tandem Library Bks.

Joyce, Jacqueline. Prickly Pete, Cody Coyote & That Bowlegged Horse. DelMar Communication International Staff, tr. 1998. (Illus.). 36p. (Orig.). (J). (ps-4). (SPA.). pap. 7.95 (978-0-9652211-9-1(9) , 11138); pap. 7.95 (978-0-9652211-8-4(0) , 11137) Bear Path, The.

—Why the Coyote Howls at the Moon. Miller, Paul, illus. 1998. 36p. (J). (ps-4). pap. 7.95 (978-1-891317-00-2(8) , 11141) Bear Path, The.

—Why the Coyote Howls at the Moon. DelMar Communications International Staff, tr. Miller, Paul, illus. 1998. (SPA.). 36p. (J). (ps-4). pap. 7.95 (978-1-891317-01-9(6) , 11142) Bear Path, The.

King, Thomas. A Coyote Columbus Story. Monkman, William Kent, illus. 2007. 32p. (J). pap. 6.95 (**978-0-88899-830-9(9)*) Groundwood Bks. CAN. *Dist:* Perseus Distribution.

—Coyote Sings to the Moon. Wales, Johnny, illus. 2002. 40p. (YA). (gr. 1-3). 15.95 (978-1-55868-642-7(8) , West Winds Pr.) Graphic Arts Ctr. Publishing Co.

King, Thomas. Coyote Sings to the Moon. Wales, Johnny, illus. 2008. 36p. pap. 9.95 (**978-1-55263-868-2(5)*) Key Porter Bks. CAN. *Dist:* Perseus Distribution.

Lund, Jillian. Two Cool Coyotes. Lund, Jillian, illus. 2001. (Illus.). 32p. (J). pap. 6.99 (978-0-14-230011-4(X) , Puffin) Penguin Group (USA) Inc.

—Two Cool Coyotes. 2001. (ps-2). lib. bdg. 14.15 (978-0-613-51420-0(3)) Tandem Library Bks.

Mattern, Joanne. The Tricky Garden. 2005. 22.00 (**978-1-4108-4191-9(X)*) Benchmark Education Co.

Mitchell, Susan K. Stone Pizza. Hayes, McNevin, illus. 2007. (J). (**978-1-891795-26-8(0)*) RGU Group, The.

Polette, Keith. Isabel & the Hungry Coyote/Isabel y el Coyote Hambriento. de la Vega, Eida, tr. Szegedy, Esther, illus. 2006. Tr. of Isabel y el coyote Hambriento. (SPA.). (J). 4.99 (978-0-9770906-4-8(7)) Raven Tree Pr.

—Isabel & the Hungry Coyote/Isabel y el Coyote Hambriento. Raven Tree Press Staff, ed. Szegedy, Esther, illus. 2004. Tr. of Isabel y el coyote Hambriento. (SPA.). 32p. (J). 16.95 (978-0-9724973-0-5(7) , 626999) Raven Tree Pr.

Ruurs, Margriet. Emma & the Coyote. Spurll, Barbara, illus. 2001. 24p. (J). pap. 8.95 (978-0-7737-6205-3(1)); 16.95 (978-0-7737-3140-0(7)) Stoddart Kids CAN. *Dist:* Fitzhenry & Whiteside, Ltd.

—Emma & the Coyote. 1999. (gr. k-3). lib. bdg. 16.40 (978-0-613-65091-5(3)) Tandem Library Bks.

Sargent, Dave & Sargent, Pat. Cody Coyote: Don't Play Tricks, 56 vols., 26. Huff, Jeane, illus. 2001. (Animal Pride Ser.: Vol. 26). 36p. (J). lib. bdg. 19.95 (978-1-56763-368-9(4)) Ozark Publishing.

Swinford, Betty. Cry of the Wild. 2004. 192p. (YA). mass mkt. 5.99 (978-1-85792-853-2(9) , Christian Focus) Christian Focus Pubns. GBR. *Dist:* Riverside.

Twinem, Neecy. Baby Coyote Counts. 2004. (New Board Book Ser.).Tr. of Bebe Coyote cuenta. (Illus.). (J). 12p. bds. 5.95 (978-0-87358-852-2(5)); (ENG & SPA., bds. 5.95 (978-0-87358-868-3(1)) Northland Publishing. (Rising Moon Bks. for Young Readers).

Vaughan, Marcia. The Treasure of Ghostwood Gully: A Southwest Mystery. Terry, Will, illus. 2004. 32p. (gr. k-4). 15.95 (978-0-87358-858-4(4) , Rising Moon Bks. for Young Readers) Northland Publishing.

Wallace, Bill. Coyote Autumn. 2002. 208p. (J). pap. 5.99 (978-0-7434-2836-1(6) , Aladdin) Simon & Schuster Children's Publishing.

—Coyote Autumn. 2002. (gr. 3-6). lib. bdg. 13.00 (978-0-613-68225-1(4)) Tandem Library Bks.

Wilson, Elizabeth. Song Dogs. 2003. (gr. 7-12). lib. bdg. 17.60 (978-0-613-78481-8(2)) Tandem Library Bks.

Wilson, Elizabeth & Wilson, Betty. Song Dogs. 2005. (Illus.). 150p. (J). pap. 8.95 (978-1-55050-216-9(6)) Coteau Bks. CAN. *Dist:* Fitzhenry & Whiteside, Ltd.

Wood, Nancy C. Old Coyote. Grafe, Max, illus. 2004. 32p. (J). (gr. k-3). 16.99 (978-0-7636-1544-4(7)) Candlewick Pr.

Woods, Shirley. Black Nell: The Adventures of a Coyote. 2000. (Illus.). (J). 13.75 (978-0-606-21882-5(3)) Tandem Library Bks.

CRABS

Binns, Tristan Boyer. Hermit Crabs. 2004. (Keeping Unusual Pets Ser.). (Illus.). 48p. (J). (gr. 2-4). lib. bdg. 22.80 (978-1-4034-0825-9(4)) Heinemann Library.

Crabs. 2006. (Under the Sea Ser.). 24p. (J). 6.95 (978-0-7368-6132-8(7)) Capstone Pr., Inc.

Crabs, 6 vols. (gr. k-2). 28.95 (978-0-7368-8256-9(1)) Red Brick Learning.

Crabs: Level M, 6 vols. (Wonder Worldtm Ser.). 16p. 34.95 (978-0-7802-2893-1(6)) Wright Group, The.

Crabs Oceans Alive. 2006. (Illus.). 24p. (J). (gr. k-2). 18.50 (**978-0-531-17867-6(6)*) Scholastic Library Publishing.

Doudna, Kelly. Hidden Hermit Crabs. Nobens, C. A., illus. 2007. (Perfect Pets Ser.). 24p. (J). (gr. k-3). lib. bdg. 19.93 (**978-1-59928-751-5(X)* , SandCastle) ABDO Publishing Co.

Douglas, Lloyd G. Crab. 2005. (Ocean Life Ser.). (Illus.). 24p. (J). (ps-2). pap. 4.95 (978-0-516-23740-4(3)); 18.00 (978-0-516-25027-4(2)) Scholastic Library Publishing. (Children's Pr.).

Dunlap, Julie. Extraordinary Horseshoe Crabs. 1999. (Nature Watch Ser.). (Illus.). 48p. (J). (gr. 3-6). lib. bdg. 25.26 (978-1-57505-293-9(8) , Carolrhoda Bks.) Lerner Publishing Group.

Fredericks, Anthony D. In One Tidepool: Crabs, Snails, & Salty Tails. DiRubbio, Jennifer, illus. 2004. (Sharing Nature with Children Book Ser.). 32p. (J). (ps-2). 16.95 (978-1-58469-039-9(9)); pap. 7.95 (978-1-58469-038-2(0)) Dawn Pubns.

Garrow, Linda, illus. Young Naturalist Field Guides, 5 bks. Incl. Berries, Nuts & Seeds. Burns, Diane L. 2000. lib. bdg. 24.67 (978-0-8368-2144-4(0)); Frogs, Toads & Turtles. Burns, Diane L. 1999. lib. bdg. 24.67 (978-0-8368-2145-1(9)); Rabbits, Squirrels & Chipmunks. Boring, Mel. 1999. lib. bdg. 24.67 (978-0-8368-2146-8(7)); Tracks, Scats & Signs. Dendy, Leslie. 1999. lib. bdg. 24.67 (978-0-8368-2147-5(5)); Wildflowers, Blooms & Blossoms. Burns, Diane L. 2000. lib. bdg. 24.67 (978-0-8368-2148-2(3)); 40p. (J). (gr. 3 up). (Illus.). Set lib. bdg. 123.35 (978-0-8368-2658-6(2)) Stevens, Gareth Inc.

Gilpin, Daniel. Lobsters, Crabs & Other Crustaceans. 2006. (Animal Kingdom Classification Ser.). (Illus.). 48p. (J). (gr. 4-6). 26.60 (978-0-7565-1612-3(9)) Compass Point Bks.

Greenaway, Theresa. Crabs. 2001. (Secret World Of... Ser.). (Illus.). 48p. (J). (gr. 4-7). lib. bdg. 27.12 (978-0-7398-3506-7(8)) Raintree.

Group/McGraw-Hill, Wright. Crabs & Frogs: Decodable Books, 6 vols. (Fasttrack Reading Ser.). 24p. (gr. 4-8). 40.95 (978-0-322-05989-4(5)) Wright Group, The.

Hall, David, photos by & text. Crabs. Hall, David, text. 2006. (Undersea Encounters Ser.). (Illus.). 48p. (J). (gr. 3-5). 27.00 (978-0-516-24390-0(X) , Children's Pr.) Scholastic Library Publishing.

Herriges, Ann. Crabs. 2006. (Blastoff! Readers Ser.). (Illus.). 24p. (J). lib. bdg. 16.95 (978-1-60014-016-7(5)) Bellwether Media.

Hollenbeck, Kathleen M. Dancing on the Sand: A Story of an Atlantic Blue Crab. Popeo, Joanie, illus. 1999. (Smithsonian Oceanic Collection: Vol. 17). (J). (ps-2). 32p. 15.95 (978-1-56899-730-8(2) , B4017); 32p. 19.95 incl. reel tape (978-1-56899-732-2(9) , BC4017); 32p. 34.95 incl. audio (978-1-56899-736-0(1)); 32p. 14.95 incl. audio (978-1-56899-737-7(X)); 31p. 4.95 (978-1-56899-731-5(0) , B4067); 32p. 29.95 (978-1-56899-734-6(5)); 32p. 9.95 incl. audio (978-1-56899-733-9(7)) Soundprints.

—Dancing on the Sand: A Story of an Atlantic Blue Crab, Includes Micro Toy, Popeo, Joanie, illus. 1999. (Smithsonian Oceanic Collection: Vol. 17). 32p. (J). (ps-2). 9.95 (978-1-56899-735-3(3) , PB4067) Soundprints.

Lewis, Brenda Ralph. Crabs & Mollusks. 2006. (Nature's Monsters Ser.). (Illus.). 32p. (J). lib. bdg. 23.33 (978-0-8368-6176-1(0)) Stevens, Gareth Inc.

Lunis, Natalie. Crawling Crabs. 2008. (J). lib. bdg. 21.28 (**978-1-59716-509-9(3)*) Bearport Publishing Co., Inc.

Morgan, Sally. Crabs & Crustaceans. 2001. (Illus.). 32p. (J). lib. bdg. 24.25 (978-1-930643-11-6(X)) Chrysalis Education.

Nelson, Robin. Pet Hermit Crab. (First Step Nonfiction). (J). (gr. k-2). 2003. (Illus.). 24p. lib. bdg. 18.60 (978-0-8225-1270-7(X)); 2002. pap. 3.95 (978-0-8225-1314-8(5)) Lerner Publishing Group.

Pascoe, Elaine. Crabs. Kuhn, Dwight, photos by. 2005. (Nature Close-up Ser.). (Illus.). 48p. (J). (ps-7). lib. bdg. 24.95 (978-1-4103-0535-0(X) , Blackbirch Pr., Inc.) Thomson Gale.

Richardson, Adele. Caring for Your Hermit Crab. 2007. (First Facts Ser.). (Illus.). 24p. (J). (gr. k-3). lib. bdg. 21.26 (978-0-7368-6388-9(5)) Capstone Pr., Inc.

Rizzati, Lorella. Crab. 1998. (Portable Pets Ser.). (Illus.). 12p. (J). (ps). bds. 5.95 (978-0-8109-5675-9(6)) Abrams, Harry N., Inc.

Schaefer, Lola M. El Cangrejo Bayoneta. 2002. (Animales Acorazados (Musty-Crusty Animals) Ser.). (SPA.). 24p. (J). (ps-1). lib. bdg. 18.50 (978-1-58810-774-9(4)); (Illus.). pap. 5.25 (978-1-58810-818-0(X) , 91558) Heinemann Library.

—El Cangrejo de Rio. 2002. (Animales Acorazados (Musty-Crusty Animals) Ser.). (SPA.). 24p. (J). (ps-1). lib. bdg. 18.50 (978-1-58810-772-5(8)); (Illus.). pap. 5.25 (978-1-58810-816-6(3) , 91559) Heinemann Library.

—El Cangrejo Ermitano. 2002. (Animales Acorazados (Musty-Crusty Animals) Ser.). (SPA.). 24p. (J). (ps-1). lib. bdg. 18.50 (978-1-58810-773-2(6)); (Illus.). pap. 5.25 (978-1-58810-817-3(1) , 91560) Heinemann Library.

—Crabs. 2005. (Ocean Life Ser.). 24p. (YA). (gr. k-3). pap. (978-0-7368-8216-3(2) , Pebble Bks.) Capstone Pr., Inc.

—Hermit Crabs. 2002. (Musty-Crusty Animals Ser.). (Illus.). 24p. (J). (ps-1). pap. 5.25 (978-1-58810-723-7(X) , 91375); lib. bdg. 17.08 (978-1-58810-514-1(8)) Heinemann Library.

Smith, Rebecca. Crabbing Time. Friar, Joanne, illus. 1999. (Books for Young Learners). 12p. (J). (gr. k-2). pap. 5.00 (978-1-57274-132-4(5)) Owen, Richard C. Pubs., Inc.

Steck-Vaughn Staff. Early Reader Program Level B: King Crab Is Coming, 6 Pack. 2004. (Illus.). pap. 33.00 (978-0-7398-8255-9(4)) Steck-Vaughn.

Sullivan, Jody. Crabs. 2005. (Illus.). 24p. (J). (ps-7). lib. bdg. 19.93 (978-0-7368-4269-3(1)) Capstone Pr., Inc.

Swain, Cynthia. The Crab. 2003. (BuildUp Ser.). (J). pap. 22.00 (978-1-4108-0746-5(0)) Benchmark Education Co.

Vining, Cindy. Crabs Are Crustaceans. 1998. (Illus.). 50p. (J). (ps-3). pap. 4.95 (978-0-9659436-0-4(7)) Omma Publishing.

World Book, Inc Staff, contrib. by. Purple Pinchers & Other Hermit Crabs. 2007. (World Book's Animals of the World Ser.). (Illus.). 64p. (J). (978-0-7166-1333-6(6)) World Bk., Inc.

CRABS—FICTION

Aloha Potter! Evaluation Guide: Evaluation Guide. 2006. (J). (978-1-55942-397-7(8)) Marsh Media.

Berkowitz, Henry. Irving, The Hermit Crab. Berkowitz, Henry, illus. 2000. (Illus.). 32p. (J). (gr. k-3). pap. 3.95 (978-0-932855-59-6(8)) Winner Enterprises.

—Irving, the Hermit Crab Visits Atlantis: A Storyteller Coloring Book. Berkowitz, Henry, illus. 2002. (Illus.). 32p. (J). (gr. k-3). pap. 4.95 (978-0-932855-70-1(9)) Winner Enterprises.

Blue Crab's Dance. 2002. (Oceanic Mini Bks.). (Illus.). 32p. (J). (978-1-59069-002-4(8) , H1003) Studio Mouse LLC.

Blumenthal, Bliss & Alarcon, Claudia. Wiley's Way: El Camino de Wiley. Gonzalez, Ricky & Gonzalez, Crysol, illus. 2004. (ENG & SPA.). 112p. pap. 9.95 (978-0-292-70615-6(4)) Univ. of Texas Pr.

Boyce, Katie. Hector the Hermit Crab. Boyce, Katie, illus. 2003. (Illus.). 32p. (J). (ps-1). 15.95 (978-1-58234-800-1(6) , Bloomsbury Children) Bloomsbury Publishing.

Bracken, Carolyn. Gets Crabby. Earhart, Kristin, ed. 2006. (Msb Science Reader Ser.). (Illus.). 32p. (J). pap. 3.99 (978-0-439-68403-3(X) , Scholastic) Scholastic, Inc.

Burgess, Karin Whiting. It's Always a Good Day for Crabbing. 2005. (J). 16.95 (978-0-9718303-4-9(7)) Flat Hammock Pr.

The Careful Crab. 2003. (J). per. (978-1-57657-935-0(2)) Paradise Pr., Inc.

Carle, Eric. A House for a Hermit Crab. Carle, Eric, illus. 2002. (Illus.). (J). 25.11 (978-0-7587-2754-1(2)) Book Wholesalers, Inc.

—A House for a Hermit Crab. Carle, Eric, illus. (Stories to Go! Ser.). (Illus.). 32p. (J). 2005. 4.99 (978-1-4169-0309-3(7) , Aladdin); 2004. bds. 8.99 (978-0-689-87064-4(7) , Little Simon); 2002. pap. 7.99 (978-0-689-84894-0(3) , Aladdin) Simon & Schuster Children's Publishing.

—A House for a Hermit Crab. 2002. (gr. k-3). lib. bdg. 15.30 (978-0-613-90187-1(8)) Tandem Library Bks.

Christie, Jean. Charlie Crab: Inflatable Bath Book. Canals, Sonia, illus. 2003. 7p. (J). 6.95 (978-1-4027-0447-5(X)) Sterling Publishing Co., Inc.

Clarke, Jane. Sherman Swaps Shells. Parker, Ant, illus. (Flying Foxes Ser.). 48p. (J). 2004. pap. (978-0-7787-1531-3(0)); 2003. (978-0-7787-1485-9(3)) Crabtree Publishing Co.

Cogdill, Jill K., illus. Cracker the Crab & the Sideways Afternoon. 2003. 40p. (J). lib. bdg. 19.95 (978-0-9725560-0-2(1)) Cracker the Crab LLC.

A Crab Called Mouse. 2006. (J). pap. 9.50 (*978-0-9787995-2-6(6)*) High-Pitched Hum Inc.

Cummings, Priscilla. Meet Chadwick & His Chesapeake Bay Friends. Cohen, A. R., illus. 1999. 30p. (J). (ps-3). 11.95 (978-0-87033-516-7(2) , Tidewater Pubs.) Cornell Maritime Pr., Inc.

Dancing on the Sand: A Story of an Atlantic Blue Crab. 2005. (Illus.). 32p. (J). (ps-2). 6.95 (978-1-59249-194-0(4) , S4017) Soundprints.

Doudna, Kelly. Crab Cakes. Haberstroh, Anne, illus. (Fact & Fiction Ser.). 24p. (J). 2007. 21.35 (978-1-59928-434-7(0)); 2006. (978-1-59928-435-4(9)) ABDO Publishing Co.

Douglas, Vincent & School Specialty Publishing Staff. Clarence Crab. 2006. (Bath Buddies Ser.). 7p. (J). 12.95 (978-0-7696-4596-4(8) , Brighter Child) School Specialty Publishing.

Fisk, Scott. Herman the Homeless Hermit Crab. 2004. 17p. 7.99 (978-1-4116-1770-4(3)) Lulu.com.

Galloway, Ruth. Clumsy Crab. Galloway, Ruth, illus. (Illus.). (J). 2007. pap. 6.95 (978-1-58925-402-2(3)); 2005. 28p. 15.95 (978-1-58925-050-5(8)) ME Media LLC. (tiger tales).

Garrido, Maria Teresa. Bernardo el Ermitano. (SPA.). (J). 7.95 (978-958-04-6487-7(1)) Norma S.A. COL. *Dist:* Distribuidora Norma, Inc.

Golden, Marcellus. The Fabulous Crabulous Family in Pee-Wee Learns about Moving. Golden, Marcellus, illus. 2004. (Illus.). 51p. (J). (gr. 2-5). pap. 12.95 (978-1-4137-2341-0(1)) PublishAmerica, Inc.

Goldy, Lynnette Godfrey. The Adventures of Periwinkle the Crab. 2000. 60p. (J). pap. 14.95 (978-1-58851-301-4(7)) PublishAmerica, Inc.

Guilfoyle, Kim. Why Do You Love Me? 2007. (J). per. 9.99 (*978-1-59886-980-4(9)*) Tate Publishing & Enterprises, L.L.C.

Hohenthal, K. D. Herman Goes Home: A Duffy Family Adventure. 2003. (Illus.). 46p. (J). per. 15.95 (978-0-9716907-3-8(1) , Ridgewood Publishing) Ridgewood Group, The.

Hollenbeck, Kathleen M. Dancing on the Sand: A Story of an Atlantic Blue Crab. 2005. (Illus.). 32p. (J). (ps-2). 8.95 incl. audio (978-1-59249-234-3(7) , SC4017) Soundprints.

—Dancing on the Sand: A Story of an Atlantic Blue Crab. Popeo, Joanie, illus. 1999. (Smithsonian Oceanic Collection: Vol. 17). 32p. (J). (ps-2). 19.95 incl. reel tape (978-1-56899-732-2(9) , BC4017) Soundprints.

Horowitz, Ruth. Crab Moon. Kiesler, Kate, illus. 2004. (Read & Wonder Ser.). 32p. (J). (gr. 1-4). pap. 6.99 (978-0-7636-2313-5(X)) Candlewick Pr.

Itoh, Shimpei. Hyper Dolls, Vol. 5. 2003. (Illus.). 208p. pap. 15.95 (978-1-929090-67-9(6)) International Comics & Entertainment L.L.C.

Kline, Trish & Donev, Mary. It's a Party! KA Reader 2. 2007. (Illus.). 32p. (J). per. 20.00 (*978-0-9717234-3-6(5)*) Ghost Hunter Productions.

Leaney, Cindy. On the Beach. Whitehouse, Patty, ed. King, Sue & Wilks, Peter, illus. 2004. (Friendly Phonics Ser.). 24p. (J). lib. bdg. 14.95 (978-1-59054-108-1(1)) Fitzgerald Bks.

Lewis, Paul Owen. Grasper. 1999. (gr. 3-6). lib. bdg. 16.40 (978-0-613-70971-2(3)) Tandem Library Bks.

—Grasper: A Young Crab's Discovery. 2004. (Illus.). 32p. (J). (gr. k-3). 8.95 (978-1-883672-98-0(8) , Tricycle Pr.) Ten Speed Pr.

Lyday, Kevin J. Albert's Shell. 2004. 32p. pap. 17.95 (978-1-4137-3158-3(9)) PublishAmerica, Inc.

Moore, Sherry. The Crab Is Back in Town. 2007. (J). per. (*978-1-894936-78-1(7)*) Saga Bks.

Moore, Sherry. Dude; You're a Crab! 2006. (YA). per. (978-1-894936-41-5(8)) Saga Bks.

Patterson, Christine. Calvin Crab's Magical Wish. 2004. 9p. (J). per. 8.88 (978-1-4116-0673-9(6)) Lulu.com.

Reasoner, Charles. I'm Just a Crab. Reasoner, Charles, illus. 2007. 12p. (J). (ps). bds. 7.99 (*978-1-84666-291-1(5)* , Tide Mill Pr.) Top That! Publishing PLC GBR. *Dist:* Random Hse., Inc.

Santillo, LuAnn. The Bad Crab. Santillo, LuAnn, ed. 2003. (Half-Pint Kids Readers Ser.). (Illus.). 7p. (J). (ps-1). pap. (978-1-59256-094-3(6)) Half-Pint Kids, Inc.

Shimberg, Elaine Fantle. Herman, the Hermit Crab. Walling, Sandy Seeley, illus. l.t. ed. 2007. 28p. (J). 7.95 (*978-0-9741940-2-8(6)*) Abernathy Hse. Publishing.

Stack, Richard L. Steamer & Shelly Go to Pot. Word, Reagan, illus. 2001. (Steamer & Shelly Ser.: Vol. 1). 32p. (J). per. 13.95 (978-0-9628262-9-0(4)) Windmill Pr.

Talley, Linda. Aloha Potter! - hardcover Book. Chase, Andra, illus. 2004. 30p. (J). (978-1-55942-200-0(9)) Marsh Media.

ToyBox Innovations, creator. Disney's Princess Little Mermaid. abr. ed. 2006. (Disney's Read along Collection). (J). (ps-3). pap. 14.99 incl. audio compact disk (978-0-7634-2184-7(7)) Walt Disney Records.

Trimble, Marcia. P. Hermit Claims a Castle. Ulrich, George, illus. 1999. 32p. (J). (ps-3). 15.95 (978-1-891577-44-4(1)) Images Pr.

Van West, Patricia E. The Crab Man. Lucas, Cedric, illus. 40p. (J). (ps-3). 2001. pap. 8.95 (978-1-890515-25-6(6)); 1998. 15.95 (978-1-890515-08-9(6)) Turtle Bks.

Voyage to Shelter Cove. 2006. (Illus.). (J). pap., act. bk. ed. 2.00 (978-0-9724425-5-8(3) , White Tiger Pr.) Homes for the Homeless, Inc.

Walsh, Ellen Stoll. Hamsters to the Rescue. 2005. (Illus.). 40p. (J). (ps-1). 16.00 (978-0-15-205202-7(X)) Harcourt Trade Pubs.

Watkins, Dawn L. Very Like a Star/The Cranky Blue Crab, 2 vols. 2000. (Illus.). (J). (ps-3). pap. 14.98 incl. audio (978-0-89084-902-6(1) , 100073) Jones, Bob Univ. Pr.

Weathers, Andrea. Hermy the Hermit Crab: The Adventure Begins. 2004. (J). pap. 15.99 (978-0-933101-22-7(8)) Legacy Pubns.

—Hermy the Hermit Crab Goes Shopping. Thames, Bob, illus. 2001. 40p. (J). 15.99 (978-0-933101-20-3(1)) Legacy Pubns.

Whatley, Bruce. Looking for Crabs. Whatley, Bruce, illus. 1999. (Illus.). 81p. (J). (ps-3). pap. 7.00 (978-0-207-17771-2(6)) HarperCollins Pubs.

Williams, Jonnie. Harry the Hopetown Hermit Crab. Kanitsch, Christine, illus. Date not set. (Abaco Ser.). (J). (ps-3). pap. 5.97 (978-0-9657849-1-7(6)) Island Ink.

Wood, Audrey. King Bidgood's in the Bathtub. Wood, Audrey, illus. 2002. (Illus.). (J). 23.40 (978-0-7587-0126-8(8)) Book Wholesalers, Inc.

CRADLE SONGS

see Lullabies

CRAFTS

see Handicraft

CRANDALL, PRUDENCE, 1803-1890

Jurmain, Suzanne. The Forbidden Schoolhouse: The True & Dramatic Story of Prudence Crandall & Her Students. 2005. (Illus.). 160p. (J). (gr. 5-6). 18.00 (978-0-618-47302-1(5)) Houghton Mifflin Co. Trade & Reference Div.

Lucas, Eileen. Prudence Crandall. Smith, Kimanne, illus. 2001. (On My Own Biographies Ser.). 48p. (J). (gr. 1-3). lib. bdg. (978-1-57505-480-3(9) , Carolrhoda Bks.) Lerner Publishing Group.

—Prudence Crandall: Teacher for Equal Rights. Smith, Kimanne, illus. 2001. (On My Own Biographies Ser.). 48p. (J). (gr. 2-5). pap. 5.95 (978-1-57505-479-7(5) , Carolrhoda Bks.) Lerner Publishing Group.

CRANE, STEPHEN, 1871-1900

Bloom, Harold. Stephen Crane. 2002. (Bloom's BioCritiques Ser.). (Illus.). 112p. (gr. 9-13). 35.00 (978-0-7910-6375-0(5) , 000886, Chelsea Hse.) Facts On File, Inc.

CRANES (BIRDS)

Benchmark Education Staff, compiled by. Bringing Back the Whooping Crane & ¡Vamos a rescatar a la grulla Blanca! 2005. 52.00 (*978-1-4108-4494-1(3)*) Benchmark Education Co.

Campbell, Jane & Hartley, Susan. Bringing Back the Whooping Crane. ed. 2004. (Shared Connections Ser.). (J). pap. 27.00 (978-1-4108-1641-2(9)) ; instr.'s gde. ed. 27.00 (978-1-4108-1617-7(6)) Benchmark Education Co.

Cook, Jean G. & Jimmie, Elsie. How the Crane Got Its Blue Eyes. (Illus.). (J). pap. 11.00 (978-1-55036-505-4(3)) Todd Communications.

Craats, Rennay. Whooping Cranes. 2003. (Endangered Plants & Animals of the United States Ser.). (J). pap. (978-1-58417-211-6(8)) ; lib. bdg. (978-1-58417-210-9(X)) Lake Street Pubs.

Cranes: Big Book: Level M, 6 vols. (Take-Twostm Ser.). 32p. 36.95 (978-0-322-03400-6(0)) Wright Group, The.

DuTemple, Lesley A. North American Cranes. 1999. (Nature Watch Ser.). (Illus.). 48p. (J). (gr. 3-6). lib. bdg. 25.26 (978-1-57505-302-8(0) , Carolrhoda Bks.) Lerner Publishing Group.

Goodman, Susan E. Saving the Whooping Crane. Saroff, Phyllis V., illus. 2007. (On My Own Science Ser.). 48p. (J). (gr. 2-4). lib. bdg. 25.26 (*978-0-8225-6748-6(2)* , Millbrook Pr.) Lerner Publishing Group.

Gray, Susan H. Whooping Crane. 2008. (J). lib. bdg. 25.26 (*978-1-60279-034-6(5)*) Cherry Lake Publishing.

Imbriaco, Alison. The Whooping Crane: Help Save This Endangered Species! 2006. (Saving Endangered Species Ser.). (Illus.). 128p. (J). lib. bdg. 33.27 (978-1-59845-032-3(8) , MyReportLinks.com Bks.) Enslow Pubs., Inc.

CRANES, DERRICKS, ETC.

Bullard, Lisa. Cranes. (Pull Ahead Books). (J). 2007. 22.60 (978-0-8225-6007-4(0) , Lerner Pubns.); 2006. (Illus.). 32p. pap. 5.95 (978-0-8225-5895-8(5) , First Avenue Editions) Lerner Publishing Group.

Dorling Kindersley Publishing Staff. Crane. 2006. (Machines at Work Ser.). 32p. (J). pap. 6.99 (978-0-7566-2266-4(2)) Dorling Kindersley Publishing, Inc.

Glover, David & Glover, Penny. Cranes. 2005. (Big Machines Ser.). (Illus.). 30p. (J). (gr. 2-5). lib. bdg. 27.10 (978-1-58340-700-4(6)) Smart Apple Media.

Granowsky, Alvin. Diggers & Cranes. 2001. 11.79 (978-0-606-22427-7(0)) Tandem Library Bks.

Martin, M. T. Cranes. 2006. (Blastoff! Readers Ser.). (Illus.). 24p. (J). lib. bdg. 16.95 (978-1-60014-045-7(9)) Bellwether Media.

Randolph, Joanne. Cranes. 2002. (PowerKids Readers Ser.). (Illus.). 24p. (J). (gr. 1). lib. bdg. 16.00 (978-0-8239-6030-9(7) , PowerKids Pr.) Rosen Publishing Group, Inc., The.

Rogers, Hal & Alinas, Marv. Cranes. 2008. (Machines at Work Ser.). 24p. (J). 22.79 (*978-1-59296-949-4(6)*) Child's World, Inc.

Star, Fleur & Dorling Kindersley Publishing Staff. Crane. 2005. (Machines at Work Ser.). (Illus.). 32p. (J). 8.99 (978-0-7566-1271-9(3)) Dorling Kindersley Publishing, Inc.

Wallace, Karen. Big Machines. 2000. (Readers Ser.). (Illus.). 32p. (J). (ps-1). pap. 3.99 (978-0-7894-5411-9(4)) Dorling Kindersley Publishing, Inc.

—Big Machines. 2000. (gr. k-3). lib. bdg. 11.80 (978-0-613-24358-2(7)) ; (Illus.). (J). 10.79 (978-0-606-18114-3(8)) Tandem Library Bks.

Wallace, Karen & Dorling Kindersley Publishing Staff. Big Machines. 2000. (Eyewitness Readers). (Illus.). 32p. (J). (ps-1). 12.99 (978-0-7894-5412-6(2)) Dorling Kindersley Publishing, Inc.

Williams, Linda D. Cranes. (Mighty MacHines Ser.). 24p. (J). pap. 6.95 (978-0-7368-5133-6(X)) Capstone Pr., Inc.

—Cranes. 2004. (Pebble Plus: Mighty Machines Ser.). (Illus.). 24p. (J). lib. bdg. 19.93 (978-0-7368-2595-5(9) , Pebble Bks.) Capstone Pr., Inc.

—Gruas: Cranes. 2006. (Pebble Plus Ser.). (ENG & SPA.). (J). (978-0-7368-5869-4(5)) Capstone Pr., Inc.

Young, Caroline. Diggers & Cranes. rev. ed. 2005. 32p. (J). pap. 6.95 (978-0-7945-0840-1(5) , Usborne) EDC Publishing.

CRANES, DERRICKS, ETC.—FICTION

Bridges, Sarah. I Drive a Crane. Muehlenhardt, Amy Bailey, illus. 2006. (Working Wheels Ser.). 24p. (J). (ps-2). 22.60 (978-1-4048-1605-3(4)) Picture Window Bks.

Fontes, Justine & Grey, Andrew. Working Hard with the Mighty Crane. Petruccio, Steven James, illus. 1998. (Tonka Ser.). 32p. (J). (ps-2). pap. 3.50 (978-0-590-13094-3(3)) Scholastic, Inc.

Iverson, Gregory. Katie's Day. Fritz, Siegfried, illus. 2006. 48p. (J). (*978-0-9755184-1-0(0)*) Sandbox Bks.

McCune, Krisha. Meet Lofty. Hot Animation Staff, Animation, illus. 2003. (Bob the Builder Ser.). 12p. (J). bds. 5.99 (978-0-689-85777-5(2) , Simon Spotlight) Simon & Schuster Children's Publishing.

Sturges, Philemon. I Love Cranes! Halpern, Shari, illus. Date not set. 32p. (J). (ps-1). 5.99 (978-0-06-443666-3(7)) HarperCollins Pubs.

—I Love Planes! Halpern, Shari, illus. 2003. 32p. (J). (ps-1). 15.99 (978-0-06-028898-3(1)) HarperCollins Pubs.

Teitelbaum, Michael. If I Could Drive a Crane! Klavins, Uldis & Walker, Jeff, illus. 2002. (Tonka Ser.). 24p. (J). (ps-3). pap. 3.50 (978-0-439-34174-5(4) , Cartwheel Bks.) Scholastic, Inc.

Titelbaum, Michael & Mada Design Staff. Tonka Tough Trucks. 2006. (Pop & Play Ser.). 10p. (J). bds. 8.99 (978-0-7944-0949-4(0)) Reader's Digest Assn., Inc., The.

Zimnik, Reiner. The Crane. Ignatowicz, Nina, tr. from GER. Zimnik, Reiner, illus. 2003. (New York Review Children's Collection). (Illus.). 96p. (J). pap. 16.95 (978-1-59017-075-5(X) , NYR Children's Collection) New York Review of Bks., Inc., The.

CRAYON DRAWING

see also Pastel Drawing

Big Bear & the Dentist. 2004. (Play Pals Ser.). (Illus.). 12p. (J). bds. (978-1-84229-638-7(8)) Top That! Publishing PLC.

Gibson, Ray. Crayon Activities Pack. 2004. (Activity Kits Ser.). 24p. (J). act. bk. ed. 14.95 (978-0-7945-0457-1(4)) EDC Publishing.

Nelson, Robin. From Wax to Crayon. 2003. (Start to Finish Ser.). (Illus.). 24p. (J). 18.60 (978-0-8225-4660-3(4) , Lerner Pubns.) Lerner Publishing Group.

Schecter, Deborah. Colorful Crayon Art. 2001. (Illus.). 32p. (J). (978-0-439-33618-5(X)) Scholastic, Inc.

—Mix It up with Crayons & Paint. 2002. (Illus.). 32p. (J). (978-0-439-33622-2(8)) Scholastic, Inc.

Woods, Samuel G. Crayons: From Start to Finish. Zucker, Gale, photos by. 1999. (Made in the U. S. A. Ser.). (Illus.). 32p. (J). (gr. 3-6). 23.70 (978-1-56711-390-7(7) , Blackbirch Pr., Inc.) Thomson Gale.

CRAYON DRAWING—FICTION

Cappelli, Susan V. The Crayons in Rainbow Land. Nehrebecki, Robert, Jr., illus. 2005. (J). pap. 9.00 (978-0-8059-6710-4(9)) Dorrance Publishing Co., Inc.

Crockett, Johns. Harold et le crayon Rose. pap. 13.95 (978-2-266-09592-1(7)) Presses Pocket FRA. *Dist:* Distribooks, Inc.

Cyr, Joe. Magical Trees & Crayons: Great Stories. 2006. (Illus.). pap. 9.95 (*978-0-9778525-6-7(3)*) Peppertree Pr., The.

Garfield, Valerie. Harold & the Purple Crayon: The Giant Garden. 2002. (ps-2). lib. bdg. 11.80 (978-0-613-50439-3(9)) Tandem Library Bks.

Gilliland, Judith Heide. Not in the House, Newton! Sayles, Elizabeth, illus. 2002. 32p. (J). (gr. k-3). 5.95 (978-0-618-24619-9(3) , Clarion Bks.) Houghton Mifflin Co. Trade & Reference Div.

—Not in the House, Newton! 2002. (gr. k-3). lib. bdg. 14.10 (978-0-613-72909-3(9)) Tandem Library Bks.

Harcourt School Publishers Staff. The Crayon Box That Talked: Library Book. 3rd ed. 2002. (Trophies Reading Program Ser.). (Illus.). pap. 13.50 (978-0-15-326527-3(2)) Harcourt Schl. Pubs.

Murawski, Kevin, illus. Harold & the Purple Crayon: Race Car. 2004. 32p. (J). (ps-ps). lib. bdg. 10.79 (978-0-606-29918-3(1)) Tandem Library Bks.

—Harold & the Purple Crayon: The Giant Garden. 128p. (J). (978-0-06-059705-4(4)) HarperCollins Pubs.

—Harold & the Purple Crayon: Under the Sea. 2004. 32p. (J). (ps-ps). lib. bdg. 10.79 (978-0-606-29924-4(6)) Tandem Library Bks.

Van Allsburg, Chris. Bad Day at Riverbend. Van Allsburg, Chris, illus. 2002. (Illus.). (J). 25.28 (978-0-7587-2026-9(2)) Book Wholesalers, Inc.

CRAZY HORSE, CA. 1842-1877

Birchfield, D. L. Crazy Horse. 2002. (Raintree Biographies Ser.). (Illus.). 32p. (J). lib. bdg. 25.69 (978-0-7398-5673-4(1)) Raintree.

Brennan, Kristine. Crazy Horse. 2001. (Famous Figures of the American Frontier Ser.). (Illus.). 64p. (J). (gr. 4-7). pap. 25.00 (978-0-7910-6494-8(8)); 25.00 (978-0-7910-6493-1(X)) Facts On File, Inc. (Chelsea Hse.).

Cunningham, Chet. Chief Crazy Horse. 2005. (Biography Ser.). (Illus.). 112p. (gr. 6-12). lib. bdg. 27.93 (978-0-8225-4978-9(6)) Lerner Publishing Group.

Hargrove, Julia. Crazy Horse. Mitchell, Judy, ed. Mohrman, Gary, illus. 2001. (Historic Monuments Ser.). 32p. (J). (gr. 4-8). pap. 5.95 (978-1-57310-310-7(1)) Teaching & Learning Co.

Landau, Elaine. Crazy Horse: American Indian Leader. 2004. (Best of the West Biographies Ser.). (Illus.). 48p. (YA). lib. bdg. 23.93 (978-0-7660-2216-4(1)) Enslow Pubs., Inc.

Oldfield, Jenny. Crazy Horse. 2001. (Illus.). 152p. (J). pap. 9.99 (978-0-340-71618-2(5) , Hodder & Stoughton) Hodder General Publishing Division GBR. *Dist:* Trafalgar Square Publishing.

Stanley, George Edward. Crazy Horse: Young War Chief. Henderson, Meryl, illus. 2005. 199p. (J). (978-1-4156-2931-4(5) , Aladdin) Simon & Schuster Children's Publishing.

Todd, Anne M. Crazy Horse 1842-1877. 2002. (American Indian Biographies Ser.). (Illus.). 32p. (J). (gr. 3-4). lib. bdg. 23.93 (978-0-7368-1210-8(5) , Blue Earth Bks.) Capstone Pr., Inc.

CREATION

see also Earth; Evolution; Geology; God; Human Beings; Mythology; Theology; Universe

Alexander, Cecil Frances. All Things Bright & Beautiful. Vojtech, Anna, illus. ed. 2006. 24p. (J). (ps-2). pap. 6.95 (978-0-7358-2045-6(7)) North-South Bks., Inc.

Alexander, Pat. What a Wonderful World! A Special Collection. Ashton-Jewell, Pythia, illus. 1998. 192p. (J). pap. 27.50 (978-0-7459-3831-8(0) , Lion) Lion Hudson plc GBR. *Dist:* Independent Pubs. Group.

All Things Bright & Beautiful. 2006. 16p. (J). pap. 1.99 (978-0-7847-1588-8(2) , 22135) Standard Publishing.

Audia, John P. The Creation Story: In Words & Sign Language. Spohn, David, illus. 2007. (J). (*978-0-8146-3174-4(6)*) Liturgical Pr.

Bicknell, Joanna. Creation Story. 2007. (Shiny, Touchy, Smelly Ser.). (Illus.). 12p. (ps-k). per., bds. 9.95 (*978-1-84610-463-3(7)*) Make Believe Ideas GBR. *Dist:* Ingram Pub. Services.

Boroson, Martin. Becoming Me: A Story of Creation. Gilvan-Cartwright, Chris, illus. 2000. (SkyLight Lives Ser.). 32p. (J). (ps-3). 16.95 (978-1-893361-11-9(X)) SkyLight Paths Publishing.

Bostrom, Kathleen Long. Song of Creation. 2003. (Illus.). 32p. (J). 12.95 (978-0-664-22418-9(0)) Westminster John Knox Pr.

Bostrom, Kathleen Long & Kucharik, Elena. Thank You, God! 2002. (Little Blessings Ser.). (Illus.). 32p. (J). bds. 6.99 (978-0-8423-5371-7(2)) Tyndale Hse. Pubs.

Bozzuti-Jones, Mark Francisco. God Created. Ishida, Jui, illus. 2003. 32p. 16.99 (978-0-8066-4568-1(7) , Augsburg Bks.) Augsburg Fortress, Pubs.

Brazzell-Robinson, Shirlye. God Created the World in 6 Days. 2006. 29.00 (978-0-8059-9794-1(6)) Dorrance Publishing Co., Inc.

Breems, Beau A. La Gran Historia: The Illustrated Gospel from Creation to Resurrection. Breems, Beau A., illus. 2005. Tr. of His Story. (SPA.). (J). 10.99 (978-0-9768680-5-7(9)) Burning Bush Creation.

Breems, Beau Alan. His Story: The Illustrated Gospel from Creation to Resurrection. Breems, Beau Alan, illus. 2005. (J). per. 14.95 (978-0-9768680-2-6(4)) Burning Bush Creation.

Bruno, Bonnie. God Thought of Everything Strange & Slimy. Brown, Kevin, illus. 2006. 128p. (YA). (gr. 3-6). pap. 8.99 (978-0-7847-1448-5(7) , 04084) Standard Publishing.

—God Thought of Everything Weird & Wacky. Brown, Kevin, illus. 2006. 128p. (YA). (gr. 3-6). pap. 8.99 (978-0-7847-1447-8(9) , 04083) Standard Publishing.

Butterworth, Nick & Inkpen, Mick. Wonderful Earth. 2003. (Illus.). 32p. 14.99 (978-1-85608-005-7(6)) Hunt, John Publishing Ltd. GBR. *Dist:* STL Distribution North America.

Caduto, Michael J. In the Beginning: The Story of Genesis & Earth Activities for Children. 2004. 48p. 16.95 (978-0-8091-6717-3(4) , 6717-4) Paulist Pr.

Carroll, Michael W., et al, illus. Animals of the World. 2005. (J). 7.99 (978-0-310-70582-6(7)) Zonderkidz.

Carroll, Michael W., et al. Fish, Bugs & Birds, Vol. 4. 2005. (God's Creation Ser.). 40p. (J). 7.99 (978-0-310-70581-9(9)) Zonderkidz.

—Rocks & Plants, Vol. 3. 2005. (God's Creation Ser.). 40p. (J). 7.99 (978-0-310-70580-2(0)) Zonderkidz.

—Sky & Sea, Vol. 2. 2005. (God's Creation Ser.). 40p. (J). 7.99 (978-0-310-70579-6(7)) Zonderkidz.

—Space & Time. 2005. (God's Creation Ser.). (Illus.). 40p. (J). 7.99 (978-0-310-70578-9(9)) Zonderkidz.

Cooper, Gilly Cameron. How the World Began: Creation in Myths & Legends. 2006. (Illus.). 48p. pap., pap. 11.99 (978-1-84476-246-0(7), Southwater) Anness Publishing GBR. *Dist:* National Bk. Network.

Dalmatian Press Staff. God's Creations: Bright Idea Book to Color. 2003. (Bright Idea Book to Color Ser.). (Illus.). 32p. (J). pap. 3.99 (978-1-57759-892-3(X)) Dalmatian Pr.

Davis, Rebecca. God's Special Creation. de Papenbrock, Dervy Romero, tr. Clement, Stacy, illus. unabr. ed. 2003. (ENG & SPA.). 30p. (J). (gr. k-3). spiral bd. 8.00 (978-0-9720881-3-8(X), B004) His Hands, Inc.

Exploring Creation Marine Biology. 2006. cd-rom 58.50 (978-1-932012-66-8(4)) Apologia Educational Ministries, Inc.

Exploring Creation Marine Biology Companion CD-ROM. 2006. cd-rom 13.50 (978-1-932012-67-5(2)) Apologia Educational Ministries, Inc.

Freed, Shirley & Moon, Louise. All My Pets. Morelan, Bill, ed. Harrell, Rob, illus. 2003. 16p. (J). (-k). pap. 3.99 (978-1-58938-099-8(1)) Concerned Communications.

—The Day God Rested. Morelan, Bill, ed. Butler, Steven, illus. 2003. 16p. (J). (gr. 1 up). pap. 3.99 (978-1-58938-102-5(5)) Concerned Communications.

—God Made Animals. Morelan, Bill, ed. Butler, Steven, illus. 2003. 16p. (J). (gr. 1 up). pap. 3.99 (978-1-58938-114-8(9)) Concerned Communications.

—God Made Birds. Morelan, Bill, ed. Butler, Steven, illus. 2003. 8p. (J). (gr. 1 up). pap. 3.99 (978-1-58938-111-7(4)) Concerned Communications.

—God Made Light. Morelan, Bill, ed. Butler, Steven, illus. 2003. 8p. (J). (gr. 1 up). pap. 3.99 (978-1-58938-109-4(2)) Concerned Communications.

—God Made Plants. Morelan, Bill, ed. Butler, Steven, illus. 2003. 16p. (J). (gr. 1 up). pap. 3.99 (978-1-58938-108-7(4)) Concerned Communications.

—God Made Sea Creatures. Morelan, Bill, ed. Butler, Steven, illus. 2003. 16p. (J). (gr. 2 up). pap. 3.99 (978-1-58938-118-6(1)) Concerned Communications.

—God Made the Sun. Morelan, Bill, ed. Butler, Steven, illus. 2003. 8p. (J). (gr. 1 up). pap. 3.99 (978-1-58938-115-5(7)) Concerned Communications.

Freed, Shirley Ann & Moon, Louise. Creation. Morelan, Bill, ed. Butler, Steven, illus. l.t. ed. 2002. 16p. (J). (gr. 1-2). pap. 3.99 (978-1-58938-036-3(3)) Concerned Communications.

Fulbright, Jeannie. Exploring Creation with Botany. Wile, Jay L., ed. 2004. 35.00 (978-1-932012-49-1(4)) Apologia Educational Ministries, Inc.

—Exploring Creation with Zoology 1: The Flying Creatures of Day Five. Wile, Jay L., ed. 2005. (Illus.). xvi, 240p. (J). 35.00 (978-1-932012-61-3(3)) Apologia Educational Ministries, Inc.

Garcia, Emmett Shkeme. Coyote & the Sky: How the Sun, Moon, & Stars Began. Pringle, Victoria, illus. 2006. 32p. (YA). (gr. 6 up). 17.95 (978-0-8263-3730-6(9)) Univ. of New Mexico Pr.

Gemmen, Heather & McNeil, Mary. Trust & Obey: Level 1. Smith, Jamie, tr. Smith, Jamie, illus. 2004. (Rocket ReaderT2 Ser.). 40p. (J). (gr. 1 up). pap., pap. 8.99 (978-0-7814-4012-7(2), 0781440122) Cook, David C. Publishing Co.

Goble, Paul. Song of Creation. Goble, Paul, illus. 2004. (Illus.). 32p. (J). 16.00 (978-0-8028-5271-7(8)) Eerdmans, William B. Publishing Co.

God Made Everything Good. 3.50 (978-0-8054-5878-7(6)) B&H Publishing Grp.

God Made Me. 3.50 (978-0-8054-5887-9(5)) B&H Publishing Grp.

God Made Outer Space. 2006. 16p. (J). pap. 1.99 (978-0-7847-1702-8(8), 04163) Standard Publishing.

Godfrey, Jan. God's Wonderful World. Adderley, Peter, illus. 2008. Orig. Title: Wonderful World. (J). 12.95 ***(978-0-8198-8317-9(4))*** Pauline Bks. & Media.

Gowensmith, Debbie & Keefer, Mikal. Creation— God's Awesome Power. 2005. (BibleVenture Centers Ser.). (Illus.). 112p. (978-0-7644-2810-4(1)) Group Publishing, Inc.

Grimes, Nikki. At Break of Day. Collier, John & Morin, Paul, illus. 2004. 32p. (ps-3). 17.00 (978-0-8028-5104-8(5)) Eerdmans, William B. Publishing Co.

Haidle, Helen. Creation. 2004. 36p. (J). pap. 4.99 (978-0-310-70824-7(9)) Zonderkidz.

—Creation. Haidle, David, illus. 2000. 40p. (J). 12.99 (978-0-310-70018-0(3)) Zonderkidz.

Haidle, Helen & Haidle, Paul. God's Amazing Creatures & Me! 2000. (Illus.). 96p. (J). (gr. 1-5). pap. 8.99 (978-0-89051-294-4(9), 303-051) Master Bks.

Ham, Ken. It's Designed to Do What It Does Do. 2006. 11p. (J). 9.99 (978-0-89051-484-9(4)) Master Bks.

—Six Days or Millions of Years? 2004. 48p. pap. 0.75 (978-1-893345-23-2(8)) Answers in Genesis Ministries.

Hansen, Janis. Creation: God's Wonderful Gift, 5 vols. Francisco, Wendy, illus. 2003. (Bible Adventure Club). 36p. wbk. ed. 19.99 incl. audio, cd-rom (978-1-58134-292-5(6)) Crossway Bks.

—Creation: God's Wonderful Gift. Francisco, Wendy, illus. 2001. (J). (978-1-58134-295-6(0)) Crossway Bks.

Harrast, Tracy. Dios Hizo a los Alimentos. 2000. (God Made...Ser.).Tr. of God Made Food. (SPA., Illus.). 14p. (J). (ps-k). pap. 2.99 (978-0-8297-2287-1(4)) Vida Pubs.

—Dios Hizo a los Animales. 2000. (God Made...Ser.).Tr. of God Made Animals. (SPA., Illus.). 12p. (J). (ps-k). pap. 2.99 (978-0-8297-2286-4(6)) Vida Pubs.

—Dios Hizo Al Mundo. 2000. (God Made...Ser.).Tr. of God Made the World. (SPA., Illus.). 12p. (J). (ps-k). pap. 2.99 (978-0-8297-2289-5(0)) Vida Pubs.

—Dios Hizo Mi Cuerpo. 2000. (God Made...Ser.).Tr. of God Made My Body. (SPA., Illus.). 12p. (J). (ps-k). pap. 2.99 (978-0-8297-2288-8(2)) Vida Pubs.

Hawksley, Gerald. Lift & Look Creation. Stanley, Mandy, illus. 2006. 8p. (J). bds. 7.99 (978-0-7847-1458-4(4), 04085) Standard Publishing.

Head, Heno, Jr. God Made the Earth. Derico, Laura, ed. Fletcher, Rusty, illus. 2000. (Happy Day Bks.). 24p. (J). (ps-2). 2.49 (978-0-7847-1060-9(0), 04332, Bean Sprouts) Standard Publishing.

Henning, Heather. Creation. Chapman, Gillian, illus. 2007. (ENG.). 16p. (J). pap. 9.99 ***(978-0-7586-1384-4(9))*** Concordia Publishing Hse.

Henning, Heather. When God Created the World. Atkins, Alison, illus. 2006. 24p. pap. 10.95 (978-1-59325-077-5(0)) Word Among Us Pr.

Hodgson, Mona Gansberg. I Wonder How Fish Sleep. 1999. (I Wonder Ser.). (Illus.). 32p. (J). (ps-2). 6.99 (978-0-570-05066-7(9)) Concordia Publishing Hse.

—I Wonder How God Hears Me. 2000. (I Wonder Ser.). (Illus.). 32p. (J). (ps-2). 6.99 (978-0-570-07029-0(5)) Concordia Publishing Hse.

—I Wonder How God Made Me. 2000. (I Wonder Ser.). (Illus.). 32p. (J). (ps-2). 6.99 (978-0-570-07030-6(9)) Concordia Publishing Hse.

—I Wonder What I Can Give God. 2000. (I Wonder Ser.). (Illus.). 32p. (J). (ps-2). 6.99 (978-0-570-07031-3(7)) Concordia Publishing Hse.

—I Wonder Who Stretched the Giraffe's Neck. 1999. (I Wonder Ser.). (Illus.). 32p. (J). (ps-2). 6.99 (978-0-570-05065-0(0)) Concordia Publishing Hse.

Horner, Susan. What Is God's Design for My Body? 2004. (Miracle of Creation Ser.). (Illus.). 64p. (J). pap. 5.99 (978-0-8024-0923-2(7)) Moody Pubs.

—Why Do Plants Grow? 2004. (Miracle of Creation Ser.). (Illus.). 32p. (J). 9.99 (978-0-8024-0921-8(0)) Moody Pubs.

In the Beginning. 2006. 16p. (J). pap. 1.99 (978-0-7847-1352-5(9), 22129) Standard Publishing.

Jablonski, Patricia Edward, ed. The Wonderful Story of Creation. Kim, Magdalena, illus. 2001. 32p. (J). pap. 6.95 (978-0-8198-8300-1(X), 332-409) Pauline Bks. & Media.

Jacobson, Matt. How Did God Make Me? 2001. 32p. (J). 9.99 (978-0-310-70106-4(6)) Zondervan.

Jeffs, Stephanie. My First Picture Book about God. Bishop, Roma, illus. 2001. 32p. (ps up). 14.99 (978-0-8066-4155-3(X), Augsburg Bks.) Augsburg Fortress, Pubs.

Jensen, Rebecca Ridges & Jensen, Daniel Loran. The Creation-From the Book of Moses. 2007. 32p. (J). 15.99 (978-1-55517-894-9(4)) Cedar Fort, Inc./CFI Distribution.

Keener, Joan N. God Thought of It First. Petrova, Valeria, illus. 2006. 28p. (J). 14.99 (978-0-7847-1432-4(0), 04016) Standard Publishing.

—God's the One Who Thought of It First. Ring, Laura, ed. Carpenter, Stephen, illus. 1998. (Happy Day Bks.). 24p. (J). (ps-2). pap. 2.49 (978-0-7847-0832-3(0), 04262, Bean Sprouts) Standard Publishing.

Kessler, Timothy. When God Made the Dakotas. Morin, Paul, illus. 2006. 32p. (J). 17.00 (978-0-8028-5275-5(0), Eerdmans Bks For Young Readers) Eerdmans, William B. Publishing Co.

LaBelle, Timothy. God Made Something Out of Nothing to Do... & So Can You! 2001. (Illus.). 32p. (gr. k-3). 9.95 (978-0-8091-6683-1(6), 6683-6) Paulist Pr.

Leunk, Thea. Fossils & Faith: Finding Our Way Through the Creation Controversy. (Other Beliefs Ser.). (gr. 11-12). pap., stu. ed. 4.95 (978-1-59255-198-9(X), 130700); pap. 12.95 (978-1-59255-199-6(8), 130705) CRC Pubns. (Faith Alive Christian Resources).

Lindbergh, Reeve. The Circle of Days. 2002. (gr. 3-6). lib. bdg. 14.15 (978-0-613-74721-9(6)) Tandem Library Bks.

Luci, Shaw & Lane, Mary. The Genesis of It All. Miao, Huai-Kuang, Sr., illus. 2006. 32p. (J). 17.95 (978-1-55725-480-1(X)) Paraclete Pr., Inc.

Mackall, Dandi Daley. God Made Me. Nakata, Hiroe, illus. 2006. 14p. (J). 6.99 (978-1-4169-1499-0(4), Little Simon Inspirations) Simon & Schuster Children's Publishing.

MacKall, Dandi Daley. Made by God. Halsey, Megan, illus. 2002. (First Things First Ser.). 12p. (ps-k). 6.99 (978-0-8066-4379-3(X), Augsburg Bks.) Augsburg Fortress, Pubs.

MacKall, Dandi Daley & Kucharik, Elena. Blessings Come in Shapes. 2005. (Tyndale Kids Ser.). (Illus.). 32p. (J). bds. 6.99 (978-1-4143-0290-4(8)) Tyndale Hse. Pubs.

Mackenzie, Catherine. God's Little Guidebooks - Creation: God Creates a Day of Rest. 2004. (Illus.). 16p. (J). pap. (978-1-85792-847-1(4), Christian Focus) Christian Focus Pubns. GBR. *Dist:* Riverside.

—God's Little Guidebooks - Creation: God Creates Animals & People. 2004. (Illus.). 16p. (J). pap. (978-1-85792-846-4(6), Christian Focus) Christian Focus Pubns. GBR. *Dist:* Riverside.

—God's Little Guidebooks - Creation: God Creates New Life in Me. 2004. (Illus.). 16p. (J). pap. (978-1-85792-848-8(2), Christian Focus) Christian Focus Pubns. GBR. *Dist:* Riverside.

—God's Little Guidebooks - Creation: God Creates the Fish & Birds. 2004. (Illus.). 16p. (J). pap. (978-1-85792-845-7(8), Christian Focus) Christian Focus Pubns. GBR. *Dist:* Riverside.

—God's Little Guidebooks - Creation: God Creates the Land, Seas & Plants. 2004. (Illus.). 16p. (J). pap. (978-1-85792-843-3(1), Christian Focus) Christian Focus Pubns. GBR. *Dist:* Riverside.

—God's Little Guidebooks - Creation: God Creates the Sun, Moon & Stars. 2004. (Illus.). 16p. (J). pap. (978-1-85792-844-0(X), Christian Focus) Christian Focus Pubns. GBR. *Dist:* Riverside.

—God's Little Guidebooks - Creation: God Creates the Water & the Sky. 2004. (Illus.). 16p. (J). pap. (978-1-85792-842-6(3), Christian Focus) Christian Focus Pubns. GBR. *Dist:* Riverside.

Maier, Paul L. The Real Story of the Creation. Barrett, Robert, illus. 2007. 32p. (J). (gr. 3 up). 16.99 ***(978-0-7586-1265-6(6))*** Concordia Publishing Hse.

Matthews, Caitlin. The Blessing Seed: A Creation Myth for the New Millennium. Dexter, Alison, illus. 2000. 32p. (J). (ps-7). pap. 6.99 (978-1-84148-154-8(8)) Barefoot Bks., Inc.

Murphy, Elspeth Campbell. Look What You Made, God! Lewis, Jim, illus. 2002. 32p. (J). 7.99 (978-0-7642-2387-7(9)) Bethany Hse. Pubs.

Najar, Qasim M. Allah Made the World. Emerick, Yahiya, ed. Meehan, Patricia, illus. l.t. ed. 2002. 36p. (J). (gr. k-2). pap. 6.95 (978-1-889720-32-6(1)) Amirah Publishing.

Nederveld, Patricia L. Adam & Eve: The Story of the First Man & Woman. 1998. (God Loves Me Ser.). (Illus.). 24p. (J). (ps-3). pap. 2.95 (978-1-56212-272-0(X), 001203, Faith Alive Christian Resources) CRC Pubns.

—Blue & Green & Purple Too! The Story of God's Colorful World. 1998. (God Loves Me Ser.). (Illus.). 24p. (J). (ps-3). pap. 2.95 (978-1-56212-270-6(3), 001201, Faith Alive Christian Resources) CRC Pubns.

—It's a Noisy Place! The Story of the First Creatures. 1998. (God Loves Me Ser.). (Illus.). 24p. (J). (ps-3). pap. 2.95 (978-1-56212-271-3(1), 001202, Faith Alive Christian Resources) CRC Pubns.

—Take Good Care of My World! The Story of Adam & Eve in the Garden. 1998. (God Loves Me Ser.). (Illus.). 24p. (J). (ps-3). pap. 2.95 (978-1-56212-273-7(8), 001204, Faith Alive Christian Resources) CRC Pubns.

Niedzviecki, Hal. The Big Book of Pop Culture: A How-To Guide for Young Artists. Ngui, Marc, illus. 2007. 183p. (YA). (gr. 7-12). 24.95 ***(978-1-55451-056-6(2));*** pap. 14.95 ***(978-1-55451-055-9(4))*** Annick Pr., Ltd. CAN. *Dist:* Firefly Bks., Ltd.

Novaskshonoff, Varlaarm. Creation of the World: For Young People. Date not set. (Illus.). 27p. (YA). (gr. 7-12). pap. 3.00 (978-1-879038-44-8(7), 9012) Synaxis Pr.

Paprocki, Joseph. In the Beginning. Sawyer, Kieran, ed. 2003. (Developing Faith Ser.). (Illus.). 80p. (gr. 9-12). stu. ed. 6.95 (978-0-87793-585-8(8)) Ave Maria Pr.

—In the Beginning, Grades 9-12. Sawyer, Kieran, ed. 2003. (Developing Faith Ser.). (Illus.). 136p. tchr. ed. 16.95 (978-0-87793-586-5(6)) Ave Maria Pr.

Parker, Robert Andrew, illus. The People with Five Fingers: A Native Californian Creation Tale. 2000. (Accelerated Reader Bks.). 32p. (J). (ps-k). 15.95 (978-0-7614-5058-0(0), Cavendish Children's Bks.) Cavendish, Marshall Corp.

Parrott, Leslie & Zondervan. God Made You Nose to Toes. Petrone, Valeria, illus. 2002. 18p. (J). bds. 6.99 (978-0-310-70216-0(X)) Zonderkidz.

Pingry, Patricia A. & Venturi-Pickett, Stacy, trs. The Story of Creation. Venturi-Pickett, Stacy, illus. 2003. (Illus.). 26p. (J). bds. 7.95 (978-0-8249-6504-4(3)) Ideals Pubns.

Poole, Susie. God Made the Garden Creatures. 2004. (Illus.). 18p. (J). 6.99 (978-0-310-70865-0(6)) Zonderkidz.

Prestofillipo, Mary Nazarene, tr. The Story of Creation. Flamini, Lorella, illus. 2005. Orig. Title: Piccola storia della Creazione. (ITA.). 36p. (J). pap. 12.95 (978-0-8198-7093-3(5)) Pauline Bks. & Media.

Pridham, Caroline. Twilight & Dawn: Simple Talks on the Six Days of Creation. 2006. 286p. pap. 13.99 (978-1-4264-2599-8(6)); 310p. pap. 17.99 (978-1-4264-2640-7(2)) BiblioBazaar.

Reeve, Penny. God Made Something Beautiful. 2002. (ps-2). lib. bdg. 11.80 (978-0-613-79989-8(5)) Tandem Library Bks.

Robb, Andy. Who Made The World?, 1. 1999. (Illus.). 26p. (J). (ps-2). 7.00 (978-0-570-05577-8(6)) Concordia Publishing Hse.

Sattgast, Linda J. When the World Was New. 2001. 48p. (J). 9.99 (978-0-310-70127-9(9)) Zondervan.

Schlitt, D. Celebrate the World God Made. 2004. 52p. 6.99 (978-0-8054-0826-3(6)) B&H Publishing Grp.

School Specialty Publishing. God Made the World. 2004. 10p. (J). 1.99 (978-0-7647-1046-9(X), In Celebration) Schaffer, Frank Pubns.

Seis Lindos Dias. 2003. (SPA.). 6.99 (978-0-7814-3598-7(6), 0781435986) Cook, David C. Publishing Co.

Seven Special Days. 2006. 16p. (J). pap. 1.99 (978-0-7847-1717-2(6), 04178) Standard Publishing.

Snellenberger, Earl & Snellenberger, Bonita. God Created the Animals. 1998. (God Created Ser.: Vol. 6). (Illus.). 32p. (J). pap. 4.95 (978-0-89051-154-1(3)) Master Bks.

—God Created the Insects. 1998. (God Created Ser.: Vol. 7). (Illus.). 32p. (J). pap. 4.95 (978-0-89051-155-8(1)) Master Bks.

—God Created the People. 1998. (God Created Ser.: Vol. 8). (Illus.). 32p. (J). pap. 4.95 (978-0-89051-157-2(8)) Master Bks.

—God Created the Plants & Trees. 1998. (God Created Ser.: Vol. 2). (Illus.). 32p. (J). pap. 4.95 (978-0-89051-150-3(0)) Master Bks.

Spirin, Gennadii, illus. Gennady Spirin's Creation. 2008. 32p. (J). ***(978-0-310-71084-4(7))*** Zonderkidz.

Stainbrook, Jess & Burr, Mark. God Made Me! The Story of Creation for Your Baby. Hom, John, illus. 2004. (Baby Faith Ser.). 18p. (J). (ps-ps). bds. 9.99 (978-1-59145-215-7(5)) Nelson, Thomas Inc.

The Story of Creation. 2000. (Illus.). (J). (ps-k). bds. 4.95 (978-0-88271-688-6(3)) Regina Pr., Malhame & Co.

The Story of Creation. 2002. (J). spiral bd. (978-0-9720158-7-5(6)) Story Reader, Inc.

Swartz, Nancy Sohn. In Our Image: God's First Creatures. Hall, Melanie, illus. 1998. 32p. (ps-3). 16.95 (978-1-879045-99-6(0)) Jewish Lights Publishing.

Tanner, Earnest D., Jr. Creation the Sixth Day. 2006. per. 11.95 (978-1-59872-563-6(7)) Instantpublisher.com.

Taylor, Jane. God Made Me. 1998. 16p. (J). 3.99 (978-1-85792-289-9(1), Christian Focus) Christian Focus Pubns. GBR. *Dist:* Riverside, Spring Arbor Distributors, Inc.

—God Made the World. 1998. (Illus.). 16p. (J). (ps-k). 3.99 (978-1-85792-292-9(1), Christian Focus) Christian Focus Pubns. GBR. *Dist:* Riverside, Spring Arbor Distributors, Inc.

Turner, Steve. In the Beginning. Newton, Jill, illus. 2002. 32p. (ps-3). 10.99 (978-0-8066-4363-2(3), Augsburg Bks.) Augsburg Fortress, Pubs.

Vander Klipp, Michael A. God Made My Body. 1999. (God Made Bks.). (Illus.). 12p. (J). (ps). bds. 2.99 (978-0-310-97859-6(9)) Zonderkidz.

Wile, Jay L. & Durnell, Marilyn F. Exploring Creation with Biology, 2 Bks., Set. 2nd ed. 2005. 85.00 (978-1-932012-57-6(5)) Apologia Educational Ministries, Inc.

Wilger, Jennifer R., ed. God Made Our World. 2003. (Bible Big Bks.). (Illus.). 8p. (ps up). pap. 15.99 (978-1-55945-436-0(9), Flagship Church Resources) Group Publishing, Inc.

Wingfield, Al. The Little Snail That Lives near a Pail. Ramey, Lisa L., illus. Ramey, Lisa L., photos by. 1999. 14p. (J). (ps-3). pap. 7.95 (978-1-930260-00-9(8)) CTS Family Pr.

CREATION (LITERARY, ARTISTIC, ETC.)

Ajmera, Maya & Ivanko, John D. To Be an Artist. 2004. (Illus.). 32p. (J). 15.95 (978-1-57091-503-1(2)) Charlesbridge Publishing, Inc.

Artic Circle Paper Doll with Stickers. 2001. (J). (978-0-89610-446-4(X)) Island Heritage Publishing.

Bao, Julie. A Loving Teacher Forever: A True Story of Loving Children, Defying Fate & Achieving Teaching Excellence. 2004. (Illus.). 32p. (J). 15.00 (978-0-9748890-0-9(8)) Dings Bks.

Berry, Joy. Be Creative. 2005. (Winning skills series, work It! Ser.). (Illus.). 48p. (J). pap. 3.95 (978-1-57687-282-6(3), PowerHouse Kids) powerHouse Cultural Entertainment, Inc.

Church, Ellen Booth. Best-Ever Circle Time Activities: Month-by-Month. 2002. (Best-ever Circle Time Activities Ser.). 64p. (ps-k). pap. 11.95 (978-0-439-31662-0(6)) Scholastic, Inc.

Creative: Building Innovative. 1999. 282p. (C). 38.40 (978-0-536-60320-3(0)) Pearson Custom Publishing.

Doyle, Jeannine. Hand to Hand Voice to Voice: Young Journeys of Courage Living with Crohn's & Colitis. Cohen, Stan, ed. unabr. ed. 2002. 334p. (YA). (gr. 1-12). spiral bd. 30.00 (978-0-9672223-2-5(X)) D&S Pubns.

Dubrovin, Vivian & Dubrovin, Barbara. Storytelling Discoveries: Favorite Activities for Young Tellers. Dubrovin, Barbara, illus. 2002. (Illus.). 72p. (J). pap. 17.50 (978-0-9638339-5-2(2)) Storycraft Publishing.

Giguere, Sarah. Ducks: Includes Fact Sheets, Bulletin Board Ideas, Songs & Finger Plays, Games, Journal Ideas, Activity Sheets & More! Bachand, Stephen, illus. 2000. 29p. (J). ring bd. 18.95 (978-1-928972-06-8(3)) Critter Pubns.

Gottlieb, Jeff & Gottlieb, Martha. Spriggles - Motivational Books for Children: Spriggles: Inspiration. Gottlieb, Alexander, illus. 2002. 32p. (J). per. 8.95 (978-1-930439-05-4(9)) Mountain Watch Pr.

Green, Marilyn, ed. My Anytime Anywhere Autograph Book. 2003. (Illus.). 66p. (J). (gr. 3 up). spiral bd. 12.95 (978-1-57054-954-0(0)) Klutz.

Haas, Carolyn B. Big Book of Fun: Creative Learning Activities for Home & School. Phillips, Jane B., illus. 2nd ed. 2003. 288p. (J). (ps-7). reprint ed. pap. 14.95 (978-1-55652-020-4(4)) Chicago Review Pr., Inc.

Haas, Carolyn Buhai. Look at Me: Creative Learning Activities for Babies & Toddlers. Phillips, Jane Bennett, illus. 2nd ed. 2003. 232p. (J). (ps). reprint ed. pap. 12.95 (978-1-55652-021-1(2)) Chicago Review Pr., Inc.

Hinkler Books Staff. My Big Book of Stickers: Fun & Educational Activity Book. rev. ed. 2004. 128p. (J). (gr. 3-7). pap. 10.95 (978-1-74121-805-3(5)) Hinkler Bks. Pty, Ltd. AUS. *Dist:* Penton Overseas, Inc.

Hirsch, Edward. The Demon & the Angel: Searching for the Source of Artistic Inspiration. 2003. (gr. 7-12). lib. bdg. 23.45 (978-0-613-61845-8(9)) Tandem Library Bks.

Houghton, Roswitha, illus. Isabella Ballerina. 2001. (J). 9.95 (978-0-9716346-0-2(2)) Dancing Words Pr., Inc.

Illing, Nancy. SPARKS Ignite Imagination. Illing, Nancy, illus. 2002. 64p. per. 14.00 (978-0-9713539-0-9(5)) Creative Genius Pubns.

Kefalos, Katina. Inspiration for Children. 1998. (Illus.). 14p. (J). (gr. 2-6). pap. 4.95 (978-0-9666822-8-1(9)) Emerald Productions.

Keiki Friends Dress-Up Dolls Activity Book. 2002. (J). 4.99 (978-0-89610-390-0(0)) Island Heritage Publishing.

Klutz Press Staff. My Fabulous Life in Pictures. 2002. (Illus.). 40p. (J). (gr. 4-7). spiral bd. 19.95 (978-1-57054-916-8(8)) Klutz.

LaBelle, Timothy. God Made Something Out of Nothing to Do... & So Can You! 2001. (Illus.). 32p. (gr. k-3). 9.95 (978-0-8091-6683-1(6), 6683-6) Paulist Pr.

Leimbach, Judy. Imagination Celebration: Adventures in Creativity. 2005. 64p. 11.95 (978-1-59363-075-1(1)) Prufrock Pr.

Leuzzi, Linda. A Creative Life: The Young Person's Guide. 1999. (Single Titles Ser.). (Illus.). 144p. (YA). (gr. 8-12). 24.00 (978-0-531-11527-5(5), Watts, Franklin) Scholastic Library Publishing.

Marsh, Carole. Heroes & Helpers. 2004. 48p. (J). (gr. 2-6). pap., act. bk. ed. 9.95 (978-0-635-01094-0(1)) Gallopade International.

Murphy, Patricia J. Creative Minds. 2005. (Real Deal Ser.). (Illus.). 32p. (J). (978-0-7608-9637-2(5)) Sundance/Newbridge Educational Publishing.

Newbery, Elizabeth. Why Make Art? 2001. (Art for All Ser.). (Illus.). 32p. (J). lib. bdg. 24.25 (978-1-930643-33-8(0)) Chrysalis Education.

Niedzviecki, Hal. The Big Book of Pop Culture: A How-To Guide for Young Artists. Ngui, Marc, illus. 2007. 183p. (YA). (gr. 7-12). 24.95 ***(978-1-55451-056-6(2))***; pap. 14.95 ***(978-1-55451-055-9(4))*** Annick Pr., Ltd. CAN. *Dist:* Firefly Bks., Ltd.

Nobisso, Josephine. Show; Don't Tell! Secrets of Writing. Montanari, Eva, illus. 2004. 40p. (J). (gr. 2-6). 24.95 (978-0-940112-13-1(2)) Gingerbread Hse.

Phillips, Vivian A. Show & Tell: Education. Date not set. (Illus.). 10p. (Orig.). (J). pap. (978-1-888413-00-7(X)) Seasoning Quilting (Arts & Crafts).

Polar (Gr. PreK-5) 2003. (J). (978-1-58232-025-0(X)) Bryan Hse. Pubs., Inc.

Rachfalski, Jane. Feeling Better about Me. Cox, Lynne, ed. Soprano, Cecilia, illus. unabr. ed. 2002. 60p. (YA). (gr. 7-12). pap. 9.95 (978-0-9631046-2-5(4)) Redwoods Pr.

Renzulli, Joseph S. New Directions in Creativity: Mark 1, 5 vols. 2000. (New Directions in Creativity: Vol. 3). 42p. (J). pap. 25.95 (978-0-936386-81-2(9)) Creative Learning Pr., Inc.

—New Directions in Creativity: Mark 2, 5 vols. 2000. (New Directions in Creativity: Vol. 4). (J). pap. 25.95 (978-0-936386-82-9(7)) Creative Learning Pr., Inc.

Renzulli, Joseph S. & Callahan, Carolyn M. New Directions in Creativity: Mark 3, 5 vols. 2nd ed. 2000. (New Directions in Creativity: Vol. 5). 42p. (J). pap. 25.95 (978-0-936386-83-6(5)) Creative Learning Pr., Inc.

Renzulli, Mary Jo, et al. New Directions in Creativity: Mark A, 5 vols., Vol. 1. 2nd rev. ed. 2000. 42p. (J). pap. 25.95 (978-0-936386-79-9(7)) Creative Learning Pr., Inc.

Showalter, Elizabeth A. Let's Do Something! Educational Crafts & Activities for Juniors & Intermediates. 1999. (Illus.). 112p. (YA). (gr. 4-9). spiral bd. 8.95 (978-0-87813-582-0(0)) Christian Light Pubns., Inc.

Smith, Linda, et al. New Directions in Creativity: Mark B, 5 vols., Vol. 2. 2nd ed. 2000. 42p. (J). pap. 25.95 (978-0-936386-80-5(0)) Creative Learning Pr., Inc.

Smith, Norma J. Write Right. 1999. (Illus.). 75p. (J). (gr. 3-9). pap. 16.99 (978-0-9672763-0-4(6)) Bookmark Pr.

Stillinger, Doug. The Spiral Draw Book. 2003. (Illus.). 38p. (J). (gr. 3 up). spiral bd. 19.95 (978-1-57054-960-1(5)) Klutz.

Striker, Susan. The Fifth Anti-Coloring Book: Creative Activities for Ages 6 & Up. rev. ed. 2004. (Illus.). 96p. (J). pap. 10.95 (978-0-8050-7648-6(4) , Owl Bks.) Holt, Henry & Co.

—The Sixth Anti-Coloring Book: Creative Activities for Ages 6 & Up. rev. ed. 2004. (Illus.). 96p. (J). pap. 11.95 (978-0-8050-7649-3(2) , Holt Paperback) Holt, Henry & Co.

Wezeman, Phyllis Vos & Finegan, Katherine. Six Seasons of Fun. 2004. (Kids & Christian Education Ser.). 15.99 (978-0-8066-4502-5(4) , Augsburg Bks.) Augsburg Fortress, Pubs.

CREATION—POETRY

Alexander, Cecil Frances. All Things Bright & Beautiful. Whatley, Bruce, illus. 2004. 32p. (J). pap. 6.99 (978-0-06-008339-7(5) , Harper Trophy) HarperCollins Pubs.

—All Things Bright & Beautiful. McDaniels, Preston, illus. 2nd ed. 2001. (Hymns for Children Ser.). 32p. (ps-2). pap. 4.95 (978-0-8192-1884-1(7)) Morehouse Publishing.

—All Things Bright & Beautiful. Heyer, Carol, illus. 2002. 26p. (ps-3). 9.95 (978-1-59093-019-9(3)) Warehousing & Fulfillment Specialists, LLC (WFS, LLC).

Carlstrom, Nancy White. Glory. Jenkins, Debra Reid, illus. 2004. 32p. (J). (ps-3). 17.00 (978-0-8028-5143-7(6)) Eerdmans, William B. Publishing Co.

CREATIVENESS

see Creation (Literary, Artistic, etc.)

CREDIBILITY

see Truthfulness and Falsehood

CREDIT

see also Banks and Banking

Green, Meg. Everything You Need to Know about Credit Cards & Fiscal Responsibilty. 2001. (Need to Know Library). (Illus.). 64p. (YA). (gr. 4-6). lib. bdg. 25.25 (978-0-8239-3327-3(X)) Rosen Publishing Group, Inc., The.

Minden, Cecilia. Using Credit Wisely. 2008. (J). lib. bdg. 25.26 ***(978-1-60279-002-5(7))*** Cherry Lake Publishing.

Prunty, James J., contrib. by. Trend Summary Analysis. 2002. (YA). cd-rom 49.50 (978-0-9740309-3-7(7)) California Capital Leasing Corp.

CREEDS—COMPARATIVE STUDIES

Baynes, Pauline, illus. I Believe: The Nicene Creed. 2004. 32p. 16.00 (978-0-8028-5258-8(0)) Eerdmans, William B. Publishing Co.

CREOLES

Fombrum, Odette Roy. Zanmi Lekol. 2000. (Big Book Ser.). (CRP., Illus.). 8p. (J). (gr. k-2). pap. 19.50 (978-1-58432-038-8(9)) Educa Vision.

—Zanmi Lekot: Camarades. 2001. (CRP & FRE., Illus.). 8p. (J). (gr. k-2). pap. 4.50 (978-1-58432-037-1(0)) Educa Vision.

Spilsbury, Louise & Spilsbury, Richard. Living on a Caribbean Island. 2007. (J). ***(978-1-4109-2819-1(5)); (978-1-4109-2828-3(4))*** Steck-Vaughn.

CRESTS

see Heraldry

CRETE (GREECE)—ANTIQUITIES

Phillips, Dee. Sunken Treasure. 2003. (History Hunters Ser.). (Illus.). 32p. (J). (gr. 3 up). lib. bdg. 24.67 (978-0-8368-3743-8(6)) Stevens, Gareth Inc.

CREWE, SARA (FICTITIOUS CHARACTER)—FICTION

Burnett, Frances Hodgson. A Little Princess: The Story of Sara Crewe. (J). 16.95 (978-0-8488-1253-9(0)) Amereon LTD.

—A Little Princess: The Story of Sara Crewe. Collier, Mary & McClintock, Barbara, illus. 2000. 32p. (J). (ps-3). 18.99 (978-0-06-027891-5(9)) HarperCollins Pubs.

—A Little Princess: The Story of Sara Crewe. Tudor, Tasha, illus. 1999. 336p. (J). (gr. 4 up). 17.99 (978-0-397-30693-0(8)) HarperCollins Pubs.

—A Little Princess: The Story of Sara Crewe. 2002. (Classics Ser.). (Illus.). 272p. pap. 10.00 (978-0-14-243701-8(8) , Penguin Classics) Penguin Group (USA) Inc.

—A Little Princess: The Story of Sara Crewe. Rust, Graham, illus. (J). pap. 22.95 (978-0-590-24079-6(X)) Scholastic, Inc.

—A Little Princess Paper Dolls. Sutton, Judith, photos by. 1999. (Illus.). 24p. (J). (ps-3). pap. 7.95 (978-0-694-00970-1(9) , Harper Festival) HarperCollins Pubs.

CRICKET

Cairns, Christopher. Way to Play. 2000. (Illus.). 88p. (J). pap. 19.95 (978-1-86950-368-0(6)) HarperCollins Pubs. New Zealand NZL. *Dist:* Antipodes Bks. & Beyond.

Gifford, Clive. So You Think You Know Test Cricket. 2005. 160p. (J). pap. (978-0-340-90293-6(0) , Hodder Children's Books) Hodder Children's Division.

Gifford, Clive. So You Think You Know Test Cricket NE. 2nd ed. 2007. 140p. pap. 9.95 ***(978-0-340-93248-3(1))*** Hodder Children's Division GBR. *Dist:* Independent Pubs. Group.

CRICKET—FICTION

Brashear-Hopper, Celia. The Curious Cricket. 2005. (J). lib. bdg. 15.95 (978-0-9765467-8-8(7)) Creative Bk. Pubs.

Cattell, Bob & Agard, John. Butter-Finger. Smy, Pam, illus. 2006. 128p. pap. 7.95 (978-1-84507-376-3(2)) Lincoln, Frances Ltd. GBR. *Dist:* Perseus Distribution.

Cattell, Bob & Agard, John. Calypso Boy. Smy, Pam, illus. 2007. 96p. (J). pap. 7.95 ***(978-1-84507-626-9(5))*** Lincoln, Frances Ltd. GBR. *Dist:* Perseus Distribution.

Cattell, Bob, et al. Shine on Butterfinger. 2007. (Illus.). 96p. (J). 15.95 ***(978-1-84507-773-0(3))*** Lincoln, Frances Ltd. GBR. *Dist:* Perseus Distribution.

English, David. Confessions English Eccentric. 2006. (Illus.). 256p. 44.50 (978-1-4050-5361-7(5)) Macmillan Publishers Ltd. GBR. *Dist:* Trans-Atlantic Pubns., Inc.

Marks, Jeannette. The Cheerful Cricket & Others. 2004. reprint ed. pap. 15.95 (978-1-4191-5649-6(7)); pap. 1.99 (978-1-4192-5649-3(1)) Kessinger Publishing, LLC.

Massucci, Joseph. There's a Cricket in the House?! Wise, Noreen, ed. Wethington, Liz, illus. 2001. (Gold Mixed Collection). 50p. (J). pap. 6.95 (978-1-58584-358-9(X)) Huckleberry Pr.

Mayfield, Marilee Joy. The Golden Cricket: A Story of Luck & Prosperity. 2004. 48p. (J). lib. bdg. 19.95 (978-0-9659222-7-2(8)) Leaping Antelope Productions.

Moxilada, J. L. Jonty Jones Takes Guard. 2005. 242p. pap. 16.88 (978-1-4116-4126-6(4)) Lulu.com.

Walker, Cindy, illus. Serenade of the Cricket. 2nd ed. 2004. (J). 12.95 (978-1-59655-000-1(7)) Cooper Publishing.

Wodehouse, P. G. Mike at Wrykyn. reprint ed. (J). lib. bdg. 98.00 (978-0-7426-3265-3(2)); 2001. pap. 28.00 (978-0-7426-8265-8(X)) Classic Bks.

CRICKETS

Berger, Melvin. Chirping Crickets. Lloyd, Megan, illus. 1998. (Let's-Read-&-Find-Out Science Bks.). 32p. (J). (gr. k-4). 15.95 (978-0-06-024961-8(7)); Stage 2. pap. 5.99 (978-0-06-445180-2(1) , Harper Trophy) HarperCollins Pubs.

—Chirping Crickets. 1998. (Let's-Read-and-Find-Out Science Ser.). (J). 11.79 (978-0-606-13270-1(8)) Tandem Library Bks.

Crickets. (Bugs, Bugs, Bugs! Ser.). 24p. (J). 6.95 (978-0-7368-5095-7(3)); 2005. (YA). (978-0-7368-8208-8(1) , Pebble Bks.) Capstone Pr., Inc.

Crickets, 6 vols. (gr. k-2). 28.95 (978-0-7368-8248-4(0)) Red Brick Learning.

Green, Emily K. Crickets. 2007. (Blastoff! Readers Ser.). (Illus.). 24p. (J). lib. bdg. (978-1-60014-011-2(4)) Bellwether Media.

—Crickets. 2006. (Blastoff! Readers Ser.). (Illus.). 24p. (J). (gr. k-2). 18.50 ***(978-0-531-17861-4(7))*** Scholastic Library Publishing.

Hall, Margaret. Crickets. 2004. (Bugs, Bugs, Bugs! Ser.). (Illus.). 24p. (J). lib. bdg. 19.93 (978-0-7368-2587-0(8) , Pebble Bks.) Capstone Pr., Inc.

Hayward, Tim & Greenaway, Theresa. Grasshoppers & Crickets. 1999. (Minipets Ser.). (Illus.). 32p. (J). (gr. 1-5). lib. bdg. 25.69 (978-0-8172-5590-9(7)) Raintree.

—Grasshoppers & Crickets. 1999. (Minipets Ser.). (Illus.). 32p. (J). (gr. 1-5). pap. 5.95 (978-0-7398-1385-0(4)) Steck-Vaughn.

Loewen, Nancy. Chirp, Chirp! Crickets in Your Backyard. Peterson, Rick, illus. 2005. (Backyard Bugs Ser.). 24p. (J). (ps). lib. bdg. 22.60 (978-1-4048-1141-6(9)) Picture Window Bks.

Meister, Cari. Crickets. 2001. (Insects Ser.). (Illus.). 24p. (J). (gr. k-6). lib. bdg. 21.35 (978-1-57765-460-5(9) , Checkerboard Library) ABDO Publishing Co.

Miller, Sara Swan. Grasshoppers & Crickets of North America. (Animals in Order Ser.). (Illus.). (J). 2003. 48p. (gr. 4-6). pap. 6.95 (978-0-531-16376-4(8)); 2002. 47p. pap. 26.50 (978-0-531-12170-2(4)) Scholastic Library Publishing. (Watts, Franklin).

—Grasshoppers & Crickets of North America. 2002. (gr. 3-6). lib. bdg. 15.25 (978-0-613-59493-6(2)) Tandem Library Bks.

Pascoe, Elaine. Crickets & Grasshoppers. Kuhn, Dwight, photos by. 1998. (Nature Close-Up Ser.). (Illus.). 48p. (J). (gr. 4-8). 23.70 (978-1-56711-176-7(9) , Blackbirch Pr., Inc.) Thomson Gale.

Ross, Michael Elsohn. Cricketology. 2003. (Backyard Buddies Ser.). 48p. (YA). (gr. 3-5). 6.95 (978-0-87614-900-3(X) , Carolrhoda Bks.) Lerner Publishing Group.

—Cricketology. 2002. (gr. 3-6). lib. bdg. 15.25 (978-0-613-77202-0(4)) Tandem Library Bks.

Squire, Ann O. Crickets & Grasshoppers. (True Bks.). (J). 2004. (gr. 3-5). pap. 6.95 (978-0-516-29357-8(5)); 2003. (Illus.). 47p. 25.00 (978-0-516-22657-6(6)) Scholastic Library Publishing. (Children's Pr.).

CRICKETS—FICTION

Barkan, Joanne & Gevry, Claudine. Little Cricket's Song. 2007. 10p. (J). bds. 6.99 (978-0-7944-1282-1(3)) Reader's Digest Assn., Inc., The.

Bunting, Eve. Christmas Cricket. Bush, Timothy, illus. 2002. 32p. (J). (gr. k-3). tchr. ed. 15.00 (978-0-618-06554-7(7) , Clarion Bks.) Houghton Mifflin Co. Trade & Reference Div.

Burt, Nancy V. Sparky the Cricket. Hower, Jack T., Jr., photos by. 2000. (Children's Self Esteem Ser.). (Illus.). 20p. (J). pap. 7.95 (978-1-931006-05-7(9)) SteppingStones BookCard Pubns., LLC.

Calloway, Troy. Clarence. 2007. 44p. (J). 16.99 (978-1-59092-377-1(4) , Little Blue Works) Windstorm Creative.

Delessert, Etienne. Yok-Yok, 12 bks., Set. Delessert, Etienne, illus. Incl. At Home. lib. bdg. 14.60 (978-0-88682-646-8(2) , 97934-098); Best Friends. lib. bdg. 14.60 (978-0-88682-639-0(X) , 97927-098); For the Birds. lib. bdg. 14.60 (978-0-88682-638-3(1) , 97926-098); Moonlight. lib. bdg. 14.60 (978-0-88682-648-2(9) , 97936-098); Nonsense. lib. bdg. 14.60 (978-0-88682-641-3(1) , 97929-098); Nuts! lib. bdg. 14.60 (978-0-88682-644-4(6) , 97932-098); Surprises. lib. bdg. 14.60 (978-0-88682-643-7(8) , 97931-098); Weird? lib. bdg. 14.60 (978-0-88682-645-1(4) , 97933-098); What a Circus! lib. bdg. 14.95 (978-0-88682-640-6(3) , 97928-098); 32p. (J). (gr. 1-5). 1993. (Illus.). lib. bdg. (978-0-88682-637-6(3) , Creative Education) Creative Co., The.

Elliot, David. The Cool Crazy Crickets to the Rescue! 2001. (Illus.). (J). (978-0-606-21642-5(1)) Tandem Library Bks.

Fine, Edith Hope. Cricket at the Manger. Pels, Winslow, illus. 2005. 32p. (J). 15.95 (978-1-56397-993-4(4)) Boyds Mills Pr.

Freeman, Mark. Cricket Nature. Friedman, David, illus. 2001. 36p. 15.00 (978-0-9662448-1-6(8)) Non Sequitur Pr.

Gifaldi, David. Listening for Crickets. 2008. 192p. (J). 16.95 (978-0-8050-7385-0(X) , Holt, Henry & Co. Bks. For Young Readers) Holt, Henry & Co.

Harcourt School Publishers Staff. Jolly Jim Crickets: Take-Home Book. 1999. (Signatures Ser.). (Illus.). (J). pap. 1.90 (978-0-15-313932-1(3)) Harcourt Schl. Pubs.

Helgerson, Kay. Crinkles the Cricket. Volion, Chris, illus. l.t. ed. 2001. 32p. (J). 14.00 (978-0-9676387-7-5(1)) L'Kayle.

Holman, Felice. The Cricket Winter. Thomas, Robyn, illus. 2006. 96p. (J). 15.00 (978-0-8028-5289-2(0) , Eerdmans Bks For Young Readers) Eerdmans, William B. Publishing Co.

Minarik, Else Holmelund. The Cricket Who Came to Dinner. Hahner, Chris, illus. 2004. 32p. (ps). lib. bdg. 11.19 (978-0-606-29910-7(6)) Tandem Library Bks.

Moulton, Mark Kimball. A Cricket's Carol. Blowers, Lisa, illus. 2004. 32p. (J). 14.95 (978-0-8249-5488-0(2)) Ideals Pubns.

—A Cricket's Carol. Blowers, Lisa, illus. 2000. 32p. (J). (gr. k-3). 18.00 (978-0-7412-0735-7(4)) Lang Graphics, Ltd.

Pfeiffer, Joseph R. & Pfeiffer, Robert J. The One-Legged, Bow-Legged Cricket: A Story in a Story. Pfeiffer, Joseph R. & Pfeiffer, Robert J., illus. 1999. (Illus.). 32p. (J). (gr. k-4). 14.93 (978-0-9659772-3-4(4)) Chessmore Publishing.

Ratoff, Michael. Caspar & the Sun: An Adventure, 3 vols. Painter, Laurie, illus. l.t. ed. 2001. (Every Thing in an Empty Box Ser.). 56p. (J). (ps-3). lib. bdg. 9.95 (978-0-9627986-3-4(0)) Rebel Butterfly Pr.

Reader's Digest Children's Books, creator. Little Cricket & Friends 3 Volume Boxed Set. 2007. (Illus.). 36p. (J). (ps-k). bds., bds. 16.99 ***(978-0-7944-1359-0(5))*** Reader's Digest Assn., Inc., The.

Reader's Digest Editors & Barkan, Joanne. Little Cricket's Song. 2004. (Illus.). 12p. (J). bds. 12.99 (978-0-7944-0367-6(0) , Reader's Digest Children's Bks.) Reader's Digest Children's Publishing, Inc.

Selden, George. Chester Cricket's Pigeon Ride. 2001. (gr. 3-6). lib. bdg. 14.10 (978-0-613-37140-7(2)) Tandem Library Bks.

—The Cricket in Times Square. Williams, Garth, illus. 1999. (Chester Cricket Ser.). 32p. (J). (gr. 3-6). 9.95 (978-1-56137-396-3(6)) Novel Units, Inc.

—The Cricket in Times Square. Williams, Garth, illus. (Chester Cricket Ser.). 151p. (J). (gr. 3-6). pap. 5.50 (978-0-8072-8311-0(8) , Listening Library) Random Hse. Audio Publishing Group.

—The Cricket in Times Square. unabr. ed. 2004. (Chester Cricket Ser.). 151p. (J). (gr. 3-7). pap. 29.00 incl. audio (978-0-8072-8310-3(X) , S YA 158 SP, Listening Library) Random Hse. Audio Publishing Group.

—The Cricket in Times Square. Williams, Garth, illus. 2008. 144p. (J). pap. 6.99 ***(978-0-312-38003-8(8))*** Square Fish.

Wheeler, Lisa. Old Cricket. Goembel, Ponder, illus. 2006. 32p. (J). reprint ed. pap. 6.99 (978-1-4169-1855-4(8) , Aladdin) Simon & Schuster Children's Publishing.

Wheeler, Lisa & Goembel, Ponder. Old Cricket. 2003. (Illus.). 32p. (J). (ps-2). 17.99 (978-0-689-84510-9(3) , Atheneum/Richard Jackson Bks.) Simon & Schuster Children's Publishing.

Wood, Audrey. Quick As a Cricket. Wood, Don, illus. 1998. (Child's Play Library). 24p. (J). (ps-1). bds. 6.99 (978-0-85953-664-6(5)) Child's Play-International.

—Veloz Como el Grillo. 1998. (SPA.). (gr. k-3). lib. bdg. 16.45 (978-0-613-77058-3(7)) Tandem Library Bks.

CRIME AND CRIMINALS

see also Assassination; Capital Punishment; Criminal Law; Detectives; Justice, Administration of; Juvenile Delinquency; Pirates; Police; Prisons; Racketeering; Riots; Robbers and Outlaws; Sex Crimes; Smuggling; Trials

Able, Deborah. Hate Groups. rev. ed. 2000. (Issues in Focus Ser.). (Illus.). 112p. (J). (gr. 6-12). lib. bdg. 26.60 (978-0-7660-1245-5(X)) Enslow Pubs., Inc.

Anderson, Angela. Crime & Punishment: A Study Across Time. 1998. (Illus.). 112p. (YA). (gr. 9-11). pap. 32.50 (978-0-7487-3057-5(5)) Nelson Thornes Ltd. GBR. *Dist:* Trans-Atlantic Pubns., Inc.

Barbour, Scott, et al, eds. Violence Against Women. 1998. (Current Controversies Ser.). (Illus.). 224p. (YA). (gr. 7-12). pap. 21.20 (978-0-7377-0014-5(9)); (gr. 9-12). lib. bdg. 32.45 (978-0-7377-0015-2(7)) Thomson Gale. (Greenhaven Pr., Inc.).

Billings. Crime & Punishment. 1998. (Wild Side Ser.). (Illus.). (YA). (gr. 6-12). 13.00 (978-0-89061-799-1(6) , R0799-6E) Jamestown.

Black, J. Anderson. Organized Crime. 2002. (Crime & Detection Ser.). (Illus.). 96p. (J). (gr. 7 up). lib. bdg. (978-1-59084-367-3(3)) Mason Crest Pubs.

Blackwood, Gary L. Bad Guys, 5 bks., Set. Incl. Gangsters. lib. bdg. 28.50 (978-0-7614-1016-4(3)); Highwaymen. lib. bdg. 29.93 (978-0-7614-1017-1(1)); Outlaws. lib. bdg. 29.93 (978-0-7614-1015-7(5)); Pirates. lib. bdg. 29.93 (978-0-7614-1019-5(8)); Swindlers. lib. bdg. 29.93 (978-0-7614-1031-7(7)); 72p. (J). (gr. 5 up). (Illus.). 2001. 142.50 (978-0-7614-1018-8(X) , Benchmark Bks.) Cavendish, Marshall Corp.

—Gangsters. 2001. (Bad Guys Ser.). (Illus.). 72p. (J). (gr. 5 up). lib. bdg. 28.50 (978-0-7614-1016-4(3) , Benchmark Bks.) Cavendish, Marshall Corp.

—Swindlers. 2001. (Bad Guys Ser.). (Illus.). 72p. (J). (gr. 5 up). lib. bdg. 29.93 (978-0-7614-1031-7(7) , Benchmark Bks.) Cavendish, Marshall Corp.

—Unsolved History, 4 bks., Set. Incl. Debatable Deaths. lib. bdg. (978-0-7614-1888-7(1)); Enigmatic Events. (J). (gr. 3-7). lib. bdg. (978-0-7614-1889-4(X)); Legends or Lies. lib. bdg. (978-0-7614-1891-7(1)); Perplexing People. (J). (gr. 3-7). lib. bdg. (978-0-7614-1890-0(3)); (Illus.). 72p. 2005. (978-0-7614-1892-4(X) , Benchmark Bks.) Cavendish, Marshall Corp.

Blue, Rose & Naden, Corinne J. Duty to Rescue. Sarat, Austin, ed. 1999. (Crime, Justice & Punishment Ser.). (Illus.). 80p. (J). (gr. 7-12). 30.00 (978-0-7910-4286-1(3) , Chelsea Hse.) Facts On File, Inc.

Brook, Henry. True Stories of Gangsters. McNee, Ian, illus. 2004. (True Adventure Stories Ser.). 144p. (J). pap. 4.95 (978-0-7945-0722-0(0) , Usborne) EDC Publishing.

Brownlie, Alison. Crime & Punishment: Changing Attitudes, 1900-2000. 1999. (Twentieth Century Issues Ser.). (Illus.). 64p. (J). (gr. 4-6). lib. bdg. 28.54 (978-0-8172-5573-2(7)) Raintree.

Campbell, Marilyn & Columbus, Curt. Crime & Punishment. 2004. (YA). pap. 6.50 (978-1-58342-225-0(0) , CB8) Dramatic Publishing Co.

Canini, Mikko. Crime. 2006. (History of Issues Ser.). (Illus.). 240p. (gr. 10-12). 36.20 (978-0-7377-2863-7(9) , Greenhaven Pr., Inc.) Thomson Gale.

Carroll, Jamuna. Cheating. 2007. (Introducing Issues with Opposing Viewpoints Ser.). (Illus.). 144p. (gr. 7-10). 33.70 ***(978-0-7377-3802-5(2)*** , Greenhaven Pr., Inc.) Thomson Gale.

Carter, K. Contra el Crimen. Palacios, Argentina, tr. 2002. (Seguridad (Safety) Ser.).Tr. of From Crime. (SPA., Illus.). 24p. mass mkt. 5.95 (978-1-58952-261-9(3) , RK31475) Rourke Publishing, LLC.

Cefrey, Holly. Bounty Hunter. 2003. (gr. 7-12). lib. bdg. 15.25 (978-0-613-67877-3(X)) Tandem Library Bks.

Charles, Robert B. Narcotics & Terrorism. 2003. (Securing the Nation Ser.). (Illus.). 112p. (J). (gr. 9-13). 30.00 (978-0-7910-7701-6(2) , Chelsea Hse.) Facts On File, Inc.

Chippendale, Neil. Crimes Against Humanity. 2002. (gr. 7-12). lib. bdg. 18.75 (978-0-613-70610-0(2)) Tandem Library Bks.

Chrisp, Peter. Victorian Crime. (Illus.). 32p. pap. (978-0-7502-3740-6(6) , Hodder Wayland) Hodder Children's Division.

Connors, Paul. Hate Crimes. 2006. (Current Controversies Ser.). (Illus.). 244p. (J). (gr. 10-12). 24.95 (978-0-7377-2209-3(6)); pap. 36.20 (978-0-7377-2208-6(8)) Thomson Gale. (Greenhaven Pr., Inc.).

Costain, Meredith & Antram, David. You Wouldn't Want to Be an 18th-Century British Convict! 2006. (Illus.). 32p. (YA). (gr. 2-5). pap. 9.95 (978-0-531-16998-8(7) , Watts, Franklin) Scholastic Library Publishing.

Crime, Justice, & Punishment. 2005. 80 - 120p. pap. 1140.00 (978-0-7910-8076-4(5) , Chelsea Hse.) Facts On File, Inc.

Dargie, Richard. Ancient Greece, Crime & Punishment. Hook, Adam, illus. 2006. (Changing Times Ser.). 32p. (J). (gr. 5-7). 27.93 (978-0-7565-2084-7(3)) Compass Point Bks.

Davis, Barbara J. Criminal Profiling. 2006. (Illus.). 48p. (J). pap. ***(978-0-8368-7717-5(9))***; lib. bdg. ***(978-0-8368-7712-0(8))*** Stevens, Gareth Inc.

DeAngelis, Gina. Cyber Crimes. 1999. (Crime, Justice & Punishment Ser.). (Illus.). (YA). (gr. 7 up). lib. bdg. 19.95 (978-0-7910-4936-5(1) , Chelsea Hse.) Facts On File, Inc.

Dupont, Ellen. Criminal Terminology. 2003. (Crime & Detection Ser.). (Illus.). 96p. (J). (gr. 7 up). lib. bdg. (978-1-59084-383-3(5)) Mason Crest Pubs.

Elgin, Kathy. Crime & Punishment. Hook, Adam, illus. 2004. (Changing Times Ser.). 32p. 26.60 (978-0-7565-0885-2(1)) Compass Point Bks.

Esherick, Joan. Criminal Psychology & Personality Profiling. 2006. (Forensics, the Science of Crime-Solving Ser.). (Illus.). 112p. (YA). (gr. 7 up). 22.95 (978-1-4222-0028-5(0)) Mason Crest Pubs.

—Prisoner Rehabilitation: Success Stories & Failures. 2007. (Incarceration Issues Ser.). (Illus.). 111p. (YA). (gr. 7 up). 22.95 (978-1-59084-994-1(9)) Mason Crest Pubs.

Fooks, Louie. The Drugs Trade. 2003. (21st Century Debates Ser.). (Illus.). 64p. (J). lib. bdg. 28.56 (978-0-7398-6033-5(X)) Raintree.

Ford, Jean. Forensics in American Culture: Obsessed with Crime. 2006. (Forensics, the Science of Crime-Solving Ser.). (Illus.). 112p. (YA). (gr. 7 up). 22.95 (978-1-4222-0037-7(X) , 1248054) Mason Crest Pubs.

—Rural Crime & Poverty: Violence, Drugs, & Other Issues. 2008. (Youth in Rural North America Ser.). (J). (978-1-4222-0016-2(7)) Mason Crest Pubs.

Gedatus, Gus. Perspectives on Violence, 8 bks. Incl. Date & Acquaintance Rape. lib. bdg. 23.93 (978-0-7368-0424-0(2)); Gangs & Violence. lib. bdg. 23.93 (978-0-7368-0423-3(4)); Hate. lib. bdg. 23.93 (978-0-7368-0427-1(7)); Stalking. lib. bdg. 23.93 (978-0-7368-0429-5(3)); Travel Safety. lib. bdg. 23.93 (978-0-7368-0426-4(9)); Violence at School. lib. bdg. 23.93 (978-0-7368-0422-6(6)); Violence in Public Places. lib. bdg. 23.93 (978-0-7368-0428-8(5)); Violence in the Media. lib. bdg. 23.93 (978-0-7368-0425-7(0)); (J). (gr. 4-6). (Illus.). 64p. 2000. Set lib. bdg. 191.44 (978-0-7368-0439-4(0) , LifeMatters Bks.) Capstone Pr., Inc.

Gibbons, Alan. Ganging Up. 2nd ed. 2006. (Illus.). 96p. (J). pap. 11.99 (***978-1-85881-194-9(5)***) Orion Publishing Group, Ltd. GBR. *Dist:* Independent Pubs. Group.

Goldenstern, Joyce. American Women Against Violence. 1998. (Collective Biographies Ser.). (Illus.). 128p. (YA). (gr. 6-12). lib. bdg. 26.60 (978-0-7660-1025-3(2)) Enslow Pubs., Inc.

Goldentyer, Debra. Street Violence. 1998. (Preteen Pressures Ser.). (Illus.). 48p. (J). (gr. 4-8). lib. bdg. 25.69 (978-0-8172-5028-7(X)) Raintree.

Greenhaven Staff. Crime & Criminals. 2002. lib. bdg. 33.25 (978-0-613-73870-5(5)) Tandem Library Bks.

Harvey, Gill. True Stories of Crime & Detection. 2004. (True Adventure Stories Ser.). 144p. (J). lib. bdg. 12.95 (978-1-58086-644-6(1) , Usborne) EDC Publishing.

—True Stories of Crime & Detection. Chisholm, Jane, ed. 2004. (True Adventure Stories Ser.). 144p. (J). pap. 4.95 (978-0-7945-0613-1(5) , Usborne) EDC Publishing.

Heinemann Educational Ltd. Publishing Staff. True Crime Package 6-Pack. 2004. pap. 275.40 (978-1-4109-1392-0(9)) Harcourt Schl. Pubs.

Hermsen, Sarah, et al. American Reference Library. 2004. (Crime & Punishment in America Reference Library). 39p. (J). lib. bdg. 5.00 (978-0-7876-9174-5(7) , UXL) Thomson Gale.

Hoehner, Jane & Macnee, Marie, eds. Outlaws, Mobsters & Crooks: From the Old West to the Internet, 3 vols. 1998. (Illus.). 495p. (J). (gr. 4-7). lib. bdg. 181.00 (978-0-7876-2803-1(4) , GML00502-112344, UXL) Thomson Gale.

Hoffman, Eric. Play Lady - La Senora Juguentona. 2004. (Anti-Bias Books for Kids). (ENG & SPA., Illus.). 32p. (J). (ps-3). pap. 11.95 (978-1-884834-61-5(2)) Redleaf Pr.

Ibrahim, Zafar Y. Folie a Deux: Shared Psychosis. Ibrahim, Zafar Y. & Ibrahim, Idore, eds. 2003. 116p. (YA). pap. (978-0-9640389-7-4(8)) Crispus Medical Pr.

Innes, Brian. Major Unsolved Crimes. 2002. (Crime & Detection Ser.). (Illus.). 96p. (J). (gr. 7 up). lib. bdg. (978-1-59084-382-6(7)) Mason Crest Pubs.

—Serial Murders. 2002. (Crime & Detection Ser.). (Illus.). 96p. (J). (gr. 7 up). lib. bdg. (978-1-59084-372-7(X)) Mason Crest Pubs.

Jacobs, Thomas A. They Broke the Law — You Be the Judge: True Cases of Teen Crime. 2003. (gr. 7-12). lib. bdg. 25.70 (978-0-613-82794-2(5)) Tandem Library Bks.

—They Broke the Law - You Be the Judge: True Cases of Teen Crime. 2004. 224p. (YA). (gr. 7 up). pap. 15.95 (978-1-57542-134-6(8)) Free Spirit Publishing, Inc.

James, Lesley. Women Who Made a Scene: Heroines, Villainesses, Eccentrics. 2002. (Remarkable Women). (Illus.). 80p. (YA). (gr. 6-9). lib. bdg. 32.85 (978-0-8172-5735-4(7)) Raintree.

Jones-Brown, Delores D. Race, Crime & Punishment. 2000. (Crime, Justice & Punishment Ser.). (Illus.). 80p. (YA). (gr. 7-12). 30.00 (978-0-7910-4273-1(1) , Chelsea Hse.) Facts On File, Inc.

Jury Trials in the Classroom. 2001, (J). per. 22.95 (978-1-883055-44-8(X)) Dandy Lion Pubns.

Kerrigan, Michael. The History of Punishment. 2002. (Crime & Detection Ser.). (Illus.). 96p. (J). (gr. 7 up). lib. bdg. (978-1-59084-386-4(X)) Mason Crest Pubs.

—Police Crime Prevention. 2002. (Rescue & Prevention Ser.). (Illus.). 96p. (J). (gr. 6 up). lib. bdg. (978-1-59084-406-9(8)) Mason Crest Pubs.

King, Andrew. Surveillance. 2007. (Crime Scene Investigations Ser.). (Illus.). 128p. (gr. 7-10). 31.20 (***978-1-59018-991-7(4)*** , Lucent Bks.) Thomson Gale.

King, David C. Al Capone: And the Roaring Twenties. 1998. (Notorious Americans & Their Times Ser.). (Illus.). 112p. (YA). (gr. 5 up). 28.70 (978-1-56711-218-4(8) , Blackbirch Pr., Inc.) Thomson Gale.

Koopmans, Andy. Crime & Criminals. 2002. (Examining Pop Culture Ser.). 176p. (J). 36.20 (978-0-7377-1431-9(X)); (Illus.). (gr. 7-10). pap. 24.95 (978-0-7377-1432-6(8)) Thomson Gale. (Greenhaven Pr., Inc.).

Lane, Brian & Buller, Laura. Crime & Detection. 2005. (Dk eyewitness Bks.). 72p. (J). lib. bdg. 19.99 (978-0-7566-1395-2(7)) Dorling Kindersley Publishing, Inc.

—Crime & Detection. Crawford, Andy, photos by. 2005. (Dk eyewitness Bks.). (Illus.). 72p. (J). (gr. 4-7). 15.99 (978-0-7566-1386-0(8)) Dorling Kindersley Publishing, Inc.

Leaney, Cindy. Wrong Stop: Safety from Crime. Wilks, Peter, illus. 2003. (Hero Club Safety Ser.). 32p. (J). 28.50 (978-1-58952-742-3(9)) Rourke Publishing, LLC.

Lewis, Michelle. Rights of the Accused. 2007. (Issues on Trial Ser.). (Illus.). 240p. (YA). (gr. 9 up). 36.20 (978-0-7377-2795-1(0) , Greenhaven Pr., Inc.) Thomson Gale.

Library in a Book Special Criminology Set. 2005. 288p. 450.00 (978-0-8160-6606-3(X)) Facts On File, Inc.

Lock, Joan. Protecting Yourself Against Criminals. 2002. (Crime & Detection Ser.). (Illus.). 96p. (J). (gr. 7 up). lib. bdg. (978-1-59084-385-7(1)) Mason Crest Pubs.

Locke, Ian. Fact Attack 5: Dastardly Deeds. 2003. (Illus.). 59p. (J). pap. 3.99 (978-0-330-35344-1(6) , Pan) Pan Macmillan GBR. *Dist:* Trafalgar Square Publishing.

MacDonald, Alan. Al Capone & His Gang. Reeve, Philip, illus. 2000. (Famous Dead People Ser.). 192p. (J). (gr. 3-7). pap. 4.50 (978-0-439-21124-6(7)) Scholastic, Inc.

—Al Capone & His Gang. Reeve, Philip, illus. 2000. (Famous Dead People Ser.). 192p. (J). (ps-7). lib. bdg. 11.15 (978-0-606-19527-0(0)) Tandem Library Bks.

MacDonald, Beverley. It's True! Crime Doesn't Pay. Weldon, Andrew, illus. 2006. (It's True! Ser.). 88p. (J). (gr. 5-8). 19.95 (978-1-55037-947-1(X)); pap. 5.95 (978-1-55037-946-4(1)) Annick Pr., Ltd. CAN. *Dist:* Firefly Bks., Ltd.

MacNee, Marie J. & Hoehner, Jane. Outlaws, Mobsters & Crooks: From the Old West to the Internet. 1998. (J). 84.00 (978-0-7876-2806-2(9) , UXL) Thomson Gale.

MacNee, Marie J. & Hoehner, Janes. Outlaws, Mobsters & Crooks: From the Old West to the Internet. 1998. (J). 84.00 (978-0-7876-2804-8(2)); pap. 84.00 (978-0-7876-2805-5(0)) Thomson Gale. (UXL).

Manaugh, Sara. Judges & Sentencing. 2001. (Crime, Justice & Punishment Ser.). (Illus.). 80p. (YA). (gr. 8 up). 30.00 (978-0-7910-4296-0(0) , Chelsea Hse.) Facts On File, Inc.

Marvis, B. & Chippendale, Neil. Crimes Against Humanity. 2000. (Crime, Justice & Punishment Ser.). 80p. (YA). (gr. 7 up). 30.00 (978-0-7910-4254-0(5) , Chelsea Hse.) Facts On File, Inc.

Marvis, B. & DeAngelis, Gina. Crimes Against Children. Sarat, Austin, ed. 1999. (Crime, Justice & Punishment Ser.). (Illus.). 80p. (YA). (gr. 7-12). 30.00 (978-0-7910-4253-3(7) , Chelsea Hse.) Facts On File, Inc.

—White-Collar Crime. Sarat, Austin, ed. 1999. (Crime, Justice & Punishment Ser.). (Illus.). 80p. (YA). (gr. 7-12). 30.00 (978-0-7910-4279-3(0) , Chelsea Hse.) Facts On File, Inc.

Marvis, B. & Worth, Richard. Great Robberies. 2000. (Crime, Justice & Punishment Ser.). (Illus.). 80p. (J). (gr. 7 up). 30.00 (978-0-7910-4265-6(0) , Chelsea Hse.) Facts On File, Inc.

Marzilli, Alan. Famous Crimes of the 20th Century. 2002. (Crime, Justice & Punishment Ser.). (Illus.). 111p. (J). 30.00 (978-0-7910-6788-8(2) , Chelsea Hse.) Facts On File, Inc.

Mauro, Paul & Melton, H. Keith. Crime Scene & Surveillance Photography. 2004. (Detective Academy Ser.). (Illus.). 48p. (J). (978-0-439-57182-1(0)) Scholastic, Inc.

—Master Case Files. Aycock, Daniel & Labat, Yancey C., illus. 2004. (Detective Academy Ser.). 48p. (J). pap. (978-0-439-57184-5(7)) Scholastic, Inc.

Moe, Barbara. Coping When You Are the Survivor of a Violent Crime. rev. ed. 1999. (Coping Ser.). (Illus.). 134p. (YA). (gr. 7-12). lib. bdg. 26.50 (978-0-8239-2873-6(X) , COSUVI) Rosen Publishing Group, Inc., The.

Moran, Paul, illus. World's Most Amazing Crime Facts for Kids. 2003. (World's Most Amazing Ser.). 112p. (J). pap. 3.99 (978-0-603-56097-2(0)) Egmont Bks., Ltd. GBR. *Dist:* Independent Pubs. Group.

Moris, Terence. Crime & Punishment. 1999. (Moral Dilemmas Ser.). (Illus.). 64p. 24.95 (978-0-237-51740-3(X) , Evans Brothers, Limited) Evans Publishing Group GBR. *Dist:* Independent Pubs. Group.

National Crime Prevention Council Staff. McGruff Wants You to Help Take a Bite Out of Crime. 1999. (Illus.). 16p. (J). (gr. k-12). pap. (978-0-934513-87-6(2)) National Crime Prevention Council.

O'Neil, Jean. Youth Action Packets. Kirby, Judy, ed. 1998. (Illus.). 18p. (YA). pap. 17.95 (978-0-934513-76-0(7)) National Crime Prevention Council.

Orme, David. Crime. 2008. (Trailblazers Ser.). (Illus.). 36p. pap. 7.95 (***978-1-84167-651-7(9)***) Ransom Publishing Ltd. GBR. *Dist:* International Publishers Marketing.

Owen, David. Police Lab: How Forensic Science Tracks down & Convicts Criminals. 2002. (Illus.). 128p. (J). (gr. 7-9). 19.95 (978-1-55297-620-3(3)) Firefly Bks., Ltd.

Parks, Peggy. Street Crime. 2007. (Ripped from the Headlines Ser.). 64p. (J). (gr. 5). 23.95 (***978-1-60217-007-0(X)***) Erickson Pr.

Platt. Organized Crime. 2004. (True Crime Ser.). (Illus.). 48p. (J). 27.14 (978-1-4109-1094-3(6)); pap. 7.95 (978-1-4109-1172-8(1)) Harcourt Schl. Pubs.

—Outlaws. 2004. (True Crime Ser.). (Illus.). 48p. (J). pap. 7.95 (978-1-4109-1173-5(X)) Harcourt Schl. Pubs.

—Poisoning. 2004. (Raintree Freestyle Ser.). (Illus.). 48p. (J). 27.14 (978-1-4109-1096-7(2)); pap. 7.95 (978-1-4109-1174-2(8)) Harcourt Schl. Pubs.

—Poisoning 6-Pack. 2004. (True Crime Ser.). pap. 42.90 (978-1-4109-1180-3(2)) Harcourt Schl. Pubs.

—True Crime, 5 bks., Set 1. 2004. 135.70 (978-1-4109-1097-4(0)); pap. 35.75 (978-1-4109-1175-9(6)) Raintree.

Platt, Richard. Villains. 2002. (ps-2). lib. bdg. 14.15 (978-0-613-57165-4(7)) Tandem Library Bks.

Powell, Phelan. Major Unsolved Crimes. Sarat, Austin, ed. 1999. (Crime, Justice & Punishment Ser.). (Illus.). 80p. (J). (gr. 7-12). 30.00 (978-0-7910-4277-9(4) , Chelsea Hse.) Facts On File, Inc.

Prentzas, G. S. & Hudson, David L. Prisoners' Rights. 2007. (Point/Counterpoint Ser.). 112p. (gr. 9). 32.95 (***978-0-7910-9277-4(1)*** , Chelsea Hse.) Facts On File, Inc.

Price, Stephen. Crime. 2006. (Illus.). 244p. (gr. 10-12). 36.20 (978-0-7377-2478-3(1)); pap. 24.95 (978-0-7377-2479-0(X)) Thomson Gale. (Greenhaven Pr., Inc.).

Raatma, Lucia. Safety in Your Neighborhood. 2004. (Living Well Ser.). 32p. (J). (gr. 2-6). 27.07 (978-1-59296-240-2(8)) Child's World, Inc.

Rafter, Nicole Hahn. Encyclopedia of Women & Crime. 2003. (gr. 7-12). lib. bdg. 30.35 (978-0-613-81045-6(7)) Tandem Library Bks.

Roleff, Tamara L. Hate Groups. 2001. (Opposing Viewpoints Digests Ser.). (Illus.). 112p. (J). 27.45 (978-0-7377-0677-2(5)); pap. 21.20 (978-0-7377-0676-5(7)) Thomson Gale. (Greenhaven Pr., Inc.).

Schroeder, Andreas. Thieves! 2005. (True Stories from the Edge Ser.). 164p. (J). (gr. 3). 18.95 (978-1-55037-933-4(X)) Annick Pr., Ltd. CAN. *Dist:* Firefly Bks., Ltd.

—Thieves! Ten Stories of Surprising Heists, Comical Capers, & Daring Escapades. 2005. (True Stories from the Edge Ser.). (Illus.). 164p. (J). (gr. 3). pap. 8.95 (978-1-55037-932-7(1)) Annick Pr., Ltd. CAN. *Dist:* Firefly Bks., Ltd.

Smith, Roger. Political Prisoners. 2007. (Incarceration Issues Ser.). (Illus.). 111p. (J). (gr. 7 up). 22.95 (978-1-59084-987-3(6)) Mason Crest Pubs.

—Prison Conditions: Overcrowding, Disease, Violence, & Abuse. 2007. (Incarceration Issues Ser.). (Illus.). 111p. (J). (gr. 7 up). 22.95 (978-1-59084-986-6(8)) Mason Crest Pubs.

Spence, David. Crime & Punishment. 2004. (Illus.). 32p. (J). (gr. 4-7). pap. (978-1-86007-010-5(8)) Ticktock Media Ltd.

Stark, Evan. Everything You Need to Know about Street Gangs. rev. ed. 2000. (Need to Know Library). (Illus.). 64p. (YA). (gr. 4-6). lib. bdg. 25.25 (978-0-8239-3305-1(9) , NTSTGA) Rosen Publishing Group, Inc., The.

Staunton, Ted. The Dreadful Truth: Canadian Crime. Geoffroi, Remie, illus. 2006. (Dreadful Truth Ser.). 104p. (J). (gr. 3-8). (***978-0-88780-705-3(4)***) Formac Publishing Co., Ltd. CAN. *Dist:* Casemate Pubs. & Bk. Distributors, LLC.

Stewart, Gail B. Forensics. 2005. (Lucent Library of Science & Technology Ser.). (Illus.). 112p. (J). (gr. 4-7). lib. bdg. 29.95 (978-1-59018-641-1(9) , Lucent Bks.) Thomson Gale.

Stockdale, Tom. Al Capone. 1999. (Life & Times of Ser.). (Illus.). 48p. (YA). (gr. 5 up). lib. bdg. 18.65 (978-0-7910-4638-8(9) , Chelsea Hse.) Facts On File, Inc.

Taylor, Robert. Profiling. 2007. (Crime Scene Investigations Ser.). (Illus.). 128p. (gr. 7-10). 32.45 (***978-1-59018-990-0(6)*** , Lucent Bks.) Thomson Gale.

Townsend, John. Breakouts & Blunders. 48p. (J). 2006. pap. 8.90 (978-1-4109-1433-0(X)); 2005. lib. bdg. 31.43 (978-1-4109-1427-9(5)) Raintree.

—Cops & Robbers. 2006. 48p. (J). pap. 8.90 (978-1-4109-1434-7(8)) Raintree.

—Crime Through Time. 2005. (Raintree Freestyle Ser.). (Illus.). 48p. (J). (978-1-4109-2051-5(8)); pap. (978-1-4109-2056-0(9)) Steck-Vaughn.

—Outlaws. 2004. (Raintree Freestyle Ser.). (Illus.). 48p. (J). (gr. 2-4). lib. bdg. 27.14 (978-1-4109-1095-0(4)) Harcourt Schl. Pubs.

—Prisons & Prisoners. 2005. (Raintree Freestyle Ser.). (Illus.). 48p. (J). (978-1-4109-2053-9(4)); (gr. 6-8). pap. 8.90 (978-1-4109-2058-4(5)) Steck-Vaughn.

—Punishment & Pain. 2005. (Raintree Freestyle Ser.). (Illus.). 48p. (J). pap. (978-1-4109-2059-1(3)); lib. bdg. (978-1-4109-2054-6(2)) Steck-Vaughn.

Uschan, Michael V. Hate Crimes. 2007. (Hot Topics Ser.). (Illus.). 128p. (gr. 7-10). 32.45 (***978-1-56006-661-3(X)*** , Lucent Bks.) Thomson Gale.

Valdez, Jannay. Bonnie & Clyde - Villains or Victims? (Illus.). 120p. (YA). (978-1-886709-09-6(2)) Outlaw Pubns.

Wilker, Josh. Organized Crime. 1999. (Crime, Justice & Punishment Ser.). (Illus.). 80p. (YA). (gr. 7-12). 30.00 (978-0-7910-4271-7(5) , Chelsea Hse.) Facts On File, Inc.

Williams, Stanley T. & Becnel, Barbara Cottman. Life in Prison. 2001. (Illus.). 80p. (J). (gr. 4-7). 14.95 (978-1-58717-093-5(0)); pap. 5.99 (978-1-58717-094-2(9)) Chronicle Bks. LLC. (SeaStar Bks.).

Wilson, Eric G. Vancouver Nightmare: A Tom Austin Mystery. Row, Richard, illus. 2000. (Tom Austin Mysteries Ser.). 112p. (J). pap. 4.99 (978-1-55143-149-9(1)) Orca Bk. Pubs. USA.

Winters, Rob. What Is a Hate Crime? 2007. 2007. (At Issue Ser.). 128p. (gr. 10-12). 29.95 (***978-0-7377-2436-3(6));*** pap. 21.20 (***978-0-7377-2437-0(4)***) Thomson Gale. (Greenhaven Pr., Inc.).

Woog, Adam. Gangsters. 2000. (History Makers Ser.). (Illus.). 112p. (YA). (gr. 7-10). 27.45 (978-1-56006-638-5(5) , Lucent Bks.) Thomson Gale.

Woolf, Alex. Why Do People Commit Crime? 2004. (Exploring Tough Issues Ser.). (Illus.). 48p. (J). lib. bdg. (978-0-7398-6682-5(6)) Raintree.

Worth, Richard. Gangs & Crime. 2001. (Crime, Justice & Punishment Ser.). (Illus.). 80p. (J). 30.00 (978-0-7910-5767-4(4) , Chelsea Hse.) Facts On File, Inc.

—Probation & Parole. 2001. (Crime, Justice & Punishment Ser.). (Illus.). 80p. (J). 30.00 (978-0-7910-5766-7(6) , Chelsea Hse.) Facts On File, Inc.

Wright, Cynthia. Everything You Need to Know about Dealing with Stalking. 2005. (Need to Know Library). (Illus.). 64p. (YA). (gr. 7-12). lib. bdg. 25.25 (978-0-8239-2841-5(1) , NTSTAL) Rosen Publishing Group, Inc., The.

Wright, John D. Hate Crimes. 2002. (Crime & Detection Ser.). (Illus.). 96p. (J). (gr. 7 up). lib. bdg. (978-1-59084-379-6(7)) Mason Crest Pubs.

—Race & Crime. 2002. (Crime & Detection Ser.). (Illus.). 96p. (J). (gr. 7 up). lib. bdg. (978-1-59084-378-9(9)) Mason Crest Pubs.

Wright, Terrell C. Home of the Body Bags. 2005. 216p. pap. 15.00 net. (978-0-9758594-0-7(4)) Senegalpress.

Yaffe, Rebecca M. & Hoade, Lonnie F. When a Parent Goes to Jail. Moody, Barbara S., illus. 2000. 48p. (J). (gr. k-7). pap., wbk. ed. 29.95 (978-1-877810-11-4(8)) Rayve Productions, Inc.

Ziff, John. Espionage & Treason. 1999. (Crime, Justice & Punishment Ser.). (Illus.). 80p. (J). (gr. 7-12). 30.00 (978-0-7910-4263-2(4) , Chelsea Hse.) Facts On File, Inc.

CRIME AND CRIMINALS—FICTION

The adventures of officer Byrd. 2007. (J). 16.99 (***978-0-9787322-0-2(0)***) Officer Byrd Publishing Co.

Ahlberg, Allan. The Cat Who Got Carried Away. McEwen, Katharine, illus. 2003. 96p. (J). (gr. 1-4). 15.99 (978-0-7636-2073-8(4)) Candlewick Pr.

Ashworth, Sherry. Something Wicked. 2004. 222p. (J). pap. 9.99 (978-0-00-712335-3(3)) HarperCollins Pubs. Ltd. GBR. *Dist:* Independent Pubs. Group.

Avi. Keep Your Eye on Amanda! 1999. (J). (978-0-606-15600-4(3)) Tandem Library Bks.

Bailey, Linda. How Come the Best Clues Are Always in the Garbage? 2004. (Stevie Diamond Mysteries Ser.). 176p. (YA). (gr. 13 up). (978-1-55337-583-8(1)) Kids Can Pr., Ltd.

Bailie, Helen. The Azura Stones. 2007. 212p. (YA). per. 18.00 (***978-1-58982-374-7(5)*** , Bedside Bks.) American Bk. Publishing Group.

Bateman, Colin. Bring Me the Head of Oliver Plunkett. 2005. 272p. (gr. 4-7). (J). 15.95 (978-0-385-73245-1(7)); lib. bdg. 17.99 (978-0-385-90269-4(7)) Random Hse. Children's Bks. (Delacorte Bks. for Young Readers).

Berry, Connie Lee. The Criminal in the Caymans. 2007. (Incredible Journey Bks.). 85p. (J). pap. 3.95 (***978-0-9772848-0-1(8)***) Kid's Fun Pr.

Bertrand, Diane Gonzales. Trino's Choice. (Illus.). 128p. (YA). (gr. 5-11). pap., stu. ed. 9.95 (978-1-55885-268-6(9)); 1999. 124p. (J). (gr. 4-7). 16.95 (978-1-55885-279-2(4)) Arte Publico Pr. (Piñata Books).

—Trino's Choice. 1999. (978-0-606-17956-0(9)); (gr. 5-8). lib. bdg. 18.75 (978-0-613-33660-4(7)) Tandem Library Bks.

Blake, Emily. No Accident. 2008. (Little Secrets Ser.: No. 2). 208p. (J). pap. 4.99 (***978-0-545-02825-7(6)*** , Scholastic Paperbacks) Scholastic, Inc.

Bone, Ian. Killer Plot. 2002. (Crime Waves Ser.). (Illus.). 96p. (YA). pap. (978-0-7344-0169-4(8) , Lothian Bks.) Hachette Livre Australia.

Boone, Jack W. Billy Box. 2000. 367p. (YA). pap. 14.95 (978-1-880719-07-7(X) , Grafco Bks.) Grafco Productions, Inc.

Brooks, Kevin. Martyn Pig. 240p. (J). 2003. pap. 6.99 (978-0-439-50752-3(9)); 2002. (gr. 5 up). pap. 16.95 (978-0-439-29595-6(5) , Chicken Hse., The) Scholastic, Inc.

—Martyn Pig. 2003. (gr. 7-12). lib. bdg. 15.30 (978-0-613-64813-4(7)) Tandem Library Bks.

Brouillet, Chrystine. Un Crime Audacieux. 2001. (Roman + — Special Editions Ser.). (FRE., Illus.). 96p. (YA). (gr. 8). pap. (978-2-89021-492-7(3)) Diffusion du livre Mirabel.

—Le Vol du Siecle. Brochard, Philippe, illus. 2001. (Roman Jeunesse Ser.). (FRE.). 96p. (J). pap. (978-2-89021-473-6(7)) Diffusion du livre Mirabel.

Brown, Jeremy. Four-Minute Forensic Mysteries: Body of Evidence. 2006. (Crime Files Ser.). (J). 19.95 (978-0-439-89554-5(5)) Scholastic, Inc.

—Shadow of a Doubt. 2006. (Crime Files Ser.). 224p. (J). pap. 5.99 (978-0-439-76935-8(3) , Scholastic Paperbacks) Scholastic, Inc.

Bumgarner, Barri L. Dregs. 2007. (YA). pap. 14.95 (***978-0-9793857-0-4(9)***) Tigress Pr.

Cadnum, Michael. Edge. 1999. (Illus.). 144p. (J). (gr. 7-12). 5.99 (978-0-14-038714-8(5) , Puffin) Penguin Group (USA) Inc.

—Edge. 1999. (gr. 7-12). lib. bdg. 14.15 (978-0-613-14695-1(6)) Tandem Library Bks.

Callaway, Phil. Jake & the Slippery Bank Robbers. 2002. (Jake Ser.). (Illus.). 36p. (J). pap. 3.99 (978-1-55305-031-5(2)) Cygnet Publishing Group, Inc./ Coolreading.com CAN. *Dist:* Orca Bk. Pubs. USA.

Carroll, Jenny, pseud. Safe House. 2007. (1-800-Where-R-You Ser.: No. 3). 272p. (YA). mass mkt. 6.99 (978-1-4169-2706-8(9) , Simon Pulse) Simon & Schuster Children's Publishing.

Carroll, Jenny, pseud & O'Neill, Jacquie. Sanctuary. 2007. (1-800-Where-R-You Ser.: No. 4). 240p. (YA). mass mkt. 6.99 (978-1-4169-2707-5(7) , Simon Pulse) Simon & Schuster Children's Publishing.

Clancy, Tom. The Ultimate Escape. 1999. (Tom Clancy's Net Force Ser.). (978-0-606-20429-3(6)) Tandem Library Bks.

—Virtual Vandals. 1999. (Tom Clancy's Net Force Ser.). (978-0-606-20430-9(X)) Tandem Library Bks.

Colfer, Eoin. The Arctic Incident. 2002. (Artemis Fowl Ser.: Bk. 2). (gr. 5-8). lib. bdg. 16.15 (978-0-613-62927-0(2)) Tandem Library Bks.

Collier, James Lincoln. The Rich & Famous. 2001. (Lost Treasures Ser.: No. 6). (Illus.). 240p. (gr. 3-7). pap. 1.99 (978-0-7868-1519-7(1) , Volo) Hyperion Bks. for Children.

Collinson, Roger. Butterfingers. 2003. (Illus.). 80p. pap. 9.99 (978-1-84270-290-1(4)) Andersen GBR. *Dist:* Independent Pubs. Group.

Coman, Carolyn. The Big House. Shepperson, Rob, illus. 2004. 224p. (J). 16.95 (978-1-932425-09-3(8) , Lemniscaat) Boyds Mills Pr.

—The Big House. Rob, Shepperson, illus. 2007. 224p. (J). (gr. 3 up). pap. 6.99 (978-0-14-240740-0(2) , Puffin) Penguin Group (USA) Inc.

Conn, Bruce. The Curse of Durgan's Reef. 2004. 142p. (YA). 21.95 (978-0-595-66223-4(4)); pap. 11.95 (978-0-595-30935-1(6)) iUniverse, Inc.

Cormier, Robert. After the First Death. 2002. 21.75 (978-0-8446-7215-1(7)) Smith, Peter Pub., Inc.

—I Am the Cheese. 2007. 256p. (J). (gr. 7). pap. 8.99 (***978-0-375-84039-5(7)*** , Knopf Bks. for Young Readers) Random Hse. Children's Bks.

Cormier, Robert. The Rag & Bone Shop. 2001. (Illus.). 160p. (YA). (gr. 7 up). 15.95 (978-0-385-72962-8(6) , Delacorte Bks. for Young Readers) Random Hse. Children's Bks.

Corr, Janice. The Aussie Time Travellers & the Cave of the Opal Eyed Snake. 2005. (Illus.). 112p. pap. (978-1-4120-4621-3(1)) Trafford Publishing.

Corrigan, Eireann. Splintering. 2005. 184p. (YA). (gr. 8-12). lib. bdg. 15.04 (978-0-606-33304-7(5)) Tandem Library Bks.

Crawford, Mary C. Suspicion of Arson. 2001. 125p. (J). (gr. 3-6). 9.99 (978-0-88092-550-1(7) , 550-7) Royal Fireworks Publishing Co.

Crime & Detection, 10 vols. rev. ed. 2005. (Fastback Ser.). 32p. (J). (gr. 6-12). pap. 44.95 (978-0-13-024445-1(7)) Globe Fearon Educational Publishing.

Deaver, Jeffery. The Bone Collector: A Lincoln Rhyme Novel. 1999. (gr. 7-12). lib. bdg. 16.45 (978-0-613-23690-4(4)) Tandem Library Bks.

Diaz, Enrique Perez. Los Pelusos, Cuentos Policiacos. Martinez, Enrique, illus. 2003. (SPA.). 95p. (J). (gr. 3-5). pap. 8.95 (978-968-19-1018-1(4)) Santillana USA Publishing Co., Inc.

Dickens, Charles. Oliver Twist. Andrew, Ian, illus. 2006. (Read & Listen Bks.). 64p. (J). 9.99 (978-0-7566-1835-3(5)) Dorling Kindersley Publishing, Inc.

—Oliver Twist. 2007. (Enriched Classics Ser.). 672p. pap. 4.95 (***978-1-4165-3475-4(X)*** , Pocket) Simon & Schuster.

Dickson, Louise. Crime Science. Cupples, Pat, illus. 1999. (Lu & Clancy Ser.). 40p. (J). (gr. k-3). (978-1-55074-552-8(2)) Kids Can Pr., Ltd.

DuPrau, Jeanne. People of Sparks. 2005. 338p. (J). (gr. k-8). per. 12.64 (978-0-606-33727-4(X)) Tandem Library Bks.

Egan, Tim. The Blunder of the Rogues. Egan, Tim, illus. (Illus.). 32p. (J). (gr. k-3). 2002. pap. 5.95 (978-0-618-25075-2(1)); 1999. tchr. ed. 15.00 (978-0-395-91007-8(2)) Houghton Mifflin Co. Trade & Reference Div.

—Blunder of the Rogues. 2002. (gr. k-3). lib. bdg. 14.10 (978-0-613-91048-4(6)) Tandem Library Bks.

Electric Chair or Taser Fried: Malicious Murder; Good Cop, Bad Cop. 2004. (YA). per. 25.00 (978-0-9760909-0-8(2)) Yost-Haynes, Melissa.

Erickson, John R. Moonshiner's Gold. (J). (gr. 5). 2003. (Illus.). 208p. 7.99 (978-0-14-250023-1(2) , Puffin); 2001. 176p. 15.99 (978-0-670-03502-1(5) , Viking Juvenile) Penguin Group (USA) Inc.

—Moonshiner's Gold. 2003. 199p. (J). (gr. 5-8). lib. bdg. 15.30 (978-0-613-61644-7(8)) Tandem Library Bks.

Ewart, Franzeska G. Sita Snake Queen of Speed. 2008. (Illus.). 96p. (J). 15.95 (***978-1-84507-779-2(2)*** **);** pap. 7.95 (***978-1-84507-748-8(2)***) Lincoln, Frances Ltd. GBR. *Dist:* Perseus Distribution.

Ferris, Jean. Love among the Walnuts. 2008. (Illus.). 240p. (YA). pap. 6.95 (***978-0-15-206227-9(0)*** , Harcourt Paperbacks) Harcourt Children's Bks.

Frye, Tom. Scratchin' on the Eight Ball. 2000. 240p. (YA). pap. 12.95 (978-0-595-12971-3(4) , Writer's Showcase Pr.) iUniverse, Inc.

Giles, Gail. What Happened to Cass Mcbride. 2007. 240p. (J). (gr. 7-17). pap. 7.99 (***978-0-316-16639-3(1)***) Little, Brown Bks. for Young Readers.

Gliori, Debi. Pure Dead Batty. 2007. (Illus.). 320p. (J). (gr. 4-7). 6.50 (***978-0-440-42074-3(1)*** , Yearling) Random Hse. Children's Bks.

Glover, Sandra. It Didn't Happen. 2006. 160p. (J). pap. 9.99 (***978-1-84270-077-8(4)***) Andersen GBR. *Dist:* Independent Pubs. Group.

Golden Books Staff & Hands, Cynthia. Cool Crime Fighters. 2001. 32p. pap. 3.99 (978-0-307-29056-4(5) , Golden Bks.) Random Hse. Children's Bks.

Gray, Nigel. Pip & the Convict. McLean, Andrew, illus. 2005. 32p. (J). 24.25 (978-1-920694-23-4(4)); pap. 15.25 (978-1-920694-66-1(8)) Univ. of Western Australia Pr. AUS. (Cygnet Bks.). *Dist:* International Specialized Bk. Services.

Greenwood, Kerry. The Three-Pronged Dagger. 2002. (Crime Waves Ser.). (Illus.). 160p. (YA). pap. (978-0-7344-0259-2(7) , Lothian Bks.) Hachette Livre Australia.

Halliday, John. Shooting Monarchs. 2003. (Illus.). 144p. (YA). 15.95 (978-0-689-84338-9(0) , McElderry, Margaret K.) Simon & Schuster Children's Publishing.

—Shooting Monarchs. l.t. ed. 2005. 157p. 20.95 (978-0-7862-7462-8(X)) Thorndike Pr.

Hamilton, Elizabeth L. Passport to Courage. 2002. (Character-in-Action Ser.: No. 1). (Illus.). 384p. (YA). per. 19.95 (978-0-9713749-3-5(7) , Character-in-Action) Quiet Impact, Inc.

Hands, Cynthia & Siefken, Paul. Unusual Suspects. 2001. 32p. pap. 3.99 (978-0-307-11357-3(4) , Golden Bks.) Random Hse. Children's Bks.

Harper, Ben, adapted by. The Movie Storybook: Batman Begins. 2005. (Batman Begins Ser.). (Illus.). 48p. 6.99 (978-0-439-72506-4(2)) Scholastic, Inc.

Harrar, George. Not As Crazy As I Seem. 2004. 240p. (J). (gr. 7). pap. 6.99 (978-0-618-49480-4(4) , Graphia) Houghton Mifflin Co. Trade & Reference Div.

Harris, Loretta. A Gangsta's Life. 2006. (YA). (***978-0-9786681-4-3(6)***) Children's Heart Publishing Co.

—Who Did It & Why? 2006. (YA). (***978-0-9786681-1-2(1)***) Children's Heart Publishing Co.

Hathaway, William. CD-Ring. 2006. 144p. (YA). (gr. 9-12). pap. (978-1-897073-29-2(1)) Lobster Pr.

Heflick, LaMonte. The Story of Boney & Clyde. 2004. (Illus.). 64p. pap. 3.99 (978-1-56175-911-8(2)) Remedia Pubns.

Hesse, Hermann. Demian. 1999. (gr. 7-12). lib. bdg. 21.10 (978-0-613-16655-3(8)) Tandem Library Bks.

Higson, Charlie. Blood Fever. 2nd rev. ed. 2007. (Young Bond Ser.). 368p. (gr. 7 up). pap. 7.99 (***978-1-4231-0029-4(8)***) Miramax Bks.

Hillenburg, Steven, creator. SpongeBob SquarePants Crime & Funishment Vol. 4, 7 vols. 2004. (Illus.). 96p. (gr. 2-5). pap. 7.99 (978-1-59182-576-0(8) , Tokyopop Kids) TOKYOPOP, Inc.

Hip Hop Criminal. 1998. (Illus.). 68p. (J). pap. 12.00 (978-0-9702945-1-7(4)) Vezun.

Howe, LeAnne. Shell Shaker. 2001. (gr. 7-12). lib. bdg. 21.05 (978-0-613-62703-0(2)) Tandem Library Bks.

Hutchens, Paul. The Cemetery Vandals. rev. ed. 1999. (Sugar Creek Gang Ser.: Vol. 32). 96p. (J). (gr. 4-7). 4.99 (978-0-8024-7037-9(8)) Moody Pubs.

Hutchinson, Emily. Oliver Twist. abr. ed. 2001. (gr. 7-12). lib. bdg. 15.25 (978-0-613-36566-6(6)) Tandem Library Bks.

Hyde, Dayton. Island of the Loons. 2002. (gr. 5-8). lib. bdg. 18.75 (978-0-613-57307-8(2)) Tandem Library Bks.

Inspector Grub & the Jelly Bean Robber: Individual Title Six-Packs. (Bookweb Ser.). 32p. (gr. 3 up). 34.00 (978-0-7635-3934-4(1)) Rigby Education.

Jenkins, Jerry B. & Fabry, Chris. Double Fault. 2005. (Tyndale Kids Ser.). 272p. (J). pap. 5.99 (978-1-4143-0146-4(4)) Tyndale Hse. Pubs.

—Hidden Riches. 2006. (Tyndale Kids Ser.). 272p. (J). pap. 5.99 (978-1-4143-0152-5(9)) Tyndale Hse. Pubs.

Jinks, Catherine. Evil Genius. 2008. (Illus.). 512p. (YA). pap. 7.95 (***978-0-15-206185-2(1)*** , Harcourt Paperbacks) Harcourt Children's Bks.

—Evil Genius. 2007. (Illus.). 496p. (YA). (gr. 7 up). 17.00 (978-0-15-205988-0(1)); 486p. (J). (***978-1-4287-3510-1(0)***) Harcourt Trade Pubs.

Johnson, Pete. Mind Reader: Blackmail. l.t. ed. 2000. (Illus.). 96p. (J). pap. (978-0-7540-6087-1(X) , CLP 289) BBC Audio.

Jones, T. W. Derth. 2006. 165p. pap. 19.95 (978-1-4241-0806-0(3)) PublishAmerica, Inc.

Karas, Phyllis. The Hate Crime. 2004. 190p. (YA). pap. 13.95 (978-0-595-33138-3(6) , Authors Choice Pr.) iUniverse, Inc.

Keene, Carolyn. Once upon a Crime. 2006. (Nancy Drew Ser.: No. 2). 192p. (J). pap. 5.99 (978-1-4169-1248-4(7) , Aladdin) Simon & Schuster Children's Publishing.

—The Wild Cat Crime. 1998. (Nancy Drew Mystery Stories: No. 141). (J). (gr. 3-6). (978-0-606-13643-3(6)) Tandem Library Bks.

Kehret, Peg. The Stranger Next Door. (J). 2003. (Illus.). 176p. (gr. 3-7). pap. 5.99 (978-0-14-250178-8(6) , Puffin); 2002. 160p. (gr. 4-8). 15.99 (978-0-525-46829-5(3) , Dutton Juvenile) Penguin Group (USA) Inc.

Korman, Gordon. Hollywood Hustle. 2006. 272p. (gr. 7-17). reprint ed. pap. 5.99 (978-0-7868-0919-6(1)) Hyperion Pr.

—Public Enemies, 2005. (On the Run Ser.: No. 5). 160p. (J). (gr. 3-7). pap. 4.99 (978-0-439-65140-0(9) , Scholastic Paperbacks) Scholastic, Inc.

—Son of the Mob. 2002. 262p. (J). 16.49 (978-0-7868-2616-2(9)) Hyperion Bks. for Children.

—The Stowaway Solution, 2005. (On the Run Ser.: No. 4). 160p. (J). (gr. 3-7). pap. 4.99 (978-0-439-65139-4(5) , Scholastic Paperbacks) Scholastic, Inc.

Korman, Gordon. Swindle. 2008. 256p. (J). pap. 16.99 (***978-0-439-90344-8(0)*** , Scholastic Pr.) Scholastic, Inc.

Krailing, Tessa. El Ladron de Gatos. (Club de las Mascotas Coleccion). (SPA.). 96p. (J). (gr. 3). (978-84-88061-89-8(7)) Serres, Ediciones, S. L. ESP. *Dist:* Lectorum Pubns., Inc.

Lavette, Lavaille. The Adventures of Roopster Roux: Escape from Vulture's Roost. Mitchell, Louis H., illus. 1998. (Adventures of Roopster Roux Ser.). 32p. (J). (ps-3). pap. 5.95 (978-1-56554-360-7(2)) Pelican Publishing Co., Inc.

—The Adventures of Roopster Roux: Slammin' Slime. Mitchell, Louis H., illus. 1998. (Adventures of Roopster Roux Ser.). 32p. (J). (ps-3). pap. 5.95 (978-1-56554-359-1(9)) Pelican Publishing Co., Inc.

Lee, Helen. Guide's Greatest Escape from Crime Stories. 2003. 141p. (J). pap. 10.99 (978-0-8280-1753-4(0) , 79-967) Review & Herald Publishing Assn.

Lenhard, Elizabeth. A New Kind of Super Spy. 2003. (Spy Kids 2 Ser.: Bk. 2). 144p. (gr. 3-7). pap. 4.99 (978-0-7868-1716-0(X) , Volo) Hyperion Bks. for Children.

—One Agent Too Many. 2nd ed. 2003. (Spy Kids 2 Ser.: Bk. 1). 144p. (J). (gr. 3-7). pap. 4.99 (978-0-7868-1715-3(1) , Volo) Hyperion Bks. for Children.

Lerangis, Peter. The Junior Novel. 2005. (Batman Begins Ser.). (Illus.). 160p. (ps-k). 4.99 (978-0-439-72509-5(7)) Scholastic, Inc.

Lisle, Janet Taylor. Black Duck. 2007. 256p. (J). (gr. 5 up). 6.99 (***978-0-14-240902-2(2)*** , Puffin) Penguin Group (USA) Inc.

Lorimer, Janet. Tuesday Raven. 2001. (PageTurner Spy Ser.). 80p. (YA). per. 3.95 (978-1-56254-140-8(4) , SP 1404) Saddleback Educational Publishing.

—Tuesday Raven. 2001. (gr. 7-12). lib. bdg. 11.80 (978-0-613-34513-2(4)) Tandem Library Bks.

Lurie, April. Brothers, Boyfriends & Other Criminal Minds. 2007. 304p. (YA). (gr. 7). 15.99 (978-0-385-73124-9(8) , Delacorte Bks. for Young Readers) Random Hse. Children's Bks.

MacDonald, Wendy. Castaway Convict. Wilson, Mark, illus. 2005. 136p. (J). pap. 15.25 (978-1-920694-35-7(8)) Univ. of Western Australia Pr. AUS. *Dist:* International Specialized Bk. Services.

Madsen, Wayne. The Case of Stolen Time: The Misadventures of Inspector Moustachio. 2007. (Misadventures of Inspector Moustachio Ser.: Bk. 1). 156p. (J). per. 16.99 (***978-0-9790878-9-9(9)***) Community Pr.

Mahy, Margaret. A Villain's Night Out. Horse, Harry, illus. l.t. ed. 1999. 144p. (J). pap. (978-0-7540-6083-3(7) , CLP 283) BBC Audio.

Martin, Nora. A Perfect Snow. 2004. 144p. (J). pap. 6.95 (978-1-58234-925-1(8) , Bloomsbury Children) Bloomsbury Publishing.

Mayowa-Harrison, Lady Paula Merry. The Buckaroos. 2006. (J). pap. 8.00 (***978-0-8059-6978-8(0)***) Dorrance Publishing Co., Inc.

McCarthy, Meghan. Steal Back the Mona Lisa! 2006. (Illus.). 40p. (J). 16.00 (978-0-15-205368-0(9)) Harcourt Trade Pubs.

McClintock, Norah. Bang. 2007. (Orca Soundings Ser.). 112p. (YA). (gr. 7 up). pap. (***978-1-55143-654-8(X)*** **);** lib. bdg. (***978-1-55143-656-2(6)***) Orca Bk. Pubs.

McRae, David. Blood of the Donnellys. 2008. 152p. (YA). pap. 9.99 (***978-1-55002-754-9(9)*** , Sandcastle Bks.) Dundurn Group, The CAN. *Dist:* Univ. of Toronto Pr.

Miller, Kirsten. The Empress's Tomb. 2007. (Kiki Strike Ser.). 350p. (J). (gr. 5-9). 16.95 (***978-1-59990-047-6(5)*** , Bloomsbury Children) Bloomsbury Publishing.

Miller, Kirsten. Kiki Strike: Inside the Shadow City. (J). 2007. 400p. (gr. 5-9). pap. 7.95 (***978-1-59990-092-6(0))***; 2006. 250p. 16.95 (978-1-58234-960-2(6)) Bloomsbury Publishing. (Bloomsbury Children).

Moloney, James. Black Taxi. 2005. 272p. (J). (gr. 7 up). 15.99 (978-0-06-055937-3(3)); lib. bdg. 16.89 (978-0-06-055938-0(1)) HarperCollins Pubs.

Morgenroth, Kate. Jude. 288p. (YA). 2004. 16.95 (978-0-689-86479-7(5)); 2006. (Illus.). reprint ed. mass mkt. 5.99 (978-1-4169-1267-5(3) , Simon Pulse) Simon & Schuster Children's Publishing.

Morrison, Grant & Millar, Mark. Skrull Kill Krew TPB. 2006. (Illus.). 120p. pap. 16.99 (978-0-7851-2120-6(X)) Marvel Enterprises, Inc.

Murphy, Barbara Beasley. Tripping the Runner. 2001. 192p. (gr. 4-7). pap. 12.95 (978-0-595-15398-5(4) , Backinprint.com) iUniverse, Inc.

Nebel, Laurel. Stop That Thief! 1999. 186p. (J). (gr. 3-5). 9.99 (978-0-88092-474-0(8) , 4748) Royal Fireworks Publishing Co.

Newton, Robert. Runner. 2007. 224p. (J). (gr. 5). lib. bdg. 18.99 (978-0-375-93744-6(7) , Knopf Bks. for Young Readers) Random Hse. Children's Bks.

Park, Barbara. Junie B. Jones's Third Boxed Set Ever!, Bks. 9-12. Brunkus, Denise, illus. 2003. (Junie B. Jones Ser.). (J). (gr. 1-4). 15.96 (978-0-375-82552-1(5) , Random Hse. Bks. for Young Readers) Random Hse. Children's Bks.

Pausacker, Jenny. Scam. 2002. (Crime Waves Ser.). (Illus.). 96p. (YA). pap. (978-0-7344-0277-6(5) , Lothian Bks.) Hachette Livre Australia.

Pennington, Kate. Charley Feather. 2007. (J). pap. (***978-0-340-87873-6(8)*** , Hodder Children's Books) Hodder Children's Division.

Peralta, Joaquin. An Almost Private Eye: Mystery of the Starfighter. 2008. 260p. (YA). per. 17.00 (***978-1-934376-17-1(5)***) Balona Bks.

Perkins, T J. In the Grand Scheme of Things: A Kim & Kelly Mystery. 2007. (Illus.). 151p. (YA). 10.99 (***978-0-9777538-4-0(0)***) GumShoe Press.

Pierce, Tamora. Terrier. 2006. (Beka Cooper Ser.: Bk. 1). (Illus.). 592p. (J). (gr. 5-8). 18.95 (978-0-375-81468-6(X) , Random Hse. Bks. for Young Readers) Random Hse. Children's Bks.

Platt. Organized Crime, 6 Packs. 2004. (Illus.). pap. 45.90 (978-1-4109-1178-0(0)) Harcourt Schl. Pubs.

Rawley, Jody. The Vicar of Church Hill. 2002. 83p. (YA). (gr. 11 up). pap. 7.66 (978-0-9721350-0-9(6)) Capital Media Enterprise.

Ray, Curtis L. Juvenile Justice 101: A Juvenile Crime Fiction Novel. 2001. 172p. (YA). (gr. 8-12). pap. 12.95 (978-0-595-19958-7(5)) iUniverse, Inc.

Return Payment. 2001. 32p. (YA). (gr. 6-12). pap. (978-0-8224-1458-2(9)) Globe Fearon Educational Publishing.

Roderman, Anna Marie. Two Tales of Courage. 2004. 116p. (YA). pap. 7.95 (978-0-87714-318-5(8)) Denlingers Pubs., Ltd.

Rowley, B. J. My Body Fell Off! 2000. (Light Traveler Adventure Ser.: Vol. 1). 206p. (YA). (gr. 6-12). pap. 11.95 (978-0-9700103-1-5(1)) Golden Wings Enterprises.

—Silver Hawk's Revenge. 2000. (Light Traveler Adventure Ser.: Vol. 2). 256p. (YA). (gr. 6-12). pap. 12.95 (978-0-9700103-2-2(X)) Golden Wings Enterprises.

Ruby, Laura. The Wall & the Wing. 2007. 352p. (J). (gr. 5 up). pap. 6.99 (***978-0-06-075257-6(2)*** , Eos) HarperCollins Pubs.

Rue, Nancy N. The Caper. 2000. (Christian Heritage Ser.). (Illus.). 192p. (J). (gr. 3-7). pap. 5.99 (978-1-56179-837-7(1)) Bethany Hse. Pubs.

Sarfati, Sonia. Maison, Prison et Folle Evasion. Durand, Pierre, illus. 2002. (Premier Roman Ser.). (FRE.). 64p. (J). (gr. 2-5). pap. (978-2-89021-257-2(2)) Diffusion du livre Mirabel.

Schirripa, Steve & Fleming, Charles. Nicky Deuce: Welcome to the Family. 2006. 176p. (gr. 5-8). 5.99 (978-0-440-42053-8(9) , Yearling) Random Hse. Children's Bks.

Schirripa, Steven R. & Fleming, Charles. Nicky Deuce: Home for the Holidays. 2006. 208p. (J). (gr. 4-7). 15.95 (978-0-385-73258-1(9)); lib. bdg. 17.99 (978-0-385-90276-2(X)) Random Hse. Children's Bks. (Delacorte Bks. for Young Readers).

Scholastic, Inc. Staff & Hernandez-Rosenblatt, Jason. Batman: The Purr-fect Crime. Burchett, Rick, illus. 2004. (Batman Ser.: No. 4). 40p. (J). 3.99 (978-0-439-47100-8(1) , Cartwheel Bks.) Scholastic, Inc.

Schraff, Anne. The Accuser: Set 2. 2002. 32p. 2.95 (978-1-56254-415-7(2) , SP 4152) Saddleback Educational Publishing.

—The Hunter. 2001. (PageTurner Mystery Ser.). 80p. (YA). per. 3.95 (978-1-56254-181-1(1) , SP 1811) Saddleback Educational Publishing.

Schwabach, Karen. A Pickpocket's Tale. 2008. 240p. (J). (gr. 3-7). 5.99 (***978-0-375-83380-9(3)*** , Yearling) Random Hse. Children's Bks.

Skillchecks for Crime & Detection. rev. ed. 2005. (Fastback Ser.). 32p. (J). (gr. 6-12). pap. 5.95 (978-0-13-024453-6(8)) Globe Fearon Educational Publishing.

Smarto, Don. Family Secrets. 2004. (Illus.). 310p. (YA). pap. 19.95 (978-0-930201-07-4(8)) Frontline Pr.

Smith, Roland. Zach's Lie. 2003. 224p. (J). (gr. 5-17). pap. 5.99 (978-0-7868-1440-4(3)) Hyperion Bks. for Children.

—Zach's Lie. 2003. (gr. 5-8). lib. bdg. 14.15 (978-0-613-63491-5(8)) Tandem Library Bks.

Snicket, Lemony, pseud & Stookey, Nathaniel. The Composer Is Dead. Ellis, Carson, illus. 2008. (J). (***978-0-06-123627-3(6)*** **);** lib. bdg. (***978-0-06-123628-0(4)***) HarperCollins Pubs.

Soto, Gary. Petty Crimes. 1998. 168p. (J). (gr. 4-7). 17.00 (978-0-15-201658-6(9)) Harcourt Children's Bks.

Stanglin, Jackie A. What Is Jail, Mommy? McGuckie, Cierra Jade, illus. l.t. ed. 2006. 40p. (J). 19.99 (***978-1-59879-252-2(0)*** **);** per. 11.99 (***978-1-59879-248-5(2)***) Lifevest Publishing, Inc.

Starke, Ruth. Dead Red. 2002. (Illus.). 96p. (YA). pap. (978-0-7344-0250-9(3) , Lothian Bks.) Hachette Livre Australia.

Stassen, Jean-Philippe. Deogratias. 2006. (Illus.). 96p. (J). pap. (***978-0-330-44467-5(0)*** , First Second Bks.) Roaring Brook Pr.

Stockton, Frank Richard. The Stories of the Three Burglars. 2004. reprint ed. pap. 15.95 (978-1-4191-8358-4(3)); pap. 1.99 (978-1-4192-8358-1(8)) Kessinger Publishing, LLC.

Strasser, Todd. Stolen Kisses, Secrets, & Lies. Trisolini, Matteo, photos by. 2007. (Mob Princess Ser.). 224p. (YA). (gr. 9 up). pap. 8.99 (***978-1-4169-3541-4(X)*** , Simon Pulse) Simon & Schuster Children's Publishing.

Strauss, Linda Leopold. Really, Truly, Everything's Fine. 2004. 160p. (YA). 15.95 (978-0-7614-5163-1(3)) Cavendish, Marshall Corp.

Stutley, Doris. Operation Foxtrot Five. 2002. 160p. (YA). pap. (978-0-7344-0180-9(9) , Lothian Bks.) Hachette Livre Australia.

Sweeney, Joyce. Takedown. 2004. 208p. (J). 15.95 (978-0-7614-5175-4(7)) Cavendish, Marshall Corp.

Talone, Augusto. The Boy Deputies: Six Short Stories about Two Young Boys Who Help Their Father, A Sheriff, Solve Crimes. 2006. 232p. (J). pap. 17.99 (978-1-59977-004-8(0)) Annotation Pr.

Teitelbaum, Michael. Justice for All. 2003. (gr. k-3). lib. bdg. 10.65 (978-0-613-72170-7(5)) Tandem Library Bks.

Torres, J. Caped Crusader. 2006. (Batman Ser.). 32p. (J). pap. 4.99 (978-0-439-83003-4(6)) Scholastic, Inc.

Updale, Eleanor. Montmorency's Revenge. 2007. 289p. (J). (***978-1-4287-3312-1(4)*** , Orchard Bks.) Scholastic, Inc.

—Montmorency's Revenge Book 4. 2008. (Montmorency's Revenge Ser.). 304p. (J). pap. 6.99 (***978-0-439-81374-7(3)*** , Scholastic Paperbacks) Scholastic, Inc.

Uwuigiaren, Omoruyi. The Adventures of Nihu. Ayalomeh, Shedrach, illus. 2007. (YA). per. 16.95 (***978-1-934138-15-1(0)***) Bouncing Ball Bks., Inc.

van Diepen, Allison. Snitch. 2007. 304p. (YA). pap. 6.99 (***978-1-4169-5030-1(3)*** , Simon Pulse) Simon & Schuster Children's Publishing.

Vrettos, A. M. Sight. 2007. 272p. (YA). (gr. 7 up). 16.99 (***978-1-4169-0657-5(6)*** , McElderry, Margaret K.) Simon & Schuster Children's Publishing.

Wagner, Paul. All Rise: The Criminal Trial of 4 Teens. 2000. 156p. (YA). pap. 10.95 (978-0-595-09151-5(2) , Writers Club Pr.) iUniverse, Inc.

Walden, Mark. H. I. V. E. Higher Institute of Villainous Education. 2007. (H. I. V. E. Ser.). 320p. (J). (gr. 5-9). 15.99 (***978-1-4169-3571-1(1)***) Simon & Schuster Children's Publishing.

Waldron, Ann. Scaredy Cat. 2000. 116p. (YA). (gr. 4-7). pap. 9.95 (978-0-595-00067-8(3)) iUniverse, Inc.

Walters, Eric. Diamonds in the Rough. 1998. (Gemini Bks.). 252p. (YA). (gr. 7-10). mass mkt. 6.95 (978-0-7736-7470-7(5)) Stoddart Kids CAN. *Dist:* Fitzhenry & Whiteside, Ltd., Stoddart Publishing.

—Diamonds in the Rough. 1998. (gr. 7-12). lib. bdg. 14.10 (978-0-613-85640-9(6)) Tandem Library Bks.

Watanabe, Taeko. Kaze Hikaru, Vol. 2. 2006. (Kaze Hikaru Ser.). 208p. (YA). pap. 8.99 (978-1-4215-0581-7(9)) Viz Media.

Wein, Elizabeth. The Empty Kingdom. 2008. (YA). (gr. 5). 16.99 (***978-0-670-06273-7(1)*** , Viking Juvenile) Penguin Group (USA) Inc.

Wells, H. G. The Invisible Man. 2004. 208p. (J). (gr. 4 up). pap. 3.99 (978-0-439-57427-3(7) , Scholastic Paperbacks) Scholastic, Inc.

Wiebe, Rudy. The Mad Trapper. rev. ed. 2004. (Illus.). 184p. (YA). (gr. 9 up). pap. 9.95 (978-0-88995-268-3(X)) Red Deer Pr. CAN. *Dist:* Fitzhenry & Whiteside, Ltd.

Wilde, Oscar. El Crimen de Lord Arthur Savile. 2001. (SPA.). (gr. 3-6). lib. bdg. 12.25 (978-0-613-82124-7(6)) Tandem Library Bks.

Wilson, Linda Miller. A Few Days Journey. 1998. 124p. (YA). (gr. 4-8). 9.99 (978-0-88092-402-3(0) , 4020) Royal Fireworks Publishing Co.

Woodson, Jacqueline. Hush. 192p. (gr. 5). 2006. (J). pap. 5.99 (978-0-14-240600-7(7) , Puffin); 2002. (YA). 15.99 (978-0-399-23114-8(5) , Putnam Juvenile) Penguin Group (USA) Inc.

Wright, Betty Ren. Princess for a Week. Rogers, Jacqueline, illus. 2007. 160p. (J). (gr. 2-5). pap. 6.95 (*978-0-8234-2111-4(2)) Holiday Hse., Inc.

Yakov y los Siete Ladrones. 2004. (SPA.). (YA). 19.95 (978-0-439-69887-0(1)) Scholastic, Inc.

CRIME AND CRIMINALS—IDENTIFICATION

Giles, Gail. What Happened to Cass McBride? 2006. 224p. (J). (gr. 7-17). 16.99 (978-0-316-16638-6(3)) Little Brown & Co.

Heath, David. Crime Lab Technician. 1999. (Careers Without College Ser.). (Illus.). 48p. (J). (gr. 3-4). lib. bdg. 21.26 (978-0-7368-0170-6(7) ; LifeMatters Bks.) Capstone Pr., Inc.

Holzer, David. Prime Suspect: Suspect Identification System. 2004. (Illus.). 48p. (J). pap. (978-0-439-68027-1(1)) Scholastic, Inc.

Joyce, Jaime. Bullet Proof! The Evidence That Guns Leave Behind. 2007. (24/7 - Science Behind the Scenes Ser.). (Illus.). 64p. (YA). (gr. 8-12). pap. 7.95 (*978-0-531-15455-7(6) , Watts, Franklin) Scholastic Library Publishing.

CRIMEAN WAR, 1853-1856

Malam, John. Mary Seacole. 2000. (Tell Me about Ser.). (Illus.). 22p. (J). 15.99 (978-0-237-51974-2(7) , Evans Brothers, Limited) Evans Publishing Group GBR. *Dist:* Independent Pubs. Group.

Ross, Stewart. Don't Say No to Flo: The Story of Florence Nightingale. Shields, Susan, illus. 32p. (J). pap. (978-0-7502-3273-9(0) , Hodder Wayland) Hodder Children's Division.

CRIMES, POLITICAL

see Political Crimes and Offenses

CRIMINAL INVESTIGATION

see also Crime and Criminals—Identification; Detectives; Police

Bauchner, Elizabeth. Document Analysis. 2006. (Forensics, the Science of Crime-Solving Ser.). (Illus.). 112p. (J). (gr. 7 up). 22.95 (978-1-4222-0029-2(9)) Mason Crest Pubs.

Beres, D. B. Dusted & Busted! The Science of Fingerprinting. 2007. (24/7 - Science Behind the Scenes Ser.). (Illus.). 64p. (J). (gr. 8-12). pap. 7.95 (*978-0-531-15457-1(2) , Watts, Franklin) Scholastic Library Publishing.

Beres, D. B. & Franklin, Watts. Dusted & Busted! The Science of Fingerprinting. 2006. (24/7 - Science Behind the Scenes Ser.). (Illus.). 64p. (J). (gr. 8-12). 25.00 (978-0-531-11822-1(3) , Watts, Franklin) Scholastic Library Publishing.

Binns, Tristan Boyer. The FBI: Federal Bureau of Investigation. 2002. (US Government Agencies Ser.). 48p. (J). (gr. 3-5). (Illus.). lib. bdg. 27.07 (978-1-58810-499-1(0)); pap. 7.95 (978-1-58810-983-5(6) , 91598) Heinemann Library.

Blohn, Craig. The D. C. Sniper Shootings. 2006. 112p. (J). (gr. 7-10). 32.45 (978-1-59018-926-9(4) , Lucent Bks.) Thomson Gale.

Bowers, Vivien. Crime Scene: How Investigators Use Science to Track down the Bad Guys. Newbigging, Martha, illus. 2nd ed. 2006. 64p. (J). 19.95 (978-1-897066-55-3(4)); pap. 9.95 (978-1-897066-56-0(2)) Maple Tree Pr. CAN. *Dist:* Perseus Distribution.

Brian, Sarah Jane. Forensics: Chemistry & Crime. 2006. (Navigators Ser.). (J). pap. 42.00 (*978-1-4108-6234-1(8)) Benchmark Education Co.

Brownlie, Alison. Crime & Punishment: Changing Attitudes, 1900-2000. 1999. (Twentieth Century Issues Ser.). (Illus.). 64p. (J). (gr. 4-6). lib. bdg. 28.54 (978-0-8172-5573-2(7)) Raintree.

Burns, Jan. Kidnapping. 2007. (Crime Scene Investigations Ser.). (Illus.). 128p. (gr. 7-10). 31.20 (*978-1-59018-989-4(2) , Lucent Bks.) Thomson Gale.

Clemson, Wendy. Using Math to Solve a Crime. 2004. (Mathworks!). (Illus.). 31p. (J). lib. bdg. 24.67 (978-0-8368-4213-5(8)) Stevens, Gareth Inc.

Croce, Nicholas. Detectives: Life of Investigating Crime. 2005. (Extreme Careers Ser.). (Illus.). 64p. (YA). (gr. 5-8). 26.50 (978-0-8239-3796-7(8)) Rosen Publishing Group, Inc., The.

Dahl, Michael. Computer Evidence. 2004. (Edge Books, Forensic Crime Solvers). (Illus.). 32p. (J). lib. bdg. 22.60 (978-0-7368-2698-3(X)) Capstone Pr., Inc.

Deary, Terry. True Detective Stories. l.t. ed. 2005. (Illus.). 192p. (J). pap. (978-0-7540-6126-7(4) , CLP 320) BBC Audio.

—True Detective Stories. unabr. l.t. ed. 2003. (Read-Along Ser.). 176p. (J). 29.95 incl. audio (978-0-7540-6240-0(6) , RAO41, Galaxy Children's Large Print) BBC Audiobooks America.

—True Mystery Stories. l.t. ed. 2005. (Illus.). 240p. (J). pap. (978-0-7540-7810-4(8) , CLP 420) BBC Audio.

DK Publishing & Cooper, Chris. Forensic Science. 2008. (DK Eyewitness Bks.). 72p. (J). (gr. 3-8). 15.99 (*978-0-7566-3383-7(4)); lib. bdg. 19.99 (*978-0-7566-3363-9(X)) Dorling Kindersley Publishing, Inc.

Domnauer, Teresa. Crime Scene Investigation, Level 3. 2007. (Extreme Readers Ser.). 32p. (J). (gr. 1-2). pap. 3.95 (*978-0-7696-6381-4(8)) School Specialty Publishing.

Donkin, Andrew. Crime Busters. Ling, Mary, ed. 2001. (Readers Ser.). (Illus.). 1p. (J). (gr. 4-7). pap. 3.95 (978-0-7894-7882-5(X)) Dorling Kindersley Publishing, Inc.

—Crime Busters. 2001. (Illus.). 48p. (J). (gr. 3-4). lib. bdg. 11.80 (978-0-613-43924-4(4)) Tandem Library Bks.

Donkin, Andrew & Dorling Kindersley Publishing Staff. Crime Busters. 2001. (Readers Ser.). (Illus.). 48p. (J). (gr. 4-7). 14.99 (978-0-7894-7881-8(1)) Dorling Kindersley Publishing, Inc.

Dowswell, Paul. Investigating Murder Mysteries. 2004. (Forensic Files Ser.). (Illus.). 48p. (J). pap. 8.50 (978-1-4034-5471-3(X)) Heinemann Library.

—Murder Mysteries. 2004. (Forensic Files Ser.). (Illus.). 48p. (J). lib. bdg. 27.07 (978-1-4034-4831-6(0)) Heinemann Library.

Dowswell, Paul, et al. Forensic Files, 6 bks. 2004. (YA). (gr. 6-8). lib. bdg. 179.57 (978-1-4034-4835-4(3)) Heinemann Library.

Dupont, Ellen. Criminal Terminology. 2003. (Crime & Detection Ser.). (Illus.). 96p. (J). (gr. 7 up). lib. bdg. (978-1-59084-383-3(5)) Mason Crest Pubs.

Fine, Jil. Undercover Agents. 2003. (High-Top Secret Ser.). (Illus.). 48p. (J). 23.00 (978-0-516-24315-3(2) , Children's Pr.) Scholastic Library Publishing.

—Undercover Agents. 2003. (gr. 7-12). lib. bdg. 15.25 (978-0-613-59752-4(4)) Tandem Library Bks.

Ford, Jean. Forensics in American Culture: Obsessed with Crime. 2006. (Forensics, the Science of Crime-Solving Ser.). (Illus.). 112p. (YA). (gr. 7 up). 22.95 (978-1-4222-0037-7(X) , 1248054) Mason Crest Pubs.

Forensic Files, 12 vols., Set. Incl. Bullet Proof! The Evidence That Guns Leave Behind. Joyce, Jaime. (Illus.). (YA). 2006. 25.00 (978-0-531-11820-7(7)); Do You Read Me? Famous Cases Solved by Handwriting Analysis! Webber, Diane. (Illus.). (J). 2006. 25.00 (978-0-531-12066-8(X)); Dusted & Busted! The Science of Fingerprinting. Beres, D. B. & Franklin, Watts. (Illus.). (J). 2006. 25.00 (978-0-531-11822-1(3)); Guilty by a Hair! Real-Life DNA Matches! Prokos, Anna. (Illus.). (YA). 2007. 25.00 (978-0-531-11821-4(5)); Killer Wallpaper : True Cases of Deadly Poisonings. Prokos, Anna. (J). 2006. 25.00 (978-0-531-12061-3(9)); Right Bite : Dentists As Detectives. Winchester, Elizabeth. (J). 2006. 25.00 (978-0-531-12062-0(7)); Shot & Framed : Photographers at the Crime Scene. Webber, Diane. (Illus.). (J). 2007. 25.00 (*978-0-531-12063-7(5)); Skulls & Skeletons : True-Life Stories of Bone Detectives. Denega, Danielle. (Illus.). (YA). 2007. 25.00 (978-0-531-12064-4(3)); 64p. (gr. 8-12). (24/7 - Science Behind the Scenes Ser.). (Illus.). 2007. 300.00 (*978-0-531-12476-5(2) , Watts, Franklin) Scholastic Library Publishing.

Forensics: The Science of Crime-Solving, 12 vols., Set. Incl. Computer Investigation. Bauchner, Elizabeth. (J). 2006. 22.95 (978-1-4222-0035-3(3)); Criminal Psychology & Personality Profiling. Esherick, Joan. (YA). 2006. 22.95 (978-1-4222-0028-5(0)); DNA Analysis. Hunter, William. (YA). 2005. lib. bdg. 22.95 (978-1-4222-0026-1(4)); Document Analysis. Bauchner, Elizabeth. (J). 2006. 22.95 (978-1-4222-0029-2(9)); Entomology & Palynology : Evidence from the Natural World. Walker, Maryalice. (YA). 2006. 22.95 (978-1-4222-0032-2(9)); Explosives & Arson Investigation. Ford, Jean. (YA). 2006. 22.95 (978-1-4222-0034-6(5)); Fingerprints, Bite Marks, Ear Prints : Human Signposts. Libal, Angela. (J). 2006. 22.95 (978-1-4222-0031-5(0) , 1248051); Forensic Anthropology. Libal, Angela. (J). 2006. 22.95 (978-1-4222-0030-8(2) , 1248052); Forensics in American Culture : Obsessed with Crime. Ford, Jean. (YA). 2006. 22.95 (978-1-4222-0037-7(X) , 1248054); Mark & Trace Analysis. Hunter, William. (YA). 2006. 22.95 (978-1-4222-0027-8(2)); Pathology. Walker, Maryalice. (YA). 2006. 22.95 (978-1-4222-0033-9(7) , 1248056); Solving Crimes with Physics. Hunter, William. (YA). 2006. 22.95 (978-1-4222-0036-0(1)); (gr. 7 up). (Forensics, the Science of Crime-Solving Ser.). (Illus.). 112p. 2006. Set lib. bdg. 275.40 (978-1-4222-0025-4(6) , 1248051) Mason Crest Pubs.

Fridell, Ron. Forensic Science. 2007. (Cool Science Ser.). (Illus.). 48p. (J). (gr. 4-8). lib. bdg. 26.60 (978-0-8225-5935-1(8) , Lerner Pubns.) Lerner Publishing Group.

Friedlander, Mark P., Jr. & Phillips, Terry M. When Objects Talk: Solving a Crime with Science. 2005. (Discovery! Ser.). (Illus.). 120p. (gr. 5-12). lib. bdg. 27.93 (978-0-8225-0649-2(1)) Lerner Publishing Group.

Frith, Alex. Forensic Science. 2007. (Forensic Science Ser.). 96p. (J). 10.99 (*978-0-7945-1689-5(0) , Usborne) EDC Publishing.

Fullick, Ann. Forensic Science. 2005. (Science at the Edge Ser.). (Illus.). 64p. (J). (978-1-4034-7763-7(9)) Heinemann Library.

Gaensslen, Robert E. Blood, Bugs, & Plants. 2008. (Essentials of Forensic Science Ser.). 176p. (gr. 6-12). 35.00 (978-0-8160-5509-8(2)) Facts On File, Inc.

Gardner, Robert. Forensic Science Projects with a Crime Lab You Can Build. 2007. (Build-a-Lab! Science Experiments Ser.). (Illus.). 128p. (J). (gr. 5). lib. bdg. 31.93 (*978-0-7660-2806-7(2)) Enslow Pubs., Inc.

Gifford, Clive. Crimebusters: Learn to Be a Scientific Supersleuth. 2007. 64p. (J). (gr. 4 up). pap. 12.99 (978-0-7641-3671-9(2)) Barron's Educational Series, Inc.

Glass, Susan. Forensic Investigator. 2007. (J). (*978-1-4109-2847-4(0)); pap. (*978-1-4109-2864-1(0)) Steck-Vaughn.

Gordon, Olivia. Cold Case File: Murder in the Mountains. 2008. (J). lib. bdg. (*978-1-59716-547-1(6)) Bearport Publishing Co., Inc.

Greenberg, Keith Elliot. Forensics. 2003. (Science on the Edge Ser.). 48p. (J). 23.70 (978-1-56711-785-1(6) , Blackbirch Pr., Inc.) Thomson Gale.

Hamilton, John. The FBI. 2007. (Defending the Nation Ser.). (Illus.). 32p. (J). (gr. 3-5). lib. bdg. 22.78 (978-1-59679-757-4(6) , Checkerboard Library) ABDO Publishing Co.

Harding, Lauri. Can DNA Testing Improve America's Legal System. 2007. (At Issue Ser.). (Illus.). 128p. (J). (gr. 10-12). 28.70 (978-0-7377-3599-4(6)); pap. 19.95 (978-0-7377-3600-7(3)) Thomson Gale. (Greenhaven Pr., Inc.).

Harris, Elizabeth Snoke. Crime Scene Science Fair Projects. 2006. (Illus.). 112p. (J). (gr. 6-10). 19.95 (978-1-57990-765-5(2)) Lark Bks.

Hopping, Lorraine Jean. The Body As Evidence. 2006. (Illus.). 48p. (J). pap. (*978-0-8368-7715-1(2)); lib. bdg. (*978-0-8368-7710-6(1)) Stevens, Gareth Inc.

—The Body As Evidence. 2006. (Illus.). 48p. (J). pap. (*978-0-8368-7716-8(0)); lib. bdg. (*978-0-8368-7711-3(X)) WRC Media, Inc.

—Investigating a Crime Scene. 2006. (Illus.). 48p. (J). pap. (*978-0-8368-7714-4(4)); lib. bdg. (*978-0-8368-7709-0(8)) Stevens, Gareth Inc.

Horn, Geoffrey M. Crime Scene Investigator. 2007. (J). pap. (*978-0-8368-8887-4(1)); lib. bdg. (*978-0-8368-8880-5(4)) Stevens, Gareth Inc.

Howard, Amanda. Robbery File: The Museum Heist. 2008. (J). lib. bdg. (*978-1-59716-550-1(6)) Bearport Publishing Co., Inc.

Hunter, William. Mark & Trace Analysis. 2006. (Forensics, the Science of Crime-Solving Ser.). (Illus.). 112p. (YA). (gr. 7 up). 22.95 (978-1-4222-0027-8(2)) Mason Crest Pubs.

Innes, Brian. DNA & Body Evidence. 2007. (Forensic Evidence Ser.). (Illus.). 96p. (gr. 6 up). 39.95 (*978-0-7656-8115-7(3)) Sharpe, M.E. Inc.

—Forensic Science. 2002. (Crime & Detection Ser.). (Illus.). 96p. (J). (gr. 7 up). lib. bdg. 22.95 (978-1-59084-373-4(8)) Mason Crest Pubs.

—Major Unsolved Crimes. 2002. (Crime & Detection Ser.). (Illus.). 96p. (J). (gr. 7 up). lib. bdg. (978-1-59084-382-6(7)) Mason Crest Pubs.

—The Search for Forensic Evidence. 2005. (Science Quest Ser.). (J). lib. bdg. 24.67 (978-0-8368-4556-3(0)) Stevens, Gareth Inc.

Inserra, Rose. Forensic Scientists. 2004. (J). lib. bdg. 27.10 (978-1-58340-545-1(3)) Smart Apple Media.

Jackson, Donna M. The Bone Detectives: How Forensic Anthropologists Solve Crimes & Uncover Mysteries of the Dead. Fellenbaum, Charlie, illus. 2001. 48p. (J). (gr. 5 up). pap. 7.99 (978-0-316-82961-8(7)) Little Brown & Co.

Jones, Charlotte Foltz. Fingerprints & Talking Bones: How Real-Life Crimes Are Solved. 1999. (Illus.). (J). (978-0-606-15908-1(8)) Tandem Library Bks.

Joyce, Jaime. Bullet Proof! The Evidence That Guns Leave Behind. 2007. (24/7 - Science Behind the Scenes Ser.). (Illus.). 64p. (YA). (gr. 8-12). pap. 7.95 (*978-0-531-15455-7(6) , Watts, Franklin) Scholastic Library Publishing.

Karlitz, Gail. Virtual Apprentice: FBI Agent. 2008. (Virtual Apprentice Ser.). 64p. (J). (gr. 6-12). 29.95 (*978-0-8160-6758-9(9) , Ferguson Publishing Co.) Facts On File, Inc.

Leimbach, Judy. Detective Club: Mysteries for Young Thinkers. 2005. 64p. 11.95 (978-1-59363-065-2(4)) Prufrock Pr.

Libal, Angela. Fingerprints, Bite Marks, Ear Prints: Human Signposts. 2006. (Forensics, the Science of Crime-Solving Ser.). (Illus.). 112p. (J). (gr. 7 up). 22.95 (978-1-4222-0031-5(0) , 1248051) Mason Crest Pubs.

Martin, Michael. Earth Evidence. 2007. 32p. (J). (978-0-7368-6787-0(2)) Capstone Pr., Inc.

—Handwriting Evidence. 2007. (Edge Books, Forensic Crime Solvers). (Illus.). 32p. (J). (*978-0-7368-6788-7(0) , 1265014); (*978-0-7368-7872-2(6) , 1265014) Capstone Pr., Inc.

—Word Evidence. 2007. (Edge Books, Forensic Crime Solvers). (Illus.). 32p. (J). (*978-0-7368-6790-0(2) , 1265019); (*978-0-7368-7874-6(2) , 1265019) Capstone Pr., Inc.

Mauro, Paul & Melton, H. Keith. Collecting & Handling Evidence. 2004. (Illus.). 48p. (J). (978-0-439-57178-4(2)) Scholastic, Inc.

—Crime Scene Investigation. 2003. (Illus.). 48p. (J). (978-0-439-57175-3(8)) Scholastic, Inc.

—Detective Mastery. 2004. (Detective Academy Ser.). (Illus.). 48p. (J). pap. (978-0-439-57185-2(5)) Scholastic, Inc.

—Interviews & Interrogations. 2003. (Detective Academy Ser.). (Illus.). 48p. (J). pap. (978-0-439-57176-0(6)) Scholastic, Inc.

—Master Case Files. Aycock, Daniel & Labat, Yancey C., illus. 2004. (Detective Academy Ser.). 48p. (J). pap. (978-0-439-57184-5(7)) Scholastic, Inc.

—Undercover Operations. Aycock, Daniel et al, illus. 2004. (Detective Academy Ser.). 48p. (J). (978-0-439-57183-8(9)) Scholastic, Inc.

Mauro, Paul, et al. Prints & Impressions. Aycock, Daniel et al, illus. 2003. (Detective Academy Ser.). 48p. (J). pap. (978-0-439-57177-7(4)) Scholastic, Inc.

Miller, Connie Colwell. Crime Scene Investigators: Uncovering the Truth. 2008. (*978-1-4296-1272-2(X)) Capstone Pr., Inc.

—The FBI: Hunting Criminals. 2008. (J). (*978-1-4296-1273-9(8)) Capstone Pr., Inc.

Morrison, Yvonne. The DNA Gave It Away: Teens Solve Crimes. 2007. (Shockwave: Science in Practice Ser.). (Illus.). 36p. (J). (gr. 4-6). lib. bdg. 25.00 (*978-0-531-17581-1(2) , Children's Pr.) Scholastic Library Publishing.

Nicholson, Edward. Murder File: A Killer's Manual. 2008. (J). lib. bdg. (*978-1-59716-549-5(2)) Bearport Publishing Co., Inc.

Orr, Tamra. Crime Scene Investigator. 2008. (J). pap. 7.95 (*978-1-60279-079-7(5)); lib. bdg. 25.26 (*978-1-60279-057-5(4)) Cherry Lake Publishing.

—Forensic Science Investigation. 2008. (J). lib. bdg. 25.26 (*978-1-60279-055-1(8)) Cherry Lake Publishing.

—Forensic Science Investigator. 2008. (J). pap. 7.95 (*978-1-60279-081-0(7)) Cherry Lake Publishing.

Owen, David. Police Lab: How Forensic Science Tracks down & Convicts Criminals. 2002. (Illus.). 128p. (J). (gr. 7-9). 19.95 (978-1-55297-620-3(3)); pap. 9.95 (978-1-55297-619-7(X)) Firefly Bks., Ltd.

Parker, Janice, contrib. by. Forgeries, Fingerprints & Forensics: The Science of Crime. 1999. (Science @ Work Ser.). (Illus.). 48p. (J). (gr. 4-6). 27.12 (978-0-7398-0133-8(3)) Raintree.

Pentland, Peter & Stoyles, Pennie. Forensic Science. 2002. (Science & Scientists Ser.). (Illus.). 32p. (gr. 4-8). 28.00 (978-0-7910-7010-9(7) , Chelsea Hse.) Facts On File, Inc.

Platt. Crime Scenes. 2004. (True Crime Ser.). (Illus.). 48p. (J). pap. 7.95 (978-1-4109-1171-1(3)) Harcourt Schl. Pubs.

Platt, Richard. Forensics. 2005. (Kingfisher Knowledge Ser.). (Illus.). 64p. (J). (gr. 5-9). 12.95 (978-0-7534-5862-4(4) , Kingfisher) Houghton Mifflin Co. Trade & Reference Div.

Rainis, Kenneth G. Fingerprints: Crime-Solving Science Experiments. 2006. (Forensic Science Projects Ser.). (Illus.). 128p. (J). (gr. 5 up). lib. bdg. 31.93 (978-0-7660-1960-7(8)) Enslow Pubs., Inc.

—Hair, Clothing, & Tire Track Evidence: Crime-Solving Science Experiments. 2006. (Forensic Science Projects Ser.). (Illus.). 128p. (J). (gr. 5 up). lib. bdg. 31.93 (978-0-7660-2729-9(5)) Enslow Pubs., Inc.

Ramaprian, Sheela. FBI. 2003. (gr. 7-12). lib. bdg. 15.25 (978-0-613-59616-9(1)) Tandem Library Bks.

Rollins, Barbara B. & Dahl, Michael. Ballistics. 2004. (Forensic Crime Solvers Ser.). (Illus.). 32p. (J). 22.60 (978-0-7368-2421-7(9)) Capstone Pr., Inc.

—A Bloody Trail: Analyzing Blood. 2004. (Forensic Crime Solvers Ser.). (Illus.). 32p. (J). 22.60 (978-0-7368-2418-7(9)) Capstone Pr., Inc.

—Finding a Match: Examining Fingerprints. 2004. (Forensic Crime Solvers Ser.). (Illus.). 32p. (J). 22.60 (978-0-7368-2419-4(7)) Capstone Pr., Inc.

—Forensic Crime Solvers. (Illus.). (J). (gr. 3-4). lib. bdg. 135.60 (978-0-7368-2699-0(8)) Capstone Pr., Inc.

Romero, Libby. Discover Forensic Chemistry. 2006. pap. 39.00 (*978-1-4108-6503-8(7)) Benchmark Education Co.

—Forensic Chemistry. 2006. pap. 42.00 (*978-1-4108-6500-7(2)) Benchmark Education Co.

Rose, Malcolm. Crime Scene Investigator. 2007. 48p. (J). (gr. 3-5). 14.95 (978-0-7534-6110-5(2) , Kingfisher) Houghton Mifflin Co. Trade & Reference Div.

Running Press Staff & Ruditis, Paul. The Hardy Boys Guide to Life. 2007. (Illus.). 128p. 4.95 (978-0-7624-2987-5(9) , Running Pr. Minature Editions) Running Pr. Bk. Pubs.

Sarat, Austin, ed. Forensic Science. 1999. (Crime, Justice & Punishment Ser.). (Illus.). 80p. (YA). (gr. 7-12). 30.00 (978-0-7910-4950-1(7) , Chelsea Hse.) Facts On File, Inc.

Schulz, Karen. Crime Scene Detective: Using Science & Critical Thinking to Solve Crimes. 2003. (J). per. 12.95 (978-1-883055-58-5(X) , 150) Dandy Lion Pubns.

—Crime Scene Detective: Using Science & Critical Thinking to Solve Crimes. 2005. 80p. 12.95 (978-1-59363-063-8(8)) Prufrock Pr.

Scott, Carey. Crime Scene Detective. 2007. 72p. (YA). (gr. 5 up). 15.99 (978-0-7566-2558-0(0)) Dorling Kindersley Publishing, Inc.

Sitford, Mikaela. Serial Killer File: The Doctor of Death Investigation. 2008. (J). lib. bdg. (*978-1-59716-551-8(4)) Bearport Publishing Co., Inc.

Stewart, Gail. Arson. 2006. (Inside the Crime Lab Ser.). (Illus.). 112p. (J). (gr. 7-10). 32.45 (978-1-59018-617-6(6) , Lucent Bks.) Thomson Gale.

Stewart, Gail B. Forensics. 2007. (KidHaven Science Library). (Illus.). 48p. (J). (gr. 3-8). 26.20 (978-0-7377-3571-0(6) , 1256751, Kidhaven) Thomson Gale.

Stewart, Gail B. Identity Theft. 2007. (Crime Scene Investigations Ser.). 128p. (gr. 7-10). 31.20 (*978-1-59018-977-1(9) , Lucent Bks.) Thomson Gale.

Teitelbaum, Michael. Batman's Guide to Crime & Detection. 2003. (Dk Readers Ser.). (Illus.). 48p. (J). pap. 3.99 (978-0-7894-9755-0(7)) Dorling Kindersley Publishing, Inc.

—Batman's Guide to Crime & Detection. 2003. (gr. k-3). lib. bdg. 11.80 (978-0-613-75252-7(X)) Tandem Library Bks.

Teitelbaum, Michael & Dorling Kindersley Publishing Staff. Batman's Guide to Crime & Detection. 2003. (Readers Ser.). (Illus.). 48p. (J). 12.99 (978-0-7894-9879-3(0)) Dorling Kindersley Publishing, Inc.

Thornburg, Linda. Cool Careers for Girls As Crime Solvers. (Illus.). 2002. 144p. pap. 12.95 (978-1-57023-174-2(5)); 2001. 120p. (J). pap. 19.95 (978-1-57023-175-9(3)) Impact Pubns.

—Cool Careers for Girls as Crime Solvers. 2002. (gr. 5-8). lib. bdg. 22.20 (978-0-613-79031-4(6)) Tandem Library Bks.

Townsend, John. Crime Scenes. 2004. (True Crime Ser.). (Illus.). 48p. (J). (gr. 3-6). lib. bdg. 27.14 (978-1-4109-1092-9(X)) Harcourt Schl. Pubs.

Wagner, Heather Lehr. The Federal Bureau of Investigation. 2007. (U. S. Government Ser.). 104p. (YA). (gr. 5-8). 30.00 (*978-0-7910-9281-1(X) , Chelsea Hse.) Facts On File, Inc.

Walker, Maryalice. Pathology. 2006. (Forensics, the Science of Crime-Solving Ser.). (Illus.). 112p. (YA). (gr. 7 up). 22.95 (978-1-4222-0033-9(7) , 1248056) Mason Crest Pubs.

Webber, Diane. Do You Read Me? Famous Cases Solved by Handwriting Analysis! 2007. (24/7, Science Behind the Scenes Ser.). (Illus.). 64p. (J). (*978-1-4287-2801-1(5) , Franklin Watts) Hodder Children's Division.

—Do You Read Me? Famous Cases Solved by Handwriting Analysis! 2007. (24/7 - Science Behind the Scenes Ser.). (Illus.). 64p. (YA). (gr. 8-12). pap. 7.95 (*978-0-531-15456-4(4) , Watts, Franklin) Scholastic Library Publishing.

—Shot & Framed: Photographers at the Crime Scene. 2007. (24/7 - Science Behind the Scenes Ser.). (Illus.). 64p. (J). (gr. 8-12). 25.00 (*978-0-531-12063-7(5) , Watts, Franklin) Scholastic Library Publishing.

Woodford, Chris. Criminal Investigation. Kossmann, Walter, ed. 2001. (Science Fact Files Ser.). (Illus.). 48p. (J). (gr. 4-7). lib. bdg. 27.12 (978-0-7398-1016-3(2)) Raintree.

Woolf, Alex. Fakes & Hoaxes. 2004. (Forensic Files Ser.). (Illus.). 48p. (J). lib. bdg. 27.07 (978-1-4034-4829-3(9)) Heinemann Library.

—Investigating Fakes & Hoaxes. 2004. (Forensic Files Ser.). (Illus.). 48p. (J). pap. 8.50 (978-1-4034-5469-0(8)) Heinemann Library.

—Investigating Thefts & Heists. 2004. (Forensic Files Ser.). (Illus.). 48p. (J). pap. 8.50 (978-1-4034-5473-7(6)) Heinemann Library.

—Thefts & Heists. 2004. (Forensic Files Ser.). (Illus.). 48p. (J). lib. bdg. (978-1-4034-4833-0(7)) Heinemann Library.

Yancey, Diane. The Forensic Anthropologist. 2006. 112p. (J). (gr. 7-10). 32.45 (978-1-59018-618-3(4) , Lucent Bks.) Thomson Gale.

—Murder: Inside the Crime Lab. 2006. (Inside the Crime Lab Ser.). (Illus.). 112p. (J). (gr. 7-10). 32.45 (978-1-59018-619-0(2) , Lucent Bks.) Thomson Gale.

Yancey, Diane. Tracking Serial Killers. 2007. (Crime Scene Investigations Ser.). 128p. (J). (gr. 7-10). 32.45 (*978-1-59018-985-6(X) , Lucent Bks.) Thomson Gale.

Yeatts, Tabatha. Forensics: Solving the Crime. Sterling, Denise, ed. 2001. (Innovators Ser.: Vol. No. 9). (Illus.). 144p. (gr. 5 up). lib. bdg. 21.95 (978-1-881508-75-5(7)) Oliver Pr., Inc.

Yount, Lisa. Forensic Science: From Fibers to Fingerprints. 2006. (Milestones in Discovery & Invention Ser.). 224p. (YA). (gr. 6-12). 35.00 (978-0-8160-5751-1(6)) Facts On File, Inc.

CRIMINAL LAW

see also Capital Punishment; Jury; Kidnapping; Trials

Anderson, Judith. Dealing with Crime. 2006. (What's You View? Ser.). 48p. (J). (978-1-58340-972-5(6)) Smart Apple Media.

Billings. Crime & Punishment. 1998. (Wild Side Ser.). (Illus.). (YA). (gr. 6-12). 13.00 (978-0-89061-799-1(6) , R0799-6E) Jamestown.

Copen, Lynn M. & Pucci, Linda M. Getting Ready for Court: Criminal Court Edition: A Book for Children. 2000. (Interpersonal Violence). (Illus.). 32p. pap. 13.95 (978-0-7619-2184-4(2) , 86538) SAGE Pubns., Inc.

Ferguson. Careers in Focus: Public Safety. 3rd rev. ed. 2007. (Careers in Focus Ser.). 224p. (gr. 6-12). 29.95 (*978-0-8160-6594-3(2) , Ferguson Publishing Co.) Facts On File, Inc.

Hunter, David. Inequities of the Justice System. 2006. (Incarceration Issues Ser.). (Illus.). 112p. (YA). (gr. 7 up). (978-1-59084-995-8(7)) Mason Crest Pubs.

Koopmans, Andy. The Leopold & Loeb Case. 2003. (Famous Trials Ser.). (Illus.). 112p. (J). 29.95 (978-1-59018-227-7(8) , Lucent Bks.) Thomson Gale.

Riley, Gail Blasser. And Justice for All. 2003. (Illus.). 60p. (J). (978-0-7398-5175-3(6)) Steck-Vaughn.

Spence, David. Crime & Punishment. 2004. (Illus.). 32p. (J). (gr. 4-7). pap. (978-1-86007-010-5(8)) Ticktock Media Ltd.

CRIMINALS

see Crime and Criminals

CRIMINOLOGY

see Crime and Criminals

CRIPPLE CREEK (COLO.)

Donlan, Leni. Strike It Rich in Cripple Creek: Gold Rush. 2006. (American History Through Primary Sources Ser.). (Illus.). 32p. (J). (978-1-4109-2419-3(X)); pap. (978-1-4109-2430-8(0)) Steck-Vaughn.

CRIPPLES

see People with Disabilities

CRITICISM

see also Book Reviews

also literature and music subjects with the subdivision History and Criticism, e.g. English Literature—History and Criticism; English Poetry—History and Criticism; Music—History and Criticism

Becnel, Kim. Bloom's How to Write about F. Scott Fitzgerald. 2007. (Bloom's How to Write about Literature Ser.). 256p. (YA). (gr. 9 up). 45.00 (*978-0-7910-9482-2(0) , Chelsea Hse.) Facts On File, Inc.

Gleed, Paul. Bloom's How to Write about William Shakespeare. 2007. (Bloom's How to Write about Literature Ser.). 256p. (YA). (gr. 9 up). 45.00 (*978-0-7910-9484-6(7) , Chelsea Hse.) Facts On File, Inc.

Kerr, Christine. Bloom's How to Write about J. D. Salinger. 2007. (Bloom's How to Write about Literature Ser.). 256p. (YA). (gr. 9 up). 45.00 (*978-0-7910-9483-9(9) , Chelsea Hse.) Facts On File, Inc.

Kordich, Catherine J. Bloom's How to Write about John Steinbeck. 2007. (Bloom's How to Write about Literature Ser.). 256p. (YA). (gr. 9 up). 45.00 (*978-0-7910-9486-0(3) , Chelsea Hse.) Facts On File, Inc.

Priddy, Anna. Bloom's How to Write about Emily Dickinson. 2007. (Bloom's How to Write about Literature Ser.). 256p. (YA). (gr. 9 up). 45.00 (*978-0-7910-9492-1(8) , Chelsea Hse.) Facts On File, Inc.

Sterling, Laurie A. Bloom's How to Write about Nathaniel Hawthorne. 2007. (Bloom's How to Write about Literature Ser.). 256p. (YA). (gr. 9 up). 45.00 (*978-0-7910-9481-5(2) , Chelsea Hse.) Facts On File, Inc.

CROCHETING

see also Beadwork

Blakley Kinsler, Gwen & Young Jackie. Crocheting. Melo, Esperanca, illus. 2004. (Kids Can Do It Ser.). 40p. (J). (gr. 4-6). (978-1-55337-177-9(1)); (978-1-55337-176-2(3)) Kids Can Pr., Ltd.

Crochet a Quick & Easy Fashion Doll Wardrobe. 2003. (Illus.). 55p. spiral bd. 14.95 (978-0-9742848-0-4(7)) Mostats, Marie C.

Davis, Jane. Kids' Crafts: Crochet: Fantastic Jewelry, Hats, Purses, Pillows & More. 2007. (Illus.). 112p. (J). pap. 9.95 (*978-1-60059-138-9(8)) Lark Bks.

Grabowski, Angela. Encyclopedia of Tunisian Crochet. 2004. (Illus.). 148p. spiral bd. 24.95 (978-0-9749725-5-8(X) , Lonestar Abilene Publishing) LoneStar Abilene Publishing, LLC.

Ivarsson, Anna-Stina Linden, et al. Second-Time Cool: The Art of Chopping up a Sweater. Lundin, Maria, tr. from SWE. 2005. (Illus.). 92p. (J). (gr. 5-12). pap. 12.95 (978-1-55037-910-5(0)) Annick Pr., Ltd. CAN. *Dist:* Firefly Bks., Ltd.

—Second-Time Cool: The Art of Chopping up a Sweater. Lundin, Maria, tr. from SWE. Guy, photos by. 2005. (Illus.). 92p. (J). (gr. 5-12). 24.95 (978-1-55037-911-2(9)) Annick Pr., Ltd. CAN. *Dist:* Firefly Bks., Ltd.

Klickmann, Flora. The Little Girl's Knitting & Crocheting Book. 2001. (Little Girl's Needlework Books Ser.: Vol. 1). 128p. (J). bds. 20.00 net. (978-1-891656-36-1(8)) Lacis Pubns.

Ronci, Kelli. Kids Crochet: Projects for Kids of All Ages. Corwin, Lena, illus. Gruen, John, photos by. 2005. (Kids Craft Ser.). 128p. 19.95 (978-1-58479-413-4(5)) Stewart, Tabori & Chang.

Warwick, Ellen. Fully Woolly. Lum, Bernice, illus. 2007. 80p. (YA). (gr. 5 up). (*978-1-55337-798-6(2)) Kids Can Pr., Ltd.

Werker, Kim Piper. Get Hooked Again: Simple Steps to Crochet More Cool Stuff. Frenette, Cynthia, illus. 2007. 96p. (YA). (gr. 7 up). pap. 11.95 (*978-0-8230-5110-6(2)) Watson-Guptill Pubns., Inc.

CROCKERY

see Pottery

CROCKETT, DAVY, 1786-1836

Allen, Charles F. David Crockett: Scout, Small Boy, Pilgrim, Mountaineer, Soldier, Bear-Hunter, & Congressman, Defender of the Alamo. (Illus.). 308p. reprint ed. lib. bdg. 98.00 (978-0-7222-4856-0(3)) Library Reprints, Inc.

—David Crockett, Scout: Small Boy, Pilgrim, Mountaineer, Soldier, Bear-Hunter & Congressman: Defender of the Alamo. McKernan, Frank, illus. 2000. (J). (978-0-89526-228-8(2)) Regnery Publishing, Inc., An Eagle Publishing Co.

Alphin, Elaine Marie. Davy Crockett. (History Maker Bios Ser.). (Illus.). (J). 2003. 48p. (gr. 3-5). lib. bdg. 26.60 (978-0-8225-0393-4(X)); 2002. 47p. pap. 6.95 (978-0-8225-1564-7(4) , Lerner Pubns.) Lerner Publishing Group.

Berger, Donna, illus. Davy Crockett. 2004. (Imagination Ser.). 32p. (J). (gr. 3 up). 22.60 (978-0-7565-0603-2(4)) Compass Point Bks.

Burke, Rick. Davy Crockett. 2003. (Illus.). 32p. (J). pap. 6.95 (978-1-4034-4198-0(7)); lib. bdg. 24.22 (978-1-4034-4190-4(1)) Heinemann Library.

Collard, Sneed B., III. David Crockett: Fearless Frontiersman. 2006. (American Heroes Ser.). (Illus.). 48p. (J). lib. bdg. 28.50 (978-0-7614-2160-3(2) , Benchmark Bks.) Cavendish, Marshall Corp.

Crockett, David & Crockett, Davy. Davy Crockett's Own Story: A Narrative of the Life of David Crockett of the State of Tennessee. Crockett, Davy, illus. 2004. (Illus.). 128p. (J). (gr. 4-7). reprint ed. per. 14.95 (978-1-55709-218-2(4)) Applewood Bks.

Davy Crocket. (Photo Illustrated Biographies Ser.). 24p. (J). 6.95 (978-0-7368-3432-2(X)) Capstone Pr., Inc.

Devillier, Christy. Davy Crockett. 2004. (First Biographies Set Iv Ser.). (Illus.). 32p. (J). (gr. k-4). lib. bdg. 22.78 (978-1-59197-512-0(3)) ABDO Publishing Co.

Feeney, Kathy. Davy Crockett. 2002. (Photo-Illustrated Biographies Ser.). (Illus.). 24p. (J). (gr. 2-3). lib. bdg. 18.60 (978-0-7368-1110-1(9) , Bridgestone Bks.) Capstone Pr., Inc.

Furstinger, Nancy. Davy Crockett. 2003. (Folk Heroes Ser.). (Illus.). 24p. (J). lib. bdg. 15.95 (978-1-59036-073-6(7)) Weigl Pubs., Inc.

Harmon, Daniel E. Davy Crockett. 2001. (Famous Figures of the American Frontier Ser.). (Illus.). 64p. (J). pap. 25.00 (978-0-7910-6482-5(4)); 25.00 (978-0-7910-6481-8(6)) Facts On File, Inc. (Chelsea Hse.).

Johnston, Marianne. Davy Crockett. 2001. (American Legends Ser.). (Illus.). 24p. (J). (gr. 3). lib. bdg. 18.75 (978-0-8239-5581-7(8) , PowerKids Pr.) Rosen Publishing Group, Inc., The.

Kellogg, Steven. Sally Ann Thunder Ann Whirlwind Crockett: A Tall Tale. 1999. (978-0-606-17396-4(X)) Tandem Library Bks.

Krensky, Stephen. Davy Crockett: A Life on the Frontier. Bandelin, Debra & Dacey, Bob, illus. 2004. (Ready-to-read SOFA Ser.). 48p. (J). pap. 3.99 (978-0-689-85944-1(9) , Aladdin) Simon & Schuster Children's Publishing.

Kunstler, James Howard. Davy Crockett. Brodner, Steve, illus. 2005. (Rabbit Ears-A Classic Tale Ser.). 40p. (J). (gr. k-5). 25.65 (978-1-59197-762-9(2)) Spotlight.

Marsh, Carole. Davy Crockett. 2002. (One Thousand Readers Ser.). (Illus.). 12p. (J). (gr. k-4). 2.95 (978-0-635-01488-7(2) , 14882) Gallopade International.

—Davy Crockett: An Ohio Experience Reader. 2001. (J). (gr. k-5). pap. 1.95 (978-0-635-00434-5(8)) Gallopade International.

—The Virginia Reader: Davy Crockett. 2001. (Virginia Experience! Ser.). (Illus.). 12p. (J). (gr. k-5). pap. 2.95 (978-0-635-00369-0(4)) Gallopade International.

Moriarty, J. T. Davy Crockett: Frontier Hero. 2003. (Primary Sources of Famous People in American History Ser.). (Illus.). 32p. (J). pap. (978-0-8239-4180-3(9)) Rosen Publishing Group, Inc., The.

Roberts, Russell. Davy Crockett. 2006. (What's So Great About... ? Ser.). (Illus.). 32p. (J). (gr. 1-4). lib. bdg. (978-1-58415-476-1(4)) Mitchell Lane Pubs., Inc.

Santillana U. S. A. Publishing Co, Inc. Staff. David Crockett. Alvarez, Jose M. & Alonso, Jesus, illus. 2003. (Historias de Siempre Ser.). (SPA.). 95p. (J). (gr. 5-8). pap. 12.95 (978-84-204-5703-1(5)) Santillana USA Publishing Co., Inc.

Sullivan, George. Davy Crockett. 2001. (gr. 3-6). lib. bdg. 12.40 (978-0-613-50786-8(X)) Tandem Library Bks.

Winders, Richard Bruce. Davy Crockett: The Legend of the Wild Frontier. 2005. (Library of American Lives & Times). (Illus.). 112p. (YA). (gr. 4-8). lib. bdg. 31.95 (978-0-8239-5747-7(0)) Rosen Publishing Group, Inc., The.

CROCKETT, DAVY, 1786-1836—FICTION

Krensky, Stephen. Davy Crockett A Life on the Frontier. Dacey, Bob & Bandelin, Debra, illus. ed. 2005. (Ready-to-Read Ser. Level 3). 48p. (J). lib. bdg. 15.00 (978-1-59054-959-9(7)) Fitzgerald Bks.

Le Sueur, Meridel. Chanticleer of Wilderness Road: A Story of Davy Crockett. Schanilec, Gaylord, illus. 2004. (Meridel Le Sueur Wilderness Bk.). 153p. (gr. 7-12). reprint ed. 13.95 (978-0-930100-35-3(2)) Holy Cow! Pr.

Lloyd, Megan, illus. Davy Gets Hitched. 2007. (J). (978-0-8234-1837-4(5)) Holiday Hse., Inc.

Meadows, Melissa. What's the Word, Thunderbird? (Illus.). 80p. (J). 2008. (ENG.). (*978-1-934517-01-7(1)); 2007. pap. 4.99 (*978-1-934517-00-0(3)) Firelight Press, Inc.

Schanzer, Rosalyn. Davy Crockett Saves the World. Schanzer, Rosalyn, illus. 2001. (Illus.). 32p. (J). 17.89 (978-0-688-16992-3(9)) HarperCollins Pubs.

CROCODILES

AnimalWays - Group 1, 5 bks., Set. Incl. Bats. Ruff, Sue & Wilson, Don E. 104p. lib. bdg. 31.36 (978-0-7614-1137-6(2)); Crocodiles. Jango-Cohen, Judith. 112p. lib. bdg. 31.36 (978-0-7614-1136-9(4)); Frogs. Greenberg, Daniel A. 112p. lib. bdg. 31.36 (978-0-7614-1138-3(0)); Gorillas. Fleisher, Paul. 112p. lib. bdg. 28.50 (978-0-7614-1140-6(2)); Horses. Stefoff, Rebecca. 112p. lib. bdg. 31.36 (978-0-7614-1139-0(9)); (J). (gr. 5 up). (Illus.). 2000. Set lib. bdg. 142.50 (978-0-7614-1135-2(6) , Benchmark Bks.) Cavendish, Marshall Corp.

Beck, Paul. Uncover a Crocodile: Take a Three-Dimensional Look Inside a Nile Crocodile. 2006. (Uncover Bks.). (Illus.). 16p. (J). 18.95 (978-1-59223-476-9(3) , Silver Dolphin Bks.) Advantage Pubs. Group.

Behler, John L. & Behler, Deborah A. Alligators & Crocodiles. rev. ed. 1998. (WorldLife Library). (Illus.). 72p. (gr. 5 up). pap. 17.95 (978-0-89658-370-2(8)) Voyageur Pr., Inc.

Bender, Lionel. Crocodile. 2005. (Illus.). 32p. (J). 18.95 (978-1-59389-192-3(X)) Chrysalis Education.

Berger, Melvin. Snap! A Book about Alligators & Crocodiles. 2001. (gr. k-3). lib. bdg. 11.80 (978-0-613-63564-6(7)) Tandem Library Bks.

Berger, Melvin & Berger, Gilda. Snap! A Book about Alligators & Crocodiles. 2002. (Hello Reader! Science Ser.). (Illus.). 40p. (J). pap. 3.99 (978-0-439-31746-7(0) , Cartwheel Bks.) Scholastic, Inc.

Bi;;, Schuyler. Crocodile Crossing. 2005. (Soundprints' Amazing Animal Adventures! Ser.). (Illus.). 36p. (J). (ps-2). 8.95 incl. audio (978-1-59249-391-3(2) , SC7104) Soundprints.

Bull, Schuyler. Crocodile Crossing. Male, Alan, illus. 2005. (Soundprints' Amazing Animal Adventures! Ser.). (J). (ps-2). 32p. 2.95 (978-1-59249-053-0(0) , S7154); 36p. 15.95 (978-1-59249-051-6(4) , B7104); 36p. pap. 6.95 (978-1-59249-052-3(2) , S7104) Soundprints.

—Crocodile Crossing. Male, Alan, illus. 2005. (Soundprints' Amazing Animal Adventures! Ser.). 36p. (J). (ps-2). 9.95 (978-1-59249-060-8(3) , PS7154) Soundprints.

Burns, Kate. Snap Like a Crocodile! 1999. (Lift-the-Flap Bk.). (Illus.). 12p. (ps-3). 6.95 (978-1-899607-40-2(4)) Sterling Publishing Co., Inc.

Los Cocodrilos (Crocodiles) 2006. (J). pap. 7.95 (978-0-8225-6629-8(X)); (SPA.). 40p. lib. bdg. 25.26 (978-0-8225-6492-8(0)) Lerner Publishing Group. (Ediciones Lerner).

Cohen, Daniel. Sarcosuchus Imperator. 2004. (Illus.). 24p. (J). 14.95 (978-0-7368-2525-2(8) , Bridgestone Bks.) Capstone Pr., Inc.

Crocodile Crossing. 2005. (Soundprints' Amazing Animal Adventures! Ser.). (Illus.). 36p. (J). (ps-2). 19.95 incl. reel tape (978-1-59249-390-6(4) , BC7104) Soundprints.

Crocodiles, 6 bks. 2005. (Animal Predators Ser.). (Illus.). 40p. (J). (gr. 3-6). pap. 46.95 (978-0-8225-5493-6(3)) Lerner Publishing Group.

Crocodiles & Alligators. 2005. (J). per. 4.99 (978-1-933581-23-1(9)) Byeway Bks.

Dennard, Deborah. Alligators & Crocodiles. Dewey, Jennifer Owings, illus. 2004. (Our Wild World Ser.). 48p. (J). (gr. 2-5). ring bd. 10.95 (978-1-55971-860-8(9)); pap. 7.95 (978-1-55971-859-2(5)) T&N Children's Publishing. (NorthWord Bks. for Young Readers).

Fairweather, Gari D. Alligators & Other Crocodilians, Vol. 1. World Book, Inc. Staff, ed. 2001. (World Book's Animals of the World Ser.: Set 2). (Illus.). 64p. (J). (978-0-7166-1218-6(6)) World Bk., Inc.

Fitzgerald, Patrick J. Croc & Alligator Attacks. 2000. (gr. 7-12). lib. bdg. 15.25 (978-0-613-52016-4(5)) Tandem Library Bks.

—Croc & Gator Attacks. 2000. (High Interest Bks.). (Illus.). 48p. (YA). (gr. 7-12). pap. 6.95 (978-0-516-23514-1(1) , Children's Pr.) Scholastic Library Publishing.

Gareth Stevens Publishing Staff, contrib. by. Crocodiles. 2004. (All about Wild Animals Ser.). (Illus.). 32p. (J). lib. bdg. 23.33 (978-0-8368-4182-4(4)) Stevens, Gareth Inc.

Harcourt School Publishers Staff. Croc! Advanced Level. 3rd ed. 2002. (Trophies Reading Program Ser.). (Illus.). pap. 5.10 (978-0-15-323199-5(8)) Harcourt Schl. Pubs.

—Croc! Below Level. 3rd ed. 2002. (Trofeos Ser.). (SPA., Illus.). pap. 6.80 (978-0-15-324110-9(1)) Harcourt Schl. Pubs.

Heller, Ruth. How to Hide a Crocodile: And Other Reptiles. unabr. ed. 2001. (How to Hide Ser.). (Illus.). (J). (gr. k-3). pap. 14.45 incl. audio Spoken Arts, Inc.

Hoff, Mary King. Crocodiles. 2006. (Illus.). 32p. (J). 18.95 (978-1-58341-431-6(2) , Creative Education) Creative Co., The.

Hunting Crocodiles with Steve Irwin. 2005. (Book Treks Ser.). (J). (gr. 3 up). stu. ed. 34.95 (978-0-673-62080-4(8)) Celebration Pr.

Jango-Cohen, Judith. Crocodiles. (Animals, Animals Ser.). (Illus.). (J). 2002. 47p. 25.64 (978-0-7614-1446-9(0)); 2000. 112p. (gr. 5 up). lib. bdg. 31.36 (978-0-7614-1136-9(4)) Cavendish, Marshall Corp. (Benchmark Bks.).

Kaufman, Gabriel. Saltwater Crocodile: The Word's Biggest Reptile. 2007. (SuperSized! Ser.). (Illus.). 24p. (J). lib. bdg. 21.28 (978-1-59716-396-5(1) , 1265941) Bearport Publishing Co., Inc.

Landau, Elaine. Alligators & Crocodiles: Hunters of the Night. 2007. (Animals after Dark Ser.). (Illus.). 32p. (J). (gr. 2-4). lib. bdg. 22.60 (*978-0-7660-2771-8(6) , Enslow Elementary) Enslow Pubs., Inc.

Legg, Gerald. Alligators & Crocodiles. Bergin, Mark, illus. 2002. (Scary Creatures Ser.). (J). (gr. 2-4). pap. 6.95 (978-0-531-14848-8(3)); 32p. pap. 22.50 (978-0-531-14670-5(7)) Scholastic Library Publishing. (Watts, Franklin).

—Alligators & Crocodiles. 2002. (gr. 3-6). lib. bdg. 15.25 (978-0-613-53901-2(X)) Tandem Library Bks.

Lewellyn, Claire. Crocodile. Mendez, Simon, illus. 2004. (Starting Life Ser.). 24p. (ps-3). 16.95 (978-1-55971-900-1(1) , NorthWord Bks. for Young Readers) T&N Children's Publishing.

Lockwood, Sophie. Crocodiles. 2006. (World of Reptiles Ser.). (Illus.). 40p. (J). (gr. 2-6). 29.93 (978-1-59296-545-8(8)) Child's World, Inc.

Lunis, Natalie & Sereno, Paul C. SuperCroc: Paul's Sereno's Dinosaur Eater. 2007. (Fossil Hunters Ser.). (J). lib. bdg. 25.27 (978-1-59716-255-5(8)) Bearport Publishing Co., Inc.

Markle, Sandra. Crocodiles. (Animal Predators Ser.). 40p. (J). 2005. (gr. 4-6). pap. 7.95 (978-1-57505-742-2(5)); 2004. (Illus.). (gr. 3-6). lib. bdg. 25.26 (978-1-57505-726-2(3)) Lerner Publishing Group.

Morgan, Sally. Alligators & Crocodiles. 2006. (QEB Animal Lives Ser.). (Illus.). 32p. (J). lib. bdg. 19.95 (978-1-59566-205-7(7)) QEB Publishing Inc.

Murray, Julie. Crocodiles. (Life Cycles Ser.). 24p. (J). (gr. k-4). 2007. lib. bdg. 21.35 (*978-1-59928-706-5(4) , Buddy Bks.); 2005. (Illus.). lib. bdg. 21.35 (978-1-59197-311-9(2)) ABDO Publishing Co.

Noonan, Diana. The Crocodile. 2002. (Life Cycle Ser.). (Illus.). 32p. (J). (gr. k-2). 23.00 (978-0-7910-6964-6(8) , Chelsea Hse.) Facts On File, Inc.

Parker, Steve. 10 Things You Should Know about Crocodiles. Gallagher, Belinda & Borton, Paula, eds. Roberts, Steve, illus. 2004. (10 Things You Should Know Ser.). 24p. (J). 6.99 (978-1-84236-121-4(X)) Miles Kelly Publishing, Ltd. GBR. *Dist:* Independent Pubs. Group.

Pohl, Kathleen. Crocodiles. 2006. (Illus.). 24p. (J). pap. (*978-0-8368-7822-6(1)); lib. bdg. (*978-0-8368-7815-8(9)) Stevens, Gareth Inc. (Weekly Reader Early Learning Library).

—Crocodiles: Cocodrilos. 2006. (ENG & SPA., Illus.). 24p. (J). pap. (*978-0-8368-8011-3(0)); lib. bdg. (*978-0-8368-8004-5(8)) Stevens, Gareth Inc. (Weekly Reader Early Learning Library).

Pope, Joyce. Crocodile. 2000. (Natural World Ser.). (Illus.). 48p. (J). (gr. 4-7). 9.95 (978-0-7398-3127-4(5)) Steck-Vaughn.

—Crocodile: Habitats, Life Cycles, Food Chains, Threats. 2000. (Natural World Ser.). (Illus.). 48p. (J). (gr. 4-7). lib. bdg. 27.12 (978-0-7398-2764-2(2)) Raintree.

Rau, Dana Meachen. When Crocodiles Attack! 2006. (When Wild Animals Attack! Ser.). (Illus.). 48p. (J). (gr. 4-10). lib. bdg. 23.93 (978-0-7660-2666-7(3)) Enslow Pubs., Inc.

Richardson, Adele. Crocodiles. 2005. (Bridgestone Books World of Reptiles). (Illus.). 24p. (J). (ps-7). lib. bdg. 21.26 (978-0-7368-4327-0(2)) Capstone Pr., Inc.

Robinson, Claire. Crocodiles. 2002. (In the Wild Ser.). (Illus.). 24p. (J). (gr. k-2). pap. 6.95 (978-1-57572-465-2(0) , 90455) Heinemann Library.

Royston, Angela. Alligators & Crocodiles. 2003. (Amazing Animals Ser.). (Illus.). 24p. (J). lib. bdg. 21.35 (978-1-58340-225-2(X)) Weigl Pubs., Inc.

C D

Rushby, Pamela. Discovering SuperCroc. 2007. (Science Chapters Ser.). 48p. (J). (gr. 1-4). lib. bdg. 17.90 (***978-1-4263-0186-5(3)***, National Geographic Children's Bks.) National Geographic Society.

Scherer, Glenn & Fletcher, Marty. The American Crocodile: Help Save This Endangered Species! 2007. (Saving Endangered Species Ser.). (Illus.). 128p. (J). (gr. 5). lib. bdg. 33.27 (978-1-59845-041-5(7), MyReportLinks.com Bks.) Enslow Pubs., Inc.

Shea, Therese. Crocodiles & Alligators. 2006. (Illus.). 24p. (J). lib. bdg. 24.77 (978-1-4042-3523-6(X), PowerKids Pr.) Rosen Publishing Group, Inc., The.

Simon, Seymour. Crocodiles & Alligators. 2001. (Illus.). 32p. (J). (gr. k up). pap. 6.99 (978-0-06-443829-2(5), Harper Trophy) HarperCollins Pubs.

—Crocodiles & Alligators. Simon, Seymour, illus. 1999. (Illus.). 32p. (J). (gr. k-3). 16.89 (978-0-06-027474-0(3)) HarperCollins Pubs.

—Crocodiles & Alligators. 2001. (ps-ps). (Illus.). (J). lib. bdg. 15.25 (978-0-613-44201-5(6)); 13.79 (978-0-606-22283-9(9)) Tandem Library Bks.

Snyder, Trish. Alligator & Crocodile Rescue: Changing the Future for Endangered Wildlife. 2006. (Firefly Animal Rescue Ser.). (Illus.). 64p. (J). (gr. 5-12). pap. 9.95 (978-1-55297-919-8(9)); lib. bdg. 19.95 (978-1-55297-920-4(2)) Firefly Bks., Ltd.

Stone, Tanya Lee. Crocodilians. 2003. (Wild Wild World Ser.). (Illus.). 24p. (J). 22.45 (978-1-4103-0037-9(4), Blackbirch Pr., Inc.) Thomson Gale.

Swanson, Diane. Alligators & Crocodiles. 2004. (Welcome to the World of Animals Ser.). (Illus.). 32p. (J). (gr. 3 up). lib. bdg. 23.33 (978-0-8368-4021-6(6)) Stevens, Gareth Inc.

—Welcome to the World of Alligators & Crocodiles. 2002. (Welcome to the World Ser.). (Illus.). 32p. (J). (ps-2). pap. 5.95 (978-1-55285-355-9(1)) Whitecap Bks., Ltd. CAN. *Dist:* Firefly Bks., Ltd.

Taylor, Barbara. Crocodiles, 3 vols. 2000. (Nature Watch Ser.). (Illus.). 64p. (gr. 3-7). 14.95 (978-1-85967-640-0(5)) Anness Publishing GBR. *Dist:* National Bk. Network.

—Dinosaur Legacy. 2005. (Illus.). 128p. pap. 17.99 (978-1-84476-081-7(2), Southwater) Anness Publishing GBR. *Dist:* National Bk. Network.

Taylor, Barbara & Griffiths, Richard. Crocodiles. 2003. (Nature Fact File Ser.). (Illus.). 64p. (gr. 3-7). pap. 7.99 (978-1-84215-737-4(X), Southwater) Anness Publishing GBR. *Dist:* National Bk. Network.

Toms, Kate. Bathtime Buddy: Colin the Crocodile. 2005. (Illus.). 8p. (J). (ps-k). 9.95 (978-1-84610-020-8(8)) Make Believe Ideas GBR. *Dist:* Ingram Pub. Services.

Tourville, Amanda Doering. A Crocodile Grows Up. Denman, Michael & Huiett, William J., illus. 2006. (Wild Animals Ser.). 24p. (J). (gr. 1-3). lib. bdg. 25.26 (978-1-4048-3157-5(6), 1265739) Picture Window Bks.

Tracqui, Valerie. Crocodile. 2000. (gr. k-3). lib. bdg. 15.25 (978-0-613-28283-3(3)); (Illus.). (J). (978-0-606-18025-2(7)) Tandem Library Bks.

—The Crocodile: Ruler of the River. Laird, Lisa, tr. from FRE. 2000. (Animal Close-Ups Ser.). (Illus.). 27p. (J). (ps-3). pap. 6.95 (978-1-57091-425-6(7)) Charlesbridge Publishing, Inc.

Trueit, Trudi Strain. Alligators & Crocodiles. 2003. (True Bks.). (gr. 3-5). pap. 6.95 (978-0-516-29353-0(2)); (Illus.). 48p. (J). 25.00 (978-0-516-22653-8(3)) Scholastic Library Publishing. (Children's Pr.).

—Alligators & Crocodiles. 2003. (Illus.). 47p. (J). (gr. 4-7). lib. bdg. 15.25 (978-0-613-67950-3(4)) Tandem Library Bks.

Walker, Sally M. Crocodiles. 2004. (Nature Watch Ser.). (Illus.). 48p. (J). (gr. 3-8). lib. bdg. 25.26 (978-1-57505-345-5(4)) Lerner Publishing Group.

—Supercroc Found. Hood, Philip, illus. 2006. (On My Own Science Ser.). (J). pap. 5.95 (978-1-57505-852-8(9), First Avenue Editions); 48p. (gr. 2-4). lib. bdg. 25.26 (978-1-57505-760-6(3)) Lerner Publishing Group.

Ward, Rebecca. Crocodile. 1999. (J). (978-1-84100-210-1(0)) Quadrillion Publishing.

Welsbacher, Anne. Crocodiles. 2002. (Predators in the Wild Ser.). (Illus.). 32p. (J). (gr. 3-4). lib. bdg. 21.26 (978-0-7368-1315-0(2), Capstone High-Interest Bks.) Capstone Pr., Inc.

Wexo, John Bonnett. Alligators & Crocodiles. (Zoobooks Ser.). (Illus.). 24p. (J). (gr. 1-6). 2001. 15.95 (978-1-888153-35-4(0)); 2003. 10.95 (978-1-932396-03-4(9), Zoo Bks.) Wildlife Education, Ltd.

Wildlife Education, Ltd. Staff & Wexo, John Bonnett. Alligators & Crocodiles. Hoopes, Barbara, illus. 2000. (Zoobooks Ser.). 18p. (Orig.). (YA). (gr. 5 up). pap. 2.95 (978-0-937934-25-8(9)) Wildlife Education, Ltd.

Woodward, John. Crocodiles & Alligators. 1999. (Endangered! Ser.). (Illus.). 32p. (J). (gr. 3-5). lib. bdg. 25.64 (978-0-7614-0322-7(1), Benchmark Bks.) Cavendish, Marshall Corp.

CROCODILES—FICTION

Ada, Alma Flor. Quien Cuida al Cocodrilo? Escriva, Viví, illus. 2003. (Alma Flor Ada Ser.). (SPA.). (J). (gr. k-1). pap. 9.95 (978-84-239-2890-3(X), EC6471) Espasa Calpe, S.A. ESP. *Dist:* Lectorum Pubns., Inc., Planeta Publishing Corp.

Alexander, Harry. Hang on, Crocodile! 2001. (Pinwheel Ser.). (Illus.). 12p. (J). bds. 5.95 (978-0-8069-2803-6(4)) Sterling Publishing Co., Inc.

Alligator Tails & Crocodile Cakes: Level L, 6 vols. 128p. (gr. 2-3). 49.95 (978-0-7699-0985-1(X)) Shortland Pubns. (U. S. A.) Inc.

Arrington, H. J. Friends Again? Kitchel, JoAnn E., illus. 2001. 32p. (J). 15.95 (978-1-56554-834-3(5)) Pelican Publishing Co., Inc.

Balzola, Asun. Munia y el Cocolilo Naranja. (SPA.). 32p. (J). (978-84-233-1335-8(2)) Ediciones Destino ESP. *Dist:* Lectorum Pubns., Inc.

Bannerman, Helen. The Story of Little Black Mingo (Illustr. 2006. pap. (***978-1-4065-0770-6(9)***) Dodo Pr.

Barsy, Kalman. El Cocodrilo Lloron. 2003. (SPA.). (gr. k-3). lib. bdg. 14.10 (978-0-613-79281-3(5)) Tandem Library Bks.

—The Crying Crocodile. Gastaldo, Walter, illus. 2004. (Yellow Ser.). (SPA.). 31p. (J). (gr. k-3). pap. 5.95 (978-1-57581-433-9(1)) Santillana USA Publishing Co., Inc.

Bedford, David. The Copy Crocs. Bolam, Emily, tr. Bolam, Emily, illus. 2004. 32p. (J). (gr. k). 15.95 (978-1-56145-304-7(8)) Peachtree Pubs., Ltd.

Beeke, Jemma & Beeke, Tiphanie. The Brand New Creature. 1999. (Illus.). (J). (ps-ps). lib. bdg. 15.25 (978-0-613-21246-5(0)) Tandem Library Bks.

Blackman, Andy. Miles the Crocodile Plays the Colors of Jazz: Baby Loves Jazz. Cunningham, Andrew, illus. 2006. 18p. (J). (ps-1). 7.99 (978-0-8431-2084-4(3), Price Stern Sloan) Penguin Group (USA) Inc.

Brown, Jo. Where's My Mommy? Brown, Jo, illus. 2006. (Illus.). 18p. (J). bds. 6.95 (978-1-58925-795-5(2), tiger tales) ME Media LLC.

—Where's My Mommy? 2004. (Illus.). 32p. (J). tchr. ed. 14.95 (978-1-58925-019-2(2), tiger tales) ME Media LLC.

Brown, Ruth. Crazy Charlie. Brown, Ruth, illus. 1998. (Illus.). 32p. (J). pap. 9.99 (978-0-86264-840-4(8)) Andersen GBR. *Dist:* Independent Pubs. Group.

Burch, Sharon. Freddie the Frog & the Thump in the Night. 2004. (Illus.). (J). 23.95 incl. audio compact disk (978-0-9747454-9-7(9)) Mystic Publishing.

Castle, Caroline. Snip, Snap, Croc. 2007. (J). lib. bdg. 16.95 (***978-1-59566-367-2(3)***) QEB Publishing Inc.

Charles, Faustin. The Selfish Crocodile. Terry, Michael, illus. 1999. 32p. (J). (gr. k-2). 14.95 (978-1-888444-56-8(8)) Little Tiger Pr.

Chen, Chih-Yuan. Guji Guji. Chen, Chih-Yuan, illus. (Illus.). (J). 2007. (SPA.). 36p. pap. 7.95 (978-1-933605-34-0(0), 05340); 2004. 32p. 15.95 (978-1-929132-67-6(0)) Kane/Miller Bk. Pubs., Inc.

Christelow, Eileen. En un Arbol Estan los Cinco Monitos / Five Little Monkeys Sitting in a Tree. 2007. Tr. of Five Little Monkeys Sitting in a Tree. (ENG & SPA., Illus.). 28p. (J). (gr. k-ps). bds. 5.95 (978-0-618-75248-5(X), Clarion Bks.) Houghton Mifflin Co. Trade & Reference Div.

—Five Little Monkeys Wash the Car. (Illus.). 40p. (J). (ps-1). 2004. 5.95 (978-0-618-48602-1(X)); 2000. tchr. ed. 15.00 (978-0-395-92566-9(5)) Houghton Mifflin Co. Trade & Reference Div. (Clarion Bks.).

Clark, Emma Chichester. Melrose & Croc: A Christmas to Remember. Clark, Emma Chichester, illus. 2006. (Illus.). 32p. (J). 16.95 (978-0-8027-9597-7(8)) Walker & Co.

The Clumsy Crocodile: Everyday Words - My Town, 3 bks., 3 discs, Set. 2004. (Make Reading Fun! Ser.: Module 3). (SPA., Illus.). (J). (ps-1). 49.95 (978-1-58086-180-9(6)) EDC Publishing.

Crocodile River. 2002. (Animal's Around the World Mini Bks.). (Illus.). 32p. (J). (978-1-59069-172-4(5), H4008) Studio Mouse LLC.

Dahl, Roald. The Enormous Crocodile. Blake, Quentin, illus. 2005. 53p. (J). (ps-3). reprint ed. 16.00 (978-0-7567-9546-7(X)) DIANE Publishing Co.

—The Enormous Crocodile. Blake, Quentin, illus. 2003. 32p. (J). pap. 7.99 (978-0-14-230245-3(7), Puffin) Penguin Group (USA) Inc.

—The Enormous Crocodile. 2003. (gr. k-3). lib. bdg. 16.45 (978-0-613-87826-5(4)) Tandem Library Bks.

de Paola, Tomie. Bill & Pete to the Rescue. 2001. (Illus.). 48p. (J). (ps-3). pap. 5.99 (978-0-698-11884-3(7), Putnam Juvenile) Penguin Group (USA) Inc.

—Bill & Pete to the Rescue. 2001. (Illus.). (J). 12.79 (978-0-606-21067-6(9)) Tandem Library Bks.

The Deer & the Crocodile: Individual Title Six-Packs. (Literatura 2000 Ser.). (gr. 1-2). 28.00 (978-0-7635-0130-3(1)) Rigby Education.

Donnio, Sylviane. I'd Really Like to Eat a Child. De Monfreid, Dorothée, illus. 2007. (Picture Book Ser.). 32p. (J). (ps-1). lib. bdg. 17.99 (978-0-375-93761-3(7), Random Hse. Bks. for Young Readers) Random Hse. Children's Bks.

—I'd Really Like to Eat a Child. Martin, Leslie, tr. from FRE. De Monfreid, Dorothée, illus. 2007. (Picture Book Ser.). 32p. (J). (ps-1). 14.99 (978-0-375-83761-6(2), Random Hse. Bks. for Young Readers) Random Hse. Children's Bks.

Douglas, Marjory Stoneman. Alligator Crossing. Nicholson, Trudy, illus. 2003. 192p. (J). (gr. 3-8). pap. 6.95 (978-1-57131-644-8(2)) Milkweed Editions.

—Alligator Crossing. 2003. (gr. 3-6). lib. bdg. 15.25 (978-0-613-79196-0(7)) Tandem Library Bks.

Easterling, Anne S. Ozzie the Great Christmas Crocodile. 2006. (Illus.). 12p. (J). 3.95 (***978-0-9768890-4-5(8)***) ASE Media.

Freedman, Claire. Where's Your Smile, Crocodile? Julian, Sean, illus. 2001. 32p. (J). (ps-k). 16.95 (978-1-56145-251-4(3)) Peachtree Pubs., Ltd.

Gerrard, Roy. Croco'nile. 2001. (Illus.). (J). 13.75 (978-0-606-21130-7(6)) Tandem Library Bks.

Golden, Kathleen M. Cleopatra's Big Birthday BBQ. Golden, Kathleen M., illus. 2003. (Illus.). 18p. (J). (ps-k). mass mkt. 14.95 (978-0-9726418-0-7(7)) Happyland Media.

Graham, Bob. Tales from the Waterhole. Graham, Bob, illus. 2004. (Illus.). 64p. (J). (ps-3). 16.99 (978-0-7636-2324-1(5)) Candlewick Pr.

Greenberg, David T. Crocs! 2008. 32p. (J). (978-0-316-07306-6(7)) Little Brown & Co.

Gwazube, Fundesile. Crocodile's Sore Tooth. Torgah, F. K. Atakpa Kple Edoh, tr. 2000. (EWE., Illus.). pap. 3.00 (978-0-521-79582-1(6)) Cambridge Univ. Pr.

—Crocodile's Sore Tooth. Ablorh, Samuel Adjei, tr. 2000. (GAA., Illus.). pap. 3.00 (978-0-521-79592-0(3) Cambridge Univ. Pr.

—Crocodile's Sore Tooth: Akwapim Twi Version. Asante, Comfort, tr. 2000. (TWI., Illus.). pap. 3.00 (978-0-521-79625-5(3)) Cambridge Univ. Pr.

—Crocodile's Sore Tooth: Asante Twi Version. Asenso, Okofo, tr. 2000. (TWI., Illus.). pap. 3.00 (978-0-521-79611-8(3)) Cambridge Univ. Pr.

—Crocodile's Sore Tooth: Dagbani Version. Abdulai, Fuseini-Bila, tr. 2000. (Illus.). pap. 3.00 (978-0-521-79601-9(6)) Cambridge Univ. Pr.

—Crocodile's Sore Tooth: Fante Version. Aggrey, Safohen J. E. K., tr. 2000. (Illus.). pap. 3.00 (978-0-521-79572-2(9)) Cambridge Univ. Pr.

Gwazube, Fundisile. Crocodile's Sore Tooth. Moyo, Sihambile, tr. 1999. (Cambridge African Language Library Ser.). (NBL & NDE., Illus.). 16p. pap. 3.70 (978-0-521-65810-2(1)) Cambridge Univ. Pr.

—Crocodile's Sore Tooth: Shona Version. Chirikure, Chirilure, tr. 1999. (Cambridge African Language Library Ser.). (SHO., Illus.). 16p. pap. 4.15 (978-0-521-65825-6(X)) Cambridge Univ. Pr.

Hamilton, Linda. The Big-Hearted Monkey & the Crocodile. 2005. (J). (978-1-933248-01-1(7)) World Quest Learning.

Hao, K. T. One Pizza, One Penny. Feldman, Roxanne Hsu, tr. from CHI. Ferri, Giuliano, illus. 2003. 32p. 15.95 (978-0-8126-2702-2(4)) Cricket Bks.

Hébert, Marie-Francine. Un Crocodile dans la Baignoire. 2002. (Premier Roman Ser.). (FRE.). 64p. (J). (gr. 2-5). pap. (978-2-89021-200-8(9)) Diffusion du livre Mirabel.

Heidbreder, Robert. Crocodiles Say... Mate, Rae, illus. 2005. 32p. (J). 16.95 (978-1-894965-42-2(6)) Simply Read Bks. CAN. *Dist:* Perseus Distribution.

Hetherington, Sands. Night Buddies. 1999. (Illus.). 64p. (J). (gr. k-6). pap. 8.00 (978-0-8059-4754-0(X)) Dorrance Publishing Co., Inc.

How to Make a Crocodile. 2005. (Early Library). (YA). (ps-3). 23.94 (978-0-8215-8952-6(0)) Sadlier, William H. Inc.

Hughes, Monica. Little Mouse Deer & the Crocodile. Moricuchi, Mique, illus. 2004. 24p. (J). lib. bdg. 22.65 (***978-1-59646-684-5(7)***) Dingles & Co.

Irly, I. R. Why Crocodile Does Not Smile. 2004. (Illus.). (J). bds. (978-0-9753075-4-0(1)) M-Graphics Publishing.

Kennen, Ally. Beast. 2006. 224p. (J). pap. 16.99 (978-0-439-86549-4(2), PUSH) Scholastic, Inc.

Kipling, Rudyard. Crocodile, Crocodile. Mogensen, Jan & Schroeder, Binnette, illus. 2003. Orig. Title: Krokodil, Krokodil. pap. 7.95 (978-1-56656-512-7(X)) Interlink Publishing Group, Inc.

Kiss, Kathrin. Que Hace un Cocodrilo por la Noche? Urberuaga, Emilio, illus. 2001. (SPA.). (J). (gr. k-3). (978-84-88342-18-8(7), KK8906) S.A. Kokinos ESP. *Dist:* Lectorum Pubns., Inc.

Kleven, Elisa. The Wishing Ball. 2006. (Illus.). 32p. (J). 16.00 (978-0-374-38449-4(5)) Farrar, Straus & Giroux.

Lakin, Patricia. Rainy Day! Nash, Scott, illus. 2007. 40p. (J). (ps-1). 16.99 (978-0-8037-3092-2(6), Dial) Penguin Group (USA) Inc.

Landay, Janet. Kangodile: A Mix-and-Match Menagerie. 2006. 29p. (J). 8.95 (978-0-8118-5178-7(8)) Chronicle Bks. LLC.

Levy, Didier & Rapaport, Giles. Ernesto. (SPA., Illus.). 32p. (J). (gr. k-2). 14.95 (978-84-95150-80-6(8), COR1529) Corimbo, Editorial S.L. ESP. *Dist:* Distribooks, Inc., Lectorum Pubns., Inc.

Lionni, Leo. Cornelius: A Fable. Lionni, Leo, illus. 2002. (Illus.). (J). 13.83 (978-0-7587-5333-5(0)) Book Wholesalers, Inc.

Lofting, Hugh. The Story of Doctor Dolittle: #2 the Circus Crocodile. 2007. (Easy Reader Classics Ser.). 32p. (J). (ps-3). 21.35 (***978-1-59961-339-0(5)***) Spotlight.

Lofting, Hugh. The Story of Doctor Dolittle Bk. 2: The Circus Crocodile. Kanzler, John, illus. 2006. (Easy Reader Classics Ser.). 32p. (J). pap. 3.95 (978-1-4027-3292-8(9)) Sterling Publishing Co., Inc.

Marcellino, Fred. I, Crocodile. Marcellino, Fred, illus. (Illus.). (J). (ps-3). 2002. 32p. pap. 7.99 (978-0-06-008859-0(1), Harper Trophy); 1999. 40p. 19.99 (978-0-06-205168-4(7)) HarperCollins Pubs.

McKendry, Sam. Are You Ticklish? A Touch & Tickle Book. Mitchell, Melanie, illus. 2005. 12p. (J). (ps up). 10.95 (978-1-58117-376-5(8), Intervisual/Piggy Toes) Dalmatian Pr.

McOmber, Rachel B., ed. McOmber Phonics Storybooks: The Invisible Crocodiles. rev. ed. (Illus.). (J). (978-0-944991-80-0(7)) Swift Learning Resources.

—McOmber Phonics Storybooks: Yellow Crocodile. rev. ed. (Illus.). (J). (978-0-944991-76-3(9)) Swift Learning Resources.

Mitton, Tony. Planet Ocky: Ham & Jam. Chatterton, Ann & Chatterton, Martin, illus. 1999. (Cambridge Reading Ser.). 14p. pap. 5.00 (978-0-521-64704-5(5)); pap., pap. 16.95 (978-0-521-66701-2(1)) Cambridge Univ. Pr.

—Planet Ocky: Jump & Bump. Chatterton, Ann & Chatterton, Martin, illus. 1999. (Cambridge Reading Ser.). 14p. pap., pap. 16.95 (978-0-521-66700-5(3)) Cambridge Univ. Pr.

Montanari, Eva. The Crocodile's True Colors. 2002. (Illus.). 32p. (J). (gr. k-3). 14.95 (978-0-8230-2435-3(0)) Watson-Guptill Pubns., Inc.

Moon, Nicola. Alligator Tales & Crocodile Cakes. Ellis, Andy, illus. 2005. (I Am Reading Ser.). 48p. (J). (gr. k-3). pap., pap. 3.95 (978-0-7534-5853-2(5), Kingfisher) Houghton Mifflin Co. Trade & Reference Div.

Moran, Rosslyn, illus. Please, Mr. Crocodile! Poems about Animals. 1999. 40p. (J). (ps-3). 16.95 (978-1-902283-62-3(7)) Barefoot Bks., Inc.

Nash, Deborah. Riddle of the Nile. 2006. (Illus.). 32p. (J). (gr. k-4). 15.95 (978-1-84507-466-1(1)) Lincoln, Frances Ltd. GBR. *Dist:* Perseus Distribution.

Noel, Genevieve. Que Amor de Cocodrilo!/Al Agua, Leo. (Torre de Papel Ser.). (SPA., Illus.). (J). 7.95 (978-958-04-5039-9(0)) Norma S.A. COL. *Dist:* Distribuidora Norma, Inc., Lectorum Pubns., Inc.

Parish, Steve, illus. The Cranky Crocodile. 2005. 24p. (J). lib. bdg. 20.67 (978-0-8368-5970-6(7)) Stevens, Gareth Inc.

Polhemus, Coleman. The Crocodile Blues. Polhemus, Coleman, illus. 2007. (Illus.). 48p. (J). (ps-1). 16.99 (***978-0-7636-3543-5(X)***) Candlewick Pr.

Postgate, Daniel. Richest Crocodile in the World. 2004. (Illus.). 32p. (J). pap. 8.95 (978-0-00-710387-4(5), HarperSport) HarperCollins Pubs. Ltd. GBR. *Dist:* Independent Pubs. Group.

—The Richest Crocodile in the World. 2003. (Illus.). 32p. (J). (gr. k-2). 17.95 (978-0-00-710388-1(3)) HarperCollins Pubs. Ltd. GBR. *Dist:* Independent Pubs. Group.

Protopopescu, Orel Odinov. Two Sticks. Wilsdorf, Anne, illus. 2007. 32p. (J). (ps-1). 16.00 (978-0-374-38022-9(8)) Farrar, Straus & Giroux.

Pugliano-Martin, Carol. Kanchil Outsmarts Crocodile: A Folktale from Malaysia & Indonesia. 2006. spiral bd. 23.00 (***978-1-4108-7165-7(7)***) Benchmark Education Co.

Rigby Education Staff. Baby Kangaroo. (Sails Literacy Ser.). (Illus.). 16p. (gr. k-1). 27.00 (978-0-7635-9879-2(8), 698798C99) Rigby Education.

—Clean My Teeth. (Sails Literacy Ser.). (Illus.). 16p. (gr. k-1). 27.00 (978-0-7635-9882-2(8), 698828C99) Rigby Education.

Roberts, Dannel. Me & Uncle Mike & the 1-Eyed Croc. Stolte, F., illus. l.t. ed. 2002. (Me & Uncle Mike Children's Book Ser.: Bk. 4). 36p. per. 14.95 net. (978-1-893459-03-8(9)) Lions & Tigers & Bears Publishing, Inc.

Robinson, Hilary. Croc by the Rock. Gordon, Mike, illus. 2005. 32p. (J). lib. bdg. 9.00 (***978-1-4242-0885-2(8)***) Fitzgerald Bks.

Rodgers, Frank. Mr. Croc's Silly Sock. 2006. (Read-It! Chapter Books). (J). 21.26 (978-1-4048-2730-1(7)) Picture Window Bks.

—Mr. Croc's Walk. 2007. (Read-It! Chapter Books). (J). 21.26 (978-1-4048-2729-5(3)) Picture Window Bks.

—What Mr. Croc Forgets. 2006. (Read-It! Chapter Books). (J). 21.26 (978-1-4048-2731-8(5)) Picture Window Bks.

Rolt, Molly. The Chocci-Croc & Other Stories. 2006. 64p. pap. (***978-1-84401-890-1(3)***) Athena Pr.

Rowe, John A. I Want a Hug. 2007. (Illus.). 32p. (J). (ps-3). 16.99 (***978-0-698-40064-1(X)***, Minedition) Penguin Group (USA) Inc.

Sarfati, Sonia & Merola, Caroline. Le Crocrodile Qui Croquait les Cauchemars. 2000. (Itait une Fois Ser.). (FRE., Illus.). 24p. (YA). (ps up). pap. (978-2-89021-397-5(8)) Diffusion du livre Mirabel.

Scheunemann, Pam. Crocodile Tears. Chawla, Neena, illus. 2007. (Fact & Fiction Ser.). 24p. (J). (978-1-59928-437-8(5)); 21.35 (978-1-59928-436-1(7)) ABDO Publishing Co.

Schubert, Ingrid & Schubert, Dieter. There's a Crocodile Under My Bed. 2nd ed. 2005. (Illus.). 32p. (J). (ps-1). 15.95 (978-1-932425-48-2(9), Lemniscaat) Boyds Mills Pr.

Shah, Naseeruddin. The Monkey & the Crocodile. 1998. (Karadi Tales Ser.). (Illus.). 24p. (YA). (gr. 1 up). 9.99 incl. audio (978-81-86838-35-8(X)) APG Sales and Fulfillment.

Shaky Crocodile. alt. ed. 2002. (J). (978-1-931312-95-0(8)) SoftPlay, Inc.

Sharratt, Nick. A Crock with a Clock: Buggy Buddies. 1999. (Illus.). 10p. (J). bds. 3.99 (978-1-58048-060-4(8)) Sandvik Publishing.

Sierra, Judy. Counting Crocodiles. Hillenbrand, Will, illus. 2001. 40p. (J). (gr. k-2). pap. 7.00 (978-0-15-216356-3(5), Voyager Bks./Libros Viajeros) Harcourt Children's Bks.

—Counting Crocodiles. 2001. (ps-2). lib. bdg. 15.30 (978-0-613-82223-7(4)); 13.80 (978-0-606-22596-0(X)) Tandem Library Bks.

—What Time Is It, Mr. Crocodile? Cushman, Doug, illus. 2007. 32p. (J). pap. 7.00 (978-0-15-205850-0(8), Voyager Bks./Libros Viajeros) Harcourt Children's Bks.

—What Time Is It, Mr. Crocodile? Cushman, Doug, tr. Cushman, Doug, illus. 2004. 32p. (J). 16.00 (978-0-15-216445-4(6), Gulliver Bks.) Harcourt Children's Bks.

Simon, Seymour. The Foolish Crocodile. 1999. (J). lib. bdg. 19.99 (978-0-517-70997-9(X)) Crown Publishing Group.

Smeeton, Miles. Alligator Tales (& Crocodiles Too) 1998. (Illus.). (J). pap. (978-1-896209-17-3(3)) Bayeux Arts, Inc.

Smith, Alexander McCall. Akimbo & the Crocodile Man. Pham, LeUyen, illus. 80p. (J). 2007. pap. 4.95 (***978-1-59990-033-9(5)***, Bloomsbury Children); 2006. 9.95 (978-1-58234-692-2(5)) Bloomsbury Publishing.

Sprott, Duncan. Daughter of the Crocodile, Vol. 2. 2006. (Illus.). 496p. (***978-0-571-20290-4(X)***) Faber & Faber, Ltd.

Stevenson, James. No Laughing, No Smiling, No Giggling: Is That Understood? 2004. (Illus.). 32p. (J). 16.00 (978-0-374-31829-1(8), Farrar, Straus & Giroux (BYR)) Farrar, Straus & Giroux.

Sturges, Philemon. Crocky Dilly. Miglio, Paige, illus. 1998. 32p. (J). (ps-3). 14.95 (978-0-87846-458-6(1)) Museum of Fine Arts, Boston.

Thomassie, Tynia. Feliciana Feydra Leroux: Cajun Tall Tale. Bowman Smith, Cat, illus. 2005. 32p. (J). 15.95 (978-1-58980-286-5(1)) Pelican Publishing Co., Inc.

Usui, Kanako. Fantastic Mr Wani. Usui, Kanako, illus. 2006. (Illus.). 32p. (J). 15.95 (978-1-58925-054-3(0) , tiger tales) ME Media LLC.

Velthuijs, Max. Crocodile's Masterpiece. 2001. (Illus.). 32p. pap. 9.95 (978-1-84270-002-0(2)) Andersen GBR. *Dist:* Trafalgar Square Publishing.

Vilarino, Andres Garcia. Un Cocodrilo en Mi Habitacion. 6th ed. 2003. (SPA., Illus.). 56p. (978-84-236-3696-9(8) , ED0976) Edebé ESP. *Dist:* Lectorum Pubns., Inc.

Vrombaut, An. Clarabella's Teeth. 2003. (Illus.). 32p. (J). (gr. k-3). 15.00 (978-0-618-33379-0(7) , Clarion Bks.) Houghton Mifflin Co. Trade & Reference Div.

Waber, Bernard. Funny, Funny Lyle. Waber, Bernard, illus. 2002. (Lyle the Crocodile Ser.). (Illus.). (J). 14.74 (978-0-7587-2559-2(0)) Book Wholesalers, Inc.

—The House on East 88th Street. Waber, Bernard, illus. 2002. (Lyle the Crocodile Ser.). (Illus.). (J). 14.74 (978-0-7587-2756-5(9)) Book Wholesalers, Inc.

—Lovable Lyle. Waber, Bernard, illus. 2002. (Lyle the Crocodile Ser.). (Illus.). (J). 14.74 (978-0-7587-3043-5(8)) Book Wholesalers, Inc.

—Lyle at Christmas. Waber, Bernard, illus. 2002. (Lyle the Crocodile Ser.). (Illus.). (J). 23.40 (978-0-7587-3058-9(6)) Book Wholesalers, Inc.

—Lyle at Christmas. 2003. (Lyle the Crocodile Ser.). (Illus.). 48p. (J). (gr. k-3). pap. 5.95 (978-0-618-38002-2(7) , Walter Lorraine) Houghton Mifflin Co. Trade & Reference Div.

—Lyle at Christmas. Waber, Bernard, illus. 1998. (Lyle the Crocodile Ser.). (Illus.). 48p. (J). (gr. k-3). tchr. ed. 16.00 (978-0-395-91304-8(7) , Walter Lorraine) Houghton Mifflin Co. Trade & Reference Div.

—Lyle at the Office. Waber, Bernard, illus. 2002. (Lyle the Crocodile Ser.). (Illus.). (J). 13.79 (978-0-7587-3059-6(4)) Book Wholesalers, Inc.

—Lyle Finds His Mother. Waber, Bernard, illus. 2002. (Lyle the Crocodile Ser.). (Illus.). (J). 14.74 (978-0-7587-3060-2(8)) Book Wholesalers, Inc.

—Lyle, Lyle, Crocodile. Waber, Bernard, illus. 2002. (Lyle the Crocodile Ser.). (Illus.). (J). 14.74 (978-0-7587-3061-9(6)) Book Wholesalers, Inc.

—Lyle, Lyle, Crocodile. 1999. (Lyle the Crocodile Ser.). (J). (ps-3). 9.95 (978-1-56137-327-7(3)) Novel Units, Inc.

Waber, Bernard & Waber, Bernard. Lyle at Christmas. Waber, Bernard, illus. 2003. (Lyle the Crocodile Ser.). (Illus.). 48p. (J). (ps-3). lib. bdg. 14.10 (978-0-613-88087-9(0)) Tandem Library Bks.

Watanabe, Etsuko. Oscar's Party. 2006. (Illus.). 12p. (J). 14.95 (978-1-58234-697-7(6) , Bloomsbury Children) Bloomsbury Publishing.

West, Colin. Have You Seen the Crocodile. West, Colin, illus. 2003. (Reading Together Ser.). (Illus.). 32p. (J). (ps). pap. 3.99 (978-0-7636-0862-0(9)) Candlewick Pr.

Widdowson, Kay, illus. Please, Mr Crocodile... 2006. 24p. (J). (978-1-84643-025-1(9)) Child's Play-International.

CROMWELL, OLIVER, 1599-1658

Aronson, Marc. John Winthrop, Oliver Cromwell, & the Land of Promise. 2004. (Illus.). 224p. (J). (gr. 5-9). tchr. ed. 20.00 (978-0-618-18177-3(6) , Clarion Bks.) Houghton Mifflin Co. Trade & Reference Div.

Ashworth, Leon. Oliver Cromwell. (Illus.). 32p. (978-0-7451-5287-5(2)); pap. (978-0-7540-9010-6(8)) Evans Publishing Group. (Cherrytree Books).

—Oliver Cromwell. 2004. (British History Makers Ser.). (Illus.). 32p. (YA). pap. 11.99 (978-1-84234-281-7(9) , Cherrytree Books) Evans Publishing Group GBR. *Dist:* Independent Pubs. Group.

Harmsworth, Andy & Dawson, Ian. King Cromwell? A Key Stage 3 Depth Study on the English Civil War. 2002. (Illus.). 72p. pap. 26.00 (***978-0-7195-8559-3(7)*** , Hodder Murray) Hodder Education GBR. *Dist:* Trans-Atlantic Pubns., Inc.

Lace, William W. Oliver Cromwell & the English Civil War in World History. 2003. (In World History Ser.). (Illus.). 128p. (J). (gr. 5-12). lib. bdg. 26.60 (978-0-7660-1937-9(3)) Enslow Pubs., Inc.

CROPS

see Farm Produce

CROSS-COUNTRY RUNNING

see Track Athletics

CROSSWORD PUZZLES

Austen, Jane. Wacky Word Search. Balloon Books Staff, ed. 2003. (Illus.). 72p. (J). (gr. 2-4). pap. 3.95 (978-0-8069-8065-2(6) , Balloon Bks.) Sterling Publishing Co., Inc.

Barbour Books Staff. Criss Cross Your Way Through the Bible: 40 Bible Crossword Puzzles for Kids. 1999. (J). pap. 0.99 (978-1-57748-440-0(1)) Barbour Publishing, Inc.

Barkan, Joanne. Games We Play. 2005. (Real Deal - Green Plus Ser.). (Illus.). 32p. (gr. 4-8). 19.00 (978-0-7910-8900-2(2)) Facts On File, Inc.

Blair, Beth & Ericsson, Jennifer. Everything Kids' Animal Puzzles. 2005. (Illus.). 144p. (J). pap., act. bk. ed. 6.95 (978-1-59337-305-4(8)) Adams Media Corp.

Blindauer, Patrick. Scrabble Jr. Sticker Crosswords. 2007. (Illus.). 32p. (J). pap. 5.95 (***978-1-4027-5066-3(8)***) Sterling Publishing Co., Inc.

Brighter Vision Publishing Staff. Crossword Puzzles. 2000. (Illus.). 32p. (J). (gr. 2). pap., act. bk. ed. 1.39 (978-1-55254-153-1(3)) Brighter Vision Pubns.

Burkett, Katherine. Super Science Crosswords. 2000. pap. 10.95 (978-0-590-64457-0(2)) Scholastic, Inc.

Charlesworth, Sylvia. 50 Great States Read-and-Solve Crossword Puzzles: Engaging Reproducible Nonfiction Passages about Each State with Fun Crosswords That Help Build Reading Comprehension & Teach Fascinating Facts about the Nifty Fifty, Grades 3-6. 2002. (Illus.). 112p. pap., tchr. ed. 14.95 (978-0-439-29707-3(9)) Scholastic, Inc.

Clifton, Chuck & Clifton, Joyce. A Crossword Walk with Lewis & Clark. 2003. 56p. (J). 9.95 (978-0-9669760-6-9(1)) Maple Canyon Co.

—Fundamentals of Freedom Crossword Puzzles - Volume 1. 2004. 50p. (YA). 9.95 (978-0-9669760-7-6(X)) Maple Canyon Co.

Cox, Emily, et al. Crosswords for a Super Brain Workout. 2002. (Illus.). 192p. (J). pap. 9.95 (978-1-4027-0417-8(8)) Sterling Publishing Co., Inc.

Crossword Puzzles: Bible Characters from the Old Testament. (Illus.). 32p. (YA). (gr. 5 up). pap. 2.25 (978-0-87162-608-0(X) , E4452) Warner Pr. Pubs.

Crossword Puzzles: New Testament. (Illus.). 32p. (YA). (gr. 5 up). pap. 2.25 (978-0-87162-495-6(8) , E4451) Warner Pr. Pubs.

Crossword Puzzles: Old Testament. (Illus.). 32p. (YA). (gr. 5 up). pap. 2.25 (978-0-87162-494-9(X) , E4450) Warner Pr. Pubs.

Dot-to-Dot, 1-100. (Classroom Helpers Ser.). 24p. (gr. 1 up). 3.99 (978-0-7682-0811-5(4) , FS194110) Schaffer, Frank Pubns.

Douglas, Vincent & School Specialty Publishing Staff. Crossword. l.t. ed. 2004. (Large Print Crosswords Ser.). (Illus.). 120p. (J). Vol. 21. pap. 2.99 (978-0-7696-3277-3(7)); Vol. 22. pap. 2.99 (978-0-7696-3278-0(5)); Vol. 23. pap. 2.99 (978-0-7696-3279-7(3)); Vol. 24. pap. 2.99 (978-0-7696-3280-3(7)) School Specialty Publishing. (Brighter Child).

Dunn, Kevin Ikim. In Search of Yourself Word Search Puzzles: Explorations into the Black Experience. Sedalia, Rajan, illus. 2005. (ENG.). 92p. per. 9.95 (978-0-9767337-0-6(6)) Invision Pubns.

DynaNotes Lab Measurement & Equipment Workbook. 2007. (J). pap. (***978-1-933854-72-4(3)***) DynaStudy, Inc.

Elite Crossword Puzzle Digest. 2003. per. (978-1-884907-18-0(0)) Paradise Pr., Inc.

Finch, Spencer. 25 Map Crossword Puzzles That Teach Map & Geography Skills. 1999. (Illus.). 64p. (J). 12.95 (978-0-590-76992-1(8)) Scholastic, Inc.

Fisk, Sally. Christian Crosswords Vol. 1: Old Testament Stories for Grades 2-3. Fisk, Sally, illus. 2000. (Illus.). 28p. (J). (gr. 2-3). pap. 8.95 (978-1-930338-00-5(7)) Praise Pubns.

—Christian Crosswords Vol. 2: New Testament Stories for Grades 2-3. Fisk, Sally, illus. 2000. (Illus.). 28p. (J). (gr. 2-3). pap. 8.95 (978-1-930338-01-2(5)) Praise Pubns.

—Christian Crosswords Vol. 3: Stories about Jesus for Grades 2-3. Fisk, Sally, illus. 2000. (Illus.). 28p. (J). (gr. 2-3). pap. 8.95 (978-1-930338-02-9(3)) Praise Pubns.

—Christian Crosswords Vol. 4: Bible Stories for Grades 2-3. Fisk, Sally, illus. 2000. (Illus.). 28p. (J). (gr. 2-3). pap. 8.95 (978-1-930338-03-6(1)) Praise Pubns.

Fremont, Victoria & Beylon, Cathy. Animal Crossword Puzzles. 1998. (Illus.). 64p. (J). pap. 1.50 (978-0-486-40153-5(5)) Dover Pubns., Inc.

Fun with Antonyms - Crossword Puzzles & Word Searches. 2004. pap. 7.99 (978-1-4206-3146-3(2)) Teacher Created Materials, Inc.

Fun with Homonyms - Crossword Puzzles & Word Searches. 2004. pap. 7.99 (978-1-4206-3143-2(8)) Teacher Created Materials, Inc.

Fun with Idioms - Crossword Puzzles & Word Searches. 2004. pap. 7.99 (978-1-4206-3144-9(6)) Teacher Created Materials, Inc.

Fun with Synonyms - Crossword Puzzles & Word Searches. 2004. pap. 7.99 (978-1-4206-3145-6(4)) Teacher Created Materials, Inc.

Gaffney, Matt. CosmoGIRL! Games: Crosswords. 2007. (Illus.). 112p. (J). pap. 5.95 (***978-1-58816-653-1(8)***) Hearst Communications, Inc.

Gamache, Dale & Gamache, Robin. La Clase Divertida (The FUN Class) Cuaderno de Actividades, Level 1. 1999. (ENG & SPA., Illus.). (J). (gr. k-6). pap., wbk. ed. 15.00 (978-0-9710190-1-0(0)) La Clase Divertida, Inc.

Glickstein, Barbara & Kennedy, Jan. Crosswords & Wordsearches. 1999. (100+ Ser.). 128p. (J). (gr. 2-4). pap. 12.99 (978-0-88012-823-0(2) , IF8724); (gr. 5-8). pap. 12.99 (978-0-88012-824-7(0) , IF8725) School Specialty Publishing.

Gogna, Ruth M. Hollywood Nineteen Eighty Crossword Puzzle. 80p. (Orig.). (J). (gr. 7 up). pap. 9.95 (978-0-931290-36-7(8)) Alchemy Bks.

Hemminger, Marcia. Comprehension Crosswords Grade 4, 6 vols. McAskin, Denice, illus. 2003. 32p. (J). 4.99 (978-1-56472-188-4(4)) Edupress, Inc.

—Comprehension Crosswords Grade 6, 6 vols. Adams Marks, Elizabeth, illus. 2003. 32p. (J). 4.99 (978-1-56472-190-7(6)) Edupress, Inc.

Hoffman, Joan. Crosswords. 2003. (Activity Zone Workbooks Ser.). 64p. (J). pap., wbk. ed. 3.79 (978-1-58947-075-0(3) , 02352) School Zone Publishing Co.

Hook, Henry. Twisted Crosswords. 2003. (Mensa Ser.). (Illus.). 96p. (J). pap. 7.95 (978-1-4027-0827-5(0)) Sterling Publishing Co., Inc.

Hovanec, Helene. More Outrageous Crossword Puzzles & Word Games for Kids. rev. ed. 2002. 96p. pap. 6.95 (978-0-312-30062-3(X) , St. Martin's Griffin) St. Martin's Pr.

—The Outrageous Crossword Puzzle & Word Game Book for Kids. rev. ed. 2002. (Illus.). 96p. pap. 6.95 (978-0-312-28915-7(4) , St. Martin's Griffin) St. Martin's Pr.

Hovanec, Helene & Shems, Ed. My First Puzzles: Letter Play. 2007. (My First Puzzles Ser.). 64p. (J). pap. 3.95 (***978-1-4027-4629-1(6)***) Sterling Publishing Co., Inc.

—My First Puzzles: Word Play. 2007. (My First Puzzles Ser.). 64p. (J). pap. 3.95 (***978-1-4027-4630-7(X)***) Sterling Publishing Co., Inc.

Joseph. Lever Crosswords. 1999. pap. (978-0-8069-6201-6(1)) Sterling Publishing Co., Inc.

Kellaher, Karen. Grammar Games & Activities Kids Can't Resist! 40 Super-Cool Crosswords, Codes, Mazes & More. 2003. (Illus.). 64p. (J). pap. 10.95 (978-0-439-07756-9(7)) Scholastic, Inc.

Koumpouras, Sally. Comprehension Crosswords Grade 5, 6 vols. Adams Marks, Elizabeth, illus. 2003. 32p. (J). 4.99 (978-1-56472-189-1(2)) Edupress, Inc.

Large Print Word Search. 2005. 120p. Bk. 36. pap. 2.99 (978-0-7696-3966-6(6)); Bk. 39. pap. 2.99 (978-0-7696-3969-7(0)) School Specialty Publishing. (American Education Publishing).

Lawrence, Linda. Crosswords for Kids, Vol. 2. 2003. 32p. pap. 14.95 (978-0-9728118-8-0(5) , 29) Inkwell Productions, LLC.

—Crosswords for Kids. unabr. ed. 2002. (ENG., Illus.). 48p. (J). (gr. 4-12). pap. 9.95 (978-0-9716039-0-5(1)) Lawrence Publishing.

—Crosswords for Kids, Two, Vol. 2. 2004. (ENG., Illus.). 56p. (YA). per. 10.95 (978-0-9716039-1-2(X)) Lawrence Publishing.

Long, Cathryn J. American History to 1900. Nolte, Larry, illus. 1998. (Crossword America Ser.). 64p. (J). (gr. 3-7). pap. 5.95 (978-1-56565-934-6(1) , 09341W) Lowell Hse. Juvenile.

—The Presidents. Nolte, Larry, illus. 2000. (Crossword America Ser.). 64p. (J). (gr. 3-7). pap. 5.95 (978-0-7373-0364-3(6) , 03646W, Roxbury Park Juvenile) Lowell Hse. Juvenile.

Mad Libs Activity Kit. 2004. (978-0-8431-0752-4(9) , Price Stern Sloan) Penguin Group (USA) Inc.

Maleska, Eugene T. Children's Word Games & Crossword Puzzles, Ages 7-9. 2003. (Illus.). 80p. pap. 6.95 (978-0-8129-3524-0(1)); Vol. 1. pap. 6.95 (978-0-8129-3521-9(7)); Vol. 2. pap. 6.95 (978-0-8129-3522-6(5)); Vol. 3. pap. 6.95 (978-0-8129-3523-3(3)) Random House Publishing Group.

Merrell, Patrick. My First Puzzles: Picture Clue Crosswords. 2007. (My First Puzzles Ser.). 64p. (J). pap. 3.95 (***978-1-4027-4725-0(X)***) Sterling Publishing Co., Inc.

My First Crosswords (Gr 1-2) 2003. (J). (978-1-58232-096-0(9)) Bryan Hse. Pubs., Inc.

New York Times Staff. The Times Jumbo Cryptic Crossword Book 7. 2007. 128p. pap. 7.95 (***978-0-00-723288-8(8)***) HarperCollins Pubs. Ltd. GBR. *Dist:* Independent Pubs. Group.

Newman-D'Amico, Fran. ABC Crosswords. 2005. 64p. (J). pap. 1.50 (978-0-486-44115-3(6)) Dover Pubns., Inc.

—Crossword Puzzles. 2001. (Illus.). 32p. (J). pap. 3.50 (978-0-486-41611-3(9)) Dover Pubns., Inc.

Payne, Trip. Amazing Crosswords for Kids. 2005. (Mensa Ser.). 96p. (J). pap. 5.95 (978-1-4027-1039-1(9)) Sterling Publishing Co., Inc.

—Awesome Crosswords for Kids. 2004. (Mensa Ser.). (Illus.). 96p. (J). pap. 5.95 (978-1-4027-1038-4(0)) Sterling Publishing Co., Inc.

—Challenging Crosswords for Kids. 2003. (Mensa Ser.). (Illus.). 96p. (J). (gr. 3-6). pap. 5.95 (978-1-4027-0555-7(7)) Sterling Publishing Co., Inc.

—Clever Crosswords for Kids. 2004. (Mensa Ser.). (Illus.). 96p. (J). pap. 5.95 (978-1-4027-0556-4(5)) Sterling Publishing Co., Inc.

—Crosswords for Kids. 1999. (Official Mensa Puzzle Book Ser.). (Illus.). 96p. (gr. 3-7). pap. 5.95 (978-0-8069-1249-3(9)) Sterling Publishing Co., Inc.

—Fantastically Fun Crosswords for Kids. Gamage, Ken, illus. 2006. (Mensa Ser.). 96p. (J). pap. 5.95 (978-1-4027-2163-2(3)) Sterling Publishing Co., Inc.

—Super Crosswords for Kids. 2003. (Mensa Ser.). (Illus.). 96p. pap. 5.95 (978-0-8069-9290-7(5)) Sterling Publishing Co., Inc.

—Trivial Pursuit for Kids Crosswords. 2007. 96p. (J). pap. 5.95 (***978-1-4027-5154-7(0)***) Sterling Publishing Co., Inc.

Payne, Trip. The 21-Foot-Long Crossword Puzzle Book: Fold-Out Fun for More Than One. 2007. 64p. (J). 9.95 (978-1-4027-4550-8(8) , Sterling Innovation) Sterling Publishing Co., Inc.

Pilkey, Dav. The All New Captain Underpants Extra-Crunchy Book O' Fun 2. 2002. (Captain Underpants Ser.). (gr. 3-6). lib. bdg. 11.80 (978-0-613-49472-4(5)) Tandem Library Bks.

Piscop, Fred, et al. Super 30-Minute Crosswords. 2003. (Illus.). 96p. (J). pap. 7.95 (978-1-4027-0542-7(5)) Sterling Publishing Co., Inc.

Preston, Roy & Preston, Sue. He Shoots, He Scores: 30 Fact-Filled Crosswords. 2003. (Illus.). 94p. (J). 5.99 (978-0-330-34106-6(5) , Pan) Pan Macmillan GBR. *Dist:* Trafalgar Square Publishing.

Price, Roger. American Idol Mad Libs. 2005. 48p. (J). (gr. 3). pap. 3.99 (978-0-8431-1391-4(X) , Price Stern Sloan) Penguin Group (USA) Inc.

Price, Roger & Stern, Leonard. Graduation Mad Libs. 2005. 48p. (J). (gr. 3). mass mkt. 3.99 (978-0-8431-1349-5(9) , Price Stern Sloan) Penguin Group (USA) Inc.

Puzzler's Giant Book of Crosswords. 2003. (YA). Vol. 10. per. 9.45 (978-1-55956-869-2(0)); Vol. 11. per. 9.45 (978-1-55956-872-2(0)) Penny Pubns., LLC. (Penny Pr.).

Samson, John M. Simon & Schuster Crossword Puzzle Book: The Original Crossword Puzzle Publisher, Vol. 229. 2002. (Illus.). 64p. pap. 9.95 (978-0-7432-2269-3(5) , Fireside) Simon & Schuster.

Schaffer, Frank. Dot-to-Dot 1 to 100. 2001. 20p. (J). (gr. 1-2). pap. 5.99 (978-0-7682-0534-3(4) , FS8521) Schaffer, Frank Pubns.

School Specialty Publishing. Large Print Word Search, Bk. 37. 2005. (Large Print Word Search Ser.). 120p. (J). pap. 2.99 (978-0-7696-3967-3(4) , American Education Publishing) School Specialty Publishing.

School Zone Publishing Company Staff. Big Activity Ages 8-Up: Word Searches, Crosswords, Puzzles, & Codes. 2004. 320p. (J). pap. 9.99 (978-1-58947-422-2(8)) School Zone Publishing Co.

School Zone Staff, ed. SZ Crosswords. 2004. (Activity Zone Workbook Ser.). 32p. (J). pap. 2.49 (978-1-58947-396-6(5) , 02198) School Zone Publishing Co.

Shiotsu, Vicki. Comprehension Crosswords Grade 1, 6 vols. McMahon, Kelly, illus. 2003. 32p. (J). 4.99 (978-1-56472-185-3(X)) Edupress, Inc.

—Comprehension Crosswords Grade 2, 6 vols. McMahon, Kelly, illus. 2003. 32p. (J). 4.99 (978-1-56472-186-0(8)) Edupress, Inc.

—Comprehension Crosswords Grade 3, 6 vols. Tunell, Ken, illus. 2003. 32p. (J). 4.99 (978-1-56472-187-7(6)) Edupress, Inc.

Sokoloff, David. My Jewish Heroes Crossword Puzzle Book. Sokoloff, David, illus. 1998. (Illus.). 24p. (Orig.). (J). (ps-5). pap. 1.00 (978-1-889655-05-5(8)) Jewish Educational Toys.

Speshock, Carl H. Crossword Puzzles & More for the Bird Watcher. 2002. 45p. spiral bd. 12.99 (978-0-9718518-0-1(8)) Joshandra Publishing, Inc.

Sterling Publishing Co., Inc. SCRABBLE Word Search for Kids. 2007. 96p. (J). pap. 5.95 (***978-1-4027-5155-4(9)***) Sterling Publishing Co., Inc.

The Sun Two-Speed Crossword Book 9. 2007. 192p. 9.95 (***978-0-00-721041-1(8)***) HarperCollins Pubs. Ltd. GBR. *Dist:* Independent Pubs. Group.

Top That Publishing Staff, ed. 101 Crossword Search Puzzles. 2005. (Illus.). 48p. pap. (978-1-84510-200-5(2)) Top That! Publishing PLC.

—101 Wordsearch Puzzles. 2005. (Illus.). 48p. pap. (978-1-84510-199-2(5)) Top That! Publishing PLC.

University Games Staff. Crosswords for Kids. 2007. 128p. (J). pap. (***978-1-57528-841-3(9)***) University Games.

—Word Searches for Kids. 2007. 128p. (J). pap. (***978-1-57528-840-6(0)***) University Games.

Walker, Jan Buckner. Kids Across, Parents Down: Crazy Critters. 2007. 32p. (J). pap. 4.95 (***978-0-7624-2930-1(5)*** , Running Pr. Kids) Running Pr. Bk. Pubs.

—Kids Across, Parents Down: On the Go. 2007. 32p. (J). pap. 4.95 (***978-0-7624-2931-8(3)*** , Running Pr. Kids) Running Pr. Bk. Pubs.

Ward, Mike. Hangman. 2005. (Sit & Solve Ser.). 96p. No. 1. pap. 5.95 (978-1-4027-2579-1(5)); Vol. 2. pap. 5.95 (978-1-4027-2580-7(9)) Sterling Publishing Co., Inc.

—Scratch & Solve Tough Hangman. 2005. (Sit & Solve Ser.). 96p. pap. 5.95 (978-1-4027-2577-7(9)); No. 2. pap. 5.95 (978-1-4027-2578-4(7)) Sterling Publishing Co., Inc.

CROWS

Bradley, James V. Ravens & Crows. 2006. (Nature Walk Ser.). (Illus.). 64p. (J). 28.00 (978-0-7910-9115-9(5) , Chelsea Hse.) Facts On File, Inc.

Jacobs, Lee. Crow. 2003. (Wild America Ser.). (Illus.). 24p. (J). 24.94 (978-1-56711-567-3(5) , Blackbirch Pr., Inc.) Thomson Gale.

Johnson, Sylvia A. Crows. 2005. (Nature Watch Ser.). (Illus.). 48p. (J). (gr. 3-8). lib. bdg. 25.26 (978-1-57505-628-9(3)) Lerner Publishing Group.

Lunis, Natalie. Crows. 2006. (Smart Animals! Ser.). (Illus.). 32p. (J). lib. bdg. 25.27 (978-1-59716-160-2(8)) Bearport Publishing Co., Inc.

Pringle, Laurence P. Crows! Strange & Wonderful. Marstall, Bob, illus. 2003. (Wildlife Ser.). 32p. (J). (gr. 2-4). 15.95 (978-1-56397-899-9(7)) Boyds Mills Pr.

Spilsbury, Louise & Spilsbury, Richard. A Murder of Crows. 2003. (Animal Groups Ser.). (Illus.). 32p. pap. 6.95 (978-1-4034-3284-1(8)); (J). lib. bdg. 24.22 (978-1-4034-0742-9(8)) Heinemann Library.

CROWS—FICTION

Aesop. The Crow & the Pitcher: A Tale about Problem Solving. Heyer, Carol, illus. 2006. (J). (***978-1-59939-096-3(5)*** , Reader's Digest Young Families, Inc.) Reader's Digest Children's Publishing, Inc.

Anastasio, Dina. Por qué el cuervo es negro y el buho tiene manchitas & How Raven Became Black & Owl Got Its Spots. 2005. spiral bd. 66.00 (***978-1-4108-5626-5(7)***) Benchmark Education Co.

Appelt, Kathi. Merry Christmas, Merry Crow. Goodell, Jon, illus. 2005. 32p. (J). (ps-ps). 16.00 (978-0-15-202651-6(7) , Harcourt Children's Bks) Harcourt Children's Bks.

Bacmeister, Rhoda Warner. Jet: The True Story of a Talking Supercrow. 2002. 63p. (J). pap. 5.99 (978-0-8280-1735-0(2) , 103-870) Review & Herald Publishing Assn.

Bailey, Arthur Scott. Tuck-Me-in Tales: The Tale of Old Mr Cro. 2006. pap. (***978-1-4065-0450-7(5)***) Dodo Pr.

Blair, Eric. El Cuervo y la Jarra: Version de la Fabula de Esopo. Silverman, Dianne, illus. 2006. (Read-It! Readers en Espanol Ser.).Tr. of Crow & the Pitcher: A Retelling of Aesop's Fable. (SPA.). 32p. (J). (ps-3). 19.95 (978-1-4048-1618-3(6)) Picture Window Bks.

Boland, Janice. Mrs. Murphy's Crows. Hartung, Susan Kathleen, illus. 1999. (Books for Young Learners). 12p. (J). (gr. k-2). pap. 5.00 (978-1-57274-141-6(4)) Owen, Richard C. Pubs., Inc.

Burgess, Thornton W. Blacky the Crow. (J). 18.95 (978-0-8488-0394-0(9)) Amereon LTD.

—Blacky the Crow. Cady, Harrison, illus. 1998. 80p. (J). pap. 2.00 (978-0-486-40550-6(8)) Dover Pubns., Inc.

—Blacky the Crow. 2004. reprint ed. pap. 15.95 (978-1-4191-1030-6(6)); pap. 1.99 (978-1-4192-1030-3(0)) Kessinger Publishing, LLC.

C D

Chorao, Kay. Pig & Crow. rev. ed. (Illus.). (J). 2005. 40p. reprint ed. pap. 6.95 (978-0-8050-7261-7(6)); 2000. 32p. 16.95 (978-0-8050-5863-5(X)) Holt, Henry & Co. (Holt, Henry & Co. Bks. For Young Readers).

Clark, Patricia Nikolina. In the Shadow of the Mammoth. LeTourneau, Anthony Alex, illus. (J). 2005. 14.99 (978-0-9674602-8-4(X)); 2003. 190p. pap. 6.99 (978-0-9674602-4-6(7)) Blue Marlin Pubns.

Cohen, Santiago, illus. Go Away, Crows! 2005. (J). (gr. 1-2). lib. bdg. 11.15 (978-0-606-33877-6(2)) Tandem Library Bks.

Croggon, Alison. The Crow. 2007. (Pellinor Ser.: Bk. 3). (Illus.). 528p. (YA). (gr. 7 up). 18.99 ***(*978-0-7636-3409-4(3))*** Candlewick Pr.

Devereux, Jan. Poe the Crow. Devereux, Jan, ed. Vanslette, Roxy, illus. 2004. 139p. (J). per. (978-0-9749677-0-7(X)) Lakeview Pr.

DeVore, Maggie. White Crow. Barron, Lynn, ed. DeVore, Jeffrey, illus. 2002. (J). 17.00 (978-0-9708940-3-8(1)) Gently Worded Bks., LLC.

Farmer Fred & the Naughty Crows. 2002. 32p. (J). 5.98 (978-0-7525-8181-1(3)) Parragon, Inc.

Fullwood, Millie F. Crow Joins the Choir. Srba, Lynne, illus. l.t. ed. 1998. 32p. (J). (ps-3). mass mkt. 9.95 (978-0-9667672-0-9(9) , 3468998-00) Fullwood Marketing Communications Co.

The Greedy Crows, 6 vols. (Multicultural Programs Ser.). 16p. (gr. 1-6). 42.50 (978-0-7802-1482-8(X)) Wright Group, The.

Griver, Jeanette A. Curio, a Shetland Sheepdog Meets the Crow: A Story of Friendship For Children of All Ages, 2004. (Illus.). 44p. (J). pap. 6.95 (978-0-929948-04-1(1)) Compsych Systems, Inc., Pubns. Div.

Haight, Angela. Crow Said No. Spurll, Barbara, illus. 2006. 36p. (J). pap. 5.25 (978-1-57874-107-6(6)) Kaeden Corp.

Hamilton, Martha & Weiss, Mitch. Two Fables of Aesop. MacDonald, Bruce, illus. 2005. 16p. (J). pap. 5.00 (978-1-57274-718-0(8) , 2788, Bks. for Young Learners) Owen, Richard C. Pubs., Inc.

Hobbs, Valerie. Carolina Crow Girl. 2000. (Illus.). 144p. (J). (gr. 5-9). pap. 5.99 (978-0-14-130976-7(8) , Puffin) Penguin Group (USA) Inc.

—Carolina Crow Girl. 2000. (J). (ps-7). 137p. per. 14.15 (978-0-613-29902-2(7)); 12.64 (978-0-606-19066-4(X)) Tandem Library Bks.

Howe, James. Bunnicula Meets Edgar Allan Crow. Fortune, Eric, illus. 2006. (Bunnicula Ser.). 160p. (J). 15.95 (978-1-4169-1458-7(7) , Ginne Seo Bks) Simon & Schuster Children's Publishing.

Huxley, Aldous. The Crows of Pearblossom. (J). 15.95 (978-0-89190-167-9(1)) Amereon LTD.

Kerven, Rosalind. Sparrow, the Crow & the Pearl. Williamson, Melanie, illus. 2005. 24p. (J). lib. bdg. 22.65 ***(*978-1-59646-754-5(1))*** Dingles & Co.

Kleven, Elisa. The Wishing Ball. 2006. (Illus.). 32p. (J). 16.00 (978-0-374-38449-4(5)) Farrar, Straus & Giroux.

Kubler, Annie. Dingle Dangle Scarecrow. 2003. (Illus.). 12p. (J). (ps). bds. 4.99 (978-0-85953-626-4(2)) Child's Play-International.

La Fontaine, Jean De. Cuervo y la Raposa. 2002. Tr. of Raven & the Fox. (SPA.). 24p. (J). 9.95 (978-84-246-1556-7(5)) La Galera, S.A. Editorial ESP. *Dist:* AIMS International Bks., Inc.

Loux, Lynn Crosbie. The Day I Could Fly. Porfirio, Guy, illus. 2003. 32p. (gr. k-3). 15.95 (978-1-55971-866-0(8) , NorthWord Bks. for Young Readers) T&N Children's Publishing.

Lowrey, Becky. Chirps. 2004. 45p. pap. 19.95 (978-1-4137-2984-9(3)) PublishAmerica, Inc.

Mackinnon, Mairi. Fox & the Crow. 2007. (First Reading Level 1 Ser.). 32p. (J). 8.99 ***(*978-0-7945-1813-4(3)*** , Usborne) EDC Publishing.

Martini, Clem. The Judgement. 2006. 304p. (978-1-55337-756-6(7)) Kids Can Pr., Ltd.

—The Mob. 2005. 240p. (978-1-55337-664-4(1)); (YA). (gr. 7 up). (978-1-55337-574-6(2)) Kids Can Pr., Ltd.

—The Plague. 272p. 2006. (978-1-55337-667-5(6)); 2005. (978-1-55337-666-8(8)) Kids Can Pr., Ltd.

Millionaire, Tony. Sock Monkey: the Inches Incident: The Inches Incident. 2007. 88p. (J). pap. 12.95 ***(*978-1-59307-842-3(0))*** Dark Horse Comics.

Mirhady, Irandought. Thorn-Bush Boy: Pesare Tigh. Mirhady, Irandought, illus. 2004. Orig. Title: Pesare Tigh. (PEO., Illus.). 63p. (YA). per. (978-0-9760323-0-4(9)) Mirhady, Farhad.

Niemela, JoAnn Huston. The Crows of Hidden Creek. Bradley, Sandy, illus. 2003. 109p. (YA). 20.00 (978-0-9716786-0-6(X)) Ten Minas Publishing.

O'Brien, May. How Crows Became Black. Leaney, Angela, illus. 2001. 40p. (J). pap. 9.95 (978-1-86368-027-1(6)) Fremantle Pr. AUS. *Dist:* International Specialized Bk. Services.

Ocker, Christa Holder. A Crow Named Robin. 2006. (J). per. ***(*978-1-59872-712-8(5))*** Instantpublisher.com.

O'Neil, Sarah. Fox & the Crow. 1999. (gr. k-3). lib. bdg. 11.80 (978-0-613-19354-2(7)) Tandem Library Bks.

Packard, Mary. The Shy Scarecrow. Huang, Benrei, illus. 2001. (Hello Reader! Ser.). (J). (978-0-439-31704-7(5)) Scholastic, Inc.

Paul, Alison. The Crow (A Not So Scary Story) 2007. (Illus.). 40p. (J). (gr. 3-5). 16.00 ***(*978-0-618-66380-4(0))*** Houghton Mifflin Co.

Renshaw, Ken. The Yosemite Adventure of Spotty Bat. Rosenthal, Robert, illus. 2005. 104p. per. 10.95 (978-0-9616620-2-8(6)) Constellation Pr.

Rex, Annmarie. Black's Adventure in the Big, Scary, Hairy World. 2007. 46p. (J). 19.99 ***(*978-1-59879-365-9(9));*** per. 15.99 ***(*978-1-59879-364-2(0))*** Lifevest Publishing, Inc. (Lifevest).

Roberts, Shelly. Sissy & the Old Crow. 2006. (Illus.). 36p. (J). per. 18.00 (978-0-9789798-2-9(6) , 978-9789798-2-9) Blackbird's World Publishing Co.

—Sissy & the Old Crow (Coloring Book) 2006. (Illus.). 36p. (J). per. 6.50 (978-0-9789798-3-6(4) , 978-0-9789798-3-6) Blackbird's World Publishing Co.

Sargent, Dave. Blackie. Lenoir, Jane, illus. 2000. (J). (978-1-56763-447-1(8)); lib. bdg. 19.95 (978-1-56763-448-8(6)) Ozark Publishing.

—Blackie Crow: Tell the Truth, 20, vol. 2. Lenoir, Jane, illus. 2003. (Feather Tales Ser.: No. 2). 42p. (J). lib. bdg. 19.95 (978-1-56763-721-2(3)); pap. 6.95 (978-1-56763-722-9(1)) Ozark Publishing.

Simmons, Lynn Sheffield. Jack Crow Said Hello. Lopez, Willie, illus. 2000. 111p. (J). (gr. 2-6). 10.95 (978-0-9642573-2-0(7)) Argyle Bks.

—Jack Crow Said Hello. 2004. (Illus.). 128p. (YA). pap. 10.95 (978-1-58980-218-6(7)) Pelican Publishing Co., Inc.

Spalding, Andrea. The Keeper & the Crows. 1999. (Young Reader Ser.). (Illus.). 128p. (J). (gr. 3-6). pap. 5.95 (978-1-55143-141-3(6)) Orca Bk. Pubs. USA.

—The Keeper & the Crows. 2000. (gr. 3-6). lib. bdg. 12.40 (978-0-613-83717-0(7)) Tandem Library Bks.

Spirin, Gennady. Martha. Spirin, Gennady, illus. 2005. (Illus.). 32p. (J). (ps-3). 14.99 (978-0-399-23980-9(4) , Philomel) Penguin Group (USA) Inc.

Sunderland, Margot & Hancock, Nicky. Helping Children Who Yearn for Someone They Love & the Frog Who Longed for the Moon to Smile, 2 vols. Armstrong, Nicky, tr. Armstrong, Nicky, illus. 76p. (978-0-86388-502-0(0) , 002-4776) Speechmark Publishing Ltd.

Swallow, Pamela C. Groundhog Gets a Say. Bunkus, Denise, illus. 2007. 40p. (J). (ps). pap. 6.99 ***(*978-0-14-240896-4(4)*** , Puffin) Penguin Group (USA) Inc.

—Groundhog Gets a Say. Brunkus, Denise, illus. 2005. 40p. (J). (ps). 15.99 (978-0-399-23876-5(X) , Putnam Juvenile) Penguin Group (USA) Inc.

Talbot, Amy. Deer & Friends: A Folktale from India. 2006. 23.00 ***(*978-1-4108-6173-3(2))*** Benchmark Education Co.

Teply, George. Lost Crown of Meleor. 2000. (gr. k-3). lib. bdg. 15.25 (978-0-613-30013-1(0)) Tandem Library Bks.

The Three Crows. 2000. (J). pap. 12.95 (978-1-891231-31-5(6)) Word Association Pubs.

Villaseñor, Victor. Little Crow to the Rescue/el Cuervito Al Rescate. Munoz, Elizabeth Cummins, tr. Alcantara, Felipe Ugalde, illus. (SPA & ENG.). 32p. (J). (ps-3). per. 15.95 (978-1-55885-430-7(4) , Piñata Books) Arte Publico Pr.

Watts, Leander. Ten Thousand Charms. 2005. 240p. (YA). (gr. 5). 16.00 (978-0-618-44897-5(7)) Houghton Mifflin Co. Trade & Reference Div.

Weeks, Sarah. Angel Face. Diaz, David, illus. 2002. 32p. (J). 17.95 (978-0-689-83302-1(4) , Atheneum) Simon & Schuster Children's Publishing.

Wheeler, Lisa. Old Cricket. Goembel, Ponder, illus. 2006. 32p. (J). reprint ed. pap. 6.99 (978-1-4169-1855-4(8) , Aladdin) Simon & Schuster Children's Publishing.

Wheeler, Lisa & Goembel, Ponder. Old Cricket. 2003. (Illus.). 32p. (J). (ps-2). 17.99 (978-0-689-84510-9(3) , Atheneum/Richard Jackson Bks.) Simon & Schuster Children's Publishing.

Wi', Raven. Inky the Raven: An Alaska Tale Based on a True Story. 2005. (J). per. 14.95 net. (978-1-59433-037-7(9)) Publication Consultants.

CRUELTY TO ANIMALS

see Animals—Treatment

CRUSADES

see also Chivalry

Crompton, Samuel Willard. The Third Crusade: Richard the Lionhearted vs. Saladin. 2003. (Great Battles Through the Ages Ser.). (Illus.). 112p. (J). (gr. 6-12). 30.00 (978-0-7910-7437-4(4) , Chelsea Hse.) Facts On File, Inc.

Davenport, John C. Saladin. 2003. (Ancient World Leaders Ser.). (Illus.). 112p. (gr. 6-12). 30.00 (978-0-7910-7223-3(1) , Chelsea Hse.) Facts On File, Inc.

Doherty, Katherine M. & Doherty, Craig A. King Richard the Lionhearted & the Crusades in World History. 2002. (In World History Ser.). (Illus.). 128p. (YA). (gr. 5-12). lib. bdg. 26.60 (978-0-7660-1459-6(2)) Enslow Pubs., Inc.

Grant, Neil. Medieval Europe. 2003. (Uncovering History Ser.). 46p. (J). lib. bdg. 28.50 (978-1-58340-254-2(3)) Smart Apple Media.

Hatt, Christine. The Crusades: Christians at War. 2001. (Documenting History Ser.). (Illus.). 64p. (J). (gr. 8-12). 24.50 (978-0-531-14610-1(3) , Watts, Franklin) Scholastic Library Publishing.

Jones, J. Sydney, et al. The Crusades Biography. 2004. (Crusades Reference Library). (Illus.). xxii, 230p. (J). lib. bdg. 67.00 (978-0-7876-9177-6(1) , UXL) Thomson Gale.

—The Crusades Primary Sources. 2004. (Crusades Reference Library). (Illus.). xxvii, 179p. lib. bdg. 67.00 (978-0-7876-9178-3(X) , UXL) Thomson Gale.

Kelman, Janet Harvey. Stories from the Crusades (Yesterday's Classics) 2005. (Illus.). 92p. (J). per. 7.95 (978-1-59915-054-3(9)) Yesterday's Classics.

Lace, William W. The Unholy Crusade: The Ransacking of Medieval Constantinople. 2006. (Lucent Library of Historical Eras). 112p. (YA). (gr. 5-9). lib. bdg. 32.45 (978-1-59018-846-0(2) , Lucent Bks.) Thomson Gale.

Lloyd-Jones, Robin. Crusaders. 2007. (Young Reading Series 3 Gift Bks). 64p. (J). 8.99 ***(*978-0-7945-1617-8(3))*** EDC Publishing.

Merrall, Irene. The Crusades. 1999. (Pathfinder History Ser.). (Illus.). 64p. (YA). (gr. 10 up). pap. 13.95 (978-0-7487-4343-8(X)) Nelson Thornes Ltd. GBR. *Dist:* Trans-Atlantic Pubns., Inc.

O'Neal, Michael J., et al. The Crusades Almanac. 2004. (Crusades Reference Library). xxv, 207p. lib. bdg. 67.00 (978-0-7876-9176-9(3) , UXL) Thomson Gale.

Scheuerman, Richard D. & Ellis, Arthur K., eds. Eleanor of Aquitaine & the Crusade of the Kings: A Medieval Journey of Discovery Travelogue. LeGette, James, illus. unabr. ed. 2000. 494p. (YA). (gr. 5-8). ring bd. 69.95 (978-1-885360-19-9(3)) Demco, Inc.

Stanley, Diane. Saladin: Noble Prince of Islam. Stanley, Diane, illus. 2002. (Illus.). 48p. (J). (gr. 5-8). 16.99 (978-0-688-17135-3(4)); lib. bdg. 18.89 (978-0-688-17136-0(2)) HarperCollins Pubs.

Streissguth, Thomas. Richard the Lionheart: Crusader King of England. 2007. (Rulers of the Middle Ages Ser.). (Illus.). 160p. (YA). (gr. 7-9). lib. bdg. 34.60 (978-0-7660-2714-5(7)) Enslow Pubs., Inc.

West, David & Gaff, Jackie. Richard the Lionheart: The Life of a King & Crusader. 2005. (Graphic Nonfiction Ser.). (Illus.). 48p. (J). lib. bdg. 26.50 (978-1-4042-0241-2(2)) Rosen Publishing Group, Inc., The.

Worth, Richard. Saladin: Sultan of Egypt & Syria. 2007. (Rulers of the Middle Ages Ser.). (Illus.). 160p. (J). (gr. 6 up). lib. bdg. 34.60 (978-0-7660-2712-1(0)) Enslow Pubs., Inc.

CRUSADES—FICTION

Grant, K. M. Blood Red Horse. 2006. 288p. (J). pap. 7.95 (978-0-8027-7734-8(1)) Walker & Co.

Henty, G. A. The Boy Knight. 2006. (Dover Value Editions Ser.). (Illus.). 272p. pap. 6.95 (978-0-486-44803-9(7)) Dover Pubns., Inc.

—A Knight of the White Cross: A Tale of the Siege of Rhodes. 1999. (gr. 3-6). lib. bdg. 26.85 (978-0-613-80289-5(6)) Tandem Library Bks.

Jewett, Eleanore M. Big John's Secret. 2nd ed. 2004. (Illus.). 207p. (J). pap. 12.95 (978-1-883937-89-8(2)) Bethlehem Bks.

Jinks, Catherine. Pagan's Scribe. De Seve, Peter, illus. 2005. (Pagan Chronicles Ser.: Bk. 4). 368p. (J). (gr. 7 up). 16.99 (978-0-7636-2022-6(X)) Candlewick Pr.

Jocson, Antonio & Christian, J. E. The Children's Crusade. Vasquez, Jorge, illus. 1998. 84p. (J). (gr. 3 up). 22.00 (978-1-890963-27-9(5) , LB Bks.) Liberty Bell Productions.

Leeds, Constance & Bennett, Constance. The Silver Cup. 2007. 240p. (YA). (gr. 6-9). 16.99 (978-0-670-06157-0(3) , Viking Adult) Penguin Group (USA) Inc.

Muschla, Gary Robert. Crusader. 2006. (YA). pap. (978-0-88092-491-7(8)) Royal Fireworks Publishing Co.

—Crusaders. 2006. (YA). lib. bdg. 9.99 (978-0-88092-490-0(X)) Royal Fireworks Publishing Co.

Reiche, Dietlof. Freddy's Final Quest Book Five in Golden Hamster. 2008. 208p. pap. 5.99 ***(*978-0-439-87415-1(7)*** , Scholastic Paperbacks) Scholastic, Inc.

Reiche, Dietlof & Brownjohn, John. Freddy's Final Quest. Cepeda, Joe, illus. 2007. (Golden Hamster Saga Ser.: Bk. 5). 304p. (J). pap. 16.99 (978-0-439-87414-4(9) , Scholastic Pr.) Scholastic, Inc.

Torres, J. Caped Crusader. 2006. (Batman Ser.). 32p. (J). pap. 4.99 (978-0-439-83003-4(6)) Scholastic, Inc.

Viguie, Debbie. Scarlet Moon. 2004. (Once upon a Time Ser.). 176p. (YA). pap. 5.99 (978-0-689-86716-3(6) , Simon Pulse) Simon & Schuster Children's Publishing.

Weil, Sylvie. My Guardian Angel. 208p. (J). 2007. pap. 5.99 ***(*978-0-439-57682-6(2)*** , Scholastic Paperbacks); 2004. (gr. 4-7). pap. 16.95 (978-0-439-57681-9(4) , Levine, Arthur A. Bks.) Scholastic, Inc.

CRUSOE, ROBINSON (FICTITIOUS CHARACTER)—FICTION

Allison, Samuel B. An American Robinson Crusoe. 2005. 136p. pap. 10.95 (978-1-4218-0186-5(8) , 1st World Library - Literary Society) 1st World Publishing, Inc.

—An American Robinson Crusoe. 2004. reprint ed. pap. 15.95 (978-1-4191-0613-2(9)); pap. 1.99 (978-1-4192-0613-9(3)) Kessinger Publishing, LLC.

Defoe, Daniel. The Farther Adventures of Robinson Crusoe. (Illus.). (J). reprint ed. 32.50 (978-0-404-07912-3(1)) AMS Pr., Inc.

—Robinson Crusoe. Heller, Julek, illus. 1998. (Eyewitness Classics Ser.).Tr. of Robinson Crusoe. 64p. (J). (gr. 3-6). 14.95 (978-0-7894-3625-2(6)) Dorling Kindersley Publishing, Inc.

—Robinson Crusoe. 2001. (Fast Track Classics Ser.).Tr. of Robinson Crusoe. (Illus.). 48p. pap. 9.99 (978-0-237-52283-4(7) , Evans Brothers, Limited) Evans Publishing Group GBR. *Dist:* Independent Pubs. Group.

—Robinson Crusoe. Exams Unlimited, Inc. Staff, ed. Paget, William, illus. 2001. Tr. of Robinson Crusoe. 104p. (J). reprint ed. cd-rom 5.20 (978-1-59132-021-0(6)) Exams Unlimited, Inc.

—Robinson Crusoe. Lindskoog, Kathryn, ed. Chitouras, Barbara, illus. 2002. (Classics for Young Readers Ser.).Tr. of Robinson Crusoe. 192p. (J). per. 7.99 (978-0-87552-735-2(3)) P & R Publishing.

—Robinson Crusoe. 2004. Tr. of Robinson Crusoe. (SPA., Illus.). 284p. (J). (ps-7). pap. (978-958-30-0091-1(4)) Panamericana Editorial.

—Robinson Crusoe. 2001. (Modern Library Classics Ser.).Tr. of Robinson Crusoe. 320p. pap. 7.95 (978-0-375-75732-7(5) , Modern Library) Random House Publishing Group.

—Robinson Crusoe. 2nd ed. 2003. (Historias de Siempre Ser.).Tr. of Robinson Crusoe. (SPA., Illus.). 92p. (J). (gr. 5-8). pap. 12.95 (978-84-204-5723-9(X)) Santillana USA Publishing Co., Inc.

—Robinson Crusoe. Grandville, J. J., illus. 2001. (Junior Classics Ser.).Tr. of Robinson Crusoe. 128p. (J). (gr. 8). mass mkt. 3.99 (978-0-439-23621-8(5)) Scholastic, Inc.

—Robinson Crusoe. 2001. (Classics Ser.).Tr. of Robinson Crusoe. 304p. (YA). (gr. 3-7). pap. 5.99 (978-0-689-84408-9(5) , Aladdin) Simon & Schuster Children's Publishing.

—Robinson Crusoe.Tr. of Robinson Crusoe. 2001. (gr. 3-6). lib. bdg. 11.80 (978-0-613-63226-3(5)); 2001. (gr. 7-12). lib. bdg. 16.45 (978-0-613-64320-7(8)); 1999. (Illus.). (J). (978-0-606-21567-1(0)); 1999. (gr. 7-12). lib. bdg. 15.25 (978-0-613-33002-2(1)) Tandem Library Bks.

—Robinson Crusoe. 2000. (Coleccion "Clasicos Juveniles" Ser.).Tr. of Robinson Crusoe. (SPA., Illus.). 288p. (YA). (gr. 4-7). pap. 13.95 (978-1-58348-782-2(4)) iUniverse, Inc.

Defoe, Daniel, et al. Robinson Crusoe. (Classics Illustrated Ser.).Tr. of Robinson Crusoe. (Illus.). 52p. (YA). pap. 4.95 (978-1-57209-021-7(9)) Classics International Entertainment, Inc.

Leavitt, Caroline. Robinhound Crusoe. l.t. ed. 1999. (Adventures of Wishbone Ser.: No. 4). (Illus.). 144p. (J). (gr. 4 up). lib. bdg. 22.60 (978-0-8368-2300-4(1)) Stevens, Gareth Inc.

Wilkes, Angela. Robinson Crusoe. 2003. (gr. 3-6). lib. bdg. 14.10 (978-0-613-90680-7(2)) Tandem Library Bks.

Wilkes, Angela & Rawson, Christopher. Robinson Crusoe. 2004. (Young Reading Ser.). (Illus.). 64p. (J). (gr. 2 up). pap. 5.95 (978-0-7945-0410-6(8) , Usborne) EDC Publishing.

Zorn, Steven & Defoe, Daniel. Robinson Crusoe. Wyeth, N. C., illus. 2002. 48p. (J). 9.98 (978-0-7624-1419-2(7) , Courage Bks.) Running Pr. Bk. Pubs.

CRYOGENICS

see Low Temperatures

CRYPTOGRAPHY

see also Ciphers

Adams, Simon. Code Breakers: From Hieroglyphs to Hackers. 2002. (gr. 3-6). lib. bdg. 14.10 (978-0-613-45731-6(5)) Tandem Library Bks.

Beissinger, Janet & Pless, Vera. The Cryptoclub: Using Mathematics to Make & Break Secret Codes. 2006. (Illus.). 300p. pap. 35.00 (978-1-56881-223-6(X)) AK Peters, Ltd.

Dickson, Louise. Lu & Clancy's Secret Languages. Cupples, Pat, illus. unabr. ed. 2001. (Lu & Clancy Ser.). 40p. (J). (gr. k-3). (978-1-55074-695-2(2)); (978-1-55337-025-3(2)) Kids Can Pr., Ltd.

James, Elizabeth. How to Keep a Secret. rev. ed. 1998. 64p. (J). (gr. 3-7). pap. 4.95 (978-0-688-16278-8(9)) HarperCollins Pubs.

Janeczko, Paul B. Top Secret: A Handbook of Codes, Ciphers, & Secret Writing. LaReau, Jenna, illus. 2004. 144p. (J). (gr. 4 up). 16.99 (978-0-7636-0971-9(4)) Candlewick Pr.

Lamb, Geoffrey Frederick. Fun with Secret Writing. 2002. (Illus.). 64p. (gr. 4-7). pap. 4.95 (978-0-486-42098-1(1)) Dover Pubns., Inc.

Levy, Janey. Breaking the Code with Cryptography: Analyzing Patterns. 2006. (Math for the Real World Ser.). (Illus.). 32p. pap. (978-1-4042-6089-4(7)); lib. bdg. (978-1-4042-3368-3(7)) Rosen Publishing Group, Inc., The.

Pincock, Stephen. Codebreaker: The History of Codes & Ciphers, from the Ancient Pharaohs to Quantum Cryptography. 2006. (Illus.). 160p. 19.95 (978-0-8027-1547-0(8)) Walker & Co.

Price Hossell, Karen. Ciphers & Codes. 2003. (Communicating Ser.). (Illus.). 48p. (J). (gr. 3-5). lib. bdg. 27.07 (978-1-58810-484-7(2)) Heinemann Library.

Raintree Steck-Vaughn Staff. All about Codes. 1999. (Illus.). (J). pap. 35.60 (978-0-7398-0908-2(3)) Steck-Vaughn.

Riley, Gail Blasser. All about Codes. 2000. (Pair-It Books). (Illus.). 40p. (978-0-7398-0877-1(X)) Steck-Vaughn.

Santella, Andrew. Navajo Code Talkers. 2004. (We the People Ser.). (Illus.). 48p. (J). (gr. 4 up). lib. bdg. 22.60 (978-0-7565-0611-7(5)) Compass Point Bks.

Sasaki, Chris. Secret Agent Codes. 2004. (Illus.). 96p. (J). pap. 4.95 (978-1-4027-1399-6(1)) Sterling Publishing Co., Inc.

Singh, Simon. Code Book: How to Make It, Break It, Hack It, Crack It. 2003. (gr. 7-12). lib. bdg. 17.60 (978-0-613-84126-9(3)) Tandem Library Bks.

Weller, Janet. Messages in Code. 1998. (Hello Out There! Ser.). (Illus.). 32p. (J). (gr. 2-5). 20.00 (978-0-531-14475-6(5) , Watts, Franklin) Scholastic Library Publishing.

Wiese, Jim & Melton, H. Keith. The Spy's Guide to Secret Codes & Ciphers. 2002. (Illus.). 48p. (J). (978-0-439-33640-6(6)) Scholastic, Inc.

CRYSTAL GAZING

see Divination

CRYSTALLINE ROCKS

see Rocks

CRYSTALLIZATION

see Crystallography

CRYSTALLOGRAPHY

see also Mineralogy

Crystal Kids Balance the World. 2003. (Illus.). (J). pap. (978-0-9745496-0-6(6)) Kid by Kid, Incorporated.

Crystal Messages from the Crystal Kids. 2003. (J). pap. (978-0-9745496-1-3(4)) Kid by Kid, Incorporated.

Dayton, Connor. Crystals. 2007. (Rocks & Minerals Ser.). (Illus.). 24p. (J). (gr. 2-5). lib. bdg. 21.25 ***(*978-1-4042-3687-5(2)*** , PowerKids Pr.) Rosen Publishing Group, Inc., The.

Faulkner, Rebecca. Crystals. 2007. (J). ***(*978-1-4109-2751-4(2));*** pap. ***(*978-1-4109-2759-0(8))*** Steck-Vaughn.

Moorey, Teresa. Crystals: Tune into Their Secret Powers. 2005. (Illus.). 128p. (J). pap. 7.99 (978-0-340-88430-0(4) , Hodder & Stoughton) Hodder General Publishing Division GBR. *Dist:* Trafalgar Square Publishing.

Squire, Ann O. Growing Crystals. 2002. (True Bks.). (Illus.). 48p. (J). (gr. 3-5). pap. 6.95 (978-0-516-26984-9(4) , Children's Pr.) Scholastic Library Publishing.

—Growing Crystals. 2002. (gr. 3-6). lib. bdg. 15.25 (978-0-613-54236-4(3)) Tandem Library Bks.

Stewart, Melissa. Crystals. 2002. (Rocks & Minerals Ser.). (Illus.). 32p. (J). (gr. 4-6). lib. bdg. 24.22 (978-1-58810-254-6(8)); pap. 7.50 (978-1-4034-0090-1(3) , 91657) Heinemann Library.

Symes, R. F. & Harding, R. R. Crystal & Gem. 2007. (DK Eyewitness Bks.). 72p. (J). (gr. 3-8). 15.99 incl. cd-rom (978-0-7566-3001-0(0)) Dorling Kindersley Publishing, Inc.

Symes, R. F. & Harding, Robert. Crystal & Gem: Eyewitness Books. Keates, Colin, photos by. 2004. (Illus.). 63p. (J). (gr. 4-8). reprint ed. 19.00 (978-0-7567-7687-9(2)) DIANE Publishing Co.

Symes, R. F., et al. Crystal & Gem. Keates, Colin, illus. 2004. (Eyewitness Books). 72p. (J). lib. bdg. 19.99 (978-0-7566-0663-3(2)) Dorling Kindersley Publishing, Inc.

CRYSTALS

see Crystallography

CUB SCOUTS

see Boy Scouts

CUBA

Ada, Alma Flor. Under the Royal Palms: A Childhood in Cuba. 1998. (Illus.). 96p. (J). (gr. 3-7). 17.99 (978-0-689-80631-5(0) , Atheneum) Simon & Schuster Children's Publishing.

Ancona, George, photos by. Cuban Kids. 2000. (Illus.). 40p. (J). (gr. 2-6). 15.95 (978-0-7614-5077-1(7) , Cavendish Children's Bks.) Cavendish, Marshall Corp.

Britton, Tamara L. Cuba. 2002. (Countries Ser.). (Illus.). 40p. (J). (gr. k-6). lib. bdg. 22.78 (978-1-57765-760-6(8) , Checkerboard Library) ABDO Publishing Co.

Campbell, Kumari. Cuba in Pictures. 2nd ed. 2005. (Visual Geography Ser.). (Illus.). 80p. (J). (gr. 5-12). 27.93 (978-0-8225-1167-0(3)) Lerner Publishing Group.

Cramer, Mark. Cuba. 1999. (Countries of the World Ser.). (Illus.). 96p. (J). (gr. 6 up). lib. bdg. 30.00 (978-0-8368-2316-5(8)) Stevens, Gareth Inc.

Crouch, Clifford W. Cuba. 1999. (Major World Nations Ser.). (Illus.). 144p. (YA). (gr. 4-7). 29.95 (978-0-7910-4736-1(9) , Chelsea Hse.) Facts On File, Inc.

Daley, Patrick. Cuba. 2002. (Steadwell Books World Tour). (Illus.). 48p. (J). lib. bdg. 24.26 (978-0-7398-5758-8(4)) Raintree.

Doak, Robin S. Cuba. 2004. (First Reports). (Illus.). 48p. (J). (gr. 3 up). lib. bdg. 22.60 (978-0-7565-0580-6(1)) Compass Point Bks.

Dubois, Muriel L. Cuba. 2005. (Fact Finders Ser.). (Illus.). 32p. (J). 22.60 (978-0-7368-3749-1(3)) Capstone Pr., Inc.

Dunn, John M. Life in Castro's Cuba. 2004. (Way People Live Ser.). (Illus.). 112p. (J). (gr. 7-10). 29.95 (978-1-59018-464-6(5)) Thomson Gale.

Frost, Helen. A Look at Cuba. Saunders-Smith, Gail, ed. (Our World Ser.). (Illus.). 24p. (J). (gr. k-3). 2005. (978-0-7368-9388-6(1)); 2002. lib. bdg. 15.93 (978-0-7368-1428-7(0)) Capstone Pr., Inc. (Pebble Bks.).

Gee, Martha B., ed. A Child's Glimpse of Cuba. 1999. 32p. (J). (gr. 1-5). pap. (978-0-377-00327-9(1)) Friendship Pr.

Gordon, Sharon. Cuba. 2003. (Discovering Cultures Ser.). (Illus.). 48p. (J). 25.64 (978-0-7614-1517-6(3)) Cavendish, Marshall Corp.

Harkrader, Lisa. Cuba: A MyReportLinks.com Book. 2004. (Top Ten Countries of Recent Immigrants Ser.). (Illus.). 48p. (J). lib. bdg. 25.26 (978-0-7660-5178-2(1) , MyReportLinks.com Bks.) Enslow Pubs., Inc.

Hernandez, Roger E. Cuba. 2003. (Discovering Latin America Ser.). (Illus.). 64p. (J). (gr. 5 up). lib. bdg. (978-1-59084-298-0(7)) Mason Crest Pubs.

Hughes, Christopher. Cuba. 2003. (Nations in Conflict Ser.). 48p. (J). (Illus.). 24.95 (978-1-4103-0079-9(X)); 26.19 (978-1-56711-511-6(X)) Thomson Gale. (Blackbirch Pr., Inc.).

Hughes, Susan & Fast, April. Cuba — The Culture. 2004. (Lands, Peoples & Cultures Ser.). (Illus.). 32p. (J). (978-0-7787-9326-7(5)); pap. (978-0-7787-9694-7(9)) Crabtree Publishing Co.

—Cuba — The Land. 2004. (Lands, Peoples, & Cultures Ser.). (Illus.). 32p. (J). (978-0-7787-9324-3(9)); pap. (978-0-7787-9692-3(2)) Crabtree Publishing Co.

Johnson, Willis Fletcher. The History of Cuba, Vol. 2. 2006. (Illus.). cd-rom (978-1-892824-20-2(5)) AFCHRON.

A Look at Cuba, 6 vols. (gr. k-2). 28.95 (978-0-7368-9389-3(X)) Red Brick Learning.

Mara, W. P. Cuba. 1998. (Countries of the World Ser.). (Illus.). 126p. (J). (gr. 2-3). 18.60 (978-0-7368-0068-6(9) , Bridgestone Bks.) Capstone Pr., Inc.

Marsh, Carole. America's Important Neighbors: Canada, Mexico & Cuba. 2001. (Here & Now Series!). (Illus.). 48p. (J). (gr. 3-8). pap. 7.95 (978-0-635-00262-4(0)) Gallopade International.

Marx, Trish. Reaching for the Sun: Kids in Cuba. 2003. (Single Titles Ser.: 6). (Illus.). 48p. lib. bdg. 25.90 (978-0-7613-2261-0(2) , Millbrook Pr.) Lerner Publishing Group.

Morris, Emily. Cuba: World in View. 2000. (Illus.). 96p. (J). (gr. 5-7). reprint ed. 17.00 (978-0-7881-9439-9(9)) DIANE Publishing Co.

Petersen, Christine. Cuba. 2001. (gr. 3-6). lib. bdg. 15.25 (978-0-613-54156-5(1)) Tandem Library Bks.

Petersen, Christine & Petersen, David. Cuba. 2002. (True Bks.). (Illus.). 48p. (J). (gr. 3-5). pap. 6.95 (978-0-516-27358-7(2) , Children's Pr.) Scholastic Library Publishing.

Petersen, David & Petersen, Christine A. Cuba. 2001. (True Geography Bks.). (Illus.). 48p. (J). (gr. 3-5). 25.00 (978-0-516-22257-8(0) , Children's Pr.) Scholastic Library Publishing.

Schreier, Alta. Cuba. (Visit to Ser.). 32p. pap. 6.50 (978-1-4034-4147-8(2)); 2000. (Illus.). (J). lib. bdg. 21.36 (978-1-57572-380-8(8)) Heinemann Library.

Stevens, Kathryn. Cuba. 2001. (Countries: Faces & Places Ser.). (Illus.). 32p. (J). (gr. 1-5). 25.64 (978-1-56766-906-0(9)) Child's World, Inc.

Walsh, Kieran. Cuba. 2005. (Countries in the News Ser.). (Illus.). 24p. (gr. 1-4). 17.95 (978-1-59515-288-6(1)) Rourke Publishing, LLC.

Yip, Dora & Cramer, Mark. Welcome to Cuba. 2001. (Welcome to My Country Ser.). (Illus.). 48p. (J). (gr. 2 up). lib. bdg. 26.00 (978-0-8368-2516-9(0)) Stevens, Gareth Inc.

Zocchi, Judy. In Cuba/en Cuba. Brodie, Neale, illus. 2005. (Global Adventures II Ser.).Tr. of En Cuba. (ENG & SPA.). 32p. (J). per. 9.95 (978-1-59646-163-5(2)) Dingles & Co.

CUBA—FICTION

Aldridge, Janet. The Meadow-Brook Girls by the Sea, or Th. 2006. pap. (***978-1-4065-0693-8(1)***) Dodo Pr.

Austin, Michael, illus. Martina the Beautiful Cockroach: A Cuban Folktale. 2007. 32p. (J). (ps-3). 16.95 (***978-1-56145-399-3(4)*** , Peachtree Junior) Peachtree Pubs., Ltd.

Cardenas, Teresa. Cartas a Mi Mama. Unger, David, tr. 2006. (SPA.). 96p. (J). 15.95 (978-0-88899-722-7(1)) Groundwood Bks. CAN. *Dist:* Perseus Distribution.

—Letters to My Mother. Unger, David, tr. from SPA. 2007. 104p. (gr. 7-9). pap. 6.95 (978-0-88899-721-0(3)) Groundwood Bks. CAN. *Dist:* Perseus Distribution.

Fernandez, Roberto G. En la Ocho Y la Doce. 2000. (Nuestra Vision Ser.). 190p. (YA). 18.36 (978-0-618-00021-0(6) , 315739) Houghton Mifflin College Div.

Figueredo, D. H. The Road to Santiago. Torrecilla, Pablo, illus. 2003. 32p. (J). 16.95 (978-1-58430-059-5(0)) Lee & Low Bks., Inc.

Flores-Galbis, Enrique. Raining Sardines. 2007. 176p. (J). (gr. 5-9). 16.95 (978-1-59643-166-9(0)) Roaring Brook Pr.

García, Cristina. The Dog Who Loved the Moon. Serra, Sebastia, illus. 2008. 32p. (J). 15.99 (***978-1-4169-1836-3(1)***) Simon & Schuster Children's Publishing.

Hamilton, Martha. Rooster's Night Out. 2007. 32p. pap. 42.95 (***978-0-87483-844-2(4)***) August Hse. Pubs., Inc.

Harcourt School Publishers Staff. The Most Amazing Place Advanced Level. 3rd ed. 2002. (Trophies Reading Program Ser.). (Illus.). pap. 5.10 (978-0-15-323206-0(4)) Harcourt Schl. Pubs.

Martinez, Raul. Rooly & Flora's Reunion: A Story of Cuba. Prieto, Antonio, illus. 2006. 32p. (J). (***978-1-59249-657-0(1)***); pap. (***978-1-59249-658-7(X)***) Soundprints.

Perera, Hilda. Cuentos de Apolo. 3rd ed. 2001. (Coleccion Caniqui Ser.). (SPA., Illus.). 103p. (gr. 6 up). 5.00 (978-0-89729-438-6(6)) Ediciones Universal.

—Cuentos Para Chicos Y Grandes. 2001. (SPA.). (gr. 3-6). lib. bdg. 16.40 (978-0-613-64478-5(6)) Tandem Library Bks.

Veciana-Suarez, Ana. Flight to Freedom. 2002. (First Person Fiction Ser.). 224p. (J). (gr. 6-9). pap. 16.95 (978-0-439-38199-4(1) , Orchard Bks.) Scholastic, Inc.

—Flight to Freedom. 2004. 215p. (YA). (gr. 8-12). lib. bdg. 13.64 (978-0-606-30967-7(5)) Tandem Library Bks.

CUBA—HISTORY

Anderson, Dale. Cuban Americans. 2006. (World Almanac Library of American Immigration). (Illus.). 48p. (J). pap. (978-0-8368-7322-1(X)); lib. bdg. (978-0-8368-7309-2(2)) Stevens, Gareth Inc. (World Almanac Library).

Butts, Ellen R. & Schwartz, Joyce R. Fidel Castro. 2005. (Biography ' Ser.). (Illus.). 112p. (J). 29.27 (978-0-8225-2371-0(X) , Lerner Pubns.); (gr. 6 up). pap. 7.95 (978-0-8225-9524-3(9)) Lerner Publishing Group.

Crooker, Richard A. Cuba. Gritzner, Charles F., ed. rev. ed. 2005. (Modern World Nations Ser.). (Illus.). 135p. (J). (gr. 6-12). lib. bdg. 30.00 (978-0-7910-8864-7(2) , Chelsea Hse.) Facts On File, Inc.

Cuba, 6 vols. (gr. 2-5). 36.95 (978-0-7368-8390-0(8)) Red Brick Learning.

Engfer, Lee. Cubans in America. 2005. (In America Ser.). (Illus.). 80p. (J). (ps-7). 27.93 (978-0-8225-4870-6(4) , Lerner Pubns.) Lerner Publishing Group.

Gibb, Tom, contrib. by. Fidel Castro: Leader of Cuba's Revolution. 2001. (Illus.). 48p. (J). (978-0-7502-3046-9(0)) Steck-Vaughn.

Green, Jen. Cuba. 2007. (Countries of the World Ser.). (Illus.). 64p. (YA). (gr. 5 up). lib. bdg. 27.90 (***978-1-4263-0057-8(3)*** , National Geographic Children's Bks.) National Geographic Society.

Hernandez, Roger E. Cuban Immigration. 2003. (Changing Face of North America Ser.). (Illus.). 112p. (YA). lib. bdg. (978-1-59084-681-0(8)) Mason Crest Pubs.

Hughes, Susan & Fast, April. Cuba — The People. 2004. (Lands, Peoples & Cultures Ser.). (Illus.). 32p. (J). (978-0-7787-9325-0(7)); pap. (978-0-7787-9693-0(0)) Crabtree Publishing Co.

Markel, Rita J. Fidel Castro's Cuba. 2007. (Dictatorships Ser.). (Illus.). 160p. (YA). (gr. 9-12). lib. bdg. 38.60 (***978-0-8225-7284-8(2)***) Lerner Publishing Group.

Marti, Jose. Jose Marti: Cuatro cuentos Infantiles. Martinez, Enrique & Graullera, Fabiola, illus. (SPA.). 28p. (J). (gr. 3-5). 9.95 (978-970-29-0522-6(2)) Santillana, S.A. de C.V., Editorial MEX. *Dist:* Santillana USA Publishing Co., Inc.

McNeese, Tim. Remember the Maine! The Spanish-American War Begins. 2004. (First Battles Ser.). (Illus.). 112p. (YA). (gr. 6-12). 23.95 (978-1-883846-79-4(X) , First Biographies) Reynolds, Morgan Inc.

Miller, Calvin Craig. Che Guevara: In Search of Revolution. 2006. (World Leaders Ser.). (Illus.). 160p. (J). (gr. 6 up). lib. bdg. 26.95 (978-1-931798-93-8(1)) Reynolds, Morgan Inc.

Naden, Corinne J. & Blue, Rose. Fidel Castro & the Cuban Revolution. 2006. (World Leaders Ser.). (Illus.). 144p. (J). (gr. 6-12). lib. bdg. 27.95 (978-1-59935-029-5(7)) Reynolds, Morgan Inc.

Platt, Richard. Fidel Castro. 2003. (20th Century History Makers Ser.). (Illus.). 112p. (J). lib. bdg. 32.85 (978-0-7398-6141-7(7)) Raintree.

Rees, Fran. Fidel Castro, Leader of Communist Cuba. 2006. (Signature Lives Ser.). (Illus.). 112p. (J). (gr. 5-7). 30.60 (978-0-7565-1580-5(7)) Compass Point Bks.

Roque-Velasco, Ismael. Cuba for Kids: Illustrated History Book/Libro de Historia Ilustrado. Montes de Oca, Gonzalo, illus. (SPA & ENG.). (J). (gr. 3-5). 16.00 net. (978-0-9706319-0-9(1)) Roque-Velasco, Dr. Ismael.

Sheehan, Sean & Jermyn, Leslie. Cuba. 2nd ed. 2005. (Cultures of the World Ser.). (Illus.). 144p. (J). (gr. 6-10). lib. bdg. (978-0-7614-1965-5(9) , Benchmark Bks.) Cavendish, Marshall Corp.

Sherrow, Victoria & Heweston, Nicholas. Cuba. 2001. (Single Titles Ser.: up). (Illus.). 144p. (gr. 7 up). lib. bdg. 24.90 (978-0-7613-1404-2(0) , Twenty-First Century Bks.) Lerner Publishing Group.

Zocchi, Judy. In Cuba. Brodie, Neale, illus. 2005. (Global Adventures II Ser.). 32p. (J). pap. 9.95 (978-1-59646-160-4(8)); lib. bdg. 20.65 (978-1-59646-079-9(2)) Dingles & Co.

—In Cuba/en Cuba. Brodie, Neale, illus. 2005. (Global Adventures II Ser.).Tr. of En Cuba. (ENG & SPA.). 32p. (J). pap. 9.95 (978-1-59646-162-8(4)); lib. bdg. 20.65 (978-1-59646-080-5(6)) Dingles & Co.

CUBAN AMERICANS

Ancona, George. Mi Familia: My Family. 2005. (Somos Latinos (We Are Latinos) Ser.). (SPA., Illus.). 32p. (J). (gr. 1-3). pap. 8.95 (978-0-516-25067-0(1) , Children's Pr.) Scholastic Library Publishing.

Anderson, Dale. Cuban Americans. 2006. (World Almanac Library of American Immigration). (Illus.). 48p. (J). pap. (978-0-8368-7322-1(X)); lib. bdg. (978-0-8368-7309-2(2)) Stevens, Gareth Inc. (World Almanac Library).

Bryan, Nichol. Cuban Americans. 2004. (One Nation Ser.). (Illus.). 31p. (J). (gr. k-6). lib. bdg. 22.78 (978-1-57765-980-8(5)) ABDO Publishing Co.

Cannarella, Deborah. Cuban Americans. 2003. (Spirit of America). (Illus.). 32p. (J). (gr. 2-6). 27.07 (978-1-59296-013-2(8)) Child's World, Inc.

Engfer, Lee. Cubans in America. 2005. (In America Ser.). (Illus.). 80p. (J). (ps-7). 27.93 (978-0-8225-4870-6(4) , Lerner Pubns.) Lerner Publishing Group.

Gay, Kathlyn. Leaving Cuba: From Operation Pedro Pan to Elian. 2000. (Single Titles Ser.: up). (Illus.). 144p. (gr. 7 up). lib. bdg. (978-0-7613-1466-0(0) , Twenty-First Century Bks.) Lerner Publishing Group.

Gonzales, Doreen. Gloria Estefan: Singer & Entertainer. 1998. (Hispanic Biographies Ser.). (Illus.). 128p. (YA). (gr. 6-12). lib. bdg. 26.60 (978-0-89490-890-3(1)) Enslow Pubs., Inc.

Hahn, Laura D. The Cuban Americans. 2002. (Welcome to America Ser.). (Illus.). 64p. (J). (gr. 5 up). lib. bdg. (978-1-59084-113-6(1)) Mason Crest Pubs.

Hernandez, Roger E. Cuban Immigration. 2003. (Changing Face of North America Ser.). (Illus.). 112p. (YA). lib. bdg. (978-1-59084-681-0(8)) Mason Crest Pubs.

Kent, Deborah. Cuban Refugees: Cuban Rooots, American Dreams. 2005. (Proud Heritage: the Hispanic Library Ser.). (Illus.). 40p. (J). (gr. 3-7). 28.50 (978-1-59296-382-9(X)) Child's World, Inc.

Libal, Autumn. Cuban Americans: Exiles from an Island Home. 2005. (Illus.). 112p. (J). (ps-7). lib. bdg. (978-1-59084-928-6(0)) Mason Crest Pubs.

Peterson, Tiffany. Cuban Americans. 2003. (We Are America Ser.). 32p. pap. 6.95 (978-1-4034-3134-9(5)); (Illus.). (J). lib. bdg. 24.22 (978-1-4034-0733-7(9)) Heinemann Library.

—Cuban Americans. 2003. (gr. 3-6). lib. bdg. 15.25 (978-0-613-67397-6(2)) Tandem Library Bks.

Philips, Jane H. Gloria Estefan. 2001. (Women of Achievement Ser.). (Illus.). (J). 111p. pap. 9.95 (978-0-7910-5884-8(0)); 112p. (gr. 4-7). 30.00 (978-0-7910-5883-1(2)) Facts On File, Inc. (Chelsea Hse.).

Sonneborn, Liz. The Cuban-Americans. 2001. (Immigrants in America Ser.). (Illus.). 104p. (YA). (gr. 4-12). 29.95 (978-1-56006-902-7(3) , LML00902-178250, Lucent Bks.) Thomson Gale.

CUBAN AMERICANS—FICTION

Bernardo, Anilu. Loves Me, Loves Me Not. 1998. 169p. (YA). (gr. 6-12). 16.95 (978-1-55885-258-7(1) , Piñata Books) Arte Publico Pr.

—Loves Me, Loves Me Not. 1999. (gr. 7-12). lib. bdg. 18.75 (978-0-613-23737-6(4)) Tandem Library Bks.

Chapra, Mimi. Amelia's Show-and-Tell Fiesta/Amelia y la Fiesta de Muestra y Cuenta. Aviles, Martha, illus. 2004. (ENG & SPA.). 32p. (J). (ps-1). lib. bdg. 17.89 (978-0-06-050256-0(8)) HarperCollins Pubs.

—Amelia's Show-and-Tell Fiesta/Amelia y la Fiesta de "Muestra y Cuenta" Aviles, Martha, illus. 2004. (ENG & SPA.). 32p. (J). (ps-1). 16.99 (978-0-06-050255-3(X)) HarperCollins Pubs.

Corbett, Sue. Free Baseball. 2008. 160p. (J). (gr. 3). 5.99 (***978-0-14-241080-6(2)*** , Puffin) Penguin Group (USA) Inc.

Dole, Mayra L. Drum, Chavi, Drum ! / Toca, Chavi, Toca! Tonel, illus. 2003. Tr. of Toca, Chavi, Toca!. (ENG & SPA.). 32p. (J). 16.95 (978-0-89239-186-8(3)) Children's Bk. Pr.

Dole, Mayra Lazara. Down to the Bone. 2008. 384p. (J). 16.99 (***978-0-06-084310-6(1)***); lib. bdg. 17.89 (***978-0-06-084311-3(X)***) HarperCollins Pubs. (HarperTeen).

Ferrer, Caridad. It's Not about the Accent. 2007. 288p. (YA). (gr. 7 up). pap. 9.95 (***978-1-4165-2491-5(6)*** , MTV) Simon & Schuster.

Heller, Marion. Paco's Perro. 2001. 163p. (J). (gr. 5-9). pap. 12.95 (978-1-56825-080-9(0) , 080.0) Rainbow Bks., Inc.

Osa, Nancy. Cuba 15. 2003. 288p. (YA). (gr. 7). lib. bdg. 17.99 (978-0-385-90086-7(4) , Delacorte Bks. for Young Readers) Random Hse. Children's Bks.

Rue, Nancy. Sophie Tracks a Thief, Vol. 8. 2005. (Faithgirlz Ser.). (Illus.). 144p. (J). pap. 6.99 (978-0-310-71023-3(5)) Zonderkidz.

Triana, Gaby. Cubanita. 2006. 208p. (J). pap. 7.99 (978-0-06-056022-5(3)) HarperCollins Pubs.

Veciana-Suarez, Ana. Flight to Freedom. 2002. (First Person Fiction Ser.). 224p. (J). (gr. 6-9). pap. 16.95 (978-0-439-38199-4(1) , Orchard Bks.) Scholastic, Inc.

—Flight to Freedom. 2004. 215p. (YA). (gr. 8-12). lib. bdg. 13.64 (978-0-606-30967-7(5)) Tandem Library Bks.

CUBAN MISSILE CRISIS, 1962

Brubaker, Paul E. The Cuban Missile Crisis in American History. 2001. (In American History Ser.). (Illus.). 128p. (YA). (gr. 5-12). lib. bdg. 26.60 (978-0-7660-1414-5(2)) Enslow Pubs., Inc.

Byrne, Paul J. The Cuban Missile Crisis: To the Brink of War. 2006. (Snapshots in History Ser.). (Illus.). 96p. (J). (gr. 5-7). 30.60 (978-0-7565-1624-6(2)) Compass Point Bks.

Carter, E. J. The Cuban Missile Crisis. 2003. (20th-Century Perspectives Ser.). (Illus.). 48p. (J). pap. (978-1-4034-4180-5(4)); lib. bdg. 27.07 (978-1-4034-3806-5(4)) Heinemann Library.

Chrisp, Peter. The Cuban Missile Crisis. 2002. (Cold War Ser.). (Illus.). 64p. (YA). (gr. 7 up). lib. bdg. 32.67 (978-0-8368-5273-8(7) , World Almanac Library) Stevens, Gareth Inc.

—Cuban Missile Crisis. 2002. (gr. 7-12). lib. bdg. 24.15 (978-0-613-52355-4(5)) Tandem Library Bks.

Finkelstein, Norman H. Thirteen Days: The Cuban Missile Crisis. 2000. Tr. of Ninety Miles: The Cuban Missile Crisis. (gr. 7-12). lib. bdg. 22.20 (978-0-613-89235-3(6)) Tandem Library Bks.

—Thirteen Days/Ninety Miles: The Cuban Missile Crisis. 2001. (Illus.). 164p. (YA). (gr. 7-12). pap. 12.95 (978-0-595-15654-2(1) , Backinprint.com) iUniverse, Inc.

Fleming, Fergus. The Cuban Missile Crisis: To the Brink of World War III. (Point of Impact Ser.). 32p. pap. 7.50 (978-1-4034-4112-6(X)) Heinemann Library.

Hanes, Sharon M., et al. Cold War: Almanac, 2 vols. 2003. (U-X-L Cold War Reference Library). (Illus.). (J). (978-0-7876-9087-8(2) , UXL) Thomson Gale.

Harris, Nathaniel. The Cuban Missile Crisis. (Illus.). 32p. 25.00 (978-0-7502-4182-3(9) , Hodder & Stoughton) Hodder General Publishing Division GBR. *Dist:* Trafalgar Square Publishing.

Ross, Stewart. The Cuban Missile Crisis: To the Brink of World War III. 2001. (Point of Impact Ser.). (Illus.). 32p. (J). (gr. 5-7). lib. bdg. 24.22 (978-1-58810-075-7(8)) Heinemann Library.

Whiting, Jim. The Cuban Missile Crisis: The Cold War Goes Hot. 2005. (Monumental Milestones Ser.). (Illus.). 48p. (J). lib. bdg. 29.95 (978-1-58415-404-4(7)) Mitchell Lane Pubs., Inc.

CUCKOOS—FICTION

Bloom, Becky. Mr. Cuckoo. Bloom, Becky, illus. 1998. (Illus.). 32p. (J). (gr. k-4). 15.95 (978-1-57255-626-3(9)) Mondo Publishing.

Rhodes, C. J. The Rabbit, the Skunk & the Cuckoo. Spears-Stewart, Reta, ed. Secca, Phillip, illus. 1998. 36p. (J). pap. 12.00 (978-0-9638648-5-7(8)) Nottinghill Bks.

CULPEPPER, DUNC (FICTITIOUS CHARACTER)—FICTION

Paulsen, Gary. Culpepper's Cannon & Dunc Gets Tweaked, Vol. 2. unabr. ed. (Culpepper Adventures Ser.). (gr. 3-5). lib. bdg. 16.95 (978-1-55656-185-6(7) , DAB 076) Dercum Audio.

CULTS AND SECTS

see Sects

CULTURAL CHANGE

see Social Change

CULTURE

see also Civilization; Education; Humanism; Learning and Scholarship; Self-Culture

Anup, A. Relativity of Morality. 2002. per. 16.99 (978-0-9657083-8-8(1)) ANUP Research & Multimedia LP.

Benchmark Education Staff, compiled by. Art & Culture. 2006. spiral bd. 159.00 (***978-1-4108-7117-6(7)***) Benchmark Education Co.

—Arts & Culture. 2006. spiral bd. 179.00 (***978-1-4108-7101-5(0)***) Benchmark Education Co.

Building Bridges: A Peace Corps Classroom Guide to Cross-Cultural Understanding. 2002. 48p. (YA). (gr. 6-12). pap. (978-0-9723579-0-6(4)) United States Peace Corps.

Cave, Kathryn. W Is for World Big Book: A Round-the-World ABC. Oxfam, illus. 2004. 32p. (J). pap. (978-1-84507-026-7(7)) Lincoln, Frances Ltd.

Chancellor, Carl C. Soul Songs. 2001. 142p. (YA). (gr. 10 up). pap. 13.95 (978-1-884242-76-2(6)); (Illus.). lib. bdg. 21.95 (978-1-884242-72-4(3)) Multicultural Pubns.

Countries & Cultures: Australia; Brazil; Canada; China; Colombia; Egypt; England; France; Germany; Haiti; Israel; Japan; Kenya; Mexico; Sweden; Thailand, 16 bks. (Illus.). (J). (gr. 3-4). lib. bdg. 382.88 (978-0-7368-1007-4(2) , Bridgestone Bks.) Capstone Pr., Inc.

Culturas Antiguas, 6 vols., Vol. 3. (Explorers. Exploradores Nonfiction Sets Ser.). (SPA.). (gr. 3-6). (978-0-7699-0659-1(1)) Shortland Pubns. (U. S. A.) Inc.

Culture. 2007. (Lucent Library of Historical Eras:Twentieth-Century Japan Ser.). (Illus.). 128p. (gr. 7-10). 31.20 (*978-1-4205-0026-4(0) , Lucent Bks.) Thomson Gale.

Culture Encyclopedia, 8 vols., Set. (Illus.). 40p. (YA). (gr. 5 up). lib. bdg. (978-1-59084-474-8(2)) Mason Crest Pubs.

Cultures of the World - Group 23, 6 Bks. 2004. (J). 222.43 (978-0-7614-1851-1(2)) Cavendish, Marshall Corp.

Cultures of the World - Group 7, 6 Bks, Set. 2nd ed. 2004. (J). 222.43 (978-0-7614-1783-5(4)) Cavendish, Marshall Corp.

Discovering Cultures - Group 2, 6 vols. 2003. 288p. (YA). (gr. 2 up). lib. bdg. 158.86 (978-0-7614-1514-5(9)) Cavendish, Marshall Corp.

Dorling Kindersley Publishing Staff. Big Book of Knowledge. 2002. (Illus.). 480p. (J). (gr. 4-7). pap. 17.99 (978-0-7894-8501-4(X)) Dorling Kindersley Publishing, Inc.

—Big Book of Knowledge. 2002. (gr. 3-6). lib. bdg. 28.05 (978-0-613-75146-9(9)) Tandem Library Bks.

Doudna, Kelly. Boys & Girls Around the World. 2004. (Around the World Ser.). (Illus.). 23p. (J). (ps-3). lib. bdg. 19.93 (978-1-59197-564-9(6)) ABDO Publishing Co.

—Culture Around the World. 2004. (Around the World Ser.). (Illus.). 23p. (J). (ps-3). lib. bdg. 19.93 (978-1-59197-566-3(2)) ABDO Publishing Co.

—People Around the World. 2004. (Around the World Ser.). (Illus.). 23p. (J). (ps-3). lib. bdg. 19.93 (978-1-59197-567-0(0)) ABDO Publishing Co.

Gay, Kathlyn. Cultural Diversity: Conflicts & Challenges. 2003. (gr. 7-12). lib. bdg. 37.30 (978-0-613-75850-5(1)) Tandem Library Bks.

Gottfried, Ted. Slovakia. 2004. (Cultures of the World Ser.). (Illus.). 144p. (J). 37.07 (978-0-7614-1856-6(3)) Cavendish, Marshall Corp.

Guile. Culture In... Set 1, 8 vols. 2003. (Illus.). (978-1-4109-0476-8(8)) Raintree.

Hill, Linda. Connecting Kids: Exploring Deversity Together. 2001. (Illus.). 192p. pap. (978-0-86571-431-1(2)) New Society Pubs., Ltd.

Kallen, Stuart A. A Travel Guide to Harlem Renaissance. 2003. (J). 29.95 (978-1-59018-358-8(4) , Lucent Bks.) Thomson Gale.

Koopmans, Andy. Crime & Criminals. 2002. (Examining Pop Culture Ser.). 176p. (J). 36.20 (978-0-7377-1431-9(X)); (Illus.). (gr. 7-10). pap. 24.95 (978-0-7377-1432-6(8)) Thomson Gale. (Greenhaven Pr., Inc.).

Landau, Elaine. All-American Companies. 2003. (Single Titles Ser.). 112p. (J). lib. bdg. 32.90 (978-0-7613-2350-1(3) , Twenty-First Century Bks.) Lerner Publishing Group.

MacDonald, Fiona. Design. 2002. (Culture Encyclopedia Ser.). (Illus.). 40p. (J). (gr. 5 up). lib. bdg. (978-1-59084-476-2(9)) Mason Crest Pubs.

—History of Culture. 2003. (Culture Encyclopedia Ser.). (Illus.). 40p. (J). (gr. 5 up). lib. bdg. (978-1-59084-477-9(7)) Mason Crest Pubs.

MacDonald, Fiona, intro. Art, Culture & Entertainment. 2001. (Through the Ages Ser.). (Illus.). 64p. (gr. 3-7). 12.95 (978-0-7548-0785-8(1)) Anness Publishing GBR. *Dist:* National Bk. Network.

Mason, Antony. Art. 2002. (Culture Encyclopedia Ser.). (Illus.). 40p. (J). (gr. 5 up). lib. bdg. (978-1-59084-475-5(0)) Mason Crest Pubs.

McGraw-Hill Staff. World Geography & Cultures, Interactive Tutor Self-Assessment. 2007. (C). cd-rom 93.32 (*978-0-07-878573-3(1) , 9780078785733) Glencoe/McGraw-Hill.

—World Geography & Cultures, Spanish Reading Essentials & Note-Taking Guide. 2007. (C). pap. 18.00 (*978-0-07-878391-3(7) , 9780078783913) Glencoe/McGraw-Hill.

—World Geography & Cultures, Standardized Test Practice Workbook. 2007. (C). pap. 14.00 (*978-0-07-878564-1(2) , 9780078785641) Glencoe/McGraw-Hill.

—World Geography & Cultures, Student Edition. 2007. (C). 93.32 (*978-0-07-874529-4(2) , 9780078745294) Glencoe/McGraw-Hill.

—World Geography & Cultures, StudentWorks Plus. 2007. (C). cd-rom 122.00 (*978-0-07-878394-4(1) , 9780078783944) Glencoe/McGraw-Hill.

Milord, Susan. Hands Around the World. Milord, Susan, illus. 1999. (Williamson Kids Can! Ser.). (Illus.). 160p. (J). (gr. 3 up). lib. bdg. 25.26 (978-0-8368-2231-1(5)) Stevens, Gareth Inc.

Popov, Linda Kavelin. The Virtues Project Educator's Guide: Simple Ways to Create a Culture of Character. 2000. (Illus.). 208p. (J). (gr. k-12). pap. 24.95 (978-1-880396-84-1(X)) Jalmar Pr.

Schaefer, Lola M. Understanding Differences, 4 bks. Saunders-Smith, Gail, ed. Incl. Some Kids Are Blind. 2001. lib. bdg. 15.93 (978-0-7368-0664-0(4)); Some Kids Are Deaf. 2001. lib. bdg. 15.93 (978-0-7368-0665-7(2)); Some Kids Use Wheelchairs. 2000. lib. bdg. 15.93 (978-0-7368-0666-4(0)); Some Kids Wear Leg Braces. 2000. lib. bdg. 15.93 (978-0-7368-0667-1(9)); 24p. (J). (gr. k-1). (Illus.). 2001. Set lib. bdg. 63.72 (978-0-7368-0691-6(1) , Pebble Bks.) Capstone Pr., Inc.

Spangenburg, Ray & Moser, Kit. Teen Fads: Fun, Foolish, or Fatal? 2003. (Teen Issues Ser.). (Illus.). 64p. (J). (gr. 6-12). lib. bdg. 22.60 (978-0-7660-1665-1(X)) Enslow Pubs., Inc.

Watson, Susan. Valuing World Heritage. 2003. 32p. (J). lib. bdg. 24.25 (978-1-58340-401-0(5)) Smart Apple Media.

Weber, Rebecca. Understanding Differences. 2004. (Spyglass Books). (Illus.). 24p. (J). (gr. 1 up). lib. bdg. 19.93 (978-0-7565-0651-3(4)) Compass Point Bks.

Williams, Mary, ed. Culture Wars. 1998. (Opposing Viewpoints Ser.). (Illus.). 208p. (YA). (gr. 8-12). lib. bdg. 32.45 (978-1-56510-939-1(2) , LML00501-177490, Greenhaven Pr., Inc.) Thomson Gale.

World Art & Culture, 4 vols., Set 1. 2003. (Illus.). 119.96 (978-0-7398-6611-5(7)) Raintree.

World Cultures & Geography. 2005. (gr. 6-12). stu. ed. (978-0-618-16841-5(9) , 2-00408) McDougal Littell Inc.

CUMBERLAND MOUNTAINS—FICTION

Murfree, Mary N. The Mystery of Witch-Face Mountain & Other Stories. 1999. (Notable American Authors Ser.). reprint ed. lib. bdg. 125.00 (978-0-7812-4601-9(6)) Reprint Services Co.

CUMMINGS, E. E. (EDWARD ESTLIN), 1894-1962

Reef, Catherine. E. E. Cummings: A Poet's Life. 2006. (Illus.). 176p. (J). (gr. 7-9). 21.00 (978-0-618-56849-9(2) , Clarion Bks.) Houghton Mifflin Co. Trade & Reference Div.

CURIE, MARIE, 1867-1934

Ardagh, Philip. Marie Curie. 2003. (Illus.). 64p. (J). pap. 6.99 (978-0-330-37571-9(7) , Pan) Pan Macmillan GBR. *Dist:* Trafalgar Square Publishing.

Beverly Birch. Marie Curie. 2005. (Gigantes de Ciencia Ser.). (gr. 5-7). 28.70 (978-1-4103-0505-3(8) , Blackbirch Pr., Inc.) Thomson Gale.

Birch, Beverley. Marie Curie: Courageous Pioneer in the Study of Radioactivity. 2000. (Giants of Science Ser.). (Illus.). 64p. (J). (gr. 5-8). 24.95 (978-1-56711-333-4(8) , Blackbirch Pr., Inc.) Thomson Gale.

Cobb, Vicki. Marie Curie. 2008. (DK Biography Ser.). 128p. (J). (gr. 3-8). 14.99 (*978-0-7566-3832-0(1)); pap. 4.99 (*978-0-7566-3831-3(3)) Dorling Kindersley Publishing, Inc.

Fullick, Ann. Marie Curie. (Groundbreakers Ser.). 48p. (J). (gr. 5-7). 2002. (Illus.). pap. 8.50 (978-1-58810-994-1(1) , 91469); 2000. lib. bdg. 25.64 (978-1-57572-374-7(3)) Heinemann Library.

Ganeri, Anita. Marie Curie. 2000. (What Would You Ask...? Ser.). (Illus.). 32p. (J). (gr. 2-6). lib. bdg. 16.95 (978-1-929298-09-9(9)) Chrysalis Education.

Gogerly, Liz. Marie Curie. 2001. (Scientists Who Made History Ser.). (Illus.). 48p. (J). lib. bdg. 27.12 (978-0-7398-4413-7(X)) Raintree.

Gormley, Beatrice. Marie Curie: Young Scientist. 2007. (Childhood of World Figures Ser.). 240p. (J). pap. 5.99 (978-1-4169-1545-4(1) , Aladdin) Simon & Schuster Children's Publishing.

Hasday, Judy L. Marie Curie: Pioneer on the Frontier of Radioactivity. 2004. (Nobel Prize-Winning Scientists Ser.). (Illus.). 112p. (YA). lib. bdg. 26.60 (978-0-7660-2440-3(7)) Enslow Pubs., Inc.

Healy, Nick. Marie Curie. 2005. (Genius Ser.). (Illus.). 48p. (gr. 5-9). 21.95 (978-1-58341-332-6(4) , Creative Education) Creative Co., The.

Krull, Kathleen. Marie Curie: Giants of Science #4. 2007. 144p. (J). (gr. 2). 15.99 (*978-0-670-05894-5(7) , Viking Juvenile) Penguin Group (USA) Inc.

Lassieur, Allison. Marie Curie: A Scientific Pioneer. 2003. (Great Life Stories Ser.). (Illus.). 112p. (J). 30.50 (978-0-531-12270-9(0) , Watts, Franklin) Scholastic Library Publishing.

Linder, Greg. Marie Curie. 1999. (Photo-Illustrated Biographies Ser.). (Illus.). 24p. (J). (gr. 2-3). lib. bdg. 18.60 (978-0-7368-0206-2(1) , Bridgestone Bks.) Capstone Pr., Inc.

MacLeod, Elizabeth. Marie Curie: A Brillant Life. 2005. (Snapshots Ser.). (Illus.). 32p. (YA). (gr. 3-7). (978-1-55337-571-5(8)); (978-1-55337-570-8(X)) Kids Can Pr., Ltd.

Marie Curie. (Compass Point Early Biographies Ser.). 32p. (J). 7.95 (978-0-7565-1176-0(3)) Compass Point Bks.

McCormick, Lisa Wade. Marie Curie. 2006. 32p. (gr. 1-2). (YA). pap. 4.95 (978-0-516-21445-0(4)); (Illus.). (J). 20.50 (978-0-516-25040-3(X)) Scholastic Library Publishing. (Children's Pr.).

McLeese, Don. Marie Curie. (Rourke Discovery Library). (Illus.). 24p. 2006. (gr. 2-5). 14.95 (978-1-59515-431-6(0)); 2005. (SPA & ENG., (978-1-59515-671-6(2)) Rourke Publishing, LLC.

Miller, Connie Colwell. Marie Curie & Radioactivity. Larson, Scott & Heike, Mark, illus. 2007. (Graphic Library). 32p. (J). 25.26 (978-0-7368-6486-2(5)); pap. (*978-0-7368-7521-9(2)) Capstone Pr., Inc.

Ogilvie, Marilyn Bailey. Marie Curie: A Biography. 2004. (Greenwood Biographies Ser.). (Illus.). 184p. 36.95 (978-0-313-32529-8(4) , GR2529, Praeger Pubs.) Greenwood Publishing Group, Inc.

Orr, Tamra. Marie Curie. 2003. (World Was Never the Same Ser.). (J). pap. (978-1-58417-263-5(0)); lib. bdg. (978-1-58417-262-8(2)) Lake Street Pubs.

Poynter, Margaret. Marie Curie: Discoverer of Radium. 2001. (Great Minds of Science Ser.). (Illus.). 128p. (YA). (gr. 4-10). pap. 13.26 (978-0-7660-1875-4(X)) Enslow Pubs., Inc.

Rau, Dana Meachen. Marie Curie. 2000. (Compass Point Early Biographies Ser.). (Illus.). 32p. (J). (gr. 2 up). lib. bdg. 21.26 (978-0-7565-0017-7(6)) Compass Point Bks.

Santella, Andrew. Marie Curie. 2001. (Trailblazers of the Modern World Ser.). (Illus.). 48p. (J). (gr. 5 up). pap. 14.95 (978-0-8368-5221-9(4)); lib. bdg. 30.00 (978-0-8368-5061-1(0)) Stevens, Gareth Inc. (World Almanac Library).

Schaefer, Lola M. Marie Curie. (First Biographies Ser.). 24p. (J). pap. 5.95 (978-0-7368-5086-5(4)) Capstone Pr., Inc.

Schaefer, Lola M. & Schaefer, Wyatt S. Marie Curie. 2004. (First Biographies Ser.). 24p. (J). lib. bdg. 15.93 (978-0-7368-2084-4(1) , Pebble Bks.) Capstone Pr., Inc.

Steele, Philip. Marie Curie: The Woman Who Changed the Course of Science. 2006. 64p. (ps-1). 17.95 (978-0-7922-5387-7(6)); 27.90 (978-0-7922-5388-4(4)) National Geographic Society. (National Geographic Children's Bks.).

Tracy, Kathleen. Pierre & Marie Curie & the Discovery of Radium. 2004. (Uncharted, Unexplored, & Unexplained Ser.). (Illus.). 48p. (J). (gr. 4-8). lib. bdg. 29.95 (978-1-58415-310-8(5)) Mitchell Lane Pubs., Inc.

Waxman, Laura Hamilton. Marie Curie. 2004. (History Maker Bios Ser.). (Illus.). 48p. (J). 26.60 (978-0-8225-0300-2(X) , Lerner Pubns.) Lerner Publishing Group.

Wishinsky, Frieda. Manya's Dream: A Story of Marie Curie. Lamontagne, Jacques, illus. 2003. 32p. (J). (gr. 3-6). pap. 6.95 (978-1-894379-54-0(3)) Maple Tree Pr. CAN. *Dist:* Firefly Bks., Ltd.

YKids Staff. Marie Curie. 2007. (Great Figures in History Ser.). 148p. (J). (gr. 4-7). pap. 14.95 (*978-981-05-4946-6(6)) Youngjin (Singapore) Pte Ltd. SGP. *Dist:* Independent Pubs. Group.

CURIE, PIERRE, 1859-1906

Tracy, Kathleen. Pierre & Marie Curie & the Discovery of Radium. 2004. (Uncharted, Unexplored, & Unexplained Ser.). (Illus.). 48p. (J). (gr. 4-8). lib. bdg. 29.95 (978-1-58415-310-8(5)) Mitchell Lane Pubs., Inc.

CURIOUS GEORGE (FICTITIOUS CHARACTER)—FICTION

Anderson, R. P. Sweet Dreams, Curious George. Obrero, Rudy, illus. 2005. (J). (ps-k). pap. (978-0-618-69493-8(5)) Houghton Mifflin Co. Trade & Reference Div.

Canetti, Yanitzia, tr. from ENG. Jorge el Curioso y el Conejito. Rey, H. A., illus. 2002. (SPA.). 26p. (J). (gr. k-ps). bds. 5.95 (978-0-618-20316-1(8)) Houghton Mifflin Co. Trade & Reference Div.

Curious George & the Puppies. 1998. (Illus.). 24p. (J). (ps-ps). lib. bdg. 10.75 (978-0-606-15497-0(3)) Tandem Library Bks.

Curious George Feeds the Animals. 1998. (Curious George Ser.). (Illus.). 24p. (J). (ps-ps). lib. bdg. 10.75 (978-0-606-16107-7(4)) Tandem Library Bks.

Dodd, Emma. Amazing Baby: Rain or Shine! Jolley, Mike, illus. 2007. (Amazing Baby Ser.). 10p. (J). bds. 6.95 (*978-1-59223-801-9(7) , Silver Dolphin Bks.) Advantage Pubs. Group.

Forrester, Emma. Monkey See, Monkey Do. Obrero, Rudy, illus. 2007. (Curious George Ser.). 96p. (J). 2.99 (*978-1-4169-3379-3(4) , Simon Scribbles) Simon & Schuster Children's Publishing.

Houghton Mifflin Company Editors. Curious George Discovery Day. 2007. (Illus.). 14p. (J). (gr. k-ps). bds. 13.95 (*978-0-618-73761-1(8)) Houghton Mifflin Co. Trade & Reference Div.

Houghton Mifflin Company Staff. Birthday Fun with Curious George. 2005. (J). (ps-k). pap. (978-0-618-69654-3(7)) Houghton Mifflin Co. Trade & Reference Div.

—Curious George & Me! 2007. (Illus.). 64p. (J). (ps-k). 9.95 (978-0-618-73762-8(6)) Houghton Mifflin Co. Trade & Reference Div.

—Curious George Cleans Up. 2007. (Illus.). 24p. (J). (gr. 3-5). 3.99 (*978-0-618-73759-8(6)) Houghton Mifflin Co. Trade & Reference Div.

—Curious George Finds a Friend. 2007. (Illus.). 16p. (J). (ps-k). 5.99 (*978-0-618-72398-0(6)) Houghton Mifflin Co. Trade & Reference Div.

—Fire Truck Fun with Curious George. 2005. (J). (ps-k). pap. (978-0-618-70499-6(X)) Houghton Mifflin Co. Trade & Reference Div.

—Splish, Splash, Curious George. 2005. (J). (ps-k). pap. (978-0-618-70498-9(1)) Houghton Mifflin Co. Trade & Reference Div.

Houghton Mifflin Company Staff & Rey, Margret. Curious George the Movie: A Junior Novel. 2006. (Illus.). 128p. (J). (gr. k-3). pap. 4.99 (978-0-618-60591-0(6)) Houghton Mifflin Co. Trade & Reference Div.

—Curious George the Movie: Curious George's Big Adventure. 2006. (Illus.). 24p. (J). (ps-k). pap. 3.99 (978-0-618-63449-1(5)) Houghton Mifflin Co. Trade & Reference Div.

—Curious George the Movie: Meet Curious George, a Picture Reader. 2006. (Illus.). 24p. (J). (gr. k-3). pap. 3.99 (978-0-618-60590-3(8)) Houghton Mifflin Co. Trade & Reference Div.

—Curious George the Movie: The Deluxe Movie Storybook. 2006. (Illus.). 48p. (J). (ps-k). 9.99 (978-0-618-60585-9(1)) Houghton Mifflin Co. Trade & Reference Div.

—Curious George the Movie: Touch & Feel Book. 2006. (Illus.). 10p. (J). (ps-k). bds. 5.99 (978-0-618-60587-3(8)) Houghton Mifflin Co. Trade & Reference Div.

Houghton Mifflin Company Staff, et al. Before & After. 2007. (Curious George Ser.). (Illus.). 12p. (J). (ps-k). bds. 6.99 (978-0-618-72399-7(4)) Houghton Mifflin Co. Trade & Reference Div.

Margaret. Curious George im Schokolade. 20.95 (978-3-8157-2329-6(9)) Coppenrath, F. Verlag KG DEU. *Dist:* Distribooks, Inc.

—Curious George und der Lastwa. 20.95 (978-3-8157-2327-2(2)) Coppenrath, F. Verlag KG DEU. *Dist:* Distribooks, Inc.

—Curious George und der Seltsa. 20.95 (978-3-8157-2330-2(2)) Coppenrath, F. Verlag KG DEU. *Dist:* Distribooks, Inc.

—Curious George und die Hundelb. 20.95 (978-3-8157-2328-9(0)) Coppenrath, F. Verlag KG DEU. *Dist:* Distribooks, Inc.

Moscovich, Rotem & Lankford, Raye. Curious George Takes a Trip. 2007. (Illus.). 24p. (J). (ps-k). pap. 3.99 (*978-0-618-88403-2(3)) Houghton Mifflin Co.

Moscovich, Rotem & Saric, Lazar. Curious George Snowy Day. 2007. (Illus.). 24p. (J). (gr. k-ps). 3.99 (*978-0-618-80043-8(3)) Houghton Mifflin Co.

Obrero, Rudy, illus. Monkey Business. 2007. (Curious George Ser.). 400p. (J). 5.99 (*978-1-4169-3374-8(3) , Simon Scribbles) Simon & Schuster Children's Publishing.

Perez, Monica & Saric, Lazar. Curious George Roller Coaster. 2007. (Illus.). 24p. (J). (ps-k). pap. 3.99 (*978-0-618-80040-7(9)) Houghton Mifflin Co.

Rey. George O Curioso. pap. 23.95 (978-85-336-0916-7(7)) Livraria Martins Editora BRA. *Dist:* Distribooks, Inc.

Rey, H. A. Curious George. Rey, H. A., illus. 2002. (Curious George Picture Bks.). (Illus.). (J). 13.79 (978-0-7587-2310-9(5)) Book Wholesalers, Inc.

—Curious George. 2000. (Curious George Ser.). (J). (ps-2). pap. 9.95 incl. audio Houghton Mifflin Co. (Schl. Div.).

—Curious George. 2000. (J). pap., tchr. ed., wbk. ed. (978-1-56137-270-6(6)) Novel Units, Inc.

—Curious George & Firefighters. Rey, Margret, illus. 2007. 24p. (J). (ps-k). bds. 9.95 (*978-0-618-89194-8(3)) Houghton Mifflin Co. Trade & Reference Div.

—Curious George & Puppies. Rey, Margret, illus. 2007. 24p. (J). (ps-k). pap. 9.95 incl. audio compact disk (*978-0-618-80065-0(4)) Houghton Mifflin Co. Trade & Reference Div.

—Curious George & the Birthday Suprise. 2003. (gr. k-3). lib. bdg. 11.80 (978-0-613-90050-8(2)) Tandem Library Bks.

—Curious George at the Zoo. Rey, Margret, illus. 2007. 12p. (J). (gr. k-ps). bds. 6.99 (*978-0-618-80042-1(5)) Houghton Mifflin Co. Trade & Reference Div.

—Curious George Flies a Kite. Rey, H. A., illus. 2002. (Curious George Picture Bks.). (Illus.). (J). 13.79 (978-0-7587-2314-7(8)) Book Wholesalers, Inc.

—Curious George Flies a Kite. ed. 2004. (J). (gr. k-3). spiral bd. (978-0-616-01770-8(7)); spiral bd. (978-0-616-01771-5(5)) Canadian National Institute for the Blind/Institut National Canadien pour les Aveugles.

—Curious George Gets a Medal. Rey, H. A., illus. 2002. (Curious George Picture Bks.). (Illus.). (J). 13.79 (978-0-7587-2315-4(6)) Book Wholesalers, Inc.

—Curious George Gets a Medal. ed. 2004. (J). (ps-2). spiral bd. (978-0-616-01772-2(3)); spiral bd. (978-0-616-01773-9(1)) Canadian National Institute for the Blind/Institut National Canadien pour les Aveugles.

—Curious George in the Big City. Weston, Martha, illus. 2001. (Curious George Ser.). 24p. (J). (ps-2). 7.95 (978-0-618-15253-7(9)) Houghton Mifflin Co.

—Curious George Learns the Alphabet. Rey, H. A., illus. 2002. (Curious George Picture Bks.). (Illus.). (J). 13.79 (978-0-7587-2318-5(0)) Book Wholesalers, Inc.

—Curious George Learns to Count from 1 to 100: Counting, Grouping, Mapping, & More! Hines, Anna Grossnickle, illus. 2005. 64p. (J). (ps-k). bds. 16.00 (978-0-618-47602-2(4)) Houghton Mifflin Co. Trade & Reference Div.

—Curious George Rides a Bike. Rey, H. A., illus. 2002. (Curious George Picture Bks.). (Illus.). 13.79 (978-0-7587-2321-5(0)) Book Wholesalers, Inc.

—Curious George Takes a Job. Rey, H. A., illus. 2002. (Curious George Picture Bks.). (Illus.). (J). 13.79 (978-0-7587-2322-2(9)) Book Wholesalers, Inc.

—Curious George Takes a Job. Rey, Margret, illus. 2007. 48p. (J). (ps-k). pap. 9.95 incl. audio compact disk (*978-0-618-72406-2(0)) Houghton Mifflin Co. Trade & Reference Div.

—Curious George Visits the Library. 2003. (gr. k-3). lib. bdg. 11.80 (978-0-613-90204-5(1)) Tandem Library Bks.

—Jorge el Curioso. 2001. (SPA., Illus.). (J). (gr. k-2). 7.96 net. (978-1-56137-558-5(6) , NU6112) Novel Units, Inc.

—Jorge el Curioso Monta en Bicicleta. Canetti, Yanitzia, tr. 2002. Tr. of Curious George Rides a Bike. (SPA., Illus.). 48p. (J). (gr. k-3). pap. 6.95 (978-0-618-19677-7(3)); tchr. ed. 14.95 (978-0-618-21615-4(4)) Houghton Mifflin Co. Trade & Reference Div.

—Jorge el Curioso Monta en Bicicleta. 2002. Tr. of Curious George Rides a Bike. (SPA.). (gr. k-3). lib. bdg. 14.10 (978-0-613-60749-0(X)) Tandem Library Bks.

Rey, H. A. & Rey, Margret. The Complete Adventures of Curious George. Rey, H. A. & Rey, Margret, illus. 60th anniv. ed. 2001. (Curious George Ser.). (Illus.). 432p. (J). (gr. k-3). tchr. ed. 30.00 (978-0-618-16441-7(3)) Houghton Mifflin Co. Trade & Reference Div.

—Curious George & Friends: Favorite Stories by Margret & H. A. Rey. 2003. (Illus.). 272p. (J). (gr. k-3). tchr. ed. 25.00 (978-0-618-22610-8(9)) Houghton Mifflin Co. Trade & Reference Div.

—Curious George & the Birthday Surprise. Weston, Martha, illus. 2003. 24p. (J). (gr. k-3). 12.95 (978-0-618-34688-2(0)); pap. 3.95 (978-0-618-34687-5(2)) Houghton Mifflin Co. Trade & Reference Div.

—Curious George Feeds the Animals. 2005. (J). (gr. k-3). 9.95 (978-0-618-55520-8(X)) Houghton Mifflin Co. Trade & Reference Div.

—Curious George Goes to the Beach. 1999. (Curious George Ser.). (Illus.). (J). (gr. k-3). 24p. tchr. ed. 12.95 (978-0-395-97834-4(3)); 32p. pap. 3.95 (978-0-395-97838-2(6)) Houghton Mifflin Co. Trade & Reference Div.

—Curious George Goes to the Movies. 2005. (J). (gr. k-3). 9.95 (978-0-618-55521-5(8)) Houghton Mifflin Co. Trade & Reference Div.

—Curious George Plants a Seed. 2007. (Illus.). 24p. (J). (ps-k). 3.99 (*978-0-618-77710-5(5)) Houghton Mifflin Co. Trade & Reference Div.

—Curious George Tadpole Trouble. 2007. (Illus.). 24p. (J). (ps-k). 3.99 (*978-0-618-77712-9(1)) Houghton Mifflin Co. Trade & Reference Div.

—Curious George to the Rescue: A Slide & Peek Adventure. 2007. (Curious George Ser.). (Illus.). 12p. (J). (ps-k). bds. 8.99 (978-0-618-72401-7(X)) Houghton Mifflin Co. Trade & Reference Div.

—Curious George Visits the Library. Weston, Martha, illus. 2003. 24p. (J). (gr. k-3). 12.95 (978-0-618-06565-3(2)) Houghton Mifflin Co. Trade & Reference Div.

—Curious George's First Day of School. 2005. (Illus.). 24p. (J). (gr. k-3). 12.95 (978-0-618-60563-7(0)) Houghton Mifflin Co. Trade & Reference Div.

—Curious George's Neighborhood: A Lift-the-Flap Adventure. Weston, Martha, illus. 2004. 10p. (J). (gr. k-3). bds. 7.99 (978-0-618-41203-7(4)) Houghton Mifflin Co. Trade & Reference Div.

—Jorge el Curioso. 2001. (Curious George Ser.). (SPA., Illus.). 48p. (J). (gr. k-3). pap. 9.95 incl. audio (978-0-618-13159-4(0) , HM30407) Houghton Mifflin Co. Trade & Reference Div.

—The New Adventures of Curious George 2006. 2006. (Illus.). 208p. (J). (ps-k). 10.99 (978-0-618-66373-6(8)) Houghton Mifflin Co. Trade & Reference Div.

—The Original Curious George. Rey, H. A., illus. 1998. (Curious George Ser.). (Illus.). 64p. (J). (gr. k-3). tchr. ed. 25.00 (978-0-395-92272-9(0)) Houghton Mifflin Co. Trade & Reference Div.

Rey, H. A. & Rey, Margret, creators. Curious George & the Rocket. 2001. (Curious George Ser.). (Illus.). 20p. (J). (gr. k-ps). bds. 5.95 (978-0-618-12069-7(6)) Houghton Mifflin Co. Trade & Reference Div.

—Curious George Rides. 2001. (Curious George Ser.). (Illus.). 20p. (J). (gr. k-ps). bds. 5.95 (978-0-618-12075-8(0)) Houghton Mifflin Co. Trade & Reference Div.

—Curious George's 1 to 10 & Back Again. 2001. (Curious George Ser.). (Illus.). 20p. (J). (gr. k-ps). bds. 5.95 (978-0-618-12074-1(2)) Houghton Mifflin Co. Trade & Reference Div.

—Opuestos con Jorge el Curioso. 2002. (SPA., Illus.). 8p. (J). (gr. k-ps). bds. 5.95 (978-0-618-20317-8(6)) Houghton Mifflin Co. Trade & Reference Div.

Rey, H. A. & Rey, Margret, illus. Curious George's 1 to 10 & Back Again. 2003. (J). bds. 9.95 (978-0-618-27711-7(0)) Houghton Mifflin Co. Trade & Reference Div.

Rey, H. A. & Vipah Interactive Staff. Curious George Goes to a Chocolate Factory. 1998. (Curious George Ser.). (Illus.). 24p. (J). (gr. k-3). pap. 3.95 (978-0-395-91214-0(8)) Houghton Mifflin Co.

Rey, H. A., et al. Curious George & the Firefighters. 2004. (Illus.). 24p. (J). (gr. k-3). 3.95 (978-0-618-49496-5(0)); 12.00 (978-0-618-49497-2(9)) Houghton Mifflin Co. Trade & Reference Div.

—Curious George's Color Fun Board Book. 2007. (Curious George Ser.). (Illus.). 14p. (J). (ps-k). bds. 6.99 (978-0-618-72400-0(1)) Houghton Mifflin Co. Trade & Reference Div.

Rey, H. A. and Margret. Curious George Hide-and-Seek CG TV shapedanimal tab Book. 2008. 10p. (J). (ps-k). bds. 6.99 (***978-0-618-89199-3(4)**) Houghton Mifflin Co. Trade & Reference Div.

—Curious George Shapes: CG TV Board Book #5. 2008. 10p. (J). (gr. k-ps). bds. 6.99 (***978-0-618-89198-6(6)**) Houghton Mifflin Co. Trade & Reference Div.

—Curious George/Jorge el curioso Bilingual Edition. 2008. 64p. (J). (gr. k-3). 16.00 (***978-0-618-88410-0(6)**); pap. 6.95 (***978-0-618-88411-7(4)**) Houghton Mifflin Co. Trade & Reference Div.

Rey, Margret. Curious George & the Dinosaur. Rey, Margret, illus. 2002. (Curious George TV Bks.). (Illus.). (J). 11.87 (978-0-7587-2311-6(3)) Book Wholesalers, Inc.

—Curious George & the Dump Truck. 1999. (gr. k-3). lib. bdg. 11.80 (978-0-613-21389-9(0)) Tandem Library Bks.

—Curious George & the Pizza. Rey, Margret, illus. 2002. (Curious George TV Bks.). (Illus.). (J). 11.87 (978-0-7587-2312-3(1)) Book Wholesalers, Inc.

—Curious George at the Fire Station. Rey, Margret, illus. 2002. (Curious George TV Bks.). (Illus.). (J). 11.87 (978-0-7587-2313-0(X)) Book Wholesalers, Inc.

—Curious George at the Parade. 1999. (gr. k-3). lib. bdg. 11.80 (978-0-613-21390-5(4)) Tandem Library Bks.

—Curious George Goes Camping. 1999. (gr. k-3). lib. bdg. 11.80 (978-0-613-21391-2(2)) Tandem Library Bks.

—Curious George Goes to a Costume Party. Vipah Interactive Staff, illus. 2001. (Curious George Ser.). 24p. (J). (gr. k-3). tchr. ed. 12.95 (978-0-618-06564-6(4)) Houghton Mifflin Co. Trade & Reference Div.

—Curious George Goes to School. Rey, Margret, illus. 2002. (Curious George TV Bks.). (Illus.). (J). 11.87 (978-0-7587-2316-1(4)) Book Wholesalers, Inc.

—Curious George Goes to the Aquarium. Rey, Margret, illus. 2002. (Curious George TV Bks.). (Illus.). (J). 11.87 (978-0-7587-2317-8(2)) Book Wholesalers, Inc.

—Curious George Goes to the Beach. 1999. (gr. k-3). lib. bdg. 11.80 (978-0-613-21392-9(0)) Tandem Library Bks.

—Curious George in the Big City. Weston, Martha, illus. 2001. (Curious George Ser.). 24p. (J). (gr. k-3). pap. 3.95 (978-0-618-15240-7(7)) Houghton Mifflin Co. Trade & Reference Div.

—Curious George, the Movie: Sticker Fun Book. 2006. (Illus.). 8p. (J). (ps-k). 6.99 (978-0-618-60586-6(X)) Houghton Mifflin Co.

—Curious George Visits the Zoo. Rey, Margret, illus. 2002. (Curious George TV Bks.). (Illus.). (J). 11.87 (978-0-7587-2323-9(7)) Book Wholesalers, Inc.

Rey, Margret & Rey, H. A. Curious George & the Bunny. 1998. (Curious George Ser.). (Illus.). 12p. (J). (gr. k-ps). bds. 5.95 (978-0-395-89922-9(2)) Houghton Mifflin Co. Trade & Reference Div.

—Curious George & the Dumptruck. 1999. (Curious George Ser.). (Illus.). 24p. (J). (gr. k-3). tchr. ed. 12.95 (978-0-395-97832-0(7)) Houghton Mifflin Co. Trade & Reference Div.

—Curious George & the Dumptruck. Vipah Interactive Staff, illus. 1999. (Curious George Ser.). 24p. (J). (gr. k-3). pap. 3.95 (978-0-395-97836-8(X)) Houghton Mifflin Co. Trade & Reference Div.

—Curious George & the Hot Air Balloon. 1998. (Curious George Ser.). (Illus.). 24p. (J). (gr. k-3). tchr. ed. 12.95 (978-0-395-91918-7(5)) Houghton Mifflin Co. Trade & Reference Div.

—Curious George & the Hot Air Balloon. Vipah Interactive Staff, illus. 1998. (Curious George Ser.). 24p. (J). (gr. k-3). pap. 3.95 (978-0-395-91909-5(6)) Houghton Mifflin Co. Trade & Reference Div.

—Curious George & the Puppies. 1998. (Curious George Ser.). (Illus.). 24p. (J). (gr. k-3). pap. 3.95 (978-0-395-91215-7(6)); tchr. ed. 12.95 (978-0-395-91217-1(2)) Houghton Mifflin Co. Trade & Reference Div.

—Curious George at the Parade. 1999. (Curious George Ser.). (Illus.). 24p. (J). (gr. k-3). pap. 3.95 (978-0-395-97837-5(8)); tchr. ed. 12.95 (978-0-395-97833-7(5)) Houghton Mifflin Co. Trade & Reference Div.

—Curious George Feeds the Animals. 1998. (Curious George Ser.). (Illus.). 24p. (J). (gr. k-3). pap. 3.95 (978-0-395-91910-1(X)) Houghton Mifflin Co. Trade & Reference Div.

—Curious George Goes Camping. 1999. (Curious George Ser.). (Illus.). 24p. (J). (gr. k-3). tchr. ed. 12.95 (978-0-395-97831-3(9)) Houghton Mifflin Co. Trade & Reference Div.

—Curious George Goes Camping. Interactive, Vipah, illus. 1999. (Curious George Ser.). 32p. (J). (gr. k-3). pap. 3.95 (978-0-395-97835-1(1)) Houghton Mifflin Co. Trade & Reference Div.

—Curious George Goes to a Chocolate Factory. 1998. (Curious George Ser.). (Illus.). 24p. (J). (gr. k-3). tchr. ed. 12.95 (978-0-395-91216-4(4)) Houghton Mifflin Co. Trade & Reference Div.

—Curious George Goes to a Movie. 1998. (Curious George Ser.). (Illus.). 24p. (J). (gr. k-3). pap. 3.95 (978-0-395-91906-4(1)); tchr. ed. 12.95 (978-0-395-91901-9(0)) Houghton Mifflin Co. Trade & Reference Div.

—Curious George in the Snow. 1998. (Curious George Ser.). (Illus.). 24p. (J). (gr. k-3). tchr. ed. 12.00 (978-0-395-91902-6(9)) Houghton Mifflin Co. Trade & Reference Div.

—Curious George Learns Phonics & Spelling. 1998. (Curious George Ser.). (J). (ps-2). 24.72 (978-0-395-85431-0(8)) Houghton Mifflin Co.

—Curious George Makes Pancakes. 1998. (Curious George Ser.). (Illus.). 24p. (J). (gr. k-3). tchr. ed. 12.95 (978-0-395-91903-3(7)) Houghton Mifflin Co. Trade & Reference Div.

—Curious George Makes Pancakes. Interactive, Vipah, illus. 1998. (Curious George Ser.). 24p. (J). (gr. k-3). pap. 3.95 (978-0-395-91908-8(8)) Houghton Mifflin Co. Trade & Reference Div.

—Curious George Visits a Toy Store. Weston, Martha, illus. 2002. 24p. (J). (gr. k-3). tchr. ed. 12.00 (978-0-618-06398-7(6)) Houghton Mifflin Co. Trade & Reference Div.

—Curious George's ABCs. Rey, H. A., illus. 1998. (Curious George Ser.). (Illus.). 12p. (J). (gr. k-ps). bds. 5.95 (978-0-395-89925-0(7)) Houghton Mifflin Co. Trade & Reference Div.

—Curious George's Are You Curious? Rey, H. A., illus. 1998. (Curious George Ser.). (Illus.). 16p. (J). (gr. k-ps). bds. 5.95 (978-0-395-89924-3(9)) Houghton Mifflin Co. Trade & Reference Div.

—Curious George's Dream. 1998. (Curious George Ser.). (Illus.). 24p. (J). (gr. k-3). tchr. ed. 12.95 (978-0-395-91905-7(3)) Houghton Mifflin Co. Trade & Reference Div.

—Curious George's Dream. Vipah Interactive Staff, illus. 1998. (Curious George Ser.). 24p. (J). (gr. k-3). pap. 3.95 (978-0-395-91911-8(8)) Houghton Mifflin Co. Trade & Reference Div.

—Curious George's First Day of School. Hines, Anna Grossnickle, illus. 2005. 24p. (J). (gr. k-3). pap. 3.95 (978-0-618-60564-4(9)) Houghton Mifflin Co. Trade & Reference Div.

—Curious George's Opposites. 1998. (Curious George Ser.). (Illus.). 16p. (J). (gr. k-ps). bds. 5.95 (978-0-395-89923-6(0)) Houghton Mifflin Co. Trade & Reference Div.

Rey, Margret & Rey, H. A., creators. Curious George Goes Fishing. 2001. (Curious George Ser.). (Illus.). 24p. (J). (gr. k-ps). bds. 5.95 (978-0-618-12071-0(8)) Houghton Mifflin Co. Trade & Reference Div.

Rey, Margret, et al. Curious George Goes to a Costume Party. Weston, Martha, illus. 2001. (Curious George Ser.). 24p. (J). (gr. k-3). pap. 3.95 (978-0-618-06569-1(5)) Houghton Mifflin Co. Trade & Reference Div.

Vipah Interactive Staff. Curious George & the Dumptruck. 1999. (Curious George Ser.). (J). (ps-2). 10.75 (978-0-606-17365-0(X)) Tandem Library Bks.

—Curious George at the Parade. 1999. (Curious George Ser.). (J). (ps-2). 10.75 (978-0-606-17366-7(8)) Tandem Library Bks.

—Curious George Goes Camping. 1999. (Curious George Ser.). (J). (ps-2). 10.75 (978-0-606-17367-4(6)) Tandem Library Bks.

—Curious George Goes to the Beach. 1999. (Curious George Ser.). (J). (ps-2). 10.75 (978-0-606-17368-1(4)) Tandem Library Bks.

Weston, Martha. Curious George Goes to a Costume Party. 2001. (Curious George Ser.). (Illus.). (J). 10.75 (978-0-606-21931-0(5)) Tandem Library Bks.

Weston, Martha, illus. Curious George in the Big City. 2001. (Curious George Ser.). 24p. (J). (gr. k-3). tchr. ed. 12.95 (978-0-618-15252-0(0)) Houghton Mifflin Co. Trade & Reference Div.

—Curious George Takes a Train. 2002. 24p. (J). (gr. k-3). pap. 3.95 (978-0-618-06567-7(9)); tchr. ed. 12.00 (978-0-618-06566-0(0)) Houghton Mifflin Co. Trade & Reference Div.

—Curious George Visits a Toy Store. 2002. 24p. (J). (gr. k-3). pap. 3.95 (978-0-618-06570-7(9)) Houghton Mifflin Co. Trade & Reference Div.

CURIOSITIES AND WONDERS

see also Disasters; Monsters; Unidentified Flying Objects; World Records

Allen, Judy. Unexplained: An Encyclopedia of Curious Phenomena, Strange Superstitions, & Ancient Mysteries. Hook, Richard & Ludlow, Patricia, illus. 2006. 144p. (J). (gr. 5-9). 19.95 (978-0-7534-5950-8(7) , Kingfisher) Houghton Mifflin Co. Trade & Reference Div.

Anthony, Susan C. Facts Plus: An Almanac of Essential Information. 4th rev. ed. 1999. (Illus.). 250p. (J). (gr. 3-8). pap. 15.95 (978-1-879478-19-0(6) , 196) Instructional Resources Co.

Arihood, Wayne. Imaginals: What in the World Is a Clockodile? A Moosepaper? A Caterputer. They're All Imaginals. Eichenbaum, Ken, ed. Schachameyer, Sher, illus. 1998. 40p. (J). (gr. k-6). lib. bdg. 15.95 (978-0-9620271-8-5(9)) Litterati Bks.

Aronson, Marc & Newquist, H. P. For Boys Only: The Biggest, Baddest, Best Book Ever! 2007. (Illus.). 160p. (J). 14.95 (***978-0-312-37706-9(1)**) Feiwel & Friends.

Ash, Russell. Great Wonders of the World. Bonson, Richard, illus. 2006. 64p. (J). pap. 10.99 (978-0-7566-1936-7(X)) Dorling Kindersley Publishing, Inc.

Barron's Educational Editorial Staff. Mysteries, True & False. 1998. (Megascope Ser.). (Illus.). 64p. (J). (gr. 5). 6.95 (978-0-7641-5095-1(2)) Barron's Educational Series, Inc.

Bathroom Readers' Institute Staff. Uncle John's Electrifying Bathroom Reader for Kids Only! 2003. (gr. 5-8). lib. bdg. 22.20 (978-0-613-67438-6(3)) Tandem Library Bks.

Bathroom Readers' Institute Staff, contrib. by. Uncle John's Electrifying Bathroom Reader for Kids Only! 2003. (Bathroom Readers Institute Ser.: 2). (Illus.). 324p. (J). pap. 12.95 (978-1-59223-021-1(0)) Advantage Pubs. Group.

Behr, Alexandra. Where Did They Go? 2005. (Illus.). 32p. (J). 18.50 (978-0-7910-8774-9(3) , Chelsea Hse.) Facts On File, Inc.

Blackwood, Gary L. Enigmatic Events. 2005. (Unsolved History Ser.). (Illus.). 72p. (J). (gr. 3-7). lib. bdg. (978-0-7614-1889-4(X) , Benchmark Bks.) Cavendish, Marshall Corp.

—Extraordinary Events & Oddball Occurrences. 1999. (Secrets of the Unexplained Ser.). (Illus.). 80p. (J). (gr. 5-9). lib. bdg. 29.93 (978-0-7614-0748-5(0) , Benchmark Bks.) Cavendish, Marshall Corp.

—Secrets of the Unexplained - Group 1, 3 bks., Set. Incl. Alien Astronauts. 80p. lib. bdg. 29.93 (978-0-7614-0469-9(4)); Fateful Forebodings. 64p. lib. bdg. 28.50 (978-0-7614-0467-5(8)); Paranormal Powers. 80p. lib. bdg. 28.50 (978-0-7614-0468-2(6)); (J). (gr. 5-9). 1998. (Illus.). 1999. Set lib. bdg. 85.50 (978-0-7614-0466-8(X) , Benchmark Bks.) Cavendish, Marshall Corp.

Blattner, Don. Seven Wonders of the World & More. 1998. (Illus.). 96p. (YA). (gr. 5). pap. 10.95 (978-1-58037-073-8(X)) Twain, Mark Media, Inc. Pubs.

Brant, Cherie. Legends of Ventura County. 2003. per. 9.99 (978-0-9722936-4-8(7) , Legends1) Del Sol Pubns.

Brassey, Richard. Nessie the Loch Ness Monster. 2003. (Illus.). 24p. (J). pap. 7.99 (978-1-85881-309-7(3)) Orion Bks. Ltd. GBR. *Dist:* Trafalgar Square Publishing.

Brettle, Jane. Lots to Do. 1999. (Illus.). 10p. (J). pap. 3.95 (978-1-57717-101-0(2)) New Line Bks.

Buckley, James. Scholastic Book of Firsts. Sheldon, David, illus. 2005. (Scholastic Book of Firsts Ser.). 320p. (J). pap. 8.95 (978-0-439-67607-6(X) , Scholastic Reference) Scholastic, Inc.

Bulloch, Ivan & James, Diane. Things We Like Best! 2004. (My Turn Ser.). (Illus.). 12p. (J). (ps-k). bds. 6.95 (978-1-58728-012-2(4) , Two Can Publishing) T&N Children's Publishing.

Bunnell, James. Night Orbs. 2003. (Illus.). 296p. per. 22.00 (978-0-9709249-2-6(5)) Lacey Publishing Co.

Burns, Jan. Crop Circles. 2005. (Wonders of the World Ser.). (Illus.). 48p. (J). (gr. 4-8). lib. bdg. 26.20 (978-0-7377-3063-0(3) , Greenhaven Pr., Inc.) Thomson Gale.

Butterfield, Moira. Why? A Child's Book of Questions & Answers. 2000. (Illus.). 64p. (YA). (ps up). 17.95 (978-1-902618-93-7(9)) Element Children's Bks.

Calkhoven, Laurie & Herndon, Ryan. Guinness World Records: Fearless Feats. 2006. (Illus.). 103p. (J). pap. 4.99 (978-0-439-71565-2(2)) Scholastic, Inc.

Campbell, Rod. What's That? 2003. (Illus.). 12p. (J). bds. 7.99 (978-1-85292-001-2(7) , Campbell Bks.) Pan Macmillan GBR. *Dist:* Trafalgar Square Publishing.

—Who's That? 2003. (Illus.). 10p. (J). pap. 7.99 (978-1-85292-031-9(9) , Campbell Bks.) Pan Macmillan GBR. *Dist:* Trafalgar Square Publishing.

Carangelo, Audrey. How Unusual! 2006. (Illus.). 16p. (***978-0-439-75712-6(6)**) Scholastic, Inc.

Carpino, Nancy. What Makes a Snowflake Grow? McNeilis, Jessica, illus. 1999. 48p. (Orig.). (J). (gr. k-7). pap. 6.95 (978-1-928675-00-6(X)) Carpino Bks.

Cerulean, Susan, et al, eds. Between Two Rivers: Stories from the Red Hills to the Gulf. Meyer, Nancy, illus. 2004. 352p. (YA). per. 21.95 (978-0-9759339-0-9(6)) Red Hills Writers Project.

A Child's First Library of Learning, 30 bks. Incl. Animal Friends. Time-Life Staff. (Illus.). 88p. (ps-4). 1999. 14.95 (978-0-8094-4849-4(1)); Animals in Action. (Illus.). 88p. (ps-2). 1999. 14.95 (978-0-8094-4869-2(6)); Dangerous Animals. Time-Life Books Editors. Kinney, Karin, ed. (Illus.). 88p. (ps-3). 1996. 16.00 (978-0-8094-9480-4(9)); Everyday Life. Cfl. (Illus.). 88p. (ps-4). 1999. 14.95 (978-0-8094-4865-4(3)); Explorers & Adventurers. Time-Life Books Editors. Fallow, Allan, ed. (Illus.). 88p. (ps-3). 1996. lib. bdg. (978-0-8094-9482-8(5)); Famous Places. Gakken Co. Ltd. Editors. Time-Life Books Editors, tr. (Illus.). 88p. (gr. 1-4). 1999. 14.95 (978-0-8094-4893-7(9)); Feelings & Manners. Time-Life Books Editors. Fallow, Allan, ed. (Illus.). 88p. (ps-3). 1997. 14.95 (978-0-8094-9483-5(3)); Flowers & Trees. Time-Life Staff. (Illus.). 88p. (gr. 1-4). 1999. 14.95 (978-0-8094-4857-9(2)); Health & Safety. Time-Life Books Editors. 1996. (978-0-8094-9479-8(5)); How Things Work in Your Home. Time-Life Books Editors. (Illus.). 88p. (gr. 1-4). 1999. 14.95 (978-0-8094-4873-9(4)); Insect World. Time-Life Books Editors. (Illus.). 88p. (ps-3). 1999. 14.95 (978-0-8094-4841-8(6)); Science Starter. Time-Life Books Editors. (Illus.). 88p. (gr. 1-4). 1999. 14.95 (978-0-8094-4881-4(5)); Sky & Earth. Time-Life Books Editors. (Illus.). 88p. (gr. 1-4). 1999. 14.95 (978-0-8094-4837-1(8)); Things Around Us. Time-Life Staff. (Illus.). 88p. (ps-2). 1999. 14.95 (978-0-8094-4845-6(9)); Things to Do. Gakken Co. Ltd. Editors & Time-Life Books Editors. (Illus.). 88p. (gr. 1-4). 1999. 14.95 (978-0-8094-4897-5(1)); Wheels & Wings. Gakken Co. Ltd. Editors. Time-Life Books Editors, tr. (Illus.). 88p. (gr. 1-4). 1999. 14.95 (978-0-8094-4861-6(0)); Where Things Come From. Time-Life Books Editors. Fallow, Allan, ed. (Illus.). 88p. (ps-3). 1997. (978-0-8094-9484-2(1)); Wind & Weather. Gakken Co. Ltd. Editors. Time-Life Books Editors, tr. (Illus.). 88p. (gr. 1-4). 1999. 14.95 (978-0-8094-4829-6(7)); World We Live In. Gakken Co. Ltd. Editors. Time-Life Books Editors, tr. (Illus.). 88p. (gr. 1-4). 1999. 14.95 (978-0-8094-4885-2(8)); (J). 403.88 (978-0-8094-9499-6(X)) Time-Life, Inc.

Clarke, Phil, et al. Mysteries & Marvels of Science - Internet Linked. 2005. (Mysteries & Marvels Ser.). 96p. (J). 19.95 (978-0-7945-0922-4(3) , Usborne) EDC Publishing.

Curiosidades y Ejemplos.Tr. of Curiosities & Examples. (SPA.). (J). (gr. 4-5). 29.95 (978-968-416-014-9(3) , 204U) Fernandez USA Publishing.

Dalby, L. Mysteries & Marvels of Nature. 2004. 128p. (J). lib. bdg. 27.95 (978-1-58086-610-1(7) , Usborne) EDC Publishing.

De Angelis, Therese. Wonders of the Ancient World. 1998. (Costume, Tradition & Culture). (Illus.). 64p. (YA). (gr. 5 up). 19.75 (978-0-7910-5170-2(6) , Chelsea Hse.) Facts On File, Inc.

Dibben, Colin. Wonders of the World. 2007. (Illus.). 48p. (J). (***978-1-60044-263-6(3)**) Rourke Publishing, LLC.

Dils, Tracey E. Real-Life Strange Encounters. 1998. (Illus.). 160p. (J). (gr. 5-8). pap. 3.99 (978-0-87406-866-5(5) , Willowisp Pr.) Darby Creek Publishing.

DK Publishing Staff. Great Wonders of the Natural World. 2007. 64p. (J). (gr. 3-6). 19.99 (978-0-7566-2980-9(2)) Dorling Kindersley Publishing, Inc.

Doherty, Gillian, et al, eds. The Usborne Book of the Paranormal. 2000. (Paranormal Guides Ser.). (Illus.). 192p. (YA). (gr. 4 up). pap. 16.95 (978-0-7460-3390-6(7)) EDC Publishing.

Dorling Kindersley Publishing Staff. DK Illustrated Factopedia. 2006. 456p. (J). 14.99 (978-0-7566-1472-0(4)) Dorling Kindersley Publishing, Inc.

—Myths & Monsters. 2003. (gr. 3-6). lib. bdg. 14.15 (978-0-613-75210-7(4)) Tandem Library Bks.

Dorling Kindersley Publishing Staff & Buller, Laura. Myths & Monsters. 2003. (Secret Worlds Ser.). (Illus.). 96p. (J). pap. 5.99 (978-0-7894-9226-5(1)) Dorling Kindersley Publishing, Inc.

Dowswell, Paul. Witches & Wizards. 2001. (Discovery Ser.). (Illus.). 64p. (gr. 4-7). 14.95 (978-0-7548-0587-8(5)) Anness Publishing GBR. *Dist:* National Bk. Network.

Duey. Freaky Facts about Natural Disasters. 2000. (J). 11.64 (978-0-606-19709-0(5)) Tandem Library Bks.

Eager, Gregory B. Wonders of the World Fact Cards. Taminga, Jean, illus. 1999. 60p. (J). (gr. 4-10). ring bd. 32.00 (978-1-884925-72-6(3)) Toucan Valley Pubns., Inc.

Eliot, Simon. Everything You Need to Know about the World. Maxey, Timon, illus. 2007. 192p. (gr. 3-7). pap. 8.95 (***978-0-312-35965-2(9)** , St. Martin's Griffin) St. Martin's Pr.

Fain, David. Spongebob Squarepants Trivia Book. 2000. (SpongeBob SquarePants Ser.). (Illus.). 48p. (J). (gr. 1-4). pap. 3.99 (978-0-689-84018-0(7) , Simon Spotlight) Simon & Schuster Children's Publishing.

—Spongebob Squarepants Trivia Book. 2000. (gr. 3-6). lib. bdg. 10.65 (978-0-613-31745-0(9)) Tandem Library Bks.

Falstein, Mark. World Geography Mysteries, Grades 4-6: Research-Based Mysteries for Super Sleuths to Solve. Clark Editorial and Design Staff, ed. Kennedy, Kelly, illus. 1998. 96p. pap., tchr. ed. 11.99 (978-0-88160-261-6(2) , LW-382, Learning Works, The) Creative Teaching Pr., Inc.

Farndon, John. Do Not Open: An Encyclopedia of the World's Best-Kept Secrets. 2007. 192p. (YA). (gr. 5-8). 24.99 (***978-0-7566-3205-2(6)**) Dorling Kindersley Publishing, Inc.

French, Jackie. The Little Book of Big Questions. Newbigging, Martha, illus. 2000. 128p. (J). (gr. 3-7). 19.95 (978-1-55037-655-5(1)); pap. 9.95 (978-1-55037-654-8(3)) Annick Pr., Ltd. CAN. *Dist:* Firefly Bks., Ltd.

Gill, Janie S. What If? Morgan, Karen O. L., illus. 1999. 23p. 5.95 (978-0-89868-436-0(6)); pap. 3.95 (978-0-89868-435-3(8)) ARO Publishing Co.

—What If...? Morgan, Karen O. L., illus. 1999. (Predictable Word Bks.). 23p. (J). (ps-3). lib. bdg. 10.95 (978-0-89868-434-6(X)) ARO Publishing Co.

C D

Gordon, Sharon. Adivina Quién, 6 bks., Set. Incl. Adivina Quién Atrapa. lib. bdg. 22.79 (978-0-7614-2383-6(4)); Adivina Quién Baja en Picada. (Illus.). lib. bdg. 22.79 (978-0-7614-2387-4(7)); Adivina Quién Cambia. (Illus.). lib. bdg. 22.79 (978-0-7614-2380-5(X)); Adivina Quién Ruge. (Illus.). lib. bdg. 22.79 (978-0-7614-2386-7(9)); Adivina Quién Se Esconde. (Illus.). lib. bdg. 22.79 (978-0-7614-2385-0(0)); Adivina Quién Se Zambulle. lib. bdg. 22.79 (***978-0-7614-2381-2(8)***); (J). 2006. (SPA.). 32p. 2007. Set lib. bdg. 136.71 (***978-0-7614-2379-9(6)***) Cavendish, Marshall Corp.

—Guess Who (Adivina Quién), 6 bks., Set. Incl. Guess Who Changes (Adivina Quién Cambia) lib. bdg. 22.79 (978-0-7614-2461-1(X)); Guess Who Dives (Adivina Quién Se Zambulle) (Illus.). lib. bdg. 22.79 (978-0-7614-2462-8(8)); Guess Who Grabs (Adivina Quién Atrapa) lib. bdg. 22.79 (978-0-7614-2464-2(4)); Guess Who Hides (Adivina Quién Se Esconde) (Illus.). lib. bdg. 22.79 (978-0-7614-2465-9(2)); Guess Who Roars (Adivina Quién Ruge) (Illus.). lib. bdg. 22.79 (978-0-7614-2466-6(0)); Guess Who Swoops (Adivina Quién Baja en Picada) (Illus.). lib. bdg. 22.79 (978-0-7614-2468-0(7)); 32p. (J). 2006. (ENG & SPA.). 2007. Set lib. bdg. 136.71 (***978-0-7614-2459-8(8)***) Cavendish, Marshall Corp.

Grabowski, John F. Mysterious Places. 2004. (Illus.). 112p. (gr. 7-10). 29.95 (978-1-59018-445-5(9)) Thomson Gale.

Guiberson, Brenda Z. Tales of the Haunted Deep. Godwin, Laura, ed. Guiberson, Brenda Z., illus. rev. ed. 2000. (Redfeather Chapter Bk.). (Illus.). 80p. (J). (gr. 3-6). 16.95 (978-0-8050-6057-7(X) , Holt, Henry & Co. Bks. For Young Readers) Holt, Henry & Co.

Guinness World Records: Activity Book. 2002. (Illus.). 96p. (J). (gr. k-7). pap. 3.99 (978-1-57759-464-2(9)) Dalmatian Pr.

Guinness World Records: Sticker Fun. 2002. (Illus.). 32p. (J). pap. 3.99 (978-1-57759-459-8(2)) Dalmatian Pr.

Hamilton, John. Fantasy & Folklore. 2005. (Fantasy & Folklore Ser.). (J). (gr. 4-8). lib. bdg. 145.26 (978-1-59197-710-0(X) , ABDO & Daughters) ABDO Publishing Co.

Harris, Pamela. Hot, cold, shy, bold: Looking at Opposites. unabr. ed. 2002. (Illus.). 32p. (J). (ps-k). (978-1-55074-322-7(8)) Kids Can Pr., Ltd.

Hegarty, Carol, ed. Strange but True Stories Book 5. 2006. (YA). per. 6.95 (***978-1-59905-014-0(5)*** , SA0145) Saddleback Educational Publishing.

Heinemann Educational Ltd. Publishing Staff. Mysteries of the Past Package. 2004. pap. 214.75 (978-1-4109-1389-0(9)) Raintree.

Henderson, Lyndsey. Fyn (Underwater Facts) 2001. (Teacher's Pet Ser.). 48p. (J). 4.95 (978-0-439-17348-3(5)) Scholastic, Inc.

—Outrageous (Weird & Fun Facts) 2001. (Teacher's Pet Ser.). 48p. (J). 4.95 (978-0-439-17347-6(7)) Scholastic, Inc.

Herbst, Judith. Lands of Mystery. (Unexplained Ser.). (Illus.). 48p. (J). 2005. lib. bdg. 26.60 (978-0-8225-1630-9(6)); 2004. pap. 7.95 (978-0-8225-2407-6(4)) Lerner Publishing Group.

Hicks, Donna E. The Most Fascinating Places on Earth. 2005. (Illus.). 48p. (J). (978-1-4027-2899-0(9) , Sterling/Main St.) Sterling Publishing Co., Inc.

Hill, Nancy S. The One Year Book of Did You Know Devotions for Kids. 2002. (Illus.). 432p. (J). per. 12.99 (978-0-8423-6184-2(7)) Tyndale Hse. Pubs.

Hobbie, K. R., et al. The Little Giant Book of Weird & Wacky Facts. 2005. (Illus.). 352p. (J). (ps-7). pap. 6.95 (978-1-4027-1548-8(X)) Sterling Publishing Co., Inc.

Horn, Randy. You Gotta be Kidding! 2006. (Illus.). 416p. (J). pap. 8.95 (978-0-7611-4365-9(3)) Workman Publishing Co., Inc.

Innes, Brian. The Cosmic Joker. 1999. (Unsolved Mysteries Ser.). 48p. (YA). (gr. 3 up). lib. bdg. 25.69 (978-0-8172-5487-2(0)) Raintree.

—The Cosmic Joker. 1999. (Unsolved Mysteries Ser.). (Illus.). 48p. (J). (gr. 3-7). pap. 8.05 (978-0-8172-5849-8(3)) Steck-Vaughn.

—Mysteries of the Ancients. 1999. (Unsolved Mysteries Ser.). (Illus.). 48p. (YA). (gr. 3 up). lib. bdg. 25.69 (978-0-8172-5481-0(1)) Raintree.

—Mysterious Healing. 1999. (Unsolved Mysteries Ser.). (Illus.). (YA). (gr. 3 up). lib. bdg. 25.69 (978-0-8172-5489-6(7)) Raintree.

—Powers of the Mind. 1999. (Unsolved Mysteries Ser.). (Illus.). 48p. (J). (gr. 3-7). pap. 8.05 (978-0-8172-5850-4(7)) Steck-Vaughn.

—Unsolved Mysteries, 8 bks., Set. 1998. (Unsolved Mysteries Ser.). (Illus.). (YA). (gr. 3). lib. bdg. 205.52 (978-0-8172-5483-4(8)) Raintree.

Jones, Victoria. Wonders of the World Dot-to-Dot. 2004. (Illus.). 80p. (J). pap. 5.95 (978-1-4027-1028-5(3)) Sterling Publishing Co., Inc.

Jr. Graphic Mysteries, 6 bks., Set. Incl. Atlantis : The Mystery of the Lost City. DeMolay, Jack. (Illus.). 24p. lib. bdg. 21.25 (978-1-4042-3407-9(1) , PowerKids Pr.); Bermuda Triangle : The Disappearance of Flight 19. DeMolay, Jack. lib. bdg. 21.25 (978-1-4042-3404-8(7) , PowerKids Pr.); Bigfoot : A North American Legend. DeMolay, Jack. (Illus.). 24p. lib. bdg. 21.25 (978-1-4042-3405-5(5)); Ghosts in Amityville : The Haunted House. Marts, Michael. (Illus.). 24p. lib. bdg. 21.25 (978-1-4042-3402-4(0) , PowerKids Pr.); Loch Ness Monster : Scotland's Mystery Beast. DeMolay, Jack. (Illus.). 24p. lib. bdg. 21.25 (978-1-4042-3406-2(3)); UFOs : The Roswell Incident. DeMolay, Jack. (Illus.). 24p. lib. bdg. 21.25 (978-1-4042-3403-1(9) , PowerKids Pr.); (J). (gr. 2-6). 2007. 2006. Set lib. bdg. 127.50 (978-1-4042-3552-6(3)) Rosen Publishing Group, Inc., The.

Kallen, Stuart A. The Highest Waterfall. 2003. (Extreme Places Ser.). (Illus.). 47p. (J). 26.20 (978-0-7377-1881-2(1)) Thomson Gale.

Kelly Publishing Staff, ed. Ripley's Believe It or Not! Expect the Unexpected. 2006. (Ripley's Believe It or Not Ser.: Bk. 3). (Illus.). 256p. (J). 27.95 (978-1-893951-12-9(X)) Ripley Entertainment, Inc.

Khan, Hena. How to Be a Know-It-All on Almost Any Subject You Can Think Of. 2004. (How to Survive Anything Club Ser.). (Illus.). 80p. (J). pap. (978-0-439-57907-0(4)) Scholastic, Inc.

Lara, Jose Luis Trueba. Descubrelas Diez Maravillas. 2006. Tr. of Discovery...The Ten Wonders. (SPA.). (J). (gr. 4-5). 18.95 (978-970-29-1058-9(7) , AT33272) Santillana, S.A. de C.V., Editorial MEX. *Dist:* Santillana USA Publishing Co., Inc.

Leslie, Jeremy & Roberts, David. Pick Me Up: Stuff You Need to Know. 2006. (Illus.). 352p. (J). 29.99 (978-0-7566-2159-9(3)) Dorling Kindersley Publishing, Inc.

Lewis, Naomi. Where Will You Be in 2000 A. D.? Averett, Cary D., illus. 1999. 32p. (J). (ps-6). pap. 5.95 (978-0-9673205-0-2(X)) Where Will You Be in 2000 A.D., Inc.

Llewellyn, Claire. Great Discoveries & Amazing Adventures: The Stories of Hidden Marvels & Lost Treasures. 2004. (Illus.). 80p. (J). (gr. 4-6). 18.95 (978-0-7534-5783-2(0) , Kingfisher) Houghton Mifflin Co. Trade & Reference Div.

—How Things Work. Kent, Phillips and Jones Assoc. Staff, illus. 2000. (First Encyclopedia Ser.). 96p. (J). (ps-3). pap. 7.95 (978-0-590-47530-3(4)) Scholastic, Inc.

Lynette, Rachel. Stonehedge. 2004. (Illus.). (gr. 4-7). 26.20 (978-0-7377-1562-0(6)) Thomson Gale.

Mann, Elizabeth. The Great Wall: The Story of 4,000 Miles of Earth & Stone That Turned a Nation into a Fortress. Witschonke, Alan, illus. 2003. (Wonders of the World Ser.). 48p. (J). (ps up). 22.95 (978-0-9650493-2-0(9)) Mikaya Pr.

Martin, Mary-Jane. Let Me Put It This Way. 2004. (Illus.). 32p. 11.95 (978-0-9730583-1-4(5)) Lion & Mouse Tales, Inc. CAN. *Dist:* Hushion Hse. Publishing, Ltd.

Martin, Michael. Near-Death Experiences. 2004. (Unexplained Ser.). (Illus.). 32p. (J). lib. bdg. 22.60 (978-0-7368-2719-5(6)) Capstone Pr., Inc.

Masoff, Joy. Oh, Yuck! The Encyclopedia of Everything Nasty. 2000. (J). (978-0-606-20303-6(6)) Tandem Library Bks.

—Oh, Yuck! The Encyclopedia of Everything Nasty. (Illus.). (J). 119.60 (978-0-7611-2529-7(9) , 22529); 2000. 224p. (gr. 3-7). pap. 14.95 (978-0-7611-0771-2(1) , 10771) Workman Publishing Co., Inc.

—Oh Yuck! The Encyclopedia of Everything Nasty. Sirrell, Terry, illus. 2000. 212p. (J). (ps-7). lib. bdg. 24.55 (978-0-613-62150-2(6)) Tandem Library Bks.

Mason, Jane & Hines Stephens, Sarah. History's Mysteries: The Dead, the Doomed, & the Buried. 2004. (History Channel Ser.). 88p. (J). pap. 4.99 (978-0-439-55706-1(2) , Scholastic Paperbacks) Scholastic, Inc.

Masters, Deborah. The Magical Wisdom of Kids. 2005. (Illus.). 108p. per. 18.95 (978-0-9740465-1-8(5)) Global Truth Publishing.

Mattern, Joanne & Herndon, Ryan, compiled by. Guinness World Records: Extraordinary Records of Unusual Facts & Feats. 2005. (Illus.). 90p. (J). pap. (978-0-439-79192-2(8)) Scholastic, Inc.

McCormick, Maggie. Terror Trail: Tales of Mystery & the Unexplained from Around the World. 1999. (978-1-84100-267-5(4)) Quadrillion Publishing.

Mericle, Charice. So Many Strange Things. 2001. (978-0-316-60000-2(8)) Little Brown & Co.

Microhabitats, 36 books,6 pack., Set. 2004. (Illus.). pap. 243.00 (978-1-4109-1264-0(7)) Raintree.

Millard, Anne. Misterios de las Piramides. (Coleccion Misterios De). (SPA., Illus.). 48p. (YA). (gr. 5-8). 19.95 (978-84-348-5690-5(5) , SM6076) SM Ediciones ESP. *Dist:* AIMS International Bks., Inc., Lectorum Pubns., Inc.

Miller, Margaret. Where Does It Go? 1998. (Illus.). 24p. (J). (ps-3). pap. 5.95 (978-0-688-15851-4(X) , Harper Trophy) HarperCollins Pubs.

—Who Uses This? 1999. (Illus.). 40p. (J). (ps-3). pap. 5.95 (978-0-688-17057-8(9) , Harper Trophy) HarperCollins Pubs.

Morgan, Matthew & Barnes, Samantha. Children's Miscellany Too. Catlow, Niki, illus. 2006. 128p. (J). 12.95 (978-0-8118-5639-3(9)) Chronicle Bks. LLC.

Morris, Neil. Wonders of Our World, 10 bks. Incl. Caves. 1995. pap. (978-0-86505-842-2(3)); Deserts. 1995. pap. (978-0-86505-839-2(3)); Earthquakes. 1998. pap. (978-0-86505-844-6(X)); Forests. 1998. pap. (978-0-86505-845-3(8)); Hurricanes & Tornadoes. 1998. pap. (978-0-86505-843-9(1)); Mountains. 1995. pap. (978-0-86505-841-5(5)); Oceans. 1995. pap. (978-0-86505-840-8(7)); Rivers & Lakes. 1998. pap. (978-0-86505-846-0(6)); Rocks & Minerals. 1998. pap. (978-0-86505-847-7(4)); Volcanoes. 1995. pap. (978-0-86505-838-5(5)); 32p. (J). (gr. 3-4). (Illus.). 2000. Set pap. (978-0-86505-849-1(0)) Crabtree Publishing Co.

Morse, Jenifer. Scholastic Book of World Records 2007. 2006. 320p. (J). pap. 9.99 (978-0-439-82766-9(3) , Scholastic Reference) Scholastic, Inc.

Morse, Jenifer. Scholastic Book of World Records Ultimate Quiz Challenge. 2007. 176p. (J). (gr. 3-7). pap. 7.99 (***978-0-439-88971-1(5)*** , Scholastic Reference) Scholastic, Inc.

Morse, Jennifer. School Book of World Records 08. 2007. 320p. (J). pap. 9.99 (***978-0-439-91658-5(5)*** , Scholastic Reference) Scholastic, Inc.

Mullin, Rita T. Animalogy; Weird & Wacky Animal Facts. 1998. (Animal Planet Ser.). (J). (978-0-606-13133-9(7)) Tandem Library Bks.

Myers, Janet Nuzum. Strange Stuff: True Stories of Odd Places & Things. Hagsted, Maj-Britt, illus. 1999. vii, 104p. (J). (gr. 4-7). 19.50 (978-0-208-02405-3(0) , Linnet Bks.) Shoe String Pr., Inc.

Mysteries of the Past, 6 Packs., Set. 2004. pap. 214.65 (978-1-4109-1269-5(8)) Raintree.

Mystery Files, 6 vols., Set. Incl. Bigfoot Caught on Film. Teitelbaum, Michael. 26.00 (978-0-531-12078-1(3)); Cities of the Dead. Rinaldo, Denise. 26.00 (978-0-531-12079-8(1)); Ghosts : Real-Life Ghost Hunter Investigations. Teitelbaum, Michael. 26.00 (978-0-531-12077-4(5)); Mind Readers : The Science of ESP. Rudy, Lisa Jo. 26.00 (978-0-531-12075-0(9)); Mummies Unwrapped. Grace, N. B. 26.00 (978-0-531-12076-7(7)); UFOs. Grace, N. B. (Illus.). 26.00 (***978-0-531-12074-3(0)***); 64p. (J). (gr. 8-12). 2007. , Watts, Franklin (24/7 Ser.). (Illus.). 2008. 150.00 (***978-0-531-12479-6(7)***) Scholastic Library Publishing.

Nathan, Emma. Lugares Conocidos. 2002. (Abre los Ojos y Aprende Serie).Tr. of Eyeopeners: Landmarks. (SPA.). 24p. (J). (-3). 24.94 (978-1-4103-0026-3(9) , Blackbirch Pr., Inc.) Thomson Gale.

Nicholaus, Bret & Lowrie, Paul. Kidchat: 222 Creative Questions to Spark Conversations. 2007. (KidChat Ser.). (Illus.). 128p. (J). pap. 6.99 (***978-1-59643-314-4(0)***) Roaring Brook Pr.

—KidChat Gone Wild! 202 Creative Questions to Unleash the Imagination. 2007. (KidChat Ser.). (Illus.). 128p. (J). (gr. 3 up). pap. 6.99 (***978-1-59643-316-8(7)***) Roaring Brook Pr.

—KidChat Oh, the Places to Go! 204 Creative Questions to Let the Imagination Travel. 2007. (KidChat Ser.). (Illus.). 128p. (J). (gr. 3 up). pap. 6.99 (***978-1-59643-317-5(5)***) Roaring Brook Pr.

—KidChat Too! All-New Questions to Fuel Young Minds & Mouths. 2nd rev. ed. 2007. (KidChat Ser.). (Illus.). 128p. (J). (gr. 3 up). pap. 6.99 (***978-1-59643-315-1(9)***) Roaring Brook Pr.

Orme, David. Don't Try This at Home. 2008. (Trailblazers Ser.). (Illus.). 36p. pap. 7.95 (***978-1-84167-652-4(7)***) Ransom Publishing Ltd. GBR. *Dist:* International Publishers Marketing.

Owl Magazine Editors. Amazing but True. 2003. (Mini-Books Ser.). (Illus.). 96p. (J). (gr. 1 up). pap. 4.95 (978-0-920775-69-1(1) , Owl Bks.) Maple Tree Pr. CAN. *Dist:* Firefly Bks., Ltd.

Oxlade, Chris. The Mystery of Crop Circles. (Can Science Solve? Ser.). (Illus.). 32p. (J). 2006. lib. bdg. 29.29 (***978-1-4034-8333-1(7)***); 1999. (gr. 4-7). lib. bdg. 22.79 (978-1-57572-804-9(4)); 2nd ed. 2006. pap. 7.85 (***978-1-4034-8342-3(6)***); Set 1. 2002. (gr. 4-7). pap. 7.50 (978-1-58810-308-6(0) , 91036) Heinemann Library.

Packard, M. & Ripley's Believe It or Not Editors. Ripley's Believe It or Not! Special Edition 2008. 2007. 144p. (J). pap. 15.99 (***978-0-439-92059-9(0)***) Scholastic, Inc.

Packard, Mary. Mysteries of the Sea. Zalme, Ron, illus. 2005. (Ripley's Believe It of Not! Ser.). 85p. (J). pap. (978-0-439-72563-7(1)) Scholastic, Inc.

—Ripley's Believe It or Not! 144p. (J). 2006. pap. 14.99 (978-0-439-82598-6(9)); 2005. (Illus.). pap. 14.99 (978-0-439-71830-1(9)) Scholastic, Inc.

—Ripley's Believe It or Not! Bizarre Collection. Franson, Leanne, illus. 2004. 361p. (J). pap. 3.99 (978-0-681-02479-3(8)) Scholastic, Inc.

—Strange School Stories. 2004. 86p. (J). pap. (978-0-439-68774-4(8)) Scholastic, Inc.

—Totally Gross. Franson, Leanne, illus. 2004. 85p. (J). (978-0-439-71739-7(6)) Scholastic, Inc.

—Weird, Weird World. Franson, Leanne, illus. 2004. 85p. (J). (978-0-439-63368-0(0)) Scholastic, Inc.

Packard, Mary, ed. Ripley's Believe It or Not! Awesome Collection. Franson, Leanne, illus. 361p. (J). pap. (978-0-681-15435-3(7)) Scholastic, Inc.

—Ripley's Believe It or Not! Bizarre Collection. Franson, Leanne, illus. 2002. (Ripley's Believe It Or Not! Ser.). 963p. (J). (gr. 3). pap. 4.99 (978-0-439-31459-6(3) , Scholastic Paperbacks) Scholastic, Inc.

—Ripley's Believe It or Not! Special Edition 2005. Franson, Leanne, illus. ed. 2001. 144p. (J). pap. 14.95 (978-0-439-26040-4(X)) Scholastic, Inc.

Parks, Peggy J. The Great Barrier Reef. 2004. (Illus.). 48p. (J). (gr. 4-7). 26.20 (978-0-7377-2054-9(9)) Thomson Gale.

Polette, Nancy. What Is This Thing? 2007. (J). pap. 11.95 (***978-1-931334-95-2(1)***) Pieces of Learning.

Poussin, Nichol. Still Spins the Spider of Rennes-le-Chateau. l.t. ed. 2004. Tr. of arraignee tisse sa toile a Rennes-le-Chateaua. (Illus.). 347p. pap. (978-0-9541527-1-0(9) , http//www.keysofantiquity.com) DEK Publishing.

Quadrillion Media Staff. Mysteries of the World (Geklarte u. Ungeklarte Phanomene), Vol. 4. 1998. (Start Me Up Ser.: Vol. 4). 48p. (J). (gr. 3-8). mass mkt. 12.95 (978-1-58185-003-1(4) , Tessloff Publishing) Quadrillion Media LLC.

Quinlan, Susan E. The Case of the Mummified Pigs: And Other Mysteries in Nature. Dewey, Jennifer Owings, illus. 2003. 128p. (YA). (gr. 4-6). 10.95 (978-1-56397-783-1(4)) Boyds Mills Pr.

Raintree Steck-Vaughn Staff. Mysteries of the Ancients. 1998. (Unsolved Mysteries Ser.). (Illus.). (J). pap. 8.05 (978-0-8172-4278-7(3)) Steck-Vaughn.

—Mysteries of the Past Series, 5 bks., Set. 2003. (Illus.). pap. 40.30 (978-1-4109-0127-9(0)) Raintree.

—Wide World, 6 bks. 1998. (Illus.). (gr. 3-7). 113.88 (978-0-8172-5066-9(2)) Raintree.

Raintree Steck-Vaughn Staff, ed. See for Yourself. 1998. 179.98 (978-0-8172-4219-0(8)) Raintree.

Ripley Publishing, creator. Ripley's Believe It or Not! Planet Eccentric! 2005. (Illus.). 256p. (YA). 27.95 (978-1-893951-10-5(3)) Ripley Entertainment, Inc.

Ripley, Robert. Ripley's Believe it or Not! 2004. (Illus.). 256p. 25.95 (978-1-893951-73-0(1)) Ripley Entertainment, Inc.

Ripley Staff. Ripley's Believe It or Not! Teasers, 8 bks. Incl. Fun & Games. lib. bdg. 19.00 (978-1-56065-062-1(1)); Great Sports Performances. lib. bdg. 19.00 (978-1-56065-063-8(X)); (Illus.). 48p. (J). (gr. 3-4). 1991. Set lib. bdg. 152.00 (978-1-56065-660-9(3) , Capstone High/Low Bks.) Capstone Pr., Inc.

Scholastic, Inc. Staff & Ripley, Robert. Awesome Animals. Nagler, Michelle, ed. 2003. (Ripley's Believe It Or Not! Ser.: No. 8). (Illus.). 96p. (J). pap. 4.99 (978-0-439-42981-8(1) , Scholastic Paperbacks) Scholastic, Inc.

Schreiber, Brad. Weird Wonders & Bizarre Blunders: The Official Book of Ridiculous Records. 1998. (Illus.). 88p. (YA). pap. 5.00 (978-0-7881-5220-7(3)) DIANE Publishing Co.

Seuling, Barbara. Three Presidents Died on the Fourth of July: And Other Freaky Facts about the First 25 Presidents. Skeens, Matthew, illus. 2007. (J). lib. bdg. (***978-1-4048-3748-5(5)***) Picture Window Bks.

Shannon, George. True Lies: 10 Tales for You to Judge. O'Brien, John, illus. 1998. 64p. (J). (gr. 3 up). reprint ed. pap. 4.99 (978-0-688-16371-6(8) , Harper Trophy) HarperCollins Pubs.

Smith, A. G. Wonders of the World Coloring Book. 2003. (Illus.). 32p. (J). pap. 3.95 (978-0-486-43044-7(8)) Dover Pubns., Inc.

Smoothey, Marion. Let's Investigate, Group 1. Evans, Ted, illus. Incl. Area & Volume. lib. bdg. 25.64 (978-1-85435-460-0(4)); Circles. lib. bdg. 25.64 (978-1-85435-456-3(6)); Number Patterns. lib. bdg. 25.64 (978-1-85435-458-7(2)); Numbers. lib. bdg. 25.64 (978-1-85435-457-0(4)); Quadrilaterals. lib. bdg. 25.64 (978-1-85435-459-4(0)); Triangles. lib. bdg. 25.64 (978-1-85435-461-7(2)); 64p. (J). (gr. 4-8). 1992. (Illus.). lib. bdg. (978-1-85435-455-6(8)); lib. bdg. (978-1-85435-463-1(9)) Cavendish, Marshall Corp. (Benchmark Bks.).

—Let's Investigate, Group 3. Incl. Calculators. Baum, Ann, illus. 1994. lib. bdg. 25.64 (978-1-85435-777-9(8)); Codes & Sequences. Baum, Ann, illus. 1994. lib. bdg. 25.64 (978-1-85435-774-8(3)); Maps & Scale Drawing. 1996. lib. bdg. 25.64 (978-1-85435-778-6(6)); Ratio & Proportion. 1996. lib. bdg. 25.64 (978-1-85435-776-2(X)); 64p. (J). (gr. 4-8). (Illus.). lib. bdg. (978-1-85435-773-1(5) , Benchmark Bks.) Cavendish, Marshall Corp.

Snyder, Bernadette McCarver. 130 Fun Facts from God's Wonder-Filled World. Sharp, Chris, illus. 2002. 144p. (J). pap. 12.95 (978-0-7648-0925-5(3) , 54528) Liguori Pubns.

Southwell, David & Twist, Sean. Unsolved Political Mysteries. 2007. (J). (***978-1-4042-1083-7(0)***) Rosen Publishing Group, Inc., The.

Spencer, John. Alienigenas. 2000. (Illus.). (J). (978-0-606-18128-0(8)) Tandem Library Bks.

Spirn, Michele Sobel. Mysterious People: A Chapter Book. 48p. (J). 2006. (gr. 2-4). pap. 4.95 (978-0-516-25464-8(5)); 2005. (Illus.). (ps-ps). 22.50 (978-0-516-25181-3(3)) Scholastic Library Publishing. (Children's Pr.).

Steck-Vaughn Staff. C. W. Cracker Sees the World/Our World of Wonders. 1999. (Take Me Home Ser.). (Illus.). (J). pap. 11.30 (978-0-7398-0945-7(8)) Steck-Vaughn.

Steele, Philip. Wonders of the World. 2007. (Kingfisher Knowledge Ser.). (Illus.). 64p. (J). (gr. 3-5). 12.95 (978-0-7534-5979-9(5) , Kingfisher) Houghton Mifflin Co. Trade & Reference Div.

Steiger, Sherry Hansen. Face to Face with the Unknown. 2001. (gr. 5-8). lib. bdg. 14.15 (978-0-613-17215-8(9)) Tandem Library Bks.

Tagliapietra, Ron. The Seven Wonders of the World. 1999. (Illus.). 238p. (J). pap. 6.95 (978-1-57924-234-3(0)) Jones, Bob Univ. Pr.

Take Five Minutes Fascinating Facts from the World Almanac(R) for Kids. 2003. pap. 13.99 (978-0-7439-3792-4(9)) Teacher Created Materials, Inc.

Taylor, Kim. Demasiado Pequeno para Verlo. (Coleccion Mundos Secretos). (SPA.). (J). (gr. k-2). 4.95 (978-84-263-2045-2(7)) Vives, Luis Editorial (Edelvives) ESP. *Dist:* Lectorum Pubns., Inc.

Thomas, Keltie. Planet Earth News Presents: Nature Shockers. Hall, Greg, illus. 2005. (Planet Earth News Ser.). 64p. (J). 16.95 (978-1-897066-29-4(5)); pap. 9.95 (978-1-897066-30-0(9)) Maple Tree Pr. CAN. *Dist:* Perseus Distribution.

Thomas, Lyn. What? What? What? Astounding, Weird, Wonderful & Just Plain Unbelievable Facts. Eastman, Dianne, illus. 2003. 128p. (J). (gr. 3-7). pap. 9.95 (978-1-894379-52-6(7)); lib. bdg. 19.95 (978-1-894379-51-9(9)) Maple Tree Pr. CAN. *Dist:* Firefly Bks., Ltd.

Townsend. Mysteries of the Deep. 2004. (Out There Ser.). (Illus.). pap. 8.95 (978-1-4109-0963-3(8)) Raintree.

—Mysterious Appearances, 6 Packs. 2004. (Out There Ser.). lib. bdg. 48.30 (978-1-4109-0975-6(1)) Raintree.

—Mysterious Disappearances, 6 Packs. 2004. (Out There Ser.). lib. bdg. 48.30 (978-1-4109-0971-8(9)); (Illus.). pap. 8.95 (978-1-4109-0962-6(X)) Raintree.

—Mysterious Encounters. 2004. (Out There Ser.). (Illus.). pap. 8.95 (978-1-4109-0964-0(6)) Raintree.

—Mysterious Encounters 6-Pack. 2004. (Out There Ser.). lib. bdg. 48.30 (978-1-4109-0973-2(5)) Raintree.

—Mysterious Signs 6-Pack. 2004. (Out There Ser.). lib. bdg. 48.30 (978-1-4109-0976-3(X)) Raintree.

—Mysterious Visitors. 2004. (Out There Ser.). (Illus.). 56p. (J). pap. 8.95 (978-1-4109-0966-4(2)) Raintree.

—Out There Series, 8 vols., Set 1. 2004. (Illus.). pap. 64.40 (978-1-4109-0969-5(7)) Raintree.

Townsend, John. Mysteries of the Deep. 2004. (Out There Ser.). (Illus.). 56p. (J). 28.56 (978-1-4109-0562-8(4)) Raintree.

—Mysterious Appearances. 2004. (Raintree Freestyle Ser.). (Illus.). 56p. (J). lib. bdg. 28.56 (978-1-4109-0565-9(9)) Raintree.

—Mysterious Encounters. 2004. (Out There Ser.). (Illus.). 56p. (J). lib. bdg. 28.56 (978-1-4109-0563-5(2)) Raintree.

Tung, Anthony M. Wonders of Civilization Fandex. 2007. (Illus.). 50p. (J). 9.95 ***(978-0-7611-4355-0(6))*** Workman Publishing Co., Inc.

Unexplained Phenomena. 2001. (978-0-307-10543-1(1) , 10543, Golden Bks.) Random Hse. Children's Bks.

Unsolved Mysteries: The Secret Files, 8 bks. Incl. Atlantis. Lewis, Ann. lib. bdg. 25.25 (978-0-8239-3559-8(0)); Bermuda Triangle. Rosenberg, Aaron. lib. bdg. 25.25 (978-0-8239-3560-4(4)); Bigfoot. Cox, Greg. lib. bdg. 25.25 (978-0-8239-3561-1(2)); Close Encounters with Aliens. Silverstein, Janna. lib. bdg. 25.25 (978-0-8239-3562-8(0)); Ghosts & Poltergeists. Watkins, Graham. lib. bdg. 25.25 (978-0-8239-3563-5(9)); Loch Ness Monster. Delrio, Martin. lib. bdg. 25.25 (978-0-8239-3564-2(7)); UFOs. Stirling, Janet. lib. bdg. 25.25 (978-0-8239-3566-6(3)); Yeti, the Abominable Snowman. Gilman, Laura Anne. lib. bdg. 25.25 (978-0-8239-3565-9(5)); 48p. (YA). (gr. 5-8). 2005. (Illus.). 2002. Set lib. bdg. 202.00 (978-0-8239-9710-7(3) , Rosen Central) Rosen Publishing Group, Inc., The.

Unter der Stadt. (GER.). (978-3-411-09241-3(6)) Bibliographisches Institut & F. A. Brockhaus AG DEU. *Dist:* i.b.d., Ltd.

Usborne Books Staff. Mysteries of the Unknown. (Illus.). 96p. (YA). (gr. 6 up). lib. bdg. 21.95 (978-1-58086-032-1(X)) EDC Publishing.

Van Til, Meaghan. Mysteries. 2005. (X-Zone Ser.). (Illus.). 30p. (gr. 4-8). 23.00 (978-0-7910-8992-7(4)) Facts On File, Inc.

Wallace, Holly. Mystery of Loch Ness Monster, Set 1. 2002. (Can Science Solve? Ser.). (Illus.). 32p. (J). (gr. 4-7). pap. 7.50 (978-1-58810-309-3(9) , 91039) Heinemann Library.

Watts, Claire & Nicholson, Robert. Great Mysteries. 2000. (Info Adventure Ser.). (Illus.). 32p. (J). (gr. 3-6). pap. 3.95 (978-1-58728-107-5(4) , Two Can Publishing) T&N Children's Publishing.

Weil, Ann. Disappearances. 2007. (J). ***(978-1-4109-2977-8(9))*** Steck-Vaughn.

Williams, Brian. Wonders of the World: Biggest & Best. 2004. (Biggest & Best Ser.). (Illus.). 40p. (J). pap. 7.95 (978-1-84236-066-8(3)) Miles Kelly Publishing, Ltd. GBR. *Dist:* Independent Pubs. Group.

Windham, Ryder. What You Don't Know about Mysterious Places. 2002. 144p. (J). (gr. 3-7). pap. 4.50 (978-0-439-22537-3(X)) Scholastic, Inc.

Wonders & Winners. (YA). (gr. 7). 48.95 (978-0-673-72660-5(6) , Scott Foresman) Addison Wesley Schl.

Woodruff, Paul. M. Monsters, Myths, & Mysteries: A Tangled Tour Maze Book. Woodruff, Paul. M, illus. 2005. (Illus.). 52p. (J). 8.95 (978-0-9764327-0-8(6)) Woodruff, Paul.

World of Horror. 2007. (YA). 290.52 ***(978-1-59928-765-2(X)*** , ABDO & Daughters) ABDO Publishing Co.

Yaccarino, Dan. Go, Go America: Oodles of Oddities from the Fifty States. 2008. 80p. (J). 17.99 ***(978-0-439-70338-3(7)*** , Scholastic Pr.) Scholastic, Inc.

Yorke, Malcolm & Davis, Lee. Beastly Tales: Big Foot, Yeti & the Loch Ness Monster. 1998. (Eyewitness Readers). (Illus.). 48p. (J). (gr. 2-3). pap. 3.99 (978-0-7894-2962-9(4) , 0-7894-4754-1) Dorling Kindersley Publishing, Inc.

Yule, Tim. Sasquatches from Outer Space: Exploring the Weirdest Mysteries Ever. Baxter, Keith, illus. 2004. (Young Readers Ser.). 130p. (gr. 3-7). 15.00 (978-1-57392-847-2(X) , Pyr Bks.) Prometheus Bks., Pubs.

CURRENCY

see Money

CURRENTS, ELECTRIC

see Electric Currents

CUSTER, ELIZABETH BACON, 1842-1933

Arruda, Suzanne Middendorf. The Girl He Left Behind: The Life & Times of Libbie Custer. 2004. (Avisson Young Adult Ser.). (Illus.). 136p. (J). pap. 19.95 (978-1-888105-67-4(4)) Avisson Pr., Inc.

CUSTER, GEORGE ARMSTRONG, 1839-1876

Anderson, Paul Christopher. George Armstrong Custer: The Indian Wars & the Battle at the Little Bighorn. 2005. (Library of American Lives & Times). (Illus.). 112p. (J). (gr. 4-8). lib. bdg. 31.95 (978-0-8239-6631-8(3)) Rosen Publishing Group, Inc., The.

Arruda, Suzanne Middendorf. The Girl He Left Behind: The Life & Times of Libbie Custer. 2004. (Avisson Young Adult Ser.). (Illus.). 136p. (J). pap. 19.95 (978-1-888105-67-4(4)) Avisson Pr., Inc.

Cox, Kurt Hamilton. Custer & His Commands. 2001. (G. I. Ser.). (Illus.). 80p. (J). 27.50 (978-0-7910-6668-3(1) , Chelsea Hse.) Facts On File, Inc.

Donovan, Jim. Custer & the Little Bighorn: The Man, the Mystery, the Myth. 2001. (Illus.). 224p. (gr. 8 up). 35.00 (978-0-89658-531-7(X)) Voyageur Pr., Inc.

Fradin, Dennis B. Custer's Last Stand. 2006. (Turning Points in U. S. History Ser.). (Illus.). 48p. (J). lib. bdg. 29.93 (978-0-7614-2124-5(6) , Benchmark Bks.) Cavendish, Marshall Corp.

George Armstrong Custer. (Compass Point Early Biographies Ser.). 32p. (J). 7.95 (978-0-7565-1169-2(0)) Compass Point Bks.

Green, Carl R. Custer's Stunning Defeat by American Indians at the Little Bighorn. 2006. (Wild History of the American West Ser.). (Illus.). 128p. (J). lib. bdg. 33.27 (978-1-59845-020-0(4) , MyReportLinks.com Bks.) Enslow Pubs., Inc.

Kent, Zachary. George Armstrong Custer: Civil War General & Western Legend. 2000. (Historical American Biographies Ser.). (Illus.). 128p. (YA). (gr. 6-12). lib. bdg. 26.60 (978-0-7660-1255-4(7)) Enslow Pubs., Inc.

Link, Theodore. George Armstrong Custer. 2003. (Primary Sources of Famous People in American History Ser.). (Illus.). 32p. (J). pap. 6.50 (978-0-8239-4182-7(5)) Rosen Publishing Group, Inc., The.

Marcovitz, Hal. George A. Custer. 2001. (Famous Figures of the American Frontier Ser.). (Illus.). 64p. (J). (gr. 5 up). pap. 25.00 (978-0-7910-6496-2(4)); 25.00 (978-0-7910-6495-5(6)) Facts On File, Inc. (Chelsea Hse.).

Rau, Dana Meachen. George Armstrong Custer. 2003. (Compass Point Early Biographies Ser.). (Illus.). 32p. (J). (gr. 2 up). lib. bdg. 21.26 (978-0-7565-0419-9(8)) Compass Point Bks.

Uschan, Michael V. The Battle of Little Bighorn. 2002. (Landmark Events in American History Ser.). (Illus.). 48p. (J). (gr. 5 up). lib. bdg. 30.00 (978-0-8368-5338-4(5)); pap. 14.60 (978-0-8368-5352-0(0)) Stevens, Gareth Inc. (World Almanac Library).

CUSTOMS, SOCIAL

see Manners and Customs

CUSTOMS ADMINISTRATION

Green, Michael. Customs Service. 1998. (Law Enforcement Ser.). 48p. (J). lib. bdg. 19.00 (978-0-531-11559-6(3) , Watts, Franklin) Scholastic Library Publishing.

CYBERNETICS

see also Bionics; Computers

Bitetto, Marco A. V. Cybernetics Laboratory. braille ed. 2000. (Illus.). (YA). (978-1-58578-025-9(1)) Institute of Cybernetics Research, Inc.

CYBERSPACE

see also Computers

Gralla, Preston. Online Kids: A Young Surfer's Guide to Cyberspace. 2nd rev. ed. 1999. (Illus.). 288p. 29.95 (978-0-471-33329-6(8) , Wiley) Wiley, John & Sons, Inc.

Sherman, Josepha. Jeff Bezos: King of Amazon. 2001. (gr. 5-8). lib. bdg. 15.25 (978-0-613-45195-6(3)) Tandem Library Bks.

Weber, Sandra. The Internet. 2003. (Transforming Power of Technology Ser.). (Illus.). 112p. (J). (gr. 9-13). 30.00 (978-0-7910-7449-7(8) , Chelsea Hse.) Facts On File, Inc.

CYCLES, MOTOR

see Motorcycles

CYCLING

see Bicycles and Bicycling; Motorcycles

CYCLOPEDIAS

see Encyclopedias and Dictionaries

CYPRUS

Etingoff, Kim. Cyprus. 2006. (European Union Ser.). (Illus.). 88p. (YA). (gr. 5 up). lib. bdg. (978-1-4222-0041-4(8) , 1247983) Mason Crest Pubs.

Spilling, Michael. Cyprus. 2000. (Cultures of the World Ser.). (Illus.). 128p. (gr. 5-12). lib. bdg. 37.07 (978-0-7614-0978-6(5) , Benchmark Bks.) Cavendish, Marshall Corp.

CYTOLOGY

see Cells

CZECHOSLOVAKIA

Docalavich, Heather. The Czech Republic. 2006. (European Union Ser.). (Illus.). 88p. (YA). (gr. 5 up). lib. bdg. (978-1-4222-0042-1(6)) Mason Crest Pubs.

Kinkade, Sheila. Children of Slovakia. Little, Elaine, photos by. 2000. (World's Children Ser.). (Illus.). 48p. (J). (gr. 3-6). (978-1-57505-446-9(9) , Carolrhoda Bks.) Lerner Publishing Group.

Milivojevic, JoAnn. Czech Republic. 2004. (Enchantment of the World, Second Ser.). (Illus.). 144p. (YA). (gr. 5-9). 36.00 (978-0-516-24255-2(5) , Children's Pr.) Scholastic Library Publishing.

Petra Press Staff. Czech Republic. 2001. (Modern Nations of the World Ser.). (Illus.). 96p. (J). (gr. 7-10). 29.95 (978-1-56006-759-7(4) , Lucent Bks.) Thomson Gale.

Sioras, Efstathia. Czech Republic. 1999. (Cultures of the World Ser.). (Illus.). 128p. (gr. 5-12). lib. bdg. 37.07 (978-0-7614-0870-3(3) , Benchmark Bks.) Cavendish, Marshall Corp.

CZECHOSLOVAKIA—FICTION

Kacer, Kathy. Clara's War. 2005. (Holocaust Remembrance Ser.). (Illus.). 196p. (YA). (gr. 5 up). pap. 5.95 (978-1-896764-42-9(8)) Second Story Pr. CAN. *Dist:* Orca Bk. Pubs. USA, Univ. of Toronto Pr., Univ. of Toronto Pr.

—Clara's War. 2001. (gr. 5-8). lib. bdg. 14.10 (978-0-613-51538-2(2)) Tandem Library Bks.

Kanefield, Teri. Rivka's Way. 2001. (Illus.). 144p. (J). (gr. 5-9). 15.95 (978-0-8126-2870-8(5)) Cricket Bks.

Melnikoff, Pamela. Prisoner in Time. 2001. 144p. (gr. 5-8). pap. 9.95 (978-0-8276-0735-4(0)) Jewish Pubn. Society.

Wolf, Joan M. Someone Named Eva. 2007. 208p. (J). (gr. 5-9). 16.00 (978-0-618-53579-8(9) , Clarion Bks.) Houghton Mifflin Co. Trade & Reference Div.

CZECHOSLOVAKIA—HISTORY

Cottrell, Robert C. Czechoslovakia & the Velvet Revolution. Matray, James I., ed. 2005. (Arbitrary Borders: Political Boundaries in World History Ser.). (Illus.). 112p. (gr. 9-13). 35.00 (978-0-7910-8255-3(5) , Chelsea Hse.) Facts On File, Inc.

Rubin, Susan Goldman. Fireflies in the Dark: The Story of Freidl Dicker-Brandeis & the Children of Terezin. (Illus.). 48p. (J). (gr. 4-6). 2005. pap. 8.95 (978-0-8234-1681-3(X)); 2000. tchr. ed. 18.95 (978-0-8234-1461-1(2)) Holiday Hse., Inc.

Sís, Peter. The Wall: Growing up Behind the Iron Curtain. 2007. (Illus.). 56p. (J). (gr. 3 up). 18.00 (978-0-374-34701-7(8) , Farrar, Straus & Giroux (BYR)) Farrar, Straus & Giroux.

CZECHS—UNITED STATES

Stotsky, Sandra, ed. The Czech Americans. 1999. (Immigrant Experience Ser.). (Illus.). 128p. (YA). (gr. 5 up). pap. 9.95 (978-0-7910-5054-5(8)); (gr. 4-7). 14.95 (978-0-7910-5052-1(1)) Facts On File, Inc. (Chelsea Hse.).

CZECHS—UNITED STATES—FICTION

Myers, Walter Dean. Game. 2008. 240p. (J). 16.99 ***(978-0-06-058294-4(4));*** lib. bdg. 17.89 ***(978-0-06-058295-1(2))*** HarperCollins Pubs. (HarperTeen).

D

DACHSHUND

see Dachshunds

DACHSHUNDS

Gray, Susan H. Dachshunds. 2008. (Domestic Dogs Ser.). 32p. (J). (gr. k-4). 27.07 ***(978-1-59296-964-7(X))*** Child's World, Inc.

Quasha, Jennifer. The Story of the Dachshund. 2000. (Dogs Throughout History Ser.). 24p. (J). (gr. k-4). lib. bdg. 18.75 (978-0-8239-5516-9(8) , PowerKids Pr.) Rosen Publishing Group, Inc., The.

Schopell, M. William. Guide to Owning a Dachshund: AKC Rank #7. 1999. (Popular Dog Library). (Illus.). 64p. (J). (gr. 4-7). 27.50 (978-0-7910-5476-5(4) , Chelsea Hse.) Facts On File, Inc.

Stone, Lynn M. Dachshunds. 2003. (Eye to Eye with Dogs Ser.). (Illus.). 24p. (gr. 2-5). 17.95 (978-1-58952-326-5(1)) Rourke Publishing, LLC.

Trumbauer, Lisa. Dachshunds. 2006. (Pebble Books). (Illus.). 24p. (J). (978-0-7368-5332-3(4) , 1252485) Capstone Pr., Inc.

Wilcox, Charlotte. The Dachshund. 2001. (Learning about Dogs Ser.). (Illus.). 48p. (J). (gr. 3-4). lib. bdg. 21.26 (978-0-7368-0763-0(2) , Capstone High-Interest Bks.) Capstone Pr., Inc.

DAEDALUS (GREEK MYTHOLOGY)

Galloway, Priscilla. Daedalus & the Minotaur. Cousineau, Normand, illus. 2003. (Tales of Ancient Lands Ser.). 112p. (J). (gr. 4-7). pap. 14.95 (978-1-55037-458-2(3)) Annick Pr., Ltd. CAN. *Dist:* Firefly Bks., Ltd.

DAFFY DUCK (FICTITIOUS CHARACTER)—FICTION

Dalmatian Press Staff. Daffy: A Sign with a Surprise. 2003. (Read-N-Snuggle Looney Tunes Ser.). 5p. (J). bds. 5.99 (978-1-57759-993-7(4)) Dalmatian Pr.

Glassman, Jackie. Looney Tunes Back in Action Reader. 2003. (gr. k-3). lib. bdg. 11.80 (978-0-613-72242-1(6)) Tandem Library Bks.

Markas, Jenny. Looney Tunes Back in Action Junior Novelization. 2003. (Looney Tunes Ser.). 80p. (J). pap. 4.99 (978-0-439-52136-9(X) , Scholastic Paperbacks) Scholastic, Inc.

Mason, Jane. Looney Tunes Back in Action Movie Storybook. 2003. (gr. k-3). lib. bdg. 14.15 (978-0-613-72238-4(8)) Tandem Library Bks.

McCann, Jesse Leon. Looney Tunes Back in Action. 2003. (gr. k-3). lib. bdg. 11.25 (978-0-613-72241-4(8)) Tandem Library Bks.

—Looney Tunes Back in Action Joke Book. 2003. (gr. 3-6). lib. bdg. 12.40 (978-0-613-72240-7(X)) Tandem Library Bks.

McCann, Jesse Leon & Mc Cann, Jesse Leon. Looney Tunes Back in Action Joke Book. 2003. (Looney Tunes Ser.). (Illus.). 64p. (J). pap. 4.50 (978-0-439-52138-3(6) , Scholastic Paperbacks) Scholastic, Inc.

DAHL, ROALD, 1916-1990

Boothroyd, Jennifer. Roald Dahl: A Life of Imagination. 2008. (Pull Ahead Books-Biographies Ser.). (J). lib. bdg. 22.60 ***(978-0-8225-8825-2(0)*** , Lerner Pubns.) Lerner Publishing Group, Inc.

Craats, Rennay. Roald Dahl. 2002. (My Favorite Writer Ser.). (Illus.). 32p. (J). lib. bdg. 18.20 (978-1-59036-029-3(X)) Weigl Pubs., Inc.

Dahl, Roald. Boy: Tales of Childhood. 1999. (Illus.). 176p. (J). (gr. 5-9). pap. 6.99 (978-0-14-130305-5(0) , Puffin) Penguin Group (USA) Inc.

Dahl, Roald. D Is for Dahl: A gloriumptious A-Z guide to the world of Roald Dahl. Blake, Quentin, illus. 2007. 160p. (J). (gr. 2). pap. 5.99 ***(978-0-14-240934-3(0)*** , Puffin) Penguin Group (USA) Inc.

Dahl, Roald & Blake, Quentin. Roald Dahl Address Book. 2004. (Illus.). 128p. 9.95 (978-1-4052-1327-1(2)) Egmont Bks., Ltd. GBR. *Dist:* Independent Pubs. Group.

—The Roald Dahl Diary 2005. 2004. (Illus.). 128p. (J). pap. 11.95 (978-1-4052-1326-4(4)) Egmont Bks., Ltd. GBR. *Dist:* Independent Pubs. Group.

—Roald Dahl Notebook. 2004. (Illus.). 128p. (J). 6.99 (978-1-4052-1328-8(0)) Egmont Bks., Ltd. GBR. *Dist:* Independent Pubs. Group.

Gaines, Ann Graham. Roald Dahl. 2001. (Real-Life Reader Biography Ser.). (Illus.). 32p. (J). (gr. 3-8). lib. bdg. 15.95 (978-1-58415-075-6(0)) Mitchell Lane Pubs., Inc.

Gelletly, LeeAnne. Gift of Imagination: The Story of Roald Dahl. 2006. (World Writers Ser.). (Illus.). 160p. (YA). (gr. 6-12). lib. bdg. 27.95 (978-1-59935-026-4(2)) Reynolds, Morgan Inc.

Gifford, Clive. So You Think You Know Roald Dahl? The Unofficial Quiz Book. 2005. (Illus.). 160p. (J). pap. (978-0-340-88448-5(7) , Hodder Children's Books) Hodder Children's Division.

Hook, Jason. Roald Dahl. 2004. (Illus.). 48p. (J). lib. bdg. 28.56 (978-0-7398-6626-9(5)) Raintree.

Houle, Michelle M. Roald Dahl: Author of Charlie & the Chocolate Factory. 2006. (Authors Teens Love Ser.). (Illus.). 104p. (YA). lib. bdg. 31.93 (978-0-7660-2353-6(2)) Enslow Pubs., Inc.

Ruffin, Frances E. Meet Roald Dahl. 2006. (About the Author Ser.). (Illus.). 24p. (J). lib. bdg. (978-1-4042-3134-4(X) , PowerKids Pr.) Rosen Publishing Group, Inc., The.

Shields, Charles J. Roald Dahl. 2002. (Who Wrote That? Ser.). (Illus.). 112p. (gr. 6-12). 30.00 (978-0-7910-6722-2(X) , Chelsea Hse.) Facts On File, Inc.

Wheeler, Jill C. Roald Dahl. 2007. (Children's Authors Ser.). (Illus.). 24p. (J). 21.35 (978-1-59679-763-5(0)) ABDO Publishing Co.

Woog, Adam. Roald Dahl. 2004. (Inventors & Creators Ser.). (Illus.). 48p. (J). (gr. 4-7). 26.20 (978-0-7377-2614-5(8) , Greenhaven Pr., Inc.) Thomson Gale.

DAIRIES

see Dairying

DAIRY CATTLE

see Cows

DAIRY PRODUCTS

see also Dairying

also names of dairy products, e.g. Milk

Christian, Eleanor & Roth-Singer, Lyzz. Let's Make Butter. 2000. (Yellow Umbrella Books). (Illus.). 16p. (J). (gr. 1). lib. bdg. 14.60 (978-0-7368-0728-9(4) , Pebble Bks.) Capstone Pr., Inc.

Derkazarian, Susan. Dairy. 2005. (Rookie Read-About Health Ser.). (Illus.). 31p. (J). (ps-ps). 20.50 (978-0-516-23672-8(5) , Children's Pr.) Scholastic Library Publishing.

DerKazarian, Susan. Dairy. 2006. 32p. (J). (gr. k-2). pap. 5.95 (978-0-516-25925-3(3) , Children's Pr.) Scholastic Library Publishing.

Feely, Jenny. Making Butter. 1999. (ps-2). lib. bdg. 11.80 (978-0-613-30588-4(4)) Tandem Library Bks.

Frost, Helen. The Dairy Group. Saunders-Smith, Gail, ed. 2000. (Food Guide Pyramid Ser.). (Illus.). 24p. (J). (gr. k-1). lib. bdg. 15.93 (978-0-7368-0540-7(0) , Pebble Bks.) Capstone Pr., Inc.

Green, Emily K. Milk, Yogurt, & Cheese. 2006. (Blastoff! Readers Ser.). (Illus.). 24p. (J). lib. bdg. 16.95 (978-1-60014-000-6(9)) Bellwether Media.

Head, Honor. Dairy. 2006. (QEB What's for Lunch? Ser.). (Illus.). 32p. (J). lib. bdg. 19.95 (978-1-59566-197-5(2)) QEB Publishing Inc.

Kalz, Jill. Dairy Products. 2003. 24p. (J). lib. bdg. 21.35 (978-1-58340-297-9(7)) Smart Apple Media.

Leeper, Angela. The Dairy. 2004. (Field Trip! Ser.). (Illus.). 24p. (J). pap. 5.75 (978-1-4034-5166-8(4)) Heinemann Library.

—To a Dairy. 2004. (Field Trip! Ser.). (Illus.). 24p. (J). lib. bdg. (978-1-4034-5160-6(5)) Heinemann Library.

Martineau, Susan. Healthy Eating. 2006. (Illus.). 32p. (J). (978-1-58340-895-7(9) , 1262658) Smart Apple Media.

Mayo, Gretchen Will. Milk. 2004. (Weekly Reader Early Learning Library). (Illus.). 24p. (gr. 2 up). (J). pap. 5.95 (978-0-8368-4074-2(7)); (YA). lib. bdg. 19.33 (978-0-8368-4067-4(4)) Stevens, Gareth Inc. (Weekly Reader Early Learning Library).

Milk Yogurt & Cheese New Food Guide Pyramid. 2006. (Illus.). 24p. (J). (gr. k-2). 18.50 ***(978-0-531-17855-3(2))*** Scholastic Library Publishing.

Nelson, Robin. Dairy. 2003. (First Step Nonfiction Ser.). (Illus.). 24p. (J). (gr. k-2). lib. bdg. 18.60 (978-0-8225-4632-0(9)) Lerner Publishing Group.

Pickering, Robin. I Like Cheese. 2000. (Welcome Bks.). (Illus.). 24p. (J). (ps-2). pap. 4.95 (978-0-516-23007-8(7) , Children's Pr.) Scholastic Library Publishing.

—I Like Cheese. 2000. (gr. k-3). lib. bdg. 12.95 (978-0-613-52084-3(X)) Tandem Library Bks.

Rondeau, Amanda. Milk Is Magnificent. 2003. (What Should I Eat? Ser.). (Illus.). 23p. (J). (ps-3). lib. bdg. 19.93 (978-1-57765-837-5(X) , SandCastle) ABDO Publishing Co.

Schuh, Mari C. The Milk Group. 2006. (Illus.). 24p. (J). (978-0-7368-5373-6(1) , Pebble Bks.) Capstone Pr., Inc.

Thomas, Ann. Dairy Products. 2002. (Food Ser.). (Illus.). 32p. (J). (gr. k-2). 23.00 (978-0-7910-6980-6(X) , Chelsea Hse.) Facts On File, Inc.

Wissolik, Richard David. Ice Cream Joe: The Valley Dairy Story—: & America's Love Affair with Ice Cream. Greubel, Joseph E., ed. 2004. (Illus.). 208p. 29.95 (978-1-885851-18-5(9)) St. Vincent College Ctr. for Northern Appalachian Studies.

DAIRYING

see also Cattle; Cows; Dairy Products; Milk

Flanagan, Alice K. Raising Cows on the Koebels' Farm. Flanagan, Romie, illus. 1999. (Our Neighborhood Ser.). 32p. (J). (gr. 1-2). 20.00 (978-0-516-21133-6(1) , Children's Pr.) Scholastic Library Publishing.

Gish, Melissa. A Dairy Farm. 2003. (Field Trips Ser.). 24p. (J). lib. bdg. 14.95 (978-1-58340-325-9(6)) Smart Apple Media.

Leeper, Angela. The Dairy. 2004. (Field Trip! Ser.). (Illus.). 24p. (J). pap. 5.75 (978-1-4034-5166-8(4)) Heinemann Library.

—To a Dairy. 2004. (Field Trip! Ser.). (Illus.). 24p. (J). lib. bdg. (978-1-4034-5160-6(5)) Heinemann Library.

Mayo, Gretchen Will. Milk. 2004. (Weekly Reader Early Learning Library). (Illus.). 24p. (gr. 2 up). (J). pap. 5.95 (978-0-8368-4074-2(7)); (YA). lib. bdg. 19.33 (978-0-8368-4067-4(4)) Stevens, Gareth Inc. (Weekly Reader Early Learning Library).

Murray, Julie. Grass to Milk. 2007. (Beginning to End Ser.). (Illus.). 24p. (J). (gr. k-3). lib. bdg. 21.35 (978-1-59679-837-3(8) , Buddy Bks.) ABDO Publishing Co.

Out & about at the Dairy Farm. (Field Trips Ser.). 24p. (J). 8.95 (978-1-4048-0166-0(9)) Picture Window Bks.

Pohl, Kathleen. What Happens at a Dairy Farm? 2006. (Illus.). 24p. (J). pap. (978-0-8368-6893-7(5)); lib. bdg. (978-0-8368-6886-9(2)) Stevens, Gareth Inc.

—What Happens at a Dairy Farm? Qué Pasa en una Granja Lechera? 2006. (ENG & SPA., Illus.). 24p. (J). pap. (978-0-8368-7394-8(7)); lib. bdg. (978-0-8368-7387-0(4)) Stevens, Gareth Inc. (Weekly Reader Early Learning Library).

Sweeney, Alyse. Let's Visit a Dairy Farm. 2007. (Scholastic News Nonfiction Readers Ser.). (Illus.). 24p. (J). (gr. k-2). 19.00 (978-0-531-16843-1(3) , Watts, Franklin) Scholastic Library Publishing.

Taus-Bolstad, Stacy. From Grass to Milk. 2004. (Start to Finish Ser.). (Illus.). 24p. (J). 18.60 (978-0-8225-4664-1(7) , Lerner Pubns.) Lerner Publishing Group.

Waidelich, Will. Dairy Learning Lab, Set. 2000. (Illus.). 60p. (YA). spiral bd. 26.95 (978-1-56502-097-9(9) , 4034K-11) Ohio State Univ., Ohio Agricultural Education Curriculum Materials Service.

DAIRYING—FICTION

Arena, Felice & Kettle, Phil. On the Farm/By Felice Arena & Phil Kettle ; Illustrated by Susy Boyer. Boyer, Susy, illus. 2004. (J). pap. (978-1-59336-363-5(X)) Mondo Publishing.

Cordsen, Carol Foskett. The Milkman. Jones, Douglas B., illus. 2007. 32p. (J). (ps). pap. 6.99 (978-0-14-240804-9(2) , Puffin) Penguin Group (USA) Inc.

Random House Disney Staff. Hero of a Horse. 2004. (ps-2). lib. bdg. 11.80 (978-0-613-73715-9(6)) Tandem Library Bks.

Schmidt, Gary. First Boy. 2007. 224p. (YA). pap. 6.99 (***978-0-312-37149-4(7)***) Square Fish.

Schmidt, Gary D. First Boy. rev. ed. 2005. 208p. (YA). (gr. 6). 17.95 (978-0-8050-7859-6(2)) Holt, Henry & Co.

DALE, SAMUEL, 1772-1841

Bailey, Tom. Sam Dale: Alabama Frontiersman. 2001. (Alabama Roots Biography Ser.). (Illus.). 107p. (J). (978-1-878561-82-4(0)) Seacoast Publishing, Inc.

DALEMARK (IMAGINARY PLACE)—FICTION

Jones, Diana Wynne. Spellcoats. 2001. (gr. 7-12). lib. bdg. 15.25 (978-0-613-36015-9(X)) Tandem Library Bks.

DALLAS (TEX.)

Carole Marsh. Dallas Coloring & Activity Book. 2004. (City Bks.). 24p. (gr. k-5). pap. 3.95 (978-0-635-02231-8(1)) Gallopade International.

Furstinger, Nancy. Dallas. 2005. (Cities Ser.). (Illus.). 32p. (J). (gr. k-6). lib. bdg. 22.78 (978-1-59197-858-9(0)) ABDO Publishing Co.

Kent, Deborah. Dallas. 2001. (Cities of the World Ser.). (Illus.). 64p. (YA). (gr. 4-9). pap. 9.95 (978-0-516-27168-2(7) , Children's Pr.) Scholastic Library Publishing.

—Dallas. 2000. (gr. 5-8). lib. bdg. 18.75 (978-0-613-51485-9(8)) Tandem Library Bks.

DALLAS COWBOYS (FOOTBALL TEAM)

Aretha, David. America's Team[97]the Dallas Cowboys. 2007. (Sensational Sports Teams Ser.). (Illus.). 128p. (J). lib. bdg. 33.27 (978-1-59845-046-0(8) , MyReportLinks.com Bks.) Enslow Pubs., Inc.

Dallas Cowboys Staff. Dallas Cowboys. CWC Sports Inc, ed. 1998. (NFL Team Yearbooks Ser.). (J). (gr. 1-12). pap. 9.99 (978-1-891613-06-7(5)) Everett Sports Publishing & Marketing.

Gatto, Kimberly. Emmitt Smith. 2003. (Stars of Sport Ser.). (Illus.). 48p. (J). 26.20 (978-0-7377-2084-6(0) , Greenhaven Pr., Inc.) Thomson Gale.

Grabowski, John F. The Dallas Cowboys. 2001. (Great Sports Teams Ser.). (Illus.). 88p. (YA). (gr. 4-12). 29.95 (978-1-56006-939-3(2) , GML12001-178251, Lucent Bks.) Thomson Gale.

—Sports Great Emmitt Smith. 1998. (Sports Great Bks.). (Illus.). 64p. (YA). (gr. 4-10). lib. bdg. 17.95 (978-0-7660-1002-4(3)) Enslow Pubs., Inc.

Halfmann, Janet. Life in a Tide Pool. 2000. (Lifeviews Ser.). (Illus.). 32p. (J). lib. bdg. (978-1-58341-076-9(7) , Creative Education) Creative Co., The.

Hawkes, Brian. The History of the Dallas Cowboys. 2004. (NFL Today Ser.). (Illus.). 32p. 18.95 (978-1-58341-294-7(8) , Creative Education) Creative Co., The.

Leboutillier, Nate. Dallas Cowboys. 2005. (Super Bowl Champions Ser.). (Illus.). 24p. (gr. 1-4). 16.95 (978-1-58341-382-1(0) , Creative Education) Creative Co., The.

Potts, Steve. Dallas Cowboys. 2001. (Championship Teams Ser.). (Illus.). (J). (978-1-58340-086-9(9)) Smart Apple Media.

Stewart, Mark. The Dallas Cowboys. 2006. (Team Spirit Ser.). (Illus.). 48p. (J). lib. bdg. 25.27 (978-1-59953-004-8(X)) Norwood Hse. Pr.

Stewart, Mark. Dallas Cowboys. 2007. 48p. pap. 9.95 (***978-1-60357-001-5(2)***) Norwood Hse. Pr.

DALTON, JOHN, 1766-1844

Kjelle, Marylou. John Dalton & the Atomic Theory. 2004. (Uncharted, Unexplored, & Unexplained Ser.). (Illus.). 48p. (J). (gr. 4-8). lib. bdg. 29.95 (978-1-58415-308-5(3)) Mitchell Lane Pubs., Inc.

DAMS

DuTemple, Lesley A. The Hoover Dam. 2003. (Great Building Feats Ser.). (Illus.). 96p. (J). (gr. 5-9). 27.93 (978-0-8225-4691-7(4)) Lerner Publishing Group.

Gresko, Marcia S. Grand Coulee Dam. 1999. (Building America Ser.). (Illus.). 48p. (J). (gr. 5-8). 23.70 (978-1-56711-174-3(2) , Blackbirch Pr., Inc.) Thomson Gale.

The Itaipu Dam: Individual Title Six-Packs. (On Deck Ser.). 24p. (gr. 4-5). 35.00 (978-0-7578-1073-2(X)) Rigby Education.

Juettner, Bonnie. Dams & Levees. 2007. (Our Environment Ser.). 48p. (gr. 4-8). 23.70 (***978-0-7377-3559-8(7)*** , Kidhaven) Thomson Gale.

Oxlade, Chris. Dams. (Building Amazing Structures Ser.). (Illus.). 32p. (J). 2000. (gr. 3-5). lib. bdg. 22.79 (978-1-57572-277-1(1)); 2nd ed. 2005. (978-1-4034-7903-7(8)) Heinemann Library.

Parks, Peggy J. Aswan High Dam. (Building World Landmarks Ser.). (J). 2004. 26.19 (978-1-4103-0204-5(0)); 2003. (Illus.). 48p. 24.95 (978-1-56711-329-7(X)) Thomson Gale. (Blackbirch Pr., Inc.).

La represa de Itaipu: Individual Title Six-Packs. (On Deck en Espanol Ser.).Tr. of Itaipu Dam. (SPA.). 24p. (gr. 4-5). 35.00 (978-0-7578-6444-5(9)) Rigby Education.

Richards, Julie. Dams. 2003. 32p. (J). lib. bdg. 24.25 (978-1-58340-345-7(0)) Smart Apple Media.

Stone, Lynn M. Dams. 2001. (How are They Built? Ser.). (Illus.). 48p. (J). (gr. 4-8). lib. bdg. 29.93 (978-1-58952-136-0(6)) Rourke Publishing, LLC.

Thomas, Mark. The Itaipu Dam: World's Biggest Dam. 2002. (Reading Power Ser.). (Illus.). 24p. (J). (gr. 1). lib. bdg. 17.25 (978-0-8239-5993-8(7) , PowerKids Pr.) Rosen Publishing Group, Inc., The.

DAMS—FICTION

Alcorn, Steve. Everything in Its Path: A Novel about the St. Francis Dam Disaster. 2003. 164p. (YA). pap. 12.99 (978-0-9729777-0-8(8)) Theme Perks, Inc.

DANA GIRLS (FICTITIOUS CHARACTERS)—FICTION

Gallego, Laura. La Llamada de Los Muertos. 2004. (Ciclo el Valle de Los Lobos the Valley of the Wolves Cycle Ser.). (SPA.). 240p. (YA). 10.99 (978-84-348-9439-6(4)) SM Ediciones ESP. *Dist:* Lectorum Pubns., Inc.

DANCE

see also Ballet; Folk Dancing

Ancona, George. Capoeira: Game! Dance! Martial Art! 2007. (Illus.). 48p. (J). (gr. 2-7). 18.95 (***978-1-58430-268-1(2)***) Lee & Low Bks., Inc.

—Let's Dance! 1998. (Illus.). 40p. (J). (ps-3). 15.89 (978-0-688-16212-2(6)) HarperCollins Pubs.

—Mis Bailes: My Dances. 2005. (Somos Latinos (We Are Latinos) Ser.). (SPA & ENG., Illus.). 32p. (J). (gr. 1-3). pap. 8.95 (978-0-516-25069-4(8) , Children's Pr.) Scholastic Library Publishing.

A bailar Flamenco! 22: Leveled Books. 2001. (McGraw-Hill Lectura Ser.). (ENG & SPA.). (gr. 2 up). (978-0-02-188071-3(9)) Macmillan/McGraw-Hill Schl. Div.

Berton, Judy & Guimond, Rick. Do a Dance Picture Book. 2006. (Illus.). (J). spiral bd. 8.95 (978-0-9761051-1-4(X)) Kidrich Corp.

Blair, Skippy. Dance Power: Own the Experience. 2nd rev. ed. 1999. Orig. Title: Dance! Dance! Dance!. (Illus.). 134p. (J). pap. 39.95 (978-0-932980-24-3(4)) Golden State Dance Teachers Assn.

Canizares, Susan. Dancing. 1999. (J). pap. 3.25 (978-0-439-04569-8(X)) Scholastic, Inc.

Canizares, Susan & Berger, Chessen. Dancing. 1999. (ps-2). lib. bdg. 10.10 (978-0-613-21402-5(1)) Tandem Library Bks.

Coachman, Mary Kaye. Dance Team. 2006. (Illus.). 64p. (J). lib. bdg. (978-1-4042-0731-8(7)) Rosen Publishing Group, Inc., The.

Collins, Pat Lowery. I Am a Dancer. Graham, Mark, illus. 2008. (Millbrook Picture Books Ser.). (J). lib. bdg. 22.60 (***978-0-8225-6369-3(X)*** , Millbrook Pr.) Lerner Publishing Group.

Compass Point Books, contrib. by. Dance for Fun! (For Fun Ser.). 48p. (YA). pap. 8.95 (978-0-7565-1153-1(4)) Compass Point Bks.

Connie's Dance: Individual Title Six-Packs. (gr. 1-2). 25.00 (978-0-7635-9143-4(2)) Rigby Education.

Craig-Quijada, Balinda. Dance for Fun! 2004. (Activities for Fun Ser.). (Illus.). 48p. (J). (gr. 3 up). lib. bdg. 21.26 (978-0-7565-0587-5(9)) Compass Point Bks.

Cranium Inc. Staff. Cranium: the Star Performer Book of Outrageous Fun! Sing it, Dance it, Act It! Baseman, illus. 2006. 38p. (J). (gr. 2-17). 14.99 (978-0-316-05759-2(2)) Little, Brown Bks. for Young Readers.

Dance Alpha. 2007. 17.95 (***978-1-58536-312-4(X)***) Sleeping Bear Pr.

Day, Eileen. I'm Good at Dancing. 2003. (Heinemann Read & Learn Ser.). (Illus.). 24p. (J). pap. 5.25 (978-1-4034-3444-9(1)); lib. bdg. 18.50 (978-1-4034-0902-7(1)) Heinemann Library.

—I'm Good at Dancing. 2003. (gr. k-3). lib. bdg. 13.30 (978-0-613-70655-1(2)) Tandem Library Bks.

Descutner, Janet. Asian Dance. 2004. (World of Dance Ser.). (Illus.). 112p. (gr. 9-13). pap. 30.00 (978-0-7910-7777-1(2) , Chelsea Hse.) Facts On File, Inc.

—Asian Dance. 2004. (gr. 5-8). lib. bdg. 18.75 (978-0-613-84046-0(1)) Tandem Library Bks.

Dillman, Lisa. Tap Dancing. 2004. (Get Going! Hobbies Ser.). (Illus.). 32p. (J). 27.79 (978-1-4034-6120-9(1)) Heinemann Library.

DK Publishing Staff. Classical Ballerina. 2007. 80p. (J). 17.99 (978-0-7566-2668-6(4)) Dorling Kindersley Publishing, Inc.

Dorling Kindersley Publishing Staff. Dance. 2005. (Eyewitness Books). (Illus.). 72p. (J). 15.99 (978-0-7566-1065-4(6) , 1241897); lib. bdg. 19.99 (978-0-7566-1066-1(4) , 1241897) Dorling Kindersley Publishing, Inc.

Dover Staff. 10 Ballet Fun Books: Stickers, Paper Dolls, Stencils & More. 162p. (J). 10.00 (978-0-486-40545-2(1)) Dover Pubns., Inc.

Dowd, Olympia. A Young Dancer's Apprenticeship. 2003. (Illus.). 128p. (J). (gr. 7 up). pap. 14.95 (978-0-7613-1898-9(4) , Twenty-First Century Bks.) Lerner Publishing Group.

Duarte, Jeffrey G. Watch & Twirl & Spin. Duarte, Jeffrey G., ed. McRae, Tylese, photos by. 2001. (Illus.). 64p. (YA). (gr. 8 up). per. 10.00 (978-0-9714433-0-3(0) , SEP-0-9714433-0-0) Speak-Easy Publishing, LLC.

Edom, Helen & Katrak, N. Starting Ballet - Internet Linked. 2005. 32p. (J). pap. 4.95 (978-0-7945-0673-5(9) , Usborne) EDC Publishing.

Feldman, Jane. We Love Ballet! 2004. (Random House Pictureback Book Ser.). (Illus.). 24p. (J). (ps-2). pap. 3.99 (978-0-375-82831-7(1) , Random Hse. Bks. for Young Readers) Random Hse. Children's Bks.

Freese, Joan. Hip-hop Dancing. 2008. (J). 25.26 (***978-1-4296-0121-4(3)***) Capstone Pr., Inc.

Garofoli, Wendy. Breakdancing. 2008. (J). (***978-1-4296-0122-1(1)***) Capstone Pr., Inc.

—Dance Team. 2008. (J). (***978-1-4296-0120-7(5)***) Capstone Pr., Inc.

—Modern Dance. 2008. (J). (***978-1-4296-1353-8(X)***) Capstone Pr., Inc.

Gibbs, Lynne. A Word about Ballet. McNicholas, Shelagh, illus. 2005. (Word About Ser.). 24p. (J). (ps-3). pap., pap. 3.95 (978-0-7696-3384-8(6) , Brighter Child) School Specialty Publishing.

Gilpin, Greg. Fame & Charleston, Set 3. 2001. (Dance Ser.). (J). (gr. 1-5). 9.95 incl. audio compact disk (978-0-7579-0740-1(7) , 0557B, Warner Bros. Pubns.) Alfred Publishing Co., Inc.

—Shake Rattle & Roll & Happy Feet!, Set 2. 2001. (Dance Ser.). (J). (gr. 1-5). 9.95 incl. audio compact disk (978-0-7579-0739-5(3) , 0556B, Warner Bros. Pubns.) Alfred Publishing Co., Inc.

Gilpin, Greg, des. I Want It That Way. 2002. (WB Dance Ser.). 9.95 (978-0-7579-9498-2(9) , Warner Bros. Pubns.) Alfred Publishing Co., Inc.

Goose, Mother. Lets Move. 2005. (Illus.). 36p. (J). bds. 7.95 (978-1-59249-534-4(6) , 1D204) Soundprints.

Graves, Karen Marie. Ballet Dance. 2008. (***978-1-4296-0119-1(1)***) Capstone Pr., Inc.

—Tap Dancing. 2008. (***978-1-4296-0124-5(8)***) Capstone Pr., Inc.

Hanley, Elizabeth A., ed. & intro. World of Dance. Hanley, Elizabeth A., intro. (Illus.). (gr. 9-13). lib. bdg. (978-0-7910-8042-9(0)); 2005. 120-164p. pap. 180.00 (978-0-7910-7639-2(3)) Facts On File, Inc. (Chelsea Hse.).

Harcourt School Publishers Staff. Dancing No Matter What Advanced Level. 3rd ed. 2002. (Trophies Reading Program Ser.). (Illus.). pap. 5.10 (978-0-15-323390-6(7)) Harcourt Schl. Pubs.

Haskins, James. Black Dance in America: A History Through It's People. 2000. (Illus.). 232p. (J). pap. 12.95 (978-1-56649-134-1(7)) Welcome Rain Pubs.

Hayward, Linda. Jobs People Do: A Day in the Life of a Dancer. 2001. (Jobs People Do Ser.). (Illus.). (J). 10.75 (978-0-606-21139-0(X)) Tandem Library Bks.

Hebach, Susan. Tap Dancing. 2001. (High Interest Bks.). (Illus.). 48p. (YA). (gr. 7-12). pap. 6.95 (978-0-516-29560-2(8)); (J). lib. bdg. (978-0-516-23259-1(2)) Scholastic Library Publishing. (Children's Pr.).

—Tap Dancing. 2001. (gr. 7-12). lib. bdg. 15.25 (978-0-613-58739-6(1)) Tandem Library Bks.

Hebach, Suzanne. Tap Dancing. 2001. (After School Ser.). (Illus.). 48p. (YA). (gr. 7-12). 23.00 (978-0-516-23156-3(1) , Children's Pr.) Scholastic Library Publishing.

Johnson, Anne E. Jazz Tap: From African Drums to American Feet. 1999. (Library of African American Arts & Culture). (Illus.). 64p. (YA). (gr. 7-12). lib. bdg. 26.50 (978-0-8239-1856-0(4) , AAJATA) Rosen Publishing Group, Inc., The.

Keeler, Patricia A. & Leitao, Julio T. Drumbeat in Our Feet. Keeler, Patricia A., illus. 2006. (Illus.). 32p. (J). lib. bdg. 16.95 (***978-1-58430-264-3(X)***) Lee & Low Bks., Inc.

Kuklin, Susan. Dance. 2020. 32p. (J). (gr. 3-7). pap. 5.99 (978-0-7868-1455-8(1)) Disney Pr.

Kuklin, Susan & Jones, Bill T. Dance! Kuklin, Susan, photos by. 1998. (Illus.). 32p. (gr. 3-7). 14.95 (978-0-7868-0362-0(2)) Hyperion Bks. for Children.

Lee Gauch, Patricia. Tanya entre Bastidores. Ichikawa, Satomi, illus. 2004. Tr. of Tanya & the Magic Wardrobe. (SPA.). (J). 16.99 (978-84-8488-083-7(4)) Serres, Ediciones, S. L. ESP. *Dist:* Lectorum Pubns., Inc.

The Library of the Choreographers, 8 bks., Set. 2006. (Illus.). (J). lib. bdg. 191.60 (978-1-4042-0618-2(3)) Rosen Publishing Group, Inc., The.

Litchman, Kristin E., ed. Let's Dance! Dances for Children from America's Melting Pot, Dance Program for Pre-School & Elementary School Children. rev. ed. 2005. (Illus.). 260p. (J). 90.00 (978-1-890034-19-1(3) , Medley Pubns.) Medley.

MacDonald, Fiona. Music & Dance. (Discovering World Cultures Ser.). (Illus.). 40p. (J). (gr. 4). 2001. pap. (978-0-7787-0249-8(9)); 2000. lib. bdg. (978-0-7787-0239-9(1)) Crabtree Publishing Co.

—Music & Dance. 2001. (gr. 3-6). lib. bdg. 17.60 (978-0-613-43477-5(3)) Tandem Library Bks.

Mason, Jane B. & Hines Stephens, Sarah. Gymboree Dance Play. rev. ed. 2007. (Illus.). 36p. (J). (ps-2). bds. 16.95 (***978-1-55263-960-3(6)***) Key Porter Bks. CAN. *Dist:* Perseus Distribution.

Maze, Stephanie. I Want to Be a Dancer. 1999. (I Want to Be Ser.). (Illus.). 48p. (J). (gr. 3-7). pap. 9.00 (978-0-15-202108-5(6) , Harcourt Paperbacks) Harcourt Children's Bks.

McAlpine, Margaret. Working in Music & Dance. 2005. (My Future Career Ser.). (Illus.). 54p. (J). lib. bdg. 26.00 (978-0-8368-4777-2(6)) Stevens, Gareth Inc.

Murphy, Liz. A Dictionary of Dance. 2007. (Illus.). 32p. (ps-3). 15.95 (***978-1-59354-613-7(0)***) Blue Apple Bks.

Peters, Craig. Dance Teams. 2003. (Let's Go Team Ser.). (Illus.). 64p. (J). (gr. 5 up). lib. bdg. (978-1-59084-540-0(4)) Mason Crest Pubs.

Porter, Tracey. A Dance of Sisters. 2002. 288p. (J). 17.89 (978-0-06-029239-3(3)) HarperCollins Pubs.

Rinaldi, Robin. European Dance: Ireland, Poland & Spain. (World of Dance Ser.). (Illus.). (gr. 9-13). 2004. 112p. pap. 30.00 (978-0-7910-7778-8(0)); 2003. 120p. 30.00 (978-0-7910-7643-9(1)) Facts On File, Inc. (Chelsea Hse.).

Seibert, Brian. George Balanchine. 2005. (Library of American Choreographers). (Illus.). 48p. (J). (ps-ps). lib. bdg. 23.95 (978-1-4042-0447-8(4)) Rosen Publishing Group, Inc., The.

Sing, Clap, & Dance with Ladybug. 2002. (J). (ps-1). 15.95 (978-0-8126-0054-4(1)) Cricket Bks.

Storey, Rita. Irish Dancing. 2006. (Get Dancing Ser.). (Illus.). 32p. (J). (978-1-59771-050-3(4)) Sea-To-Sea Pubns.

—Line Dancing. 2006. (Get Dancing Ser.). (Illus.). 32p. (J). (978-1-59771-052-7(0)) Sea-To-Sea Pubns.

—Rock 'n' Roll. 2006. (Get Dancing Ser.). (Illus.). 32p. (J). (978-1-59771-051-0(2)) Sea-To-Sea Pubns.

—Street Jazz. 2006. (Get Dancing Ser.). (Illus.). 32p. (978-1-59771-049-7(0)) Sea-To-Sea Pubns.

Thomas, Mark. African Dancing. 2001. (Let's Dance Ser.). (Illus.). 24p. (J). (ps-2). 17.00 (978-0-516-23141-9(3) , Children's Pr.) Scholastic Library Publishing.

—Irish Step Dancing. 2001. (Welcome Bks.). (Illus.). 24p. (J). (ps-2). pap. 4.95 (978-0-516-23068-9(9)); 17.00 (978-0-516-23143-3(X)) Scholastic Library Publishing. (Children's Pr.).

—Irish Step Dancing. 2001. (gr. k-3). lib. bdg. 12.95 (978-0-613-52096-6(3)) Tandem Library Bks.

—Jazz Dancing. 2001. (Let's Dance Ser.). (Illus.). 24p. (J). (ps-2). 17.00 (978-0-516-23144-0(8) , Children's Pr.) Scholastic Library Publishing.

—Jazz Dancing. 2001. (gr. k-3). lib. bdg. 12.95 (978-0-613-52101-7(3)) Tandem Library Bks.

—Square Dancing. 2001. (Let's Dance Ser.). (Illus.). 24p. (J). (ps-2). 17.00 (978-0-516-23145-7(6) , Children's Pr.) Scholastic Library Publishing.

—Square Dancing. 2001. (gr. k-3). lib. bdg. 12.95 (978-0-613-52187-1(0)) Tandem Library Bks.

—Tap Dancing. 2001. (Welcome Bks.). (Illus.). 24p. (J). (ps-2). pap. 4.95 (978-0-516-23071-9(9)); 17.00 (978-0-516-23146-4(4)) Scholastic Library Publishing. (Children's Pr.).

—Tap Dancing. 2001. (gr. k-3). lib. bdg. 12.95 (978-0-613-52194-9(3)) Tandem Library Bks.

Tierney, Tom. Ballet Princesses Paper Doll. 2005. 16p. (J). (gr. 3-6). pap. 4.95 (978-0-486-44468-0(6)) Dover Pubns., Inc.

Tobey, Cheryl. Modern Dance. 2001. (After School Ser.). (Illus.). 48p. (YA). (gr. 7-12). 23.00 (978-0-516-23152-5(9)); pap. 6.95 (978-0-516-29556-5(X)) Scholastic Library Publishing. (Children's Pr.).

—Modern Dance. 2001. (gr. 7-12). lib. bdg. 15.25 (978-0-613-58717-4(0)) Tandem Library Bks.

What tap dancing's all about according to Dr. Jeni Legon, 1. 2007. (Illus.). 38p. (J). spiral bd. 25.00 (***978-0-9795696-0-9(5)***) Haver, Nancy.

DANCE—FICTION

Advantage Publishers Group & Saidens, Amy. Ballerina Girl Sticker Book. 2007. (Illus.). 24p. (J). 14.95 (978-1-59223-633-6(2) , Silver Dolphin Bks.) Advantage Pubs. Group.

Aikins, Dave, illus. Bailando al Rescate (Dance to the Rescue) 2005. (Dora la Exploradora Ser.). (SPA.). 24p. (J). pap. 3.99 (978-1-4169-1504-1(4) , Libros Para Ninos) Simon & Schuster Children's Publishing.

Andersen, Hans Christian. The Red Shoes. ed. 2004. (Illus.). (J). (gr. 1-4). spiral bd. (978-0-616-14558-6(6)) Canadian National Institute for the Blind/Institut National Canadien pour les Aveugles.

Anderson, Doug. Too Big to Dance. Anderson, Sara, illus. 2004. 32p. (J). 15.95 (978-1-59354-046-3(9)) Handprint Bks.

Andreae, Giles. Giraffes Can't Dance. Parker-Rees, Guy, illus. (J). (ps-1). 2001. 32p. pap. 16.95 (978-0-439-28719-7(7) , Orchard Bks.); 2007. 29.95 incl. audio compact disk (***978-0-439-02734-2(9)***); 2007. 24.95 incl. audio (***978-0-439-02733-5(0)***) Scholastic, Inc.

Andrews, Sylvia. Dancing in My Bones. Mueller, Ellen, illus. 2001. (Growing Tree Ser.). 24p. (J). (ps-k). 10.99 (978-0-694-01316-6(1) , Harper Festival) HarperCollins Pubs.

Anholt, Laurence. Degas & the Little Dancer. 2007. (Anholt's Artists Books for Children Ser.). 32p. (J). (ps-3). pap. 7.99 (***978-0-7641-3852-2(9)***) Barron's Educational Series, Inc.

Appelt, Kathi. Rain Dance. Chollat, Emilie, illus. 2001. (Growing Tree Ser.). 24p. (J). (ps up). 9.95 (978-0-694-01291-6(2) , Harper Festival) HarperCollins Pubs.

Arnold, Marsha Diane. Prancing, Dancing Lily. Manders, John, illus. 2004. 32p. (J). (gr. k-3). 16.99 (978-0-8037-2823-3(9) , Dial) Penguin Group (USA) Inc.

Asch, Frank. Moondance. Asch, Frank, illus. 2002. (Moonbear Ser.). (Illus.). 13.83 (978-1-4046-0169-7(4)) Book Wholesalers, Inc.

Atkinson, Sally. The Tales of Tango Bk. III: The Fair of the Pharaohs. Netzel, Lee, illus. 1999. 32p. (J). 14.95 (978-0-9653034-2-2(X)) Tango's Grove Publishing.

Axelrod, Amy & McGinley-Nally, Sharon. Pigs in the Corner. 2001. (Pigs Will Be Pigs Ser.). (Illus.). 40p. (J). (ps-4). 15.95 (978-0-689-82470-8(X)) Simon & Schuster Children's Publishing.

Backx, Patsy. Skippy & Jack. Backx, Patsy, illus. 2002. (Illus.). 32p. (J). (ps up). lib. bdg. 24.67 (978-0-8368-3080-4(6)) Stevens, Gareth Inc.

Bader, Amanda. Havana Nights. 2004. (gr. 7-12). lib. bdg. 14.15 (978-0-613-71571-3(3)) Tandem Library Bks.

Barber, Antonia. Dancing Shoes: Into the Spotlight. (Illus.). 96p. (J). 5.95 (978-0-14-038683-7(1)) Penguin Group (USA) Inc.

—Dancing Shoes: Lucy's Next Step. (Illus.). 96p. (J). 6th ed. 5.95 (978-0-14-130150-1(3)); Vol. 4. 5.95 (978-0-14-038685-1(8)) Penguin Bks., Ltd. GBR. *Dist:* Trafalgar Square Publishing.

—Dancing Shoes: Making the Grade. (Illus.). 96p. (J). 5.95 (978-0-14-130149-5(X)) Penguin Bks., Ltd. GBR. *Dist:* Trafalgar Square Publishing.

—Dancing Shoes Friends & Rivals. (Illus.). 96p. (J). 5.95 (978-0-14-038684-4(X)) Penguin Group (USA) Inc.

—Lessons for Lucy. (Illus.). 96p. (J). 5.95 (978-0-14-038681-3(5)) Penguin Group (USA) Inc.

Barker, Cicely Mary. Flower Fairy Springtime Dance. 2006. (Flower Fairies Ser.). (Illus.). 24p. (J). 4.99 (978-0-7232-5726-4(4) , Warne) Penguin Group (USA) Inc.

Bazilian, Barbara. The Red Shoes. 2001. 40p. (J). (gr. 1-4). pap. 6.95 (978-1-58089-069-4(5)) Charlesbridge Publishing, Inc.

Bell, Cece. Sock Monkey Boogie-Woogie: A Friend Is Made. Bell, Cece, illus. 2004. (Illus.). 32p. (J). (ps-2). 14.99 (978-0-7636-2392-0(X)) Candlewick Pr.

Beller, Jasmine. Bring It On. 2006. (Hip-Hop Kidz Ser.: Vol. 1). 160p. (J). (gr. 4-7). pap. 4.99 (978-0-448-44362-1(7) , Grosset & Dunlap) Penguin Group (USA) Inc.

—Bust a Move. 2006. 156p. (J). ***(978-1-4156-9619-4(5)** , Grosset & Dunlap) Penguin Group (USA) Inc.

—Freaky #3. 2007. (Illus.). 160p. (J). pap. 4.99 (978-0-448-44364-5(3) , Grosset & Dunlap) Penguin Group (USA) Inc.

—Raise the Roof, No. 4. 2007. 160p. (J). pap. 4.99 (978-0-448-44445-1(3) , Grosset & Dunlap) Penguin Group (USA) Inc.

Bergman, Mara & Monks, Lydia. Glitter Kitty. 2007. (Illus.). 32p. (J). pap. 8.99 ***(978-0-689-87306-5(9))** Simon & Schuster, Ltd. GBR. *Dist:* Independent Pubs. Group.

Berton, Judy. City Dancin' Dancin' at Peppy's. Hernandez, Steven, illus. 2004. 36p. (J). per. 16.95 (978-0-9761051-0-7(1)) Kidrich Corp.

Brisson, Pat. Tap-Dance Fever. Cote, Nancy, illus. 2005. 32p. (J). (ps-ps). 15.95 (978-1-59078-290-3(9)) Boyds Mills Pr.

Brown, Marc. Buster & the Dance Contest. 2005. (Postcards from Buster Ser.). (Illus.). 32p. (J). (gr. 1-4). 14.99 (978-0-316-15889-3(5)); pap., pap. 3.99 (978-0-316-00118-2(X)) Little, Brown Bks. for Young Readers.

Brownrigg, Sheri. Todos los Tutus Deberian Ser Rosas. Johnson, Meredith, illus. 2002. (Coleccion "Hola, Lector" Ser.). (SPA.). 32p. (J). (gr. k-2). pap. 3.99 (978-0-439-25985-9(1) , SO30499, Scholastic en Espanol) Scholastic, Inc.

Bruna, Dick. Miffy Dances. 2004. 24p. 7.99 (978-1-59226-024-9(1)); (Illus.). pap. 4.99 (978-1-59226-010-2(1)) Big Tent Entertainment, Inc.

Bryant, Ann. Ballet Magic (Combined Volume) 2007. (Ballerina Dreams Ser.). 336p. (J). pap. 7.99 ***(978-0-7945-1740-3(4)** , Usborne) EDC Publishing.

—Dancing Friends (Combined Volume) 2007. (Ballerina Dreams Ser.). 336p. (J). pap. 7.99 ***(978-0-7945-1741-0(2)** , Usborne) EDC Publishing.

—Jasmine's Lucky Star. Benton, Tim, illus. 2006. 112p. (J). pap. 4.99 (978-0-7945-1295-8(X) , Usborne) EDC Publishing.

—Poppy's Secret Wish. Benton, Tim, illus. 2006. 112p. (J). pap. 4.99 (978-0-7945-1294-1(1) , Usborne) EDC Publishing.

—Rose's Big Decision. Benton, Tim, illus. 2006. 112p. (J). pap. 4.99 (978-0-7945-1296-5(8) , Usborne) EDC Publishing.

Bryant, Megan E. Dance with Me! 2007. (All Aboard Reading Ser.). 32p. (J). (ps-1). pap. 3.99 ***(978-0-448-44665-3(0)** , Grosset & Dunlap) Penguin Group (USA) Inc.

Burgard, Anna Marlis. Flying Feet: A Story of Irish Dance. Dees, Leighanne, illus. 2006. 31p. (J). (gr. 4-8). 16.00 (978-1-4223-5255-7(2)) DIANE Publishing Co.

Burgess, Melvin. Billy Elliot. 2001. 224p. (J). (gr. 5-12). pap. 4.50 (978-0-439-31228-8(0)) Scholastic, Inc.

Butler, Dori Hillestad. Trading Places with Tank Talbott. 2003. 136p. (J). (gr. 3-6). 15.95 (978-0-8075-1708-6(9)); pap. 6.95 (978-0-8075-8060-8(0)) Whitman, Albert & Co.

Calhoun, Dia. Aria of the Sea. 2003. 272p. (J). pap. 7.95 (978-0-374-40454-3(2) , Sunburst) Farrar, Straus & Giroux.

—Aria of the Sea. 2003. (gr. 5-8). lib. bdg. 16.40 (978-0-613-59572-8(6)) Tandem Library Bks.

—Aria of the Sea. (Illus.). (gr. 5-9). 2002. 340p. (YA). pap. 5.95 (978-1-58837-019-8(4)); 2000. 264p. (J). 15.95 (978-1-890817-25-1(2)) Winslow Pr.

—The Phoenix Dance. 2005. (Illus.). 288p. (YA). (gr. 9). 17.00 (978-0-374-35910-2(5) , Farrar, Straus & Giroux (BYR)) Farrar, Straus & Giroux.

Carlson, Nancy L. Harriet's Recital. 2006. (Illus.). (J). 15.95 (978-1-57505-898-6(7) , Carolrhoda Bks.) Lerner Publishing Group.

Carman, Debby. Cha Cha the Dancing Dog. 2006. (J). (978-0-9777340-5-4(6)) Faux Paw Media Group.

Carville, Declan & Ellis, Brandan. Kathleen O'Byrne: Irish Dancer. 2003. (Illus.). 32p. (C). 16.95 (978-1-57768-671-2(3) , Gingham Dog Pr.) School Specialty Publishing.

Cazet, Denys. Minnie & Moo Go Dancing. Cazet, Denys, illus. 2002. (Minnie & Moo Ser.). (Illus.). (J). 11.49 (978-0-7587-1443-5(2)) Book Wholesalers, Inc.

—Minnie & Moo Go Dancing. 1999. (Illus.). 48p. (J). pap. 15.95 (978-0-7737-3105-9(9)) Dorling Kindersley Publishing, Inc.

—Minnie & Moo Go Dancing. 2001. (Live Oak Readalong Ser.). (Illus.). (J). (ps-4). pap. 16.95 incl. audio (978-0-87499-721-7(6)) Live Oak Media.

Cirrone, Dorian. Dancing in Red Shoes Will Kill You. 2005. 224p. (J). (gr. 7 up). 15.99 (978-0-06-055701-0(X)) HarperCollins Pubs.

Clement, Rod. Olga the Brolga. Clement, Rod, illus. 2004. (Illus.). 32p. 14.95 (978-0-207-19701-7(6)) HarperCollins Pubs. AUS. *Dist:* Consortium Bk. Sales & Distribution.

Contijoch, Josefa. Mariquilla va de Fiesta. Filella, Lluis, illus. 2003. (Caballo Alado Ser.). (SPA & ENG.). 24p. 6.95 (978-84-7864-648-7(5)) Combel Editorial, S.A. ESP. *Dist:* Independent Pubs. Group.

Conway, Celeste. The Melting Season. 2006. 288p. (YA). (gr. 7). 17.99 (978-0-385-90357-8(X)); 15.95 (978-0-385-73339-7(9)) Random Hse. Children's Bks. (Delacorte Bks. for Young Readers).

Corbett, Kat. First-String Future. 2000. (gr. 7-12). lib. bdg. 22.20 (978-0-613-83507-7(7)) Tandem Library Bks.

—First-String Future. 2000. 220p. (YA). (gr. 7-12). pap. 12.95 (978-0-595-12738-2(X)) iUniverse, Inc.

Coxe, Molly. Fox Trot. 1999. (Road to Reading Ser.). (J). lib. bdg. (978-0-03-074629-1(9) , Saunders) Elsevier - Health Sciences Division.

Crimi, Carolyn. Tessa's Tip-Tapping Toes. Carrington, Marsha Gray, illus. 2002. 32p. (J). (ps-2). pap. 16.95 (978-0-439-31768-9(1) , Orchard Bks.) Scholastic, Inc.

Cronin, Doreen. Wiggle. Menchin, Scott, illus. 2005. 40p. (J). 12.95 (978-0-689-86375-2(6) , Atheneum) Simon & Schuster Children's Publishing.

Dadey, Debbie & Jones, Marcia Thornton. Wolfmen Don't Hula Dance. 1999. (Bailey School Kids Ser.: No.36). (gr. 3-6). lib. bdg. 11.80 (978-0-613-17044-4(X)) Tandem Library Bks.

Dalecki, Linden. Kid B. 2006. 178p. (J). (gr. 8). pap. 7.99 (978-0-618-60566-8(5)) Houghton Mifflin Co.

Daly, Niki & Turkington, Nola. Dancer. 2004. (Illus.). 36p. (J). pap. 7.95 (978-1-84507-181-3(6)) Lincoln, Frances Ltd. GBR. *Dist:* Perseus Distribution.

De Anda, Diane. Dancing Miranda. Castilla, Julia Mercedes, tr. from ENG. Alvarez, Lamberto, illus. 2001. Tr. of Baila, Miranda, Baila. (SPA & ENG.). 32p. (J). (ps-3). 14.95 (978-1-55885-323-2(5) , Piñata Books) Arte Publico Pr.

de Paola, Tomie. Oliver Button Es una Nena. 2001. (SPA., Illus.). (J). (gr. k-2). 8.95 (978-84-355-0631-1(2) , LEC6312) Minon, S.A. ESP. *Dist:* Continental Bk. Co., Inc., Lectorum Pubns., Inc.

DePrisco, Dorothea. Dinosaur Dance. 2006. 12p. 9.95 (978-1-58117-480-9(2) , Intervisual/Piggy Toes) Dalmatian Pr.

Derrick, Patricia. Montgomery the Moose. 2007. 32p. 18.95 (978-1-933818-18-4(2)) Animalations.

Doyle, Bill. Betrayed! The 1977 Journal of Zeke Moorie. Hoskins, Brian, illus. 2006. 139p. (J). lib. bdg. 18.46 ***(978-1-4242-1733-5(4))** Fitzgerald Bks.

—Betrayed! The 1977 Journal of Zeke Moorie. 4th ed. 2006. (Crime Through Time Ser.: No. 4). 144p. (J). (gr. 3-7). pap. 5.99 (978-0-316-05741-7(X)) Little Brown & Co.

—ICED: The 2007 Journal of Nick Fitzmorgan. 5th ed. 2006. (Crime Through Time Ser.: No. 5). (Illus.). 144p. (J). (gr. 3-7). pap. 5.99 (978-0-316-05753-0(3)) Little Brown & Co.

—Trapped: The 2031 Journal of Otis Fitzmorgan. 6th ed. 2006. (Crime Through Time Ser.: No. 6). 144p. (J). (gr. 3-7). pap. 5.99 (978-0-316-05754-7(1)) Little Brown & Co.

Driscoll, Laura. Dance to the Rescue. Aikins, Dave, illus. 2005. 24p. (J). lib. bdg. 9.00 ***(978-1-4242-0981-1(1))** Fitzgerald Bks.

DuJardin, Rosamond. Senior Prom. 2003. (YA). pap. 12.95 (978-1-930009-77-6(1) , 800-691-7779) Image Cascade Publishing.

Elliott, David. Evangeline Mudd & the Great Mink Escapade. Wesson, Andrea, illus. 2006. 192p. (J). (gr. 2-5). 15.99 (978-0-7636-2295-4(8)) Candlewick Pr.

Elliott, David. One Little Chicken: A Counting Book. Long, Ethan, illus. 2007. 24p. (J). (ps-k). 16.95 ***(978-0-8234-1983-8(5))** Holiday Hse., Inc.

Finsterbusch, Monika. Princess Lillifee. 2006. (Illus.). 28p. (J). (ps-3). 12.95 (978-0-8109-5722-0(1) , Abrams Bks. for Young Readers) Abrams, Harry N. , Inc.

Fitzgerald, Kevin. Dancing in the Moonlight. Fitzgerald, Anita, illus. 2005. (J). (978-0-9765987-4-9(4)) Foundation, Pr. The.

Fox, Paula. The Slave Dancer. Eros, Keith, illus. 2002. (J). 14.47 (978-0-7587-0214-2(0)) Book Wholesalers, Inc.

—The Slave Dancer. unabr. ed. 2004. 152p. (J). (gr. 5-9). pap. 38.00 incl. audio (978-0-8072-0458-0(7) , Listening Library) Random Hse. Audio Publishing Group.

French, Jackie. Josephine Wants to Dance. Whatley, Bruce, illus. 2007. 32p. (J). (ps-1). 15.95 ***(978-0-8109-9431-7(3)** , Abrams Bks. for Young Readers) Abrams, Harry N. , Inc.

French, Vivian. Princess Sophia & the Prince's Party. Gibb, Sarah, illus. 2007. (J). ***(978-0-06-112450-1(8));** (Tiara Club Ser.: No. 11). 80p. pap. 3.99 ***(978-0-06-112449-5(4)** , Harper Trophy) HarperCollins Pubs.

Freymann-Weyr, Garret. The Kings Are Already Here. 2003. 160p. (YA). (gr. 7). tchr. ed. 15.00 (978-0-618-26363-9(2)) Houghton Mifflin Co. Trade & Reference Div.

Friedlander, Tim. The I Like Me Dance. 2007. 32p. (J). (ps-3). 14.95 ***(978-1-933721-07-1(3))** Playdate Kids Publishing.

Friedman, Dawn. Dance, Annie. Bosch, Nicole in den, illus. 2001. (Rookie Reader Skill Set Ser.). 24p. (J). (gr. k-2). pap. 4.95 (978-0-516-27289-4(6) , Children's Pr.) Scholastic Library Publishing.

—Dance, Annie. 2001. (gr. k-3). lib. bdg. 12.95 (978-0-613-54158-9(8)) Tandem Library Bks.

Fruchter, Jason, illus. Let's Dance! 2005. (Paint Box Book Ser.). 32p. (J). (ps-2). 3.99 (978-0-375-83478-3(8) , Golden Bks.) Random Hse. Children's Bks.

Galjanic, Lisa. When Flowers Dance. Hope, Michelle, illus. 2007. (J). 9.95 (978-1-933532-05-9(X)) LSG Pubns.

Gallagher, Diana G. Dance Trap: The Complicated Life of Claudia Cristina Cortez. Garvey, Brann, illus. 2008. (J). pap. ***(978-1-59889-879-8(5));** 81p. (gr. 4-8). lib. bdg. 23.93 ***(978-1-59889-841-5(8))** Stone Arch Bks.

Gambassi, Rod. The Boy Who Wanted to be a Dancer. Brownlee, Kelly Jackson, illus. 2007. 22p. (J). 23.95 ***(978-1-889829-18-0(8))** Window Bks.

Gauch, Patricia Lee. Tanya & Emily in a Dance for Two. 1998. (978-0-606-13838-3(2)) Tandem Library Bks.

Geras, Adèle. Like a Real Ballerina. McNicholas, Shelagh, illus. 2008. 32p. (J). (ps). 16.99 ***(978-0-8037-3237-7(6)** , Dial) Penguin Group (USA) Inc.

Gerber, Carole. Jessica Mcbean, Tap Dance Queen. Barton, Patrice, illus. 144p. (J). 2007. per. (978-0-9718348-9-7(X)); 2006. 13.95 (978-0-9718348-7-3(3)) Blooming Tree Pr.

Giff, Patricia Reilly. Fancy Feet. 77p. (J). (gr. 1-2). pap. 3.99 (978-0-8072-1279-0(2) , Listening Library) Random Hse. Audio Publishing Group.

Gloria Whelan. The Turning. l.t. ed. 2006. 190p. (YA). 21.95 (978-0-7862-9035-2(8)) Thorndike Pr.

Golden Books Staff. Rising Stars. Duarte, Pamela, illus. 2004. (Barbie Ser.). 64p. (J). (ps-2). 2.99 (978-0-375-82649-8(1) , Golden Bks.) Random Hse. Children's Bks.

Golembe, Carla. The Story of Hula. 2004. (Illus.). 32p. (J). 16.95 incl. audio compact disk (978-1-57306-185-8(9)) Bess Pr., Inc.

Graves, Keith. Frank Was a Monster Who Wanted to Dance. 1999. (Illus.). 32p. (J). (ps-3). 13.95 (978-0-8118-2169-8(2)) Chronicle Bks. LLC.

Gray, Libba Moore. My Mama Had a Dancing Heart. Colon, Raul, illus. 2001. pap. 35.95 incl. audio compact disk (978-1-59112-543-3(X)) Live Oak Media.

—My Mama Had a Dancing Heart. 1999. (gr. k-3). lib. bdg. 14.10 (978-0-613-28968-9(4)) Tandem Library Bks.

Greaves, Margaret. Stories from the Ballet. Kopper, Lisa, illus. 2004. 72p. (J). pap. 12.95 (978-1-84507-269-8(3)) Lincoln, Frances Ltd. GBR. *Dist:* Perseus Distribution.

—Stories from the Ballet. Kopper, Lisa, tr. Kopper, Lisa, illus. 2003. 72p. (J). pap. 12.95 (978-0-7112-2162-8(6)) Lincoln, Frances Ltd. GBR. *Dist:* Transition Vendor.

—Stories from the Ballet. Kopper, Lisa, illus. 2002. 72p. (J). pap. 13.95 (978-0-7112-1356-2(9)) Lincoln, Frances Ltd. GBR. *Dist:* Raincoast Bk. Distribution, Star Bright Bks., Inc.

Griffin, Margot. Dance of Life. Burden, John, illus. 2004. 112p. (J). pap. (978-1-55005-125-4(3)) Fitzhenry & Whiteside, Ltd.

Gruska, Denise Eliana. The Only Boy in Ballet Class. Wummer, Amy, illus. 2007. 32p. (J). (ps-3). 15.95 ***(978-1-4236-0220-0(X))** Gibbs Smith, Publisher.

Hager, Sarah. Dancing Matilda. Murphy, Kelly, illus. 2005. 40p. (J). (ps-2). 15.99 (978-0-06-051452-5(3)); lib. bdg. 16.89 (978-0-06-051453-2(1)) HarperCollins Pubs.

Hall, Kirsten. Ballerina Girl. Kennedy, Anne, illus. 2003. 32p. (J). 18.50 (978-0-516-22921-8(4) , Children's Pr.) Scholastic Library Publishing.

Hanson, Warren. Bugtown Boogie. 2008. 32p. (J). 16.99 ***(978-0-06-059937-9(5));** lib. bdg. 17.89 ***(978-0-06-059938-6(3))** HarperCollins Pubs. (Geringer, Laura Book).

Harcourt School Publishers Staff. I Want to Be Me. 3rd ed. 2002. (Trophies English Language Learners Ser.). (Illus.). pap. 5.10 (978-0-15-327829-7(3)) Harcourt Schl. Pubs.

—Ready to Dance! Take-Home Book. rev. ed. 2001. (Collections Ser.: Bk. 18). (Illus.). (J). pap. 1.90 (978-0-15-319076-6(0)) Harcourt Schl. Pubs.

Hardy, Lorien. The Snow Dance. Trover, Zachary, illus. 2006. (Read-It! Readers Ser.). (J). 19.93 (978-1-4048-2421-8(9)) Picture Window Bks.

Havill, Juanita. Brianna, Jamaica, & the Dance of Spring. O'Brien, Anne Sibley, illus. 2002. 32p. (J). (gr. 4-6). 16.00 (978-0-618-07700-7(6)) Houghton Mifflin Co. Trade & Reference Div.

Hedderwick, Mairi. Katie Morag & the Dancing Class. 32p. (J). 2008. pap. 12.95 ***(978-1-86230-221-1(9));** 2007. (Illus.). 17.95 ***(978-0-370-32910-9(4))** Transworld Publishers Ltd. GBR. *Dist:* Independent Pubs. Group.

Heidbreder, Robe. Drumheller Dinosaur Dance. Slavin, Bill, illus. 2006. 32p. (978-1-55337-982-9(9)) Kids Can Pr., Ltd.

Heidbreder, Robert. Drumheller Dinosaur Dance. Slavin, Bill & Melo, Esperanca, illus. 2005. 32p. (J). (ps-1). (978-1-55337-393-3(6)) Kids Can Pr., Ltd.

Helldorfer, M. C. Got to Dance. Nakata, Hiroe, illus. 2004. 32p. (J). (gr. k-k). lib. bdg. 17.99 (978-0-385-90865-8(2) , Doubleday Bks. for Young Readers) Random Hse. Children's Bks.

Hoff, Syd. Oliver! Hoff, Syd, illus. 2002. (Illus.). pap. 18.95 incl. audio compact disk (978-1-59112-660-7(6)); pap. 31.95 incl. audio compact disk (978-1-59112-661-4(4)); (J). pap. 16.95 incl. audio (978-0-87499-902-0(2)) Live Oak Media.

Holabird, Katharine. All Dancers on Deck. Craig, Helen, illus. 2006. (Angelina Ballerina Ser.). 32p. (J). (ps-1). 3.99 (978-0-448-44388-1(0) , Grosset & Dunlap) Penguin Group (USA) Inc.

—The Angelina's Diary No. 4. Craig, Helen, illus. 2006. (Angelina Ballerina Ser.). 80p. (J). (gr. 1-3). 3.99 (978-0-448-44386-7(4) , Grosset & Dunlap) Penguin Group (USA) Inc.

—Let's Dance! Craig, Helen, illus. 2007. (Angelina Ballerina Ser.). 14p. (J). 10.99 (978-0-448-44470-3(4) , Grosset & Dunlap) Penguin Group (USA) Inc.

Hula Girl. 2000. (YA). 3.49 (978-0-89610-391-7(9)) Island Heritage Publishing.

Isadora, Rachel. Max. Isadora, Rachel, illus. 2002. (Illus.). (J). 13.40 (978-0-7587-6689-2(0)) Book Wholesalers, Inc.

James, Brian. Everybody Hates School Dances. 2007. (Everybody Hates Chris Ser.). 96p. (J). pap. 5.99 ***(978-1-4169-3562-9(2)** , Simon Spotlight) Simon & Schuster Children's Publishing.

James, Susan. This Is My Dance: Sing, Dance & Read with Me, Read-Along with Big Book & Cassette. 2000. 16p. (J). (ps-3). pap. 14.95 incl. audio (978-1-931127-32-5(8) , 986-011) Kindermusik International.

—This Is My Dance: Sing, Dance & Read with Me, Read-Along with Big Book, & Instrument. 2000. 16p. (J). (ps-3). pap. 29.95 incl. audio compact disk (978-1-931127-34-9(4) , 986-012) Kindermusik International.

—This Is My Dance: Sing, Dance & Read with Me, Read-Along with Small Book. 2000. 16p. (J). (ps-3). pap. 9.95 incl. audio (978-1-931127-33-2(6) , 986-010) Kindermusik International.

Jennings, Sharon. Priscilla's Paw de Deux. Hendry, Linda, illus. 2002. 36p. (J). (ps-2). (978-1-55041-718-0(5)) Fitzhenry & Whiteside, Ltd.

Joachimowski, Paula L. Swamp Band Lullaby. 2007. (J). per. 12.99 ***(978-1-59879-211-9(3))** Lifevest Publishing, Inc.

Jones, Sally Lloyd. Farmyard Boogie. Abel, Simone, illus. 2001. (Flip Flap Ser.). 10p. (J). bds. 8.95 (978-1-57145-547-5(7) , Silver Dolphin Bks.) Advantage Pubs. Group.

Jones, Sally Lloyd & Abel, Simone, illus. Jungle Jive! 2001. (Flip Flap Ser.). 10p. (J). bds. 8.95 (978-1-57145-548-2(5) , Silver Dolphin Bks.) Advantage Pubs. Group.

Kaldor, Connie. A Duck in New York City. 2005. (Illus.). 36p. (J). (ps-3). 16.95 incl. audio compact disk (978-2-923163-02-4(8)) La Montagne Secrete CAN. *Dist:* National Bk. Network.

Kalkipsakis, Thalia. Go Girl! #7 - Dancing Queen. Oswald, Ash, illus. 2008. (Go Girl! Ser.). 96p. (J). pap. 3.99 ***(978-0-312-34651-5(4))** Feiwel & Friends.

Kanter, Angela. My Ballerina Sister. 2002. (Illus.). 64p. pap. 8.99 (978-0-09-941702-6(2)) Random Hse. GBR. *Dist:* Trafalgar Square Publishing.

—My Ballerina Sister on Stage. 2002. (Illus.). 64p. (J). pap. 8.99 (978-0-09-941703-3(0)) Random Hse. GBR. *Dist:* Independent Pubs. Group.

Kenrick, Joanna & Weir, Doffy. Moondance. 2004. (Illus.). 32p. (J). 19.99 (978-1-84270-324-3(2)) Andersen GBR. *Dist:* Independent Pubs. Group.

Kinerk, Robert. Clorinda. Kellogg, Steven, illus. 2007. 40p. (J). (ps-3). pap. 6.99 ***(978-1-4169-3964-1(4)** , Aladdin) Simon & Schuster Children's Publishing.

Knister. Sophie's Dance. Schlundt, Mandy, illus. 2007. 32p. (J). 16.99 ***(978-0-698-40056-6(9)** , Minedition) Penguin Group (USA) Inc.

Kurtis-Kleinman, Eileen. When Aunt Lena Did the Rhumba. 1999. (978-0-606-16664-5(5)) Tandem Library Bks.

Ladybird Books Staff. Daisy, Little Dancer: Little Stories. 1998. (Little Dancing Stories Ser.). (Illus.). 32p. (J). 2.50 (978-0-7214-1924-4(0) , Dutton Juvenile) Penguin Group (USA) Inc.

Lee, Kathy. Phoebe Finds Her Feet. 2004. 128p. 6.49 (978-1-85999-701-7(5)) Scripture Union GBR. *Dist:* Gabriel Resources.

Lee, Quinlan B. Bungee Boo Dance! 2004. (Boohbah Ser.). (Illus.). 22p. (J). bds. 4.99 (978-0-439-59089-1(2)) Scholastic, Inc.

Lehr, Norma. Dance of the Crystal Skull. rev. exp. ed. 2003. (Illus.). 238p. (J). (gr. 3-7). lib. bdg. 15.95 (978-0-87358-724-2(3) , Rising Moon Bks. for Young Readers) Northland Publishing.

—Dance of the Crystal Skull. 1999. (Illus.). (J). (978-0-606-18310-9(8)) Tandem Library Bks.

Let's Dance. 2003. (J). per. (978-1-57657-875-9(5)) Paradise Pr., Inc.

Levy, Elizabeth. Seventh-Grade Tango. 2001. (J). (978-0-606-22571-7(4)) Tandem Library Bks.

—Seventh-Grade Tango. l.t. ed. 2001. (Illus.). 174p. (J). (gr. 3-7). 20.95 (978-0-7862-3105-8(X)) Thorndike Pr.

Lincoln, Rosalie. Arnat Castun Pillerkat Assigeskuneng. Lincoln, Rosalie & Nevak, Caroline, illus. l.t. ed. 1999. Tr. of What Girls Should Do When Eskimo Dancing. (ESK.). 16p. (J). (gr. k-3). pap. 21.00 (978-1-58084-111-5(2)) Lower Kuskokwim Schl. District.

—Nasaurluum Yurallra. Lincoln, Rosalie & Nevak, Caroline, illus. l.t. ed. 1999. Tr. of What Girls Should Do When Eskimo Dancing. (ESK.). 16p. (J). (gr. k-3). pap. 21.00 (978-1-58084-065-1(5)) Lower Kuskokwim Schl. District.

—What Girls Should Do When Eskimo Dancing. Lincoln, Rosalie & Nevak, Caroline, illus. l.t. ed. 1999. 16p. (J). (gr. k-3). pap. 20.00 (978-1-58084-064-4(7)) Lower Kuskokwim Schl. District.

Lord, Michelle. Little Sap & Monsieur Rodin. Hoshino, Felicia, illus. 2006. 32p. (J). (ps-3). 16.95 (978-1-58430-248-3(8)) Lee & Low Bks., Inc.

Lukas, Sarah. Dragon Dance. 2003. (Illus.). (J). bds. 6.99 (978-0-375-82340-4(9)) Random Hse. Children's Bks.

Malcolm, Jahnna N. Battle of the Bunheads. 2000. (Bad News Ballet Ser.: Vol. 2). Tr. of fantome d'Ivan Scapinsky. 160p. (J). (gr. 4-6). pap. 3.95 (978-0-9700164-1-6(7)) Starcatcher Pr.

Marzollo, Jean. Shanna's Ballerina Show. Evans, Shane, illus. 2003. 24p. (ps-2). pap. 3.50 (978-0-7868-1758-0(5)) Hyperion Bks. for Children.

—Shanna's Ballerina Show. 2003. (gr. k-3). lib. bdg. 11.25 (978-0-613-68386-9(2)) Tandem Library Bks.

Masurel, Claire. Emily's Dance Class. Peskin, Joy, ed. Calitri, Susan, illus. 2001. (Picture Puffin Ser.). 16p. (J). (ps-k). pap. 6.99 (978-0-14-056758-8(5) , Puffin) Penguin Group (USA) Inc.

Mathers, Petra. Sophie & Lou. 2001. (978-0-606-22257-0(X)) Tandem Library Bks.

May, Tessa. Bella Wishes. Rodriguez, Dave, illus. 2004. 35p. pap. 13.95 incl. audio compact disk (978-0-9759325-0-6(0)) CarLou Interactive Media & Publishing.

McCoy, Karen Kawamoto. Bon Odori Dancer. Yao, Carolina, illus. 1998. 32p. (J). (gr. 1-4). pap. 14.95 (978-1-879965-16-4(X)) Polychrome Publishing Corp.

McDaniel, Lurlene. Last Dance. 2006. (YA). pap. 4.99 (978-1-58196-031-0(X)) Darby Creek Publishing.

McKissack, Patricia C. Mirandy & Brother Wind. 2002. (Illus.). (J). 14.79 (978-0-7587-3143-2(4)) Book Wholesalers, Inc.

McLaren, Clemence. Dance for the Aina. 2003. 160p. 9.95 (978-1-57306-151-3(4)) Bess Pr., Inc.

Medearis, Angela Shelf. Dancing with the Indians. Byrd, Samuel, illus. 2000. pap. 18.95 incl. audio compact disk (978-1-59519-248-6(4)); pap. 39.95 incl. audio compact disk (978-1-59519-249-3(2)) Live Oak Media.

Meyer, Carolyn. Marie, Dancing. 2007. (Illus.). 272p. (YA). (gr. 7 up). pap. 6.95 (978-0-15-205879-1(6) , Harcourt Paperbacks) Harcourt Children's Bks.

Michalak, Jamie. Larry & Rita. Newton, Jill, illus. 2007. (Brand New Readers Ser.). 1p. (J). (ps-2). pap. 5.99 (***978-0-7636-2964-9(2)***) Candlewick Pr.

Michelson, Richard. Happy Feet: The Savoy Ballroom Lindy Hoppers & Me. Lewis, E. B., illus. 2005. 32p. (J). (ps-ps). 16.00 (978-0-15-205057-3(4)) Harcourt Children's Bks.

Mills, Liz, ed. Little Lamb: A Pull-the Tab Cloth Book. 2005. (Little Lamb Ser.). (J). 7.99 (978-0-439-71013-8(8) , Cartwheel Bks.) Scholastic, Inc.

Mills, Nancy Libbey. And Dance with the Orange Cow. Wells, Shan, illus. 2003. 32p. (J). pap. 7.95 (978-1-893815-10-0(2)); per. 12.95 (978-1-893815-09-4(9)) Pie in the Sky Publishing, LLC.

Milord, Susan. If I Could. Denise, Christopher, illus. 2008. 32p. (J). (gr. k-1). 15.99 (978-0-7636-2348-7(2)) Candlewick Pr.

Mitton, Tony. Down by the Cool of the Pool. Parker-Rees, Guy, illus. 2002. 32p. (J). (ps-k). pap. 15.95 (978-0-439-30915-8(8) , Orchard Bks.) Scholastic, Inc.

Morgan, Richard & Rose, Maddy. Dance Fever. 2007. (Illus.). 24p. (J). pap. 9.95 (***978-1-86230-161-0(1)***) Transworld Publishers Ltd. GBR. *Dist:* Independent Pubs. Group.

Morris, Oradel N. Little Angel Dancer. Morris, Oradel N., ed. 1999. (Illus.). (Orig.). (J). (gr. 1-8). pap. (978-0-944064-06-1(X)) Paupieres Publishing Co.

Moss, Alexandra. Belle's Best Move, No. 3. 2005. (Royal Ballet School Diaries: No. 3). 144p. (gr. 3-5). mass mkt. 4.99 (978-0-448-43769-9(4) , Grosset & Dunlap) Penguin Group (USA) Inc.

—Sophie's Flight of Fancy, No. 4. 2005. (Royal Ballet School Diaries: No. 4). 144p. (gr. 3-5). mass mkt. 4.99 (978-0-448-43770-5(8) , Grosset & Dunlap) Penguin Group (USA) Inc.

Mouse Works Staff. Noodle Dance! Chunky Roly Poly. 1999. (P B & J Otter Noodle Stories Ser.). (Illus.). 16p. (J). bds. 3.50 (978-0-7364-0011-4(7)) Mouse Works.

Munoz, Claudio, illus. Dream Dancer. 2002. 32p. (J). (ps-3). 15.95 (978-0-06-000932-8(2)) HarperCollins Pubs.

Newsome, Jill. Dream Dancer. 2002. (Illus.). 32p. (J). (ps-3). 15.89 (978-0-06-001322-6(2)) HarperCollins Pubs.

Nobisso, Josephine. The Numbers Dance: A Counting Comedy. Ziborova, Dasha, illus. 2005. 32p. (J). (ps-4). 16.95 (978-0-940112-11-7(6)); pap. 8.95 (978-0-940112-12-4(4)) Gingerbread Hse.

Nolan, Han. Dancing on the Edge. 1999. 256p. (gr. 3-6). pap. 6.99 (978-0-14-130203-4(8) , Puffin) Penguin Group (USA) Inc.

—Dancing on the Edge. 1999. (J). 12.64 (978-0-606-16836-6(2)); (gr. 7-12). lib. bdg. 14.15 (978-0-613-15338-6(3)) Tandem Library Bks.

Norton, Jack, Jr. Natasha Goes to the Brush Dance. 2000. pap. 16.50 (978-0-9740071-3-0(0)) Ctr. for the Affirmation of Responsible Education.

Numeroff, Laura Joffe & Evans, Nate. The Jellybeans. 2008. 32p. (J). 15.95 (***978-0-8109-9352-5(X)*** , Abrams Bks. for Young Readers) Abrams, Harry N., Inc.

O'Connor, Ilett. The Dancer 2 Cristina & the Magic Ball. unabr. ed. 2002. 45p. (J). pap. 12.00 (978-0-9717003-5-2(4)) O'Connor, Ilett K.

O'Connor, Jane. Nina, Nina & the Copycat Ballerina. DiSalvo-Ryan, DyAnne, illus. 2000. (All Aboard Reading Ser.). 32p. (J). (ps-1). pap. 3.99 (978-0-448-42151-3(8) , Grosset & Dunlap) Penguin Group (USA) Inc.

—Nina, Nina & the Copycat Ballerina. 2000. (All Aboard Reading Ser.). (978-0-606-18472-4(4)) Tandem Library Bks.

—Nina, Nina, & the Copycat Ballerina. 2000. (gr. k-3). lib. bdg. 11.80 (978-0-613-26400-6(2)) Tandem Library Bks.

Ormerod, Jan & Gardiner, Lindsey. Doing the Animal Bop. 2005. 32p. (J). pap. 8.99 incl. audio compact disk (978-0-7641-7899-3(7)) Barron's Educational Series, Inc.

Osborne. The Boy who Loved to Shim-sham Shimmy. 2004. (Illus.). 40p. (J). lib. bdg. 14.95 (978-0-9762852-0-5(7)) Wooden Shoe Pr.

Ostow, Micol. Emily Goldberg Learns to Salsa. 2006. 288p. (YA). (gr. 7-12). 16.99 (978-1-59514-081-4(6) , Razorbill) Penguin Group (USA) Inc.

Oxenbury, Helen. La Clase de Baile (Dance Class) (SPA.). 16p. (J). 7.50 (978-84-261-1947-6(6)) Juventud, Editorial ESP. *Dist:* AIMS International Bks., Inc.

Phipps, Alisha. Growing up with Allie: The Dance. 2005. 58p. pap. 12.95 (978-1-4137-9713-8(X)) PublishAmerica, Inc.

Pinkwater, Daniel M. Dancing Larry. Pinkwater, Daniel M. & Pinkwater, Jill, illus. 2006. 32p. (J). 16.95 (978-0-7614-5220-1(6)) Cavendish, Marshall Corp.

Porter, Tracey. A Dance of Sisters. 288p. (J). (gr. 3-7). 2002. 15.99 (978-0-06-028182-3(0) , Cotler, Joanna Books); 2005. reprint ed. pap. 5.99 (978-0-06-440751-9(9)) HarperCollins Pubs.

Princess Aurora: A Special Day in Her Life. l.t. ed. 2005. (Illus.). 32p. (J). 5.95 (978-0-9766640-0-0(3) , 212-279-3492) Attitudes in Dressing, Inc.

Quattlebaum, Mary. Sparks Fly High: The Legend of Dancing Point. Gore, Leonid, illus. 2006. 40p. (J). 16.00 (978-0-374-34452-8(3)) Farrar, Straus & Giroux.

Rachael's First Year at Dance School. 2000. (J). 10.95 (978-0-9764071-8-8(3)) Torbert, Margot.

Raczek, Linda Theresa. Rainy's Powwow. Bennett, Gary, illus. 1999. 32p. (J). (gr. k-3). 15.95 (978-0-87358-686-3(7) , Rising Moon Bks. for Young Readers) Northland Publishing.

Reader's Digest Staff. Ballerina Zoe. 2006. (Sesame Street Ser.). 12p. (J). 14.99 (978-0-7944-1111-4(8)) Reader's Digest Assn., Inc., The.

Redbank, Tennant. Barbie in the Twelve Dancing Princesses. 2006. (Step into Reading Ser.). (Illus.). 32p. (J). (ps-2). lib. bdg. 11.99 (978-0-375-93780-4(3) , Random Hse. Bks. for Young Readers) Random Hse. Children's Bks.

Redbank, Tennant & Golden Books Staff. Barbie in the Twelve Dancing Princesses. 2006. (Step into Reading Ser.: No. 2). (Illus.). 32p. (J). (ps-2). pap. 3.99 (978-0-375-83780-7(9) , Random Hse. Bks. for Young Readers) Random Hse. Children's Bks.

Reilly, Dee Dee. Teaching Agnes to Dance. Walker, Betsy, illus. l.t. ed. 1999. 40p. (J). (ps-3). 14.95 (978-0-9669497-0-4(6)) Reilly Enterprises.

Ricci, Christine. Dance with Uniqua! Hall, Susan', illus. 2006. (Backyardigans Ser.). 10p. (J). bds. 9.99 (978-1-4169-1535-5(4) , Simon Spotlight/Nickelodeon) Simon & Schuster Children's Publishing.

Roberts, Brenda C. Jazzy Miz Mozetta. Morrison, Frank, illus. 2004. 32p. (J). 16.50 (978-0-374-33674-5(1)) Farrar, Straus & Giroux.

Rodda, Emily. The Flower Fairies. Vitale, Raoul, illus. 2003. (Fairy Realm Ser.: No. 2). 128p. (J). 8.99 (978-0-06-009586-4(5)); lib. bdg. 15.89 (978-0-06-009587-1(3)) HarperCollins Pubs.

Rovetch, Lissa. Frog Went A-Dancing. Berry, Holly, illus. 2006. (J). (978-1-58987-008-6(5)) Kindermusik International.

Ryder, Joanne. Dance by the Light of the Moon. Francis, Guy, illus. 2007. 40p. (ps-1). 15.99 (978-0-7868-1820-4(4)) Hyperion Pr.

Samuels, Barbara. Dolores on Her Toes. Samuels, Barbara, illus. 2003. (Dolores Ser.). (Illus.). 40p. (J). 16.50 (978-0-374-31818-5(2) , Farrar, Straus & Giroux (BYR)) Farrar, Straus & Giroux.

Sargent, Dave, et al. Tattoos of Honor Vol. 17: (Osage) Be Gentle & Giving, 20 bks. Lenoir, Jane, illus. l.t. ed. 2004. (Story Keeper Ser.: Vol. 17). 42p. (J). pap. 6.95 (978-1-56763-936-0(4)); lib. bdg. 22.60 (978-1-56763-935-3(6)) Ozark Publishing.

Say, Allen. Music for Alice. 2004. (Illus.). 32p. (J). (gr. k-3). tchr. ed. 17.00 (978-0-618-31118-7(1) , Walter Lorraine) Houghton Mifflin Co. Trade & Reference Div.

Schaefer, Carole Lexa. Dragon Dancing. Morgan, Pierr, illus. 2006. 40p. (J). (ps-1). 16.99 (978-0-670-06084-9(4) , Viking Juvenile) Penguin Group (USA) Inc.

Schick, Eleanor. I Am: I Am a Dancer. 2002. (Illus.). 32p. (J). (gr. k-3). 15.95 (978-0-7614-5097-9(1) , Cavendish Children's Bks.) Cavendish, Marshall Corp.

School Specialty Publishing. My Very Best Coloring & Activity Book: Hippo Dance. 2002. 120p. (J). (gr. k-3). pap. 1.99 (978-0-7696-2789-2(7) , American Education Publishing) School Specialty Publishing.

Schulz. Permetti Questo Ballo Charl. pap. 19.95 (978-88-451-8058-3(1)) Fabbri - RCS Libri ITA. *Dist:* Distribooks, Inc.

Schutz, Samantha & Burr, Daniela. Barbie in the Twelve Dancing Princesses. 2006. (Illus.). 80p. (J). pap. 3.99 (978-0-439-87003-0(8) , Scholastic Paperbacks) Scholastic, Inc.

Schwartz, Fletcher. Willim was a Dancer. 2003. 60p. per. 12.95 (978-1-932344-48-6(9)) Thornton Publishing.

Shearer, Alex. The Summer Sisters & the Dance Disaster. Kenyon, Tony, illus. 1998. 103p. (J). (gr. 3-7). lib. bdg. 15.99 (978-0-531-33080-7(X) , Orchard Bks.) Scholastic, Inc.

Sheldon, Dyan. Clara & Buster Go Moondancing. 2001. (978-0-606-22329-4(0)) Tandem Library Bks.

Shields, Carol Diggory. Saturday Night at the Dinosaur Stomp. 2002. (gr. k-3). lib. bdg. 14.15 (978-0-613-74752-3(6)) Tandem Library Bks.

Shiva's Fire. 2002. stu. ed. (978-1-58130-747-4(0)) Novel Units, Inc.

Siegel, Siena Cherson. To Dance: A Ballerina's Graphic Novel. Siegel, Mark, illus. 2006. 64p. (J). (gr. 3-9). 17.95 (978-0-689-86747-7(6) , Atheneum/Richard Jackson Bks.); pap. 9.99 (978-1-4169-2687-0(9) , Aladdin) Simon & Schuster Children's Publishing.

Silver Dolphin en Español Editors, creator. El Baile de las Princesas. 2005. (SPA., Illus.). 16p. (J). (ps-7). 14.95 (978-970-718-288-2(1) , Silver Dolphin en Español) Advanced Marketing, S. de R. L. de C. V. MEX. *Dist:* Perseus Distribution.

Slater, Teddy. The Bunny Hop. Di Fiori, Larry, illus. 2004. 32p. (J). lib. bdg. 15.00 (978-1-59054-342-9(4)) Fitzgerald Bks.

Smith, Cynthia Leitich. Jingle Dancer. Van Wright, Cornelius & Hu, Ying-Hwa, illus. 2000. 32p. (J). (ps-5). 16.99 (978-0-688-16241-2(X)) HarperCollins Pubs.

—Jingle Dancer. Van Wright, Cornelius, illus. 2000. 32p. (J). (ps-5). lib. bdg. 17.89 (978-0-688-16242-9(8)) HarperCollins Pubs.

Sollinger, Emily. Dance! Dora's Pop-up Dancing Adventure. Aikins, Dave, illus. 2007. (Dora the Explorer Ser.). 12p. (J). 12.99 (***978-1-4169-4717-2(5)*** , Simon Spotlight/Nickelodeon) Simon & Schuster Children's Publishing.

Soto, Gary. Marisol. 2004. (American Girl Today Ser.). (Illus.). 160p. pap. 6.95 (978-1-58485-972-7(5)) American Girl Publishing, Inc.

Squillace, Elisa, illus. Down in the Jungle. 2005. (Classic Books with Holes). 16p. (J). bds. 5.99 (978-1-904550-61-7(4)) Child's Play-International.

Stadler, Alexander. Lila Bloom. 2004. (Illus.). 40p. (J). 16.00 (978-0-374-34474-0(4) , Farrar, Straus & Giroux (BYR)) Farrar, Straus & Giroux.

Staples, Suzanne Fisher. Shiva's Fire. 2000. (Illus.). 288p. (YA). (gr. 7-12). 18.00 (978-0-374-36824-1(4) , Farrar, Straus & Giroux (BYR)) Farrar, Straus & Giroux.

—Shiva's Fire. 2001. 288p. (J). (gr. 5 up). pap. 6.99 (978-0-06-440979-7(1) , Harper Trophy) HarperCollins Pubs.

—Shiva's Fire. 2001. (978-0-606-22295-2(2)) Tandem Library Bks.

Steck-Vaughn Staff. Dancing: The King who Loves Dancing. 1998. (Illus.). (J). pap. 11.50 (978-0-8172-8638-5(1)) Steck-Vaughn.

Stevenson, James. Flying Feet: A Mud Flat Story. Stevenson, James, illus. 2004. (Illus.). 48p. (J). 15.99 (978-0-06-051975-9(4)) HarperCollins Pubs.

Striegel, Jana. Homeroom Exercise. 2002. 176p. (J). (gr. 4-6). tchr. ed. 16.95 (978-0-8234-1579-3(1)) Holiday Hse., Inc.

Sullivan, Jenny. The Caterpillar That Couldn't. 2002. (Illus.). 32p. pap. 12.95 (978-1-84323-071-7(2)) Beekman Bks., Inc.

Symes, Ruth. Harriet Dancing. Church, Caroline, illus. 2008. 32p. (J). 16.99 (***978-0-545-03204-9(0)*** , Chicken Hse., The) Scholastic, Inc.

Taylor, Ann & HarperCollins Staff. Baby Dance. Van Heerden, Marjorie, illus. 1999. (Growing Tree Ser.). 16p. (J). (ps up). 6.99 (978-0-694-01206-0(8) , Harper Festival) HarperCollins Pubs.

Thomas, Peggy. Snow Dance. Facklam, Paul, illus. 2007. 32p. (J). 15.95 (***978-1-58980-478-4(3)***) Pelican Publishing Co., Inc.

Todd, Traci N. Wiggle, Waggle, Loop-De-Loo! Barner, Bob, illus. 2006. (J). (978-1-58987-009-3(3)) Kindermusik International.

Tripathi, Namrata. Dance Disaster. 2004. (Festival Reader Ser.). (Illus.). 32p. (J). (ps-2). pap. 3.99 (978-0-06-054867-4(3) , Harper Festival) HarperCollins Pubs.

Turner, J. Hale. I Love to Sing & Dance. 2005. 41p. (J). pap. 12.00 (978-1-4116-3270-7(2)) Lulu.com.

Ure, Jean. Becky Bananas: This Is Your Life! Brownfield, Mick & Player, Stephen, illus. l.t. ed. 2005. 206p. (J). (gr. 4-7). pap. (978-1-4056-6017-4(1)) BBC Audio.

Vail, Rachel. Please, Please, Please. (Friendship Ring Ser.: No. 2). 240p. (J). (gr. 4-8). 1999. pap. 3.99 (978-0-439-08762-9(7)); 1998. pap. 14.95 (978-0-590-00327-8(5)); 1998. pap. 4.99 (978-0-590-37452-1(4)) Scholastic, Inc.

Veit, Kimberly Michelle. To Be Thirteen. 2006. 57p. pap. 12.95 (978-1-4241-1392-7(X)) PublishAmerica, Inc.

Walker, Susan Eileen. Secret of the Dance. 2006. 232p. pap. 15.00 (978-0-9766805-4-3(8)) Keene Publishing.

Wallace, Ian. Chin Chiang & the Dragon's Dance. 1998. (Illus.). 32p. (J). (ps-2). pap. 5.95 (978-0-88899-167-6(3)) Groundwood Bks. CAN. *Dist:* Perseus Distribution.

Wallace, Ian, illus. Chin Chiang & the Dragon's Dance. 1998. 32p. (J). (ps-2). 19.95 (978-0-88899-020-4(0)) Groundwood Bks. CAN. *Dist:* Perseus Distribution.

Walton, Rick. How Can You Dance? Lopez-Escriva, Ana, illus. 2001. 1p. (J). (ps-3). 13.99 (978-0-399-23229-9(X) , Putnam Juvenile) Penguin Group (USA) Inc.

Weeks, Sarah. Danger! Boys Dancing! 2006. (Boyds Will Be Boyds Ser.: No. 3). 160p. (J). pap. 4.99 (978-0-439-57471-6(4) , Scholastic Paperbacks) Scholastic, Inc.

—Ella, of Course! Cushman, Doug, illus. 2007. 32p. (J). (ps). 16.00 (978-0-15-204943-0(6)) Harcourt Trade Pubs.

Welch, Willy. Dancing with Daddy. Woodruff, Liza, illus. 2004. 32p. (J). (ps-3). pap. 6.95 (978-1-58089-078-6(4)) Charlesbridge Publishing, Inc.

Wheeler, Lisa. Hokey Pokey: Another Prickly Love Story. Bynum, Janie, illus. 2006. 32p. (J). (ps-1). 15.99 (978-0-316-00090-1(6)) Little Brown & Co.

Whelan, Gloria. The Turning. 2006. 224p. (J). 15.99 (978-0-06-075593-5(8)) HarperCollins Pubs.

Winston, Sherri. Kayla Chronicles. 2008. 208p. (YA). (gr. 7-17). 16.99 (***978-0-316-11430-1(8)***) Little, Brown Bks. for Young Readers.

Winthrop, Elizabeth. Dancing Granny. Murdocca, Sal, illus. 2003. 32p. (J). 16.95 (978-0-7614-5141-9(2)) Cavendish, Marshall Corp.

—Dumpy la Rue. Lewin, Betsy, illus. 2004. 48p. (J). (ps-4). lib. bdg. 14.15 (978-0-606-30292-0(1)) Tandem Library Bks.

Yee, T. Leilani's Hula. 2002. (J). pap. 3.99 (978-0-89610-379-5(X)) Island Heritage Publishing.

Young, Amy. Belinda & the Glass Slipper. Young, Amy, illus. 2006. (Illus.). 34p. (J). (ps). 15.99 (978-0-670-06082-5(8) , Viking Juvenile) Penguin Group (USA) Inc.

—Belinda in Paris. 2005. (Illus.). 32p. (J). 15.99 (978-0-670-03693-6(5) , Viking Juvenile) Penguin Group (USA) Inc.

—Belinda the Ballerina. 2005. (Illus.). 30p. (J). (ps-ps). lib. bdg. 12.79 (978-0-606-33108-1(5)) Tandem Library Bks.

—Belinda, the Ballerina. 2005. (Illus.). 32p. (J). (gr. k-2). reprint ed. pap. 5.99 (978-0-14-240272-6(9) , Puffin) Penguin Group (USA) Inc.

Ziefert, Harriet. Dancing Class. Haley, Amanda, illus. 2006. (I'm Going to Read Ser.). 32p. (J). pap. 3.95 (978-1-4027-3427-4(1)) Sterling Publishing Co., Inc.

Ziefert, Harriet & Ehrlich, H. M. Dancing Class. Rader, Laura, illus. 2001. 32p. (J). (ps-1). pap. 12.95 (978-0-531-30300-9(4) , Orchard Bks.) Scholastic, Inc.

DANCE—VOCATIONAL GUIDANCE

Maze, Stephanie. I Want to Be a Dancer. 2000. (I Want to Be Ser.). (Illus.). 48p. (YA). (gr. 4-9). lib. bdg. 27.12 (978-0-7398-1104-7(5)) Raintree.

—I Want to Be a Dancer. 1999. (Illus.). (J). (ps-7). 47p. lib. bdg. 17.65 (978-0-613-19516-4(7)); 15.80 (978-0-606-18176-1(8)) Tandem Library Bks.

Reeves, Diane Lindsey. Career Ideas for Kids Who Like Music & Dance. 2nd rev. ed. (Career Ideas for Kids Ser.). 208p. (J). (gr. 4-9). pap. 16.95 (***978-0-8160-6538-7(1)*** , Checkmark Bks.); 2007. 32.95 (***978-0-8160-6537-0(3)*** , Ferguson Publishing Co.) Facts On File, Inc.

Reeves, Diane Lindsey & Bryan, Gayle. Career Ideas for Kids Who Like Music & Dance. Bond, Nancy, illus. 2001. (Career Ideas for Kids Ser.). 192p. (J). (gr. 4-9). 23.00 (978-0-8160-4323-1(X)) Facts On File, Inc.

DANCERS

Ada, Alma Flor & Campoy, F. Isabel, contrib. by. Pasos. (Literature Collection of Puertas Al Sol Ser.). (SPA.). 32p. (J). (gr. k-6). pap. 13.95 (978-1-59437-704-4(9)) Santillana USA Publishing Co., Inc.

Allman, Barbara & Haas, Shelly O. Dance of the Swan: A Story about Anna Pavlova. 2006. (Creative Minds Biographies Ser.). (Illus.). 64p. (gr. 4-8). lib. bdg. 22.60 (978-1-57505-463-6(9)) Lerner Publishing Group.

Barasch, Lynne. Knockin' on Wood: Starring Peg Leg Bates. 2004. (Illus.). 32p. (J). 16.95 (978-1-58430-170-7(8)) Lee & Low Bks., Inc.

Cady, Jennifer. Jose Limon. 2005. (Library of American Choreographers). (Illus.). 48p. (J). (ps-ps). lib. bdg. 23.95 (978-1-4042-0449-2(0)) Rosen Publishing Group, Inc., The.

Collins, Pat Lowery. I Am a Dancer. Graham, Mark, illus. 2008. (Millbrook Picture Books Ser.). (J). lib. bdg. 22.60 (***978-0-8225-6369-3(X)*** , Millbrook Pr.) Lerner Publishing Group.

Cruz, Barbara C. Alvin Ailey: Celebrating African-American Culture in Dance. 2004. (African-American Biographies Ser.). (Illus.). 112p. (J). lib. bdg. 26.60 (978-0-7660-2293-5(5)) Enslow Pubs., Inc.

De Angelis, Gina. Gregory Hines. 1999. (Black Americans of Achievement Ser.). (YA). (gr. 4 up). lib. bdg. 19.95 (978-0-7910-4965-5(5) , Chelsea Hse.) Facts On File, Inc.

Derezinski, Amelia. Twyla Tharp. 2005. (Library of American Choreographers). (Illus.). 48p. (J). (ps-ps). lib. bdg. 23.95 (978-1-4042-0451-5(2)); (978-1-4042-0646-5(9)) Rosen Publishing Group, Inc., The.

Dorling Kindersley Publishing Staff. Ballet School. 2003. (Illus.). 48p. (J). 12.99 (978-0-7894-9228-9(8)) Dorling Kindersley Publishing, Inc.

Dowd, Olympia. A Young Dancer's Odyssey. 2001. (Illus.). 50p. (YA). (gr. 5 up). pap. (978-1-55192-326-0(2)) Raincoast Bk. Distribution.

Dyro, Janniche, illus. Forever Dancing. 32p. (J). (gr. 4 up). 16.00 (978-0-9675413-8-9(7)) Libros, Encouraging Cultural Literacy.

Fandel, Jennifer. Rudolf Nureyev. 2005. (Extraordinary Artists Ser.). (Illus.). 48p. (J). (gr. 5-9). 21.95 (978-1-58341-380-7(4) , Creative Education) Creative Co., The.

Ford, Carin T. Legends of American Dance & Choreography. 2000. (Collective Biographies Ser.). (Illus.). 112p. (YA). (gr. 6-12). lib. bdg. 26.60 (978-0-7660-1378-0(2)) Enslow Pubs., Inc.

Freedman, Russell. Martha Graham: A Dancer's Life. 1998. (Illus.). 176p. (J). (gr. 4-6). tchr. ed. 19.00 (978-0-395-74655-4(8) , Clarion Bks.) Houghton Mifflin Co. Trade & Reference Div.

Garfunkel, Trudy. Letter to the World: The Life & Dances of Martha Graham. 1999. (Illus.). 92p. (YA). (gr. 7-12). reprint ed. 17.00 (978-0-7881-6064-6(8)) DIANE Publishing Co.

Gitenstein, Judy. Alvin Ailey. 2005. (Library of American Choreographers). (Illus.). 48p. (J). (ps-ps). lib. bdg. 23.95 (978-1-4042-0445-4(8)); pap. (978-1-4042-0639-7(6)) Rosen Publishing Group, Inc., The.

Glover, Savion & Weber, Bruce. Savion! My Life in Tap. 2000. (Illus.). 80p. (J). (gr. 5 up). 19.99 (978-0-688-15629-9(0)) HarperCollins Pubs.

Guest, Ann Hutchinson. The Adventures of Klig & Gop: In Rotation-Land. 2001. (Illus.). 84p. (J). (ps-6). pap. (978-1-930798-05-2(9)) National Dance Education Organization.

—The Adventures of Klig & Gop: In Spring-Up-Land. 2001. 59p. (J). (ps-6). pap. (978-1-930798-06-9(7)) National Dance Education Organization.

—The Adventures of Klig & Gop: In Support-Land. 2001. 54p. (J). (ps-6). pap. (978-1-930798-07-6(5)) National Dance Education Organization.

Guest, Ann Hutchinson, et al. The Adventures of Klig & Gop No. 2: Parent & Teacher Guide. 2001. (Illus.). 76p. (J). (ps-6). pap. (978-1-930798-04-5(0)) National Dance Education Organization.

Harcourt School Publishers Staff. The Life of Alvin Ailey Advanced Level. 3rd ed. 2002. (Trophies Reading Program Ser.). (Illus.). pap. 5.10 (978-0-15-323477-4(6)) Harcourt Schl. Pubs.

Hasday, Judy L. Agnes de Mille. 2003. (Women in the Arts Ser.). (Illus.). 112p. (gr. 6-12). 30.00 (978-0-7910-7457-2(9) , Chelsea Hse.) Facts On File, Inc.

—Savion Glover. 2006. (Black Americans of Achievement, Legacy Edition Ser.). (Illus.). 112p. (J). (gr. 6-12). 30.00 (978-0-7910-9223-1(2) , Chelsea Hse.) Facts On File, Inc.

Hayward, Linda. Day in the Life of a Dancer. 2001. (gr. k-3). lib. bdg. 11.80 (978-0-613-35097-6(9)) Tandem Library Bks.

Jones, Jen. Cheer Professionals. 2008. (J). (*978-1-4296-1349-1(1)) Capstone Pr., Inc.

Kessel, Kristin. Martha Graham. 2005. (Library of American Choreographers). (Illus.). 48p. (J). pap. (978-1-4042-0644-1(2)); lib. bdg. 23.95 (978-1-4042-0450-8(4)) Rosen Publishing Group, Inc., The.

Krohn, Katherine E. Evelyn Cisneros: Prima Ballerina. 2006. (Fact Finders Ser.). (Illus.). 32p. (J). (gr. 1-3). 22.60 (978-0-7368-6416-9(4)) Capstone Pr., Inc.

Loibl, Marianne. Little Ballerina Book & Tutu. Suetens, Clara, illus. 2007. 48p. (J). (ps). 17.95 (*978-0-7358-2148-4(8)) North-South Bks., Inc.

McMahon, Patricia. Dancing Wheels. Godt, John, photos by. 2000. (Illus.). 48p. (J). (gr. 4-6). tchr. ed. 16.00 (978-0-395-88889-6(1)) Houghton Mifflin Co. Trade & Reference Div.

My Dolly Dressing Book of Ballerinas. 2002. 16p. (J). pap. 2.98 (978-0-7525-8042-5(6)) Parragon, Inc.

O'Connor, Barbara. Barefoot Dancer: The Story of Isadora Duncan. 2003. (Illus.). 96p. (J). pap. 8.95 (978-0-87614-911-9(5) , Carolrhoda Bks.) Lerner Publishing Group.

—Katherine Dunham: Pioneer of Black Dance. 2005. (Trailblazers Biographies Ser.). (Illus.). 112p. (gr. 5-9). 27.93 (978-1-57505-353-0(5)) Lerner Publishing Group.

Orgill, Roxane. Footwork: The Story of Fred & Adele Astaire. Jorisch, Stephane, illus. 2007. 48p. (J). (gr. 1-5). 17.99 (978-0-7636-2121-6(8)) Candlewick Pr.

Paskevska, Anna. Ballet Beyond Tradition. 2004. (Illus.). 200p. 24.95 (978-0-415-97018-1(0)) Routledge.

Peters, Craig. Techniques of Dance for Cheerleading. 2003. (Let's Go Team Ser.). (Illus.). 64p. (J). (gr. 5 up). lib. bdg. (978-1-59084-531-8(5)) Mason Crest Pubs.

Reich, Susanna. Jose! Born to Dance: The Story of Jose Limon. Colon, Raul, illus. 2005. 32p. (J). (gr. 2-4). 16.95 (978-0-689-86576-3(7) , Simon & Schuster Children's Publishing) Simon & Schuster Children's Publishing.

Schroeder, Alan & Wagner, Heather Lehr. Josephine Baker. 2006. (Black Americans of Achievement Ser.). (Illus.). 128p. (J). (gr. 6-12). 30.00 (978-0-7910-9212-5(7) , Chelsea Hse.) Facts On File, Inc.

Schubert, Leda. Ballet of the Elephants. Parker, Robert Andrew, illus. 2006. 34p. (J). 17.95 (978-1-59643-075-4(3)) Roaring Brook Pr.

Seibert, Brian. George Balanchine. 2006. (Library of American Choreographers). (Illus.). 48p. (J). pap. (978-1-4042-0641-0(8) , Rosen Central) Rosen Publishing Group, Inc., The.

—Jerome Robbins. 2005. (Library of American Choreographers). (J). pap. (978-1-4042-0642-7(6)) Rosen Publishing Group, Inc., The.

Shahan, Sherry. Willie Covan Loved to Dance. Van Wright, Cornelius & Ha, Ying-Hwa, trs. Van Wright, Cornelius & Ha, Ying-Hwa, illus. 2004. (J). 15.95 (978-1-59034-445-3(6)); pap. (978-1-59034-580-1(0)) Mondo Publishing.

Siempre Bailando. (SPA.). (J). (978-0-9675413-9-6(5)) Libros, Encouraging Cultural Literacy.

Tallchief, Maria. Tallchief: America's Prima Ballerina. 2001. (J). (978-0-606-22511-3(0)) Tandem Library Bks.

Tallchief, Maria & Well, Rosemary. Tallchief: America's Prima Ballerina. Kelley, Gary, illus. 2001. 28p. (J). (gr. k-4). lib. bdg. 15.30 (978-0-613-44420-0(5)) Tandem Library Bks.

Tallchief, Maria & Wells, Rosemary. Tallchief: America's Prima Ballerina. Kelley, Gary, illus. 1999. 32p. (J). (gr. k-4). 16.99 (978-0-670-88756-9(0) , Viking Juvenile) Penguin Group (USA) Inc.

Tierney, Tom. Great Movie Dance Couples Paper Dolls. 2004. (Paper Dolls Ser.). (Illus.). 16p. (J). pap. 6.95 (978-0-486-43054-6(5)) Dover Pubns., Inc.

Trenton, Trisha. Trisha Trenton: Dance Diva Dance! 2007. mass mkt. 39.95 (978-0-9727410-0-2(3)) TEG Publishing.

Wells, Rosemary & Tallchief, Maria. Tallchief: America's Prima Ballerina. Kelley, Gary F., illus. 2001. 32p. (J). pap. 6.99 (978-0-14-230018-3(7) , Puffin) Penguin Group (USA) Inc.

White, Diana. Ballerina Dreams. Rogers, Jacqueline, illus. (Scholastic Reader Ser.). (J). 2006. 32p. pap. 3.99 (978-0-439-83302-8(7) , Cartwheel Bks.); Level 3. 1998. 48p. (gr. 1-3). pap. 3.99 (978-0-590-37233-6(5)) Scholastic, Inc.

Zannos, Susan. Paula Abdul. 1998. (Real-Life Reader Biographies Ser.). (Illus.). 32p. (J). (gr. 4-7). lib. bdg. 15.95 (978-1-883845-74-2(2)) Mitchell Lane Pubs., Inc.

DANCERS—FICTION

Anonymous. Confessions of a Backup Dancer. 2004. 272p. (J). pap. 8.99 (978-0-689-87075-0(2) , Simon Pulse) Simon & Schuster Children's Publishing.

—Confessions of a Backup Dancer. l.t. ed. 2005. 360p. (YA). (gr. 8-12). per. 20.95 (978-0-7862-7881-7(1) , Large Print Pr.) Thorndike Pr.

Bornstein, Ruth Lercher. The Dancing Man. rev. ed. 1998. (Illus.). 32p. (J). (gr. k-3). tchr. ed. 16.00 (978-0-395-83429-9(5) , Clarion Bks.) Houghton Mifflin Co. Trade & Reference Div.

Brandeis, Madeline. The Little Spanish Dancer. 2005. reprint ed. pap. 22.95 (978-1-4191-4096-9(5)) Kessinger Publishing, LLC.

Clark, Sherryl. Bites:The Too-Tight Tutu: Will Practice Make Merry Perfect? Wilcox, Cathy, illus. 2007. 96p. (J). pap. 3.95 (*978-0-7624-3046-8(X) , Running Pr. Kids) Running Pr. Bk. Pubs.

Corbett, Kat. Future Perfect. 2000. (gr. 7-12). lib. bdg. 22.20 (978-0-613-83510-7(7)) Tandem Library Bks.

—Future Perfect. 2000. 228p. (YA). (gr. 7-12). pap. 12.95 (978-0-595-12886-0(6)) iUniverse, Inc.

Cowley, Joy. Agapanthus Hum & the Eyeglasses. 1999. (YA). pap. 30.99 incl. audio (978-0-7887-3788-6(0) , 41032) Recorded Bks., LLC.

Dancing Dilemma. 2005. 46p. (J). 3.99 (978-0-9763213-1-6(9)) OHC Group LLC.

DePalma, Johnny & Crabapple, Molly. Once upon a Christmas Tree - A Holiday Fairy Tale. 2007. 88p. pap. 10.50 (*978-0-615-15448-0(4)) Umbrelly Bks.

Dillon, Leo & Dillon, Diane. Rap a Tap Tap: Here's Bojangles - Think of That! 2005. (J). 25.95 incl. audio (978-1-59519-365-0(0)); 28.95 incl. audio compact disk (978-1-59519-369-8(3)) Live Oak Media.

—Rap a Tap Tap: Here's Bojangles - Think of That! Dillon, Leo & Dillon, Diane, illus. 2002. (Illus.). 32p. (J). pap. 15.95 (978-0-590-47883-0(4) , Blue Sky Pr., The) Scholastic, Inc.

Dominguez, Barbara. La Hija de la Manaa. 2001. Tr. of Child of the Morning. (SPA.). 152p. (J). 7.95 (978-84-348-1979-5(1)) SM Ediciones ESP. *Dist:* AIMS International Bks., Inc.

Downs, Celise. Dance Jam Productions. Colston, Steven, illus. 2004. 140p. (YA). per. (978-0-9752907-1-2(1)) Gemini Mojo Pr.

Drayton, Kat, illus. Nantucket's Night Magic. 1998. 32p. (J). 14.95 (978-0-9667090-0-1(4)) Dionis Bound Publishing.

Dube, Jasmine & Paré, Roger. Elvis Aime Danser. 2001. (Elvis Ser.). (FRE., Illus.). 24p. (YA). (ps up). pap. (978-2-89021-462-0(1)) Diffusion du livre Mirabel.

Fox, Paula. The Slave Dancer. Eros, Keith, illus. 2002. (J). 14.47 (978-0-7587-0214-2(0)) Book Wholesalers, Inc.

—The Slave Dancer. 1998. (Assessment Packs Ser.). 15p. pap., tchr.'s training gde. ed. 15.95 (978-1-58303-061-5(1)) Pathways Publishing.

—The Slave Dancer. unabr. ed. 2004. 152p. (J). (gr. 5-9). pap. 38.00 incl. audio (978-0-8072-0458-0(7) , Listening Library) Random Hse. Audio Publishing Group.

—The Slave Dancer. Keith, Eros, illus. 2001. 192p. (YA). 18.99 (978-0-689-84505-5(7) , Atheneum/Richard Jackson Bks.) Simon & Schuster Children's Publishing.

Gauch, Patricia Lee. Tanya & the Red Shoes. Ichikawa, Satomi, illus. 2002. 40p. (J). 16.99 (978-0-399-23314-2(8) , Philomel) Penguin Group (USA) Inc.

Giff, Patricia Reilly. Not-So-Perfect Rosie, No. 4. Durrell, Julie, illus. 1998. (Ballet Slippers Ser.: Vol. 4). 80p. (J). (gr. 2-5). pap. 4.99 (978-0-14-130060-3(4) , Puffin) Penguin Group (USA) Inc.

Harcourt School Publishers Staff. Darci's Ballet Dream Advanced Level. 3rd ed. 2002. (Trophies Reading Program Ser.). (Illus.). pap. 5.10 (978-0-15-323194-0(7)) Harcourt Schl. Pubs.

Helbrough, Emma, retold by. Tweleve Dancing Princesses. 2005. (Young Reading Gift Books Ser.). 48p. (J). (gr. 2 up). 8.95 (978-0-7945-0824-1(3) , Usborne) EDC Publishing.

Hewett, Lorri. Dancer: Everybody Has a Dream. 2001. 224p. (YA). (gr. 8-12). pap. 5.99 (978-0-14-131085-5(5) , Puffin) Penguin Group (USA) Inc.

Holabird, Katharine. Christmas in Mouseland. Craig, Helen, illus. 2007. (Angelina Ballerina Ser.). 24p. (J). (ps-1). 6.99 (*978-0-448-44663-9(4) , Grosset & Dunlap) Penguin Group (USA) Inc.

Isadora, Rachel. Lili on Stage. Isadora, Rachel, illus. 2002. (Illus.). (J). 14.04 (978-0-7587-2988-0(X)) Book Wholesalers, Inc.

Jefferies, Cindy. Lucky Break #6. 2008. (Fame School Ser.). 128p. (J). (gr. 1-3). pap. 5.99 (*978-0-14-241102-5(7) , Puffin) Penguin Group (USA) Inc.

Johnson, Sarah. Time to Dance. Lew, Willie, illus. Lew, Willie, photos by. 2003. (J). 16.98 (978-0-7853-8811-1(7)) Publications International, Ltd.

Lasky, Kathryn. Dancing Through Fire. 2005. (Portraits Ser.: No. 1). 176p. (J). (gr. 4-7). pap. 9.99 (978-0-439-71009-1(X) , Scholastic Paperbacks) Scholastic, Inc.

Lowell, Susan. Josefina Javelina: A Hairy Tale. MacPherson, Bruce, illus. 2005. 32p. (ps-3). 15.95 (978-0-87358-790-7(1) , Rising Moon Bks. for Young Readers) Northland Publishing.

Marshall, James. Swine Lake. ed. 2004. (Illus.). (J). (gr. k-5). spiral bd. (978-0-616-01712-8(X)) Canadian National Institute for the Blind/Institut National Canadien pour les Aveugles.

—Swine Lake. Sendak, Maurice, illus. 2002. 45p. (YA). (gr. 6-8). 16.00 (978-0-7567-5267-5(1)) DIANE Publishing Co.

—Swine Lake. Sendak, Maurice, illus. 1999. (Michael di Capua Bks.). (ps-3). 40p. (J). 15.89 (978-0-06-205172-1(5)); 40p. 16.95 (978-0-06-205171-4(7)); (J). 15.95 (978-0-06-028430-5(7)) HarperCollins Pubs.

Maybarduk, Linda. James the Dancing Dog. Johnson, Gillian, illus. 2004. 24p. (J). (ps-3). 15.95 (978-0-88776-619-0(6)) Tundra Bks., Inc./Livres Toundra, Inc. CAN. *Dist:* Random Hse., Inc.

Moss, Alexandra. Boys or Ballet? 2006. 142p. (J). (*978-1-4156-8361-3(1) , Grosset & Dunlap) Penguin Group (USA) Inc.

Murphy, Kelly. The Boll Weevil Ball. rev. ed. 2002. (Illus.). 32p. (J). (ps-2). 15.95 (978-0-8050-6712-5(4) , Holt, Henry & Co. Bks. For Young Readers) Holt, Henry & Co.

Murray, C. J. Different Dancers. 2001. (J). pap. 9.95 (978-0-89992-152-5(3)) Council for Indian Education.

Ormerod, Jan. Ballet Sisters No. 1: The Duckling & the Swan. 2007. (Scholastic Reader Ser.). 32p. (J). (gr. k-2). pap. 5.99 (978-0-439-82281-7(5)) Scholastic, Inc.

Ormerod, Jan. The Newest Dancer. 2008. (Ballet Sisters Ser.: No. 2). 32p. (J). pap. 5.99 (*978-0-439-82282-4(3)) Scholastic, Inc.

Plante, Raymond. Une Curieuse Invasion de Picots-les-Bains par les Zhbres. Franson, Leanne, illus. 2002. (Il etait une Fois Ser.). (FRE.). 24p. (J). (ps up). pap. (978-2-89021-597-9(0)) Diffusion du livre Mirabel.

Resnick, Mike. Club in Montmartre. 2006. (Art Encounters Ser.). (Illus.). 176p. (YA). 16.95 (978-0-8230-0420-1(1)) Watson-Guptill Pubns., Inc.

Smith, Charles R., Jr. Dance with Me. 2004. (J). 16.99 (978-0-7636-2246-6(X)) Candlewick Pr.

Staples, Suzanne Fisher. Shiva's Fire. 2001. (gr. 7-12). lib. bdg. 14.10 (978-0-613-44414-9(0)) Tandem Library Bks.

The Willow Tree. 2001. 336p. (J). pap. 14.95 (978-0-9678340-0-9(7)) B G & J Pubs.

Winthrop, Elizabeth. Dumpy la Rue. Lewin, Betsy, illus. rev. ed. 2004. 40p. (J). reprint ed. pap. 7.95 (978-0-8050-7535-9(6) , Holt, Henry & Co. Bks. For Young Readers) Holt, Henry & Co.

DANDELIONS

Himmelman, John. A Dandelion's Life. Himmelman, John, illus. (Nature Upclose Ser.). (Illus.). 32p. (J). (gr. k-2). 1999. pap. 6.95 (978-0-516-26402-8(8)); 1998. 25.00 (978-0-516-21177-0(3)) Scholastic Library Publishing. (Children's Pr.).

Kite, L. Patricia. Dandelion Adventures. Hariton, Anca, illus. 1998. (Our World Ser.). 32p. (ps-1). lib. bdg. 21.90 (978-0-7613-0037-3(6) , Millbrook Pr.) Lerner Publishing Group.

Kottke, Jan. From Seed to Dandelion. 2000. (gr. k-3). lib. bdg. 12.95 (978-0-613-52063-8(7)) Tandem Library Bks.

Kudlinski, Kathleen V. Dandelions. Wexler, Jerome, photos by. 1999. (Early Bird Nature Bks.). (Illus.). 48p. (J). (gr. 2-4). lib. bdg. 25.26 (978-0-8225-3016-9(3) , Lerner Pubns.) Lerner Publishing Group.

Long, Olivia. The Dandelion Queen. Long, Olivia, illus. Date not set. (Our Precious Planet Ser.). (Illus.). 32p. (J). (ps-4). 9.95 (978-1-880042-08-3(8) , SL12461) Shelf-Life Bks.

Posada, Mia. Dandelions: Stars in the Grass. Posada, Mia, illus. 2003. (Picture Bks.). (Illus.). 32p. (J). (ps-3). 15.95 (978-1-57505-383-7(7)) Lerner Publishing Group.

—Dandelions: Stars in the Grass. 2000. (gr. k-3). lib. bdg. 15.25 (978-0-613-58897-3(5)) Tandem Library Bks.

Weiss, Ellen. From Seed to Dandelion. 2007. (Scholastic News Nonfiction Readers: How Things Grow—NEW SUBSET Ser.). 24p. (J). pap. 6.95 (*978-0-531-18792-0(6)); (Illus.). (gr. 1-2). lib. bdg. 20.00 (*978-0-531-18539-1(7)) Scholastic Library Publishing. (Children's Pr.).

DANGER JOE (FICTITIOUS CHARACTER)—FICTION

Schade, Susan. Bungee Baboon Rescue. Buller, Jon, illus. 2002. (Danger Joe Show Ser.: No. 2). 112p. (J). pap. 3.99 (978-0-439-40976-6(4) , Scholastic Paperbacks) Scholastic, Inc.

—Bungee Baboon Rescue. 2002. (gr. k-3). lib. bdg. 11.80 (978-0-613-72067-0(9)) Tandem Library Bks.

DANIEL (BIBLICAL CHARACTER)

Ammerman, Mark & Wheeler, Ron. Daniel & the Lion's Den. 1999. (Little Bible Bks.). (Illus.). 24p. (J). 1.99 (978-1-57748-660-2(9)) Barbour Publishing, Inc.

Auld, Mary. Daniel in the Lions' Den. 2000. (Bible Stories Ser.). (Illus.). 32p. (J). (gr. 2-4). pap. 7.95 (978-0-531-15385-7(1) , Watts, Franklin) Scholastic Library Publishing.

Bek, et al. Daniel in the Dangerous Den & Paul & Silas & the Prison Prayer. Bek et al, illus. 2006. (Upside down Bible Stories Ser.). 62p. (J). pap. 7.99 (978-0-7814-4391-3(1)) Cook, David C. Publishing Co.

Dalmatian Press Staff, ed. Daniel in the Lion's Den. 2004. (Illus.). 24p. (J). 2.99 (978-1-4037-0965-3(3) , Spirit Pr.) Dalmatian Pr.

Daniel in the Lion's Den. Date not set. (J). stu. ed., act. bk. ed. 1.49 (978-0-88271-233-8(0) , 1749) Regina Pr., Malhame & Co.

De Graaf, Anne. Daniel. Montero, Jose Perez, illus. 1999. (Little Children's Bible Bks.). 38p. (J). 5.99 (978-0-8054-1898-9(9)) B&H Publishing Grp.

DeBoer, Rondl & Tangvald, Christine. Daniel & the Lions. Conger, Holli, illus. 2007. (J). 5.99 (*978-0-7847-1948-0(9)) Standard Publishing.

Donaher, D F. & Bibleco. Daniel & the Lions. 2004. (Illus.). (J). bds. (978-0-9746058-2-1(4) , Biblemania) Bibleco, Inc.

Fogle, Robin. Daniel & the Lions' Den Coloring Book. 2007. (Illus.). 16p. (J). pap. 1.89 (*978-1-59317-191-9(9)) Warner Pr. Pubs.

Hartman, Bob. Dinner in the Lions' Den. Raglin, Tim, illus. 2007. 32p. (J). (ps-2). 16.99 (978-0-399-24674-6(6) , Putnam Juvenile) Penguin Group (USA) Inc.

Murdock, Hy. Daniel. (Bible Stories Ser.: No. S846-6). (Illus.). (J). (ps-2). pap. 3.95 (978-0-7214-5069-8(5) , Dutton Juvenile) Penguin Group (USA) Inc.

Nederveld, Patricia L. Lions, Lions! The Story of Daniel. 1998. (God Loves Me Ser.: Vol. 23). (Illus.). 24p. (J). (ps-3). pap. 2.95 (978-1-56212-292-8(4) , 001223, Faith Alive Christian Resources) CRC Pubns.

Pingry, Patricia A. The Story of Daniel. Britt, Stephanie McFetridge, illus. 1999. 26p. (J). (ps-k). bds. 6.95 (978-0-8249-4163-5(2) , Ideals Children's Bks.) Ideals Pubns.

Pulley, Kelly, illus. Daniel & the Lions: My First I Can Read! 2008. 32p. (J). pap. (*978-0-310-71551-1(2)) Zonderkidz.

Rabbit. Daniel in the Lion's Den. 2005. (J). 10.95 (978-0-689-80239-3(0) , Simon & Schuster Children's Publishing) Simon & Schuster Children's Publishing.

Ramirez, Frank. Apocalypse When? Daniel & Revelation. 1998. (Generation Why Ser.: No. 4, Pt. 1). 40p. (YA). (gr. 9-12). pap. 12.95 (978-0-87303-281-0(0)) Faith & Life Pr.

Stories about Daniel. (Old Testament Pict-O-Graph Ser.). (J). 10.99 (978-0-7847-1040-1(6)) Standard Publishing.

Taylor, Damon J. A Little Man with a Big Plan: The Story of Young David. 2003. (Child Sockology Ser.). (Illus.). 36p. (J). 10.99 (978-0-8254-3861-5(6)) Kregel Pubns.

DANTE ALIGHIERI, 1265-1321

Dante Alighieri. Inferno. 2000. (Bloom's Notes Ser.). (YA). pap. 4.95 (978-0-7910-6018-6(7) , Chelsea Hse.) Facts On File, Inc.

Davenport, John C. Dante: Poet, Author & Proud Florentine. 2005. (Makers of the Middle Ages & Renaissance Ser.). (Illus.). 140p. (J). (gr. 4-8). lib. bdg. 30.00 (978-0-7910-8634-6(8) , Chelsea Hse.) Facts On File, Inc.

DARK AGES

see Middle Ages

DARWIN, CHARLES, 1809-1882

Adamson, Heather. Charles Darwin & the Theory of Evolution. Purcell, Gordon & Milgrom, Al, illus. 2008. (J). (*978-1-4296-0145-0(0)) Capstone Pr., Inc.

Anderson, Margaret J. Charles Darwin: Naturalist. 2001. (Great Minds of Science Ser.). (Illus.). 128p. (YA). (gr. 4-10). pap. 13.26 (978-0-7660-1868-6(7)) Enslow Pubs., Inc.

Anderson, Margaret Jean. Charles Darwin: Naturalist, Revised Edition. 2008. (Great Minds of Science Ser.). (Illus.). 128p. (J). (gr. 5 up). lib. bdg. 31.93 (*978-0-7660-2794-7(5)) Enslow Pubs., Inc.

Cook, Diane. Charles Darwin: British Naturalist. 2002. (Great Names Ser.). (Illus.). 32p. (J). (gr. 3 up). lib. bdg. (978-1-59084-145-7(X)) Mason Crest Pubs.

Fullick, Ann. Charles Darwin. (Groundbreakers Ser.). (Illus.). 48p. (J). (gr. 5-7). 2002. pap. 8.50 (978-1-58810-990-3(9) , 91465); 2000. lib. bdg. 25.64 (978-1-57572-368-6(9)) Heinemann Library.

Hopkinson, Deborah. Who Was Charles Darwin? Harrison, Nancy, illus. 2005. (Who Was— ? Ser.). 112p. (J). (gr. 2-5). pap. 4.99 (978-0-448-43764-4(3) , Grosset & Dunlap) Penguin Group (USA) Inc.

King, David C. Charles Darwin. (DK Biography Ser.). (Illus.). 128p. (J). 2007. (*978-1-4287-1710-7(2)); 2006. 14.99 (978-0-7566-2555-9(6)); 2006. pap. 4.99 (978-0-7566-2554-2(8)) Dorling Kindersley Publishing, Inc.

Lasky, Kathryn. Charles Darwin. Sorel, Edward, illus. 2004. (J). (978-0-7636-1436-2(X)) Candlewick Pr.

Lawson, Kristan. Darwin & Evolution for Kids: His Life & Ideas with 21 Activities. 2003. (For Kids Ser.). (Illus.). 160p. (J). pap. 16.95 (978-1-55652-502-5(8)) Chicago Review Pr., Inc.

MacDonald, Fiona. Inside the Beagle with Charles Darwin. 2005. (Illus.). 48p. (J). (gr. 4-6). 19.95 (978-1-59270-041-7(1)) Enchanted Lion Bks., LLC.

Nardo, Don. Charles Darwin. 2004. (Importance of Ser.). (Illus.). 112p. (YA). (gr. 7-10). lib. bdg. 32.45 (978-1-59018-339-7(8) , Lucent Bks.) Thomson Gale.

Senker, Cath. Charles Darwin. 2001. (Scientists Who Made History Ser.). (Illus.). 48p. (J). lib. bdg. 27.12 (978-0-7398-4843-2(7)) Raintree.

Sis, Peter. The Tree of Life: Charles Darwin. Sis, Peter, illus. 2003. (Illus.). 44p. (J). (gr. 3 up). 18.00 (978-0-374-45628-3(3) , Farrar, Straus & Giroux (BYR)) Farrar, Straus & Giroux.

—The Tree of Life: Charles Darwin. (Illus.). 22.95 (978-0-88899-564-3(4)) Groundwood Bks. CAN. *Dist:* Transition Vendor.

Sproule, Anna. Charles Darwin: Visionary Behind the Theory of Evolution. 2002. (Scientists Who Have Changed the World Ser.). (Illus.). 64p. (J). 26.20 (978-1-56711-655-7(8) , Blackbirch Pr., Inc.) Thomson Gale.

Weaver, Anne H. The Voyage of the Beetle: A Journey Around the World with Charles Darwin & the Search for the Solution to the Mystery of Mysteries, As Narrated by Rosie, an Articulate Beetle. Lawrence, George, illus. 2007. 80p. (YA). (gr. 5 up). 16.95 (*978-0-8263-4304-8(X)) Univ. of New Mexico Pr.

Whiting, Jim. Charles Darwin & the Origin of the Species. 2005. (Uncharted, Unexplored, & Unexplained Ser.). (Illus.). 48p. (J). (gr. 8). lib. bdg. 29.95 (978-1-58415-364-1(4)) Mitchell Lane Pubs., Inc.

DARWIN, CHARLES, 1809-1882—FICTION

Johnson, Vargie. Charles Darwin, the Discoverer: What Made Them Famous? 2006. (Illus.). 152p. (J). per. 15.00 (978-1-931195-91-1(9)) KiwE Publishing, Ltd.

Weaver, Anne H. The Voyage of the Beetle: A Journey Around the World with Charles Darwin & the Search for the Solution to the Mystery of Mysteries, as Narrated by Rosie, an Articulate Beetle. Lawrence, George, tr. Lawrence, George, illus. 2004. (Roman Mysteries Ser.). 80p. (J). (gr. 5-8). lib. bdg. 26.90 (978-0-7613-2923-7(4) , Millbrook Pr.) Lerner Publishing Group.

DARWINISM

see Evolution

DATA (FICTITIOUS CHARACTER)—FICTION

Weiss, Bobbi J. G. & Weiss, David Cody. Deceptions. 1998. (Star Trek, The Next Generation: No. 14). (J). (gr. 3-6). (978-0-606-13812-3(9)) Tandem Library Bks.

DATA PROCESSING

see Information Storage and Retrieval Systems

DATA STORAGE AND RETRIEVAL SYSTEMS

see Information Storage and Retrieval Systems

DATE ETIQUETTE

see Dating (Social Customs)

DATING (SOCIAL CUSTOMS)

see also Love; Marriage

Acevedo, Eddie. The Ultimate Teen Relationship Guide! Step-by-Step Handbook for Love & Dating That Young People Can Really Use! 2002. (gr. 7-12). lib. bdg. 32.70 (978-0-613-77555-7(4)) Tandem Library Bks.

C D

Aldrich, Vickie. Mom Has a New Boyfriend, What about Me? Crow, Madge, illus. 2000. vi, 26p. (J). (ps-3). pap. 7.95 (978-0-615-11547-4(0)) Aldrich/Crow.

Bailey, Lorilyn. The Original Dating Questionnaire for Teens: A Great Way to Get to Know Each Other. (Illus.). 128p. (Orig.). (YA). (gr. 7-12). pap. (978-0-9641239-7-7(5)) Lormax Communications.

Baish, Vanessa. Frequently Asked Questions about Dating: Teen Life. 2006. (FAQ Ser.). (Illus.). 64p. (J). (gr. 7-12). lib. bdg. 27.95 (***978-1-4042-1969-4(2)***) Rosen Publishing Group, Inc., The.

Beisswenger, Iffer & Eldred, Margaret. The Way We See Things: Middle Schoolers Look at Themselves & Issues They Face Everyday. Krusi, Carolynne, ed. 2004. 96p. pap. 14.95 (978-0-9759264-0-6(3)) Rope Ferry Pr.

Burrows, David. Sex & Dating: A Guide to Relationships for Teens & Young Adults y Dave Burrows. 2001. (gr. 7-12). lib. bdg. 19.95 (978-0-613-85880-9(8)) Tandem Library Bks.

Camron, Roxanne. 60 Clues about Guys: A Guide to Feelings, Flirting, & Falling in Like. Elsammak, Ariane, illus. 2002. 96p. pap. 8.95 (978-0-9678285-5-8(4)) Lunchbox Pr.

Carey, Joely. Boys & Sex. 2002. (gr. 7-12). lib. bdg. 15.25 (978-0-613-81891-9(1)) Tandem Library Bks.

Clark, Chap. Next Time I Fall in Love: How to Handle Sex, Intimacy, & Feelings in Dating Relationships. 2004. 144p. pap. 18.00 (978-1-59244-684-1(1) , Wipf and Stock) Wipf & Stock Pubs.

Cobb, Carlene. Coping with an Abusive Relationship. 2005. (Coping Ser.). (Illus.). 192p. (YA). (gr. 7-12). lib. bdg. 26.50 (978-0-8239-2822-4(5)) Rosen Publishing Group, Inc., The.

Conley, Erin. Psst - Dumped: A Girl's Guide to Happiness after Heartbreak. 2007. (PSST! Ser.). (Illus.). 128p. (J). pap. 9.95 (***978-0-9772660-1-2(X)*** , Zest Bks.) Orange Avenue Publishing.

CosmoGIRL! Editors. All about Guys. Cosmopolitan Editors, ed. 2004. (CosmoGIRL Quiz Book Ser.). (Illus.). 128p. pap. 5.95 (978-1-58816-382-0(2)) Hearst Bks.

—All about You. Cosmopolitan Editors, ed. 2004. (CosmoGIRL Quiz Book Ser.). (Illus.). 128p. pap. 5.95 (978-1-58816-381-3(4)) Hearst Bks.

Eisenbise, Debbie & Krahenbuhl, Lee. Dating: The Art of Respect. 1998. (Generation Why Ser.: Vol. 3:8). 40p. (J). (gr. 9-12). pap. 14.95 (978-0-87303-280-3(2)) Faith & Life Pr.

Ethridge, Shannon & Arterburn, Stephen. Every Young Woman's Battle Workbook: How to Pursue Purity in a Sex-Saturated World. 2004. 112p. pap., wbk. ed. 7.99 (978-1-57856-855-0(2) , WaterBrook Pr.) WaterBrook Pr.

Evert, J. Pure Love. 2004. pap. 1.33 (978-1-888992-13-7(1)) Catholic Answers, Inc.

Feltes, Kim & Chen, Grace. Yo, Yolanda! Advice from an Expert. 2002. (Read 180 Ser.). (Illus.). 70p. (J). (978-0-439-12333-4(X)) Scholastic, Inc.

The FrogBuster Dating Diary: The Perfect Dating Companion. 2004. 169p. (YA). spiral bd. (978-0-9703102-1-7(8)) Intralife Systems Publishing.

Garcia, David. Don't Awaken Love Before the Time: Why Young People Lose When They Date. 2003. (YA). pap. 7.99 (978-1-889893-99-0(4) , Ambassador-Emerald, International) Emerald Hse. Group, Inc.

Goodnough, David. Stalking. 2000. (Hot Issues Ser.). (Illus.). 64p. (YA). (gr. 6-12). lib. bdg. 27.93 (978-0-7660-1364-3(2)) Enslow Pubs., Inc.

Grapes, Bryan J. Violence. 2001. (Teen Decisions Ser.). (Illus.). 142p. (YA). (gr. 10 up). lib. bdg. 36.20 (978-0-7377-0574-4(4) , Greenhaven Pr., Inc.) Thomson Gale.

Haugen, David M. Interracial Relationships. 2006. 128p. (YA). (gr. 7 up). 21.20 (978-0-7377-2391-5(2)); pap. 29.95 (978-0-7377-2390-8(4)) Thomson Gale. (Greenhaven Pr., Inc.).

Hauver, Sandy. Dating & Relationships, 8 vols., Vol. 4. 2002. (Illus.). (J). per. (978-1-932062-29-8(7)) Hability Solution Services, Inc.

Henley, Joy. But it Only Happened Once. 2002. 108p. pap. 16.95 (978-1-59129-762-8(1)) PublishAmerica, Inc.

Holyoke, Nancy. A Smart Girl's Guide to Boys: Surviving Crushes, Staying True to Yourself & Other Stuff! Timmons, Bonnie, illus. 2001. (American Girl Library). 112p. (J). (gr. 3 up). 9.95 (978-1-58485-368-8(9)) American Girl Publishing, Inc.

—A Smart Girl's Guide to Boys: Surviving Crushes, Staying True to Yourself & Other Stuff! 2001. (gr. 3-6). lib. bdg. 18.75 (978-0-613-50064-7(4)) Tandem Library Bks.

Hopkins, Cathy. The Mates, Dates Guide to Life, Love, & Looking Luscious. 2005. (Mates, Dates Ser.). (Illus.). 160p. (YA). pap. 6.99 (978-1-4169-0279-9(1) , Simon Pulse) Simon & Schuster Children's Publishing.

Hormachea, David. Cartas Al Joven Tentado: Consejos Practicos para Evitar las Caídas Sexuales. 2002. (SPA.). 160p. pap. 9.99 (978-0-88113-714-9(6)) Grupo Nelson.

Hovanec, Erin M. Everything You Need to Know about Dating & Relationships. 2005. (Need to Know Library). (Illus.). 64p. (YA). (gr. 7-12). lib. bdg. 25.25 (978-0-8239-3081-4(5) , NTDARE) Rosen Publishing Group, Inc., The.

Hunt, Angela Elwell. Now That He's Asked You Out: Straight Talk for Girls. 2000. (gr. 7-12). lib. bdg. 18.75 (978-0-613-84102-3(6)) Tandem Library Bks.

Hunt, Gary. Now That You've Asked Her Out: Straight Talk for Guys. 2000. (gr. 7-12). lib. bdg. 18.75 (978-0-613-84101-6(8)) Tandem Library Bks.

—Now That You've Asked Her Out: Straight Talk for Guys. 2000. 136p. (YA). (gr. 7-12). pap. 9.95 (978-0-595-09225-3(X)) iUniverse, Inc.

Karres, Erika V. Shearin. Crushes, Flirts, & Friends: A Real Girl's Guide to Boy Smarts. 2005. 160p. (YA). (gr. 8-12). pap. 8.95 (978-1-59337-363-4(5)) Adams Media Corp.

Kirberger, Kimberly. Teen Love, on Relationships: A Book for Teenagers. 1999. (Teen Love Ser.). (Illus.). 300p. (YA). (gr. 8-12). pap. 14.95 (978-1-55874-734-0(6)) Health Communications, Inc.

Kreiner, Anna. In Control: Learning to Say No to Sexual Pressure. rev. ed. 1999. (Teen Pregnancy Prevention Library). (Illus.). 64p. (YA). (gr. 4-6). lib. bdg. 23.95 (978-0-8239-2996-2(5) , TPINCO) Rosen Publishing Group, Inc., The.

Landau, Elaine. Date Violence. (Life Balance Ser.). 80p. (J). 2005. (Illus.). (gr. 5-8). pap. 6.95 (978-0-531-16613-0(9)); 2004. 19.50 (978-0-531-12214-3(X)) Scholastic Library Publishing. (Watts, Franklin).

Levy, Barrie. In Love & in Danger: A Teen's Guide to Breaking Free of Abusive Relationships. 3rd rev. ed. 2006. (Illus.). 150p. (Orig.). (YA). pap. 12.95 (978-1-58005-187-3(1)) Seal Pr.

Lookadoo, Justin & DiMarco, Hayley. The Dateable Rules: A Guide to the Sexes. 2004. (Illus.). 176p. (YA). reprint ed. pap. 11.99 (978-0-8007-5915-5(X)) Revell.

Lookadoo, Justin & Morgan, Hayley. The Dirt on Breaking Up: A Dateable Book. 2004. (Dirt Ser.). 120p. (YA). (gr. 10-12). reprint ed. pap. 9.99 (978-0-8007-5918-6(4)) Revell.

Mayall, Beth. What's Your Guy-Q? 25+ Cool Quizzes to Help Discover the Real You! 2000. 128p. (YA). (gr. 7-12). pap. 4.99 (978-0-439-11466-0(7)) Scholastic, Inc.

Mayo, Jeanne. Uncensored: Dating, Relationship, & Sex. 2007. 224p. pap. 14.99 (978-1-57794-821-6(1)) Harrison Hse., Inc.

McCarthy, Tara. Dating & Relating: A Guy's Guide to Girls. 1999. (Guys' Guides Ser.). (Illus.). 48p. (YA). (gr. 5-8). lib. bdg. 17.95 (978-0-8239-3110-1(2) , GUDARE, Rosen Central) Rosen Publishing Group, Inc., The.

Olsen, Mary-Kate. Girl's Guide to Guys. 2003. (gr. 5-8). lib. bdg. 13.00 (978-0-613-66506-3(6)) Tandem Library Bks.

Ouffy, Jan. Recuerdos de las Montanas. 2000. (Reunited Ser.: Vol. 3). (SPA.). (J). (gr. 8-12). mass mkt. 3.99 (978-0-7899-0804-9(2)) Spanish Hse. Distributors.

Palardy, Debra J. Sweetie, Here's the Best Reason on the Planet to Say No to Your Boyfriend: Even If You've Already Said Yes. 2000. 56p. (YA). pap. 8.00 (978-0-8059-4875-2(9)) Dorrance Publishing Co., Inc.

Peacock, Judith. Dating & Sex: Defining & Setting Boundaries. (Perspectives on Healthy Sexuality Ser.). pap. 8.95 (978-0-7368-8845-5(4)); 2000. (Illus.). 64p. (J). (gr. 4-6). lib. bdg. 23.93 (978-0-7368-0716-6(0)) Capstone Pr., Inc. (LifeMatters Bks.).

Powell. Is Kissing a Girl Who Smokes Like Licking an Ashtray? 2003. (gr. 7-12). lib. bdg. 14.10 (978-0-613-71864-6(X)) Tandem Library Bks.

Rabens, Susan. Complete Idiot's Guide to Dating for Teens. 2001. (gr. 7-12). lib. bdg. 22.20 (978-0-613-83253-3(1)) Tandem Library Bks.

Radziszewicz, Tina. Ready or Not: A Girl's Guide to Making Her Own Decisions about Dating, Love, & Sex. 2006. (Illus.). 288p. (YA). (gr. 7 up). 16.95 (978-0-8027-9613-4(3)); pap. 9.95 (978-0-8027-9612-7(5)) Walker & Co.

Rasmussen, Klayne, et al. The FrogBuster: A Girl's Guide for Survival in the Dating Swamp. 2002. 214p. (YA). per. 16.95 (978-0-9703102-0-0(X)) Intralife Systems Publishing.

Real Teens Vol. 5: Diary of A Junior Year. 2000. (gr. 7-12). lib. bdg. 13.00 (978-0-613-26722-9(2)) Tandem Library Bks.

Riera, Mike. Surviving High School: Making the Most of the High School Years. 2004. (Illus.). 160p. (gr. 8-12). pap. 12.95 (978-0-89087-825-5(0) , Celestial Arts Publishing Company) Ten Speed Pr.

Rose, Lyman Hinckley. Pure & Chased. 2004. ix, 86p. (978-1-55517-774-4(3)) Cedar Fort, Inc./CFI Distribution.

Scheer, Scott. Talking to Teens about Dating & Sex. 2002. (YA). per. (978-1-931600-09-5(0)) Faith Printing Co.

Seventeen Magazine. True Love. 2007. 128p. (J). pap. 4.95 (978-1-58816-629-6(5)) Hearst Communications, Inc.

Spencer, Lauren. Everything You Need to Know about Falling in Love. 2001. (Need to Know Library). (Illus.). 64p. (YA). (gr. 4-6). lib. bdg. 25.25 (978-0-8239-3395-2(4)) Rosen Publishing Group, Inc., The.

Sperekas, Nicole B. But He Says He Loves Me: Girls Speak Out on Dating Abuse. 2002. viii, 162p. (J). 15.00 (978-1-884444-66-1(0)) Safer Society Pr.

Stanley, Barb. What Catholics Teens Should Know When Dating Turns Violent. Larkin, Jean K., ed. 2004. (What Catholic Teens Should Know Ser.). (Illus.). 8p. (YA). 7.95 (978-0-89837-239-7(9) , 441210) Pflaum Publishing Group.

Stewart, Arlene Hamilton, et al. The Love & Romance Teen Quiz Book. 2001. 240p. pap. 9.95 (978-0-7407-1988-2(2)) Andrews McMeel Publishing.

Taylor, Paula. Run Farrah Run: Detecting, Ditching & Dealing with Dating Dopes. von Seeburg, Kate, ed. Foster, Frank, illus. 2004. 128p. (YA). pap. 12.95 (978-0-9749173-0-6(3)) Tea Party Pr.

Theisen, Michael. Dating & Love. Zanzig, Thomas, ed. Thiewes, Sam, illus. 2003. (Horizons Program : Vol. Level II, Minicourse 5). 64p. (Orig.). (YA). (gr. 10). pap., stu. ed. 9.95 (978-0-88489-362-2(6)) St. Mary's Pr.

Thomas Nelson Publishing Staff & Eastham, Chad. The Truth about Guys. 2006. (Illus.). 232p. (YA). pap. 12.99 (978-1-4003-0968-9(9)) Nelson, Thomas Inc.

Watkins, James. When Can I Start Dating? The Why Files. 2000. (ENG., Illus.). 222p. (YA). (gr. 7-12). pap. 9.99 (978-0-570-05249-4(1)) Concordia Publishing Hse.

Watkins, James N. When Can I Start Dating? Questions about Love, Sex, & a Cure for Zits. 2000. (gr. 7-12). lib. bdg. 18.80 (978-0-613-72646-7(4)) Tandem Library Bks.

White, Katherine. Everything You Need to Know about Relationship Violence. 2001. (Need to Know Library). (Illus.). 64p. (YA). (gr. 4-6). lib. bdg. 25.25 (978-0-8239-3398-3(9)) Rosen Publishing Group, Inc., The.

Winkler, Kathleen. Date Rape. 1999. (Hot Issues Ser.). (Illus.). 64p. (YA). (gr. 6-12). lib. bdg. 27.93 (978-0-7660-1198-4(4)) Enslow Pubs., Inc.

Youth Specialties Staff. Outrageous Dates. 1998. pap. 6.00 (978-0-310-67949-3(4)) HarperCollins Pubs.

DATING (SOCIAL CUSTOMS)—FICTION

Abbot, Hailey. After Summer. 2006. (Summer Boys Ser.). 224p. (J). pap. 8.99 (978-0-439-86367-4(8) , Scholastic Paperbacks) Scholastic, Inc.

Abbott, Hailey. Getting Lost with Boys. 2006. 240p. (J). pap. 8.99 (978-0-06-082432-7(8)) HarperCollins Pubs.

—Next Summer: A Summer Boys Novel. 2005. (Summer Boys Ser.). 224p. (YA). (gr. 10 up). 8.99 (978-0-439-75540-5(9)) Scholastic, Inc.

—The Secrets of Boys. 2006. 272p. (J). pap. 8.99 (978-0-06-082433-4(6)) HarperCollins Pubs.

Abbott, Hailey. Waking up to Boys. 2007. 256p. (J). pap. 8.99 (***978-0-06-082435-8(2)*** , HarperTeen) HarperCollins Pubs.

Adams, Kendall. Don't Do Anything I Wouldn't Do. 2007. (Hook up or Break Up Ser.: No. 4). 256p. (J). pap. 8.99 (***978-0-06-088566-3(1)*** , HarperTeen) HarperCollins Pubs.

Adams, Kendall. If You Can't Be Good, Be Good at It. 2006. (Hook up or Break Up Ser.: No. 2). 256p. (J). pap. 8.99 (978-0-06-088564-9(5) , HarperTeen) HarperCollins Pubs.

Appelt, Kathi. Kissing Tennessee: And Other Stories from the Stardust Dance. 2004. (Illus.). 132p. (YA). reprint ed. pap. 5.95 (978-0-15-205127-3(9) , Harcourt Paperbacks) Harcourt Children's Bks.

Applegate, Katherine. Always Loving Zoey. 2000. (Making Out Ser.: No. 22). 192p. (YA). (gr. 7-12). pap. 3.99 (978-0-380-81311-7(4)) HarperCollins Pubs.

—Don't Tell Zoey. 1999. (Making Out Ser.: No. 13). 176p. (YA). (gr. 7 up). pap. 3.99 (978-0-380-80869-4(2)) HarperCollins Pubs.

—Falling for Claire. 2000. (Making Out Ser.: No. 27). 176p. (YA). (gr. 7-12). pap. 3.99 (978-0-380-81531-9(1)) HarperCollins Pubs.

—Jake Finds Out. 1998. (Making Out Ser.: No. 2). 224p. (YA). (gr. 7-12). reprint ed. pap. 3.99 (978-0-380-80212-8(0)) HarperCollins Pubs.

—Nina Won't Tell, No. 3. 1998. (Making Out Ser.: No. 3). 224p. (YA). (gr. 7-12). reprint ed. pap. 3.99 (978-0-380-80213-5(9)) HarperCollins Pubs.

—Once upon a Date. 2001. (True Love Ser.: No. 6). 208p. (YA). pap. 4.99 (978-1-931497-39-8(7)) 17th Street Productions, An Alloy Online Inc. Co.

—Zoey Comes Home. 2000. (Making Out Ser.: No. 28). 176p. (YA). (gr. 7-12). pap. 3.99 (978-0-380-81532-6(X)) HarperCollins Pubs.

Ashton, Victoria. Confessions of a Teen Nanny. 2006. (Confessions of a Teen Nanny Ser.). 208p. (J). reprint ed. pap. 8.99 (978-0-06-073178-6(8)) HarperCollins Pubs.

—Juicy Secrets. 2006. (Confessions of a Teen Nanny Ser.). 208p. (J). 15.99 (978-0-06-073181-6(8)); lib. bdg. 16.89 (978-0-06-077526-1(2)) HarperCollins Pubs. (HarperTeen).

—Rich Girls. 2006. (Confessions of a Teen Nanny Ser.). 224p. (J). pap. 8.99 (978-0-06-073180-9(X) , HarperTeen); 15.99 (978-0-06-073179-3(6)) HarperCollins Pubs.

Ashworth, Sherry. Is He Worth It? 2000. 144p. (J). pap. 9.99 (978-0-7043-4970-4(1)) Women's Pr., Ltd., The GBR. *Dist:* Independent Pubs. Group.

Baer, Judy. No Me Digas Mentiras. 1999. (Reunited Ser.: Vol. 1). (SPA.). (J). (gr. 4-7). mass mkt. 3.99 (978-0-7899-0644-1(9)) Spanish Hse. Distributors.

Bagert, Brod. Hormone Jungle: Coming of Age in Middle School. 2006. (Illus.). 121p. (J). (gr. 5-8). 23.95 (978-0-929895-87-1(8)) Maupin Hse. Publishing.

Banks, Piper. Geek High. 2007. 256p. (gr. 12 up). 9.99 (***978-0-451-22225-1(3)*** , N A L Trade) Penguin Group (USA) Inc.

Barnholdt, Lauren. Reality Chick. 2006. 288p. (YA). pap. 8.99 (978-1-4169-1317-7(3) , Simon Pulse) Simon & Schuster Children's Publishing.

Beam, Matt. Getting to First Base with Danalda Chase. 2007. (Illus.). 192p. (J). (gr. 5-8). 16.99 (978-0-525-47578-1(8) , Dutton Juvenile) Penguin Group (USA) Inc.

Berenstain, Stan & Berenstain, Jan. The Berenstain Bears & the Big Date. 1998. (Berenstain Bears Big Chapter Bks.). (J). (gr. 2-6). (978-0-606-13951-9(6)) Tandem Library Bks.

Blume, Judy. Forever... 2007. 208p. (YA). pap. 8.99 (978-1-4169-3400-4(6) , Simon Pulse) Simon & Schuster Children's Publishing.

Bonin, Liane. Pretty on the Outside: Fame Unlimited. 2007. 288p. (YA). pap. 9.99 (***978-0-451-22122-3(2)*** , N A L Trade) Penguin Group (USA) Inc.

Bradley, Alex. 24 Girls in 7 Days. 2006. 272p. (YA). (gr. 7). reprint ed. pap. 5.99 (978-0-14-240543-7(4) , Puffin) Penguin Group (USA) Inc.

—24 Girls in 7 Days (Splashproof Ed) 2007. 1p. (YA). (gr. 7). pap. 5.99 (978-0-14-240834-6(4) , Puffin) Penguin Group (USA) Inc.

Brian, Kate. Fake Boyfriend. 2007. 272p. (YA). (gr. 9 up). 16.99 (***978-1-4169-1367-2(X)*** Simon & Schuster Children's Publishing.

—Inner Circle. 2007. (Private Ser.). 224p. (YA). (gr. 9 up). pap. 9.99 (***978-1-4169-5041-7(9)*** , Simon Pulse) Simon & Schuster Children's Publishing.

—Invitation Only. 2006. (Private Ser.). 272p. (YA). (gr. 9 up). pap. 8.99 (978-1-4169-1874-5(4) , Simon Pulse) Simon & Schuster Children's Publishing.

—Sweet 16. 2006. 272p. (YA). 15.99 (978-1-4169-0032-0(2)) Simon & Schuster Children's Publishing.

—The V Club: Wanna Join? 2004. 288p. (YA). 14.95 (978-0-689-86764-4(6)) Simon & Schuster Children's Publishing.

Brown, Amanda. Family Trust. 2004. 336p. (gr. 12). pap. 14.00 (978-0-452-28553-8(4) , Plume) Penguin Group (USA) Inc.

Brown, Hobson, et al. Miss Educated. 2007. (Upper Class Ser.). 288p. (J). (gr. 9 up). pap. 8.99 (***978-0-06-085083-8(3)*** , HarperTeen) HarperCollins Pubs.

—The Upper Class. 2007. (Upper Class Ser.). 304p. (J). (gr. 9 up). pap. 8.99 (***978-0-06-085082-1(5)*** , HarperTeen) HarperCollins Pubs.

Brown, Marc. Muffy's Secret Admirer. 1999. (Arthur Chapter Bks. : Bk. 17). (J). (gr. 3-6). pap. 3.95 (978-0-316-12047-0(2)) Little, Brown Bks. for Young Readers.

—Muffy's Secret Admirer. Brown, Marc, illus. 17th ed. 1999. (Arthur Chapter Bks. : Bk. 17). (Illus.). 64p. (J). (gr. 2-4). 13.95 (978-0-316-12017-3(0)); pap. 3.95 (978-0-316-12230-6(0)) Little, Brown Bks. for Young Readers.

—Muffy's Secret Admirer. 1999. (Arthur Chapter Bks.: Bk. 17). (gr. k-3). lib. bdg. 11.80 (978-0-613-22040-8(4)); (J). (gr. 3-6). (978-0-606-17237-0(8)) Tandem Library Bks.

Burke, Morgan. Get It Started. 2005. (Party Room Ser.: No. 1). 272p. (YA). (gr. 11 up). pap. 5.99 (978-0-689-87725-9(9) , Simon Pulse) Simon & Schuster Children's Publishing.

Burnham, Niki. Sticky Fingers. 2005. 278p. (YA). (gr. 7 up). pap. 6.99 (978-0-689-87649-3(1) , Simon Pulse) Simon & Schuster Children's Publishing.

Burns, Laura. A Fine State of Affairs, No. 3. 2006. (Darcy's Wild Life Ser.: Bk. 3). 176p. (J). (gr. 4-7). pap. 4.99 (978-0-448-44260-0(4) , Grosset & Dunlap) Penguin Group (USA) Inc.

Busby, Cylin. The Campfire Crush: A Choose Your Boyfriend Book. 2007. (Date Him or Dump Him? Ser.). 176p. (J). (gr. 5-8). pap. 6.95 (***978-1-59990-083-4(1)***) Bloomsbury Publishing.

—The Dance Dilemma: A Choose Your Boyfriend Book. 2007. (Date Him or Dump Him? Ser.). 192p. (J). (gr. 5 up). pap. 6.95 (***978-1-59990-084-1(X)*** , Bloomsbury Children) Bloomsbury Publishing.

—The Ski Trip Trouble: A Choose Your Boyfriend Book. 2007. (Date Him or Dump Him? Ser.). 192p. (J). (gr. 5 up). pap. 6.95 (***978-1-59990-106-0(4)***) Bloomsbury Publishing.

Byars, Betsy. The Cybil War. l.t. ed. 2003. (LRS Large Print Heritage Ser.). 122p. (J). lib. bdg. 27.95 (978-1-58118-111-1(6)) LRS.

Cabot, Meg. Pants on Fire. 2007. 272p. (gr. 7-10). (J). lib. bdg. 17.89 (978-0-06-088016-3(3)); (YA). 16.99 (978-0-06-088015-6(5)) HarperCollins Pubs. (HarperTeen).

—The Princess Diaries Box Set Vols. I-III: Princess in Love; Princess in the Spotlight; The Princess Diaries. 2003. (Princess Diaries). 304p. (gr. 7 up). pap. 19.99 (978-0-06-058745-1(8)) HarperCollins Pubs.

—Princess in Waiting. (Princess Diaries: Vol. 4). (YA). (gr. 7 up). 2004. 288p. pap. 6.99 (978-0-06-009609-0(8) , Harper Trophy); 2003. pap. 6.99 (978-0-06-054065-4(6)) HarperCollins Pubs.

Cann, Kate. Mediterranean Holiday. 2007. 336p. (J). pap. 5.99 (***978-0-06-115216-0(1)*** , HarperTeen) HarperCollins Pubs.

Carlson, Melody. Torch Red: Color Me Torn. 2004. 196p. (YA). pap. 12.99 (978-1-57683-531-9(6)) NavPress Publishing Group.

Chandler, Elizabeth. Summer in the City. 2006. 384p. (J). pap. 5.99 (978-0-06-084734-0(4)) HarperCollins Pubs.

Cheung, Dave. Chugworth Academy, Vol. 1. 2006. (Illus.). 160p. pap. 13.99 (978-1-933164-17-5(4)) Seven Seas Entertainment, LLC.

Clairday, Robynn. Confessions of a Boyfriend Stealer. 2005. 240p. (YA). (gr. 7-12). pap. 7.95 (978-0-385-73242-0(2) , Delacorte Bks. for Young Readers) Random Hse. Children's Bks.

Clark, Catherine. Frozen Rodeo. 2003. 304p. (J). (gr. 8 up). 15.99 (978-0-06-009070-8(7)) HarperCollins Pubs.

—Frozen Rodeo. 2004. lib. bdg. 15.30 (978-0-613-71502-7(0)) Tandem Library Bks.

Clark, Catherine. So Inn Love. 2007. 336p. (J). pap. 5.99 (***978-0-06-113904-8(1)*** , HarperTeen) HarperCollins Pubs.

Coffey, Jan. Tropical Kiss. 2005. 304p. (J). (gr. 8 up). pap. 5.99 (978-0-06-076003-8(6)) HarperCollins Pubs.

Colasanti, Susane. Take Me There. 2008. 304p. (YA). (gr. 7). 17.99 (***978-0-670-06333-8(9)*** , Viking Juvenile) Penguin Group (USA) Inc.

Condie, Allyson. First Day. 2007. 304p. (YA). pap. 15.95 (***978-1-59038-775-7(9)***) Deseret Bk. Co.

Condie, Allyson B. Yearbook. 2006. 208p. (YA). pap. 14.95 (978-1-59038-690-3(6)) Deseret Bk. Co.

Craft, Elizabeth. Prom Season: Three Novels. 2007. 560p. (YA). (gr. 7-11). lib. bdg. 11.99 (978-0-375-94074-3(X) , Laurel Leaf) Random Hse. Children's Bks.

—Prom Season: Three Stories. 2007. 560p. (YA). (gr. 7-11). mass mkt. 7.99 (978-0-375-84074-6(5) , Laurel Leaf) Random Hse. Children's Bks.

Cross, Cecil, II. First Semester. 2007. 256p. pap. 9.99 (***978-0-373-83082-4(3)*** , Kimani) Harlequin Enterprises, Ltd. CAN. *Dist:* Simon & Schuster, Inc.

Davis, Cynthia. Drink the Rain. 2007. 256p. (YA). per. 12.95 (***978-0-9712163-1-0(2)***) Greenroom Bks.

de la Cruz, Melissa. The Au Pairs. (Au Pairs Ser.: Bk. 1). (YA). 2004. 304p. 14.95 (978-0-689-87066-8(3)); 2005. 320p. reprint ed. pap. 8.99 (978-0-689-87319-5(0) , Simon Pulse) Simon & Schuster Children's Publishing.

—Crazy Hot. 2007. (Au Pairs Ser.: No. 4). 288p. (YA). 16.99 (978-1-4169-3961-0(X)) Simon & Schuster Children's Publishing.

—Sun-Kissed. 2006. (Au Pairs Ser.: No. 3). 320p. (YA). (gr. 9 up). 15.95 (978-1-4169-1746-5(2)) Simon & Schuster Children's Publishing.

Dessen, Sarah. Dreamland. 2000. (Illus.). 256p. (J). (gr. 7-12). 15.99 (978-0-670-89122-1(3) , Viking Juvenile) Penguin Group (USA) Inc.

—Someone Like You. ed. 2004. 288p. (YA). (gr. 7 up). pap. 7.99 (978-0-14-240177-4(3) , Puffin) Penguin Group (USA) Inc.

—This Lullaby. 2002. 304p. (J). 16.99 (978-0-670-03530-4(0) , Viking Juvenile) Penguin Group (USA) Inc.

Disney Press Staff. Head over Heels. 2001. (gr. 3-6). lib. bdg. 13.00 (978-0-613-74997-8(9)) Tandem Library Bks.

Dower, Laura. Rewind. 2006. 256p. (J). pap. 8.99 (978-0-439-70340-6(9) , Scholastic Paperbacks) Scholastic, Inc.

Ellerbee, Linda. Girl Reporter Snags Crush! 2000. (Get Real Ser.: No. 4). (Illus.). 229p. (J). (gr. 3-7). 14.89 (978-0-06-028248-6(7)) HarperCollins Pubs.

Emery, Anne. Dinny Gordon, Freshman. 2004. (J). per. 9.95 (978-1-930009-97-4(6)) Image Cascade Publishing.

—Dinny Gordon Sophomore. 2004. (J). per. 9.95 (978-1-930009-98-1(4)) Image Cascade Publishing.

Emery, Anne. Senior Year. 2006. (YA). per. 11.95 (***978-1-59511-005-3(4)***) Image Cascade Publishing.

Ferraro, Tina. How to Hook a Hottie. 2008. 208p. (J). pap. (***978-0-385-73438-7(7)*** , Delacorte Pr.) Dell Publishing.

—How to Hook a Hottie. 2008. 208p. (YA). (gr. 7). lib. bdg. 11.99 (***978-0-385-90444-5(4)*** , Delacorte Bks. for Young Readers) Random Hse. Children's Bks.

Ferrer, Caridad. It's Not about the Accent. 2007. 288p. (YA). (gr. 7 up). pap. 9.95 (***978-1-4165-2491-5(6)*** , MTV) Simon & Schuster.

Fleming, Maria. Where Do Kisses Come From? DRI Artworks Staff & Kinnealy, Janice, illus. 1999. (Little Golden Bks.). 16p. (J). (gr. k-k). 2.99 (978-0-307-99503-2(8) , Golden Bks.) Random Hse. Children's Bks.

Flinn, Alex. Breathing Underwater. 272p. (J). 2002. (gr. 5 up). pap. 8.99 (978-0-06-447257-9(4)); 2001. (Illus.). (gr. 8 up). 18.99 (978-0-06-029198-3(2)) HarperCollins Pubs.

—Breathing Underwater. unabr. ed. 2004. (Young Adult Cassette Librariestm Ser.). 272p. (J). (gr. 7 up). pap. 36.00 incl. audio (978-0-8072-0992-9(9) , S YA 346 SP, Listening Library) Random Hse. Audio Publishing Group.

—Breathing Underwater. 2002. (gr. 7-12). lib. bdg. 16.45 (978-0-613-60383-6(4)) Tandem Library Bks.

Fox, Red. The Big Book of Summer Love. 2001. 480p. (J). pap. 11.99 (978-0-09-941758-3(8)) Random Hse. GBR. *Dist:* Independent Pubs. Group.

Franklin, Emily. Balancing Acts: Chalet Girls. 2007. 244p. (YA). (gr. 12 up). per. 9.99 (***978-0-451-22219-0(9)*** , N A L Trade) Penguin Group (USA) Inc.

—The Other Half of Me. 2007. 256p. (YA). (gr. 9). 15.99 (***978-0-385-73445-5(X)*** ***);*** lib. bdg. 18.99 (***978-0-385-90449-0(5)***) Random Hse. Children's Bks. (Delacorte Bks. for Young Readers).

Fredericks, Mariah. Head Games. 2006. (Illus.). 272p. (YA). pap. 6.99 (978-1-4169-1335-1(1) , Simon Pulse) Simon & Schuster Children's Publishing.

Freeman, Martha. 1,000 Reasons Never to Kiss a Boy. 2007. 240p. (YA). (gr. 7 up). 16.95 (978-0-8234-2044-5(2)) Holiday Hse., Inc.

Friedman, Aimee. French Kiss. 2006. 336p. (J). pap. 8.99 (978-0-439-79281-3(9) , Scholastic Paperbacks) Scholastic, Inc.

Friedman, Robin. The Girlfriend Project. 2007. 192p. (YA). (gr. 7 up). 15.95 (978-0-8027-9624-0(9)) Walker & Co.

Gallagher, Liz. The Opposite of Invisible. 2008. (YA). (***978-0-375-84152-1(0)*** ***);*** (***978-0-375-94329-4(3)***) Dell Publishing. (Delacorte Pr.).

Garfield, Valerie. Sergeant Sniff's Secret Valentine Mystery. 2001. (Sergeant Sniff Scratch-and-Sniff Mystery Ser.). (Illus.). 16p. (J). (ps-k). 6.95 (978-0-694-01507-8(5) , Harper Festival) HarperCollins Pubs.

Garfinkle, Debra. The Band: Holding On. 2007. 240p. (YA). (gr. 12 up). pap. 9.99 (***978-0-425-21562-3(8)*** , Berkley Trade) Penguin Group (USA) Inc.

—The Band: Trading Guys: Trading Guys. 2007. 256p. (YA). (gr. 12). pap. 9.99 (***978-0-425-21513-5(X)*** , Berkley Trade) Penguin Group (USA) Inc.

Garfinkle, Debra. Storky: How I Lost My Nickname & Won the Girl. 192p. (YA). 2007. (gr. 7 up). pap. 5.99 (978-0-14-240782-0(8) , Puffin); 2005. (gr. 6). 16.99 (978-0-399-24284-7(8) , Putnam Juvenile) Penguin Group (USA) Inc.

Gavril, David. Penelope Nuthatch & the Big Surprise. 2006. (Illus.). 32p. (J). (ps-2). 14.95 (978-0-8109-5762-6(0)) Abrams, Harry N. , Inc.

Goldblatt, Stacey. Stray. 2007. 288p. (YA). (gr. 7-10). 15.99 (978-0-385-73443-1(3)); lib. bdg. 18.99 (978-0-385-90448-3(7)) Random Hse. Children's Bks. (Delacorte Bks. for Young Readers).

Haft, Erin. Pool Boys. 2006. 240p. (J). pap. 8.99 (978-0-439-83523-7(2) , Scholastic Paperbacks) Scholastic, Inc.

Hale, Stephanie. Revenge of the Homecoming Queen. 2007. 272p. (YA). (gr. 6 up). pap. 9.99 (***978-0-425-21615-6(2)*** , Berkley Trade) Penguin Group (USA) Inc.

Hall, John. Where the Boys Are. 1998. 208p. (J). (gr. 5-9). pap. 4.50 (978-0-590-05960-2(2)) Scholastic, Inc.

HarperCollins Staff, ed. Calling All Boys. 2000. (gr. 3-6). lib. bdg. 13.00 (978-0-613-21280-9(0)) Tandem Library Bks.

Harrison, Emma. Tourist Trap. 2006. 384p. (J). pap. 5.99 (978-0-06-084735-7(2)) HarperCollins Pubs.

Harrison, Emma, et al. Slipping Away. 2005. 163p. (YA). (978-1-4155-8181-0(9) , Simon Spotlight) Simon & Schuster Children's Publishing.

Hawthorne, Rachel. The Boyfriend League. 2007. 336p. (J). pap. 5.99 (***978-0-06-113837-9(1)*** , HarperTeen) HarperCollins Pubs.

—Snowed In. 2007. 272p. (YA). (gr. 9 up). pap. 5.99 (***978-0-06-113836-2(3)*** , HarperTeen) HarperCollins Pubs.

Hawthorne, Rachel. Thrill Ride. 2006. 320p. (J). pap. 5.99 (978-0-06-083954-3(6)) HarperCollins Pubs.

Henderson, Lauren. Kiss Me Kill Me. 2008. 256p. (YA). (gr. 9). 15.99 (***978-0-385-73487-5(5)*** , Delacorte Bks. for Young Readers) Random Hse. Children's Bks.

Hewett, Lorri. Lives of Our Own. 2000. (J). (978-0-606-19695-6(1)) Tandem Library Bks.

Hoang, Hoa X. My First Boyfriend: An Unforgettable Obsession. 2002. (gr. 7-12). lib. bdg. 21.05 (978-0-613-81382-2(0)) Tandem Library Bks.

—My First Boyfriend: An Unforgettable Obsession. 2002. 146p. (YA). pap. 11.95 (978-0-595-22842-3(9) , Writers Club Pr.) iUniverse, Inc.

Hoffmann, Kerry Cohen. Easy. 2006. 176p. (YA). (gr. 9 up). 15.95 (978-1-4169-1425-9(0)) Simon & Schuster Children's Publishing.

Hogan, Mary. Pretty Face. 2008. 224p. (J). 16.99 (***978-0-06-084111-9(7)*** ***);*** lib. bdg. 17.89 (***978-0-06-084112-6(5)***) HarperCollins Pubs. (HarperTeen).

Hopkins, Cathy. Mates, Dates & Cosmic Kisses. 2003. (Mates, Dates Ser.). (Illus.). 208p. (YA). mass mkt. 5.99 (978-0-689-85545-0(1) , Simon Pulse) Simon & Schuster Children's Publishing.

—Mates, Dates & Cosmic Kisses. 2003. (Mates, Dates Ser.). (YA). (gr. 7-12). lib. bdg. 13.00 (978-0-613-61796-3(7)) Tandem Library Bks.

—Mates, Dates & Diamond Destiny. 2006. (Mates, Dates Ser.). (Illus.). 272p. (YA). mass mkt. 6.99 (978-0-689-87697-4(1) , Simon Pulse) Simon & Schuster Children's Publishing.

—Mates, Dates & Inflatable Bras. 2003. (Mates, Dates Ser.: No. 1). 176p. (YA). pap. 5.99 (978-0-689-85544-3(3) , Simon Pulse) Simon & Schuster Children's Publishing.

—Mates, Dates & Inflatable Bras. 2003. (Mates, Dates Ser.: No. 1). (YA). (gr. 7-12). lib. bdg. 13.00 (978-0-613-61797-0(5)) Tandem Library Bks.

—Mates, Dates & Sizzling Summers. 2006. (Mates, Dates Ser.). 224p. (YA). mass mkt. 5.99 (978-0-689-87698-1(X) , Simon Pulse) Simon & Schuster Children's Publishing.

—Mates, Dates & Sleepover Secrets. 2003. (Mates, Dates Ser.). 208p. (YA). mass mkt. 5.99 (978-0-689-85991-5(0) , Simon Pulse) Simon & Schuster Children's Publishing.

—Mates, Dates & Sleepover Secrets. 2003. (gr. 7-12). lib. bdg. 13.00 (978-0-613-73417-2(3)) Tandem Library Bks.

—The Princess of Pop. 2004. (Truth or Dare Ser.: No. 2). 224p. (YA). mass mkt. 5.99 (978-0-689-87002-6(7) , Simon Pulse) Simon & Schuster Children's Publishing.

—Teen Queens & Has-Beens. 2004. (Truth or Dare Ser.: No. 3). 192p. (YA). pap. 5.99 (978-0-689-87129-0(5) , Simon Pulse) Simon & Schuster Children's Publishing.

I Met a Boy I Used to Know. 2000. (Katie Rose/Stacy Belford Ser.). (YA). pap. 12.95 (978-1-930009-13-4(5)) Image Cascade Publishing.

Ikumi, Mia & Yoshida, Reiko. Tokyo Mew Mew (en Español), Vol. 1. 2006. (SPA., Illus.). 176p. reprint ed. pap. 10.95 (978-1-59497-155-6(2)) Public Square Bks.

Jahn-Clough, Lisa. Me, Penelope. 2007. 208p. (YA). (gr. 7 up). 16.00 (***978-0-618-77366-4(5)*** , Walter Lorraine) Houghton Mifflin Co. Trade & Reference Div.

Johnson, Kathleen Jeffrie. Dumb Love. 2005. 176p. (YA). (gr. 7-17). 16.95 (978-1-59643-062-4(1)) Roaring Brook Pr.

Johnson, Lissa Halls & Lambert, David. Opportunity Knocks Twice, Vol. 3. 2005. (Brio Girls Ser.). 192p. (YA). pap. 7.99 (978-1-56179-953-4(X)) Focus on the Family Publishing.

Jones, Carrie. Tips on Having a Gay (ex) Boyfriend. 2008. 264p. (J). pap. 9.95 (***978-0-7387-1341-0(4)*** , Flux) Llewellyn Pubns.

Jones, Patrick. Things Change. 2006. 228p. (J). reprint ed. pap. 7.95 (978-0-8027-7746-1(5)) Walker & Co.

Juby, Susan. Alice MacLeod, Realist at Last. (J). 2006. 320p. pap. 8.99 (978-0-06-051552-2(X)); 2005. 15.99 (978-0-06-051549-2(X)); 2005. 320p. lib. bdg. 16.89 (978-0-06-051550-8(3)) HarperCollins Pubs. (HarperTeen).

Kantor, Melissa. Confessions of a Not It Girl. 2006. 256p. (gr. 7-17). pap. 8.99 (978-0-7868-1808-2(5)) Hyperion Pr.

Katschke, Judy. The Facts about Flirting. 2003. (Two of a Kind Ser.: Vol. 27). (Illus.). 112p. mass mkt. 4.99 (978-0-06-009323-5(4) , Harper Entertainment) HarperCollins Pubs.

Killian, Beth. Everything She Wants. 2006. (310 Ser.). 240p. pap. 9.95 (978-1-4165-2168-6(2) , MTV) Simon & Schuster.

Kornreich, Leron. Ivory Towers. 2001. (YA). 7.99 (978-0-9707509-0-7(0)) Banana Peel Bks.

Kraut, Julie & Lester, Shallon. Hot Mess: Summer in the City. 2008. 256p. (YA). (gr. 9). pap. 8.99 (***978-0-385-73506-3(5)*** ***);*** lib. bdg. 12.99 (***978-0-385-90499-5(1)***) Random Hse. Children's Bks. (Delacorte Bks. for Young Readers).

Landon, Kristen. Life in the Pit. Johnson, Regan, illus. 2007. 192p. (YA). (gr. 8-12). 16.95 (***978-1-933831-08-4(1)***) Blooming Tree Pr.

Lantz, Francess L. Current Affairs. 2004. (Luna Bay Ser.: No. 9). 176p. mass mkt. 4.99 (978-0-06-059521-0(3) , Harper Entertainment) HarperCollins Pubs.

Lawton, Wendy. Dating Do-Over. 2005. (Real Tv Ser.: Take 4). (Illus.). 192p. (J). (gr. 8-12). pap. 10.99 (978-0-8024-5416-4(X)) Moody Pubs.

Le, Ny Jeanine. Once upon A Prom #1 Dream. 2008. 240p. pap. 5.99 (***978-0-545-02815-8(9)*** , Scholastic Paperbacks) Scholastic, Inc.

—Once upon A Prom #2 Dress. 2008. (Once upon A Prom Ser.). 240p. (J). pap. 5.99 (***978-0-545-03181-3(8)*** , Scholastic Paperbacks) Scholastic, Inc.

Leblanc, Louise. Sophie Est en Orbite. Gay, Marie-Louise, tr. 2003. (Premier Roman Ser.). (FRE., Illus.). 64p. (J). (gr. 1-4). pap. (978-2-89021-670-9(5)) Diffusion du livre Mirabel.

Levithan, David & Cohn, Rachel. Naomi & Ely's No Kiss List. 2007. (YA). (gr. 9 up). 240p. 16.99 (***978-0-375-84440-9(6)*** ***);*** 192p. lib. bdg. 19.99 (***978-0-375-94440-6(0)***) Random Hse. Children's Bks. (Knopf Bks. for Young Readers).

Levithan, David & Ehrenhaft, Daniel, eds. 21 Proms. 2007. 304p. (J). pap. 8.99 (***978-0-439-89029-8(2)*** , Scholastic Paperbacks) Scholastic, Inc.

Limb, Sue. Girl, 15, Charming but Insane. 2004. (Girl, 15 Ser.). 214p. (J). (gr. 5). per. 16.00 (978-0-606-33729-8(6)) Tandem Library Bks.

—Girl 15, Charming but Insane. 2007. (Girl, 15 Ser.). 224p. (YA). (gr. 7-11). mass mkt. 5.99 (978-0-440-23896-6(X) , Laurel Leaf) Random Hse. Children's Bks.

—Girl, (Nearly) 16: Absolute Torture. (Girl, 15 Ser.). 224p. (YA). (gr. 5-11). 2008. mass mkt. 6.50 (***978-0-440-23897-3(8)*** , Laurel Leaf); 2006. pap. 8.95 (978-0-385-73217-8(1) , Delacorte Bks. for Young Readers) Random Hse. Children's Bks.

Lockhart, E. The Boy Book: A Study of Habits & Behaviors, Plus Techniques for Taming Them. (YA). (gr. 7). 2008. 224p. pap. 8.99 (***978-0-385-73209-3(0));*** 2006. 208p. 15.95 (978-0-385-73208-6(2)); 2006. 208p. 17.99 (978-0-385-90239-7(5)) Random Hse. Children's Bks. (Delacorte Bks. for Young Readers).

—The Boyfriend List. (gr. 7). 2005. 240p. (J). lib. bdg. 17.99 (978-0-385-90238-0(7)); 2006. 256p. (YA). reprint ed. pap. 8.95 (978-0-385-73207-9(4)) Random Hse. Children's Bks. (Delacorte Bks. for Young Readers).

—The Boyfriend List: (15 Guys, 11 Shrink Appointments, 4 Ceramic Frogs, & Me, Ruby Oliver) 2005. 240p. (YA). (gr. 7). 15.95 (978-0-385-73206-2(6) , Delacorte Bks. for Young Readers) Random Hse. Children's Bks.

MacKall, Dandi Daley. Crazy in Love. 2007. 192p. (J). (gr. 8 up). 16.99 (978-0-525-47780-8(2) , Dutton Juvenile) Penguin Group (USA) Inc.

Mackall, Dandi Daley. Love, Annie. 2006. (Faithgirlz Ser.: Bk. 2). 128p. (J). pap. 6.99 (978-0-310-71094-3(4)) Zonderkidz.

Mackler, Carolyn. Love & Other Four-Letter Words. 2002. (Laurel-Leaf Books). 256p. (YA). (gr. 7). pap. 5.99 (978-0-440-22831-8(X) , Laurel Leaf) Random Hse. Children's Bks.

MacLean, Christine Kole. How It's Done. 2006. 336p. (J). (gr. 9 up). 15.95 (978-0-7387-1029-7(6) , Flux) Llewellyn Pubns.

MacLeod, Doug. I'm Being Stalked by a Moonshadow. 2007. 212p. (YA). (gr. 8 up). 16.95 (***978-1-59078-501-0(0)*** , Front Street) Boyds Mills Pr.

Manning, Sarra. French Kiss. 2006. 224p. (YA). (gr. 9). pap. 6.99 (978-0-14-240632-8(5) , Puffin) Penguin Group (USA) Inc.

—Kiss & Make Up. 2006. 272p. (YA). (gr. 9). pap. 6.99 (978-0-14-240642-7(2) , Puffin) Penguin Group (USA) Inc.

—Sealed with a Kiss. 2006. 288p. (YA). (gr. 9). pap. 6.99 (978-0-14-240648-9(1) , Puffin) Penguin Group (USA) Inc.

Marrone, Amanda. Uninvited. 2007. 224p. (YA). (gr. 9 up). pap. 8.99 (***978-1-4169-3978-8(4)*** , Simon Pulse) Simon & Schuster Children's Publishing.

Martin, Ann M. Mary Anne's Big Breakup. 1999. (Baby-Sitters Club Friends Forever Ser.: No. 3). 144p. (J). (gr. 3-7). pap. 4.50 (978-0-590-52326-4(0)) Scholastic, Inc.

—Stacey's Ex-Boyfriend. 1998. (Baby-Sitters Club Ser.: No. 119). (J). (gr. 3-7). pap. 3.99 (978-0-590-05997-8(1)) Scholastic, Inc.

—Stacey's Ex-Boyfriend. 1998. (Baby-Sitters Club Ser.: No. 119). (J). (gr. 3-7). (978-0-606-13163-6(9)) Tandem Library Bks.

Maxwell, Katie. Eyeliner of the Gods. 2004. (YA). mass mkt. 5.99 (978-0-8439-5378-7(0)) Dorchester Publishing Co., Inc.

McCann, James. Rancour. 2005. (Illus.). 240p. (J). (gr. 10). pap. 10.95 (978-1-894965-31-6(0)) Simply Read Bks. CAN. *Dist:* Perseus Distribution.

McClintock, Norah. Down. 2007. (Orca Soundings Ser.). 112p. (YA). (gr. 7 up). pap. (***978-1-55143-766-8(X)*** ***);*** lib. bdg. (***978-1-55143-768-2(6)***) Orca Bk. Pubs.

McClymer, Kelly. Getting to Third Date. 2006. (Romantic Comedies Ser.). (Illus.). 304p. (YA). (gr. 9 up). pap. 5.99 (978-1-4169-1479-2(X) , Simon Pulse) Simon & Schuster Children's Publishing.

Meacham, Margaret. A Fairy's Guide to Understanding Humans. 2007. 160p. (YA). (gr. 5 up). 16.95 (***978-0-8234-2078-0(7)***) Holiday Hse., Inc.

Minter, J. Inside Girl: A Novel. 2007. (Insiders Novel Ser.). 240p. (YA). (gr. 7 up). pap. 8.95 (***978-1-59990-086-5(0)***) Bloomsbury Publishing.

—The Insiders. 2004. 200p. (gr. 9 up). pap. 8.95 (978-1-58234-895-7(2) , Bloomsbury Children) Bloomsbury Publishing.

—Pass It On. 2004. (Insiders Ser.). 200p. (YA). pap. 8.95 (978-1-58234-954-1(1) , Bloomsbury Children) Bloomsbury Publishing.

Minter, J. The Sweetest Thing: An Inside Girl Novel. 2007. (Insiders Novel Ser.). 224p. (J). (gr. 7 up). pap. 8.95 (***978-1-59990-087-2(4)*** , Bloomsbury Children) Bloomsbury Publishing.

Moore, Stephanie Perry. Purity Reigns. 2002. (Laurel Shadrach Ser.: Vol. 1). 240p. (YA). pap. 6.99 (978-0-8024-4035-8(5)) Moody Pubs.

—Purity Reigns. 2002. (gr. 7-12). lib. bdg. 15.30 (978-0-613-90559-6(8)) Tandem Library Bks.

Namioka, Lensey. Mismatch. 224p. (gr. 5-9). 2007. (YA). mass mkt. 6.50 (978-0-440-23879-9(X) , Laurel Leaf); 2006. (J). 15.95 (978-0-385-73183-6(3) , Delacorte Bks. for Young Readers) Random Hse. Children's Bks.

Nash, Naomi. Beaner O'Brian's Absolutely Ginormous Guidebook to Guys. 2004. (YA). mass mkt. 5.99 (978-0-8439-5403-6(5)) Dorchester Publishing Co., Inc.

—Chloe, Queen of Denial. 2004. (YA). mass mkt. 5.99 (978-0-8439-5377-0(2)) Dorchester Publishing Co., Inc.

Noonan, Rosalind. Turning Seventeen: Any Guy You Want, Bk. 1. 2000. (Turning Seventeen Ser.: No. 1). 208p. (YA). (gr. 7 up). pap. 4.95 (978-0-06-447237-1(X)) HarperCollins Pubs.

O'Connell, Jenny. The Book of Luke. 2007. 304p. pap. 9.95 (978-1-4165-2040-5(6) , MTV) Simon & Schuster.

—Plan B. 2006. 288p. pap. 9.95 (978-1-4165-2033-7(3) , MTV) Simon & Schuster.

Odell, Jeri. La Sonadora Escarlata. 1999. (Reunited Ser.: Vol. 2). (SPA.). (J). (gr. 8-12). mass mkt. 3.99 (978-0-7899-0803-2(4)) Spanish Hse. Distributors.

Olsen, Ashley. Dating Game. 2003. (gr. 5-8). lib. bdg. 13.00 (978-0-613-64704-5(1)) Tandem Library Bks.

Olsen, Mary-Kate. Boy Crazy. 2003. (gr. 5-8). lib. bdg. 13.00 (978-0-613-68407-1(9)) Tandem Library Bks.

Olsen, Mary-Kate & Olsen, Ashley. Boy Crazy. 2003. (So Little Time Ser.: No. 11). 128p. mass mkt. 4.99 (978-0-06-009315-0(3) , Harper Entertainment) HarperCollins Pubs.

—Love & Kisses. 2004. (Mary-Kate & Ashley Sweet 16 Ser.: No. 13). 144p. 4.99 (978-0-06-059066-1(1) , Harper Entertainment) HarperCollins Pubs.

—Love & Kisses. 2004. (gr. 7-12). lib. bdg. 13.00 (978-0-613-71466-2(0)) Tandem Library Bks.

Ostow, Micol. Gettin' Lucky. 2007. (Romantic Comedies Ser.). 256p. (YA). (gr. 6-9). mass mkt. 5.99 (978-1-4169-3536-0(3) , Simon Pulse) Simon & Schuster Children's Publishing.

Penny, Patricia G. Chelsea's Ride. 2006. 144p. (J). (gr. 8-12). pap. (978-1-897073-44-5(5)) Lobster Pr.

—Rica's Summer. 2006. 144p. (J). (gr. 8-12). pap. (978-1-897073-45-2(3)) Lobster Pr.

Perez, Marlene. Unexpected Development. rev. ed. 2004. 176p. (YA). 16.95 (978-1-59643-006-8(0)) Roaring Brook Pr.

Peters, Kimberly Joy. Painting Caitlyn. 2006. 192p. (J). (gr. 9-12). pap. (978-1-897073-40-7(2)) Lobster Pr.

Plaisted, Caroline. 10 Ways to Cope with Boys. 2007. 160p. (YA). mass mkt. 5.99 (978-1-4169-3476-9(6) , Simon Pulse) Simon & Schuster Children's Publishing.

Portman, Frank. Andromeda Klein. 2008. 256p. (YA). (gr. 9). 16.99 (***978-0-385-73525-4(1)*** ***);*** lib. bdg. 19.99 (***978-0-385-90512-1(2)***) Random Hse. Children's Bks. (Delacorte Bks. for Young Readers).

Poulsen, David A. Blind Date. 2002. (Lawrence High Yearbook Ser.). (Illus.). 106p. (YA). pap. 3.99 (978-1-55305-010-0(X)) Cygnet Publishing Group, Inc./ Coolreading.com CAN. *Dist:* Orca Bk. Pubs. USA.

Powell, Randy. Is Kissing a Girl Who Smokes Like Licking an Ashtray? 2003. 208p. (YA). pap. 5.95 (978-0-374-43628-5(2) , Sunburst) Farrar, Straus & Giroux.

Qualey, Marsha. Just Like That. 240p. (YA). (gr. 7). 2007. pap. 6.99 (978-0-14-240830-8(1) , Puffin); 2005. 16.99 (978-0-8037-2840-0(9) , Dial) Penguin Group (USA) Inc.

Quin-Harkin, Janet. Love Potion. 1999. (Enchanted Hearts Ser.: No. 4). (Illus.). 192p. (YA). (gr. 7 up). pap. 4.50 (978-0-380-80122-0(1)) HarperCollins Pubs.

—Love Potion. 1999. (Enchanted Hearts Ser.). (Illus.). (J). (978-0-606-17966-9(6)) Tandem Library Bks.

Rallison, Janette. How to Take the Ex Out of Ex-Boyfriend. 2007. 272p. (YA). (gr. 7 up). 15.99 (978-0-399-24617-3(7) , Putnam Juvenile) Penguin Group (USA) Inc.

Rallison, Janette. Revenge of the Cheerleaders. 2007. (Illus.). 247p. (YA). (gr. 7 up). 16.95 (***978-0-8027-8999-0(4)***) Walker & Co.

Reisfeld, Randi. CC (Cape Cod) 2005. (Summer Share Ser.). 304p. (YA). pap. 8.99 (978-1-4169-0036-8(5) , Simon Pulse) Simon & Schuster Children's Publishing.

—Partiers Preferred. 2007. (Summer Share Ser.). 288p. (YA). pap. 8.99 (978-1-4169-0037-5(3) , Simon Pulse) Simon & Schuster Children's Publishing.

Rennison, Louise. Dancing in My Nuddy-Pants: Even Further Confessions of Georgia Nicolson. (Confessions of Georgia Nicolson Ser.). 2003. 224p. (J). 15.99 (978-0-06-009746-2(9)); 2004. 240p. (YA). reprint ed. pap. 7.99 (978-0-06-009748-6(5)) HarperCollins Pubs. (HarperTeen).

—On the Bright Side, I'm Now the Girlfriend of a Sex God: Further Confessions Of. 2002. (gr. 7-12). lib. bdg. 15.30 (978-0-613-49344-4(3)) Tandem Library Bks.

—On the Bright Side, I'm Now the Girlfriend of a Sex God: Further Confessions of Georgia Nicolson. (Confessions of Georgia Nicolson Ser.). 2003. 256p. (J). pap. 6.99 (978-0-06-052185-1(6)); 2002. 272p. (YA). pap. 7.99 (978-0-06-447226-5(4)); 2001. 256p. (J). (gr. 7 up). 17.99 (978-0-06-028813-6(2)) HarperCollins Pubs.

—Then He Ate My Boy Entrancers: More Mad, Marvy Confessions of Georgia Nicolson. (Confessions of Georgia Nicolson Ser.). 2006. 336p. (J). pap. 7.99 (978-0-06-058939-4(6)); 2005. 320p. (J). lib. bdg. 16.89 (978-0-06-058938-7(8)); No. 6. 2005. 320p. (YA). 15.99 (978-0-06-058937-0(X)) HarperCollins Pubs. (HarperTeen).

Rivers, Karen. The Cure for Crushes: And Other Deadly Plagues. 2005. 304p. (J). (gr. 10 up). pap. 6.95 (978-1-55192-779-4(9)) Raincoast Bk. Distribution CAN. *Dist:* Perseus Distribution.

—The Healing Time of Hickeys. 2004. 304p. pap. 6.95 (978-1-55192-600-1(8)) Raincoast Bk. Distribution CAN. *Dist:* Perseus Distribution.

Robar, Serena. Dating4Demons. 2007. 224p. (YA). (gr. 12). pap. 9.99 (*978-0-425-21514-2(8)) , Berkley Trade) Penguin Group (USA) Inc.

Robins, Eleanor. One Date Too Many. 2003. (Illus.). 48p. (YA). per. (978-1-56254-689-2(9) , SP6899) Saddleback Educational Publishing.

Robinson, Timberly. Undercover STD Police. 2002. (ENG.). 112p. 19.95 (*978-0-595-65366-9(9)); 108p. (YA). pap. 9.95 (978-0-595-25833-8(6)) iUniverse, Inc. (Writers Club Pr.).

Rottman, S. L. Head above Water. 192p. (YA). 2003. pap. 6.95 (978-1-56145-238-5(6) , Q21186); 1999. (gr. 7-11). 14.95 (978-1-56145-185-2(1) , Q21186) Peachtree Pubs., Ltd.

Ruditis, Paul. Rainbow Party. 2005. 256p. (YA). (gr. 9 up). pap. 12.95 (978-1-4169-0235-5(X) , Simon Pulse) Simon & Schuster Children's Publishing.

Rushton, Rosie. How Could You Do This to Me, Mum? 2005. 224p. (J). pap. 5.99 (978-0-7868-5187-4(2)) Hyperion Bks. for Children.

—What a Week to Fall in Love. (Illus.). 144p. (J). 7.95 (978-0-14-038760-5(9)) Penguin Bks., Ltd. GBR. *Dist:* Trafalgar Square Publishing.

—Where Do We Go from Here? 2005. 224p. (J). pap. 5.99 (978-0-7868-5189-8(9)) Hyperion Bks. for Children.

Sachs, Marilyn. First Impressions. 2006. 128p. (YA). 16.95 (978-1-59643-117-1(2)) Roaring Brook Pr.

Salter, Helen. Does Snogging Count As Exercise? 2007. 256p. (YA). (gr. 7 up). mass mkt. 5.99 (*978-1-4169-3801-9(X) , Simon Pulse) Simon & Schuster Children's Publishing.

Scott, Elizabeth. Bloom. 2007. 240p. (YA). (gr. 7 up). pap. 8.99 (978-1-4169-2683-2(6) , Simon Pulse) Simon & Schuster Children's Publishing.

Scott, Kieran. Boy Crazy! 2nd ed. 2001. pap. 4.99 (978-0-06-441050-2(1)) HarperCollins Pubs.

Scott, Kieran. Geek Magnet. 2008. 256p. (YA). (gr. 7). 16.99 (*978-0-399-24760-6(2) , Putnam Juvenile) Penguin Group (USA) Inc.

Scott, Nyomi. Gettin' Hooked. 2007. 256p. pap. 9.99 (*978-0-373-83086-2(6)) Harlequin Enterprises, Ltd. CAN. *Dist:* Simon & Schuster, Inc.

Shaw, Tucker. The Hookup Artist. 2007. 208p. (J). pap. 7.99 (978-0-06-075622-2(5) , HarperTeen) HarperCollins Pubs.

—The Hookup Artist: Mysterious Mating Rituals of the American Teen. 2006. 208p. (J). lib. bdg. 16.89 (978-0-06-075621-5(7)) HarperCollins Pubs.

Shulman, Polly. Enthusiasm. 2006. 212p. (YA). (gr. 6). 15.99 (978-0-399-24389-9(5) , Putnam Juvenile) Penguin Group (USA) Inc.

Snadowsky, Daria. Anatomy of a Boyfriend. 2007. 272p. (YA). (gr. 9). 16.99 (978-0-385-73320-5(8)); 16.99 (978-0-385-90339-4(1)) Random Hse. Children's Bks. (Delacorte Bks. for Young Readers).

Sones, Sonya. What My Girlfriend Doesn't Know. 2007. 304p. (YA). (gr. 7 up). 16.99 (978-0-689-87602-8(5)) Simon & Schuster Children's Publishing.

Soto, Gary. Accidental Love. 2006. 192p. (YA). 16.00 (978-0-15-205497-7(9)) Harcourt Children's Bks.

Stahl, Mary Louise. Louie. 2003. 122p. (YA). 20.95 (978-0-595-74889-1(9)); pap. 10.95 (978-0-595-28750-5(6)) iUniverse, Inc.

Standiford, Natalie. The Dating Game, No. 1. 2005. 224p. (YA). (gr. 8-17). pap. 9.99 (978-0-316-11040-2(X)) Little Brown & Co.

—Dating Game: Breaking Up Is Really, Really Hard to Do, No. 2. 2005. 224p. (YA). (gr. 8-17). pap. 9.99 (978-0-316-11041-9(8)) Little Brown & Co.

—Dating Game: Can True Love Survive High School?, No. 3. 2005. 224p. (YA). (gr. 8-17). pap. 9.99 (978-0-316-11042-6(6)) Little Brown & Co.

—Ex Rating. 6th ed. 2006. (Dating Game Ser.: No. 6). 224p. (J). (gr. 8-17). pap. 9.99 (978-0-316-11531-5(2)) Little Brown & Co.

—Speed Dating. 5th ed. 2006. (Dating Game Ser.: No. 5). 224p. (J). (gr. 8-17). pap. 9.99 (978-0-316-11530-8(4)) Little Brown & Co.

Stephens, Nia. Boy Shopping. 2007. 224p. pap. 9.95 (978-0-7582-1929-9(6) , Dafina) Kensington Publishing Corp.

Stine, R.L. Boy Next Door. 2006. 147p. (J). lib. bdg. 13.00 (*978-1-4242-1008-4(9)) Fitzgerald Bks.

Stoks, Peggy. Sonido de las Aguas. 2000. (Reunited Ser.: Vol. 4). (SPA.). (J). (gr. 8-12). mass mkt. 3.99 (978-0-7899-0805-6(0)) Spanish Hse. Distributors.

Stone, Tanya Lee. A Bad Boy Can Be Good for a Girl. 2006. 240p. (YA). (gr. 9). 14.95 (978-0-385-74702-8(0)); lib. bdg. 16.99 (978-0-385-90946-4(2)) Random Hse. Children's Bks. (Lamb, Wendy).

Sumpolec, Sarah Anne. The Passage. 2005. (Becoming Beka Ser.). 256p. (J). pap. 12.99 (978-0-8024-6453-8(X)) Moody Pubs.

Takanashi, Mitsuba. The Devil Does Exist, Vol. 4. 2006. 192p. pap. 9.99 (978-1-4012-0548-5(8)) DC Comics.

Tashjian, Janet. Fault Line. 256p. (YA). 2006. reprint ed. pap. 7.95 (978-0-8050-8063-6(5)); 2003. (Illus.). 16.95 (978-0-8050-7200-6(4) , Holt, Henry & Co. Bks. For Young Readers) Holt, Henry & Co.

Taylor, Michelle. What's Happily Ever After, Anyway? 2005. (Illus.). 192p. (YA). pap. 10.95 (978-0-9746481-3-2(2)) Brown Barn Bks.

Thomson, Sarah L. The Manny. 2007. 192p. (YA). pap. 6.99 (978-0-14-240803-2(4) , Puffin) Penguin Group (USA) Inc.

Truth or Dairy Bound Galley. 2000. (J). pap. (978-0-06-029055-9(2) , Harper Trophy) HarperCollins Pubs.

Ueda, Miwa, creator. Peach Vol. 1: Miwa Ueda Illustrations. 2004. (Illus.). 92p. pap. 29.99 (978-1-59182-042-0(1) , Tokyopop Adult) TOKYOPOP, Inc.

Vail, Rachel. If We Kiss. 2005. 272p. (J). 15.99 (978-0-06-056914-3(X)) HarperCollins Pubs.

Vogel, Jane, et al. Good-Bye to All That, Vol. 5. 2005. (Brio Girls Ser.). 192p. (YA). pap. 7.99 (978-1-58997-051-9(9)) Focus on the Family Publishing.

von Ziegesar, Cecily. Unforgettable. 2007. (It Girl Ser.: No. 4). 288p. (YA). (gr. 10-17). pap. 9.99 (*978-0-316-11348-9(4) , Poppy) Little, Brown Bks. for Young Readers.

Voorhees, Coert. Los Torres. 2008. 320p. 16.99 (*978-1-4231-0304-2(1)) Hyperion Pr.

Vos, Jacob. What Are the Odds? 2002. 304p. (YA). pap. 16.95 (978-0-595-21974-2(8) , Writers Club Pr.) iUniverse, Inc.

Wallington, Aury. Pop! 2006. 288p. (YA). (gr. 9-12). pap. 8.99 (978-1-59514-092-0(1) , Razorbill) Penguin Group (USA) Inc.

Wasserman, Robin. Envy. 2005. (Seven Deadly Sins Ser.). 256p. (YA). pap. 7.99 (978-0-689-87783-4(8) , Simon Pulse) Simon & Schuster Children's Publishing.

Wasserman, Robin. Greed. 2007. (Seven Deadly Sins Ser.). 256p. (YA). pap. 8.99 (*978-1-4169-0720-6(3) , Simon Pulse) Simon & Schuster Children's Publishing.

Wells, Pamela. Heartbreakers. 2007. 304p. (YA). (gr. 9 up). pap. 16.99 (*978-0-439-02691-8(1)) Scholastic, Inc.

Wierenga, Kathy & Johnson, Lissa Halls. Double Exposure, Vol. 4. 2005. (Brio Girls Ser.). 192p. (YA). pap. 7.99 (978-1-56179-954-1(8)) Focus on the Family Publishing.

Wilkins, Rose. So Super Stylish. 2006. 288p. (J). (gr. 6). 16.99 (978-0-8037-3064-9(0) , Dial) Penguin Group (USA) Inc.

Wilson, Jacqueline. Girls in Love. 2002. 192p. (YA). (gr. 7). pap. 5.50 (978-0-440-22957-5(X) , Laurel Leaf) Random Hse. Children's Bks.

—Girls in Love. 2002. (gr. 7-12). lib. bdg. 13.00 (978-0-613-72336-7(8)) Tandem Library Bks.

—Girls in Love. (Illus.). (J). 2003. 160p. mass mkt. (978-0-552-54521-1(X) , Corgi); 2000. (Girlfriends Trilogy Ser.: No. 1). 156p. 17.95 (978-0-385-40804-2(8)) Transworld Publishers Ltd. GBR. *Dist:* Random Hse. of Canada, Ltd., Trafalgar Square Publishing.

Withrow, Sarah. What Gloria Wants. 2006. 176p. pap. 6.95 (978-0-88899-692-3(6)) Groundwood Bks. CAN. *Dist:* Perseus Distribution.

Wittlinger, Ellen. Sandpiper. 2005. 240p. (YA). (gr. 7 up). 16.95 (978-0-689-86802-3(2) , Simon & Schuster Children's Publishing) Simon & Schuster Children's Publishing.

Woodson, Jacqueline. If You Come Softly. 2006. 192p. (YA). (gr. 5). pap. 5.99 (978-0-14-240601-4(5) , Puffin) Penguin Group (USA) Inc.

Zarr, Sara. Sweethearts. 2008. 224p. (J). 16.99 (*978-0-316-01455-7(9)) Little, Brown Bks. for Young Readers.

Zimmerman, Zoe. Johnny. 2000. (gr. 7-12). lib. bdg. 12.40 (978-0-613-25817-3(7)) Tandem Library Bks.

Zindel, Paul. My Darling, My Hamburger. 2005. 176p. (J). (gr. 7 up). pap. 6.99 (978-0-06-075736-6(1) , Harper Trophy) HarperCollins Pubs.

DAVID, KING OF ISRAEL

Abingdon. Samuel, Paul & David, Unit 5. 1998. (Children's Teaching Pictures Ser.). (Illus.). 22p. (J). 16.00 (978-0-687-09537-7(9)) Abingdon Pr.

Behnken, Patricia A. Bayless. A Story of David: David & Goliath. Hultberg, Sharon Elanie, illus. 2002. (Story of David Ser.: Vol. 1). (J). (gr. 1-8). 5.95 (978-0-9637811-3-0(8)) Morning Joy Publishing.

—A Story of David 2: Mighty Warrior / David's Friend / Man after God's Heart. Butler, James R., illus. 2002. (Story of David Ser.: Vol. 2). (J). (gr. 1-8). 5.95 (978-0-9637811-4-7(6)) Morning Joy Publishing.

—A Story of David 3: Praise & Obedience / Son of David. Combs, Crystal, illus. 2002. (Story of David Ser.: Vol. 3). (J). (gr. 1-8). 5.95 (978-0-9637811-5-4(4)) Morning Joy Publishing.

—A Story of David Set, 3 vols., Set. 2002. (Story of David Ser.). (J). (gr. 1-8). 15.95 (978-0-9637811-6-1(2)) Morning Joy Publishing.

Blyton, Enid. David, el Nino Pastor. 2nd ed. 1999. (Historias Biblicas Ilustradas; Illustrated Bible Stories Ser.). (SPA., Illus.). 32p. (ps-3). pap. 4.99 (978-0-8254-1064-2(9) , Editorial Portavoz) Kregel Pubns.

—David, el Nino Pastor. 1999. (SPA.). (gr. k-3). lib. bdg. 13.00 (978-0-613-76711-8(X)) Tandem Library Bks.

Cohen, Barbara. David: A Biography. 2000. 108p. (J). (gr. 4-6). reprint ed. 16.00 (978-0-7881-9501-3(8)) DIANE Publishing Co.

Dalmatian Press Staff. David & Goliath. 2004. (Illus.). 24p. (J). 2.99 (978-1-4037-0971-4(8) , Spirit Pr.) Dalmatian Pr.

David. (Divertidas Historias Biblicas para Ninos Ser.). (SPA.). (J). 3.49 (978-0-7899-0598-7(1) , 496645) Editorial Unilit.

David. 2004. (Junior Bible Ser.: Vol. 5). 36p. pap. 5.95 (978-1-58516-133-1(0)) American Bible Society.

David & Goliath. Date not set. (J). act. bk. ed. 1.49 (978-0-88271-235-2(7) , 1751) Regina Pr., Malhame & Co.

David & Goliath. 2006. 16p. (J). pap. 1.99 (978-0-7847-1712-7(5) , 04173) Standard Publishing.

David & Goliath: A Bible Story to Color. (Illus.). 16p. (J). pap. 1.50 (978-0-87162-825-1(2) , E6018) Warner Pr. Pubs.

David & Goliath Bible Sticker Book. 2003. (Illus.). 16p. (J). 2.98 (978-1-4054-1554-5(1)) Parragon, Inc.

De Graaf, Anne. David. Montero, Jose Perez, illus. 1999. (Little Children's Bible Bks.). 38p. (J). 5.99 (978-0-8054-1899-6(7)) B&H Publishing Grp.

DeBoer, Rondi & Tangvald, Christine. David & Goliath. Conger, Holli, illus. 2007. (J). 5.99 (*978-0-7847-1950-3(0)) Standard Publishing.

Dietrich, Julie. David & His Friend, Jonathan. Ramsey, Marcy, illus. 2005. (Arch Books). (ENG.). 16p. (J). 1.99 (978-0-7586-0723-2(7)) Concordia Publishing Hse.

Frank, Penny. David & Goliath. (Illus.). 24p. 2.99 (978-0-7459-4111-0(7) , Lion) Lion Hudson plc GBR. *Dist:* Trafalgar Square Publishing.

Ham, Ken. David: The Shepard Who Became a Great King. 2000. (Awesome Adventure Bible Stories Ser.). (Illus.). (J). (gr. 2-7). pap. 5.99 (978-0-89051-329-3(5)) Master Bks.

Hansen, Janis. David & His Giant Battle, 5 vols. Francisco, Wendy, illus. (Bible Adventure Club). 2003. 36p. wbk. ed. 19.99 incl. audio, cd-rom (978-1-58134-321-2(3)); 2001. (J). (978-1-58134-324-3(8)) Crossway Bks.

Harrast, Tracy. Little David & Big Goliath. 1999. (Peek-A-Boo Ser.). 6.99 (978-0-310-97586-1(7)) Zondervan.

Murdock, Hy. David. (Bible Stories Ser.: No. S846-5). (Illus.). (J). (ps-2). pap. 3.95 (978-0-7214-5068-1(7) , Dutton Juvenile) Penguin Group (USA) Inc.

Nederveld, Patricia L. David & the Giant: The Story of David & Goliath. 1998. (God Loves Me Ser.). (Illus.). 24p. (J). (ps-3). pap. 2.95 (978-1-56212-288-1(6) , 001219, Faith Alive Christian Resources) CRC Pubns.

—Lions & Bears! The Story of David the Shepherd Boy. 1998. (God Loves Me Ser.). (Illus.). 24p. (J). (ps-3). pap. 2.95 (978-1-56212-287-4(8) , 001218, Faith Alive Christian Resources) CRC Pubns.

Perry, Marilyn. The Adventures of David: The Story of a Shepherd Who Became King, 4 bklts., Set. 2003. (Illus.). 208p. (J). 69.95 (978-1-55145-483-2(1)) Northstone Publishing, Inc. CAN. *Dist:* Pilgrim Pr., The/ United Church Pr.

Pingry, Patricia A. David & Goliath: A Story about Trusting in God: Based on 1 Samuel 17:1/50. Munger, Nancy, illus. 2005. (Children of the Bible Ser.). 23p. (J). bds. 6.95 (978-0-8249-6570-9(1)) Ideals Pubns.

Pulley, Kelly, illus. David & the Giant: My First I Can Read! 2008. 32p. (J). pap. (*978-0-310-71550-4(4)) Zonderkidz.

Round, Graham. David. 2001. (Your Favorite Bible Stories Ser.). 16p. (J). (ps-5). pap. 4.99 (978-0-8254-7219-0(9)) Kregel Pubns.

Simon, Mary Mans. David & Goliath: Read & Learn the Bible. 2005. (Illus.). 24p. (J). pap. 2.99 (978-1-4037-1161-8(5) , Spirit Pr.) Dalmatian Pr.

Slater, Teddy. The Story of David. Simpson, Fiona, ed. 2006. (Illus.). 32p. (J). pap. 3.99 (978-0-439-85426-9(1) , Little Shepherd) Scholastic, Inc.

Smart Kids Publishing Staff. David & Goliath: All about Courage. 2006. (Illus.). 12p. (ps). bds. 14.95 (978-0-8249-6659-1(7) , Candy Cane Pr.) Ideals Pubns.

The Story of David. 2000. (Illus.). 24p. (J). (ps-k). bds. 6.95 (978-0-8249-4171-0(3)) Ideals Pubns.

van Rijswijk, Cor. David & Goliath. Visser, Rino, illus. 2003. 43p. (J). (978-1-894666-23-7(2)) Inheritance Pubns.

Youngs, C. R. David: Prince of Israel. 2004. 203p. (YA). mass mkt. 9.95 (978-0-9760451-0-6(9)) Youngs, C. R.

DAVID, KING OF ISRAEL—FICTION

Booth, Bradley. Shepherd Warrior. 2007. 127p. (J). (*978-0-8163-2161-2(2)) Pacific Pr. Pubns.

Borchard, Therese Johnson. Whitney Coaches David on Fighting Goliath: And Learns to Stand up for Herself. 2000. (Emerald Bible Collection). (Illus.). 80p. (gr. 3-7). 5.95 (978-0-8091-6669-5(0) , 6669-0) Paulist Pr.

Braddon, Mary Elizabeth. Thou art the Man. fac. ed. 2002. 282p. pap. 15.95 (978-1-4021-9102-2(2)); Vol. 2. 288p. pap. 15.95 (978-1-4021-9101-5(4)) Adamant Media. (Elibron Classics).

The David & Goliath, Beginner's Biblereg; 2007. 24p. (J). 5.99 (978-0-8297-4937-3(3)) Vida Pubs.

Goldsboro, Bobby. Noah & the Ark/David & Goliath. Stewart, Toni D., illus. 2003. (Adventures of Cheze & Kwackers Ser.: Bk. 1). 48p. (J). (gr. k-3). pap. 8.95 (978-1-889658-27-8(8)) New Canaan Publishing Co. LLC.

Page, Nick & Page, Claire. David & Goliath. Loy, Nikki, illus. 2006. (Read with Me (Make Believe Ideas) Ser.). 31p. (J). (gr. k-2). 3.95 (978-1-84610-173-1(5)) Make Believe Ideas GBR. *Dist:* Ingram Pub. Services.

Pakulak, Eric. At the Side of David: A Multiple-Ending Bible Adventure. Fielding, David, illus. 2000. 87p. (J). pap. 6.95 (978-0-8198-0768-7(0)) Pauline Bks. & Media.

Veranos, Sandi. David, the Giant Fighter. 2003. (Pencil Fun Bks.: Vol. 10). 16p. (J). (gr. 7-4). pap. 9.90 (978-1-55513-026-8(7) , 1555130267) Cook, David C. Publishing Co.

DAVIS, JEFFERSON, 1808-1889

Burch, Joann Johansen. Jefferson Davis: President of the Confederacy. 1998. (Historical American Biographies Ser.). (Illus.). 128p. (YA). (gr. 6-12). lib. bdg. 26.60 (978-0-7660-1064-2(3)) Enslow Pubs., Inc.

Carter, E. J. Jefferson Davis. 2004. (American War Biographies Ser.). (Illus.). 48p. (J). pap. 8.50 (978-1-4034-5089-0(7)); lib. bdg. 27.07 (978-1-4034-5082-1(X)) Heinemann Library.

Frazier, Joey. Jefferson Davis: Confederate President. (Famous Figures of the Civil War Era Ser.). (Illus.). 80p. (J). (gr. 4-7). 2001. 25.00 (978-0-7910-6006-3(3)); 2000. pap. 25.00 (978-0-7910-6144-2(2)) Facts On File, Inc. (Chelsea Hse.).

Hale, Sarah Elder, ed. Jefferson Davis & the Confederacy. 2005. (Cobblestone the Civil War Ser.). (Illus.). 48p. (J). 17.95 (978-0-8126-7908-3(3)) Cobblestone Publishing Co.

Jefferson Davis. (Civil War Biographies Ser.). 48p. (YA). 7.95 (978-0-7368-4524-3(0)) Capstone Pr., Inc.

Jefferson Davis, 6 vols. (gr. 2-5). 39.95 (978-0-7368-4604-2(2)) Red Brick Learning.

Williams, Jean Kinney. Jefferson Davis: President of the Confederate States. 2004. (Signature Lives Ser.). (Illus.). 112p. (J). 30.60 (978-0-7565-0817-3(7) , 1240142) Compass Point Bks.

DAVIS, JEFFERSON, 1803-1889—FICTION

Dixon, Thomas. The Victim: A Romance of the Real Jefferson Davis. Marchand, J. N., illus. 2004. reprint ed. pap. 41.95 (978-1-4179-1462-3(9)) Kessinger Publishing, LLC.

DAY—FICTION

Alter, Anna. Francine's Day. Alter, Anna, illus. 2003. (Illus.). 32p. (J). lib. bdg. 16.89 (978-0-06-623937-8(0)) HarperCollins Pubs.

Anderson, Sara. Noisy City Day. 2005. (Illus.). 6p. (J). bds. 7.95 (978-1-59354-054-8(X)) Handprint Bks.

Ashman, Linda. Just Another Morning. Munoz, Claudio, illus. 2004. 32p. (J). (ps-3). 15.99 (978-0-06-029053-5(6)) HarperCollins Pubs.

Awdry, Wilbert V. Blue Train, Green Train. Stubbs, Tommy, illus. 2006. 36p. (J). (gr. k-1). 8.99 (978-0-375-83463-9(X) , Random Hse. Bks. for Young Readers) Random Hse. Children's Bks.

—Blue Train, Green Train. Stubbs, Tommy, illus. (J). (gr. k-ps). 2007. 24p. bds. 4.99 (*978-0-375-83984-9(4)); 2006. 36p. lib. bdg. 12.99 (978-0-375-93463-6(4)) Random Hse. Children's Bks. (Random Hse. Bks. for Young Readers).

Baicker, Karen. Tumble Me Tumbily. Williams, Sam, illus. 2002. 40p. (J). 15.95 (978-1-929766-61-1(0)) Handprint Bks.

Beck, Scott. Little House, Little Town. 2004. (Illus.). 32p. (J). (ps-1). 14.95 (978-0-8109-4930-0(X)) Abrams, Harry N., Inc.

Bernardo, Anilu. Un Dia con Mis Tias: Day with My Aunts. Rodriguez, Christina, illus. (ENG & SPA.). 32p. (J). 15.95 (978-1-55885-374-4(X) , Piñata Books) Arte Publico Pr.

Boulter, Steve, illus. My Day. 2007. (Rattle Bks.). 8p. (J). (ps). bds. 4.99 (*978-0-7641-6078-3(8)) Barron's Educational Series, Inc.

Braun, Sebastien. I Love My Daddy. Braun, Sebastien, illus. 2004. (Illus.). 32p. (J). (ps-2). 12.99 (978-0-06-054311-2(6)) HarperCollins Pubs.

Bullard, Lisa. My Day: Morning, Noon & Night. Wesley, Omarr, illus. 2004. (All about Me Ser.). 24p. (C). (gr. k-1). 21.26 (978-1-4048-0045-8(X)) Picture Window Bks.

Charlip, Remy. A Perfect Day. Charlip, Remy, illus. 2007. 40p. (J). lib. bdg. 17.89 (978-0-06-051973-5(8)) HarperCollins Pubs.

Colors All Day. (J). 26.20 (978-0-8136-8399-7(8)) ; 59.50 (978-0-8136-7918-1(4)); 1998. pap. (978-0-8136-8292-1(4)) Modern Curriculum Pr.

Coop, Kay. Gertrude's Moving Day. 2003. (Illus.). 42p. (J). per. (978-1-931456-70-8(4)); 2nd ed. 48p. per. (978-1-932077-61-2(8)) Athena Pr.

Dalmatian Press Staff. Sesame Street Rise & Shine. 2007. 24p. pap. 3.50 (*978-1-4037-3233-0(7)) Dalmatian Pr.

De Regniers, Beatrice Schenk. What Did You Put in Your Pocket? Date not set. 32p. (J). (ps-1). pap. 5.95 (978-0-06-443700-4(0)) HarperCollins Pubs.

DePaola, Tomie. Angels, Angels Everywhere. DePaola, Tomie, illus. 2005. (Illus.). 28p. (J). (ps-3). 14.99 (978-0-399-24370-7(4) , Putnam Juvenile) Penguin Group (USA) Inc.

Dougherty, Terri. Days of the Week. Greathouse, Justin, illus. 2006. (Read-It! Readers Ser.). 32p. (J). (ps-3). 18.60 (978-1-4048-1581-0(3)) Picture Window Bks.

Downing, Julie. No Hugs till Saturday. 2008. (J). (*978-0-618-91078-6(6) , Clarion Bks.) Houghton Mifflin Co. Trade & Reference Div.

DuBurke, Randy. Alex. 2006. (Illus.). 22p. (J). bds. 6.95 (978-0-8118-4954-8(6)) Chronicle Bks. LLC.

Fisher, Doris & Sneed, Dani. My Even Day, 2 bks., Bk. 2. Lee, Karen, illus. 2007. 32p. (J). (ps-3). 15.95 (978-0-9777423-3-2(4)) Sylvan Dell Pubng.

Franco, Betsy. Birdsongs: A Backwards Counting Book. Jenkins, Steve, illus. 2007. 40p. (J). (ps-2). 16.99 (978-0-689-87777-3(3) , McElderry, Margaret K.) Simon & Schuster Children's Publishing.

Freedman, Claire. One Magical Day. Macnaughton, Tina, illus. 2007. 28p. (J). (ps-1). 16.95 (*978-1-56148-567-3(5)) Good Bks.

Freeman, Don. Corduroy. 2007. (Puffin Storytime Ser.). 32p. (J). (ps). pap. 9.99 (978-0-14-240839-1(5) , Puffin) Penguin Group (USA) Inc.

Gershator, Phillis & Gershator, David. Greetings, Sun. 2000. (978-0-606-17809-9(0)) Tandem Library Bks.

Hebert, Marie-Francine. John's Day. Hamel, Caroline, illus. 2005. (Read-It! Readers Ser.). 32p. (C). (gr. k-3). 18.60 (978-1-4048-1071-6(4)) Picture Window Bks.

Heo, Yumi. One Afternoon. 2000. (Metro Reading Program Ser.). (J). (gr. k). 7.98 (978-1-58120-971-6(1)); 45.95 (978-1-58830-029-4(3)) Metropolitan Teaching & Learning Co.

Hill, Susan. Ruby's Perfect Day. Moore, Margie, illus. 2006. (I Can Read Bks.). 32p. (J). 15.99 (978-0-06-008982-5(2)); lib. bdg. 16.89 (978-0-06-008983-2(0)) HarperCollins Pubs.

Himmelman, John. Chickens to the Rescue. 2006. (Illus.). 32p. (J). (ps-3). 16.95 (978-0-8050-7951-7(3)) Holt, Henry & Co.

I Can Say- My Day. 2005. (J). bds. (978-1-4194-0034-6(7)) Paradise Pr., Inc.

Jackson, Ellen. Earth Mother. Dillon, Leo & Dillon, Diane, illus. 2005. 32p. (J). (ps-2). 16.95 (978-0-8027-8992-1(7)) Walker & Co.

Jenkins, Emily. What Happens on Wednesdays. Castillo, Lauren, illus. 2007. 40p. (J). (ps-1). 16.00 (978-0-374-38303-9(0)) Farrar, Straus & Giroux.

Jocelyn, Marthe. A Day with Nellie. 2008. 16p. 7.95 (***978-0-88776-869-9(5)***) Tundra Bks., Inc./Livres Toundra, Inc. CAN. *Dist:* Random Hse., Inc.

Jordan, Deloris & Jordan, Roslyn. Did I Tell You I Love You Today? Evans, Shane, tr. Evans, Shane, illus. 2004. 32p. (J). 16.95 (978-0-689-85271-8(1)) Simon & Schuster Children's Publishing.

Juan, Ana. The Night Eater. Juan, Ana, illus. 2004. (Illus.). 40p. (J). (ps-3). pap. 16.95 (978-0-439-48891-4(5) , Levine, Arthur A. Bks.) Scholastic, Inc.

Kavanagh, Peter. I Love My Mama. Chapman, Jane, illus. 2003. 32p. (J). (ps-1). 14.99 (978-0-689-85691-4(1)) Simon & Schuster Children's Publishing.

—I Love My Mama. Chapman, Jane, tr. Chapman, Jane, illus. 2003. 32p. (J). 12.95 (978-1-85430-806-1(8) , Simon & Schuster Children's Publishing) Simon & Schuster Children's Publishing.

Klingel, Cynthia Fitterer & Noyed, Robert B. Yesterday & the Letter Y. 2003. (Alphaphonics Ser.). (Illus.). 24p. (J). (ps-2). 21.36 (978-1-59296-115-3(0)) Child's World, Inc.

Koller, Jackie French. Seven Spunky Monkeys. Munsinger, Lynn M., illus. 2005. 32p. (J). (ps-ps). 16.00 (978-0-15-202519-9(7)) Harcourt Trade Pubs.

Kontis, Alethea. AlphaOops! The Day Z Went First. Kolar, Bob, illus. 2006. 56p. (J). (ps-3). 16.99 (978-0-7636-2728-7(3)) Candlewick Pr.

Kupchella, Rick. Tell Me What We Did Today. Hanson, Warren, illus. 32p. (J). 15.95 (978-0-9726504-0-3(7)) Tristan Publishing, Inc.

Lewman, David. Day in the Life of Chuckie. 1999. (gr. k-3). lib. bdg. 10.65 (978-0-613-21415-5(3)) Tandem Library Bks.

Lizzie Doodle's Beary Special Day. 2003. (J). 7.95 (978-0-9713174-8-2(8)) Boyds Collection Ltd., The.

Ljungkvist, Laura. Follow the Line. Ljungkvist, Laura, illus. 2006. (Illus.). 32p. (J). (ps). 16.99 (978-0-670-06049-8(6) , Viking Juvenile) Penguin Group (USA) Inc.

London, Jonathan & Moore, Margie. Do Your ABCs, Little Brown Bear. 2007. 32p. (J). pap. 5.99 (978-0-14-240713-4(5) , Puffin) Penguin Group (USA) Inc.

Lorenz Editors. My Day, 4 vols. 2002. Tr. of Mi dia. (Illus.). 48p. pap. 12.95 (978-0-7548-0876-3(9) , Lorenz Bks.) Anness Publishing, Inc.

Marshall, Judy. Morning. Annelli, Nikki, illus. l.t. ed. 2005. 21p. (J). per. 9.99 (978-1-59879-050-4(1)) Lifevest Publishing, Inc.

Mayer, Mercer. Mercer Mayer's Little Critter's Series, 2 bks. (Illus.). (J). (gr. k-1). lib. bdg. 27.90 (978-1-56674-943-5(3)) Forest Hse. Publishing Co., Inc.

McGee, Marni. The Noisy Farm. Shearing, Leonie, tr. Shearing, Leonie, illus. 2004. 32p. (J). (ps-1). 15.95 (978-1-58234-879-7(0) , Bloomsbury Children) Bloomsbury Publishing.

McKay, Sindy. We Both Read-My Day (Picture Book Edition) Johnson, Meredith, illus. 2007. (We Both Read Ser.). 44p. (J). 14.95 (***978-1-60115-005-9(9)***) Treasure Bay, Inc.

McKee, David. Elmer's Day. 2004. (Elmer Ser.). (ENG & SOM., Illus.). 16p. (J). bds. 6.95 (978-1-84059-400-3(4)) Milet Publishing.

Meyers, Susan. This Is the Way a Baby Rides. Nakata, Hiroe, illus. 2005. 32p. (J). (ps-1). 15.95 (978-0-8109-5763-3(9) , Abrams Bks. for Young Readers) Abrams, Harry N., Inc.

Milgrim, David. Time to Get up, Time to Go. 2006. (Illus.). 32p. (J). (ps-k). 15.00 (978-0-618-51998-9(X) , Clarion Bks.) Houghton Mifflin Co. Trade & Reference Div.

Mitton, Tony. Playful Little Penguins. Parker-Rees, Guy, illus. 2007. 32p. (J). (ps-1). 15.95 (***978-0-8027-9710-0(5)***) Walker & Co.

Modesitt, Jeanne. Oh, What a Beautiful Day! Spowart, Robin, illus. 2008. (J). (***978-1-56397-409-0(6)***) Boyds Mills Pr.

Montardre, Helene. Night & Day. 2003. (Illus.). 8p. (J). bds. 7.95 (978-1-58728-481-6(2) , Two Can Publishing) T&N Children's Publishing.

Ormerod, Jan. Miss Mouse's Day. Ormerod, Jan, illus. 2002. (Illus.). (J). 24.00 (978-0-7587-6481-2(2)) Book Wholesalers, Inc.

Paul, Ann W. Hello Toes! Hello Feet! Wescott, Nadine Bernard, illus. 2000. (J). (978-0-606-19770-0(2)) Tandem Library Bks.

Rainey, L. E. Sad Sam, Glad Sam. 2006. (Illus.). 32p. (J). 16.95 (978-0-9785521-0-7(5)) Shoetree Publishers, Inc.

Rau, Dana. Rise & Shine. 2007. 12p. 10.95 (***978-1-58117-559-2(0)***) Dalmatian Pr.

Reynolds, Peter H. My Very Big Little World: A SugarLoaf Book. 2006. (Illus.). 40p. (J). (ps-2). 15.95 (978-0-689-87621-9(1) , Atheneum) Simon & Schuster Children's Publishing.

Ritchie, Alison. Me & My Dad! Edgson, Alison, illus. 2007. 28p. (J). (ps-2). 16.95 (***978-1-56148-565-9(9)***) Good Bks.

Rong, Yu. A Lovely Day for Amelia Goose. Rong, Yu, illus. 2004. (Illus.). 32p. (J). (gr. k-k). 14.99 (978-0-7636-2309-8(1)) Candlewick Pr.

Rosenthal, Amy Krouse. One of Those Days. Doughty, Rebecca, illus. 2006. 32p. (J). (ps-3). 13.99 (978-0-399-24365-3(8)) Penguin Group (USA) Inc.

Ryder, Joanne. My Mother's Voice. Catalanotto, Peter, illus. 2006. 32p. (J). 15.99 (978-0-06-029509-7(0)); lib. bdg. 17.89 (978-0-06-029510-3(4)) HarperCollins Pubs.

Schaefer, Carole Lexa. Someone Says. Morgan, Pierr, illus. 2003. 32p. (J). (gr. k-2). 15.99 (978-0-670-03664-6(1) , Viking Juvenile) Penguin Group (USA) Inc.

Schwartz, Amy. A Glorious Day. Schwartz, Amy, illus. 2004. (Illus.). 32p. (J). 16.95 (978-0-689-84802-5(1) , Atheneum/Richard Jackson Bks.) Simon & Schuster Children's Publishing.

Seuss, Dr. My Many Colored Days. Johnson, Stephen T. & Fancher, Lou, illus. 1998. 16p. (J). (gr. k-ps). bds. 6.99 (978-0-679-89344-8(X) , Knopf Bks. for Young Readers) Random Hse. Children's Bks.

Shannon, David. Huy! David en Paneles! Shannon, David, illus. 2005. (Oops! Ser.). (SPA., Illus.). 12p. (J). 6.99 (978-0-439-70972-9(5) , Scholastic en Espanol) Scholastic, Inc.

—Oops! A Diaper David Book. Shannon, David, illus. 2005. (Oops! Ser.). (Illus.). 12p. (J). (gr. k). bds. 6.99 (978-0-439-68882-6(5) , Blue Sky Pr., The) Scholastic, Inc.

Simon, Charnan. Luna the Wake-Up Cat. Huang, Benrei, illus. 2007. (Rookie Reader Ser.). 31p. (J). pap. (***978-0-531-12489-5(4)***) Children's Pr., Ltd.

Slate, Joseph. Miss Bindergarten Has a Wild Day in Kindergarten. Wolff, Ashley, illus. 2006. 40p. (J). (ps). reprint ed. pap. 6.99 (978-0-14-240709-7(7) , Puffin) Penguin Group (USA) Inc.

Spanyol, Jessica. Little Neighbors of Sunnyside Street. Spanyol, Jessica, illus. 2007. 64p. (J). (ps-1). 16.99 (978-0-7636-2986-1(3)) Candlewick Pr.

Spinelli, Eileen. The Best Time of Day. Lango, Bryan, illus. 2007. 32p. (J). pap. 6.00 (978-0-15-205862-3(1) , Voyager Bks./Libros Viajeros) Harcourt Children's Bks.

—The Best Time of Day. Lango, Bryan, illus. 2005. 32p. (J). (ps-ps). 16.00 (978-0-15-205051-1(5)) Harcourt Trade Pubs.

A Story of Faith: Mary Ann's Book — My Bestest Day. 2006. (J). 19.95 (978-0-9787761-0-7(0)) Mountain Ministries.

Tompert, Ann. Harry's Hats. Elizalde, Marcelo, illus. (Rookie Reader Skill Set Ser.). (J). (gr. k-2). 2005. 32p. pap. 4.95 (978-0-516-24647-5(X)); 2004. 31p. 19.50 (978-0-516-23613-1(X)) Scholastic Library Publishing. (Children's Pr.).

Tullet, Herve. El Dia y la Noche. (SPA.). 148p. (J). (978-84-233-3236-6(5)) Ediciones Destino ESP. *Dist:* Lectorum Pubns., Inc.

Uff, Caroline. Lulu's Busy Day. Uff, Caroline, illus. 2004. (Illus.). 14p. (J). bds. 5.95 (978-0-8027-8929-7(3)) Walker & Co.

—Lulu's Busy Day. 2000. (Illus.). (J). (978-0-8027-8717-0(7)) Walker & Co.

Van Fleet, Matthew. Monday the Bullfrog. 2006. (J). (978-978-141-691-0(2) , Simon & Schuster Children's Publishing) Simon & Schuster Children's Publishing.

—Monday the Bullfrog. Van Fleet, Matthew, illus. 2006. (Illus.). 20p. (J). 17.99 (978-1-4169-1231-6(2)) Simon & Schuster Children's Publishing.

Waite, Lance. A Day with My Dad. 2008. (Illus.). 24p. (J). 15.99 (***978-1-60131-015-6(3)***) Big Tent Bks.

Yolen, Jane. Baby Bear's Books. Sweet, Melissa, illus. 2006. 40p. (J). 16.00 (978-0-15-205290-4(9)) Harcourt Trade Pubs.

DAYS

see Birthdays; Fasts and Feasts; Holidays

DEAD SEA SCROLLS

Allon, Hagit & Zehavi, Lena. The Mystery of the Dead Sea Scrolls. Abolafia, Yossi, illus. 2004. 60p. pap. 12.95 (978-0-8276-0800-9(4)) Jewish Pubn. Society.

Burnham, Brad. Qumran Caves: Hiding Place for the Dea Sea Scrolls. 2003. (Famous Caves of the World Ser.). (Illus.). 24p. (J). lib. bdg. 18.75 (978-0-8239-6259-4(8) , PowerKids Pr.) Rosen Publishing Group, Inc., The.

Weintraub, Aileen. The Dead Sea: The Saltiest Sea. 2001. (Great Record Breakers in Nature Ser.). (Illus.). 24p. (J). lib. bdg. 18.75 (978-0-8239-5637-1(7) , PowerKids Pr.) Rosen Publishing Group, Inc., The.

DEAF

Adler, David A. Helen Keller. Wallner, John, illus. 32p. (J). 4.95 (978-0-8234-2042-1(6)) Holiday Hse., Inc.

Baldwin, Carol. Hearing Loss. 2003. (Illus.). 32p. (J). (gr. 3-5). lib. bdg. (978-1-4034-0251-6(5)) Heinemann Library.

Basinger, Carol. Everything You Need to Know about Deafness. 2005. (Need to Know Library). (Illus.). 64p. (J). (gr. 7-12). lib. bdg. 25.25 (978-0-8239-3165-1(X) , NT-DEAF) Rosen Publishing Group, Inc., The.

Brearley, Sue. Talk to Me. (Illus.). 26p. (J). (gr. 1-4). 10.95 (978-0-7136-3192-0(9)) A & C Black GBR. *Dist:* Lubrecht & Cramer, Ltd.

Carroll, Cathryn. Clerc: The Story of His Early Years. 2002. (Orig.). (gr. 7-12). lib. bdg. 21.05 (978-0-613-88531-7(7)) Tandem Library Bks.

De Silva-Nijkamp, Tineke. Samaya: The Deaf Baby Elephant. Maters, Ingrid, illus. 2005. 33p. (J). (***978-955-599-438-5(2)***) Sarvodaya Bk. Publishing Services.

Devillier, Christy. Helen Keller. 2004. (First Biographies Set Iv Ser.). (Illus.). 32p. (J). (gr. k-4). lib. bdg. 22.78 (978-1-59197-514-4(X)) ABDO Publishing Co.

Fetty, Margaret. Helen Keller: Break down the Walls! 2007. (Defining Moments Ser.). (Illus.). 32p. (J). lib. bdg. 25.27 (978-1-59716-271-5(X)) Bearport Publishing Co., Inc.

Gordon, Melanie Apel. Let's Talk about Deafness. 1999. (Let's Talk Library). (Illus.). 24p. (J). (gr. 3). lib. bdg. 18.75 (978-0-8239-5198-7(7) , PowerKids Pr.) Rosen Publishing Group, Inc., The.

Greene, Laura. Discovering Sign Language. 2002. (gr. 5-8). lib. bdg. 18.75 (978-0-613-86447-3(6)) Tandem Library Bks.

—Sign-Me-Fine: Experiencing American Sign Language. 2002. (gr. 7-12). lib. bdg. 21.05 (978-0-613-88924-7(X)) Tandem Library Bks.

Heelan, Jamee Riggio. Can You Hear a Rainbow? The Story of a Deaf Boy Named Chris. Simmonds, Nicola, illus. 2002. (Rehabilitation Institute of Chicago Learning Book Ser.). 32p. (J). (gr. 1-5). 14.95 (978-1-56145-268-2(8) , Q34265) Peachtree Pubs., Ltd.

Koestler-Grack, Rachel A. The Story of Helen Keller. 2003. (Breakthrough Biographies Ser.). (Illus.). 32p. (J). (gr. 3-5). 23.00 (978-0-7910-7315-5(7) , Chelsea Hse.) Facts On File, Inc.

Lakin, Patricia. Helen Keller & the Big Storm. Magnuson, Diana, illus. 2002. (Ready-to-Read Ser.: Level 2). 32p. (J). pap. 3.99 (978-0-689-84104-0(3) , Aladdin) Simon & Schuster Children's Publishing.

Levene, Anna. My Friend Is Deaf. 2003. (Illus.). (J). (gr. 3-5). lib. bdg. 16.95 (978-1-932333-27-5(4)) Chrysalis Education.

Libal, Autumn. The Ocean Inside: Youth Who Are Deaf & Hard of Hearing. 2004. (Youth with Special Needs Ser.). (Illus.). 128p. (J). (978-1-59084-729-9(6)) Mason Crest Pubs.

Marsh, Carole. Helen Keller. 2002. (One Thousand Readers Ser.). (Illus.). 12p. (J). (gr. k-4). 2.95 (978-0-635-01478-8(5) , 14785) Gallopade International.

McLeese, Don. Helen Keller. 2002. (J). lib. bdg. 20.64 (978-1-58952-302-9(4)) Rourke Publishing, LLC.

O'Neill, Linda. Imagine Being Deaf. 2000. (Imagine Ser.). (Illus.). 32p. (J). (gr. 1-4). lib. bdg. 26.60 (978-1-57103-377-2(7)) Rourke Publishing, LLC.

Sabin, Francene. Helen Keller: Una Chica Valiente. abr. ed. 2007. 64p. (J). pap. 3.99 (***978-0-439-87999-6(X)*** , Scholastic en Espanol) Scholastic, Inc.

Schaefer, Lola M. Some Kids Are Deaf. 2008. (J). (***978-1-4296-0811-4(0)***); (***978-1-4296-0812-1(9)***) Capstone Pr., Inc.

—Some Kids Are Deaf. Saunders-Smith, Gail, ed. 2001. (Understanding Differences Ser.). (Illus.). 24p. (J). (gr. k-1). lib. bdg. 15.93 (978-0-7368-0665-7(2) , Pebble Bks.) Capstone Pr., Inc.

Sheen, Barbara. Deafness. 2005. (Diseases & Disorders Ser.). (Illus.). 112p. (J). (gr. 7-10). lib. bdg. 32.45 (978-1-59018-408-0(4) , Lucent Bks.) Thomson Gale.

Sutcliffe, Jane. Helen Keller. Verstraete, Elaine, illus. 2002. (On My Own Biographies Ser.). 48p. (J). lib. bdg. 23.93 (978-0-87614-600-2(0) , Carolrhoda Bks.) Lerner Publishing Group.

—Helen Keller. 2002. (gr. 3-6). lib. bdg. 14.10 (978-0-613-52398-1(9)) Tandem Library Bks.

Woodhouse, Jayne. Helen Keller. 2002. (Lives & Times Ser.). (Illus.). 24p. (J). (gr. k-3). pap. 6.50 (978-1-4034-0030-7(X) , 91474) Heinemann Library.

—Helen Keller. 2002. (gr. k-3). lib. bdg. 12.95 (978-0-613-88095-4(1)) Tandem Library Bks.

Woolley, Maggie. Being Deaf. 1999. (Think about Ser.). (Illus.). 32p. (J). (gr. 2-5). lib. bdg. 16.95 (978-1-887068-85-7(6)) Smart Apple Media.

DEAF—EDUCATION

Bodkin, Odds. Doing, Doing, Doing. 2003. (Illus.). 14p. spiral bd. (978-0-9657170-6-9(2)) Perkins Schl. for the Blind.

Carroll, Cathryn. Clerc: The Story of His Early Years. 2002. (Orig.). (gr. 7-12). lib. bdg. 21.05 (978-0-613-88531-7(7)) Tandem Library Bks.

Katschka, Gustav. Mr. Cue's Zoo: Phonics & Cued Speech. Katschka, Gustav, illus. 1998. (Illus.). 53p. (J). (gr. k-5). spiral bd. 30.00 (978-1-892917-05-8(X)) Cued Speech for Integrated Communication, Inc.

Schneider, Elaine Ernst. Taking Hearing Impairment to School. Schader, Karen, ed. Dineen, Tom, illus. 2004. (Special Kids in School Ser.: Fifteenth). (J). per. 11.95 (978-1-891383-23-6(X) , 70015) JayJo Bks., LLC.

DEAF—FICTION

Addabbo, Carole. Dina the Deaf Dinosaur. Valentine, illus. 1998. 32p. (J). (ps-5). 19.95 (978-1-889262 04 8(8)) Hannacroix Creek Bks., Inc.

Beamish, Diane. Amy's Silent World. 2006. 24p. 10.25 (978-1-4116-5759-5(4)) Lulu.com.

Blatchford, Claire H. Going with the Flow. 1998. (Illus.). 40p. (J). (gr. 2-4). pap. 7.95 (978-1-57505-284-7(9) , Carolrhoda Bks.) Lerner Publishing Group.

Bodkin, Odds. Perkins Goes Out. 2003. (Illus.). 22p. spiral bd. (978-0-9657170-7-6(0)) Perkins Schl. for the Blind.

Bronzaft, Arline L. Listen to the Raindrops. Parton, Steven, illus. unabr. ed. 2000. 26p. (J). (gr. 1-5). pap. 9.95 (978-0-9677843-1-1(X)) League for The Hard of Hearing.

Broski, Julie & Vigla, Vincent. Being Me. 2006. (Illus.). 32p. (YA). pap. 4.95 (978-0-516-24913-1(4) , Children's Pr.) Scholastic Library Publishing.

Carey, Keelin. A Princess, a Tiger, & Other Deaf Tales. 2005. (Illus.). 50p. (J). pap. 7.95 (978-1-896764-90-0(8)) Second Story Pr. CAN. *Dist:* Orca Bk. Pubs. USA.

Chorost, Susan & Stock, Susan. Herbie Hears the Horn. Parton, Steven, illus. 2001. 32p. (J). 9.95 (978-0-88200-212-5(0) , I2005) Bell, Alexander Graham Assn. for the Deaf & Hard of Hearing, Inc.

Death Be Not Proud. 1999. (J). 9.95 (978-1-56137-149-5(1)) Novel Units, Inc.

Dunbar, Joyce & Ray, Jane. Moonbird. Ray, Jane, illus. (Illus.). 32p. (J). 2008. pap. 9.95 (***978-0-552-55003-1(5)***); 2007. 15.99 (***978-0-385-60589-2(7)***) Transworld Publishers Ltd. GBR. *Dist:* Independent Pubs. Group.

Ferris, Jean. Of Sound Mind. 224p. (YA). 2001. (gr. 8 up). 16.00 (978-0-374-35580-7(0) , Farrar, Straus & Giroux (BYR)); 2004. reprint ed. pap. 6.95 (978-0-374-45584-2(8) , Sunburst) Farrar, Straus & Giroux.

—Of Sound Mind. l.t. ed. 2004. 225p. 21.95 (978-0-7862-7036-1(5) , Large Print Pr.) Thorndike Pr.

Glass Menagerie. 1999. (YA). (gr. 10-12). 9.95 (978-1-56137-186-0(6) , BK8244) Novel Units, Inc.

Hanlon, Emily. The Swing. 2001. 224p. (YA). (gr. 7-11). pap. 14.95 (978-0-595-16913-9(9) , Backinprint.com) iUniverse, Inc.

Imagination Stage Teacher's Study Guide: The Garden Wall. 2005. (J). pap. 3.95 (978-0-9723729-2-3(X)) Imagination Stage, Inc.

Jordan, Sherryl. The Raging Quiet. 2004. 368p. (YA). mass mkt. 5.99 (978-0-689-87004-0(3) , Simon Pulse) Simon & Schuster Children's Publishing.

—The Raging Quiet. 2000. (YA). (978-0-606-20093-6(2)) Tandem Library Bks.

—The Raging Quiet. l.t. ed. 2005. 416p. 22.95 (978-0-7862-7313-3(5) , Large Print Pr.) Thorndike Pr.

—The Raging Quiet. l.t. ed. 2000. (Illus.). 464p. (978-0-7089-9535-8(7)) Ulverscroft Large Print Bks.

Klein, Adria F. Max Learns Sign Language. 2007. (Read-It! Readers Ser.). (Illus.). 24p. (J). (***978-1-4048-3545-0(8)*** , 1265795) Picture Window Bks.

—Max Learns Sign Language. Gallagher-Cole, Mernie, illus. 2006. (Read-It! Readers Ser.). 24p. (J). (gr. k-2). lib. bdg. 19.93 (***978-1-4048-3148-3(7)*** , 1265795) Picture Window Bks.

Lea, M. E. The Squiggle Kids Get Ice Cream. Z - N Staff, illus. 2002. (Squiggle Kids Ser.). 32p. (J). (gr. k-4). 14.95 (978-1-932053-01-2(8)) Nonetheless Pr.

Look, Lenore. Ruby Lu, Empress of Everything. Wilsdorf, Anne, illus. (J). (gr. 1-5). 2007. 164p. per. 4.99 (***978-1-4169-5003-5(6)*** , Aladdin); 2006. 176p. 15.95 (978-0-689-86460-5(4) , Atheneum) Simon & Schuster Children's Publishing.

Lowell, Gloria Roth. Elana's Ears: Or How I Became the Best Big Sister in the World. Brooks, Karen Stormer, illus. 2000. 32p. (J). (ps-3). (978-1-55798-598-9(7) , 441-5987); pap. (978-1-55798-702-0(5) , 441-7025) American Psychological Assn. (Magination Pr.).

Matlin, Marlee. Deaf Child Crossing. (Illus.). 208p. (J). 2004. pap. 4.99 (978-0-689-86696-8(8) , Aladdin); 2002. (gr. 3-6). 15.95 (978-0-689-82208-7(1)) Simon & Schuster Children's Publishing.

—Deaf Child Crossing. 2004. (gr. 3-6). lib. bdg. 13.00 (978-0-613-88068-8(4)) Tandem Library Bks.

Matlin, Marlee & Cooney, Doug. Leading Ladies. 2007. 288p. (J). (gr. 3-7). 15.99 (***978-0-689-86987-7(8)*** , Simon & Schuster Children's Publishing) Simon & Schuster Children's Publishing.

Matlin, Marlee & Cooney, Doug. Nobody's Perfect. 2006. (Illus.). 240p. (J). (gr. 3-7). 15.95 (978-0-689-86986-0(X) , Simon & Schuster Children's Publishing) Simon & Schuster Children's Publishing.

McDonald, Megan. Changes for Julie, Bk. 6. McAliley, Susan, illus. 2007. 104p. (YA). (gr. 3 up). 12.95 (***978-1-59369-355-8(9)***) American Girl Publishing, Inc.

—Changes for Julie, Bk. 6. McAliley, Susan & Hunt, Robert, illus. 2007. 104p. (YA). (gr. 3 up). pap. 6.95 (***978-1-59369-354-1(0)***) American Girl Publishing, Inc.

McElfresh, Lynn E. Can You Feel the Thunder? 1999. (YA). pap., stu. ed. 52.00 incl. audio (978-0-7887-3837-1(2) , 41031) Recorded Bks., LLC.

Miller, Sarah Elizabeth. Miss Spitfire: Reaching Helen Keller. 2007. 240p. (J). (gr. 5-9). 16.99 (978-1-4169-2542-2(2)) Simon & Schuster Children's Publishing.

Millman, Isaac. Moses Goes to a Concert. Millman, Isaac, illus. (Moses Goes To Ser.). (Illus.). 40p. (J). 2002. pap. 6.95 (978-0-374-45366-4(7) , Sunburst); 1998. 17.00 (978-0-374-35067-3(1) , Farrar, Straus & Giroux (BYR)) Farrar, Straus & Giroux.

—Moses Goes to a Concert. 2002. (gr. k-3). lib. bdg. 14.10 (978-0-613-53841-1(2)) Tandem Library Bks.

—Moses Goes to School. Millman, Isaac, illus. 2000. (Moses Goes To Ser.). (Illus.). 32p. (J). (gr. k-3). 16.00 (978-0-374-35069-7(8) , Farrar, Straus & Giroux (BYR)) Farrar, Straus & Giroux.

—Moses Goes to the Circus. Millman, Isaac, illus. 2003. (Moses Goes To Ser.). (Illus.). 32p. (J). (ps-3). 16.00 (978-0-374-35064-2(7) , Farrar, Straus & Giroux (BYR)) Farrar, Straus & Giroux.

—Moses Sees a Play. Millman, Isaac, illus. 2004. (Moses Goes To Ser.). (Illus.). 32p. (J). 16.00 (978-0-374-35066-6(3) , Farrar, Straus & Giroux (BYR)) Farrar, Straus & Giroux.

Myers, Anna. Hoggee. 2004. 160p. (J). 16.95 (978-0-8027-8926-6(9)) Walker & Co.

Nanette. Buddy & Muddy: The Twin Brown Skunks. 2004. (J). 12.95 (978-0-9741269-5-1(0)) St. Bernard Publishing, LLC.

Napoli, Donna Jo. Friends Everywhere. 1999. (Angelwings Ser.: No. 1). (Illus.). (J). 10.79 (978-0-606-17904-1(6)) Tandem Library Bks.

Napoli, Donna Jo & Ben-Ami, Doron. Friends Everywhere. Klementz-Harte, Lauren, illus. 1999. (Angelwings Ser.: No. 1). 96p. (J). (gr. 2-5). pap. 7.95 (978-0-689-82694-8(X) , Aladdin) Simon & Schuster Children's Publishing.

New Mexico School for the Deaf Staff, 2nd Grade. Too Many Hands??? l.t. ed. 2004. (Illus.). 32p. (J). 16.95 (978-1-929115-10-5(5)) Azro Pr., Inc.

Podmore, Ron. A Sign to Remember. 2002. (YA). per. 9.95 (978-0-9723537-0-0(4)) Puget Sound Pubns.

Ray, Delia. Singing Hands. 2006. (Illus.). 224p. (J). (gr. 5-9). 16.00 (978-0-618-65762-9(2) , Clarion Bks.) Houghton Mifflin Co. Trade & Reference Div.

Riggio, Anita. Secret Signs: An Escape Through the Underground Railroad. Riggio, Anita, illus. 2003. 32p. (J). (gr. k-3). 15.95 (978-1-56397-555-4(6)) Boyds Mills Pr.

Riskind, Mary. Apple Is My Sign. 1999. (J). (gr. 4-7). 21.00 (978-0-8446-7004-1(9)) Smith, Peter Pub., Inc.

C D

Rorby, Ginny. Hurt Go Happy. 2007. 272p. (J). 5.99 (***978-0-7653-5304-7(0)***, Starscape) Doherty, Tom Assocs., LLC.

Seeger, Pete & Jacobs, Paul DuBois. The Deaf Musicians. Christie, Gregory, illus. 2006. 32p. (J). (ps-3). 16.99 (978-0-399-24316-5(X)) Penguin Group (USA) Inc.

Smith, D. James. The Boys of San Joaquin. 240p. (J). (gr. 3-7). 2006. pap. 5.99 (978-1-4169-1619-2(9), Aladdin); 2005. (Illus.). 16.99 (978-0-689-87606-6(8), Atheneum) Simon & Schuster Children's Publishing.

—Probably the World's Best Story about a Dog & the Girl Who Loved Me. 2006. 240p. (J). (gr. 4-7). 15.95 (978-1-4169-0542-4(1)) Simon & Schuster Children's Publishing.

Somebody Moved in Next Door: Individual Chapter Book Title Six-Pack. Vol. 29. 32p. (gr. 5 up). 44.00 (978-0-7578-0978-1(2)) Rigby Education.

Stryer, Andrea Stenn. Kami & the Yaks. Dodson, Bert, illus. 2007. 48p. (J). (gr. k-3). 16.95 (***978-0-9778961-0-3(2)***); pap. 9.95 (***978-0-9778961-1-0(0)***) Bay Otter Pr.

Suskind, Patrick. Die Taube. (GER.). pap. 15.95 (978-3-257-21846-6(X)) Diogenes Verlag AG CHE. *Dist:* Distribooks, Inc.

Uhlberg, Myron. Dad, Jackie, & Me. Bootman, Colin, illus. 2005. 32p. (J). (ps-3). 16.95 (978-1-56145-329-0(3)) Peachtree Pubs., Ltd.

—The Printer. Sorensen, Henri, tr. Sorensen, Henri, illus. 2003. 32p. (J). (gr. 1-5). 16.95 (978-1-56145-221-7(1)) Peachtree Pubs., Ltd.

Ure, Jean. Muddy Four Paws. 1999. (We Love Animals Bks.). (Illus.). 128p. (J). (gr. 4-7). pap. 3.95 (978-0-7641-0968-3(5)) Barron's Educational Series, Inc.

Wahl, Jan. Rosa's Parrot. Howard, Kim, illus. 1999. (J). (ps-3). 15.95 (978-1-58089-011-3(3)) Charlesbridge Publishing, Inc.

Woodson, Jacqueline. Feathers. 2007. 128p. (J). (gr. 3-7). 15.99 (978-0-399-23989-2(8), Putnam Juvenile) Penguin Group (USA) Inc.

DEATH

Agnew, Kate, ed. Classic Collections of Poetry & Prose Life & Death. 2007. 208p. pap. 8.95 (***978-1-84046-567-9(0)***) Totem Bks. GBR. *Dist:* National Bk. Network.

Albom, Mitch. Tuesdays with Morrie. 2002. 192p. (gr. 7-12). lib. bdg. 21.05 (978-0-613-55075-8(7)) Tandem Library Bks.

Altman, Linda Jacobs. Death: An Introduction to Medical-Ethical Dilemmas. 2000. (Illus.). 112p. (J). (gr. 6-12). lib. bdg. 26.60 (978-0-7660-1246-2(8)) Enslow Pubs., Inc.

Amidei, Kathie, et al. Dealing with Death. Cannizzo, Karen A., ed. 1999. (Conversations with Teens Ser.). 16p. (YA). pap. 7.95 (978-0-937997-64-2(1), 3822) Pflaum Publishing Group.

Amos, Janine. Death. Green, Gwen, illus. Hampton, Angela, photos by. 2002. (Separations Ser.). 32p. (J). (gr. 3 up). lib. bdg. 23.33 (978-0-8368-3089-7(X)) Stevens, Gareth Inc.

Answers to a Child's Questions about Death. 2005. (J). 3.99 (978-1-882951-25-3(5)) Guideline Pubns. Co.

Berry, Joy Wilt. Death: Good Answers to Tough Questions. Bartholomew, illus. rev. ed. 2000. (Good Answers to Tough Questions Ser.: Vol. 16). 48p. (J). (gr. 4-7). pap. 4.95 (978-1-58634-226-5(6), 01-0901-16) Goldstar Publishing, Inc.

Biale, Rachel. My Pet Died: A Let's Make a Book about It Book. 2004. (Let's Make a Book about It Ser.). (Illus.). 48p. (ps-3). 7.95 (978-1-883672-51-5(1), Tricycle Pr.) Ten Speed Pr.

Boritzer, Etan. What Is Death? Forrest, Nancy, illus. 2001. (Love & Feeling for Kids Ser.). 36p. (J). lib. bdg. 15.95 (978-1-56674-292-4(7)) Forest Hse. Publishing Co., Inc.

—What Is Death? Forrest, Nancy, illus. 2004. (What Is? Ser.). 32p. (ps-4). 14.95 (978-0-9637597-4-0(4)); 6.95 (978-0-9637597-5-7(2)) Lane, Veronica Bks.

—What Is Death? 1999. (gr. 3-6). lib. bdg. 15.25 (978-0-613-77789-6(1)) Tandem Library Bks.

Bray, Jeannine D. My Poppie. Kenyatta, Imani, ed. Mitchell, Denise B., illus. 1998. 80p. (J). (gr. k-6). 14.95 (978-1-886580-62-6(6)) Pinnacle-Syatt Pubns.

Britain, Lory. My Grandma Died: A Child's Story about Grief & Loss. Deach, Carol, illus. 2002. 32p. (J). 16.95 (978-1-884734-27-4(8)); pap. 6.95 (978-1-884734-26-7(X)) Parenting Pr., Inc.

Broadbent, Lynne & Chaplin, Denise. Life's End. Sloan, Frank, ed. 2001. (Ceremonies & Celebrations Ser.). (Illus.). 32p. (J). (ps-3). lib. bdg. 25.69 (978-0-7398-3270-7(0)) Raintree.

Brown, Laurie Krasny. When Dinosaurs Die: A Guide to Understanding Death. Brown, Marc, illus. 1998. 32p. (J). (ps-3). 7.99 (978-0-316-11955-9(5)) Little, Brown Bks. for Young Readers.

—When Dinosaurs Die: A Guide to Understanding Death. Brown, Marc, illus. 1998. (gr. k-3). lib. bdg. 16.40 (978-0-613-71802-8(X)) Tandem Library Bks.

Coerr, Eleanor. Sadako. Young, Ed, illus. 2002. (J). 24.55 (978-0-7587-3544-7(8)) Book Wholesalers, Inc.

—Sadako & the Thousand Paper Cranes. Himler, Ronald, illus. 2004. 80p. (gr. 8). pap. 5.99 (978-0-14-240113-2(7), Puffin) Penguin Group (USA) Inc.

—Sadako & the Thousand Paper Cranes. Himler, Ronald, illus. 1999. 79p. (J). (ps-ps). lib. bdg. 13.00 (978-0-613-23029-2(9)) Tandem Library Bks.

—Sadako & the Thousand Paper Cranes. 1999. (978-0-606-17425-1(7)) Tandem Library Bks.

Coping with Death. 2003. 160p. (J). (ps-7). lib. bdg. 33.25 (978-0-613-73881-1(0)) Tandem Library Bks.

Coping with the Loss of a Loved One: An Inspiring New Book about Appreciating Human Life & Death. 2003. 60p. per. 10.00 net. (978-0-9620180-3-9(1)) Black, Clinton L.

Cunningham, Alan Blain, compiled by. Goodbye My Good Friend: Memories of Lost Animal Companions & Loved Ones. 2007. (ENG., Illus.). 112p. per. 15.95 (***978-0-9777072-2-5(9)***) Agreka Bks., LLC.

Cunningham, Alexis. A Child's Simple Guide Through Grief. 2000. 48p. (J). (ps-3). pap. 9.95 (978-1-880396-88-9(2)) Jalmar Pr.

Davidson, Judy. Grief Skills for Life: A Personal Journal about Loss for Adolescents. rev. ed. 2002. (Illus.). 112p. (YA). (gr. 7-12). pap. 11.95 (978-0-9719569-1-9(X)) RENEW: Ctr. for Personal Recovery, Inc.

—My Own Grief Journal: A Personal Journal About Loss for the Young Child. rev. ed. 2002. (Illus.). 48p. (J). (gr. 1-5). pap. 11.95 (978-0-9719569-2-6(8)) RENEW: Ctr. for Personal Recovery, Inc.

—My Own Grief Journal: A Personal Journal for Children Ages 7-11 about Loss. rev. ed. 2002. (Illus.). 32p. (J). (gr. 4-5). pap. 11.95 (978-0-9719569-9-5(5)) RENEW: Ctr. for Personal Recovery, Inc.

Dennison, Amy, et al, as told by. Our Dad Died: The True Story of Three Kids Whose Lives Changed. 2004. (Illus.). 112p. (J). pap. 9.95 (978-1-57542-135-3(6)) Free Spirit Publishing, Inc.

Dokas, Dara. Remembering Mama. Chostner, Angela L., illus. 2002. 32p. 15.99 (978-0-8066-4352-6(8), Augsburg Bks.) Augsburg Fortress, Pubs.

Edwards, Dianna. Meet Patou. 2006. (J). pap. 29.95 (978-0-9767756-0-7(3)) Patou Bks., LLC.

—My Journal & Drawings. 2004. (J). spiral bd. (978-0-9767756-4-5(6)) Patou Bks., LLC.

—Why Can't Everything Just Stay the Same? Book Three. 2004. (J). (978-0-9767756-3-8(8)) Patou Bks., LLC.

Edwards, Nicola. A Pet. 2003. (Saying Goodbye to Ser.). (Illus.). 32p. (J). (ps-2). lib. bdg. 16.95 (978-1-932333-19-0(3)) Chrysalis Education.

Eubanks, Sonja. Death & Dying. 2006. (Social Issues Firsthand Ser.). (Illus.). 224p. (YA). (gr. 10-12). 29.95 (978-0-7377-2885-9(X), Greenhaven Pr., Inc.) Thomson Gale.

Fitchett, Jilda, 4th. Aunt Molly's Transition—Seeing Death in A New Light. 2006. (Illus.). 91p. (J). per. 15.95 (***978-0-9773244-0-8(0)***) Light Line.

Fitzgerald, Helen. The Grieving Teen: A Guide for Teenagers & Their Friends. 2000. 18.65 (978-0-606-20685-3(X)) Tandem Library Bks.

Ganeri, Anita. Journey's End: Death & Mourning. 1999. (Life Times Ser.). (Illus.). 30p. (YA). (gr. 2 up). 15.95 (978-0-87226-289-8(8), 62898B, Bedrick, Peter Bks.) School Specialty Publishing.

Gaughen, Shasta. Coping with Death. 2003. (Contemporary Issues Companion Ser.). (YA). 176p. pap. 24.95 (978-0-7377-1521-7(9)); 160p. lib. bdg. 36.20 (978-0-7377-1520-0(0)) Thomson Gale. (Greenhaven Pr., Inc.).

Gay, Kathlyn. Death & Dying A-Z: By Kathlyn Gay. 2004. (Greenhaven Encyclopedias Ser.). (J). 74.95 (978-0-7377-1495-1(6), Greenhaven Pr., Inc.) Thomson Gale.

Gootman, Marilyn E. When a Friend Dies: A Book for Teens about Grieving & Healing. Espeland, Pamela, ed. 2004. 120p. (YA). (gr. 6 up). pap. 9.95 (978-0-915793-66-2(0), FS209) Free Spirit Publishing, Inc.

Gravelle, Karen. Teenagers Face to Face with Bereavement. 2000. 148p. (YA). (gr. 7-12). pap. 10.95 (978-0-595-15278-0(3), Backinprint.com) iUniverse, Inc.

Grebin, Margaret. Baseball Forever! A Boy's Book on Grief, Loss, & Healing. 2004. (J). per. 10.95 (978-1-59094-076-1(8)) Jawbone Publishing Corp.

Harper, Kimberly. Stepping Stones Through Grief: A Children's Workbook on Death, Grief & Loss. Stratton, David, ed. Carroll, Michelle, illus. 2000. (J). spiral bd., wbk. ed. 5.00 (978-0-9703035-1-6(3)) United Medical Ctr.

Himler, Ronald, illus. Sadako & the Thousand Paper Cranes. 2005. 80p. (J). pap. 3.99 (978-0-14-240440-9(3), Puffin) Penguin Group (USA) Inc.

Holford, Karen. I Miss Grandpa: A Story to Help Your Child Understand Death— & Eternal Life. 2004. (Illus.). 32p. (J). (978-0-8163-2030-1(6)) Pacific Pr. Publishing Assn.

Holmes, Margaret M. Molly's Mom Died: A Child's Book of Hope Through Grief. Aitken, Susan, illus. 1999. (J). 6.95 (978-1-56123-122-5(3), MMDC) Centering Corp.

Holmes, Margaret M., et al. Sam's Dad Died: A Child's Book of Hope Through Grief. 1999. (J). 6.95 (978-1-56123-123-2(1)) Centering Corp.

House, Catherine. Where Did Grandad Go? Ayres, Honor, illus. 2007. (J). 9.95 (978-0-8198-8312-4(3)) Pauline Bks. & Media.

Hughes, Lynn. Teens Talk about Life after the Loss of a Parent. 2005. (You Are Not Alone Ser.). 208p. (J). pap. 8.99 (978-0-439-58591-0(0), Scholastic Paperbacks) Scholastic, Inc.

Hughes, Lynne. You Are Not Alone: Teens Talk about Life after the Loss of a Parent. 2005. (You Are Not Alone Ser.). (Illus.). 208p. (J). pap. 16.99 (978-0-439-58590-3(2), Scholastic Pr.) Scholastic, Inc.

Jackson, Aariane R. Can You Hear Me Smiling? A Child Grieves a Sister. 2004. (New Child & Family Press Titles Ser.). (Illus.). 40p. (J). pap. 9.95 (978-0-87868-835-7(8), 8358, Child & Family Pr.) Child Welfare League of America, Inc.

Jackson, Ellen B. Sometimes Bad Things Happen. Rotner, Shelley, illus. 2002. 32p. (ps-1). pap. 7.95 (978-0-7613-1734-0(1), Millbrook Pr.) Lerner Publishing Group.

Johnson, Joy & Grollman, Earl, texts. A Child's Book about Death. 2001. (J). (gr. k-5). 4.95 (978-1-56123-147-8(9), CADC) Centering Corp.

Joseph, Judith C. I Hate Strawberry Jam. Spitzer, Hillary, illus. 2002. 120p. (YA). (gr. 3 up). pap. 14.95 (978-0-9715420-0-6(7)) JCJoseph, Ltd.

Joslin, Mary. The Goodbye Boat. St. Louis Little, Claire, illus. 1999. 28p. (ps-k). 16.00 (978-0-8028-5186-4(X)) Eerdmans, William B. Publishing Co.

Kane, Darlene. Missing Hannah: Based on a True Story O. 2006. pap. 26.49 (***978-1-4259-0136-3(0)***) AuthorHouse.

Kuehn, Eileen. Death: Coping with the Pain. 2001. (Grief & Loss Ser.). (Illus.). 64p. (J). (gr. 4-6). lib. bdg. 23.93 (978-0-7368-0745-6(4), LifeMatters Bks.) Capstone Pr., Inc.

Kwalwasser, Eugene I. Beyond Tears. 2006. 112p. (YA). pap. 12.95 (978-1-932687-33-0(5)) Pitspopany Pr.

Latta, Sara L. Dealing with the Loss of a Loved One: Focus on Family Matters. 2002. (Focus on Family Matters Ser.). (Illus.). 64p. (J). 25.00 (978-0-7910-6955-4(9)) Facts On File, Inc.

LaVelle, Steven. Just Passing Through: A Grown-Up Book for Kids. 2003. (Illus.). 32p. (Orig.). (gr. k-3). 6.95 (978-0-87516-402-1(1), Devorss Pubns.) DeVorss & Co.

LeCount, Darren. The Death Next Door: A Story & Activity Book to Help Children Cope with the Death of Someone Close to Them. Johnson, Cari, illus. Harper, Shawn, photos by. 2000. 34p. (J). (ps-6). pap. 14.95 (978-1-931273-01-5(4)) Rainbow Project, Inc., The.

Lichtman, Wendy. Blew & the Death of the Mag. 2001. 72p. pap. 9.50 (978-0-939266-34-0(2)) Gestalt Journal Pr.

Liss-Levinson, Nechama & Baskette, Molly Phinney. Remembering My Grandparent: A Kid's Own Grief Workbook in the Christian Tradition. 2006. (Illus.). 48p. (J). wbk. ed. 16.99 (978-1-59473-212-6(4)) SkyLight Paths Publishing.

—Remembering My Pet: A Kid¿s Own Spiritual Workbook for When a Pet Dies. 2007. 48p. (J). wbk. ed. 16.99 (978-1-59473-221-8(3)) SkyLight Paths Publishing.

Marsh, Dilleen, tr. & illus. What Happens When People Die? Marsh, Dilleen, illus. 2003. (J). 12.95 (978-1-57008-954-1(X)) Deseret Bk. Co.

McDowell, Josh & Stewart, Ed. Friendship 911 Collection: My Friend Is Struggling With... Death of a Loved One. 2000. (Friendship 911 Ser.). (Illus.). 64p. (gr. 8-12). pap. 7.98 (978-0-8499-3791-0(4)) Nelson, Thomas Inc.

Monhollon, Lake P. A Child Asks... What Does Dying Mean? 1998. (Illus.). 36p. (J). (ps up). 14.95 (978-0-9657561-1-2(4)) Reflection Publishing Co.

Munoz-Kiehnel, Marisol. Since My Brother Died - Desde Que Murio Mi Hermano. Dietrich, Glanda, illus. 2000. (SPA & ENG.). 20p. (J). (gr. k-4). pap. 5.95 (978-1-56123-135-5(5)) Centering Corp.

Murphy, Patricia J. Death. 2007. (J). (***978-1-4034-9778-9(8)***); pap. (***978-1-4034-9783-3(4)***) Heinemann Library.

Perl, Lila & Heweston, Nicholas. Dying to Know: About Death, Funeral Customs, & Final Resting Places. 2001. (Single Titles Ser.). (Illus.). 96p. (gr. 5-7). lib. bdg. 25.90 (978-0-7613-1564-3(0), Millbrook Pr.) Lerner Publishing Group.

Rock, Lois. When Goodbye Is Forever. Moxley, Sheila, illus. 2004. 32p. (J). (ps-3). 7.95 (978-1-56148-449-2(0)) Good Bks.

Rogers, Fred. When a Pet Dies. Judkis, Jim, photos by. 1998. (First Experience Bks.). (Illus.). 32p. (J). (ps-k). pap. 5.99 (978-0-698-11666-5(6), Putnam Juvenile) Penguin Group (USA) Inc.

—When a Pet Dies. 1998. (ps-2). lib. bdg. 14.15 (978-0-613-90031-7(6)) Tandem Library Bks.

Romain, Trevor. What on Earth Do You Do When Someone Dies? Romain, Trevor, illus. 1999. (Illus.). 72p. (J). (gr. k-5). pap. 7.95 (978-1-57542-055-4(4), FS571) Free Spirit Publishing, Inc.

Royston, Angela. Living & Non-Living. 2003. (My World of Science Ser.). (Illus.). 32p. (J). (gr. k-2). lib. bdg. 22.79 (978-1-4034-0854-9(8)) Heinemann Library.

Rugg, Sharon. When Death Knocks at the Schoolhouse Door. Foster, Andrea R., illus. 1998. 38p. (J). (gr. k-6). 25.00 (978-0-9652410-2-1(5)) Rising Sun Ctr. for Loss & Renewal.

Ruiz, Ruth Anne. Coping with the Death of a Brother or Sister. 2005. (Coping Ser.). (Illus.). 192p. (J). (gr. 7-12). lib. bdg. 26.50 (978-0-8239-2851-4(9)) Rosen Publishing Group, Inc., The.

Ryan, Victoria. When Your Pet Dies: A Healing Handbook for Kids. Ryan, Victoria & Alley, R. W., illus. 2003. (Elf-Help Books for Kids). 32p. (J). per. 7.95 (978-0-87029-376-4(1)) Abbey Pr.

Sadako & the Thousand Paper Cranes. 1999. (J). 9.95 (978-1-56137-178-5(5)); 11.95 (978-1-56137-631-5(0)) Novel Units, Inc.

Sanders, Bruce. Death & Dying. 2007. (Illus.). 32p. (J). (***978-1-59604-087-8(4)***) Stargazer Bks.

Sanders, Pete & Myers, Steve. When People Die. 2005. (Choices & Decisions Ser.). (Illus.). 32p. (J). (gr. 4-7). lib. bdg. 27.10 (978-1-59604-076-2(9)) Stargazer Bks.

Shavatt, Donna. My Grieving Journey Book. 2002. (Illus.). 48p. 9.95 (978-0-8091-6695-4(X), 6695-x) Paulist Pr.

Silverman, Janis. Help Me Say Goodbye: Activities for Helping Kids Cope When a Special Person Dies. 1999. (Illus.). 32p. (ps-4). pap. 9.95 (978-1-57749-085-2(1)) Fairview Pr.

Simon, Annette Dauphin. Libby Died: This Book Is for All Kids, but Especially My Sister, Libby. Simon, Annette Dauphin, illus. 2000. (Illus.). 32p. (J). (ps-6). 15.99 (978-0-9701853-0-3(8), 00088AGPres) GSD&M.

Slough, Rebecca & Bachrach, Ann W. Deal with It: The Bible on Death & Dying. 1999. (Generation Why Ser.). 44p. (YA). (gr. 9-12). pap. 12.95 (978-0-87303-382-4(5)) Faith & Life Pr.

Stalfelt, Pernilla. The Death Book. 2003. (Illus.). (J). (gr. 3 up). 15.95 (978-0-88899-482-0(6)) Groundwood Bks. CAN. *Dist:* Transition Vendor.

Stenson, Lila & Stenson, Anna. Daddy, up & Down: Sisters Grieve the Loss of Their Daddy. Ferre', Heidi, ed. Biddix, Cheryl L., illus. 2002. 32p. (J). per. 16.95 (978-0-9658061-1-4(1)) Peaceful Village Publishing.

Summer, Paulette. In the Stillness of the Night: Learning to Grow Beyond the Fear of Death. Nozik, Ira, photos by. 2000. (Illus.). 56p. (YA). (gr. 5 up). pap. 8.95 (978-0-9627610-0-3(1)) Millennium Pubns.

Thomas, Pat. I Miss You: A First Look at Death. Harker, Leslie, illus. 2001. (First Look at Bks.). 32p. (ps-2). pap. 6.99 (978-0-7641-1764-0(5)) Barron's Educational Series, Inc.

—I Miss You: First Look at Death. 2001. (gr. k-3). lib. bdg. 15.25 (978-0-613-81901-5(2)) Tandem Library Bks.

Thornhill, Jan. I Found a Dead Bird: The Kids' Guide to the Cycle of Life & Death. 2006. (Illus.). 64p. 21.95 (978-1-897066-70-6(8)); pap. 9.95 (978-1-897066-71-3(6)) Maple Tree Pr. CAN. *Dist:* Perseus Distribution.

Torr, James D. Problems of Death. 2000. (Opposing Viewpoints Ser.). (Illus.). 189p. (YA). (gr. 10-12). pap. 24.95 (978-0-7377-0349-8(0)); 36.20 (978-0-7377-0350-4(4)) Thomson Gale. (Greenhaven Pr., Inc.).

Tubbs, Janet. Death. 2000. (Spud Packs Ser.). 16p. (J). pap. 19.95 (978-1-881185-13-0(3)) Arcadia Pr.

Watkins, James N. Is There Really Life after Death? 2000. (5 Minute Bible Studies). (Illus.). 160p. (YA). (gr. 7-11). 9.99 (978-0-570-05247-0(5)) Concordia Publishing Hse.

Wezeman, Phyllis Vos, et al. Wipe the Tears: 30 Children's Sermons on Death. 2005. (New Brown Bag Ser.). (Illus.). 96p. 10.00 (978-0-8298-1520-7(1)) Pilgrim Pr., The/United Church Pr.

Why Is There Death & Suffering. 2001. (YA). 0.75 (978-1-893345-21-8(1)) Answers in Genesis Ministries.

Williams, Mary E. Terminal Illness. 2001. (Opposing Viewpoints Ser.). (Illus.). 208p. (YA). (gr. 10-12). 32.45 (978-0-7377-0526-3(4), Greenhaven Pr., Inc.) Thomson Gale.

Williams, Mary E., ed. Terminal Illness. 2001. (Opposing Viewpoints Ser.). (Illus.). 208p. (YA). (gr. 10-12). pap. 21.20 (978-0-7377-0525-6(6), Greenhaven Pr., Inc.) Thomson Gale.

Wilson, Antoine. You & a Death in Your Family. 2005. (Family Matters Ser.). (Illus.). 48p. (YA). (gr. 5-8). lib. bdg. 23.95 (978-0-8239-3355-6(5)) Rosen Publishing Group, Inc., The.

Wolfelt, Alan. Healing Your Grieving Heart: 100 Practical Ideas for Kids. (Healing Your Grieving Heart Ser.). 128p. (gr. 1-7). 2001. pap. 11.95 (978-1-879651-27-2(0)); 2000. (J). pap. 9.95 (978-1-879651-19-7(X)) Companion Pr.

—Healing Your Grieving Heart for Teens: 100 Practical Ideas. 2001. (Healing Your Grieving Heart Ser.). 128p. (gr. 8 up). pap. 11.95 (978-1-879651-23-4(8)) Companion Pr.

Worth, Richard. Elisabeth Kubler-Ross: Encountering Death & Dying. 2004. (Women in Medicine Ser.). (Illus.). 112p. (gr. 6-12). 30.00 (978-0-7910-8027-6(7), Chelsea Hse.) Facts On File, Inc.

Zagdanski, Doris. What's Dead Mean? How to Help Children Cope with Death. 2005. (Illus.). 32p. pap. 11.95 (978-0-85572-316-3(5)) Warwick Publishing CAN. *Dist:* Perseus Distribution.

DEATH—FICTION

Abelove, Joan. Saying It Out Loud. 2001. 144p. (YA). (gr. 7 up). pap. 5.99 (978-0-14-131227-9(0), Puffin) Penguin Group (USA) Inc.

—Saying It Out Loud. 2001. (YA). 136p. (gr. 8-12). lib. bdg. 14.15 (978-0-613-44252-7(0)); (978-0-606-21410-0(0)) Tandem Library Bks.

Acampora, Paul. Defining Dulcie. 176p. (gr. 7). 2008. (YA). pap. 6.99 (***978-0-14-241183-4(3)***, Puffin); 2006. (J). 16.99 (978-0-8037-3046-5(2), Dial) Penguin Group (USA) Inc.

Ahlberg, Allan. My Brother's Ghost. l.t. ed. 2005. (Illus.). 64p. (J). pap. (978-0-7540-6181-6(7), CLP 372) BBC Audio.

Aitken, Susan. Anna's Scrapbook: Journal of a Sister's Love. Aitken, Sarah, illus. 2000. (J). (978-1-56123-134-8(7)) Centering Corp.

Al-Chokhachy, Elissa. The Angel with the Golden Glow: A Family's Journey Through Loss & Healing. Graf, Ulrike, illus. 2001. 32p. (J). (ps up). 15.95 (978-1-893356-00-9(0), Penny Bear Publishing) Penny Bear Co., Inc., The.

—How Can I Help, Papa? A Child's Journey Through Loss & Healing. Graf, Ulrike, illus. 2002. 32p. (J). (ps-7). 15.95 (978-0-9712481-0-6(9)) Works of Hope Publishing.

Alexander Greene, Alesia. A Mural for Mamita. Lara, Susana, tr. Teis, Kyra, illus. 2001. Tr. of Mural Para Mamita. (ENG & SPA.). (J). 8.95 (978-1-56123-154-6(1), MFMC) Centering Corp.

Allan, Nicholas. Heaven. 2006. (Illus.). 32p. (J). pap. 9.99 (***978-0-09-948814-9(0)***) Transworld Publishers Ltd. GBR. *Dist:* Independent Pubs. Group.

Anderson, Laurie Halse. Catalyst. 240p. (YA). 2003. (gr. 6). pap. 7.99 (978-0-14-240001-2(7), Puffin); 2002. (gr. 7 up). 17.99 (978-0-670-03566-3(1), Viking Juvenile) Penguin Group (USA) Inc.

—Catalyst. 2003. (gr. 7-12). lib. bdg. 15.30 (978-0-613-70575-2(0)) Tandem Library Bks.

Angell, Judie. Ronnie & Rosey. 223p. (YA). (gr. 7 up). pap. 3.95 (978-0-8072-1377-3(2), Listening Library) Random Hse. Audio Publishing Group.

Angle, Kimberly Greene. Hummingbird. 2008. 256p. (J). 16.95 (***978-0-374-33376-8(9)***) Farrar, Straus & Giroux.

Ardagh, Philip. Heir of Mystery. 2006. (Unlikely Exploits Trilogy Ser.). 144p. (J). pap. 5.99 (978-0-439-73017-4(1), Scholastic Paperbacks) Scholastic, Inc.

Arenella, Betsy Bottino. Isabelle's Dream: A Story & Activity Book for a Child's Grief Journey. Henderson, Dana, illus. 2007. 48p. (J). per. 7.95 (***978-0-9675532-9-0(6)***) Quality of Life Publishing Co.

Aveni, Louise Rose. Can I Ride My Bike to Heaven? Maddox, Simone, illus. 1999. 16p. (J). (ps-6). 14.95 (978-0-9675124-0-2(9)) Angel Hse. Publishing, Inc.

Badart, Della. Two Coins. 2007. (Illus.). (J). per. 18.95 (978-0-9788985-2-6(4)) A Better Be Write Pub.

Bagert, Brod. Hormone Jungle: Coming of Age in Middle School. 2006. (Illus.). 121p. (J). (gr. 5-8). 23.95 (978-0-929895-87-1(8)) Maupin Hse. Publishing.

Bahr, Mary. If Nathan Were Here. Jerome, Karen A., illus. 2004. 32p. (J). (gr. 1-7). 16.00 (978-0-8028-5187-1(8)); (ps-4). pap. 8.00 (978-0-8028-5235-9(1)) Eerdmans, William B. Publishing Co.

—If Nathan Were Here. 2002. (gr. k-3). lib. bdg. 16.45 (978-0-613-75337-1(2)) Tandem Library Bks.

Banerjee, Anjali. Looking for Bapu. 2006. 176p. (J). (gr. 3-6). 15.95 (978-0-385-74657-1(1)); lib. bdg. 17.99 (978-0-385-90894-8(6)) Random Hse. Children's Bks. (Lamb, Wendy).

Banks, Kate. Friends of the Heart: Amici Del Cuore. 2005. 144p. (J). 16.00 (978-0-374-32455-1(7)) Farrar, Straus & Giroux.

—Walk Softly, Rachel. 2003. 160p. (YA). (gr. 7-9). 16.00 (978-0-374-38230-8(1) , Farrar, Straus & Giroux (BYR)) Farrar, Straus & Giroux.

Banting, Celia. I only said I couldn't Cope. 2006. 240p. (YA). per. 14.99 (***978-0-9786648-2-4(5)*** Wighita Pr.

Barron, T. A. Where is Grandpa? 2000. (978-0-606-22527-4(7)) Tandem Library Bks.

—Where Is Grandpa? Soentpiet, Chris K., illus. 2000. 1p. (J). (ps-3). 16.99 (978-0-399-23037-0(8) , Philomel) Penguin Group (USA) Inc.

Baskin, Nora Raleigh. What Every Girl. 2002. (gr. 5-8). lib. bdg. 13.00 (978-0-613-89779-2(X)) Tandem Library Bks.

Bateman, Teresa. Keeper of Soles. Yayo, illus. 2005. 32p. (J). 16.95 (978-0-8234-1734-6(4)) Holiday Hse., Inc.

Baugher, Kristina, illus. & text. Death Turns Allie's Family Upside Down. Baugher, Kristina, text. l.t. ed. 1999. 27p. (J). pap. 8.00 (978-0-9635975-2-6(3)) Caring People Pr.

Bayne, Nancy. Great-Grandpa's Chair: A Story about Living & Dying, Shared Between A Great-Grandpa & His 10-year-old Grandson! Graber, Vickie, illus. l.t. ed. 2005. 22p. (J). per. 9.99 (978-1-59879-046-7(3)) Lifevest Publishing, Inc.

Belton, Sandra. Store-Bought Baby. 2006. 256p. (J). 15.99 (978-0-06-085086-9(8)); lib. bdg. 16.89 (978-0-06-085087-6(6)) HarperCollins Pubs.

Bingley, Margaret. A Dramatic Death. l.t. ed. 1998. 294p. (J). pap. 16.95 (978-0-7540-6019-2(5) , Galaxy Children's Large Print) BBC Audiobooks America.

Blacker, Terence. Boy2Girl. 2005. 304p. (J). 16.00 (978-0-374-30926-8(4) , Farrar, Straus & Giroux) Farrar, Straus & Giroux.

—Boy2Girl. 2007. 304p. (YA). pap. 6.99 (***978-0-312-37146-3(2)*** Square Fish.

Blain Parker, Marjorie. Jaspers Day. Wilson, Janet, illus. 2004. 32p. (J). (gr. k-3). (978-1-55337-764-1(8)) Kids Can Pr., Ltd.

Bock, Caren J. Wings: A Story of Transformation. Schwinghammer, Judy C., illus. 2005. 32p. (J). 16.95 (978-1-932279-12-2(1)) Wyatt-MacKenzie Publishing.

Bostrom, Kathleen Long. The Day Scooter Died: A Book about the Death of a Pet. Bladholm, Cheri, illus. 2005. (Helping Kids Heal Ser.). 32p. (J). 9.99 (978-0-310-70902-2(4)) Zonderkidz.

—Papa's Gift: An Inspirational Story of Love & Loss. Porfirio, Guy, illus. ed. 2004. 32p. (J). pap. 6.99 (978-0-310-70923-7(7)) Zonderkidz.

Bowler, Tim. Firmament. 2004. (Illus.). 320p. (YA). 16.95 (978-0-689-86161-1(3) , McElderry, Margaret K.) Simon & Schuster Children's Publishing.

—River Boy. 2002. (Illus.). 160p. (YA). mass mkt. 4.99 (978-0-689-84804-9(8) , Simon Pulse) Simon & Schuster Children's Publishing.

—River Boy. l.t. ed. 2001. 190p. (J). 22.95 (978-0-7862-3507-0(1)) Thorndike Pr.

Boyd, David. Closer to Hamlet. 2003. 120p. (YA). pap. 4.95 (978-0-921156-93-2(6)) Rubicon Publishing, Inc. CAN. *Dist:* International Publishers Marketing.

—Closer to Hamlet. 2003. (gr. 7-12). lib. bdg. 12.95 (978-0-613-77672-1(0)) Tandem Library Bks.

Boyden, Linda. The Blue Roses. Cordova, Amy, illus. 2002. 32p. (J). (gr. 1-5). 16.95 (978-1-58430-037-3(X)) Lee & Low Bks., Inc.

Bradbury, Martha Todd. My Friend Christopher Is Dead. 2005. 48p. pap. 12.95 (978-1-4137-6908-1(X)) PublishAmerica, Inc.

Bradley, Kimberly Brubaker. Halfway to the Sky. 2003. 176p. (J). (gr. 3-7). pap. 5.99 (978-0-440-41830-6(5) , Yearling) Random Hse. Children's Bks.

—Halfway to the Sky. 2003. (gr. 5-8). lib. bdg. 13.00 (978-0-613-62771-9(7)) Tandem Library Bks.

Brandis, Marianne & Brender a Brandis, G. The Tinderbox. 2003. Orig. Title: Fyrtojet. (Illus.). 176p. (J). (gr. 6-9). pap. 9.95 (978-0-88776-626-8(9)) Tundra Bks., Inc./Livres Toundra, Inc. CAN. *Dist:* Random Hse., Inc.

Brisson, Pat. I Remember Miss Perry. Jorisch, Stephane, illus. 2006. 32p. (J). (ps). 16.99 (978-0-8037-2981-0(2) , Dial) Penguin Group (USA) Inc.

Brooks, Bruce. All That Remains. 2002. 176p. (YA). (gr. 7 up). pap. 6.99 (978-0-689-83442-4(X) , Simon Pulse) Simon & Schuster Children's Publishing.

—All That Remains: 3 Stories. 2001. (Illus.). 176p. (J). (gr. 7 up). 16.00 (978-0-689-83351-9(2) , Atheneum) Simon & Schuster Children's Publishing.

—All That Remains: 3 Stories. 2002. (gr. 7-12). lib. bdg. 15.30 (978-0-613-62371-1(1)) Tandem Library Bks.

Brooks, Kevin. Martyn Pig. 240p. (J). 2003. pap. 6.99 (978-0-439-50752-3(9)); 2002. (gr. 5 up). pap. 16.95 (978-0-439-29595-6(5) , Chicken Hse., The) Scholastic, Inc.

—Martyn Pig. 2003. (gr. 7-12). lib. bdg. 15.30 (978-0-613-64813-4(7)) Tandem Library Bks.

Bunting, Eve. Blackwater. 1999. (Illus.). 160p. (YA). (gr. 5 up). 15.95 (978-0-06-027838-0(2) , Cotler, Joanna Books) HarperCollins Pubs.

—Rudi's Pond. Himler, Ronald, illus. 2004. 32p. (J). (gr. k-3). pap. 5.95 (978-0-618-48604-5(6) , Clarion Bks.) Houghton Mifflin Co. Trade & Reference Div.

—A Sudden Silence. 2007. (Illus.). 144p. (YA). pap. 6.95 (978-0-15-205868-5(0) , Harcourt Paperbacks) Harcourt Children's Bks.

Burrowes, Adjoa J. Grandma's Purple Flowers. 2000. (Illus.). 32p. (J). (ps-3). 15.95 (978-1-880000-73-1(3)) Lee & Low Bks., Inc.

Buscaglia, Leo. The Fall of Freddie the Leaf: A Story of Life for All Ages. annot. rev. ed. 2002. (Illus.). 30p. (J). 14.95 (978-0-8050-7195-5(4)) SLACK, Inc.

Butcher, Kristin. Hemingway Tradition. 2002. (gr. 7-12). lib. bdg. 16.40 (978-0-613-62955-3(8)) Tandem Library Bks.

—The Hemingway Tradition. 2002. (Orca Soundings Ser.). 96p. (J). (gr. 7-12). pap. 7.95 (978-1-55143-242-7(0)) Orca Bk. Pubs. USA.

Byars, Betsy. A Blossom Promise. (Blossom Ser.). (J). (gr. 4-6). 145p. pap. 4.50 (978-0-8072-1444-2(2)); Set. 2000. pap. 29.00 incl. audio (978-0-8072-7322-7(8) , YA826SP) Random Hse. Audio Publishing Group. (Listening Library).

Cabot, Meg. Twilight. 2005. (Mediator Ser.: Bk. 6). 256p. (J). 15.99 (978-0-06-072467-2(6)); (gr. 7 up). lib. bdg. 16.89 (978-0-06-072468-9(4)) HarperCollins Pubs.

Caldwell, Lindsay. Don't Let Me Die. 1998. (gr. 8-12). pap. 4.99 (978-0-590-56735-0(7)) Scholastic, Inc.

Call, Brian D., tr. & illus. Sarah's Cloud. Call, Brian D., illus. 2003. (J). 15.95 (978-1-57008-955-8(8)) Deseret Bk. Co.

Carey, Janet Lee. Wenny Has Wings. 2004. 240p. (J). reprint ed. pap. 4.99 (978-0-689-86759-0(X) , Aladdin) Simon & Schuster Children's Publishing.

Carlson, Melody. Beyond Reach. 2007. (Secret Life Samantha Mcgregor Ser.). 258p. (YA). pap. 11.99 (978-1-59052-693-4(7) , Multnomah Fiction) WaterBrook Pr.

Carlson, Melody. Beyond Reach: A Novel. 2007. 250p. (YA). (***978-1-4287-2412-9(5)*** , Multnomah) WaterBrook Pr.

Carnevale, Michael. The Hotel Coolidge. 2007. 91p. pap. 10.95 (***978-0-7414-3752-5(X))*** Infinity Publishing.

Carney, Karen L. Everything Changes, but Love Endures: Explaining Hospice to Children. Carney, Karen L., illus. 2000. (Barklay & Eve Ser.: Bk. 6). (Illus.). (J). pap. 6.95 (978-0-9667820-5-9(4)) Dragonfly Publishing.

—Honoring Our Loved Ones: Going to a Funeral. Carney, Karen L., illus. 3rd ed. 2001. (Barklay & Eve Ser.: Bk. 2). (Illus.). (J). pap. 6.95 (978-0-9667820-1-1(1)) Dragonfly Publishing.

—Our Special Garden: Understanding Cremation. Carney, Karen L., illus. 1999. (Barklay & Eve Ser.: Bk. 4). (Illus.). (J). pap. 6.95 (978-0-9667820-3-5(8)) Dragonfly Publishing.

—Precious Gifts: The Katie Coolican Story. Carney, Karen L., illus. 2002. (Barklay & Eve Ser.: Bk. 7). (Illus.). (J). pap. 6.95 (978-0-9667820-6-6(2)) Dragonfly Publishing.

—They're Part of the Family: Barklay & Eve Talk to Children about Pet Loss. Carney, Karen L., illus. 2002. (Barklay & Eve Ser.: Bk. 8). (Illus.). (J). pap. 6.95 (978-0-9667820-8-0(9)) Dragonfly Publishing.

—Together, We'll Get Through This! Learning to Cope with Loss & Transition. Carney, Karen L., illus. 1999. (Barklay & Eve Ser.: Bk. 1). (Illus.). (J). pap. 6.95 (978-0-9667820-0-4(3)) Dragonfly Publishing.

—What Is the Meaning of Shiva. Carney, Karen L., illus. rev. ed. 2001. (Barklay & Eve Ser.: Bk. 3). Orig. Title: Barklay & Eve. (Illus.). (J). pap. 6.95 (978-0-9667820-2-8(X)) Dragonfly Publishing.

Caseley, Judith. Praying to A. L. 2000. 64p. (J). (gr. 5 up). 15.95 (978-0-688-15934-4(6)) HarperCollins Pubs.

Chalifour, Francis. Le Fils du Pendu. 2006. (FRE.). 168p. (J). (gr. 7). pap. 7.95 (978-0-88776-795-1(8) , Livres Toundra) Tundra Bks., Inc./Livres Toundra, Inc. CAN. *Dist:* Random Hse., Inc.

Chotjewitz, David & Orgel, Doris. Crazy Diamond. 2008. 272p. (YA). 17.99 (***978-1-4169-1176-0(6))*** Simon & Schuster Children's Publishing.

Clark, Clara Gillow. Hill Hawk Hattie. Clark, Clara Gillow, illus. 2004. (Illus.). 176p. (J). (gr. 5 up). pap. 5.99 (978-0-7636-2559-7(0)) Candlewick Pr.

Clements, Andrew. Things Hoped For. 176p. (gr. 5). 2008. (J). 6.99 (***978-0-14-241073-8(X)*** , Puffin); 2006. (YA). 16.99 (978-0-399-24350-9(X) , Philomel) Penguin Group (USA) Inc.

Cochran, Bill. The Forever Dog. Andreasen, Dan, illus. 2007. 32p. (J). (ps-3). 15.99 (978-0-06-053939-9(9)); lib. bdg. 16.89 (978-0-06-053940-5(2)) HarperCollins Pubs.

Collins, Chris. A Mary Little Christmas. Brimer, Molly, illus. l.t. ed. 2002. 32p. (J). lib. bdg. (978-0-9722799-0-1(3)) Words of Grace, Inc.

Coman, Carolyn. Many Stones. 2002. 160p. (YA). pap. 5.99 (978-0-14-230148-7(5) , Puffin) Penguin Group (USA) Inc.

—Many Stones. 2002. 157p. (YA). (gr. 7-9). lib. bdg. 14.15 (978-0-613-45291-5(7)) Tandem Library Bks.

—Many Stones. l.t. ed. 2001. 24.95 (978-0-7862-3399-1(0)) Thorndike Pr.

—Tell Me Everything. 2006. 160p. (YA). pap. 6.95 (978-0-374-40005-7(9) , Farrar, Straus & Giroux (BYR)) Farrar, Straus & Giroux.

Comor-Jacobs, Annie. Reesy: A Little Girl Learning Life's Lessons: Reesy Learning about Divorce; Reesy Learning about the Deep South; Reesy Learning about Deafness; Reesy Learning about Death, 4 vols. Price, Chris, illus. 2000. 40p. (J). (gr. 2-5). pap. 30.00 (978-1-889743-18-9(6)) Robbie Dean Pr.

Coombs, Corinne. My Brother Sam Is Dead. Chaney, Howard, illus. 1999. (Literature Units Ser.). 48p. (J). pap., tchr. ed. 7.99 (978-1-57690-507-4(1) , TCA2507) Teacher Created Materials, Inc.

Cooney, Caroline B. Driver's Ed. 2004. 192p. (YA). (gr. 7). lib. bdg. 17.99 (978-0-385-90236-6(0) , Delacorte Bks. for Young Readers) Random Hse. Children's Bks.

Cosby, Bill. The Day I Saw My Father Cry. 2000. (Little Bill Books for Beginning Readers Ser.). (Illus.). (J). 10.79 (978-0-606-20470-5(9)) Tandem Library Bks.

—The Day I Saw My Father Cry. Honeywood, Varnette P., illus. 2000. (J). (ps-k). lib. bdg. 11.80 (978-0-613-21412-4(9)) Tandem Library Bks.

Cosby, Bill & Honeywood, Varnette P. The Day I Saw My Father Cry. 2000. (Little Bill Books for Beginning Readers Ser.). (Illus.). 40p. (J). (gr. k-3). pap. 15.95 (978-0-590-52197-0(7)) Scholastic, Inc.

Couloumbis, Audrey. Getting near to Baby. 2002. (Illus.). (J). 13.19 (978-0-7587-6515-4(0)) Book Wholesalers, Inc.

—Getting near to Baby. 224p. (J). (gr. 5-9). 2001. pap. 5.99 (978-0-698-11892-8(8)); 1999. 17.99 (978-0-399-23389-0(X)) Penguin Group (USA) Inc. (Putnam Juvenile).

—Getting near to Baby. 2001. (gr. 5-8). lib. bdg. 14.15 (978-0-613-44208-4(3)) Tandem Library Bks.

—Getting near to Baby. l.t. ed. 2000. (Juvenile Ser.). (Illus.). 215p. (J). (gr. 4-7). 22.95 (978-0-7862-2705-1(2)) Thorndike Pr.

Crane, E. M. Skin Deep. 2008. (YA). (***978-0-385-73479-0(4)*** , Delacorte Pr.) Dell Publishing.

Creech, Sharon. Chasing Redbird. l.t. ed. 2005. 259p. (J). (gr. 3-7). per. 22.95 (978-0-7862-7779-7(3) , Large Print Pr.) Thorndike Pr.

—Walk Two Moons. 2002. (Illus.). (J). 15.00 (978-0-7587-0223-4(X)) Book Wholesalers, Inc.

—Walk Two Moons. 2004. 304p. (J). (gr. 7 up). pap. 6.99 (978-0-06-056013-3(4) , Harper Trophy) HarperCollins Pubs.

—Walk Two Moons. 1999. (J). 9.95 (978-1-56137-770-1(8)); 11.95 (978-1-56137-771-8(6)) Novel Units, Inc.

—Walk Two Moons. 1998. (Assessment Packs Ser.). 15p. (J). pap., tchr.'s training gde. ed. 15.95 (978-1-58303-067-7(0)) Pathways Publishing.

—Walk Two Moons. 280p. (J). (gr. 4-6). pap. 4.95 (978-0-8072-1509-8(0) , Listening Library) Random Hse. Audio Publishing Group.

—Walk Two Moons. 2004. (gr. 7-12). lib. bdg. 14.75 (978-0-613-81971-8(3)) Tandem Library Bks.

—Walk Two Moons. l.t. ed. 287p. 2003. pap. 10.95 (978-0-7862-6185-7(4)); 2000. (Illus.). (J). 21.95 (978-0-7862-2773-0(7)) Thorndike Pr.

Croall, Marie P. & Lago, Ray, texts. Marwe: Into the Land of the Dead: An East African Folktale. 2007. (Graphic Myths & Legends Ser.). (J). 26.60 (***978-0-8225-7134-6(X)*** , Graphic Universe) Lerner Publishing Group.

Crossley, Diana. Muddles, Puddles & Sunshine: Your Activity Book to Help When Someone Has Died. Sheppard, Kate, illus. 2000. 32p. (ps-3). pap. 8.95 (978-1-869890-58-2(2)) Hawthorn Pr. GBR. *Dist:* SteinerBooks, Inc.

Crowley, James. The Magic Hour. 2003. (Illus.). 280p. (J). pap. 17.95 (978-1-55517-713-3(1) , 77131) Cedar Fort, Inc./CFI Distribution.

Crutcher, Chris. The Sledding Hill. 2005. 240p. (J). (gr. 7 up). 16.99 (978-0-06-050243-0(6)); lib. bdg. 17.89 (978-0-06-050244-7(4)) HarperCollins Pubs.

—Sledding Hill. 2006. 256p. (J). pap. 6.99 (978-0-06-050245-4(2) , HarperTeen) HarperCollins Pubs.

—The Sledding Hill. l.t. ed. 2005. 181p. (YA). 20.95 (978-0-7862-8091-9(3)) Thorndike Pr.

Cummings, Priscilla. Red Kayak. (gr. 5). 2006. 224p. (YA). pap. 6.99 (978-0-14-240573-4(6) , Puffin); 2004. 192p. (J). 15.99 (978-0-525-47317-6(3) , Dutton Juvenile) Penguin Group (USA) Inc.

Cusick, Richie Tankersley. The Unseen II. 2004. 288p. (YA). pap. (***978-0-439-96799-0(6))*** Scholastic, Inc.

Danziger, Paula. United Tates of America. 2006. 144p. (J). pap. 5.99 (978-0-439-83883-2(5) , Scholastic Paperbacks) Scholastic, Inc.

—United Tates of America. Danziger, Paula, illus. 2002. (Illus.). 144p. (J). (gr. 3-7). pap. 17.95 (978-0-590-69221-2(6) , Scholastic Pr.) Scholastic, Inc.

—United Tates of America: The Story & the Scrapbook. 2002. (gr. 3-6). lib. bdg. 14.15 (978-0-613-67042-5(6)) Tandem Library Bks.

De Groot, Bob & Turk. 7 Days to Die. 2007. (Illus.). 48p. pap. 9.99 (***978-1-905460-08-3(2))*** CineBook GBR. *Dist:* Biblio Distribution.

de Paola, Tomie. Nana Upstairs & Nana Downstairs. 2000. (Illus.). 32p. (J). (ps-3). pap. 6.99 (978-0-698-11836-2(7) , Putnam Juvenile) Penguin Group (USA) Inc.

—Nana Upstairs & Nana Downstairs. unabr. ed. 2006. (J). (gr. k-3). pap. 17.95 incl. audio (978-0-8045-6943-9(6)); pap. 19.95 incl. audio compact disk (978-0-8045-4157-2(4)) Spoken Arts, Inc.

—Nana Upstairs & Nana Downstairs. 2000. (gr. k-3). lib. bdg. 15.30 (978-0-8085-2686-5(3)) Tandem Library Bks.

Deem, James M. 3 NBs of Julian Drew. 2004. 208p. (YA). (gr. 7 up). pap. 6.99 (978-0-618-43907-2(2) , Graphia) Houghton Mifflin Co. Trade & Reference Div.

Demas, Corinne. Saying Goodbye to Lulu. Hoyt, Ard, tr. Hoyt, Ard, illus. 2004. 40p. (J). (ps-3). 15.99 (978-0-316-70278-2(1)) Little Brown & Co.

Dessen, Sarah. The Truth about Forever. 2006. 400p. (YA). (gr. 7). reprint ed. pap. 7.99 (978-0-14-240625-0(2) , Puffin) Penguin Group (USA) Inc.

Devries, Karen. Peekaboo, Pearly Moon. Myers, Stan, illus. 2004. 32p. (ps-2). 12.99 (978-0-8254-2448-9(8)) Kregel Pubns.

Dickerson, Karle & Campbell, Joanna. The Forgotten Filly. 1998. (Ashleigh's Thoroughbred Collection). 192p. (gr. 3-7). mass mkt. 4.99 (978-0-06-106486-9(6)) HarperCollins Pubs.

Dingles, Molly. Jinka, Jinka Jelly Bean. Bingler, Aimee, illus. 1998. 38p. (J). (ps-6). 23.00 (978-1-891997-03-7(3)) Dingles & Co.

DiSalvo-Ryan, DyAnne. A Dog Like Jack. unabr. ed. 2005. (Illus.). (J). (ps-2). pap. 16.95 incl. audio (978-0-87499-758-3(5)) BBC Audiobooks America.

—A Dog Like Jack. DiSalvo-Ryan, DyAnne, illus. 1999. (Illus.). 32p. (J). (gr. k-3). tchr. ed. 16.95 (978-0-8234-1369-0(1)); pap. 6.95 (978-0-8234-1680-6(1)) Holiday Hse., Inc.

—A Dog Like Jack. 2005. (Live Oak Readalong Ser.). (J). pap. 18.95 incl. audio compact disk (978-1-59519-298-1(0)) Live Oak Media.

—A Dog Like Jack. DiSalvo-Ryan, DyAnne, illus. 2001. (Illus.). pap. 25.95 incl. audio (978-0-87499-759-0(3)); pap. 37.95 incl. audio (978-0-87499-760-6(7)) Live Oak Media.

DiSunno, Rebecca, et al. Jeremy Goes to Camp Good Grief. l.t. ed. 2004. (Illus.). 48p. (J). per. 14.95 (978-0-9754932-0-5(5)) East End Hospice, Inc.

Doggy Heaven's in the Sky! 2004. (J). 4.95 (***978-0-9791362-0-7(2))*** Tony Tales.

Dokey, Cameron. How Not to Spend Your Senior Year. 2004. (gr. 7-12). lib. bdg. 14.15 (978-0-613-73455-4(6)) Tandem Library Bks.

Dokey, Cameron & Saidens, Amy. How Not to Spend Your Senior Year. 2003. (Romantic Comedies Ser.). 304p. (YA). mass mkt. 5.99 (978-0-689-86703-3(4) , Simon Pulse) Simon & Schuster Children's Publishing.

Doray, Malika. One More Wednesday. Freeman, Suzanne, tr. Doray, Malika, illus. 2001. (Illus.). 32p. (J). (ps up). 15.89 (978-0-06-029590-5(2)) HarperCollins Pubs.

Douglas, Eileen. Rachel & the Upside down Heart. 2006. (J). per. 14.95 (978-0-9790041-0-0(1)) Dancing Magic Heart Bk.

Dow, Unity. Far & Beyon' 2002. 208p. (YA). (gr. 7 up). pap. 11.95 (978-1-879960-64-0(8)) Aunt Lute Bks.

Dowell, Frances O'Roark. Dovey Coe. 192p. (J). 2001. (Illus.). pap. 5.99 (978-0-689-84667-0(3) , Aladdin); 2000. (gr. 4-7). 16.99 (978-0-689-83174-4(9) , Atheneum) Simon & Schuster Children's Publishing.

—Dovey Coe. 2001. 11.64 (978-0-606-22127-6(1)) Tandem Library Bks.

—Dovey Coe. l.t. ed. 2001. 171p. (J). 22.95 (978-0-7862-3590-2(X)) Thorndike Pr.

Draper, Sharon M. The Battle of Jericho. 2003. (Illus.). 304p. (YA). 17.95 (978-0-689-84232-0(5) , Atheneum) Simon & Schuster Children's Publishing.

—Tears of a Tiger. l.t. ed. 219p. 2006. pap. 10.95 (978-0-7862-8361-3(0)); 2005. 20.95 (978-0-7862-7418-5(2) , Large Print Pr.) Thorndike Pr.

Draper, Sharon M. & Bascoul, Eric. The Battle of Jericho. 2004. 352p. (YA). mass mkt. 6.99 (978-0-689-84233-7(3) , Simon Pulse) Simon & Schuster Children's Publishing.

Duckworth, Liz. Ragtail Remembers. Barnes, Jeff, illus. 2002. (J). (978-1-56123-163-8(0)) Centering Corp.

Durant, Alan. Always & Forever. Gliori, Debi, tr. Gliori, Debi, illus. 2004. 32p. (J). 16.00 (978-0-15-216636-6(X)) Harcourt Children's Bks.

Durrant, George D. The Christmas Marble: A Christmas Story. 2004. 70p. (J). 4.95 (978-1-55517-824-6(3) , Bonneville Bks.) Cedar Fort, Inc./CFI Distribution.

Ebeling, Vicki. The Winners Group. 2007. (J). per. 7.95 (978-0-9779768-0-5(7)) Pier Avenue Publishing.

Edwards, Michelle. Stinky Stern Forever: A Jackson Friends Book. 2007. (Jackson Friends Ser.). (Illus.). 56p. (J). pap. 5.95 (***978-0-15-206101-2(0)*** , Harcourt Paperbacks) Harcourt Children's Bks.

—Stinky Stern Forever: A Jackson Friends Book. 2005. (Jackson Friends Ser.). (Illus.). 56p. (J). (gr. 1-3). 14.00 (978-0-15-216389-1(1)) Harcourt Trade Pubs.

Eenie Meanie Me & the Very Sad Day. 2005. (J). (978-0-9772878-0-2(7)) Bishop, Susan Lynn.

Ellsworth, Loretta. Shrouding Woman. 2007. 160p. (YA). pap. 6.95 (***978-0-8050-8185-5(2)*** , Holt, Henry & Co. Bks. For Young Readers) Holt, Henry & Co.

Ellsworth, Loretta. The Shrouding Woman. rev. ed. 2002. 160p. (J). (gr. 5-8). 16.95 (978-0-8050-6651-7(9) , Holt, Henry & Co. Bks. For Young Readers) Holt, Henry & Co.

Enderle, Dotti. Hidden. Gentry, T. Kyle, illus. 2007. 120p. (YA). (gr. 5-9). pap. 8.95 (***978-1-58980-481-4(3))*** Pelican Publishing Co., Inc.

Ephron, Delia. Frannie in Pieces. 2007. 384p. (YA). (gr. 7 up). 16.99 (***978-0-06-074716-9(1)*** , HarperTeen) HarperCollins Pubs.

—Frannie in Pieces. Beckerman, Chad, illus. 2007. 384p. (YA). (gr. 7 up). lib. bdg. 17.89 (***978-0-06-074717-6(X)*** , HarperTeen) HarperCollins Pubs.

Erb, Sharlyne. A Hug from Daddy. 2005. 43p. pap. 12.97 (978-1-4116-5576-8(1)) Lulu.com.

Evenson, Inge, text. Serafina's Silver Web: A Project to Benefit Noah's Children. 1999. (Illus.). 40p. (J). (978-0-9674273-0-0(4)) Noah's Children, Inc.

Ewing, Lynne. Drive-By. 1998. 96p. (J). (gr. 5 up). pap. 4.99 (978-0-06-440649-9(0) , Harper Trophy) HarperCollins Pubs.

Fallon, Kevin A. Rest in Peas: What Does that Mean? 2005. per. 12.95 (978-1-59196-943-3(3)) Instantpublisher.com.

Farnes, Catherine. Out of Hiding. 2000. 174p. (YA). (gr. 9 up). pap. 6.49 (978-1-57924-329-6(0) , 122085) Jones, Bob Univ. Pr.

—Out of Hiding. 2000. (gr. 7-12). lib. bdg. 14.70 (978-0-613-83927-3(7)) Tandem Library Bks.

—The Way of Escape. 2000. (J). 166p. (gr. 8-12). pap. 6.49 (978-1-57924-453-8(X)) ; (Illus.). 157p. (gr. 9 up). 6.49 (978-1-57924-454-5(8) , 126599) Jones, Bob Univ. Pr.

Ferber, Brenda A. Julia's Kitchen. 2006. (Illus.). 160p. (J). 16.00 (978-0-374-39932-0(8)) Farrar, Straus & Giroux.

Fletcher, Ralph J. Flying Solo. 1998. (Illus.). 144p. (J). (gr. 4-6). tchr. ed. 15.00 (978-0-395-87323-6(1) , Clarion Bks.) Houghton Mifflin Co. Trade & Reference Div.

—Flying Solo. 2000. (gr. 5-8). lib. bdg. 13.00 (978-0-613-28491-2(7)) Tandem Library Bks.

Foreman, Michael. Evie & the Man Who Helped God. 2003. (Illus.). 32p. (J). 18.00 (978-1-84270-219-2(X)) Andersen GBR. *Dist:* Independent Pubs. Group.

Forever Friends. 2002. (Illus.). 32p. 16.95 (978-1-931290-12-8(1) , Smallfellow Pr.) Tallfellow Pr.

Frank, E. R. Wrecked. 256p. (YA). (gr. 7 up). 2007. pap. 8.99 (978-0-689-87384-3(0) , Simon Pulse); 2005. (Illus.). 16.99 (978-0-689-87383-6(2) , Atheneum) Simon & Schuster Children's Publishing.

Franklin, Kristine L. Lone Wolf. 224p. (J). (gr. 4-8). 2006. 5.99 (978-0-7636-2996-0(0)); 1998. (Illus.). pap. 6.99 (978-0-7636-0480-6(1)) Candlewick Pr.

—Lone Wolf. 1998. (J). (978-0-606-13578-8(2)) Tandem Library Bks.

Freymann-Weyr, Garret. When I Was Older. 2000. (Illus.). 176p. (YA). (gr. 5-9). tchr. ed. 15.00 (978-0-618-05545-6(2)) Houghton Mifflin Co. Trade & Reference Div.

—When I Was Older. l.t. ed. 2001. 159p. (J). 22.95 (978-0-7862-3546-9(2)) Thorndike Pr.

Fried, Amelie. Is Grandpa Wearing a Suit? Gleich, Jacky, illus. 2007. 32p. (J). (gr. 4-7). 16.95 (***978-0-9787550-4-1(9)***) Heryin Publishing Corp.

Friend, Natasha. Perfect. 2004. 232p. (J). 16.95 (978-1-57131-652-3(3)) ; pap. 6.95 (978-1-57131-651-6(5)) Milkweed Editions.

Frink-Hunter, Chene I. Grandma Died & Mommy Really, Really Cried: Death - Dying. Robertson, Michael, illus. (J). (ps-6). (978-0-9654185-1-5(0)) Hunter Pubns.

Garrick, Lainie. Losing Papou: One Child's Journey Towards Understanding & Accepting Death. Mandarino, Gene, illus. l.t. ed. 2003. 32p. (J). (978-0-9765725-0-3(8)) printONDEMANDpublisher.com.

Gibbons, Alan. The Lost Boys' Appreciation Society. 2006. 176p. (J). pap. 11.99 (***978-1-84255-095-3(0)***) Orion Publishing Group, Ltd. GBR. *Dist:* Independent Pubs. Group.

Gilbert, Sheri. The Legacy of Gloria Russell. 2004. 224p. (J). (gr. 3-7). 15.95 (978-0-375-82823-2(0) , Knopf Bks. for Young Readers) Random Hse. Children's Bks.

Giles, Gail. Dead Girls Don't Write Letters. rev. ed. 2003. 144p. (YA). (gr. 7 up). 16.95 (978-0-7613-1727-2(9)) Roaring Brook Pr.

—Dead Girls Don't Write Letters. 2004. 128p. (YA). reprint ed. pap. 6.99 (978-0-689-86624-1(0) , Simon Pulse) Simon & Schuster Children's Publishing.

Glowatsky, Phyllis. The Light of Stars. Stringer, Karen, illus. 2003. 32p. (J). 19.95 (978-1-931650-18-2(7)) Coastal Publishing Carolina, Inc.

Going, K. L. The Garden of Eve. 2007. (Illus.). 240p. (J). (gr. 3-7). 17.00 (***978-0-15-205986-6(5)***) Harcourt Children's Bks.

Golden, Christopher. Body Bags. 1999. (YA). 11.64 (978-0-606-20505-4(5)) Tandem Library Bks.

Gostick, Adrian R. Jessica's Search: The Secret of Ballycater Cove. 1998. (J). 1.99 (978-1-57345-436-0(2)) Deseret Bk. Co.

Grandma Is Now A Butterfly. 2005. (Illus.). 24p. (J). 8.00 (978-0-9767077-0-7(5)) Carson, Tracy.

Gray, Nigel. Little Bear's Grandad. Cabban, Vanessa, illus. 2001. 28p. (J). (ps-k). tchr. ed. 14.95 (978-1-58925-008-6(7) , tiger tales) ME Media LLC.

Green, John. Looking for Alaska. 2005. 160p. (YA). (gr. 8-12). 15.99 (978-0-525-47506-4(0) , Dutton Juvenile) Penguin Group (USA) Inc.

Greene, Constance C. Beat the Turtle Drum. 128p. (J). (gr. 4-6). pap. 3.99 (978-0-8072-1411-4(6) , Listening Library) Random Hse. Audio Publishing Group.

Gregory, Nan. Wild Girl & Gran. ed. 2004. (Illus.). (J). (gr. k-3). spiral bd. (978-0-616-11112-3(6)) Canadian National Institute for the Blind/Institut National Canadien pour les Aveugles.

—Wild Girl & Gran. Lightburn, Ron, illus. 2004. (Northern Lights Books for Children Ser.). 32p. (J). (ps-3). pap. 16.95 (978-0-88995-221-8(3)) Red Deer Pr. CAN. *Dist:* Fitzhenry & Whiteside, Ltd.

Grekul, Lisa. Kalyna's Song. 2nd ed. 2007. 472p. (YA). (gr. 10 up). pap. 12.95 (***978-1-55050-355-5(3)***) Coteau Bks. CAN. *Dist:* Fitzhenry & Whiteside, Ltd.

Griffin, Adele. Rainy Season. 1998. (978-0-606-13726-3(2)) Tandem Library Bks.

Griffin, Adele. Where I Want to Be. 160p. (gr. 7). 2007. (YA). 6.99 (***978-0-14-240948-0(0)*** , Puffin); 2005. (J). 15.99 (978-0-399-23783-6(6) , Putnam Juvenile) Penguin Group (USA) Inc.

Haas, Jessie. Unbroken. 2001. 208p. (J). (gr. 5 up). pap. 6.99 (978-0-380-73313-2(7) , Harper Trophy) HarperCollins Pubs.

—Unbroken. 2001. (J). (978-0-606-20962-5(X)) ; (gr. 5-8). lib. bdg. 14.10 (978-0-613-33735-9(2)) Tandem Library Bks.

—Unbroken. l.t. ed. 2000. (Juvenile Ser.). 248p. (J). (gr. 4-7). 21.95 (978-0-7862-2769-3(9)) Thorndike Pr.

Hall, S.C. Turns of Fortune & Other Tales. 2007. (ENG.). 116p. per. (***978-1-4065-1586-2(8)***) Dodo Pr.

Harness, Cheryl. Just for You to Know. 2008. (J). pap. (***978-0-06-078315-0(X)***) HarperCollins Pubs.

Harrar, George. Not as Crazy as I Seem. 2003. 208p. (J). (gr. 7). tchr. ed. 15.00 (978-0-618-26365-3(9)) Houghton Mifflin Co. Trade & Reference Div.

—Not As Crazy As I Seem. 2004. 240p. (J). (gr. 7). pap. 6.99 (978-0-618-49480-4(4) , Graphia) Houghton Mifflin Co. Trade & Reference Div.

Harrison, Josephine Chaudoin. The Magical Master Snowman & the Black Dragon: A Fairy Tale for All Ages. Harrison, Josephine Chaudoin, illus. 2002. (Illus.). 100p. (J). pap. (978-1-894694-12-4(0)) Granville Island Publishing.

Hartling, Peter. La Abuela. 1998. (SPA., Illus.). 112p. (gr. 4-7). 9.95 (978-84-204-4768-1(4)) Alfaguara, Ediciones, S.A.- Grupo Santillana ESP. *Dist:* Santillana USA Publishing Co., Inc.

—La Abuela. Mizsenko, Ingrid, illus. 2003. (SPA.). 103p. (J). (gr. 5-8). pap. 9.95 (978-968-19-0730-3(2)) Santillana USA Publishing Co., Inc.

Harvey, Jacqueline. The Sound of the Sea. Crossett, Warren, illus. 2005. 32p. (J). (***978-0-7344-0742-9(4)*** , Lothian Bks.) Hachette Livre Australia.

Haufsk, Violet. The Gathering Spot: A Story for Children about Death. 2001. 24p. (J). 14.99 (978-0-933675-96-4(8)) Scratch & Scribble Pr., Inc.

Hawes, Louise. Rosey in the Present Tense. 1999. (Illus.). (J). (978-0-606-20488-0(1)) Tandem Library Bks.

—Rosey in the Present Tense. l.t. ed. 2002. 186p. (J). 22.95 (978-0-7862-4418-8(6)) Thorndike Pr.

—Rosey in the Present Tense. 1999. 176p. (YA). (gr. 7). 16.95 (978-0-8027-8685-2(5)) Walker & Co.

Hayes, Daniel. Flyers. 1998. (978-0-606-13392-0(5)) Tandem Library Bks.

Haynes, India K. Sweet Shana. 2007. (ENG.). 56p. per. 27.99 (***978-1-4134-1175-1(4)***) Xlibris Corp.

Haynes, Max. Grandma's Gone to Live in the Stars. 2000. (Concept Book Ser.). (Illus.). 32p. (J). (ps-3). 15.95 (978-0-8075-3026-9(3)) Whitman, Albert & Co.

Heide, Florence Parry & Pierce, Roxanne H. Tio Armando. Grifalconi, Ann, illus. 1998. 32p. (YA). (gr. 5 up). 15.00 (978-0-688-12107-5(1)) HarperCollins Pubs.

Hemery, Kathleen Maresh. The Healing Tree. Teis, Kyra, illus. 2001. (J). (978-1-56123-153-9(3) , HTRC) Centering Corp.

—Sunflower Promise. Bordelois, Augusto, illus. 2005. (J). (978-1-56123-188-1(6)) Centering Corp.

Henderson, Lauren. Kiss Me Kill Me. 2008. 256p. (YA). (gr. 9). 15.99 (***978-0-385-73487-5(5)*** , Delacorte Bks. for Young Readers) Random Hse. Children's Bks.

Henkes, Kevin. Sun & Spoon. 2007. 144p. (J). pap. 5.99 (***978-0-06-128875-3(6)*** , Harper Trophy) HarperCollins Pubs.

—Sun & Spoon. 1998. (Puffin Novel Ser.). 144p. (J). (gr. 3-7). pap. 4.99 (978-0-14-130095-5(7) , Puffin) Penguin Group (USA) Inc.

Hereford, L. F. Gerry the Grape. Skardarasy, Doreen L., illus. 2005. (J). pap. (978-0-9728969-9-3(6)) Acorn Publishing.

Hermes, Patricia. Sweet by & By. 2002. 208p. (J). (gr. 3-6). 15.99 (978-0-380-97452-8(5)) HarperCollins Pubs.

Herrick, Steven. By the River. 2006. 240p. (YA). 16.95 (978-1-932425-72-7(1) , Lemniscaat) Boyds Mills Pr.

Hest, Amy. Remembering Mrs. Rossi. Maione, Heather, illus. 2007. 192p. (J). (gr. 3-7). 14.99 (978-0-7636-2163-6(3)) Candlewick Pr.

Hester, John C. Three Days in Hell. 2003. (J). 7.95 (978-1-59196-311-0(7)) Instantpublisher.com.

Hill, Frances. The Bug Cemetery. Rosenberry, Vera, illus. rev. ed. 2002. 32p. (J). (gr. k-2). 16.95 (978-0-8050-6370-7(6)) , Holt, Henry & Co. Bks. For Young Readers) Holt, Henry & Co.

Hite, Sid. A Hole in the World. 208p. (J). 2001. (Illus.). pap. 16.95 (978-0-439-09830-4(0)); 2004. (gr. 5 up). reprint ed. pap. 5.99 (978-0-439-09831-1(9) , Scholastic Pr.) Scholastic, Inc.

Hobbs, Valerie. Defiance. 2005. 128p. (J). 16.00 (978-0-374-30847-6(0)) Farrar, Straus & Giroux.

—Defiance. l.t. ed. 2006. 147p. 22.95 (978-0-7862-8667-6(9)) Thorndike Pr.

—Sonny's War. 2002. 224p. (YA). (gr. 7 up). 16.00 (978-0-374-37136-4(9) , Farrar, Straus & Giroux (BYR)) Farrar, Straus & Giroux.

—Sonny's War. 2006. 224p. (YA). pap. 7.95 (978-0-374-46970-2(9)) Macmillan.

Hodge, John. Finding Grandpa Everywhere: A Young Child Discovers Memories of a Grandparent. Aitken, Susan, illus. 1999. (J). 6.95 (978-1-56123-125-6(8)) Centering Corp.

Holt, Kimberly Willis. Keeper of the Night. rev. ed. 2003. (Illus.). 180p. (YA). (gr. 5-8). 16.95 (978-0-8050-6361-5(7) , Holt, Henry & Co. Bks. For Young Readers) Holt, Henry & Co.

—Keeper of the Night. 2005. 336p. (YA). (gr. 7). reprint ed. mass mkt. 6.50 (978-0-553-49441-9(4) , Laurel Leaf) Random Hse. Children's Bks.

—Keeper of the Night. 2005. 309p. (YA). (gr. 7-12). lib. bdg. 13.55 (978-0-606-33249-1(9)) Tandem Library Bks.

—Keeper of the Night. l.t. ed. 2004. 336p. (J). 23.95 (978-0-7862-6431-5(4)) Thorndike Pr.

Holubitsky, Katherine. Alone at Ninety Foot. 2001. 192p. (J). (gr. 7-12). mass mkt. 6.95 (978-1-55143-204-5(8)) Orca Bk. Pubs. USA.

—Alone at Ninety Foot. 2001. (gr. 7-12). lib. bdg. 15.25 (978-0-613-23678-2(5)); 1999. (J). 13.60 (978-0-606-21583-1(2)); 1999. (Illus.). (J). (978-0-606-18327-7(2)) Tandem Library Bks.

Honeycutt, Natalie. Twilight in Grace Falls. 1999. 192p. (J). (gr. 3-7). pap. 4.50 (978-0-380-73128-2(2)) HarperCollins Pubs.

—Twilight in Grace Falls. 1999. (978-0-606-15928-9(2)) Tandem Library Bks.

Honeywood, Varnette P., illus. The Day I Saw My Father Cry. 2002. (Little Bill Ser.). (J). 11.91 (978-0-7587-1093-2(3)) Book Wholesalers, Inc.

Hooper, Mary. Newes from the Dead: Being a True Story of Anne Green, Hanged for Infanticide at Oxford Assizes in 1650, Restored to the World & Died Again 1665. 2008. 256p. (YA). 15.95 (***978-1-59643-355-7(8)***) Roaring Brook Pr.

Horvath, Polly. The Corps of the Bare-Boned Plane. 2007. 272p. (J). (gr. 7 up). 17.00 (***978-0-374-31553-5(1)*** , Farrar, Straus & Giroux (BYR)) Farrar, Straus & Giroux.

Hubler, Marsha. A True Test for Skye. 2004. (Keystone Stables Ser.). (Illus.). 144p. (J). pap. 4.99 (978-0-310-70573-4(8)) Zonderkidz.

Hughes, Carol. Dirty Magic. 2006. (Illus.). 432p. (J). (gr. 4-9). 17.95 (978-0-375-83187-4(8)) ; (gr. 5-8). lib. bdg. 19.99 (978-0-375-93187-1(2)) Random Hse. Children's Bks. (Random Hse. Bks. for Young Readers).

—Dirty Magic. 2008. (Illus.). 432p. (J). (gr. 5-9). 5.99 (978-0-375-83188-1(6)) Random Hse., Inc.

Hughes, Shirley. Alfie & the Birthday Surprise. 1998. (Illus.). 32p. (J). (ps-1). 16.00 (978-0-688-15187-4(6)) HarperCollins Pubs.

—Alfie & the Birthday Surprise. 2007. (Illus.). 32p. (J). pap. 8.95 (***978-0-09-920862-4(8)*** , Red Fox) Random Hse. Children's Bks. GBR. *Dist:* Independent Pubs. Group.

—Alfie & the Birthday Surprise. Hughes, Shirley, illus. 1999. (Illus.). 30p. (J). 9.99 (978-1-58048-086-4(1)) Sandvik Publishing.

Hurwin, Davida Lewis. The Farther You Run. 2005. 224p. (YA). (gr. 7). pap. 6.99 (978-0-14-240294-8(X) , Puffin) Penguin Group (USA) Inc.

Hurwin, Davida Wills. The Farther You Run. 2005. 217p. (YA). (gr. 9-12). per. 14.04 (978-0-606-33126-5(3)) Tandem Library Bks.

Jacobs, Deborah Lynn. Choices. 2007. 208p. (YA). (gr. 7 up). 16.95 (***978-1-59643-217-8(9)***) Roaring Brook Pr.

James, Gill. Nick's Gallery. 2004. 149p. pap. 19.95 (978-1-4137-2186-7(9)) PublishAmerica, Inc.

Jeffs, Stephanie. Josh: Coming to Terms with the Death of a Friend. Thomas, Jacqui, illus. 2006. 32p. (ps-3). 14.00 (978-0-687-49719-5(1)) Abingdon Pr.

Johnston, Tony. That Summer. Moser, Barry, illus. 2007. 32p. (J). (gr. 1-4). pap. 6.00 (978-0-15-205856-2(7) , Voyager Bks./Libros Viajeros) Harcourt Children's Bks.

Kadohata, Cynthia. Kira-Kira. 2004. (Illus.). 256p. 16.95 (978-0-689-85639-6(3) , Atheneum); 2006. 272p. (J). reprint ed. pap. 6.99 (978-0-689-85640-2(7) , Aladdin) Simon & Schuster Children's Publishing.

—Kira-Kira. l.t. ed. 2005. 201p. 23.95 (978-0-7862-7616-5(9) , Large Print Pr.) Thorndike Pr.

Kaplow, Julie B. & Pincus, Donna. Samantha Jane's Missing Smile: A Story about Coping with the Loss of a Parent. Spiegel, Beth, illus. 2007. 32p. (J). (ps-3). 14.95 (***978-1-59147-808-9(1)***); pap. 8.95 (***978-1-59147-809-6(X)***) American Psychological Assn. (Magination Pr.).

Katz, Welwyn W. Out of the Dark. 2001. 185p. (J). (gr. 4). pap. 5.95 (978-0-88899-262-8(9)) Groundwood Bks. CAN. *Dist:* Perseus Distribution.

Keeling, Annie E. Andrew Golding A Tale of the Great Plague. 2004. reprint ed. pap. 15.95 (978-1-4191-0694-1(5)) ; pap. 1.99 (978-1-4192-0694-8(X)) Kessinger Publishing, LLC.

Keeling, E. Annie. Andrew Golding (a Tale of the Great Plag. 2006. 40.99 (***978-1-4280-0516-7(1)***); pap. 34.99 (***978-1-4280-0515-0(3)***) IndyPublish.com.

Kelly, David. Canoes of the Dead. 144p. pap. 11.95 (978-0-7022-2509-3(6)) Univ. of Queensland Pr. AUS. *Dist:* International Specialized Bk. Services.

Kelly, Tom. Finn's Going. 2007. 288p. (J). (gr. 5-9). 16.99 (***978-0-06-121453-0(1)***); lib. bdg. 17.89 (***978-0-06-121454-7(X)***) HarperCollins Pubs. (Greenwillow Bks.).

Kemper, Bebe. Seeing Zach. 1999. (Illus.). 32p. (J). 14.95 (978-0-9674363-0-2(3) , Rainy Day Bks.) Purple Chickie Pr.

Kitty Heaven's in the Sky! 2004. (J). 4.95 (***978-0-9791362-1-4(0)***) Tony Tales.

Klause, Annette Curtis. The Silver Kiss. 2007. 224p. (J). pap. 8.99 (***978-0-385-73422-6(0)***); lib. bdg. 11.99 (***978-0-385-90435-3(5)***) Random Hse. Children's Bks. (Delacorte Bks. for Young Readers).

—The Silver Kiss. 1999. (J). (gr. 7-12). lib. bdg. 13.55 (978-0-8335-9378-8(1)) Tandem Library Bks.

Kolie & the Funeral. 2005. (J). 3.99 (978-1-882951-40-6(9)) Guideline Pubns. Co.

Koller, Jackie French. The Promise. Rogers, Jacqueline, illus. 2001. 80p. (gr. 5-8). 4.99 (978-0-440-41658-6(2) , Yearling) Random Hse. Children's Bks.

Kornblatt, Marc. Izzy's Place. 2003. (Illus.). 128p. (J). 16.95 (978-0-689-84639-7(8) , McElderry, Margaret K.) Simon & Schuster Children's Publishing.

—Understanding Buddy. l.t. ed. 2002. 100p. (J). 21.95 (978-0-7862-3712-8(0)) Thomson Gale.

Koss, Amy Goldman. Stolen Words. 2001. (978-0-606-22775-9(X)) Tandem Library Bks.

Kroll, Steven. When I Dream of Heaven: Angelina's Story. 2000. (978-0-606-21879-5(3)) Tandem Library Bks.

Kubler-Ross, Elisabeth. Remember the Secret. 2004. (Illus.). 32p. (ps-3). pap. 9.95 (978-1-883672-79-9(1) , Tricycle Pr.) Ten Speed Pr.

Kuns, Judith Irvin. While You Were Out. 2006. 144p. (J). (gr. 3). pap. 5.99 (978-0-14-240628-1(7) , Puffin) Penguin Group (USA) Inc.

Laird, Elizabeth. Secret Friends. 2002. (Illus.). 96p. (J). pap. (978-0-340-66473-5(8) , Hodder Children's Books) Hodder Children's Division.

Lanton, Sandy. Daddy's Chair. Haas, Shelly O., illus. 2000. 32p. (J). (gr. k-2). 14.95 (978-0-9702482-0-6(2)) ; pap. 6.95 (978-0-9702482-1-3(0)) Lanton Haas Pr.

Larson, K. D. That Place. 2005. (Illus.). 32p. (J). (978-0-615-12555-8(7)) Monkeytoes Pr.

Laughter in the Wind. 2004. (Illus.). (J). 17.95 (978-0-9753417-0-4(7)) Cheerful Cherub.

Lawrence, Iain. Gemini Summer. 2006. 272p. (J). (gr. 3-7). 15.95 (978-0-385-73089-1(6)) ; lib. bdg. 17.99 (978-0-385-90111-6(9)) Random Hse. Children's Bks. (Delacorte Bks. for Young Readers).

Layefsky, Virginia. Impossible Things. 1998. (Accelerated Reader Bks.). 208p. (J). (gr. 5-9). 14.95 (978-0-7614-5038-2(6) , Cavendish Children's Bks.) Cavendish, Marshall Corp.

Leavitt, Martine. Keturah & Lord Death. 2006. 216p. (YA). (gr. 7 up). 16.95 (978-1-932425-29-1(2) , Front Street) Boyds Mills Pr.

Lemieux, Jean. Toby's Very Important Question. Casson, Sophia, illus. 2004. 61p. (J). lib. bdg. 12.00 (***978-1-4242-1246-0(4)***) Fitzgerald Bks.

—Toby's Very Important Question. Cummins, Sarah, tr. from FRE. Casson, Sophie, illus. 2004. (First Novels Ser.: Vol. 51). 64p. (J). (gr. 1-5). 4.95 (978-0-88780-636-0(8)) ; (***978-0-88780-637-7(6)***) Formac Publishing Co., Ltd. CAN. *Dist:* Casemate Pubs. & Bk. Distributors, LLC.

L'Engle, Madeleine. A Ring of Endless Light. 2006. (Austin Family Ser.: No. 5). 21.75 (978-0-8446-7285-4(8)) Smith, Peter Pub., Inc.

Levithan, David. Marly's Ghost. Selznick, Brian, illus. 176p. 2007. (YA). (gr. 7). 6.99 (***978-0-14-240912-1(X)*** , Puffin); 2005. (J). 14.99 (978-0-8037-3063-2(2) , Dial) Penguin Group (USA) Inc.

Linko, G. J. Tess's Touchstone. 2004. (Seekers Ser.: No. 5). 108p. 5.99 (978-0-8066-4189-8(4) , Augsburg Bks.) Augsburg Fortress, Pubs.

Lion, Melissa. Swollen. 2006. 192p. (YA). pap. 6.50 (978-0-553-49408-2(2) , Laurel Leaf) Random Hse. Children's Bks.

—Upstream. 160p. (YA). (gr. 7). 2006. pap. 8.95 (978-0-375-83954-2(2)); 2005. 15.95 (978-0-385-74643-4(1)) Random Hse. Children's Bks. (Lamb, Wendy).

Lisle, Janet Taylor. The Lost Flower Children. 2001. (J). (978-0-606-21305-9(8)) Tandem Library Bks.

Lowry, Lois. A Summer to Die. 2007. 160p. (YA). (gr. 7). pap. 7.99 (978-0-385-73420-2(4) , Delacorte Bks. for Young Readers) Random Hse. Children's Bks.

—A Summer to Die. 1999. mass mkt. (978-0-553-14304-1(2)) ; mass mkt. (978-0-553-24389-5(6)) ; mass mkt. (978-0-553-25447-1(2)) Random Hse., Inc.

Luenn, Nancy. A Gift for Abuelita: Celebrating the Day of the Dead. Chapman, Robert, illus. 1998. Tr. of Un Regalo para Abuelita: En Celebration del Dia de los Muertos. (ENG & SPA.). 32p. (gr. k-3). 15.95 (978-0-87358-688-7(3) , Rising Moon Bks. for Young Readers) Northland Publishing.

Lynch, Chris. Freewill. 2002. 160p. (J). (gr. 8 up). pap. 6.99 (978-0-06-447202-9(7)) HarperCollins Pubs.

—Freewill. 2002. 148p. (YA). (gr. 8-12). lib. bdg. 15.30 (978-0-613-56380-2(8)) Tandem Library Bks.

MacLachlan, Patricia. Edward's Eyes. 2007. 128p. (J). (gr. 3-7). 15.99 (***978-1-4169-2743-3(3)*** , Atheneum) Simon & Schuster Children's Publishing.

Maddern, Eric. Death in a Nut. Hess, Paul, illus. 2005. 32p. (J). 15.95 (978-1-84507-081-6(X)) Lincoln, Frances Ltd. GBR. *Dist:* Perseus Distribution.

Mangal, Roshni. The Stray Bullet. Hammond, Amanda, illus. 1999. 48p. (J). (ps-3). pap. 17.95 (978-0-9644695-3-2(7)) Image Maker Publishing Co., The.

Mangum, Kay Lynn. A Love Like Lilly. 2006. 336p. (YA). pap. 15.95 (978-1-59038-580-7(2)) Deseret Bk. Co.

Manning, Sarra. Let's Get Lost. 2006. 320p. (YA). (gr. 9). 16.99 (978-0-525-47666-5(0) , Dutton Juvenile) Penguin Group (USA) Inc.

Manns, Nick. Dead Negative. 2003. mass mkt. (978-0-340-85566-9(5) , Hodder Children's Books) Hodder Children's Division.

Mansfield, Katherine. The Garden Party. l.t. ed. 2006. pap. (***978-1-84702-354-4(1)***) Echo Library.

Mansur, Motesem. The Terry Tornado Story: The Wake-up Call. 2004. 25p. pap. 14.95 (978-1-4137-2133-1(8)) PublishAmerica, Inc.

Marsh, Katherine. The Night Tourist. rev. ed. 2007. 240p. (YA). (gr. 7 up). 17.99 (***978-1-4231-0689-0(X)***) Hyperion Pr.

Martin, Ann M. Sunny: Diary Three. 1999. (California Diaries: Bk. 12). 160p. (YA). (gr. 6-8). pap. 4.50 (978-0-590-02390-0(X)) Scholastic, Inc.

—Sunny: Diary Three. 1999. (California Diaries: Bk. 12). (Illus.). (YA). (gr. 6-8). (978-0-606-18523-3(2)) Tandem Library Bks.

Martin, Cheryl. I Love You, Son. 2004. pap. 7.95 (978-0-533-14673-4(9)) Vantage Pr., Inc.

Martinez, Agnes. Poe Park. 2004. 128p. (J). (ps-7). tchr. ed. 16.95 (978-0-8234-1834-3(0)) Holiday Hse., Inc.

Mass, Wendy. A Mango-Shaped Space. 2005. 240p. (J). (gr. 5-8). pap. 6.99 (978-0-316-05825-4(4)) Little Brown & Co.

Masson, Sophie. Sooner or Later. 115p. pap. 11.95 (978-0-7022-2336-5(0)) Univ. of Queensland Pr. AUS. *Dist:* International Specialized Bk. Services.

Masters, Susan Rowan. Summer Song. 2000. 148p. (YA). (gr. 4-7). pap. 9.95 (978-0-595-14407-5(1)) iUniverse, Inc.

Matthews, Kezi. Flying Lessons. 2002. 160p. (J). (gr. 5-9). 16.95 (978-0-8126-2671-1(0)) Cricket Bks.

Mayfield, Sue. On Eagles' Wings. 2004. 144p. (J). pap. 8.99 (***978-0-7459-4890-4(1)***) Lion Hudson plc GBR. *Dist:* Independent Pubs. Group.

Mazer, Norma Fox. After the Rain. l.t. ed. 2005. 359p. (YA). pap. 10.95 (978-0-7862-7913-5(3)) Thorndike Pr.

—Girlhearts. 2001. 224p. (J). (gr. 5 up). 15.99 (978-0-688-13350-4(9)) HarperCollins Pubs.

—Girlhearts. 2002. (gr. 7-12). lib. bdg. 15.30 (978-0-613-58571-2(2)) Tandem Library Bks.

—When She Was Good. 2000. (Illus.). 240p. (J). (gr. 7 up). pap. 5.99 (978-0-590-31990-4(6) , Scholastic Paperbacks) Scholastic, Inc.

McCombie, Karen. Indie Kidd: Are We Having Fun Yet? (Hmmm?) Monks, Lydia, illus. 2008. (J). ***(*978-0-440-42201-3(9));*** 160p. (gr. 2-5). lib. bdg. 9.99 ***(*978-0-440-42202-0(7))*** Random Hse. Children's Bks. (Yearling).

McDaniel, Lurlene. Always & Forever. 2004. 352p. (YA). (gr. 7). pap. 7.50 (978-0-553-49419-8(8) , Laurel Leaf) Random Hse. Children's Bks.

—Briana's Gift. 2006. 176p. (YA). (gr. 7). 10.95 (978-0-385-73160-7(4)); lib. bdg. 12.99 (978-0-385-90197-0(6)) Random Hse. Children's Bks. (Delacorte Bks. for Young Readers).

—Dawn Rochelle: Four Novels. 2000. (Dawn Rochelle Ser.). (Illus.). (J). (978-0-606-17994-2(1)) Tandem Library Bks.

—The Girl Death Left Behind. 1999. 192p. (YA). (gr. 7-12). pap. 5.50 (978-0-553-57091-5(9) , Laurel Leaf) Random Hse. Children's Bks.

—The Girl Death Left Behind. 1999. (J). 11.64 (978-0-606-16371-2(9)); (gr. 7-12). lib. bdg. 13.00 (978-0-613-16116-9(5)) Tandem Library Bks.

—How Do I Love Thee: Three Stories. 272p. (YA). (gr. 7). 2002. pap. 5.50 (978-0-553-57107-3(9) , Laurel Leaf); 2001. 9.95 (978-0-553-57154-7(0) , Starfire) Random Hse. Children's Bks.

—I Want to Live. 2005. (Dawn Rochelle Ser.: No. 2). (Illus.). 160p. (gr. 6-12). reprint ed. pap. 4.99 (978-1-58196-004-4(2)) Lerner Publishing Group.

—I Want to Live. 2003. (Dawn Rochelle Ser.: No. 2). (gr. 7-12). lib. bdg. 13.00 (978-0-613-84378-2(9)) Tandem Library Bks.

—Kathleen's Story. (Angels in Pink Ser.). (YA). 2006. 256p. mass mkt. 6.50 (978-0-440-23865-2(X) , Laurel Leaf); 2004. 240p. (gr. 7). 10.95 (978-0-385-73156-0(6) , Delacorte Bks. for Young Readers); 2004. 240p. (gr. 7). lib. bdg. 12.99 (978-0-385-90193-2(3) , Delacorte Bks. for Young Readers) Random Hse. Children's Bks.

—Mother, Please Don't Die. 2005. 128p. (Orig.). (J). (gr. 5-8). pap. 4.99 (978-1-58196-028-0(X)) Darby Creek Publishing.

—One Last Wish: Three Novels: Mother, Help Me Live; Let Him Live; Sixteen & Dying. 1998. (One Last Wish Ser.). (gr. 7-12). lib. bdg. 15.30 (978-0-613-88880-6(4)) Tandem Library Bks.

—Six Months to Live. 2005. (Dawn Rochelle Ser.: No. 1). (Illus.). 160p. (gr. 6-12). reprint ed. pap. 4.99 (978-1-58196-003-7(4)) Lerner Publishing Group.

—Six Months to Live. 2003. (Dawn Rochelle Ser.: No. 1). (gr. 7-12). lib. bdg. 13.00 (978-0-613-82291-6(9)) Tandem Library Bks.

—To Live Again. 2001. (Dawn Rochelle Ser.: No. 5). (YA). (978-0-606-21491-9(7)) Tandem Library Bks.

—Why Did She Have to Die? 2005. 128p. (J). (gr. 6-12). pap. 4.99 (978-1-58196-029-7(8)) Darby Creek Publishing.

McDonald, Joyce. Swallowing Stones. 1999. 272p. (YA). (gr. 7-12). mass mkt. 6.99 (978-0-440-22672-7(4) , Laurel Leaf) Random Hse. Children's Bks.

—Swallowing Stones. 1999. 245p. lib. bdg. 13.55 (978-0-606-16721-5(8)); (gr. 7-12). lib. bdg. 13.55 (978-0-613-19465-5(9)) Tandem Library Bks.

McFarlane, Sheryl. Waiting for the Whales. 1998. (gr. k-3). lib. bdg. 16.40 (978-0-613-86453-4(0)) Tandem Library Bks.

McGhee, Alison. All Rivers Flow to the Sea. 176p. (YA). (gr. 9 up). 2007. (Illus.). pap. 7.99 ***(*978-0-7636-3372-1(0));*** 2005. 15.99 (978-0-7636-2591-7(4)) Candlewick Pr.

McGhee, Alison. Snap. 2006. 144p. (J). (gr. 4-7). reprint ed. pap. 5.99 (978-0-7636-2617-4(1)) Candlewick Pr.

Mckeever Stacia & Beyer Ingrid. Why Is Keiko Sick? 2006. 32p. 12.99 (978-0-89051-463-4(1)) Master Bks.

McLaughlin, Kirsten. The Memory Box. Rudolph, Adrienne, illus. 2000. (J). 5.95 (978-1-56123-136-2(3) , MEBC) Centering Corp.

McMillion, Gloria. Whirlwinds Whirl Around. 2007. 136p. per. 11.95 ***(*978-0-595-42248-7(9))*** iUniverse, Inc.

McNish, Cliff. Breathe: A Ghost Story 2006. 264p. (J). 15.95 (978-0-8225-6443-0(2) , Carolrhoda Bks.) Lerner Publishing Group.

Mendes, Valerie. Lost & Found. 2004. 256p. pap. 8.99 (978-0-689-86049-2(8)) Simon & Schuster, Ltd. GBR. *Dist:* Independent Pubs. Group.

Messer, Celeste M. Forever & Always. Hoeffner, Deb, illus. 2004. 82-92p. 4.95 (978-0-9710145-0-3(7)) AshleyAlan Enterprises.

Metzger, Lois. Missing Girls. 2001. (J). (978-0-606-21334-9(1)) Tandem Library Bks.

Michaels, Rune. Genesis Alpha. 2007. 208p. (YA). (gr. 7-10). 14.99 (978-1-4169-1886-8(8) , Ginne Seo Bks) Simon & Schuster Children's Publishing.

Miller, Mary Beth. Aimee. 2004. (Illus.). 288p. (YA). (gr. 9). pap. 6.99 (978-0-14-240025-8(4) , Puffin) Penguin Group (USA) Inc.

—Aimee. 2004. (gr. 7-12). lib. bdg. 15.30 (978-0-613-89043-4(4)) Tandem Library Bks.

Mills, Joyce C. Gentle Willow: A Story for Children about Dying. Pillo, Cary, illus. 2nd ed. 2004. 32p. (J). 14.95 (978-1-59147-071-7(4)); pap. 8.95 (978-1-59147-072-4(2)) American Psychological Assn. (Magination Pr.).

Miracles, Max. Los Milagros de Max. Rubio, Gabriela, illus. (SPA.). 84p. (J). (978-84-392-8700-1(3)) Gaviota Ediciones ESP. *Dist:* Lectorum Pubns., Inc.

Mitchell, Marianne. Finding Zola. 144p. 2005. (J). (ps-7). pap. 9.95 (978-1-59078-370-2(0)); 2003. (Illus.). (YA). (gr. 4-6). 16.95 (978-1-59078-070-1(1)) Boyds Mills Pr.

Monk, Isabell. Blackberry Stew. Porter, Janice Lee, illus. 2005. 32p. (J). (ps-ps). lib. bdg. 15.95 (978-1-57505-605-0(4)) Lerner Publishing Group.

Montoya, Louis R. Camilla. 2007. (J). pap. 8.00 ***(*978-0-8059-7424-9(5))*** Dorrance Publishing Co., Inc.

Morgenroth, Kate. Echo. 2007. 144p. (YA). pap. 15.99 (978-1-4169-1438-9(2)) Simon & Schuster Children's Publishing.

Moyer, Bernadette A. Angel Stacey Earth Angel to Guardian Angel - Daddy in Heaven, It Is Me, Your Daughter. Moyer, Ariane M., illus. 1998. 96p. (J). (ps-6). pap. 20.95 (978-0-9666183-9-6(4)) Two Bee-A-TwinBee Publishing, LLC.

Murphy, Barbara. Life! How I Love You! Baca, Elena, illus. 2004. (Museo Kids Ser.). 1p. 16.95 (978-0-89013-468-9(5)) Museum of New Mexico Pr.

Newth, Mette. The Dark Light. Ingwersen, Faith, tr. 2004. 256p. (YA). reprint ed. pap. 6.95 (978-0-374-41688-1(5) , Sunburst) Farrar, Straus & Giroux.

Nobisso, Josephine. Grandpa Loved. Hyde, Maureen, illus. 2nd rev. ed. 2000. 32p. (J). (gr. 2 up). pap. 8.95 (978-0-940112-04-9(3)); reprint ed. 16.95 (978-0-940112-01-8(9)) Gingerbread Hse.

—Grandpa Loved. 2000. (gr. k-3). lib. bdg. 17.60 (978-0-613-70807-4(5)) Tandem Library Bks.

Noel, Alyson. Saving Zoe: A Novel. 2007. 240p. (YA). (gr. 8 up). pap. 8.95 ***(*978-0-312-35510-4(6)*** , St. Martin's Griffin) St. Martin's Pr.

Nora, David, Jr. Happy Balloon to You. 2005. 9.00 (978-0-8059-9870-2(5)) Dorrance Publishing Co., Inc.

Oates, Joyce Carol. After the Wreck, I Picked Myself up, Spread My Wings, & Flew Away. 2007. 320p. (J). (gr. 9 up). pap. 7.99 ***(*978-0-06-073527-2(9));*** 2006. 304p. (YA). lib. bdg. 17.89 (978-0-06-073526-5(0)) HarperCollins Pubs. (HarperTeen).

Oates, Joyce Carol. After the Wreck, I Picked Myself Up, Spread My Wings, & Flew Away. 2006. 304p. (YA). 16.99 (978-0-06-073525-8(2) , HarperTeen) HarperCollins Pubs.

Oliviero, Jamie. Som See & the Magic Elephant. Kelly, Jo'Anne, illus. 2005. 27p. (J). (ps-2). reprint ed. 17.00 (978-0-7567-8929-9(X)) DIANE Publishing Co.

Osborn, Kelly. The Green Knight. 2006. 64p. pap. 12.95 (978-1-4241-1741-3(0)) PublishAmerica, Inc.

Owens, Connie S. My Heart Is Sad: When Someone Special Dies. 2005. pap. 7.99 (978-1-59317-088-2(2)) Warner Pr. Pubs.

Park, Barbara. Mick Harte Was Here. 88p. (J). (gr. 4-6). pap. 4.99 (978-0-8072-1502-9(3) , Listening Library) Random Hse. Audio Publishing Group.

Park, Barbara, ed. Mick Harte Was Here. unabr. ed. 2004. (Middle Grade Cassette Librariestm Ser.). 88p. (J). (gr. 3-7). pap. 29.00 incl. audio (978-0-8072-7797-3(5) , S YA 922 SP, Listening Library) Random Hse. Audio Publishing Group.

Parkinson, Siobhan. Second Fiddle: Or How to Tell a Blackbird from a Sausage. 2007. 192p. (J). (gr. 6-9). 16.95 (978-1-59643-122-5(9)) Roaring Brook Pr.

Pastor, Melanie Joy. Wishes for One More Day. Grantford, Jacqui, illus. 2006. 32p. (J). 15.95 (978-0-9729225-7-9(1)) Flashlight Pr.

Paterson, Katherine. Bridge to Terabithia. Diamond, Donna, illus. 2002. (J). 14.47 (978-0-7587-0003-2(2)) Book Wholesalers, Inc.

—Bridge to Terabithia. Diamond, Donna, illus. (J). 2005. 208p. (gr. 7 up). pap. 6.99 (978-0-06-073401-5(9) , Harper Trophy); 2007. 176p. pap. 6.99 (978-0-06-122728-8(5)) HarperCollins Pubs.

—Bridge to Terabithia. Diamond, Donna, illus. l.t. ed. 1999. (LRS Large Print Cornerstone Ser.). 250p. (YA). (gr. 5-12). lib. bdg. 28.95 (978-1-58118-053-4(5) , 22769) LRS.

—Bridge to Terabithia. Diamond, Donna, illus. 1998. (J). pap. 3.95 (978-0-439-04477-6(4)) Scholastic, Inc.

—Bridge to Terabithia Movie Tie-in Edition (rack) Diamond, Donna, illus. 2007. 208p. (J). pap. 6.99 (978-0-06-125370-6(7) , Harper Entertainment) HarperCollins Pubs.

—Un Puente Hasta Terabithia. 1999. (SPA.). (gr. 5-8). lib. bdg. 17.60 (978-0-613-64582-9(0)) Tandem Library Bks.

Pérez, Alfredo. Sueno de Novela. (SPA.). (J). 8.95 (978-958-04 6870-7(2)) Norma S.A. COL. *Dist:* Distribuidora Norma, Inc.

Perry, Sarah. Clara's Road. 2005. 64p. (J). per. (978-1-55306-945-4(5) , Epic Pr.) Essence Publishing.

Pickard, W. Raymond. When an Angel Cries: (but I Don't Want to Be an Angel) 2006. 67p. pap. 14.95 (978-1-4241-0243-3(X)) PublishAmerica, Inc.

Pittar, Gill. Milly, Molly & Jimmy's Seeds (book W/dolls) 2006. 28p. pap. (978-1-86972-091-9(1)) Milly Molly Bks.

Portnoy, Mindy Avra. Where Do People Go When They Die? Haas, Shelly O., illus. 2004. (Carolrhoda Picture Books Ser.). 24p. (J). (ps-3). 15.95 (978-1-58013-081-3(X)) Kar-Ben Publishing.

Potter, Ellen. Olivia Kidney & the Exit Academy. Reynolds, Peter H., illus. 2005. 256p. (J). (gr. 4-6). 15.99 (978-0-399-24162-8(0) , Philomel) Penguin Group (USA) Inc.

Prestine, Joan Singleton. Someone Special Died. Kylberg, Virginia, illus. 2002. 32p. (J). pap. 6.95 (978-1-57768-655-2(1)) School Specialty Publishing.

Price, Dianne D. Enemy in the House: The Story of a Young Friendship Born of War in America. 2003. 123p. pap. 14.95 (978-1-59286-483-6(X)) PublishAmerica, Inc.

Price, Reynolds. A Perfect Friend. 2002. 176p. pap. 11.00 (978-0-7432-2521-2(X) , Scribner) Simon & Schuster.

—A Perfect Friend. l.t. ed. 2001. 150p. (J). (gr. 4-7). 21.95 (978-0-7862-3589-6(0)) Thorndike Pr.

Prose, Francine. Bullyville. 2007. 272p. (J). (gr. 5-8). 16.99 ***(*978-0-06-057497-0(6));*** lib. bdg. 17.89 ***(*978-0-06-057498-7(4))*** HarperCollins Pubs. (HarperTeen).

Qualey, Marsha. Thin Ice. 2007. (YA). ***(*978-0-9793444-0-4(9))*** Quercus Pr.

—Thin Ice. 1999. (978-0-606-17348-3(X)) Tandem Library Bks.

Rabb, Margo. Cures for Heartbreak. 2007. 256p. (YA). (gr. 9). 15.99 (978-0-385-73402-8(6)); lib. bdg. 18.99 (978-0-385-90414-8(2)) Random Hse. Children's Bks. (Delacorte Bks. for Young Readers).

Ramos, Ian. Adventures of the G.C. Boys: The Cure for Death. 2001. 188p. (J). pap. 19.95 (978-1-58851-040-2(9)) PublishAmerica, Inc.

Ranulfo. Joker. 2006. 208p. (J). 15.99 (978-0-06-054158-3(X)); lib. bdg. 16.89 (978-0-06-054159-0(8)) HarperCollins Pubs. (Cotler, Joanna Books).

Raphael, Taffy E. Missing May. 2002. (Book Club Novel Guide Ser.). 48p. 17.95 (978-1-931376-08-2(5)) Small Planet Communications, Inc.

Rapp, Adam. Under the Wolf, under the Dog. 320p. (YA). (gr. 9). 2007. pap. 8.99 (978-0-7636-3365-3(8)); 2004. 16.99 (978-0-7636-1818-6(7)) Candlewick Pr.

Raschka, Chris. The Purple Balloon. 2007. (Illus.). 32p. (J). (ps-2). 16.99 (978-0-375-84146-0(6)); lib. bdg. 19.99 (978-0-375-94259-4(9)) Random Hse. Children's Bks. (Schwartz & Wade Bks.).

Regenold, Theresa. Not Your Average Princess: A Real-Life Fairy Tale. 2005. 117p. pap. 16.95 (978-1-4137-9308-6(8)) PublishAmerica, Inc.

Rivers, Karen. Surviving Sam. 2002. (Illus.). 176p. (YA). (gr. 9 up). pap. 6.95 (978-1-55192-506-6(0)) Raincoast Bk. Distribution CAN. *Dist:* Perseus Distribution.

Roberts, Willo Davis. The One Left Behind. (J). 2007. 139p. (gr. 3-7). per. 5.99 (978-0-689-85083-7(2)); 2006. (Illus.). 144p. 16.95 (978-0-689-85075-2(1) , Atheneum) Simon & Schuster Children's Publishing.

Rodowsky, Colby. The Turnabout Shop. 2000. (978-0-606-17885-3(6)) Tandem Library Bks.

Roper, Janice. Dancing on the Moon. Grimm, Laurence G., illus. 2001. iv, 31p. (J). (ps-3). 19.95 (978-0-9641218-6-7(7)) SIDS Educational Services, Inc.

Rosen, Michael. Lovely Old Roly. Lamont, Priscilla, illus. 2004. (J). 25p. (978-0-7112-1488-0(3)); 32p. pap. 7.95 (978-1-84507-144-8(1)) Lincoln, Frances Ltd. GBR. *Dist:* Transition Vendor, Perseus Distribution.

—Michael Rosen's Sad Book. Blake, Quentin, illus. 2005. 32p. (J). 16.99 (978-0-7636-2597-9(3)) Candlewick Pr.

Rosenbloom, Eileen. Stuck Down. 2005. 240p. pap. 8.95 (978-0-7387-0658-0(2)) Llewellyn Pubns.

Rozek, Kathy. Rudy & the Magical Twin Balloons. 2002. 32p. (J). 15.95 (978-0-9720871-0-0(9)) Brookline Merrimac Pubs.

Runyon, Brent. Maybe. 2006. 208p. (YA). (gr. 9). 18.99 (978-0-375-93543-5(6)); 16.95 (978-0-375-83543-8(1)) Random Hse. Children's Bks. (Knopf Bks. for Young Readers).

Rutledge, Linda Austin. Without Dad: Written & Illustrated by Linda Austin Rutledge. 2002. (gr. 7-12). lib. bdg. 20.50 (978-0-613-74649-6(X)) Tandem Library Bks.

Ryan, Patrick. Saints of Augustine. 2007. 320p. (J). lib. bdg. 17.89 ***(*978-0-06-085811-7(7));*** (gr. 7 up). 16.99 ***(*978-0-06-085810-0(9))*** HarperCollins Pubs. (HarperTeen).

Rylant, Cynthia. The Heavenly Village: A Novel. 1999. 96p. (J). (gr. 5-9). pap. 15.95 (978-0-439-04096-9(5) , Blue Sky Pr., The) Scholastic, Inc.

—The Heavenly Village: A Novel. 2000. (gr. 5-8). lib. bdg. 13.00 (978-0-613-53819-0(6)) Tandem Library Bks.

—Missing May. unabr. ed. 2004. 89p. (J). (gr. 5 up). pap. 29.00 incl. audio (978-0-8072-8701-9(6) , YA240SP, Listening Library) Random Hse. Audio Publishing Group.

—Missing May. 2004. 112p. (J). pap. 5.99 (978-0-439-61383-5(3) , Scholastic Paperbacks) Scholastic, Inc.

Saenz, Benjamin Alire. Sammy & Juliana in Hollywood. 2006. 368p. (J). pap. 7.99 (978-0-06-084374-8(8)) HarperCollins Pubs.

Salonen, Roxane Beauclair. First Salmon. 2005. (Illus.). 29p. (J). (gr. 3-7). 15.95 (978-1-59078-171-5(6)) Boyds Mills Pr.

Sample, Jewel. Flying Hugs & Kisses Activity Book. 2007. (J). per. 10.99 ***(*978-1-59879-377-2(2))*** Lifevest Publishing, Inc.

Schick, Eleanor. Mama. 2000. (Accelerated Reader Bks.). (Illus.). 32p. (J). (gr. k-3). 15.95 (978-0-7614-5060-3(2) , Cavendish Children's Bks.) Cavendish, Marshall Corp.

Schroeder, Lisa. I Heart You, You Haunt Me. 2008. 240p. (YA). pap. 7.99 ***(*978-1-4169-5520-7(8)*** , Simon Pulse) Simon & Schuster Children's Publishing.

Schwiebert, Pat. We Were Gonna Have a Baby, but We Had an Angel Instead. Bills, Taylor, illus. 2004. 24p. pap. 7.95 (978-0-9724241-1-0(3) , 717) Perinatal Loss.

Scott, James. Flowers for Algernon: Reproducible Teaching Unit. 1999. 43p. tchr. ed., ring bd. 29.50 (978-1-58049-088-7(3) , TU85) Prestwick Hse., Inc.

Seidler, Tor. Brothers below Zero. McCarty, Peter, illus. 2003. 144p. (J). (gr. 5 up). pap. 5.99 (978-0-06-440936-0(8) , Harper Trophy) HarperCollins Pubs.

—Brothers below Zero. 2002. (Illus.). 144p. (J). (gr. 3 up). 14.95 (978-0-06-029179-2(6) , Geringer, Laura Book) HarperCollins Pubs.

—Brothers below Zero. McCarty, Peter, illus. 2002. 144p. (J). (gr. 5 up). lib. bdg. 15.89 (978-0-06-029180-8(X) , Geringer, Laura Book) HarperCollins Pubs.

—Brothers below Zero. 2003. (gr. 3-6). lib. bdg. 14.15 (978-0-613-57705-2(1)) Tandem Library Bks.

Seuffert, Marie. Tiny Red's Trip to Earth. Palmer, Frances, illus. 2002. 32p. (J). (ps-1). 12.95 (978-0-9639838-7-9(3)) Little Treasure Pubns., Inc.

Sherrard, Valerie. Kate. 2004. 200p. pap. 8.99 (978-1-55002-476-0(0)) Dundurn Group, The CAN. *Dist:* Univ. of Toronto Pr.

—Kate. 2003. (gr. 7-12). lib. bdg. 17.60 (978-0-613-88193-7(1)) Tandem Library Bks.

Shewver, Margaret. Without a Trace & Other Stories. 2005. 91p. (YA). (gr. 6-12). pap. 17.95 (978-0-936389-59-2(1)) Tudor Pubs., Inc.

Shriver, Maria. What's Heaven? ed. 2004. (Illus.). (J). (gr. k-3). spiral bd. (978-0-616-03056-1(8)) Canadian National Institute for the Blind/Institut National Canadien pour les Aveugles.

—What's Heaven? Speidel, Sandra, illus. 1999. (J). 15.00 (978-1-58238-100-8(3)); 10th ed. 32p. reprint ed. 15.00 (978-0-307-44043-3(5) , NHC 0190) St. Martin's Pr. (Golden Bks. Adult Publishing Group).

Shusterman, Neal. Everlost. 2007. 384p. (YA). mass mkt. 6.99 ***(*978-0-689-87238-9(0)*** , Simon Pulse); 2006. 320p. (J). (gr. 7 up). 16.95 (978-0-689-87237-2(2)) Simon & Schuster Children's Publishing.

Slade, Arthur. Megiddo's Shadow. 2006. (Illus.). 304p. (J). (gr. 7). 15.95 (978-0-385-74701-1(2) , Lamb, Wendy) Random Hse. Children's Bks.

Sleator, William. The Boy Who Couldn't Die. 2004. 174p. (J). (gr. 7-11). 16.95 (978-0-8109-4824-2(9)) Abrams, Harry N. , Inc.

Smith, Cynthia Leitich. Rain Is Not My Indian Name. Earley, Lori, illus. 2001. 144p. (J). (gr. 5-9). 16.99 (978-0-688-17397-5(7)) HarperCollins Pubs.

Smith, Jane Denitz. Mary by Myself. 1999. (J). (978-0-606-16701-7(3)) Tandem Library Bks.

Smith, Patricia. Janna & the Kings. Boyd, Aaron, illus. 2003. 32p. (J). 16.95 (978-1-58430-088-5(4)) Lee & Low Bks., Inc.

Smith, Walter. Grandad's Ashes. 2007. (Illus.). 32p. (J). ***(*978-1-84310-517-6(9))*** Kingsley, Jessica Ltd.

Sneve, Virginia Driving Hawk. Lana's Lakota Moons. 2007. (Illus.). 127p. (J). (gr. 3 up). pap. 12.95 ***(*978-0-8032-6028-3(8))*** Univ. of Nebraska Pr.

Snyder, Zilpha Keatley. Spyhole Secrets. 2005. 192p. (J). (gr. 3-7). pap. 5.99 (978-0-440-41708-8(2) , Yearling) Random Hse. Children's Bks.

—Spyhole Secrets. 2002. (gr. 3-6). lib. bdg. 13.00 (978-0-613-88326-9(8)) Tandem Library Bks.

Sophie Maye. 2000. (Illus.). 20p. (J). (gr. k-3). pap. 10.00 (978-0-9679561-1-4(0)); 18.00 (978-0-9679561-0-7(2)) Debbie-Lou Productions.

Soros, Barbara. Grandmother's Song. Morris, Jackie, illus. 1998. 32p. (J). (gr. 3-7). 15.95 (978-1-902283-02-9(3)) Barefoot Bks., Inc.

Spencer, Katherine. Saving Grace. (Saving Grace Ser.). (Illus.). 256p. (YA). 2007. pap. 6.95 ***(*978-0-15-206096-1(0)*** , Harcourt Paperbacks); 2006. 15.00 (978-0-15-205740-4(4)) Harcourt Children's Bks.

Spillebeen, Geert. Kipling's Choice. Edelstein, Terese, tr. 160p. (YA). (gr. 7 up). 2007. pap. 7.99 ***(*978-0-618-80035-3(2)*** , Graphia); 2005. 16.00 (978-0-618-43124-3(1)) Houghton Mifflin Co. Trade & Reference Div.

Springer, Nancy. Sky Rider. 2000. 128p. (J). (gr. 7 up). pap. 4.95 (978-0-380-79565-9(5) , Harper Trophy) HarperCollins Pubs.

Steele, James M. Sadie Listens: An Inward Journey. l.t. ed. 2003. (Inward Journey Ser.: Vol. 1). (Illus.). iv, 48p. 17.95 (978-0-9716811-3-2(9)) Steele Studios.

Sternthal, Sherry. How Do You Get to Heaven? Thornton-Haas, Barbara, illus. 2000. 36p. (J). (gr. 3-9). pap. 11.95 (978-0-9700375-0-3(3)) Schlifer, Sherry.

Stone, B. J. Ola's Wake. 2002. (gr. 3-6). lib. bdg. 12.40 (978-0-613-55345-2(4)) Tandem Library Bks.

Stroud, Jonathan. The Leap. 2004. 240p. (gr. 5-17). pap. 6.95 (978-0-7868-5195-9(3)) Miramax Bks.

Sweeney, Joyce. Spirit Window. 1999. (978-0-606-16717-8(X)) Tandem Library Bks.

Thong, Roseanne. The Wishing Tree. McLennan, Connie, illus. 2004. 32p. (J). 16.95 (978-1-885008-26-8(0)) Shen's Bks.

Thottam, Meena, adapted by. Death, Where are You? 2006. (J). 3.95 ***(*978-0-9776917-5-3(6)*** , Curcumin Bks.) Davlaw Press.

Tolan, Stephanie S. Listen! 2006. 208p. (J). 15.99 (978-0-06-057935-7(8)); lib. bdg. 16.89 (978-0-06-057936-4(6)) HarperCollins Pubs.

Toledo, Natalia. Light Foot/Pies Ligeros. Amado, Elisa, tr. from CAI. Toledo, Francisco, illus. 2007. (ENG & SPA.). 56p. (gr. 1 up). 17.95 ***(*978-0-88899-789-0(2))*** Groundwood Bks. CAN. *Dist:* Perseus Distribution.

Tomey, Ingrid. Grandfather's Day. 2001. (J). 16.75 (978-0-606-20682-2(5)); (gr. 3-6). lib. bdg. 18.75 (978-0-613-63598-1(1)) Tandem Library Bks.

Town, Nathan. Ned Stapleton & the Wrath of the Death Gods. 2006. 174p. (YA). ***(*978-0-9781040-0-9(5))*** Emerald City Storytellers.

Trembath, Don. Rooster. 2005. 208p. (J). (gr. 7-12). pap. 7.95 (978-1-55143-261-8(7)) Orca Bk. Pubs. USA.

Turner, Ann. Hard Hit. l.t. ed. 2006. (YA). 21.95 (978-0-7862-8745-1(4)) Thorndike Pr.

Turner, Ann Warren. Hard Hit. 2006. 128p. (J). (gr. 7 up). pap. 16.99 (978-0-439-29680-9(3)) Scholastic, Inc.

Umphenour, Terry. Across a Broken Sky. 2001. 176p. (YA). pap. 12.95 (978-0-595-17949-7(5) , Writer's Showcase Pr.) iUniverse, Inc.

Valentine, Jenny. Me, the Missing, & the Dead. 2008. 208p. (J). 16.99 ***(*978-0-06-085068-5(X));*** lib. bdg. 17.89 ***(*978-0-06-085069-2(8))*** HarperCollins Pubs.

Van Steenwyk, Elizabeth. Three Dog Winter. 1999. (978-0-606-16440-5(5)) Tandem Library Bks.

VanHook, Natalie. The Little Fish Who Prayed. 2002. (Illus.). 36p. (J). per. 5.95 (978-1-930648-36-4(7)) Goose River Pr.

Velde, Vivian Vande. Remembering Raquel. 2007. (Illus.). 160p. (YA). (gr. 7 up). 16.00 ***(*978-0-15-205976-7(8))*** Harcourt Trade Pubs.

Viorst, Judith. The Tenth Good Thing about Barney. Cruz, Ray, illus. 2002. (J). 13.40 (978-0-7587-3778-6(5)) Book Wholesalers, Inc.

Volponi, Paul. Rooftop. (gr. 7). 2007. 224p. (J). pap. 6.99 (978-0-14-240844-5(1) , Puffin); 2006. 208p. (YA). 15.99 (978-0-670-06069-6(0) , Viking Adult) Penguin Group (USA) Inc.

Walde, Christine. The Candy Darlings. 2006. 320p. (YA). (gr. 10). pap. 8.99 (978-0-618-58969-2(4) , Graphia) Houghton Mifflin Co. Trade & Reference Div.

Walker, Pamela. Pray Hard. 2001. 176p. (Illus.). (J). (gr. 4-7). pap. 15.95 (978-0-439-21586-2(2)); (YA). (gr. 5-9). pap. 4.50 (978-0-439-21587-9(0) , Scholastic Pr.) Scholastic, Inc.

Wallace, Bill. No Dogs Allowed! 2004. 214p. (J). (gr. 4-6). tchr. ed. 16.95 (978-0-8234-1818-3(9)) Holiday Hse., Inc.

Wallace-Brodeur, Ruth. Blue Eyes Better. 2003. (Illus.). 112p. (J). (gr. 4-7). pap. 5.99 (978-0-14-250086-6(0) , Puffin) Penguin Group (USA) Inc.

—Blue Eyes Better. 2003. (gr. 5-8). lib. bdg. 14.15 (978-0-613-67139-2(2)) Tandem Library Bks.

Walters, Eric & Spreekmeester, Kevin. Death by Exposure: An Interactive Mystery. 2005. (Illus.). 64p. (YA). pap. (978-0-88878-442-1(2) , Sandcastle Bks.) Dundurn Group, The.

Warfel, Elizabeth Stuart. The Blue Pearls. Giarrusso, Veronique, illus. 2001. 32p. (J). (gr. k-4). 16.99 (978-1-902283-78-4(3)) Barefoot Bks., Inc.

Warner, Sally. This Isn't about the Money. 2002. 224p. (J). (gr. 3-6). 15.99 (978-0-670-03574-8(2) , Viking Juvenile) Penguin Group (USA) Inc.

Weigelt, Udo. Bear's Last Journey. Kazeroid, Sibylle, tr. from GER. Kadmon, Cristina, illus. 2003. 32p. (J). (gr. k-3). 15.95 (978-0-7358-1799-9(5)) North-South Bks., Inc.

Weigelt, Udo. Bears Last Journey. Kadmon, Christina, illus. 2007. 0032p. pap. 6.95 (***978-0-7358-2155-2(0)***) North-South Bks., Inc.

Wheeler, Karla. Timmy's Christmas Surprise. Wheeler, Jenny Lee, illus. l.t. ed. 2001. 24p. 4.95 (978-0-9675532-0-7(2)) Quality of Life Publishing Co.

Whelan, Gloria. A Time to Keep Silent. 2004. 144p. (J). pap. 8.00 (978-0-8028-5255-7(6)) Eerdmans, William B. Publishing Co.

—Time to Keep Silent. 2003. (gr. 5-8). lib. bdg. 16.45 (978-0-613-75511-5(1)) Tandem Library Bks.

White, Marjorie Pellegrino. I Don't Have an Uncle Phil Anymore. Kempf, Christine, illus. 1998. 32p. (J). (ps-5). (978-1-55798-559-0(6) , 441-5596, Magination Pr.) American Psychological Assn.

Wiles, Deborah. The Aurora County All-Stars. 2007. (Illus.). 256p. (J). (gr. 5 up). 16.00 (***978-0-15-206068-8(5)***) Harcourt Children's Bks.

—Each Little Bird That Sings. (Illus.). (J). 2005. 272p. 16.00 (978-0-15-205113-6(9)); 2006. 276p. reprint ed. pap. 5.95 (978-0-15-205657-5(2) , Harcourt Paperbacks) Harcourt Children's Bks.

—Love, Ruby Lavender. (Illus.). (J). 2001. 200p. (gr. 3-7). 16.00 (978-0-15-202314-0(3)); 2005. 228p. reprint ed. pap. 5.95 (978-0-15-205478-6(2)) Harcourt Children's Bks. (Gulliver Bks.).

—Love, Ruby Lavender. 2004. 216p. (J). (gr. 3-7). pap. 36.00 incl. audio (978-0-8072-2096-2(5) , Listening Library) Random Hse. Audio Publishing Group.

Williams, Lori Aurelia. Broken China. (YA). (gr. 7 up). 2005. 272p. 16.95 (978-0-689-86878-8(2) , Simon & Schuster Children's Publishing); 2006. 336p. reprint ed. mass mkt. 5.99 (978-1-4169-1618-5(0) , Simon Pulse) Simon & Schuster Children's Publishing.

Wilson, Jacqueline. Vicky Angel. l.t. ed. 2001. (Illus.). 232p. (J). 16.95 (978-0-7540-6165-6(5) , Galaxy Children's Large Print) BBC Audiobooks America.

—Vicky Angel. 2003. (Illus.). 176p. (gr. 3-7). reprint ed. 5.50 (978-0-440-41808-5(9) , Yearling) Random Hse. Children's Bks.

—Vicky Angel. 2003. (gr. 3-6). lib. bdg. 13.00 (978-0-613-88328-3(4)) Tandem Library Bks.

Winn, Laura Rocke. Margie Asks Why Do People Have to Die? 2002. 156p. (J). pap. 9.99 (978-0-8280-1730-5(1) , 132-100) Review & Herald Publishing Assn.

Wittlinger, Ellen. Blind Faith. (YA). 2007. 304p. pap. 8.99 (***978-1-4169-4906-0(2)*** , Simon Pulse); 2006. 288p. (gr. 7 up). 16.99 (978-1-4169-0273-7(2) , Simon & Schuster Children's Publishing) Simon & Schuster Children's Publishing.

Wolff, Virginia. Probably Still Nick Swansen. 2002. (gr. 5-8). lib. bdg. 16.45 (978-0-613-57323-8(4)) Tandem Library Bks.

Wood, Debra. Just A Little Child. Blake, Joshua Aaron, illus. l.t. ed. 2006. 33p. (J). per. 12.95 (978-1-59879-087-0(0)) Lifevest Publishing, Inc.

Wood, Douglas. Grandad's Prayers for the Earth. Lynch, P. J., illus. 1999. 32p. (J). (gr. 1-4). 17.99 (978-0-7636-0660-2(X)) Candlewick Pr.

—Grandad's Prayers of the Earth. Lynch, P. J., illus. 2004. 28p. (J). (gr. k-4). reprint ed. 17.00 (978-0-7567-7101-0(3)) DIANE Publishing Co.

Wood, June Rae. Turtle on a Fence Post. 2001. 272p. (J). pap. 6.99 (978-0-698-11783-9(2) , Putnam Juvenile) Penguin Group (USA) Inc.

Wood, Nancy C. Old Coyote. Grafe, Max, illus. 2004. 32p. (J). (gr. k-3). 16.99 (978-0-7636-1544-4(7)) Candlewick Pr.

Woodson, Jacqueline. Behind You. 128p. (YA). 2006. (gr. 7). pap. 5.99 (978-0-14-240390-7(3) , Puffin); 2004. (gr. 5-12). 15.99 (978-0-399-23988-5(X) , Putnam Juvenile) Penguin Group (USA) Inc.

—Last Summer with Maizon. 2002. 112p. (J). 17.99 (978-0-399-23755-3(0)); (Illus.). (gr. 3-7). pap. 5.99 (978-0-698-11929-1(0)) Penguin Group (USA) Inc. (Putnam Juvenile).

—Last Summer with Maizon. 2002. (gr. 3-6). lib. bdg. 13.00 (978-0-613-45286-1(0)) Tandem Library Bks.

Wooldridge, Frosty. Strike Three! Take Your Base. Petri, Freeman, illus. 2001. 160p. (YA). (gr. 6-12). pap. 6.95 (978-1-930093-07-2(1)) Brookfield Reader, Inc., The.

—Strike Three! Take Your Base. Freeman, Pietri, illus. 2001. 160p. (YA). (gr. 6-12). 16.95 (978-1-930093-01-0(2)) Brookfield Reader, Inc., The.

Wrenn, Elizabeth. The Christmas Cactus. Aitken, Susan, illus. 2001. (J). (978-1-56123-158-4(4)) Centering Corp.

Yeomans, Ellen. Rubber Houses. 2007. 160p. (J). (gr. 7-17). 15.99 (978-0-316-10647-4(X)) Little Brown & Co.

Yoemans, Ellen. Lost & Found: Remembering a Sister. Johnson, Joy, ed. DeRosa, Dee, illus. 2000. 32p. (J). (gr. k-4). pap. 8.95 (978-1-56123-129-4(0) , LAFC) Centering Corp.

Youmans, Marly. Little Jordan. 1999. 112p. (YA). (gr. 7-12). pap. 6.99 (978-0-380-73136-7(3)) HarperCollins Pubs.

Younger, Marshal. The Last Days of Eugene Meltsner. 2000. (Adventures in Odyssey Ser.). (Illus.). 96p. (J). (gr. 3-7). pap. 4.99 (978-1-56179-911-4(4)) Focus on the Family Publishing.

Yumoto, Kazumi. The Letters. 2003. 176p. (YA). (gr. 7). pap. 5.50 (978-0-440-23822-5(6) , Laurel Leaf) Random Hse. Children's Bks.

—Letters. 2003. (gr. 7-12). lib. bdg. 13.55 (978-0-613-72256-8(6)) Tandem Library Bks.

Zalben, Jane Breskin. The Fortuneteller in 5B. 2001. 160p. (gr. 4-7). pap. 11.95 (978-0-595-14657-4(0) , Backinprint.com) iUniverse, Inc.

Zevin, Gabrielle & McGhee, Alison. Elsewhere. 2005. 288p. (YA). (gr. 7-17). 16.00 (978-0-374-32091-1(8)) Farrar, Straus & Giroux.

—Elsewhere. 2007. 304p. (YA). pap. 6.95 (***978-0-312-36746-6(5)***) Square Fish.

Zimmerman, George G. Dougie & the Dane: Chelsea the Great Dane. 2004. (Illus.). 36p. 21.99 (978-1-4134-4139-0(4)) Xlibris Corp.

Zindel, Paul. The Undertaker's Gone Bananas. 1999. mass mkt. (978-0-553-20172-7(7)) Random Hse., Inc.

Zitelman, Jem. Ventures Tested: One Teenager's Story . . . to Happiness. 2000. viii, 206p. (J). 24.95 (978-1-891612-00-8(X) , 9701); pap. 15.95 (978-1-891612-01-5(8) , 9701); lib. bdg. 24.95 (978-1-891612-02-2(6) , 9701) Celjon Bks.

Zusak, Markus. The Book Thief. (YA). (gr. 7 up). 2007. 576p. pap. 11.99 (***978-0-375-84220-7(9)***); 2006. 560p. 16.95 (978-0-375-83100-3(2)); 2006. 560p. lib. bdg. 18.99 (978-0-375-93100-0(7)) Random Hse. Children's Bks. (Knopf Bks. for Young Readers).

DEATH, MERCY

see Euthanasia

DEATH PENALTY

see Capital Punishment

DEATH VALLEY (CALIF. AND NEV.)

Cooper, Jason. Death Valley. Date not set. (Natural Wonders Discovery Library). 24p. (J). (gr. k-4). lib. bdg. 10.95 (978-0-86625-015-3(8)) Rourke Publishing, LLC.

Dell, Pamela. Surviving Death Valley: Desert Adaptation. 2008. (J). (***978-1-4296-1266-1(5)***) Capstone Pr., Inc.

Levinson, Nancy Smiler. Death Valley Level 2: A Day in the Desert. Hearn, Diane Dawson, illus. (Reader Ser.). 32p. (J). (gr. k-3). tchr. ed. 14.95 (978-0-8234-1566-3(X)) Holiday Hse., Inc.

Pancella, Peggy. Death Valley National Park. 2006. (Symbols of Freedom Ser.). (Illus.). 32p. (J). (978-1-4034-7793-4(0)) Heinemann Library.

DEBATES AND DEBATING

see also Parliamentary Practice

Burgett, Cindy. Policy Debate. 2007. (National Forensic League Library of Public Speaking & Debate). (Illus.). 48p. (J). (gr. 5-8). lib. bdg. 26.50 (***978-1-4042-1024-0(5)***) Rosen Publishing Group, Inc., The.

Great Historic Debates & Speeches, 6 Bks, Set. 2004. (J). 175.50 (978-1-4042-0350-1(8)) Rosen Publishing Group, Inc., The.

Hensley, Dana & Carlin, Diana B. Mastering Competitive Debate. 5th ed. 1999. (YA). (gr. 10-12). 38.00 (978-0-931054-58-7(3)); pap. 25.00 (978-0-931054-59-4(1)) Clark Publishing, Inc.

Open for Debate Group 3, 5 bks., Set. Incl. Affirmative Action. Kowalski, Kathiann M. 143p. (J). (gr. 6-9). lib. bdg. 39.93 (978-0-7614-2300-3(1)); Arab-Israeli Conflict. Worth, Richard. 127p. (J). (gr. 7 up). lib. bdg. 39.93 (978-0-7614-2295-2(1)); Marriage. Stefoff, Rebecca. 143p. (YA). (gr. 9 up). lib. bdg. 39.93 (978-0-7614-2299-0(4)); Media Bias. Streissguth, Thomas. 127p. (YA). (gr. 8 up). lib. bdg. 39.93 (978-0-7614-2296-9(X)); Racial Profiling. Kops, Deborah. 127p. (YA). (gr. 6-9). lib. bdg. 39.93 (978-0-7614-2298-3(6)); (Illus.). 2006. 2007. Set lib. bdg. 199.64 (***978-0-7614-2294-5(3)*** , Benchmark Bks.) Cavendish, Marshall Corp.

Orr, Tamra B. Extraordinary Debates. 2006. 128p. (gr. 8-12). pap. 9.95 (978-0-531-13905-9(0) , Watts, Franklin) Scholastic Library Publishing.

Touchstones Discussion Project, prod. Touchpebbles Volume A - Student's Guide, Vol. A. 2003. 76p. per. 17.95 (978-1-878461-65-0(6)) Touchstones Discussion Project.

—Touchpebbles Volume A - Teacher's Guide, Vol. A. 2003. 234p. tchr. ed., per. 34.95 (978-1-878461-64-3(8)) Touchstones Discussion Project.

—Touchpebbles Volume B - Teacher's Guide, Vol. B. 2003. per., instr.'s gde. ed. 34.95 (978-1-878461-66-7(4)) Touchstones Discussion Project.

Wolfson, Jonathan. The Great Debate! Freedom to Communicate! A Handbook for Policy Debate. 2003. 144p. per. 25.00 (978-0-9746398-1-9(8)) LightningBolt Pr.

DEBS, EUGENE V. (EUGENE VICTOR), 1855-1926

Carey, Charles W. Eugene V. Debs: Outspoken Labor Leader & Socialist. 2003. (Historical American Biographies Ser.). (Illus.). 128p. (J). lib. bdg. 26.60 (978-0-7660-1979-9(9)) Enslow Pubs., Inc.

DEBTS, PUBLIC

Bussing-Burks, Maire. The Young Zillionaire's Guide to Taxation & Government Spending. 2000. (Be a Zillionaire Ser.). (Illus.). 48p. (YA). (gr. 5-8). lib. bdg. 23.95 (978-0-8239-3258-0(3) , ZITASP, Rosen Central) Rosen Publishing Group, Inc., The.

DECALOGUE

see Ten Commandments

DECATHLON

Gutman, Bill. Dan O'Brien. 1998. (Overcoming the Odds Ser.). (Illus.). 48p. (J). (gr. 3-8). (978-0-8172-4129-2(9)) Raintree.

U. S. Olympic Committee. A Basic Guide to Decathlon. 2001. (Olympic Guides). (Illus.). 160p. (J). (gr. 6 up). lib. bdg. 23.33 (978-0-8368-2796-5(1)) Stevens, Gareth Inc.

DECIMAL SYSTEM

Aihara, Masaaki & Sarris, Eno, eds. Grade 4 Decimals & Fractions: Kumon Math Workbooks. 2008. (J). per. 6.95 (***978-1-933241-58-6(6)***) Kumon Publishing North America, Inc.

—Grade 5 Decimals & Fractions: Kumon Math Workbooks. 2008. (J). per. 6.95 (***978-1-933241-59-3(4)***) Kumon Publishing North America, Inc.

Decimals & Fractions. 2003. 16.95 (978-0-7690-0837-0(2)) Seymour, Dale Pubns.

Findlay, Diane. Digging into Dewey. 2005. (Illus.). 126p. (J). pap. 16.95 (978-1-932146-18-9(0) , Upstart Bks.) Highsmith Inc.

HSP. Decimal Operations, Bk. B. 2nd ed. 2002. (First-Place Math Ser.). (gr. 5 up). pap. 12.60 (978-0-15-334634-7(5)); (gr. 6 up). pap. 12.60 (978-0-15-334640-8(X)) Harcourt Schl. Pubs.

—Decimals, Bk. D. 2nd ed. 2002. (First-Place Math Ser.). (gr. 4 up). pap. 12.60 (978-0-15-334630-9(2)) Harcourt Schl. Pubs.

Kompelien, Tracy. Can You Count More Than Before? (Math Made Fun Ser.). (Illus.). 24p. (J). 2007. 19.93 (978-1-59928-511-5(8)); 2006. pap. (978-1-59928-512-2(6)) ABDO Publishing Co.

Miles Moran, Andrea. Fractions, Decimals, Percents. 1999. (Homework Booklets Ser.). (Illus.). 80p. (J). (gr. 5-5). pap. 2.99 (978-1-56822-068-0(5) , IF0281); (J). (gr. 6-6). pap. 2.99 (978-1-56822-069-7(3) , IF0282); (YA). (gr. 7-8). pap. 2.99 (978-1-56822-070-3(7) , IF0283) Schaffer, Frank Pubns. (Instructional Fair).

Mitchell, Cindi. Math Skills Made Fun: Great Graph Art Decimals & Fractions. 2000. (Illus.). 64p. (J). pap. 10.95 (978-0-590-64375-7(4)) Scholastic, Inc.

New Decimal Dog. 2004. (J). (978-1-59242-144-2(X)) Delta Education, LLC.

O'Donnell, Kerri. A Trip Around the World. 2004. (PowerMath Ser.). (J). lib. bdg. (978-0-8239-8871-6(6) , PowerKids Pr.) Rosen Publishing Group, Inc., The.

—A Trip Around the World: Using Expanded Notation to Represent Numbers. 2004. (PowerMath Ser.). 24p. (J). lib. bdg. 21.25 (978-0-8239-8966-9(6) , PowerKids Pr.) Rosen Publishing Group, Inc., The.

Pallotta, Jerry. Count to a Million: 1,000,000. Bolster, Rob, tr. Bolster, Rob, illus. 2003. (J). (978-0-439-38915-0(1)) Scholastic, Inc.

Realtime Associates and Mazer Corporation Staff & LeapFrog Staff, compiled by. Add Decimals. 2002. (J). (gr. 3). 66.75 (978-1-58605-394-9(9) , LeapFrog Schl. Hse.) LeapFrog Enterprises, Inc.

—Multiply Decimals. 2002. (J). (gr. 5). 66.75 (978-1-58605-515-8(1) , LeapFrog Schl. Hse.) LeapFrog Enterprises, Inc.

—Read, Write, & Compare Decimals Using Place Value. 2002. (J). (gr. 4). 66.75 (978-1-58605-451-9(1) , LeapFrog Schl. Hse.) LeapFrog Enterprises, Inc.

School Specialty Publishing. Mathematics: A Step-by-Step Approach. 1999. (Homework Booklets Ser.). 86p. (J). (gr. 6-6). pap. 2.99 (978-0-88012-481-2(4) , IF0160); (YA). (gr. 7-7). pap. 2.99 (978-0-88012-484-3(9) , IF0170) Schaffer, Frank Pubns. (Instructional Fair).

Schwartz, David M. On Beyond a Million: An Amazing Math Journey. Meisel, Paul, illus. 2001. 32p. (J). (gr. 1-5). pap. 6.99 (978-0-440-41177-2(7) , Dragonfly Bks.) Random Hse. Children's Bks.

—On Beyond a Million: An Amazing Math Journey. 2001. (978-0-606-22416-1(5)) Tandem Library Bks.

Steck-Vaughn Staff. Decimals: Concepts & Problem Solving. 2000. (Illus.). (J). (gr. 3). pap. (978-0-7398-3398-8(7)); (gr. 4). pap. (978-0-7398-3399-5(5)) Steck-Vaughn.

—Focus on Math Level F: Decimals. 2005. pap. 2.99 (978-1-4190-0284-7(8)) Harcourt Schl. Pubs.

—Focus on Math Level F 10-pack: Decimals. 2005. pap. 29.95 (978-1-4190-0308-0(9)) Harcourt Schl. Pubs.

—Top Line Math: Decimals. 2005. pap. 5.49 (978-1-4190-0367-7(4)); pap., tchr. ed. 5.95 (978-1-4190-0377-6(1)) Harcourt Schl. Pubs.

—Top Line Math 10-Pack: Decimals. 2005. pap. 54.95 (978-1-4190-0388-2(7)) Harcourt Schl. Pubs.

Wells, Robert E. Can You Count to a Googol? 2000. (Illus.). (J). 13.75 (978-0-606-18773-2(1)) Tandem Library Bks.

—Can You Count to a Googol? Wells, Robert E., illus. 2000. (Illus.). 32p. (J). (gr. 1-5). 15.95 (978-0-8075-1060-5(2)) Whitman, Albert & Co.

—Can You Count to a Googol? 2000. (Illus.). 32p. (J). (gr. 1-5). pap. 6.95 (978-0-8075-1061-2(0)) Whitman, Albert & Co.

Wickett, Maryann. Lessons for Extending Place Value: Grade 3. 2005. (Teaching Arithmetic Ser.). (Illus.). 256p. pap. 26.95 (978-0-941355-57-5(8)) Math Solutions Pubns.

Zuravicky, Orli. When There Were Dinosaurs: Using Expanded Notation to Represent Numbers in the Millions. 2004. (PowerMath Ser.). (Illus.). 32p. (J). lib. bdg. (978-0-8239-8901-0(1)); lib. bdg. 22.50 (978-0-8239-8988-1(7)) Rosen Publishing Group, Inc., The. (PowerKids Pr.).

DECISION MAKING

Adams, Phillip G. Decisions, Decisions, Decisions. 2004. 160p. per. 12.95 (978-0-9762723-0-4(X)) Rhizoo Publishing.

Berry, Joy Wilt. Saying No. Smith, Maggie, illus. 2001. (J). (978-0-439-34150-9(7)) Scholastic, Inc.

Bunnell, Jean. You Decide! Making Responsible Choices. 1999. (Middle School Teacher Resource Book Ser.). (Illus.). 128p. (J). (gr. 5-8). pap. 13.99 (978-1-56822-457-2(3) , IF2543) School Specialty Publishing.

Burns, Jim. Tough Problems, Real Solutions. 181p. pap. 10.99 (978-0-8307-3508-2(9) , Regal Bks.) Gospel Light Pubns.

Clued in! on Saying No. 2005. (J). 4.95 (978-1-55548-051-6(9) , 675) Human Relations Media.

Decision Making. 1999. (Overcoming Obstacles). 32p. (YA). (gr. 6-9). pap. 11.50 (978-1-929393-04-6(0)) Community for Education Foundation.

Decision Making Skills. 1999. (Overcoming Obstacles). 26p. (YA). (gr. 9-12). pap. 9.38 (978-1-929393-17-6(2)) Community for Education Foundation.

Holt, Rinehart and Winston Staff. Decisions for Health Blue: Decision-Making. 4th ed. Date not set. pap., wbk. ed. 7.20 (978-0-03-068356-5(4)) Holt, Rinehart & Winston.

Making Good Moral Choices, 6 booklets. 1998. (Illus.). (YA). (gr. 7-10). stu. ed. 6.95 (978-0-89837-217-5(8)) Pflaum Publishing Group.

Matlock, Mark. Avoiding Stupidity: The Art & Science of Decision-Making. 1998. (Wise Guides Ser.). 48p. (YA). pap. 5.95 (978-1-888237-20-7(1)) Baxter Pr.

McKelvey, Brian. Oath of I Can Man: Characters with Concepts. 2005. (J). 7.95 (978-1-57921-786-0(9)) WinePress Publishing.

PowerXpress Living God's Word Making Choices. 2005. 115.00 (978-0-687-06311-6(6)) Abingdon Pr.

Pritchard, M. Ann. Phil the Pill & Friends: Making Positive Choices. 2005. (Illus.). 75p. (J). per. 11.99 (978-0-9772210-0-4(8)) MAMP Creations.

Rozema, Bob & Vander Ark, Dan. No Easy Answers: Making Good Decisions in an Anything-Goes World. 2002. (LifeWise Ser.). stu. ed. 8.25 (978-1-56212-844-9(2) , 138620, Faith Alive Christian Resources) CRC Pubns.

Sheindlin, Judy. Win or Lose by How You Choose! Judge Judy Sheindlin's. Tore, Bob, illus. 2001. 80p. (J). (gr. 2-7). pap. 6.95 (978-0-06-446239-6(0) , Harper Trophy) HarperCollins Pubs.

Straight Talk About Sex, Gender & Media. (YA). (gr. 6-8). 69.95 (978-1-55942-198-0(3) , 9240V9) Marsh Media.

Teal, Joyce Willard. Don't Sweat It, Kid. 2002. 152p. (J). 7.95 (978-1-56315-292-4(4)) SterlingHouse Pubs., Inc.

Tubbs, Janet. Making Decisions. 2000. (Spud Packs Ser.). (Illus.). 16p. (J). (ps-4). pap. 19.95 (978-1-881185-21-5(4)) Arcadia Pr.

Wandberg, Robert. Making Tough Decisions: Working Through Hard Choices. 2000. (Life Skills-Contemporary Issues Ser.). (Illus.). 64p. (J). (gr. 4-6). lib. bdg. 23.93 (978-0-7368-0697-8(0) , LifeMatters Bks.) Capstone Pr., Inc.

Wesley, Sonya L. Game Plan Ethical Decision Making: A Discussion & Activity Tool. 2000. (Illus.). (YA). spiral bd. (978-1-931377-08-9(1)) Game Plan Pubns.

DECLARATION OF INDEPENDENCE

see United States—Declaration of Independence

DECORATION, INTERIOR

see Interior Decoration

DECORATION AND ORNAMENT

see also Art, Decorative; Bronzes; Design; Design, Decorative; Flower Arrangement; Furniture; Gems; Illustration of Books; Interior Decoration; Jewelry; Leatherwork; Lettering; Metalwork; Mosaics; Pottery; Sculpture; Tapestry; Wood-Carving

Andrich, Tom. Decorate Yourself: Cool Designs for Temporary Tattoos, Face Painting, Henna & More. 2004. (Illus.). 96p. pap. 9.95 (978-1-895569-71-1(0)) Tamos Bks., Inc. CAN. *Dist:* Sterling Publishing Co., Inc.

Berger, Thomas & Berger, Petra. Crafts Through the Year. Lawson, Polly, tr. from DUT. 2000. (Illus.). 118p. 19.95 (978-0-86315-322-8(4)) Floris Bks. GBR. *Dist:* Gryphon Hse., Inc., SteinerBooks, Inc.

Gibson, Ray. Easter Activities. (Activity Bks.). (Illus.). 32p. (J). pap. 6.95 (978-0-7460-4234-2(5)) EDC Publishing.

Gooden, Clare. Customize Your Clothes. 2007. (Illus.). 512p. 24.99 (978-0-7548-1393-4(2) , Lorenz Bks.) Anness Publishing GBR. *Dist:* National Bk. Network.

Hodge, Susie. Picture Frames. 2006. (Illus.). 32p. (J). (978-1-58340-953-4(X)) Smart Apple Media.

Klutz Blossom Bracelets Kit. 8.95 (978-1-57054-750-8(5)) Klutz.

Noble, Marty. Art Nouveau Patterns. 2007. 32p. pap., pap. 3.95 (***978-0-486-46198-4(X)***) Dover Pubns., Inc.

Noble, Marty. Decorative Tile Designs Coloring Book. 2006. 32p. pap. 3.95 (978-0-486-45195-4(X)) Dover Pubns., Inc.

Obrochta, Dale. Faces, Faces, Balloon Faces. 2003. (Illus.). 32p. (YA). (978-0-9728793-0-9(7)) DEO Consulting, Inc.

Phillips, Matt. Make Your Own Fun Frames! Jaskiel, Stan, illus. 2001. (Quick Starts for Kids! Ser.). 64p. (YA). (gr. 3 up). pap. 8.95 (978-1-885593-64-1(3) , Williamson Bks.) Ideals Pubns.

Pressler, Rudolf, et al. Antique Biedermeier Furniture. 2002. (Schiffer Book for Collectors Ser.). (Illus.). 256p. 39.95 (978-0-7643-1648-7(6)) Schiffer Publishing, Ltd.

Sample, Ann. Houses & Homes in Colonial America. 2003. (Everyday Life Long Ago Ser.). (J). (978-0-7368-2163-6(5) , Blue Earth Bks.) Capstone Pr., Inc.

Yates, Irene. Pattern. 2002. (All about Ser.). (Illus.). 32p. (J). lib. bdg. 24.25 (978-1-931983-00-6(3)) Chrysalis Education.

DECORATION ART

see Art, Decorative

DECORATIONS OF HONOR

see also Heraldry

Lloyd, Mark. Military Badges & Insignia. 1999. (Illus.). 46p. (gr. 8-12). 20.00 (978-0-7881-6443-9(0)) DIANE Publishing Co.

O'Connor, Neal W. Aviation Awards of Imperial Germany in WWI & the Men Who Earned Them, Vol. 7. 2002. (Illus.). 528p. (gr. 10-13). 69.95 (978-0-7643-1626-5(5)) Schiffer Publishing, Ltd.

DECORATIVE ARTS

see Art, Decorative; Art Industries and Trade; Decoration and Ornament; Design, Decorative; Interior Decoration

DECOUPAGE

Elton, Candice & Elton, Richard. Every Kid Needs Mod Podge. 2006. (Illus.). 48p. (J). spiral bd., spiral bd. 19.95 (978-1-58685-709-7(6)) Gibbs Smith, Publisher.

DEDUCTION LOGIC

see Logic

DEEP DIVING

see also Scuba Diving; Skin Diving

Baker, Beth. Sylvia Earle: Guardian of the Sea. 2000. (Lerner Biographies Ser.). (Illus.). 112p. (YA). (gr. 6-12). lib. bdg. 27.93 (978-0-8225-4961-1(0) , Lerner Pubns.) Lerner Publishing Group.

Chapman, Simon. Under the Sea. Chapman, Simon, illus. 2005. (Illus.). 112p. (J). lib. bdg. 20.00 ***(*978-1-4242-0631-5(6))*** Fitzgerald Bks.

Hitchcock, Susan Tyler. Sylvia A. Earle: Deep Sea Explorer. 2004. (Women Explorers Ser.). (Illus.). 120p. 30.00 (978-0-7910-7712-2(8) , Chelsea Hse.) Facts On File, Inc.

Hyland, Tony. Divers. 2006. (Extreme Jobs Ser.). 32p. (J). (gr. 4-6). lib. bdg. 27.10 (978-1-58340-744-8(8)) Smart Apple Media.

Matsen, Bradford. An Extreme Dive under the Antarctic Ice. 2003. (Incredible Deep-Sea Adventures Ser.). (Illus.). 48p. (J). lib. bdg. 23.93 (978-0-7660-2190-7(4)) Enslow Pubs., Inc.

Vander Hook, Sue. Deep Diving Adventures. 2000. (Dangerous Adventures Ser.). (Illus.). 48p. (J). (gr. 3-4). lib. bdg. 21.26 (978-0-7368-0573-5(7) , Capstone High-Interest Bks.) Capstone Pr., Inc.

DEEP-SEA TECHNOLOGY

see Oceanography

DEER

see also Reindeer

Arnosky, Jim. All about Deer. 1999. (All About... Ser.). (Illus.). 32p. (J). (ps-4). pap. 5.99 (978-0-439-05874-2(0)) Scholastic, Inc.

Cooper, Jason. Fawn to Deer. 2003. (Rourke Discovery Library). (Illus.). 24p. (J). 20.64 (978-1-58952-693-8(7)) Rourke Publishing, LLC.

Creative Publishing international Editors. Forest Animals. 2004. (Our Wild World Ser.). (Illus.). 192p. (J). (gr. 2-5). ring bd. 16.95 (978-1-55971-708-3(4) , NorthWord Bks. for Young Readers) T&N Children's Publishing.

Deer Have Fawns. (Animals & Their Young Ser.). 24p. (J). 7.95 (978-0-7565-1239-2(5)) Compass Point Bks.

Evert, Laura. Whitetail Deer. McGee, John F., illus. 2004. (Our Wild World Ser.). 48p. (J). (gr. 2-5). pap. 7.95 (978-1-55971-743-4(2) , NorthWord Bks. for Young Readers) T&N Children's Publishing.

—Whitetail Deer. 2000. (gr. 3-6). lib. bdg. 16.40 (978-0-613-24805-1(8)) Tandem Library Bks.

Frahm, Randy. Deer Hunting. 2008. (J). ***(*978-1-4296-0817-6(X))*** Capstone Pr., Inc.

Frisch, Aaron. Deer. 2000. (Northern Trek Ser.). (Illus.). 24p. (J). (gr. 2-7). lib. bdg. 15.95 (978-1-58340-036-4(2)) Smart Apple Media.

George, Jean Craighead. Autumn Moon. 2003. (J). (gr. 3-7). 20.75 (978-0-8446-7241-0(6)) Smith, Peter Pub., Inc.

—Autumn Moon. 2001. (gr. 3-6). lib. bdg. 14.10 (978-0-613-50407-2(0)) Tandem Library Bks.

Hinshaw Patent, Dorothy. White-Tailed Deer. 2005. (Early Bird Nature Bks.). (J). 25.26 (978-0-8225-3052-7(X) , Lerner Pubns.) Lerner Publishing Group.

Hodge, Deborah. Deer, Moose, Elk & Caribou. 1999. (J). 12.75 (978-0-606-19013-8(9)) Tandem Library Bks.

—Deer, moose, elk & caribou. 2004. (Kids Can Press Wildlife Ser.). (Illus.). 32p. (J). (gr. k-3). (978-1-55074-667-9(7)) Kids Can Pr., Ltd.

—Deer, moose, elk & caribou. Stephens, Pat, illus. 1998. (Kids Can Press Wildlife Ser.). 32p. (J). (gr. k-3). (978-1-55074-435-4(6)) Kids Can Pr., Ltd.

Jaffe, Elizabeth Dana. Deer Have Fawns. 2002. (Animals & Their Young Ser.). (Illus.). 24p. (J). (gr. 1 up). lib. bdg. 18.60 (978-0-7565-0169-3(5)) Compass Point Bks.

Johnson, Jinny. Deer. Ch'en-Ling, illus. 2001. (Busy Baby Animals Ser.). 16p. (J). (ps up). lib. bdg. 19.33 (978-0-8368-2922-8(0)) Stevens, Gareth Inc.

Leach, Michael. Deer. 2003. (Animal Neighbours Ser.). (Illus.). 32p. (978-0-7502-4169-4(1) , Hodder Wayland) Hodder Children's Division.

Macken, JoAnn Early. Deer. 2005. (Illus.). 24p. (J). pap. (978-0-8368-4488-7(2)); (YA). lib. bdg. 19.33 (978-0-8368-4481-8(5)) Stevens, Gareth Inc.

Murray, Julie. Deer. 2005. (Animal Kingdom Set Ii Ser.). (Illus.). 24p. (J). (gr. k-4). lib. bdg. 21.35 (978-1-59197-312-6(0)) ABDO Publishing Co.

Open Court Staff. We Feed Deer. (J). pap. (978-0-8126-1002-4(4) , 61002) Open Court Publishing Co.

Schaefer, Lola M. Deer. 2004. (J). pap. (978-1-4034-5733-2(6)); lib. bdg. (978-1-4034-5045-6(5)) Heinemann Library.

Stefoff, Rebecca. Deer. 2007. (Animalways Ser.). 112p. (J). lib. bdg. 34.21 ***(*978-0-7614-2534-2(9)*** , Benchmark Bks.) Cavendish, Marshall Corp.

Sullivan, Jody. Deer: Graceful Grazers. 2002. (Wild World of Animals Ser.). (Illus.). 24p. (J). (gr. 1-2). lib. bdg. 18.60 (978-0-7368-1394-5(2) , Bridgestone Bks.) Capstone Pr., Inc.

Townsend, Emily Rose. Deer. Saunders-Smith, Gail, ed. 2004. (Woodland Animals Ser.). (Illus.). 24p. (J). (gr. k-1). lib. bdg. 15.93 (978-0-7368-2067-7(1) , Pebble Bks.) Capstone Pr., Inc.

Webster, Christine. Deer. 2007. (J). ***(*978-1-59036-675-2(1)); (*978-1-59036-676-9(X))*** Weigl Pubs., Inc.

The White-Tailed Deer. (Wildlife of North America Ser.). 48p. (YA). 7.95 (978-0-7368-8490-7(4)) Capstone Pr., Inc.

The White-Tailed Deer, 6 vols. (gr. 4 up). 39.95 (978-0-7368-8502-7(1)) Red Brick Learning.

Wilsdon, Christina. White-Tailed Deer. 2006. (Illus.). 45p. (J). (978-1-59939-073-4(6) , Reader's Digest Young Families, Inc.) Reader's Digest Children's Publishing, Inc.

DEER—FICTION

Baglio, Ben M. Deer in the Darkness. Baum, Ann, tr. Baum, Ann, illus. 2003. 125p. (J). pap. (978-0-439-52103-1(3)) Scholastic, Inc.

Bambi: A Little Spring Shower. unabr. ed. Date not set. (My First Read Along Ser.). (Illus.). 18p. (J). 7.99 incl. audio (978-1-55723-749-1(2)) Walt Disney Records.

Bartlett, Susan. Opening Day. Wrenn, Luanne, illus. 2007. 32p. (J). 16.95 ***(*978-0-88448-288-8(X))*** Tilbury Hse. Pubs.

Bender, Esther. Search for a Fawn. Bender, Edna, illus. 1998. 32p. (J). (gr. k-5). pap. 8.99 (978-0-8361-9099-1(8)) Herald Pr.

Bennett, Dean. Finding a Friend in the Forest: A True Story. 2005. (Illus.). 15.95 (978-0-89272-662-2(8)) Down East Bks.

Blair's Deer. (Early Intervention Levels Ser.). 31.86 (978-0-7362-0624-2(8)) Hampton-Brown Bks.

Brantley, Steven & Brantley, Judi. The Legend of Snowflake, the Messenger Deer. McDaniel-Clark, Carol, illus. l.t. ed. 2002. 40p. (J). 16.95 (978-1-892570-04-8(1)) Spring Hse. Bks.

Brooks, Dawn Marie. Cat-Ice. 2004. 175p. pap. 13.95 (978-0-7414-2240-8(9)) Infinity Publishing.

Burgess, Thornton W. The Adventures of Lightfoot the Deer. (J). 19.95 (978-0-8488-0393-3(0)) Amereon LTD.

—Lightfoot the Deer. Cady, Harrison, illus. 1998. (Dover Children's Thrift Classics Ser.). 96p. (J). (gr. 3-6). pap. 2.00 (978-0-486-40100-3(6)) Dover Pubns., Inc.

Burns, Joanne. Don't Fear Little Deer. 2005. 23p. (J). 9.99 (978-1-4116-4798-5(X)) Lulu.com.

Charlotte Latin School Staff. Ann & the Fawn. Sher, illus. 2001. 32p. (J). per. 4.95 (978-0-9707920-4-4(2)) Charlotte's Storybooks.

Dalmatian Press Staff. Disney's Bambi. 2007. 18p. pap. 11.99 ***(*978-1-4037-3223-1(X))*** Dalmatian Pr.

The Deer & the Crocodile: Individual Title Six-Packs. (Literatura 2000 Ser.). (gr. 1-2). 28.00 (978-0-7635-0130-3(1)) Rigby Education.

The Deer Report. 2005. (J). (978-1-58453-311-5(0)) Pioneer Valley Educational Pr., Inc.

Doerr, Bonnie J. Kenzie's Key. Aberle, Xylena Apotheloz, illus. 2003. 211p. (J). 16.95 (978-0-9619155-6-8(0)) Laurel & Herbert, Inc.

Francis, Margaret Thornton. Bucky Roo. Springer, Becky Francis, illus. 1998. (J). (978-1-882194-43-8(8)) Tennessee Valley Publishing.

Hughes, Monica. Little Mouse Deer & the Crocodile. Moricuchi, Mique, illus. 2004. 24p. (J). lib. bdg. 22.65 ***(*978-1-59646-684-5(7))*** Dingles & Co.

—More Little Mouse Deer Tales. Clemenston, John, illus. 2005. 24p. (J). lib. bdg. 22.65 ***(*978-1-59646-730-9(4))*** Dingles & Co.

Ikeda, Daisaku. Kanta & the Deer. Selden, Kyoko, tr. Sun, Christina, illus. 2001. (J). (gr. 2-3). reprint ed. 15.00 (978-0-7567-5157-9(8)) DIANE Publishing Co.

Joyce, Rita. Deer of the Dawn. 2004. (Illus.). 40p. (J). per. 8.95 (978-1-59094-067-9(9) , Jawbreakers for Kids) Jawbone Publishing Corp.

Kalar, Bonnie. Kirk & the Deer. Spreen, Kathe, illus. Date not set. 12p. (J). (ps-2). pap. (978-1-891619-43-4(8)) Corona Pr.

Kerr, Rita. Dearie Deer: Wild & Free. Kerr, Rita, illus. 1998. (Illus.). 40p. (gr. 1-4). 13.95 (978-1-57168-273-4(2)) Eakin Pr.

Keyes, Shirley. Diffee, the White Deer. 2003. (J). (978-0-9747755-0-0(9)) Wilkes Publishing Co., Inc.

LaBounty, David. Eye of the Deer. 2004. (J). pap. 4.95 (978-0-9745900-1-1(0) , Castle Builder Pr.) Blue Cubicle Pr., LLC.

Liput, Andrew L. Evie the Evergreen's Christmas Adventure. 2002. 31p. (J). pap. 9.95 (978-0-7414-1034-4(6)) Infinity Publishing.

Little Fawn's Summer Day. 2002. (Backyard Mini Bks.). (Illus.). 32p. (J). (978-1-59069-012-3(5) , H2001) Studio Mouse LLC.

Luna, Rachel Nickerson. Darinka, the Little Artist Deer. Luna, Rachel Nickerson, illus. 1999. (Illus.). 36p. (J). (gr. 3-4). 12.95 (978-1-886551-06-0(5)) Howard, Emma Bks.

Martin, Ann M. Karen's Reindeer. 1999. (Baby-Sitters Little Sister Ser.: No. 116). (Illus.). 128p. (J). (gr. 3-7). pap. 3.99 (978-0-590-52454-4(2)) Scholastic, Inc.

Marzollo, Jean. Once upon a Springtime. 1998. (978-0-606-13680-8(0)) Tandem Library Bks.

Mayfield, Helen, illus. The Enchanted Deer. 77p. (Orig.). (J). (gr. 6 up). pap. 4.00 (978-1-884993-03-9(6)) Koldarana Pubns.

Mora, Pat. The Race of Toad & Deer. Domi, illus. 2001. 32p. (J). (ps-k). 15.95 (978-0-88899-434-9(6)) Groundwood Bks. CAN. *Dist:* Perseus Distribution.

Mora, Pat, et al. La Carrera del Sapa y el Venado. Domi, illus. 2001. (SPA.). (J). (ps-k). 15.95 (978-0-88899-435-6(4) , GRO30719) Groundwood Bks. CAN. *Dist:* Lectorum Pubns., Inc., Transition Vendor.

Mouse Works Staff. The Jungle Book/Bambi, 2 vols. 75th anniv. ed. 1998. (978-0-7364-0090-9(7)) Mouse Works.

Oates, Joyce Carol. Come Meet Muffin! Graham, Mark, illus. 1998. 32p. (ps-1). 18.00 (978-0-88001-556-1(X)) HarperCollins Pubs.

Paulsen, Gary. Tracker. 2007. 96p. (J). pap. 4.99 ***(*978-1-4169-3940-5(7)*** , Aladdin) Simon & Schuster Children's Publishing.

Peck, Del. Deer Jack. 2000. (Illus.). 720p. (J). (ps-5). pap. 12.95 (978-0-9676844-2-0(0)) Pex Castle.

Random House Disney Staff. Bambi. (FRE.). (J). (gr. 3-8). 13.95 (978-0-7859-0613-1(4) , S26622) French & European Pubns., Inc.

—Bambi. 2001. (978-84-305-7629-6(0)) Lectorum Pubns., Inc.

—Bambi. unabr. ed. (Read-Along Ser.). (J). 7.99 incl. audio (978-1-55723-008-9(0)) Walt Disney Records.

—Bambi's Hide & Seek. 2002. (ps-2). lib. bdg. 11.80 (978-0-613-73649-7(4)) Tandem Library Bks.

Rawlings, Marjorie Kinnan. The Yearling. 1999. (Illus.). 444p. (J). 17.90 (978-0-03-054778-2(4)) Holt, Rinehart & Winston.

—The Yearling. 2002. 480p. pap. 15.00 (978-0-7432-2525-0(2) , Scribner) Simon & Schuster.

—The Yearling. 2001. (Aladdin Classics Ser.). 528p. mass mkt. 5.99 (978-0-689-84623-6(1) , Aladdin) Simon & Schuster Children's Publishing.

—Yearling. 2001. (gr. 3-6). lib. bdg. 14.15 (978-0-613-90195-6(9)) Tandem Library Bks.

—The Yearling, Level 3. 2001. 64p. (C). pap. 9.00 (978-0-582-34439-6(5)) Pearson ESL.

Reich, J. J. Snort, Wheeze, Rattle & Grunt. Hillmann, Joe & Cox, Chad, illus. 2006. (J). 8.99 (978-0-9762971-1-6(6)) Outdoor Originals LLC.

Reich, J. J. Snort, Wheeze, Rattle & Grunt: Kampp Tales, Outdoor Adventures. Johnathan, Kuehl, illus. 2006. 64p. (J). ***(*978-0-9762971-2-3(4))*** Outdoor Originals LLC.

Ryder, Joanne. A Fawn in the Grass. Narahashi, Keiko, illus. rev. ed. 2001. 32p. (J). (ps-k). 16.95 (978-0-8050-6236-6(X) , Holt, Henry & Co. Bks. For Young Readers) Holt, Henry & Co.

Salten, Felix. Bambi - Life in the Woods. (J). 20.95 (978-0-8488-1467-0(3)) Amereon LTD.

Sams, Carl R., II & Stoick, Jean, photos by. Lost in the Woods: A Photographic Fantasy. 2004. (Illus.). 48p. (J). pap. 19.95 (978-0-9671748-8-4(0)) Sams, II, Carl R. Photography, Inc.

Sargent, Dave & Sargent, Pat. Dawn the Deer: Family & Friends, 56 vols., 8. Huff, Jeane, illus. 2nd rev. ed. 2003. (Animal Pride Ser.: Vol. 8). 42p. (J). lib. bdg. 19.95 (978-1-56763-773-1(6)) Ozark Publishing.

Shepard, Aaron. The Adventures of Mouse Deer. Gamble, Kim, illus. 2005. 56p. (J). pap. 6.00 (978-0-938497-32-5(4) , Skyhook Pr.) Shepard Pubns.

—The Adventures of Mouse Deer: Tales of Indonesia & Malaysia (or Indonesian & Malaysian Folktales) Gamble, Kim, illus. 2006. 56p. (J). lib. bdg. 15.00 (978-0-938497-31-8(6) , Skyhook Pr.) Shepard Pubns.

Simon-Kerr, Julia. Best Buddies. 2006. (Open Season Ser.). 24p. (J). pap. 3.99 (978-0-06-084602-2(X)) HarperCollins Pubs.

So-un, Kim. Deer & the Woodcutter: A Korean Folktale. 2005. (Illus.). 32p. (J). 15.95 (978-0-8048-3655-5(8)) Tuttle Publishing.

Soros, Barbara. Tenzin's Deer: A Tibetan Tale. Mayer, Danuta, illus. 2003. 32p. (J). (gr. 2-5). 16.99 (978-1-84148-811-0(9)) Barefoot Bks., Inc.

Sternkopf, Susan. My Deer My Dear. Meehan, David, illus. 2001. 14p. (J). (gr. k-6). pap. 9.99 (978-0-9677130-1-4(3)) Sternkopf, Susan.

Storie Tree Inc, Staff. A Pocket Pearl of Light: Twinkle & Shinmet Come Home. l.t. ed. 2003. (Illus.). 27p. pap. 6.00 (978-0-9679014-9-7(9)) Storie Tree, Inc., The.

Talbot, Amy. Deer & Friends: A Folktale from India. 2006. 23.00 ***(*978-1-4108-6173-3(2))*** Benchmark Education Co.

Wade, Mary H. Swift Fawn the Little Foundling. Betts, Louis, illus. 2005. reprint ed. pap. 15.95 (978-1-4179-1811-9(X)) Kessinger Publishing, LLC.

Wallace, Robert E. The Adventures of Ichi, the Baby Deer Bk. 1: The Rescue. Wallace, Robert E., photos by. 2004. (Adventures of Ichi the Baby Deer Ser.: Bk. 1). (Illus.). (J). lib. bdg. 16.95 (978-0-9755678-0-7(2)) Cirrus Publishing, LLC.

Whiteside, Sandra M. A Train Named McSwain. Stancil, Mary H., ed. Ritter, Donna C., illus. 1998. 40p. (J). (gr. k-2). pap. 5.95 (978-1-892212-03-0(X)) Love Publishing Co.

Wilder, Laura Ingalls. The Deer in the Wood. Graef, Renee, illus. 1999. (My First Little House Bks.). 32p. (J). (ps-3). pap. 6.99 (978-0-06-443498-0(2) , Harper Trophy) HarperCollins Pubs.

—The Deer in the Wood. 1999. (My First Little House Bks.). (J). 12.79 (978-0-606-15841-1(3)); lib. bdg. 14.15 (978-0-613-11467-7(1)) Tandem Library Bks.

Wilson, Karen Collett. Autumn Rescue. Zerga, Susan A., photos by. 2004. (Deer Tales Ser.). (Illus.). (J). (gr. k-6). 15.95 (978-0-9722570-1-5(2)) Snowbound Bks.

—Pogonip Magic. Zerga, Susan A., illus. 2002. 40p. (J). (ps-3). 14.95 (978-0-9722570-0-8(4)) Snowbound Bks.

Wolfbear, Jessie. Tales of Bear & Deer: Native American Teaching Stories for Children of All Age. 2001. (gr. k-3). lib. bdg. 24.55 (978-0-613-74718-9(5)) Tandem Library Bks.

DEERE, JOHN, 1804-1886

Collins, David R. Pioneer Plowmaker: A Story about John Deere. 2003. (Creative Minds Biographies Ser.). (Illus.). 64p. (J). (gr. 3-6). pap. 22.60 (978-0-87614-909-6(3) , Carolrhoda Bks.) Lerner Publishing Group.

Hall, Margaret. John Deere. 2004. (Illus.). 32p. (J). pap. 6.50 (978-1-4034-5335-8(7)); lib. bdg. 22.79 (978-1-4034-5327-3(6)) Heinemann Library.

Marsh, Carole. John Deere. 2002. (One Thousand Readers Ser.). (Illus.). 12p. (J). (gr. k-4). 2.95 (978-0-635-01517-4(X) , 1517X) Gallopade International.

Mauser, Tracy & Beemer, Rod. John Deere. rev. ed. 2006. (Illus.). 80p. (J). pap. 9.95 (978-0-7603-2325-0(9) , Motorbooks) MBI Publishing Co. LLC.

Sutcliffe, Jane. John Deere. 2007. (History Maker Biographies Ser.). (J). 26.60 (978-0-8225-6579-6(X) , Lerner Pubns.) Lerner Publishing Group.

DEGAS, EDGAR, 1834-1917

Cocca-Leffler, Maryann. Edgar Degas: Paintings That Dance. Cocca-Leffler, Maryann, illus. 2001. (Smart about Art Ser.). (Illus.). 32p. (J). (gr. k-4). pap. 5.99 (978-0-448-42520-7(3) , Grosset & Dunlap) Penguin Group (USA) Inc.

—Edgar Degas: Paintings That Dance. 2001. (gr. k-3). lib. bdg. 14.15 (978-0-613-45259-5(3)) Tandem Library Bks.

Mattern, Joanne. Edgar Degas. 2005. (Checkerboard Biography Library). (Illus.). 32p. (J). (gr. k-6). lib. bdg. 22.78 (978-1-59197-843-5(2)) ABDO Publishing Co.

Merberg, Julie & Bober, Suzanne. Dancing with Degas. 2003. (Illus.). 22p. (J). bds. 6.95 (978-0-8118-4047-7(6)) Chronicle Bks. LLC.

Mis, Melody S. Edgar Degas. 2008. (J). lib. bdg. ***(*978-1-4042-3839-8(5)*** , PowerKids Pr.) Rosen Publishing Group, Inc., The.

Muhlberger, Richard. What Makes a Degas a Degas? 2002. (Illus.). 48p. (YA). 16.99 (978-0-670-03571-7(8) , Viking Juvenile) Penguin Group (USA) Inc.

Rubin, Susan Goldman. Degas & the Dance: The Painter & the Petits Rats, Perfecting Their Art. 2005. (Illus.). 31p. (J). (gr. 4-8). reprint ed. 18.00 (978-0-7567-9291-6(6)) DIANE Publishing Co.

Rubin, Susan Goldman & Degas, Edgar. Degas & the Dance: The Painter & the Petits Rats, Perfecting their Art. 2002. (Illus.). 32p. (J). (gr. k-4). 17.95 (978-0-8109-0567-2(1)) Abrams, Harry N., Inc.

Spence, David. Degas. 1998. (Great Artists Ser.). (Illus.). 32p. (J). pap. 6.95 (978-0-7641-0626-2(0)) Barron's Educational Series, Inc.

Venezia, Mike. Edgar Degas. Venezia, Mike, illus. 2001. (Getting to Know the World's Greatest Artists Ser.). (Illus.). 32p. (J). (gr. 3-4). pap. 6.95 (978-0-516-27172-9(5) , Children's Pr.) Scholastic Library Publishing.

—Edgar Degas. 2000. (Getting to Know the World's Greatest Artists Ser.). (Illus.). 32p. (J). (gr. 3-4). 27.00 (978-0-516-21593-8(0) , Children's Pr.) Scholastic Library Publishing.

—Edgar Degas. Venezia, Mike, illus. 2001. (Illus.). 31p. (J). (ps-ps). lib. bdg. 15.25 (978-0-613-50683-0(9)) Tandem Library Bks.

Wenzel, Angela. Edgar Degas: Dance Like a Butterfly. Jackson, Rosie, tr. from GER. 2002. (Adventures in Art Ser.). (Illus.). 30p. (gr. 4-6). 14.95 (978-3-7913-2736-5(4)) Prestel Publishing.

Woodhouse, Jayne. Edgar Degas. 2002. (Life & Work of. . . Ser.). (Illus.). 32p. (J). (gr. k-2). lib. bdg. 22.79 (978-1-58810-602-5(0)) Heinemann Library.

—The Life & Work of Edgar Degas, Set 2. 2002. (Illus.). 32p. (J). (gr. k-2). pap. 6.50 (978-1-4034-0000-0(8) , 91618) Heinemann Library.

DELACROIX, EUGENE, 1798-1863

Julio, Paredes. Eugéne Delacroix. 2005. 132p. pap. (978-958-30-1358-4(7)) Panamericana Editorial.

Venezia, Mike. Eugene Delacroix. Venezia, Mike, illus. 2003. (Getting to Know the World's Greatest Artists Ser.). (Illus.). pap. 6.95 (978-0-516-26976-4(3) , Children's Pr.) Scholastic Library Publishing.

—Eugene Delacroix. 2003. (Getting to Know World Artists Ser.). (Illus.). 32p. (J). 27.00 (978-0-516-22576-0(6) , Children's Pr.) Scholastic Library Publishing.

—Eugene Delacroix. 2003. (gr. 3-6). lib. bdg. 15.25 (978-0-613-67888-9(5)) Tandem Library Bks.

DELAWARE

Bennett, Kelly. Delaware. 2005. (Rookie Read-About Geography Ser.). (Illus.). 32p. (J). (gr. 1-2). pap. 5.95 (978-0-516-25156-1(2) , Children's Pr.) Scholastic Library Publishing.

Bennett, Kelly & Vargus, Nanci Reginelli. Delaware. 2004. (Rookie Read-About Geography Ser.). (J). 20.50 (978-0-516-22752-8(1) , Children's Pr.) Scholastic Library Publishing.

Bennett, Kelly & Wormser, Richard. Delaware. 2004. (Life in the Thirteen Colonies Ser.). (Illus.). 124p. (J). 36.00 (978-0-516-24569-0(4) , Children's Pr.) Scholastic Library Publishing.

Brown, Dottie. Delaware. (Hello U. S. A. Ser.). (Illus.). (gr. 3-6). 1999. 72p. pap. 5.95 (978-0-8225-9785-8(3)); 2nd rev. exp. ed. 2002. 84p. (J). lib. bdg. 25.26 (978-0-8225-4079-3(7)) Lerner Publishing Group.

—Delaware. rev. ed. 2002. (gr. 3-6). lib. bdg. 15.25 (978-0-613-46065-1(0)) Tandem Library Bks.

Brown, Jonatha A. Delaware. 2006. (Portraits of the States Ser.). (J). pap. (978-0-8368-4715-4(6)); lib. bdg. (978-0-8368-4698-0(2)) Stevens, Gareth Inc.

Brown, Vanessa. Delaware. 2005. (Bilingual Library of the United States of America: Set 1). (ENG & SPA., Illus.). 32p. (J). (ps-k). lib. bdg. 22.50 (978-1-4042-3073-6(4) , Buenas Letra) Rosen Publishing Group, Inc., The.

Crane, Carol. F Is for First State: A Delaware Alphabet. Traynor, Elizabeth, illus. 2005. (State Ser.). 40p. (J). (ps-3). 17.95 (978-1-58536-154-0(2)) Sleeping Bear Pr.

Delaware. 2000. (Switched on Schoolhouse Ser.). (Illus.). (YA). (gr. 7-12). pap. 24.95 incl. cd-rom (978-0-7403-0260-2(4) , SOSDE) Alpha Omega Pubns., Inc.

Fontes, Justine & Fontes, Ron. Delaware: The First State. 2003. (World Almanac Library of the States). (Illus.). 48p. (J). (gr. 5 up). pap. 14.95 (978-0-8368-5319-3(9) , World Almanac Library) Stevens, Gareth Inc.

Heinrichs, Ann. Delaware. 2005. (Welcome to the USA Ser.). 40p. (J). (gr. 1-5). 27.07 (978-1-59296-470-3(2)) Child's World, Inc.

—Delaware. 2003. (This Land Is Your Land Ser.). (Illus.). 48p. (J). (gr. 3 up). lib. bdg. 22.60 (978-0-7565-0341-3(8)) Compass Point Bks.

King, David C. Delaware. 2004. (It's My State! Ser.). (Illus.). 80p. (J). 27.07 (978-0-7614-1826-9(1) , Benchmark Bks.) Cavendish, Marshall Corp.

Kule, Elaine A. Delaware Facts & Symbols. (States & Their Symbols Ser.). 24p. (J). 2000. (Illus.). (gr. 2-3). lib. bdg. 18.60 (978-0-7368-0635-0(0) , Bridgestone Bks.); 2003. lib. bdg. 19.93 (978-0-7368-2238-1(0)) Capstone Pr., Inc.

Kummer, Patricia K. Delaware. rev. ed. 2002. (One Nation Ser.). (Illus.). 48p. (J). (gr. 3-4). lib. bdg. 22.60 (978-0-7368-1232-0(6) , Bridgestone Bks.) Capstone Pr., Inc.

Marsh, Carole. The Big Delaware Reproducible Acvitity Book. 2001. (Carole Marsh Delaware Bks.). (Illus.). 96p. (J). (gr. 2-6). pap. 9.95 (978-0-7933-9938-3(6)) Gallopade International.

—Delaware Classic Christmas Trivia. 2002. (Carole Marsh Delaware Bks.). (Illus.). 32p. pap. 6.95 (978-0-635-01383-5(5) , 13835); lib. bdg. 21.95 (978-0-635-01384-2(3) , 13843) Gallopade International. (Marsh, Carole Bks.).

—Delaware Current Events Projects: 30 Cool, Activities, Crafts, Experiments & More for Kids to Do to Learn about Your State! 2003. (Delaware Experience Ser.). 32p. (gr. k-8). pap. 5.95 (978-0-635-02027-7(0) , Marsh, Carole Bks.) Gallopade International.

—The Delaware Experience Pocket Guide. 2001. (Carole Marsh Delaware Bks.). (Illus.). 96p. (J). (gr. 3-8). pap. 6.95 (978-0-7933-9909-3(2)) Gallopade International.

—Delaware Geography Projects: 30 Cool Activities, Crafts, Experiments & More for Kids to Do to Learn about Your State! 2003. (Delaware Experience Ser.). 32p. (gr. k-5). pap. 5.95 (978-0-635-01827-4(6) , Marsh, Carole Bks.) Gallopade International.

—Delaware Government Projects: 30 Cool, Activities, Crafts, Experiments & More for Kids to Do to Learn about Your State! 2003. (Delaware Experience Ser.). 32p. (gr. k-5). pap. 5.95 (978-0-635-01927-1(2) , Marsh, Carole Bks.) Gallopade International.

—Delaware Jeopardy! Answers & Questions about Our State! 2001. (Illus.). 32p. (J). (gr. 3-8). pap. 7.95 (978-0-7933-9793-8(6)) Gallopade International.

—Delaware "Jography" A Fun Run Thru Our State! 2001. (Carole Marsh Delaware Bks.). (Illus.). 32p. (J). (gr. 3-8). pap. 7.95 (978-0-7933-9822-5(3)) Gallopade International.

—Delaware Millionaire: Game Book. 2001. (Carole Marsh Delaware Bks.). (Illus.). 32p. (J). (gr. 3-8). pap., act. bk. ed. 9.95 (978-0-635-00032-3(6)) Gallopade International.

—Delaware People Projects: 30 Cool, Activities, Crafts, Experiments & More for Kids to Do to Learn about Your State! 2003. (Delaware Experience Ser.). 32p. (gr. k-5). pap. 5.95 (978-0-635-01977-6(9) , Marsh, Carole Bks.) Gallopade International.

—Delaware Survivor: Game Book. 2001. (Carole Marsh Delaware Bks.). (Illus.). 32p. (J). (gr. 3-8). pap., act. bk. ed. 9.95 (978-0-635-00529-8(8)) Gallopade International.

—Delaware Symbols & Facts Projects: 30 Cool, Activities, Crafts, Experiments & More for Kids to Do to Learn about Your State! 2003. (Delaware Experience Ser.). 32p. (gr. k-5). pap. 5.95 (978-0-635-01877-9(2) , Marsh, Carole Bks.) Gallopade International.

—My First Book about Delaware. 2001. (Carole Marsh Delaware Bks.). (Illus.). 32p. (J). (gr. k-4). pap. 7.95 (978-0-7933-9880-5(0)) Gallopade International.

—My First Pocket Guide Delaware. 2000. (Delaware Experience! Ser.). (Illus.). 96p. (J). (gr. 3-8). 12.95 (978-0-635-01298-2(7) , 12987) Gallopade International.

—The Survivor: A Class Challenge. 2001. (Carole Marsh Delaware Bks.). lib. bdg. 29.95 (978-0-635-00654-7(5)) Gallopade International.

—Who Wants to Be a Delaware Millionaire? 2001. (Carole Marsh Delaware Bks.). lib. bdg. 29.95 (978-0-635-00033-0(4)) Gallopade International.

Miller, Amy. Delaware. 2002. (From Sea to Shining Sea Ser.: 2). (Illus.). 80p. (J). (gr. 3-5). pap. 30.50 (978-0-516-22482-4(4) , Children's Pr.) Scholastic Library Publishing.

Moose, Katherine. Uniquely Delaware. 2003. (Heinemann State Studies). (Illus.). 48p. (J). pap. 8.50 (978-1-4034-4713-5(6)); lib. bdg. 27.07 (978-1-4034-4644-2(X)) Heinemann Library.

Murray, Julie. Delaware. 2005. (Buddy Book Ser.). (Illus.). 32p. (J). (gr. k-4). lib. bdg. 22.78 (978-1-59197-667-7(7) , Buddy Bks.) ABDO Publishing Co.

Reiter, Chris. Delaware: A MyReportLinks.com Book. 2003. (States Ser.). (Illus.). 48p. (J). (gr. 4-10). lib. bdg. 25.26 (978-0-7660-5019-8(X) , MyReportLinks.com Bks.) Enslow Pubs., Inc.

Schuman, Michael A. Delaware. 2000. (Celebrate the States Ser.). (Illus.). 144p. (gr. 4-8). lib. bdg. 37.07 (978-0-7614-0645-7(X) , Benchmark Bks.) Cavendish, Marshall Corp.

Welsbacher, Anne. Delaware. 2003. (Land of Liberty Ser.). (Illus.). 64p. (J). (gr. 3-4). lib. bdg. 23.93 (978-0-7368-1576-5(7) , Bridgestone Bks.) Capstone Pr., Inc.

Wimmer, Teresa. Delaware. 2008. (J). (*978-1-58341-633-4(1) , Creative Education) Creative Co., The.

Winans, Jay D. A Guide to Delaware. 2001. (American States Ser.). (Illus.). 32p. (J). lib. bdg. 16.95 (978-1-930954-99-1(9)) Weigl Pubs., Inc.

DELAWARE—FICTION

Anderson, M. T. Jasper Dash & the Flame-Pits of Delaware: M. T. Anderson's Thrilling Tales. Cyrus, Kurt, illus. 2008. (M. T. Anderson's Thrilling Tales Ser.). 300p. (J). 16.00 (*978-0-15-205346-8(8)) Harcourt Children's Bks.

Blair, Margaret Whitman. The Sand Castle: Blockade Running & the Battle of Fort Fisher. 2004. (White Mane Kids Ser.: 17). (Illus.). 200p. (J). pap. 8.95 (978-1-57249-346-9(1) , White Mane Kids) White Mane Publishing Co., Inc.

Hogan, Mary. Perfect Girl. 2008. 208p. (J). 7.99 (*978-0-06-084110-2(9) , HarperTeen) HarperCollins Pubs.

Laird, Marnie. Water Rat. 2001. 192p. (J). (gr. 4-7). pap. 5.95 (978-1-58837-002-0(X)) Winslow Pr.

Maxson, H. A. & Young, Claudia H. Kalmar Nyckel & Fort Christina. Kosits, Andrew, illus. 2002. (J). per. 8.95 (978-0-9704692-6-7(8)) Bay Oak Pubs., Ltd.

—Lenapehoking: Land of the Delawares. Etherson, Lesley, illus. 2001. 64p. (J). per. 8.95 (978-0-9704692-1-2(7)) Bay Oak Pubs., Ltd.

—Lenapehoking: Resource Guide. Etherson, Lesley, illus. 2001. 13.95 (978-0-9704692-3-6(3)) Bay Oak Pubs., Ltd.

Noble, Trinka Hakes. The Legend of the Cape May Diamond. Lewis, Earl B, illus. rev. ed. 2007. 40p. (J). 17.95 (*978-1-58536-279-0(4)) Sleeping Bear Pr.

Zeises, Lara M. Anyone but You. 256p. (YA). (gr. 9). 2007. mass mkt. 6.50 (*978-0-440-23858-4(7) , Laurel Leaf); 2005. 15.95 (978-0-385-73145-4(0) , Delacorte Bks. for Young Readers) Random Hse. Children's Bks.

Zeises, Lara M. Contents under Pressure. 2004. 256p. (YA). (gr. 7). 15.95 (978-0-385-73047-1(0) , Delacorte Bks. for Young Readers) Random Hse. Children's Bks.

DELAWARE—HISTORY

Blashfield, Jean F. The Delaware Colony. 2003. (Spirit of America). (Illus.). 40p. (J). (gr. 2-6). 28.50 (978-1-56766-610-6(8)) Child's World, Inc.

Britton, Tamara L. The Delaware Colony. 2001. (Colonies Ser.). (Illus.). 32p. (J). (gr. k-6). lib. bdg. 22.78 (978-1-57765-577-0(X) , Checkerboard Library) ABDO Publishing Co.

Doherty, Craig A. & Doherty, Katherine M. Delaware. 2005. (Thirteen Colonies Ser.). (Illus.). 144p. (J). (gr. 4-9). 35.00 (978-0-8160-5414-5(2)) Facts On File, Inc.

Dubois, Muriel L. The Delaware Colony. 2005. (Fact Finders Ser.). (Illus.). 32p. (J). (gr. 2-4). 22.60 (978-0-7368-2673-0(4)) Capstone Pr., Inc.

Fontes, Justine & Fontes, Ron. Delaware: The First State. 2003. (World Almanac Library of the States). (Illus.). 48p. (J). (gr. 5 up). lib. bdg. 30.00 (978-0-8368-5148-9(X) , World Almanac Library) Stevens, Gareth Inc.

Hoffecker, Carol E. Delaware: The First State. 2nd rev. ed. 2005. (Illus.). 215p. (YA). (gr. 6-9). pap. (978-0-9705804-0-5(1)) Middle Atlantic Pr.

Hossell, Karen & National Geographic Society Staff. Delaware 1638-1776. 2006. (Voices from Colonial America Ser.). (Illus.). 112p. (J). (gr. 5-9). 21.95 (978-0-7922-6408-8(8)); lib. bdg. 32.90 (978-0-7922-6864-2(4)) National Geographic Society. (National Geographic Children's Bks.).

Marsh, Carole. Delaware History Projects: 30 Cool, Activities, Crafts, Experiments & More for Kids to Do to Learn about Your State! 2003. (Delaware Experience Ser.). 32p. (gr. k-5). pap. 5.95 (978-0-635-01777-2(6) , Marsh, Carole Bks.) Gallopade International.

Miller, Jake. The Colony of Delaware: A Primary Source History. 2006. (Primary Source Library of the Thirteen Colonies & the Lost Colony). (Illus.). 24p. (J). lib. bdg. (978-1-4042-3033-0(5) , PowerKids Pr.) Rosen Publishing Group, Inc., The.

Quasha, Jennifer. How to Draw Delawares Sights & Symbols. 2002. (Kids Guide to Drawing America Ser.). 32p. (J). lib. bdg. 25.25 (978-0-8239-6062-0(5) , PowerKids Pr.) Rosen Publishing Group, Inc., The.

Raymond, Aaron. A Primary Source History of the Colony of Delaware. 2005. (Primary Sources of the Thirteen Colonies & the Lost Colony Ser.). (Illus.). 64p. (J). (gr. 3-7). pap. 14.60 (978-1-4042-0670-0(1)); (YA). (gr. 5-8). lib. bdg. 29.25 (978-1-4042-0425-6(3)) Rosen Publishing Group, Inc., The.

Whitehurst, Susan. The Colony of Delaware. 2000. (Library of the Thirteen Colonies & the Lost Colony). (Illus.). 24p. (J). (gr. 3). lib. bdg. 19.95 (978-0-8239-5482-7(X) , PowerKids Pr.) Rosen Publishing Group, Inc., The.

Wiener. The 13 Colonies Pack: Delaware, 6. 2004. (Illus.). 48.30 (978-1-4109-0365-5(6)) Harcourt Schl. Pubs.

Wiener, Roberta & Arnold, James R. Delaware. 2004. (Thirteen Colonies Ser.). (Illus.). 64p. (J). 31.36 (978-0-7398-6878-2(0)); 9.50 (978-1-4109-0302-0(8)) Harcourt Schl. Pubs.

DELHI (INDIA)

Rowe, Percy. Delhi. 2004. (Great Cities of the World Ser.). (J). pap. 11.95 (978-0-8368-5197-7(8)); (Illus.). 48p. (YA). lib. bdg. 30.00 (978-0-8368-5037-6(8)) Stevens, Gareth Inc. (World Almanac Library).

DELINQUENCY, JUVENILE

see Juvenile Delinquency

DELINQUENTS

see Crime and Criminals; Juvenile Delinquency

DELTORA (IMAGINARY PLACE)—FICTION

Rodda, Emily. Cavern of the Fear. McBride, Marc, illus. 2002. (Deltora Quest Ser.: No. 1). 144p. (J). (gr. 3-7). pap. 5.99 (978-0-439-39491-8(0)) Scholastic, Inc.

—Cavern of the Fear. 2002. (gr. 3-6). lib. bdg. 13.00 (978-0-613-50594-9(8)) Tandem Library Bks.

—City of the Rats. 2001. (Deltora Quest Ser.: No. 3). (Illus.). 144p. (J). (gr. 3-7). pap. 5.99 (978-0-439-25325-3(X)) Scholastic, Inc.

—City of the Rats. 2001. (gr. 5-8). lib. bdg. 13.00 (978-0-613-36052-4(4)) Tandem Library Bks.

—The Deltora Book of Monsters. McBride, Marc, illus. 2002. (Deltora Quest Ser.). 48p. (J). (gr. 3-7). pap. 7.99 (978-0-439-39084-2(2)) Scholastic, Inc.

—The Deltora Book of Monsters. 2002. (gr. 5-8). lib. bdg. 16.45 (978-0-613-50600-7(6)) Tandem Library Bks.

—Dread Mountain. 2001. (Deltora Quest Ser.: No. 5). 144p. (J). pap. 4.99 (978-0-439-25327-7(6) , Scholastic Paperbacks) Scholastic, Inc.

—Dread Mountain. 2001. (gr. 5-8). lib. bdg. 13.00 (978-0-613-35715-9(9)) Tandem Library Bks.

—The Forests of Silence. 2001. (Deltora Quest Ser.: No. 1). (Illus.). 144p. (J). (gr. 3-7). pap. 5.99 (978-0-439-25323-9(3)) Scholastic, Inc.

—The Isle of Illusion. 2002. (Deltora Quest Ser.: No. 2). (Illus.). 160p. (J). pap. 4.99 (978-0-439-39492-5(9) , Scholastic Paperbacks) Scholastic, Inc.

—The Isle of Illusion. 2002. (gr. 3-6). lib. bdg. 13.00 (978-0-613-50624-3(3)) Tandem Library Bks.

—The Lake of Tears. 2001. (Deltora Quest Ser.: No. 2). (Illus.). 144p. (J). (gr. 3-7). pap. 4.99 (978-0-439-25324-6(1)) Scholastic, Inc.

—The Maze of the Beast. 2001. (Deltora Quest Ser.: No. 6). (Illus.). 144p. (J). pap. 4.99 (978-0-439-25328-4(4) , Scholastic Paperbacks) Scholastic, Inc.

—Return to Del. (Illus.). (J). 2002. 136p. (978-0-439-41951-2(4)); 2001. (Deltora Quest Ser.: No. 8). 144p. (gr. 8). pap. 4.99 (978-0-439-25330-7(6)) Scholastic, Inc.

—Return to Del. 2001. (gr. 5-8). lib. bdg. 13.00 (978-0-613-43874-2(4)) Tandem Library Bks.

—The Shadowlands. McBride, Marc, illus. 2002. (Deltora Quest Ser.: No. 3). 160p. (J). (gr. 4-9). pap. 4.99 (978-0-439-39493-2(7) , Scholastic Paperbacks) Scholastic, Inc.

—The Shifting Sands. 2001. (Deltora Quest Ser.: No. 4). (Illus.). 144p. (J). (gr. 4-7). pap. 4.99 (978-0-439-25326-0(8)) Scholastic, Inc.

—The Sister of the South. McBride, Marc, illus. 2005. (Deltora Quest Ser.: Vol. 4). 224p. (J). pap. 4.99 (978-0-439-63376-5(1) , Scholastic Paperbacks) Scholastic, Inc.

—The Valley of the Lost. 2001. (Deltora Quest Ser.: No. 7). (Illus.). 143p. (J). pap. 4.99 (978-0-439-25329-1(2) , Scholastic Paperbacks) Scholastic, Inc.

DELUSIONS

see Superstition; Witchcraft

DEMILLE, AGNES, 1908-1993

Gaskill, Rachel. Agnes de Mille. 2005. (Library of American Choreographers). (Illus.). 48p. (J). pap. (978-1-4042-0645-8(0)) Rosen Publishing Group, Inc., The.

—Agnes Demille. 2005. (Library of American Choreographers). (Illus.). 48p. (J). (ps-ps). lib. bdg. 23.95 (978-1-4042-0444-7(X)) Rosen Publishing Group, Inc., The.

DEMOCRACY

see also Equality; Liberty; Socialism; Suffrage

Downing, David & Tames, Richard. Democracy. 2003. (Political & Economic Systems Ser.). (Illus.). 64p. (J). (gr. 6-8). lib. bdg. 28.50 (978-1-4034-0317-9(1)) Heinemann Library.

Einfeld, Jann, ed. Can Democracy Succeed in the Middle East? 2006. (At Issue Ser.). (Illus.). 128p. (YA). (gr. 6 up). pap. 21.20 (978-0-7377-3394-5(2)); lib. bdg. 29.95 (978-0-7377-3393-8(4)) Thomson Gale. (Greenhaven Pr., Inc.).

Grodin, Elissa. A Citizen's Alphabet. 2007. 40p. pap. 7.95 (*978-1-58536-328-5(6)) Sleeping Bear Pr.

Harcourt School Publishers Staff. Pericles & the First Democracy Below Level. 3rd ed. 2002. (Trophies Reading Program Ser.). (Illus.). pap. 5.10 (978-0-15-323415-6(6)) Harcourt Schl. Pubs.

Harris, Nathaniel. Democracy. 2001. (Ideas of the Modern World Ser.). (Illus.). 64p. (J). lib. bdg. 25.69 (978-0-7398-3160-1(7)) Raintree.

Lansford, Tom. Democracy. 2007. (Political Systems of the World Ser.). 160p. (YA). (gr. 9 up). lib. bdg. 39.93 (978-0-7614-2629-5(9) , Benchmark Bks.) Cavendish, Marshall Corp.

McGraw-Hill Staff. United States Government, Democracy in Action, Spanish Reading Essentials. 2nd ed. 2005. (SPA.). pap., stu. ed., wbk. ed. 26.60 (978-0-07-865920-1(5) , 9780078659201) Glencoe/McGraw-Hill.

Neitzel, Shirley. Liberty & Justice for All: A First Look at Core Democratic Values. l.t. ed. 2002. 48p. (J). per. 9.95 (978-0-938682-70-7(9) , 682-70-9) River Road Pubns., Inc.

Rees, Peter. Liberty: Blessing or Burden? 2007. (Shockwave: the Human Experience Ser.). (Illus.). 36p. (J). (gr. 4-6). lib. bdg. 25.00 (*978-0-531-17760-0(2) , Children's Pr.) Scholastic Library Publishing.

Smith, Ruth J. Self Government: A Child's History of the United States of America. Mikler, Lisa M., illus. 2002. 160p. (J). per. 17.95 (978-0-9705618-1-7(4)) Bradford Pr.

—Self Government Teacher's Guide. 2002. 192p. (J). tchr. ed., per. 34.95 (978-0-9705618-2-4(2)) Bradford Pr.

Stites, Bill. Democracy: A Primary Source Analysis. 2003. (Primary Sources of Political Systems Ser.). (Illus.). 64p. (J). lib. bdg. 29.25 (978-0-8239-4518-4(9)) Rosen Publishing Group, Inc., The.

Sullivan, Erin Ash. Matematicas en una democracia & Math in a Democracy. 2005. spiral bd. 84.00 (*978-1-4108-5715-6(8)) Benchmark Education Co.

Travis, Cathy. Constitution Translated For Kids. 2nd ed. 2001. (Illus.). 69p. (J). per. 14.95 (978-1-59165-000-3(3)) Oakwood Publishing.

—Constitution Translated for Kids. 3rd ed. 2006. (Illus.). 100p. (J). 16.95 (978-1-933538-01-3(5)) Synergy Bks.

Woolf, Alex. Democracy. 2005. (Systems of Government Ser.). (Illus.). 48p. (J). (978-0-8368-5888-4(3)); lib. bdg. 30.00 (978-0-8368-5883-9(2)) Stevens, Gareth Inc. (World Almanac Library).

DEMOCRATIC PARTY (U.S.)

Anderson, Dale. The Democratic Party: America's Oldest Party. 2007. (Illus.). 96p. (J). pap. (*978-0-7565-3169-0(1)); (YA). (gr. 5-8). lib. bdg. 31.93 (*978-0-7565-2450-0(4)) Compass Point Bks.

Landau, Elaine. Friendly Foes: A Look at Political Parties. 2004. (How Government Works Ser.). (Illus.). 56p. (J). (gr. 4-8). lib. bdg. 25.26 (978-0-8225-1349-0(8)) Lerner Publishing Group.

Schlesinger, Arthur M., Jr., ed. The History of the Democratic Party. 2000. (Your Government Ser.). (Illus.). 64p. (YA). (gr. 3-7). 25.00 (978-0-7910-5539-7(6) , Chelsea Hse.) Facts On File, Inc.

Zilber, Jeremy. Why Mommy Is a Democrat. Firsova, Yuliya, illus. 2005. 28p. (J). 8.00 (978-0-9786688-0-8(4)) Zilber, Jeremy.

DEMONOLOGY

Osborne, Rick & Strauss, Ed. Bible Angels & Demons. 2004. (2:52 Ser.). (Illus.). 112p. (J). pap. 7.99 (978-0-310-70775-2(7)) Zonderkidz.

DEMONOLOGY—FICTION

Aryal, Aimee. Hello Demon Deacon! Cooper, Blair, illus. 2004. (J). 19.95 (978-1-932888-14-0(4)) Mascot Bks., Inc.

Bass, L. G. The Outlaws of Moonshadow Marsh No. 1, Bk.1: The Sign of Qin. 2004. (Illus.). 400p. (gr. 5-17). 17.99 (978-0-7868-1918-8(9)) Hyperion Bks. for Children.

—The Outlaws of Moonshadow Marsh the Sign of Qin, Bk. 1. 2006. 400p. (gr. 5-17). reprint ed. pap. 7.99 (978-0-7868-5566-7(5)) Hyperion Pr.

—Sign of the Qin. l.t. ed. 2004. 513p. 23.95 (978-0-7862-6772-9(0) , Large Print Pr.) Thorndike Pr.

Buckingham, Royce. Demonkeeper. 2007. 192p. (J). (gr. 4-7). 15.99 (978-0-399-24649-4(5) , Putnam Juvenile) Penguin Group (USA) Inc.

Chris Wooding. The Haunting of Alaizabel Cray. l.t. ed. 2006. 463p. (YA). 22.95 (978-0-7862-8739-0(X)) Thorndike Pr.

Clare, Cassandra. City of Ashes. 2008. (Mortal Instruments Ser.). 480p. (YA). 17.99 (*978-1-4169-1429-7(3) , McElderry, Margaret K.) Simon & Schuster Children's Publishing.

Clare, Cassandra. City of Bones. 2007. (Mortal Instruments Ser.). (YA). 496p. (gr. 9 up). 17.99 (978-1-4169-1428-0(5)); 485p. (*978-1-4287-3999-4(8)) Simon & Schuster Children's Publishing. (McElderry, Margaret K.).

Clement-Moore, Rosemary. Hell Week. 2008. 336p. (YA). 16.99 (*978-0-385-73414-1(X)); lib. bdg. 19.99 (*978-0-385-90429-2(0)) Dell Publishing. (Delacorte Pr.).

—Prom Dates from Hell. 2008. 304p. (YA). pap. 8.99 (*978-0-385-73413-4(1) , Delacorte Bks. for Young Readers) Random Hse. Children's Bks.

Enthoven, Sam. The Black Tattoo. 2006. 512p. (J). (gr. 5-12). 19.99 (978-1-59514-114-9(6) , Razorbill) Penguin Group (USA) Inc.

Ewing, Lynne. Divine One. 2nd rev. ed. 2007. (Sisters of Isis Ser.: No. 2). 272p. (gr. 7 up). 9.99 (*978-1-4231-0343-1(2)) Hyperion Pr.

—The Summoning. 2007. (Sisters of Isis Ser.: No. 1). 272p. (gr. 7 up). 9.99 (*978-1-4231-0342-4(4)) Hyperion Pr.

Fujishima, Kosuke. Oh My Goddess! Ninja Master. 2000. (gr. 7-12). lib. bdg. 23.40 (978-0-613-55182-3(6)) Tandem Library Bks.

Galouchko, Annouchka. Sho & the Demons of the Deep. Galouchko, Annouchka, illus. 1998. (Illus.). 32p. (J). (gr. 2-3). lib. bdg. 17.95 (978-1-55037-398-1(6)) Annick Pr., Ltd. CAN. *Dist:* Firefly Bks., Ltd.

Golden, Christopher & Sniegoski, Thomas E. Monster Island. 2004. (Buffy the Vampire Slayer & Angel Crossover Ser.). 448p. (YA). pap. 7.99 (978-0-689-86699-9(2) , Simon & Schuster Children's Publishing) Simon & Schuster Children's Publishing.

Jenkins, Jerry B. & Perrodin, John. Demons Bluff. 2007. 288p. (YA). (gr. 4-7). 9.99 (978-1-59145-397-0(6)) Nelson, Thomas Inc.

Johnson, Maureen. Devilish. 2007. 272p. (YA). (gr. 7 up). pap. 8.99 (*978-1-59514-132-3(4) , Razorbill) Penguin Group (USA) Inc.

Jones, Willie. Demonology. 2004. 110p. (YA). per. (978-1-932496-13-0(0)) Penman Publishing, Inc.

Kikuchi, Hideyuki. Demon City Hunter, Vol. 1. 2003. 216p. (YA). pap. (978-1-4139-0003-3(8)) ADV Manga.

Lewis, Richard. The Demon Queen. 2008. 252p. (J). (*978-1-4169-3589-6(4) , Simon & Schuster Children's Publishing) Simon & Schuster Children's Publishing.

Murphy, Jim. Fergus & the Night-Demon: An Irish Ghost Story. Manders, John, illus. 2006. 32p. (J). (gr. 3-5). 16.00 (978-0-618-33955-6(8) , Clarion Bks.) Houghton Mifflin Co. Trade & Reference Div.

Paver, Michelle. Chronicles of Ancient Darkness #3: Soul Eater. Taylor, Geoff, illus. 2008. (Chronicles of Ancient Darkness). 352p. (J). pap. 6.99 (*978-0-06-072833-5(7) , Harper Trophy) HarperCollins Pubs.

Ratnett, Michael. Dracula Steps Out. Goulding, June, illus. 1998. 12p. (J). (ps-1). pap. 15.95 (978-0-531-30100-5(1) , Orchard Bks.) Scholastic, Inc.

Shan, Darren, pseud. Bec. 2007. (Demonata Ser.: No. 4). 256p. (J). (gr. 7 up). 16.99 (978-0-316-01389-5(7)) Little Brown & Co.

—Blood Beast. 2007. (Demonata Ser.: No. 5). 240p. (YA). (gr. 10-17). 16.99 (*978-0-316-00377-3(8)) Little, Brown Bks. for Young Readers.

—Demon Thief. 2006. (Demonata Ser.: No. 2). 256p. (J). (gr. 10-17). 15.99 (978-0-316-01237-9(8)) Little Brown & Co.

—Demon Thief. 2007. (Demonata Ser.: No. 2). 256p. (J). (gr. 10-17). pap. 8.99 (*978-0-316-01238-6(6)) Little, Brown Bks. for Young Readers.

—The Demonata. 2007. (YA). (gr. 10-12). pap., per. 26.99 (*978-0-316-02141-8(5)) Little, Brown Bks. for Young Readers.

—Lord Loss. (Demonata Ser.: No. 1). 240p. (J). 2006. (gr. 10-17). pap. 8.99 (978-0-316-01233-1(5)); 2005. (gr. 7-17). 15.99 (978-0-316-11499-8(5)) Little Brown & Co.

—Slawter. 2006. (Demonata Ser.: No. 3). 240p. (J). (gr. 10-17). 16.99 (978-0-316-01387-1(0)) Little Brown & Co.

—Slawter. 2007. (Demonata Ser.: No. 3). 240p. (J). (gr. 10-17). pap. 8.99 (*978-0-316-01388-8(9)) Little, Brown Bks. for Young Readers.

Sisters of Isis3 & Ewing, Lynne. Enchantress. 3rd rev. ed. 2007. 256p. (gr. 7 up). 9.99 (*978-1-4231-0684-5(9)) Hyperion Bks. for Children.

Webb, Mack H., Jr. Danny & the Detention Demons. Espinola, Nicole & Nealon, Eve, illus. l.t. ed. 2007. 52p. (J). per. 15.95 (*978-0-9779576-2-0(4)) Pilinut Pr., Inc.

Yep, Laurence. The Imp That Ate My Homework. 2000. 11.75 (978-0-606-17671-2(3)) Tandem Library Bks.

DENMARK

Britton, Tamara L. Denmark. 2004. (Countries Ser.). (Illus.). 40p. (J). (gr. k-6). lib. bdg. 22.78 (978-1-59197-291-4(4)) ABDO Publishing Co.

Docalavich, Heather. Denmark. 2006. (European Union Ser.). (Illus.). 88p. (YA). (gr. 5 up). lib. bdg. (978-1-4222-0043-8(4)) Mason Crest Pubs.

Dorling Kindersley Publishing Staff, contrib. by. Denmark. 2005. (Illus.). 32p. (YA). (gr. 3 up). lib. bdg. 27.10 (978-1-59389-228-9(4)) Chrysalis Education.

Kwek, Karen & Trapp, Clayton. Welcome to Denmark. 2003. (Welcome to My Country Ser.). (Illus.). 48p. (J). (gr. 2 up). lib. bdg. 26.00 (978-0-8368-2550-3(0)) Stevens, Gareth Inc.

Murphy, Patricia J. Denmark. 2002. (Countries of the World Ser.). (Illus.). 24p. (J). (gr. 2-3). lib. bdg. 18.60 (978-0-7368-1371-6(3) , Bridgestone Bks.) Capstone Pr., Inc.

Stein, R. Conrad. Denmark. 2003. (Enchantment of the World, Second Ser.). (Illus.). 144p. (J). (gr. 5-9). 36.00 (978-0-516-24213-2(X) , Children's Pr.) Scholastic Library Publishing.

Trapp, Clayton. Denmark. 2002. (Countries of the World Ser.). (Illus.), 96p. (J). (gr. 6 up). lib. bdg. 30.00 (978-0-8368-2350-9(8)) Stevens, Gareth Inc.

DENMARK—FICTION

Burglon, Nora. Sticks Across the Chimney: A Story of Denmark. 2005. (Illus.). 224p. (J). per. 11.95 (978-1-892857-13-2(8)) Whole Spirit Pr.

Coville, Bruce & Shakespeare, William. Hamlet. Gore, Leonid, illus. 2004. 40p. (J). (gr. 3). 18.99 (978-0-8037-2708-3(9) , Dial) Penguin Group (USA) Inc.

Deedy, Carmen Agra. The Yellow Star: The Legend of King Christian X of Denmark. Sorensen, Henri, illus. 2000. 32p. (J). (gr. 3-7). 16.95 (978-1-56145-208-8(4) , Q24691) Peachtree Pubs., Ltd.

Lowry, Lois. Compte les Etoiles. pap. 16.95 (978-2-211-03436-4(5)) Archimede Editions FRA. *Dist:* Distribooks, Inc.

—Number the Stars. 2004. 144p. (J). (gr. 5-9). pap. 29.00 incl. audio (978-1-4000-8637-5(X) , Listening Library) Random Hse. Audio Publishing Group.

—Number the Stars. 1998. 144p. (YA). (gr. 5-7). reprint ed. mass mkt. 6.50 (978-0-440-22753-3(4) , Laurel Leaf) Random Hse. Children's Bks.

—Number the Stars. 1998. (J). (978-0-606-13670-9(3)); (gr. 5-8). lib. bdg. 14.15 (978-0-613-72319-0(8)) Tandem Library Bks.

—Number the Stars - Musical. 1998. 33p. (J). pap. 6.95 (978-0-87129-834-8(1) , N03) Dramatic Publishing Co.

—Quien Cuenta las Estrellas. 5th ed. 1998. (SPA., Illus.). 152p. (J). 8.95 (978-84-239-8867-9(8)) Espasa Calpe, S.A. ESP. *Dist:* Continental Bk. Co., Inc.

Lutzen, Hanna. Vlad the Undead. 2001. (gr. 7-12). lib. bdg. 14.10 (978-0-613-88930-8(4)) Tandem Library Bks.

Morpurgo, Michael. Beowulf. Foreman, Michael, illus. 2006. 96p. (J). (gr. 3-7). 17.99 (978-0-7636-3206-9(6)) Candlewick Pr.

Richard, Derrik. The Diamonds of Denmark. ed. 2005. (Illus.). (YA). 24.95 (978-0-9644758-5-4(5)) Peebco Publishing Hse., The.

Roberts, Judson. Viking Warrior. (Strongbow Saga Ser.: Bk. 1). 368p. 2007. (J). pap. 7.99 (*978-0-06-079999-1(4) , HarperTeen); 2006. (Illus.). (YA). 16.99 (978-0-06-079996-0(X)); Bk. 1. 2006. (Illus.). (YA). lib. bdg. 17.89 (978-0-06-079997-7(8)) HarperCollins Pubs.

Shakespeare, William, et al. Hamlet. 2007. (Manga Shakespeare Ser.). 204p. (J). (gr. 2-8). pap. 9.95 (*978-0-8109-9324-2(4) , Abrams Bks. for Young Readers) Abrams, Harry N. , Inc.

Stuchner, Joan Betty. Honey Cake. Nugent, Cynthia, illus. 2008. (J). (*978-0-375-85189-6(5)); pap. (*978-0-375-85190-2(9)); lib. bdg. (*978-0-375-95189-3(X)) Random Hse., Inc.

Toksvig, Sandi. Hitler's Canary. 2007. 192p. (J). (gr. 6 up). 16.95 (978-1-59643-247-5(0)) Roaring Brook Pr.

DENMARK—HISTORY

Harcourt School Publishers Staff. Sail Like a Viking Advanced Level. 3rd ed. 2002. (Trophies Reading Program Ser.). (Illus.). pap. 5.10 (978-0-15-323129-2(7)) Harcourt Schl. Pubs.

Levine, Ellen. Darkness over Denmark: The Danish Resistance & the Rescue of the Jews. 2005. (Illus.). 178p. (YA). (gr. 7 up). pap. 14.95 (978-0-8234-1755-1(7)) Holiday Hse., Inc.

Wild, Mary Campbell. Denmark. 2004. (Modern Nations of the World Ser.). (Illus.). 112p. (YA). (gr. 7-12). lib. bdg. 29.95 (978-1-59018-112-6(3) , 1234025, Lucent Bks.) Thomson Gale.

DENOMINATIONS, RELIGIOUS

see Sects

DENTAL ASSISTANTS

Hodgkins, Fran. Dental Hygienists. 2001. (Community Helpers Ser.). (Illus.). 24p. (J). (gr. 1-2). lib. bdg. 18.60 (978-0-7368-0808-8(6) , Bridgestone Bks.) Capstone Pr., Inc.

DENTISTRY

see also Teeth

Adamson, Heather. A Day in the Life of a Dentist. 2003. (First Facts Ser.). (Illus.). 24p. (J). lib. bdg. 21.26 (978-0-7368-2282-4(8)) Capstone Pr., Inc.

Bagley, Katie. Brush Well: A Look at Dental Care. 2001. (Your Health Ser.). (Illus.). 24p. (J). (gr. 1-2). lib. bdg. 18.60 (978-0-7368-0969-6(4) , Bridgestone Bks.) Capstone Pr., Inc.

Dember-Paige, Judith. Smile Wide Look Inside. 2005. (Illus.). 16p. (J). (gr. k-5). 15.00 (978-0-9754008-0-7(0)) ABCDE Academic Bks. for Children's Development Through Education.

Dental Health Kit. 2006. (J). pap. (*978-1-57332-390-1(X)) HighReach Learning, Inc.

Dental Health Set. (gr. k-2). 114.95 (978-0-7368-9035-9(1)) Red Brick Learning.

Dentists. (Community Helpers Ser.). 24p. (J). 6.95 (978-0-7368-8452-5(1)) Capstone Pr., Inc.

Dentists, 6 vols. (gr. 2-5). 36.95 (978-0-7368-8467-9(X)) Red Brick Learning.

DK Publishing Staff. Going to the Dentist. 2007. 12p. (J). (ps-2). bds. 6.99 (*978-0-7566-3102-4(5)) Dorling Kindersley Publishing, Inc.

Dorling Kindersley Publishing Staff. A Trip to the Dentist. 2006. (Dk Readers Ser.). (Illus.). 32p. (J). 14.99 (978-0-7566-1915-2(7)); pap. 3.99 (978-0-7566-1914-5(9)) Dorling Kindersley Publishing, Inc.

Douglas, Lloyd G. My Mouth. 2004. (Wel-My Body Ser.). (J). 18.00 (978-0-516-24061-9(7) , Children's Pr.) Scholastic Library Publishing.

Ehrlich, Fred. Does a Tiger Open Wide? 2006. (Illus.). 32p. pap. 5.95 (978-1-59354-144-6(9)) Blue Apple Bks.

—Does a Tiger Open Wide? Bolam, Emily, illus. 2003. (Early Experiences Ser.). 32p. 10.95 (978-1-929766-78-9(5)) Blue Apple Bks.

Frost, Helen. Going to the Dentist. Saunders-Smith, Gail, ed. 1998. (Dental Health Ser.). (Illus.). 24p. (J). (gr. k-1). lib. bdg. 15.93 (978-0-7368-0114-0(6) , Pebble Bks.) Capstone Pr., Inc.

—Going to the Dentist. 1998. (Dental Health Ser.). (J). lib. bdg. 13.25 (978-0-516-21494-8(2) , Children's Pr.) Scholastic Library Publishing.

Going to the Dentist, 6 vols. (gr. k-2). 28.95 (978-0-7368-8139-5(5)) Red Brick Learning.

Gorman, Jacqueline Laks. Dentist. Andersen, Gregg, illus. 2002. (People in My Community Ser.). 24p. (J). (ps up). lib. bdg. 19.33 (978-0-8368-3293-8(0) , Weekly Reader Early Learning Library) Stevens, Gareth Inc.

—Dentist/El Dentista. Acosta, Tatiana & Gutiérrez, Guillermo, trs. 2002. (Weekly Reader Early Learning Library). (SPA & ENG., Illus.). 24p. (J). (ps up). lib. bdg. 19.33 (978-0-8368-3307-2(4) , Weekly Reader Early Learning Library) Stevens, Gareth Inc.

Gorman, Jacqueline Laks & Macken, JoAnn Early. Dentist. Andersen, Gregg, photos by. 2002. (Weekly Reader Early Learning Library). (Illus.). 24p. (J). (ps up). pap. 7.93 (978-0-8368-3300-3(7) , Weekly Reader Early Learning Library) Stevens, Gareth Inc.

—Dentist/El Dentista. Coffey, Colleen & Carrillo, Consuelo, trs. Andersen, Gregg, photos by. 2002. (Weekly Reader Early Learning Library). (ENG & SPA., Illus.). 24p. (J). (ps up). pap. 5.95 (978-0-8368-3341-6(4) , Weekly Reader Early Learning Library) Stevens, Gareth Inc.

Harcourt School Publishers Staff. Trofeos On Level: El Dr. Flores. 3rd ed. 2002. (SPA., Illus.). pap. 6.80 (978-0-15-323907-6(7)) Harcourt Schl. Pubs.

—Your Health Reader: The Dentist. 3rd ed. 2003. (Illus.). (ps). pap. 9.40 (978-0-15-338775-3(0)) Harcourt Schl. Pubs.

Hewitt, Sally. First Experiences: Going to the Dentist. 2004. (Illus.). 24p. (J). lib. bdg. 15.95 (978-1-59566-011-4(9)) QEB Publishing Inc.

Hughes, Monica. First Visit to the Dentist. 2003. 24p. (J). pap. 5.50 (978-1-4109-0671-7(X)); (Illus.). lib. bdg. 18.56 (978-1-4109-0645-8(0)) Raintree.

—First Visit to the Dentist. 2003. (ps-2). lib. bdg. 13.55 (978-0-613-78207-4(0)) Tandem Library Bks.

Hunter, Rebecca. Dentist. Fairclough, Chris, photos by. 2007. (People Who Help Us Ser.). (Illus.). 32p. (J). 22.95 (*978-1-84234-386-9(6) , Evans Brothers, Limited) Evans Publishing Group GBR. *Dist:* Independent Pubs. Group.

Ichord, Loretta Frances. Toothworms & Spider Juice: An Illustrated History of Dentistry. 2000. (Twenty-First Century Medical Library). (Illus.). 96p. (gr. 4-8). lib. bdg. (978-0-7613-1465-3(2) , Millbrook Pr.) Lerner Publishing Group.

Keller, Laurie. Open Wide: Tooth School Inside. Keller, Laurie, illus. rev. ed. 2003. (Illus.). 40p. (J). pap. 6.95 (978-0-8050-7268-6(3) , Holt, Henry & Co. Bks. For Young Readers) Holt, Henry & Co.

—Open Wide: Tooth School Inside. rev. ed. 2000. (Illus.). 40p. (J). (gr. k-5). 17.95 (978-0-8050-6192-5(4) , Holt, Henry & Co. Bks. For Young Readers) Holt, Henry & Co.

—Open Wide: Tooth School Inside. Keller, Laurie, illus. unabr. ed. 2006. (Illus.). (J). (gr. k-5). 24.95 incl. audio (*978-0-439-84917-3(9) , WHRA650); 29.95 incl. audio compact disk (*978-0-439-84918-0(7) , WHCD650); pap. 14.95 incl. audio (*978-0-439-84919-7(5) , WPRA650); pap. 18.95 incl. audio compact disk (*978-0-439-84920-3(9) , WPCD650) Weston Woods Studios, Inc.

Kemper, Bitsy. Out & about at the Dentist. Trover, Zachary, illus. 2006. (J). 25.26 (978-1-4048-2278-8(X)) Picture Window Bks.

Libal, Autumn & Hovius, Christopher. Taking Care of Your Smile: A Teen's Guide to Dental Care. 2005. (Science of Health Ser.). (Illus.). 128p. (J). lib. bdg. 24.95 (978-1-59084-846-3(2)) Mason Crest Pubs.

Mackenzie, Michael. Lower Denture Problems? The Worlds Only Self-Help Book on Dentures. 1999. (Illus.). 136p. 19.95 (978-0-9668234-9-3(4)) First Bite Publishing.

McGinty, Alice B. Dental Care. 1999. (Staying Healthy Ser.). (978-0-606-18160-0(1)) Tandem Library Bks.

Miller, Heather. What Does a Dentist Do? 2006. (What Does a Community Helper Do? Ser.). (Illus.). 24p. (J). lib. bdg. 21.26 (978-0-7660-2323-9(0) , Enslow Elementary) Enslow Pubs., Inc.

Minden, Cecilia & Armantrout, Linda M. Dentists. 2006. (Neighborhood Helpers Ser.). (Illus.). 32p. (J). (gr. k-4). 22.79 (978-1-59296-562-5(8)) Child's World, Inc.

Murkoff, Heidi. What to Expect When You Go to the Dentist. Rader, Laura, illus. 2002. (What to Expect Kids Ser.). 32p. (J). (ps-k). 10.99 (978-0-694-01328-9(5) , Harper Festival) HarperCollins Pubs.

Murphy, Patricia J. The Dentist's Office. 2004. (Visit To Ser.). (Illus.), 24p. (J). lib. bdg. 19.93 (978-0-7368-2580-1(0) , Pebble Bks.) Capstone Pr., Inc.

Open Wide: Individual Title Six-Packs. (gr. k-1). 23.00 (978-0-7635-8835-9(0)) Rigby Education.

Petty, Kate. Going to the Dentist. 2007. (J). (*978-1-59604-158-5(7)) Stargazer Bks.

QEB Start Reading Together National Book Stores Edition: First Experiences: Going to the Dentist. 2006. (J). per. (978-1-59566-260-6(X)) QEB Publishing Inc.

Radabaugh, Melinda Beth. Going to the Dentist. 2003. (First Time Ser.). (Illus.). 24p. (J). pap. 5.50 (978-1-4034-0467-1(4)); lib. bdg. 18.50 (978-1-4034-0228-8(0)) Heinemann Library.

Rogers, Josephine. Dental Health, Beautiful Teeth. 2000. (Illus.). 32p. (J). (ps-7). pap., act. bk. ed. 7.00 (978-0-9679975-0-6(X)) Rogers, Josephine H.

Royston, Angela. Tooth Decay. 2004. (Heinemann First Library). (Illus.). 32p. (J). lib. bdg. (978-1-4034-4827-9(2)) Heinemann Library.

Schaefer, Lola M. Helpers in Our Community: We Need Dentists; We Need Doctors; We Need Farmers; We Need Fire Fighters; We Need Mail Carriers; We Need Nurses; We Need Police Officers; We Need Veterinarians, 8 bks. Saunders-Smith, Gail, ed. 2000. (Illus.). (J). (gr. k-1). lib. bdg. 116.80 (978-0-7368-0451-6(X) , Pebble Bks.) Capstone Pr., Inc.

—We Need Dentists. Saunders-Smith, Gail, ed. 1999. (Helpers in Our Community Ser.). (Illus.). 24p. (J). (gr. k-1). lib. bdg. 15.93 (978-0-7368-0388-5(2) , Pebble Bks.) Capstone Pr., Inc.

—We Need Dentists. 1999. pap. 13.25 (978-0-516-21901-1(4) , Children's Pr.) Scholastic Library Publishing.

Schuh, Mari C. At the Dentist. 2008. (J). (*978-1-4296-1242-5(8) , Pebble Bks.) Capstone Pr., Inc.

—Brushing Teeth. 2008. (J). (*978-1-4296-1240-1(1) , Pebble Bks.) Capstone Pr., Inc.

—Flossing Teeth. 2008. (J). (*978-1-4296-1241-8(X) , Pebble Bks.) Capstone Pr., Inc.

—Snacks for Healthy Teeth. 2008. (J). (*978-1-4296-1239-5(8) , Pebble Bks.) Capstone Pr., Inc.

Sessler, Peter & Sessler, N. Sports Cars. 1999. (Off to the Races Ser.). (Illus.). 24p. (J). (gr. 2-6). lib. bdg. 25.64 (978-1-57103-282-9(7)) Rourke Publishing, LLC.

Simon, Charnan. Dentist. 2003. (Wonder Books Level 3: Careers Ser.). (Illus.). 32p. (J). (ps-2). 22.79 (978-1-56766-463-8(6)) Child's World, Inc.

Swanson, Diane. The Dentist & You. Cowles, Rose, illus. 2002. 32p. (J). (ps-2). pap. 7.95 (978-1-55037-728-6(0)) Annick Pr., Ltd. CAN. *Dist:* Firefly Bks., Ltd.

—Dentist & You. 2002. (gr. 5-8). lib. bdg. 16.40 (978-0-613-78435-1(9)) Tandem Library Bks.

The Tooth Chicken. (J). 8.40 (978-0-934510-24-0(5) , W013) American Dental Assn.

Tuggle, Diane. Spencer's Toothbrush Vol. 1: An Adventure in Preventive Dental Health. 1999. (Illus.). 48p. (J). (gr. k-10). pap. 12.99 (978-0-9674450-1-4(9)) Forerunner Pr.

Vittorini, Candace & Boyer-Quick, Sara. Joey Goes to the Dentist. 2007. (Illus.). 28p. (J). (*978-1-84310-854-2(2)) Kingsley, Jessica Ltd.

We Need Dentists, 6 vols. (gr. k-2). 28.95 (978-0-7368-8598-0(6)) Red Brick Learning.

Winchester, Elizabeth. The Right Bite: Dentists As Detectives. (24/7 - Science Behind the Scenes Ser.). 64p. (J). (gr. 8-12). 2007. pap. 7.95 (*978-0-531-18734-0(9)); 2006. 25.00 (978-0-531-12062-0(7)) Scholastic Library Publishing. (Watts, Franklin).

DENTISTRY—FICTION

Adventure of My Dentist & the Tooth Fairy Activity & Coloring Book, First Edition. 2005. (978-1-59649-533-3(2)) Whispering Pine Pr., Inc.

Adventures of My Dentist & the Tooth Fairy A Daily Journal. 2005. (J). spiral bd. 19.95 (978-1-59649-532-6(4)); per. 19.95 (978-1-59649-531-9(6)) Whispering Pine Pr., Inc.

Adventures of My Dentist & the Tooth Fairy Activity & Coloring Book Second Edition. 2nd ed. 2005. (J). per. 19.95 (978-1-59649-535-7(9)) Whispering Pine Pr., Inc.

Adventures of My Dentist & the Tooth Fairy Adventures in Learning Book. 2005. (J). per. 19.95 (978-1-59649-537-1(5)) Whispering Pine Pr., Inc.

Adventures of My Dentist & the Tooth Fairy Educational Curriculum Book. 2005. per. 19.95 (978-1-59649-540-1(5)) Whispering Pine Pr., Inc.

Adventures of My Dentist & the Tooth Fairy Story Book. 2005. (J). 9.95 (978-1-59649-412-1(3)); spiral bd. 9.95 (978-1-59649-542-5(1)); per. 9.95 (978-1-59649-541-8(3)); cd-rom 9.95 (978-1-59649-543-2(X)) Whispering Pine Pr., Inc.

Barber, Tom. Open Wide. Chapman, Lynne, illus. 2007. 24p. (J). pap. 6.99 (*978-1-84458-053-8(9)) Anova Bks. GBR. *Dist:* Independent Pubs. Group.

Barber, Tom & Chapman, Lynne. Open Wide! 2004. (Illus.). 32p. 14.95 (978-1-84458-241-9(8)) Chrysalis Children's Bks. GBR. *Dist:* Transition Vendor.

Civardi, Anne. Going to the Dentist. rev. ed. 2005. (First Experiences Ser.). 16p. (J). pap. 4.95 (978-0-7945-1007-7(8) , Usborne) EDC Publishing.

Clarke, Jane. Tooth Trouble. Johansson, Cecilia, illus. 2005. (J). (978-0-439-74496-6(2)) Scholastic, Inc.

Clarke, Jane & Johansson, Cecilia. Tusk Trouble. (Illus.). 25p. (J). (978-0-340-87725-8(1) , Hodder Children's Books) Hodder Children's Division.

—Tusk Trouble. 2004. (Illus.). 32p. (J). pap. 8.99 (978-0-340-86079-3(0) , Hodder & Stoughton) Hodder General Publishing Division GBR. *Dist:* Trafalgar Square Publishing.

Cousins, Lucy. Maisy, Charley, & the Wobbly Tooth. Cousins, Lucy, illus. 2006. (Illus.). 32p. (J). (gr. k-k). 12.99 (978-0-7636-2904-5(9)) Candlewick Pr.

Dalmatian Press Staff. Elmo Visits the Dentist. 2007. 24p. pap. 3.50 (*978-1-4037-3430-3(5)) Dalmatian Pr.

The Dentist, 2 Packs. (Chiquilibros Ser.). (ps-1). 12.00 (978-0-7635-8545-7(9)) Rigby Education.

Deslauriers, Anne. La Fee Dentiste. Begin, Jean-Guy, illus. 2004. (Collection des 6 Ans). (FRE.). 64p. (J). 7.95 (978-2-922565-99-7(8)) Editions de la Paix CAN. *Dist:* World of Reading, Ltd.

Doctor de Soto. 2004. (J). 24.95 incl. audio (978-0-89719-770-0(4)) Weston Woods Studios, Inc.

Doctor Desoto. 2004. (J). pap. 18.95 incl. audio compact disk (978-0-7882-0950-5(7)); pap. 32.75 incl. audio (978-1-55592-219-1(8)); pap. 32.75 incl. audio (978-1-55592-220-7(1)); pap. 14.95 incl. audio (978-1-55592-937-4(0)) Weston Woods Studios, Inc.

Fiedler, S. & Kraushaar, S. Say Ahh! 2006. (Illus.). 12p. (J). 8.95 (978-0-7358-2095-1(3)) North-South Bks., Inc.

Finnegan, Evelyn M. My Little Friend Goes to the Dentist. Houghton, Diane R., illus. 2006. 32p. (J). (ps-3). reprint ed. pap. 7.00 (978-1-4223-5404-9(0)) DIANE Publishing Co.

Florie, Christine. Braces for Cori. Tripp, Christine, illus. 2005. (Rookie Reader Skill Set Ser.). (J). 31p. (gr. k-2). pap. 4.95 (978-0-516-25286-5(0)); 32p. (gr. 1-2). 19.50 (978-0-516-25136-3(8)) Scholastic Library Publishing. (Children's Pr.).

Greig, Allison. Stacey's Adventures. 2006. (Illus.). 64p. pap. (*978-1-84401-035-6(X)) Athena Pr.

Harcourt School Publishers Staff. Dr. Brown at Work: On Level. 3rd ed. 2002. (Trophies Reading Program Ser.). (Illus.). pap. 5.10 (978-0-15-322996-1(9)) Harcourt Schl. Pubs.

Hood, Karen Jean Matsko. My Dentist & the Tooth Fairy A Daily Journal. 2002. cd-rom 13.95 (978-1-59210-597-7(1)) Whispering Pine Pr., Inc.

—My Dentist & the Tooth Fairy Activity & Coloring Book. 2002. (J). per. 17.95 (978-1-59210-596-0(3)) Whispering Pine Pr., Inc.

Jarrell, Pamela R. Dr. Danny Checks My Teeth. Bicking, Judith, illus. l.t. ed. 2001. (Big Bks.). 8p. (J). (ps-1). pap. 10.95 (978-1-57332-217-1(2)); pap. 10.95 (978-1-57332-218-8(0)) HighReach Learning, Inc.

Klein, Adria F. Max Goes to the Dentist. Gallagher-Cole, Mernie, illus. 2005. (Read-It! Readers Ser.). 24p. (J). (ps). lib. bdg. 18.60 (978-1-4048-1181-2(8)) Picture Window Bks.

Maloney, Peter & Zekauskas, Felicia. Lose That Tooth! 2005. (Illus.). 32p. (J). (*978-0-439-67639-7(8)) Scholastic, Inc.

Mayer, Mercer. Just Going to the Dentist. Mayer, Mercer, illus. 2001. (Little Critter Ser.). (Illus.). 24p. (J). (gr. k-k). pap. 3.29 (978-0-307-12583-5(1) , 12583, Random Hse. Bks. for Young Readers) Random Hse. Children's Bks.

—Just Going to the Dentist. Mayer, Mercer, illus. 1998. (Little Critter Ser.). (J). (ps-3). 10.09 (978-0-606-12374-7(1)) Tandem Library Bks.

Moffatt, Julia. Mi dentista no es un Monstruo. Axworthy, Anni, illus. 2005. (Lightning Readers Ser.). 32p. (J). (gr. k-1). pap. 3.95 (978-0-7696-4070-9(2) , Gingham Dog Pr.) School Specialty Publishing.

—My Dentist Is Not a Monster. Axworthy, Anni, illus. 2005. (Lightning Readers Ser.). 32p. (J). (gr. k-1). pap. 3.95 (978-0-7696-4030-3(3) , Gingham Dog Pr.) School Specialty Publishing.

My Dentist & the Tooth Fairy Christian Adventures in Learning Book. 2005. (J). cd-rom 13.95 (978-1-59649-319-3(4)) Whispering Pine Pr., Inc.

My Dentist & the Tooth Fairy Hood Christian Educational Curriculum Book. 2005. (J). cd-rom 13.95 (978-1-59649-320-9(8)) Whispering Pine Pr., Inc.

My Dentist & the Tooth Fairy Story Book. 2005. (J). 15.95 (978-1-59649-432-9(8)) Whispering Pine Pr., Inc.

My Dentist, My Friend. 2002. (Illus.). 24p. (J). (ps-3). 5.95 (978-0-8249-5388-1(6)) Ideals Pubns.

Nathanson, Laura. El Problema de los Miercoles. (SPA.). 160p. (YA). (gr. 5-8). (978-84-279-3181-7(6) , NG3677) Noguer y Caralt Editores, S. A. ESP. *Dist:* Lectorum Pubns., Inc.

—El Problema de los Miercoles. 2001. (SPA.). (gr. 5-8). lib. bdg. 17.60 (978-0-613-80655-8(7)) Tandem Library Bks.

Ricci, Christine. Show Me Your Smile! A Visit to the Dentist. Roper, Robert, illus. 2005. (Dora the Explorer Ser.). 24p. (J). pap. 3.99 (978-0-689-87169-6(4) , Simon Spotlight/Nickelodeon) Simon & Schuster Children's Publishing.

Robinson, Robert, et al. Danny Goes to the Dentist. Smee, Nicola, illus. 2002. (First Experiences Ser.). 32p. (J). (gr. k-2). 15.00 (978-1-57768-987-4(9) , Waterbird Bks.) School Specialty Publishing.

Rosenberry, Vera. Vera Goes to the Dentist. rev. ed. 2002. (Illus.). 32p. (J). (ps-3). 16.95 (978-0-8050-6668-5(3) , Holt, Henry & Co. Bks. For Young Readers) Holt, Henry & Co.

Schoberle, Cecile. Open Wide: A Visit to the Dentist. Goldberg, Barry, illus. 2000. (Rugrats Ser.). 24p. (J). (ps-2). per. (978-0-671-77361-8(5) , Simon & Schuster Children's Publishing) Simon & Schuster Children's Publishing.

—Open Wide! a Visit to the Dentist. 2000. (gr. k-3). lib. bdg. 11.25 (978-0-613-22138-2(9)) Tandem Library Bks.

Steig, William. Doctor De Soto. 2003. (Picture Books Collection). (SPA.). 32p. (J). (gr. k-3). 16.95 (978-84-372-6616-9(5)) Altea, Ediciones, S.A. - Grupo Santillana ESP. *Dist:* Santillana USA Publishing Co., Inc.

—Doctor De Soto. Steig, William, illus. 2002. (Illus.). (J). 14.43 (978-0-7587-0256-2(6)) Book Wholesalers, Inc.

—Doctor De Soto. ed. 2004. (J). (gr. k-3). spiral bd. (978-0-616-01784-5(7)); spiral bd. (978-0-616-01785-2(5)) Canadian National Institute for the Blind/Institut National Canadien pour les Aveugles.

—Doctor De Soto. Puncel, María, tr. 1998. (SPA., Illus.). pap., tchr. ed. 37.95 incl. audio (978-0-87499-459-9(4)); (J). pap. 16.95 incl. audio (978-0-87499-458-2(6)) Live Oak Media.

—Doctor De Soto. 2004. (J). (gr. k-5). pap. 14.95 incl. audio (978-0-89719-771-7(2) , PRA284) Weston Woods Studios, Inc.

Suarez Romero, Alfonso. Maraca. Alvarado, Dalia & Pacheco, Luis Gabriel, illus. rev. ed. 2006. (Castillo de la Lectura Verde Ser.). (SPA.). 120p. (J). pap. 7.95 (978-970-20-0128-7(5)) Castillo, Ediciones, S. A. de C. V. MEX. *Dist:* Macmillan.

Thaler, Mike. Fang the Dentist. 2000. (J). (978-0-606-19674-1(9)) Tandem Library Bks.

Williams-Reyes, Inez. Kimani's Visit to the Dentist. 2003. per. 5.00 (978-0-9669289-3-8(8)) Publish To Go Pubns., LLC.

Willson, Sarah. Behold, No Cavities! A Visit to the Dentist. Moore, Harry, illus. 2007. (SpongeBob SquarePants Ser.). 24p. (J). pap. 3.99 (***978-1-4169-3566-7(5)*** , Simon Spotlight/Nickelodeon) Simon & Schuster Children's Publishing.

Wilson, Sarah. Dragon Tooth Trouble. 2006. (Illus.). 64p. (J). 15.95 (978-0-8050-7830-5(4) , Holt, Henry & Co. Bks. For Young Readers) Holt, Henry & Co.

Wurm, Kristine K. Truman's Loose Tooth, Chesworth, Michael, illus. 2006. 32p. (J). per. 16.95 (978-0-9768513-0-1(X)) Spirited Publishing, LLC.

DENTISTRY—VOCATIONAL GUIDANCE

Nelson, Kristin L. Dentists. 2005. (Pull Ahead Bks.). (Illus.). 32p. (J). (gr. k-2). 22.60 (978-0-8225-1688-0(8)) Lerner Publishing Group.

Ready, Dee. Dentistas. Ferrer, Martín Luis Guzman, tr. from ENG. 1998. (Servidores Comunitarios Ser.). (SPA., Illus.). 24p. (J). (gr. 1-2). lib. bdg. 18.60 (978-1-56065-795-8(2) , Bridgestone Bks.) Capstone Pr., Inc.

Schaefer, Lola M. Dental Office. 2000. (Who Works Here? Ser.). (Illus.). 32p. (J). (gr. 1-3). lib. bdg. 21.36 (978-1-57572-517-8(7)) Heinemann Library.

Wallner, Rosemary. Dental Assistant. 2000. (Career Exploration Ser.). (Illus.). 48p. (J). (gr. 3-4). lib. bdg. 21.26 (978-0-7368-0593-3(1) , LifeMatters Bks.) Capstone Pr., Inc.

DENVER (COLO.)

Baker, Gayle. Denver: A Boomtown History. 2004. (Illus.). 96p. per. 9.95 (978-0-9710984-4-2(1)) HarborTown Histories.

Nelson, Elizabeth. I Live in Denver: A Guided Tour of Denver's Past & Present. Nelson, Elizabeth, illus. 2002. (Illus.). 64p. (J). bds. 19.95 (978-0-9714078-0-0(0)) Greenwich Pr.

Rich, D. The Denver Hiking Guide: 45 Hikes Within 45 Minutes of Denver. 2nd rev. ed. 1999. (Illus.). 104p. (Orig.). (J). pap. 12.95 (978-1-889593-58-6(3)) 3D Pr., Inc.

Sutton, Carolyn. The Preschooler's Guide to Denver: Best Outings for Kids under 6 Years Old. 2002. 160p. pap. 15.95 (978-0-9715543-0-6(7) , Lil' Pardner Pr.) Fire Creek Publishing Corp.

DENVER BRONCOS (FOOTBALL TEAM)

Christopher, Matt. In the Huddle with... John Elway. 1999. (J). (978-0-606-16726-0(9)) Tandem Library Bks.

—John Elway. 1999. (J). pap. (978-0-316-14283-0(2)) Little Brown & Co.

Denver Broncos Organization Staff. Denver Broncos. CWC Sports Inc., ed. 1998. (NFL Team Yearbooks Ser.). (J). (gr. 1-12). pap. 9.99 (978-1-891613-07-4(3)) Everett Sports Publishing & Marketing.

Dougherty, Denis. John Elway. 1999. (Jam Session Ser.). (Illus.). 32p. (J). (gr. 4). lib. bdg. 24.21 (978-1-57765-040-9(9) , ABDO & Daughters) ABDO Publishing Co.

Leboutillier, Nate. Denver Broncos. 2005. (Super Bowl Champions Ser.). (Illus.). 24p. (gr. 1-4). 16.95 (978-1-58341-383-8(9) , Creative Education) Creative Co., The.

Macnow, Glen. The Denver Broncos Football Team. 2001. (Great Sports Teams Ser.). (Illus.). 48p. (J). (gr. 4-10). lib. bdg. 23.93 (978-0-7660-1489-3(4)) Enslow Pubs., Inc.

Schmalzbauer, Adam. The History of the Denver Broncos. 2004. (NFL Today Ser.). (Illus.). 32p. 18.95 (978-1-58341-295-4(6) , Creative Education) Creative Co., The.

Stewart, Mark. Denver Broncos. 2006. (Team Spirit Ser.). (Illus.). 48p. (J). lib. bdg. 25.27 (978-1-59953-066-6(X)) Norwood Hse. Pr.

—Terrell Davis: Toughing It Out. 1999. (New Wave Ser.). (Illus.). 48p. (gr. 4 up). lib. bdg. 22.90 (978-0-7613-1514-8(4) , Millbrook Pr.) Lerner Publishing Group.

DEOXYRIBONUCLEIC ACID

see DNA

DEPARTMENT STORES—FICTION

Bond, Michael. Paddington Bear & the Christmas Surprise. 1999. (ps-2). lib. bdg. 14.10 (978-0-613-22917-3(7)); (J). (978-0-606-17305-6(6)) Tandem Library Bks.

Corey, Shana. Milly & the Macy's Parade. Helquist, Brett, illus. 2006. 38p. (J). (gr. 4-8). reprint ed. 17.00 (978-1-4223-5174-1(2)) DIANE Publishing Co.

Kavanagh, Terry. Batman: Tell-A-Riddle Telephone Book. Doescher, Erik et al, illus. 2002. (J). (978-0-7853-6402-3(1)) Publications International, Ltd.

Pratchett, Terry. The Bromeliad: Truckers, Diggers, & Wings. 2003. 512p. (J). (gr. 5 up). 18.99 (978-0-06-009493-5(1)); 18.89 (978-0-06-054855-1(X)) HarperCollins Pubs.

—Diggers. 2004. (Bromeliad Trilogy Ser.). 224p. (J). (gr. 5 up). reprint ed. pap. 5.99 (978-0-06-009494-2(X) , Harper Trophy) HarperCollins Pubs.

—Wings. 2004. (Bromeliad Trilogy Ser.). 224p. (J). (gr. 5 up). reprint ed. pap. 5.99 (978-0-06-009495-9(8) , Harper Trophy) HarperCollins Pubs.

Sharmat, Marjorie Weinman. Nate the Great & the Big Sniff. Weston, Martha, illus. 2003. (Nate the Great Ser.). 48p. (gr. 1-4). pap. 4.50 (978-0-440-41502-2(0) , Yearling) Random Hse. Children's Bks.

—Nate the Great & the Big Sniff. 2003. (gr. k-3). lib. bdg. 12.40 (978-0-613-63966-8(9)) Tandem Library Bks.

Sharmat, Marjorie Weinman, et al. Nate the Great & the Big Sniff. Weston, Martha, illus. 2001. (Nate the Great Ser.). 48p. (J). (gr. 1-4). 13.95 (978-0-385-32604-9(1) , Delacorte Bks. for Young Readers) Random Hse. Children's Bks.

Vinopol, Corinne & Bednarczyk, Angela. ASL Tales & Games for Kids - Biscuit Blvd: Computer Software in American Sign Language. 2004. (J). cd-rom 34.95 (978-0-9667589-9-3(4)) Institute for Disabilities Research & Training, Inc.

Wax, Wendy. Valentine for Tommy. 2003. (gr. k-3). lib. bdg. 11.80 (978-0-613-57563-8(6)) Tandem Library Bks.

Wells, Helen. Cherry Ames, Department Store Nurse. 2007. (YA). (***978-0-8261-0415-1(0)***) Springer.

DEPENDENT CHILDREN

see Child Welfare

DEPRESSION, MENTAL

Adams, Jacqueline. Obsessive-Compulsive Disorder. 2007. (Diseases & Disorders Ser.). (Illus.). 128p. (gr. 7-10). 31.20 (***978-1-4205-0000-4(7)*** , Lucent Bks.) Thomson Gale.

Andrews, Beth. Why Are You So Sad? A Child's Book about Parental Depression. Wong, Nicole A., illus. 2002. 32p. (J). pap. 8.95 (978-1-55798-887-4(0)); 14.95 (978-1-55798-836-2(6)) American Psychological Assn. (Magination Pr.).

Ayer, Eleanor H. Everything You Need to Know about Depression. rev. ed. 2001. (Need to Know Library). (Illus.). 64p. (YA). (gr. 4-6). lib. bdg. 25.25 (978-0-8239-3439-3(X)) Rosen Publishing Group, Inc., The.

Benziger, Katherine. Overcoming Depression: The Easy to Read Simple to Use Little Book You Can Use to Turn Your Life Around. 2005th ed. 2005. (Illus.). 59p. spiral bd., wbk. ed. 15.00 (978-1-880931-46-2(X)) KBA, LLC.

Berne, Emma Carlson, ed. Depression. 2007. (Contemporary Issues Companion Ser.). 184p. (gr. 10-12). lib. bdg. 36.20 (***978-0-7377-3645-8(3)*** , Greenhaven Pr., Inc.) Thomson Gale.

Clarke, Julie & Kirby-Payne, Ann. Understanding Weight & Depression. 2005. (Teen Eating Disorder Prevention Book Ser.). (Illus.). 192p. (J). (gr. 7-12). lib. bdg. 25.25 (978-0-8239-2994-8(9) , E2WEDE) Rosen Publishing Group, Inc., The.

Cobain, Bev. When Nothing Matters Anymore: A Survival Guide for Depressed Teens. Verdick, Elizabeth, ed. Tolbert, Jeff, illus. 1998. 176p. (YA). (gr. 8 up). pap. 13.95 (978-1-57542-036-3(8)) Free Spirit Publishing, Inc.

Cobain, Bev & Verdick, Elizabeth. When Nothing Matters Anymore: A Survival Guide for Depressed Teens. 2007. (Illus.). 176p. (J). pap. (***978-1-57542-235-0(2)*** Free Spirit Publishing, Inc.

Copeland, Mary Ellen & Copans, Stuart. Recovering from Depression: A Workbook for Teens. rev. ed. 2002. 192p. (YA). pap. 22.95 (978-1-55766-592-8(3)) Brookes, Paul H. Publishing Co.

Crist, James. What to Do When Youre Sad & Lonely: A Guide for Kids. 2005. (What to Do When Ser.). (Illus.). 128p. (J). (gr. 4-8). pap. 9.95 (978-1-57542-189-6(5)) Free Spirit Publishing, Inc.

Demetriades, Helen A. Bipolar Disorder, Depression, & Other Mood Disorders. 2002. (Diseases & People Ser.). (Illus.). 112p. (YA). (gr. 6-12). lib. bdg. 26.60 (978-0-7660-1898-3(9)) Enslow Pubs., Inc.

Docalavich, Heather. Antidepressants & Psychology: Talk Therapy vs. Medication. 2006. (Antidepressants Ser.). (Illus.). 120p. (J). (gr. 7 up). (978-1-4222-0096-4(5)) Mason Crest Pubs.

Esherick, Joan. Drug Therapy & Mood Disorders. 2003. (Encyclopedia of Psychiatric Drugs & Their Disorders Ser.). (Illus.). 128p. (J). lib. bdg. (978-1-59084-568-4(4)) Mason Crest Pubs.

Gold, Susan Dudley. Bipolar Disorder & Depression. 2000. (Health Watch Ser.). (Illus.). 48p. (YA). (gr. 4-10). lib. bdg. 23.93 (978-0-7660-1654-5(4)) Enslow Pubs., Inc.

Helmer, Diana Star. Let's Talk about When Your Mom or Dad Is Unhappy. 1999. (Let's Talk Library). (Illus.). 24p. (J). (gr. 3). lib. bdg. 18.75 (978-0-8239-5192-5(8) , PowerKids Pr.) Rosen Publishing Group, Inc., The.

Hirschmann, Kris. Depression. 2006. (Understanding Diseases & Disorders Ser.). (J). (978-0-7377-3171-2(0) , Greenhaven Pr., Inc.) Thomson Gale.

Hyde, Margaret O. & Forsyth, Elizabeth Held. Depression. 2002. (Single Title - Science Ser.). (Illus.). 112p. (YA). (gr. 8-12). pap. 25.00 (978-0-531-11892-4(4) , Watts, Franklin) Scholastic Library Publishing.

Irwin, Cait. Depression: Challenge the Beast Within Yourself & Win. Shaughnessy, Patrick S. et al, eds. 2nd rev. ed. 1998. (Illus.). 112p. (J). (gr. 6-12). pap. 12.95 (978-0-9663665-1-8(4)) AVI Communications, Inc.

Irwin, Cait, et al. Monochrome Days: A First-Hand Account of One Teenager's Experience with Depression. 2007. (Adolescent Mental Health Initiative Ser.). (Illus.). 184p. (gr. 8 up). 30.00 (978-0-19-531004-7(7)); pap. 9.95 (978-0-19-531005-4(5)) Oxford Univ. Pr., Inc.

Jaffe, Steven L. Prozac & Other Antidepressants. 1999. (Junior Drug Awareness Ser.). (Illus.). 80p. (J). (gr. 4-8). 32.00 (978-0-7910-5204-4(4) , Chelsea Hse.) Facts On File, Inc.

Lennard-Brown, Sarah. Stress & Depression. 2001. (Health Issues Ser.). (Illus.). 64p. (YA). (gr. 6-8). lib. bdg. 28.54 (978-0-7398-4419-9(9)) Raintree.

Libal, Autumn. Drug Therapy & Postpartum Disorders. 2003. (Encyclopedia of Psychiatric Drugs & Their Disorders Ser.). (Illus.). 128p. (J). lib. bdg. (978-1-59084-570-7(6)) Mason Crest Pubs.

McIntosh, Kenneth. The History of Depression: The Mind-Body Connection. 2006. (Antidepressants Ser.). (Illus.). 120p. (J). (gr. 7 up). lib. bdg. 24.95 (978-1-4222-0104-6(X)) Mason Crest Pubs.

McIntosh, Kenneth & Livingston, Phyllis. Youth with Depression & Anxiety: Moods That Overwhelm. 2008. (J). (978-1-4222-0142-8(2)) Mason Crest Pubs.

Moragne, Wendy. Depression. 2001. (Medical Library: up). (Illus.). 112p. (gr. 7 up). lib. bdg. (978-0-7613-1774-6(0) , Twenty-First Century Bks.) Lerner Publishing Group.

Peacock, Judith. Bipolar Disorder. 2000. (Perspectives on Mental Health Ser.). (Illus.). 64p. (J). (gr. 4-6). lib. bdg. 23.93 (978-0-7368-0434-9(X) , LifeMatters Bks.) Capstone Pr., Inc.

Perrier, Pascale, et al. Flying Solo: How to Soar above Your Lonely Feelings, Make Friends, & Find the Happiest You. 2007. (Sunscreen Book Ser.). 112p. (J). (gr. 2-8). pap. 9.95 (***978-0-8109-9281-8(7)*** , Abrams Bks. for Young Readers) Abrams, Harry N. , Inc.

Roy, Jennifer Rozines. Depression. 2004. (Illus.). 64p. (J). 28.50 (978-0-7614-1800-9(8) , Benchmark Bks.) Cavendish, Marshall Corp.

Scowen, Kate. My Kind of Sad: What It's Like to Be Young & Depressed. Szuc, Jeff, illus. 2006. 168p. (YA). (gr. 8-12). 19.95 (978-1-55037-941-9(0)); pap. 10.95 (978-1-55037-940-2(2)) Annick Pr., Ltd. CAN. *Dist:* Firefly Bks., Ltd.

Silverstein, Alvin, et al. The Depression & Bipolar Disorder Update. 2008. (J). (***978-0-7660-2801-2(1)***) Enslow Pubs., Inc.

Smith, Linda Wasmer. Depression: What It Is, How to Beat It. 2000. (Teen Issues Ser.). (Illus.). 64p. (YA). (gr. 6-12). lib. bdg. 22.60 (978-0-7660-1357-5(X)) Enslow Pubs., Inc.

Thakkar, Vatsal. Depression & Bipolar Disorder. 2006. (Psychological Disorders Ser.). (Illus.). 100p. (J). (gr. 6-12). 37.50 (978-0-7910-8542-4(2) , Chelsea Hse.) Facts On File, Inc.

Thomas, Peggy. Post-Traumatic Stress Disorder. 2007. (Diseases & Disorders Ser.). (Illus.). 128p. (gr. 7-10). 31.20 (***978-1-4205-0002-8(3)*** , Lucent Bks.) Thomson Gale.

—Postpartum Depression. 2007. (Diseases & Disorders Ser.). (Illus.). 128p. (gr. 7-10). 31.20 (***978-1-4205-0001-1(5)*** , Lucent Bks.) Thomson Gale.

Walker, Maryalice. The Development of Antidepressants: The Chemistry of Depression. 2007. (Antidepressants Ser.). (Illus.). 112p. (J). (gr. 7 up). 24.95 (978-1-4222-0102-2(3)) Mason Crest Pubs.

Wallerstein, Claire. Depression. 2003. (Just the Facts Ser.). (Illus.). 56p. (YA). lib. bdg. 25.64 (978-1-4034-0818-1(1)) Heinemann Library.

Weaver, Mary Wenger. Mommy Stayed in Bed This Morning: Helping Children Understand Depression. Chambers, Mary, illus. 2002. 40p. (J). (ps-3). pap. 12.99 (978-0-8361-9150-9(1)) Herald Pr.

Wilde, Jerry. Hot Stuff to Help Kids Cheer U. 2007. 80p. (J). pap. 9.95 (***978-1-4022-0926-0(6)*** , Sourcebooks Jabberwocky) Sourcebooks, Inc.

Wilkinson, Beth. Drugs & Depression. rev. ed. 1999. (Drug Abuse Prevention Library). (Illus.). 64p. (YA). (gr. 7-12). 25.25 (978-0-8239-3004-3(1) , DRDEPR) Rosen Publishing Group, Inc., The.

Winkler, Kathleen. Teens, Depression & the Blues. 2000. (Hot Issues Ser.). (Illus.). 64p. (YA). (gr. 6-12). lib. bdg. 27.93 (978-0-7660-1369-8(3)) Enslow Pubs., Inc.

Wolff, Lisa. Teen Depression. 1998. (Teen Issues Ser.). (Illus.). 112p. (YA). (gr. 4-12). lib. bdg. 27.45 (978-1-56006-519-7(2) , LML00902-177877, Lucent Bks.) Thomson Gale.

Zucker, Faye. Depression. (Life Balance Ser.). 2004. (YA). (gr. 5-8). pap. 6.95 (978-0-531-15578-3(1)); 2003. (Illus.). 80p. (J). 20.50 (978-0-531-12259-4(X)) Scholastic Library Publishing. (Watts, Franklin).

DEPRESSION, MENTAL—FICTION

Bang, Molly Garrett. Tiger's Fall. Bang, Molly Garrett, illus. rev. ed. 2001. (Illus.). 112p. (J). (gr. 4-7). 15.95 (978-0-8050-6689-0(6) , Holt, Henry & Co. Bks. For Young Readers) Holt, Henry & Co.

Dellasega, Cheryl. Nugrl90 (Sadie) LaPierre, Karina, illus. 2007. (Bloggrls Ser.). (YA). (gr. 7 up). 200p. 15.99 (***978-0-7614-5375-8(X)*** ***);*** 190p. per. 6.99 (***978-0-7614-5396-3(2)***) Cavendish, Marshall Corp.

Dreyer, Ellen. The Glow Stone. 2006. 186p. (J). 15.95 (978-1-56145-370-2(6) , Peachtree Junior) Peachtree Pubs., Ltd.

Haas, Dan. You Can Call Me Worm. 1999. (978-0-606-16790-1(0)) Tandem Library Bks.

Holmes, Sarah. Letters from Rapunzel. 2007. 192p. (J). (gr. 5-8). 15.99 (978-0-06-078073-9(8)); lib. bdg. 16.89 (978-0-06-078074-6(6)) HarperCollins Pubs.

Houk, Randy. Rico's Hawk. Lane, Nancy, illus. 1998. 32p. (J). 12.95 (978-1-58021-029-4(5)); pap. 5.95 (978-1-58021-030-0(9)); (gr. 1-4). pap. 9.95 incl. audio (978-1-58021-033-1(3)); (gr. 1-4). pap. 19.95 incl. audio (978-1-58021-031-7(7)) Benefactory, Inc., The.

—Rico's Hawk: Includes Plush Toy Animal. Lane, Nancy, illus. 1998. 32p. (J). 29.95 (978-1-58021-038-6(4)); pap. 14.95 (978-1-58021-032-4(5)) Benefactory, Inc., The.

—Rico's Hawk: Includes Tape & Plush Toy Animal. Lane, Nancy, illus. 1998. 32p. (J). 34.95 incl. audio (978-1-58021-037-9(6)) Benefactory, Inc., The.

Jenkins, A. M. Damage. 2003. (Illus.). 192p. (J). (gr. 7 up). pap. 7.99 (978-0-06-447255-5(8)) HarperCollins Pubs.

—Damage. 2003. (gr. 7-12). lib. bdg. 15.30 (978-0-613-62741-2(5)) Tandem Library Bks.

—Damage. l.t. ed. 2002. 221p. (YA). 24.95 (978-0-7862-4749-3(5)) Thorndike Pr.

Khalsa, Kathy. Taking Depression to School. Dineen, Tom, illus. 2002. (Special Kids in School Ser.: 14). 32p. (J). per. 11.95 (978-1-891383-22-9(1) , 70014) JayJo Bks., LLC.

Kienzle, Patricia Taylor. Chocolate Syrup on Your Arm. 2000. (Illus.). 16p. (J). (gr. 4-7). pap. 3.50 (978-1-890798-13-0(4)) Kienzle, Patricia Taylor.

Lewandowski, Lisa & Trost, Shannon. Darcy Daisy & the Firefly Festival: Learning about Bipolar Disorder & Community. Shaw-Peterson, Kimberly, illus. 2005. 32p. (J). pap. 9.95 (978-0-9785075-2-7(5) , Ferne Pr.) Nelson Publishing & Marketing.

Marchetta, Melina. Saving Francesca. 2006. 256p. (YA). (gr. 7). reprint ed. pap. 8.95 (978-0-375-82983-3(0) , Knopf Bks. for Young Readers) Random Hse. Children's Bks.

Maynard, Joyce. The Cloud Chamber. 288p. (YA). 2006. (gr. 9). pap. 7.99 (978-1-4169-2699-3(2) , Simon Pulse); 2005. (gr. 6-9). 16.95 (978-0-689-87152-8(X) , Atheneum) Simon & Schuster Children's Publishing.

Messer, Celeste M. A Message from Teddy. Hoeffner, Deb, illus. 2004. 82-92p. 4.95 (978-0-9702171-5-8(3)) AshleyAlan Enterprises.

Rapp, Adam. Under the Wolf, under the Dog. 320p. (YA). (gr. 9). 2007. pap. 8.99 (978-0-7636-3365-3(8)); 2004. 16.99 (978-0-7636-1818-6(7)) Candlewick Pr.

Spollen, Anne. The Shape of Water. 2008. 312p. (J). pap. 9.95 (***978-0-7387-1101-0(2)*** , Flux) Llewellyn Pubns.

Vizzini, Ned. It's Kind of a Funny Story: A Novel. 448p. (gr. 8 up). 2007. pap. 8.99 (***978-0-7868-5197-3(X));*** 2006. 16.95 (978-0-7868-5196-6(1)) Miramax Bks.

Wittlinger, Ellen. Blind Faith. (YA). 2007. 304p. pap. 8.99 (***978-1-4169-4906-0(2)*** , Simon Pulse); 2006. 288p. (gr. 7 up). 16.99 (978-1-4169-0273-7(2) , Simon & Schuster Children's Publishing) Simon & Schuster Children's Publishing.

Young, Janet Ruth. The Opposite of Music. 2007. 352p. (YA). 15.99 (978-1-4169-0040-5(3) , Atheneum) Simon & Schuster Children's Publishing.

DEPRESSIONS

Appelt, Kathi & Schmitzer, Jeanne Cannella. Down Cut Shin Creek: The Pack Horse Librarians of Kentucky. 2001. (Illus.). 64p. (J). (gr. 3-7). 16.99 (978-0-06-029135-8(4)) HarperCollins Pubs.

Bednarz, Robert, et al. TIME for Kids Readers: The Big Crash. 3rd ed. 2002. (Harcourt Horizons Ser.). (gr. k-7). pap. 38.10 (978-0-15-335298-0(1)) Harcourt Schl. Pubs.

Berg, Rebecca L. The Great Depression in Literature for Youth: A Geographical Study of Families & Young Lives. 2004. 210p. pap. 35.00 (978-0-8108-5093-4(1)) Scarecrow Pr., Inc.

Blumenthal, Karen. Six Days in October: The Stock Market Crash of 1929; A Wall Street Journal Book for Children. 2002. (Wall Street Journal Book Ser.). (Illus.). 160p. (J). (gr. 6 up). 17.95 (978-0-689-84276-4(7) , Atheneum) Simon & Schuster Children's Publishing.

Brown, Harriet. Welcome to Kit's World, 1934: Growing up During America's Great Depression. Rane, Walter et al, illus. Young, Jamie, photos by. 2002. (American Girls Collection). 64p. (J). 16.95 (978-1-58485-359-6(X)) American Girl Publishing, Inc.

Burg, David F. The Great Depression. 2nd rev. ed. 2005. (Eyewitness History Ser.). (Illus.). 464p. (J). (gr. 9). 75.00 (978-0-8160-5709-2(5)) Facts On File, Inc.

Burgan, Michael. The Great Depression. 2001. (We the People Ser.). (Illus.). 48p. (J). (gr. 4 up). lib. bdg. 22.60 (978-0-7565-0152-5(0)) Compass Point Bks.

Clements, Peter. Prosperity, Depression & the New Deal. 2nd ed. 2001. (Illus.). vi, 168p. pap. 13.99 (978-0-340-80429-2(7)) Hodder Education GBR. *Dist:* Trafalgar Square Publishing.

Collier, Christopher & Collier, James Lincoln. Progressivism, the Great Depression & the New Deal: 1901-1941. 2000. (Drama of American History Ser.). (Illus.). 96p. (J). (gr. 5-9). lib. bdg. 31.36 (978-0-7614-1054-6(6), Benchmark Bks.) Cavendish, Marshall Corp.

Connell, Kate. Dust Bowl Days: Hard Times for Farmers. 2004. (Illus.). 40p. (J). pap. (978-0-7922-4557-5(1)) National Geographic Society.

—Hoping for Rain: The Dust Bowl Adventures of Patty & Earl Buckler. 2004. (I Am American Ser.). (Illus.). 40p. (J). (gr. 3-7). pap. 6.99 (978-0-7922-6903-8(9), National Geographic Children's Bks.) National Geographic Society.

Cooper, Michael L. Dust to Eat: Drought & Depression in the 1930s. 2004. (Illus.). 96p. (J). (gr. 7-9). tchr. ed. 17.00 (978-0-618-15449-4(3), Clarion Bks.) Houghton Mifflin Co. Trade & Reference Div.

Crewe, Sabrina & Ingram, Scott. The Stock Market Crash of 1929. 2005. (Events That Shaped America Ser.). (Illus.). 32p. (J). lib. bdg. 24.67 (978-0-8368-3416-1(X)) Stevens, Gareth Inc.

A Deadly Secret Set. 1999. (Illus.). (J). 10.00 (978-1-892421-87-6(9), 119SET) Boulden Publishing.

DeAngelis, Therese & DeAngelis, Gina. The Dust Bowl. 2001. (Great Disasters, Reforms & Ramifications Ser.). (Illus.). 112p. (J). 30.00 (978-0-7910-6323-1(2), Chelsea Hse.) Facts On File, Inc.

DeGezelle, Terri. Franklin D. Roosevelt & the Great Depression. 2007. (J). ***(978-1-4034-9670-6(6)***); pap. ***(978-1-4034-9678-2(1))*** Heinemann Library.

Doak, Robin S. Black Tuesday: Prelude to the Great Depression. 2007. (J). lib. bdg. ***(978-0-7565-3327-4(9))*** Compass Point Bks.

Downing, David. The Great Depression. (20th Century Perspectives Ser.). (Illus.). 48p. (J). 2001. (gr. 4-7). lib. bdg. 25.64 (978-1-57572-435-5(9)); Set 1. 2002. (gr. 5-7). pap. 7.95 (978-1-58810-374-1(9), 91126) Heinemann Library.

—The Great Depression. 2001. (YA). 15.30 (978-0-606-22492-5(0)) Tandem Library Bks.

Freedman, Russell. Children of the Great Depression. 2005. (Illus.). 128p. (J). (gr. 5-8). 20.00 (978-0-618-44630-8(3), Clarion Bks.) Houghton Mifflin Co. Trade & Reference Div.

Gale Research Staff. Great Depression & New Deal: Primary Sources, 3 vols., Vol. lll. 2002. (U-X-L Great Depression & New Deal Reference Library). (Illus.). 225p. (J). lib. bdg. 67.00 (978-0-7876-6535-7(5), GML00502-182437, UXL) Thomson Gale.

Gedney, Mona K. The Story of the Great Depression. 2005. (Monumental Milestones Ser.). (Illus.). 48p. (YA). (ps-7). lib. bdg. (978-1-58415-403-7(9)) Mitchell Lane Pubs., Inc.

Gerdes, Louise I. The Crash of 1929. 2001. (At Issue in History Ser.). (Illus.). 104p. (YA). (gr. 7-10). lib. bdg. 27.45 (978-0-7377-0819-6(0), GML12001-179091, Greenhaven Pr., Inc.) Thomson Gale.

Gitlin, Marty. The Great Depression & World War II. 2007. (J). ***(978-1-59036-749-0(9)***); ***(978-1-59036-750-6(2))*** Weigl Pubs., Inc.

Gow, Mary. The Stock Market Crash Of 1929: Dawn of the Great Depression. 2003. (American Disasters Ser.). (Illus.). 48p. (J). lib. bdg. 23.93 (978-0-7660-2111-2(4)) Enslow Pubs., Inc.

Graves, Kerry A. Going to School During the Great Depression. 2001. (Blue Earth Books). (Illus.). 32p. (J). (gr. 3-4). lib. bdg. 22.60 (978-0-7368-0800-2(0), Bridgestone Bks.) Capstone Pr., Inc.

Grolier Educational Staff, contrib. by. Boom & Bust, 6 vols., Vol. 1. 2001. (Illus.). (YA). (978-0-7172-5503-0(4), Grolier) Scholastic Library Publishing.

—Countryside & City, 6 vols., Vol. 3. 2001. (Illus.). (YA). (978-0-7172-5505-4(0), Grolier) Scholastic Library Publishing.

—Depression America: Boom or Bust, 6 vols., Vol. 1. Incl. Vol. 1. Boom & Bust. (978-0-7172-5503-0(4)); Vol. 2. Roosevelt's First Term. (978-0-7172-5504-7(2)); Vol. 3. Countryside & City. (978-0-7172-5505-4(0)); Vol. 4. Political Tensions. (978-0-7172-5506-1(9)); Vol. 5. U. S. Society. (978-0-7172-5507-8(7)); Vol. 6. War Years & Economic Boom. (978-0-7172-5508-5(5)); (YA). (Illus.). 768p. 2001. 319.00 (978-0-7172-5502-3(6), Grolier) Scholastic Library Publishing.

—Political Tensions, 6 vols., Vol. 4. 2001. (Illus.). (YA). (978-0-7172-5506-1(9), Grolier) Scholastic Library Publishing.

—Roosevelt's First Term, 6 vols., Vol. 2. 2001. (Illus.). (YA). (978-0-7172-5504-7(2), Grolier) Scholastic Library Publishing.

—U. S. Society, 6 vols., Vol. 5. 2001. (Illus.). (YA). (978-0-7172-5507-8(7), Grolier) Scholastic Library Publishing.

—The War Years & Economic Boom, 6 vols., Vol. 6. 2001. (Illus.). (YA). (978-0-7172-5508-5(5), Grolier) Scholastic Library Publishing.

Gunderson, Cory. Great Depression. 2005. (American Moments Ser.). (Illus.). 48p. (J). (gr. 4-8). lib. bdg. 25.65 (978-1-59197-286-0(8), ABDO & Daughters) ABDO Publishing Co.

Hazen, Walter A. The Great Depression. 1999. (Eye on History Ser.). 32p. (J). (gr. 5-12). pap. 5.99 (978-1-56822-628-6(4), IF2668) School Specialty Publishing.

Ingram, Scott. The Stock Market Crash of 1929. 2004. (Landmark Events in American History Ser.). (J). pap. 11.95 (978-0-8368-5425-1(X)); lib. bdg. 30.00 (978-0-8368-5397-1(0)) Stevens, Gareth Inc. (World Almanac Library).

King, David C. The Great Depression. Deitch, JoAnne Weisman, ed. 2000. (Researching American History Ser.). (Illus.). 56p. (J). 7.95 (978-1-57960-067-9(0)) History Compass, LLC.

Kupperberg, Paul. Critical Perspectives on the Great Depression. 2005. (Critical Anthologies of Nonfiction Writing Ser.). 176p. (gr. 7-12). lib. bdg. 30.60 (978-1-4042-0061-6(4)) Rosen Publishing Group, Inc., The.

Landau, Elaine. The Great Depression. 2007. (Cornerstones of Freedomtrade;, Second Ser.). 48p. (J). pap. 5.95 ***(978-0-531-18767-8(5)***, Children's Pr.) Scholastic Library Publishing.

Malchik, E., Antonia. The Los numeros de la Gran Depresion & Great Depression by the Numbers. 2005. spiral bd. 88.00 ***(978-1-4108-5730-9(1))*** Benchmark Education Co.

McArthur, Debra. The Dust Bowl & the Depression in American History. 2002. (In American History Ser.). (Illus.). 128p. (J). (gr. 5-12). lib. bdg. 26.60 (978-0-7660-1838-9(5)) Enslow Pubs., Inc.

McDougal, Littell Staff & Nextext Staff, contrib. by. World War, Boom & Bust. 2004. (Stories in History Ser.). (Illus.). 224p. (J). (gr. 6-12). (978-0-618-22202-5(2), 2-00308) McDougal Littell Inc.

McNeill, Allison & Hanes, Sharon M. Great Depression & New Deal. 2002. 48p. (J). 5.00 (978-0-7876-6536-4(3), UXL) Thomson Gale.

Nishi, Dennis. The Great Depression. 2001. (History Firsthand Ser.). (Illus.). 234p. (YA). (gr. 7-10). pap. 21.20 (978-0-7377-0410-5(1), Greenhaven Pr., Inc.) Thomson Gale.

Parks, Peggy J. The Great Depression. 2003. (Daily Life Ser.). (Illus.). 48p. (J). 26.20 (978-0-7377-1399-2(2), Greenhaven Pr., Inc.) Thomson Gale.

Price, Sean. The Dirty Thirties: Documenting the Dust Bowl. 2006. (American History Through Primary Sources Ser.). (Illus.). 32p. (J). (978-1-4109-2416-2(5)); pap. (978-1-4109-2427-8(0)) Steck-Vaughn.

Ross, Stewart. The Great Depression. 1998. (Causes & Consequences Ser.). (Illus.). 80p. (J). (gr. 5-9). lib. bdg. 29.97 (978-0-8172-4059-2(4)) Raintree.

Ruggiero, Adriane. The Great Depression. 2004. (American Voices From Ser.). (Illus.). xxi, 116p. (J). 34.21 (978-0-7614-1696-8(X), Benchmark Bks.) Cavendish, Marshall Corp.

Ruth, Amy. Growing up in the Great Depression, 1929 to 1941. 2003. (Our America Ser.). (Illus.). 64p. (J). (gr. 4-7). lib. bdg. 26.60 (978-0-8225-0655-3(6)) Lerner Publishing Group.

Schultz, Stanley. The Great Depression: A Primary Source History. 2005. lib. bdg. 26.00 (978-0-8368-5978-2(2)) Stevens, Gareth Inc.

Stanley, George Edward. The Great Depression & World War II (1929-1949) 2005. (Illus.). 48p. (J). pap. (978-0-8368-5838-9(7)); lib. bdg. 30.00 (978-0-8368-5829-7(8)) Stevens, Gareth Inc. (World Almanac Library).

Stein, R. Conrad. The New Deal: Pulling America Out of the Great Depression. 2006. (American Saga Ser.). (Illus.). 128p. (J). (gr. 6-9). lib. bdg. 31.93 (978-0-7660-2570-7(5)) Enslow Pubs., Inc.

Stone, Tanya Lee. The Great Depression & World War II. 2001. (Making of America Ser.). (Illus.). 96p. (J). (gr. 4-7). lib. bdg. 28.54 (978-0-8172-5710-1(1)) Raintree.

Turck, Mary. The Dirty Thirties: The United States from 1929-1941. 2002. (Cover-To-Cover Books). (Illus.). 72p. (J). pap. (978-0-7891-5673-0(3)); (gr. 4-7). lib. bdg. 17.95 (978-0-7569-0637-5(7)) Perfection Learning Corp.

Webster, Christine. Valleys. 2005. (Illus.). 24p. (J). 21.26 (978-0-7368-3716-3(7)) Capstone Pr., Inc.

Woolf, Alex. The Wall Street Crash. 2002. (Days That Shook the World Ser.). (Illus.). 48p. (J). lib. bdg. (978-0-7398-5237-8(X)) Raintree.

Wright, John & Waugh, Steven. The USA 1929-1980. 2005. (Illus.). 144p. pap. 38.50 ***(978-0-340-88903-9(9)***, Hodder Murray) Hodder Education GBR. *Dist:* Trans-Atlantic Pubns., Inc.

Wroble, Lisa A. Kids During the Great Depression. 1999. (Kids Throughout History Ser.). (Illus.). 24p. (J). (gr. 3). lib. bdg. 18.75 (978-0-8239-5255-7(X), PowerKids Pr.) Rosen Publishing Group, Inc., The.

—The New Deal & the Great Depression in American History. 2002. (In American History Ser.). (Illus.). 128p. (J). (gr. 5-12). lib. bdg. 26.60 (978-0-7660-1421-3(5)) Enslow Pubs., Inc.

Yancey, Diane. Life During the Dust Bowl. 2004. (Way People Live Ser.). (J). 29.95 (978-1-59018-265-9(0), Lucent Bks.) Thomson Gale.

DEPRESSIONS—FICTION

Adler, David A. The Babe & I. Widener, Terry, illus. 1999. 32p. (J). (gr. k-4). 17.00 (978-0-15-201378-3(4), Gulliver Bks.) Harcourt Children's Bks.

Alexander, Lloyd. The Gawgon & the Boy. 2003. (gr. 3-6). lib. bdg. 14.15 (978-0-613-59809-5(1)) Tandem Library Bks.

Austin, Lynn. Hidden Places. 2001. (gr. 5-8). lib. bdg. 22.25 (978-0-613-55604-0(6)) Tandem Library Bks.

Ayres, Katherine. Macaroni Boy. 2004. 192p. (J). (gr. 3-7). pap. 5.99 (978-0-440-41884-9(4), Yearling) Random Hse. Children's Bks.

Blackwood, Gary L. Moonshine. 1999. (Accelerated Reader Bks.). 160p. (J). (gr. 3-7). 14.95 (978-0-7614-5056-6(4), Cavendish Children's Bks.) Cavendish, Marshall Corp.

Blume, Lesley M. M. Tennyson. 2008. 240p. (J). (gr. 3-7). 15.99 ***(978-0-375-84703-5(0)***, Knopf Bks. for Young Readers) Random Hse. Children's Bks.

Brookins, Cara. Doris Free. Barrow, Ann, illus. 2006. 127p. (J). pap. (978-1-59336-333-8(8)) Mondo Publishing.

Burch, Robert. Ida Early Comes over the Mountain. 2001. (J). (gr. 3-6). 20.75 (978-0-8446-7171-0(1)) Smith, Peter Pub., Inc.

Carville, James & McKissack, Patricia C. Lu & the Swamp Ghost. Catrow, David, tr. Catrow, David, illus. 2004. 40p. (J). 17.95 (978-0-689-86560-2(0), Atheneum) Simon & Schuster Children's Publishing.

Center for Learning Network Staff. A Long Way from Chicago/A Year down Yonder: Curriculum Unit. 2002. (Novel Ser.). 84p. (J). tchr. ed., spiral bd. 19.95 (978-1-56077-723-6(0)) Ctr. for Learning, The.

Collier, James Lincoln. The Worst of Times: A Story of the Great Depression. 2004. (Jamestown's American Portraits Ser.). (Illus.). 144p. (J). (gr. 5-7). pap. 4.95 (978-0-7696-3447-0(8), Waterbird Bks.) School Specialty Publishing.

Collins, Pat L. Just Imagine. 2001. (Illus.). 224p. (J). (gr. 5-9). tchr. ed. 15.00 (978-0-618-05603-3(3)) Houghton Mifflin Co. Trade & Reference Div.

Curtis, Christopher. Bud Not Buddy. l.t. ed. 2003. 278p. pap. 10.95 (978-0-7862-6191-8(9)) Thorndike Pr.

De Young, C. Coco. A Letter to Mrs. Roosevelt. 2000. 112p. (J). (gr. 3-7). pap. 5.50 (978-0-440-41529-9(2), Yearling) Random Hse. Children's Bks.

de Young, C. Coco. Letter to Mrs. Roosevelt. 2000. 105p. (J). (ps-7). lib. bdg. 12.40 (978-0-613-28551-3(4)) Tandem Library Bks.

DeFelice, Cynthia C. Nowhere to Call Home. 2000. (YA). pap., stu. ed. 60.00 incl. audio (978-0-7887-4179-1(9), 41113) Recorded Bks., LLC.

—Nowhere to Call Home. 2001. (gr. 5-8). lib. bdg. 14.10 (978-0-613-35992-4(5)) Tandem Library Bks.

Early, Tony. Jim the Boy. 2001. (gr. 7-12). lib. bdg. 21.95 (978-0-613-33827-1(8)) Tandem Library Bks.

Ernst, Kathleen. Midnight in Lonesome Hollow: A Kit Mystery. Tibbles, Jean-Paul, illus. 2007. 192p. (J). 10.95 ***(978-1-59369-161-5(0)***); pap. 6.95 ***(978-1-59369-160-8(2))*** American Girl Publishing, Inc. (American Girl).

Fenton, Edward. Duffy's Rocks. 1999. (gr. 7-12). lib. bdg. 22.20 (978-0-613-76650-0(4)) Tandem Library Bks.

Fitz-Gibbon, Sally. Lizzie's Storm. Wood, Muriel, illus. (J). 2004. 64p. pap. (978-1-55041-795-1(9)); 2003. 67p. (978-1-55041-793-7(2)) Fitzhenry & Whiteside, Ltd.

Friedrich, Elizabeth. Leah's Pony. 1999. (gr. k-3). lib. bdg. 17.60 (978-0-613-78901-1(6)); (J). (978-0-606-17333-9(1)) Tandem Library Bks.

Friedrich, Elizabeth & Boyds Mills Press Staff. Leah's Pony. Garland, Michael, illus. 2003. 32p. (J). (gr. 2-4). pap. 9.95 (978-1-56397-828-9(8)) Boyds Mills Pr.

Grote, JoAnn A. Anna's Fight for Hope: The Great Depression. 2004. (Sisters in Time Ser.). 144p. (J). pap. 4.97 (978-1-59310-208-1(9)) Barbour Publishing, Inc.

Guest, Jacqueline. Secret Signs. 2006. (Illus.). 144p. (J). pap. 5.95 (978-1-55143-599-2(3)) Orca Bk. Pubs. USA.

Hale, Marian. The Truth about Sparrows. rev. ed. 2004. (Illus.). 272p. (J). 16.95 (978-0-8050-7584-7(4), Holt, Henry & Co. Bks. For Young Readers) Holt, Henry & Co.

—The Truth about Sparrows. 2007. 288p. (J). pap. 6.99 ***(978-0-312-37133-3(0))*** Square Fish.

Harcourt School Publishers Staff. Student of the Week On Level. 3rd ed. 2002. (Trophies Reading Program Ser.). (Illus.). pap. 5.10 (978-0-15-323181-0(5)) Harcourt Schl. Pubs.

Harper, Jo & Harper, Josephine. Finding Daddy: A Story of the Great Depression. Mazellan, Ron, illus. 2005. 48p. (J). 16.95 (978-1-890515-31-7(0)) Turtle Bks.

Harris, Dorothy Joan. Ellen: Hobo Jungle. 2002. (Our Canadian Girl Ser.). (Illus.). 96p. (J). pap. (978-0-14-100270-5(0)) Penguin Group (USA) Inc.

Hesse, Karen. Out of the Dust. 2002. (Illus.). (J). 13.19 (978-0-7587-0207-4(8)) Book Wholesalers, Inc.

—Out of the Dust. 240p. (gr. 5 up). (YA). pap. 4.99 (978-0-8072-1526-5(0)); 1998. (J). pap. 29.00 incl. audio (978-0-8072-8013-3(5), YA967SP) Random Hse. Audio Publishing Group. (Listening Library).

—Out of the Dust. 1999. (Apple Signature Edition Ser.). 240p. (gr. 4-7). mass mkt. 5.99 (978-0-590-37125-4(8)) Scholastic, Inc.

—Out of the Dust. 1999. (978-0-606-15665-3(8)); (gr. 5-8). lib. bdg. 13.00 (978-0-613-11953-5(3)) Tandem Library Bks.

—Out of the Dust. l.t. ed. 2004. 180p. 22.95 (978-0-7862-7006-4(3), Large Print Pr.) Thorndike Pr.

Hoobler, Dorothy & Hoobler, Thomas. The 1930s: Directions. Hoffman, Robin, illus. 2000. (Century Kids Ser.). 160p. (J). (gr. 5-8). lib. bdg. 22.90 (978-0-7613-1603-9(5), Twenty-First Century Bks.) Lerner Publishing Group.

Horvath, Polly. The Happy Yellow Car. 2004. (Illus.). 128p. (J). pap. 5.95 (978-0-374-42879-2(4), Sunburst) Farrar, Straus & Giroux.

Ingold, Jeanette. Hitch. 288p. (YA). 2006. (Illus.). pap. 6.95 (978-0-15-205619-3(X), Harcourt Paperbacks); 2005. (gr. 7-12). 17.00 (978-0-15-204747-4(6)) Harcourt Children's Bks.

Kerr, Rita. The Good Old Days. 1999. (Illus.). 120p. 13.95 (978-1-57168-362-5(3)) Eakin Pr.

Kytle, Calvin. Like a Tree. 2007. 430p. 28.95 ***(978-1-58838-220-7(6)***, NewSouth Bks.) NewSouth, Inc.

Laskas, Gretchen Moran. The Miner's Daughter. 2007. 256p. (YA). 15.99 (978-1-4169-1262-0(2)) Simon & Schuster Children's Publishing.

Lied, Kate. Potato: A Tale from the Great Depression. Ernst, Lisa Campbell, illus. 2002. 32p. (J). (gr. k-5). pap. 7.95 (978-0-7922-6946-5(2), National Geographic Children's Bks.) National Geographic Society.

—Potato: A Tale from the Great Depression. 2002. (gr. 3-6). lib. bdg. 16.40 (978-0-613-81334-1(0)) Tandem Library Bks.

Lincoln Collier, James. The Worst of Times. 2004. 142p. (J). lib. bdg. 16.92 ***(978-1-4242-0766-4(5))*** Fitzgerald Bks.

Littlesugar, Amy. Tree of Hope. 2001. (gr. k-3). lib. bdg. 15.30 (978-0-613-44423-1(X)) Tandem Library Bks.

Mackall, Dandi Daley. The Legend of the Christmas Cookie: An Inspirational Story of Sharing. Chabrian, Deborah L., illus. 2008. (J). ***(978-0-310-71328-9(5))*** Zonderkidz.

—Rudy Rides the Rails: A Depression Era Story. Ellison, Chris, illus. rev. ed. 2007. (Tales of Young Americans Ser.). 40p. (J). (gr. 3-6). 17.95 ***(978-1-58536-286-8(7))*** Sleeping Bear Pr.

Mangin, John F. Squirt Blossom Jubilation. 2006. pap. 13.00 (978-0-8059-9885-6(3), RoseDog Bks.) Dorrance Publishing Co., Inc.

Mangum, Kay Lynn. A Love Like Lilly. 2006. 336p. (YA). pap. 15.95 (978-1-59038-580-7(2)) Deseret Bk. Co.

Marsh, Carole. The Puzzle of the Indian Arrowhead. 2006. 64p. (gr. 1-3). 14.95 ***(978-0-635-06201-7(1))*** Gallopade International.

McKissack, Pat. The All-I'll-Ever-Want Christmas Doll. Pinkney, Jerry, illus. 2007. (J). ***(978-0-375-83615-2(2)***, Schwartz & Wade Bks.) Random Hse. Children's Bks.

McKissack, Patricia. The All-I'll-Ever-Want Christmas Doll. Pinkney, Jerry, illus. 2007. 40p. (J). (ps-3). lib. bdg. 19.99 ***(978-0-375-93759-0(5)***); 16.99 ***(978-0-375-83759-3(0))*** Random Hse. Children's Bks. (Schwartz & Wade Bks.).

Meltzer, Milton. Tough Times. 2007. 176p. (J). (gr. 7 up). 16.00 ***(978-0-618-87445-3(3)***, Clarion Bks.) Houghton Mifflin Co. Trade & Reference Div.

Miller, William. Rent Party Jazz. Riley-Webb, Charlotte, illus. 2001. 32p. (J). (gr. 1-5). 16.95 (978-1-58430-025-0(6)) Lee & Low Bks., Inc.

Montgomery, Bobbie. Fruit Tramp Kids. 2000. (Pathfinder Junior Book Club Ser.). 143p. (J). (gr. 4-7). pap. 6.99 (978-0-8280-1422-9(1)) Review & Herald Publishing Assn.

Moss, Marissa. Rose's Journal: The Story of a Girl in the Great Depression. 2003. (Young American Voices Ser.). (Illus.). 56p. (J). pap. 7.00 (978-0-15-204605-7(4), Silver Whistle) Harcourt Trade Pubs.

—Rose's Journal: The Story of a Girl in the Great Depression. Moss, Marissa, illus. 2001. (Young American Voices Ser.). (Illus.). 56p. (YA). (gr. 3-7). 15.00 (978-0-15-202423-9(9), Silver Whistle) Harcourt Trade Pubs.

—Rose's Journal: The Story of A Girl in the Great Depression. 2003. (gr. 3-6). lib. bdg. 15.30 (978-0-613-59923-8(3)) Tandem Library Bks.

Osborne, Mary Pope. Blizzard of the Blue Moon. Murdocca, Sal, illus. 2007. (Magic Tree House Ser.: No. 36). 144p. (J). (gr. 2-5). pap. 4.99 (978-0-375-83038-9(3), Random Hse. Bks. for Young Readers) Random Hse. Children's Bks.

—Blizzard of the Blue Moon. 2006. (Magic Tree House Ser.: No. 36). (Illus.). 128p. (J). (gr. k-3). lib. bdg. 13.99 (978-0-375-93037-9(X)); (gr. 2-5). 11.95 (978-0-375-83037-2(5)) Random Hse. Children's Bks. (Random Hse. Bks. for Young Readers).

Peck, Richard. A Long Way from Chicago. 2002. (Illus.). (J). 13.19 (978-0-7587-6520-8(7)) Book Wholesalers, Inc.

—A Long Way from Chicago. (Puffin Modern Classics Ser.). 2004. 160p. (gr. 3-6). pap. 6.99 (978-0-14-240110-1(2), Puffin); 2000. (Illus.). 176p. (J). (gr. 5-9). pap. 6.99 (978-0-14-130352-9(2), Puffin); 1998. 192p. (J). (gr. 4-7). 16.99 (978-0-8037-2290-3(7), Dial) Penguin Group (USA) Inc.

—A Long Way from Chicago. 2000. (J). (978-0-606-19769-4(9)) Tandem Library Bks.

—A Year down Yonder. 2002. (Illus.). (YA). 13.19 (978-1-4046-1795-7(7)) Book Wholesalers, Inc.

—A Year down Yonder. 2002. 144p. (gr. 5-8). pap. 6.99 (978-0-14-230070-1(5), Puffin) Penguin Group (USA) Inc.

—A Year down Yonder. Cieslawski, Steve, illus. 2000. 144p. (J). (gr. 5-9). 16.99 (978-0-8037-2518-8(3), Dial) Penguin Group (USA) Inc.

—A Year down Yonder. unabr. ed. 2004. (Middle Grade Cassette Librariestm Ser.). 144p. (J). (gr. 5-9). pap. 29.00 incl. audio (978-0-8072-0991-2(0), S YA 256 SP, Listening Library) Random Hse. Audio Publishing Group.

—A Year down Yonder. 2002. (gr. 5-8). lib. bdg. 14.15 (978-0-613-57934-6(8)) Tandem Library Bks.

—A Year down Yonder. l.t. ed. 2001. 160p. (J). 24.95 (978-0-7862-3282-6(X)) Thorndike Pr.

Peck, Robert Newton. Weeds in Bloom: Autobiography of an Ordinary Man. 2007. (Illus.). 224p. (YA). (gr. 7-11). mass mkt. 6.50 (978-0-375-82802-7(8), Laurel Leaf) Random Hse. Children's Bks.

Ryan, Pam Muñoz. Esperanza Rising. unabr. ed. 2004. (Middle Grade Cassette Librariestm Ser.). 272p. (J). (gr. 4-7). pap. 36.00 incl. audio (978-0-8072-1726-9(3), S YA 281 SP, Listening Library) Random Hse. Audio Publishing Group.

Sanders, Scott Russell. Bad Man Ballad. 2004. (Library of Indiana Classics). 256p. (J). reprint ed. pap. 32.95 (978-0-253-21688-5(5)) Indiana Univ. Pr.

Schraff, Anne. Hear That Whistle Blow. 1999. (Passages Ser.). 119p. (J). (gr. 5-12). lib. bdg. 13.95 (978-0-7807-8970-8(9)) Perfection Learning Corp.

Simons, Joseph. Under a Living Sky. 2005. (Orca Young Readers Ser.). (Illus.). 144p. (J). (gr. 3-6). pap. 5.95 (978-1-55143-355-4(9)) Orca Bk. Pubs. USA.

Swain, Gwenyth. Chig & the Second Spread. 2003. 208p. (J). (gr. 3-7). 14.95 (978-0-385-73065-5(9) , Delacorte Bks. for Young Readers) Random Hse. Children's Bks.

Taylor, Kim. Cissy Funk. 2001. 224p. (J). (gr. 5 up). 15.95 (978-0-06-029041-2(2)); 15.89 (978-0-06-029042-9(0)) HarperCollins Pubs.

Taylor, Mildred D. Roll of Thunder, Hear My Cry. 2004. 276p. (gr. 4-8). reprint ed. pap. 10.00 (978-0-7567-7955-9(3)) DIANE Publishing Co.

—Roll of Thunder, Hear My Cry. l.t. ed. 2000. (LRS Large Print Cornerstone Ser.). 348p. (YA). (gr. 5-12). lib. bdg. 32.95 (978-1-58118-057-2(8) , 23471) LRS.

—Roll of Thunder, Hear My Cry. 1999. (Masterpiece Series Access Editions). xvii, 205p. (J). pap. 10.95 (978-0-8219-1985-9(7) , 35335) Paradigm Publishing, Inc.

—Roll of Thunder, Hear My Cry. Pinkney, Jerry, illus. 25th anniv. ed. 2001. 296p. (J). (gr. 5 up). 17.99 (978-0-8037-2647-5(3) , Dial) Penguin Group (USA) Inc.

—Roll of Thunder, Hear My Cry. 1999. 60p. (J). (gr. 6-8). stu. ed., ring bd. 12.99 (978-1-58609-152-1(2)) Progeny Pr.

—Roll of Thunder, Hear My Cry. 1998. (J). (gr. 5). pap. 3.95 (978-0-439-04476-9(6)) Scholastic, Inc.

—Song of the Trees. 2003. (Illus.). 64p. (J). pap. 5.99 (978-0-14-250075-0(5) , Puffin) Penguin Group (USA) Inc.

—Song of the Trees. 2003. (gr. 3-6). lib. bdg. 14.15 (978-0-613-67301-3(8)) Tandem Library Bks.

Thrasher, Crystal. The Dark Didn't Catch Me. 2004. (Library of Indiana Classics). 192p. (J). reprint ed. pap. 14.95 (978-0-253-21685-4(0)) Indiana Univ. Pr.

Tripp, Valerie. Changes for Kit: A Winter Story. Rane, Walter & McAliley, Susan, illus. 2001. (American Girls Collection: Bk. 6). 86p. (J). (gr. 2 up). 12.95 (978-1-58485-027-4(2)); 6.95 (978-1-58485-026-7(4)) American Girl Publishing, Inc.

—Changes for Kit: A Winter Story. 2001. (American Girls Collection). (Illus.). (J). 12.75 (978-0-606-21107-9(1)) Tandem Library Bks.

—Changes for Kit: A Winter Story 1934. Rane, Walter & McAliley, Susan, illus. 2001. 64p. (J). (gr. 3-6). lib. bdg. 14.10 (978-0-613-44636-5(4)) Tandem Library Bks.

—Happy Birthday, Kit! A Springtime Story, Bk. 4. 2000. (American Girls Collection: Bk. 4). (Illus.). 80p. (J). (gr. 2 up). 12.95 (978-1-58485-023-6(X)) American Girl Publishing, Inc.

—Happy Birthday, Kit! A Springtime Story, Bk. 4. Rane, Walter, illus. 2000. (American Girls Collection: Bk. 4). 80p. (YA). (gr. 2 up). pap. 6.95 (978-1-58485-022-9(1)) American Girl Publishing, Inc.

—Happy Birthday, Kit! A Springtime Story. (American Girls Collection). (J). 2001. (Illus.). 12.75 (978-0-606-21225-0(6)); 2000. (978-0-606-22805-3(5)) Tandem Library Bks.

—Happy Birthday Kit! A Springtime Story 1934. 2001. (gr. 3-6). lib. bdg. 14.10 (978-0-613-44661-7(5)) Tandem Library Bks.

—Kit Learns a Lesson: A School Story, Bk. 2. Rane, Walter, illus. 2000. (American Girls Collection: Bk. 2). 80p. (J). (gr. 2 up). 6.95 (978-1-58485-018-2(3)); 12.95 (978-1-58485-121-9(X)) American Girl Publishing, Inc.

—Kit Learns a Lesson: A School Story. 2000. (gr. 3-6). lib. bdg. 14.10 (978-0-613-28917-7(X)); (American Girls Collection: Bk. 2). (YA). (gr. 2 up). (978-0-606-18943-9(2)) Tandem Library Bks.

—Kit Saves the Day! A Summer Story, Bk. 5. Rane, Walter & McAliley, Susan, illus. 2001. (American Girls Collection: Bk. 5). 80p. (J). (gr. 2 up). 12.95 (978-1-58485-025-0(6)) American Girl Publishing, Inc.

—Kit Saves the Day! A Summer Story, Bk. 5. Rane, Walter, illus. 2001. (American Girls Collection: Bk. 5). 80p. (YA). (gr. 2 up). pap. 6.95 (978-1-58485-024-3(8)) American Girl Publishing, Inc.

—Kit Saves the Day! A Summer Story. 2001. (American Girls Collection). (Illus.). (J). (978-0-606-21283-0(3)) Tandem Library Bks.

—Kit Saves the Day: A Summer Story 1934. 2001. (gr. 3-6). lib. bdg. 14.10 (978-0-613-44682-2(8)) Tandem Library Bks.

—Kit's Boxed Set: Happy Birthday, Kit!; Kit Saves the Day; Meet Kit; Kit Learns a Lesson; Changes for Kit; Kit's Surprise, 6 bks. 2001. (American Girls Collection). (J). 39.95 (978-1-58485-357-2(3)) American Girl Publishing, Inc.

—Kit's Short Story Collection. Rane, Walter & Graef, Renee, illus. 2006. 256p. (J). 12.95 (***978-1-59369-126-4(2)***) American Girl Publishing, Inc.

—Kit's Surprise: A Christmas Story, Bk. 3. Rane, Walter & McAliley, Susan, illus. 2000. (American Girls Collection: Bk. 3). 80p. (J). (gr. 2 up). 12.95 (978-1-58485-021-2(3)) American Girl Publishing, Inc.

—Kit's Surprise: A Christmas Story, Bk. 3. Rane, Walter, illus. 2000. (American Girls Collection: Bk. 3). 80p. (YA). (gr. 2 up). pap. 6.95 (978-1-58485-020-5(5)) American Girl Publishing, Inc.

—Kit's Surprise: A Christmas Story. 2000. (gr. 3-6). lib. bdg. 14.10 (978-0-613-28918-4(8)); (American Girls Collection: Bk. 3). (YA). (gr. 2 up). (978-0-606-18944-6(0)) Tandem Library Bks.

—Meet Kit: An American Girl. Rane, Walter & McAliley, Susan, illus. 2000. (American Girls Collection: Bk. 1). 80p. (J). (gr. 2 up). 12.95 (978-1-58485-017-5(5)) American Girl Publishing, Inc.

—Meet Kit: An American Girl. Rane, Walter, illus. 2000. (American Girls Collection: Bk. 1). 80p. (YA). (gr. 2 up). pap. 6.95 (978-1-58485-016-8(7)) American Girl Publishing, Inc.

—Meet Kit: An American Girl. 2000. (American Girls Collection: Bk.1). (YA). (gr. 2 up). (978-0-606-18942-2(4)) Tandem Library Bks.

Uchida, Yoshiko. A Jar of Dreams. 1998. (J). pap. 3.95 (978-0-87628-469-8(1)) Ctr. for Applied Research in Education, The.

Wells, Rosemary. Wingwalker. Selznick, Brian, illus. 2002. 80p. (gr. 2-5). 15.99 (978-0-7868-0397-2(5)); 16.49 (978-0-7868-2347-5(X)) Hyperion Bks. for Children.

White, Joseph C. Forged in a Country Crucible. 2003. (Illus.). 278p. per. 19.95 (978-0-9726095-1-7(2) , FCC2003) Crossing Trails Pubns.

Whitmore, Arvella. The Bread Winner. 2004. 144p. (J). (gr. 4-6). pap. 5.95 (978-0-618-49479-8(0)) Houghton Mifflin Co. Trade & Reference Div.

Willis, Patricia. The Barn Burner. 2000. 208p. (J). (gr. 5-9). tchr. ed. 15.00 (978-0-395-98409-3(2) , Clarion Bks.) Houghton Mifflin Co. Trade & Reference Div.

Winthrop, Elizabeth. Dear Mr. President - Franklin Delano Roosevelt: Letters from a Mill Town Girl. Winthrop, Elizabeth, illus. unabr. ed. 2003. (Illus.). (J). (gr. 4-7). 25.95 incl. audio (978-1-59112-213-5(9)) Live Oak Media.

Wyatt, Leslie J. Poor Is Just a Starting Place. 2005. 192p. (J). (gr. 6-17). 16.95 (978-0-8234-1884-8(7)) Holiday Hse., Inc.

DERMATOLOGY

see Skin—Diseases

DESERT ANIMALS

see also Camels

Animales del Desierto: Aventuras (Adventure Books) 2000. (Aventuras A Traves Del Tiempo Ser.). (ENG & SPA.). (gr. 3 up). (978-0-02-148695-3(6)) Macmillan/McGraw-Hill Schl. Div.

Animals & Birds of the Desert. (Butterfly Bks.). (ARA., Illus.). 32p. (J). (gr. 4-8). 9.95 (978-0-86685-398-9(7) , LDL251) International Bk. Ctr., Inc.

Auch, Alison. Desert Animals. 2003. (Spyglass Books). (Illus.). 24p. (J). (gr. 1 up). lib. bdg. 18.60 (978-0-7565-0445-8(7)) Compass Point Bks.

Bailey, Jill. Life in a Desert Cactus. (Microhabitats Ser.). (Illus.). 32p. (J). (ps-ps). 2004. lib. bdg. 24.28 (978-0-7398-6801-0(2)); 2003. pap. 7.50 (978-1-4109-0347-1(8)) Raintree.

—Life in a Desert Cactus. 2003. (gr. k-3). lib. bdg. 15.90 (978-0-613-78241-8(0)) Tandem Library Bks.

Barlowe, Sy. Learning about Desert Animals. 1998. (Learning about Ser.). 16p. (J). (gr. 3-5). pap. 1.50 (978-0-486-40333-5(5) , 40333-5) Dover Pubns., Inc.

Bateman, Helen & Denshire, Jayne. Of the Deserts. 2005. (Illus.). 32p. (J). (gr. 4-7). lib. bdg. 27.10 (978-1-58340-770-7(7)) Smart Apple Media.

Bessesen, Brooke. Look Who Lives in the Desert. 2004. (Illus.). 48p. (J). 16.95 (978-1-932082-09-8(3)) Arizona Highways.

Bullard, Lisa. Wet & Dry: An Animal Opposites Book. Saunders-Smith, Gail, ed. 2005. (Illus.). 32p. (J). (ps-7). 22.60 (978-0-7368-4278-5(0)) Capstone Pr., Inc.

Butterfield, Moira. Animals in Hot Places. 1999. (Looking at...Ser.). (Illus.). 32p. (J). (gr. k-3). pap. 5.95 (978-0-7398-0715-6(3)) Steck-Vaughn.

Chanko, Pamela & Moreton, Daniel. Who Beats the Heat? 1998. (Science Emergent Readers Ser.). (J). 3.25 (978-0-590-63873-9(4)) Scholastic, Inc.

Darling, Kathy. Desert Babies. Darling, Tara, photos by. 2002. (Illus.). 32p. (J). (gr. k-3). pap. 6.95 (978-0-8027-7533-7(0)) Walker & Co.

de Lambilly-Bresson, Elisabeth. Animals in the Desert. 2007. (Animal Show & Tell Ser.). 16p. (J). (ps-2). lib. bdg. 17.27 (***978-0-8368-8204-9(0)***) Stevens, Gareth Inc.

Fredericks, Anthony D. Around One Cactus: Owls, Bats, & Leaping Rats. DiRubbio, Jennifer, tr. DiRubbio, Jennifer, illus. 2004. (Sharing Nature with Children Book Ser.). 32p. (J). 16.95 (978-1-58469-051-1(8)); pap. 7.95 (978-1-58469-052-8(6)) Dawn Pubns.

Galko, Francine. Desert Animals. 2003. (Animals in Their Habitats Ser.). (Illus.). 32p. (J). (gr. k-2). lib. bdg. 21.36 (978-1-4034-0178-6(0)); pap. 6.95 (978-1-4034-0435-0(6)) Heinemann Library.

—Desert Animals. 2003. (gr. k-3). lib. bdg. 14.75 (978-0-613-45737-8(4)) Tandem Library Bks.

George, Jean Craighead. Summer Moon. 2002. (Seasons of the Moon Ser.). (Illus.). 112p. (J). pap. 5.95 (978-0-06-440995-7(3) , Harper Trophy) HarperCollins Pubs.

—Summer Moon. 2003. (J). (gr. 3-7). 20.75 (978-0-8446-7243-4(2)) Smith, Peter Pub., Inc.

—Summer Moon. 2002. (gr. 3-6). lib. bdg. 14.10 (978-0-613-50513-0(1)) Tandem Library Bks.

Helman, Andrea. C Is for Coyote. Wolfe, Art & Jecan, Gavriel, illus. Wolfe, Art & Jecan, Gavriel, photos by. 2002. 32p. (ps-3). 15.95 (978-0-87358-798-3(7) , Rising Moon Bks. for Young Readers) Northland Publishing.

Hine, Eileen, illus. Desert Opposites. 2005. 12p. (J). bds. 5.95 (978-0-87358-890-4(8) , Rising Moon Bks. for Young Readers) Northland Publishing.

Jango-Cohen, Judith. Desert Iguanas. (Pull Ahead Bks.). (Illus.). 32p. (gr. k-3). 2005. lib. bdg. 22.60 (978-0-8225-3635-2(8)); 2003. (J). pap. 5.95 (978-0-8225-3642-0(0)) Lerner Publishing Group.

—Desert Iguanas. 2001. (gr. k-3). lib. bdg. 14.10 (978-0-613-58830-0(4)) Tandem Library Bks.

Keating, Brian. Amazing Animal Adventures in the Desert. 2006. (Illus.). 48p. (J). pap. 12.95 (978-1-894856-72-0(4)) Fifth Hse. Pubs. CAN. *Dist:* F & W Pubns., Inc.

Landstrom, Lee Ann & Shragg, Karen. Nature's Yucky! 2: The Desert Southwest. Rogge, Rachel, illus. 48p. (J). pap. 12.00 (***978-0-87842-529-7(2)***) Mountain Pr. Publishing Co., Inc.

Longnecker, Theresa. Who Grows Up in the Desert? A Book about Desert Animals & Their Offspring. Carpenter, Melissa, illus. 2004. (Who Grows Up Here? Ser.). 24p. (C). (gr. k-4). 21.26 (978-1-4048-0024-3(7)) Picture Window Bks.

Macken, JoAnn Early. Animals That Live in the Desert. 24p. (YA). 115.98 (978-0-8368-4825-0(X)) Stevens, Gareth Inc.

—Anmials That Live in the Desert. 24p. (YA). 115.98 (978-0-8368-4839-7(X)) Stevens, Gareth Inc.

Mattern, Joanne. What Desert Animals Eat. 2006. (Illus.). 24p. (J). pap. (978-0-8368-6877-7(3)); lib. bdg. (978-0-8368-6870-8(6)) Stevens, Gareth Inc.

—What Desert Animals Eat: Qué Comen Los Animales Del Desierto? 2006. (ENG & SPA., Illus.). 24p. (J). pap. (978-0-8368-7378-8(5)); lib. bdg. (978-0-8368-7371-9(8)) Stevens, Gareth Inc. (Weekly Reader Early Learning Library).

McKissack, Fredrick, Jr. & McKissack, Lisa Beringer. Counting in the Desert. 2008. (Counting in the Biomes Ser.). 32p. (J). (gr. 1-3). lib. bdg. 22.60 (***978-0-7660-2988-0(3)***) Enslow Pubs., Inc.

Merlin, Pinau. A Guide to Southern Arizona Bird Nests & Eggs Vol. 1: Desert Areas. 2001. (Illus.). 182p. (J). 14.95 (978-1-886679-17-7(7)) Arizona Sonora Desert Museum Pr.

Murphy, Stuart J. Coyotes All Around. Bjorkman, Steve, illus. 2003. (MathStart Ser.). 40p. (J). (gr. 1 up). 15.99 (978-0-06-051529-4(5)); pap. 5.99 (978-0-06-051531-7(7)) HarperCollins Pubs.

—Coyotes All Around. 2003. (gr. k-3). lib. bdg. 13.00 (978-0-613-68415-6(X)) Tandem Library Bks.

Nicholson, Sue. Animal Babies in Deserts. 2006. (Animal Babies Ser.). (Illus.). 24p. (J). (ps-k). bds. 6.95 (978-0-7534-5942-3(6) , Kingfisher) Houghton Mifflin Co. Trade & Reference Div.

NorthWord Books for Young Readers Editors, contrib. by. Desert Babies. (J). 2005. (SPA.). bds. 5.95 (978-1-55971-907-0(9)); 2003. (Illus.). 22p. bds. 5.95 (978-1-55971-872-1(2)) T&N Children's Publishing. (NorthWord Bks. for Young Readers).

Oliver, Narelle. Baby Bilby, Where Do You Sleep? Oliver, Narelle, illus. 2002. (Illus.). 32p. (J). (978-0-7344-0230-1(9) , Lothian Bks.) Hachette Livre Australia.

—Sand Swimmers. 2002. (Illus.). 32p. (YA). (978-0-85091-768-0(9) , Lothian Bks.) Hachette Livre Australia.

Phillips, Dee. Find It in the Desert. 2005. (Can You Find It? Ser.). (Illus.). 24p. (J). lib. bdg. 22.00 (978-0-8368-6300-0(3)) Stevens, Gareth Inc.

Radley, Gail. Grasslands & Deserts. Sherlock, Jean, illus. (Vanishing from Ser.). 2005. 32p. (gr. 6-12). lib. bdg. 22.60 (978-1-57505-406-3(X)); 2003. 32p. (YA). (gr. 3-5). 6.95 (978-1-57505-568-8(6) , Carolrhoda Bks.); 1998. (J). lib. bdg. (978-0-8225-1936-2(4)) Lerner Publishing Group.

—Grasslands & Deserts. 2001. (gr. 3-6). lib. bdg. 15.25 (978-0-613-64517-1(0)) Tandem Library Bks.

Rivera, Sheila. Desert. 2005. (First Step Nonfiction Ser.). (Illus.). 23p. (J). (ps-7). 18.60 (978-0-8225-2597-4(6) , Lerner Pubns.) Lerner Publishing Group.

Schwartz, David M. In the Desert. Kuhn, Dwight, photos by. 1998. (Springboards into Science Ser.). (Illus.). 24p. (J). (gr. 1 up). lib. bdg. 20.67 (978-0-8368-2220-5(X)) Stevens, Gareth Inc.

Steele, Christy. Desert Animals. 2002. (Animals of the Biomes Ser.). (Illus.). 48p. (J). lib. bdg. 24.26 (978-0-7398-5686-4(3)) Raintree.

—Desert Animals. 2003. (Animals of the Biomes Ser.). (Illus.). 48p. (J). pap. 6.95 (978-0-7398-6406-7(8)) Steck-Vaughn.

Stewart, Pat. Invisible Desert Animals Magic Picture Book. 2003. (Dover Little Activity Bks.). (Illus.). 16p. (J). pap. 1.50 (978-0-486-43023-2(5)) Dover Pubns., Inc.

Townsend, Emily Rose. Desert Animals. Saunders-Smith, Gail, ed. 2005. (Pebble Ser.). (Illus.). (J). (gr. k-1). lib. bdg. 127.44 (978-0-7368-3799-6(X)) Capstone Pr., Inc.

—Desert Animals, 4 bks. Saunders-Smith, Gail, ed. Incl. Armadillos. lib. bdg. 15.93 (978-0-7368-2075-2(2)); Jackrabbits. lib. bdg. 15.93 (978-0-7368-2076-9(0)); Lizards. lib. bdg. 15.93 (978-0-7368-2077-6(9)); Rattlesnakes. lib. bdg. 15.93 (978-0-7368-2078-3(7)); 24p. (J). (gr. k-1). 2003. (Illus.). 2003. Set lib. bdg. 63.72 (978-0-7368-2320-3(4) , Pebble Bks.) Capstone Pr., Inc.

Whitehouse, Patricia. Hiding in a Desert. 2003. (Animal Camouflage Ser.). (Illus.). 32p. (J). lib. bdg. 22.79 (978-1-4034-0796-2(7)) Heinemann Library.

Whitehouse, Patricia, tr. Hiding in a Desert. 2003. (Heinemann First Library). (Illus.). 32p. (J). pap. 6.50 (978-1-4034-3186-8(8)) Heinemann Library.

Who Grows up in the Desert? (Who Grows up Here? Ser.). 24p. (J). 7.95 (978-1-4048-0206-3(1)) Picture Window Bks.

Wickings, Ruth. Animals in the Desert. 2006. (First Fun Pop-ups Ser.). (Illus.). 12p. bds. 8.95 (978-1-84560-021-1(5)) Mercury Bks. Ltd. GBR. *Dist:* International Publishers Marketing.

Windsor, Jo. Animals in the Desert: Emergent Level Satellite Individual Title Six-Packs. (Sails Literacy Ser.). (gr. k-1). 27.00 (978-0-7578-7940-1(3)) Rigby Education.

DESERT PLANTS

Barlowe, Dorothy & Barlowe, Dot. Learning about Desert Plants. 2000. (Learning about Ser.). (Illus.). 16p. (J). pap. 1.50 (978-0-486-41292-4(X)) Dover Pubns., Inc.

Betanzos, Sue, illus. My New Backyard Garden. 2006. Tr. of Mi Nuevo Jardin del Traspatio. (SPA & ENG.). (J). (***978-0-9792253-0-7(2)***) Tucson Botanical Gardens.

Giesecke, Ernestine. Desert Plants. 1999. (Plants Ser.). (Illus.). 32p. (J). (gr. k-2). lib. bdg. 21.36 (978-1-57572-821-6(4)) Heinemann Library.

Harcourt School Publishers Staff. The Giant of the Desert Below Level. 3rd ed. 2002. (Trophies Reading Program Ser.). (Illus.). pap. 5.10 (978-0-15-323053-0(3)) Harcourt Schl. Pubs.

—The Land of Little Water: Take-Home Book. 2001. (Collections Ser.). (Illus.). (J). (gr. 4). pap. 1.90 (978-0-15-319497-9(9)) Harcourt Schl. Pubs.

—The Land of Little Water Below Level. 3rd ed. 2002. (Trophies Reading Program Ser.). (Illus.). pap. 5.10 (978-0-15-323243-5(9)) Harcourt Schl. Pubs.

Merlin, Pinau. A Guide to Southern Arizona Bird Nests & Eggs Vol. 1: Desert Areas. 2001. (Illus.). 182p. (J). 14.95 (978-1-886679-17-7(7)) Arizona Sonora Desert Museum Pr.

Nelson, Cyndi. Desert Blooms. Miller, Millie, illus. 2007. 38p. pap. 7.95 (***978-1-55566-405-3(9)***) Johnson Bks.

Phillips, Dee. Find It in the Desert. 2005. (Can You Find It? Ser.). (Illus.). 24p. (J). lib. bdg. 22.00 (978-0-8368-6300-0(3)) Stevens, Gareth Inc.

Plants & Flowers of Desert. (Butterfly Bks.). (ARA., Illus.). 32p. (J). (gr. 3-5). 8.95 (978-0-86685-402-3(9) , LDL252) International Bk. Ctr., Inc.

Rivera, Sheila. Desert. 2005. (First Step Nonfiction Ser.). (Illus.). 23p. (J). (ps-7). 18.60 (978-0-8225-2597-4(6) , Lerner Pubns.) Lerner Publishing Group.

Welch, Catherine A. Desert Plants. 2006. (Life in the World's Biomes Ser.). (Illus.). 24p. (J). (978-0-7368-4321-8(3) , Bridgestone Bks.) Capstone Pr., Inc.

DESERTS

see also Desert Animals; Desert Plants

Adil, Janeen R. Why Is the Sahara So Dry? A Book about Deserts. 2007. (First Facts Ser.). (Illus.). 24p. (J). 21.26 (978-0-7368-6382-7(6)) Capstone Pr., Inc.

Allaby, Michael. Deserts & Semideserts. 2003. (Biomes Atlas Ser.). (Illus.). 64p. pap. 9.50 (978-1-4109-0021-0(5)); pap. 48.30 (978-1-4109-0256-6(0)) Raintree.

American Deserts. 2001. (J). cd-rom 69.95 (978-1-56791-297-5(4)) Environmental Media Corp.

Arnosky, Jim. Parrotfish & Sunken Ships: Exploring a Tropical Reef. Arnosky, Jim, illus. 2007. (Illus.). 32p. (J). (gr. k-5). 16.99 (978-0-688-17123-0(0)) HarperCollins Pubs.

Baker, Lucy. Deserts. 2004. (Life In... Ser.). (SPA., Illus.). (gr. 3-6). 32p. (J). pap. 6.95 (978-1-58728-567-7(3)); 31p. 12.95 (978-1-58728-552-3(5)) T&N Children's Publishing. (Two Can Publishing).

—Los Desiertos. 2004. (Ecologia Ser.). (SPA., Illus.). 32p. (gr. 3-6). 12.95 (978-1-58728-974-3(1) , Two Can Publishing) T&N Children's Publishing.

—Life in the Deserts. 2001. (World Book Ecology Ser.). (Illus.). 32p. (J). (978-0-7166-5220-5(X)) World Bk., Inc.

—Vida en las Desiertos. 2000. Tr. of Life in the Deserts. (Illus.). (J). (978-0-606-20970-0(0)) Tandem Library Bks.

Baldwin, Carol. Living in a Desert. 2003. (Living Habitats Ser.). (Illus.). 32p. (J). lib. bdg. 24.22 (978-1-4034-0840-2(8)); pap. 6.95 (978-1-4034-3224-7(4)) Heinemann Library.

Banting, Erinn. Deserts. 2005. (Illus.). 32p. (J). (ps-6). lib. bdg. 24.45 (978-1-59036-344-7(2)); pap. 7.95 (978-1-59036-350-8(7)) Weigl Pubs., Inc.

Barnes, Julia. 101 Facts about Deserts. 2003. (One Hundred One Facts about Our World Ser.). (Illus.). 32p. (J). (gr. 3 up). lib. bdg. 23.33 (978-0-8368-3706-3(1)) Stevens, Gareth Inc.

Benchmark Education Staff. Dry as a Desert. 2005. 2.00 (***978-1-4108-4642-6(3)***) Benchmark Education Co.

Benduhn, Tea. Living in Deserts. 2007. (J). pap. (***978-0-8368-8346-6(2)***); 24p. (gr. 2-4). lib. bdg. 19.93 (***978-0-8368-8341-1(1)***) Stevens, Gareth Inc. (Weekly Reader Early Learning Library).

Bennett, Paul. Desert Habitats. 2006. (Exploring Habitats Ser.). (Illus.). 36p. (J). lib. bdg. (978-0-8368-7253-8(3)) Stevens, Gareth Inc.

Bodden, Valerie. Deserts. 2006. (Our World Ser.). (Illus.). 24p. 16.95 (978-1-58341-461-3(4) , Creative Education) Creative Co., The.

Brannon, Barbara. Discover Deserts. 2005. 39.00 (***978-1-4108-5129-1(X)***) Benchmark Education Co.

Brewer, Duncan. Deserts. (Illus.). 64p. (YA). (gr. 4 up). lib. bdg. 29.95 (978-1-59389-128-2(8)) Chrysalis Education.

Brooks, David. You Can Count in the Desert. 2005. (You Can Count Ser.). (Illus.). 24p. (J). (978-1-55971-910-0(9) , Two Can Publishing) T&N Children's Publishing.

Brown, Harriett. Geography: Deserts. 2006. (Illus.). 32p. (J). (978-1-59604-101-1(3)) Stargazer Bks.

Butterfield, Moira. Desert. 1999. (Where Am I? Ser.). 32p. (J). (gr. 2-6). lib. bdg. 16.95 (978-1-929298-35-8(8)) Chrysalis Education.

Castaldo, Nancy F. Deserts: An Activity Guide for Ages 6-9. 2004. (Illus.). 128p. (J). pap. 14.95 (978-1-55652-524-7(9)) Chicago Review Pr., Inc.

Cefrey, Holly. Deserts. 2003. (Reading Power Ser.). (Illus.). 24p. (J). lib. bdg. 17.25 (978-0-8239-6456-7(6) , PowerKids Pr.) Rosen Publishing Group, Inc., The.

Chambers, Catherine & Lapthorn, Nicholas. Deserts. 2nd ed. 2007. (J). (***978-1-4034-9689-8(7)***); pap. (***978-1-4034-9609-6(9)***) Heinemann.

Champion, Neil. Deserts. 2005. (Caring for the Planet Ser.). (Illus.). 48p. (J). (978-1-58340-513-0(5)) Smart Apple Media.

Cheshire, Gerard. Nature Unfolds Mountains & Deserts. Barrett, Peter, illus. 2002. (Nature Unfolds Ser.). 40p. (J). (gr. 4). pap. (978-0-7787-0323-5(1)); lib. bdg. (978-0-7787-0311-2(8)) Crabtree Publishing Co.

—Nature Unfolds the Rocky Mountains & Deserts. 2002. (gr. 5-8). lib. bdg. 18.75 (978-0-613-81340-2(5)) Tandem Library Bks.

Claybourne, Anna. Deserts. 2004. (Geography Fact Files Ser.). (J). lib. bdg. 28.50 (978-1-58340-425-6(2)) Smart Apple Media.

Cole, Joanna. The Magic School Bus Gets All Dried Up: A Book about Deserts. 2002. (Magic School Bus Ser.). (Illus.). (J). 11.45 (978-0-7587-6956-5(3)) Book Wholesalers, Inc.

Cole, Melissa S. Desert. 2003. (Wild America Habitats Ser.). (Illus.). 24p. (J). 24.94 (978-1-56711-799-8(6) , Blackbirch Pr., Inc.) Thomson Gale.

Costain, Meredith. Desert Life. 2000. (gr. k-3). lib. bdg. 11.80 (978-0-613-30354-5(7)) Tandem Library Bks.

Davies, Nicola. Deserts. 2005. (Kingfisher Young Knowledge Ser.). (Illus.). 48p. (J). (gr. k-3). 9.95 (978-0-7534-5866-2(7) , Kingfisher) Houghton Mifflin Co. Trade & Reference Div.

Delano, Marfe Ferguson. Deserts. 1999. (Nature Library). (Illus.). (J). (978-0-7922-7544-2(6)) National Geographic Society.

Dell, Pamela. Surviving Death Valley: Desert Adaptation. 2008. (J). ***978-1-4296-1266-1(5))** Capstone Pr., Inc.

The Desert: First Grade Guided Reading Level A. (On Our Way to English Ser.). (gr. 1 up). 27.75 (978-0-7578-7027-9(9)) Rigby Education.

Desert Clowns: Second Grade Guided Reading Level I. (On Our Way to English Ser.). (gr. 2 up). 34.50 (978-0-7578-7088-0(0)) Rigby Education.

Deserts, 6 vols. (gr. 2-5). 36.95 (978-0-7368-9262-9(1)) Red Brick Learning.

Deserts: Individual Title Six-Packs. (On Deck Ser.: Vol. 2). 24p. (gr. 4-5). 35.00 (978-0-7578-5825-3(2)) Rigby Education.

Deserts Learning about the Earth. 2006. (Illus.). 24p. (J). (gr. k-2). 18.50 ***978-0-531-17887-4(0))** Scholastic Library Publishing.

DK Publishing Staff. Desert. 2007. (Eye Wonder Ser.). 48p. (J). (gr. 1-3). 9.99 (978-0-7566-2908-3(X)); lib. bdg. 17.99 (978-0-7566-2909-0(8)) Dorling Kindersley Publishing, Inc.

Dorling Kindersley Publishing Staff. Desert. 2006. (Dk 24 Hours Ser.). (Illus.). 48p. (J). 12.99 (978-0-7566-1984-8(X)) Dorling Kindersley Publishing, Inc.

Dunphy, Madeleine. Here Is the Southwestern Desert. Coe, Anne, illus. 2006. (Web of Life Ser.). 32p. (J). 16.95 (978-0-9773795-7-6(4)); pap. 9.95 (978-0-9773795-6-9(6)) Web of Life Children's Bks.

Fine, Jill. The Sahara: World's Largest Desert. 2002. (Reading Power Ser.). (Illus.). 24p. (J). (gr. 2). lib. bdg. 17.25 (978-0-8239-6013-2(7) , PowerKids Pr.) Rosen Publishing Group, Inc., The.

Fridell, Ron. Life in the Desert. 2005. (Watts Library). (Illus.). 63p. (J). (gr. k-7). 25.50 (978-0-531-12384-3(7) , Watts, Franklin) Scholastic Library Publishing.

Gaff, Jackie. I Wonder Why the Sahara Is Cold at Night? And Other Questions about Deserts. 2002. (I Wonder Why Ser.). (Illus.). 32p. (J). (gr. k-3). tchr. ed. 11.95 (978-0-7534-5434-3(3) , Kingfisher) Houghton Mifflin Co. Trade & Reference Div.

—I Wonder Why the Sahara Is Cold at Night & Other Questions about Deserts. 2004. (I Wonder Why Ser.). (Illus.). 32p. (J). (gr. k-3). pap. 6.95 (978-0-7534-5764-1(4) , Kingfisher) Houghton Mifflin Co. Trade & Reference Div.

Galko, Francine. Desert Animals. 2003. (Heinemann First Library). (Illus.). 32p. (J). pap. 6.95 (978-1-4034-0435-0(6)) Heinemann Library.

—Desert Animals. 2003. (gr. k-3). lib. bdg. 14.75 (978-0-613-45737-8(4)) Tandem Library Bks.

Ganeri, Anita. Deserts. 2003. (Science Files Ser.). (Illus.). 32p. (J). (gr. 3 up). lib. bdg. 24.67 (978-0-8368-3566-3(2)) Stevens, Gareth Inc.

—Esos Desesperantes Desiertos. (Coleccion Esa Horrible Geografia). (SPA.). (YA). (gr. 5-8). pap. (978-84-272-2155-0(X) , ML31292) Molino, Editorial ESP. *Dist:* Lectorum Pubns., Inc.

George, Michael. Deserts: Gardens of Sand. 2003. (Life-Views Ser.). (Illus.). 32p. (J). lib. bdg. (978-1-58341-251-0(4) , Creative Education) Creative Co., The.

Gilkerson, Patricia. My Adventure in the Desert. 2006. 44p. (J). 8.99 (978-1-59092-278-1(6) , Orchard Academy Pr.) Windstorm Creative.

Gordon, Sharon. At Home in the Desert. 2005. (Bookworms Ser.). (ENG & SPA., Illus.). 32p. (J). (gr. 3-7). lib. bdg. (978-0-7614-1963-1(2) , Benchmark Bks.) Cavendish, Marshall Corp.

—At Home in the Desert (Mi Casa en el Desierto) 2006. (Bookworms Ser.). (ENG & SPA., Illus.). 32p. (J). lib. bdg. 22.79 (978-0-7614-2453-6(9)) Cavendish, Marshall Corp.

—Mi Casa en el Desierto. 2006. (Bookworms Ser.). (SPA & ENG., Illus.). 32p. (J). lib. bdg. 22.79 (978-0-7614-2373-7(7)) Cavendish, Marshall Corp.

Gray, Susan Heinrichs. Deserts. 2000. (First Reports). (Illus.). 48p. (J). (gr. 3 up). lib. bdg. 21.26 (978-0-7565-0019-1(2)) Compass Point Bks.

Green, Emily K. Deserts. 2006. (Blastoff! Readers Ser.). (Illus.). 24p. (J). lib. bdg. 16.95 (978-1-60014-035-8(1)) Bellwether Media.

Gritzner, Charles F. Deserts. 2007. (Geography of Extreme Environments Ser.). 128p. (J). (gr. 6-12). 24.95 (978-0-7910-9234-7(8) , Chelsea Hse.) Facts On File, Inc.

Group/McGraw-Hill, Wright. Life in the Deserts, 6 vols. (Book2WebTM Ser.). (gr. 4-8). 36.50 (978-0-322-04436-4(7)) Wright Group, The.

Guiberson, Brenda Z. Cactus Hotel. 2007. (Illus.). 32p. (J). 23.95 ***978-0-8050-8228-9(X)** , Holt, Henry & Co. Bks. For Young Readers) Holt, Henry & Co.

Gunzi, Christiane. Deserts. (Collectafact Ser.). (J). 2002. 14.95 (978-1-58728-673-5(4)); 2002. pap. 7.95 (978-1-58728-769-5(2)); 2001. (Illus.). 48p. (gr. 1-5). 4.95 (978-1-58728-757-2(9)) T&N Children's Publishing. (Two Can Publishing).

Harcourt School Publishers Staff. The Land of Little Water: Take-Home Book. 2001. (Collections Ser.). (Illus.). (J). (gr. 4). pap. 1.90 (978-0-15-319497-9(9)) Harcourt Schl. Pubs.

—The Land of Little Water Below Level. 3rd ed. 2002. (Trophies Reading Program Ser.). (Illus.). pap. 5.10 (978-0-15-323243-5(9)) Harcourt Schl. Pubs.

—Trofeos Advanced Level: Que Es para Desiert? 3rd ed. 2002. (SPA., Illus.). pap. 6.80 (978-0-15-324127-7(6)) Harcourt Schl. Pubs.

—What Is a Desert? Advanced Level. 3rd ed. 2002. (Trophies Reading Program Ser.). (Illus.). pap. 5.10 (978-0-15-323216-9(1)) Harcourt Schl. Pubs.

Harvey, Gill. True Desert Adventures. Woodcock, John, illus. 2004. (True Adventure Stories Ser.). 144p. (J). pap. 4.95 (978-0-7945-0381-9(0) , Usborne) EDC Publishing.

Hoena, B. A. A Desert ABCs: An Alphabet Book. 2004. (A+ Alphabet Books). (Illus.). 17p. (J). 22.60 (978-0-7368-2605-1(X) , Aplus Bks.) Capstone Pr., Inc.

Holland, Gini. I Live in the Desert. 2004. (Weekly Reader Early Learning Library). (Illus.). 24p. (gr. k up). (J). pap. (978-0-8368-4087-2(9)); (YA). lib. bdg. 19.33 (978-0-8368-4080-3(1)) Stevens, Gareth Inc. (Weekly Reader Early Learning Library).

—I Live in the Desert/Vivo en el Desierto. Coffey, Colleen & Carrillo, Consuelo, trs. 2004. (Weekly Reader Early Learning Library). (ENG & SPA., Illus.). 24p. (J). (gr. k up). pap. 5.95 (978-0-8368-4135-0(2)); lib. bdg. 19.33 (978-0-8368-4128-2(X)) Stevens, Gareth Inc. (Weekly Reader Early Learning Library).

Howard, Fran. Deserts. 2007. (Habitats Ser.). (Illus.). 32p. (J). (gr. k-4). lib. bdg. 22.78 (978-1-59679-776-5(2)) ABDO Publishing Co.

In the Desert. 2002. (Illus.). (J). pap. 5.43 (978-0-7398-5919-3(6)) Steck-Vaughn.

Jackson, Kay. Deserts. 2006. (Illus.). 24p. (J). (978-0-7368-5404-7(5) , 1252617) Capstone Pr., Inc.

—Explore the Desert. 2007. (Fact Finders Ser.). (Illus.). 32p. (J). 22.60 (978-0-7368-6404-6(0)) Capstone Pr., Inc.

James, Ian, ed. Deserts. 1998. (Living Planet Ser.). (Illus.). 32p. (J). 17.99 (978-0-7540-9030-4(2) , Cherrytree Books) Evans Publishing Group GBR. *Dist:* Independent Pubs. Group.

Johansson, Philip. The Dry Desert: A Web of Life. 2004. (World of Biomes Ser.). (Illus.). 48p. (J). lib. bdg. 23.93 (978-0-7660-2200-3(5)) Enslow Pubs., Inc.

Johnson, Rebecca L. A Walk in the Desert. Saroff, Phyllis V., illus. Braasch, Gary, photos by. 2005. (Biomes of North America Ser.). 48p. (gr. 3-6). 23.93 (978-1-57505-152-9(4)) Lerner Publishing Group.

Kalman, Bobbie & MacAulay, Kelley. Cadenas Alimentarias del Desierto. 2006. (Cadenas Alimentarias Ser.). (SPA., Illus.). 32p. (J). pap. (978-0-7787-8546-0(7)) Crabtree Publishing Co.

—Desert Food Chains. 2004. (Food Chains Ser.). (Illus.). 32p. (J). (978-0-7787-1944-1(8)); pap. (978-0-7787-1990-8(1)) Crabtree Publishing Co.

Klingel, Cynthia Fitterer & Noyed, Robert B. Deserts. 2001. (Wonder Books Level 2: Habitats Ser.). (Illus.). 24p. (J). (ps-3). 22.79 (978-1-56766-972-5(7)) Child's World, Inc.

Knowlton, Jack. Deserts of the World. Barton, Harriett, illus. 1999. 48p. (J). (gr. 2-5). lib. bdg. 14.89 (978-0-06-021310-7(8)); 15.00 (978-0-06-021309-1(4)) HarperCollins Pubs.

Kottke, Jan. Living in a Desert. 2000. (Welcome Bks.). (Illus.). 24p. (J). (ps-2). 17.00 (978-0-516-23300-0(9) , Children's Pr.) Scholastic Library Publishing.

—Living in a Desert. 2000. (Illus.). 24p. (J). (ps-3). lib. bdg. 12.95 (978-0-613-52130-7(7)) Tandem Library Bks.

Lalley. Desert Scientists. 2001. (Scientists of the Biomes Ser.). (Illus.). (J). pap. (978-0-7398-4935-4(2)) Steck-Vaughn.

Lalley, Pat & Lalley, Janet. Desert Scientists. 2001. (Scientists of the Biomes Ser.). (Illus.). 48p. (J). (gr. 4-7). lib. bdg. 24.26 (978-0-7398-4754-1(6)) Raintree.

Lambert, David. People of the Deserts. 1999. (Wide World Ser.). (Illus.). 48p. (J). (gr. 3-7). 18.98 (978-0-8172-5063-8(8)) Raintree.

Le Rochais, Marie-Ange. Desert Trek: An Eye-Opening Journey Through the World's Driest Places. Newman, George L., tr. 2001. (Illus.). 40p. (J). (gr. 1-5). lib. bdg. 18.85 (978-0-8027-8766-8(5)) Walker & Co.

Legg, Gerald. Life in the Desert. 2005. (What on Earth? Ser.). (Illus.). 32p. (J). 25.50 (978-0-516-25317-6(4) , Children's Pr.) Scholastic Library Publishing.

Life Cycles, Vol. 2. 2005. (Animals, Animals, Animals Ser.). (YA). (gr. k-3). 267.30 (978-0-7368-4208-2(X) , Pebble Bks.) Capstone Pr., Inc.

Llewellyn, Claire. Deserts & Rainforests. 1998. (Illus.). 24p. (J). (gr. 1-6). (978-1-57572-196-5(1)) Heinemann Library.

Lynch, Wayne, photos by. Sonoran Desert. 2008. (J). ***978-1-55971-984-1(2));** pap. ***978-1-55971-985-8(0))** T&N Children's Publishing. (NorthWord Bks. for Young Readers).

MacAulay, Kelley. Un Habitat de Desierto. 2007. (SPA.). 32p. (J). (gr. 1-2). ***978-0-7787-8326-8(X))** Crabtree Publishing Co.

MacAulay, Kelley & Kalman, Bobbie. A Desert Habitat. 2006. (Illus.). 32p. (J). (978-0-7787-2950-1(8)) Crabtree Publishing Co.

MacAulay, Kelley & Kalman, Bobbie. Un Habitat de Desierto. rev. ed. 2007. (SPA & ENG.). 32p. (J). (gr. 1-2). pap. ***978-0-7787-8350-3(2))** Crabtree Publishing Co.

MacAuley, Kelley. A Desert Habitat. 2006. (Illus.). 32p. (J). (gr. 2). pap. (978-0-7787-2978-5(8)) Crabtree Publishing Co.

Macken, JoAnn Early. Deserts. 2006. (Illus.). 24p. (J). pap. (978-0-8368-6400-7(X)); lib. bdg. 19.33 (978-0-8368-6393-2(3)) Stevens, Gareth Inc.

MacLeod, Beatrice. Deserts. 2002. (Animal Homes Ser.). (Illus.). 40p. (J). (gr. 1 up). 9.95 (978-0-87226-695-7(8) , Bedrick, Peter Bks.) School Specialty Publishing.

MacQuitty, Miranda. Desert. 2000. (Eyewitness Bks.). (Illus.). 64p. (J). (gr. 4-7). 15.99 (978-0-7894-5862-9(4)) Dorling Kindersley Publishing, Inc.

MacQuitty, Miranda & Dorling Kindersley Publishing Staff. Desert. 2000. (Eyewitness Bks.). (Illus.). 64p. (J). (gr. 4-7). lib. bdg. 19.99 (978-0-7894-6600-6(7)) Dorling Kindersley Publishing, Inc.

Mayer, Cassie. Desert. 2007. (J). ***978-1-4034-9429-0(0));** pap. ***978-1-4034-9435-1(5))** Heinemann Library.

McKissack, Fredrick, Jr. & McKissack, Lisa Beringer. Counting in the Desert. 2008. (Counting in the Biomes Ser.). 32p. (J). (gr. 1-3). lib. bdg. 22.60 ***978-0-7660-2988-0(3))** Enslow Pubs., Inc.

McNeil, Niki, et al. HOCPP 1083 Desert Habitats. 2006. spiral bd. 22.50 ***978-1-60308-083-5(X))** In the Hands of a Child.

Merlin, Pinau. A Guide to Southern Arizona Bird Nests & Eggs Vol. 1: Desert Areas. 2001. (Illus.). 182p. (J). 14.95 (978-1-886679-17-7(7)) Arizona Sonora Desert Museum Pr.

Morris. Earth's Changing Deserts 6-Pack. 2003. (Illus.). pap. 40.50 (978-1-4109-0406-5(7)) Raintree.

Morris, Neil. Earth's Changing Deserts. 2003. (Illus.). 32p. (J). 7.50 (978-1-4109-0343-3(5)); lib. bdg. 25.70 (978-1-4109-0176-7(9)) Raintree.

—Earth's Changing Deserts. 2003. (gr. 3-6). lib. bdg. 15.90 (978-0-613-78238-8(0)) Tandem Library Bks.

Mullican, Judy. In the Desert. Linke, Don, Jr., illus. l.t. ed. 1998. (Cuddle Bks.). 10p. (J). (ps-k). pap. 10.95 (978-1-57332-119-8(2)) HighReach Learning, Inc.

Nadeau, Isaac. Food Chains in a Desert Habitat. Kuhn, Dwight, photos by. 2002. (Library of Food Chains & Food Webs). (Illus.). 24p. (J). lib. bdg. 18.75 (978-0-8239-5760-6(8) , PowerKids Pr.) Rosen Publishing Group, Inc., The.

National Wildlife Federation Staff. Discovering Deserts. 1998. (Ranger Rick's Naturescope Ser.). (Illus.). 96p. (gr. k-3). pap. 12.95 (978-0-07-047100-9(2) , 9780070471009) McGraw-Hill Cos., The.

—Discovering Deserts. 1998. (gr. k-3). lib. bdg. 22.20 (978-0-613-71553-9(5)) Tandem Library Bks.

Nester, Tony. Desert Survival Tips, Tricks, & Skills. 2003. per. 10.95 (978-0-9713811-1-7(9)) Diamond Creek Publishing.

Owen, Andy, et al. Deserts. 2002. (Geography Starts Ser.). (Illus.). 32p. (J). (gr. k-2). pap. 6.95 (978-1-58810-970-5(4) , 91453) Heinemann Library.

Parker, Steve. Deserts. 1998. (Take 5 Geography Ser.). (Illus.). 32p. (J). (gr. 3-5). 21.00 (978-0-531-14460-2(7) , Watts, Franklin) Scholastic Library Publishing.

Parker, Steve & Harris, Nathaniel. Atlas of the World's Deserts. 2003. (Illus.). 192p. (gr. 6 up). 135.00 (978-1-57958-310-1(5)) Fitzroy Dearborn Pubs., Inc.

Pfeffer, Wendy. Hot Deserts. 2002. (Living on the Edge Ser.). (J). 25.64 (978-0-7614-1440-7(1) , Benchmark Bks.) Cavendish, Marshall Corp.

Pipe, Jim. Desert Survival. 2007. (Extreme Habitats Ser.). 32p. (J). (gr. 4-6). lib. bdg. 25.27 ***978-0-8368-8245-2(8))** Stevens, Gareth Inc.

Pyers. Desert Explorer. 2004. (Habitat Explorer Ser.). (Illus.). pap. 7.50 (978-1-4109-0906-0(9)); pap. 40.50 (978-1-4109-0911-4(5)) Raintree.

Raintree Steck-Vaughn Staff. True Tales from the Deserts. 1999. (Illus.). (J). pap. 13.00 (978-0-7398-0856-6(7)) Steck-Vaughn.

Raskin, Lawrie & Pearson, Debora. 52 Days by Camel: My Sahara Adventure. Raskin, Lawrie, photos by. 1998. (Adventure Travel Ser.). (Illus.). 88p. (J). (gr. 3-7). pap. 14.95 (978-1-55037-518-3(0)) Annick Pr., Ltd. CAN. *Dist:* Firefly Bks., Ltd.

Rau, Dana Meachen. Deserts. 2007. (Wonders of Nature Ser.). 32p. (J). lib. bdg. 22.79 ***978-0-7614-2667-7(1)** , Benchmark Bks.) Cavendish, Marshall Corp.

—Deserts/Los Desiertos. 2007. (Wonders of Nature/ Maravillas de la Naturaleza Ser.). (SPA & ENG.). 32p. (J). lib. bdg. 22.79 ***978-0-7614-2830-5(5)** , Benchmark Bks.) Cavendish, Marshall Corp.

—Los Desiertos. 2007. (Maravillas de la Naturaleza Ser.). (SPA.). 32p. (J). lib. bdg. 22.79 ***978-0-7614-2806-0(2)** , Benchmark Bks.) Cavendish, Marshall Corp.

Reid, Greg. Deserts. 2004. (Ecosystems Ser.). (Illus.). 32p. (J). (gr. 3-5). 23.00 (978-0-7910-7938-6(4) , Chelsea Hse.) Facts On File, Inc.

Riley, Peter D. Survivor's Science in the Desert. 2004. (Survivor's Science Ser.). (Illus.). 48p. (J). (gr. 6-8). lib. bdg. 28.56 (978-1-4109-0224-5(2)) Harcourt Schl. Pubs.

Rivera, Sheila. Desert. 2005. (First Step Nonfiction Ser.). (Illus.). 23p. (J). (ps-7). 18.60 (978-0-8225-2597-4(6) , Lerner Pubns.) Lerner Publishing Group.

Roca, Nuria. Deserts. 2002. (Living Planet Ser.). (Illus.). 32p. (J). 23.70 (978-1-56711-667-0(1) , Blackbirch Pr., Inc.) Thomson Gale.

Romero, Libby. Dry as a Desert. 2005. 39.00 ***978-1-4108-4594-8(X))** Benchmark Education Co.

Royston, Angela. Deserts. 2004. (Heinemann First Library). (Illus.). 32p. (J). 24.21 (978-1-4034-5588-8(0)) Heinemann Library.

—Deserts. (Extreme Survival Ser.). (Illus.). 32p. (J). 2004. pap. 7.95 (978-1-4109-0359-4(1)); 2003. lib. bdg. 25.70 (978-1-4109-0000-5(2)) Raintree.

Rozario, Paul. Spreading Deserts. 2004. (Green Alert Ser.). (Illus.). 48p. (J). lib. bdg. 28.56 (978-0-7398-7013-6(0)) Raintree.

Ruth, Maria M. The Deserts of the Southwest. 1999. (Ecosystems of North America Ser.). (Illus.). 64p. (YA). (gr. 6 up). lib. bdg. 28.50 (978-0-7614-0899-4(1) , Benchmark Bks.) Cavendish, Marshall Corp.

Salas, Laura Purdie. Deserts. 2007. (Amazing Science Ser.). (Illus.). 24p. (J). ***978-1-4048-3469-9(9)** , 1265689) Picture Window Bks.

—Deserts: Thirsty Wonderlands. Yesh, Jeff, illus. 2006. (Amazing Science Ser.). 24p. (J). ***978-1-4048-3095-0(2)** , 1265689) Picture Window Bks.

Salzmann, Mary Elizabeth. In the Desert. l.t. ed. 2001. (What Do You See? Ser.). (Illus.). 24p. (J). (ps-3). lib. bdg. 19.93 (978-1-57765-564-0(8) , SandCastle) ABDO Publishing Co.

Sandler, Michael. Deserts: Surviving in the Sahara. 2005. (X-treme Places Ser.). (Illus.). 32p. (J). (gr. 3-7). lib. bdg. 25.27 (978-1-59716-085-8(7)) Bearport Publishing Co., Inc.

Saunders-Smith, Gail, ed. Earth Features, 8 bks. Incl. What Are Caves? Schuh, Mari C. 2002. lib. bdg. 15.93 (978-0-7368-1169-9(9)); What Are Deserts? Trumbauer, Lisa. 2001. lib. bdg. 15.93 (978-0-7368-0987-0(2)); What Are Forests? Trumbauer, Lisa. 2001. lib. bdg. 15.93 (978-0-7368-0988-7(0)); What Are Lakes? Schuh, Mari C. 2002. lib. bdg. 15.93 (978-0-7368-1170-5(2)); What Are Mountains? Trumbauer, Lisa. 2001. lib. bdg. 15.93 (978-0-7368-0989-4(9)); What Are Oceans? Trumbauer, Lisa. 2001. lib. bdg. 15.93 (978-0-7368-0990-0(2)); What Are Rivers? Schuh, Mari C. 2002. lib. bdg. 15.93 (978-0-7368-1171-2(0)); What Are Volcanoes? Schuh, Mari C. 2002. lib. bdg. 15.93 (978-0-7368-1172-9(9)); 24p. (J). (gr. k-1). (Illus.). 2001. Set lib. bdg. 127.44 (978-0-7368-1198-9(2) , Pebble Bks.) Capstone Pr., Inc.

Schwartz, David M. In the Desert. Kuhn, Dwight, photos by. 1998. (Springboards into Science Ser.). (Illus.). 24p. (J). (gr. 1 up). lib. bdg. 20.67 (978-0-8368-2220-5(X)) Stevens, Gareth Inc.

Seddon, Tony. Deserts: South African Edition. 1998. (Cambridge Reading Routes Ser.). (Illus.). 16p. pap. 5.00 (978-0-521-63665-0(5)) Cambridge Univ. Pr.

Sill, Cathryn P. & Sill, John. About Habitats: Deserts. Sill, Cathryn P. & Sill, John, illus. 2007. 48p. (J). (ps-2). lib. bdg. 16.95 ***978-1-56145-390-0(0)** , Peachtree Junior) Peachtree Pubs., Ltd.

Smithee, Allan. Los Desiertos. 2002. (Interfact Ser.). (SPA.). (J). spiral bd. 14.95 incl. cd-rom (978-1-58728-988-0(1) , Two Can Publishing) T&N Children's Publishing.

Somervill, Barbara A. Our Living World: Earth's Biomes, 7 vols., Set. 2005. (Illus.). (J). (gr. 4-8). 350.00 (978-1-59187-052-4(6)) Tradition Publishing Co.

Spilsbury, Louise & Spilsbury, Richard. Desert Food Chains. 2004. (Food Webs Ser.). (Illus.). 32p. (J). 24.22 (978-1-4034-5855-1(3)); pap. (978-1-4034-5862-9(6)) Heinemann Library.

Steele. Deserts. 2000. (Biomes Ser.). (Illus.). (J). pap. (978-0-7398-4157-0(2)) Steck-Vaughn.

Steele, Christy. Deserts. Sloan, Frank, ed. 2001. (Biomes Ser.). (Illus.). 32p. (J). (gr. 4-7). lib. bdg. 22.83 (978-0-7398-3560-9(2)) Raintree.

Stille, Darlene R. Deserts. 2000. (True Bks.). (Illus.). 48p. (J). (gr. 3-5). pap. 6.95 (978-0-516-26760-9(4) , Children's Pr.) Scholastic Library Publishing.

—Deserts. 1999. (gr. 3-6). lib. bdg. 15.25 (978-0-613-37325-8(1)) Tandem Library Bks.

Stone, Lynn M. Deserts. 2003. (Rourke Discovery Library). (Illus.). 24p. (J). 20.64 (978-1-58952-683-9(X)) Rourke Publishing, LLC.

Tarbox, A. D. The Desert. 2007. (J). ***978-1-58341-597-9(1)** , Creative Education) Creative Co., The.

Trumbauer, Lisa. What Are Deserts? Saunders-Smith, Gail, ed. 2001. (Earth Features Ser.). (Illus.). 24p. (J). (gr. k-1). lib. bdg. 15.93 (978-0-7368-0987-0(2) , Pebble Bks.) Capstone Pr., Inc.

Tull, Mary. Deserts. 2004. (Illus.). 32p. (J). pap. (978-0-7922-4565-0(2)) National Geographic Society.

Warhol, Tom. Desert. 2006. (Earth's Biomes Ser.). (Illus.). 80p. (YA). (gr. 5-8). lib. bdg. 32.79 (978-0-7614-2194-8(7) , Benchmark Bks.) Cavendish, Marshall Corp.

What Are Deserts?, 6 vols., Vol. 2. 2005. (Earth & Outer Space Ser.). (gr. k-2). 28.95 (978-0-7368-3274-8(2)) Red Brick Learning.

Whitehouse, Patricia. Living in a Desert. 2007. (Illus.). 24p. (J). (978-1-60044-183-7(1)) Rourke Publishing, LLC.

Wilkins, Sally. Deserts. 2001. (Bridgestone Science Library). (Illus.). 24p. (J). (gr. 2-3). lib. bdg. 18.60 (978-0-7368-0835-4(3) , Bridgestone Bks.) Capstone Pr., Inc.

Wood, Jennifer. Deserts. 2004. (Interfact Ser.). (SPA., Illus.). 48p. (J). (gr. 3-6). pap. 14.95 incl. cd-rom (978-1-58728-457-1(X) , Two Can Publishing) T&N Children's Publishing.

Woodford. Arctic Tundra & Polar Deserts. 2003. (Biomes Atlas Ser.). (Illus.). 64p. pap. 9.50 (978-1-4109-0020-3(7)) Raintree.

—Arctic Tundra Polar Desert. 2003. (Biomes Atlas Ser.). (Illus.). pap. 48.30 (978-1-4109-0255-9(2)) Raintree.

Wright-Frierson, Virginia. A Desert Scrapbook. 2002. (Illus.). 40p. (J). (gr. 1 up). pap. 6.99 (978-0-689-85055-4(7) , Aladdin) Simon & Schuster Children's Publishing.

—Desert Scrapbook: Dawn to Dusk in the Sonoran Desert. 2002. (gr. 3-6). lib. bdg. 15.30 (978-0-613-51815-4(2)) Tandem Library Bks.

Zollman, Pam. Life Cycles, 6 bks., Set. Incl. Bear Cub Grows Up. 19.00 (978-0-516-24943-8(6)); Chick Grows Up. 19.00 (978-0-516-24944-5(4)); Shark Pup Grows Up. 19.00 (978-0-516-24945-2(2)); Spiderling Grows Up. 19.00 (978-0-516-24946-9(0)); Tadpole Grows Up. 19.00 (978-0-516-24947-6(9)); Turtle

Hatchling Grows Up. 19.00 (978-0-516-24948-3(7)); (Illus.). 24p. (J). (gr. 1-2). 2005. (Scholastic News Nonfiction Readers Ser.). 2005. 108.00 (978-0-516-25393-0(X) , Children's Pr.) Scholastic Library Publishing.

DESERTS—FICTION

Alexander, Lloyd. The Jedera Adventure. 2001. (Vesper Holly Ser.). (Illus.). 160p. (J). (gr. 5-9). pap. 5.99 (978-0-14-131238-5(6) , Puffin) Penguin Group (USA) Inc.

Blanco, Alberto. The Desert Mermaid (La Sirena del Desierto) Revah, Patricia, illus. 2002. (ENG & SPA.). 32p. (J). (gr. 1 up). pap. 7.95 (978-0-89239-173-8(1)) Bellerophon Bks.

Campbell, Joanna. Cindy's Desert Adventure. 2001. (Thoroughbred Ser.: No. 47). 176p. (gr. 4-7). mass mkt. 4.99 (978-0-06-106671-9(0) , Harper Entertainment) HarperCollins Pubs.

—Cindy's Desert Adventure. 2001. (gr. 3-6). lib. bdg. 12.40 (978-0-613-67181-1(3)) Tandem Library Bks.

Campbell, Roy. Song of the Jackalope. Bosworth, David, illus. 2nd ed. 2006. 140p. (YA). pap. 12.95 (978-1-933538-04-4(X)) Bridgeway Bks.

Carroll, Thomas L. The Colony: A Novel for the Young Reader. 2000. 152p. (J). (gr. 4-7). 18.95 (978-0-86534-295-8(4)) Sunstone Pr.

Farber, Erica. Golden Eagle. Mayer, Mercer, illus. 2006. (Critter Kids Adventure Ser.). 32p. (J). (gr. 2-5). pap. 4.95 (978-0-7696-4764-7(2) , Gingham Dog Pr.) School Specialty Publishing.

Fox, Mary Virginia. A Desert Adventure. McMahon, Kelly, illus. 2002. (Two Can Read Ser.). 16p. (J). 2.99 (978-1-56472-659-9(2)) Edupress, Inc.

Freed, Rachael A. Blessing Our Daughters & Our Sons: The Story of Zelophehad's Daughters in the Desert. Stillman, Deborah L., illus. 2000. 32p. (J). (gr. k-3). pap. 6.95 (978-0-9637795-8-8(3)) MinervaPress.

Frieders, Robert. American Elves - The Yankoos Vol. 1: The Yankoos & Life in the Sonoran Desert. Olin, George & Robinson, Earle, photos by. 1998. (Illus.). 152p. (J). (gr. 4 up). 16.00 (978-0-9639284-6-7(5)) Yankoo Publishing Co.

Gelsey, James. Scooby-Doo! & the Cactus Creature. 2005. (Illus.). 58p. (J). lib. bdg. 15.00 (****978-1-4242-0304-8(X)***) Fitzgerald Bks.

—Scooby-Doo! & the Cactus Creature. 2005. (Illus.). 58p. (J). (****978-1-4155-9742-2(1)***) Scholastic, Inc.

Greenburg, J. C. In the Desert. Gerardi, Jan, illus. 2008. (Andrew Lost: 17). 96p. (J). (****978-0-375-84667-0(0)***) Random Hse., Inc.

Hanson, Ed. Desert Ordeal. 2003. (Barclay Family Adventure Ser.: Bk. 3). 64p. (J). (gr. k-6). per. 3.95 (978-1-56254-552-9(3) , SP 5523) Saddleback Educational Publishing.

Hapka, Cathy. Oasis. 2002. (Dinotopia Ser.: Vol. 16). 208p. (J). (gr. 3-8). pap. 3.99 (978-0-375-82295-7(X) , Random Hse. Bks. for Young Readers) Random Hse. Children's Bks.

Harcourt School Publishers Staff. Desert Letters On Level. 3rd ed. 2002. (Trophies Reading Program Ser.). (Illus.). pap. 5.10 (978-0-15-323280-0(3)) Harcourt Schl. Pubs.

—Desert Night. 3rd ed. 2002. (Trophies English Language Learners Ser.). (Illus.). pap. 5.10 (978-0-15-327772-6(6)) Harcourt Schl. Pubs.

—In the Desert: Take-Home Book. rev. ed. 2001. (Collections Ser.: Bk. 17). (Illus.). (J). pap. 1.90 (978-0-15-319075-9(2)) Harcourt Schl. Pubs.

Hausman, Sid. Cactus Critter Bash. Hausman, Sid, illus. 2007. (Illus.). 32p. (J). 21.95 (****978-1-929115-15-0(6)***) Azro Pr., Inc.

Have You Seen a Javelina? Individual Title Six-Packs. (Literatura 2000 Ser.). (gr. 2-3). 33.00 (978-0-7635-0201-0(4)) Rigby Education.

Hiscock, Bruce. Coyote & Badger: Desert Hunters of the Southwest. 2003. (Illus.). 32p. (J). (gr. 2-4). 15.95 (978-1-56397-848-7(2)) Boyds Mills Pr.

Hodgson, Mona Gansberg. Desert Critter Friends Set, 12 vols. (Desert Critter Friends Ser.). (J). 54.99 (978-0-7586-0007-3(0)) Concordia Publishing Hse.

—Goofy Glasses. 2000. (ps-2). lib. bdg. 13.00 (978-0-613-72834-8(3)) Tandem Library Bks.

—Jumping Jokers. 1999. (Desert Critter Friends Ser.: Vol. 7). (Illus.). 48p. (J). (ps-2). 4.99 (978-0-570-05481-8(8)) Concordia Publishing Hse.

—Jumping Jokers. 1999. (ps-2). lib. bdg. 13.00 (978-0-613-72657-3(X)) Tandem Library Bks.

Hodgson, Mona Gansberg & Sharp, Chris. Goofy Glasses. 2000. (Desert Critter Friends Ser.: Vol. 10). (Illus.). 48p. (J). (ps-2). 4.99 (978-0-570-07011-5(2)) Concordia Publishing Hse.

Howey, Paul M. Freckles: The Mystery of the Little White Dog in the Desert. Zabriskie, Judy Mehn, illus. 2003. 72p. (gr. 2-5). lib. bdg. 14.95 (978-0-9677292-1-3(1)) AZTexts Publishing, Inc.

Jackson, Barry. Danny Diamondback. 2008. 40p. (J). 17.89 (****978-0-06-113185-1(7));*** 16.99 (****978-0-06-113184-4(9)***) HarperCollins Pubs.

Johnson, Angela. Toning the Sweep. 2002. (J). 13.19 (978-0-7587-0401-6(1)) Book Wholesalers, Inc.

—Toning the Sweep. 2003. 112p. (J). (gr. 7 up). pap. 5.99 (978-0-590-48142-7(8) , Scholastic Paperbacks) Scholastic, Inc.

Johnson, Frances A. Coyote Tales: How Coyote Brought Color to the Desert. Zweiger, Jackie Gulledge, illus. 2000. (J). 15.95 (978-1-57168-377-9(1)) Eakin Pr.

Johnston, Tony. Desert Dog. Weatherford, Robert, illus. 2001. 32p. (J). (gr. 1-5). 15.95 (978-0-87156-979-0(5)) Gibbs Smith, Publisher.

Jones, Christianne C. & Kipling, Rudyard. How the Camel Got Its Hump: A Retelling of the Classic Folktale. Rooney, Ronnie, illus. 2005. (Read-It! Readers Ser.). 32p. (J). (gr. k-3). 18.60 (978-1-4048-1003-7(X)) Picture Window Bks.

Karr, Kathleen. Exiled: Memoirs of a Camel. 2004. 240p. (J). 15.95 (978-0-7614-5164-8(1)) Cavendish, Marshall Corp.

Keats, Ezra Jack. Clementina's Cactus. Keats, Ezra Jack, illus. 2002. (Illus.). (J). 21.81 (978-0-7587-2249-2(4)) Book Wholesalers, Inc.

—Clementina's Cactus. Keats, Ezra Jack, illus. 1999. (Illus.). 40p. (J). (ps-3). 16.99 (978-0-670-88545-9(2) , Viking Juvenile) Penguin Group (USA) Inc.

Lazaroff, David Wentworth. Correctamundo! Prickly Pete's Guide to Desert Facts & Cactifracts. Neel, Preston, illus. 2001. 32p. (J). per. 9.95 (978-1-886679-16-0(9)) Arizona Sonora Desert Museum Pr.

Leaney, Cindy. Desert Dream. Whitehouse, Patty, ed. King, Sue & Wilks, Peter, illus. 2004. (Friendly Phonics Ser.). 24p. (J). lib. bdg. 14.95 (978-1-59054-117-3(0)) Fitzgerald Bks.

Leinster, Murray. Space Tug. 2006. 95.99 (****978-1-4280-4342-8(X));*** pap. 89.99 (****978-1-4280-4295-7(4)***) Indy-Publish.com.

The Living Desert: Third Grade Guided Reading Level H. (On Our Way to English Ser.). (gr. 3 up). 34.50 (978-0-7578-7110-8(0)) Rigby Education.

Mason, Prue. Camel Rider. 2007. 204p. (J). (gr. 5-9). 15.95 (****978-1-58089-314-5(7)***) Charlesbridge Publishing, Inc.

Masters, Anthony. The Desert Pirates. Buckley, Harriet, illus. 2008. (J). pap. (****978-1-59889-906-1(6));*** lib. bdg. (****978-1-59889-870-5(1)***) Stone Arch Bks.

Morris, Gilbert. Dixie & Sandy. 1998. (Dixie Morris Animal Adventure Ser.: No. 4). 128p. (Orig.). (J). (gr. 4-7). pap. 5.99 (978-0-8024-3366-4(9)) Moody Pubs.

Osborne, Mary Pope. Season of the Sandstorms. Murdocca, Sal, illus. 2005. (Magic Tree House Ser.: No. 34). 128p. (J). (gr. k-3). lib. bdg. 13.99 (978-0-375-93031-7(0)); (gr. 2-6). 11.95 (978-0-375-83031-0(6)) Random Hse. Children's Bks. (Random Hse. Bks. for Young Readers).

Otis, James. Dick in the Desert. 2005. reprint ed. pap. 15.95 (978-1-4179-0335-1(X)) Kessinger Publishing, LLC.

Parpan, Justin. Gwango's Lonesome Trail. Parpan, Justin, illus. 2006. (Illus.). 32p. (J). 15.95 (978-1-60108-004-2(2)) Red Cygnet Pr.

Raintree Steck-Vaughn Staff. Desert Trek. 2000. (Read All about It Ser.). (Illus.). (J). pap. 4.95 (978-0-8114-3796-7(5)) Steck-Vaughn.

Rau, Dana Meachen. Visit the Desert. (J). (gr. k-2). 2001. (Illus.). 24p. lib. bdg. 19.27 (978-1-57103-321-5(1)); 2000. lib. bdg. (978-0-86625-321-5(1)) Rourke Publishing, LLC.

Rodda, Emily. The Shifting Sands. 2001. (Deltora Quest Ser.: No. 4). (Illus.). 144p. (J). (gr. 4-7). pap. 4.99 (978-0-439-25326-0(8)) Scholastic, Inc.

Stein, David Ezra. Cowboy Ned & Andy. Stein, David Ezra, illus. 2006. (Illus.). 32p. (J). (ps-1). 14.95 (978-1-4169-0041-2(1) , Simon & Schuster Children's Publishing) Simon & Schuster Children's Publishing.

Still, Wayne Anthony, illus. Desert Treasure. 1999. (J). 30.00 (978-0-8172-7296-8(8)) Steck-Vaughn.

Storad, Conrad J. Lizards for Lunch: A Roadrunner's Tale. 1999. 32p. (J). (ps-3). 15.95 (978-1-891795-02-2(3)) RGU Group, The.

—Lizards for Lunch: A Roadrunner's Tale. 1999. (gr. k-3). lib. bdg. 15.25 (978-0-613-61916-5(1)) Tandem Library Bks.

Strasser, Todd. Buzzard's Feast. 1999. (gr. 3-6). lib. bdg. 11.80 (978-0-613-17125-0(X)) Tandem Library Bks.

Temple, Frances. The Beduins' Gazelle. Bowers, David, illus. 1998. (Harper Trophy Bks.). 160p. (J). (gr. 7 up). pap. 5.99 (978-0-06-440669-7(5) , Harper Trophy) HarperCollins Pubs.

Tibo, Gilles & Vaillancourt, Francois. El Senor Patapum. (Barril Sin Fondo Ser.). (SPA.). (J). (gr. 3-5). pap. (978-968-6465-58-7(8)) Casa de Estudios de Literatura y Talleres Artisticos Amaquemecan A.C. MEX. *Dist:* Lectorum Pubns., Inc.

Tsinajinnie, Veronica, et al. Johonaa'éí: Bringer of Dawn. Howard, Winston, illus. 2008. (ENG & NAV.). 32p. 17.95 (978-1-893354-54-8(7)) Salina Bookshelf.

Van Zant, Dawn. Bradford & the Journey to the Desert of Lop. 2005. (Illus.). 36p. (J). pap. 17.99 (978-0-9761768-2-4(3)) Wild Heart Ranch, Inc.

Vaughan, Marcia. Night Dancer: Mythical Piper of the Native American Southwest. Desimini, Lisa, illus. 2002. 32p. (J). (ps-2). pap. 16.95 (978-0-439-35248-2(7) , Orchard Bks.) Scholastic, Inc.

Ward, Jennifer. The Seed & the Giant Saguaro. Rangner, Mike, illus. 2003. 32p. (gr. 4-8). 15.95 (978-0-87358-845-4(2) , Rising Moon Bks. for Young Readers) Northland Publishing.

Winderman, Jay B. Thunder on the Desert. Becker, LuAnne E. & Becker, Lisa E., illus. 2005. 152p. (J). (gr. 3-7). per. 13.95 (978-0-9761623-1-5(8)) Pill Bug Pr.

Winderman, Jay B. Thunder on the Reservation. Becker, LuAnne E., illus. 2007. 147p. (J). (gr. 3-7). per. 13.95 (****978-0-9761623-2-2(6)***) Pill Bug Pr.

DESIGN

see also Costume Design

also subdivision Design under topical headings where the subdivision Design and Construction is not appropriate

Biggs, Andy, et al. Product Design for Key Stage 3. 2000. (Design & Make It Ser.). (Illus.). 144p. (J). (gr. 6-9). pap. 22.50 (978-0-7487-4429-9(0)) Nelson Thornes Ltd. GBR. *Dist:* Trans-Atlantic Pubns., Inc.

—Product Design for Key Stage 3: Teacher Support Pack. 2000. (Design & Make It Ser.). (Illus.). 244p. (J). (gr. 6-9). 99.50 (978-0-7487-4430-5(4)) Nelson Thornes Ltd. GBR. *Dist:* Trans-Atlantic Pubns., Inc.

Bigham, Julia. The 60s: The Plastic Age. 2000. (Twentieth Century Design Ser.). (Illus.). 32p. (J). (gr. 5 up). lib. bdg. 26.00 (978-0-8368-2708-8(2)) Stevens, Gareth Inc.

Canizares, Susan & Berger, Samantha. Patterns. 1999. (J). pap. 2.50 (978-0-439-04596-4(7)) Scholastic, Inc.

Cassagnau, Pascale & Pillet, Christophe, texts. Starck's Kid: The Influence of Philippe Starck. 1999. (Illus.). 128p. pap. 23.50 (978-2-906571-84-6(9)) Dis Voir Editions FRA. *Dist:* D.A.P./Distributed Art Pubs.

Cosway, Ted, et al. Design & Make It! Resistant Materials Technology. 1998. (Illus.). 144p. pap. 30.00 (978-0-7487-2470-3(2)) State Mutual Bk. & Periodical Service, Ltd.

—Resistant Materials Technology. 2nd rev. ed. 2001. (Design & Make It Ser.). (Illus.). 152p. (YA). pap. 27.50 (978-0-7487-6083-1(0)) Nelson Thornes Ltd. GBR. *Dist:* Trans-Atlantic Pubns., Inc.

eraill, Sian Evans ac & Cymru, Addysg Cyfryngau. Gweithgareddau Dylunio a Thechnoleg CA1/2. 2005. (978-1-902346-02-1(5)) Addysg Y Cyfryngau Cymru.

Ford, Hannah. The 90s: The Digital Age. 2000. (Twentieth Century Design Ser.). (Illus.). 32p. (J). (gr. 5 up). lib. bdg. 26.00 (978-0-8368-2710-1(4)) Stevens, Gareth Inc.

Gaff, Jackie. 20s & 30s: Between the Wars. 2000. (Twentieth Century Design Ser.). (Illus.). 32p. (J). (gr. 5 up). lib. bdg. 26.00 (978-0-8368-2706-4(6)) Stevens, Gareth Inc.

—1900-20: The Birth of Modernism. 2000. (Twentieth Century Design Ser.). (Illus.). 32p. (J). (gr. 5 up). lib. bdg. 26.00 (978-0-8368-2705-7(8)) Stevens, Gareth Inc.

Gonyea, Mark. Another Book about Design: Complicated Doesn't Make It Bad. rev. ed. 2007. (Illus.). 160p. (J). (gr. 4 up). 19.95 (978-0-8050-7576-2(3)) Holt, Henry & Co.

—A Book About Design: Complicated Doesn't Make It Good. rev. ed. 2005. (Illus.). 144p. (J). 18.95 (978-0-8050-7575-5(5)) Holt, Henry & Co.

Harris, Trudy. Pattern Bugs. Green, Anne Canevari, illus. 2001. (Fun Early Math Concepts Ser.). 40p. (J). (gr. k-3). 22.60 (978-0-7613-2107-1(1) , Millbrook Pr.) Lerner Publishing Group.

Hendler, Muncie. Infinite Designs Coloring Book. 2006. 32p. (J). pap. 3.95 (978-0-486-44892-3(4)) Dover Pubns., Inc.

J. G. Ferguson Publishing Company Staff. Careers in Focus: Design. 2002. (Careers in Focus Ser.). (Illus.). 176-192p. (YA). (gr. 7 up). lib. bdg. 22.95 (978-0-89434-410-7(2) , F725, Ferguson Publishing Co.) Facts On File, Inc.

J. G. Ferguson Publishing Company Staff, contrib. by. Design. 2nd ed. 2005. (Careers in Focus Ser.). (Illus.). 192p. (YA). (gr. 6-12). 22.95 (978-0-8160-5865-5(2) , Ferguson Publishing Co.) Facts On File, Inc.

Jones, Helen. 40s & 50s: War & Post-War Years. 2000. (Twentieth Century Design Ser.). (Illus.). 32p. (J). (gr. 5 up). lib. bdg. 26.00 (978-0-8368-2707-1(4)) Stevens, Gareth Inc.

LaCoste, Michael, ed. & frwd. Design Denied: The Dynamics of Withholding Good Design & its Ethical Implications: The Dynamics of Withholding Good Design & its Ethical ImplicationsThe Withholding of Good Design & its Ethical Implications, LaCoste, Michael, frwd. 2005. (Illus.). 120p. per. 20.00 (978-0-9753405-2-3(2)) Archeworks.

Making Amazing Art: 40 Activities Using the 7 Elements of Art Design. 2007. (Illus.). 128p. (J). (gr. 2-8). pap. 12.99 (****978-0-8249-6795-6(X)*** , Williamson Bks.) Ideals Pubns.

McArthur, Alex & Shepard, Tristram. Textiles Technology for Key Stage 3. 2000. (Design & Make It Ser.). (Illus.). 144p. (J). (gr. 6-9). pap., stu. ed. 22.50 (978-0-7487-4431-2(2)) Nelson Thornes Ltd. GBR. *Dist:* Trans-Atlantic Pubns., Inc.

Nagel, Rob. Body by Design: From the Digestive System to the Skeleton, 2 vols., Set. 2000. (Illus.). 416p. (J). (gr. 8 up). lib. bdg. 120.00 (978-0-7876-3897-9(8) , GML00502-113693, UXL) Thomson Gale.

Nsrc. Science & Technology for Children Books, Motion & Design: Motion & Design. 2004. (Illus.). 64p. (J). (978-1-933008-03-5(2)) National Science Resources Ctr.

Science & Technology for Children Books, Motion & Design Set, 8 vols. 2004. (Illus.). 64p. (J). (978-1-933008-15-8(6)) National Science Resources Ctr.

Shepard, Tristram, et al. Design & Make It! Product Design. 1998. (Illus.). 176p. pap. 115.00 (978-0-7487-3513-6(5)) Nelson Thornes Ltd. GBR. *Dist:* Trans-Atlantic Pubns., Inc.

Steck-Vaughn Staff. Patterns Across the Curriculum. 2000. (Illus.). (J). (gr. 1). pap. (978-0-7398-3424-4(X)); (gr. 2). pap. (978-0-7398-3425-1(8)); (gr. 3). pap. (978-0-7398-3426-8(6)) Steck-Vaughn.

Stephens, Pamela Geiger. Tessellations: The History & Making of Symmetrical Designs. McNeill, Jim, illus. 2001. 40p. (J). pap. 14.95 net. (978-1-56290-243-8(1)) Crystal Productions.

Willacy, David M. Craft & Design in Wood. 1998. (Illus.). 224p. pap. 36.00 (978-0-7487-1066-9(3)) State Mutual Bk. & Periodical Service, Ltd.

Yes Mag Editors. Fantastic Feats & Failures. Kurisu, Jane, illus. 2005. 52p. (YA). (gr. 3-7). (978-1-55337-634-7(X)); (978-1-55337-633-0(1)) Kids Can Pr., Ltd.

DESIGN, DECORATIVE

see also Art, Decorative; Decoration and Ornament; Drawing; Lettering; Tapestry

Noble, Marty. African Designs Coloring Book. 2003. (Illus.). 32p. (J). pap. 3.95 (978-0-486-43037-9(5)) Dover Pubns., Inc.

Rainbow & You Temporary Tattoo. 2000. (J). pap. (978-0-688-18033-1(7) , Harper Trophy) HarperCollins Pubs.

Random House Disney Staff. Showers of Flowers. 2006. (Stickerific Ser.). (Illus.). 32p. (J). (ps-2). pap. 2.99 (978-0-7364-2357-1(5) , Golden/Disney) Random Hse. Children's Bks.

20th Century Design, 6 bks. Incl. 20s & 30s : Between the Wars. Gaff, Jackie. lib. bdg. 26.00 (978-0-8368-2706-4(6)); 40s & 50s : War & Post-War Years. Jones, Helen. lib. bdg. 26.00 (978-0-8368-2707-1(4)); 60s : The Plastic Age. Bigham, Julia. lib. bdg. 26.00 (978-0-8368-2708-8(2)); 70s & 80s : The High-Tech Age. Gaff, Jackie & Tyrrell, John. lib. bdg. 26.00 (978-0-8368-2709-5(0)); 90s : The Digital Age. Ford, Hannah. lib. bdg. 26.00 (978-0-8368-2710-1(4)); 1900-20 : The Birth of Modernism. Gaff, Jackie. lib. bdg. 26.00 (978-0-8368-2705-7(8)); (J). (gr. 5 up). (Illus.). 32p. 2000. Set lib. bdg. 52.00 (978-0-8368-2704-0(X)) Stevens, Gareth Inc.

DESSERTS

Ashworth, Sue. Desserts. 2004. (World of Recipes Ser.). (Illus.). 48p. (J). lib. bdg. (978-1-4034-4698-5(9)) Heinemann Library.

Beery, Barbara. Delicious Desserts. Snortum, Marty, photos by. 2004. (Illus.). 68p. (J). (gr. 1-7). 19.95 (978-1-58685-365-5(1)) Gibbs Smith, Publisher.

Beery, Barbara. Pink Princess Cookbook. Snortum, Marty, photos by. 2006. (Illus.). 64p. (J). spiral bd. 14.95 (****978-1-4236-0173-9(4)***) Gibbs Smith, Publisher.

Cooper, Hilda. Mother Estelle's Old Southern Recipe Dessert Cookbook. 2001. 376p. per. 18.95 (978-0-9701466-6-3(3)) Athenean Pr., Inc.

Desserts from Three Generations. 2004. 128p. per. 25.00 (978-0-9754003-0-2(4)) Ivy Fund, The.

Engfer, Lee, ed. Desserts Around the World. 2nd rev. ed. 2004. (Easy Menu Ethnic Cookbooks). (Illus.). 72p. (J). 25.26 (978-0-8225-4126-4(2)) Lerner Publishing Group.

Gilpin, Rebecca & Atkinson, Catherine. Yummy Little Cookbook. rev. ed. 2007. (Children's Cooking Ser.). 96p. (J). 7.99 (****978-0-7945-1655-0(6)*** , Usborne) EDC Publishing.

Kalman, Bobbie. Delicious Desserts. 2003. (Kid Power Ser.). (Illus.). 32p. (J). pap. (978-0-7787-1276-3(1)); (gr. 3). (978-0-7787-1254-1(0)) Crabtree Publishing Co.

—Delicious Desserts. 2003. (gr. 3-6). lib. bdg. 17.60 (978-0-613-70815-9(6)) Tandem Library Bks.

Linton, Marilyn. Just Desserts: And Other Treats for Kids to Make. Reid, Barbara, illus. 1998. (Kids Can Do It Ser.). 160p. (J). (gr. 4-6). (978-0-921103-02-8(6)) Kids Can Pr., Ltd.

—Just Desserts: And Other Treats for Kids to Make. Reid, Barbara, illus. 1998. 64p. (J). (ps-ps). lib. bdg. 12.95 (978-0-613-16368-2(0)) Tandem Library Bks.

Martineau, Susan. Healthy Eating. 2006. (Illus.). 32p. (J). (978-1-58340-897-1(5)) Smart Apple Media.

Wagner, Lisa. Cool Sweets & Treats to Eat: Easy Recipes for Kids to Cook. 2007. (Cool Cooking Ser.). (Illus.). 32p. (J). (gr. 3-6). lib. bdg. 22.78 (****978-1-59928-726-3(9)*** , Checkerboard Library) ABDO Publishing Co.

Weil, Carolyn Beth. Williams-Sonoma Kids in the Kitchen: Sweet Treats. 2006. (Illus.). 128p. 19.95 (978-0-7432-7857-7(7) , Free Pr.) Simon & Schuster.

DETECTIVE AND MYSTERY STORIES

see Mystery and Detective Stories

DETECTIVES

see also Criminal Investigation; Police; Secret Service

Arnone, Marilyn P. & Coatney, Sharon. Mac, Information Detective, in the Curious Kids... Digging for Answers: A Storybook Approach to Introducing Research Skills. 2006. (Illus.). 104p. (J). 35.00 (978-1-59158-397-4(7) , LU3977) Libraries Unlimited, Inc.

Croce, Nicholas. Detectives: Life of Investigating Crime. 2005. (Extreme Careers Ser.). (Illus.). 64p. (YA). (gr. 5-8). 26.50 (978-0-8239-3796-7(8)) Rosen Publishing Group, Inc., The.

Gaines, Ann Graham. Detectives, Private Investigators, & Bounty Hunters. 1999. (Crime, Justice & Punishment Ser.). (Illus.). 80p. (YA). (gr. 7-12). 30.00 (978-0-7910-4285-4(5) , Chelsea Hse.) Facts On File, Inc.

Goldberg, Jan. Private Investigator. 1998. (Careers Without College Ser.). (Illus.). 48p. (J). (gr. 3-4). lib. bdg. 21.26 (978-0-7368-0038-9(7) , LifeMatters Bks.) Capstone Pr., Inc.

Kilby, Janice Eaton. The Master Detective Handbook: Help Our Daring Detectives Use Gadgets & Super Sleuthing Skills to Solve the Mystery & Catch the Crooks. Chin, Jason, illus. 2007. 96p. (J). (gr. 5-7). 17.95 (978-1-57990-849-2(7)) Lark Bks.

Klein, Hilary Dole. A Day with a Chef. 2007. (Boys Rock! Ser.). 32p. (J). (gr. 1-5). 24.21 (****978-1-59296-857-2(0)***) Child's World, Inc.

Mauro, Paul & Melton, H. Keith. Master Case Files. Aycock, Daniel & Labat, Yancey C., illus. 2004. (Detective Academy Ser.). 48p. (J). pap. (978-0-439-57184-5(7)) Scholastic, Inc.

Running Press Staff & Oxlade, Chris. Detective Tool Kit. 2005. (Action Bks.). (Illus.). 32p. (J). pap. 24.95 (978-0-7624-1980-7(6) , Running Pr. Kids) Running Pr. Bk. Pubs.

Teitelbaum, Michael. Batman's Guide to Crime & Detection. 2003. (gr. k-3). lib. bdg. 11.80 (978-0-613-75252-7(X)) Tandem Library Bks.

Teitelbaum, Michael & Dorling Kindersley Publishing Staff. Batman's Guide to Crime & Detection. 2003. (Readers Ser.). (Illus.). 48p. (J). 12.99 (978-0-7894-9879-3(0)) Dorling Kindersley Publishing, Inc.

DETECTIVES—FICTION

Ace Lacewing: Bug Detective. 2005. (Illus.). 40p. (J). (ps-k). 15.95 (978-1-57091-569-7(5)) Charlesbridge Publishing, Inc.

Adler, David A. The Mystery of the Stolen Corn Popper. Natti, Susanna, illus. 2004. (Cam Jansen Ser.: No. 11). 64p. (J). (gr. 2-4). pap. 3.99 (978-0-14-240178-1(1) , Puffin) Penguin Group (USA) Inc.

Akiyama, Tamayo, illus. & creator. Secret Chaser. Akiyama, Tamayo, creator. 2006. 192p. pap. 9.99 (978-1-59816-341-4(8) , Tokyopop Adult) TOKYOPOP, Inc.

Alexander, Heather. The Case of the Easter Egg Race. 2004. 84p. (J). (ps-17). 11.79 (978-0-606-32976-7(5)) Tandem Library Bks.

Alexander, Liza & Santomero, Angela C. Blue y Tu, Detective de Colores. Ziegler, Argentina Palacios, tr. Speer-Lyon, Tammie, illus. 2004. (Blue's Clues Ser.).Tr. of Blue & the Color Detectives. (SPA.). 24p. (J). pap. 3.99 (978-0-689-86979-2(7) , Libros Para Ninos) Simon & Schuster Children's Publishing.

Anderson, Jane. Inspector Insector. 2005. 22.00 (***978-1-4108-4196-4(0)***) Benchmark Education Co.

Ardagh, Philip. The Fall of Fergal: Or Not So Dingly in the Dell. Roberts, David, illus. 2005. (Unlikely Exploits Trilogy Ser.). 144p. (J). (ps-7). reprint ed. pap. 5.99 (978-0-439-73014-3(7) , Scholastic Paperbacks) Scholastic, Inc.

Bailey, Linda. How Can a Brilliant Detective Shine in the Dark? (Stevie Diamond Mystery Ser.). 200p. (YA). (gr. 13 up). 1999. (978-1-55074-750-8(9)); No. 6. 2004. (978-1-55074-896-3(3)) Kids Can Pr., Ltd.

Banscherus, Jurgen. Detective's Duel. Baron, Daniel C., tr. from GER. Butschkow, Ralf, illus. 2007. 65p. (J). (gr. 3-6). lib. bdg. 22.60 (***978-1-59889-339-7(4)***) Stone Arch Bks.

Banscherus, Jurgen & Baron, Daniel C. Detective's Duel. Butschkow, Ralf, illus. 2007. 65p. (J). pap. (***978-1-59889-434-9(X)***) Stone Arch Bks.

Bikfalvy, Andrea. The Junkyard Club. 2002. 148p. pap. 15.00 (978-1-59146-055-8(7)) Crystal Dreams Publishing.

Bingham, Jane, retold by. Around the World in Eighty Days. 2004. (Young Reading Gift Books Ser.). 64p. (J). (gr. 2 up). 8.95 (978-0-7945-0826-5(X) , Usborne) EDC Publishing.

The Blind Alley. 2001. 32p. (YA). (gr. 6-12). pap. (978-0-8224-1453-7(8)) Globe Fearon Educational Publishing.

Brook, H. & Doyle, Arthur Conan. The Hound of the Baskervilles. 2004. (Paperback Classics Ser.). 144p. (J). lib. bdg. 12.95 (978-1-58086-605-7(0)) EDC Publishing.

Brooks, Walter R. Freddy & Mr. Camphor. Wiese, Kurt, illus. 2000. 234p. (J). (gr. 3-7). 23.95 (978-1-58567-027-7(8)) Overlook Pr., The.

—Freddy & the Baseball Team from Mars. Wiese, Kurt, illus. 1999. 256p. (J). (gr. 3-7). 23.95 (978-0-87951-942-1(8)) Overlook Pr., The.

—Freddy & the Baseball Team from Mars. 2000. (J). pap. 67.95 incl. audio (978-0-7887-4461-7(5) , 41150) Recorded Bks., LLC.

—Freddy & the Dragon. Wiese, Kurt, illus. 2000. 239p. (J). (gr. 3 up). 23.95 (978-1-58567-026-0(X)) Overlook Pr., The.

—Freddy & the Flying Saucer Plans. Wiese, Kurt, illus. 1998. (Freddy Ser.). 243p. (J). (gr. 3-7). 23.95 (978-0-87951-883-7(9)) Overlook Pr., The.

—Freddy & the Flying Saucer Plans. unabr. ed. 2000. (J). pap. 66.95 incl. audio (978-0-7887-3639-1(6) , 41004X4) Recorded Bks., LLC.

—Freddy & the Ignormus. Wiese, Kurt, illus. 1998. (Freddy Ser.). 288p. (J). (gr. 3-7). 23.95 (978-0-87951-882-0(0)) Overlook Pr., The.

—Freddy & the Ignormus. 1999. (J). pap. 66.95 incl. audio (978-0-7887-2996-6(9) , 40878) Recorded Bks., LLC.

Buckeridge, Anthony. Jennings & Darbishire. 2002. 196p. pap. (978-0-7551-0153-5(7)) House of Stratus, Inc.

Byars, Betsy. Dead Letter. 2006. (Herculeah Jones Mystery Ser.). 160p. (J). (gr. 3). pap. 5.99 (978-0-14-240564-2(7) , Puffin) Penguin Group (USA) Inc.

Campbell, Julie. Trixie Belden, 3 bks., Bk. 1. 2004. (J). (gr. 3). 20.97 (978-0-375-83109-6(6) , Random Hse. Bks. for Young Readers) Random Hse. Children's Bks.

Christie, Agatha. Misterio del Guia. 2000. (gr. 7-12). lib. bdg. 17.60 (978-0-613-63631-5(7)) Tandem Library Bks.

Conrad, Hy. Whodunit Crime Mysteries. 2003. (Illus.). 96p. (J). pap. 6.95 (978-1-4027-0646-2(4)) Sterling Publishing Co., Inc.

Cormier, Robert. The Rag & Bone Shop. 2001. (Illus.). 160p. (YA). (gr. 7 up). 15.95 (978-0-385-72962-8(6) , Delacorte Bks. for Young Readers) Random Hse. Children's Bks.

—The Rag & Bone Shop. l.t. ed. 2002. 141p. (J). 24.95 (978-0-7862-3873-6(9)) Thomson Gale.

Danko, Dan. Scooby-Doo: The Complete Movie Scrapbook. 2002. (gr. k-3). lib. bdg. 14.15 (978-0-613-50741-7(X)) Tandem Library Bks.

del Sur, Duendes. Catnapped Caper. 2000. (gr. k-3). lib. bdg. 11.80 (978-0-613-24507-4(5)) Tandem Library Bks.

The Detective Business. 2005. (J). (978-1-932570-45-8(4)) Literacy Footprints Inc.

Dickson, Louise. Lu & Clancy's Crime Science. Cupples, Pat, illus. 1999. 40p. (J). (ps-k). lib. bdg. 14.10 (978-0-613-21938-9(4)) Tandem Library Bks.

Dixon, Franklin W. & Walker, Jeff. Typhoon Island, Vol. 180. 2003. (Hardy Boys Ser.). (Illus.). 160p. (J). pap. 4.99 (978-0-689-85884-0(1) , Aladdin) Simon & Schuster Children's Publishing.

Doyle, Arthur Conan. A Study in Scarlet. 2001. (gr. 7-12). lib. bdg. 15.30 (978-0-613-64328-3(3)) Tandem Library Bks.

Doyle, Patrick H. T. Edgar Font's Hunt for a House to Haunt: Adventure One: the Castle Tower Lighthouse. 2006. (Illus.). 232p. (J). per. 6.99 (978-0-9786132-0-4(1)) Armadillo Bks.

Dunlop, Ed. Sherlock Jones: The Assassination Plot. 2004. 116p. (J). (978-1-59166-315-7(6)) Jones, Bob Univ. Pr.

Ferguson, Dwayne. The Werewolf of PS 40, Vol. 2. 1998. (Kid Caramel: Vol. 2). 72p. (J). (gr. 4-7). pap. 4.50 (978-0-940975-82-8(3) , Sankofa Bks.) Just Us Bks., Inc.

Friesen, Ray. Another Dirt Sandwich: Some Rambling & Hilarious Exploits of Tbyrd Fearlessness, 2008. (ENG., Illus.). 100p. pap. 12.95 (978-0-9728177-4-5(3)) Don't Eat Any Bugs Prodns.

—RQW, Vol. 3. 2003. (YA). 2.95 (978-0-9728177-2-1(7)) Don't Eat Any Bugs Prodns.

Funke, Cornelia. The Thief Lord. Latsch, Oliver, tr. from GER. Burmingham, Christian, illus. (J). 2002. 352p. (gr. 4-7). pap. 16.95 (978-0-439-40437-2(1)); 2003. 376p. (gr. 3-6). reprint ed. 6.99 (978-0-439-42089-1(X)) Scholastic, Inc. (Chicken Hse., The).

Funke, Cornelia. Thief Lord ('el Senor de Los Ladrones) 2007. 352p. (J). pap. 7.99 (***978-0-545-00517-3(5)*** , Scholastic en Espanol) Scholastic, Inc.

Funke, Cornelia & Latsch, Oliver. The Thief Lord. l.t. ed. 2004. 422p. (J). 23.95 (978-0-7862-7084-2(5)) Thorndike Pr.

Gaetz, Dayle Campbell. Barkerville Gold. 2004. 144p. (J). (gr. 3-7). pap. 7.95 (978-1-55143-306-6(0)) Orca Bk. Pubs. USA.

Hale, Bruce. Farewell, My Lunchbag. unabr. ed. 2004. (Chet Gecko, Private Eye Ser.: No. 3). 128p. (J). (gr. 3-6). pap. 17.00 incl. audio (978-0-8072-1708-5(5) , S FTR 273 SP, Listening Library) Random Hse. Audio Publishing Group.

Harcourt School Publishers Staff. The Missing Case 5-Pack, On Level. 3rd ed. 2002. (Trophies Reading Program Ser.). (Illus.). (gr. 3). pap. 25.60 (978-0-15-327019-2(5)) Harcourt Schl. Pubs.

—Mysteries of Nature Advanced Level. 3rd ed. 2002. (Trophies Reading Program Ser.). (Illus.). pap. 5.10 (978-0-15-323297-8(8)) Harcourt Schl. Pubs.

—The Thing That Visited Our Camp 5-Pack, Below Level. 3rd ed. 2002. (Trophies Reading Program Ser.). (Illus.). (gr. 1). pap. 20.10 (978-0-15-326818-2(2)) Harcourt Schl. Pubs.

—The Thing That Visited the Camp: Below Level. 3rd ed. 2002. (Trophies Reading Program Ser.). (Illus.). (J). pap. 4.10 (978-0-15-322968-8(3)) Harcourt Schl. Pubs.

—Watch the Eggs: Take-Home Book. rev. ed. 2001. (Collections Ser.: Bk. 14). (Illus.). (J). pap. 1.90 (978-0-15-319072-8(8)) Harcourt Schl. Pubs.

Harris, Thomas. Hannibal. 2000. (gr. 7-12). lib. bdg. 16.45 (978-0-613-27865-2(8)) Tandem Library Bks.

Heisler, Edith. Mystery at the Old Estate. 2002. 129p. pap. 17.95 (978-1-59129-275-3(1)) PublishAmerica, Inc.

Herman, Gail. Scooby Doo: Mummies at the Mall. 2002. (gr. k-3). lib. bdg. 11.80 (978-0-613-51319-7(3)) Tandem Library Bks.

—Scooby-Doo: Racecar Monster. 2001. (gr. k-3). lib. bdg. 11.80 (978-0-613-43872-8(8)) Tandem Library Bks.

—Scooby Doo: Sea Monster Scare. 2002. (gr. k-3). lib. bdg. 11.80 (978-0-613-51324-1(X)) Tandem Library Bks.

—Scooby-Doo! Snack Snatcher. 2001. (gr. k-3). lib. bdg. 11.80 (978-0-613-36675-5(1)) Tandem Library Bks.

—Scooby Doo! The Haunted Ski Lodge. 2001. (gr. k-3). lib. bdg. 11.80 (978-0-613-43831-5(0)) Tandem Library Bks.

—Scooby Doo! & the Football Fright. 2002. (gr. k-3). lib. bdg. 11.80 (978-0-613-58152-3(0)) Tandem Library Bks.

—Scooby Doo! Valentine's Day Dognapping. 2002. (gr. k-3). lib. bdg. 11.80 (978-0-613-54717-8(9)) Tandem Library Bks.

Itoh, Shimpei. Hyper Dolls, Vol. 4. 2003. 218p. pap. 15.95 (978-1-929090-44-0(7)) International Comics & Entertainment L.L.C.

Jardine, Quintin. Wearing Purple. 1999. (Oz Blackstone Mysteries Ser.). 344p. pap. 9.99 (978-0-7472-5666-3(7)) Headline Bk. Publishing GBR. *Dist:* Independent Pubs. Group.

Jennings, Sharon. Franklin the Detective. Gagnon, Celeste et al, illus. 2004. 32p. (J). lib. bdg. 15.38 (***978-1-4242-1171-5(9)***) Fitzgerald Bks.

Joosse, Barbara M. Dead Guys Talk: A Wild Willie Mystery. Truesdell, Sue & Carter, Abby, illus. 2006. 112p. (J). (gr. 3-5). 15.00 (978-0-618-30666-4(8) , Clarion Bks.) Houghton Mifflin Co. Trade & Reference Div.

Keane, Dave. The Phantom at Eve's Hollow. Keane, Dave, illus. 2007. (Joe Sherlock Ser.). 96p. (J). pap. 3.99 (***978-0-06-085473-7(1)*** , Harper Trophy) HarperCollins Pubs.

Keene, Carolyn. Nancy Drew Girl Detective (Boxed Set) Sleuth Set: Without a Trace; A Race Against Time; False Notes; High Risk. 2004. (Nancy Drew Ser.). (Illus.). 640p. (J). pap. 19.99 (978-0-689-03691-0(4) , Aladdin) Simon & Schuster Children's Publishing.

—Pit of Vipers. 2006. (Nancy Drew Ser.: No. 18). 160p. (J). pap. 4.99 (978-1-4169-1180-7(4) , Aladdin) Simon & Schuster Children's Publishing.

—Riverboat Ruse, Vol. 11. 2005. (Nancy Drew Ser.). 160p. (ps-7). pap. 4.99 (978-0-689-87335-5(2) , Aladdin) Simon & Schuster Children's Publishing.

—Snowman Surprise. Casale, Paul, illus. Frost, Michael, photos by. 2004. (Nancy Drew Notebooks: No. 63). 80p. (J). pap. 3.99 (978-0-689-87411-6(1) , Aladdin) Simon & Schuster Children's Publishing.

Klim, Christopher. Firecracker Jones Is on the Case. 2006. (Illus.). 116p. (J). lib. bdg. 19.95 (978-1-933435-11-4(9)) Hopewell Pubns., LLC.

Labatt, Mary. Weekend at the Grand Hotel. 2001. (gr. 3-6). lib. bdg. 12.95 (978-0-613-37071-4(6)) Tandem Library Bks.

Ladd, Debbie. Ethan the Ending Eater. Nakasone, Shaun, illus. 2007. 64p. (J). 16.95 (978-0-9727615-2-9(7)) Deb on Air Bks.

Landon, Lucinda. Meg Mackintosh & the Stage Fright Secret: A Solve-It-Yourself Mystery. 2004. (Meg Mackintosh Mystery Ser.). (Illus.). 48p. (J). pap. 5.95 (978-1-888695-07-6(2)) Secret Passage Pr.

Leather, Sue. Dead Cold Book/Audio CD Pack: Level 2 Elementary/Lower Intermediate. 2007. (Cambridge English Readers Ser.). (Illus.). 48p. pap. 11.00 incl. audio compact disk (978-0-521-69392-9(6)) Cambridge Univ. Pr.

Lement, Wendy. Keri Tarr: Cat Detective. Burrows, Jeffrey Scott, illus. 2004. 80p. pap. 9.95 (978-1-891369-52-0(0)) Breakaway Bks.

Lerangis, Peter. Tunnel Vision. 4th ed. 2005. (Spy X Ser.: No. 4). 160p. 4.99 (978-0-439-50728-6(8) , Scholastic Paperbacks) Scholastic, Inc.

Lorimer, Janet. The Tiger Lily Code: Set 2. 2002. 32p. (YA). 2.95 (978-1-56254-422-5(5) , SP 4225) Saddleback Educational Publishing.

Marini, Enrico & Dufaux, Jean. Rapaces, Vol. 4. 2005. (SPA., Illus.). 56p. pap. 17.95 (978-1-59497-107-5(2)) Public Square Bks.

Mason, Adrienne. Secret Codes. Cupples, Pat, illus. 1999. 40p. (J). (ps-k). lib. bdg. 14.10 (978-0-613-21939-6(2)) Tandem Library Bks.

McCann, Jesse Leon. Scooby-Doo! & Santa's Bake Shop. 2000. (gr. 3-6). lib. bdg. 14.15 (978-0-613-54349-1(1)) Tandem Library Bks.

—Scooby-Doo & the Cyber Chase. 2001. (gr. k-3). lib. bdg. 11.25 (978-0-613-50734-9(7)) Tandem Library Bks.

—Scooby-Doo! & the Eerie Ice Monster. 2000. (gr. k-3). lib. bdg. 14.15 (978-0-613-54351-4(3)) Tandem Library Bks.

—Scooby-Doo & the Phantom Cowboy. 2002. (gr. k-3). lib. bdg. 11.25 (978-0-613-50736-3(3)) Tandem Library Bks.

McCann, Jesse Leon, et al. The Scrapyard Detectives: Collected Cases Volume 1. 2007. 106p. (J). pap. 5.00 (***978-0-9797193-0-1(5)***) Diversity Foundation, The.

Miller, Michael. Hilde und Gunter Level Two Reader, 2 books. 2003. (GER., Illus.). 53p. 6.00 (978-0-9743522-0-6(9) , 0-9743522-0-9) Miller, Michael.

Mitchelhill, Barbara & Ross, Tony. How to Be a Detective. 2004. (Illus.). 64p. (J). pap. 8.99 (978-1-84270-360-1(9)) Andersen GBR. *Dist:* Independent Pubs. Group.

Obrist, Jurg. Case Closed?! 40 Mini-Mysteries for You to Solve. 2003. (Single Titles Ser.). 96p. (J). pap. 6.95 (978-0-7613-1999-3(9)); 22.90 (978-0-7613-2739-4(8)) Lerner Publishing Group. (Millbrook Pr.).

—Complex Cases: Three Major Mysteries for You to Solve. 2006. (Illus.). (J). pap. 6.95 (978-0-8225-5975-7(7) , First Avenue Editions) Lerner Publishing Group.

Odgers, Sally & Odgers, Darrel. The Buried Biscuits. Dawson, Janine, illus. 2008. (Jack Russell: Dog Detective Ser.: 7). 84p. (J). pap. 4.95 (***978-1-933605-77-7(4)***) Kane/Miller Bk. Pubs., Inc.

—The Lying Postman: Jack Russell: Dog Detective. 2007. (Jack Russell: Dog Detective Ser.: 4). (Illus.). 80p. (J). pap. 4.95 (978-1-933605-31-9(6) , 05319) Kane/Miller Bk. Pubs., Inc.

—The Mugged Pug: Jack Russell: Dog Detective. 2007. (Jack Russell: Dog Detective Ser.: 3). (Illus.). 80p. (J). pap. 4.95 (978-1-933605-32-6(4) , 05326) Kane/Miller Bk. Pubs., Inc.

O'Mahony, Carol. A Dee Dee & Clark Delay Magical Myster. 2006. 73p. pap. 14.95 (***978-1-4241-5119-6(8)***) PublishAmerica, Inc.

Platt, Richard. Shipwreck Detective. Cameron, Duncan, illus. 2006. 96p. (J). 24.99 (978-0-7566-2218-3(2)) Dorling Kindersley Publishing, Inc.

Pommaux, Yvan. El Sueno Interminable: Una Investigacion de John Chatterton. Iribarren, Leopoldo, tr. from FRE. 2002. (SPA., Illus.). 42p. (J). (978-980-257-271-7(3)) Ekare, Ediciones.

Poulsen, David A. The Hunk Machine No. 2: The Salt & Pepper Chronicles. 2nd rev. ed. 2007. 160p. pap. 6.95 (***978-1-55263-723-4(9)***) Key Porter Bks. CAN. *Dist:* Perseus Distribution.

Preller, James. The Case of the Double Trouble Detectives. Smith, Jamie C., illus. 2005. 79p. (J). (***978-1-4155-7908-4(3)***) Scholastic, Inc.

—The Case of the Double Trouble Detectives. 2005. (Illus.). 80p. (J). (ps-ps). lib. bdg. 10.79 (978-0-606-33280-4(4)) Tandem Library Bks.

—The Case of the Glow-in-the-Dark Ghost. 2004. (Jigsaw Jones Ser.: No. 24). (Illus.). 80p. (J). pap. 3.99 (978-0-439 55998-0(7) , Scholastic Paperbacks) Scholastic, Inc.

—The Case of the Perfect Prank. Smith, Jamie & Alley, R. W., illus. 2004. 66p. (J). (ps). 11.19 (978-0-606-33039-8(9)) Tandem Library Bks.

Rigby Education Staff. Mickey Maloney. (Sails Literacy Ser.). (Illus.). 16p. (gr. 1-2). 27.00 (978-0-7635-9929-4(8) , 699298C99) Rigby Education.

—The Sausage Spy. (Sails Literacy Ser.). (Illus.). 16p. (gr. 1-2). 27.00 (978-0-7635-9909-6(3) , 699093C99) Rigby Education.

Rosellini, Eleanor. Mystery of the Ancient Coins. 2003. (Illus.). 116p. 18.95 (978-1-57860-122-6(3)) Emmis Bks.

Rylant, Cynthia. The Case of the Climbing Cat. Karas, G. Brian, illus. 2003. (High-Rise Private Eyes Ser.: No. 2). (J). (gr. k-3). pap. 16.95 incl. audio (978-1-59112-189-3(2)); pap. 18.95 incl. audio compact disk (978-1-59112-610-2(X)); 25.96 incl. audio (978-1-59112-190-9(6)); pap. 29.95 incl. audio (978-1-59112-191-6(4)) Live Oak Media.

—The Case of the Climbing Cat. 2001. (High-Rise Private Eyes Ser.: No. 2). (J). (gr. k-3). lib. bdg. 11.80 (978-0-613-44193-3(1)) Tandem Library Bks.

—The Case of the Missing Monkey. Karas, G. Brian, illus. 2003. (High-Rise Private Eyes Ser.: No. 1). (J). 25.95 incl. audio (978-1-59112-194-7(9)); pap. 29.95 incl. audio (978-1-59112-195-4(7)); pap. 18.95 incl. audio compact disk (978-1-59112-614-0(2)); pap. 16.95 incl. audio (978-1-59112-193-0(0)) Live Oak Media.

—The Case of the Missing Monkey. Karas, G. Brian, illus. 2002. (High-Rise Private Eyes Ser.: No. 1). 46p. (J). (ps-17). lib. bdg. 11.80 (978-0-613-44194-0(X)) Tandem Library Bks.

—The Case of the Puzzling Possum. Karas, G. Brian, illus. (High-Rise Private Eyes Ser.: No. 3). (J). (ps-2). 2004. 48p. pap. 18.95 incl. audio compact disk (978-1-59112-618-8(5)); 2003. pap. 29.95 incl. audio (978-1-59112-199-2(X)); 2003. pap. 16.95 incl. audio (978-1-59112-197-8(3)); 2003. 25.95 incl. audio (978-1-59112-198-5(1)) Live Oak Media.

—The Case of the Puzzling Possum. 2002. (High-Rise Private Eyes Ser.: No. 3). (J). (gr. k-3). lib. bdg. 11.80 (978-0-613-44514-6(7)) Tandem Library Bks.

Scheunemann, Pam. Cat Tails. Chawla, Neena, illus. 2006. (Fact & Fiction Ser.). 24p. (J). pap. (978-1-59679-928-8(5)); (gr. 1-3). 21.35 (978-1-59679-927-1(7) , Sand-Castle) ABDO Publishing Co.

Schroder, Jack. The Nasty Affair at the Lake, 1 bk. 2004. 152p. (J). per. 9.95 (978-0-9745665-8-0(6)) Catalpa Pr.

Stanley, George Edward. The Clue of the Left-Handed Envelope. Murdocca, Salvatore, illus. 2000. (Third Grade Detectives Ser.: No. 1). 64p. (J). (gr. 1-4). pap. 3.99 (978-0-689-82194-3(8) , Aladdin) Simon & Schuster Children's Publishing.

—The Cobweb Confession. Murdocca, Salvatore, illus. 2001. (Third Grade Detectives Ser.: No. 4). 80p. (J). (gr. 1-4). pap. 3.99 (978-0-689-82197-4(2) , Aladdin) Simon & Schuster Children's Publishing.

Stevenson, James. Mud Flat Mystery. Stevenson, James, illus. 2003. (Illus.). 64p. (J). pap. 4.99 (978-0-06-051181-4(8) , Harper Trophy) HarperCollins Pubs.

Talbert, Marc. The Paper Knife. 2001. 196p. (YA). pap. 14.95 (978-0-595-19803-0(1) , Backinprint.com) iUniverse, Inc.

Tashjian, Janet. Marty Frye, Private Eye. Keller, Laurie, illus. rev. ed. 1998. (Redfeather Bks.). 64p. (J). (gr. 1-3). 15.95 (978-0-8050-5888-8(5) , Holt, Henry & Co. Bks. For Young Readers) Holt, Henry & Co.

—Marty Frye, Private Eye. 2000. (978-0-606-18880-7(0)) Tandem Library Bks.

Tosal, Oscar. Asesinato en el Barrio Gotico Level 2. 1998. (SPA.). (gr. 7-12). lib. bdg. 14.10 (978-0-613-80706-7(5)) Tandem Library Bks.

Trembath, Don. Emville Confidential. 2007. 192p. (J). (gr. 4-8). pap. (***978-1-55143-671-5(X)***) Orca Bk. Pubs.

Van Draanen, Wendelin. Sammy Keyes & the Hotel Thief. 1998. (Sammy Keyes Ser.: Bk. 1). 176p. (gr. 5-8). 15.00 (978-0-679-88839-0(X) , Knopf Bks. for Young Readers) Random Hse. Children's Bks.

Weyn, Suzanne. Scooby-Doo Movie Novelization. 2002. (gr. k-3). lib. bdg. 13.00 (978-0-613-50739-4(8)) Tandem Library Bks.

Whybrow, Ian. Little Wolf, Forest Detective. Ross, Tony, illus. 2005. (Middle Grade Fiction Ser.). 112p. (J). (gr. 3-6). 14.95 (978-1-57505-413-1(2)) Lerner Publishing Group.

Woodbury, Mary. Incredible Polly Mcdoodle. 2003. (gr. 3-6). lib. bdg. 16.40 (978-0-613-78479-5(0)) Tandem Library Bks.

—The Intrepid Polly McDoodle. 1999. (Polly McDoodle Ser.: Vol. 2). 180p. (J). (gr. 3 up). pap. 6.95 (978-1-55050-133-9(X)) Coteau Bks. CAN. *Dist:* Fitzhenry & Whiteside, Ltd.

Wright, Elsie. Patty & Jo, Detectives. 2005. reprint ed. pap. 24.95 (978-1-4179-9752-7(4)) Kessinger Publishing, LLC.

Yee, Wong Herbert. Detective Small in the Amazing Banana Caper. 2007. (Illus.). 32p. (J). (gr. k-3). 15.00 (978-0-618-47285-7(1)) Houghton Mifflin Co.

DETROIT (MICH.)

Knudsen, Anders. Antoine de la Mothe Cadillac: French Settlements at Detroit & Louisiana. 2006. (In the Footsteps of Explorers Ser.). (Illus.). 32p. (J). (gr. 3-9). (978-0-7787-2429-2(8)); pap. (978-0-7787-2465-0(4)) Crabtree Publishing Co.

DETROIT (MICH.)—FICTION

Fisher, Marcy Heller. The Outdoor Museum: The Magic of Michigan's Marshall M. Fredericks. Woomer, Christine Collins, illus. 2001. (Great Lakes Bks.). 72p. (J). (gr. 3 7). 18.95 (978-0-8143-2969-6(1) , Great Lakes Bks.); 29.95 (978-0-8143-2932-0(2)) Wayne State Univ. Pr.

Portis, Nathanial. Things in Between. 2005. 268p. (YA). per. 14.75 (978-0-9760372-0-0(3)) Quick Quest Pubns. LLC.

DETROIT LIONS (FOOTBALL TEAM)

Detroit Lions Staff. Detroit Lions. CWC Sports Inc., ed. 1998. (NFL Team Yearbooks Ser.). (J). (gr. 1-12). pap. 9.99 (978-1-891613-08-1(1)) Everett Sports Publishing & Marketing.

Dougherty, Terri. Barry Sanders. 1999. (Jam Session Ser.). (Illus.). 32p. (J). (gr. 3-8). lib. bdg. 24.21 (978-1-57765-037-9(9) , ABDO & Daughters) ABDO Publishing Co.

Frisch, Aaron. The History of the Detroit Lions. 2004. (NFL Today Ser.). (Illus.). 32p. 18.95 (978-1-58341-296-1(4) , Creative Education) Creative Co., The.

Griffin, Gwen. Barry Sanders. 1999. (Ovations Ser.). (Illus.). 32p. (YA). (gr. 4-7). pap. (978-0-88682-938-4(0) , Creative Education) Creative Co., The.

Knapp, Ron. Sports Great Barry Sanders. rev. ed. 1999. (Sports Great Bks.). (Illus.). 64p. (YA). (gr. 4-10). lib. bdg. 22.60 (978-0-7660-1067-3(8)) Enslow Pubs., Inc.

DETROIT TIGERS (BASEBALL TEAM)

Eldridge, Grant & Bush, Karen Elizabeth. Willie Horton: Detroit's Own "Willie the Wonder" 2001. (Detroit Biography Series for Young Readers). (Illus.). 160p. (J). (gr. 5). 27.95 (978-0-8143-3013-5(4)); pap. 16.00 (978-0-8143-3025-8(8)) Wayne State Univ. Pr.

Epstein, Brad M. Detroit Tigers 101: My first Team-board-book. l.t. ed. 2007. (101—My First Text-Board Books). (Illus.). 22p. (J). bds. 10.95 (***978-1-932530-96-4(7)*** , 101 Bk.) Michaelson Entertainment.

Gilbert, Sara. The Story of the Detroit Tigers. 2007. (J). (***978-1-58341-487-3(8)*** , Creative Education) Creative Co., The.

Rambeck, Richard. The History of the Detroit Tigers. 1998. (Baseball, the Great American Game Ser.). (Illus.). 32p. (YA). (gr. 3-12). pap. 21.30 (978-0-88682-908-7(9) , Creative Education) Creative Co., The.

Stewart, Mark. The Detroit Tigers. 2007. (Team Spirit Ser.). (Illus.). 48p. (J). lib. bdg. 25.27 (***978-1-59953-093-2(7)*** Norwood Hse. Pr.

Stewart, Wayne. Detroit Tigers. 2002. 32p. (J). pap. 5.95 (978-0-89812-342-5(9) , Creative Paperbacks); (Illus.). (978-1-58341-208-4(5)) Creative Co., The.

DEVELOPING COUNTRIES

Economically Developing Countries, 12 vols., set. 1999. 203.76 (978-0-8172-4532-0(4)) Raintree.

Entwicklungslaender. (Duden Abiturhilfen Ser.). (GER.). (YA). (gr. 12-13). (978-3-411-70752-2(6)) Bibliographisches Institut & F. A. Brockhaus AG DEU. *Dist:* International Bk. Import Service, Inc.

Garlake, Teresa. Global Debt. 2003. (21st Century Debates Ser.). (Illus.). 64p. (J). lib. bdg. 28.56 (978-0-7398-6035-9(6)) Raintree.

Suen, Anastasia. Doctors Without Borders. 2002. (Reading Power Ser.). (Illus.). 24p. (J). (gr. k-3). lib. bdg. 17.25 (978-0-8239-6002-6(1) , PowerKids Pr.) Rosen Publishing Group, Inc., The.

Torr, James D. Civil Rights. 2004. (Current Controversies Ser.). 200p. (YA). (gr. 7-12). pap. 24.95 (978-0-7377-1177-6(9) , Greenhaven Pr., Inc.) Thomson Gale.

DEVELOPMENT

see Embryology; Evolution; Growth

DEVELOPMENTAL READING

Miller, Karen. Simple Steps: Developmental Activities for Infants, Toddlers & Two-Year-Olds. 2004. (Illus.). 256p. (ps). pap. 24.95 (978-0-87659-204-5(3) , 18274) Gryphon Hse., Inc.

DEVIL

Bible Visuals International, compiled by. Satan & His Demons Vol. 08: New Testament. 2006. (Illus.). (J). pap. (978-1-932381-38-2(4) , 1008) Bible Visuals International, Inc.

—Satan, the Enemy of God Vol. 2: New Testament. 2006. (Illus.). (J). pap. (978-1-932381-22-1(8) , 1002) Bible Visuals International, Inc.

Robson, David. The Devil. 2007. (Mysterious Encounters Ser.). (Illus.). 48p. (J). (gr. 4-8). 23.70 (***978-0-7377-3780-6(8)*** , Kidhaven) Thomson Gale.

Turner, Tracey. Whos Who of Horrors. 2006. (Illus.). pap. 8.99 (978-0-340-90294-3(9) , Hodder & Stoughton) Hodder General Publishing Division GBR. *Dist:* Trafalgar Square Publishing.

DEVIL—FICTION

Aryal, Aimee. Hello Blue Devil! Cooper, Blair, illus. 2004. (J). 19.95 (978-1-932888-26-3(8)) Mascot Bks., Inc.

Barunga, Albert. About This Little Devil. 2000. (Illus.). 32p. pap. 12.95 (978-1-875641-42-0(4)) Magabala Bks. AUS. *Dist:* International Specialized Bk. Services.

Bugmann, Marlies. Tazzie Devil Double Trouble. 2003. (Green Heart Ser.: Bk. 3). 200p. (J). pap. 13.00 (978-1-55410-025-5(9)) Zumaya Pubns. LLC.

Cantrell, Pam Bullman. The Three Little Boys & the Big Bad Devil. 2004. pap. 6.95 (978-0-533-14193-7(1)) Vantage Pr., Inc.

Cho, Jerry, et al. Stray Little Devil. 2006. (Illus.). 200p. (YA). pap. 9.95 (978-1-59796-043-4(8)) DrMaster Pubns. Inc.

Dalmatian Press Staff. Taz: Devils & Martians. 2003. (Read-N-Snuggle Looney Tunes Ser.). 5p. (J). bds. 5.99 (978-1-57759-992-0(6)) Dalmatian Pr.

Falcone, L. M. The Devil, the Banshee & Me. 2006. 192p. (J). (gr. 4-7). (978-1-55337-894-5(6)) Kids Can Pr., Ltd.

—The Devil, the Banshee & Me. 2006. 192p. 6.95 (978-1-55337-895-2(4)) Kids Can Pr., Ltd. CAN. *Dist:* Wybel Marketing Group.

Fort, Gloria. Liapesadillas. 2000. (Dulces Suenos Collection). (SPA., Illus.). 10p. (J). 7.95 (978-84-348-6257-9(3)) SM Ediciones ESP. *Dist:* Distribooks, Inc.

Gripari, Pierre. Gentil Petit Diable.Tr. of Nice Little Devil. (FRE.). (J). pap. 16.95 (978-2-07-051343-7(2)) Gallimard, Editions FRA. *Dist:* Distribooks, Inc.

Hale, Nathan. The Devil You Know. Hale, Nathan, illus. 2005. (Illus.). 32p. (J). (ps-3). 17.85 (978-0-8027-8983-9(8)) ; 16.95 (978-0-8027-8981-5(1)) Walker & Co.

Jubert, Hervé. Devil's Tango. Bell, Anthea, tr. from FRE. 2006. (Devil's Dances Trilogy Ser.). 384p. (J). (gr. 7 up). 16.99 (978-0-06-077720-3(6) , Eos); lib. bdg. 17.89 (978-0-06-077721-0(4)) HarperCollins Pubs.

Meidell, Sherry. The Devil with the Three Golden Hairs: The Classic Brothers Grimm Folktale. 2006. (Illus.). 32p. (J). 16.95 (978-1-933317-50-2(7)) Silverleaf Pr.

Mori, Kotaro. Stray Little Devil. 2006. (Illus.). 200p. (YA). Vol. 2. pap. 9.95 (***978-1-59796-044-1(6))***; Vol. 3. pap. 9.95 (***978-1-59796-045-8(4))*** DrMaster Pubns. Inc.

—Stray Little Devil Volume 4. 2007. (Illus.). 200p. (YA). pap. 9.95 (***978-1-59796-046-5(2))*** DrMaster Pubns. Inc.

Petrucha, Stefan. Snared. 2008. (Wicked Dead Ser.: No.3). 224p. (J). pap. 7.99 (***978-0-06-113851-5(7)*** , HarperTeen) HarperCollins Pubs.

Potters, Harry. Tory the Little Dust Devil. 2006. pap. 15.30 (***978-1-84728-571-3(6))*** Lulu.com.

Potters, Harry P. Tory. 2006. 85p. 22.96 (978-1-4116-7958-0(X)) Lulu.com.

Quattlebaum, Mary. Sparks Fly High: The Legend of Dancing Point. Gore, Leonid, illus. 2006. 40p. (J). 16.00 (978-0-374-34452-8(3)) Farrar, Straus & Giroux.

Rousseau, Paul. Lucifer, Mon Grand-Pere: Tome 2. Guenette, Genevieve, illus. 2004. (Mon Roman Ser.). (FRE.). 184p. (J). (gr. 2). pap. (978-2-89021-703-4(5)) Diffusion du livre Mirabel.

Sengupta, Poile. Vikram & Vetal. 2005. 144p. (J). pap. 8.00 (978-0-14-333498-9(0) , Penguin Global) Penguin Group (USA) Inc.

Simon, Francesca. Pablo Diablo y el Dinero. 2005. (Pablo Diablo Ser.). (SPA., Illus.). 96p. (J). (gr. 2-3). 8.95 (978-84-348-9124-1(7)) SM Ediciones ESP. *Dist:* Iaconi, Mariuccia Bk. Imports.

—Pablo Diablo Y la Bomba Fetida. Ross, Tony, illus. 2005. (Pablo Diablo Ser.).Tr. of Horrid Harry & the Stink Bomb. (SPA.). (J). (gr. 2-3). pap. 8.95 (978-84-348-9683-3(4)) SM Ediciones ESP. *Dist:* Iaconi, Mariuccia Bk. Imports.

—Pablo Diablo y la Cangura Fantasma. Ross, Tony, illus. 2005. (Pablo Diablo Ser.).Tr. of Horrid Harry & the Kangaroo Ghost. (SPA.). (J). (gr. 2-3). pap. 8.95 (978-84-348-9684-0(2)) SM Ediciones ESP. *Dist:* Iaconi, Mariuccia Bk. Imports.

—Pablo Diablo y la Maldicion de la Momia. 2005. (Pablo Diablo Ser.). (SPA., Illus.). 94p. (J). (gr. 2-3). 8.95 (978-84-348-9072-5(0)) SM Ediciones ESP. *Dist:* Iaconi, Mariuccia Bk. Imports.

—Pablo Diablo Y Los Piojos. Ross, Tony, illus. 2005. (Pablo Diablo Ser.).Tr. of Horrid Harry & the Lice. (SPA.). (J). (gr. 2-3). pap. 8.95 (978-84-348-8673-5(1)) SM Ediciones ESP. *Dist:* Iaconi, Mariuccia Bk. Imports.

—La Venganza de Pablo Diablo. 2005. (Pablo Diablo Ser.). (SPA., Illus.). 94p. (J). (gr. 2-3). 8.95 (978-84-348-9017-6(8)) SM Ediciones ESP. *Dist:* Iaconi, Mariuccia Bk. Imports.

Small, David. Paper John. Small, David, illus. 1998. (Illus.). pap. 18.95 incl. audio compact disk (978-1-59519-066-6(X) ; pap. 39.95 incl. audio compact disk (978-1-59519-067-3(8)) Live Oak Media.

Smith, M. J. Kevin Murphy Takes on the Father of Lies. 2005. (Illus.). 311p. (J). (gr. 4-8). pap. 10.95 (978-0-9765066-0-7(2)) B & S Publishing Corp.

Smith, Rick. Shuck Unmasked. 2003. (Illus.). 168p. pap. 14.95 (978-1-891830-47-1(3)) Top Shelf Productions.

Takenaga, Francis. Omnibus Vol. 1. 2003. (Illus.). 264p. (gr. 11 up). pap. 19.95 (978-1-58240-302-1(3)) Image Comics.

Wilde, Gloria. Lucifer, Good Angel Gone Bad. Bauer, John, illus. 2007. 36p. (J). 14.95 (***978-1-57258-462-4(9)*** , 945-6323) TEACH Services, Inc.

DE VIL, CRUELLA (FICTITIOUS CHARACTER)—FICTION

Disney Press Staff. 102 Dalmatians. 2001. (Illus.). 96p. (J). pap. (978-0-7868-4463-0(9)) Disney Pr.

Disney Staff. 101 Dalmatians. (FRE.). 96p. (J). (gr. k-5). pap. 9.95 (978-0-7859-8847-2(5)) French & European Pubns., Inc.

Gomez, Rebecca. 102 Dalmatians: Pull-Out Posters & Trading Cards Book. 2000. (Illus.). 32p. (J). (ps-2). lib. bdg. 7.99 (978-0-7364-1066-3(X)) Mouse Works.

Hogan, Mary. 102 Dalmatians: Colors. 2000. (Lift the Flaps Bks.). (Illus.). 12p. (J). (ps). bds. 4.99 (978-0-7364-0228-6(4) , RH/Disney) Random Hse. Children's Bks.

Katschke, Judy. 102 Dalmations: Where's Oddball? Hogan, Mary, ed. 2000. (Disney's First Readers Ser.). (Illus.). 32p. (J). (gr. 1-3). pap. 3.99 (978-0-7868-1479-4(9)) Disney Pr.

Odom, Mel. 102 Dalmatians: Prima's Official Strategy Guide. 2000. (Illus.). (J). pap. 14.99 (978-0-7615-2997-2(7) , Prima Lifestyles) Crown Publishing Group.

102 Dalmations Read Along. unabr. ed. 2000. (J). pap. incl. audio compact disk (978-0-7634-0709-4(7)) Walt Disney Records.

DEVON (ENGLAND : COUNTY)—FICTION

Phillips, Michael. New Dawn over Devon. 2001. (gr. 5-8). lib. bdg. 23.40 (978-0-613-55639-2(9)) Tandem Library Bks.

DEVOTION

see Worship

DIABETES

Allman, Toney. From Gecko Feet to Sticky Tape. 2006. (Imitating Nature Ser.). (Illus.). 32p. (J). (gr. 3-6). 24.95 (978-0-7377-3487-4(6) , Greenhaven Pr., Inc.) Thomson Gale.

—From Lizard Saliva to Diabetes Drugs. 2006. 32p. (gr. 3-6). 24.95 (978-0-7377-3489-8(2) , Kidhaven) Thomson Gale.

Apel, Melanie Ann. Everything You Need to Know about Diabetes. 2005. (Need to Know Library). (Illus.). 64p. (YA). (gr. 7-12). lib. bdg. 25.25 (978-0-8239-3090-6(4) , NTDIAB) Rosen Publishing Group, Inc., The.

Bankston, John. Frederick Banting & the Discovery of Insulin. 2002. (Unlocking the Secrets of Science Ser.). (Illus.). 56p. (gr. 4-10). lib. bdg. 25.70 (978-1-58415-094-7(7)) Mitchell Lane Pubs., Inc.

Betschart, Jean. In Control: A Guide for Teens with Diabetes for Eli Lilly. 2001. (Illus.). 128p. pap. 10.95 (978-0-471-21260-7(1)) Wiley, John & Sons, Inc.

—It's Time to Learn about Diabetes: A Workbook on Diabetes for Children for Eli Lilly. 2nd ed. 2001. (Illus.). 112p. pap. 12.95 (978-0-471-21261-4(X)) Wiley, John & Sons, Inc.

Betschart-Roemer, Jean. Type 2 Diabetes in Teens: Secrets for Success. 2002. (Illus.). 240p. pap. 14.95 (978-0-471-15056-5(8) , Wiley) Wiley, John & Sons, Inc.

Block, Jed. The Best Year of My Life Bk. 1: Getting Diabetes. Block, Caitlin, illus. 1999. 28p. (J). (gr. 2-6). pap. 10.95 (978-0-9672728-0-1(7)) Block, Jed.

Bolar, Katrina. Living with Diabetes. 2007. (Teen's Guides Ser.). 176p. (gr. 6-12). 34.95 (***978-0-8160-6346-8(X))*** Facts On File, Inc.

Brill, Marlene Targ. Diabetes. 2007. lib. bdg. (***978-0-8225-6785-1(7))*** Twenty First Century Bks.

Bryan, Jenny. Diabetes. 2003. (Just the Facts Ser.). (Illus.). 56p. (J). lib. bdg. (978-1-4034-4600-8(8)) Heinemann Library.

Carter, Alden R. I'm Tougher Than Diabetes! Carter, Carol S., illus. Carter, Carol S., photos by. 2001. 32p. (J). (gr. k-4). 15.95 (978-0-8075-1572-3(8)) Whitman, Albert & Co.

Chase, H. Peter. A Book for Coloring & Learning about Diabetes. Reece, Regina, ed. United Artists Corporation Staff, illus. 4th ed. 2000. Orig. Title: A Coloring Book about Diabetes. (SPA.). 102p. (YA). (gr. 9 up). pap. 5.00 (978-0-9675398-1-2(1)) Children's Diabetes Foundation at Denver, The.

Geil, Patricia Bazel & Ross, Tami A. Cooking up Fun for Kids with Diabetes. 2003. (Illus.). 128p. pap. 14.95 (978-1-58040-134-0(1) , 9781580401340) McGraw-Hill/Contemporary.

Glaser, Jason. Juvenile Diabetes. 2007. (First Facts Ser.). (Illus.). 24p. (J). 21.26 (978-0-7368-6392-6(3)) Capstone Pr., Inc.

Gordon, Melanie Apel. Let's Talk about Diabetes. 1999. (Let's Talk Library). (Illus.). 24p. (J). (gr. 3). lib. bdg. 18.75 (978-0-8239-5196-3(0) , PowerKids Pr.) Rosen Publishing Group, Inc., The.

Gosselin, Kim. Taking Diabetes to School. Mitchell, Barbara, ed. Freedman, Moss, illus. 2nd rev. ed. 1998. (Special Kids in School Ser.: Vol. 1). 32p. (J). (gr. k-5). pap. 11.95 (978-1-891383-00-7(0)) JayJo Bks., LLC.

Gray, Shirley W. Living with Diabetes. 2002. (Living Well: Chronic Conditions Ser.). (Illus.). 32p. (J). (gr. 2-6). 27.07 (978-1-56766-102-6(5)) Child's World, Inc.

Haney, Johannah. Juvenile Diabetes. 2004. (Illus.). 63p. (J). 28.50 (978-0-7614-1798-9(2) , Benchmark Bks.) Cavendish, Marshall Corp.

Hautman, Pete. Sweetblood. Williams, Brooke, photos by. 2004. 256p. (YA). reprint ed. mass mkt. 5.99 (978-0-689-87324-9(7) , Simon Pulse) Simon & Schuster Children's Publishing.

Hollerorth, Hugo J., et al. Everyone Likes to Eat: How Children Can Eat Most of the Foods They Enjoy & Still Take Care of Their Diabetes. 2nd rev. ed. 1998. (Illus.). 128p. (ps-1). pap. 14.95 (978-0-471-34682-1(9) , Wiley) Wiley, John & Sons, Inc.

Hyde, Margaret O. & Forsyth, Elizabeth. Diabetes. 2004. (Single Titles-Science Ser.). (YA). (gr. 8-12). pap. 8.95 (978-0-531-16607-9(4) , Watts, Franklin) Scholastic Library Publishing.

Hyde, Margaret O. & Forsyth, Elizabeth Held. Diabetes. 2003. (Single Title: Science Ser.). (Illus.). 96p. (J). 26.00 (978-0-531-12209-9(3) , Watts, Franklin) Scholastic Library Publishing.

Kelly, Pat. Coping with Diabetes. (Coping Ser.). (Illus.). 192p. (YA). (gr. 7-12). 2005. lib. bdg. 26.50 (978-0-8239-3756-1(9)); 2000. lib. bdg. 25.25 (978-0-8239-3203-0(6) , CODIAB) Rosen Publishing Group, Inc., The.

Lawton, Sandra Augustyn, ed. Diabetes Information for Teens: Health Tips about Managing Diabetes & Preventing Related Complications; Including Information about Insulin, Glucose Control, Healthy Eating, Physical Activity, & Learning to Live with Diabetes. 2006. (Teen Health Ser.). (Illus.). xiii, 410p. (J). lib. bdg. 65.00 (978-0-7808-0811-9(8)) Omnigraphics, Inc.

Life with Diabetes, Lacie the Lizard's Adventure. 2004. (J). 11.95 (978-0-9745997-0-0(0)) CrittersInc.

Llewellyn, Claire. Diabetes. 2001. (Illus.). 32p. (J). lib. bdg. 24.25 (978-1-929298-97-6(8)) Chrysalis Education.

Loy, Spike Nasmyth & Loy, Bo Nasmyth. Getting a Grip on Your Diabetes: A Guide for Kids. 2000. (Illus.). 128p. pap. 14.95 (978-1-58040-053-4(1) , 9781580400534) McGraw-Hill/Contemporary.

Loy, Spike Nasmyth & Loy, Virginia Nasmyth. Getting a Grip on Diabetes. 2nd ed. 2007. 135p. (J). pap. 14.95 (978-1-58040-255-2(0) , 9781580402552) McGraw-Hill Cos., The.

Making the Best of Life: Learning to Live with Diabetes, Bk. 2. 2000. 107p. (J). per. 14.95 (978-0-9672728-1-8(5)) Block, Jed.

Mayo Clinic Staff, contrib. by. 20 Tasty Recipes for People with Diabetes. 2002. (Mayo Clinic on Health Ser.). (Illus.). 36,52p. (YA). (gr. 8 up), lib. bdg. (978-1-59084-247-8(2)) Mason Crest Pubs.

McAuliffe. Growing up with Diabetes. 2002. 128p. pap. 49.95 (978-0-471-26592-4(6)) Wiley, John & Sons, Inc.

Moran, Katherine J. Diabetes: The Ultimate Teen Guide. 2006. (Illus.). 192p. pap. 14.95 (978-0-8108-5642-4(5)) Scarecrow Pr., Inc.

—Diabetes: The Ultimate Teen Guide. Merriman, Lisa P., illus. 2004. (It Happened to Me Ser.: No. 7). 208p. 39.50 (978-0-8108-4806-1(6)) Scarecrow Pr., Inc.

Morrill, Rania. How Many Carbs Is a Booger: Make Carb Counting Fun. 2006. (J). 15.00 (978-1-4276-0140-7(2)) Aardvark Global Publishing.

Olson, Karen. Cooper Has Diabetes. Pritchett and Hull Associates, Inc., illus. 2003. (J). 4.50 (978-0-939838-82-0(6)) Pritchett & Hull Assocs., Inc.

Olson, Michael Keith. How I Feel: A Book about Diabetes. 2002. (Illus.). 48p. 15.00 (978-1-59056-037-2(X)) Lantern Bks.

O'Neill, Linda. Imagine Having Diabetes. 2000. (Imagine Ser.). (Illus.). 32p. (J). (gr. 1-4). lib. bdg. 26.60 (978-1-57103-380-2(7)) Rourke Publishing, LLC.

Peacock, Carol Antoinette. Sugar Was My Best Food: Diabetes & Me. 2000. (978-0-606-18776-3(6)) Tandem Library Bks.

Peacock, Carol Antoinette, et al. Sugar Was My Best Food: Diabetes & Me. Jones, Mary, illus. 2004. (Concept Book Ser.). 56p. (J). (gr. 3-8). pap. 4.95 (978-0-8075-7648-9(4)) Whitman, Albert & Co.

Peacock, Judith. Diabetes. 1999. (Perspectives on Disease & Illness Ser.). (Illus.). 64p. (J). (gr. 4-6). lib. bdg. 23.93 (978-0-7368-0277-2(0) , LifeMatters Bks.) Capstone Pr., Inc.

Rodgers, Jill & Walker, Rosemary. Diabetes: A Practical Guide to Managing Your Life. 2004. (Illus.). 224p. 25.00 (978-0-7566-0359-5(5) , 1236007) Dorling Kindersley Publishing, Inc.

Semple, Carol McCormick. Diabetes. rev. ed. 2000. (Health Watch Ser.). (Illus.). 48p. (YA). (gr. 4-10). lib. bdg. 23.93 (978-0-7660-1660-6(9)) Enslow Pubs., Inc.

Sheen, Barbara. Diabetes. 2003. (Diseases & Disorders Ser.). (Illus.). 112p. (J). 32.45 (978-1-59018-244-4(8) , Lucent Bks.) Thomson Gale.

Silverstein, Alvin. Diabetes. 2002. (gr. 3-6). lib. bdg. 15.25 (978-0-613-59464-6(9)) Tandem Library Bks.

Silverstein, Alvin, et al. Diabetes. (My Health Ser.). 48p. (J). (gr. 3-5). 2003. pap. 6.95 (978-0-531-16638-3(4)); 2002. (Illus.). pap. 25.50 (978-0-531-12049-1(X)) Scholastic Library Publishing. (Watts, Franklin).

—The Diabetes Update. 2006. (Disease Update Ser.). (Illus.). 128p. (J). (gr. 5 up). lib. bdg. 31.93 (978-0-7660-2483-0(0)) Enslow Pubs., Inc.

Vander Hook, Sue. Diabetes. 2000. (Understanding Illness Ser.). (Illus.). 32p. (J). lib. bdg. 16.95 (978-1-58340-023-4(0)) Smart Apple Media.

Whelan, Jo. Diabetes. 2002. (Health Issues Ser.). (Illus.). 64p. (J). (gr. 6-8). lib. bdg. 28.54 (978-0-7398-5220-0(5)) Raintree.

Yuwiler, Janice. Insulin. 2005. (Great Medical Discoveries Ser.). (Illus.). 112p. (YA). (gr. 7-10). lib. bdg. 29.95 (978-1-56006-930-0(9) , Lucent Bks.) Thomson Gale.

DIABETES—FICTION

Carr, Sheryl. Little Drop & the Healing Place. Harris, La Verne Abe, illus. 2006. (J). 10.00 (***978-0-9791383-0-0(2))*** Reliant Energy.

Deem, Saitofi Anne. Myrtle Learns about Diabetes. 1998. (Teachable Moments Ser.). (Illus.). 12p. (J). (ps-3). pap. 7.95 (978-1-930694-04-0(0)) Myrtle Learns.

Dennis, Anne. Taming the Diabetes Dragon. Mitchell, Barb, ed. Buttner, Thom, illus. 1998. 24p. (J). (gr. 3-7). pap. 14.95 (978-1-891383-03-8(5)) JayJo Bks., LLC.

Gosselin, Kim. Rufus Comes Home: Rufus, the Bear with Diabetes. Mitchell, Barbara, ed. Ravanelli, Terry, illus. 1998. 32p. (J). (ps-5). pap. 11.95 (978-1-891383-02-1(7)) JayJo Bks., LLC.

—Trick or Treat for Diabetes: A Halloween Story for Kids Living with Diabetes. Ditto, Laura, ed. Dineen, Tom, illus. 1999. 28p. (J). (gr. k-6). pap. 11.95 (978-1-891383-07-6(8)) JayJo Bks., LLC.

Hautman, Pete. Sweetblood. 2003. (Illus.). 192p. (YA). 16.95 (978-0-689-85048-6(4)) Simon & Schuster Children's Publishing.

Hume, Stephen. A Miracle for Maggie. 2004. (Illus.). 144p. (YA). pap., tchr. ed. (978-0-88878-415-5(5) , Sandcastle Bks.) Dundurn Group, The.

Kent, Deborah. Living with a Secret. 2001. (gr. 7-12). lib. bdg. 13.00 (978-0-613-74124-8(2)) Tandem Library Bks.

Martin, Ann M. The Truth about Stacey. 2006. (Baby-Sitters Club Ser.: No. 3). (Illus.). 144p. (J). (gr. 3-7). pap. 8.99 (978-0-439-73936-8(5)); pap. 16.99 (978-0-439-86724-5(X)) Scholastic, Inc. (Graphix).

Morgan, Melissa J. Alex's Challenge. 2007. 22.78 (978-1-59961-150-1(3)) Spotlight.

Morgan, Nicola. Chicken Friend. 2005. 160p. (J). (gr. 4-7). 15.99 (978-0-7636-2735-5(6)) Candlewick Pr.

Robert, G. Sillwee Wobbert, Diabetes & Jose at School & Play. 2002. (Illus.). 32p. (J). per. 9.95 (978-0-9704861-5-8(4)) Dream Publishing Co.

Schultz Nicholson, Lorna. Interference. 2004. (Sports Stories Ser.). 96p. (J). (gr. 3-8). 7.95 (978-1-55028-822-3(9)); (***978-1-55028-823-0(7))*** Lorimer, James & Co., Ltd., Pubs. CAN. *Dist:* Casemate Pubs. & Bk. Distributors, LLC.

Steinberg, Howard. Jackie's Got Game! A Story about Diabetes. Chris, Healey, illus. 2005. (J). 9.99 (978-0-9777463-0-9(5)) dLife - For Your Diabetes Life.

Stern, Rochelle. Can Mom Have a Piece of My Birthday Cake: What It Means to a Child When a Member of the Family Has Diabetes. 2002. (J). per. 14.95 (978-1-891231-95-7(2)) Word Association Pubs.

Tirey, Rodney. Coppershoo Saves the Sarge's Saddle! Tirey, Rodney, illus. 2007. (Illus.). 32p. (J). 16.95 (***978-0-9789591-0-4(8))*** MirthMarks Publishing.

DIAGRAMS, STATISTICAL

see Statistics—Graphic Methods

DIALECTICS

see Logic

DIAMONDS

Edwards, Ron & Dickie, Lisa. Diamonds & Gemstones. 2004. (Rocks, Minerals, & Resources Ser.). (Illus.). 32p. (J). (978-0-7787-1414-9(4)); pap. (978-0-7787-1446-0(2)) Crabtree Publishing Co.

Franck, Irene M. & Brownstone, David M. Diamonds. 2003. (Illus.). 32p. (J). (978-0-7172-5715-7(0) , Grolier) Scholastic Library Publishing.

Milne, Jean. The Story of Diamonds. 2000. (Illus.). v, 113p. (J). (gr. 3-7). 21.50 (978-0-208-02476-3(X) , Linnet Bks.) Shoe String Pr., Inc.

Morris, Neil. Diamonds & Other Gems. 2005. (Earth's Resources Ser.). (Illus.). 32p. (J). (gr. 4-7). lib. bdg. 27.10 (978-1-58340-629-8(8)) Smart Apple Media.

Murray, Peter. Diamonds. 2001. (From the Earth Ser.). (Illus.). 24p. (J). 21.35 (978-1-58340-111-8(3)) Smart Apple Media.

Ungaro, Ellen. Diamonds. 2006. (Navigators Ser.). (J). pap. 42.00 (***978-1-4108-6235-8(6))*** Benchmark Education Co.

DIANA, PRINCESS OF WALES, 1961-1997

Cox, Vicki. Diana, Princess of Wales. 2000. (They Died Too Young Ser.). (Illus.). 48p. (J). (gr. 4-7). 27.00 (978-0-7910-5854-1(9) , Chelsea Hse.) Facts On File, Inc.

Dorling Kindersley Publishing Staff. Princess Diana. 2006. (Biography Ser.). (Illus.). 128p. (J). 14.99 (978-0-7566-1613-7(1)); (gr. 8). pap. 4.99 (978-0-7566-1614-4(X)) Dorling Kindersley Publishing, Inc.

Gormley, Beatrice. Diana, Princess of Wales: Young Royalty. 2005. 204p. (J). lib. bdg. 18.46 ***(978-1-4242-1728-1(8))*** Fitzgerald Bks.

—Diana, Princess of Wales: Young Royalty. 2005. (Childhood of World Figures Ser.). 192p. (J). pap. 5.99 (978-1-4169-0021-4(7) , Aladdin) Simon & Schuster Children's Publishing.

Horner, Matina S., intro. Diana, Princess of Wales: Humanitarian. 1999. (Women of Achievement Ser.). (Illus.). 112p. (YA). (gr. 8-12). pap. 30.00 (978-0-7910-4715-6(6)); (gr. 4-7). 32.00 (978-0-7910-4714-9(8)) Facts On File, Inc. (Chelsea Hse.).

Krohn, Katherine E. Princess Diana. 1998. (Biography Ser.). (Illus.). 112p. (YA). (gr. 6-12). lib. bdg. 27.93 (978-0-8225-4941-3(7) , Lerner Pubns.) Lerner Publishing Group.

Levchuck, Caroline M. Learning about Charity from the Life of Princess Diana. 1999. (Character Building Book Ser.). (Illus.). 24p. (J). (gr. 3). lib. bdg. 18.75 (978-0-8239-5344-8(0) , PowerKids Pr.) Rosen Publishing Group, Inc., The.

Oleksy, Walter G. Princess Diana. 2000. (People in the News Ser.). (Illus.). 112p. (YA). (gr. 6-9). 27.45 (978-1-56006-579-1(6) , Lucent Bks.) Thomson Gale.

Weinberger, Kimberly. Princess Diana - Forever in Our Hearts: A Scrapbook of Memories. 439th ed. 1998. (Illus.). 48p. (gr. 1-4). pap. 5.99 (978-0-439-04529-2(0)) Scholastic, Inc.

Wheeler, Jill C. Princess Diana. 2002. (Women of the World Ser.). (J). lib. bdg. 21.35 (978-1-57765-314-1(9)) ABDO Publishing Co.

DIARIES

see Autobiographies

DIARIES—FICTION

Adams, Anne Tyra. Songbird of the Nile: The Diary of Miriam's Best Friend, Egypt, 1527 B. C. -1526 B. C. 2004. (Promised Land Diaries). (Illus.). 192p. (J). 10.99 (978-0-8010-4525-7(8)) Baker Bks.

Adlington, L. J. The Diary of Pelly D. 2008. 304p. (J). pap. 8.99 ***(978-0-06-076617-7(4)*** , HarperTeen); 2005. 288p. (YA). (gr. 8 up). 16.99 (978-0-06-076615-3(8)); 2005. 288p. (YA). (gr. 8 up). lib. bdg. 17.89 (978-0-06-076616-0(6)) HarperCollins Pubs.

Alford, Jan. I Can't Believe I Have to Do This. 1999. (J). (978-0-606-16801-4(X)); (gr. 5-8). lib. bdg. 14.15 (978-0-613-19374-0(1)) Tandem Library Bks.

—I Can't Believe I Have to Do This! 1999. (Illus.). 192p. (J). (gr. 3-7). pap. 5.99 (978-0-698-11785-3(9) , Putnam Juvenile) Penguin Group (USA) Inc.

Amato, Mary. The Naked Mole Rat Letters. 208p. (J). (Illus.). 16.95 (978-0-8234-1927-2(4)); 2007. (gr. 3-7). pap. 6.95 ***(978-0-8234-2098-8(1))*** Holiday Hse., Inc.

Anonymous. Confessions of a Backup Dancer. l.t. ed. 2005. 360p. (YA). (gr. 8-12). per. 20.95 (978-0-7862-7881-7(1) , Large Print Pr.) Thorndike Pr.

—Go Ask Alice. 1998. 11.64 (978-0-606-13431-6(X)) Tandem Library Bks.

—Go Ask Alice: A Real Diary. 2005. 224p. (YA). pap. 8.99 (978-1-4169-1463-1(3) , Simon Pulse) Simon & Schuster Children's Publishing.

Ayres, Katherine. North by Night. 2000. (gr. 3-6). lib. bdg. 12.40 (978-0-613-23020-9(5)) Tandem Library Bks.

Baglio, Ben M. Following the Rainbow. 2003. (Dolphin Diaries Ser.: No. 7). (Illus.). 160p. (J). (gr. 3-6). pap. 4.99 (978-0-439-44614-3(7) , Scholastic Paperbacks) Scholastic, Inc.

—Following the Rainbow. 2003. (gr. 3-6). lib. bdg. 12.40 (978-0-613-72206-3(X)) Tandem Library Bks.

—Racing the Wind. 2003. (Dolphin Diaries: No. 6). 160p. (J). pap. 4.99 (978-0-439-31952-2(8)) Scholastic, Inc.

—Racing the Wind. 2003. (gr. 3-6). lib. bdg. 12.40 (978-0-613-72053-3(9)) Tandem Library Bks.

Bateson, Catherine. The Boyfriend Rules of Good Behavior. 2006. 192p. (YA). 16.95 (978-0-8234-2026-1(4)) Holiday Hse., Inc.

Bauer, Marion Dane. Land of the Buffalo Bones: The Diary of Mary Elizabeth Rodgers, an English Girl in Minnesota. 2003. (Dear America Ser.). (Illus.). 224p. (J). pap. 12.95 (978-0-439-22027-9(0)) Scholastic, Inc.

Benton, Jim. Hagamos Come Si Esto Nunca Hubiera Pasado. Benton, Jim, illus. 2006. (Querido Diario Tonto Ser.: Bk. 1). (SPA.). 112p. (J). pap. 4.99 (978-0-439-78374-3(7) , Scholastic en Espanol) Scholastic, Inc.

—Let's Pretend This Never Happened. 2007. (Dear Dumb Diary Ser.: Bk. 1). 128p. (J). pap. 2.99 ***(978-0-545-01030-6(6))*** Scholastic, Inc.

—Let's Pretend This Never Happened. Benton, Jim, illus. 2004. (Dear Dumb Diary Ser.: Bk. 1). (Illus.). 80p. (J). 4.99 (978-0-439-62904-1(7) , Scholastic Paperbacks) Scholastic, Inc.

—The Problem with Here Is That It's Where I'm From. 2007. (Dear Dumb Diary Ser.: Bk. 6). (Illus.). 128p. (J). 4.99 (978-0-439-79622-4(9) , Scholastic Paperbacks) Scholastic, Inc.

Bernasconi, Pablo. Captain Arsenio: Inventions & (Mis)adventures in Flight. 2005. (Illus.). 40p. (J). (gr. 3-5). 16.00 (978-0-618-50749-8(3)) Houghton Mifflin Co. Trade & Reference Div.

Bloor, Edward. Tangerine. 2006. (Illus.). 324p. (YA). pap. 6.95 (978-0-15-205780-0(3) , Harcourt Paperbacks) Harcourt Children's Bks.

Boelter, Ashaki. Diaries of the Doomed. Boelter, Ashaki, illus. 2004. 88p. (YA). per. 6.95 (978-0-9721067-4-0(X) , Writing Wild & Crazy) Shakalot High Entertainment.

Brighton, Catherine. My Napoleon. Brighton, Catherine, illus. 2005. (Illus.). 26p. (J). (gr. k-4). reprint ed. 17.00 (978-0-7567-8931-2(1)) DIANE Publishing Co.

Brill, Marlene Targ. Diary of A Drummer Boy. Garland, Michael, illus. 1998. 48p. (gr. 4-6). lib. bdg. 23.90 (978-0-7613-0118-9(6) , Millbrook Pr.) Lerner Publishing Group.

Brown, Marc. Arthur & the Lost Diary. ed. 2005. (Arthur Chapter Bks.: Bk. 9). (Illus.). 55p. (J). lib. bdg. 15.00 (978-1-59054-723-6(3)) Fitzgerald Bks.

—Arthur & the Lost Diary. 2001. (Arthur Chapter Bks. : Bk. 9). (J). (ps-2). spiral bd. 14.99 (978-1-58605-129-7(6)) LeapFrog Enterprises, Inc.

Brunelle, Lynn. Elmo's Movie Star Diary. Walz, Richard, illus. Bridges, James, photos by. 1999. (J). 7.99 (978-0-375-80132-7(4) , Random Hse. Bks. for Young Readers) Random Hse. Children's Bks.

Bryant, Bonnie. Lisa: The Inside Story. 1999. (J). (978-0-606-19289-7(1)) Tandem Library Bks.

Bryant, Jennifer. Pieces of Georgia. 176p. (J). 2007. (gr. 5-9). 5.99 ***(978-0-440-42055-2(5)*** , Yearling); 2006. (gr. 6-9). 15.95 (978-0-375-83329-8(9) , Knopf Bks. for Young Readers); 2006. (gr. 6-9). lib. bdg. 17.99 (978-0-375-93259-5(3) , Knopf Bks. for Young Readers) Random Hse. Children's Bks.

Buckeridge, Anthony. Jennings' Diary. 2002. 179p. pap. (978-0-7551-0163-4(4)) House of Stratus, Inc.

Burchett, Jan, et al. Exile. 2006. (Lady Grace Mysteries, from the Daybookes of Lady Grace Cavendish Ser.). 208p. (J). (gr. 3-7). 7.95 (978-0-385-73322-9(4)); lib. bdg. 9.99 (978-0-385-90341-7(3)) Random Hse. Children's Bks. (Delacorte Bks. for Young Readers).

Byrd, Sandra. Cross My Heart. 2001. (Hidden Diary Ser.). 112p. (J). (gr. 3-7). reprint ed. pap. 5.99 (978-0-7642-2480-5(8)) Bethany Hse. Pubs.

—Cross My Heart. 2001. (gr. 3-6). lib. bdg. 13.00 (978-0-613-84512-0(9)) Tandem Library Bks.

—Hidden Diary, Vols. 5-8. 2001. (Hidden Diary Ser.). (J). pap. 19.99 (978-0-7642-8056-6(2)) Bethany Hse. Pubs.

—Make a Wish. 2001. (Hidden Diary Ser.). 112p. (J). (gr. 3-7). reprint ed. pap. 5.99 (978-0-7642-2481-2(6)) Bethany Hse. Pubs.

Cabot, Meg. In Love. 2002. (Princess Diaries: Vol. 3). 240p. (YA). (gr. 7 up). 16.99 (978-0-06-029467-0(1)) HarperCollins Pubs.

—In Love, Vol. 3. 2004. (Princess Diaries: Vol. 3). 288p. (J). (gr. 7 up). pap. 38.00 incl. audio (978-0-8072-2284-3(4) , Listening Library) Random Hse. Audio Publishing Group.

—Party Princess. (Princess Diaries: Vol. 7). (J). 2007. 368p. pap. 6.99 (978-0-06-072455-9(2) , Harper Trophy); 2006. 304p. 16.99 (978-0-06-072453-5(6)) HarperCollins Pubs.

—Party Princess. l.t. rev. ed. 2007. (Princess Diaries: Vol. 7). 335p. (YA). 23.95 ***(978-0-7862-9273-8(3))*** Thorndike Pr.

—The Princess Diaries. (Princess Diaries: Vol. 1). 2000. 240p. (J). (gr. 7 up). lib. bdg. 17.89 (978-0-06-029210-2(5)); 2001. 320p. (YA). (gr. 7 up). pap. 6.99 (978-0-380-81402-2(1) , Harper Trophy); 2000. (Illus.). 240p. (J). (gr. 7 up). 16.99 (978-0-380-97848-9(2)); Vols. 1-3, Set. 2006. (J). pap., pap. 19.99 (978-0-06-115389-1(3) , HarperTeen) HarperCollins Pubs.

—The Princess Diaries. unabr. ed. 2004. (Princess Diaries: Vol. I). 240p. (J). (gr. 7 up). pap. 38.00 incl. audio (978-0-8072-0669-0(5) , Listening Library) Random Hse. Audio Publishing Group.

—The Princess Diaries. 2001. (Princess Diaries: Vol. I). (gr. 7-12). lib. bdg. 15.30 (978-0-613-37165-0(8)); (Illus.). (J). (978-0-606-21844-3(0)) Tandem Library Bks.

—The Princess Diaries. l.t. ed. 2002. (Princess Diaries: Vol. I). 325p. (J). 24.95 (978-0-7862-4058-6(X)) Thomson Gale.

—Princess diaries, volume Ii: 2008. (Princess Diaries). 240p. (J). pap. 7.99 ***(978-0-06-147994-6(2)*** , HarperTeen) HarperCollins Pubs.

—Princess diaries, volume Iii. 2008. (Princess Diaries). 240p. (J). pap. 7.99 ***(978-0-06-147995-3(0)*** , HarperTeen) HarperCollins Pubs.

—The Princess Diaries, Volume IX: Princess Mia (international Edition) 2008. (Princess Diaries). 288p. (J). pap. 12.00 ***(978-0-06-156819-0(8)*** , HarperTeen) HarperCollins Pubs.

—Princess in Pink. (Princess Diaries: Vol. 5). (J). (gr. 7 up). 2004. 272p. 15.99 (978-0-06-009610-6(1)); 2005. (Illus.). 304p. reprint ed. pap. 6.99 (978-0-06-009612-0(8) , Harper Trophy) HarperCollins Pubs.

—Princess in Pink. l.t. ed. 2004. (Princess Diaries: Vol. 5). 304p. 23.95 (978-0-7862-6735-4(6) , Large Print Pr.) Thorndike Pr.

—Princess in the Spotlight. (Princess Diaries: Vol. II). (J). (gr. 7 up). 2002. 288p. pap. 6.99 (978-0-06-447279-1(5) , Harper Trophy); 2001. 240p. 16.99 (978-0-06-029465-6(5)) HarperCollins Pubs.

—Princess in the Spotlight. unabr. ed. 2004. (Princess Diaries: Vol. II). 272p. (J). (gr. 7 up). pap. 38.00 incl. audio (978-0-8072-1197-7(4) , S YA 332 SP, Listening Library) Random Hse. Audio Publishing Group.

—Princess in the Spotlight. 2002. (Princess Diaries: Vol. II). (gr. 7-12). lib. bdg. 15.30 (978-0-613-62987-4(6)) Tandem Library Bks.

—Princess in the Spotlight. l.t. ed. 2003. (Princess Diaries: Vol. II). 285p. 24.95 (978-0-7862-4845-2(9)) Thomson Gale.

—Princess in Training. (Princess Diaries: Vol. 6). (Illus.). (J). 2006. 320p. pap. 6.99 (978-0-06-009615-1(2) , Harper Trophy); 2005. 288p. (gr. 7 up). 16.99 (978-0-06-009613-7(6)) HarperCollins Pubs.

—Princess in Training. l.t. ed. 2005. (Princess Diaries: Vol. 6). 355p. (YA). (gr. 7-12). per. 22.95 (978-0-7862-7753-7(X) , Large Print Pr.) Thorndike Pr.

—Princess in Waiting. (Princess Diaries: Vol. 4). (gr. 7 up). 2004. 288p. (YA). pap. 6.99 (978-0-06-009609-0(8) , Harper Trophy); 2003. (Illus.). 240p. (J). 16.99 (978-0-06-009607-6(1)); 2003. (YA). pap. 6.99 (978-0-06-054065-4(6)) HarperCollins Pubs.

—Princess in Waiting. l.t. ed. 2003. (Princess Diaries: Vol. 4). 287p. (J). 25.95 (978-0-7862-5682-2(6)) Thorndike Pr.

—Princess Mia. 2008. (Princess Diaries: Vol. 9). 288p. (J). lib. bdg. 17.89 ***(978-0-06-072462-7(5))*** HarperCollins Pubs.

—Princess on the Brink. (Princess Diaries: Vol. 8). (J). 2008. 288p. 16.99 ***(978-0-06-072461-0(7))***; 2008. 272p. pap. 7.99 ***(978-0-06-072460-3(9)*** , Harper Trophy); 2007. 256p. 16.99 (978-0-06-072456-6(0)); 2007. 256p. lib. bdg. 17.89 (978-0-06-072457-3(9)) HarperCollins Pubs.

Cabot, Meg. Project Princess. 2003. (Princess Diaries: Vol. 4 1/2). 64p. (J). (gr. 7 up). pap. 2.99 (978-0-06-057131-3(4)) HarperCollins Pubs.

—Project Princess. 2003. (Princess Diaries: Vol. 4 1/2). (gr. 7-12). lib. bdg. 10.65 (978-0-613-67515-4(0)) Tandem Library Bks.

Carlson, Melody. Becoming Me. 2000. (Diary of a Teenage Girl Ser.: Bk. 1). (Illus.). 256p. (YA). pap. 12.99 (978-1-57673-735-4(7) , Multnomah) WaterBrook Pr.

—Diary of a Teenage Girl - It's My Life: Diary Number 2. 2002. (gr. 7-12). lib. bdg. 22.25 (978-0-613-88463-1(9)) Tandem Library Bks.

—I Do. 2005. (Diary of a Teenage Girl Ser.). 272p. (YA). pap. 12.99 (978-1-59052-320-9(2) , Multnomah) WaterBrook Pr.

—Just Ask. 2005. (Diary of a Teenage Girl Ser.). 256p. (J). pap. 12.99 (978-1-59052-321-6(0) , Multnomah) WaterBrook Pr.

—My Name Is Chloe. 2005. 288p. (YA). mass mkt. 7.99 (978-1-59052-736-8(4) , Multnomah) WaterBrook Pr.

—My Name Is Chloe: Diary of a Teenage Girl. 2003. (gr. 7-12). lib. bdg. 22.25 (978-0-613-87416-8(1)) Tandem Library Bks.

—On My Own. 2002. (gr. 7-12). lib. bdg. 22.25 (978-0-613-85855-7(7)) Tandem Library Bks.

—On My Own: Diary Number 4. 2002. (Diary of a Teenage Girl Ser.: Bk. 4). 300p. (J). pap. 12.99 (978-1-59052-017-8(3) , Multnomah) WaterBrook Pr.

Carpenter, Phyllis & Ford, Marti. Sparky's Excellent Misadventures: My A. D. D. Journal by Me (Sparky) Horjas, Peter, illus. 1999. 32p. (J). (gr. k-6). pap. (978-1-55798-606-1(1) , 441-6061, Magination Pr.) American Psychological Assn.

Cary, Kate. Bloodline. 2006. 352p. (YA). (gr. 7-12). pap. 8.99 (978-1-59514-078-4(6) , Razorbill) Penguin Group (USA) Inc.

—Reckoning. 2007. (Bloodline Ser.: Bk. 2). 320p. (YA). (gr. 9 up). 16.99 (978-1-59514-013-5(1) , Razorbill) Penguin Group (USA) Inc.

Caseley, Judith. The Kissing Diary. 2007. 208p. (J). (gr. 5 up). 16.00 (978-0-374-36346-8(3)) Farrar, Straus & Giroux.

Cavendish, Grace. Conspiracy. 2005. (Lady Grace Mysteries, from the Daybookes of Lady Grace Cavendish Ser.). 208p. (J). (gr. 3-7). 6.95 (978-0-385-73153-9(1) , Delacorte Bks. for Young Readers) Random Hse. Children's Bks.

—The Lady Grace Mysteries: Assassin. l.t. ed. 2006. pap. 16.95 (978-1-4056-6068-6(6)) BBC Audio GBR. *Dist:* BBC Audiobooks America.

Chan, Gillian. An Ocean Apart: The Gold Mountain Diary of Chin Mei-Ling. 2004. (Dear Canada Ser.). (Illus.). 217p. (J). pap. (978-0-7791-1353-8(5)) Scholastic Canada, Ltd.

Child, Lauren, et al. Fi'n Hollol, Carys Blodyn. 2005. (WEL., Illus.). 192p. pap. (978-1-85596-675-8(1)) Dref Wen.

Clark, Catherine. Wurst Case Scenario. 2001. 320p. (J). (gr. 8 up). 16.89 (978-0-06-029525-7(2)) HarperCollins Pubs.

Creel, Ann Howard. A Ceiling of Stars. 2000. (Illus.). (J). (978-0-606-18354-3(X)) Tandem Library Bks.

Crist-Evans, Craig. Moon over Tennessee: A Boy's Civil War Journal. Christensen, Bonnie, illus. 64p. (J). (gr. 4-6). 2003. pap. 6.95 (978-0-618-31107-1(6)); 1999. tchr. ed. 15.00 (978-0-395-91208-9(3)) Houghton Mifflin Co. Trade & Reference Div.

—Moon over Tennessee: A Boy's Civil War Journal. 1999. (gr. 3-6). lib. bdg. 15.25 (978-0-613-60819-0(4)) Tandem Library Bks.

Cronin, Doreen. Diary of a Fly. Bliss, Harry, illus. 2007. 40p. (J). (ps-3). 15.99 ***(978-0-06-000156-8(9));*** lib. bdg. 16.89 ***(978-0-06-000157-5(7))*** HarperCollins Pubs. (Cotler, Joanna Books).

—Diary of a Spider. Bliss, Harry, illus. 2005. 40p. (J). (ps-3). 15.99 (978-0-06-000153-7(4)); lib. bdg. 16.89 (978-0-06-000154-4(2)) HarperCollins Pubs. (Cotler, Joanna Books).

—Diary of a Spider. Bliss, Harry, illus. unabr. ed. 2006. (Picture Book Readalong Ser.). (J). (ps-3). 25.95 incl. audio (978-1-59519-482-4(7)); 28.95 incl. audio compact disk (978-1-59519-486-2(X)) Live Oak Media.

—Diary of a Spider. Bliss, Harry, illus. unabr. ed. 2006. (J). (ps-3). 24.95 incl. audio ***(978-0-439-90573-2(7));*** 29.95 incl. audio compact disk ***(978-0-439-90579-4(6))*** Weston Woods Studios, Inc.

Cronin, Doreen. Diary of a Worm. 2003. (Illus.). (J). (978-0-06-056884-9(4)); (J). 127.92 (978-0-06-056900-6(X)); 127.92 (978-0-06-056901-3(8)) HarperCollins Pubs.

—Diary of a Worm. Bliss, Harry, illus. 2003. 40p. (J). (ps-3). 15.99 (978-0-06-000150-6(X)); lib. bdg. 16.89 (978-0-06-000151-3(8)) HarperCollins Pubs. (Cotler, Joanna Books).

—Diary of a Worm. Bliss, Harry, illus. pap. 16.95 incl. audio (978-1-59112-867-0(6)); pap. incl. audio (978-1-59112-869-4(2)); pap. 18.95 incl. audio compact disk (978-1-59112-871-7(4)); pap. incl. audio compact disk (978-1-59112-873-1(0)) Live Oak Media.

—Diary of a Worm. 2004. (Illus.). (J). 25.95 incl. audio (978-1-59112-868-7(4)); 28.95 incl. audio compact disk (978-1-59112-872-4(2)) Live Oak Media.

Cross, Gillian. The Monster from Underground. Priestley, Chris, illus. 2002. (Yellow Bananas Ser.). 48p. (J). (gr. 3-4). pap. (978-0-7787-0981-7(7)); lib. bdg. (978-0-7787-0935-0(3)) Crabtree Publishing Co.

—Monster from Underground. 2002. (gr. 3-6). lib. bdg. 12.95 (978-0-613-52882-5(4)) Tandem Library Bks.

Cruise, Robin. Fiona's Private Pages. 2002. (gr. 3-6). lib. bdg. 14.15 (978-0-613-46254-9(8)) Tandem Library Bks.

—Top-Secret Journal of Fiona Claire Jardin. 2000. (978-0-606-18192-1(X)) Tandem Library Bks.

Cruise, Robin & Cruise, Roberta Ann. Fiona's Private Pages. 2002. 200p. (YA). (gr. 3-7). pap. 6.95 (978-0-15-216572-7(X) , Harcourt Paperbacks) Harcourt Children's Bks.

Cunningham, Laura Shaine. The Midnight Diary of Zoya Blume. 2006. 176p. (J). pap. 5.99 (978-0-06-072261-6(4) , Harper Trophy) HarperCollins Pubs.

Cushman, Karen. Catherine, Called Birdy. 2002. (Illus.). (J). 15.00 (978-0-7587-0246-3(9)) Book Wholesalers, Inc.

Danticat, Edwidge. Anacaona: Golden Flower, Haiti 1490. 2005. (Royal Diaries). (Illus.). 192p. (J). pap. 10.95 (978-0-439-49906-4(2)) Scholastic, Inc.

Davies, Nicola. Tangled Webs. 2000. 120p. (YA). pap. 12.95 (978-1-85902-847-6(0)) Beekman Bks., Inc.

Davis, Terry. Mysterious Ways. 2002. 284p. (YA). pap. 15.95 (978-0-910055-81-9(5)) Eastern Washington Univ. Pr.

DeCesare, Angelo. Flip's Fantastic Journal. DeCesare, Angelo, illus. 1999. (Illus.). 48p. (J). (gr. 1-4). pap. 6.99 (978-0-14-056655-0(4) , Puffin) Penguin Group (USA) Inc.

—Flip's Fantastic Journal. 1999. (gr. 3-6). lib. bdg. 14.15 (978-0-613-21547-3(8)) Tandem Library Bks.

Deem, James M. 3 NBs of Julian Drew. 2004. 208p. (YA). (gr. 7 up). pap. 6.99 (978-0-618-43907-2(2) , Graphia) Houghton Mifflin Co. Trade & Reference Div.

DeFelice, Cynthia C. The Ghost of Fossil Glen. 1998. (Ghost Mysteries Ser.). 176p. (J). (gr. 3-7). 16.00 (978-0-374-31787-4(9) , Farrar, Straus & Giroux (BYR)) Farrar, Straus & Giroux.

—The Ghost of Fossil Glen. 1999. 160p. (J). (gr. 3-7). pap. 5.99 (978-0-380-73175-6(4) , Harper Trophy) HarperCollins Pubs.

—The Ghost of Fossil Glen. 2000. (YA). (gr. 6 up). pap. 52.00 incl. audio (978-0-7887-4334-4(1) , 41129) Recorded Bks., LLC.

—The Ghost of Fossil Glen. 1999. (J). 11.60 (978-0-606-16359-0(X)); (gr. 5-8). lib. bdg. 14.15 (978-0-7857-0557-4(0)) Tandem Library Bks.

—The Ghost of Fossil Glen. l.t. ed. 2000. (Juvenile Ser.). (Illus.). 185p. (J). (gr. 4-7). 21.95 (978-0-7862-2768-6(0)) Thorndike Pr.

Denenberg, Barry. One Eye Laughing, the Other Weeping: The Diary of Julie Weiss, Vienna, Austria to New York, 1938. 2000. (Dear America Ser.). (Illus.). 256p. (J). (gr. 4-9). pap. 12.95 (978-0-439-09518-1(2)) Scholastic, Inc.

DeVillers, Julia. How My Private, Personal Journal Became a Bestseller. 2004. 224p. (J). (gr. 5). 15.99 (978-0-525-47283-4(5) , Dutton Juvenile) Penguin Group (USA) Inc.

—How My Private Personal Journal Became a Bestseller. 2005. 224p. (J). (gr. 5). pap. 5.99 (978-0-14-240332-7(6) , Puffin) Penguin Group (USA) Inc.

Diary of a Worm. 2004. (J). 24.95 incl. audio (978-0-7882-0536-1(6)) Weston Woods Studios, Inc.

Dockray, Tracy. My Life Story. Dockray, Tracy, illus. 2003. (Illus.). 40p. (J). lib. bdg. 15.95 (978-1-58717-218-2(6) , SeaStar Bks.) Chronicle Bks. LLC.

Douglas, Lola. True Confessions of a Hollywood Starlet. (YA). (gr. 7-12). 2007. 272p. 6.99 (978-1-59514-153-8(7)); 2006. 288p. pap. 6.99 (978-1-59514-093-7(X)); 2005. 272p. 16.99 (978-1-59514-035-7(2)) Penguin Group (USA) Inc. (Razorbill).

Dower, Laura. Scribbles & Secrets. Torrecilla, Pablo, illus. 2004. 96p. (J). 9.99 (978-0-439-56126-6(4) , Tangerine Pr.) Scholastic, Inc.

Draper, Sharon M. Jazz Imagination: A Journal to Read & Write. 2000. 81p. (J). (gr. 3-7). pap. 12.95 (978-0-439-06130-8(X)) Scholastic, Inc.

—Jazzimagination: A Journal to Read & Write. 2002. 128p. (J). pap. 4.50 (978-0-439-26577-5(0)) Scholastic, Inc.

Durrant, Sabine. Bon Voyage, Connie Pickles. 2008. 240p. (J). 16.99 ***(978-0-06-085482-9(0));*** lib. bdg. 17.89 ***(978-0-06-085483-6(9))*** HarperCollins Pubs. (HarperTeen).

Easton, Kelly. The Life History of a Star. 2002. (gr. 7-12). lib. bdg. 15.30 (978-0-613-60641-7(8)) Tandem Library Bks.

Ehrlich, Gretel. A Blizzard Year. Kiesler, Kate A., illus. 2001. 128p. (gr. 4-8). pap. 5.99 (978-0-7868-1245-5(1)) Hyperion Bks. for Children.

Everett Hale, Edward. Last of the Peterkins with Others of the. 2006. pap. ***(978-1-4068-1087-5(8))*** Echo Library.

Fergus, Maureen. Exploits of a Reluctant (But Extremely Goodlooking) Hero. 2007. 216p. (YA). (gr. 7 up). ***(978-1-55453-025-0(3)); (978-1-55453-024-3(5))*** Kids Can Pr., Ltd.

Finney, Patricia & Cavendish, Grace. Assasin, No. 1. 2004. (Lady Grace Mysteries, from the Daybookes of Lady Grace Cavendish Ser.). 208p. (J). (gr. 3-7). lib. bdg. 12.99 (978-0-385-90189-5(5) , Delacorte Bks. for Young Readers) Random Hse. Children's Bks.

CD

—Assassin, No. 1. 2004. (Lady Grace Mysteries, from the Daybookes of Lady Grace Cavendish Ser.). 208p. (J). (gr. 3-7). 9.95 (978-0-385-73151-5(5) , Delacorte Bks. for Young Readers) Random Hse. Children's Bks.

—Deception. 2005. (Lady Grace Mysteries, from the Daybookes of Lady Grace Cavendish Ser.). 224p. (J). (gr. 3-7). 7.95 (978-0-385-73321-2(6)); lib. bdg. 9.99 (978-0-385-90340-0(5)) Random Hse. Children's Bks. (Delacorte Bks. for Young Readers).

—Feud. 2006. (Lady Grace Mysteries, from the Daybookes of Lady Grace Cavendish Ser.). 192p. (J). (gr. 3-7). 7.95 (978-0-385-73323-6(2)); lib. bdg. 9.99 (978-0-385-90342-4(1)) Random Hse. Children's Bks. (Delacorte Bks. for Young Readers).

Flinn, Alex. Breathing Underwater. 272p. (J). 2002. (gr. 5 up). pap. 8.99 (978-0-06-447257-9(4)); 2001. (Illus.). (gr. 8 up). 18.99 (978-0-06-029198-3(2)) HarperCollins Pubs.

—Breathing Underwater. unabr. ed. 2004. (Young Adult Cassette Librariestm Ser.). 272p. (J). (gr. 7 up). pap. 36.00 incl. audio (978-0-8072-0992-9(9) , S YA 346 SP, Listening Library) Random Hse. Audio Publishing Group.

—Breathing Underwater. 2002. (gr. 7-12). lib. bdg. 16.45 (978-0-613-60383-6(4)) Tandem Library Bks.

Flint, Garrison. Sanity in Search of Peter Alexander. 2003. 198p. (YA). per. 13.95 (978-1-885631-73-2(1)) Hutchison, G.F. Pr.

Foland, Constance M. Flying High, Pogo! 2002. (gr. 3-6). lib. bdg. 14.10 (978-0-613-89603-0(3)) Tandem Library Bks.

French, Jackie. Diary of a Wombat. Whatley, Bruce, illus. 2003. 32p. (J). (gr. k-3). 14.00 (978-0-618-38136-4(8) , Clarion Bks.) Houghton Mifflin Co. Trade & Reference Div.

Friedman, Laurie. Heart to Heart with Mallory. Pollak, Barbara, illus. 2007. (Mallory Ser.). 160p. (J). (gr. 2-7). pap. 5.95 (*978-0-8225-7133-9(1) , First Avenue Editions) Lerner Publishing Group.

Friedman, Laurie B. Heart to Heart with Mallory. Pollak, Barbara, illus. 2006. 160p. (J). (gr. 2-5). 15.95 (978-1-57505-932-7(0) , Twenty-First Century Bks.) Lerner Publishing Group.

Fullerton, Alma. Walking on Glass. 2007. 144p. (J). (gr. 9 up). 15.99 (978-0-06-077851-4(2)); lib. bdg. 16.89 (978-0-06-077852-1(0)) HarperCollins Pubs. (HarperTeen).

Garfinkle, Debra. Storky: How I Lost My Nickname & Won the Girl. 192p. (YA). 2007. (gr. 7 up). pap. 5.99 (978-0-14-240782-0(8) , Puffin); 2005. (gr. 6). 16.99 (978-0-399-24284-7(8) , Putnam Juvenile) Penguin Group (USA) Inc.

Garland, Sherry. Valley of the Moon: The Diary of Maria Rosalia de Milagros, Sonoma Valley, Alta California, 1846. 2001. (Dear America Ser.). (Illus.). 208p. (J). (gr. 4-9). pap. 10.95 (978-0-439-08820-6(8)) Scholastic, Inc.

Gray, Dianne. Holding up the Earth. 2006. 224p. (J). (gr. 5-9). pap. 6.95 (978-0-618-73747-5(2)) Houghton Mifflin Co. Trade & Reference Div.

Gray, Dianne E. Holding up the Earth. 2000. 224p. (J). (gr. 5-9). tchr. ed. 15.00 (978-0-618-00703-5(2)) Houghton Mifflin Co. Trade & Reference Div.

—Holding up the Earth. l.t. ed. 2002. 198p. (J). 22.95 (978-0-7862-3889-7(5)) Thomson Gale.

Green, Jessica. Diary of a Would-Be Princess: The Journal of Jillian James, 5B. 2007. (Illus.). 236p. (J). (gr. 4-7). 15.95 (978-1-58089-166-0(7)) Charlesbridge Publishing, Inc.

Gregory, Kristiana. Catherine: The Great Journey, Russia, 1743. 2005. (Royal Diaries). (Illus.). 176p. (J). (gr. 4-9). pap. 10.99 (978-0-439-25385-7(3)) Scholastic, Inc.

—Cleopatra VII: Daughter of the Nile, Egypt, 57 B. C. 1999. (Royal Diaries Ser.). (Illus.). 224p. (J). (gr. 4-8). pap. 10.95 (978-0-590-81975-6(5) , Scholastic Pr.) Scholastic, Inc.

—Eleanor: Crown Jewel of Aquitaine: France 1136. 2002. (Royal Diaries Ser.). (Illus.). 192p. (gr. 4-9). pap. 10.95 (978-0-439-16484-9(2) , Scholastic Pr.) Scholastic, Inc.

—The Great Railroad Race: The Diary of Libby West, Utah Territory, 1868. 1999. (Dear America Ser.). (Illus.). 208p. (J). (gr. 4-9). pap. 10.95 (978-0-590-10991-8(X)) Scholastic, Inc.

—We Are Patriots: Hope's Revolutionary War Diary. 2002. (gr. 3-6). lib. bdg. 13.00 (978-0-613-45633-3(5)) Tandem Library Bks.

—We Are Patriots Bk. 2: Hope's Revolutionary War Diary. 2002. (My America Ser.). (Illus.). 112p. (J). (gr. 2-5). pap. 10.95 (978-0-439-21039-3(9)); pap. 4.99 (978-0-439-36906-0(1)) Scholastic, Inc. (Scholastic Pr.).

—When Freedom Comes: Hope's Revolutionary War Diary, Bk. 3. 2004. (My America Ser.). (Illus.). 112p. (J). pap. 4.99 (978-0-439-37054-7(X)) Scholastic, Inc.

—The Winter of Red Snow: The Revolutionary War Story of Abigail Jane Stewart, Valley Forge, Pa, 1777. 2000. (Dear America Ser.). (J). 9.95 (978-0-439-17969-0(6)) Scholastic, Inc.

Grimes, Nikki. Jazmin's Notebook. 2002. (Illus.). (J). 12.34 (978-0-7587-0368-2(6)) Book Wholesalers, Inc.

—Jazmin's Notebook. 112p. (J). 1998. (gr. 8-12). 15.99 (978-0-8037-2224-8(9) , Dial); 2000. (gr. 5-9). reprint ed. pap. 5.99 (978-0-14-130702-2(1) , Puffin) Penguin Group (USA) Inc.

—Jazmin's Notebook. 2000. (gr. 7-12). lib. bdg. 14.15 (978-0-613-23623-2(8)); (Illus.). (J). 12.64 (978-0-606-18414-4(7)) Tandem Library Bks.

Gutman, Dan. Race for the Sky. 2003. (Illus.). 192p. (J). (gr. 3-6). 16.99 (978-0-689-84554-3(5)) Simon & Schuster Children's Publishing.

—Race for the Sky: The Kitty Hawk Diaries of Johnny Moore. l.t. ed. 2004. 299p. 22.95 (978-0-7862-6466-7(7)) Thorndike Pr.

Haase, Tony. Mr. Bean's Diary. 2002. (Illus.). 128p. (J). pap. 15.00 (978-1-84222-656-8(8)) Carlton Bks., Ltd. GBR. *Dist:* Independent Pubs. Group.

Harcourt School Publishers Staff. Greetings from Ancient Greece On Level. 3rd ed. 2002. (Trophies Reading Program Ser.). (Illus.). pap. 5.10 (978-0-15-323445-3(8)) Harcourt Schl. Pubs.

Harper, Charise Mericle. Flashcards of My Life. (J). 2007. 224p. (gr. 3-7). pap. 6.99 (978-0-316-16676-8(6)); 2006. (Illus.). 240p. (gr. 4-7). 15.99 (978-0-316-75621-1(0)) Little Brown & Co.

Hausman, Gerald. Tom Cringle: Battle on the High Seas. Hills, Tad, illus. 2000. 224p. (J). (gr. 4-6). 28.99 (978-0-689-82810-2(1)) Simon & Schuster Children's Publishing.

Hays, Anna Jane. Smarty Sara. Kantorovitz, Sylvie, illus. 2008. (J). pap. (*978-0-375-83512-4(1)); lib. bdg. (*978-0-375-95054-4(0)) Random Hse., Inc.

Herbst, Judith. Ivy's Journal. O'Gorman, Molly, illus. 2000. 32p. (J). (gr. 3-7). 15.95 (978-1-57255-839-7(3)) Mondo Publishing.

Hermes, Patricia. Our Strange New Land: Elizabeth's Jamestown Colony Diary, Bk. 1. 2002. (My America Ser.: Bk. 1). 112p. (J). (gr. 2-5). 4.99 (978-0-439-36898-8(7) , Scholastic Pr.) Scholastic, Inc.

—Our Strange New Land: Elizabeth's Jamestown Colony Diary. 2002. (gr. 3-6). lib. bdg. 13.00 (978-0-613-53849-7(8)) Tandem Library Bks.

—A Perfect Place Bk. 2: Joshua's Oregon Trail Diary. 2002. (My America Ser.: Bk. 2). 112p. (J). (gr. 2-5). pap. 10.95 (978-0-439-19999-5(9) , Scholastic Pr.) Scholastic, Inc.

—A Perfect Place Bk. 2: Joshua's Oregon Trail Diary. 2002. (gr. 3-6). lib. bdg. 13.00 (978-0-613-57261-3(0)) Tandem Library Bks.

—Season of Promise: Elizabeth's Jamestown Colony Diary. 2002. (My America Ser.: Bk. 3). (Illus.). 112p. (J). (gr. 2-5). pap. 10.95 (978-0-439-38898-6(8)); pap. 4.99 (978-0-439-27206-3(8)) Scholastic, Inc. (Scholastic Pr.).

—Season of Promise: Elizabeth's Jamestown Colony Diary. 2002. (gr. 3-6). lib. bdg. 13.00 (978-0-613-57130-2(4)) Tandem Library Bks.

—The Starving Time Bk. 2: Elizabeth's Jamestown Colony Diary. 2002. (My America Ser.: Bk. 2). (Illus.). 112p. (J). (gr. 2-5). pap. 4.99 (978-0-439-36902-2(9) , Scholastic Pr.) Scholastic, Inc.

—The Starving Time Bk. 2: Elizabeth's Jamestown Colony Diary. 2002. (gr. 3-6). lib. bdg. 13.00 (978-0-613-53867-1(6)) Tandem Library Bks.

—Westward to Home Bk. 1: Joshua's Oregon Trail Diary. 2002. (Joshua's Oregon Trail Diary Ser.: Bk. 1). 112p. (J). (gr. 2-5). 4.99 (978-0-439-38899-3(6) , Scholastic Pr.) Scholastic, Inc.

—Westward to Home Bk. 1: Joshua's Oregon Trail Diary. 2002. (gr. 3-6). lib. bdg. 13.00 (978-0-613-60738-4(4)) Tandem Library Bks.

Hesse, Karen. Stowaway. unabr. ed. 2004. 328p. (J). (gr. 5-9). pap. 48.00 incl. audio (978-0-8072-8760-6(1) , LYA 259 SP, Listening Library) Random Hse. Audio Publishing Group.

—Stowaway. Parker, Robert Andrew, illus. 2002. 320p. (J). (gr. 5-9). pap. 6.99 (978-0-689-83989-4(8) , Aladdin) Simon & Schuster Children's Publishing.

—Stowaway. Parker, Robert Andrew & Prato, Rodica, illus. 2000. 328p. (J). (gr. 5-9). 17.95 (978-0-689-83987-0(1) , McElderry, Margaret K.) Simon & Schuster Children's Publishing.

—Stowaway. 2002. (gr. 5-8). lib. bdg. 15.30 (978-0-613-45110-9(4)) Tandem Library Bks.

Hite, Sid. I'm Exploding Now. 2007. 192p. (YA). (gr. 5-9). 16.99 (*978-0-7868-3757-1(8)) Hyperion Pr.

Holabird, Katharine. Angelina's Diary. Craig, Helen, illus. 2006. (Angelina Ballerina Ser.). 80p. (J). (gr. 1-3). 3.99 (978-0-448-44016-3(4) , Grosset & Dunlap) Penguin Group (USA) Inc.

Hopkinson, Deborah. Birdie's Lighthouse. Root, Kimberly B., illus. 2000. 32p. (J). (ps-3). 6.99 (978-0-689-83529-2(9) , Aladdin) Simon & Schuster Children's Publishing.

—Birdie's Lighthouse. 2000. (gr. 3-6). lib. bdg. 14.15 (978-0-613-28424-0(0)); (Illus.). (J). (978-0-606-17913-3(5)) Tandem Library Bks.

Hurwitz, Johanna. The Unsigned Valentine: And Other Events in the Life of Emma Meade. Azarian, Mary, illus. 2006. 176p. (J). 15.99 (978-0-06-056053-9(3)); lib. bdg. 16.89 (978-0-06-056054-6(1)) HarperCollins Pubs.

Janke, Katelan. Survival in the Storm: The Dust Bowl Diary of Grace Edwards. 2002. (Dear America Ser.). (Illus.). 192p. (J). (gr. 4-9). pap. 10.95 (978-0-439-21599-2(4)) Scholastic, Inc.

Jocelyn, Marthe. Mable Riley: A Reliable Record of Humdrum, Peril, & Romance. 2007. 288p. (J). (gr. 5). 6.99 (978-0-7636-3287-8(2)) Candlewick Pr.

The Journey. 2003. 170p. (YA). per. 10.95 (978-0-9713292-8-7(1)) Aim Higher Bks.

Juby, Susan. Alice, I Think. (J). 2003. (Illus.). 304p. lib. bdg. 16.89 (978-0-06-051544-7(9)); 2004. 320p. reprint ed. pap. 7.99 (978-0-06-051545-4(7)) HarperCollins Pubs. (HarperTeen).

—Alice, I Think. 2000. 224p. (YA). pap. (978-1-894345-12-5(6)) Thistledown Pr., Ltd.

—Miss Smithers. 2004. (Illus.). 336p. (J). 15.99 (978-0-06-051546-1(5)); lib. bdg. 16.89 (978-0-06-051547-8(3)) HarperCollins Pubs. (HarperTeen).

Kallok, Emma. Diary of Chickabiddy Baby. 1999. (gr. 3-6). lib. bdg. 12.95 (978-0-613-18577-6(3)) Tandem Library Bks.

Kalman, Esther. Tchaikovsky Discovers America. Fernandez, Laura & Jacobson, Rick, illus. 2000. 48p. (J). (gr. k-3). pap. 6.95 (978-0-531-07168-7(5) , Orchard Bks.) Scholastic, Inc.

Kaufman, Sue. Diary of a Mad Housewife: A Novel. 2005. 320p. pap. 14.95 (978-1-56025-687-8(7)) Seal Pr.

Keep, Linda Lowery. Peace, Love, & Rock 'n' Roll. Field, Ann, illus. 2005. 144p. (J). 9.95 (978-0-307-10519-6(9) , Golden Bks.) Random Hse. Children's Bks.

—Red, White, & Blue Jeans: By Linda Lowery: Illustrated by Ann Field. Field, Ann, illus. 2005. 144p. (J). 9.95 (978-0-375-82540-8(1) , Golden Bks.) Random Hse. Children's Bks.

Kelly, Katy. Busy Like You Can't Believe. Rex, Adam, illus. 2006. (Lucy Rose Ser.). 176p. (J). (gr. 3-7). 12.95 (978-0-385-73319-9(4) , Delacorte Bks. for Young Readers) Random Hse. Children's Bks.

—Lucy Rose: Big on Plans. Rex, Adam, illus. 2005. 176p. (gr. 3-7). (J). 12.95 (978-0-385-73204-8(X)); lib. bdg. 14.99 (978-0-385-90235-9(2)) Random Hse. Children's Bks. (Delacorte Bks. for Young Readers).

—Lucy Rose: Here's the Thing about Me. Rex, Adam, illus. 2004. 144p. (J). (gr. 3-7). 12.95 (978-0-385-73203-1(1)); lib. bdg. 14.99 (978-0-385-90234-2(4)) Random Hse. Children's Bks. (Delacorte Bks. for Young Readers).

—Lucy Rose: Working Myself to Pieces & Bits. Ferguson, Peter, illus. 2007. (J). (gr. 3-7). 208p. 12.99 (*978-0-385-73408-0(5)); 128p. lib. bdg. 15.99 (*978-0-385-90425-4(8)) Random Hse. Children's Bks. (Delacorte Bks. for Young Readers).

—Lucy Rose: Big on Plans. Rex, Adam, illus. 2007. 192p. (gr. 3-5). 5.50 (978-0-440-42027-9(X) , Yearling) Random Hse. Children's Bks.

—Lucy Rose: Busy Like You Can't Believe. Rex, Adam, illus. 2006. 176p. (J). (gr. 3-7). lib. bdg. 14.99 (978-0-385-90338-7(3) , Delacorte Bks. for Young Readers) Random Hse. Children's Bks.

Kimmel, Elizabeth Cody. Lily B. on the Brink of Cool. 2003. 256p. (J). (gr. 3-7). 15.99 (978-0-06-000586-3(6)) HarperCollins Pubs.

Kinney, Jeff. Diary of a Wimpy Kid. 2007. (Illus.). 224p. (J). (gr. 2-8). 12.95 (*978-0-8109-9313-6(9) , Abrams Bks. for Young Readers) Abrams, Harry N. , Inc.

Kirkpatrick, Katherine. The Voyage of the Continental. 2002. (Illus.). 256p. (J). (gr. 7 up). tchr. ed. 16.95 (978-0-8234-1580-9(5)) Holiday Hse., Inc.

Klein, Rachel. The Moth Diaries. 2002. 256p. (YA). (978-1-58243-205-2(8)) Counterpoint.

Klingel, Cynthia Fitterer & Noyed, Robert B. Josef's Journal & the Letter J. 2003. (Alphaphonics Ser.). (Illus.). 24p. (J). (ps-2). 21.36 (978-1-59296-100-9(2)) Child's World, Inc.

Klise, Kate. Trial by Journal. Klise, M. Sarah, illus. 256p. (J). 2002. (gr. 3-6). pap. 6.99 (978-0-380-81672-9(5)); 2001. (gr. 4-6). 15.95 (978-0-380-97880-9(6)); 2001. (gr. 4-6). 16.89 (978-0-06-029541-7(4)) HarperCollins Pubs.

—Trial by Journal. 2002. (gr. 5-8). lib. bdg. 15.30 (978-0-613-60649-3(3)) Tandem Library Bks.

Knight, Joan. Charlotte in Paris. Sweet, Melissa, illus. 2003. 52p. (J). 16.95 (978-0-8118-3766-8(1)) Chronicle Bks. LLC.

Koertge, Ronald. Shakespeare Bats Clean-Up. 2003. 128p. (YA). (gr. 7). 15.99 (978-0-7636-2116-2(1)) Candlewick Pr.

Koja, Kathe. Going Under. 2006. 128p. (YA). 16.00 (978-0-374-30393-8(2) , Frances Foster Bks.) Farrar, Straus & Giroux.

Koss, Amy Goldman. Stolen Words. 2001. (978-0-606-22775-9(X)) Tandem Library Bks.

Lasky, Kathryn. Dreams in the Golden Country: The Diary of Zipporah Feldman, a Jewish Immigrant Girl, New York City, 1903. 1998. (Dear America Ser.). (Illus.). 192p. (J). (gr. 4-9). pap. 10.95 (978-0-590-02973-5(8)) Scholastic, Inc.

—Home at Last: Sofia's Immigrant Diary. 2003. (My America Ser.). (Illus.). 112p. (J). pap. 12.95 (978-0-439-44963-2(4)); (gr. 3-4). pap. 4.99 (978-0-439-20644-0(8)) Scholastic, Inc.

—Jahanara: Princess of Princesses, India, 1627. 2002. (Royal Diaries Ser.). 192p. (J). (gr. 4-8). pap. 10.95 (978-0-439-22350-8(4) , Scholastic Pr.) Scholastic, Inc.

—A Journey to the New World: The Diary of Remember Patience Whipple, Mayflower, 1620. 1999. (Dear America Ser.). (J). 9.95 (978-0-439-15601-1(7)) Scholastic, Inc.

—Kazunomiya: Prisoner of Heaven, Japan, 1858. 2004. (Royal Diaries). (Illus.). 160p. (J). (gr. 4-7). pap. 10.95 (978-0-439-16485-6(0)) Scholastic, Inc.

—Marie Antoinette: Princess of Versailles, Austria-France, 1769. 2000. (Royal Diaries Ser.). (Illus.). 240p. (J). (gr. 4-8). pap. 10.95 (978-0-439-07666-1(8)) Scholastic, Inc.

—Mary, Queen of Scots: Queen Without a Country, France 1553. 2002. (Royal Diaries Ser.). (Illus.). 112p. (J). (gr. 4-8). pap. 10.95 (978-0-439-19404-4(0) , Scholastic Pr.) Scholastic, Inc.

Lee, Tanith. Indigara: Firebird Novella. 2007. 192p. (YA). (gr. 7 up). 11.99 (*978-0-14-240922-0(7) , Puffin) Penguin Group (USA) Inc.

Levine, Beth Seidel. When Christmas Comes Again: The World War I Diary of Simone Spencer. 2002. (Dear America Ser.). (Illus.). 176p. (J). (gr. 4-9). pap. 10.95 (978-0-439-43982-4(5)) Scholastic, Inc.

Levine, Ellen. The Journal of Jedediah Barstow: An Emigrant on the Oregon Trail. 2002. (My Name Is America Ser.). (Illus.). 176p. (J). (gr. 4-8). pap. 10.95 (978-0-439-06310-4(8) , Scholastic Pr.) Scholastic, Inc.

Lewis, Cynthia C. Dilly's Summer Camp Diary. 2000. 4. (Illus.). 32p. (J). (gr. 2-4). pap. 6.95 (978-0-7613-0990-1(X) , First Avenue Editions) Lerner Publishing Group.

—Dilly's Summer Camp Diary. 1999. (gr. 3-6). lib. bdg. 15.25 (978-0-613-28464-6(X)) Tandem Library Bks.

Lisa's Diary: Individual Title Six-Packs. (gr. k-1). 23.00 (978-0-7635-9066-6(5)) Rigby Education.

Lutzen, Hanna. Vlad the Undead. 2001. (gr. 7-12). lib. bdg. 14.10 (978-0-613-88930-8(4)) Tandem Library Bks.

MacHale, D. J. The Quillan Games. 2007. (Pendragon Ser.: Bk. 7). 496p. (J). pap. 8.99 (*978-0-689-86913-6(4) , Aladdin) Simon & Schuster Children's Publishing.

MacHale, D. J. The Rivers of Zadaa. (Pendragon Ser.: Bk. 6). 416p. (J). 2006. pap. 6.99 (978-0-689-86912-9(6) , Aladdin); 2005. 14.95 (978-1-4169-0710-7(6)) Simon & Schuster Children's Publishing.

May, Kyla. Introducing Kyla May Miss. Behaves. 2005. (Illus.). 64p. (J). (gr. 4-7). pap. 4.99 (978-0-8431-1370-9(7) , Price Stern Sloan) Penguin Group (USA) Inc.

Mazer, Anne. Every Cloud Has a Silver Lining. Gesue, Monica, illus. 2000. (Amazing Days of Abby Hayes Ser.: No. 1). 128p. (gr. 4-7). mass mkt. 4.99 (978-0-439-14977-8(0)) Scholastic, Inc.

—Every Cloud Has a Silver Lining. 2000. (Amazing Days of Abby Hayes Ser.: No. 1). (J). 11.79 (978-0-606-19559-1(9)); (gr. 3-6). lib. bdg. 12.40 (978-0-613-25048-1(6)) Tandem Library Bks.

—That's the Way the Cookie Crumbles. 2005. (Amazing Days of Abby Hayes Ser.: No. 16). (Illus.). 128p. (J). (gr. 3-7). pap. 4.99 (978-0-439-68067-7(0) , Scholastic Paperbacks) Scholastic, Inc.

McKissack, Patricia C. Color Me Dark: The Diary of Nellie Lee Love, the Great Migration North, Chicago, Illinois, 1919. 2000. (Dear America Ser.). (J). 9.95 (978-0-439-26653-6(X)) Scholastic, Inc.

—Color Me Dark: The Diary of Nellie Lee Love, the Great Migration North, Chicago, Illinois, 1919. 2000. (Dear America Ser.). (Illus.). 224p. (J). (gr. 4-9). pap. 10.95 (978-0-590-51159-9(9)) Scholastic, Inc.

—Nzingha, Warrior Queen of Matamba - Angola 1595. 2000. (Royal Diaries Ser.). (Illus.). 144p. (J). (gr. 4-8). pap. 10.95 (978-0-439-11210-9(9)) Scholastic, Inc.

McMullan, Kate. As Far As I Can See Bk. 1: Meg's Prairie Diary. (My America Ser.). 112p. (J). 2002. (gr. 3-5). pap. 10.95 (978-0-439-42517-9(4)); 2001. (Illus.). (gr. 2-5). pap. 10.95 (978-0-439-18895-1(4)) Scholastic, Inc. (Scholastic Pr.).

—A Fine Start Bk. 3: Meg's Prairie Diary. 2003. (My America Ser.: No. 3). 112p. (J). pap. 12.95 (978-0-439-37061-5(2)) Scholastic, Inc.

—For This Land Bk. 2: Meg's Prairie Diary. 2003. (My America Ser.). (Illus.). 112p. (J). pap. 10.95 (978-0-439-37059-2(0) , Scholastic Pr.) Scholastic, Inc.

—For This Land Bk. 2: Meg's Prairie Diary. 2003. (gr. 3-6). lib. bdg. 19.90 (978-0-613-63038-2(6)) Tandem Library Bks.

McNamee, Graham. Acceleration. (YA). (gr. 7). 2003. 224p. lib. bdg. 17.99 (978-0-385-90144-4(5) , Lamb, Wendy); 2005. 240p. reprint ed. pap. 6.50 (978-0-440-23836-2(6) , Laurel Leaf) Random Hse. Children's Bks.

Mechling, Lauren, et al. The Rise & Fall of a 10th Grade Social Climber. 2005. 304p. (YA). (gr. 7). pap. 7.99 (978-0-618-55519-2(6) , Graphia) Houghton Mifflin Co. Trade & Reference Div.

Mercati, Cynthia. Wagons Ho! A Diary of the Oregon Trail. Kabel, Larassa, illus. 2000. (Cover-to-Cover Bks.). 56p. (J). pap. (978-0-7891-5039-4(5)); (gr. 1-4). lib. bdg. 16.95 (978-0-7807-9011-7(1)) Perfection Learning Corp.

Meyer, Carolyn. Anastasia: The Last Grand Duchess: Russia 1914. 2000. (Royal Diaries Ser.). (Illus.). 224p. (J). (gr. 4-8). pap. 10.95 (978-0-439-12908-4(7)) Scholastic, Inc.

—Isabel: Jewel of Castilla, Spain 1466. 2000. (Royal Diaries Ser.). (Illus.). 208p. (J). (gr. 4-8). pap. 10.95 (978-0-439-07805-4(9)) Scholastic, Inc.

—Kristina, the Girl King, Sweden 1638. 2003. (Royal Diaries Ser.). 176p. (J). pap. 10.95 (978-0-439-24976-8(7) , Scholastic Pr.) Scholastic, Inc.

Mills, Claudia. The Totally Made-Up Civil War Diary of Amanda MacLeish. 2008. 208p. (J). 16.00 (*978-0-374-37696-3(4)) Farrar, Straus & Giroux.

Moerbeek, Kees. The Diary of Hansel & Gretel. Moerbeek, Kees, illus. 2002. (Illus.). 12p. (J). (gr. k-3). 12.95 (978-0-689-84602-1(9) , Little Simon) Simon & Schuster Children's Publishing.

Montano, Josie. Chicken Pox. . . Yuck! 2005. (Illus.). 160p. pap. (978-0-7344-0335-3(6) , Lothian Bks.) Hachette Livre Australia.

Montes, Juan Mari. Diario del Autobus a de la Linea 3. Fra, Irene, illus. 2006. (SPA.). 96p. (J). (978-84-667-5192-6(0)) Grupo Anaya, S.A.

Moonshower, Candie. The Legend of Zoey. 2007. 224p. (J). (gr. 4-7). 5.99 (*978-0-440-23924-6(9) , Yearling) Random Hse. Children's Bks.

Morpurgo, Michael. The Amazing Story of Adolphus Tips. 2006. 208p. (J). (gr. 2-5). 16.99 (978-0-439-79661-3(X) , Scholastic Pr.) Scholastic, Inc.

—The Wreck of the Zanzibar. l.t. ed. 2003. (J). 16.95 (978-0-7540-7846-3(9) , Galaxy Children's Large Print) BBC Audiobooks America.

Moss, Alexandra. Kate's Special Secret, No. 5. 2005. (Royal Ballet School Diaries). 144p. (J). (gr. 3-5). pap. 4.99 (978-0-448-43771-2(6) , Grosset & Dunlap) Penguin Group (USA) Inc.

Moss, Marissa. Amelia Hits the Road. 1999. (Amelia's Notebooks). (J). (gr. 3-5). 12.75 (978-0-606-19867-7(9)) Tandem Library Bks.

—Amelia Takes Command. 1999. (Amelia's Notebooks). (Illus.). 48p. (J). (ps-7). lib. bdg. 12.75 (978-0-606-19868-4(7)) Tandem Library Bks.

—Amelia Writes Again. Moss, Marissa, illus. 2006. (Amelia's Notebooks). (Illus.). 32p. (J). 9.95 (978-1-4169-0904-0(4) , Simon & Schuster/Paula Wiseman Bks.) Simon & Schuster Children's Publishing.

—Amelia Writes Again. 1999. (Amelia's Notebooks). (Illus.). 48p. (gr. 3-5). lib. bdg. 12.75 (978-0-606-17252-3(1)) Tandem Library Bks.

—Amelia's 5th-Grade Notebook. Moss, Marissa, illus. 2006. (Amelia's Notebooks). (Illus.). 40p. (J). 9.95 (978-1-4169-0912-5(5) , Simon & Schuster/Paula Wiseman Bks.) Simon & Schuster Children's Publishing.

—Amelia's 5th-Grade Notebook. Moss, Marissa, illus. 2006. (Amelia's Notebooks). (J). 5.99 (978-1-4169-1292-7(4)) Simon & Schuster, Inc.

—Amelia's 6th Grade Notebook. Moss, Marissa, illus. 2005. (Amelia's Notebooks). (Illus.). 80p. (J). (gr. k-8). 9.95 (978-0-689-87040-8(X) , Simon & Schuster Children's Publishing) Simon & Schuster Children's Publishing.

—Amelia's Are-We-There-yet Longest Ever Car Trip. Moss, Marissa, illus. 2006. (Amelia's Notebooks). (Illus.). 40p. (J). 9.95 (978-1-4169-0906-4(0) , Simon & Schuster/Paula Wiseman Bks.) Simon & Schuster Children's Publishing.

—Amelia's Family Ties. Moss, Marissa, illus. 2007. (Amelia's Notebooks). 40p. (J). (gr. 2-5). 9.99 (***978-1-4169-0914-9(1)*** , Simon & Schuster/Paula Wiseman Bks.) Simon & Schuster Children's Publishing.

—Amelia's Family Ties. 2000. (Amelia's Notebooks). (Illus.). (J). (gr. 3-5). 12.75 (978-0-606-18352-9(3)) Tandem Library Bks.

—Amelia's Longest, Biggest, Most-Fights-Ever Family Reunion. Moss, Marissa, illus. 2006. (Amelia's Notebooks). (Illus.). 80p. (J). 9.95 (978-0-689-87447-5(2) , Simon & Schuster Children's Publishing) Simon & Schuster Children's Publishing.

—Amelia's Most Unforgettable Embarrassing Moments. Moss, Marissa, illus. 2005. (Amelia's Notebooks). (Illus.). 80p. (J). 9.95 (978-0-689-87041-5(8) , Simon & Schuster Children's Publishing) Simon & Schuster Children's Publishing.

—Amelia's Notebook. Moss, Marissa, illus. 2006. (Amelia's Notebooks). (Illus.). 40p. (J). 9.95 (978-1-4169-0905-7(2)) Simon & Schuster Children's Publishing.

—Amelia's Notebook. Moss, Marissa, illus. 2006. (Amelia's Notebooks). (J). 5.99 (978-1-4169-1286-6(X)) Simon & Schuster, Inc.

—Amelia's Notebook. 1999. (Amelia's Notebooks). (Illus.). (J). (gr. 3-5). 12.75 (978-0-606-18353-6(1)) Tandem Library Bks.

—Emma's Journal: The Story of a Colonial Girl. Moss, Marissa, illus. 2001. (Young American Voices Ser.: Bk. 2). (Illus.). 56p. (YA). (gr. 3-7). pap. 7.00 (978-0-15-216325-9(5) , Silver Whistle) Harcourt Trade Pubs.

—Galen: My Life in Imperial Rome. Moss, Marissa, illus. 2002. (Ancient World Journals). (Illus.). 48p. (YA). (gr. 3-7). 15.00 (978-0-15-216535-2(5) , Silver Whistle) Harcourt Trade Pubs.

—Hannah's Journal: The Story of an Immigrant Girl. 2002. (Young American Voices Ser.). (Illus.). 56p. (YA). (gr. 3-7). pap. 7.00 (978-0-15-216329-7(8) , Silver Whistle) Harcourt Trade Pubs.

—Hannah's Journal: The Story of an Immigrant Girl. 2002. (gr. 3-6). lib. bdg. 15.30 (978-0-613-53818-3(8)) Tandem Library Bks.

—Rachel's Journal: The Story of A Pioneer Girl. 2001. (gr. 3-6). lib. bdg. 15.30 (978-0-613-35560-5(1)) Tandem Library Bks.

—Rose's Journal: The Story of a Girl in the Great Depression. 2003. (Young American Voices Ser.). (Illus.). 56p. (J). pap. 7.00 (978-0-15-204605-7(4) , Silver Whistle) Harcourt Trade Pubs.

—Rose's Journal: The Story of a Girl in the Great Depression. Moss, Marissa, illus. 2001. (Young American Voices Ser.). (Illus.). 56p. (YA). (gr. 3-7). 15.00 (978-0-15-202423-9(9) , Silver Whistle) Harcourt Trade Pubs.

Murphy, Stuart J. Pepper's Journal: A Kitten's First Year. Winborn, Marsha, illus. 2000. (Trophy Picture Bk.). 40p. (J). (gr. 1 up). pap. 5.99 (978-0-06-446723-0(6) , Harper Trophy) HarperCollins Pubs.

—Pepper's Journal: A Kitten's First Year. 2000. (Math Start Ser.). (978-0-606-18711-4(1)); lib. bdg. 13.00 (978-0-613-22167-2(2)) Tandem Library Bks.

Myers, Walter Dean. The Journal of Biddy Owens: The Negro Leagues, Birmingham, Alabama 1948. 2001. (978-0-606-22807-7(1)) Tandem Library Bks.

—The Journal of Joshua Loper: A Black Cowboy: The Chisholm Trail, 1871. 1999. (My Name Is America Ser.). (Illus.). 160p. (J). (gr. 4-8). pap. 10.95 (978-0-590-02691-8(7)) Scholastic, Inc.

—The Journal of Scott Pendelton Collins: A World War II Soldier. 1999. (My Name Is America Ser.). (Illus.). 144p. (J). (gr. 4-8). 10.95 (978-0-439-05013-5(8)) Scholastic, Inc.

Oke, Janette. Spunky's Diary. Munger, Nancy, illus. rev. ed. 2000. (Animal Friends Ser.). 64p. (J). (gr. 1-5). pap. 6.99 (978-0-7642-2405-8(0)) Bethany Hse. Pubs.

Oldfield, Jenny. When Dad Went on a Date. (Illus.). (J). mass mkt. 8.99 (978-0-340-85075-6(2) , Hodder & Stoughton) Hodder General Publishing Division GBR. *Dist:* Independent Pubs. Group.

—When Ellie Cheated. (Illus.). (YA). mass mkt. 8.99 (978-0-340-85072-5(8) , Hodder & Stoughton) Hodder General Publishing Division GBR. *Dist:* Independent Pubs. Group.

—When Geri & I Fell Out. (Illus.). (J). mass mkt. 8.99 (978-0-340-85074-9(4) , Hodder & Stoughton) Hodder General Publishing Division GBR. *Dist:* Independent Pubs. Group.

—When I Won a Prize. (Illus.). (J). mass mkt. 8.99 (978-0-340-85076-3(0) , Hodder & Stoughton) Hodder General Publishing Division GBR. *Dist:* Independent Pubs. Group.

—When Scott Got Lost No. 2. (Illus.). (J). mass mkt. 8.99 (978-0-340-85073-2(6)) Macmillan Publishers Ltd. GBR. *Dist:* Trafalgar Square Publishing.

—When Shah Went Weird. (Illus.). (J). mass mkt. 8.99 (978-0-340-85077-0(9) , Hodder & Stoughton) Hodder General Publishing Division GBR. *Dist:* Independent Pubs. Group.

Olsson, Soren & Jacobsson, Anders. In Ned's Head. Read, Kevin, tr. 2004. 144p. (J). reprint ed. pap. 4.99 (978-0-689-87355-3(7) , Aladdin) Simon & Schuster Children's Publishing.

Ortiz, Michael J. Swan Town: The Secret Journal of Susanna Shakespeare. 2006. 208p. (J). lib. bdg. 16.89 (978-0-06-058127-5(1)); (Illus.). 15.99 (978-0-06-058126-8(3)) HarperCollins Pubs.

Osborne, Mary Pope. After the Rain Bk. 2: Virginia's Civil War Diary. 2002. (My America Ser.). 112p. (J). (gr. 2-5). pap. 10.95 (978-0-439-20138-4(1)); (Illus.). pap. 4.99 (978-0-439-36904-6(5)) Scholastic, Inc. (Scholastic Pr.).

Osborne, Mary Pope, et al. A Time to Dance Bk. 3: Virginia's Civil War Diary. 2003. (My America Ser.). 112p. (J). pap. 12.95 (978-0-439-44341-8(5)) Scholastic, Inc.

Park, Barbara. Junie B. , First Grader: Shipwrecked. Brunkus, Denise, illus. 2004. 88p. (J). lib. bdg. 18.46 (***978-1-4242-0360-4(0)***) Fitzgerald Bks.

Park, Barbara. Junie B., First Grader: Aloha-Ha-Ha! Brunkus, Denise, illus. 2007. (Junie B. Jones Ser.: No. 26). 128p. (J). (gr. 1-4). 4.99 (978-0-375-83404-2(4) , Random Hse. Bks. for Young Readers) Random Hse. Children's Bks.

—Junie B., First Grader: Aloha-Ha-Ha! 2006. (Junie B. Jones Ser.: No. 26). (Illus.). 128p. (J). (gr. k-3). lib. bdg. 13.95 (978-0-375-93403-2(0)); (gr. 2-5). 11.95 (978-0-375-83403-5(6)) Random Hse. Children's Bks. (Random Hse. Bks. for Young Readers).

Paton, Ian, illus. Margaret's Magnificent Colorado Adventure. 1999. 48p. (J). (gr. 4-7). 14.95 (978-1-56579-329-3(3) , A176) Westcliffe Pubs.

Paulsen, Gary. The Amazing Life of Birds: The Twenty-Day Puberty Journal of Duane Homer Leech. 2006. (Illus.). 96p. (J). (gr. 5-9). 13.95 (978-0-385-74660-1(1) , Lamb, Wendy) Random Hse. Children's Bks.

Perez, Amada Irma. My Diary from Here to There / Mi Diario de Aqui Hasta Alla. Gonzalez, Maya Christina, illus. 2002. Tr. of Mi Diario de Aqui Hasta Alla. (ENG & SPA.). 32p. (J). (gr. 2-5). 16.95 (978-0-89239-175-2(8)) Children's Bk. Pr.

Perrin, Randy, et al. Time Like a River. 2004. 144p. (gr. 5 up). 14.95 (978-1-57143-061-8(X)) RDR Bks.

Pfeffer, Susan Beth. Beth's Story. 2001. (Portraits of Little Women Ser.). (Illus.). (J). (978-0-606-21063-8(6)) Tandem Library Bks.

—Life As We Knew It. 2006. (Illus.). 352p. (J). 17.00 (978-0-15-205826-5(5)) Harcourt Children's Bks.

Philbrick, Rodman. The Journal of Douglas Allen Deeds: The Donner Party Expedition, 1846. 2001. (My Name Is America Ser.). (Illus.). 160p. (J). (gr. 4-9). pap. 10.95 (978-0-439-21600-5(1)) Scholastic, Inc.

Platt, Richard. Castle Diary: The Journal of Tobias Burgess. Riddell, Chris, illus. 2003. 128p. (J). (gr. 4). 6.99 (978-0-7636-2164-3(1)) Candlewick Pr.

—Castle Diary: The Journal of Tobias Burgess. 2003. (gr. 3-6). lib. bdg. 15.30 (978-0-613-74821-6(2)) Tandem Library Bks.

—Castle Diary: The Journal of Tobias Burgess, Page. 2001. (J). (978-0-606-22543-4(9)) Tandem Library Bks.

Raham, Gary, et al. The Deep Time Diaries: As Recorded by Neesha & Jon Olifee. 2000. (Illus.). 96p. (J). (gr. 3-4). pap. 17.95 (978-1-55591-415-8(2)) Fulcrum Publishing.

Ravel, Edeet. The Secret Journey of Pauline Siddhartha. 2007. 224p. pap. 9.95 (***978-1-55192-974-3(0)***) Raincoast Bk. Distribution CAN. *Dist:* Perseus Distribution.

Rees, Celia. Witch Child. 272p. (YA). (gr. 7 up). 2002. pap. 8.99 (978-0-7636-1829-2(2)); 2001. (Illus.). 15.99 (978-0-7636-1421-8(1)) Candlewick Pr.

—Witch Child. unabr. ed. 2004. (Young Adult Cassette Librariestm Ser.). 304p. (J). (gr. 5-9). pap. 40.00 incl. audio (978-0-8072-1198-4(2) , S YA 343 SP, Listening Library) Random Hse. Audio Publishing Group.

—Witch Child. 2002. (gr. 7-12). lib. bdg. 16.45 (978-0-613-60740-7(6)) Tandem Library Bks.

—Witch Child. l.t. ed. 2002. 284p. (J). 22.95 (978-0-7862-3896-5(8)) Thomson Gale.

Reiche, Dietlof. Ghost Ship. Brownjohn, John, tr. from GER. 2005. 320p. (J). pap. 16.95 (978-0-439-59704-3(8)) Scholastic, Inc.

Rempel, Leah. Hey, Hmong Girl, Whassup? The Journal of Choua Vang. 2004. (Illus.). v, 138p. (YA). pap. (***978-0-9723721-5-2(6)***) Hamline Univ. Pr.

Rennison, Louise. Angus, Thongs & Full-Frontal Snogging. 2000. (Confessions of Georgia Nicolson Ser.). (Illus.). 256p. (J). (gr. 7 up). lib. bdg. 17.89 (978-0-06-028871-6(X)) HarperCollins Pubs.

—Angus, Thongs & Full-Frontal Snogging: Confessions of Georgia Nicolson. 2001. (Confessions of Georgia Nicolson Ser.). 272p. (J). (gr. 7 up). pap. 7.99 (978-0-06-447227-2(2) , HarperTeen) HarperCollins Pubs.

—Angus, Thongs & Full-Frontal Snogging: Confessions of Georgia Nicolson. 2003. (gr. 7-12). lib. bdg. 15.30 (978-0-613-71444-0(X)) Tandem Library Bks.

—Dancing in My Nuddy-Pants: Even Further Confessions of Georgia Nicolson. (Confessions of Georgia Nicolson Ser.). 2003. 224p. (J). 15.99 (978-0-06-009746-2(9)); 2004. 240p. (YA). reprint ed. pap. 7.99 (978-0-06-009748-6(5)) HarperCollins Pubs. (HarperTeen).

—Further Confessions of Georgia Nicolson. ed. 2004. (Confessions of Georgia Nicolson Ser.). 416p. (J). pap. 13.99 (978-0-06-059007-9(6)) HarperCollins Pubs.

—Knocked Out by My Nunga-Nungas: Further, Further Confessions of Georgia Nicolson. 2002. (Confessions of Georgia Nicolson Ser.). 192p. (J). (gr. 8-10). 15.99 (978-0-06-623656-8(8)) HarperCollins Pubs.

—Knocked Out by My Nunga-Nungas: Further, Further Confessions of Georgia Nicolson. 2003. (gr. 7-12). lib. bdg. 15.30 (978-0-613-67208-5(9)) Tandem Library Bks.

—On the Bright Side, I'm Now the Girlfriend of a Sex God: Further Confessions Of. 2002. (gr. 7-12). lib. bdg. 15.30 (978-0-613-49344-4(3)) Tandem Library Bks.

—On the Bright Side, I'm Now the Girlfriend of a Sex God: Further Confessions of Georgia Nicolson. (Confessions of Georgia Nicolson Ser.). 2003. 256p. (J). pap. 6.99 (978-0-06-052185-1(6)); 2002. 272p. (YA). pap. 7.99 (978-0-06-447226-5(4)); 2001. 256p. (J). (gr. 7 up). 17.99 (978-0-06-028813-6(2)) HarperCollins Pubs.

—Startled by His Furry Shorts. 2007. (Confessions of Georgia Nicolson Ser.). 304p. (J). pap. 7.99 (***978-0-06-085386-0(7)*** , HarperTeen) HarperCollins Pubs.

—Startled by His Furry Shorts! 2006. (Confessions of Georgia Nicolson Ser.). 288p. (J). 16.99 (978-0-06-085384-6(0)); lib. bdg. 17.89 (978-0-06-085385-3(9)) HarperCollins Pubs. (HarperTeen).

—Then He Ate My Boy Entrancers: More Mad, Marvy Confessions of Georgia Nicolson. (Confessions of Georgia Nicolson Ser.). 2006. 336p. (J). pap. 7.99 (978-0-06-058939-4(6)); 2005. 320p. (J). lib. bdg. 16.89 (978-0-06-058938-7(8)); No. 6. 2005. 320p. (YA). 15.99 (978-0-06-058937-0(X)) HarperCollins Pubs. (HarperTeen).

Rettig, Liz. My Desperate Love Diary. 2007. 314p. (YA). (gr. 9 up). 16.95 (978-0-8234-2033-9(7)) Holiday Hse., Inc.

Rigby Education Staff. Cat's Diary. (Sails Literacy Ser.). (Illus.). 16p. (gr. 2-3). 27.00 (978-0-7635-9937-9(9) , 699379C99) Rigby Education.

Rinaldi, Ann. The Journal of Jasper Jonathan Pierce: A Pilgrim Boy, Plymouth, 1620. 2000. (My Name Is America Ser.). (Illus.). 160p. (J). (gr. 4-8). pap. 10.95 (978-0-590-51078-3(9)) Scholastic, Inc.

—Sarah's Ground. 2004. (Illus.). 192p. (YA). 15.95 (978-0-689-85924-3(4)) Simon & Schuster Children's Publishing.

Rivers, Karen. The Cure for Crushes: And Other Deadly Plagues. 2005. 304p. (J). (gr. 10 up). pap. 6.95 (978-1-55192-779-4(9)) Raincoast Bk. Distribution CAN. *Dist:* Perseus Distribution.

Rogers, Lisa Waller. Get along Little Dogies: The Chisholm Trail Diary of Hallie Lou Wells. 2001. (Lone Star Journals: Vol. 1). (Illus.). 174p. (J). (gr. 4-7). 14.50 (978-0-89672-446-4(8)) Texas Tech Univ. Pr.

—Get along, Little Dogies: The Chisholm Trail Diary of Hallie Lou Wells, South Texas 1878. 2001. (Lone Star Journals). (Illus.). 174p. (J). (gr. 4-7). 8.95 (978-0-89672-448-8(4)) Texas Tech Univ. Pr.

—The Great Storm: The Hurricane Diary of J. T. King, Galveston, Texas, 1900. 2002. (Lone Star Journals). (Illus.). 192p. (J). 14.50 (978-0-89672-478-5(6)) Texas Tech Univ. Pr.

—Remember the Alamo! The Runaway Scrape Diary of Belle Wood. 2003. (Lone Star Journals: Bk. 3). 208p. (J). 15.95 (978-0-89672-497-6(2)) Texas Tech Univ. Pr.

Rosen, Michael J. Shakespeare: His Work & His World. Ingpen, Robert R., illus. 2001. 104p. (J). (gr. 7-11). 19.99 (978-0-7636-1568-0(4)) Candlewick Pr.

Scholastic, Inc. Staff. Elizabeth I: Red Rose of the House of Tudor, England 1544. 2000. (Royal Diaries Ser.). (J). lthr. 9.95 (978-0-439-26654-3(8)) Scholastic, Inc.

—Isabel: Jewel of Castilla, Spain 1466. 2000. (Royal Diaries Ser.). (J). lthr. 9.95 (978-0-439-26656-7(4)) Scholastic, Inc.

Schumacher, Julie. The Book of One Hundred Truths. 192p. (gr. 4-7). 2008. 5.99 (***978-0-440-42085-9(7)*** , Yearling); 2006. (J). 15.95 (978-0-385-73290-1(2) , Delacorte Bks. for Young Readers); 2006. (J). lib. bdg. 17.99 (978-0-385-90311-0(1) , Delacorte Bks. for Young Readers) Random Hse. Children's Bks.

Segal, Zoe. Confessions of a Tenth-Grade Social Climber. 2005. 290p. (YA). (978-0-618-44981-1(7)) Houghton Mifflin Co.

Shields, Gillian. The Actual Real Reality of Jennifer James: A Reality TV Novel. 2006. 384p. (J). lib. bdg. 17.89 (978-0-06-082241-5(4) , Tegen, Katherine Bks) HarperCollins Pubs.

Skye, Obert. Professor Winsnicker's Book of Proper Etiquette for Well-Mannered Sycophants. 2007. 167p. (J). (***978-1-59038-716-0(3)*** , Shadow Mountain) Deseret Bk. Co.

Smith, Debra West. Yankees on the Doorstep: The Story of Sarah Morgan. 2001. (Illus.). 176p. (J). (gr. 3-7). pap. 10.95 (978-1-56554-872-5(8)) Pelican Publishing Co., Inc.

Smith Dinbergs, Holly. Diary Disaster. Stewart, Chantal, illus. 2005. (Girlz Rock! Ser.). (J). pap. (978-1-59336-700-8(7)) Mondo Publishing.

Smith, Eunice Geil. Treasure Hunt: A Shenandoah Valley Mystery. 2006. 119p. (J). pap. 9.99 (978-0-8361-9332-9(6)) Herald Pr.

Sommerdorf, Norma. Red River Girl. 2006. (Illus.). 192p. (J). 16.95 (978-0-8234-1903-6(7)) Holiday Hse., Inc.

Sparks, Beatrice. Kim: Empty Inside. 2002. (gr. 7-12). lib. bdg. 14.15 (978-0-613-56919-4(9)) Tandem Library Bks.

Sparks, Beatrice, ed. Kim: Empty Inside: The Diary of an Anonymous Teenager. 2002. 176p. (YA). (gr. 7 up). pap. 5.99 (978-0-380-81460-2(9)) HarperCollins Pubs.

Speltz, Ann. The Year My Mother Was Bald. Sternberg, Kate, illus. 2003. 64p. (YA). (gr. 3-8). 14.95 (978-1-55798-837-9(4)); (ps-8). pap. 8.95 (978-1-55798-888-1(9)) American Psychological Assn. (Magination Pr.).

—Year My Mother Was Bald. 2003. (gr. 3-6). lib. bdg. 17.60 (978-0-613-61137-4(3)) Tandem Library Bks.

Spinelli, Jerry. Love, Stargirl. 2007. (J). 192p. (gr. 5-8). lib. bdg. 19.99 (***978-0-375-91375-4(0));*** 288p. (gr. 7-8). 16.99 (***978-0-375-81375-7(6)***) Random Hse. Children's Bks. (Knopf Bks. for Young Readers).

Stevermer, Caroline & Wrede, Patricia C. The Grand Tour: Being a Revelation of Matters of High Confidentiality & Greatest Importance, Including Extracts from the Intimate Diary of a Noblewoman & the Sworn Testimony of a Lady of Quality. 2006. (Illus.). 480p. (J). pap. 6.95 (978-0-15-205556-1(8) , Magic Carpet Bks.) Harcourt Children's Bks.

Stewart, Sarah. The Journey. Small, David, illus. 40p. (J). 2001. (gr. 2-6). 16.00 (978-0-374-33905-0(8)); 2006. reprint ed. pap. 6.95 (978-0-374-40010-1(5)) Farrar, Straus & Giroux. (Farrar, Straus & Giroux (BYR)).

—The Journey. Smalls, David, illus. pap. 16.95 incl. audio (978-0-87499-922-8(7)); pap. incl. audio (978-0-87499-924-2(3)); pap. 18.95 incl. audio compact disk (978-1-59112-344-6(5)); pap. incl. audio compact disk (978-1-59112-556-3(1)) Live Oak Media.

—The Journey. 2002. (Illus.). (J). 28.95 incl. audio compact disk (978-1-59112-345-3(3)); 25.95 incl. audio (978-0-87499-923-5(5)) Live Oak Media.

Stine, R. L. Dear Diary, I'm Dead. 2001. (Nightmare Room Ser.: Vol. 5). (J). 10.64 (978-0-606-20068-4(1)) Tandem Library Bks.

Strawberry Shortcake Berry Loveable Diary. 2005. 7.95 (978-1-59487-083-5(7)) Artist Studios, Ltd.

Tashjian, Janet. Tru Confessions. 1999. (Illus.). 176p. (J). pap. 4.99 (978-0-590-96047-2(4)) Scholastic, Inc.

—Tru Confessions. 2007. 176p. (J). pap. 6.99 (***978-0-312-37273-6(6)***) Square Fish.

—Tru Confessions. 1999. (978-0-606-16611-9(4)) Tandem Library Bks.

Ting, Renee. The Prince's Diary. Dulemba, Elizabeth, illus. 2005. 32p. (J). (978-1-885008-27-5(9)) Shen's Bks.

Townson, Hazel. Two Weird Weeks. 2003. (Illus.). 80p. (YA). pap. 8.99 (978-1-84270-073-0(1)) Andersen GBR. *Dist:* Independent Pubs. Group.

Trottier, Maxine. Death of My Country: The Plains of Abraham Diary of Geneviève Aubuchon. 2005. (Dear Canada Ser.). (Illus.). 208p. pap. (***978-0-439-96762-4(7)***) Scholastic Canada, Ltd.

Trueit, Trudi. Julep O' Toole: Miss Independent. 2006. (Illus.). 160p. (J). (gr. 3). 15.99 (978-0-525-47637-5(7) , Dutton Juvenile) Penguin Group (USA) Inc.

—Julep O' Toole: Miss Independent: Miss Independent. 2007. 176p. (J). 5.99 (978-0-14-240829-2(8) , Puffin) Penguin Group (USA) Inc.

—Julep O'Toole: What I Really Want to Do Is Direct. 2007. 160p. (J). (gr. 3 up). 16.99 (978-0-525-47781-5(0) , Dutton Juvenile) Penguin Group (USA) Inc.

—Julep O'Toole: Confessions of a Middle Child: Confessions of a Middle Child. 2007. 192p. (J). 5.99 (978-0-14-240798-1(4) , Puffin) Penguin Group (USA) Inc.

Turner, Nancy E. These Is My Words: The Diary of Sarah Agnes Prine, 1881-1902 Arizona Territories. 1999. (978-0-606-17597-5(0)) Tandem Library Bks.

Ure, Jean. Boys on the Brain. l.t. ed. 2005. (Illus.). 184p. (J). pap. incl. audio (978-0-7540-7859-3(0) , CLP 450) BBC Audio.

—Boys on the Brain. 2002. (Diary Ser.). (Illus.). 208p. (J). pap. 9.99 (978-0-00-711373-6(0)) HarperCollins Pubs. Ltd. GBR. *Dist:* Independent Pubs. Group.

—The Flower Power Collection: Passion Flower, Shrinking Violet & Pumpkin Pie. 2006. (Illus.). 544p. (J). pap. 16.99 (978-0-00-720155-6(9) , HarperCollins Children's Bks.) HarperCollins Pubs. Ltd. GBR. *Dist:* Independent Pubs. Group.

—Secret Life of Sally Tomato. 2001. (Diary Ser.). (Illus.). 160p. (J). pap. 9.99 (978-0-00-675150-2(4) , Collins) HarperCollins Pubs. Ltd. GBR. *Dist:* Independent Pubs. Group.

Valgardson, W. D. Frances. (J). (gr. 6-9). 2002. 172p. pap. 5.95 (978-0-88899-397-7(8)); 2000. 190p. 15.95 (978-0-88899-386-1(2)) Groundwood Bks. CAN. *Dist:* Perseus Distribution, Transition Vendor.

van de Ruit, John. Spud. 2007. 352p. (YA). (gr. 7 up). 16.99 (***978-1-59514-170-5(7)*** , Razorbill) Penguin Group (USA) Inc.

Van Draanen, Wendelin. Runaway. 2006. 256p. (J). (gr. 5). 15.95 (978-0-375-83522-3(9)); lib. bdg. 17.99 (978-0-375-93522-0(3)) Random Hse. Children's Bks. (Knopf Bks. for Young Readers).

Veciana-Suarez, Ana. Flight to Freedom. 2002. (First Person Fiction Ser.). 224p. (J). (gr. 6-9). pap. 16.95 (978-0-439-38199-4(1) , Orchard Bks.) Scholastic, Inc.

—Flight to Freedom. 2004. 215p. (YA). (gr. 8-12). lib. bdg. 13.64 (978-0-606-30967-5(5)) Tandem Library Bks.

Ware-Holmes, Barbara. Letters to Julia. 1999. (J). (978-0-606-17466-4(4)) Tandem Library Bks.

Watts, Leander. Stonecutter. 2006. 182p. (J). (gr. 5-9). reprint ed. pap. 7.99 (978-0-618-60577-4(0) , Graphia) Houghton Mifflin Co. Trade & Reference Div.

Weston, Carol. The Diary of Melanie Martin. 2001. (Illus.). 144p. (J). (ps-7). per. 13.00 (978-0-613-33751-9(4)) Tandem Library Bks.

—The Diary of Melanie Martin: Or How I Survived Matt the Brat, Michelangelo & the Leaning Tower of Pizza. Roth, Marci Doane, illus. 2001. 160p. (gr. 3-7). 5.50 (978-0-440-41667-8(1) , Yearling) Random Hse. Children's Bks.

—The Diary of Melanie Martin: Or How I Survived Matt the Brat, Michelangelo & the Leaning Tower of Pizza. 2001. 11.64 (978-0-606-21144-4(6)) Tandem Library Bks.

—Melanie in Manhattan. 288p. (J). (gr. 3-7). 2006. 5.99 (978-0-440-42040-8(7) , Yearling); 2005. (Illus.). 15.95 (978-0-375-83028-0(6) , Knopf Bks. for Young Readers) Random Hse. Children's Bks.

—Melanie Martin Goes Dutch: The Private Diary of My Almost Bummer Summer with Cecily, Matt the Brat, & Vincent van Go Go Go. 2003. (Illus.). 240p. (J). (gr. 3-7). 5.99 (978-0-440-41899-3(2) , Yearling) Random Hse. Children's Bks.

C D

—Melanie Martin Goes Dutch: The Private Diary of My Almost Bummer Summer with Cecily, Matt the Brat, & Vincent van Go Go Go. 2003. (gr. 3-6). lib. bdg. 25.70 (978-0-613-62527-2(7)) Tandem Library Bks.

Whelan, Gloria. Fruitlands: Louisa May Alcott Made Perfect. 2002. 128p. (J). (gr. 4-7). 15.99 (978-0-06-623815-9(3)) HarperCollins Pubs.

Whicker, Mike. Proper Suda. 2003. 162p. (YA). 21.95 (978-0-595-65727-8(3)) iUniverse, Inc.

Whicker, Mike & Scribes, F. J. Proper Suda. 2003. 162p. (YA). pap. 11.95 (978-0-595-28034-6(X) , iUniverse, Inc.) iUniverse, Inc.

White, Ellen Emerson. The Journal of Patrick Seamus Flaherty: United States Marine Corps, Khe Sanh, Vietnam, 1968. 2002. (My Name Is America Ser.). (Illus.). 192p. (J). (gr. 4-9). pap. 10.95 (978-0-439-14890-0(1) , Scholastic Pr.) Scholastic, Inc.

Whitmore, Benette. Shelter. 2006. 304p. (YA). 16.95 (978-0-8027-8884-9(X)) Walker & Co.

Wilbourne, David. Summers Diary. 2002. (Illus.). 288p. (J). pap. 14.99 (978-0-00-710007-1(8)) HarperCollins Pubs. Ltd. GBR. *Dist:* Trafalgar Square Publishing.

Wildner, Martina & Skofield, James. Shooting Stars Everywhere. 2006. 192p. (J). (gr. 7). 15.95 (978-0-385-73250-5(3) , Delacorte Bks. for Young Readers) Random Hse. Children's Bks.

Wilson, Nancy Hope. Mountain Pose. 2001. 240p. (J). (gr. 5 up). 17.00 (978-0-374-35078-9(7) , Farrar, Straus & Giroux (BYR)) Farrar, Straus & Giroux.

Windle, Jeanette. Jana's Journal: A Novel for Teens. 2002. 256p. pap. 12.99 (978-0-8254-4117-2(X)) Kregel Pubns.

Wolfer, Dianne. Border Line. 1998. 190p. (J). pap. 11.95 (978-1-86368-208-4(2)) Fremantle Pr. AUS. *Dist:* International Specialized Bk. Services.

Wooters, Duane. The Unnamed Manuscript. 2003. 70p. (YA). pap. 8.95 (978-0-595-29612-5(2)) iUniverse, Inc.

Wright, Betty Ren. Crandall's Castle. 2005. 184p. (YA). (gr. 4-6). tchr. ed. 16.95 (978-0-8234-1726-1(3)) Holiday Hse., Inc.

Wyeth, Sharon Dennis. Flying Free: Corey's Underground Railroad Diary. 2002. (My America Ser.: Bk. 2). (Illus.). 112p. (J). (gr. 2-5). pap. 10.95 (978-0-439-24443-5(9) , Scholastic Pr.) Scholastic, Inc.

—Freedom's Wings: Corey's Underground Railroad Diary. 2002. (gr. 3-6). lib. bdg. 13.00 (978-0-613-53813-8(7)) Tandem Library Bks.

Yee, Lisa. Millicent Min, Girl Genius. 256p. 2003. (YA). (gr. 5-8). 16.95 (978-0-439-42519-3(0)); 2004. (J). (gr. 4-7). reprint ed. pap. 4.99 (978-0-439-42520-9(4)) Scholastic, Inc. (Levine, Arthur A. Bks.).

Yep, Laurence. My Name Is America: The Journal of Wongming-chun, A Chinese Miner. 2000. (My Name Is America Ser.). (Illus.). 224p. (J). (gr. 4-8). pap. 10.95 (978-0-590-38607-4(7)) Scholastic, Inc.

DICKENS, CHARLES, 1812-1870

Browne, Barber & Browne, Lee. Charles Dickens. (Illus.). 32p. (J). (978-0-237-51742-7(6) , Evans Brothers, Limited) Evans Publishing Group.

Caravantes, Peggy. Best of Times: The Story of Charles Dickens. 2005. (World Writers Ser.). (Illus.). 160p. (J). (gr. 3-7). lib. bdg. 26.95 (978-1-931798-68-6(0)) Reynolds, Morgan Inc.

Champion, Neil. Charles Dickens. 2001. (Creative Lives Ser.). (Illus.). 64p. (YA). (gr. 6-8). lib. bdg. 27.07 (978-1-58810-207-2(6)) Heinemann Library.

Chin, Mei & Bloom, Harold. Charles Dickens. 2nd rev. ed. 2006. (Bloom's Modern Critical Views Ser.). 296p. (gr. 9). 45.00 (978-0-7910-8568-4(6) , Chelsea Hse.) Facts On File, Inc.

Dickens, Charles. A Christmas Carol. 2001. (CliffsComplete Ser.). 192p. (J). pap. 9.99 (978-0-7645-8722-1(6)) Wiley, John & Sons, Inc.

Orr, Tamra. Charles Dickens. 2006. (J). lib. bdg. (978-1-58415-456-3(X)) Mitchell Lane Pubs., Inc.

Rosen, Michael. Dickens: His Work & His World. Ingpen, Robert R., illus. 2005. 96p. (YA). (gr. 7-11). 19.99 (978-0-7636-2752-2(6)) Candlewick Pr.

A Tale of Two Cities: Novel Units. 1998. 40p. (YA). 9.95 (978-1-56137-432-8(6) , NU4326) Novel Units, Inc.

Williams, Brian. The Story Behind Charles Dickens' Oliver Twist. 2006. (History in Literature Ser.). (Illus.). 56p. (J). lib. bdg. (978-1-4034-8209-9(8)) Heinemann Library.

DICKENS, CHARLES, 1812-1870—CHARACTERS

Sweetser, Kate Dickinson. Ten Boys from Dickens. 2004. reprint ed. pap. 21.95 (978-1-4191-5096-8(0)); pap. 1.99 (978-1-4192-5096-5(5)) Kessinger Publishing, LLC.

—Ten Girls from Dickens. Williams, George Alfred, illus. 2004. reprint ed. pap. 27.95 (978-1-4179-3165-1(5)) Kessinger Publishing, LLC.

—Ten Girls from Dickens. 2004. reprint ed. pap. 1.99 (978-1-4192-5098-9(1)) Kessinger Publishing, LLC.

DICKENS, EDDIE (FICTITIOUS CHARACTER)—FICTION

Ardagh, Philip. Dreadful Acts. 2002. (Eddie Dickens Trilogy: Bk. 2). (Illus.). 144p. (J). (gr. 3-6). 5.99 (978-0-571-20947-7(5)) Faber & Faber, Inc.

—Dreadful Acts. Roberts, David, illus. 2003. (Eddie Dickens Trilogy: Bk. 2). 144p. (J). (gr. 4-9). 12.95 (978-0-8050-7155-9(5) , Holt, Henry & Co. Bks. For Young Readers) Holt, Henry & Co.

—Dreadful Acts. Roberts, David, illus. 2004. (Eddie Dickens Trilogy Ser.: Bk. 2). 144p. (J). reprint ed. mass mkt. 5.99 (978-0-439-53760-5(6)) Scholastic, Inc.

—A House Called Awful End. Roberts, David, illus. 2002. (Eddie Dickens Trilogy: Bk. 1). 144p. (J). (gr. 4-7). 14.95 (978-0-8050-6828-3(7) , Holt, Henry & Co. Bks. For Young Readers) Holt, Henry & Co.

—Terrible Times. Roberts, David, illus. 2003. (Eddie Dickens Trilogy: Bk. 3). 160p. (J). (gr. 3-6). 12.95 (978-0-8050-7156-6(3) , Holt, Henry & Co. Bks. For Young Readers) Holt, Henry & Co.

Ardagh, Philip, et al. A House Called Awful End. Roberts, David, illus. 2003. (Eddie Dickens Trilogy Ser.: Bk. 1). 144p. (J). (gr. 3-6). mass mkt. 5.99 (978-0-439-53759-9(2) , Scholastic Paperbacks) Scholastic, Inc.

DICKINSON, EMILY, 1830-1886

Bedard, Michael. Emily. Cooney, Barbara, illus. 2002. 40p. (J). (gr. k-3). pap. 6.99 (978-0-440-41740-8(6) , Dragonfly Bks.) Random Hse. Children's Bks.

Daly, Mary, ed. & illus. Into Deep Eternity: An Introduction to Emily Dickinson. Daly, Mary, illus. 2001. 110p. (YA). per. 20.00 (978-0-9723239-1-8(0)) Ye Hedge Schl.

Dommermuth-Costa, Carol. Emily Dickinson: Singular Poet. 1998. (Lerner Biographies Ser.). (Illus.). 128p. (gr. 6-12). lib. bdg. 27.93 (978-0-8225-4958-1(1)) Lerner Publishing Group.

Griskey, Michele. Emily Dickinson. 2006. (Poets & Playwrights Ser.). (Illus.). 112p. (YA). (gr. 6-12). lib. bdg. 37.10 (978-1-58415-429-7(2)) Mitchell Lane Pubs., Inc.

Herstek, Amy Paulson. Emily Dickinson: Solitary & Celebrated Poet. 2003. (Historical American Biographies Ser.). (Illus.). 128p. (J). lib. bdg. 26.60 (978-0-7660-1977-5(2)) Enslow Pubs., Inc.

McChesney, Sandra. Emily Dickinson. 2003. (gr. 7-12). lib. bdg. 21.05 (978-0-613-57178-4(9)) Tandem Library Bks.

McChesney, Sandra, ed. Emily Dickinson. 2003. (Bloom's Bio Critiques Ser.). (Illus.). 128p. (gr. 9-13). pap. 35.00 (978-0-7910-7112-0(X) , Chelsea Hse.) Facts On File, Inc.

Meltzer, Milton. Emily Dickinson: A Biography. 2006. (American Literary Greats Ser.). 128p. (YA). (gr. 7 up). lib. bdg. 31.93 (978-0-7613-2949-7(8) , Millbrook Pr.) Lerner Publishing Group.

Priddy, Anna. Bloom's How to Write about Emily Dickinson. 2007. (Bloom's How to Write about Literature Ser.). 256p. (YA). (gr. 9 up). 45.00 (***978-0-7910-9492-1(8)*** , Chelsea Hse.) Facts On File, Inc.

Winter, Jeanette. Emily Dickinson's Letters to the World. Winter, Jeanette, illus. 2002. (Illus.). 40p. (J). (gr. 2-5). 16.00 (978-0-374-32147-5(7) , Farrar, Straus & Giroux (BYR)) Farrar, Straus & Giroux.

DICTATORS

Dowswell, Paul. Dictatorship. 2005. (Systems of Government Ser.). (Illus.). 48p. (J). pap. (978-0-8368-5889-1(1)); lib. bdg. 30.00 (978-0-8368-5884-6(0)) Stevens, Gareth Inc. (World Almanac Library).

Ruby, India. Tres dictadores del siglo XX & Three Twentieth Century Dictators. 2005. spiral bd. 88.00 (***978-1-4108-5739-2(5)***) Benchmark Education Co.

Scandiffio, Laura. Evil Masters: The Frightening World of Tyrants. 2005. (Illus.). 160p. (J). (gr. 7-12). 24.95 (978-1-55037-895-5(3)); pap. 12.95 (978-1-55037-894-8(5)) Annick Pr., Ltd. CAN. *Dist:* Firefly Bks., Ltd.

Tames, Richard & Downing, David. Dictatorship. 2003. (Political & Economic Systems Ser.). (Illus.). 64p. (YA). (gr. 6-8). lib. bdg. 28.50 (978-1-4034-0318-6(X)) Heinemann Library.

Thomson Gale Staff. Prejudice in the Modern World: Biographies. Hanes, Richard C. & Rudd, Kelly, eds. rev. ed. 2007. (Prejudice Throughout History Reference Library). 920p. (YA). 67.00 (978-1-4144-0207-9(4) , UXL) Thomson Gale.

DIET

see also Beverages; Cookery; Digestion; Food; Menus; Vegetarianism; Weight Control

Ballard, Carol. Special Diets & Food Allergies. 2006. (Making Healthy Food Choices Ser.). (Illus.). 56p. (J). (978-1-4034-8572-4(0)) Heinemann Library.

Benduhn, Tea. Fruit: Fruta. 2007. (SPA & ENG.). (J). pap. (***978-0-8368-8462-3(0)*** , Weekly Reader Early Learning Library) Stevens, Gareth Inc.

—Fruit/Fruta. 2007. (Find Out about Food/Conoce la Comida Ser.). (SPA & ENG.). 24p. (J). (gr. k-2). lib. bdg. 19.93 (***978-0-8368-8455-5(8)*** , Weekly Reader Early Learning Library) Stevens, Gareth Inc.

Boaz, Claire Kreger. Dieting. 2007. (Issues that Concern You Ser.). 144p. (gr. 7-10). 32.45 (***978-0-7377-3644-1(5)*** , Greenhaven Pr., Inc.) Thomson Gale.

Carol Ballard. Special Diets & Food Allergies. 2006. (Making Healthy Food Choices Ser.). (Illus.). 56p. (J). pap. (***978-1-4034-8578-6(X)***) Heinemann Library.

Constant. Diet. 2004. (Teen Issues Ser.). (Illus.). 56p. (J). 31.36 (978-1-4109-0610-6(8)); 56p. (J). pap. 8.95 (978-1-4109-0881-0(X)); Pk. 6. (YA). pap. 48.30 (978-1-4109-0888-9(7)) Harcourt Schl. Pubs.

Cruise, Jorge. The 3-Hour Diet for Teens: Lose Weight & Feel Great in Two Weeks! 2007. (Illus.). 85p. (YA). (gr. 7 up). pap. 15.99 (978-0-06-117143-7(3)) HarperCollins Pubs.

Dawson, Susan H. & Norton, Susan R. Pyramid Pal's Adventures in Eating: Eating Should Always Be Fun for a Kid, 7 vols., Set. O'Hare, Mark, illus. 2000. (Adventures in Eating with the Nutrition Champion of Kids Ser.). 140p. (J). pap. 22.50 (978-1-58000-070-3(3)) Griffin Publishing Group.

Deal, Darlene. Play with Your Food & Learn How to Eat Right: Nutritional Book about Fruits & Vegetables. 2004. (ENG & SPA., Illus.). 22p. (J). (gr. 1-4). pap. 9.95 (978-0-9747299-0-9(6)) Deal, Darlene.

Graham, Ian. Diet. 2006. (Illus.). 36p. (J). lib. bdg. 16.95 (978-1-59566-191-3(3)) QEB Publishing Inc.

Having a Healthy Baby - Diet & Nutrition. 2004. (YA). pap. 4.00 net. (978-1-930996-57-1(8)) Planned Parenthood Federation of America, Inc.

Hunt, Charles. The Perfect Diet: The Ultimate Weight Solution for Every Body. 2004. (978-0-9630377-2-5(2)) HeartQuake Publishing.

Leedy, Loreen. The Edible Pyramid: Good Eating Every Day. Leedy, Loreen, illus. rev. ed. (Illus.). 32p. (J). (gr. k-3). 17.95 (***978-0-8234-2074-2(4)***); 6.95 (***978-0-8234-2075-9(2)***) Holiday Hse., Inc.

Llewellyn, Claire. Estoy Sano? Aprender Sobre Alimentacion y Actividad Fisica. Gordon, Mike, illus. (SPA.). (J). (gr. k-2). pap. (978-950-24-0945-0(0)) Albatros ARG. *Dist:* Lectorum Pubns., Inc.

Longe, Jacqueline L. Gale Encyclopedia Diet. 2007. 360.00 (***978-1-4144-2991-5(6)***) Thomson Gale.

Naik, Anita. Eating. 2nd ed. 2005. (Illus.). 144p. (YA). pap. 12.00 (978-0-340-88393-8(6) , Hodder & Stoughton) Hodder General Publishing Division GBR. *Dist:* Trafalgar Square Publishing.

Olson, Karen W. Eat, Run & Live Healthy. Hamelin, Marie-Micheline, illus. 2006. 20p. (J). pap. 10.95 (978-1-894778-32-9(4)) Theytus Bks., Ltd. CAN. *Dist:* Orca Bk. Pubs. USA.

Randall, Ronne. What's So Good about Vegetables? 2003. (What? Where? Why? Ser.). (Illus.). 24p. (J). (gr. 1 up). lib. bdg. 20.67 (978-0-8368-3789-6(4)) Stevens, Gareth Inc.

Roberts, Jeremy. Drugs & Dieting. 2005. (Drug Abuse Prevention Library). (Illus.). 64p. (YA). (gr. 7-12). lib. bdg. 25.25 (978-0-8239-3357-0(1)) Rosen Publishing Group, Inc., The.

Ross, Veronica. Eating. 2002. (My Healthy Body Ser.). (Illus.). 32p. (J). lib. bdg. 24.25 (978-1-930643-83-3(7)) Chrysalis Education.

Simpson, Carolyn. Coping with Compulsive Eating. 1998. (Coping Skills Library). 96p. (YA). (gr. 7 up). reprint ed. pap. 6.95 (978-1-56838-215-9(4)) Hazelden Publishing & Educational Services.

Trumbauer, Lisa. Comiendo Bien. Ramos, Gloria, tr. 2005. (SPA., Illus.). 20p. (J). 15.93 (978-0-7368-4159-7(8) , Yellow Umbrella Bks.) Capstone Pr., Inc.

Turner, Keith. H Is for Healthy Diet: H Is for Hope Book Series, 1. 2007. (Illus.). 24p. (J). 8.00 (***978-0-9794377-1-7(7)***) Turngroup Technologies, LLC.

Westcott, Patsy. Diet & Nutrition. 2000. (Health & Fitness Ser.). (Illus.). 48p. (J). (gr. 4-6). lib. bdg. 27.12 (978-0-7398-1344-7(7)) Raintree.

DIETETICS

see Diet

DIGESTION

see also Diet; Food; Nutrition

Andrews, Barbara. Discover the Nervous & Digestive Systems. 2006. pap. 39.00 (***978-1-4108-6515-1(0)***) Benchmark Education Co.

Angliss, Sarah. The Food Processor: Digestive System. 1999. (Human Machine Ser.). (Illus.). 32p. (J). lib. bdg. 16.95 (978-1-929298-17-4(X)) Chrysalis Education.

Arnold, Nick & Saules, Tony de. Esa Repugnante Digestion. Saules, Tony de, tr. 2003. (Coleccion Esa Horrible Cienca). (SPA., Illus.). 156p. (YA). pap. (978-84-272-2057-7(X) , ML4090) Molino, Editorial ESP. *Dist:* Lectorum Pubns., Inc.

Avraham, Regina. Digestive System. 1999. (Twenty-First Century Health & Wellness Ser.). (Illus.). 100p. (J). (gr. 7 up). 16.00 (978-0-7910-5526-7(4) , Chelsea Hse.) Facts On File, Inc.

Ballard, Carol. The Digestive System. 2002. (Body Focus Ser.). (Illus.). 48p. (J). pap. (978-1-4034-0451-0(8)) Heinemann Library.

—The Stomach & Digestion. 2005. (Exploring the Human Body Ser.). (Illus.). 32p. (J). (gr. 4-7). lib. bdg. 24.95 (978-0-7377-3023-4(4) , Greenhaven Pr., Inc.) Thomson Gale.

Blevins, Wiley. Where Does Your Food Go? 2004. (Rookie Read-About Health Ser.). 31p. (J). (gr. k-2). pap. 5.95 (978-0-516-27854-4(1) , Children's Pr.) Scholastic Library Publishing.

Brynie, Faith Hickman. 101 Questions about Food & Digestion That Have Been Eating at You until Now. Holm, Sharon Lane, illus. 2002. (One Hundred One Questions... Ser.). 176p. (gr. 7 up). lib. bdg. 27.90 (978-0-7613-2309-9(0) , Twenty-First Century Bks.) Lerner Publishing Group.

Cho, Shinta. The Gas We Pass: The Story of Farts. Stinchecum, Amanda M., tr. 2004. (My Body Science Ser.). (Illus.). 28p. (J). (ps up). pap. 6.95 (978-1-929132-15-7(8)) Kane/Miller Bk. Pubs., Inc.

Corcoran, Mary K. The Quest to Digest. Czekaj, Jef, illus. 2006. 32p. (J). 16.95 (978-1-57091-664-9(0)); pap. 6.95 (978-1-57091-665-6(9)) Charlesbridge Publishing, Inc.

Creative Media Applications Staff. The Human Body & Environment: Digestive Systems, 4 vols., Vol. 3. 2003. (Middle School Reference Ser.). (Illus.). (J). (978-0-313-32561-8(8)) Greenwood Publishing Group, Inc.

Delaunois, Angele. The Fantastic Voyage of Senor Caca: El Viaje Fantastico de Senor Caca. Lafrance, Marie, illus. 2007. (SPA.). 24p. (J). 14.95 (***978-1-933693-07-1(X)***) Cinco Puntos Pr.

The Digestive System. (Human Body Systems Ser.). 24p. (J). 5.95 (978-0-7368-8777-9(6)) Capstone Pr., Inc.

Frost, Helen. The Digestive System. Saunders-Smith, Gail, ed. 2000. (Human Body Systems Ser.). (Illus.). 24p. (J). (gr. k-1). lib. bdg. 15.93 (978-0-7368-0649-7(0) , Pebble Bks.) Capstone Pr., Inc.

Ganeri, Anita. Your Digestive System. Shott, Steve, photos by. 2003. (How Your Body Works). (Illus.). 32p. (J). (gr. 2 up). lib. bdg. 23.33 (978-0-8368-3633-2(1)) Stevens, Gareth Inc.

Gordon, Sharon. My Stomach. 2004. (Bookworms Ser.). (ENG & SPA., Illus.). 31p. (J). 21.36 (978-0-7614-1782-8(6)) Cavendish, Marshall Corp.

Green, Jen. Digestion. 2005. (Illus.). 32p. (J). (gr. 4-7). lib. bdg. 27.10 (978-1-59604-057-1(2)) Stargazer Bks.

Houghton, Gillian. The Digestive System. 2007. (How Your Body Works). (Illus.). 24p. (J). pap. (978-1-4042-2179-6(4)); lib. bdg. (978-1-4042-3470-3(5)) Rosen Publishing Group, Inc., The. (PowerKids Pr.).

Jakab, Cheryl. The Digestive System. 2006. (Our Body Ser.). (Illus.). 32p. (J). (gr. 3-5). lib. bdg. 27.10 (978-1-58340-737-0(5)) Smart Apple Media.

Johnson, Rebecca L. Digestive System. 2005. (Illus.). 48p. (YA). pap. (978-0-8225-2519-6(4) , Lerner Pubns.) Lerner Publishing Group.

King, John E., ed. Guia de la Clinica Mayo Sobre Salud Digestiva. 2002. (Mayo Clinic on Health Ser.). (SPA.). 196p. lib. bdg. (978-1-59084-234-8(0)) Mason Crest Pubs.

LeapFrog Staff, compiled by. I Know Where My Food Goes. 2001. (J). (ps-1). spiral bd. 14.99 (978-1-58605-082-5(6)) LeapFrog Enterprises, Inc.

Libra, Anna. Why Does My Stomach Ache? An Inside Look at the Digestive System. 2003. (J). pap. (978-1-58417-068-6(9)) Lake Street Pubs.

Lindeen, Carol. My Stomach. 2007. 24p. (J). (***978-0-7368-6694-1(9)*** , Pebble Bks.) Capstone Pr., Inc.

Llamas, Andreu. Digestion & Reproduction. Rizo, Luis, illus. 1998. (Human Body Ser.). 32p. (J). (gr. 5 up). lib. bdg. 24.67 (978-0-8368-2111-6(4)) Stevens, Gareth Inc.

Llewellyn, Claire. Eating. 2004. (J). pap. 27.10 (978-1-58340-436-2(8)) Smart Apple Media.

Maurer, Tracy. Digestion. 1999. (Bodyworks Discovery Library). (Illus.). 24p. (J). (gr. 1-4). lib. bdg. 19.27 (978-0-86593-584-6(X)) Rourke Publishing, LLC.

McGregor, Emily. Enjoy Your Meal: What Happens When You Eat? 2008. (J). (***978-1-60044-603-0(5)***) Rourke Publishing, LLC.

Monroe, Judy. Coping with Ulcers, Heartburn & Stress-Related Stomach Disorders. 2005. (Coping Ser.). (Illus.). 192p. (YA). (gr. 7-12). lib. bdg. 26.50 (978-0-8239-2971-9(X) , COULCE) Rosen Publishing Group, Inc., The.

Morrison, Ben. The Digestive System. 2001. (Insider's Guide to the Body Ser.). (Illus.). 48p. (YA). (gr. 5-8). lib. bdg. 23.95 (978-0-8239-3337-2(7) , Rosen Central) Rosen Publishing Group, Inc., The.

Nardo, Don. Eating Disorders. 2003. (Understanding Issues Ser.). (Illus.). 48p. (J). (gr. 3-5). 26.20 (978-0-7377-1384-8(4) , Kidhaven) Thomson Gale.

Nettleton, Pamela Hill & Shipe, Becky. Gurgles & Growls: Learning about Your Stomach. 2004. (Amazing Body Ser.). (Illus.). 24p. (C). (gr. k-3). 22.60 (978-1-4048-0253-7(3)) Picture Window Bks.

Parker, Steve. Break It Down! The Digestive System. 2006. (Illus.). 48p. (J). pap. (978-1-4109-1886-4(6)); lib. bdg. (978-1-4109-1879-6(3)) Steck-Vaughn.

—Digestion. 2004. (Our Bodies Ser.). (Illus.). 48p. (J). lib. bdg. 28.56 (978-0-7398-6620-7(6)) Raintree.

Petrie, Kristin. The Digestive System. 2007. (Checkerboard Science Library). (Illus.). 32p. (J). 22.78 (978-1-59679-710-9(X)) ABDO Publishing Co.

Rau, Dana Meachen. El Estomago. 2006. (Bookworms Ser.). (SPA & ENG., Illus.). 32p. (J). lib. bdg. 22.79 (978-0-7614-2407-9(5)) Cavendish, Marshall Corp.

—My Stomach (El Estomago) 2006. (Bookworms Ser.). (ENG & SPA., Illus.). 32p. (J). lib. bdg. 22.79 (978-0-7614-2485-7(7)) Cavendish, Marshall Corp.

Rosewarne, Graham, illus. The Food Processor. 1999. (J). (978-0-382-42180-8(9)) Cobblestone Publishing Co.

Royston. Eating. 2004. (My Amazing Body Ser.). (Illus.). pap. 7.50 (978-1-4109-0949-7(2)) Raintree.

Royston, Angela. Eating. 2004. (My Amazing Body Ser.). (Illus.). 32p. (J). 25.70 (978-1-4109-0480-5(6)) Raintree.

—Why Do I Vomit? And Other Questions about Digestion. 2003. (Body Matters Ser.). (Illus.). 32p. (J). (gr. 3-5). lib. bdg. 24.22 (978-1-4034-0206-6(X)); pap. 7.50 (978-1-4034-0461-9(5)) Heinemann Library.

Sheps, Sheldon G., ed. Mayo Clinic on Digestive Health: Enjoy Better Digestion with Answers to More Than 12 Common Conditions. 2002. (Mayo Clinic on Health Ser.). (Illus.). 178,248p. (YA). (gr. 8 up). lib. bdg. (978-1-59084-223-2(5)) Mason Crest Pubs.

Showers, Paul. What Happens to a Hamburger? Rockwell, Anne F. & Miller, Edward, illus. 2001. (Let's-Read-and-Find-Out Science Ser.). 40p. (J). (gr. k-4). 15.95 (978-0-06-027947-9(8)); 15.89 (978-0-06-027948-6(6)) HarperCollins Pubs.

—What Happens to a Hamburger? Miller, Edward, illus. 2001. (Let's-Read-and-Find-Out Science Ser.). 40p. (J). (ps-ps). pap., pap. 5.99 (978-0-06-445183-3(6) , Harper Trophy) HarperCollins Pubs.

—What Happens to a Hamburger? Miller, Edward, illus. 2001. 33p. (J). (ps-ps). lib. bdg. 13.00 (978-0-613-36026-5(5)) Tandem Library Bks.

Silverstein, Alvin. Stomachaches. 2003. (gr. 3-6). lib. bdg. 15.25 (978-0-613-67935-0(0)) Tandem Library Bks.

Silverstein, Alvin, et al. Stomachaches. 2003. (My Health Ser.). 48p. 25.50 (978-0-531-12192-4(5) , Watts, Franklin) Scholastic Library Publishing.

Simon, Seymour. Guts: Our Digestive System. 2005. (Illus.). 32p. (J). lib. bdg. 17.89 (978-0-06-054652-6(2)); 16.99 (978-0-06-054651-9(4)) HarperCollins Pubs.

Stille, Darlene R. The Digestive System. 1998. (True Bks.). (Illus.). 48p. (J). (gr. 3-5). pap. 6.95 (978-0-516-26262-8(9) , Children's Pr.) Scholastic Library Publishing.

Sullivan, Robert J. Digestion & Nutrition. 2004. (Your Body, How It Works). (Illus.). 112p. (gr. 9-13). 31.95 (978-0-7910-7739-9(X) , Chelsea Hse.) Facts On File, Inc.

Swanson, Diane. Burp! The Most Interesting Book You'll Ever Read about Eating. Cowles, Rose, illus. 2004. (Mysterious You Ser.). 40p. (J). (gr. 4-6). (978-1-55074-601-3(4)); (978-1-55074-599-3(9)) Kids Can Pr., Ltd.

—Burp! The Most Interesting Book You'll Ever Read about Eating. 2001. (Illus.). (J). 13.75 (978-0-606-21092-8(X)) Tandem Library Bks.

—Burp! The Most Interesting Book You'll Ever Read about Eating. 2001. (gr. 3-6). lib. bdg. 15.25 (978-0-613-36243-6(8)) Tandem Library Bks.

Taylor-Butler, Christine. The Digestive System. 2007. (True Booktrade;: Health & the Human Body Ser.). 48p. (J). spiral bd. 26.00 (*978-0-531-16857-8(3), Children's Pr.) Scholastic Library Publishing.

Thames, Susan. Our Digestion System. 2008. (J). (*978-1-60044-510-1(1)) Rourke Publishing, LLC.

Toriello, James. The Stomach: Learning How We Digest. 2002. (3-D Library of the Human Body). (Illus.). 48p. (YA). (gr. 5-8). lib. bdg. 26.50 (978-0-8239-3536-9(1), Rosen Central) Rosen Publishing Group, Inc., The.

Vv. Nuestro Sistema Digestivo. (SPA.). 96p. (J). 10.00 (978-84-342-1807-9(0)) Parramon Ediciones S.A. ESP. *Dist:* Distribuidora Norma, Inc.

World Book, Inc Staff, contrib. by. The Digestive System/ The Urinary System. 2006. (World Book's Human Body Works). (Illus.). 48p. (J). (978-0-7166-4429-3(0)) World Bk., Inc.

Ylvisaker, Anne. Your Stomach. 2002. (Bridgestone Science Library). (Illus.). 24p. (J). (gr. 1-2). lib. bdg. 18.60 (978-0-7368-1151-4(6), Bridgestone Bks.) Capstone Pr., Inc.

Your Stomach. (Your Body Ser.). 24p. (J). 6.95 (978-0-7368-3355-4(2)) Capstone Pr., Inc.

DIGIMON (FICTITIOUS CHARACTERS)—FICTION

Bright, J. E. Digimon No. 3: Andromon's Attack. 2000. (Digimon Ser.: No. 3). 96p. (gr. 4-7). pap. 4.50 (978-0-06-107188-1(9), Harper Entertainment) HarperCollins Pubs.

—The Quest for Crests. 2001. (Digimon Ser.). (Illus.). 96p. (J). (gr. 1-4). pap. 4.50 (978-0-06-107199-7(4), Harper Entertainment) HarperCollins Pubs.

—Return to Infinity Mountain. 2000. (Digimon Ser.). 144p. (J). (gr. 1-4). pap. 8.95 (978-0-06-107196-6(X), Harper Entertainment) HarperCollins Pubs.

Digital Monster Madness. 1999. (Digimon 8x8 Storybooks Ser.). (Illus.). 24p. (J). (ps-2). pap. (978-0-7666-0554-1(X)) Modern Publishing.

Dobbyn, Nigel, et al. Digimon: Adventures in the Digital World. 2001. 88p. (YA). (gr. 4-7). pap. 9.95 (978-1-56971-532-1(7)) Dark Horse Comics.

HarperEntertainment Staff, contrib. by. Map of File Island. 2000. (Digimon Ser.). (J). (gr. 1-6). pap. 7.95 (978-0-06-107194-2(3), Harper Entertainment) HarperCollins Pubs.

Hongo, Akiyoshi. Digimon, 5, 3. Sheh, Stephanie, tr. rev. ed. 2003. (Illus.). 164p. (gr. 2 up). pap. 9.99 (978-1-59182-158-8(4)) TOKYOPOP, Inc.

—Digimon, 5 vols., Vol. 1. Yuen Wong Yu, illus. 2003. 164p. (gr. 2 up). pap. 9.99 (978-1-59182-076-5(6)) TOKYOPOP, Inc.

—Digimon, 5 vols., Vol. 4. 4th rev. ed. 2003. (Illus.). 164p. (gr. 2 up). pap. 9.99 (978-1-59182-159-5(2)) TOKYOPOP, Inc.

Nerz, A. Ryan. Invasion of the Black Gears! 2000. (Digimon Ser.: No. 2). (Illus.). 96p. (J). (gr. 4-7). pap. 4.50 (978-0-06-107187-4(0), Harper Entertainment) HarperCollins Pubs.

Next Stop... Digiworld. 1999. (Digimon 8x8 Storybooks Ser.). (Illus.). 24p. (J). (ps-2). pap. (978-0-7666-0553-4(1)) Modern Publishing.

Sullivan, Michael J. The Ultimate Adventures New Digidestined, 2. 2001. (Digimon Ser.). 96p. (J). (gr. 4-7). pap. 4.50 (978-0-06-107206-2(0), Harper Entertainment) HarperCollins Pubs.

Whitman, John. Adventures on File Island. 2000. (Digimon Ser.: No. 1). (Illus.). 96p. (J). (gr. 4-7). pap. 4.50 (978-0-06-107186-7(2), Harper Entertainment) HarperCollins Pubs.

—Legend Digidestined. 2001. (Digimon Ser.). (Illus.). 96p. (J). (gr. 4-7). pap. 4.50 (978-0-06-107198-0(6), Harper Entertainment) HarperCollins Pubs.

—Leomon's Challenge. 2000. (Digimon Ser.: No. 4). 96p. (J). (gr. 1-6). pap. 4.50 (978-0-06-107189-8(7), Harper Entertainment) HarperCollins Pubs.

Yo, Yuen Wong, illus. Digimon: Digital Monsters, 5 vols., Vol. 5. rev. ed. 2003. 164p. pap. 9.99 (978-1-59182-160-1(6)) TOKYOPOP, Inc.

Yu, Yuen Wong. Digimon, 5 vols., Vol. 2. rev. ed. 2003. (Illus.). 164p. (gr. 2 up). pap. 9.99 (978-1-59182-090-1(1)) TOKYOPOP, Inc.

DIGIMON (GAME)

Arnold, J. Douglas, et al. Digimon Cards! Player's & Collector's Guide. 2000. (Illus.). 144p. (J). pap. 12.95 (978-1-884364-52-5(7)) Sandwich Islands Publishing.

Schlesinger, Hank. Digimon Power. 2000. (J). 71.88 (978-0-312-97652-1(6), St. Martin's Paperbacks) St. Martin's Pr.

Triumph Books Staff. Total Digimon. 2000. (Illus.). 112p. (J). (ps-3). pap. 12.95 (978-1-57243-371-7(X)) Triumph Bks.

DIMAGGIO, JOE, 1914-1999

Dunn, Herb. Joe DiMaggio: Young Sports Hero. 1999. (Childhood of Famous Americans Ser.). (Illus.). 208p. (J). (gr. 3-7). mass mkt. 5.99 (978-0-689-83186-7(2), Aladdin) Simon & Schuster Children's Publishing.

—Joe DiMaggio: Young Sports Hero. 1999. 11.64 (978-0-606-17509-8(1)) Tandem Library Bks.

—Joe Dimaggio: Young Sports Hero. 1999. (gr. 3-6). lib. bdg. 13.00 (978-0-613-21813-9(2)) Tandem Library Bks.

Jensen, Luke. Joltin' Joe Baseball Hero: The Amazing True Story of Joe DiMaggio. 1999. (J). (978-0-606-18666-7(2)) Tandem Library Bks.

Viola, Kevin. Joe Dimaggio. 2006. (Sports Heroes & Legends Ser.). (Illus.). 106p. (J). (gr. 3-7). 27.93 (978-0-8225-3081-7(3), Lerner Pubns.) Lerner Publishing Group.

DINERS

see Restaurants

DINOSAURS

Acorn, John. Deep Alberta: Fossil Facts & Dinosaur Digs. 2007. (Illus.). 200 p. (YA). (gr. 7 up). pap. 26.95 (*978-0-88864-481-7(7)) Univ. of Alberta Pr. CAN. *Dist:* Michigan State Univ. Pr.

Adam, Winky. Little Dinosaur ABC Coloring Book. 1998. (Illus.). 64p. (J). pap. 1.50 (978-0-486-40301-4(7)) Dover Pubns., Inc.

Adams, Pam, illus. Diplodocus. 2002. 12p. (J). 4.99 (978-0-85953-114-6(7)) Child's Play-International.

—Stegosaurus. 2002. 12p. (J). 4.99 (978-0-85953-113-9(9)) Child's Play-International.

—Triceratops. 2002. 12p. (J). 4.99 (978-0-85953-115-3(5)) Child's Play-International.

—Tyrannosaurus. 2002. 12p. (J). 4.99 (978-0-85953-112-2(0)) Child's Play-International.

Advantage Publishers Group & Beck, Paul. 3D Paint by Number Dinosaurs. 2006. (3-D Paint by Numbers Ser.). (Illus.). 40p. (J). 17.95 (978-1-59223-462-2(3), Silver Dolphin Bks.) Advantage Pubs. Group.

After the Dinosaurs: Level P, 6 vols. (Wonder Worldtm Ser.). 48p. 39.95 (978-0-7802-7084-8(3)) Wright Group, The.

The Age of Dinosaurs. 2004. (Sticker Timelines Ser.). (Illus.). 12p. (J). pap. (978-1-84229-843-5(7)) Top That! Publishing PLC.

Aliki. Digging up Dinosaurs. 33p. (J). (gr. 1-3). pap. 4.95 (978-0-8072-1339-1(X), Listening Library) Random Hse. Audio Publishing Group.

Allosaurus. (Dinosaurs & Prehistoric Animals Ser.). 24p. (J). 6.95 (978-0-7368-5104-6(6)) Capstone Pr., Inc.

American Education Publishing Staff & School Specialty Publishing Staff. Dinosaurs: 54 Cards. 2001. (Brighter Child Fact Card Ser.). (Illus.). 54p. (J). (-5). 2.99 (978-1-56189-685-1(3), 31381, American Education Publishing) School Specialty Publishing.

Amery, Heather. Dinosaurs. 2007. (Up Close Ser.). (Illus.). 24p. (J). (gr. 3-5). lib. bdg. 23.95 (*978-1-4042-3759-9(3), PowerKids Pr.) Rosen Publishing Group, Inc., The.

Amery, Heather. 3D Dinosaurs. 2001. (Illus.). 16p. (J). pap. (978-1-84193-006-0(7)) Arcturus Publishing.

Ankylosaurus. (Discovering Dinosaurs Ser.). 24p. (J). 6.95 (978-0-7368-3463-6(X)) Capstone Pr., Inc.

Armentrout, David & Armentrout, Patricia. Dinosaurs. 2003. (50 Words about Ser.). (Illus.). 32p. (gr. 2-4). 19.95 (978-1-58952-342-5(3)) Rourke Publishing, LLC.

Arnold, Caroline. Pterosaurs: Rulers of the Skies in the Dinosaur Age. Caple, Laurie A., illus. 2004. 40p. (J). (gr. 4-6). tchr. ed. 16.00 (978-0-618-31354-9(0), Clarion Bks.) Houghton Mifflin Co. Trade & Reference Div.

Ashby, Ruth. My Favorite Dinosaurs. Sibbick, John, illus. 2005. 32p. (J). (gr. 1-3). 16.95 (978-0-689-03921-8(2)) ibooks, Inc.

—Pteranodon: The Life Story of a Pterosaur. Wilson, Phil, illus. 2005. 32p. (J). (gr. k-4). 14.95 (978-0-8109-5778-7(7)) Abrams, Harry N., Inc.

Asimov, Isaac & Hantula, Richard. What Killed the Dinosaurs? 2004. (Isaac Asimov's 21st Century Library of the Universe). (Illus.). 32p. (J). lib. bdg. 24.67 (978-0-8368-3955-5(2)) Stevens, Gareth Inc.

Aylmore, Angela. I Like Dinosaurs. 2007. (Illus.). 24p. (J). (978-1-4034-9273-9(5)); lib. bdg. 21.36 (978-1-4034-9264-7(6)) Heinemann Library.

Bailer, Darice. Dinomite! All about Dinisaurs. 2006. (Illus.). 32p. (J). (*978-0-439-83862-7(2)) Scholastic, Inc.

Bailey, Jacqui. The Day of the Dinosaurs, 4 vols., Vol. 3. Lilly, Matthew, illus. 2001. (Cartoon History of the Earth Ser.). 32p. (J). (gr. 4-6). (978-1-55337-082-6(1)); (978-1-55337-073-4(2)) Kids Can Pr., Ltd.

—Monster Bones: The Story of a Dinosaur Fossil. Lilly, Matthew, illus. 2004. (Science Works Ser.). 32p. (J). (gr. 3-6). 23.93 (978-1-4048-0565-1(6)) Picture Window Bks.

Bakker, Robert T. Dinosaurs! Rey, Luis V., illus. 2005. (Random House Pictureback Reader Ser.). 24p. (J). (ps-2). pap. 3.99 (978-0-375-83141-6(X)); lib. bdg. 8.99 (978-0-375-93141-3(4)) Random Hse. Children's Bks. (Random Hse. Bks. for Young Readers).

—Raptor Pack. Skrepnick, Michael William, illus. 2003. (Step into Reading Ser.). 48p. (J). (gr. 2-4). 3.99 (978-0-375-82303-9(4)); lib. bdg. 11.99 (978-0-375-92303-6(9)) Random Hse. Children's Bks. (Random Hse. Bks. for Young Readers).

Balloon Dinosaurs. 2004. (Formula Fun Ser.). (Illus.). 48p. (J). pap. (978-1-84229-876-3(3)) Top That! Publishing PLC.

Barner, Bob. Dinosaur Bones. 2001. (Illus.). 36p. (J). (ps-3). 15.95 (978-0-8118-3158-1(2)) Chronicle Bks. LLC.

—Dinosaur Bones. Barner, Bob, illus. unabr. ed. 2006. (J). (ps-2). 24.95 incl. audio (*978-0-439-90574-9(5)); 29.95 incl. audio compact disk (*978-0-439-90580-0(X)) Weston Woods Studios, Inc.

Barnett, Michelle Noble, et al. Theme Pockets - May: Cinco de Mayo; Dinosaurs; Plants. Evans, Marilyn, ed. Larsen, Jo, illus. 1999. (Making Books with Pockets). 96p. (J). pap., tchr. ed. 12.99 (978-1-55799-702-9(0), EMC 588) Evan-Moor Educational Pubs.

Barrett, Paul M., et al. National Geographic Dinosaurs. Martin, Raoul, illus. 2001. 192p. (J). (gr. 5-9). 29.95 (978-0-7922-8224-2(8), National Geographic Children's Bks.) National Geographic Society.

Baugh, Bryan. 50 Nifty Dinosaurs to Draw. 1999. (Fifty Nifty Ser.). (Illus.). 96p. (J). (gr. 2-6). pap. 6.95 (978-0-7373-0198-4(8), 01988W) McGraw-Hill/Contemporary.

BBC Wildlife Magazine Staff, Magazine Wildlife. Walking with Prehistoric Beasts: Photo Journal. 2001. (gr. k-3). lib. bdg. 15.25 (978-0-613-75134-6(5)) Tandem Library Bks.

Beall, Pamela Conn & Nipp, Susan Hagen. Wee Sing & Learn Dinosaurs. 2005. (Wee Sing & Learn Ser.). 20p. (J). (ps). 9.99 (978-0-8431-1664-9(1), Price Stern Sloan) Penguin Group (USA) Inc.

Benchmark Education Staff. Dinosaurs. 2005. 2.00 (*978-1-4108-4662-4(8)) Benchmark Education Co.

Bennett, Leonie. Amazing Dinosaur Facts. 2008. (J). lib. bdg. (*978-1-59716-546-4(8)) Bearport Publishing Co., Inc.

—Dinosaur Babies. 2008. (J). lib. bdg. (*978-1-59716-544-0(1)) Bearport Publishing Co., Inc.

—Dinosaur Fossils. 2008. (J). lib. bdg. (*978-1-59716-555-6(7)) Bearport Publishing Co., Inc.

—Dinosaur Hunting. 2008. (I Love Reading Ser.). (J). lib. bdg. 19.96 (*978-1-59716-554-9(9)) Bearport Publishing Co., Inc.

—Dinosaurs that Ate Meat. 2006. (I Love Reading Ser.). (Illus.). 24p. (J). lib. bdg. 19.96 (978-1-59716-151-0(9)) Bearport Publishing Co., Inc.

—Dinosaurs that Ate Plants. 2006. (I Love Reading Ser.). (Illus.), 24p. (J). lib. bdg. 19.96 (978-1-59716-152-7(7)) Bearport Publishing Co., Inc.

Bentley, Dawn. Dinosaur Adventure: Facts & Fun! Wilson, Phil, illus. 2001. (J). (ps-3). pap. 19.95 incl. VHS (978-1-58117-116-7(1), Intervisual/Piggy Toes) Dalmatian Pr.

—Dinosaur & More Travel Pack. Carr, Karent, illus. rev. ed. 2006. 60p. (J). 12.95 (978-1-59069-487-9(2)) Soundprints.

Benton, M. J. Dinosaurs. 1998. (Single Subject References Ser.). (Illus.). 64p. (J). (gr. 5-9). tchr. ed. 16.95 (978-0-7534-5131-1(X), Kingfisher) Houghton Mifflin Co. Trade & Reference Div.

—The Great Book of Dinosaurs. 2004. (Illus.). 128p. (YA). (978-1-904516-08-8(4)) Chrysalis Children's Bks.

—The World of Dinosaurs. 2004. (World Of Ser.). (Illus.). 64p. (J). (gr. 4-6). pap. 8.95 (978-0-7534-5785-6(7), Kingfisher) Houghton Mifflin Co. Trade & Reference Div.

Benton, Michael. Deinonychus - Dinoclub. 2000. (SPA.). (gr. 3-6). lib. bdg. 12.90 (978-0-613-83020-1(2)) Tandem Library Bks.

—Flying Monsters. (Illus.). 32p. (YA). (gr. 3 up). lib. bdg. 27.10 (978-1-932333-61-9(4)) Chrysalis Education.

—Mighty Giants. (Illus.). 32p. (YA). (gr. 3 up). lib. bdg. 27.10 (978-1-932333-58-9(4)) Chrysalis Education.

Benton, Michael J. Dinosaurios y Otros Animales Prehistoricos de la A a la Z. 2003. (SPA., Illus.). 256p. (J). (gr. 4-6). pap. 11.95 (978-970-607-302-0(7)) Larousse, Ediciones, S. A. de C. V. MEX. *Dist:* Houghton Mifflin Co. Trade & Reference Div.

Beres, Samantha & Fischman, Josh. 101 Things Every Kid Should Know about Dinosaurs. 2000. (Illus.). 128p. (J). (gr. 3-7). pap. 9.95 (978-0-7373-0496-1(0)) Lowell Hse. Juvenile.

Beres, Samantha, et al. 101 Things Every Kid Should Know about Dinosaurs. 2000. (Illus.). 128p. (J). (gr. 3-7). 14.95 (978-0-7373-0518-0(5)) Lowell Hse. Juvenile.

Bergen. Triceratops. 1999. (Prehistoric Creatures Then & Now Ser.). (Illus.). pap. 7.20 (978-0-7398-2148-0(2)) Steck-Vaughn.

Bergen, David. Life-Size Dinosaurs. 2004. (Life-Size Ser.). (Illus.). 28p. (J). 9.95 (978-1-4027-1775-8(X)) Sterling Publishing Co., Inc.

Bergen, Lara Rice. Triceratops. 2000. (Prehistoric Creatures Then & Now Ser.). (Illus.). 32p. (J). (ps-3). lib. bdg. 22.83 (978-0-7398-0103-1(1)) Raintree.

Berger, Melvin. Did Dinosaurs Live in Your Backyard? 1999. (Question & Answer Ser.). (J). 12.75 (978-0-606-20053-0(3)) Tandem Library Bks.

Berger, Melvin & Berger, Gilda. Did Dinosaurs Live in Your Backyard? Male, Alan, illus. 1999. (Scholastic Question & Answer Ser.). 48p. (J). (gr. 2-4). pap. 12.95 (978-0-590-13078-3(1), Scholastic Reference) Scholastic, Inc.

—Did Dinosaurs Live in Your Backyard? Questions & Answers about Dinosaurs. Male, Alan, illus. 1999. (Scholastic Question & Answer Ser.). 48p. (J). (gr. 2-4). 5.95 (978-0-439-08568-7(3), Scholastic Reference) Scholastic, Inc.

—Why Did the Dinosaurs Disappear? The Great Dinosaur Mystery. Harrison, Susan J., illus. 1999. (Discovery Readers Ser.). 48p. (YA). (gr. 4-7). lib. bdg. 17.55 (978-0-7910-5074-3(2), Chelsea Hse.) Facts On File, Inc.

Berkowitz, Jacob. Jurassic Poop: What Dinosaurs (And Others) Left Behind. 2006. (Illus.). 40p. (J). (978-1-55337-860-0(1)) Kids Can Pr., Ltd.

—Jurassic Poop: What Dinosaurs (And Others) Left Behind. Mack, Steve, illus. 2006. 40p. (978-1-55337-867-9(9)) Kids Can Pr., Ltd.

Bernstein, Rosemary R. & Shepherd, Annis M. Kid's Solve World's Great Dinosaur Mysteries: An Interdisciplinary Unit for 4th to 8th Grade Students. 2001. (Kid's Solve World Great... Mysteries Ser.). ring bd. 30.00 (978-0-9713992-0-4(4)) Academic Power Ctr.

Bertch, David P. & Bertch, Barbara A. The Dynamic Dinosaur of Faith's History Vol. I: From Christ to 1000 AD. Martin, Terry & Martin, Dyna, eds. Hopper, Billy, illus. (Roots of the Past Ser.: Bk. 1). 150p. (J). (gr. 6). stu. ed. 9.95 (978-0-9634472-4-1(6)) Good Works Pr.

BHB International Staff. Dinosaurs. 1998. (Our Animal World in Pictures Ser.). (J). (978-2-215-06172-4(3)) Editions Fleurus.

Bicknell, Joanna & Pountney, Beth. Bedtime Buddy: Roarasaurus Loves Buddies. 2005. (Illus.). 8p. (J). (ps-k). 9.95 (978-1-84610-017-8(8)) Make Believe Ideas GBR. *Dist:* Ingram Pub. Services.

—Bedtime Buddy: Snugglesaurus Loves Cuddles. 2005. (Illus.). 8p. (J). (ps-k). 9.95 (978-1-84610-018-5(6)) Make Believe Ideas GBR. *Dist:* Ingram Pub. Services.

Bilgrami, Shaheen. A Magic Skeleton Book: Amazing Dinosaur Discovery. Tamblin, Treve & Phillips, Mike, illus. 2002. (Magic Color Bks.). 24p. (J). (ps-2). 9.95 (978-0-8069-8591-6(7)) Sterling Publishing Co., Inc.

Bingham, Caroline. First Dinosaur Encyclopedia. 2006. (Illus.). 128p. (J). (gr. 2-5). 15.99 (978-0-7566-2539-9(4)) Dorling Kindersley Publishing, Inc.

Bingham, Jane. Escenas de la Prehistoria. 2004. (Titles in Spanish Ser.). (SPA.). 32p. (J). 8.95 (978-0-7460-6107-7(2), Usborne) EDC Publishing.

Birch, Robin. Bird-Footed Dinosaurs. 2002. (Chelsea Clubhouse Science Exploration Ser.). (Illus.). 32p. (gr. k-2). 23.00 (978-0-7910-6989-9(3), 104202, Chelsea Hse.) Facts On File, Inc.

—Bony-Skinned Dinosaurs. 2002. (Chelsea Clubhouse Science Exploration Ser.). (Illus.). 32p. (gr. k-2). 23.00 (978-0-7910-6990-5(7), Chelsea Hse.) Facts On File, Inc.

—Dinosaur World, 6 vols., Set. 2005. (Illus.). 32p. (gr. 2-4). pap. 138.00 (978-0-7910-7055-0(7), Chelsea Hse.) Facts On File, Inc.

—Hard-Headed Dinosaurs. 2002. (Chelsea Clubhouse Science Exploration Ser.). (Illus.). 32p. (gr. k-2). 23.00 (978-0-7910-7051-2(4), Chelsea Hse.) Facts On File, Inc.

—Long-Necked Dinosaurs. 2002. (Chelsea Clubhouse Science Exploration Ser.). (Illus.). 32p. (gr. k-2). 23.00 (978-0-7910-6988-2(5), Chelsea Hse.) Facts On File, Inc.

—Meat-Eating Dinosaurs. 2002. (Chelsea Clubhouse Science Exploration Ser.). (Illus.). 32p. (gr. k-2). 23.00 (978-0-7910-6987-5(7), Chelsea Hse.) Facts On File, Inc.

Bishop, Nic. Digging for Bird Dinosaurs: An Expedition to Madagascar. 2002. (Scientists in the Field Ser.). (Illus.). 48p. (J). (gr. 4-6). pap. 4.95 (978-0-618-19682-1(X)) Houghton Mifflin Co. Trade & Reference Div.

Black, Jessica L. Dinosaur Opposites. Ruminski, Jeff, illus. 2003. 10p. (J). (ps-1). bds. 10.95 (978-1-57332-230-0(X)) HighReach Learning, Inc.

—Dinosaurs Were We. Linke, Don, Jr., illus. l.t. ed. 2001. (Little Bks.). 8p. (J). (ps-1). pap. 10.95 (978-1-57332-188-4(5)); pap. 10.95 (978-1-57332-187-7(7)) HighReach Learning, Inc.

Bony Back. (Dinosaur World Ser.). 24p. (J). 7.95 (978-1-4048-0497-5(8)) Picture Window Bks.

Book Studio Staff, ed. Dinosaur Discovery Kit. 2007. 32p. (J). (gr. k-4). pap. 19.99 (978-0-7566-2915-1(2)) Dorling Kindersley Publishing, Inc.

Brachiosaurus. (Discovering Dinosaurs Ser.). 24p. (J). 6.95 (978-0-7368-3464-3(8)) Capstone Pr., Inc.

Brachiosaurus (Dinosaur Profiles) 2004. 11.20 (978-1-4103-0500-8(7), Blackbirch Pr., Inc.) Thomson Gale.

Bradley, Timothy J. The Care & Feeding of Dinosaurs. 2000. (All about Animals Ser.). (Illus.). 48p. (gr. 2-4). lib. bdg. 23.90 (978-0-7613-1305-2(2), Millbrook Pr.) Lerner Publishing Group.

Branley, Franklyn M. What Happened to the Dinosaurs? 2001. 24.75 (978-0-06-000343-2(X)) HarperCollins Pubs.

—What Happened to the Dinosaurs? Simont, Marc, illus. 2000. (Let's-Read-and-Find-Out Science Ser.). 32p. (J). (gr. k-4). 15.89 (978-0-690-04749-3(5)) HarperCollins Pubs.

Brannon, Barbara. Discover Dinosaurs. 2005. 39.00 (*978-1-4108-5120-8(6)) Benchmark Education Co.

Brett-Surman, Michael K. & Holtz, Thomas. The World of Dinosaurs: A North American Selection. Gurney, James, illus. 1998. 48p. (J). (gr. 5-8). pap. 19.95 (978-0-86713-046-1(6)) Greenwich Workshop Pr.

Brighter Minds. 3-D Dinos! 2007. (Illus.). 15p. (J). 9.95 (978-1-57791-209-5(8)) Brighter Minds Children's Publishing.

Brighter Vision Publishing Staff. About Dinosaurs. (My Discovery Bks.). (Illus.). 20p. (J). (ps). 2000. pap. 2.95 (978-1-55254-207-1(6)); 1999. pap. 3.99 (978-1-55254-055-8(3)) Brighter Vision Pubns.

—Dinosaurs. 2000. (Learning Adventures Kindergarten Ser.). (Illus.). (J). (gr. k-1). pap. 2.25 (978-1-55254-147-0(9)) Brighter Vision Pubns.

Brighton, Catherine. The Fossil Girl: Mary Anning's Dinosaur Discovery. 1999. (Illus.). 32p. (gr. k-3). lib. bdg. 22.90 (978-0-7613-1468-4(7), Millbrook Pr.) Lerner Publishing Group.

Brilliant, Ken. Digital Dinosaurs. 2002. (Charles River Media Graphics Ser.). (Illus.). 375p. 49.95 (978-1-58450-209-8(6)) Charles River Media.

Brochu, Christopher A., et al. Dinosaurs. Brett-Surman, Michael K., ed. 2003. (Guides). (Illus.). 256-288p. pap. (978-1-877019-12-8(7)) Fog City Pr.

Brooks, Felicity. Dinosaurios. Litchfield, Jo, illus. 2004. (Titles in Spanish Ser.). (SPA.). 10p. (J). 4.95 (978-0-7460-6111-4(0), Usborne) EDC Publishing.

Brown, Charlotte Lewis. The Day the Dinosaurs Died. Wilson, Phil, illus. (I Can Read Bks.). 48p. (J). 2007. pap. 3.99 (*978-0-06-000530-6(0), Harper Trophy); 2006. 15.99 (978-0-06-000528-3(9)); 2006. lib. bdg. 16.89 (978-0-06-000529-0(7)) HarperCollins Pubs.

Brown, Susan. Dinosaurios/Dinosaurs. 2005. 80p. (J). per. 9.99 (978-1-59441-496-1(3), FI-704009) Carson-Dellosa Publishing Co., Inc.

Bryant-Mole, Karen. Dot-to-Dot Dinosaurs. 2005. 24p. (J). pap. 3.99 (978-0-7945-0491-5(4), Usborne) EDC Publishing.

Bulletpoints Dinosaurs up Close. 2005. (Illus.). (J). per. 4.99 (978-1-933581-02-6(6)) Byeway Bks.

Burnie, David. The Concise Dinosaur Encyclopedia. 2004. (Concise Ser.). (Illus.). 224p. (J). (gr. 4-8). 12.95 (978-0-7534-5754-2(7) , Kingfisher) Houghton Mifflin Co. Trade & Reference Div.

—The Kingfisher Illustrated Dinosaur Encyclopedia. 2001. (Kingfisher Encyclopedias Ser.). (Illus.). 224p. (J). (gr. 4-6). tchr. ed. 24.95 (978-0-7534-5287-5(1) , Kingfisher) Houghton Mifflin Co. Trade & Reference Div.

Butz, Steve. The Bone Race: A Quest for Dinosaur Fossils. 2007. 248p. (YA). pap. 16.95 (***978-1-933255-30-9(7))*** DNA Pr.

Calvetti, Leonello & Massini, Luca, illus. Brachiosaurus. 2004. 32p. (J). (gr. 2-4). 23.70 (978-1-4103-0327-1(6) , Blackbirch Pr., Inc.) Thomson Gale.

—Deinonychus. 2004. 32p. (J). (gr. 2-4). 23.70 (978-1-4103-0328-8(4) , Blackbirch Pr., Inc.) Thomson Gale.

—Edmontosaurus. 2004. 32p. (J). (gr. 2-4). 23.70 (978-1-4103-0329-5(2) , Blackbirch Pr., Inc.) Thomson Gale.

—Plateosaurus. 2007. (Dinosaur Profiles Ser.). 32p. (J). (gr. 2-6). 23.70 (***978-1-4103-0744-6(1)*** , Blackbirch Pr., Inc.) Thomson Gale.

—Scipionyx. 2004. (J). (gr. 2-4). 23.70 (978-1-4103-0334-9(9) , Blackbirch Pr., Inc.) Thomson Gale.

—Stegosaurus. 2004. 32p. (J). (gr. 2-4). 23.70 (978-1-4103-0330-1(6) , Blackbirch Pr., Inc.) Thomson Gale.

—Triceratops. 2004. 32p. (J). (gr. 2-4). 23.70 (978-1-4103-0331-8(4) , Blackbirch Pr., Inc.) Thomson Gale.

—Tyrannosaurus. 2004. 32p. (J). (gr. 2-4). 23.70 (978-1-4103-0332-5(2) , Blackbirch Pr., Inc.) Thomson Gale.

Canfield, Judy. How to Draw a Dinosaur. 2000. (gr. k-3). lib. bdg. 11.80 (978-0-613-29644-1(3)) Tandem Library Bks.

Carpenter, Elizabeth. Dinomaze: Colossal Fossil Maze Book. 2001. (Illus.). 50p. (J). (gr. 10 up). pap. 14.95 (978-0-7611-1275-4(8) , 11275) Workman Publishing Co., Inc.

Carpenter, Kenneth. The Carnivorous Dinosaurs. 2005. (Life of the Past Ser.). (Illus.). 352p. 49.95 (978-0-253-34539-4(1)) Indiana Univ. Pr.

Carr, Karen. Dinosaur Hunt: Texas - 115 Million Years Ago. Carr, Karen, illus. 2002. (Illus.). 48p. (J). (gr. 1 up). 17.99 (978-0-06-029703-9(4)) HarperCollins Pubs.

—My Dinosaur Book. 2007. (Illus.). 16p. (J). 5.99 (978-0-06-089949-3(2)) HarperCollins Pubs.

Casalis, Anna & Tempesta, Franco. Dinosaurs: The World of Dinosaurs with Lift-the-Flaps. 2002. (Illus.). 24p. (J). (ps-1). bds. 9.99 (978-0-689-85130-8(8) , Little Simon) Simon & Schuster Children's Publishing.

Caudipteryx (Dinosaur Profiles) 2004. 11.20 (978-1-4103-0499-5(X) , Blackbirch Pr., Inc.) Thomson Gale.

Chaikin, Andrew. When Dinosaurs Walked. Wynne, Patricia, illus. 2004. (Treasure Tree Ser.). 32p. (J). (978-0-7166-1607-8(6)) World Bk., Inc.

Chambers, Sally. Zippy Dinosaur: Diplodocus. 2000. (Illus.). 10p. (J). (ps-k). 6.95 (978-1-86233-178-5(2)) David & Charles Children's Bks. GBR. *Dist:* Sterling Publishing Co., Inc.

—Zippy Dinosaur: Stegosaurus. 2000. (Illus.). 10p. (J). (ps-k). 6.95 (978-1-86233-188-4(X)) David & Charles Children's Bks. GBR. *Dist:* Sterling Publishing Co., Inc.

—Zippy Dinosaur: Triceratops. 2000. (Illus.). 10p. (J). (ps-k). 6.95 (978-1-86233-193-8(6)) David & Charles Children's Bks. GBR. *Dist:* Sterling Publishing Co., Inc.

—Zippy Dinosaur: Tyrannosaurus Rex. 2000. (Illus.). 10p. (J). (ps-k). 6.95 (978-1-86233-183-9(9)) David & Charles Children's Bks. GBR. *Dist:* Sterling Publishing Co., Inc.

Chancellor, Deborah & Waddell, Martin. Dinosaurs. 2007. (I-read Ser.). (Illus.). 48p. pap. (***978-0-521-70488-5(X))*** Cambridge Univ. Pr.

Cheney, Martha C. Dinosaurs: A Science. Gorman, Linda & Siebert, Joanna, eds. Auckland, Jim, illus. 1999. (Gifted & Talented Ser.). 64p. (J). (gr. 1-3). pap., wbk. ed. 5.95 (978-0-7373-0054-3(X)) Lowell Hse. Juvenile.

Chin, Karen & Holmes, Thom. Dino Dung. Carr, Karen, illus. 2005. (Step into Reading Ser.: Vol. 5). 48p. (J). (gr. 2-5). pap. 3.99 (978-0-375-82702-0(1) , Random Hse. Bks. for Young Readers) Random Hse. Children's Bks.

—Dino Dung: The Scoop on Fossil Feces. Carr, Karen, illus. 2005. (Step into Reading Ser.). 48p. (J). (gr. 2-5). lib. bdg. 11.99 (978-0-375-92702-7(6) , Random Hse. Bks. for Young Readers) Random Hse. Children's Bks.

Ciencin, Scott. Dino Defenses. 2006. (Illus.). 32p. (J). pap. (***978-0-439-83871-9(1))*** Scholastic, Inc.

Clark, Neil & Lindsay, William. Dinosaurs. 2nd rev. ed. 2003. (DK Pockets Ser.). (Illus.). 160p. pap. 6.99 (978-0-7894-9589-1(9)) Dorling Kindersley Publishing, Inc.

Clark, Neil, et al. 1,001 Facts about Dinosaurs. Mugford, Simon, ed. 2002. (Backpack Book Ser.). (Illus.). 192p. (J). (gr. 8-3). pap. 8.99 (978-0-7894-8448-2(X)) Dorling Kindersley Publishing, Inc.

Clemson, Wendy & Clemson, David. Digging for Dinosuars. 2006. (J). pap. (***978-0-8368-8137-0(0));*** lib. bdg. (***978-0-8368-7838-7(8))*** Stevens, Gareth Inc.

Cohen, Daniel. Allosaurus. 2003. (Bridgestone Science Library). (Illus.). 24p. (J). (gr. 1-2). lib. bdg. 18.60 (978-0-7368-1618-2(6) , Bridgestone Bks.) Capstone Pr., Inc.

—Ankylosaurus. 2003. (Bridgestone Science Library). (Illus.). 108p. (J). (gr. 1-2). 18.60 (978-0-7368-1619-9(4) , Bridgestone Bks.) Capstone Pr., Inc.

—Apatosaurus. 2000. (Bridgestone Science Library). (Illus.). 108p. (J). (gr. 1-2). 18.60 (978-0-7368-0616-9(4) , Bridgestone Bks.) Capstone Pr., Inc.

—Brachiosaurus. 2003. (Bridgestone Science Library). (Illus.). 108p. (J). (gr. 1-2). 18.60 (978-0-7368-1620-5(8) , Bridgestone Bks.) Capstone Pr., Inc.

—The Bridgestone Science Library: Discovering Dinosaurs, 12 bks. Incl. Allosaurus. 24p. 2003. lib. bdg. 18.60 (978-0-7368-1618-2(6)); Ankylosaurus. 108p. 2003. 18.60 (978-0-7368-1619-9(4)); Apatosaurus. 108p. 2000. 18.60 (978-0-7368-0616-9(4)); Brachiosaurus. 108p. 2003. 18.60 (978-0-7368-1620-5(8)); Diplodocus. 108p. 2003. 18.60 (978-0-7368-1621-2(6)); Ichthyosaurus. 24p. 2003. lib. bdg. 18.60 (978-0-7368-1622-9(4)); Iguanodon. 108p. 2003. 18.60 (978-0-7368-1623-6(2)); Pteranodon. 108p. 2000. 18.60 (978-0-7368-0617-6(2)); Stegosaurus. 108p. 2000. 18.60 (978-0-7368-0618-3(0)); Triceratops. 108p. 2000. 18.60 (978-0-7368-0619-0(9)); Tyrannosaurus Rex. 108p. 2000. 18.60 (978-0-7368-0620-6(2)); Velociraptor. 108p. 2000. 18.60 (978-0-7368-0621-3(0)); (J). (gr. 1-2). (Illus.). Set lib. bdg. 223.20 (978-0-7368-1637-3(2) , Bridgestone Bks.) Capstone Pr., Inc.

—The Bridgestone Science Library - Discovering Dinosaurs: Apatosaurus; Pteranodon; Stegosaurus; Triceratops; Tyrannosaurus Rex; Velociraptor, 6 bks. 2000. (Illus.). (J). (gr. 1-2). lib. bdg. 111.60 (978-0-7368-0683-1(0) , Bridgestone Bks.) Capstone Pr., Inc.

—Dinosaurs of North America, 4 bks. Incl. Allosaurus & Other Jurassic Meat-Eaters. lib. bdg. 21.26 (978-1-56065-286-1(1)); Stegosaurus & Other Jurassic Plant-Eaters. lib. bdg. 21.26 (978-1-56065-287-8(X)); Triceratops & Other Cretaceous Plant-Eaters. lib. bdg. 21.26 (978-1-56065-289-2(6)); Tyrannosaurus Rex & Other Cretaceous Meat-Eaters. lib. bdg. 21.26 (978-1-56065-288-5(8)); 48p. (J). (gr. 3-4). 1996. (Illus.). Set lib. bdg. 85.04 (978-1-56065-641-8(7) , Capstone High-Interest Bks.) Capstone Pr., Inc.

—Diplodocus. 2003. (Bridgestone Science Library). (Illus.). 108p. (J). (gr. 1-2). 18.60 (978-0-7368-1621-2(6) , Bridgestone Bks.) Capstone Pr., Inc.

—Discovering Dinosaurs. (Illus.). (J). (gr. 2-3). lib. bdg. 382.68 (978-0-7368-2568-9(1)) Capstone Pr., Inc.

—Ichthyosaurus. 2003. (Bridgestone Science Library). (Illus.). 24p. (J). (gr. 1-2). lib. bdg. 18.60 (978-0-7368-1622-9(4) , Bridgestone Bks.) Capstone Pr., Inc.

—Iguanodon. 2003. (Bridgestone Science Library). (Illus.). 108p. (J). (gr. 1-2). 18.60 (978-0-7368-1623-6(2) , Bridgestone Bks.) Capstone Pr., Inc.

—Maiasaura. 2004. (Bridgestone Science Library). (Illus.). 24p. (J). 14.95 (978-0-7368-2522-1(3) , Bridgestone Bks.) Capstone Pr., Inc.

—Pachycephalosaurus. 2004. (Bridgestone Science Library). (Illus.). 24p. (J). 14.95 (978-0-7368-2523-8(1) , Bridgestone Bks.) Capstone Pr., Inc.

—Parasaurolophus. 2004. (Illus.). 108p. (J). 14.95 (978-0-7368-2524-5(X) , Bridgestone Bks.) Capstone Pr., Inc.

—Pteranodon. 2000. (Bridgestone Science Library). (Illus.). 108p. (J). (gr. 1-2). 18.60 (978-0-7368-0617-6(2) , Bridgestone Bks.) Capstone Pr., Inc.

—Spinosaurus. 2004. (Illus.). 24p. (J). 14.95 (978-0-7368-2526-9(6) , Bridgestone Bks.) Capstone Pr., Inc.

—Stegosaurus. 2000. (Bridgestone Science Library). (Illus.). 108p. (J). (gr. 1-2). 18.60 (978-0-7368-0618-3(0) , Bridgestone Bks.) Capstone Pr., Inc.

—Triceratops. 2000. (Bridgestone Science Library). (Illus.). 108p. (J). (gr. 1-2). 18.60 (978-0-7368-0619-0(9) , Bridgestone Bks.) Capstone Pr., Inc.

—Troodon. 2004. (Illus.). 24p. (J). 14.95 (978-0-7368-2527-6(4) , Bridgestone Bks.) Capstone Pr., Inc.

—Tyrannosaurus Rex. 2000. (Bridgestone Science Library). (Illus.). 108p. (J). (gr. 1-2). 18.60 (978-0-7368-0620-6(2) , Bridgestone Bks.) Capstone Pr., Inc.

—Velociraptor. 2000. (Bridgestone Science Library). (Illus.). 108p. (J). (gr. 1-2). 18.60 (978-0-7368-0621-3(0) , Bridgestone Bks.) Capstone Pr., Inc.

Cole, Stephen. Allosaurus! The Life & Death of Big Al. 2001. (J). (978-0-606-21023-2(7)) Tandem Library Bks.

—Allosaurus! the Life & Death of Big Al. 2001. (gr. 3-6). lib. bdg. 16.45 (978-0-613-72583-5(2)) Tandem Library Bks.

Cole, Stephen & Dorling Kindersley Publishing Staff. Walking with Dinosaurs: 3D Dinosaurs. 2000. (Illus.). 24p. (J). (gr. 4-7). pap. 11.99 (978-0-7894-5207-8(3)) Dorling Kindersley Publishing, Inc.

Cole, Steven Roger. How Big Is a Dinosaur? 2000. 24p. (J). pap. 4.95 (978-0-7894-5209-2(X)) Dorling Kindersley Publishing, Inc.

Color All About: A Giant Coloring Book about Dinosaurs: Dinosaurs. 2004. (SPA & ENG., Illus.). 36p. (J). (978-1-59949-001-4(3)) Food Marketing Consultants, Inc.

Conklin, Tom. Soar! All about Pterosaurs. 2006. (Illus.). 32p. (J). pap. (***978-0-439-83872-6(X))*** Scholastic, Inc.

Conway, Brian. My First Big Book of Questions & Answers: Dinosaurs. Wilson, Phil, illus. 2005. 10p. bds. 9.98 (978-0-7853-6778-9(0) , 7166900) Publications International, Ltd.

Cooley, Brian. Make-a-saurus: My Life with Raptors & Other Dinosaurs. 2000. (J). (978-0-606-20139-1(4)) Tandem Library Bks.

Cooley, Brian & Wilson, Mary Ann. Make-a-saurus: My Life with Raptors & Other Dinosaurs. Campbell, Gary, photos by. 2000. (Illus.). 64p. (J). (gr. 3-6). pap. 14.95 (978-1-55037-644-9(6)) Annick Pr., Ltd. CAN. *Dist:* Firefly Bks., Ltd.

Cooper, John. Dinosaurs. 2006. (Illus.). 24p. (YA). (gr. 1 up). lib. bdg. 22.80 (978-1-931983-58-7(5)) Chrysalis Education.

—Dinosaurs. Bergin, Mark, illus. 2002. (Scary Creatures Ser.). 32p. (J). (gr. 2-4). pap. 22.50 (978-0-531-14669-9(3)); pap. 6.95 (978-0-531-14851-8(3)) Scholastic Library Publishing. (Watts, Franklin).

—Dinosaurs. 2002. (gr. 3-6). lib. bdg. 15.25 (978-0-613-53599-1(5)) Tandem Library Bks.

Cooper, John A. Dinosaurs. 2003. (Knowledge Masters Ser.). (Illus.). 32p. (YA). pap. incl. cd-rom (978-1-903954-08-9(8)) Chrysalis Children's Bks.

Copyright Paperback Collection (Library of Congress) Staff, contrib. by. Dinosaurs. 2005. (Twenty4Sevens Ser.). (Illus.). 48p. (J). pap. (978-0-439-78526-6(X)) Scholastic, Inc.

Cosson, M. J. Troodon. 2007. (North American Dinosaurs Ser.). (Illus.). 24p. (J). (978-1-60044-254-4(4)) Rourke Publishing, LLC.

Court, Rob. How to Draw Dinosaurs. 2007. (Doodle Bks.). 32p. (J). 21.36 (***978-1-59296-806-0(6))*** Child's World, Inc.

Cox, Geoffrey & Wiffen, Joan. Dinosaur New Zealand. 2002. (Illus.). 39p. (J). pap. 19.95 (978-1-86950-404-5(6)) HarperCollins Pubs. New Zealand NZL. *Dist:* Antipodes Bks. & Beyond.

Currie, Phillip & Martin, Colleayan. The Newest & Coolest Dinosaurs. Sovak, Jan, illus. 1998. 32p. (J). (gr. 4-8). (978-1-895910-41-4(2)) Grasshopper Bks.

Cutchins, Judy & Johnston, Ginny. Dinosaurs of the South: Southern Fossil Discoveries. 2002. (Southern Fossil Discoveries Ser.: Vol. 3). (Illus.). 64p. (J). (gr. 3-7). 14.95 (978-1-56164-266-3(5)) Pineapple Pr., Inc.

Dahl, Michael. Bony Back: The Adventure of Stegosaurus. Yesh, Jeff, illus. 2004. (Dinosaur World Ser.). 24p. (C). (gr. k-3). 22.60 (978-1-4048-0135-6(9)) Picture Window Bks.

—Dinosaur World, 6 bks. Yesh, Jeff, illus. Incl. Bony Back : The Adventure of Stegosaurus. 22.60 (978-1-4048-0135-6(9)); Long-Neck : The Adventure of Apatosaurus. 22.60 (978-1-4048-0134-9(0)); Swift Thief : The Adventure of Velociraptor. 22.60 (978-1-4048-0138-7(3)); T-Rex : The Adventure of Tyrannosaurus Rex. 22.60 (978-1-4048-0139-4(1)); Three-Horn : The Adventure of Triceratops. 22.60 (978-1-4048-0136-3(7)); Winged & Toothless : The Adventure of Pterandon. 22.60 (978-1-4048-0137-0(5)); 24p. (C). (gr. k-3). 2004. (Illus.). 2003. Set lib. bdg. 135.60 (978-1-4048-0133-2(2)) Picture Window Bks.

—Double Bones: The Adventure of Diplodocus. Yesh, Jeff, illus. 2004. (Dinosaur World Ser.). 24p. (C). (gr. k-3). 22.60 (978-1-4048-0940-6(6)) Picture Window Bks.

—Lizard Tooth: The Adventure of Iguanodon. Yesh, Jeff, illus. 2004. 24p. (C). (gr. k-3). 22.60 (978-1-4048-0942-0(2)) Picture Window Bks.

—Long Arm: The Adventure of Brachiosaurus. Yesh, Jeff, illus. 2004. (Dinosaur World Ser.). 24p. (C). (gr. k-3). 22.60 (978-1-4048-0939-0(2)) Picture Window Bks.

—Long-Neck: The Adventure of Apatosaurus. Yesh, Jeff, illus. 2004. (Dinosaur World Ser.). 24p. (C). (gr. k-3). 22.60 (978-1-4048-0134-9(0)) Picture Window Bks.

—Stiff Armor: The Adventure of Ankylosaurus. Yesh, Jeff, illus. 2004. (Dinosaur World Ser.). 24p. (C). (gr. k-3). 22.60 (978-1-4048-0938-3(4)) Picture Window Bks.

—Strange Lizard: The Adventure of Allosaurus. Yesh, Jeff, illus. 2004. (Dinosaur World Ser.). 24p. (C). (gr. k-3). 22.60 (978-1-4048-0937-6(6)) Picture Window Bks.

—Swift Thief: The Adventure of Velociraptor. Yesh, Jeff, illus. 2004. (Dinosaur World Ser.). 24p. (C). (gr. k-3). 22.60 (978-1-4048-0138-7(3)) Picture Window Bks.

—T-Rex: The Adventure of Tyrannosaurus Rex. Yesh, Jeff, illus. 2004. (Dinosaur World Ser.). 24p. (C). (gr. k-3). 22.60 (978-1-4048-0139-4(1)) Picture Window Bks.

—Three-Horn: The Adventure of Triceratops. Yesh, Jeff, illus. 2004. (Dinosaur World Ser.). 24p. (C). (gr. k-3). 22.60 (978-1-4048-0136-3(7)) Picture Window Bks.

—Winged & Toothless: The Adventure of Pterandon. Yesh, Jeff, illus. 2004. (Dinosaur World Ser.). 24p. (C). (gr. k-3). 22.60 (978-1-4048-0137-0(5)) Picture Window Bks.

Dalmatian Press, ed. Dinosaur Discovery. rev. ed. 2007. 48p. pap. 3.99 (***978-1-4037-3383-2(X))*** Dalmatian Pr.

Dalmatian Press Staff. Big Dino Fun. 2002. (Pop-Up & Flap Board Bks.). (Illus.). 10p. (J). (ps). pap. 4.99 (978-1-57759-791-9(5)) Dalmatian Pr.

—Growing Dinosaurs. 2006. 48p. (J). pap. 3.99 (978-1-4037-1971-3(3)) Dalmatian Pr.

Dalmatian Press Staff, contrib. by. Barney All Year Long. 1998. (Big Best Book to Color Ser.). (Illus.). 96p. (J). (ps-3). 2.99 (978-1-57759-012-5(0)) Dalmatian Pr.

—Barney Better Than Ever! 1998. (Big Best Book to Color Ser.). (Illus.). 96p. (J). (ps-3). 2.99 (978-1-57759-109-2(7)) Dalmatian Pr.

Dalmatian Press Staff, ed. Dinosaurs. rev. ed. 2006. 48p. (J). 3.99 (978-1-4037-2417-5(2)) Dalmatian Pr.

Daly, Kathleen & Golden Books Staff. Bob's Best Christmas. Ruth, Rod & Baker, Darrell, illus. 2003. 32p. (J). (ps-2). pap. 3.99 (978-0-307-10501-1(6) , Golden Bks.) Random Hse. Children's Bks.

Davidson, Susanna. Dinosaurios Atlas Con Pegatinas/ Dinosaur Sticker Atlas. 2005. (SPA.). 30p. (J). pap. 8.95 (978-0-7460-6624-9(4) , Usborne) EDC Publishing.

Davidson, Susanna, et al. The Usborne Internet-Linked World Atlas of Dinosaurs. Rey, Luis V., illus. 2003. 144p. (J). (978-0-439-81840-7(0)) Scholastic, Inc.

Davidson, Susannah. Dinosaur Sticker Atlas. Turnbull, Stephanie, ed. 2004. (Sticker Atlas Ser.). (Illus.). 24p. (J). pap. 8.95 (978-0-7945-0668-1(2) , Usborne) EDC Publishing.

—World Atlas of Dinosaurs: Internet-Linked. 2004. 144p. (J). lib. bdg. 30.95 (978-1-58086-635-4(2) , Usborne) EDC Publishing.

Davies, Francis & Faleschini, Gian P. Dinosaurs. 2000. (Nature's Record-Breakers Ser.). (Illus.). 32p. (J). (gr. 3 up). lib. bdg. 23.33 (978-0-8368-2474-2(1)) Stevens, Gareth Inc.

Davis, Kenneth C. Don't Know Much about Dinosaurs. Date not set. 48p. (J). (gr. 1-4). pap. 5.99 (978-0-06-446233-4(1)) HarperCollins Pubs.

—Don't Know Much about Dinosaurs. Martin, Pedro, illus. 2004. (Picture Bks.: No. 7). 48p. (J). 15.99 (978-0-06-028619-4(9)) HarperCollins Pubs.

Davis, Lee. Dinosaur Dinners, Vol. 2. 1998. (Eyewitness Readers). (Illus.). 32p. (J). (gr. 1-3). pap. 3.99 (978-0-7894-2959-9(4)) Dorling Kindersley Publishing, Inc.

Degen, Bruce, illus. The Magic School Bus in the Time of the Dinosaurs. (Magic School Bus Ser.). (FRE.). (J). (gr. 1-4). pap. 6.99 (978-0-590-24641-5(0)) Scholastic, Inc.

Deinonychus (Dinosaur Profiles) 2004. 11.20 (978-1-4103-0498-8(1) , Blackbirch Pr., Inc.) Thomson Gale.

del Nevo, Annapaola. Dimetrodon. 2000. (Portable Pets Ser.). (Illus.). 12p. (J). (ps). 6.95 (978-0-8109-5663-6(2)) Abrams, Harry N. , Inc.

Devillier, Christy. Carnotaurus. 2004. (Dinosaurs Set Iii Ser.). (Illus.). 32p. (J). (gr. k-4). lib. bdg. 22.78 (978-1-59197-536-6(0)) ABDO Publishing Co.

—Corythosaurus. 2004. (Dinosaurs Set Iii Ser.). (Illus.). 32p. (J). (gr. k-4). lib. bdg. 22.78 (978-1-59197-537-3(9)) ABDO Publishing Co.

—Deinonychus. 2004. (Dinosaurs Set Iii Ser.). (Illus.). 32p. (J). (gr. k-4). lib. bdg. 22.78 (978-1-59197-538-0(7)) ABDO Publishing Co.

—Dinosaurs Set III, 6 vols. 2004. (Illus.). (J). (gr. k-4). lib. bdg. 136.68 (978-1-59197-535-9(2) , Buddy Bks.) ABDO Publishing Co.

—Spinosaurus. 2004. (Dinosaurs Set Iii Ser.). (Illus.). 32p. (J). (gr. k-4). lib. bdg. 22.78 (978-1-59197-539-7(5)) ABDO Publishing Co.

—Styracosaurus. 2004. (Dinosaurs Set Iii Ser.). (Illus.). 32p. (J). (gr. k-4). lib. bdg. 22.78 (978-1-59197-540-3(9)) ABDO Publishing Co.

—Troodon. 2004. (Dinosaurs Set Iii Ser.). (Illus.). 32p. (J). (gr. k-4). lib. bdg. 22.78 (978-1-59197-541-0(7)) ABDO Publishing Co.

Di Blasi, Lidia, et al. Soy un Gran Tiranosauro. 2002. (I Am Ser.).Tr. of I Am a Big Tyrannosaurus. (SPA & ENG., Illus.). 24p. (J). (ps). bds. 9.95 (978-0-7641-5504-8(0)) Barron's Educational Series, Inc.

Dig the Dinosaurs. 2000. (Learning Fun for Little Ones Ser.). 64p. (J). (ps-1). pap. 8.99 (978-0-88724-588-6(9)) Carson-Dellosa Publishing Co., Inc.

Dinoclub: Deinonychus.Tr. of Dinosaur Book. (SPA.). (J). 5.98 (978-970-607-992-3(0)) Larousse, Ediciones, S. A. de C. V. MEX. *Dist:* Continental Bk. Co., Inc.

Dinoclub: Stegasaurus.Tr. of Stegasaurus Dino Book. (SPA.). (J). 5.98 (978-970-607-991-6(2)) Larousse, Ediciones, S. A. de C. V. MEX. *Dist:* Continental Bk. Co., Inc.

Dinosaur Alphabet Dinosaur Alphabet. bds. (978-1-58394-099-0(5)) North Atlantic Bks.

Dinosaur Atlas. 2002. 32p. (J). 4.98 (978-0-7525-7878-1(2)) Parragon, Inc.

Dinosaur Balloons. 2004. (Whizz Kits Ser.). (Illus.). 48p. (J). (978-1-84229-961-6(1)) Top That! Publishing PLC.

The Dinosaur Boogie. (Sails Literacy Ser.). 24p. (gr. 2-3). 8.00 (978-0-7635-7035-4(4)) Rigby Education.

Dinosaur Coloring Book. (Illus.). (J). Bk. 1. pap. 1.99 (978-1-59340-008-8(X)); Bk. 2. pap. 1.99 (978-1-59340-009-5(8)) Grandreams Bks., Inc.

Dinosaur Construction Kit: Tyrannosaurus Rex. (J). (gr. 4-6). 10.75 (978-0-669-15886-1(0)) Houghton Mifflin Co. (Schl. Div.).

Dinosaur Dig. 2003. (Science Card Games Ser.). (gr. 1-3). 9.99 (978-0-7682-1994-4(9) , J53022) School Specialty Publishing.

Dinosaur Discovery: Individual Title, 6 packs. (Story Steps Ser.). (gr. k-2). 32.00 (978-0-7635-9829-7(1)) Rigby Education.

The dinosaur Fan: Individual Title, 6 packs. (gr. 1-2). 25.00 (978-0-7635-9129-8(7)) Rigby Education.

Dinosaur Nests: Individual Title, 6 packs. (Sails Literacy Ser.). (gr. 1-2). 36.00 (978-0-7578-6773-6(1)) Rigby Education.

Dinosaur World. (Illus.). (C). (gr. k-3). 271.20 (978-1-4048-0991-8(0)) Picture Window Bks.

Dinosaurio. 2000. (McGraw-Hill Ciencias Ser.). (ENG & SPA.). (gr. 5 up). (978-0-02-279683-9(5)) Macmillan/ McGraw-Hill Schl. Div.

Dinosaurios. (Coleccion Adventuras con la Ciencia).Tr. of Dinosaurs. (SPA.). (J). (gr. 3-5). pap. (978-950-24-0522-3(6) , AL5080) Albatros ARG. *Dist:* Lectorum Pubns., Inc.

Dinosaurios. 2005. Tr. of Dinosaurs. 97p. (J). spiral bd. 14.99 (978-1-59441-461-9(0) , K04012) Carson-Dellosa Publishing Co., Inc.

Dinosaurios. 2003. (Megabites Ser.).Tr. of Dinosaurs. (SPA., Illus.). (J). pap. 8.95 (978-0-9715256-9-6(2)) Planeta Publishing Corp.

Dinosaurios. (My First Big Book of Questions & Answers Ser.).Tr. of Dinosaurs. (SPA.). 22p. (J). bds. (978-1-4127-3586-5(6) , 7166902) Publications International, Ltd.

Dinosaurios. 2005. (Collection Abre Tus Ojos, Collection Eye Openers Ser.).Tr. of Dinosaurs. (SPA.). (J). (gr. k-2). 6.95 (978-950-11-0963-4(1)) Sigmar ARG. *Dist:* Iaconi, Mariuccia Bk. Imports.

Los Dinosaurios: Big Book Packages. 2003. 64.95 (978-0-673-58597-4(2)) Celebration Pr.

Dinosaurios con plumas (Feathered Dinosaurs) 2006. (J). 23.93 (978-0-8225-6242-9(1)); pap. 6.95 (978-0-8225-6641-0(9)) Lerner Publishing Group. (Ediciones Lerner).

Los dinosaurios mas inteligentes (the Smartest Dinosaurs) 2006. (J). 23.93 (978-0-8225-6245-0(6)); pap. 6.95 (978-0-8225-6636-6(2)) Lerner Publishing Group. (Ediciones Lerner).

Los dinosaurios mas mortíferos (the Deadliest Dinosaurs) 2006. (J). 23.93 (978-0-8225-6240-5(5)); pap. 6.95 (978-0-8225-6639-7(7)) Lerner Publishing Group. (Ediciones Lerner).

Los dinosaurios mas rapidos (the Fastest Dinosaurs) 2006. (J). 23.93 (978-0-8225-6241-2(3)); pap. 6.95 (978-0-8225-6640-3(0)) Lerner Publishing Group. (Ediciones Lerner).

Dinosaur/Libro De Dinosaurios Con Actividades. 2006. 64p. (J). pap., act. bk. ed. (978-0-9762071-9-1(2) , 371-009) Big City Publishing.

Dinosaurs. (Color & Learn Ser.). (J). 36p. (gr. 1-5). pap. (978-1-882210-04-6(2)); 42p. (gr. 4-8). pap. (978-1-882210-51-0(4)) Action Publishing, Inc.

Dinosaurs. (Illus.). 24p. (J). 1.99 (978-1-59445-055-6(2)) Dogs in Hats Children's Publishing Co.

Dinosaurs. 2003. (Eye Wonder Ser.). 48p. (J). pap. 5.99 (978-0-7566-0094-5(4)) Dorling Kindersley Publishing, Inc.

Dinosaurs. 2003. (Little Guides). (Illus.). 320p. pap. 8.95 (978-1-877019-53-1(4)); 256-288p. (978-1-876778-63-7(6)) Fog City Pr.

Dinosaurs. (Illus.). (J). (ps-6). pap. 2.95 (978-0-565-01078-2(6)) Natural History Museum Pubns. GBR. *Dist:* Parkwest Pubns., Inc.

Dinosaurs. 2003. (J). per. (978-1-884907-32-6(6)); per. (978-1-884907-33-3(4)) Paradise Pr., Inc.

Dinosaurs. (Question & Answers of the Natural World Ser.). Date not set. 32p. 4.98 (978-0-7525-4332-1(6)); Date not set. (Illus.). 12p. (J). 3.98 (978-1-4054-0497-6(3)); Date not set. (Illus.). 40p. (J). 3.98 (978-1-4054-0173-9(7)); 2002. 32p. (J). 7.95 (978-0-7525-7248-2(2)); 2002. 32p. (J). 7.98 (978-0-7525-4438-0(1)); 2002. 32p. (J). 9.95 (978-0-7525-7576-6(7)); 2001. 64p. (YA). 8.65 (978-0-7525-4881-4(6)) Parragon, Inc.

Dinosaurs. 2000. (Illus.). (J). (gr. 1-5). pap. (978-1-57584-709-2(4)) Reader's Digest Children's Publishing, Inc.

Dinosaurs. 2001. (SPA., Illus.). 32p. (J). 6.95 (978-0-9727833-3-0(4)) Really Big Coloring Bks., Inc.

Dinosaurs. 32p. 1.99 (978-0-7682-0242-7(6) , FS144004); 3.99 (978-0-7682-0178-9(0) , FS83144); 4.29 (978-0-7682-0228-1(0) , FS130306) Schaffer, Frank Pubns.

Dinosaurs. 2007. (First Discovery Book Ser.). 24p. (J). pap. 5.99 (***978-0-439-91089-7(7)***) Scholastic, Inc.

Dinosaurs. 2007. (My First Sticker Encyclopedia Ser.). (Illus.). 18p. (J). pap. 5.95 (***978-1-59496-143-4(3)***) Teora USA LLC.

Dinosaurs. gif. ed. (Illus.). (J). (ps-k). 6.95 (978-1-55254-258-3(0) , BV50001) Brighter Vision Pubns.

Dinosaurs: Eye to Eye. (Illus.). 32p. (J). (978-1-57755-674-9(7)) Allied Publishing.

Dinosaurs Action. 2002. 12p. (J). pap. 3.98 (978-0-7525-8035-7(3)) Parragon, Inc.

Dinosaurs & Monsters. Date not set. (Illus.). 64p. (J). 2.98 (978-1-4054-0448-8(5)) Parragon, Inc.

Dinosaurs & Other Prehistoric Reptiles. 2002. (Wild, Wild World Ser.).Tr. of Los Dinosaurios. 32p. (J). 9.95 (978-0-7525-4681-0(3)) Parragon, Inc.

Dinosaurs & the Bible. 2003. (BUL.). (YA). 0.75 (978-1-893345-11-9(4)) Answers in Genesis Ministries.

Dinosaurs (Gr. PreK-5) 2003. (J). (978-1-58232-019-9(5)) Bryan Hse. Pubs., Inc.

Dinosaurs Guide Kid Kit. 2004. (Kid Kits Ser.). (Illus.). 32+64p. (J). 12.99 (978-1-58086-415-2(5) , Usborne); 12.99 (978-1-58086-405-3(8)) EDC Publishing.

Dinosaurs Learning Kits Know It Alls. 2001. (Illus.). 24p. (YA). 7.95 (978-1-58610-500-6(0) , 85010) Learning Horizons, Inc.

Dinosaurs Set 4. 2007. (J). 136.68 (***978-1-59928-693-8(9)*** , Buddy Bks.) ABDO Publishing Co.

The Dinosaurs with Book & Puzzle. 2000. (Illus.). 16p. (J). (ps-3). 9.95 (978-1-878427-82-3(2)) Cimino Publishing Group.

Discovering Dinosaurs, Vol. 2. 2005. (Fluent Library). (YA). (ps-3). 29.34 (978-0-8215-8966-3(0)) Sadlier, William H. Inc.

Discovery Kids Staff. Dangerous Dinosaurs. 2000. (Illus.). (J). (978-0-606-18465-6(1)) Tandem Library Bks.

DiSpezio, Michael Anthony. Dino Mania: Discovering Who's Who in the Jurassic Zoo. Garbot, Dave, illus. 2003. 80p. (J). pap. 6.95 (978-1-4027-0855-8(6)) Sterling Publishing Co., Inc.

—Dino Mania: Discovering Who's Who in the Jurassic Zoo. 2003. (gr. 3-6). lib. bdg. 15.25 (978-0-613-77948-7(7)) Tandem Library Bks.

Dixon, Dougal. Agustinia & Other Dinosaurs of Central & South America. 2007. (Illus.). 24p. (J). (***978-1-4048-2269-6(0)*** , 1265746) Picture Window Bks.

—Agustinia & Other Dinosaurs of Central & South America. Weston, Steve & Field, James, illus. 2006. 24p. (J). lib. bdg. (***978-1-4048-2263-4(1)*** , 1265746) Picture Window Bks.

—Aletopelta & Other Dinosaurs of the West Coast. Weston, Steve & Field, James, illus. 2006. (J). 23.93 (978-1-4048-2744-8(7)) Picture Window Bks.

—Allosaurus & Other Dinosaurs of the Rockies. Weston, Steve & Field, James, illus. 2006. (Dinosaur Find Ser.). (J). 23.93 (978-1-4048-2748-6(X)) Picture Window Bks.

—Ankylosaurus & Other Mountain Dinosaurs. Field, James & Weston, Steve, illus. 2004. (Dinosaur Find Ser.). 24p. (C). (gr. k-3). 22.60 (978-1-4048-0670-2(9)) Picture Window Bks.

—Carnivores. 2001. (Dinosaurs Ser.). (Illus.). 36p. (J). (gr. 4 up). lib. bdg. 24.67 (978-0-8368-2915-0(8)) Stevens, Gareth Inc.

—Centrosaurus & Other Dinosaurs of Cold Places. Field, James & Weston, Steve, illus. 2004. (Dinosaur Find Ser.). 24p. (C). (gr. k-3). 22.60 (978-1-4048-0672-6(5)) Picture Window Bks.

—Ceratosaurus & Other Fierce Dinosaurs. Weston, Steve & Field, James, illus. 2006. 24p. (J). (gr. k-3). 22.60 (978-1-4048-1327-4(6)) Picture Window Bks.

—Coelophysis & Other Dinosaurs of the South. Weston, Steve & Field, James, illus. 2006. 23.93 (978-1-4048-2747-9(1)) Picture Window Bks.

—Cretaceous Life. 2006. (Prehistoric World Bks.). 32p. (J). pap. 4.99 (978-0-7641-3483-8(3)) Barron's Educational Series, Inc.

—Deltadromeus & Other Shoreline Dinosaurs. Field, James & Weston, Steve, illus. 2004. (Dinosaur Find Ser.). 24p. (C). (gr. k-3). 22.60 (978-1-4048-0669-6(5)) Picture Window Bks.

—Dinosaur. (Google E Guides Ser.). (Illus.). (J). 2006. 96p. (gr. 8). pap. 9.99 (978-0-7566-2228-2(X)); 2003. 40p. 12.99 (978-0-7894-9749-9(2)) Dorling Kindersley Publishing, Inc.

—Dinosaur Dig. 2003. (History Hunters Ser.). (Illus.). 32p. (J). (gr. 3 up). lib. bdg. 24.67 (978-0-8368-3739-1(8)) Stevens, Gareth Inc.

—Dinosaur Find, 6 bks. Field, James & Weston, Steve, illus. Incl. Ankylosaurus & Other Mountain Dinosaurs. (C). 22.60 (978-1-4048-0670-2(9)); Centrosaurus & Other Dinosaurs of Cold Places. (C). 22.60 (978-1-4048-0672-6(5)); Deltadromeus & Other Shoreline Dinosaurs. (C). 22.60 (978-1-4048-0669-6(5)); Plateosaurus & Other Desert Dinosaurs. (C). 22.60 (978-1-4048-0667-2(9)); Stegosaurus & Other Plains Dinosaurs. (C). 22.60 (978-1-4048-0668-9(7)); Triceratops & Other Forest Dinosaurs. (J). 22.60 (978-1-4048-0671-9(7)); 24p. (gr. k-3). (Illus.). 2004. 135.60 (978-1-4048-0673-3(3)) Picture Window Bks.

—Dinosaurs, 4 bks. Incl. Carnivores. lib. bdg. 24.67 (978-0-8368-2915-0(8)); Herbivores. lib. bdg. 24.67 (978-0-8368-2916-7(6)); In the Sea. lib. bdg. 24.67 (978-0-8368-2917-4(4)); In the Sky. lib. bdg. 24.67 (978-0-8368-2918-1(2)); 36p. (J). (gr. 4 up). (Illus.). 2001. Set lib. bdg. 98.68 (978-0-8368-2914-3(X)) Stevens, Gareth Inc.

—Dinosaurs: A Closer Look. rev. ed. 1998. (New Dinosaur Dynasty Ser.). (Illus.). 32p. (J). (gr. 2-6). lib. bdg. 21.27 (978-1-884756-62-7(X)) Davidson Titles, Inc.

—Dinosaurs: All Shapes & Sizes. 1998. (New Dinosaur Dynasty Ser.). (Illus.). 32p. (J). (gr. 2-6). lib. bdg. 21.27 (978-1-884756-60-3(3)) Davidson Titles, Inc.

—Dinosaurs: Giants of the Earth. rev. ed. 1998. (New Dinosaur Dynasty Ser.). (Illus.). 32p. (J). (gr. 2-6). lib. bdg. 21.27 (978-1-884756-63-4(8)) Davidson Titles, Inc.

—Dinosaurs: The Fossil Hunters. rev. ed. 1998. (New Dinosaur Dynasty Ser.). (Illus.). 32p. (J). (gr. 2-6). lib. bdg. 21.27 (978-1-884756-61-0(1)) Davidson Titles, Inc.

—Dinosaurs: The Real Monsters. rev. ed. 1998. (New Dinosaur Dynasty Ser.). (Illus.). 32p. (J). (gr. 2-6). lib. bdg. 21.27 (978-1-884756-64-1(6)) Davidson Titles, Inc.

—Dinosaurs in the Sea: Dinosaurs in the Sky. 2003. (J). pap. (978-0-8368-3329-4(5)) Stevens, Gareth Inc.

—Dinosaurs, the World of the. 2007. (Illus.). 96p. pap. 14.99 (***978-1-84476-375-7(7)*** , Southwater) Anness Publishing GBR. *Dist:* National Bk. Network.

—The Discovery of T. Rex. 2006. (Stories from History Ser.). 48p. (J). 14.95 (***978-0-7696-4712-8(X)***); pap. 6.95 (***978-0-7696-4693-0(X)***) School Specialty Publishing.

—Dougal Dixon's Amazing Dinosaurs: The Fiercest, the Tallest, the Toughest, the Smallest. (Illus.). 128p. 2003. (YA). (gr. 4-6). 17.95 (978-1-56397-773-2(7)); 2nd ed. 2007. (J). (gr. 1 up). 19.95 (***978-1-59078-537-9(1)***) Boyds Mills Pr.

—Dougal Dixon's Dinosaurs. (Illus.). 160p. 2nd ed. 2003. (YA). (gr. 4-6). 19.95 (978-1-56397-722-0(2)); 3rd ed. 2007. (J). (***978-1-59078-470-9(7)***) Boyds Mills Pr.

—Dromaeosaurus & Other Dinosaurs of the North. Weston, Steve & Field, James, illus. 2006. (Dinosaur Find Ser.). (J). 23.93 (978-1-4048-2745-5(5)) Picture Window Bks.

—Giganotosaurus & Other Big Dinosaurs. Weston, Steve & Field, James, illus. 2006. 24p. (J). (gr. k-3). 22.60 (978-1-4048-1325-0(X)) Picture Window Bks.

—Herbivores. 2001. (Dinosaurs Ser.). (Illus.). 36p. (J). (gr. 4 up). lib. bdg. 24.67 (978-0-8368-2916-7(6)) Stevens, Gareth Inc.

—The Ice Age. 2006. (Prehistoric World Bks.). 32p. (J). pap. 4.99 (978-0-7641-3479-1(5)) Barron's Educational Series, Inc.

—In the Sea. 2001. (Dinosaurs Ser.). (Illus.). 36p. (J). (gr. 4 up). lib. bdg. 24.67 (978-0-8368-2917-4(4)) Stevens, Gareth Inc.

—In the Sky. 2001. (Dinosaurs Ser.). (Illus.). 36p. (J). (gr. 4 up). lib. bdg. 24.67 (978-0-8368-2918-1(2)) Stevens, Gareth Inc.

—Jurassic Life. 2006. (Prehistoric World Bks.). 32p. (J). pap. 4.99 (978-0-7641-3478-4(7)) Barron's Educational Series, Inc.

—Maiasaura & Other Dinosaurs of the Midwest. Weston, Steve & Field, James, illus. 2006. 23.93 (978-1-4048-2749-3(8)) Picture Window Bks.

—Minmi & Other Dinosaurs of Australia. Weston, Steve & Field, James, illus. 2006. 24p. (J). lib. bdg. (***978-1-4048-2262-7(3)***) Picture Window Bks.

—My First Book of Dinosaurs. 2004. (Illus.). 48p. (J). 9.95 (978-1-86007-267-3(4)) Ticktock Media Ltd. GBR. *Dist:* Consortium Bk. Sales & Distribution.

—Neovenator & Other Dinosaurs of Europe. Weston, Steve & Field, James, illus. 2006. 24p. (J). lib. bdg. (***978-1-4048-2264-1(X)***) Picture Window Bks.

—Nodosaurs & Other Dinosaurs of the East Coast. Weston, Steve & Field, James, illus. 2006. (J). 23.93 (978-1-4048-2746-2(3)) Picture Window Bks.

—Ornithomimus & Other Fast Dinosaurs. Weston, Steve & Field, James, illus. 2006. 24p. (J). (gr. k-3). 22.60 (978-1-4048-1326-7(8)) Picture Window Bks.

—Plateosaurus & Other Desert Dinosaurs. Field, James & Weston, Steve, illus. 2004. (Dinosaur Find Ser.). 24p. (C). (gr. k-3). 22.60 (978-1-4048-0667-2(9)) Picture Window Bks.

—Saltopus & Other First Dinosaurs. Weston, Steve & Field, James, illus. 2006. 24p. (J). (gr. k-3). 22.60 (978-1-4048-1328-1(4)) Picture Window Bks.

—Scutellosaurus & Other Small Dinosaurs. Weston, Steve & Field, James, illus. 2006. 24p. (J). (gr. k-3). 22.60 (978-1-4048-1330-4(6)) Picture Window Bks.

—Spinosaurus & Other Dinosaurs of Africa. Weston, Steve & Field, James, illus. 2006. 24p. (J). lib. bdg. (***978-1-4048-2260-3(7)***) Picture Window Bks.

—Stegosaurus & Other Plains Dinosaurs. Field, James & Weston, Steve, illus. 2004. (Dinosaur Find Ser.). 24p. (C). (gr. k-3). 22.60 (978-1-4048-0668-9(7)) Picture Window Bks.

—Styracosaurus & Other Last Dinosaurs. Weston, Steve & Field, James, illus. 2006. 24p. (J). (gr. k-3). 22.60 (978-1-4048-1329-8(2)) Picture Window Bks.

—Therizinosaurus & Other Dinosaurs of Asia. Weston, Steve & Field, James, illus. 2006. 24p. (J). lib. bdg. (***978-1-4048-2261-0(5)***) Picture Window Bks.

—Triassic Life. 2006. (Prehistoric World Bks.). 32p. (J). pap. 4.99 (978-0-7641-3481-4(7)) Barron's Educational Series, Inc.

—Triceratops & Other Forest Dinosaurs. Field, James & Weston, Steve, illus. 2004. (Dinosaur Find Ser.). 24p. (J). (gr. k-3). 22.60 (978-1-4048-0671-9(7)) Picture Window Bks.

Dixon, Dougal. Tyrannosaurus & Other Dinosaurs of North America. Weston, Steve & Field, James, illus. 2006. 24p. (J). (***978-1-4048-2265-8(8)***) Picture Window Bks.

DK Publishing. Dangerous Dinosaurs Q & A. 2008. 64p. (J). 12.99 (***978-0-7566-3502-2(0)***) Dorling Kindersley Publishing, Inc.

—Dinosaur. 2008. (J). 48p. (gr. 2-8). pap. 9.99 (***978-0-7566-3820-7(8)***); 24p. 8.99 (***978-0-7566-3439-1(3)***) Dorling Kindersley Publishing, Inc.

—Dinosaur Adventure. 2008. 14p. (J). (ps-2). 19.99 (***978-0-7566-3745-3(7)***) Dorling Kindersley Publishing, Inc.

—Dinosaurs. 2008. 10p. (J). 8.99 (***978-0-7566-3379-0(6)***) Dorling Kindersley Publishing, Inc.

—My Terrific Dinosaur Book. 2008. 14p. (J). (ps-k). 12.99 (***978-0-7566-3757-6(0)***) Dorling Kindersley Publishing, Inc.

DK Publishing Staff. Dinosaurium. 2007. 22p. (YA). (gr. 5-8). 24.99 (***978-0-7566-3206-9(4)***) Dorling Kindersley Publishing, Inc.

—Dinosaurs. 2007. (Let's Look Ser.).Tr. of Los Dinosaurios. (Illus.). 36p. (J). 4.99 (978-0-7566-2593-1(9)) Dorling Kindersley Publishing, Inc.

—Dinosaurs! 2007. 14p. (J). (gr. k-2). 12.99 (978-0-7566-2994-6(2)) Dorling Kindersley Publishing, Inc.

—Farm. 2007. 12p. (J). (ps-1). bds. 8.99 (978-0-7566-2586-3(6)) Dorling Kindersley Publishing, Inc.

—Pop-Up Dinosaur 123. 2007. (DK Toys & Games Ser.). (Illus.). (J). (ps-2). 12.99 (978-0-7566-2728-7(1)) Dorling Kindersley Publishing, Inc.

¿Donde Fueron los Dinosaurios? (Coleccion Primeros Pasos en la Ciencia). (SPA., Illus.). (J). (gr. 1-3). pap. (978-950-724-217-5(1) , LMA8220) Lumen ARG. *Dist:* Lectorum Pubns., Inc.

Dorling Kindersley Publishing Staff. Deadly Dinosaurs. 1999. (Animal Fun Ser.). (Illus.). 8p. (J). pap. 3.95 (978-0-7894-4783-8(5)) Dorling Kindersley Publishing, Inc.

—Dinosaur Atlas. 2006. 96p. (J). (gr. 8). 19.99 (978-0-7566-2235-0(2)) Dorling Kindersley Publishing, Inc.

—Dinosaurio. 2004. (Dk Eyewitness Books Ser.). 72p. (J). 15.99 (978-0-7566-0632-9(2)); lib. bdg. 19.99 (978-0-7566-0797-5(3)) Dorling Kindersley Publishing, Inc.

—Dinosaurs. 2002. (Touch & Feel Ser.). (Illus.). 12p. (J). bds. 6.99 (978-0-7894-8854-1(X)) Dorling Kindersley Publishing, Inc.

—Dinosaurs & How They Lived: See & Explore Library. 1998. (See & Explore Library). (Illus.). 64p. (J). (gr. 4-7). pap. 7.95 (978-0-7894-3447-0(4) , D K Ink) Dorling Kindersley Publishing, Inc.

—Meet the Dinosaurs. 2006. (Dk Readers Ser.). (Illus.). 32p. (J). 14.99 (978-0-7566-1911-4(4)); pap. 3.99 (978-0-7566-1910-7(6)) Dorling Kindersley Publishing, Inc.

—Mighty Dinosaurs. 1999. (Animal Fun Ser.). (Illus.). 8p. (J). pap. 3.95 (978-0-7894-4784-5(3)) Dorling Kindersley Publishing, Inc.

—Spiky, Scary, Scaly Dinosaurs. 2006. (Touchables Ser.). (Illus.). 14p. (J). bds. 8.99 (978-0-7566-2020-2(1)) Dorling Kindersley Publishing, Inc.

—Tyrannosaurus. 2000. (Dinosaur Board Bks.). (Illus.). 12p. (J). (ps-2). bds. 6.99 (978-0-7894-5403-4(3)) Dorling Kindersley Publishing, Inc.

—Visual Encyclopedia of Dinosaurs. 2005. (Illus.). 512p. (J). (gr. 8). pap. 12.99 (978-0-7566-0858-3(9)) Dorling Kindersley Publishing, Inc.

—1001 Facts about Dinosaurs. 2002. (gr. 3-6). lib. bdg. 17.60 (978-0-613-75142-1(6)) Tandem Library Bks.

Dorling Kindersley Publishing Staff, ed. Dangerous Dinosaurs. 2004. (Ultimate Sticker Bks.). 16p. (J). pap. 6.99 (978-0-7566-0565-0(2)) Dorling Kindersley Publishing, Inc.

—My First Dinosaur. 2004. (Touch & Feel Ser.). 12p. (J). bds. 9.99 (978-0-7566-0585-8(7)) Dorling Kindersley Publishing, Inc.

—Summer Vacation Dinosaur!, 2 vols., Set. 2000. (Illus.). (J). (gr. 3-7). pap. 25.00 (978-0-7894-6065-3(3) , D K Ink) Dorling Kindersley Publishing, Inc.

Dot-to-Dots, Mazes & More: Dinosaurs. (gr. k-1). 2.99 (978-0-7424-0171-6(5) , IF0404) School Specialty Publishing.

Double Bones. 2006. (Dinosaur World Ser.). 24p. (J). 7.95 (978-1-4048-1833-0(2)) Picture Window Bks.

Douglas, Vincent & School Specialty Publishing Staff. The Complete Book of Dinosaurs. 2003. (Complete Book Ser.). (Illus.). 352p. (J). (gr. k-6). pap. 14.95 (978-1-57768-606-4(3) , American Education Publishing) School Specialty Publishing.

Dover Staff. Dinosaur Fun Books. 1998. (J). pap. 10.00 (978-0-486-40343-4(2)) Dover Pubns., Inc.

Draw 50 Dinosaurs & Other Prehistoric Animals. 2002. (Draw 50 Ser.). (Illus.). (J). 17.60 (978-0-7587-4163-9(4)) Book Wholesalers, Inc.

Due, Andrea. Anklyosaurus. 2007. (Dinosaur Profiles Ser.). (Illus.). 32p. (J). (gr. 2-6). 23.70 (978-1-4103-0738-5(7) , Blackbirch Pr., Inc.) Thomson Gale.

—Diplodocus. 2007. (Dinosaur Profiles Ser.). (Illus.). 32p. (J). (gr. 2-6). 23.70 (978-1-4103-0734-7(4) , Blackbirch Pr., Inc.) Thomson Gale.

—Giganatosaurus. 2007. (Dinosaur Profiles Ser.). (Illus.). 32p. (J). (gr. 2-6). 23.70 (978-1-4103-0735-4(2) , Blackbirch Pr., Inc.) Thomson Gale.

—Iguanadon. 2007. (Dinosaur Profiles Ser.). (Illus.). 32p. (J). (gr. 2-6). 23.70 (978-1-4103-0736-1(0) , Blackbirch Pr., Inc.) Thomson Gale.

—Ornitholestes. 2007. (Dinosaur Profiles Ser.). (Illus.). 32p. (J). (gr. 2-6). 23.70 (978-1-4103-0740-8(9) , Blackbirch Pr., Inc.) Thomson Gale.

—Pachycephalosaurus. 2007. (Dinosaur Profiles Ser.). (Illus.). 32p. (J). (gr. 2-6). 23.70 (978-1-4103-0741-5(7) , Blackbirch Pr., Inc.) Thomson Gale.

—Velociraptor. 2007. (Dinosaur Profiles Ser.). (Illus.). 32p. (J). (gr. 2-6). 23.70 (978-1-4103-0737-8(9) , Blackbirch Pr., Inc.) Thomson Gale.

Duhig, Lee. Draw Dinosaurs! 2006. (Illus.). 64p. (J). pap. (***978-1-59412-158-6(3)***) Mud Puddle, Inc.

Dungworth, Richard. Dinosaurs. Pledger, Maurice, illus. 2006. (Nature Trails Ser.). 16p. (J). 12.95 (978-1-59223-470-7(4) , Silver Dolphin Bks.) Advantage Pubs. Group.

Dunn, Mary. My Adventure on a Dinosaur Dig. 2006. 44p. (J). 8.99 (978-1-59092-281-1(6) , Orchard Academy Pr.) Windstorm Creative.

Dussling, Jennifer. Dinosaur Eggs. Johnson, Pamela, illus. 2000. (All Aboard Reading Ser.). 48p. (J). (ps-3). pap. 3.99 (978-0-448-42093-6(7) , Grosset & Dunlap) Penguin Group (USA) Inc.

—Dinosaur Eggs: Level 2. 2000. (All Aboard Reading Ser.). (Illus.). (J). 10.79 (978-0-606-18850-0(9)) Tandem Library Bks.

Edmontosaurus (Dinosaur Profiles) 2004. 11.20 (978-1-4103-0497-1(3) , Blackbirch Pr., Inc.) Thomson Gale.

Encyclopedia of Dinosaurs. 2003. (Illus.). 256p. (J). 12.98 (978-1-4054-0944-5(4)) Parragon, Inc.

Equipo Staff. Mi Primer Libro de Dinosaurios. (SPA.). 16p. 12.95 (978-84-272-1736-2(6)) Molino, Editorial ESP. *Dist:* Distribooks, Inc.

Fact & Opinion. 2003. 48p. (J). (gr. 5-5). pap. 6.99 (978-0-7424-1835-6(9) , FS99153) School Specialty Publishing.

Farlow, James Orville. Bringing Dinosaur Bones to Life: How Do We Know What Dinosaurs Were Really Like? Whitcraft, Jim, illus. 2001. (Single Title - Science Ser.). 64p. (J). (gr. 5-7). 26.00 (978-0-531-11403-2(1) , Watts, Franklin) Scholastic Library Publishing.

Field, James, illus. Dinosaurs. 2001. (Trackpack Ser.).Tr. of Dinosaurios. 32p. (J). 4.99 (978-0-439-37479-8(0)) Scholastic, Inc.

Fiesta de Dinosaurios, 6 Pks. (Chiquilibros Ser.). (SPA.). (gr. k-1). 23.00 (978-0-7635-8786-4(9)) Rigby Education.

First Dinosaur. Date not set. (Illus.). (J). bds. 9.98 (978-0-7525-9893-2(7)) Parragon, Inc.

Firth, Rachel. Dinosaurs. 2004. (Discovery Program Ser.). (SPA., Illus.). 64p. (J). (gr. 2 up). pap. 8.99 (978-0-7945-0024-5(2) , Usborne); lib. bdg. 16.99 (978-1-58086-354-4(X)) EDC Publishing.

—Dinosaurs. 2001. (gr. 3-6). lib. bdg. 17.60 (978-0-613-91002-6(8)) Tandem Library Bks.

Fisher, Enid Broderick. The Great Dinosaur Record Book. Grant, Richard, illus. 1998. 32p. (J). (gr. 4 up). lib. bdg. 22.60 (978-0-8368-2176-5(9)) Stevens, Gareth Inc.

—They Lived with the Dinosaurs. Grant, Richard, illus. 1999. (World of Dinosaurs Ser.). 32p. (J). (gr. 4 up). lib. bdg. 21.26 (978-0-8368-2292-2(7)) Stevens, Gareth Inc.

Folder, Alan. Paper Dinosaurs. Galvani, Maureen, illus. 2001. (Paper Magic Ser.). 48p. (J). (gr. 3-7). 7.95 (978-0-439-22762-9(3)) Scholastic, Inc.

Foran, Jill. Dinosaurs. 2004. (Prehistoric Life Ser.). (J). pap. 7.95 (978-1-59036-171-9(7)); (Illus.). 32p. lib. bdg. 15.95 (978-1-59036-110-8(5)) Weigl Pubs., Inc.

Foster, Walter, ed. Dinosaurs: Step-by-Step Instructions for 27 Prehistoric Creatures. Shelly, Jeff, illus. 2004. (Draw & Color Ser.). 40p. pap. 4.95 (978-1-56010-817-7(7)) Foster, Walter Publishing, Inc.

Francis, Suzanne. Extreme Dinos. 2006. (Illus.). 32p. (J). pap. (***978-0-439-83873-3(8)***) Scholastic, Inc.

—Prehistoric Hunters. 2006. (Illus.). 32p. (J). (***978-0-439-83863-4(0)***) Scholastic, Inc.

Frank, Marjorie Slavick, et al. Science Leveled Libraries: Titanosaur Treasure. 3rd ed. 2002. (Harcourt Science Ser.). (gr. 4 up). pap. 25.60 (978-0-15-327347-6(X)) Harcourt Schl. Pubs.

Fraser, Mary Ann, illus. Dinosaurs. 1999. (Science Crosswords Ser.). 48p. (J). (gr. 3-7). pap. 4.95 (978-0-7373-0167-0(8)) Lowell Hse.

French, Vivian. T Rex. Bartlett, Alison, illus. 2004. 32p. (J). (gr. k-3). 15.99 (978-0-7636-2184-1(6)) Candlewick Pr.

—T. Rex. Bartlett, Alison, illus. 2006. 32p. (J). (gr. k-3). reprint ed. pap. 6.99 (978-0-7636-3177-2(9)) Candlewick Pr.

Frith, Alex. See Inside the World of Dinosaurs. Scott, Peter, illus. 2007. 16p. (J). bds. 12.99 (978-0-7945-1436-5(7) , Usborne) EDC Publishing.

Frost, Helen. Allosaurus. 2005. (Dinosaurs & Prehistoric Animals Ser.). (Illus.). 24p. (J). 19.93 (978-0-7368-3646-3(2)) Capstone Pr., Inc.

—Alosaurio: Allosaurus. 2006. (SPA & ENG.). (J). 19.93 (978-0-7368-6683-5(3)) Capstone Pr., Inc.

—Estegosaurio: Stegosaurus. 2006. (SPA & ENG.). (J). 19.93 (978-0-7368-6684-2(1)) Capstone Pr., Inc.

—Stegosaurus. 2005. (Dinosaurs & Prehistoric Animals Ser.). (Illus.). 24p. (J). 19.93 (978-0-7368-3647-0(0)) Capstone Pr., Inc.

—Tiranosaurio Rex. 2006. (SPA & ENG.). (J). 19.93 (978-0-7368-6688-0(4)) Capstone Pr., Inc.

—Triceratops. 2005. (Dinosaurs & Prehistoric Animals Ser.). (Illus.). 24p. (J). 19.93 (978-0-7368-3650-0(0)) Capstone Pr., Inc.

C D

—Triceratops. 2006. (SPA & ENG.). (J). 19.93 (978-0-7368-6687-3(6) , Pebble Bks.) Capstone Pr., Inc.

—Tyrannosaurus Rex. Saunders-Smith, Gail, ed. 2005. (Dinosaurs & Prehistoric Animals Ser.). (Illus.). 24p. (J). (ps). lib. bdg. 19.93 (978-0-7368-3651-7(9)) Capstone Pr., Inc.

Furgang, Kathy. Let's Look at the Dinosaurs. 2003. (Early Connections Ser.). (J). pap. 33.00 (978-1-4108-1074-8(7)) Benchmark Education Co.

Gabriele, Joseph. The First Days of the Dinosaurs: Text Edition. Hurst, Margaret, illus. 32p. (Orig.). (J). (gr. 1-3). pap. 1.95 (978-0-911211-55-9(1)) Penny Lane Pubns., Inc.

Gaines, Richard. Apatosaurus. 2001. (Dinosaurs Ser.). (Illus.). 32p. (J). (gr. k-4). lib. bdg. 22.78 (978-1-57765-487-2(0) , Buddy Bks.) ABDO Publishing Co.

—Archaeopteryx. 2001. (Dinosaurs Ser.). (Illus.). 32p. (J). (gr. k-4). lib. bdg. 22.78 (978-1-57765-486-5(2) , Buddy Bks.) ABDO Publishing Co.

—Coelophysis. 2001. (Dinosaurs Ser.). (Illus.). 32p. (J). (gr. k-4). lib. bdg. 22.78 (978-1-57765-488-9(9) , Buddy Bks.) ABDO Publishing Co.

—Dinosaurs Set I, 6 vols. Incl. Apatosaurus. lib. bdg. 22.78 (978-1-57765-487-2(0)); Archaeopteryx. lib. bdg. 22.78 (978-1-57765-486-5(2)); Coelophysis. lib. bdg. 22.78 (978-1-57765-488-9(9)); Triceratops. lib. bdg. 22.78 (978-1-57765-489-6(7)); Tyrannosaurus Rex. lib. bdg. 22.78 (978-1-57765-485-8(4)); Velociraptor. lib. bdg. 22.78 (978-1-57765-490-2(0)); 32p. (J). (gr. k-4). 2001. (Illus.). 2001. Set lib. bdg. 136.68 (978-1-57765-509-1(5) , Buddy Bks.) ABDO Publishing Co.

—Triceratops. 2001. (Dinosaurs Ser.). (Illus.). 32p. (J). (gr. k-4). lib. bdg. 22.78 (978-1-57765-489-6(7) , Buddy Bks.) ABDO Publishing Co.

—Tyrannosaurus Rex. 2001. (Dinosaurs Ser.). (Illus.). 32p. (J). (gr. k-4). lib. bdg. 22.78 (978-1-57765-485-8(4) , Buddy Bks.) ABDO Publishing Co.

—Velociraptor. 2001. (Dinosaurs Ser.). (Illus.). 32p. (J). (gr. k-4). lib. bdg. 22.78 (978-1-57765-490-2(0) , Buddy Bks.) ABDO Publishing Co.

Gardom, Tim & Milner, Angela. Book of Dinosaurs. 2002. (Illus.). 136p. (gr. 4-7). pap. 12.95 (978-1-84222-256-0(2)) Carlton Bks., Ltd. GBR. *Dist:* Ingram Pub. Services, Simon & Schuster, Inc.

Gee & Rey. Dinosaurios Guia de Campo. 2003. (SPA.). 144p. (978-84-7556-268-1(X) , 1500) Oceano Difusion Editorial, S. A.

Gee, Henry. A Field Guide to Dinosaurs: The Essential Handbook for Travelers in the Mesozoic. Rey, Luis V., illus. 2003. 192p. 24.95 (978-0-7641-5511-6(3)) Barron's Educational Series, Inc.

Gerth, Melanie. My First Jumbo Book of Dinosaurs. Diaz, James, illus. 2004. (My First Jumbo Book Ser.). 10p. (J). pap. 9.95 (978-0-439-57675-8(X)) Scholastic, Inc.

Gibbons, Gail. Dinosaur Discoveries. Gibbons, Gail, illus. 2006. (Illus.). 32p. (J). 6.95 (978-0-8234-2030-8(2)) Holiday Hse., Inc.

—Dinosaur Discoveries. 2005. (Illus.). 32p. (J). (ps-ps). 16.95 (978-0-8234-1971-5(1)) Holiday Hse., Inc.

—Dinosaurs. 34p. (J). (ps-2). pap. 6.95 (978-0-8072-1271-4(7) , Listening Library) Random Hse. Audio Publishing Group.

Gibbons, Tony & Snedden, Robert. Dinosaur Atlas. 2003. (J). bds. 5.98 (978-0-7525-8919-0(9)) Parragon, Inc.

Gigantes marinos de la época de los dinosaurios (Sea Giants of Dinosaur Time) 2006. (J). 23.93 (978-0-8225-6244-3(8) , Ediciones Lerner) Lerner Publishing Group.

Gigantes voladores de la época de los dinosaurios (Flying Giants of Dinosaur Time) 2006. (J). 23.93 (978-0-8225-6243-6(X)); pap. 6.95 (978-0-8225-6637-3(0)) Lerner Publishing Group. (Ediciones Lerner).

Glut, Donald F., tr. Discover Dinosaurs. 2005. (Discover Ser.). (Illus.). 48p. (J). 7.98 (978-0-7853-6109-1(X) , 3073307) Publications International, Ltd.

God Made Dinosaurs. 2006. 16p. (J). pap. 1.99 (978-0-7847-1703-5(6) , 04164) Standard Publishing.

Goecke, Michael P. Allosaurus. 2002. (Dinosaurs Ser.). (Illus.). 32p. (J). (gr. k-4). lib. bdg. 22.78 (978-1-57765-636-4(9) , Buddy Bks.) ABDO Publishing Co.

—Ankylosaurus. 2002. (Dinosaurs Ser.). (Illus.). 32p. (J). (gr. k-4). lib. bdg. 22.78 (978-1-57765-637-1(7) , Buddy Bks.) ABDO Publishing Co.

—Baryonyx. 2007. (Illus.). 32p. (J). 22.78 (***978-1-59928-694-5(7)***) ABDO Publishing Co.

—Brachiosaurus. 2002. (Dinosaurs Ser.). (Illus.). 32p. (J). (gr. k-4). lib. bdg. 22.78 (978-1-57765-632-6(6) , Buddy Bks.) ABDO Publishing Co.

—Camarasaurus. 2007. (Illus.). 32p. (J). 22.78 (***978-1-59928-695-2(5)***) ABDO Publishing Co.

—Compsognathus. 2007. (Illus.). 32p. (J). 22.78 (***978-1-59928-696-9(3)***) ABDO Publishing Co.

—Dinosaurs Set II, 6 vols. Incl. Allosaurus. lib. bdg. 22.78 (978-1-57765-636-4(9)); Ankylosaurus. lib. bdg. 22.78 (978-1-57765-637-1(7)); Brachiosaurus. lib. bdg. 22.78 (978-1-57765-632-6(6)); Diplodocus. lib. bdg. 22.78 (978-1-57765-633-3(4)); Iguanodon. lib. bdg. 22.78 (978-1-57765-634-0(2)); Stegosaurus. lib. bdg. 22.78 (978-1-57765-635-7(0)); 32p. (J). (gr. k-4). (Illus.). 2002. Set lib. bdg. 136.68 (978-1-57765-512-1(5) , Buddy Bks.) ABDO Publishing Co.

—Diplodocus. 2002. (Dinosaurs Ser.). (Illus.). 32p. (J). (gr. k-4). lib. bdg. 22.78 (978-1-57765-633-3(4) , Buddy Bks.) ABDO Publishing Co.

—Giganotosaurus. 2007. (Illus.). 32p. (J). 22.78 (***978-1-59928-697-6(1)***) ABDO Publishing Co.

—Iguanodon. 2002. (Dinosaurs Ser.). (Illus.). 32p. (J). (gr. k-4). lib. bdg. 22.78 (978-1-57765-634-0(2) , Buddy Bks.) ABDO Publishing Co.

—Oviraptor. 2007. (Illus.). 32p. (J). 22.78 (***978-1-59928-698-3(X)***) ABDO Publishing Co.

—Pachycephalosaurus. 2007. 32p. (J). 22.78 (***978-1-59928-699-0(8)***) ABDO Publishing Co.

Goecke, Michael P. Stegosaurus. 2002. (Dinosaurs Ser.). (Illus.). 32p. (J). (gr. k-4). lib. bdg. 22.78 (978-1-57765-635-7(0) , Buddy Bks.) ABDO Publishing Co.

Golden Books Staff. Fire in the Sky: Glow in the Dark Sticker Book. 2000. (Disney Ser.). (Illus.). (J). (ps-3). pap. 3.99 (978-0-307-10469-4(9) , Golden Bks.) Random Hse. Children's Bks.

Goldish, Meish. The Oviraptor Adventure: Mark Norell & the Egg Thief. 2007. (Fossil Hunters Ser.). (J). lib. bdg. 25.27 (978-1-59716-258-6(2)) Bearport Publishing Co., Inc.

Goldsmith, Andrew. Killer Dinosaurs. 2005. (Top Tens Ser.). (Illus.). 32p. (J). (gr. 3-7). lib. bdg. 25.27 (978-1-59716-066-7(0)) Bearport Publishing Co., Inc.

Graham-Kennedy, Elaine. Dinosaurs: Where Did They Come from & Where Did They Go? 2006. (Illus.). 80p. (J). (978-0-8163-2155-1(8)) Pacific Pr. Publishing Assn.

Grambo, Rebecca L. Digging Canadian Dinosaurs. Bonder, Dianna, illus. 2004. 64p. (J). (gr. 2-6). pap. 12.95 (978-1-55285-395-5(0)) Whitecap Bks., Ltd. CAN. *Dist:* Firefly Bks., Ltd.

—Dinosaurs. 2000. (Eyes on Nature Ser.). (Illus.). 109p. (J). 19.95 (978-1-56156-707-2(8)) Kidsbooks, Inc.

Granowsky, Alvin. Dinosaurs. 2000. (gr. k-3). lib. bdg. 13.00 (978-0-613-45176-5(7)) Tandem Library Bks.

Grant, Richard, illus. World of Dinosaurs, 6 bks. Incl. Great Dinosaur Hunters. Green, Tamara. 1999. lib. bdg. 21.26 (978-0-8368-2291-5(9)); They Lived with the Dinosaurs. Fisher, Enid Broderick. 1999. lib. bdg. 21.26 (978-0-8368-2292-2(7)); Triassic Dinosaur World. Green, Tamara. 1998. lib. bdg. 21.26 (978-0-8368-2175-8(0)); True-Life Monsters of the Prehistoric Seas. Fisher, Enid Broderick. 1999. lib. bdg. 21.26 (978-0-8368-2293-9(5)); True-Life Monsters of the Prehistoric Skies. Fisher, Enid Broderick. 1999. lib. bdg. 21.26 (978-0-8368-2294-6(3)); What Dinosaurs Ate. Green, Tamara. 1999. lib. bdg. 21.26 (978-0-8368-2295-3(1)); 32p. (J). (gr. 4 up). (Illus.). Set lib. bdg. 135.60 (978-0-8368-2378-3(8)) Stevens, Gareth Inc.

Gray, Samantha & Walker, Sarah. Dinosaurs. Ling, Mary, ed. 2001. (Eye Wonder Ser.). (Illus.). 48p. (J). (gr. k-3). 9.99 (978-0-7894-7851-1(X)) Dorling Kindersley Publishing, Inc.

Gray, Samantha, et al. Dinosaurs. 2001. (Eye Wonder Ser.). (Illus.). 48p. (J). (gr. k-3). lib. bdg. 17.99 (978-0-7894-8179-5(0)) Dorling Kindersley Publishing, Inc.

Gray, Susan H. Ammonites. 2005. (Exploring Dinosaurs & Prehistoric Creatures Ser.). (Illus.). 32p. (J). (gr. 2-6). 27.07 (978-1-59296-407-9(9)) Child's World, Inc.

—Dinosaur Armor. 2007. (Scholastic News Nonfiction Readers: Prehistoric World Ser.). 24p. (J). pap. 6.95 (***978-0-531-18775-3(6)*** , Children's Pr.) Scholastic Library Publishing.

—Dinosaur Dig! 2007. (Scholastic News Nonfiction Readers: Prehistoric World Ser.). 24p. (J). pap. 6.95 (***978-0-531-18776-0(4)*** , Children's Pr.) Scholastic Library Publishing.

—Dinosaur Eggs. 2007. (Scholastic News Nonfiction Readers: Prehistoric World Ser.). 24p. (J). pap. 6.95 (***978-0-531-18777-7(2)*** , Children's Pr.) Scholastic Library Publishing.

—Dinosaur Teeth. 2007. (Scholastic News Nonfiction Readers: Prehistoric World Ser.). 24p. (J). pap. 6.95 (***978-0-531-18778-4(0)*** , Children's Pr.) Scholastic Library Publishing.

—Dinosaur Tracks. 2007. (Scholastic News Nonfiction Readers: Prehistoric World Ser.). 24p. (J). pap. 6.95 (***978-0-531-18779-1(9)*** , Children's Pr.) Scholastic Library Publishing.

—Ichthyosaurs. 2005. (Exploring Dinosaurs & Prehistoric Creatures Ser.). (Illus.). 32p. (J). (gr. 2-6). 27.07 (978-1-59296-366-9(8)) Child's World, Inc.

—Is It a Dinosaur? 2007. (Scholastic News Nonfiction Readers: Prehistoric World Ser.). 24p. (J). pap. 6.95 (***978-0-531-18780-7(2)*** , Children's Pr.) Scholastic Library Publishing.

—Megatherium. 2005. (Exploring Dinosaurs & Prehistoric Creatures Ser.). (Illus.). 32p. (J). (gr. 2-6). 27.07 (978-1-59296-410-9(9)) Child's World, Inc.

—Pelycosaurs. 2005. (Exploring Dinosaurs & Prehistoric Creatures Ser.). (Illus.). 32p. (J). (gr. 2-6). 27.07 (978-1-59296-411-6(7)) Child's World, Inc.

—Plesiosaurs. 2005. (Exploring Dinosaurs & Prehistoric Creatures Ser.). (Illus.). 32p. (J). (gr. 2-6). 27.07 (978-1-59296-367-6(6)) Child's World, Inc.

—Pterosaurs. 2005. (Exploring Dinosaurs & Prehistoric Creatures Ser.). 32p. (J). (gr. 2-6). 27.07 (978-1-59296-368-3(4)) Child's World, Inc.

—Saber-Toothed Cats. 2005. (Exploring Dinosaurs & Prehistoric Creatures Ser.). (Illus.). 32p. (J). (gr. 2-6). 27.07 (978-1-59296-412-3(5)) Child's World, Inc.

—Trilobites. 2005. (Exploring Dinosaurs & Prehistoric Creatures Ser.). 32p. (J). (gr. 2-6). 27.07 (978-1-59296-369-0(2)) Child's World, Inc.

Gray, Susan Heinrichs. Allosaurus. 2004. (Exploring Dinosaurs Ser.). 32p. (J). (gr. 2-6). 27.07 (978-1-59296-184-9(3)) Child's World, Inc.

—Ankylosaurus. 2004. (Science of Dinosaurs Ser.). 32p. (J). (gr. 2-6). 27.07 (978-1-59296-042-2(1)) Child's World, Inc.

—Apatosaurus. 2004. (Science of Dinosaurs Ser.). 32p. (J). (gr. 2-6). 27.07 (978-1-59296-043-9(X)) Child's World, Inc.

—Coelophysis. 2004. (Exploring Dinosaurs Ser.). 32p. (J). (gr. 2-6). 27.07 (978-1-59296-185-6(1)) Child's World, Inc.

—Compsognathus. 2004. (Exploring Dinosaurs Ser.). 32p. (J). (gr. 2-6). 27.07 (978-1-59296-233-4(5)) Child's World, Inc.

—Dinosaur Armor. 2007. (Scholastic News Nonfiction Readers Ser.). (Illus.). 24p. (J). (gr. 1-2). 19.00 (978-0-531-17481-4(6) , Children's Pr.) Scholastic Library Publishing.

—Dinosaur Dig! 2007. (Scholastic News Nonfiction Readers Ser.). (Illus.). 24p. (J). (gr. 1-2). 19.00 (***978-0-531-17482-1(4)*** , Children's Pr.) Scholastic Library Publishing.

—Dinosaur Eggs. 2007. (Scholastic News Nonfiction Readers Ser.). (Illus.). 24p. (J). (gr. 1-2). 19.00 (***978-0-531-17483-8(2)*** , Children's Pr.) Scholastic Library Publishing.

—Dinosaur Teeth. 2007. (Scholastic News Nonfiction Readers Ser.). (Illus.). 24p. (J). (gr. 1-2). 19.00 (978-0-531-17484-5(0) , Children's Pr.) Scholastic Library Publishing.

—Dinosaur Tracks. 2007. (Scholastic News Nonfiction Readers Ser.). (Illus.). 24p. (J). (gr. 1-2). 19.00 (***978-0-531-17485-2(9)*** , Children's Pr.) Scholastic Library Publishing.

—Diplodocus. 2004. (Exploring Dinosaurs Ser.). (Illus.). 32p. (J). (gr. 2-6). 27.07 (978-1-59296-186-3(X)) Child's World, Inc.

—Edmontosaurus. 2004. (Exploring Dinosaurs Ser.). 32p. (J). (gr. 2-6). 27.07 (978-1-59296-235-8(1)) Child's World, Inc.

—Iguanodon. 2004. (Exploring Dinosaurs Ser.). 32p. (J). (gr. 2-6). 27.07 (978-1-59296-187-0(8)) Child's World, Inc.

—Is It a Dinosaur? 2007. (Scholastic News Nonfiction Readers Ser.). (Illus.). 24p. (J). (gr. 1-2). 19.00 (***978-0-531-17486-9(7)*** , Children's Pr.) Scholastic Library Publishing.

—Maiasaura. 2004. (Exploring Dinosaurs Ser.). 32p. (J). (gr. 2-6). 27.07 (978-1-59296-188-7(6)) Child's World, Inc.

—Megalosaurus. 2004. (Exploring Dinosaurs Ser.). 32p. (J). (gr. 2-6). 27.07 (978-1-59296-236-5(X)) Child's World, Inc.

—Oviraptor. 2004. (Exploring Dinosaurs Ser.). (Illus.). 32p. (J). (gr. 2-6). 27.07 (978-1-59296-189-4(4)) Child's World, Inc.

—Psittacosaurus. 2004. (Exploring Dinosaurs Ser.). 32p. (J). (gr. 2-6). 27.07 (978-1-59296-237-2(8)) Child's World, Inc.

—Spinosaurus. 2004. (Exploring Dinosaurs Ser.). (Illus.). 32p. (J). (gr. 2-6). 27.07 (978-1-59296-234-1(3)) Child's World, Inc.

—Stegosaurus. 2004. (Science of Dinosaurs Ser.). 32p. (J). (gr. 2-6). 27.07 (978-1-59296-044-6(8)) Child's World, Inc.

—Triceratops. 2004. (Science of Dinosaurs Ser.). (Illus.). 32p. (J). (gr. 2-6). 27.07 (978-1-59296-045-3(6)) Child's World, Inc.

—Troodon. 2004. (Exploring Dinosaurs Ser.). 32p. (J). (gr. 2-6). 27.07 (978-1-59296-238-9(6)) Child's World, Inc.

—Tyrannosaurus Rex. 2004. (Science of Dinosaurs Ser.). 32p. (J). (gr. 2-6). 27.07 (978-1-59296-046-0(4)) Child's World, Inc.

—Velociraptor. 2004. (Science of Dinosaurs Ser.). 32p. (J). (gr. 2-6). 27.07 (978-1-59296-047-7(2)) Child's World, Inc.

Green, Jen. Dinosaur Hunters: Discover the Incredible Lost World of Dinosaurs. 2007. (Illus.). 29p. (J). 19.95 (***978-0-7624-3008-6(7)***) Running Pr. Bk. Pubs.

Green, Tamara. Cretaceous Dinosaur World. Grant, Richard, illus. 1998. 32p. (J). (gr. 4 up). lib. bdg. 22.60 (978-0-8368-2173-4(4)) Stevens, Gareth Inc.

—Dinosaur Babies. Grant, Richard, illus. 1999. 32p. (J). (gr. 4 up). lib. bdg. 22.60 (978-0-8368-2290-8(0)) Stevens, Gareth Inc.

—Great Dinosaur Hunters. Grant, Richard, illus. 1999. (World of Dinosaurs Ser.). 32p. (J). (gr. 4 up). lib. bdg. 21.26 (978-0-8368-2291-5(9)) Stevens, Gareth Inc.

—Jurassic Dinosaur World. Grant, Richard, illus. 1998. 32p. (J). (gr. 4 up). lib. bdg. 22.60 (978-0-8368-2174-1(2)) Stevens, Gareth Inc.

—Triassic Dinosaur World. Grant, Richard, illus. 1998. (World of Dinosaurs Ser.). 32p. (J). (gr. 4 up). lib. bdg. 21.26 (978-0-8368-2175-8(0)) Stevens, Gareth Inc.

—What Dinosaurs Ate. Grant, Richard, illus. 1999. (World of Dinosaurs Ser.). 32p. (J). (gr. 4 up). lib. bdg. 21.26 (978-0-8368-2295-3(1)) Stevens, Gareth Inc.

Griffin, Georgene. Dinosaurs. 2001. (How to Draw Ser.). (Illus.). 32p. (J). (gr. 2-5). lib. bdg. 25.27 (978-1-58952-153-7(6)) Rourke Publishing, LLC.

Group/McGraw-Hill, Wright. I Dig Dinosaurs: Level K, 6 vols., Vol. 2. (First Explorers Ser.). 24p. (J). (gr. 1-2). 34.95 (978-0-7699-1460-2(8)) Shortland Pubns. (U. S. A.) Inc.

—Set 2: Los Dinosaurios, 6 vols., Vol. 2. (First Explorers. Primeros Exploradores Nonfiction Sets Ser.). (SPA.). (gr. 1-2). 34.95 (978-0-7699-1484-8(5)) Shortland Pubns. (U. S. A.) Inc.

Gunzi, Christiane. Dinosaurs. 2007. (Feels Real Ser.). (Illus.). 10p. (J). 4.99 (***978-0-7641-6051-6(6)***) Barron's Educational Series, Inc.

Gussoni, Clizia. The Awesome Book of Dinosaurs! McDonnell, Luke, illus. 2005. 288p. pap. 9.95 (978-0-7624-2643-0(8) , Running Pr. Kids) Running Pr. Bk. Pubs.

Habiger, Geoff. Dinosaur Learning Activity Book. Habiger, Geoff & Gower, Jim, illus. 2005. 80p. (J). per. 7.95 (978-1-932926-96-5(8)) Artemesia Publishing, LLC.

Hall, Katy, pseud. Dino Riddles. 2003. (gr. k-3). lib. bdg. 11.80 (978-0-613-70800-5(8)) Tandem Library Bks.

Hall, Katy, pseud & Eisenberg, Lisa. Dino Riddles. Rubel, Nicole, illus. (J). (gr. k-3). 2003. 48p. pap. 3.99 (978-0-14-250179-5(4) , Puffin); 2002. 40p. 13.99 (978-0-8037-2239-2(7) , Dial) Penguin Group (USA) Inc.

Halls, Kelly Milner. Dinosaur Mummies: Beyond Bare-Bone Fossils. 2007. (J). pap. 8.95 (***978-1-58196-034-1(4)***) Darby Creek Publishing.

—Dinosaur Mummies: Beyond Bare-Bone Fossils. Spears, Rick, illus. 2003. (Junior Library Guild Selection Ser.). 48p. (J). (gr. 4 up). 17.95 (978-1-58196-000-6(X)) Darby Creek Publishing.

—The Random House Dinosaur Travel Guide. Rey, Luis, illus. 2006. 224p. (J). (gr. 1). 10.99 (978-0-375-82715-0(3) , Random Hse. Bks. for Young Readers) Random Hse. Children's Bks.

Ham, Ken & Snelling. Dinosaurs of Eden: A Biblical Journey through Time. 2000. (Illus.). 64p. (J). (gr. 4-7). 13.99 (978-0-89051-340-8(6)) Master Bks.

Hammerslough, J. Fandex Family Guide: Dinosaurs. (Illus.). 119.40 (978-0-7611-3621-7(5) , 23621) Workman Publishing Co., Inc.

Hammerslough, Jane. The Dinosaurs. 2004. (Illus.). 50p. (J). 9.95 (978-0-7611-2976-9(6) , 12976) Workman Publishing Co., Inc.

Hanrahan, Brendan. Great Day Trips in the Connecticut Valley of the Dinosaurs. 2004. (Road to Discovery Guides Ser.). (Illus.). 256p. pap. (978-0-9630181-1-3(6) , A Road to Discovery Series Guide) Perry Heights Pr.

Harcourt School Publishers Staff. Dinosaur Times On Level. 3rd ed. 2002. (Trophies Reading Program Ser.). (Illus.). pap. 5.10 (978-0-15-323169-8(6)) Harcourt Schl. Pubs.

Harpster, Steve. Dinosaurs. 2006. (Pencil, Paper, Draw! Ser.). (Illus.). 64p. (J). pap., pap., spiral bd. 5.95 (978-1-4027-2974-4(X)) Sterling Publishing Co., Inc.

Harris, Jerald D. Dino Finder Dot-to-Dot. 2002. (Connect the Dots & Color Ser.). (Illus.). 80p. (J). (gr. 1-4). pap. 5.95 (978-0-8069-9093-4(7)) Sterling Publishing Co., Inc.

—Dinosaur Discovery Dot-to-Dot: Connect the Dots & Color. 2004. (Illus.). 80p. (J). pap. 5.95 (978-1-4027-0815-2(7)) Sterling Publishing Co., Inc.

Harris, Nicholas. Dinosaurs & Other Prehistoric Life. 2006. (First Library of Knowledge). 32p. (J). (gr. 2-4). 23.70 (978-1-4103-0350-9(0) , Blackbirch Pr., Inc.) Thomson Gale.

—Incredible Journey Through the World of Dinosaurs. 2003. (Incredible Journey Ser.). 32p. (gr. 3 up). 9.95 (978-1-57768-958-4(5) , Bedrick, Peter Bks.) School Specialty Publishing.

Harrison, Carol. Dinosaurs Everywhere. Courtney, Richard, illus. 1998. 40p. (J). (ps-1). pap. 14.95 (978-0-590-00089-5(6) , Cartwheel Bks.) Scholastic, Inc.

Harrub, Brad. God Made Dinosaurs. 2005. (Illus.). 32p. (J). pap. 3.00 (978-0-932859-71-6(2)) Apologetics Pr., Inc.

Hartzog, Brooke. The Dinosaur Footprints & Roland T. Bird. 1999. (Dinosaurs & Their Discoverers Ser.). (Illus.). 24p. (J). (gr. k-4). lib. bdg. 18.75 (978-0-8239-5330-1(0) , PowerKids Pr.) Rosen Publishing Group, Inc., The.

Haslam, Andrew. Dinosaurs. 2004. (Make It Work! Science Ser.). (Illus.). 48p. (J). (gr. 3-6). 12.95 (978-1-58728-364-2(6) , Two Can Publishing) T&N Children's Publishing.

Haslam, Andrew & Benton, M. J. Dinosaurs. 2004. (Make It Work! Science Ser.). (Illus.). 48p. (J). (gr. 3-6). pap. 6.95 (978-1-58728-352-9(2) , Two Can Publishing) T&N Children's Publishing.

Hawcock, David & Brampton, Clare. Dinosaurs: With Six Amazing Dinosaur Models. 2004. (Illus.). 16p. (J). bds. 24.95 (978-1-4052-0801-7(5)) Egmont Bks., Ltd. GBR. *Dist:* Trafalgar Square Publishing.

Haywood, R. Los Dinosaurios. 2004. (Great Searches Ser.).Tr. of Great Dinosaur Search. (SPA., Illus.). 32p. (J). (ps up). pap. 8.95 (978-0-7460-4500-8(X)); lib. bdg. 16.95 (978-1-58086-339-1(6)) EDC Publishing.

Heins, Edward. Drawing Dinosaurs. 2001. (gr. k-3). lib. bdg. 15.30 (978-0-613-72458-6(5)) Tandem Library Bks.

Helm, Charles. Daniel's Dinosaurs: A True Story of Discovery. Zimmer, Joan, illus. 2004. 32p. (J). (gr. k-3). 16.95 (978-1-897066-06-5(6)); pap. 6.95 (978-1-897066-07-2(4)) Maple Tree Pr. CAN. *Dist:* Perseus Distribution.

Henderson, Doug. Asteroid Impact. 2000. (Illus.). 40p. (J). (gr. 1-5). 16.99 (978-0-8037-2500-3(0) , Dial) Penguin Group (USA) Inc.

Henry, Michel. Raptor: The Life of a Young Deinonychus. Penney, Rich, illus. 2007. 32p. (J). (gr. 2-8). 15.95 (978-0-8109-5775-6(2)) Abrams, Harry N. , Inc.

Heywood, Rosie. Great Dinosaur Search. rev. ed. 2005. (Illus.). 32p. (J). pap. 7.99 (978-0-7945-1046-6(9) , Usborne) EDC Publishing.

—Great Dinosaur Search. 2000. (ps-2). lib. bdg. 17.60 (978-0-613-50314-3(7)) Tandem Library Bks.

Hincks, Joseph. Dinosaur Dictionary. 1999. (Illus.). 96p. (J). (gr. 1-8). lib. bdg. 27.95 (978-0-86593-586-0(6)) Rourke Publishing, LLC.

Hinkler Books Staff. Dinosaurs. Penton Overseas, Inc. Staff, ed. Kiely, Robert, illus. rev. ed. 2006. (Touch, Feel & Hear Ser.). 6p. (J). (gr. 2-5). 9.95 (978-1-74157-725-9(X)) Hinkler Bks. Pty, Ltd. AUS. *Dist:* Penton Overseas, Inc.

Hixson, Bryce. Get Your Poop in a Group. Hixson, Bryce, illus. 2003. (Illus.). (J). per. 9.95 (978-1-931801-01-0(0)) Loose In The Lab.

Holmes & Thom. Dawn of the Dinosaur Age: The Triassic Period. 2008. (Prehistoric Earth Ser.). 208p. (gr. 6-12). 35.00 (***978-0-8160-5959-1(4)*** , Chelsea Hse.) Facts On File, Inc.

—Last of the Dinosaurs: The Late Cretaceous Period. 2008. (Prehistoric Earth Ser.). 208p. (gr. 6-12). 35.00 (***978-0-8160-5962-1(4)*** , Chelsea Hse.) Facts On File, Inc.

—Time of the Giants: The Mid-Late Jurassic Periods. 2008. (Prehistoric Earth Ser.). 208p. (gr. 6-12). 35.00 (***978-0-8160-5960-7(8)*** , Chelsea Hse.) Facts On File, Inc.

Holmes, Thom & Holmes, Laurie. Baby Dinosaurs: Eggs, Nests, & Recent Discoveries. Skrepnick, Michael William, illus. 2003. (Dinosaur Library). 104p. (J). (gr. 6-12). lib. bdg. 26.60 (978-0-7660-2074-0(6)) Enslow Pubs., Inc.

—Feathered Dinosaurs: The Origin of Birds. Skrepnick, Michael William, illus. 2002. (Dinosaur Library). 112p. (YA). (gr. 6-12). lib. bdg. 26.60 (978-0-7660-1454-1(1)) Enslow Pubs., Inc.

—Gigantic Long-Necked Plant-Eating Dinosaurs: The Prosauropods & Sauropods. Skrepnick, Michael William, illus. 2001. (Dinosaur Library). 128p. (J). (gr. 6-12). lib. bdg. 26.60 (978-0-7660-1449-7(5)) Enslow Pubs., Inc.

—Great Dinosaur Expeditions & Discoveries: Adventures with the Fossil Hunters. Skrepnick, Michael William, illus. 2003. (Dinosaur Library). 112p. (J). lib. bdg. 26.60 (978-0-7660-2078-8(9)) Enslow Pubs., Inc.

—Meat-Eating Dinosaurs: The Theropods. Skrepnick, Michael William, illus. 2001. (Dinosaur Library). 128p. (YA). (gr. 6-12). lib. bdg. 26.60 (978-0-7660-1452-7(5)) Enslow Pubs., Inc.

Holmes, Thom, et al. Armored, Plated, & Bone-Headed Dinosaurs: The Ankylosaurs, Stegosaurs & Pachycephalosaurs. Skrepnick, Michael William, illus. 2002. (Dinosaur Library). 128p. (YA). (gr. 6-12). lib. bdg. 26.60 (978-0-7660-1453-4(3)) Enslow Pubs., Inc.

—Horned Dinosaurs: The Ceratopsians. Skrepnick, Michael William, illus. 2001. (Dinosaur Library). 128p. (YA). (gr. 6-12). lib. bdg. 26.60 (978-0-7660-1451-0(7)) Enslow Pubs., Inc.

—Peaceful Plant-Eating Dinosaurs: The Iguanodonts, Duckbills & Other Ornithopods. Skrepnick, Michael William, illus. 2001. (Dinosaur Library). 128p. (YA). (gr. 6-12). lib. bdg. 26.60 (978-0-7660-1450-3(9)) Enslow Pubs., Inc.

Holtz, Thomas. T Rex: Hunter or Scavenger? 2003. (gr. k-3). lib. bdg. 11.80 (978-0-613-70804-3(0)) Tandem Library Bks.

Holtz, Thomas & Benton, Michael J., contrib. by. Dinosaurs of the World, 11 vols., Set. 1999. (Illus.). 700p. (gr. 4 up). 471.36 (978-0-7614-7072-4(7) , Cavendish, Marshall Reference Bks.) Cavendish, Marshall Corp.

Holtz, Thomas R. Dinosaurs: The Most Complete, Up-To-Date Encyclopedia for Dinosaur Lovers of All Ages. Rey, Luis V., illus. 2007. 432p. (gr. 7). (J). lib. bdg. 37.99 (****978-0-375-92419-4(1));*** (YA). 34.99 (****978-0-375-82419-7(7))*** Random Hse. Children's Bks. (Random Hse. Bks. for Young Readers).

—A Little Giant Book: Dinosaurs. Riley, Terry, illus. 2007. 360p. (J). pap. 6.95 (****978-1-4027-4982-7(1))*** Sterling Publishing Co., Inc.

—The Little Giant Book of Dinosaurs. Riley, Terry, illus. 2001. (Little Giant Bks.). 352p. (J). (gr. 3-7). pap. 6.95 (978-0-8069-7391-3(9)) Sterling Publishing Co., Inc.

—T. Rex: Hunter or Scavenger? Jurassic Park Institute. Skrepnick, Michael William, illus. 2003. 48p. (J). (gr. 2-5). lib. bdg. 11.99 (978-0-375-91297-9(5) , Random Hse. Bks. for Young Readers) Random Hse. Children's Bks.

—T. Rex: Hunter or Scavenger?: Jurassic Park Institute. Skrepnick, Michael William, illus. 2003. (Step into Reading Ser.). 48p. (J). (gr. 2-5). pap. 3.99 (978-0-375-81297-2(0) , Random Hse. Bks. for Young Readers) Random Hse. Children's Bks.

Holub, Joan. Dinosaurs. 2003. (ps-2). lib. bdg. 14.15 (978-0-613-84475-8(0)) Tandem Library Bks.

Hopkins, Bruce R. Dinosaur Discovery 3-D: Construct Your Own Velociraptor. Wilson, Phil, illus. 2000. 32p. (J). (gr. k up). act. bk. ed. 19.95 (978-1-58117-085-6(8) , Intervisual/Piggy Toes) Dalmatian Pr.

Horner, John R. Digging up Dinosaurs with Jack Horner. 2007. 48p. (J). (gr. 3-7). 12.95 (978-1-56037-396-4(2)) Farcountry Pr.

Hort, Lenny. Did Dinosaurs Eat Pizza? Mysteries Science Hasn't Solved. O'Brian, John, illus. rev. ed. 2006. 32p. (J). 15.95 (978-0-8050-6757-6(4) , Holt, Henry & Co. Bks. For Young Readers) Holt, Henry & Co.

Hughes, Monica. Fighting Dinosaurs. 2008. (J). lib. bdg. (****978-1-59716-545-7(X))*** Bearport Publishing Co., Inc.

—Really Big Dinosaurs. 2008. (I Love Reading Ser.). (J). lib. bdg. (****978-1-59716-543-3(3))*** Bearport Publishing Co., Inc.

Husted, Russell. Hey Mom, What about Dinosaurs? 2000. (Illus.). 240p. (J). pap. 12.95 (978-1-57921-234-6(4)) WinePress Publishing.

Hutton, Simon. Brilliant Billy's Big Book of Dinosaurs. Glicksman, Caroline, illus. 2008. 80p. (J). pap. 8.95 (****978-1-84270-569-8(5))*** Andersen GBR. *Dist:* Independent Pubs. Group.

Jacobs, Marian B. Why Did the Dinosaurs Become Extinct? 1999. (Library of Why). (Illus.). 24p. (J). (gr. k-4). lib. bdg. 18.75 (978-0-8239-5276-2(2) , PowerKids Pr.) Rosen Publishing Group, Inc., The.

Jay, Michael. Age of Dinosaurs. 2003. (Illus.). 32p. (J). lib. bdg. 25.70 (978-1-4109-0006-7(1)) Raintree.

—Flying Creatures. 2003. (Illus.). 32p. (J). lib. bdg. 25.70 (978-1-4109-0007-4(X)) Raintree.

—Rise of the Reptiles. 2003. (Illus.). 32p. (J). lib. bdg. 25.70 (978-1-4109-0009-8(6)) Raintree.

Jeffus, Richard & Jeffus, Sharon. Dinosaur Art Project Book. 1999. (Illus.). 30p. (J). pap. 12.95 (978-0-9677386-7-3(9)) Visual Manna.

Jenkins, Steve. Prehistoric Actual Size. 2005. (Illus.). 36p. (J). (gr. 3-5). 16.00 (978-0-618-53578-1(0)) Houghton Mifflin Co. Trade & Reference Div.

Jeunesse, Gallimard. Dinosaurs. 1998. (Discovery Box Ser.). 32p. (J). (gr. 1-5). 11.95 (978-0-590-92685-0(3) , Scholastic Reference) Scholastic, Inc.

Johnson, Jay. Dinosaurs. Harris, Greg, illus. 2005. 24p. (J). (ps-ps). pap. 5.99 incl. audio compact disk (978-1-58610-930-1(8)) Learning Horizons, Inc.

Johnson, Jinny. Brachiosaurus & Other Dinosaur Giants. 2007. (J). (****978-1-59920-065-1(1))*** Smart Apple Media.

—The Children's Dinosaur Encyclopedia. 2004. (Illus.). 96p. (J). (978-0-681-02672-8(3)) Marshall Editions.

—Dino Wars: Discover the Deadliest Dinosaurs, Bloodiest Battles, & Super Survival Strategies of the Prehistoric World. 2005. (Illus.). 144p. (J). (gr. 1-7). 17.95 (978-0-8109-5798-5(1) , Abrams Bks. for Young Readers) Abrams, Harry N. , Inc.

—Dinosaur Skeletons & Other Prehistoric Animals. 1999. (Weird & Wonderful! Ser.). (Illus.). 46p. (YA). (gr. 3). pap. 7.99 (978-0-7681-0184-3(0) , 57004, McClanahan Bk.) Learning Horizons, Inc.

—Iguanodon & Other Plant-Eating Dinosaurs. 2007. (J). (****978-1-59920-067-5(8))*** Smart Apple Media.

—Triceratops & Other Horned & Armoured Dinosaurs. Rosewarne, Graham, illus. 2007. (J). (****978-1-59920-064-4(3))*** Smart Apple Media.

—Velociraptor & Other Speedy Killers. 2007. (J). (****978-1-59920-066-8(X))*** Smart Apple Media.

Johnson, Rebecca L. & Sereno, Paul C. Paul Sereno: Digging for Dinosaurs. 2003. (National Geographic Reading Expeditions Ser.). (Illus.). 32p. (J). pap. (978-0-7922-8887-9(4)) National Geographic Society.

Johnston, Marianne. From the Dinosaurs of the Past to the Birds of the Present. 2000. (Prehistoric Animals & Their Modern-Day Relatives Ser.). 24p. (J). (gr. k-4). lib. bdg. 18.75 (978-0-8239-5204-5(5) , PowerKids Pr.) Rosen Publishing Group, Inc., The.

Josephs, Ben. Where Dinosaurs Walked. 2003. (Compass Point Phonics Readers Ser.). (Illus.). 16p. (J). (gr. 1 up). 13.26 (978-0-7565-0531-8(3)) Compass Point Bks.

Kalman, Bobbie. What Is a Dinosaur? 1999. (Science of Living Things Ser.). (Illus.). 32p. (J). (gr. 2-3). pap. (978-0-86505-949-8(7)); (978-0-86505-921-4(7)) Crabtree Publishing Co.

Kalman, Bobbie & Walker, Niki. What Is a Dinosaur? 1999. (Illus.). 32p. (J). (ps-ps). lib. bdg. 14.10 (978-0-613-19537-9(X)) Tandem Library Bks.

Kavanagh, James. Dinosaurs Nature Activity Book. 2004. (Pocket Naturalist Ser.). (Illus.). 32p. pap. 6.95 (978-1-58355-257-5(X)) Waterford Pr., Ltd.

Kchodl, Joseph 'PaleoJoe'. Hidden Dinosaurs. DeWildt, Jim, illus. 2006. 32p. (J). (978-1-934133-00-2(0)) Mackinac Island Pr., Inc.

Kearns, Kimberly & Amaral, Gayla. BJ's Rub a Dub Dub. Davis, Guy, ed. Johnson, Jay B., illus. 1999. (Barney Ser.). 14p. (J). (ps-k). 5.95 (978-1-57064-612-6(0)) Scholastic, Inc.

Keiran, Monique. Albertosaurus: Death of a Predator. 2002. (Discoveries in Palaeontology Ser.: No. 1). (Illus.). 56p. (J). (gr. 5 up). pap. 9.95 (978-1-55192-550-9(8)) Raincoast Bk. Distribution CAN. *Dist:* Perseus Distribution.

—Pachyrhinosaurus: The Mystery of the Horned Dinosaur. 2006. (Illus.). 56p. 21.95 (978-1-894974-03-5(4)) Heritage Hse. Publishing Co., Ltd. CAN. *Dist:* Midpoint Trade Bks., Inc.

Keller. Theme Pack: Dinosaurs. 2002. (Pair-It Bks.). (Illus.). (J). pap. (978-0-7398-6374-9(6)) Steck-Vaughn.

Kelley, K. C. Deadly Dinos. 2006. (Boys Rock! Ser.). (Illus.). 32p. (J). (gr. 1-5). 24.21 (978-1-59296-728-5(0)) Child's World, Inc.

Kelly, Harold G. How the Dinosaurs Disappeared. 2006. (Rosen Publishing Group's Reading Room Collection). (J). lib. bdg. (978-1-4042-3340-9(7) , PowerKids Pr.) Rosen Publishing Group, Inc., The.

Kelsey, Elin. Canadian Dinosaurs. (Wow Canada! Ser.). (Illus.). 96p. (J). (gr. 3-7). 2003. pap. 19.95 (978-1-894379-56-4(X)); 2007. 29.95 (****978-1-897349-08-3(4));*** 2007. pap. 19.95 (****978-1-897066-85-0(6))*** Maple Tree Pr. CAN. *Dist:* Firefly Bks., Ltd., Perseus Distribution.

—Finding Out about Dinosaurs. 2000. (Science Explorers Ser.). (Illus.). 40p. (J). (gr. 3-7). 19.95 (978-1-895688-97-9(3) , Owl Bks.) Maple Tree Pr. CAN. *Dist:* Firefly Bks., Ltd.

Kerley, Barbara. The Dinosaurs of Waterhouse Hawkins: An Illuminating History of Mr. Warehouse Hawkins, Artist & Lecturer. Selznick, Brian, illus. 2001. 48p. (J). (gr. 2-5). pap. 16.95 (978-0-439-11494-3(2) , Levine, Arthur A. Bks.) Scholastic, Inc.

Kim, F. S. Dig Deep! Looking for Dinosaurs. 2006. (Illus.). 32p. (J). pap. (****978-0-439-83877-1(0))*** Scholastic, Inc.

Kranking, Kathy. Gone! Dino Extinction. 2006. (Illus.). 32p. (J). pap. (****978-0-439-83878-8(9))*** Scholastic, Inc.

Kranz, Peter M. Dinosaurs of the District of Columbia. 2003. (Illus.). vii, 31p. per. 14.95 (978-0-9748618-0-7(4)) Dinosaur Fund.

Kronstadt, Jonathan. Dinosaur Dig It! Jankowski, Dan, illus. 2007. 48p. (J). (gr. 2 up). 9.99 (****978-0-439-92634-8(3)*** , Tangerine Pr.) Scholastic, Inc.

Kudlinski, Kathleen V. Boy, Were We Wrong about Dinosaurs! Schindler, S. D., illus. 2005. 32p. (J). (ps-4). 15.99 (978-0-525-46978-0(8) , Dutton Juvenile) Penguin Group (USA) Inc.

Kurtz, Jane. Mister Bones: Dinosaur Hunter. Haverfield, Mary, illus. 2004. (Ready-to-Read Ser.). 32p. (J). pap. 3.99 (978-0-689-85960-1(0) , Aladdin) Simon & Schuster Children's Publishing.

Lakeshore Learning Materials Staff, contrib. by. Dinosaurs, Dinosaurs Packet. 2000. (J). pap. 34.95 (978-1-929255-47-4(0)) Lakeshore Learning Materials.

Lambert, David. Dinosaurs. 2006. (DK Guides Ser.). 64p. (J). (gr. 8). pap. 7.99 (978-0-7566-1793-6(6)) Dorling Kindersley Publishing, Inc.

—Guide to Dinosaurs. 2000. (Illus.). 64p. (J). (gr. 1-10). 19.99 (978-0-7894-5237-5(5)) Dorling Kindersley Publishing, Inc.

Lambert, David & Diagram Visual Staff. Super Little Giant Book of Prehistoric Creatures. 2006. (Illus.). 288p. (J). pap. 6.95 (978-1-4027-2593-7(0)) Sterling Publishing Co., Inc.

Lambert, David, et al. Dinosaur Encyclopedia: From Dinosaurs to the Dawn of Man. 2001. (Illus.). 376p. (J). (gr. 5 up). 29.99 (978-0-7894-7935-8(4)) Dorling Kindersley Publishing, Inc.

—Super Little Giant Book of Dinosaurs. 2005. (Illus.). 288p. (J). (gr. 4-7). pap., pap. 6.95 (978-1-4027-2595-1(7)) Sterling Publishing Co., Inc.

Landau, Elaine. Apatosaurus. rev. ed. 2006. (True Book Ser.). (Illus.). 47p. (J). (978-0-531-16799-1(2)) Children's Pr., Ltd.

—Apatosaurus. 1999. (True Bks.). (Illus.). 48p. (J). (gr. 3-5). 25.00 (978-0-516-20434-5(3) , Children's Pr.) Scholastic Library Publishing.

—Apatosaurus. 1999. (gr. 3-6). lib. bdg. 15.25 (978-0-613-37271-8(9)) Tandem Library Bks.

—Dinosaurs, 6 vols. 2006. (True Booktm Ser.). (Illus.). (J). (gr. 3-5). 150.00 (****978-0-531-16789-2(5))*** Scholastic Library Publishing.

—Pterosaurs. 1999. (True Bks.). (Illus.). 48p. (J). (gr. 3-5). 25.00 (978-0-516-20447-5(5) , Children's Pr.) Scholastic Library Publishing.

—Pterosaurs. 1999. (gr. 3-6). lib. bdg. 15.25 (978-0-613-37515-3(7)) Tandem Library Bks.

—Stegosaurus. 2006. (True Book Ser.). (Illus.). 47p. (J). (978-0-531-16830-1(1)) Children's Pr., Ltd.

—Stegosaurus. 1999. (True Bks.). (Illus.). 48p. (J). (gr. 3-5). 25.00 (978-0-516-20452-9(1) , Children's Pr.) Scholastic Library Publishing.

—Stegosaurus. 1999. (gr. 3-6). lib. bdg. 15.25 (978-0-613-37552-8(1)) Tandem Library Bks.

—Triceratops. 2006. (True Book Ser.). (Illus.). 47p. (J). (978-0-531-16831-8(X)) Children's Pr., Ltd.

—Triceratops. 1999. (True Bks.). (Illus.). 48p. (J). (gr. 3-5). pap. 6.95 (978-0-516-26506-3(7)); 25.00 (978-0-516-20453-6(X)) Scholastic Library Publishing. (Children's Pr.).

—Tyrannosaurus Rex. rev. ed. 2006. (True Book Ser.). (Illus.). 47p. (J). (978-0-531-16832-5(8)) Children's Pr., Ltd.

—Tyrannosaurus Rex. 1999. (gr. 3-6). lib. bdg. 15.25 (978-0-613-37570-2(X)) Tandem Library Bks.

—Velociraptor. rev. ed. 2006. (True Book Ser.). (Illus.). 47p. (J). (978-0-531-16833-2(6)) Children's Pr., Ltd.

—Velociraptor. 1999. (Dinosaurs Ser.). (Illus.). 48p. (J). (gr. 3-5). 25.00 (978-0-516-20437-6(8) , Children's Pr.) Scholastic Library Publishing.

—Velociraptor. 1999. (gr. 3-6). lib. bdg. 15.25 (978-0-613-37576-4(9)) Tandem Library Bks.

Landis, Beth, ed. My First Dinosaur Board Book. 2004. (Illus.). 36p. (J). bds. 5.99 (978-0-7566-0281-9(5)) Dorling Kindersley Publishing, Inc.

Larousse Kingfisher Chambers Staff & Madgwick, Wendy. Dinosaurs. 2000. (Questions & Answers about... Ser.). (Illus.). 40p. (J). (gr. 4-6). pap. 7.95 (978-0-7534-5309-4(6) , Kingfisher) Houghton Mifflin Co. Trade & Reference Div.

Larousse Mexico Staff, ed. Los Dinosaurios. 2005. (Mi Pequena Enciclopedia Ser.). (SPA.). 38p. (ps-k). pap. 3.95 (978-970-22-0861-7(0)) Larousse, Ediciones, S. A. de C. V. MEX. *Dist:* Houghton Mifflin Co. Trade & Reference Div.

Lauber, Patricia. News about Dinosaurs. 1998. (J). pap. 6.95 (978-0-87628-976-1(6)) Ctr. for Applied Research in Education, The.

LeapFrog Staff, compiled by. Leap into Science: Dinosaurs. 2001. (J). (ps-2). spiral bd. 14.99 (978-1-58605-049-8(4)) LeapFrog Enterprises, Inc.

Lee, Brian, illus. The World of Dinosaurs. 2005. (J). (978-0-7607-6569-2(3)) backpackbook.

Leigh, Susannah. Puzzle Dinosaurs. 2007. (Young Puzzles Ser.). 32p. (J). pap. 6.99 (****978-0-7945-1778-6(1)*** , Usborne) EDC Publishing.

Less, Emma. Little Scribbles: Dinosaur Fun. Harpster, Steve, illus. 2006. (Little Scribbles Ser.). 12p. (J). bds. 5.95 (978-1-4027-3805-0(6)) Sterling Publishing Co., Inc.

Lessem, Dino Don. Baby Dinosaurs. Bindon, John, illus. 2001. (When Dinosaurs Lived Ser.). 16p. (J). pap. 5.99 (978-0-448-42536-8(X) , Grosset & Dunlap) Penguin Group (USA) Inc.

—Baby Dinosaurs. 2001. (gr. k-3). lib. bdg. 14.15 (978-0-613-64430-3(1)) Tandem Library Bks.

—Biggest Dinosaurs. Bindon, John, illus. 2001. (When Dinosaurs Lived Ser.). 40p. (J). pap. 5.99 (978-0-448-42535-1(1) , Grosset & Dunlap) Penguin Group (USA) Inc.

—Biggest Dinosaurs. 2001. (gr. k-3). lib. bdg. 14.15 (978-0-613-64431-0(X)) Tandem Library Bks.

Lessem, Don. Armored Dinosaurs. Bindon, John, illus. 2005. (Meet the Dinosaurs Ser.). 32p. (J). (gr. 2-4). lib. bdg. 23.93 (978-0-8225-1374-2(9)) Lerner Publishing Group.

—Carnivoros Gigantes. Bindon, John, illus. 2005. Tr. of Giant Meat-Eating Dinosaurs. (SPA.). 32p. (J). (gr. 2-4). pap. 6.95 (978-0-8225-2963-7(7)); (ps-7). lib. bdg. 23.93 (978-0-8225-2962-0(9) , Ediciones Lerner) Lerner Publishing Group.

—The Deadliest Dinosaurs. Bindon, John, illus. 2005. (Meet the Dinosaurs Ser.). 32p. (J). (gr. 2-4). 23.93 (978-0-8225-1421-3(4)); pap. 6.95 (978-0-8225-2619-3(0)) Lerner Publishing Group.

—The Dinosaur Atlas. Bindon, John, illus. 2003. 64p. (J). (gr. 3-7). 18.95 (978-1-55297-830-6(3)) Firefly Bks., Ltd.

—Dinosaur Worlds: New Dinosaurs - New Discoveries. 2003. (Illus.). 192p. (YA). (gr. 4-6). 19.95 (978-1-56397-597-4(1)) Boyds Mills Pr.

—Dinosaurios Acorazados. Bindon, John, illus. 2005. Tr. of Armored Dinosaurs. (SPA.). 32p. (J). (gr. 2-4). pap. 6.95 (978-0-8225-2958-3(0)); (gr. 3-7). lib. bdg. 23.93 (978-0-8225-2949-1(1) , Ediciones Lerner) Lerner Publishing Group.

—Dinosaurios Cornudos. Bindon, John, illus. 2005. Tr. of Horned Dinosaurs. (SPA.). 32p. (J). (gr. 2-4). pap. 6.95 (978-0-8225-2967-5(X)); (gr. 3-7). lib. bdg. 23.93 (978-0-8225-2966-8(1) , Ediciones Lerner) Lerner Publishing Group.

—Los Dinosaurios Mas Pequenos. Bindon, John, illus. 2005. Tr. of Smallest Dinosaurs. (SPA.). 32p. (J). (gr. 2-4). pap. 6.95 (978-0-8225-2969-9(6)); (gr. 4-7). lib. bdg. 23.93 (978-0-8225-2968-2(8) , Ediciones Lerner) Lerner Publishing Group.

—Dinosaurios Pico de Pato. Bindon, John, illus. 2005. Tr. of Duck-Billed Dinosaurs. (SPA.). 32p. (J). (gr. 2-4). pap. 6.95 (978-0-8225-2961-3(0)); (gr. 3-7). lib. bdg. 23.93 (978-0-8225-2959-0(9) , Ediciones Lerner) Lerner Publishing Group.

—Dinosaurs. 2005. (Time for Learning Ser.). (Illus.). 96p. 12.98 (978-0-7853-8504-2(5) , 7190500) Publications International, Ltd.

—Dinosaurs A to Z: The Ultimate Dinosaur Encyclopedia. Sovak, Jan, illus. 2003. (Reference Ser.). 224p. (J). 22.95 (978-0-439-16591-4(1)) Scholastic, Inc.

—Duck-Billed Dinosaurs. Bindon, John, illus. 2005. (Meet the Dinosaurs Ser.). 32p. (J). (gr. 2-4). lib. bdg. 23.93 (978-0-8225-1369-8(2)) Lerner Publishing Group.

—The Fastest Dinosaurs. Bindon, John, illus. 2005. (Meet the Dinosaurs Ser.). 32p. (J). (gr. 2-4). 23.93 (978-0-8225-1422-0(2)); pap. 6.95 (978-0-8225-2620-9(4)) Lerner Publishing Group.

—Feathered Dinosaurs. Bindon, John, illus. 2005. (Meet the Dinosaurs Ser.). 32p. (J). (gr. 2-4). 23.93 (978-0-8225-1423-7(0)); pap. 6.95 (978-0-8225-2621-6(2)) Lerner Publishing Group.

—Giant Meat-Eating Dinosaurs. Bindon, John, illus. (Meet the Dinosaurs Ser.). (J). 2005. 32p. (gr. 2-4). lib. bdg. 23.93 (978-0-8225-3925-4(X)); 2004. pap. 7.95 (978-0-8225-5326-7(0) , Lerner Pubns.) Lerner Publishing Group.

—Giant Plant-Eating Dinosaurs. Bindon, John, illus. 2005. (Meet the Dinosaurs Ser.). 32p. (J). (gr. 2-4). lib. bdg. 23.93 (978-0-8225-1371-1(4)) Lerner Publishing Group.

—Herbivoros Gigantes. Bindon, John, illus. 2005. Tr. of Giant Plant-Eating Dinosaurs. (SPA.). 32p. (J). (gr. 2-4). pap. 6.95 (978-0-8225-2965-1(3)); (gr. 3-7). lib. bdg. 23.93 (978-0-8225-2964-4(5) , Ediciones Lerner) Lerner Publishing Group.

—Horned Dinosaurs. Bindon, John, illus. 2005. (Meet the Dinosaurs Ser.). 32p. (J). (gr. 2-4). lib. bdg. 23.93 (978-0-8225-1370-4(6)) Lerner Publishing Group.

—Raptors! The Nastiest Dinosaurs. Peters, David, illus. 1998. 32p. (J). (gr. 1-5). pap. 5.95 (978-0-316-56428-1(1)) Little Brown & Co.

—The Smallest Dinosaurs. Bindon, John, illus. 2005. (Meet the Dinosaurs Ser.). 32p. (J). (gr. 2-4). lib. bdg. 23.93 (978-0-8225-1372-8(2)) Lerner Publishing Group.

—The Smartest Dinosaurs. Bindon, John, illus. 2005. (Meet the Dinosaurs Ser.). 32p. (J). (gr. 2-4). 23.93 (978-0-8225-1373-5(0)); pap. 6.95 (978-0-8225-2618-6(2)) Lerner Publishing Group.

Lessem, Don & Dodson, Peter. Dinosaurs: Facts, Profiles, & Amazing Information. 2007. (Illus.). 32p. (J). (****978-1-4127-1343-6(9)); (*978-1-4127-1344-3(7))*** Publications International, Ltd.

Levin, Freddie. 1-2-3 Draw Dinosaurs & Other Prehistoric Animals: Step-by-Step Guide. 2000. (One-Two-Three Draw Ser.). (Illus.). 64p. (J). (gr. 1-5). pap. 8.99 (978-0-939217-41-0(4)) Peel Productions, Inc.

Levy, Barbara Soloff. Dinosaurs Dot-to-Dot. 2006. 32p. (J). pap. 2.95 (978-0-486-45320-0(0)) Dover Pubns., Inc.

Lewis, Brenda Ralph. Meat-Eating Dinosaurs. 2006. (Nature's Monsters Ser.). (Illus.). 32p. lib. bdg. (978-0-8368-6843-2(9)) Stevens, Gareth Inc.

—Plant-Eating Dinosaurs. 2006. (Nature's Monsters Ser.). (Illus.). 32p. (J). lib. bdg. (978-0-8368-6844-9(7)) Stevens, Gareth Inc.

—Small & Deadly Dinosaurs. 2006. (Nature's Monsters Ser.). (Illus.). 32p. (J). lib. bdg. (978-0-8368-6846-3(3)) Stevens, Gareth Inc.

Liflander, Pamela. Dinosaurs. deluxe ed. 2006. (Start Exploring Ser.). (Illus.). 16p. (J). (gr. 3 up). pap. 19.95 (978-0-7624-1591-5(6) , Running Pr. Kids) Running Pr. Bk. Pubs.

Lindeen, Carol. Apatosaurio: Apatosaurus. 2007. (ENG & SPA.). 24p. (J). (978-0-7368-7635-3(9)) Capstone Pr., Inc.

—Braquiosaurio: Brachiosaurus. 2007. (ENG & SPA.). 24p. (J). (978-0-7368-7636-0(7)) Capstone Pr., Inc.

—Velociraptor: Velociraptor. 2007. (ENG & SPA.). (J). (978-0-7368-7641-4(3)) Capstone Pr., Inc.

Lindeen, Carol K. Apatosaurus. 2006. (Pebble Plus—Dinosaurs & Prehistoric Animals Ser.). (Illus.). 23p. (J). (978-0-7368-4256-3(X)) Capstone Pr., Inc.

—Brachiosaurus. 2006. (Pebble Plus—Dinosaurs & Prehistoric Animals Ser.). (Illus.). 24p. (J). (978-0-7368-4257-0(8)) Capstone Pr., Inc.

Lindsay, William. On the Trail of Incredible Dinosaurs. 1998. (American Museum of Natural History Ser.). (Illus.). 96p. (J). (gr. k-3). pap. 14.99 (978-0-7894-3628-3(0)) Dorling Kindersley Publishing, Inc.

Litchfield, J. & Brooks, F. Dinosaurs. 2004. (Illus.). 10p. (J). 4.95 (978-0-7945-0590-5(2)) EDC Publishing.

Litchfield, Jo. First Picture Dinosaurs. 2007. (First Picture Board Bks). 16p. (J). bds. 11.99 (****978-0-7945-1752-6(8)*** , Usborne) EDC Publishing.

Llewellyn, Claire. Ask Dr. K. Fisher about Dinosaurs. Sheppard, Kate, illus. 2007. (Ask Dr. K. Fisher about... Ser.). 32p. (J). (gr. k-3). 10.95 (978-0-7534-6106-8(4) , Kingfisher) Houghton Mifflin Co. Trade & Reference Div.

Long, John. Dinosaurs. 2007. (Insiders Ser.). 64p. (J). (gr. 3-7). 16.99 (****978-1-4169-3857-6(5))*** Simon & Schuster Children's Publishing.

Long-Neck. (Dinosaur World Ser.). 24p. (J). 7.95 (978-1-4048-0496-8(X)) Picture Window Bks.

Long, Olivia. There's a Dinosaur in My Bathtub! Long, Olivia, illus. Date not set. (World of Dinosaurs Ser.). (Illus.). 32p. (J). (ps-4). (978-1-880042-11-3(8)) Shelf-Life Bks.

Longhurst, Terry. I Can Draw Dinosaurs. 2002. (I Can Draw Ser.). 32p. (J). 9.95 (978-0-7525-7277-2(6)) Parragon, Inc.

Lorbiecki, Marybeth. Triceratops. 2007. (North American Dinosaurs Ser.). (Illus.). 24p. (J). (978-1-60044-253-7(6)) Rourke Publishing, LLC.

Lunis, Natalie. A T. Rex Named Sue: Sue Hendrickson's Huge Discovery. 2007. (Fossil Hunters Ser.). 32p. (J). (gr. 3-7). lib. bdg. 25.27 (978-1-59716-259-3(0)) Bearport Publishing Co., Inc.

—The Tiny Titanosaurs: Luis Chiappe's Dinosaur Nests. 2007. (Fossil Hunters Ser.). (Illus.). 32p. (J). lib. bdg. 25.27 (978-1-59716-373-6(2)) Bearport Publishing Co., Inc.

Lunis, Natalie & Sereno, Paul C. SuperCroc: Paul's Sereno's Dinosaur Eater. 2007. (Fossil Hunters Ser.). (J). lib. bdg. 25.27 (978-1-59716-255-5(8)) Bearport Publishing Co., Inc.

Maccarone, Grace. Dinosaurs. Courtney, Richard, illus. 2001. (Hello Reader! Ser.). 32p. (J). (gr. k-2). pap. 3.99 (978-0-439-20060-8(1) , Cartwheel Bks.) Scholastic, Inc.

—Dinosaurs. 2001. (gr. k-3). lib. bdg. 11.80 (978-0-613-35504-9(0)); (Illus.). (J). 10.79 (978-0-606-21148-2(9)) Tandem Library Bks.

Maccarone, Grace & Lopez, Erika. Dinosaurs. 2007. (Scholastic Reader Collection). 144p. (J). pap. 6.99 (*978-0-439-93251-6(3)) Scholastic, Inc.

MacLeod, Elizabeth. What Did Dinosaurs Eat? And Other Things You Want to Know about Dinosaurs. Sauve, Gordon, illus. 32p. (J). (gr. k-3). 2002. (978-1-55337-460-2(6)); 2001. (978-1-55337-063-5(5)) Kids Can Pr., Ltd.

—What Did Dinosaurs Eat? And Other Things You Want to Know about Dinosaurs. 2002. (gr. k-3). lib. bdg. 14.10 (978-0-613-89641-2(6)) Tandem Library Bks.

Malam, John. Dinosaur. (Experience Ser.). (J). 2006. (Illus.). 64p. (gr. 5-8). 15.99 (978-0-7566-1412-6(0)); 2004. 5.99 (978-0-7566-0402-8(8)); 2003. (Illus.). 16p. pap. 3.99 (978-0-7894-9825-0(1)); 2003. (Illus.). 14.99 (978-0-7894-9777-2(8)) Dorling Kindersley Publishing, Inc.

Malm, John, et al. Atlas de Dinosaurios: Dinosaur Atlas. 2007. (Illus.). 96p. (J). 19.99 (*978-970-718-509-8(0) , Silver Dolphin en Español) Advanced Marketing, S. de R. L. de C. V. MEX. *Dist:* Perseus Distribution.

Mammals; Dinosaurs; Human Body, 3 vols., Set. 2001. 192p. (J). 25.95 (978-0-7525-5456-3(5)) Parragon, Inc.

Manning, Linda & van Kampen, Vlasta. Dinosaur Days. 2002. (Illus.). 15p. (J). 8.95 (978-0-7737-3333-6(7)) Stoddart Kids CAN. *Dist:* Fitzhenry & Whiteside, Ltd.

Manning, Mick. Dino-Dinners. Granstrom, Brita, illus. 2007. 32p. (J). (ps-3). 16.95 (*978-0-8234-2089-6(2)) Holiday Hse., Inc.

Manning, Mick & Granstrom, Brita. Dinomania: Things to Do with Dinosaurs. 2002. (Illus.). 32p. (J). (gr. k-3). 16.95 (978-0-8234-1641-7(0)) Holiday Hse., Inc.

Manning, Phillip Lars. Dinomummy. 2007. (Illus.). 64p. (J). (gr. 4-6). 18.95 (*978-0-7534-6047-4(5) , Kingfisher) Houghton Mifflin Co. Trade & Reference Div.

Markle, Sandra. Outside & Inside Dinosaurs. 2003. (Outside Inside Ser.). (Illus.). 40p. (J). 7.99 (978-0-689-85778-2(0) , Aladdin) Simon & Schuster Children's Publishing.

—Outside & Inside Dinosaurs. 2003. (gr. 3-6). lib. bdg. 15.30 (978-0-613-66531-5(7)) Tandem Library Bks.

Marrin, Albert. Secrets from the Rocks: Dinosaur Hunting with Roy Chapman Andrews. Marrin, Albert, illus. 2002. (Illus.). 64p. (J). (gr. 4-8). 18.99 (978-0-525-46743-4(2) , Dutton Juvenile) Penguin Group (USA) Inc.

Marven, Nigel. Dinosaurs. 2007. (Kingfisher Knowledge Ser.). (Illus.). 64p. (J). 12.95 (*978-0-7534-6102-0(1) , Kingfisher) Houghton Mifflin Co. Trade & Reference Div.

Marzollo, Jean & Wick, Walter. I Spy a Dinosaur's Eye. 2003. (ps-2). lib. bdg. 11.80 (978-0-613-72243-8(4)) Tandem Library Bks.

Mash, Robert. Extreme Dinosaurs. Martin, Stuart, illus. 2007. 32p. (J). (gr. 1-7). 21.99 (*978-1-4169-3952-8(0) , Atheneum) Simon & Schuster Children's Publishing.

Masiello, Ralph. Ralph Masiello's Dinosaur Drawing Book. 2005. (Illus.). 32p. (J). (ps-k). pap. 6.95 (978-1-57091-528-4(8)); 16.95 (978-1-57091-527-7(X)) Charlesbridge Publishing, Inc.

Mattern, Joanne. Apatosaurus. 2006. (J). pap. (*978-0-8368-7702-1(0)); lib. bdg. (*978-0-8368-7695-6(4)) Stevens, Gareth Inc. (Weekly Reader Early Learning Library).

—Apatosaurus: Apatosaurio. 2006. (ENG & SPA.). (J). pap. (*978-0-8368-8025-0(0)); lib. bdg. (*978-0-8368-8018-2(8)) Stevens, Gareth Inc. (Weekly Reader Early Learning Library).

—Dinosaur Claws & Crests. 2005. (Prehistoric Creatures Ser.). (Illus.). 24p. (J). pap. (978-0-8368-4903-5(5)); lib. bdg. 19.33 (978-0-8368-4896-0(9)) Stevens, Gareth Inc.

—Dinosaur Skeletons & Skulls. 2005. (Prehistoric Creatures Ser.). (Illus.). 24p. (J). pap. (978-0-8368-4904-2(3)); lib. bdg. 19.33 (978-0-8368-4897-7(7)) Stevens, Gareth Inc.

—Dinosaur Spikes & Necks. 2005. (Prehistoric Creatures Ser.). (Illus.). 24p. (J). pap. (978-0-8368-4905-9(1)); lib. bdg. 19.33 (978-0-8368-4898-4(5)) Stevens, Gareth Inc.

—Dinosaur Tails & Armor. 2005. (Prehistoric Creatures Ser.). (Illus.). 24p. (J). pap. (978-0-8368-4906-6(X)); lib. bdg. 19.33 (978-0-8368-4899-1(3)) Stevens, Gareth Inc.

—Dinosaur Teeth & Beaks. 2005. (Prehistoric Creatures Ser.). (Illus.). 24p. (J). pap. (978-0-8368-4907-3(8)); lib. bdg. 19.33 (978-0-8368-4900-4(0)) Stevens, Gareth Inc.

—Dinosaur Wings & Fins. 2005. (Prehistoric Creatures Ser.). (Illus.). 24p. (J). pap. (978-0-8368-4908-0(6)); lib. bdg. 19.33 (978-0-8368-4901-1(9)) Stevens, Gareth Inc.

—Dinosaurios: Alas y Aletas. 2006. (SPA.). 24p. (J). pap. 5.95 (978-0-8368-6020-7(9)); lib. bdg. 19.33 (978-0-8368-6013-9(6)) Stevens, Gareth Inc.

—Dinosaurios: Colas y Corazas. 2006. (SPA.). 24p. (J). pap. 5.95 (978-0-8368-6021-4(7)); lib. bdg. 19.33 (978-0-8368-6014-6(4)) Stevens, Gareth Inc.

—Dinosaurios: Espinas Oseas y Cuellos. 2006. (SPA.). 24p. (J). pap. 5.95 (978-0-8368-6023-8(3)); lib. bdg. 19.33 (978-0-8368-6016-0(0)) Stevens, Gareth Inc.

—Dinosaurios, Dientes y Picos. 2005. (J). (SPA.). pap. (978-0-8368-6022-1(5)); (ENG & SPA.). lib. bdg. 19.33 (978-0-8368-6015-3(2)) Stevens, Gareth Inc.

—Dinosaurios, Equeletos y Craneos. 2005. (SPA.). (J). pap. (978-0-8368-6024-5(1)) Stevens, Gareth Inc.

—Dinosaurios: Esqueletos y Craneos. 2005. (ENG & SPA., Illus.). 24p. (J). (ps). lib. bdg. 19.33 (978-0-8368-6017-7(9)) Stevens, Gareth Inc.

—Dinosaurios, Garras y Crestas. 2005. (J). (SPA.). pap. (978-0-8368-6025-2(X)); (ENG & SPA.). lib. bdg. 19.33 (978-0-8368-6018-4(7)) Stevens, Gareth Inc.

—Giganotosaurus. 2006. (J). pap. (*978-0-8368-7703-8(9)); (ENG & SPA.). pap. (*978-0-8368-8026-7(9)); lib. bdg. (*978-0-8368-7696-3(2)); (ENG & SPA.). lib. bdg. (*978-0-8368-8019-9(6)) Stevens, Gareth Inc. (Weekly Reader Early Learning Library).

—Stegosaurus. 2006. (J). pap. (*978-0-8368-7704-5(7)); lib. bdg. (*978-0-8368-7697-0(0)) Stevens, Gareth Inc. (Weekly Reader Early Learning Library).

—Stegosaurus: Estegosaurio. 2006. (ENG & SPA.). pap. (*978-0-8368-8027-4(7)); lib. bdg. (*978-0-8368-8020-5(X)) Stevens, Gareth Inc. (Weekly Reader Early Learning Library).

—Triceratops. 2006. (J). pap. (*978-0-8368-7705-2(5)); lib. bdg. (*978-0-8368-7698-7(9)) Stevens, Gareth Inc. (Weekly Reader Early Learning Library).

—Triceratops: Triceratops. 2006. (ENG & SPA., Illus.). 24p. (J). pap. (*978-0-8368-8028-1(5)); lib. bdg. (*978-0-8368-8021-2(8)) Stevens, Gareth Inc. (Weekly Reader Early Learning Library).

—Tyrannosaurus Rex. 2006. (J). pap. (*978-0-8368-7706-9(3)); lib. bdg. (*978-0-8368-7699-4(7)) Stevens, Gareth Inc. (Weekly Reader Early Learning Library).

—Tyrannosaurus Rex: Tiranosaurio Rex. 2006. (ENG & SPA.). (J). pap. (*978-0-8368-8029-8(3)); lib. bdg. (*978-0-8368-8022-9(6)) Stevens, Gareth Inc. (Weekly Reader Early Learning Library).

—Velociraptor. 2006. (J). pap. (*978-0-8368-7707-6(1)); lib. bdg. (*978-0-8368-7700-7(4)) Stevens, Gareth Inc. (Weekly Reader Early Learning Library).

—Velociraptor: Velociraptor. 2006. (ENG & SPA.). (J). pap. (*978-0-8368-8030-4(7)); lib. bdg. (*978-0-8368-8023-6(4)) Stevens, Gareth Inc. (Weekly Reader Early Learning Library).

Matthews, Rupert. Ankylosaurus. 2004. (Illus.). 32p. (J). pap. 6.50 (978-1-4034-4916-0(3)); lib. bdg. (978-1-4034-4909-2(0)) Heinemann Library.

—Apatosaurus. 2004. (Illus.). 32p. (J). pap. 6.50 (978-1-4034-4917-7(1)); lib. bdg. (978-1-4034-4910-8(4)) Heinemann Library.

—Baryonyx. 2004. (Illus.). 32p. (J). pap. 6.50 (978-1-4034-4918-4(X)); lib. bdg. (978-1-4034-4911-5(2)) Heinemann Library.

—Brachiosaurus. 2003. (Gone Forever Ser.). (Illus.). 32p. (J). pap. 6.50 (978-1-4034-3667-2(3)); 22.79 (978-1-4034-3660-3(6)); lib. bdg. 22.79 (978-1-4034-3656-6(8)) Heinemann Library.

—Cretaceous Dinosaurs. Stalio, Ivan, illus. 2002. (Dinosaurs Undercover Ser.). 40p. (J). 29.94 (978-1-56711-602-1(7) , Blackbirch Pr., Inc.) Thomson Gale.

—Diplodocus. 2003. (Gone Forever Ser.). (Illus.). 32p. pap. 6.50 (978-1-4034-3416-6(6)); (J). lib. bdg. 22.79 (978-1-4034-0788-7(6)) Heinemann Library.

—Edmontosaurus. 2004. (Illus.). 32p. (J). pap. 6.50 (978-1-4034-4920-7(1)) Heinemann Library.

—End of the Dinosaurs. 2002. (Dinosaurs Undercover Ser.). (Illus.). 40p. (J). 29.94 (978-1-56711-603-8(5) , Blackbirch Pr., Inc.) Thomson Gale.

—Iguanodon. 2003. (Heinemann First Library). (Illus.). 32p. (J). lib. bdg. 22.79 (978-1-4034-3657-3(6)); (978-1-4034-3668-9(1)) Heinemann Library.

—Jurassic Dinosaurs. Stalio, Ivan, illus. 2002. (Dinosaurs Undercover Ser.). 40p. (J). 29.94 (978-1-56711-601-4(9) , Blackbirch Pr., Inc.) Thomson Gale.

—Pterodactyl. 2003. (Illus.). 32p. pap. 6.50 (978-1-4034-3418-0(2)); (J). lib. bdg. 22.79 (978-1-4034-0790-0(8)) Heinemann Library.

—Seismosaurus. 2004. (Illus.). 32p. (J). pap. 6.50 (978-1-4034-4919-1(8)); lib. bdg. (978-1-4034-4912-2(0)) Heinemann Library.

—Stegosaurus. 2003. (Heinemann First Library). (Illus.). 32p. (J). lib. bdg. 22.79 (978-1-4034-3658-0(4)); (978-1-4034-3669-6(X)) Heinemann Library.

—Trachodon. 2004. (Illus.). 32p. (J). lib. bdg. (978-1-4034-4913-9(9)) Heinemann Library.

—Triceratops. 2003. (Gone Forever Ser.). (Illus.). 32p. pap. 6.50 (978-1-4034-3420-3(4)); (J). lib. bdg. 22.79 (978-1-4034-0792-4(4)) Heinemann Library.

—Troodon. 2004. (Illus.). 32p. (J). pap. 6.50 (978-1-4034-4921-4(X)); lib. bdg. (978-1-4034-4914-6(7)) Heinemann Library.

—Tyrannosaurus Rex. 2003. (Gone Forever Ser.). (Illus.). 32p. pap. 6.50 (978-1-4034-3421-0(2)); (J). lib. bdg. 22.79 (978-1-4034-0793-1(2)) Heinemann Library.

—Velociraptor. 2003. (Illus.). 32p. (J). lib. bdg. 22.79 (978-1-4034-3659-7(2)); (978-1-4034-3670-2(3)) Heinemann Library.

Matthies, Don-Oliver. Dinosaur Mazes. 2004. (Maze Craze Book Ser.). (Illus.). 40p. pap. 3.95 (978-1-4027-1292-0(8)) Sterling Publishing Co., Inc.

Mayes, Susan. The Usborne Book of Dinosaurs. Rey, Luis & Trotter, Stuart, illus. rev. ed. 2005. 32p. (J). pap. 6.95 (978-0-7945-0849-4(9) , Usborne) EDC Publishing.

Maynard, Christopher. The Best Book of Dinosaurs. (Best Book of... Ser.). 32p. (J). (gr. k-3). 2005. pap. 6.95 (978-0-7534-5872-3(1)); 1998. (Illus.). tchr. ed. 12.95 (978-0-7534-5116-8(6)) Houghton Mifflin Co. Trade & Reference Div. (Kingfisher).

McGraw-Hill Staff, ed. Dinosaurs. 2000. (Factfinders Ser.). (Illus.). 32p. (J). (gr. k-5). pap. 9.95 incl. cd-rom (978-1-57768-765-8(5)) School Specialty Publishing.

McGraw-Hill Staff & School Specialty Publishing Staff. Dinosaur: Dot-to-Dot. 2001. (Homework Helpers Activity Bks.). (Illus.). 56p. (J). (gr. k-1). pap., act. bk. ed. 2.99 (978-0-7682-0687-6(1) , FS109016, Schaffer, Frank) Schaffer, Frank Pubns.

McLaughlin, AnnMarie. Dinos! Filipowich, Bob, illus. 2001. (Textured Soft Shapes Ser.). 8p. (J). (ps-ps). 10.99 (978-1-58476-066-5(4)) Innovative Kids.

McMorrow, Annalisa. Dinosaurs. Chalk, Philip, illus. 1998. 48p. (J). (gr. 1-3). pap. 7.95 (978-1-57612-055-2(4) , MM2069) Monday Morning Bks., Inc.

McMullan, Kate. Dinosaur Hunters. Jones, John Randolph, illus. 2005. (Step into Reading Ser.: No. 5). 48p. (J). (gr. 2-4). pap. 3.99 (978-0-375-82450-0(2) , Random Hse. Bks. for Young Readers) Random Hse. Children's Bks.

—Dinosaur Hunters. Jones, John R., illus. 2005. 48p. (J). (gr. 2-4). lib. bdg. 11.19 (978-0-606-33717-5(2)) Tandem Library Bks.

Mehling, Carl. Dinosaurs. 2001. (It's All about! Ser.). (Illus.). 32p. (J). (gr. 2-5). lib. bdg. 25.27 (978-1-58952-159-9(5)) Rourke Publishing, LLC.

Mehling, Randi. Great Extinctions of the Past. 2007. (Scientific American Ser.). 72p. (J). (gr. 5-8). 30.00 (978-0-7910-9049-7(3) , Chelsea Hse.) Facts On File, Inc.

Meredith Books Staff, ed. Prehistoric Park. 2007. 48p. pap. 6.99 (*978-0-696-23691-4(5)) Meredith Bks.

Milbourne, Anna. Dinosaur. 2005. (First Discovery Ser.). 24p. (J). 9.95 (978-0-7945-0906-4(1) , Usborne) EDC Publishing.

Miles, Lisa. Dinosaurs Sticker Book. rev. ed. 2006. 24p. (J). pap. 8.99 (978-0-7945-1323-8(9) , Usborne) EDC Publishing.

Mini Dinosaurs: Brontosaurus. (Mini Dinosaurs Ser.). 10p. (J). 4.95 (978-1-58117-289-8(3) , Intervisual/Piggy Toes) Dalmatian Pr.

Mini Dinosaurs: Stegosaurus. (Mini Dinosaurs Ser.). 10p. (J). 4.95 (978-1-58117-290-4(7) , Intervisual/Piggy Toes) Dalmatian Pr.

Mini Dinosaurs: Triceratops. (Mini Dinosaurs Ser.). 10p. (J). 4.95 (978-1-58117-291-1(5) , Intervisual/Piggy Toes) Dalmatian Pr.

Mini Dinosaurs: Tyrannosaurus. (Mini Dinosaurs Ser.). 10p. (J). 4.95 (978-1-58117-292-8(3) , Intervisual/Piggy Toes) Dalmatian Pr.

Mitzo Thompson, Kim. Dinosaurs. 2006. (Sing along Activity Books with CDs Ser.). 32p. (J). pap. 4.99 (978-0-7696-4578-0(X)) School Specialty Publishing.

Monster Bones. (Science Works). 32p. (YA). 8.95 (978-1-4048-1126-3(5)) Picture Window Bks.

Morris, Ting & Morris, Neil. Dinosaurs. Levy, Ruth & Cowne, Joanne, illus. 2007. 32p. (J). (*978-1-59771-029-9(6)) Sea-To-Sea Pubns.

Most, Bernard. Dinosaur Cousins? Most, Bernard, illus. 2002. (Illus.). (J). 13.19 (978-0-7587-2377-2(6)) Book Wholesalers, Inc.

—Happy Holidaysaurus! Most, Bernard, illus. 2002. (Illus.). (J). 22.34 (978-0-7587-2695-7(3)) Book Wholesalers, Inc.

—How Big Were the Dinosaurs? Most, Bernard, illus. 2002. (Illus.). (J). 14.04 (978-0-7587-2758-9(5)) Book Wholesalers, Inc.

—Where to Look for a Dinosaur. Most, Bernard, illus. 2002. (Illus.). (J). 13.19 (978-0-7587-3995-7(8)) Book Wholesalers, Inc.

Mravec, James. Dinosaurs. 2005. Tr. of Dinosaurios. (Illus.). 96p. spiral bd. 9.98 (978-0-7853-8301-7(8) , 3460800) Publications International, Ltd.

Mullican, Judy. Dinosaurs Dinosaurs. Cress, Michelle H., illus. l.t. ed. 2000. (Cuddle Bks.). 6p. (J). (ps-1). pap. 10.95 (978-1-57332-184-6(2)) HighReach Learning, Inc.

—Like a Dinosaur. Gray, Stacy A., illus. l.t. ed. 2004. (HRL Board Book Ser.). 10p. (J). (ps-k). bds. 10.95 (978-1-57332-266-9(0)) HighReach Learning, Inc.

Murawski, Laura. How to Draw Dinosaurs. 2001. (Kid's Guide to Drawing Ser.). (Illus.). 24p. (J). (gr. 3). lib. bdg. 21.25 (978-0-8239-5550-3(8) , PowerKids Pr.) Rosen Publishing Group, Inc., The.

Murphy. Dinosaur Deals. 2002. (Illus.). pap. (978-0-7398-6793-8(8)) Steck-Vaughn.

Murphy, Stuart J. Dinosaur Deals. 2001. (gr. k-3). lib. bdg. 12.95 (978-0-613-59233-8(6)) Tandem Library Bks.

Murphy, Stuart J. & Henson, Heather. Dinosaur Deals. O'Malley, Kevin, illus. 2001. (MathStart Ser.). 40p. (J). (gr. 2 up). pap. 5.99 (978-0-06-446251-8(X) , Harper Trophy) HarperCollins Pubs.

Murray, Peter. Apatosaurus. 2001. (J). (978-1-58340-078-4(8)) Smart Apple Media.

—Pterodactyls. 2001. (J). (978-1-58340-079-1(6)) Smart Apple Media.

—Stegosaurus. 2001. (J). (978-1-58340-080-7(X)) Smart Apple Media.

—Triceratops. 2001. (J). (978-1-58340-081-4(8)) Smart Apple Media.

—Tyrannosaurus Rex. 2001. (J). (978-1-58340-082-1(6)) Smart Apple Media.

—Velociraptor. 2001. (J). (978-1-58340-083-8(4)) Smart Apple Media.

Myers, Tim. If You Give a T-Rex a Bone. Hovemann, Anisa Claire, illus. 2007. 32p. (J). pap. 8.95 (*978-1-58469-098-6(4)); 16.95 (*978-1-58469-097-9(6)) Dawn Pubns.

Nardo, Don. The Extinction of the Dinosaur. 2004. (KidHaven Science Library). (Illus.). (J). (gr. 4-7). 26.20 (978-0-7377-2637-4(7) , Greenhaven Pr., Inc.) Thomson Gale.

—The Extinction of the Dinosaurs. 2001. (Mystery Library). (Illus.). 112p. (YA). (gr. 4-12). 27.45 (978-1-56006-890-7(6) , Lucent Bks.) Thomson Gale.

Nash, Dylan. Dinosaurs. 2007. 12p. 19.95 (*978-1-58117-580-6(9) , Intervisual/Piggy Toes) Dalmatian Pr.

Nichols, V. The Incredible Dionsaur. M. J. Studios Staff, illus. 128p. (J). (gr. k-6). pap., act. bk. ed. 2.95 (978-1-879424-64-7(9)) Nickel Pr.

Norman, D. Dinosaurs Sticker & Puzzle Kid Kit (Bag) 2007. (Kid Kits Ser.). 24p. (J). pap. 14.99 (*978-1-60130-054-6(9)) EDC Publishing.

Norman, David. The Big Book of Dinosaurs. (Illus.). 448p. (gr. 5 up). 29.95 (978-0-941807-48-7(7) , Welcome Bks.) Welcome Enterprises, Inc.

Norman, David. Dinosaur. 2008. (DK Eyewitness Bks.). 72p. (J). (gr. 3-8). 15.99 (*978-0-7566-3772-9(4)) Dorling Kindersley Publishing, Inc.

Norman, David, et al. Dinosaur. Keates, Colin, illus. 2004. (Eyewitness Books). 72p. (J). lib. bdg. 19.99 (978-0-7566-0665-7(9)) Dorling Kindersley Publishing, Inc.

Norris, Richard. Meteorite! The Last Days of the Dinosaurs. 1999. (Turnstone Ocean Explorer Ser.). 64p. (YA). (gr. 4-7). 19.98 (978-0-7398-1240-2(8)) Raintree.

Nunn, Daniel. Brachiosaurus. 2007. (Illus.). 24p. (J). (*978-1-4034-9449-8(5)); pap. (*978-1-4034-9456-6(8)) Heinemann Library.

—Braquiosaurio. 2007. (SPA & ENG.). (J). pap. (*978-1-4329-0535-4(X)); lib. bdg. (*978-1-4329-0528-6(7)) Heinemann Library.

—Diplodocus. 2007. (Illus.). 24p. (J). (*978-1-4034-9447-4(9)); pap. (*978-1-4034-9454-2(1)) Heinemann Library.

—Tiranosaurio Rex. 2007. (SPA & ENG.). (J). pap. (*978-1-4329-0530-9(9)); lib. bdg. (*978-1-4329-0523-1(6)) Heinemann Library.

—Triceratops. 2007. (Illus.). 24p. (J). (*978-1-4034-9445-0(2)); pap. (*978-1-4034-9452-8(5)) Heinemann Library.

—Tyrannosaurus Rex. 2007. (Illus.). 24p. (J). (*978-1-4034-9444-3(4)); pap. (*978-1-4034-9451-1(7)) Heinemann Library.

—Velociraptor. 2007. (J). (SPA & ENG.). pap. (*978-1-4329-0534-7(1)); (SPA & ENG.). lib. bdg. (*978-1-4329-0527-9(9)); (Illus.). 24p. (*978-1-4034-9448-1(7)); (Illus.). 24p. pap. (*978-1-4034-9455-9(X)) Heinemann Library.

O'Brien, Patrick. Gigantic! How Big Were the Dinosaurs? rev. ed. 2002. (Illus.). 32p. (J). (gr. k-3). pap. 6.95 (978-0-8050-6899-3(6) , Holt, Henry & Co. Bks. For Young Readers) Holt, Henry & Co.

Oburkova, Eva. Toby's Travels Through Time: Puzzle Adventures in Dinosaur Days. 2006. (J). lib. bdg. (*978-0-8368-7497-6(8)) Stevens, Gareth Inc.

O'Donnell, Kerri. Birds: Modern-Day Dinosaurs. 2002. (Reading Room Collection). (Illus.). 24p. (J). pap. 4.40 (978-0-8239-8170-0(3)); lib. bdg. 18.75 (978-0-8239-3733-2(X)) Rosen Publishing Group, Inc., The.

Olien, Rebecca. What Happened to the Dinosaurs? A Book about Extinction. 2007. (First Facts Ser.). (Illus.). 24p. (J). 21.26 (978-0-7368-6378-0(8)) Capstone Pr., Inc.

Oliver, Martin. Esos Extintos Dinosaurios. Postgate, Daniel, tr. Postgate, Daniel, illus. 2003. (Coleccion Esa Gran Cultura).Tr. of Dead Dinosaurs. (SPA.). 134p. (YA). 7.96 (978-84-272-2137-6(1)) Molino, Editorial ESP. *Dist:* Lectorum Pubns., Inc.

Oliver, Rupert. Ankylosaurus. Long, Bernard, illus. 2001. (Dinosaur Library). 24p. (J). (gr. 3-6). lib. bdg. 25.27 (978-1-58952-027-1(0)) Rourke Publishing, LLC.

—Brachiosaurus. Payne, Roger, illus. 2001. (Dinosaur Library). 24p. (J). (gr. 3-6). lib. bdg. 25.27 (978-1-58952-028-8(9)) Rourke Publishing, LLC.

—Chasmosaurus. Long, Bernard, illus. 2001. (Dinosaur Library). 24p. (J). (gr. 3-6). lib. bdg. 25.27 (978-1-58952-029-5(7)) Rourke Publishing, LLC.

—Dilophosaurus. Howatt, Andrew, illus. 2001. (Dinosaur Library). 24p. (J). (gr. 3-6). lib. bdg. 25.27 (978-1-58952-030-1(0)) Rourke Publishing, LLC.

Olshevsky & Fritz, Sandy. Velociraptor. 2002. (Illus.). 32p. (J). lib. bdg. 24.25 (978-1-58340-176-7(8)) Smart Apple Media.

Olshevsky, George & Fritz, Sandy. Diplodocus. 2002. (Illus.). 32p. (J). lib. bdg. 24.25 (978-1-58340-177-4(6)) Smart Apple Media.

—Iguanodon. 2002. (Illus.). 32p. (J). lib. bdg. 24.25 (978-1-58340-180-4(6)) Smart Apple Media.

—Stegosaurus. 2002. (Illus.). 32p. (J). lib. bdg. 24.25 (978-1-58340-179-8(2)) Smart Apple Media.

—Triceratops. 2002. (Illus.). 32p. (J). lib. bdg. 24.25 (978-1-58340-178-1(4)) Smart Apple Media.

—Tyrannosaurus Rex. 2002. (Illus.). 32p. (J). lib. bdg. 24.25 (978-1-58340-175-0(X)) Smart Apple Media.

O'Malley, Kevin. Dinosaur Deals: Equivalent Values. 2001. 11.79 (978-0-606-22289-1(8)) Tandem Library Bks.

On the Trail of Incredible Dinosaurs. 1998. (Illus.). 96p. (J). (ps-ps). lib. bdg. 24.55 (978-0-613-75058-5(6)) Tandem Library Bks.

Opperman, Joachim. Dinosaurs (Dinosaurier) 1998. (Start Me Up Ser.: Vol. 2). (Illus.). 48p. (J). (gr. 4-7). pap. 12.95 (978-1-58185-001-7(8) , Tessloff Publishing) Quadrillion Media LLC.

Orme, David. Dinosaur. 2007. (Trailblazers Ser.). (Illus.). 36p. pap. 7.95 (***978-1-84167-426-1(5)***) Ransom Publishing Ltd. GBR. *Dist:* International Publishers Marketing.

Osborne, Mary Pope. Dinosaurs: A Nonfiction Companion to Dinosaurs Before Dark. 2000. (Magic Tree House Research Guide Ser.: No. 1). (J). (gr. k-3). lib. bdg. 13.00 (978-0-613-50295-5(7)) Tandem Library Bks.

Osborne, Mary Pope & Osborne, Will. Dinosaurs: A Companion to Dinosaurs Before Dark. Murdocca, Sal, illus. 2000. (Magic Tree House Research Guide Ser.: No. 1). 128p. (J). (gr. k-3). pap. 4.99 (978-0-375-80296-6(7) , Random Hse. Bks. for Young Readers) Random Hse. Children's Bks.

—Dinosaurs: A Nonfiction Companion to Dinosaurs Before Dark. 2000. (Magic Tree House Research Guide Ser.: No. 1). (J). (gr. k-3). 11.64 (978-0-606-18856-2(8)) Tandem Library Bks.

Owens, L. L. Ankylosaurus. 2007. (North American Dinosaurs Ser.). (Illus.). 24p. (J). (978-1-60044-251-3(X)) Rourke Publishing, LLC.

Owl Magazine Editors. Dinosaur Question & Answer Book: Everything Kids Want to Know about Dinosaurs, Fossils & Pa. 1998. (J). (978-0-606-13333-3(X)) Tandem Library Bks.

Oxlade, Chris. The Mystery of the Death of the Dinosaurs. 2002. (Can Science Solve? Ser.). 32p. (J). (gr. 4-7). (Illus.). lib. bdg. 22.79 (978-1-58810-664-3(0)); pap. 7.50 (978-1-58810-931-6(3) , 91567) Heinemann Library.

Parker, Steve. The Age of the Dinosaurs, 12 vols., Set. 1999. (Illus.). 768p. (YA). (gr. 5-10). lib. bdg. 249.00 (978-0-7172-9406-0(4) , Grolier) Scholastic Library Publishing.

—10 Things You Should Know about Dinosaurs. Gallagher, Belinda & Borton, Paula, eds. Bozer, Chris, illus. 2004. (10 Things You Should Know Ser.). 24p. (J). 6.99 (978-1-84236-120-7(1)) Miles Kelly Publishing, Ltd. GBR. *Dist:* Independent Pubs. Group.

Parker, Steve & Dewan, Ted. Inside Dinosaurs & Other Prehistoric Creatures. (Illus.). (J). pap. 18.95 (978-0-590-74839-1(4)) Scholastic, Inc.

Parker, Steve & Flegg, Jim. Dinosaurs: Great Little Fact Books. 2003. (Great Little Fact Books Ser.). (Illus.). 40p. (J). pap. 7.95 (978-1-84236-110-8(4)) Miles Kelly Publishing, Ltd. GBR. *Dist:* Independent Pubs. Group.

Patent, Dorothy Hinshaw. In Search of the Maiasaurs. 1998. (Frozen in Time Ser.). (Illus.). (J). (gr. 5-9). lib. bdg. 28.50 (978-0-7614-0787-4(1) , Benchmark Bks.) Cavendish, Marshall Corp.

Pearce, Querida L. The Land Before Time: How to Draw Dinosaurs. 1999. (Illus.). 64p. (YA). (gr. 2 up). pap. 6.95 (978-0-7373-0237-0(2) , 02372W) McGraw-Hill/Contemporary.

—The Land Before Time Dinosaur Q & A. Baugh, Bryan, illus. 1999. (Roxbury Park Bks.). 63p. (J). (gr. 1-3). pap. 7.95 (978-0-7373-0281-3(X) , 0281XW, Roxbury Park) Lowell Hse.

Pearcey, Alice. Dinosaur Stencil Book. Kushii, Tetsuo, illus. 2006. 14p. (J). bds. 12.99 (978-0-7945-1138-8(4) , Usborne) EDC Publishing.

Pearcey, Alice, ed. Dinosaur Jigsaw Atlas. Bird, Glen, illus. 2004. 20p. (J). 14.95 (978-0-7945-0913-2(4) , Usborne) EDC Publishing.

Penguin Books Staff, ed. Dinosaurs. (Learners Ser.). (Illus.). 48p. (J). 3.50 (978-0-7214-1701-1(9) , Dutton Juvenile) Penguin Group (USA) Inc.

Penner, Lucille Recht. Dinosaur Babies. 1999. (J). (gr. k-3). lib. bdg. 11.80 (978-0-8335-8503-5(7)) Tandem Library Bks.

Penton Overseas, Inc. Staff & Bater, Lucy. Dinosaur Stenciling Book: Learn to Draw Dinosaurs & Discover Dinosaur Facts. Robbins, Jim, illus. 2007. (J). (gr. 3-7). bds. 12.95 (978-1-59125-563-5(5) , Penton Kids) Penton Overseas, Inc.

Peponi, Inc. Staff. Beanosaurs Collectors Book. Werndl, Bruno, illus. 1998. 32p. (J). (ps up). pap. 6.00 (978-0-9662990-0-7(0)) Peponi, Inc.

Perez, Jessica. Who's Hiding Inside? Dinosaurs. Lensch, Chris, illus. 2005. (Who's Hiding Inside Ser.). 12p. (J). bds. 7.95 (978-1-58117-246-1(X) , Intervisual/Piggy Toes) Dalmatian Pr.

Peter Pauper Press Staff. Scratch & Sketch Dino Dudes: An Art Activity Book for Fossil Hunters of All Ages. 2005. (Activity Journal Ser.). 60p. 14.99 (978-1-59359-973-7(0)) Peter Pauper Pr. Inc.

Plant, Andrew. Could a Tyrannosaurus Play Table Tennis? Plant, Andrew, illus. 2006. (Illus.). 32p. (J). pap. 8.95 (978-1-929132-97-3(2)) Kane/Miller Bk. Pubs., Inc.

Plesiosaurs. 2004. 25.70 (978-1-4109-1060-8(1)); pap. 7.50 (978-1-4109-1228-2(0)); Pack. pap. 40.50 (978-1-4109-1235-0(3)) Raintree.

Poddington, L. World of Dinosaurs. 2004. (Interfact Play & Discover Ser.). (Illus.). 48p. (J). (ps-2). 14.95 incl. cd-rom (978-1-58728-627-8(0) , Two Can Publishing) T&N Children's Publishing.

Pomaska, Anna. Dinosaurs. 2005. 32p. (J). pap. 2.95 (978-0-486-44701-8(4)) Dover Pubns., Inc.

Potts, Aidan. Uneversaurus. 2007. 48p. (J). (gr. k-3). lib. bdg. 19.99 (978-0-385-75120-9(6)); (Illus.). 16.99 (978-0-385-75119-3(2)) Random Hse. Children's Bks. (Fickling, David Bks.).

Prehistoric Creatures Then & Now Series, 6 bks., Set. 2000. (Prehistoric Creatures Then & Now Ser.). (Illus.). 136.98 (978-0-7398-4168-6(8)) Steck-Vaughn.

Prehistoric Record Breakers, 6 Packs. (Discovery World Ser.). 24p. (gr. 1-2). 33.00 (978-0-7635-8477-1(0)) Rigby Education.

Priddy Books Staff. Picture Pops Dinosaur. 2004. (Illus.). 16p. (J). 12.95 (978-0-312-49343-1(6) , Priddy Bks.) St. Martin's Pr.

—Sticker Activity Dinosaur. 2004. (Illus.). 20p. (J). act. bk. ed. 5.95 (978-0-312-49354-7(1) , Priddy Bks.) St. Martin's Pr.

Priddy Books Staff & Priddy, Roger. Dinosaur ABC. l.t. rev. ed. 2004. (Illus.). 32p. (J). bds. 9.95 (978-0-312-49254-0(5) , Priddy Bks.) St. Martin's Pr.

—My Big Dinosaur Book. rev. ed. 2004. (Illus.). 12p. (J). bds. 5.95 (978-0-312-49328-8(2) , Priddy Bks.) St. Martin's Pr.

Priddy, Roger. Dino IQ. 2006. (J). 14p. bds. 9.95 (978-0-312-49884-9(5)); 18p. bds. 14.95 (978-0-312-49698-2(2)) St. Martin's Pr. (Priddy Bks.).

—Dinosaurs. 2005. (Sticker Activity Fun Workbooks). (J). (Illus.). 48p. (J). pap. 3.47 (978-0-312-49662-3(1)); 12p. bds. 0.97 (978-0-312-49608-1(7)) St. Martin's Pr. (Priddy Bks.).

—Dinosaurs ABC. rev. ed. 2004. 16p. (J). pap. 6.95 (978-0-312-49353-0(3) , Priddy Bks.) St. Martin's Pr.

—Pop up Dino IQ. 2007. 12p. (J). pap. 5.95 (***978-0-312-50046-7(7)*** , Priddy Bks.) St. Martin's Pr.

—Sticker Fun: Dinosaurs. rev. ed. 2004. (Illus.). 20p. (J). 3.95 (978-0-312-49310-3(X) , Priddy Bks.) St. Martin's Pr.

—Trucks, Bugs, Dinosaurs. 2006. 132p. (J). act. bk. ed. 12.95 (978-0-312-49741-5(5) , Priddy Bks.) St. Martin's Pr.

—3 in 1: My Big Animal,World,Dinosaur. 2005. (J). bds. 16.95 (978-0-312-49562-6(5) , Priddy Bks.) St. Martin's Pr.

Priddy, Roger & Priddy Books Staff. Dinosaurs. rev. ed. 2006. 48p. (J). bds. 3.47 (978-0-312-49797-2(0) , Priddy Bks.) St. Martin's Pr.

Pterosaurs. 2004. 25.70 (978-1-4109-1061-5(X)); pap. 7.50 (978-1-4109-1229-9(9)) Raintree.

Pterosaurs 6 Pack. 2004. pap. 40.50 (978-1-4109-1236-7(1)) Raintree.

Punter, Russell. Dinosaurs. Decker, Cynthia, illus. 2006. 48p. (J). pap. 5.99 (978-0-7945-1363-4(8) , Usborne) EDC Publishing.

Quigley, Mary. Dinosaur Digs. 2005. (Excavating the Past Ser.). (J). (978-1-4034-5996-1(7)) Heinemann Library.

Raintree Steck-Vaughn Staff. ¿Como Eran los Dinosaurios? 1999. (SPA.). (J). pap., stu. ed. 31.05 (978-0-7398-0764-4(1)) Steck-Vaughn.

Reader's Digest Editors. Build It Dinosaurs: Book & 3-D Models. 2007. (Illus.). 24p. (J). bds. 12.99 (978-0-7944-1167-1(3)) Reader's Digest Assn., Inc., The.

Red Bird Press Staff. Dinosaurs. 2004. (Mission Xtreme 3D Ser.). 18p. (J). pap. 5.95 (978-1-902626-61-1(3)) Red Bird Publishing GBR. *Dist:* Weatherhill, Inc.

—Secret Spex Dinosaurs. 2004. (Secret Picture Search Ser.). 18p. (J). pap. 5.95 (978-1-902626-65-9(6)) Red Bird Publishing GBR. *Dist:* Weatherhill, Inc.

Redmond, Shirley Raye. The Dog That Dug for Dinosaurs. Sullivan, Simon, illus. 2004. (Ready-to-Read Ser.). 32p. (J). pap. 3.99 (978-0-689-85708-9(X) , Aladdin) Simon & Schuster Children's Publishing.

Redmond, Shirley-Raye. The Dog That Dug for Dinosaurs: A True Story. Sullivan, Simon, illus. 2005. (Ready-to-Read Ser. Level 3). 32p. (J). lib. bdg. 15.00 (978-1-59054-993-3(7)) Fitzgerald Bks.

Reinhart, Matthew & Sabuda, Robert. Encyclopedia Prehistorica Dinosaurs: The Definitive Pop-up. Reinhart, Matthew & Sabuda, Robert, illus. 2005. (Sabuda Encyclopedias Ser.). (Illus.). 12p. (J). (gr. k). 27.99 (978-0-7636-2228-2(1)) Candlewick Pr.

Relf, Patricia. A Dinosaur Named Sue: The World's Most Complete T. Rex. 2000. (Hello Reader Ser.). (Illus.). 64p. (J). (gr. 1-5). pap. 15.95 (978-0-439-09985-1(4)) Scholastic, Inc.

Rey, Luis. Extreme Dinosaurs. 2001. (Illus.). 64p. (J). (gr. 3-7). 16.95 (978-0-8118-3086-7(1)) Chronicle Bks. LLC.

Richardson, Hazel. Dinosaurs & Other Prehistoric Life. 2003. (Smithsonian Handbooks Ser.). (Illus.). 224p. pap. 20.00 (978-0-7894-9361-3(6)) Dorling Kindersley Publishing, Inc.

Riehecky, Janet. Diplodocus. 2006. (Pebble Plus Ser.). (Illus.). 24p. (J). (978-0-7368-5352-1(9) , Pebble Bks.) Capstone Pr., Inc.

—Diplodocus: Diplodocus. 2007. (ENG & SPA.). (J). (978-0-7368-7637-7(5)) Capstone Pr., Inc.

—Giganotosaurus. 2008. (J). (***978-1-4296-0038-5(1)*** , Pebble Bks.) Capstone Pr., Inc.

—Iguanodon. 2006. (Pebble Plus Ser.). (Illus.). 24p. (J). (978-0-7368-5353-8(7) , 1252533, Pebble Bks.) Capstone Pr., Inc.

—Iguanodonte: Iguanodon. 2007. (ENG & SPA.). (J). (978-0-7368-7638-4(3)) Capstone Pr., Inc.

Riehecky, Janet. Megalosaurus. 2008. (J). (***978-1-4296-0039-2(X)*** , Pebble Bks.) Capstone Pr., Inc.

Rigby Education Staff. Discovery World Red Prehistoric. (Discovery World Ser.). (Illus.). 12p. (gr. 1-2). 31.00 (978-0-7635-2705-1(X)) Rigby Education.

Ripley, Esther. The Big Dinosaur Dig, Vol. 3. 2003. (DK Readers Ser.). (Illus.). 48p. (J). pap. 3.99 (978-0-7894-9290-6(3)) Dorling Kindersley Publishing, Inc.

—The Big Dinosaur Dig. 2003. (Illus.). 48p. (J). (ps-3). lib. bdg. 11.80 (978-0-613-62432-9(7)) Tandem Library Bks.

Ripley, Esther & Dorling Kindersley Publishing Staff. The Big Dinosaur Dig. 2003. (Readers Ser.). (Illus.). 48p. (J). 12.99 (978-0-7894-9540-2(6)) Dorling Kindersley Publishing, Inc.

Roberts, Russell. Where Did All the Dinosaurs Go? 2005. (Natural Disasters Ser.). (Illus.). 32p. (J). (gr. 1-4). lib. bdg. (978-1-58415-420-4(9)) Mitchell Lane Pubs., Inc.

Robins, Harry S. Dinosaur Alphabet. 2006. (Illus.). 80p. (J). (978-1-58394-167-6(3) , Frog Ltd.) North Atlantic Bks.

Robinson, Fay. A Dinosaur Named Sue: The Find of the Century. Sloan, Portia, illus. 1999. (Hello Reader! Ser.). 48p. (J). (gr. 1-4). pap. 3.99 (978-0-439-09983-7(8)) Scholastic, Inc.

—A Dinosaur Named Sue: The Find of the Century. Sloan, Portia, illus. 1999. 48p. (J). (ps-ps). lib. bdg. 11.80 (978-0-613-21435-3(8)) Tandem Library Bks.

—A Dinosaur Named Sue: The Find of the Century. 1999. 10.79 (978-0-606-17539-5(3)) Tandem Library Bks.

Rodriguez. Ichthyosaurus. 1999. (Prehistoric Creatures Then & Now Ser.). (Illus.). pap. 7.20 (978-0-7398-2145-9(8)) Steck-Vaughn.

—Iguanodon. 1999. (Prehistoric Creatures Then & Now Ser.). (Illus.). pap. 7.20 (978-0-7398-2146-6(6)) Steck-Vaughn.

—Pterodon. 1999. (Prehistoric Creatures Then & Now Ser.). (Illus.). pap. 7.20 (978-0-7398-2147-3(4)) Steck-Vaughn.

—Stegosaurus. 1999. (Prehistoric Creatures Then & Now Ser.). (Illus.). pap. 7.20 (978-0-7398-2149-7(0)) Steck-Vaughn.

—Tyrannosaurus Rex. 1999. (Prehistoric Creatures Then & Now Ser.). (Illus.). pap. 7.20 (978-0-7398-2150-3(4)) Steck-Vaughn.

Rodriguez, K. S. Iguanodon. 2000. (Prehistoric Creatures Then & Now Ser.). (Illus.). 32p. (J). (ps-3). lib. bdg. 22.83 (978-0-7398-0100-0(7)) Raintree.

—Pteranodon. 2000. (Prehistoric Creatures Then & Now Ser.). (Illus.). 32p. (J). (ps-3). lib. bdg. 22.83 (978-0-7398-0101-7(5)) Raintree.

—Stegosaurus. 2000. (Prehistoric Creatures Then & Now Ser.). (Illus.). 32p. (J). (ps-3). lib. bdg. 22.83 (978-0-7398-0102-4(3)) Raintree.

—Tyrannosaurus Rex. 1998. (Prehistoric Creatures Then & Now Ser.). (Illus.). 32p. (J). (ps-3). lib. bdg. 22.83 (978-0-7398-0104-8(X)) Raintree.

Rohr, Ian. Dinosaur Dig. 2006. (Real Deal - Yellow Ser.). (Illus.). 32p. (gr. 4-8). 19.00 (978-0-7910-9059-6(0)) Facts On File, Inc.

Rolland, Claudine. Dinosaurs. Saillard, Remi et al, illus. 2006. (Explore Your World Ser.). 28p. (J). (ps-1). 15.95 (978-1-55407-005-3(8)) Firefly Bks., Ltd.

Romero, Libby. Dinosaurs. 2005. 39.00 (***978-1-4108-4614-3(8)***) Benchmark Education Co.

Rooney, Anne. Dinosaurs. 2003. (Wicked Wallets Ser.). (Illus.). 96p. (YA). pap. (978-1-84347-037-3(3)) Chrysalis Children's Bks.

Rosenberg, Pam. Dinosaur Jokes. 2004. (Laughing Matters Ser.). 24p. (J). (gr. k-4). 22.79 (978-1-59296-073-6(1)) Child's World, Inc.

Rowe, Erna. Giant Dinosaurs. Smith, Merle, illus. 2000. 32p. (J). (ps-3). pap. 4.99 (978-0-590-40262-0(5)) Scholastic, Inc.

Royston. Dinosaurs Eye Openers. 1998. (J). pap. 7.95 (978-0-87628-162-8(5)) Ctr. for Applied Research in Education, The.

Rugg, Michael & Kieffer, Steve. Dinosaur Coloring Book. 2005. (Illus.). 24p. (J). pap. 4.95 (978-0-88839-593-1(0)) Hancock Hse. Pubs., Ltd. CAN. *Dist:* Hancock Hse. Pubs.

Running Press Staff & Daeschler, Ted. The Dinosaur Hunter's Kit: Discover a Lost World. 2001. (Illus.). 64p. (J). pap. 22.95 (978-0-7624-0967-9(3) , Running Pr. Kids) Running Pr. Bk. Pubs.

Sabertooth Cat. (Dinosaurs & Prehistoric Animals Ser.). 24p. (J). 6.95 (978-0-7368-5105-3(4)) Capstone Pr., Inc.

Saffer, Barbara. Science Questions & Answers: Dinosaurs. 2000. (Gifted & Talented Ser.). (Illus.). 64p. (J). (gr. 1-3). pap. 5.95 (978-0-7373-0348-3(4) , 03484W) Lowell Hse.

Sansone, Adele. El Pequeno Ganso Verde. 2001. (978-0-606-22736-0(9)) Tandem Library Bks.

Saunders-Smith, Gail, ed. Dinosaurs & Prehistoric Animals. 2005. (Pebble Plus Ser.). (Illus.). (J). (gr. k-1). lib. bdg. 199.30 (978-0-7368-4405-5(8)) Capstone Pr., Inc.

Sautter, Aaron. How to Draw Ferocious Dinosaurs. Martin, Cynthia, illus. 2008. (J). (***978-1-4296-0076-7(4)*** Capstone Pr., Inc.

Schatz, Dennis. Al Descubierto T Rex. 2003. (Al Descubierto Ser.). 16p. (J). bds. 18.95 (978-970-718-121-2(4) , Silver Dolphin en Español) Advanced Marketing, S. de R. L. de C. V. MEX. *Dist:* Perseus Distribution.

Schatz, Dennis. King of the Dinosaurs. 2005. (Illus.). 32p. (J). pap. (***978-0-439-77757-5(7)***) Scholastic, Inc.

Schatz, Dennis & Bonadonna, Davide. Uncover a T-Rex. Keitzmueller, Christian, illus. 2003. (Uncover Bks.). 16p. (J). 18.95 (978-1-57145-790-5(9)) Advantage Pubs. Group.

Schlein, Miriam. What the Dinosaurs Saw: Animals Living Then & Now. 1998. (Hello Reader! Science Ser.). (J). (978-0-606-13903-8(6)) Tandem Library Bks.

Schmidtling, Ron. Dinosounds. 2002. (Illus.). 44p. (J). per. 24.95 incl. audio compact disk (978-0-9717154-0-0(8)) Dinosounds, Inc.

Schoedel, Todd S. Dinosaurs & Dinosaur Babies: An Educational Coloring - Activity Book. Schoedel, Todd S., illus. 1998. (Illus.). 36p. (J). (gr. 1-6). pap. 4.95 (978-0-9664734-1-4(8)) Coloring Bk. Co., The.

Scholastic, Inc. Staff. Dinosaurs: Teaching Kit. 2000. (Super Science Readers Ser.). (Illus.). 16p. (J). 10.95 (978-0-439-18626-1(9)) Scholastic, Inc.

—My First Jumbo Book of Dinosaurs. 2007. (Little Scholastic Ser.). 10p. (J). 9.99 (***978-0-545-03041-0(2)***) Scholastic, Inc.

Scholastic, Inc. Staff. Wheel of Dinosaurs Pack. 1998. (Wheel Ser.). (Illus.). (J). (gr. 4-7). 3.95 (978-0-590-02723-6(9) , Scholastic Reference) Scholastic, Inc.

Schomp, Virginia. Ankylosaurus & Other Armored Plant-Eaters. 2002. (Prehistoric World Ser.). (Illus.). 32p. (J). 25.64 (978-0-7614-1023-2(6) , Benchmark Bks.) Cavendish, Marshall Corp.

—Apatosaurus & Other Giant Long-Necked Plant-Eaters. 2002. (Prehistoric World Ser.). (Illus.). 32p. (J). 25.64 (978-0-7614-1022-5(8) , Benchmark Bks.) Cavendish, Marshall Corp.

—Ceratosaurus: And Other Horned Meat-Eaters. 2005. (Prehistoric World Ser.). (Illus.). 31p. (J). (gr. 3-7). lib. bdg. (978-0-7614-2009-5(6) , Benchmark Bks.) Cavendish, Marshall Corp.

—Iguanodon: And Other Spiky-Thumbed Plant-Eaters. 2005. (Prehistoric World Ser.). (Illus.). 31p. (J). (gr. 3-7). lib. bdg. (978-0-7614-2005-7(3) , Benchmark Bks.) Cavendish, Marshall Corp.

—Ornithomimus: And Other Speedy Ostrich Dinosaurs. 2005. (Prehistoric World Ser.). (Illus.). 31p. (J). (gr. 3-7). lib. bdg. (978-0-7614-2006-4(1) , Benchmark Bks.) Cavendish, Marshall Corp.

—Plateosaurus: And Other Early Long-Necked Plant-Eaters. 2005. (Prehistoric World Ser.). (Illus.). 31p. (J). (gr. 3-7). lib. bdg. (978-0-7614-2008-8(8) , Benchmark Bks.) Cavendish, Marshall Corp.

—Therizinosaurus: And Other Colossal-Clawed Plant-Eaters. 2005. (Prehistoric World Ser.). (Illus.). 31p. (J). (gr. 3-7). lib. bdg. (978-0-7614-2007-1(X) , Benchmark Bks.) Cavendish, Marshall Corp.

—Triceratops & Other Horned Plant-Eaters. 2002. (Prehistoric World Ser.). (Illus.). 32p. (J). 25.64 (978-0-7614-1024-9(4) , Benchmark Bks.) Cavendish, Marshall Corp.

—Tyrannosaurus & Other Giant Meat-Eaters. 2002. (Prehistoric World Ser.). (Illus.). 32p. (J). 25.64 (978-0-7614-1020-1(1) , Benchmark Bks.) Cavendish, Marshall Corp.

—Velociraptor & Other Small, Speedy, Meat-Eaters. 2002. (Prehistoric World Ser.). (Illus.). 32p. (J). 25.64 (978-0-7614-1025-6(2) , Benchmark Bks.) Cavendish, Marshall Corp.

School Specialty Publishing. Dinosaurs. 2004. (Theme-A-Saurus(R) Ser.). 80p. (J). pap. 12.99 (978-1-57029-483-9(6) , WPH99049, Totline Pubns.) Schaffer, Frank Pubns.

—Dinosaurs. 2003. (Brighter Child Activity Bks.). 32p. (J). (ps-1). pap. 2.99 (978-0-7696-3217-9(3) , Brighter Child) School Specialty Publishing.

—Fact & Opinion. 2003. 48p. (J). (gr. 2 up). pap. 6.99 (978-0-7424-1832-5(4) , FS99150); (gr. 3 up). pap. 6.99 (978-0-7424-1833-2(2) , FS99151); (gr. 4 up). pap. 6.99 (978-0-7424-1834-9(0) , FS99152) School Specialty Publishing.

—Learn about Dinosaurs. 2005. (Learn about Coloring Bks.). 32p. (J). (ps-3). pap. 1.99 (978-0-7696-4157-7(1) , Brighter Child) School Specialty Publishing.

Scipionyx (Dinosaur Profiles) 2004. 11.20 (978-1-4103-0496-4(5) , Blackbirch Pr., Inc.) Thomson Gale.

Scott, Foresman and Company Staff. Dinosaurs, Dinosaurs, Vol. 8. 2001. (J). pap. 29.36 (978-0-673-80902-5(1) , Scott Foresman) Addison Wesley Schl.

Scott, Janine. Discovering Dinosaurs. 2002. (Spyglass Books). (Illus.). 24p. (J). (gr. 1 up). lib. bdg. 18.60 (978-0-7565-0231-7(4)) Compass Point Bks.

Scott, Peter David, illus. Dinosaur. 2006. 31p. (J). (***978-0-7607-7524-0(9)***) backpackbook.

The Search for Dinosaurs. 2000. (Digging Up the Past Ser.). 48p. (J). (gr. 4-7). lib. bdg. (978-0-8172-4640-2(1)) Raintree.

Searl, Duncan. The Maiasaura Nests: Jack Horner's Dinosaur Eggs. 2007. (Fossil Hunters Ser.). (J). lib. bdg. 18.95 (978-1-59716-257-9(4)) Bearport Publishing Co., Inc.

Shade, Laurie, illus. & text. The Little Buckeye Discovers Dinosaurs. Shade, Laurie, text. 2nd l.t. ed. 2002. (Little Buckeye Ser.: 1,2). 32p. (J). per. 6.95 (978-0-9703936-1-6(X) , 3000) Little Buckeye Publishing Co., The.

Sheen, Martin, contrib. by. Dinosaur. 2007. 16p. (J). pap. 29.99 (***978-0-7566-3135-2(1)***) Dorling Kindersley Publishing, Inc.

Sheldon, David. Barnum Brown: Dinosaur Hunter. Sheldon, David, illus. 2006. (Illus.). 32p. (J). (gr. 1-3). 16.95 (978-0-8027-9602-8(8)); 17.85 (978-0-8027-9603-5(6)) Walker & Co.

Shi, Sharon. Dinosaurs & Other Creatures. Montgomery, Tim, illus. rev. ed. 2000. 23p. (J). (ps-2). pap. 4.99 (978-0-9678636-2-7(7) , B003, Tattootles Bks.) Tattoo Manufacturing.

Shulman, Mark. Dinosaurs Then & Wow! Ostrom, Bob, illus. 2005. (Storytime Stickers Ser.). 16p. (J). pap. 4.95 (978-1-4027-1805-2(5)) Sterling Publishing Co., Inc.

Siamon, Sharon. Dinosaurs! Battle of the Bones. 2007. (Dk Readers Ser.). 48p. (J). (gr. 3-4). 14.99 (***978-0-7566-3142-0(4)***); pap. 3.99 (***978-0-7566-3139-0(4)***) Dorling Kindersley Publishing, Inc.

Silver Dolphin en Español Staff, ed. Libro y modelos 3-D: Dinosaurios: Book & 3-D Models: Dinosaurs. 2007. (Illus.). 24p. (J). 12.95 (***978-970-718-507-4(4)*** , Silver Dolphin en Español) Advanced Marketing, S. de R. L. de C. V. MEX. *Dist:* Perseus Distribution.

Skrepnick, Michael W. Sinosauropteryx: Mysterious Feathered Dinosaur. 2005. (I Like Dinosaurs! Ser.). (Illus.). 24p. (J). (ps-ps). lib. bdg. 21.26 (978-0-7660-2623-0(X) , Enslow Elementary) Enslow Pubs., Inc.

Skrepnick, Michael William. Diplodocus—Gigantic Long-Necked Dinosaur. Skrepnick, Michael William, illus. 2005. (I Like Dinosaurs! Ser.). (Illus.). 24p. (J). lib. bdg. 21.26 (978-0-7660-2622-3(1) , Enslow Elementary) Enslow Pubs., Inc.

—Triceratops—Mighty Three-Horned Dinosaur. Skrepnick, Michael William, illus. 2005. (I Like Dinosaurs! Ser.). (Illus.). 24p. (J). lib. bdg. 21.26 (978-0-7660-2620-9(5) , Enslow Elementary) Enslow Pubs., Inc.

—Tyrannosaurus Rex—Fierce King of the Dinosaurs. Skrepnick, Michael William, illus. 2005. (I Like Dinosaurs! Ser.). (Illus.). 24p. (J). lib. bdg. 21.26 (978-0-7660-2621-6(3) , Enslow Elementary) Enslow Pubs., Inc.

Slade, Suzanne. What Do You Know about Fossils? 2008. (J). lib. bdg. (***978-1-4042-4197-8(3)*** , PowerKids Pr.) Rosen Publishing Group, Inc., The.

Sladen, Louisa. Dinosaurs. Rinaldo, Luana, illus. 2005. (Magic Color Bks.). 10p. (J). 3.95 (978-1-4027-2055-0(6) , Sterling/Pinwheel) Sterling Publishing Co., Inc.

Sloan, Christopher. Feathered Dinosaurs. 2000. (Illus.). 64p. (J). (gr. 3-7). 17.95 (978-0-7922-7219-9(6) , National Geographic Children's Bks.) National Geographic Society.

—How Dinosaurs Took Flight: The Fossils, the Science, What We Think We Know, & Mysteries yet Unsolved. 2005. (Illus.). 64p. (J). (gr. 5-9). 17.95 (978-0-7922-7298-4(6)); 27.90 (978-0-7922-7404-9(0)) National Geographic Society. (National Geographic Children's Bks.).

Smith, A. G. Glow-in-the-Dark Dinosaurs Stickers. 2006. 2p. (J). 1.50 (978-0-486-44997-5(1)) Dover Pubns., Inc.

—Jurassic Dinosaurs Sticker Activity Book. 2002. (Shiny Stickers Ser.). (Illus.). 4p. (J). 1.50 (978-0-486-42345-6(X)) Dover Pubns., Inc.

Smith, Alastair & Tatchell, Judy. Dinosaurs. 2004. (Jumbo Lift-the-Flap Learners Ser.). (Illus.). 16p. (J). (gr. 1 up). 11.95 (978-0-7945-0418-2(3) , Usborne) EDC Publishing.

—Dinosaurs. Scott, Peter David, illus. 2005. (J). (*978-0-439-68903-8(1)*) Scholastic, Inc.

Smithee, Allan. Dinosaurs. 2004. (Interfact Ser.). (SPA., Illus.). 48p. (J). (gr. 3-6). 14.95 incl. cd-rom (978-1-58728-343-7(3) , Two Can Publishing) T&N Children's Publishing.

SoftPlay Staff, contrib. by. Dinosaur Park. 2000. (SoftPlay Felt Playset Book Ser.). (Illus.). (J). (978-1-56156-937-3(2)) Kidsbooks, Inc.

Sommers, Joan. Dinosaur Tunnel Book: Take a Peek at Cretaceous Creatures. Sibbick, John, illus. 2007. (Take a Peek Ser.). 16p. (J). 14.95 (*978-0-9754150-4-7(2)*) Tunnel Vision.

Sovak, Jan. Dinosaurs Stained Glass Coloring Book. 2005. (Illus.). 16p. (J). (gr. 1). pap. 5.95 (978-0-486-44668-4(9)) Dover Pubns., Inc.

Spizzirri, Linda, ed. Counting & Coloring Dinosaurs. (Illus.). 32p. (J). (gr. 1-8). pap. 4.98 incl. audio (978-0-86545-044-8(7)) Spizzirri Pr., Inc.

—Dinosaurs. Kohn, Arnie, illus. 32p. (J). (gr. 1-8). pap. 4.98 incl. audio (978-0-86545-019-6(6)) Spizzirri Pr., Inc.

Stegosaurus. (Dinosaurs & Prehistoric Animals Ser.). 24p. (J). 6.95 (978-0-7368-5106-0(2)) Capstone Pr., Inc.

Stegosaurus (Dinosaur Profiles) 2004. 11.20 (978-1-4103-0495-7(7) , Blackbirch Pr., Inc.) Thomson Gale.

Sterling, Mary E. Dinosaurs Photo Fun Activities. Rogers, Kathy, ed. Carrozza, John, illus. 1998. (Science Photo Fun Activities Ser.). 8p. (J). pap. 6.95 (978-1-56472-090-0(X)) Edupress, Inc.

Sterling Publishing Company Staff. Pocket Factfiles: Dinosaurs. 2004. (Illus.). 256p. (J). 4.98 (978-1-4027-1849-6(7)) Sterling Publishing Co., Inc.

Stewart, David. Dinosaurs! (World of Wonder Ser.). 32p. (J). 2008. pap. 9.95 (*978-0-531-20541-9(X)*); 2007. spiral bd. 29.00 (*978-0-531-20450-4(2)*) Scholastic Library Publishing. (Children's Pr.).

Stewart, Jennifer, ed. Dinosaurs! McLeod, Liz, illus. 1999. 28p. (J). (ps-2). pap. 3.49 (978-0-7847-1091-3(0) , 22075) Standard Publishing.

Stille, Darlene R. Allosaurus. 2007. (North American Dinosaurs Ser.). (Illus.). 24p. (J). (978-1-60044-250-6(1)) Rourke Publishing, LLC.

—Hadrosaurus. 2007. (North American Dinosaurs Ser.). (Illus.). 24p. (J). (978-1-60044-252-0(8)) Rourke Publishing, LLC.

Storrs, Glenn W. Stegosaurus - Dinoclub. 2000. (SPA.). (gr. 3-6). lib. bdg. 12.90 (978-0-613-83019-5(9)) Tandem Library Bks.

Suen, Anastasia. Tyrannosaurus Rex. 2007. (North American Dinosaurs Ser.). (Illus.). 24p. (J). (978-1-60044-255-1(2)) Rourke Publishing, LLC.

Svarney, Thomas E. & Barnes-Svarney, Patricia L. The Handy Dinosaur Answer Book. 2000. (Handy Answer Book Ser.). (Illus.). 528p. pap. 19.95 (978-1-57859-072-8(8) , GML14099-112780) Visible Ink Pr.

Swift-Thief. (Dinosaur World Ser.). 24p. (J). 7.95 (978-1-4048-0500-2(1)) Picture Window Bks.

T Rex. (Dinosaur World Ser.). 24p. (J). 7.95 (978-1-4048-0501-9(X)) Picture Window Bks.

Tallarico, Tony. A-Maze-Ing Dinosaurs. 2001. (Illus.). 96p. (J). (978-1-58865-025-2(1)) Kidsbooks, Inc.

Tanaka, Shelley. Graveyards of the Dinosaurs: What It Is Like to Discover Prehistoric Creatures. 2001. (I Was There Bk.). (Illus.). (J). 14.79 (978-0-606-20684-6(1)) Tandem Library Bks.

Taplin, Sam. First Encyclopedia of Dinosaurs - Internet Linked. Hancock, David, illus. 2004. (First Encyclopedias Ser.). 64p. (J). (gr. 3 up). pap. 9.99 (978-0-7945-0696-4(8) , Usborne) EDC Publishing.

—Little Encyclopedia of Dinosaurs. 2005. (Illus.). 64p. (J). (ps-ps). 6.95 (978-0-7945-1087-9(6) , Usborne) EDC Publishing.

—Mi Primera Enciclopedia de Dinosaurios y el Mundo Prehistorico Internet Linked. 2005. (SPA.). 64p. (J). pap. 9.99 (978-0-7460-6639-3(2) , Usborne) EDC Publishing.

Targo Publishing Staff. Dinosaur Travel Pad. 1999. (My Art Ser.). pap. 2.50 (978-1-894307-10-9(0)) Sterling Publishing.

Taylor, Barbara. Oxford First Book of Dinosaurs. 2001. (Illus.). 48p. (YA). (gr. k-3). 21.95 (978-0-19-521847-3(7)) Oxford Univ. Pr., Inc.

Temperley, Howard. In The Days of the Dinosaurs. Kline, Michael P., illus. 2005. (Tales Alive Bks.). 64p. (J). pap. 9.95 (978-0-8249-6759-8(3) , Williamson Bks.) Ideals Pubns.

Theodorou, Rod. Dinosaurs. 2002. (Curious Kids Guides). (Illus.). 32p. (J). tchr. ed. 6.95 (978-0-7534-5474-9(2) , Kingfisher) Houghton Mifflin Co. Trade & Reference Div.

—I Wonder Why Triceratops Had Horns: And Other Questions about Dinosaurs. 2003. (I Wonder Why Ser.). (Illus.). 32p. (J). (gr. k-3). pap. 6.95 (978-0-7534-5615-6(X) , Kingfisher) Houghton Mifflin Co. Trade & Reference Div.

—I Wonder Why Triceratops Had Horns: And Other Questions about Dinosaurs. 2003. (gr. k-3). lib. bdg. 14.10 (978-0-613-63166-2(8)) Tandem Library Bks.

Thomson, Sarah L. Extreme Dinosaurs! Q&A. 2007. 48p. (J). (gr. k-4). 16.99 (*978-0-06-089971-4(9)*); pap. 6.99 (*978-0-06-089967-7(0)*) HarperCollins Pubs.

Three-Horn. (Dinosaur World Ser.). 24p. (J). 7.95 (978-1-4048-0498-2(6)) Picture Window Bks.

Ticktock Media. If Dinosaurs Were Alive Today. 2007. (Illus.). 96p. (J). (gr. 2 up). 15.95 (*978-0-7624-3142-7(3)* , Running Pr. Kids) Running Pr. Bk. Pubs.

Tierra de Dinosaurios 6: Leveled Books. 2001. (McGraw-Hill. Lectura Ser.). (ENG & SPA.). (gr. 3 up). (978-0-02-188127-7(8)) Macmillan/McGraw-Hill Schl. Div.

Toms, Kate. Dinosaur Tails. 2006. (Illus.). 12p. (ps-k). per., bds. 5.95 (978-1-84610-097-0(6)) Make Believe Ideas GBR. *Dist:* Ingram Pub. Services.

Top That Publishing Staff, ed. Dinosaurs. 2004. (Know How Know Why Ser.). (Illus.). (J). 48p. pap. (978-1-84510-031-5(X)); 24p. pap. (978-1-84510-116-9(2)) Top That! Publishing PLC.

—Lets Learn Dinosaurs. 2004. (Fun Kits Ser.). (Illus.). 48p. (J). (978-1-84510-245-6(2)) Top That! Publishing PLC.

Triassic. 2002. (Dinosaurs Undercover Ser.). (Illus.). 40p. 29.94 (978-1-56711-600-7(0) , Blackbirch Pr., Inc.) Thomson Gale.

Triceratops. (Dinosaurs & Prehistoric Animals Ser.). 24p. (J). 6.95 (978-0-7368-5107-7(0)) Capstone Pr., Inc.

Tucker Slingsby Ltd., Staff. Ask Me About Animals. 2002. (Illus.). 12p. bds. (978-1-902272-17-7(X)) Tucker Slingsby, Ltd.

Turnbull, Stephanie. Los Dinosaurios Con Cuatro Puzzles Sencillos. Scott, Peter, illus. 2004. (Titles in Spanish Ser.). (SPA.). 6p. (J). 8.95 (978-0-7460-6109-1(9) , Usborne) EDC Publishing.

—Dinosaurs. 2004. (Beginners Ser.). 32p. (J). (gr. 1 up). lib. bdg. 12.95 (978-1-58086-606-4(9) , Usborne) EDC Publishing.

—Dinosaurs. Kushii, Tetsuo, illus. 2003. 32p. (J). (*978-0-439-88995-7(2)*) Scholastic, Inc.

Turnbull, Stephanie. Dinosaurs (Level 2) - Internet Referenced. 2006. (Illus.). 32p. (J). 4.99 (978-0-7945-1334-4(4) , Usborne) EDC Publishing.

Turnbull, Stephanie & Helbrough, Emma. World Atlas Of Dinosaurs (Reduced) rev. ed. 2007. (World Atlas of Dinosaurs Ser.). 144p. (J). 16.99 (*978-0-7945-1739-7(0)* , Usborne) EDC Publishing.

The Ultimate Book of Dinosaurs. 2002. 256p. (J). 12.98 (978-0-7550-0020-3(X)) Parragon, Inc.

Ultimate Book of Dinosaurs. 2002. 256p. (J). pap. 25.95 (978-0-7525-4813-5(1)) Parragon, Inc.

University Games Staff, compiled by. Spinner Books Kids: Dinomite. 2005. (Illus.). 160p. (J). pap. (978-1-57528-948-9(2)) University Games.

Unwin, Mike. Where Did Dinosaurs Go? 2006. 24p. (J). pap. 4.99 (978-0-7945-1410-5(3) , Usborne) EDC Publishing.

Upgrade kit dsm-3 Dinos&fossils. (J). 2004. (978-1-59242-528-0(3)); 2003. (978-1-59242-411-5(2)) Delta Education, LLC.

Vail, Rachel. Mama Rex & T: The Reading Champion. Bjorkman, Steve, illus. (Scholastic Reader Ser.). (J). 2004. 32p. pap. 3.99 (978-0-439-57822-6(1) , Cartwheel Bks.); 2003. (978-0-439-47193-0(1) , Orchard Bks.) Scholastic, Inc.

Valdivia, Manny & Valdivia, Rochelle. Dinosaurs: Let's Draw. Valdivia, Manny & Valdivia, Rochelle, illus. 2000. (Let's Draw Ser.). (Illus.). 32p. (J). (gr. 1-7). mass mkt. 2.99 (978-0-7681-0221-5(9) , 67302, McClanahan Bk.) Learning Horizons, Inc.

Wagner, Kathi & Racine, Sheryl. Everything Kids' Dinosaurs Book. 2005. (Illus.). 144p. (J). pap. 6.95 (978-1-59337-360-3(0)) Adams Media Corp.

Walker, Niki & Kalman, Bobbie. Les Dinosaures. 2005. (FRE., Illus.). 32p. (J). pap. (978-2-89579-050-1(7)) Crabtree Publishing Co.

—Qué Es un Dinosaurio? 2006. (ENG & SPA., Illus.). 32p. (J). (978-0-7787-8764-8(8)) Crabtree Publishing Co.

—Ques es un Dinosaurio? 2006. (ENG & SPA., Illus.). 32p. (gr. 2-3). pap. (978-0-7787-8810-2(5)) Crabtree Publishing Co.

Walker, Sally M. The Search for Antarctic Dinosaurs. Bindon, John, illus. 2007. (On My Own Science Ser.). 48p. (J). (gr. 2-4). lib. bdg. 25.26 (*978-0-8225-6749-3(0)* , Millbrook Pr.) Lerner Publishing Group.

Wallace, B. L. Noisy Dinosaur. 2007. (Touch & Feel Ser.). (Illus.). 12p. (ps). per., bds. 6.95 (978-1-84610-444-2(0)) Make Believe Ideas GBR. *Dist:* Ingram Pub. Services.

Wallace, Karen. I Am a Diplodocus. Bostock, Mike, illus. 2005. (J). (ps-ps). (978-0-340-89381-4(8) , Hodder Children's Books) Hodder Children's Division.

—I Am an Ankylosaurus. Bostock, Mike, illus. 2005. 32p. (J). 15.95 (978-0-689-87318-8(2) , Atheneum) Simon & Schuster Children's Publishing.

Walsh, Patricia. Dinosaurs. Westerfield, David, illus. 2006. (Draw It! Ser.). 32p. (J). (*978-1-4034-8923-4(8)*) Heinemann Library.

—Dinosaurs. 2nd ed. 2006. (Draw It! Ser.). (Illus.). 32p. (J). pap. (*978-1-4034-8930-2(0)*) Heinemann Library.

Walt & Wells. Este No Es Mi Dinosaurio. 2004. (Touchy-Feely Board Bks.).Tr. of This Is Not My Dinosaur. (SPA., Illus.). 12p. (J). (ps up). 7.95 (978-0-7460-5079-8(8)) EDC Publishing.

Walters, Robert, illus. Big Book of Dinosaurs. 2001. 128p. (J). (ps up). 9.98 (978-0-7624-0720-0(4) , Courage Bks.) Running Pr. Bk. Pubs.

Warner Press Staff. Dinosaurs. 2000. (J). pap. (978-0-87162-569-4(5)) Warner Pr. Pubs.

Watt, Fiona. Baby Dinosaur Cloth Bk. Wells, Rachel, illus. 2006. 10p. (J). 10.99 (978-0-7945-1429-7(4) , Usborne) EDC Publishing.

—Los Dinosaurios. 2007. (Titles in Spanish Ser.). 32p. (J). pap. 8.99 (*978-0-7460-8373-4(4)* , Usborne) EDC Publishing.

Watt, Fiona. How to Draw Dinosaurs. Figg, Non et al, illus. 2005. 31p. (J). (ps-ps). pap. 8.95 (978-0-7945-1056-5(6) , Usborne) EDC Publishing.

Weinberger, Kimberly. A Dinosaur Named Sue. 2001. (Jurassic Park Ser.). (Illus.). 24p. (J). (ps-2). pap. 5.99 (978-0-439-28367-0(1)) Scholastic, Inc.

Wenzell, Gregory. Feathered Dinosaurs of China. 2004. (Illus.). 32p. (J). 16.95 (978-1-57091-561-1(X)) Charlesbridge Publishing, Inc.

—Giant Dinosaurs of the Jurassic. Wenzell, Gregory, illus. 2004. (Illus.). 32p. (J). 16.95 (978-1-57091-563-5(6)); pap. 6.95 (978-1-57091-564-2(4)) Charlesbridge Publishing, Inc.

Wenzell, Gregory, illus. The Feathered Dinosaurs of China. 2004. 32p. (J). pap. 6.95 (978-1-57091-562-8(8)) Charlesbridge Publishing, Inc.

West, David. Triceratops: The Three Horned Dinosaur. 2008. (J). lib. bdg. (*978-1-4042-3896-1(4)* , PowerKids Pr.) Rosen Publishing Group, Inc., The.

—Tyrannosaurus: The Tyrant Lizard. 2008. (J). lib. bdg. (*978-1-4042-3897-8(2)* , PowerKids Pr.) Rosen Publishing Group, Inc., The.

—Velociraptor: The Speedy Thief. 2008. (J). lib. bdg. (*978-1-4042-3898-5(0)* , PowerKids Pr.) Rosen Publishing Group, Inc., The.

Wexo, John Bonnett. Dinosaurs. (Zoobooks Ser.). (Illus.). 24p. (J). (gr. 1-6). 2001. 15.95 (978-1-888153-37-8(7)); 2003. 10.95 (978-1-932396-02-7(0) , Zoo Bks.) Wildlife Education, Ltd.

Where Dinosaurs Walked Set C, 6 vols. (Phonics Readers Ser.). (gr. k-2). 17.50 (978-0-7368-3206-9(8)) Red Brick Learning.

White, David. Parasaurolophus. Mara, Pamela, illus. 2001. (Dinosaur Library). 24p. (J). (gr. 3-6). lib. bdg. 25.27 (978-1-58952-031-8(9)) Rourke Publishing, LLC.

Whitfield, Philip. Scholastic's Children's Guide to Dinosaurs. (Illus.). 96p. (J). pap. 21.95 (978-0-590-24329-2(2)) Scholastic, Inc.

Wick, Walter. Can You See What I See? Dinosaurs. 2006. (Illus.). 16p. (J). bds. 4.99 (978-0-439-83297-7(7) , Cartwheel Bks.) Scholastic, Inc.

Wickings, Ruth. Make & Meet Dinosaurs. 2006. (Make & Meet Kits Ser.). (Illus.). 24p. 8.95 (978-1-84560-029-7(0)) Mercury Bks. Ltd. GBR. *Dist:* International Publishers Marketing.

Wildlife Education, Ltd. Staff & Wexo, John Bonnett. Dinosaurs. Hallett, Mark, illus. 1999. (Zoobooks Ser.). 18p. (Orig.). (J). (gr. k-12). pap. 2.95 (978-0-937934-34-0(8)) Wildlife Education, Ltd.

Wilkes, Angela. The Big Book of Dinosaurs. (Illus.). 32p. (J). pap. 16.95 (978-0-590-24371-1(3)) Scholastic, Inc.

Williams, Judith. The Discovery & Mystery of a Dinosaur Named Jane. 2007. (Prime Ser.). (Illus.). 48p. (J). (gr. 3-7). pap. 13.26 (*978-0-7660-2709-1(0)*); lib. bdg. 23.93 (978-0-7660-2730-5(9)) Enslow Pubs., Inc.

Willis, Paul M. A. Dinosaurs. 2002. (Reader's Digest Pathfinders Ser.). (Illus.). 64p. (J). pap. 7.99 (978-1-57584-984-3(4) , Reader's Digest Children's Bks.) Reader's Digest Children's Publishing, Inc.

—Dinosaurs. 2002. (gr. 3-6). lib. bdg. 16.45 (978-0-613-45029-4(9)) Tandem Library Bks.

Wilson, Mary Ann & Cooley, Brian. Make-A-Saurus: My Life with Raptors & Other Dinosaurs. 2000. (Illus.). 58p. (J). (ps-6). lib. bdg. 24.55 (978-0-613-78401-6(4)) Tandem Library Bks.

Wilson, Ron. Allosaurus. Edwards, Doreen, illus. 2001. (Dinosaur Library). 24p. (J). (gr. 3-6). lib. bdg. 25.27 (978-1-58952-026-4(2)) Rourke Publishing, LLC.

Windsor, Jo. Dinosaurs: Early Level Satellite Individual Title Six-Packs. (Sails Literacy Ser.). 16p. (gr. 1-2). 27.00 (978-0-7578-2913-0(9)) Rigby Education.

Wingate, Philippa. Dinosaurs. 2004. (Usborne Spotter's Guides). (Illus.). 64p. (J). (ps up). lib. bdg. 13.95 (978-1-58086-311-7(6)); pap. 5.95 (978-0-7460-4068-3(7)) EDC Publishing.

Winged & Toothless. (Dinosaur World Ser.). 24p. (J). 7.95 (978-1-4048-0499-9(4)) Picture Window Bks.

Winner, Cherie. Little Book of Dinosaurs. Chesterman, Al, illus. 2005. 24p. (J). 5.95 (978-1-58728-516-5(9)) T&N Children's Publishing.

—The Little Book of Dinosaurs. 2005. (Illus.). 24p. (978-1-58728-484-7(7) , Two Can Publishing) T&N Children's Publishing.

World Book, Inc Staff, contrib. by. World of Dinosaurs. 2007. (J). (*978-0-7166-7734-5(2)*) World Bk., Inc.

Wormell, Christopher. Wings, Horns, & Claws: A Dinosaur Book of Epic Proportions. 2007. (Illus.). 64p. (*978-0-7624-3213-4(6)* , Running Pr.); (J). 18.95 (*978-0-7624-2419-1(2)* , Running Pr. Kids) Running Pr. Bk. Pubs.

Wynne, Patricia J. Easy Dinosaur Mazes. 2006. 48p. (J). pap. 3.95 (978-0-486-45363-7(4)) Dover Pubns., Inc.

—Feathered Dinosaurs: Flying Reptiles & Ancient Birds. 2005. (Illus.). 32p. (J). (ps-ps). pap. 3.95 (978-0-486-44224-2(1)) Dover Pubns., Inc.

Yelagalawadi, Jyoti. Laugh with Dinosaurs. Nagaraju, Harsha, illus. 2004. 32p. (J). 14.99 (978-0-9725901-1-2(0)) Lekha Pubs., LLC.

You Can Name 100 Dino Dis. 2003. (J). 53.70 (978-0-590-69063-8(9)) Scholastic, Inc.

Zappler, Georg. Learn about... Texas Dinosaurs. Ivy, Elena T., illus. rev. ed. 2001. (Learn about Texas Ser.). 48p. (J). pap. 9.95 (978-1-885696-37-3(X)) Texas Parks & Wildlife Pr.

Zermeno, Rebeca M. Dinosaurios.Tr. of Dinosaurs. (SPA.). (J). 6.98 (978-970-643-266-7(3)) Selector, S.A. de C.V. MEX. *Dist:* AIMS International Bks., Inc., Giron Bks.

Zimmerman, Howard. Dinosaurs! 2000. (Illus.). 64p. (J). (ps-3). 19.95 (978-0-689-83276-5(1) , Atheneum) Simon & Schuster Children's Publishing.

Zoehfeld, Kathleen Weidner. Did Dinosaurs Have Feathers? Washburn, Lucia, illus. 2004. (Let's-Read-and-Find-Out Science Ser.). 40p. (J). (gr. k-4). 15.99 (978-0-06-029026-9(9)); pap. 5.99 (978-0-06-445218-2(2) , Harper Trophy); lib. bdg. 16.89 (978-0-06-029027-6(7)) HarperCollins Pubs.

—Dinosaur Babies. Washburn, Lucia, illus. 1999. (Let's-Read-and-Find-Out Science Ser.). 40p. (J). (gr. k-4). 15.89 (978-0-06-027142-8(6)); pap. 4.99 (978-0-06-445162-8(3) , Harper Trophy) HarperCollins Pubs.

—Dinosaur Babies. 1999. (Let's-Read-and-Find-Out Science Ser.). (Illus.). 40p. (J). (gr. k-4). 15.95 (978-0-06-027141-1(8)) HarperCollins Pubs.

—Dinosaur Babies. 1999. (Let's-Read-and-Find-Out Ser.). 11.79 (978-0-606-17490-9(7)); lib. bdg. 13.00 (978-0-613-21433-9(1)) Tandem Library Bks.

—Dinosaur Parents, Dinosaur Young: Uncovering the Mystery of Dinosaur Families. 2007. (Illus.). 64p. (J). (gr. 4-6). pap. 6.95 (978-0-618-75244-7(7) , Clarion Bks.) Houghton Mifflin Co. Trade & Reference Div.

—Dinosaur Parents, Dinosaur Young: Uncovering the Mystery of Dinosaur Families. Carrick, Paul & Shillinglaw, Bruce, illus. 2001. 64p. (J). (gr. 4-6). tchr. ed. 17.00 (978-0-395-91338-3(1) , Clarion Bks.) Houghton Mifflin Co. Trade & Reference Div.

—Dinosaur Times. Date not set. 40p. (J). 15.99 (978-0-06-029022-1(6)); lib. bdg. 16.89 (978-0-06-029023-8(4)); pap. 4.99 (978-0-06-445216-8(6)) HarperCollins Pubs.

—Dinosaur Tracks. Washburn, Lucia, illus. 2007. (Let's-Read-and-Find-Out Science Ser.). 40p. (J). (gr. k-4). 15.99 (978-0-06-029024-5(2)); pap. 5.99 (978-0-06-445217-5(4)) HarperCollins Pubs.

—Dinosaurs Big & Small. Washburn, Lucia, illus. 2002. (Let's-Read-and-Find-Out Science Ser.). 40p. (J). (ps-1). pap. 5.99 (978-0-06-445182-6(8) , Harper Trophy) HarperCollins Pubs.

—Dinosaurs Big & Small. 2002. (gr. k-3). lib. bdg. 12.95 (978-0-613-59378-6(2)) Tandem Library Bks.

—Terrible Tyrannosaurs. Washburn, Lucia, illus. 2001. (Let's-Read-&-Find-Out Science Bks.). 40p. (J). (gr. k-4). 15.95 (978-0-06-027933-2(8)) HarperCollins Pubs.

—Terrible Tyrannosaurs. Washburn, Lucas, illus. 2001. (Let's-Read-and-Find-Out Science Ser.). 40p. (J). (gr. k-4). 15.89 (978-0-06-027934-9(6)) HarperCollins Pubs.

—Terrible Tyrannosaurs. Washburn, Lucia, illus. 2001. (Let's-Read-and-Find-Out Science Ser.). 40p. (J). (gr. k-4). pap. 5.99 (978-0-06-445181-9(X) , Harper Trophy) HarperCollins Pubs.

—Terrible Tyrannosaurs. 2001. (Let's-Read-and-Find-Out Ser.). (Illus.). (J). (978-0-606-20937-3(9)) Tandem Library Bks.

—Terrible Tyrannosaurs. Washburn, Lucia, illus. 2001. 32p. (J). (ps-ps). lib. bdg. 13.00 (978-0-613-31793-1(9)) Tandem Library Bks.

Zuravicky, Orli. When There Were Dinosaurs: Using Expanded Notation to Represent Numbers in the Millions. 2004. (PowerMath Ser.). (Illus.). 32p. (J). lib. bdg. (978-0-8239-8901-0(1)); lib. bdg. 22.50 (978-0-8239-8988-1(7)) Rosen Publishing Group, Inc., The. (PowerKids Pr.).

DINOSAURS—FICTION

Addabbo, Carole. Dina the Deaf Dinosaur. Valentine, illus. 32p. (J). 2005. pap. 19.95 (978-1-889262-92-5(7)); 1998. 19.95 (978-1-889262-04-8(8)) Hannacroix Creek Bks., Inc.

Adler, David A. Bones & the Dinosaur Mystery. 2005. (Jeffrey Bones Mystery Ser.: No. 4). (Illus.). 32p. (J). (gr. k-3). 13.99 (978-0-670-06010-8(0) , Viking Juvenile) Penguin Group (USA) Inc.

—Bones & the Dinosaur Mystery. Newman, Barbara Johansen, illus. 2005. (Jeffrey Bones Mystery Ser.: No. 4). 32p. (J). (978-0-670-05970-6(6) , Viking Adult) Penguin Group (USA) Inc.

—Cam Jansen & the Mystery of the Dinosaur Bones. 2004. (Cam Jansen Ser.: No. 3). (Illus.). 64p. (J). (gr. 2-4). pap. 3.99 (978-0-14-240012-8(2) , Puffin) Penguin Group (USA) Inc.

Albee, Sarah. My New Pet Is the Greatest. 1999. (Road to Reading Ser.). (Illus.). (J). (978-0-606-20816-1(X)) Tandem Library Bks.

Albrecht, Jeff. Barney Says. Albrecht, Jeff, illus. 2006. (Barney Ser.). 5p. (J). bds. 9.99 (978-0-439-74410-2(5)) Scholastic, Inc.

Alphin, Elaine Marie. Dinosaur Hunter. Bolognese, Don, illus. (I Can Read Bks.). (J). 2004. 48p. (gr. k-3). pap. 3.99 (978-0-06-444256-5(X)); 2003. 48p. 15.99 (978-0-06-028303-2(3)); 2003. 64p. (gr. 2-3). 16.89 (978-0-06-028304-9(1)) HarperCollins Pubs.

Amaral, Gayla. Barney's Sing-Along Stories: B-i-n-g-o! 2002. (gr. k-3). lib. bdg. 11.25 (978-0-613-89904-8(0)) Tandem Library Bks.

—Hooray for Mommies! Babies & BarneyTM. Full, Dennis, photos by. 2002. (Barney Ser.). (Illus.). 22p. (J). (ps-k). bds. 5.99 (978-1-58668-220-0(2)) Scholastic, Inc.

Amaral, Gayla & Lyrick Publishing Staff. Barney's C Is for Christmas. Yingling, Kathryn, illus. 2001. (Barney Ser.). 16p. (J). (ps-k). bds. 6.99 (978-1-57064-726-0(7)) Scholastic, Inc.

Andreae, Giles. Captain Flinn & the Pirate Dinosaurs. Ayto, Russell, illus. 2005. 32p. (J). (gr. k-3). 15.95 (978-1-4169-0713-8(0) , McElderry, Margaret K.) Simon & Schuster Children's Publishing.

Anholt, Laurence & Moxley, Sheila. Stone Girl Bone Girl: The Story of Mary Anning. 2006. (Illus.). 32p. (J). pap. 7.95 (***978-1-84507-700-6(8)***) Lincoln, Frances Ltd. GBR. *Dist:* Perseus Distribution.

Applegate, Katherine. In the Time of Dinosaurs. 1998. (Animorphs Ser.: No. 2). (J). (gr. 3-7). (978-0-606-13142-1(6)) Tandem Library Bks.

Baby Stegosaurus. 2007. (J). per. (***978-1-932570-66-3(7)***) Literacy Footprints Inc.

Baker, Liza. Harold & the Purple CrayonTM: Dinosaur Days. Chiang, Andy, illus. 2002. (Harold & the Purple Crayon Ser.). 40p. (J). (ps-1). 12.99 (978-0-06-000541-2(6)) HarperCollins Pubs.

Banks, Steven. In Search of Reptar. 2002. (gr. 3-6). lib. bdg. 11.80 (978-0-613-50538-3(7)) Tandem Library Bks.

—In Search of Reptar: A Time Travel Adventure. Artful Doodlers Limited Staff, illus. 2002. (Rugrats Files: Bk. 5). 96p. (J). (gr. 3-7). pap. 3.99 (978-0-689-84609-0(6) , Simon Spotlight) Simon & Schuster Children's Publishing.

Bardhan-Quallen, Sudipta. The Mine-O-Saur. Clark, David, illus. 2007. 32p. (J). (ps). 16.99 (***978-0-399-24642-5(8)*** , Putnam Juvenile) Penguin Group (USA) Inc.

Barney & BJ Go to the Police Station. 2002. (Barney's Go to Ser.). 32p. (J). (ps-k). bds. 5.95 (978-1-58668-231-6(8)) Lyrick Studios.

Barney Goes to the Dentist. 2002. (Barney's Go to Ser.). 32p. (J). (ps-k). bds. 5.95 (978-1-58668-248-4(2)) Scholastic, Inc.

Barney Let's Go to the Zoo. 2001. (Barney Ser.). (Illus.). 60p. (J). (ps-k). 1.99 (978-1-57064-940-0(5)) Scholastic, Inc.

Barney Meets the New Baby. 2002. (Barney Ser.). 32p. (J). (ps-k). bds. 5.95 (978-1-58668-246-0(6)) Scholastic, Inc.

Barney Publishing Staff & Bernthal, Mark S. Barney's Book of Colors. McKee, Darren, illus. 1999. (Barney Ser.). 22p. (J). (ps-3). bds. 5.99 (978-1-57064-454-2(3)) Scholastic, Inc.

Barney Yummy Songs. 2003. 10p. (J). bds. 9.98 (978-0-7853-8283-6(6) , 7182100) Publications International, Ltd.

Barney's ABC Animals! 1999. (Barney Ser.). (Illus.). 32p. (J). (ps-k). 6.95 (978-1-57064-624-9(4)) Scholastic, Inc.

Bateman, Teresa. Hunting the Daddyosaurus. Huang, Benrei, illus. 2004. 29p. (J). (gr. k-4). reprint ed. 16.00 (978-0-7567-7796-8(8)) DIANE Publishing Co.

—Hunting the Daddyosaurus. Huang, Benrei, illus. 2002. 32p. (J). (ps-1). 15.95 (978-0-8075-1433-7(0)) Whitman, Albert & Co.

Bearden, Candace N. & Bearden, Michael D. Marus the Longneck & the Journey to Stone Mountain. Bearden, Michael D., illus. 1998. (Marus the Longneck Ser.). (Illus.). 25p. (J). (ps-6). pap. 8.95 (978-0-9667619-2-4(8)) Dino Tales.

—Marus the Longneck & the Rescue at Moss Hill. Bearden, Michael D., illus. 1998. (Marus the Longneck Ser.). (Illus.). 25p. (J). (ps-6). pap. 8.95 (978-0-9667619-1-7(X)) Dino Tales.

Bearden, Michael D. & Bearden, Candace N. Marus the Longneck Saves the Day. Bearden, Michael D., illus. 1998. (Marus the Longneck Ser.). (Illus.). 25p. (J). (ps-6). pap. 8.95 (978-0-9667619-0-0(1)) Dino Tales.

Bedford, David & Worthington, Leonie. In-O-Saur, Out-O-Saur. 2007. (Illus.). 24p. (J). (ps-k). 9.95 (***978-1-877003-85-1(9)***) Little Hare Bks. AUS. *Dist:* Independent Pubs. Group.

—One-O-Saur, Two-O-Saur. 2007. (Illus.). 22p. (J). (ps-k). 9.95 (***978-1-877003-84-4(0)***) Little Hare Bks. AUS. *Dist:* Independent Pubs. Group.

Bentley, Dawn. A Busy Day for Stegosaurus. Carr, Karen, illus. 2005. (Smithsonian's Prehistoric Pals Ser.). (J) (ps-?). 36p. 9.95 (978-1-59249-156-8(1) , PS2451); 30p. 8.95 incl. cd-rom (978-1-59249-210-7(X) , SD2401) Soundprints.

—A Busy Day for Stegosaurus. Carr, Karen, tr. Carr, Karen, illus. 2005. (Smithsonian's Prehistoric Pals Ser.). (J). (ps-2). 30p. 2.95 (978-1-59249-155-1(3) , S2451); 36p. 14.95 incl. cd-rom (978-1-59249-153-7(7) , H2401); 36p. pap. 6.95 (978-1-59249-154-4(5) , S2401) Soundprints.

—It's Tyrannosaurus Rex! Carr, Karen, illus. 2005. (Smithsonian's Prehistoric Pals Ser.). (J). (ps-2). 36p. 9.95 (978-1-59249-160-5(X) , PS2450); 30p. 8.95 incl. cd-rom (978-1-59249-212-1(6) , SD2400) Soundprints.

—It's Tyrannosaurus Rex! Carr, Karen, tr. Carr, Karen, illus. 2005. (Smithsonian's Prehistoric Pals Ser.). (J). (ps-2). 32p. 2.95 (978-1-59249-159-9(6) , S2450); 36p. pap. 6.95 (978-1-59249-158-2(8) , S2400) Soundprints.

—Lead the Way, Velociraptor!/By Dawn Bentley ; Illustrated by Karen Carr. Carr, Karen, illus. 2005. (Read & Discover (Soundprints) Ser.). 32p. (J). (ps-1). pap. 3.95 (978-1-59249-304-3(1) , S2031) Soundprints.

—Parasaurolophus Escapes. McIntosh, Gabe, illus. 2006. (Smithsonian's Prehistoric Pals Ser.). 36p. (J). (978-1-59249-645-7(8)); pap. (978-1-59249-643-3(1)) Soundprints.

—Pteranodon Soars. Carr, Karen, illus. 2005. (Smithsonian's Prehistoric Pals Ser.). (J). (ps-2). 36p. 8.95 incl. cd-rom (978-1-59249-371-5(8) , SD2405); 32p. 9.95 (978-1-59249-373-9(4) , PS2455); 36p. 14.95 incl. cd-rom (978-1-59249-369-2(6) , H2405); 36p. 6.95 (978-1-59249-370-8(X) , S2405); 32p. 2.95 incl. cd-rom (978-1-59249-372-2(6) , S2455) Soundprints.

—Snack Time, Tyrannosaurus Rex! Carr, Karen, illus. 2005. (Soundprints' Read-and-Discover Ser.). 32p. (J). (ps-1). pap. 3.95 (978-1-59249-302-9(5) , S2033) Soundprints.

—Surprise, Stegosaurus! Carr, Karen, illus. 2005. (Read & Discover (Soundprints) Ser.). 32p. (J). (ps-1). pap. 3.95 (978-1-59249-305-0(X) , S2032) Soundprints.

—Triceratops Gets Lost. Carr, Karen, illus. 2005. (Smithsonian's Prehistoric Pals Ser.). 32p. (J). (ps-2). 8.95 incl. cd-rom (978-1-59249-216-9(9) , SD2403) Soundprints.

—Triceratops Gets Lost. Carr, Karen, tr. Carr, Karen, illus. 2005. (Smithsonian's Prehistoric Pals Ser.). (J). (ps-2). 32p. 2.95 (978-1-59249-167-4(7) , S2453); 36p. pap. 6.95 (978-1-59249-166-7(9) , S2403) Soundprints.

—Velociraptor: Small & Speedy. Carr, Karen, illus. 2005. (Smithsonian's Prehistoric Pals Ser.). 30p. (J). (ps-2). 8.95 incl. cd-rom (978-1-59249-214-5(2) , SD2402) Soundprints.

—Velociraptor: Small & Speedy. Carr, Karen, tr. Carr, Karen, illus. 2005. (Smithsonian's Prehistoric Pals Ser.). (J). (ps-2). 32p. 2.95 (978-1-59249-163-6(4) , S2452); 36p. 6.95 (978-1-59249-162-9(6) , S2402); 36p. 14.95 incl. cd-rom (978-1-59249-161-2(8) , H2402) Soundprints.

—Velociraptor: Small & Speedy. Carr, Karen, illus. 2004. 27p. (J). (ps-ps). lib. bdg. 13.75 (978-0-606-32581-3(6)) Tandem Library Bks.

—Watch Out, Triceratops! Carr, Karen, illus. 2005. (Read & Discover (Soundprints) Ser.). 32p. (J). (ps-1). pap. 3.95 (978-1-59249-303-6(3) , S2030) Soundprints.

Berenstain, Stan & Berenstain, Jan. The Berenstain Bears & the G-Rex Bones. 2001. (Berenstain Bears Big Chapter Bks.). (J). (gr. 2-6). lib. bdg. 11.99 (978-0-679-98949-3(8) , Random Hse. Bks. for Young Readers) Random Hse. Children's Bks.

—The Berenstain Bears' Dinosaur Coloring Adventure. 2005. (Berenstain Bears Ser.). (Illus.). 32p. (J). pap. 3.99 (978-0-06-057413-0(5) , Harper Festival) HarperCollins Pubs.

Berger, Gilda & Berger, Melvin. Vivio Algun Dinosaurio Cerca de Tu Casa. 2007. 48p. (J). pap. 5.99 (***978-0-439-85314-9(1)*** , Scholastic en Espanol) Scholastic, Inc.

Berk, Sheryl. Barney's Little Lessons: The New Babysitter. Yingling, Kathryn, illus. 2003. (Barney Ser.). 224p. (J). (ps-1). bds. 5.99 (978-1-58668-302-3(0)) Scholastic, Inc.

Bernstein, Lee. Barney's Sing-Along Stories: I Love You. Valentine-Ruppe, June, illus. 2003. (Barney Ser.). 24p. (J). (ps-1). pap. 3.50 (978-1-58668-299-6(7)) Scholastic, Inc.

Bernthal, Mark S. Barney's 12 Days of Christmas. 1998. (Barney Ser.). 26p. (J). (ps-k). bds. 13.95 (978-1-57064-241-8(9)) Scholastic, Inc.

Bernthal, Mark S. & Lyrick Publishing Staff. Barney & BJ Go to the Zoo. Full, Dennis, photos by. 1999. (Barney's Go to Ser.). (Illus.). 24p. (J). (ps-k). pap. 3.50 (978-1-57064-446-7(2)) Scholastic, Inc.

—Barney's Book of Shapes. 1998. (Barney Ser.). (Illus.). 22p. (J). (ps). bds. 5.95 (978-1-57064-242-5(7)) Scholastic, Inc.

Bernthal, Mark S. & Scholastic, Inc. Staff. Barney's ABC Animals! Baker, Darrell, illus. 1999. (Barney Ser.). 32p. (J). (ps-k). pap. 3.50 (978-1-57064-453-5(5)) Scholastic, Inc.

Blackstone, Stella. I Dreamt I Was a Dinosaur. Beaton, Clare, illus. 2005. 32p. (J). (ps-3). 15.99 (978-1-84148-238-5(2)) Barefoot Bks., Inc.

Blasing, George. Uno and the Raptor Pack: The Journey Begins! Ramirez, Alberto, illus. 2007. (J). 4.95 (***978-0-9797304-1-2(4)***) Raining Popcorn Media.

—Dinosaur George Prehistoric Safari: Raptor Island. Ramirez, Alberto, illus. 2007. (J). 4.95 (***978-0-9797304-2-9(2)***) Raining Popcorn Media.

Blasing, George & Blasing, George. The Prehistoric Adventures of Dinosaur George: Jurassic Tigers. Smith, David, illus. 2007. 16p. (J). 4.95 (***978-0-9797304-0-5(6)***) Raining Popcorn Media.

Blathwayt, Benedict. Dinosaur Chase. 2006. (Illus.). 32p. (J). (gr. 1-2). 16.99 (978-0-09-189293-7(7)) Transworld Publishers Ltd. GBR. *Dist:* Independent Pubs. Group.

Blathwayt, Benedict. Dinosaur Chase! 2007. (Illus.). 32p. pap. 5.99 (***978-0-09-945644-5(3)*** , Red Fox) Random Hse. Children's Bks. GBR. *Dist:* Independent Pubs. Group.

Bodkin, Odds. Little Proto's T-Rex Adventure: A Musical Dinosaur Story. (Odds Bodkin Musical Story Collection). (J). 9.95 incl. audio (978-1-882412-27-3(3) , Odds Bodkin Storytelling Library, The) Rivertree Productions, Inc.

Book Company Staff. Are You a Dinosaur? 2003. (Novelty Bks.). (J). 12.95 (978-1-74047-319-4(1)) Book Co. Publishing Pty, Ltd., The AUS. *Dist:* Penton Overseas, Inc.

—Lift & Learn Dinosaurs. 2005. (J). bds. 10.95 (978-1-74047-619-5(0)) Book Co. Publishing Pty, Ltd., The AUS. *Dist:* Penton Overseas, Inc.

—Little Dinosaur Goes to School. 2002. (Novelty Bks.). (J). 7.95 (978-1-74047-262-3(4)) Book Co. Publishing Pty, Ltd., The AUS. *Dist:* Penton Overseas, Inc.

Book Company Staff & Book Company Staff, illus. Little Dinosaur Goes to School. 2002. (Novelty Bks.). (J). 7.95 (978-1-74047-263-0(2)) Book Co. Publishing Pty, Ltd., The AUS. *Dist:* Penton Overseas, Inc.

Bourgeois, Paulette. Franklin en el Museo. Clark, Brenda, illus. 1999. (Franklin Ser.). (SPA.). (J). (ps-3). pap. 5.95 (978-1-880507-57-5(9) , LC2801) Lectorum Pubns., Inc.

—Franklin's Class Trip. Clark, Brenda, illus. (Franklin Ser.). (J). (ps-3). 1999. 30p. (978-1-55074-472-9(0)); 2004. 32p. (978-1-55074-470-5(4)) Kids Can Pr., Ltd.

—Franklin's Class Trip. Clark, Brenda, illus. 1999. (Franklin Ser.). 32p. (J). (ps-3). pap. 4.50 (978-0-590-13002-8(1)) Scholastic, Inc.

Boynton, Sandra. Dinos to Go. Boynton, Sandra, illus. 2000. (Illus.). 18p. (J). (ps-k). 7.99 (978-0-689-84007-4(1)) Simon & Schuster Children's Publishing.

—Dinos to Go: 7 Nifty Dinosaurs in 1 Swell Book. 2001. (J). bds. 7.99 (978-0-689-83510-0(8) , Little Simon) Simon & Schuster Children's Publishing.

—Dinosaur's Binkit. 1998. (Illus.). 14p. (J). (ps-k). bds. 10.95 (978-0-689-82203-2(0) , Little Simon) Simon & Schuster Children's Publishing.

Bradbury, Ray. Dinosaur Tales. 2003. (Illus.). 144p. pap. (978-0-7434-5897-9(4)) ibooks, Inc.

Brimner, Larry Dane. Dinosaurs Dance. Rau, Dana, ed. Girouard, Patrick, illus. 1998. (Rookie Reader Skill Set Ser.). 32p. (J). (gr. k-2). pap. 4.95 (978-0-516-26358-8(7) , Children's Pr.) Scholastic Library Publishing.

Broach, Elise. When Dinosaurs Came with Everything. Small, David, illus. 2007. (Junior Library Guild Selection Ser.). 40p. (J). (ps-2). 16.99 (978-0-689-86922-8(3)) Simon & Schuster Children's Publishing.

Brookes, Diane & Osborne, Mary Pope. A Novel Study for Grades Two & Three Based on Dinosaurs Before Dark, 25 vols. 1998. (J). pap., tchr. ed. (978-0-9683234-6-5(4)) Raven Rock Publishing.

Brown, Laurie Krasny. Rex & Lilly Schooltime: A Dino Easy Reader. Brown, Marc, illus. 2001. 32p. (J). (ps-1). pap. 4.95 (978-0-316-13535-1(6)) Little, Brown Bks. for Young Readers.

Brown, Marc. Buster Hunts for Dinosaurs. 2006. (Postcards from Buster Ser.). 32p. (J). (gr. 1-4). 14.99 (978-0-316-15914-2(X)) Little Brown & Co.

—Buster's Dino Dilemma. ed. 2005. (Arthur Chapter Bks.: Bk. 7). (Illus.). 58p. (J). lib. bdg. 15.00 (978-1-59054-738-0(1)) Fitzgerald Bks.

Bully Dinosaur. 2004. (J). (978-1-932570-28-1(4)) Literacy Footprints Inc.

Butterworth, Oliver. The Enormous Egg. unabr. ed. 2000. (J). pap. 29.00 incl. audio (978-0-8072-8776-7(8) , YA264SP, Listening Library) Random Hse. Audio Publishing Group.

Byars, Betsy. Boo's Dinosaur. Brooks, Erik, illus. 2006. 48p. (J). 15.95 (978-0-8050-7958-6(0) , Holt, Henry & Co. Bks. For Young Readers) Holt, Henry & Co.

Carmine, Mary & Baynton, Martin. Daniel et Ses Dinosaures.Tr. of Daniel et Ses Dinosaures. (FRE., Illus.). (J). 13.99 (978-0-590-74149-1(7)); bds. 29.99 (978-0-590-74124-8(1)) Scholastic, Inc.

Carrick, Carol. Patrick's Dinosaurs. Carrick, Donald, illus. 2002. (J). 13.79 (978-0-7587-3380-1(1)) Book Wholesalers, Inc.

—Patrick's Dinosaurs on the Internet. Milgrim, David, illus. 1999. 32p. (J). (gr. k-3). tchr. ed. 16.00 (978-0-395-50949-4(1) , Clarion Bks.) Houghton Mifflin Co. Trade & Reference Div.

—What Happened to Patrick's Dinosaurs? Carrick, Donald, illus. 2002. (J). 13.79 (978-0-7587-3960-5(5)) Book Wholesalers, Inc.

Carter, David A. Flapdoodle Dinosaurs. 2001. (Illus.). 16p. (J). (ps-3). 16.95 (978-0-689-84643-4(6) , Little Simon) Simon & Schuster Children's Publishing.

Castor, H. The Dinosaurs Next Door. (Young Reading Ser.: Vol. 1). 48p. (J). (gr. 2 up). lib. bdg. 13.95 (978-1-58086-787-0(1)); 2004. (Illus.). pap. 5.95 (978-0-7945-0251-5(2)) EDC Publishing. (Usborne).

Chronicle Books LLC Staff. Dinosaur Wings. 2008. (J). 15.95 (978-0-8118-5663-8(1)) Chronicle Bks. LLC.

—Hide-and-Seek Dinosaurs! 2008. 8p. (J). bds. 6.99 (978-0-8118-5202-9(4)) Chronicle Bks. LLC.

Ciencin, Scott. Beverly Hills Brontosaurus. Fredericks, Mike, illus. 2000. (Dinoverse Ser.: Vol. 5). (J). (978-0-606-19891-2(1)) Tandem Library Bks.

—I Was a Teenage T. Rex. 2000. (Dinoverse Ser.: No. 1). (978-0-606-17873-0(2)) Tandem Library Bks.

—Jurassic Park Adventures, Bk. 1. 2001. (Step into Reading Ser.). (Illus.). (J). (978-0-606-21274-8(4)) Tandem Library Bks.

—Raptor Without a Cause. 2000. (gr. 3-6). lib. bdg. 13.00 (978-0-613-26714-4(1)) Tandem Library Bks.

—Return to Lost City. 2000. (Dinotopia Ser.). (Illus.). (J). (978-0-606-20466-8(0)) Tandem Library Bks.

—Sky Dance. 1999. (Dinotopia Ser.: No. 10). (Illus.). 264p. (J). (gr. 3-6). pap. 4.99 (978-0-679-80417-8(X)) Random Hse., Inc.

—Sky Dance. 1999. (Dinotopia Ser.). (Illus.). (J). (978-0-606-20468-2(7)) Tandem Library Bks.

—The Teens Time Forgot. 2000. (Dinoverse Ser.: No. 2). (978-0-606-17874-7(0)) Tandem Library Bks.

Clark, Brenda, illus. Franklin's Class Trip. 2002. (Franklin Ser.). 12.40 (978-1-4046-0325-7(5)) Book Wholesalers, Inc.

Clarke, Jane. Dippy's Sleepover: A Reassuring Story for Kids Who Have a Bedwetting Problem. McQuillan, Mary, illus. 2006. 32p. (J). pap. 6.99 (978-0-7641-3425-8(6)) Barron's Educational Series, Inc.

Cohn, Arlen. Dino 2 News. 2006. 34p. (J). 15.99 (978-1-57939-249-9(0)) Accord Publishing, Ltd.

Cole, Jennifer. Tyler & the Megasaurous. 2007. (J). 16.95 (978-1-933872-21-6(7)) Lima Bear Pr LLC, The.

Cole, Steve. The Hatching Horror. Fowkes, Charlie, illus. 2006. (Astrosaurs Ser.). 144p. (J). pap. 4.99 (978-0-689-87842-8(7) , Aladdin) Simon & Schuster Children's Publishing.

—The Mind-Swap Menace. Fox, Woody, illus. 2007. (Astrosaurs Ser.). 128p. (Orig.). (J). pap. 4.99 (978-0-689-87844-2(3) , Aladdin) Simon & Schuster Children's Publishing.

—Riddle of the Raptors. Fowkes, Charlie, illus. 2006. (Astrosaurs Ser.). 144p. (J). (gr. 3-7). pap. 4.99 (978-0-689-87841-1(9) , Aladdin) Simon & Schuster Children's Publishing.

—The Seas of Doom. Fox, Woody, illus. 2006. (Astrosaurs Ser.). 128p. (Orig.). (J). pap. 4.99 (978-0-689-87843-5(5) , Aladdin) Simon & Schuster Children's Publishing.

Coll, Ivar Da, illus. Los Dinosaurios. 2000. (Coleccion Buenas Noches Ser.).Tr. of Great Dinosaur Search. (SPA.). (J). (gr. 1-3). 8.95 (978-958-04-4645-3(8)) Norma S.A. COL. *Dist:* Distribuidora Norma, Inc., Lectorum Pubns., Inc.

Cook, Gerri. Where the Buffalo Jump. Yu, Chao & Wang, Jue, illus. 2003. (Dinosaur Soup Ser.). 120p. (YA). (gr. 3-5). pap. 9.95 (978-1-895836-95-0(6)) River Bks. CAN. *Dist:* Fitzhenry & Whiteside, Ltd.

Cooner, Donna D. Barney Makes Music. Davis, Guy, ed. 1999. (Barney Ser.). (Illus.). 24p. (J). (ps-k). 4.95 (978-1-57064-461-0(6)) Scholastic, Inc.

—Barney's Toolbox. Hernandez, Joseph, illus. 1998. (Barney Ser.). 14p. (J). (ps-k). 5.95 (978-1-57064-244-9(3)) Scholastic, Inc.

Cooner, Donna D. & Scholastic, Inc. Staff. Barney's Easter Basket. Valentine-Ruppe, June, illus. 2001. (Barney Ser.). 14p. (J). (ps-k). bds. 5.99 (978-1-58668-045-9(5)) Scholastic, Inc.

Cowley, Joy, contrib. by. Dinosaur Morning. 2004. (Story Basket Ser.: Vol. 5). 8 or 16p. (gr. k-2). pap. 31.50 (978-0-322-01923-2(0)) Wright Group, The.

Cowley, Stewart. Bronty: Share the Adventures of Bronty Brontosaurus & His Friends. 2001. (Dinosaur Friends Ser.). (Illus.). 32p. (J). 7.95 (978-1-57717-178-2(0)) New Line Bks.

—Steggy: Share the Adventures of Steggy Stegasaurus & Her Friends. 2001. (Dinosaur Friends Ser.). (Illus.). 32p. (J). 7.95 (978-1-57717-179-9(9)) New Line Bks.

—Trisha: Share the Adventures of Trisha Triceratops & Her Friends. 2001. (Dinosaur Friends Ser.). (Illus.). 32p. (J). 7.95 (978-1-57717-177-5(2)) New Line Bks.

—Tyro: Share the Adventures of Tyro Tyrannosaurus & His Friends. 2001. (Dinosaur Friends Ser.). (Illus.). 32p. (J). 7.95 (978-1-57717-180-5(2)) New Line Bks.

Cross, Gillian. The Monster from Underground. Priestley, Chris, illus. 2002. (Yellow Bananas Ser.). 48p. (J). (gr. 3-4). pap. (978-0-7787-0981-7(7)); lib. bdg. (978-0-7787-0935-0(3)) Crabtree Publishing Co.

—Monster from Underground. 2002. (gr. 3-6). lib. bdg. 12.95 (978-0-613-52882-5(4)) Tandem Library Bks.

Crowson, Andrew. Flip Flap Prehistoric. Crowson, Andrew, illus. 2003. (Illus.). 12p. (J). pap. (978-1-85602-474-7(1)) Chrysalis Children's Bks.

Cunningham, Kay. Bucky, the Adventures of the Dinosaur Cowboy. Wilson, Mary Ann, illus. 2004. 32p. (J). 18.99 (978-1-57860-173-8(8) , Guild Pr. of Indiana); pap. 12.99 (978-1-57860-174-5(6)) Emmis Bks.

Currie, Philip J. & Koppelhus, Eva B. Centrosaurus. Sovak, Jan, illus. 2001. (Moment in Time Ser.). 56p. (J). (gr. 2-9). pap. (978-0-9682512-2-5(6)) Red Deer Pr.

—Sinosauropteryx. Sovak, Jan, illus. 2001. (Moment in Time Ser.). 56p. (J). (gr. 2-9). (978-0-9682512-3-2(4)) Red Deer Pr.

Cyrus, Kurt. Tadpole Rex. 2008. (J). (***978-0-15-205990-3(3)***) Harcourt Trade Pubs.

Dalmatian Press Staff. Jungle Book/Dinosaurs. 2007. 64p. pap. 4.99 (***978-1-4037-3593-5(X)***) Dalmatian Pr.

Daniels, Teri. G-Rex. Pearson, Tracey Campbell, illus. 2000. 32p. (J). (gr. k-4). 17.99 (978-0-531-33243-6(8)); pap. 16.95 (978-0-531-30243-9(1)) Scholastic, Inc. (Orchard Bks.).

Davis, Guy. Barney Says "Night-Night" McKee, Darren, illus. 1998. (Barney Ser.). 12p. (J). (ps-k). 6.95 (978-1-57064-455-9(1)) Scholastic, Inc.

—Barney's ABC, 123 & More. McKee, Darren, illus. 1999. (Barney Ser.). 14p. (J). (ps-k). bds. 9.99 (978-1-57064-243-2(5)) Scholastic, Inc.

—Barney's Neighborhood. Davis, Guy, illus. Dipold, Jane, photos by. 1999. (Barney Ser.). (Illus.). 18p. (J). (ps-k). 6.95 (978-1-57064-463-4(2)) Scholastic, Inc.

—Freddi Fish & the Pirate's Treasure. Winslow, Becky, illus. 2001. (Humongous Ser.). 12p. (J). bds. 9.99 incl. cd-rom (978-1-58668-066-4(8)) Lyrick Studios.

Davis, Guy, ed. Barney's We Wish You a Merry Christmas. 1999. (Barney Ser.). (Illus.). 14p. (J). (ps-k). pap. 5.95 (978-1-57064-750-5(X)) Scholastic, Inc.

Davis, Guy & Valentine-Ruppe, June. Baby Bop's Blankey. 1999. (Barney Ser.). (Illus.). 14p. (J). (ps-k). 5.95 (978-1-57064-613-3(9)) Scholastic, Inc.

Davis, Lee & Dorling Kindersley Publishing Staff. Dinosaur Dinners. 1999. (Eyewitness Readers). (Illus.). 32p. (J). (gr. 1-3). 12.99 (978-0-7894-4252-9(3)) Dorling Kindersley Publishing, Inc.

de Paola, Tomie. Little Grunt & the Big Egg: A Prehistoric Fairy Tale. 2007. 27.95 incl. audio (***978-0-8045-6944-6(4)***); 29.95 incl. audio compact disk (***978-0-8045-4158-9(2)***) Spoken Arts, Inc.

—T-Rex Is Missing! 2002. (gr. k-3). lib. bdg. 11.80 (978-0-613-50544-4(1)) Tandem Library Bks.

—T-Rex Is Missing! A Barkers Book. 2002. (All Aboard Reading Ser.). (Illus.). 32p. (J). pap. 3.99 (978-0-448-42870-3(9) , Grosset & Dunlap) Penguin Group (USA) Inc.

Dell, Patricia. Zander. Dell, Patricia, illus. 2000. (Illus.). 12p. (J). (gr. k-6). pap. 10.00 (978-0-9702221-0-7(6)) Zanderbooks.

DePaola, Tomie. Little Grunt & the Big Egg: A Prehistoric Fairy Tale. 2006. 32p. (J). (ps-3). 16.99 (978-0-399-24529-9(4)) Penguin Group (USA) Inc.

DePrisco, Dorothea. Dinosaur Dance. 2006. 12p. 9.95 (978-1-58117-480-9(2) , Intervisual/Piggy Toes) Dalmatian Pr.

Desrosiers, Sylvie. Ou Sont Passes les Dinosaures? 2002. (Roman Jeunesse Ser.). (FRE.). 96p. (YA). (gr. 4-7). pap. (978-2-89021-119-3(3)) Diffusion du livre Mirabel.

Dinges, Jason. Paleo Pals: The Adventures of Bill & Beryl. 2004. (Illus.). 34p. (J). pap. 14.95 (978-1-932373-71-4(3) , Cedar Hill Pr.) Cedar Hill Publishing.

Dino Detective. Date not set. 9.95 (978-0-89868-271-7(1)); pap. 3.95 (978-0-89868-272-4(X)) ARO Publishing Co.

The Dinosaur Dance. 2005. (Emergent Library: Vol. 2). (YA). (ps-1). 23.94 (978-0-8215-8927-4(X)) Sadlier, William H. Inc.

The Dinosaur Dance: Take-Home Book. 2005. (Emergent Library: Vol. 2). (YA). (ps-1). 12.60 (978-0-8215-7257-3(1)) Sadlier, William H. Inc.

Dinosaur Girl: Individual Title, 6 packs. (Action Packs Ser.). 120p. (gr. 3-5). 44.00 (978-0-7635-8394-1(4)) Rigby Education.

Dinosaur Party: Individual Title, 6 packs. (Chiquilibros Ser.). (gr. k-1). 23.00 (978-0-7635-0432-8(7)) Rigby Education.

Dinosaur Quest at Diamond Peak, , 2001. (Truth Seeker's Mystery Ser.: Vol. 2). 208p. per. 7.99 (978-0-9700385-6-2(9)) Media Angels, Inc.

Dinosaur Read Along: With 3-D Dinosound with Book. 2000. (J). (ps-3). pap. 6.98 incl. audio (978-0-7634-0609-7(0)) Walt Disney Records.

A Dinosaur Snack. 2004. (J). (978-1-932570-24-3(1)) Literacy Footprints Inc.

Dinosaur Tales. (My Animal Library). (Illus.). 10p. (J). bds. (978-2-7643-0104-3(9)) Phidal Publishing, Inc./Editions Phidal, Inc.

Dinosaurio Chiquito: Individual Title Six-Packs. (Coleccion Pm Ser.).Tr. of Lucky Day for Little Dinosaur. (SPA.). 16p. (gr. 1 up). 26.00 (978-0-7578-3002-0(1)) Rigby Education.

DiPucchio, Kelly. Dinosnores. Goembel, Ponder, illus. 2005. 32p. (J). (ps-1). lib. bdg. 16.89 (978-0-06-051578-2(3)); 15.99 (978-0-06-051577-5(5)) HarperCollins Pubs.

Disney Dinosaur Play-a-sound. 15.98 (978-0-7853-4190-1(0)) Publications International, Ltd.

Dolby, Karen. The Incredible Dinosaur Expedition. Haw, Brenda, illus. 2004. (Puzzle Adventures Ser.). 48p. (J). pap. 4.95 (978-0-7945-0022-1(6) , Usborne) EDC Publishing.

Donaldson, Julia. The Dinosaur's Diary. l.t. ed. 2005. (Illus.). 96p. (J). pap. (978-0-7540-7835-7(3) , CLP 426) BBC Audio.

Donaldson, Julia. Tyrannosaurus Drip. 2008. (Illus.). 32p. (J). 16.95 (***978-0-312-37747-2(9)***) Feiwel & Friends.

Donnelly, Liza. Dinosaur Garden. 2000. (J). 19.95 (978-0-590-72598-9(X)) Scholastic, Inc.

Donnie Dinosaur's Tobacco Trouble. (J). 29.50 (978-1-56230-276-4(0)) Syndistar, Inc.

Dorling Kindersley Publishing Staff. Glow in the Dark: Dinosaur. Parsons, Jayne, ed. 2002. (Ultimate Sticker Bks.). (Illus.). 16p. (J). (gr. k-3). pap. 6.99 (978-0-7894-8458-1(7)) Dorling Kindersley Publishing, Inc.

Doyle, Arthur Conan. The Lost World & Other Thrilling Tales. 2001. (gr. 7-12). lib. bdg. 17.65 (978-0-613-64299-6(6)) Tandem Library Bks.

Draper, Sharon M. Stars & Sparks on Stage. Watson, Jesse Joshua, illus. 2007. (Ziggy & the Black Dinosaurs Ser.). 160p. (J). lib. bdg. 11.89 (978-1-4169-2755-6(7) , Aladdin Library) Simon & Schuster Children's Publishing.

—Stars & Sparks Onstage. Watson, Jesse Joshua, illus. 2007. (Ziggy & the Black Dinosaurs Ser.). 160p. (J). pap. 4.99 (978-1-4169-0001-6(2) , Aladdin) Simon & Schuster Children's Publishing.

Dudko, Mary Ann & Larsen, Margie. Barney's in, Out & All Around. Full, Dennis, illus. 1999. (Barney Ser.). 24p. (J). (ps-k). bds. 4.99 (978-1-57064-445-0(4)) Scholastic, Inc.

Duey, Kathleen. Rex. Epstein, Eugene, illus. Gould, Robert, photos by. 2000. (Time Soldiers Ser.: Bk. 1). 48p. (J). (ps-5). 12.95 (978-1-929945-18-4(3)) Big Guy Bks., Inc.

—Rex. Epstein, Eugene, illus. Gould, Robert, photos by. (Time Soldiers Ser.: Bk. 1). (J). 2005. 96p. (gr. 3-4). pap. 5.95 (978-1-929945-53-5(1)); 2003. 48p. (ps-5). pap. 7.95 (978-1-929945-20-7(5)) Big Guy Bks., Inc.

—Rex 2. Epstein, Eugene, illus. Gould, Robert, photos by. 2003. (Time Soldiers Ser.: Bk. 2). 48p. (J). (ps-5). pap. 8.95 (978-1-929945-27-6(2)) Big Guy Bks., Inc.

—Rex 2. 2007. (Illus.). 96p. (J). 24.21 (978-1-59961-228-7(3)) Spotlight.

—Rex 2. 2003. (gr. k-3). lib. bdg. 17.60 (978-0-613-70796-1(6)) Tandem Library Bks.

—Rex 2. Epstein, Eugene, illus. Gould, Robert, photos by. (Time Soldiers Ser.: Bk. 2). (J). 2005. (ENG.). 96p. (gr. 3-4). pap. 5.95 (978-1-929945-54-2(X)); 2nd rev. ed. 2000. 48p. (ps-5). 12.95 (978-1-929945-19-1(1)) Big Guy Bks., Inc.

Duey, Kathleen & Gould, Robert. Rex. Epstein, Eugene, illus. 2007. (Time Soldiers Ser.: Bk. 1). 96p. (J). (gr. k-5). 24.21 (978-1-59961-227-0(5)) Spotlight.

—Rex 2. Epstein, Eugene, illus. Gould, Robert, photos by. 2003. (Soldados de Tiempo Libro : Vol. 2). (SPA.). 48p. (J). pap. 8.95 (978-1-929945-36-8(1)) Big Guy Bks., Inc.

Edwards, Pamela Duncan. Dinorella: A Prehistoric Fairy Tale. 1999. (gr. k-3). lib. bdg. 14.15 (978-0-613-74987-9(1)) Tandem Library Bks.

Edwards, Wallace. The Extinct Files: My Science Project. 2006. (Illus.). 32p. (J). (978-1-55337-971-3(3)) Kids Can Pr., Ltd.

Emmett, Jonathan. Dino Boulder Ball. Rutherford, Peter, illus. 2006. 32p. (J). (***978-1-4048-3116-2(9)***) Picture Window Bks.

—Terry Takes Off. Rutherford, Peter, illus. 2006. 32p. (J). (***978-1-4048-3132-2(0)***) Picture Window Bks.

Everson, Chance. Beginnings Vol. 2: Tales of the Mandrasaurs, Volume the Second. Geary, Steve, illus. 2004. cd-rom 9.95 (978-0-9760303-1-7(4)) R.A.R.E. TALES.

—Discoveries: Tales of the Mandrasaurs, Volume the Third. Geary, Steve, illus. 2004. cd-rom 9.95 (978-0-9760303-2-4(2)) R.A.R.E. TALES.

—Forever & a Day Vol. 1: Tales of the Mandrasaurs, Volume the First. Geary, Steve, illus. 2004. cd-rom 9.95 (978-0-9760303-0-0(6)) R.A.R.E. TALES.

—Verlin's Magical Blunder: Tales of the Mandrasaurs, Volume the Seventh. Geary, Steve, illus. 2004. cd-rom 9.95 (978-0-9760303-6-2(5)) R.A.R.E. TALES.

Ewart, Claire. Fossil. Ewart, Claire, illus. 2004. (Illus.). 32p. (J). 16.95 (978-0-8027-8890-0(4)) Walker & Co.

Explorers in Dinosaur World. 2005. (J). audio, cd-rom 25.95 (978-0-9771381-2-8(7)) Williams, Geoffrey T.

Fearnley, Jan. Colin & the Curly Claw. Fearnley, Jan, illus. 2001. (Blue Bananas Ser.). (Illus.). 48p. (J). (gr. 1-2). (978-0-7787-0840-7(3)); pap. (978-0-7787-0886-5(1)) Crabtree Publishing Co.

—Colin & the Curly Claw. 2002. (gr. k-3). lib. bdg. 12.95 (978-0-613-52821-4(2)) Tandem Library Bks.

Felber, Eric P. & Currie, Philip J. Albertosaurus. Sovak, Jan, illus. 2001. (Moment in Time Ser.). 56p. (J). (gr. 2-9). (978-0-9682512-1-8(8)) Red Deer Pr.

Ferrone, John M. Gus & the Pteranodon. Ferrone, John M., illus. 1999. (Illus.). 36p. (ps-5). pap. 16.95 (978-1-928811-00-8(0)) Story Stuff, Inc.

Fisher, Valorie. How High Can a Dinosaur Count? ...and Other Math Mysteries. Fisher, Valorie, illus. 2006. 40p. (J). (gr. k-4). lib. bdg. 18.99 (978-0-375-93608-1(4) , Schwartz & Wade Bks.) Random Hse. Children's Bks.

Fitch, Sheree. When Dinosaurs Dine by Moonlight. 2002. (Illus.). 13.95 (978-0-385-25875-3(5) , Delta) Dell Publishing.

—When Dinosaurs Dine by Moonlight. 2002. (Illus.). (J). pap. 6.95 (978-0-385-25933-0(6)) Doubleday Canada, Ltd. CAN. *Dist:* Random Hse. of Canada, Ltd.

Fleischman, Paul. Time Train. 2002. (Illus.). (J). 15.49 (978-0-7587-3814-1(5)) Book Wholesalers, Inc.

Foreman, Michael. Dinosaur Time. 2002. (Illus.). 32p. (J). (978-1-84270-183-6(5)) Andersen GBR. *Dist:* Random Hse. of Canada, Ltd.

—A Trip to Dinosaur Time. Foreman, Michael, illus. 2003. (Illus.). 32p. (J). (ps-3). 16.99 (978-0-7636-2104-9(8)) Candlewick Pr.

Foster, Alan Dean. The Hand of Dinotopia. Gurney, James, illus. 1999. (Dinotopia Ser.). 416p. (J). (gr. 5 up). 22.99 (978-0-06-028005-5(0)) HarperCollins Pubs.

—Hand of Dinotopia. 2002. (Dinotopia Ser.). (Illus.). 416p. (J). (gr. 5 up). pap. 7.99 (978-0-06-051851-6(0)) HarperCollins Pubs.

Fotonovel Publications Staff. Dinosaur. 2000. (Illus.). 176p. (J). pap. 7.95 (978-0-89752-012-6(2)) Fotonovel Pubns.

Fox, Diane & Fox, Christyan. Tyson the Terrible. Fox, Diane, illus. 2006. (Illus.). 24p. (J). (ps-2). 12.95 (978-1-58234-734-9(4)) Bloomsbury Publishing.

Frederick, Mary. Peeka, Pooka, & the Dinosaur. Williams, Allen, illus. 2000. 108p. (ps-3). pap. 9.95 (978-0-595-12812-9(2)) iUniverse, Inc.

French, Jackie. My Dog the Dinosaur. King, Stephen Michael, illus. 2007. (J). 112p. (***978-1-59889-344-1(0)***); 107p. pap. (***978-1-59889-437-0(4)***) Stone Arch Bks.

Galvin, Laura Gates. Ankylosaurus Fights Back. Chesterman, Adrian, illus. 2007. 36p. 14.95 (***978-1-59249-679-2(2)***); 2.95 (***978-1-59249-682-2(2)***); pap. 6.95 (***978-1-59249-680-8(6)***) Soundprints.

—Ankylosaurus Fights Back: Paperback with CD. Chesterman, Adrian, illus. 2007. 36p. 8.95 (***978-1-59249-681-5(4)***) Soundprints.

Garland, Michael. Miss Smith Reads Again! Garland, Michael, illus. 2006. (Illus.). 32p. (J). (ps). 15.99 (978-0-525-47722-8(5) , Dutton Juvenile) Penguin Group (USA) Inc.

—Miss Smith Reads Again! 2006. (Illus.). (J). (***978-1-4156-8098-8(1)*** , Dutton Juvenile) Penguin Group (USA) Inc.

Geraghty, Paul. Dinosaur in Danger. 2005. (Illus.). 32p. (J). pap. (***978-0-09-943865-6(8)*** , Red Fox) Random Hse. Children's Bks.

Geraghty, Paul. Rotten & Rascal: The Two Terrible Pterosaur Twins. 2006. (Illus.). 32p. (J). 12.99 (978-0-7641-5918-3(6)) Barron's Educational Series, Inc.

Gerwitz, Felice. Literature No. 2: Dinosaur Quest at Diamond Peak. 2003. (Truth Seeker's Mystery Ser.: 2). (YA). stu. ed., per. 6.50 (978-1-931941-05-1(X)) Media Angels, Inc.

Gerwitz, Felice & Gerwitz, Christina. Dinosaur Quest at Diamond Peak, 3, Vol. 2. 2nd rev. ed. 2007. (Truth Seeker's Mystery Ser.). 208p. (YA). per. 8.99 (***978-1-931941-11-2(4)***) Media Angels, Inc.

Giff, Patricia Reilly. En las Garras del Dinosaurio. 2000. (SPA.). (YA). (gr. 1 up). 3.95 (978-0-922852-42-0(1)) AIMS International Bks., Inc.

Gilmore, Rachna & Watts, Leslie Elizabeth. Making Grizzle Grow. 2008. (Illus.). 32p. (J). (ps-2). (***978-1-55041-885-9(8)***) Fitzhenry & Whiteside, Ltd.

Girling, Brough. Granddad's Dinosaur. Dell, Stephen, illus. 2005. (I Am Reading Ser.). 48p. (J). (gr. k-3). pap. 3.95 (978-0-7534-5897-6(7) , Kingfisher) Houghton Mifflin Co. Trade & Reference Div.

Glossop, Jennifer & Russell, Jay. Hypacrosaurus. 1999. (Tiny Perfect Dinosaur Ser.). (Illus.). 32p. 12.95 (978-0-8362-7910-8(7)) Andrews McMeel Publishing.

Glut, Donald F. Chomper. 2000. (Dinotopia Ser.: No. 11). (J). (gr. 3-6). 10.64 (978-0-606-17872-3(4)) Tandem Library Bks.

Golden Books Staff. Colorful Dino World! 2008. (Illus.). 48p. (J). (ps-2). pap. 3.99 (978-0-375-83715-9(9) , Golden Bks.) Random Hse. Children's Bks.

Goode, Diane. The Dinosaur's New Clothes. 1999. Orig. Title: Kejserens nye klaeder. (Illus.). 40p. (YA). (ps-3). pap. 15.95 (978-0-590-38360-8(4) , Blue Sky Pr., The) Scholastic, Inc.

Gorgo Meets Her Match: Individual Title Six-Packs. 16p. (gr. 2 up). 35.00 (978-0-7635-9238-7(2)) Rigby Education.

Gould, Robert. Dinosaurs. Epstein, Eugene, illus. Gould, Robert, photos by. 2005. (Big Stuff Ser.: 7). 16p. (J). bds. 7.95 (978-1-929945-58-0(2)) Big Guy Bks., Inc.

Gould, Robert & Duey, Kathleen. Time Soldiers. 2005. 384p. pap. 16.95 (978-1-929945-60-3(4)) Big Guy Bks., Inc.

Grace, Will. Five Little Dinosaurs. Vere Hodgkinson, Ed, illus. 2004. 7p. (J). bds. 6.99 (978-0-439-58393-0(4) , Cartwheel Bks.) Scholastic, Inc.

Grambling, Lois G. Big Dog. San Diego, Andy, illus. 2001. 32p. (J). (gr. k-3). 15.95 (978-0-7614-5045-0(9) , Cavendish Children's Bks.) Cavendish, Marshall Corp.

—Can I Bring My Pterodactyl to School, Ms. Johnson? Love, Judy, illus. 2006. 32p. (J). pap. 6.95 (978-1-58089-141-7(1)) Charlesbridge Publishing, Inc.

—Can I Have a Stegosaurus, Mom? Can I? Please? 1998. (J). (978-0-606-13243-5(0)) Tandem Library Bks.

—Can I Have a Tyrannosaurus, Mom? Can I? Please!? 2001. (Illus.). (J). (978-0-606-21099-7(7)) Tandem Library Bks.

—Here Comes T. Rex Cottontail. Davis, Jack E., illus. 2007. 32p. (J). lib. bdg. 16.89 (978-0-06-053131-7(2)); 15.99 (978-0-06-053129-4(0)) HarperCollins Pubs.

—T. Rex Trick-or-Treats. Davis, Jack E., illus. 2005. 32p. (J). 12.99 (978-0-06-050252-2(5) , Tegen, Katherine Bks) HarperCollins Pubs.

—T-Rex Trick-or-Treats. Davis, Jack E., illus. 2005. 32p. (J). lib. bdg. 13.89 (978-0-06-050253-9(3) , Tegen, Katherine Bks) HarperCollins Pubs.

Grandad's Dinosaur: Level M, 6 vols. 128p. (gr. 2-3). 49.95 (978-0-7699-0984-4(1)) Shortland Pubns. (U. S. A.) Inc.

Gray, Susan H. Mammoths & Mastodons. 2005. (Exploring Dinosaurs & Prehistoric Creatures Ser.). (Illus.). 32p. (J). (gr. 2-6). 27.07 (978-1-59296-409-3(5)) Child's World, Inc.

The Great Dinosaur Hunt, 6 vols. (Woodland Mysteriestm Ser.). 133p. (gr. 3-7). 42.50 (978-0-7802-7929-2(8)) Wright Group, The.

Greenburg, Dan. Green Eggs & Dinosaurs. Davis, Jack, illus. 2001. (Zack Files Ser.: No. 23). 64p. (J). (gr. 2-5). mass mkt. 4.99 (978-0-448-42546-7(7) , Grosset & Dunlap) Penguin Group (USA) Inc.

—Green Eggs & Dinosaurs. 2001. (gr. 3-6). lib. bdg. 13.00 (978-0-613-58366-4(3)) Tandem Library Bks.

Greenburg, J. C. With the Dinosaurs. Gerardi, Jan, illus. 2005. (Andrew Lost Ser.: Bk. 11). 96p. (J). (gr. 2-5). pap. 3.99 (978-0-375-82951-2(2)); lib. bdg. 11.99 (978-0-375-92951-9(7)) Random Hse. Children's Bks. (Random Hse. Bks. for Young Readers).

—With the Dinosaurs. Gerardi, Jan, illus. 2005. (Andrew Lost Ser.: Bk. 11). 85p. (J). (gr. 2-5). lib. bdg. 11.04 (978-0-606-33719-9(0)) Tandem Library Bks.

Griffith, Helen V. Dinosaur Habitat. 1999. (Avon Camelot Bks.). (Illus.). 112p. (J). (gr. 3-7). pap. 4.95 (978-0-380-73225-8(4)) HarperCollins Pubs.

—Dinosaur Habitat. 1999. (J). (978-0-606-17327-8(7)) Tandem Library Bks.

Griffiths, Andy. What Buttosaur Is That? 2008. (Teacher's Essential Guide Ser.). 208p. (J). (gr. 4-7). pap. 5.99 (***978-0-439-92622-5(X)*** , Scholastic Paperbacks) Scholastic, Inc.

Guettier, Benedicte. Dinosaurs. Guettier, Benedicte, illus. 2005. (Illus.). 14p. (J). (ps-k). bds. 11.95 (978-1-929132-86-7(7)) Kane/Miller Bk. Pubs., Inc.

Gurney, James. Dinotopia: Journey to Chandara. 2007. (Illus.). 160p. 29.95 (***978-0-7407-6431-8(4)***) Andrews McMeel Publishing.

—Dinotopia: The World Beneath. Gurney, James, illus. 2003. (Dinotopia Ser.). (Illus.). 160p. (J). pap. 19.99 (978-0-06-053065-5(0)) HarperCollins Pubs.

—A Land Apart from Time. Gurney, James, illus. 2003. (Dinotopia Ser.). (Illus.). 160p. (J). pap. 21.99 (978-0-06-053064-8(2)) HarperCollins Pubs.

—Land Apart from Time. 2003. (gr. 3-6). lib. bdg. 30.40 (978-0-613-85748-2(8)) Tandem Library Bks.

Gurney, John Steven. Dinosaur Train. Date not set. 32p. (J). (ps-1). pap. 5.99 (978-0-06-443738-7(8)) HarperCollins Pubs.

—Dinosaur Train. Gurney, John Steven, illus. 2002. (Illus.). 32p. (J). (ps-1). 15.99 (978-0-06-029245-4(8)) HarperCollins Pubs.

Hahn, Victor H. The Adventures of Frank the Friendly Frogasaurus & Family. Twiner, Stacy, illus. 2000. (Frank the Friendly Frogasaurus Ser.). 32p. (J). (ps-3). 15.95 (978-0-929765-76-1(1) , Papa & Noelle Stories) Seven Locks Pr.

—Frank the Frogasaurus Meets T-Rex in the Forest. Twiner, Stacey, illus. 2000. (Frank the Friendly Frogasaurus Ser.). 32p. (J). (ps-3). 15.95 (978-0-929765-78-5(8) , Papa & Noelle Stories) Seven Locks Pr.

Halfmann, Janet. Barney's Four Seasons. Davis, Guy, ed. Sharp, Chris, illus. 1999. 80p. (J). (ps-3). 1.99 (978-1-57064-465-8(9)) Scholastic, Inc.

Halfmann, Janet & Scholastic, Inc. Staff. Barney's Christmas Fun: A Dino-Mite Color & Activity Book. Davis, Guy, ed. Valentine-Ruppe, June, illus. 1999. (Barney Ser.). 80p. (J). (ps-k). 1.99 (978-1-57064-466-5(7)) Scholastic, Inc.

Halfmann, Janet, et al. Barney's Favorite Songs. Davis, Guy, ed. Valentine-Ruppe, June, illus. 1999. (Barney Ser.). 112p. (J). (ps-k). act. bk. ed. 2.99 (978-1-57064-457-3(8)) Scholastic, Inc.

Ham, Ken. What Really Happened to the Dinosaurs? 2004. 48p. pap. 0.75 (978-1-893345-22-5(X)) Answers in Genesis Ministries.

Hapka, Catherine. The Land Before Time: Cera's Shiny Stone. Grosvenor, Charles, illus. 2007. (I Can Read Bks.). 32p. (J). pap. 3.99 (***978-0-06-134777-1(9)*** , Harper Trophy) HarperCollins Pubs.

—Land Before Time: The Lonely Dinosaur. 2008. (I Can Read Bks.). 32p. (J). pap. 3.99 (***978-0-06-135293-5(4)*** , Harper Trophy) HarperCollins Pubs.

Hapka, Cathy. Oasis. 2002. (Dinotopia Ser.: Vol. 16). 208p. (J). (gr. 3-8). pap. 3.99 (978-0-375-82295-7(X) , Random Hse. Bks. for Young Readers) Random Hse. Children's Bks.

Harcourt School Publishers Staff. A Trip on Dinosaur Airlines Below Level. 3rd ed. 2002. (Trophies Reading Program Ser.). (Illus.). pap. 5.10 (978-0-15-323068-4(1)) Harcourt Schl. Pubs.

Hartmann, Wendy. The Dinosaurs Are Back & It's All Your Fault Edward! 2000. (Illus.). (J). (978-0-606-17918-8(6)) Tandem Library Bks.

Harvey, Damian. Oggy & the Dinosaur. Hall, Francois, illus. 2005. (Reading Corner Ser.). 24p. (J). (gr. k-3). lib. bdg. 22.80 (978-1-59771-008-4(3)) Sea-To-Sea Pubns.

Hawkins, Colin. Dance of Dinosaurs. 2002. (Illus.). 30p. (J). pap. 9.99 (978-0-00-711444-3(3)) HarperCollins Pubs. Ltd. GBR. *Dist:* Independent Pubs. Group.

Hay DeSimone, Corkey. Dinosaur Explore Activity & Coloring Book: Dinosaurs designed for their littlest Fans. Hay DeSimone, Corkey, illus. 2006. (J). 4.95 (978-0-9777394-0-0(6)) Gentle Giraffe Pr.

—Dinosaur Explore Board Book: Dinosaurs Designed for Their Littlest Fans. Hay DeSimone, Corkey, illus. 2006. (J). bds. 7.95 (978-0-9777394-1-7(4)) Gentle Giraffe Pr.

Hayes, Fiona. What's up with Trinny? 2007. (Illus.). 10p. (J). 4.95 (978-1-4027-4478-5(1)) Sterling Publishing Co., Inc.

Hearn, Diane Dawson. Dad's Dinosaur Day. Hearn, Diane Dawson, illus. 1999. (Illus.). 32p. (J). (ps-3). pap. 5.99 (978-0-689-82611-5(7) , 076714005990, Aladdin) Simon & Schuster Children's Publishing.

—Dad's Dinosaur Day. 1999. (J). 12.79 (978-0-606-16309-5(3)); lib. bdg. 14.15 (978-0-613-18246-1(4)) Tandem Library Bks.

Heffernan, Colleen. Dinosaurs in the Attic. Clark, Dan, illus. 2001. (Early Chapters Bks.). 48p. (J). (gr. 1-4). pap. (978-1-896184-68-5(5)) Roussan Pubs., Inc./Roussan Editeur, Inc.

Hegeman, Andrew. The Last Dinosaur Egg. Hegeman, Andrew, illus. 1998. (Illus.). 36p. (J). (ps-3). 15.95 (978-1-890817-04-6(X)) Winslow Pr.

Heidbreder, Robe. Drumheller Dinosaur Dance. Slavin, Bill, illus. 2006. 32p. (978-1-55337-982-9(9)) Kids Can Pr., Ltd.

Heidbreder, Robert. Drumheller Dinosaur Dance. Slavin, Bill & Melo, Esperanca, illus. 2005. 32p. (J). (ps-1). (978-1-55337-393-3(6)) Kids Can Pr., Ltd.

Helmer, Marilyn. Dinosaurs on the Beach. 2003. (Orca Young Readers Ser.). (Illus.). 144p. (J). (gr. 3-6). pap. 4.99 (978-1-55143-260-1(9)) Orca Bk. Pubs. USA.

—Dinosaurs on the Beach. 2003. (gr. 3-6). lib. bdg. 13.00 (978-0-613-87472-4(2)) Tandem Library Bks.

Hennessy, B. G. Busy Dinah Dinosaur. Martín Larrañaga, Ana, illus. 2000. (Brand New Readers Ser.). (J). (ps-2). 48p. 10.99 (978-0-7636-1140-4(9)); Set. 32p. pap. 4.99 (978-0-7636-1141-5(7)) Candlewick Pr.

—Dinah Hide & See. 2000. (Brand New Readers Ser.). (Illus.). (J). (978-0-7636-1136-1(0)) Candlewick Pr.

—Dinah Likes to Eat. 2000. (Brand New Readers Ser.). (Illus.). (J). (978-0-7636-1134-7(4)) Candlewick Pr.

—Dinah Little Big. 2000. (Brand New Readers Ser.). (Illus.). (J). (978-0-7636-1135-4(2)) Candlewick Pr.

—Dinah Muddy Dinosaur. 2000. (Brand New Readers Ser.). (Illus.). (J). (978-0-7636-1144-6(1)) Candlewick Pr.

—Dinahs Dream. 2000. (Brand New Readers Ser.). (Illus.). (J). (978-0-7636-1137-8(9)) Candlewick Pr.

—Dinahs Pretty Rose. 2000. (Brand New Readers Ser.). (Illus.). (J). (978-0-7636-1143-9(3)) Candlewick Pr.

—Dinahs Walk. 2000. (Brand New Readers Ser.). (Illus.). (J). (978-0-7636-1142-2(5)) Candlewick Pr.

—Good Night Dinah. 2000. (Brand New Readers Ser.). (Illus.). (J). (978-0-7636-1145-3(X)) Candlewick Pr.

Herbert Hilligan's Prehistoric Adventure Curriculum Guide. 2004. ring bd. 24.95 (978-0-9743335-5-7(7)) Imaginative Publishing, Ltd.

Herman, Gail. Spike at Halloween. 2002. (ps-2). lib. bdg. 11.80 (978-0-613-64113-5(2)) Tandem Library Bks.

Hiebert, Elfrieda H. Five Little Dinosaurs. (Little Book Practice Reader Ser.). (J). (978-0-8136-0788-7(4)) Modern Curriculum Pr.

Hoff, Syd. Danny & the Dinosaur. Hoff, Syd, illus. 2002. (Illus.). (J). 11.91 (978-0-7587-1089-5(5)) Book Wholesalers, Inc.

—Danny & the Dinosaur. 1999. (I Can Read Bks.). 64p. (J). (ps-3). 14.95 (978-0-694-01297-8(1)) HarperCollins Pubs.

—Danny & the Dinosaur Go to Camp. Hoff, Syd, illus. 2002. (Illus.). (J). 11.91 (978-0-7587-6062-3(0)) Book Wholesalers, Inc.

—Danny & the Dinosaur Go to Camp. Hoff, Syd, illus. 1998. (I Can Read Bks.). (Illus.). 32p. (J). (ps-2). pap. 3.99 (978-0-06-444244-2(6) , Harper Trophy) HarperCollins Pubs.

—Danny & the Dinosaur Go to Camp. 1998. (I Can Read Bks.). (J). (ps-1). 10.79 (978-0-606-13313-5(5)) Tandem Library Bks.

—Happy Birthday, Danny & the Dinosaur! Hoff, Syd, illus. 2002. (Illus.). (J). 11.87 (978-0-7587-4360-2(2)) Book Wholesalers, Inc.

Hogan, Mary. Dinosaur. 2000. (Dinosaur Ser.). (Illus.). (J). (ps-3). 96p. 3.99 (978-0-7364-1045-8(7)); 32p. 7.99 (978-0-7364-1061-8(9)) Mouse Works.

Holcomb, Sue A. & Holcomb, J. Paul. Tex R Masaur: Down in the Dump. Holcomb, Sue A., illus. (Tex R Masaur, Dinodillo Bks.). (Illus.). 32p. (Orig.). (J). (gr. k-3). pap. 3.95 (978-0-9636122-2-9(0)) Post Oak Hill.

Holmquist, Delano. Santasauras. Galey, Chuck, illus. 2002. 32p. (J). (ps-2). 15.95 (978-1-56554-933-3(3)) Pelican Publishing Co., Inc.

Hooke, R. Schuyler. Harry & His Bucket Full of Dinosaurs: X Marks the Spot. Mawhinney, Art, illus. 2007. (Bright & Early Bks.). 36p. (J). (ps-2). lib. bdg. 12.99 (978-0-375-94243-3(2) , Random Hse. Bks. for Young Readers) Random Hse. Children's Bks.

—Harry & his Bucket Full of Dinosaurs: X Marks the Spot. Mawhinney, Art, illus. 2007. (Bright & Early Bks.). 36p. (J). (ps-2). 8.99 (978-0-375-84141-5(5) , Random Hse. Bks. for Young Readers) Random Hse. Children's Bks.

—Harry & the Bucketful of Dinosaurs Uh-Oh! Mawhinney, Art, illus. 2007. (Step into Reading Ser.). 32p. (J). (ps-2). pap. 3.99 (978-0-375-83977-1(1)); lib. bdg. 11.99 (978-0-375-94056-9(1)) Random Hse. Children's Bks. (Random Hse. Bks. for Young Readers).

Hooke, R. Schuyler & Mawhinney, Art. Harry & His Bucket Full of Dinosaurs: Into the Bucket. 2006. (Illus.). 24p. (J). (ps-2). pap. 3.99 (978-0-375-83867-5(8) , Random Hse. Bks. for Young Readers) Random Hse. Children's Bks.

Hope, Laura Lee. The Mystery of the Dinosaur in the Forest. Ruppert, Larry, illus. 2005. (Bobbsey Twins Ser.). 24p. (J). pap. 3.99 (978-1-4169-0705-3(X) , Little Simon) Simon & Schuster Children's Publishing.

Horner, John R. & Gorman, James. Maia: A Dinosaur Grows Up. Walton, Jeri D. & Blumer, Terrance L., eds. Henderson, Douglas, illus. anniv. ed. 1998. 56p. (YA). reprint ed. 14.95 (978-0-933819-02-3(1)) Museum of the Rockies, Inc.

How to clean a Dinosaur: Individual Title Six-Packs. (gr. 1-2). 25.00 (978-0-7635-9136-6(X)) Rigby Education.

Hunt, Elizabeth Singer. The Escape of the Deadly Dinosaur. 2007. (Secret Agent Jack Stalwart Ser.). 128p. (J). (gr. 1-4). pap. 4.99 ***978-1-60286-004-9(1))*** Weinstein Bks.

James, B. J. Supertwins Meet the Dangerous Dino-Robots. 2003. (gr. k-3). lib. bdg. 11.80 (978-0-613-72179-0(9)) Tandem Library Bks.

James, B. J., et al. Supertwins Meet the Dangerous Dino-Robots, No. 3. Demarest, Chris L., illus. 2003. (Scholastic Reader Ser.). 32p. (J). pap. 3.99 (978-0-439-46625-7(3) , Cartwheel Bks.) Scholastic, Inc.

Joyce, William. Dinosaur Bob & His Adventures with the Family Lazardo. Joyce, William, illus. ltd. ed. (Laura Geringer Bks.). (Illus.). 48p. (J). (ps-3). 1998. 150.00 (978-0-06-025429-2(7)); 1999. pap. 4.95 (978-0-06-443247-4(5) , Harper Trophy) HarperCollins Pubs.

Jurassic Park III: Movie Storybook. 2002. (Jurassic Park III Ser.). (Illus.). (J). 14.79 (978-0-7587-5765-4(4)) Book Wholesalers, Inc.

Jurassic Park III: Rescue Mission. 2002. (Jurassic Park III Ser.). (Illus.). (J). 11.91 (978-0-7587-5675-6(5)) Book Wholesalers, Inc.

Kasser, Carol. Broccoliosaur Stories. 2007. pap. 26.49 ***(*978-1-4259-7933-1(5))*** AuthorHouse.

Kastner, Jill. Merry Christmas, Princess Dinosaur! 2002. (Illus.). 32p. (J). 17.89 (978-0-06-000472-9(X)) HarperCollins Pubs.

—Princess Dinosaur. 2001. (Illus.). 32p. (J). (gr. k up). 15.89 (978-0-688-17046-2(3)) HarperCollins Pubs.

Katschke, Judy & Hogan, Mary. Dinosaurs: Two of a Kind. 2000. (Dinosaur Ser.). (Illus.). 32p. (J). (gr. k-2). pap. 3.99 (978-0-7868-4388-6(8)) Disney Pr.

Kchodl, Joseph 'PaleoJoe' & Caszatt-Allen, Wendy. The Disappearance of Dinosaur Sue. 2006. (PaleoJoe's Dinosaur Detective Club Ser.: 1). (Illus.). 150p. (J). pap. (978-1-934133-03-3(5)) Mackinac Island Pr., Inc.

—Raptor's Revenge. 2007. (Illus.). 160p. (J). pap. 6.95 ***(*978-1-934133-37-8(X))*** Mackinac Island Pr., Inc.

Kchodl, Joseph 'PaleoJoe' & Caszatt-Allen, Wendy. Stolen Stegosaurus. 2006. (PaleoJoe's Dinosaur Detective Club Ser.: 2). (Illus.). 150p. (J). pap. (978-1-934133-04-0(3)) Mackinac Island Pr., Inc.

Khan, Joe. The Forest Eggimals. 2006. pap. 26.49 ***(*978-1-4208-9589-6(3))*** AuthorHouse.

Knife and Packer Staff. Dinosaur Adventure. 2005. (Captain Fact Ser.: Bk. 2). (Illus.). 112p. (gr. 2-5). pap. 4.99 (978-0-7868-5512-4(6) , Volo) Hyperion Bks. for Children.

Kurokawa, Mitsuhiro. Dinosaur Valley. 2006. 56p. (J). 16.95 (978-0-8118-5231-9(8)); reprint ed. pap. 7.95 (978-0-8118-5232-6(6)) Chronicle Bks. LLC.

Kurtz, Jane. Mister Bones Dinosaur Hunter. Haverfield, Mary, illus. ed. 2005. (Ready-to-Read Ser. Level 1). 32p. (J). lib. bdg. 15.00 (978-1-59054-929-2(5)) Fitzgerald Bks.

Lampman, Evelyn Sibley. The Shy Stegosaurus of Cricket Creek. Buel, Hubert, illus. 2001. 220p. (J). 17.95 (978-1-930900-09-7(0)) Purple Hse. Pr.

Landau, Elaine. Tyrannosaurus Rex. 1999. (True Bks.). (Illus.). 48p. (J). (gr. 3-5). 25.00 (978-0-516-20454-3(8) , Children's Pr.) Scholastic Library Publishing.

Larsen, Margie & Dudko, Mary Ann. Barney's "Let's Learn" Boxed Set, Set. Full, Dennis, photos by. 1998. (Barney Ser.). (Illus.). (J). (ps-k). 9.99 (978-1-57064-517-4(5)) Scholastic, Inc.

Lawson, Jim & Dooney, Michael. Paleo: Tales of the Late Cretaceous. 2003. (Illus.). 172p. (YA). reprint ed. pap. 12.95 (978-0-9661985-3-9(0) , Empty Sky) Zeromayo Studios, LLP.

Leach, Sheryl. Barney's Sharing & Caring Treasury. McKee, Darren, illus. 2001. 168p. (J). 10.99 (978-1-58668-283-5(0)) Scholastic, Inc.

LeapFrog Staff, compiled by & des. Magic Tree House - Dinosaurs Before Dark. LeapFrog Staff, des. 2002. (J). spiral bd. 14.99 (978-1-58605-818-0(5)) LeapFrog Enterprises, Inc.

Lester, Tyler. Welcome to Dyslexic Park. Russell, Diane & Eskola, Toby Alice, illus. l.t. ed. 1999. 25p. (J). 15.00 (978-0-938911-16-6(3)) Individualized Education Systems/Poppy Lane Publishing.

Lewis, Kevin. Dinosaur, Dinosaur. Kirk, Daniel, illus. 2006. (J). (978-0-439-78228-9(7)); 32p. pap. 15.99 (978-0-439-60371-3(4)) Scholastic, Inc. (Orchard Bks.).

Lewisson, Helene. Hem: The Duckbill Dinosaur. 2003. (J). pap. (978-1-885275-41-7(2)) Howie, C.J. Co.

Little Dinosaur Chapter Books. 2007. (J). per. ***(*978-1-932570-65-6(9))*** Literacy Footprints Inc.

Little Dinosaur Runs Away. 2007. (J). per. ***(*978-1-932570-67-0(5))*** Literacy Footprints Inc.

Little Dinosaur Snack. 2004. (978-1-932570-22-9(5)) Literacy Footprints Inc.

Little Dinosaur, the Hero. 2004. (J). (978-1-932570-26-7(8)) Literacy Footprints Inc.

Little Dinosaur's Skateboard. 2005. (J). (978-1-932570-42-7(X)) Literacy Footprints Inc.

Longyear, Barry B. The Homecoming. 2002. 146p. pap. 12.95 (978-0-595-21309-2(X) , Backinprint.com) iUniverse, Inc.

Lost in Dinosaur World. 2005. (J). audio, cd-rom 29.95 (978-0-9771381-1-1(9)) Williams, Geoffrey T.

Lou Weber Staff, ed. Dinosaurs Play a Puzzle. 2004. 12p. (J). bds. 9.98 (978-1-4127-3150-8(X) , 7232000) Publications International, Ltd.

Lucas, Sally. Dancing Dinos. Lueas, Margeaux, illus. 1998. (Road to Reading Ser.). 32p. (J). (ps-k). pap. 3.99 (978-0-307-26200-4(6) , 26200, Random Hse. Bks. for Young Readers) Random Hse. Children's Bks.

Lucas, Sally & Lucas, Margeaux. Dancing Dinos Go to School. 2006. (Step into Reading Ser.). (Illus.). 32p. (J). (ps-1). lib. bdg. 11.99 (978-0-375-93241-0(0)); pap. 3.99 (978-0-375-83241-3(6)) Random Hse. Children's Bks. (Random Hse. Bks. for Young Readers).

Lund, Deb. Dinosailors. Fine, Howard, illus. 2003. 40p. (J). (ps-2). 16.00 (978-0-15-204609-5(7)) Harcourt Children's Bks.

Lund, Deborah. All Aboard the Dinotrain. Fine, Howard, illus. 2006. 40p. (J). 16.00 (978-0-15-205237-9(2)) Harcourt Trade Pubs.

Lynne Enden, Rebecca. Ryan's Dinosaur & the Neon Fish: Two Stories from Rebecca's. 2006. (ENG.). 44p. per. 16.99 ***(*978-1-4208-5670-5(7))*** AuthorHouse.

Maccarone, Grace. Magic Matt & the Dinosaur. Bridwell, Norman, illus. 2004. (Scholastic Reader Ser.). 32p. (J). 3.99 (978-0-439-37607-5(6) , Cartwheel Bks.) Scholastic, Inc.

MacHado, Ana Maria. Un Deseo Loco. (Torre de Papel Ser.). (SPA.). (YA). (gr. 6 up). 8.95 (978-958-04-4529-6(X) , NR30565) Norma S.A. COL. *Dist:* Distribuidora Norma, Inc., Lectorum Pubns., Inc.

Mansell, Dom. If Dinosaurs Came to Town. 1998. (J). 13.50 (978-0-606-13513-9(8)); lib. bdg. 15.25 (978-0-613-71780-9(5)) Tandem Library Bks.

Marsh, Carole. The Mystery of the Chicago Dinosaurs. 2003. lib. bdg. 14.10 (978-0-613-73040-2(2)) Tandem Library Bks.

Marsoli, Lisa Ann. Dinosaurs are Big Babies. Smitherton, Jeb, illus. 2005. (J). bds. 14.99 (978-0-9767325-0-1(5)) Toy Quest.

Martin, Linda. When Dinosaurs Go to School. 2002. (Illus.). 32p. (J). (gr. k-1). pap. 6.95 (978-0-8118-3514-5(6)) Chronicle Bks. LLC.

—When Dinosaurs Go to School. 2002. (ps-2). lib. bdg. 15.25 (978-0-613-51424-8(6)) Tandem Library Bks.

Marzollo, Jean. I Spy a Dinosaur's Eye. Wick, Walter, photos by. 2003. (Scholastic Reader Ser.). (Illus.). 32p. (J). pap. 3.99 (978-0-439-52471-1(7) , Cartwheel Bks.) Scholastic, Inc.

Mattern, Joanne. Dino Disaster! Spaziante, Patrick & Giles, Mike, illus. ed. 2005. (Adventures of Jimmy Neutron Ser.: 9). 24p. (J). lib. bdg. 15.00 (978-1-59054-782-3(9)) Fitzgerald Bks.

Mayhew, James. Carlota y los Dinosaurios. 2000. (J). (CAT.). 38p. (ps-3). 14.95 (978-84-8488-000-4(1)); (SPA., Illus.). 32p. (gr. 1-2). 14.95 (978-84-88061-93-5(5) , RR8019) Serres, Ediciones, S. L. ESP. *Dist:* Lectorum Pubns., Inc.

McAdam, Christine. Barney's Shapes. McKee, Darren, illus. 1999. (Barney Ser.). 22p. (J). (ps-k). 5.95 (978-1-57064-651-5(1)) Scholastic, Inc.

McCarty, Peter. T Is for Terrible. rev. ed. 2004. (Illus.). 32p. (J). 15.95 (978-0-8050-7404-8(X) , Holt, Henry & Co. Bks. For Young Readers) Holt, Henry & Co.

—T Is for Terrible. McCarty, Peter, illus. unabr. ed. 2005. (J). (ps-3). 29.95 incl. audio compact disk (978-0-439-80479-0(5) , WHCD679) Scholastic, Inc.

McClements, George. Ridin' Dinos with Buck Bronco. 2007. (Illus.). 40p. (J). (ps-2). 16.00 (978-0-15-205989-7(X)) Harcourt Trade Pubs.

McDonnell, David, ed. Dinosaurs Dinosaurs: Starlog Movie Magic. 2000. (Starlog Movie Magic Ser.: No. 1). (J). pap. 5.99 (978-0-88013-010-3(5)) Profile Entertainment, Inc.

McKay, Sindy. We Both Read-about Dinosaurs. Walters, Robert, illus. 2004. (We Both Read Ser.). 44p. (J). (gr. 1-2). 7.99 (978-1-891327-53-7(4)); pap. 3.99 (978-1-891327-54-4(2)) Treasure Bay, Inc.

McKee, Darren, illus. Barney's Musical Fun Fair. 2004. (Deluxe Jukebox Ser.). 24p. (J). bds. (978-0-7853-9958-2(5) , 7209200) Publications International, Ltd.

McKinlay, Penny. Bumposaurus. Teckentrup, Britta, illus. 2006. 32p. (J). pap. 7.95 (978-1-84507-516-3(1)) Lincoln, Frances Ltd. GBR. *Dist:* Perseus Distribution.

McMahon, Jean. Rex Finally Finds a Friend. 2005. (J). pap. 8.00 (978-0-8059-6909-2(8)) Dorrance Publishing Co., Inc.

McMahon, P. J. The Mystery of the Disappearing Dinosaurs. Manders, John, illus. 2005. (Freaky Joe Club Ser.: No. 5). 128p. (J). pap. 3.99 (978-1-4169-0049-8(7) , Aladdin) Simon & Schuster Children's Publishing.

McMullan, Kate. Fluffy Meets the Dinosaurs. Smith, Mavis, illus. 2004. 40p. (J). lib. bdg. 15.00 (978-1-59054-459-4(5)) Fitzgerald Bks.

—Fluffy Meets the Dinosaurs. 2000. (Hello Reader! Ser.). (Illus.). (J). 10.79 (978-0-606-18545-5(3)) Tandem Library Bks.

McNaughton, Colin. Potty Poo-Poo Wee-Wee! McNaughton, Colin, illus. 2005. (Illus.). 40p. (J). (gr. k-ps). 9.99 (978-0-7636-2781-2(X)) Candlewick Pr.

Meister, Cari. Luther's Halloween. Petrone, Valeria, illus. 2004. 32p. (J). (ps-1). 15.99 (978-0-670-03555-7(6) , Viking Juvenile) Penguin Group (USA) Inc.

Metzger, Steve. Dinofours Bind Up. Wilhelm, Hans, illus. 2002. (J). 9.99 (978-0-439-48284-4(4)) Scholastic, Inc.

—Dinofours, Our Holiday Show! Wilhelm, Hans, illus. 2002. (J). 3.50 (978-0-439-38218-2(1)) Scholastic, Inc.

—I'm Having a Bad Day! Wilhelm, Hans, illus. 1998. (Dinofours Ser.: No. 2). 32p. (J). (ps-1). pap. 3.25 (978-0-590-03551-4(7)) Scholastic, Inc.

—I'm So Grumpy! Wilhelm, Hans, illus. 2000. (Dinofours Ser.: No. 4). (J). (ps-1). pap. 3.25 (978-0-439-17959-1(9)) Scholastic, Inc.

—I'm the Boss! Wilhelm, Hans, illus. 1998. (Dinofours Ser.: No. 6). 32p. (J). (ps-1). pap. 3.25 (978-0-590-37458-3(3)) Scholastic, Inc.

—I'm the Winner! Wilhelm, Hans, illus. 1999. (Dinofours Ser.: No. 7). (J). (ps-1). 3.25 (978-0-439-06327-2(2)) Scholastic, Inc.

—It's Apple Picking Day! Wilhelm, Hans, illus. 1998. (Dinofours Ser.: No. 8). (J). (ps-1). 3.25 (978-0-590-03549-1(5)) Scholastic, Inc.

—It's Beach Day! Wilhelm, Hans, illus. 1998. (Dinofours Ser.: No. 9). 32p. (J). (ps-1). pap. 3.25 (978-0-590-03267-4(4)) Scholastic, Inc.

—It's Halloween! Wilhelm, Hans, illus. 1999. (Dinofours Ser.: No. 13). (J). (ps-1). (978-0-439-06326-5(4)) Scholastic, Inc.

—It's Pumpkin Day! Wilhelm, Hans, illus. 2001. (Dinofours Ser.). (J). (ps-1). pap. 3.25 (978-0-439-29569-7(6)) Scholastic, Inc.

—It's Snowing. Wilhelm, Hans, illus. 1998. (Dinofours Ser.: No. 14). (J). (ps-1). pap. 3.25 (978-0-590-03550-7(9)) Scholastic, Inc.

—It's Thanksgiving! Wilhelm, Hans, illus. 2001. (Dinofours Ser.). (J). (ps-1). 3.25 (978-0-439-29570-3(X)) Scholastic, Inc.

—It's Valentine's Day! Wilhelm, Hans, illus. 2001. (Dinofours Ser.: No. 17). (J). (ps-1). pap. 3.25 (978-0-439-17960-7(2)) Scholastic, Inc.

—Let's Go Sledding! Wilhelm, Hans, illus. 2002. (Dinofours Ser.). (J). (ps-1). pap. 3.25 (978-0-439-29571-0(8)) Scholastic, Inc.

—My Seeds Won't Grow! Wilhelm, Hans, illus. 2000. (Dinofours Ser.: No. 18). (J). (ps-1). (978-0-439-06329-6(9)) Scholastic, Inc.

—Rain! Rain! Go Away! Wilhelm, Hans, illus. 2002. (J). pap. 3.25 (978-0-439-29572-7(6)) Scholastic, Inc.

—That's My Dino! Wilhelm, Hans, illus. 2002. (J). (978-0-439-32052-8(6)) Scholastic, Inc.

Metzger, Steve & Wilhelm, Hans. We Love Bugs! 2001. (Dinofours Ser.: No. 1). (Illus.). (J). (ps-1). pap. (978-0-439-17961-4(0)) Scholastic, Inc.

Michaels, Julie. Dinosaurs. Hogan, Mary, ed. 2000. (Giant Lift-the-Flap Ser.). (Illus.). 10p. (J). (ps-2). 9.99 (978-0-7364-1041-0(4)) Mouse Works.

Miller, Austin. Sam Is Special. ed. 2003. (Early Connections Ser.). (J). pap. 33.00 (978-1-4108-1358-9(4)) Benchmark Education Co.

Milnes, Margaret. Dinosaur Alive. 2000. (Pull a Page Ser.). (Illus.). 14p. (J). (ps-1). 9.99 (978-0-7364-1039-7(2)) Mouse Works.

Mitton, Tony. Dinosaurumpus! Parker-Rees, Guy, illus. 2003. 32p. (J). (ps-1). pap. 15.95 (978-0-439-39514-4(3) , Orchard Bks.) Scholastic, Inc.

Mody, Monica. Barney's Easter Party! Baker, Darrell, illus. 2000. (Barney Ser.). 22p. (J). (ps-k). pap. 5.99 (978-1-57064-714-7(3)) Scholastic, Inc.

Moncure, Jane Belk. Word Bird's Dinosaur Days. 2002. (New Word Bird Library). (Illus.). 32p. (J). (ps-3). 22.79 (978-1-56766-999-2(9)) Child's World, Inc.

Monica, Carol. Fisher Price Let's Go on a Class Trip Lift the Flap. SI Artists, illus. 2007. 10p. (J). bds. 8.99 ***(*978-0-7944-1291-3(2))*** Reader's Digest Assn., Inc., The.

Moses, Brian. Trouble at the Dinosaur Cafe. Parsons, Garry, illus. 2006. 32p. (J). 16.95 (978-0-8027-9599-1(4)) Walker & Co.

Most, Bernard. ABC T-Rex. (Illus.). 32p. (J). 2004. pap. 6.00 (978-0-15-205028-3(0) , Voyager Bks./Libros Viajeros); 2000. 14.00 (978-0-15-202007-1(1)) Harcourt Children's Bks.

—ABC T-Rex. 2004. (ps-2). lib. bdg. 14.15 (978-0-613-83875-7(0)); (Illus.). 32p. (J). lib. bdg. 13.20 (978-0-606-30395-8(2)) Tandem Library Bks.

—Catch Me If You Can!/A que no me Alcanzas! Campoy, F. Isabel & Ada, Alma Flor, trs. from ENG. 2007. (Green Light Reader Ser.). (ENG & SPA., Illus.). 28p. (J). 12.95 (978-0-15-205964-4(4)); pap. 3.95 (978-0-15-205967-5(9)) Harcourt Trade Pubs.

—If the Dinosaurs Came Back. Most, Bernard, illus. 2002. (Illus.). (J). 13.83 (978-0-7587-2829-6(8)) Book Wholesalers, Inc.

—A Trio of Triceratops. Most, Bernard, illus. 2002. (Illus.). (J). 17.45 (978-0-7587-3860-8(9)) Book Wholesalers, Inc.

—Whatever Happened to the Dinosaurs? Most, Bernard, illus. 2002. (Illus.). (J). 12.30 (978-0-7587-3970-4(2)) Book Wholesalers, Inc.

—Whatever Happened to the Dinosaurs? 1999. (Illus.). (J). (gr. k-3). lib. bdg. 12.95 (978-0-8335-2103-3(9)) Tandem Library Bks.

Mullican, Judy. Caillou Plays Dinosaur Hide-and-Seek. Storch, Ellen N., illus. 2006. (J). pap. (978-1-57332-376-5(4)) HighReach Learning, Inc.

Murail, Marie-Aude. Un Domingo Con Los Dinosaurios. (la Orilla Del Viento Ser.). (SPA., Illus.). 48p. (J). reprint ed. 6.99 (978-968-16-5798-7(5) , 108) Fondo de Cultura Economica USA.

Murdocca, Sal & Osborne, Mary Pope. Dinosaurs Before Dark Book & CD. 2008. (Stepping Stone Book(TM) Ser.). (J). (gr. k-3). 9.99 ***(*978-0-375-84405-8(8)*** , Random Hse. Bks. for Young Readers) Random Hse. Children's Bks.

Murphy, Jane. My Pet Tyrannosaurus. 2001. (Illus.). 32p. (J). (ps-2). 8.95 incl. audio (978-0-937124-17-8(6) , KIM 11C) Kimbo Educational.

My Day with the Dinosaurs. 2004. (J). ring bd. 3.25 (978-0-9762740-2-5(7) , Flat Kids) Smart Smiles Co., The.

Nash, David. A Pete & Charley Adventure: The Sheri. 2005. 131p. pap. 19.95 (978-1-4137-9449-6(1)) PublishAmerica, Inc.

Neuschafer-Carlon, Mercedes. Dani y Dino. Saez, Bea, illus. Tr. of Dani & Dino. (SPA.). 48p. (J). (978-84-241-7897-0(1)) Everest de Ediciones y Distribucion, S.L. ESP. *Dist:* Lectorum Pubns., Inc.

—Dani y Dino. 2000. Tr. of Dani & Dino. (SPA.). (ps-2). lib. bdg. 15.90 (978-0-613-80608-4(5)) Tandem Library Bks.

Neusner, Dena Wallenstein. Barney Is Sooo Big! McKee, Darren, illus. 2003. (Barney Ser.). 5p. (J). bds. 6.99 (978-1-58668-301-6(2)) Scholastic, Inc.

Neusner, Dena Wallenstein & McKee, Darren. Barney's Colors of Spring: Paint with Water Color Activity Book. 2003. (Barney Ser.). (Illus.). 32p. (J). act. bk. ed. 3.99 (978-1-58668-305-4(5)) Scholastic, Inc.

North, Ryan. Dinosaur Comics. North, Ryan, illus. 2005. 112p. 14.99 (978-0-7560-0518-4(3)) Teacher's Discovery.

Novacek, Michael J. Time Traveler: In Search of Dinosaurs & Other Fossils from Montana to Mongolia. 2002. (Illus.). 352p. 26.00 (978-0-374-27880-9(6)) Farrar, Straus & Giroux.

Nussbaum, Ben. Is Apatosaurus Okay? Reaveley, Trevor, illus. 2005. (Smithsonian's Prehistoric Pals Ser.). 32p. (J). (ps-2). 9.95 (978-1-59249-510-8(9) , PS2458); 14.95 incl. cd-rom (978-1-59249-506-1(0) , H2408) Soundprints.

—Is Apatosaurus Okay? Reavely, Trevor, illus. 2005. 30p. (J). (ps-2). 8.95 incl. cd-rom (978-1-59249-508-5(7) , SD2408) Soundprints.

—Is Apatosaurus Okay? Reaveley, Trevor, illus. 2005. (Smithsonian's Prehistoric Pals Ser.). (J). (ps-2). 36p. pap. 6.95 (978-1-59249-507-8(9) , S2408); 32p. pap. 2.95 (978-1-59249-509-2(5) , S2458) Soundprints.

—Spinosaurus in the Storm. Scalf, Christopher, illus. 2005. (Smithsonian's Prehistoric Pals Ser.). 36p. (J). (ps-ps). pap. 6.95 (978-1-59249-459-0(5) , S2407) Soundprints.

Nussbaum, Ben & McIntosh, G. B. Spinosaurus in the Storm. Scalf, Chris, illus. 2005. (Smithsonian's Prehistoric Pals Ser.). 36p. (J). (ps-2). 14.95 (978-1-59249-458-3(7) , H2407); 2.95 (978-1-59249-461-3(7) , S2457) Soundprints.

Nye, Bill & Saunders, Ian G. Bill Nye the Science Guy's Great Big Book of Science: Featuring Oceans & Dinosaurs. Dykes, John & Koelsch, Michael, illus. 2005. 96p. (gr. 2-5). pap., pap. 12.99 (978-0-7868-5591-9(6)) Hyperion Pr

O'Brien, Patrick & O'Malley, Kevin. Captain Raptor & the Space Pirates. O'Brien, Patrick, illus. 2007. (Illus.). 32p. (J). (gr. k-3). 17.85 ***(*978-0-8027-9572-4(2));*** 16.95 ***(*978-0-8027-9571-7(4))*** Walker & Co.

O'Connor, Ilett. Thomas & the Big Dog & Natie & the Dinosaur Egg. 2002. 50p. (J). (ps-5). pap. 12.00 (978-0-9717003-6-9(2)) O'Connor, Ilett K.

O'Malley, Kevin. Captain Raptor & the Moon Mystery. O'Brien, Patrick, illus. 2005. 32p. (J). 17.85 (978-0-8027-8936-5(6)); 16.95 (978-0-8027-8935-8(8)) Walker & Co.

Oram, Hiawyn & Kitamura, Satoshi. A Boy Wants a Dinosaur. 2007. (Illus.). 32p. (J). pap. 8.95 ***(*978-1-84270-580-3(6))*** Andersen GBR. *Dist:* Independent Pubs. Group.

Orme, David. Dinosaur Planet. Fiorin, Fabiano, illus. 2005. 32p. (J). (gr. 1-2). lib. bdg. 11.15 (978-0-606-33601-7(X)) Tandem Library Bks.

—Dinosaur Planet. Fiorin, Fabiano, illus. 2005. (Lightning Readers Ser.). 32p. (J). (gr. 1-2). pap. 3.95 (978-0-7696-4031-0(1) , Gingham Dog Pr.) School Specialty Publishing.

—Planeta Dinosaurio. Fiorin, Fabiano, illus. 2005. (Lightning Readers Ser.). 32p. (J). (gr. 1-2). pap. 3.95 (978-0-7696-4071-6(0) , Gingham Dog Pr.) School Specialty Publishing.

Osborne, Mary Pope. Dinosaurios al Atardecer. 2004. (Coleccion la Casa Del Arbol the Magic Tree House Ser.). (SPA.). (J). pap. 4.95 (978-1-930332-49-2(1)) Lectorum Pubns., Inc.

—Dinosaurios al Atardecer. 2003. (SPA.). (gr. 3-6). lib. bdg. 12.95 (978-0-613-64486-0(7)) Tandem Library Bks.

—Dinosaurs Before Dark. 2002. (Magic Tree House Ser.: No. 1). (J). (gr. k-3). 14.95 (978-1-58605-925-5(4) , LeapFrog Schl. Hse.) LeapFrog Enterprises, Inc.

—Dinosaurs Before Dark. unabr. ed. 2004. (Magic Tree House Ser.: No. 1). 68p. (J). (gr. k-5). pap. 17.00 incl. audio (978-0-8072-0330-9(0) , FTR208SP, Listening Library) Random Hse. Audio Publishing Group.

Osorio, Rick. The Great Adventure of Sally Rock & the Cretaceous Chicken. 2006. 65p. pap. 12.95 (978-1-4241-0971-5(X)) PublishAmerica, Inc.

Palatini, Margie. Gorgonzola. Bowers, Tim, illus. 2008. 32p. (J). 16.99 (978-0-06-073897-6(9)); lib. bdg. 17.89 (978-0-06-073898-3(7)) HarperCollins Pubs.

Parent, Nancy. Barney's Zoo Friends. Yee, Josie, illus. 2001. (Barney Ser.). 12p. (J). (ps-1). bds. 9.99 (978-1-58668-233-0(4)) Scholastic, Inc.

Park, Melanie. No Dinosaurs at Church. Black, Elise, illus. 2005. (J). bds. (978-1-932898-37-8(9)) Spring Creek Bk. Co.

Parpan, Justin. Gwango's Lonesome Trail. Parpan, Justin, illus. 2006. (Illus.). 32p. (J). 15.95 (978-1-60108-004-2(2)) Red Cygnet Pr.

Penton, ed. Little Dinosaur Gets Dressed (English) 2000. (J). (978-1-58805-081-6(5)) DS-Max USA, Inc.

Perry, Janet & Gentle, Victor. Dragons & Dinosaurs. 1999. (Imagination Library). (Illus.). 24p. (J). (gr. 2 up). lib. bdg. 22.00 (978-0-8368-2436-0(9)) Stevens, Gareth Inc.

Pez, Alberto. Mimosaurio! Cubillas, Roberto, illus. (SPA.). (J). 8.95 (978-958-04-6035-0(3)) Norma S.A. COL. *Dist:* Distribuidora Norma, Inc., Lectorum Pubns., Inc.

Pfister, Marcus. Dazzle the Dinosaur. 2000. (Illus.). 32p. (J). (gr. k-3). pap. 7.95 (978-0-7358-1370-0(1)) North-South Bks., Inc.

—Dazzle the Dinosaur. 2000. (J). 14.75 (978-0-606-19470-9(3)); lib. bdg. 16.40 (978-0-613-29922-0(1)) Tandem Library Bks.

—Destello el Dinosuario. 2000. (SPA.). (gr. k-3). lib. bdg. 16.40 (978-0-613-29928-2(0)) Tandem Library Bks.

A Picnic Lunch. 2004. (J). (978-1-932570-23-6(3)) Literacy Footprints Inc.

Pilkey, Dav. Mighty Robot vs. the Jurassic Jackrabbits from Jupiter. Ontiveros, Martin, illus. 2002. (Ricky Ricotta Ser.: No. 5). 128p. (J). (ps-3). pap. 16.95 (978-0-439-37642-6(4) , Blue Sky Pr., The); pap. 3.99 (978-0-439-37643-3(2)) Scholastic, Inc.

Plourde, Lynn. Dino Pets. Kendall, Gideon, illus. 2007. 32p. (J). (ps-1). 15.99 (978-0-525-47778-5(0) , Dutton Juvenile) Penguin Group (USA) Inc.

Pope, Jerald. Madeleine Claire & the Dinosaur. 2006. (J). 16.00 (978-0-9700125-6-2(X)) Brave Ulysses Bks.

Pope, Psborne. Vallee des Dinosaurs. pap. 15.95 (978-2-7470-0496-1(1)) Bayard Editions FRA. *Dist:* Distribooks, Inc.

Preller, James. The Case of the Disappearing Dinosaur. Smith, Jamie & Alley, R. W., illus. 2002. (Jigsaw Jones Mystery Ser.: No. 17). 96p. (J). pap. 3.99 (978-0-439-30639-3(6)) Scholastic, Inc.

—Case of the Disappearing Dinosaur. 2002. (gr. 3-6). lib. bdg. 11.80 (978-0-613-50420-1(8)) Tandem Library Bks.

Punter, Russell. Dinosaur Who Lost His Roar. 2007. 48p. (J). 8.99 (978-0-7945-1547-8(9) , Usborne) EDC Publishing.

Quisenberry, Stacey. Dinosaur George Pre-hysterical Adventures: What Color Were Dinosaurs? Browning, Suzan, illus. 2007. (J). 3.95 ***(978-0-9797304-3-6(0))*** Raining Popcorn Media.

Raintree Steck-Vaughn Staff. Muestra y Cuenta Entre Dinosaurios. 1999. (SPA.). (J). pap., stu. ed. 31.05 (978-0-7398-0763-7(3)) Steck-Vaughn.

Rand, Jonathan. Dinosaurs Destroy Detroit. 2001. (Michigan Chillers: Vol. 8). 215p. (YA). pap. 5.99 (978-1-893699-14-4(5)) AudioCraft Publishing, Inc.

Ransom, Candice. Bones in the Badlands. Call, Greg, illus. 2006. 128p. (J). (gr. 2-4). pap. 4.99 (978-0-7869-4028-8(X) , Mirrorstone) Wizards of the Coast.

Rauchwerger, Diane Levin. Dinosaur on Hanukkah. Wolff, Jason, illus. 2005. 24p. (J). (ps-6). pap. 6.95 (978-1-58013-143-8(3)); 15.95 (978-1-58013-145-2(X)) Kar-Ben Publishing.

—Dinosaur on Passover. 2006. (J). pap. 6.95 (978-1-58013-161-2(1)) Kar-Ben Publishing.

—Dinosaur on Passover. Wolff, Jason, illus. 2006. (J). 15.95 (978-1-58013-156-8(5)) Kar-Ben Publishing.

—Dinosaur on Shabbat. Wolff, Jason, illus. 2006. (J). 15.95 (978-1-58013-159-9(X)) Kar-Ben Publishing.

Reid, Suzan & Hendry, Linda. Meat Eaters Arrive. (Tell Me a Story Ser.). (Illus.). 32p. (J). 12.99 (978-0-590-24540-1(6)) Scholastic, Inc.

Reimer, Ramon. Were There Dinosaurs in My Past? Kilgore, Jeannette Vrlin, illus. 2002. 32p. (J). (gr. k-6). 14.95 (978-1-931650-16-8(0)) Coastal Publishing Carolina, Inc.

Richler, Mordecai. Jacob Two-Two & the Dinosaur. Eyolfson, Norman, illus. 2004. 96p. (J). (gr. 3-7). pap. 6.95 (978-0-88776-712-8(5)) Tundra Bks., Inc./Livres Toundra, Inc. CAN. *Dist:* Random Hse., Inc.

Ring, Susan. Dinosaurs: An Adventure Back in Time, Level 3. Wilson, Phil, illus. 2006. (innovativeKids readers ser.: level 3). 32p. (J). (gr. 1-3). pap., pap. 6.99 (978-1-58476-478-6(3) , IKIDS) Innovative Kids.

Rizner, Staci. Last Chance Out. 2002. (gr. 7-12). lib. bdg. 24.55 (978-0-613-81754-7(0)) Tandem Library Bks.

Robinson, Fay. Un Dinosaurio Llamado Sue: El Hallazgo del Siglo. 2002. Tr. of Dinosaur Named Sue. (gr. k-3). lib. bdg. 11.80 (978-0-613-85119-0(6)) Tandem Library Bks.

—Un Dinosaurio Llamado Sue: El Hallzgo del Siglo. 2002. (SPA., Illus.). 48p. (J). (gr. k-2). pap. 3.99 (978-0-439-42110-2(1) , Scholastic en Espanol) Scholastic, Inc.

Rodgers, Frank. Little T & Lizard the Wizard. 2007. (Read-It! Chapter Books). (J). 21.26 (978-1-4048-2725-7(0)) Picture Window Bks.

—Little T & the Crown Jewels. 2007. (Read-It! Chapter Books). (J). 21.26 (978-1-4048-2726-4(9)) Picture Window Bks.

—Little T & the Dragon's Tooth. 2007. (Read-It! Chapter Books). (J). 21.26 (978-1-4048-2727-1(7)) Picture Window Bks.

—Royal Roar. 2007. (Read-It! Chapter Books). (J). 21.26 (978-1-4048-2728-8(5)) Picture Window Bks.

Rossacci, Jacob. Dinosaurs Live Together. 2003. (J). 8.95 (978-1-932205-14-5(4)) Word Association Pubs.

Roy, Ron. The Talking T. Rex. Gurney, John Steven, illus. 2003. (A to Z Mysteries Ser.: No. 20). (J). (gr. 3-6). lib. bdg. 11.80 (978-0-613-85127-5(7)) Tandem Library Bks.

Russey, Nancy. Doing the Dinosaur Dip. 2002. pap. (978-0-9718565-9-2(1)) Playbooks, Inc.

Russo, Monica. Dinosaur Dots. 2003. (Connect the Dots & Color Ser.). (Illus.). 96p. (J). (ps-3). pap. 5.95 (978-0-8069-7388-3(9)) Sterling Publishing Co., Inc.

Ryder, Joanne. A Just for a Day Book: Tyrannosaurus Time. 1999. (Just for a Day Book Ser.). (Illus.). 32p. (J). (gr. k-3). 15.95 (978-0-688-13682-6(6)); 15.89 (978-0-688-13683-3(4)) HarperCollins Pubs.

Sabretooth: A Dinosaur World Adventure. 2005. (J). audio, cd-rom 24.95 (978-0-9771381-3-5(5)) Williams, Geoffrey T.

Salmon, Michael. Dinosaur. 2006. (Illus.). 32p. (J). ***(978-1-74178-213-4(9))*** Five Mile Pr. Pty Ltd. The.

Sander, Sonia. Getting Ready for 123 Fun. McKee, Darren, illus. 2003. (Barney Ser.). 64p. (J). pap. 2.99 (978-1-58668-310-8(1)) Scholastic, Inc.

Sander, Sonia. Let's Go Look & See. 2007. (Barney Ser.). 40p. (J). bds. 9.99 ***(978-0-439-89610-8(X))*** Scholastic, Inc.

Sanders, Nancy I. Hidden Treasure. 2000. (Parables in Action Ser.: Vol. 2). (Illus.). 48p. (J). (ps-2). 4.99 (978-0-570-07013-9(9)) Concordia Publishing Hse.

—Hidden Treasure. 2000. (ps-2). lib. bdg. 13.00 (978-0-613-72836-2(X)) Tandem Library Bks.

Sansone, Adele. The Little Green Goose. James, J. Alison, tr. Marks, Alan, illus. 2001. (J). (ps-ps). lib. bdg. 15.25 (978-0-613-36468-3(6)) Tandem Library Bks.

Savage, Derek. Cool Cat Learns Karate. Bustamante, Denny, illus. 2001. (Donny the Dinosaur Ser.: Vol. 1). Tr. of Cool Cat Aprende Karate. (ENG & SPA.). 32p. (J). lib. bdg. 9.95 (978-0-9673000-8-5(8)) Savage Bks.

Schachner, Judith Byron. Skippyjon Jones & the Big Dig. 2007. 32p. (J). (ps). 16.99 ***(978-0-525-47884-3(1)*** , Dutton Juvenile) Penguin Group (USA) Inc.

Schade, Susan. Dinosaur Ed, Level 2. Buller, Jon, illus. 2000. (All-Star Readers Ser.). 32p. (J). (gr. 1-2). pap. 3.99 (978-1-57584-385-8(4) , Reader's Digest Children's Bks.) Reader's Digest Children's Publishing, Inc.

—Dinosaur Ed. 2000. (gr. k-3). lib. bdg. 11.80 (978-0-613-24839-6(2)) Tandem Library Bks.

Schneider, John Lee. Extinction: Dragons of Earth: A Novel. 2005. 173p. (YA). pap. (978-1-890109-79-0(7) , Cross Time) Crossquarter Publishing Group.

Schnetzler, Pattie L. Ten Little Dinosaurs. Harris, Jim, illus. 28p. (J). 2000. bds. 9.99 (978-1-57939-074-7(9)); 2002. bds. 24.99 (978-1-57939-115-7(X)) Accord Publishing, Ltd.

Schoberle, Cecile. Reptar's Surprise Visit. Haefele, Steve, illus. 1999. 24p. (J). (gr. k-3). per. 3.50 (978-0-671-02881-7(2) , Simon & Schuster Children's Publishing) Simon & Schuster Children's Publishing.

—Reptar's Surprise Visit. 1999. (gr. k-3). lib. bdg. 11.25 (978-0-613-15954-8(3)) Tandem Library Bks.

Scholastic, Inc. Staff. Barney's Paint & Play. Amaral, Gayla, ed. McKee, Darren & Winslow, Becky, illus. 2001. (Barney Ser.). 32p. (J). (ps-1). pap., act. bk. ed. 2.99 (978-1-58668-142-5(7)) Scholastic, Inc.

Scholastic, Inc. Staff, et al. Barney's Colorful World. McKee, Darren, illus. 2003. (Barney Ser.). 32p. (J). pap. 3.99 (978-0-439-56881-4(1)) Scholastic, Inc.

Schwabacher, Martin. The Magic School Bus Flies with the Dinosaurs. Bracken, Carolyn, illus. 2008. (Scholastic Reader Ser.). 32p. (J). pap. 3.99 ***(978-0-439-80106-5(0))*** Scholastic, Inc.

Sciarra, John. Shoestrings-Paradox. 2006. (Illus.). 128p. (J). per. 14.95 (978-0-9769555-1-1(2)) Wild Animal Publishing Co.

Sciarra, John Benjamin. Shoestrings—No Time for Dinosaurs. 2005. 128p. (J). per. 12.95 (978-0-9769555-0-4(4)) Wild Animal Publishing Co.

Scott, Kim & Kendall, Peter. The Dredgersaurus. 2001. (Illus.). 16p. (J). pap. 11.95 (978-1-86368-307-4(0)) Fremantle Pr. AUS. *Dist:* International Specialized Bk. Services.

Scruton, Clive, illus. The Kingfisher Treasury of Dinosaur Stories. 2004. (Kingfisher Treasury of Stories Ser.). 160p. (J). (gr. k-3). pap. 5.95 (978-0-7534-5728-3(8) , Kingfisher) Houghton Mifflin Co. Trade & Reference Div.

Seidler, Tor. The Tar Pit. 2000. (J). 15.95 (978-0-06-623611-7(8)); lib. bdg. 15.89 (978-0-06-623612-4(6)) HarperCollins Pubs.

—The Tar Pit. 2001. (978-0-606-22299-0(5)) Tandem Library Bks.

Seidman, David. Kong: The 8th Wonder of the World Deluxe Sound Storybook. Curry, Don, ed. Bollinger, Peter & Papp, Robert, illus. 2005. 22p. (J). (ps-3). 15.95 (978-0-696-22813-1(0)) Meredith Bks.

Sharfe, Elaine. There's a Dinosaur in My Room. Share, Brian, illus. 2005. 24p. 7.95 (978-1-894601-05-4(X)) Chestnut Publishing Group CAN. *Dist:* Hushion Hse. Publishing, Ltd.

Sharkey, Niamh. Santasaurus. Sharkey, Niamh, illus. 2005. (Illus.). 32p. (J). (ps-1). 15.99 (978-0-7636-2671-6(6)) Candlewick Pr.

Sharmat, Marjorie Weinman. Mitchell Is Moving. Aruego, Jose, illus. 2002. (J). 11.91 (978-0-7587-1449-7(1)) Book Wholesalers, Inc.

—Mitchell Is Moving. Aruego, Jose & Dewey, Ariane, illus. 2000. (J). pap. 19.97 incl. audio (978-0-7366-9209-0(6)) Books on Tape, Inc.

Sharratt, Nick. Dinosaurs' Day Out. Sharratt, Nick, illus. 1999. (Read & Share Ser.). (Illus.). 32p. (J). (gr. k). pap. 3.99 (978-0-7636-0874-3(2)) Candlewick Pr.

Shields, Carol Diggory. Saturday Night at the Dinosaur Stomp. 2002. (gr. k-3). lib. bdg. 14.15 (978-0-613-74752-3(6)) Tandem Library Bks.

—The Saturday Night at the Dinosaur Stomp. Nash, Scott, illus. 2002. 32p. (J). (ps-3). pap. 5.99 (978-0-7636-0696-1(0)) Candlewick Pr.

Sibbick, John. My Favorite Dinosaurs. 2007. 32p. (978-1-59687-180-9(6) , Milk & Cookies) ibooks, Inc.

Silver Dolphin en Español Editors. Dinosaurios. 2005. (Mezcla y Divierte Ser.). (SPA., Illus.). 5p. (J). 7.95 (978-970-718-292-9(X) , Silver Dolphin en Español) Advanced Marketing, S. de R. L. de C. V. MEX. *Dist:* Perseus Distribution.

Silver Dolphin en Español Staff. Imanes Magicos: un Dia Con los Dinosaurios: Magical Magnets: A Day with Dinos. 2006. (Illus.). 8p. (J). bds. 12.95 (978-970-718-369-8(1) , Silver Dolphin en Español) Advanced Marketing, S. de R. L. de C. V. MEX. *Dist:* Perseus Distribution.

Silverthorne, Judith. Dinosaur Breakout. 2004. (Dinosaur Adventure Ser.). 180p. (J). (gr. 4-6). pap. 6.95 (978-1-55050-294-7(8)) Coteau Bks. CAN. *Dist:* Fitzhenry & Whiteside, Ltd.

—Dinosaur Hideout. 2003. (Dinosaur Adventure Ser.). 192p. (J). (gr. 4-6). pap. 6.95 (978-1-55050-226-8(3)) Coteau Bks. CAN. *Dist:* Fitzhenry & Whiteside, Ltd.

Silverthorne, Judith. Dinosaur Stakeout. 2006. (Dinosaur Adventure Ser.). 212p. (J). (gr. 4-6). pap. ***(978-1-55050-344-9(8))*** Coteau Bks.

Simont, Marc, illus. Nate the Great & the Sticky Case. 2002. (Nate the Great Ser.). (J). 12.87 (978-0-7587-0702-4(9)) Book Wholesalers, Inc.

Sis, Peter. Dinosaur! Sis, Peter, illus. (J). (ps-1). 2005. 28p. bds. 6.99 (978-0-06-075967-4(4) , Harper Festival); 2000. (Illus.). 24p. 16.99 (978-0-688-17049-3(8)) HarperCollins Pubs.

Skofield, James. Detective Dinosaur. Alley, R. W., illus. 1998. (I Can Read Bks.). 48p. (J). (gr. k-3). pap. 3.99 (978-0-06-444235-0(7) , Harper Trophy) HarperCollins Pubs.

—Detective Dinosaur. 1998. (I Can Read Bks.). (J). (gr. 1-3). 10.79 (978-0-606-12912-1(X)) Tandem Library Bks.

—Detective Dinosaur Lost & Found. Alley, R. W., illus. 1999. (I Can Read Bks.). 48p. (J). (ps-3). pap. 3.99 (978-0-06-444257-2(8) , Harper Trophy) HarperCollins Pubs.

—Detective Dinosaur Lost & Found. 1999. (I Can Read Bks.). (J). 10.79 (978-0-606-16693-5(9)); lib. bdg. 11.80 (978-0-613-16089-6(4)) Tandem Library Bks.

Skvarch, Angela & Skvarch, Jeffrey. Dinosaurs in Space. 2004. 48p. (J). per. 9.95 (978-1-932560-35-0(1)) Media Creations, Inc.

Smith, Donna. Dinosaur: Zini's Big Adventure. 2000. (Dinosaur Ser.). (Illus.). 48p. (J). (gr. 2-4). pap. 3.99 (978-0-7868-4408-1(6)) Disney Pr.

Smith, Mark S. Lost World Adventures. 2000. (Illus.). 96p. (J). pap. 10.99 (978-0-89051-277-7(9)) Master Bks.

Smith, Stu. Dinosaur Hide-and-Seek. Santoro, Christopher, illus. 2004. 20p. (J). (ps-3). 8.99 (978-0-694-01305-0(6) , Harper Festival) HarperCollins Pubs.

Soderberg, Erin. Dinosaur Dig. 2000. (gr. k-3). lib. bdg. 11.80 (978-0-613-54167-1(7)) Tandem Library Bks.

Sorrentino, Scott & McCormack, Erin. Dinosaur Junior Novel. 2000. (Dinosaur Ser.). (Illus.). 96p. (J). (gr. 3-7). pap. 4.99 (978-0-7868-4407-4(8)) Disney Pr.

Spalding, Andrea & Spalding, David A. E. The Disappearing Dinosaur. 2002. (Adventure Net Ser.: Vol. 3). 128p. (J). (gr. 3-2). pap. 6.95 (978-1-55285-311-5(X)) Whitecap Bks., Ltd. CAN. *Dist:* Firefly Bks., Ltd.

Sperring, Mark. Find-A-Saurus. Steele-Morgan, Alexandra, tr. Steele-Morgan, Alexandra, illus. 2003. 32p. (J). pap. 15.95 (978-0-439-53162-7(4)) Scholastic, Inc.

St. Aubin, Bruno. Daddy Is a Dinosaur. St. Aubin, Bruno, illus. 1999. (Little Wolf Bks.). (Illus.). 32p. (J). (gr. k-1). pap. (978-1-894363-19-8(1)) Dominique & Friends.

St-Aubin, Bruno, illus. Daddy's a Dinosaur. 2005. (Read-It! Readers Ser.). 32p. (J). (gr. k-3). 18.60 (978-1-4048-1028-0(5)) Picture Window Bks.

Stamper, Judith Bauer. Dinosaur Detectives. 2001. (gr. 3-6). lib. bdg. 11.80 (978-0-613-50679-3(0)) Tandem Library Bks.

—Dinosaur Detectives: Reading Comprehension & Activities. Enik, Ted, illus. 2002. (Magic School Bus Chapter Bks.: No. 9). 96p. (J). pap. 4.99 (978-0-439-20423-1(2) , Scholastic Paperbacks) Scholastic, Inc.

Stark, Barbara. Blue Dinosaur's Friends. l.t. ed. 2006. (Illus.). 24p. (J). E-Book 9.95 incl. cd-rom (978-1-933090-20-7(0)) Guardian Angel Publishing, Inc.

Steinberg, Laya. Thesaurus Rex. Harter, Debbie, illus. 2005. 24p. (J). 15.99 (978-1-84148-042-8(8)); pap. 6.99 (978-1-84148-180-7(7)) Barefoot Bks., Inc.

—Thesaurus Rex Finds a Friend. Harter, Debbie, illus. 2006. (J). (978-1-905236-48-0(4)) Barefoot Bks., Inc.

Stemach, Jerry. The Night of the Loch Ness Monster. Venable, Gail Portnuff, ed. Ham, Jeff, illus. l.t. ed. 124p. 2002. 150.00 (978-1-58702-037-7(8)); 2000. 50.00 (978-1-58702-457-3(8)); 2000. 65.00 incl. audio, cd-rom (978-1-893376-78-6(8)) Johnston, Don Inc.

Stickland, Paul. Dinosaur Roar! Stickland, Henrietta, illus. 2002. (J). 13.19 (978-1-4046-0857-3(5)) Book Wholesalers, Inc.

—Dinosaur Roar. 2001. (ps-2). lib. bdg. 14.15 (978-0-613-35933-7(X)) Tandem Library Bks.

—Ten Terrible Dinosaurs. Stickland, Paul, illus. 2000. (Illus.). 48p. (J). (ps-1). pap. 7.99 (978-0-14-056770-0(4) , Puffin) Penguin Group (USA) Inc.

—Ten Terrible Dinosaurs. 2000. (ps-1). (Illus.). lib. bdg. 15.19 (978-0-606-20376-0(1)); lib. bdg. 16.45 (978-0-613-31792-4(0)) Tandem Library Bks.

Stickland, Paul & Stickland, Henrietta. Dinosaur Roar! 2002. (Illus.). 32p. (J). (ps-2). pap. 6.99 (978-0-14-056808-0(5) , Puffin) Penguin Group (USA) Inc.

—Dinosaur Roar! 2001. (Illus.). (J). 12.79 (978-0-606-21147-5(0)) Tandem Library Bks.

Stier, Roy E. Son of Bunyon & the Swamp Angel. 2002. (J). pap. 11.95 (978-1-58151-082-9(9)) BookPartners, Inc.

Strickland, Brad. Survive! 2001. (Dinotopia Ser.). (Illus.). (J). (978-0-606-21475-9(5)) Tandem Library Bks.

Strickland, Paul. Ten Terrible Dinosaurs. 2000. (J). (978-0-606-20260-2(9)) Tandem Library Bks.

Strong, Jeremy. Dinosaur Pox. l.t. ed. 2000. (Illus.). 112p. (J). pap. (978-0-7540-6122-9(1) , CLP 317) BBC Audio.

—Dinosaur Pox. (Illus.). 128p. (J). 7.95 (978-0-14-038979-1(2)) Penguin Bks., Ltd. GBR. *Dist:* Trafalgar Square Publishing.

Stuart, W. Howard. Journey to the Undiscovered World, Vol. 5. 1998. (T-Rex Ser.). pap. (978-0-9696800-4-8(X)) Youth Academy Books, Limited.

Suhay, Lisa. Haddy the Doorstopasaurus: North America's First Dinosaur. 2003. 160p. 5.95 (978-0-9679227-8-2(X) , 329-006) Franklin Mason Pr.

Sutton, Scott E. Danger: Dinky Diplodocus. 2007. (Adventures of Dinosaur Dog Ser.). 144p. (J). pap. 5.99 ***(978-1-888045-52-9(3))*** Action Publishing, LLC.

—Death by Deinonychus. 2007. (Adventures of Dinosaur Dog Ser.). 144p. (J). pap. 5.99 ***(978-1-888045-54-3(X))*** Action Publishing, LLC.

—Trouble with Pteranodons. 2007. (Adventures of Dinosaur Dog Ser.). 144p. (Orig.). (J). pap. 5.99 ***(978-1-888045-53-6(1))*** Action Publishing, LLC.

—Tyrannosaurus Forest. 2007. (Adventures of Dinosaur Dog Ser.). 144p. (J). (gr. 3-6). pap. 5.99 ***(978-1-888045-51-2(5))*** Action Publishing, LLC.

Sykes, Julie. Great Dinosaur Mystery. 2001. (gr. k-3). lib. bdg. 11.25 (978-0-613-53511-3(1)) Tandem Library Bks.

Tagel, Peggy, illus. Dinosaurs. 2003. (Squishy Shapes Ser.). 10p. (J). 12.95 (978-1-57145-740-0(2) , Silver Dolphin Bks.) Advantage Pubs. Group.

Tanaka, Shelley. I Was There: Graveyard of the Dinosaurs School Market Edition. 1998. 48p. (J). (gr. 4-7). pap. 16.95 (978-0-7868-1332-2(6)) Disney Pr.

Thaler, Mike. School Bus Driver from the Black Lagoon. 1999. (gr. 3-6). lib. bdg. 10.95 (978-0-613-17939-3(0)) Tandem Library Bks.

There's a Dinosaur. (Early Intervention Levels Ser.). 28.38 (978-0-7362-0417-0(2)) Hampton-Brown Bks.

Thomas, Jerry D. Danger at Dinosaur Camp. 2002. (Detective Zack Ser.). (Illus.). 132p. (J). pap., pap. 6.99 (978-0-7814-3732-5(6) , 0781437326) Cook, David C. Publishing Co.

—Danger at Dinosaur Camp. 2002. (gr. 3-6). lib. bdg. 14.15 (978-0-613-74879-7(4)) Tandem Library Bks.

Thompson, Kay & McClatchy, Lisa. Eloise & the Dinosaurs. Lyon, Tammie, illus. 2007. (Ready-to-Reads Ser.). 32p. (J). pap. 3.99 (978-0-689-87453-6(7) , Aladdin) Simon & Schuster Children's Publishing.

Thompson, Lisa. Bony Puzzle. Thompson, Lisa & Stapleton, Matthew, illus. 2005. (Read-It! Chapter Bks.). 48p. (J). (ps-k). lib. bdg. 19.95 (978-1-4048-1345-8(4)) Picture Window Bks.

Thomson, Ruth. Dinosaur's Day. Martin, Linda, ed. 2000. (Readers Ser.). (Illus.). 32p. (J). (ps-1). pap. 3.99 (978-0-7894-6634-1(1)) Dorling Kindersley Publishing, Inc.

—Dinosaur's Day. 2000. (gr. k-3). lib. bdg. 11.80 (978-0-613-32466-3(8)) Tandem Library Bks.

Thomson, Ruth & Dorling Kindersley Publishing Staff. Dinosaur's Day. 2000. (Readers Ser.). (Illus.). 1p. (J). (ps-1). 12.99 (978-0-7894-6635-8(X)) Dorling Kindersley Publishing, Inc.

Time Soldiers Book: Rex. 2003. tchr. ed. (978-1-929945-30-6(2)) Big Guy Bks., Inc.

Time Soldiers Book Vol. 2: Rex 2. 2003. tchr. ed. (978-1-929945-31-3(0)) Big Guy Bks., Inc.

Todd, John S. The Goodfellow Boys & the Talking Dinosaur. 2004. (Illus.). 32p. (gr. 3-5). 10.95 (978-1-57197-190-6(4)) Pentland Pr., Inc.

Torres, Daniel. Tom Tu Gran Amigo: Juega al Futbol, Vol. 5. 2005. (SPA., Illus.). 32p. 17.95 (978-1-59497-120-4(X)) Public Square Bks.

—Tom Tu Gran Amigo Vol. 6: Descubre el Carnaval. 2005. (SPA., Illus.). 32p. 17.95 (978-1-59497-121-1(8)) Public Square Bks.

—Tom Tu Gran Amigo en París, Vol. 4. 2005. (SPA., Illus.). 32p. 19.95 (978-1-59497-119-8(6)) Public Square Bks.

Triebwasser, Wayne & Squires, Elizabeth. Willy the Dinosaur Lies. Solum, Lisbeth J., illus. 2005. 32p. (J). pap. 9.95 (978-1-930572-39-3(5)) Educational Media Corp.

—Willy the Dinosaur Steals. Solum, Lisbeth J., illus. 2005. 32p. (J). pap. 9.95 (978-1-930572-40-9(9)) Educational Media Corp.

A Troop of Little Dinosaurs: Individual Title Six-Packs. 16p. (gr. 2 up). 35.00 (978-0-7635-9233-2(1)) Rigby Education.

Upton, Deborah. World of Words. 2001. (Illus.). (J). (978-0-7853-4798-9(4)) Publications International, Ltd.

Vail, Rachel. The (Almost) Perfect Mother's Day. Bjorkman, Steve, illus. 2003. (Mama Rex & T Ser.: No. 8). 32p. (J). pap. 14.95 (978-0-439-40718-2(4) , Orchard Bks.) Scholastic, Inc.

—Homework Trouble. Bjorkman, Steve, illus. 2002. (Mama Rex & T Ser.). 32p. (J). (gr. k-2). pap. 14.95 (978-0-439-40628-4(5)); pap. 4.99 (978-0-439-33281-1(8)) Scholastic, Inc. (Orchard Bks.).

—The Horrible Play Date. Bjorkman, Steve, illus. 2002. (Mama Rex & T Ser.). 32p. (J). pap. 14.95 (978-0-439-40627-7(7)); pap. 4.99 (978-0-439-28335-9(3)) Scholastic, Inc. (Orchard Bks.).

—Mama Rex & T: Lose a Waffle. Bjorkman, Steve, illus. 2000. (Mama Rex & T Ser.). (J). (978-0-439-19918-6(2)) Scholastic, Inc.

—Mama Rex & T: Run Out of Tape. Bjorkman, Steve, illus. 2001. (Mama Rex & T Ser.). (J). (978-0-439-19920-9(4)) Scholastic, Inc.

—The Prize. Bjorkman, Steve, illus. 2003. 32p. (J). (978-0-439-47191-6(5) , Orchard Bks.) Scholastic, Inc.

Vail, Rachel & Bjorkman, Steve. Halloween Knight. 2004. (Illus.). (J). (ps-2). lib. bdg. 12.19 (978-0-606-29858-2(4)) Tandem Library Bks.

Valvassori, Maureen M. My Day with Barney. Hill, Nelson, illus. 2001. (Barney Ser.). 12p. (J). bds. 5.99 (978-1-58668-139-5(7)) Scholastic, Inc.

Valvassori, Maureen M. & Scholastic, Inc. Staff. What Will I Be When I Grow Up? Alvord, R. & Greenfield, Nelson, illus. 2000. (Barney Ser.). 16p. (J). (ps). pap. 5.99 (978-1-57064-712-3(7) , 97963) Scholastic, Inc.

Volke, Gordon. Dizzy Dinos. Cassettari, Noeline, illus. 2006. 14p. (J). 8.99 (978-0-439-85673-7(6) , Cartwheel Bks.) Scholastic, Inc.

Von Sholly, Peter. Dinosaur Circus. 2001. (Illus.). 32p. (Orig.). (J). (gr. 2-6). pap. 9.95 (978-0-9709368-0-6(X)) Vonshollywood.

Vornholt, John. Dolphin Watch. 2002. (gr. 5-8). lib. bdg. 11.80 (978-0-613-70888-3(1)) Tandem Library Bks.

Wahl, Jan. I Met a Dinosaur. 2002. (gr. k-3). lib. bdg. 16.40 (978-0-613-77489-5(2)) Tandem Library Bks.

Wahl, Jan & Sheban, Chris. I Met a Dinosaur. 2002. (Illus.). 32p. (J). (gr. 1-5). pap. 7.95 (978-0-89812-331-9(3) , Creative Paperbacks) Creative Co., The.

Waite, Judy. Digging for Dinosaurs. Parsons, Garry, illus. (Flying Foxes Ser.). 32p. (J). 2004. pap. (978-0-7787-1529-0(9)); 2003. (978-0-7787-1483-5(7)) Crabtree Publishing Co.

Walker, E. G. Mario & the Dinosaur. Graffam, Merle H., illus. 2002. 50p. (J). (gr. 5-12). pap. 6.95 (978-0-9716071-1-8(7)) Walker, Esther.

Wallace, Karen. I Am a Tyrannosaurus. Bostock, Mike, illus. 2004. 32p. (J). 15.95 (978-0-689-87317-1(4) , Atheneum) Simon & Schuster Children's Publishing.

Walt Disney Company Staff, contrib. by. Walt Disney Pictures Presents Dinosaur. 2000. (Disney's Wonderful World of Reading Ser.). (Illus.). (J). (978-0-7172-6447-6(5) , Grolier) Scholastic Library Publishing.

—Walt Disney Pictures Presents Dinosaur. 2000. (Colorforms Books). (Illus.). (J). (978-1-57528-397-5(2)) University Games.

Walton, Rick. Why the Banana Split. Holder, Jimmy, illus. 2005. 32p. (J). (ps-3). pap. 6.95 (978-1-58685-841-4(6)) Gibbs Smith, Publisher.

Warnes, Tim. The Great Dinosaur Mystery. 2001. (Illus.). 24p. (J). 3.50 (978-1-58925-361-2(2) , tiger tales) ME Media LLC.

Washington, LaVonne & LaShawn. The World That Then Was - Dinosaurs. 2005. 32p. 11.20 (978-1-4116-2428-3(9)) Lulu.com.

Wasserman, Veronica. The Dinosaur Dig. 2008. 32p. (J). (ps-k). pap. 3.99 (***978-0-448-44710-0(X)** , Grosset & Dunlap) Penguin Group (USA) Inc.

Watt, F. & Wells, R. That's Not My Dinosaur... It's Body Is Too Squashy. 2004. (Touchy-Feely Board Bks.). (SPA., Illus.). 10p. (J). (ps up). 7.95 (978-0-7945-0129-7(X) , Usborne) EDC Publishing.

Weatherby, Mark Alan. Mi Dinosaurio. 2001. (SPA., Illus.). (J). (978-84-88342-22-5(5) , KK3700) S.A. Kokinos ESP. *Dist:* Lectorum Pubns., Inc.

Webster-Stratton, Carolyn. Wally Meets Dina Dinosaur. Mostyn, David, illus. 1998. (Dina Dinosaur Ser.). (J). (ps-3). pap. (978-1-892222-03-9(5)) Incredible Years Pr.

—Wally's Detective Book for Solving Problems at Home. Mostyn, David, illus. 1998. (Dina Dinosaur Ser.). (J). (ps-3). pap. (978-1-892222-00-8(0)) Incredible Years Pr.

—Wally's Detective Book for Solving Problems at School. Mostyn, David, illus. 1998. (Dina Dinosaur Ser.). (J). (ps-3). pap. (978-1-892222-01-5(9)) Incredible Years Pr.

Wells, Rosemary. Doris's Dinosaur. Wheeler, Jody & Nez, John, illus. 2001. (Yoko & Friends School Days Ser.: No. 4). 32p. (gr. k-2). 9.99 (978-0-7868-0726-0(1) , Volo) Hyperion Bks. for Children.

—Doris's Dinosaur. 2001. (J). 10.79 (978-0-606-22550-2(1)) Tandem Library Bks.

Westell, Kerry. Dinosaur Dreams. Ritchie, Scot, illus. 2003. (Annikins Ser.: Vol. 8). 32p. (J). (ps-2). pap. 0.99 (978-1-55037-049-2(9)) Annick Pr., Ltd. CAN. *Dist:* Firefly Bks., Ltd.

Weston, Martha. The Dinosaurs Meet Dr. Clock: A Holiday House Reader. 2002. (Reader Level 1 Ser.). (Illus.). 32p. (J). (gr. k-3). tchr. ed. 14.95 (978-0-8234-1661-5(5)) Holiday Hse., Inc.

Wheeler, Lisa. Dino-Hockey. Gott, Barry, illus. 2007. (Carolrhoda Picture Bks.). 32p. (J). (gr. k-4). 16.95 (***978-0-8225-6191-0(3)** , Carolrhoda Bks.) Lerner Publishing Group.

White, Stephen. Barney's Storybook Treasury. Sharp, Chris & McGlothin, David, illus. 1999. (Barney Ser.). 176p. (J). (ps-k). pap. 10.95 (978-1-57064-579-2(5)) Scholastic, Inc.

White, Stephen & Scholastic, Inc. Staff. Barney's Night Before Christmas. Davis, Guy, ed. Grayson, Rick, illus. 1999. (Barney Ser.). 24p. (J). (ps-k). pap. 3.50 (978-1-57064-462-7(4)) Scholastic, Inc.

White, Steve. Come on over to Barney's House. McKee, Darren & Greenfield, Nelson, illus. 2001. (Barney Ser.). 24p. (J). (ps-k). pap. 3.50 (978-1-58668-046-6(3)) Scholastic, Inc.

Whitehead, Pete, illus. Hungry Dinosaur. 2006. (I'm Going to Read Ser.). 32p. (J). pap. 3.95 (978-1-4027-3418-2(2)) Sterling Publishing Co., Inc.

Whybrow, Ian. Harry & the Bucketful of Dinosaurs. Reynolds, Adrian, illus. 2003. (Harry & the Dinosaurs Ser.). 32p. (J). (ps-3). 14.95 (978-0-375-82541-5(X) , Random Hse. Bks. for Young Readers) Random Hse. Children's Bks.

—Harry & the Dinosaurs at the Museum. Reynolds, Adrian, illus. 2005. 32p. (J). (ps-2). 15.95 (978-0-375-83338-0(2) , Random Hse. Bks. for Young Readers) Random Hse. Children's Bks.

—Harry & the Dinosaurs Go to School. Reynolds, Adrian, illus. 2007. 32p. (J). (ps-2). 15.99 (978-0-375-84180-4(6) , Random Hse. Bks. for Young Readers) Random Hse. Children's Bks.

—Harry & the Dinosaurs Make a Christmas Wish. Reynolds, Adrian, illus. 2004. 32p. (J). (ps-2). 15.95 (978-0-375-83111-9(8) , Random Hse. Bks. for Young Readers) Random Hse. Children's Bks.

—Harry & the Dinosaurs Say "Raahh!" Reynolds, Adrian, illus. 2004. 32p. (J). (ps-3). 14.95 (978-0-375-82542-2(8) , Random Hse. Bks. for Young Readers) Random Hse. Children's Bks.

—Sammy & the Dinosaurs. Reynolds, Adrian, illus. 1999. 32p. (J). (ps-1). pap. 15.95 (978-0-531-30207-1(5) , Orchard Bks.) Scholastic, Inc.

—Sammy & the Dinosaurs: Deluxe Gift Set. Reynolds, Adrian, illus. 2000. (J). (ps-3). 14.95 (978-0-531-30337-5(3) , Orchard Bks.) Scholastic, Inc.

Whybrow, Ian, et al. Owain A'r Cloc. 2005. (WEL., Illus.). 18p. 6.99 (978-1-84323-366-4(5)) Gomer Pr. GBR. *Dist:* Gomer Pr.

Wilhelm, Hans. Tyrone the Double Dirty Rotten Cheater. (FRE.). (J). pap. 6.99 (978-0-590-74141-5(1)) Scholastic, Inc.

Willems, Mo. Edwina: The Dinosaur Who Didn't Know She Was Extinct. Willems, Mo, illus. 2006. (Illus.). 40p. (ps-2). 16.99 (978-0-7868-3748-9(9)) Hyperion Pr.

Williams, Mark London. Ancient Fire. 2004. (Danger Boy Ser.: No. 1). (Illus.). 224p. (J). (gr. 4-8). 12.99 (978-0-7636-2152-0(8)) Candlewick Pr.

—Ancient Fire: Danger Boy Episode 1. 2006. 232p. (J). (gr. 4-8). pap. 4.99 (978-0-7636-3092-8(6)) Candlewick Pr.

Williams, Mark London. Trail of Bones: Danger Boy Episode 3. 2007. (Illus.). 320p. (J). (gr. 4-8). 5.99 (***978-0-7636-3410-0(7)*** Candlewick Pr.

Williams, Mary. The Little Boy Who Wanted a Dinosaur Tail. Brittain, Angela, ed. Takatch, Bob, illus. 2001. 12p. (J). (ps-2). pap. 8.95 (978-0-9706232-0-1(8)) Mogdrmombooks.

Williams, Rozanne Lanczak. Writing Dino-Mite Poems. Maio, Barbara & Faulkner, Stacey, eds. Adnet, Bernard, illus. 2006. (Learn to Write Ser.). 8p. (J). pap. 1.99 (978-1-59198-285-2(5) , 6179) Creative Teaching Pr., Inc.

Willson, Sarah. Up & Away, Reptar! Rillo, Cary, illus. 1999. (Ready-to-Read Ser.). 32p. (J). (ps-3). pap. 3.99 (978-0-689-82631-3(1) , 076714003996, Simon Spotlight/ Nickelodeon) Simon & Schuster Children's Publishing.

Wilson, David Henry. Please Keep off the Dinosaur. l.t. ed. 2005. 112p. (J). pap. (978-0-7540-6135-9(3) , CLP 330) BBC Audio.

—Please Keep off the Dinosaur. unabr. l.t. ed. 2003. (Read-Along Ser.). (J). pap. 24.95 incl. audio (978-0-7540-6232-5(5) , RAO33, Galaxy Children's Large Print) BBC Audiobooks America.

—Please Keep off the Dinosaur. (Illus.). 98p. (J). pap. 8.99 (978-0-330-34571-2(0) , Pan) Pan Macmillan GBR. *Dist:* Trafalgar Square Publishing.

Wilson, Jacqueline. The Dinosaur's Packed Lunch. 2001. (Illus.). 32p. (J). 6.99 (978-0-552-52818-4(8) , Corgi) Transworld Publishers Ltd. GBR. *Dist:* Independent Pubs. Group.

Wilson, Pauline Hutchens & Dengler, Sandy. The Case of the Dinosaur in the Desert, Vol. 4. 2001. (New Sugar Creek Gang Ser.: Vol. #4). (Illus.). 144p. (J). 5.99 (978-0-8024-8664-6(9)) Moody Pubs.

Wishinsky, Frieda. Danger, Dinosaurs! Griffiths, Dean, illus. 2007. (Canadian Flyer Adventures Ser.: No. 2). 96p. (J). (gr. 1-4). 16.95 (978-1-897066-81-2(3)); pap. 6.95 (978-1-897066-82-9(1)) Maple Tree Pr. CAN. *Dist:* Perseus Distribution.

Wiskur, Darrell. Dinky Dinosaur: Creation Days. 2002. (Illus.). 16p. (J). (ps-1). 6.99 (978-0-89051-361-3(9) , 303-075) Master Bks.

Wiskur, Darrell, told to. Dinky Dinosaur - Who's My Friend? 2001. (Illus.). 16p. (J). 6.99 (978-0-89051-362-0(7)) Master Bks.

Woodruff, Paul M. Monsters, Myths & Mysteries: A Tangled Tour Maze Book. 2007. (Illus.). 80p. (J). pap. 5.95 (978-1-4027-3803-6(X)) Sterling Publishing Co., Inc.

Woodson, Marion. Dinosaur Fever. 2007. 168p. (YA). pap. 11.99 (***978-1-55002-690-0(9)** , Sandcastle Bks.) Dundurn Group, The CAN. *Dist:* Univ. of Toronto Pr.

Worth, Bonnie. Oh, Say Can You Say Di-No-Saur. 1999. (Cat in the Hat's Learning Library Ser.). (Illus.). 48p. (gr. k-3). 8.99 (978-0-679-89114-7(5) , Random Hse. Bks. for Young Readers) Random Hse. Children's Bks.

Yeh, Phil. Dinosaurs Across America. 2007. (Illus.). 32p. (J). (gr. 1-5). 12.95 (***978-1-56163-509-2(X))** NBM Publishing Co.

Yolen, Jane. Como Dan las Buenas Noches los Dinoaurios? Teague, Mark, illus. 2002. (SPA.). 40p. (J). (gr. k-2). pap. 5.99 (978-0-439-31735-1(5) , SO30538, Scholastic en Espanol) Scholastic, Inc.

—Como Dan las Buenas Noches los Dinosaurios? 2002. Tr. of How Do Dinosaurs Say Goodnight?. (SPA.). (gr. k-3). lib. bdg. 14.15 (978-0-613-84113-9(1)) Tandem Library Bks.

—Como Ordenan sus Habitaciones los Dinosaurios? Teague, Mark, illus. 2004. (SPA.). 12p. (J). (ps up). bds. 6.99 (978-0-439-66202-4(8) , Blue Sky Pr., The) Scholastic, Inc.

—Como Se Curan los Dinosaurios? 2004. Tr. of How Do Dinosaurs Get Well Soon?. (SPA.). (ps-2). lib. bdg. 13.00 (978-0-613-87299-7(1)) Tandem Library Bks.

—How Do Dinosaurs Clean Their Rooms? Teague, Mark, illus. 2004. 12p. (J). (ps up). bds. 6.99 (978-0-439-64950-6(1) , Blue Sky Pr., The) Scholastic, Inc.

—How Do Dinosaurs Count to Ten? Teague, Mark, illus. 2004. 12p. (J). (ps up). bds. 6.99 (978-0-439-64949-0(8) , Blue Sky Pr., The) Scholastic, Inc.

—How Do Dinosaurs Eat Their Food? Teague, Mark, illus. 40p. (J). 2006. (SPA.). pap. 4.99 (978-0-439-76404-9(1) , Scholastic en Espanol); 2005. pap. 15.99 (978-0-439-24102-1(2) , Blue Sky Pr., The) Scholastic, Inc.

—How Do Dinosaurs Get Well Soon? Teague, Mark, illus. 40p. (J). 2004. pap. 4.99 (978-0-439-54563-1(3)); 2003. pap. 15.95 (978-0-439-24100-7(6) , Blue Sky Pr., The) Scholastic, Inc.

—How Do Dinosaurs Go to School? Teague, Mark, illus. 2007. 40p. (J). (ps-2). 16.99 (***978-0-439-02081-7(6)*** Scholastic, Inc.

—How Do Dinosaurs Learn Their Colors? Teague, Mark, illus. 2006. 12p. (J). bds. 6.99 (978-0-439-85653-9(1) , Blue Sky Pr., The) Scholastic, Inc.

—How Do Dinosaurs Learn Their Colors (Como Aprenden los Dinosaurios los Colores) 2006. 12p. (J). bds. 6.99 (978-0-439-87192-1(1) , Scholastic en Espanol) Scholastic, Inc.

—How Do Dinosaurs Play with Their Friends? Teague, Mark, illus. 2006. 12p. (J). bds. 6.99 (978-0-439-85654-6(X) , Blue Sky Pr., The) Scholastic, Inc.

—How Do Dinosaurs Play with Their Friends (Como Juegan los Dinosaurios con Sus Amigos) 2006. 12p. (J). bds. 6.99 (978-0-439-87193-8(X) , Scholastic en Espanol) Scholastic, Inc.

—How Do Dinosaurs Say Good Night? Teague, Mark, illus. 2000. 40p. (J). (ps up). pap. 15.95 (978-0-590-31681-1(8) , Blue Sky Pr., The) Scholastic, Inc.

—How Do Dinosaurs Say Good Night? Book & Plush Set. 2002. (Illus.). (J). 25.04 (978-0-7587-2759-6(3)) Book Wholesalers, Inc.

—How Do Dinosaurs Say Good Night? Book & Plush Set. 2004. (J). (ps-1). 24.95 incl. audio (978-1-55592-099-9(3)) Weston Woods Studios, Inc.

—How Do Dinosaurs Say Good Night? Book & Plush Set. Teague, Mark, illus. 2004. (J). 29.95 incl. cd-rom (978-1-55592-138-5(8)) Weston Woods Studios, Inc.

Zala Runs for Her Life: Individual Title Six-Packs. 16p. (gr. 2 up). 35.00 (978-0-7635-9229-5(3)) Rigby Education.

Zindel, Paul. Raptor, No. 1. 1999. (Raptor Ser.: Vol. 1). 176p. (gr. 5-9). pap. 4.99 (978-0-7868-1224-0(9)) Disney Pr.

—Raptor. unabr. ed. 2000. (J). pap., stu. ed. 42.24 incl. audio (978-0-7887-4185-2(3) , 41098) Recorded Bks., LLC.

—Raptor. 1999. 170p. (J). (ps-7). per. 11.64 (978-0-606-17385-8(4)); (gr. 5-8). lib. bdg. 13.00 (978-0-613-22241-9(5)) Tandem Library Bks.

—Raptor Paperback Club. 1999. (Illus.). 176p. (J). pap. 4.99 (978-0-7868-1471-8(3)) Disney Pr.

Zoehfeld, Kathleen Weidner. Dinosaur: Aladar's Story. Clarke, Judith et al, illus. 2000. (Dinosaur Ser.). 32p. (J). (ps-3). 12.99 (978-0-7868-3259-0(2)) Disney Pr.

—Fossil Fever. 2000. (gr. 3-6). lib. bdg. 11.80 (978-0-613-27833-1(X)); (Illus.). (J). 10.79 (978-0-606-20435-4(0)) Tandem Library Bks.

Zoehfeld, Kathleen Weidner & Bogan, Paulette. Fossil Fever. 1999. (Stepping Stone Bks.). (Illus.). 48p. (J). (gr. 1-4). pap. 3.99 (978-0-307-26400-8(9) , Random Hse. Bks. for Young Readers) Random Hse. Children's Bks.

DINOSAURS—POETRY

Andreae, Giles. Dinosaurs Galore! Wojtowycz, David, illus. 32p. (J). 2006. pap. 7.95 (978-1-58925-399-5(X)); 2005. 16.95 (978-1-58925-044-4(3)) ME Media LLC. (tiger tales).

Beall, Pamela Conn & Nipp, Susan Hagen. Wee Sing Dinosaurs. 2006. (Wee Sing Ser.). 60p. (J). (ps-2). 9.99 (978-0-8431-2097-4(5) , Price Stern Sloan) Penguin Group (USA) Inc.

Greenfield, Eloise. I Can Draw a Weeposaur & Other Dinosaurs. Spivey-Gilchrist, Jan, illus. 2001. 32p. (J). (gr. k-3). lib. bdg. 14.89 (978-0-688-17635-8(6)) HarperCollins Pubs.

Hopkins, Lee Bennett. Dino-Roars. Fisher, Cynthia, illus. 1999. (Road to Reading Ser.). 10.95 (978-0-307-26304-9(5)) Whitman Publishing LLC.

Prelutsky, Jack. Tyrannosaurus Was a Beast: Dinosaur Poems. unabr. ed. 1999. (Follow the Reader Ser.). (J). (gr. 1-3). pap. 17.00 incl. audio (978-0-8072-0226-5(6) , EFTR169SP, Listening Library) Random Hse. Audio Publishing Group.

Sierra, Judy. Good Night, Dinosaurs. Chess, Victoria, illus. 2002. 32p. (J). (gr. k-3). pap. 5.95 (978-0-618-19600-5(5) , Clarion Bks.) Houghton Mifflin Co. Trade & Reference Div.

—Good Night, Dinosaurs. 2002. (gr. k-3). lib. bdg. 14.10 (978-0-613-60677-6(9)) Tandem Library Bks.

Temperley, Howard. In the Days of Dinosaurs: A Rhyming Romp Through Dino History. Kline, Michael P., illus. 2004. (J). pap. 9.95 (978-1-885593-81-8(3) , Williamson Bks.) Ideals Pubns.

DIPHTHERIA

Kimmel, Elizabeth Cody. Balto & the Great Race. 2004. (Stepping Stone Bks.). (Illus.). 112p. (J). (gr. k-3). lib. bdg. 11.99 (978-0-679-99198-4(0) , Random Hse. Bks. for Young Readers) Random Hse. Children's Bks.

—Balto & the Great Race. Koerber, Nora, illus. 1999. (Stepping Stone Bks.). 112p. (J). (gr. k-3). pap. 3.99 (978-0-679-89198-7(6) , Random Hse. Bks. for Young Readers) Random Hse. Children's Bks.

—Balto & the Great Race. 1999. (Step into Reading Ser.). 10.64 (978-0-606-17522-7(9)) Tandem Library Bks.

Margulies, Phillip. Diphtheria. 2004. (Epidemics Ser.). (Illus.). 64p. (J). lib. bdg. 26.50 (978-1-4042-0253-5(6)) Rosen Publishing Group, Inc., The.

Miller, Debbie S. The Great Serum Race. Van Zyle, Jon, illus. 2006. 40p. (J). pap. 8.95 (978-0-8027-7723-2(6)) Walker & Co.

Standiford, Natalie. Bravest Dog Ever: Story of Balto. Cook, Donald, illus. 2003. (Step into Reading Ser.: Step 3). 48p. (J). (gr. 1-3). lib. bdg. 11.99 (978-0-394-99695-0(X) , Random Hse. Bks. for Young Readers) Random Hse. Children's Bks.

DIPLOMATIC AND CONSULAR SERVICE—FICTION

Hale, Shannon. River Secrets. 2006. (Illus.). 304p. (J). 17.95 (978-1-58234-901-5(0)) Bloomsbury Publishing.

DIPLOMATS

Acker, Kerry. Madeleine Albright. 2004. (Women in Politics Ser.). (Illus.). 120p. 30.00 (978-0-7910-7734-4(9)); 116p. pap. 30.00 (978-0-7910-7998-0(8)) Facts On File, Inc. (Chelsea Hse.).

Blashfield, Jean F. Shirley Temple Black: Actor & Diplomat. 2000. (Career Biographies Ser.). (Illus.). 128p. (J). (gr. 6-12). 25.00 (978-0-89434-338-4(6) , F408, Ferguson Publishing Co.) Facts On File, Inc.

Blue, Rose, et al. Madeleine Albright: U. S. Secretary of State. 1998. (Library of Famous Women). (Illus.). 64p. (J). 26.20 (978-1-56711-253-5(6) , Blackbirch Pr., Inc.) Thomson Gale.

Burgan, Michael. Madeleine Albright. 1998. (Single Titles Ser.: up). (Illus.). 144p. (gr. 7-12). lib. bdg. 24.90 (978-0-7613-0367-1(7) , Millbrook Pr.) Lerner Publishing Group.

Byman, Jeremy. Madam Secretary: The Story of Madeleine Albright. (Notable Americans Ser.). (Illus.). 1998. 96p. (gr. 5 up). 21.95 (978-1-883846-23-7(4)); 2004. 128p. (YA). (gr. 6-12). 23.95 (978-1-931798-34-1(6)) Reynolds, Morgan Inc.

Friedman, Lita. Mary Robinson: Fighter for Human Rights. 2004. (Avisson Young Adult Ser.). (Illus.). 142p. (YA). pap. 19.95 (978-1-888105-65-0(8)) Avisson Pr., Inc.

Gold, Alison Leslie. A Special Fate: Chiune Sugihara: Hero of the Holocaust. 2000. (Illus.). 176p. (YA). (gr. 4-9). pap. 15.95 (978-0-590-39525-0(4) , Scholastic Reference) Scholastic, Inc.

Jones, Gerald Colman. Mary Robinson: Citizen of the World. 2000. (Contemporary Profiles & Policy Series for the Younger Reader). (Illus.). 72p. (J). (gr. 8 up). 24.00 (978-0-934272-63-6(8)); pap. 15.00 (978-0-934272-64-3(6)) Burke, John Gordon Pub., Inc.

Kramer, Barbara. Madeleine Albright: First Woman Secretary of State. 2000. (People to Know Ser.). (Illus.). 112p. (J). (gr. 6-12). lib. bdg. 26.60 (978-0-7660-1143-4(7)) Enslow Pubs., Inc.

McArthur, Debra. Raoul Wallenberg: Rescuing Thousands from the Nazis' Grasp. 2005. (Holocaust Heroes & Nazi Criminals Ser.). (Illus.). 160p. (J). (gr. 6-12). lib. bdg. 27.93 (978-0-7660-2530-1(6)) Enslow Pubs., Inc.

Mochizuki, Ken. Pasajea la Libertad. ed. 2004. (SPA., Illus.). (J). (gr. k-4). spiral bd. (978-0-616-03091-2(6)) Canadian National Institute for the Blind/Institut National Canadien pour les Aveugles.

—Passage to Freedom: The Sugihara Story. Lee, Dom, illus. 2003. 32p. (J). 6.95 (978-1-58430-157-8(0)) Lee & Low Bks., Inc.

Streissguth, Thomas. Raoul Wallenberg: Swedish Diplomat & Humanitarian. 2005. (Holocaust Biographies Ser.). (Illus.). 112p. (J). (gr. 7-12). lib. bdg. 26.50 (978-0-8239-3318-1(0) , HBRAWA) Rosen Publishing Group, Inc., The.

Watson, Marilyn Myrick. Raul Castro: Arizona's First Hispanic Governor. 2007. (J). (***978-0-9790826-5-8(X)); (*978-0-9790826-6-5(8))*** Acacia Publishing, Inc.

Wheeler, Jill C. Madeleine Albright. 2002. (Women of the World Ser.). (J). lib. bdg. 21.35 (978-1-57765-316-5(5)) ABDO Publishing Co.

—Mary Robinson. 2004. (Women of the World Ser.). (J). (978-1-59197-617-2(0)) ABDO Publishing Co.

DIPSOMANIA

see Alcoholism

DIPTERA

see Flies; Mosquitoes

DIRECTION, SENSE OF

see Orientation

DIRIGIBLE BALLOONS

see Airships

DISABLED PEOPLE

see People with Disabilities

DISARMAMENT

see also Peace; Security, International

Bingley, Richard. The Arms Trade. 2003. (Face the Facts Ser.). (Illus.). 56p. (J). lib. bdg. 28.56 (978-0-7398-6431-9(9)) Raintree.

Cheney, Glenn A. Nuclear Proliferation: The Problems & Possibilities. 1999. (Impact Bks.). (Illus.). 144p. (YA). (gr. 8-12). 22.00 (978-0-531-11431-5(7) , Watts, Franklin) Scholastic Library Publishing.

Minneus, Steve. Nukes: The Spread of Nuclear Weapons. 2007. (J). ***(978-1-4042-1916-8(1))*** Rosen Publishing Group, Inc., The.

Parks, Peggy J. North Korea. 2003. (Nations in Conflict Ser.). (Illus.). 48p. (J). 24.95 (978-1-4103-0077-5(3) , Blackbirch Pr., Inc.) Thomson Gale.

DISASTERS

see also Accidents; Aircraft Accidents; Fires; Natural Disasters; Shipwrecks

American Disasters, 29 bks., Set. Incl. Challenger Disaster : Tragic Space Flight. Bredeson, Carmen. (YA). 1999. lib. bdg. 23.93 (978-0-7660-1222-6(0)); Exxon Valdez : Tragic Oil Spill. Sherrow, Victoria. (YA). 1998. lib. bdg. 23.93 (978-0-7660-1058-1(9)); Fire in Oakland, California : Billion-Dollar Blaze. Bredeson, Carmen. (YA). 1999. lib. bdg. 23.93 (978-0-7660-1220-2(4)); Hurricane Andrew : Nature's Rage. Sherrow, Victoria. (YA). 1998. lib. bdg. 23.93 (978-0-7660-1057-4(0)); L. A. Riots : Rage in the City of Angels. Cole, Michael D. (YA). 1999. lib. bdg. 23.93 (978-0-7660-1219-6(0)); Love Canal : Toxic Waste Tragedy. Sherrow, Victoria. (J). 2001. lib. bdg. 23.93 (978-0-7660-1553-1(X)); Mighty Midwest Flood : Raging Rivers. Bredeson, Carmen. (YA). 1999. lib. bdg. 23.93 (978-0-7660-1221-9(2)); Mount St. Helens Volcano : Violent Eruption. Bredeson, Carmen. (YA). 2001. lib. bdg. 23.93 (978-0-7660-1552-4(1)); Oklahoma City Bombing : Terror in the Heartland. Sherrow, Victoria. (YA). 1998. lib. bdg. 23.93 (978-0-7660-1061-1(9)); Plains Outbreak Tornadoes : Killer Twisters. Sherrow, Victoria. (YA). 1998. lib. bdg. 23.93 (978-0-7660-1059-8(7)); Polio Epidemic : Crippling Virus Outbreak. Sherrow, Victoria. (YA). 2001. lib. bdg. 23.93 (978-0-7660-1555-5(6)); San Francisco Earthquake, 1989 : Death & Destruction. Sherrow, Victoria. (YA). 1998. lib. bdg. 23.93 (978-0-7660-1060-4(0)); Siege at Waco : Deadly Inferno. Cole, Michael D. (YA). 1999. lib. bdg. 23.93 (978-0-7660-1218-9(2)); Titanic : Disaster at Sea. Cole, Michael D. (YA). 2001. lib. bdg. 23.93 (978-0-7660-1557-9(2)); TWA Flight 800 : Explosion in Midair. Cole, Michael D. (YA). 1999. lib. bdg. 23.93 (978-0-7660-1217-2(4)); World Trade Center Bombing : Terror in the Towers. Sherrow, Victoria. (YA). 1998. lib. bdg. 23.93 (978-0-7660-1056-7(2)); 48p. (gr. 4-10). (Illus.). Set lib. bdg. 549.55 (978-0-7660-1190-8(9)) Enslow Pubs., Inc.

Berry, Joy Wilt. Disasters: Good Answers to Tough Questions. Bartholomew, illus. rev. ed. 1999. (Good Answers to Tough Questions Ser.: Vol. 14). 48p. (J). pap. 4.95 (978-1-58634-224-1(X) , 01-0901-14) Goldstar Publishing, Inc.

Blackwood, Gary L. Enigmatic Events. 2005. (Unsolved History Ser.). (Illus.). 72p. (J). (gr. 3-7). lib. bdg. (978-0-7614-1889-4(X) , Benchmark Bks.) Cavendish, Marshall Corp.

Blattner, Don & Howerton, Lisa. Disasters. 1999. (Illus.). 144p. (YA). (gr. 5-8). pap. 12.95 (978-1-58037-101-8(9)) Twain, Mark Media, Inc. Pubs.

Bryan, Nichol. Chernobyl: Nuclear Disaster. 2003. (Environmental Disasters Ser.). (Illus.). 48p. (gr. 5 up). (YA). lib. bdg. 30.00 (978-0-8368-5504-3(3)); (J). pap. 11.95 (978-0-8368-5511-1(6)) Stevens, Gareth Inc. (World Almanac Library).

Butts, Ed. SOS: Stories of Survival: Tales of Disaster, Tragedy & Courage. 2007. (Illus.). 128p. (YA). (gr. 6 up). pap. 12.95 (978-0-88776-786-9(9)) Tundra Bks., Inc./ Livres Toundra, Inc. CAN. *Dist:* Random Hse., Inc.

Calamities: Events That Touched the World. (Critical Reading Ser.). (YA). (gr. 6-12). pap. (978-0-8092-1111-1(4)) Jamestown.

Cruise, Robin. The Nuclear Disaster at Chernobyl. Taylor, Marjorie, illus. rev. ed. 1999. (Take Ten Ser.). 46p. (YA). (gr. 4 up). pap. 3.95 (978-1-58659-022-2(7)) Artesian Pr.

Davis, Lee A. Man-Made Catastrophes. 2nd rev. ed. 2002. (Illus.). 416p. (YA). (gr. 6-12). 60.00 (978-0-8160-4418-4(X)) Facts On File, Inc.

Destination Disaster: Individual Title Six-Packs. (Action Packs Ser.). 104p. (gr. 3-5). 44.00 (978-0-7635-3300-7(9)) Rigby Education.

Diamond, Arthur. The Bhopal Chemical Leak. 2002. (World Disasters Ser.). (Illus.). 64p. (YA). (gr. 4-12). lib. bdg. 26.20 (978-1-56006-009-3(3) , Lucent Bks.) Thomson Gale.

Disaster!, 4 bks. Incl. Challenger : The Explosion on Liftoff. Chandler, Gil. lib. bdg. 21.26 (978-0-7368-1322-8(5)); Exxon Valdez : The Oil Spill off the Alaskan Coast. Chandler, Gil. lib. bdg. 21.26 (978-0-7368-1320-4(9)); Hindenburg : The Fiery Crash of a German Airship. Deady, Kathleen W. lib. bdg. 21.26 (978-0-7368-1321-1(7)); Titanic : The Tragedy at Sea. Deady, Kathleen W. lib. bdg. 21.26 (978-0-7368-1323-5(3)); 32p. (J). (gr. 3-4). 2002. (Illus.). 2002. Set lib. bdg. 85.04 (978-0-7368-1324-2(1) , Capstone High-Interest Bks.) Capstone Pr., Inc.

Fallout: Nuclear Disasters in Our World: Individual Title, 6 pack. (On Deck Ser.: Vol. 2). 24p. (gr. 4-5). 35.00 (978-0-7578-5831-4(7)) Rigby Education.

Halley, Ned. Disasters. 1999. (Single Subject References Ser.). (Illus.). 64p. (J). (gr. 5-9). tchr. ed. 16.95 (978-0-7534-5221-9(9) , Kingfisher) Houghton Mifflin Co. Trade & Reference Div.

—The World of Disasters. 2005. (World Of Ser.). (Illus.). 64p. (J). (gr. 4-6). pap., pap. 8.95 (978-0-7534-5835-8(7) , Kingfisher) Houghton Mifflin Co. Trade & Reference Div.

Higginson, Sheila Sweeny. Desastres de la tecnología & Disasters of Technology. 2005. spiral bd. 88.00 ***(978-1-4108-5731-6(X))*** Benchmark Education Co.

Ingram, Scott. The Chernobyl Nuclear Disaster. 2005. (Environmental Disasters Ser.). (Illus.). 112p. (J). (gr. 6-12). 35.00 (978-0-8160-5755-9(9)) Facts On File, Inc.

Kenah, Katharine. Destruction Earth. 2004. (Extreme Readers Ser.). (Illus.). 32p. (J). (gr. k-1). pap. 3.95 (978-0-7696-3185-1(1)) School Specialty Publishing.

Landau, Elaine. Maritime Disasters. 1999. (Watts Library). (Illus.). 64p. (J). (gr. 5-7). 25.50 (978-0-531-20344-6(1) , Watts, Franklin) Scholastic Library Publishing.

—Maritime Disasters. 1999. (gr. 3-6). lib. bdg. 17.60 (978-0-613-29471-3(8)) Tandem Library Bks.

Leroe, Ellen. Disaster! Three Real-Life Stories of Survival. 2000. (gr. 5-8). lib. bdg. 14.15 (978-0-613-36304-4(3)) Tandem Library Bks.

Lieurance, Suzanne. The Space Shuttle Challenger Disaster in American History. 2001. (In American History Ser.). (Illus.). 128p. (J). (gr. 5-12). lib. bdg. 26.60 (978-0-7660-1419-0(3)) Enslow Pubs., Inc.

Louis, Nancy. Ground Zero. 2002. (War on Terrorism Ser.). (Illus.). 64p. (J). (gr. 4-8). lib. bdg. 25.65 (978-1-57765-657-9(1) , ABDO & Daughters) ABDO Publishing Co.

Mayell, Mark. Building Collapses. 2004. (Man-Made Disasters Ser.). (Illus.). 112p. (J). 29.95 (978-1-59018-055-6(0)) Thomson Gale.

McDaniel, Melissa. Disaster Search Dogs. 2005. (Dog Heroes Ser.). (Illus.). 32p. (J). lib. bdg. 25.27 (978-1-59716-012-4(1)) Bearport Publishing Co., Inc.

Roza, Greg. Disaster Relief Workers. 2006. (Extreme Careers Ser.). (Illus.). 64p. (J). (gr. 5-8). lib. bdg. 26.50 (978-1-4042-0943-5(3)) Rosen Publishing Group, Inc., The.

Saari, Peggy. Great Misadventures. 1998. (J). 99.00 (978-0-7876-2799-7(2)); 99.00 (978-0-7876-2800-0(X)); 99.00 (978-0-7876-2801-7(8)); 99.00 (978-0-7876-2802-4(6)) Thomson Gale. (UXL).

—Great Misadventures: Bad Ideas That Led to Big Disasters, 4 vols. Betz, Des Chenes, ed. 1998. (Illus.). 729p. (J). (gr. 4-7). lib. bdg. 235.00 (978-0-7876-2798-0(4) , GML00502-112339, UXL) Thomson Gale.

Sandler, Martin W. America's Great Disasters. Sandler, Martin W., illus. 2003. (Illus.). 96p. (J). (gr. 3 up). 17.99 (978-0-06-029107-5(9)) HarperCollins Pubs.

Scher, Linda. The Texas City Disaster. 2007. (Code Red Ser.). (Illus.). 32p. (J). (gr. 3-7). lib. bdg. 25.27 (978-1-59716-363-7(5)) Bearport Publishing Co., Inc.

Sherrow, Victoria. The Exxon Valdez: Tragic Oil Spill. 1998. (American Disasters Ser.). (Illus.). 48p. (YA). (gr. 4-10). lib. bdg. 23.93 (978-0-7660-1058-1(9)) Enslow Pubs., Inc.

—The Oklahoma City Bombing: Terror in the Heartland. 1998. (American Disasters Ser.). (Illus.). 48p. (YA). (gr. 4-10). lib. bdg. 23.93 (978-0-7660-1061-1(9)) Enslow Pubs., Inc.

Simms, Mattie. The "Q" Kids: A Disaster Safety Workbook for Children of All Ages. 1998. 64p. (J). (gr. 1-6). pap. 7.00 (978-0-8059-4307-8(2)) Dorrance Publishing Co., Inc.

Stephen Currie. Escapes from Man-Made Disasters. 2004. (Great Escapes Ser.). (Illus.). 112p. (J). 29.95 (978-1-59018-277-2(4)) Thomson Gale.

Stewart, Gail B. America under Attack: September 11, 2001. 2002. (Terrorism Library). (Illus.). 112p. (J). 29.95 (978-1-59018-208-6(1) , LML00902-182195, Lucent Bks.) Thomson Gale.

Suen, Anastasia. Helping Organizations, 6 bks. Incl. American Society for the Prevention of Cruelty to Animals (ASPCA) (gr. k-3). lib. bdg. 17.25 (978-0-8239-6004-0(8)); Doctors Without Borders. (gr. k-3). lib. bdg. 17.25 (978-0-8239-6002-6(1)); Habitat for Humanity. (gr. 2). lib. bdg. 17.25 (978-0-8239-6006-4(4)); Peace Corps. (gr. 2). lib. bdg. 17.25 (978-0-8239-6001-9(3)); Red Cross. (gr. 2). lib. bdg. 17.25 (978-0-8239-6003-3(X)); UNICEF : United Nations Children's Fund. (gr. 2). lib. bdg. 17.25 (978-0-8239-6005-7(6)); 24p. (J). 2002. (Illus.). 2001. Set lib. bdg. 96.00 (978-0-8239-7175-6(9) , PowerKids Pr.) Rosen Publishing Group, Inc., The.

—The Red Cross. 2002. (Reading Power Ser.). (Illus.). 24p. (J). (gr. 2). lib. bdg. 17.25 (978-0-8239-6003-3(X) , PowerKids Pr.) Rosen Publishing Group, Inc., The.

Survivor Stories, 6 bks., Set. Incl. Earthquake : True Stories of Survival. Roza, Greg. (J). lib. bdg. 26.50 (978-1-4042-0997-8(2) , 1267007); Hurricane : True Stories of Survival. Wolny, Philip. (J). lib. bdg. 26.50 (978-1-4042-0998-5(0) , 1267008); Plane Crash : True Stories of Survival. Spalding, Frank. (J). lib. bdg. 26.50 (978-1-4042-0999-2(9) , 1267009); Shipwreck : True Stories of Survival. Porterfield, Jason. (J). lib. bdg. 26.50 (978-1-4042-1000-4(8)); Terrorist Attack : True Stories of Survival. Silate, Jennifer. (YA). lib. bdg. 26.50 (978-1-4042-1001-1(6)); Tsunamis : True Stories of Survival. Sommers, Michael A. (YA). lib. bdg. 26.50 (978-1-4042-1002-8(4)); (Illus.). 48p. (gr. 5-8). 2006. 2007. Set lib. bdg. 159.00 ***(978-1-4042-0938-1(7))*** Rosen Publishing Group, Inc., The.

Weil, Ann. Sea Disasters. 2003. (Illus.). 64p. (YA). per. (978-1-56254-660-1(0) , SP6600) Saddleback Educational Publishing.

—Space Disasters. 2003. (Illus.). 64p. (YA). per. 3.95 (978-1-56254-662-5(7) , SP6627) Saddleback Educational Publishing.

Wheeler, Jill C. September 11, 2001: The Day That Changed America. 2002. (War on Terrorism Ser.). (Illus.). 64p. (J). (gr. 4-8). lib. bdg. 25.65 (978-1-57765-656-2(3) , ABDO & Daughters) ABDO Publishing Co.

Woods, Michael & Woods, Mary B. Environmental Disasters. 2008. (Disasters up Close Ser.). (J). lib. bdg. 27.93 ***(978-0-8225-6774-5(1)*** , Lerner Pubns.) Lerner Publishing Group.

DISASTERS—FICTION

Boelter, Ashaki. Diaries of the Doomed 2: Fair of the Fatal. 2007. (Illus.). 114p. (J). per. 11.95 ***(978-0-9796219-0-1(9)*** , Writing Wild & Crazy) Shakalot High Entertainment.

Evans, Greg. Dates & Other Disasters: A Luann Collection. 2004. (Illus.). 128p. (J). pap. 10.95 (978-0-7407-4664-2(2)) Andrews McMeel Publishing.

Finney, Townsend. Disaster Run Amok. 2002. 35p. (J). per. 9.95 (978-0-9725830-0-8(9)) Buchavina Pr.

Hanson, Ed. Disaster in Oceania. 2004. 64p. (YA). per. 3.95 (978-1-56254-801-8(8) , SP8018) Saddleback Educational Publishing.

Harlow, Joan Hiatt. Joshua's Song. (Illus.). (J). 2003. 160p. pap. 4.99 (978-0-689-85542-9(7) , Aladdin); 2001. 192p. (gr. 3-7). 16.95 (978-0-689-84119-4(1) , McElderry, Margaret K.) Simon & Schuster Children's Publishing.

—Joshua's Song. 2003. (gr. 3-6). lib. bdg. 13.00 (978-0-613-61785-7(1)) Tandem Library Bks.

Kehret, Peg & Beckoff, Samuel. The Volcano Disaster. 1998. (FRIGHTMARES). 144p. (J). (gr. 4-7). pap. 4.99 (978-0-671-00968-7(0) , Aladdin) Simon & Schuster Children's Publishing.

McCaughrean, Geraldine. Ghosts, Rogues & Highwaymen. l.t. ed. 2006. pap. 16.95 (978-1-4056-6013-6(9)) BBC Audio GBR. *Dist:* BBC Audiobooks America.

Nilsson, Per. Seventeen. Chace, Tara, tr. 2007. 264p. (YA). (gr. 7 up). 17.95 ***(978-1-932425-89-5(6))*** Boyds Mills Pr.

Random House Disney Staff. Chicken Little. 2006. (Disney Read-Aloud Board Books). (Illus.). 24p. (J). (gr. k-k). bds. 4.99 (978-0-7364-2290-1(0) , RH/Disney) Random Hse. Children's Bks.

Seuling, Barbara. Robert & the Happy Endings. Brewer, Paul, illus. 2007. (Robert Bks.). 160p. (J). (gr. 2-4). 16.95 (978-0-8126-2748-0(2)) Cricket Bks.

DISCIPLINE OF CHILDREN

see Child Rearing

DISCOVERERS

see Discoveries in Geography; Explorers

DISCOVERIES IN GEOGRAPHY

see also America—Discovery and Exploration; Antarctica; Arctic Regions; Explorers; Northwest Passage; Scientific Expeditions; Voyages and Travels

also names of countries with the subdivision description and travel, e.g. United States—Description and Travel

Adams, Simon. Exploration & Discovery: The Amazing Journeys of the People Who Travelled Our World. 2003. (History Detectives Ser.). (Illus.). 64p. (gr. 3-7). pap. 7.99 (978-1-84215-781-7(7) , Southwater) Anness Publishing GBR. *Dist:* National Bk. Network.

Age of Exploration DBA. 2003. spiral bd. 16.95 (978-1-56004-169-6(2)) Social Studies Schl. Service.

Alphin, Elaine Marie. Around the World in 1500. 2001. (Around the World Ser.: Vol. 1). (Illus.). 96p. (J). lib. bdg. 29.93 (978-0-7614-1082-9(1) , Benchmark Bks.) Cavendish, Marshall Corp.

Aronson, Marc, et al. The World Made New: Why the Age of Exploration Happened & How It Changed the World. 2007. (National Geographic Timelines Ser.). (Illus.). 64p. (J). (gr. 4-6). 17.95 (978-0-7922-6454-5(1)); lib. bdg. 27.90 (978-0-7922-6978-6(0)) National Geographic Society. (National Geographic Children's Bks.).

Bergin, Mark. You Wouldn't Want to Travel with Captain Cook! A Voyage You'd Rather Not Make. Antram, David, illus. 2006. (You Wouldn't Want To Ser.). 32p. (J). (gr. 2-5). 28.50 (978-0-531-12421-5(5) , Watts, Franklin) Scholastic Library Publishing.

Bowman, John S. Exploration in the World of the Ancients, 10 vols. 2004. (Discovery & Exploration Ser.). (Illus.). 160p. (YA). (gr. 6-12). 40.00 (978-0-8160-5257-8(3)) Facts On File, Inc.

Bowman, John S. & Isserman, Maurice, eds. Discovery & Exploration, 5 Vols., Set. 2004. (Discovery & Exploration Ser.). 160-192p. (gr. 9-12). 200.00 (978-0-8160-5938-6(1)) Facts On File, Inc.

—Discovery & Exploration Set. 2005. (Discovery & Exploration Ser.). 160-224p. (gr. 6-12). 400.00 (978-0-8160-5255-4(7)) Facts On File, Inc.

Bridgman, Roger Francis. 1,000 Inventions & Discoveries. 2006. (Illus.). 256p. (J). ***(978-1-4156-4955-8(3))*** Dorling Kindersley Publishing, Inc.

Brooks, Philip. Exploration & Discovery. 2002. (Questions & Answers about... Ser.). (Illus.). 40p. (J). (gr. 4-8). pap. 7.95 (978-0-7534-5492-3(0) , Kingfisher) Houghton Mifflin Co. Trade & Reference Div.

Calvert, Patricia. Vasco Da Gama: So Strong a Spirit. 2003. (Great Explorations Ser.). (Illus.). 96p. (J). 29.93 (978-0-7614-1611-1(0) , Benchmark Bks.) Cavendish, Marshall Corp.

Cannarella, Deborah & Fournier, Jane. Exploration. 1999. (Into the Next Millennium Ser.). (Illus.). 32p. (J). (gr. 4-8). lib. bdg. 27.93 (978-1-57103-273-7(8)) Rourke Publishing, LLC.

Clements, Gillian. The Picture History of Great Explorers. 2005. (Illus.). 96p. (J). (gr. 3-17). 19.95 (978-1-84507-075-5(5)) Lincoln, Frances Ltd. GBR. *Dist:* Perseus Distribution.

Currie, Stephen. Travels to Distant Lands: 1000-1400. 2004. (Reading Expeditions Ser.). (Illus.). 32p. (J). (978-0-7922-4542-1(3)) National Geographic Society.

Dalgleish, Sharon & Turner, Garda. People & the Sea. 2003. (Ocean Facts Ser.). (Illus.). 24p. (gr. 2-4). 23.00 (978-0-7910-7287-5(8) , Chelsea Hse.) Facts On File, Inc.

Davis, Kenneth C. Don't Know Much about Planet Earth. 2001. (gr. 3-6). lib. bdg. 15.25 (978-0-613-36148-4(2)) Tandem Library Bks.

Doak, Robin S. Da Gama: Vasco Da Gama Sails Around the Cape of Good Hope. 2001. (Exploring the World Ser.). (Illus.). 48p. (J). (gr. 4 up). lib. bdg. 22.60 (978-0-7565-0124-2(5)) Compass Point Bks.

Douglas, Vincent & School Specialty Publishing Staff. Renaissance & Discovery. 2001. (History of the World Ser.). (Illus.). 48p. (J). (gr. 3 up). 18.95 (978-1-57768-953-9(4) , Bedrick, Peter Bks.) School Specialty Publishing.

Exploration, 4 Bks. 2004. 96.00 (978-0-531-12399-7(5) , Watts, Franklin) Scholastic Library Publishing.

Exploration & Discovery. (J). tchr. ed. 41.95 (978-0-382-40667-6(2)) Cobblestone Publishing Co.

Exploration & Discovery, 15 vols., Set. 2002. (Illus.). 64p. (YA). (gr. 5 up). lib. bdg. (978-1-59084-042-9(9)) Mason Crest Pubs.

Exploration & Discovery. 2004. (Sticker Timelines Ser.). (Illus.). 12p. (J). pap. (978-1-84229-845-9(3)) Top That! Publishing PLC.

Fritz, Jean. Around the World in a Hundred Years: From Henry the Navigator to Magellan. Venti, Anthony B., illus. 1998. 128p. (J). (gr. 2-6). pap. 8.99 (978-0-698-11638-2(0) , Putnam Juvenile) Penguin Group (USA) Inc.

Gallagher, Jim. Vasco da Gama & the Portuguese Explorers. 1999. (Explorers of the New World Ser.). (Illus.). 63p. (J). (gr. 4 up). 31.00 (978-0-7910-5514-4(0) , Chelsea Hse.) Facts On File, Inc.

Goodman, Joan Elizabeth. A Long & Uncertain Journey: The 27,000 Mile Voyage of Vasco Da Gama. McNeely, Tom, illus. 2001. (Great Explorers Ser.). 48p. (ps-12). 22.95 (978-0-9650493-7-5(X)) Mikaya Pr.

Gough, Barry M., ed. Geographers & Explorers. 2001. (Scribner Science Reference Ser.: Vol. 4). (Illus.). 225p. (J). 115.00 (978-0-684-80662-4(2) , GML00502-173594, Charles Scribner's Sons) Thomson Gale.

Grant, Kevin Patrick. Exploration in the Age of Empire, 1750-1953, 10 vols. 2004. (Discovery & Exploration Ser.). (Illus.). 176p. (J). (gr. 6-12). 40.00 (978-0-8160-5260-8(3)) Facts On File, Inc.

Great Explorations Group 4, 6 bks., Set. Incl. Christopher Columbus : To the New World. Collier, James Lincoln. (J). 2006. lib. bdg. 32.79 (978-0-7614-2221-1(8)); David Livingstone : Deep in the Heart of Africa. Otfinoski, Steven. (YA). (gr. 5-9). 2006. lib. bdg. 32.79 (978-0-7614-2226-6(9)); Edmund Hillary : First to the Top. Elish, Dan. (YA). (gr. 5-9). 2007. lib. bdg. 32.79 ***(978-0-7614-2224-2(2));*** Henry Hudson : In Search of the Northwest Passage. Otfinoski, Steven. (J). 2007. lib. bdg. 32.79 ***(978-0-7614-2225-9(0));*** Kit Carson : He Led the Way. Calvert, Patricia. (J). 2006. lib. bdg. 32.79 (978-0-7614-2223-5(4)); Richard Francis Burton : Explorer, Scholar, Spy. Young, Serenity. (YA). (gr. 5-9). 2007. lib. bdg. 32.79 ***(978-0-7614-2222-8(6));*** (Illus.). 80p. 2007. Set lib. bdg. 196.71 ***(978-0-7614-2219-8(6)*** , Benchmark Bks.) Cavendish, Marshall Corp.

Greenwood, Rosie. I Wonder Why Columbus Crossed the Ocean: And Other Questions about Explorers. 2005. (I Wonder Why Ser.). (Illus.). 32p. (J). (gr. k-3). 11.95 (978-0-7534-5860-0(8) , Kingfisher) Houghton Mifflin Co. Trade & Reference Div.

Harcourt School Publishers Staff. Grand Explorations: Intervention Reader & Practice Book. 2001. (Collections Ser.). (Illus.). (gr. 6). pap. 6.00 (978-0-15-324949-5(8)) Harcourt Schl. Pubs.

Harmon, Daniel E. Explorers of the South Pacific. 2002. (Exploration & Discovery Ser.). (Illus.). 64p. (YA). (gr. 5 up). lib. bdg. (978-1-59084-057-3(7)) Mason Crest Pubs.

Harris, Laurie Lanzen, ed. Biography for Beginners: World Explorers. 2003. (Illus.). xxi, 598p. (J). (gr. 3-6). 55.00 (978-1-931360-20-3(0)) Favorable Impressions.

Harris, Nicholas. Cultures of the Past. 2006. 32p. (gr. 2-4). 23.70 (978-1-4103-0344-8(6) , Blackbirch Pr., Inc.) Thomson Gale.

Haskins, Jim. Against All Opposition: Black Explorers in America. 2003. (gr. 5-8). lib. bdg. 17.60 (978-0-613-91054-5(0)) Tandem Library Bks.

Heckschler, Melissa & Shulman, Mark. The Explorer's Gazette: Amazing Stories of 30 Real-Life Journeys. 2004. (Illus.). (J). pap. (978-0-439-67653-3(3)) Scholastic, Inc.

High-Low Reading: Explorers & Exploration, 11 bks., Set. Incl. Travels of Ferdinand Magellan. Mattern, Joanne. 2000. lib. bdg. 22.83 (978-0-7398-1484-0(2)); Travels of Francisco de Coronado. Crisfield, Deborah. 1999. lib. bdg. 22.83 (978-0-7398-1493-2(1)); Travels of Francisco Pizarro. Bergen, Lara Rice. 2000. lib. bdg. 22.83 (978-0-7398-1487-1(7)); Travels of Hernan Cortes. Crisfield, Deborah. 2000. lib. bdg. 22.83 (978-0-7398-1488-8(5)); Travels of John & Sebastian Cabot. Mattern, Joanne. 1999. lib. bdg. 22.83 (978-0-7398-1492-5(3)); Travels of Juan Ponce de Leon. Crisfield, Deborah. 1999. lib. bdg. 22.83 (978-0-7398-1491-8(5)); Travels of Lewis & Clark. Bergen, Lara Rice. 2000. lib. bdg. 22.83 (978-0-7398-1486-4(9)); Travels of Marco Polo. Bandon, Alex & O'Brien, Patrick. 1999. lib. bdg. 22.83 (978-0-7398-1485-7(0)); Travels of Samuel de Champlain. Mattern, Joanne. 1999. lib. bdg. 22.83 (978-0-7398-1494-9(X)); Travels of Sieur de la Salle. Bergen, Lara Rice. 1999. lib. bdg. 22.83 (978-0-7398-1495-6(8)); Travels of Vasco da Gama. Mattern, Joanne. 1999. lib. bdg. 22.83 (978-0-7398-1490-1(7)); 48p. (J). (gr. 4-7). (Illus.). 1999. Set lib. bdg. 273.96 (978-0-7398-1496-3(6)) Raintree.

Koestler-Grack, Rachel A. Vasco Da Gama: And the Sea Route to India. Goetzmann, William H., ed. 2005. (Explorers of New Lands Ser.). (Illus.). 146p. (J). (ps-8). lib. bdg. 30.00 (978-0-7910-8611-7(9) , Chelsea Hse.) Facts On File, Inc.

Larkin, Tanya. Vasco da Gama. 2001. (Famous Explorers Ser.). (Illus.). 24p. (J). (gr. 3). lib. bdg. 18.75 (978-0-8239-5555-8(9) , PowerKids Pr.) Rosen Publishing Group, Inc., The.

The Library of Explorers & Exploration: Sets 1 & 2, 12 bks. 2002. (Illus.). (YA). (gr. 5-8). lib. bdg. 273.00 (978-0-8239-4073-8(X) , Rosen Central) Rosen Publishing Group, Inc., The.

Lorenz Books Staff & Adams, Simon. Exploration & Discovery: Charts Extraordinary Journeys into the Unknown, 4 vols. 2000. (Exploring History Ser.). (Illus.). 64p. (gr. 3-7). 12.95 (978-0-7548-0443-7(7)) Anness Publishing GBR. *Dist:* National Bk. Network.

Marzollo, Jean. En 1492. 2002. (SPA., Illus.). 32p. (J). (ps-3). pap. 4.99 (978-0-590-49442-7(2) , SO5713, Scholastic en Espanol) Scholastic, Inc.

Mattern, Joanne. The Travels of Vasco da Gama. 1999. (Explorers & Exploration Ser.). (Illus.). 48p. (J). (gr. 4-7). lib. bdg. 22.83 (978-0-7398-1490-1(7)) Raintree.

McFarren, Kathleen. Vasco Da Gama. 2004. (Fact Finders Ser.). (Illus.). 32p. (J). 16.95 (978-0-7368-2491-0(X)) Capstone Pr., Inc.

National Geographic Society Staff. Cultural & Geographical Exploration: Chronicles from National Geographic, 8 bks. 1998. (gr. 5-12). 19.95 (978-0-7910-5096-5(3) , Chelsea Hse.) Facts On File, Inc.

Neufeld, David. Great Explorations. Koerber, Nora, illus. 2002. 16p. (J). pap. (978-0-439-35178-2(2)) Scholastic, Inc.

Parks, Peggy J. Exploration. 2005. (Yesterday & Today Ser.). (Illus.). 32p. (J). (ps-7). lib. bdg. 23.70 (978-1-56711-831-5(3) , Blackbirch Pr., Inc.) Thomson Gale.

Petrie, Kristin. Vasco Da Gama. 2004. (Explorers Ser.). (Illus.). 32p. (J). (gr. k-6). lib. bdg. 22.78 (978-1-59197-603-5(0) , Checkerboard Library) ABDO Publishing Co.

Place, Francois. A Voyage of Discovery Vol. 1: From the Land of the Amazons to the Indigo Isles. 2001. (Illus.). 144p. (YA). (gr. 3 up). 22.99 (978-1-86205-213-0(1) , Pavilion Bks., Ltd.) Anova Bks. GBR. *Dist:* Trafalgar Square Publishing.

Puckett, Katie, ed. My World of Discovery. Suter, Gina, illus. 2005. 192p. (J). (gr. k-3). 14.95 (978-0-7534-5931-7(0) , Kingfisher) Houghton Mifflin Co. Trade & Reference Div.

Raum, Elizabeth. Explorers. 2007. (J). (***978-1-4109-2963-1(9)***); pap. (***978-1-4109-2984-6(1)***) Steck-Vaughn.

Rutsala, David. The Sea Route to Asia. 2002. (Exploration & Discovery Ser.). (Illus.). 64p. (YA). (gr. 5 up). lib. bdg. (978-1-59084-046-7(1)) Mason Crest Pubs.

St. George, Judith. So You Want to Be an Explorer? Small, David, illus. 2005. 56p. (J). (gr. 3-6). 16.99 (978-0-399-23868-0(9) , Philomel) Penguin Group (USA) Inc.

Stefoff, Rebecca. Exploration. 2004. (J). 27.07 (978-0-7614-1640-1(4) , Benchmark Bks.) Cavendish, Marshall Corp.

Streissguth, Thomas. Lewis & Clark: Explorers of the Northwest. 1998. (Historical American Biographies Ser.). (Illus.). 128p. (YA). (gr. 6-12). lib. bdg. 26.60 (978-0-7660-1016-1(3)) Enslow Pubs., Inc.

Time Traveler. (Guided Discovery Activity Workbooks Ser.). (Illus.). 32p. (J). (gr. 3-7). pap. 4.95 (978-0-88110-181-2(8)) EDC Publishing.

Wilkinson, Paul & Wilkinson, Philip. Explorers. 2002. (Best Ever Ser.). (Illus.). 64p. (J). (gr. 5-9). tchr. ed. 16.95 (978-0-7534-5452-7(1) , Kingfisher) Houghton Mifflin Co. Trade & Reference Div.

Wilkinson, Philip. Civilizations, Exploration & Conquest: The Illustrated History Encyclopedia. 2001. (gr. 3-6). lib. bdg. 30.35 (978-0-613-82097-4(5)) Tandem Library Bks.

—The World of Exploration. 2006. (World Of Ser.). (Illus.). 64p. (J). (gr. 4-6). pap. 8.95 (978-0-7534-6007-8(6) , Kingfisher) Houghton Mifflin Co. Trade & Reference Div.

Young, Ian. Amazing Journeys: Following in History's Footsteps. 2003. (High Five Reading Ser.). (Illus.). (J). 64p. lib. bdg. 22.60 (978-0-7368-2790-4(0)); 48p. pap. 23.93 (978-0-7368-2831-4(1)) Capstone Pr., Inc.

DISCOVERIES IN GEOGRAPHY—FICTION

Brown, Carl & Brown, Kay. The Little Star. 2006. 123p. pap. (***978-1-4120-9079-7(2)***) Trafford Publishing.

Hoffman, Alice. Aquamarine. 2001. (gr. 5-8). lib. bdg. 13.00 (978-0-613-49420-5(2)) Tandem Library Bks.

Lancaster, Susan. Hell's Gate. 2004. 200p. pap. 12.95 (978-0-9730350-2-5(1)) Snosrap Publishing CAN. *Dist:* Hushion Hse. Publishing, Ltd.

—Hell's Gate. 2003. (gr. 7-12). lib. bdg. 22.20 (978-0-613-86097-0(7)) Tandem Library Bks.

Rocca, Al. Explorer Courage: The First Voyage of Christopher Columbus. l.t. ed. 2006. (Illus.). 72p. (J). pcr. 4.95 (***978-0-9643378-1-7(9)***) Renown Publishing Co.

DISCOVERIES IN SCIENCE

Ben Franklin's Big Shock. 2007. (J). pap. 5.95 (***978-0-8225-6450-8(5)*** , First Avenue Editions) Lerner Publishing Group.

Berger, Melvin & Berger, Gilda. Did It Take Creativity to Find Relativity, Albert Einstein? 2007. (Scholastic Science Supergiants Ser.). 48p. (J). pap. 4.99 (978-0-439-83384-4(1) , Scholastic Nonfiction) Scholastic, Inc.

Beshore, George W. Science in Ancient China. 1998. (Science of the Past Ser.). (Illus.). 64p. (J). (gr. 5-7). pap. 8.95 (978-0-531-15914-9(0) , Watts, Franklin) Scholastic Library Publishing.

—Science in Ancient China. 1998. (gr. 3-6). lib. bdg. 17.60 (978-0-613-72684-9(7)) Tandem Library Bks.

Bridgman, Roger. 1,000 Inventions & Discoveries. 2006. (Illus.). 256p. (J). pap. 14.99 (978-0-7566-1705-9(7)) Dorling Kindersley Publishing, Inc.

Bridgman, Roger Francis. 1,000 Inventions & Discoveries. 2006. (Illus.). 256p. (J). (***978-1-4156-4955-8(3)***) Dorling Kindersley Publishing, Inc.

Casanellas, Antonio. Great Discoveries & Inventions, 5 bks. Garousi, Ali, illus. Incl. Great Discoveries & Inventions That Advanced Industry & Technology. lib. bdg. 24.67 (978-0-8368-2583-1(7)); Great Discoveries & Inventions That Helped Explore Earth & Space. lib. bdg. 24.67 (978-0-8368-2584-8(5)); Great Discoveries & Inventions That Improved Human Health. lib. bdg. 24.67 (978-0-8368-2585-5(3)); Great Discoveries & Inventions That Improved Our Daily Lives. lib. bdg. 24.67 (978-0-8368-2586-2(1)); Great Discoveries & Inventions That Improved Transportation. lib. bdg. 24.67 (978-0-8368-2587-9(X)); 32p. (J). (gr. 4 up). (Illus.). 2000. Set lib. bdg. 123.35 (978-0-8368-2582-4(9)) Stevens, Gareth Inc.

Douglas, Vincent & School Specialty Publishing Staff. Inventions & Discoveries. 2006. (Just the Facts Ser.). (Illus.). 64p. (J). (gr. 5-8). pap. 9.95 (978-0-7696-4256-7(X)) School Specialty Publishing.

Henderson & Yount. Milestones in Discovery & Invention, 4 Vols., Set. 2006. 176p. (gr. 6-12). 140.00 (978-0-8160-7014-5(8)) Facts On File, Inc.

Inventions & Discoveries. (Action Bks.). 64p. (J). (gr. 3-7). pap. (978-1-882210-68-8(9)) Action Publishing, Inc.

Jones, Charlotte Foltz. Accidents May Happen. 1998. (Illus.). 96p. (J). (gr. 3-7). reprint ed. pap. 11.95 (978-0-385-32240-9(2) , Delacorte Bks. for Young Readers) Random Hse. Children's Bks.

—Accidents May Happen: 50 Inventions Discovered by Mistake. 1998. (J). 18.60 (978-0-606-13109-4(4)) Tandem Library Bks.

Kozar, Richard. Inventors & Their Discoveries. 1999. (Costume, Tradition & Culture). (Illus.). 64p. (YA). (gr. 5 up). 28.00 (978-0-7910-5163-4(3) , Chelsea Hse.) Facts On File, Inc.

Llewellyn, Claire. Great Discoveries & Amazing Adventures: The Stories of Hidden Marvels & Lost Treasures. 2004. (Illus.). 80p. (J). (gr. 4-6). 18.95 (978-0-7534-5783-2(0) , Kingfisher) Houghton Mifflin Co. Trade & Reference Div.

Mercury Books, creator. Early Discoveries. (Crafty Inventions Ser.). (Illus.). 48p. (J). (ps-9). 12.95 (978-1-904668-70-1(4)) Mercury Bks. Ltd. GBR. *Dist:* International Publishers Marketing.

Pobst, Sandy. Scientific Discovery in the Renaissance. 2006. (Navigators Ser.). (J). pap. 44.00 (***978-1-4108-6267-9(4)***) Benchmark Education Co.

Ross, Frank. Oracle Bones, Stars, & Wheelbarrows: Ancient Chinese Science & Technology. (gr. 5-8). lib. bdg. 15.25 (978-0-8335-6082-7(4)) Tandem Library Bks.

Science Discoveries. 2005. pap. 131.70 (978-0-7910-9149-4(X) , Chelsea Hse.) Facts On File, Inc.

Shuter, Jane. Discoveries & Inventions. 1999. (Ancient Egypt Ser.). 32p. (J). (gr. 3-5). lib. bdg. 22.79 (978-1-57572-729-5(3)) Heinemann Library.

Snedden, Robert. Scientists & Discoveries. 2000. (Microlife Ser.). 48p. (YA). (gr. 6-8). lib. bdg. 22.79 (978-1-57572-244-3(5)) Heinemann Library.

Voyages Through Scientific Discoveries Gr 6-9. 2002. (YA). (gr. 6-9). pap. 8.94 (978-1-889369-50-1(0)) Teaching Ink, Inc.

DISCOVERIES, MARITIME

see Discoveries in Geography

DISCRIMINATION

Here are entered general works on social discrimination based on race, religion, sex, social minority status, or other factors.

see also Civil Rights; Minorities; Toleration

Cockcroft, James D. Latinos in Beisbol. 2004. (Illus.). 207p. (J). (gr. 4-9). reprint ed. pap. 10.00 (978-0-7567-7347-2(4)) DIANE Publishing Co.

Connolly, Sean. Gender Equality. 2005. (Campaigns for Change Ser.). (Illus.). 48p. (J). (gr. 6-9). lib. bdg. 29.95 (978-1-58340-515-4(1)) Smart Apple Media.

Davidson, Tish. Prejudice. 2003. (Life Balance Ser.). (Illus.). 80p. (J). 20.50 (978-0-531-12252-5(2) , Watts, Franklin) Scholastic Library Publishing.

Friedman, Lauri S. Discrimination. 2007. (Issues that Concern You Ser.). (Illus.). 144p. (gr. 7-10). 33.70 (***978-0-7377-3813-1(8)*** , Greenhaven Pr., Inc.) Thomson Gale.

MacDonald, Fiona. Equal Opportunities. (World Issues Ser.). (Illus.). 57p. (J). lib. bdg. 28.50 (978-1-931983-30-3(5)) Chrysalis Education.

—Equal Opportunities. 2006. (Global Issues Ser.). 64p. (J). (gr. 4-12). pap. 12.95 (978-1-55285-744-1(1) , Walrus Bks.) Whitecap Bks., Ltd. CAN. *Dist:* Firefly Bks., Ltd.

McKissack, Patricia C. & Zarembka, Arlene. To Establish Justice: Citizenship & the Constitution. 2004. (Illus.). 160p. (YA). (gr. 9-11). lib. bdg. 20.99 (978-0-679-99308-7(8) , Knopf Bks. for Young Readers) Random Hse. Children's Bks.

McKissack, Patricia C., et al. To Establish Justice: Citizenship & the Constitution. 2004. (Illus.). 160p. (YA). (gr. 9-11). 18.95 (978-0-679-89308-0(3) , Knopf Bks. for Young Readers) Random Hse. Children's Bks.

Middleton, Don. Dealing with Discrimination. 1999. (Conflict Resolution Library). 24p. (J). lib. bdg. 18.75 (978-0-8239-5270-0(3) , PowerKids Pr.) Rosen Publishing Group, Inc., The.

Senker, Cath. Why Are People Prejudiced? 2002. (Exploring Tough Issues Ser.). 48p. (J). lib. bdg. 25.69 (978-0-7398-4959-0(X)) Raintree.

Stewart, Gail B. Racism. 2002. (Understanding Issues Ser.). (Illus.). 48p. (J). (gr. 3-5). 26.20 (978-0-7377-1025-0(X) , Kidhaven) Thomson Gale.

Williams, Mary E. Capital Punishment. 2000. (Current Controversies Ser.). (Illus.). 320p. (YA). (gr. 7-12). pap. 21.20 (978-0-7377-0140-1(4) , Greenhaven Pr., Inc.) Thomson Gale.

Williams, Mary E., ed. Discrimination. 2002. (Illus.). 200p. (J). 36.20 (978-0-7377-1226-1(0) , Greenhaven Pr., Inc.) Thomson Gale.

DISCRIMINATION—FICTION

Hewitt, William. Across the Wide River. 2004. 104p. (J). 11.95 (978-0-8263-2978-3(0)) Univ. of New Mexico Pr.

Hirsch, Odo. Have Courage, Hazel Green! (J). 2007. (Illus.). 256p. pap. 6.95 (978-1-59990-003-2(3)); 2006. 262p. 15.95 (978-1-58234-659-5(3)) Bloomsbury Publishing. (Bloomsbury Children).

Horowitz, Jeanine. Toady Toad's Move. 2006. (Illus.). 32p. (J). lib. bdg. 17.95 (***978-1-934190-03-6(9)***) Ocean Front Bk. Publishing, Inc.

Maddox, Jake. Snowboard Duel. Tiffany, Sean, illus. 2008. (J). pap. (***978-1-59889-895-8(7)***); lib. bdg. (***978-1-59889-843-9(4)***) Stone Arch Bks.

Myers, Walter Dean. The Glory Field. 1999. 420p. (J). 15.60 (978-0-03-054616-7(8)) Holt, Rinehart & Winston.

Rue, Nancy N. The Stunt. 1999. (Christian Heritage Ser.). 208p. (J). (gr. 3-7). pap. 5.99 (978-1-56179-833-9(9)) Bethany Hse. Pubs.

Tunis, John R. Keystone Kids. 2006. (Illus.). 252p. (J). pap. 5.95 (978-0-15-205634-6(3) , Odyssey Classics) Harcourt Children's Bks.

Winston, Sherri. Kayla Chronicles. 2008. 208p. (YA). (gr. 7-17). 16.99 (***978-0-316-11430-1(8)***) Little, Brown Bks. for Young Readers.

Wood, Frances M. Becoming Rosemary. 1998. (J). (978-0-606-13186-5(8)) Tandem Library Bks.

DISCRIMINATION IN EDUCATION

see also Segregation in Education

Anderson, Sonya, et al, eds. Facing Racism in Education. 3rd ed. 2005. (Harvard Educational Review Ser.: No. 39). (Illus.). 315p. (YA). pap. 29.95 (978-0-916690-42-7(3)) Harvard Educational Review.

Cushman, Clare & Urofsky, Melvin I., eds. Black, White, & Brown: The Landmark School Desegregation Case in Retrospect. 2004. (Illus.). 352p. (gr. 9 up). 45.00 (978-1-56802-911-5(X)) CQ Pr.

Kowalski, Kathiann M. Affirmative Action. 2006. (Open for Debate Ser.). (Illus.). 143p. (J). (gr. 6-9). lib. bdg. 39.93 (978-0-7614-2300-3(1) , Benchmark Bks.) Cavendish, Marshall Corp.

Lucas, Eileen. Prudence Crandall. Smith, Kimanne, illus. 2001. (On My Own Biographies Ser.). 48p. (J). (gr. 1-3). lib. bdg. (978-1-57505-480-3(9) , Carolrhoda Bks.) Lerner Publishing Group.

McNeese, Tim. Regents of the University of California V. Bakke. 2007. (Great Supreme Court Decisions Ser.). (Illus.). 152p. (J). (gr. 5-8). 30.00 (978-0-7910-9260-6(7) , Chelsea Hse.) Facts On File, Inc.

Morrison, Toni. Remember: The Journey to School Integration. 2004. (Illus.). 80p. (J). (gr. k-3). tchr. ed. 18.00 (978-0-618-39740-2(X)) Houghton Mifflin Co. Trade & Reference Div.

Telgen, Diane. Brown V. Board of Education. 2005. (Defining Moments Ser.). (Illus.). 246p. (YA). (gr. 8 up). lib. bdg. 49.00 (978-0-7808-0775-4(8)) Omnigraphics, Inc.

DISCRIMINATION IN EMPLOYMENT

Kowalski, Kathiann M. Affirmative Action. 2006. (Open for Debate Ser.). (Illus.). 143p. (J). (gr. 6-9). lib. bdg. 39.93 (978-0-7614-2300-3(1) , Benchmark Bks.) Cavendish, Marshall Corp.

DISCUSSION

see Debates and Debating

DISEASE (PATHOLOGY)

see Pathology

DISEASE GERMS

see Bacteriology

DISEASES

see also Sick

see also names of diseases and groups of diseases; and subjects with the subdivision Diseases

Aaseng, Nathan. Multiple Sclerosis. 2000. (Single Title - Science Ser.). (Illus.). 112p. (YA). (gr. 8-12). 21.00 (978-0-531-11531-2(3) , Watts, Franklin) Scholastic Library Publishing.

Abramovitz, Melissa. Cystic Fibrosis. 2003. (Diseases & Disorders Ser.). (Illus.). 96p. (J). 32.45 (978-1-59018-299-4(5) , Lucent Bks.) Thomson Gale.

—Multiple Sclerosis. 2002. (Diseases & Disorders Ser.). (Illus.). 120p. (J). (gr. 6-9). 27.45 (978-1-59018-042-6(9) , Lucent Bks.) Thomson Gale.

—Parkinson's Disease. 2004. (Illus.). 109p. (J). (gr. 7-10). 32.45 (978-1-59018-300-7(2) , Lucent Bks.) Thomson Gale.

—West Nile Virus. 2003. (Illus.). 96p. (J). 32.45 (978-1-59018-343-4(6) , Lucent Bks.) Thomson Gale.

Ackermann, Abigail & Ackermann, Adrienne. Our Mom Has Cancer. 2001. (Illus.). 32p. 12.95 (978-0-944235-31-7(X) , 9780944235317) American Cancer Society, Inc.

—Our Mom Has Cancer. 2002. 32p. pap. 8.95 (978-0-944235-16-4(6) , 9780944235164) McGraw-Hill Cos., The.

Alcamo, I. Edward, ed. Deadly Diseases & Epidemics. (Illus.). (gr. 9-13). pap. 47.80 (978-0-7910-8398-7(5)); lib. bdg. 467.10 (978-0-7910-8326-0(8)) Facts On File, Inc. (Chelsea Hse.).

Alcamol, I. Edward, ed. Deadly Diseases & Epidemics. (Illus.). (J). 155.70 (978-0-7910-7301-8(7) , Chelsea Hse.) Facts On File, Inc.

Ali, Rasheda. I'll Hold Your Hand So You Won't Fall: A Child's Guide to Parkinson's Disease. 2005. (Illus.). 40p. (J). pap. 19.95 (978-1-873413-13-5(0)) Merit Publishing International, Inc.

Allman, Toney. Tuberculosis. 2006. 112p. (J). (gr. 7-10). 32.45 (978-1-59018-968-9(X) , Lucent Bks.) Thomson Gale.

Anderson, Judith. Me & My Body. 2007. (J). (***978-1-59771-086-2(5)***) Sea-To-Sea Pubns.

Apel, Melanie Ann. Let's Talk about When You Have to Have Your Appendix Out. 2002. (Let's Talk Library). (Illus.). 24p. (J). lib. bdg. 18.75 (978-0-8239-5865-8(5) , PowerKids Pr.) Rosen Publishing Group, Inc., The.

Apte, Sunita. Michael J. Fox: I Can Make a Difference! 2006. (Defining Moments Ser.). (Illus.). 32p. (J). lib. bdg. 25.27 (978-1-59716-269-2(8)) Bearport Publishing Co., Inc.

Aronson, Virginia. Everything You Need to Know about Hepatitis. 2005. (Need to Know Library). (Illus.). 64p. (YA). (gr. 7-12). lib. bdg. 25.25 (978-0-8239-3100-2(5) , NTHEPA) Rosen Publishing Group, Inc., The.

Baldwin, Carol. Sickle Cell Disease. 2003. (Health Matters Ser.). (Illus.). 32p. (J). (gr. 3-5). lib. bdg. (978-1-4034-0252-3(3)) Heinemann Library.

Balkwill, Fran & Rolph, Mic. Staying Alive: Fighting HIV/AIDS. 2002. (Illus.). 30p. (J). pap. 8.95 (978-0-87969-651-1(6)) Cold Spring Harbor Laboratory Pr.

Bayer, Linda N. Sleep Disorders. 2000. (Encyclopedia of Psychological Disorders Ser.). (Illus.). 88p. (J). (gr. 7 up). 35.00 (978-0-7910-5314-0(8) , Chelsea Hse.) Facts On File, Inc.

Benchmark Education Staff. Fighting Disease. 2005. 2.00 (***978-1-4108-4657-0(1)***) Benchmark Education Co.

Betschart, Jean. A Magic Ride in Foozbah-Land: Custom Edition for Eli Lilly. 2001. (Illus.). 48p. pap. 12.95 (978-0-471-21259-1(8)) Wiley, John & Sons, Inc.

Bjorklund, Ruth. Food Borne Illnesses. 2005. (Health Alert Ser.). (Illus.). 64p. (J). (978-0-7614-1917-4(9) , Benchmark Bks.) Cavendish, Marshall Corp.

Bohland, Mark. Mystery Disease. 2003. pap. 12.95 (978-1-883055-56-1(3)) Dandy Lion Pubns.

—Mystery Disease. 2005. 88p. 12.95 (978-1-59363-110-9(3)) Prufrock Pr.

Brannon, Barbara. Discover Disease. 2005. 39.00 (***978-1-4108-5137-6(0)***) Benchmark Education Co.

Brill, Marlene Targ. Multiple Sclerosis. 2007. (Health Alert Ser.). 64p. (J). lib. bdg. 31.36 (***978-0-7614-2699-8(X)*** , Benchmark Bks.) Cavendish, Marshall Corp.

Bryan, Jenny. Asthma. 2003. (Just the Facts Ser.). (Illus.). 56p. (J). lib. bdg. (978-1-4034-4599-5(0)) Heinemann Library.

Bueche, Shelley. The Ebola Virus. 2003. (Parasites Ser.). (Illus.). 32p. (J). 24.95 (978-0-7377-1780-8(7) , Greenhaven Pr., Inc.) Thomson Gale.

Bunch, Bryan H., ed. Diseases, 8 vols. 2nd rev. ed. 2003. (Illus.). (J). Set. (978-0-7172-5688-4(X)); Vol. 1. (978-0-7172-5689-1(8) , Grolier); Vol. 2. (978-0-7172-5690-7(1) , Grolier); Vol. 3. (978-0-7172-5691-4(X) , Grolier); Vol. 4. (978-0-7172-5692-1(8) , Grolier); Vol. 5. (978-0-7172-5693-8(6) , Grolier); Vol. 6. (978-0-7172-5694-5(4) , Grolier); Vol. 7. (978-0-7172-5695-2(2) , Grolier); Vol. 8. (978-0-7172-5696-9(0) , Grolier) Scholastic Library Publishing.

Bunch, Bryan H. & Tesar, Jenny E. Diseases. 3rd ed. 2006. (J). (978-0-7172-6206-9(5)); (J). (978-0-7172-6207-6(3)); (J). (978-0-7172-6208-3(1)); (J). (978-0-7172-6209-0(X)); (J). (978-0-7172-6210-6(3)); (J). (978-0-7172-6211-3(1)); (J). (978-0-7172-6212-0(X)); (J). (978-0-7172-6213-7(8)); Set. (YA). (gr. 6 up). 309.00 (978-0-7172-6205-2(7)) Scholastic Library Publishing. (Grolier).

Burnett, Betty & Gevertz, Rob. Coping with Multiple Sclerosis. 2005. (Coping Ser.). (Illus.). 192p. (YA). (gr. 7-12). lib. bdg. 26.50 (978-0-8239-3204-7(4)) Rosen Publishing Group, Inc., The.

Burnett, Gail Lemley. Muscular Dystrophy. rev. ed. 2000. (Health Watch Ser.). (Illus.). 48p. (YA). (gr. 4-10). lib. bdg. 23.93 (978-0-7660-1651-4(X)) Enslow Pubs., Inc.

Burnfield, Alexander. Multiple Sclerosis. 2003. (Just the Facts Ser.). (Illus.). 56p. (J). lib. bdg. (978-1-4034-4602-2(4)) Heinemann Library.

Burstein, John. Staying Well. McGinnis, Ben, illus. Pinchbeck, Chris, photos by. 2006. (Slim Goodbody's Good Health Guides Ser.). 32p. (J). (gr. 2-4). lib. bdg. 25.27 (***978-0-8368-7744-1(6)***) Stevens, Gareth Inc.

Butler, Dori Hillestad. My Grandpa Had a Stroke. Wong, Nicole, illus. 2007. 32p. (J). (ps-2). 14.95 (***978-1-59147-806-5(5)***); pap. 8.95 (***978-1-59147-807-2(3)***) American Psychological Assn. (Magination Pr.).

Cohen, Joel H. Tuberculosis. 2002. (Great Medical Discoveries Ser.). (Illus.). 120p. (YA). (gr. 6-9). 29.95 (978-1-56006-931-7(7) , GML12001-178709, Lucent Bks.) Thomson Gale.

Coleman, William L. Cholera. 2003. (Deadly Diseases & Epidemics Ser.). (Illus.). 112p. (gr. 9-13). 31.95 (978-0-7910-7303-2(3) , Chelsea Hse.) Facts On File, Inc.

Day, Nancy. Killer Superbugs: The Story of Drug-Resistant Diseases. 2001. (Issues in Focus Ser.). (Illus.). 128p. (YA). (gr. 6-12). lib. bdg. 26.60 (978-0-7660-1588-3(2)) Enslow Pubs., Inc.

—Malaria, West Nile & Other Mosquito-Borne Diseases. 2001. (Diseases & People Ser.). (Illus.). 128p. (YA). (gr. 6-12). lib. bdg. 26.60 (978-0-7660-1597-5(1)) Enslow Pubs., Inc.

Deadly Diseases & Epidemics. 2005. 958.50 (978-0-7910-9166-1(X) , Chelsea Hse.) Facts On File, Inc.

Decker, Janet I. Anthrax. 2003. (Deadly Diseases & Epidemics Ser.). (Illus.). 112p. (gr. 9-13). 31.95 (978-0-7910-7302-5(5) , Chelsea Hse.) Facts On File, Inc.

Decker, Janet M. Mononucleosis. 2003. (Deadly Diseases & Epidemics Ser.). (Illus.). 112p. (gr. 9-13). 31.95 (978-0-7910-7700-9(4) , Chelsea Hse.) Facts On File, Inc.

Derkins, Susie. Legionnaire's Disease. 2002. (Epidemics Ser.). (Illus.). 64p. (YA). (gr. 7-12). lib. bdg. 26.50 (978-0-8239-3497-3(7)) Rosen Publishing Group, Inc., The.

Doak, Robin. Genetic Disorders. 2006. (Navigators Ser.). (J). pap. 44.00 (***978-1-4108-6239-6(9)***) Benchmark Education Co.

C D

Draper, Allison Stark. Ebola. 2002. (Epidemics Ser.). (Illus.). 64p. (YA). (gr. 7-12). lib. bdg. 26.50 (978-0-8239-3496-6(9)) Rosen Publishing Group, Inc., The.

Emmelu, Donald. Influenza. 2003. (Deadly Diseases & Epidemics Ser.). (Illus.). 112p. (gr. 9-13). 31.95 (978-0-7910-7305-6(X) , Chelsea Hse.) Facts On File, Inc.

Emmeluth, Donald. Typhoid Fever. 2003. (Deadly Diseases & Epidemics Ser.). (Illus.). 112p. (gr. 9-13). 31.95 (978-0-7910-7464-0(1) , Chelsea Hse.) Facts On File, Inc.

Epidemic! Series, 5 Bks, Set. 2004. (J). 149.64 (978-0-7614-1632-6(3)) Cavendish, Marshall Corp.

Epidemics: Deadly Diseases Throughout History, 6 bks. 2005. (YA). (gr. 7-12). Set 4. lib. bdg. 159.00 (978-1-4042-0375-4(3)); Sets 1-4. lib. bdg. 598.50 (978-1-4042-0502-4(0)) Rosen Publishing Group, Inc., The.

Epidemics: Deadly Diseases Throughout History, 8 vols. Incl. AIDS. Cefrey, Holly. (YA). lib. bdg. 26.50 (978-0-8239-3344-0(X)); Cholera. Hayhurst, Chris. (YA). lib. bdg. 26.50 (978-0-8239-3345-7(8)); Influenza. Ramen, Fred. (YA). lib. bdg. 26.50 (978-0-8239-3347-1(4)); Malaria. Isle, Mick. (J). lib. bdg. 26.50 (978-0-8239-3342-6(3)); Plague. Cefrey, Holly. (YA). lib. bdg. 26.50 (978-0-8239-3343-3(1)); Polio. Draper, Allison Stark. (YA). lib. bdg. 26.50 (978-0-8239-3348-8(2)); Smallpox. Ridgway, Tom. (YA). lib. bdg. 26.50 (978-0-8239-3346-4(6)); Tuberculosis. Ramen, Fred. (J). lib. bdg. 26.50 (978-0-8239-3349-5(0)); 64p. (gr. 4-6). 2001. (Illus.). 2000. Set lib. bdg. 212.00 (978-0-8239-9202-7(0)) Rosen Publishing Group, Inc., The.

C D

Finer, Kim. Tuberculosis. 2003. (Deadly Diseases & Epidemics Ser.). (Illus.). 112p. (gr. 9-13). 31.95 (978-0-7910-7309-4(2) , Chelsea Hse.) Facts On File, Inc.

Forrest, Stuart. Genital Herpes. 2006. (Library of Sexual Health). (Illus.). 64p. (J). (978-1-4042-0907-7(7)) Rosen Publishing Group, Inc., The.

Frender, Sam & Schiffmiller, Robin. Brotherly Feelings: Me, My Emotions, & My Brother with Asperger's Syndrome. Dittrich, Dennis, illus. 2007. 64p. (J). pap. (***978-1-84310-850-4(X)***) Kingsley, Jessica Ltd.

Friedlander, Mark P., Jr. Outbreak: Disease Detectives at Work. 2000. (Discovery! Ser.). (Illus.). 120p. (YA). (gr. 7-12). 25.26 (978-0-8225-2860-9(6) , Lerner Pubns.) Lerner Publishing Group.

Friedlander, Mark P. Outbreak: Disease Detectives at Work. 2nd enl. rev. ed. 2005. (Discovery! Ser.). (Illus.). 120p. (gr. 5-12). 27.93 (978-0-8225-0948-6(2)) Lerner Publishing Group.

Gareth Stevens Publishing Staff, contrib. by. Viruses. 2003. (Discovery Channel School Science Ser.). (Illus.). 32p. (J). (gr. 5 up). lib. bdg. 24.67 (978-0-8368-3375-1(9)) Stevens, Gareth Inc.

Gay, Kathlyn & McGarrahan, Sean. Epilepsy: The Ultimate Teen Guide. 2002. (It Happened to Me Ser.). (Illus.). 112p. 37.50 (978-0-8108-4339-4(0)) Scarecrow Pr., Inc.

Gelone, Steven, et al. Pelvic Inflammatory Disease. 2007. (Deadly Diseases & Epidemics Ser.). (Illus.). 88p. (J). (gr. 9-12). 31.95 (978-0-7910-8507-3(4) , Chelsea Hse.) Facts On File, Inc.

Getz, David. Purple Death: The Mysterious Flu of 1918. McCarty, Peter, illus. rev. ed. 2000. 96p. (J). (gr. 3-6). 17.95 (978-0-8050-5751-5(X) , Holt, Henry & Co. Bks. For Young Readers) Holt, Henry & Co.

Giddens, Sandra. Suicide. 2006. (Coping in a Changing World Ser.). 112p. (YA). (gr. 7-12). lib. bdg. 31.95 (978-1-4042-0952-7(2)) Rosen Publishing Group, Inc., The.

Giddens, Sandra & Giddens, Owen. Everything You Need to Know about Crohn's Disease & Colitis. 2005. (Need to Know Library). (Illus.). 64p. (YA). lib. bdg. 25.25 (978-0-8239-3996-1(0)) Rosen Publishing Group, Inc., The.

Gillie, Oliver. Cancer. 2004. (Just the Facts Ser.). (J). lib. bdg. 27.07 (978-1-4034-5144-6(3)) Heinemann Library.

—Sickle Cell Disease. 2003. (Just the Facts Ser.). (Illus.). 56p. (J). lib. bdg. (978-1-4034-4603-9(2)) Heinemann Library.

Glaser, Jason. Colds. 2005. (First Facts Ser.). (Illus.). 24p. (J). (ps-7). lib. bdg. 21.26 (978-0-7368-4289-1(6)) Capstone Pr., Inc.

—Flu. 2005. (First Facts Ser.). (Illus.). 24p. (J). (gr. 1-3). lib. bdg. 21.26 (978-0-7368-4290-7(X) , 1243925) Capstone Pr., Inc.

—Pinkeye. 2005. (First Facts Ser.). (Illus.). 24p. (J). (gr. 1-3). lib. bdg. 21.26 (978-0-7368-4292-1(6)) Capstone Pr., Inc.

—Strep Throat. 2007. (First Facts Ser.). (J). 21.26 (978-0-7368-6393-3(1)) Capstone Pr., Inc.

Gold, Susan Dudley. Cystic Fibrosis. 2000. (Health Watch Ser.). (Illus.). 48p. (YA). (gr. 4-10). lib. bdg. 23.93 (978-0-7660-1655-2(2)) Enslow Pubs., Inc.

—Multiple Sclerosis. rev. ed. 2001. (Health Watch Ser.). (Illus.). 48p. (YA). (gr. 4-10). lib. bdg. 23.93 (978-0-7660-1658-3(7)) Enslow Pubs., Inc.

Goldsmith, Connie. Meningitis. 2007. (J). lib. bdg. (***978-0-8225-7034-9(3)***) Twenty First Century Bks.

Goldstein, Margaret J. Everything You Need to Know about Multiple Sclerosis. 2005. (Need to Know Library). (Illus.). 64p. (YA). (gr. 7-12). 25.25 (978-0-8239-3292-4(3) , NTMUSC) Rosen Publishing Group, Inc., The.

Gordon, Melanie Apel. Let's Talk about Epilepsy. 2000. (Let's Talk Library). (Illus.). 24p. (J). (gr. 3). lib. bdg. 18.75 (978-0-8239-5414-8(5) , PowerKids Pr.) Rosen Publishing Group, Inc., The.

—Let's Talk about Sickle Cell Anemia. 2000. (Let's Talk Library). (Illus.). 24p. (J). (gr. 3). lib. bdg. 18.75 (978-0-8239-5417-9(X) , PowerKids Pr.) Rosen Publishing Group, Inc., The.

Gordon, Sharon. Asthma. 2003. (Rookie Read-About Health Ser.). (Illus.). 32p. (J). (-2). 20.50 (978-0-516-22582-1(0) , Children's Pr.) Scholastic Library Publishing.

—Pinkeye. 2003. (Rookie Read-About Health Ser.). (Illus.). 32p. (J). (-2). 20.50 (978-0-516-22583-8(9) , Children's Pr.) Scholastic Library Publishing.

Gosselin, Kim. Patrick Learns about Parkinson's Disease: A Story of a Special Bond Between Friends. Dineen, Tom, illus. 2002. (Special Family & Friends Ser.: Vol. 2). 32p. (J). pap. 14.95 (978-1-891383-18-2(3)) JayJo Bks., LLC.

Goulding, Sylvia. Illness & Injury. 2005. (Healthy Kids Ser.). (Illus.). 32p. (gr. 3-6). 19.95 (978-1-59515-206-0(7)) Rourke Publishing, LLC.

Gregson, Susan R. High Blood Pressure. 2001. (Perspectives on Disease & Illness Ser.). (Illus.). 64p. (J). (gr. 4-6). lib. bdg. 23.93 (978-0-7368-0750-0(0) , LifeMatters Bks.) Capstone Pr., Inc.

Harris, Jacqueline L. Sickle Cell Disease. 2001. (Medical Library: up). (Illus.). 96p. (gr. 7 up). lib. bdg. 26.90 (978-0-7613-1459-2(8) , Twenty-First Century Bks.) Lerner Publishing Group.

Hawkins, Trisha. Everything You Need to Know about Measles & Rubella. 2005. (Need to Know Library). (Illus.). 64p. (YA). (gr. 7-12). 25.25 (978-0-8239-3322-8(9)) Rosen Publishing Group, Inc., The.

Hayhurst, Chris. Cholera. 2001. (Epidemics Ser.). (Illus.). 64p. (YA). (gr. 4-6). lib. bdg. 26.50 (978-0-8239-3345-7(8)) Rosen Publishing Group, Inc., The.

—Everything You Need to Know about Hepatitis C. 2005. (Need to Know Library). (Illus.). 64p. (YA). (gr. 4-6). lib. bdg. 25.25 (978-0-8239-3613-7(9)) Rosen Publishing Group, Inc., The.

Health Alert Series, 6 Bks, Set. 2004. (J). 171.00 (978-0-7614-1797-2(4)) Cavendish, Marshall Corp.

Herbst, Judith. Germ Theory. 2005. (Great Ideas of Science Ser.). (J). lib. bdg. (978-0-8225-2909-5(2)) Twenty First Century Bks.

Hicks, Terry Allan. The Common Cold. 2005. (Health Alert Ser.). (Illus.). 64p. (J). (978-0-7614-1913-6(6) , Benchmark Bks.) Cavendish, Marshall Corp.

Hill, Eric M. Deliverance from Demons & Diseases: Freedom from Incurable Diseases & Persistent Problems, 2004. 256p. per. 12.99 net. (978-0-9673189-1-2(2)) SunHill Pubs.

Hirschmann, Kris. Salmonella. 2003. (Parasites Ser.). (Illus.). 32p. (J). 24.95 (978-0-7377-1785-3(8) , Greenhaven Pr., Inc.) Thomson Gale.

Hoff, Brent H. Mapping Epidemics: A Historical Atlas of Disease. 2000. (gr. 7-12). lib. bdg. 30.35 (978-0-613-72661-0(8)) Tandem Library Bks.

Hoffmann, Gretchen. Mononucleosis. 2005. (Health Alert Ser.). (Illus.). 64p. (J). (978-0-7614-1915-0(2) , Benchmark Bks.) Cavendish, Marshall Corp.

Hoffmann, Gretchen. Osteoporosis. 2007. (Health Alert Ser.). 64p. (J). lib. bdg. 31.36 (***978-0-7614-2702-5(3)*** , Benchmark Bks.) Cavendish, Marshall Corp.

Holt, Rinehart and Winston Staff. Decisions for Health Blue, Chptr. 18: Noninfectious Diseases. 4th ed. 2004. pap. 11.20 (978-0-03-068053-3(0)) Holt, Rinehart & Winston.

—Decisions for Health Red Chptr. 15: Noninfectious Diseases. 4th ed. 2004. pap. 11.20 (978-0-03-068042-7(5)) Holt, Rinehart & Winston.

—A Lifetime of Health Chptr. 13: Prevention of Diseases. 4th ed. Date not set. pap. 11.20 (978-0-03-068106-6(5)) Holt, Rinehart & Winston.

—A Lifetime of Health Chptr. 14: Lifestyle Diseases. 4th ed. Date not set. pap. 11.20 (978-0-03-068107-3(3)) Holt, Rinehart & Winston.

—A Lifetime of Health Chptr. 15: Other Diseases. 4th ed. Date not set. pap. 11.20 (978-0-03-068108-0(1)) Holt, Rinehart & Winston.

Huebner, Dawn. What to Do When Your Brain Gets Stuck: A Kid's Guide to Overcoming OCD. Matthews, Bonnie, illus. 2007. 95p. (J). (***978-1-59147-805-8(7)*** , Magination Pr.) American Psychological Assn.

Izenberg, Neil, ed. Human Diseases & Conditions, 3 vols., Set. 1999. (Illus.). 912p. (J). 355.00 (978-0-684-80543-6(X) , GML00502-167276, Charles Scribner's Sons) Thomson Gale.

—Human Diseases & Disorders, 3 vols. 1999. (Illus.). (J). Vol. 1. 125.00 (978-0-684-80541-2(3)); Vol. 2. vii, 311p. 125.00 (978-0-684-80542-9(1)) Simon & Schuster.

Jacobs, Marian B. Coping with Hereditary Diseases. 1999. (Coping Ser.). (Illus.). 152p. (YA). (gr. 7-12). lib. bdg. 26.50 (978-0-8239-2823-1(3) , COHEDI) Rosen Publishing Group, Inc., The.

Jarrow, Gail. Hookworms. 2003. (Parasites Ser.). (Illus.). 32p. (J). 24.95 (978-0-7377-1781-5(5) , Greenhaven Pr., Inc.) Thomson Gale.

Jerome, Kate Boehm. Fighting Disease. 2003. (Human Body Ser.). (Illus.). 32p. (J). pap. (978-0-7922-8865-7(3)) National Geographic Society.

Keen, Jared, ed. The Conquest of Disease: Understanding Global Issues. 2002. (Understanding Global Issues). (Illus.). 56p. (YA). (gr. 10-12). lib. bdg. 19.95 (978-1-58340-166-8(0)) Weigl Pubs., Inc.

Kienzle, Thomas E. & Heymann, David. Rabies. 2007. (Deadly Diseases & Epidemics Ser.). 144p. (J). (gr. 9). 31.95 (978-0-7910-9261-3(5) , Chelsea Hse.) Facts On File, Inc.

Kittredge, Mary. Common Cold. 2000. (Twenty-First Century Health & Wellness Ser.). (Illus.). 104p. (J). (gr. 7-12). 24.95 (978-0-7910-5985-2(5) , Chelsea Hse.) Facts On File, Inc.

Klosterman, Lorrie. Rabies. 2007. (Health Alert Ser.). 64p. (J). lib. bdg. 31.36 (***978-0-7614-2704-9(X)*** , Benchmark Bks.) Cavendish, Marshall Corp.

Knowles, Johanna. Huntington's Disease. 2006. (Genetic Diseases Ser.). (Illus.). 64p. (J). (978-1-4042-0694-6(9)) Rosen Publishing Group, Inc., The.

Korneluk, Yolanda G., et al. CF & You: A Guide for Adolescents. MacDonald, Kyla, illus. 2nd ed. 64p. (YA). (978-0-88629-309-3(X)) McGill-Queen's Univ. Pr.

Krueger, Tira. Taking Tourette Syndrome to School. Dineen, Tom, illus. 2001. (Special Kids in School Ser.: Vol. 9). 32p. (J). pap. 11.95 (978-1-891383-12-0(4)) JayJo Bks., LLC.

Kruszka, Bonnie J. Eating Gluten-Free with Emily: A Story for Children with Celiac Disease. Cihlar, Richard S., illus. 2004. 32p. (J). pap. 14.95 (978-1-890627-62-1(3)) Woodbine Hse.

Kupperberg, Paul. How Do We Know the Nature of Disease. 2005. (Great Scientific Questions & the Scientists Who Answered Them Ser.). (Illus.). 112p. (J). (gr. 7-12). lib. bdg. 26.50 (978-1-4042-0075-3(4)) Rosen Publishing Group, Inc., The.

Lamb, Kirsten. Cancer. 2002. (Health Issues Ser.). (Illus.). 64p. (J). (gr. 6-8). lib. bdg. 28.54 (978-0-7398-5219-4(1)) Raintree.

Laskey, Elizabeth. Fifth Disease. 2003. (It's Catching Ser.). (Illus.). 32p. (J). (gr. k-2). lib. bdg. 22.79 (978-1-4034-0272-1(8)) Heinemann Library.

—Flu. 2003. (It's Catching Ser.). (Illus.). 32p. (J). (gr. k-2). lib. bdg. 22.79 (978-1-4034-0273-8(6)) Heinemann Library.

—Impetigo. 2003. (It's Catching Ser.). (Illus.). 32p. (J). (gr. k-2). lib. bdg. 22.79 (978-1-4034-0274-5(4)) Heinemann Library.

—It's Catching, Set 2. 2003. (Illus.). (J). (gr. k-2). lib. bdg. 134.74 (978-1-4034-0279-0(5)) Heinemann Library.

—Strep Throat. 2003. (It's Catching Ser.). (Illus.). 32p. (J). (gr. k-2). lib. bdg. 22.79 (978-1-4034-0276-9(0)) Heinemann Library.

—Whooping Cough. 2003. (It's Catching Ser.). (Illus.). 32p. (J). (gr. k-2). lib. bdg. 22.79 (978-1-4034-0277-6(9)) Heinemann Library.

Latta, Sara L. Food Poisoning & Foodborne Diseases. 1999. (Diseases & People Ser.). (Illus.). 128p. (YA). (gr. 6-12). lib. bdg. 26.60 (978-0-7660-1183-0(6)) Enslow Pubs., Inc.

Lee, Justin. Everything You Need to Know about Cystic Fibrosis. 2001. (Need to Know Library). (Illus.). 64p. (YA). (gr. 4-6). lib. bdg. 25.25 (978-0-8239-3321-1(0)) Rosen Publishing Group, Inc., The.

Lennard-Brown, Sarah. Asthma. 2002. (Health Issues Ser.). (Illus.). 64p. (J). (gr. 6-8). lib. bdg. 28.54 (978-0-7398-5218-7(3)) Raintree.

The Let's Talk Library, Set 9 (Accelerated Reader) Health Challenges, 6 bks. Incl. Let's Talk about Being Overweight. Gordon, Melanie Apel. lib. bdg. 18.75 (978-0-8239-5413-1(7)); Let's Talk about Epilepsy. Gordon, Melanie Apel. lib. bdg. 18.75 (978-0-8239-5414-8(5)); Let's Talk about Poison Ivy. Gordon, Melanie Apel, contrib. by. lib. bdg. 18.75 (978-0-8239-5415-5(3)); Let's Talk about Scratches, Scrapes & Bug Bites. Gordon, Melanie Apel. lib. bdg. 18.75 (978-0-8239-5416-2(1)); Let's Talk about Sickle Cell Anemia. Gordon, Melanie Apel. lib. bdg. 18.75 (978-0-8239-5417-9(X)); Let's Talk about When You Have to Have Your Tonsils Out. Gordon, Melanie Apel. lib. bdg. 18.75 (978-0-8239-5418-6(8)); 24p. (J). (gr. 3). (Illus.). 2000. Set lib. bdg. 103.50 (978-0-8239-7009-4(4) , PowerKids Pr.) Rosen Publishing Group, Inc., The.

Leuenroth, Stephanie. Hantavirus Pulmonary Syndrome. 2006. (Deadly Diseases & Epidemics Ser.). (Illus.). 104p. (J). (gr. 9-12). 31.95 (978-0-7910-8676-6(3) , Chelsea Hse.) Facts On File, Inc.

Libal, Autumn. Chained: Youth with Chronic Illness. 2004. (Youth with Special Needs Ser.). (Illus.). 128p. (J). lib. bdg. (978-1-59084-735-0(0)) Mason Crest Pubs.

Libal, Joyce. Drug Therapy for Mental Disorders Caused by a Medical Condition. 2003. (Encyclopedia of Psychiatric Drugs & Their Disorders Ser.). (Illus.). 128p. (J). lib. bdg. (978-1-59084-567-7(6)) Mason Crest Pubs.

Mahony, Mary. There's an "S" on My Back, "S" Is for Scoliosis. 1999. (Illus.). 196p. (YA). (gr. 5-8). pap. 14.95 (978-0-9658879-1-5(X)) Redding Pr.

Margulies, Phillip. Everything You Need to Know about Rheumatic Fever. 2005. (Need to Know Library). (Illus.). 64p. (YA). lib. bdg. 25.25 (978-0-8239-4509-2(X)) Rosen Publishing Group, Inc., The.

Martin, Carrie & Martin, Chia. The Rainbow Feelings of Cancer: A Book of Children Who Have a Loved One with Cancer. 2001. (Illus.). 32p. wbk. ed. 14.95 (978-1-890772-16-1(X)) Hohm Pr.

Masoff, Joy. All Better Now. Dickason, Jack, illus. 2008. 20p. (J). 9.95 (***978-1-60059-128-0(0)***) Lark Bks.

Massari, Francesca. Everything You Need to Know about Cancer. 2005. (Need to Know Library). (Illus.). 64p. (YA). (gr. 7-12). lib. bdg. 25.25 (978-0-8239-3164-4(1) , NTCANC) Rosen Publishing Group, Inc., The.

McGuigan, Jim. Alzheimer's Disease. 2004. (Just the Facts Ser.). (Illus.). 56p. (J). lib. bdg. 27.07 (978-1-4034-5143-9(5)) Heinemann Library.

Moe, Barbara. Coping with Eating Disorders. rev. ed. 1999. (Coping Ser.). (Illus.). 149p. (YA). (gr. 7-12). lib. bdg. 26.50 (978-0-8239-2974-0(4) , COEADI) Rosen Publishing Group, Inc., The.

—Everything You Need to Know about Migraines & Other Headaches. 2005. (Need to Know Library). (Illus.). 64p. (YA). (gr. 7-12). lib. bdg. 25.25 (978-0-8239-3291-7(5) , NTMIHE) Rosen Publishing Group, Inc., The.

Moehn, Heather. Everything You Need to Know When Someone You Know Has Leukemia. 2005. (Need to Know Library). (Illus.). 64p. (YA). (gr. 7-12). lib. bdg. 25.25 (978-0-8239-3121-7(8) , NTLEUK) Rosen Publishing Group, Inc., The.

Monroe, Judy. Cystic Fibrosis. 2000. (Perspectives on Disease & Illness Ser.). (Illus.). 64p. (J). (gr. 4-6). lib. bdg. 23.93 (978-0-7368-1026-5(9) , LifeMatters Bks.) Capstone Pr., Inc.

—Influenza & Other Viruses. 2000. (Perspectives on Disease & Illness Ser.). (Illus.). 64p. (J). (gr. 4-6). lib. bdg. 23.93 (978-0-7368-1025-8(0) , LifeMatters Bks.) Capstone Pr., Inc.

Moore, Eva. The Giant Germ. 2001. (Magic School Bus Chapter Bks.). (Illus.). (J). 11.79 (978-0-606-21310-3(4)) Tandem Library Bks.

Moran, Katherine J. Diabetes: The Ultimate Teen Guide. Merriman, Lisa P., illus. 2004. (It Happened to Me Ser.: No. 7). 208p. 39.50 (978-0-8108-4806-1(6)) Scarecrow Pr., Inc.

Morgan, Sally. Germ Killers: Fighting Disease. (Science at the Edge Ser.). 64p. 8.95 (978-1-4034-4121-8(9)) Heinemann Library.

Murphy, Patricia J. Illness. 2007. (J). (***978-1-4034-9777-2(X)***); pap. (***978-1-4034-9782-6(6)***) Heinemann Library.

Murphy, Wendy B. Asthma. 1998. (Medical Library: up). (Illus.). 112p. (gr. 7 up). lib. bdg. (978-0-7613-0364-0(2) , Twenty-First Century Bks.) Lerner Publishing Group.

—Orphan Diseases: New Hope for Rare Medical Conditions. 2002. (Twenty-First Century Medical Library). (Illus.). 144p. (gr. 7 up). lib. bdg. 26.90 (978-0-7613-1919-1(0) , Twenty-First Century Bks.) Lerner Publishing Group.

Nardo, Don. Malnutrition. 2007. (Diseases & Disorders Ser.). 128p. (J). (gr. 7-10). 32.45 (***978-1-59018-677-0(X)*** , Lucent Bks.) Thomson Gale.

Newton, David E., ed. Sick! Diseases & Disorders, Injuries & Infections, 4 vols., Set. 2000. (Illus.). 814p. (J). (gr. 6 up). lib. bdg. 235.00 (978-0-7876-3922-8(2) , GML00502-1137193719, UXL) Thomson Gale.

—Sick! Diseases & Disorders, Injuries & Infections, 4 vols. 2000. (Illus.). (J). (978-0-7876-3923-5(0)); (978-0-7876-3924-2(9)); (978-0-7876-3925-9(7)); (978-0-7876-3926-6(5)) Thomson Gale. (UXL).

O'Shei, Tim. The World's Deadliest Diseases. 2006. (Edge Books, the World's Top Ten). (Illus.). 32p. (J). (978-0-7368-5452-8(5)) Capstone Pr., Inc.

Paquette, Penny Hutchins. Asthma: The Ultimate Teen Guide. 2003. (It Happened to Me Ser.: No. 5). (Illus.). 184p. 37.50 (978-0-8108-4633-3(0)) Scarecrow Pr., Inc.

Parsons, Michelle Hyde. Fighting Disease. 2005. 42.00 (***978-1-4108-4609-9(1)***) Benchmark Education Co.

Pascoe, Elaine, ed. Spreading Menace: Salmonella Attack & the Hunger Craving. 2003. (Body Story Ser.). (Illus.). 48p. (J). 24.95 (978-1-4103-0064-5(1)); 11.20 (978-1-4103-0185-7(0)) Thomson Gale. (Blackbirch Pr., Inc.).

Perspectives on Disease & Illness, 16 bks. Incl. Allergies. Monroe, Judy. (J). (gr. 4-6). 2001. lib. bdg. 23.93 (978-0-7368-0752-4(7)); Asthma. Peacock, Judith. (J). (gr. 4-6). 1999. lib. bdg. 23.93 (978-0-7368-0283-3(5)); Breast Cancer. Peacock, Judith. (J). (gr. k-9). 2001. lib. bdg. 23.93 (978-0-7368-1028-9(5)); Cerebral Palsy. Peacock, Judith. (J). (gr. 4-6). 1999. lib. bdg. 23.93 (978-0-7368-0280-2(0)); Cystic Fibrosis. Monroe, Judy. (J). (gr. 4-6). 2000. lib. bdg. 23.93 (978-0-7368-1026-5(9)); Diabetes. Peacock, Judith. (J). (gr. 4-6). 1999. lib. bdg. 23.93 (978-0-7368-0277-2(0)); Epilepsy. Peacock, Judith. (J). (gr. 4-6). 1999. lib. bdg. 23.93 (978-0-7368-0278-9(9)); Heart Disease. Gregson, Susan R. (J). (gr. 4-6). 2001. lib. bdg. 23.93 (978-0-7368-0749-4(7)); High Blood Pressure. Gregson, Susan R. (J). (gr. 4-6). 2001. lib. bdg. 23.93 (978-0-7368-0750-0(0)); HIV & AIDS. Gedatus, Gustav Mark. (J). (gr. 4-6). 1999. lib. bdg. 23.93 (978-0-7368-0281-9(9)); Hodgkin's Disease. Peacock, Judith. (YA). (gr. 4-6). 2000. lib. bdg. 23.93 (978-0-7368-1027-2(7)); Influenza & Other Viruses. Monroe, Judy. (J). (gr. 4-6). 2000. lib. bdg. 23.93 (978-0-7368-1025-8(0)); Juvenile Arthritis. Peacock, Judith. (J). (gr. 4-6). 1999. lib. bdg. 23.93 (978-0-7368-0279-6(7)); Leukemia. Peacock, Judith. (J). (gr. 4-6). 1999. lib. bdg. 23.93 (978-0-7368-0282-6(7)); Lyme Disease. Monroe, Judy. (J). (gr. 4-6). 2001. lib. bdg. 23.93 (978-0-7368-0751-7(9)); Mononucleosis. Gedatus, Gustav Mark. (J). (gr. 4-6). 1999. lib. bdg. 23.93 (978-0-7368-0284-0(3)); 64p. (Illus.). Set lib. bdg. 382.88 (978-0-7368-1038-8(2) , LifeMatters Bks.) Capstone Pr., Inc.

Peters, Stephanie True. Smallpox in the New World. 2003. (J). 29.93 (978-0-7614-1637-1(4) , Benchmark Bks.) Cavendish, Marshall Corp.

—The 1918 Influenza Pandemic. 2003. (Illus.). ix, 69p. (J). 29.93 (978-0-7614-1636-4(6) , Benchmark Bks.) Cavendish, Marshall Corp.

Potter, Christina. Coping with Crohn's Disease & Ulcerative Colitis. 2005. (Coping Ser.). 192p. (YA). (gr. 7-12). lib. bdg. 26.50 (978-0-8239-3962-6(6)) Rosen Publishing Group, Inc., The.

Powell, Jillian. Sore Throat. 2007. (J). (***978-1-84234-473-6(0)***) Cherrytree Pubns., Inc.

Preventing Food-Borne Illness: What Can You Do? (AVA) 2001. (YA). pap. 5.00 (978-1-57078-004-2(8)) C E V Multimedia, Ltd.

Ramen, Fred. Influenza. 2001. (Epidemics Ser.). (Illus.). 64p. (YA). (gr. 4-6). lib. bdg. 26.50 (978-0-8239-3347-1(4)) Rosen Publishing Group, Inc., The.

—Tuberculosis. 2001. (Epidemics Ser.). (Illus.). 64p. (J). (gr. 4-6). lib. bdg. 26.50 (978-0-8239-3349-5(0)) Rosen Publishing Group, Inc., The.

Ray, Kurt. Typhoid Fever. 2002. (Epidemics Ser.). 64p. (YA). (gr. 7-12). lib. bdg. 26.50 (978-0-8239-3572-7(8)) Rosen Publishing Group, Inc., The.

Rocha, Toni L. Understanding Recovery from Eating Disorders. 1999. (Teen Eating Disorder Prevention Book Ser.). (Illus.). 192p. (YA). (gr. 7-12). lib. bdg. 25.25 (978-0-8239-2884-2(5) , E2UNRE) Rosen Publishing Group, Inc., The.

Routh, Kristina. Meningitis. 2004. (Just the Facts Ser.). (J). lib. bdg. 27.07 (978-1-4034-5146-0(X)) Heinemann Library.

—Tuberculosis. 2004. (Just the Facts Ser.). (Illus.). 56p. (J). lib. bdg. 27.07 (978-1-4034-5147-7(8)) Heinemann Library.

Royston, Angela. Colds. 2001. (It's Catching Ser.). (Illus.). 32p. (J). (gr. k-2). lib. bdg. 21.36 (978-1-58810-227-0(0)) Heinemann Library.

—It's Not Catching, 8 bks. 2004. (J). (gr. k-2). lib. bdg. 193.71 (978-1-4034-4828-6(0)) Heinemann Library.

—Pink Eye. 2001. (It's Catching Ser.). (Illus.). 32p. (J). (gr. k-2). lib. bdg. 21.36 (978-1-58810-230-0(0)) Heinemann Library.

Royston, Angela, contrib. by. Clean & Healthy. 1999. 32p. (J). (gr. k-2). lib. bdg. 21.36 (978-1-57572-981-7(4)) Heinemann Library.

Sheen, Barbara. Asthma. 2002. (Diseases & Disorders Ser.). (Illus.). 120p. (J). (gr. 6-9). 32.45 (978-1-59018-235-2(9) , Lucent Bks.) Thomson Gale.

—Cerebral Palsy. 2003. (Illus.). 96p. (J). 32.45 (978-1-59018-038-9(0) , Lucent Bks.) Thomson Gale.

—Headaches. 2004. (Illus.). 96p. (J). 32.45 (978-1-59018-346-5(0) , Lucent Bks.) Thomson Gale.

—Hepatitis. 2002. (Illus.). 144p. (J). 32.45 (978-1-59018-041-9(0) , Lucent Bks.) Thomson Gale.

—Mad Cow Disease. 2004. (Illus.). 112p. (J). (gr. 7-10). 32.45 (978-1-59018-635-0(4) , Lucent Bks.) Thomson Gale.

—Toxic Shock Syndrome. 2006. (Diseases & Disorders Ser.). 112p. (J). (gr. 7-10). 32.45 (978-1-59018-859-0(4) , Lucent Bks.) Thomson Gale.

Shmaefsk, Brian. Syphilis. 2003. (Deadly Diseases & Epidemics Ser.). (Illus.). 112p. (gr. 9-13). 31.95 (978-0-7910-7308-7(4) , Chelsea Hse.) Facts On File, Inc.

Shmaefsky, Brian. Toxic Shock Syndrome. 2003. (Your Body, How It Works). (Illus.). 112p. (gr. 9-13). 31.95 (978-0-7910-7465-7(X) , Chelsea Hse.) Facts On File, Inc.

Sileo, Frank J. & Gradisher, Martha. Toilet Paper Flowers: A Story for Children about Crohn's Disease. 2005. (Illus.). (J). (978-0-929173-47-4(3)) Health Pr. NA, Inc.

Silverstein, Alvin. Diseases & People, 40 bks., Set. (Illus.). (YA). (gr. 6-12). lib. bdg. 838.00 (978-0-89490-571-1(6)) Enslow Pubs., Inc.

—Earaches. 2002. (gr. 3-6). lib. bdg. 15.25 (978-0-613-54181-7(2)) Tandem Library Bks.

—Scoliosis. (gr. 3-6). 2003. lib. bdg. 15.25 (978-0-613-72731-0(2)); 2002. lib. bdg. 15.25 (978-0-613-59546-9(7)) Tandem Library Bks.

—Sore Throats & Tonsillitis. 2000. (gr. 3-6). lib. bdg. 15.25 (978-0-613-34485-2(5)) Tandem Library Bks.

—Stomachaches. 2003. (gr. 3-6). lib. bdg. 15.25 (978-0-613-67935-0(0)) Tandem Library Bks.

Silverstein, Alvin, et al. Bites & Stings. 2001. (My Health Ser.). (Illus.). 48p. (J). (gr. 3-5). 25.50 (978-0-531-11861-0(4) , Watts, Franklin) Scholastic Library Publishing.

—Chicken Pox & Shingles. 1998. (Diseases & People Ser.). (Illus.). 128p. (YA). (gr. 6-12). lib. bdg. 26.60 (978-0-89490-715-9(8)) Enslow Pubs., Inc.

—Common Colds. 1999. (My Health Ser.). (Illus.). 48p. (J). (gr. 3-5). 25.50 (978-0-531-11579-4(8) , Watts, Franklin) Scholastic Library Publishing.

—Earaches. 2002. (My Health Ser.). (Illus.). 48p. (J). (gr. 3-5). pap. 6.95 (978-0-531-15562-2(5) , Watts, Franklin) Scholastic Library Publishing.

—The Flu & Pneumonia Update. 2006. (Disease Update Ser.). (Illus.). 104p. (YA). (gr. 5 up). lib. bdg. 31.93 (978-0-7660-2480-9(6)) Enslow Pubs., Inc.

—Headaches. Stromoski, Rick, illus. 2001. (My Health Ser.). 48p. (J). (gr. 3-5). 25.50 (978-0-531-11872-6(X) , Watts, Franklin) Scholastic Library Publishing.

—Parkinson's Disease. 2002. (Diseases & People Ser.). (Illus.). 128p. (YA). (gr. 6-12). lib. bdg. 26.60 (978-0-7660-1593-7(9)) Enslow Pubs., Inc.

—Scoliosis. (My Health Ser.). 48p. (J). (gr. 3-5). 2003. pap. 6.95 (978-0-531-16639-0(2)); 2002. (Illus.). pap. 25.50 (978-0-531-12046-0(5)) Scholastic Library Publishing. (Watts, Franklin).

—Stomachaches. 2003. (My Health Ser.). 48p. 25.50 (978-0-531-12192-4(5) , Watts, Franklin) Scholastic Library Publishing.

—The Tuberculosis Update. 2006. (Disease Update Ser.). (Illus.). 112p. (J). (gr. 5 up). lib. bdg. 31.93 (978-0-7660-2481-6(4)) Enslow Pubs., Inc.

Smith, Jennifer Crown. Dad's Falling Apart: Keeping It Together When a Family Member Has Multiple Sclerosis. Williams, Ron, illus. 2003. 32p. (J). per. 14.95 (978-0-929173-36-8(8)) Health Pr. NA, Inc.

Smith, Tara C. Streptococcus (Group B) 2007. (Deadly Diseases & Epidemics Ser.). 88p. (gr. 9). 31.95 (*978-0-7910-9243-9(7) , Chelsea Hse.) Facts On File, Inc.

Sommers, Michael A. Everything You Need to Know about Colds & Flu. 2005. (Need to Know Library). (Illus.). 64p. (YA). (gr. 7-12). lib. bdg. 25.25 (978-0-8239-3297-9(4) , NTCOFL) Rosen Publishing Group, Inc., The.

Stangl, Jean. What Makes You Cough, Sneeze, Burp, Hiccup, Yawn, Blink, Sweat, & Shiver? 2001. (Illus.). 48p. (J). (gr. 3-5). lib. bdg. 15.25 (978-0-613-34546-0(0)) Tandem Library Bks.

Stanley, Debbie. Coping with Vision Disorders. 2005. (Coping Ser.). (Illus.). 192p. (YA). (gr. 7-12). lib. bdg. 26.50 (978-0-8239-3198-9(6)) Rosen Publishing Group, Inc., The.

—Understanding Anorexia Nervosa. 1999. (Teen Eating Disorder Prevention Book Ser.). (Illus.). 192p. (YA). (gr. 7-12). lib. bdg. 25.25 (978-0-8239-2877-4(2) , E2ANNE) Rosen Publishing Group, Inc., The.

—Understanding Bulimia Nervosa. 1999. (Teen Eating Disorder Prevention Book Ser.). (Illus.). 192p. (YA). (gr. 7-12). lib. bdg. 25.25 (978-0-8239-2878-1(0) , E2BULI) Rosen Publishing Group, Inc., The.

Stewart, Gail. Sars. 2004. (gr. 4-7). 26.20 (978-0-7377-2642-8(3)) Thomson Gale.

Stewart, Gail B. Sleep Disorders. 2002. (Diseases & Disorders Ser.). (Illus.). 112p. (YA). (gr. 6-9). 32.45 (978-1-56006-909-6(0) , Lucent Bks.) Thomson Gale.

Stewart, Gregory. The Immune System. 2003. (Your Body, How It Works). (Illus.). 112p. (gr. 9-13). 31.95 (978-0-7910-7630-9(X) , Chelsea Hse.) Facts On File, Inc.

Storad, Conrad J. Inside AIDS: HIV Attacks the Immune System. 1998. (Discovery! Ser.). (Illus.). 120p. (gr. 5-12). lib. bdg. 27.93 (978-0-8225-2857-9(6)) Lerner Publishing Group.

Susman, Edward. Multiple Sclerosis. 1999. (Diseases & People Ser.). (Illus.). 128p. (YA). (gr. 6-12). lib. bdg. 26.60 (978-0-7660-1185-4(2)) Enslow Pubs., Inc.

Twenty-First Century Medical Library, 11 vols. 2004. (Health & Medicine Ser.). (YA). (gr. 7 up). (978-0-7613-3105-6(0) , Twenty-First Century Bks.) Lerner Publishing Group.

Uschan, Michael V. Forty Years of Medical Racism: The Tuskegee Experiments. 2005. (American Secrets & Scandals Ser.). (Illus.). 112p. (J). (gr. 7-10). lib. bdg. 32.45 (978-1-59018-486-8(6) , Lucent Bks.) Thomson Gale.

Vander Hook, Sue. Epilepsy. 2000. (Understanding Illness Ser.). (Illus.). 32p. (J). lib. bdg. 16.95 (978-1-58340-025-8(7)) Smart Apple Media.

—Parkinson's Disease. 2000. (Understanding Illness Ser.). (Illus.). 32p. (J). (gr. 4-10). lib. bdg. 16.95 (978-1-58340-055-5(9)) Smart Apple Media.

—Understanding Illness, 6 vols., Set. 1999. (Illus.). (YA). (gr. 3-10). lib. bdg. 101.70 (978-1-58340-028-9(1)) Smart Apple Media.

Votava, Andrea. Coping with Migraines & Other Headaches. rev. ed. 2000. (Coping Ser.). (Illus.). 162p. (YA). (gr. 7-12). lib. bdg. 26.50 (978-0-8239-3197-2(8)) Rosen Publishing Group, Inc., The.

Wade, Mary Dodson. ALS: Lou Gehrig's Disease. 2001. (Diseases & People Ser.). (Illus.). 128p. (YA). (gr. 6 up). lib. bdg. 26.60 (978-0-7660-1594-4(7)) Enslow Pubs., Inc.

Walker, Richard. Epidemics & Plagues. 2007. (Kingfisher Knowledge Ser.). (Illus.). 64p. (J). pap. 8.95 (*978-0-7534-6161-7(7) , Kingfisher) Houghton Mifflin Co. Trade & Reference Div.

—KFK Epidemics & Plagues. 2007. (Kingfisher Knowledge Ser.). 8.95 (*978-0-7534-6181-5(1) , Kingfisher) Houghton Mifflin Co. Trade & Reference Div.

Watson, Stephanie. Endometriosis. 2006. (Library of Sexual Health). (Illus.). 64p. (J). (978-1-4042-0904-6(2)) Rosen Publishing Group, Inc., The.

Weitzman, Elizabeth. Let's Talk about Having Asthma. 1998. (Conflict Resolution Library). (Illus.). 24p. (J). (gr. k-4). pap. 6.95 (978-1-56838-272-2(3)) Hazelden Publishing & Educational Services.

Whelan, Jo. Diabetes. 2002. (Health Issues Ser.). (Illus.). 64p. (J). (gr. 6-8). lib. bdg. 28.54 (978-0-7398-5220-0(5)) Raintree.

When Someone You Love Has. 2004. (J). lib. bdg. 18.75 (978-0-8239-6813-8(8) , PowerKids Pr.) Rosen Publishing Group, Inc., The.

Willett, Edward. Ebola Virus. 2003. (Diseases & People Ser.). (Illus.). 112p. (J). lib. bdg. 26.60 (978-0-7660-1595-1(5)) Enslow Pubs., Inc.

—Hemophilia. 2001. (Diseases & People Ser.). (Illus.). 128p. (YA). (gr. 6-12). lib. bdg. 26.60 (978-0-7660-1684-2(6)) Enslow Pubs., Inc.

—Meningitis. 1999. (Diseases & People Ser.). (Illus.). 112p. (YA). (gr. 6-12). lib. bdg. 26.60 (978-0-7660-1187-8(9)) Enslow Pubs., Inc.

Winkler, Peter. Keeping Fit. 2003. (Human Body Ser.). (Illus.). 32p. (J). pap. (978-0-7922-8863-3(7)) National Geographic Society.

Winter, Barbara. The 10 Most Extraordinary Medical Conditions. 2008. (Tentrade; Ser.). 48p. (J). pap. 14.99 (*978-1-55448-481-2(2) , Watts, Franklin) Scholastic Library Publishing.

Winters, Adam. Everything You Need to Know about Lupus. 2005. (Need to Know Library). (Illus.). 64p. (YA). (gr. 7-12). lib. bdg. 25.25 (978-0-8239-3288-7(5) , NT-LUPU) Rosen Publishing Group, Inc., The.

Yancey, Diane. Tuberculosis. 2001. (Medical Library). (Illus.). 128p. (gr. 7 up). lib. bdg. 26.90 (978-0-7613-1624-4(8) , Twenty-First Century Bks.) Lerner Publishing Group.

Yannielli, Len. Lyme Disease. 2003. (Deadly Diseases & Epidemics Ser.). (Illus.). 112p. (gr. 9-13). 31.95 (978-0-7910-7463-3(3) , Chelsea Hse.) Facts On File, Inc.

Yount, Lisa. Epidemics. 2000. (Overview Ser.). (Illus.). 112p. (YA). (gr. 6-9). lib. bdg. 29.95 (978-1-56006-441-1(2) , LML00902-177810, Lucent Bks.) Thomson Gale.

Zonderman, Jon & Shader, Laurel. Legionnaire's Disease. 2006. (Deadly Diseases & Epidemics Ser.). (Illus.). 80p. (J). (gr. 9-12). 31.95 (978-0-7910-8885-2(5) , Chelsea Hse.) Facts On File, Inc.

DISEASES, COMMUNICABLE

see Communicable Diseases

DISEASES—FICTION

Abdullah, Patricia Noor. Saving Daddy. Cabri, Alexandra, illus. 2006. 32p. (J). (gr. 2-5). 17.95 (*978-1-933193-16-8(6)) EECI, Inc.

Allen, Lynn Marie. Asperger's? God Bless You! 2004. 31p. pap. 17.95 (978-1-4137-3435-5(9)) PublishAmerica, Inc.

Arrington, Gladys. Dallas: On Book One: Jo/Jo KIDS. Arrington, Chiquila, illus. 2006. 49p. pap. 12.95 (978-1-4241-1162-6(5)) PublishAmerica, Inc.

Brenna, Beverley A. The Moon Children. 2007. 144p. (J). (gr. 4-7). pap. 8.95 (*978-0-88995-378-9(3)) Red Deer Pr. CAN. *Dist:* Fitzhenry & Whiteside, Ltd.

Brinker, Julie. Rachel's Night. 1999. 44p. (J). (gr. k-5). mass mkt. 4.00 (978-1-58193-174-7(3)) Brown Bag Productions.

Brugman, Alyssa. Finding Grace. 2004. 240p. (YA). (gr. 7). lib. bdg. 17.99 (978-0-385-90142-0(9) , Delacorte Bks. for Young Readers) Random Hse. Children's Bks.

Clement, Hal. Half Life. 2000. (gr. 7-12). lib. bdg. 15.30 (978-0-613-27864-5(X)) Tandem Library Bks.

Cooney, Caroline B. Code Orange. 2007. 208p. (YA). (gr. 7). pap. 6.50 (978-0-385-73260-4(0) , Laurel Leaf) Random Hse. Children's Bks.

Deem, Saitofi Anne. Myrtle Learns about Seizures. 1998. (Teachable Moments Ser.). (Illus.). 8p. (J). (ps-3). pap. 7.95 (978-1-930694-14-9(8)) Myrtle Learns.

—Myrtle Learns How You Catch an Illness. 1998. (Teachable Moments Ser.). (Illus.). 8p. (J). (ps-3). pap. 7.95 (978-1-930694-10-1(5)) Myrtle Learns.

Dowd, Siobhan. The London Eye Mystery. 2008. 336p. (J). (*978-0-375-84976-3(9)); lib. bdg. (*978-0-375-94976-0(3)) Random Hse. Children's Bks. (Fickling, David Bks.).

Etlinger, Rebecca. To Be Me. 2005. pap. (*978-0-87424-452-6(8)) Western Psychological Services.

Fanning, Tena. Booger Boogie. 2007. 32p. (ps-3). 14.95 (*978-1-933721-13-2(8)) Playdate Kids Publishing.

Grab, Daphne. Alive & Well in Prague, NY. 2008. 256p. (J). 16.99 (*978-0-06-125670-7(6)); lib. bdg. 17.89 (*978-0-06-125671-4(4)) HarperCollins Pubs. (Geringer, Laura Book).

Grindley, Sally. Hurricane Wills. 2008. 250p. (J). pap. 8.95 (*978-0-7475-9095-8(8)) Bloomsbury Publishing Plc GBR. *Dist:* Independent Pubs. Group.

Haddix, Margaret Peterson. Because of Anya. 2004. 128p. (J). reprint ed. pap. 5.99 (978-0-689-86993-8(2) , Aladdin) Simon & Schuster Children's Publishing.

Hamilton, Virginia. Bluish. 2002. 128p. (J). (gr. 4-6). pap. 5.99 (978-0-439-36786-8(7) , Scholastic Paperbacks) Scholastic, Inc.

Hansen, Lynne. Reckless Revolution. 2007. (YA). (*978-1-4114-9672-9(8)) Spark Publishing Group.

Hatkoff, Craig & Hatkoff, Juliana. Good-Bye Tonsils! Mets, Marilyn, illus. 2004. 32p. (J). (gr. k up). pap. 6.99 (978-0-14-240133-0(1) , Puffin) Penguin Group (USA) Inc.

Hull, Rod. Mr. Betts & Mr. Potts. Davies, Jo, illus. 2000. 32p. (J). (ps-5). 15.99 (978-1-84148-106-7(8)) Barefoot Bks., Inc.

I'm Not Afraid of Needles. 2004. (J). 4.99 (978-0-9776144-0-0(9)) Kidstalk, LLC.

James, Brian. Treasure Trouble. Zivoin, Jennifer, illus. 2008. (Pirate School Ser.). 64p. (J). (gr. 1-3). 3.99 (*978-0-448-44782-7(7) , Grosset & Dunlap) Penguin Group (USA) Inc.

Johnson, Angela. A Cool Moonlight. 2005. 133p. (J). (ps-7). per. 12.64 (978-0-606-33124-1(7)) Tandem Library Bks.

Kay, Elizabeth, et al. The Divide. 2003. 320p. (J). (gr. 3-6). pap. 15.95 (978-0-439-45696-8(7) , Chicken Hse., The) Scholastic, Inc.

Koertge, Ronald. Shakespeare Bats Cleanup. 2006. 128p. (YA). (gr. 7). reprint ed. pap. 5.99 (978-0-7636-2939-7(1)) Candlewick Pr.

Mahony, Mary. Harry Scores A Hat Trick, Pawns, Pucks, & Scoliosis: The Sequel to Stand Tall, Harry. Pasternack, Susan, ed. Larkin, Catherine, illus. 2003. 130p. (YA). (gr. 5-8). per. 14.95 (978-0-9658879-4-6(4)) Redding Pr.

—Stand Tall, Harry. Pasternack, Susan, ed. Larkin, Catherine, illus. 2002. 200p. (J). (gr. 4). pap. 14.95 (978-0-9658879-2-2(8)) Redding Pr.

Marien, Donna. Waiting at the Bay: A Young Woman's Reflections on Journeys in the Sea of Life. 2003. 108p. (YA). pap. 10.95 (978-0-595-26304-2(6) , Writers Club Pr.) iUniverse, Inc.

Marsh, Carole. The Puzzle of the Indian Arrowhead. 2006. 64p. (gr. 1-3). 14.95 (*978-0-635-06201-7(1)) Gallopade International.

May, Cynthia. Ryan's Vitiligo. Nelson, Shannon, illus. 2003. (J). pap. 8.95 (978-0-615-12578-7(6)) May, Cynthia D.

McDaniel, Lurlene. To Live Again. 2001. (Dawn Rochelle Ser.: No. 5). (gr. 5-8). lib. bdg. 13.00 (978-0-613-57927-8(5)) Tandem Library Bks.

McFarlane, Sheryl. The Smell of Paint. 2006. 192p. (YA). (gr. 7 up). pap. (*978-1-55041-457-8(7)) Fitzhenry & Whiteside, Ltd.

Morpurgo, Michael. Out of the Ashes. Foreman, Michael, illus. l.t. ed. 2005. 144p. (J). pap. (978-0-7540-6190-8(6) , CLP 382) BBC Audio.

—Out of the Ashes. 2003. (Illus.). 128p. (J). pap. 9.99 (978-0-330-40017-6(7) , Macmillan Children's Bks.) Pan Macmillan GBR. *Dist:* Trafalgar Square Publishing.

Newth, Mette. The Dark Light. Ingwersen, Faith, tr. 2004. 256p. (YA). reprint ed. pap. 6.95 (978-0-374-41688-1(5) , Sunburst) Farrar, Straus & Giroux.

Niner, Holly L. Mr. Worry: A Story about OCD. Swearingen, Greg, illus. 2003. 32p. (J). (gr. 2-5). 15.95 (978-0-8075-5182-0(1)) Whitman, Albert & Co.

Reynolds, Marilynn. The Name of the Child. Kilby, Don, illus. 2002. 32p. (J). (ps-2). 16.95 (978-1-55143-221-2(8)) Orca Bk. Pubs. USA.

Roberts, G. Sillwee Wobbert the Happy Heart Kid. Lucas, Glenn E., illus. 2001. (Sillwee Wobbert Ser.: 1). 32p. (J). (ps-5). pap. 10.00 (978-0-9704861-1-0(1)) Dream Publishing Co.

Roberts, Kerry Daniel. Mark of the Yuan-Ti, Bk. 12. 2006. (Knights of the Silver Dragon Ser.: Bk. 12). (Illus.). 192p. (J). pap. 5.99 (978-0-7869-4033-2(6) , Mirrorstone) Wizards of the Coast.

Rockwood, Joyce. To Spoil the Sun. l.t. ed. 2004. 259p. 20.95 (978-0-7862-6433-9(0)) Thorndike Pr.

Saramago, José. Blindness. 1999. (gr. 7-12). lib. bdg. 23.45 (978-0-613-21232-8(0)) Tandem Library Bks.

Speltz, Ann. The Year My Mother Was Bald. Sternberg, Kate, illus. 2003. 64p. (YA). (gr. 3-8). 14.95 (978-1-55798-837-9(4)); (ps-8). pap. 8.95 (978-1-55798-888-1(9)) American Psychological Assn. (Magination Pr.).

—Year My Mother Was Bald. 2003. (gr. 3-6). lib. bdg. 17.60 (978-0-613-61137-4(3)) Tandem Library Bks.

To Wait Is to Win. 2004. (J). (978-0-9762904-7-6(2)) Layne Morgan Media, Inc.

Vejjajiva, Jane. The Happiness of Kati. Borthwick, Prudence, tr. from THA. 2006. 144p. (J). (gr. 6-8). 15.95 (978-1-4169-1788-5(8) , Atheneum) Simon & Schuster Children's Publishing.

DISEASES—HISTORY

Aronson, Virginia. Influenza Pandemic of 1918-1919. 2000. (Great Disasters, Reforms & Ramifications Ser.). (Illus.). 120p. (J). (gr. 6-8). 30.00 (978-0-7910-5263-1(X) , Chelsea Hse.) Facts On File, Inc.

De Hahn, Tracee. The Black Death. 2001. (Great Disasters, Reforms & Ramifications Ser.). (Illus.). 112p. (J). 30.00 (978-0-7910-6326-2(7) , Chelsea Hse.) Facts On File, Inc.

Draper, Allison Stark. Polio. 2001. (Epidemics Ser.). (Illus.). 64p. (YA). (gr. 4-6). lib. bdg. 26.50 (978-0-8239-3348-8(2)) Rosen Publishing Group, Inc., The.

Marrin, Albert. Dr. Jenner & the Speckled Monster: The Search for the Smallpox Vaccine. 2002. (Illus.). 96p. (J). 19.99 (978-0-525-46922-3(2) , Dutton Juvenile) Penguin Group (USA) Inc.

Medical Files, 6 vols., Set. Incl. Belly-Busting Worm Invasions! Parasites That Love Your Insides. Lewis Tilden, Thomasine E. 26.00 (978-0-531-12068-2(6)); Blood Suckers! Deadly Mosquito Bites! DiConsiglio, John. 26.00 (978-0-531-12070-5(8)); Cute, Furry, & Deadly : Diseases You Can Catch from Your Pet! Brownlee, Christen. 26.00 (978-0-531-12072-9(4)); Help! What's Eating My Flesh? Runaway Staph & Strep Infections! Lewis Tilden, Thomasine E. 26.00 (978-0-531-12073-6(2)); Theres a Fungus among Us! True Stories of Killer Molds. DiConsiglio, John. 26.00 (978-0-531-12071-2(6)); When Birds Get Flu & Cows Go Mad! How Safe Are We? DiConsiglio, John. 26.00 (978-0-531-12069-9(4)); 64p. (YA). (gr. 8-12). (24/7 Ser.). (Illus.). 2007. 150.00 (*978-0-531-12478-9(9) , Watts, Franklin) Scholastic Library Publishing.

Peters, Stephanie True. Cholera: Curse of the Nineteenth Century. 2004. (Illus.). ix, 69p. (J). 29.93 (978-0-7614-1634-0(X) , Benchmark Bks.) Cavendish, Marshall Corp.

Ridgway, Tom. Smallpox. 2001. (Epidemics Ser.). (Illus.). 64p. (YA). (gr. 4-6). lib. bdg. 26.50 (978-0-8239-3346-4(6)) Rosen Publishing Group, Inc., The.

Sherrow, Victoria. Polio Epidemic: Crippling Virus Outbreak. 2001. (American Disasters Ser.). (Illus.). 48p. (YA). (gr. 4-10). lib. bdg. 23.93 (978-0-7660-1555-5(6)) Enslow Pubs., Inc.

Townsend, John. Disease: Pox, Pus & Plague. 2005. (Raintree Freestyle Ser.). (Illus.). 56p. (J). pap. (978-1-4109-1338-8(4)) Steck-Vaughn.

—Pox, Pus & Plague: A History of Disease & Infection. (J). 2006. (978-1-4109-2541-1(2)); 2006. 48p. pap. (978-1-4109-2546-6(3)); 2005. (Illus.). 56p. lib. bdg. 32.86 (978-1-4109-1333-3(3)) Steck-Vaughn.

Yount, Lisa. Disease Detectives. 2000. (History Makers Ser.). (Illus.). 112p. (YA). (gr. 7-10). 28.70 (978-1-56006-738-2(1) , Lucent Bks.) Thomson Gale.

DISEASES, INFECTIONS

see Communicable Diseases

DISEASES, MENTAL

see Mental Illness; Psychology, Pathological

DISEASES, TROPICAL

see Tropics—Diseases and Hygiene

DISEASES AND PESTS

see Fungi; Insects, Injurious and Beneficial; Parasites

see names of individual pests (e.g. Locusts)

DISEASES OF ANIMALS

see Veterinary Medicine

DISEASES OF CHILDREN

see Children—Diseases

DISEASES OF THE BLOOD

see Blood—Diseases

DISHES

see Glassware; Porcelain; Pottery

DISHONESTY

see Honesty

DISNEY, WALT, 1901-1966

Broggie, Michael. Walt Disney's Happy Place. Byerley, Bob, illus. 2001. (J). (978-1-57864-152-9(7)) Donning Co. Pubs.

Brown, Jonatha A. Walt Disney. (People We Should Know Ser.). 24p. (J). 2006. pap. 5.95 (978-0-8368-4767-3(9)); 2006. lib. bdg. 19.33 (978-0-8368-4760-4(1)); 2005. (Illus.). pap. (978-0-8368-4753-6(9)); 2005. (Illus.). lib. bdg. 19.33 (978-0-8368-4746-8(6)) Stevens, Gareth Inc.

Feinstein, Stephen. Read about Walt Disney. 2005. (I Like Biographies! Ser.). (Illus.). 24p. (J). (ps-ps). lib. bdg. 21.26 (978-0-7660-2595-0(0) , Enslow Elementary) Enslow Pubs., Inc.

Ford, Carin T. Walt Disney: Meet the Cartoonist. 2003. (Meeting Famous People Ser.). (Illus.). 32p. (J). (gr. 1-4). lib. bdg. 22.60 (978-0-7660-1857-0(1)) Enslow Pubs., Inc.

Greene, Katherine & Greene, Richard. Inside the Dream: The Personal Story of Walt Disney. 2001. (Illus.). 192p. 60.00 (978-0-7868-5350-2(6) , Disney Editions) Disney Pr.

Jaffe, Elizabeth Dana. Walt Disney. 2001. (Trailblazers of the Modern World Ser.). (Illus.). 48p. (J). (gr. 5 up). pap. 14.95 (978-0-8368-5222-6(2)); lib. bdg. 30.00 (978-0-8368-5062-8(9)) Stevens, Gareth Inc. (World Almanac Library).

Josephson, Judith Pinkerton. Walt Disney: Genius of Entertainment. 2006. (People to Know Today Ser.). (Illus.). 128p. (J). lib. bdg. 31.93 (978-0-7660-2624-7(8)) Enslow Pubs., Inc.

Marsh, Carole. Walt Disney. 2002. (One Thousand Readers Ser.). (Illus.). 12p. (J). (gr. k-4). 2.95 (978-0-635-01496-2(3) , 14963) Gallopade International.

Preszler, June. Walt Disney. 2003. (Photo-Illustrated Biographies Ser.). (Illus.). 24p. (J). lib. bdg. 19.93 (978-0-7368-2226-8(7) , Bridgestone Bks.) Capstone Pr., Inc.

Richardson, Adele D. The Story of Disney. 2003. (Built for Success Ser.). (Illus.). 48p. (J). 19.95 (978-1-58340-291-7(8)) Smart Apple Media.

Simon, Charnan. Walt Disney: Creator of Magical Worlds. 2000. (Community Builders Ser.). (Illus.). 48p. (J). (gr. 3-5). pap. 6.95 (978-0-516-26515-5(6) , Children's Pr.) Scholastic Library Publishing.

Walt Disney. (Photo Illustrated Biographies Ser.). 24p. (J). 6.95 (978-0-7368-3442-1(7)) Capstone Pr., Inc.

DISPLACED PERSONS

see Refugees

DISPOSAL OF REFUSE

see Refuse and Refuse Disposal

DISRAELI, BENJAMIN, EARL OF BEACONSFIELD, 1804-1881

Lee, Stephen J. Gladstone & Disraeli. 2005. (Questions & Analysis in History Ser.). (Illus.). 208p. 20.95 (978-0-415-32357-4(6)); 90.00 (978-0-415-32356-7(8)) Routledge.

DISSENT

Engelbert, Phillis. Activists, Rebels & Reformers, 3 vols. Sawinski, Diane M., ed. (Illus.). (J). 2001. 600p. (gr. 6 up). lib. bdg. 181.00 net. (978-0-7876-4847-3(7) , GML00502-114891); 2000. xxx, 596p. (978-0-7876-4848-0(5)); 2000. xxx, 596p. (978-0-7876-4849-7(3)) Thomson Gale. (UXL).

Engelbert, Phillis & Sawinski, Diane M. Activists, Rebels & Reformers, 3 vols., Set. 2000. (Illus.). xxx, 596p. (J). (978-0-7876-4850-3(7)) Visible Ink Pr.

Hacker, Carlotta. Rebels. 1998. (Women in Profile Ser.). (Illus.). 48p. (J). (gr. 4). lib. bdg. (978-0-7787-0014-2(3)) Crabtree Publishing Co.

Kallen, Stuart A. The Home Front: Americans Protest the War. 2001. (American War Library). (Illus.). 112p. (YA). (gr. 4-12). lib. bdg. 29.95 (978-1-56006-718-4(7) , LML00902-178070, Lucent Bks.) Thomson Gale.

DISTRIBUTION (ECONOMICS)

see Commerce; Marketing

DISTRIBUTION OF ANIMALS AND PLANTS

see Geographical Distribution of Animals and Plants

DISTRIBUTION OF WEALTH

see Economics

DISTRICT NURSES

see Nurses and Nursing

DIVERSITY, BIOLOGICAL

see Biodiversity

DIVIDENDS

see Securities; Stocks

DIVINATION

see also Astrology; Dreams; Fortune-Telling; Occultism; Superstition

Adcock, Will. Guia Practica Del I Ching. (SPA.). 64p. (J). 12.00 (978-84-342-3019-4(4)) Parramon Ediciones S.A. ESP. *Dist:* Distribuidora Norma, Inc.

Burns, Jane & Gottlieb, Dale. Wise Gal Tarot: Amazing Ways to Read Your Fortune! Slattery, Joan, ed. 2000. (Illus.). 64p. (J). (gr. 3-7). lib. bdg. 15.99 (978-0-375-90644-2(4) , Random Hse. Bks. for Young Readers) Random Hse. Children's Bks.

DIVINE HEALING

see Christian Science

DIVING

Bailer, Darice. Dive! 2002. (gr. 3-6). lib. bdg. 17.60 (978-0-613-81332-7(4)) Tandem Library Bks.

—Dive! Extreme Sports. 2002. (Extreme Sports Ser.). (Illus.). 64p. (J). (gr. 4-9). pap. 8.95 (978-0-7922-6743-0(5) , National Geographic Children's Bks.) National Geographic Society.

Covert, Kim. Extreme Diving. 2005. (X-Sports Ser.). (Illus.). 32p. (J). 22.60 (978-0-7368-3782-8(5)) Capstone Pr., Inc.

Deep Diving Adventures, 6 vols. (gr. 4 up). 39.95 (978-0-7368-9027-4(0)) Red Brick Learning.

Fine, John Christopher. Diving for Treasure. Fine, John Christopher, photos by. 2000. (Books for Young Learners). 16p. (J). pap. 5.00 (978-1-57274-391-5(3)) Owen, Richard C. Pubs., Inc.

Harcourt School Publishers Staff. Diving with Sylvia Earle On Level. 3rd ed. 2002. (Trophies Reading Program Ser.). pap. 5.10 (978-0-15-323353-1(2)) Harcourt Schl. Pubs.

Jarrell, Pamela R. Diving at the Reef. Ruminski, Jeff, illus. 2002. (Big Bks.). 8p. (J). (ps-1). pap. 10.95 (978-1-57332-200-3(8)); pap. 10.95 (978-1-57332-201-0(6)) HighReach Learning, Inc.

Kehm, Greg. Olympic Swimming & Diving. 2007. (Great Moments in Olympic History Ser.). (Illus.). 48p. (J). (gr. 5-8). lib. bdg. 26.50 (978-1-4042-0970-1(0) , Rosen Central) Rosen Publishing Group, Inc., The.

Keiser, Howard. Superstars of Men's Swimming & Diving. 1999. (Male Sports Stars Ser.). (Illus.). 64p. (YA). (gr. 4-7). 18.65 (978-0-7910-4589-3(7) , Chelsea Hse.) Facts On File, Inc.

Norman, Tony. Diving. 2006. (Illus.). 32p. (J). 24.67 (978-0-8368-6367-3(4)) Stevens, Gareth Inc.

Verrier, John. Swimming & Diving. 1998. (Olympic Library). (J). pap. (978-1-57572-039-5(6)) Heinemann Library.

Yoo, Paula. Sixteen Years in Sixteen Seconds: The Sammy Lee Story. Lee, Dom, illus. 2005. 32p. (J). (ps-k). 16.95 (978-1-58430-247-6(X)) Lee & Low Bks., Inc.

DIVING—FICTION

Alba, Gene. Mutley Goes Diving! 1998. (Mutley's True Life Adventures Ser.). (Illus.). 32p. (ps-3). 14.95 (978-0-89346-878-1(9)) Heian International Publishing, Inc.

Christopher, Matt. Dive Right In. ed. 2005. (Sports Classics IV Ser.). 133p. (J). lib. bdg. 15.00 (978-1-59054-753-3(5)) Fitzgerald Bks.

—Dive Right In. 2002. (#1 Sports Series for Kids). 144p. (J). (gr. 3-7). pap. 4.50 (978-0-316-34921-5(6)) Little, Brown Bks. for Young Readers.

—Dive Right In. 2002. (gr. 3-6). lib. bdg. 12.40 (978-0-613-50602-1(2)) Tandem Library Bks.

Cox, Buddy. Quicksilver Deep. 2004. 401p. per. 19.95 (978-0-9709104-3-1(6)) Hickory Tales Publishing.

Donovan, Stacey. Dive. 2000. (gr. 7-12). lib. bdg. 25.70 (978-0-613-87317-8(3)) Tandem Library Bks.

—Dive. 2001. 256p. (gr. 7-12). pap. 15.95 (978-0-595-16557-5(5) , Backinprint.com) iUniverse, Inc.

Hobbs, Valerie. Tender. 2001. 256p. (YA). (gr. 7 up). 18.00 (978-0-374-37397-9(3) , Farrar, Straus & Giroux (BYR)) Farrar, Straus & Giroux.

Johnson, Julia. The Pearl Diver. Al Fakhri, Patricia, illus. 2003. 56p. (J). pap. 15.95 (978-1-900988-58-2(5)) Interlink Publishing Group, Inc.

—The Pearl Diver. Al-Fakhri, Patricia, illus. 2003. (ARA.). 52p. (J). (gr. 3-6). pap. 15.95 (978-1-900988-62-9(3)) Stacey International Pubs. GBR. *Dist:* Interlink Publishing Group, Inc.

Korman, Gordon. The Danger. 2003. (Dive Ser.: No. 3). 144p. (J). pap. 4.99 (978-0-439-50724-0(3)) Scholastic, Inc.

—The Deep. 2003. (Dive Ser.: No. 2). 144p. (J). (gr. 3-6). pap. 4.99 (978-0-439-50723-3(5) , Scholastic Paperbacks) Scholastic, Inc.

—The Discovery. 2003. (Dive Ser.: No. 1). 144p. (J). (gr. 3-7). pap. 4.99 (978-0-439-50722-6(7) , Scholastic Paperbacks) Scholastic, Inc.

Streib, Sally. Octopus Encounter. 2007. (J). (***978-0-8163-2210-7(4)***) Pacific Pr. Publishing Assn.

Tromp, Janyre. That Sinking Feeling: Blue Water Mysteries. 2006. 128p. (J). pap. (978-0-8254-3887-5(X)) Kregel Pubns.

Wildner, Martina & Skofield, James. Shooting Stars Everywhere. 2006. 192p. (J). (gr. 7). 15.95 (978-0-385-73250-5(3) , Delacorte Bks. for Young Readers) Random Hse. Children's Bks.

DIVING, SKIN

see Skin Diving

DIVING, SUBMARINE

see Bathyscaphe; Deep Diving

DIVORCE

see also Marriage

Abrams, Liesa. Divorce. 2003. (Lucent Overview Ser.). (Illus.). 96p. (J). 29.95 (978-1-56006-197-7(9) , Lucent Bks.) Thomson Gale.

Aldrich, Vickie. Mom Has a New Boyfriend, What about Me? Crow, Madge, illus. 2000. vi, 26p. (J). (ps-3). pap. 7.95 (978-0-615-11547-4(0)) Aldrich/Crow.

Amos, Janine. Divorce. Green, Gwen, illus. Hampton, Angela, photos by. 2002. (Separations Ser.). 32p. (J). (gr. 3 up). lib. bdg. 23.33 (978-0-8368-3090-3(3)) Stevens, Gareth Inc.

Aydt, Rachel. Why Me? A Teen Guide to Divorce & Your Feelings. 2005. (Divorce Resource Ser.). (Illus.). 64p. (YA). (gr. 7-12). lib. bdg. 26.50 (978-0-8239-3113-2(7) , DIWHME) Rosen Publishing Group, Inc., The.

Beyer, Roberta & Winchester, Kent. Juggling Act: Handling Divorce Without Dropping the Ball: A Survival Kit for Parents & Kids. 2004. (Illus.). (YA). 39.95 (978-1-57542-097-4(X)) Free Spirit Publishing, Inc.

—Speaking of Divorce: How to Talk to Your Kids & Help Them Cope. 2004. (Illus.). 136p. (YA). (gr. 7 up). pap. 10.95 (978-1-57542-093-6(7)) Free Spirit Publishing, Inc.

—What in the World Do You Do When Your Parents Divorce? A Survival Guide for Kids. 2004. (Illus.). 128p. (YA). (gr. 2-7). pap. 9.95 (978-1-57542-092-9(9)) Free Spirit Publishing, Inc.

Beyl, Charles, illus. My Parents Are Divorced Too: A Book for Kids by Kids. 2nd ed. 2006. 71p. (J). 14.95 (978-1-59147-241-4(5)); pap. 9.95 (978-1-59147-242-1(3)) American Psychological Assn. (Magination Pr.).

Bianchi, Anne. Understanding the Law: A Teen Guide to Family Court & Minors' Rights. 2005. (Divorce Resource Ser.). (Illus.). 64p. (YA). (gr. 7-12). lib. bdg. 26.50 (978-0-8239-3152-1(8) , DIUNLA) Rosen Publishing Group, Inc., The.

Bingham, Jane. Why Do Families Break Up? 2004. (Exploring Tough Issues Ser.). (J). lib. bdg. 29.93 (978-0-7398-6683-2(4)) Raintree.

Bishop, Keeley & Tripp, Penny. Family Break Up. 2003. (Just the Facts Ser.). (Illus.). 56p. (YA). lib. bdg. 25.64 (978-1-4034-0819-8(X)) Heinemann Library.

Brotherton, Marcus. Split: A Graphic Reality Check for Teens Dealing with Divorce. 2006. 64p. pap. 7.00 (978-1-59052-716-0(X) , Multnomah) WaterBrook Pr.

Burchett, Mary. When Mommy & Daddy Divorce. 2004. (Illus.). 38p. pap. 12.95 (978-0-9748244-0-6(2)) Tate Publishing & Enterprises, L.L.C.

Cadier, Florence & Daly, Melissa. My Parents Are Getting Divorced: How to Keep It Together When Your Mom & Dad Are Splitting Up, 4 vols. Gandini, Claire, illus. 2004. (Sunscreen Ser.). 112p. (J). (gr. 6-11). pap. 9.95 (978-0-8109-9163-7(2) , Amulet Bks.) Abrams, Harry N. , Inc.

Calhoun, Florence. No Easy Answers: A Teen Guide to Why Divorce Happens. 2005. (Divorce Resource Ser.). (Illus.). 64p. (YA). (gr. 7-12). lib. bdg. 26.50 (978-0-8239-3153-8(6) , DINOEA) Rosen Publishing Group, Inc., The.

Cann, Kate. Breaking Up. 2002. 150p. pap. 9.95 (978-0-7043-4976-6(0)) Women's Pr., Ltd., The GBR. *Dist:* Trafalgar Square Publishing.

Cassella, Lynn. When Parents Divorce. 2003. (YA). pap. 1.95 net. (978-0-7648-1061-9(8)) Liguori Pubns.

Charlish, Anne. Divorce. 1999. (Talking Points Ser.). (Illus.). 64p. (YA). (gr. 5-9). lib. bdg. 27.12 (978-0-8172-5310-3(6)) Raintree.

Clark, Betty. When Your Parents Divorce: A Handbook for Children Whose Parents Are Divorcing. Kaiser, Cyndee, illus. 1998. 148p. (YA). (gr. 8 up). pap. 7.95 (978-0-932796-89-9(3)) Educational Media Corp.

Cole, Babette. Todo Doble o Como Divorciarse con Buen Humor. 2001. (SPA.). 34p. (J). (gr. 1-3). (978-84-233-2961-8(5)) Ediciones Destino ESP. *Dist:* Lectorum Pubns., Inc.

Crews, June T. Can Anyone Fix My Broken Heart? Hope for Children of Divorce. 2000. (Illus.). 32p. (Orig.). (J). (ps-3). pap. 6.99 (978-1-57921-228-5(X)) WinePress Publishing.

The Divorce Resource Series, 6 bks. Incl. Caught in the Middle : A Teen Guide to Custody. Isler, Claudia. (YA). lib. bdg. 26.50 (978-0-8239-3109-5(9) , DICAMI); Finding Your Place : A Teen Guide to Life in a Blended Family. Leibowitz, Julie. (YA). lib. bdg. 26.50 (978-0-8239-3114-9(5) , DIFIPL); Money Matters : A Teen Guide to the Economics of Divorce. Frisch, Carlienne A. (J). lib. bdg. 26.50 (978-0-8239-3151-4(X) , DIMOMA); No Easy Answers : A Teen Guide to Why Divorce Happens. Calhoun, Florence. (YA). lib. bdg. 26.50 (978-0-8239-3153-8(6) , DINOEA); Understanding the Law : A Teen Guide to Family Court & Minors' Rights. Bianchi, Anne. (YA). lib. bdg. 26.50 (978-0-8239-3152-1(8) , DIUNLA); Why Me? A Teen Guide to Divorce & Your Feelings. Aydt, Rachel. (YA). lib. bdg. 26.50 (978-0-8239-3113-2(7) , DIWHME); 64p. (gr. 7-12). (Illus.). 2005. Set lib. bdg. 159.00 (978-0-8239-9050-4(8) , DIVRES) Rosen Publishing Group, Inc., The.

Dotterweich, Kass. What Catholic Teens Should Know about Divorce. Larkin, Jean, ed. 2003. (What Catholic Teens Should Know Ser.). (Illus.). 8p. (YA). 7.95 (978-0-89837-189-5(9) , 440210) Pflaum Publishing Group.

Edwards, Nicola. Divorce. (Illus.). 32p. (YA). (gr. 1 up). lib. bdg. 27.10 (978-1-932333-05-3(3)) Chrysalis Education.

Feelings Only I Know: Mom & Dad Are Getting Divorced. 2007. (J). 14.95 (***978-0-9789965-0-5(X)***) Wayfarer Pr., LLC.

Friedler, Anna Dunwell. My Very Own Family Divorce. 2000. (Illus.). 16p. (J). (gr. k-12). spiral bd. 29.95 (978-1-891657-35-1(6) , S3091) Lift Every Voice.

Frisch, Carlienne A. Money Matters: A Teen Guide to the Economics of Divorce. 2005. (Divorce Resource Ser.). (Illus.). 64p. (J). (gr. 7-12). lib. bdg. 26.50 (978-0-8239-3151-4(X) , DIMOMA) Rosen Publishing Group, Inc., The.

Garon, Risa J. A Kid's Guide to Coming toTerms with Separation & Divorce. 2000. (Illus.). 23p. (YA). pap. 10.00 (978-0-9729415-1-8(7)) National Family Resiliency Ctr., Inc.

Goldentyer, Debra. Divorce. 1998. (Preteen Pressures Ser.). (Illus.). 48p. (J). (gr. 4-8). lib. bdg. 25.69 (978-0-8172-5030-0(1)) Raintree.

Grollman, Earl A. Talking about Divorce & Separation: A Dialogue Between Parent & Child. Pitzer, Suzanne, illus. 2005. (J). (978-1-56123-155-3(X)) Centering Corp.

Hunt, Angela Elwell. Keeping Your Life Together When Your Parents Pull Apart: A Teen's Guide to Survi. 2000. (gr. 7-12). 1998. lib. bdg. 19.90 (978-0-613-86214-1(7)) Tandem Library Bks.

Isler, Claudia. Caught in the Middle: A Teen Guide to Custody. 2005. (Divorce Resource Ser.). (Illus.). 64p. (YA). (gr. 7-12). lib. bdg. 26.50 (978-0-8239-3109-5(9) , DICAMI) Rosen Publishing Group, Inc., The.

Katie & Coco: A Color Book for Parents & Preschoolers about Divorce. 2004. (J). 5.00 (978-0-9767215-0-5(3)) Family Guidance & Outreach Ctr. of Lubbock.

Kuehn, Eileen. Divorce: Finding a Place. 2001. (Grief & Loss Ser.). (Illus.). 64p. (J). (gr. 4-6). lib. bdg. 23.93 (978-0-7368-0747-0(0) , LifeMatters Bks.) Capstone Pr., Inc.

Lansky, Vicki. It's Not Your Fault, KoKo Bear Package: A Book & a Bear, 2 vols. 1999. (Lansky, Vicki Ser.). (Illus.). 21.95 (978-0-916773-74-8(4)) Book Peddlers.

Lebowitz, Marcia L. I Think Divorce Stinks. Borguald, Pamela M., illus. 3rd rev. ed. 1999. 32p. (J). (gr. 1-8). pap. 9.95 (978-0-935769-05-0(6)) CDC Pr.

Levins, Sandra. Was It the Chocolate Pudding? A Story for Little Kids about Divorce. Langdo, Bryan, illus. 2005. 40p. (J). 14.95 (978-1-59147-308-4(X)); pap. 8.95 (978-1-59147-309-1(8)) American Psychological Assn. (Magination Pr.).

MacGregor, Cynthia. The Divorce Helpbook for Kids. 2001. (Rebuilding Books, for Divorce & Beyond). 112p. (J). (gr. 4-8). pap. 12.95 (978-1-886230-39-2(0) , Rebuilding Bks.) Impact Pubs., Inc.

—The Divorce Helpbook for Teens. 2004. (Rebuilding Books, for Divorce & Beyond). 144p. (J). pap. 13.95 (978-1-886230-57-6(9)) Impact Pubs., Inc.

McDowell, Josh & Stewart, Ed. Friendship 911 Collection: My Friend Is Struggling with... Divorce of Parents. 2000. (Friendship 911 Ser.). (Illus.). 64p. (gr. 8-12). pap. 7.98 (978-0-8499-3794-1(9)) Nelson, Thomas Inc.

Menendez-Aponte, Emily. When Mom & Dad Divorce: A Kid's Resource. Alley, R. W., illus. 1999. 32p. (J). (ps-3). pap. 5.95 (978-0-87029-333-7(8)) Abbey Pr.

Moore-Mallions, Jennifer & Roca, Nuria. Mi Papa se Casa: Daddy's Getting Married, Spanish Edition. Fabrega, Marta, illus. 2006. (Let's Talk about It Bks.). (SPA.). 32p. (J). pap. 6.99 (978-0-7641-3505-7(8)) Barron's Educational Series, Inc.

Moser, Adolph J. Don't Fall Apart on Saturdays! The Children's Divorce-Survival Book. Melton, David, illus. 2000. (Emotional Impact Ser.). 60p. (J). (gr. 4-7). lib. bdg. 19.95 (978-0-933849-77-8(X)) Landmark Editions, Inc.

Murphy, Patricia J. Divorce & Separation. 2007. (***978-1-4034-9775-8(3)***); pap. (***978-1-4034-9780-2(X)***) Heinemann Library.

Pleasant Company Staff. Help! A Girl's Guide to Divorce & Stepfamilies. 1999. (J). (978-0-606-19870-7(9)) Tandem Library Bks.

Powell, Jillian. Family Breakup. 1999. (Talking about Ser.). (Illus.). 32p. (J). (gr. k-4). lib. bdg. 25.69 (978-0-8172-5542-8(7)) Raintree.

Price, Elizabeth. Divorce & Teens: When a Family Splits Apart. 2004. (Teen Issues Ser.). (Illus.). 64p. (J). lib. bdg. 22.60 (978-0-7660-1670-5(6)) Enslow Pubs., Inc.

Prokop, Michael S. Kids Divorce Workbook: A Book by, for & about Kids. Peters, Robert C., ed. McCullough, Dennis J. et al, illus. rev. ed. 2001. 112p. (J). (ps-7). pap., wbk. ed. 9.95 (978-0-933879-42-3(3)) Alegra Hse. Pubs.

Reilly, Natalie June. My Stick Family: Helping Children Cope with Divorce. 2003. (gr. k-3). lib. bdg. 22.20 (978-0-613-87999-6(6)) Tandem Library Bks.

Ripley, Nancy & Rebowe, Darlene. K. I. D. S. Kids in Divorce Support. 2002. 12.95 (978-1-930572-19-5(0)) Educational Media Corp.

Rogers, Fred. Divorce. Judkis, Jim, illus. 1998. (Let's Talk about It Ser.). 32p. (J). (ps-3). pap. 6.99 (978-0-698-11670-2(4) , Putnam Juvenile) Penguin Group (USA) Inc.

Rubin, Judith. My Mom & Dad Don't Live Together Anymore: A Drawing Book for Children of Separated or Divorced Parents. Matthews, Bonnie, illus. 2002. 80p. (J). (ps-6). pap. 14.95 (978-1-55798-835-5(8) , Magination Pr.) American Psychological Assn.

Sam & Sarge. 2004. (J). 5.00 (978-0-9767215-1-2(1)) Family Guidance & Outreach Ctr. of Lubbock.

Sanders, Pete & Myers, Steve. When Parents Separate. 2006. (Choices & Decisions Ser.). (Illus.). 32p. (J). (978-1-59604-096-0(3)) Stargazer Bks.

Sommers-Flanagan, Rita, et al. Don't Divorce Us! Kid's Advice to Divorcing Parents. 2000. (Illus.). 157p. pap. 23.95 (978-1-55620-175-2(3) , 72663) American Counseling Assn.

Stern, Ellen S., et al. Divorce Is Not the End of the World: Zoe's & Evan's Coping Guide for Kids. 2004. (Illus.). 96p. (YA). (gr. 4-8). pap. 8.95 (978-1-883672-44-7(9) , Tricycle Pr.) Ten Speed Pr.

Thomas, Pat. My Family's Changing: A First Look at Family Break-Up. Harker, Lesley, illus. 1999. (First Look at Bks.). 32p. (J). (ps-2). pap. 6.95 (978-0-7641-0995-9(2)) Barron's Educational Series, Inc.

—My Family's Changing: A First Look at Family Break Up. 1999. (978-0-606-18004-7(4)) Tandem Library Bks.

Trueit, Trudi Strain. Surviving Divorce: Teens Talk about What Hurts & What Helps. 2005. (Scholastic Choices Ser.). (Illus.). 112p. (J). (gr. 7-12). 22.50 (978-0-531-12368-3(5) , Watts, Franklin) Scholastic Library Publishing.

Tubbs, Janet. Divorce, Set. 2000. (Spud Packs Ser.). 16p. (J). pap. 19.95 (978-1-881185-15-4(X)) Arcadia Pr.

Whyman, Matthew. Family Breakup. 2nd ed. 2005. (Illus.). (YA). pap. 12.00 (978-0-340-88394-5(4) , Hodder & Stoughton) Hodder General Publishing Division GBR. *Dist:* Trafalgar Square Publishing.

Winchester, Kent. My Two Homes Magic Words Handbook for Kids. 1998. (Illus.). 28p. (J). (gr. 2-6). spiral bd. 5.95 (978-0-9650296-1-2(1)) LadyBug Pr.

DIVORCE—FICTION

Adams, Eric J. & Adams, Kathleen. On the Day His Daddy Left. Johnson, Layne, illus. 2000. (Concept Book Ser.). 24p. (J). (gr. k-4). 15.95 (978-0-8075-6072-3(3)); pap. 6.95 (978-0-8075-6073-0(1)) Whitman, Albert & Co.

Aldrich, Vickie. Dad Has a New Girlfriend, What about Me? Crow, Madge, illus. 2000. VI, 25p. (J). (ps-3). pap. 7.95 (978-0-9706093-0-4(2)) Aldrich/Crow.

—Mom & Dad Divorce, What about Me? Crow, Madge, illus. 2000. 32p. (J). (ps-3). pap. 7.95 (978-0-9706093-1-1(0) , 003) Aldrich/Crow.

Alki Zei Staff. Tina's Web. 2007. 300p. pap. 18.95 (***978-0-9551566-1-8(0)***) Aurora Metro Pubns. Ltd. GBR. *Dist:* Consortium Bk. Sales & Distribution.

Alvarez, Julia. Cuando Tia Lola Vino (de Visita) a Quedarse. Valenzuela, Liliana, tr. 2004. Tr. of How Tia Lola Came to (Visit) Stay. (SPA.). 144p. (gr. 3-7). pap. 5.50 (978-0-375-81552-2(X) , Yearling) Random Hse. Children's Bks.

—Cuando Tía Lola Vino (De Visita) a Quedarse. Valenzuela, Liliana, tr. 2004. (SPA.). 144p. (J). (gr. 3-7). lib. bdg. 17.99 (978-0-375-91552-9(4) , Yearling) Random Hse. Children's Bks.

—How Tia Lola Came to Stay. 2002. (Illus.). 160p. (gr. 3-7). 5.99 (978-0-440-41870-2(4) , Yearling) Random Hse. Children's Bks.

—How Tia Lola Came to (Visit) Stay. Cascardi, Andrea, ed. 2001. (Illus.). 160p. (J). (gr. 3-5). 15.95 (978-0-375-80215-7(0)); lib. bdg. 17.99 (978-0-375-90215-4(5)) Random Hse. Children's Bks. (Knopf Bks. for Young Readers).

Andrews, V. C. Jade. 1999. (Wildflower Ser.). (978-0-606-17531-9(8)) Tandem Library Bks.

—Jade. l.t. ed. 1999. (Core Ser.). 176p. (YA). 29.95 (978-0-7838-8804-0(X) , Macmillan Reference USA) Thomson Gale.

—Misty. 1999. (Wildflower Ser.). (978-0-606-17532-6(6)) Tandem Library Bks.

—Star. 1999. (978-0-606-17533-3(4)) Tandem Library Bks.

Atkinson, Elizabeth. Lisa's Totally Unforgettable Winter. 2006. (ENG.). 56p. per. 12.95 ***(978-1-4241-6249-9(1))*** PublishAmerica, Inc.

Bateman, Colin. Running with the Reservoir Pups. 2005. 272p. (J). (gr. 5-9). lib. bdg. 17.99 (978-0-385-90268-7(9) , Delacorte Bks. for Young Readers) Random Hse. Children's Bks.

Bateson, Catherine. Rain May & Captain Daniel. 2002. 144p. (YA). pap. 15.50 (978-0-7022-3337-1(4)) Univ. of Queensland Pr. AUS. *Dist:* International Specialized Bk. Services.

Bateson, Catherine. Stranded in Boringsville. 144p. (gr. 5-9). (J). 16.95 (978-0-8234-1969-2(X)); 2007. (YA). pap. 6.95 ***(978-0-8234-2113-8(9))*** Holiday Hse., Inc.

Bauer, Joan. Stand Tall. 192p. (YA). 2005. (gr. 5). pap. 7.99 (978-0-14-240427-0(6) , Puffin); 2002. (gr. 6-9). 16.99 (978-0-399-23473-6(X) , Putnam Juvenile) Penguin Group (USA) Inc.

Bernhard, Durga. To & Fro, Fast & Slow. 2001. (Illus.). 32p. (J). (ps-2). 15.95 (978-0-8027-8782-8(7)); lib. bdg. 16.85 (978-0-8027-8783-5(5)) Walker & Co.

Blume, Judy. It's Not the End of the World. 2002. (Illus.). (J). 13.94 (978-0-7587-9132-0(1)) Book Wholesalers, Inc.

—It's Not the End of the World. 174p. (YA). (gr. 5 up). pap. 4.50 (978-0-8072-1365-0(9) , Listening Library) Random Hse. Audio Publishing Group.

—It's Not the End of the World. 2002. 176p. (J). 17.99 (978-0-689-84293-1(7) , Atheneum/Richard Jackson Bks.) Simon & Schuster Children's Publishing.

Boles, Philana Marie. Little Divas. 2006. 176p. (J). 15.99 (978-0-06-073299-8(7) , Amistad); lib. bdg. 16.89 (978-0-06-073300-1(4)) HarperCollins Pubs.

Bradley, Kimberly Brubaker. Halfway to the Sky. 176p. (gr. 3-7). 2003. (J). pap. 5.99 (978-0-440-41830-6(5) , Yearling); 2002. 15.95 (978-0-385-72960-4(X) , Delacorte Bks. for Young Readers) Random Hse. Children's Bks.

—Halfway to the Sky. 2003. (gr. 5-8). lib. bdg. 13.00 (978-0-613-62771-9(7)) Tandem Library Bks.

Brinkerhoff, Shirley. Tangled Web. 2000. (Nikki Sheridan Ser.: Vol. 5). 176p. (J). (gr. 9-12). pap. 5.99 (978-1-56179-737-0(5)) Bethany Hse. Pubs.

—Tangled Web. 2000. (gr. 7-12). lib. bdg. 14.15 (978-0-613-84406-2(8)) Tandem Library Bks.

Brown, Marc. Arthur & the 1,001 Dads. Brown, Marc, illus. 28th ed. 2003. (Arthur Chapter Bks. : Bk. 28). (Illus.). 64p. (J). (gr. 1-4). 14.95 (978-0-316-12516-1(4)); pap. 4.25 (978-0-316-12280-1(7)) Little, Brown Bks. for Young Readers.

—Arthur & the 1,001 Dads. 2003. (Arthur Chapter Bks.: Bk. 28). (Illus.). 57p. (J). (ps). lib. bdg. 12.10 (978-0-613-58311-4(6)) Tandem Library Bks.

Brugman, Alyssa. Being Bindy. 2006. 208p. (YA). (gr. 7). 15.95 (978-0-385-73294-9(5)); lib. bdg. 17.99 (978-0-385-90315-8(4)) Random Hse. Children's Bks. (Delacorte Bks. for Young Readers).

Bunting, Eve. The Days of Summer. Low, William, illus. 2001. 40p. (J). (gr. k-3). 16.00 (978-0-15-201840-5(9)) Harcourt Children's Bks.

—My Mom's Wedding. Papp, Lisa, illus. 2006. 32p. (J). (gr. 1-5). 16.95 (978-1-58536-288-2(3)) Sleeping Bear Pr.

—Some Frog! Medlock, Scott, illus. 2002. 48p. (J). (gr. 1-4). pap. 6.00 (978-0-15-216384-6(0) , Voyager Bks./Libros Viajeros) Harcourt Children's Bks.

—Some Frog! 2002. (gr. 3-6). lib. bdg. 14.15 (978-0-613-53865-7(X)) Tandem Library Bks.

—The Summer of Riley. 2002. (gr. 3-6). lib. bdg. 14.10 (978-0-613-44482-8(5)) Tandem Library Bks.

Carney, Karen L. Together, We'll Get Through This! Learning to Cope with Loss & Transition. Carney, Karen L., illus. 1999. (Barklay & Eve Ser.: Bk. 1). (Illus.). (J). pap. 6.95 (978-0-9667820-0-4(3)) Dragonfly Publishing.

Caseley, Judith. The Kissing Diary. 2007. 208p. (J). (gr. 5 up). 16.00 (978-0-374-36346-8(3)) Farrar, Straus & Giroux.

Clarke, Jane. The Best of Both Nests. Kennedy, Anne, illus. 2007. 32p. (J). 15.95 ***(978-0-8075-0668-4(0))*** Whitman, Albert & Co.

Cleary, Beverly. Dear Mr. Henshaw. 2002. (Illus.). (J). 13.83 (978-0-7587-9140-5(2)) Book Wholesalers, Inc.

—Dear Mr. Henshaw. Zelinsky, Paul O., illus. 2000. (Cleary Reissue Ser.). 160p. (J). (gr. 5 up). pap. 5.99 (978-0-380-70958-8(9) , Harper Trophy) HarperCollins Pubs.

Clements, Andrew. Head of the Class: Frindle; the Landry News; the Janitor's Boy. Selznick, Brian, illus. 2007. 416p. (J). 17.99 ***(978-1-4169-4974-9(7)*** , Aladdin) Simon & Schuster Children's Publishing.

—The Landry News. 2000. (gr. 3-6). lib. bdg. 13.00 (978-0-613-30001-8(7)) Tandem Library Bks.

—El Periodico Landry. Selznick, Brian, illus. 2004. Tr. of Landry News. (SPA.). (YA). pap. 9.99 (978-84-241-7886-4(6)) Everest de Ediciones y Distribucion, S.L. ESP. *Dist:* Lectorum Pubns., Inc.

Clements, Bruce. What Erika Wants. 2005. 224p. (YA). (gr. 7-17). 16.00 (978-0-374-32304-2(6) , Farrar, Straus & Giroux (BYR)) Farrar, Straus & Giroux.

Cockerill, Pamela. Finders Keepers. 2000. 137p. pap. 12.95 (978-1-85902-816-2(0)) Beekman Bks., Inc.

Comor-Jacobs, Annie. Reesy: A Little Girl Learning Life's Lessons: Reesy Learning about Divorce; Reesy Learning about the Deep South; Reesy Learning about Deafness; Reesy Learning about Death. 4 vols. Price, Chris, illus. 2000. 40p. (J). (gr. 2-5). pap. 30.00 (978-1-889743-18-9(6)) Robbie Dean Pr.

Cooney, Caroline B. Tune in Anytime. 2001. (J). (978-0-606-21495-7(X)) Tandem Library Bks.

Cruise, Robin. Top-Secret Journal of Fiona Claire Jardin. 2000. (978-0-606-18192-1(X)) Tandem Library Bks.

Curtis, Patricia Gregory. A Secret from the Deep. 2004. 154p. pap. 19.95 (978-1-4137-2293-2(8)) PublishAmerica, Inc.

Danziger, Paula. Amber Brown Goes Fourth. Ross, Tony, illus. 2002. (Amber Brown Ser.: No. 3). (J). (gr. 3-6). 12.17 (978-0-7587-0417-7(8)) Book Wholesalers, Inc.

—Amber Brown Goes Fourth. 2007. (Amber Brown Ser.: No. 3). 112p. (J). (gr. 2-6). 4.99 ***(978-0-14-240901-5(4)*** , Puffin) Penguin Group (USA) Inc.

—Amber Brown Goes Fourth. (Amber Brown Ser.: No. 3). 112p. (J). (gr. 3-6). pap. 3.99 (978-0-8072-1291-2(1) , Listening Library) Random Hse. Audio Publishing Group.

—Amber Brown Is Feeling Blue. Ross, Tony, illus. 2002. (Amber Brown Ser.: No. 7). (J). (gr. 3-6). 12.17 (978-0-7587-0418-4(6)) Book Wholesalers, Inc.

—Amber Brown Is Feeling Blue. Ross, Tony, illus. 1998. (Amber Brown Ser.: No. 7). 128p. (J). (gr. 3-6). 14.99 (978-0-399-23179-7(X) , Putnam Juvenile) Penguin Group (USA) Inc.

—Amber Brown Is Feeling Blue. 2004. (Amber Brown Ser.: No. 7). 131p. (J). (gr. 2-4). pap. 17.00 incl. audio (978-0-8072-2063-4(9) , Listening Library) Random Hse. Audio Publishing Group.

—Amber Brown Is Feeling Blue. Ross, Tony & Rogers, Jacqueline, illus. 1999. (Amber Brown Ser.: No. 7). 144p. (J). (gr. 3-6). pap. 3.99 (978-0-439-07168-0(2)) Scholastic, Inc.

—Amber Brown Is Feeling Blue. 1999. (Amber Brown Ser.: No. 7). (J). (gr. 3-6). 10.64 (978-0-606-17275-2(0)); lib. bdg. 11.80 (978-0-613-20096-7(9)) Tandem Library Bks.

—Amber Brown Is Green with Envy. Ross, Tony, illus. 2003. (Amber Brown Ser.: No. 9). 160p. (J). (gr. 2-5). 15.99 (978-0-399-23181-0(1) , Putnam Juvenile) Penguin Group (USA) Inc.

—Amber Brown Is Green with Envy. Ross, Tony, illus. 2004. (Amber Brown Ser.: No. 9). 160p. (J). (gr. 3-6). pap. 4.99 (978-0-439-07171-0(2) , Scholastic Paperbacks) Scholastic, Inc.

—Amber Brown Sees Red. Ross, Tony, illus. 2002. (Amber Brown Ser.: No. 6). (J). (gr. 3-6). 12.17 (978-0-7587-0420-7(8)) Book Wholesalers, Inc.

—Amber Brown Sees Red. (Amber Brown Ser.: No. 6). 116p. (J). (gr. 3-6). pap. 3.99 (978-0-8072-1294-3(6) , Listening Library) Random Hse. Audio Publishing Group.

—Amber Brown Sees Red. Ross, Tony, illus. 1998. (Amber Brown Ser.: No. 6). 130p. (J). (gr. 3-6). pap. 3.99 (978-0-590-94728-2(1)) Scholastic, Inc.

—Amber Brown Sees Red. 1998. (Amber Brown Ser.: No. 6). (J). (gr. 3-6). 10.64 (978-0-606-12874-2(3)) Tandem Library Bks.

—Amber Brown Wants Extra Credit. Ross, Tony, illus. 2002. (Amber Brown Ser.: No. 4). (J). (gr. 3-6). 12.17 (978-0-7587-0421-4(6)) Book Wholesalers, Inc.

—Amber Brown Wants Extra Credit. Ross, Tony, illus. 2008. (Amber Brown Ser.: No. 4). 128p. (J). (gr. 2-6). 4.99 ***(978-0-14-241049-3(7)*** , Puffin) Penguin Group (USA) Inc.

—Amber Brown Wants Extra Credit. (Amber Brown Ser.: No. 4). 120p. (J). (gr. 3-6). pap. 3.99 (978-0-8072-1292-9(X) , Listening Library) Random Hse. Audio Publishing Group.

—The Divorce Express. 2007. 160p. (J). (gr. 5). pap. 5.99 (978-0-14-240712-7(7) , Puffin) Penguin Group (USA) Inc.

—The Divorce Express. 160p. (J). pap. 3.99 (978-0-8072-1376-6(4) , Listening Library) Random Hse. Audio Publishing Group.

—I, Amber Brown. Ross, Tony, illus. 1999. (Amber Brown Ser.: No. 8). 144p. (J). (gr. 3-6). 14.99 (978-0-399-23180-3(3) , Putnam Juvenile) Penguin Group (USA) Inc.

—I, Amber Brown. 2004. (Amber Brown Ser.: No. 8). 144p. (J). (gr. 2-4). pap. 17.00 incl. audio (978-0-8072-2064-1(7) , Listening Library) Random Hse. Audio Publishing Group.

—I, Amber Brown. 2000. (Amber Brown Ser.: No. 8). (gr. 3-6). lib. bdg. 11.80 (978-0-613-28528-5(X)) Tandem Library Bks.

—It's an Aardvark-Eat-Turtle World. 2007. 144p. (J). (gr. 5). pap. 5.99 (978-0-14-240679-3(1) , Puffin) Penguin Group (USA) Inc.

—It's an Aardvark-Eat-Turtle World. 2000. (Illus.). (J). 11.64 (978-0-606-18469-4(4)) Tandem Library Bks.

—You Can't Eat Your Chicken Pox, Amber Brown. (Amber Brown Ser.: No. 2). 101p. (J). (gr. 3-6). pap. 3.50 (978-0-8072-1290-5(3) , Listening Library) Random Hse. Audio Publishing Group.

—You Can't Eat Your Chicken Pox, Amber Brown. Ross, Tony, illus. 2006. (Amber Brown Ser.). 112p. (J). (gr. 2). pap. 4.99 (978-0-14-240629-8(5) , Puffin) Penguin Group (USA) Inc.

Davidson, Barbara. Billys Most Difficult Choice. 2007. 49p. 12.95 ***(978-1-4241-6153-9(3))*** PublishAmerica, Inc.

de Oliveira, Eddie. Johnny Hazzard. 2005. 352p. (J). (gr. 7-12). pap. 16.95 (978-0-439-67361-7(5) , PUSH) Scholastic, Inc.

Dellasega, Cheryl. Nugrl90 (Sadie) LaPierre, Karina, illus. 2007. (Bloggrls Ser.). (YA). (gr. 7 up). 200p. 15.99 ***(978-0-7614-5375-8(X));*** 190p. per. 6.99 ***(978-0-7614-5396-3(2))*** Cavendish, Marshall Corp.

Deuker, Carl. Night Hoops. 2001. 256p. (gr. 7 up). pap. 6.99 (978-0-06-447275-3(2) , Harper Trophy) HarperCollins Pubs.

—Night Hoops. 2000. (Illus.). 224p. (J). (gr. 7-12). tchr. ed. 15.00 (978-0-395-97936-5(6)) Houghton Mifflin Co. Trade & Reference Div.

—Night Hoops. 2001. (978-0-606-22927-2(2)); 250p. (gr. 7-12). lib. bdg. 14.15 (978-0-613-61919-6(6)) Tandem Library Bks.

Dhami, Narinder. Genius Games. 2001. 160p. (gr. 3-7). 15.99 (978-0-7868-0616-4(8)) Hyperion Bks. for Children.

Doherty, Berlie. Holly Starcross. 2002. 192p. (J). (gr. 7 up). 17.89 (978-0-06-001342-4(7)) HarperCollins Pubs.

Doodle, Nanny. Divorced at Six. 2006. 158p. pap. 19.95 (978-1-4241-3963-7(5)) PublishAmerica, Inc.

Dower, Laura. From the Files of Madison Finn: Sink or Swim. 2003. (gr. 3-6). lib. bdg. 13.00 (978-0-613-88965-0(7)) Tandem Library Bks.

—From the Files of Madison Finn No.15: Off the Wall. 2004. (gr. 3-6). lib. bdg. 13.00 (978-0-613-91008-8(7)) Tandem Library Bks.

—Sink or Swim. rev. ed. 2003. (From the Files of Madison Finn Ser.: No. 13). 176p. (J). (gr. 3-7). pap. 4.99 (978-0-7868-1735-1(6) , Volo) Hyperion Bks. for Children.

Dumont, Virginie & Soria, Bernard. Enredos de Familia. Boucher, Michel, illus. 2004. (Arbol de la Vida Ser.). (SPA.). 64p. (J). 13.99 (978-84-8488-098-1(2)) Serres, Ediciones, S. L. ESP. *Dist:* Lectorum Pubns., Inc.

Ernst, Kathleen. Highland Fling. 2006. 192p. (J). 15.95 (978-0-8126-2742-8(3)) Cricket Bks.

Falk, Jennifer & Morgan. A Heart Daddy for Chrissie. 2005. 43p. (J). pap. 16.00 (978-1-4116-3585-2(X)) Lulu.com.

Fitch, Sheree. One More Step. (Orca Soundings Ser.). 2006. 112p. (YA). lib. bdg. 14.95 (978-1-55143-554-1(3)); 2002. 96p. (J). (gr. 7-12). pap. 7.95 (978-1-55143-248-9(X)) Orca Bk. Pubs. USA.

—One More Step. 2002. (gr. 7-12). lib. bdg. 16.40 (978-0-613-62978-2(7)) Tandem Library Bks.

Forbes. Sinking Sam. 2002. 115p. pap. 16.95 (978-1-59129-852-6(0)) PublishAmerica, Inc.

Franklin, Kristine L. Lone Wolf. 224p. (J). (gr. 4-8). 2006. 5.99 (978-0-7636-2996-0(0)); 1998. (Illus.). pap. 6.99 (978-0-7636-0480-6(1)) Candlewick Pr.

—Lone Wolf. 1998. (J). (978-0-606-13578-8(2)) Tandem Library Bks.

Fritz, T. J. Katey's Dream List. 1999. 90p. (gr. 4-7). 7.95 (978-1-56315-084-5(0)) SterlingHouse Pubs., Inc.

Gallagher, Mary Collins. Ginny Morris & Dad's New Girlfriend. Martin, Whitney, illus. 2006. 63p. (J). (gr. 3-5). 14.95 (978-1-59147-386-2(1)); pap. 8.95 (978-1-59147-387-9(X)) American Psychological Assn. (Magination Pr.).

—Nine Is Not an Even Number. Martin, Whitney, illus. 2004. 48p. (J). 14.95 (978-1-59147-157-8(5)); pap. 8.95 (978-1-59147-158-5(3)) American Psychological Assn. (Magination Pr.).

Garfinkle, Debra. Storky: How I Lost My Nickname & Won the Girl. 192p. (YA). 2007. (gr. 7 up). pap. 5.99 (978-0-14-240782-0(8) , Puffin); 2005. (gr. 6). 16.99 (978-0-399-24284-7(8) , Putnam Juvenile) Penguin Group (USA) Inc.

Garon, Risa J. Snowman. 2000. (Illus.). 5p. (J). pap. 5.00 (978-0-9729415-0-1(9)) National Family Resiliency Ctr., Inc.

Gasparro, Marie & Falletta, Bernadette. The Magnificent Hole. 2005. 13p. (J). 12.95 (978-1-4116-5924-7(4)) Lulu.com.

Haas, Dan. You Can Call Me Worm. 1999. (978-0-606-16790-1(0)) Tandem Library Bks.

Hobbs, Valerie. Charlie's Run. 2000. (Illus.). 176p. (YA). (gr. 4-7). 16.00 (978-0-374-34994-3(0) , Farrar, Straus & Giroux (BYR)) Farrar, Straus & Giroux.

—Charlie's Run. 2002. (gr. 3-6). lib. bdg. 14.15 (978-0-613-85722-2(4)) Tandem Library Bks.

—Charlie's Run. l.t. ed. 2001. (Illus.). 166p. (J). (gr. 4-7). 21.95 (978-0-7862-3104-1(1)) Thorndike Pr.

Hood, Ann. How I Saved My Father's Life (and Ruined Everything Else) 2008. 224p. (J). pap. 16.99 ***(978-0-439-92819-9(2)*** , Scholastic Pr.) Scholastic, Inc.

Hubler, Marsha. The Winning Summer. 2005. (Keystone Stables Ser.: Bk. 5). (Illus.). 144p. (J). pap. 4.99 (978-0-310-70798-1(6)) Zonderkidz.

Hurwitz, Johanna. One Small Dog. deGroat, Diane, illus. (J). (gr. 2 up). 2002. 112p. pap. 5.99 (978-0-380-73293-7(9)); 2000. 128p. 15.89 (978-0-06-029220-1(2)); 2000. 128p. 15.95 (978-0-688-17382-1(9)) HarperCollins Pubs.

—One Small Dog. 2002. (gr. 3-6). lib. bdg. 13.00 (978-0-613-62113-7(1)) Tandem Library Bks.

Jenkins, A. M. Beating Heart: A Ghost Story. 2006. 256p. (YA). 16.99 (978-0-06-054607-6(7)); (Illus.). (J). lib. bdg. 16.89 (978-0-06-054608-3(5)) HarperCollins Pubs.

Johnson, Angela. Songs of Faith. 1998. (Illus.). 112p. (J). (gr. 3-7). 16.99 (978-0-531-33023-4(0)); pap. 15.95 (978-0-531-30023-7(4)) Scholastic, Inc. (Orchard Bks.).

Jones, Jennifer B. Dear Mrs. Ryan, You're Ruining My Life. 2004. 144p. (J). pap. 5.95 (978-0-8027-7653-2(1)) Walker & Co.

Judd-Leisten, Betty. Tell It for a Toll, Toll It for a Tale. 2005. 102p. per. 7.95 (978-1-59824-057-3(9)) E-BookTime LLC.

Kelly, Katy. Busy Like You Can't Believe. Rex, Adam, illus. 2006. (Lucy Rose Ser.). 176p. (J). (gr. 3-7). 12.95 (978-0-385-73319-9(4) , Delacorte Bks. for Young Readers) Random Hse. Children's Bks.

—Lucy Rose: Big on Plans. Rex, Adam, illus. 2005. 176p. (gr. 3-7). (J). 12.95 (978-0-385-73204-8(X)); lib. bdg. 14.99 (978-0-385-90235-9(2)) Random Hse. Children's Bks. (Delacorte Bks. for Young Readers).

—Lucy Rose: Big on Plans. Rex, Adam, illus. 2007. 192p. (gr. 3-5). 5.50 (978-0-440-42027-9(X) , Yearling) Random Hse. Children's Bks.

—Lucy Rose: Busy Like You Can't Believe. Rex, Adam, illus. 2006. 176p. (J). (gr. 3-7). lib. bdg. 14.99 (978-0-385-90338-7(3) , Delacorte Bks. for Young Readers) Random Hse. Children's Bks.

Kienzle, Patricia Taylor. The Parrot Parents Part. Coffey, Peg, illus. 2001. 24p. (J). (gr. k-2). pap. 4.00 (978-1-890798-17-8(7)) Kienzle, Patricia Taylor.

Kimmel, Haven. Kaline Klattermaster's Tree House. Brown, Peter, illus. 2008. 160p. (J). 15.99 ***(978-0-689-87402-4(2)*** , Atheneum) Simon & Schuster Children's Publishing.

Klassen, Kirsten L. Katelyn's Affection. 2004. 280p. pap. 11.99 (978-0-8361-9281-0(8)) Herald Pr.

Klein, Adria F. Max Stays Overnight. 2007. (Read-It! Readers Ser.). (Illus.). 24p. (J). ***(978-1-4048-3547-4(4)*** , 1265795) Picture Window Bks.

—Max Stays Overnight. Gallagher-Cole, Mernie, illus. 2006. (Read-It! Readers Ser.). 24p. (J). ***(978-1-4048-3149-0(5)*** , 1265796) Picture Window Bks.

Komaiko, Leah. Malibu Carmie. 2007. 256p. (YA). (gr. 7-11). mass mkt. 5.99 (978-0-440-42014-9(8) , Laurel Leaf) Random Hse. Children's Bks.

Krishnaswami, Uma. Naming Maya. 2004. (Illus.). 192p. (J). 16.00 (978-0-374-35485-5(5) , Farrar, Straus & Giroux (BYR)) Farrar, Straus & Giroux.

Krueger, Kathryn L. Road to Grandma's House. 2005. 128p. pap. 13.95 (978-1-59800-366-6(6)) Outskirts Press, Inc.

LaFaye, A. The Year of the Sawdust Man. 1999. (978-0-606-17947-8(X)) Tandem Library Bks.

Laskin, Pamela L. Getting to Know You. 2003. (YA). 16.95 (978-0-936389-92-9(3)) Tudor Pubs., Inc.

Lems, Kristin. Piano Teacher's Daughter. Daoudi, Karima Lems & Daoudi, Kennan Lems, illus. 2002. pap. 18.00 (978-0-9637048-2-5(6)) Lems-Dworkin, Carol Pubs.

Levinson, Marilyn. No Boys Allowed. 2005. 144p. (J). pap. 4.99 (978-0-439-71965-0(8) , Scholastic Paperbacks) Scholastic, Inc.

Lewis, Beverly. Secret Summer Dreams. rev. ed. 2001. (Holly's Heart Ser.: Bk. 2). 144p. (YA). (gr. 6-9). pap. 6.99 (978-0-7642-2501-7(4)) Bethany Hse. Pubs.

Linko, G. J. Holden's Heart. 2004. (Seekers Ser.). 5.99 (978-0-8066-4180-5(0) , Augsburg Bks.) Augsburg Fortress, Pubs.

Losier, Dave. Fred's Prayer Machine. 2002. (Illus.). 152p. (J). pap. 11.95 (978-1-929039-07-4(7)) Ambassador Bks., Inc.

Lowry, Danielle. What Can I Do? A Book for Children of Divorce. Matthews, Bonnie, illus. 2001. 46p. (J). (gr. 3-7). 14.95 (978-1-55798-769-3(6)); pap. 8.95 (978-1-55798-770-9(X)) American Psychological Assn. (Magination Pr.).

Ly, Many. Home Is East. 304p. 2007. (YA). (gr. 7-11). mass mkt. 6.50 ***(978-0-440-23900-0(1)*** , Laurel Leaf); 2005. (J). (gr. 5 up). lib. bdg. 17.99 (978-0-385-73223-9(6) , Delacorte Bks. for Young Readers) Random Hse. Children's Bks.

Mack, Tracy. Drawing Lessons. (Illus.). 176p. (J). 2002. (gr. 5-9). pap. 4.99 (978-0-439-11203-1(6) , Scholastic Paperbacks); 2000. (gr. 7-12). pap. 15.95 (978-0-439-11202-4(8) , Scholastic Reference) Scholastic, Inc.

—Drawing Lessons. 2002. (gr. 5-8). lib. bdg. 13.00 (978-0-613-72015-1(6)) Tandem Library Bks.

Margolis, Bette S. A Heart Full of Love: With Workshop for Children of Divorce. Cline, Christie L., illus. 1999. 80p. (J). (gr. 1-4). pap. 14.95 (978-0-9676360-0-9(0)) Bette's Bks.

Marino, Peter. Dough Boy. 176p. (YA). (gr. 7-12). 16.95 (978-0-8234-1873-2(1)) Holiday Hse., Inc.

Martin, Ann M. Dawn on the Coast. (Baby-Sitters Club Ser.: No. 23). 10p. (J). (gr. 3-7). pap. 3.95 (978-0-590-42007-5(0)) Scholastic, Inc.

McDonald, Megan. Happy New Year, Julie, Bk. 3. McAliley, Susan, illus. 2007. 88p. (YA). (gr. 3 up). 12.95 ***(978-1-59369-292-6(7))*** American Girl Publishing, Inc.

—Happy New Year, Julie, Bk. 3. McAliley, Susan & Hunt, Robert, illus. 2007. 88p. (YA). (gr. 3 up). pap. 6.95 ***(978-1-59369-291-9(9))*** American Girl Publishing, Inc.

—Meet Julie. McAliley, Susan & Hunt, Robert, illus. 2007. 104p. (YA). (gr. 3 up). pap. 6.95 ***(978-1-59369-257-5(9))*** American Girl Publishing, Inc.

—Meet Julie. McAliley, Susan, illus. 2007. 104p. (YA). (gr. 3 up). 12.95 ***(978-1-59369-287-2(0))*** American Girl Publishing, Inc.

Mills, Sam. The Viper Within. 2008. 304p. (J). (gr. 7). 16.99 ***(978-0-375-84465-2(1));*** lib. bdg. 19.99 ***(978-0-375-94465-9(6))*** Random Hse. Children's Bks. (Knopf Bks. for Young Readers).

Moss, Marissa. Amelia's Family Ties. Moss, Marissa, illus. 2007. (Amelia's Notebooks). 40p. (J). (gr. 2-5). 9.99 ***(978-1-4169-0914-9(1)*** , Simon & Schuster/Paula Wiseman Bks.) Simon & Schuster Children's Publishing.

—Amelia's Family Ties. 2000. (Amelia's Notebooks). (Illus.). (J). (gr. 3-5). 12.75 (978-0-606-18352-9(3)) Tandem Library Bks.

—Max's Mystical Logbook. 2004. (J). 12.95 (978-0-439-46663-9(6)) Scholastic, Inc.

Murphy, Claire Rudolf. To the Summit. 1998. 208p. pap. 3.99 (978-0-380-79537-6(X)) HarperCollins Pubs.

Napoli, Donna Jo. Changing Tunes. 2000. (Illus.). (J). (978-0-606-18394-9(9)) Tandem Library Bks.

Neale, Jonathan. Himalaya. 2004. 160p. (J). (gr. 5-9). tchr. ed. 16.00 (978-0-618-41200-6(X)) Houghton Mifflin Co. Trade & Reference Div.

Park, Barbara. Don't Make Me Smile. 2002. 144p. (gr. 3-7). 5.50 (978-0-375-81555-3(4) , Yearling) Random Hse. Children's Bks.

—Don't Make Me Smile. 2002. (gr. 3-6). lib. bdg. 13.00 (978-0-613-87819-7(1)) Tandem Library Bks.

Parkinson, Siobhan. Second Fiddle: Or How to Tell a Blackbird from a Sausage. 2007. 192p. (J). (gr. 6-9). 16.95 (978-1-59643-122-5(9)) Roaring Brook Pr.

Paulsen, Gary. Hatchet. 2002. (Illus.). (J). 14.47 (978-0-7587-0017-9(2)) Book Wholesalers, Inc.

—Hatchet. 1999. 235p. (J). 17.90 (978-0-03-054626-6(5)) Holt, Rinehart & Winston.

—Hatchet. l.t. ed. 2000. (LRS Large Print Cornerstone Ser.). 205p. (YA). (gr. 4-12). lib. bdg. 28.95 (978-1-58118-055-8(1) , 23469) LRS.

—Hatchet. 2003. 151p. (J). 9.99 (978-0-330-31045-1(3) , Pan) Pan Macmillan GBR. *Dist:* Trafalgar Square Publishing.

—Hatchet. 2000. 195p. (J). (gr. 4-6). pap. 4.99 (978-0-8072-8320-2(7) , Listening Library) Random Hse. Audio Publishing Group.

—Hatchet. 2006. 192p. (J). pap. 6.99 (978-1-4169-3647-3(5) , Aladdin); 2006. 208p. (YA). (gr. 5-9). mass mkt. 6.99 (978-1-4169-3646-6(7) , Simon Pulse); 2000. (Illus.). 208p. (YA). 17.99 (978-0-689-84092-0(6) , Atheneum/Richard Jackson Bks.) Simon & Schuster Children's Publishing.

—Hatchet. Willis, Drew, illus. 20th ed. 2007. 188p. (J). (gr. 5-9). 19.99 ***(978-1-4169-2508-8(2))*** Simon & Schuster Children's Publishing.

Paulsen, Gary. Hatchet: With Related Readings. 2004. (EMC Masterpiece Series Access Editions). (J). (978-0-8219-2960-5(7)) EMC/Paradigm Publishing.

Perry, Anne M. Just Like Always. Lyon, Tammie, illus. 2005. (Rookie Reader Skill Set Ser.). (J). 31p. (gr. k-2). pap. 4.95 (978-0-516-25287-2(9)); 32p. (gr. 1-2). 19.50 (978-0-516-25154-7(6)) Scholastic Library Publishing. (Children's Pr.).

Prestine, Joan Singleton. Mom & Dad Break Up. Kylberg, Virginia, illus. 2002. 32p. (J). pap. 6.95 (978-1-57768-656-9(X)) School Specialty Publishing.

Prosek, James. The Day My Mother Left. Prosek, James, illus. 2007. (Illus.). 304p. (J). 15.99 (978-1-4169-0770-1(X)) Simon & Schuster Children's Publishing.

Quarles, Heather. A Door Near Here. 2000. 11.64 (978-0-606-17796-2(5)) Tandem Library Bks.

—Door near Here. 2000. (gr. 7-12). lib. bdg. 13.00 (978-0-613-22981-4(9)) Tandem Library Bks.

—A Door near Here. 2000. (Illus.). 240p. (YA). (gr. 7 up). pap. 5.50 (978-0-440-22761-8(5) , Laurel Leaf) Random Hse. Children's Bks.

Ransom, Jeanie Franz. I Don't Want to Talk about It. Finney, Kathryn Kunz, illus. 2000. 28p. (J). (ps-3). (978-1-55798-664-1(9) , 441-6649); pap. (978-1-55798-703-7(3) , 441-7033) American Psychological Assn. (Magination Pr.).

—I Don't Want to Talk about It. 2000. (gr. k-3). lib. bdg. 17.60 (978-0-613-78683-6(1)) Tandem Library Bks.

Ranulfo. Joker. 2006. 208p. (J). 15.99 (978-0-06-054158-3(X)); lib. bdg. 16.89 (978-0-06-054159-0(8)) HarperCollins Pubs. (Cotler, Joanna Books).

Ravel, Edeet. The Mysterious Adventures of Pauline Bovary. 2007. 168p. (J). (gr. 5-10). pap. 9.95 ***(978-1-55192-986-6(4))*** Raincoast Bk. Distribution CAN. *Dist:* Perseus Distribution.

Ray, Belinda & SparkNotes Staff. Sun-Kissed. 2004. (SparkNotes SAT Vocabulary Novels Ser.). (Illus.). 200p. pap. 7.95 (978-1-4114-0080-1(1)) Spark Publishing Group.

Reilly, Natalie June & Pavese, Brandi J. My Stick Family: Helping Children Cope with Divorce. 2002. (Let's Talk Ser.). (Illus.). 48p. (J). pap. 12.95 (978-0-88282-207-5(1) , Small Horizons) New Horizon Pr. Pubs., Inc.

Reinhardt, Dana. How to Build a House. 2008. 240p. (YA). (gr. 7). lib. bdg. 18.99 ***(978-0-375-94454-3(0)*** , Lamb, Wendy) Random Hse. Children's Bks.

Richardson, Faith. Angel Walker. 2003. Orig. Title: The Sea, the Song & the Trumpetfish. (Illus.). 172p. (J). 19.95 (978-0-9744989-2-8(0)); pap. 12.95 (978-0-9744989-3-5(9)) Fox Song Bks.

Roth, Rhonda. The Most Important Thing. Grajczyk, Shane, illus. 2007. 32p. (J). 16.95 ***(978-0-9770141-0-1(X)*** , Crossing Guard Bks.) Longs Peak Publishing, Inc.

Royal, Randal. Spirit Mountain: Wounded-Fox. 2004. (YA). per. 10.00 (978-0-9747918-1-4(4)) 153 Fish Publishing.

Rue, Nancy N. Ask Lily. 2001. (gr. 3-6). lib. bdg. 13.00 (978-0-613-71720-5(1)) Tandem Library Bks.

Santucci, Barbara. Loon Summer. Shine, Andrea, illus. 2004. 32p. (J). (gr. k-3). 16.00 (978-0-8028-5182-6(7)) Eerdmans, William B. Publishing Co.

Schnur, Steven. The Koufax Dilemma. Treatner, Meryl, illus. 2001. 196p. (YA). pap. 14.95 (978-0-595-19998-3(4) , Backinprint.com) iUniverse, Inc.

—Koufax Dilemma. 2001. (gr. 3-6). lib. bdg. 24.55 (978-0-613-85103-9(X)) Tandem Library Bks.

Scholastic, Inc. Staff & Grimes, Nikki. Day with Daddy. Tadgell, Nicole, illus. 2004. (Just for You! Ser.). 32p. pap. 3.99 (978-0-439-56850-0(1) , Teaching Resources) Scholastic, Inc.

Schraff, Anne. Once upon a Crime. 2001. (PageTurner Mystery Ser.). 80p. (YA). per. 3.95 (978-1-56254-179-8(X) , SP 179X) Saddleback Educational Publishing.

—Once upon a Crime. 2001. (gr. 7-12). lib. bdg. 11.80 (978-0-613-32914-9(7)) Tandem Library Bks.

Shen, Michele. The Spider & the Bee. Shen, Michele, illus. 2002. (Illus.). 32p. (J). 4.95 (978-1-929132-25-6(5)) Kane/Miller Bk. Pubs., Inc.

Simner, Janni Lee. Secret of the Three Treasures. 2005. 160p. (J). 16.95 (978-0-8234-1914-2(1)) Holiday Hse., Inc.

Southgate, Martha. Another Way to Dance. 1998. (978-0-606-12878-0(6)) Tandem Library Bks.

Spalding, Andrea. Me & Mr Mah. 2001. (gr. k-3). lib. bdg. 16.40 (978-0-613-88504-1(X)) Tandem Library Bks.

Spelman, Cornelia Maude. Mama & Daddy Bear's Divorce. Parkinson, Kathy, illus. 2004. (Concept Book Ser.). 24p. (J). (ps-1). pap. 6.95 (978-0-8075-5222-3(4)) Whitman, Albert & Co.

Springer, Pat. A Mirror Image. 2005. 57p. pap. 12.95 (978-1-4137-7939-4(5)) PublishAmerica, Inc.

Spyropolous, Angelo. RV. 2005. pap. 12.99 (978-1-894869-98-0(2) , PO 00128) Zumaya Pubns. LLC.

Staunton, Ted. Stinky. Gardos, Susan, illus. 2004. (Northern Lights Young Novels Ser.). 64p. (J). (gr. 2-5). pap. 4.95 (978-0-88995-263-8(9)) Red Deer Pr. CAN. *Dist:* Fitzhenry & Whiteside, Ltd.

—Stinky. 2003. (gr. 3-6). lib. bdg. 12.95 (978-0-613-84450-5(5)) Tandem Library Bks.

Steindal, Yvonne L. D. Holden's Heart. ldr.'s ed. 2004. (Seekers Ser.). 3.99 (978-0-8066-4183-6(5)) Augsburg Fortress, Pubs.

Stinson, Kathy. Mom & Dad Don't Live Together Anymore. Reynolds, Nancy L., illus. 2003. 32p. (J). (ps-2). lib. bdg. 15.95 (978-0-920236-92-5(8)) Annick Pr., Ltd. CAN. *Dist:* Firefly Bks., Ltd.

—Mom & Dad Don't Live Together Anymore. Oelofsen, Vlan, illus. rev. ed. 2007. 24p. (J). (ps-2). pap. 6.95 ***(978-1-55451-093-1(7))***; lib. bdg. 19.95 ***(978-1-55451-094-8(5))*** Annick Pr., Ltd. CAN. *Dist:* Firefly Bks., Ltd.

Stinson, Kathy. One Year Commencing. 2004. 152p. pap. (978-1-895449-65-5(0)) Thistledown Pr., Ltd.

Talbert, Marc. Thin Ice. 2001. 216p. pap. 15.95 (978-0-595-20019-1(2) , Backinprint.com) iUniverse, Inc.

Taylor, Jeannie St. John. Out at Home: A Novel. 2004. 144p. (J). pap. 6.99 (978-0-8254-3724-3(5)) Kregel Pubns.

Thiel, Annie. Cosmos' Mom & Dad Are Moving Apart. 2006. (Playdate Kids Ser.). (Illus.). 32p. 14.95 (978-1-933721-04-0(9)) Playdate Kids Publishing.

Thomas, Rob. Rats Saw God. 2007. 208p. (YA). pap. 6.99 (978-1-4169-3897-2(4) , Simon Pulse) Simon & Schuster Children's Publishing.

Tobesman, Rachmiel. The Magic Glasses: Stories & Other Activities for Children of Separation & Divorce. 1998. (Illus.). 38p. (J). (ps-12). spiral bd. 12.95 (978-0-9677266-0-1(3)) Project Shalom.

Ullman, Barb Bentler. The Fairies of Nutfolk Wood. 256p. (J). 2008. pap. 5.99 ***(978-0-06-134563-0(6)*** , Harper Trophy); 2006. 15.99 (978-0-06-073614-9(3) , Tegen, Katherine Bks); 2006. lib. bdg. 16.89 (978-0-06-073615-6(1) , Tegen, Katherine Bks) HarperCollins Pubs.

Venable, Leslie Allgood. The Not So Wicked Stepmother. Harrison, Julie M., illus. 1999. 24p. (J). (gr. 1-7). per. 9.95 (978-0-9666817-0-3(3)) Venable, L.A. Publishing Co.

Vivian, Siobhan. A Little Friendly Advice. 2008. 256p. (J). pap. 16.99 ***(978-0-545-00404-6(7)*** , PUSH) Scholastic, Inc.

Voigt, Cynthia. Bad, Badder, Baddest. 1999. (Bad Girls Ser.). 272p. (J). (gr. 4-7). pap. 4.99 (978-0-439-08096-5(7) , Scholastic Paperbacks) Scholastic, Inc.

—Bad, Badder, Baddest. 1999. (Bad Girls Ser.). (J). (978-0-606-17038-3(3)) Tandem Library Bks.

—A Solitary Blue. 2003. (Tillerman Cycle Ser.: Bk. 3). 256p. (J). pap. 6.99 (978-0-689-86360-8(8) , Aladdin); (YA). mass mkt. 6.99 (978-0-689-86434-6(5) , Simon Pulse) Simon & Schuster Children's Publishing.

—A Solitary Blue. 2003. (Tillerman Cycle Ser.: Bk. 3). (gr. 7-12). lib. bdg. 14.15 (978-0-613-73441-7(6)) Tandem Library Bks.

—A Solitary Blue. l.t. ed. 2005. (Tillerman Cycle Ser.: Bk. 3). 359p. (J). pap. 10.95 (978-0-7862-7912-8(5)) Thorndike Pr.

Wallace, Rich. Southpaw. 2006. 105p. (J). lib. bdg. 15.38 ***(978-1-4242-2166-0(8))*** Fitzgerald Bks.

—Southpaw. (Winning Season Ser.: Vol. 6). 128p. (J). 2007. pap. 4.99 (978-0-14-240785-1(2) , Puffin); 2006. (gr. 4). 14.99 (978-0-670-06053-5(4) , Viking Juvenile) Penguin Group (USA) Inc.

Warner Press Staff. Divorce Comes to Our House. 2003. pap. (978-1-59317-009-7(2)) Warner Pr. Pubs.

Warner, Sally. Sister Split. 2001. (gr. 3-6). lib. bdg. 14.10 (978-0-613-85509-9(4)) Tandem Library Bks.

Weatherly, Lee. Child X. 2003. 224p. (gr. 4-9). 5.99 (978-0-440-41904-4(2) , Yearling) Random Hse. Children's Bks.

Weber, Lori. Split. 2005. (SideStreets Ser.). 152p. (YA). (gr. 7-12). ***(978-1-55028-879-7(2));*** 7.95 (978-1-55028-878-0(4)) Lorimer, James & Co., Ltd., Pubs. CAN. *Dist:* Casemate Pubs. & Bk. Distributors, LLC.

Weber, Lori. Tattoo Heaven. 2005. (SideStreets Ser.). 168p. (YA). (gr. 7-12). ***(978-1-55028-903-9(9));*** 7.95 (978-1-55028-902-2(0)) Lorimer, James & Co., Ltd., Pubs. CAN. *Dist:* Casemate Pubs. & Bk. Distributors, LLC.

Weeks, Sarah. Guy Time. 2001. 176p. (J). (gr. 3-7). pap. 5.99 (978-0-06-440783-0(7) , Harper Trophy) HarperCollins Pubs.

—Guy Time. 2001. (J). 12.64 (978-0-606-21222-9(1)); (gr. 3-6). lib. bdg. 14.15 (978-0-613-35956-6(9)) Tandem Library Bks.

White, Ruth. Buttermilk Hill. 2004. 176p. (J). 16.00 (978-0-374-35112-0(0) , Farrar, Straus & Giroux (BYR)) Farrar, Straus & Giroux.

—Buttermilk Hill. 2006. 176p. (J). reprint ed. pap. 6.95 (978-0-374-41003-2(8)) Macmillan.

Wilkins, Rose. So Super Starry. 2006. (YA). 230p. ***(978-1-4156-6975-4(9));*** 240p. (gr. 7). reprint ed. pap. 6.99 (978-0-14-240581-9(7)) Penguin Group (USA) Inc. (Puffin).

Willey, Margaret. The Melinda Zone. 2003. 146p. (YA). pap. 14.95 (978-0-595-28984-4(3) , Backinprint.com) iUniverse, Inc.

Wilson, Jacqueline. The Bed & Breakfast Star. Sharratt, Nick, illus. l.t. ed. 2000. 255p. (J). pap. (978-0-7540-6090-1(X) , CLP 292) BBC Audio.

—The Bed & Breakfast Star. Sharratt, Nick, illus. unabr. ed. 2000. (Read-Along Ser.). 242p. (J). pap. 29.95 incl. audio (978-0-7540-6231-8(7) , RA032, Chivers Children's Audio Bks.) BBC Audiobooks America.

—The Bed & Breakfast Star. Sharratt, Nick, illus. 2001. (Yearling Book Ser.). 32p. pap. 9.99 (978-0-440-86324-3(4) , Corgi) Transworld Publishers Ltd. GBR. *Dist:* Trafalgar Square Publishing.

—The Suitcase Kid. Hu, Ying-Hwa, illus. 1998. 144p. (gr. 3-7). 5.50 (978-0-440-41371-4(0) , Yearling) Random Hse. Children's Bks.

Wilson, Jacqueline & Sharratt, Nick. Candyfloss. 2007. (Illus.). 352p. (J). (gr. 4-7). 14.95 ***(978-1-59643-241-3(1))*** Roaring Brook Pr.

Wittlinger, Ellen. Hard Love. 2001. (Illus.). 240p. (YA). (gr. 8-12). reprint ed. pap. 8.99 (978-0-689-84154-5(X) , Simon Pulse) Simon & Schuster Children's Publishing.

Wright, Bil. When the Black Girl Sings. 2008. 272p. (YA). (gr. 7 up). 16.99 ***(978-1-4169-3995-5(4)*** , Simon & Schuster Children's Publishing) Simon & Schuster Children's Publishing.

Yee, Lisa. So Totally Emily Ebers. 2008. 304p. (J). 5.99 (978-0-439-83848-1(7) , Levine, Arthur A. Bks.) Scholastic, Inc.

—So Totally Emily Embers. 2007. 304p. (J). (gr. 4-7). pap. 16.99 (978-0-439-83847-4(9) , Levine, Arthur A. Bks.) Scholastic, Inc.

Zimmer, Tracie Vaughn. Sketches from a Spy Tree. Glass, Andrew, illus. 2005. 64p. (J). (gr. 4-6). 16.00 (978-0-618-23479-0(9) , Clarion Bks.) Houghton Mifflin Co. Trade & Reference Div.

DIX, DOROTHEA LYNDE, 1802-1887

Muckenhoupt, Margaret. Dorothea Dix: Advocate for Mental Health Care. 2004. (Oxford Portraits Ser.). (Illus.). 128p. (YA). 28.00 (978-0-19-512921-2(0)) Oxford Univ. Pr., Inc.

DIXON, JOHNNY (FICTITIOUS CHARACTER)—FICTION

Bellairs, John. The Chessmen of Doom. Gorey, Edward, illus. 2000. (John Bellairs Ser.). 160p. (J). (gr. 3-7). pap. 5.99 (978-0-14-130697-1(1) , Puffin) Penguin Group (USA) Inc.

—The Curse of the Blue Figurine. 2004. (Johnny Dixon Ser.). (Illus.). 208p. (J). pap. 5.99 (978-0-14-240258-0(3) , Puffin) Penguin Group (USA) Inc.

—The Curse of the Blue Figurine. 2000. (J). (gr. 4-8). 21.50 (978-0-8446-7138-3(X)) Smith, Peter Pub., Inc.

—The Eyes of the Killer Robot. 1998. (Johnny Dixon Mystery Ser.). 12.64 (978-0-606-13371-5(2)) Tandem Library Bks.

—The Mummy, the Will, & the Crypt. 2001. (J). (gr. 4-8). 21.75 (978-0-8446-7170-3(3)) Smith, Peter Pub., Inc.

—The Revenge of the Wizard's Ghost. 1999. (J). (gr. 3 up). 20.25 (978-0-8446-7010-2(3)) Smith, Peter Pub., Inc.

—The Spell of the Sorcerer's Skull. 2002. (J). (gr. 3 up). 21.50 (978-0-8446-7206-9(8)) Smith, Peter Pub., Inc.

DNA

Allan, Tony. Understanding DNA: A Breakthrough in Medicine. 2002. (Point of Impact Ser.). 32p. (J). (gr. 5-7). pap. 7.50 (978-1-4034-0074-1(1) , 91555) Heinemann Library.

—Understanding DNA: A Breakthrough in Science Medicine. 2002. (Point of Impact Ser.). (Illus.). 32p. (J). (gr. 5-7). lib. bdg. 25.64 (978-1-58810-557-8(1)) Heinemann Library.

Balkwill, Fran & Rolph, Mic. Have a Nice DNA. 2002. (Enjoy Your Cells Ser.: Vol. 3). (Illus.). 32p. (J). 13.95 (978-0-87969-614-6(1)); pap. 8.95 (978-0-87969-610-8(9)) Cold Spring Harbor Laboratory Pr.

Boon, Kevin Alexander. The Human Genome Project: What Does Decoding DNA Mean for Us? 2002. (Issues in Focus Ser.). (Illus.). 128p. (YA). (gr. 8-12). lib. bdg. 26.60 (978-0-7660-1685-9(4)) Enslow Pubs., Inc.

Building Blocks of Science: Understanding Cells & DNA Teacher's Guide (Firsthand Learning) 2007. ring bd. ***(978-0-89278-338-0(9))*** Carolina Biological Supply Co.

Building Blocks of Science: Understanding Cells & DNA Unit Kit (Firsthand Learning) 2007. ring bd. ***(978-0-89278-433-2(4))*** Carolina Biological Supply Co.

Claybourne, Anna. Introduction to Genes & DNA. 2004. (Genes & Dna Ser.). (Illus.). 64p. (J). pap. 11.95 (978-0-7945-0444-1(2) , Usborne) EDC Publishing.

De la Bédoyère, Camilla. The Discovery of DNA. 2005. (Milestones in Modern Science Ser.). 48p. (J). pap. (978-0-8368-5858-7(1)); (Illus.). lib. bdg. 30.00 (978-0-8368-5851-8(4)) Stevens, Gareth Inc. (World Almanac Library).

Edelson, Edward. Francis Crick & James Watson: And the Building Blocks of Life. 1998. (Oxford Portraits in Science Ser.). (Illus.). 112p. (YA). (gr. 9 up). 30.00 (978-0-19-511451-5(5)) Oxford Univ. Pr., Inc.

Fridell, Ron. DNA Fingerprinting: The Ultimate Identity. 2001. (Single Title - Science Ser.). (Illus.). 112p. (J). (gr. 9-12). 26.00 (978-0-531-11858-0(4) , Watts, Franklin) Scholastic Library Publishing.

Hamilton, Janet. James Watson: Solving the Mystery of DNA. 2004. (Nobel Prize-Winning Scientists Ser.). (Illus.). 104p. (J). lib. bdg. 26.60 (978-0-7660-2258-4(7)) Enslow Pubs., Inc.

Holt, Rinehart and Winston Staff. Holt Science & Technology Chapter 6: Life Science: Genes & DNA. 5th ed. 2004. (Illus.). pap. 12.86 (978-0-03-030186-5(6)) Holt, Rinehart & Winston.

Innes, Brian. DNA & Body Evidence. 2007. (Forensic Evidence Ser.). (Illus.). 96p. (gr. 6 up). 39.95 ***(978-0-7656-8115-7(3))*** Sharpe, M.E. Inc.

Johnson, Rebecca L. Amazing DNA. Desrocher, Jack, illus. 2007. (Microquests Ser.). 48p. (J). (gr. 3-5). lib. bdg. 29.27 ***(978-0-8225-7139-1(0)*** , Millbrook Pr.) Lerner Publishing Group.

Kafka, Tina. DNA on Trial. 2004. (Overview Ser.). (Illus.). 112p. (J). (gr. 7-10). 29.95 (978-1-59018-337-3(1) , Lucent Bks.) Thomson Gale.

Marx, Christy. Watson & Crick & DNA. 2004. (Primary Sources of Revolutionary Scientific Discoveries & Theories Ser.). (Illus.). 64p. (J). lib. bdg. 29.25 (978-1-4042-0312-9(5)) Rosen Publishing Group, Inc., The.

Meredith, Susan. Genes & Dna - Internet Linked. rev. ed. 2006. 64p. (J). pap. 11.99 (978-0-7945-1562-1(2) , Usborne) EDC Publishing.

Morrison, Yvonne. The DNA Gave It Away: Teens Solve Crimes. 2007. (Shockwave: Science in Practice Ser.). (Illus.). 36p. (J). (gr. 4-6). lib. bdg. 25.00 ***(978-0-531-17581-1(2)*** , Children's Pr.) Scholastic Library Publishing.

Phelan, Glen. Double Helix: The Quest to Uncover the Structure of DNA. 2006. (Science Quest Ser.). (Illus.). 64p. (J). (gr. 5-9). 17.95 (978-0-7922-5541-3(0)); lib. bdg. 25.90 (978-0-7922-5542-0(9)) National Geographic Society. (National Geographic Children's Bks.).

Prokos, Anna. Guilty by a Hair! Real-Life DNA Matches! 2007. (24/7 - Science Behind the Scenes Ser.). (Illus.). 64p. (YA). (gr. 8-12). pap. 7.95 ***(978-0-531-18733-3(0));*** 25.00 (978-0-531-11821-4(5)) Scholastic Library Publishing. (Watts, Franklin).

Rainis, Kenneth G. Blood & DNA Evidence: Crime-Solving Science Experiments. 2006. (Forensic Science Projects Ser.). (Illus.). 104p. (J). lib. bdg. 31.93 (978-0-7660-1958-4(6)) Enslow Pubs., Inc.

Senker, Cath. Rosalind Franklin. 2002. (Scientists Who Made History Ser.). (Illus.). 48p. (J). 27.12 (978-0-7398-5226-2(4)) Raintree.

Severs, Vesta-Nadine. Oswald Avery & the Story of DNA. l.t. ed. 2002. (Unlocking the Secrets of Science Ser.). (Illus.). 56p. (gr. 4-10). lib. bdg. 25.70 (978-1-58415-110-4(2)) Mitchell Lane Pubs., Inc.

Silverstein, Alvin & Silverstein, Virginia. DNA. 2002. (Science Concepts Ser.). (Illus.). 64p. (gr. 5-8). lib. bdg. 26.90 (978-0-7613-2257-3(4) , Twenty-First Century Bks.) Lerner Publishing Group.

Snedden, Robert. DNA & Genetic Engineering. 2003. (Cells & Life Ser.). (Illus.). 48p. (gr. 6-8). (J). lib. bdg. 27.86 (978-1-58810-674-2(8)); (YA). pap. 8.50 (978-1-58810-936-1(4)) Heinemann Library.

Stille, Darlene R. DNA: The Master Molecule of Life. 2006. (Exploring Science Ser.). (Illus.). 48p. (J). (gr. 5-7). 25.27 (978-0-7565-1617-8(X)) Compass Point Bks.

Walker, Richard. Genes & DNA. 2007. (Kingfisher Knowledge Ser.). (Illus.). 64p. (J). (gr. 4-6). pap. 8.95 ***(978-0-7534-6121-1(8)*** , Kingfisher) Houghton Mifflin Co. Trade & Reference Div.

Wilcox, Frank H. DNA: The Thread of Life. 1998. (Discovery! Ser.). (Illus.). 80p. (J). (gr. 5 up). 23.93 (978-0-8225-1584-5(9) , Lerner Pubns.) Lerner Publishing Group.

DOCKS

see also Harbors

Canizares, Susan. Where Does It Park? 1999. (J). pap. 2.50 (978-0-439-04583-4(5)) Scholastic, Inc.

DOCTOR SEUSS, 1904-1991

see Seuss, Dr., 1904-1991

DOCTORS

see Physicians

DOCTRINAL THEOLOGY

see Theology

DOCTRINES

see Theology

DODGSON, CHARLES LUTWIDGE, 1832-1898

see Carroll, Lewis, 1832-1898

DODO

Green, Tamara. The Dodo: Extinct Species. Gibbons, Tony, illus. 2007. 24p. (J). reprint ed. 15.00 ***(978-1-4223-6677-6(4))*** DIANE Publishing Co.

DODO—FICTION

Cheke. The Lost Land of the Dodo. 2002. (Illus.). 250p. (978-0-12-170660-9(5) , Academic Pr.) Elsevier Science & Technology Bks.

Nishimura, Kae. I Am Dodo: Not a True Story. Nishimura, Kae, illus. 2005. (Illus.). 32p. (J). (ps-k). 15.00 (978-0-618-33614-2(1) , Clarion Bks.) Houghton Mifflin Co. Trade & Reference Div.

DOG

see Dogs

DOG GUIDES

see Guide Dogs

DOG SHOWS

Rauen, Amy. Measuring at the Dog Show. 2007. (J). pap. ***(978-0-8368-8483-8(3));*** 24p. (gr. 1-3). lib. bdg. 19.93 ***(978-0-8368-8474-6(4))*** Stevens, Gareth Inc. (Weekly Reader Early Learning Library).

DOGMATIC THEOLOGY

see Theology

DOGS

see also Beagle (Dog Breed); Chihuahua (Dog Breed); Collie; German Shepherd Dog; Guide Dogs; Police Dogs; Poodles

Adelman, Beth. Good Dog! Dog Care for Kids. 2006. (Girls Rock! Ser.). (Illus.). 32p. (J). (gr. 1-5). 24.21 (978-1-59296-743-8(4)) Child's World, Inc.

Adkins, Linda. The Dog Who Couldn't Wag His Tail: A True Story about a Stray Who Made a Difference. Dilworth, Kristopher & Rhodes, Sean C., eds. 2003. (J). 13.95 (978-0-9718632-0-0(2)) Keep Me Company Publishing Co.

Ajmera, Maya & Fisher, Alex. A Kid's Best Friend. 2004. (It's a Kid's World Ser.). (Illus.). 32p. (J). (ps-2). 15.95 (978-1-57091-513-0(X)); pap. 6.95 (978-1-57091-514-7(8)) Charlesbridge Publishing, Inc.

Alcott, Louisa May. Under the Lilacs. l.t. ed. 2005. 444p. pap. (978-1-84637-059-5(0)) Echo Library.

Alderton, David. Dog. 2003. (Looking after My Pet Ser.). (Illus.). 20p. 7.99 (978-0-7548-1222-7(7)) Anness Publishing GBR. *Dist:* National Bk. Network.

Allberti, Frances C. Finding Rover. Gremillion, Barry, illus. 2006. (J). per. (978-0-9785937-1-1(5)) Open Pages Publishing.

Altman, Linda Jacobs. Big Dogs. 2000. (Perfect Pets Ser.). (Illus.). 32p. (J). (gr. 3-5). lib. bdg. 25.64 (978-0-7614-1101-7(1) , Benchmark Bks.) Cavendish, Marshall Corp.

—Small Dogs. 1999. (Perfect Pets Ser.). (Illus.). 32p. (J). (gr. 3-5). lib. bdg. 25.64 (978-0-7614-0795-9(2) , Benchmark Bks.) Cavendish, Marshall Corp.

American Kennel Club Dog Care & Training. 2002. (gr. 7-12). lib. bdg. 26.90 (978-0-613-70580-6(7)) Tandem Library Bks.

Andres, Patricia. Maggie: A Savannah Dog. Abbott, Jason, illus. 1998. (J). (gr. k-8). 4.75 (978-0-9703795-0-4(1)) Maggie's D.O.G. Co.

Anjou, Colette. Westie the Dog. Niles, Kim, illus. 2005. 28p. (J). (ps-3). per. 15.95 (978-0-9748933-6-5(6)) E & E Publishing.

Arraras, Maria Celeste. Dogs. 2008. (Scholastic First Discovery Ser.). 24p. (J). pap. 5.99 (*978-0-545-00139-7(0)* , Scholastic Reference) Scholastic, Inc.

Ashton, Anna. Our New Puppy. 2006. 80p. pap. (*978-1-84401-164-3(X)*) Athena Pr.

Augello, Barbara. Dogs. 2005. (Illus.). 32p. (J). (978-0-439-78475-7(1)) Scholastic, Inc.

Axelrod, Herbert R. Adopting a Dog. 1999. (Cats & Dogs). (Illus.). 84p. (YA). (gr. 3-7). 19.95 (978-0-7910-4813-9(6) , Chelsea Hse.) Facts On File, Inc.

—Skin & Coat Care for Dogs. 1999. (Cats & Dogs). (Illus.). 84p. (YA). (gr. 3-7). 21.95 (978-0-7910-4815-3(2) , Chelsea Hse.) Facts On File, Inc.

—You & Your Puppy. 1999. (Cats & Dogs). (Illus.). 84p. (YA). (gr. 3-7). lib. bdg. 19.95 (978-0-7910-4823-8(3) , Chelsea Hse.) Facts On File, Inc.

—Your Healthy Puppy. 1999. (Cats & Dogs). (Illus.). 84p. (YA). (gr. 4-7). lib. bdg. 19.95 (978-0-7910-4820-7(9) , Chelsea Hse.) Facts On File, Inc.

Aylmore, Angela. I Like Dogs. 2007. (Illus.). 24p. (J). (978-1-4034-9278-4(6)); lib. bdg. 21.36 (978-1-4034-9269-2(7)) Heinemann Library.

Baillie, Marilyn. My Pet Puppy. Kurisu, Jane, illus. 2005. 32p. (J). (gr. k-3). (978-1-55337-651-4(X)) Kids Can Pr., Ltd.

Baldwin, Sage & Wolfe, Rita M. A Puppy's Life. 2007. (Illus.). 40p. (J). 18.95 (*978-0-9792439-9-8(8)*) Maximus Publishing.

Balloon Books Staff, ed. Small Dog, Big Dog. 2003. (Animal Bring-Along Bks.). (Illus.). 16p. (J). bds. 3.50 (978-0-8069-7695-2(0) , Balloon Bks.) Sterling Publishing Co., Inc.

Barnes, Julia. Dogs at Work. 2006. (Illus.). 32p. (J). 23.33 (978-0-8368-6223-2(6)) Stevens, Gareth Inc.

—Pet Dogs. 2006. (Pet Pals Ser.). (Illus.). 32p. (J). (gr. 2-5). lib. bdg. 23.93 (978-0-8368-6777-0(7)) Stevens, Gareth Inc.

Barnes, Julia, et al. 101 Facts about Puppies. 2001. (One Hundred One Facts about Pets Ser.). (Illus.). 32p. (J). (gr. 3 up). lib. bdg. 23.33 (978-0-8368-2890-0(9)) Stevens, Gareth Inc.

Barrett, John E., photos by. Puppies! 2000. (Elmo's World Ser.). (Illus.). 12p. (J). (gr. k-ps). bds. 4.99 (978-0-375-80575-2(3) , Random Hse. Bks. for Young Readers) Random Hse. Children's Bks.

Bass, Rick. Colter: The True Story of the Best Dog I Ever Had. 2001. (Illus.). (J). 16.65 (978-0-606-21720-0(7)) Tandem Library Bks.

Bennett, Leonie. My Dog's a Mommy! 2006. (I Love Reading Ser.). (Illus.). 24p. (J). lib. bdg. 19.96 (978-1-59716-158-9(6)) Bearport Publishing Co., Inc.

Berman, Ruth. My Pet Dog. Hustace, Billy, photos by. 2005. (All about Pets Ser.). (Illus.). 64p. (gr. 2-6). lib. bdg. 22.60 (978-0-8225-2259-1(4)) Lerner Publishing Group.

BHB International Staff. Dogs. 1998. (Our Animal World in Pictures Ser.). (J). (978-2-215-06166-3(9)) Editions Fleurus.

Bidner, Jenni. Is My Dog a Wolf? How Your Pet Compares to Its Wild Cousin. 2006. (Illus.). 64p. 9.95 (978-1-57990-732-7(6)) Lark Bks.

Biel, Timothy Levi. Wild Dogs. 2001. (Zoobooks Ser.). 24p. (J). (gr. 1-7). 15.95 (978-1-888153-04-0(0)) Wildlife Education, Ltd.

Blackaby, Susan. A Dog for You: Caring for Your Dog. DeLage, Charlene, illus. 2004. (Pet Care Ser.). 24p. (C). (gr. k-3). 22.60 (978-1-4048-0114-1(6)) Picture Window Bks.

Blankenhorn, Rebecca. The World of Dogs. 1999. (Pair-It Books). (Illus.). 40p. (J). pap. 5.65 (978-0-7398-0873-3(7)) Steck-Vaughn.

Bourgeois, Kim. Puppy's First Year: A Record & Keepsake Book. Sarrazin, Marisol, illus. 2000. (Abby & Tess Pet-Sitters Ser.). 22p. (J). pap. 7.95 (978-1-894222-25-9(3)) Lobster Pr. CAN. *Dist:* Univ. of Toronto Pr.

Bowdish, Lynea. Dog for Each Day. 2003. (gr. k-3). lib. bdg. 12.95 (978-0-613-67609-0(2)) Tandem Library Bks.

Boynton, Sandra. Perritos: Un Libro para Contar y Ladrar. Boynton, Sandra, illus. 2004. Tr. of Doggies. (SPA., Illus.). 14p. (J). bds. 5.99 (978-0-689-86303-5(9) , Libros Para Ninos) Simon & Schuster Children's Publishing.

Bozzo, Linda. My First Dog. 2007. (My First Pet Library from the American Humane Association Ser.). (Illus.). 32p. (J). (gr. 1-3). lib. bdg. 22.60 (978-0-7660-2754-1(6) , Enslow Elementary) Enslow Pubs., Inc.

Branigan, Cynthia. Living with a Greyhound. 2002. (Living with a Pet Ser.). (Illus.). 128p. 16.99 (978-0-7641-5428-7(1)) Barron's Educational Series, Inc.

Brooks. Come Back, Energy Man. Date not set. 224p. (J). 14.99 (978-0-06-020670-3(5)); 15.89 (978-0-06-020671-0(3)) HarperCollins Pubs.

Burris, Andrea M. & Schad, Anna M. A Dog Lover's Alphabet Book. Burris, Andrea M., illus. 2007. 32p. (J). 14.95 (*978-0-9743294-1-3(X)*) A & D Bks.

Burton, Frances. That's Me, Tyler! Thompson, Karmen, illus. 2002. 32p. (J). (ps-3). lib. bdg. 15.95 (978-0-9650769-2-0(X)) Stonehill Publishing.

Buttler, Elizabeth, illus. Girls & Their Dogs. 2007. 64p. (YA). (gr. 3 up). pap. 8.95 (*978-1-59369-169-1(6)*) American Girl Publishing, Inc.

Calmenson, Stephanie. Rosie: A Visiting Dog's Story. Sutcliffe, Justin, photos by. 1998. (Illus.). 48p. (J). (gr. k-3). pap. 6.95 (978-0-395-92722-9(6) , Clarion Bks.) Houghton Mifflin Co. Trade & Reference Div.

—Shaggy, Waggy Dogs (and Others) Sutcliffe, Justin, illus. 1998. 48p. (J). (gr. k-3). tchr. ed. 15.00 (978-0-395-77605-6(8) , Clarion Bks.) Houghton Mifflin Co. Trade & Reference Div.

—Shaggy, Waggy Dogs (and Others) Sutcliffe, Justin, illus. 2002. 48p. (J). (gr. k-3). pap. 5.95 (978-0-618-19466-7(5) , Clarion Bks.) Houghton Mifflin Co. Trade & Reference Div.

Cary, Bob. Born to Pull. De Marcken, Gail, illus. 2001. 96p. (J). (gr. k-4). pap. 26.95 (978-0-439-22086-6(6)) Scholastic, Inc.

Cary, Bob & De Marcken, Gail. Born to Pull. 2003. (Illus.). 96p. (J). (gr. 3 up). reprint ed. pap. 9.99 (978-0-439-28682-4(4)) Scholastic, Inc.

Cats & Dogs (Gr. PreK-5) 2003. (J). (978-1-58232-018-2(7)) Bryan Hse. Pubs., Inc.

Chien. 1999. (Pocket Pals Ser.). (FRE.). (J). (ps-1). pap. 1.99 (978-0-85953-731-5(5)) Child's Play International Ltd. GBR. *Dist:* Child's Play-International.

Chuse, Patricia Jepsen. Six Lessons with Delphi: How to Live Happily with All Life. 2002. 124p. 12.95 (978-0-9667560-2-9(9)) Chuse, Patricia Jepsen.

Clements, Andrew. Brave Norman: A True Story. 2002. (ps-2). lib. bdg. 11.80 (978-0-613-57568-3(7)) Tandem Library Bks.

—Tara & Tiree, Fearless Friends: A True Story. 2002. (gr. k-3). lib. bdg. 11.80 (978-0-613-66607-7(0)) Tandem Library Bks.

Clements, Andrew & Beier, Ellen. Brave Norman: A True Story. 2002. (Pets to the Rescue Ser.). 32p. (J). pap. 3.99 (978-0-689-83438-7(1) , Aladdin) Simon & Schuster Children's Publishing.

Clever Coyote & other Wild Dogs: Level L, 6 vols. 128p. (gr. 2-3). 40.50 (978-0-7699-1033-8(5)) Shortland Pubns. (U. S. A.) Inc.

Clutton-Brock, Juliet. Dog. 2004. (Dk Eyewitness Books Ser.). (Illus.). 72p. 15.99 (978-0-7566-0678-7(0)) Dorling Kindersley Publishing, Inc.

Coile, D. Caroline. How Smart Is Your Dog? 30 Fun Science Activities with Your Pet. 2004. (Illus.). 96p. (J). pap. 7.95 (978-1-4027-1363-7(0)) Sterling Publishing Co., Inc.

—The Jack Russell Terrier Handbook. Earle-Bridges, Michele, illus. 2000. (Pet Handbooks). 144p. pap. 11.99 (978-0-7641-1411-3(5)) Barron's Educational Series, Inc.

—Silly Dog Tricks: Fun for You & Your Best Friend. 2007. (Illus.). 112p. (J). 14.95 (978-1-4027-1431-3(9)) Sterling Publishing Co., Inc.

Cole, Joanna & Calmenson, Stephanie, compiled by. Give a Dog a Bone: Stories, Poems, Jokes & Riddles about Dogs. 1999. (J). lib. bdg. 14.79 (978-0-606-17057-4(X)) Tandem Library Bks.

Cole, Lynn. My Dog. 2001. (Pet Pals Ser.). (Illus.). 48p. (J). (gr. 1-5). pap. 8.95 (978-1-55971-793-9(9) , NorthWord Bks. for Young Readers) T&N Children's Publishing.

Collard, Sneed B., III. Shep: Our Most Loyal Dog. Yardley, Joanne, illus. 2006. 40p. (J). (gr. k-5). 16.95 (978-1-58536-259-2(X)) Sleeping Bear Pr.

Colombo, Luann. World's Coolest Dog Tricks. McFarlane, James, illus. 2001. 24p. (J). 6.95 (978-0-9700346-6-3(0)) becker&mayer! books.

Conditt, Margaret K. Gifts from God: What Our Dogs Teach Us about God's Love. 2007. 64p. pap. 16.99 (*978-1-57921-883-6(0)*) WinePress Publishing.

Coon, Kathy. Dog Intelligence Test: Kathy Coon's Dog Intelligence Test. rev. ed. 2003. Orig. Title: The Dog Intelligence Test. (Illus.). 88p. (J). pap. (978-0-9741300-0-2(1)) Coon, Kathy.

Coren, Stanley. Why Do Dogs Have Wet Noses? 2008. (Illus.). 64p. pap. (*978-1-55337-658-3(7)*) Kids Can Pr., Ltd.

—Why Do Dogs Have Wet Noses? 2006. (Illus.). 64p. 12.95 (978-1-55337-657-6(9)) Kids Can Pr., Ltd. CAN. *Dist:* Wybel Marketing Group.

Cotton, Jack. A Dog's Guide to Life: Lessons from "Moose" 2005. (Illus.). 32p. (J). (978-1-59490-025-9(6)) Tide-Mark Pr., Ltd.

Crisp, Marty. Everything Dog. 2003. (Everything Kids Ser.). (Illus.). 64p. (gr. 2-6). 10.95 (978-1-55971-839-4(0)); (YA). pap. 6.95 (978-1-55971-854-7(4)) T&N Children's Publishing. (NorthWord Bks. for Young Readers).

—Everything Dog: What Kids Really Want to Know about Dogs. 2003. (gr. 3-6). lib. bdg. 15.25 (978-0-613-67959-6(8)) Tandem Library Bks.

Crosby, Jeff & Jackson, Shelley Ann. Little Lions, Bull Baiters & Hunting Hounds: A History of Dog Breeds. 2008. 72p. 19.95 (*978-0-88776-815-6(6)*) Tundra Bks., Inc./Livres Toundra, Inc. CAN. *Dist:* Random Hse. of Canada, Ltd.

Crump, A. K., ed. The Dog's Guide to Surfing: Hanging Ten with Man's Best Friend. 2004. (Illus.). 128p. (gr. 5 up). pap. 14.95 (978-0-9674898-7-2(3)) TCB-Cafe Publishing.

Cummins, Judi, creator. Ginger & Snoops, 1. 2006. (Illus.). 22p. (J). per. (978-0-9760377-0-5(X)) Cummins, Judi.

—Ginger the Wonder Beagle. 2005. (Illus.). 26p. (J). per. (978-0-9760377-1-2(8)) Cummins, Judi.

Dalgleish, Sharon. Working Dogs. 2005. (Farm Animals Ser.). (Illus.). 32p. (J). (gr. 2-4). 23.00 (978-0-7910-8275-1(X) , Chelsea Hse.) Facts On File, Inc.

Dalmatian Press Staff. Caring for Your Puppy: Pet Care Guide. 2005. (Illus.). 64p. (J). pap. 5.99 (978-1-4037-0884-7(3)) Dalmatian Pr.

—Puppy Dogs. 2002. (Pop-Up & Flap Board Bks.). (Illus.). 10p. (J). (ps). pap. 4.99 (978-1-57759-792-6(3)) Dalmatian Pr.

Daronco, Mickey & Ohanesian, Diane. My Pet Pup. 2nd rev. ed. 2003. (BuildUp Ser.). (J). pap. 22.00 (978-1-4108-0744-1(4)) Benchmark Education Co.

De Bourgoing, Pascale & Jeunesse, Gallimard. Dogs. Galeron, Henri, illus. 1999. (First Discovery Book Ser.). 24p. (J). (ps-2). 12.95 (978-0-590-87608-7(2)) Scholastic, Inc.

Dell, Pamela. Mustangs. 2007. (Majestic Horses Ser.). 32p. (J). (gr. k-4). 27.07 (978-1-59296-783-4(3)) Child's World, Inc.

Dennis-Bryan, Kim & Dorling Kindersley Publishing Staff. Puppy Care: A Guide for Young Pet Owners. 2004. 48p. (J). 9.99 (978-0-7566-0389-2(7)) Dorling Kindersley Publishing, Inc.

Detector Dog, 6 Pack. (Bookweb Ser.). 32p. (gr. 3 up). 34.00 (978-0-7635-3953-5(8)) Rigby Education.

Dewin, Howie. Do You Know Your Dog? 2007. (Nintendogs Ser.). (Illus.). 48p. (J). pap. 3.99 (*978-0-439-84367-6(7)*) Scholastic, Inc.

Dilly Dog & the Party. 2004. (Play Pals Ser.). (Illus.). 12p. (J). bds. (978-1-84229-642-4(6)) Top That! Publishing PLC.

DK Publishing. Puppies & Kittens. 2008. 14p. (J). (ps-k). bds. 5.99 (*978-0-7566-3835-1(6)*) Dorling Kindersley Publishing, Inc.

—Soft, Fluffy, Playful Puppies. 2008. (Touchables Ser.). 10p. (J). (ps-ps). bds. 8.99 (*978-0-7566-3793-4(7)*) Dorling Kindersley Publishing, Inc.

DK Publishing Staff. Touch & Feel Puppy. 1999. (Touch & Feel Ser.). (Illus.). 12p. (J). (ps-k). bds. 6.99 (978-0-7894-3991-8(3)) Dorling Kindersley Publishing, Inc.

Do Dogs Make Desert? (Animals All Around Ser.). 24p. (J). 7.95 (978-1-4048-0378-7(5)) Picture Window Bks.

Dodd, Emma. Dog's: Farmyard Friends. (Illus.). 140p. (J). bds. (978-1-902272-43-6(9)) Tucker Slingsby, Ltd.

Dog. 2003. (Quick Kiss Guides Ser.). 160p. (YA). pap. 10.00 (978-0-7894-9309-5(8)) Dorling Kindersley Publishing, Inc.

The Dog: Why are Dogs' Noses Wet? 2007. 32p. (J). pap. 3.99 (*978-0-439-92214-2(3)*) Scholastic, Inc.

Dog Artlist Collection Staff. The Dog from Arf! Arf! to Zzzzzz. 2007. (Illus.). 40p. (J). (ps-3). pap. 6.99 (*978-0-06-059859-4(X)* , Harper Trophy) HarperCollins Pubs.

—The Dog from Arf! Arf! to Zzzzzz. Dog Artlist Collection Staff, illus. 2004. (Illus.). 40p. (J). 14.99 (978-0-06-059857-0(3)); lib. bdg. 16.89 (978-0-06-059858-7(1)) HarperCollins Pubs.

The Dog Family: Individual Title Six-Packs. (Story Steps Ser.). (gr. k-2). 32.00 (978-0-7635-9835-8(6)) Rigby Education.

A Dog for You. (Pet Care Ser.). 24p. (J). 7.95 (978-1-4048-0392-3(0)) Picture Window Bks.

Dogs. 2007. (My First Sticker Encyclopedia Ser.). (Illus.). 18p. (J). pap. 5.95 (*978-1-59496-145-8(X)*) Teora USA LLC.

Dogs & Puppies. 2006. (Illus.). (J). cd-rom 9.99 (*978-0-9795190-0-0(4)*) Color & Learn.

Dogs & Puppies Kid Kit. 2003. (Illus.). 32p. 14.95 (978-1-58086-525-8(9)) EDC Publishing.

Dogs & Puppies Sticker Activity Book. Date not set. (Illus.). 12p. (J). 2.98 (978-1-4054-1180-6(5)) Parragon, Inc.

Dogs Have Puppies. (Animals & Their Young Ser.). 24p. (J). 7.95 (978-0-7565-1240-8(9)) Compass Point Bks.

Dogs on the Farm, 6 vols. (gr. k-2). 28.95 (978-0-7368-9379-4(2)) Red Brick Learning.

Dolbear, Emily J. & Primm, E. Russell. Dogs Have Puppies. 2001. (Animals & Their Young Ser.). (Illus.). 24p. (J). (gr. 1 up). lib. bdg. 18.60 (978-0-7565-0060-3(5)) Compass Point Bks.

Dorling Kindersley Publishing Staff. Dog. 2005. (Ultimate sticker Bks.). 16p. (J). pap. 6.99 (978-0-7566-1457-7(0)) Dorling Kindersley Publishing, Inc.

—Puppy. (See How They Grow Ser.). (J). (ps-1). 2007. 24p. pap. 3.99 (978-0-7566-3019-5(3)); 2005. 16p. pap. 6.99 (978-0-7566-1458-4(9)) Dorling Kindersley Publishing, Inc.

Dorling Kindersley Publishing Staff, ed. Puppies. 2004. (Dk Picture Stickers Ser.). 16p. (J). pap. 3.99 (978-0-7566-0560-5(1)) Dorling Kindersley Publishing, Inc.

Dorling Kindersley Publishing Staff & Taylor, David. Dogs. 2nd rev. ed. 2003. (DK Pockets Ser.). (Illus.). 128p. (J). pap. 6.99 (978-0-7894-9591-4(0)) Dorling Kindersley Publishing, Inc.

Draw 50 Dogs. 2002. (Draw 50 Ser.). (Illus.). (J). 17.60 (978-0-7587-4164-6(2)) Book Wholesalers, Inc.

Driscoll, Laura. All about Dogs & Puppies. 1998. (Grossett & Dunlap All Aboard Books & Cassettes Ser.). (Illus.). 32p. (J). (ps-3). pap. 3.99 (978-0-448-41841-4(X) , Grosset & Dunlap) Penguin Group (USA) Inc.

Dunlap, Julie & Lorbiecki, Marybeth. John Muir & the Stickeen: An Icy Adventure with a No Good Dog. Farnsworth, Bill, illus. 2004. 32p. (gr. k-3). 16.95 (978-1-55971-903-2(6) , NorthWord Bks. for Young Readers) T&N Children's Publishing.

Edah, Omatseyin Mark. The Runaway Dog. Eda, Martin M., ed. Edoja, Oke-Wiskee, illus. 2000. 45p. (J). (gr. 3 up). pap. (978-1-928903-01-7(0)) Edah Bks.

Eggleton, Jill. Davy D's Dog: 3-in-1 Package. Gibson, Dave, illus. (Sails Literacy Ser.). 24p. (gr. k up). 57.00 (978-0-7578-8615-7(9)) Rigby Education.

—Davy D's Dog: 6 Small Books. Gibson, Dave, illus. (Sails Literacy Ser.). 24p. (gr. k up). 25.00 (978-0-7578-7728-5(1)) Rigby Education.

—Davy D's Dog: Big Book Only. Gibson, Dave, illus. (Sails Literacy Ser.). 24p. (gr. k up). 27.00 (978-0-7578-6198-7(9)) Rigby Education.

Einhorn, Kama. Sesame Subjects: My First Book about Dogs. Mathieu, Joe, illus. 2006. (Sesame Street Ser.). 24p. (J). (gr. k). 7.99 (978-0-375-83514-8(8) , Random Hse. Bks. for Young Readers) Random Hse. Children's Bks.

Endres, Hollie. Dogs. 2007. (Illus.). 24p. (J). lib. bdg. 19.95 (978-1-60014-083-9(1)) Bellwether Media.

Evans, Mark. Puppy. 2001. (ASPCA Pet Care Guides for Kids). (Illus.). (J). (978-0-606-21389-9(9)) Tandem Library Bks.

Fahiner, Paul. Dog & Cat. 2004. (My First Reader Ser.). (Illus.). 29p. (J). (gr. k-1). pap. 3.95 (978-0-516-24626-0(7) , Children's Pr.) Scholastic Library Publishing.

Falk, Laine. Let's Explore the Five Senses with City Dog & Country Dog. 2007. (Let's Find Out Early Learning Bks.). (Illus.). 24p. (J). (ps-k). 18.00 (978-0-531-14873-0(4) , Children's Pr.) Scholastic Library Publishing.

Feldman, Heather. My Dog: A Book about a Special Pet. 2000. (PowerKids Readers Ser.). (Illus.). 24p. (J). (gr. 1). lib. bdg. 16.00 (978-0-8239-5524-4(9) , PKMYDO, PowerKids Pr.) Rosen Publishing Group, Inc., The.

—The Story of the Golden Retriever. 2000. (Dogs Throughout History Ser.). 24p. (J). (gr. k-4). lib. bdg. 18.75 (978-0-8239-5514-5(1) , PowerKids Pr.) Rosen Publishing Group, Inc., The.

Fernandez, Amy. Puppies: A Guide to Caring for Your Puppy. 2006. (Complete Care Made Easy Ser.). (Illus.). 200p. (J). pap. 9.95 (978-1-931993-76-0(9)) BowTie Pr.

Fiedler, Julie. Bulldogs. 2006. (Illus.). 24p. (J). lib. bdg. (978-1-4042-3119-1(6) , PowerKids Pr.) Rosen Publishing Group, Inc., The.

—Doberman Pinschers. 2006. (Illus.). 24p. lib. bdg. (978-1-4042-3120-7(X) , PowerKids Pr.) Rosen Publishing Group, Inc., The.

—Great Danes. 2006. (Illus.). 24p. (J). lib. bdg. (978-1-4042-3122-1(6) , PowerKids Pr.) Rosen Publishing Group, Inc., The.

—Rottweilers. 2006. (Illus.). 24p. (J). lib. bdg. (978-1-4042-3118-4(8) , PowerKids Pr.) Rosen Publishing Group, Inc., The.

Fink, Jeri, et al. The Gizmo Tales: Working Dogs. 2004. (Illus.). (J). per. 14.94 (978-0-9716567-3-4(8)) Book Web Publishing, Ltd.

FLOWERS, P. A. M. Douggie. Van Zyle, Jon, illus. 2008. 0032p. (J). 15.95 (*978-0-88240-654-1(X)* , Alaska Northwest Bks.) Graphic Arts Ctr. Publishing Co.

Flowers, Pam. Big-Enough Anna: The Little Sled Dog Who Braved the Arctic. 2003. (gr. k-3). lib. bdg. 17.60 (978-0-613-77220-4(2)) Tandem Library Bks.

Flowers, Pam. Douggie's Story. Rubin, David, illus. 2007. (J). pap. (*978-0-88240-655-8(8)* , Alaska Northwest Bks.) Graphic Arts Ctr. Publishing Co.

Flowers, Pam & Dixon, Ann. Big-Enough Anna: The Little Sled Dog Who Braved the Arctic. Farnsworth, Bill, illus. 2005. (Seldovia Sam Ser.). 32p. (ps up). 15.95 (978-0-88240-577-3(2)) Graphic Arts Ctr. Publishing Co.

—Big-Enough Anna: The Little Sled Dog Who Braved the Arctic. Farnsworth, Bill, tr. Farnsworth, Bill, illus. 2005. 32p. pap. 8.95 (978-0-88240-580-3(2)) Graphic Arts Ctr. Publishing Co.

Fogle, Bruce. Kiss Guide to Living with a Dog. 2000. (gr. 7-12). lib. bdg. 29.20 (978-0-613-32746-6(2)) Tandem Library Bks.

Foran, Jill. Caring for Your Dog. Marshall, Diana & Nault, Jennifer, eds. 2003. (Caring for Your Pet Ser.). (Illus.). 32p. (J). pap. 7.95 (978-1-59036-063-7(X)) Weigl Pubs., Inc.

Fordham, Kate. Me & My Puppy. 2007. 80p. (J). (ps-3). pap. 9.99 (*978-0-439-91882-4(0)* , Tangerine Pr.) Scholastic, Inc.

Frisch, Joy. Bulldogs. 2003. (Dog Breeds Ser.). 24p. (J). lib. bdg. 21.35 (978-1-58340-316-7(7)) Smart Apple Media.

—Retrievers. 2003. (Dog Breeds Ser.). 24p. (J). lib. bdg. 21.35 (978-1-58340-312-9(4)) Smart Apple Media.

Frost, Helen. Dogs. 2000. (All about Pets Ser.). (Illus.). 24p. (J). (gr. k-1). lib. bdg. 15.93 (978-0-7368-0656-5(3) , Pebble Bks.) Capstone Pr., Inc.

Furfur, Christopher. How Should I Care for My Doggy? 2005. (Illus.). 64p. (J). 15.95 (978-0-9742845-6-9(4)) Mystic Ridge Bks.

Furstinger, Nancy. Dogs Set VI. 2006. (J). (gr. k-6). 128.10 (978-1-59679-270-8(1) , Checkerboard Library) ABDO Publishing Co.

—Fun Stuff with Your Best Friend: The Interactive Dog Book. Anderson, Mark, ed. Ebdon, Bob, illus. 2000. 112p. (ps-3). pap. 14.95 (978-0-944875-66-7(1)) Doral Publishing, Inc.

—Lhasa Apsos. 2006. (Checkerboard Animal Library). (Illus.). 24p. (J). (gr. k-6). 21.35 (978-1-59679-271-5(X) , Checkerboard Library) ABDO Publishing Co.

—Maltese. 2006. (Checkerboard Animal Library). 24p. (J). (gr. k-6). 21.35 (978-1-59679-272-2(8) , Checkerboard Library) ABDO Publishing Co.

—Mastiffs. 2006. (Illus.). 24p. (J). (gr. k-6). 21.35 (978-1-59679-273-9(6) , Checkerboard Library) ABDO Publishing Co.

—Miniature Schnauzers. 2006. (Illus.). 24p. (J). (gr. k-6). 21.35 (978-1-59679-274-6(4) , Checkerboard Library) ABDO Publishing Co.

—Pointers. 2006. (Checkerboard Animal Library). (Illus.). 24p. (J). (gr. k-6). 21.35 (978-1-59679-275-3(2) , Checkerboard Library) ABDO Publishing Co.

Gaines, Ann. Top 10 Dogs for Kids. 2008. (J). (*978-0-7660-3070-1(9)) Enslow Pubs., Inc.

Ganeri, Anita. Dogs. 2003. (Heinemann First Library). (Illus.). 32p. (J). pap. (978-1-4034-4270-3(3)) Heinemann Library.

—Dogs & Puppies. 2007. (J). (*978-1-58340-806-3(1)) Smart Apple Media.

—From Puppy to Dog. 2006. (Heinemann First Library). (Illus.). 32p. (J). (978-1-4034-7856-6(2)); pap. (978-1-4034-7865-8(1)) Heinemann Library.

—A Pet's Life: Dogs. 2003. (Heinemann First Library). (Illus.). 32p. (J). lib. bdg. 22.79 (978-1-4034-3994-9(X)) Heinemann Library.

Gebauer, Roland. Lass. Bladholm, Cheri, illus. 2004. 32p. 12.99 (978-0-8254-2694-0(4)) Kregel Pubns.

Gentle, Victor & Perry, Janet. African Wild Dogs. 2002. (Imagination Library). (Illus.). 24p. (J). (gr. 2 up). lib. bdg. 22.00 (978-0-8368-3094-1(6)) Stevens, Gareth Inc.

—Dingoes. 2002. (Imagination Library). (Illus.). 24p. (J). (gr. 2 up). lib. bdg. 22.00 (978-0-8368-3096-5(2)) Stevens, Gareth Inc.

—Wild Dogs, 6 bks. Incl. African Wild Dogs. lib. bdg. 22.00 (978-0-8368-3094-1(6)); Coyotes. lib. bdg. 22.00 (978-0-8368-3095-8(4)); Dingoes. lib. bdg. 22.00 (978-0-8368-3096-5(2)); Jackals. lib. bdg. 22.00 (978-0-8368-3097-2(0)); Red Foxes. lib. bdg. 22.00 (978-0-8368-3098-9(9)); Wolves. lib. bdg. 22.00 (978-0-8368-3099-6(7)); 24p. (J). (gr. 2 up). (Illus.). 2002. Set lib. bdg. 132.00 (978-0-8368-3093-4(8)) Stevens, Gareth Inc.

George, Charles. Dogs at Work. 1998. pap. 76.00 (978-0-531-19416-4(7) , Watts, Franklin) Scholastic Library Publishing.

George, Jean Craighead. How to Talk to Your Dog. Truesdell, Sue & Meisel, Paul, illus. 2003. 40p. (J). (gr. 1-3). pap. 6.99 (978-0-06-000623-5(4) , Harper Trophy) HarperCollins Pubs.

—How to Talk to Your Dog. Truesdell, Sue, illus. 2000. 40p. (J). (gr. 1-4). 14.99 (978-0-06-027092-6(6)) HarperCollins Pubs.

—How to Talk to Your Dog. 2003. (gr. 3-6). lib. bdg. 14.15 (978-0-613-62959-1(0)) Tandem Library Bks.

George, Linda & George, Charles. Bomb Detection Dogs. 1998. (Riverfront Dogs at Work Ser.). 48p. (J). lib. bdg. 19.00 (978-0-531-11554-1(2) , Watts, Franklin) Scholastic Library Publishing.

—Search & Rescue Dogs. 1998. (Dogs at Work Ser.). 48p. (J). pap. 19.00 (978-0-531-11557-2(7) , Watts, Franklin) Scholastic Library Publishing.

Gersten, Dan, creator. Ask Curtis: Dog-Sense Advice from Curtis the Dog, 1. 2005. (Illus.). 146p. per. (978-0-9766846-0-2(8)) Dogwalk Pr.

Getting Lucky. 2003. (J). lib. bdg. 25.00 (978-0-9747527-0-9(3)) Nicoll Creations.

Gilkerson, Patricia. My Adventure with Dogs. 2007. 44p. (J). 8.99 (978-1-59092-451-8(7) , Orchard Academy Pr.) Windstorm Creative.

Gillis, Jennifer Blizin. Dogs. 2004. (Heinemann Read & Learn Ser.). (Illus.). 24p. (J). 18.50 (978-1-4034-5052-4(8)); pap. 5.50 (978-1-4034-6020-2(5)) Heinemann Library.

Glaser, Rebecca Stromstad. Border Collies. 2006. (Pebble Books). (Illus.). 24p. (J). (978-0-7368-5331-6(6) , 1252484) Capstone Pr., Inc.

Glover, A. Libro de Pegatinas Perros. 2004. (Spotter's Guides Sticker Bks.).Tr. of Dogs Sticker Book. (SPA., Illus.). 24p. (J). (gr. 2 up). pap. 7.95 (978-0-7460-3643-3(4)) EDC Publishing.

Glover, Harry. Dogs. 2004. (Spotter's Guides). 64p. (J). pap. 5.95 (978-0-7945-0620-9(8)) EDC Publishing.

God Made Puppies. 2006. 16p. (J). pap. 1.99 (978-0-7847-1685-4(4) , 02987) Standard Publishing.

Goldish, Meish. Dogs. 2007. (Smart Animals! Ser.). (J). lib. bdg. 25.27 (978-1-59716-368-2(6)) Bearport Publishing Co., Inc.

—Hollywood Dogs. 2007. (Dog Heroes Ser.). (Illus.). 32p. (J). lib. bdg. 25.27 (978-1-59716-404-7(6) , 1265962) Bearport Publishing Co., Inc.

Good Morning Miss Prin. 2002. (J). pap. 7.95 (978-0-9722555-0-9(8)) Sblendido, Barbara.

Gordon, Bob. Noisy Puppy. 2006. (Touch & Feel Noisy Ser.). (Illus.). 10p. (ps). per., bds. 6.95 (978-1-84610-285-1(5)) Make Believe Ideas GBR. *Dist:* Ingram Pub. Services.

Gorrell, Gena K. Working Like a Dog: The Story of Working Dogs Through History. 2003. (gr. 5-8). lib. bdg. 26.85 (978-0-613-77330-0(6)) Tandem Library Bks.

—Working Like a Dog: The Story of Working Dogs Through History. 2003. (Illus.). 160p. (J). (gr. 5 up). pap. 16.95 (978-0-88776-589-6(0)) Tundra Bks., Inc./Livres Toundra, Inc. CAN. *Dist:* Random Hse., Inc.

Gray, Susan H. Basset Hounds. 2007. (Domestic Dogs Ser.). 32p. (J). (gr. k-4). 27.07 (978-1-59296-771-1(X)) Child's World, Inc.

—Border Collies. 2007. (Domestic Dogs Ser.). 32p. (J). (gr. k-4). 27.07 (978-1-59296-772-8(8)) Child's World, Inc.

—Bulldogs. 2008. (Domestic Dogs Ser.). 32p. (J). (gr. k-4). 27.07 (*978-1-59296-962-3(3)) Child's World, Inc.

—Cocker Spaniels. 2008. (Domestic Dogs Ser.). 32p. (J). (gr. k-4). 27.07 (*978-1-59296-963-0(1)) Child's World, Inc.

—Golden Retrievers. 2007. (Domestic Dogs Ser.). 32p. (J). (gr. k-4). 27.07 (978-1-59296-774-2(4)) Child's World, Inc.

—Labradors. 2007. (Domestic Dogs Ser.). 32p. (J). (gr. k-4). 27.07 (978-1-59296-775-9(2)) Child's World, Inc.

—Pomeranians. 2008. (Domestic Dogs Ser.). 32p. (J). (gr. k-4). 27.07 (*978-1-59296-966-1(6)) Child's World, Inc.

—Pugs. 2007. (Domestic Dogs Ser.). 32p. (J). (gr. k-4). 27.07 (978-1-59296-776-6(0)) Child's World, Inc.

—Rottweilers. 2008. (Domestic Dogs Ser.). 32p. (J). (gr. k-4). 27.07 (*978-1-59296-967-8(4)) Child's World, Inc.

—Scottish Terriers. 2008. (Domestic Dogs Ser.). 32p. (J). (gr. k-4). 27.07 (*978-1-59296-968-5(2)) Child's World, Inc.

—Shih Tzus. 2007. (Domestic Dogs Ser.). 32p. (J). (gr. k-4). 27.07 (978-1-59296-777-3(9)) Child's World, Inc.

—Yorkshire Terriers. 2007. (Domestic Dogs Ser.). 32p. (J). (gr. k-4). 27.07 (978-1-59296-778-0(7)) Child's World, Inc.

Greenberg, Daniel A. Wilderness Search Dogs. 2005. (Dog Heroes Ser.). (Illus.). 32p. (J). lib. bdg. 25.27 (978-1-59716-019-3(9)) Bearport Publishing Co., Inc.

Gregoire, Caroline. Apollo. 2006. 32p. 7.95 (978-1-933605-04-3(9)) Kane/Miller Bk. Pubs., Inc.

Grogan, John. Marley: A Dog Like No Other. 208p. (J). 2008. pap. 6.99 (*978-0-06-124035-5(4)); 2007. (Illus.). (gr. 3-7). 16.99 (*978-0-06-124033-1(8)); 2007. (Illus.). (gr. 3-7). lib. bdg. 17.89 (*978-0-06-124034-8(6)) HarperCollins Pubs.

Grolier Educational Staff, contrib. by. Wild Dogs. 2001. (Nature's Children Ser.). (Illus.). 48p. (J). (978-0-7172-5551-1(4) , Grolier) Scholastic Library Publishing.

Gruber, Beth. Dog Days. 2004. (Pet's Point of View Ser.). (Illus.). 32p. (J). (gr. 4 up). lib. bdg. 22.60 (978-0-7565-0698-8(0)) Compass Point Bks.

Gunter, Veronika & Newcomb, Rain. Pet Science: Purr-Fectly Woof-Worthy Activities for You & Your Pets. 2006. (Illus.). 80p. (J). 14.95 (978-1-57990-786-0(5)) Lark Bks.

Gunzi, Christiane. The Best Book of Wolves & Wild Dogs. Rowe, Mike, illus. 2003. (Best Book of... Ser.). 32p. (J). (gr. k-3). tchr. ed. 12.95 (978-0-7534-5574-6(9) , Kingfisher) Houghton Mifflin Co. Trade & Reference Div.

Gutman, Bill. Adopting Pets: How to Choose Your New Best Friend. 2001. (Pet Friends Ser.). (Illus.). 64p. (gr. 4-6). lib. bdg. (978-0-7613-1863-7(1) , Millbrook Pr.) Lerner Publishing Group.

Haigh, Jane. Gold Rush Dogs. 2001. (gr. 7-12). lib. bdg. 26.85 (978-0-613-58217-9(9)) Tandem Library Bks.

Hall, Lynn. Barry: The Bravest Saint Bernard. Castro, Antonio, illus. 2007. 48p. (J). (gr. 2-4). 3.99 (*978-0-375-84439-3(2)); lib. bdg. 11.99 (*978-0-375-94439-0(7)) Random Hse. Children's Bks. (Random Hse. Bks. for Young Readers).

Halls, Kelly Milner. Wild Dogs: Past & Present. 2005. (Illus.). 64p. (J). (gr. 6-12). 18.95 (978-1-58196-027-3(1)) Darby Creek Publishing.

Halpern, Monica. Look at Dogs. 1998. (Look at Ser.). (Illus.). 24p. (gr. k-3). pap. 4.95 (978-0-8172-7986-8(5)) Steck-Vaughn.

Hamilton, Lynn A. Caring for Your Dog. 2002. (Caring for Your Pet Ser.). (Illus.). 32p. (J). lib. bdg. 16.95 (978-1-59036-033-0(8)) Weigl Pubs., Inc.

Hansen, Jennifer. Lucy's Grade School Adventure. Marsden, Ken, illus. 2006. (J). (978-0-9774822-7-6(8)) Crosam Pr.

Harcourt School Publishers Staff. Big Dogs, Little Dogs: Take-Home Book. 1999. (Signatures Ser.). (Illus.). (J). pap. 1.70 (978-0-15-313822-5(X)) Harcourt Schl. Pubs.

—Dogs to the Rescue Advanced Level. 3rd ed. 2002. (Trophies Reading Program Ser.). (Illus.). pap. 5.10 (978-0-15-323468-2(7)) Harcourt Schl. Pubs.

—Guide Dog Heroes: Take-Home Book. 1999. (Signatures Ser.). (Illus.). (J). pap. 1.90 (978-0-15-313908-6(0)) Harcourt Schl. Pubs.

Harpster, Steve. Dogs. 2006. (Pencil, Paper, Draw! Ser.). (Illus.). 64p. (J). pap., spiral bd. 5.95 (978-1-4027-2973-7(1)) Sterling Publishing Co., Inc.

Hart, Joyce. Big Dogs. 2007. (Great Pets Ser.). 48p. (J). lib. bdg. 28.50 (*978-0-7614-2707-0(4) , Benchmark Bks.) Cavendish, Marshall Corp.

Haskins, Lori. Sled Dogs. 2006. (Dog Heroes Ser.). (Illus.). 32p. (J). lib. bdg. 25.27 (978-1-59716-171-8(3) , 1251393) Bearport Publishing Co., Inc.

—Too Many Dogs! Mathieu, Joe, illus. 1998. 32p. (J). (ps-ps). lib. bdg. 11.80 (978-0-613-08924-1(3)) Tandem Library Bks.

Hawkes, Chris. All about Dogs. 2005. (Illus.). 38p. (J). (ps-8). lib. bdg. 28.00 (978-0-7910-8686-5(0) , Chelsea Hse.) Facts On File, Inc.

Head, Honor. Puppy. Burton, Jane, photos by. 2000. (My Pet Ser.). (Illus.). 32p. (J). (gr. 3-5). lib. bdg. 25.69 (978-0-7398-2885-4(1)) Raintree.

—Puppy. 2000. (My Pet Ser.). (Illus.). 32p. (J). (gr. 3-5). pap. 8.95 (978-0-7398-3012-3(0)) Steck-Vaughn.

Helbrough, Emma. Dogs (Level 1) - Internet Referenced. 2006. 32p. (J). 4.99 (978-0-7945-1395-5(6) , Usborne) EDC Publishing.

Helms, Jo. Grizz's Story-A Greater Courage: A Dog's Journey. ltd. ed. 2003. 86p. 14.95 (978-0-9745319-0-8(1)) Helms, Jo Publishing.

Hendry, Linda. Dog Crafts. Hendry, Linda, illus. 2004. (Kids Can Do It Ser.). (Illus.). 40p. (J). (gr. 4-6). (978-1-55074-960-1(9)); (978-1-55074-962-5(5)) Kids Can Pr., Ltd.

Hibbert, Clare. Life of a Dog. 2004. (Raintree Perspectives Ser.). (Illus.). 32p. (J). lib. bdg. 25.70 (978-1-4109-0535-2(7)) Raintree.

—The Life of a Dog. 2004. (Illus.). pap. 7.50 (978-1-4109-0923-7(9)) Raintree.

—The Life of a Dog 6-Pack. 2004. (Illus.). pap. 40.50 (978-1-4109-0930-5(1)) Raintree.

Hirschmann, Kris. The Dog: Is a Paw a Foot? Learn Measurement. 2007. (Illus.). 32p. (J). pap. 3.99 (*978-0-439-92213-5(5)) Scholastic, Inc.

Hirshberg, Jackie. Nicky the Swamp Dog: A True Story. Guillory, D. Ray, photos by. 2000. (Illus.). 40p. (J). (gr. 3-5). 14.95 (978-0-925417-36-7(X)) Acadian Hse. Publishing.

Hodge, Deborah. Wild Dogs: Wolves, Coyotes & Foxes. Stephens, Pat, illus. 1999. 32p. (J). (ps-ps). lib. bdg. 14.10 (978-0-613-16446-7(6)) Tandem Library Bks.

Hodge, Judith. Surprise Puppy! 1998. (Eyewitness Readers). (Illus.). 32p. (J). (gr. 5-3). pap. 3.99 (978-0-7894-3624-5(8)) Dorling Kindersley Publishing, Inc.

Hodge, Judith & Dorling Kindersley Publishing Staff. Surprise Puppy! 1998. (Eyewitness Readers). (Illus.). 32p. (J). (ps-3). 12.99 (978-0-7894-3765-5(1)) Dorling Kindersley Publishing, Inc.

Hoena, B. A. Dogs ABC: An Alphabet Book. 2004. (A+ Alphabet Books). (Illus.). 32p. (J). lib. bdg. 22.60 (978-0-7368-2606-8(8) , Aplus Bks.) Capstone Pr., Inc.

Holub, Joan. Why Do Dogs Bark? Holub, Joan & DiVito, Anna, illus. 2001. (Easy-to-Read Ser.). 48p. (J). (ps-3). pap. 3.99 (978-0-14-056789-2(5) , Puffin) Penguin Group (USA) Inc.

—Why Do Dogs Bark? DiVito, Anna, illus. 2001. 48p. (J). (ps-ps). lib. bdg. 11.80 (978-0-613-35607-7(1)) Tandem Library Bks.

Horenstein, Henry. Arf! Beg! Catch! Dogs from A to Z. Horenstein, Henry, illus. 1999. (Illus.). 40p. (J). (ps-1). pap. 12.95 (978-0-590-03380-0(8) , Cartwheel Bks.) Scholastic, Inc.

Hosley, Maria. Dogs. 2007. (Illus.). 24p. (J). 21.35 (*978-1-59679-803-8(3)) ABDO Publishing Co.

Hughes, Sarah. My Dog. 2001. (My Pets Ser.). (Illus.). 24p. (J). (ps-2). 17.00 (978-0-516-23184-6(7) , Children's Pr.) Scholastic Library Publishing.

—My Dog. 2001. (gr. k-3). lib. bdg. 12.95 (978-0-613-58861-4(4)) Tandem Library Bks.

Jeffrey, Laura S. Dogs: How to Choose & Care for a Dog. 2004. (American Humane Pet Care Library). (Illus.). 48p. (J). lib. bdg. 23.93 (978-0-7660-2520-2(9)) Enslow Pubs., Inc.

Jenkins, Steve. Dogs & Cats. 2007. (Illus.). 40p. (J). (gr. 1-5). 16.00 (*978-0-618-50767-2(1)) Houghton Mifflin Co. Trade & Reference Div.

Jobs for Dogs, 6, Pack. (Rigby Focus Ser.). 16p. (gr. 1 up). 30.00 (978-0-7578-5548-1(2)) Rigby Education.

Jobs for Dogs: Individual Title Six-Packs. (Rigby Focus Ser.). 16p. (gr. 1 up). 28.00 (978-0-7578-5316-6(1)) Rigby Education.

Johnston, Tony. It's about Dogs. 2000. (Illus.). 48p. (J). (gr. k-3). 16.98 (978-0-7398-2200-5(4)) Raintree.

Kallen, Stuart A. Dogs, Set V. 2003. (J). (gr. k-6). lib. bdg. 128.10 (978-1-57765-918-1(X) , Checkerboard Library) ABDO Publishing Co.

—Dogs - Set II, 6 bks. l.t. ed. Incl. Beagles. (Illus.). lib. bdg. 21.35 (978-1-56239-572-8(6)); Collies. (Illus.). lib. bdg. 21.35 (978-1-56239-573-5(4)); Dachshunds. (Illus.). lib. bdg. 21.35 (978-1-56239-574-2(2)); Golden Retrievers. (Illus.). lib. bdg. 21.35 (978-1-56239-576-6(9)); Old English Sheepdogs. (Illus.). lib. bdg. 21.35 (978-1-56239-575-9(0)); Yorkshire Terriers. lib. bdg. 21.35 (978-1-56239-577-3(7)); 24p. (J). (gr. k-6). 1998. (Illus.). 1998. Set lib. bdg. 128.10 (978-1-56239-929-0(2) , Checkerboard Library) ABDO Publishing Co.

Kalman, Bobbie & Sotzek, Hannelore. Les Chiens. 2002. (FRE., Illus.). 32p. (J). pap. (978-2-920660-84-7(5)) Crabtree Publishing Co.

—Que es un Perro? 2006. (SPA., Illus.). 32p. (gr. 2-3). pap. (978-0-7787-8811-9(3)) Crabtree Publishing Co.

—What Is a Dog? 2000. (Science of Living Things Ser.). (Illus.). 32p. (J). (gr. 2-3). (978-0-86505-979-5(9)); pap. (978-0-86505-956-6(X)) Crabtree Publishing Co.

—What Is a Dog? 2000. (Illus.). 32p. (J). (gr. 2-8). lib. bdg. 14.10 (978-0-613-28130-0(6)) Tandem Library Bks.

Kast, Edie. Heroic Animals. 2005. (Illus.). 24p. (J). (*978-0-328-13606-3(9) , Scott Foresman) Addison-Wesley Educational Pubs., Inc.

Katz, Jon. Dog Year: Twelve Months, Four Dogs, & Me. 2003. (gr. 7-12). lib. bdg. 22.20 (978-0-613-58362-6(0)) Tandem Library Bks.

Kehret, Peg. Shelter Dogs: Amazing Stories of Adopted Strays. 1999. (gr. 3-6). lib. bdg. 14.10 (978-0-613-61854-0(8)) Tandem Library Bks.

—Shelter Dogs: Amazing Stories of Adopted Strays. Farrar, Greg, photos by. (Illus.). 144p. (J). (gr. 3-8). 2004. pap. 6.95 (978-0-8075-7336-5(1)); 1999. 15.95 (978-0-8075-7334-1(5)) Whitman, Albert & Co.

Kennedy, Edward M. My Senator & Me: A Dog's Eye View of Washington, D. C. Small, David, illus. 2006. 56p. (J). (ps-3). pap. 16.99 (978-0-439-65077-9(1) , Scholastic) Scholastic, Inc.

The Kids Guide to Pet Jokes, Rhymes & Riddles: For Kids Who Love Pets. 2006. (J). 7.95 (*978-0-9744749-3-9(2)) Crazy Pet Pr., The.

Kip & Tip 6 Packs. KinderReaders Individual Title. (Kinderstarters Ser.). 8p. (ps-1). 21.00 (978-0-7635-8650-8(1)) Rigby Education.

Kishel, Ann-Marie. Dogs & Puppies. 2006. (First Step Nonfiction Ser.). (Illus.). 8p. (J). lib. bdg. (978-0-8225-5650-3(2) , Lerner Pubns.) Lerner Publishing Group.

Kittens & Puppies. 2002. (Three Minute Tales Ser.). 32p. (J). 12.98 (978-0-7525-5467-9(0)) Parragon, Inc.

Knight, K. R. Puppy. 2002. (Cuddly Pups Board Bks.). (Illus.). 18p. (J). bds. 4.99 (978-1-57759-787-2(7)) Dalmatian Pr.

Koehler-Pentacoff, Elizabeth. John Muir & Stickeen: An Alaskan Adventure. Swanson, Karl W., illus. 2003. (Single Titles Ser.). 32p. (J). 14.95 (978-0-7613-1997-9(2) , Millbrook Pr.) Lerner Publishing Group.

Kunhardt, Katharine. Let's Count the Puppies. 2004. (Illus.). 32p. (J). (ps-1). 13.89 (978-0-06-054337-2(X)) HarperCollins Pubs.

Landau, Elaine. Your Pet Dog. rev. ed. 2006. (True Book Ser.). (Illus.). 47p. (J). (978-0-531-16767-0(4)) Children's Pr., Ltd.

—Your Pet Dog. 1998. (True Bks.). (Illus.). 48p. (J). (gr. 3-5). pap. 6.95 (978-0-516-26263-5(7) , Children's Pr.) Scholastic Library Publishing.

Lane, Judith. Buster, Where Are You? Lane, Nancy, illus. 1998. 32p. (J). (gr. 1-5). 12.95 (978-1-58021-019-5(8)); pap. 5.95 (978-1-58021-020-1(1)); pap. 9.95 incl. audio (978-1-58021-023-2(6)); pap. 19.95 incl. audio (978-1-58021-021-8(X)) Benefactory, Inc., The.

—Buster, Where Are You? Includes Plush Toy Animal. Lane, Nancy, illus. 1998. 32p. (J). (gr. 1-5). 29.95 (978-1-58021-028-7(7)); pap. 14.95 (978-1-58021-022-5(8)) Benefactory, Inc., The.

—Buster, Where Are You? Includes Tape & Plush Toy Animal. Lane, Nancy, illus. 1998. 32p. (J). (gr. 1-5). 34.95 incl. audio (978-1-58021-027-0(9)) Benefactory, Inc., The.

Laroyster, Angela. Puppy. (See How They Grow Ser.). (Illus.). (J). 10.95 (978-0-590-73805-7(4)) Scholastic, Inc.

Latham, Donna. Fire Dogs. 2005. (Dog Heroes Ser.). (Illus.). 32p. (J). lib. bdg. 25.27 (978-1-59716-141-1(1)) Bearport Publishing Co., Inc.

Lauber, Patricia. The True-or-False Book of Dogs. Schanzer, Rosalyn, illus. 2003. 32p. (J). 15.99 (978-0-06-029767-1(0)) HarperCollins Pubs.

Leduc-Lenmark, MaryAlice. Meet Mister Muttley. Speas, Joann, illus. 2004. 25p. (J). 16.95 (978-0-9760733-0-7(7)) Heartstrings Publishing.

LeFrak, Karen. Jake the Philharmonic Dog. Baranski, Marcin, illus. 2006. 32p. (J). 17.85 (978-0-8027-9553-3(6)) Walker & Co.

Lewis, David, contrib. by. Puppies. 1999. (Junior Pet Care Ser.). (Illus.). 48p. (YA). (gr. 4-7). 18.65 (978-0-7910-4905-1(1) , Chelsea Hse.) Facts On File, Inc.

The Life Cycle of a Dog, Vol. 2. 2005. (Animals, Animals, Animals Ser.). (YA). (gr. k-3). (978-0-7368-3394-3(3) , Pebble Bks.) Capstone Pr., Inc.

Linden, Joanne. Yorkshire Terriers. 2007. (Illus.). 24p. (J). 15.93 (978-0-7368-6329-2(X)) Capstone Pr., Inc.

Lloyd, Sam. Happy Dog, Sad Dog. 2005. (Illus.). 14p. (J). (ps). 5.95 (978-1-56148-455-3(5)) Good Bks.

Lodien, Jennie, des. A Doggie Diary: The story of our Dog. 2003. (Illus.). 48p. (YA). ring bd. 16.95 (978-0-9746341-7-3(4)) Chin & A Pr.

—Life on a Leash: My Dog's Story. 2003. (Illus.). 48p. (YA). ring bd. 16.95 (978-0-9746341-6-6(6)) Chin & A Pr.

Loewen, Nancy. Dalmatians. 2003. (Dog Breeds Ser.). 24p. (J). lib. bdg. 21.35 (978-1-58340-317-4(5)) Smart Apple Media.

London, Jonathan. Sled Dogs Run. Van Zyle, Jon, illus. 2005. 32p. (J). 17.85 (978-0-8027-8958-7(7)); 16.95 (978-0-8027-8957-0(9)) Walker & Co.

Lorenz Books Staff & Tuxworth, Nicola. Puppies. 1999. (Very First Picture Bks.). (Illus.). 12p. (ps). bds. 4.95 (978-0-7548-0384-3(8) , Lorenz Bks.) Anness Publishing GBR. *Dist:* National Bk. Network.

Los Perros. 2004. (Los Mascotas de mi Casa). 24p. (J). 14.95 (978-1-4034-6033-2(7)) Heinemann Library.

Loves, June. Dogs. 2003. (Pets Ser.). (Illus.). 32p. (gr. 2-4). 23.00 (978-0-7910-7549-4(4) , Chelsea Hse.) Facts On File, Inc.

Lubka, S. Ruth. Pupniks: The Story of Two Space Dogs. 2003. (Illus.). 32p. (J). 16.95 (978-0-7614-5137-2(4)) Cavendish, Marshall Corp.

MacAulay, Kelley. Los Cocker Spaniel. 2007. (SPA.). 32p. (J). (gr. 2-3). (*978-0-7787-8458-6(4)) Crabtree Publishing Co.

—Los Dalmatas. 2007. (SPA.). 32p. (J). (gr. 2-3). (*978-0-7787-8459-3(2)) Crabtree Publishing Co.

—Los Perros Labrador. 2007. (SPA & ENG.). 32p. (J). (gr. 2-3). (*978-0-7787-8460-9(6)) Crabtree Publishing Co.

MacAulay, Kelley & Kalman, Bobbie. Los Cocker Spaniel. rev. ed. 2007. (SPA.). 32p. (J). (gr. 2-3). pap. (*978-0-7787-8480-7(0)) Crabtree Publishing Co.

—Cocker Spaniels. 2006. (Pet Care Ser.). (Illus.). 32p. (J). (978-0-7787-1760-7(7) , 1259503) Crabtree Publishing Co.

—Los Dalmatas. rev. ed. 2007. (SPA.). 32p. (J). (gr. 2-3). pap. (*978-0-7787-8481-4(9)) Crabtree Publishing Co.

—Dalmatians. 2006. (Pet Care Ser.). (Illus.). 32p. (J). (978-0-7787-1761-4(5) , 1259504) Crabtree Publishing Co.

—Labrador Retrievers. 2006. (Pet Care Ser.). (Illus.). 32p. (J). (978-0-7787-1762-1(3)) Crabtree Publishing Co.

MacAulay, Kelley & Kalman, Bobbie. Los Perros Labrador. rev. ed. 2007. (SPA & ENG.). 32p. (J). (gr. 2-3). pap. (*978-0-7787-8482-1(7)) Crabtree Publishing Co.

MacAuley, Kelley. Cocker Spaniels. 2006. (Pet Care Ser.). (Illus.). 32p. (J). (gr. 2-3). pap. (978-0-7787-1792-8(5) , 1259503) Crabtree Publishing Co.

—Dalmatians. 2006. (Pet Care Ser.). (Illus.). 32p. (J). (gr. 2-3). pap. (978-0-7787-1793-5(3) , 1259504) Crabtree Publishing Co.

—Labrador Retrievers. 2006. (Pet Care Ser.). (Illus.). 32p. (gr. 2-3). pap. (978-0-7787-1794-2(1)) Crabtree Publishing Co.

Macken, JoAnn Early. Puppies. 2003. (Let's Read about Pets Ser.). (Illus.). 24p. (J). (ps up). lib. bdg. 19.33 (978-0-8368-3801-5(7)); pap. 7.93 (978-0-8368-3848-0(3)) Stevens, Gareth Inc. (Weekly Reader Early Learning Library).

Magloff, Lisa & Dorling Kindersley Publishing Staff. Puppy. 2005. (Watch me Grow Ser.). (Illus.). 24p. (J). 7.99 (978-0-7566-1273-3(X)) Dorling Kindersley Publishing, Inc.

Makowski, Robin Lee. Dogs. 2001. (How to Draw Ser.). (Illus.). 32p. (J). (gr. 2-5). lib. bdg. 25.27 (978-1-58952-154-4(4)) Rourke Publishing, LLC.

Makowski, Robin Lee, illus. Dogs. 2004. (J). (978-1-59203-088-0(2)) Learning Challenge, Inc.

Marie, Christian. Little Dogs. 2006. (Born to Be Wild Ser.). (Illus.). 23p. (J). lib. bdg. 22.00 (978-0-8368-6164-8(7)) Stevens, Gareth Inc.

Markle, Sandra. Tasmanian Devils. 2005. (Animal Scavengers Ser.). (Illus.). 40p. (J). (ps-7). 25.26 (978-0-8225-3199-9(2) , Lerner Pubns.) Lerner Publishing Group.

Marlin, Debrah. Yellowdog. 2000. (Illus.). 96p. pap. (978-0-8212-2692-6(4)) Bulfinch Pr.

Marshall, Diana. Caring for Your Dog. 2003. (gr. 3-6). lib. bdg. 16.40 (978-0-613-79809-9(0)) Tandem Library Bks.

Mayes, Katie. Puppies. 2006. (Touch & Sparkle Ser.). (Illus.). 12p. (ps). per., bds. 5.95 (978-1-84610-078-9(X)) Make Believe Ideas GBR. *Dist:* Ingram Pub. Services.

McDaniel, Melissa. Disaster Search Dogs. 2005. (Dog Heroes Ser.). (Illus.). 32p. (J). lib. bdg. 25.27 (978-1-59716-012-4(1)) Bearport Publishing Co., Inc.

McGinty, Alice B. Detector Dogs: Sniffing Out Trouble. 1999. (Dogs Helping People Ser.). 24p. (J). (gr. k-4). lib. bdg. 18.75 (978-0-8239-5217-5(7) , PowerKids Pr.) Rosen Publishing Group, Inc., The.

—Sheep-Herding Dogs: Rounding up the Herd. 1999. (Dogs Helping People Ser.). 24p. (J). (gr. k-4). lib. bdg. 18.75 (978-0-8239-5219-9(3) , PowerKids Pr.) Rosen Publishing Group, Inc., The.

—Sled Dogs: Speeding Through Snow. 1999. (Dogs Helping People Ser.). 24p. (J). (gr. k-4). lib. bdg. 18.75 (978-0-8239-5216-8(9) , PowerKids Pr.) Rosen Publishing Group, Inc., The.

McNeil, Niki, et al. HOCPP1029 the Iditarod. 2004. spiral bd. 15.50 (***978-1-60308-029-3(5)***) In the Hands of a Child.

Meadows, Graham. Dogs. Meadows, Graham, photos by. 1998. (Animals Are Not Like Us Ser.). (Illus.). 24p. (J). (ps up). lib. bdg. 21.26 (978-0-8368-2252-6(8)) Stevens, Gareth Inc.

Mehus-Roe, Kristin. Dogs for Kids: Everything You Need to Know about Dogs. 2007. (Illus.). 384p. (J). (gr. 3-8). pap. 14.95 (978-1-931993-83-8(1)) BowTie Pr.

Meister, Cari. Basset Hounds. l.t. ed. 2001. (Dogs Ser.). (Illus.). 24p. (J). (gr. k-6). lib. bdg. 21.35 (978-1-57765-478-0(1) , Checkerboard Library) ABDO Publishing Co.

—Boxers. l.t. ed. 2001. (Dogs Ser.). (Illus.). 24p. (J). (gr. k-6). lib. bdg. 21.35 (978-1-57765-477-3(3) , Checkerboard Library) ABDO Publishing Co.

—Bulldogs. l.t. ed. 2001. (Dogs Ser.). (Illus.). 24p. (J). (gr. k-6). lib. bdg. 21.35 (978-1-57765-476-6(5) , Checkerboard Library) ABDO Publishing Co.

—Cavalier King Charles Spaniels. l.t. ed. 2001. (Dogs Ser.). (Illus.). 24p. (J). (gr. k-6). lib. bdg. 21.35 (978-1-57765-475-9(7) , Checkerboard Library) ABDO Publishing Co.

—Dogs - Set IV, 6 bks. l.t. ed. Incl. Basset Hounds. lib. bdg. 21.35 (978-1-57765-478-0(1)); Boxers. lib. bdg. 21.35 (978-1-57765-477-3(3)); Bulldogs. lib. bdg. 21.35 (978-1-57765-476-6(5)); Cavalier King Charles Spaniels. lib. bdg. 21.35 (978-1-57765-475-9(7)); Greyhounds. lib. bdg. 21.35 (978-1-57765-473-5(0)); Saint Bernards. lib. bdg. 21.35 (978-1-57765-474-2(9)); 24p. (J). (gr. k-6). 2001. (Illus.). 2001. Set lib. bdg. 128.10 (978-1-57765-501-5(X) , Checkerboard Library) ABDO Publishing Co.

—Greyhounds. l.t. ed. 2001. (Dogs Ser.). (Illus.). 24p. (J). (gr. k-6). lib. bdg. 21.35 (978-1-57765-473-5(0) , Checkerboard Library) ABDO Publishing Co.

—Saint Bernards. l.t. ed. 2001. (Dogs Ser.). (Illus.). 24p. (J). (gr. k-6). lib. bdg. 21.35 (978-1-57765-474-2(9) , Checkerboard Library) ABDO Publishing Co.

Mi Perrito, 6 Packs. (Coleccion Pm Ser.: Vol. 2). (SPA.). 16p. (gr. k-1). 26.00 (978-0-7578-0685-8(6)) Rigby Education.

Mi Perro. 2000. (SPA.). (J). 3.25 net. (978-1-58453-102-9(9)) Pioneer Valley Educational Pr., Inc.

Mi Perro, 6 Packs. (Literatura 2000 Ser.). (SPA.). (ps-1). 28.00 (978-0-7635-1197-5(8)) Rigby Education.

Millard, Anne. Perritos Juguietones/Playful Puppies. 2005. (Soft-to-touch Bks.). 16p. (J). bds. 4.99 (978-0-7566-1201-6(2)) Dorling Kindersley Publishing, Inc.

Miller, Connie Colwell. Basset Hounds. 2007. (Pebble Ser.). (Illus.). 24p. (J). (978-0-7368-6741-2(4) , 1264852) Capstone Pr., Inc.

—Bichons Frises. 2007. (Pebble Ser.). (Illus.). 24p. (J). (978-0-7368-6697-2(3) , 1264853) Capstone Pr., Inc.

—Bloodhounds. 2007. (Pebble Ser.). (Illus.). 24p. (J). (978-0-7368-6698-9(1) , 1264854) Capstone Pr., Inc.

—Cocker Spaniels. 2007. (Pebble Ser.). (Illus.). 24p. (J). (978-0-7368-6700-9(7) , 1264856) Capstone Pr., Inc.

—Great Danes. 2007. (Pebble Ser.). (Illus.). 24p. (J). (978-0-7368-6742-9(2) , 1264858) Capstone Pr., Inc.

Miller, Connie Colwell & Capstone Press Staff. Labradors. 2007. (Pebble Ser.). (Illus.). 24p. (J). (978-0-7368-6699-6(X) , 1264861) Capstone Pr., Inc.

Miller, M. Dogs. 2002. (Pets Ser.). (Illus.). 24p. (J). (gr. k-3). pap. 6.50 (978-1-57572-478-2(2) , 90467) Heinemann Library.

Miller, Marie-Therese. Distinguished Dogs. 2007. (Dog Tales: True Stories about Amazing Dogs Ser.). 80p. (J). 28.00 (***978-0-7910-9039-8(6)*** , Chelsea Hse.) Facts On File, Inc.

—Hunting & Herding Dogs. 2007. (Dog Tales: True Stories about Amazing Dogs Ser.). 80p. (J). 28.00 (***978-0-7910-9038-1(8)*** , Chelsea Hse.) Facts On File, Inc.

—Search & Rescue Dogs. 2007. (Dog Tales: True Stories about Amazing Dogs Ser.). 80p. (J). 28.00 (***978-0-7910-9037-4(X)*** , Chelsea Hse.) Facts On File, Inc.

Miller, Michaela. Puppies & Dogs. 2007. (Illus.). 32p. (J). lib. bdg. 19.95 (978-1-59566-218-7(9)) QEB Publishing Inc.

Miller, Michelle. Aggie & Rowdy Say No Way to Cigarettes: Dog Tales, Cancer Stories for Kids. 2007. 53p. pap. 12.99 (***978-1-58752-258-1(6)***) Timberwolf Pr., Inc.

—I Can Make Healthy Choices: Dog Tales, Cancer Stories for Kids. 2007. 37p. pap. 9.99 (***978-1-58752-261-1(6)***) Timberwolf Pr., Inc.

Mongrel. 2003. 160p. (YA). pap. 20.00 (978-0-7894-9683-6(6)) Dorling Kindersley Publishing, Inc.

Morley, Christine & Orbell, Carole. Mon Chien. Granstrom, Brita, illus. 2001. (Me & My Pet Ser.). (FRE.). 32p. (J). (gr. 1-5). pap. 4.95 (978-1-58728-141-9(4) , Two Can Publishing) T&N Children's Publishing.

Muir, John. Stickeen. Buell, Carl Dennis, illus. Date not set. 94p. (J). 16.95 (978-0-8488-2803-5(8)) Amereon LTD.

Mulvany, Martha. The Story of the Beagle. 2000. (Dogs Throughout History Ser.). 24p. (J). (gr. k-4). lib. bdg. 18.75 (978-0-8239-5518-3(4) , PowerKids Pr.) Rosen Publishing Group, Inc., The.

—The Story of the Boxer. 2000. (Dogs Throughout History Ser.). 24p. (J). (gr. k-4). lib. bdg. 18.75 (978-0-8239-5519-0(2) , PowerKids Pr.) Rosen Publishing Group, Inc., The.

Murdico, Suzanne J., contrib. by. Wild Dog Attacks. 2000. (J). (978-0-531-12104-7(6)); (978-0-531-17604-7(5)) Scholastic Library Publishing. (Watts, Franklin).

Murdoch, J. D., et al. The African Wild Dog. 2002. (Library of Wolves & Wild Dogs). (Illus.). 24p. (J). (gr. 2-4). lib. bdg. 18.75 (978-0-8239-5769-9(1) , PowerKids Pr.) Rosen Publishing Group, Inc., The.

Murray, Julie. Airedale Terrier. 2003. (Dogs Ser.). (Illus.). 24p. (J). (gr. k-6). lib. bdg. 21.35 (978-1-57765-919-8(8)) ABDO Publishing Co.

—Beagles. 2002. (Buddy Book Ser.). (Illus.). 24p. (J). (gr. k-4). lib. bdg. 21.35 (978-1-57765-643-2(1)) ABDO Publishing Co.

—Bichon Frise. 2003. (Dogs Ser.). (Illus.). 24p. (J). (gr. k-6). lib. bdg. 21.35 (978-1-57765-921-1(X)) ABDO Publishing Co.

—Bloodhound. 2003. (Dogs Ser.). (Illus.). 24p. (J). (gr. k-6). lib. bdg. 21.35 (978-1-57765-920-4(1)) ABDO Publishing Co.

—Brittany Spaniel. 2003. (Dogs Ser.). (Illus.). 24p. (J). (gr. k-6). lib. bdg. 21.35 (978-1-57765-922-8(8)) ABDO Publishing Co.

—Cocker Spaniels. 2005. (Animal Kingdom Set Ii Ser.). (Illus.). 24p. (J). (gr. k-4). lib. bdg. 21.35 (978-1-59197-307-2(4)) ABDO Publishing Co.

—Dalmatians. 2002. (Buddy Book Ser.). (Illus.). 24p. (J). (gr. k-4). lib. bdg. 21.35 (978-1-57765-642-5(3)) ABDO Publishing Co.

—Golden Retrievers. 2005. (Animal Kingdom Set Ii Ser.). (J). (gr. k-4). lib. bdg. 21.35 (978-1-59197-316-4(3)) ABDO Publishing Co.

—Great Dane. 2003. (Dogs Ser.). (Illus.). 24p. (J). (gr. k-6). lib. bdg. 21.35 (978-1-57765-923-5(6)) ABDO Publishing Co.

—Irish Setter. 2003. (Dogs Ser.). (Illus.). 24p. (J). (gr. k-6). lib. bdg. 21.35 (978-1-57765-924-2(4)) ABDO Publishing Co.

—Jack Russell Terriers. 2005. (Animal Kingdom Set Ii Ser.). (Illus.). 24p. (J). (gr. k-4). lib. bdg. 21.35 (978-1-59197-321-8(X)) ABDO Publishing Co.

—Labrador Retrievers. 2005. (Animal Kingdom Set Ii Ser.). (Illus.). 24p. (J). (gr. k-4). lib. bdg. 21.35 (978-1-59197-324-9(4)) ABDO Publishing Co.

—Mutts. 2002. (Buddy Book Ser.). (Illus.). 24p. (J). (gr. k-4). lib. bdg. 21.35 (978-1-57765-641-8(5)) ABDO Publishing Co.

Myers, Jack. How Dogs Came from Wolves: And Other Explorations of Science in Action. Rice, John, illus. 2004. 64p. (YA). (gr. 4-6). 17.95 (978-1-56397-411-3(8)) Boyds Mills Pr.

Myers, Scott. 101 Dumb Dog Deaths. 2001. pap. 10.00 (978-0-9724047-0-9(8)) Myers, Ralph.

Nye, Penny. My Dog. Eargle, Michelle, photos by. 1999. (Illus.). (J). (ps-5). pap. 12.00 (978-1-890703-17-2(6) , Bookmates) Penny Laine Papers, Inc.

Olson, Gillia M. Siberian Huskies. 2008. (J). (***978-1-4296-0017-0(9)*** , Pebble Bks.) Capstone Pr., Inc.

O'Neill, Amanda. Dog Biz: A Compendium of Amazing Facts & Anecdotes from the Dog World. 2006. 208p. pap. 14.99 (978-0-7641-3466-1(3)) Barron's Educational Series, Inc.

—Dogs. (Single Subject References Ser.). (Illus.). 64p. (J). (gr. 4-8). 2001. pap. 10.95 (978-0-7534-5383-4(5)); 1999. tchr. ed. 16.95 (978-0-7534-5175-5(1)) Houghton Mifflin Co. Trade & Reference Div. (Kingfisher).

—Dogs. 2001. (gr. 3-6). lib. bdg. 19.90 (978-0-613-90906-8(2)) Tandem Library Bks.

O'Sullivan, Robyn. Science Chapters: More Than Man's Best Friend: The Story of Working Dogs. 2006. (National Geographic Science Chapters Ser.). 48p. (gr. 1-4). 17.90 (978-0-7922-5940-4(8) , National Geographic Children's Bks.) National Geographic Society.

Otto, Carolyn B. Our Puppies Are Growing. Morgan, Mary, illus. 1998. (Let's-Read-and-Find-Out Science Ser.). 32p. (J). (ps-1). 15.89 (978-0-06-027272-2(4)) HarperCollins Pubs.

—Our Puppies Are Growing. 1998. (Let's-Read-and-Find-Out Science Ser.). (J). (978-0-606-13684-6(3)) Tandem Library Bks.

Otto, Crolyn. Our Puppies Are Growing. Morgan, Mary, illus. 1998. (Let's-Read-and-Find-Out Science Ser.). 32p. (J). (ps-1). pap. 4.95 (978-0-06-445169-7(0)) HarperCollins Pubs.

Page, Gill. I Am Your Puppy. 2004. (gr. 3-6). lib. bdg. 14.10 (978-0-613-74929-9(4)) Tandem Library Bks.

Pata, Sharae & Linzy, Jan. Poodle (Standard) Champions, 1983-2003. 2004. (Illus.). 198p. spiral bd. 46.95 (978-1-55893-154-1(6)) Camino E.E. & Bk. Co.

Patent, Dorothy Hinshaw. Right Dog for the Job: Ira's Path from Service Dog to Guide Dog. 2004. (Illus.). 32p. (J). 17.85 (978-0-8027-8915-0(3)); 16.95 (978-0-8027-8914-3(5)) Walker & Co.

Paulsen, Gary. My Life in Dog Years. l.t. ed. 2003. 176p. pap. 10.95 (978-0-7862-6188-8(9)) Thorndike Pr.

—Woodsong. unabr. ed. 2004. 132p. (J). (gr. 6 up). pap. 29.00 incl. audio (978-0-8072-0460-3(9) , Listening Library) Random Hse. Audio Publishing Group.

Perry, Phyllis Jean. Sherlock Hounds: Our Heroic Search & Rescue Dogs. 2006. (Illus.). 32p. (J). pap. (978-1-59336-728-2(7)) Mondo Publishing.

Petty, Kate. Dog. 2005. (Illus.). 24p. (J). (gr. 2-5). lib. bdg. 22.80 (978-1-59604-026-7(2)) Stargazer Bks.

Pickett, Robert & Pickett, Justine, illus. Dog. Pickett, Robert & Pickett, Justine, photos by. 2004. 32p. (J). lib. bdg. 27.10 (978-1-58340-430-0(9)) Smart Apple Media.

Pinkwater, Daniel M. Superpuppy: How to Choose, Raise, & Train the Best Possible Dog for You. Pinkwater, Jill, illus. rev. ed. 2002. 208p. (YA). (gr. 5). pap. 7.95 (978-0-618-13050-4(0) , Clarion Bks.) Houghton Mifflin Co. Trade & Reference Div.

Pinkwater, Jill. Superpuppy: How to Choose, Raise & Train the Best Possible Dog for You. 2002. (gr. 3-6). lib. bdg. 16.40 (978-0-613-60724-7(4)) Tandem Library Bks.

Pipe, Jim. Dogs. 2006. (Read & Play Ser.). (Illus.). 24p. (J). (ps-k). lib. bdg. 22.80 (978-1-59604-113-4(7)) Stargazer Bks.

Popular Dog Library. 2005. pap. 137.50 (978-0-7910-9190-6(2) , Chelsea Hse.) Facts On File, Inc.

Powell, Jillian. From Puppy to Dog. 2001. (How Do They Grow? Ser.). (Illus.). 32p. (J). lib. bdg. 25.69 (978-0-7398-4423-6(7)) Raintree.

Powell, R. This Little Doggy. Curry, Peter, illus. 2004. (Mini Movers Ser.). 14p. (J). bds. 3.50 (978-0-7641-5741-7(8)) Barron's Educational Series, Inc.

Presnall, Judith Janda. Hearing Dogs. 2004. (Animals with Jobs Ser.). (Illus.). 48p. (J). (gr. 4-7). 26.20 (978-0-7377-1826-3(9)) Thomson Gale.

—Rescue Dogs. 2002. (Animals with Jobs Ser.). (Illus.). 48p. (J). (gr. 3-5). 23.70 (978-0-7377-1361-9(5) , Kidhaven) Thomson Gale.

Preszler, June. Caring for Your Dog. 2007. (First Facts Ser.). (Illus.). 24p. (J). (978-0-7368-6385-8(0)) Capstone Pr., Inc.

Priddy, Roger. Baby Tales: Dotty Dog. rev. ed. 2005. 8p. (J). 6.95 (978-0-312-49540-4(4) , Priddy Bks.) St. Martin's Pr.

—Puppies. 2005. 12p. (J). bds. 0.97 (978-0-312-49609-8(5) , Priddy Bks.) St. Martin's Pr.

Puppies. 2003. (Three Minute Tales Ser.). 32p. (J). 5.98 (978-0-7525-8918-3(0)); 7.95 (978-0-7525-5538-6(3)) Parragon, Inc.

Puppies Know it All. 2005. (J). pap. 2.79 (***978-1-59545-003-6(3)***) Learning Horizons, Inc.

Puppies Know it All with CD. 2006. (J). pap. 5.99 (***978-1-59545-166-8(8)***) Learning Horizons, Inc.

Puppy. 2004. (J). per. (978-1-57657-397-6(4)) Paradise Pr., Inc.

Puppy. (Buggy Buddies Ser.). (Illus.). (J). (ps). bds. (978-1-56021-351-2(5) , 202) W.J. Fantasy, Inc.

Quasha, Jennifer. The Story of the Dachshund. 2000. (Dogs Throughout History Ser.). 24p. (J). (gr. k-4). lib. bdg. 18.75 (978-0-8239-5516-9(8) , PowerKids Pr.) Rosen Publishing Group, Inc., The.

—The Story of the Dalmatian. 2000. (Dogs Throughout History Ser.). 24p. (J). (gr. k-4). lib. bdg. 18.75 (978-0-8239-5515-2(X) , PowerKids Pr.) Rosen Publishing Group, Inc., The.

—The Story of the Saint Bernard. 2000. (Dogs Throughout History Ser.). 24p. (J). (gr. k-4). lib. bdg. 18.75 (978-0-8239-5517-6(6) , PowerKids Pr.) Rosen Publishing Group, Inc., The.

Raintree Steck-Vaughn Staff. A World of Dogs. 1999. (Illus.). (J). pap. 35.60 (978-0-7398-0904-4(0)) Steck-Vaughn.

Rake, Jody Sullivan. Airedale Terriers. 2008. (J). (***978-1-4296-0808-4(0)*** , Pebble Bks.) Capstone Pr., Inc.

—Boxers. 2008. (J). (***978-1-4296-0809-1(9)*** , Pebble Bks.) Capstone Pr., Inc.

—Bulldogs. 2008. (J). (***978-1-4296-0014-9(4)***) Capstone Pr., Inc.

—English Springer Spaniels. 2007. (J). (***978-0-7368-6744-3(9)*** , Pebble Bks.) Capstone Pr., Inc.

—Jack Russell Terriers. 2007. (Pebble Ser.). (Illus.). 24p. (J). (***978-0-7368-6743-6(0)*** , 1264860, Pebble Bks.) Capstone Pr., Inc.

—Mutts. 2008. (J). (***978-1-4296-0016-3(0)***) Capstone Pr., Inc.

Rayner, Matthew & BVetMed MRCVS Staff. Dog. Burton, Jane & Greenaway, Frank, photos by. 2004. (I Am Your Pet Ser.). (Illus.). 32p. (J). (gr. 2 up). lib. bdg. 23.33 (978-0-8368-4103-9(4)) Stevens, Gareth Inc.

Redmond, Shirley Raye. The Dog That Dug for Dinosaurs. Sullivan, Simon, illus. 2004. (Ready-to-Read Ser.). 32p. (J). pap. 3.99 (978-0-689-85708-9(X) , Aladdin) Simon & Schuster Children's Publishing.

Redmond, Shirley-Raye. The Dog That Dug for Dinosaurs: A True Story. Sullivan, Simon, illus. 2005. (Ready-to-Read Ser. Level 3). 32p. (J). lib. bdg. 15.00 (978-1-59054-993-3(7)) Fitzgerald Bks.

Rende, Thomas & Rende, Crystal. Novel Ideas 3 Great Dog Stories. 2007. (J). spiral bd. 12.99 (***978-0-9793576-3-3(2)***) New Learning Publishing.

Rescue Rover! 101 Ways You Can Help Abandoned Dogs. 2002. 218p. per. 16.95 (978-0-9675381-0-5(6)) HoundHut Pr.

Richmond, Marianne R. Goodbye, Faithful Friend: Remembering Your Dog with Love. 2005. (Illus.). 40p. (YA). 7.95 (978-0-9770000-1-2(X)) Marianne Richmond Studios, Inc.

Ring, Susan. Good Dog! (Yellow Umbrella Ser.). (J). 2006. (Illus.). 17p. 15.93 (978-0-7368-5839-7(3)); 2005. (978-0-7368-5305-7(7)); 2005. (Illus.). 17p. (978-0-7368-5269-2(7)) Capstone Pr., Inc.

Robb, Jackie & Stringle, Berny. The Story of Dog. Duncan, Karen & Stringle, Sam, illus. 2004. (Bang on the Door Ser.). 32p. (YA). pap. (978-1-85602-315-3(X)) Chrysalis Children's Bks.

Roca, Nuria. Let's Take Care of Our New Dog. Curto, Rosa M., illus. 2006. (Let's Take Care of Bks.). 36p. (J). (ps-2). pap. 6.99 (978-0-7641-3455-5(8)) Barron's Educational Series, Inc.

Rock, Maxine. Totally Fun Things to Do with Your Dog. 1998. (Play with Your Pet). (Illus.). 128p. (gr. 3-7). pap. 12.95 (978-0-471-19574-0(X) , Frommers) Wiley, John & Sons, Inc.

Rondinone, Craig. Jeepers. Simonton, Tom, illus. 2005. 16p. (J). pap. 5.00 (978-1-57274-755-5(2) , 2750, Bks. for Young Learners) Owen, Richard C. Pubs., Inc.

Rosenthal, Lisa. A Dog's Best Friend: An Activity Book for Kids & Their Dogs. Matthews, Bonnie, illus. 1999. 176p. (J). (gr. 1-7). pap. 12.95 (978-1-55652-362-5(9)) Chicago Review Pr., Inc.

Ross, Veronica. Dog. 2002. (My First Ser.). (Illus.). 32p. (J). lib. bdg. 24.95 (978-1-930643-71-0(3)) Chrysalis Education.

Royston, Angela. Dog. 2002. (Life Cycle of a... Ser.). (Illus.). 32p. (J). (gr. k-2). pap. 6.95 (978-1-58810-328-4(5) , 91060) Heinemann Library.

—Dog. 2000. 13.30 (978-0-606-21989-1(7)) Tandem Library Bks.

—Life Cycle of a Dog. 2000. (Illus.). 32p. (J). (gr. k-2). lib. bdg. 21.36 (978-1-57572-209-2(7)) Heinemann Library.

—Puppy. 2004. (J). lib. bdg. 27.10 (978-1-59389-159-6(8)) Chrysalis Education.

Rozakis, Laurie. Where the Red Fern Grows. 2003. (Bookfiles Ser.). 64p. (J). pap. 4.99 (978-0-439-46375-1(0)) Scholastic, Inc.

Ruffin, Frances E. Military Dogs. 2006. (Dog Heroes Ser.). (Illus.). 32p. (J). lib. bdg. 25.27 (978-1-59716-273-9(6)) Bearport Publishing Co., Inc.

—Water Rescue Dogs. 2005. (Dog Heroes Ser.). (Illus.). 32p. (J). (gr. 3-7). lib. bdg. 25.27 (978-1-59716-142-8(X)) Bearport Publishing Co., Inc.

Ruffin, Francis E. Medical Detective Dogs. 2006. (Dog Heroes Ser.). (Illus.). 32p. (J). lib. bdg. 25.27 (978-1-59716-251-7(5)) Bearport Publishing Co., Inc.

Saltis, Nicki. Dogs. 1999. (ps-2). lib. bdg. 11.20 (978-0-613-30358-3(X)) Tandem Library Bks.

Salzmann, Mary Elizabeth. Dandy Dogs. Nobens, C. A., illus. 2007. (Perfect Pets Ser.). 24p. (J). (gr. k-3). lib. bdg. 19.93 (***978-1-59928-746-1(3)*** , SandCastle) ABDO Publishing Co.

Schaefer, Peggy. More Stories of Dogs. 2005. (Illus.). 205p. 12.95 (978-0-8249-4639-5(1)) Ideals Pubns.

Schick-Jacobowitz, Jean & Schick-Pierce, Susan. You're My Friend Bepaws. gif. ed. 2006. (Illus.). 48p. 7.95 (978-1-4022-0738-9(7)) Sourcebooks, Inc.

Schindel, John. Busy Doggies. Sparks, Beverly, photos by. 2004. (Illus.). 20p. (J). bds. 6.95 (978-1-58246-090-1(6) , Tricycle Pr.) Ten Speed Pr.

Schmidt, Karen Lee. Dogs & Puppies. 1998. (Nature Sticker Stories Ser.). (Illus.). 20p. (J). (ps-3). pap. 4.99 (978-0-448-41747-9(2) , Grosset & Dunlap) Penguin Group (USA) Inc.

Scholastic, Inc. Staff. Happy Howliday Book. 2007. (Dog Ser.). 80p. (J). pap. 4.99 (***978-0-545-00008-6(4)***) Scholastic, Inc.

Schuh, Mari C. Dogs on the Farm. 2002. (On the Farm Ser.). (Illus.). 24p. (J). (gr. k-1). lib. bdg. 15.93 (978-0-7368-1187-3(7) , Pebble Bks.) Capstone Pr., Inc.

—Dogs on the Farm. (On the Farm Ser.). 24p. (J). pap. 5.95 (978-0-7368-9378-7(4)) Capstone Pr., Inc.

Seibold, J. Otto. Quincy, the Hobby Photographer Vol. 1: Dogs. 2006. (Illus.). 68p. (J). 16.00 (978-0-15-216331-0(X)) Harcourt Children's Bks.

Shaggy Sheepdog & the Hairdresser's. 2004. (Play Pals Ser.). (Illus.). 12p. (J). bds. (978-1-84229-648-6(5)) Top That! Publishing PLC.

Shahan, Sherry, photos by. Dashing Through the Snow: The Story of the Jr. Iditarod. 2nd ed. 2006. (J). pap. (978-1-59336-714-5(7)) Mondo Publishing.

Sherman, T. Mershon. My Name Is Willy, G. P. 2002. pap. 7.95 (978-0-533-14030-5(7)) Vantage Pr., Inc.

Sidman, Joyce. The World According to Dog: Poems & Teen Voices. Mindell, Doug, illus. 2003. 80p. (J). (gr. 5). tchr. ed. 15.00 (978-0-618-17497-3(4)) Houghton Mifflin Co. Trade & Reference Div.

Siegal, Mordecai & Margolis, Matthew. I Just Got a Puppy, What Do I Do? How to Buy, Train, Understand & Enjoy Your Puppy. Margolis, Matthew & Darling, Tara, photos by. anniv. ed. 2002. (Illus.). 224p. pap. 14.00 (978-0-684-85520-2(8) , Fireside) Simon & Schuster.

Silverman, Maida. Snow Search Dogs. 2005. (Dog Heroes Ser.). 32p. (J). lib. bdg. 25.27 (978-1-59716-017-9(2)) Bearport Publishing Co., Inc.

Silverstein, Alvin, et al. Different Dogs. 2000. (What a Pet! Ser.). (Illus.). 48p. (gr. 5-8). lib. bdg. 23.90 (978-0-7613-1371-7(0) , Millbrook Pr.) Lerner Publishing Group.

Simon, Dominique & Simon, Serge. Dog: Faithful Friend. 1998. (Little Nature Bks.). (Illus.). 10p. (J). (ps-k). bds. 4.95 (978-0-88106-316-5(9)) Charlesbridge Publishing, Inc.

Simon, Seymour. Dogs. Simon, Seymour, illus. (Illus.). (J). (ps-1). Date not set. 32p. 6.99 (978-0-06-446255-6(2)); 2004. 40p. 16.99 (978-0-06-028942-3(2)); 2004. 40p. lib. bdg. 17.89 (978-0-06-028943-0(0)) HarperCollins Pubs.

Simont, Marc. El Perro Vagabundo. 2003. (SPA.). (gr. k-3). lib. bdg. 15.30 (978-0-613-66988-7(6)) Tandem Library Bks.

Sjonger, Rebecca & Kalman, Bobbie. Los Cachorros. 2005. (ENG & SPA., Illus.). 32p. (J). (978-0-7787-8455-5(X)) Crabtree Publishing Co.

—Las Cachorros: Puppies. 2006. (Illus.). 32p. pap. (978-0-7787-8477-7(0)) Crabtree Publishing Co.

—Puppies. (Pet Care Ser.). (Illus.). 32p. (J). 2004. pap. (978-0-7787-1783-6(6)); 2003. (978-0-7787-1751-5(8)) Crabtree Publishing Co.

Sled Dogs of Denali National Park. 2nd ed. 2002. Orig. Title: Sled Dogs of Denali. (Illus.). 44p. pap. 8.00 (978-0-930931-37-7(8)) Alaska Natural History Assn.

Solberg, Jessica L. First Dog: Unleashed in the Montana Capitol. Rath, Robert, illus. 2007. (J). (*978-1-56037-419-0(5)) Farcountry Pr.

Spilsbury, Louise & Spilsbury, Richard. Dogs. 2006. (Keeping Pets Ser.). (Illus.). 48p. (J). (978-1-4034-7699-9(3)) Heinemann Library.

Spizzirri, Linda. Dogs of the Wild: An Educational Coloring Book. (J). pap. 1.99 (978-0-86545-216-9(4)) Spizzirri Pr., Inc.

Standiford, Natalie. Bravest Dog Ever: Story of Balto. Cook, Donald, illus. 2003. (Step into Reading Ser.: Step 3). 48p. (J). (gr. 1-3). lib. bdg. 11.99 (978-0-394-99695-0(X) , Random Hse. Bks. for Young Readers) Random Hse. Children's Bks.

Starke, Katherine. Dogs & Puppies. Watt, Fiona, ed. rev. ed. 2004. (First Pets Ser.). 32p. (J). (gr. 1 up). pap. 5.99 (978-0-7945-0790-9(5) , Usborne) EDC Publishing.

Starke, Katherine, ed. Dogs & Puppies. 1999. (First Pets Ser.). (Illus.). 32p. (YA). (gr. k-3). lib. bdg. 12.95 (978-1-58086-159-5(8)) EDC Publishing.

Starke, Katherine & Watt, Fiona. Dogs & Puppies. Fox, Christyan, illus. 2004. 31p. (J). (978-0-439-78715-4(7)) Scholastic, Inc.

Stefoff, Rebecca. Dogs. 2002. (Animalways Ser.). (Illus.). 112p. (J). 31.36 (978-0-7614-1393-6(6) , Benchmark Bks.) Cavendish, Marshall Corp.

Stewart, Pat. Invisible Dogs Magic Picture Book. 2001. (Invisible Magic Picture Bks.). (Illus.). 16p. (J). (ps up). pap. 1.50 (978-0-486-41848-3(0)) Dover Pubns., Inc.

Stone, Lynn M. Alaskan Malamutes. 2005. (Eye to Eye with Dogs II). (Illus.). 24p. (gr. 2-5). 17.95 (978-1-59515-290-9(3)) Rourke Publishing, LLC.

—Basset Hounds. 2005. (Eye to Eye with Dogs Ser.). (Illus.). 24p. (gr. 2-5). 17.95 (978-1-59515-291-6(1)) Rourke Publishing, LLC.

—Boxers. 2005. (Eye to Eye with Dogs Ser.). (Illus.). 24p. (gr. 2-5). 17.95 (978-1-59515-158-2(3)) Rourke Publishing, LLC.

—Bulldog. 2007. (Illus.). 24p. (J). (978-1-60044-238-4(2)) Rourke Publishing, LLC.

—Chesapeake Bay Retriever. 2007. (Illus.). 24p. (J). (978-1-60044-239-1(0)) Rourke Publishing, LLC.

—Chihuahuas. 2005. (Eye to Eye with Dogs Ser.). (Illus.). 24p. (gr. 2-5). 17.95 (978-1-59515-159-9(1)) Rourke Publishing, LLC.

—Dalmatians. 2005. (Eye to Eye with Dogs Ser.). (Illus.). 24p. (gr. 2-5). 17.95 (978-1-59515-160-5(5)) Rourke Publishing, LLC.

—Doberman Pinscher. 2007. (Illus.). 24p. (J). (978-1-60044-240-7(4)) Rourke Publishing, LLC.

—Golden Retrievers. 2003. (Eye to Eye with Dogs Ser.). (Illus.). 24p. (gr. 2-5). 17.95 (978-1-58952-328-9(8)) Rourke Publishing, LLC.

—Labrador Retrievers. 2003. (Eye to Eye with Dogs Ser.). (Illus.). 24p. (gr. 2-5). 17.95 (978-1-58952-329-6(6)) Rourke Publishing, LLC.

—Rottweilers. 2005. (Eye to Eye with Dogs Ser.). (Illus.). 24p. (gr. 2-5). 17.95 (978-1-59515-161-2(3)) Rourke Publishing, LLC.

—Shetland Sheepdogs. 2007. (Illus.). 24p. (J). (978-1-60044-243-8(9)) Rourke Publishing, LLC.

—Siberian Huskies. 2005. (Eye to Eye with Dogs Ser.). (Illus.). 24p. (gr. 2-5). 17.95 (978-1-59515-162-9(1)) Rourke Publishing, LLC.

Storer, Pat. Your Puppy, Your Dog: A Kid's Guide to Raising a Happy, Healthy Dog. 2003. (Storey's Your Ser.). (Illus.). 172p. (Orig.). (J). (gr. 3-8). pap. 14.95 (978-0-88266-959-5(1) , 66959) Storey Publishing, LLC.

Strother, Ruth. W Is for Woof: A Dog Alphabet. Frankenhuyzen, Gijsbert van, illus. 2008. (J). (*978-1-58536-343-8(X)) Sleeping Bear Pr.

Tagliaferro, Linda. Dogs & Their Puppies. 2004. (Animal Offspring Ser.). (Illus.). 24p. (J). 13.95 (978-0-7368-2388-3(3) , Pebble Bks.) Capstone Pr., Inc.

—Service Dogs. 2005. (Dog Heroes Ser.). (Illus.). 32p. (J). lib. bdg. 25.27 (978-1-59716-016-2(4)) Bearport Publishing Co., Inc.

—Therapy Dogs. 2005. (Dog Heroes Ser.). (Illus.). 32p. (J). lib. bdg. 25.27 (978-1-59716-018-6(0)) Bearport Publishing Co., Inc.

Taylor, Andrea. Kadee's Capers. 2002. pap. 9.00 (978-0-8059-5926-0(2)) Dorrance Publishing Co., Inc.

Tedesco, Leah/Hollis. Junior Showmanship How to get started in One of the Best Family Sports. 2007. (YA). 6.95 (*978-0-9792059-0-3(5)) JBT Publishing.

Temple, Bob. Chihuahuas. l.t. ed. 2000. (Dogs Ser.). (Illus.). 24p. (J). (gr. k-6). lib. bdg. 21.35 (978-1-57765-419-3(6) , Checkerboard Library) ABDO Publishing Co.

—Dogs - Set III, 6 bks. l.t. ed. Incl. Chihuahuas. lib. bdg. 21.35 (978-1-57765-419-3(6)); Jack Russell Terriers. lib. bdg. 21.35 (978-1-57765-424-7(2)); Pugs. lib. bdg. 21.35 (978-1-57765-422-3(6)); Scottish Terriers. lib. bdg. 21.35 (978-1-57765-421-6(8)); Shih Tzus. lib. bdg. 21.35 (978-1-57765-423-0(4)); Siberian Huskies. lib. bdg. 21.35 (978-1-57765-420-9(X)); 24p. (J). (gr. k-6). 2000. (Illus.). 2000. Set lib. bdg. 128.10 (978-1-57765-291-5(6) , Checkerboard Library) ABDO Publishing Co.

—Jack Russell Terriers. l.t. ed. 2000. (Dogs Ser.). (Illus.). 24p. (J). (gr. k-6). lib. bdg. 21.35 (978-1-57765-424-7(2) , Checkerboard Library) ABDO Publishing Co.

—Pugs. 2000. (Dogs Ser.). (Illus.). 24p. (J). (gr. k-6). lib. bdg. 21.35 (978-1-57765-422-3(6) , Checkerboard Library) ABDO Publishing Co.

—Scottish Terriers. l.t. ed. 2000. (Dogs Ser.). (Illus.). 24p. (J). (gr. k-6). lib. bdg. 21.35 (978-1-57765-421-6(8) , Checkerboard Library) ABDO Publishing Co.

—Shih Tzus. l.t. ed. 2000. (Dogs Ser.). (Illus.). 24p. (J). (gr. k-6). lib. bdg. 21.35 (978-1-57765-423-0(4) , Checkerboard Library) ABDO Publishing Co.

—Siberian Huskies. l.t. ed. 2000. (Dogs Ser.). (Illus.). 24p. (J). (gr. k-6). lib. bdg. 21.35 (978-1-57765-420-9(X) , Checkerboard Library) ABDO Publishing Co.

Todd, Christopher. Sled Dogs. 2002. (Illus.). 16p. (J). (978-0-439-35094-5(8)) Scholastic, Inc.

Top That Publishing Staff, ed. Puppies & Dogs. 2005. (Illus.). 24p. (978-1-84510-540-2(0)) Top That! Publishing PLC.

Top That! Team Staff, contrib. by. I [Love] Dogs & Puppies. 2002. (Art Rom Ser.). (Illus.). 48p. (J). (978-0-439-53072-9(5)) Scholastic, Inc.

Touch & Feel 24-Copy Spring Display. 2005. pap. 190.80 (978-0-7624-2283-8(1)) Running Pr. Bk. Pubs.

Tough Dogs. (Illus.). (J). (gr. k-6). 112.50 (978-1-4042-3297-6(4)) Rosen Publishing Group, Inc., The.

Tracqui, Valerie. Face-to-Face with the Dog: Loyal Companion. Laird, Lisa, tr. from FRE. Hubert, Marie-Luce & Klein, Jean-Louis, photos by. 2004. (Face-to-Face Ser.). (Illus.). 28p. (J). (gr. 2-4). 9.95 (978-1-57091-452-2(4)) Charlesbridge Publishing, Inc.

Trumbauer, Lisa. Golden Retrievers. 2006. (Pebble Books). (Illus.). 24p. (J). (978-0-7368-5334-7(0)) Capstone Pr., Inc.

—The Life Cycle of a Dog. 2002. (Life Cycles Ser.). (Illus.). 24p. (J). (gr. k-1). lib. bdg. 15.93 (978-0-7368-1184-2(2) , Pebble Bks.) Capstone Pr., Inc.

Twine, Alice. Puppies. 2008. (J). lib. bdg. (*978-1-4042-4143-5(4) , PowerKids Pr.) Rosen Publishing Group, Inc., The.

Tytell, Mellon. My Lucky Dog. 2008. 96p. 19.95 (*978-0-06-147307-4(3) , Morrow, William &Co.) HarperCollins Pubs.

Urbigkit, Cat. Brave Dogs, Gentle Dogs: How They Guard Sheep. 2004. (Illus.). 32p. (J). 15.95 (978-1-59078-317-7(4)) Boyds Mills Pr.

Wales, Dirk. A Lucky Dog: Owney, U.S. Rail Mail Mascot. Kenna, Diane, illus. 2003. 32p. (J). 15.95 (978-0-9632459-0-8(2)) Great Plains Pr.

Walker-Hodge, Judith. Surprise Puppy! 1998. (Illus.). 32p. (J). (ps-ps). lib. bdg. 11.80 (978-0-613-12166-8(X)) Tandem Library Bks.

Waters, Jo. The Wild Side of Pet Dogs. 2004. (Raintree Perspectives Ser.). (Illus.). 32p. (J). 7.50 (978-1-4109-1158-2(6)); 25.70 (978-1-4109-1018-9(0)) Harcourt Schl. Pubs.

Watt, Fiona. Puppies. rev. ed. 2005. 10p. (J). 11.99 (978-0-7945-0958-3(4) , Usborne) EDC Publishing.

Watt, Fiona & Wells, Rachel, eds. That's Not My Puppy: Its Coat Is Too Hairy. 2004. (Touchy-Feely Board Bks.). (SPA., Illus.). 10p. (J). (ps up). bds. 7.99 (978-0-7460-3778-2(3)) EDC Publishing.

Webb, Willyn. Baby, the Poodle Cow Dog. Theobald, Denise, illus. 2007. 32p. (J). 13.95 (*978-1-932738-40-7(1)) Western Reflections Publishing Co.

Weide, Bruce & Tucker, Pat. Tales of Two Canines - Koani & Indy: The Adventures of a Wolf & a Dog. Sidhu, Amber, illus. 1998. 168p. (J). pap. 10.00 (978-0-87842-392-7(3)) Mountain Pr. Publishing Co., Inc.

Whaley, Simon. Puppytalk: 50 Ways to Make Friends with Your Puppy. 2006. (Illus.). 96p. (J). pap. 4.99 (978-0-340-90306-3(6) , Hodder & Stoughton) Hodder General Publishing Division GBR. *Dist:* Trafalgar Square Publishing.

Where's the Dog?, 6 Pack. (gr. 1-2). 22.00 (978-0-7635-9157-1(2)) Rigby Education.

Wilcox, Charlotte. The Bloodhound. 2001. (Learning about Dogs Ser.). (Illus.). 48p. (J). (gr. 3-4). lib. bdg. 21.26 (978-0-7368-0761-6(6) , Capstone High-Interest Bks.) Capstone Pr., Inc.

—The Boxer. 2001. (Learning about Dogs Ser.). (Illus.). 48p. (J). (gr. 3-4). lib. bdg. 21.26 (978-0-7368-0762-3(4) , Capstone High-Interest Bks.) Capstone Pr., Inc.

—The Bulldog. 1998. (Learning about Dogs Ser.). (Illus.). 48p. (J). (gr. 3-4). lib. bdg. 21.26 (978-0-7368-0004-4(2) , Capstone High-Interest Bks.) Capstone Pr., Inc.

—The Chow Chow. 1999. (Learning about Dogs Ser.). (Illus.). 48p. (J). (gr. 3-4). lib. bdg. 21.26 (978-0-7368-0159-1(6) , Capstone High-Interest Bks.) Capstone Pr., Inc.

—The Collie. 1998. (Learning about Dogs Ser.). (Illus.). 48p. (J). (gr. 3-4). lib. bdg. 21.26 (978-0-7368-0005-1(0) , Capstone High-Interest Bks.) Capstone Pr., Inc.

—The Dachshund. 2001. (Learning about Dogs Ser.). (Illus.). 48p. (J). (gr. 3-4). lib. bdg. 21.26 (978-0-7368-0763-0(2) , Capstone High-Interest Bks.) Capstone Pr., Inc.

—The Greyhound. 2001. (Learning about Dogs Ser.). (Illus.). 48p. (J). (gr. 3-4). lib. bdg. 21.26 (978-0-7368-0764-7(0) , Capstone High-Interest Bks.) Capstone Pr., Inc.

—The Irish Setter. 1998. (Learning about Dogs Ser.). (Illus.). 48p. (J). (gr. 3-4). lib. bdg. 21.26 (978-0-7368-0006-8(9) , Capstone High-Interest Bks.) Capstone Pr., Inc.

—Learning about Dogs, 24 bks. Incl. Beagle. 1997. lib. bdg. 21.26 (978-1-56065-539-8(9)); Bloodhound. 2001. lib. bdg. 21.26 (978-0-7368-0761-6(6)); Boxer. 2001. lib. bdg. 21.26 (978-0-7368-0762-3(4)); Bulldog. 1998. lib. bdg. 21.26 (978-0-7368-0004-4(2)); Chihuahua. 1999. lib. bdg. 21.26 (978-0-7368-0158-4(8)); Chow Chow. 1999. lib. bdg. 21.26 (978-0-7368-0159-1(6)); Cocker Spaniel. 1997. lib. bdg. 21.26 (978-1-56065-540-4(2)); Collie. 1998. lib. bdg. 21.26 (978-0-7368-0005-1(0)); Dachshund. 2001. lib. bdg. 21.26 (978-0-7368-0763-0(2)); Dalmatian. 1997. lib. bdg. 21.26 (978-1-56065-541-1(0)); Doberman Pinscher. 1997. lib. bdg. 21.26 (978-1-56065-542-8(9)); German Shepherd. 1996. lib. bdg. 21.26 (978-1-56065-398-1(1)); Golden Retriever. 1996. lib. bdg. 21.26 (978-1-56065-397-4(3)); Great Dane. 1997. lib. bdg. 21.26 (978-1-56065-543-5(7)); Greyhound. 2001. lib. bdg. 21.26 (978-0-7368-0764-7(0)); Irish Setter. 1998. lib. bdg. 21.26 (978-0-7368-0006-8(9)); Labrador Retriever. 1996. lib. bdg. 21.26 (978-1-56065-396-7(5)); Newfoundland. 1999. lib. bdg. 21.26 (978-0-7368-0160-7(X)); Rottweiler. 1996. lib. bdg. 21.26 (978-1-56065-395-0(7)); Saint Bernard. 1997. lib. bdg. 21.26 (978-1-56065-544-2(5)); Samoyed. 1999. lib. bdg. 21.26 (978-0-7368-0161-4(8)); Shetland Sheepdog. 1999. lib. bdg. 21.26 (978-0-7368-0162-1(6)); Siberian Husky. 1998. lib. bdg. 21.26 (978-0-7368-0007-5(7)); Weimaraner. 1999. lib. bdg. 21.26 (978-0-7368-0163-8(4)); 48p. (J). (gr. 3-4). (Illus.). Set lib. bdg. 510.24 (978-0-7368-0870-5(1) , Capstone High-Interest Bks.) Capstone Pr., Inc.

—The Shetland Sheepdog. 1999. (Learning about Dogs Ser.). (Illus.). 48p. (J). (gr. 3-4). lib. bdg. 21.26 (978-0-7368-0162-1(6) , Capstone High-Interest Bks.) Capstone Pr., Inc.

—The Siberian Husky. 1998. (Learning about Dogs Ser.). (Illus.). 48p. (J). (gr. 3-4). lib. bdg. 21.26 (978-0-7368-0007-5(7) , Capstone High-Interest Bks.) Capstone Pr., Inc.

—The Weimaraner. 1999. (Learning about Dogs Ser.). (Illus.). 48p. (J). (gr. 3-4). lib. bdg. 21.26 (978-0-7368-0163-8(4) , Capstone High-Interest Bks.) Capstone Pr., Inc.

Williams, Chris. One Incredible Dog! Lady. Friedman, Judith, illus. 2004. 32p. (J). (gr. k-3). 15.95 (978-0-9724853-3-3(3) , 845-987-7750) Keene Publishing.

Wilsdon, Christina. Dogs. 2007. (J). (*978-1-59939-135-9(X) , Reader's Digest Young Families, Inc.) Reader's Digest Children's Publishing, Inc.

The Wisdom of Zeus. 2005. (J). (978-0-9765840-0-1(X)) Zeus Media LLC.

Wood, Selina. Dog. 2006. (Owning a Pet Ser.). (J). (978-1-59771-056-5(3)) Sea-To-Sea Pubns.

Wood, Ted. Bear Dogs: Canines with a Mission. 2001. (Illus.). 32p. (J). (gr. 8-12). 16.95 (978-0-8027-8758-3(4)) Walker & Co.

World Book, Inc Staff, contrib. by. Golden Retrievers & Other Sporting Dogs. 2007. (World Book's Animals of the World Ser.). (Illus.). 64p. (J). (978-0-7166-1328-2(X)) World Bk., Inc.

Yarnelle, Darlene. Dan the Dog. Sheets, L. K., illus. 1998. (J). (ps-3). 8.50 (978-1-891883-02-6(X)) Make Pretend, Inc.

Young, Ian. The Iditarod: The Last Great Race. 2002. (High Five Reading Ser.). (Illus.). 48p. (J). (gr. 3-4). lib. bdg. 22.60 (978-0-7368-9545-3(0) , Capstone High-Interest Bks.); pap. (978-0-7368-9523-1(X)) Capstone Pr., Inc.

DOGS—DICTIONARIES

Cisco: The High Tailed Dog. 2001. 76p. (J). per. 4.99 (978-0-9707924-1-9(7)) Tail it Like it is, Publishing.

DOGS—FICTION

AaronG, Driftin'. Claude Henry, the Iditarod Mouse: The Adventures Begin. 2007. 108p. (J). per. 9.95 (*978-0-595-44990-3(5)) iUniverse, Inc.

Abadzis, Nick. Laika Collector's Edition. 2007. (Illus.). 208p. (YA). 29.95 (*978-1-59643-302-1(7) , First Second Bks.) Roaring Brook Pr.

Abbott, Raymond. Rosie Finds A Home. 2004. 92p. pap. 14.95 (978-1-4137-3680-9(7)) PublishAmerica, Inc.

Abbott, Roger. Sniffer's Golden Nose. West, Colin, illus. 2006. (I Am Reading Ser.). 48p. (J). (gr. k-3). pap. 3.95 (978-0-7534-5959-1(0) , Kingfisher) Houghton Mifflin Co. Trade & Reference Div.

Abercrombie, Barbara & Gustavson, Adam. Bad Dog, Dodger! 2002. (Illus.). 40p. (J). (gr. 1-5). 14.95 (978-0-689-83782-1(8) , McElderry, Margaret K.) Simon & Schuster Children's Publishing.

Aboff, Marcie & Preller, James. All the Way Home. Kurtz, John, illus. 2005. (Clifford's Puppy Days Ser.). 80p. (J). (ps-ps). pap. 2.99 (978-0-439-73380-9(4)) Scholastic, Inc.

About Town with Benny Be. 2005. (J). bds. 15.99 (978-0-9774752-0-9(4)) Bentley, Trish.

Accorsi, William. Apple, Apple, Alligator: A Picture-Puzzle Book. 2000. (Illus.). 20p. (J). (ps). bds. 14.95 (978-0-7611-1787-2(3)) Workman Publishing Co., Inc.

Adams, Jean Ekman. Clarence & the Great Surprise. Adams, Jean Ekman, illus. 2001. (Illus.). 32p. (J). (gr. k-2). 15.95 (978-0-87358-795-2(2) , Rising Moon Bks. for Young Readers) Northland Publishing.

Adler, David A. Bones & the Dog Gone Mystery. Newman, Barbara, illus. 2008. (Jeffrey Bones Mystery Ser.: No. 2). 32p. (J). (gr. k). pap. 3.99 (*978-0-14-241043-1(8) , Puffin) Penguin Group (USA) Inc.

—Bones & the Dog Gone Mystery. Newman, Barbara Johansen, illus. 2004. (Jeffrey Bones Mystery Ser.: No. 2). 32p. (J). (gr. k-3). 13.99 (978-0-670-05948-5(X) , Viking Juvenile) Penguin Group (USA) Inc.

—Cam Jansen & the Mystery of the Television Dog. 2004. (Cam Jansen Ser.: No. 4). (Illus.). 64p. (J). (gr. 2-4). pap. 3.99 (978-0-14-240013-5(0) , Puffin) Penguin Group (USA) Inc.

Adventures of Wishbone, 14 bks. l.t. ed. Incl. Digging to the Center of the Earth. Steele, Michael Anthony. Punchatz, Don, illus. (gr. 4 up). lib. bdg. 22.60 (978-0-8368-2595-4(0)); Digging up the Past. Sathre, Vivian. 144p. (gr. 4 up). lib. bdg. 22.60 (978-0-8368-2302-8(8)); Dog Overboard! Sathre, Vivian. (gr. 4 up). lib. bdg. 22.60 (978-0-8368-2590-9(X)); Dr. Jekyll & Mr. Dog. Butcher, Nancy. (gr. 4 up). lib. bdg. 22.60 (978-0-8368-2592-3(6)); Gullifur's Travels. Strickland, Brad & Strickland, Barbara. (gr. 4 up). lib. bdg. 22.60 (978-0-8368-2596-1(9)); Homer Sweet Homer. Jablonski, Carla. Punchatz, Don, illus. (gr. 4 up). lib. bdg. 22.60 (978-0-8368-2591-6(8)); Hunchdog of Notre Dame. Friedman, Michael Jan. 139p. (gr. 4 up). lib. bdg. 22.60 (978-0-8368-2301-1(X)); Last of the Breed. Steele, Alexander. Punchatz, Don, illus. 163p. (gr. 4 up). lib. bdg. 22.60 (978-0-8368-2594-7(2)); Mutt in the Iron Muzzle. Friedman, Michael Jan. 144p. (gr. 4 up). lib. bdg. 22.60 (978-0-8368-2303-5(6)); Pawloined Paper. Litowinsky, Olga. (gr. 4 up). lib. bdg. 22.60 (978-0-8368-2589-3(6)); Prince & the Pooch. Leavitt, Caroline. 144p. (gr. 4 up). lib. bdg. 22.60 (978-0-8368-2299-1(4)); Pup in King Arthur's Court. Barkan, Joanne. 164p. (gr. 2-5). lib. bdg. 22.60 (978-0-8368-2593-0(4)); Robinhound Crusoe. Leavitt, Caroline. 144p. (gr. 4 up). lib. bdg. 22.60 (978-0-8368-2300-4(1)); Tale of Two Sitters. Barkan, Joanne. 144p. (gr. 4 up). lib. bdg. 22.60 (978-0-8368-2305-9(2)); (J). 1999. (Illus.). 1999. Set lib. bdg. 316.40 (978-0-8368-2654-8(X)) Stevens, Gareth Inc.

Aguila, Priscilla. As Different As Can Be. 2006. 48p. pap. 17.96 (978-1-4116-5609-3(1)) Lulu.com.

Aguillo, Don Ellis, illus. Boomer, the Missing Pomeranian. 2005. 34p. (J). pap. (*978-1-932864-45-8(8)) Masthof Pr.

Ahlberg, Allan. Slow Dog's Nose, Bk. 5. 2000. (Illus.). 32p. (J). pap. 9.95 (978-0-14-056401-3(2)) Penguin Group (USA) Inc.

—Woof! (Illus.). 160p. (J). 9.95 (978-0-14-038669-1(6)) Penguin Bks., Ltd. GBR. *Dist:* Trafalgar Square Publishing.

Aigner-Clark, Julie. Dogs. 2002. (Baby Einstein Ser.). (Illus.). 20p. (ps-17). 3.99 (978-0-7868-0839-7(X)) Hyperion Bks. for Children.

Alba, Gene. Mutley Goes Diving! 1998. (Mutley's True Life Adventures Ser.). (Illus.). 32p. (ps-3). 14.95 (978-0-89346-878-1(9)) Heian International Publishing, Inc.

—Mutley Goes to Snow Mountain. 1999. (Mutley's True Life Adventures Ser.). (Illus.). 32p. (J). (ps-3). 14.95 (978-0-89346-877-4(0)) Heian International Publishing, Inc.

Albee, Sarah. Blue's Bad Dream. Chernichaw, Ian, illus. 2006. (Blue's Clues Ser.). 24p. (J). pap. 3.99 (978-1-4169-1553-9(2) , Simon Spotlight/Nickelodeon) Simon & Schuster Children's Publishing.

—Hello, Cat, Hello, Dog. Leigh, Tom, illus. 2006. (Step-By-Step Readers Ser.). (J). pap. (978-1-59939-054-3(X) , Reader's Digest Young Families, Inc.) Reader's Digest Children's Publishing, Inc.

Albers, Everett C. Lewis & Clark Meet the American Indians: As Told by Seaman the Dog. Eslinger, Kimberly, illus. 1999. 32p. (J). (ps-11). pap. 3.95 (978-0-9674002-0-4(1)) United Printing.

Alborough, Jez. Some Dogs Do. Alborough, Jez, illus. 2003. (Illus.). 40p. (J). (ps-2). 15.99 (978-0-7636-2201-5(X)) Candlewick Pr.

Alcantra, Ricardo. Dog & Cat. Gusti, illus. 1999. 32p. (gr. k-2). lib. bdg. 19.90 (978-0-7613-1420-2(2) , Millbrook Pr.) Lerner Publishing Group.

Alderton, Sylvia. A Real Name for Puppy. McCartney, Michael David, illus. 2006. (J). (978-1-930566-58-3(1) , WestWind Pr.) Scott, D.&F. Publishing, Inc.

Alen, Antonia. My Three Little Dogs. 2003. 32p. pap. 8.00 (978-0-8059-5490-6(2)) Dorrance Publishing Co., Inc.

Alexander, DeHaven. Smokey's Big Move. 2002. 32p. pap. 9.00 (978-0-8059-5714-3(6)) Dorrance Publishing Co., Inc.

Alexander, Liza & Santomero, Angela C. Blue y Tu, Detective de Colores. Ziegler, Argentina Palacios, tr. Speer-Lyon, Tammie, illus. 2004. (Blue's Clues Ser.).Tr. of Blue & the Color Detectives. (SPA.). 24p. (J). pap. 3.99 (978-0-689-86979-2(7) , Libros Para Ninos) Simon & Schuster Children's Publishing.

Alfonsi, Alice, adapted by. What You See Is What You Get. novel ed. 2004. (That's So Raven Ser.: Bk. 1). (Illus.). 144p. (gr. 3-7). pap. 4.99 (978-0-7868-4639-9(9)) Disney Pr.

Allan, Nicholas. Heaven. 2006. (Illus.). 32p. (J). pap. 9.99 (*978-0-09-948814-9(0)) Transworld Publishers Ltd. GBR. *Dist:* Independent Pubs. Group.

Allee, Ann. "Colt" a Dog's Story. Hirchert, Richard A., ed. Kovelant, Lindsey, illus. 2001. 68p. (J). (ps-3). pap. 6.95 (978-0-9708638-0-5(2)) 3 Millennium Publishing.

Altan. Here Comes Timpa. Altan, illus. 2007. (Illus.). 48p. (J). pap. 14.95 (*978-1-933372-28-0(1)) Europa Editions, Inc.

Alumenda, Stephen. Toko & the Lost Kittens. 2004. (Illus.). 19p. 13.95 (978-9966-25-170-1(7)) Heinemann Kenya, Limited (East African Educational Publishers Ltd E.A.E.P.) KEN. *Dist:* Michigan State Univ. Pr.

Amery, H. & Cartwright, S. Where's Rusty? 2004. (Treasury of Farmyard Tales Ser.). 10p. (J). 7.95 (978-0-7945-0545-5(7)) EDC Publishing.

Amery, Heather. Rusty's Train Ride. rev. ed. 2007. 16p. (J). pap. 5.99 (*978-0-7945-0802-9(2) , Usborne) EDC Publishing.

Amico, Tom & Proimos, James. The Day the Dog Dressed Like Dad. 2004. (Illus.). 32p. (J). 16.95 (978-1-58234-877-3(4) , Bloomsbury Children) Bloomsbury Publishing.

Amundson, Susan. Free to Be Me: The Eskimo Way. Geiken, Brenda, illus. 2003. 56p. lib. bdg. 16.95 (978-1-883477-65-3(4)) Lone Oak Pr., Ltd.

Anderson, C. W. Blaze & the Lost Quarry. 1999. (J). (gr. 1-4). 21.75 (978-0-8446-7001-0(4)) Smith, Peter Pub., Inc.

Anderson, Joan F. Buster B. Basset Hound, the Label Buster (Book & Music CD) Labeled as ADHD (Attention Deficit Hyperactive Dog) by the Sneaky Label Maker Buster B. Basset Hound Turns into a Hero, the Label Buster. 2004. (Illus.). (J). per. 15.00 (978-0-9665545-5-7(8)) Block System, The.

Anderson, Laurie Halse. Fight for Life, Vol. 1. 2007. (Vet Volunteers Ser.). 144p. (J). (gr. 3). pap. 6.99 (978-0-14-240862-9(X), Puffin) Penguin Group (USA) Inc.

—Fight for Life. 2003. (Wild at Heart Ser.). (Illus.). 127p. (J). (gr. 4 up). lib. bdg. 23.33 (978-0-8368-3256-3(6)) Stevens, Gareth Inc.

—Fight for Life. 2000. (American Girl Wild at Heart Ser.: Bk. 1). (YA). (978-0-606-18358-1(2)) Tandem Library Bks.

—Say Good-Bye. 2003. (Wild at Heart Ser.). (Illus.). 129p. (J). (gr. 4 up). lib. bdg. 23.33 (978-0-8368-3259-4(0)) Stevens, Gareth Inc.

—Say Good-Bye. 2001. (American Girl Wild at Heart Ser.: Bk. 5). (Illus.). (YA). (978-0-606-21527-5(1)) Tandem Library Bks.

—Teacher's Pet. 2003. (Wild at Heart Ser.). (Illus.). 132p. (J). (gr. 4 up). lib. bdg. 23.33 (978-0-8368-3261-7(2)) Stevens, Gareth Inc.

—Trapped. 2003. (Wild at Heart Ser.). (Illus.). 113p. (J). (gr. 4 up). lib. bdg. 23.33 (978-0-8368-3263-1(9)) Stevens, Gareth Inc.

Anderson, Scoular. Stan the Dog & the Crafty Cats. 2006. (Read-It! Chapter Books). (J). 21.26 (978-1-4048-2739-4(0)) Picture Window Bks.

—Stan the Dog & the Golden Goals. 2006. (Read-It! Chapter Books). (J). 21.26 (978-1-4048-2740-0(4)) Picture Window Bks.

—Stan the Dog & the Major Makeover. 2006. (Read-It! Chapter Books). (J). (978-1-4048-2741-7(2)) Picture Window Bks.

—Stan the Dog & the Sneaky Snacks. 2006. (Read-It! Chapter Books). (J). 21.26 (978-1-4048-2742-4(0)) Picture Window Bks.

Anderson, Scoular, illus. Stan the Dog Becomes Superdog. 2006. 52p. (J). lib. bdg. (*978-1-4048-3131-5(2)) Picture Window Bks.

Anderson, Wayne R. Paula's Perilous Adventure. 2006. 48p. (YA). 12.95 (978-0-9773478-0-3(X)); 19.95 incl. DVD (978-0-9773478-2-7(6)) IMAGECRAFTERS.

Anfousse, Ginette. Le Chien d'Arthur. 2002. (Premier Roman Ser.). (FRE.). 64p. (J). (gr. 2-5). pap. (978-2-89021-186-5(X)) Diffusion du livre Mirabel.

Angelo, Alyssa. Sherlock the Circus Dog. 2007. 108p. pap. 11.95 (*978-1-60145-137-8(7)); pap. 21.95 (*978-1-60145-133-0(4)) Booklocker.com, Inc.

Angus & the Cat. 2004. (J). 24.95 incl. audio (978-0-89719-699-4(0)) Weston Woods Studios, Inc.

Angus & the Ducks. 2004. (J). pap. 18.95 incl. audio compact disk (978-1-55592-369-3(0)); pap. 38.75 incl. audio compact disk (978-1-55592-370-9(4)); pap. 32.75 incl. audio (978-1-55592-187-3(6)) Weston Woods Studios, Inc.

Animal Friends Squeaky- Dog. 2005. (J). bds. (978-1-4194-0093-3(2)) Paradise Pr., Inc.

Anonymous. Arthur Hamilton & His Dog. 2004. reprint ed. pap. 15.95 (978-1-4191-0774-0(7)); pap. 1.99 (978-1-4192-0774-7(1)) Kessinger Publishing, LLC.

Appelt, Kathi. Bubba & Beau, Best Friends. Howard, Arthur, illus. 2006. (Bubba & Beau Ser.). 32p. (J). pap. 6.00 (978-0-15-205580-6(0), Voyager Bks./Libros Viajeros) Harcourt Children's Bks.

—Bubba & Beau Go Night-Night. Howard, Arthur, illus. 2003. (Bubba & Beau Ser.). 32p. (J). 16.00 (978-0-15-204593-7(7)) Harcourt Children's Bks.

—Bubba & Beau Go Night-Night. Howard, Arthur, illus. 2006. (Bubba & Beau Ser.). 32p. (J). pap. 6.00 (978-0-15-205815-9(X), Voyager Bks./Libros Viajeros) Harcourt Children's Bks.

—Bubba & Beau Meet the Relatives. Howard, Arthur, tr. Howard, Arthur, illus. 2004. (Bubba & Beau Ser.). 32p. (J). 16.00 (978-0-15-216630-4(0)) Harcourt Children's Bks.

Aragones, Sergio. Groo & Rufferto. 2000. (Groo Ser.). (Illus.). 112p. (YA). (gr. 7 up). pap. 9.95 (978-1-56971-447-8(9)) Dark Horse Comics.

—The Groo Inferno. 1999. (Groo Ser.). 96p. (YA). (gr. 5 up). pap. 9.95 (978-1-56971-430-0(4)) Dark Horse Comics.

—Sergio Aragones Groo Handbook. 1999. (Illus.). 96p. (YA). (gr. 5 up). pap. 9.95 (978-1-56971-385-3(5)) Dark Horse Comics.

Ardizzone, Edward. Tims Friend Towser. 2000. (J). 15.89 (978-0-06-029205-8(9)) HarperCollins Pubs.

Ardizzone, Edward. Tims Friend Towser. 2008. (Illus.). 48p. (J). 16.95 (*978-1-84507-560-6(9)) Lincoln, Frances Ltd. GBR. *Dist:* Perseus Distribution.

Arguello, Tito. A Dog in Love. 2005. 114p. (J). pap. 8.95 (978-1-4116-2287-6(1)) Lulu.com.

Armstrong, William H. Sounder. 2001. (Perennial Classics Ser.). 96p. (gr. 4-7). pap. 7.00 (978-0-06-093548-1(0)) HarperCollins Pubs.

—Sounder. Barkley, James, illus. l.t. ed. 1999. (LRS Large Print Cornerstone Ser.). 230p. (YA). (gr. 6-12). lib. bdg. 27.95 (978-1-58118-054-1(3), 22768) LRS.

—Sounder. 2001. (gr. 3-6). lib. bdg. 15.30 (978-0-613-85745-1(3)) Tandem Library Bks.

—Sounder. l.t. ed. 2005. 111p. (YA). pap. 10.95 (978-0-7862-7915-9(X)) Thorndike Pr.

Arnosky, Jim. Little Lions. 1998. (Illus.). 1p. (J). (ps-1). 17.99 (978-0-399-22944-2(2), Putnam Juvenile) Penguin Group (USA) Inc.

Arruzza, Rick. El Paseo de Sparky. Newton, Pilar, illus. 2003. (SPA.). 24p. mass mkt. 7.95 (978-0-9744509-1-9(X)) Three Spots Productions.

—Sparky's Walk. Newton, Pilar, illus. 2003. 24p. (J). mass mkt. 7.95 (978-0-9744509-0-2(1)) Three Spots Productions.

Arsenault, Elaine. Doggie in the Window. Fanny, illus. 2004. 32p. (J). (ps-2). 14.95 (978-0-88899-619-0(5)) Groundwood Bks. CAN. *Dist:* Perseus Distribution.

As Told by Milo: My Very Own Family. 2005. (J). 14.95 (978-0-9772000-0-9(0)) Andrus, Ashley.

Asare, Meshack. Sosu's Call. Asare, Meshack, illus. 2002. (Illus.). 40p. (J). (gr. k-4). 15.95 (978-1-929132-21-8(2)) Kane/Miller Bk. Pubs., Inc.

Ashworth, Susan M. Jo-Jo Helps with the Housework. l.t. ed. 2003. (Illus.). 20p. (J). per. 8.95 (978-1-932338-35-5(7)) Lifevest Publishing, Inc.

—Jo-Jo Santa's Naughty Puppy. l.t. ed. 2002. (Illus.). 29p. (J). per. 8.95 (978-1-932338-00-3(4)) Lifevest Publishing, Inc.

Auch, Mary Jane. I Was a Third Grade Spy. Auch, Herm, illus. 2001. 96p. (J). (gr. 4-6). tchr. ed. 15.95 (978-0-8234-1576-2(7)) Holiday Hse., Inc.

—I Was a Third Grade Spy. Auch, Herm, illus. 2003. 96p. (J). (gr. 2-5). pap. 5.50 (978-0-440-41871-9(2), Yearling) Random Hse. Children's Bks.

—I Was a Third Grade Spy. 2003. (gr. 3-6). lib. bdg. 13.00 (978-0-613-60388-1(5)) Tandem Library Bks.

Auch, Mary Jane & Auch, Herm, illus. I Was a Third Grade Bodyguard. 2003. 80p. (J). (gr. 4-6). tchr. ed. 15.95 (978-0-8234-1775-9(1)) Holiday Hse., Inc.

Auerbach, Annie. Most World Records. 2000. (gr. 3-6). lib. bdg. 11.80 (978-0-613-26278-1(6)) Tandem Library Bks.

Avi. The Good Dog. 256p. 2003. mass mkt. 5.99 (978-0-689-83825-5(5), Aladdin); 2001. (Illus.). (J). (gr. 3-6). 17.99 (978-0-689-83824-8(7), Atheneum/Richard Jackson Bks.) Simon & Schuster Children's Publishing.

—The Good Dog. 2003. (gr. 3-6). lib. bdg. 14.15 (978-0-613-61770-3(3)) Tandem Library Bks.

—The Good Dog. l.t. ed. 2003. 176p. (J). 23.95 (978-0-7862-5600-6(1)) Thorndike Pr.

Axelrod, Amy. The News Hounds Catch a Wave: A Geography Adventure. Bowers, Tim, illus. 2001. (J). 13.00 (978-0-689-82410-4(6), Simon & Schuster Children's Publishing) Simon & Schuster Children's Publishing.

Ayoub, Susan. Hockey Pups, 1. 1999. (Illus.). (J). pap. 6.50 (978-0-9665637-1-9(9)) Smirk Productions.

Babee says No. 2006. (YA). spiral bd. (978-1-59872-479-0(7)) Instantpublisher.com.

Backx, Patsy. Josie & Mr. Fernandez. Backx, Patsy, illus. 2002. (Illus.). 32p. (J). (ps up). lib. bdg. 24.67 (978-0-8368-3079-8(2)) Stevens, Gareth Inc.

—Skippy & Jack. Backx, Patsy, illus. 2002. (Illus.). 32p. (J). (ps up). lib. bdg. 24.67 (978-0-8368-3080-4(6)) Stevens, Gareth Inc.

Bader, Bonnie. Play Ball. Ruppert, Larry, illus. 2007. 24p. (J). pap. 3.99 (978-0-448-44466-6(6), Grosset & Dunlap) Penguin Group (USA) Inc.

Baek, Matthew J. Be Gentle with the Dog, Dear. 2008. 32p. (J). (ps-k). 14.99 (*978-0-8037-3250-6(3), Dial) Penguin Group (USA) Inc.

Baglio, Ben M. Beagle in a Backpack. Baum, Ann, illus. 2005. 142p. (J). pap. (*978-0-439-77521-2(3)) Scholastic, Inc.

—Collie with a Card. Baum, Ann, illus. 2004. 136p. (J). pap. (*978-0-439-68760-7(8)) Scholastic, Inc.

—Come Back, Buddy! 2004. (Illus.). 118p. (J). pap. (978-0-439-68883-3(3)) Scholastic, Inc.

—Dog at the Door. Gregory, Jenny, illus. 2002. (Animal Ark Ser.: No. 25). 160p. (J). mass mkt. 3.99 (978-0-439-34386-2(0)) Scholastic, Inc.

—Dog at the Door. 2002. (gr. 3-6). lib. bdg. 11.80 (978-0-613-57036-7(3)) Tandem Library Bks.

—The Dog with No Name. 2005. (Illus.). 148p. (J). (978-0-439-74617-5(5)) Scholastic, Inc.

—Doggy Dare. 2000. (Animal Ark Pets Ser.: No. 12). (Illus.). 128p. (J). (gr. 4-7). pap. 3.99 (978-0-439-05169-9(X)) Scholastic, Inc.

—Hound at the Hospital. Baum, Ann & Gregory, Jenny, illus. 2004. (Animal Ark Hauntings Ser.). 144p. (J). pap. 3.99 (978-0-439-44891-8(3)) Scholastic, Inc.

—Husky with a Heart. 2006. 139p. (978-0-439-77523-6(X)) Scholastic, Inc.

—Labrador on the Lawn. Gregory, Jenny, illus. 2005. (Animal Ark Hauntings Ser.: No. 38). 144p. (J). (gr. 2-5). pap. 3.99 (978-0-439-68488-0(9)) Scholastic, Inc.

—Pup at the Palace. 2003. (Animal Ark Ser.: No. 30). 144p. (J). pap. 3.99 (978-0-439-34391-6(7), Scholastic Paperbacks) Scholastic, Inc.

—Puppies in the Pantry. McNicholas, Shelagh, illus. 1998. (Animal Ark Ser.: No. 3). 144p. (gr. 3-5). 3.99 (978-0-590-18751-0(1)) Scholastic, Inc.

—Puppy in a Puddle, No. 28. Baum, Ann, illus. 2003. (Animal Ark Ser.: No. 28). 144p. (J). mass mkt. 3.99 (978-0-439-34389-3(5), Scholastic Paperbacks) Scholastic, Inc.

—Puppy in a Puddle. 2002. (gr. 3-6). lib. bdg. 11.80 (978-0-613-63336-9(9)) Tandem Library Bks.

—Puppy Puzzle. Howard, Paul, illus. 1999. (Animal Ark Pets Ser.: No. 1). 112p. (J). (gr. 3-6). 3.99 (978-0-439-05158-3(4)) Scholastic, Inc.

—Puppy Puzzle. 1999. (gr. 3-6). lib. bdg. 11.80 (978-0-613-12010-4(8)) Tandem Library Bks.

—Spaniel in a Stocking. 2007. (Animal Ark Ser.: No. 50). (Illus.). 160p. (J). pap. 3.99 (*978-0-439-87118-1(2)) Scholastic, Inc.

Baglio, Ben M. Terrier in the Tinsel. Baum, Ann & Gregory, Jenny, illus. 2004. (Animal Ark Hauntings Ser.). 160p. (J). (gr. 2-5). pap. 3.99 (978-0-439-44892-5(1), Scholastic Paperbacks) Scholastic, Inc.

Bailey, Linda. Stanley at Sea. Slavin, Bill, illus. 2008. 32p. (*978-1-55453-193-6(4)) Kids Can Pr., Ltd.

—Stanley's party. Slavin, Bill, illus. 32p. (J). (gr. k-3). 2004. (978-1-55337-768-9(0)); 2003. (978-1-55337-382-7(0)) Kids Can Pr., Ltd.

—Stanley's Wild Ride. Slavin, Bill, illus. 2006. 32p. (J). 14.95 (978-1-55337-960-7(8)) Kids Can Pr., Ltd. CAN. *Dist:* Wybel Marketing Group.

Bailey's Birthday - Evaluation Guide: Evaluation Guide. 2006. (J). (978-1-55942-399-1(4)) Marsh Media.

Bajoria, Paul. The Printer's Devil. 2007. 400p. (J). (gr. 4-8). pap. 6.99 (978-0-316-10678-8(X)) Little Brown & Co.

Baker, Barbara. Digby & Kate 1-2-3. Winborn, Marsha, illus. 2004. (Dutton Easy Reader Ser.). 48p. (J). (gr. 1-4). 14.99 (978-0-525-46854-7(4), Dutton Juvenile) Penguin Group (USA) Inc.

—Digby & Kate & the Beautiful Day. Winborn, Marsha, illus. 2004. (Easy-to-Read Ser.). 48p. (J). (gr. 1-4). pap. 3.99 (978-0-14-240035-7(1), Puffin) Penguin Group (USA) Inc.

—Digby & Kate & the Beautiful Day. 2004. (gr. k-3). lib. bdg. 11.80 (978-0-613-86706-1(8)) Tandem Library Bks.

Baker, Cristal. Popsicle Goes to Church. 2006. 2p. 9.83 (978-1-4116-8288-7(2)) Lulu.com.

Balaam, Lisa & Balaam, Steven. Abbey the Cavi in Miami Beach. 2006. 52p. (J). 19.95 (978-1-4196-1004-2(X)) BookSurge, LLC.

Balaam, Steven & Balaam, Lisa. Abbey the Cavi: And Friends. 2007. (Illus.). 102p. (J). per. 9.95 (978-0-9785885-0-5(2)) Balaam Books LLC.

Balaban, Bob. Beware of Dog. 2002. (gr. 3-6). lib. bdg. 13.00 (978-0-613-72091-5(1)) Tandem Library Bks.

—It's a Dog-Eat-Dog World. 2004. (McGrowl Ser.). 176p. (J). (gr. 4-7). pap. 4.99 (978-0-439-43458-4(0), Scholastic Paperbacks) Scholastic, Inc.

—Puppy Tales. 2005. (McGrowl Ser.: No. 6). 176p. (J). pap. 4.99 (978-0-439-43459-1(9), Scholastic Paperbacks) Scholastic, Inc.

Ball, Brian. Hop It Duggy Dog. (Illus.). 32p. (J). pap. 7.95 (978-0-14-038158-0(9)) Penguin Bks., Ltd. GBR. *Dist:* Trafalgar Square Publishing.

Ball, Justin & Croker, Evan. Space Dogs. 2006. 272p. (J). (gr. 3-7). 15.95 (978-0-375-83256-7(4)); lib. bdg. 17.99 (978-0-375-93256-4(9)) Random Hse. Children's Bks. (Knopf Bks. for Young Readers).

Ballantyne, R. M. The Dog Crusoe (Illustrated Edition) (Do. 2006. pap. (*978-1-4065-0529-0(3)) Dodo Pr.

Bampton, Bob. Animal Friends Little Puppy Board Book. 1999. (Illus.). 14p. (ps-k). 7.95 (978-1-58185-220-2(7)) Quadrillion Media LLC.

Banim, Lisa. In the Doghouse. 2005. 124p. (J). lib. bdg. 16.92 (*978-1-4242-0685-8(5)) Fitzgerald Bks.

Banks, Kate. Monkeys & Dog Days. Bogacki, Tomasz, illus. 2008. (J). (*978-0-374-35029-1(9)) Farrar, Straus & Giroux.

Banks, Steven. Catdog Undercover. 2000. (gr. 3-6). lib. bdg. 11.80 (978-0-613-21308-0(4)) Tandem Library Bks.

—Space Oddity. 2000. (gr. 3-6). lib. bdg. 11.80 (978-0-613-27021-2(5)) Tandem Library Bks.

Banscherus, Jurgen & Baron, Daniel C. The Snarling Suspect. Butschkow, Ralf, illus. 2008. (J). pap. (*978-1-59889-911-5(2)); lib. bdg. (*978-1-59889-875-0(2)) Stone Arch Bks.

Barham, Olivia. It's Puppy Time: Sticker Storybook. Kaminski, Karol, illus. 2002. (Chubby Puppies Ser.). 16p. (J). (ps-3). pap. 4.99 (978-0-439-35588-9(5)) Scholastic, Inc.

—Springtime in Chubbytown. 2002. (Chubby Puppies Ser.: Vol. 1). (Illus.). 32p. (J). (ps-3). pap. 3.50 (978-0-439-35566-7(4)) Scholastic, Inc.

—Summer Picnic. Kaminski, Karol, illus. 2002. (Chubby Puppies Ser.: Vol. 2). 32p. (J). (ps-3). pap. 3.50 (978-0-439-35586-5(9)) Scholastic, Inc.

Bark, George. 2004. (J). pap. 38.75 incl. audio compact disk (978-1-55592-713-4(0)); pap. 32.75 incl. audio (978-1-55592-709-7(2)) Weston Woods Studios, Inc.

Barkan, Joanne. A Pup in King Arthur's Court. l.t. ed. 1999. (Adventures of Wishbone Ser.: No. 15). (Illus.). 164p. (J). (gr. 2-5). lib. bdg. 22.60 (978-0-8368-2593-0(4)) Stevens, Gareth Inc.

—A Tale of Two Sitters. l.t. ed. 1999. (Adventures of Wishbone Ser.: No. 9). (Illus.). 144p. (J). (gr. 4 up). lib. bdg. 22.60 (978-0-8368-2305-9(2)) Stevens, Gareth Inc.

Barkly, Bob. A Puppy to Love. Kurtz, John, illus. 2001. (Clifford, the Big Red Dog Ser.). (J). (gr. k-2). pap. (978-0-439-22004-0(1)) Scholastic, Inc.

Barracca, Debra. The Adventures of Taxi Dog. Buehner, Mark, illus. 2002. (J). 13.19 (978-0-7587-1907-2(8)) Book Wholesalers, Inc.

—Adventures of Taxi Dog. 2000. (ps-2). lib. bdg. 14.15 (978-0-613-28397-7(X)) Tandem Library Bks.

—Maxi, the Hero. Buehner, Mark, illus. 2002. (J). 14.04 (978-0-7587-3112-8(4)) Book Wholesalers, Inc.

Barracca, Debra & Barracca, Sal. The Adventures of Taxi Dog. Buehner, Mark, illus. 2000. 32p. (J). (ps-3). pap. 5.99 (978-0-14-056665-9(1), Puffin) Penguin Group (USA) Inc.

—The Adventures of Taxi Dog. 2000. (Illus.). (J). 12.79 (978-0-606-18386-4(8)) Tandem Library Bks.

Bartoletti, Susan Campbell. Nobody's Diggier Than a Dog. Giacobbe, Beppe, illus. 2005. 40p. (ps-17). 15.99 (978-0-7868-1824-2(7)) Hyperion Bks. for Children.

Baruffi, Andrea, illus. If I Had a Robot Dog. 2005. (I'm Going to Read Ser.). 32p. (J). (ps). pap. 3.95 (978-1-4027-3027-6(6)); 11.95 (978-1-4027-3026-9(8)) Sterling Publishing Co., Inc.

Bastedo, Jaya. A Winter Walk with Haley. Macintosh, Tessa, illus. Macintosh, Tessa, photos by. l.t. ed. 1999. 24p. (J). (ps-5). pap. (978-1-894303-06-4(7)) Raven Rock Publishing.

Bateman, Teresa. Fluffy, Scourge of the Sea. Chesworth, Michael, illus. 32p. (J). 2006. pap. 6.95 (978-1-58089-152-3(7)); 2005. 14.95 (978-1-58089-099-1(7)) Charlesbridge Publishing, Inc.

Batson, Susann. A Duck at the Dog Pound. 2007. (Illus.). 32p. (J). E-Book 5.00 incl. cd-rom (*978-1-933090-23-8(5)) Guardian Angel Publishing, Inc.

Bauer, Jutta. Selma. Bauer, Jutta, illus. 2004. (Illus.). 56p. (J). 7.95 (978-1-929132-50-8(6)) Kane/Miller Bk. Pubs., Inc.

Baum, Roger S. Toto in Candy Land of Oz. Berkovitz, Ronit, illus. 2002. 32p. (J). 14.95 (978-1-57072-224-0(2)) Overmountain Pr.

Baum, Roger S. & Seitzinger, Victoria. Toto of Oz & the Surprise Party. 2004. 32p. (J). 13.95 (978-1-57072-284-4(6)) Overmountain Pr.

Baumgart, Klaus. Don't Be Afraid, Tommy. 1998. (Illus.). 28p. (J). (ps-2). 14.95 (978-1-888444-32-2(0), 21150) Little Tiger Pr.

Be Kind, Be Friendly, Be Thankful: The Adventures of Brisky Bear & Trooper Dog. 2007. Orig. Title: Friends for Always. (J). pap. 7.95 incl. audio compact disk (*978-0-9795127-0-4(0)) Glory Be Collectibles.

Bea, Holly & Howard, Kim. God Believes in You. 2004. (Illus.). 32p. (J). 15.00 (978-1-932073-08-9(6)) Kramer, H.J. Inc.

Bean, Shelly. Rooty Toot Rambler: Finds a Home. 2003. (Illus.). 20p. (J). per. 5.95 (978-0-9674915-4-7(1)) Day By Day.

Beaumont, Karen. Doggone Dogs! Catrow, David, illus. 2008. (J). (*978-0-8037-3157-8(4), Dial) Penguin Group (USA) Inc.

—Move Over, Rover! Dyer, Jane, illus. 2006. (J). (ps-2). 40p. 16.00 (978-0-15-201979-2(0)); (*978-1-4287-0246-2(6)) Harcourt Trade Pubs.

Bechtold, Lisze. Buster: The Very Shy Dog. 2001. (Illus.). 48p. (J). (gr. k-3). pap. 5.95 (978-0-618-11122-0(0)) Houghton Mifflin Co. Trade & Reference Div.

—Buster: The Very Shy Dog. 1999. (gr. 3-6). lib. bdg. 14.10 (978-0-613-35495-0(8)); (Illus.). (J). 12.75 (978-0-606-21095-9(4)) Tandem Library Bks.

—Buster & Phoebe: The Great Bone Game. 48p. (J). 2010. pap. 5.95 (978-0-618-58547-2(8)); 2003. (Illus.). tchr. ed. 15.00 (978-0-618-20862-3(3)) Houghton Mifflin Co. Trade & Reference Div.

Beckwith, Lillian. The Spuddy. 2002. 108p. 9.95 (978-0-7551-0276-1(2)) House of Stratus, Inc. GBR. *Dist:* Midpoint Trade Bks., Inc.

Bedford, David. Hound Dog. Williamson, Melanie, illus. 2006. (J). pap. 6.95 (978-1-58925-397-1(3), tiger tales) ME Media LLC.

—Hound Dog. (Illus.). 32p. (978-0-19-279132-0(X)) Oxford Univ. Pr., Inc.

—The Way I Love You. James, Ann, illus. 2004. 32p. (J). 12.95 (978-0-689-87625-7(4)) Simon & Schuster Children's Publishing.

Bedford, David & Williamson, Gwyneth. Shaggy Dog & the Terrible Itch. 2001. (Illus.). 28p. (J). (ps-1). 12.95 (978-0-7641-5391-4(9)) Barron's Educational Series, Inc.

Bedford, David & Williamson, Melanie. Hound Dog. (Illus.). 32p. (978-0-19-272567-7(X)) Oxford Univ. Pr., Inc.

Behar, Joy. Sheetzucacapoopoo: My Kind of Dog. Barretta, Gene, illus. 2006. 32p. (J). (ps). 15.99 (978-0-525-47718-1(7), Dutton Juvenile) Penguin Group (USA) Inc.

Beil, Karen Magnuson. Jack's House. Wohnoutka, Mike, illus. 2008. (J). (*978-0-8234-1913-5(4)) Holiday Hse., Inc.

Bell, Joanne. Breaking Trail. 2005. 136p. (J). pap. 6.95 (978-0-88899-662-6(4)) Groundwood Bks. CAN. *Dist:* Perseus Distribution.

Bella & Rosie Beach Stories. 2007. (J). per. (*978-1-932570-83-0(7)) Literacy Footprints Inc.

Bella & Rosie Chapter Set 1. 2005. (J). (978-1-932570-48-9(9)) Literacy Footprints Inc.

Bella & Rosie Play Hide & Seek. 2003. (J). (978-1-932570-11-3(X)) Literacy Footprints Inc.

Bella & Rosie Set 1. 2003. (J). (978-1-932570-08-3(X)) Literacy Footprints Inc.

Bella & Rosie Set 2. 2004. (J). (978-1-932570-15-1(2)) Literacy Footprints Inc.

Bella & Rosie, Set 3. 2006. (J). (*978-1-932570-59-5(4)) Literacy Footprints Inc.

Bella & Rosie Trick or Treat. 2004. (J). (978-1-932570-17-5(9)) Literacy Footprints Inc.

Bella Is a Bad Dog. 2003. (J). (978-1-932570-14-4(4)) Literacy Footprints Inc.

Bella's Birthday. 2003. (J). (978-1-932570-09-0(8)) Literacy Footprints Inc.

Bellingham, Brenda. Lilly's Clever Puppy. Owen, Elizabeth, illus. 2002. 64p. (gr. 1-5). (First Novel Ser.). (J). (*978-0-88780-563-9(9)); (First Novels Ser.: Vol. 22). 4.95 (978-0-88780-562-2(0)) Formac Publishing Co., Ltd. CAN. *Dist:* Casemate Pubs. & Bk. Distributors, LLC.

Belzunce, Philip R. & Gutierrez, Lalei E. Once upon a Doggie: A Dog Named Kan-Li. Giolekas, Charity Matty & Matty, Susan, illus. 2001. 32p. (J). pap. 13.95 (978-1-888683-01-1(5)) Wooster Bk. Co., The.

Bemelmans, Ludwig. Madeline's Rescue. ed. 2004. (J). (ps-2). spiral bd. (978-0-616-11864-1(3)) Canadian National Institute for the Blind/Institut National Canadien pour les Aveugles.

Benjamin, A. H. Shamwood. 2006. 140p. pap. 19.95 (978-1-4137-9193-8(X)) PublishAmerica, Inc.

Bennett, Dean. Finding a Friend in the Forest: A True Story. 2005. (Illus.). 15.95 (978-0-89272-662-2(8)) Down East Bks.

Bennett, Jeffrey. Max Goes to the Moon. Okamoto, Alan, illus. 2003. (Science Adventures with Max the Dog Ser.). 32p. (J). (ps-7). 16.95 (978-0-9721819-0-7(3)) Big Kid Science.

Bennett, Marian. God Made Puppies. Derico, Laura, ed. Lash-Ruff, Michelle, illus. 2000. (Happy Day Bks.). 24p. (J). (ps-2). 2.49 (978-0-7847-1186-6(0) , 04336, Bean Sprouts) Standard Publishing.

Bennett, Paul. Tale of a Waggish Dog: Max. 2003. 192p. pap. 12.95 (978-1-878044-64-8(8)) Mayhaven Publishing.

Benson, Linda. Finding Chance. Lane, Nancy, illus. 2006. 112p. (J). (978-1-59336-696-4(5)) Mondo Publishing.

Bentley, Dawn. Patchwork Puppies. Winston, Jeannie, illus. 1999. (Cuddly Cloth Book Ser.). 8p. (J). bds. 9.95 (978-1-58117-044-3(0) , Intervisual/Piggy Toes) Dalmatian Pr.

Bentley, Dawn & Diefendorf, Cathy. Jack Lights Camera Action. 2005. (Illus.). 32p. (J). (ps-2). 4.95 incl. cd-rom (978-1-59249-502-3(8) , 1B039); 2.95 incl. cd-rom (978-1-59249-503-0(6) , 1B040) Soundprints.

Benton, Jim. Attack of the 50-Ft. Cupid. Benton, Jim, illus. 2003. (Franny K. Stein, Mad Scientist Ser.: Bk. 2). (Illus.). 112p. (J). (gr. 2-5). 14.95 (978-0-689-86292-2(X)) Simon & Schuster Children's Publishing.

Berenstain, Stan & Berenstain, Jan. The Berenstain Bears' New Pup. Berenstain, Stan & Berenstain, Jan, illus. 2005. (Berenstain Bears Ser.). (Illus.). 32p. (J). (gr. k-3). 15.99 (978-0-06-058343-9(6)) HarperCollins Pubs.

—The Berenstain Bears' New Pup. 2005. (Berenstain Bears Ser.). (Illus.). 32p. (J). (gr. k-3). pap. 3.99 (978-0-06-058344-6(4)) HarperCollins Pubs.

—The Berenstain Bears' New Pup. Berenstain, Stan & Berenstain, Jan, illus. 2005. (Berenstain Bears Ser.). (Illus.). 32p. (J). (ps-3). lib. bdg. 11.19 (978-0-606-33614-7(1)) Tandem Library Bks.

—Berenstain Bears' New Pup. Berenstain, Stan, illus. 2005. (Illus.). 32p. (J). lib. bdg. 13.85 (***978-1-4242-0816-6(5)***) Fitzgerald Bks.

Berenstain, Stan & Berenstain, Jan. The Runamuck Dog Show. 2001. (Berenstain Bears Ser.). (Illus.). (J). (gr. k-3). 10.79 (978-0-606-21059-1(8)) Tandem Library Bks.

Berlitz Publishing Staff, ed. Five Crayons French. 2005. (Berlitz Adventures with Nicholas Ser.). (ENG & FRE., Illus.). 64p. 16.95 (978-981-246-751-5(3) , 467513) Berlitz Publishing.

—Five Crayons Spanish. 2005. (Berlitz Adventures with Nicholas Ser.). (ENG & SPA., Illus.). 64p. 16.95 (978-981-246-752-2(1) , 467521) Berlitz Publishing.

Bern, Dave. Best Friends. 2006. 28p. pap. 9.95 (***978-1-4327-0036-2(7)***) Outskirts Press, Inc.

Best, Cari. Montezuma's Revenge. Palmisciano, Diane, illus. 1999. 32p. (J). (ps-2). 16.99 (978-0-531-33198-9(9) , Orchard Bks.) Scholastic, Inc.

Bester, Maryanne. Three Friends & a Taxi. Bester, Shayle, illus. 2007. 24p. (J). pap. 12.00 (***978-1-77009-265-5(X)***) Jacana Media ZAF. *Dist:* Independent Pubs. Group.

Betancourt, Jeanne. The Pony & the Missing Dog. 2000. (Pony Pals Ser.: Vol. 27). (Illus.). 96p. (J). (gr. 2-5). pap. 3.99 (978-0-439-21639-5(7)) Scholastic, Inc.

Beth, Hodder. The Ghost of Schafer Meadows. 2007. (J). per. 7.99 (***978-0-9793963-0-4(1)***) Grizzly Ridge Publishing.

Bethany: Adventures of the Mighty Mustard Seed. 2004. Orig. Title: Bethany in Beulah Land. (J). mass mkt. 12.95 (978-0-9745440-0-7(0)) McKatlib Pr.

Bevan, Jan Atchley. Zachary Cooks up Some Fun. Garfinkel, Dana Kleiman, illus. l.t. ed. 2004. 32p. (J). 15.95 (978-0-9717641-6-3(6)) Ocean Publishing.

Big Red's Greatest Find. ed. 2006. (J). per. (978-0-9725286-5-8(2)) Sheppard Publishing.

Billy & Baxter at the Airport, 4 vols. 2005. (Illus.). 24p. (J). (ps-7). 8.95 (978-1-58087-100-6(3)) Stampley, C.D. Enterprises, Inc.

Bird, Janie. Freddy in the City: Memorable Monday. Treffeisen, Brian, photos by. 2nd rev. ed. 2005. Tr. of Freddy en la Ciudad un Lunes Memorble. (SPA., Illus.). 32p. (J). 10.95 (978-1-59494-005-7(3)) CPCC Pr.

Biros, Florence W. Dog Jack: Heart-Warming Story of a Slave Boy & His Best Friend. 2nd rev. ed. 2001. (Illus.). (YA). (gr. 5 up). pap. 9.95 (978-0-936369-47-1(7)) Son-Rise Pubns. & Distribution Co.

Bischoff, Linda L. Ben & the Big Black Dog. 2000. (Illus.). 24p. (J). (gr. 2-4). pap. 9.95 (978-1-892614-32-2(4)) Briarwood Pubns.

Bishop, Rose. Arielle's Pursuit. 2007. 100p. pap. 10.95 (***978-0-7414-3804-1(6)***) Infinity Publishing.

Bistricean, Karen. The Adventures of Fergus & Lady: Home Sweet Home. Bistricean, Claudius, illus. 2006. (J). (978-0-9786975-1-8(0)) Fergus & Lady Publishing.

—The Adventures of Fergus & Lady: The Beginning. Bistricean, Claudius, illus. 2006. (J). (978-0-9786975-0-1(2)) Fergus & Lady Publishing.

Bix, Daisy. At the Dog Park with Sam & Lucy. Hansen, Amelia, illus. 2006. (Sit! Stay! Read! Ser.). 24p. (J). (gr. k-2). 15.95 (978-0-940719-00-2(2)) Gryphon Pr., The.

—Buddy Unchained. Hyatt, Joel, illus. 2006. (Sit! Stay! Read! Ser.). 24p. (gr. k-2). 15.95 (978-0-940719-01-9(0)) Gryphon Pr., The.

Black, Robyn Hood. Sir Mike. Murphy, David, illus. (J). (gr. k-2). 2006. 32p. pap. 4.95 (978-0-516-25020-5(5)); 2005. 31p. 19.50 (978-0-516-24862-2(6)) Scholastic Library Publishing. (Children's Pr.).

Black, Simon. Dog-Child. Robledo, Honorio, illus. 2006. 32p. (J). 17.95 (978-0-938317-42-5(3)) Consortium Bk. Sales & Distribution.

Blackaby, Susan. Bess & Tess. Rooney, Ronnie, illus. 2005. (Read-It! Readers Ser.). 32p. (J). (gr. k-3). 18.60 (978-1-4048-1013-6(7)) Picture Window Bks.

—Bess y Tess. Rooney, Ronnie, illus. 2006. (Read-It! Readers en Espanol Ser.).Tr. of Bess & Tess. (SPA.). 32p. (J). (ps-3). 19.95 (978-1-4048-1689-3(5)) Picture Window Bks.

—The Best Soccer Player. Haugen, Ryan, illus. 2005. (Read-It! Readers Ser.). 32p. (J). (gr. k-3). 18.60 (978-1-4048-1055-6(2)) Picture Window Bks.

—Coco on the Go. Muehlenhardt, Amy Bailey, illus. 2006. (Read-It! Readers Ser.). 24p. (J). (ps-3). 18.60 (978-1-4048-1580-3(5)) Picture Window Bks.

—Lost on Owl Lane. Muehlenhardt, Amy Bailey, illus. 2007. (J). lib. bdg. (***978-1-4048-2333-4(6)***) Picture Window Bks.

—Meg Sale a Pasear. Holme, Sharon, illus. 2006. (Read-It! Readers en Espanol Ser.).Tr. of Meg Takes a Walk. (SPA.). 32p. (J). (ps-3). 19.95 (978-1-4048-1685-5(2)) Picture Window Bks.

—Meg Takes a Walk. Holme, Sharon, illus. 2005. (Read-It! Readers Ser.). 32p. (J). (gr. k-3). 18.60 (978-1-4048-1005-1(6)) Picture Window Bks.

—El Mejor Futbolista. Haugen, Ryan, illus. 2006. (Read-It! Readers en Espanol Ser.).Tr. of Best Soccer Player. (SPA.). 32p. (J). (ps-3). 19.95 (978-1-4048-1690-9(9)) Picture Window Bks.

—A Pup Shows Up. Muehlenhardt, Amy Bailey, illus. 2004. (Read-It! Readers Classroom Tales Ser.). 32p. (C). (gr. k-3). 18.60 (978-1-4048-0586-6(9)) Picture Window Bks.

Blackstone, Stella. Cleo & Caspar. Mockford, Caroline, illus. 24p. (J). (gr. k-2). 2002. bds. 6.99 (978-1-84148-973-5(5)); 2001. 14.99 (978-1-84148-440-2(7)) Barefoot Bks., Inc.

—Una Isla Bajo el Sol (An Island in the Sun) Ceccoli, Nicoletta, illus. 2003. (SPA.). 24p. (J). pap. 6.99 (978-1-84148-144-9(0)) Barefoot Bks., Inc.

—An Island in the Sun. Ceccoli, Nicoletta, illus. 2005. 24p. (J). pap. 6.99 (978-1-84148-079-4(7)); 15.99 (978-1-84148-193-7(9)) Barefoot Bks., Inc.

Blain Parker, Marjorie. Jaspers Day. Wilson, Janet, illus. 2004. 32p. (J). (gr. k-3). (978-1-55337-764-1(8)) Kids Can Pr., Ltd.

Blair, Eric. El Lobo y el Perro: Version de la Fabula de Esopo. Silverman, Dianne, illus. 2006. (Read-It! Readers en Espanol Ser.).Tr. of Dog & the Wolf: A Retelling of Aesop's Fable. (SPA.). 32p. (J). (ps-3). 19.95 (978-1-4048-1619-0(4)) Picture Window Bks.

Blake, Bronwyn. Nick Riley's Ninth Life. 100p. (YA). pap. (978-0-7344-0333-9(X) , Lothian Bks.) Hachette Livre Australia.

Blake, Robert J. Akiak: A Tale from the Iditarod. Blake, Robert J., illus. 2004. (Illus.). 32p. (J). (gr. k-3). reprint ed. pap. 6.99 (978-0-14-240185-9(4) , Puffin) Penguin Group (USA) Inc.

—Swift. Blake, Robert J., illus. 2007. (Illus.). 48p. (J). (gr. k). 16.99 (***978-0-399-23383-8(0)*** , Philomel) Penguin Group (USA) Inc.

Blake, Robert J. Togo. Blake, Robert J., illus. 2002. (Illus.). 48p. (J). 16.99 (978-0-399-23381-4(4) , Philomel) Penguin Group (USA) Inc.

Blalock, Rachel. The dog & the Flea. 2005. 15p. 8.97 (978-1-4116-2784-0(9)) Lulu.com.

Bland, Steve. Playtime Puppy. 2001. (Phone Friends Ser.). (Illus.). 12p. (J). bds. 4.95 (978-0-7641-5378-5(1)) Barron's Educational Series, Inc.

Bleck, Linda. Pepper Goes to School. Bleck, Linda, illus. 2006. (Pepper plays, pulls, & Pops! Ser.). (Illus.). 18p. (J). 8.99 (978-1-4169-0944-6(3) , Little Simon) Simon & Schuster Children's Publishing.

—Pepper Picks a Pumpkin. Bleck, Linda, illus. 2007. (Pepper plays, pulls, & Pops! Ser.). 18p. (J). 8.99 (***978-1-4169-1773-1(X)*** , Little Simon) Simon & Schuster Children's Publishing.

Bleck, Linda. Pepper's Snow Day. Bleck, Linda, illus. 2006. (Pepper plays, pulls, & Pops! Ser.). 18p. (J). 8.99 (978-1-4169-1772-4(1) , Little Simon) Simon & Schuster Children's Publishing.

Blenkhorn, Les. The Adventures of Tracker. 2006. 26.99 (***978-1-4259-6605-8(5)***); pap. 16.99 (***978-1-4259-6604-1(7)***) AuthorHouse.

The Blind Alley. 2001. 32p. (YA). (gr. 6-12). pap. (978-0-8224-1453-7(8)) Globe Fearon Educational Publishing.

Bloch, Beth. My Oh My Sweet Potato Pie. Bloch, Beth, illus. 2005. (Illus.). 32p. (J). 16.00 (978-0-9771515-0-9(6)) Dream Creek Pr.

Blotcky, Mark. Cameron & Her Missing Shoes. 2006. 28p. pap. 9.95 (***978-1-4327-0035-5(9)***) Outskirts Press, Inc.

—Erin & Her Shoe Laces. 2006. 28p. pap. 9.95 (***978-1-4327-0034-8(0)***) Outskirts Press, Inc.

Bluemle, Elizabeth. My Father the Dog. Cecil, Randy, illus. 2006. 32p. (J). (ps-2). 15.99 (978-0-7636-2222-0(2)) Candlewick Pr.

Blum, Marilyn E. Mollie the Mutt. 2004. pap. 7.95 (978-0-533-14800-4(6)) Vantage Pr., Inc.

Blyton, Enid. Bumpy-Dog Helps Out. 1998. (Toyland Stories Ser.). (Illus.). 32p. (J). (ps-k). pap. 7.99 (978-0-00-136084-6(1)) Zondervan.

Boase, Susan. Lucky Boy. 2002. (Illus.). 32p. (J). (gr. k-3). 15.00 (978-0-618-13175-4(2)) Houghton Mifflin Co. Trade & Reference Div.

Bob, Uncle. Tobi the Little Puppy Dog. 2006. (Illus.). 12p. (J). pap. 3.95 (978-1-930596-61-0(8)) Amherst Pr.

Bocanegra, Haley. New Dog Food for Mozart. 2005. 14p. 9.76 (978-1-4116-3896-9(4)) Lulu.com.

Bodalski, Gerard S. Lucy's Legacy. 2004. 137p. pap. 19.95 (978-1-4137-4692-1(6)) PublishAmerica, Inc.

Boelts, Maribeth. Before You Were Mine. Walker, David, illus. 2007. 32p. (J). (ps). 15.99 (***978-0-399-24526-8(X)*** , Putnam Juvenile) Penguin Group (USA) Inc.

—Dogerella. Wu, Donald, illus. 2008. (J). (***978-0-375-83393-9(5)***); lib. bdg. (***978-0-375-93393-6(X)***) Random Hse., Inc.

Boelts, Maribeth. Starlight Lullaby. Sarrazin, Marisol, illus. 2006. 12p. (J). 9.99 (978-1-4169-0633-9(9) , Little Simon) Simon & Schuster Children's Publishing.

Bogacki, Tomek. Cat & Mouse in the Snow. Bogacki, Tomek, illus. 1999. (Illus.). 26p. (J). (gr. 2-4). reprint ed. 16.00 (978-0-7567-6125-7(5)) DIANE Publishing Co.

Bogardus, Ray & Bogardus, Karin. Hannah the Magic Shelter Dog. Seltzer, Jerry, illus. 2005. 143p. (J). pap. 14.99 (***978-1-932864-30-4(X)***) Masthof Pr.

Bojunga, Lygia. Los Amigos. (SPA.). (J). 8.95 (978-958-04-6262-0(3)) Norma S.A. COL. *Dist:* Distribuidora Norma, Inc.

Bolam, Emily. Dog. 2003. (Chunky Pet Bks.). (Illus.). 14p. (J). bds. 5.99 (978-0-7641-5610-6(1)) Barron's Educational Series, Inc.

Bonder, Dianna. Dogabet. Bonder, Dianna, illus. 2007. (Illus.). 32p. (J). (ps-2). 16.95 (978-1-55285-797-7(2) , Walrus Bks.) Whitecap Bks., Ltd. CAN. *Dist:* Firefly Bks., Ltd.

Bonk, John J. Subway Crush. Trissler, Rebecca Johns, ed. Kubic, Ginger, illus. (Adventures of Storydog Ser.). 75p. (J). pap. (978-0-9722690-1-8(0) , 1001) Storydog, Inc.

Book, Jennie Hale. Baby Dog Beans Comes Home: A Paul & Beans Adventure. 2005. (J). per. 13.95 (978-0-9767514-2-7(9) , 2000) Abbott Avenue Pr.

Borden, Louise. Just in Time for Christmas. 2000. (Illus.). (J). pap. 5.99 (978-0-590-45356-1(4)) Scholastic, Inc.

—Just in Time for Christmas. 2000. (J). 12.79 (978-0-606-19573-7(4)) Tandem Library Bks.

Borkin, Jeff. Blue's Beach Day. Craig, Karen, illus. 2004. (Blue's Clues Ser.: Vol. 9). 24p. (J). pap. 3.99 (978-0-689-86499-5(X) , Simon Spotlight/Nickelodeon) Simon & Schuster Children's Publishing.

Borsky, Mary. Benny Bensky & the Perogy Palace. 2001. (978-0-606-22811-4(X)); (gr. 3-6). lib. bdg. 16.40 (978-0-613-50180-4(2)) Tandem Library Bks.

—Benny Bensky & the Perogy Palace. Hendry, Linda, illus. 2001. 128p. (J). (gr. 3-7). pap. 7.95 (978-0-88776-523-0(8)) Tundra Bks., Inc./Livres Toundra, Inc. CAN. *Dist:* Random Hse., Inc.

Bostrom, Kathleen Long. The Day Scooter Died: A Book about the Death of a Pet. Bladholm, Cheri, illus. 2005. (Helping Kids Heal Ser.). 32p. (J). 9.99 (978-0-310-70902-2(4)) Zonderkidz.

Bottner, Barbara. Be Brown! Gott, Barry, illus. 2004. 32p. (ps-ps). lib. bdg. 13.19 (978-0-606-30365-1(0)) Tandem Library Bks.

Boulden, Jim & Boulden, Joan. Bulldog vs Monstros. Tate, Susan, ed. Prudhomme, Suzanne, illus. 1999. 22p. (J). (gr. 4-6). 4.95 (978-1-892421-10-4(0) , 10-0AB) Boulden Publishing.

Bourgeois, Paulette. Benjamin et Son Voisinage. ed. 2004. Tr. of Franklin's Neighborhood. (FRE., Illus.). (J). (ps-2). spiral bd. (978-0-616-01826-2(6)) Canadian National Institute for the Blind/Institut National Canadien pour les Aveugles.

Bousman, Cindy. Pete & P. J. Sing, Dance & Read with Me, Read-Along with Big Book & Cassette. 2000. 12p. (J). (ps-3). pap. 14.95 incl. audio (978-1-931127-36-3(0) , 986-005) Kindermusik International.

—Pete & P. J. Sing, Dance & Read with Me, Read-Along with Big Book, CD & Instrument. 2000. 14p. (J). (ps-3). pap. 29.95 incl. audio compact disk (978-1-931127-38-7(7) , 986-006) Kindermusik International.

Bowdish, Lynea. A Dog for Each Day. Brooks, Karen Stormer, illus. 2003. (Rookie Reader Espanol Ser.). (J). (gr. k-2). pap. 4.95 (978-0-516-27399-0(X)); 32p. 19.50 (978-0-516-22849-5(8)) Scholastic Library Publishing. (Children's Pr.).

—Un Perro Para Cada Dia. 2004. (Rookie Reader Espanol Ser.). (J). (gr. k-2). pap. 4.95 (978-0-516-24615-4(1) , Children's Pr.) Scholastic Library Publishing.

—Un Perro para Cada Dia. Brooks, Karen Stormer, illus. 2003. (Rookie Reader Espanol Ser.). (SPA.). (J). 19.50 (978-0-516-25888-1(5) , Children's Pr.) Scholastic Library Publishing.

—Thunder Doesn't Scare Me! Wallace, John, illus. 2001. (Rookie Reader Espanol Ser.). 32p. (J). (gr. k-2). pap. 4.95 (978-0-516-27291-7(8) , Children's Pr.) Scholastic Library Publishing.

—Thunder Doesn't Scare Me! 2001. (gr. k-3). lib. bdg. 12.95 (978-0-613-54706-2(3)) Tandem Library Bks.

—Los Truenos No Me Asustan! Wallace, John, illus. 2001. (Rookie Espanol Ser.). (SPA.). 32p. (J). (gr. k-2). 19.50 (978-0-516-22354-4(2) , Children's Pr.) Scholastic Library Publishing.

—Truenos No Me Asustan! 2001. (SPA.). (gr. k-3). lib. bdg. 12.95 (978-0-613-54434-4(X)) Tandem Library Bks.

Bowering, George. Diamondback Dog. 1998. (Out of This World Ser.). 200p. (J). (gr. 7-9). pap. 9.95 (978-1-896184-48-7(0)) Roussan Pubs., Inc./Roussan Editeur, Inc. CAN. *Dist:* Orca Bk. Pubs. USA.

Bowman, Vicki. Julie Through the Looking Glass. 2005. 55p. pap. 12.95 (978-1-4137-4679-2(9)) PublishAmerica, Inc.

Bowness, Kim. The Brave Engineers. 2007. (Illus.). 30p. (J). lib. bdg. 19.95 (***978-1-933732-36-7(9)*** , Bear Hug Bks.) MidAmerica Publishing Co.

Boxall, Ed. Scoot on Top of the World. Boxall, Ed, illus. 2004. (Illus.). 32p. (J). (ps-1). 15.99 (978-0-7636-2375-3(X)) Candlewick Pr.

Boynton, Sandra. My Puppy Book. Boynton, Sandra, illus. 2005. (Illus.). 10p. (J). 16.95 (978-1-4169-0844-9(7) , Little Simon) Simon & Schuster Children's Publishing.

—Snuggle Puppy! A Love Song. 2003. (Illus.). 24p. (J). bds. 6.95 (978-0-7611-3067-3(5) , 13067) Workman Publishing Co., Inc.

Bracken, Carolyn & Edwards, Ken, illus. The Big Bad Cold. 2002. (Big Red Reader Ser.). 32p. (J). (978-0-439-38989-1(5)) Scholastic, Inc.

Bradford, Karleen. Ghost Wolf. Cormack, Allan & Drew-Brook, Deborah, illus. 2005. (Orca Echoes Ser.). 64p. (J). (gr. 2-3). pap. 4.99 (978-1-55143-341-7(9)) Orca Bk. Pubs. USA.

Bradley, Kimberly Brubaker. Ballerino Nate. Alley, R. W., illus. 2006. 32p. (J). (ps). 16.99 (978-0-8037-2954-4(5) , Dial) Penguin Group (USA) Inc.

Brandon, Anthony G. Moving Day. Yee, Wong Herbert, illus. 2005. (Green Light Readers Level 2 Ser.). 32p. (J). (ps-ps). 12.95 (978-0-15-205646-9(7)); pap. 3.95 (978-0-15-205652-0(1)) Harcourt Trade Pubs.

Brandy, a Puppy from a Broken Home. 2001. (J). per. (978-1-931413-50-3(9)) Fundcraft Publishing.

Branford, Henrietta. Fire, Bed, & Bone. 2006. 128p. (J). (gr. 5-9). reprint ed. 5.99 (978-0-7636-2992-2(8)) Candlewick Pr.

Breakfast for Pickles. 2002. (J). (978-1-58453-199-9(1)); (978-1-58453-186-9(X)) Pioneer Valley Educational Pr., Inc.

Breathed, Berkeley. Flawed Dogs: The Year-End Leftovers at the Piddleton Last Chance Dog Pound. 2003. (Illus.). 48p. (J). (ps-17). 18.95 (978-0-316-71359-7(7)) Little Brown & Co.

Bremmer, Patricia A. The Christmas Westie. 2007. 48p. (J). kivar 17.99 (***978-0-9745884-5-2(8)***) Windcall Publishing.

Brenner, Harriett A. Corky's Humane Tail Tale. Kelly, Julia, illus. 2006. 32p. (J). bds. 16.95 (978-0-9768667-0-1(6)) M & D Publishing, Inc.

Brett, Jan. The Trouble with Trolls. Brett, Jan, illus. 2002. (Illus.). (J). 14.04 (978-0-7587-3862-2(5)) Book Wholesalers, Inc.

—The Trouble with Trolls. Brett, Jan, illus. 1999. (Illus.). 32p. (J). (ps-3). pap. 6.99 (978-0-698-11791-4(3) , Putnam Juvenile) Penguin Group (USA) Inc.

—The Trouble with Trolls. 1999. (978-0-606-17433-6(8)); lib. bdg. 15.30 (978-0-613-22953-1(3)) Tandem Library Bks.

Brewer, Dottie A. Jessie's Walk. Naenix, Robin, illus. 2004. 20p. (J). 4.95 (978-0-9707945-7-4(6)) Billion $ Baby Pubns.

Bridwell, Norman. Bertrand le Chien de Pompiers. Bridwell, Norman, illus. 2002. (Clifford, the Big Red Dog Ser.). (Illus.). (J). 11.45 (978-1-4046-0071-3(X)) Book Wholesalers, Inc.

—Bertrand le Chien de Pompiers. (Clifford, the Big Red Dog Ser.). (J). (gr. k-2). (FRE., Illus.). pap. 5.99 (978-0-590-24375-9(6)); 2005. 40p. pap. 3.99 (978-0-439-72524-8(0) , Cartwheel Bks.) Scholastic, Inc.

—The Big Leaf Pile. Bridwell, Norman, illus. 2002. (Big Red Readers Ser.). (Illus.). (J). 11.91 (978-0-7587-6773-8(0)) Book Wholesalers, Inc.

—Big Leaf Pile. 2000. (ps-2). lib. bdg. 11.80 (978-0-613-35664-0(0)) Tandem Library Bks.

—The Big Red Reader: The Egg Hunt. Bridwell, Norman, illus. 2002. (Big Red Readers Ser.). (Illus.). (J). 11.91 (978-0-7587-9315-7(4)) Book Wholesalers, Inc.

—Camping Out. Bracken, Carolyn & Edwards, Ken, illus. 2003. (Big Red Reader Ser.). (J). (978-0-439-45810-8(2)) Scholastic, Inc.

—Clifford. 2006. (Scholastic Reader Collection Level 2 Ser.). 144p. (J). pap. 6.99 (978-0-439-84800-8(8) , Cartwheel Bks.) Scholastic, Inc.

—Clifford al Rescate. 2000. (Clifford, the Big Red Dog Ser.). (SPA., Illus.). 32p. (J). (gr. k-2). pap. 3.50 (978-0-439-12956-5(7) , SO2943, Scholastic en Espanol) Scholastic, Inc.

—Clifford al Rescate. 2000. (SPA.). (gr. k-3). lib. bdg. 11.25 (978-0-613-24609-5(8)); (Illus.). (J). 10.30 (978-0-606-18534-9(8)) Tandem Library Bks.

—Clifford & His Friends. 2007. 48p. (J). pap. 4.99 (***978-0-545-00064-2(5)*** , Cartwheel Bks.) Scholastic, Inc.

—Clifford & the Big Parade. Bridwell, Norman, illus. 2002. (Clifford, the Big Red Dog Ser.). (Illus.). (J). 11.45 (978-0-7587-6372-3(7)) Book Wholesalers, Inc.

—Clifford & the Big Parade. Bridwell, Norman, illus. 1998. (Clifford, the Big Red Dog Ser.). (Illus.). 32p. (J). (gr. k-2). pap. 3.50 (978-0-590-10811-9(5)) Scholastic, Inc.

—Clifford & the Big Parade. 1998. (Clifford, the Big Red Dog Ser.). (J). (gr. k-2). 10.30 (978-0-606-13284-8(8)) Tandem Library Bks.

—Clifford & the Big Storm. Bridwell, Norman, illus. 2002. (Clifford, the Big Red Dog Ser.). (Illus.). (J). 11.45 (978-0-7587-0008-7(3)) Book Wholesalers, Inc.

—Clifford & the Grouchy Neighbors. Bridwell, Norman, illus. 2005. 40p. (J). pap. 3.99 (978-0-439-73432-5(0) , Cartwheel Bks.) Scholastic, Inc.

—Clifford & the Halloween Parade: Level 1. Bridwell, Norman, illus. 2004. (Clifford, the Big Red Dog Ser.). (Illus.). 32p. (J). (gr. k-3). pap. 3.99 (978-0-439-09834-2(3)) Scholastic, Inc.

—Clifford at the Circus. Bridwell, Norman, illus. 2002. (Clifford, the Big Red Dog Ser.). (Illus.). (J). 11.45 (978-0-7587-6707-3(2)) Book Wholesalers, Inc.

—Clifford at the Circus. (Clifford, the Big Red Dog Ser.). (Illus.). (J). (gr. k-2). 6.95 (978-0-590-68639-6(9)) Scholastic, Inc.

—Clifford Barks! Bridwell, Norman, illus. 2000. (Clifford, the Big Red Dog Ser.). (Illus.). 7p. (J). (ps-k). bds. 3.95 (978-0-439-14999-0(1) , Cartwheel Bks.) Scholastic, Inc.

—Clifford Celebrates the Year. 2002. (Clifford Ser.). (Illus.). 256p. (J). pap. 10.99 (978-0-439-46770-4(5)) Scholastic, Inc.

—Clifford Counts 1-2-3. 1998. (Clifford, the Big Red Dog Ser.). (Illus.). 14p. (J). (ps-k). bds. 6.99 (978-0-590-37928-1(3) , Cartwheel Bks.) Scholastic, Inc.

—Clifford, el Cachorrito. Suarez, Ana, tr. from ENG. 2003. (Clifford Ser.). (SPA., Illus.). 32p. (J). 3.50 (978-0-439-54566-2(8) , Scholastic en Espanol) Scholastic, Inc.

—Clifford Gets a Job. Bridwell, Norman, illus. 2002. (Clifford, the Big Red Dog Ser.). (Illus.). (J). 11.45 (978-0-7587-6390-7(5)) Book Wholesalers, Inc.

—Clifford Goes to Dog School. Bridwell, Norman, illus. 2002. (Clifford, the Big Red Dog Ser.). (Illus.). 32p. (J). (ps-3). pap. 3.50 (978-0-439-32788-6(1)) Scholastic, Inc.

—Clifford Goes to Dog School. 2002. (ps-2). lib. bdg. 11.25 (978-0-613-45580-0(0)) Tandem Library Bks.

—Clifford Goes to Hollywood. Bridwell, Norman, illus. 2002. (Clifford, the Big Red Dog Ser.). (Illus.). (J). 11.45 (978-0-7587-7061-5(8)) Book Wholesalers, Inc.

—Clifford' Keeps Cool. 1999. (Clifford, the Big Red Dog Ser.). (Illus.). 32p. (J). (gr. k-2). pap. 3.99 (978-0-439-04394-6(8)) Scholastic, Inc.

—Clifford Makes a Friend. Bridwell, Norman, illus. 2002. (Clifford, the Big Red Dog Ser.). (Illus.). (J). 11.91 (978-0-7587-5017-4(X)) Book Wholesalers, Inc.

—Clifford Makes a Friend. 2004. 32p. (J). lib. bdg. 15.00 (978-1-59054-547-8(8)) Fitzgerald Bks.

—Clifford Makes a Friend. Bridwell, Norman, illus. 1998. (Clifford, the Big Red Dog Ser.). (Illus.). 32p. (J). (gr. k-2). pap. 3.99 (978-0-590-37930-4(5)) Scholastic, Inc.

—Clifford Makes a Friend. 1998. (Illus.). (J). (ps-ps). lib. bdg. 11.80 (978-0-613-11422-6(1)) Tandem Library Bks.

—Clifford Takes a Trip. Bridwell, Norman, illus. 2002. (Clifford, the Big Red Dog Ser.). (Illus.). (J). 11.45 (978-0-7587-9335-5(9)) Book Wholesalers, Inc.

—Clifford Takes A Trip Library. 2007. (J). 18.95 (****978-0-545-00409-1(8)***) Scholastic, Inc.

—Clifford, the Big Red Dog. Bridwell, Norman, illus. 2002. (Clifford, the Big Red Dog Ser.). (Illus.). (J). 11.45 (978-0-7587-4114-1(6)) Book Wholesalers, Inc.

—Clifford the Big Red Dog Read Along. unabr. ed. 2006. (J). 9.95 (978-0-439-87587-5(0)) Scholastic, Inc.

—Clifford the Big Red Dog Read along Library. 2006. (J). 18.95 (978-0-439-87593-6(5)) Scholastic, Inc.

—Clifford the Small Red Puppy. (J). 2007. 9.95 (978-0-439-92492-4(8)); 2005. 40p. pap. 3.99 (978-0-439-72526-2(7) , Cartwheel Bks.) Scholastic, Inc.

—Clifford the Small Red Puppy - Library Edition. 2007. (J). 18.95 (****978-0-439-02313-9(0)***) Scholastic, Inc.

—Clifford to the Rescue. Bridwell, Norman, illus. 2002. (Clifford, the Big Red Dog Ser.). (Illus.). (J). 11.45 (978-0-7587-5005-1(6)) Book Wholesalers, Inc.

—Clifford to the Rescue. Bridwell, Norman, illus. 2000. (Clifford, the Big Red Dog Ser.). (Illus.). 32p. (J). (gr. k-2). pap. 3.99 (978-0-439-14038-6(2) , Cartwheel Bks.) Scholastic, Inc.

—Clifford to the Rescue. 2000. (ps-2). lib. bdg. 11.25 (978-0-613-24611-8(X)); (Illus.). (J). 10.30 (978-0-606-18535-6(6)) Tandem Library Bks.

—Clifford Va A la Escuela. Bridwell, Norman, illus. 1999. (Clifford, the Big Red Dog Ser.). (Illus.). 32p. (J). (gr. k-2). 3.50 (978-0-439-08284-6(6) , Cartwheel Bks.); (SPA., pap. 3.50 (978-0-439-08729-2(5) , SO4319, Scholastic en Espanol) Scholastic, Inc.

—Clifford Visita el Hospital. Bridwell, Norman, illus. 2000. (Clifford, the Big Red Dog Ser.). (SPA., Illus.). 32p. (J). (ps-k). pap. 3.50 (978-0-439-18897-5(0) , SO4989, Scholastic en Espanol) Scholastic, Inc.

—Clifford Visita el Hospital. 2000. (SPA., Illus.). (J). 10.05 (978-0-606-18869-2(X)) Tandem Library Bks.

—Clifford Visits the Hospital. Bridwell, Norman, illus. 2002. (Clifford, the Big Red Dog Ser.). (Illus.). (J). 11.45 (978-0-7587-5004-4(8)) Book Wholesalers, Inc.

—Clifford Visits the Hospital. Bridwell, Norman, illus. 2000. (Clifford, the Big Red Dog Ser.). (Illus.). 32p. (J). (ps-k). pap. 3.50 (978-0-439-14096-6(X)) Scholastic, Inc.

—Clifford Visits the Hospital. 2000. (ps-2). lib. bdg. 11.25 (978-0-613-24612-5(8)); (Illus.). (J). 10.30 (978-0-606-18868-5(1)) Tandem Library Bks.

—Clifford Vista el Hospital. 2000. (SPA.). (gr. k-3). lib. bdg. 10.95 (978-0-613-24613-2(6)) Tandem Library Bks.

—Clifford y el Dia de Pascua. 2003. (Clifford, the Big Red Dog Ser.). (SPA., Illus.). 32p. (J). (ps-k). pap. 3.50 (978-0-590-11740-1(8) , SO7533, Scholastic en Espanol) Scholastic, Inc.

—Clifford y el Gran Desfile. Bridwell, Norman, illus. 1998. (Clifford, the Big Red Dog Ser.). (SPA., Illus.). 32p. (J). (ps-k). pap. 3.50 (978-0-590-50663-2(3) , SO7528, Scholastic en Espanol) Scholastic, Inc.

—Clifford y el Gran Desfile. 1998. (Clifford, the Big Red Dog Ser.). (SPA.). (J). (gr. k-2). 10.30 (978-0-606-13285-5(6)) Tandem Library Bks.

—Clifford y el Verano Calurosa. 1999. (Cifford,the Big Red Dog in Spanish Ser.).Tr. of Cifford Keeps Cool. (J). 10.30 (978-0-606-16627-0(0)) Tandem Library Bks.

—Clifford y la Hora del Bano. 2003. (Clifford Ser.).Tr. of Clifford's Bathtime. (SPA., Illus.). 16p. (J). pap. 3.95 (978-0-439-54567-9(6) , Scholastic en Espanol) Scholastic, Inc.

—Clifford y los Opuestos. 2003. (Clifford Ser.).Tr. of Clifford's Opposites. (SPA., Illus.). 7p. (J). bds. 3.95 (978-0-439-55110-6(2) , Scholastic en Espanol) Scholastic, Inc.

—Clifford y los Sondios de los Animales. 2003. (Clifford Ser.).Tr. of Clifford's Animal Sounds. (SPA.). 7p. (J). bds. 3.95 (978-0-439-55109-0(9) , Scholastic en Espanol) Scholastic, Inc.

—Clifford's.Tr. of Mots Preferes de Bertrand. (FRE., Illus.). (J). pap. 5.99 (978-0-590-74326-6(0)) Scholastic, Inc.

—Clifford's Bedtime. (Naked Brothers Band Ser.). (J). 2008. 10p. pap. 6.99 (****978-0-545-03513-2(9)*** , Cartwheel Bks.); 2003. (SPA., Illus.). 7p. pap. 3.95 (978-0-439-54568-6(4) , Scholastic en Espanol) Scholastic, Inc.

—Clifford's Best Friend: A Story about Emily Elizabeth. Bridwell, Norman, illus. 2001. (Clifford, the Big Red Dog Ser.). (Illus.). 32p. (J). (ps-k). pap. 3.50 (978-0-439-21997-6(3)) Scholastic, Inc.

—Clifford's Big Book of Things to Know: A Book of Fun Facts. Bridwell, Norman, illus. 1999. (Clifford, the Big Red Dog Ser.). (Illus.). 40p. (J). (gr. k-2). pap. 10.95 (978-0-590-00385-8(2) , Cartwheel Bks.) Scholastic, Inc.

—Clifford's Birthday Party. Bridwell, Norman, illus. 2002. (Clifford, the Big Red Dog Ser.). (Illus.). (J). 11.45 (978-0-7587-6391-4(3)) Book Wholesalers, Inc.

—Clifford's Class Trip. Bridwell, Norman, illus. 2003. (Clifford, the Big Red Dog Ser.). (Illus.). 32p. (J). pap. 3.50 (978-0-439-44931-1(6)) Scholastic, Inc.

—Clifford's Class Trip. 2003. (gr. k-3). lib. bdg. 11.25 (978-0-613-70577-6(7)) Tandem Library Bks.

—Clifford's Family. Bridwell, Norman, illus. 2002. (Clifford, the Big Red Dog Ser.). (Illus.). (J). 11.45 (978-0-7587-6708-0(0)) Book Wholesalers, Inc.

—Clifford's First Christmas. (Clifford, the Big Red Dog Ser.). (FRE., Illus.). (J). (gr. k-2). pap. 5.99 (978-0-590-24374-2(8)) Scholastic, Inc.

—Clifford's First Christmas (Gel Pack Book) 2007. 32p. (J). pap. 7.99 (****978-0-545-02022-0(0)***) Scholastic, Inc.

—Clifford's First Sleepover. Bridwell, Norman, illus. 2004. (Clifford Ser.). (Illus.). 32p. (J). 3.50 (978-0-439-47285-2(7)) Scholastic, Inc.

—Clifford's' First Snow Day. Bridwell, Norman, illus. 1998. (Clifford, the Big Red Dog Ser.). (Illus.). 32p. (J). (gr. k-2). 3.99 (978-0-590-03480-7(4) , Cartwheel Bks.) Scholastic, Inc.

—Clifford's First Valentine's Day. Bridwell, Norman, illus. 2002. (Clifford, the Big Red Dog Ser.). (Illus.). (J). 11.45 (978-0-7587-6533-8(9)) Book Wholesalers, Inc.

—Clifford's Funny Adventures. 2007. 48p. (J). pap. 4.99 (****978-0-439-93438-1(9)*** , Cartwheel Bks.) Scholastic, Inc.

—Clifford's Glow-in-the-Dark Halloween. 2001. (Clifford, the Big Red Dog Ser.). (Illus.). 12p. (J). (ps-k). pap. 6.95 (978-0-439-30566-2(7) , Cartwheel Bks.) Scholastic, Inc.

—Clifford's Good Deeds. Bridwell, Norman, illus. 2002. (Clifford, the Big Red Dog Ser.). (Illus.). (J). 11.45 (978-0-7587-6638-0(6)) Book Wholesalers, Inc.

—Clifford's Good Deeds. (J). 2007. audio compact disk 9.95 (****978-0-545-01483-0(2)***); 2005. 40p. pap. 3.99 (978-0-439-73561-2(0) , Cartwheel Bks.) Scholastic, Inc.

—Clifford's Good Deeds Library Edition. 2007. (J). 18.95 (****978-0-545-01779-4(3)***) Scholastic, Inc.

—Clifford's Happy Mother's Day. 2001. (Clifford, the Big Red Dog Ser.). (Illus.). 32p. (J). (gr. k-2). 3.50 (978-0-439-22229-7(X)) Scholastic, Inc.

—Clifford's Happy Mother's Day. (ps-2). 2001. lib. bdg. 11.25 (978-0-613-35665-7(9)); 2000. (Illus.). (J). 10.30 (978-0-606-21114-7(4)) Tandem Library Bks.

—Clifford's Neighborhood: Lots to Learn Around Town. Bracken, Carolyn & Edwards, Ken, illus. 2002. (Clifford, the Big Red Dog Ser.). 10p. (J). (ps-k). pap. 10.99 (978-0-439-33242-2(7) , Cartwheel Bks.) Scholastic, Inc.

—Clifford's Opposites. Bridwell, Norman, illus. 2000. (Clifford, the Big Red Dog Ser.). (Illus.). 7p. (J). (ps-k). bds. 3.95 (978-0-439-15000-2(0) , Cartwheel Bks.) Scholastic, Inc.

—Clifford's Pals. 2005. 40p. (J). pap. 3.99 (978-0-439-72523-1(2) , Cartwheel Bks.) Scholastic, Inc.

—Cliffords Pals Audio. 2008. pap. 9.95 (****978-0-545-05247-4(5)*** , Scholastic) Scholastic, Inc.

—Clifford's Riddles. Bridwell, Norman, illus. 2002. (Clifford, the Big Red Dog Ser.). (Illus.). (J). 11.45 (978-0-7587-6709-7(9)) Book Wholesalers, Inc.

—Clifford's Schoolhouse. Bridwell, Norman, illus. 2000. (Clifford, the Big Red Dog Ser.). (Illus.). 10p. (J). (ps-k). bds. 10.95 (978-0-439-16252-4(1)) Scholastic, Inc.

—Clifford's Schoolhouse. 2000. (Clifford, the Big Red Dog Ser.). (Illus.). (J). (gr. k-2). 87.60 (978-0-439-21185-7(9)) Scholastic, Inc.

—Clifford's Sports Day. Bridwell, Norman, illus. 2002. (Clifford, the Big Red Dog Ser.). (Illus.). (J). 11.45 (978-0-7587-6710-3(2)) Book Wholesalers, Inc.

—Clifford's Sports Day. (Clifford, the Big Red Dog Ser.). (Illus.). 32p. (J). (gr. k-2). pap. 5.99 (978-0-590-16002-5(8)) Scholastic, Inc.

—Clifford's Spring Carnival. 2002. (Clifford, the Big Red Dog Ser.). (Illus.). 24p. (J). (gr. k-2). pap. 5.99 (978-0-439-34022-9(5)) Scholastic, Inc.

—Clifford's Thanksgiving Visit. Bridwell, Norman, illus. 2002. (Clifford, the Big Red Dog Ser.). (Illus.). (J). 11.45 (978-0-7587-6640-3(8)) Book Wholesalers, Inc.

—Clifford's Tricks. Bridwell, Norman, illus. 2002. (Clifford, the Big Red Dog Ser.). (Illus.). (J). 11.45 (978-0-7587-7031-8(6)) Book Wholesalers, Inc.

—Clifford's Tricks. (Clifford, the Big Red Dog Ser.). (FRE., Illus.). (J). (gr. k-2). pap. 5.99 (978-0-590-73954-2(9)) Scholastic, Inc.

—Clifford's Valentines. 2004. 32p. (J). lib. bdg. 15.00 (978-1-59054-548-5(6)) Fitzgerald Bks.

—Clifford's Valentines. Bridwell, Norman, illus. 2002. (Hello Reader! Ser.). (Illus.). 32p. (J). (ps-3). pap. 3.99 (978-0-439-18300-0(6) , Cartwheel Bks.) Scholastic, Inc.

—Clifford's Valentines. 2001. 10.79 (978-0-606-22241-9(3)) Tandem Library Bks.

—Cooking with Clifford. 1999. (Clifford, the Big Red Dog Ser.). 24p. (J). (gr. k-2). 9.95 (978-0-590-68931-1(2) , Cartwheel Bks.) Scholastic, Inc.

—The Dog Who Cried "Woof!" Kurtz, John & Bridwell, Norman, illus. 2001. (Big Red Reader Ser.). 32p. (J). (ps-1). pap. 3.99 (978-0-439-28978-8(5) , Cartwheel Bks.) Scholastic, Inc.

—The Dog Who Cried "Woof!" Bridwell, Norman, illus. 2002. (Big Red Readers Ser.). (Illus.). (J). 11.91 (978-0-7587-6772-1(2)) Book Wholesalers, Inc.

—Glow-in-the-Dark Christmas. Marderosian, Mark, illus. 2001. (Clifford, the Big Red Dog Ser.). 12p. (J). (ps-k). pap. 6.95 (978-0-439-30567-9(5) , Cartwheel Bks.) Scholastic, Inc.

—My Dog Clifford Plush Book. 2000. (Clifford, the Big Red Dog Ser.). (Illus.). 12p. (J). (ps-k). bds. 7.95 (978-0-439-06046-2(X) , Cartwheel Bks.) Scholastic, Inc.

—Oops, Clifford! 1999. (Clifford, the Big Red Dog Ser.). (Illus.). 32p. (J). (gr. k-2). pap. 3.25 (978-0-590-63117-4(9) , Cartwheel Bks.) Scholastic, Inc.

—The Runaway Rabbit. Bridwell, Norman, illus. 2002. (Big Red Readers Ser.). (Illus.). (J). 11.91 (978-0-7587-5219-2(9)) Book Wholesalers, Inc.

—School Days Treasury. 2007. (Clifford Ser.). 96p. (J). pap. 7.99 (****978-0-439-91568-7(6)***) Scholastic, Inc.

—The Show & Tell Surprise. Bridwell, Norman, illus. 2002. (Big Red Readers Ser.). (Illus.). (J). 11.91 (978-0-7587-5217-8(2)) Book Wholesalers, Inc.

—The Stormy Day Rescue. Bridwell, Norman, illus. 2002. (Big Red Readers Ser.). (Illus.). (J). 11.91 (978-0-7587-5220-8(2)) Book Wholesalers, Inc.

—A Tiny Family. 1999. (Hello Reader! Ser.). 32p. (J). (ps-1). pap. 3.99 (978-0-439-04019-8(1)) Scholastic, Inc.

—Tummy Trouble. Bridwell, Norman, illus. 2002. (Big Red Readers Ser.). (Illus.). (J). 11.91 (978-0-7587-5218-5(0)) Book Wholesalers, Inc.

—What Time Is It, Clifford? Book & Clock Set. 1998. (Clifford, the Big Red Dog Ser.). (Illus.). 32p. (J). (ps-2). 9.95 (978-0-590-76338-7(5)) Scholastic, Inc.

—Where's the Big Red Doggie? Bridwell, Norman, illus. 1998. (Clifford, the Big Red Dog Ser.). (Illus.). 14p. (J). (ps-k). bds. 5.99 (978-0-590-04710-4(8) , Cartwheel Bks.) Scholastic, Inc.

Bridwell, Norman, illus. Clifford the Big Red Dog. 40th anniv. deluxe ed. 2002. (Clifford Ser.). 32p. (J). (ps-1). pap. 14.95 (978-0-439-40396-2(0) , Cartwheel Bks.) Scholastic, Inc.

Bridwell, Norman & Fry, Sonali. Take Me to School with You! Thompson Brothers Staff, illus. 2002. (Clifford, the Big Red Dog Ser.). 16p. (J). pap. 3.99 (978-0-439-39454-3(6)) Scholastic, Inc.

Bridwell, Norman & Lewison, Wendy Cheyette. Clifford's Loose Tooth. Kurtz, Sandrina & Kurtz, John, illus. 2002. (Clifford Big Red Readers Ser.). 32p. (J). (ps-1). pap. 3.99 (978-0-439-33245-3(1)) Scholastic, Inc.

Bridwell, Norman & Page, Josephine. The Big Leaf Pile. Durk, Jim, illus. 2001. (Clifford Big Red Readers Ser.). 32p. (J). (ps-1). 3.99 (978-0-439-21357-8(6) , Cartwheel Bks.) Scholastic, Inc.

Bridwell, Norman & Scholastic, Inc. Staff. Clifford Plush, Big Red Dog. 1999. (Clifford, the Big Red Dog Ser.). (J). (gr. k-2). 16.99 (978-0-590-27359-6(0) , Sidekicks TM) Scholastic, Inc.

—El Dolor de Barriga. Navarro, Carmen, ed. 2003. (Big Red Reader Ser.). (SPA., Illus.). 32p. (J). (gr. k-2). pap. 3.99 (978-0-439-55113-7(7) , Scholastic en Espanol) Scholastic, Inc.

Bridwell, Norman, et al. T-Bone Tells the Truth. Binder, Eric & Lloyd, Gita, illus. 2002. (Clifford's Big Red Ideas Ser.). 7p. (J). bds. 4.99 (978-0-439-39450-5(3)) Scholastic, Inc.

Briggs-Ward, Barbara. Snarly Sally's Garden of ABC. (Illus.). 32p. 14.95 (978-1-890621-30-8(7)) Landauer Corp.

Brimner, Larry Dane. Everybody's Best Friend. 2002. (gr. k-3). lib. bdg. 14.10 (978-0-613-59470-7(3)) Tandem Library Bks.

—The Pet Show. Tripp, Christine, illus. (Rookie Choices Ser.). 32p. (J). (gr. 1-2). 2003. pap. 5.95 (978-0-516-27793-6(6)); 2002. pap. 20.50 (978-0-516-22541-8(3)) Scholastic Library Publishing. (Children's Pr.).

—Pet Show. 2002. (gr. k-3). lib. bdg. 14.10 (978-0-613-59539-1(4)) Tandem Library Bks.

Broach, Elise. Wet Dog! Catrow, David, illus. 32p. (J). (gr. k). 2007. pap. 5.99 (978-0-14-240855-1(7) , Puffin); 2005. 16.99 (978-0-8037-2809-7(3) , Dial) Penguin Group (USA) Inc.

Brodkin, Adele M. The Lonely Only Dog. Di Fiori, Lawrence, illus. 1998. (Hello Reader! Ser.). 32p. (J). (gr. 1-3). pap. 3.99 (978-0-590-52280-9(9)) Scholastic, Inc.

Brook, H. & Doyle, Arthur Conan. The Hound of the Baskervilles. 2004. (Paperback Classics Ser.). 144p. (J). lib. bdg. 12.95 (978-1-58086-605-7(0)) EDC Publishing.

Brooks, Ron. Oscar y la Gata de Medianoche. 2nd ed. 2002. (Rosa y Manzana Ser.). (SPA.). 32p. (J). (978-84-89804-05-0(2)) Loguez Ediciones ESP. *Dist:* Lectorum Pubns., Inc.

Brown, Alan. I Am a Dog. Allen, Jonathan, illus. 2002. 32p. (J). pap. 7.95 (978-1-929132-37-9(9)) Kane/Miller Bk. Pubs., Inc.

—I Am a Dog. 2002. (gr. k-3). lib. bdg. 16.40 (978-0-613-62780-1(6)) Tandem Library Bks.

Brown, Gladys M. Home Away from Home. 2005. 36p. pap. 6.95 (978-1-4116-3026-0(2)) Lulu.com.

Brown, Janet Allison. Puppy Backpack. O'Neill, Rachael, illus. 2007. 10p. (J). bds. 12.95 (978-1-4027-4480-8(3)) Sterling Publishing Co., Inc.

Brown, Ken. Monster Mucky Pup. 2005. (Illus.). 32p. (J). 19.99 (****978-0-86264-875-6(0)***) Transworld Publishers Ltd. GBR. *Dist:* Independent Pubs. Group.

—Mucky Pup. 2007. (Illus.). 32p. (J). pap. 9.95 (****978-1-84270-652-7(7)***) Andersen GBR. *Dist:* Independent Pubs. Group.

Brown, Marc. Arthur & the Dog Show. 14th rev. ed. 2006. (Arthur's 8 x 8 Bks.). (Illus.). 24p. (J). (ps-1). mass mkt. 3.99 (978-0-316-05774-5(6)) Little Brown & Co.

—Arthur's Adventures Four Book Set: Arthur's Computer Disaster, Arthur's TV Troubles, Arthur's Teacher Troubles, Arthur's New Puppy. 2002. pap. 23.80 (978-0-316-16961-5(7)) Little Brown & Co.

—Arthur's Lost Puppy. 2001. (Arthur Ser.). (J). (ps-1). spiral bd. 14.99 (978-1-58605-223-2(3)) LeapFrog Enterprises, Inc.

—Arthur's Lost Puppy. Brown, Marc, illus. 2000. (Arthur Ser.). (Illus.). 24p. (J). (gr. k-3). lib. bdg. 11.99 (978-0-679-98466-5(6) , Random Hse. Bks. for Young Readers) Random Hse. Children's Bks.

—Arthur's Lost Puppy. 2000. (Arthur Ser.). (gr. k-3). lib. bdg. 11.80 (978-0-613-34588-0(6)) Tandem Library Bks.

—Arthur's New Puppy. Brown, Marc, illus. 2002. (Arthur Adventure Ser.). (Illus.). (J). 13.15 (978-0-7587-1984-3(1)) Book Wholesalers, Inc.

—Arthur's New Puppy. Brown, Marc, illus. 2005. (Arthur Adventure Ser.). 32p. (J). (ps-1). pap. 10.99 (978-0-316-05955-8(2)) Little Brown & Co.

—Arthur's New Puppy. 1998. (Arthur Adventure Ser.). (Illus.). 32p. (J). (ps-3). 9.95 (978-0-316-11949-8(0)) Little, Brown Bks. for Young Readers.

—Arthur's New Puppy. (Arthur Adventure Ser.). (J). (gr. k-3). 7.98 incl. audio NewSound, LLC.

—Arthur's Pet Business. Brown, Marc, illus. rev. ed. 2007. (Arthur Adventure Ser.). (Illus.). 32p. (J). (ps-1). pap. 10.99 incl. audio compact disk (****978-0-316-11863-7(X)***) Little, Brown Bks. for Young Readers.

—Arturo y el Negocio de Mascotas. Sarfatti, Esther, tr. (SPA.). (J). (gr. k-2). pap. 6.95 (978-1-880507-94-0(3) , LC8511) Lectorum Pubns., Inc.

—Arturo y el Negocio de Mascotas. 2001. (Arthur's Adventures in Spanish Ser.). (SPA., Illus.). (J). 13.75 (978-0-606-21045-4(8)) Tandem Library Bks.

—Cachorrito de Arturo. 1999. Tr. of Arthur's New Puppy. (SPA.). (gr. k-3). lib. bdg. 15.25 (978-0-613-18090-0(9)) Tandem Library Bks.

Brown, Marc & LeapFrog Staff, compiled by. Arthur's Lost Puppy. 2002. (Arthur Ser.). (J). (gr. k-3). 14.95 (978-1-58605-911-8(4) , LeapFrog Schl. Hse.) LeapFrog Enterprises, Inc.

Brown, Margaret Wise. Mister Dog. Williams, Garth, illus. 2003. (Little Golden Book Classics). 24p. (J). (gr. k-k). 2.99 (978-0-307-10336-9(6) , Golden Bks.) Random Hse. Children's Bks.

—The Sailor Dog. Williams, Garth, illus. 2001. (Little Golden Bks.). 24p. (J). (gr. k-k). 2.99 (978-0-307-00143-6(1) , 98284, Golden Bks.) Random Hse. Children's Bks.

Brown, Peter. Chowder. 2006. (Illus.). 32p. (J). (ps-1). 15.99 (978-0-316-01180-8(0)) Little Brown & Co.

Brown, Peter. The Fabulous Bouncing Chowder. 2007. 32p. (J). (ps-1). 15.99 (****978-0-316-01179-2(7)***) Little, Brown Bks. for Young Readers.

Brown, Ruth, retold by. The Ghost of Greyfriar's Bobby. 1999. (Illus.). (J). pap. 5.99 (978-0-14-056190-6(0) , Puffin) Penguin Group (USA) Inc.

Brown, Tricia, ed. Sled Dog Wisdom. 2005. 64p. pap. 4.95 (978-0-9745014-5-1(X)) Epicenter Pr., Inc.

Browne, Anthony. Voices in the Park. 2001. (gr. 3-6). lib. bdg. 16.45 (978-0-613-75141-4(8)) Tandem Library Bks.

Browne, Anthony & Dorling Kindersley Publishing Staff. Voices in the Park. 2001. 32p. (J). (gr. 2-6). pap. 7.99 (978-0-7894-8191-7(X)) Dorling Kindersley Publishing, Inc.

Bruce, Lisa. Fran's Friend. Beardshaw, Rosalind, illus. 2003. 32p. (J). (ps-1). 15.95 (978-1-58234-777-6(8) , Bloomsbury Children) Bloomsbury Publishing.

Bruel, Nick. Poor Puppy. 2007. (Illus.). 40p. (J). (ps up). 16.95 (****978-1-59643-270-3(5)***) Roaring Brook Pr.

Brumett, Jonas O. Peegus Learned to Bark: A Learning Storybook. Johnson, Sandra L., illus. l.t. ed. 2002. 64p. (J). (ps-3). 16.95 (978-1-892812-04-9(5)) Froginhood & Friends, Inc.

Bruna, Dick. Snuffy. 2004. (Illus.). 24p. (J). 7.99 (978-1-59226-028-7(4)) Big Tent Entertainment, Inc.

Bruno's Birthday: Individual Title Six-Packs. (Literatura 2000 Ser.). (gr. 1-2). 28.00 (978-0-7635-0086-3(0)) Rigby Education.

Bryan, Marcia. Dandy Lion: The Adventure Begins. Bowden, CeCelia, illus. 2006. (J). 18.95 (****978-1-57736-376-7(0)*** , Hillsboro Pr.) Providence Hse Pubs.

Bryant, Megan E. Little Engine That Could & the Fire Rescue: Based on Original Story by Watty Piper. Ong, Cristina & Lustig, Loretta, illus. 2003. (Reading Railroad Bks.). 32p. (J). pap. 3.49 (978-0-448-43279-3(X) , Grosset & Dunlap) Penguin Group (USA) Inc.

BubbleGirl, Season. A Doggy Diary. 2006. 93p. (J). per. (****978-0-9775120-0-3(2)***) Carpe Diem Publishing.

Buchanan, Paul. Dog Days, Vol. 14. 1999. (Misadventures of Willie Plummett Ser.: Vol. 14). (Illus.). 128p. (J). (gr. 3-7). 5.99 (978-0-570-07054-2(6)) Concordia Publishing Hse.

—Dog Days. 1999. (gr. 3-6). lib. bdg. 14.15 (978-0-613-72786-0(X)) Tandem Library Bks.

Buchwald, Claire. Max Talks to Me. Ritz, Karen, illus. 2007. (Sit! Stay! Read! Ser.). 24p. (J). 15.95 (****978-0-940719-03-3(7)***) Gryphon Pr., The.

Buehner, Caralyn. Dex: The Heart of a Hero. Buehner, Mark, illus. 2007. 32p. (J). (ps-3). pap. 6.99 (****978-0-06-443845-2(7)*** , Harper Trophy) HarperCollins Pubs.

Buehner, Caralyn. Superdog: The Heart of a Hero. Buehner, Mark, illus. 2004. 32p. (J). (ps-3). 16.99 (978-0-06-623620-9(7)); lib. bdg. 17.89 (978-0-06-623621-6(5)) HarperCollins Pubs.

Buffy: Individual Title Six-Packs. (Literatura 2000 Ser.). (ps-1). 28.00 (978-0-7635-0002-3(X)) Rigby Education.

Buffy's Tricks: Individual Title Six-Packs. (Literatura 2000 Ser.). (gr. 1-2). 28.00 (978-0-7635-0087-0(9)) Rigby Education.

Buggs, Michael A. Tabard. Buggs, Michael A., illus. (Illus.). 64p. (Orig.). (J). (gr. 2-6). pap. 15.00 (978-0-9657723-0-3(6)) Mogul Comics.

C
D

Bullard, Lisa. My Home: Walls, Floors, Ceilings & Doors. Wesley, Omarr, illus. 2004. (All about Me Ser.). 24p. (C). (gr. k-1). 21.26 (978-1-4048-0046-5(8)) Picture Window Bks.

Bullert, Annie. Sparkle Spots. 2004. (J). 14.95 (978-1-931945-11-0(X)) Expert Publishing, Inc.

Bumpy Slide Books Staff. Blue Looks for Books. Nickelodeon/Viacom International Staff, ed. 2000. (Blue's Clues: No. 16). (Illus.). 32p. (J). (ps-1). 3.49 (978-1-57973-082-6(5)) Advance Pubs. LLC.

—Blue Puts on a Play. Nickelodeon/Viacom International Staff, ed. 2000. (Blue's Clues: No. 11). (Illus.). 32p. (J). (ps-1). 3.49 (978-1-57973-077-2(9)) Advance Pubs. LLC.

—Blue Skidoos to the Beach. Nickelodeon/Viacom International Staff, ed. 2000. (Blue's Clues: No. 15). (Illus.). 32p. (J). (ps-1). 3.49 (978-1-57973-081-9(7)) Advance Pubs. LLC.

—Blue's Big Week. Nickelodeon/Viacom International Staff, ed. 2000. (Blue's Clues: No. 14). (Illus.). 32p. (J). (ps-1). 3.49 (978-1-57973-080-2(9)) Advance Pubs. LLC.

—Blue's Frustrating Day. Nickelodeon/Viacom International Staff, ed. 2000. (Blue's Clues: No. 18). (Illus.). 32p. (J). (ps-1). 3.49 (978-1-57973-084-0(1)) Advance Pubs. LLC.

—Count & Save with Blue. Nickelodeon/Viacom International Staff, ed. 2000. (Blue's Clues: No. 17). (Illus.). 32p. (J). (ps-1). 3.49 (978-1-57973-083-3(3)) Advance Pubs. LLC.

—Home Sweet Home. Nickelodeon/Viacom International Staff, ed. 2000. (Blue's Clues: No. 5). (Illus.). 32p. (J). (ps-1). 3.49 (978-1-57973-071-0(X)) Advance Pubs. LLC.

—A Picnic with Blue. Nickelodeon/Viacom International Staff, ed. 2000. (Blue's Clues: No. 12). (Illus.). 32p. (J). (ps-1). 3.49 (978-1-57973-078-9(7)) Advance Pubs. LLC.

—Where Is Magenta. Nickelodeon/Viacom International Staff, ed. 2000. (Blue's Clues: No. 3). (Illus.). 32p. (J). (ps-1). 3.49 (978-1-57973-069-7(8)) Advance Pubs. LLC.

Bunting, Eve. Reggie. Burkett, D. Brent, illus. 2006. 112p. 16.95 (978-0-8126-2746-6(6)) Cricket Bks.

—The Summer of Riley. 2002. (gr. 3-6). lib. bdg. 14.10 (978-0-613-44482-8(5)) Tandem Library Bks.

Burchett, Loni. Bear & Katie in A Riverboat Ride, 4 vols., Vol. 4. 2006. (Illus.). 104p. (J). per. 12.95 (978-0-9742815-3-7(0)) Black Lab Publishing LLC.

Burchett, Loni R. Bear & Katie in a Day with Friends, Vol. 3. l.t. ed. 2005. (Illus.). 68p. (J). per. 11.95 (978-0-9742815-2-0(2) , bk003) Black Lab Publishing LLC.

Burgess, Karin Whiting. It's Always a Good Day for Crabbing. 2005. (J). 16.95 (978-0-9718303-4-9(7)) Flat Hammock Pr.

Burgess, M. Lady. 2001. 208p. (J). (978-0-86264-770-4(3)) Andersen.

Burgess, Melvin. Lady: My Life As A Bitch. 2002. (gr. 7-12). lib. bdg. 15.30 (978-0-613-68355-5(2)) Tandem Library Bks.

Burgess, Thornton W. Bowser the Hound. (J). 19.95 (978-0-8488-0391-9(4)) Amereon LTD.

—Bowser the Hound. 2003. (Dover Children's Thrift Classics Ser.). (Illus.). 96p. (J). (gr. 3-6). pap. 1.50 (978-0-486-42847-5(8)) Dover Pubns., Inc.

—Bowser the Hound. 2004. reprint ed. pap. 24.95 (978-1-4179-2323-6(7)) Kessinger Publishing, LLC.

Burgess, W. Thornton. Bowser the Hound. 2006. 77.99 ***978-1-4280-3737-3(3))**; pap. 70.99 ***978-1-4280-3759-5(4))** IndyPublish.com.

Burke, Tina. Fly Little Bird. Burke, Tina, illus. 2006. (Illus.). 32p. (J). 14.95 (978-1-933605-02-9(2)) Kane/Miller Bk. Pubs., Inc.

Burnford, Sheila. Bel Ria: Dog of War. 2006. 256p. (J). (gr. 5). 17.95 (978-1-59017-211-7(6) , NYR Children's Collection) New York Review of Bks., Inc., The.

—The Incredible Journey. unabr. ed. 2004. 145p. (J). (gr. 5-9). pap. 29.00 incl. audio (978-0-8072-8322-6(3) , YA162SP, Listening Library) Random Hse. Audio Publishing Group.

Burns, Joanne. Frog's Dog Days. 2005. 30p. 9.99 (978-1-4116-4829-6(3)) Lulu.com.

Butcher, Nancy. Dr. Jekyll & Mr. Dog. l.t. ed. 1999. (Adventures of Wishbone Ser.: No. 14). (Illus.). (J). (gr. 4 up). lib. bdg. 22.60 (978-0-8368-2592-3(6)) Stevens, Gareth Inc.

—Lights! Camera! Action Dog! l.t. ed. 2000. (Wishbone Mysteries Ser.: No. 11). (Illus.). 139p. (J). (gr. 4 up). lib. bdg. 23.33 (978-0-8368-2694-4(9)) Stevens, Gareth Inc.

Butler, Kristi T. Rip's Secret Spot. Cepeda, Joe, illus. 2003. (Green Light Readers Level 1 Ser.). 24p. (J). 11.95 (978-0-15-204809-9(X)); pap. 3.95 (978-0-15-204849-5(9)) Harcourt Children's Bks. (Green Light Readers).

—Rip's Secret Spot. 2000. (Green Light Readers Ser.). (J). (978-0-606-20035-6(5)); lib. bdg. 11.80 (978-0-613-66374-8(8)) Tandem Library Bks.

Butterworth, A. N. Jake Again. (Illus.). 60p. (J). pap. 7.99 (978-0-340-68728-4(2) , Hodder & Stoughton) Hodder General Publishing Division GBR. *Dist:* Trafalgar Square Publishing.

Butts, Christina. Horse & the Dog A Grand Fairy Tale A. 2006. pap. 15.38 ***978-1-4116-1235-8(3))** Lulu.com.

Byars, Betsy, et al. My Dog, My Hero. Long, Loren, illus. rev. ed. 2000. 64p. (J). (gr. 3-6). 16.95 (978-0-8050-6327-1(7) , Holt, Henry & Co. Bks. For Young Readers) Holt, Henry & Co.

Byars, Betsy Cromer, et al. The Dog Diaries: Secret Writings of the WOOF Society. Brooks, Erik, illus. 2007. 80p. (J). 15.95 (978-0-8050-7957-9(2)) Holt, Henry & Co.

Byars, Betsy Cromer, et al. Dog Diaries: Secret Writings of the WOOF Society. Brooks, Erik, illus. 2007. 72p. (J). ***978-1-4287-4611-4(0))** Holt, Henry & Co.

Byng, Georgia. Molly Moon, Micky Minus, & the Mind Machine. 2007. 416p. (J). (gr. 3-7). 16.99 ***978-0-06-075036-7(7))**; lib. bdg. 17.89 ***978-0-06-075037-4(5))** HarperCollins Pubs.

Byrd, Sandra. Just Between Friends. 2001. (Hidden Diary Ser.). 112p. (J). (gr. 3-7). pap. 4.99 (978-0-7642-2482-9(4)) Bethany Hse. Pubs.

—Just Between Friends. 2001. (gr. 3-6). lib. bdg. 13.00 (978-0-613-82434-7(2)) Tandem Library Bks.

Byrne, John. Mad Mag's Woof. (Illus.). 80p. (J). 7.95 (978-0-14-130043-6(4)) Penguin Bks., Ltd. GBR. *Dist:* Trafalgar Square Publishing.

C D Stampley Enterprises, creator. Billy & Baxter Learn to Build, 4 vols. 2005. (Illus.). 24p. (J). (ps-ps). 8.95 (978-1-58087-099-3(6)) Stampley, C.D. Enterprises, Inc.

—Billy & Baxter on City Streets, 4 vols. 2005. (Illus.). 24p. (J). (ps-ps). 8.95 (978-1-58087-101-3(1)) Stampley, C.D. Enterprises, Inc.

Cabrera, Jane. Dog's Day. Cabrera, Jane, illus. 2000. (Illus.). 32p. (J). (ps-k). 12.95 (978-0-531-30262-0(8) , Orchard Bks.) Scholastic, Inc.

Cain, Barbara S. I Don't Know Why... I Guess I'm Shy. Smith-Moore, J. J., illus. 1999. 32p. (J). (ps-3). (978-1-55798-596-5(0) , 441-5960, Magination Pr.) American Psychological Assn.

Calhoun, Mary. High-Wire Henry. 2000. (YA). pap. 33.00 incl. audio (978-0-7887-4175-3(6) , 41090) Recorded Bks., LLC.

Calmenson, Stephanie. May I Pet Your Dog? The How-to Guide for Kids Meeting Dogs (And Dogs Meeting Kids) Ormerod, Jan, illus. 2007. 32p. (J). (gr. k-3). 9.95 (978-0-618-51034-4(6) , Clarion Bks.) Houghton Mifflin Co. Trade & Reference Div.

—May I Pet Your Dog? The How-To Guide for Kids Meeting Dogs (and Dogs Meeting Kids) Ormerod, Jan, illus. 2007. 32p. (J). ***978-1-4287-3952-9(1)** , Clarion Bks.) Houghton Mifflin Co. Trade & Reference Div.

—My Dog's the Best. Dunn Ramsey, Marcy, illus. 2004. 32p. (J). lib. bdg. 15.00 (978-1-59054-549-2(4)) Fitzgerald Bks.

—Perfect Puppy. Yezerski, Thomas F., illus. 2001. 32p. (J). (gr. k-3). tchr. ed. 15.00 (978-0-618-01139-1(0) , Clarion Bks.) Houghton Mifflin Co. Trade & Reference Div.

Calvert, Patricia. Bigger. 2003. 144p. (J). pap. 8.95 (978-0-689-86003-4(X) , Aladdin) Simon & Schuster Children's Publishing.

Camp, Joe. Benji: Off the Leash! 2004. (Benji Returns Ser.). (Illus.). 144p. (J). pap. 4.99 (978-0-06-073084-0(6) , Harper Festival) HarperCollins Pubs.

Capeci, Anne. Case of the Cyber-Hacker. l.t. ed. 2000. (Wishbone Mysteries Ser.: No. 19). (Illus.). 141p. (J). (gr. 4 up). lib. bdg. 23.33 (978-0-8368-2702-6(3)) Stevens, Gareth Inc.

—Case of the Cyber-Hacker. 2000. (gr. 3-6). lib. bdg. 11.80 (978-0-613-27764-8(3)) Tandem Library Bks.

—Key to the Golden Dog. l.t. ed. 1999. (Wishbone Mysteries Ser.: No. 8). 144p. (J). (gr. 4 up). lib. bdg. 23.33 (978-0-8368-2389-9(3)) Stevens, Gareth Inc.

—The Maltese Dog. l.t. ed. 1999. (Wishbone Mysteries Ser.: No. 6). 144p. (J). (gr. 4 up). lib. bdg. 23.33 (978-0-8368-2387-5(7)) Stevens, Gareth Inc.

Capucilli, Alyssa Satin. Bathtime for Biscuit. Schories, Pat, illus. (My First I Can Read Bks.). 32p. (J). (ps up). 1999. pap. 3.99 (978-0-06-444264-0(0) , Harper Trophy); 1998. lib. bdg. 16.89 (978-0-06-027938-7(9)) HarperCollins Pubs.

—Bathtime for Biscuit. 1999. (gr. k-3). lib. bdg. 11.80 (978-0-613-22819-0(7)) Tandem Library Bks.

—Biscuit. Schories, Pat, illus. 2005. 24p. (J). (ps-1). bds. 6.99 (978-0-06-076596-5(8) , Harper Festival) HarperCollins Pubs.

—Biscuit & the Baby. Schories, Pat, illus. 2005. (My First I Can Read Bks.). 32p. (J). (ps up). 14.99 (978-0-06-009459-1(1)); lib. bdg. 15.89 (978-0-06-009460-7(5)) HarperCollins Pubs.

—Biscuit & the Little Pup. Schories, Pat, illus. 2008. (My First I Can Read Bks.). 32p. (J). pap. 3.99 ***978-0-06-074172-3(4)** , Harper Trophy) HarperCollins Pubs.

—Biscuit Big Book. Schories, Pat, illus. 2007. (My First I Can Read Bks.). 32p. (J). pap. 24.99 ***978-0-06-111973-6(3)** , Harper Festival) HarperCollins Pubs.

—Biscuit Finds a Friend. Schories, Pat, illus. 1998. (My First I Can Read Bks.). 32p. (J). (ps up). pap. 3.99 (978-0-06-444243-5(8) , Harper Trophy) HarperCollins Pubs.

—Biscuit Finds a Friend. Schories, Pat, illus. 1998. (My First I Can Read Bks.). (J). (ps-k). 10.79 (978-0-606-13203-9(1)) Tandem Library Bks.

—Biscuit Gives a Gift. Schories, Pat, illus. 2004. 16p. (J). (ps-1). 4.99 (978-0-06-009467-6(2) , Harper Festival) HarperCollins Pubs.

—Biscuit Goes to School. Schories, Pat, illus. (Biscuit Ser.). 32p. (J). (ps up). 2003. pap. 3.99 (978-0-06-443616-8(0)); 2002. 15.99 (978-0-06-028682-8(2)); 2002. lib. bdg. 16.89 (978-0-06-028683-5(0)) HarperCollins Pubs.

—Biscuit Goes to School. Schories, Pat, illus. 2003. 21p. (J). (ps-ps). lib. bdg. 11.80 (978-0-613-66941-2(X)) Tandem Library Bks.

—Biscuit Is Thankful. Schories, Pat, illus. 2003. (Biscuit Ser.). 16p. (J). (ps-1). 4.99 (978-0-694-01519-1(9)) HarperCollins Pubs.

—Biscuit Loves Father's Day. Schories, Pat, illus. 2004. 20p. (J). 6.99 (978-0-06-009463-8(X) , Harper Festival) HarperCollins Pubs.

—Biscuit Loves Mother's Day. Schories, Pat & Young, Mary O'Keefe, illus. 2004. 20p. (J). pap. 6.99 (978-0-06-009462-1(1) , Harper Festival) HarperCollins Pubs.

—Biscuit Loves... Reusable Sticker Book. Berlin, Rose Mary, illus. 2007. (Biscuit Ser.). 12p. (J). (ps-1). pap. 6.99 ***978-0-06-112838-7(4)** , Harper Festival) HarperCollins Pubs.

—Biscuit Mini Book & Puppy. Schories, Pat, illus. 1999. (Biscuit Ser.). (J). (ps-1). 14.95 (978-0-694-01444-6(3)) HarperCollins Pubs.

—Biscuit Storybook Collection. Schories, Pat, illus. 2005. (Biscuit Ser.). 192p. (J). (ps-1). 10.99 (978-0-06-075904-9(6) , Harper Festival) HarperCollins Pubs.

—Biscuit Treasury. Schories, Pat, illus. 2000. (Biscuit Ser.). (J). (ps-1). (978-0-06-029128-0(1)) HarperCollins Pubs.

—Biscuit Visits the Big City. Schories, Pat, illus. (My First I Can Read Bks.). 32p. (J). 2007. pap. 3.99 (978-0-06-074166-2(X) , Harper Trophy); 2006. 15.99 (978-0-06-074164-8(3)); 2006. lib. bdg. 15.89 (978-0-06-074165-5(1)) HarperCollins Pubs.

—Biscuit Wants to Play. Schories, Pat, illus. (My First I Can Read Bks.). 32p. (J). (ps-k). 2002. pap. 3.99 (978-0-06-444315-9(9) , Harper Trophy); 2001. 15.99 (978-0-06-028069-7(7)); 2001. lib. bdg. 15.89 (978-0-06-028070-3(0)) HarperCollins Pubs.

—Biscuit Wants to Play. 2002. (gr. k-3). lib. bdg. 11.80 (978-0-613-44508-5(2)) Tandem Library Bks.

—Biscuit Wins a Prize. Schories, Pat, illus. (My First I Can Read Bks.). 32p. (J). (ps up). 2005. 3.99 (978-0-06-009458-4(3) , Harper Trophy); 2004. 15.99 (978-0-06-009455-3(9)); 2004. lib. bdg. 15.89 (978-0-06-009457-7(5)) HarperCollins Pubs.

—Biscuit's Big Friend. Schories, Pat, illus. (My First I Can Read Bks.). 32p. (J). (ps up). 2004. pap. 3.99 (978-0-06-444288-6(8) , Harper Trophy); 2003. 16.99 (978-0-06-029167-9(2)); 2003. lib. bdg. 17.89 (978-0-06-029168-6(0)) HarperCollins Pubs.

—Biscuit's Busy Day Reusable Sticker Book. Berlin, Rose Mary, illus. 2007. (Biscuit Ser.). 12p. (J). pap. 6.99 (978-0-06-112831-8(7) , Harper Festival) HarperCollins Pubs.

—Biscuit's Christmas. Schories, Pat, illus. 2000. (Biscuit Ser.). 16p. (J). (ps-1). pap. 6.99 (978-0-694-01516-0(4) , Harper Festival) HarperCollins Pubs.

—Biscuit's Christmas. 2003. (gr. k-3). lib. bdg. 15.25 (978-0-613-70855-5(5)) Tandem Library Bks.

—Biscuit's Christmas Eve. Young, Mary O'Keefe, illus. 2007. (Biscuit Ser.). 20p. (J). (ps-1). pap. 6.99 ***978-0-06-112836-3(8)** , Harper Festival) HarperCollins Pubs.

—Biscuit's Day at the Farm. Schories, Pat, illus. 2007. (My First I Can Read Bks.). 32p. (J). 15.99 (978-0-06-074167-9(8)); lib. bdg. 16.89 (978-0-06-074168-6(6)) HarperCollins Pubs.

—Biscuit's Fourth of July. Schories, Pat, illus. 2005. (Biscuit Ser.). 20p. (J). (ps-ps). pap., pap. 6.99 (978-0-06-009464-5(8) , Harper Festival) HarperCollins Pubs.

—Biscuit's Fun with Friends. Schories, Pat, illus. 2007. (Biscuit Ser.). 32p. (J). (ps-2). pap. 3.99 ***978-0-06-112837-0(6)** , Harper Festival) HarperCollins Pubs.

—Biscuits Graduation Day. Schories, Pat, illus. 2005. (Biscuit Ser.). 20p. (J). (ps-ps). bds. 6.99 (978-0-06-009465-2(6) , Harper Festival) HarperCollins Pubs.

—Biscuit's New Trick. Schories, Pat, illus. 2000. (My First I Can Read Bks.). 32p. (J). (ps-k). 16.99 (978-0-06-028067-3(0)); lib. bdg. 15.89 (978-0-06-028068-0(9)) HarperCollins Pubs.

—Biscuit's New Trick. 2001. (gr. k-3). lib. bdg. 11.80 (978-0-613-35489-9(3)); (Illus.). (J). 10.79 (978-0-606-21071-3(7)) Tandem Library Bks.

—Biscuit's Pet & Play Halloween. Andreasen, Dan, illus. 2007. (Biscuit Ser.). 12p. (J). (ps-1). pap. 6.99 ***978-0-06-112833-2(3)** , Harper Festival) HarperCollins Pubs.

—Biscuit's Picnic. Schories, Pat, illus. 1998. (Biscuit Ser.). 24p. (J). (ps-1). 12.95 (978-0-06-028072-7(7)) HarperCollins Pubs.

—Biscuit's Show & Share Day. Young, Mary O'Keefe, illus. 2007. (Biscuit Ser.). 24p. (J). pap. 3.99 (978-0-06-112832-5(5) , Harper Festival) HarperCollins Pubs.

—Biscuit's Vacation. Schories, Pat, illus. 2002. (Biscuit Ser.). 24p. (J). (ps-1). lib. bdg. 12.89 (978-0-06-028681-1(4)) HarperCollins Pubs.

—Bizcocho. 2001. (SPA.). (ps-2). lib. bdg. 12.95 (978-0-613-35909-2(7)) Tandem Library Bks.

—Happy Easter, Biscuit! Schories, Pat, illus. 2000. (Biscuit Ser.). 20p. (J). (ps-1). pap. 6.99 (978-0-694-01223-7(8) , Harper Festival) HarperCollins Pubs.

—Happy Easter, Biscuit! 2000. (gr. k-3). lib. bdg. 15.25 (978-0-613-70589-9(0)) Tandem Library Bks.

—Happy Halloween, Biscuit! Schories, Pat, illus. 1999. (Biscuit Ser.). 20p. (J). (ps-1). pap. 6.99 (978-0-694-01220-6(3) , Harper Festival) HarperCollins Pubs.

—Happy Thanksgiving, Biscuit! Schories, Pat, illus. 1999. (Biscuit Ser.). 20p. (J). (ps-1). pap. 6.99 (978-0-694-01221-3(1) , Harper Festival) HarperCollins Pubs.

—Meet Biscuit! Schories, Pat, illus. 2005. (Biscuit Ser.). 24p. (J). (ps-1). 3.99 (978-0-06-057846-6(7) , Harper Festival) HarperCollins Pubs.

—Mind Your Manners, Biscuit! Young, Mary O'Keefe, illus. 2007. (Biscuit Ser.). 24p. (J). pap. 3.99 ***978-0-06-112835-6(X)** , Harper Festival) HarperCollins Pubs.

—Reading Is Fun with Biscuit: Biscuit Wants to Play; Biscuit Finds a Friend. Schories, Pat, illus. 2003. (My First I Can Read Bks.). (J). (ps-k). pap. 11.99 (978-0-06-058933-2(7) , Harper Trophy) HarperCollins Pubs.

—Time for School, Biscuit! Back Lane Studio, illus. 2007. (Biscuit Ser.). 32p. (J). pap. 3.99 ***978-0-06-112834-9(1)** , Harper Festival) HarperCollins Pubs.

Capucilli, Alyssa Satin. What Is Love, Biscuit? Schories, Pat, illus. 2002. (Biscuit Ser.). 16p. (J). (ps-1). bds. 4.99 (978-0-694-01517-7(2)) HarperCollins Pubs.

Carabine, Sue. A Dog's Night Before Christmas. Kawasaki, Shauna Mooney, illus. 2001. 60p. 5.95 (978-0-87905-762-6(9)) Gibbs Smith, Publisher.

Carbone, Elisa. Night Running: How James Escaped with the Help of His Faithful Dog. Lewis, Earl, illus. 2007. (J). (978-0-375-82247-6(X)); lib. bdg. (978-0-375-92247-3(4)) Knopf, Alfred A. Inc.

Carlson, Nancy. Harriet & George's Christmas Treat. Carlson, Nancy, illus. 2005. (Picture Bks.). (Illus.). 32p. (J). (gr. k-2). 15.95 (978-1-57505-506-0(6)) Lerner Publishing Group.

—Harriet & George's Christmas Treat. 2003. (Illus.). 32p. (J). (gr. k-2). pap. 6.95 (978-1-57505-639-5(9)) Lerner Publishing Group.

—Harriet & George's Christmas Treat. 2001. (gr. k-3). lib. bdg. 15.25 (978-0-613-68088-2(X)) Tandem Library Bks.

—Harriet & the Roller Coaster. 20th anniv. ed. (Nancy Carlson's Neighborhood Ser.). (Illus.). 32p. (gr. k-2). 2005. 15.95 (978-1-57505-053-9(6)); 2003. (J). (978-1-57505-202-1(4)) Lerner Publishing Group.

—Harriet & the Roller Coaster. 2003. (gr. k-3). lib. bdg. 15.25 (978-0-613-68089-9(8)) Tandem Library Bks.

—Harriet & Walt. rev. ed. (Carolrhoda Picture Books Ser.). (Illus.). 32p. (J). (gr. k-2). 2005. 15.95 (978-1-57505-672-2(0)); 2004. pap. (978-1-57505-723-1(9)) Lerner Publishing Group.

—Harriet's Halloween Candy. (Illus.). 32p. (gr. k-2). anniv. ed. 2003. (J). pap. 6.95 (978-0-87614-926-3(3) , Carolrhoda Bks.); 20th anniv. ed. 2005. 15.95 (978-0-87614-913-3(1)) Lerner Publishing Group.

—Harriet's Halloween Candy. 2002. (gr. k-3). lib. bdg. 15.25 (978-0-613-77204-4(0)) Tandem Library Bks.

—Harriet's Recital. 2006. (J). pap. 6.95 (978-1-57505-929-7(0) , First Avenue Editions) Lerner Publishing Group.

Carlson, Nancy L. Harriet's Recital. 2006. (Illus.). (J). 15.95 (978-1-57505-898-6(7) , Carolrhoda Bks.) Lerner Publishing Group.

Carman, Debby. Cha Cha the Dancing Dog. 2006. (J). (978-0-9777340-5-4(6)) Faux Paw Media Group.

—Chewdalootie, Doing My Duty. 2006. (J). (978-0-9777340-3-0(X)) Faux Paw Media Group.

Carmody, Isobelle. Night Gate. 2006. 272p. (gr. 4-7). 6.50 (978-0-375-83017-4(0) , Yearling) Random Hse. Children's Bks.

Carr, Roger. Big Dog. 2000. (gr. k-3). lib. bdg. 11.80 (978-0-613-29561-1(7)) Tandem Library Bks.

—Lost in the Park. 2001. (gr. k-3). lib. bdg. 11.95 (978-0-613-33390-0(X)) Tandem Library Bks.

Carson, William C. Peter Becomes a Trail Man: The Story of a Boy's Journey on the Santa Fe Trail. Oliphant, Pat, illus. 2002. 192p. (J). (gr. 6 up). 12.95 (978-0-8263-2895-3(4)) Univ. of New Mexico Pr.

Carter, Christine R. The Collie of Castle Hill. Carter, Christine R., illus. 2002. 48p. (J). per. 10.95 (978-0-9717964-1-6(6) , TCCH-PB16); (Illus.). 16.95 (978-0-9717964-0-9(8) , TCCH-HC08) Polt Mountain Pr.

Carter, David A. Woof! Woof! Carter, David A., illus. 2006. 32p. (J). 12.95 (978-1-4169-0805-0(6) , Little Simon) Simon & Schuster Children's Publishing.

Cartwright, Stephen & Zeff, Claudia. Find the Puppy. 2000. (Kid Kits Ser.). (Illus.). 10p. (J). (ps). 10.95 (978-0-88110-801-9(4)) EDC Publishing.

Carville, Declan. A Day to Remember at the Giant's Causeway. Ellis, Brendan, illus. 29p. (J). (gr. 2-5). pap. 7.95 (978-0-9538222-0-1(6)) Discovery Pubns. GBR. *Dist:* Irish Bks. & Media, Inc.

Casanova, Mary. Danger at Snow Hill. Rayyan, Omar, illus. 2006. (Dog Watch Ser.: No. 3). 128p. (J). pap. 4.99 (978-0-689-86812-2(X) , Aladdin) Simon & Schuster Children's Publishing.

—Dog-Napped! Rayyan, Omar, illus. 2006. (Dog Watch Ser.: No. 2). 144p. (J). pap. 4.99 (978-0-689-86811-5(1) , Aladdin) Simon & Schuster Children's Publishing.

—Extreme Stunt Dogs. Rayyan, Omar, illus. 2007. (Dog Watch Ser.). 133p. (J). (gr. 3-7). per. 4.99 ***978-1-4169-4782-0(5)** , Aladdin) Simon & Schuster Children's Publishing.

—Some Dog! Hoyt, Ard, illus. 2007. 40p. (J). (ps-2). 16.00 (978-0-374-37133-3(4) , Farrar, Straus & Giroux (BYR)) Farrar, Straus & Giroux.

—To Catch a Burglar. Rayyan, Omar, illus. 2007. (Dog Watch Ser.: No. 4). 144p. (J). pap. 4.99 (978-0-689-86813-9(8) , Aladdin) Simon & Schuster Children's Publishing.

—Trouble in Pembrook. Rayyan, Omar, illus. 2006. (J). (Dog Watch Ser.: No. 1). 128p. pap. 4.99 (978-0-689-86810-8(3)); 117p. ***978-1-4156-7757-5(3))** Simon & Schuster Children's Publishing. (Aladdin).

Casanova, Mary. The Turtle-Hatching Mystery. Rayyan, Omar, illus. 2008. (Dog Watch Ser.: No. 6). 144p. (J). pap. 4.99 ***978-1-4169-4783-7(3)** , Aladdin) Simon & Schuster Children's Publishing.

Case, Layne. Charlie. 2007. (J). 14.95 ***978-0-9789546-9-7(6))** Back Channel Pr.

Case, Linda. Brigits Day of Fun. 2006. 28p. pap. 9.95 ***978-1-4327-0001-0(4))** Outskirts Press, Inc.

Cason, Anjanette. Praise Puppy's Adventure in Praise. 2007. (J). ***978-0-9755234-7-6(3))** DOMINIONHOUSE Publishing & Design.

Cassidy, Anne. Cleo & Leo. Norman, Philip, illus. 2004. (Read-It! Readers Ser.). 32p. (C). (gr. k-3). 18.60 (978-1-4048-0049-6(2)) Picture Window Bks.

—Jasper & Jess. Hall, Francois, illus. 2004. (Read-It! Readers Ser.). 32p. (C). (gr. k-3). 18.60 (978-1-4048-0061-8(1)) Picture Window Bks.

Castelli, Jeanette. The cats on the Moon / Los gatos en la Luna. 2005. 48p. pap. (978-958-30-1767-4(1)) Panamericana Editorial.

Caszatt-Allen, Wendy. Fort Brokenheart. 2007. 120p. (J). pap. 6.95 ***978-1-934133-09-5(4))** Mackinac Island Pr., Inc.

—Last Voyage of the Griffon. 2007. (Illus.). 140p. (J). pap. 6.95 ***978-1-934133-08-8(6))** Mackinac Island Pr., Inc.

Cat & Dog Talk: Individual Title Six-Packs. (Sails Literacy Ser.). (gr. 1-2). 36.00 (978-0-7578-4021-0(3)) Rigby Education.

Catalano, Dominic. Mr. Basset Plays. Catalano, Dominic, illus. 2003. (Illus.). 32p. (YA). (gr. k-2). 15.95 (978-1-59078-007-7(8)) Boyds Mills Pr.

Catalanotto, Peter. Daisy 1, 2, 3. Catalanotto, Peter, illus. 2003. (Illus.). 32p. (J). 15.95 (978-0-689-85457-6(9) , Atheneum/Richard Jackson Bks.) Simon & Schuster Children's Publishing.

—Dylan's Day Out. Catalanotto, Peter, illus. 2006. pap. 7.99 (978-0-9777720-0-1(4)) Southpaw Books LLC.

—Ivan the Terrier. Catalanotto, Peter, illus. 2007. 32p. (J). (ps-k). 16.99 (978-1-4169-1247-7(9)) Simon & Schuster Children's Publishing.

Cavanna, Betty. Going on Sixteen. 1998. 192p. (YA). (gr. 7-12). reprint ed. pap. 5.95 (978-0-688-16324-2(6)) HarperCollins Pubs.

Cave, Kathryn & Dhami, Narinder. Emperors Gruckle Hound. 2nd ed. 2002. (Illus.). 144p. pap. 8.99 (978-0-340-85463-1(4) , Hodder & Stoughton) Hodder General Publishing Division GBR. *Dist:* Trafalgar Square Publishing.

Cazet, Denys. Grandpa Spanielson's Chicken Pox Stories No. 1: The Octopus. Cazet, Denys, illus. 2005. (I Can Read Bks.). (Illus.). 48p. (J). (ps-3). lib. bdg. 16.89 (978-0-06-051089-3(7)) HarperCollins Pubs.

—Octopus. Cazet, Denys, illus. 2005. (I Can Read Bks.). (Illus.). 48p. (J). (ps-3). 15.99 (978-0-06-051088-6(9)) HarperCollins Pubs.

—Octopus No. 1: Grandpa Spanielson's Chicken Pox Stories. Cazet, Denys, illus. 2006. (I Can Read Bks.). 48p. (J). pap. 3.99 (978-0-06-051092-3(7) , Harper Trophy) HarperCollins Pubs.

—Shrunken Head. Cazet, Denys, illus. 2008. (I Can Read Bks.: No. 3). 48p. (J). pap. 3.99 (***978-0-06-073015-4(3)*** , Harper Trophy) HarperCollins Pubs.

—Shrunken Head No. 3: Grandpa Spanielson's Chicken Pox Stories. Cazet, Denys, illus. 2007. (I Can Read Bks.). (Illus.). 48p. (J). (gr. k-2). 15.99 (978-0-06-073013-0(7)); lib. bdg. 16.89 (978-0-06-073014-7(5)) HarperCollins Pubs.

—Snout for Chocolate: Grandpa Spanielson's Chicken Pox Stories. Cazet, Denys, illus. 2007. (I Can Read Bks.). 48p. (J). pap. 3.99 (978-0-06-051095-4(1) , Harper Trophy) HarperCollins Pubs.

—Snout for Chocolate No. 2: Grandpa Spanielson's Chicken Pox Stories. Cazet, Denys, illus. 2006. (I Can Read Bks.). (Illus.). 48p. (J). 15.99 (978-0-06-051093-0(5)); lib. bdg. 16.89 (978-0-06-051094-7(3)) HarperCollins Pubs.

Chan, Gillian. The Carved Box. Fernandez, Laura, illus. 2001. 232p. (YA). (gr. 13 up). (978-1-55074-895-6(5)) Kids Can Pr., Ltd.

Chanda, J-P. Healthy Snacks with Blue! Kanemoto, Dan, illus. 2007. (Blue's Clues Ser.). 24p. (J). pap. 3.99 (978-1-4169-2778-5(6) , Simon Spotlight/Nickelodeon) Simon & Schuster Children's Publishing.

Chao, Eileen. Go Away, Sam! 2004. (J). pap. 8.00 (978-0-8059-6505-6(X)) Dorrance Publishing Co., Inc.

Chapman, Cynthia. Dog Gone. 2008. 224p. (J). 16.95 (***978-0-312-37123-4(3)***) Feiwel & Friends.

Chapman, Nancy Kapp. Tripper's Travels: An International Scrapbook. Chapman, Lee, illus. 2005. 48p. (J). (gr. k-4). per. 16.95 (978-0-7614-5240-9(0)) Cavendish, Marshall Corp.

Chapra, Mimi. Sparky's Bark. Escriva, Vivi, illus. 2006. Tr. of Ladrido de Sparky. (ENG & SPA.). 32p. (J). lib. bdg. 17.89 (978-0-06-053173-7(8) , Rayo) HarperCollins Pubs.

—Sparky's Bark/El Ladrido de Sparky. Escriva, Vivi, illus. 2006. (ENG & SPA.). 32p. (J). 16.99 (978-0-06-053172-0(X)) HarperCollins Pubs.

Charles, Norma M. Fuzzy Wuzzy. 2005. (Illus.). 80p. (J). 5.95 (978-0-9730831-2-5(3)) Hodgepog Bks. CAN. *Dist:* Coteau Bks., Fitzhenry & Whiteside, Ltd.

Charlotte Latin School Staff. Ann & the Puppy. Sher, illus. 2001. 32p. (J). per. 4.95 (978-0-9707920-2-0(6)) Charlotte's Storybooks.

Chase, Diana. Daisy Street. Bradley, Vanessa, illus. 2005. 128p. (Orig.). (J). pap. 13.50 (978-1-920731-11-3(3)) Fremantle Pr. AUS. *Dist:* International Specialized Bk. Services.

Chatterton, Martin. Bad Dog: Bad Dog & the Curse of the President's Knee. 2005. (Bad Dog Ser.). (Illus.). 176p. (J). 4.99 (978-0-439-66160-7(9) , Scholastic Paperbacks) Scholastic, Inc.

—Bad Dog & All That Hollywood Hoohah. 2005. (Bad Dog Ser.: No. 1). (Illus.). 176p. (J). pap. 4.99 (978-0-439-57370-2(X) , Scholastic Paperbacks) Scholastic, Inc.

—Bad Dog & Those Crazee Martians. 2nd ed. 2005. (Bad Dog Ser.: Vol. 02). (Illus.). 176p. (J). pap. 4.99 (978-0-439-66159-1(5) , Scholastic Paperbacks) Scholastic, Inc.

—Bad Dog Goes Barktastic. 2005. (Bad Dog Ser.: No. 4). (Illus.). 192p. (ps-7). mass mkt. 4.99 (978-0-439-67714-1(9) , Scholastic Paperbacks) Scholastic, Inc.

—Can Dogs Fly? Fido's Book of Pop-up Transportation Surprises. 2005. (Illus.). 12p. (J). (gr. k-4). reprint ed. 10.00 (978-0-7567-8838-4(2)) DIANE Publishing Co.

Cherrington, Janelle. Tale of Two Catdogs. 2000. (gr. 3-6). lib. bdg. 11.80 (978-0-613-27166-0(1)) Tandem Library Bks.

Cheryl, Bustle. Ralphie Goes on a Boat Ride. 2007. (J). pap. 7.99 (***978-1-60247-243-3(2)***) Tate Publishing & Enterprises, L.L.C.

Chester. 2007. (Illus.). 32p. (J). (ps-3). 16.99 (***978-0-698-40062-7(3)*** , Minedition) Penguin Group (USA) Inc.

Chetkowski, Emily. Mabel Takes a Sail. 2000. (gr. k-3). lib. bdg. 19.35 (978-0-613-85830-4(1)) Tandem Library Bks.

—Mabel Takes a Sail. Peterson, Dawn, illus. 2000. 64p. (J). (ps-3). pap. 10.50 (978-1-880158-26-5(4)) Townsend, J.N. Publishing.

—Mabel Takes the Ferry. Peterson, Dawn, illus. 2001. 40p. (J). pap. 11.95 (978-1-880158-37-1(X)) Townsend, J.N. Publishing.

Chichester Clark, Emma. Piper. Chichester Clark, Emma, illus. 2007. (Illus.). 32p. (J). 17.00 (978-0-8028-5314-1(5) , Eerdmans Bks For Young Readers) Eerdmans, William B. Publishing Co.

Child, Lauren. Sizzles Is Completely Not Here. 2007. (Charlie & Lola Ser.). 10p. (J). (ps-1). bds. 7.99 (978-0-448-44501-4(8) , Grosset & Dunlap) Penguin Group (USA) Inc.

—We Honestly Can Look after Your Dog. 2006. (Charlie & Lola Ser.). (Illus.). 32p. (J). (ps-2). pap. 5.99 (978-0-448-44414-7(3) , Grosset & Dunlap) Penguin Group (USA) Inc.

Chin, Oliver. The Year of the Dog: Tales from the Chinese Zodiac. Alcorn, Miah, illus. 2006. (Tales from the Chinese Zodiac Ser.). 36p. 15.95 (978-1-59702-002-2(8)) Immedium.

Choldenko, Gennifer. Notes from a Liar & Her Dog. (J). (gr. 5-7). 2003. 224p. pap. 6.99 (978-0-14-250068-2(2) , Puffin); 2001. (Illus.). 1p. 16.99 (978-0-399-23591-7(4) , Putnam Juvenile) Penguin Group (USA) Inc.

—Notes from a Liar & Her Dog. 2004. 224p. (J). (gr. 4-7). pap. 38.00 incl. audio (978-0-8072-2097-9(3) , Listening Library) Random Hse. Audio Publishing Group.

—Notes from a Liar & Her Dog. 2001. lib. bdg. 14.15 (978-0-613-67468-3(5)) Tandem Library Bks.

Christelow, Eileen. The Five-Dog Night. Christelow, Eileen, illus. 1998. (Illus.). 40p. (J). (gr. k-3). 6.95 (978-0-395-92862-2(1) , Clarion Bks.) Houghton Mifflin Co. Trade & Reference Div.

—Letters from a Desperate Dog. 2006. (Illus.). 32p. (J). (gr. 3-5). 16.00 (978-0-618-51003-0(6) , Clarion Bks.) Houghton Mifflin Co. Trade & Reference Div.

—Not until Christmas, Walter! Christelow, Eileen, illus. 2002. (Illus.). 40p. (J). (gr. k-3). pap. 5.95 (978-0-618-24618-2(5) , Clarion Bks.) Houghton Mifflin Co. Trade & Reference Div.

—Not until Christmas, Walter! 2002. (Illus.). 40p. (J). (ps-3). lib. bdg. 14.10 (978-0-613-70984-2(5)) Tandem Library Bks.

—The Robbery at the Diamond Dog Diner. 1999. (Illus.). (J). (ps-2). lib. bdg. 15.25 (978-0-8335-2149-1(7)) Tandem Library Bks.

—Where's the Big Bad Wolf? Christelow, Eileen, illus. 2002. (Illus.). 40p. (J). (gr. k-3). tchr. ed. 16.00 (978-0-618-18194-0(6) , Clarion Bks.) Houghton Mifflin Co. Trade & Reference Div.

Christian, Cheryl. Where's the Puppy? (Korean) Dwight, Laura, photos by. 2004. (KOR., Illus.). 12p. (J). bds. 5.50 (978-1-932065-79-4(2)) Star Bright Bks., Inc.

—Where's the Puppy? (Simplified Chinese) Dwight, Laura, photos by. 2004. (CHI., Illus.). 12p. (J). bds. 5.50 (978-1-932065-67-1(9)) Star Bright Bks., Inc.

—Where's the Puppy? (Traditional Chinese) Dwight, Laura, photos by. 2004. (CHI., Illus.). 12p. (J). bds. 5.50 (978-1-932065-61-9(X)) Star Bright Bks., Inc.

—Where's the Puppy? (Vietnamese) Dwight, Laura, photos by. 2004. (VIE., Illus.). 12p. (J). bds. 5.50 (978-1-932065-73-2(3)) Star Bright Bks., Inc.

—Where's the Puppy?/Kote Ti Toutous la Ye? Dwight, Laura, photos by. 2005. (CRP., Illus.). 12p. (J). (ps). per. 5.50 (978-1-59572-029-0(4)) Star Bright Bks., Inc.

Christie, Jacky. The Wind Blows North. 2007. (ENG.). 56p. per. 10.99 (***978-1-4141-0835-3(4)***) Pleasant Word.

Christopher, Matt. You Lucky Dog. Vasconcellos, Daniel, illus. 8th ed. 2003. (Soccer 'Cats Ser.: No. 8). 64p. (J). (gr. 1-4). pap. 4.99 (978-0-316-73805-7(0)) Little, Brown Bks. for Young Readers.

—You Lucky Dog. 2003. (gr. k-3). lib. bdg. 13.00 (978-0-613-71888-2(7)) Tandem Library Bks.

Church, Caroline Jayne. Digby Takes Charge. 2007. 32p. (J). (ps-2). 14.99 (978-1-4169-3441-7(3) , McElderry, Margaret K.) Simon & Schuster Children's Publishing.

Chuse, Patricia Jepsen. Delphi: What Being on Earth Is All About. 2002. 200p. 15.95 (978-0-9667560-3-6(7)) Chuse, Patricia Jepsen.

Ciminera, Siobhan. Love Your Pup. 2007. 24p. (J). pap. 4.99 (978-0-448-44551-9(4) , Grosset & Dunlap) Penguin Group (USA) Inc.

Ciminera, Siobhan & Faulkner, Keith. A Yummy Mystery: A Scratch-and-Sniff Story. 2007. (Puppy Scooby-Doo Ser.). 16p. (J). pap. 5.99 (978-0-448-44406-2(2) , Grosset & Dunlap) Penguin Group (USA) Inc.

Citra, Becky. Dog Days. 2003. (Orca Young Readers Ser.). (Illus.). 144p. (J). (gr. 3-6). pap. 4.99 (978-1-55143-256-4(0)) Orca Bk. Pubs. USA.

—Dog Days. 2003. (gr. 3-6). lib. bdg. 13.00 (978-0-613-87471-7(4)) Tandem Library Bks.

Civardi, Anne. New Puppy. 2001. (gr. k-3). lib. bdg. 12.95 (978-0-613-67655-7(6)) Tandem Library Bks.

Clanchy, Kate. Our Cat Henry Comes to the Swings. Bird, Jemima, illus. 2007. 32p. (J). (ps-1). 16.00 (***978-1-56148-563-5(2)***) Good Bks.

Clark, Dan. Puppies for Sale. 1999. (Illus.). 28p. (J). (gr. k-5). 6.99 (978-1-57759-262-4(X)) Dalmatian Pr.

Clark, Emma Chichester. Melrose & Croc: A Christmas to Remember. Clark, Emma Chichester, illus. 2006. (Illus.). 32p. (J). 16.95 (978-0-8027-9597-7(8)) Walker & Co.

Clark Jordan Sarah. Bossqueen Little Bigbark & Sentinel Pup. 2006. 144p. (J). 5.95 (978-1-58246-170-0(8) , Tricycle Pr.) Ten Speed Pr.

Clarke, Gus. Lucky. Clarke, Gus, illus. 2005. (Illus.). 32p. (J). pap. 7.95 (978-1-929132-84-3(0)) Kane/Miller Bk. Pubs., Inc.

—Nervous Norris. 2002. (Illus.). 64p. (J). pap. (978-1-84270-049-5(9)) Andersen.

—Scratch N' Sniff. 1998. (Illus.). 27p. (J). pap. 9.95 (978-0-86264-810-7(6)) Andersen GBR. *Dist:* Trafalgar Square Publishing.

—Suerte. Clarke, Gus, illus. 2006. (SPA., Illus.). 32p. (J). pap. 4.95 (978-1-933605-08-1(1)) Kane/Miller Bk. Pubs., Inc.

The Clay Dog: Individual Title Six-Pack Pouch - Level L. (Lighthouse Ser.). 16p. (gr. 2 up). 28.00 (978-0-7578-0871-5(9)) Rigby Education.

Claycomb, Patty. If Dogs Ruled the World. McMahon, Kelly, illus. 2002. (Two Can Read Ser.). 16p. (J). 2.99 (978-1-56472-650-6(9)) Edupress, Inc.

Cleary, Beverly. Henry Huggins. Darling, Louis, illus. 2004. (SPA.). 160p. (J). pap. 6.99 (978-0-06-073600-2(3) , Rayo) HarperCollins Pubs.

Clement, Gary. The Great Poochini. ed. 2004. (J). (gr. 1-4). spiral bd. (978-0-616-03027-1(4)) Canadian National Institute for the Blind/Institut National Canadien pour les Aveugles.

—The Great Poochini. Clement, Gary, illus. 1999. (Illus.). 32p. (J). (ps-3). 15.95 (978-0-88899-331-1(5) , Libros Tigrillo) Groundwood Bks. CAN. *Dist:* Perseus Distribution.

Clement, Rod. Frank's Great Museum Adventure. Clement, Rod, illus. 1999. (Illus.). 32p. (J). (ps-3). 14.95 (978-0-06-027673-7(8)) HarperCollins Pubs.

Clements, Andrew. Circus Family Dog. Truesdell, Sue, illus. 2000. 32p. (J). (gr. k-3). tchr. ed. 16.00 (978-0-395-78648-2(7) , Clarion Bks.) Houghton Mifflin Co. Trade & Reference Div.

—Naptime for Slippers. Bynum, Janie, illus. 2005. 32p. (J). (ps). 12.99 (978-0-525-47287-2(8) , Dutton Juvenile) Penguin Group (USA) Inc.

—Slippers at Home. Bynum, Janie, illus. 2005. 32p. (J). (ps-2). 12.99 (978-0-525-47138-7(3) , Dutton Juvenile) Penguin Group (USA) Inc.

—Slippers at School. Bynum, Janie, illus. 2005. 32p. (J). (ps-1). 12.99 (978-0-525-47189-9(8) , Dutton Juvenile) Penguin Group (USA) Inc.

—Slippers Loves to Run. Bynum, Janie, illus. 2006. 32p. (J). (ps-1). 12.99 (978-0-525-47648-1(2) , Dutton Juvenile) Penguin Group (USA) Inc.

Clements, Andrew & Bynum, Janie. Slippers at Home. 2007. 32p. (J). pap. 5.99 (978-0-14-240781-3(X) , Puffin) Penguin Group (USA) Inc.

Clemesha, David & Zimmerman, Andrea. My Dog Toby. Kelley, True, illus. 2000. 32p. (J). (ps-2). 15.00 (978-0-15-202014-9(4) , Silver Whistle) Harcourt Trade Pubs.

Clifford the Big Red Dog: Play Time! 2002. (J). (978-1-931312-78-3(8)) SoftPlay, Inc.

Clover, Peter. Hercules: New Pup on the Block. l.t. ed. 2005. (Illus.). 200p. (J). pap. (978-0-7540-6162-5(0) , CLP 353) BBC Audio.

The Clubhouse, 6 Packs. 16p. (gr. 2 up). 35.00 (978-0-7635-9372-8(9)) Rigby Education.

Cneut, Carll. The Amazing Love Story of Mr. Morf: An Astonishing Circus Romance. Cneut, Carll, illus. 2003. (Illus.). 32p. (J). (gr. k-3). tchr. ed. 15.00 (978-0-618-33170-3(0) , Clarion Bks.) Houghton Mifflin Co. Trade & Reference Div.

Cobb, Debbie. Gracie's Big Adventure... with Augustine the Beaver. Ferchaud, Steve, illus. 2006. (J). per. 10.95 (978-0-9787376-0-3(1)) Laurob Pr.

Cocca-Leffler, Maryann. Dog Wash Day: All Aboard Picture Reader. 2004. (All Aboard Reading Ser.). (Illus.). 32p. (J). (ps-1). pap. 3.99 (978-0-448-43370-7(2) , Grosset & Dunlap) Penguin Group (USA) Inc.

Cochran, Bill. The Forever Dog. Andreasen, Dan, illus. 2007. 32p. (J). (ps-3). 15.99 (978-0-06-053939-9(9)); lib. bdg. 16.89 (978-0-06-053940-5(2)) HarperCollins Pubs.

Cochran, Thomas. Running the Dogs. 2007. 160p. (J). (gr. 3-7). 16.00 (***978-0-374-36360-4(9)***) Farrar, Straus & Giroux.

Coffelt. Dogs in Space. 1998. (Illus.). 40p. (J). pap. 23.95 (978-0-15-201015-7(7)) Harcourt Trade Pubs.

Coffelt, Nancy. Pug in a Truck. 2006. (Illus.). (J). (***978-0-16-856319-7(3)***) Houghton Mifflin Co.

—Pug in a Truck. 2006. (Illus.). 40p. (J). (ps-k). 12.95 (978-0-618-56319-7(9)) Houghton Mifflin Co. Trade & Reference Div.

Cohen, Barbara S. Forever Friends. Hall, Dorothy Louise, illus. 2004. 32p. (J). reprint ed. 9.95 (978-1-931290-54-8(7)) Tallfellow Pr.

Cohen, Shari. Alfie's Bark Mitzvah. 2006. (Illus.). (J). per. 18.00 net. (978-1-58985-055-2(6)) Five Star Pubns., Inc.

Cohen, Sonia. Gigi. l.t. ed. 2005. (Illus.). 34p. (J). 14.95 (978-0-615-12926-6(9)) Gigi Enterprises.

Cole, Babette. Lady Lupin's Book of Etiquette. 2002. (Illus.). 32p. (J). (gr. 1-5). 14.95 (978-1-56145-257-6(2)) Peachtree Pubs., Ltd.

—El Libro de Etiqueta de Lady Lupina. 2003. (Babette Cole Ser.). (SPA.). (J). 18.95 (978-84-233-3337-0(X)) Ediciones Destino ESP. *Dist:* Planeta Publishing Corp.

—Mi Amor. Filipetto, Celia, illus. 2003. (Babette Cole Ser.). (SPA.). 28p. (J). (gr. k-2). 18.95 (978-84-233-3283-0(7) , DS30975) Ediciones Destino ESP. *Dist:* AIMS International Bks., Inc., Lectorum Pubns., Inc., Planeta Publishing Corp.

Cole, Barbara. Anna & Natalie. Himler, Ronald, illus. 2007. 32p. (J). 16.95 (***978-1-59572-105-1(3)***) Star Bright Bks., Inc.

Cole, Joanna & Calmenson, Stephanie. Stories, Poems, Jokes & Riddles about Dogs. 1999. (Give A Dog A Bone Ser.). (Illus.). 96p. (J). (gr. 2-5). pap. 7.99 (978-0-439-08708-7(2)) Scholastic, Inc.

Coleman, David R. Old Troop, Rainbow Fairies, & the Forget-Me-Now Potion. 2007. (J). pap. 8.99 (***978-1-60247-054-5(5)***) Tate Publishing & Enterprises, L.L.C.

Collard, Sneed B., III. Dog Sense. 2005. 192p. (J). 14.95 (978-1-56145-351-1(X)) Peachtree Pubs., Ltd.

Collins, Jenny. Puppy Love. 2007. (First Kisses Ser.: No. 3). 192p. (J). pap. 5.99 (***978-0-06-114312-0(X)*** , HarperTeen) HarperCollins Pubs.

Collins, Terry. High-Flying Sam. Date not set. (Rocket Power Ready-to-Read Ser.: Vol. 5). (J). pap. 3.50 (978-0-689-86582-4(1) , Simon Spotlight/Nickelodeon) Simon & Schuster Children's Publishing.

Collins, Tom. Perfect Bone. 1999. (gr. 3-6). lib. bdg. 11.80 (978-0-613-22168-9(0)) Tandem Library Bks.

Come Here Puppy. 2006. (J). (***978-1-932570-53-3(5)***) Literacy Footprints Inc.

Comfort, Philip. Rescued Retriever. 2005. 129p. pap. 17.95 (978-1-4137-6536-6(X)) PublishAmerica, Inc.

Conahan, Carolyn. The Twelve Days of Christmas Dogs. Conahan, Carolyn, illus. 2005. (Illus.). 32p. (J). (ps). 15.99 (978-0-525-47486-9(2) , Dutton Juvenile) Penguin Group (USA) Inc.

Condon, Bill. Holly & Mac. Gordon, Gus, illus. 1999. (Supa Doopers Ser.). 64p. (J). (978-0-7608-1924-1(6)) Sundance/Newbridge Educational Publishing.

—Holly & Mac. 1999. (gr. 3-6). lib. bdg. 12.60 (978-0-613-19373-3(3)) Tandem Library Bks.

Cone, Breanna. The Adventures of Pirate & Black Bart. 2006. 41p. pap. 8.25 (978-1-4116-6494-4(9)) Lulu.com.

Cone, Molly. Mishmash & the Substitute Teacher. 2000. (gr. 3-6). lib. bdg. 12.95 (978-0-613-27978-9(6)) Tandem Library Bks.

Conford, Ellen. Hound of the Barkervilles. Andriani, Renee W., illus. (Annabel the Actress Ser.). 96p. (J). 2003. pap. 3.99 (978-0-689-84791-2(2) , Aladdin); 2002. (gr. 2-5). 15.00 (978-0-689-84734-9(3)) Simon & Schuster Children's Publishing.

—Hound of the Barkervilles. 2003. (gr. 3-6). lib. bdg. 11.80 (978-0-613-66394-6(2)) Tandem Library Bks.

Connolley, Matthew & Rovetch, Bob. Hot Dog & Bob Adventure, Bk. 1. 2006. (Illus.). 96p. (J). 15.50 (978-0-8118-4463-5(3)) Chronicle Bks. LLC.

Cook, Sherry & Johnson, Terri. Nosey Nina, 26 vols. Kuhn, Jesse, illus. l.t. ed. 2006. (Quirkles—Exploring Phonics through Science Ser.: 14). 32p. (J). 7.99 (978-1-933815-13-8(2) , Quirkles, The) Creative 3, LLC.

Cooper, Ilene. Absolutely Lucy. Harvey, Amanda, illus. 1999. (Stepping Stones Ser.). 80p. (J). (gr. 1-4). pap. 3.99 (978-0-307-26502-9(1) , Random Hse. Bks. for Young Readers) Random Hse. Children's Bks.

—Absolutely Lucy. 2000. (Road to Reading Ser.). (J). 10.79 (978-0-606-20434-7(2)); (gr. 3-6). lib. bdg. 11.80 (978-0-613-27694-8(9)) Tandem Library Bks.

—Lucy on the Loose. Harvey, Amanda, illus. 2000. (Road to Reading Ser.). 80p. (J). (gr. 2-5). 11.99 (978-0-307-46508-5(X)); pap. 3.99 (978-0-307-26508-1(0)) Random Hse. Children's Bks. (Golden Bks.).

—Lucy on the Loose. 2000. (J). (978-0-606-18929-3(7)) Tandem Library Bks.

Coplans, Peta. Cat & Dog. 2000. (Illus.). (J). pap. (978-0-14-056140-1(4) , Puffin) Penguin Group (USA) Inc.

Coppel, Chris. Far from Burden Dell. 2005. 286p. (J). pap. 4.95 (978-0-9746481-6-3(7)) Brown Barn Bks.

Corey's Web Unleashed. 2003. (J). (978-0-9716567-8-9(9)) Book Web Publishing, Ltd.

Coste, Marion. Wild Beach. Gray, Cissy, illus. 2005. 32p. (J). pap. 8.25 (978-0-89317-062-2(3) , WW-623); lib. bdg. 17.95 (978-0-89317-061-5(5) , WW-0615) Finney Co., Inc. (Windward Publishing).

Costello, Emily. Abandoned Puppy. 1999. (gr. 3-6). lib. bdg. 11.80 (978-0-613-17066-6(0)) Tandem Library Bks.

Cottringer, Anne. Hot Dog. Walker, Katherine, illus. 2005. 24p. (J). lib. bdg. 22.65 (***978-1-59646-738-5(X)***) Dingles & Co.

—Mary Is Scary. Gale, Cathy, illus. 2007. 32p. (J). pap. 9.99 (***978-0-7475-7927-4(X)***) Bloomsbury Publishing Plc GBR. *Dist:* Independent Pubs. Group.

Coulton, Mia. Danny & Abby Are Friends. Coulton, Mia, photos by. 2001. 16p. (J). 4.95 (978-0-9713518-1-3(3)) Maryruth Bks., Inc.

—Danny & the Bully. Coulton, Mia, photos by. 2002. (J). 4.95 (978-0-9713518-7-5(2)) Maryruth Bks., Inc.

—Danny & the Four Seasons. Coulton, Mia, photos by. 2001. (J). 4.95 (978-0-9713518-5-1(6)) Maryruth Bks., Inc.

—Danny Gets Fit. Coulton, Mia, photos by. 2001. (J). (978-0-9713518-3-7(X)) Maryruth Bks., Inc.

—Danny Likes Red. Coulton, Mia, photos by. 2003. (J). 4.95 (978-0-9720295-2-0(4)) Maryruth Bks., Inc.

—Danny Likes to Help. Coulton, Mia, photos by. 2005. (J). 4.95 (978-0-9746475-9-3(4)) Maryruth Bks., Inc.

—Danny Looks for Abby. Coulton, Mia, photos by. 2002. (J). 4.95 (978-0-9713518-6-8(4)) Maryruth Bks., Inc.

—Danny's Castle. Coulton, Mia, photos by. 2005. (J). 4.95 (978-1-933624-00-6(0)) Maryruth Bks., Inc.

—Danny's Dinner. Coulton, Mia, photos by. 2001. 12p. (J). 4.95 (978-0-9713518-2-0(1)) Maryruth Bks., Inc.

—Danny's Groundhog Day. Coulton, Mia, photos by. 2002. (J). (978-0-9713518-9-9(9)) Maryruth Bks., Inc.

—Danny's New Toy. Coulton, Mia, photos by. 2002. (J). (978-0-9713518-8-2(0)) Maryruth Bks., Inc.

—Danny's Window. Coulton, Mia, photos by. 2005. (J). 4.95 (978-0-9746475-8-6(6)) Maryruth Bks., Inc.

—Five Danny Dogs. Coulton, Mia, photos by. 2005. (J). 4.95 (978-1-933624-01-3(9)) Maryruth Bks., Inc.

—Get down Danny. Coulton, Mia, photos by. 2003. (J). 4.95 (978-0-9720295-5-1(9)) Maryruth Bks., Inc.

—Halloween Danny. Coulton, Mia, photos by. 2001. 12p. (J). 4.95 (978-0-9713518-4-4(8)) Maryruth Bks., Inc.

—Look at Danny. Coulton, Mia, photos by. 2001. 12p. (J). 4.95 (978-0-9713518-0-6(5)) Maryruth Bks., Inc.

C D

—Spy Danny. Coulton, Mia, photos by. 2005. (J). 4.95 (978-1-933624-03-7(5)) Maryruth Bks., Inc.

Counce, Paula. A Journey Remembered. l.t. ed. 2004. (Illus.). 135p. (J). 19.95 (978-0-9762776-0-6(3)) Counce, Paula.

Counts, Elizabeth. Buffy Visits the Beach. 1998. (Illus.). 24p. (J). (gr. k-2). pap. 7.00 (978-0-8059-4472-3(9)) Dorrance Publishing Co., Inc.

Cowley, Joy. Agapanthus Hum & Major Bark. Plecas, Jennifer, illus. 2001. 1p. (J). (ps-3). 14.99 (978-0-399-23322-7(9) , Philomel) Penguin Group (USA) Inc.

Cox, David. Hello Puppy! Cox, David, illus. 2004. (Illus.). 32p. 12.99 (978-0-670-04056-8(8) , Penguin Global) Penguin Group (USA) Inc.

Cox, Phil Roxbee & Cartwright, S. Rusty's Bone. 2004. (Farmyard Tales Touchy Feely Board Bks.). (Illus.). 10p. (J). 7.95 (978-0-7945-0012-2(9) , Usborne) EDC Publishing.

Coxe, Molly. Hot Dog. Coxe, Molly, illus. 1998. (Road to Reading Ser.). (Illus.). 32p. (J). (ps-1). pap. 3.99 (978-0-307-26101-4(8) , 26101, Random Hse. Bks. for Young Readers) Random Hse. Children's Bks.

—Hot Dog. (Road to Reading Ser.). 1999. (Illus.). (J). 10.79 (978-0-606-16255-5(0)); 1998. lib. bdg. 11.80 (978-0-613-71623-9(X)) Tandem Library Bks.

Coxon, Michele. It's Mine. 2002. (Illus.). 16p. (J). 13.95 (978-1-903285-05-3(4)); pap. 5.95 (978-1-903285-04-6(6)) Happy Cat Bks. GBR. *Dist:* Star Bright Bks., Inc.

Craig, Helen. This Is the Bear. 2003. (ps-2). lib. bdg. 11.80 (978-0-613-74748-6(8)) Tandem Library Bks.

Craighill, Lina. Buster Teases Emily. 2006. 16p. (J). 12.00 (978-1-4116-8404-1(4)) Lulu.com.

Crane, E. M. Skin Deep. 2008. (YA). (*978-0-385-73479-0(4) , Delacorte Pr.) Dell Publishing.

Crebbin, June. The Dog Show. 2005. (Cambridge Storybooks Ser.). 32p. pap. 7.00 (978-0-521-67474-4(3)) Cambridge Univ. Pr.

Creel, Ann Howard. Nicki. 2006. 136p. (J). pap. 6.95 (*978-1-59369-259-9(5) , Pleasant Co.) American Girl Publishing, Inc.

—Thanks to Nicki. 2007. (J). pap. 6.95 (*978-1-59369-290-2(0) , Pleasant Co.) American Girl Publishing, Inc.

Crider, Bill. Muttketeer! l.t. ed. 1999. (Adventures of Wishbone Ser.: No. 8). (Illus.). 144p. (J). (gr. 4 up). lib. bdg. 22.60 (978-0-8368-2304-2(4)) Stevens, Gareth Inc.

Crimi, Carolyn. No Necesito Amigos. 2004. (SPA.). 32p. (978-84-7720-798-6(4)) Obelisco, Ediciones S.A.

Crisp, Marty. The Most Precious Gift. Cooper, Floyd, illus. 2006. 32p. (J). (gr. k). 16.99 (978-0-399-24296-0(1) , Philomel) Penguin Group (USA) Inc.

—White Star: A Dog on the Titanic. 2006. 160p. (J). pap. 4.99 (978-0-439-71265-1(3) , Scholastic Paperbacks) Scholastic, Inc.

Cross, Nicholas. The Boy & the Dog Who Walked to the Moon. 2000. (Illus.). 160p. (J). (gr. 3 up). pap. (978-0-86315-314-3(3)) Floris Bks. GBR. *Dist:* SteinerBooks, Inc.

Crummel, Susan Stevens. Ten-Gallon Bart. Donohue, Dorothy, illus. 2006. 32p. (J). 16.95 (978-0-7614-5246-1(X)) Cavendish, Marshall Corp.

Crummel, Susan Stevens. Ten-Gallon Bart & the Wild West Show. Donohue, Dorothy, illus. 2008. (J). (*978-0-7614-5391-8(1)) Cavendish, Marshall Corp.

Crummel, Susan Stevens & Donohue, Dorothy. City Dog & Country Dog. Donohue, Dorothy, illus. unabr. ed. 2006. (Illus.). (J). (gr. k-3). 27.95 incl. audio (978-0-8045-6942-2(8) , SAC6942); 29.95 incl. audio compact disk (978-0-8045-4156-5(6)) Spoken Arts, Inc.

—City Dog, Country Dog. Donohue, Dorothy, illus. 2004. (Illus.). 32p. (J). 16.95 (978-0-7614-5156-3(0)) Cavendish, Marshall Corp.

Crunk, Tony. Grandpa's Overall. Nash, Scott, illus. 2001. 32p. (J). (ps). pap. 15.95 (978-0-531-30321-4(7) , Orchard Bks.) Scholastic, Inc.

—Grandpa's Overalls. Nash, Scott, illus. 2001. (J). lib. bdg. (978-0-531-33321-1(3) , Orchard Bks.) Scholastic, Inc.

Crusoe, Kristen. The Maggie Tales: Morgan & the Sneaker Wave. 2007. (Illus.). 20p. pap. 14.95 (*978-1-59299-286-7(2)) Inkwater Pr.

Cruzan, Patricia & Solly, Gloria, illus. Molly's Mischievous Dog. l.t. ed. 2004. 121p. (J). per. (978-0-9653543-3-2(4)) Clear Creek Pubs.

Cuddy, Robbin, illus. Amazing Animals! 2004. (Clifford Ser.). 24p. (J). pap. 8.99 (978-0-439-62748-1(6)) Scholastic, Inc.

Cullen, Lynn. Little Scraggly Hair: A Dog on Noah's Ark. Rogers, Jacqueline, illus. 2003. 32p. (J). (gr. k-3). tchr. ed. 16.95 (978-0-8234-1772-8(7)) Holiday Hse., Inc.

—Moi & Marie Antoinette. Young, Amy, illus. 2006. 32p. (J). 16.95 (978-1-58234-958-9(4)) Bloomsbury Publishing.

Curtis, Christopher Paul. Mr. Chickee's Funny Money. 160p. 2007. (gr. 4-7). 6.50 (978-0-440-22919-3(7) , Yearling); 2005. (Illus.). (J). (gr. 3-7). 15.95 (978-0-385-32772-5(2) , Lamb, Wendy); 2005. (Illus.). (J). (gr. 3-7). lib. bdg. 17.99 (978-0-385-90936-5(5) , Lamb, Wendy) Random Hse. Children's Bks.

—Mr. Chickee's Funny Money. l.t. ed. 2006. 190p. 23.95 (978-0-7862-8670-6(9)) Thorndike Pr.

—Mr. Chickee's Messy Mission. 240p. (J). (gr. 4-7). 2008. 6.50 (*978-0-440-22922-3(7) , Yearling); 2007. (Illus.). 15.99 (978-0-385-32775-6(7) , Lamb, Wendy); 2007. (Illus.). lib. bdg. 18.99 (978-0-385-90942-6(X) , Lamb, Wendy) Random Hse. Children's Bks.

Curwood, James Oliver. Baree Son of Kazan. 2004. reprint ed. pap. 21.95 (978-1-4191-0891-4(3)); pap. 1.99 (978-1-4192-0891-1(8)) Kessinger Publishing, LLC.

—Kazan: Father of Baree. 2005. 240p. (YA). (gr. 4-7). pap. 5.95 (978-1-55704-225-5(X)) Newmarket Pr.

Custard, P. T. Jules the Lighthouse Dog, 1. Greer, Ana, illus. 2006. 32p. (J). 12.95 (978-0-9785317-0-6(1)) Black Plum Bks.

Cuyler, Margery. Reading Worries. Howard, Arthur, illus. 2008. (J). (*978-0-689-86188-8(5) , Simon & Schuster Children's Publishing) Simon & Schuster Children's Publishing.

Dadey, Debbie. Bobby & the Big, Blue Bulldog. Gordon, Mike, illus. 1998. (Bobby Ser.). 48p. (J). (gr. 2-4). pap. 3.50 (978-0-87406-889-4(4) , Willowisp Pr.) Darby Creek Publishing.

Dadey, Debbie. The Worst Name in Third Grade. 2007. 80p. (J). pap. 3.99 (*978-0-439-72000-7(1)) Scholastic, Inc.

Daggett, Wade. Coco's New Friend. 2004. 35p. pap. 17.95 (978-1-4137-2001-3(3)) PublishAmerica, Inc.

Dahl, Michael. Fables Whistle. Lee, Ji Sun, illus. 2005. (Read-It! Readers Ser.). 32p. (J). (ps). lib. bdg. 18.60 (978-1-4048-1169-0(9)) Picture Window Bks.

—Fito y el Pito. Lee, Ji Sun, illus. 2006. (Read-It! Readers en Espanol Ser.).Tr. of Fables Whistle. (SPA.). 32p. (J). (ps-3). 19.95 (978-1-4048-1691-6(7)) Picture Window Bks.

Dakin, Glenn. Wallace & Gromit Curse of the Were-Rabbit: The Essential Guide. 2005. (Illus.). 48p. (J). (ps-7). 12.99 (978-0-7566-1153-8(9)) Dorling Kindersley Publishing, Inc.

Dale, Jenny. Abandoned! 2000. (Puppy Patrol Ser.: Vol. 3). (Illus.). 112p. (J). (gr. 3-6). pap. 3.99 (978-0-439-11325-0(3)) Scholastic, Inc.

—Abandoned! 2000. (gr. 3-6). lib. bdg. 11.80 (978-0-613-24082-6(0)) Tandem Library Bks.

—Barney's Rescue. Reid, Mick, illus. 2003. 100p. (J). (978-0-439-45356-1(9)) Scholastic, Inc.

—Best of Friends. 2002. (gr. 3-6). lib. bdg. 11.80 (978-0-613-63253-9(2)) Tandem Library Bks.

—Double Trouble. 2000. (Puppy Patrol Ser.: Vol. 4). (Illus.). 112p. (J). (gr. 4-7). pap. 3.99 (978-0-439-11326-7(1)) Scholastic, Inc.

—The Great Escape. 2001. (Puppy Patrol Ser.). 112p. (YA). (gr. 8-10). pap. 3.99 (978-0-439-21811-5(X)) Scholastic, Inc.

—Gus the Greedy Puppy. 2000. (Puppy Tales Ser.). (J). 10.79 (978-0-606-19248-4(4)) Tandem Library Bks.

—King of the Castle. Reid, Mick, illus. 2003. (Puppy Patrol Ser.: No. 18). 112p. (J). (gr. 3-6). pap. 3.99 (978-0-439-31911-9(0)) Scholastic, Inc.

—Lost & Found. Reid, Mick, illus. 2003. 108p. (J). (978-0-439-54359-0(2)) Scholastic, Inc.

—Murphy's Mystery. Reid, Mick, illus. 2003. 110p. (J). (978-0-439-54364-4(9)) Scholastic, Inc.

—Perfect Puppy. 2001. (Puppy Patrol Ser.: No. 11). 112p. (J). pap. 3.99 (978-0-439-21812-2(8)) Scholastic, Inc.

—Posh Pup. 2002. (gr. 3-6). lib. bdg. 11.80 (978-0-613-65053-3(0)) Tandem Library Bks.

—The Puppy Express. Reid, Mick, illus. 2003. 108p. (J). (978-0-439-45355-4(0)) Scholastic, Inc.

—Puppy Love. Reid, Mike, illus. 2002. (Puppy Patrol Ser.: No. 16). 128p. (J). pap. 3.99 (978-0-439-31909-6(9)) Scholastic, Inc.

—Puppy Patrol: Teachers Pet. Reid, Mick, illus. l.t. ed. 1999. 184p. (J). pap. (978-0-7540-6086-4(1) , CLP 285) BBC Audio.

—Puppy Power. Reid, Mick, illus. 2003. 105p. (J). (978-0-439-45351-6(8)) Scholastic, Inc.

—Red Alert. 2001. (Puppy Patrol Ser.: Vol. 9). (Illus.). 112p. (J). (gr. 3-6). pap. 3.99 (978-0-439-21810-8(1)) Scholastic, Inc.

—The Sea Dog. 2002. (Puppy Patrol Ser.: No. 13). 128p. (J). (gr. 3-6). pap. 3.99 (978-0-439-21814-6(4) , Scholastic Paperbacks) Scholastic, Inc.

—Snowy the Surprise Puppy. Hellard, Susan, illus. 2005. 60p. (J). (*978-0-439-79124-3(3)) Scholastic, Inc.

—Spot the Sporty Puppy. 2000. (Puppy Friends Ser.). (J). (978-0-606-19725-0(7)) Tandem Library Bks.

—Star Paws. 2000. (Puppy Patrol Ser.: Vol. 5). (Illus.). 112p. (J). (gr. 4-7). pap. 3.99 (978-0-439-11327-4(X)) Scholastic, Inc.

—Superdog! Reid, Mick & Rowe, Michael, trs. Reid, Mick, illus. 2003. 110p. (J). (978-0-439-38921-1(6)) Scholastic, Inc.

—Teacher's Pet. 2000. (Puppy Patrol Ser.: Vol. 1). 128p. (J). (gr. 3-6). pap. 3.99 (978-0-439-11323-6(7)) Scholastic, Inc.

—Teacher's Pet. 1999. (gr. 3-6). lib. bdg. 11.80 (978-0-613-27181-3(5)) Tandem Library Bks.

—Top Dog! Reid, Mick, illus. 2003. 107p. (J). (978-0-439-54360-6(6)) Scholastic, Inc.

—Trick or Treat? Reid, Mick, illus. 2003. 107p. (J). (978-0-439-54362-0(2)) Scholastic, Inc.

—Tuff's Luck. 2001. (Puppy Patrol Ser.: Vol. 8). 128p. (J). (gr. 3-6). pap. 3.99 (978-0-439-11330-4(X)) Scholastic, Inc.

—Tug of Love. 2000. (Puppy Patrol Ser.: Vol. 6). 112p. (J). (gr. 4-7). mass mkt. 3.99 (978-0-439-11328-1(8)) Scholastic, Inc.

—Winter's Tale. 2001. (gr. 3-6). lib. bdg. 11.80 (978-0-613-65065-6(4)) Tandem Library Bks.

Dale, Jenny & Reid, Mick. Puppy School. 2002. (Puppy Pâtrol Ser.: No. 14). 112p. (J). per. 3.99 (978-0-439-21815-3(2)) Scholastic, Inc.

Dalmatian Press Staff. Disney 101 Dalmatians. rev. ed. 2007. 24p. 3.50 (*978-1-4037-3316-0(3)) Dalmatian Pr.

—Lady & the Tramp. 2006. 48p. 3.99 (978-1-4037-2194-5(7)) Dalmatian Pr.

—Playful Puppy: Little Pups Board Book. 2003. (Little Pups Board Bks.). (Illus.). 20p. (J). bds. 2.99 (978-1-57759-661-5(7)) Dalmatian Pr.

—Scooby Doo: A Dog's Best Friend. 2005. (Big Best Book to Color Ser.). (Illus.). 80p. (J). pap. 2.99 (978-1-4037-1179-3(8)) Dalmatian Pr.

Dalmatian Press Staff, adapted by. The Call of the Wild. 2002. (Spot the Classics Ser.). (Illus.). 182p. (J). (gr. k-5). 4.99 (978-1-57759-545-8(9)) Dalmatian Pr.

Dalmatian Press Staff, ed. 101 Dalmatian/Lady & the Tramp. 2006. 64p. pap. 4.99 (978-1-4037-2340-6(0)) Dalmatian Pr.

Damschroder, Scott. Small Dog, Small Dog, Small, Small, Dog. Faust, Laurie, illus. 2004. 24p. (J). lib. bdg. 19.95 (978-0-9754728-2-8(8)) MidAmerica Publishing Co.

Danega, Danielle. Reader. Cecil, Lauren, ed. 2007. (Firehouse Dog Ser.). 32p. (J). pap. 3.99 (978-0-439-89643-6(6)) Scholastic, Inc.

Daniels, Lucy. Puppies in the Pantry. McNicholas, Shelagh, illus. l.t. ed. 1999. (Animal Ark Ser.: No. 3). 178p. (J). (gr. 3-5). pap. (978-0-7540-6058-1(6) , CLP 264) BBC Audio.

Dann, Colin. Nobody's Dog. 2000. 144p. pap. 7.99 (978-0-09-926707-2(1)) Random Hse. GBR. *Dist:* Trafalgar Square Publishing.

Danner, Pamela. Andre' Angel in a Poodle Suit. Neuburger, Jenny, illus. 2003. 32p. (J). per. (978-0-9728429-0-7(X) , 4290X) Poodle Suit Publishing.

Dark Horse Comics Staff & Aragones, Sergio. Jamboree. 2000. (Groo Ser.). (Illus.). 96p. (YA). (gr. 5 up). pap. 9.95 (978-1-56971-462-1(2)) Dark Horse Comics.

Dart, Iris Rainer & Brotman, Joyce. Larry: The King of Rock & Roll. 2007. 176p. (J). (gr. 4-6). 16.99 (978-0-399-24546-6(4) , Putnam Juvenile) Penguin Group (USA) Inc.

David, Luke. Sight for Sore Eyes. Goldberg, Barry, tr. Goldberg, Barry, illus. 1999. (Rugrats Ser.). 32p. (J). (ps-3). per. 3.50 (978-0-671-02866-4(9) , Simon & Schuster Children's Publishing) Simon & Schuster Children's Publishing.

—Sight for Sore Eyes. 1999. (gr. k-3). lib. bdg. 11.25 (978-0-613-15977-7(2)) Tandem Library Bks.

Davidson, Margaret. Five True Dog Stories. (FRE.). (J). pap. 4.99 (978-0-590-73687-9(6)) Scholastic, Inc.

Davies, Tristan. Anoraknophobia. 1999. (Illus.). 48p. (J). pap. (978-0-340-72834-5(5) , Hodder & Stoughton) Hodder General Publishing Division.

—Wallace & Gromit: The Lost Slipper & The Curse of the Ramsbottoms. 1998. (Wallace & Gromit Comic Strip Bks.). (J). (ps-3). pap. 9.95 (978-0-8417-3035-9(0)) Adventure Medical Kits.

Davies, Tristan & Newman, Nick. Wallace & Gromit: Anoraknophobia. 1998. (Wallace & Gromit Comic Strip Bks.). (Illus.). 48p. (J). 9.95 (978-0-8417-2031-2(2)) Adler's Foreign Bks., Inc.

Davies, Tristan, et al. Crackers in Space. 2000. (Illus.). 48p. (J). pap. (978-0-340-71290-0(2) , Hodder & Stoughton) Hodder General Publishing Division.

—Crackers in Space. 2000. (Illus.). 48p. (J). 16.99 (978-0-340-71289-4(9) , Hodder & Stoughton) Hodder General Publishing Division GBR. *Dist:* Trafalgar Square Publishing.

Davis, Cathy Durbin. Big Dog Winnie. Pulley, Jan Jones, illus. 1999. 40p. (J). 19.95 (978-0-943335-18-6(3)) Marblehead Publishing.

Davis, Christine. For Every Dog an Angel. 2nd ed. 2004. (Illus.). 32p. (J). 9.95 (978-0-9659225-2-4(9)) Lighthearted Press Inc.

Davis, David. Rock n Roll Dogs. 2006. (Illus.). (J). 15.95 (978-1-58980-349-7(3)) Pelican Publishing Co., Inc.

Davis, Dayna. All White Dogs Love Mud. Osker, Denise, illus. 14p. (J). (gr. 1-5). pap. (978-0-9660350-1-8(1)) Suzalooz Pr.

Davis, Jim. K-Niner: Dog of Doom. 1998. (Garfield's Pet Force Ser.: Vol. 3). (J). (gr. 3-7). pap. 4.50 (978-0-590-05944-2(0)) Scholastic, Inc.

Davis, Lee. Spooky Game: Bear Read Alone. 2001. (Pajama Bedtime Bear Ser.). (Illus.). 24p. (J). (ps-1). pap. 6.95 (978-0-7894-4945-0(5) , D K Ink) Dorling Kindersley Publishing, Inc.

Dawe, Bruce. Luke & Lulu: Lulu Likes to Always Do Things Luke Doesn't Want Her To! 2006. (Bites Ser.). (Illus.). 86p. (J). (gr. 2-5). pap. 3.95 (978-0-7624-2623-2(3) , Running Pr. Kids) Running Pr. Bk. Pubs.

Day, Alexandra. Carl's Birthday. Day, Alexandra, illus. 2002. (Illus.). (J). 22.13 (978-0-7587-2194-5(3)) Book Wholesalers, Inc.

—Carl's Summer Vacation. Day, Alexandra, illus. 2008. (Carl Ser.). (Illus.). 32p. (J). 12.95 (*978-0-374-31085-1(8) , Farrar, Straus & Giroux (BYR)) Farrar, Straus & Giroux.

—Follow Carl! Day, Alexandra, illus. 1998. (Carl Ser.). (Illus.). 32p. (J). (ps-1). 12.95 (978-0-374-34380-4(2) , Farrar, Straus & Giroux (BYR)) Farrar, Straus & Giroux.

—Puppy Trouble: A Pop-up Book. Day, Alexandra & Meyer, Dennis K., illus. 2005. 12p. (J). (gr. k-4). reprint ed. 17.00 (978-0-7567-9662-4(8)) DIANE Publishing Co.

Day, Alexandra. You're a Good Dog, Carl! 2007. (Carl Ser.). (Illus.). 200p. 29.95 (*978-0-312-37130-2(6)) Farrar, Straus & Giroux.

Day, Ed D. Why Dogs Bark: And Other Tall Tales Told by Ted. Scott, Sarah Chamberlin, illus. 2006. (J). per. 12.95 (978-1-933002-20-0(4)) PublishingWorks.

de Beer, Hans. Little Polar Bear & the Husky Pup. de Beer, Hans, illus. (Illus.). 32p. (J). (ps-3). 2004. pap. 6.95 (978-0-7358-1904-7(1)); 1999. 15.95 (978-0-7358-1154-6(7)) North-South Bks., Inc.

De La Rame, Louisa. Dog of Flanders. 2007. pap. 87.99 (*978-1-4280-5277-2(1)) IndyPublish.com.

De Lint, Charles. Dingo. 2008. 192p. (YA). (gr. 7). 11.99 (*978-0-14-240816-2(6) , Puffin) Penguin Group (USA) Inc.

de Paola, Tomie. Hide-and-Seek All Week. de Paola, Tomie, illus. 2001. (All Aboard Reading Ser.). (Illus.). 32p. (J). (ps-2). 13.89 (978-0-448-42617-4(X)); pap. 3.99 (978-0-448-42545-0(9)) Penguin Group (USA) Inc. (Grosset & Dunlap).

—Hide-and-Seek All Week. 2001. 10.79 (978-0-606-22475-8(0)) Tandem Library Bks.

—Meet the Barkers. 2003. (Barker Twins Ser.). (Illus.). 32p. (J). (gr. k-1). pap. 5.99 (978-0-14-250083-5(6) , Puffin) Penguin Group (USA) Inc.

—Meet the Barkers: Morgan & Moffat Go to School. de Paola, Tomie, illus. 2001. (Illus.). 1p. (J). (ps-1). 13.99 (978-0-399-23708-9(9) , Putnam Juvenile) Penguin Group (USA) Inc.

—Meet the Barkers: Morgan & Moffat Go to School. 2005. (J). (gr. k-3). pap. 17.95 incl. audio (978-0-8045-6934-7(7) , SAC6934); pap. 19.95 incl. audio compact disk (978-0-8045-4129-9(9) , SACD4129) Spoken Arts, Inc.

—Morgan & Moffat Go to School. 2003. (gr. k-3). lib. bdg. 14.15 (978-0-613-66367-0(5)) Tandem Library Bks.

—A New Barker in the House. 2004. (Illus.). 32p. (J). (ps up). pap. 5.99 (978-0-14-240141-5(2) , Puffin) Penguin Group (USA) Inc.

Dear Santa- 2005. (Illus.). 24p. (J). (ps-1). bds. 6.95 (978-0-8249-6618-8(X)) Ideals Pubns.

Debra's Dog: 6 Small Books. (gr. k-3). 24.00 (978-0-7635-6229-8(7)) Rigby Education.

DeCesare, Angelo. Flip's Fantastic Journal. DeCesare, Angelo, illus. 1999. (Illus.). 48p. (J). (gr. 1-4). pap. 6.99 (978-0-14-056655-0(4) , Puffin) Penguin Group (USA) Inc.

—Flip's Fantastic Journal. 1999. (gr. 3-6). lib. bdg. 14.15 (978-0-613-21547-3(8)) Tandem Library Bks.

DeFelice, Cynthia. The Ghost of Cutler Creek. 2006. (Ghost Mysteries Ser.). 192p. (J). pap. 5.95 (978-0-374-40004-0(0) , Farrar, Straus & Giroux (BYR)) Farrar, Straus & Giroux.

DeFelice, Cynthia C. The Ghost of Cutler Creek. 2004. (Ghost Mysteries Ser.). 192p. (J). 16.00 (978-0-374-38058-8(9)) Farrar, Straus & Giroux.

—The Ghost of Cutler Creek. l.t. ed. 2005. 20.95 (978-0-7862-7190-0(6)) Thorndike Pr.

DeJong, Meindert. Y Entonces Llego un Perro. (SPA.). 144p. (YA). (gr. 5-9). (978-84-279-3220-3(0) ; NG3490) Noguer y Caralt Editores, S. A. ESP. *Dist:* Lectorum Pubns., Inc.

DeKok, Joy. Room for Bandit. 2006. (ENG.). 36p. (J). per. 16.99 (978-1-4141-0585-7(1)) Pleasant Word.

De'Leon, Lunden. Oops Loops. 2006. 28p. pap. 9.95 (*978-1-4327-0114-7(2)) Outskirts Press, Inc.

Demas, Corinne. Saying Goodbye to Lulu. Hoyt, Ard, tr. Hoyt, Ard, illus. 2004. 40p. (J). (ps-3). 15.99 (978-0-316-70278-2(1)) Little Brown & Co.

Demas, Corinne. Yuck! Stuck in the Muck. 2006. (Illus.). 32p. (J). lib. bdg. 9.00 (*978-1-4242-0985-9(4)) Fitzgerald Bks.

—Yuck! Stuck in the Muck. Rader, Laura, illus. 2006. (Scholastic Reader Ser.). 32p. (J). pap. 3.99 (978-0-439-79431-2(5) , Cartwheel Bks.) Scholastic, Inc.

Demers, Dominique, et al. Old Thomas & the Little Fairy. Poulin, Stephane, illus. 2001. 29p. (J). (ps-3). pap. (978-1-894363-45-7(0)) Dominique & Friends.

Deming, Lynette. Day in Matthews Shoes. 2006. 28p. pap. 9.95 (*978-1-4327-0100-0(2)) Outskirts Press, Inc.

DePaola, Tomie. Hide-and-Seek All Week. 2001. (Illus.). 32p. (J). (ps-3). lib. bdg. 11.80 (978-0-613-50319-8(8)) Tandem Library Bks.

DePrisco, Dorothea. Willie & Buster Take the Train. Ansley, Frank, illus. 2003. (Stories to Share Ser.). 10p. (J). 10.95 (978-1-58117-183-9(8) , Intervisual/Piggy Toes) Dalmatian Pr.

Derksen, Barbara Ann. Alexis Learns to Trust: Shih-Tzu Puppy Adventures. 2007. (J). 9.99 (*978-1-59872-845-3(8)) Instantpublisher.com.

Derrick, Patricia. Dody the Dog Has a Rainbow. 2007. 32p. 18.95 (978-1-933818-10-8(7)) Animalations.

Desimini, Lisa. Spot the Fire Dog. Desimini, Lisa, illus. 2001. (Illus.). 40p. (J). (ps up). pap. 16.95 (978-0-439-23322-4(4) , Blue Sky Pr., The) Scholastic, Inc.

Desrosiers, Sylvie. Les Enquetes de l'Agence Notdog. 2000. (Roman Jeunesse Ser.). (FRE.). 288p. (J). (gr. 4-7). pap. (978-2-89021-390-6(0)) Diffusion du livre Mirabel.

Desrosiers, Sylvie & Sylvestre, Daniel. Peut-On Dessiner un Souvenir? 2001. (FRE., Illus.). 96p. (J). pap. (978-2-89021-510-8(5)) Diffusion du livre Mirabel.

—Quelqu'un A-T-Il Vu Notdog? 2001. (Roman Jeunesse Ser.). (FRE., Illus.). 96p. (J). pap. (978-2-89021-453-8(2)) Diffusion du livre Mirabel.

Dewdney, Anna. Grumpy Gloria. Dewdney, Anna, illus. 2006. (Illus.). 28p. (J). (ps). 15.99 (978-0-670-06123-5(9) , Viking Juvenile) Penguin Group (USA) Inc.

Un Dia de Perros!, 6 packs. (Chiquilibros Ser.). (SPA.). (gr. k-1). 23.00 (978-0-7635-8602-7(1)) Rigby Education.

DiCamillo, Kate. Because of Winn-Dixie. 2002. (Illus.). (J). 13.83 (978-0-7587-6512-3(6)) Book Wholesalers, Inc.

—Because of Winn-Dixie. braille ed. 2003. (J). (gr. 2). spiral bd. (978-0-616-15263-8(9)) Canadian National Institute for the Blind/Institut National Canadien pour les Aveugles.

—Because of Winn-Dixie. (Because of Winn-Dixie Ser.). (J). 2001. 192p. (gr. 3 up). pap. 5.99 (978-0-7636-1605-2(2)); 2000. 184p. (gr. 4-7). 15.99 (978-0-7636-0776-0(2)); 2004. 184p. 19.99 (978-0-7636-2557-3(4)); 2004. (Illus.). 192p. (gr. 3). mass mkt. 5.99 (978-0-7636-2558-0(2)) Candlewick Pr.

—Because of Winn-Dixie. unabr. ed. 2004. 192p. (J). (gr. 4-7). pap. 29.00 incl. audio (978-0-8072-0707-9(1) , Listening Library) Random Hse. Audio Publishing Group.

—Because of Winn-Dixie. 2001. (gr. 3-6). lib. bdg. 14.15 (978-0-613-39503-8(4)) Tandem Library Bks.

C
D

—Because of Winn-Dixie. l.t. ed. 2002. 125p. (J). 23.95 (978-0-7862-3665-7(5)) Thomson Gale.

—Il Cane Piu Brutto del Mondo. pap. 22.95 (978-88-04-50721-5(7)) Mondadori ITA. *Dist:* Distribooks, Inc.

—Gracias a Winn-Dixie. 2005. (SPA.). pap. 4.99 (978-84-279-3254-8(5)) Noguer y Caralt Editores, S. A. ESP. *Dist:* Lectorum Pubns., Inc.

Dickinson, Peter. Chuck & Danielle. 115p. (J). (gr. 3-5). pap. 3.99 (978-0-8072-1504-3(X) , Listening Library) Random Hse. Audio Publishing Group.

—Chuck & Danielle. 2001. (Illus.). 128p. (gr. 4-7). pap. 12.00 (978-0-375-89505-0(1) , Yearling) Random Hse. Children's Bks.

—Chuck & Danielle. 2001. lib. bdg. 21.10 (978-0-613-87813-5(2)) Tandem Library Bks.

Dickson, Louise. Lu & Clancy's Crime Science. Cupples, Pat, illus. 1999. 40p. (J). (ps-k). lib. bdg. 14.10 (978-0-613-21938-9(4)) Tandem Library Bks.

—Vanishing Cat. 2002. (gr. 3-6). lib. bdg. 15.25 (978-0-613-53331-7(3)) Tandem Library Bks.

Diehl, Jean Heilprin. Loon Chase. Freeman, Kathryn, illus. 2006. 32p. (J). 15.95 (978-0-9764943-8-6(8)) Sylvan Dell Pubng.

Dig: KinderReaders Individual Title Six-Packs. (Kinderstarters Ser.). 8p. (ps-1). 21.00 (978-0-7635-8659-1(5)) Rigby Education.

Dillingham, Mike. Rivers Book Two: Through the Eyes of a Blind Sled Dog. 2003. 13.95 (978-1-59433-004-9(2)) Publication Consultants.

DiMare, Loren Spiotta. Rockwell: A Boy & His Dog. Miller, Cliff, illus. 2005. 32p. (J). 14.95 (978-0-7641-5790-5(6)) Barron's Educational Series, Inc.

Dirty & Wet Dogs. 2005. (J). (978-1-932570-49-6(7)) Literacy Footprints Inc.

DiSalvo-Ryan, DyAnne. A Dog Like Jack. unabr. ed. 2005. (Illus.). (J). (ps-2). pap. 16.95 incl. audio (978-0-87499-758-3(5)) BBC Audiobooks America.

—A Dog Like Jack. DiSalvo-Ryan, DyAnne, illus. 1999. (Illus.). 32p. (J). (gr. k-3). tchr. ed. 16.95 (978-0-8234-1369-0(1)); pap. 6.95 (978-0-8234-1680-6(1)) Holiday Hse., Inc.

—A Dog Like Jack. 2005. (Live Oak Readalong Ser.). (J). pap. 18.95 incl. audio compact disk (978-1-59519-298-1(0)) Live Oak Media.

—A Dog Like Jack. DiSalvo-Ryan, DyAnne, illus. 2001. (Illus.). pap. 25.95 incl. audio (978-0-87499-759-0(3)); pap. 37.95 incl. audio (978-0-87499-760-6(7)) Live Oak Media.

Disney Press Staff. 102 Dalmatians. 2001. (Illus.). 96p. (J). pap. (978-0-7868-4463-0(9)) Disney Pr.

Disney Staff. 101 Dalmatas. 2000. Tr. of One Hundred One Dalmatians. (SPA.). 112p. (J). 19.95 (978-84-406-6841-7(4)) Ediciones B ESP. *Dist:* AIMS International Bks., Inc.

—101 Dalmatians. (FRE.). 96p. (J). (gr. k-5). pap. 9.95 (978-0-7859-8847-2(5)) French & European Pubns., Inc.

Divine, Gloria Jill. Sissy & Scooter's Things to Do When You're Blue. 2002. (Illus.). per. 14.95 (978-0-9711773-0-7(9)) Moondoggie Publishing.

D'Lacey, Chris. Dexter's Journey. Roberts, David, illus. 2001. (Blue Bananas Ser.). 48p. (J). (gr. 1-2). (978-0-7787-0846-9(2)); pap. (978-0-7787-0892-6(6)) Crabtree Publishing Co.

—Dexter's Journey. 2002. (gr. k-3). lib. bdg. 12.95 (978-0-613-52829-0(8)) Tandem Library Bks.

Dodd, Emma. Dog's ABC: A Silly Story about the Alphabet. Dodd, Emma, illus. 2002. (Illus.). 32p. (J). 14.99 (978-0-525-46837-0(4) , Dutton Juvenile) Penguin Group (USA) Inc.

—Dog's Colorful Day: A Messy Story about Colors & Counting. Dodd, Emma, illus. 2003. (Illus.). 32p. (J). (gr. k-3). pap. 5.99 (978-0-14-250019-4(4) , Puffin) Penguin Group (USA) Inc.

Dodd, Lynley. A Dragon in a Wagon. Dodd, Lynley, illus. 2000. (Gold Star First Readers Ser.). (Illus.). 32p. (J). (gr. 1 up). lib. bdg. 22.00 (978-0-8368-2687-6(6)) Stevens, Gareth Inc.

—Hairy Maclary & Zachary Quack. Dodd, Lynley, illus. 2000. (Gold Star First Readers Ser.). (Illus.). 32p. (J). (gr. 1 up). lib. bdg. 22.00 (978-0-8368-2676-0(0)) Stevens, Gareth Inc.

—Hairy Maclary & Zachary Quack. 2005. (Illus.). 32p. (J). reprint ed. 5.95 (978-1-58246-147-2(3) , Tricycle Pr.) Ten Speed Pr.

—Hairy Maclary from Donaldson's Dairy. Dodd, Lynley, illus. 2000. (Gold Star First Readers Ser.). (Illus.). 32p. (J). (gr. 1 up). lib. bdg. 21.26 (978-0-8368-2688-3(4)) Stevens, Gareth Inc.

—Hairy Maclary from Donaldson's Dairy. 2005. (Illus.). 36p. (J). 5.95 (978-1-58246-059-8(0) , Tricycle Pr.) Ten Speed Pr.

—Hairy Maclary Scattercat. Dodd, Lynley, illus. 2000. (Gold Star First Readers Ser.). (Illus.). 32p. (J). (gr. 1 up). lib. bdg. 22.00 (978-0-8368-2689-0(2)) Stevens, Gareth Inc.

—Hairy Maclary Scattercat. 2005. (Illus.). 32p. (J). 5.95 (978-1-58246-095-6(7) , Tricycle Pr.) Ten Speed Pr.

—Hairy Maclary, Sit. Dodd, Lynley, illus. 2001. (Gold Star First Readers Ser.). (Illus.). 32p. (J). (gr. 1 up). lib. bdg. 22.00 (978-0-8368-2808-5(9)) Stevens, Gareth Inc.

—Hairy Maclary's Bone. Dodd, Lynley, illus. 2001. (Gold Star First Readers Ser.). (Illus.). 32p. (J). (gr. 1 up). lib. bdg. 22.00 (978-0-8368-2782-8(1)) Stevens, Gareth Inc.

—Hairy Maclary's Bone. 2001. (ps-2). lib. bdg. 14.10 (978-0-613-57835-6(X)) Tandem Library Bks.

—Hairy Maclary's Bone. 2005. (Illus.). 36p. (J). 5.95 (978-1-58246-060-4(4) , Tricycle Pr.) Ten Speed Pr.

—Hairy Maclary's Caterwaul Caper. Dodd, Lynley, illus. 2000. (Gold Star First Readers Ser.). (Illus.). 32p. (J). (gr. 1 up). lib. bdg. 22.00 (978-0-8368-2690-6(6)) Stevens, Gareth Inc.

—Hairy Maclary's Showbusiness. 2006. (Illus.). 32p. (J). 5.95 (***978-1-58246-208-0(9)*** , Tricycle Pr.) Ten Speed Pr.

—Schnitzel Von Krumm, Dogs Never Climb Trees. 2004. (Gold Star First Readers Ser.). (Illus.). 32p. (J). (gr. 1 up). lib. bdg. 22.00 (978-0-8368-4092-6(5)) Stevens, Gareth Inc.

—Schnitzel Von Krumm's Basketwork. Dodd, Lynley, illus. 2001. (Gold Star First Readers Ser.). (Illus.). 32p. (J). (gr. 1 up). lib. bdg. 22.00 (978-0-8368-2783-5(X)) Stevens, Gareth Inc.

Doder, Joshua. A Dog Called Grk. (Grk Bks.). (J). (gr. 4-7). 2008. 240p. 6.50 (***978-0-440-42147-4(0)*** , Yearling); 2007. 272p. 14.99 (978-0-385-73359-5(3) , Delacorte Bks. for Young Readers); 2007. 272p. lib. bdg. 18.99 (978-0-385-90374-5(X) , Delacorte Bks. for Young Readers) Random Hse. Children's Bks.

—Grk & the Hotdog Trail. 2008. (J). (***978-0-385-73361-8(5)***); (***978-0-385-90376-9(6)***); pap. (***978-0-440-42150-4(0)***) Dell Publishing. (Delacorte Pr.).

—Grk & the Pelotti Gang. 2007. (Grk Bks.). 208p. (J). (gr. 4-7). 14.99 (***978-0-385-73360-1(7)***); lib. bdg. 17.99 (***978-0-385-90375-2(8)***) Random Hse. Children's Bks. (Delacorte Bks. for Young Readers).

Dodson, Emma. Badly Drawn Dog. 2004. (Illus.). 32p. (J). 14.95 (978-0-7641-5814-8(7)) Barron's Educational Series, Inc.

The Dog & the Bone, Set 2. l.t. ed. 1999. (Illus.). 19p. (J). (gr. k-6). reprint ed. pap. 2.50 (978-1-893688-02-5(X)) Carroll Schl., The.

The Dog & the Wolf, Set 1. l.t. ed. 1999. (Illus.). 25p. (J). (gr. k-6). reprint ed. pap. 2.50 (978-1-893688-04-9(6)) Carroll Schl., The.

Dog Artlist Collection Staff. The Dog: From Arf! Arf! to Zzzzzz. Dog Artlist Collection Staff, illus. 2005. (Illus.). 32p. (J). (ps up). bds. 6.99 (978-0-06-077181-2(X) , Harper Festival) HarperCollins Pubs.

Dog Artlist Collection Staff, contrib. by. Dog Princess Fairy Tails. 2008. (Illus.). 32p. (J). 16.99 (978-0-06-078310-5(9)); lib. bdg. 17.89 (978-0-06-078311-2(7)) HarperCollins Pubs.

A Dog Called Bear: Individual Title Six-Packs. 16p. (gr. 2 up). 35.00 (978-0-7635-9228-8(5)) Rigby Education.

A Dog Day! Individual Title Six-Packs. (Chiquilibros Ser.). (gr. k-1). 23.00 (978-0-7635-0419-9(X)) Rigby Education.

The Dog from Outer Space: Individual Title Six-Pack Pouch - Level J. (Lighthouse Ser.). 16p. (gr. 2 up). 28.00 (978-0-7578-0864-7(6)) Rigby Education.

A Dog to Walk. 2005. (J). (978-1-58453-294-1(7)) Pioneer Valley Educational Pr., Inc.

Doggie Daze. (Illus.). 12p. (J). bds. (978-2-7643-0126-5(X)) Phidal Publishing, Inc./Editions Phidal, Inc.

A Doggone Good Story. 2006. (J). (978-0-9779606-0-6(9)) Isaacs, John.

Doggy Heaven's in the Sky! 2004. (J). 4.95 (***978-0-9791362-0-7(2)***) Tony Tales.

Donat, Jaclynne. Ribbons for Randi. 2006. (ENG.). 52p. per. 12.95 (***978-1-4241-5307-7(7)***) PublishAmerica, Inc.

Don't Worry: Individual Title Six-Packs. (Literatura 2000 Ser.). (gr. 2-3). 33.00 (978-0-7635-0167-9(0)) Rigby Education.

Doogie, Doogie. The Lot: Doogie's Survival. 2002. 48p. pap. 9.00 (978-0-8059-5641-2(7)) Dorrance Publishing Co., Inc.

Doris, Fisher & Dani, Sneed. One Odd Day. Karen, Lee, illus. 2006. 32p. (J). 15.95 (978-0-9768823-3-6(7)) Sylvan Dell Pubng.

Dorling Kindersley Publishing Staff. Wallace & Gromit: Curse of the Were-Rabbit. 2005. (Ultimate sticker Bks.). (Illus.). 16p. (J). 6.99 (978-0-7566-1154-5(7)) Dorling Kindersley Publishing, Inc.

Dot the Fire Dog. 2004. (J). 29.95 incl. cd-rom (978-1-55592-623-6(1)); 24.95 incl. audio (978-1-55592-621-2(5)) Weston Woods Studios, Inc.

Dotty Dog: Shaky Sound Book. 2003. (J). (978-1-59292-020-4(9)) SoftPlay, Inc.

Doudna, Kelly. Doggie Pants. Haberstroh, Anne, illus. 2006. (Fact & Fiction Ser.). (J). 21.35 (978-1-59679-931-8(5) , SandCastle); pap. (978-1-59679-932-5(3)) ABDO Publishing Co.

Dougherty, Terri. The Bath. Yi, Hye Won, illus. 2006. (Read-It! Readers Ser.). 32p. (J). (ps-3). 18.60 (978-1-4048-1576-6(7)) Picture Window Bks.

Dower, Laura. Monkey See, Doggy Do. 2000. (ps-2). lib. bdg. 11.25 (978-0-613-32842-5(6)) Tandem Library Bks.

Downes, Alice. 102 Dalmatians: Junior Novel. 2000. (Illus.). 96p. (J). (gr. 3-7). pap. 4.99 (978-0-7868-4440-1(X)) Disney Pr.

Doyle, Arthur Conan. Le Chien des Baskerville. (FRE.). pap. 16.95 (978-2-07-051346-8(7)) Gallimard, Editions FRA. *Dist:* Distribooks, Inc.

—The Hound of the Baskervilles: Another Adventure of Sherlock Holmes. 2001. (gr. 7-12). lib. bdg. 16.45 (978-0-613-64290-3(2)); 2001. (gr. 7-12). lib. bdg. 12.95 (978-0-613-37148-3(8)); 2000. (gr. 3-6). lib. bdg. 11.80 (978-0-613-63203-4(6)) Tandem Library Bks.

—The Hounds of the Baskervilles. abr. ed. 2001. (gr. 7-12). lib. bdg. 15.25 (978-0-613-43833-9(7)) Tandem Library Bks.

—Sherlock Holmes & the Case of the Hound of the Baskervilles. 2005. (Great Illustrated Classics Ser.). (Illus.). 237p. (J). (gr. 3-8). 21.35 (978-1-59679-250-0(7) , ABDO & Daughters) ABDO Publishing Co.

Doyle, Malachy. Albert & Sarah Jane. 2007. (J). lib. bdg. 16.95 (***978-1-59566-336-8(3)***) QEB Publishing Inc.

Doyle, Malachy. Sleepy Pendoodle. Vivas, Julie, illus. 2001. 32p. (J). (ps-1). 12.99 (978-0-7636-1561-1(7)) Candlewick Pr.

Doyle, Roddy. The Giggler Treatment. 2001. (gr. 3-6). lib. bdg. 11.80 (978-0-613-44359-3(4)) Tandem Library Bks.

Doyle, Roddy. Wilderness. 2007. (J). (***978-0-439-02357-3(2)***); 224p. (gr. 7 up). pap. 16.99 (***978-0-439-02356-6(4)***) Scholastic, Inc. (Levine, Arthur A. Bks.).

DPWW. Porkchop Pup. 1999. 32p. (J). 8.95 (978-0-7868-3219-4(3)) Disney Pr.

Draper, Melissa J. Holly the Christmas Collie. Kravanek, J. Elise, illus. 2004. 63p. (J). (978-0-9741081-3-1(8)) Acres Publishing.

Drew, Rosa. Cat & Dog Go Shopping, Vol. 4476. Kupperstein, Joel, ed. Leary, Catherine, illus. 1998. (Learn to Read Math Ser.). 16p. (J). pap. 2.75 (978-1-57471-383-1(3) , 4476) Creative Teaching Pr., Inc.

Dubowski, Cathy East. Dog's Life. 1998. (gr. 7-12). lib. bdg. 13.00 (978-0-613-73049-5(6)) Tandem Library Bks.

Duchess of Windsor: The Dog Who Thinks She's a Person & Sometimes a Cat. 1999. (ps-2). pap. (978-0-9668780-0-4(0)) Lighthouse Literary Pr., Inc.

Duffy, Daniel M., illus. The Magic Show Mystery, Vol. 4. 1998. (Adventures of Benny & Watch: Vol. No. 4). 32p. (J). (ps-2). pap. 3.95 (978-0-8075-4939-1(8)) Whitman, Albert & Co.

Dumin, Jennifer. Wolfie & Freddie: the New Puppy. 2006. (ENG.). 44p. per. 22.65 (***978-1-4257-0680-7(0)***) Xlibris Corp.

Dunbar, Polly. Dog Blue. Dunbar, Polly, illus. 2004. (Illus.). 40p. (J). (gr. k-k). 14.99 (978-0-7636-2476-7(4)) Candlewick Pr.

Duncan, Al. Rescue Dog. Panse, Sonal, illus. 2005. (J). per. 10.00 (978-0-9754298-6-0(8) , Ithaca Pr.) Authors & Artists Publishers of New York, Inc.

Dunfey, Beth, ed. Scooby-Doo, 4 Pack. 2001. (Teacher's Pets Ser.). 32p. (J). lthr. 19.80 (978-0-439-31810-5(6) , Scholastic Paperbacks) Scholastic, Inc.

Dunlap, Maggie, illus. The Four Dog Blues Band, or, How Chester, Boy, Dog in the Fog, & Diva Took the Big City by Storm. 2007. (J). (***978-1-887422-13-0(7)***) Mississippi Museum of Art.

Dunn-Dern, Lisa. Dr. Duncan Dog on Duty! 2007. (J). per. 16.99 (***978-1-933156-20-0(1)*** , Visikid Bks.) GSVQ Publishing.

Dunwoodie, Helen. Dogspell. 2003. (Young Corgi Ser.). (Illus.). 89p. pap. 8.99 (978-0-552-54853-3(7) , Corgi) Transworld Publishers Ltd. GBR. *Dist:* Independent Pubs. Group.

Eagle, Rita. Sniffy the Beagle. Rasmussen, Gerry, illus. 2007. (ENG.). 44p. per. 13.95 (***978-1-59800-537-0(5)***) Outskirts Press, Inc.

East, Jacqueline. Ed the Pup I Can't. 1999. (Ed the Pup Ser.). (J). (ps-3). (978-1-894155-66-3(1)) Cethial & Bossche Co.

—Ed the Pup I Won't Eat That. 1999. (Ed the Pup Ser.). (ps-3). (978-1-894155-76-2(9)) Cethial & Bossche Co.

—Ed the Pup I'm Scared of the Dark. 1999. (Ed the Pup Ser.). (ps-3). (978-1-894155-77-9(7)) Cethial & Bossche Co.

East, Jacqueline, illus. Puppy. 2007. (Wiggle-Waggles Ser.). 8p. (J). (ps). bds. 4.99 (***978-0-7641-6074-5(5)***) Barron's Educational Series, Inc.

Eastman, P. D. Big Dog ... Little Dog. 2006. (Bright & Early Board Bks.). (Illus.). 24p. (J). (gr. k-ps). bds. 4.99 (978-0-375-87539-7(5) , Random Hse. Bks. for Young Readers) Random Hse. Children's Bks.

—Big Dog... Little Dog. 2003. (I Can Read It All by Myself Ser.). (Illus.). 48p. (J). (gr. k-3). 8.99 (978-0-375-82297-1(6) , Random Hse. Bks. for Young Readers) Random Hse. Children's Bks.

—Big Dog... Little Dog. Eastman, P. D. & Eastman, Tony, illus. 2003. (I Can Read It All by Myself Ser.). 48p. (J). (gr. k-3). lib. bdg. 13.99 (978-0-375-92297-8(0) , Random Hse. Bks. for Young Readers) Random Hse. Children's Bks.

—Ve, Perro, Ve! Go, Dog. Go! Perdomo, Adolfo Perez, tr. 2003. Tr. of Go, Dog, Go!. (SPA & ENG., Illus.). 24p. (J). (gr. k-ps). bds. 4.99 (978-0-375-82361-9(1) , RH Para Ninos) Random Hse. Children's Bks.

Eastman, Peter. Fred & Ted Go Camping. 2005. (Bright & Early Bks.). (Illus.). 48p. (J). (gr. k-3). 8.99 (978-0-375-82965-9(2)); lib. bdg. 12.99 (978-0-375-92965-6(7)) Random Hse. Children's Bks. (Random Hse. Bks. for Young Readers).

Eavy, Tiki. Life Through Tiki's Eyes: With Comments by Tiger. 2000. (Illus.). 16p. (J). pap. (978-1-931311-00-7(5)) Exceptional Innovations, Inc.

Eding, June. Easter Showers. Chauhan, Manhar, illus. 2007. (Puppy Scooby-Doo Ser.). 32p. (J). pap. 3.99 (978-0-448-44485-7(2) , Grosset & Dunlap) Penguin Group (USA) Inc.

Edwards, Frank B. Robin Hood with Lots of Dogs. Bianchi, John, illus. 1999. (Dog Eared Classics Ser.). 32p. (J). (gr. 3-6). pap. 15.95 (978-1-894323-09-3(2)) Pokeweed Pr. CAN. *Dist:* Fitzhenry & Whiteside, Ltd.

Edwards, Frank B. & Bianchi, John. Robin Hood with Lots of Dogs. 1999. (Dog Eared Classics Ser.). (Illus.). 32p. (J). (gr. 3-6). pap. 5.95 (978-1-894323-08-6(4)) Pokeweed Pr. CAN. *Dist:* Fitzhenry & Whiteside, Ltd.

—Treasure Island with Lots of Dogs. 1999. (Dog Eared Classics Ser.). (Illus.). 32p. (J). (gr. 3-6). pap. 5.95 (978-1-894323-10-9(6)); lib. bdg. 15.95 (978-1-894323-11-6(4)) Pokeweed Pr. CAN. *Dist:* Fitzhenry & Whiteside, Ltd.

Edwards, Kris. Santa Paws #8 Santa Paws & the Christmas Storm. 2005. 144p. (J). pap. (***978-0-439-78115-2(9)***) Scholastic, Inc.

—Santa Paws on Christmas Island. 2007. (Santa Paws Ser.). 144p. (J). pap. 4.99 (***978-0-439-88812-7(3)*** , Scholastic Paperbacks) Scholastic, Inc.

Edwards, Kris. Santa Paws Saves the Day. 2005. (Santa Paws Ser.: No. 7). 144p. (J). (gr. 3-7). pap. 4.99 (978-0-439-57354-2(8) , Scholastic Paperbacks) Scholastic, Inc.

Edwards, Nicholas. Our Hero. 2002. (gr. k-3). lib. bdg. 12.40 (978-0-613-72041-0(5)) Tandem Library Bks.

—Santa Paws, Come Home. 2000. (Santa Paws Ser.: No. 4). 208p. (J). (gr. 3-7). pap. 4.99 (978-0-590-37990-8(9) , Scholastic Paperbacks) Scholastic, Inc.

—Santa Paws, Our Hero. 2002. (Santa Paws Ser.: No. 5). 176p. (J). pap. 4.99 (978-0-439-37283-1(6)) Scholastic, Inc.

Edwards, Pamela Duncan. Muldoon. 2002. 32p. (ps-2). 14.99 (978-0-7868-0360-6(6)); 15.49 (978-0-7868-2305-5(4)) Hyperion Bks. for Children.

Edwards, S. Neil. My Dog, Digger. 2006. 122p. pap. 17.95 (978-1-4241-0514-4(5)) PublishAmerica, Inc.

Egan, Tim. Burnt Toast on Davenport Street. Egan, Tim, illus. 2001. (Sandpiper Bks.). (Illus.). 32p. (J). (gr. k-3). pap. 6.95 (978-0-618-11121-3(2)) Houghton Mifflin Co. Trade & Reference Div.

Eggleton, Jill. Cat & Dog: Emergent Level Satellite Individual Title Six-Packs. (Sails Literacy Ser.). (gr. k-1). 27.00 (978-0-7578-7915-9(2)) Rigby Education.

Ehlert, Lois. Wag a Tail. 2007. (Illus.). 40p. (J). (ps-2). 16.00 (978-0-15-205843-2(5)) Harcourt Trade Pubs.

Ehrenhaft, Daniel. The Last Dog on Earth. 2004. 240p. (J). (gr. 4-7). pap. 5.50 (978-0-440-41950-1(6) , Yearling) Random Hse. Children's Bks.

Ellis, Andy. Scaredy Dog. 2006. (I Am Reading Ser.). (Illus.). 48p. (J). (gr. k-3). pap. 3.95 (978-0-7534-6028-3(9) , Kingfisher) Houghton Mifflin Co. Trade & Reference Div.

Ellis, Rolant. Castell Marwolaeth Boenus Ac Erchyll. 2005. (WEL., Illus.). 75p. pap. (978-0-86243-377-2(0)) Y Lolfa.

Ellsberry, Sharon. The Spaniel Family Goes to the State Fair. Espinosa, Chris, illus. 2004. 24p. (J). 9.00 (978-0-9724637-2-0(0)) Sky Rocket Pr.

Elmer, Robert. Wired Wonder Woof. 2001. (SpaceKids Ser.: Vol. 3). (Illus.). 112p. (J). (gr. 2-6). pap. 4.99 (978-0-7642-2358-7(5)) Bethany Hse. Pubs.

—Wired Wonder Woof. 2001. (gr. 3-6). lib. bdg. 13.00 (978-0-613-82426-2(1)) Tandem Library Bks.

Eman, Leisa M. Pugsley's Imagination. 2007. 52p. per. 8.95 (***978-0-595-44247-8(1)***) iUniverse, Inc.

Emerson, Scott. The Brotherhood of the Moon: From the Notebooks of Edward R. Smithfield, D.V.M. Glasauer, Willi, illus. 2005. (J). 9.95 (978-0-689-87630-1(0) , Simon & Schuster Children's Publishing) Simon & Schuster Children's Publishing.

Emigh, Karen. Bookworm. 2007. (Illus.). 21p. (J). (ps-3). pap. 9.95 (***978-1-932565-42-3(6)***) Future Horizons, Inc.

Emily Breaks Free - Evaluation Guide. 2006. (J). (978-1-55942-404-2(4)) Marsh Media.

Emily Breaks Free - Teaching Guide. 2000. 17.95 (978-1-55942-157-7(6)) Marsh Media.

Equipo Staff. El Perro. 2000. (SPA., Illus.). 12p. (J). (ps-k). 7.95 (978-84-488-0892-1(4)) Beascoa, Ediciones S.A. ESP. *Dist:* Distribooks, Inc., Lectorum Pubns., Inc.

Erickson, John R. The Case of the Black-Hooded Hangmans. Holmes, Gerald L., illus. 1998. (Hank the Cowdog Ser.: No. 24). 144p. (J). (gr. 2-5). 15.99 (978-0-670-88431-5(6) , Viking Juvenile); Vol. 24. pap. 4.99 (978-0-14-130400-7(6) , Puffin) Penguin Group (USA) Inc.

—The Case of the Black-Hooded Hangmans. 1999. (Hank the Cowdog Ser.: No. 24). (gr. 3-6). lib. bdg. 13.00 (978-0-7857-6345-1(7)) Tandem Library Bks.

—The Case of the Blazing Sky, No. 51. Holmes, Gerald L., illus. 2008. (Hank the Cowdog Ser.). 144p. (J). (gr. 3). 5.99 (***978-0-14-241015-8(2)*** , Puffin) Penguin Group (USA) Inc.

—The Case of the Blazing Sky #51. Holmes, Gerald L., illus. 2008. (Hank the Cowdog Ser.). 144p. (J). (gr. 3). 15.99 (***978-0-670-06260-7(X)*** , Viking Juvenile) Penguin Group (USA) Inc.

—The Case of the Booby-Trapped Pickup. Holmes, Gerald L., illus. 2007. (Hank the Cowdog Ser.: No. 49). 144p. (J). 4.99 (978-0-14-240755-4(0) , Puffin); 15.99 (978-0-670-06186-0(7) , Viking Juvenile) Penguin Group (USA) Inc.

—The Case of the Burrowing Robot, Vol. 42. Holmes, Gerald L., illus. 2003. (Hank the Cowdog Ser.: No. 42). 144p. (J). (gr. 3). 15.99 (978-0-670-03632-5(3) , Viking Juvenile); (gr. 4-6). pap. 4.99 (978-0-14-250063-7(1) , Puffin) Penguin Group (USA) Inc.

—The Case of the Burrowing Robot. 2003. (Hank the Cowdog Ser.: No. 42). (gr. 3-6). lib. bdg. 13.00 (978-0-613-66353-3(5)) Tandem Library Bks.

—The Case of the Car-Barkaholic Dog. Holmes, Gerald L., illus. (Hank the Cowdog Ser.: No. 17). 144p. (J). (gr. 2-5). 2000. 14.99 (978-0-670-88424-7(3) , Viking Juvenile); 1998. pap. 4.99 (978-0-14-130393-2(X) , Puffin) Penguin Group (USA) Inc.

—The Case of the Deadly Ha-Ha Game. Holmes, Gerald L., illus. 2001. (Hank the Cowdog Ser.: No. 37). 144p. (J). (gr. 2-5). 14.99 (978-0-670-89640-0(3) , Viking Juvenile) Penguin Group (USA) Inc.

—The Case of the Deadly Ha-Ha Game, Vol. 37. Gilson, K., ed. Holmes, Gerald L., illus. 2001. (Hank the Cowdog Ser.: No. 37). 144p. (J). (gr. 2-5). pap. 4.99 (978-0-14-131048-0(0) , Puffin) Penguin Group (USA) Inc.

—The Case of the Deadly Ha-Ha Game. 2001. (Hank the Cowdog Ser.: No. 37). (gr. 3-6). lib. bdg. 13.00 (978-0-613-33649-9(6)) Tandem Library Bks.

—The Case of the Double Bumblebee Sting. Holmes, Gerald L., illus. 1998. (Hank the Cowdog Ser.: No. 22). 144p. (J). (gr. 2-5). 14.99 (978-0-670-88429-2(4) , Viking Juvenile); Vol. 22. pap. 4.99 (978-0-14-130398-7(0) , Puffin) Penguin Group (USA) Inc.

—The Case of the Falling Sky. Holmes, Gerald L., illus. 2005. (Hank the Cowdog Ser.: No. 45). 129p. (J). lib. bdg. 17.00 (***978-1-4242-1602-4(8)***) Fitzgerald Bks.

C D

—The Case of the Falling Sky. Holmes, Gerald L., illus. 2005. (Hank the Cowdog Ser.: No. 45). (J). 144p. pap. 4.99 (978-0-14-240296-2(6) , Puffin); 160p. (gr. 3-7). 15.99 (978-0-670-05999-7(4) , Viking Juvenile) Penguin Group (USA) Inc.

—The Case of the Fiddle-Playing Fox, Vol. 12. Holmes, Gerald L., illus. 1998. (Hank the Cowdog Ser.: No. 12). 144p. (J). (gr. 2-5). pap. 4.99 (978-0-14-130388-8(3) , Puffin) Penguin Group (USA) Inc.

—The Case of the Garbage Monster from Outer Space. Holmes, Gerald L., illus. 1999. (Hank the Cowdog Ser.: No. 32). 144p. (J). (gr. 2-5). 13.99 (978-0-670-88488-9(X) , Viking Juvenile) Penguin Group (USA) Inc.

—The Case of the Halloween Ghost. Holmes, Gerald L., illus. 1998. (Hank the Cowdog Ser.: No. 9). 144p. (J). (gr. 2-5). 14.99 (978-0-670-88416-2(2) , Viking Juvenile); No. 9. pap. 4.99 (978-0-14-130385-7(9) , Puffin) Penguin Group (USA) Inc.

—The Case of the Haystack Kitties. Holmes, Gerald L., illus. 1998. (Hank the Cowdog Ser.: No. 30). 144p. (J). (gr. 2-5). 14.99 (978-0-670-88437-7(5) , Viking Juvenile); Vol. 30. pap. 4.99 (978-0-14-130406-9(5) , Puffin) Penguin Group (USA) Inc.

—The Case of the Haystack Kitties. 1999. (Hank the Cowdog Ser.: No. 30). (gr. 3-6). lib. bdg. 13.00 (978-0-613-07442-1(4)) Tandem Library Bks.

—The Case of the Hooking Bull, Vol. 18. Holmes, Gerald L., illus. 1998. (Hank the Cowdog Ser.: No. 18). 144p. (J). (gr. 2-5). pap. 4.99 (978-0-14-130394-9(8) , Puffin) Penguin Group (USA) Inc.

—The Case of the Kidnapped Collie. Holmes, Gerald L., illus. 1998. (Hank the Cowdog Ser.: No. 26). 144p. (J). (gr. 2-5). 14.99 (978-0-670-88433-9(2) , Viking Juvenile); Vol. 26. pap. 4.99 (978-0-14-130402-1(2) , Puffin) Penguin Group (USA) Inc.

—The Case of the Kidnapped Collie. 1999. (Hank the Cowdog Ser.: No. 26). (gr. 3-6). lib. bdg. 13.00 (978-0-7857-9075-4(6)) Tandem Library Bks.

—The Case of the Kidnapped Collie. Holmes, Gerald L., illus. 1999. (Hank the Cowdog Ser.: No. 26). (J). (gr. 2-5). 11.64 (978-0-606-09375-0(3)) Tandem Library Bks.

—The Case of the Measled Cowboy. Holmes, Gerald L., illus. 1999. (Hank the Cowdog Ser.: No. 33). 144p. (J). (gr. 2-5). 13.99 (978-0-670-88489-6(8) , Viking Juvenile); Vol. 33. pap. 4.99 (978-0-14-130423-6(5) , Puffin) Penguin Group (USA) Inc.

—The Case of the Measled Cowboy. 1999. (Hank the Cowdog Ser.: No. 33). (J). (gr. 2-5). 11.64 (978-0-606-17534-0(2)); (gr. 3-6). lib. bdg. 13.00 (978-0-613-14613-5(1)) Tandem Library Bks.

—The Case of the Midnight Rustler. Holmes, Gerald L., illus. 1998. (Hank the Cowdog Ser.: No. 19). 144p. (J). (gr. 2-5). 14.99 (978-0-670-88426-1(X) , Viking Juvenile); pap. 4.99 (978-0-14-130395-6(6) , Puffin) Penguin Group (USA) Inc.

—The Case of the Missing Bird Dog, Vol. 40. Holmes, Gerald L., illus. 2002. (Hank the Cowdog Ser.: No. 40). 144p. (J). 15.99 (978-0-670-03558-8(0) , Viking Juvenile); pap. 4.99 (978-0-14-230141-8(8) , Puffin) Penguin Group (USA) Inc.

—The Case of the Missing Bird Dog. 2002. (Hank the Cowdog Ser.: No. 40). (gr. 3-6). lib. bdg. 13.00 (978-0-613-50279-5(5)) Tandem Library Bks.

—The Case of the Missing Cat. Holmes, Gerald L., illus. (Hank the Cowdog Ser.: No. 15). 144p. (J). (gr. 2-5). 2000. 14.99 (978-0-670-88422-3(7) , Viking Juvenile); 1998. pap. 4.99 (978-0-14-130391-8(3) , Puffin) Penguin Group (USA) Inc.

—The Case of the Missing Cat. 1999. (Hank the Cowdog Ser.: No. 15). (gr. 3-6). lib. bdg. 13.00 (978-0-8335-6828-1(0)) Tandem Library Bks.

—The Case of the Monkey Burglar. Holmes, Gerald L., illus. 2006. (Hank the Cowdog Ser.: No. 48). 144p. (J). (gr. 3). 4.99 (978-0-14-240636-6(8) , Puffin); 15.99 (978-0-670-06098-6(4) , Viking Juvenile) Penguin Group (USA) Inc.

—The Case of the Most Ancient Bone. Homes, Gerald L., illus. 2007. (Hank the Cowdog Ser.). 192p. (J). (gr. 3). 16.99 (978-0-670-06224-9(3) , Viking Juvenile) Penguin Group (USA) Inc.

—The Case of the Most Ancient Bone, No. 50. Holmes, Gerald L., illus. 2007. (Hank the Cowdog Ser.: No. 50). 256p. (J). (gr. 3). pap. 5.99 (978-0-14-240800-1(X) , Puffin) Penguin Group (USA) Inc.

—The Case of the Night-Stalking Bone Monster. Holmes, Gerald L., illus. 1998. (Hank the Cowdog Ser.: No. 27). 144p. (J). (gr. 2-5). 14.99 (978-0-670-88434-6(0) , Viking Juvenile); Vol. 27. pap. 4.99 (978-0-14-130403-8(0) , Puffin) Penguin Group (USA) Inc.

—The Case of the One-Eyed Killer Stud Horse, Vol. 8. Holmes, Gerald L., illus. 1998. (Hank the Cowdog Ser.: No. 8). 144p. (gr. 2-5). pap. 4.99 (978-0-14-130384-0(0) , Puffin) Penguin Group (USA) Inc.

—The Case of the Raging Rottweiler. 2000. (Hank the Cowdog Ser.: No. 36). (gr. 3-6). lib. bdg. 13.00 (978-0-613-31048-2(9)) Tandem Library Bks.

—The Case of the Saddle House Robbery. Holmes, Gerald L., illus. 2000. (Hank the Cowdog Ser.: No. 35). 144p. (J). (gr. 2-5). 14.99 (978-0-670-88890-0(7) , Viking Juvenile); Vol. 35. pap. 4.99 (978-0-14-130678-0(5) , Puffin) Penguin Group (USA) Inc.

—The Case of the Saddle House Robbery. unabr. ed. 2000. (Hank the Cowdog Ser.: No. 35). (J). (gr. 2-5). pap. 23.00 incl. audio (978-0-8072-8376-9(2) , YA172SP, Listening Library) Random Hse. Audio Publishing Group.

—The Case of the Saddle House Robbery. 2000. (Hank the Cowdog Ser.: No. 35). (gr. 3-6). lib. bdg. 13.00 (978-0-613-24495-4(8)); (Illus.). (J). (gr. 2-5). 11.64 (978-0-606-18409-0(0)) Tandem Library Bks.

—The Case of the Shipwrecked Tree. Holmes, Gerald L., illus. 2003. (Hank the Cowdog Ser.: No. 41). 144p. (J). (gr. 3-7). 14.99 (978-0-670-03603-5(X) , Viking Juvenile); (gr. 4-6). pap. 4.99 (978-0-14-230225-5(2) , Puffin) Penguin Group (USA) Inc.

—The Case of the Shipwrecked Tree. 2003. (Hank the Cowdog Ser.: No. 41). (gr. 3-6). lib. bdg. 13.00 (978-0-613-61613-3(8)) Tandem Library Bks.

—The Case of the Swirling Killer Tornado. Holmes, Gerald L., illus. 1998. (Hank the Cowdog Ser.: No. 25). 144p. (J). (gr. 2-5). 14.99 (978-0-670-88432-2(4) , Viking Juvenile); Vol. 25. pap. 4.99 (978-0-14-130401-4(4) , Puffin) Penguin Group (USA) Inc.

—The Case of the Tender Cheeping Chickies. Holmes, Gerald L., illus. 2005. (Hank the Cowdog Ser.: No. 47). 129p. (J). lib. bdg. 17.00 (*978-1-4242-1605-5(2)) Fitzgerald Bks.

—The Case of the Tender Cheeping Chickies. 2006. (Hank the Cowdog Ser.: No. 47). (Illus.). 144p. (J). (gr. 3). 15.99 (978-0-670-06097-9(6) , Viking Juvenile) Penguin Group (USA) Inc.

—The Case of the Tender Cheeping Chickies. Holmes, Gerald L., illus. 2006. (Hank the Cowdog Ser.: No. 47). 144p. (J). (gr. 3). pap. 4.99 (978-0-14-240553-6(1) , Puffin) Penguin Group (USA) Inc.

—The Case of the Tricky Trap. Holmes, Gerald L., illus. 2005. (Hank the Cowdog Ser.: No. 46). 126p. (J). lib. bdg. 17.00 (*978-1-4242-1603-1(6)) Fitzgerald Bks.

—The Case of the Tricky Trap. Holmes, Gerald L., illus. 2005. (Hank the Cowdog Ser.: No. 46). 144p. (J). (gr. 4). pap. 4.99 (978-0-14-240325-9(3) , Puffin) Penguin Group (USA) Inc.

—The Case of the Twisted Kitty. Holmes, Gerald L., illus. 2004. (Hank the Cowdog Ser.: No. 43). 131p. (J). lib. bdg. 17.00 (*978-1-4242-1600-0(1)) Fitzgerald Bks.

—The Case of the Twisted Kitty, Vol. 43. Holmes, Gerald L., tr. Holmes, Gerald L., illus. 2004. (Hank the Cowdog Ser.: No. 43). 144p. (J). pap. 4.99 (978-0-14-240041-8(6) , Puffin) Penguin Group (USA) Inc.

—The Case of the Vampire Cat. Holmes, Gerald L., illus. 1998. (Hank the Cowdog Ser.: No. 21). 144p. (J). (gr. 2-5). 14.99 (978-0-670-88428-5(6) , Viking Juvenile); Vol. 21. pap. 4.99 (978-0-14-130397-0(2) , Puffin) Penguin Group (USA) Inc.

—The Case of the Vampire Vacuum Sweeper. Holmes, Gerald L., illus. 1998. (Hank the Cowdog Ser.: No. 29). 144p. (J). (gr. 2-5). 14.99 (978-0-670-88436-0(7) , Viking Juvenile); (gr. 3-7). pap. 4.99 (978-0-14-130405-2(7) , Puffin) Penguin Group (USA) Inc.

—The Case of the Vanishing Fishhook. Holmes, Gerald L., illus. 1999. (Hank the Cowdog Ser.: No. 31). 144p. (J). (gr. 2-5). 14.99 (978-0-670-88438-4(3) , Viking Juvenile); Vol. 31. pap. 4.99 (978-0-14-130356-7(5) , Puffin) Penguin Group (USA) Inc.

—The Case of the Vanishing Fishhook. Holmes, Gerald L., illus. 1999. (Hank the Cowdog Ser.: No. 31). (J). (gr. 2-5). 11.64 (978-0-606-16826-7(5)) Tandem Library Bks.

—The Case of the Vanishing Fishhook. 1999. (Hank the Cowdog Ser.: No. 31). (gr. 3-6). lib. bdg. 13.00 (978-0-613-11389-2(6)) Tandem Library Bks.

—The Curse of the Incredible Priceless Corncob. Holmes, Gerald L., illus. 1998. (Hank the Cowdog Ser.: No. 7). 144p. (J). (gr. 2-5). 14.99 (978-0-670-88414-8(6) , Viking Juvenile); Vol. 7. pap. 4.99 (978-0-14-130383-3(2) , Puffin) Penguin Group (USA) Inc.

—The Dungeon of Doom. Holmes, Gerald L., illus. 2004. (Hank the Cowdog Ser.: No. 44). 122p. (J). lib. bdg. 17.00 (*978-1-4242-1601-7(X)) Fitzgerald Bks.

—The Dungeon of Doom. Holmes, Gerald L., illus. 2004. (Hank the Cowdog Ser.: No. 44). 144p. (J). (gr. 3-7). 15.99 (978-0-670-05881-5(5) , Viking Juvenile); pap. 4.99 (978-0-14-240134-7(X) , Puffin) Penguin Group (USA) Inc.

—Every Dog Has His Day. Holmes, Gerald L., illus. 1998. (Hank the Cowdog Ser.: No. 10). 144p. (J). (gr. 2-5). 15.99 (978-0-670-88417-9(0) , Viking Juvenile); pap. 4.99 (978-0-14-130386-4(7) , Puffin) Penguin Group (USA) Inc.

—Faded Love. Holmes, Gerald L., illus. 1998. (Hank the Cowdog Ser.: No. 5). 144p. (J). (gr. 2-5). 14.99 (978-0-670-88412-4(X) , Viking Juvenile); Vol. 5. pap. 4.99 (978-0-14-130381-9(6) , Puffin) Penguin Group (USA) Inc.

—The Fling. Holmes, Gerald L., illus. 2001. (Hank the Cowdog Ser.: No. 38). 144p. (J). (gr. 2-5). 14.99 (978-0-670-89694-3(2) , Viking Juvenile); Vol. 38. pap. 4.99 (978-0-14-131174-6(6) , Puffin) Penguin Group (USA) Inc.

—The Fling. 2001. (Hank the Cowdog Ser.: No. 38). (gr. 3-6). lib. bdg. 13.00 (978-0-613-35805-7(8)) Tandem Library Bks.

—The Fling Robbery. 2001. (Hank the Cowdog Ser.: No. 38). (Illus.). (J). (978-0-606-21223-6(X)) Tandem Library Bks.

—The Further Adventures of Hank the Cowdog. Holmes, Gerald L., illus. (Hank the Cowdog Ser.: No. 2). 144p. (J). 1999. (gr. 2-5). pap. 4.99 (978-0-14-130378-9(6) , Puffin); 1998. (gr. 3-5). 14.99 (978-0-670-88409-4(X) , Viking Juvenile) Penguin Group (USA) Inc.

—The Further Adventures of Hank the Cowdog. Holmes, Gerald L., illus. 1999. (Hank the Cowdog Ser.: No. 2). (J). (gr. 2-5). lib. bdg. 13.00 (978-0-8335-6816-8(7)) Tandem Library Bks.

—The Garbage Monster from Outer Space, Vol. 32. Holmes, Gerald L., illus. 1999. (Hank the Cowdog Ser.: No. 32). 144p. (J). (gr. 2-5). pap. 4.99 (978-0-14-130422-9(7) , Puffin) Penguin Group (USA) Inc.

—The Garbage Monster from Outer Space. 1999. (Hank the Cowdog Ser.: No. 32). (J). (gr. 2-5). 11.64 (978-0-606-16827-4(3)); (gr. 3-6). lib. bdg. 13.00 (978-0-613-14748-4(0)) Tandem Library Bks.

—Hank Cowdog 50. Holmes, Gerard L., illus. 2007. 256p. 16.99 (*978-0-670-62249-8(4) , Viking Adult) Penguin Group (USA) Inc.

—Hank the Cowdog & Monkey Business. Holmes, Gerald L., illus. 1999. (Hank the Cowdog Ser.: No. 14). (J). (gr. 3-6). lib. bdg. 13.00 (978-0-8335-6827-4(2)) Tandem Library Bks.

—It's a Dog's Life. Holmes, Gerald L., illus. (Hank the Cowdog Ser.: No. 3). 100p. (J). (gr. 2-5). 9.95 (978-0-916941-04-8(3)); pap. 5.95 (978-0-9608612-9-3(7)) Maverick Bks., Inc.

—It's a Dog's Life. Holmes, Gerald L., illus. 1998. (Hank the Cowdog Ser.: No. 3). 144p. (J). (gr. 2-5). 14.99 (978-0-670-88410-0(3) , Viking Juvenile); pap. 4.99 (978-0-14-130379-6(4) , Puffin) Penguin Group (USA) Inc.

—Let Sleeping Dogs Lie. Holmes, Gerald L., illus. 1998. (Hank the Cowdog Ser.: No. 16). 144p. (J). (gr. 2-5). 15.99 (978-0-670-88413-1(8) , Viking Juvenile); pap. 4.99 (978-0-14-130382-6(4) , Puffin) Penguin Group (USA) Inc.

—Lost in the Blinded Blizzard. Holmes, Gerald L., illus. 1998. (Hank the Cowdog Ser.: No. 16). 144p. (J). (gr. 2-5). 14.99 (978-0-670-88423-0(5) , Viking Juvenile); pap. 4.99 (978-0-14-130392-5(1) , Puffin) Penguin Group (USA) Inc.

—Lost in the Dark Unchanted Forest, Vol. 11. Holmes, Gerald L., illus. 1998. (Hank the Cowdog Ser.: No. 11). 144p. (J). (gr. 2-5). pap. 4.99 (978-0-14-130387-1(5) , Puffin) Penguin Group (USA) Inc.

—Monkey Business. Holmes, Gerald L., illus. 1998. (Hank the Cowdog Ser.: No. 14). 144p. (J). (gr. 2-5). 14.99 (978-0-670-88421-6(9) , Viking Juvenile); Vol. 14. pap. 4.99 (978-0-14-130390-1(5) , Puffin) Penguin Group (USA) Inc.

—Moonlight Madness. Holmes, Gerald L., illus. 1998. (Hank the Cowdog Ser.: No. 23). 144p. (J). (gr. 2-5). 15.99 (978-0-670-88430-8(8) , Viking Juvenile); Vol. 23. pap. 4.99 (978-0-14-130399-4(9) , Puffin) Penguin Group (USA) Inc.

—The Mopwater Files. Holmes, Gerald L., illus. 1998. (Hank the Cowdog Ser.: No. 28). 144p. (J). (gr. 2-5). 14.99 (978-0-670-88435-3(9) , Viking Juvenile); pap. 4.99 (978-0-14-130404-5(9) , Puffin) Penguin Group (USA) Inc.

—Murder in the Middle Pasture. Holmes, Gerald L., illus. 1998. (Hank the Cowdog Ser.: No. 4). 144p. (J). (gr. 2-5). 14.99 (978-0-670-88411-7(1) , Viking Juvenile); Vol. 4. pap. 4.99 (978-0-14-130380-2(8) , Puffin) Penguin Group (USA) Inc.

—Murder in the Middle Pasture. Holmes, Gerald L., illus. 1999. (Hank the Cowdog Ser.: No. 4). (J). (gr. 3-6). lib. bdg. 13.00 (978-0-8335-6817-5(5)) Tandem Library Bks.

—Las Nuevas Aventuras de Hank el Perro Vaquero. 2000. (SPA., Illus.). (J). (978-0-606-18416-8(3)) Tandem Library Bks.

—The Original Adventures. Holmes, Gerald L., illus. 1999. (Hank the Cowdog Ser.: No. 1). 144p. (J). (gr. 3-5). 14.99 (978-0-670-88408-7(1) , Viking Juvenile) Penguin Group (USA) Inc.

—The Original Adventures of Hank the Cowdog. Holmes, Gerald L., illus. 1998. (Hank the Cowdog Ser.: No. 1). 144p. (J). (gr. 2-5). pap. 4.99 (978-0-14-130377-2(8) , Puffin) Penguin Group (USA) Inc.

—The Original Adventures of Hank the Cowdog. Holmes, Gerald L., illus. 1999. (Hank the Cowdog Ser.: No. 1). (J). (gr. 3-6). lib. bdg. 13.00 (978-0-8335-6815-1(9)) Tandem Library Bks.

—The Phantom in the Mirror. Holmes, Gerald L., illus. (Hank the Cowdog Ser.: No. 20). 144p. (J). (gr. 2-5). 2000. 14.99 (978-0-670-88427-8(8) , Viking Juvenile); Vol. 20. 1998. pap. 4.99 (978-0-14-130396-3(4) , Puffin) Penguin Group (USA) Inc.

—The Secret Laundry Monster Files. 2000. (Hank the Cowdog Ser.: No. 39). (Illus.). (J). (gr. 2-5). pap. (978-5-550-03190-2(6)) Nairi.

—The Secret Laundry Monster Files, Vol. 39. Holmes, Gerald L., illus. 2002. (Hank the Cowdog Ser.: No. 39). 144p. (J). pap. 4.99 (978-0-14-230076-3(4) , Puffin) Penguin Group (USA) Inc.

—The Secret Laundry Monster Files. 2002. (Hank the Cowdog Ser.: No. 39). (gr. 3-6). lib. bdg. 13.00 (978-0-613-43642-7(3)) Tandem Library Bks.

—Slim's Good-Bye. Holmes, Gerald L., illus. 2000. (Hank the Cowdog Ser.: No. 34). 144p. (J). (gr. 2-5). 15.99 (978-0-670-88889-4(3) , Viking Juvenile); Vol. 34. pap. 4.99 (978-0-14-130677-3(7) , Puffin) Penguin Group (USA) Inc.

—Slim's Good-Bye. 2000. (Hank the Cowdog Ser.: No. 34). (Illus.). (J). (gr. 2-5). (978-0-606-18408-3(2)) Tandem Library Bks.

—Las Verdaderas Aventuras de Hank el Perro Vaquero. 2000. (SPA., Illus.). (J). (978-0-606-18840-1(1)) Tandem Library Bks.

—The Wounded Buzzard on Christmas Eve. Holmes, Gerald L., illus. 1998. (Hank the Cowdog Ser.: No. 13). 144p. (J). (gr. 2-5). 14.99 (978-0-670-88420-9(0) , Viking Juvenile); pap. 4.99 (978-0-14-130389-5(1) , Puffin) Penguin Group (USA) Inc.

Erickson, Mary Ellen. Snowstorm. 2005. (J). (978-0-9765453-3-0(0)) Dr. Mary's Bks.

Estefan, Gloria & Garland, Michael. The Magically Mysterious Adventures of Noelle the Bulldog. 32p. 2006. pap. 6.99 (978-0-06-082625-3(8)); 2005. (Illus.). 17.99 (978-0-06-082623-9(1)) HarperCollins Pubs. (Rayo).

—Las Magicas y Misteriosas Aventuras de una Bulldog Llamada Noelle. 2005. (Illus.). 32p. (ps). 17.99 (978-0-06-082626-0(6) , Rayo) HarperCollins Pubs.

—Noelle's Treasure Tale: A New Magically Mysterious Adventure. 2006. (Illus.). 32p. (ps-1). 17.95 (978-0-06-112614-7(4) , Rayo) HarperCollins Pubs.

Estes, Eleanor. Ginger Pye. Estes, Eleanor, illus. 2000. (Illus.). 320p. (YA). (gr. 3 up). 17.00 (978-0-15-202499-4(9) , Odyssey Classics); (gr. 4-7). pap. 6.00 (978-0-15-202505-2(7)) Harcourt Children's Bks.

—Ginger Pye. unabr. ed. 2000. (YA). pap. 69.00 incl. audio (978-0-7887-3179-2(3) , 40914X4) Recorded Bks., LLC.

—Ginger Pye. 2000. (Illus.). 306p. (J). (ps-7). lib. bdg. 14.15 (978-0-613-29963-3(9)) Tandem Library Bks.

Eubank, Patricia Reeder. Seaman's Journal. Barrett, Robert, illus. 2002. 32p. (J). 15.95 (978-0-8249-5442-0(4)) Ideals Pubns.

Evans, Karen & Urmston, Kathleen. Sammy Gets a Ride. 2005. (J). cd-rom 7.95 (978-1-57874-102-1(5)) Kaeden Corp.

Evans, Nate & Numeroff, Laura Nate. Sherman Crunchley. Bowers, Tim, illus. 2005. 32p. (J). pap. 5.99 (978-0-14-240385-3(7) , Puffin) Penguin Group (USA) Inc.

Exelby, Kathy. My Dog Harpo: The Biggest Kid I Know. Wall Darby, Colleen, illus. 2007. (J). per. 20.00 (*978-1-932583-39-7(4)) digital@batesjackson llc.

Fair, Sherry. The Best Parade Day: Spatz. Rutland, Jarrett, illus. 2006. 40p. (J). 18.95 (978-1-57736-375-0(2) , Providence Hse. Pubs.) Providence Hse Pubs.

Fair, Sherry W. The Scratching Sound: Spatz. Rutland, Jarrett, illus. 2005. 28p. (J). (ps-7). 16.98 (978-1-57736-348-4(5)) Providence Hse Pubs.

Faith, Susan. Purple Puppy. Offner, Naomi, illus. 2005. 32p. (J). 19.95 (978-0-9707793-0-4(5)) Purple People, Inc.

Faller, Régis. The Adventures of Polo. Faller, Régis, illus. 2006. (Illus.). 80p. (J). (gr. k-2). 16.95 (978-1-59643-160-7(1)) Roaring Brook Pr.

Faller, Regis. Polo: The Runaway Book. Faller, Regis, illus. rev. ed. 2007. (Illus.). 80p. (J). (gr. k-3). 16.95 (978-1-59643-189-8(X)) Roaring Brook Pr.

Falletta, Bernadette & Gasparro, Marie. Reflections of the Dog That Learned English. 2005. 16p. (J). 14.95 (978-1-4116-6524-8(4)) Lulu.com.

Fann, Linsey. Puppy Love. Abdulai, David, ed. Fann, Linsey, illus. Date not set. (Illus.). 32p. (J). (gr. 4-6). pap. 19.95 (978-0-9647012-6-7(X) , Dawn of a New Day Pubns., The) Konkori International.

Faust, Laurie, illus. A New Home for Honey. 2006. (J). 9.95 (*978-0-9789227-0-2(0)) Weeping Willow Publishing.

Faye. Jazzy Shoes. l.t. ed. 2006. (ENG., Illus.). 28p. per. 9.95 (*978-1-4327-0176-5(2)) Outskirts Press, Inc.

Fearnley, Jan. The Search for the Perfect Child. Fearnley, Jan, illus. 2006. (Illus.). 40p. (J). (ps-1). 15.99 (978-0-7636-3231-1(7)) Candlewick Pr.

Fehlner, Paul. Dog & Cat. Chambliss, Maxie, illus. 2003. (My First Reader Ser.). 32p. (J). 18.50 (978-0-516-22924-9(9) , Children's Pr.) Scholastic Library Publishing.

Feiffer, Jules. Bark, George. Feiffer, Jules, illus. 2002. (Illus.). (J). 25.11 (978-0-7587-6808-7(7)) Book Wholesalers, Inc.

—Bark, George. ed. 2004. (J). (ps-k). spiral bd. (978-0-616-01637-4(9)); spiral bd. (978-0-616-01638-1(7)) Canadian National Institute for the Blind/Institut National Canadien pour les Aveugles.

—Bark, George. 2000. 32p. (J). (ps-1). pap. 5.95 (978-0-06-205930-7(0)) HarperCollins Pubs.

—Bark, George. Feiffer, Jules, illus. 1999. (Michael di Capua Bks.). (Illus.). 32p. (J). (ps-1). lib. bdg. 17.89 (978-0-06-205186-8(5)); 16.99 (978-0-06-205185-1(7)) HarperCollins Pubs.

Feiffer, Kate & Feiffer, Jules. Henry, the Dog with No Tail. 2007. 32p. (J). (ps-1). 16.99 (978-1-4169-1614-7(8) , Simon & Schuster Children's Publishing) Simon & Schuster Children's Publishing.

Feinstein, Stephen. Call of the Wild. abr. ed. 1999. (gr. 7-12). lib. bdg. 15.25 (978-0-613-32365-9(3)) Tandem Library Bks.

Feldman, Eve B. Dog Crazy. 2000. (Illus.). 116p. (J). (gr. 4-7). pap. 9.95 (978-0-595-09197-3(0) , Backinprint-.com) iUniverse, Inc.

Feldman, Thea. Backyard Pirates: Magnix Imagination. 2007. 6p. bds. 5.99 (*978-1-932915-40-2(0)) Sandvik Innovations, LLC.

Feldman, Thea. Don't Wake the Puppies! Goldberg, Barry, illus. 2003. (Clifford Ser.). 24p. (J). pap. 10.95 (978-0-439-44941-0(3)) Scholastic, Inc.

Felton, Jerilyn E. The Master's Companion: A Christian Midrash. 2007. (YA). (*978-0-88489-936-5(5)) St. Mary's Pr.

Fenton, Karen B. It's Raining Outside & I'm Gonna Be Bored! Roth, Stacy Schulstrom, illus. 2006. (J). lib. bdg. 16.82 (978-0-9778196-4-5(7)) Harbour Arts, LLC.

Ferreira, Anton. Zulu Dog. 2002. (Illus.). 208p. (J). (gr. 5 up). 16.00 (978-0-374-39223-9(4) , Farrar, Straus & Giroux (BYR)) Farrar, Straus & Giroux.

Fickling, Phillip. Fillmore & Geary Take Off! Shulman, Mark, illus. 2003. 40p. (J). lib. bdg. (978-1-58717-258-8(5) , SeaStar Bks.) Chronicle Bks. LLC.

Fine, Anne. Notso Hotso. Ross, Tony, illus. 2006. 96p. (J). 15.00 (978-0-374-35550-0(9)) Farrar, Straus & Giroux.

Finney, Patricia. I, Jack. Bailey, Peter, illus. 192p. (J). 2005. pap. 5.99 (978-0-06-052209-4(7) , Harper Trophy); 2004. 15.99 (978-0-06-052207-0(0)); 2004. lib. bdg. 16.89 (978-0-06-052208-7(9)) HarperCollins Pubs.

Finney, Patricia. Jack & Rebel, the Police Dog. 2007. (Illus.). 208p. (J). 15.99 (*978-0-06-088049-1(X)); lib. bdg. 16.89 (*978-0-06-088050-7(3)) HarperCollins Pubs.

Fiorentini, Paolo, illus. My House. 2005. (J). 16.95 (978-0-7641-7846-7(6)) Barron's Educational Series, Inc.

Fisch, Sarah & Bridwell, Norman. Backpack Puppy. Durk, Jim, illus. 2005. (J). pap. (*978-0-439-73379-3(0)) Scholastic, Inc.

Fitzgerald, Laurie. My Dog Wears Shoes & Her Name Is Maggie Mae. 2006. 32p. 17.95 (978-1-887542-30-2(2)) Seven Locks Pr.

Five Little Dogs. 2004. (J). (978-1-932570-19-9(5)) Literacy Footprints Inc.

Five O'Clock Dog: Firestorm Trail, 5 vols. 2005. (J). pap. 9.95 (978-0-9767887-0-6(5)) Five O'clock Dog.

Flack, Marjorie. Angus & the Ducks. Flack, Marjorie, illus. 2002. (Illus.). (J). 14.43 (978-0-7587-9219-8(0)) Book Wholesalers, Inc.

—Angus & the Ducks. unabr. ed. 1998. (J). (ps-2). pap. 14.95 incl. audio (978-0-7882-0694-8(X) , PRA039) Weston Woods Studios, Inc.

—Angus Lost. Flack, Marjorie, illus. 2002. (Illus.). (J). 14.43 (978-0-7587-9220-4(4)) Book Wholesalers, Inc.

Flather, Lisa, contrib. by. Ten Silly Dogs: A Countdown Story. 1999. (J). (ps-2). lib. bdg. (978-0-531-33192-7(X) , Watts, Franklin) Scholastic Library Publishing.

Fleischman, Sid. Jim Ugly. Smith, Jos. A., illus. 2003. 144p. (J). (gr. 3-6). pap. 6.99 (978-0-06-052121-9(X) , Harper Trophy) HarperCollins Pubs.

Fleming, Denise. Buster Goes to Cowboy Camp. 2008. 40p. (J). 16.95 (****978-0-8050-7892-3(4)***) Holt, Henry & Co.

Fleming, Sarah. My Dog's Check-Up. 2000. (Cambridge Reading Ser.). (Illus.). 10p. pap. 5.00 (978-0-521-77456-7(X)) Cambridge Univ. Pr.

Flesher, Vivienne. Alfred's Nose. Flesher, Vivienne, illus. 2008. 32p. (J). 16.99 (****978-0-06-084313-7(6));*** lib. bdg. 17.89 (****978-0-06-084314-4(4)***) HarperCollins Pubs.

Florence, Leigh Anne. Woody, the Kentucky Wiener: The Adoption. Asher, James, illus. 2003. 32p. (J). (gr. 1-3). pap. 12.95 (978-0-9741417-0-1(4)) HotDiggetyDog Pr.

—Woody, the Kentucky Wiener Welcomes a Dad, Vol. 2. Asher, James, illus. 2004. 32p. (J). (gr. 1-3). pap. 12.95 (978-0-9741417-1-8(2)) HotDiggetyDog Pr.

Floyd, Marla K. The Pink Poodle. 2000. (Illus.). 28p. (J). (ps-6). pap. 9.95 (978-0-9704399-0-1(3)) Daisy Pubns.

The Flying Pig & the Daredevil Dog: Individual Title Six-Packs. (Action Packs Ser.). 104p. (gr. 3-5). 44.00 (978-0-7635-2985-7(0)) Rigby Education.

Fontes, Justine. 101 Dalmatians. Langley, Bill & Dias, Ron, illus. 2000. (Little Golden Bks.). 24p. (J). (ps-3). bds. 2.99 (978-0-307-00116-0(4) , 98069, Golden Bks.) Random Hse. Children's Bks.

Fontes, Justine & Korman, Justine. The Luckiest Leprechaun: A Tail-Wagging Tale of Friendship. 2001. (Illus.). (J). (978-0-606-20779-9(1)) Tandem Library Bks.

Forbush, Kyle. Balto: The Dog Hero. Forbush, Lisa, illus. 2004. (J). pap. 14.95 (978-1-57833-267-0(2)) Todd Communications.

Ford, Laura. Buster Brown & Tige in Misfit Heroes. 2004. (Illus.). 320p. 19.95 (978-1-881554-28-8(7)) Skyward Publishing Co.

Ford, Sally. Bungee's Voyage. Dudley, Peter, illus. 2002. (J). 14.95 (978-1-931807-04-3(3)) Randall, Peter E. Pub.

Foreman, Michael. Mia's Story: A Sketchbook of Hopes & Dreams. Foreman, Michael, illus. 2006. (Illus.). 32p. (J). (gr. k-3). 15.99 (978-0-7636-3063-8(2)) Candlewick Pr.

—Saving Sinbad! 2002. (Illus.). 32p. (J). 15.95 (978-1-929132-34-8(4)) Kane/Miller Bk. Pubs., Inc.

Forney, Melissa. A Medal for Murphy. Rice, James, illus. 2000. 32p. (J). (ps-3). pap. 7.95 (978-1-56554-832-9(9)) Pelican Publishing Co., Inc.

Forton-Barnes, Therese, Zaki & Venus. 2007. 13.95 (****978-1-59526-388-9(8)***) Media Creations, Inc.

Fox & the Hound. (Read-Along Ser.). (J). 7.99 incl. audio (978-1-55723-019-5(6)) Walt Disney Records.

Fox, Dorothea Warren. Miss Twiggley's Tree. Fox, Dorothea Warren, illus. 2002. 17.95 (978-1-930900-17-2(1)) Purple Hse. Pr.

Fox, Paula. Gus Cara de Piedra. (SPA.). 128p. (J). (gr. 3-5). (978-84-279-3450-4(5) , NG4694) Noguer y Caralt Editores, S. A. ESP. *Dist:* Lectorum Pubns., Inc.

The Stone-Faced Boy. 2005. 83p. (J). (gr. 4-7). pap. 8.95 (978-1-932425-42-0(X) , Lemniscaat) Boyds Mills Pr.

Francis, Pauline & London, Jack. White Fang. 2003. (Fast Track Classics Ser.). (Illus.). 48p. (YA). pap. 9.99 (978-0-237-52532-3(1) , Evans Brothers, Limited) Evans Publishing Group GBR. *Dist:* Independent Pubs. Group.

Franks, T. S. ZZ Dogs. d'Obrin, Felix, illus. 2003. (J). 15.99 (978-0-9722304-0-7(8) , 5000, ZZ Dogs Pr.) That's Life Publishing, Inc.

Freeman, Don & McCue, Lisa. Corduroy Goes to the Fire Station. 2003. (Illus.). 24p. (J). (gr. 1). 11.99 (978-0-670-03600-4(5) , Viking Juvenile) Penguin Group (USA) Inc.

Freeman, Martha. Mrs. Wow Never Wanted a Cow. Salerno, Steven, illus. 2006. 48p. (J). (gr. k-3). 8.99 (978-0-375-83418-9(4)); lib. bdg. 11.99 (978-0-375-93418-6(9)) Random Hse. Children's Bks. (Random Hse. Bks. for Young Readers).

—Mrs. Wow Never Wanted a Cow. Salerno, Steven, illus. 2006. (J). (978-0-375-83419-6(2)) Random Hse., Inc.

French, Jackie. Pete the Sheep-Sheep. Whatley, Bruce, illus. 2005. 32p. (J). (gr. k-3). 14.00 (978-0-618-56862-8(X) , Clarion Bks.) Houghton Mifflin Co. Trade & Reference Div.

French, Vivian. Space Dog Visits Planet Earth. Heap, Sue, illus. 2000. (Space Dog Ser.: No. 4). 64p. (J). (ps-3). pap. 3.99 (978-0-439-13086-8(7) , Scholastic Paperbacks) Scholastic, Inc.

French, Vivian & Heap, Sue. Space Dog Finds Treasure. 2000. (Space Dog Ser.: No. 2). (Illus.). 64p. (J). (ps-3). pap. 3.99 (978-0-439-13084-4(0)) Scholastic, Inc.

—Space Dog to the Rescue. 2000. (Space Dog Ser.: No. 1). (Illus.). 64p. (J). (ps-3). pap. 3.99 (978-0-439-13083-7(2)) Scholastic, Inc.

Freymann, Saxton & Elffers, Joost. Gus & Button. Freymann, Saxton & Elffers, Joost, illus. 2001. (Illus.). 40p. (J). pap. 15.95 (978-0-439-11015-0(7) , Levine, Arthur A. Bks.) Scholastic, Inc.

Friedman, Laurie. Mallory vs. Max. Schmitz, Tamara, illus. 2006. (J). pap. 5.95 (978-1-57505-863-4(4) , First Avenue Editions) Lerner Publishing Group.

Friedman, Laurie B. Mallory vs. Max. Schmitz, Tamara, illus. 2005. 160p. (J). (ps-k). 15.95 (978-1-57505-795-8(6)) Lerner Publishing Group.

Friedman, Michael Jan. Hunchdog of Notre Dame. l.t. ed. 1999. (Adventures of Wishbone Ser.: No. 5). (Illus.). 139p. (J). (gr. 4 up). lib. bdg. 22.60 (978-0-8368-2301-1(X)) Stevens, Gareth Inc.

—The Sirian Conspiracy. 1999. (Wishbone Mysteries Ser.: No. 16). (J). (gr. 2-5). (978-0-606-17768-9(X)) Tandem Library Bks.

—The Stolen Trophy. l.t. ed. 1999. (Wishbone Mysteries Ser.: No. 5). 144p. (J). (gr. 4 up). lib. bdg. 23.33 (978-0-8368-2386-8(9)) Stevens, Gareth Inc.

—The Stolen Trophy. 1998. (Wishbone Mysteries Ser.: No. 5). (J). (gr. 2-5). (978-0-606-12859-9(X)) Tandem Library Bks.

Friedman, Michael Jan, et al. The Sirian Conspiracy. l.t. ed. 2000. (Wishbone Mysteries Ser.: No. 16). (Illus.). 141p. (J). (gr. 4 up). lib. bdg. 23.33 (978-0-8368-2699-9(X)) Stevens, Gareth Inc.

Friedman, Rainey L. Monsters in Your Bed... Monsters in Your Head. Dill, Betsy, illus. 1999. 32p. (J). 15.95 (978-0-9666199-1-1(9)) DreamDog Pr.

Frith, Michael. I'll Teach My Dog a Lot of Words. Eastman, P. D., illus. 1999. (Bright & Early Board Bks.). 12p. (J). (gr. k-ps). bds. 4.99 (978-0-375-80099-3(9) , Random Hse. Bks. for Young Readers) Random Hse. Children's Bks.

Fritz, Jean & Clute, Tom. Champion Dog Prince Tom. 10.00 (978-0-89064-070-8(X)) National Assn. for Visually Handicapped.

Fritz, Kevin. The Newf & the Dane. 2003. 108p. (J). pap. 9.95 (978-0-595-27050-7(6) , Writers Club Pr.) iUniverse, Inc.

Frost, Helen. Diamond Willow. 2008. 128p. (J). 16.00 (****978-0-374-31776-8(3)***) Farrar, Straus & Giroux.

Fry, Sonali. Best in Show! 2003. (Illus.). 32p. (gr. k-3). lib. bdg. 11.25 (978-0-613-64461-7(1)) Tandem Library Bks.

Fry, Sonali, ed. The Missing Beach Ball. 2002. (Clifford, the Big Red Dog Ser.). (Illus.). 24p. (J). (ps-3). pap. 3.95 (978-0-439-33799-1(2) , Cartwheel Bks.) Scholastic, Inc.

Fuge, Charles. Yip! Snap! Yap! 2004. (Illus.). (J). 22p. bds. 6.95 (978-1-58246-097-0(3)); 24p. 14.95 (978-1-58246-046-8(9)) Ten Speed Pr. (Tricycle Pr.).

Fun in the Snow. 2003. (J). (978-1-932570-13-7(6)) Literacy Footprints Inc.

Fun Wherever We Are. 2004. (Dick & Jane Ser.). (Illus.). 144p. (J). (ps-2). 7.99 (978-0-448-43614-2(0) , Grosset & Dunlap) Penguin Group (USA) Inc.

Funk, Bev. Wool E. Woola. 2006. spiral bd. 9.45 (978-0-9789092-0-8(0)) Moonbow Pr., LLc.

Gabby Goes up & Down. 2005. (J). (978-1-58453-115-9(0)) Pioneer Valley Educational Pr., Inc.

Gaetz, Dayle. Sea Dog. Meissner, Amy, illus. 2006. 64p. (gr. 2-3). pap. 4.99 (978-1-55143-406-3(7)) Orca Bk. Pubs. USA.

Gaetz, Dayle Campbell. Sea Dog. Meissner, Amy, illus. 2006. 62p. (J). lib. bdg. 20.00 (****978-1-4242-1249-1(9)***) Fitzgerald Bks.

Ga'g, Wanda. Nothing at All. 2004. (Illus.). 32p. 14.95 (978-0-8166-4418-6(7)) Univ. of Minnesota Pr.

El Gallo, la Zorra, y el Perro. (Coleccion Fabulas y Cuentos Populares). (SPA.). (J). (gr. 2-4). (978-84-246-1559-8(X) , GL0414) La Galera, S.A. Editorial ESP. *Dist:* Lectorum Pubns., Inc.

Gantt, Leticia. Phantom of the Video Store. l.t. ed. 2000. (Wishbone Mysteries Ser.: No. 18). (Illus.). 141p. (J). (gr. 4 up). lib. bdg. 23.33 (978-0-8368-2701-9(5)) Stevens, Gareth Inc.

Ganzer, Diane. Patrick the Wayward Setter. 2005. 69p. pap. 14.95 (978-1-4137-5855-9(X)) PublishAmerica, Inc.

—Patrick the Wayward Setter: A Christmas Miracle. 2005. 60p. pap. 12.95 (978-1-4137-8351-3(1)) PublishAmerica, Inc.

García, Cristina. The Dog Who Loved the Moon. Serra, Sebastia, illus. 2008. 32p. (J). 15.99 (****978-1-4169-1836-3(1)***) Simon & Schuster Children's Publishing.

Gardiner, John Reynolds. Stone Fox. 48p. (J). pap. 4.50 (978-0-8072-1267-7(9) , Listening Library) Random Hse. Audio Publishing Group.

Gardiner, Lindsey. Here Come Poppy & Max. Gardiner, Lindsey, illus. 2000. (Illus.). 24p. (J). (ps-1). 12.95 (978-0-316-60346-1(5)) Little Brown & Co.

—When Poppy & Max Grow Up. Gardiner, Lindsey, illus. 2001. (Illus.). 24p. (J). (gr. k-1). 12.95 (978-0-316-60342-3(2)) Little, Brown Bks. for Young Readers.

Gardner, Wendy. Dig, Ivan Dig! Gardner, Wendy, illus. 2002. (Naughty Naughty Pets Ser.). (Illus.). 32p. (ps-17). 10.99 (978-0-7868-0884-7(5)) Hyperion Bks. for Children.

Garland, Sarah. Doing the Garden. 2008. (Illus.). 32p. (J). 9.95 (****978-1-84507-721-1(0)***) Lincoln, Frances Ltd. GBR. *Dist:* Perseus Distribution.

Garn, Laura Aimee. Bella Basset Ballerina. Sokolova, Valerie, illus. 2006. 32p. (J). (ps-3). 15.95 (978-0-9759378-0-8(4)) Pretty Please Pr., Inc.

Garr, Hillary. Dino the Dog & His Day in the Country. Kirton, Pamela T., illus. Date not set. 15.95 (978-0-9637143-3-6(3)) Amicus Pr.

Gauthier, Gail. A Girl, a Boy, & a Monster Cat. Cepeda, Joe, illus. 2007. 96p. (J). (gr. 2-4). 14.99 (978-0-399-24689-0(4) , Putnam Juvenile) Penguin Group (USA) Inc.

Gauthier, Gilles. En Souvenir de Babouche. 2000. (Premier Roman Ser.). (FRE.). 192p. (J). (gr. 2-5). pap. (978-2-89021-383-8(8)) Diffusion du livre Mirabel.

Gauthier, Gilles & Derome, Pierre-Andre. Mon Cher Chausson. 2000. (Premier Roman Ser.). (FRE.). 64p. (J). (gr. 2-5). pap. (978-2-89021-416-3(8)) Diffusion du livre Mirabel.

Gautier, Gary. Spaghetti & Peas. Bailey, Sheila, illus. 2007. (ENG.). 40p. (J). pap. 15.95 (978-0-9744446-1-1(8)) All About Kids Publishing.

Gave, Marc. Fox & the Hound: Read Aloud Storybook. 2000. (Illus.). 64p. (J). (ps-3). 6.99 (978-0-7364-0194-4(6)) Mouse Works.

Gay, Marie-Louise. Buenas Noches Samuel. 2004. (SPA.). (J). (gr. k up). pap. 7.99 (978-980-257-296-0(9)) Ekare, Ediciones VEN. *Dist:* Lectorum Pubns., Inc., Iaconi, Mariuccia Bk. Imports.

—What Are You Doing, Sam? 2006. (Illus.). 32p. 14.95 (978-0-88899-734-0(5)) Groundwood Bks. CAN. *Dist:* Perseus Distribution.

Gee, Genese. The Story of Jack, Sprat, & the Backpack. Gee, Genese, illus. (Illus.). 20p. (J). (ps-1). 2002. 14.99 (978-0-9719935-1-8(3)); 2001. pap. 10.49 (978-0-9719935-0-1(5)) Gee, Genese Celeste.

Gelsey, James. The Scary Scooby. 2007. (Scooby-Doo Case Files Ser.). 80p. (J). pap. 3.99 (****978-0-439-91594-6(5)***) Scholastic, Inc.

—Scooby-Doo! & the Cactus Creature. 2005. (Illus.). 58p. (J). lib. bdg. 15.00 (****978-1-4242-0304-8(X)***) Fitzgerald Bks.

—Scooby-Doo! & the Cactus Creature. 2005. (Illus.). 58p. (J). (****978-1-4155-9742-2(1)***) Scholastic, Inc.

—Scooby-Doo & the Carnival Creeper. 1999. (Scooby-Doo Mysteries Ser.: No. 7). (Illus.). 64p. (J). (ps-3). 3.99 (978-0-439-11346-5(6)) Scholastic, Inc.

—Scooby-Doo & the Groovy Ghost. 8th ed. 2000. (Scooby-Doo Mysteries Ser.: No. 8). (Illus.). 64p. (J). (ps-3). pap. 3.99 (978-0-439-11347-2(4) , Scholastic Paperbacks) Scholastic, Inc.

—Scooby-Doo & the Groovy Ghost. 2000. (gr. 3-6). lib. bdg. 11.80 (978-0-613-22338-6(1)) Tandem Library Bks.

—Scooby-Doo! & the Gruesome Goblin. 2004. (Illus.). 60p. (J). lib. bdg. 15.00 (****978-1-4242-0303-1(1)***) Fitzgerald Bks.

—Scooby-Doo & the Haunted Castle. 1998. (Scooby-Doo Mysteries Ser.: No. 1). (Illus.). 64p. (ps-3). pap. 3.99 (978-0-590-81909-1(7)) Scholastic, Inc.

—Scooby-Doo & the Mummy's Curse. 1998. (Scooby-Doo Mysteries Ser.: No. 2). (Illus.). 64p. (ps-3). 3.99 (978-0-590-81910-7(0)) Scholastic, Inc.

—Scooby-Doo & the Snow Monster. 1999. (Scooby-Doo Mysteries Ser.: No. 3). (Illus.). 57p. (J). (ps-3). 3.99 (978-0-590-81914-5(3) , Scholastic Paperbacks) Scholastic, Inc.

—Scooby-Doo & the Snow Monster. 1999. (gr. 3-6). lib. bdg. 11.80 (978-0-613-12085-2(X)) Tandem Library Bks.

—Scooby-Doo & the Spooky Strikeout. 2000. (gr. 3-6). lib. bdg. 11.80 (978-0-613-26854-7(7)) Tandem Library Bks.

—Scooby-Doo! & the Spooky Strikeout. del Sur, Duendes, illus. 2000. (Scooby-Doo Mysteries Ser.: No. 10). 64p. (J). (ps-3). 3.99 (978-0-439-11349-6(0)) Scholastic, Inc.

—Scooby-Doo & the Sunken Ship. 1999. (Scooby-Doo Mysteries Ser.: No. 4). (Illus.). 64p. (J). (ps-3). pap. 3.99 (978-0-590-81917-6(8)) Scholastic, Inc.

—Scooby-Doo & the Sunken Ship. 1999. (gr. 3-6). lib. bdg. 11.80 (978-0-613-17004-8(0)) Tandem Library Bks.

—Scooby-Doo & the Vampire's Revenge. 1999. (Scooby-Doo Mysteries Ser.: No. 6). (Illus.). 64p. (J). (ps-3). mass mkt. 3.99 (978-0-439-08278-5(1)) Scholastic, Inc.

—Scooby-Doo & the Vampire's Revenge. 1999. (gr. 3-6). lib. bdg. 11.80 (978-0-613-17940-9(4)) Tandem Library Bks.

—Scooby Doo! & the Zombie's Treasure. 2000. (gr. 3-6). lib. bdg. 11.80 (978-0-613-27677-1(9)) Tandem Library Bks.

—Scooby-Doo! & You. del Sur, Duendes, illus. 2001. (Collect the Clues Mystery Ser.). 60p. (J). (978-0-439-23155-8(8)) Scholastic, Inc.

—Scooby-Doo!TM & the Fairground Phantom. del Sur, Duendes, illus. 2000. (Scooby-Doo Mysteries Ser.: No. 11). 64p. (J). (ps-3). 3.99 (978-0-439-10664-1(8)) Scholastic, Inc.

—The Zombie's Treasure. 2000. (Scooby-Doo Mysteries Ser.: No. 9). (Illus.). 64p. (J). (ps-3). pap. 3.99 (978-0-439-11348-9(2)) Scholastic, Inc.

Geoghegan, Adrienne. Dogs Don't Wear Glasses. 2000. (Illus.). 32p. (J). (ps-3). pap. 7.95 (978-1-56656-274-4(0) , Crocodile Bks.) Interlink Publishing Group, Inc.

—Dogs Don't Wear Glasses. 2000. (gr. k-3). lib. bdg. 16.40 (978-0-613-81226-9(3)) Tandem Library Bks.

George, Jean Craighead. Cliff Hanger. Minor, Wendell, illus. 2002. (Outdoor Adventures Ser.). 32p. (J). (ps-4). 15.99 (978-0-06-000260-2(3)) HarperCollins Pubs.

George, Olivia. The Bravest Girls in the World. DuBurke, Randy, illus. 2004. 32p. (J). lib. bdg. 15.00 (****978-1-4242-0241-6(8)***) Fitzgerald Bks.

Gerlach-Babb nee Maines, Mary & Gerlach, Susan. Best Christmas Gift. 2007. (ENG.). 52p. per. 12.95 (****978-1-4241-6389-2(7)***) PublishAmerica, Inc.

Gerrit & His Dog. unabr. ed. 1998. (Children's Heritage Ser.). (Illus.). 83p. (J). (ps-6). reprint ed. pap. 5.75 (978-1-58339-138-9(X) , D38) Grace & Truth Bks.

Gerson, Corinne. Cyberdog. 1999. 62p. (J). (gr. 3-5). pap. 9.99 (978-0-88092-447-4(0) , 4470) Royal Fireworks Publishing Co.

Ghent, Natale. Piper. 2001. (J). (978-0-606-21772-9(X)); (gr. 5-8). lib. bdg. 15.25 (978-0-613-36600-7(X)) Tandem Library Bks.

Giancamilli, Vanessa. Patches Finds a Home. Hatala, Dan, illus. 2006. (Pet Tales Ser.). 32p. (J). (978-1-59249-641-9(5)); pap. (978-1-59249-640-2(7)); pap. incl. audio compact disk (978-1-59249-639-6(3)) Soundprints.

Giff, Patricia Reilly. Good Luck, Ronald Morgan! 1999. (J). (978-0-606-16778-9(1)) Tandem Library Bks.

A Gift to Share. 2005. (J). 17.00 (978-0-9721457-1-8(0)) Silent Moon Bks.

Giglio, Judy. The Tapping Tale. Cepeda, Joe, illus. 2003. (Green Light Readers Level 1 Ser.). 24p. (J). 11.95 (978-0-15-204812-9(X)); pap. 3.95 (978-0-15-204852-5(9)) Harcourt Children's Bks. (Green Light Readers).

Gilbert, Frances. Sleepy Dog. Sterling Publishing Company Staff, ed. 2003. (Illus.). 16p. (J). bds. 4.95 (978-1-4027-0576-2(X)) Sterling Publishing Co., Inc.

Giles, S. A. A Home for All: How a Little Black Puppy Gets a Name. 2007. 23.00 (****978-0-8059-8864-2(5)***) Dorrance Publishing Co., Inc.

Giles, S. A. A Home for All: How a Little Puppy Finds a Home. 2006. 20.00 (978-0-8059-9076-8(3)) Dorrance Publishing Co., Inc.

Gill-Brown, Vanessa & Stanley, Mandy. Rufferella. 2001. (Illus.). 32p. (J). (ps-5). pap. 12.95 (978-0-439-25617-9(8)) Scholastic, Inc.

Gillham, Bill. My Dog's Party ELT Edition. Snow, Alan, illus. 2001. (Cambridge Storybooks Ser.). 8p. pap. 3.00 (978-0-521-00654-5(6)) Cambridge Univ. Pr.

Gilmer, Evelyn. Maggie: The Beagle with a Broken Tail. 2007. (J). per. 6.99 (****978-1-60247-310-2(2)***) Tate Publishing & Enterprises, L.L.C.

Ginsberg, Martha. The Three Buddies in Hideaway Land. Loughran, Tony, illus. l.t. ed. 2003. 38p. (J). (ps-7). per. 9.95 (978-1-59453-054-8(8) , 1368) Airleaf Publishing & Bookselling.

Gipson, Fred. Old Yeller. Date not set. 192p. (J). 20.95 (978-0-8488-2273-6(0)) Amereon LTD.

—Old Yeller. 2001. 132p. (J). (ps-7). lib. bdg. 16.45 (978-0-613-85744-4(5)) Tandem Library Bks.

—Old Yeller. 1999. (J). lib. bdg. 21.95 (978-1-56723-204-2(3)) Yestermorrow, Inc.

—Savage Sam. Date not set. pap. 371.40 (978-0-671-75819-6(5) , Atria) Simon & Schuster.

Gipson, Fred & Polson, Steven. Old Yeller. 2001. (Perennial Classics Ser.). (Illus.). 144p. (gr. 4-7). pap. 8.00 (978-0-06-093547-4(2)) HarperCollins Pubs.

Gipson, Frederick. Old Yeller. Burger, Carl, illus. 2002. 14.47 (978-0-7587-0299-9(X)) Book Wholesalers, Inc.

Gizmo Gets His Wish. 2005. (J). pap. (978-0-9716567-5-8(4)) Book Web Publishing, Ltd.

The Gizmo Tales: Hero Dogs. 2005. (YA). pap. 14.94 (978-0-9716567-6-5(2)) Book Web Publishing, Ltd.

Glass, Timothy. Sleepytown Beagles: Oh Brother! 2007. 24p. per. 13.95 (****978-1-59594-178-7(9)*** , Wingspan Pr.) WingSpan Publishing.

—Sleepytown Beagles Penny's 4th of July. Mikle, Toby, illus. 2006. 24p. (J). per. 15.95 (****978-1-888461-10-7(1));*** 16.95 (****978-1-888461-11-4(X)***) Islewest Publishing.

Glenn, Sharlee Mullins. Just What Mama Needs. Hirao, Amiko, illus. 2008. 32p. (J). 16.00 (978-0-15-205759-6(5)) Harcourt Trade Pubs.

Glymph, Rikimah. Are You My Friend? 2006. (Illus.). 32p. (J). lib. bdg. 17.95 (****978-1-934190-00-5(4)***) Ocean Front Bk. Publishing, Inc.

Godwin, Laura. The Best Fall of All. Chapman, Jane, illus. 2002. (Happy Honey Ser.). 32p. (J). pap. 3.99 (978-0-689-84763-9(7) , Aladdin); 14.95 (978-0-689-84713-4(0) , McElderry, Margaret K.) Simon & Schuster Children's Publishing.

—Best Fall of All. 2002. (ps-2). lib. bdg. 11.80 (978-0-613-57495-2(8)) Tandem Library Bks.

—Happy & Honey. Chapman, Jane, illus. 2001. (Happy Honey Ser.: Vol. 1). 32p. (J). pap. 3.99 (978-0-689-84235-1(X) , Aladdin) Simon & Schuster Children's Publishing.

—Happy & Honey. 2001. (gr. k-3). lib. bdg. 11.80 (978-0-613-36968-8(8)); (Illus.). (J). 10.79 (978-0-606-22029-3(1)) Tandem Library Bks.

—Happy & Honey: Honey Helps. 2001. (gr. k-3). lib. bdg. 11.80 (978-0-613-36969-5(6)) Tandem Library Bks.

—Happy Christmas, Honey. 2002. (ps-2). lib. bdg. 11.80 (978-0-613-57505-8(9)) Tandem Library Bks.

—Honey Helps. Chapman, Jane, illus. 2001. (Happy Honey Ser.: Vol. 2). 32p. (J). pap. 3.99 (978-0-689-84234-4(1) , Aladdin) Simon & Schuster Children's Publishing.

—Honey Helps. 2001. (Illus.). (J). 10.79 (978-0-606-22030-9(5)) Tandem Library Bks.

Godwin, Laura & Chapman, Jane. Happy Christmas, Honey! 2002. (Ready-to-Read Ser.). (Illus.). 32p. (J). 14.95 (978-0-689-84714-1(9) , McElderry, Margaret K.) Simon & Schuster Children's Publishing.

Goertzen, Glenda. City Dogs. Hudecki, Peter, illus. 2007. 128p. (J). (gr. 2-4). pap. (****978-1-55455-005-0(X)***) Fitzhenry & Whiteside, Ltd.

Goertzen, Glenda. The Prairie Dogs. Béha, Philippe, illus. 2004. 164p. pap. (978-1-55005-113-1(X)) Fitzhenry & Whiteside, Ltd.

Goldblatt, Stacey. Stray. 2007. 288p. (YA). (gr. 7-10). 15.99 (978-0-385-73443-1(3)); lib. bdg. 18.99 (978-0-385-90448-3(7)) Random Hse. Children's Bks. (Delacorte Bks. for Young Readers).

Golden Books Staff. Welcome to Blue's Room! Miller, Victoria A., illus. 2004. 32p. (J). (ps-2). pap. 3.99 (978-0-375-83061-7(8) , Golden Bks.) Random Hse. Children's Bks.

—Which Way Do I Go? Saunders, Zina, illus. 2004. 32p. (J). (ps-2). pap. 4.99 (978-0-375-83062-4(6) , Golden Bks.) Random Hse. Children's Bks.

—102 Dalmatians: Coloring Book. 2000. (Illus.). 80p. (J). (ps-3). pap. 3.99 (978-0-307-25253-1(1) , Golden Bks.) Random Hse. Children's Bks.

—102 Dalmatians: Mutts in a Mess. 2000. (Illus.). 32p. (J). (ps-3). pap. 3.99 (978-0-307-29901-7(5) , 29901, Golden Bks.) Random Hse. Children's Bks.

Goldfinger, Jennifer P. My Dog Lyle. Goldfinger, Jennifer P., illus. 2007. (Illus.). 32p. (J). (ps-k). 16.00 (978-0-618-63983-0(7) , Clarion Bks.) Houghton Mifflin Co. Trade & Reference Div.

Golding, Sally. Foley & Jem. Mark, Oliver, illus. 2004. 32p. (J). 14.95 (978-1-4027-1364-4(9)) Sterling Publishing Co., Inc.

Goldstein, Arline. Keeping Time with JouJou. 2006. pap. 23.99 (***978-1-4259-5043-9(4)***) AuthorHouse.

Golembe, Carla. Annabelle's Big Move. Golembe, Carla, illus. 1999. (Illus.). 32p. (J). (gr. k-3). tchr. ed. 16.00 (978-0-395-91543-1(0)) Houghton Mifflin Co. Trade & Reference Div.

Gomez, Rebecca. 102 Dalmatians: Pull-Out Posters & Trading Cards Book. 2000. (Illus.). 32p. (J). (ps-2). lib. bdg. 7.99 (978-0-7364-1066-3(X)) Mouse Works.

The Good-for-Nothing Dog, 6 vols., Vol. 2. (Woodland Mysteriestm Ser.). 133p. (gr. 3-7). 42.50 (978-0-7802-7936-0(0)) Wright Group, The.

Goodale, Rebecca, illus. Island Dog. 1999. 38p. (J). (ps up). 17.95 (978-1-891090-03-5(8)) Two Dog Pr.

Goodall, Jane. Rickie & Henri: A True Story. Marks, Alan, illus. 2004. 32p. (J). (ps). 15.99 (978-0-698-40002-3(X) , Minedition) Penguin Group (USA) Inc.

Goode, Diane. Thanksgiving Is Here! Goode, Diane, illus. 2005. 32p. (J). (ps-3). pap. 6.99 (978-0-06-051590-4(2) , Harper Trophy) HarperCollins Pubs.

Goodhart, Pippa. Rescued by a Dog Called Flow. 2006. (Illus.). 128p. (J). pap. 6.95 (978-1-903015-47-6(2)) Barn Owl Bks, London GBR. *Dist:* Independent Pubs. Group.

Goodman, David & Copp, Rick. Scooby-Doo & the Hex Files. 1999. (Scooby-Doo Movie Storybooks). (Illus.). 32p. (J). (ps-3). pap. 3.50 (978-0-439-08787-2(2)) Scholastic, Inc.

Goose, Mother. Puppy Dog Tails Travel Pack. 2005. (Illus.). (J). 12.95 (978-1-59249-474-3(9) , 1D101) Soundprints.

Gordon, Wendy. I'm Safe! at the Mall. Gordon, Paul, illus. 1998. (I'm Safe! Ser.). 32p. (J). (ps-3). pap. 6.95 (978-1-891596-00-1(4)) BackYard Bks.

Gormley, Greg. The Yawn That Wouldn't Stop. 2006. (Illus.). 10p. (J). bds. 12.95 (978-0-7696-4637-4(9) , Gingham Dog Pr.) School Specialty Publishing.

Gosney, Joy. Hey Scruffy! 2001. (Illus.). 32p. (YA). (ps up). 16.95 (978-0-7475-4877-5(3)) Bloomsbury Publishing Plc GBR. *Dist:* Trafalgar Square Publishing.

Graham, Bob. Benny: An Adventure Story. Graham, Bob, illus. 2003. (Illus.). 32p. (J). (ps-2). pap. 6.99 (978-0-7636-1703-5(2)) Candlewick Pr.

—Benny: An Adventure Story. 2006. (J). (gr. k-3). pap. 19.95 incl. audio compact disk (978-0-8045-4138-1(8)); pap. 17.95 incl. audio (978-0-8045-6939-2(8)) Spoken Arts, Inc.

—Benny: An Adventure Story. 2003. (gr. k-3). lib. bdg. 14.15 (978-0-613-60334-8(6)) Tandem Library Bks.

—Let's Get a Pup! Said Kate. Graham, Bob, illus. 2003. (Illus.). 32p. (J). (ps-ps). pap. 6.99 (978-0-7636-2193-3(5)) Candlewick Pr.

Graham, Bob. The "Trouble with Dogs..." Said Dad. Graham, Bob, illus. 2007. (Illus.). 32p. (J). (ps). 12.99 (***978-0-7636-3316-5(X)***) Candlewick Pr.

Graham, Georgia. A Team Like No Other. Graham, Georgia, illus. 2004. (Illus.). 32p. (J). (gr. 1-3). 17.95 (978-0-88995-290-4(6)) Red Deer Pr. CAN. *Dist:* Fitzhenry & Whiteside, Ltd.

Grambling, Lois G. Big Dog. San Diego, Andy, illus. 2001. 32p. (J). (gr. k-3). 15.95 (978-0-7614-5045-0(9) , Cavendish Children's Bks.) Cavendish, Marshall Corp.

La Gran Perrera Galactica: Los Perros Galactica. adapted l.t. ed. 2000. (SPA.). 36p. (J). pap. 5.00 (978-1-883772-90-1(7)) Flying Rhinoceros, Inc.

Gravdahl, John. The Tale of Dog Giovanni. 2000. (Illus.). 32p. (J). (gr. k-4). 16.95 (978-0-9678577-9-4(1)) Propeller Pr.

Graves, Sue. Dog in the Fog. 2007. (Fun with Phonics Ser.). 20p. (J). pap. 4.99 (***978-0-439-02551-5(6)***) Scholastic, Inc.

Gray, Nigel. My Dog, My Cat, My Mama, & Me! Graham, Bob, illus. 2007. 24p. (J). (gr. k-ps). 8.99 (***978-0-7636-3639-5(8)***) Candlewick Pr.

Graybill, Guy, Jr. The Dogs of Saint George: The Dogs of St George, 1 vol. 2005. 101p. (YA). per. (978-0-9747039-2-3(3)) Ironhorse Publishing Co.

The Great Race. 2002. (Thomas the Tank Engine Ser.). (Illus.). (J). 11.91 (978-0-7587-4754-9(3)) Book Wholesalers, Inc.

Green-Armytage, Stephen. Dudley: The Little Terrier That Could. 1999. (Illus.). 32p. (gr. 8-17). 12.95 (978-0-8109-4098-7(1)) Abrams, Harry N. , Inc.

Green, Jonathan, illus. Amadeus, the Leghorn Rooster. 2004. (J). 17.95 (978-0-87844-174-7(3)) Sandlapper Publishing Co., Inc.

Greenaway, Elizabeth. Night Is the Time. Weston, Martha, illus. 1999. (Jellybean Bks.). 24p. (J). (ps-k). 1.99 (978-0-375-89274-5(5) , Random Hse. Bks. for Young Readers) Random Hse. Children's Bks.

Greenburg, J. C. On the Dog. Palen, Debbie, illus. 2002. (Andrew Lost Ser.: Bk. 1). 96p. (J). (gr. 1-4). pap. 3.99 (978-0-375-81277-4(6) , Random Hse. Bks. for Young Readers) Random Hse. Children's Bks.

—On the Dog. 2002. (Andrew Lost Ser.: Bk. 1). (J). (ps-2). lib. bdg. 11.80 (978-0-613-50405-8(4)) Tandem Library Bks.

Greene, Brenda. Dog Gone: Boomer's Story. Cheryl H. Hahn, illus. 2005. 127p. (YA). per. 8.99 (978-0-9770279-0-3(2)) Three Willows Pr.

Greene, Daryl C. Benjamin's Dog Joseph: A Three Legged Hero. Akers-Bell, Mary, illus. 2003. 48p. (J). (gr. 2-4). pap. 9.95 (978-0-9700827-4-9(6)); lib. bdg. 17.95 (978-0-9700827-5-6(4)) Densmore-Reid Pubns.

Greenlee, Don. This Countryboy Guardian Was Heaven Sent. 2007. (Illus.). 114p. (YA). per. 14.95 net. (***978-0-9795574-0-8(2)***) Country Boy Publishing Co.

Greer, Tom C. Honey's Peanut Butter Adventure. Faust, Laurie A., illus. 2007. (J). per. 9.95 (***978-0-9789227-1-9(9)***) Weeping Willow Publishing.

Gregg, John Hunter. Where Dogs Run. 2006. (YA). per. (978-0-9790165-5-4(X)) 302 Publishing.

Grégoire, Caroline. Apolo. Grégoire, Caroline, illus. 2006. (SPA., Illus.). 28p. (J). pap. 7.95 (978-1-933605-20-3(0)) Kane/Miller Bk. Pubs., Inc.

—Counting with Apollo. Grégoire, Caroline, illus. 2007. (Illus.). 32p. (J). pap. 7.95 (978-1-933605-42-5(1)) Kane/Miller Bk. Pubs., Inc.

Gregory, Jillian Louise. Dobbs Dog Detective: Operation Fido & Fifi. 2003. 67p. pap. 11.95 (978-1-4137-0644-4(4)) PublishAmerica, Inc.

Gregory, Nan & Lightburn, Ron. How Smudge Came. 1999. (Northern Lights Books for Children Ser.). (Illus.). 32p. (J). (ps-3). (978-0-88995-143-3(8)) Red Deer Pr.

Gretz, Susanna. Riley & Rose in the Picture. Gretz, Susanna, illus. 2005. (Illus.). 32p. (J). (gr. k-3). 16.99 (978-0-7636-2681-5(3)) Candlewick Pr.

Griebel, Roberta L. Joyful Noise! 2007. (ENG.). 56p. per. 12.95 (***978-1-4241-6037-2(5)***) PublishAmerica, Inc.

Griggs, Joyce. Imanis Good Deed. 2006. pap. 9.95 (***978-1-4327-0071-3(5)***) Outskirts Press, Inc.

Griver, Jeanette A. CURIO a Shetland Sheepdog & Friends: A Story of Change for Children of All Ages. 2005. (Illus.). 64p. (J). per. 6.95 (978-0-929948-05-8(X)) Compsych Systems, Inc., Pubns. Div.

Griver, Jeanette A. CURIO a Shetland Sheepdog & her Pals: All ages Will enjoy the Tales of Friendship. 2007. (J). per. 8.50 (***978-0-929948-06-5(8)***) Compsych Systems, Inc., Pubns. Div.

Grogan, John. Bad Dog, Marley! Cowdrey, Richard, illus. 2007. 40p. (J). (ps-3). 16.99 (***978-0-06-117114-7(X)***); lib. bdg. 17.89 (***978-0-06-117115-4(8)***) HarperCollins Pubs.

—Bad Dog, Marley! Book & Puppy. Cowdrey, Richard, illus. 2007. 40p. (J). (ps-3). 24.99 (***978-0-06-143496-9(5)***) HarperCollins Pubs.

Grooms, Molly. We Are Puppies. 2005. 40p. bds. 12.95 (978-90-5843-815-7(5)) YoYo Bks. BEL. *Dist:* National Bk. Network.

Group/McGraw-Hill, Wright. Seiko the Watchdog: Level N, 6 vols. 128p. (gr. 3-6). 36.95 (978-0-322-05883-5(X)) Wright Group, The.

Grovet, Heather. Petunia the Ugly Pug. 2002. (Julius & Friends Ser.: Vol. 7). (Illus.). 94p. (J). 6.99 (978-0-8163-1871-1(9)) Pacific Pr. Publishing Assn.

Grovet, Heather Marie. Marvelous Mark & His No-Good Dog. 2003. 128p. (J). pap. 7.99 (978-0-8280-1734-3(4) , 132-670) Review & Herald Publishing Assn.

Gruelle, Johnny. Raggedy Ann & Rags: Adapted from Stories by Johnny Gruelle. Palmer, illus. 2003. 40p. (J). 15.00 (978-0-689-86162-8(1) , Simon & Schuster Children's Publishing) Simon & Schuster Children's Publishing.

Gruelle, Johnny & Palmer, Jan. Raggedy Ann & Rags: Adapted from Stories by Johnny Gruelle. 2002. (My First Raggedy Ann Ser.). (Illus.). 40p. (J). 15.00 (978-0-689-82977-2(9)) Simon & Schuster Children's Publishing.

Gruffudd, Elena. Gelert. 2005. (WEL., Illus.). 34p. (978-0-86381-291-0(0)) Gwasg Carreg Gwalch.

Gumbo Goes Downtown - Evaluation Guide: Evaluation Guide. 2006. (J). (978-1-55942-407-3(9)) Marsh Media.

Gummelt, Donna & Melchiorre, Dondino. Cow Puppies. Wall, Randy Hugh, ed. Varela, Juan D., tr. Varela, Juan D., illus. 2006. Tr. of Cachorros Vaqueros. (SPA.). 32p. (J). 14.95 (978-0-9764798-7-1(7)) Story Store Collection Publishing.

Gurney, Stella. The Silly Hot Dog. Million, Liz, illus. 2006. (Lightning Readers Ser.). 32p. (J). pap. 3.95 (978-0-7696-4195-9(4) , Gingham Dog Pr.) School Specialty Publishing.

Gutman, Anne. Gaspard & Lisa at the Museum. Hallensleben, Georg, illus. 2001. 32p. (J). (ps-3). 9.95 (978-0-375-81117-3(6) , Knopf Bks. for Young Readers) Random Hse. Children's Bks.

—Gaspard & Lisa, Friends Forever. Hallensleben, Georg, illus. 2003. 32p. (J). (ps-3). 9.95 (978-0-375-82253-7(4) , Knopf Bks. for Young Readers) Random Hse. Children's Bks.

—Gaspard & Lisa's Rainy Day. Hallensleben, Georg, illus. 2003. (Misadventures of Gaspard & Lisa Ser.). 32p. (J). (ps-3). 9.95 (978-0-375-82252-0(6) , Knopf Bks. for Young Readers) Random Hse. Children's Bks.

—Gaspard in the Hospital. Hallensleben, Georg, illus. 2001. (Misadventures of Gaspard & Lisa Ser.). 32p. (J). (ps-3). 9.95 (978-0-375-81116-6(8) , Knopf Bks. for Young Readers) Random Hse. Children's Bks.

—Lisa in the Jungle. Hallensleben, Georg, illus. 2003. (Misadventures of Gaspard & Lisa Ser.). 32p. (J). (ps-3). 9.95 (978-0-375-82254-4(2) , Knopf Bks. for Young Readers) Random Hse. Children's Bks.

—Lisa's Baby Sister. Hallensleben, Georg, illus. 2003. (Misadventures of Gaspard & Lisa Ser.). 32p. (J). (ps-3). 9.95 (978-0-375-82251-3(8) , Knopf Bks. for Young Readers) Random Hse. Children's Bks.

Gutman, Anne & Hallensleben, Georg. Gaspard at the Seashore. 2002. (Illus.). 32p. (J). (gr. k-3). 9.95 (978-0-375-81118-0(4) , Knopf Bks. for Young Readers) Random Hse. Children's Bks.

—Gaspard on Vacation. 2001. (Illus.). 32p. (J). (ps-1). 9.95 (978-0-375-81115-9(X) , Knopf Bks. for Young Readers) Random Hse. Children's Bks.

—Lisa in New York. 2002. (Illus.). 32p. (J). (gr. k-3). 9.95 (978-0-375-81119-7(2) , Knopf Bks. for Young Readers) Random Hse. Children's Bks.

Guzman, Lila. Kichi in Jungle Jeopardy. Johnson, Regan, illus. (J). 2007. per. 8.95 (978-0-9769417-2-9(4)); 2006. 144p. 13.95 (978-0-9769417-1-2(6)) Blooming Tree Pr.

Haas, Jessie. Shaper. 2002. 192p. (J). (gr. 5 up). 16.99 (978-0-06-000170-4(4)); lib. bdg. 17.89 (978-0-06-000171-1(2)) HarperCollins Pubs.

Haddock, Martin. Winston of Winnacle Farm. 2001. 32p. per. (978-1-930493-00-1(2)) Athena Pr.

Haig, Matt. Samuel Blink & the Forbidden Forest. 2007. 352p. (J). 16.99 (978-0-399-24739-2(4) , Putnam Juvenile) Penguin Group (USA) Inc.

Haircuts for Bella & Rosie. 2004. (J). (978-1-932570-18-2(7)) Literacy Footprints Inc.

Halbur, Donna. The Puppy & the Guppy. 2nd ed. 2005. (YA). per. 9.95 (978-0-9603520-1-2(5)) Halbur Publishing.

Hall, Margaret. Sebastian in Central Park. Wenzel, David, illus. 2001. (Suitcase Bear Adventures Ser.: Vol. 1). (J). (978-0-9713174-0-6(2) , Bear & Co.) Bear & Co.

Hamilton, Elizabeth L. Pandora Puppy's Caring Circle. 2004. (Character Critters Ser.: No. 5). (Illus.). 32p. (J). per. 5.95 (978-0-9754629-0-4(3) , Character-in-Action) Quiet Impact, Inc.

Hamilton, Martha & Weiss, Mitch. Why Animals Never Got Fire: A Story of the Couer d'Alene Indians. MacDonald, Bruce, illus. 2005. 12p. (J). pap. 5.00 (978-1-57274-715-9(3) , 2793, Bks. for Young Learners) Owen, Richard C. Pubs., Inc.

Hamilton, Richard. Cal & the Amazing Anti-Gravity Machine. Hearn, Sam, illus. 2006. 128p. (J). 14.95 (978-1-58234-723-3(9) , Bloomsbury Children); pap. 5.95 (978-1-58234-714-1(X)) Bloomsbury Publishing.

Hanel, Wolfram. Mary & the Mystery Dog. 2000. (gr. 3-6). lib. bdg. 14.10 (978-0-613-30020-9(3)) Tandem Library Bks.

Hanson, Paige & Hanson, Jon. Harry Spotter: The Incontinent Puppy, Sellers, Amy, illus. l.t. ed. 2005. 44p. (J). per. 20.00 (978-0-9721146-1-5(0)) Monroe Educational Media.

Harcourt School Publishers Staff. Are We Having Fun Yet? 3rd ed. 2002. (Trophies English Language Learners Ser.). (Illus.). (gr. 5). pap. 5.10 (978-0-15-327812-9(9)) Harcourt Schl. Pubs.

—Autobiography of a Dog On Level. 3rd ed. 2002. (Trophies Reading Program Ser.). (Illus.). pap. 5.10 (978-0-15-323438-5(5)) Harcourt Schl. Pubs.

—The Best Stunt of All: Take-Home Book. 1999. (Collections Ser.). (Illus.). (J). pap. 1.90 (978-0-15-317287-8(8)) Harcourt Schl. Pubs.

—The Best Stunt of All Below Level. 3rd ed. 2002. (Trophies Reading Program Ser.). (Illus.). (gr. 3). pap. 5.10 (978-0-15-323131-5(9)) Harcourt Schl. Pubs.

—The Black Dog: Take-Home Book. rev. ed. 2001. (Collections Ser.: Vol. 4). (Illus.). (J). pap. 1.90 (978-0-15-317817-7(5)) Harcourt Schl. Pubs.

—Bravo! On Level. 3rd ed. 2002. (Trophies Reading Program Ser.). (Illus.). pap. 5.10 (978-0-15-323260-2(9)); (SPA., pap. 6.80 (978-0-15-324170-3(5)) Harcourt Schl. Pubs.

—A Bug & a Pup: Below Level. 3rd ed. 2002. (Trophies Reading Program Ser.). (Illus.). (J). pap. 3.20 (978-0-15-322947-3(0)) Harcourt Schl. Pubs.

—The Dog & His Shadow On Level. 3rd ed. 2002. (Trophies Reading Program Ser.). (Illus.). pap. 5.10 (978-0-15-323074-5(6)) Harcourt Schl. Pubs.

—The Encounter Advanced Level. 3rd ed. 2002. (Trophies Reading Program Ser.). (Illus,). pap. 5.10 (978-0-15-323385-2(0)) Harcourt Schl. Pubs.

—The Girl Who Spoke Dog: Take-Home Book. 2001. (Collections Ser.). (Illus.). (J). pap. 1.90 (978-0-15-319550-1(9)) Harcourt Schl. Pubs.

—The Girl Who Spoke Dog Below Level. 3rd ed. 2002. (Illus.). pap. 5.10 (978-0-15-323408-8(3)) Harcourt Schl. Pubs.

—The Legend of the Arctic Ice Advanced Level. 3rd ed. 2002. (Trophies Reading Program Ser.). (Illus.). pap. 5.10 (978-0-15-323378-4(8)) Harcourt Schl. Pubs.

—The Lost Dog: Independent Reader. 3rd ed. 2002. (Trophies Reading Program Ser.). (Illus.). (J). pap. 2.90 (978-0-15-325492-5(0)) Harcourt Schl. Pubs.

—Mr. Smart's Big Dog Book Advanced Level. 3rd ed. 2002. (Trophies Reading Program Ser.). (Illus.). pap. 5.10 (978-0-15-323020-2(7)) Harcourt Schl. Pubs.

—My Friend, Boots 5-Pack, Advanced Level. 3rd ed. 2002. (Trophies Reading Program Ser.). (Illus.). (gr. 12). pap. 20.10 (978-0-15-326864-9(6)) Harcourt Schl. Pubs.

—The Mystery at Wolf River Level D: Library Edition. 2001. (Collections Ser.). (Illus.). pap. 12.10 (978-0-15-314433-2(5)) Harcourt Schl. Pubs.

—Our Best Friend Advanced Level. 3rd ed. 2002. (Trophies Reading Program Ser.). (Illus.). (gr. 3). pap. 5.10 (978-0-15-323197-1(1)) Harcourt Schl. Pubs.

—Space Dogs: Take-Home Book. 1999. (Signatures Ser.). (Illus.). (J). pap. 1.90 (978-0-15-313901-7(3)) Harcourt Schl. Pubs.

—Spike: Library Book. 1999. (Collections Ser.). (Illus.). pap. 13.60 (978-0-15-313398-5(8)) Harcourt Schl. Pubs.

—Ten Dogs in the Window Little Book. 3rd ed. 2002. (Trophies Reading Program Ser.). (Illus.). (J). pap. 10.20 (978-0-15-329350-4(0)) Harcourt Schl. Pubs.

—Trofeos Advanced Level: Cuando/Cacharro. 3rd ed. 2002. (SPA., Illus.). pap. 5.50 (978-0-15-323926-7(3)) Harcourt Schl. Pubs.

—Trofeos Advanced Level: Donde Estamos? 3rd ed. 2002. (SPA., Illus.). pap. 6.80 (978-0-15-323934-2(4)) Harcourt Schl. Pubs.

—Trofeos Advanced Level: Guillerno/Panzen. 3rd ed. 2002. (SPA., Illus.). pap. 6.80 (978-0-15-323931-1(X)) Harcourt Schl. Pubs.

—Trofeos Below Level: Jugamos, Julita? 3rd ed. 2002. (SPA., Illus.). (J). pap. 3.50 (978-0-15-323860-4(7)) Harcourt Schl. Pubs.

—When I Was a Pup, 5-Pack, Advanced Level. 3rd ed. 2002. (Trophies Reading Program Ser.). (Illus.). (gr. 1). pap. 20.10 (978-0-15-326865-6(4)) Harcourt Schl. Pubs.

—When I Was a Pup Advanced Level. 3rd ed. 2002. (Trophies Reading Program Ser.). (Illus.). (J). pap. 3.70 (978-0-15-323015-8(0)) Harcourt Schl. Pubs.

Harder Tangvald, Christine. Bow Wow Puppy Learns to Share. Gambill, Henrietta, ed. Fletcher, Rusty, illus. 1998. (Shaped Paperback Bks.). 24p. (J). (ps-k). pap. 3.99 (978-0-7847-0836-1(3) , 03996, Bean Sprouts) Standard Publishing.

Hardin, Suzanne. Dogs at School. Friar, Joanne, illus. 1999. (Books for Young Learners). 16p. (J). (gr. k-2). pap. 5.00 (978-1-57274-256-7(9)) Owen, Richard C. Pubs., Inc.

—No Se Permiten Perros. Romo, Alberto, tr. Friar, Joanne, illus. 1998. (Books for Young Learners).Tr. of No Dogs Allowed. (SPA.). 12p. (J). (gr. k-2). pap. 5.00 (978-1-57274-201-7(1) , A2886) Owen, Richard C. Pubs., Inc.

Harlow, Joan Hiatt. Star in the Storm. 160p. 2005. pap. 2.99 (978-1-4169-0530-1(8)); 2001. (gr. 3-7). mass mkt. 5.99 (978-0-689-84621-2(5)) Simon & Schuster Children's Publishing. (Aladdin).

—Star in the Storm. 2001. (978-0-606-22107-8(7)); (gr. 3-6). lib. bdg. 13.00 (978-0-613-53446-8(8)) Tandem Library Bks.

—Thunder from the Sea. (Illus.). 256p. (J). 2005. pap. 5.99 (978-0-689-86404-9(3) , Aladdin); 2004. 16.99 (978-0-689-86403-2(5) , McElderry, Margaret K.) Simon & Schuster Children's Publishing.

Harlow, Joan Hiatt & Minor, Wendell. Star in the Storm. 2000. (Illus.). 160p. (J). (gr. 3-7). 16.00 (978-0-689-82905-5(1) , McElderry, Margaret K.) Simon & Schuster Children's Publishing.

Harper, Dan. Sit, Truman! Moser, Barry & Moser, Cara, illus. 2004. 32p. (J). reprint ed. pap. 6.00 (978-0-15-205068-9(X) , Voyager Bks./Libros Viajeros) Harcourt Children's Bks.

Harper, Isabelle. Our New Puppy. Moser, Barry, illus. 2001. 32p. (J). pap. 5.99 (978-0-439-19993-3(X)) Scholastic, Inc.

—Our New Puppy. 2001. (Illus.). (J). (978-0-606-21370-7(8)) Tandem Library Bks.

Harper, Isabelle & Moser, Barry. My Dog Rosie. 1999. (Illus.). 32p. (J). (ps-2). pap. 5.99 (978-0-590-48634-7(9)) Scholastic, Inc.

Harper, Jessica. I'm Not Going to Chase the Cat Today! 2000. (Illus.). 32p. (J). (ps-3). 15.89 (978-0-688-17637-2(2)) HarperCollins Pubs.

—I'm Not Going to Chase the Cat Today! Dupont, Lindsay Harper, illus. 2000. 32p. (J). (ps-3). 15.95 (978-0-688-17636-5(4)) HarperCollins Pubs.

Harper, Meg. My Mum & the Hound from Hell. 2003. (My Mum Ser.). 160p. (J). pap. 9.99 (978-0-7459-4799-0(9) , Lion) Lion Hudson plc GBR. *Dist:* Independent Pubs. Group.

Harperfestival. Good Boy! Dog's Best Friend. 2003. (ps-2). lib. bdg. 11.80 (978-0-613-71419-8(9)) Tandem Library Bks.

—Good Boy! The Movie Novel. 2003. (gr. 3-6). lib. bdg. 13.00 (978-0-613-71420-4(2)) Tandem Library Bks.

Harrington, Sean P. Patterson & the Great Green Greedy Galumpus. 2000. (Illus.). 20p. (J). (gr. k-4). pap. 10.95 (978-0-9672290-2-7(2)) Harrington, Adventure in, Denis J. Pub.

Harris, Mark J. The Amazing Adventure in Tovia. 2001. 168p. pap. 12.95 (978-0-595-19230-4(0) , Writers Club Pr.) iUniverse, Inc.

Harris, Trudy. Over, under, in, & Ouch! 2003. (Silly Millies Ser.). 32p. lib. bdg. 17.90 (978-0-7613-2912-1(9)); (Illus.). (J). (gr. 1-3). pap. 4.99 (978-0-7613-1946-7(8)) Lerner Publishing Group. (Millbrook Pr.).

Harrison, Cora. Milleniumdrumshee. 1999. (Drumshee Timeline Ser.). (Illus.). 143p. (J). (978-0-86327-715-3(2)) Wolfhound Pr.

—Two Mad Dogs. Myler, Terry, illus. 2003. 64p. (YA). pap. 8.95 (978-1-901737-44-8(6)) Anvil Bks., Ltd. IRL. *Dist:* Dufour Editions, Inc.

Harrison, David Lee. The Big Sleepover. Edwards, Ken, illus. 2001. (Clifford, the Big Red Dog Ser.). (J). pap. (978-0-439-22364-5(4)) Scholastic, Inc.

Harry How Books. Just Luke. l.t. ed. 2006. (ENG., Illus.). 28p. per. 9.95 (***978-1-4327-0178-9(9)***) Outskirts Press, Inc.

Harry the Dirty Dog. 2004. (J). pap. 38.75 incl. audio (978-1-55592-430-0(1)) Weston Woods Studios, Inc.

Hart, Christopher. Police Puppies. 2003. (Illus.). 32p. (gr. k-3). 14.95 (978-0-8230-4063-6(1)) Watson-Guptill Pubns., Inc.

Harter, Lois. Where's the Boss. 2005. 32p. 9.95 (978-1-888125-63-4(2)) Publication Consultants.

Hartley, Susan. Get the Gum. 2003. (StartUp Ser.). (J). pap. 22.00 (978-1-4108-0707-6(X)) Benchmark Education Co.

Hartnett, Sonya. Stripes of Sidestep Wolf. 2007. (Illus.). 208p. (YA). (gr. 7). pap. 7.99 (***978-0-7636-3416-2(6)***) Candlewick Pr.

Hartnett, Sonya. Surrender. 2006. 256p. (YA). (gr. 9). 16.99 (978-0-7636-2768-3(2)) Candlewick Pr.

Harvey, Amanda. Dog Eared: Starring Otis. Harvey, Amanda, illus. 2004. (Illus.). 32p. (J). (ps-1). reprint ed. pap. 6.99 (978-0-440-41763-7(5) , Dragonfly Bks.) Random Hse. Children's Bks.

Harvey, Sarah N. Puppies on Board. Cowles, Rose, illus. 2005. 32p. (J). (ps-2). 17.95 (978-1-55143-390-5(7)) Orca Bk. Pubs. USA.

Haskins, Lori & Jordan, Hannah. Too Many Dogs! Mathieu, Joe & Fuge, Charles, illus. 1998. (Early Step into Reading Ser.). 32p. (J). (gr. k-ps). pap. 3.99 (978-0-679-86443-1(1) , Random Hse. Bks. for Young Readers) Random Hse. Children's Bks.

—Too Many Dogs! Mathieu, Joe & Fuge, Charles, illus. 1998. (Early Step into Reading Ser.). (J). (ps-k). (978-0-606-13971-7(0)) Tandem Library Bks.

Hassett, John & Hassett, Ann. Charles of the Wild. 2000. (J). (978-0-606-19361-0(8)) Tandem Library Bks.

Hassett, John & Hassett, Ann. The Nine Lives of Dudley Dog. 2008. 32p. (J). (gr. k-3). 16.00 (***978-0-618-81153-3(2)***) Houghton Mifflin Co.

Hassler, Donald & Hassler, Sara. Loving Marley. Newsom, Carol, illus. 2007. 32p. (J). (ps-3). 14.99 (***978-0-9766390-7-7(6)***) PugTale Publishing.

Hatley, Julie. Dasher Gets Adopted: A Story of Love, Trust & Family. Jones, Shay, illus. 2000. 32p. (J). (ps-3). 14.95 (978-0-9705188-0-4(3)) Shine Pubns.

Hattersley, Ray. Buster's Diaries: The True Story of A Dog & His Man. 2001. (gr. 3-6). lib. bdg. 21.05 (978-0-613-51806-2(3)) Tandem Library Bks.

Hauman, Carrie. Zoe the Magic Love Dog. 2003. (Illus.). 32p. (J). 16.00 (978-0-9746333-8-1(0)) Alma Pr.

Hawksley, Gerald. Good Puppy. Stanley, Mandy, illus. 2005. (J). (978-1-890647-14-8(4)) RC2 Corp.

Hayes, Malcolm. The Dreamcatchers. 2006. 282p. pap. (***978-1-4120-8320-1(6)***) Trafford Publishing.

Hayes, Sarah. El Solo y la Merienda. 2000. (Easy Readers Ser.).Tr. of Bear & the Snack. (SPA., Illus.). 32p. (J). 11.95 (978-84-207-3401-9(2)) Grupo Anaya, S.A. ESP. *Dist:* Distribooks, Inc.

Hays, Anna Jane. The Pup Speaks Up: A Phonics Reader. Petrone, Valeria, illus. 2003. (Early Step into Reading Ser.). 32p. (J). (ps-1). pap. 3.99 (978-0-375-81232-3(6) , Random Hse. Bks. for Young Readers) Random Hse. Children's Bks.

Hazen, Barbara Shook. Digby. Phillips-Duke, Barbara J., illus. 1998. (I Can Read Bks.). 32p. (J). (ps-2). pap. 4.99 (978-0-06-444239-8(X) , Harper Trophy) HarperCollins Pubs.

—Digby. Phillips-Duke, Barbara J., illus. 1998. 32p. (J). (ps-ps). lib. bdg. 13.00 (978-0-613-07618-0(4)) Tandem Library Bks.

—The New Dog. 2000. (Illus.). (J). pap. (978-0-14-056531-7(0) , Puffin) Penguin Group (USA) Inc.

Heape, David. R. That's What Friends Do. 1st. ed. 2006. (ENG., Illus.). 28p. per. 9.95 (***978-1-4327-0177-2(0)***) Outskirts Press, Inc.

Hearne, Betsy Gould. The Canine Connection: Stories about Dogs & People. 2003. (Illus.). 128p. (YA). 15.95 (978-0-689-85258-9(4) , McElderry, Margaret K.) Simon & Schuster Children's Publishing.

Heflick, LaMonte. The Story of Big Dog. 2004. (Illus.). 64p. pap. 3.99 (978-1-56175-888-3(4)) Remedia Pubns.

—The Story of Boney & Clyde. 2004. (Illus.). 64p. pap. 3.99 (978-1-56175-911-8(2)) Remedia Pubns.

Hegarty, Sue. Barnaby & Thor. Shaw, Alice, illus. 2002. (J). 16.95 (978-0-939549-53-5(0)) ZON International Publishing Co.

Heiligman, Deborah. Fun Dog, Sun Dog/Deborah Heiligman ; Illustrated by Tim Bowers. Bowers, Tim, illus. 2005. 32p. (J). 14.95 (978-0-7614-5162-4(5)) Cavendish, Marshall Corp.

Heller, Marion. Paco's Perro. 2001. 163p. (J). (gr. 5-9). pap. 12.95 (978-1-56825-080-9(0) , 080.0) Rainbow Bks., Inc.

Hellmann-Hurpol, Odile. Devuelvanme Mi Perro. (Torre de Papel Ser.). (SPA., Illus.). (J). 7.95 (978-958-04-5637-7(2)) Norma S.A. COL. *Dist:* Distribuidora Norma, Inc.

Help for Rosie. 2003. (J). (978-1-932570-10-6(1)) Literacy Footprints Inc.

Henderson, Kathy. Dog Story. Granstrom, Brita, illus. 32p. 2005. pap., pap. 12.99 (978-0-7475-7133-9(3)); 2004. 17.95 (978-0-7475-5071-6(9)) Bloomsbury Publishing Plc GBR. *Dist:* Independent Pubs. Group.

Henity, Kristi. Kimi's Grand Adventures, Vol. 1. 2004. 55p. pap. 12.95 (978-1-4137-2869-9(3)) PublishAmerica, Inc.

Henkes, Kevin. Circle Dogs. Yaccarino, Dan, illus. 32p. (J). 2001. (ps up). pap. 6.99 (978-0-06-443757-8(4) , Harper Trophy); 1998. (gr. k-3). 17.99 (978-0-688-15446-2(8)); 1998. (gr. 3 up). 14.89 (978-0-688-15447-9(6)) HarperCollins Pubs.

—Circle Dogs. 2001. (J). 13.79 (978-0-606-20607-5(8)) Tandem Library Bks.

—Circle Dogs. Yaccarino, Dan, illus. 2001. (ps-k). lib. bdg. 14.10 (978-0-613-34644-3(0)) Tandem Library Bks.

Henkes, Kevin. Protecting Marie. 2007. 208p. (J). pap. 5.99 (***978-0-06-128876-0(4)*** , Harper Trophy) HarperCollins Pubs.

Henry & Mudge. 2006. (J). (gr. 1-6). 145.26 (978-1-59961-080-1(9)) Spotlight.

Henry, Ragene. The Barefoot Boys of Fayette. Stich, Carolyn R., illus. 2005. 184p. (YA). per. 9.95 (978-0-9749412-3-3(9)) EDCO Publishing, Inc.

Hensley, Terri Anne. The silliest bug & insect book Ever. 2007. (J). per. 6.95 (***978-0-9789057-7-4(6)***) Huntington Ludlow Media Group.

Herbert, Martha. Bloomer. 2004. pap. 7.95 (978-0-533-14538-6(4)) Vantage Pr., Inc.

Herfurtner, Ralph. Niki y el Perrito. (Torre de Papel Ser.). (SPA., Illus.). (J). 7.95 (978-958-04-5034-4(X)) Norma S.A. COL. *Dist:* Distribuidora Norma, Inc.

Herge. Tintin Boxed Set Of 8. 2007. (ps-17). 150.00 (***978-0-316-00668-2(8)***) Little, Brown Bks. for Young Readers.

Herman, Gail. Fall Fright. del Sur, Duendes, illus. 2005. (Hello Reader! Ser.). 32p. (J). pap. (978-0-439-78358-3(5)) Scholastic, Inc.

—New Dog in Town. Nez, John, illus. 2006. 32p. (J). lib. bdg. 20.00 (***978-1-4242-1110-4(7)***) Fitzgerald Bks.

—New Dog in Town. Nez, John A., illus. 2006. (Social Studies Connects). 32p. (J). pap. 4.99 (978-1-57565-165-1(3)) Kane Pr., The.

—Scooby Doo! Shiny Spooky Knights. 2000. (gr. k-3). lib. bdg. 11.80 (978-0-613-33053-4(6)) Tandem Library Bks.

—Scooby-Doo & Aliens Too! del Sur, Duendes, illus. 2000. (Scooby-Doo Movie Storybooks). 32p. (J). (ps-3). 3.50 (978-0-439-17701-6(4)) Scholastic, Inc.

—Scooby-Doo & Aliens Too! 2000. (gr. k-3). lib. bdg. 11.25 (978-0-613-33034-3(X)) Tandem Library Bks.

—Scooby Doo! & the Howling on the Playground. 2000. (gr. k-3). lib. bdg. 11.80 (978-0-613-32658-2(X)) Tandem Library Bks.

—Scooby Doo! & the Map in the Mystery Machine. 2000. (gr. k-3). lib. bdg. 11.80 (978-0-613-26117-3(8)) Tandem Library Bks.

—The Shaggy Dog: The Junior Novelization. 2006. 144p. (gr. 3-7). pap. 4.99 (978-0-7868-4863-8(4)) Disney Pr.

—Valentine's Day Dognapping. del Sur, Duendes, illus. 2002. (Scooby-Doo! Reader Ser.: No. 10). 32p. (J). (gr. k-2). pap. 3.99 (978-0-439-34113-4(2) , Cartwheel Bks.) Scholastic, Inc.

Herman, Gail & del Sur, Duendes. Football Fright. 2002. (Scooby-Doo! Reader Ser.: No. 14). (Illus.). 32p. (J). (gr. k-3). pap. 3.99 (978-0-439-34116-5(7)) Scholastic, Inc.

Herman, Gail & Hughes, Francine. Cats & Dogs. 2001. (Illus.). 32p. (J). (gr. k-3). pap. 3.50 (978-0-439-22573-1(6)) Scholastic, Inc.

Hernandez, Regina. Jail Break Spells Double the Trouble: Jake the Beagle's Crazy Adventures. Woods, Carol, ed. 2003. (Jake the Beagle Crazy Adventure Ser.: 5). (Illus.). 90p. (J). pap. 5.99 (978-0-9727771-8-6(0)) Regal Enterprises.

—Texas Roundup: Jake the Beagle's Crazy Adventures. Woods, Carol, ed. Fetherston, Catherine & Miller, Tom, illus. 2003. (Jake the Beagle Crazy Adventure Ser.: 2). 90p. (J). pap. 5.99 (978-0-9727771-2-4(1)) Regal Enterprises.

Hersey, Paul. The Dog That Grew. Hersey, Deborah, illus. 2001. 25p. (J). pap. 14.95 (978-0-931619-08-3(4)) Ctr. for Leadership Studies.

Hesse, Karen. Sable. Sewall, Marcia, illus. rev. ed. 1998. 96p. (J). (gr. 4 up). pap. 7.95 (978-0-8050-5772-0(2) , Holt, Henry & Co. Bks. For Young Readers) Holt, Henry & Co.

—Sable. 1998. (YA). (gr. 4 up). (978-0-606-13755-3(6)) Tandem Library Bks.

—Sable. Sewall, Marcia, illus. 1998. 81p. (J). (ps-k). lib. bdg. 16.40 (978-0-613-08689-9(9)) Tandem Library Bks.

Hessel, Brooke. Clifford the Big Red Dog Telephone Book. 2002. (Illus.). (J). 16.98 (978-0-7853-6401-6(3)) Publications International, Ltd.

Hest, Amy. The Dog Who Belonged to No One. 2008. (J). (***978-0-8109-9483-6(6)*** , Abrams Bks. for Young Readers) Abrams, Harry N. , Inc.

Hickey, Tony & Myler, Terry. Flip 'n' Flop & the Movies. 1998. 112p. pap. 7.95 (978-1-901737-05-9(5)) Anvil Bks., Ltd. IRL. *Dist:* Dufour Editions, Inc.

Higdon, Hal. Run, Dogs, Run! Summers, Dana, illus. 2003. 56p. (J). (978-0-9636346-3-4(1)) Roadrunner Pr.

Higgins, Kitty. Mushing in Alaska. 2005. 40.00 (***978-1-4108-4228-2(2)***) Benchmark Education Co.

High, Linda Oatman. Hound Heaven. 2004. (Illus.). 208p. (J). (gr. 4-6). pap. 9.95 (978-1-59078-244-6(5)) Boyds Mills Pr.

Highet, Alistair. Lucas. 2001. 8.95 (978-1-56846-127-4(5)) Creative Co., The.

—Lucas. Delessert, Etienne, illus. 2000. 40p. (J). (gr. 3). pap. 8.95 (978-0-89812-014-1(4) , Creative Paperbacks) Creative Co., The.

Hill, Amye Rose. The Amazing Mr. Buddy. 10th ed. 2005. (Illus.). (J). 6.99 (978-0-9769234-0-4(8)) Zany Angel Projects LLC.

Hill, Becky. The Duck That Stayed Behind. 2007. (J). per. 8.99 (***978-1-60247-417-8(6)***) Tate Publishing & Enterprises, L.L.C.

Hill, Eric. Donde Esta Spot. (SPA.). pap. 10.95 (978-950-07-1960-5(6)) Editorial Sudamericana S.A. ARG. *Dist:* Distribooks, Inc.

—Good Night Spot. 2004. (Illus.). 14p. (J). (ps-1). bds. 3.99 (978-0-399-24319-6(4) , Putnam Juvenile) Penguin Group (USA) Inc.

—Los Juguetes de Spot. (SPA.). pap. 4.95 (978-950-07-1963-6(0)) Editorial Sudamericana S.A. ARG. *Dist:* Distribooks, Inc.

—My First Spot Library. Hill, Eric, illus. 2002. (Illus.). 60p. (J). pap. 12.95 (978-0-7232-8460-4(1) , Putnam Juvenile) Penguin Group (USA) Inc.

—La Primera Navidad de Spot.Tr. of Spot's First Christmas. (SPA.). pap. 10.95 (978-950-07-2016-8(7)) Editorial Sudamericana S.A. ARG. *Dist:* Distribooks, Inc.

—Spot: 10 Stories. 2001. (Illus.). (J). 15.98 (978-0-7853-4809-2(3)) Publications International, Ltd.

—Spot: Night-Night, Spot. Hill, Eric, illus. 2005. (Spot Ser.). 32p. (J). (ps). pap. 3.99 (978-0-448-43810-8(0) , Grosset & Dunlap) Penguin Group (USA) Inc.

—Spot at Home. 2004. (Illus.). 14p. (J). (ps-k). bds. 3.99 (978-0-399-24318-9(6) , Putnam Juvenile) Penguin Group (USA) Inc.

—Spot at the Beach. Hill, Eric, illus. 2005. (Illus.). 10p. (J). (ps-ps). bds. 7.99 (978-0-399-24394-3(1) , Putnam Juvenile) Penguin Group (USA) Inc.

—Spot Bakes a Cake. Hill, Eric, illus. (J). 2005. 20p. pap. 6.99 (978-0-14-240329-7(6) , Puffin); 2003. (Illus.). 22p. bds. 7.99 (978-0-399-24013-3(6) , Putnam Juvenile) Penguin Group (USA) Inc.

—Spot Can Count. Hill, Eric, illus. (Illus.). (J). (ps-1). 2005. 12p. bds. 6.99 (978-0-399-24361-5(5) , Putnam Juvenile); 2003. 24p. pap. 6.99 (978-0-14-250121-4(2) , Puffin) Penguin Group (USA) Inc.

—Spot Can Count. 1999. (Spot Ser.). (Illus.). 32p. (J). (ps). 12.99 (978-0-399-23454-5(3) , Putnam Juvenile) Penguin Group (USA) Inc.

—Spot Counts from 1 to 10. Hill, Eric, illus. 2003. (Illus.). 12p. (J). (ps-1). bds. 3.99 (978-0-399-24043-0(8) , Putnam Juvenile) Penguin Group (USA) Inc.

—Spot Goes Splash! Hill, Eric, illus. 2003. (Illus.). 5p. (J). (ps-1). 5.99 (978-0-399-24032-4(2) , Putnam Juvenile) Penguin Group (USA) Inc.

—Spot Goes to School. Hill, Eric, illus. 2004. (Illus.). (J). (ps-1). (SPA.). 12p. bds. 7.99 (978-0-399-24246-5(5) , Putnam Juvenile); 24p. pap. 6.99 (978-0-14-240167-5(6) , Puffin) Penguin Group (USA) Inc.

—Spot Goes to School. Hill, Eric, illus. 2006. 22p. (J). (ps-k). 12.99 (978-0-399-24613-5(4) , Putnam Juvenile) Penguin Group (USA) Inc.

—Spot Goes to the Beach. Hill, Eric, illus. 2003. (Illus.). 24p. (J). pap. 6.99 (978-0-14-250122-1(0) , Puffin) Penguin Group (USA) Inc.

—Spot Goes to the Farm. Hill, Eric, illus. 2003. (Illus.). 24p. (J). pap. 6.99 (978-0-14-250123-8(9) , Puffin) Penguin Group (USA) Inc.

—Spot Goes to the Farm. 2001. (Spot Ser.). (Illus.). 12p. (J). (ps-1). bds. 7.99 (978-0-399-23647-1(3) , Putnam Juvenile) Penguin Group (USA) Inc.

—Spot Goes to the Farm. 2003. (ps-2). lib. bdg. 15.30 (978-0-613-86708-5(4)) Tandem Library Bks.

—Spot Goes to the Farm. Hill, Eric, illus. 2006. 22p. (J). (ps-k). bds. 12.99 (978-0-399-24614-2(2) , Putnam Juvenile) Penguin Group (USA) Inc.

—Spot Goes to the Park. Hill, Eric, illus. 2003. (Illus.). 24p. (J). pap. 6.99 (978-0-14-250124-5(7) , Puffin) Penguin Group (USA) Inc.

—Spot Sleeps Over. Hill, Eric, illus. 2004. (Spot Ser.). (Illus.). 24p. (J). (ps-1). pap. 6.99 (978-0-14-240168-2(4) , Puffin) Penguin Group (USA) Inc.

—Spot Sleeps Over. 2007. 10p. 6.99 (***978-0-399-24780-4(7)*** , Putnam Adult) Penguin Group (USA) Inc.

—Spot Sleeps Over. Hill, Eric, illus. 2007. 12p. (J). (ps-k). bds. 6.99 (***978-0-399-24769-9(6)*** , Putnam Juvenile) Penguin Group (USA) Inc.

—Spot Va a la Escuela. Brant Drake, Alexandra, tr. from ENG. 1998. (Spot Ser.). (SPA., Illus.). 20p. (J). (ps). pap. 6.99 (978-0-14-056411-2(X) , Puffin) Penguin Group (USA) Inc.

—Spot Va a la Escuela. 1998. (SPA.). (ps-2). lib. bdg. 15.30 (978-0-613-85730-7(5)) Tandem Library Bks.

—Spot Visits His Grandparents. 2005. 20p. (J). pap. 6.99 (978-0-14-240360-0(1) , Puffin) Penguin Group (USA) Inc.

—Spot's Baby Sister. Hill, Eric, illus. 2004. (Spot Ser.). (Illus.). 24p. (J). (ps-1). pap. 6.99 (978-0-14-240169-9(2) , Puffin) Penguin Group (USA) Inc.

—Spot's Bedtime Storybook. 1998. (Spot Ser.). (Illus.). 32p. (J). (ps). 12.99 (978-0-399-23353-1(9) , Putnam Juvenile) Penguin Group (USA) Inc.

—Spot's Big Lift-the-flap Book. Hill, Eric, illus. 2004. (Illus.). 24p. (J). pap. 8.99 (978-0-14-240083-8(1) , Puffin) Penguin Group (USA) Inc.

—Spot's Birthday Party. Hill, Eric, illus. 2003. (Illus.). 24p. (J). pap. 6.99 (978-0-14-250125-2(5) , Puffin) Penguin Group (USA) Inc.

—Spot's Birthday Party. 2003. (gr. k-3). lib. bdg. 15.30 (978-0-613-87829-6(9)) Tandem Library Bks.

—Spot's Birthday Party. Hill, Eric, illus. 2007. 12p. (J). (ps-ps). bds. 6.99 (***978-0-399-24770-5(X)*** , Putnam Juvenile) Penguin Group (USA) Inc.

—Spot's Christmas. Hill, Eric, illus. 2004. (Illus.). 12p. (J). (ps-1). bds. 5.99 (978-0-399-24320-2(8) , Putnam Juvenile) Penguin Group (USA) Inc.

—Spot's Christmas Book & Toy. Hill, Eric, illus. 2005. 10p. (J). (ps). 15.99 (978-0-399-24470-4(0) , Putnam Juvenile) Penguin Group (USA) Inc.

—Spot's Colors, Shapes, & Numbers. Hill, Eric, illus. 2007. 18p. (J). (ps-k). bds. 12.99 (***978-0-399-24779-8(3)*** , Putnam Juvenile) Penguin Group (USA) Inc.

—Spot's First Christmas. Hill, Eric, illus. (Spot Ser.). (Illus.). (J). 2004. 20p. pap. 6.99 (978-0-14-240202-3(8) , Puffin); 2003. 22p. bds. 7.99 (978-0-399-23597-9(3) , Putnam Juvenile) Penguin Group (USA) Inc.

—Spot's First Easter: A Lift-the-flap Book. Hill, Eric, illus. 2004. (Illus.). 12p. (J). (ps-1). bds. 7.99 (978-0-399-24245-8(7) , Putnam Juvenile) Penguin Group (USA) Inc.

—Spot's First Easter: A Lift-the-flap Book. 2004. (Illus.). 24p. (J). pap. 6.99 (978-0-14-240084-5(X) , Puffin) Penguin Group (USA) Inc.

—Spot's First Picnic & Other Stories. 2001. (gr. k-3). lib. bdg. 11.25 (978-0-613-72403-6(8)) Tandem Library Bks.

—Spot's First Walk. Hill, Eric, illus. 2004. (Illus.). 20p. (J). pap. 6.99 (978-0-14-240085-2(8) , Puffin) Penguin Group (USA) Inc.

—Spot's First Walk. Hill, Eric, illus. 2005. (Illus.). 12p. (J). (ps-k). bds. 6.99 (978-0-399-24482-7(4) , Putnam Juvenile) Penguin Group (USA) Inc.

—Spot's First Words. Hill, Eric, illus. 2006. 12p. (J). (ps-k). bds. 12.99 (978-0-399-24616-6(9) , Putnam Juvenile) Penguin Group (USA) Inc.

—Spot's Giant Treasury. 2005. (Spot Ser.). 192p. (J). (ps-2). 10.99 (978-0-448-43973-0(5) , Grosset & Dunlap) Penguin Group (USA) Inc.

—Spot's Halloween. Hill, Eric, illus. 2003. (Spot Ser.). (Illus.). 10p. (J). (ps-1). bds. 5.99 (978-0-399-24185-7(X) , Putnam Juvenile) Penguin Group (USA) Inc.

—Spot's Halloween Party. Hill, Eric, illus. 2007. 6p. (J). (ps-ps). pap. 7.99 (***978-0-399-24778-1(5)*** , Putnam Juvenile) Penguin Group (USA) Inc.

—Spot's Little Book of Fun at the Farm. Hill, Eric, illus. 2003. (Spots Little Book of Fun Ser.). (Illus.). 10p. (J). (ps-k). 5.99 (978-0-399-23893-2(X) , Putnam Juvenile) Penguin Group (USA) Inc.

—Spot's Little Book of Fun in the Garden. Hill, Eric, illus. 2003. (Spots Little Book of Fun Ser.). (Illus.). 10p. (J). (ps-k). 5.99 (978-0-399-23894-9(8) , Putnam Juvenile) Penguin Group (USA) Inc.

—Spot's Thanksgiving. Hill, Eric, illus. 2003. (Spot Ser.). (Illus.). 10p. (J). (ps-1). bds. 5.99 (978-0-399-24186-4(8) , Putnam Juvenile) Penguin Group (USA) Inc.

—Spot's Walk in the Woods. Hill, Eric, illus. 2004. (Spot Ser.). (Illus.). 24p. (J). (ps-1). pap. 6.99 (978-0-14-240170-5(6) , Puffin) Penguin Group (USA) Inc.

—Where's Spot? Hill, Eric, illus. 2003. (Illus.). (J). (ps-1). (SPA.). 22p. bds. 7.99 (978-0-399-24046-1(5) , 53517281, Putnam Juvenile); 24p. pap. 7.99 (978-0-14-250126-9(3) , Puffin) Penguin Group (USA) Inc.

—Where's Spot. Hill, Eric, illus. 25th anniv. ed. 2005. (Illus.). 24p. (J). (gr. k-ps). 12.99 (978-0-399-24373-8(9) , Putnam Juvenile) Penguin Group (USA) Inc.

—Who's There, Spot? 2007. 22p. (J). pap. 6.99 (978-0-14-240864-3(6) , Puffin) Penguin Group (USA) Inc.

—Who's There, Spot? Hill, Eric, illus. 2005. (Illus.). 12p. (J). (ps-k). 12.99 (978-0-399-24484-1(0) , Putnam Juvenile) Penguin Group (USA) Inc.

Hill, Sandi. Detective Dog & the Search for Cat, Vol. 4415. Kupperstein, Joel, ed. Leary, Catherine, illus. 1998. (Learn to Read Social Studies). 16p. (J). (gr. 2). pap. 2.75 (978-1-57471-338-1(8) , 4415) Creative Teaching Pr., Inc.

Hills, Jodi. Hope-So. Bjornson, Barbara, illus. 2004. 36p. (J). 16.95 (978-0-9726504-2-7(3)) Tristan Publishing, Inc.

Hinds, Ruth McNaughton. Puppy & I. 2006. (J). per. 7.95 (978-0-9764232-2-5(7)) River City Pr.

Hirsch, Ron. No, No Jack! 2003. (Illus.). (J). 10.99 (978-0-8037-2997-1(9) , Dial) Penguin Group (USA) Inc.

Hirshfield, Lynn & Fishbein, Dena. Sassafras Goes to Hollywood. 2007. 32p. (J). 15.99 (978-0-8431-2191-9(2) , Price Stern Sloan) Penguin Group (USA) Inc.

—Sassie: The True Confessions of a Poodle Princess. 2006. (Illus.). 32p. (J). (ps-2). 15.99 (978-0-8431-2125-4(4) , Price Stern Sloan) Penguin Group (USA) Inc.

Hobbs, Valerie. Sheep. 2006. 128p. (J). 16.00 (978-0-374-36777-0(9) , Farrar, Straus & Giroux (BYR)) Farrar, Straus & Giroux.

Hobbs, William. Down the Yukon. unabr. ed. 2004. (Middle Grade Cassette Librariestm Ser.). 208p. (J). (gr. 5-9). pap. 36.00 incl. audio (978-0-8072-0786-4(1) , S YA 310 SP, Listening Library) Random Hse. Audio Publishing Group.

—Wild Man Island. 192p. (J). (gr. 5 up). 2003. pap. 5.99 (978-0-380-73310-1(2) , Harper Trophy); 2002. (Illus.). 19.99 (978-0-688-17473-6(6)); 2002. (Illus.). lib. bdg. 16.89 (978-0-06-029810-4(3)) HarperCollins Pubs.

—Wild Man Island. 2003. (gr. 5-8). lib. bdg. 14.15 (978-0-613-61741-3(X)) Tandem Library Bks.

Hoberman, Mary Ann. One of Each. Priceman, Marjorie, illus. 2000. 32p. (J). (ps-3). pap. 7.99 (978-0-316-36644-1(7)) Little, Brown Bks. for Young Readers.

—One of Each. Priceman, Marjorie, illus. 2000. (J). (ps-ps). lib. bdg. 14.10 (978 0 613-30077-3(7)) Tandem Library Bks.

—One of Each. 2000. (978-0-606-22189-4(1)) Tandem Library Bks.

Hobrecker, Ginny. Magic Memories of Mutts & More. 2006. 49p. per. 8.95 (***978-1-59824-371-0(3)***) E-BookTime LLC.

Hodge, Marie. Are You Sleepy yet, Petey? Graef, Renee, illus. 2005. 24p. (J). 12.95 (978-1-4027-1265-4(0) , 1241713) Sterling Publishing Co., Inc.

Are You Sleepy Yet, Petey? Graef, Renee, illus. 2006. 24p. (J). bds. 5.95 (978-1-4027-4025-1(5)) Sterling Publishing Co., Inc.

Hodgkins, Fran. The Cat of Strawberry Hill: A True Story. Sochor, Lesia, illus. 2005. (ps-3). 15.95 (978-0-89272-684-4(9)) Down East Bks.

Hoffman, Alice & Martin, Wolfe. Moondog. Heo, Yumi, illus. 2004. (J). pap. (978-0-439-09862-5(9)); 32p. pap. 16.95 (978-0-439-09861-8(0)) Scholastic, Inc.

Hoffmann, Catherine E. & Hoffmann, Dana Marie. Here Little Teacup! up! Up! O'Leary Brown, Erin, illus. 2005. 16p. (J). 6.95 (978-0-9753106-2-5(3)) Hoffmann Partnership, The.

Hogan, Mary. 102 Dalmatians: Colors. 2000. (Lift the Flaps Bks.). (Illus.). 12p. (J). (ps). bds. 4.99 (978-0-7364-0228-6(4) , RH/Disney) Random Hse. Children's Bks.

Hollander, Cass & Scholastic, Inc. Staff. Word Family Tales -Ack: A Snack for Mack. Brown, Rick, illus. 2002. (Word Family Tales Ser.). 16p. (ps-2). pap. 2.95 (978-0-439-26255-2(0) , Teaching Resources) Scholastic, Inc.

Holmes, Laura. Baby Grady: The First Year. 2004. 84p. pap. 14.95 (978-1-4137-3202-3(X)) PublishAmerica, Inc.

Holmes, Linda. Jazz & Sam. 2002. (Reading Explosion Beginner Readers: Book 2). 32p. (J). pap. 9.95 (978-1-57921-445-6(2)) WinePress Publishing.

Holt, Rinehart and Winston Staff. Where the Red Fern Grows: With Connections. 1998. pap., stu. ed. 13.20 (978-0-03-054053-0(4)) Holt, Rinehart & Winston.

Homework, 6 Packs. (ps-2). 27.00 (978-0-7635-9453-4(9)) Rigby Education.

Hong, Seonna & Hahn, Shenne. Animus. 2005. (Illus.). 34p. 25.00 (978-0-9729388-5-3(0)) Baby Tattoo Bks.

Hood, Susan. Pup & Hound. Hendry, Linda, illus. 2004. 32p. (J). lib. bdg. 15.38 (***978-1-4242-1164-7(6)***) Fitzgerald Bks.

—Pup & Hound. Hendry, Linda, illus. 2005. (Kids Can Read! Ser.). 32p. (J). (gr. k-1). (978-1-55337-673-6(0)); (978-1-55337-572-2(6)) Kids Can Pr., Ltd.

—Pup & Hound at Sea. Hendry, Linda, illus. 2006. 32p. (J). lib. bdg. 15.38 (***978-1-4242-0249-2(3)***) Fitzgerald Bks.

—Pup & Hound at Sea. Hendry, Linda, illus. 32p. (978-1-55337-804-4(0)) Kids Can Pr., Ltd.

—Pup & Hound at Sea. Hendry, Linda, illus. 2006. 32p. 3.95 (978-1-55337-805-1(9)) Kids Can Pr., Ltd. CAN. *Dist:* Wybel Marketing Group.

—Pup & Hound Catch a Thief. Hendry, Linda, illus. 2007. (Kids Can Read Ser.). 32p. (J). (gr. k-1). (***978-1-55337-972-0(1)***); (***978-1-55337-973-7(X)***) Kids Can Pr., Ltd.

—Pup & Hound Hatch an Egg. Hendry, Linda, illus. 2007. (Kids Can Read Ser.). 32p. (J). (gr. k-1). (***978-1-55337-974-4(8)***); (***978-1-55337-975-1(6)***) Kids Can Pr., Ltd.

—Pup & Hound in Trouble. Hendry, Linda, illus. 2005. 32p. (J). lib. bdg. 15.38 (***978-1-4242-1162-3(X)***) Fitzgerald Bks.

—Pup & Hound in Trouble. Hendry, Linda, illus. 2005. (Kids Can Read! Ser.). 32p. (J). (gr. k-1). (978-1-55337-677-4(3)); (978-1-55337-676-7(5)) Kids Can Pr., Ltd.

—Pup & Hound in Trouble. Hendry, Linda, illus. 2005. 32p. (J). (gr. k-1). lib. bdg. 11.15 (978-0-606-33686-4(9)) Tandem Library Bks.

—Pup & Hound Lost & Found. Hendry, Linda, illus. 2006. 32p. (J). lib. bdg. 15.38 (***978-1-4242-0250-8(7)***) Fitzgerald Bks.

—Pup & Hound Lost & Found. Hendry, Linda, illus. 32p. (978-1-55337-806-8(7)) Kids Can Pr., Ltd.

—Pup & Hound Lost & Found. Hendry, Linda, illus. 2006. 32p. 3.95 (978-1-55337-807-5(5)) Kids Can Pr., Ltd. CAN. *Dist:* Wybel Marketing Group.

—Pup & Hound Move In. Hendry, Linda, illus. 2004. 32p. (J). lib. bdg. 15.38 (***978-1-4242-1165-4(4)***) Fitzgerald Bks.

—Pup & Hound Move In. Hendry, Linda, illus. 2005. (Kids Can Read! Ser.). 32p. (J). (gr. k-1). (978-1-55337-675-0(7)); (978-1-55337-674-3(9)) Kids Can Pr., Ltd.

—Pup & Hound Play Copycats. 2007. 32p. pap. (***978-1-55453-145-5(4)***) Kids Can Pr., Ltd.

—Pup & Hound Scare a Ghost. Hendry, Linda, illus. 2007. 32p. pap. (***978-1-55453-143-1(8)***) Kids Can Pr., Ltd.

—Pup & Hound Stay up Late. Hendry, Linda, illus. 2005. 32p. (J). lib. bdg. 15.38 (***978-1-4242-1163-0(8)***) Fitzgerald Bks.

—Pup & Hound Stay up Late. Hendry, Linda, illus. 2005. (Kids Can Read! Ser.). 32p. (J). (gr. k-1). (978-1-55337-679-8(X)); (978-1-55337-678-1(1)) Kids Can Pr., Ltd.

Hooks, William H. Little Poss & Horrible Hound. Newsom, Carol, illus. 1998. (Bank Street Reader Collection). 48p. (J). (gr. 2-4). lib. bdg. 22.60 (978-0-8368-1773-7(7)) Stevens, Gareth Inc.

—Where's Lulu? Alley, R. W., illus. 1998. (Bank Street Reader Collection). 48p. (J). (ps-2). lib. bdg. 22.60 (978-0-8368-1768-3(0)) Stevens, Gareth Inc.

Hooper, Meredith. Dog's Night. Curless, Allan, illus. 32p. (gr. k-3). 2002. pap. (978-0-7613-1649-7(3)); 2000. lib. bdg. 22.90 (978-0-7613-1824-8(0)) Lerner Publishing Group. (Millbrook Pr.).

—La Gran Noche de los Perros. Curless, Allan, illus. 2000. Tr. of Dogs' Night. (CAT.). 32p. (J). (gr. 1-3). 14.95 (978-84-95040-31-2(X)) Serres, Ediciones, S. L. ESP. *Dist:* Lectorum Pubns., Inc.

—La Gran Noche de los Perros. Curless, Allan & Burgess, Mark, illus. 2000. Tr. of Dogs' Night. (SPA.). 32p. (J). (gr. 1-3). 14.95 (978-84-95040-30-5(1)) Serres, Ediciones, S. L. ESP. *Dist:* Lectorum Pubns., Inc.

Hooper, Meredith & Curless, Allan. Dogs' Night. Burgess, Mark, illus. 2006. 36p. pap. 7.95 (978-1-84507-688-7(5)) Lincoln, Frances Ltd. GBR. *Dist:* Perseus Distribution.

Hope, Laura Lee. Freddie & Flossie & Snap. Pyle, Chuck, illus. 2005. (Ready-To-Read Ser.). 32p. (J). pap. 3.99 (978-1-4169-0267-6(8) , Aladdin) Simon & Schuster Children's Publishing.

—Freddie & Flossie & Snap. 2006. (Ready-To-Read Ser.). (J). (ps-2). 21.35 (978-1-59961-096-2(5)) Spotlight.

—Freddie & Flossie & the Easter Egg Hunt. Downer, Maggie, illus. 2006. 32p. (J). lib. bdg. 15.00 (***978-1-4242-0966-8(8)***) Fitzgerald Bks.

—Freddie & Flossie & the Easter Egg Hunt. Downer, Maggie, illus. 2006. (Bobbsey Twins Ser.). 32p. (J). pap. 3.99 (978-1-4169-1029-9(8) , Aladdin) Simon & Schuster Children's Publishing.

—Freddie & Flossie & the Easter Egg Hunt. 2006. (Ready-To-Read Ser.). (Illus.). 32p. (J). (ps-2). 21.35 (978-1-59961-100-6(7)) Spotlight.

—Freddie & Flossie & the Leaf Monster. Ruppert, Larry, illus. 2005. 32p. (J). lib. bdg. 15.00 (***978-1-4242-0965-1(X)***) Fitzgerald Bks.

—Freddie & Flossie & the Leaf Monster. Ruppert, Larry, illus. 2005. (Ready-To-Read Ser.). 32p. (J). (ps-k). pap. 3.99 (978-1-4169-0271-3(6) , Aladdin) Simon & Schuster Children's Publishing.

—Freddie & Flossie & the Leaf Monster. 2006. (Ready-To-Read Ser.). 32p. (J). (ps-2). 21.35 (978-1-59961-099-3(X)) Spotlight.

—Freddie & Flossie & the Little Seed. Downer, Maggie, illus. 2006. (Bobbsey Twins Ser.). 32p. (J). (ps-k). pap. 3.99 (978-1-4169-1766-3(7) , Aladdin) Simon & Schuster Children's Publishing.

—Freddie & Flossie at the Beach. Pyle, Chuck, illus. 2005. (Ready-To-Read Ser.). 32p. (J). (ps-ps). pap. 3.99 (978-1-4169-0268-3(6) , Aladdin) Simon & Schuster Children's Publishing.

—Freddie & Flossie at the Beach. 2006. (Ready-To-Read Ser.). (J). (ps-2). 21.35 (978-1-59961-098-6(1)) Spotlight.

Hopper, Celia. Blade & the Story of the Little Spotted Dog. 2006. (J). lib. bdg. (978-0-9779662-3-3(2)) Creative Bk. Pubs.

Hornsey, Chris. Why Do I Have to Eat off the Floor? Perkins, Gwyn, illus. 2007. 24p. (J). (ps-2). 15.95 (978-0-8027-9617-2(6)) Walker & Co.

Horse, Harry, illus. The Last Polar Bears. 2007. 76p. (J). (gr. 1-5). 12.95 (***978-1-56145-379-5(X)*** , Peachtree Junior) Peachtree Pubs., Ltd.

Howard, Arthur. Cosmo Zooms. (Illus.). 32p. (J). 2003. pap. 6.00 (978-0-15-204765-8(4) , Voyager Bks./Libros Viajeros); 1999. 15.00 (978-0-15-201788-0(7)) Harcourt Children's Bks.

—Cosmo Zooms. 2003. (gr. k-3). lib. bdg. 14.15 (978-0-613-70499-1(1)) Tandem Library Bks.

Howe, Deborah & Howe, James. A Rabbit-Tale of Mystery. unabr. ed. 2004. (Bunnicula Ser.). 98p. (J). (gr. 3-7). pap. 29.00 incl. audio (978-0-8072-8204-5(9) , YYA139SP, Listening Library) Random Hse. Audio Publishing Group.

Howe, James. Bonicula: Una Historia de Misterio Conejil. 2000. Tr. of Bunnicula. (SPA.). (gr. 3-6). lib. bdg. 14.15 (978-0-613-85443-6(8)) Tandem Library Bks.

—Bud Barkin, Private Eye. Helquist, Brett, illus. (Tales from the House of Bunnicula Ser.). (J). 2004. 112p. pap. 3.99 (978-0-689-86989-1(4) , Aladdin); 2003. 96p. 9.95 (978-0-689-85632-7(6) , Atheneum) Simon & Schuster Children's Publishing.

—Bunnicula & Friends: Hot Fudge. Mack, Jeff, illus. 2004. 42p. (J). lib. bdg. 15.00 (***978-1-4242-1149-4(2)***) Fitzgerald Bks.

—Bunnicula-in-a-Box: Bunnicula, the Celery Stalks at Midnight, Howliday Inn. 2006. 496p. (J). pap. 14.99 (978-1-4169-3498-1(7) , Aladdin) Simon & Schuster Children's Publishing.

—Bunnicula Strikes Again! 2004. (Bunnicula Ser.). 116p. (J). (gr. 3-7). pap. 29.00 incl. audio (978-0-8072-8213-7(8) , Listening Library) Random Hse. Audio Publishing Group.

—Bunnicula Strikes Again! Daniel, Alan, illus. 2007. (Bunnicula Ser.). 144p. (J). pap. 5.99 (***978-1-4169-3968-9(7)*** , Aladdin) Simon & Schuster Children's Publishing.

—Bunnicula Strikes Again! 2001. (Bunnicula Ser.). (gr. 3-6). lib. bdg. 13.00 (978-0-613-49480-9(6)); (Illus.). (J). 11.64 (978-0-606-21090-4(3)) Tandem Library Bks.

—Hot Fudge. Mack, Jeff, illus. 2006. (Bunnicula & Friends Ser.). 48p. (J). pap. 3.99 (978-0-689-85750-8(0) , Aladdin) Simon & Schuster Children's Publishing.

—Hot Fudge. Mack, Jeff, tr. Mack, Jeff, illus. 2004. (Bunnicula & Friends Ser.). 48p. (J). 14.95 (978-0-689-85725-6(X) , Atheneum) Simon & Schuster Children's Publishing.

—Houndsley & Catina. Gay, Marie-Louise, illus. 2006. 48p. (J). (gr. k-2). 14.99 (978-0-7636-2404-0(7)) Candlewick Pr.

—Houndsley & Catina. Gay, Marie-Louise, illus. 2007. (Candlewick Sparks Ser.). 48p. (J). (gr. k-2). pap. 4.99 (978-0-7636-3293-9(7)) Candlewick Pr.

—Houndsley & Catina & the Birthday Surprise. Gay, Marie-Louise, illus. 2006. 48p. (J). (gr. k-3). 14.99 (978-0-7636-2405-7(5)) Candlewick Pr.

—Houndsley & Catina & the Birthday Surprise. Gay, Marie-Louise, illus. 2007. 48p. (J). (gr. k-3). pap. 4.99 (***978-0-7636-3640-1(1)***) Candlewick Pr.

—Howie Monroe & the Doghouse of Doom. Helquist, Brett, illus. 2002. (Tales from the House of Bunnicula Ser.). 96p. (J). 9.95 (978-0-689-83951-1(0) , Atheneum) Simon & Schuster Children's Publishing.

—Howie Monroe & the Doghouse of Doom. 2002. (Tales from the House of Bunnicula Ser.). (Illus.). 90p. (J). (gr. 3-6). 9.95 (978-0-689-88395-8(1) , Atheneum) Simon & Schuster Children's Publishing.

—Howie Monroe & the Doghouse of Doom. 2003. (Tales from the House of Bunnicula Ser.). (gr. 3-6). lib. bdg. 11.80 (978-0-613-73267-3(7)) Tandem Library Bks.

—Howie Monroe & the Doghouse of Doom. Helquist, Brett, illus. 2003. (Tales from the House of Bunnicula Ser.). 112p. (J). pap. 3.99 (978-0-689-83952-8(9) , Aladdin) Simon & Schuster Children's Publishing.

—Howie Monroe & the Doghouse of Doom. 2004. (Tales from the House of Bunnicula Ser.). 85p. (J). (gr. 3-6). pap. 17.00 incl. audio (978-1-4000-8634-4(5) , Listening Library) Random Hse. Audio Publishing Group.

—Howliday Inn. Munsinger, Lynn, illus. 2nd ed. 2006. 224p. (J). pap. 5.99 (978-1-4169-2815-7(4) , Aladdin) Simon & Schuster Children's Publishing.

—Howliday Inn. 2001. (Bunnicula Ser.). 11.64 (978-0-606-22105-4(0)) Tandem Library Bks.

—Invasion of the Mind Swappers from Asteroid 6! 2004. (Tales from the House of Bunnicula Ser.). 112p. (J). (gr. 3-6). pap. 17.00 incl. audio (978-1-4000-8633-7(7) , Listening Library) Random Hse. Audio Publishing Group.

—Invasion of the Mind Swappers from Asteroid 6! Helquist, Brett, illus. (Tales from the House of Bunnicula Ser.). (J). 2003. 112p. pap. 3.99 (978-0-689-83950-4(2) , Aladdin); 2002. 96p. (gr. 2-4). 9.95 (978-0-689-83949-8(9) , Atheneum) Simon & Schuster Children's Publishing.

—Invasion of the Mind Swappers from Asteroid 6! 2003. (Tales from the House of Bunnicula Ser.). (gr. 3-6). lib. bdg. 11.80 (978-0-613-66414-1(0)) Tandem Library Bks.

—It Came from Beneath the Bed! Helquist, Brett, illus. (Tales from the House of Bunnicula Ser.). (J). 2003. 112p. pap. 3.99 (978-0-689-83948-1(0) , Aladdin); 2002. 96p. (gr. 2-4). 9.95 (978-0-689-83947-4(2) , Atheneum) Simon & Schuster Children's Publishing.

—It Came from Beneath the Bed! 2003. (Tales from the House of Bunnicula Ser.). lib. bdg. 11.80 (978-0-613-66415-8(9)) Tandem Library Bks.

—It Came from Beneath the Bed! 2004. (Tales from the House of Bunnicula Ser.). 112p. (J). (gr. 3-6). pap. 17.00 incl. audio (978-1-4000-8632-0(9) , Listening Library) Random Hse. Audio Publishing Group.

—Nighty-Nightmare. unabr. ed. 2004. (Bunnicula Ser.). 128p. (J). (gr. 3-7). pap. 29.00 incl. audio (978-0-8072-8397-4(5) , YA201SP, Listening Library) Random Hse. Audio Publishing Group.

—Nighty-Nightmare. Morrill, Leslie, illus. 2007. 144p. (J). pap. 5.99 (***978-1-4169-3966-5(0)*** , Aladdin) Simon & Schuster Children's Publishing.

—The Odorous Adventures of Stinky Dog. Helquist, Brett, illus. (Tales from the House of Bunnicula Ser.). 112p. (J). 2004. pap. 3.99 (978-0-689-87412-3(X) , Aladdin); 2003. bds. 9.95 (978-0-689-85633-4(4) , Atheneum) Simon & Schuster Children's Publishing.

—Rabbit-Cadabra! Daniel, Alan, illus. 1999. (Bunnicula & Friends Ser.). 48p. (J). (gr. k-3). pap. 5.95 (978-0-688-16699-1(7)) HarperCollins Pubs.

—Rabbit-Cadabra! Mack, Jeff, illus. 2006. (Bunnicula & Friends Ser.: Vol. 4). 48p. (J). 14.95 (978-0-689-85727-0(6) , Atheneum) Simon & Schuster Children's Publishing.

—Rabbit-cadabra! Mack, Jeff, illus. 2007. (Bunnicula & Friends Ser.). 48p. (J). pap. 3.99 (***978-0-689-85752-2(7)*** , Aladdin) Simon & Schuster Children's Publishing.

—Return to Howliday Inn. unabr. ed. 2004. (Bunnicula Ser.). 128p. (J). (gr. 3-7). pap. 29.00 incl. audio (978-0-8072-8416-2(5) , YA192SP, Listening Library) Random Hse. Audio Publishing Group.

—Return to Howliday Inn. Daniel, Alan, illus. 2007. (Bunnicula Ser.). 192p. (J). pap. 5.99 (***978-1-4169-3967-2(9)*** , Aladdin) Simon & Schuster Children's Publishing.

—Scared Silly. Mack, Jeff, illus. (Bunnicula & Friends Ser.). (J). 2006. 40p. pap. 3.99 (978-0-689-85751-5(9) , Aladdin); 2005. 48p. 14.95 (978-0-689-85726-3(8) , Atheneum) Simon & Schuster Children's Publishing.

—Screaming Mummies of the Pharaoh's Tomb II. Helquist, Brett, illus. 2003. (Tales from the House of Bunnicula Ser.). 112p. (J). pap. 3.99 (978-0-689-83954-2(5) , Aladdin); 9.95 (978-0-689-83953-5(7) , Atheneum) Simon & Schuster Children's Publishing.

—The Vampire Bunny. Mack, Jeff, illus. 2005. (Bunnicula & Friends Ser.). 48p. (J). pap. 3.99 (978-0-689-85749-2(7) , Aladdin) Simon & Schuster Children's Publishing.

Howe, Peter. Waggit's Tale. Rayyan, Omar, illus. 2008. 288p. (J). 16.99 (***978-0-06-124261-8(6)***); lib. bdg. 17.89 (***978-0-06-124262-5(4)***) HarperCollins Pubs.

Howell, Trisha Adelena. Addie, the Playful Pekingese. Hohn, David, illus. 2005. 128p. (YA). pap. 11.95 (978-1-931210-27-0(6)) Howell Canyon Pr.

—The Poopy Pekinese. Marshall, Jamie, illus. 2005. 32p. (J). 15.95 (978-1-931210-09-6(8)) Howell Canyon Pr.

—The Princess & the Pekinese. 2003. (Illus.). 32p. 15.95 (978-1-931210-03-4(9)) Howell Canyon Pr.

Howey, Paul M. Freckles: The Mystery of the Little White Dog in the Desert. Zabriskie, Judy Mehn, illus. 2003. 72p. (gr. 2-5). lib. bdg. 14.95 (978-0-9677292-1-3(1)) AZTexts Publishing, Inc.

Howie. Have You Seen Christmas? 2006. (Illus.). 32p. 18.00 (978-0-687-49678-5(0)) Abingdon Pr.

Hubbard, Coleen. Great Spaniel Escape. 2000. (Dog Tales Ser.: Vol. 4). (Illus.). 160p. (J). (gr. 3-7). pap. 4.50 (978-0-590-18978-1(6)) Scholastic, Inc.

—Mountain Dog Rescue. 2000. (Dog Tales Ser.: No. 3). (Illus.). 160p. (J). (gr. 3-7). pap. 4.50 (978-0-590-18977-4(8) , Scholastic Paperbacks) Scholastic, Inc.

—Mountain Dog Rescue. 1999. (978-0-606-18578-3(X)) Tandem Library Bks.

—One Golden Year. 1999. (Dog Tales Ser.). (Illus.). 128p. (J). (gr. 3-7). pap. 4.50 (978-0-590-18975-0(1)) Scholastic, Inc.

—Westie Winter: A Story of a West Highland Terrier. 1999. (Dog Tales Ser.: 2). (Illus.). 163p. (J). pap. 4.50 (978-0-590-18976-7(X)) Scholastic, Inc.

Hughes, Monica. Jan on the Trail. Freire, Carlos, illus. 2000. (New First Novels Ser.). 61p. (gr. 1-5). 4.95 (978-0-88780-502-8(7)); (J). (978-0-88780-503-5(5)) Formac Publishing Co., Ltd. CAN. *Dist:* Casemate Pubs. & Bk. Distributors, LLC.

Hughes, Shirley. Dogger. 2007. (Illus.). 32p. (J). pap. 8.95 (***978-0-09-992790-7(X)*** , Red Fox) Random Hse. Children's Bks. GBR. *Dist:* Independent Pubs. Group.

Huneck, Stephen. Sally Gets a Job. 2008. 32p. (J). 16.95 (***978-0-8109-9493-5(3)*** , Abrams Bks. for Young Readers) Abrams, Harry N. , Inc.

—Sally Goes to the Beach. Huneck, Stephen, illus. 2000. (Illus.). 38p. (J). (ps-3). 17.95 (978-0-8109-4186-1(4)) Abrams, Harry N. , Inc.

—Sally Goes to the Farm. Huneck, Stephen, illus. 2002. (Illus.). 40p. (J). (ps-3). 17.95 (978-0-8109-4498-5(7)) Abrams, Harry N. , Inc.

—Sally Goes to the Mountains. 2001. (Illus.). 38p. (J). (ps-3). 17.95 (978-0-8109-4485-5(5)) Abrams, Harry N. , Inc.

—Sally Goes to the Vet. Huneck, Stephen, illus. 2004. (Illus.). 32p. (J). (ps-3). 17.95 (978-0-8109-4813-6(3)) Abrams, Harry N. , Inc.

—Sally's Snow Adventure. 2006. (J). (978-0-8109-5781-7(7)); (Illus.). 32p. 15.95 (978-0-8109-7061-8(9)) Abrams, Harry N. , Inc.

A Hungry Puppy. 2006. (J). (***978-1-932570-54-0(3)***) Literacy Footprints Inc.

Hunter, Erin. A Dangerous Path. 2004. (Warriors Ser.: Bk. 5). 336p. (J). (gr. 5 up). 16.99 (978-0-06-000006-6(6)); lib. bdg. 17.89 (978-0-06-052564-4(9)) HarperCollins Pubs.

Hunter, John P. Red Thunder: Secrets, Spies, & Scoundrels at Yorktown. 2006. (J). (***978-0-87935-231-8(0)***) Colonial Williamsburg Foundation.

Hurd, Clement. The Merry Chase. 2005. (Illus.). 32p. (J). 15.95 (978-0-8118-4967-8(8)) Chronicle Bks. LLC.

Hurd, Thacher. Art Dog. 2000. (J). pap. 19.97 incl. audio (978-0-7366-9194-9(4)) Books on Tape, Inc.

—Art Dog. 2004. (Live Oak Readalong Ser.). (Illus.). (J). pap. 18.95 incl. audio compact disk (978-1-59112-308-8(9)) Live Oak Media.

—Art Dog. Hurd, Thacher, illus. 1999. (Illus.). pap. 43.95 incl. audio compact disk (978-1-59112-526-6(X)) Live Oak Media.

—Art Dog. 1999. (Illus.). (J). (gr. k-3). 24.95 incl. audio (978-0-87499-509-1(4)); pap. 16.95 incl. audio (978-0-87499-508-4(6)); pap., tchr. ed. 41.95 incl. audio (978-0-87499-510-7(8)) Live Oak Media.

Hurricane Katrina Dogs. 2006. (J). per. (***978-1-932570-78-6(0)***) Literacy Footprints Inc.

Hurwitz, Johanna. One Small Dog. deGroat, Diane, illus. (J). (gr. 2 up). 2002. 112p. pap. 5.99 (978-0-380-73293-7(9)); 2000. 128p. 15.89 (978-0-06-029220-1(2)); 2000. 128p. 15.95 (978-0-688-17382-1(9)) HarperCollins Pubs.

—One Small Dog. 2002. (gr. 3-6). lib. bdg. 13.00 (978-0-613-62113-7(1)) Tandem Library Bks.

Hutchens, Paul. The Ghost Dog. rev. ed. 1998. (Sugar Creek Gang Ser.: No. 25). 128p. (J). (gr. 4-7). 4.99 (978-0-8024-7029-4(7)) Moody Pubs.

Hyland, Hilary. The Wreck of the Ethie. 1999. (978-0-606-22861-9(6)) Tandem Library Bks.

—Wreck of the Ethie. 1999. (gr. 3-6). lib. bdg. 16.40 (978-0-613-23823-6(0)) Tandem Library Bks.

I Am Danny. 2003. (J). 4.95 (978-0-9720295-7-5(5)) Maryruth Bks., Inc.

I Dream of Sleeping Dogs. 2006. (J). 24.95 (978-0-9789633-0-9(X)) Village Monkey LLC, The.

Icelandic Sheepdog Activity & Coloring Book. 2005. (J). 15.95 (978-1-59210-342-3(1)) Whispering Pine Pr., Inc.

Icelandic Sheepdog Story Book. 2005. (J). 15.95 (978-1-59649-427-5(1)) Whispering Pine Pr., Inc.

Ichikawa, Satomi. Come Fly with Me. Ichikawa, Satomi, illus. 2008. 40p. (J). (ps). 15.99 (***978-0-399-24679-1(7)*** , Philomel) Penguin Group (USA) Inc.

Inches, Alison. The Big Itch. Cuddy, Robbin, illus. 2003. (Big Red Reader Ser.). 32p. (J). pap. 3.99 (978-0-439-44943-4(X) , Cartwheel Bks.) Scholastic, Inc.

—Big Itch. 2003. (ps-2). lib. bdg. 11.80 (978-0-613-64793-9(9)) Tandem Library Bks.

—Hello, Spring! Chernichaw, Ian, illus. 2004. (Blue's Clues Ser.: Vol. 8). 24p. (J). pap. 3.99 (978-0-689-86316-5(0) , Simon Spotlight/Nickelodeon) Simon & Schuster Children's Publishing.

—Hello, Spring! 2004. (ps-2). lib. bdg. 11.80 (978-0-613-73462-2(9)) Tandem Library Bks.

—Hooray for Polka Dots! Chernichaw, Ian, illus. 2005. (Blue's Clues Ser.: Vol. 10). 24p. (J). pap. 3.99 (978-0-689-87210-5(0) , Simon Spotlight/Nickelodeon) Simon & Schuster Children's Publishing.

—My Visit with Periwinkle. Levy, David B., illus. ed. 2005. 22p. (J). lib. bdg. 15.00 (978-1-59054-970-4(8)) Fitzgerald Bks.

—My Visit with Periwinkle. Levy, David B., illus. 2003. (Ready-to-Read Ser.). 24p. (J). pap. 3.99 (978-0-689-85230-5(4) , Simon Spotlight/Nickelodeon) Simon & Schuster Children's Publishing.

—My Visit with Periwinkle. 2003. (gr. k-3). lib. bdg. 11.80 (978-0-613-58161-5(X)) Tandem Library Bks.

—Off to School with Periwinkle & Blue. Oxley, Jennifer, illus. 2003. (Blue's Clues Ser.). 24p. (J). 5.99 (978-0-689-85498-9(6) , 53560712, Simon Spotlight/ Nickelodeon) Simon & Schuster Children's Publishing.

—Spring Is Here! Chernichaw, Ian, illus. 2006. (Blue's Clues Ser.). 16p. (J). pap. 5.99 (978-1-4169-0920-0(6) , Simon Spotlight/Nickelodeon) Simon & Schuster Children's Publishing.

Inkpen, Mick. A to Z: An Alphabet Adventure. 2001. (Kipper Ser.). (Illus.). 64p. (J). (ps-2). 16.95 (978-0-15-202594-6(4) , Red Wagon Bks.) Harcourt Children's Bks.

—Beachmoles & Bellvine. 2006. (Blue Nose Island Ser.: Bk. 2). (Illus.). (J). (ps). 19.99 (978-0-340-87865-1(7) , Hodder & Stoughton) Hodder General Publishing Division GBR. *Dist:* Trafalgar Square Publishing.

—Beachmoles & Bellvine, 1 CD. MC, ed. 2006. (Blue Nose Island Ser.: Bk. 2). (Illus.). 34p. (J). (ps). audio compact disk 13.95 (978-1-84456-225-1(5) , Hodder & Stoughton) Hodder General Publishing Division GBR. *Dist:* Trafalgar Square Publishing.

—Hissss! 2000. 11.75 (978-0-606-22337-9(1)); 1999. lib. bdg. 12.95 (978-0-613-25527-1(5)) Tandem Library Bks.

—Kipper. Inkpen, Mick, illus. 2002. (Illus.). (J). 13.15 (978-0-7587-6464-5(2)) Book Wholesalers, Inc.

—Kipper. (ENG & FRE., Illus.). 32p. (J). (978-1-85430-330-1(9) , 93450); (978-1-85430-333-2(3) , 93451) Magi Pubns.

—Kipper. 1999. (978-0-606-17487-9(7)) Tandem Library Bks.

—Kipper & Roly. 2003. (gr. k-3). lib. bdg. 14.10 (978-0-613-70494-6(0)) Tandem Library Bks.

—Kipper's Birthday. 2000. (Illus.). (J). (978-0-606-18181-5(4)) Tandem Library Bks.

—Kipper's Book of Numbers. Inkpen, Mick, illus. 2002. (Kipper Ser.). (Illus.). (J). 13.19 (978-0-7587-6465-2(0)) Book Wholesalers, Inc.

—Kipper's Book of Opposites. Inkpen, Mick, illus. 2002. (Kipper Ser.). (Illus.). (J). 13.19 (978-0-7587-6466-9(9)) Book Wholesalers, Inc.

—Kipper's Snowy Day. Inkpen, Mick, illus. 2002. (Kipper Ser.). (Illus.). (J). 13.15 (978-0-7587-2935-4(9)) Book Wholesalers, Inc.

—Kipper's Snowy Day. 1999. (978-0-606-17488-6(5)) Tandem Library Bks.

—Kipper's Toybox. Inkpen, Mick, illus. 2002. (Kipper Ser.). (Illus.). (J). 13.15 (978-0-7587-6467-6(7)) Book Wholesalers, Inc.

—Kipper's Toybox. (Illus.). 25p. (J). (CHI, ENG, URD, VIE & FRE.). (978-1-85430-350-9(3) , 93452); (ENG, FRE, URD, VIE & CHI., (978-1-85430-351-6(1) , 93453) Magi Pubns.

—Kipper's Toybox. 2000. (Illus.). (J). (978-0-606-18182-2(2)) Tandem Library Bks.

—Picnic. Inkpen, Mick, illus. 2002. (Kipper Ser.). (Illus.). (J). 12.30 (978-0-7587-6469-0(3)) Book Wholesalers, Inc.

—Picnic. 2001. (978-0-606-22345-4(2)) Tandem Library Bks.

—Rocket. 2001. (gr. k-3). lib. bdg. 12.95 (978-0-613-53550-2(2)) Tandem Library Bks.

—Sandcastle. Inkpen, Mick, illus. 2002. (Kipper Ser.). (Illus.). (J). 12.30 (978-0-7587-6470-6(7)) Book Wholesalers, Inc.

—Splosh. 1999. (978-0-606-22347-8(9)) Tandem Library Bks.

—Thing! 2001. (ps-2). lib. bdg. 12.95 (978-0-613-35474-5(5)) Tandem Library Bks.

Intrater, Roberta Grobel. Christmas Puppy. 1999. (Illus.). (J). 65.70 (978-0-439-11755-5(0)) Scholastic, Inc.

Ioan, Elwyn & Gruffudd, Garmon. Llywelyn a Gelert: Llyfr Lliwio. 2005. (WEL., Illus.). 16p. pap. (978-0-86243-379-6(7)) Y Lolfa.

Ip, Ivy S. Clues at the Carnival. 2001. (ps-2). lib. bdg. 11.80 (978-0-613-54137-4(5)) Tandem Library Bks.

Irbinskas, Heather & King, Andra. Morgan the Dog: An Egyptian Adventure. 2002. 33p. 14.95 (978-0-9711970-2-2(4)) Morgan Hse. Publishing.

Isaacs, Michael. The Fuzzy Escape Artists. 2005. (Illus.). 40p. (J). 15.95 (978-0-9742845-8-3(0)) Mystic Ridge Bks.

It's Hard to Say Good-Bye: The Story of How the Only Hearts Club Was Formed. 2005. 40p. (J). 3.99 (978-0-9763213-0-9(0)) OHC Group LLC.

Jablonski, Carla. Homer Sweet Homer. Punchatz, Don, illus. l.t. ed. 1999. (Adventures of Wishbone Ser.: No. 13). (J). (gr. 4 up). lib. bdg. 22.60 (978-0-8368-2591-6(8)) Stevens, Gareth Inc.

Jack's Special Day. 2003. lib. bdg. 12.95 (978-0-9741295-0-1(X)) Crowther, Debra.

Jackson, Carolyn. If I Had a Dog. Brassard, France, illus. 2006. 32p. (J). (ps-2). 16.95 (978-0-88776-725-8(7)) Tundra Bks., Inc./Livres Toundra, Inc. CAN. *Dist:* Random Hse., Inc.

Jackson, Debra Ann. Canines on Patrol. 2005. (J). pap. 8.00 (978-0-8059-6896-5(2)) Dorrance Publishing Co., Inc.

Jacobs, Susan. Meggie the Pup's Summer Adventure. Jacobs, Susan, illus. 2000. (Illus.). 56p. (J). (gr. 3 up). pap. 9.95 (978-0-9702604-0-6(7)) Blissful Biscuits.

Jacques, Brian. The Angel's Command. Elliot, David & Schoenherr, Ian, illus. 2005. (Castaways of the Flying Dutchman Ser.: No. 2). 384p. (J). (gr. 5-9). pap. 7.99 (978-0-14-240285-6(0) , Puffin) Penguin Group (USA) Inc.

—The Angel's Command. Elliot, David, illus. 2003. (Castaways of the Flying Dutchman Ser.: No. 2). 384p. (J). (gr. 5-6). 23.99 (978-0-399-23999-1(5) , Philomel) Penguin Group (USA) Inc.

—Castaways of the Flying Dutchman. Schoenherr, Ian, illus. 2001. (Castaways of the Flying Dutchman Ser.: No. 1). 1p. (J). (gr. 4-7). 23.99 (978-0-399-23601-3(5) , Philomel) Penguin Group (USA) Inc.

—Castaways of the Flying Dutchman. (Castaways of the Flying Dutchman Ser.: No. 1). 2002. (gr. 3-6). lib. bdg. 15.30 (978-0-613-72303-9(1)); 2001. (gr. 5-8). lib. bdg. 16.45 (978-0-613-62934-8(5)) Tandem Library Bks.

—Voyage of Slaves. 2006. (Castaways of the Flying Dutchman Ser.: No. 3). (Illus.). 368p. (YA). (gr. 5). 23.99 (978-0-399-24549-7(9) , Philomel) Penguin Group (USA) Inc.

Jahn-Clough, Lisa. Little Dog. 2006. (Illus.). 32p. (J). (gr. k-3). 16.00 (978-0-618-57405-6(0) , Walter Lorraine) Houghton Mifflin Co. Trade & Reference Div.

James, Nathaniel. Debbie Mumm's Mummford Adventures. Mumm, Debbie, illus. 2002. 32p. (gr. k-3). 14.95 (978-1-890621-33-9(1)) Landauer Corp.

Jammes, Francis. Romance of the Rabbit. 2006. 77.99 (***978-1-4280-0048-3(8)***); pap. 70.99 (***978-1-4280-0047-6(X))*** IndyPublish.com.

Jane, Pamela. Milo & the Fire Engine Parade. Johnson, Meredith, ed. Johnson, Meredith, illus. 2002. 32p. (J). pap. 13.95 (978-1-59034-036-3(1)); (gr. 1-4). 13.95 (978-1-59034-192-6(9)) Mondo Publishing.

Jax, T. L. Fraidy-Frieda's Light Show. Jax, T. L., illus. l.t. ed. 2004. (Illus.). 30p. (J). 9.95 (978-0-9743890-2-8(1)) Flaxenfluff Pr., LLC.

Jenisch, Betty. Rennie. 2007. 9.00 (***978-0-8059-8947-2(1))*** Dorrance Publishing Co., Inc.

Jenkins, Emily. Skunkdog. Pratt, Pierre, illus. 2008. 32p. (J). 16.95 (***978-0-374-37009-1(5)*** , Farrar, Straus & Giroux (BYR)) Farrar, Straus & Giroux.

Jenkins, Emily. That New Animal. Pratt, Pierre, illus. 2005. 32p. (J). 16.00 (978-0-374-37443-3(0) , Farrar, Straus & Giroux (BYR)) Farrar, Straus & Giroux.

—That New Animal. Jenkins, Emily, illus. 2006. (Illus.). (J). (ps-4). 29.95 incl. audio compact disk (978-0-439-84925-8(X) , WHCD687); 24.95 incl. audio (978-0-439-84924-1(1) , WHRA687) Weston Woods Studios, Inc.

Jennings, Linda. Duna y Dan. Chapman, Jane, illus. (SPA.). 28p. (J). (gr. k-1). (978-84-8418-027-2(1) , ZZ4481) Zendrera Zariquiey, Editorial ESP. *Dist:* Lectorum Pubns., Inc.

Jennings, Patrick. Faith & the Electric Dogs. 1998. 144p. (J). pap. 4.99 (978-0-590-69769-9(2)) Scholastic, Inc.

—The Pup Tent: An Ike & Mem Story. O'Neill, Catharine, illus. 2005. (J). (978-0-8234-1938-8(X)) Holiday Hse., Inc.

Jennings, Patti. The Fleecy Puppy. 2003. (Fleecy Friends Ser.). (Illus.). 10p. (J). (ps). 9.99 (978-0-8431-7788-6(8) , Price Stern Sloan) Penguin Group (USA) Inc.

Jennings, Richard W. Scribble: A Dog Story, a Ghost Story, a Love Story. 2004. 160p. (YA). (gr. 5-9). tchr. ed. 15.00 (978-0-618-43367-4(8) , Walter Lorraine) Houghton Mifflin Co. Trade & Reference Div.

Jessup, Diane. The Dog Who Spoke with Gods Easel. 2002. (J). (978-0-312-30126-2(X) , St. Martin's Griffin) St. Martin's Pr.

Johansen, K. V. Pippin & Pudding. Lum, Bernice, illus. unabr. ed. 2002. (Pippin & Mabel Ser.). 32p. (J). (gr. k-3). (978-1-55074-631-0(6)) Kids Can Pr., Ltd.

—Pippin & Pudding. 2001. (ps-2). lib. bdg. 14.10 (978-0-613-57114-2(2)) Tandem Library Bks.

Johansen, K. V. & Lum, Bernice. Pippin Takes a Bath. 1999. (Pippin & Mabel Ser.). (Illus.). 32p. (J). (gr. k-3). (978-1-55074-627-3(8)) Kids Can Pr., Ltd.

Johansen, Zdenka. When You Give of Yourself. 2006. 28p. pap. 9.95 (***978-1-4327-0059-1(6))*** Outskirts Press, Inc.

Johns, Linda. Carmen's Crystal Ball. 2006. (Star Sisterz Ser.: Bk. 7). 144p. (YA). pap. 4.99 (978-0-7869-4029-5(8) , Mirrorstone) Wizards of the Coast.

—Hannah West in the Center of the Universe. 2007. (Hannah West Ser.). 176p. (J). pap. 5.99 (978-0-14-240756-1(9) , Puffin) Penguin Group (USA) Inc.

Johnson, Gillian. My Sister Gracie. 2005. (Illus.). 32p. (J). (ps-k). pap. 7.95 (978-0-88776-750-0(8)) Tundra Bks., Inc./Livres Toundra, Inc. CAN. *Dist:* Random Hse., Inc.

—My Sister Gracie. Johnson, Gillian, illus. 2000. (Illus.). 32p. (J). (ps-k). 16.95 (978-0-88776-514-8(9)) Tundra Bks., Inc./Livres Toundra, Inc. CAN. *Dist:* Random Hse., Inc.

Johnson, Pete. Ghost Dog. 2000. (Yearling Book Ser.). (Illus.). 143p. (J). pap. 8.99 (978-0-440-86341-0(4)) Transworld Publishers Ltd. GBR. *Dist:* Trafalgar Square Publishing.

—The Ghost Dog. l.t. ed. 2005. pap. 16.95 (978-1-4056-6028-0(7)) BBC Audio GBR. *Dist:* BBC Audiobooks America.

Johnson, Sandi. Black Ridge Mountain. Johnson, Britt, ed. Sturgen, Bobbi, illus. 2000. 21p. (J). (gr. k-5). spiral bd. 5.99 (978-1-929063-66-6(0) , 165) Moons & Stars Publishing For Children.

Johnson, Sharon. Therapy Dog & Other Stories. 2003. 118p. pap. 16.95 (978-1-4137-0285-9(6)) PublishAmerica, Inc.

Johnston-Brown, A. M. The Chronicles of Pleasant Grove. 2006. (J). pap. 12.95 (978-0-9760718-5-3(1)) Retriever Pr.

—The Chronicles of Pleasant Grove (Glossary of Terms) 2006. (J). pap. 1.95 (978-0-9760718-6-0(X)) Retriever Pr.

Johnston, Tony. Desert Dog. Weatherford, Robert, illus. 2001. 32p. (J). (gr. 1-5). 15.95 (978-0-87156-979-0(5)) Gibbs Smith, Publisher.

Jolin, Dominique. Little Red Washington. Perkes, Carolyn, tr. from FRE. Jolin, Dominique, illus. 2001. (Bee-Bop Bks.). (Illus.). 24p. (J). bds. (978-1-894363-70-9(1)) Dominique & Friends.

—Super Washington. Perkes, Carolyn, tr. from FRE. Jolin, Dominique, illus. 2001. (Bee-Bop Bks.). (Illus.). 24p. (J). bds. (978-1-894363-71-6(X)) Dominique & Friends.

Jones, Diana Wynne. Dogsbody. 2001. 256p. (J). (gr. 5 up). 16.95 (978-0-06-029880-7(4)) HarperCollins Pubs.

—Dogsbody. 2001. (gr. 7-12). lib. bdg. 15.25 (978-0-613-57404-4(4)) Tandem Library Bks.

Jones, Jasmine, adapted by. Tell It Like It Is, Vol. 7. rev. ed. 2005. (That's So Raven Ser.: Bk. 7). (Illus.). 128p. (J). (gr. 3-7). pap. 4.99 (978-0-7868-4684-9(4)) Disney Pr.

Jones, Jolie. Little Kisses. Downing, Julie, illus. 2005. (Julie Andrews Collection). 32p. (J). lib. bdg. 16.89 (978-0-06-058699-7(0) , Julie Andrews Collection) HarperCollins Pubs.

Jones, Katina. Cool School Story: Little Lucy & Friends. Ottinger, Jon, illus. Zaidan, Rick, photos by. 2001. (Little Lucy & Friends Ser.). 24p. (J). (ps-3). 9.99 (978-1-57151-700-5(6)) Playhouse Publishing.

Jones, Katina, et al. Cowdog Caper: Little Lucy & Friends. Ottinger, Jon, illus. Zaidan, Rick, photos by. 2001. (Little Lucy & Friends Ser.). 24p. (J). (ps-3). 9.99 (978-1-57151-701-2(4)) Playhouse Publishing.

Jones, Lara. Fun at the Park. Jones, Lara, illus. 2003. (Lola & Binky Bks.). (Illus.). 8p. (J). bds. 5.95 (978-0-7641-5689-2(6)) Barron's Educational Series, Inc.

—Fun on the Beach. Jones, Lara, illus. 2003. (Lola & Binky Bks.). (Illus.). 8p. (J). bds. 5.95 (978-0-7641-5685-4(3)) Barron's Educational Series, Inc.

—Fun on the Farm. Jones, Lara, illus. 2003. (Lola & Binky Bks.). (Illus.). 8p. (J). bds. 5.95 (978-0-7641-5688-5(8)) Barron's Educational Series, Inc.

—Me Divierto en el Parque. 2003. (Lola y Bony Ser.). (SPA., Illus.). 8p. 8.95 (978-84-7864-628-9(0)) Combel Editorial, S.A. ESP. *Dist:* Independent Pubs. Group.

—Me Divierto en la Granja. 2003. (Lola y Bony Ser.). (SPA., Illus.). 8p. 8.95 (978-84-7864-630-2(2)) Combel Editorial, S.A. ESP. *Dist:* Independent Pubs. Group.

Jones, Marcia Thornton & Dadey, Debbie. Puppies on Parade. 2002. (Barkley's School for Dogs Ser.: Vol. 12). (gr. 3-6). lib. bdg. 11.80 (978-0-613-57435-8(4)) Tandem Library Bks.

—Tattle Tails. 2001. (gr. 3-6). lib. bdg. 11.80 (978-0-613-57448-8(6)) Tandem Library Bks.

Jones, Nancy. The Grandpaws. 2005. 57p. pap. 12.95 (978-1-4137-4778-2(7)) PublishAmerica, Inc.

Joosse, Barbara M. Bad Dog School. Plecas, Jennifer, illus. 2004. 40p. (J). (gr. k-3). 15.00 (978-0-618-13331-4(3) , Clarion Bks.) Houghton Mifflin Co. Trade & Reference Div.

—Nugget & Darling. Truesdell, Sue, illus. 2001. 32p. (J). (gr. k-3). 5.95 (978-0-618-11141-1(7) , Clarion Bks.) Houghton Mifflin Co. Trade & Reference Div.

—Wind Wild Dog. Kiesler, Kate, illus. 2006. 40p. (J). 16.95 (978-0-8050-7053-8(2) , Holt, Henry & Co. Bks. For Young Readers) Holt, Henry & Co.

Jordan, Apple. Clifford Helps Out. Bracken, Carolyn, illus. 2004. (Clifford Ser.). 80p. (J). pap. 2.99 (978-0-439-55670-5(8)) Scholastic, Inc.

Jordan, Evora. Annie Love: A Hannah Gray Dog Story. 2003. (Hannah Gray Mysteries). (J). per. (978-0-9725071-2-7(4)) EvoraBooks, LLC.

Jordan, Sarah Clark. The BossQueen, Little BigBark, & the Sentinel Pup. 2004. (Illus.). 144p. (J). 14.95 (978-1-58246-115-1(5) , Tricycle Pr.) Ten Speed Pr.

Jorden, Edwin W. Cookie Paws. Waywell, Valerie B., illus. 2007. (J). 9.95 (***978-0-9793483-0-3(7))*** Gilded Dog Enterprises LLC.

Joy, Angela. My Dog. Slater, Nicola, illus. 2005. 14p. (J). 12.95 (978-1-58925-759-7(6) , tiger tales) ME Media LLC.

Joyce, Samantha & Joyce, Caroline. Fluffy's Story Part 1 Fluffy's Journey. Moore, Debra, illus. 2005. 48p. (J). 16.95 (978-0-9770898-0-2(0)) Paw Print Publishing.

Joyce, William. Rolie Polie Olie. 2001. (Rolie Polie Olie Ser.). (Illus.). (J). (ps). 5p. 3.99 (978-0-7364-0163-0(6)); Vol. 2. 10p. bds. 3.99 (978-0-7364-0164-7(4)) Mouse Works.

Jugran, Jan. Nose Knows: Puppy Love. Kolanovic, Dubravka, illus. 2007. 10p. (J). (ps-17). 9.99 (978-1-58476-550-9(X)) Innovative Kids.

Julian-Ottie, Vanessa. My Name Is Lucy. 2003. (Illus.). 24p. (J). (gr. k-1). 12.95 (978-0-7696-3007-6(3) , Gingham Dog Pr.) School Specialty Publishing.

Julian, Russell. Busy Dog. 2005. (Farm Board Book Ser.). (Illus.). 12p. (J). bds. 9.99 (978-1-4052-1031-7(1)) Egmont Bks., Ltd. GBR. *Dist:* Trafalgar Square Publishing.

The Junkyard Dog: Individual Chapter Book Title Six-Packs. Vol. 26. 32p. (gr. 3-4). 44.00 (978-0-7635-4478-2(7)) Rigby Education.

Kadohata, Cynthia. Cracker! The Best Dog in Vietnam. 2007. 320p. (J). (gr. 5-8). 16.99 (978-1-4169-0637-7(1) , Atheneum) Simon & Schuster Children's Publishing.

Kahn, Peggy, et al. Welcome to Birdwell Island. 2001. (Clifford, the Big Red Dog Ser.). (Illus.). (J). pap. (978-0-439-22005-7(X)) Scholastic, Inc.

Kalman, Maira. Smartypants: Pete in School. 2005. (J). 27.95 incl. audio (978-0-8045-6929-3(0) , SAC6929); 29.95 incl. audio compact disk (978-0-8045-4105-3(1) , SACD4105) Spoken Arts, Inc.

—Smartypants (Pete in School) Kalman, Maira, illus. 2003. (Illus.). 32p. (J). (gr. k-3). 15.99 (978-0-399-23478-1(0) , Putnam Juvenile) Penguin Group (USA) Inc.

—What Pete Ate from a to Z. 2003. (gr. k-3). lib. bdg. 15.30 (978-0-613-86703-0(3)) Tandem Library Bks.

—What Pete Ate from A-Z. 2003. (Illus.). 48p. (J). pap. 6.99 (978-0-14-250159-7(X) , Puffin) Penguin Group (USA) Inc.

—What Pete Ate from A-Z. Kalman, Maira, illus. 2001. (Illus.). 40p. (J). (ps-4). 15.99 (978-0-399-23362-3(8) , Putnam Juvenile) Penguin Group (USA) Inc.

Kalz, Jill. Tuckerbean. Mahan, Ben, illus. 2006. (Read-It! Readers Ser.). 24p. (J). (ps-3). 18.60 (978-1-4048-1591-9(0)) Picture Window Bks.

—Tuckerbean at Waggle World. 2007. (Illus.). 32p. (J). (***978-1-4048-3389-0(7))*** Picture Window Bks.

—Tuckerbean at Waggle World. Mahan, Ben, illus. 2006. 32p. (J). lib. bdg. (***978-1-4048-3388-3(9))*** Picture Window Bks.

Kalz, Jill. Tuckerbean in the Kitchen. Mahan, Ben, illus. 2007. (Read-It! Readers Ser.). (J). 19.93 (978-1-4048-2402-7(2)) Picture Window Bks.

Kamens, Gerald. Leopold & Clinton. 2007. 44p. (J). pap. 8.99 (978-1-59092-395-5(2) , Little Blue Works) Windstorm Creative.

Kaminski, Tom. Miss Olivia, the Little Red Poodle: Her First Big Adventure. Fallon, Lisa, illus. 2006. (J). pap. 16.00 (***978-0-8059-7253-5(6))*** Dorrance Publishing Co., Inc.

Kapelos, Joe. Patience the Herd Dog. Bretschneider, Jeanne, ed. Leeman, Linda, photos by. 1998. 28p. (J). (ps-3). pap. 11.95 (978-0-9668001-0-4(9)) Leeman, Linda.

Kaplan, Kathy Walden. The Dog of Knots. 2005. 139p. (J). pap. 7.50 (978-0-8028-5274-8(2)) Eerdmans, William B. Publishing Co.

Kapper, Jon. Bow Wow Blast Off: Little Lucy & Friends. Ottinger, Jon, illus. Zaidan, Rick, photos by. 2001. (Little Lucy & Friends Ser.). 24p. (J). (gr. k-3). 9.99 (978-1-57151-702-9(2)) Playhouse Publishing.

Kapper, R. Jon & D'Andrea, Deborah. Bow Wow Blast Off: Little Lucy & Friends. Ottinger, Jon & Zaidan, Rick, illus. 2001. (Little Lucy & Friends Ser.). 24p. (J). pap. 4.99 (978-1-57151-707-4(3)) Playhouse Publishing.

Karbo, Karen. Minerva Clark Goes to the Dogs. 2006. 244p. (YA). 16.95 (978-1-58234-678-6(X) , Bloomsbury Children) Bloomsbury Publishing.

Karwoski, Gail Langer. Seaman: The Dog Who Explored the West with Lewis & Clark. 1999. (gr. 3-6). lib. bdg. 17.60 (978-0-613-23470-2(7)) Tandem Library Bks.

Kashino, Mark. The Journey of Mobius & Sidh: An Interactive Journey of Self Discovery. Kashino, Mark, illus. 2nd l.t. ed. 2001. 48p. 19.95 (978-0-9715709-0-0(6) , KEI Publishing) Kashino Enterprises, Inc.

Kasza, Keiko. The Dog Who Cried Wolf. Kasza, Keiko, illus. 2005. (Illus.). 32p. (J). (ps-3). 15.99 (978-0-399-24247-2(3) , Putnam Juvenile) Penguin Group (USA) Inc.

Katey, Miss. Jelly Bean: A Puppy's Tale. 2005. (ENG., Illus.). 28p. (J). (ps-3). per. 13.99 (978-1-4134-8093-1(4)) Xlibris Corp.

Kathleen, Jo Ann. NATALIA, O' MIA, WHITE LACES & SHOES. l.t. ed. 2006. (ENG., Illus.). 28p. per. 9.95 (***978-1-4327-0314-1(5))*** Outskirts Press, Inc.

Katschke, Judy. 102 Dalmations: Where's Oddball? Hogan, Mary, ed. 2000. (Disney's First Readers Ser.). (Illus.). 32p. (J). (gr. 1-3). pap. 3.99 (978-0-7868-1479-4(9)) Disney Pr.

—102 Dalmations First Reader. 2001. (gr. k-3). lib. bdg. 11.80 (978-0-613-31551-7(0)) Tandem Library Bks.

Keane, Dave. The Neighborhood Stink. Keane, Dave, illus. 2006. (Joe Sherlock Ser.). 112p. (J). pap. 3.99 (978-0-06-076186-8(5) , Harper Trophy) HarperCollins Pubs.

—The Neighborhood Stink: Case 000002. Keane, Dave, illus. 2006. (Joe Sherlock Ser.). (Illus.). 112p. (J). 15.99 (978-0-06-076187-5(3)) HarperCollins Pubs.

Keats, Ezra Jack. Kitten for a Day. Keats, Ezra Jack, illus. 2002. (Illus.). (J). 14.04 (978-1-4046-0836-8(2)) Book Wholesalers, Inc.

—Kitten for a Day. Keats, Ezra Jack, illus. 2002. (Illus.). 32p. (J). pap. 6.99 (978-0-14-230054-1(3) , Puffin) Penguin Group (USA) Inc.

—My Dog Is Lost. Keats, Ezra Jack, illus. 1999. (Picture Puffin Ser.). (Illus.). 32p. (J). (ps-3). pap. 6.99 (978-0-14-056569-0(8) , Puffin) Penguin Group (USA) Inc.

—My Dog Is Lost. 1999. (gr. k-3). lib. bdg. 15.30 (978-0-613-15019-4(8)) Tandem Library Bks.

—My Dog Is Lost! Keats, Ezra Jack, illus. 2002. (Illus.). (J). 14.04 (978-0-7587-4531-6(1)) Book Wholesalers, Inc.

—The Snowy Day/Whistle for Willie DVD & Book Gift Set. 2007. 64p. (J). (gr. 12). 19.99 (***978-0-670-06253-9(7)*** , Viking Juvenile) Penguin Group (USA) Inc.

Keats, Ezra Jack. Whistle for Willie. Keats, Ezra Jack, illus. 2002. (Illus.). (J). 13.19 (978-0-7587-4003-8(4)) Book Wholesalers, Inc.

—Whistle for Willie. 2000. (J). pap. 19.97 incl. audio (978-0-7366-9211-3(8)) Books on Tape, Inc.

—Whistle for Willie. Keats, Ezra Jack, illus. 1998. (Illus.). 32p. (J). (ps-k). bds. 7.99 (978-0-670-88046-1(9) , Viking Juvenile) Penguin Group (USA) Inc.

Keene, Carolyn. The Puppy Problem. Accardo, Anthony, illus. 2005. 69p. (J). lib. bdg. 15.00 (***978-1-4242-0373-4(2))*** Fitzgerald Bks.

Keeping Watch. 2005. (J). (978-1-932570-50-2(0)) Literacy Footprints Inc.

Kelleher, Victor. Dogboy. 2006. (YA). (gr. 9 up). 16.95 (978-1-932425-76-5(4) , Lemniscaat) Boyds Mills Pr.

Keller, Holly. Sophie's Window. Keller, Holly, illus. 2005. (Illus.). 32p. (J). 15.99 (978-0-06-056282-3(X)); 16.89 (978-0-06-056283-0(8)) HarperCollins Pubs.

Kelley, Lynn. The First Boykin Spaniels: The Story of Dumpy & Singo. Gardiner, Lisa, illus. 2004. (Orig.). (J). per. 13.50 (978-0-9761463-0-8(4)) Berke Bks.

Kellogg, Steven. A Penguin Pup for Pinkerton. 2003. (Picture Puffin Ser.). (Illus.). 32p. (J). (gr. k-3). pap. 6.99 (978-0-14-250170-2(0) , Puffin) Penguin Group (USA) Inc.

—Penguin Pup for Pinkerton. 2003. (gr. k-3). lib. bdg. 15.30 (978-0-613-87825-8(6)) Tandem Library Bks.

—Pinkerton, Behave! Kellogg, Steven, illus. 2002. (Illus.). (J). 14.04 (978-1-4046-0250-2(X)) Book Wholesalers, Inc.

—Pinkerton, Behave! Kellogg, Steven, illus. 2002. (Illus.). 32p. (J). 17.99 (978-0-8037-2722-9(4) , Dial); pap. 6.99 (978-0-14-230007-7(1) , Puffin) Penguin Group (USA) Inc.

—Pinkerton, Behave! 2002. (gr. k-3). lib. bdg. 15.30 (978-0-613-44891-8(X)) Tandem Library Bks.

—Prehistoric Pinkerton. Kellogg, Steven, illus. 2002. (Illus.). 32p. (J). pap. 6.99 (978-0-14-230008-4(X) , Puffin) Penguin Group (USA) Inc.

—Prehistoric Pinkerton! 2002. (gr. k-3). lib. bdg. 15.30 (978-0-613-85725-3(9)) Tandem Library Bks.

—A Rose for Pinkerton. Kellogg, Steven, illus. 2002. (Illus.). (J). 14.04 (978-0-7587-3531-7(6)) Book Wholesalers, Inc.

—A Rose for Pinkerton. Kellogg, Steven, illus. 2002. (Illus.). 32p. (J). 16.99 (978-0-8037-2723-6(2) , Dial); pap. 6.99 (978-0-14-230009-1(8) , Puffin) Penguin Group (USA) Inc.

—Rose for Pinkerton. 2002. (ps-2). lib. bdg. 15.30 (978-0-613-43641-0(5)) Tandem Library Bks.

—Tallyho, Pinkerton! Kellogg, Steven, illus. 2002. (Illus.). 14.04 (978-1-4046-0249-6(6)) Book Wholesalers, Inc.

—Tallyho, Pinkerton! Kellogg, Steven, illus. 2002. (Illus.). 32p. (J). 16.99 (978-0-8037-2724-3(0) , Dial); pap. 6.99 (978-0-14-230010-7(1) , Puffin) Penguin Group (USA) Inc.

Kelly, Irene. A Small Dog's Big Life: Around the World with Owney. 2005. (Illus.). 32p. (J). 16.95 (978-0-8234-1863-3(4)) Holiday Hse., Inc.

Kelly, Sharon L. C. M. Coco's Vineyard Vacation: Double Fun on Martha's Vineyard. Galbraith, Alison L., illus. 2005. 40p. (J). 16.95 (978-0-9766283-0-9(9)) Secret Garden Bookworks.

Kemper, Bebe. Seeing Zach. 1999. (Illus.). 32p. (J). 14.95 (978-0-9674363-0-2(3) , Rainy Day Bks.) Purple Chickie Pr.

Kendall, Stan P. Samson Gets a Family. 2005. 22p. (J). 13.50 (978-1-4116-5756-4(X)) Lulu.com.

Kerby, Mona. Owney, the Mail Pouch Pooch. Barasch, Lynne, illus. 2008. 40p. (J). 16.95 (978-0-374-35685-9(8)) Farrar, Straus & Giroux.

Kerry's Double: Individual Title Six-Packs. (gr. 3 up). 35.00 (978-0-7635-9660-6(4)) Rigby Education.

Ketter-Brust, Sandra. Sir Guinness of Wildridge. 2006. 48p. pap. 12.95 (*978-1-4241-4626-0(7)) PublishAmerica, Inc.

Keylocke, Andrew, illus. Whizzy Woof. 2004. (Crazy Racers Ser.). 12p. (J). bds. 4.95 (978-0-7641-5748-6(5)) Barron's Educational Series, Inc.

Khalsa, Dayal Kaur. Julian. 2000. (gr. k-3). lib. bdg. 18.75 (978-0-613-27919-2(0)) Tandem Library Bks.

—Julian. 1999. (Illus.). 24p. (J). (gr. 1-4). pap. 6.95 (978-0-88776-513-1(0)) Tundra Bks., Inc./Livres Toundra, Inc. CAN. *Dist:* Random Hse., Inc.

Kilgras, Heidi. Peanut. Reed, Mike, illus. 2003. (Step into Reading Ser.). 32p. (J). (ps-2). pap. 3.99 (978-0-375-80618-6(0) , Random Hse. Bks. for Young Readers) Random Hse. Children's Bks.

Kimmel, Haven. Orville: A Dog Story. Parker, Robert Andrew, illus. 2003. 32p. (J). (gr. k-3). 15.00 (978-0-618-15955-0(X) , Clarion Bks.) Houghton Mifflin Co. Trade & Reference Div.

Kimmelman, Leslie. In the Doghouse: An Emma & Bo Story. Kelley, True, illus. (Holiday House Reader Ser.: Level 2). 32p. (J). (gr. k-3). 14.95 (978-0-8234-1882-4(0)) Holiday Hse., Inc.

Kindig, Tess Eileen. March Mania, Vol. 6. 2000. (Slam Dunk Ser.: Vol. 6). 96p. (J). (gr. 1-4). 4.99 (978-0-570-07092-4(9)) Concordia Publishing Hse.

—March Mania. 2000. (gr. k-3). lib. bdg. 13.00 (978-0-613-72796-9(7)) Tandem Library Bks.

Kinerk, Robert. Timothy Cox Will Not Change His Socks. Gammell, Stephen, illus. 2005. 32p. (J). 16.95 (978-0-689-87181-8(3) , Simon & Schuster Children's Publishing) Simon & Schuster Children's Publishing.

King-Smith, Dick. Titus Rules! Eastwood, John, illus. 96p. (gr. 2-4). 2003. (J). lib. bdg. 17.99 (978-0-375-91461-4(7) , Knopf Bks. for Young Readers); 2004. reprint ed. 5.50 (978-0-440-42000-2(8) , Yearling) Random Hse. Children's Bks.

King, Stephen Michael. Mutt Dog! 2005. (Illus.). 32p. (J). (ps-ps). 16.00 (978-0-15-205561-5(4)) Harcourt Children's Bks.

—Mutt Dog! King, Stephen Michael, illus. 2005. (Illus.). 32p. (J). (978-1-86504-636-5(1) , Scholastic Pr.) Scholastic, Inc.

—Mutt Dog! 2005. (Illus.). 32p. (J). pap. (978-1-86504-637-2(X) , Scholastic Pr.) Scholastic, Inc.

Kingsley, Carmen. Ten Little Puppies. Cassidy, Sean, illus. 2001. 32p. (J). (ps-k). bds. (978-1-55041-654-1(5)) Fitzhenry & Whiteside, Ltd.

Kirk, Daniel. Moondogs. 1999. (Illus.). 1p. (J). (ps-3). 16.99 (978-0-399-23128-5(5) , Putnam Juvenile) Penguin Group (USA) Inc.

Kirwan, Wednesday. Nobody Notices Minerva. 2007. (Illus.). 32p. (J). (ps up). 14.95 (*978-1-4027-4728-1(4)) Sterling Publishing Co., Inc.

Kitamura, Satoshi. Perro Tiene SED. 1998. (SPA., Illus.). (J). (ps). per. (978-968-16-5536-5(2)) Fondo de Cultura Economica MEX. *Dist:* Lectorum Pubns., Inc.

Klass, David. Firestorm. 2006. (Caretaker Trilogy Ser.: Bk. 1). 304p. (YA). 17.00 (978-0-374-32307-3(0) , Frances Foster Bks.) Farrar, Straus & Giroux.

Klass, David. Firestorm: The Caretaker Trilogy: Book 1. 2008. (Caretaker Trilogy Ser.). 320p. (YA). pap. 8.99 (*978-0-312-38018-2(6)) Square Fish.

Klein, Adria F. Max & Buddy Go to the Vet. Gallagher-Cole, Mernie, illus. 2007. (J). lib. bdg. (*978-1-4048-3679-2(9)) Picture Window Bks.

Kleven, Elisa. Hooray, a Pinata! 2000. (J). 13.79 (978-0-606-19775-5(3)) Tandem Library Bks.

—The Paper Princess Flies Again: With Her Dog! 2005. (Illus.). 32p. (J). (gr. k-2). 15.95 (978-1-58246-146-5(5) , Tricycle Pr.) Ten Speed Pr.

Kline, Trish & Donev, Mary. Coming Home: KA Reader 8. 2007. (Illus.). 32p. (J). per. 20.00 (*978-1-934307-01-4(7)) Ghost Hunter Productions.

Klingel, Cynthia Fitterer & Noyed, Robert B. Daisy, My Dad & the Letter D. 2003. (Alphaphonics Ser.). (Illus.). 24p. (J). (ps-2). 21.36 (978-1-59296-094-1(4)) Child's World, Inc.

Klobuchar, Rose. Dunda. 2002. (J). per. 6.95 (978-1-891231-85-8(5)) Word Association Pubs.

Knapp, Jennifer F. A Walk with Ovid. 2003. (Illus.). 30p. (YA). per. 14.95 (978-0-9742249-0-9(1)) JFK Online Studios, LLC.

Knapp, Susan. Bells Goes to the Fair. l.t. ed. 2002. (Illus.). 44p. (J). 12.95 (978-1-888223-34-7(0)) McMillen Publishing.

Knight, Eric. Lassie Come-Home. Kirmse, Marguerite, illus. rev. ed. 2003. 256p. (J). (gr. 4-12). 18.95 (978-0-8050-7206-8(3) , Holt, Henry & Co. Bks. For Young Readers) Holt, Henry & Co.

—Lassie Come-Home. Kirmse, Marguerite, illus. 2007. 256p. (J). pap. 6.99 (*978-0-312-37131-9(4)) Square Fish.

Knight, Kathryn. Bow-Wow! Peep! rev. ed. 2006. 10p. 5.99 (*978-1-4037-2956-9(5)) Dalmatian Pr.

Knipe, Floyd P. Forest & Grandpa Go Fishing. Jackson, James K., illus. 2000. (Forest the Huggable Dog Ser.: Vol. 2). 23p. (J). (ps-3). pap. 4.95 (978-1-930130-06-7(6)) Nature's Nest Bks.

—Forest & Grandpa Go Fishing Coloring Book. Jackson, James K., illus. 2000. (Forest the Huggable Dog Ser.: Vol. 2). 23p. (J). (ps-3). pap. 2.00 (978-1-930130-07-4(4)) Nature's Nest Bks.

—Forest & the Family Reunion. Jackson, James K., illus. 2000. (Forest the Huggable Dog Ser.: Vol. 5). 23p. (J). (ps-3). pap. 4.95 (978-1-930130-08-1(2)) Nature's Nest Bks.

—Forest & the Family Reunion Coloring Book. Jackson, James K., illus. 2000. (Forest the Huggable Dog Ser.: Vol. 5). 23p. (J). (ps-3). pap. 2.00 (978-1-930130-09-8(0)) Nature's Nest Bks.

—Forest Goes Snow Skiing. Jackson, James K., illus. 2000. (Forest the Huggable Dog Ser.: Vol. 4). 23p. (J). (ps-3). pap. 4.95 (978-1-930130-10-4(4)) Nature's Nest Bks.

—Forest Goes Snow Skiing Coloring Book. Jackson, James K., illus. 2000. (Forest the Huggable Dog Ser.: Vol. 4). 23p. (J). (ps-3). pap. 2.00 (978-1-930130-11-1(2)) Nature's Nest Bks.

—Forest Visits the Daycare. Jackson, James K., illus. 1999. (Forest the Huggable Dog Ser.: Vol. 3). 23p. (J). (ps-3). pap. 4.95 (978-1-930130-02-9(3)) Nature's Nest Bks.

—Forest Visits the Daycare Coloring Book. Jackson, James K., illus. 1999. (Forest the Huggable Dog Ser.: Vol. 3). 23p. (J). (ps-3). pap. 2.00 (978-1-930130-03-6(1)) Nature's Nest Bks.

Kochka. The Boy Who Ate Stars. Adams, Sarah, tr. from FRE. 2006. 112p. (J). 12.95 (978-1-4169-0038-2(1)) Simon & Schuster Children's Publishing.

Koeppel, Ruth & Sander, Sonia. Let's Spell. 2006. (Clifford Ser.). 8p. (J). bds. 12.99 (978-0-439-73376-2(6) , Scholastic) Scholastic, Inc.

Koja, Kathe. Straydog. 2002. (Illus.). 112p. (YA). (gr. 8-10). 16.00 (978-0-374-37278-1(0) , Farrar, Straus & Giroux (BYR)) Farrar, Straus & Giroux.

—Straydog. 2004. 128p. (YA). reprint ed. pap. 5.99 (978-0-14-240071-5(8) , Puffin) Penguin Group (USA) Inc.

Kolar, Bob. Racer Dogs. Kolar, Bob, illus. 2003. (Illus.). 32p. (J). (ps-2). 15.99 (978-0-525-45939-2(1) , Dutton Juvenile) Penguin Group (USA) Inc.

Koller, Jackie French. The Promise. Rogers, Jacqueline, illus. 2001. 80p. (gr. 5-8). 4.99 (978-0-440-41658-6(2) , Yearling) Random Hse. Children's Bks.

Koontz, Dean. Watchers. 2003. (gr. 7-12). lib. bdg. 16.45 (978-0-613-57487-7(7)) Tandem Library Bks.

Koontz, Robin Michal. Why a Dog? By A. Cat. 2000. (Hello Reader! Ser.). (978-0-606-18892-0(4)) Tandem Library Bks.

Kopper, Lisa. Daisy Is a Mommy. Kopper, Lisa, illus. 2002. (Illus.). (J). 21.36 (978-0-7587-2336-9(9)) Book Wholesalers, Inc.

Korbel, Wendy. Gus: Adventures on the Farm. 2007. 24p. (J). pap. 8.99 (*978-1-59886-999-6(X)) Tate Publishing & Enterprises, L.L.C.

Kotzwinkle, William. Rough Weather Ahead for Walter the Farting Dog. Andrews, Colman, illus. 2007. 32p. (J). (gr. k up). pap. 6.99 (978-0-14-240845-2(X) , Puffin) Penguin Group (USA) Inc.

Kotzwinkle, William & Murray, Glenn. Walter Canis Inflatus. Dobbin, Rob, tr. from ENG. Colman, Audrey, illus. 2004. Tr. of Walter the Farting Dog (LAT.). 32p. (978-1-58394-110-2(X) , Frog Ltd.) North Atlantic Bks.

—Walter el Perro Pedorrero. Bohorquez, Eduardo, tr. from ENG. Colman, Audrey, illus. 2004. Tr. of Walter the Farting Dog. (SPA.). 32p. (J). (978-1-58394-103-4(7) , Frog Ltd.) North Atlantic Bks.

—Walter le Chien Qui Pete. Choquette, Michel, tr. from ENG. Colman, Audrey, illus. 2004. Tr. of Walter the Farting Dog. (FRE.). 32p. (J). (978-1-58394-104-1(5) , Frog Ltd.) North Atlantic Bks.

—Walter the Farting Dog. Colman, Audrey, illus. 2001. 32p. (J). (ps-2). 15.95 (978-1-58394-053-2(7) , Frog Ltd.) North Atlantic Bks.

—Walter the Farting Dog: Trouble at the Yard Sale. Colman, Audrey, illus. 2004. 32p. (J). (gr. k). 16.99 (978-0-525-47217-9(7) , Dutton Juvenile) Penguin Group (USA) Inc.

—Walter the Farting Dog: Trouble at the Yard Sale. Coleman, Audrey, illus. 2006. 32p. (J). (gr. k). reprint ed. pap. 6.99 (978-0-14-240626-7(0) , Puffin) Penguin Group (USA) Inc.

Kotzwinkle, William, et al. Rough Weather Ahead for Walter the Farting Dog. Coleman, Audrey, illus. ed. 2005. 32p. (J). (gr. k). 16.99 (978-0-525-47218-6(5) , Dutton Juvenile) Penguin Group (USA) Inc.

—Walter the Farting Dog: Banned from the Beach. Colman, Audrey, illus. 2007. 32p. (J). (gr. k up). 16.99 (978-0-525-47812-6(4) , Dutton Juvenile) Penguin Group (USA) Inc.

—Walter the Farting Dog Goes on a Cruise. Coleman, Audrey, illus. 2006. 32p. (J). (gr. k-4). 16.99 (978-0-525-47714-3(4) , Dutton Juvenile) Penguin Group (USA) Inc.

Kovacs, Deborah. Catie Copley. Williams, Jared T., illus. 2007. 32p. (J). (gr. k-3). 17.95 (*978-1-56792-332-2(1)) Godine, David R. Pub.

Kovalski, Maryann. Martha et Edouard. ed. Tr. of Martha et Edouard. (FRE.). (J). pap. 3.99 (978-0-590-74819-3(X)) Scholastic, Inc.

Krailing, Tessa. Trixie & the Cyber Pet. Lewis, Jan & Eastwood, John, illus. 1998. (Petsitters Club Ser.: No. 6). 96p. (J). (gr. 1-4). pap. 4.50 (978-0-7641-0614-9(7)) Barron's Educational Series, Inc.

Krakow, Amy. The Mutt & the Monster. Williams, Steve, illus. 2002. 24p. (J). (gr. 2-7). 15.00 (978-0-9715224-0-4(5)) Wagging Tales Publishing.

Kranowitz, Carol Stock. The Goodenoughs Get in Sync: A Story for Kids about the Tough Day When Filibuster Grabbed Darwin's Rabbit's Foot... Wylie, T. J., illus. 2004. 86p. (J). 14.95 (978-1-931615-17-4(9) , 978-1-931615-17-4) Sensory Resources.

Krantz Stewart, Kathy. Rani, the Ugly Dogling. 2002. 118p. (J). pap. 9.95 (978-0-595-22608-5(6) , Writers Club Pr.) iUniverse, Inc.

Krauser, Susan A. Lilith A. Wilith. 2002. (J). lib. bdg. 16.95 (978-0-9717860-0-4(3)) Lilith & Co.

Kravitz, Cathy. A Dog's Day. 2005. (J). 24.95 (978-1-59858-025-9(6)); per. 16.95 (978-1-59858-009-9(4)) Dog Ear Publishing, LLC.

Kristiansen, Kate. Black Dog White Dog. 2004. (Illus.). 16p. (J). 13.99 (978-0-9764175-0-7(2)) Winking Moon Pr.

Kroll, Steven. Pooch on the Loose: A Christmas Adventure. Garland, Michael, illus. 2005. 32p. (J). (ps-3). per. 14.95 (978-0-7614-5239-3(7)) Cavendish, Marshall Corp.

—A Tale of Two Dogs. Reed, Mike, tr. Reed, Mike, illus. 2004. 32p. (J). 16.95 (978-0-7614-5161-7(7)) Cavendish, Marshall Corp.

Kroll, Virginia L. Selvakumar Knew Better. Li, Xiaojun, illus. 2006. (J). 17.95 (978-1-885008-29-9(5)) Shen's Bks.

Krueger, Kathryn L. Road to Grandma's House. 2005. 128p. pap. 13.95 (978-1-59800-366-6(6)) Outskirts Press, Inc.

Krulik, Nancy E. Cat's Big Night. 1999. Tr. of Dog Behind Bars. (gr. 3-6). lib. bdg. 11.80 (978-0-613-21313-4(0)) Tandem Library Bks.

—Doggone It!, No. 8. John and Wendy Staff, illus. 2003. (Katie Kazoo, Switcheroo Ser.: No. 8). 80p. (J). (gr. 2-4). pap. 3.99 (978-0-448-43172-7(6) , Grosset & Dunlap) Penguin Group (USA) Inc.

—Doggone It!, No. 8. 2003. (Katie Kazoo, Switcheroo Ser.: No. 8). (gr. 3-6). lib. bdg. 11.80 (978-0-613-67541-3(X)) Tandem Library Bks.

Kubik, Dorothy. The Adventures of Elbert & Leopoldina. James, Annie, illus. 2006. 104p. (J). per. 15.00 (*978-0-9790775-1-7(6)) Touchstone Communications.

Kunhardt, Edith. Pat the Puppy. 2001. (Touch & Feel Bks.). (Illus.). 20p. (J). (gr. k-ps). pap. 9.99 (978-0-307-12004-5(X) , 12004, Golden Bks.) Random Hse. Children's Bks.

Kuskin, Karla. City Dog. Kuskin, Karla, illus. 1998. (Illus.). 32p. (J). (gr. k-3). 6.95 (978-0-395-90016-1(6) , Clarion Bks.) Houghton Mifflin Co. Trade & Reference Div.

Kutchinski, Marjorie. Liberty, Justice & F'Rall: The Dog Heroes of the Texas Republic. 1998. 152p. (gr. k-5). 15.95 (978-1-57168-217-8(1)) Eakin Pr.

Kwon, Jean. Because of Winn Dixie Movie Scrapbook. Tenner, Suzanne, photos by. 2004. (Because of Winn-Dixie Ser.). (Illus.). 48p. (J). pap. 6.99 (978-0-7636-2817-8(4)) Candlewick Pr.

La Fontaine, Jean De. The Falcon & the Little Dog. 2004. reprint ed. pap. 15.95 (978-1-4191-6181-0(4)) Kessinger Publishing, LLC.

Labatt, Mary. Aliens in Woodford. 2000. (gr. 3-6). lib. bdg. 12.95 (978-0-613-30214-2(1)); (Illus.). (J). 11.60 (978-0-606-21020-1(2)) Tandem Library Bks.

—Friend for Sam. 2003. (gr. k-3). lib. bdg. 11.80 (978-0-613-84410-9(6)) Tandem Library Bks.

—The Ghost of Captain Briggs. Hill-Jackson, Troy, illus. 1999. (Sam Ser.). 120p. (J). (gr. 4-6). (978-1-55074-636-5(7)) Kids Can Pr., Ltd.

—The Ghost of Captain Briggs. Jackson, Troy, illus. 1999. (Sam Ser.). 120p. (J). (gr. 4-6). (978-1-55074-638-9(3)) Kids Can Pr., Ltd.

—The Ghost of Captain Briggs. 1999. (J). 11.60 (978-0-606-19016-9(3)) Tandem Library Bks.

—Mummy Lives! 2002. (gr. 3-6). lib. bdg. 12.95 (978-0-613-62530-2(7)) Tandem Library Bks.

—The Mummy Lives! unabr. ed. 2002. (Sam Ser.). (Illus.). 120p. (J). (gr. 4-6). (978-1-55337-042-0(2)) Kids Can Pr., Ltd.

—The Mummy Lives! Hill-Jackson, Troy, illus. unabr. ed. 2002. (Sam Ser.). 120p. (J). (gr. 4-6). (978-1-55337-023-9(6)) Kids Can Pr., Ltd.

—A Parade for Sam. Sarrazin, Marisol, illus. 2005. 32p. (J). lib. bdg. 15.38 (*978-1-4242-1154-8(9)) Fitzgerald Bks.

—A Parade for Sam. Sarrazin, Marisol, illus. 2005. (Kids Can Start to Read Ser.). 32p. (J). (978-1-55337-788-7(5)); (978-1-55337-787-0(7)) Kids Can Pr., Ltd.

—A Puppy Is for Loving. Liwska, Renata, illus. 2007. (Orca Echoes Ser.). 64p. (J). (gr. 2-4). pap. (*978-1-55143-477-3(6)) Orca Bk. Pubs.

—Sam at the Seaside. Sarrazin, Marisol, illus. 2006. 32p. (978-1-55337-877-8(6)); (978-1-55337-876-1(8)) Kids Can Pr., Ltd.

—Sam Finds a Monster. 2003. (gr. k-3). lib. bdg. 11.80 (978-0-613-82321-0(4)) Tandem Library Bks.

—Sam Gets Lost. Sarrazin, Marisol, illus. 2004. 32p. (J). lib. bdg. 15.38 (*978-1-4242-1159-3(X)) Fitzgerald Bks.

—Sam Gets Lost. Sarrazin, Marisol, tr. Sarrazin, Marisol, illus. 2004. (Kids Can Read! Ser.: Vol. 1). 32p. (J). (gr. k-3). (978-1-55337-563-0(7)); (978-1-55337-562-3(9)) Kids Can Pr., Ltd.

—Sam Goes Next Door. Sarrazin, Marisol, illus. 2006. 32p. (978-1-55337-879-2(2)); (978-1-55337-878-5(4)) Kids Can Pr., Ltd.

—Sam Goes to School. Sarrazin, Marisol, illus. 2004. 31p. (J). lib. bdg. 15.38 (*978-1-4242-1160-9(3)) Fitzgerald Bks.

—Sam Goes to School. Sarrazin, Marisol, tr. Sarrazin, Marisol, illus. 2004. (Kids Can Read! Ser.: Vol. 1). 32p. (J). (gr. k-3). (978-1-55337-565-4(3)); (978-1-55337-564-7(5)) Kids Can Pr., Ltd.

—Sam's Snowy Day. Sarrazin, Marisol, illus. 2005. 32p. (J). lib. bdg. 10.00 (*978-1-4242-1155-5(7)) Fitzgerald Bks.

—Sam's Snowy Day. Sarrazin, Marisol, illus. 2005. (Kids Can Start to Read Ser.). 32p. (J). (ps-ps). (978-1-55337-790-0(7)); (978-1-55337-789-4(3)) Kids Can Pr., Ltd.

—The Secret of Sagawa Lake. Hill-Jackson, Troy, illus. 2001. (Sam Ser.). 120p. (J). (gr. 4-6). (978-1-55074-887-1(4)); (978-1-55074-889-5(0)) Kids Can Pr., Ltd.

—Secret of Sagawa Lake. 2001. (gr. 3-6). lib. bdg. 12.95 (978-0-613-51586-3(2)) Tandem Library Bks.

—Spying on Dracula. Jackson, Troy, illus. 1999. (Sam Ser.). 120p. (J). (gr. 4-6). (978-1-55074-632-7(4)) Kids Can Pr., Ltd.

—Spying on Dracula. Hill-Jackson, Troy, illus. 1999. (Sam Ser.). 120p. (J). (gr. 4-6). (978-1-55074-634-1(0)) Kids Can Pr., Ltd.

—Spying on Dracula. 1999. (J). (978-0-606-19023-7(6)) Tandem Library Bks.

—Strange Neighbors. Hill-Jackson, Troy, illus. unabr. ed. 2000. (Sam Ser.). 120p. (J). (gr. 4-6). (978-1-55074-603-7(0)); (978-1-55074-605-1(7)) Kids Can Pr., Ltd.

—A Weekend at the Grand Hotel. 2000. (Sam Dog Detective Ser.). (Illus.). (J). (978-0-606-21512-1(3)) Tandem Library Bks.

—Weekend at the Grand Hotel. 2001. (gr. 3-6). lib. bdg. 12.95 (978-0-613-37071-4(6)) Tandem Library Bks.

—A Weekend at the Grand Hotel. Hill-Jackson, Troy, illus. unabr. ed. 2001. (Sam Ser.). 120p. (J). (gr. 4-6). (978-1-55074-885-7(8)); (978-1-55074-883-3(1)) Kids Can Pr., Ltd.

Lacombe, Benjamin. Cherry & Olive. 2007. (J). (*978-0-8027-9708-7(3)) Walker & Co.

—Cherry & Olive. Lacombe, Benjamin, illus. 2007. (Illus.). 32p. (J). (ps-2). 16.95 (*978-0-8027-9707-0(5)) Walker & Co.

Ladd, Debbie. Ethan the Ending Eater. Nakasone, Shaun, illus. 2007. 64p. (J). 16.95 (978-0-9727615-2-9(7)) Deb on Air Bks.

Laden, Nina. Romeow & Drooliet. 2005. (Illus.). 44p. (J). 16.95 (978-0-8118-3973-0(7)) Chronicle Bks. LLC.

Lady & the Tramp. 2000. (Read-Along Ser.). (Illus.). 24p. (J). 7.99 incl. audio (978-1-55723-016-4(1)) Walt Disney Records.

Laguna, Sofie. Bad Buster: Being Bad Is Not Just for the Dogs! Hobbs, Leigh, illus. 2006. (Nibbles Ser.). 72p. (J). (gr. 1-4). pap. 3.95 (978-0-7624-2626-3(8) , Running Pr. Kids) Running Pr. Bk. Pubs.

Lambert, Billy. Dog on a Surfboard (and the Rest of the Adventure) 2003. 174p. pap. 12.95 (978-0-595-26290-8(2) , Writers Club Pr.) iUniverse, Inc.

Landolf, Diane Wright. Hog & Dog. Harris, Jennifer Beck, illus. 2005. (Step into Reading Ser.: Vol. 1). 32p. (J). (ps-1). pap. 3.99 (978-0-375-83165-2(7) , Random Hse. Bks. for Young Readers) Random Hse. Children's Bks.

Landy, Sarah. Blue's Snack Party. Cardinali, Kevin, illus. 2000. (Blue's Clues Ser.). 16p. (J). (ps-k). 5.99 (978-0-689-83432-5(2) , Simon Spotlight/Nickelodeon) Simon & Schuster Children's Publishing.

Lang, Andrew. The Violet Fairy Book. 2005. 404p. pap. 16.95 (978-1-4218-0107-0(8) , 1st World Library - Literary Society) 1st World Publishing, Inc.

Langford, Jane. Hero. Vince, Dawn, illus. 2005. 24p. (J). lib. bdg. 22.65 (*978-1-59646-720-0(7)) Dingles & Co.

Langreuter, Jutta & Hebrock, Andrea. Belly Buttons. 1999. (Illus.). 32p. (J). (ps-2). 12.95 (978-0-7641-5216-0(5)) Barron's Educational Series, Inc.

Langston, Laura. Perfect Blue. 2008. 220p. pap. (*978-1-55455-058-6(0)) Fitzhenry & Whiteside, Ltd.

—A Taste of Perfection. 2002. (Illus.). 190p. (J). (gr. 5 up). pap. 6.95 (978-0-7737-6274-9(4)) Stoddart Kids CAN. *Dist:* Fitzhenry & Whiteside, Ltd.

Langston, Laura. The Trouble with Cupid. 2008. 240p. (YA). (gr. 5-8). pap. (*978-1-55455-059-3(9)) Fitzhenry & Whiteside, Ltd.

Lanier, Virginia. Blind Bloodhound Justice. 1999. 337p. (gr. 7-12). per. 15.30 (978-0-613-23687-4(4)) Tandem Library Bks.

Larochelle, David. The Best Pet of All. Wakiyama, Hanako, illus. 2004. 32p. (J). (ps). 16.99 (978-0-525-47129-5(4) , Dutton Juvenile) Penguin Group (USA) Inc.

Laschutza, Susanne. Nat the Bat. Laschutza, Susanne, illus. 2003. (Illus.). 24p. (J). (gr. 1 up). lib. bdg. 23.33 (978-0-8368-3573-1(5)) Stevens, Gareth Inc.

Lassiter, Nancy. Proud Racer: Blind Faith. 2003. 48p. (YA). per. 12.00 (978-1-932496-07-9(6)) Penman Publishing, Inc.

Lastoka, Mariann. Pete & Patricia Prairie Dog & their Pack of Prairie Pups. Carpenter, Debra, illus. 2003. 40p. 6.50 (978-1-892860-05-7(8) , 5) MRL, Inc.

Lawlor, Laurie. He Will Go Fearless. 2006. 224p. (J). 15.95 (978-0-689-86579-4(1)) Simon & Schuster Children's Publishing.

Lawrence, Iain. Gemini Summer. 2006. 272p. (J). (gr. 3-7). 15.95 (978-0-385-73089-1(6)); lib. bdg. 17.99 (978-0-385-90111-6(9)) Random Hse. Children's Bks. (Delacorte Bks. for Young Readers).

Lawrence, Jennifer B. Sad Doggy. Ering, Tim, illus. 2001. 24p. (J). (ps-k). 13.95 (978-1-58117-066-5(1) , Intervisual/Piggy Toes) Dalmatian Pr.

Lawrence, Peter. Colleen Smoothflow of Coneve: From Central Africa to Southern England, The True Adventures of a Wire Hair Terier. Rowe, David, illus. 2001. 137p. (J). pap. 9.95 (978-1-930702-01-1(9) , Smart Kids Studio Productions) Literary Assocs. Pr.

Lawson, Julie. The Klondike Cat. Mombourquette, Paul, illus. 2002. 32p. (J). (gr. k-3). (978-1-55337-013-0(9)) Kids Can Pr., Ltd.

Lawson, Rob, illus. Duke Finds a Home. 2006. (Duke's Tails Ser.). 32p. (J). (978-0-9779308-0-7(7)) Bush Brothers & Co.

LeapFrog Staff, compiled by. Clifford. 2002. (YA). (ps up). spiral bd. 9.99 (978-1-58605-798-5(7)) LeapFrog Enterprises, Inc.

Leavitt, Caroline. The Haunted Clubhouse. l.t. ed. 1999. (Wishbone Mysteries Ser.: No. 2). 144p. (J). (gr. 4 up). lib. bdg. 22.60 (978-0-8368-2383-7(4)) Stevens, Gareth Inc.

—The Prince & the Pooch. l.t. ed. 1999. (Adventures of Wishbone Ser.: No. 3). (Illus.). 144p. (J). (gr. 4 up). lib. bdg. 22.60 (978-0-8368-2299-1(4)) Stevens, Gareth Inc.

—Robinhound Crusoe. l.t. ed. 1999. (Adventures of Wishbone Ser.: No. 4). (Illus.). 144p. (J). (gr. 4 up). lib. bdg. 22.60 (978-0-8368-2300-4(1)) Stevens, Gareth Inc.

Lee, Chinlun. Good Dog, Paw! Lee, Chinlun, illus. 2004. (Illus.). 40p. (J). (ps-1). 15.99 (978-0-7636-2178-0(1)) Candlewick Pr.

Lee, Kara, illus. Chelsea & the New Puppy. 2001. (J). (ps-3). 14.00 (978-1-892657-03-9(1)) Town Bk. Pr. The.

Lee, Quinlan B. Christmas Angel. 2006. (Clifford's Puppy Days Ser.). (Illus.). 24p. (J). pap. 3.99 (978-0-439-75533-7(6)) Scholastic, Inc.

Leedy, Loreen. Mapping Penny's World. rev. ed. 2003. (Illus.). 32p. (J). (gr. k-3). pap. 6.95 (978-0-8050-7262-4(4) , Holt, Henry & Co. Bks. For Young Readers) Holt, Henry & Co.

—Mapping Penny's World. Leedy, Loreen, illus. rev. ed. 2000. (Illus.). 32p. (J). (gr. k-3). 17.00 (978-0-8050-6178-9(9) , Holt, Henry & Co. Bks. For Young Readers) Holt, Henry & Co.

Leeson, Robert. Dog Who Changed the World. 96p. (J). 17.95 (978-0-241-00244-5(3) , Hamilton, Hamish) Penguin Bks., Ltd. GBR. *Dist:* Trafalgar Square Publishing.

LeFrak, Karen. Jake the Philharmonic Dog. Baranski, Marcin, illus. 2006. 32p. (J). 16.95 (978-0-8027-9552-6(8)) Walker & Co.

LeLeu, Lisa. Diggity the Dog Puppet Show Play Set. ed. 2004. (Lisa Leleu Puppet Show Books Ser.). (J). 19.95 (***978-0-9710537-2-4(3)*** , LeLeu, Lisa Puppet Show Bks.) LeLeu, Lisa Studios! Inc.

Lemieux, Jean. Pas de S pour Copernic. Casson, Sophie, illus. 2001. (Premier Roman Ser.). (FRE.). 64p. (J). (gr. 1-4). pap. (978-2-89021-454-5(0)) Diffusion du livre Mirabel.

Lemieux, Jean & Casson, Sophie. Le Bonheur Est une Tempjte Avec un Chien. 2002. (Premier Roman Ser.). (FRE., Illus.). 64p. pap. (978-2-89021-568-9(7)) Diffusion du livre Mirabel.

L'Engle, Madeleine. The Other Dog. Davenier, Christine, illus. 2006. 48p. (J). reprint ed. pap. 6.95 (978-0-8118-5228-9(8) , SeaStar Bks.) Chronicle Bks. LLC.

—The Other Dog. Davenier, Christine, illus. 2003. 37p. (J). (gr. 2-5). reprint ed. 16.00 (978-0-7567-6970-3(1)) DIANE Publishing Co.

Lenhard, Elizabeth. Cats & Dogs. 2001. (Illus.). 144p. (J). (gr. 2-5). pap. 4.99 (978-0-439-22569-4(8)) Scholastic, Inc.

Leonard, Elmore. A Coyote's in the House. 2004. (Illus.). 160p. 15.95 (978-0-06-054404-1(X) , Harper Entertainment) HarperCollins Pubs.

Leonard, Marcia. Get the Ball, Slim. Handelman, Dorothy, photos by. 1998. (Real Kids Readers Ser.). (Illus.). 32p. (gr. k-1). (J). pap. 4.99 (978-0-7613-2025-8(3)); lib. bdg. 18.90 (978-0-7613-2000-5(8)) Lerner Publishing Group. (Millbrook Pr.).

—Trae la Pelota, Tito. Handelman, Dorothy, photos by. 2005. (Lecturas para Niños de Verdad (Real Kids Readers) Ser.). (Illus.). 32p. (J). (ps-1). (SPA.). pap. 4.99 (978-0-8225-3292-7(1) , Ediciones Lerner); (ENG & SPA., pap. 4.99 (978-0-8225-3293-4(X)) Lerner Publishing Group.

Leonard, Mary T. Three Best Friends. Russell, Terry, illus. 2004. 96p. (J). per. 12.00 (978-0-9740683-8-1(1)) Authors & Artists Publishers of New York, Inc.

LePage, Deborah. Scary Stories to Tell Your Pet: The Kitty Man. 2003. 108p. pap. 13.95 (978-1-59286-878-0(9)) PublishAmerica, Inc.

Lerman, Rory S. Charlie's Checklist. Bartlett, Alison, illus. 2000. 32p. (J). (ps-3). pap. 6.95 (978-0-531-07173-1(1) , Orchard Bks.) Scholastic, Inc.

Leslie, Amanda. Who's That Scratching at My Door? A Peekaboo Riddle Book. 2001. (Illus.). 24p. (J). (ps-k). pap. 12.95 (978-1-929766-19-2(X)) Handprint Bks.

Lesynski, Loris. Dirty Dog Boogie. Lesynski, Loris, illus. rev. ed. 1999. (Illus.). 32p. (J). (gr. 1-4). pap. 6.95 (978-1-55037-572-5(5)); lib. bdg. 18.95 (978-1-55037-573-2(3)) Annick Pr., Ltd. CAN. *Dist:* Firefly Bks., Ltd.

—Dirty Dog Boogie. 2002. (gr. k-3). lib. bdg. 15.25 (978-0-613-78365-1(4)) Tandem Library Bks.

Levin, Betty. Look Back, Moss. 1998. (Illus.). 160p. (J). (gr. 3 up). 15.00 (978-0-688-15696-1(7)) HarperCollins Pubs.

Levin, Betty. The Unmaking of Duncan Veerick. 2007. 204p. (YA). (gr. 5 up). 16.95 (***978-1-932425-96-3(9)*** , Front Street) Boyds Mills Pr.

Levine, Nancy. Letters to a Young Pug. 2006. (Illus.). 128p. (gr. 12). 19.95 (978-0-670-03809-1(1) , Studio) Penguin Group (USA) Inc.

Levy, Elizabeth. A Hare-Raising Tale: A Fletcher Mystery. Gorstein, Mordicai, illus. unabr. ed. 2006. (First Chapter Bks.). (J). (gr. 2-4). pap. 17.95 incl. audio (***978-1-59519-704-7(4));*** pap. 20.95 incl. audio compact disk (***978-1-59519-705-4(2))*** Live Oak Media.

—The Mixed-Up Mask Mystery: A Fletcher Mystery. Gorstein, Mordicai, illus. unabr. ed. 2006. (First Chapter Bks.). (J). (gr. 2-4). pap. 20.95 incl. audio compact disk (***978-1-59519-711-5(7));*** pap. 17.95 incl. audio (***978-1-59519-710-8(9))*** Live Oak Media.

Levy, Elizabeth. The Principal's on the Roof. Gerstein, Mordicai, illus. ed. 2005. 74p. (J). lib. bdg. 15.00 (978-1-59054-912-4(0)) Fitzgerald Bks.

—The Principal's on the Roof. Gerstein, Mordicai, illus. unabr. ed. 2006. (First Chapter Bks.). (J). (gr. 2-4). 20.95 incl. audio compact disk (***978-1-59519-699-6(4));*** pap. 17.95 incl. audio (***978-1-59519-698-9(6))*** Live Oak Media.

Levy, Elizabeth & Brunkus, Denise. The Mystery of the Missing Dog. (Hello Reader! Ser.). (FRE., Illus.). (J). pap. 5.99 (978-0-590-16010-0(9)) Scholastic, Inc.

Levy, Elizabeth & Coville, Bruce. The Dragon of Doom. Gerstein, Mordicai & Coville, Katherine, illus. ed. 2005. 71p. (J). lib. bdg. 15.00 (978-1-59054-903-2(1)) Fitzgerald Bks.

Levy, Elizabeth & Gerstein, Mordicai. A Hare-Raising Tail. 2002. (Fletcher Mystery Ser.: No. 1). (Illus.). 80p. (J). (gr. 2-5). pap. 3.99 (978-0-689-84626-7(6) , Aladdin) Simon & Schuster Children's Publishing.

—The Principal's on the Roof. 2002. (Ready-for-Chapters Ser.). (Illus.). 80p. (J). pap. 3.99 (978-0-689-84627-4(4) , Aladdin) Simon & Schuster Children's Publishing.

Lewis, Beverly. The Midnight Mystery. 2007. (Cul-de-Sac Kids Ser.: Vol. 24). (Illus.). 80p. (J). (gr. 2-5). pap. 3.99 (978-0-7642-2129-3(9)) Bethany Hse. Pubs.

—Mystery Mutt. 2000. (Cul-de-Sac Kids Ser.: Vol. 21). (Illus.). 80p. (J). (gr. 2-5). pap. 3.99 (978-0-7642-2126-2(4)) Bethany Hse. Pubs.

Lewis, Kevin. My Truck Is Stuck! Kirk, Daniel, illus. 2006. 30p. (ps-ps). 6.99 (978-0-7868-3739-7(X)) Hyperion Bks. for Children.

Lewis, Kim. A Puppy for Annie. Lewis, Kim, illus. 2006. (Illus.). 32p. (J). (ps). 15.99 (978-0-7636-3200-7(7)) Candlewick Pr.

Lewis, Larry. Laddie's Tales & Travels. 2005. 38p. pap. 17.95 (978-1-4137-3390-7(5)) PublishAmerica, Inc.

Lewis, Marla. Rescued: Benny's Story. 2005. 38p. (J). 10.23 (978-1-4116-6172-1(9)) Lulu.com.

Lewis, Sian. Billy Jones, Dog Star. Roberts, Maggy, tr. Roberts, Maggy, illus. 2003. 48p. pap. 11.95 (978-1-84323-169-1(7)) Beekman Bks., Inc.

Lewis, Wendy A. In Abby's Hands. Mets, Marilyn & Ledwon, Peter, illus. 2004. 32p. (J). (gr. k-1). pap. 17.95 (978-0-88995-282-9(5)) Red Deer Pr. CAN. *Dist:* Fitzhenry & Whiteside, Ltd.

Lewison, Wendy Cheyette. The Prince & the Potty. Motoyama, Keiko, illus. 2006. 40p. (J). (ps). 12.95 (978-0-689-87808-4(7) , Simon & Schuster Children's Publishing) Simon & Schuster Children's Publishing.

—Raindrop, Plop! Paparone, Pamela, tr. Paparone, Pamela, illus. 2004. 32p. (J). (ps-3). 15.99 (978-0-670-03620-2(X) , Viking Juvenile) Penguin Group (USA) Inc.

Lide, Emily. Zimbabwe. 2006. per. 11.95 (978-1-59094-120-1(9)) Jawbone Publishing Corp.

Lilley, Andrew, Sr. The Story of Old Dog. 2005. (J). pap. 8.00 (978-0-8059-6744-9(3)) Dorrance Publishing Co., Inc.

Linamen, Karen Scalf. Princess Madison & the Paisley Puppy. 2007. (Princess Madison Trilogy Ser.). (Illus.). 32p. (J). 12.99 (978-0-8007-1841-1(0)) Revell.

Lincoln, Jacqueline Michelle. The Adventures of Sheila the Awesome (Aussie) Dog. 2005. (J). 7.95 (978-0-9748426-3-9(X)) Accent Pubns.

Lisle, Rebecca. The Dog in the Diamond Collar. Archbold, Tim, illus. 2006. 74p. (J). (gr. 1-2). 8.99 (978-1-84270-366-3(8)) Andersen GBR. *Dist:* Independent Pubs. Group.

Literature Connections English: Where the Red Fern Grows. 2004. (gr. 6-12). (978-0-395-77528-8(0) , 2-80097) McDougal Littell Inc.

Litowinsky, Olga. The Pawloined Paper. l.t. ed. 1999. (Adventures of Wishbone Ser.: No. 11). (Illus.). (J). (gr. 4 up). lib. bdg. 22.60 (978-0-8368-2589-3(6)) Stevens, Gareth Inc.

Little, Jean. Birdie for Now. 2002. (gr. 3-6). lib. bdg. 13.00 (978-0-613-53482-6(4)) Tandem Library Bks.

—Different Dragons. 2007. (Illus.). 112p. (J). (gr. 3). pap. 5.99 (978-0-14-331230-7(8) , Puffin) Penguin Group (USA) Inc.

—Forward, Shakespeare! 2005. (Orca Young Readers Ser.). (Illus.). 144p. (J). (gr. 3-6). pap. 5.95 (978-1-55143-339-4(7)) Orca Bk. Pubs. USA.

—I Know an Old Laddie. ed. 2004. (Illus.). (J). (gr. k-3). spiral bd. (978-0-616-01703-6(0)) Canadian National Institute for the Blind/Institut National Canadien pour les Aveugles.

Little Puppy. 2003. (Goodnight Mr. Moon Ser.). (Illus.). (J). bds. 2.98 (978-0-7525-4742-8(9)) Parragon, Inc.

Lloyd, Ellen. Freckles. 2000. (Illus.). 36p. (J). (ps-2). 14.95 (978-0-9650449-0-5(4)) Butterfly Creations, Inc.

Lloyd, Gita & Binder, Eric, illus. Clifford's Doodle Pad: Scribble Pad. 2004. (Clifford Ser.). (J). bds. 2.49 (978-0-439-55671-2(6)) Scholastic, Inc.

Lloyd, Sam. Farting Fred & the Dog Show. 2005. (Illus.). 10p. (J). (ps-7). 12.95 (978-0-7624-2497-9(4) , Running Pr. Kids) Running Pr. Bk. Pubs.

Lloyd, Stacy K. A Girl & Her Dog. 2005. 32p. pap. 12.00 (978-1-4116-1359-1(7)) Lulu.com.

Lo, Jim. Showing Love to Other. Lo, Jim, illus. 2000. (Illus.). 30p. (J). (gr. 1-3). pap. 6.99 (978-0-89827-208-6(4)) Wesleyan Publishing Hse.

Logan, Wanda. Caesar, A Story about a Dog. 2005. (Illus.). 116p. (J). per. 13.95 (978-1-59405-055-8(4)) New Age World Publishing.

Logue, Stephanie. Mango's Revenge. Murphy, Chris, illus. 2006. (J). pap. (978-1-59336-769-5(4)) Mondo Publishing.

London, Jack. Call of the Wild. 2003. (gr. 3-6). lib. bdg. 11.80 (978-0-613-61610-2(3)); 2000. (gr. 5-8). lib. bdg. 11.80 (978-0-613-66693-0(3)) Tandem Library Bks.

—The Call of the Wild. Pablo Marcos Studio Staff, illus. 2002. (Great Illustrated Classics Ser.). 240p. (J). (gr. 3-8). 21.35 (978-1-57765-682-1(2) , ABDO & Daughters) ABDO Publishing Co.

—The Call of the Wild. 2002. 11.49 (978-0-7587-7808-6(2)) Book Wholesalers, Inc.

—The Call of the Wild. 2001. (Fast Track Classics Ser.). (Illus.). 48p. pap. 9.99 (978-0-237-52285-8(3) , Evans Brothers, Limited) Evans Publishing Group GBR. *Dist:* Independent Pubs. Group.

—The Call of the Wild. 1999. (HRW Library). 161p. (YA). (978-0-03-054457-6(2)) Holt, Rinehart & Winston.

—The Call of the Wild. Davidson, Andrew, illus. 2002. (Kingfisher Classics Ser.). 208p. (J). (gr. k-3). tchr. ed. 15.95 (978-0-7534-5493-0(9) , Kingfisher) Houghton Mifflin Co. Trade & Reference Div.

—The Call of the Wild. 2003. (Aladdin Classics Ser.). 160p. mass mkt. 4.99 (978-0-689-85674-7(1) , Aladdin) Simon & Schuster Children's Publishing.

—The Call of the Wild. Minor, Wendell, illus. 1999. (Scribner Illustrated Classics Ser.). 128p. (YA). (gr. 4-7). 24.00 (978-0-689-81836-3(X) , Atheneum) Simon & Schuster Children's Publishing.

—The Call of the Wild. Clift, Eva, tr. Clift, Eva, illus. 2003. (Values in Action Illustrated Classics Ser.). (J). (978-1-59203-047-7(5)) Learning Challenge, Inc.

—The Call of the Wild. Corvino, Lucy, illus. 2005. (Classic Starts Ser.). 160p. 4.95 (978-1-4027-1274-6(X)) Sterling Publishing Co., Inc.

—The Call of the Wild. unabr. ed. 2002. (YA). pap. incl. audio compact disk (978-1-58472-221-2(5) , In Audio) Sound Room Pubs., Inc.

—The Call of the Wild: Prestwick House Literary Touchstone Edition. 2005. 100p. (YA). per. 3.99 (978-1-58049-584-4(2) , PWH5842) Prestwick Hse., Inc.

—The Call of the Wild - Spotlight Edition. Grudzina, Douglas, ed. 2005. 100p. (YA). per. 5.95 (978-1-58049-552-3(4) , PWH5524) Prestwick Hse., Inc.

—The Call of the Wild & Selected Short Stories. 2006. (Scholastic Classics Ser.). (Illus.). iv, 260p. (J). (gr. 9-12). 25.00 (978-0-531-16982-7(0) , Watts, Franklin) Scholastic Library Publishing.

—Jack London/the Call of the Wild. Carrillo, Fred, illus. 2005. 48p. (gr. 5-8). 25.50 (978-0-7910-9104-3(X)) Facts On File, Inc.

—To Build a Fire. abr. ed. 1999. mass mkt. 3.99 (978-0-8125-6993-3(8) , Tor Bks.) Doherty, Tom Assocs., LLC.

—White Fang. Vera, Ross, illus. 2002. (Great Illustrated Classics Ser.). 240p. (J). (gr. 3-8). 21.35 (978-1-57765-810-8(8) , ABDO & Daughters) ABDO Publishing Co.

—White Fang. 2003. 192p. (J). 4.99 (978-1-57759-566-3(1)) Dalmatian Pr.

—White Fang. (J). 9.95 (978-1-56156-306-7(4)) Kidsbooks, Inc.

—White Fang. (gr. 7-12). 2001. lib. bdg. 11.80 (978-0-613-39272-3(8)); 1999. lib. bdg. 29.20 (978-0-613-88083-1(8)) Tandem Library Bks.

—White Fang. Andreasen, Dan, illus. 2006. (Classic Starts Ser.). 160p. 4.95 (978-1-4027-2500-5(0)) Sterling Publishing Co., Inc.

—White Fang. 1999. 200p. (YA). reprint ed. pap. 9.95 (978-1-57002-095-7(7)) University Publishing Hse., Inc.

—White Fang: The Whole Story. 1999. (Whole Story Ser.). (Illus.). 248p. (J). (gr. 7-12). pap. 18.99 (978-0-670-88480-3(4) , Viking Juvenile) Penguin Group (USA) Inc.

—White Fang: With a Discussion of Resilience. Walker, Karen, illus. 2003. (Values in Action Illustrated Classics Ser.). 191p. (J). (978-1-59203-038-5(6)) Learning Challenge, Inc.

London, Jack & Access Matrix Staff. The Call of the Wild. adapted ed. (YA). (gr. 5-12). 8.50 (978-0-8359-0040-9(1)) Globe Fearon Educational Publishing.

London, Jonathan. Shawn & Keeper: Show & Tell. 2000. (Puffin Easy-to-Read Ser.). (978-0-606-18450-2(3)) Tandem Library Bks.

—Shawn & Keeper & the Birthday Party. 1999. (Easy-to-Read Ser.). (J). (978-0-606-19507-2(6)); lib. bdg. 11.80 (978-0-613-22368-3(3)) Tandem Library Bks.

Long, Ethan. Stop Kissing Me. 2007. 30p. (J). (ps). 10.99 (***978-0-316-00143-4(0))*** Little, Brown Bks. for Young Readers.

—Stop Kissing Me! 2007. 24p. bds. 7.99 (***978-0-316-01921-7(6))*** Little, Brown Bks. for Young Readers.

Long, Olivia. The Boy & the Dog. Long, Olivia, illus. Date not set. (Pets & Their People Ser.). (Illus.). 32p. (J). (gr. k-5). (978-1-880042-07-6(X)) Shelf-Life Bks.

Long-Vermillion, Jeri L. The Little Dog Who Taught the Lessons of Life. Lautzenheiser, Mary, ed. Long-Vermillion, Jeri L., photos by. 2001. (Illus.). 36p. (J). (ps-3). pap. 6.95 (978-0-9708533-0-1(0)) Pom Publishing.

Look at Pickles. 2002. (J). (978-1-58453-184-5(3)) Pioneer Valley Educational Pr., Inc.

Looking for Lewis. 1999. (Books to Go Ser.). (J). pap. (978-0-8136-7879-5(X)) Modern Curriculum Pr.

Losi, Carol A. Salt & Pepper at the Pike Place Market. Meissner, Amy, illus. 2004. 32p. (J). 15.95 (978-1-55868-800-1(5)); pap. 8.95 (978-1-55868-801-8(3)) Graphic Arts Ctr. Publishing Co. (West Winds Pr.).

Lost in the Woods. 2003. (J). (978-1-932570-12-0(8)) Literacy Footprints Inc.

Lottridge, Celia Barker. Berta: A Remarkable Dog. Myotte, Elsa, illus. 104p. (J). 2003. (gr. 1-4). pap. 4.95 (978-0-88899-469-1(9)); 2002. (gr. 2-5). 14.95 (978-0-88899-461-5(3)) Groundwood Bks. CAN. *Dist:* Perseus Distribution.

—Berta: A Remarkable Dog. 2002. (gr. 3-6). lib. bdg. 12.95 (978-0-613-62441-1(6)) Tandem Library Bks.

Lou Weber Staff, ed. Puppy: Wipe-off Activity Boards. 2004. 6p. (J). spiral bd., bds. 7.98 (978-1-4127-0039-9(6) , 7212201) Publications International, Ltd.

Loupy, Christophe. Hugs & Kisses. James, J. Alison, tr. from GER. Tharlet, Eve, illus. 2001. 36p. (J). (ps-k). 15.95 (978-0-7358-1484-4(8)) North-South Bks., Inc.

Lovascio, Jane. Casey & Bella Go to New York City. 2007. (J). 15.95 (***978-1-60131-007-1(2))*** Big Tent Bks.

Lovett, Darrell. Hi, I'm Alex. l.t. ed. 2006. (ENG., Illus.). 28p. per. 9.95 (***978-1-4327-0195-6(9))*** Outskirts Press, Inc.

—My Dog Tony. l.t. ed. 2006. (ENG., Illus.). 28p. per. 9.95 (***978-1-4327-0187-1(8))*** Outskirts Press, Inc.

Lovett, Darrell F. Darrell's Lake Franklin. 2007. 13.00 (***978-0-8059-8807-9(6))*** Dorrance Publishing Co., Inc.

Lowe, Ellen. Judge: The Angel Dog of Happiness. 2002. 40p. (J). pap. 12.00 (978-0-8059-5506-4(2)) Dorrance Publishing Co., Inc.

Lowell, Gloria Roth. Elana's Ears: Or How I Became the Best Big Sister in the World. Brooks, Karen Stormer, illus. 2000. 32p. (J). (ps-3). (978-1-55798-598-9(7) , 441-5987); pap. (978-1-55798-702-0(5) , 441-7025) American Psychological Assn. (Magination Pr.).

Lowrey, Janette Sebring. The Poky Little Puppy. Tenggren, Gustaf, illus. deluxe ed. Date not set. 23p. (J). (ps-2). reprint ed. (978-1-929566-56-3(5)) Cronies.

—The Poky Little Puppy. Tenggren, Gustaf, illus. (J). (gr. k-k). 2003. 32p. 10.99 (978-0-307-90328-0(1)); 2001. 24p. 2.99 (978-0-307-02134-2(3) , 98100); 2003. 32p. reprint ed. 8.99 (978-0-307-10328-4(5)) Random Hse. Children's Bks. (Golden Bks.).

—The Poky Little Puppy: Classic Edition. Tenggren, Gustaf, illus. Date not set. 23p. (J). (ps-1). reprint ed. (978-1-929566-50-1(6)) Cronies.

Lowry, Lois. Stay! Keeper's Story. 1999. (978-0-606-16584-6(3)); (gr. 3-6). lib. bdg. 13.00 (978-0-613-17863-1(7)) Tandem Library Bks.

—Stay Keeper's Story. annual Kelley, True, illus. 1999. 128p. (J). (gr. 4-7). 5.50 (978-0-440-41524-4(1) , Yearling) Random Hse. Children's Bks.

Lueck, Andrew. Chicabee. 2006. 32p. 16.95 (978-0-9774547-0-9(3)) Lueck Studios.

Luke, Melinda. The Green Dog. Manning, Jane K., illus. 2002. (Science Solves It! Ser.). 32p. (J). 4.99 (978-1-57565-115-6(7)) Kane Pr., The.

—The Green Dog. Manning, Jane K., illus. 2002. 32p. (J). (gr. 4-7). lib. bdg. 13.00 (978-0-613-53732-2(7)) Tandem Library Bks.

Lum, Bernice, illus. Pippin & Pudding. 2002. (Pippin Ser.). 32p. (J). (gr. k-3). (978-1-55337-418-3(5)) Kids Can Pr., Ltd.

—Pippin Takes a Bath. 2002. (Pippin Ser.). 32p. (J). (gr. k-3). (978-1-55337-420-6(7)) Kids Can Pr., Ltd.

Lundell, Margo. Lad is Lost. 1998. (Lad a Dog Ser.). (J). (978-0-606-13560-3(X)) Tandem Library Bks.

Luthardt, Kevin, tr. & illus. Larabee. Luthardt, Kevin, illus. 2004. 32p. (J). 15.95 (978-1-56145-300-9(5)) Peachtree Pubs., Ltd.

Lynn, Diana & Arroyo, George. Dog's Scratch: Los Perritos Se Rascan. 2003. (SPA & ENG.). (J). 4.95 (978-0-9745864-0-3(4)) Brookteam Corp.

Lynn, Diana & Arroyo, George, creators. Dogs Scratch: Les Chiens Se Grattent. l.t. ed. 2003. (FRE & ENG., Illus.). 6p. (J). 4.95 (978-0-9745864-2-7(0) , Shirt Tales) Brookteam Corp.

Lynn, Tammy. Happy Birthday Puppy: An I See Puppy Book. Stewart, Elaine, ed. Lynn, Tammy, illus. 2006. (Illus.). 12p. (J). bds. 6.99 (978-0-9774277-0-3(6) , 0-9774277-0-6) I See Puppy, LLP.

Maccarone, Grace. Mr. Rover Takes Over. Johnson, Meredith, illus. 2001. (Hello Reader! Ser.). 32p. (J). (ps-1). pap. 3.99 (978-0-439-20057-8(1) , Cartwheel Bks.) Scholastic, Inc.

—Mr. Rover Takes Over. 2001. (Illus.). (J). (978-0-606-21338-7(4)); 2000. lib. bdg. 11.80 (978-0-613-35537-7(7)) Tandem Library Bks.

MacDonald, James. Levi, Adventures of a Police Dog. 2005. 96p. (J). 16.95 (978-0-9716923-1-2(9)) Regency Hse., Ltd.

Mack, Lizzie. Hello, Spring! G Studios, illus. 2008. (Land of Milk & Honey Ser.). 12p. (J). bds. 7.99 (***978-1-4169-4933-6(X)*** , Little Simon Inspirations) Simon & Schuster Children's Publishing.

MacKenzie, Catherine. The Lonely Grey Dog at No. 6: Tammy & Jake Learn about Love & Loyalty. 2005. (Illus.). 157p. (J). mass mkt. (978-1-84550-103-7(9) , Christian Focus) Christian Focus Pubns.

Mackey, CousCous. Memoirs of a Dog. Stautberg, M. A. S., ed. Mayor, Michael, illus. 2002. 180p. (YA). (gr. 4-12). 21.95 (978-0-9701137-5-7(7)); pap. 15.95 (978-0-9701137-6-4(5)) Artistic Origins Pubns.

MacLachlan, Patricia & MacLachlan, Emily. Bittle. Yaccarino, Dan, illus. 2004. 40p. (J). (ps-3). 16.99 (978-0-06-000961-8(6)); lib. bdg. 16.89 (978-0-06-000962-5(4)) HarperCollins Pubs. (Cotler, Joanna Books).

Maddox, Tony & Wen, Dref. Ffred ar y Dwr. 2005. (WEL., Illus.). 28p. (978-1-85596-666-6(2)) Dref Wen.

Mahy, Margaret. Dashing Dog! 2002. (Illus.). 32p. (J). 15.89 (978-0-06-000457-6(6)) HarperCollins Pubs.

Maldonado, Helen. Big Dog & His Family. 2003. (J). pap. 8.00 (978-0-8059-5812-6(6)) Dorrance Publishing Co., Inc.

Mamatas, Emanuel. By My Side: A Tale of the Heart. 2000. (Illus.). 132p. (YA). (gr. 5-10). pap. 8.95 (978-0-9706247-4-1(3)) Ikarian Pr. Of America.

—By My Side: A Tale of the Heart. 2000. (Illus.). 132p. (YA). (gr. 7-12). pap. 8.95 (978-1-891231-20-9(0)) Word Association Pubs.

Mankell, Henning. A Bridge to the Stars. 2005. 160p. pap. (978-1-84270-439-4(7)) Andersen.

Manos, Helen. Samsara Dog. Vivas, Julie, illus. 2007. 48p. (J). (gr. 3 up). 17.95 (***978-1-933605-51-7(0))*** Kane/Miller Bk. Pubs., Inc.

Manuel, Lynn. The Trouble with Tilly Trumble. Greenseid, Diane, illus. 2006. 32p. (J). (ps-3). 16.95 (978-0-8109-5972-9(0)) Abrams, Harry N. , Inc.

Manus, Willard. A Dog Called Leka. 2007. (ENG.). 122p. pap. 7.99 (***978-0-9740551-3-8(1))*** Smith, Viveca Publishing.

Manzano, Sonia. No Dogs Allowed! Muth, Jon J., illus. 2005. (J). 27.95 incl. audio (978-0-8045-6927-9(4) , SAC6927); 29.95 incl. audio compact disk (978-0-8045-4101-5(9) , SACD4101) Spoken Arts, Inc.

Manzano, Sonia & Muth, Jon J. No Dogs Allowed! 2004. (Illus.). 32p. (J). (ps-3). 15.95 (978-0-689-83088-4(2) , Atheneum) Simon & Schuster Children's Publishing.

Manzur, Salvador S. Black Dog of Clearmountain. 2005. pap. 7.95 (978-0-533-15016-8(7)) Vantage Pr., Inc.

Margolis, Alysia. Sit! Stay! Sign! Miller, Paton, illus. 2007. 32p. (J). (***978-1-4257-5919-3(X))*** Margolis, Marion.

Margulies, Teddy Slater. Show-and-Tell Surprise. 2001. (ps-2). lib. bdg. 11.80 (978-0-613-33054-1(4)) Tandem Library Bks.

Margulies, Teddy Slater & Bridwell, Norman. Clifford & the Runaway Rabbit. Studio Orlando Staff, illus. 2001. (Clifford, the Big Red Dog Ser.). 32p. (J). (gr. k-2). pap. 3.99 (978-0-439-21361-5(4)) Scholastic, Inc.

—Clifford & the Show-and-tell Surprise. Studio Orlando Staff, illus. 2001. (Clifford, the Big Red Dog Ser.). 32p. (J). (gr. k-2). pap. 3.99 (978-0-439-21359-2(2)) Scholastic, Inc.

Markoe, Merrill. The Day My Dogs Became Guys. 2001. (978-0-606-20622-8(1)) Tandem Library Bks.

Marks, Nancy Freeman. Just As You Are: The Story of Leon & Sam. Buchheim, Su Jen, illus. 2003. 32p. (J). 15.00 (978-0-9722430-1-8(1)) Wave Publishing.

Marks, William C. Lawrence the Laughing Cookie Jar. Taylor, Josephine, illus. 2003. 16.95 (978-0-9715541-0-8(2)) MPC Pr. International.

Marlow, Herb. Bruno to the Rescue. Rainbolt, Juliette, illus. l.t. ed. 2000. 26p. (J). (gr. k-9). lib. bdg. 14.95 (978-0-9666858-6-2(5)) Four Seasons Bks., Inc.

—Jack, the Border Collie. Sadler, Steve, illus. 2001. 113p. (J). per. 16.95 (978-1-893595-09-5(9)) Four Seasons Bks., Inc.

—Jack the Border Collie. Sadler, Steve, illus. 2001. 113p. (J). lib. bdg. 24.95 (978-1-893595-10-1(2)) Four Seasons Bks., Inc.

—Sisters, Wild Dogs & Catfish Bait. Caffee, Julie, illus. 2005. 122p. (J). lib. bdg. 24.95 (978-1-893595-45-3(5)); per. 16.95 (978-1-893595-48-4(X)) Four Seasons Bks., Inc.

Marr, Ella J. The Adventures of Curtis & Grammy. 2006. 57p. pap. 12.95 (***978-1-4241-4743-4(3))*** PublishAmerica, Inc.

Marsh, Carole. The Adventure Diaries of Riley, the Rescue Dog!, 8 vols. 48p. (J). 2004. (gr. 1-4). pap. 5.95 (978-0-635-01151-0(4)); 2002. (Illus.). lib. bdg. 9.95 (978-0-635-01277-7(4)) Gallopade International.

Marsh, Carole. The Riddle of the Missing Puppies. 2006. 64p. (gr. 1-3). 14.95 (***978-0-635-06203-1(8))*** Gallopade International.

Marshall, James. Speedboat. 1999. (978-0-606-16540-2(1)) Tandem Library Bks.

Marshall, Mark. Imagine! 2006. (Illus.). 10p. (J). (gr. k-k). bds. 12.95 (978-0-7696-4647-3(6) , Gingham Dog Pr.) School Specialty Publishing.

Martelli, Dawn. Like Me. Wharton, Jennifer Heyd, illus. 2004. (J). (978-1-893516-01-4(6)) Our Child Pr.

Martin, Ann M. A Dog's Life. 192p. (J). 2007. pap. 5.99 (978-0-439-71700-7(0) , Scholastic Paperbacks); 2005. (gr. 4-7). pap. 16.99 (978-0-439-71559-1(8)) Scholastic, Inc.

—Kristy Thomas, Dog Trainer. 1998. (Baby-Sitters Club Ser.: No. 118). (J). (gr. 3-7). (978-0-606-13162-9(0)) Tandem Library Bks.

Martin, Anne E. Flip Flops for Paige. 2007. (Illus.). 48p. (J). per. 14.99 (***978-1-59879-243-0(1))*** Lifevest Publishing, Inc.

Martin, Paul. The Search for the Golden Bone: The Adventures of the Blacktail Kids. 2004. 235p. 15.95 (978-0-944875-96-4(3)) Doral Publishing, Inc.

Martin, Timothy. Legend of Boomer Jack. 2007. 113p. 16.95 (***978-1-4241-0886-2(1))*** PublishAmerica, Inc.

Marty the Dog Staff. I Am Found by Marty. 2004. (Illus.). 36p. (J). 3.99 (978-0-9746587-7-3(4) , Beacon Street Girls) B*tween Productions, Inc.

Martyr, Andrew & Martyr, Paula, illus. Space Dog Shock. 32p. (J). pap. 7.95 (978-0-14-038839-8(7)) Penguin Bks., Ltd. GBR. *Dist:* Trafalgar Square Publishing.

Masaurel, Claire. Ten Dogs in the Window. 2000. (978-0-606-18323-9(X)) Tandem Library Bks.

Mason, Adrienne. Secret Codes. Cupples, Pat, illus. 1999. 40p. (J). (ps-k). lib. bdg. 14.10 (978-0-613-21939-6(2)) Tandem Library Bks.

Mason, Adrienne & Cupples, Pat. The Carnival Caper. 2002. (Illus.). 39p. (J). (gr. 3-7). lib. bdg. 15.25 (978-0-613-57708-3(6)) Tandem Library Bks.

Masrud, Judy. Second Chance: A Tale of Two Puppies, 1 vol. Pool, Cathy, illus. 2006. 96p. (J). pap. 9.95 (978-0-9774142-0-8(5) , Birdseed Books for Kids) Birdseed Bks.

Masters, Susan Rowan. Night Journey to Vicksburg. Killcoyne, Hope L., ed. Smith, Duane A., illus. 2003. (Adventures in America Ser.). 74p. (J). 14.95 (978-1-893110-30-4(3)) Silver Moon Pr.

Masurel, C. & Halpern, S. No Tito No!/No No Titus! 2006. (Illus.). 32p. (J). 16.50 (978-0-7358-2074-6(0)); pap. 6.95 (978-0-7358-2075-3(9)) North-South Bks., Inc.

Masurel, Claire. A Cat & a Dog. Kolar, Bob, illus. 2003. 32p. (J). (ps). pap. 6.95 (978-0-7358-1780-7(4)) North-South Bks., Inc.

—A Cat & a Dog BB W/sound. 2007. (J). bds. 11.95 (978-0-7358-2118-7(6)) North-South Bks., Inc.

—Cat & Dog Bilingual BB W/sou. 2007. (J). bds. 11.95 (978-0-7358-2114-9(3)) North-South Bks., Inc.

—Diez Perros en la Tienda: Un Libro Para Contar. 2000. (SPA., Illus.). (J). 13.75 (978-0-606-18318-5(3)) Tandem Library Bks.

—Diez Perros en la Tienda: Un Libro para Contar. Moro, Elena, tr. from ENG. Paparone, Pamela, illus. 2000. (SPA.). 32p. (J). (ps-1). pap. 6.95 (978-0-7358-1303-8(5) , NS3643) North-South Bks., Inc.

—Domino. Walker, David, illus. 2007. (Super Sturdy Picture Book Ser.). 24p. (J). (gr. k-ps). 8.99 (978-0-7636-2862-8(X)) Candlewick Pr.

—Un Gato y un Perro. Antreasyan, Andres, tr. Kolar, Bob, illus. 2003. Tr. of Cat & a Dog. (SPA & ENG.). 32p. (J). (ps). pap. 6.95 (978-0-7358-1784-5(7)); 13.95 (978-0-7358-1835-4(5)) North-South Bks., Inc.

—No, Tito, No! No, No, Titus! Lasconi, Diego, tr. Halpern, Shari, illus. 1999. (SPA.). 32p. (J). (ps-1). 15.95 (978-0-7358-1208-6(X) , NS3699); pap. 6.95 (978-0-7358-1209-3(8) , NS3707) North-South Bks., Inc.

—Ten Dogs in the Window: A Countdown Book. Paparone, Pamela, illus. 2000. 32p. (J). (ps-1). pap. 6.95 (978-0-7358-1301-4(9)) North-South Bks., Inc.

—Ten Dogs in the Window: A Countdown Book. Paparone, Pamela, illus. 2000. (J). (ps-1). lib. bdg. 15.25 (978-0-613-27195-0(5)) Tandem Library Bks.

Matott, Justin, Jr., illus. The Tales of Mr. Murphy. 2005. 145p. (YA). 17.50 (978-1-889191-17-1(5)) Clove Pubns.

Matthews, Gill. Benito pasea y cuenta, Level P. Worsley, Belinda, illus. 2006. (Lightning Readers Ser.). 32p. (J). pap. 3.95 (978-0-7696-4208-6(X) , Gingham Dog Pr.) School Specialty Publishing.

—Ben's Counting Walk, Level P. Worsley, Belinda, illus. 2006. (Lightning Readers Ser.). 32p. (J). pap. 3.95 (978-0-7696-4178-2(4) , Gingham Dog Pr.) School Specialty Publishing.

Matthews, L. S. A Dog for Life. 2006. 176p. (J). (gr. 5). 16.99 (978-0-385-90381-3(2)); 14.95 (978-0-385-73366-3(6)) Random Hse. Children's Bks. (Delacorte Bks. for Young Readers).

Matthews/Worsley, Bill/Belinda. Ben's Counting Walk. 2005. (Illus.). 32p. (J). lib. bdg. 9.00 (***978-1-4242-0877-7(7))*** Fitzgerald Bks.

Mauner, Claudia & Smalley, Elisa. Zoe Sophia's Scrapbook: An Adventure in Venice. Mauner, Claudia, illus. 2003. (Illus.). 40p. (J). (ps-1). 14.95 (978-0-8118-3606-7(1)) Chronicle Bks. LLC.

Maxwell, Corey. The Mixed-Up Pup. Vitale, Steve & Turnbaugh, Paul, illus. 1999. 32p. (J). 12.95 (978-1-890145-03-3(3) , Paw Island Entertainment, Inc.) PetCare, Inc.

—The Paperdog Surprise. Turnbaugh, Paul & Vitale, Steve, illus. 2000. (Paw Island Presents...Ser.). 32p. (J). (gr. k-3). 12.95 (978-1-890145-06-4(8) , Paw Island Entertainment, Inc.) PetCare, Inc.

Maybarduk, Linda. James the Dancing Dog. Johnson, Gillian, illus. 2004. 24p. (J). (ps-3). 15.95 (978-0-88776-619-0(6)) Tundra Bks., Inc./Livres Toundra, Inc. CAN. *Dist:* Random Hse., Inc.

Maycock, Dianne. Lucky's Mountain. 2007. (Orca Young Readers Ser.). 112p. pap. (***978-1-55143-682-1(5))*** Orca Bk. Pubs.

Mayer, Mercer. A Boy, a Dog & a Frog. Mayer, Mercer, illus. 2003. (Illus.). 32p. (J). (ps). 5.99 (978-0-8037-2880-6(8) , Dial) Penguin Group (USA) Inc.

—Just Me & My Puppy. Mayer, Mercer, illus. 1998. (Little Critter Ser.). (Illus.). 24p. (J). (gr. k-k). pap. 3.99 (978-0-307-11937-7(8) , 11937, Random Hse. Bks. for Young Readers) Random Hse. Children's Bks.

—Play Ball. 2002. (Little Critter Ser.). (Illus.). 24p. (J). (ps-k). pap. 3.95 (978-1-57768-803-7(1)) School Specialty Publishing.

—Play Ball. 2001. (gr. k-3). lib. bdg. 11.80 (978-0-613-86831-0(5)) Tandem Library Bks.

Mayer, Mercer & Mayer, Marianna. A Boy, a Dog, a Frog & a Friend. Mayer, Mercer & Mayer, Marianna, illus. 2003. (Illus.). 32p. (J). (ps). 6.99 (978-0-8037-2882-0(4) , Dial) Penguin Group (USA) Inc.

Mayfield, Sue. Shoot! Cox, Ken, illus. 2001. (Blue Bananas Ser.). 48p. (J). (gr. 1-2). (978-0-7787-0847-6(0)); pap. (978-0-7787-0893-3(4)) Crabtree Publishing Co.

—Shoot! 2002. lib. bdg. 12.95 (978-0-613-52906-8(5)) Tandem Library Bks.

McAllister, Angela. Harry's Box. Jones, Jenny, illus. 2003. 32p. (J). (gr. k-3). 16.95 (978-1-58234-772-1(7) , Bloomsbury Children) Bloomsbury Publishing.

McCann, Jesse Leon. Case of the Disappeared Doggie. 2001. (gr. 3-6). lib. bdg. 11.80 (978-0-613-32375-8(0)) Tandem Library Bks.

—The Case of the Hollywood Hound. Fantascope Staff, illus. 2001. (Ace Ventura Chapter Book Ser.: Vol. 4). 64p. (J). (gr. 1-4). pap. 3.99 (978-0-439-20862-8(9)) Scholastic, Inc.

—Scooby-Doo & Santa's Bake Shop. del Sur, Duendes, illus. 2000. (Scooby-Doo Ser.). 24p. (J). (ps-3). pap. 5.99 (978-0-439-20999-1(4)) Scholastic, Inc.

—Scooby-Doo & the Alien Invaders. 2000. (Golden Book Ser.). (Illus.). 32p. (J). (ps-3). pap. 3.99 (978-0-307-10474-8(5) , 10474, Golden Bks.) Random Hse. Children's Bks.

—Scooby-Doo & the Alien Invaders. 2000. (gr. k-3). lib. bdg. 11.25 (978-0-613-33035-0(8)) Tandem Library Bks.

—Scooby-Doo & the Creepy Carnival. 1998. (Scooby-Doo 3-D Storybooks: No. 1). (Illus.). 16p. (J). (ps-3). pap. 5.99 (978-0-590-38654-8(9)) Scholastic, Inc.

—Scooby-Doo! & the Creepy Chef. 2005. (Illus.). 24p. (J). (978-1-4155-9752-1(9)) Scholastic, Inc.

—Scooby-Doo & the Fantastic Puppet Factory. 2000. (gr. k-3). lib. bdg. 11.25 (978-0-613-26852-3(0)) Tandem Library Bks.

—Scooby-Doo & the Halloween Hotel Haunt: A Glow in the Dark Mystery! del Sur, Duendes, illus. 1999. (Scooby-Doo Ser.). 24p. (J). (ps-3). pap. 5.99 (978-0-439-11768-5(2)) Scholastic, Inc.

—Scooby-Doo & the Tiki's Curse. 2004. (Scooby-Doo Ser.). (Illus.). 24p. (J). 3.50 (978-0-439-54604-1(4) , Scholastic Paperbacks) Scholastic, Inc.

—Scooby-Doo & the Weird Water Park. 2000. (Scooby-Doo Original Titles Ser.: No. 3). (Illus.). 32p. (J). (ps-3). 3.50 (978-0-439-17253-0(5)) Scholastic, Inc.

—Scooby-Doo & the Weird Water Park. 2000. (gr. k-3). lib. bdg. 11.25 (978-0-613-26855-4(5)) Tandem Library Bks.

—Scooby-Doo! & You. del Sur, Duendes, illus. 2001. (Collect the Clues Mystery Ser.). 60p. (J). (978-0-439-23156-5(6)) Scholastic, Inc.

—Scooby-Doo!TM & the Eerie Ice Monster. 2000. (Scooby-Doo Ser.). (Illus.). 24p. (J). (ps-3). 5.99 (978-0-439-20667-9(7)) Scholastic, Inc.

—Scooby-Doo!TM & the Fantastic Puppet Factory. 2000. (Scooby-Doo Original Titles Ser.: No. 4). (Illus.). 32p. (J). (ps-3). 3.50 (978-0-439-17254-7(3)) Scholastic, Inc.

McCann, Jesse Leon, adapted by. Scooby-Doo & the Alien Invaders. 2000. (Scooby-Doo Movie Storybooks). (Illus.). 32p. (J). (ps-3). 3.50 (978-0-439-17700-9(6)) Scholastic, Inc.

McCann, Jesse Leon & Markas, Jenny. Scooby-Doo & the Cyber Chase. del Sur, Duendes, illus. 2001. (Scooby-Doo Ser.). 96p. (J). pap. 3.99 (978-0-439-31391-9(0)) Scholastic, Inc.

McCarty, Jerry. A Dog to Treasure. 2003. 130p. per. 14.95 (978-1-59196-228-1(5)) Instantpublisher.com.

McCarty, Peter. Fabian Escapes. rev. ed. 2007. (Illus.). 40p. (J). (ps-1). 16.95 (***978-0-8050-7713-1(8)*** , Holt, Henry & Co. Bks. For Young Readers) Holt, Henry & Co.

—Hondo & Fabian. McCarty, Peter, illus. rev. ed. 2002. (Illus.). 32p. (J). (ps-1). 16.95 (978-0-8050-6352-3(8) , Holt, Henry & Co. Bks. For Young Readers) Holt, Henry & Co.

—Hondo & Fabian. 2007. (Illus.). 32p. (J). pap. 6.95 (***978-0-312-36747-3(3))*** Square Fish.

—Hondo & Fabian. unabr. ed. 2006. (Illus.). (J). (ps-3). 24.95 incl. audio (978-0-439-84905-0(5) , WHRA688); 29.95 incl. audio compact disk (978-0-439-84906-7(3) , WHCD688) Weston Woods Studios, Inc.

McCaughrean, Geraldine. Dog Days. 2005. (Illus.). pap. 24.95 incl. audio (978-0-7540-6290-5(2) , Chivers Children's Audio Bks.) BBC Audiobooks America.

McClear, Preston. Frannie & Pickles. Dollak, Nicholas, illus. 2003. 48p. (J). (gr. k-5). 16.95 (978-1-929084-13-5(7)) Malibu Bks. for Children.

McCloskey, John J. Warrior Ching. 2006. 179p. pap. 19.95 (978-1-4241-2389-6(5)) PublishAmerica, Inc.

McCombie, Karen. How to Be Goodish. Monks, Lydia, illus. 2007. (Indie Kidd Ser.). 160p. (J). (gr. 2-5). lib. bdg. 11.99 (978-0-440-42196-2(9) , Yearling) Random Hse. Children's Bks.

—Indie Kidd: How to Be Goodish. Monks, Lydia, illus. 2007. (Indie Kidd Ser.). 160p. (J). (gr. 2-5). 5.99 (978-0-440-42195-5(0) , Yearling) Random Hse. Children's Bks.

McConnell, Robert. Perfect Pals. Bradford, June, illus. 2004. (Napples Ser.). 34p. (J). (ps-k). pap. 7.95 (978-0-929141-72-5(5)) Napoleon Publishing/Rendezvous Pr. CAN. *Dist:* AtlasBooks Distribution.

McCorkle, Barbara. Brutis' New Friend. 2005. (Illus.). 23p. (J). per. 8.99 (978-1-932338-60-7(8)) Lifevest Publishing, Inc.

McCormack, Ann. Letters to Lucy from Kizzy. 2004. pap. 8.95 (978-0-533-14693-2(3)) Vantage Pr., Inc.

McDermott, Michael. Jingle Cats. 2004. (Illus.). 32p. (J). 9.99 (978-1-4003-0471-4(7)) Nelson, Thomas Inc.

McDonald, Megan. Beezy & Funnybone. Poydar, Nancy, illus. 2000. 48p. (J). (gr. 1-4). 15.99 (978-0-531-33211-5(X)); pap. 14.95 (978-0-531-30211-8(3)) Scholastic, Inc. (Orchard Bks.).

—Beezy & Funnybone. 2000. (J). (978-0-606-19481-5(9)) Tandem Library Bks.

McDonnell, Flora. Sparky. McDonnell, Flora, illus. 2004. (Illus.). 32p. (J). (gr. k-ps). 15.99 (978-0-7636-2208-4(7)) Candlewick Pr.

McDonnell, Patrick. The Gift of Nothing. 2005. (Illus.). 52p. (J). (ps-1). 14.99 (978-0-316-11488-2(X)) Little Brown & Co.

—Just Like Heaven: A Mutts Children's Book. 2006. (Illus.). 44p. (J). (ps-1). 14.99 (978-0-316-11493-6(6)) Little Brown & Co.

McElroy, Laurie. Drake & Josh: Chapter Book. 2007. (Teenick Ser.: No. 6). 112p. (J). pap. 4.99 (***978-0-439-91645-5(3))*** Scholastic, Inc.

McFall, Jessica & McFall, Ernest. Unselfish Love. l.t. ed. 2006. (ENG., Illus.). 28p. per. 9.95 (***978-1-4327-0076-8(6))*** Outskirts Press, Inc.

McFarland, Lyn Rossiter. Widget. McFarland, Jim, illus. ed. 2004. (J). (ps-k). spiral bd. (978-0-616-11121-5(5)); spiral bd. (978-0-616-11122-2(3)) Canadian National Institute for the Blind/Institut National Canadien pour les Aveugles.

—Widget. McFarland, Jim, illus. 2001. 32p. (J). (ps-1). 16.00 (978-0-374-38428-9(2) , Farrar, Straus & Giroux (BYR)) Farrar, Straus & Giroux.

—Widget. McFarland, Jim, illus. 2006. 32p. (J). pap. 5.95 (978-0-374-48386-9(8)) Macmillan.

—Widget & the Puppy. McFarland, Jim, illus. 2004. 32p. (J). 16.00 (978-0-374-38429-6(0) , Farrar, Straus & Giroux (BYR)) Farrar, Straus & Giroux.

McFarlane, Sheryl. This is the Dog. Wysotski, Chrissie, illus. 32p. (978-1-55041-551-3(4)) Fitzhenry & Whiteside, Ltd.

—This Is the Dog. Wysotti, Chrissie, illus. 2004. 32p. (J). (gr. k-2). (978-1-55041-806-4(8)) Fitzhenry & Whiteside, Ltd.

McGarrahan, Margaret. Nessie's California Adventures. Wright, Kathleen, illus. 2002. 55p. (J). (gr. k-4). pap. 12.50 (978-0-9672639-2-2(1)) Smith Lane Pubs.

—Nessie's Manhattan Holiday. Wright, Kathleen, illus. 2000. 57p. (J). (gr. k-5). pap. 12.50 (978-0-9672639-1-5(3)) Smith Lane Pubs.

McGeorge, Constance W. Boomer Goes to School. Whyte, Mary, illus. 1998. 32p. (J). (ps-1). pap. 6.95 (978-0-8118-2020-2(3)) Chronicle Bks. LLC.

—Boomer Va a la Escuela. 1999. Tr. of Boomer Goes to School. (SPA., Illus.). (J). 13.75 (978-0-606-18040-5(0)) Tandem Library Bks.

—Boomer's Big Surprise. Whyte, Mary, illus. 2005. 32p. (J). pap. 6.95 (978-0-8118-4907-4(4)) Chronicle Bks. LLC.

McGrath, Carmelita. The Dog-Next-Year. Keating, Nancy, illus. 2001. 32p. (J). (gr. k-4). pap. (978-1-894294-33-1(5) , Tuckamore Bks) Creative Bk. Publishing.

McGuirk, Leslie. Ho, Ho, Ho, Tucker! McGuirk, Leslie, illus. 2007. (Illus.). 30p. (J). (gr. k-k). pap. 4.99 (***978-0-7636-3663-0(0))*** Candlewick Pr.

—Tucker's Spooky Halloween. McGuirk, Leslie, illus. 2007. (Illus.). 28p. (J). (ps-k). bds. 7.99 (***978-0-7636-3181-9(7))*** Candlewick Pr.

McHenry, E. B. Has Anyone Seen Winnie & Jean? McHenry, E. B., illus. 2007. (Illus.). 32p. (J). (gr. k-2). 16.95 (978-1-58234-999-2(1)) Bloomsbury Publishing.

—Poodlena. McHenry, E. B., illus. 2005. (Illus.). 32p. (J). (ps-3). pap. 6.95 (978-1-58234-698-4(4) , Bloomsbury Children) Bloomsbury Publishing.

—Poodlena. 2004. (Illus.). (J). (978-1-58234-962-6(2)); 32p. (gr. 1 up). 16.95 (978-1-58234-824-7(3) , Bloomsbury Children) Bloomsbury Publishing.

McKay, Hilary. El Perro Viernes. (Barco de Vapor). (SPA.). (YA). (gr. 5-8). pap. (978-84-348-6214-2(X)) SM Ediciones.

McKay, Sindy. We Both Read-My Car Trip. Johnson, Meredith, illus. 2005. (We Both Read Ser.). 44p. (J). (gr. k up). 7.99 (978-1-891327-63-6(1)); pap. 3.99 (978-1-891327-64-3(X)) Treasure Bay, Inc.

McKenna, Colleen O'Shaughnessy. Doggone... Third Grade! Roth, Stephanie, illus. 2002. 80p. (J). (gr. 4-6). tchr. ed. 15.95 (978-0-8234-1696-7(8)) Holiday Hse., Inc.

McKibben, Marion A. Pearl the Rodeo Queen. 2006. 24p. (J). per. 12.00 (978-1-59971-711-1(5)) Aardvark Global Publishing.

McKissack, Patricia C. Tippy Lemmey. Keeter Susan, illus. ed. 2005. 60p. (J). lib. bdg. 15.00 (978-1-59054-919-3(8)) Fitzgerald Bks.

—Tippy Lemmey. Keeter, Susan, illus. 2003. (Ready-for-Chapters Ser.). 64p. (J). lib. bdg. 11.89 (978-0-689-85594-8(X) , Aladdin Library); (gr. 2-4). pap. 3.99 (978-0-689-85019-6(0) , Aladdin) Simon & Schuster Children's Publishing.

—Tippy Lemmey. 2003. (gr. 3-6). lib. bdg. 11.80 (978-0-613-61590-7(5)) Tandem Library Bks.

McLaughlin, Marilyn. Fierce Milly & the Amazing Dog. Shearing, Leonie, illus. 2001. 55p. (J). pap. 6.99 (978-0-7497-4239-3(9)) Egmont Bks., Ltd. GBR. *Dist:* Independent Pubs. Group.

McLean, Janet. Josh & Thumper. McLean, Andrew, illus. 2000. (Josh Ser.). 32p. (J). (ps-k). mass mkt. 4.95 (978-1-86448-491-5(8)) Allen & Unwin AUS. *Dist:* Independent Pubs. Group.

McMenemy, Sarah. Waggle! McMenemy, Sarah, illus. 2003. (Illus.). 32p. (J). (gr. k-k). 14.99 (978-0-7636-2059-2(9)) Candlewick Pr.

McMullan, Kate. Knight for a Day. 2007. (Dragon Slayers' Academy Ser.: No. 5). 112p. (J). (gr. 1-6). 24.21 (***978-1-59961-377-2(8))*** Spotlight.

McMullen, Jill. Toby & Friends: Therapy Dogs. 2007. (J). pap. 7.99 (***978-1-60247-241-9(6))*** Tate Publishing & Enterprises, L.L.C.

McNamara, Margaret. The First Day of School. Gordon, Mike, illus. 2005. (Ready-To-Read Ser.). 32p. (J). (ps-1). pap. 3.99 (978-0-689-86914-3(2)); lib. bdg. 11.89 (978-0-689-86915-0(0)) Simon & Schuster Children's Publishing. (Aladdin).

McNamee, Graham. Nothing Wrong with a Three-Legged Dog. 2001. (Illus.). (J). (978-0-606-21358-5(9)) Tandem Library Bks.

McNicholas, Shelagh, illus. Puppies in the Pantry. 1998. (Animal Ark Ser.: No. 3). (J). (gr. 3-5). (978-0-606-13131-5(0)) Tandem Library Bks.

McNicoll, Sylvia. Beauty Returns. 2006. 208p. (J). 17.95 (978-1-55005-149-0(0)) Fitzhenry & Whiteside, Ltd. CAN. *Dist:* F & W Pubns., Inc.

—Bringing up Beauty. 2000. (Illus.). 204p. (gr. 4-7). mass mkt. 5.95 (978-0-7736-7479-0(9)) Stoddart Kids CAN. *Dist:* Fitzhenry & Whiteside, Ltd.

—A Different Kind of Beauty. 2003. 224p. (J). pap. (978-1-55005-060-8(5)); 208p. (YA). (978-1-55005-059-2(1)) Fitzhenry & Whiteside, Ltd.

McNulty, Faith. If Dogs Ruled the World. Durrell, Julie, illus. 2002. (Hello Reader! Ser.). 32p. (J). (gr. 1-3). pap. 3.99 (978-0-439-08752-0(X) , Cartwheel Bks.) Scholastic, Inc.

—The Silly Story of a Flea & His Dog. Smith, Mavis, illus. 1999. (Hello Reader! Ser.). (J). (978-0-590-22860-2(9)) Scholastic, Inc.

McPhail, David M. El D_a Que el Perro Dijo Quiquiriqu_! 1999. (Coleccion "Hola, Lector" Ser.). (SPA., Illus.). 32p. (J). (gr. k-2). pap. 3.99 (978-0-439-07164-2(X) , SO3288, Scholastic en Espanol) Scholastic, Inc.

—Dia Que el Perro Dijo, Quiquiriqui! 1999. (Hello Reader! Ser.). (J). (978-0-606-16654-6(8)) Tandem Library Bks.

McPherson, Dottie. Kizzi's Special Friends. 2003. (Illus.). (J). 14.95 (978-0-9724979-0-9(0) , Advocate Hse.) A Cappela Publishing.

McSpadden, J. Walker. Famous Dogs in Fiction. 2005. reprint ed. pap. 31.95 (978-1-4179-0414-3(3)) Kessinger Publishing, LLC.

McVeigh, Mark. Clifford for President. LaPadula, Tom, illus. 2004. (Big Red Reader Ser.). 32p. (J). pap. 3.99 (978-0-439-69391-2(8)) Scholastic, Inc.

McVeity, Jen. Joe Cocker Spaniel. Axelsen, Stephen, illus. 1999. (Supa Doopers Ser.). 64p. (J). (978-0-7608-3291-2(9)) Sundance/Newbridge Educational Publishing.

—Joe Cocker Spaniel. 1999. (gr. 3-6). lib. bdg. 12.60 (978-0-613-30532-7(9)) Tandem Library Bks.

Meddaugh, Susan. Martha & Skits. 2005. (Illus.). 32p. (J). (gr. k-3). pap. 5.95 (978-0-618-60917-8(2) , Walter Lorraine) Houghton Mifflin Co. Trade & Reference Div.

—Martha Blah Blah. Meddaugh, Susan, illus. 2002. (Martha Ser.). (Illus.). (J). 13.79 (978-0-7587-3094-7(2)) Book Wholesalers, Inc.

—Martha Blah Blah. Meddaugh, Susan, illus. 1998. (Illus.). 32p. (J). (gr. k-3). pap. 6.95 (978-0-395-90118-2(9) , Walter Lorraine) Houghton Mifflin Co. Trade & Reference Div.

—Martha Habla. 1999. (SPA., Illus.). (J). (gr. k-2). pap. 6.95 (978-1-880507-55-1(2) , LC2799) Lectorum Pubns., Inc.

—Martha Speaks. Meddaugh, Susan, illus. 2002. (Martha Ser.). (Illus.). (J). 13.79 (978-0-7587-3096-1(9)) Book Wholesalers, Inc.

—Martha Walks the Dog. Meddaugh, Susan, illus. 2002. (Martha Ser.). (Illus.). (J). 22.45 (978-0-7587-3097-8(7)) Book Wholesalers, Inc.

—Martha Walks the Dog. (Illus.). 32p. (J). (gr. k-3). 2003. pap. 5.95 (978-0-618-38005-3(1)); 1998. tchr. ed. 15.00 (978-0-395-90494-7(3)) Houghton Mifflin Co. Trade & Reference Div. (Walter Lorraine).

—Martha Walks the Dog. 2003. (gr. k-3). lib. bdg. 14.10 (978-0-613-73023-5(2)) Tandem Library Bks.

—Perfectly Martha. 2004. (Illus.). 32p. (J). (gr. k-3). tchr. ed. 15.00 (978-0-618-37857-9(X) , Walter Lorraine) Houghton Mifflin Co. Trade & Reference Div.

Meek, Nora. Sniffing for Democracy. 2004. (J). per. (978-0-9753852-0-3(8)) PM, INK.

Meister, Cari. Tiny Goes Camping. Davis, Rich, illus. (Viking Easy-To-Read Ser.). 32p. (J). (ps-k). 2006. 13.99 (978-0-670-89250-1(5) , Viking Adult); 2000. pap. 3.99 (978-0-14-056741-0(0) , Puffin) Penguin Group (USA) Inc.

—Tiny Goes to the Library. Davis, Rich, illus. 2000. (Easy-to-Read Ser.). 32p. (J). (ps-2). pap. 3.99 (978-0-14-130488-5(X) , Puffin); 13.89 (978-0-670-88556-5(8) , Viking Juvenile) Penguin Group (USA) Inc.

—Tiny Goes to the Library. 2000. (Puffin Easy-to-Read Ser.). (978-0-606-18458-8(9)) Tandem Library Bks.

—Tiny on the Farm. Davis, Rich, illus. 2008. 32p. (J). (ps). 15.99 (***978-0-670-06246-1(4)*** , Viking Juvenile) Penguin Group (USA) Inc.

—The Tiny the Snow Dog. Davis, Rich, illus. 2001. (Easy-to-Read Ser.). 32p. (J). pap. 3.99 (978-0-14-056708-3(9) , Puffin) Penguin Group (USA) Inc.

—Tiny the Snow Dog. 2001. (gr. k-3). lib. bdg. 11.80 (978-0-613-64426-6(3)) Tandem Library Bks.

—Tiny, the Snow Dog: Level 1. Davis, Rich, illus. 2001. (Viking Easy-to-Read Ser.). 32p. (J). (gr. k-1). 13.99 (978-0-670-89117-7(7) , Viking Juvenile) Penguin Group (USA) Inc.

—Tiny's Bath. Davis, Rich, illus. 1999. (Viking Easy-to-Read Ser.). 32p. (J). (ps-2). 13.89 (978-0-670-87962-5(2) , Viking Juvenile); pap. 3.99 (978-0-14-130267-6(4) , Puffin) Penguin Group (USA) Inc.

—Tiny's Bath. Davis, Rich, illus. 1999. (J). (ps-ps). lib. bdg. 11.80 (978-0-613-15238-9(7)) Tandem Library Bks.

Menchen, Antonio Martinez. Fosco. (SPA.). 104p. (YA). (gr. 5-8). (978-84-204-4101-6(5) , AF1750) Alfaguara, Ediciones, S.A.- Grupo Santillana ESP. *Dist:* Lectorum Pubns., Inc.

Merello, Gwyn. La Piccola Pooch. 2003. 135p. (J). pap. 13.95 (978-0-595-29260-8(7)) iUniverse, Inc.

Meserve, Adria. No Room for Napoleon. 2006. (Illus.). 32p. (J). 16.00 (978-0-374-35536-4(3)) Farrar, Straus & Giroux.

Meyer, Franklyn E. Me & Caleb. Smith, Lawrence Beall, illus. 2006. (J). kivar 16.95 (***978-0-9789388-0-2(1)***) Hester Publishing.

—Me & Caleb Again. Liese, Charles, illus. 2006. (J). kivar 16.95 (***978-0-9789388-1-9(X)***) Hester Publishing.

Meyer, Kathy. Daisy & Digger. 2007. 41p. 15.95 (***978-1-4243-1507-9(7)***) Independent Publisher Services.

Meyers, Susan. Puppies! Puppies! Puppies! Walker, David, illus. 2005. 32p. (J). (ps-1). 15.95 (978-0-8109-5856-2(2)) Abrams, Harry N., Inc.

Michael, Livi. City of Dogs. 2007. 250p. (J). (gr. 5). 16.99 (***978-0-399-24356-1(9)*** , Putnam Juvenile) Penguin Group (USA) Inc.

Michaels, Vaughn. Dodi's Prince. Rogers, Jacqueline, illus. 2003. 96p. (J). (gr. 2-5). 15.99 (978-0-525-47034-2(4) , Dutton Juvenile) Penguin Group (USA) Inc.

Middleton, Charlotte. Do You Still Love Me? Middleton, Charlotte, illus. 2003. (Illus.). 32p. (J). (gr. k-1). 15.99 (978-0-7636-2254-1(0)) Candlewick Pr.

Miles, Ellen. Buddy. 2007. (Puppy Place Ser.: No. 5). 96p. (J). pap. 3.99 (***978-0-439-87410-6(6)***) Scholastic, Inc.

—Flash. 2007. (Puppy Place Ser.: No. 6). 96p. (J). pap. 3.99 (***978-0-439-87411-3(4)***) Scholastic, Inc.

—Goldie. 2006. (Puppy Place Ser.: Vol. 1). (Illus.). 80p. (J). pap. 4.99 (978-0-439-79379-7(3) , Scholastic Paperbacks) Scholastic, Inc.

—Patches. 2007. (Puppy Place Ser.). 80p. (J). pap. 3.99 (***978-0-439-87413-7(0)*** , Scholastic Paperbacks) Scholastic, Inc.

—Pugsley. 2008. (Owen & Mzee Ser.). 96p. (J). pap. 4.99 (***978-0-545-03455-5(8)*** , Scholastic Paperbacks) Scholastic, Inc.

—Rascal. 2007. (Puppy Place Ser.: No. 4). 80p. (J). pap. 3.99 (978-0-439-79382-7(3) , Scholastic Paperbacks) Scholastic, Inc.

—Scout. 2007. (Puppy Place Ser.: No. 7). 80p. (J). pap. 3.99 (***978-0-439-87412-0(2)*** , Scholastic Paperbacks) Scholastic, Inc.

—Shadow. 2007. (Little Apple Ser.: No. 3). 80p. (J). pap. 3.99 (978-0-439-79381-0(5)) Scholastic, Inc.

—Snowball. 2006. (Puppy Place Ser.: Vol. 2). (Illus.). 80p. (J). pap. 4.99 (978-0-439-79380-3(7) , Scholastic Paperbacks) Scholastic, Inc.

Milgrim, David. My Dog, Buddy. 2008. (J). pap. (***978-0-545-03593-4(7)***) Scholastic, Inc.

Militzer, Jill. Kizzy's Castle. 2005. 35p. 13.24 (978-1-4116-5538-6(9)) Lulu.com.

Millard, Anne. Puppies at Play. 2001. (Soft-to-Touch Bk.). (Illus.). 18p. (J). (ps-3). bds. 4.99 (978-0-7894-7401-8(8)) Dorling Kindersley Publishing, Inc.

Miller, Paula. One-Eyed Jack. Forrest, Chris, illus. 144p. (J). 2007. per. 8.95 (978-0-9769417-0-5(8)); 2006. 13.95 (978-0-9718348-8-0(1)) Blooming Tree Pr.

Miller, Sara Swan. Three More Stories You Can Read to Your Cat. 2000. (gr. k-3). lib. bdg. 14.10 (978-0-613-44269-5(5)) Tandem Library Bks.

—Three More Stories You Can Read to Your Dog. Kelley, True, illus. 48p. (J). 2001. (gr. 4-6). pap. 5.95 (978-0-618-15244-5(X)); 2000. (gr. k-3). tchr. ed. 15.00 (978-0-395-92293-4(3)) Houghton Mifflin Co. Trade & Reference Div.

—Three Stories You Can Read to Your Teddy Bear. Kelley, True, tr. Kelley, True, illus. 2004. 48p. (J). (gr. k-3). tchr. ed. 15.00 (978-0-618-30397-7(9)) Houghton Mifflin Co. Trade & Reference Div.

Miller, Scott. Prairie Whispers. 2006. 99p. pap. 14.95 (***978-1-4241-4790-8(5)***) PublishAmerica, Inc.

Mills, Enos A. Stories of Scotch: Large Print Edition. l.t. ed. 2006. (Illus.). 43p. pap. 9.50 (978-1-928878-36-0(9)) Temporal Mechanical Pr.

Mills, Eva. Simon & the Aliens. 1999. (gr. 3-6). lib. bdg. 12.60 (978-0-613-30734-5(8)) Tandem Library Bks.

Mills, Lauren A. The Dog Prince. Mills, Lauren A. & Nolan, Dennis, illus. 2001. 32p. (J). (gr. 1-3). 15.95 (978-0-316-57417-4(1)) Little, Brown Bks. for Young Readers.

Minarik, Else Holmelund. Cat & Dog. Langdo, Bryan, illus. 2005. (My First I Can Read Bks.). 32p. (J). (ps up). 14.99 (978-0-06-074247-8(X)); lib. bdg. 15.89 (978-0-06-074248-5(8)) HarperCollins Pubs.

Miner, Audrey. Rebbie. 2006. pap. 10.00 (***978-1-4257-2710-9(7)***) Xlibris Corp.

Mini Cuentos: Hazanas de Baltazar, Pipo, el Perro Fiel.Tr. of Mini Faiy Tales: Pipo, the Loyal Dog. (SPA.). (J). (gr. k-4). 4.98 (978-970-607-622-9(0)) Larousse, Ediciones, S. A. de C. V. MEX. *Dist:* Continental Bk. Co., Inc.

The Misadventures of Wags & Freckles. (J). 4.00 (978-1-56230-043-2(1)) Syndistar, Inc.

The Missing Puppy. 2006. (J). (***978-1-932570-56-4(X)***) Literacy Footprints Inc.

Mitchell, Melanie. Mommy & Baby: Pets. 2006. (Illus.). 8p. (J). bds. 6.95 (978-0-8027-8982-2(X)) Walker & Co.

Mitchell, Sharon Kay, VIII. What Great Thing Can Patches Do? l.t. ed. 2005. (Illus.). 40p. (J). 12.95 (978-0-9772222-0-9(9)) KOBZ.

Mitzo Thompson, Kim. My Family. 2006. (Dual Language Readers Ser.). 32p. (J). pap., pap. 4.99 incl. audio compact disk (978-0-7696-4613-8(1)) School Specialty Publishing.

Mobley, Cyn. A Very Airey Christmas. 2004. pap. 16.00 (978-0-9724136-0-2(X)) Greyhound Bks.

Modica, Cathy & Van Eyck, Laura. Niik & Bling: The Friendship Begins. Modica, Cathy, photos by. l.t. ed. 2005. (Illus.). 40p. (J). 19.95 (978-0-9762466-0-2(0)) Wholesome Puppy Tales.

Mohr, Michale & Geer, Debi. Stephy Lynns' My Puppy. Archambault, A. J., illus. l.t. ed. 2002. 22p. per. 9.95 (978-0-9719597-8-1(1)) Thornton Publishing.

Mokosso, Henry Efesoa. One Child - One Wish: The Agony of a Single Child Family. 2006. 71p. per. 8.95 (978-1-59824-351-2(9)) E-BookTime LLC.

Monninger, Joseph. Baby. 2007. 204p. (YA). (gr. 8 up). 16.95 (***978-1-59078-502-7(9)*** , Front Street) Boyds Mills Pr.

Montardre, Helene. The Cat & the Dog. 2003. (Illus.). 8p. (J). bds. 7.95 (978-1-58728-483-0(9) , Two Can Publishing) T&N Children's Publishing.

Montgomery, R. A. The Haunted House. 2007. (Choose Your Own Adventure Ser.). (Illus.). 64p. (J). pap. 5.99 (***978-1-933390-51-2(4)***) Chooseco LLC.

Montgomery, Rutherford G. Broken Fang. Hunt, Lynn Bogue, illus. 2004. (Classic Ser.). 312p. (gr. 4-7). pap. 15.95 (978-0-87004-416-8(8)) Caxton Pr.

Montparker, Carol. Polly & the Piano. 2004. (Illus.). 40p. 19.95 incl. audio compact disk (978-1-57467-093-6(X) , 157467093X, Amadeus Press) Leonard, Hal Corp.

Moody-Luther, Jacqui. Word World Dog. 2005. NAp. 11.95 (978-0-7624-2462-7(1)) Running Pr. Bk. Pubs.

Mooney, Margaret. Cat & Dog. 2001. (gr. k-3). lib. bdg. 11.80 (978-0-613-33346-7(2)) Tandem Library Bks.

Moore, Stephen. Skin & Bone. mass mkt. 8.99 (978-0-340-70455-4(1) , Hodder & Stoughton) Hodder General Publishing Division GBR. *Dist:* Trafalgar Square Publishing.

Moost, Nele. El Perro en la Luna. Lopez, L. Rodriguez, tr. Becker, Jutta, illus. 2002. (Rosa y Manzana Ser.). (SPA.). 24p. 16.95 (978-84-89804-35-7(4) , LG30440) Loguez Ediciones ESP. *Dist:* Baker & Taylor Bks., Lectorum Pubns., Inc.

More Trouble. 2006. (J). (***978-1-932570-58-8(6)***) Literacy Footprints Inc.

Morgan, Allen. Quackadack Duck. Beder, John, illus. 2003. 32p. (J). (ps-2). lib. bdg. 18.95 (978-1-55037-761-3(2)) Annick Pr., Ltd. CAN. *Dist:* Firefly Bks., Ltd.

Morgan, Clay. The Boy Who Spoke Dog. (J). (gr. 4-7). 2005. 176p. pap. 5.99 (978-0-14-240343-3(1) , Puffin); 2003. 192p. 15.99 (978-0-525-47159-2(6) , Dutton Juvenile) Penguin Group (USA) Inc.

Morgan, Clay. The Boy Who Spoke Dog: Return to Dog Island. 2007. 176p. (J). (gr. 4). 16.99 (***978-0-525-47401-2(3)*** , Dutton Juvenile) Penguin Group (USA) Inc.

Morgan, Margaret. Wuffy the Wonder Dog. Knight, Vanessa, illus. 2005. 60p. (J). per. 9.95 (978-1-59594-034-6(0) , Wingspan Pr.) WingSpan Publishing.

Morgan, Michaela. Silly Sausage & the Little Visitor. Shulman, Dee, illus. 2006. (Read-It! Chapter Books). (J). 21.26 (978-1-4048-2735-6(8)) Picture Window Bks.

—Silly Sausage & the Spooks. Shulman, Dee, illus. 2006. (Read-It! Chapter Books). (J). 21.26 (978-1-4048-2736-3(6)) Picture Window Bks.

—Silly Sausage Goes to School. Shulman, Dee, illus. 2006. (Read-It! Chapter Books). (J). 21.26 (978-1-4048-2738-7(2)) Picture Window Bks.

—Silly Sausage in Trouble. Shulman, Dee, illus. 2006. (Read-It! Chapter Books). (J). 21.26 (978-1-4048-2737-0(4)) Picture Window Bks.

Morgan, Ruth. Sglod & Chips: A Story. Carpenter, Suzanne, illus. 2002. 30p. pap. 12.95 (978-1-85902-807-0(1)) Beekman Bks., Inc.

—Sglod & the Sand Dragon. Carpenter, Suzanne, illus. 2000. 32p. pap. 12.95 (978-1-85902-831-5(4)) Beekman Bks., Inc.

Morgan, Ruth & Carpenter, Suzanne. Sglod at Sea. 2001. (Illus.). 32p. pap. 12.95 (978-1-85902-937-4(X)) Beekman Bks., Inc.

Morina, Frances. Tiko at the Seashore. Morina, Frances, illus. Morina, Joseph A., photos by. l.t. ed. 1998. (Illus.). 24p. (J). (ps-2). pap. 3.95 (978-0-9664657-0-9(9) , Redbird Bks.) Redbird Enterprises.

Morpurgo, Michael. It's a Dog's Life. Allibone, Judith, illus. 2007. (J). (***978-0-374-33620-2(2)***) Farrar, Straus & Giroux.

Morris, Garvin. Dump Dog. Morris, Garvin, illus. 2007. 32p. (J). (ps-2). 15.95 (***978-1-60108-012-7(3)***) Red Cygnet Pr.

Moscovich, Rotem & Saric, Lazar. Curious George Snowy Day. 2007. (Illus.). 24p. (J). (gr. k-ps). 3.99 (***978-0-618-80043-8(3)***) Houghton Mifflin Co.

Moss, Miriam. Wiley & Jasper. Bucker, Jutta, tr. Bucker, Jutta, illus. 2003. (J). 25p. pap. (978-1-59336-061-0(4)); 32p. 15.95 (978-1-59336-060-3(6)) Mondo Publishing.

A Mother Dog & Her Puppies. 2006. (J). per. (***978-1-932570-79-3(9)***) Literacy Footprints Inc.

Mouse Works Staff. Cars, Boats, Planes & Trains. 2001. 48p. (J). 12.99 (978-0-7364-0114-2(8)) Mouse Works.

—Goofy. 1998. (Friendly Tales Ser.). (Illus.). 10p. (J). (ps). 6.99 (978-1-57082-928-4(4)) Mouse Works.

—The Lady & the Tramp: We're All Different. 1999. (Illus.). (J). 2.99 (978-0-7364-0044-2(3)) Mouse Works.

—The Lady & the Tramp Easy Reader. 1998. 48p. (J). 3.95 (978-0-7364-0039-8(7)) Mouse Works.

—Lucky Classic Friendly Tale. 1999. 10p. (J). 6.99 (978-0-7364-1010-6(4)) Mouse Works.

—Mulan - Lady & the Tramp, 2. 75th anniv. ed. 1998. (Illus.). (ps-3). (978-0-7364-0089-3(3)) Mouse Works.

—102 Dalmatians. 2000. 32p. (J). 3.99 (978-0-7868-4464-7(7)) Disney Pr.

—102 Dalmatians. 2000. 10p. (J). pap. 4.99 (978-0-7364-0236-1(5)) Microsoft Pr.

Mowat, Farley. The Dog Who Wouldn't Be. (J). 21.95 (978-0-89190-819-7(6)) Amereon LTD.

—The Dog Who Wouldn't Be. 1999. mass mkt. (978-0-553-20951-8(5)) Random Hse., Inc.

Moyer, Marshall M. Rollo Bones, Canine Hypnotist. Moyer, Marshall M., illus. 2004. (Illus.). 32p. (J). (gr. k-3). 14.95 (978-1-883672-65-2(1) , Tricycle Pr.) Ten Speed Pr.

Muffin Is Trapped, 6 vols., Pack. 16p. (gr. 2 up). 35.00 (978-0-7635-9235-6(8)) Rigby Education.

Muir, John. Stikeen: An Adventure with a Dog & a Glacier. 2003. (gr. k-3). lib. bdg. 12.95 (978-0-613-88678-9(X)) Tandem Library Bks.

Muncy, Brenda. Truly Lucky. 2006. (ENG.). 32p. per. 16.49 (***978-1-4259-6289-0(0)***) AuthorHouse.

Munoz-Kiehne, Marisol, text. Big Bad News! Terrorism, Hate Crime, Gang Violence, War. 2001. (SPA.). 2.95 (978-1-56123-160-7(6) , BBNC) Centering Corp.

Murdocca, Sal. Lucy Takes a Holiday. Murdocca, Sal, illus. 1998. (Illus.). 32p. (J). (gr. 1-5). 15.95 (978-1-57255-560-0(2)) Mondo Publishing.

Murphy, Barbara Beasley. Annie & the Animals. 2000. 112p. (gr. 4-7). pap. 9.95 (978-0-595-00443-0(1) , Backinprint.com) iUniverse, Inc.

Murphy, Julie. Barks & Bytes by Mulligan. McArtor, Barbara, illus. 2006. (ENG.). 40p. per. 21.99 (***978-1-4208-9187-4(1)***) AuthorHouse.

Murphy, Mary. Comet the Fairy Dog. (Illus.). 32p. pap. 8.99 (***978-0-09-943932-5(8)*** , Red Fox) Random Hse. Children's Bks. GBR. *Dist:* Trafalgar Square Publishing.

Murphy, Peg. I Can Do Anything. l.t. ed. 2006. (ENG., Illus.). 28p. per. 9.95 (***978-1-4327-0175-8(4)***) Outskirts Press, Inc.

Murray, Guillermo. Que, Miedo! rev. ed. 2006. (Castillo del Terror Ser.). (SPA.). 112p. (J). (gr. 2-6). pap. 6.95 (978-970-20-0338-0(5)) Castillo, Ediciones, S. A. de C. V. MEX. *Dist:* Macmillan.

Mustaine Hettinger, Cynthia. Penelope, the Busy Hen. Ramsey, Jayne, illus. 2004. (Electra's Acres Ser.: Bk. 3). 32p. (J). per. 14.95 (978-0-9746330-4-6(6)) Anton Berkshire Publishing.

My Dog & Other Stories, 6 Packs. (Story Steps Ser.). (gr. k-2). 48.00 (978-0-7635-9833-4(X)) Rigby Education.

My Dog Rusty, 6 Packs. (ps-2). 27.00 (978-0-7635-9464-0(4)) Rigby Education.

My Name Is Baxter, Bk. 1. 2001. (J). lib. bdg. 24.95 (978-0-9715864-0-6(3) , Bax-1) Baxter & Friends.

My Way Sally: Evaluation Guide. 2006. (J). (978-1-55942-418-9(4)) Marsh Media.

Mycek-Wodecki, Anna. Minutka: The Bilingual Dog. 2007. (POL & ENG., Illus.). 48p. (J). (ps). 9.95 (***978-1-84059-504-8(3)***) Milet Publishing.

Myers, Bill. Phantom of the Haunted Church. 1998. (Bloodhounds, Inc. Ser.: Vol. 3). (Illus.). 128p. (J). (gr. 3-8). pap. 5.99 (978-1-55661-892-5(1)) Bethany Hse. Pubs.

Myers, Walter Dean. The Blues of Flats Brown. Laden, Nina, illus. 32p. (J). (gr. k-3). 2005. pap. 6.95 (978-0-8234-1679-0(8)); 2000. tchr. ed. 16.95 (978-0-8234-1480-2(9)) Holiday Hse., Inc.

—Blues of Flats Brown. 2002. (Live Oak Readalong Ser.). (Illus.). (J). pap. 18.95 incl. audio compact disk (978-1-59112-404-7(2)); pap. 16.95 incl. audio (978-0-87499-940-2(5)) Live Oak Media.

—The Blues of Flats Brown. Laden, Nina, illus. 2002. 28.95 incl. audio compact disk (978-1-59112-424-5(7)); pap. 39.95 incl. audio compact disk (978-1-59112-601-0(0)); (J). 25.95 incl. audio (978-0-87499-941-9(3)); (J). pap., tchr.'s planning gde. ed. 37.95 incl. audio (978-0-87499-942-6(1)) Live Oak Media.

—Three Swords for Granada. Speirs, John, illus. 2002. 112p. (J). (gr. 4-6). tchr. ed. 15.95 (978-0-8234-1676-9(3)) Holiday Hse., Inc.

The Mystery of the Missing Dog, 6 vols. (Woodland Mysteriestm Ser.). 133p. (gr. 3-7). 42.50 (978-0-7802-7930-8(1)) Wright Group, The.

Nadja. Perro Azul. (SPA.). 40p. (978-84-95150-30-1(1)); (978-84-95150-40-0(9)) Corimbo, Editorial S.L.

Nagler, Michelle H. Meet Big Foot. 2002. (gr. k-3). lib. bdg. 11.80 (978-0-613-54285-2(1)) Tandem Library Bks.

A name for a Dog: Individual Title Six-Packs. (gr. 1-2). 25.00 (978-0-7635-9127-4(0)) Rigby Education.

Nanette. Sunny the Orange Puppy. 2004. (Life on Granny's Farm Ser.). (J). 12.95 (978-0-9741269-6-8(9)) St. Bernard Publishing, LLC.

Nanny & I Meet Odie. 2006. (J). lib. bdg. 18.99 (978-0-9724394-1-1(2)) Sylables.

Napoli, Donna Jo. Partners. 2001. (Angelwings Ser.: No. 15). 80p. (J). (gr. 2-5). pap. 7.95 (978-0-689-83972-6(3) , Aladdin) Simon & Schuster Children's Publishing.

—Playing Games. Ben-Ami, Doron & Klementz-Harte, Lauren, illus. 2000. (Angelwings Ser.: No. 8). 80p. (J). (gr. 2-5). mass mkt. 7.95 (978-0-689-83208-6(7) , Aladdin) Simon & Schuster Children's Publishing.

—Playing Games. 2000. (Angelwings Ser.: No. 8). (Illus.). (J). (978-0-606-20386-9(9)) Tandem Library Bks.

Nara, Yoshitomo. The Lonesome Puppy. 2008. (J). 17.99 (978-0-8118-5640-9(2)) Chronicle Bks. LLC.

Nastasi, Michael. It's a Dog's Life. 2006. (Illus.). 96p. 14.95 (978-0-8118-4981-4(3)) Chronicle Bks. LLC.

Naylor, Phyllis Reynolds. Saving Shiloh. 144p. (J). 1999. (Shiloh Ser.: No. 3). (gr. 4-7). reprint ed. pap. 5.99 (978-0-689-81461-7(5)); 2nd ed. 2006. (Illus.). (gr. 3-7). pap. 5.99 (978-1-4169-1422-8(6)) Simon & Schuster Children's Publishing. (Aladdin).

—Saving Shiloh. 1999. (978-0-606-14310-3(6)); (Shiloh Ser.: No. 3). (J). (gr. 3-6). lib. bdg. 13.55 (978-0-613-12073-9(6)) Tandem Library Bks.

—Saving Shiloh. l.t. ed. 2002. 193p. (J). 22.95 (978-0-7862-3713-5(9)) Thorndike Pr.

—Shiloh. (SPA.). 146p. (YA). (gr. 5-8). (978-968-16-5805-2(1) , FC0086) Fondo de Cultura Economica MEX. *Dist:* Lectorum Pubns., Inc.

—Shiloh. l.t. ed. 2000. (Shiloh Ser.: No. 1). 155p. (J). (gr. 4-7). lib. bdg. 27.95 (978-1-58118-058-9(6) , 23472) LRS.

—Shiloh. 144p. (J). (Shiloh Ser.: No. 1). (gr. 4-7). pap. 4.99 (978-0-8072-8330-1(4)); No. 1. 2004. (gr. 3-7). pap. 29.00 incl. audio (978-0-8072-8329-5(0) , YA164SP) Random Hse. Audio Publishing Group. (Listening Library).

—Shiloh. Moser, Barry, illus. 2000. (Shiloh Ser.: No. 1). 144p. (J). (gr. 3-7). pap. 5.99 (978-0-689-83582-7(5) , Aladdin) Simon & Schuster Children's Publishing.

—Shiloh. movie tie-in ed. 2000. (Shiloh Ser.: No. 6). (Illus.). 144p. (J). (gr. 4-7). pap. 5.99 (978-0-689-83583-4(3) , Aladdin) Simon & Schuster Children's Publishing.

—Shiloh. 2000. (gr. 3-6). lib. bdg. 14.15 (978-0-613-73274-1(X)); (J). (978-0-606-19724-3(9)); (gr. 3-6). lib. bdg. 14.15 (978-0-613-30125-1(0)) Tandem Library Bks.

—Shiloh Season. unabr. ed. 2004. (Shiloh Ser.: No. 2). 120p. (J), (gr. 3-7). pap. 29.00 incl. audio (978-0-8072-8707-1(5) , YA242SP, Listening Library) Random Hse. Audio Publishing Group.

—Shiloh Season. Moser, Barry, illus. (Shiloh Ser.: No. 2). 128p. (J). 1999. (gr. 3-7). pap. 5.99 (978-0-689-82931-4(0)); 1998. (gr. 4-7). pap. 5.99 (978-0-689-80646-9(9)) Simon & Schuster Children's Publishing. (Aladdin).

—Shiloh Season. 1999. (gr. 3-6). lib. bdg. 13.55 (978-0-613-90607-4(1)); 1998. (Shiloh Ser.: No. 2). (J). (gr. 4-7). (978-0-606-13085-1(3)) Tandem Library Bks.

—Shiloh Trilogy. (J). 2000. 432p. (gr. 3-7). pap. 16.99 (978-0-689-01525-0(9) , Aladdin); 1998. (Shiloh Ser.: Nos. 1-3). (gr. 4-7). 35.00 (978-0-689-82327-5(4) , Atheneum) Simon & Schuster Children's Publishing.

Nebel, Laurel. Stop That Thief! 1999. 186p. (J). (gr. 3-5). 9.99 (978-0-88092-474-0(8) , 4748) Royal Fireworks Publishing Co.

Neftzger, Amy. All That the Dog Ever Wanted. 2005. (Illus.). 32p. (J). lib. bdg. 21.99 (978-0-9746296-1-2(8) , FOG104) Fields of Gold Publishing, Inc.

Neimark, Susie. The Adventures of Sunny & the Chocolate Dog: Sunny & the Chocolate Dog Go to the Beach. Hammerstrom, Kent, illus. 2003. per. (978-0-9725945-1-6(5)) Sunny & The Chocolate Dog, LLC.

—The Adventures of Sunny & the Chocolate Dog: Sunny & the Chocolate Dog Go to the Doctor. Hammerstrom, Kent, illus. 2003. per. (978-0-9725945-2-3(3)) Sunny & The Chocolate Dog, LLC.

—The Adventures of Sunny & the Chocolate Dog: Sunny Meets Her Baby Sister. Hammerstrom, Kent, illus. 2003. per. (978-0-9725945-0-9(7)) Sunny & The Chocolate Dog, LLC.

Nettrour, Nelani. Welcoming Garcon Vol. 1: Dog Tails. Nettrour, Heather, illus. 2002. (J). pap. 11.95 (978-1-929381-07-4(7) , 07, Third Millennium Publishing) Sci Fi-Arizona, Inc.

C
D

Nettrour, Nelani A. All about Krammer: Dogtails 2. Nettrour, Heather, illus. 2005. 100p. pap. 11.95 (978-1-932657-30-2(4)) Third Millennium Pubns.

Neusner, Dena Wallenstein. Clifford's Touch & Feel Day. Lloyd, Gita & Binder, Eric, illus. 2003. (Clifford Ser.). 5p. (J). bds. 9.99 (978-0-439-44936-6(7)) Scholastic, Inc.

Neveloff, Arlene. Jackson Finds a Home. Bolam, Emily, illus. 2007. (I'm Going to Read Ser.). 32p. (J). (gr. 2-3). pap. 3.95 (***978-1-4027-3078-8(0)***) Sterling Publishing Co., Inc.

A New Friend at the Beach. 2007. (J). per. (***978-1-932570-87-8(X)***) Literacy Footprints Inc.

Newbery, Linda & Ripper, Georgie. A Dog Called Whatnot. 2006. (Red Bananas Ser.). (Illus.). (J). 48p. pap. (978-0-7787-1094-3(7)); 46p. (978-0-7787-1078-3(5)) Crabtree Publishing Co.

Newell, Jeff. Skimper-Scamper. Hranilovich, Barbara J., illus. 2005. (Green Light Readers Level 2 Ser.). 24p. (J). 12.95 (978-0-15-205166-2(X)); pap. 3.95 (978-0-15-205165-5(1)) Harcourt Children's Bks. (Green Light Readers).

Newgarden, Mark & Cash, Megan Montague. Bow-Wow attracts Opposites. 2008. (Illus.). 18p. (J). bds. 4.95 (***978-0-15-205847-0(8)*** , Red Wagon Bks.) Harcourt Children's Bks.

—Bow-Wow Bugs a Bug. 2007. (Illus.). 56p. (J). (ps-2). 12.95 (978-0-15-205813-5(3)) Harcourt Trade Pubs.

—Bow-Wow hears Things. 2008. (Illus.). 18p. (J). bds. 4.95 (***978-0-15-205841-8(9)*** , Red Wagon Bks.) Harcourt Children's Bks.

—Bow-Wow Naps by Number. 2007. (Illus.). 18p. (J). (ps). bds. 4.95 (***978-0-15-205835-7(4)*** , Red Wagon Bks.) Harcourt Children's Bks.

—Bow-Wow Orders Lunch. 2007. (Illus.). 18p. (J). (ps). bds. 4.95 (***978-0-15-205829-6(X)*** , Red Wagon Bks.) Harcourt Children's Bks.

Newman, Leslea & Oller, Erika. Dogs, Dogs, Dogs! 2002. (Illus.). 32p. (J). (ps-3). 16.00 (978-0-689-84492-8(1)) Simon & Schuster Children's Publishing.

Newsome, Jill. Night Walk. Munoz, Claudio, illus. 2003. (J). (gr. k-3). 15.00 (978-0-618-32458-3(5) , Clarion Bks.) Houghton Mifflin Co. Trade & Reference Div.

Nez, John A., illus. One Smart Cookie. 2006. 32p. (J). lib. bdg. 15.95 (978-0-8075-6099-0(5)) Whitman, Albert & Co.

Nguyen, Duke & Kuon, Vuthy. Elmer Dog. 2004. 29p. 15.95 (978-0-9675803-0-2(7)) Providence Publishing.

Nichols, S. L. How Minnie Came to Be Queen. 2006. (Illus.). pap. 11.99 (***978-1-4259-6238-8(6)***) AuthorHouse.

Nielsen-Fernlund, Susin. Hank & Fergus. Laliberte, Louise-Andree, illus. 2005. 32p. (J). (ps-2). 7.95 (978-1-55143-343-1(5)) Orca Bk. Pubs. USA.

Nielsen, Susin. Hank & Fergus. Laliberte, Louise-Andree, illus. 2003. 32p. (J). (ps-2). 16.95 (978-1-55143-245-8(5)) Orca Bk. Pubs. USA.

Niland, Deborah. When I Was a Baby. Niland, Deborah, illus. 2007. (Illus.). 24p. (J). (ps). pap. 4.99 (***978-1-933605-49-4(9)***) Kane/Miller Bk. Pubs., Inc.

Nodset, Joan L. Go Away, Dog. Meisel, Paul, illus. 1999. (My First I Can Read Bks.). 32p. (J). (ps up). pap. 3.99 (978-0-06-444231-2(4) , Harper Trophy) HarperCollins Pubs.

—Go Away, Dog. Meisel, Paul, illus. 1999. 32p. (J). (ps-ps). lib. bdg. 11.80 (978-0-613-13602-0(0)) Tandem Library Bks.

Nolan, Carrie Stewart. My Little Miracle. 2007. (J). per. 10.99 (***978-1-59886-848-7(9)***) Tate Publishing & Enterprises, L.L.C.

Nolan, Lucy A. Down Girl & Sit: Smarter Than Squirrels. Reed, Mike, illus. 2004. 64p. (J). 14.95 (978-0-7614-5184-6(6)) Cavendish, Marshall Corp.

—On the Road. Reed, Mike, illus. 2005. 54p. (J). (gr. 1-4). per. 14.95 (978-0-7614-5234-8(6)) Cavendish, Marshall Corp.

Nolen, Jerdine. Max & Jax Plant a Garden. Schmidt, Katen, illus. Date not set. (J). 14.00 (978-0-15-201672-2(4) , Silver Whistle) Harcourt Children's Bks. CAN. *Dist:* Harcourt Trade Pubs.

Noonan, Julia. Breakfast Time. 2000. (Puppy & Me Ser.). (Illus.). 20p. (YA). (ps up). pap. 6.99 (978-0-439-11490-5(X) , Cartwheel Bks.) Scholastic, Inc.

—Going to the Corner. Noonan, Julia, illus. 2000. (Puppy & Me Ser.). (Illus.). 20p. (J). (ps-1). pap. 6.99 (978-0-439-17323-0(X)) Scholastic, Inc.

Norfolk, Booby. The Great Smelly, Slobbery, Small-Tooth Dog: A Folktale from Great Britain. Paschkis, Julie, illus. 2008. 32p. (***978-0-87483-831-2(2)***) August Hse. Pubs., Inc.

Nuestro perro Sam 6 Packs. Individual Title. (Literatura 2000 Ser.). (SPA.). (gr. k-1). 28.00 (978-0-7635-1025-1(4)) Rigby Education.

Nugent, Cynthia. Francesca & the Magic Bike Teacher Guide. 2005. 4p. (J). pap. (978-1-55192-825-8(6)) Raincoast Bk. Distribution CAN. *Dist:* Transition Vendor.

Nunn, Paul E. Puppy Fun. 2007. (Puppy Scooby-Doo Ser.). 24p. (J). 4.99 (978-0-448-44483-3(6) , Grosset & Dunlap) Penguin Group (USA) Inc.

Nye, Julie & Nye, Julie. Scout: The Secret at les Cheneaux. 2007. (Illus.). 160p. (YA). per. (***978-0-9767762-1-5(9)***) Fieldstone Hill Pr.

O'Brien, Jack. The Return of Silver Chief. (J). 21.95 (978-0-89190-398-7(4)) Amereon LTD.

O'Brien, John. Mother Hubbard's Christmas. O'Brien, John, illus. 2003. (Illus.). 32p. (J). (ps-1). 14.95 (978-1-56397-139-6(9)) Boyds Mills Pr.

O'Byrne, Tim. Cowboys & Dog Tales. unabr. ed. 164p. (J). pap. (978-0-920576-65-6(6)) Caitlin Pr., Inc.

Ochiltree, Dianne & D'Allance, Mireille. Pillow Pup. 2002. (Illus.). 32p. (J). (gr. k-3). 14.95 (978-0-689-83408-0(X) , McElderry, Margaret K.) Simon & Schuster Children's Publishing.

O'Connor, Barbara. How to Steal a Dog. 2007. 176p. (J). (gr. 3-7). 16.00 (978-0-374-33497-0(8)) Farrar, Straus & Giroux.

O'Connor, Ilett. Thomas & the Big Dog & Natie & the Dinosaur Egg. 2002. 50p. (J). (ps-5). pap. 12.00 (978-0-9717003-6-9(2)) O'Connor, Ilett K.

O'Connor, Jane. Fancy Nancy & the Posh Puppy. Glasser, Robin Preiss, illus. 2007. (Fancy Nancy Ser.). 32p. (J). lib. bdg. 17.89 (***978-0-06-054215-3(2)***); 16.99 (***978-0-06-054213-9(6)***) HarperCollins Pubs.

O'Connor, Jane. The Perfect Puppy for Me! Hartland, Jessie, illus. 32p. (J). (ps-3). 2003. 15.99 (978-0-670-03614-1(5) , Viking Juvenile); 2005. reprint ed. pap. 5.99 (978-0-14-240335-8(0) , Puffin) Penguin Group (USA) Inc.

Odgers, Darrel & Odgers, Sally. The Awful Pawful: Jack Russell: Dog Detective. Dawson, Janine, illus. 2007. (Jack Russell: Dog Detective Ser.: No. 5). 80p. (J). (gr. 2-6). pap. 4.95 (***978-1-933605-53-1(7)***) Kane/Miller Bk. Pubs., Inc.

—The Sausage Situation: Jack Russell: Dog Detective. Dawson, Janine, illus. 2007. (Jack Russell: Dog Detective Ser.: No. 6). 80p. (J). (gr. 2-6). 4.95 (***978-1-933605-54-8(5)***) Kane/Miller Bk. Pubs., Inc.

Odgers, Sally & Odgers, Darrel. The Buried Biscuits. Dawson, Janine, illus. 2008. (Jack Russell: Dog Detective Ser.: 7). 84p. (J). pap. 4.95 (***978-1-933605-77-7(4)***) Kane/Miller Bk. Pubs., Inc.

—Jack Russell: Dog Detective Dog Den Mystery. 2006. (Jack Russell: Dog Detective Ser.: 1). (Illus.). 84p. (J). pap. 4.95 (978-1-933605-18-0(9)) Kane/Miller Bk. Pubs., Inc.

—Jack Russell: Dog Detective the Phantom Mudder. 2006. (Jack Russell: Dog Detective Ser.: 2). (Illus.). 84p. (J). pap. 4.95 (978-1-933605-19-7(7)) Kane/Miller Bk. Pubs., Inc.

—The Lying Postman: Jack Russell: Dog Detective. 2007. (Jack Russell: Dog Detective Ser.: 4). (Illus.). 80p. (J). pap. 4.95 (978-1-933605-31-9(6) , 05319) Kane/Miller Bk. Pubs., Inc.

—The Mugged Pug: Jack Russell: Dog Detective. 2007. (Jack Russell: Dog Detective Ser.: 3). (Illus.). 80p. (J). pap. 4.95 (978-1-933605-32-6(4) , 05326) Kane/Miller Bk. Pubs., Inc.

Odom, Mel. 102 Dalmatians: Prima's Official Strategy Guide. 2000. (Illus.). (J). pap. 14.99 (978-0-7615-2997-2(7) , Prima Lifestyles) Crown Publishing Group.

O'Donnell, Liam. Duncan, a Brave Rescue. Hynes, Robert, illus. 2005. (Pet Tales Ser.). 32p. (J). (ps-2). 4.95 incl. cd-rom (978-1-59249-291-6(6) , 1B001); 2.95 (978-1-59249-292-3(4) , 1B003) Soundprints.

—Ginger Leads Way. Diefendorf, Cathy, illus. 2005. (Pet Tales Ser.). 32p. (J). (ps-2). 9.95 (978-1-59249-360-9(2) , 1B025); 2.95 (978-1-59249-359-3(9) , 1B024); 4.95 incl. cd-rom (978-1-59249-358-6(0) , 1B023) Soundprints.

—Tracker: On the Job. Hynes, Robert, illus. 2005. (Pet Tales Ser.). 32p. (J). (ps-2). 2.95 (978-1-59249-294-7(0) , 1B009) Soundprints.

—Tracker; on the Job. Hynes, Robert, illus. 2005. (Pet Tales Ser.). 32p. (J). (ps-2). 9.95 (978-1-59249-318-0(1) , 1B010) Soundprints.

—Winston in the City. (Pet Tales Ser.). (Illus.). 32p. (J). (ps-2). 9.95 (978-1-59249-449-1(8) , 1B033) Soundprints.

—Winston in the City. Hatala, Dan, illus. 2005. (Pet Tales Ser.). 32p. (J). (ps-2). 2.95 (978-1-59249-448-4(X) , 1B032) Soundprints.

—Winston in the City. Hatala, Dan, illus. 2005. (Pet Tales Ser.). 32p. (J). (ps-ps). pap. 4.95 (978-1-59249-447-7(1) , 1B031) Soundprints.

Offley, Nancy. The Story of Snickers. 2004. (Illus.). 40p. (J). pap. 9.95 (978-0-9748081-0-9(5)) Classroom Enrichment Assocs.

O'Hair, Margaret. My Pup. Lyon, Tammie, illus. 2008. (J). (***978-0-7614-5389-5(X)***) Cavendish, Marshall Corp.

Oke, Janette. Spunky's Diary. Munger, Nancy, illus. rev. ed. 2000. (Animal Friends Ser.). 64p. (J). (gr. 1-5). pap. 6.99 (978-0-7642-2405-8(0)) Bethany Hse. Pubs.

Old Yeller. 1999. (J). 9.95 (978-1-56137-081-8(9)) Novel Units, Inc.

Oldfield, Jenny. Speckled & Sinbad 2-1 Bind Up. (Illus.). mass mkt. 11.99 (978-0-340-70880-4(8) , Hodder & Stoughton) Hodder General Publishing Division GBR. *Dist:* Trafalgar Square Publishing.

Oliver, Mark. Robot Dog. 2005. (Illus.). 28p. (J). 16.00 (978-1-56148-489-8(X)) Good Bks.

One Special Dog. 2002. (Illus.). (J). pap. 6.25 (978-0-7398-6159-2(X)) Steck-Vaughn.

O'Neill, Catharine. Annie & Simon. O'Neill, Catharine, illus. 2008. (Illus.). 64p. (J). (gr. k-2). 15.99 (978-0-7636-2688-4(0)) Candlewick Pr.

oneones. Happy Birthday Coco. oneones, illus. 2006. (Illus.). 56p. (J). 12.95 (978-1-933605-13-5(8)) Kane/Miller Bk. Pubs., Inc.

Operation: Lost Puppy. 2003. (J). per. (978-1-57657-825-4(9)) Paradise Pr., Inc.

Osborne, Mary Pope. Tigers at Twilight, Vol. 19. unabr. ed. 2004. (Magic Tree House Ser.: No. 19). 72p. (J). (gr. k-3). pap. 17.00 incl. audio (978-0-8072-0928-8(7) , S FTR 251 SP, Listening Library) Random Hse. Audio Publishing Group.

—Tigers at Twilight. Murdocca, Sal, illus. 1999. (Magic Tree House Ser.: No. 19). 96p. (J). (gr. k-3). lib. bdg. 11.99 (978-0-679-99065-9(8)); mass mkt. 3.99 (978-0-679-89065-2(3)) Random Hse. Children's Bks. (Random Hse. Bks. for Young Readers).

—Tigers at Twilight. 1999. (Magic Tree House Ser.: No. 19). (J). (gr. k-3). (Illus.). 71p. lib. bdg. 10.79 (978-0-606-16957-8(1)); lib. bdg. 11.80 (978-0-613-16224-1(2)) Tandem Library Bks.

Osborne, Susan Titus. Dog Paws & Sandy Claws. Durrell, Julie, illus. 2001. (Parables in Action Ser.: Vol. 8). 48p. (J). (ps-2). 4.99 (978-0-570-07140-2(2)) Concordia Publishing Hse.

O'Shea, Pat. Hounds of the Morrigan. 1999. (gr. 7-12). lib. bdg. 16.45 (978-0-613-16125-1(4)) Tandem Library Bks.

—The Hounds of the Morrigon. 1999. (J). (978-0-606-16707-9(2)) Tandem Library Bks.

Ouida. A Dog of Flanders. 2000. (J). 19.95 (978-0-8488-2957-5(3)) Amereon LTD.

Our Dog Sam, 6, Pack. (Literatura 2000 Ser.). (gr. k-1). 28.00 (978-0-7635-0036-8(4)) Rigby Education.

Owens, Connie S. My Heart Is Sad: When Someone Special Dies. 2005. pap. 7.99 (978-1-59317-088-2(2)) Warner Pr. Pubs.

Paco Dog's When I Get Home from School! 2003. 3.99 (978-0-915960-30-9(3)) Ebon Research Systems Publishing, LLC.

Page, Gail. How to Be a Good Dog. Page, Gail, illus. 2007. (Illus.). 32p. (J). (ps-3). pap. 6.95 (***978-1-59990-151-0(X)*** , Bloomsbury Children) Bloomsbury Publishing.

—How to Be a Good Dog. 2006. (Illus.). 32p. (J). 15.95 (978-1-58234-683-0(6) , Bloomsbury Children) Bloomsbury Publishing.

Page, Josephine. Tummy Trouble. Edwards, Ken, illus. 2001. (Clifford, the Big Red Dog Ser.). 32p. (J). (gr. k-2). pap. 3.99 (978-0-439-21358-5(4)) Scholastic, Inc.

Palmer, Amy. In the Doghouse. 2004. 29p. pap. 14.95 (978-1-4137-3085-2(X)) PublishAmerica, Inc.

Palmer, C. Everard. A Dog Called Houdini.Tr. of Houdini, le Chien. (FRE.). (J). pap. 5.99 (978-0-590-73092-1(4)) Scholastic, Inc.

Palmer, D. Tia. 2005. 48p. pap. 12.95 (978-1-4137-8188-5(8)) PublishAmerica, Inc.

Pandell, Karen. Where's Stretch? McElmurry, Jill, illus. 2004. 18p. (J). (gr. k-k). 9.99 (978-0-7636-1594-9(3)) Candlewick Pr.

Pannell, Michael. Wilbur the Brushhound. 2005. 312p. (J). per. 14.95 (978-1-59453-920-6(0) , Airleaf Publishing) Airleaf Publishing & Bookselling.

The Paper Pup. 2004. 39p. pap. 17.95 (978-1-4137-3012-8(4)) PublishAmerica, Inc.

Paraskevas, Betty. Chocolate at the Four Seasons. Paraskevas, Mickey, illus. 2007. 32p. (J). (ps-1). 16.99 (978-0-316-01375-8(7)) Little Brown & Co.

Parent, Nancy. Clifford's Big Red Easter. Cuddy, Robin, illus. 2003. (Clifford, the Big Red Dog Ser.). 7p. (J). (ps up). bds. 4.99 (978-0-439-43428-7(9)) Scholastic, Inc.

Park, Nick, et al. Close Shave. 2006. 31.95 (978-0-19-459239-0(1)) Oxford Univ. Pr., Inc.

Parker, Linda & Langdon, Katie. Austin & Charlie Adventures: Washington DC Adventure. 2007. 32p. (J). 14.95 (***978-0-9785473-1-8(4)*** , Austin & Charlie Adventures) Paw Print Pubns.

Parker, Marjorie Blain. Hello, Freight Train! Kolar, Bob, illus. 2005. (Scholastic Reader Ser.). (J). (***978-1-4155-7966-4(0)***) Scholastic, Inc.

—Hello, Freight Train! Kolar, Bob, illus. 2005. 28p. (J). (ps-ps). lib. bdg. 10.79 (978-0-606-33279-8(0)) Tandem Library Bks.

—Jasper's Day. Wilson, Janet, illus. 2002. 32p. (J). (gr. k-3). (978-1-55074-957-1(9)) Kids Can Pr., Ltd.

Parr, Todd. I Love You Just Because. 2006. (Toddworld Ser.). 24p. (J). (ps-3). pap. 3.99 (978-0-316-05710-3(X)) Little Brown & Co.

—Otto Goes to Bed. 2003. (Illus.). 24p. (J). (ps-3). 9.95 (978-0-316-73873-6(5) , Tingley, Megan Bks.) Little, Brown Bks. for Young Readers.

—Otto Goes to Camp. 2004. (Illus.). 24p. (J). (ps-3). 9.95 (978-0-316-73900-9(6)) Little Brown & Co.

—Otto Goes to School. Parr, Todd, illus. 2005. (Illus.). 24p. (J). (ps-1). 9.99 (978-0-316-83533-6(1)) Little Brown & Co.

—Otto Goes to the Beach. 2003. (Illus.). 24p. (J). (ps-1). 9.95 (978-0-316-73870-5(0) , Tingley, Megan Bks.) Little, Brown Bks. for Young Readers.

—Otto Has a Birthday Party. 2004. (Illus.). 24p. (J). (ps-3). 9.95 (978-0-316-73907-8(3)) Little Brown & Co.

Parsons, Garry. Krong! Parsons, Garry, illus. 2006. (Illus.). 36p. (J). 15.95 (978-1-58925-061-1(3) , tiger tales) ME Media LLC.

Paschkis, Julie, illus. The Great Smelly, Slobbery, Small-Tooth Dog: A Folktale from Great Britain. 2007. 32p. (ps-3). 16.95 (***978-0-87483-808-4(8)***) August Hse. Pubs., Inc.

Pataki, Libby & Kimball, Wilson, texts. Madison in New York. l.t. ed. 2005. (Illus.). 32p. (J). 16.95 (978-1-893622-15-9(0) , VSP Bks.) Vacation Spot Publishing.

Paterson, Katherine. El Clan de los Perros. 2003. Tr. of Field of the Dogs. (SPA.). 464p. (J). 7.95 (978-84-279-3854-0(3)) Noguer y Caralt Editores, S. A. ESP. *Dist:* Lectorum Pubns., Inc.

—The Field of the Dogs. McCully, Emily Arnold, illus. (J). 2002. 112p. pap. 5.99 (978-0-06-442147-8(3)); 2001. 96p. (gr. 4-7). 14.89 (978-0-06-029475-5(2)) HarperCollins Pubs.

—The Field of the Dogs. 2002. (gr. 3-6). lib. bdg. 13.00 (978-0-613-62947-8(7)) Tandem Library Bks.

Patrick Book & Plush Dog. (J). (978-1-58209-078-8(5)) Books Are Fun, Ltd.

Patterson, Nancy Ruth. The Winner's Walk. Yezerski, Thomas, illus. 2006. 128p. (J). 16.00 (978-0-374-38445-6(2)) Farrar, Straus & Giroux.

Paulsen, Gary. Brian's Hunt. 2005. 112p. (J). (gr. 5). pap. 5.99 (978-0-553-49415-0(5) , Laurel Leaf) Random Hse. Children's Bks.

—Brian's Hunt: A Novel. 2005. 103p. (YA). (gr. 4-8). reprint ed. 15.00 (978-0-7567-9570-2(2)) DIANE Publishing Co.

—Dogsong. 1999. (YA). 9.95 (978-1-56137-342-0(7)) Novel Units, Inc.

—Dogsong. 192p. 2007. (J). pap. 6.99 (978-1-4169-3962-7(8) , Aladdin); 2007. (YA). mass mkt. 6.99 (978-1-4169-3919-1(9) , Simon Pulse); 2000. (YA). (gr. 7 up). 17.99 (978-0-689-83960-3(X) , Atheneum/Richard Jackson Bks.) Simon & Schuster Children's Publishing.

—Dogsong. 1999. (J). 11.64 (978-0-606-16328-6(X)) Tandem Library Bks.

—Dogsong. l.t. ed. 2000. (Illus.). 184p. (J). (gr. 8-12). 21.95 (978-0-7862-2845-4(8)) Thorndike Pr.

—Puppies, Dogs, & Blue Northers: Reflections on Being Raised by a Pack of Sled Dogs. 1998. (978-0-606-13019-6(5)) Tandem Library Bks.

Payne, Helen. Vacation Paws. Youngblood, Carol, illus. 2006. 50p. per. 10.00 (***978-0-9786276-6-9(0)***) Mentzer Printing Ink.

Pearce, Jacqueline. Dog House Blues. 2005. 176p. (J). (gr. 3-7). pap. 6.95 (978-1-55143-360-8(5)) Orca Bk. Pubs. USA.

Pearce, Philippa. A Dog So Small. Maitland, Anthony, illus. l.t. ed. 2005. 256p. (J). pap. (978-0-7540-7806-7(X) , CLP 402) BBC Audio.

—A Dog So Small. 2003. (Read-Along Ser.). (J). pap. 29.95 incl. audio (978-0-7540-6255-4(4) , Galaxy Children's Large Print) BBC Audiobooks America.

Pease, J. L. Barnabas the Shaggedy, Raggedy Dog. 2005. (J). pap. 9.00 (978-0-8059-6880-4(6)) Dorrance Publishing Co., Inc.

Pennac, Daniel. Cabot-Caboche. 2000. (FRE.). (J). pap. 13.95 (978-2-09-282119-0(9)) Nathan, Fernand FRA. *Dist:* Distribooks, Inc.

Pennac, Daniel & Adams, Sarah. Dog. Teckentrup, Britta, illus. 2004. 192p. (J). (gr. 7 up). 15.99 (978-0-7636-2421-7(7)) Candlewick Pr.

Penner, Lucille Recht. Where's That Bone? Adams, Lynn, illus. 2005. (Math Matters Ser.). 32p. (ps). pap. 4.95 (978-1-57565-097-5(5)) Kane Pr., The.

—Where's That Bone? 2000. (Math Matters Ser.). (J). (978-0-606-20183-4(1)); lib. bdg. 12.95 (978-0-613-39374-4(0)) Tandem Library Bks.

Penston, Gail. Playful Puppies: Picnic in the Park. Tarbett, Debbie, illus. 2006. 12p. (J). (gr. 3-9). 12.95 (978-1-59125-636-6(4) , Penton Kids) Penton Overseas, Inc.

Pepin, Rebecca. Bobby Dog & the Flying Frog. Fuller, Cari, illus. 2004. (J). (gr. 4 up). 16.99 (978-0-9760684-0-2(0)); pap. 11.99 (978-0-9760684-1-9(9)) FullofPep Pubns.

Perez, Monica, et al. Dog Show: Early Reader. 2007. (Curious George Ser.). (Illus.). 24p. (J). (gr. k-3). 3.99 (978-0-618-72397-3(8)) Houghton Mifflin Co.

Perkins, Lynne Rae. Snow Music. Perkins, Lynne Rae, illus. 2003. (Illus.). 40p. (J). 15.99 (978-0-06-623956-9(7)); lib. bdg. 16.89 (978-0-06-623958-3(3)) HarperCollins Pubs.

—Snow Music. 2000. pap. 4.95 (978-0-06-443875-9(9)) HarperCollins Pubs.

Perrow, Angeli. Captain's Castaway. Harris, Emily, illus. 1998. 32p. (J). (ps-3). 15.95 (978-0-89272-419-2(6)) Down East Bks.

—Sirius, the Dog Star. Harris, Emily, illus. 2002. 32p. (gr. k-3). 15.95 (978-0-89272-545-8(1)) Down East Bks.

Perry, Tristan. Furry Tails: The Adventures of Cinnamon Persimmon. 2006. (ENG.). 108p. per. 16.95 (***978-1-4241-4788-5(3)***) PublishAmerica, Inc.

Peruski, Steven. My Friend & Teacher Sammie. 2006. (YA). 21.99 (***978-0-615-13428-4(9)***) Compassion Pets Publishing.

Petheram, Florence. Word: A Real Dog Locked in a Shelter Cage for Eight Years Until... 2006. 72p. (J). pap. 9.99 (978-1-4141-0518-5(5)) Pleasant Word.

Petit, Karen. The Mystery of the Screecher Creature: A Shandon's Ivy League Mystery. 2006. (J). per. 14.95 (***978-1-59872-666-4(8)***) Instantpublisher.com.

Petticoffer, Carl L. Howard Saves a Hound. Warfel, David M. H., illus. 2000. per. 3.00 (978-1-930710-41-2(0)) Veritas Pr., Inc.

Pfister, Marcus. El Erizo Feliz. 2003. Tr. of Happy Hedgehog. (SPA.). (gr. k-3). lib. bdg. 15.25 (978-0-613-73630-5(3)) Tandem Library Bks.

Phelps, Karen. Grass Is Always Greener, the & Let Sleeping Dogs Lie: Two Original Fairy Tales. 2006. spiral bd. 23.00 (***978-1-4108-7155-8(X)***) Benchmark Education Co.

Philipson, Sandra. Max's Rules. Campbell, Jenny, illus. 2004. (J). 9.95 (978-1-929821-10-5(7)) Chagrin River Publishing Co.

Phillips, Don. I, Tutus: Book One: the Son of Heaven. 2005. 263p. pap. 21.95 (978-1-4137-5932-7(7)) PublishAmerica, Inc.

Phillips, Vivian A. My Dog & His Bone. Date not set. (Illus.). (J). Vol. I. 15p. pap. (978-1-888413-03-8(4)); Vol. II. 14p. (978-1-888413-07-6(7)) Seasoning Quilting (Arts & Crafts).

Pichon, Liz. Bored Bill. Pichon, Liz, illus. 2006. (Illus.). 32p. (J). 15.95 (978-1-58925-053-6(2) , tiger tales) ME Media LLC.

Pickering, Jimmy. Skelly the Skeleton Girl. Pickering, Jimmy, illus. 2007. 32p. (J). (ps-2). 12.99 (978-1-4169-1192-0(8) , Simon & Schuster Children's Publishing) Simon & Schuster Children's Publishing.

Pickles Gets Lost. 2002. (J). (978-1-58453-187-6(8)) Pioneer Valley Educational Pr., Inc.

Pickles Goes to School. 2002. (J). (978-1-58453-183-8(5)) Pioneer Valley Educational Pr., Inc.

Pickles Helps Out. 2002. (J). (978-1-58453-188-3(6)) Pioneer Valley Educational Pr., Inc.

Pickles the Dog Set 1. 2002. (J). (978-1-58453-182-1(7)) Pioneer Valley Educational Pr., Inc.

Pieniozek, Lillian & Family. Meet the Knucklepuppies. 2003. (J). 10.95 (978-0-9708959-4-3(1)) Accent Pubns.

Pierce, Craig. A Greyhound's Tale: Running for Glory, Walking for Home. Santiago, Tony, illus. 2004. (J). per. 15.00 (978-0-9762564-0-3(1) , American Dog) Ideate Prairie.

—A Labrador's Tale: An Eye for Heroism. Santiago, Tony, illus. 2006. 30p. 15.00 (978-0-9762564-3-4(6) , American Dog) Ideate Prairie.

—A Labrador's Tale 2: The Incredible Thank You Gift, 1. Santiago, Tony, illus. 2006. 32p. 15.00 (978-0-9762564-4-1(4) , 2500, American Dog) Ideate Prairie.

Piggy Toes Press Staff & Haskamp, Steve. Good Morning, Good Night! 2006. (Illus.). 12p. (J). 12.95 (978-1-58117-461-8(6) , Intervisual/Piggy Toes) Dalmatian Pr.

Pilkey, Dav. Big Dog & Little Dog Making a Mistake. 1999. (Big Dog & Little Dog Ser.). (Illus.). 14p. (J). (ps-1). bds. 5.95 (978-0-15-200354-8(1) , Red Wagon Bks.) Harcourt Children's Bks.

—Big Dog & Little Dog Wearing Sweaters. 1998. (Big Dog & Little Dog Ser.). (Illus.). 14p. (J). (ps-1). bds. 5.95 (978-0-15-200361-6(4) , Red Wagon Bks.) Harcourt Children's Bks.

—The Complete Adventures of Big Dog & Little Dog. 2003. (Big Dog & Little Dog Ser.). (Illus.). 88p. (J). 16.00 (978-0-15-204708-5(5)) Harcourt Children's Bks.

—Dog Breath! The Horrible Trouble with Hally Tosis. Pilkey, Dav, illus. 2002. (Illus.). (J). 23.98 (978-0-7587-2398-7(9)) Book Wholesalers, Inc.

—Dog Breath! The Horrible Trouble with Hally Tosis. 2004. (Scholastic Bookshelf Ser.). 32p. (J). pap. 6.99 (978-0-439-59839-2(7) , Scholastic Paperbacks) Scholastic, Inc.

—Dogzilla. Pilkey, Dav, illus. 2002. (Illus.). (J). 14.04 (978-0-7587-2405-2(5)) Book Wholesalers, Inc.

—Dogzilla. 2003. (Illus.). 32p. (J). 14.00 (978-0-15-204948-5(7)); pap. 5.95 (978-0-15-204949-2(5) , Harcourt Paperbacks) Harcourt Children's Bks.

—Dogzilla. 2003. lib. bdg. 12.95 (978-0-613-71633-8(7)) Tandem Library Bks.

—The Hallo-Wiener. Pilkey, Dav, illus. 1999. (Illus.). 32p. (J). (ps-2). pap. 5.99 (978-0-439-07946-4(2)) Scholastic, Inc.

—The Hallo-Wiener. 1999. (J). 12.79 (978-0-606-17288-2(2)); lib. bdg. 14.15 (978-0-613-22864-0(2)) Tandem Library Bks.

Pinkwater, Daniel M. Mush, a Dog from Space. Pinkwater, Jill, illus. 2002. (Ready-for-Chapters Ser.). 64p. (J). (gr. 1-4). lib. bdg. 11.89 (978-0-689-84801-8(3) , Aladdin Library) Simon & Schuster Children's Publishing.

—Mush's Jazz Adventure. Pinkwater, Jill, illus. ed. 2005. 42p. (J). lib. bdg. 15.00 (978-1-59054-909-4(0)) Fitzgerald Bks.

—Mush's Jazz Adventure. 2002. (gr. 3-6). lib. bdg. 11.80 (978-0-613-57577-5(6)) Tandem Library Bks.

—Rainy Morning. Pinkwater, Jill, illus. 1999. (Pinkwater Ser.: Vol. 1). 32p. (J). (gr. k-3). 16.00 (978-0-689-81143-2(8) , Atheneum) Simon & Schuster Children's Publishing.

Pinkwater, Daniel M. & Pinkwater, Jill. Mush's Jazz Adventure. 2002. (Ready-for-Chapters Ser.). (Illus.). 48p. (J). pap. 6.99 (978-0-689-84572-7(3) , Aladdin) Simon & Schuster Children's Publishing.

Pinto va a la Escuela: Individual Title Six-Packs. (Coleccion Pm Ser.).Tr. of Lucky goes to dog school. (SPA.). 16p. (gr. 1 up). 26.00 (978-0-7578-2991-8(0)) Rigby Education.

Pintozzi, Nick. Bentley & the Cactus Rustlers. Pintozzi, Nick & Pintozzi, Connie, illus. 2006. per. 11.00 (***978-0-9749465-4-2(0)***) BentDaiSha, LLC.

Pintozzi, Nick. Bentley & the Great Fire. Pintozzi, Nick et al, illus. 2004. 16.95 (978-0-9749465-2-8(4)) BentDaiSha, LLC.

Pippa's Pet Pest, 6 Packs. (ps-2). 23.00 (978-0-7635-8794-9(X)) Rigby Education.

Pitts, Constance. Chulita the Blind Cat. 2007. (Illus.). 48p. (J). (***978-0-9652902-2-7(0)***) Beevinwood, Inc.

Pitzer, Susanna. Not Afraid of Dogs. Day, Larry, illus. 2006. 32p. (J). 16.95 (978-0-8027-8067-6(9)) Walker & Co.

Pitzer, Susanna & Day, Larry. Not Afraid of Dogs. 2006. (Illus.). 32p. (J). 17.85 (978-0-8027-8068-3(7)) Walker & Co.

Pogo the Clown. Along Little Dogie: Harley's Great Adventures. Miller, Richard, illus. 2005. (J). 12.95 (978-0-9755253-3-3(6)) Chiliric Pubns.

Policeman Dog: New Heroes Backpack Story. 2002. (J). (978-1-931312-59-2(1)) SoftPlay, Inc.

Pomerantz, Charlotte. The Birthday Letters. Adinolfi, JoAnn, illus. 2000. 32p. (J). (gr. k-3). 15.95 (978-0-688-16335-8(1)); 15.89 (978-0-688-16336-5(X)) HarperCollins Pubs.

Porter, Pamela. The Crazy Man. 2006. 176p. pap. 6.95 (978-0-88899-695-4(0)) Groundwood Bks. CAN. *Dist:* Perseus Distribution.

Postgate, Daniel. Smelly Bill. 2007. (Illus.). 24p. (J). (ps-2). 16.95 (***978-0-7358-2135-4(6)***) North-South Bks., Inc.

Posthuma, Sieb. Benny. Posthuma, Sieb, illus. (Illus.). (J). 2006. (SPA.). 24p. pap. 7.95 (978-1-933605-21-0(9)); 2002. 32p. 15.95 (978-1-929132-43-0(3)) Kane/Miller Bk. Pubs., Inc.

Potter, Beatrix. Jemima Puddle-Duck. 2007. 12p. (J). bds. 3.99 (978-0-7232-5856-8(2) , Warne) Penguin Group (USA) Inc.

Potter, Beatrix, text. Jemima Puddle-Duck. 2003. (Play-A-Sound Ser.). (Illus.). (J). (978-0-7853-7970-6(3)); (978-0-7853-7969-0(X)) Publications International, Ltd.

Potter, Tony. Hide & Seek Puppy. 1998. (J). (ps). 9.95 (978-1-902553-02-3(0)) Grimond FRA. *Dist:* Continental Enterprises Group, Inc. (CEG).

Powell, Jillian. The Naughty Puppy. Durantz, Summer, illus. 2004. (Read-It! Readers Ser.). 32p. (C). (gr. k-3). 18.60 (978-1-4048-0067-0(0)) Picture Window Bks.

Powell, Richard. Playful Pup. Martín Larrañaga, Ana, illus. 2001. 10p. bds. 5.95 (978-1-58925-664-4(6) , tiger tales) ME Media LLC.

—Puppy's Tail. Davis, Carolina A., illus. 2003. (Animal Tails Ser.). 12p. (J). 3.95 (978-1-58925-674-3(3) , tiger tales) ME Media LLC.

Powers-Fish, Amy Rose. Buddy's Forever Home. l.t. ed. 2006. (Illus.). 42p. (J). per. 11.99 (***978-1-59879-192-1(3)***) Lifevest Publishing, Inc.

Pratcher, Birgit. Matt & Spencer in Their Great Adventur. 2005. 153p. pap. 19.95 (978-1-4137-6638-7(2)) PublishAmerica, Inc.

Preiss, Thomas. The Other Side of the Window. 2005. pap. 7.95 (978-0-533-15028-1(0)) Vantage Pr., Inc.

Preller, James. The Case of the Runaway Dog. 1999. (Jigsaw Jones Mystery Ser.: No. 7). (Illus.). (J). (gr. 1-4). 10.79 (978-0-606-18529-5(1)) Tandem Library Bks.

Preller, James, et al. The Case of the Runaway Dog. Alley, R. W., illus. 2001. (Jigsaw Jones Mystery Ser.: No. 7). 80p. (J). (gr. 1-4). pap. 3.99 (978-0-439-11426-4(8)) Scholastic, Inc.

Priddy, Roger. Funny Faces Rocky Dog. 2007. (J). bds. 14.95 (***978-0-312-50113-6(7)*** , Priddy Bks.) St. Martin's Pr.

—Happy Dog Activity Cloth Book. rev. ed. 2007. 24p. (J). 9.95 (***978-0-312-49999-0(X)*** , Priddy Bks.) St. Martin's Pr.

—Happy Dog Activity Cloth Book in Bag. 2007. 24p. (J). 9.95 (***978-0-312-50076-4(9)*** , Priddy Bks.) St. Martin's Pr.

—Rocky Dog Large Format. 2007. 10p. (J). bds. 14.95 (***978-0-312-50116-7(1)*** , Priddy Bks.) St. Martin's Pr.

Priestley, Holly. Moonbeam, Precious Moonbeam. 2002. 12.95 (978-1-891231-96-4(0)) Word Association Pubs.

Prince, Alison. A Dog Called You. 2003. (Illus.). 64p. (J). pap. 6.99 (978-0-330-32708-4(9) , Pan) Pan Macmillan GBR. *Dist:* Trafalgar Square Publishing.

Pringle, Cindy & Pringle, Kirby. Happy Tails: Earl & Pearl on the Farm. l.t. ed. 2006. (Illus.). 32p. (J). 16.95 (978-0-9777126-0-1(5)) Dogtown Artworks.

Prins, Piet. The Flying Phantom. 2006. (Illus.). 142p. (J). pap. (978-1-894666-45-9(3)) Inheritance Pubns.

—The Haunted Castle. 2006. (Illus.). 139p. (J). pap. (978-1-894666-44-2(5)) Inheritance Pubns.

—The Mystery of the Abandoned Mill. Kramer, Jaap, illus. 2006. 127p. (J). pap. (978-1-894666-48-0(8)) Inheritance Pubns.

—The Sailing Sleuths. Kramer, Jaap, illus. 2006. 137p. (J). pap. (978-1-894666-46-6(1)) Inheritance Pubns.

—Scout's Distant Journey. 2006. (Illus.). 141p. (J). pap. (978-1-894666-49-7(6)) Inheritance Pubns.

—The Search for Sheltie. Kramer, Jaap, illus. 2006. 137p. (J). pap. (978-1-894666-43-5(7)) Inheritance Pubns.

—The Treasure of Rodensteyn Castle. Kramer, Jaap, illus. 2006. 132p. (J). pap. (978-1-894666-47-3(X)) Inheritance Pubns.

Provensen, Alice. A Day in the Life of Murphy. Provensen, Alice, illus. unabr. rev. ed. 2005. (Illus.). (J). 25.95 incl. audio (978-1-59519-534-0(3)); 28.95 incl. audio compact disk (978-1-59519-538-8(6)) Live Oak Media.

—A Day in the Life of Murphy. Provensen, Alice, illus. 40p. (J). (ps-2). 2003. (Illus.). 16.95 (978-0-689-84884-1(6)); 2006. reprint ed. pap. 6.99 (978-1-4169-1800-4(0) , Aladdin) Simon & Schuster Children's Publishing.

Pullen, Ken. Rescue Me. 2006. 139p. per. 11.95 (978-1-60002-170-1(0) , 4133, Airleaf Publishing) Airleaf Publishing & Bookselling.

Puppy Love. 2003. (J). per. (978-1-57657-890-2(9)) Paradise Pr., Inc.

Puppy Play. 2001. (978-1-58453-162-3(2)) Pioneer Valley Educational Pr., Inc.

Puppy Trouble. 2006. (J). (***978-1-932570-57-1(8)***) Literacy Footprints Inc.

Puppy's Busy Day. 2002. 10p. (J). bds. 2.50 (978-1-56021-398-7(1)) W.J. Fantasy, Inc.

Puppy's House. Date not set. (Illus.). (J). bds. 4.98 (978-1-4054-0787-8(5)) Parragon, Inc.

Quattlebaum, Mary. Magic Squad & the Dog of Great Potential. 1998. (978-0-606-13592-4(8)) Tandem Library Bks.

Raber-Luna, Robin. My Name Is No No Bad Dog. 2002. (J). pap. 7.95 (978-0-9715065-7-2(4)) Dog Days Publishing.

Radford, Tom. Healing Rex. 2007. (Illus.). pap. (***978-1-84426-417-9(3)***) Upfront Publishing Ltd.

Rae, Jennifer. Dog Tales. 2003. (Illus.). 32p. (J). (gr. 1-6). 14.95 (978-1-58246-011-6(6) , Tricycle Pr.) Ten Speed Pr.

Rakusin, Sudie. Dear Calla Roo. . . Love, Savannah Blue: A Letter to a Pen Pal. Rakusin, Sudie, illus. 2000. (Illus.). 36p. (J). (ps-4). 16.95 (978-0-9664805-1-1(1)) Winged Willow Pr.

—Dear Calla Roo... Love, Savannah Blue No. 2: A Letter about Getting Sick & Feeling Better. Rakusin, Sudie, illus. 2003. (Illus.). 32p. (J). (ps-4). 16.95 (978-0-9664805-3-5(8)) Winged Willow Pr.

Randall, MarilynMae. Wellington's Windows. McCarter, Zack, illus. 2003. 146p. (J). per. 15.00 (978-0-9713589-6-6(6)) Ubaviel's Gifts.

Rankin, Laura. Fluffy & Baron. 2006. (Illus.). 32p. (J). (ps). 16.99 (978-0-8037-2953-7(7) , Dial) Penguin Group (USA) Inc.

Ranville, Myralene. Tex. Dobson, Clive, illus. 1999. 32p. (J). (ps-3). pap. 6.95 (978-1-55209-291-0(7)) Firefly Bks., Ltd.

—Tex. 1999. (J). (978-0-606-18997-2(1)); lib. bdg. 15.25 (978-0-613-23819-9(2)) Tandem Library Bks.

Raschka, Chris. Can't Sleep. Raschka, Chris, illus. 1999. (Illus.). (J). (ps-1). 32p. 15.99 (978-0-531-08779-4(4)); 16p. bds. 6.95 (978-0-531-30201-9(6)); 32p. pap. 14.95 (978-0-531-09479-2(0)) Scholastic, Inc. (Orchard Bks.).

Rathmann, Peggy. Officer Buckle & Gloria. Rathmann, Peggy, illus. 2002. (Illus.). (J). 23.64 (978-0-7587-0061-2(X)) Book Wholesalers, Inc.

Rawls, Wilson. Where the Red Fern Grows. 1999. (Masterpiece Series Access Editions). (Illus.). xvii, 235p. (J). 10.95 (978-0-8219-1987-3(3) , 35337) Paradigm Publishing, Inc.

—Where the Red Fern Grows. 249p. (YA). (gr. 5 up). pap. 5.99 (978-0-8072-1467-1(1)); pap. 5.99 (978-0-8072-1358-2(6)) Random Hse. Audio Publishing Group. (Listening Library).

—Where the Red Fern Grows. l.t. ed. 2005. 376p. pap. 10.95 (978-0-7862-7312-6(7) , Large Print Pr.) Thorndike Pr.

Reader's Digest Editors. Puppy & Me. 2004. (Small Miracles Ser.: No. 5). 10p. (J). 7.99 (978-1-4003-0318-2(4)) Nelson, Thomas Inc.

Reading Friends Staff. Puppies Single. (J). (978-0-8136-3766-2(X)) Modern Curriculum Pr.

Reber, Deborah. Blue's Best Rainy Day. Cardinali, Kevin, illus. 2000. (Blue's Clues Ser.). 24p. (J). (ps-k). pap. 3.50 (978-0-689-83279-6(6) , Simon Spotlight/Nickelodeon) Simon & Schuster Children's Publishing.

—Blue's Best Rainy Day. 2000. (gr. k-3). lib. bdg. 11.25 (978-0-613-24387-2(0)) Tandem Library Bks.

—Blue's Egg Hunt. Norden, Carolyn, illus. 2001. (Blue's Clues Ser.). 24p. (J). (ps-k). pap. 3.50 (978-0-689-83873-6(5) , Simon Spotlight/Nickelodeon) Simon & Schuster Children's Publishing.

—Blue's Egg Hunt. 2001. (gr. k-3). lib. bdg. 11.25 (978-0-613-31009-3(8)) Tandem Library Bks.

—Blue's Valentines Day. Pontillo, Jenine, illus. 2000. (Blue's Clues Ser.). 16p. (J). (ps-k). pap. 3.99 (978-0-689-83062-4(9) , Simon Spotlight/Nickelodeon) Simon & Schuster Children's Publishing.

—Magenta & Me. Bishop, Don, illus. 2000. (Blues Clue's Ready to Read Ser.: No. 2). 24p. (J). (ps-1). pap. 3.99 (978-0-689-83123-2(4) , Simon Spotlight/Nickelodeon) Simon & Schuster Children's Publishing.

—Magenta & Me. 2000. (gr. k-3). lib. bdg. 11.80 (978-0-613-26094-7(5)) Tandem Library Bks.

—Meet My Family. 2001. (ps-2). lib. bdg. 11.80 (978-0-613-35671-8(3)) Tandem Library Bks.

Redmond, Pamela Woods. Elf Dog. LaFrance, Debbie, illus. 2005. 44p. (J). 15.95 (978-0-9760767-0-4(5)) Redmond, Pamela.

Reed, Wendy. Little Lilly's Polka Dot World. 2006. (Illus.). 28p. (J). 15.95 (978-0-9755490-0-1(6)) BookMasters, Inc.

Reid, Jim, as told by. Schultze's Stories: Celebrating Friends Through a Puppy's Eyes. 2006. (J). pap. (***978-0-86534-494-5(9)***) Sunstone Pr.

Reinen, Judy. Bow Wow: A Day in the Life of Dogs. Reinen, Judy, illus. 2001. (Illus.). 32p. (J). (gr. k-3). 13.95 (978-0-316-83290-8(1)) Little, Brown Bks. for Young Readers.

Reiser, Lynn. Hardworking Puppies. 2006. (Illus.). 40p. (J). 16.00 (978-0-15-205404-5(9)) Harcourt Trade Pubs.

Reneaux, J. J. Why Alligator Hates Dog: A Cajun Folktale. 2001. (ps-2). lib. bdg. 15.25 (978-0-613-49793-0(7)) Tandem Library Bks.

Repp, Gloria. Mik-Shrok. 1998. 133p. (J). (gr. 4-7). pap. 7.49 (978-1-57924-069-1(0) , 113902) Jones, Bob Univ. Pr.

Rey. Attention aux Chiens. pap. 16.95 (978-2-09-250164-1(X)) Nathan, Fernand FRA. *Dist:* Distribooks, Inc.

Rey, H. A. Curious George & Puppies. Rey, Margret, illus. 2007. 24p. (J). (ps-k). pap. 9.95 incl. audio compact disk (***978-0-618-80065-0(4)***) Houghton Mifflin Co. Trade & Reference Div.

Rey, Margret & Rey, H. A. Curious George & the Puppies. 1998. (Curious George Ser.). (Illus.). 24p. (J). (gr. k-3). pap. 3.95 (978-0-395-91215-7(6)); tchr. ed. 12.95 (978-0-395-91217-1(2)) Houghton Mifflin Co. Trade & Reference Div.

Reynolds, Mignon C. Life as Bonkers. 2006. 137p. pap. 12.95 (978-1-4116-7357-1(3)) Lulu.com.

Ricci, Christine. Puppy Takes a Bath. Mangano, Tom, illus. 2006. (Ready-To-Read Ser.). 24p. (J). pap. 3.99 (978-1-4169-1483-9(8) , Simon Spotlight/Nickelodeon) Simon & Schuster Children's Publishing.

Richardson, Bill. Sally Dog Little. Malepart, Celine, illus. 2002. 24p. (J). (ps-2). lib. bdg. 14.95 (978-1-55037-759-0(0)) Annick Pr., Ltd. CAN. *Dist:* Firefly Bks., Ltd.

—Sally Dog Little Undercover Agent. Malépart, Céline, illus. 2003. 24p. (J). (ps-2). pap. 6.95 (978-1-55037-824-5(4)) Annick Pr., Ltd. CAN. *Dist:* Firefly Bks., Ltd.

—Sally Dog Little Undercover Agent. Malepart, Celine, illus. 2003. 24p. (J). (ps-2). lib. bdg. 18.95 (978-1-55037-825-2(2)) Annick Pr., Ltd. CAN. *Dist:* Firefly Bks., Ltd.

Richardson, Kara, illus. Simon & Barklee in Mexico. 2002. (Simon & Barklee in Mexico). 64p. (J). per. 15.00 (978-0-9714502-0-2(X) , Explorer Media) Simon & Barklee, Inc./ExplorerMedia.

Ries, Lori. Aggie & Ben: Three Stories. Dormer, Frank W., illus. 48p. (J). (ps-2). 2007. pap. 5.95 (***978-1-57091-649-6(7)***); 2006. 12.95 (978-1-57091-594-9(6)) Charlesbridge Publishing, Inc.

Rigby Education Staff. The Cat Show. (Sails Literacy Ser.). (Illus.). 16p. (gr. k-1). 27.00 (978-0-7635-9881-5(X) , 698819C99) Rigby Education.

—Dog's Diary. (Sails Literacy Ser.). (Illus.). 16p. (gr. 2-3). 27.00 (978-0-7635-9936-2(0) , 699360C99) Rigby Education.

—The Happy House. (Sails Literacy Ser.). (Illus.). 16p. (gr. 1-2). 27.00 (978-0-7635-9908-9(5) , 699085C99) Rigby Education.

—Marvins Woolly Mammoth. (Sails Literacy Ser.). (Illus.). 16p. (gr. 1-2). 27.00 (978-0-7635-9926-3(3) , 699263C99) Rigby Education.

—Shar. (Sails Literacy Ser.). (Illus.). 16p. (gr. 1-2). 27.00 (978-0-7635-9888-4(7) , 698887C99) Rigby Education.

—Snow. (Sails Literacy Ser.). (Illus.). 16p. (gr. 1-2). 27.00 (978-0-7635-9927-0(1) , 699271C99) Rigby Education.

Riser, Winifred. Max Goes to Moscow. 2006. (Illus.). 40p. (J). (ps-1). 15.95 (978-1-84507-482-1(3)) Lincoln, Frances Ltd. GBR. *Dist:* Perseus Distribution.

Risk, Mary, et al. Puppy Finds a Friend: Cachorrito Encuentra a un Amigo. Bendall-Brunello, John, illus. 2000. (I Can Read Bks.). (SPA, ENG & FRE.). 28p. (J). (gr. k-2). 6.95 (978-0-7641-5283-2(1)) Barron's Educational Series, Inc.

—Puppy Finds a Friend: Le Petit chien Trouve un Copain. Bendall-Brunello, John, illus. 2000. (I Can Read Bks.). (FRE & ENG.). 28p. (J). (ps-2). 8.99 (978-0-7641-5285-6(8)) Barron's Educational Series, Inc.

Rizzati, Lorella. Pochacco. 2001. (Portable Pets Ser.). (Illus.). 12p. (J). (ps-ps). bds. 6.95 (978-0-8109-5682-7(9)) Abrams, Harry N. , Inc.

Roberts, Allyson. Leroy the Labrador - the Big Move. 2005. 14.95 (978-0-9759305-1-9(6)) Maximum Potential, Inc.

Roberts, Curt. The Story of Scruffy of Smithfield, Virginia. Traylor, Waverley, ed. Roberts, Curt & Traylor, Waverley, illus. l.t. ed. 2005. 14p. (J). (gr. k-6). pap. 3.95 (978-0-9715068-4-8(1)) Traylor, Waverley Publishing.

Roberts, Phyllis. Teeny Tiny Star. 2007. (Illus.). 30p. (J). lib. bdg. 19.95 (***978-1-933732-40-4(7)*** , Bear Hug Bks.) MidAmerica Publishing Co.

Roberts, Willo Davis. Rebel. 160p. (J). 2005. pap. 5.99 (978-0-689-85081-3(6) , Aladdin); 2003. (Illus.). 16.95 (978-0-689-85073-8(5) , Atheneum) Simon & Schuster Children's Publishing.

Robertson, Susan, illus. Little Puppy. 2005. (Bedtime Babies Ser.). 8p. (J). (ps). per. 6.99 (978-1-57755-501-8(5)) Allied Publishing.

Robison, Peggy. Prince Cody Meets A Monster. Clay, Doris, illus. 2004. 40p. (J). 9.95 (978-0-9708395-7-2(X)) Legacy Publishing Services, Inc.

—Prince Cody Runs Ahead of the Hurricane. Clay, Doris, illus. 2005. 64p. (J). per. 9.95 (978-0-9764982-7-8(8)) Legacy Publishing Services, Inc.

Rocklin, Joanne. The Very Best Hanukkah Gift. 2001. (978-0-606-22400-0(9)) Tandem Library Bks.

—Very Best Hanukkah Gift. 2001. (gr. 3-6). lib. bdg. 12.40 (978-0-613-85709-3(7)) Tandem Library Bks.

Rodowsky, Colby. The Next-Door Dogs. Bates, Amy June, illus. 2005. 112p. (J). 15.00 (978-0-374-36410-6(9) , Farrar, Straus & Giroux (BYR)) Farrar, Straus & Giroux.

—Not My Dog. Yezerski, Thomas F., illus. 1999. 80p. (J). (gr. 2-5). 15.00 (978-0-374-35531-9(2) , Farrar, Straus & Giroux (BYR)) Farrar, Straus & Giroux.

—Not My Dog. 2001. (gr. 3-6). lib. bdg. 12.95 (978-0-613-53444-4(1)); (Illus.). (J). (978-0-606-21357-8(0)) Tandem Library Bks.

Rodowsky, Colby F. Not My Dog. Yezerski, Thomas F., illus. 2001. (Sunburst Bks.). 80p. (J). (ps-k). pap. 4.95 (978-0-374-45538-5(4) , Sunburst) Farrar, Straus & Giroux.

Romanova, Yelena. The Perfect Friend. Kulikov, Boris, illus. 2005. 32p. (J). (ps-1). 15.00 (978-0-374-35821-1(4) , Frances Foster Bks.) Farrar, Straus & Giroux.

Romer, Ruth. Los cuidadores de mascotas & Pet Care Kids. 2005. spiral bd. 76.00 (***978-1-4108-5795-8(6)***) Benchmark Education Co.

Roop, Peter. Abe Lincoln's Dog. 2003. (Illus.). 14.95 (978-1-59319-020-0(4)) LeapFrog Enterprises, Inc.

A Rose for Pinkerton. 2004. (J). 24.95 incl. audio (978-0-7882-0644-3(3)); pap. 14.95 incl. audio (978-0-7882-0643-6(5)) Weston Woods Studios, Inc.

Rose, J. R. More Fun with Pup! Activity Book. 1998. (Illus.). 64p. (J). (gr. k-3). pap. 5.95 (978-1-56554-368-3(8)) Pelican Publishing Co., Inc.

Rosen, Michael. Howler. Layton, Neal, illus. 2004. 32p. (J). (ps-2). 15.95 (978-1-58234-851-3(0) , Bloomsbury Children) Bloomsbury Publishing.

Rosie Is Cold. 2004. (J). (978-1-932570-20-5(9)) Literacy Footprints Inc.

Ross, Thea. Lucy Wants to Help. 2005. 16p. (J). bds. 3.99 (978-1-59384-028-0(4)) Parklane Publishing.

Ross, Theodore J. Lucy Wants to Play. 2003. (Illus.). 16p. (J). 3.99 (978-1-59384-029-7(2)) Parklane Publishing.

Ross, Tony. Is It Because? 2005. (Illus.). 32p. (J). 9.95 (978-0-7641-5830-8(9)) Barron's Educational Series, Inc.

Rotenberg, Lisa. Rodeo Pup. 1998. (Illus.). 32p. (J). (gr. k-2). 14.95 (978-1-55209-245-3(3)) Firefly Bks., Ltd.

Roth, Susan L. It's a Dog's New York. 2001. (Illus.). 32p. (J). (gr. 5-3). 16.95 (978-0-7922-7054-6(1) , National Geographic Children's Bks.) National Geographic Society.

—It's Still a Dogs New York: A Book of Healing. 2001. 32p. (J). (gr. k-7). 12.00 (978-0-7922-7050-8(9) , National Geographic Children's Bks.) National Geographic Society.

Rovetch, L. Bob. Hot Dog & Bob: And the Particularly Pesky Attack of the Pencil People. Whamond, Dave, illus. 2006. 96p. (J). pap. 4.95 (978-0-8118-5322-4(5)) Chronicle Bks. LLC.

—Hot Dog & Bob: And the Seriously Scary Attack of the Evil Alien Pizza Person. Whamond, Dave, illus. 2006. 96p. (J). pap. 4.95 (978-0-8118-5156-5(7)) Chronicle Bks. LLC.

—Hot Dog & Bob & the Surprisingly Slobbery Attack of the Dog-Wash Doggies. Whamond, Dave, illus. 2007. (Hot Dog & Bob Ser.: No. 5). 96p. (J). (gr. 1-5). 15.50 (978-0-8118-5745-1(X)); pap. 4.95 (978-0-8118-5746-8(8)) Chronicle Bks. LLC.

Rovetch, Lissa. Hot Dog & Bob Adventure, Bk. 2. 2006. (Illus.). 96p. (J). 15.50 (978-0-8118-4464-2(1)) Chronicle Bks. LLC.

—Hot Dog & Bob Adventure, No. 6. Whamond, Dave, illus. 2008. (J). pap. 4.95 (978-0-8118-5748-2(4)) Chronicle Bks. LLC.

—Hot Dog & Bob Adventure 6 Le. Whamond, Dave, illus. 2008. (J). 15.50 (978-0-8118-5747-5(6)) Chronicle Bks. LLC.

Rowe, Jeannette. YoYo Goes Next Door. Rowe, Jeannette, illus. 2003. (Illus.). 16p. (J). 5.95 (978-1-58925-368-1(X) , tiger tales) ME Media LLC.

—YoYo Goes to the Park. Rowe, Jeannette, illus. 2003. (Illus.). 12p. (J). pap. 5.95 (978-1-58925-369-8(8) , tiger tales) ME Media LLC.

—YoYo's Animal Friends. Rowe, Jeannette, illus. 2002. (Illus.). 12p. (J). 3.95 (978-1-58925-681-1(6) , tiger tales) ME Media LLC.

Rowe, Jeannette, illus. YoYo's Colors. 2002. 10p. (J). 3.95 (978-1-58925-682-8(4) , tiger tales) ME Media LLC.

—YoYo's Numbers. 2002. 10p. (J). 3.95 (978-1-58925-683-5(2) , tiger tales) ME Media LLC.

—YoYo's Toys. 2002. 10p. (J). 3.95 (978-1-58925-684-2(0) , tiger tales) ME Media LLC.

Rowen, Amy & Rowen, Tyla Marie. Waggin' Tails. 2003. 182p. 23.95 (978-0-595-65740-7(0)); pap. 13.95 (978-0-595-28171-8(0)) iUniverse, Inc.

—Waggin' Tales. 2003. 182p. (YA). 23.95 (978-0-595-66087-2(8)); pap. 13.95 (978-0-595-29955-3(5)) iUniverse, Inc.

Roxbee-Cox, Phil. Find the Puppy. 2007. (Find-its Board Bks). 12p. (J). bds. 6.99 (***978-0-7945-1802-8(8)*** , Usborne) EDC Publishing.

—Find the Puppy. Cartwright, Stephen, illus. rev. ed. 2004. (Treasury of Farmyard Tales Ser.). 10p. (J). 3.99 (978-0-7460-3824-6(0)) EDC Publishing.

Rudisill, J. J., et al, illus. Shaggy's Visit. 1999. (Wimzie's House Bks.). 24p. (J). pap. 3.99 (978-0-88724-540-4(4) , CD-4846) Carson-Dellosa Publishing Co., Inc.

Russell, Christopher. Dogboy. 2006. 272p. (J). 15.99 (978-0-06-084116-4(8)); lib. bdg. 16.89 (978-0-06-084117-1(6)) HarperCollins Pubs.

—Hunted. 2007. 272p. (J). (gr. 5-8). 15.99 (978-0-06-084119-5(2)); lib. bdg. 16.89 (978-0-06-084120-1(6)) HarperCollins Pubs.

Russell, Lisa. The Farm Puppy. 2007. 16p. (J). per. 9.99 (***978-1-59886-810-4(1)***) Tate Publishing & Enterprises, L.L.C.

Ryan, Margaret. Scratch & Sniff. Reed, Nathan, illus. 2006. 48p. (J). lib. bdg. (***978-1-4048-3130-8(4)***) Picture Window Bks.

Ryan, Pam Muñoz. Doug Counts Down. 1998. (Doug Ser.). (Illus.). 32p. (J). (gr. k-4). 8.95 (978-0-7868-3141-8(3)) Disney Pr.

Rylant, Cynthia. Annie & Snowball & the Tea Cup Club. Stevenson, Sucie, illus. 2008. (Annie & Snowball Ser.). 32p. (J). 15.99 (***978-1-4169-0940-8(0)*** , Simon & Schuster Children's Publishing) Simon & Schuster Children's Publishing.

—Dog Heaven. 2002. (Illus.). (J). 25.06 (978-0-7587-2400-7(4)) Book Wholesalers, Inc.

—The Eagle. McDaniels, Preston, illus. 2004. (Lighthouse Family Ser.). 64p. (J). 14.95 (978-0-689-86243-4(1)) Simon & Schuster Children's Publishing.

—Family Time with Henry & Mudge. Stevenson, Sucie, illus. 2002. pap. 61.95 incl. audio (978-0-87499-997-6(9)); pap. 68.95 incl. audio compact disk (978-1-59112-854-0(4)) Live Oak Media.

—The Great Gracie Chase: Stop That Dog! Teague, Mark, illus. 2001. 40p. (J). (ps-3). pap. 15.95 (978-0-590-10041-0(6) , Blue Sky Pr., The) Scholastic, Inc.

—The Great Gracie Chase: Stop That Dog! abr. ed. 2002. (J). (gr. k-3). 26.90 (978-0-8045-6890-6(1)) Spoken Arts, Inc.

—Henry & Mudge. Stevenson, Sucie, illus. 2002. (Henry & Mudge Ser.). (J). 11.91 (978-0-7587-1269-1(3)) Book Wholesalers, Inc.

—Henry & Mudge: The First Book. 2006. (Henry & Mudge Ser.). (J). (gr. 1-6). 24.21 (978-1-59961-082-5(5)) Spotlight.

—Henry & Mudge & a Very Merry Christmas. Stevenson, Sucie, illus. (Henry & Mudge Ser.). 40p. (J). 2005. pap. 3.99 (978-0-689-83448-6(9) , Aladdin); 2004. 14.95 (978-0-689-81168-5(3)) Simon & Schuster Children's Publishing.

—Henry & Mudge & Annie's Good Move. Stevenson, Sucie, illus. 2002. (Henry & Mudge Ser.). (J). 11.91 (978-0-7587-1260-8(X)) Book Wholesalers, Inc.

—Henry & Mudge & Annie's Good Move. Stevenson, Sucie, illus. 2002. (Henry & Mudge Ser.). 28.95 incl. audio compact disk (978-1-59112-648-5(7)); pap. 31.95 incl. audio compact disk (978-1-59112-647-8(9)) Live Oak Media.

—Henry & Mudge & Annie's Good Move. Stevenson, Sucie, illus. (Henry & Mudge Ser.). (J). (gr. k-3). 2000. 48p. pap. 3.99 (978-0-689-83284-0(2) , Aladdin); 1998. 40p. 15.95 (978-0-689-81174-6(8)) Simon & Schuster Children's Publishing.

—Henry & Mudge & Annie's Perfect Pet. Stevenson, Sucie, illus. 2002. (Henry & Mudge Ser.). (J). 11.91 (978-0-7587-5054-9(4)) Book Wholesalers, Inc.

—Henry & Mudge & Annie's Perfect Pet. (Henry & Mudge Ser.). 2001. (Illus.). (J). 10.79 (978-0-606-20699-0(X)); 2000. lib. bdg. 11.80 (978-0-613-33701-4(8)) Tandem Library Bks.

—Henry & Mudge & Mrs. Hopper's House. Bracken, Carolyn, illus. 2003. (Henry & Mudge Ser.). 40p. (J). pap. 3.99 (978-0-689-83446-2(2) , Aladdin); 14.95 (978-0-689-81153-1(5)) Simon & Schuster Children's Publishing.

—Henry & Mudge & Mrs. Hopper's House. 2006. (Henry & Mudge Ser.). (J). (gr. 1-6). 24.21 (978-1-59961-084-9(1)) Spotlight.

—Henry & Mudge & Mrs. Hopper's House. Bracken, Carolyn, illus. 2004. (Henry & Mudge Ser.). 40p. (J). (gr. k-2). lib. bdg. 11.80 (978-0-613-90376-9(5)) Tandem Library Bks.

—Henry & Mudge & the Bedtime Thumps. Stevenson, Sucie, illus. 2002. (Henry & Mudge Ser.). (J). 11.91 (978-0-7587-1265-3(0)) Book Wholesalers, Inc.

—Henry & Mudge & the Bedtime Thumps. 2006. (Henry & Mudge Ser.). (J). (gr. 1). 24.21 (978-1-59961-081-8(7)) Spotlight.

—Henry & Mudge & the Best Day of All. Stevenson, Sucie, illus. 2002. (Henry & Mudge Ser.). (J). 11.91 (978-0-7587-1268-4(5)) Book Wholesalers, Inc.

—Henry & Mudge & the Big Sleepover. Stevenson, Sucie, illus. (Henry & Mudge Ser.). 40p. (J). 2007. pap. 3.99 (978-0-689-83451-6(9) , Aladdin); 2006. 14.95 (978-0-689-81171-5(3) , Simon & Schuster Children's Publishing) Simon & Schuster Children's Publishing.

—Henry & Mudge & the Careful Cousin. Stevenson, Sucie, illus. 1999. (Henry & Mudge Ser.). 28.95 incl. audio compact disk (978-1-59112-571-6(5)); pap. 31.95 incl. audio compact disk (978-1-59112-570-9(7)) Live Oak Media.

—Henry & Mudge & the Careful Cousin. Stevenson, Sucie, illus. 1999. (Henry & Mudge Ser.). 48p. (J). (gr. k-3). 15.99 (978-0-689-81007-7(5)) Simon & Schuster Children's Publishing.

—Henry & Mudge & the Forever Sea. Stevenson, Sucie, illus. 2000. (Henry & Mudge Ser.). 28.95 incl. audio compact disk (978-1-59112-575-4(8)); pap. 31.95 incl. audio compact disk (978-1-59112-574-7(X)) Live Oak Media.

—Henry & Mudge & the Funny Lunch. Bracken, Carolyn, illus. 2005. (Henry & Mudge Ser.). 40p. (J). (gr. k-2). lib. bdg. 12.10 (978-1-4176-7107-6(6)) Tandem Library Bks.

—Henry & Mudge & the Great Grandpas. Stevenson, Sucie, illus. (Henry & Mudge Ser.). 40p. (J). (gr. k-2). 2006. pap. 3.99 (978-0-689-83447-9(0) , Aladdin); 2005. 14.95 (978-0-689-81170-8(5) , Simon & Schuster Children's Publishing) Simon & Schuster Children's Publishing.

—Henry & Mudge & the Long Weekend. Stevenson, Sucie, illus. 2000. (Henry & Mudge Ser.). 28.95 incl. audio compact disk (978-1-59112-577-8(4)); pap. 18.95 incl. audio compact disk (978-1-59112-376-7(3)); pap. 31.95 incl. audio compact disk (978-1-59112-576-1(6)) Live Oak Media.

—Henry & Mudge & the Long Weekend. 2006. (Henry & Mudge Ser.). (J). (gr. 1-6). 24.21 (978-1-59961-083-2(3)) Spotlight.

—Henry & Mudge & the Sneaky Crackers. Stevenson, Sucie, illus. 2002. (Henry & Mudge Ser.). (J). 11.91 (978-0-7587-1271-4(5)) Book Wholesalers, Inc.

—Henry & Mudge & the Sneaky Crackers. 2002. (Henry & Mudge Ser.). (Illus.). (J). pap., tchr.'s planning gde. ed. 29.95 incl. audio (978-0-87499-958-7(8)) Live Oak Media.

—Henry & Mudge & the Sneaky Crackers. Stevenson, Sucie, illus. 2002. (Henry & Mudge Ser.). 28.95 incl. audio compact disk (978-1-59112-639-3(8)); pap. 31.95 incl. audio compact disk (978-1-59112-640-9(1)); (J). pap. 18.95 incl. audio compact disk (978-1-59112-638-6(X)) Live Oak Media.

—Henry & Mudge & the Sneaky Crackers. abr. ed. 2002. (Henry & Mudge Ser.). (Illus.). (J). pap. 16.95 incl. audio (978-0-87499-956-3(1)) Live Oak Media.

—Henry & Mudge & the Sneaky Crackers. Stevenson, Sucie, illus. abr. ed. 2002. (Henry & Mudge Ser.). (J). 25.95 incl. audio (978-0-87499-957-0(X)) Live Oak Media.

—Henry & Mudge & the Sneaky Crackers. Stevenson, Sucie, illus. 1999. (Henry & Mudge Ser.). 48p. (J). (gr. k-3). pap. 3.99 (978-0-689-82525-5(0) , Aladdin) Simon & Schuster Children's Publishing.

—Henry & Mudge & the Sneaky Crackers. 1999. (Henry & Mudge Ser.). (gr. k-3). lib. bdg. 11.80 (978-0-613-11622-0(4)); (J). 10.79 (978-0-606-15925-8(8)) Tandem Library Bks.

—Henry & Mudge & the Snowman Plan. Stevenson, Sucie, illus. 2002. (Henry & Mudge Ser.). (J). 11.91 (978-0-7587-4471-5(4)) Book Wholesalers, Inc.

—Henry & Mudge & the Snowman Plan. 2002. (Henry & Mudge Ser.). (Illus.). (J). pap., tchr.'s planning gde. ed. 29.95 incl. audio (978-0-87499-970-9(7)) Live Oak Media.

—Henry & Mudge & the Snowman Plan. Stevenson, Sucie, illus. 2002. (Henry & Mudge Ser.). 28.95 incl. audio compact disk (978-1-59112-651-5(7)); pap. 31.95 incl. audio compact disk (978-1-59112-652-2(5)) Live Oak Media.

—Henry & Mudge & the Snowman Plan. abr. ed. 2002. (Henry & Mudge Ser.). (Illus.). (J). 25.95 incl. audio (978-0-87499-969-3(3)); pap. 16.95 incl. audio (978-0-87499-968-6(5)) Live Oak Media.

—Henry & Mudge & the Snowman Plan. Stevenson, Sucie, illus. (Henry & Mudge Ser.). 40p. (J). (gr. k-3). 2000. pap. 3.99 (978-0-689-83449-3(7) , Aladdin); 1999. 15.95 (978-0-689-81169-2(1)) Simon & Schuster Children's Publishing.

—Henry & Mudge & the Snowman Plan. 2000. (Henry & Mudge Ser.). (gr. k-3). lib. bdg. 11.80 (978-0-613-29977-0(9)); (J). 10.79 (978-0-606-19711-3(7)) Tandem Library Bks.

—Henry & Mudge & the Starry Night. Stevenson, Sucie, illus. 2002. (Henry & Mudge Ser.). (J). 11.91 (978-0-7587-1272-1(3)) Book Wholesalers, Inc.

—Henry & Mudge & the Starry Night. Stevenson, Sucie, illus. 2002. (Henry & Mudge Ser.). 28.95 incl. audio compact disk (978-1-59112-643-0(6)); pap. 31.95 incl. audio compact disk (978-1-59112-644-7(4)); (J). pap. 18.95 incl. audio compact disk (978-1-59112-642-3(8)) Live Oak Media.

—Henry & Mudge & the Starry Night. abr. ed. 2002. (Henry & Mudge Ser.). (Illus.). (J). 25.95 incl. audio (978-0-87499-961-7(8)); pap. 16.95 incl. audio (978-0-87499-960-0(X)); pap., tchr.'s planning gde. ed. 29.95 incl. audio (978-0-87499-962-4(6)) Live Oak Media.

—Henry & Mudge & the Starry Night. Stevenson, Sucie, illus. 1999. (Henry & Mudge Ser.). 48p. (J). (gr. k-3). pap. 3.99 (978-0-689-82586-6(2) , 076714003996, Aladdin) Simon & Schuster Children's Publishing.

—Henry & Mudge & the Starry Night. 1999. (Henry & Mudge Ser.). (gr. k-3). lib. bdg. 11.80 (978-0-613-18179-2(4)); (J). 10.79 (978-0-606-16305-7(0)) Tandem Library Bks.

—Henry & Mudge & the Tall Tree House. Bracken, Carolyn, illus. 2003. (Henry & Mudge Ser.). 40p. (J). pap. 3.99 (978-0-689-83445-5(4) , Aladdin) Simon & Schuster Children's Publishing.

—Henry & Mudge & the Tall Tree House. 2003. (Henry & Mudge Ser.). (gr. k-3). lib. bdg. 11.80 (978-0-613-90605-0(5)) Tandem Library Bks.

—Henry & Mudge & the Tumbling Trip. Bracken, Carolyn, illus. 2006. (Henry & Mudge Ser.). 40p. (J). pap. 3.99 (978-0-689-83452-3(7) , Aladdin) Simon & Schuster Children's Publishing.

—Henry & Mudge & the Wild Goose Chase. Bracken, Carolyn, illus. 2004. (Henry & Mudge Ser.). 40p. (J). pap. 3.99 (978-0-689-83450-9(0) , Aladdin) Simon & Schuster Children's Publishing.

—Henry & Mudge & the Wild Goose Chase. Bracken, Carolyn, illus. 2004. (Henry & Mudge Ser.). 40p. (J). (gr. k-2). lib. bdg. 12.10 (978-1-4176-4340-0(4)) Tandem Library Bks.

—Henry & Mudge Get the Cold Shivers. Stevenson, Sucie, illus. (Henry & Mudge Ser.). 9.95 (978-1-59112-290-6(2)); 1999. 28.95 incl. audio compact disk (978-1-59112-573-0(1)); 1999. pap. 31.95 incl. audio compact disk (978-1-59112-572-3(3)) Live Oak Media.

—Henry & Mudge in Puddle Trouble. Stevenson, Sucie, illus. 2002. (Henry & Mudge Ser.). (J). 11.91 (978-0-7587-1261-5(8)) Book Wholesalers, Inc.

—Henry & Mudge in Puddle Trouble. 2006. (Henry & Mudge Ser.). (J). (gr. 1-6). 24.21 (978-1-59961-085-6(X)) Spotlight.

—Henry & Mudge in the Family Trees. Stevenson, Sucie, illus. 2002. (Henry & Mudge Ser.). (J). 11.91 (978-0-7587-1273-8(1)) Book Wholesalers, Inc.

—Henry & Mudge in the Family Trees. Stevenson, Sucie, illus. 1998. (Henry & Mudge Ser.). 40p. (J). (gr. k-3). pap. 3.99 (978-0-689-82317-6(7) , Aladdin) Simon & Schuster Children's Publishing.

—Henry & Mudge in the Green Time. Stevenson, Sucie, illus. 2002. (Henry & Mudge Ser.). (J). 11.91 (978-0-7587-1264-6(2)) Book Wholesalers, Inc.

—Henry & Mudge in the Green Time. Stevenson, Sucie, illus. 1999. (Henry & Mudge Ser.). 28.95 incl. audio compact disk (978-1-59112-579-2(0)); pap. 31.95 incl. audio compact disk (978-1-59112-578-5(2)) Live Oak Media.

—Henry & Mudge in the Sparkle Days. Stevenson, Sucie, illus. 2002. (Henry & Mudge Ser.). (J). 11.91 (978-0-7587-1270-7(7)) Book Wholesalers, Inc.

—Henry & Mudge in the Sparkle Days. Stevenson, Sucie, illus. 1999. (Henry & Mudge Ser.). 28.95 incl. audio compact disk (978-1-59112-583-9(9)); pap. 31.95 incl. audio compact disk (978-1-59112-582-2(0)) Live Oak Media.

—Henry & Mudge in the Sparkle Days. 2006. (Henry & Mudge Ser.). (J). (gr. 1-6). 24.21 (978-1-59961-086-3(8)) Spotlight.

—Henry & Mudge Take the Big Test. Stevenson, Sucie, illus. 2002. (Henry & Mudge Ser.). (J). 11.91 (978-0-7587-1266-0(9)) Book Wholesalers, Inc.

—Henry & Mudge under the Yellow Moon. Stevenson, Sucie, illus. 1998. (Henry & Mudge Ser.). 28.95 incl. audio compact disk (978-1-59112-585-3(5)); pap. 31.95 incl. audio compact disk (978-1-59112-584-6(7)) Live Oak Media.

—Mr. Putter & Tabby Spin the Yarn. Howard, Arthur, illus. 2007. (Mr. Putter & Tabby Ser.). 44p. (J). pap. 5.95 (***978-0-15-206095-4(2)*** , Harcourt Paperbacks) Harcourt Children's Bks.

—Mr. Putter & Tabby Spin the Yarn. Howard, Arthur, illus. 2006. (Mr. Putter & Tabby Ser.). 44p. (J). (gr. k-2). 14.00 (978-0-15-205067-2(1)) Harcourt Trade Pubs.

—Mr. Putter & Tabby Stir the Soup. Howard, Arthur, illus. (Mr. Putter & Tabby Ser.). 44p. (J). 2004. pap. 5.95 (978-0-15-205058-0(2) , Harcourt Paperbacks); 2003. 14.00 (978-0-15-202637-0(1)) Harcourt Children's Bks.

—Mr. Putter & Tabby Take the Train. Howard, Arthur, illus. 1998. (Mr. Putter & Tabby Ser.). 44p. (J). (gr. 1-5). 14.00 (978-0-15-201786-6(0)) Harcourt Children's Bks.

—Puppy Mudge Finds a Friend. Stevenson, Sucie, illus. (Puppy Mudge Ser.). (J). (ps-k). 2005. 32p. pap. 3.99 (978-1-4169-0369-7(0) , Aladdin); 2005. (***978-1-4156-3675-6(3)*** , Aladdin); 2004. 32p. 14.95 (978-0-689-83982-5(0)) Simon & Schuster Children's Publishing.

—Puppy Mudge Has a Snack. Mones, Isidre, illus. 2003. (Puppy Mudge Ser.). 32p. (J). (ps-k). 14.95 (978-0-689-83981-8(2)) Simon & Schuster Children's Publishing.

—Puppy Mudge Loves His Blanket. Mones, Isidre, illus. 2005. (Puppy Mudge Ser.). 32p. (J). (ps). pap. 3.99 (978-1-4169-0336-9(4) , Aladdin) Simon & Schuster Children's Publishing.

—Puppy Mudge Loves His Blanket. Mones, Isidre, illus. 2005. (Puppy Mudge Ser.). 32p. (J). (ps). lib. bdg. 11.19 (978-0-606-33855-4(1)) Tandem Library Bks.

—Puppy Mudge Takes a Bath. 2004. (Puppy Mudge Ser.). (ps-2). lib. bdg. 11.80 (978-0-613-90714-9(0)) Tandem Library Bks.

—Puppy Mudge Wants to Play. Stevenson, Sucie, illus. (Puppy Mudge Ser.). 32p. (J). 2006. pap. 3.99 (978-1-4169-1556-0(7) , Aladdin); 2005. 14.95 (978-0-689-83984-9(7)) Simon & Schuster Children's Publishing.

—Seasons with Henry & Mudge. Stevenson, Sucie, illus. 2000. (Henry & Mudge Ser.). pap. 68.95 incl. audio compact disk (978-1-59112-855-7(2)); (J). pap. 61.95 incl. audio (978-0-87499-573-2(6)) Live Oak Media.

—Tulip Sees America. Desimini, Lisa, illus. 32p. (J). (ps up). 2002. pap. 6.99 (978-0-439-39978-4(5)); 1998. pap. 15.95 (978-0-590-84744-5(9) , Blue Sky Pr., The) Scholastic, Inc.

—Tulip Sees America. 2002. (gr. k-3). lib. bdg. 14.15 (978-0-613-53874-9(9)) Tandem Library Bks.

Rylant, Cynthia & Bracken, Carolyn. Henry & Mudge & the Funny Lunch. 2004. (Henry & Mudge Ser.). (Illus.). 40p. (J). (gr. k-3). 14.95 (978-0-689-81178-4(0)) Simon & Schuster Children's Publishing.

—Henry & Mudge & the Tall Tree House. 2002. (Henry & Mudge Ser.). (Illus.). 40p. (J). (gr. k-3). 15.95 (978-0-689-81173-9(X)) Simon & Schuster Children's Publishing.

—Henry & Mudge & the Tumbling Trip. Stevenson, Sucie, illus. 2005. (Henry & Mudge Ser.). 40p. (J). (gr. k-3). 14.95 (978-0-689-81180-7(2)) Simon & Schuster Children's Publishing.

—Henry & Mudge & the Wild Goose Chase. 2003. (Henry & Mudge Ser.). (Illus.). 40p. (J). (gr. k-3). 14.95 (978-0-689-81172-2(1)) Simon & Schuster Children's Publishing.

Rylant, Cynthia & McDaniels, Preston. The Storm. 2003. (Lighthouse Family Ser.). (Illus.). 80p. (J). pap. 3.99 (978-0-689-84882-7(X) , Aladdin) Simon & Schuster Children's Publishing.

Rylant, Cynthia & Mones, Isidre. Puppy Mudge Has a Snack. 2004. (Puppy Mudge Ser.). (Illus.). 32p. (J). pap. 3.99 (978-0-689-86995-2(9) , Aladdin) Simon & Schuster Children's Publishing.

—Puppy Mudge Loves His Blanket. 2004. (Puppy Mudge Ser.). (Illus.). 32p. (J). (ps-k). 14.95 (978-0-689-83983-2(9)) Simon & Schuster Children's Publishing.

—Puppy Mudge Takes a Bath. (Puppy Mudge Ser.). (Illus.). 32p. (J). 2004. pap. 3.99 (978-0-689-86621-0(6) , Aladdin); 2002. 14.95 (978-0-689-83980-1(4)) Simon & Schuster Children's Publishing.

The Sacrament Series. 2005. (J). (978-0-9772007-0-2(1)) Layne Morgan Media, Inc.

Sadler, Judy Ann. Sandwiches for Duke. Bennett, Lorna, illus. 2007. 32p. (J). pap. (978-1-55005-062-2(1)) Fitzhenry & Whiteside, Ltd.

—Sandwiches for Duke. Bennett, Lorna, illus. 2002. 30p. (ps-3). 15.95 (978-0-7737-3313-8(2)) Stoddart Kids CAN. *Dist:* Fitzhenry & Whiteside, Ltd.

Sager, Elizabeth R. Clif & Simmons: A Tale of Two Puppies. l.t. ed. 1999. (Illus.). 20p. (J). (gr. k-5). pap. 6.95 (978-0-9678386-0-1(6)) C.S. Publishing.

—Clif & Simmons: And Pet the Puppies. Gladden, Dawn, photos by. l.t. ed. 2001. (Illus.). 16p. (J). (ps-3). pap. 9.95 (978-0-9678386-4-9(9)) C.S. Publishing.

—Clify Simmons: El Cuento de dos Puerritos. Wheatley, Olga, tr. from ENG. Gladden, Dawn, photos by. 2000. Tr. of Clif & Simmons: A Tale of Two Puppies. (SPA., Illus.). 20p. (J). (gr. k-6). pap. 6.95 (978-0-9678386-1-8(4)) C.S. Publishing.

Said, S. F. The Outlaw Varjak Paw. McKean, Dave, illus. 2007. 272p. (J). (gr. 3-7). 6.50 (978-0-440-42172-6(1) , Yearling) Random Hse. Children's Bks.

Salas, Macarena, ed. What A Mess, Little Puppies!/vaya Desorden, Cachorritos! 2005. (Disney Bil Ser.). (SPA.). 10p. (J). bds. 3.99 (978-0-439-66367-0(9) , Scholastic en Espanol) Scholastic, Inc.

Salisbury, Graham. Eyes of the Emperor. (YA). (gr. 7-11). 2007. 256p. mass mkt. 6.50 (978-0-440-22956-8(1) , Laurel Leaf); 2005. 240p. 15.95 (978-0-385-72971-0(5) , Lamb, Wendy); 2005. 240p. lib. bdg. 17.99 (978-0-385-90874-0(1) , Lamb, Wendy) Random Hse. Children's Bks.

—Jungle Dogs. unabr. ed. 2000. (YA). (gr. 5 up). pap., stu. ed. 59.95 incl. audio (978-0-7887-4336-8(8) , 41131) Recorded Bks., LLC.

—Jungle Dogs. 1999. 11.64 (978-0-606-17837-2(6)) Tandem Library Bks.

Saltzberg, Barney. I Love Dogs. Saltzberg, Barney, illus. 2005. (Super Sturdy Picture Book Ser.). (Illus.). 24p. (J). (ps up). 8.99 (978-0-7636-2587-0(6)) Candlewick Pr.

Salvador, Thomas W., II. Suitcase the Dog. 1999. 24p. (J). (ps-2). pap. 4.95 (978-0-9678030-0-5(4)) Caribbean Scene.

Sam the Dog. (Chunky Animal Shaped Boards Ser.). (J). 2003. 10p. bds. 9.95 (978-0-7525-7856-9(1)); 2003. (Illus.). bds. 1.98 (978-0-7525-7777-7(8)); 2002. bds. 4.98 (978-0-7525-4632-2(5)) Parragon, Inc.

Sampson, Brent. Aidan's Shoes. Switzer, Bobbi, illus. 2006. (ENG.). 28p. per. 12.95 (***978-1-59800-684-1(3)***) Outskirts Press, Inc.

Sampson, Michael R. Caddie the Golf Dog. Cooper, Floyd, illus. 2000. 32p. (J). 14.99 (978-0-8499-5823-6(7)) Nelson, Thomas Inc.

Sander, Heather. Whatever Happened to My Dog Cuddles. 2004. (Illus.). 176p. (J). (gr. 3-7). pap. 6.95 (978-1-55143-307-3(9)) Orca Bk. Pubs. USA.

Santiago, Tony, illus. A Greyhound's Tale: Running for Glory, Walking for Home. 2006. 32p. 15.00 (978-0-9762564-2-7(8)) Ideate Prairie.

Santillo, LuAnn. The Dog. Santillo, LuAnn, ed. 2003. (Half-Pint Kids Readers Ser.). (Illus.). 7p. (J). (ps-1). pap. (978-1-59256-065-3(2)) Half-Pint Kids, Inc.

—Go West. Santillo, LuAnn, ed. 2003. (Half-Pint Kids Readers Ser.). (Illus.). 7p. (J). (ps-1). pap. (978-1-59256-071-4(7)) Half-Pint Kids, Inc.

Santomero, Angela C. Blue Goes to School. Levy, David B., illus. 2000. (Blue's Clues Ser.). 24p. (J). (ps-k). pap. 3.99 (978-0-689-83280-2(X) , Simon Spotlight/ Nickelodeon) Simon & Schuster Children's Publishing.

—Blue Goes to School. 2000. (gr. k-3). lib. bdg. 11.25 (978-0-613-24384-1(6)) Tandem Library Bks.

—Blue Is My Name: My First Preschool Ready to Read. 2000. (gr. k-3). lib. bdg. 11.80 (978-0-613-24386-5(2)) Tandem Library Bks.

—Blue Is My Name! My First Preschool Ready to Read, Level 1. Craig, Karen, illus. 2000. (Blues Clue's Ready to Read Ser.: No. 1). 24p. (J). (ps-1). pap. 3.99 (978-0-689-83122-5(6) , Simon Spotlight/Nickelodeon) Simon & Schuster Children's Publishing.

—Blue Va a la Escuela. 2003. Tr. of Blue Goes to School. (SPA.). (ps-2). lib. bdg. 11.25 (978-0-613-90465-0(6)) Tandem Library Bks.

—Blue va a la escuela. Levy, David B., illus. 2003. (Blue's Clues Ser.).Tr. of Blue Goes to School. (SPA.). 24p. (J). 3.99 (978-0-689-86308-0(X) , Libros Para Ninos) Simon & Schuster Children's Publishing.

—Blue's Big Birthday. 2002. (gr. k-3). lib. bdg. 11.25 (978-0-613-51292-3(8)) Tandem Library Bks.

—Blue's Big Treasure Hunt. Johnson, Traci Paige & Kim, Soo Kyung, illus. 1999. (Blue's Clues Ser.). 24p. (J). (ps-k). 5.99 (978-0-689-82540-8(4) , Simon Spotlight/ Nickelodeon) Simon & Schuster Children's Publishing.

—Blue's Big Treasure Hunt. 1999. (gr. k-3). lib. bdg. 14.15 (978-0-613-63255-3(9)) Tandem Library Bks.

—Buenas Noches, Blue. Pontillo, Jenine, illus. 2003. (Blue's Clues Ser.). (SPA.). 22p. (J). bds. 4.99 (978-0-689-86309-7(8) , Libros Para Ninos) Simon & Schuster Children's Publishing.

—Crayon World. Johnson, Traci Paige & Kim, Soo Kyung, illus. 1999. (Blue's Clues Ser.). 6p. (J). (ps-k). bds. 4.99 (978-0-689-82448-7(3) , Simon Spotlight/Nickelodeon) Simon & Schuster Children's Publishing.

—Farley's Crayon World. Kim, illus. 2001. 8p. mass mkt. 0.06 (978-0-689-84796-7(3) , Simon Spotlight/ Nickelodeon) Simon & Schuster Children's Publishing.

—Good Night Blue. Pontillo, Jenine, illus. 1999. (Blue's Clues Ser.). 10p. (J). (ps-k). bds. 4.99 (978-0-689-82950-5(7) , Simon Spotlight/Nickelodeon) Simon & Schuster Children's Publishing.

—Lights On! Lights Off! 1999. (Blue's Clues Ser.). (Illus.). 140p. (J). (ps-k). pap. 9.00 (978-0-7416-1009-6(4)) Havoc Publishing.

—What to Do, Blue? Johnson, Traci Paige & Craig, Karen, illus. 1999. (Blue's Clues Ser.: Vol. 2). 24p. (J). (ps-k). pap. 3.50 (978-0-689-82444-9(0) , 076714003507, Simon Spotlight/Nickelodeon) Simon & Schuster Children's Publishing.

—What to Do, Blue? 1999. (gr. k-3). lib. bdg. 11.25 (978-0-613-16035-3(5)) Tandem Library Bks.

Santomero, Angela C., et al. Lights On! Lights Off! Rillo, Cary, illus. 1998. (Blue's Clues Ser.). 20p. (J). (ps-k). bds. 4.99 (978-0-689-81909-4(9) , Simon Spotlight/ Nickelodeon) Simon & Schuster Children's Publishing.

—What to Do, Blue? 1999. (Blue's Clues Ser.). (Illus.). 24p. (J). (gr. k-3). pap. 3.50 (978-0-689-83214-7(1) , Simon Spotlight/Nickelodeon) Simon & Schuster Children's Publishing.

Sargent, Dave. Autumn's Emergency. Huff, Jean Lirley, illus. 2000. (J). pap. (978-1-56763-566-9(0)) Ozark Publishing.

Sargent, Dave & Sargent, Pat. Cammie Camel: Endurance, 56 bks, Vol. 42. Lenoir, Jane, illus. 2000. (Animal Pride Ser.). 36p. (J). lib. bdg. 19.95 (978-1-56763-525-6(3)) Ozark Publishing.

—A Puppy for Bobby/un cachorro para Robertito, 10. Robinson, Laura, illus. 2004. (Learn to Read Ser.: 10). (ENG & SPA.). 18p. (J). pap. 9.95 (978-1-56763-982-7(8)) Ozark Publishing.

—Puppy for Bobby/un cachorro para Robertito, 10, 11. Robinson, Laura, illus. 2004. (Learn to Read Ser.: 10). (ENG & SPA.). 18p. (J). lib. bdg. 19.95 (978-1-56763-981-0(X)) Ozark Publishing.

—Samone the Siamese: Lazybones!, 56 vols., 36. Huff, Jeane, illus. 2001. (Animal Pride Ser.: Vol. 36). 36p. (J). lib. bdg. 19.95 (978-1-56763-388-7(9)) Ozark Publishing.

—Young Chrissy: Mind Your Mama!, 7. Woodword, Elaine, illus. 2005. (Young Animal Pride Ser.). 24p. (J). pap. 6.95 (978-1-56763-876-9(7)) Ozark Publishing.

—Young Dawn: Friends Care!, 8. Woodword, Elaine, illus. 2005. (Young Animal Pride Ser.: 8). 24p. (J). pap. 6.95 (978-1-56763-878-3(3)); lib. bdg. 19.95 (978-1-56763-877-6(5)) Ozark Publishing.

—Young Sammy: I'm a Little Stinker, 9. Woodword, Elaine, illus. 2005. (Young Animal Pride Ser.). 24p. (J). lib. bdg. 19.95 (978-1-56763-879-0(1)) Ozark Publishing.

—Young Sammy: I'm a Little Stinker!, 9. Woodword, Elaine, illus. 2005. (Young Animal Pride Ser.). 24p. (J). pap. 6.95 (978-1-56763-880-6(5)) Ozark Publishing.

—Young White Thunder: I'm a Leader!, 6. Woodword, Elaine, illus. 2005. (Young Animal Pride Ser.). 24p. (J). pap. 6.95 (978-1-56763-874-5(0)); lib. bdg. 19.95 (978-1-56763-873-8(2)) Ozark Publishing.

Sargent, Dave, et al. Cammie Camel: Endurance, 17, 42. 2000. (Animal Pride Ser.: 42). (Illus.). (J). pap. 6.95 (978-1-56763-526-3(1)) Ozark Publishing.

—A Puppy for Bobby, 10. 2004. (Learn to Read Ser.: 10). (Illus.). 18p. (J). pap. 9.95 (978-1-56763-818-9(X)); lib. bdg. 19.95 (978-1-56763-817-2(1)) Ozark Publishing.

—Young Chrissy: Mind Your Mama!, 7. 2005. (Young Animal Pride Ser.). (Illus.). 24p. (J). lib. bdg. 19.95 (978-1-56763-875-2(9)) Ozark Publishing.

Sargent, Dave M., Jr. Buffy's Haircut, 9. Huff, Jeane Lirley, illus. 2004. (Doggie Tails Ser.: 9). (J). pap. 9.95 (978-1-56763-860-8(0)) Ozark Publishing.

—Vicious Vera, 9. Huff, Jeane Lirley, illus. 2004. (Doggie Tails Ser.: 9). (J). pap. 9.95 (978-1-56763-854-7(6)); lib. bdg. 19.95 (978-1-56763-853-0(8)) Ozark Publishing.

Sargent, David M., Jr. Autumn's Emergency. Huff, Jeane Lirley, illus. 2003. (Doggie Tails Ser.). 32p. (J). pap. 6.95 (978-1-56763-846-2(5)) Ozark Publishing.

—Buffy's Haircut, 9. Huff, Jeane Lirley, illus. 2004. (Doggie Tails Ser.: 9). (J). lib. bdg. 19.95 (978-1-56763-859-2(7)) Ozark Publishing.

—Buffy's Revenge. Huff, Jeane Lirley, illus. 2003. (Doggie Tails Ser.). 32p. (J). pap. 6.95 (978-1-56763-844-8(9)) Ozark Publishing.

—Guard Dog Mary. Huff, Jeane Lirley, illus. 2003. (Doggie Tails Ser.). 32p. (J). lib. bdg. 19.95 (978-1-56763-843-1(0)); pap. 6.95 (978-1-56763-850-9(3)); lib. bdg. 19.95 (978-1-56763-849-3(X)) Ozark Publishing.

—Portia's Prank, 9. Huff, Jeane Lirley, illus. 2003. (Doggie Tails Ser.). 32p. (J). pap. 6.95 (978-1-56763-848-6(1)); lib. bdg. 19.95 (978-1-56763-847-9(3)) Ozark Publishing.

Sargent, Pat. The Black Panther, 6. Lenoir, Jane, illus. 2003. (Barney the Bear Killer Ser.: Vol. 2). 137p. (J). 2. pap. 9.95 (978-1-56763-966-7(6)); Vol. 2. lib. bdg. 25.25 (978-1-56763-965-0(8)) Ozark Publishing.

—The Bobcat, 8, Vol. 5. Lenoir, Jane, illus. 2003. (Barney the Bear Killer Ser.: Vol. 5). 136p. (J). lib. bdg. 25.25 (978-1-56763-971-1(2)) Ozark Publishing.

—Cougar Holler. Lenoir, Jane, illus. 2000. (J). lib. bdg. 19.95 (978-1-56763-563-8(6)); pap. 6.95 (978-1-56763-564-5(4)) Ozark Publishing.

—Cougar Holler, 8, Vol. 4. Lenoir, Jane, illus. 2004. (Barney the Bear Killer Ser.: 6). (J). lib. bdg. 25.25 (978-1-56763-969-8(0)) Ozark Publishing.

Sargent, Pat L. Jaguar #8 (PB), 6 vols. 2007. (Barney the Bear Killer Ser.: 8). (YA). pap. 9.95 (*978-1-59381-425-0(9)) Ozark Publishing.

Sarnoff, Lolo. Dara: Autobiography of a Chesapeake Bay Retriever. 1999. (Illus.). 94p. (YA). (gr. 4 up). 16.95 (978-0-9700667-9-4(1)) Dara's Canine Foundation, Inc.

Sarrazin, Marisol. Peppy, Patch, & the Postman. 2005. (Read-It! Readers Ser.). (Illus.). 32p. (C). (gr. k-3). 18.60 (978-1-4048-1034-1(X)) Picture Window Bks.

—Peppy, Patch, & the Socks. 2005. (Read-It! Readers Ser.). (Illus.). 32p. (C). (gr. k-3). 18.60 (978-1-4048-1023-5(4)) Picture Window Bks.

Sarrazin, Marisol, illus. Peppy, Patch, & the Bath. 2005. (Read-It! Readers Ser.). 32p. (C). (gr. k-3). 18.60 (978-1-4048-1032-7(3)) Picture Window Bks.

Sarrazin, Marisol & Homel, David. Peppy, Phlox & the Bath. 2000. (Illus.). 32p. (J). (gr. 1-4). pap. (978-1-894363-42-6(6)) Dominique & Friends.

Sathre, Vivian. Digging up the Past. l.t. ed. 1999. (Adventures of Wishbone Ser.: No. 6). (Illus.). 144p. (J). (gr. 4 up). lib. bdg. 22.60 (978-0-8368-2302-8(8)) Stevens, Gareth Inc.

—Dog Overboard! l.t. ed. 1999. (Adventures of Wishbone Ser.: No. 12). (Illus.). (J). (gr. 4 up). lib. bdg. 22.60 (978-0-8368-2590-9(X)) Stevens, Gareth Inc.

—Stage Invader. l.t. ed. 2000. (Wishbone Mysteries Ser.: No. 15). (Illus.). 140p. (J). (gr. 4 up). lib. bdg. 23.33 (978-0-8368-2698-2(1)) Stevens, Gareth Inc.

—Stage Invader. 1999. (Wishbone Mysteries Ser.: No. 15). (J). (gr. 2-5). (978-0-606-15826-8(X)) Tandem Library Bks.

Sattler, Jennifer Gordon. All Aboard, Owney! The Adirondack Mail Dog. Sattler, Jennifer Gordon, illus. 2003. (Illus.). 32p. (J). per. 10.95 (978-0-9713069-7-4(4)) Burns, Nicholas K. Publishing.

Saunders, Margaret Marshall. Beautiful Joe. 2001. (Fiction Treasures Ser.). (Illus.). 326p. pap., pap., pap. (978-0-88780-540-0(X)) Formac Publishing Co., Ltd. CAN. *Dist:* Casemate Pubs. & Bk. Distributors, LLC.

Saunders, Marshall. Beautiful Joe: An AutoBiography of a Dog. 2007. 244p. pap. 12.99 (*978-1-4264-4034-2(0)); 266p. pap. 16.99 (*978-1-4264-4093-9(6)) BiblioBazaar.

—Beautiful Joe a Dog's Own Story. 2006. 256p. pap. 18.45 (978-1-59462-284-7(1) , 320, Book Jungle) Standard Pubns., Inc.

—Beautiful Joe a Dog's Own Story - 1893. 2006. 256p. pap. 18.45 (978-1-59462-261-8(2) , 297, Book Jungle) Standard Pubns., Inc.

Saunders, Susan. All-American Puppies: On The Scent of Trouble. 2001. (All-American Puppies Ser.: Vol. 2). (Illus.). 96p. (J). (gr. 2-5). pap. 3.99 (978-0-06-440885-1(X)) HarperCollins Pubs.

—All-American Puppies No. 1: New Pup on the Block. 2001. (gr. 3-6). lib. bdg. 11.80 (978-0-613-71454-9(7)) Tandem Library Bks.

Savarese, Peter. The Smartest Dog in the Neighborhood. 2005. (J). pap. 7.95 (978-0-533-14951-3(7)) Vantage Pr., Inc.

Sawyer, Dawn. Good Dog! Haefele, Steve, illus. 2004. (Clifford Ser.). 32p. (J). (ps up). pap. 3.99 (978-0-439-62690-3(0)) Scholastic, Inc.

Scarry, Huck & Scarry, Richard. A Day at the Police Station. 2004. (Illus.). 24p. (J). (ps-2). pap. 3.99 (978-0-375-82822-5(2) , Golden Bks.) Random Hse. Children's Bks.

Schaap, Martine & De Wolf, Alex. Mop's Backyard Concert. 2003. (Mop & Family Ser.). (Illus.). 32p. (J). (ps-3). 12.95 (978-1-57768-892-1(9) , Cricket) School Specialty Publishing.

Schachner, Judith Byron. Skippyjon Jones & the Big Dig. 2007. 32p. (J). (ps). 16.99 (*978-0-525-47884-3(1) , Dutton Juvenile) Penguin Group (USA) Inc.

Schachner, Judy. Skippyjon Jones: Color Crazy. 2007. 12p. (J). (ps). pap. 6.99 (978-0-525-47782-2(9) , Dutton Juvenile) Penguin Group (USA) Inc.

—Skippyjon Jones in Mummy Trouble. Schachner, Judy, illus. 2006. (Illus.). 36p. (J). (ps). 16.99 (978-0-525-47754-9(3) , Dutton Juvenile) Penguin Group (USA) Inc.

—Skippyjon Jones in the Doghouse. Schachner, Judy, illus. 2007. 32p. (J). pap. 6.99 (978-0-14-240749-3(6) , Puffin) Penguin Group (USA) Inc.

—Skippyjon Jones in the Doghouse. Wilhelm, James J., ed. Schachner, Judy, illus. 2005. (Illus.). 32p. (J). (ps). 16.99 (978-0-525-47297-1(5) , Dutton Juvenile) Penguin Group (USA) Inc.

Schade, Susan. Space Dog Jack. 2001. (Hello Reader! Ser.). (Illus.). (J). (978-0-606-21443-8(7)) Tandem Library Bks.

Schade, Susan & Buller, Jon. Space Dog Jack. 2001. (Hello Reader! Ser.). (Illus.). 32p. (J). (ps-1). pap. (978-0-439-20541-2(7)) Scholastic, Inc.

—Space Dog Jack & the Haunted Spaceship. 2002. (Hello Reader! Ser.). (Illus.). 32p. (J). pap. 3.99 (978-0-439-32315-4(0) , Cartwheel Bks.) Scholastic, Inc.

Schaefer, Lola M. Baron: Rescue Dog. Butterfield, Ned, illus. 2000. (Books for Young Learners). 16p. (J). 20.00 (978-1-57274-743-2(9) , BB2427) Owen, Richard C. Pubs., Inc.

—Baron, Perro de Rescate. de la Vega, Eida, tr. Butterfield, Ned, illus. 2001. (Books for Young Learners).Tr. of Baron: Rescue Dog. (SPA.). 16p. (J). (gr. k-2). pap. 5.00 (978-1-57274-437-0(5) , 2828) Owen, Richard C. Pubs., Inc.

Schaefer, Lola M. What's That, Mittens? Hartung, Susan Kathleen, illus. 2008. (My First I Can Read Bks.). 32p. (J). 16.99 (*978-0-06-054662-5(X)); lib. bdg. 17.89 (*978-0-06-054663-2(8)) HarperCollins Pubs.

Schaefer, Peggy. My Puppy's First Year. Bates, Amy June, illus. 2007. 24p. (J). (gr. k-3). pap. 12.99 (*978-0-8249-5571-7(4) , Ideals Children's Bks.) Ideals Pubns.

Scherer, Catherine W. Simon & Barklee in China, Book 1 - the Southeast. 2007. (Another Country Calling Ser.). (J). per. 15.00 (978-0-9714502-6-4(9) , Explorer Media) Simon & Barklee, Inc./ExplorerMedia.

Scheunemann, Pam. Cat Tails. Chawla, Neena, illus. 2006. (Fact & Fiction Ser.). 24p. (J). pap. (978-1-59679-928-8(5)); (gr. 1-3). 21.35 (978-1-59679-927-1(7) , SandCastle) ABDO Publishing Co.

Schieber, Barry J. An Open Heart: A Story about Moritz. 2006. (Illus.). 32p. (J). 17.00 (*978-0-9721457-2-5(9)) Silent Moon Bks.

Schiller, Gerald A. The Dog That Belonged to No One. Schiller, Dawn, illus. unabr. ed. 1998. 105p. (J). (gr. 3-7). pap. 5.95 (978-1-881164-91-3(8)) Intercontinental Publishing, Inc.

—Two Dogs, an Emperor, & Me. Schiller, Dawn, illus. 2000. 108p. (J). (gr. 4-7). pap. 7.50 (978-1-881164-92-0(6)) Intercontinental Publishing, Inc.

Schiller, Pam. My Doggie Brought to Me. Sanford, Robert, illus. 2006. (Noodlebug Ser.). (J). 12.95 (978-0-7696-4276-5(4)) School Specialty Publishing.

Schmidt, Karen. Carl's Nose. 2006. (Illus.). 40p. (J). 16.00 (978-0-15-205049-8(3)) Harcourt Trade Pubs.

Schmidt, Werner. Prisoners of the Witchaliks. 2005. 173p. pap. 12.50 (978-1-4116-4728-2(9)) Lulu.com.

Schneider, Howie. Chewy Louie. Schneider, Howie, illus. 2000. (Illus.). 32p. (ps-3). 15.95 (978-0-87358-765-5(0) , Rising Moon Bks. for Young Readers) Northland Publishing.

Scholastic, Inc. Staff. The Christmas Cookie Case. del Sur, Duendes, illus. 2004. (Scooby Doo Ser.). 32p. (J). pap. 3.99 (978-0-439-55714-6(3)) Scholastic, Inc.

—Cleo Plush. 2001. (Clifford Ser.). (J). 10.99 (978-0-439-30184-8(X) , Sidekicks TM) Scholastic, Inc.

—Clifford Reduced Floppy. 2001. (Clifford Ser.). (J). 18.99 (978-0-439-30186-2(6) , Sidekicks TM) Scholastic, Inc.

—Clifford the Big Red Dog: The Big Leaf Pile. 2001. (Clifford, the Big Red Dog Ser.). (Illus.). (J). 10.79 (978-0-606-21112-3(8)) Tandem Library Bks.

—Clifford the Big Red Dog: The Dog Who Cried "Woof!" 2001. (Clifford, the Big Red Dog Ser.). (Illus.). (J). 10.79 (978-0-606-21113-0(6)) Tandem Library Bks.

—Clifford the Big Red Dog Collectible Plush. 2001. (Clifford Ser.). (J). 10.99 (978-0-439-29696-0(X) , Sidekicks TM) Scholastic, Inc.

—Clifford the Small Red Puppy: Beanbag. 2004. (Sidekicks Ser.). (J). 8.99 (978-0-439-64991-9(9) , Sidekicks TM) Scholastic, Inc.

—Clifford's Puppy Days Attachable Jiggler. 2004. (Sidekicks Ser.). (J). 11.99 (978-0-439-63683-4(3) , Sidekicks TM) Scholastic, Inc.

—Clifford's Puppy Days (Daffodil Beanbag) 2004. (Sidekicks Ser.). (J). 8.99 (978-0-439-64990-2(0) , Sidekicks TM) Scholastic, Inc.

—Clifford's Puppy Days (Jorge Beanbag) 2004. (Sidekicks Ser.). (J). 8.99 (978-0-439-64988-9(9) , Sidekicks TM) Scholastic, Inc.

—Clifford's Puppy Days (Norville Beanbag) 2004. (Sidekicks Ser.). (J). 8.99 (978-0-439-64989-6(7) , Sidekicks TM) Scholastic, Inc.

—Clifford's Puppy Days Wrist Rattle, 12, Pack. 2004. (Sidekicks Ser.). (J). 71.88 (978-0-439-62731-3(1) , Sidekicks TM) Scholastic, Inc.

—Dear Mrs. Larue. 2005. (J). pap. 550.00 (978-0-439-70787-9(0) , Sidekicks TM) Scholastic, Inc.

—Dog Who Cried Woof: El Perro Que Grito Socorrol. Salas, Macarena, ed. 2002. (Clifford Big Red Readers Ser.). (SPA., Illus.). 32p. (J). pap. 3.99 (978-0-439-31734-4(7) , SO0084, Scholastic en Espanol) Scholastic, Inc.

—Me Gusta el Invierno! Winter Ice Is Nice. Salas, Macarena, ed. 2003. (Clifford Big Red Readers Ser.). (SPA., Illus.). 32p. (J). (ps-k). pap. 3.99 (978-0-439-39523-6(2) , Scholastic en Espanol) Scholastic, Inc.

—Scooby Doo Storybook Collection, 8 vols., Set. 2002. (Scooby-Doo Ser.). (Illus.). 256p. (J). (ps-1). 10.99 (978-0-439-51320-3(0) , Scholastic Paperbacks) Scholastic, Inc.

—The Small Red Puppy Teether Rattle, 12, Pack. 2003. (Clifford Ser.). (J). 83.88 (978-0-439-20131-5(4) , Sidekicks TM) Scholastic, Inc.

—T-Bone Plush. 2001. (Clifford Ser.). (J). 10.99 (978-0-439-30185-5(8) , Sidekicks TM) Scholastic, Inc.

Scholastic, Inc. Staff, contrib. by. Teacher's Pet: Clifford. 2002. (Illus.). 32p. (J). pap. 6.99 (978-0-439-36411-9(6)) Scholastic, Inc.

Scholastic, Inc. Staff & Bridwell, Norman. Finger Puppet. 1999. (Clifford Ser.). (J). 6.99 (978-0-439-09261-6(2) , Sidekicks TM) Scholastic, Inc.

Scholastic, Inc. Staff & Hooks, Gwendolyn. The Mystery of the Missing Dog. Devard, Nancy, illus. 2004. (Just for You! Ser.). 32p. (gr. k-3). pap. 3.99 (978-0-439-56864-7(1) , Teaching Resources) Scholastic, Inc.

Scholastic, Inc. Staff & Mills, Liz. Go, Clifford, Go! Bracken, Carolyn & Edwards, Ken, illus. 2002. (Clifford, the Big Red Dog Ser.). 10p. (J). bds. 9.99 (978-0-439-39447-5(3)) Scholastic, Inc.

Scholastic, Inc. Staff, et al. Scooby-Doo & the Witch's Ghost. 1999. (Scooby-Doo Movie Storybooks). (Illus.). 32p. (J). (ps-3). pap. 3.50 (978-0-439-08786-5(4)) Scholastic, Inc.

—28 Floppy Clifford with Barking Mechanism. 2003. (Clifford Ser.). (J). 49.99 (978-0-439-48643-9(2) , Sidekicks TM) Scholastic, Inc.

Schories, Pat. Breakfast for Jack. 2004. (Illus.). 32p. (J). 13.95 (978-1-932425-16-1(0) , Lemniscaat) Boyds Mills Pr.

—Jack & the Missing Piece. 2004. (Illus.). 32p. (J). 13.95 (978-1-932425-17-8(9) , Lemniscaat) Boyds Mills Pr.

—Jack & the Night Visitors. 2006. (Illus.). 32p. (J). 13.95 (978-1-932425-33-8(0) , Lemniscaat) Boyds Mills Pr.

Schories, Pat, illus. Bathtime for Biscuit. 2002. (Biscuit Ser.). (J). 11.91 (978-0-7587-6003-6(5)) Book Wholesalers, Inc.

—Biscuit. 2002. (Biscuit Ser.). (J). 12.34 (978-0-7587-0002-5(4)) Book Wholesalers, Inc.

—Biscuit & the Little Pup. 2008. (My First I Can Read Bks.). 32p. (J). 17.89 (*978-0-06-074171-6(6)); 16.99 (*978-0-06-074170-9(8)) HarperCollins Pubs.

—Biscuit Wants to Play. 2002. (Biscuit Ser.). (J). 11.87 (978-0-7587-8903-7(3)) Book Wholesalers, Inc.

—Biscuit's Fourth of July. 2005. (J). (*978-1-4156-0311-6(1) , Harper Festival) HarperCollins Pubs.

—Biscuit's Graduation Day. 2005. (J). (*978-1-4155-9660-9(3) , Harper Festival) HarperCollins Pubs.

Schories, Pat, illus. Biscuit's New Trick. 2002. (Biscuit Ser.). (J). 11.91 (978-0-7587-5673-2(9)) Book Wholesalers, Inc.

Schrader, Jessica R. Carrie's New Puppy. 2006. (J). pap. 17.50 (978-0-9776440-6-3(5)) Working Title Publishing.

Schroeder, Erin, illus. & des. Oh no! it's the helpful hound... & the days of the Week. Schroeder, Erin, des. 2006. (FRE, JPN, SPA & GER.). 27p. (J). per. 7.95 (*978-0-9779155-0-7(6)) Erinsillart.

Schroeder, Frauna. Elwood: A Dog with Heart. Carlson, Kim, illus. 2006. 32p. (J). per. 9.95 (978-1-892076-20-5(9)) Dancing Moon Pr.

Schubert, Leda. Winnie All Day Long. Benedict, William, illus. 2000. (Brand New Readers Ser.). 1p. (J). (ps-2). pap. 5.99 (978-0-7636-0774-6(6)) Candlewick Pr.

—Winnie Plays Ball. Benedict, William, illus. 2000. (Brand New Readers Ser.). 1p. (J). (ps-2). pap. 4.99 (978-0-7636-0673-2(1)) Candlewick Pr.

Schultz, Kathy. Get Out of My Chair. Payne, Tom, illus. 2002. (Rookie Reader Skill Set Ser.). 24p. (J). (gr. k-2). pap. 4.95 (978-0-516-25965-9(2) , Children's Pr.) Scholastic Library Publishing.

—Get Out of My Chair. 2001. (gr. k-3). lib. bdg. 12.95 (978-0-613-54233-3(9)) Tandem Library Bks.

Schulz, C. Snoopy: Flying Ace to the Rescue. LoBianco, Peter & LoBianco, Nick, illus. 2002. 31p. (gr. k-3). lib. bdg. 11.80 (978-0-613-57583-6(0)) Tandem Library Bks.

Schulz, Charles M. Friends Forever, Snoopy. 2001. (gr. k-3). lib. bdg. 11.80 (978-0-613-61768-0(1)) Tandem Library Bks.

—Snoopy, Flying Ace to the Rescue! Schulz, Charles M., illus. 2002. (Peanuts Ser.). 32p. (J). pap. 3.99 (978-0-689-85148-3(0) , Little Simon) Simon & Schuster Children's Publishing.

Schulz, Charles M., illus. Friends Forever, Snoopy. 2001. (Ready-to-Read Ser.). 32p. (J). pap. 3.99 (978-0-689-84597-0(9) , Little Simon) Simon & Schuster Children's Publishing.

Scimone, Diana. Adventures with Pawpaw: China. Wiedemer, Leah, illus. 2003. 32p. (J). 8.95 (978-0-9729507-0-1(2)) Peapod Publishing, Inc.

Scooby-Doo & the Hex Files. 1999. (gr. k-3). lib. bdg. 11.25 (978-0-613-22339-3(X)) Tandem Library Bks.

Scooby-Doo & the Witch's Ghost. 1999. (gr. k-3). lib. bdg. 11.25 (978-0-613-22340-9(3)) Tandem Library Bks.

Scooby Doo Storybook Box Set. 2003. (Illus.). 14.00 (978-0-439-55194-6(3)) Scholastic, Inc.

Scott, Adam. Joe Moves In. 2002. (gr. k-3). lib. bdg. 11.25 (978-0-613-51310-4(X)) Tandem Library Bks.

Scott, James. Sounder: Reproducible Teaching Unit. 1999. 29p. (YA). (gr. 7-12). ring bd. 29.50 (978-1-58049-125-9(1) , TU96) Prestwick Hse., Inc.

Scott, Terrence. Bryce Coris Blessing. 2006. 28p. pap. 9.95 (*978-1-4327-0000-3(6)) Outskirts Press, Inc.

Scruggs, Sandy. Ode to the Wart Hog. Scruggs, Sandy, illus. 1999. (Illus.). 56p. (YA). (gr. 3 up). pap. 11.95 (978-0-9660239-7-8(8)) Azro Pr., Inc.

Sdoia-Satz, Phyllis & Satz, Barry. The Husky Gang Tales. 2002. 21.95 incl. audio compact disk (978-0-7579-9918-5(2) , Warner Bros. Pubns.) Alfred Publishing Co., Inc.

Seawall: Individual Chapter Book Title Six-Packs. Vol. 27. 32p. (gr. 4 up). 44.00 (978-0-7635-4494-2(9)) Rigby Education.

Sebring Lowrey, Janette. The Poky Little Puppy. Tenggren, Gustaf, illus. 2007. 26p. (J). (gr. k-ps). bds. 4.99 (978-0-375-83925-2(9) , Golden Bks.) Random Hse. Children's Bks.

Sebring Lowrey, Janette. The Poky Little Puppy Special Anniversary Edition LGB. Tenggren, Gustaf, illus. 2007. (Special Edition LGB Ser.). 52p. (J). (gr. k-k). 8.99 (***978-0-375-83920-7(8)** , Golden Bks.) Random Hse. Children's Bks.

Sebring Lowrey, Janette & Crampton, Gertrude. The Poky Little Puppy & Other Stories to Color. Tenggren, Gustaf & Gergely, Tibor, illus. 2007. 96p. (J). (ps-2). 2.99 (978-0-375-83536-0(9) , Golden Bks.) Random Hse. Children's Bks.

Secret Agent Cat Purse: The Case of the Dog with Golden Wings. 2006. (J). (978-0-9743359-3-3(2)) Murdock Publishing Co.

Seeger, Laura Vaccaro. Dog & Bear. Seeger, Laura Vaccaro, illus. 2007. (Illus.). 32p. (J). (ps-3). 12.95 (978-1-59643-053-2(2)) Roaring Brook Pr.

Seeger, Laura Vaccaro. Dog & Bear, Too! 2008. 32p. (J). 12.95 (***978-1-59643-273-4(X)**) Roaring Brook Pr.

Seibold, J. Otto. Quincy, the Hobby Photographer. 2006. (Illus.). 64p. 14.95 (978-0-15-101494-1(9)) Harcourt Trade Pubs.

Seibold, J. Otto & Walsh, Vivian. Olive, the Other Reindeer. 10th deluxe anniv. ed. 2007. (Illus.). 40p. (J). (ps up). 19.95 (978-0-8118-5719-2(0)) Chronicle Bks. LLC.

Seltzer, Eric. Doodle Dog. ed. 2005. (Illus.). 32p. (J). lib. bdg. 15.00 (978-1-59054-979-7(1)) Fitzgerald Bks.

—Doodle Dog. Seltzer, Eric, illus. 2005. (Ready-to-Reads Ser.). (Illus.). 32p. (J). pap. 3.99 (978-0-689-85910-6(4) , Aladdin) Simon & Schuster Children's Publishing.

—Doodle Dog. 2005. (Ready-to-Reads Ser.). (Illus.). 32p. (J). lib. bdg. 11.89 (978-0-689-85913-7(9) , Aladdin Library) Simon & Schuster Children's Publishing.

—Doodle Dog in Space. Seltzer, Eric, illus. 2005. (Ready-to-Reads Ser.). (Illus.). 32p. (J). (ps-3). pap. 3.99 (978-0-689-85912-0(0) , Aladdin) Simon & Schuster Children's Publishing.

—Granny Doodle Day. Seltzer, Eric, illus. 2006. (Ready-to-Reads Ser.). (Illus.). 32p. (J). pap. 3.99 (978-0-689-85911-3(2) , Aladdin) Simon & Schuster Children's Publishing.

Sendak, Maurice. Didola Pidola Pon! O la Vida Debe Ofrecer Algo Mas. (SPA.). 80p. (J). (gr. 2-4). (978-84-204-3107-9(9)) Alfaguara, Ediciones, S.A.- Grupo Santillana ESP. *Dist:* Lectorum Pubns., Inc.

Serfozo, Mary. What's What? a Guessing Game. 2000. (gr. k-3). lib. bdg. 15.30 (978-0-613-22614-1(3)) Tandem Library Bks.

Serrano, Esteban & Spotorno, Lucia. Leo & His Dog Lou. Serrano, Esteban & Spotorno, Lucia, illus. 2005. (Illus.). 28p. (J). (ps-ps). 12.95 (978-9974-7896-0-9(5)) Hardenville SA URY. *Dist:* Independent Pubs. Group.

Servi Machlin, Edda. My Puppy Marrano. 2007. (YA). 19.95 (***978-1-878857-13-2(4)**) Giro Pr.

Seuling, Barbara. Robert & the Great Pepperoni. Brewer, Paul, illus. 2001. (Robert Bks.). 128p. (J). (gr. 2-5). 15.95 (978-0-8126-2825-8(X)) Cricket Bks.

Seuss, Dr. The Grinch Meets His Max. 1998. (J). (ps-3). lib. bdg. 11.99 (978-0-679-98836-6(X) , Random Hse. Bks. for Young Readers) Random Hse. Children's Bks.

Seward, Angela. Maxx & the Wishing Bone. Easter, Avery, illus. 2001. 42p. (J). (ps-3). 15.95 (978-0-9710809-0-4(9)) Summer Sun Publishing.

Shaffert, Charles F. Googus to the Rescue. Stringer, Margaret, illus. l.t. ed. 2005. 31p. (J). per. 10.00 (978-1-59879-043-6(9)) Lifevest Publishing, Inc.

The Shaggy Dog: The Movie Storybook. 2006. 48p. (gr. 2-7). pap. 6.99 (978-0-7868-4862-1(6)) Disney Pr.

Shanks, Ronnie. Oh Where, Oh Where Is My Teddy Bear? 2004. 22p. pap. 14.95 (978-1-4137-2693-0(3)) PublishAmerica, Inc.

Shannon, David. Good Boy, Fergus! Shannon, David, illus. 2006. (Illus.). 40p. (J). (ps-1). pap. 15.99 (978-0-439-49027-6(8) , Blue Sky Pr., The) Scholastic, Inc.

—Good Boy, Fergus! (muy Bien, Fergus!) 2006. 40p. (J). pap. 3.99 (978-0-439-80294-9(6) , Scholastic en Espanol) Scholastic, Inc.

Shannon, George. Tippy-Toe Chick, Go! Dronzek, Laura, illus. 2003. 32p. (J). lib. bdg. 16.89 (978-0-06-029824-1(3)); 16.99 (978-0-06-029823-4(5)) HarperCollins Pubs.

Sharmat, Marjorie Weinman. A Dog Star Is Born. 2000. (Illus.). (J). (978-0-606-18494-6(5)) Tandem Library Bks.

—Hollywood Hound. 2000. (Illus.). (J). 10.79 (978-0-606-18493-9(7)) Tandem Library Bks.

—Nate the Great & the Big Sniff. Weston, Martha, illus. 2003. (Nate the Great Ser.). 48p. (gr. 1-4). pap. 4.50 (978-0-440-41502-2(0) , Yearling) Random Hse. Children's Bks.

—Nate the Great & the Big Sniff. 2003. (gr. k-3). lib. bdg. 12.40 (978-0-613-63966-8(9)) Tandem Library Bks.

—Nate the Great on the Owl Express. Sharmat, Mitchell & Weston, Martha, illus. 2004. 80p. (J). (gr. 1-4). 4.50 (978-0-440-41927-3(1) , Yearling) Random Hse. Children's Bks.

Sharmat, Marjorie Weinman, et al. Nate the Great & the Big Sniff. Weston, Martha, illus. 2001. (Nate the Great Ser.). 48p. (J). (gr. 1-4). 13.95 (978-0-385-32604-9(1) , Delacorte Bks. for Young Readers) Random Hse. Children's Bks.

Shaskan, Trisha Speed. Another Pet. Vincent, Kenneth, illus. 2006. (Read-It! Readers Ser.). (J). 19.93 (978-1-4048-2404-1(9)) Picture Window Bks.

Shaw, Janet Beeler. Kaya & Lone Dog. 2002. (gr. 3-6). lib. bdg. 14.10 (978-0-613-46221-1(1)) Tandem Library Bks.

—Kaya & Lone Dog Bk. 4: A Friendship Story. Farnsworth, Bill & McAliley, Susan, illus. 2002. (American Girls Collection: Bk. 4). 96p. (J). (gr. 2-7). 12.95 (978-1-58485-430-2(8)); 6.95 (978-1-58485-429-6(4)) American Girl Publishing, Inc.

Sheeley, Jill. Rescue on Star Mountain. 2000. (Adventures of Fraser the Yellow Dog Ser.). (Illus.). (J). 15.95 (978-0-9609108-6-1(7)) Courtney Pr.

—Rescue on Vail Mountain. 2000. (Adventures of Fraser the Yellow Dog Ser.). (Illus.). (J). 14.95 (978-0-9609108-5-4(9)) Courtney Pr.

Sheldon, Dyan. Clara & Buster Go Moondancing. 2001. (978-0-606-22329-4(0)) Tandem Library Bks.

Sherlock, Patti. Letters from Wolfie. 2007. 240p. (YA). (gr. 5 up). pap. 6.99 (978-0-14-240358-7(X) , Puffin); 2004. 256p. (J). (gr. 3-7). 16.99 (978-0-670-03694-3(3) , Viking Juvenile) Penguin Group (USA) Inc.

Shiloh. 2000. 144p. (J). (gr. 4-6). 5.50 (978-0-689-83930-6(8) , Aladdin) Simon & Schuster Children's Publishing.

Shoemaker, Sharon. Sir Waltie of Shoe. Whiting, Sandra, illus. 2004. (J). per. 12.95 (978-0-9759499-0-0(X)) Water Shoe Pr.

Shortridge, Retha. Gnome in the House. 2005. 78p. pap. 14.95 (978-1-4137-5188-8(1)) PublishAmerica, Inc.

Shott, Stephen & Dorling Kindersley Publishing Staff. Puppy. 2000. (Animal Board Bks.). (Illus.). 12p. (J). (ps-2). bds. 6.95 (978-0-7894-5402-7(5)) Dorling Kindersley Publishing, Inc.

Shrom, LaJoyce. Learning about Life. 2005. (ENG., Illus.). 28p. per. 15.99 (978-1-4141-0338-9(7)) Pleasant Word.

Shuff, Lana Tanaka. Kira Helps A Friend. l.t. ed. 2007. (ENG., Illus.). 28p. (J). per. 9.95 (***978-1-4327-0810-8(4)**) Outskirts Press, Inc.

Shugars, Betty. Smokey the Tailess Dog. 2004. pap. 14.00 (978-0-8059-6324-3(3)) Dorrance Publishing Co., Inc.

Shulman, Mark. Fillmore & Geary Take Off! Fickling, Phillip, illus. 2004. 40p. (J). 14.95 (978-1-58717-256-4(9) , SeaStar Bks.) Chronicle Bks. LLC.

Shyer, Marlene Fanta. Fleabiscuit Sings! 2005. 160p. (J). 15.95 (978-0-7614-5213-3(3)) Cavendish, Marshall Corp.

Sidle, Christian. Murphy Dog at the Circus. Lynn, Dianne, illus. l.t. ed. 2001. 80p. (J). (ps-3). per. 12.50 (978-0-9708053-6-2(5)) Authors & Artists Publishers of New York, Inc.

—Murphy Dog Bedtime Story. Lynn, Dianne, illus. l.t. ed. 2001. 48p. (J). (ps-3). per. 12.50 (978-0-9708053-3-1(0)) Authors & Artists Publishers of New York, Inc.

Silver Dolphin en Español Editors. All about Dogs. 2006. (Baby Einstein Ser.). (Illus.). 8p. (J). bds. 9.95 (978-970-718-402-2(7) , Silver Dolphin en Español) Advanced Marketing, S. de R. L. de C. V. MEX. *Dist:* Perseus Distribution.

Silver, Karren L. Chi Chi in Cyberspace: The E-mailing Chihuahuas - Chichi@mcn.org. Phillips, Marc, illus. Isadore Press Staff, photos by. l.t. ed. 1999. (Growing up with Chihuahua Puppies Ser.: Vol. 1). 30p. (J). (gr. k-2). pap. 10.00 (978-0-9602600-3-4(X)) Isadore Pr.

Silverhardt, Lauryn. Blue's Hugs. Style Guide Staff, illus. 2005. (Blue's Clues Ser.). 8p. (J). 6.99 (978-0-689-87693-6(9) , Simon Spotlight/Nickelodeon) Simon & Schuster Children's Publishing.

—Christmas in Blue's Room. Craig, Karen, illus. 2006. (Blue's Room Ser.). 14p. (J). bds. 6.99 (978-1-4169-1569-0(9) , Simon Spotlight/Nickelodeon) Simon & Schuster Children's Publishing.

Simmie, Lois. Mister Got to Go & Arnie. Nugent, Cynthia, illus. 2004. 32p. pap. 6.95 (978-1-55192-636-0(9)) Raincoast Bk. Distribution CAN. *Dist:* Perseus Distribution.

Simmons, Jane. Ebb & Flo & the Greedy Gulls. 2003. (gr. k-3). lib. bdg. 15.30 (978-0-613-66401-1(9)) Tandem Library Bks.

—Ebb & Flo & the New Friend. Simmons, Jane, illus. 2002. (Illus.). 32p. (J). (ps-2). 6.99 (978-0-689-84890-2(0) , Aladdin) Simon & Schuster Children's Publishing.

—Ebb & Flo & the New Friend. 2002. (ps-2). lib. bdg. 15.30 (978-0-613-50532-1(8)) Tandem Library Bks.

—Together. 2007. (Illus.). 32p. (J). (ps-3). 15.99 (978-0-375-84339-6(0)); lib. bdg. 18.99 (978-0-375-94339-3(0)) Random Hse. Children's Bks. (Knopf Bks. for Young Readers).

Simmons, Jane, illus. Ebb & Flo & the Greedy Gulls. 2003. 32p. (J). pap. 6.99 (978-0-689-85810-9(8) , Aladdin) Simon & Schuster Children's Publishing.

Simmons, Lynn. Bo & the Night Intruder. 2005. (Illus.). 104p. (J). 8.95 (978-1-58980-266-7(7)) Pelican Publishing Co., Inc.

Simmons, Lynn Sheffield. Bo & the Missing Dogs. Hampton, Lin, illus. 2002. 117p. (J). (gr. 4-7). pap. 6.95 (978-0-9642573-3-7(5)) Argyle Bks.

—Bo & the Missing Dogs. 2004. (Illus.). 128p. (YA). 8.95 (978-1-58980-219-3(5)) Pelican Publishing Co., Inc.

—Bo, the Famous Retriever. Hampton, Lin, illus. 2004. 128p. (YA). (gr. 3-6). pap. 10.95 (978-1-58980-217-9(9)) Pelican Publishing Co., Inc.

Simon & Barklee in Mexico. 2002. 70p. tchr. ed. 20.00 (978-0-9714502-2-6(6) , Explorer Media) Simon & Barklee, Inc./ExplorerMedia.

Simon, Charnan. Big Bad Buzz. Epstein, Len, illus. 2006. (Magic Door to Learning Ser.). 24p. (J). (gr. 1-3). 21.36 (978-1-59296-617-2(9)) Child's World, Inc.

—Guard the House, Sam! Rau, Dana, ed. Bialke, Gary, illus. 1998. (Rookie Reader Skill Set Ser.). 32p. (J). (gr. k-2). pap. 4.95 (978-0-516-26359-5(5) , Children's Pr.) Scholastic Library Publishing.

—Sam's Pet. Bialke, Gary, illus. 2000. (Rookie Reader Skill Set Ser.). 32p. (J). (gr. k-2). pap. 4.95 (978-0-516-26553-7(9) , Children's Pr.) Scholastic Library Publishing.

—Sam's Pet. Bialke, Gary, illus. 2000. 31p. (J). (ps-3). lib. bdg. 12.95 (978-0-613-54642-3(3)) Tandem Library Bks.

—Show-and-Tell Sam. Bialke, Gary, illus. 1998. (Rookie Readers Ser.). 32p. (J). (gr. 1-2). 19.50 (978-0-516-20945-6(0) , Children's Pr.) Scholastic Library Publishing.

—Show-and-Tell Sam. Bialke, Gary, illus. 1999. 31p. (J). (gr. k-3). lib. bdg. 12.95 (978-0-613-37537-5(8)) Tandem Library Bks.

Simon, Charnan & Bialke, Gary. Sam the Dog Boxed Set. 2006. 9.95 (978-0-531-16922-3(7) , Children's Pr.) Scholastic Library Publishing.

Simon, Francesca. Little Yellow Dog Bites the Builder. Lucas, James E., illus. 2004. (Little Yellow Dog Ser.). 32p. (J). pap. 7.99 (978-1-84255-246-9(5)) Orion Children's Bks. GBR. *Dist:* Independent Pubs. Group.

—Little Yellow Dog Gets a Shock. Lucas, James E., tr. Lucas, James E., illus. 2004. (Little Yellow Dog Ser.). 32p. (J). pap. 7.99 (978-1-84255-243-8(0)) Orion Children's Bks. GBR. *Dist:* Independent Pubs. Group.

—Little Yellow Dog Meets His Match. Lucas, James E., illus. 2004. (Little Yellow Dog Ser.). 32p. (J). pap. 7.99 (978-1-84255-245-2(7)) Orion Children's Bks. GBR. *Dist:* Independent Pubs. Group.

—Little Yellow Dog Says Look at Me. Lucas, James E., illus. 2004. (Little Yellow Dog Ser.). 32p. (J). pap. 7.99 (978-1-84255-244-5(9)) Orion Children's Bks. GBR. *Dist:* Independent Pubs. Group.

—Where Are You? Melling, David, illus. 1998. 32p. (J). (ps-1). 12.95 (978-1-56145-179-1(7)) Peachtree Pubs., Ltd.

Simon, Mary Manz. Puppy Makes Friends. Couri, Kathy & Clearwater, Linda, illus. 2006. (First Virtues for Toddlers Ser.). 20p. (J). 5.99 (978-0-7847-1414-0(2) , 04066) Standard Publishing.

Simont, Marc. El Perro Vagabundo. Simont, Marc, illus. 2003. (SPA., Illus.). 32p. (J). (ps-3). pap. 6.99 (978-0-06-052274-2(7) , Rayo) HarperCollins Pubs.

—El Perro Vagabundo. (Picture Book Readalong in Spanish Ser.). (J). 2005. (SPA.). pap. 18.95 incl. audio compact disk (978-1-59112-939-4(7)); 2004. (SPA., Illus.). pap. 16.95 incl. audio (978-1-59112-935-6(4)); 2004. (Illus.). pap. 37.95 incl. audio (978-1-59112-937-0(0)); 2004. pap. 39.95 incl. audio compact disk (978-1-59112-941-7(9)) Live Oak Media.

—The Stray Dog. Simont, Marc, illus. (Illus.). 32p. (J). (ps-3). 2003. pap. 6.99 (978-0-06-443669-4(1)); 2001. 15.99 (978-0-06-028933-1(3)); 2001. lib. bdg. 17.89 (978-0-06-028934-8(1)) HarperCollins Pubs.

—The Stray Dog. 2002. (Illus.). (J). pap. 16.95 incl. audio (978-0-87499-926-6(X)); pap. 18.95 incl. audio compact disk (978-1-59112-356-9(9)) Live Oak Media.

—Stray Dog. 2003. (gr. k-3). lib. bdg. 15.30 (978-0-613-62849-5(7)) Tandem Library Bks.

—The Stray Dog. Simont, Marc, illus. Tr. of El Perro Vagabundo. (Illus.). 2004. pap. 33.95 incl. audio (978-1-59112-092-6(6)); 2002. 28.95 incl. audio compact disk (978-1-59112-357-6(7)); 2002. pap. 37.95 incl. audio (978-0-87499-928-0(6)); 2002. pap. 39.95 incl. audio compact disk (978-1-59112-560-0(X)); 2002. (J). 25.95 incl. audio (978-0-87499-927-3(8)) Live Oak Media.

Simont, Marc, illus. Nate the Great & the Crunchy Christmas. 2002. (Nate the Great Ser.). (J). 12.87 (978-0-7587-0704-8(5)) Book Wholesalers, Inc.

Simpson, Peggy. Moca, the Chocolate Puppy. 2001. 24p. pap. 6.95 (978-1-58597-077-3(8)) Leathers Publishing.

Sims, Matt. Red Cap. 1999. (gr. 3-6). lib. bdg. 10.85 (978-0-613-30696-6(1)) Tandem Library Bks.

Sinclair, Nicholas, et al. The Cookie Story. Wall, Randy Hugh, ed. Varela, Juan D., tr. Varela, Juan D., illus. l.t. ed. 2005. Tr. of Cuent de Galletas. (SPA.). 33p. (J). 14.95 (978-0-9764798-1-9(8)) Story Store Collection Publishing.

Singh, Bally B. Jako—the Dog that Survived 9/11. 2005. pap. 7.95 (978-0-533-15134-9(1)) Vantage Pr., Inc.

Sis, Peter. Madlenka's Dog. Sis, Peter, illus. 2002. (Illus.). 40p. (J). (ps-1). 17.00 (978-0-374-34699-7(2) , Farrar, Straus & Giroux (BYR)) Farrar, Straus & Giroux.

—Madlenka's dog. (Illus.). 19.95 (978-0-88899-462-2(1)) Groundwood Bks. CAN. *Dist:* Transition Vendor.

Sitzenstock, Gabriele. Raising Puppy. 2006. (J). spiral bd. 12.95 (***978-1-59872-721-0(4)**) Instantpublisher.com.

Skewes, John & Schwartz, Robert. Larry Gets Lost in Seattle. 2007. (Illus.). 32p. 16.95 (***978-1-57061-483-5(0)**) Sasquatch Bks.

Skinner, Daphne. 101 Dalmations & Cruella de Vil. Disney Storybook Artists Staff, illus. 2005. (My Side of the Story Ser.). 72p. (ps-17). 12.99 (978-0-7868-3520-1(6)) Disney Pr.

Skolsky, Mindy Warshaw. You're the Best Hannah! 2000. (978-0-606-18733-6(2)) Tandem Library Bks.

Slater, Teddy & Kindert, Jennifer. The Christmas Puppy. 2005. (Illus.). 24p. (J). (ps-ps). 6.95 (978-1-4027-1980-6(9)) Sterling Publishing Co., Inc.

Sleepy Pup: KinderConcepts Individual Title Six-Packs. (Kinderstarters Ser.). 8p. (ps-1). 21.00 (978-0-7635-8733-8(8)) Rigby Education.

Slifka, Linda. Where's My Puppy? 2004. 32p. 14.95 (978-1-932820-11-9(6)) Outland Communications, LLC.

Slusser, Janet S. Smokey & the Big Snow. 2003. (Illus.). 32p. (J). per. 15.95 (978-0-9745171-0-0(0)) RiverCreek Bks., Inc.

Smee, Nicola. Funny Face. 2006. (Illus.). 24p. (J). 8.95 (978-1-58234-710-3(7) , Bloomsbury Children) Bloomsbury Publishing.

Smerek, Kim. What Is Zazu?, 1 bk. Smerek, Kim, illus. 2003. (Illus.). 24p. (J). bds. 7.95 (978-0-9745116-0-3(9)) Sunshine Bks. for Children.

Smith, Alexander McCall. Max & Maddy & the Chocolate Money Mystery. Pamintuan, Macky, illus. 2007. 128p. (J). (gr. 2-4). 9.95 (978-1-59990-036-0(X) , Bloomsbury Children) Bloomsbury Publishing.

Smith, D. James. Probably the World's Best Story about a Dog & the Girl Who Loved Me. 2006. 240p. (J). (gr. 4-7). 15.95 (978-1-4169-0542-4(1)) Simon & Schuster Children's Publishing.

Smith, Dodie. 101 Dalmatians. 2004. (Illus.). 192p. (J). (gr. 3-5). pap. 36.00 incl. audio (978-0-8072-0791-8(8) , LYA 345 SP, Listening Library) Random Hse. Audio Publishing Group.

Smith, Dona. Cross Country with Lewis & Clark. 2004. (Tall Tails Ser.: No. 2). 144p. (J). pap. 3.99 (978-0-439-43441-6(6) , Scholastic Paperbacks) Scholastic, Inc.

—Wingin' It with the Wright Brothers. 2003. (gr. 3-6). lib. bdg. 11.80 (978-0-613-72060-1(1)) Tandem Library Bks.

Smith, Linda. The Inside Tree. Brown, Kathryn, illus. Date not set. 32p. (J). (ps-3). 5.99 (978-0-06-443542-0(3)) HarperCollins Pubs.

—The Inside Tree. 2002. 32p. (J). (ps-3). 14.95 (978-0-06-028241-7(X)) HarperCollins Pubs.

Smith, Michael. I Want to Be in the Show. 2000. (gr. k-3). lib. bdg. 11.25 (978-0-613-31346-9(1)) Tandem Library Bks.

—Magenta's Visit. 1999. (gr. k-3). lib. bdg. 11.25 (978-0-613-15894-7(6)) Tandem Library Bks.

Smith, Peggy. The Champ: The Adventures of a Boy & His New Puppy. Told in One-syllable Words for the Barton Reading & Spelling System. 2003. (J). pap. 7.95 (978-0-9744343-3-9(7) , SA-304) Bright Solutions for Dyslexia, LLC.

Smith, Roland. The Captain's Dog: My Journey with the Lewis & Clark Tribe. 2000. (Great Episodes Ser.). (Illus.). 304p. (YA). (gr. 4-7). pap. 6.00 (978-0-15-202696-7(7) , Harcourt Paperbacks) Harcourt Children's Bks.

—The Captain's Dog: My Journey with the Lewis & Clark Tribe. 2000. (J). 12.65 (978-0-606-19000-8(7)); (gr. 3-6). lib. bdg. 14.15 (978-0-613-29900-8(0)) Tandem Library Bks.

Smith, W. Bryan. Buddy & the Jack: A Novel. 2002. 182p. 22.95 (978-1-59286-207-8(1)); pap. 19.95 (978-1-59129-224-1(7)) PublishAmerica, Inc.

Snowman, Sally R. Sammy the Boston Lighthouse Dog. 2005. (J). (gr. 3-5). 15.00 (978-0-9674666-2-0(8)) Snowman Learning Center, The.

Soderberg, Erin. Dinosaur Dig. 2000. (gr. k-3). lib. bdg. 11.80 (978-0-613-54167-1(7)) Tandem Library Bks.

Soling, Cevin. Boris the Dog. Kille, Steve, illus. 2008. 16.95 (978-0-9767771-6-8(9)) Spectacle Films, Inc.

Sollinger, Emily & Ken Karp Photography Staff. Let's Play, Baby! 2006. (Baby Nick Jr Ser.). (Illus.). 10p. (J). bds. 9.99 (978-1-4169-1209-5(6) , Simon Spotlight/Nickelodeon) Simon & Schuster Children's Publishing.

Some Dog! Individual Chapter Book Title Six-Packs. Vol. 27. 32p. (gr. 4 up). 44.00 (978-0-7635-4495-9(7)) Rigby Education.

Soto, Gary. Chato Goes Cruisin' Guevara, Susan, tr. Guevara, Susan, illus. 2005. 32p. (J). (ps-3). 16.99 (978-0-399-23974-8(X) , Putnam Juvenile) Penguin Group (USA) Inc.

—Chato Goes Cruisin' Guevara, Susan, illus. 2007. 32p. (J). (ps). pap. 6.99 (978-0-14-240810-0(7) , Puffin) Penguin Group (USA) Inc.

Spafford-Fitz, Karen. Dog Walker. 2006. 112p. (J). (gr. 5-10). pap. 7.95 (978-1-55143-522-0(5)); lib. bdg. 14.95 (978-1-55143-533-6(0)) Orca Bk. Pubs. USA.

Spain, Frederick. Missy the Mutt. Garlets, Peggy L., illus. 2nd rev. ed. 1999. i, 28p. (J). (ps-6). 12.95 (978-1-929792-00-9(X)) Roehm Pubs.

—Missy the Mutts Surprise Birthday Party. Garlets, Peggy L., illus. 1999. i, 26p. (J). (ps-6). 12.95 (978-1-929792-02-3(6)) Roehm Pubs.

Spangler, Brie. Peg Leg Peke. 2008. 40p. (J). (ps-1). lib. bdg. 18.99 (***978-0-375-94888-6(0)** , Knopf Bks. for Young Readers) Random Hse. Children's Bks.

Spearman, Andy. Barry Boyhound. 2007. 240p. (J). (gr. 3-7). 5.50 (***978-0-440-42058-3(X)** , Yearling) Random Hse. Children's Bks.

Spinelli, Patti. Mackenzie & Emma Get a Puppy. 2004. (Illus.). (YA). (gr. k up). lib. bdg. 11.95 (978-0-9742328-2-9(3)) Spinelli, Patti.

—Mackenzie & Emma Visit York Beach. Spinelli, Patti, illus. 2003. (J). (978-0-9742328-0-5(7)) Spinelli, Patti.

Spiotta-DiMare, Loren. Norman. 1998. (J). 12.95 (978-1-58021-058-4(9)); pap. 5.95 (978-1-58021-053-9(8)) Benefactory, Inc., The.

Spohn, Kate. Dog & Cat Shake a Leg. 2000. 32p. (J). pap. 3.99 (978-0-14-038374-4(3) , Puffin) Penguin Group (USA) Inc.

Spooner, J. B. The Little Black Dog Buccaneer. Seeley, Terre Lamb, illus. 1998. 32p. (ps-3). 15.95 (978-1-55970-448-9(9)) Arcade Publishing, Inc.

Stadler, John. Ready, Set, Go! Stadler, John, illus. 1998. (Trophy I Can Read Bks.). (Illus.). 32p. (J). (ps-2). pap. 3.99 (978-0-06-444238-1(1) , Harper Trophy) HarperCollins Pubs.

—Ready, Set, Go! 1998. (I Can Read Bks.). (J). (ps-1). (978-0-606-13022-6(5)) Tandem Library Bks.

Stagno, Laura, illus. Yo Tenia 10 Perritos. 2004. (SPA.). 24p. (J). (gr. k up). pap. 6.50 (978-980-257-277-9(2)) Ekare, Ediciones VEN. *Dist:* Lectorum Pubns., Inc., Iaconi, Mariuccia Bk. Imports.

Stamper, Judith Bauer. Bowwow Bake Sale. 2002. (gr. k-3). lib. bdg. 11.80 (978-0-613-64026-8(8)) Tandem Library Bks.

—The Bowwow Bake Sale. Demarest, Chris L., illus. 2002. (All Aboard Math Reader Ser.: Vol. 3). 48p. (J). pap. 3.99 (978-0-448-42845-1(8) , Grosset & Dunlap) Penguin Group (USA) Inc.

Standiford, Natalie. Space Dog & Roy. Howell, Kathleen C., illus. 1998. (Space Dog Ser.). (J). (gr. k-3). (978-0-606-13035-6(7)) Tandem Library Bks.

—Space Dog the Hero. 1999. (Space Dog Ser.). (J). (gr. k-3). (978-0-606-16119-0(8)) Tandem Library Bks.

Stanley, George Edward. Adam Sharp, the Spy Who Barked. 2002. (gr. 3-6). lib. bdg. 11.80 (978-0-613-50173-6(X)) Tandem Library Bks.

—The Mystery of the Hairy Tomatoes. Murdocca, Salvatore, illus. 2001. (Third Grade Detectives Ser.: No. 3). 80p. (J). (gr. 1-4). pap. 3.99 (978-0-689-82209-4(X) , Aladdin) Simon & Schuster Children's Publishing.

—The Mystery of the Hairy Tomatoes. 2001. (gr. 3-6). lib. bdg. 11.80 (978-0-613-31518-0(9)); No. 3. (Illus.). (J). (978-0-606-20941-0(7)) Tandem Library Bks.

Stanton, Andy. You're a Bad Man, Mr. Gum! Dezern, Chad, illus. 2008. 144p. (J). 9.99 (*978-0-06-115240-5(4)); lib. bdg. 14.89 (*978-0-06-115243-6(9)) HarperCollins Pubs.

Staples, Suzanne Fisher. The Green Dog: A Mostly True Story. 2003. (Illus.). 128p. (J). 16.00 (978-0-374-32779-8(3) , Farrar, Straus & Giroux (BYR)) Farrar, Straus & Giroux.

—The Green Dog: A Mostly True Story. 2005. 144p. (J). (ps-7). reprint ed. pap. 5.99 (978-0-06-076045-8(1) , Harper Trophy) HarperCollins Pubs.

—The Green Dog: A Mostly True Story. l.t. ed. 2004. 140p. (J). 21.95 (978-0-7862-6577-0(9)) Thorndike Pr.

Starbuck, Veronica Anne. Heart of the Savannah. 2000. 267p. (YA). (gr. 9 up). pap. 12.95 (978-0-9658488-3-1(3)) Windigo Harbor Media.

Starr, Claire. They Called Me Beautiful: A Dog's Search for Love & the Family That Rescued Him. Starr, Claire, illus. 2002. (Illus.). 128p. (J). (ps-4). pap. 10.95 (978-0-9706377-1-0(3)) Lucky Pr., LLC.

Staunton, Ted. Morgan's Pet Plot. Slavin, Bill, illus. 2003. (First Novel Ser.). 64p. (J). (gr. 1-5). 4.95 (978-0-88780-587-5(6)); (*978-0-88780-588-2(4)) Formac Publishing Co., Ltd. CAN. *Dist:* Casemate Pubs. & Bk. Distributors, LLC.

Stead, Vince. Rusty the Runaway Golden Retriever. 2007. 73p. 14.95 (*978-1-4241-5739-6(0)) PublishAmerica, Inc.

Stead, Vince. Sammy, the Runaway Mastiff: Sammy Breaks Out of His Kennel. 2006. 102p. per. 8.95 (978-1-59824-314-7(4)) E-BookTime LLC.

Steck-Vaughn Staff. Early Reader Program Level A: The Puppy That Sniffed Too Much, 6 Pack. 2004. (Illus.). pap. 30.00 (978-0-7398-8151-4(5)) Steck-Vaughn.

—My Dog. 1999. (Illus.). pap. (978-0-8172-8722-1(1)) Steck-Vaughn.

—Special Friends: My Dog/Sister. 1998. (Illus.). (J). pap. (978-0-8172-8645-3(4)) Steck-Vaughn.

Steele, Alexander. Case of the Breaking Story. l.t. ed. 2000. (Wishbone Mysteries Ser.: No. 20). (Illus.). 144p. (J). (gr. 4 up). lib. bdg. 23.33 (978-0-8368-2703-3(1)) Stevens, Gareth Inc.

—Case of the On-Line Alien. l.t. ed. 1999. (Wishbone Mysteries Ser.: No. 9). 144p. (J). (gr. 4 up). lib. bdg. 23.33 (978-0-8368-2449-0(0)) Stevens, Gareth Inc.

—Case of the Unsolved Case. l.t. ed. 2000. (Wishbone Mysteries Ser.: No. 13). (Illus.). 139p. (J). (gr. 4 up). lib. bdg. 23.33 (978-0-8368-2696-8(5)) Stevens, Gareth Inc.

—The Last of the Breed. Punchatz, Don, illus. l.t. ed. 1999. (Adventures of Wishbone Ser.: No. 16). 163p. (J). (gr. 4 up). lib. bdg. 22.60 (978-0-8368-2594-7(2)) Stevens, Gareth Inc.

—Moby Dog. l.t. ed. 1999. (Adventures of Wishbone Ser.: No. 10). (Illus.). 144p. (J). (gr. 4 up). lib. bdg. 22.60 (978-0-8368-2306-6(0)) Stevens, Gareth Inc.

—Tale of the Missing Mascot. l.t. ed. 1999. (Wishbone Mysteries Ser.: No. 4). 144p. (J). (gr. 4 up). lib. bdg. 23.33 (978-0-8368-2385-1(0)) Stevens, Gareth Inc.

—Unleashed in Space. 1999. (Super Adventures of Wishbone Ser.: No. 3). (J). (gr. 4-7). (978-0-606-19032-9(5)) Tandem Library Bks.

Steele, Michael Anthony. Case of the Impounded Hounds. l.t. ed. 2000. (Wishbone Mysteries Ser.: No. 17). 138p. (J). (gr. 4 up). lib. bdg. 23.33 (978-0-8368-2700-2(7)) Stevens, Gareth Inc.

—Case of the Impounded Hounds. 1999. (Wishbone Mysteries Ser.: No. 17). (978-0-606-17769-6(8)) Tandem Library Bks.

—Digging to the Center of the Earth. Punchatz, Don, illus. l.t. ed. 1999. (Adventures of Wishbone Ser.: No. 17). (J). (gr. 4 up). lib. bdg. 22.60 (978-0-8368-2595-4(0)) Stevens, Gareth Inc.

—Forgotten Heroes. l.t. ed. 2000. (Wishbone Mysteries Ser.: No. 12). (Illus.). 139p. (J). (gr. 4 up). lib. bdg. 23.33 (978-0-8368-2695-1(7)) Stevens, Gareth Inc.

—The Ghost of Camp Ka Nowato. 1999. (Wishbone Super Mysteries Ser.: No. 2). (J). (gr. 2-5). (978-0-606-19033-6(3)) Tandem Library Bks.

—Movie Novel. Cecil, Lauren, ed. 2007. (Firehouse Dog Ser.). 160p. (J). pap. 4.99 (978-0-439-89642-9(8)) Scholastic, Inc.

Steig, William. Dominic. 146p. (J). (gr. 3-6). pap. 4.95 (978-0-8072-1512-8(0)); 1998. pap. 28.00 incl. audio (978-0-8072-7894-9(7) , YA945SP) Random Hse. Audio Publishing Group. (Listening Library).

—Dominic. 2007. (Illus.). 160p. (J). pap. 5.99 (*978-0-312-37144-9(6)) Square Fish.

Stejskal, Susan. The Little Dog Who Did Big Things. 2006. (J). (*978-0-615-13395-9(9)) Stejskal, Susan M.

Stelljes, Susan. Wonder Dog: The Story of Silverton Bobbie. 2005. (Illus.). 167p. (YA). pap. 14.95 (978-0-9761124-7-1(7)) For The Love of Dog Bks.

Stephens, Helen. Ahoyty-Toyty. 2004. (Illus.). 32p. (J). (ps-3). 14.95 (978-0-385-75039-4(0) , Fickling, David Bks.) Random Hse. Children's Bks.

—Poochie-Poo. 2003. (Illus.). 32p. (J). (ps-3). 14.95 (978-0-385-75012-7(9) , Fickling, David Bks.) Random Hse. Children's Bks.

Sterling Publishing Co., Inc. Playful Puppy: A Touch & Feel Adventure. 2005. (Illus.). 16p. (J). 12.95 (978-1-4027-2455-8(1)) Sterling Publishing Co., Inc.

Stern, Maggie. George & Diggety. Sims, Blanche, illus. 2000. (Orchard Chapters Ser.). 47p. (J). (gr. 1-4). 15.99 (978-0-531-33295-5(0)); pap. 14.95 (978-0-531-30295-8(4)) Scholastic Library Publishing. (Watts, Franklin).

—George & Diggety. Sims, Blanche, illus. 2000. (Orchard Chapters Ser.). 47p. (J). (gr. 1-4). pap. 4.95 (978-0-531-07172-4(3)) Scholastic, Inc.

—George & Diggety. 2000. (George & Diggety Ser.). (Illus.). (J). (978-0-606-21775-0(4)) Tandem Library Bks.

—Singing Diggety. Sims, Blanche, illus. 2001. 46p. (J). lib. bdg. (978-0-531-33318-1(3) , Orchard Bks.) Scholastic, Inc.

Sternberg, Demetria. Hey, What's Going on down There? 2005. 23p. pap. 14.95 (978-1-4137-3806-3(0)) PublishAmerica, Inc.

Stetson, Street Dog of Park City. 2002. (J). per. 18.95 (978-0-9717019-0-8(3)) Le Petit Chien.

Stevens, Beverly. This Dog Team Lives in the House. 2005. (J). pap. 9.95 (*978-1-57833-317-2(2)) Todd Communications.

Stevens, Janet & Crummel, Susan Stevens. Help Me, Mr. Mutt! Expert Answers for Dogs with People Problems. 2008. 56p. (J). 17.00 (*978-0-15-204628-6(3)) Harcourt Trade Pubs.

Stevens, Janet & Stevens Crummel, Susan. My Big Dog. Stevens, Janet, illus. 2005. (Illus.). 40p. (J). (gr. k-k). 12.95 (978-0-375-83297-0(1)); lib. bdg. 14.99 (978-0-375-93297-7(6)) Random Hse. Children's Bks. (Golden Bks.).

Stewart, Dana. God Made My Puppy. Stewart, Jennifer, ed. Haantz, Carol, illus. 1999. (Tall Shape Board Bks.). 10p. (J). (ps-1). 4.99 (978-0-7847-0961-0(0) , 04301, Bean Sprouts) Standard Publishing.

Stewart, Paul. Hot Dog & the Talent Competition. Ward, Nick, illus. 2006. (Read-It! Chapter Books). 48p. (J). (*978-1-4048-3129-2(0) , 1265809) Picture Window Bks.

Stierle, Cynthia. The Mysterious Pup. Nunn, Paul E., illus. 2007. 32p. (J). pap. 3.99 (978-0-448-44484-0(4) , Grosset & Dunlap) Penguin Group (USA) Inc.

Stine, R.L. Night of the Creepy Things. Park, Trip, illus. 2007. (Rotten School Ser.: No. 14). 128p. (J). lib. bdg. 14.89 (*978-0-06-123273-2(4)); (gr. 3-7). 6.99 (*978-0-06-123272-5(6)) HarperCollins Pubs.

Stocksdale, Rosie. Along the Way. Stocksdale, Mike, illus. 2005. (J). pap. 8.00 (978-0-8059-6916-0(0)) Dorrance Publishing Co., Inc.

Stoffle, Eric D. Adventure on Wild Horse Mountain. 1999. (Shoebox Kids Ser.: Vol. 10). (J). (gr. 2-7). pap. 6.99 (978-0-8163-1683-0(X)) Pacific Pr. Publishing Assn.

The Storm Dog of the Koolaus. 2004. (HAW.). (J). 11.95 (978-0-9729905-3-0(4)) Beachhouse Publishing, LLC.

Stormer, Kate. Casey's Unexpected Friend. Lowes, Tom, illus. l.t. ed. 2003. 38p. (J). 16.95 (978-0-9722099-7-7(2) , CUF) Caseys World Bks.

Straight, Susan. The Friskative Dog. 2007. 160p. (J). (gr. 3-7). 14.99 (978-0-375-83777-7(9)); lib. bdg. 17.99 (978-0-375-93777-4(3)) Random Hse. Children's Bks. (Knopf Bks. for Young Readers).

Strasser, Todd. Y2K-9: The Dog Who Saved the World. 1999. (YA). pap. 4.50 (978-0-439-14247-2(4)) Scholastic, Inc.

—Y2K-9: The Dog Who Saved the World. 1999. (978-0-606-18619-3(0)) Tandem Library Bks.

Strickland, Brad. Be a Wolf! l.t. ed. 1999. (Adventures of Wishbone Ser.: No. 1). (Illus.). 144p. (J). (gr. 4 up). lib. bdg. 22.60 (978-0-8368-2297-7(8)) Stevens, Gareth Inc.

—Salty Dog. l.t. ed. 1999. (Adventures of Wishbone Ser.: No. 2). (Illus.). 140p. (J). (gr. 4 up). lib. bdg. 22.60 (978-0-8368-2298-4(6)) Stevens, Gareth Inc.

—Terrier of the Lost Mines. 1999. (Adventures of Wishbone Ser.: No. 19). (J). (gr. 2-5). (978-0-606-19457-0(6)) Tandem Library Bks.

—When Mack Came Back. 2003. (Illus.). 112p. (J). (gr. 3-7). pap. 5.99 (978-0-14-230075-6(6) , Puffin) Penguin Group (USA) Inc.

—When Mack Came Back. 2003. (gr. 3-6). lib. bdg. 14.15 (978-0-613-85719-2(4)) Tandem Library Bks.

Strickland, Brad & Fuller, Thomas E. The Disappearing Dinosaurs. l.t. ed. 1999. (Wishbone Mysteries Ser.: No. 10). 144p. (J). (gr. 4 up). lib. bdg. 23.33 (978-0-8368-2450-6(4)) Stevens, Gareth Inc.

—The Riddle of the Wayward Books. l.t. ed. 1999. (Wishbone Mysteries Ser.: No. 3). 144p. (J). (gr. 4 up). lib. bdg. 23.33 (978-0-8368-2384-4(2)) Stevens, Gareth Inc.

Strickland, Brad & Strickland, Barbara. Gullifur's Travels. l.t. ed. 1999. (Adventures of Wishbone Ser.: No. 18). (Illus.). (J). (gr. 4 up). lib. bdg. 22.60 (978-0-8368-2596-1(9)) Stevens, Gareth Inc.

Strickland, Brad, et al. Disoriented Express. l.t. ed. 2000. (Wishbone Mysteries Ser.: No. 14). 167p. (J). (gr. 4 up). lib. bdg. 23.33 (978-0-8368-2697-5(3)) Stevens, Gareth Inc.

—Drive-In of Doom. l.t. ed. 1999. (Wishbone Mysteries Ser.: No. 7). 144p. (J). (gr. 4 up). lib. bdg. 23.33 (978-0-8368-2388-2(5)) Stevens, Gareth Inc.

Stroll with Mr. Emmett: A Walk Through Charleston. 2004. (J). lib. bdg. 15.95 (978-0-9759346-0-9(0)) Mr. Emmett Publishing.

Strong, Beverly Jean. Gypsy the Circus Dog: A Story for Children. Strong, Beverly Jean, illus. 1999. (Illus.). 48p. (J). (ps-3). 24.95 (978-0-86534-300-9(4)) Sunstone Pr.

Stroud, Scott. Baby Kong. Hunt, Jim, illus. 2006. (J). 12.95 (978-1-60131-001-9(3)) Big Tent Bks.

Studley, Wanda Jean. Shorty Stories: A Story about a Dog & Her Famous Wheels. 2006. (J). pap. 9.00 (*978-0-8059-7149-1(1)) Dorrance Publishing Co., Inc.

Stutson, Caroline. Pirate Pup. Rayevsky, Robert, illus. 2005. 32p. (J). 15.95 (978-0-8118-4239-6(8)) Chronicle Bks. LLC.

Suarez, Ana, tr. from ENG. Le Semana Atareada de Clifford'. Bridwell, Norman, illus. 2002. (Clifford, the Big Red Dog Ser.). (SPA.). 32p. (J). (ps-1). pap. 3.50 (978-0-439-41833-1(X) , Scholastic en Espanol) Scholastic, Inc.

Suarez Romero, Alfonso. Maraca. Alvarado, Dalia & Pacheco, Luis Gabriel, illus. rev. ed. 2006. (Castillo de la Lectura Verde Ser.). (SPA.). 120p. (J). pap. 7.95 (978-970-20-0128-7(5)) Castillo, Ediciones, S. A. de C. V. MEX. *Dist:* Macmillan.

Suen, Anastasia & Keats, Ezra Jack. Willie's Birthday. Eitzen, Allan, illus. 2001. (Easy-to-Read Ser.). 32p. (J). (gr. k-3). 13.99 (978-0-670-88943-3(1) , Viking Juvenile) Penguin Group (USA) Inc.

Sukach, Jim, Elliott's Talking Dog: And Other Quicksolve Mini-Mysteries. Flinn, Alan, illus. 2005. 80p. (J). (gr. 4-7). pap. 6.95 (978-1-4027-2366-7(0)) Sterling Publishing Co., Inc.

Sutcliff, Rosemary. The Hound of Ulster. 2002. (Illus.). 192p. (J). pap. 8.99 (978-0-09-943859-5(3)) Random Hse. GBR. *Dist:* Independent Pubs. Group.

Sutton, Scott E. Danger: Dinky Diplodocus. 2007. (Adventures of Dinosaur Dog Ser.). 144p. (J). pap. 5.99 (*978-1-888045-52-9(3)) Action Publishing, LLC.

—Death by Deinonychus. 2007. (Adventures of Dinosaur Dog Ser.). 144p. (J). pap. 5.99 (*978-1-888045-54-3(X)) Action Publishing, LLC.

—Trouble with Pteranodons. 2007. (Adventures of Dinosaur Dog Ser.). 144p. (Orig.). (J). pap. 5.99 (*978-1-888045-53-6(1)) Action Publishing, LLC.

—Tyrannosaurus Forest. 2007. (Adventures of Dinosaur Dog Ser.). 144p. (J). (gr. 3-6). pap. 5.99 (*978-1-888045-51-2(5)) Action Publishing, LLC.

Swaim, Jessica. The Hound from the Pound. McElmurry, Jill, illus. 2007. 32p. (J). (ps-3). 15.99 (*978-0-7636-2330-2(X)) Candlewick Pr.

Sweet, Melissa. Carmine: A Little More Red. 2005. (Illus.). 40p. (J). (gr. k-3). 16.00 (978-0-618-38794-6(3)) Houghton Mifflin Co. Trade & Reference Div.

Sweet, Melissa, illus. Tupelo Rides the Rails. 2008. (J). (*978-0-618-71714-9(5)) Houghton Mifflin Co.

Swerling, Lisa & Lazar, Ralph. Dogs Going Places. 2004. 64p. 9.95 (978-1-84072-604-6(0)) M Q Pubns. GBR. *Dist:* Weatherhill, Inc., Wybel Marketing Group.

Sykes, Julie. Dora's Eggs. Chapman, Jane, illus. 2007. (J). bds. 6.95 (978-1-58925-801-3(0) , tiger tales) ME Media LLC.

—Smudge. Chapman, Jane, illus. 1998. 32p. (J). (ps-2). 14.95 (978-1-888444-44-5(4)) Little Tiger Pr.

—Smudge. Chapman, Jane, illus. 2001. 32p. (J). (ps-k). 5.95 (978-1-58925-355-1(8) , tiger tales) ME Media LLC.

—Smudge. 2001. (gr. k-3). lib. bdg. 14.10 (978-0-613-42439-4(5)) Tandem Library Bks.

Taeckens, Geri. Walking along with My Dog. Carney, Deborah, illus. 2005. (J). 16.99 (978-0-9774546-0-0(6)) Accessibilities.

Taha, Karen T. Hotdog on TV. Takahashi, Hideko, illus. 2005. (Easy-to-Read, Dial Ser.). 40p. (J). (ps). 14.99 (978-0-8037-2933-9(2) , Dial) Penguin Group (USA) Inc.

Talone, Augusto. The Adventures of Max & Sandy: Three Short Stories about a Yellow Labrador Retriever Named Max & a Simese House Cat Named Sandy, Who Solve Mysteries. 2006. 96p. (J). pap. 11.99 (978-1-59977-005-5(9)) Annotation Pr.

Tanaka, Shinsuke, illus. Wings. 2006. 80p. (J). 14.95 (978-1-933327-19-8(7)) Purple Bear Bks., Inc.

Tavano, Joe. A Dachshund's Wish. Yu, Ji Yon, illus. 2006. 80p. (J). pap. 13.95 (978-0-9744287-1-0(X)) Traitor Dachshund Bks.

Taylor, Alastair. Mr. Blewitt's Nose. 2005. (J). (gr. k-3). 16.00 (978-0-618-58111-5(1)); (Illus.). 32p. 16.00 (978-0-618-42353-8(2)) Houghton Mifflin Co. Trade & Reference Div.

—Swollobog. 2001. (Illus.). 32p. (J). (gr. k-3). tchr. ed. 15.00 (978-0-618-04348-4(9)) Houghton Mifflin Co. Trade & Reference Div.

Taylor, G. P. The Tizzle Sisters & Erik. 2007. 188p. (*978-1-905692-22-4(6)) Markosia Enterprises Ltd.

Taylor, Joyce. My Dog & I 6 Packs. Pouch - Level B. Garner, Phil, illus. (Lighthouse Ser.). 12p. (gr. k-1). 24.00 (978-0-7578-0816-6(6)) Rigby Education.

Taylor, Theodore. The Trouble with Tuck. 2000. (978-0-606-18791-6(X)) Tandem Library Bks.

—The Trouble with Tuck: The Inspiring Story of a Dog Who Triumphs Against All Odds. 2000. (Illus.). 128p. (J). (gr. 4-7). 5.99 (978-0-440-41696-8(5) , Yearling) Random Hse. Children's Bks.

Taylor, Yvonne. Hartlie: The Streak. Taylor, Yvonne, ed. (Hartlie: Vol. 1). (Illus.). 32p. (J). 10.99 (978-0-9709187-0-3(4)) Peaceable Productions.

Tazewell, Charles. The Littlest Uninvited One. Tribble, Gail, illus. 2001. (J). (ps-3). 16.95 (978-0-8249-5404-8(1) , Ideals Children's Bks.) Ideals Pubns.

Teague, Mark. Dear Mrs. La Rue: Letters from Obedience School. Teague, Mark, illus. 2002. (Dear Mrs. Larue Ser.). (Illus.). 32p. (J). (gr. k-3). 16.99 (978-0-439-20663-1(4) , Scholastic Pr.) Scholastic, Inc.

—Dear Mrs. Larue: Querida Sra. Larue. Teague, Mark, illus. 2004. (SPA., Illus.). 32p. (J). (ps-3). pap. 4.99 (978-0-439-66128-7(5) , Scholastic en Espanol) Scholastic, Inc.

—Detective LaRue: Letters from the Investigation. Teague, Mark, illus. 2004. (Detective Larue Ser.). (Illus.). 32p. (J). (ps-3). pap. 15.95 (978-0-439-45868-9(4) , Scholastic Pr.) Scholastic, Inc.

—Larue para Alcalde: Cartas de la Campana: Cartas de la Campana. 2008. (Larue for Mayor Ser.). 32p. (J). pap. 4.99 (*978-0-545-02214-9(2) , Scholastic en Espanol) Scholastic, Inc.

—The Letters from the Campaign. 2008. (Larue for Mayor Ser.). 32p. (J). pap. 16.99 (*978-0-439-78315-6(1) , Blue Sky Pr., The) Scholastic, Inc.

Terhume, Albert Pays. Further Adventures of Lad. 2006. pap. (*978-1-4068-1162-9(9)) Echo Library.

—His Dog. 2006. pap. (*978-1-4068-1163-6(7)) Echo Library.

Terhune, Albert Payson. A Dog Named Chips. l.t. ed. 2000. (Wheeler Large Print Bks.). (Illus.). 166p. (J). (gr. 4-7). pap. 22.95 (978-1-56895-820-0(X) , Wheeler Publishing, Inc.) Thomson Gale.

—Gray Dawn. 2nd ed. 2002. (Illus.). 208p. (gr. 4-7). pap. 15.00 (978-1-880158-35-7(3)) Townsend, J.N. Publishing.

—Lad of Sunnybank. l.t. ed. 1999. (Perennial Ser.). 287p. (gr. 4-7). 26.95 (978-0-7838-8552-0(0)) Thorndike Pr.

—The Way of a Dog. l.t. ed. 1999. (Perennial Bestsellers Ser.). 337p. (YA). (gr. 5-9). 26.95 (978-0-7838-8743-2(4)) Thorndike Pr.

—Wolf. 2nd ed. 2004. 200p. pap. (978-1-880158-46-3(9)) Townsend, J.N. Publishing.

Terhune, Payson Albe. Further Adventures of Lad. 2006. 78.99 (*978-1-4280-1186-1(2)) IndyPublish.com.

Texas Golden Retriever, Casanova & Jason, Daniel. I Can't Do That I Have Paws. 2005. (J). per. 9.99 (978-0-9659470-4-6(1)) 5 Star Stories, Inc.

Thayer, Jane. Part-Time Dog. Barasch, Lynne & McCue, Lisa, illus. 2004. 32p. (J). (ps-3). 14.99 (978-0-06-029693-3(3)) HarperCollins Pubs.

—The Puppy Who Wanted a Boy. McCue, Lisa, illus. 2005. 32p. (J). pap. 6.99 (978-0-06-052698-6(X) , Harper Trophy) HarperCollins Pubs.

Thiele, Colin. The Cave & the Glory of Galumph. (Illus.). 160p. pap. (978-0-7344-0413-8(1) , Lothian Bks.) Hachette Livre Australia.

Thierry, Raphael. Green Butterfly: A Superdog Adventure. 2007. (Illus.). 24p. (J). 7.95 (*978-1-59354-198-9(8)) Handprint Bks.

—Green Butterfly: A Superdog Adventure. 2007. (Superdog Adventure Ser.). (Illus.). 32p. (J). (ps-k). pap. 6.99 (*978-1-84270-449-3(4)) Transworld Publishers Ltd. GBR. *Dist:* Independent Pubs. Group.

Thomas, Marjorie W. White Nose the Sheep Dog: Chiilgai, Na'nilkaadii. 2000. (ENG & NAV., Illus.). 40p. (J). pap. 9.00 (978-1-893354-17-3(2)) Salina Bookshelf.

Thompson, Laura J. Joseph's Charleston Adventure. Thompson, Laura J., illus. 1998. (Illus.). 28p. (J). (ps-4). 16.95 (978-0-9607854-1-4(8)) Junior League of Charleston, South Carolina, Inc.

Thorn, David. Dollypogs. 2002. (J). cd-rom (978-0-9724995-8-3(X)) Alcazar AudioWorks.

Thornton-Jones, Marcia. Champ. 2007. 192p. (J). (gr. 4-7). pap. 4.99 (*978-0-439-79399-5(8)) Scholastic, Inc.

The Three Pups. (Lexile Levels Ser.). 47.88 (978-1-56334-092-5(5)) Hampton-Brown Bks.

Tibo, Gilles. Alex & Sarah. Germain, Philippe, illus. 2005. (Read-It! Readers Ser.). 32p. (J). (ps). lib. bdg. 18.60 (978-1-4048-1352-6(7)) Picture Window Bks.

—Alex & the Team Jersey. Germain, Philippe, illus. 2005. (Read-It! Readers Ser.). 32p. (J). (gr. k-3). 18.60 (978-1-4048-1024-2(2)) Picture Window Bks.

—Alex & Toolie. Germain, Philippe, illus. 2005. (Read-It! Readers Ser.). 32p. (C). (gr. k-3). 18.60 (978-1-4048-1027-3(7)) Picture Window Bks.

Tibo, Gilles & Perkes, Carolyn. Alex & Sarah. Germain, Philippe, illus. 2001. (Little Wolf Bks.; Level 3). 32p. (J). (gr. 1 up). pap. (978-1-894363-76-1(0)) Dominique & Friends.

Tibo, Gilles, et al. Alex & Hockey-Playing Dog. 2000. (Illus.). (J). (gr. 1-4). pap. (978-1-894363-43-3(4)) Dominique & Friends.

Tiger Tales Staff. Little Puppy. Finn, Rebecca, illus. 2005. (Cuddly Cuffs Ser.). 6p. (J). 6.95 (978-1-58925-761-0(8) , tiger tales) ME Media LLC.

Tisopulos, Tara. Finding a Family. Tokar, Rob, photos by. 1999. (Adventures of Buddi the Greyhound Ser.). (Illus.). 22p. (J). (gr. 1-5). 14.95 (978-0-9678057-0-2(8)) Great Dog Publishing.

Tofte, Mavis. Doogie Dork & Marta. 2005. (Illus.). 64p. (J). per. 5.75 (978-0-9709906-4-8(2)) Creative Quill Publishing, Inc.

—Doogie Dork & the Storm. Tofte, Mavis, illus. 2006. (Illus.). 64p. (J). per. 6.75 (978-0-9709906-5-5(0)) Creative Quill Publishing, Inc.

Tolan, Stephanie S. Listen! 2006. 208p. (J). 15.99 (978-0-06-057935-7(8)); lib. bdg. 16.89 (978-0-06-057936-4(6)) HarperCollins Pubs.

Tolkien, J. R. R. Roverandom. Scull, Christina & Hammond, Wayne G., eds. (Illus.). 1999. 106p. pap. 12.00 (978-0-395-95799-8(0)); 1998. 128p. (gr. 3-5). 17.00 (978-0-395-89871-0(4)) Houghton Mifflin Co. Trade & Reference Div.

Tolkien, J. R. R., et al. Roverandom. Scull, Christina & Hammond, Wayne G., eds. 783rd l.t. ed. 1998. (Illus.). 191p. (J). 25.95 (978-0-7838-0299-2(4)) Thorndike Pr.

Tomkins, Jasper. The Camelback Dogs! 2004. (Illus.). 48p. (J). 15.95 (978-1-57061-420-0(2)) Sasquatch Bks.

Tompkins, Robyn Lee. Miss Molly's Adventure at the Beach: Another Great Adventure Brought to You by Miss Molly & Her Dog Reyburn, 10 vols. Kantz, Bill, illus. 2004. (J). per. (978-0-9741647-5-5(5)) NRG Pubns.

—Miss Molly's Adventure in the Park: Another Great Adventure Brought to You by Miss Molly & Her Dog Reyburn, 10 vols. Carson, Shawn K., illus. l.t. ed. 2005. (ENG.). 60p. (J). per. (978-0-9741647-6-2(3)) NRG Pubns.

Toms, Kate. Funny Faces Cloth Book: Jogger Dog. 2006. (Funny Faces (Make Believe Ideas) Ser.). (Illus.). 4p. (ps). 8.95 (978-1-84610-289-9(8)) Make Believe Ideas GBR. *Dist:* Ingram Pub. Services.

Toms, Kate & Funny Faces Staff. Jogger Dog. 2007. (Funny Faces (Make Believe Ideas) Ser.). (Illus.). (ps). 8.95 ***(978-1-84610-268-4(5))*** Make Believe Ideas GBR. *Dist:* Ingram Pub. Services.

Toole, Darlene. Cajun's Song. 2004. (ENG & SPA., Illus.). 56p. (978-1-884362-67-5(2)) Butte Pubns., Inc.

Trapani, Iza. My Jack. 1999. (J). (ps-3). pap. 7.95 (978-1-58089-013-7(X)) Charlesbridge Publishing, Inc.

—Oh Where, Oh Where Has My Little Dog Gone? Trapani, Iza, illus. 1998. (Illus.). 28p. (J). (ps-k). bds. 6.95 (978-1-58089-016-8(4)) Charlesbridge Publishing, Inc.

—Oh Where, Oh Where Has My Little Dog Gone? 1998. (Illus.). 32p. (J). (ps-2). pap. 6.95 (978-1-58089-005-2(9)) Charlesbridge Publishing, Inc.

Treadaway, Angie. Banah for Kids&. The Master's Workshop. 2003. 25 p. pap. 14.95 (978-1-59286-866-7(5)) PublishAmerica, Inc.

Trimble, Marcia. Peppy's Shadow. Pellegrini, Will, illus. 2003. 32p. (J). (ps-3). 15.95 (978-1-891577-70-3(0)); pap. 7.95 (978-1-891577-71-0(9)) Images Pr.

A Trip to the Beach. 2007. (J). per. ***(978-1-932570-85-4(3))*** Literacy Footprints Inc.

Tripp, Jenny. Pete & Fremont. Manders, John, illus. 2007. 192p. (J). (gr. 2-4). 16.00 (978-0-15-205629-2(7)) Harcourt Trade Pubs.

Trissler, Rebecca Johns. Vinny's Secret. (Adventures of Storydog Ser.). 75p. (J). pap. (978-0-9722690-0-1(2), 1000) Storydog, Inc.

Trottier, Maxine. Little Dog Moon. Fernandez, Laura & Jacobson, Rick, illus. 2000. 20p. (J). (ps-3). 14.95 (978-0-7737-3220-9(9)) Stoddart Kids CAN. *Dist:* Fitzhenry & Whiteside, Ltd.

Truax, Doug. A Good Day for Ducks. Smith, Jack K., illus. 2003. 32p. (gr. k-4). 16.95 (978-1-932052-12-1(7)) Ducks Unlimited, Inc.

Tucker Goes to Heaven. 2006. pap. 13.95 ***(978-1-59526-457-2(4))*** Media Creations, Inc.

Tudor, Tasha. Corgiville Christmas. 2004. (Corgiville Ser.: Bk. 3). (Illus.). 48p. (J). 15.95 (978-1-932425-00-0(4), Lemniscaat) Boyds Mills Pr.

—Corgiville Fair. Tudor, Tasha, illus. 1998. (Illus.). 48p. (J). (ps-17). 17.99 (978-0-316-85312-5(7)) Little Brown & Co.

Turner, Deborah & Mohler, Diana. How Willy Got His Wings: The Continuing Adventures of Wheely Willy. Ahrends, Susan, illus. 2003. 30p. 15.95 (978-0-944875-88-9(2)) Doral Publishing, Inc.

Turner, Pamela S. Hachiko: The True Story of a Loyal Dog. Nascimbene, Yan, illus. 2004. 32p. (J). (gr. k-3). tchr. ed. 15.00 (978-0-618-14094-7(8)) Houghton Mifflin Co. Trade & Reference Div.

Turner, Sandy. Cool Cat, Hot Dog. Turner, Sandy, illus. 2005. (Illus.). 48p. (J). (ps-ps). 16.95 (978-0-689-84946-6(X), Atheneum) Simon & Schuster Children's Publishing.

Tuxworth, Nicola. Puppies: A Very First Picture Book. 1999. (Pictures & Words Ser.). (Illus.). 24p. (J). (ps up). lib. bdg. 22.00 (978-0-8368-2380-6(X)) Stevens, Gareth Inc.

Twain, Mark. Personal Recollections of Joan of Arc. 1999. reprint ed. pap. 28.00 (978-1-4047-1122-8(8)); pap. 28.00 (978-1-4047-1123-5(6)) Classic Textbooks.

Tyo, Courtney. Shamrock Scare. del Sur, Duendes, illus. 2004. (Scooby-Doo Ser.: No. 19). 32p. (J). pap. 3.99 (978-0-439-55715-3(1), Scholastic Paperbacks) Scholastic, Inc.

Typaldos, Sylvia. Don't Call Me Lassie! The Fascinating Lives of Seven Family Dogs. 2003. Orig. Title: Family Dogs: an Animal Rights Novel about Dogs. 192p. (YA). per. 16.95 (978-0-9729863-0-4(8)) Haven Harbor.

Tyrell, Michael. Krypto: Test Pilot Puppy. 2006. 96p. (J). pap. 2.99 (978-0-439-74404-1(0)) Scholastic, Inc.

—Krypto Dog Star Patrol. 2006. 48p. (J). pap. 3.99 (978-0-439-72508-8(9)) Scholastic, Inc.

Ugly Pugsy: Individual Title Six-Packs. (Bookweb Ser.). 32p. (gr. 5 up). 34.00 (978-0-7635-3779-1(9)) Rigby Education.

Umansky, Kaye. I Don't Like Gloria! Chamberlain, Margaret, illus. 2007. 32p. (J). (ps-1). 15.99 (978-0-7636-3202-1(3)) Candlewick Pr.

Underwood, Ralph Kim. His Dogness Finds a Blue Heart. Goldman, Garnet, illus. 2004. 32p. (J). 16.95 (978-0-89587-304-0(4)) Blair, John F. Pub.

Unger, Pam. Fly, Greyhound Racer: A Special Dog's Tale. 2005. (Illus.). 60p. (YA). pap. 14.99 (978-1-933570-38-9(5)) Aardvark Global Publishing.

Upton, Deborah. Scooby-Doo! Telephone Book. 2001. (Illus.). (J). 15.98 (978-0-7853-4755-2(0)) Publications International, Ltd.

Urbigkit, Cat. Puppies, Puppies Everywhere! Urbigkit, Cat, photos by. (Illus.). 24p. (J). (ps-1). 12.95 (978-1-59078-363-4(8)) Boyds Mills Pr.

Ure, Jean. Muddy Four Paws. 1999. (We Love Animals Bks.). (Illus.). 128p. (J). (gr. 4-7). pap. 3.95 (978-0-7641-0968-3(5)) Barron's Educational Series, Inc.

Urmston, Kathleen. Sammy. Gedeon, Gloria, illus. 2005. (J). pap. 4.95 (978-1-57874-089-5(4)) Kaeden Corp.

Urmston, Kathleen & Urmston, Craig. Sammy's Hamburger Caper. Gedeon, Gloria, illus. 2002. 24p. (J). (gr. k-2). pap. 5.25 (978-1-57874-035-2(5)) Kaeden Corp.

—Sammy's Slippery Day. Gedeon, Gloria, illus. 2002. 24p. (J). (gr. k-2). pap. 5.25 (978-1-57874-033-8(9)) Kaeden Corp.

Utton, Peter. Duncan & the Pirates. Utton, Peter, illus. 2005. (Read-It! Chapter Bks.). (Illus.). 52p. (J). (ps-k). lib. bdg. 19.95 (978-1-4048-1277-2(6)) Picture Window Bks.

Van de Velde, Vivian. Smart Dog. 2000. (Illus.). 160p. (gr. 4-7). 4.99 (978-0-440-41610-4(8), Yearling) Random Hse. Children's Bks.

Van Draanen, Wendelin. Sammy Keyes & the Runaway Elf. VanDraanen, Wendelin, illus. 2001. (Sammy Keyes Ser.: Bk. 4). pap. 39.95 incl. audio compact disk (978-0-87499-858-0(1)) Live Oak Media.

—Sammy Keyes & the Runaway Elf. 2000. (Sammy Keyes Ser.: Bk. 4). (Illus.). 208p. (J). (gr. 5-8). pap. 5.99 (978-0-375-80255-3(X), Yearling) Random Hse. Children's Bks.

—Sammy Keyes & the Runaway Elf. 2000. (Sammy Keyes Ser.: Bk. 4). (gr. 5-8). lib. bdg. 13.00 (978-0-613-28240-6(X)) Tandem Library Bks.

Van Dusen, Chris. A Camping Spree with Mr. Magee. 2003. (Illus.). 36p. (J). 14.95 (978-0-8118-3603-6(7)) Chronicle Bks. LLC.

Van Fleet, Matthew. Dog. Stanton, Brian, photos by. 2007. (Illus.). 20p. (J). (ps up). 14.99 (978-1-4169-4137-8(1), Simon & Schuster/Paula Wiseman Bks.) Simon & Schuster Children's Publishing.

Van Patter, Bruce. Farley Found It. (Illus.). (J). 16.95 (978-1-59078-351-1(4)) Boyds Mills Pr.

Van Steenwyk, Elizabeth. Three Dog Winter. 1999. (978-0-606-16440-5(5)) Tandem Library Bks.

Van Stockum, Hilda, illus. Pamela Walks the Dog. 2002. 32p. 9.95 (978-1-883937-61-4(2)) Bethlehem Bks.

Vandalay, Martha. Pittsburgh a to Z. 2003. per. 6.95 (978-1-932205-18-3(7)) Word Association Pubs.

Vande Velde, Vivian. Smart Dog. 160p. 2007. (Illus.). (J). pap. 5.95 ***(978-0-15-206172-2(X)***, Magic Carpet Bks.); 1998. (YA). (gr. 3-7). 16.00 (978-0-15-201847-4(6)) Harcourt Children's Bks.

—Smart Dog. 2002. (J). (gr. 4-8). 20.00 (978-0-8446-7231-1(9)) Smith, Peter Pub., Inc.

—Smart Dog. 2000. (978-0-606-18790-9(1)); (gr. 3-6). lib. bdg. 12.40 (978-0-613-28646-6(4)) Tandem Library Bks.

Vaniko, K. L. Why the Dog Chases the Cat & the Cat C. 2006. 30.99 ***(978-1-59926-863-7(9))*** Xlibris Corp.

Vassallo, Rebecca. Listen to Luther. 2006. 24p. (J). 10.87 (978-1-4116-8169-9(X)) Lulu.com.

Venn, Cecilia. Puppy Parade, Level 2. 1998. (Disney's First Readers Ser.). (Illus.). 32p. (J). (gr. 1-3). pap. 2.95 (978-0-7868-4170-7(2)) Disney Pr.

Verville, Linda. For Pete's Sake. Pelletier, Melissa, illus. 2002. 24p. (J). (gr. k-5). pap. 7.95 (978-0-9721472-0-0(9)) For Pete's Sake Publishing.

Villaloz, ChiChi & Etheridge, Katy. Do Dogs Dream? Villaloz, ChiChi & Etheridge, Katy, illus. 2003. (Illus.). 32p. (J). 16.95 (978-0-9722180-5-4(X)) Malamute Pr.

Villet, Olivia. Chester's Big Surprise. 2001. (Illus.). 32p. (J). 17.99 (978-0-7475-5247-5(9)) Bloomsbury Publishing Plc GBR. *Dist:* Trafalgar Square Publishing.

Vinopol, Corinne & Bednarczyk, Angela. ASL Tales & Games for Kids - Biscuit Blvd: Computer Software in American Sign Language. 2004. (J). cd-rom 34.95 (978-0-9667589-9-3(4)) Institute for Disabilities Research & Training, Inc.

Voigt, Cynthia. Angus & Sadie. Leigh, Tom, illus. 2005. 208p. (J). lib. bdg. 16.89 (978-0-06-074583-7(5)); 15.99 (978-0-06-074582-0(7)) HarperCollins Pubs.

—The Rosie Stories. Smith, Cat Bowman, illus. 2003. 48p. (J). (gr. k-3). tchr. ed. 16.95 (978-0-8234-1625-7(9)) Holiday Hse., Inc.

Volker, Kerstin. Henry Builds a Tree House. 2003. (Funny Friends Lift-and-Learn Bks.). (Illus.). 14p. (J). 5.99 (978-1-59384-023-5(3)) Parklane Publishing.

Von Sholly, Peter. Dinosaur Circus. 2001. (Illus.). 32p. (Orig.). (J). (gr. 2-6). pap. 9.95 (978-0-9709368-0-6(X)) Vonshollywood.

Waddell, James M. Puppy Dog Tails. 2005. 217p. pap. 19.95 (978-0-7414-2438-9(X)) Infinity Publishing.

Wag & Woof. 2002. 10p. (J). 9.95 (978-0-7525-5578-2(2)) Parragon, Inc.

Wagner, Jenny. High Hopes on Sea. Rogers, Gregory, illus. 2005. (UQP Children's Fiction Ser.). 80p. (Orig.). (J). pap. 16.95 (978-0-7022-3525-2(3)) Univ. of Queensland Pr. AUS. *Dist:* International Specialized Bk. Services.

Waite, Judy. Digging for Dinosaurs. Parsons, Garry, illus. (Flying Foxes Ser.). 32p. (J). 2004. pap. (978-0-7787-1529-0(9)); 2003. (978-0-7787-1483-5(7)) Crabtree Publishing Co.

Wales, Dirk. Penny House. Kenna, Diane, illus. 2005. 32p. (J). 16.95 (978-0-9632459-1-5(0)) Great Plains Pr.

A Walk for Pickles. 2002. (J). (978-1-58453-185-2(1)) Pioneer Valley Educational Pr., Inc.

Walker, Russell D. Michelle & the Magic Timepiece. 2006. 108p. pap. 16.95 (978-1-4241-3143-3(X)) PublishAmerica, Inc.

Walking the Dogs, 6 Pack. (ps-2). 27.00 (978-0-7635-9481-7(4)) Rigby Education.

Wallace, Bill. Coyote Autumn. 2002. 208p. (J). pap. 5.99 (978-0-7434-2836-1(6), Aladdin) Simon & Schuster Children's Publishing.

—Coyote Autumn. 2002. (gr. 3-6). lib. bdg. 13.00 (978-0-613-68225-1(4)) Tandem Library Bks.

—A Dog Called Kitty. 153p. (J). (gr. 3-5). pap. 3.99 (978-0-8072-1492-3(2), Listening Library) Random Hse. Audio Publishing Group.

—The Dog Who Thought He Was Santa. 2007. 224p. (J). (gr. 3-7). 16.95 ***(978-0-8234-2114-5(7))*** Holiday Hse., Inc.

—Goosed! Rogers, Jacqueline, illus. 2002. 128p. (J). (gr. 4-6). tchr. ed. 16.95 (978-0-8234-1757-5(3)) Holiday Hse., Inc.

—Goosed! Rogers, Jacqueline, illus. 2004. 128p. (J). pap. 4.99 (978-0-689-86681-4(X), Aladdin) Simon & Schuster Children's Publishing.

—No Dogs Allowed! 2004. 214p. (J). (gr. 4-6). tchr. ed. 16.95 (978-0-8234-1818-3(9)) Holiday Hse., Inc.

—Pick of the Litter. 2005. 160p. (J). (ps-7). 16.95 (978-0-8234-1921-0(5)) Holiday Hse., Inc.

—Pick of the Litter. 2006. 176p. (J). pap. 4.99 (978-1-4169-2511-8(2), Aladdin) Simon & Schuster Children's Publishing.

—Red Dog. 2002. 192p. (J). pap. 5.99 (978-0-689-85394-4(7), Aladdin) Simon & Schuster Children's Publishing.

—Red Dog. 2002. (gr. 3-6). lib. bdg. 13.00 (978-0-613-64447-1(6)) Tandem Library Bks.

Wallace, Carol. One Nosy Pup. Bjorkman, Steve, illus. 40p. (J). 15.95 (978-0-8234-1917-3(7)) Holiday Hse., Inc.

—The Santa Secret. Bjorkman, Steve, illus. 2007. 40p. (J). (gr. k-3). 15.95 ***(978-0-8234-2022-3(1)***; pap. 4.95 ***(978-0-8234-2126-8(0))*** Holiday Hse., Inc.

—That Furball Puppy & Me. 2000. (gr. 3-6). lib. bdg. 12.40 (978-0-613-84059-0(3)) Tandem Library Bks.

—Turkeys Together. Rogers, Jaqueline, illus. 40p. (J). (ps). 15.95 (978-0-8234-1895-4(2)) Holiday Hse., Inc.

Wallace, Carol & Wallace, Bill. The Meanest Hound Around. Gurney, John Steven, illus. 160p. (J). 2004. pap. 4.99 (978-0-7434-3786-8(1), Aladdin); 2003. 15.95 (978-0-7434-3785-1(3)) Simon & Schuster Children's Publishing.

—That Furball Puppy & Me. 2000. (Illus.). 96p. (J). (gr. 3-6). reprint ed. pap. 4.50 (978-0-7434-1029-8(7), Aladdin) Simon & Schuster Children's Publishing.

—That Furball Puppy & Me. Wolff, Jason, illus. 2000. 83p. (J). (ps-ps). lib. bdg. 11.30 (978-0-606-20668-6(X)) Tandem Library Bks.

Wallace, Karen. Ooh la la, Lottie! Parsons, Garry, illus. 2004. (I Am Reading Ser.). 48p. (J). (gr. k-3). pap. 3.95 (978-0-7534-5716-0(4), Kingfisher) Houghton Mifflin Co. Trade & Reference Div.

Wallace, Nikki. Stubby & the Puppy Pack. 2000. (Illus.). 96p. (J). (gr. 4-7). pap. 3.99 (978-0-671-02589-2(9), Aladdin) Simon & Schuster Children's Publishing.

—Stubby & the Puppy Pack. 2000. (gr. 3-6). lib. bdg. 11.80 (978-0-613-34025-0(6)) Tandem Library Bks.

—Stubby & the Puppy Pack to the Rescue. Gurney, John Steven, illus. 144p. (J). 2003. pap. 4.99 (978-0-7434-2695-4(9), Aladdin); 2002. (gr. 3-6). 16.00 (978-0-7434-2694-7(0)) Simon & Schuster Children's Publishing.

—Stubby & the Puppy Pack to the Rescue. 2003. (gr. 3-6). lib. bdg. 13.00 (978-0-613-66546-9(5)) Tandem Library Bks.

Walsh, Laurence & Walsh, Suella. In the Middle of the Night. 2006. (J). pap. ***(978-0-88092-473-3(X))*** Royal Fireworks Publishing Co.

Walsh, Vivian & Seibold, J. Otto. Olive, My Love. 2004. (Illus.). 40p. (J). 15.00 (978-0-15-204720-7(4)) Harcourt Children's Bks.

Walt Disney's Lady & the Tramp. 2002. (J). spiral bd. (978-0-9720651-5-3(6)) Story Reader, Inc.

Walton, Rick. Bertie Was a Watchdog. Robins, Arthur, illus. 2002. 56p. (J). (ps-2). 12.99 (978-0-7636-1385-3(1)) Candlewick Pr.

—Dog Day Detectives: Mini-Mysteries for a Summer Day. 2006. (Illus.). 80p. (J). pap. 6.95 (978-1-933317-49-6(3)) Leatherwood Pr.

Walton, Van. From the Pound to the Palace. 2006. (ENG., Illus.). 32p. per. 15.99 (978-1-4141-0579-6(7)) Pleasant Word.

Wang, Margaret. Five Little Puppies. 2006. (Illus.). 12p. (J). 9.95 (978-1-58117-487-8(X), Intervisual/Piggy Toes) Dalmatian Pr.

Ward, Carla Ward. Emily Finds a Dog. Ward, Megan, illus. 2007. (J). 15.95 ***(978-0-9793124-0-3(X))*** Tinkertown Museum.

Ward, Damian, illus. Captain Cur & Wonder Flea. 2006. 48p. (J). 16.99 (978-1-57687-342-7(0)) powerHouse Cultural Entertainment, Inc.

Ward, Helen. Moon Dog. 2005. (Illus.). 40p. (J). ***(978-1-84011-864-3(4))*** Templar Publishing, Dorking.

Ward, Jean Elizabeth. A Barbara Anne Bushy Tale: Book #2 in a Series. 2007. 188p. per. 16.95 ***(978-0-595-45726-7(6))*** iUniverse, Inc.

Warden, Evelyn. Oh, Please, Cricket. 2006. 144p. pap. 19.95 (978-1-4241-1860-1(3)) PublishAmerica, Inc.

Wardlaw, Lee. Bow-Wow Birthday. Johnson-Petrov, Arden, illus. 1998. 32p. (J). (gr. k-3). 14.95 (978-1-56397-489-2(4)) Boyds Mills Pr.

Warner, Cheryl Ware. Chunkerella. 2006. (J). pap. 8.00 ***(978-0-8059-7060-9(6))*** Dorrance Publishing Co., Inc.

Warner, Gertrude Chandler. Benny's Saturday Surprise, Vol. 8. Life, Kay, illus. 2004. (Adventures of Benny & Watch: Vol. 8). 32p. (J). (ps-2). pap. 3.95 (978-0-8075-0642-4(7)) Whitman, Albert & Co.

—Mystery of the Midnight Dog. 2001. (gr. 3-6). lib. bdg. 11.80 (978-0-613-35789-0(2)) Tandem Library Bks.

—The Mystery of the Midnight Dog, Vol. 81. 2004. (Boxcar Children Ser.: No. 81). (Illus.). 122p. (J). (gr. 2-7). pap. 4.50 (978-0-8075-5476-0(6)) Whitman, Albert & Co.

—The Secret under the Tree. 2001. (Boxcar Children Early Reader Ser.). (Illus.). (J). (978-0-606-21083-6(0)) Tandem Library Bks.

—Watch, the Superdog! 2002. (gr. k-3). lib. bdg. 11.80 (978-0-613-70864-7(4)) Tandem Library Bks.

—Watch, the Superdog!, Vol. 10. Life, Kay, illus. 2004. (Adventures of Benny & Watch: Vol. 10). 32p. (J). (ps-2). pap. 3.95 (978-0-8075-0647-9(8)) Whitman, Albert & Co.

Warnes, Tim. Can't You Sleep, Dotty? Warnes, Tim, illus. 2003. (Illus.). 32p. (J). pap. 5.95 (978-1-58925-376-6(0), tiger tales) ME Media LLC.

—Can't You Sleep, Dotty? 2001. (Illus.). 28p. (J). tchr. ed. 14.95 (978-1-58925-010-9(9), tiger tales) ME Media LLC.

—Can't You Sleep, Dotty? 2003. (ps-2). lib. bdg. 14.10 (978-0-613-84706-3(7)) Tandem Library Bks.

—Chalk & Cheese. 2008. (J). ***(978-1-4169-1378-8(5)***, Simon & Schuster Children's Publishing) Simon & Schuster Children's Publishing.

Warnes, Tim. Happy Birthday, Dotty. Warnes, Tim, illus. 2003. (Illus.). 32p. (J). tchr. ed. 15.95 (978-1-58925-026-0(5), tiger tales) ME Media LLC.

Warren, Adrian. Caminando a Orillas Del Rio. de la Vega, Eida, tr. Brown, Craig, illus. 2001. (Books for Young Learners).Tr. of Walking by the Rio. (SPA.). 16p. (J). (gr. k-2). pap. 5.00 (978-1-57274-439-4(1), 2832) Owen, Richard C. Pubs., Inc.

Warren, Celia. The Ghost Dog. Smith, Pete, illus. 2008. (J). pap. ***(978-1-59889-899-6(X)***; 33p. (YA). (gr. 5-9). lib. bdg. 21.26 ***(978-1-59889-847-7(7))*** Stone Arch Bks.

Warriner, Mercer. Hounded by Baskervilles. 2002. (gr. 5-8). lib. bdg. 13.00 (978-0-613-74233-7(8)) Tandem Library Bks.

Wasserman, Shannon & Wasserman, Curt. The Adventures of Ruff-n-Rescue. 2006. 40p. 16.95 ***(978-1-931643-87-0(3))*** Seven Locks Pr.

Watkins, Patricia. Boyd-Friend: His Yippie-Skippie Journey to a Forever Home. Watkins, Christopher, illus. l.t. ed. 2004. 44p. 10.95 (978-0-9753397-0-1(2)) Frayed Pages Publishing.

Watson, Don. Amazing Graci & River Bottom Goats. 2005. 144p. pap. 9.95 (978-0-9764026-0-2(2)) Longhorn Creek Pr.

Watt, Fiona. Este No Es Mi Perrito. 2004. Tr. of That's Not My Puppy. (SPA., Illus.). 10p. (J). (ps up). 7.95 (978-0-7460-3898-7(4)) EDC Publishing.

Wattenberg, Jane & Aesop. Never Cry Woof! A Dog-U-Drama. Wattenberg, Jane, illus. 2005. (Illus.). 40p. (J). pap. 16.95 (978-0-439-21675-3(3)) Scholastic, Inc.

Waucaush, Clair. Pokey's World. 2004. 72p. pap. 14.95 (978-1-4137-3923-7(7)) PublishAmerica, Inc.

We Adopted a Greyhound. 2001. 36p. per. 16.95 (978-0-9713838-0-7(4)) Hawaiian Publishing.

We Adopted a Greyhound: A Coloring Book. 2001. 36p. (J). pap. 8.95 (978-0-9713838-1-4(2)) Hawaiian Publishing.

Weale, David. The True Meaning of Crumbfest. McNevin, Dale, illus. 28p. pap. 5.95 (978-0-9698606-4-8(1)) Acorn Pr., The CAN. *Dist:* Goose Lane Editions.

Weare, Tim. I'm A Little Puppy: A Finger-Puppet Pal. 2002. (I'm A Little Ser.). (Illus.). 12p. (J). (ps-k). bds. 6.95 (978-0-439-40642-0(0), Cartwheel Bks.) Scholastic, Inc.

Weaver, Griz. Along Came Lizzie. 2005. 36p. (J). 12.43 (978-1-4116-3933-1(2)) Lulu.com.

—How It Came to Be Seven Cats, A Woman, A Man & Me. 2005. 55p. (J). 15.28 (978-1-4116-0630-2(2)) Lulu.com.

Weber, Lou. Puppy Tales Four Book Carry Case. 2005. 20p. 10.98 (978-1-4127-3808-8(3), PIL Kids) Publications International, Ltd.

Weber, Richard D. Elvis & Me. 2004. 511p. (YA). per. 17.41 (978-1-4116-0549-7(7)) Lulu.com.

Weeks, Sarah. Oh My Gosh, Mrs. McNosh. Westcott, Nadine Bernard, illus. 2002. 32p. (J). (ps up). 15.99 (978-0-694-01204-6(1)); lib. bdg. 15.89 (978-0-06-008858-3(3)) HarperCollins Pubs. (Geringer, Laura Book).

—Ruff! Ruff! Where's Scruff? A Lift the Flap Adventure. Carter, David A., illus. 2006. 16p. (J). 13.95 (978-0-15-205575-2(4), Red Wagon Bks.) Harcourt Children's Bks.

Wegman, William. Dress up Batty. Wegman, William, illus. 2004. (Illus.). 18p. (ps-17). 19.99 (978-0-7868-1849-5(2)) Hyperion Bks. for Children.

—My Town. Wegman, William, photos by. 1998. (Illus.). 40p. (ps-17). 16.95 (978-0-7868-0410-8(6)) Hyperion Bks. for Children.

—Surprise Party. Wegman, William, photos by. 2000. (Illus.). 32p. (ps-17). 16.99 (978-0-7868-0585-3(4)) Hyperion Bks. for Children.

Weigand, Edith S. Scottie-Robbie: The Story of a True Champion. Cleaveland, Caroline A., illus. 2000. 77p. (J). (gr. 3-7). pap. 12.95 (978-0-9618904-5-2(2)) Zhera Pubns.

Weil, Zoe. Claude & Medea: The Hellburn Dogs. 2007. 112p. (J). (gr. 4-7). pap. 30.00 ***(978-1-59056-105-8(8))*** Lantern Bks.

Weinberger, Jane. That Dog. 2002. (J). pap. 8.00 (978-1-883650-57-5(7)) Windswept Hse. Pubs.

Weinberger, Kimberly. Be-a-Good-Friend Sticker Book. 2001. (Clifford, the Big Red Dog Ser.). (Illus.). 24p. (J). (gr. k-2). 5.99 (978-0-439-22945-6(6)) Scholastic, Inc.

—Clifford el Dia de la Tormenta. 2003. (Big Red Reader Ser.). (SPA., Illus.). 32p. (J). (gr. k-3). pap. 3.99 (978-0-439-55114-4(5), Scholastic en Espanol) Scholastic, Inc.

—Share-and-Be-Fair Sticker Book. 2001. (Clifford, the Big Red Dog Ser.). (J). pap. 5.99 (978-0-439-28681-7(6)) Scholastic, Inc.

—The Stormy Day Rescue. Thompson, Del, illus. 2001. (J). 10.79 (978-0-606-19914-8(4)) Tandem Library Bks.

—Stormy Day Rescue. 2001. (ps-2). lib. bdg. 11.80 (978-0-613-33106-7(0)) Tandem Library Bks.

Weinberger, Kimberly & Bridwell, Norman. The Stormy Day Rescue. 2001. (Clifford, the Big Red Dog Ser.). (Illus.). 32p. (J). (gr. k-2). pap. 3.99 (978-0-439-21360-8(6)) Scholastic, Inc.

Weisman, Debbie. The Lady & the Tramp. 2000. (Read-Aloud Storybook Ser.). 64p. (J). 6.99 (978-0-7364-0162-3(8)) Mouse Works.

Weissman, Sandy. Abby & Rileys First Day Home. 2006. pap. 12.99 ***(978-1-4259-8241-6(7))*** AuthorHouse.

Wells, Angela. Tales of Albie the Talking Dog. 2008. (J). per. 12.95 (978-0-9767047-0-6(6)) Anystar Publishing.

Wells, Rosemary. Lassie Come-Home. Jeffers, Susan, illus. rev. ed. 1998. 48p. (J). (ps up). reprint ed. pap. 8.95 (978-0-8050-5995-3(4) , Holt, Henry & Co. Bks. For Young Readers) Holt, Henry & Co.

—McDuff & the Baby. Jeffers, Susan, illus. 2006. 32p. (ps-k). 9.99 (978-0-7868-3834-9(5)) Hyperion Bks. for Children.

—McDuff & the Baby. Jeffers, Susan, illus. 2020. 24p. (J). pap. 4.99 (978-0-7868-1191-5(9)) Hyperion Paperbacks for Children.

—McDuff Comes Home. Jeffers, Susan, illus. 2006. 32p. (ps-k). 9.99 (978-0-7868-3833-2(7)) Hyperion Bks. for Children.

—McDuff Encuentra un Hogar. Jeffers, Susan, illus. 2000. (SPA.). (J). (ps-k). pap. 7,95 (978-958-04-4696-5(2) , NR2168) Norma S.A. COL. *Dist:* Distribuidora Norma, Inc., Lectorum Pubns., Inc.

—McDuff Goes to School. Jeffers, Susan, illus. ed. 2005. 32p. (ps-k). 9.99 (978-0-7868-5676-3(9)) Hyperion Bks. for Children.

—McDuff Moves In. Jeffers, Susan, illus. Date not set. 24p. (J). pap. 4.99 (978-0-7868-1190-8(0)) Hyperion Paperbacks for Children.

—McDuff Moves In. Jeffers, Susan, illus. ed. 2005. 32p. (ps-k). 9.99 (978-0-7868-5677-0(7)) Hyperion Bks. for Children.

—McDuff Saves the Day. Jeffers, Susan, illus. 32p. (ps-k). 2002. 15.49 (978-0-7868-2311-6(9)); 2005. 9.99 (978-0-7868-5675-6(0)) Hyperion Bks. for Children.

—McDuff's New Friend. 1998. 8.95 (978-0-7868-0493-1(9)) Hyperion Bks. for Children.

—McDuff's New Friend: Includes Stuffed Toy Puppy. 1998. (Illus.). (J). 219.00 (978-0-7868-2825-8(0)) Hyperion Pr.

—McDuff's New Friend with Plush Box Set. 2003. (Illus.). 28p. (J). 14.99 (978-0-7868-1866-2(2) , Disney Editions) Disney Pr.

—Mini McDuff & the Baby McDuff & Friends. 2001. 32p. (J). 9.99 (978-0-7868-0695-9(8)) Disney Pr.

Wert, Richard. The Boxer's Backyard. 2007. (J). pap. 8.99 ***(978-1-60247-023-1(5))*** Tate Publishing & Enterprises, L.L.C.

West, Jill Marie. Smokey. 2002. (Illus.). 32p. (J). per. (978-0-9719283-2-9(0)) Mishe-Mokwa Design Prepress & Publishing.

West, Kim. A Home for Pup E. Dog. West, Kim, illus. l.t. ed. 2002. (Illus.). 39p. (J). 9.50 (978-0-9743905-0-5(X) , 1500) West, Kim.

West, Nancy. Chips - the War Dog: Based on the True-Life Adventures of the World War II K-9 Hero. 2nd ed. 2004. 183p. (J). per. 8.95 (978-0-9743659-1-6(2)) Hero Dog Pubns.

West, Tracey. Double Trouble Dwarfs. 2006. (Pixie Tricks Ser.: No. 7). (Illus.). 96p. (J). (gr. 1-4). 3.99 (978-0-439-17983-6(1) , Scholastic Paperbacks) Scholastic, Inc.

—Double Trouble Dwarfs. 2000. (gr. 3-6). lib. bdg. 11.80 (978-0-613-32485-4(4)) Tandem Library Bks.

Westfeldt, Linda M. Buttons' Big Ears. l.t. ed. 2004. 32p. (J). spiral bd. (978-1-59196-686-9(8)) Instantpublisher.com.

Weston, Martha. Jack & Jill & Big Dog Bill. 2002. (Step into Reading Early Bks.). (Illus.). 32p. (J). (ps-2). pap. 3.99 (978-0-375-81248-4(2)); lib. bdg. 11.99 (978-0-375-91248-1(7)) Random Hse. Children's Bks. (Random Hse. Bks. for Young Readers).

—Jack & Jill & Big Dog Bill. 2002. (ps-2). lib. bdg. 11.80 (978-0-613-86247-9(3)) Tandem Library Bks.

Weyn, Suzanne & Bridwell, Norman. Clifford's Hiccups. Bracken, Carolyn et al, illus. 2001. (Clifford, the Big Red Dog Ser.). 24p. (J). (ps-1). pap. 3.50 (978-0-439-28337-3(X) , Cartwheel Bks.) Scholastic, Inc.

Whatley, Bruce. That Magnetic Dog. 2001. (Illus.). 81p. (J). (ps-3). pap. 6.95 (978-0-207-18420-8(8)) HarperCollins Pubs.

Wheatley, Bill. Mr. Bumble & the Hippo: A Story for Anyone Who Has Ever Loved a Pet. Duderstadt, Jane, illus. 2001. 100p. (J). pap. 24.95 (978-1-888683-10-3(4)) Wooster Bk. Co., The.

Wheatley, Marylou. Calypso & Strange Lands. 2004. 119p. pap. 16.95 (978-1-4137-1012-0(3)) PublishAmerica, Inc.

Wheeler, Isabelle. Many a Mickle: Little Things Not to Be Forgotten. 2003. 202p. 24.95 (978-0-595-66007-0(X)); pap. 14.95 (978-0-595-29487-9(1)) iUniverse, Inc.

Wheeler, Lisa. Seadogs: An Epic Ocean Operetta. Siegel, Mark, illus. 2006. 40p. (J). reprint ed. 7.99 (978-1-4169-4103-3(7) , Aladdin) Simon & Schuster Children's Publishing.

Whelan, Gloria. Silver. Marchesi, Stephen, illus. 2004. (Stepping Stone Bks.). 64p. (J). (gr. 1-4). pap. 3.99 (978-0-394-89611-3(4) , Random Hse. Bks. for Young Readers) Random Hse. Children's Bks.

Where Red Fern Grows. 1998. (J). pap. 3.95 (978-0-439-04478-3(2)) Scholastic, Inc.

Where's the Puppy? (English/Russian) 2005. (Photo Flap Bks.). (RUS., Illus.). 12p. (J). bds. 5.50 (978-1-932065-85-5(7)) Star Bright Bks., Inc.

Whitaker, Kent. Big Mo's Tennis Ball Hunt. 2007. (J). ***(978-0-9779053-8-6(1))*** Great American Pubs.

White, Amanda. Rip & Rap. Harter, Debbie, illus. 2002. 24p. (J). (gr. k-2). 14.99 (978-1-84148-944-5(1)) Barefoot Bks., Inc.

White, Ellen Emerson. Santa Paws: Picture Book. Blake, Robert, illus. 2003. (Santa Paws Ser.). 40p. (J). (gr. k-3). pap. 16.95 (978-0-439-32438-0(6)) Scholastic, Inc.

White Fang Study Guide. 2002. (Illus.). 48p. (YA). per. 17.95 (978-1-56254-536-9(1) , SP5361) Saddleback Educational Publishing.

White, Herman H. Valley of the Flames. 2004. 96p. (J). 19.95 (978-1-932278-09-5(5)) Mayhaven Publishing.

Whitehead, Catherine. Skookumchuck. 2002. (Illus.). 156p. (J). (gr. 5-12). pap. 11.95 (978-1-58151-064-5(0)) BookPartners, Inc.

Whitehead, David. Odd Story Mr Bloggs & His 17 Dogs. 2007. (Illus.). 56p. 16.95 ***(978-1-905636-08-2(3))*** Beautiful Bks. GBR. *Dist:* International Publishers Marketing.

Wigersma, Tanneke. Baby Brother. Talsma, Nynke Mare, illus. 2005. 32p. (J). (ps-ps). 16.95 (978-1-932425-55-0(1) , Lemniscaat) Boyds Mills Pr.

Wignell, Edel & Argent, Leanne. I Wonder Who Lives Upstairs. (Illus.). 32p. pap. 10.95 (978-1-875560-55-4(6)) Univ. of Western Australia Pr. AUS. *Dist:* International Specialized Bk. Services.

Wilbur, Frances. The Dog with Golden Eyes. Coyle, Mark, illus. 1998. (Milkweed Prize for Children's Literature Ser.). 160p. (J). (gr. 3-9). pap. 6.95 (978-1-57131-615-8(9)) Milkweed Editions.

Wild, Margaret. Fox. Brooks, Ron, illus. 2000. 40p. (J). (978-1-86448-465-6(9)); mass mkt. (978-1-86448-933-0(2)) Allen & Unwin.

—Fox. Brooks, Ron, illus. 2006. 32p. (J). pap. 7.95 (978-1-933605-15-9(4)) Kane/Miller Bk. Pubs., Inc.

—The Pocket Dogs. King, Stephen Michael, illus. 2001. 40p. (J). (ps-2). pap. 15.95 (978-0-439-23973-8(7)) Scholastic, Inc.

Wild, Margaret & King, Stephen Michael. The Pocket Dogs. 2001. (Illus.). (J). pap. (978-0-439-23974-5(5)) Scholastic GBR. *Dist:* Scholastic, Inc.

Wilder, Alice. Magenta's Visit. 1999. (Blue's Clues Ser.). (J). (ps-k). mass mkt. 3.99 (978-0-689-83355-7(5) , Simon Spotlight/Nickelodeon) Simon & Schuster Children's Publishing.

Wilder, Alice & Smith, Michael T. Magenta's Visit. Johnson, Traci Paige & Craig, Karen, illus. 1999. (Blue's Clues Ser.: Vol. 1). 24p. (J). (ps-k). pap. 3.50 (978-0-689-82443-2(2) , 076714003507, Simon Spotlight/Nickelodeon) Simon & Schuster Children's Publishing.

Wilhelm, Hans. I Lost My Tooth! 2004. 32p. (J). lib. bdg. 15.00 (978-1-59054-366-5(1)) Fitzgerald Bks.

—I Lost My Tooth! Wilhelm, Hans, illus. 1999. (Hello Reader! Ser.). (Illus.). 32p. (J). (ps-1). pap. 3.99 (978-0-590-64230-9(8) , Cartwheel Bks.) Scholastic, Inc.

—I Lost My Tooth! 1999. (Hello Reader! Ser.). (J). 10.79 (978-0-606-16613-3(0)); lib. bdg. 11.80 (978-0-613-11664-0(X)) Tandem Library Bks.

—I Love Colors! 2000. (gr. k-3). lib. bdg. 11.80 (978-0-613-54811-3(6)) Tandem Library Bks.

—I Love Snow! 2007. (Scholastic Reader Level 1 Ser.). 32p. (J). pap. 3.99 ***(978-0-439-79594-4(X))*** , Cartwheel Bks.) Scholastic, Inc.

Wilhelm, Hans. It's Too Windy! 2004. 32p. (J). lib. bdg. 15.00 (978-1-59054-367-2(X)) Fitzgerald Bks.

—It's Too Windy! 2000. (Hello Reader! Ser.). (Illus.). 32p. (J). (gr. 1-3). pap. 3.99 (978-0-439-10849-2(7)) Scholastic, Inc.

—It's Too Windy! 2000. (gr. k-3). lib. bdg. 11.80 (978-0-613-25758-9(8)); (Illus.). (J). 10.79 (978-0-606-18571-4(2)) Tandem Library Bks.

Wilhelm, Hans, illus. I Love Colors! 2001. (Hello Reader! Ser.). 32p. (J). (ps-1). pap. 3.99 (978-0-439-19288-0(9) , Cartwheel Bks.) Scholastic, Inc.

Will, Nocolas. Finders Keepers. 1999. (J). (gr. k-3). lib. bdg. 15.30 (978-0-8335-0345-9(6)) Tandem Library Bks.

Williams, Rozanne Lanczak. Cat Can't Write: A Cat & Dog Story. Maio, Barbara, ed. Leary, Catherine, illus. 2006. (J). per. 6.99 ***(978-1-59198-344-6(4))*** Creative Teaching Pr., Inc.

—Cat's Fairy Tale: A Cat & Dog Story. Maio, Barbara, ed. Leary, Catherine, illus. 2006. (Learn to Write Ser.). (J). 16p. pap. 2.99 (978-1-59198-294-4(4) , 6191); per. 6.99 ***(978-1-59198-348-4(7))*** Creative Teaching Pr., Inc.

—Lost Puppy, Found Puppy. Maio, Barbara, ed. Motoyama, Keiko, illus. 2006. (Learn to Write Ser.). (J). 8p. pap. 2.99 (978-1-59198-296-8(0) , 6190); per. 6.99 ***(978-1-59198-347-7(9))*** Creative Teaching Pr., Inc.

Williams, Suzanne. My Dog Never Says Please. 2000. (978-0-606-18435-9(X)) Tandem Library Bks.

Williamson, Peggy. Jake's American Story. 2003. 35 p. pap. 14.95 (978-1-4137-0428-0(X)) PublishAmerica, Inc.

Willson, Sarah. Rugrats' Easter Surprise. 2002. (gr. k-3). lib. bdg. 14.15 (978-0-613-51321-0(5)) Tandem Library Bks.

—Simon Says. Ulrich, George, illus. 2006. (Step-By-Step Readers Ser.). (J). pap. (978-1-59939-057-4(4) , Reader's Digest Young Families, Inc.) Reader's Digest Children's Publishing, Inc.

—What's with Dad? Marantz, Larissa & DiPaolo, Katharine, illus. 2006. (All Grown Up! Ser.). 32p. (J). pap. 3.99 (978-1-4169-0669-8(X) , Simon Spotlight/Nickelodeon) Simon & Schuster Children's Publishing.

Wilson, Shelliah. Samuel's Little Brother. 2005. 12p. 9.72 (978-1-4116-4789-3(0)) Lulu.com.

Winthrop, Elizabeth. The Biggest Parade. Ulriksen, Mark, illus. rev. ed. 2006. 32p. (J). 16.95 (978-0-8050-7685-1(9)) Holt, Henry & Co.

—Dog Show. Ulriksen, Mark, illus. rev. ed. 2004. 32p. (J). 15.95 (978-0-8050-7111-5(3) , Holt, Henry & Co. Bks. For Young Readers) Holt, Henry & Co.

The Wishbone Mysteries, 20 bks. l.t. ed. Incl. Case of the Breaking Story. Steele, Alexander. (Illus.). 144p. 2000. lib. bdg. 23.33 (978-0-8368-2703-3(1)); Case of the Cyber-Hacker. Capeci, Anne. (Illus.). 141p. 2000. lib. bdg. 23.33 (978-0-8368-2702-6(3)); Case of the Impounded Hounds. Steele, Michael Anthony. 138p. 2000. lib. bdg. 23.33 (978-0-8368-2700-2(7)); Case of the On-Line Alien. Steele, Alexander. 144p. 1999. lib. bdg. 23.33 (978-0-8368-2449-0(0)); Case of the Unsolved Case. Steele, Alexander. (Illus.). 139p. 2000. lib. bdg. 23.33 (978-0-8368-2696-8(5)); Disappearing Dinosaurs. Strickland, Brad & Fuller, Thomas E. 144p. 1999. lib. bdg. 23.33 (978-0-8368-2450-6(4)); Disoriented Express. Strickland, Brad. 167p. 2000. lib. bdg. 23.33 (978-0-8368-2697-5(3)); Drive-In of Doom. Strickland, Brad & Fuller, Thomas E. 144p. 1999. lib. bdg. 23.33 (978-0-8368-2388-2(5)); Forgotten Heroes. Steele, Michael Anthony. (Illus.). 139p. 2000. lib. bdg. 23.33 (978-0-8368-2695-1(7)); Haunted Clubhouse. Leavitt, Caroline. 144p. 1999. lib. bdg. 22.60 (978-0-8368-2383-7(4)); Key to the Golden Dog. Capeci, Anne. 144p. 1999. lib. bdg. 23.33 (978-0-8368-2389-9(3)); Lights! Camera! Action Dog! Butcher, Nancy. (Illus.). 139p. 2000. lib. bdg. 23.33 (978-0-8368-2694-4(9)); Maltese Dog. Capeci, Anne. 144p. 1999. lib. bdg. 23.33 (978-0-8368-2387-5(7)); Phantom of the Video Store. Gantt, Leticia. (Illus.). 141p. 2000. lib. bdg. 23.33 (978-0-8368-2701-9(5)); Riddle of the Wayward Books. Strickland, Brad & Fuller, Thomas E. 144p. 1999. lib. bdg. 23.33 (978-0-8368-2384-4(2)); Sirian Conspiracy. Friedman, Michael Jan. (Illus.). 141p. 2000. lib. bdg. 23.33 (978-0-8368-2699-9(X)); Stage Invader. Sathre, Vivian. (Illus.). 140p. 2000. lib. bdg. 23.33 (978-0-8368-2698-2(1)); Stolen Trophy. Friedman, Michael Jan. 144p. 1999. lib. bdg. 23.33 (978-0-8368-2386-8(9)); Tale of the Missing Mascot. Steele, Alexander. 144p. 1999. lib. bdg. 23.33 (978-0-8368-2385-1(0)); Treasure of Skeleton Reef. Strickland, Brad & Fuller, Thomas E. 144p. 1999. lib. bdg. 23.33 (978-0-8368-2382-0(6)); (J). (gr. 4 up). Set lib. bdg. 443.27 (978-0-8368-2752-1(X)) Stevens, Gareth Inc.

Wishinsky, Frieda. Please, Louise! Gay, Marie-Louise, illus. 2007. 32p. (J). (ps-k). 17.95 ***(978-0-88899-796-8(5))*** Groundwood Bks. CAN. *Dist:* Perseus Distribution.

Witschen, Kay. Clinker's Christmas Star. Witschen, Kay, illus. 2004. (Illus.). 24p. (J). 6.95 (978-0-9741352-1-2(6)) Dwitt Publishing.

Wojtusik, Elizabeth. Kitty Up! Yoshikawa, Sachiko, illus. 2008. (J). (978-0-8037-3045-8(4) , Dial) Penguin Group (USA) Inc.

Wolff, Nancy. It's Time for School with Tallulah. 2007. (Illus.). 40p. (J). (ps-3). 16.95 ***(978-0-8050-7962-3(9))*** Holt, Henry & Co.

Wood, Audrey. A Dog Needs a Bone. 2007. (J). pap. ***(978-0-545-00006-2(8))*** Blue Sky Pr.

—A Dog Needs a Bone. 2007. (Illus.). 40p. (J). (ps-k). pap. 16.99 ***(978-0-545-00005-5(X)*** , Blue Sky Pr., The) Scholastic, Inc.

Wood, Beverley & Wood, Chris. DogStar. 2004. 4p. (J). pap., tchr. ed. (978-1-55192-608-7(3) , Polestar Book Pubs.) Raincoast Bk. Distribution CAN. *Dist:* Transition Vendor.

Wood, Beverley. DogStar. rev. ed. 2004. (Sirius Mystery Ser.). 320p. (J). pap. 7.95 (978-1-55192-638-4(5)) Raincoast Bk. Distribution CAN. *Dist:* Perseus Distribution.

Wooldridge, S. & Wooldridge, J. Seven Day Dog. Wooldridge, Jack, illus. 1999. 32p. (J). (gr. k-5). pap. 7.00 (978-1-887963-16-9(2)) Pota Pr.

Wormell, Chris. The Wild Girl. Wormell, Chris, illus. 2006. (Illus.). 32p. (J). 17.00 (978-0-8028-5311-0(0) , Eerdmans Bks For Young Readers) Eerdmans, William B. Publishing Co.

Wurzburg, Robert. Dogshark Readers: Red Set. 2005. (Illus.). 96p. (ps-ps). 14.95 (978-1-59354-074-6(4)) Handprint Bks.

Wurzburg, Robert, illus. Where Are the Dogsharks? 2005. (I'm Going to Read Ser.). 28p. (J). (ps-k). pap., pap. 3.95 (978-1-4027-2616-3(3)) Sterling Publishing Co., Inc.

Yaccarino, Dan. Unlovable. rev. ed. 2004. (Illus.). 32p. (J). reprint ed. pap. 6.95 (978 0 8050 7532-8(1) , Owlet Paperbacks for Young Readers) Holt, Henry & Co.

Yang, James. Joey & Jet. Yang, James, illus. 2004. (Adventures Ser.: Bk. 1). (Illus.). 32p. (J). 15.95 (978-0-689-86926-6(6) , Atheneum/Richard Jackson Bks.) Simon & Schuster Children's Publishing.

—Joey & Jet in Space. Yang, James, illus. 2006. (Illus.). 32p. (J). (ps-k). 15.95 (978-0-689-86927-3(4) , Atheneum/Richard Jackson Bks.) Simon & Schuster Children's Publishing.

Yanuchi, Lori. Running with the Big Dogs: A Sled Dog Puppy Grows up in Denali National Park, Alaska. Brown, Wendy, illus. 1999. 32p. (J). 8.95 (978-0-9670177-0-9(X)) Ridge Rock Pr.

Yates, Elizabeth. The Seventh One. 2003. 115p. (J). (978-1-57924-981-6(7)) Jones, Bob Univ. Pr.

Yates, Irene. Ollie. 1998. (Cambridge Reading Ser.). (Illus.). 32p. (gr. 2-6). pap. 9.00 (978-0-521-63944-6(1)) Cambridge Univ. Pr.

Yee, Wong Herbert. Did You See Chip? Ovresat, Laura, illus. 2004. (Green Light Readers Level 2 Ser.). 24p. (J). 12.95 (978-0-15-205095-5(7)); pap. 3.95 (978-0-15-205096-2(5)) Harcourt Children's Bks. (Green Light Readers).

—Did You See Chip? 2004. (gr. k-3). lib. bdg. 11.80 (978-0-613-81965-7(9)) Tandem Library Bks.

Yerges, Karen. The Adventures of Scooper the Beagle Dog: Las aventuras de Scooper el perrito Beagle. 2004. (SPA., Illus.). 60p. (J). per. 19.95 (978-0-9764384-0-3(2)) Mitre's Touch Gallery, The.

Ylvisaker, Anne. Little Klein. 2007. (Illus.). 192p. (J). (gr. 3-7). 15.99 ***(978-0-7636-3359-2(3))*** Candlewick Pr.

Yobe, Marjorie. The Adventures of Little Tyke: A Loveab. 2006. 48p. pap. 12.95 ***(978-1-4241-3920-0(1))*** PublishAmerica, Inc.

Yocum, Randi. Cowpie Corgi: A Dog's Tale. Yocum, Sam, 2nd, photos by. 2007. 32p. (J). lib. bdg. 16.98 (978-0-9663629-3-0(4)) By Grace Enterprises.

Yorinks, Arthur. Harry & Lulu. braille ed. 2004. (Illus.). (J). (gr. k-3). spiral bd. (978-0-616-07249-3(X)); spiral bd. (978-0-616-07250-9(3)) Canadian National Institute for the Blind/Institut National Canadien pour les Aveugles.

—Harry & Lulu. Matje, Martin, illus. 2020. 32p. (J). pap. 4.99 (978-0-7868-1221-9(4)) Hyperion Paperbacks for Children.

—Hey, Al. Egielski, Richard, illus. 2002. (J). 14.43 (978-0-7587-0051-3(2)) Book Wholesalers, Inc.

—Hey, Al. Egielski, Richard, illus. 2001. (J). (gr. k-3). pap. 15.90 incl. audio (978-0-8045-6872-2(3)) Spoken Arts, Inc.

Young, Selina. Big Dog & Little Dog Go Sailing. Young, Selina, illus. 2001. (Blue Bananas Ser.). (Illus.). 48p. (J). (gr. 1-2). (978-0-7787-0845-2(4)); pap. (978-0-7787-0891-9(8)) Crabtree Publishing Co.

—Big Dog & Little Dog Go Sailing. 2002. (gr. k-3). lib. bdg. 12.95 (978-0-613-52810-8(7)) Tandem Library Bks.

—Big Dog & Little Dog Visit the Moon. Young, Selina, illus. 2001. (Blue Bananas Ser.). (Illus.). 48p. (J). (gr. 1-2). (978-0-7787-0849-0(7)); pap. (978-0-7787-0895-7(0)) Crabtree Publishing Co.

—Big Dog & Little Dog Visit the Moon. 2002. (gr. k-3). lib. bdg. 12.95 (978-0-613-52811-5(5)) Tandem Library Bks.

Zarchi, Nurit. No Echeis A Nanny! 2002. 90p. (978-84-85334-87-2(6)) Loguez Ediciones ESP. *Dist:* Lectorum Pubns., Inc.

Zarin, Cynthia & Pratt, Pierre. Albert, the Dog Who Liked to Ride in Taxis. 2004. (Illus.). 32p. (J). 17.95 (978-0-689-84762-2(9) , Atheneum/Richard Jackson Bks.) Simon & Schuster Children's Publishing.

Ziefert, Harriet. Hey Irma! It's a Contest! 2004. (Illus.). 36p. pap. 7.95 (978-1-59354-060-9(4)) Blue Apple Bks.

—Hey Irma! It's Mother's Day. 2004. (Illus.). 36p. pap. 7.95 (978-1-59354-027-2(2)) Blue Apple Bks.

—Murphy Jumps a Hurdle. 2006. (Illus.). 40p. (J). 15.95 (978-1-59354-174-3(0)) Blue Apple Bks.

—Murphy Meets the Treadmill. Bolam, Emily, illus. 2001. 32p. (J). (gr. k-3). tchr. ed. 15.00 (978-0-618-11357-6(6) , Walter Lorraine) Houghton Mifflin Co. Trade & Reference Div.

Ziefert, Harriet & Ehrlich, H. M. Dancing Class. Rader, Laura, illus. 2001. 32p. (J). (ps-1). pap. 12.95 (978-0-531-30300-9(4) , Orchard Bks.) Scholastic, Inc.

Ziegler, Jennifer. Alpha Dog. 2006. 336p. (YA). (gr. 7). pap. 7.95 (978-0-385-73285-7(6)); lib. bdg. 9.99 (978-0-385-90302-8(2)) Random Hse. Children's Bks. (Delacorte Bks. for Young Readers).

Zimmerman, Andrea Griffing & Clemesha, David. Dig! Rosenthal, Marc, tr. Rosenthal, Marc, illus. 2004. 32p. (J). 16.00 (978-0-15-216785-1(4) , Silver Whistle) Harcourt Trade Pubs.

Zimmerman, George G. Dougie & the Dane: Chelsea the Great Dane. 2004. (Illus.). 36p. 21.99 (978-1-4134-4139-0(4)) Xlibris Corp.

Zinnen, Linda. The Truth about Rats, Rules, & Seventh Grade. 2001. 160p. (J). (gr. 3-7). 14.95 (978-0-06-028799-3(3)); (gr. 4-7). lib. bdg. 15.89 (978-0-06-028800-6(0)) HarperCollins Pubs.

Zion, Gene. Harry & the Lady Next Door. Graham, Margaret Bloy, illus. 2002. (J). 12.34 (978-0-7587-6128-6(7)) Book Wholesalers, Inc.

—Harry the Dirty Dog. unabr. ed. 2006. (SPA.). (J). (ps-2). pap. 18.95 incl. audio compact disk ***(978-0-439-90593-0(1))*** Weston Woods Studios, Inc.

Zion, Gene. Harry the Dirty Dog Board Book. Graham, Margaret Bloy, illus. 50th ed. 2006. 32p. (J). 6.99 (978-0-06-084244-4(X) , Harper Festival) HarperCollins Pubs.

101 Dalmatians. 2007. 18p. bds. 11.99 ***(978-1-4037-3591-1(3))*** Dalmatian Pr.

102 Dalmations Read Along. unabr. ed. 2000. (J). pap. incl. audio compact disk (978-0-7634-0709-4(7)) Walt Disney Records.

DOGS—HABITS AND BEHAVIOR

Dorling Kindersley Publishing Staff & Millard, Anne. The Puppy. 2000. (Stroller Bks.). (Illus.). 16p. (J). (ps-k). bds. 4.95 (978-0-7894-6656-3(2)) Dorling Kindersley Publishing, Inc.

Dromgoole, Glenn. What Puppies Teach Us: Life's Lessons Learned from Our Little Friends. 2003. (Illus.). 32p. tchr. ed. 12.95 (978-1-57223-684-4(1) , 6841) Willow Creek Pr., Inc.

George, Jean Craighead. How to Talk to Your Dog. Truesdell, Sue & Meisel, Paul, illus. 2003. 40p. (J). (gr. 1-3). pap. 6.99 (978-0-06-000623-5(4) , Harper Trophy) HarperCollins Pubs.

—How to Talk to Your Dog. Truesdell, Sue, illus. 2000. 40p. (J). (gr. 1-4). 14.99 (978-0-06-027092-6(6)) HarperCollins Pubs.

—How to Talk to Your Dog. 2003. (gr. 3-6). lib. bdg. 14.15 (978-0-613-62959-1(0)) Tandem Library Bks.

Harvey, Bev. The Dog Family. 2003. (Animal Families Ser.). (Illus.). 32p. (gr. 2-4). 23.00 (978-0-7910-7542-5(7) , Chelsea Hse.) Facts On File, Inc.

Murdico, Suzanne J. Wild Dog Attacks. 2000. (gr. 7-12). lib. bdg. 15.25 (978-0-613-52236-6(2)) Tandem Library Bks.

Whitehead, Sarah. How to Speak Dog. 2008. 96p. (J). pap. 6.99 ***(978-0-545-02078-7(6)*** , Scholastic Reference) Scholastic, Inc.

DOGS—HISTORY

Dorling Kindersley Publishing Staff. Dog. 2004. (Eyewitness Books). 72p. (J). lib. bdg. 19.99 (978-0-7566-0677-0(2)) Dorling Kindersley Publishing, Inc.

C
D

Greatest Dog Stories Ever (Omnibus) 2000. (J). (978-0-06-029127-3(3)) HarperCollins Pubs.

Kimmel, Elizabeth Cody. Balto & the Great Race. 2004. (Stepping Stone Bks.). (Illus.). 112p. (J). (gr. k-3). lib. bdg. 11.99 (978-0-679-99198-4(0) , Random Hse. Bks. for Young Readers) Random Hse. Children's Bks.

—Balto & the Great Race. Koerber, Nora, illus. 1999. (Stepping Stone Bks.). 112p. (J). (gr. k-3). pap. 3.99 (978-0-679-89198-7(6) , Random Hse. Bks. for Young Readers) Random Hse. Children's Bks.

—Balto & the Great Race. 1999. (Step into Reading Ser.). 10.64 (978-0-606-17522-7(9)) Tandem Library Bks.

Murphy, Frank. George Washington & the General's Dog. Walz, Richard, illus. 2002. (Step into Reading Ser.). 48p. (J). (gr. 1-3). pap. 3.99 (978-0-375-81015-2(3)); lib. bdg. 11.99 (978-0-375-91015-9(8)) Random Hse. Children's Bks. (Random Hse. Bks. for Young Readers).

Myers, Jack. How Dogs Came from Wolves: And Other Explorations of Science in Action. Rice, John, illus. 2004. 64p. (YA). (gr. 4-6). pap. 9.95 (978-1-59078-278-1(X)) Boyds Mills Pr.

DOGS—PICTORIAL WORKS

Aigner-Clark, Julie. Perros. 2004. (Baby Einstein Ser.). (SPA., Illus.). 20p. (J). bds. 3.95 (978-970-718-156-4(7) , Silver Dolphin en Español) Advanced Marketing, S. de R. L. de C. V. MEX. *Dist:* Perseus Distribution.

Barbaresi, Nina. Little Dogs. 2002. (Dover Little Activity Bks.). (Illus.). 4p. (J). (ps-5). pap. 1.50 (978-0-486-42620-4(3)) Dover Pubns., Inc.

Bauman, Liana, et al. Dog Breeds: An Illustrated Guide. 2002. (Illus.). 66p. (J). pap. 14.95 (978-1-58779-480-3(2) , Anatomical Chart Co.) Lippincott Williams & Wilkins.

Glover, Harry. Dogs. 2004. (Spotter's Guides Sticker Bks.). (SPA., Illus.). 32p. (J). pap. 7.95 (978-0-7945-0212-6(1) , Usborne) EDC Publishing.

Kojima, Toyoharu. Legacy of the Dog: The Ultimate Illustrated Guide. 2nd rev. ed. 2005. (Illus.). 344p. pap. 24.95 (978-0-8118-5113-8(3)) Chronicle Bks. LLC.

Murawski, Laura. How to Draw Dogs. 2001. (Kid's Guide to Drawing Ser.). (Illus.). 24p. (J). (gr. 3). lib. bdg. 21.25 (978-0-8239-5551-0(6) , PowerKids Pr.) Rosen Publishing Group, Inc., The.

Pfloog, Jan. Puppy Book: Shape Book. 1999. (gr. k-3). lib. bdg. 11.00 (978-0-613-81152-1(6)) Tandem Library Bks.

Rosen, Michael J., ed. Speak! Children's Book Illustrators Brag about Their Dogs. 2004. (Illus.). 43p. (J). (gr. k-4). reprint ed. 17.00 (978-0-7567-8069-2(1)) DIANE Publishing Co.

Sforza, Daniella, ed. Savannah Blue's Activity Book/Libro de Actividades de Savannah Azul. Spagnoli, Maria Eugenia, tr. Rakusin, Sudie, illus. 2005. Tr. of Libro de Actividades de Savannah Azul. (SPA & ENG.). 48p. (J). 10.95 (978-0-9664805-4-2(6)) Winged Willow Pr.

Tuxworth, Nicola. Puppies, 12 vols. (Illus.). 2006. 12p. bds. 6.99 (978-0-7548-1365-1(7)); 2002. 20p. 5.99 (978-0-7548-1047-6(X)) Anness Publishing GBR. (Lorenz Bks.). *Dist:* National Bk. Network.

Watt, Fiona & Wells, Rachel. Perritos. 2004. (SPA., Illus.). 10p. (J). 11.95 (978-0-7460-5090-3(9)) EDC Publishing.

The Wisdom of Zeus. 2005. (J). (978-0-9765840-0-1(X)) Zeus Media LLC.

DOGS—POETRY

Cabrera, Jane. Old Mother Hubbard. 2008. (J). ***(978-0-8234-2132-9(5))*** Holiday Hse., Inc.

Clements, Andrew. Dogku. Bowers, Tim, illus. 2007. 40p. (J). (ps-3). 16.99 (978-0-689-85823-9(X) , Simon & Schuster Children's Publishing) Simon & Schuster Children's Publishing.

Crawley, Dave. Dog Poems. Petrosino, Tamara, illus. 2007. 32p. (J). (gr. 4-7). 16.95 ***(*978-1-59078-454-9(5)*** , Wordsong) Boyds Mills Pr.

George, Kristine O'Connell. Little Dog Poems. Otani, June, illus. 1999. 40p. (J). (gr. k-3). tchr. ed. 13.00 (978-0-395-82266-1(1) , Clarion Bks.) Houghton Mifflin Co. Trade & Reference Div.

Gottfried, Maya. Good Dog. 2008. 32p. (J). (ps-3). pap. 6.99 ***(*978-0-553-11383-9(6)*** , Dragonfly Bks.) Random Hse. Children's Bks.

—Good Dog. Zakanitch, Robert Rahway, illus. 2005. 40p. (J). (ps-3). 15.95 (978-0-375-83049-5(9)); lib. bdg. 17.99 (978-0-375-93049-2(3)) Random Hse. Children's Bks. (Knopf Bks. for Young Readers).

Harrison, David L. Farmer's Dog Goes to the Forest: Rhymes for Two Voices. Johnson-Petrov, Arden, illus. 2005. 32p. (J). 15.95 (978-1-59078-242-2(9)) Boyds Mills Pr.

Kirk, Daniel F. Dogs Rule! Kirk, Daniel F., illus. 2003. (Illus.). 56p. (ps-3). 18.99 incl. cd-rom (978-0-7868-1949-2(9) , Disney Editions) Disney Pr.

MacLachlan, Patricia & MacLachlan, Emily. Once I Ate a Pie. Schneider, Katy, illus. 2006. 40p. (J). 16.99 (978-0-06-073531-9(7) , Cotler, Joanna Books) HarperCollins Pubs.

MacLachlan, Patricia, et al. Once I Ate a Pie. Schneider, Katy, illus. 2006. 40p. (J). lib. bdg. 17.89 (978-0-06-073532-6(5) , Cotler, Joanna Books) HarperCollins Pubs.

Sargent, David M., Jr. Buffy's Anger. 2003. (Doggie Tails Ser.). (Illus.). 23p. (J). pap. 6.95 (978-1-56763-856-1(2)); lib. bdg. 19.95 (978-1-56763-855-4(4)) Ozark Publishing.

—Emma's Law, 9. 2003. (Doggie Tails Ser.). (Illus.). 24p. (J). pap. 6.95 (978-1-56763-862-2(7)); lib. bdg. 19.95 (978-1-56763-861-5(9)) Ozark Publishing.

—Vera's Talent, 9. 2003. (Doggie Tails Ser.). (Illus.). 25p. (J). pap. 6.95 (978-1-56763-858-5(9)); lib. bdg. 19.95 (978-1-56763-857-8(0)) Ozark Publishing.

Sidman, Joyce. World According to Dog. Mindell, Doug, photos by. 2008. (Illus.). 80p. (J). (gr. 5). pap. 7.95 ***(*978-0-618-28381-1(1))*** Houghton Mifflin Co. Trade & Reference Div.

Sklansky, Amy E. From the Doghouse: Poems to Chew On. Firehammer, Karla et al, illus. rev. ed. 2002. 48p. (J). (gr. 1-4). 17.95 (978-0-8050-6673-9(X) , Holt, Henry & Co. Bks. For Young Readers) Holt, Henry & Co.

Turner, Nancy Byrd. When It Rained Cats & Dogs. Jerome, Karen A., illus. rev. ed. 2000. 24p. (J). (ps-1). 14.95 (978-0-9665564-1-4(0)) Meadow Geese Pr.

DOGS—TRAINING

Axelrod, Herbert R. Housebreaking & Other Puppy Problems. 1999. (Cats & Dogs). (Illus.). 84p. (YA). (gr. 4-7). 19.95 (978-0-7910-4818-4(7) , Chelsea Hse.) Facts On File, Inc.

—The Perfect Retriever. 1999. (Cats & Dogs). (Illus.). 84p. (YA). (gr. 3-7). 21.95 (978-0-7910-4814-6(4) , Chelsea Hse.) Facts On File, Inc.

—Training Older Dogs. 1999. (Cats & Dogs). (Illus.). 84p. (YA). (gr. 3-7). 19.95 (978-0-7910-4817-7(9) , Chelsea Hse.) Facts On File, Inc.

Basic Canine Grooming. 2004. (YA). cd-rom 59.00 (978-1-56918-000-6(8) , CEV70145) Visual Education Productions.

Dog Heroes, 8 vols., Set. 2005. (Dog Heroes Ser.). (Illus.). (J). lib. bdg. 263.56 (978-1-59716-022-3(9)) Bearport Publishing Co., Inc.

Dog School: Individual Title Six-Packs. (Story Steps Ser.). (gr. k-2). 32.00 (978-0-7635-9834-1(8)) Rigby Education.

Dorling Kindersley Publishing Staff, et al. Training Your Dog. 2003. (101 Essential Tips Ser.). (Illus.). 72p. pap. 5.00 (978-0-7894-9688-1(7)) Dorling Kindersley Publishing, Inc.

Ereth, Mary. Meet CJ, the Guide Dog Puppy. 1999. 39p. (J). (978-0-9672071-0-0(X)) Southeastern Guide Dogs, Inc.

Haas, Jessie. Shaper. 2002. 192p. (J). (gr. 5 up). 16.99 (978-0-06-000170-4(4)); lib. bdg. 17.89 (978-0-06-000171-1(2)) HarperCollins Pubs.

Harcourt School Publishers Staff. Good Dog! 3rd ed. 2002. (Trophies English Language Learners Ser.). (Illus.). pap. 5.10 (978-0-15-327818-1(8)) Harcourt Schl. Pubs.

—Helping Dogs Advanced Level. 3rd ed. 2002. (Trophies Reading Program Ser.). (Illus.). pap. 5.10 (978-0-15-323107-0(6)) Harcourt Schl. Pubs.

Kadlec, Pamela Owen. Retriever Training for Spaniels: Working with Hard-Headed, Soft-Tempered, Intelligent Dogs. 2002. (Illus.). 150p. per. 19.95 (978-0-9717103-0-6(9)) Just Ducky Publishing.

LeTourneau, Anthony Alex, illus. Hanni & Beth: Safe & Sound. 2007. (J). ***(*978-0-9792918-0-7(1))*** Blue Marlin Pubns.

Levin, Betty. That'll Do, Moss. 2002. (Illus.). 128p. (J). (gr. 3 up). 15.89 (978-0-06-000532-0(7)) HarperCollins Pubs.

McGinty, Alice B. Sheep-Herding Dogs: Rounding up the Herd. 1999. (Dogs Helping People Ser.). 24p. (J). (gr. k-4). lib. bdg. 18.75 (978-0-8239-5219-9(3) , PowerKids Pr.) Rosen Publishing Group, Inc., The.

Presnall, Judith Janda. Canine Companions. 2003. (Animals with Jobs Ser.). (Illus.). 48p. (J). 26.20 (978-0-7377-2050-1(6) , Greenhaven Pr., Inc.) Thomson Gale.

Shahan, Sherry. Working Dogs. 2001. (Planet Reader Ser.). (Illus.). (J). (978-0-606-21534-3(4)) Tandem Library Bks.

Simmons-Moake, Jane. Excelling at Dog Agility Bk. 3: Advanced Skills Training. 2003. (Illus.). 192p. 25.95 (978-0-9674929-2-6(0)) FlashPaws Productions.

Whitehead, Sarah. Puppy Training for Kids. Burton, Jane, photos by. 2001. (Illus.). 96p. pap. 14.95 (978-0-7641-1940-8(0)) Barron's Educational Series, Inc.

Williams, Chris. One Incredible Dog! Kizzy. Friedman, Judith, illus. 2006. 32p. (ps-3). 15.95 (978-0-9766805-5-0(6) , Moo Pr.) Keene Publishing.

Wombacher, Michael. There's a Puppy in the House: Surviving the First Five Months. 2003. pap. 16.95 (978-0-9713033-1-7(2)) Wombacher, Michael.

DOGS—TREATMENT

McLaine, Susan, et al. Can I Pat That Dog? Power, Margaret, illus. 2005. 32p. (ps-17). 14.95 (978-0-207-19804-5(7)) HarperCollins Pubs.

DOGS FOR THE BLIND

see Guide Dogs

DOLITTLE, DOCTOR (FICTITIOUS CHARACTER)—FICTION

Baker, Elliott, adapted by. The Adventures of Doctor Dolittle. 2002. 104p. (YA). pap. 6.95 (978-1-58342-113-0(0) , A03) Dramatic Publishing Co.

Dalmatian Press Staff, adapted by. The Story of Doctor Dolittle. 2003. (Spot the Classics Ser.). 180p. (J). 4.99 (978-1-57759-695-0(1)) Dalmatian Pr.

Glasser, Robin Preiss, illus. Doctor Dolittle & His Animal Family: Based on the Original Text & Illustrations of Hugh Lofting. 1999. (Doctor Dolittle Chapter Bks.). (J). (gr. 1-4). (978-0-606-16445-0(6)) Tandem Library Bks.

—Doctor Dolittle & Tommy Stubbins. 1999. (Doctor Dolittle Chapter Bks.). (J). (gr. 1-4). (978-0-606-16719-2(6)) Tandem Library Bks.

—Doctor Dolittle Meets the Pushmi-Pullyu. 1999. (Doctor Dolittle Chapter Bks.). (J). (gr. 1-4). (978-0-606-16718-5(8)) Tandem Library Bks.

—Doctor Dolittle's Journey. 1999. (Doctor Dolittle Chapter Bks.). (J). (gr. 1-4). (978-0-606-16446-7(4)) Tandem Library Bks.

Lofting, Hugh. The Story of Doctor Dolittle. Exams Unlimited, Inc. Staff, ed. 2001. 116p. (J). reprint ed. cd-rom 5.95 (978-1-885343-94-9(9)) Exams Unlimited, Inc.

—The Story of Doctor Dolittle: #1 Animal Talk. 2007. (Easy Reader Classics Ser.). 32p. (J). (ps-3). 21.35 ***(*978-1-59961-338-3(7))*** Spotlight.

—The Story of Doctor Dolittle: #2 the Circus Crocodile. 2007. (Easy Reader Classics Ser.). 32p. (J). (ps-3). 21.35 ***(*978-1-59961-339-0(5))*** Spotlight.

—Viages de Doctor Dolittle. 1999. (Espasa Juvenil Ser.: Vol. 94). Tr. of Voyages of Doctor Dolittle. (SPA., Illus.). 376p. (J). (gr. 4-7). 11.95 (978-84-239-7060-5(4)) Espasa Calpe, S.A. ESP. *Dist:* Planeta Publishing Corp.

—The Voyages of Doctor Dolittle. 2004. (Illus.). 224p. (J). pap. 3.95 (978-0-486-43491-9(5)) Dover Pubns., Inc.

—The Voyages of Doctor Dolittle. Hague, Michael, illus. 2001. (Doctor Dolittle Ser.). 368p. (J). (gr. 4-6). 28.99 (978-0-688-14002-1(5)) HarperCollins Pubs.

—The Voyages of Doctor Dolittle. 2000. (Doctor Dolittle Ser.). (Illus.). 272p. (gr. 4-6). mass mkt. 4.95 (978-0-451-52769-1(0) , Signet Classics) Penguin Group (USA) Inc.

—The Voyages of Doctor Dolittle. Lamut, Sonja, illus. 1998. (Doctor Dolittle Ser.). 288p. (J). (gr. 1-6). 16.99 (978-0-448-41863-6(0) , Grosset & Dunlap) Penguin Group (USA) Inc.

—Voyages of Dr Dolittle. 2000. (gr. 5-8). lib. bdg. 12.95 (978-0-613-27681-8(7)) Tandem Library Bks.

Miles, Ellen. Dr. Doolittle. 2004. 144p. (J). (gr. 3 up). pap. 3.99 (978-0-439-57425-9(0) , Scholastic Paperbacks) Scholastic, Inc.

DOLL

see Dolls

DOLLHOUSES

Balloon Books. Balloon: Make A Doll House. 1999. (Press Out & Play Bks.). (Illus.). 20p. (J). (gr. k-2). pap. 5.95 (978-0-8069-3792-2(0) , Balloon Bks.) Sterling Publishing Co., Inc.

Goossens, Linda. Micro Minis: Create Teeny Tiny Rooms with Your Own Style & Flair! 2004. (Americangirl Library(R) Ser.). (Illus.). 48p. (J). (gr. 4 up). 17.95 (978-1-58485-872-0(9)) American Girl Publishing, Inc.

Jablow, Renee. A Three-Dimensional Victorian Doll House. Wilson, Phil, illus. 1999. (Classics Ser.). (J). (ps-3). 22.00 (978-1-58117-029-0(7) , Intervisual/Piggy Toes) Dalmatian Pr.

May, Darcy. Victorian Dollhouse Sticker Picture. 1998. (J). pap. 5.95 (978-0-486-40375-5(0)) Dover Pubns., Inc.

Warner, Barbara. The ABC's of Dollhouse Finishing. 2nd ed. 2003. (Illus.). 124p. (YA). per. 19.95 (978-1-893625-05-1(2)) Scott Pubns., Inc.

DOLLHOUSES—FICTION

Bunting, Eve. The Lambkins. Keegan, Jonathan, illus. 2006. 192p. (J). pap. 5.99 (978-0-06-059908-9(1) , Harper Trophy) HarperCollins Pubs.

Dress up Dolls Fairies Princess. rev. ed. 2007. 64p. pap. 7.95 ***(*978-1-74181-498-9(7))*** Hinkler Bks. Pty, Ltd. AUS. *Dist:* Penton Overseas, Inc.

Godden, Rumer. Miss Happiness & Miss Flower. 2002. (Illus.). 128p. (J). (gr. 3-7). 14.89 (978-0-06-029193-8(1)) HarperCollins Pubs.

Green, Dan, illus. Let's Pretend Rose's Doll House. 2007. 24p. (J). (ps-1). 14.95 ***(*978-0-312-50017-7(3)*** , Priddy Bks.) St. Martin's Pr.

Herman, Gail & Bratun, Katy. Hay una Cuidad. Bratun, Katy, illus. 2003. (SPA.). (J). lib. bdg. (978-0-375-91499-7(4)) Random House Publishing Group.

Hoffman, Elizabeth Stokes. Miss Renee's Mice. Peterson, Dawn, illus. 2001. (Miss Rene's Mice Ser.: No. 1). 32p. (ps-3). 15.95 (978-0-89272-505-2(2)) Down East Bks.

Holub, Joan. Danielle's Dollhouse Wish. Isa, Ann W., illus. 2003. (Doll Hospital Ser.: No. 5). 128p. (J). pap. 3.99 (978-0-439-40182-1(8) , Scholastic Paperbacks) Scholastic, Inc.

—Danielle's Dollhouse Wish. 2003. (gr. 3-6). lib. bdg. 11.80 (978-0-613-72098-4(9)) Tandem Library Bks.

Keene, Carolyn. The Dollhouse Mystery. Jones, Jan Naimo, illus. 2004. 68p. (J). lib. bdg. 15.00 ***(*978-1-4242-0927-9(7))*** Fitzgerald Bks.

—The Dollhouse Mystery. Jones, Jan Naimo, illus. 2004. (Nancy Drew Notebooks). 80p. (J). pap. 4.99 (978-0-689-86534-3(1) , Aladdin) Simon & Schuster Children's Publishing.

—The Dollhouse Mystery. Jones, Jan Naimo, illus. 2004. 68p. (J). (gr. 1-4). lib. bdg. 12.10 (978-0-613-95311-5(8)) Tandem Library Bks.

McDonough, Yona Zeldis. Dollhouse Magic. Palmisciano, Diane, illus. 2002. 96p. (J). (gr. 2-4). pap. 3.99 (978-0-439-34049-6(7)) Scholastic, Inc.

McKain, Kelly. Fairy Friends. 2008. (Fairy House Ser.). 112p. (J). pap. 6.99 ***(*978-0-545-04237-6(2))*** Scholastic, Inc.

O'Rourke, Page Eastburn. The Dollhouse Family. 1998. (Sticker Stories Ser.). (Illus.). 16p. (J). (ps-3). pap. 4.99 (978-0-448-41831-5(2) , Grosset & Dunlap) Penguin Group (USA) Inc.

Penton & Twinem, Neecy. Giggly Wiggly Worms. rev. ed. 2007. (ENG.). (Illus.). (J). bds. 7.95 ***(*978-1-59354-191-0(0))*** Handprint Bks.

Petrucha, Stefan. Haunted Dollhouse. 2006. (J). (gr. 3-8). 24.21 (978-1-59961-059-7(0)) Spotlight.

Pollack, Pam. Incredible Shrinking Dexter. 2003. (gr. 3-6). lib. bdg. 11.80 (978-0-613-72108-0(X)) Tandem Library Bks.

Potter, Beatrix. A Tale of Two Bad Mice. McClintock, Barbara, illus. 2007. (J). 25.65 (978-1-59961-314-7(X)) ABDO Publishing Co.

Reiss, Kathryn. Sweet Miss Honeywell's Revenge: A Ghost Story. 2005. 444p. (J). (gr. 7-17). pap. 6.95 (978-0-15-205471-7(5) , Harcourt Paperbacks) Harcourt Children's Bks.

Rylant, Cynthia. In Aunt Lucy's Kitchen. 2000. (Cobble Street Cousins Ser.: No. 1). (J). 10.79 (978-0-606-16211-1(9)); (gr. 3-6). lib. bdg. 11.80 (978-0-613-28533-9(6)) Tandem Library Bks.

Scamell, Ragnhild. Toby's Doll's House. Reynolds, Adrian, illus. 1999. 32p. (J). (ps-3). 14.95 (978-1-86233-026-9(3)) Sterling Publishing Co., Inc.

Scamell, Ragnhild & Reynolds, Adrian. Toby's Doll's House. 2000. (Illus.). 32p. (J). (ps-1). pap. 6.95 (978-1-86233-067-2(0)) Sterling Publishing Co., Inc.

Swanson, Maggie, illus. The Tale of Two Bad Mice. 2006. (J). 6.99 (978-1-59939-030-7(2)) Reader's Digest Young Families, Inc.

Wright, Betty Ren. The Dollhouse Murders. unabr. ed. 1999. (Illus.). (J). (gr. 4-6). 39.95 incl. audio (978-0-87499-521-3(3)); pap. 30.95 incl. audio (978-0-87499-520-6(5)) Live Oak Media.

—The Dollhouse Murders, Grades 4-6. unabr. ed. 1999. (Illus.). (J). pap., tchr. ed. 41.95 incl. audio (978-0-87499-522-0(1)) Live Oak Media.

Young, Miriam. Miss Suzy. Lobel, Arnold, illus. 40th anniv. ed. 2004. 44p. (J). 17.95 (978-1-930900-28-8(7)) Purple Hse. Pr.

DOLLS

Adams, Lynn. Penguin Sticker Paper Doll. 2003. (Dover Little Activity Bks.). (Illus.). 4p. (J). pap. 1.50 (978-0-486-42629-7(7)) Dover Pubns., Inc.

AGC Editors. Addy's Paper Dolls. 2003. (American Girls Collection Ser.). (Illus.). 28p. (J). 9.95 (978-1-58485-704-4(8)) American Girl Publishing, Inc.

—Josefina's Paper Dolls. 2003. (American Girls Collection Ser.). (Illus.). 28p. (J). 9.95 (978-1-58485-705-1(6)) American Girl Publishing, Inc.

—Kirsten's Paper Dolls: Kirsten & Her Friends with Outfits to Cut out & Scenes to Play With. 2003. (American Girls Collection Ser.). (Illus.). 28p. (J). pap. 9.95 (978-1-58485-703-7(X)) American Girl Publishing, Inc.

—Kit's Paper Dolls. 2003. (American Girls Collection Ser.). (Illus.). 28p. (J). 9.95 (978-1-58485-706-8(4)) American Girl Publishing, Inc.

—Molly's Paper Dolls. 2003. (American Girls Collection Ser.). (Illus.). 28p. (J). pap. 9.95 (978-1-58485-702-0(1)) American Girl Publishing, Inc.

Allert, Kathy. Helen Scot Sticker Paper Doll. 2001. (Illus.). 4p. (J). pap. 1.50 (978-0-486-41631-1(3)) Dover Pubns., Inc.

—Nurse Paper Doll. 2000. (J). pap. 1.00 (978-0-486-41307-5(1)) Dover Pubns., Inc.

—Teacher Paper Doll. 2000. (J). pap. 1.00 (978-0-486-41311-2(X)) Dover Pubns., Inc.

Amerikaner, Phyllis. Paper Doll Dress-Up. Clark, Kim, ed. Fribley, Rae, illus. 2001. 56p. (J). (ps-3). pap. 9.99 (978-0-88160-351-4(1) , LW390, Learning Works, The) Creative Teaching Pr., Inc.

Ansary, Mir Tamim. Dolls. 1998. (Cool Collections). (J). 18.50 (978-1-57572-118-7(X)) Heinemann Library.

Artic Circle Paper Doll with Stickers. 2001. (J). (978-0-89610-446-4(X)) Island Heritage Publishing.

Balducci, Rita. Disney Princess Movie Theater: Storybook & Movie Projector. 2002. (Disney Princess Ser.). (Illus.). 48p. (J). 24.99 incl. audio compact disk (978-1-57584-939-3(9) , Reader's Digest Children's Bks.) Reader's Digest Children's Publishing, Inc.

—Mix & Match Fashions: Storybook & Key Chain Craft Kit. Chapmanworks Staff, illus. 1999. (Barbie Ser.). 16p. (J). (ps-1). bds. 8.99 (978-1-57584-334-6(X) , Reader's Digest Children's Bks.) Reader's Digest Children's Publishing, Inc.

Barker, Cicely Mary. Flower Fairies Paper Dolls. 2005. 13p. (J). 6.99 (978-0-7232-5432-4(X) , Warne) Penguin Group (USA) Inc.

Burnett, Frances Hodgson. A Little Princess Paper Dolls. Sutton, Judith, photos by. 1999. (Illus.). 24p. (J). (ps-3). pap. 7.95 (978-0-694-00970-1(9) , Harper Festival) HarperCollins Pubs.

—The Secret Garden Paper Dolls. adapted ed. 1998. (Illus.). 24p. (J). (ps-3). 7.95 (978-0-694-00969-5(5)) HarperCollins Pubs.

Carabetta, Natalie. Arianna from Greece. 2003. (Dover Little Activity Bks.). (Illus.). 4p. (J). (gr. k-5). pap. 1.50 (978-0-486-42630-3(0)) Dover Pubns., Inc.

Carroll, William C. Stories of Little Girls & Their Dolls: Classics from an Age of Remembered Joy. 2003. (Illus.). 192p. (J). (gr. 3-7). 19.95 (978-1-56397-738-1(9)) Boyds Mills Pr.

Cherry, Winky. My First Doll Book Level 3: Hand Sewing. Palmer, Pati & Wisner, Linda, eds. Cherry, Winky, illus. 2003. (My First Sewing Book Ser.). (Illus.). 40p. (J). (gr. k-5). pap. 14.95 (978-0-935278-36-1(2)) Palmer-Pletsch Assocs.

Collections, Linda A. Limited Edition Ethnic Doll Educational Pak: Adventures in Learning about Others. 2000. (Illus.). 10p. (J). (gr. k up). 49.95 (978-1-877983-07-8(1)) Data-Lynn Bk. Co.

Collings, Julie. Pocket Paper Dolls Fairies. 2007. 30p. (J). pap. 6.95 ***(*978-1-59174-480-1(6))*** Klutz.

—Pocket Paper Dolls Princesses. 2007. 30p. (J). pap. 6.95 ***(*978-1-59174-482-5(2))*** Klutz.

Dalmatian Press Staff. Princess Glitter Paper Dolls. 2003. 10p. (J). pap. 3.99 (978-1-4037-0352-1(3)) Dalmatian Pr.

Doney, Meryl. Toys. 2004. (Crafts from Many Cultures Ser.). (Illus.). 32p. (J). (gr. 3 up). lib. bdg. 23.33 (978-0-8368-4048-3(8)) Stevens, Gareth Inc.

Dorling Kindersley Publishing Staff. Barbie International Dolls. (Barbie sticker Bks.). (J). 2005. 20p. pap. 6.99 (978-0-7566-1119-4(9)); 2000. (Illus.). 16p. pap. 6.99 (978-0-7894-5450-8(5)) Dorling Kindersley Publishing, Inc.

—Barbie Sports Doll. 2000. (Ultimate Sticker Bks.). (Illus.). 16p. (J). pap. 6.99 (978-0-7894-5451-5(3)) Dorling Kindersley Publishing, Inc.

Dorling Kindersley Publishing Staff, ed. The Ultimate Fashion Show Sticker Book. 2004. (Barbie Sticker Books Ser.). 20p. (J). pap. 6.99 (978-0-7566-0571-1(7)) Dorling Kindersley Publishing, Inc.

Falligant, Erin & Evert, Jodi, eds. Felicity's Paper Dolls. Graef, Renee & Wimmer, Mike, illus. 2005. (American Girls Collection). 22p. (J). (gr. 2-6). pap. 9.95 (978-1-59369-054-0(1) , American Girl) American Girl Publishing, Inc.

Fisher, Phyllis Mae Richardson, illus. Janae, #3 in the 1989 Family Friends Paper Doll Set, Vol. 3. l.t. ed. 2003. 24p. (J). 10.00 (978-0-9745615-7-8(6)) PJs Corner.

Gathings, Evelyn. Twin Tots of the Twenties Paper Dolls. 2000. (J). pap. 6.95 (978-0-486-41332-7(2)) Dover Pubns., Inc.

Golden Books Staff. Sleeping Beauty: Paper Doll. 1999. (Sleeping Beauty Ser.). 12p. (J). (ps-3). pap. 3.29 (978-0-307-02011-6(8) , 02011, Golden Bks.) Random Hse. Children's Bks.

Green, Yuko. Camina from Brazil Sticker Paper Doll. 2004. (Sticker Paper Dolls Ser.). (Illus.). 4p. (J). (gr. k-5). pap. 1.50 (978-0-486-43311-0(0)) Dover Pubns., Inc.

—Greek Girl & Boy Paper Dolls. 2003. 16p. (J). pap. 3.95 (978-0-486-42389-0(1)) Dover Pubns., Inc.

—Northwest Indian Girl & Boy Paper Dolls. 2003. (Paper Dolls Ser.). (Illus.). 16p. (J). 3.95 (978-0-486-43051-5(0)) Dover Pubns., Inc.

—Traditional African Costumes Paper Dolls. 1999. (J). pap. 6.95 (978-0-486-40810-1(8)) Dover Pubns., Inc.

Hall, Patricia. Honest-to-Goodness Story of Raggedy Andy. Wanamaker, Joni, illus. 2005. 32p. (J). 15.95 (978-1-58980-251-3(9)) Pelican Publishing Co., Inc.

—The Real-for-Sure Story of Raggedy Ann. Wannamaker, Joni Gruelle, illus. 2001. 32p. (J). (ps-3). 14.95 (978-1-56554-763-6(2)) Pelican Publishing Co., Inc.

Henry, Marilyn. Marilyn Monroe Paper Dolls. Taliadoros, Jenny, ed. Henry, Marilyn, illus. 2007. (ENG., Illus.). 8p. pap. 12.00 (***978-0-9790668-8-7(3)*** Paper Studio Pr.

Hilton, Nanette. Teddy Twins Sticker Paper Doll. 2001. 4p. (J). pap. 1.50 (978-0-486-41844-5(8)) Dover Pubns., Inc.

Hinkler Books Staff. Dress up Dolls. Penton Overseas, Inc. Staff, ed. rev. ed. 2006. 64p. (J). (gr. 3-3). pap. 7.95 (978-1-74157-930-7(9)) Hinkler Bks. Pty, Ltd. AUS. *Dist:* Penton Overseas, Inc.

Holzer, David. Make & Play Airplanes. Galvani, Maureen, illus. 2005. 48p. (J). (ps-3). (978-1-84510-549-5(4)) Top That! Publishing PLC.

Hooks, Kristine. Dolls. 2000. (High Interest Bks.). (Illus.). 48p. (J). (gr. 7-12). 24.00 (978-0-516-23330-7(0)); pap. 6.95 (978-0-516-23530-1(3)) Scholastic Library Publishing. (Children's Pr.).

Houghton, Roswitha, illus. Isabella Ballerina. 2001. (J). 9.95 (978-0-9716346-0-2(2)) Dancing Words Pr., Inc.

Houston-Montgomery, Beauregard. Designer Fashion Dolls. 1999. (Illus.). (J). pap. 14.95 (978-0-87599-524-3(1)) Phillips, S.G. Inc.

Jacobs, Laurie Barbie. Barbie: Four Decades of Fashion. 1999. (MiniSer.). (Illus.). 192p. 5.95 (978-0-7892-0552-0(1)) Abbeville Pr., Inc.

Johnson, Robyn. Enchanted Dolls' Wedding. 2007. 32p. (J). 24.95 (***978-1-59354-197-2(X)*** Handprint Bks.

Kassirer, Sue & Golden Books Staff. Barbie: Cinderella. 2002. (Illus.). 16p. (J). (gr. k-k). 2.99 (978-0-307-96040-5(4) , Golden Bks.) Random Hse. Children's Bks.

Keiki Friends Dress-Up Dolls Activity Book. 2002. (J). 4.99 (978-0-89610-390-0(0)) Island Heritage Publishing.

Krulik, Nancy E. What a Doll! 2003. (gr. 3-6). lib. bdg. 13.00 (978-0-613-66475-2(2)) Tandem Library Bks.

Krulik, Nancy E. & Ladybird Books Staff. Jade: Xtreme Kool! 2003. (Bratz Ser.). (Illus.). 32p. pap. 2.99 (978-1-84422-188-2(1) , Putnam Juvenile) Penguin Group (USA) Inc.

Lehri, R. M. Girl & Boy from India Paper Dolls. 2002. (Illus.). 16p. (J). pap. 3.95 (978-0-486-42189-6(9)) Dover Pubns., Inc.

Lorenz Books Staff. Teddy Bears: With over 50 Reusable Stickers. 1999. (Sticker Fun Ser.). (Illus.). 16p. (ps-k). pap. 4.95 (978-0-7548-0049-1(0) , Lorenz Bks.) Anness Publishing GBR. *Dist:* National Bk. Network.

Mahren, Sue. Make Your Own Teddy Bears & Bear Clothes. Jaskiel, Stan, illus. 2000. (Quick Starts for Kids! Ser.). 64p. (YA). (gr. 3 up). pap. 8.95 (978-1-885593-75-7(9) , Williamson Bks.) Ideals Pubns.

—Make Your Own Teddy Bears & Bear Clothes. 2001. (gr. 3-6). lib. bdg. 16.40 (978-0-613-57610-9(1)) Tandem Library Bks.

Massey, Cal. Whitney the TV Star Paper Doll. 2001. 8p. (J). pap. 1.50 (978-0-486-41666-3(6)) Dover Pubns., Inc.

Mattox, Brenda Sneathen. Three Antique Paper Dolls. 2000. (J). pap. 5.95 (978-0-486-41045-6(5)) Dover Pubns., Inc.

May, Darcy. Fairy of the Seasons Sticker Paper Doll. 2004. (Sticker Paper Dolls Ser.). (Illus.). 4p. (J). (gr. k-5). 1.50 (978-0-486-43312-7(9)) Dover Pubns., Inc.

Noble, Marty. Priscilla the Pilgrim Girl Sticker Paper Doll. 2003. (Dover Little Activity Bks.). (Illus.). 4p. (J). 1.50 (978-0-486-42769-0(2)) Dover Pubns., Inc.

Novell, Cappi. Barbie Magnetic Fashions: Book & Playset. 2005. (Barbie Magnet Kit Ser.). (Illus.). 16p. (J). bds. 14.99 (978-0-7944-0673-8(4)) Reader's Digest Assn., Inc., The.

O'Neill, Cynthia, ed. Barbie: Fashion Dolls. 2000. (Ultimate Sticker Bks.). (Illus.). 16p. (J). pap. 6.99 (978-0-7894-6668-6(6)) Dorling Kindersley Publishing, Inc.

—Barbie: Hobbies. 2001. (Ultimate Sticker Bks.). (Illus.). 20p. (J). pap. 6.99 (978-0-7894-7337-0(2)) Dorling Kindersley Publishing, Inc.

Polacco, Patricia. Betty Doll. Polacco, Patricia, illus. (Illus.). (J). (ps-3). 2001. 1p. 16.99 (978-0-399-23638-9(4) , Philomel); 2004. 40p. reprint ed. pap. 6.99 (978-0-14-240196-5(X) , Puffin) Penguin Group (USA) Inc.

Princess Sweetwater Paper Doll. 2006. 24p. (J). pap. (978-0-9762071-0-8(9) , 371-010) Big City Publishing.

Reinckens, Sunnhild. Making Dolls. 2nd rev. ed. 2003. (Illus.). 80p. pap. 15.95 (978-0-86315-415-7(8)) Floris Bks. GBR. *Dist:* SteinerBooks, Inc.

Ross, Kathy. Things to Make for Your Doll. Garvin, Elaine, illus. 2003. 48p. (J). (gr. k-2). lib. bdg. (978-0-7613-2861-2(0) , Millbrook Pr.); pap. 7.95 (978-0-7613-1781-4(3) , First Avenue Editions) Lerner Publishing Group.

Schiffer, Nancy N. Contemporary Hopi Kachina Dolls. 2003. (Illus.). 208p. (gr. 10-13). 39.95 (978-0-7643-1848-1(9)) Schiffer Publishing, Ltd.

Simons, Suzanne. Trouble Dolls: Chase Your Cares Away with These Six Handmade Dolls! Mendez, Diego Isaias Hernandez, illus. 2000. 62p. (J). (gr. 3-7). pap. 12.95 (978-0-439-12948-0(6)) Scholastic, Inc.

Steadman, Barbara. Bride & Bridesmaid Paper Dolls. 2002. (Sticker Paper Dolls Ser.). (Illus.). 8p. (J). pap. 4.95 (978-0-486-42394-4(8)) Dover Pubns., Inc.

—Bride & Groom Sticker Paper Dolls. 2004. (Sticker Paper Dolls Ser.). (Illus.). 4p. (J). (gr. k-5). pap. 1.50 (978-0-486-43313-4(7)) Dover Pubns., Inc.

—Storybook Princess Sticker Paper Doll. 2004. (Illus.). 4p. (J). pap. 1.50 (978-0-486-43726-2(4)) Dover Pubns., Inc.

—Sweet Valentine Sticker Paper Doll. 2004. 4p. (J). pap. 1.50 (978-0-486-43751-4(5)) Dover Pubns., Inc.

—Vera the Fashion Designer Paper Doll. 2001. (Illus.). 8p. (J). pap. 1.50 (978-0-486-41663-2(1)) Dover Pubns., Inc.

Stewart, Pat. Jennifer the Career Girl Paper Doll. 2001. 8p. (J). pap. 1.50 (978-0-486-41664-9(X)) Dover Pubns., Inc.

Stillerman, Robbie. Candie the Circus Girl Sticker Paper Doll. 2000. (Illus.). 4p. (J). pap. 1.00 (978-0-486-40991-7(0)) Dover Pubns., Inc.

—Everybody Loves Emma Sticker Paper Doll. 2004. (Sticker Paper Dolls Ser.). (Illus.). 4p. (J). (gr. k-5). pap. 1.50 (978-0-486-43314-1(5)) Dover Pubns., Inc.

—Little King & Queen Sticker Paper Dolls. 2003. (Dover Little Activity Bks.). (Illus.). 4p. (J). pap. 1.50 (978-0-486-42631-0(9)) Dover Pubns., Inc.

—Princess Paper Doll. 2000. (J). pap. 1.00 (978-0-486-41314-3(4)) Dover Pubns., Inc.

—Wendy Works Out Sticker Paper Doll. 2003. (Dover Little Activity Bks.). (Illus.). 4p. (J). 1.50 (978-0-486-42632-7(7)) Dover Pubns., Inc.

Sun, Ming-Ju. Godey's Early Victorian Fashions Paper Dolls. 2004. (Illus.). 32p. (J). pap. 5.95 (978-0-486-43687-6(X)) Dover Pubns., Inc.

—Japanese Warrior Costumes Paper Dolls. 2000. (J). pap. 6.95 (978-0-486-41046-3(3)) Dover Pubns., Inc.

—Old-Time Children's Fashions Paper Dolls. 2004. (Illus.). 16p. (J). pap. 5.95 (978-0-486-43344-8(7)) Dover Pubns., Inc.

—Russian Folk Costumes Paper Dolls. 2003. 32p. (J). pap. 5.95 (978-0-486-42390-6(5)) Dover Pubns., Inc.

—Traditional Japanese Fashions Paper Dolls. 2003. (Paper Dolls Ser.). (Illus.). 32p. (J). pap. 6.95 (978-0-486-42654-9(8)) Dover Pubns., Inc.

Taliadoros, Jenny, ed. Alice Faye: Glamorous Movie Star Paper Dolls & Costumes. Mingo, Norman & Ernst, Clara, illus. 2007. 8p. pap. 12.00 (***978-0-9795053-0-0(5)*** Paper Studio Pr.

—Bette Davis Paper Dolls. Mingo, Norman & Ernst, Clara, illus. 2007. 8p. (J). pap. 12.00 (***978-0-9790668-2-5(4)*** Paper Studio Pr.

—Betty Grable Paper Dolls. 2007. 8p. pap. 12.00 (***978-0-9790668-7-0(5)*** Paper Studio Pr.

—Deanna Durbin Paper Dolls. Mingo, Norman & Ernst, Clara, illus. 2007. 8p. pap. 12.00 (***978-0-9790668-5-6(9)*** Paper Studio Pr.

—Doris Day Paper Dolls. 2007. 8p. pap. 12.00 (***978-0-9790668-4-9(0)*** Paper Studio Pr.

—Greer Garson Paper Dolls. Madan, Fredric & Ernst, Clara, illus. 2007. 8p. pap. 12.00 (***978-0-9790668-6-3(7)*** Paper Studio Pr.

—Judy Garland Cut-Out Dolls. 2007. (Illus.). 8p. pap. 12.00 (***978-0-9790668-9-4(1)*** Paper Studio Pr.

—Lana Turner Paper Dolls. Valliant, Regina & Meixner, Jo Hedwig, illus. 2007. 8p. (J). pap. 12.00 (***978-0-9790668-1-8(6)*** Paper Studio Pr.

—The Lollypop Crowd Stand-up Paper Dolls. 2007. (Illus.). 8p. pap. 12.00 (***978-0-9795053-1-7(3)*** Paper Studio Pr.

—Navy Scouts Paper Dolls. Mingo, Norman & Ernst, Clara, illus. 2007. 8p. (J). pap. 12.00 (***978-0-9790668-3-2(2)*** Paper Studio Pr.

—Rita Hayworth Paper Doll: Dancing Star Dolls & Clothes. Mingo, Norman & Ernst, Clara, illus. 2007. 8p. (J). pap. 12.00 (***978-0-9790668-0-1(8)*** Paper Studio Pr.

Tierney, Tom. American Family of the 1970s Paper Dolls. 2001. 32p. (J). (gr. 3). pap. 5.95 (978-0-486-41872-8(3)) Dover Pubns., Inc.

—American Family Paper Dolls. 2002. (Illus.). 68p. (J). pap. 12.95 (978-0-486-42740-9(4)) Dover Pubns., Inc.

—Byzantine Costume Paper Dolls. 2002. (Illus.). 16p. (J). pap. 4.95 (978-0-486-42077-6(9)) Dover Pubns., Inc.

—Camelot Paper Dolls. 2002. (Illus.). 32p. (J). pap. 5.95 (978-0-486-42393-7(X)) Dover Pubns., Inc.

—Campus Fashions Paper Dolls: 1900s-1980s. 2001. 32p. (J). pap. 5.95 (978-0-486-41674-8(7)) Dover Pubns., Inc.

—The Dalai Lama Paper Doll. 2006. 32p. pap. 6.95 (978-0-486-45181-7(X)) Dover Pubns., Inc.

—Edwardian Costumes Paper Dolls. 2001. (Illus.). 16p. (J). pap. 3.95 (978-0-486-41556-7(2)) Dover Pubns., Inc.

—Elizabeth the Queen Mother Paper Dolls. 2001. (Illus.). 32p. (J). pap. 5.95 (978-0-486-41771-4(9)) Dover Pubns., Inc.

—Famous Movie Wedding Gowns Paper Dolls. 2007. 32p. pap. 6.95 (***978-0-486-45800-7(8)***) Dover Pubns., Inc.

—Fashion Parade Paper Dolls: 4 Decades of Great Designs, from 1960 To 2000. 2002. (Illus.). 136p. (J). pap. 12.95 (978-0-486-42738-6(2)) Dover Pubns., Inc.

—Ferdinand & Isabella Paper Dolls. 2004. (Illus.). 16p. (J). pap. 4.95 (978-0-486-43345-5(5)) Dover Pubns., Inc.

—George W. Bush & His Family Paper Dolls. 2001. 32p. (J). (gr. 3). pap. 5.95 (978-0-486-42190-2(2)) Dover Pubns., Inc.

—Glamorous Movie Stars of the Seventies Paper Dolls. 2001. 32p. (J). pap. 5.95 (978-0-486-41557-4(0)) Dover Pubns., Inc.

—Gothic Costumes Paper Dolls. 2001. (J). pap. 5.95 (978-0-486-41329-7(2)) Dover Pubns., Inc.

—Great Characters from Shakespeare Paper Dolls. 2000. (Illus.). 32p. (J). pap. 6.95 (978-0-486-41330-3(6)) Dover Pubns., Inc.

—Great Costumes from Classic Movies Paper Dolls: 30 Fashions by Adrian, Edith Head, Walter Plunkett, & Others. 2003. (Paper Dolls Ser.). (Illus.). 32p. (J). pap. 6.95 (978-0-486-42772-0(2)) Dover Pubns., Inc.

—Great Fashion Designs of the Nineties Paper Dolls. 2000. (Illus.). 16p. (J). pap. 6.95 (978-0-486-41331-0(4)) Dover Pubns., Inc.

—Hollywood Movie Star Paper Dolls. 2002. (Illus.). 120p. (J). pap. 12.95 (978-0-486-42739-3(0)) Dover Pubns., Inc.

—Mae West Paper Doll. 2005. (Illus.). 32p. (J). pap. 5.95 (978-0-486-44099-6(0)) Dover Pubns., Inc.

—Marie Antoinette Paper Dolls. 2001. (Illus.). 32p. (J). (gr. 3). pap. 6.95 (978-0-486-41874-2(X)) Dover Pubns., Inc.

—Mikado Paper Dolls. 2003. (Paper Dolls Ser.). (Illus.). 32p. (J). pap. 5.95 (978-0-486-42656-3(4)) Dover Pubns., Inc.

—Queen Elizabeth I Paper Doll. 2002. (Illus.). 16p. (J). (gr. 3). pap. 4.95 (978-0-486-42192-6(9)) Dover Pubns., Inc.

—Rock 'n' Pop Stars of the Sixties Paper Dolls. 2001. (Illus.). 32p. (J). pap. 5.95 (978-0-486-41558-1(9)) Dover Pubns., Inc.

—Royal Weddings: Paper Dolls. 2005. (Illus.). 32p. (ps-ps). pap. 6.95 (978-0-486-44178-8(4)) Dover Pubns., Inc.

—Sarah Bernhardt Paper Dolls. 2002. 16p. (J). pap. 4.95 (978-0-486-42391-3(3)) Dover Pubns., Inc.

—Ziegfeld Girls Paper Dolls. 2004. (Illus.). 32p. (J). pap. 5.95 (978-0-486-43679-1(9)) Dover Pubns., Inc.

—16 Great Stars of the Broadway Musical Paper Dolls. 2004. (Illus.). 32p. (J). pap. 5.95 (978-0-486-43684-5(5)) Dover Pubns., Inc.

Ulmer, Louise. Fashion Folio: Designs by Me, Paper Doll Design & Coloring Book. Ulmer, Louise, illus. 1999. (Illus.). 28p. (J). (gr. 2-6). mass mkt. 4.95 (978-0-941367-08-0(8)) Peach Blossom Pubns.

Witkowski, Teri, ed. Addy's Magnetic Mini World. 2007. (J). (ps-2). pap. 9.95 (***978-1-59369-180-6(7)*** , Pleasant Co.) American Girl Publishing, Inc.

—Felicity's Magnetic Mini World. 2007. (J). (ps-2). pap. 9.95 (***978-1-59369-175-2(0)*** , Pleasant Co.) American Girl Publishing, Inc.

—Josefina's Magnetic Mini World. 2007. (J). (ps-2). pap. 9.95 (***978-1-59369-178-3(5)*** , Pleasant Co.) American Girl Publishing, Inc.

—Kaya's Magnetic Mini World. 2007. (J). (ps-2). pap. 9.95 (***978-1-59369-182-0(3)*** , Pleasant Co.) American Girl Publishing, Inc.

—Kirsten's Magnetic Mini World. 2007. (J). (ps-2). pap. 9.95 (***978-1-59369-179-0(3)*** , Pleasant Co.) American Girl Publishing, Inc.

—Kit's Magnetic Mini World. 2007. (J). (ps-2). pap. 9.95 (***978-1-59369-181-3(5)*** , Pleasant Co.) American Girl Publishing, Inc.

—Molly's Magnetic Mini World. 2007. (J). (ps-2). pap. 9.95 (***978-1-59369-176-9(9)*** , Pleasant Co.) American Girl Publishing, Inc.

—Samantha's Magnetic Mini World. 2007. (J). (ps-2). pap. 9.95 (***978-1-59369-177-6(7)*** , Pleasant Co.) American Girl Publishing, Inc.

Zondervan. Elsie's Paper Doll Collection. 2004. (Life of Faith Ser.). (YA). pap. 9.99 (978-1-928749-33-2(X)) Zonderkidz.

DOLLS—FICTION

Baker, Deb. Dolly Departed. 2008. 288p. (gr. 12). mass mkt. 6.99 (***978-0-425-22051-1(6)*** , Berkley) Penguin Group (USA) Inc.

Balloon Books Staff. Go to Sleep: Book & Doll. 1999. (Balloon Ser.). (Illus.). 4p. (ps-k). 6.95 (978-0-8069-5925-2(8)) Sterling Publishing Co., Inc.

—Let's Go: Book & Doll. 1999. (Balloon Ser.). (Illus.). 4p. (J). 6.95 (978-0-8069-5926-9(6) , Balloon Bks.) Sterling Publishing Co., Inc.

Barbie: Hatbox. 2001. (Illus.). 24p. (J). 14.99 (978-0-307-20024-2(8) , 20024, Golden Bks.) Random Hse. Children's Bks.

Bartels, Alice. Grandmother Doll. 2001. (ps-2). lib. bdg. 15.25 (978-0-613-78378-1(6)) Tandem Library Bks.

Bartels, Alice & Petricic, Dusan. The Grandmother Doll. 2001. (Illus.). 24p. (J). (ps-2). lib. bdg. 17.95 (978-1-55037-667-8(5)); pap. 6.95 (978-1-55037-666-1(7)) Annick Pr., Ltd. CAN. *Dist:* Firefly Bks., Ltd.

Bauer, Marion Dane. The Red Ghost. Ferguson, Peter, illus. 2008. (J). (***978-0-375-84081-4(8)***); pap. (***978-0-375-84082-1(6)***); lib. bdg. (***978-0-375-94081-1(2)***) Random Hse., Inc.

Bently, Dawn. Kelly's Great Day. 2005. (Woodkins Ser.). (Illus.). 12p. (J). bds. 14.95 (978-1-59354-048-7(5)) Handprint Bks.

Berger, Barbara Helen. The Jewel Heart. 1998. (978-0-606-13537-5(5)) Tandem Library Bks.

Bergsmer. Dragon. 2004. (SPA.). 32p. (978-84-7720-840-2(9)) Obelisco, Ediciones S.A.

Bertrand, Diane Gonzales. The Last Doll/la ultima Muñeca. Balestra, Alejandra, tr. Accardo, Anthony, illus. 2001. Tr. of Ultima Muneca. (ENG & SPA.). 32p. (J). (ps-2). 14.95 (978-1-55885-290-7(5) , Piñata Books) Arte Publico Pr.

Blake, Quentin. Clown. 1998. (Illus.). 32p. (J). (ps-3). pap. 8.95 (978-0-8050-5933-5(4) , Holt, Henry & Co. Bks. For Young Readers) Holt, Henry & Co.

Blauberg, Alyssa. Teddy Bear Soap on a Rope. 1998. (Illus.). 4p. (J). (gr. 1-6). pap. 4.95 (978-1-58295-016-7(4) , Beehive Bk.) Pace Products, Inc.

Bliss, Corine Demas. The Littlest Matryoshka. Brown, Kathryn, illus. 1999. 32p. (ps-17). 15.99 (978-0-7868-0153-4(0)) Hyperion Bks. for Children.

Bodel, Garrett. Dare, Dare, Double-Dare! Bodel, Garrett, photos by. 2002. (Doll's Life Story Ser.: Vol. 5). (Illus.). 28p. (J). (gr. 2-3). pap. 7.90 (978-0-9720072-1-2(9)) Doll's Life.

—A Day at the Fair. 2002. (Doll's Life Story Ser.: Vol. 4). (Illus.). 32p. (J). pap. 7.90 (978-0-9720072-1-4(0)) Doll's Life.

—The St. Patrick's Day Dance. Bodel, Garrett, photos by. 2002. (Doll's Life Story Ser.: Vol. 3). (Illus.). 28p. (J). (gr. 2-3). pap. 7.90 (978-0-9720072-0-7(2)) Doll's Life.

—Trick or Treat! Bodel, Garrett, photos by. 2002. (Doll's Life Story Ser.: Vol. 7). (Illus.). 32p. (J). (gr. 2-4). pap. 7.90 (978-0-9720072-3-8(7)) Doll's Life.

—A Trip to the City. Bodel, Garrett, photos by. 2002. (Doll's Life Story Ser.: Vol. 2). (Illus.). 32p. (J). (gr. 2-4). pap. 7.90 (978-0-9720072-4-5(5)) Doll's Life.

Bond, Belle Bacon. Drusilla & Her Dolls. 2005. 58p. (J). (ps-3). 16.95 (978-1-55709-598-5(1)) Applewood Bks.

Book Company Staff. Catch That Hat! 2002. (Magical World of Teddies Ser.). 14p. (J). bds. 12.95 (978-1-74047-162-6(8)) Book Co. Publishing Pty, Ltd., The AUS. *Dist:* Penton Overseas, Inc.

Brown, Marc. Arthur in New York. 2008. (J). (***978-0-375-82976-5(8)***) Random Hse., Inc.

Browne, Anthony. Silly Billy. Browne, Anthony, illus. 2006. (Illus.). 32p. (J). (ps-2). 15.99 (978-0-7636-3124-6(8)) Candlewick Pr.

Bunting, Eve. The Ghost Children. 2005. 166p. (J). (***978-1-4156-2991-8(9)*** , Clarion Bks.) Houghton Mifflin Co. Trade & Reference Div.

Burke, Janine. The Deadly Doll. Tan, Shaun, illus. 2008. 80p. (J). pap. (***978-1-59889-914-6(7)***); (YA). (gr. 5-9). lib. bdg. 16.95 (***978-1-59889-858-3(2)***) Stone Arch Bks.

Burnett, Frances Hodgson. The Racketty-Packetty House. Halperin, Wendy Anderson, illus. 100th anniv. ed. 2006. 96p. (J). 17.95 (978-0-689-86974-7(6)) Simon & Schuster Children's Publishing.

—RackettyPacketty House. l.t. ed. 2006. 52p. pap. (978-1-84637-262-9(3)) Echo Library.

But You Promised! A Book about Keeping Your Word. 1998. (Big Comfy Couch Ser.). (Illus.). 32p. (J). 5.95 (978-0-7370-1001-5(0)) Time-Life Inc.

Channell, Jim. Quien Vive en el Nido? 2000. (SPA.). 10p. (J). (ps-k). 7.95 (978-84-392-8314-0(8)) Lectorum Pubns., Inc.

Cheney, Cora. The Doll of Lilac Valley. Cassidy, Nancy White, illus. 2003. 128p. 11.95 (978-0-9714612-5-3(2)) Green Mansion Pr. LLC.

Clements, Andrew. Sound Story Format Snowden Raggedy Ann & Andy. 1998. (J). 9.99 (978-0-689-82369-5(X) , Little Simon) Simon & Schuster Children's Publishing.

Collins-Varni, H. Elizabeth. The Doll Lady. Kuusisto, Judy, illus. 2001. 32p. (J). (ps-3). 15.95 (978-0-935699-24-1(4) , 0935699244) Illumination Arts Publishing Co., Inc.

Coristine, Philip. Serena & the Wild Doll. Gukova, Julia, illus. 2000. 32p. (J). (ps-2). pap. 6.95 (978-1-55037-648-7(9)); lib. bdg. 19.95 (978-1-55037-649-4(7)) Annick Pr., Ltd. CAN. *Dist:* Firefly Bks., Ltd.

Cuno, Sabine. Abre, cierra y Aprende: Open, Close, & Learn, Spanish-Lanaguage Edition. 2007. (Illus.). 12p. (J). 14.95 (***978-970-718-489-3(2)*** , Silver Dolphin en Español) Advanced Marketing, S. de R. L. de C. V. MEX. *Dist:* Perseus Distribution.

Cutler, Jane. The Birthday Doll. Nakata, Hiroe, illus. 2004. 32p. (J). 16.00 (978-0-374-30719-6(9) , Farrar, Straus & Giroux (BYR)) Farrar, Straus & Giroux.

Davidson, Susanna. Dolls. Wanert, Amandine, illus. 2006. 48p. (J). 8.99 (978-0-7945-1327-6(1) , Usborne) EDC Publishing.

De Guzman, Michael. Finding Stinko. 2007. 144p. (J). (gr. 5 up). 16.00 (978-0-374-32305-9(4)) Farrar, Straus & Giroux.

DeBellis, Thea. Miss Anne & Her Doll Collection. 2004. pap. 8.00 (978-0-8059-6407-3(X)) Dorrance Publishing Co., Inc.

Dillard, Mary Gregory. Finding Betsyanna. 2006. (ENG.). 48p. per. 12.95 (***978-1-4241-5492-0(8)***) PublishAmerica, Inc.

Dillon, Jana. Sasha's Matrioshka Dolls. Lattimore, Deborah Nourse, illus. 2007. 28p. (J). reprint ed. 16.00 (***978-1-4223-6684-4(7)***) DIANE Publishing Co.

Dockweiler, Sharon. No Buttons for Suzy Cow. Silbert, Barbara Briggs, illus. 1999. (J). (978-1-929453-00-9(0)) Sharon's Small Pr.

Dorling Kindersley Publishing Staff. Barbie Hobbies. 2005. (Barbie sticker Bks.). 20p. (J). pap. 6.99 (978-0-7566-1120-0(2)) Dorling Kindersley Publishing, Inc.

C D

Doty, Linda. The Christmas Doll. 2005. 124p. pap. 17.95 (978-1-4137-7790-1(2)) PublishAmerica, Inc.

Dracker, Pune. Doll & Teddy Bear Activity Book. Bart, Kathleen & Hofmann, Ginnie, illus. 2005. 96p. (J). pap. (978-1-932485-24-0(4)) Reverie Publishing Co.

Earl, Janice. Jan Has a Doll. Tusa, Tricia, illus. 2005. (Green Light Readers Level 1 Ser.). 24p. (J). (ps-ps). 12.95 (978-0-15-205168-6(6)); pap. 3.95 (978-0-15-205167-9(8)) Harcourt Trade Pubs.

Edwards, Pamela Duncan. Miss Polly Has a Dolly. Castaldi, Elicia, illus. 2003. 32p. (J). (ps-2). 15.99 (978-0-399-23857-4(3) , Putnam Juvenile) Penguin Group (USA) Inc.

Elizabeti's Doll. 2004. 24.95 incl. audio (978-1-55592-053-1(5)); (J). pap. 14.95 incl. audio (978-1-55592-716-5(5)) Weston Woods Studios, Inc.

Entara Ltd. Staff, photos by. Piggley & the Magic Doll. 2006. (Jakers! Ser.). 24p. (J). pap. 3.99 (978-0-689-87611-0(4) , Simon Spotlight) Simon & Schuster Children's Publishing.

Equipo Staff. El Vuelo de Igor. 2000. (Adventures of Winnie the Pooh! Ser.). (SPA., Illus.). 114p. (J). 12.95 (978-84-488-0733-7(2)) Beascoa, Ediciones S.A. ESP. *Dist:* Distribooks, Inc.

Ferguson, Sarah. Little Red. Williams, Sam, illus. 2006. 40p. (J). 6.99 (978-1-4169-1853-0(1) , Aladdin) Simon & Schuster Children's Publishing.

—Little Red's Christmas Story. Williams, Sam, illus. 2004. 40p. (J). 15.95 (978-0-689-85561-0(3)) Simon & Schuster Children's Publishing.

—Little Red's Summer Adventure. Williams, Sam, illus. 2006. 40p. (J). (ps-2). 15.95 (978-0-689-85562-7(1)) Simon & Schuster Children's Publishing.

Ferguson, Sarah The Duchess of York. Little Red's Christmas Story. Williams, Sam, illus. 2007. 40p. (J). 6.99 ***(978-1-4169-5002-8(8)*** , Aladdin) Simon & Schuster Children's Publishing.

Field, Rachel. Hitty: Her First Hundred Years. Lathrop, Dorothy P., illus. 2005. reprint ed. pap. 24.95 (978-1-4179-0581-2(6)) Kessinger Publishing, LLC.

Field, Rachel & Lathrop, Dorothy P. Hitty: Her First Hundred Years. 1998. (Illus.). 256p. (J). (ps-7). pap. 5.99 (978-0-689-82284-1(7) , Aladdin) Simon & Schuster Children's Publishing.

Fine, Anne. Jamie & Angus Stories. Dale, Penny, illus. 2007. 176p. (J). (ps-1). pap. 5.99 ***(978-0-7636-3312-7(7))*** Candlewick Pr.

Fonteyn, Margot. Coppelia. Johnson, Steve & Fancher, Lou, illus. 1998. 36p. (YA). reprint ed. 17.00 (978-0-7567-6160-8(3)) DIANE Publishing Co.

—Coppelia. 1998. (Easy to Read Folktales Ser.). (Illus.). 48p. (ps-3). lib. bdg. 27.12 (978-0-8172-5740-8(3)) Raintree.

Ford, Mike. The Dollhouse That Time Forgot. 1998. (Eerie Indiana Ser.: No. 11). 144p. (J). (gr. 3-7). pap. 3.99 (978-0-380-79787-5(9)) HarperCollins Pubs.

Gardner, Sally. Boolar's Big Day Out. 2003. (Tales from the Box Ser.: Vol. 2). (Illus.). 128p. (J). 14.95 (978-1-58234-833-9(2) , Bloomsbury Children) Bloomsbury Publishing.

—Countess's Calamity. 2003. (gr. 3-6). lib. bdg. 15.25 (978-0-613-63271-3(0)) Tandem Library Bks.

—The Countess's Calamity: Tales from the Box. Gardner, Sally, illus. 2003. (Tales from the Box Ser.). (Illus.). 160p. (J). (gr. 1-6). 14.95 (978-1-58234-812-4(X)); pap. 6.95 (978-1-58234-855-1(3)) Bloomsbury Publishing. (Bloomsbury Children).

Gates, Josephine Scribner. The April fool Doll. Keep, Virginia, illus. 2007. 152p. (J). lib. bdg. 59.00 ***(978-1-60304-009-9(9))*** Dollworks.

—Captain Billie: Leads the way to the land of I don't want To. Sichel, Harold, illus. 2007. 96p. (J). lib. bdg. 59.00 ***(978-1-60304-019-8(6))*** Dollworks.

—The dolls in Fairyland. Keep, Virginia, illus. 2007. 136p. (J). lib. bdg. 59.00 ***(978-1-60304-013-6(7))*** Dollworks.

—Little girl Blue: Lives in the woods till she learns to say Please. Keep, Virginia, illus. 2007. 54p. (J). lib. bdg. 59.00 ***(978-1-60304-012-9(9))*** Dollworks.

—Little Girl Blue plays I Spy. 2007. (Illus.). 64p. (J). lib. bdg. 59.00 ***(978-1-60304-017-4(X))*** Dollworks.

—Little red white & Blue. Keep, Virginia, illus. 2007. 118p. (J). lib. bdg. 59.00 ***(978-1-60304-006-8(4))*** Dollworks.

—The Live Doll Series, 4 vols., 9bks. 2006. (Illus.). (YA). lib. bdg. 349.00 (978-0-9760064-4-2(8)) Dollworks.

—The live dolls' busy Days. Keep, Virginia, illus. 2007. 106p. (J). lib. bdg. 59.00 ***(978-1-60304-007-5(2))*** Dollworks.

—The live dolls' house Party. Keep, Virginia, illus. 2007. 104p. (J). lib. bdg. 59.00 ***(978-1-60304-005-1(6))*** Dollworks.

—The live dolls in Wonderland. Keep, Virginia, illus. 2007. 150p. (J). lib. bdg. 59.00 ***(978-1-60304-015-0(3))*** Dollworks.

—The live dolls' play Days. Keep, Virginia, illus. 2007. 110p. (J). lib. bdg. 59.00 ***(978-1-60304-008-2(0))*** Dollworks.

—More about live Dolls. Keep, Virginia, illus. 2007. 106p. (J). lib. bdg. 59.00 ***(978-1-60304-002-0(1))*** Dollworks.

—Nannette & the baby Monkey. 2007. (Illus.). 50p. (J). lib. bdg. 59.00 ***(978-1-60304-020-4(X))*** Dollworks.

—Nannette goes to visit her Grandmother. 2007. (J). lib. bdg. 59.00 ***(978-1-60304-021-1(8))*** Dollworks.

—One day in Betty,s Life. Stuart, B. S., illus. 2007. 58p. (J). lib. bdg. 59.00 ***(978-1-60304-018-1(8))*** Dollworks.

—The secret of the live Dolls. Archibald, A. L., illus. 2007. (J). lib. bdg. 59.00 ***(978-1-60304-024-2(2))*** Dollworks.

—The Story of Live Dolls: Being an account by Josephine Scribner Gates of how, on a certian June morning, all of the dolls in the Cloverdale came Alive. Keep, Virginia, illus. 2007. 102p. (J). lib. bdg. 59.00 ***(978-1-60304-001-3(3))*** Dollworks.

—The story of the lost Doll. Keep, Virginia, illus. 2007. 108p. (J). lib. bdg. 59.00 ***(978-1-60304-003-7(X))*** Dollworks.

—The Story of the three Dolls. Keep, Virginia, illus. 2007. 148p. (J). lib. bdg. 59.00 ***(978-1-60304-004-4(8))*** Dollworks.

—Sunshine Annie. Cory, Fanny Y., illus. 2007. 148p. (J). lib. bdg. 59.00 ***(978-1-60304-011-2(0))*** Dollworks.

—Tommy Sweet-Tooth & Little girl Blue. Churbuck, Esther V., illus. 2007. 64p. (J). lib. bdg. 59.00 ***(978-1-60304-014-3(5))*** Dollworks.

—The Turkey Doll. Flass, E. C., illus. 2007. 62p. (J). lib. bdg. 59.00 ***(978-1-60304-016-7(1))*** Dollworks.

Geddes, Anne. 10 en la Cama. 2005. (SPA.). 34p. 7.95 (978-84-406-9855-1(0)) Ediciones B ESP. *Dist:* Independent Pubs. Group.

Geter, Maurice. My Friend Buddy. Geter, Maurice, illus. 2006. (Illus.). 24p. (J). (978-1-4120-9646-1(4)) Trafford Publishing.

Gipson, Morrell. The Surprise Doll. Lerch, Steffie, illus. 2005. 46p. (J). (ps-ps). reprint ed. 15.00 (978-1-930900-18-9(X)) Purple Hse. Pr.

Godden, Rumer. Miss Happiness & Miss Flower. 2002. (Illus.). 128p. (J). (gr. 3-7). 14.89 (978-0-06-029193-8(1)) HarperCollins Pubs.

—Story of Holly & Ivy, the R/I. Cooney, Barbara, illus. 2006. 32p. (J). (gr. k). 17.99 (978-0-670-06219-5(7) , Viking Juvenile) Penguin Group (USA) Inc.

Golden Books Staff. Barbie: The Nutcracker. 2002. (Illus.). 16p. (J). (gr. k-k). 2.99 (978-0-307-99512-4(7) , Golden Bks.) Random Hse. Children's Bks.

—Blue's Dress-up Day. Miller, Victoria, illus. 2005. 48p. (J). (ps-2). pap. 2.99 (978-0-375-83172-0(X) , Golden Bks.) Random Hse. Children's Bks.

—Happy Holiday Surprise. 2000. (Barbie Ser.). (Illus.). 64p. (J). (ps-2). pap. 2.99 (978-0-307-25706-2(1) , 25706, Golden Bks.) Random Hse. Children's Bks.

Goldstein, Alrica, ed. Polly Pocket. 2007. (I Can Find It Ser.). 22p. (J). 7.99 (978-0-696-23197-1(2)) Meredith Bks.

—Polly Pocket & the Tricky Tryouts. 2007. 64p. (J). pap. 4.99 (978-0-696-23198-8(0)) Meredith Bks.

Gordh, Bill. Barbie: Two Princesses. S. I. International Staff, illus. 2000. (Road to Reading Ser.). 32p. (J). (ps-2). pap. 3.99 (978-0-307-26206-6(5) , Random Hse. Bks. for Young Readers) Random Hse. Children's Bks.

Green, Yuko. Christina from Sweden Sticker Paper Doll. 2003. (Dover Little Activity Bks.). (Illus.). 4p. (J). pap. 1.50 (978-0-486-43015-7(4)) Dover Pubns., Inc.

Gregory, Nan. Pink. Melanson, Luc, illus. 2007. 32p. (J). (ps-2). 17.95 ***(978-0-88899-781-4(7))*** Groundwood Bks. CAN. *Dist:* Perseus Distribution.

Gruelle, Johnny. How Raggedy Ann Got Her Candy Heart. 2001. (ps-2). lib. bdg. 15.30 (978-0-613-90801-6(5)) Tandem Library Bks.

—Marcella: A Raggedy Ann Story. Gruelle, Johnny, illus. 2004. (Illus.). 95p. (J). (gr. k-4). reprint ed. 17.00 (978-0-7567-8151-4(5)) DIANE Publishing Co.

—The Paper Dragon: A Raggedy Ann Adventure. Gruelle, Johnny, illus. 2003. (Raggedy Ann Ser.). (Illus.). 96p. (J). 17.95 (978-0-689-84969-5(9)) Simon & Schuster Children's Publishing.

—Raggedy Andy Stories. 2006. pap. 87.99 ***(978-1-4280-2889-0(7))*** IndyPublish.com.

—Raggedy Ann & Andy: A Read-Aloud Treasury. 2005. (Raggedy Ann Ser.). (Illus.). 96p. (J). 9.99 (978-1-4169-0752-7(1) , Little Simon) Simon & Schuster Children's Publishing.

—Raggedy Ann & Andy & the Camel with the Wrinkled Knees. Moerbeek, Kees, illus. ltd. ed. 2003. (Raggedy Ann Ser.). 14p. (J). 150.00 (978-0-689-86370-7(5) , Little Simon) Simon & Schuster Children's Publishing.

—Raggedy Ann & Andy & the Camel with the Wrinkled Knees. abr. ed. 2001. (gr. k-3). lib. bdg. 15.30 (978-0-613-62571-5(4)) Tandem Library Bks.

—Raggedy Ann & Rags: Adapted from Stories by Johnny Gruelle. Palmer, illus. 2003. 40p. (J). 15.00 (978-0-689-86162-8(1) , Simon & Schuster Children's Publishing) Simon & Schuster Children's Publishing.

—Raggedy Ann in Cookie Land. Gruelle, Johnny, illus. 2002. (Classic Edition Ser.). (Illus.). 96p. (J). 17.95 (978-0-689-85096-7(4)) Simon & Schuster Children's Publishing.

—Raggedy Ann Stories. 2006. pap. 87.99 ***(978-1-4280-2426-7(3))*** IndyPublish.com.

Gruelle, Johnny. Raggedy Ann's Wishing Pebble. Gruelle, Johnny, illus. 2004. reprint ed. pap. 15.95 (978-1-4179-0709-0(6)) Kessinger Publishing, LLC.

—Raggedy Ann's Wishing Pebble. Palmer, Jan, illus. 2002. (My First Raggedy Ann Ser.). 40p. (J). (ps-2). pap. 6.99 (978-0-689-85117-9(0) , Aladdin) Simon & Schuster Children's Publishing.

—Raggedy Ann's Wishing Pebble. 2002. (ps-2). lib. bdg. 15.30 (978-0-613-90193-2(2)) Tandem Library Bks.

Gruelle, Johnny & Palmer, Jan. Raggedy Ann & Andy & the Nice Police Officer. 2002. (My First Raggedy Ann Ser.). (Illus.). 40p. (J). pap. 6.99 (978-0-689-85344-9(0) , Aladdin) Simon & Schuster Children's Publishing.

—Raggedy Ann & Rags: Adapted from Stories by Johnny Gruelle. 2002. (My First Raggedy Ann Ser.). (Illus.). 40p. (J). 15.00 (978-0-689-82977-2(9)) Simon & Schuster Children's Publishing.

Hahn, Mary Downing. The Doll in the Garden: A Ghost Story. 2007. 144p. (J). (gr. 4-6). pap. 5.95 ***(978-0-618-87315-9(5)*** , Clarion Bks.) Houghton Mifflin Co. Trade & Reference Div.

Haley, Gail E. Marguerite. Haley, Gail E., illus. 2001. (Illus.). (J). (ps-3). pap. 19.95 (978-0-87460-262-3(9)) Lion Bks.

Hall, Patricia. A Day at the Fair. Mitter, Kathryn & Winfield, Alison, illus. 2000. (Classic Raggedy Ann & Andy Ser.). 32p. (J). (ps-3). pap. 3.99 (978-0-689-83248-2(6) , Little Simon) Simon & Schuster Children's Publishing.

—Day at the Fair. 2000. (gr. k-3). lib. bdg. 11.80 (978-0-613-31111-3(6)) Tandem Library Bks.

—Hooray for Reading! Mitter, Kathryn, illus. 2005. (Ready-to-Read Ser. Level 1). 32p. (J). lib. bdg. 15.00 (978-1-59054-927-8(9)) Fitzgerald Bks.

—Hooray for Reading! Mitter, Kathryn, illus. 2002. (Classic Raggedy Ann & Andy Ser.). 32p. (J). (ps-3). pap. 3.99 (978-0-689-85178-0(2) , Little Simon) Simon & Schuster Children's Publishing.

—Hooray for Reading! 2002. (ps-2). lib. bdg. 11.80 (978-0-613-45064-5(7)) Tandem Library Bks.

—School Day Adventure. Mitter, Kathryn & Winfield, Alison, illus. 2000. (Classic Raggedy Ann & Andy Ser.). 32p. (J). (ps-3). pap. 3.99 (978-0-689-83247-5(8) , Little Simon) Simon & Schuster Children's Publishing.

—School Day Adventure. 2000. (gr. k-3). lib. bdg. 11.80 (978-0-613-31660-6(6)) Tandem Library Bks.

Hall, Patricia & Winfield, Alison. Old Friends, New Friends. 2002. (Raggedy Ann Ser.). 32p. (J). pap. 3.99 (978-0-689-85224-4(X) , Little Simon) Simon & Schuster Children's Publishing.

Halter, Pam. Beatrice Loses Her Doll. Sponaugle, Kim, tr. Sponaugle, Kim, illus. 2001. 32p. (J). 6.99 (978-0-570-07117-4(8)) Concordia Publishing Hse.

Hammerschlag, Carl A. The Go-Away Doll. Havill, Juanita, ed. Soasey, Beverly E., illus. l.t. ed. 1998. (Dr. H. Bks.). 32p. (J). (ps-12). 16.95 (978-1-889166-22-3(7) , 299-5425, Dr. H Bks.) Turtle Island Pr., Inc.

Harcourt School Publishers Staff. A Corn Husk Doll Advanced Level. 3rd ed. 2002. (Trophies Reading Program Ser.). (Illus.). (J). pap. 3.70 (978-0-15-323012-7(6)) Harcourt Schl. Pubs.

—Corn Husk Doll 5-Pack, Advanced Level. 3rd ed. 2002. (Trophies Reading Program Ser.). (Illus.). (J). (gr. 1). pap. 20.10 (978-0-15-326862-5(X)) Harcourt Schl. Pubs.

—Jan Has a Doll: Below Level. 3rd ed. 2002. (Trophies Reading Program Ser.). (Illus.). (J). pap. 3.20 (978-0-15-322944-2(6)) Harcourt Schl. Pubs.

Hassler, Kurt. Hannah & the Homunculus. Darnell, K. L., illus. 2001. 32p. (J). 15.95 (978-1-58536-043-7(0)) Sleeping Bear Pr.

Hayes-Knoll, Carolyn. Ista Cante. 2004. (Illus.). 32p. (J). (978-0-9755646-6-0(8)) Westview Publishing Co., Inc.

Henson, John, illus. Sarah Lynn's Christmas Present. 2002. (J). 24.95 (978-0-9711706-8-1(1)) Waiver Publishing.

Hill, Eric. Spot's Christmas Plush Doll. Hill, Eric, illus. 2005. (J). 11.00 (978-0-399-24472-8(7) , Putnam Juvenile) Penguin Group (USA) Inc.

Holabird, Katharine. Angelina & the Rag Doll. Craig, Helen, illus. 2006. (Angelina Ballerina Ser.). 24p. (J). (ps-1). 3.99 (978-0-448-44331-7(7) , Grosset & Dunlap) Penguin Group (USA) Inc.

—Angelina Ballerina Book & Doll Set. Craig, Helen, illus. 2006. (Angelina Ballerina Ser.). 32p. (J). 27.99 (978-0-670-06088-7(7) , Viking Juvenile) Penguin Group (USA) Inc.

Holub, Joan. Charlotte's Choice. 2003. (gr. 3-6). lib. bdg. 11.80 (978-0-613-72096-0(2)) Tandem Library Bks.

—Tatiana Comes to America: An Ellis Island Story. 2002. (gr. 3-6). lib. bdg. 11.80 (978-0-613-70904-0(7)) Tandem Library Bks.

Horner, Dwana. Amanda's Toybox. 2001. 21p. pap. 9.95 (978-0-7414-0793-1(0)) Infinity Publishing.

Innovative Kids Staff. Sugar & Spice - Fashion Girls. Perrett, Lisa, illus. 2006. 10p. (J). (ps-1). 19.99 (978-1-58476-487-8(2) , IKIDS) Innovative Kids.

Irbinskas, Heather. The Lost Kachina. Albert, Robert & Anthis, Brian, illus. 2004. 32p. (J). 15.95 (978-1-885772-33-6(5)) Kiva Publishing, Inc.

Itoh, Shimpei. Hyper Dolls. 2003. Vol. 4. 218p. pap. 15.95 (978-1-929090-44-0(7)); Vol. 5. (Illus.). 208p. pap. 15.95 (978-1-929090-67-9(6)) International Comics & Entertainment L.L.C.

Jackson, Jill L. Fine Feathers Don't Make a Peacock. Kirby, Bertha, illus. 2000. (Lessons for Lucile Ser.). 79p. (J). 24.95 (978-0-9700692-0-7(0)) Noble Endeaver.

James, Annabelle. Abigail's Bedtime. Beckes, Shirley, illus. 2004. (J). bds. 12.99 (978-1-883043-53-7(0) , 6022) Straight Edge Pr., The.

Jane, Pamela. Noelle of the Nutcracker. Brett, Jan, illus. 2003. 64p. (J). (gr. 4-6). pap. 5.95 (978-0-618-36922-5(8)) Houghton Mifflin Co. Trade & Reference Div.

Jennings, Paul. The Gizmo. Smith, Craig, illus. 2005. 72p. (YA). pap. 9.00 (978-0-14-037090-4(0) , Penguin Global) Penguin Group (USA) Inc.

—The Gizmo Again. McEwan, Keith, illus. 2005. 72p. (YA). pap. 9.00 (978-0-14-037807-8(3) , Penguin Global) Penguin Group (USA) Inc.

Johnson, Robyn. The Enchanted Dolls' House. Johnson, Robyn, illus. 2006. (Illus.). 32p. (J). (gr. k-3). 24.95 (978-1-59354-182-8(1)) Handprint Bks.

Jones, Elizabeth Orton. Big Susan. Jones, Elizabeth Orton, illus. anniv. ed. 2001. (Illus.). 88p. (J). (gr. 1-6). 18.95 (978-1-930900-06-6(6)) Purple Hse. Pr.

Jordan, Apple. Barbie: School Days. Wolcott, Karen, illus. 2004. (Step into Reading Ser.). 32p. (J). (ps-1). pap. 3.99 (978-0-375-82723-5(4) , Random Hse. Bks. for Young Readers) Random Hse. Children's Bks.

Jordan, Apple & Random House Staff. Barbie: On Your Toes. Wolcott, Karen, illus. 2005. (Step into Reading Ser.: No. 1). 32p. (J). (ps-1). pap. 3.99 (978-0-375-83142-3(8) , Random Hse. Bks. for Young Readers) Random Hse. Children's Bks.

Karpinski, David. Sarah's Christmas Presence. 2006. 58p. pap. 8.95 (978-0-7414-3411-1(3)) Infinity Publishing.

Kassirer, Norma. Magic Elizabeth. Krush, Joe, illus. 1999. 224p. (J). (gr. 3-7). pap. 4.95 (978-0-06-440748-9(9) , Harper Trophy) HarperCollins Pubs.

—Magic Elizabeth. 1999. (J). (978-0-606-16700-0(5)) Tandem Library Bks.

Kawahara, Yumiko. Dolls, Vol. 2. Kawahara, Yumiko, illus. 2005. (Dolls Ser.). (Illus.). 216p. (YA). pap. 9.99 (978-1-59116-670-2(5)) Viz Media.

Keene, Carolyn. The Kachina Doll Mystery, Vol. 62. 2005. (Nancy Drew Mystery Stories). (Illus.). 192p. (J). (gr. 3-8). 6.99 (978-0-448-43693-7(0) , Grosset & Dunlap) Penguin Group (USA) Inc.

Keene, Carolyn. Sleepover Sleuths. 2007. (Nancy Drew & the Clue Crew Ser.). 96p. (J). (gr. 2-4). 24.21 ***(978-1-59961-348-2(4))*** Spotlight.

Kehret, Peg. Wally Amos Presents Chip & Cookie - The First Adventure: No More Chocolate Chips. 2002. (Illus.). 40p. (J). (ps-3). 14.95 (978-1-58497-018-7(9)) Addax Publishing Group, Inc.

Kim, Sun-Min & Horvath, David. The Ugly Guide to the Uglyverse. 2008. (Illus.). 64p. (J). (gr. 1). lib. bdg. 12.99 ***(978-0-375-93683-8(1)*** , Random Hse. Bks. for Young Readers) Random Hse. Children's Bks.

Kleven, Elisa. The Apple Doll. 2007. (Illus.). 40p. (J). (ps-3). 16.00 (978-0-374-30380-8(0)) Farrar, Straus & Giroux.

Koeppel, Ruth. Brought to You by the Number 1. 1999. (gr. k-3). lib. bdg. 10.95 (978-0-613-82501-6(2)) Tandem Library Bks.

Kunhardt, Dorothy. Kitty's New Doll. 2004. (Little Golden Book Ser.). (Illus.). 24p. (J). (gr. k-k). 2.99 (978-0-375-82936-9(9) , Golden Bks.) Random Hse. Children's Bks.

Leavitt, Martine. The Dollmage. 2004. (Illus.). 160p. (YA). (gr. 7 up). pap. 8.95 (978-0-88995-233-1(7)) Red Deer Pr. CAN. *Dist:* Fitzhenry & Whiteside, Ltd.

The live dolls' party Days. 2007. (Illus.). 160p. (J). lib. bdg. 59.00 ***(978-1-60304-010-5(2))*** Dollworks.

Luke, Michelle. Victoria Elizabeth's Magical Dream Paper Dolls. Luke, Michelle, illus. 1998. (Illus.). 32p. (J). (gr. 2-5). 7.99 (978-0-9660672-2-4(3)) It's a Girl Pubns.

Lunn, Janet. Double Spell. 2003. 144p. (J). (gr. 3-7). pap. 8.95 (978-0-88776-660-2(9)) Tundra Bks., Inc./Livres Toundra, Inc. CAN. *Dist:* Random Hse., Inc.

Malanga, Tara & O'Keefe, Susan Heyboer. Sleepy Angel's First Bedtime Story. 2000. (Illus.). 32p. (ps-2). 9.95 (978-0-8091-6670-1(4) , 6670-4) Paulist Pr.

Man-Kong, Mary & Posner-Sanchez, Andrea. Barbie of Swan Lake. movie tie-in ed. 2003. (Barbie Ser.). (Illus.). 24p. (J). (ps-2). pap. 3.99 (978-0-375-82640-5(8) , Golden Bks.) Random Hse. Children's Bks.

Manson, Ainslie. Leaving the Log House. 2003. 144p. (J). (gr. 3-7). pap. 6.95 (978-1-55143-258-8(7)) Orca Bk. Pubs. USA.

—Leaving the Log House. 2003. (gr. 3-6). lib. bdg. 16.40 (978-0-613-87474-8(9)) Tandem Library Bks.

Martin, Ann M. & Godwin, Laura. The Doll People. Selznick, Brian, illus. (gr. 3-7). 2003. 288p. (J). pap. 6.99 (978-0-7868-1240-0(0)); 2000. 272p. 15.99 (978-0-7868-0361-3(4)) Hyperion Bks. for Children.

—The Doll People. 2004. 288p. (J). (gr. 3-7). pap. 37.00 incl. audio (978-1-4000-9021-1(0) , Listening Library) Random Hse. Audio Publishing Group.

—The Meanest Doll in the World. Selznick, Brian, illus. 2005. 304p. (gr. 3-7). pap. 7.99 (978-0-7868-5297-0(6)) Hyperion Bks. for Children.

McClintock, Barbara. Dahlia. McClintock, Barbara, illus. 2002. (Illus.). 32p. (J). (ps-3). 16.00 (978-0-374-31678-5(3) , Farrar, Straus & Giroux (BYR)) Farrar, Straus & Giroux.

McDonough, Yona Zeldis. Doll Named Dora Anne. 2002. (gr. k-3). lib. bdg. 11.80 (978-0-613-45257-1(7)) Tandem Library Bks.

—The Doll with the Yellow Star. Root, Kimberly Bulcken, illus. 2005. 64p. (J). (gr. 3-5). 17.95 (978-0-8050-6337-0(4) , Holt, Henry & Co. Bks. For Young Readers) Holt, Henry & Co.

McDonough, Yona Zeldis & Ryan, Dyanne DiSalvo, illus. A Doll Named Dora Anne. 2002. (All Aboard Reading Ser.). 48p. (J). pap. 3.99 (978-0-448-42678-5(1) , Grosset & Dunlap) Penguin Group (USA) Inc.

McElreath, Kim. Pouring in Love. l.t. ed. 2005. (Illus.). 30p. (J). 13.95 (978-0-9769271-0-5(1)) McElreath, K.M.

McKissack, Pat. The All-I'll-Ever-Want Christmas Doll. Pinkney, Jerry, illus. 2007. (J). ***(978-0-375-83615-2(2)*** , Schwartz & Wade Bks.) Random Hse. Children's Bks.

McKissack, Patricia. The All-I'll-Ever-Want Christmas Doll. Pinkney, Jerry, illus. 2007. 40p. (J). (ps-3). lib. bdg. 19.99 ***(978-0-375-93759-0(5));*** 16.99 ***(978-0-375-83759-3(0))*** Random Hse. Children's Bks. (Schwartz & Wade Bks.).

McKissack, Patricia C. Nettie Jo's Friends. 2002. (Illus.). (J). 15.74 (978-0-7587-3246-0(5)) Book Wholesalers, Inc.

McPhail, David M. Emma in Charge. McPhail, David M., illus. 2005. (Illus.). 32p. (J). (ps). 12.99 (978-0-525-47411-1(0) , Dutton Juvenile) Penguin Group (USA) Inc.

Medearis, Michael & Medearis, Angela Shelf. Daisy & the Doll. Johnson, Larry, illus. (Family Heritage Ser.). 32p. (J). 2000. (gr. 1-5). 14.95 (978-0-916718-15-2(8)); 2005. reprint ed. pap. 7.95 (978-0-916718-23-7(9)) Vermont Folklife Ctr.

Metzger, Steve. My Bossy Dolly. Demarest, Chris L., illus. 2006. 24p. (J). pap. 3.50 (978-0-439-74055-5(X) , Cartwheel Bks.) Scholastic, Inc.

Mihara, Mitsukazu. Doll, Vol. 1. 2004. (Illus.). 192p. pap. 9.99 (978-1-59182-710-8(8) , Tokyopop Adult) TOKYOPOP, Inc.

Mihara, Mitsukazu, illus. & creator. Doll, Vol. 5. Mihara, Mitsukazu, creator. rev. ed. 2005. 176p. pap. 9.99 (978-1-59532-391-0(0) , Tokyopop Adult) TOKYOPOP, Inc.

Miller, Sara Swan. Barbie Super Fun. O'Brien, Jeff & Yuh, Ramona, photos by. 2001. (Barbie Friendship Craft Kit Ser.). (Illus.). (J). (gr. 1-3). (978-1-57584-812-9(0)) Reader's Digest Children's Publishing, Inc.

Millionaire, Tony. Sock Monkey: the Inches Incident: The Inches Incident. 2007. 88p. (J). pap. 12.95 (***978-1-59307-842-3(0)***) Dark Horse Comics.

Mitchell, Robin. Windy. Mitchell, Robin & Steedman, Judith, illus. l.t. ed. 2002. 48p. (J). (ps-2). 14.95 (978-0-9688768-2-4(X)) Simply Read Bks. CAN. *Dist:* Perseus Distribution.

Moerbeek, Kees, illus. Raggedy Ann & Andy & the Camel with the Wrinkled Knees. collector's ed. 2003. (Raggedy Ann Ser.). 14p. (J). 21.99 (978-0-689-85775-1(6) , Little Simon) Simon & Schuster Children's Publishing.

Montanari, Eva. My First... 2007. (Illus.). 32p. (J). (ps-k). 17.00 (***978-0-618-64644-9(2)***) Houghton Mifflin Co.

Muldrow, Diane. Barbie: Rapunzel. 2001. (Little Golden Book Ser.). 24p. (J). (gr. k-k). 2.99 (978-0-307-98782-2(5) , Golden Bks.) Random Hse. Children's Bks.

—Ice Skating Dreams. 2000. (gr. k-3). lib. bdg. 11.00 (978-0-613-83883-2(1)) Tandem Library Bks.

Munoz, Claudio, illus. Dream Dancer. 2002. 32p. (J). (ps-3). 15.95 (978-0-06-000932-8(2)) HarperCollins Pubs.

Musick, Brenda Crissman. The Dolls on the Old Stairway. 2000. 24p. (J). 9.95 (978-1-891029-41-7(X)) Henderson Publishing.

Necochea, Kristi Landry. The First Day of Forever. 2007. (J). (***978-0-9792361-0-5(X)***) Inspire U., LLC.

Nelson, Vaunda Micheaux. Almost to Freedom. Bootman, Colin, illus. 2003. (Carolrhoda Picture Books Ser.). 40p. (J). (gr. 1-5). 15.95 (978-1-57505-342-4(X)) Lerner Publishing Group.

Nesbit, E. My School Days. 2006. pap. (***978-1-4250-0678-5(7)***) Assistedreadingbooks.com Inc.

Newsome, Jill. Dream Dancer. 2002. (Illus.). 32p. (J). (ps-3). 15.89 (978-0-06-001322-6(2)) HarperCollins Pubs.

Oram, Hiawyn. Rubbaduck & Ruby Roo. Lucas, David, illus. 2004. 28p. (J). 15.95 (978-1-59078-356-6(5)) Boyds Mills Pr.

O'Rourke, Page Eastburn. The Dollhouse Family. 1998. (Sticker Stories Ser.). (Illus.). 16p. (J). (ps-3). pap. 4.99 (978-0-448-41831-5(2) , Grosset & Dunlap) Penguin Group (USA) Inc.

Orr, Salile. One Pink Shoe. S. I. International Staff, illus. 1998. (Barbie Ser.). 32p. (J). (ps-1). pap. 3.99 (978-0-307-26106-9(9) , Random Hse. Bks. for Young Readers) Random Hse. Children's Bks.

Orr, Salile & Golden Books Staff. One Pink Shoe. 1999. 70p. (J). pap. 0.99 (978-0-307-20021-1(3) , Golden Bks.) Random Hse. Children's Bks.

O'ryan, Ellie. Life's Littlest Lessons. 2007. (Littlest Pet Shop Ser.). 56p. (J). pap. 6.99 (978-0-439-89753-2(X)) Scholastic, Inc.

Palmer, Jan, illus. How Raggedy Ann Got Her Candy Heart. 2001. (My First Raggedy Ann Ser.). 32p. (J). pap. 6.99 (978-0-689-80887-6(9) , Aladdin) Simon & Schuster Children's Publishing.

Parker, Helen. Clover, the Fairy of Luck. Prole, Helen, illus. 2007. 10p. (J). (ps-2). 9.99 (978-1-58476-563-9(1) , IKIDS) Innovative Kids.

—Ivy, the Fairy of Friendship. Prole, Helen, illus. 2007. 10p. (J). (ps-2). 9.99 (978-1-58476-562-2(3) , IKIDS) Innovative Kids.

—Rose, the Fairy of Love. Prole, Helen, illus. 2007. 10p. (J). (ps-2). 9.99 (978-1-58476-561-5(5) , IKIDS) Innovative Kids.

—Willow, the Fairy of Bravery. Prole, Helen, illus. 2007. 10p. (J). (ps-2). 9.99 (978-1-58476-560-8(7) , IKIDS) Innovative Kids.

Parker, Jessie, et al. Barbie: A Dress-up Day. S. I. International Staff, illus. 2003. (Step into Reading Ser.: Vol. 1). 32p. (J). (ps-1). pap. 3.99 (978-0-375-82501-9(0) , Random Hse. Bks. for Young Readers) Random Hse. Children's Bks.

Pattison, Darcy. The Journey of Oliver K. Woodman. Cepeda, Joe, illus. 2003. 56p. (J). (gr. k-3). 16.00 (978-0-15-202329-4(1)) Harcourt Children's Bks.

—Searching for Oliver K. Woodman. Cepeda, Joe, illus. 2005. 56p. (J). 16.00 (978-0-15-205184-6(8)) Harcourt Children's Bks.

Pausacker, Jenny. Looking for Blondie. 2002. (Crime Waves Ser.). (Illus.). 96p. (YA). pap. (978-0-7344-0167-0(1) , Lothian Bks.) Hachette Livre Australia.

Pearlman, Bobby & Gruelle, Johnny. Leaf Dance. Mitter, Kathryn & Winfield, Alison, illus. 2001. (Classic Raggedy Ann & Andy Ser.). 32p. (J). pap. 3.99 (978-0-689-84679-3(7) , Little Simon) Simon & Schuster Children's Publishing.

Pilgrim, Elza. The China Doll. Segovia, Carmen, illus. 2005. 32p. (J). (gr. k-2). 14.95 (978-1-4027-2223-3(0)) Sterling Publishing Co., Inc.

Pittar, Gill. Milly & Molly Go Camping (book W/dolls) 2006. 28p. pap. (978-1-86972-097-1(0)) Milly Molly Bks.

—Milly, Molly & Alf (book W/dolls) 2006. 28p. pap. (978-1-86972-100-8(4)) Milly Molly Bks.

Ponko, Cindy A. Busy Busy Days. 2006. (J). (978-0-9768230-1-8(2)) Some Kids I Know.

Poulsen, Kathleen Phillips. Apple Doll. Poulsen, Kathleen Phillips, illus. 2002. (Illus.). 32p. (J). 9.95 (978-1-57072-222-6(6)) Overmountain Pr.

A Prairie Heart. 2007. (Illus.). (J). per. 19.95 (***978-0-9793668-0-2(1)***) Prairie Heart Publishing.

Pugliano-Martin, Carol. BarbieTM: A Day at the Fair. S. I. International Staff, illus. 2003. (Step into Reading Ser.). 32p. (J). (ps-1). pap. 3.99 (978-0-375-82368-8(9) , Random Hse. Bks. for Young Readers) Random Hse. Children's Bks.

Ransom, Candice F. The Christmas Dolls. Fain, Moira, illus. 1998. 32p. (J). (gr. k-3). 15.95 (978-0-8027-8659-3(6)); lib. bdg. 16.85 (978-0-8027-8661-6(8)) Walker & Co.

Rees, Douglas. The Janus Gate: An Encounter with John Singer Sargent. 2006. (Art Encounters Ser.). (Illus.). 176p. (YA). 15.95 (978-0-8230-0406-5(6)) Watson-Guptill Pubns., Inc.

Regelson, Abraham. The Dolls' Journey to Eretz-yisrael. Sharona, Tel-Oren, tr. 2003. Tr. of Masa Habubot L'eretz-yisrael. pap. (978-0-9729545-8-7(9)) Biblio Bks. International.

—The Doll's Journey to Eretz Yisrael. Tel-Oren, Sharona, tr. from HEB. 2006. (J). lib. bdg. 25.00 (978-0-9766681-8-3(1)) Biblio Bks. International.

Richards, Barbara. Barbie Com: Ballet Buddies. 2000. (gr. 3-6). lib. bdg. 11.80 (978-0-613-27723-5(6)) Tandem Library Bks.

Robinson, Ida. Sally's Doll. 2004. (J). pap. 15.00 (978-0-8059-6563-6(7)) Dorrance Publishing Co., Inc.

Roper, Robert, illus. Dolls of Danger. ed. 2005. 32p. (J). lib. bdg. 15.00 (978-1-59054-989-6(9)) Fitzgerald Bks.

Ross, Jil. Marie Plays Homeless: Another installment in the Shenanigans Series. 2004. (Illus.). 62p. (J). pap. 6.95 (978-1-932373-66-0(7)) Cedar Hill Publishing.

Rubins, Diane Teitel. Sarah the Best Bridesmaid: Paper Doll Storybook. Shanahan, Sue, illus. 2004. 24p. (J). pap. 5.95 (978-0-486-43531-2(8)) Dover Pubns., Inc.

Russo, Marisabina. The Trouble with Baby. Russo, Marisabina, illus. 2003. (Illus.). 32p. (J). (ps up). 16.89 (978-0-06-008925-2(3)) HarperCollins Pubs.

Rylant, Cynthia. The Ticky-Tacky Doll. Stevenson, Harvey, illus. 2002. 32p. (J). (gr. k-2). 16.00 (978-0-15-201078-2(5)) Harcourt Children's Bks.

Salas, Macarena, ed. A New Doll for Baby Daisy/Un Mueco para Beb Daisy: A Book about Classifying/Un Libro Sobre Clasificaciones. 2005. (SPA.). 10p. (J). bds. 3.99 (978-0-439-66361-8(X) , Scholastic en Espanol) Scholastic, Inc.

San Souci, Robert D. Zigzag. Czernecki, Stefan, illus. 2005. 32p. (gr. 9). 16.95 (978-0-87483-764-3(2)) August Hse. Pubs., Inc.

Santiago, Esmeralda. A Doll for Navidades. Sanchez, Enrique O., illus. 2005. 32p. (J). (ps-3). pap. 16.99 (978-0-439-55398-8(9) , Scholastic Pr.) Scholastic, Inc.

Say, Allen. Allison. 2004. (Illus.). 32p. (J). (ps-ps). lib. bdg. 13.75 (978-0-606-32838-8(6)) Tandem Library Bks.

Schiller, Pam. This Little Train. Janes, Joshua, illus. 2006. (Noodlebug Ser.). (J). 12.95 (978-0-7696-4278-9(0)) School Specialty Publishing.

Scholastic, Inc. Staff. Cleo Clip-On. 2002. (Sidekicks Ser.). (J). 6.99 (978-0-439-36579-6(1) , Sidekicks TM) Scholastic, Inc.

—Clifford Barking Beanbag. 2002. (Sidekicks Ser.). (J). 9.99 (978-0-439-36582-6(1) , Sidekicks TM) Scholastic, Inc.

—Clifford the Big Red Dog Poseable Plush. 2002. (Sidekicks Ser.). (J). 15.99 (978-0-439-36201-6(6) , Sidekicks TM) Scholastic, Inc.

—Emily Elizabeth Clip-On. 2002. (Sidekicks Ser.). (J). 6.99 (978-0-439-36581-9(3) , Sidekicks TM) Scholastic, Inc.

—Emily Elizabeth Playwear - Pajama Outfit. 2002. (Sidekicks Ser.). (J). 12.99 (978-0-439-36578-9(3) , Sidekicks TM) Scholastic, Inc.

—Gingerbread Man Activity Developmental Toy. 2004. (Sidekicks Ser.). (J). 16.99 (978-0-439-62729-0(X) , Sidekicks TM) Scholastic, Inc.

—Gingerbread Man Attachable Toy. 2004. (Sidekicks Ser.). (J). 7.99 (978-0-439-63535-6(7) , Sidekicks TM) Scholastic, Inc.

—Gingerbread Man Security Blanket. 2004. (Sidekicks Ser.). (J). 14.99 (978-0-439-62337-7(5) , Sidekicks TM) Scholastic, Inc.

—Mary Had a Little Lamb Plush. 2003. (Sidekicks Ser.). (J). 23.99 (978-0-590-03416-6(2) , Sidekicks TM) Scholastic, Inc.

—Real Mother Goose. 2001. (Sidekicks Ser.). (J). 23.99 (978-0-590-03420-3(0) , Sidekicks TM) Scholastic, Inc.

Scholastic, Inc. Staff, et al. Emily Elizabeth Playwear - Cheerleading Outfit. 2003. (Clifford Ser.). (J). 12.99 (978-0-439-20237-4(X) , Sidekicks TM) Scholastic, Inc.

Small, David. Eulalie & the Hopping Head. Small, David, illus. 2001. (Illus.). 32p. (J). 16.00 (978-0-374-32230-4(9) , Farrar, Straus & Giroux (BYR)) Farrar, Straus & Giroux.

—Eulalie & the Hopping Head. (Illus.). (J). 2005. pap. 16.95 incl. audio (978-1-59112-216-6(3)); 2005. pap. 18.95 incl. audio compact disk (978-1-59112-509-9(X)); 2003. 28.95 incl. audio compact disk (978-1-59112-510-5(3)); 2003. 25.95 incl. audio (978-1-59112-217-3(1)) Live Oak Media.

—Eulalie & the Hopping Head. Small, David, illus. 2003. (Illus.). (J). pap. 33.95 incl. audio (978-1-59112-218-0(X)) Live Oak Media.

—Eulalie & the Hopping Head. Small, David, illus. l.t. ed. 2001. (Illus.). 32p. (J). pap. 5.95 (978-0-374-42202-8(8) , Sunburst) Farrar, Straus & Giroux.

Spohn, Kate. Mermaid Swim. 2002. (ps-2). lib. bdg. 14.15 (978-0-613-86240-0(6)) Tandem Library Bks.

Steadman, Barbara. Little Flower Girls Sticker Paper Dolls. 2003. (Dover Little Activity Bks.). (Illus.). 4p. (J). pap. 1.50 (978-0-486-43019-5(7)) Dover Pubns., Inc.

Stephens, Monique. Berry Merry Christmas. Thomas, Laura & Ungrey, Tom, illus. 2003. (Strawberry Shortcake Ser.). 32p. (J). (gr. k-1). 9.99 (978-0-448-43200-7(5) , Grosset & Dunlap) Penguin Group (USA) Inc.

Stevenson, James. Night after Christmas. 2003. (J). pap. 2.95 (978-0-590-41600-9(6)) Scholastic, Inc.

Stillerman, Robbie. Twin Sisters Sticker Paper Dolls. 2003. (Dover Little Activity Bks.). (Illus.). 4p. (J). pap. 1.50 (978-0-486-43018-8(9)) Dover Pubns., Inc.

Stuve-Bodeen, Stephanie. Elizabeti's Doll. Hale, Christy, illus. 2002. (J). 23.19 (978-0-7587-2449-6(7)) Book Wholesalers, Inc.

—Elizabeti's Doll. Hale, Christy, illus. 32p. (YA). 2002. (978-1-58430-081-6(7)); 2000. 19.95 (978-1-880000-70-0(9)) Lee & Low Bks., Inc.

—La Muneca de Elizabeti. Sarfatti, Esther, tr. from ENG. Hale, Christy, illus. 2000. (SPA.). 32p. (J). (gr. k-1). pap. 6.95 (978-1-58430-001-4(9) , LW5012); lib. bdg. 15.95 (978-1-58430-000-7(0) , LW5352) Lee & Low Bks., Inc.

—La Muneca de Elizabeti. 2000. (978-0-606-17847-1(3)) Tandem Library Bks.

—Muneca de Elizabeti. 2000. (SPA.). (gr. k-3). lib. bdg. 15.25 (978-0-613-27986-4(7)) Tandem Library Bks.

—La Muneca de Elizabeti. Sarfatti, Esther, tr. Hale, Christy, illus. braille ed. 2004. (SPA.). (J). (gr. k-3). spiral bd. (978-0-616-08966-8(X)) Canadian National Institute for the Blind/Institut National Canadien pour les Aveugles.

Tews, Susan. The Gingerbread Doll. Lloyd, Megan, illus. 2001. 32p. (J). (gr. k-3). pap. 5.95 (978-0-618-13059-7(4) , Clarion Bks.) Houghton Mifflin Co. Trade & Reference Div.

Thompson, Julian F. Hard Time. 2003. (Illus.). 256p. (YA). 16.95 (978-0-689-85424-8(2) , Atheneum) Simon & Schuster Children's Publishing.

Thompson, Lauren. A Christmas Gift for Mama. Burke, Jim, illus. 2003. (J). 48p. pap. 16.95 (978-0-590-30725-3(8)); pap. 16.95 (978-0-590-30726-0(6)) Scholastic, Inc.

Tudor, Tasha. The Dolls' Christmas. unabr. ed. 2000. (YA). (ps). pap. 29.95 incl. audio (978-0-7887-3795-4(3) , 41039X4) Recorded Bks., LLC.

—A Is for Annabelle: A Doll's Alphabet. Tudor, Tasha, illus. 2004. (Illus.). 64p. (J). reprint ed. pap. 6.99 (978-0-689-86996-9(7) , Aladdin) Simon & Schuster Children's Publishing.

Turk, Ruth. The Doll on the Top Shelf. Volquartz, Per, illus. 1998. 32p. (J). (gr. k-3). 15.95 (978-1-891992-02-5(3)) Owl's Hse. Pr.

Udry, Janice May. Thump & Plunk. Hayes, Geoffrey, illus. (My First I Can Read Bks.). 32p. (J). (ps up). 2001. pap. 3.99 (978-0-06-444267-1(5) , Harper Trophy); 2000. 12.95 (978-0-06-028528-9(1)) HarperCollins Pubs.

Ungerer, Tomi. Otto: Biography of a Teddy Bear. 1999. (Illus.). 32p. (J). (gr. 1-5). 16.95 (978-1-57098-304-7(6)) Rinehart, Roberts Pubs.

Van Walsum-Quispel, J. M. Tina's Island Home. Leeflang-Oudenarden, C., illus. 36p. (J). (gr. k-5). 12.95 (978-0-87592-053-5(5)) Scroll Pr., Inc.

Vaughn, Margaret Britton, et al. The Birthday Dolly. 2000. (Illus.). 47p. (J). pap. (978-1-882845-09-5(9)) Bell Buckle Pr.

Vv. Las Cosas Del Jardin. (SPA.). 24p. 7.95 (978-84-488-1109-9(7)) Beascoa, Ediciones S.A. ESP. *Dist:* Distribooks, Inc.

—Las Cosas Del Salon. (SPA.). 24p. 7.95 (978-84-488-1108-2(9)) Beascoa, Ediciones S.A. ESP. *Dist:* Distribooks, Inc.

Waddell, Martin. The Toymaker. 1999. (J). (978-0-606-19322-1(7)) Tandem Library Bks.

Wainwright, Richard M. A New Life for Sir Christopher. Drorsack, Carolyn S., illus. 2nd ed. 1998. 48p. (J). reprint ed. 17.00 (978-0-9619566-4-6(X)) Family Life Publishing/Richard Wainright Bks.

Watt, Fiona. Este No Es Mi Osito. 2004. (Touchy-Feely Board Bks.).Tr. of That's Not My Teddy. (SPA., Illus.). 10p. (J). (ps up). 7.99 (978-0-7460-3897-0(6)) EDC Publishing.

Waugh, Sylvia. Mennyms Alive. 1999. 224p. (J). (gr. 3-7). pap. 4.50 (978-0-380-72943-2(1) , Harper Trophy) HarperCollins Pubs.

—Mennyms Alone. 1998. 224p. (J). (gr. 3-7). pap. 4.50 (978-0-380-78867-5(5) , Harper Trophy) HarperCollins Pubs.

Weiss, Ellen. Hitty's Travels: Civil War Days. 2001. 10.79 (978-0-606-22091-0(7)) Tandem Library Bks.

Williams, Margery. Little Wooden Doll. (Illus.). (J). 2003. 32p. 15.95 (978-0-06-028277-6(0)); 2000. lib. bdg. 15.89 (978-0-06-623877-7(3)) HarperCollins Pubs.

Woodruff, Elvira. The Christmas Doll. McClintock, Barbara, illus. 2002. 160p. (J). pap. 4.99 (978-0-590-31879-2(9) , Scholastic Paperbacks) Scholastic, Inc.

Wright, Betty Ren. The Dollhouse Murders. unabr. ed. 1999. (Illus.). (J). (gr. 4-6). 39.95 incl. audio (978-0-87499-521-3(3)); pap. 30.95 incl. audio (978-0-87499-520-6(5)) Live Oak Media.

—The Dollhouse Murders, Grades 4-6. unabr. ed. 1999. (Illus.). (J). pap., tchr. ed. 41.95 incl. audio (978-0-87499-522-0(1)) Live Oak Media.

Wright, Dale. Edith & Mr Bear: A Lonely Doll Story. 2000. (gr. k-3). lib. bdg. 15.25 (978-0-613-27801-0(1)) Tandem Library Bks.

Wright, Dare. A Gift from the Lonely Doll. 2001. (Illus.). 64p. (J). (gr. k-3). tchr. ed. 16.00 (978-0-618-07181-4(4)); pap. 6.95 (978-0-618-07182-1(2)) Houghton Mifflin Co. Trade & Reference Div.

—Gift from the Lonely Doll. 2001. (gr. k-3). lib. bdg. 15.25 (978-0-613-35517-9(2)) Tandem Library Bks.

—The Lonely Doll. 1998. (Illus.). 64p. (J). (gr. k-3). tchr. ed. 16.00 (978-0-395-89926-7(5)); pap. 6.95 (978-0-395-90112-0(X)) Houghton Mifflin Co. Trade & Reference Div.

Zendrera, Concepcion. Yaci y Su Muneca. (SPA.). 16p. (J). 9.95 (978-84-261-5604-4(5) , JV3576) Juventud, Editorial ESP. *Dist:* AIMS International Bks., Inc., Lectorum Pubns., Inc.

DOLLS—POETRY

Warren-Turner, Ann. Secrets from the Dollhouse. Colon, Raul, illus. 2000. 32p. (J). (gr. k-3). 15.95 (978-0-06-024564-1(6)); 15.89 (978-0-06-024567-2(0)) HarperCollins Pubs.

DOLLY (SHEEP)

Morgan, Sally. From Sea Urchins to Dolly the Sheep: Discovering Cloning. 2006. (Chain Reactions Ser.). (Illus.). 64p. (YA). (gr. 6-9). lib. bdg. 34.29 (978-1-4034-8838-1(X)) Heinemann Library.

Wimmer, Teresa. Dolly the Sheep. 2008. (J). (***978-1-58341-652-5(8)*** , Creative Education) Creative Co., The.

DOLPHINS

Adamson, Deborah. Stormy the Baby Dolphin. 2000. (Illus.). 32p. (ps-3). (J). 15.95 (978-1-57168-386-1(0)); 15.95 (978-1-57168-402-8(6)) Eakin Pr.

Albee, Sarah. Dolphins. 2006. (Illus.). 45p. (J). (978-1-59939-064-2(7) , Reader's Digest Young Families, Inc.) Reader's Digest Children's Publishing, Inc.

Allen, Elizabeth. Dolphins. 2004. (World Discovery Science Readers Ser.). (Illus.). 32p. (J). pap. (978-0-439-67650-2(9)) Scholastic, Inc.

Barlowe, Sy. Learning about Dolphins. 2001. 16p. (J). (gr. 3-5). pap. 1.50 (978-0-486-41643-4(7)) Dover Pubns., Inc.

Barnes, Julia. The Secret Lives of Dolphins. 2006. (Illus.). 32p. (J). lib. bdg. (***978-0-8368-7656-7(3)***) Stevens, Gareth Inc.

Berger, Melvin. Do Whales Have Belly Buttons? Questions & Answers about Whales & Dolphins. 1999. (Question & Answer Ser.). (J). 12.75 (978-0-606-20055-4(X)) Tandem Library Bks.

Berger, Melvin & Berger, Gilda. Do Whales Have Belly Buttons? Questions & Answers about Whales & Dolphins. Bond, Higgins, illus. 1999. (Scholastic Question & Answer Ser.). 48p. (J). (gr. 2-4). 5.95 (978-0-439-08571-7(3)); pap. 12.95 (978-0-590-13081-3(1)) Scholastic, Inc. (Scholastic Reference).

—Dolphins. 2003. (Scholastic Readers Ser.). (Illus.). 16p. (J). (978-0-439-47389-7(6)) Scholastic, Inc.

Bingham, Caroline. Whales & Dolphins. 2003. (Eye Wonder Ser.). (Illus.). 48p. (J). 9.99 (978-0-7894-9269-2(5)) Dorling Kindersley Publishing, Inc.

Bingham, Caroline & Dorling Kindersley Publishing Staff. Whales & Dolphins. 2003. (Eye Wonder Ser.). (Illus.). 48p. (J). lib. bdg. 17.99 (978-0-7894-9613-3(5)) Dorling Kindersley Publishing, Inc.

Bright, Michael & Kerrod, Robin. Giants of the Ocean. 2004. (Illus.). 128p. pap. 17.99 (978-1-84215-989-7(5) , Southwater) Anness Publishing GBR. *Dist:* National Bk. Network.

Brust, Beth. Dolphins & Porpoises. 2001. (Zoobooks Ser.). (Illus.). (J). (gr. 1-6). 15.95 (978-1-888153-49-1(0)) Wildlife Education, Ltd.

Brust, Beth Wagner. Dolphins. rev. ed. 2003. (Illus.). 24p. 10.95 (978-1-888153-94-1(6) , Zoo Bks.) Wildlife Education, Ltd.

Buettner, Debi. Discover Bottlenose Dolphins Vol. 3: The Dangers of Dolphin Life. Karecki, Jason & Williams, Sandra, illus. 1998. 24p. (J). (gr. k-5). (978-1-890716-06-6(5)) K&M International.

Camm, Martin, illus. Meyers Buch der Wale und Delfine. (GER.). 48p. (978-3-411-07451-8(5)) Bibliographisches Institut & F. A. Brockhaus AG DEU. *Dist:* i.b.d., Ltd.

Chessen, Betsey & Chanko, Pamela. A Dolphin Is Not a Fish. 1998. (Science Emergent Readers Ser.). (J). pap. 3.25 (978-0-05-906388-1(2)) Scholastic, Inc.

Cole. El Delfin. 2002. Tr. of Wild Marine Animals: The Dolphin. (SPA.). 24p. (J). (gr. 3-5). 24.94 (978-1-4103-0006-5(4) , Blackbirch Pr., Inc.) Thomson Gale.

Crisp, Marty. Everything Dolphin: What Kids Really Want to Know About Dolphins. 2004. (Kids' FAQs Ser.). (Illus.). 64p. (J). (gr. 2-6). pap. 7.95 (978-1-55971-049-7(7) , NorthWord Bks. for Young Readers) T&N Children's Publishing.

—Everything Dolphin: What Kids Really Want to Know about Dolphins. 2004. (Kids' FAQs Ser.). (Illus.). 64p. (gr. 2-6). 10.95 (978-1-55971-042-8(X) , NorthWord Bks. for Young Readers) T&N Children's Publishing.

Davidson, Margaret & Wilson, Roger. Nine True Dolphin Stories.Tr. of Neuf Histoires Vraies de Dauphins. (FRE.). (J). pap. 4.99 (978-0-590-71188-3(1)) Scholastic, Inc.

Davidson, Susannah. Whales & Dolphins. 2004. (Discovery Program Ser.). (Illus.). 48p. (J). pap. 8.95 (978-0-7945-0316-1(0) , Usborne); lib. bdg. 16.95 (978-1-58086-478-7(3)) EDC Publishing.

—Whales & Dolphins. 2002. (gr. 3-6). lib. bdg. 17.60 (978-0-613-67679-3(3)) Tandem Library Bks.

Davidson, Susannah, et al. Whales & Dolphins. Woodcock, John, illus. 2003. (Usborne Discovery Ser.). 48p. (J). pap. (978-0-439-56060-3(8)); pap. (978-0-439-57780-9(2)) Scholastic, Inc.

Davies, Nic. Dolphin. 2000. (Natural World Ser.). (Illus.). 48p. (J). (gr. 4-7). 9.95 (978-0-7398-3125-0(9)) Steck-Vaughn.

Davies, Nicola. Dolphin: Habitats, Life Cycles, Food Chains, Threats. 2000. (Natural World Ser.). (Illus.). 48p. (J). (gr. 3-7). lib. bdg. 27.12 (978-0-7398-2766-6(9)) Raintree.

Dolphin in the Sea. Date not set. (Illus.). (J). bds. 1.98 (978-0-7525-9840-6(6)) Parragon, Inc.

Dolphins. (Under the Sea Ser.). (J). 24p. 6.95 (978-0-7368-5111-4(9)); 32p. 6.95 (978-0-7368-8071-8(2)) Capstone Pr., Inc.

Dolphins, 6 vols. (gr. k-2). 28.95 (978-0-7368-9101-1(3)); (gr. 2-5). 36.95 (978-0-7368-8181-4(6)) Red Brick Learning.

Dolphins. 2006. (J). 4.95 (978-1-932396-18-8(7)) Wildlife Education, Ltd.

C D

Dolphins. 2007. (My First Sticker Encyclopedia Ser.). (Illus.). 18p. (J). pap. 5.95 (*978-1-59496-149-6(2)) Teora USA LLC.

Dolphins: Level L, 6 vols. (Wonder Worldtm Ser.). 16p. 34.95 (978-0-7802-2895-5(2)) Wright Group, The.

Dolphins Oceans Alive. 2006. (Illus.). 24p. (J). (gr. k-2). 18.50 (*978-0-531-17868-3(4)) Scholastic Library Publishing.

Dolphins Set II. 2006. (J). (gr. k-6). 128.10 (978-1-59679-298-2(1) , Checkerboard Library) ABDO Publishing Co.

Donovan. Amazon River Dolphins. 2002. pap. (978-0-7398-5809-7(2)) Steck-Vaughn.

Donovan, Sandy. Amazon River Dolphins. 2002. (Animals of the Rain Forest Ser.). (Illus.). 32p. (YA). lib. bdg. 22.83 (978-0-7398-5367-2(8)) Raintree.

Dorling Kindersley Publishing Staff, contrib. by. Diving Dolphin. 2001. (Readers Ser.). (Illus.). 32p. (J). (ps-k). 14.99 (978-0-7894-7356-1(9)) Dorling Kindersley Publishing, Inc.

Driscoll, Laura. Do Dolphins Really Smile? Station Stop 2. Wald, Christina, illus. 2006. (All Aboard Science Reader Ser.). 48p. (J). (gr. 1-3). pap. 3.99 (978-0-448-44341-6(4) , Grosset & Dunlap) Penguin Group (USA) Inc.

Dudzinski, Kathleen. Meeting Dolphins. 2000. (Illus.). 64p. (J). (gr. 3-7). 17.95 (978-0-7922-7129-1(7) , National Geographic Children's Bks.) National Geographic Society.

Eckart, Edana. Bottlenose Dolphin. 2003. (Welcome Book Ser.). (Illus.). 24p. (J). 17.00 (978-0-516-24302-3(0) , Children's Pr.) Scholastic Library Publishing.

—Bottlenose Dolphin. 2003. (gr. k-3). lib. bdg. 12.95 (978-0-613-67697-7(1)) Tandem Library Bks.

Ericson, Anton. Whales & Dolphins. 2001. (Nature's Wild Ser.). (J). lib. bdg. (978-1-58952-206-0(0)) Rourke Publishing, LLC.

Francis, Dorothy Brenner. Dolphins. 2001. (Animal Adventures Ser.). (Illus.). (J). 55p. pap. (978-0-7891-5243-5(6)); 56p. (gr. 1-4). lib. bdg. 16.95 (978-0-7807-9656-0(X)) Perfection Learning Corp.

Gareth Stevens Publishing Staff, contrib. by. Dolphins. 2004. (All about Wild Animals Ser.). (Illus.). 32p. (J). (gr. 2 up). lib. bdg. 23.33 (978-0-8368-4115-2(8)) Stevens, Gareth Inc.

Gentle, Victor & Perry, Janet. Bottlenose Dolphins. 2001. (Whales & Dolphins Ser.). (Illus.). 24p. (YA). (gr. 2 up). lib. bdg. 22.00 (978-0-8368-2881-8(X)) Stevens, Gareth Inc.

—Whales & Dolphins, 6 bks. Incl. Blue Whales. lib. bdg. 22.00 (978-0-8368-2880-1(1)); Bottlenose Dolphins. lib. bdg. 22.00 (978-0-8368-2881-8(X)); Humpback Whales. lib. bdg. 22.00 (978-0-8368-2882-5(8)); Orcas : Killer Whales. lib. bdg. 22.00 (978-0-8368-2883-2(6)); Right Whales. lib. bdg. 22.00 (978-0-8368-2884-9(4)); Sperm Whales. lib. bdg. 22.00 (978-0-8368-2885-6(2)); 24p. (YA). (gr. 2 up). 2001. (Illus.). Set lib. bdg. 132.00 (978-0-8368-2879-5(8)) Stevens, Gareth Inc.

Gordon, Sharon. Adivina Quién Cambia. 2006. (Bookworms Ser.). (SPA & ENG., Illus.). 32p. (J). lib. bdg. 22.79 (978-0-7614-2380-5(X)) Cavendish, Marshall Corp.

—Adivina Quién Se Zambulle. 2006. (Bookworms Ser.). (SPA.). 32p. (J). lib. bdg. 22.79 (*978-0-7614-2381-2(8)) Cavendish, Marshall Corp.

—Guess Who Changes (Adivina Quién Cambia) 2006. (Bookworms Ser.). (ENG & SPA.). 32p. (J). lib. bdg. 22.79 (978-0-7614-2461-1(X)) Cavendish, Marshall Corp.

—Guess Who Dives (Adivina Quién Se Zambulle) 2006. (Bookworms Ser.). (SPA & ENG., Illus.). 32p. (J). lib. bdg. 22.79 (978-0-7614-2462-8(8)) Cavendish, Marshall Corp.

Gowell, Elizabeth Tayntor. Whales & Dolphins: What They Have in Common. 2000. (Animals in Order Ser.). (Illus.). 48p. (J). (gr. 4-6). pap. 6.95 (978-0-531-16454-9(3)); 26.50 (978-0-531-20396-5(4)) Scholastic Library Publishing. (Watts, Franklin).

Grooms, Molly. We Are Dolphins. Oda, Takashi, illus. 2004. 32p. (ps-2). 15.95 (978-1-55971-814-1(5) , NorthWord Bks. for Young Readers) T&N Children's Publishing.

Grover, Wayne. Dolphin Adventure: A True Story. Fowler, Jim, illus. 2000. 80p. (J). (gr. 3-7). pap. 4.99 (978-0-380-73252-4(1) , Harper Trophy) HarperCollins Pubs.

—Dolphin Adventure: A True Story. 2000. (Illus.). (J). 11.79 (978-0-606-18688-9(3)) Tandem Library Bks.

—Dolphin Treasure. 2001. (J). (978-0-606-21549-7(2)); (gr. 3-6). lib. bdg. 12.95 (978-0-613-35934-4(8)) Tandem Library Bks.

Guidoux, Valerie. Little Dolphins. 2005. (Born to Be Wild Ser.). (Illus.). 23p. (J). (ps-17). 22.00 (978-0-8368-4735-2(0)) Stevens, Gareth Inc.

Gunzi, Christiane. The Best Book of Whales & Dolphins. (Best Book of... Ser.). 32p. (J). (gr. k-3). 2006. pap. 6.95 (978-0-7534-5987-4(6)); 2001. (Illus.). tchr. ed. 12.95 (978-0-7534-5369-8(X)) Houghton Mifflin Co. Trade & Reference Div. (Kingfisher).

Gustafson, Sarah. Whales, Dolphins, & More Marine Mammals. 2005. (Illus.). 48p. (J). pap. (978-0-439-71189-0(4)) Scholastic, Inc.

Harris, Caroline. Whales & Dolphins. 2005. (Kingfisher Young Knowledge Ser.). (Illus.). 48p. (J). (gr. k-3). 9.95 (978-0-7534-5869-3(1) , Kingfisher) Houghton Mifflin Co. Trade & Reference Div.

Harris, Greg, illus. Whales & Dolphins. 1998. (At Your Fingertips Ser.). 10p. (J). (ps-3). 6.95 (978-0-7681-0031-0(3) , McClanahan Bk.) Learning Horizons, Inc.

Harvey, Bev. The Dolphin Family. 2003. (Animal Families Ser.). (Illus.). 32p. (gr. 2-4). 23.00 (978-0-7910-7543-2(5) , Chelsea Hse.) Facts On File, Inc.

Herriges, Ann. Dolphins. 2006. (Oceans Alive! Ser.). (Illus.). 24p. (J). lib. bdg. 16.95 (978-1-60014-017-4(3)) Bellwether Media.

Hirschi, Ron. Dolphins. 2002. (Animals, Animals Ser.). (Illus.). 47p. (J). 25.64 (978-0-7614-1443-8(6) , Benchmark Bks.) Cavendish, Marshall Corp.

Hirschmann, Kris. Dolphins. 2003. (Illus.). 48p. (J). 26.20 (978-0-7377-1555-2(3) , Greenhaven Pr., Inc.) Thomson Gale.

Hodge, Judith. Dolphins Vol. 1: Animals of the Oceans. 1999. (Animals of the Ocean Ser.: No. 3). (Illus.). 32p. (J). (gr. 2-6). lib. bdg. 14.95 (978-1-56674-231-3(5)) Forest Hse. Publishing Co., Inc.

Ingram, Scott. Dolphins. 2006. (Smart Animals! Ser.). (Illus.). 32p. (J). lib. bdg. 25.27 (978-1-59716-161-9(6)) Bearport Publishing Co., Inc.

James, Sylvia M. Dolphins. 2002. (Illus.). 24p. (J). (gr. k-3). pap. 6.00 (978-1-59034-010-3(8)) Mondo Publishing.

John, Victoria. Dolphins: Level N, 6 vols. 128p. (gr. 3-6). 36.95 (978-0-322-05902-3(X)) Wright Group, The.

Kallen, Stuart A. Dolphins & Porpoises. 2001. (Endangered Animals & Habitats Ser.). (Illus.). 112p. (YA). (gr. 4-12). 27.45 (978-1-56006-729-0(2) , Lucent Bks.) Thomson Gale.

Kalman, Bobbie. Dolphin Worlds, 4 bks. Incl. Dolphins Around the World. (978-0-7787-1162-9(5)); Dolphin's Body. (978-0-7787-1163-6(3)); Fun with Dolphins. (978-0-7787-1165-0(X)); Life in a Dolphin Pod. (978-0-7787-1164-3(1)); 32p. (J). (gr. 4-5). 2002. (Illus.). 2002. (978-0-7787-1160-5(9)); Set pap. (978-0-7787-1180-3(3)) Crabtree Publishing Co.

—Dolphins Around the World. 2002. (Dolphin Worlds Ser.). (Illus.). 32p. (J). (gr. 4-5). (978-0-7787-1162-9(5)); pap. (978-0-7787-1182-7(X)) Crabtree Publishing Co.

—Dolphins Around the World. 2003. (gr. 3-6). lib. bdg. 15.25 (978-0-613-52830-6(1)) Tandem Library Bks.

—A Dolphin's Body. 2002. (Dolphin Worlds Ser.). (Illus.). 32p. (J). (gr. 4-5). (978-0-7787-1163-6(3)); pap. (978-0-7787-1183-4(8)) Crabtree Publishing Co.

—Dolphin's Body. 2003. (gr. 3-6). lib. bdg. 15.25 (978-0-613-52831-3(X)) Tandem Library Bks.

—Fun with Dolphins. 2002. (Dolphin Worlds Ser.). (Illus.). 32p. (J). (gr. 4-5). (978-0-7787-1165-0(X)); pap. (978-0-7787-1185-8(4)) Crabtree Publishing Co.

—Life in a Dolphin Pod. 2002. (Dolphin Worlds Ser.). (Illus.). 32p. (J). (gr. 4-5). (978-0-7787-1164-3(1)); pap. (978-0-7787-1184-1(6)) Crabtree Publishing Co.

—Life in a Dolphin Pod. 2003. (gr. 3-6). lib. bdg. 15.25 (978-0-613-52867-2(0)) Tandem Library Bks.

—Swimming with Dolphins. 2003. (gr. 3-6). lib. bdg. 15.25 (978-0-613-52919-8(7)) Tandem Library Bks.

Kalz, Jill. Dolphins. 2006. (Wild World of Animals Ser.). (Illus.). 32p. (J). (gr. 5). lib. bdg. 18.95 (978-1-58341-432-3(0) , Creative Education) Creative Co., The.

Kelley, K. C. Secrets of the Dolphins. 2006. (Girls Rock! Ser.). (Illus.). 32p. (J). (gr. 1-5). 24.21 (978-1-59296-747-6(7)) Child's World, Inc.

Kendell, Patricia. Dolphins. 2002. (In the Wild Ser.). (Illus.). 32p. (J). lib. bdg. 25.69 (978-0-7398-4905-7(0)) Raintree.

Kerrod, Robin. Whales & Dolphins. (Illus.). 64p. (gr. 3-7). 2001. pap. 7.95 (978-1-84215-424-3(9) , Southwater); 1998. 14.99 (978-1-85967-611-0(1) , Lorenz Bks.) Anness Publishing GBR. *Dist:* National Bk. Network.

Laskey, Elizabeth. Dolphins. 2003. (Sea Creatures Ser.). 32p. (J). (gr. 3-5). lib. bdg. 22.79 (978-1-4034-0961-4(7)); (Illus.). pap. 6.95 (978-1-4034-3562-0(6)) Heinemann Library.

Lebloas-Julienne, Renee. The Dolphin. 2004. (Animal Close-Ups Ser.). (Illus.). 28p. (J). pap. 6.95 (978-1-57091-627-4(6)) Charlesbridge Publishing, Inc.

Lever, E., et al. Dolphins. Parish, Steve, photos by. 1999. (Animals Are Fun! Ser.). (Illus.). 16p. (J). (ps up). lib. bdg. 19.33 (978-0-8368-2612-8(4)) Stevens, Gareth Inc.

Lindeen, Carol K. Dolphins. 2004. (Under the Sea Ser.). (Illus.). 24p. (J). lib. bdg. 19.93 (978-0-7368-2599-3(1) , Pebble Bks.) Capstone Pr., Inc.

MacAulay, Kelley & Kalman, Bobbie. Dolphins & Other Marine Mammals. 2005. (What Kind of Animal Is It? Ser.). (Illus.). 32p. (J). (gr. k-6). pap. (978-0-7787-2222-9(8)) Crabtree Publishing Co.

Miles, Elizabeth. Watching Dolphins in the Ocean. 2006. (Illus.). 32p. (J). (978-1-4034-7229-8(7)); pap. (978-1-4034-7242-7(4)) Heinemann Library.

Miller, Connie Colwell. Dolphins. 2005. (World of Mammals Ser.). (Illus.). 24p. (J). (ps-7). lib. bdg. 21.26 (978-0-7368-4310-2(8)) Capstone Pr., Inc.

Miller-Schroeder, Patricia. Bottlenose Dolphins. 2002. (Untamed World Ser.). (Illus.). 64p. (J). 28.54 (978-0-7398-4970-5(0)) Raintree.

Mitter, Matt. Dolly Dolphin Can't Stop Clicking. Goode, Jon, illus. 2003. (Snappy Fun Bks.). 12p. (J). bds. 4.99 (978-0-7944-0123-8(6) , Reader's Digest Children's Bks.) Reader's Digest Children's Publishing, Inc.

Molter, Carey. Dolphins. l.t. ed. 2001. (Zoo Animals Ser.). (Illus.). 24p. (J). (ps-3). lib. bdg. 19.93 (978-1-57765-559-6(1) , SandCastle) ABDO Publishing Co.

Montgomery, Sy. Encantado: Pink Dolphin of the Amazon. Taylor-Snow, Dianne, photos by. 2002. (Illus.). 80p. (J). (gr. 4-6). 18.00 (978-0-618-13103-7(5)) Houghton Mifflin Co. Trade & Reference Div.

Murray, Julie. Bottle-Nosed Dolphins. 2005. (Animal Kingdom Set Ii Ser.). (Illus.). 24p. (J). (gr. k-4). lib. bdg. 21.35 (978-1-59197-304-1(X)) ABDO Publishing Co.

—Common Dolphins. 2005. (Animal Kingdom Set Ii Ser.). (Illus.). 24p. (J). (gr. k-4). lib. bdg. 21.35 (978-1-59197-308-9(2)) ABDO Publishing Co.

—Spotted Dolphins. 2002. (Animal Kingdom Ser.). (Illus.). 24p. (J). (gr. k-4). lib. bdg. 21.35 (978-1-57765-707-1(1)) ABDO Publishing Co.

Nowacek, Douglas & Nowacek, Stephanie. Discovering Dolphins. rev. ed. 2006. (Illus.). 48p. pap. 9.95 (978-0-7603-2561-2(8)) Voyageur Pr., Inc.

Nuzzolo, Deborah. Dolphin Discovery: Bottlenose Dolphin Training & Interaction. 2nd rev. ed. 2003. (Seaworld Education Ser.). (Illus.). 76p. (gr. 4-12). per. 7.99 (978-1-893698-03-1(3) , B03, SeaWorld Education Dept.) SeaWorld, Inc.

—This Is a Dolphin: SeaWorld Books for Young Learners. 2002. (Illus.). 28p. (J). per. 3.99 (978-1-893698-22-2(X) , E03, SeaWorld Bks. for Young Learners) SeaWorld, Inc.

Osborne, Mary Pope & Boyce, Natalie Pope. Dolphins & Sharks. Murdocca, Sal, illus. 2003. (Magic Tree House Research Guide Ser.: No. 9). 128p. (J). (gr. k-3). pap. 4.99 (978-0-375-82377-0(8) , Random Hse. Bks. for Young Readers) Random Hse. Children's Bks.

—Dolphins & Sharks: A Nonfiction Companion to Dolphins at Daybreak. Murdocca, Sal, illus. 2003. (Magic Tree House Research Guide Ser.: No. 9). 128p. (J). (gr. k-3). lib. bdg. 11.99 (978-0-375-92377-7(2) , Random Hse. Bks. for Young Readers) Random Hse. Children's Bks.

Our Friend the Dolphin: Level P, 6 vols. (Wonder Worldtm Ser.). 48p. 39.95 (978-0-7802-7078-7(9)) Wright Group, The.

Petrie, Kristin. Amazon River Dolphins. 2006. (Illus.). 24p. (J). (gr. k-6). 21.35 (978-1-59679-299-9(X) , Checkerboard Library) ABDO Publishing Co.

—Atlantic Humpbacked Dolphins. 2006. (Illus.). 24p. (J). (gr. k-6). 21.35 (978-1-59679-300-2(7) , Checkerboard Library) ABDO Publishing Co.

—Chinese River Dolphins. 2006. (Illus.). 24p. (J). (gr. k-6). 21.35 (978-1-59679-301-9(5) , Checkerboard Library) ABDO Publishing Co.

—Ganges River Dolphins. 2006. (Illus.). 24p. (J). (gr. k-6). 21.35 (978-1-59679-302-6(3) , Checkerboard Library) ABDO Publishing Co.

—Risso's Dolphins. 2006. (Illus.). 24p. (J). (gr. k-6). 21.35 (978-1-59679-303-3(1) , Checkerboard Library) ABDO Publishing Co.

—Striped Dolphins. 2006. (Checkerboard Animal Library). (Illus.). 24p. (J). (gr. k-6). 21.35 (978-1-59679-304-0(X) , Checkerboard Library) ABDO Publishing Co.

Pfeffer, Wendy. Dolphin Talk: Whistles, Clicks, & Clapping Jaws. Davie, Helen K., illus. 2003. (Let's-Read-and-Find-Out Science Ser.). 40p. (J). (gr. k-4). 15.99 (978-0-06-028801-3(9)); pap. 5.99 (978-0-06-445210-6(7)); lib. bdg. 16.89 (978-0-06-028802-0(7)) HarperCollins Pubs.

—Dolphin Talk: Whistles, Clicks, & Clapping Jaws. 2003. (gr. k-3). lib. bdg. 13.00 (978-0-613-68419-4(2)) Tandem Library Bks.

Pohl, Kathleen. Dolphins. 2006. (Illus.). 24p. (J). pap. (*978-0-8368-7823-3(X)); lib. bdg. (*978-0-8368-7816-5(7)) Stevens, Gareth Inc. (Weekly Reader Early Learning Library).

—Dolphins: Delfines. 2006. (ENG & SPA., Illus.). 24p. pap. (*978-0-8368-8012-0(9)); lib. bdg. (*978-0-8368-8005-2(6)) Stevens, Gareth Inc. (Weekly Reader Early Learning Library).

Presnall, Judith Janda. Navy Dolphins. 2001. (Animals with Jobs Ser.). (Illus.). 48p. (J). (gr. 3-5). 23.70 (978-0-7377-0675-8(9) , LML00902-178561, Kidhaven) Thomson Gale.

Pringle, Laurence P. Dolphin Man: Exploring the World of Dolphins. Wells, Randall S., photos by. 2003. (Illus.). 48p. (YA). (gr. 4-6). pap. 10.95 (978-1-59078-004-6(3)) Boyds Mills Pr.

—Dolphin Man: Exploring the World of Dolphins. 2002. (gr. 5-8). lib. bdg. 18.75 (978-0-613-51819-2(5)) Tandem Library Bks.

Quadrillion Media Staff. Whales & Dolphins. 1998. (Start Me Up Ser.: Vol. 5). Orig. Title: Wale und Delphine. 48p. (J). (gr. 3-8). mass mkt. 12.95 (978-1-58185-005-5(0) , Tessloff Publishing) Quadrillion Media LLC.

Ripley's Whales & Dolphins, 6 vols., Vol. 2. 2nd ed. 2000. 64p. (YA). 14.95 (978-1-893951-01-3(4)) Ripley Entertainment, Inc.

Robinson, Claire. Dolphin. 1999. (In the Wild Ser.). (Illus.). 24p. (J). (gr. k-2). lib. bdg. 21.36 (978-1-57572-862-9(1)) Heinemann Library.

—Dolphins. 2002. (In the Wild Ser.). (Illus.). 24p. (J). (gr. k-2). pap. 6.95 (978-1-58810-326-0(9) , 91047) Heinemann Library.

—Dolphins. 1999. (gr. k-3). lib. bdg. 14.75 (978-0-613-36094-4(X)); (Illus.). (J). 13.75 (978-0-606-21990-7(0)) Tandem Library Bks.

Roop, Peter. Whales & Dolphins. 2000. (gr. k-3). lib. bdg. 11.80 (978-0-613-63573-8(6)) Tandem Library Bks.

Roop, Peter & Roop, Connie. Whales & Dolphins. Schwartz, Carol, illus. 2002. (Hello Reader! Science Ser.). 32p. (J). (ps-1). pap. 3.99 (978-0-439-09912-7(9) , Cartwheel Bks.) Scholastic, Inc.

Rustad, Martha E. Dolphins. 2005. (Ocean Life Ser.). 24p. (YA). (gr. k-3). pap. (978-0-7368-9080-9(7) , Pebble Bks.) Capstone Pr., Inc.

Rustad, Martha E. H. Dolphins. Saunders-Smith, Gail, ed. 2001. (Ocean Life Ser.). (Illus.). 24p. (J). (gr. k-1). lib. bdg. 15.93 (978-0-7368-0857-6(4) , Pebble Bks.) Capstone Pr., Inc.

Samuels, Amy. Follow That Fin! Studying Dolphin Behavior. 1999. (Turnstone Ocean Pilot Bks.). (Illus.). 48p. (J). (gr. 3-7). pap. 7.95 (978-0-7398-1231-0(9)) Steck-Vaughn.

—Follow That Fin! Studying Dolphin Behavior. 1999. (Illus.). (J). (978-0-606-18479-3(1)) Tandem Library Bks.

Schaefer, Lola M. Dolphins: Fins, Flippers & Flukes. 2001. (Wild World of Animals Ser.). (Illus.). 24p. (J). (gr. 1-2). lib. bdg. 18.60 (978-0-7368-0825-5(6) , Bridgestone Bks.) Capstone Pr., Inc.

Shivley, Julie. Baby Dolphin. Sharp, Chris & Seaworld, Chris, illus. Seaworld, Chris, photos by. 2005. (Seaworld Animal Library: Vol. 4). 26p. (J). (ps-k). bds. 6.95 (978-0-8249-6614-0(7)) Ideals Pubns.

Skog, Jason. Dolphins. 2008. (J). (*978-1-58341-653-2(6) , Creative Education) Creative Co., The.

Spilsbury, Louise & Spilsbury, Richard. A School of Dolphins. 2004. 32p. (J). pap. 6.95 (978-1-4034-5420-1(5)); (Illus.). lib. bdg. 24.22 (978-1-4034-4692-3(X)) Heinemann Library.

Stille, Darlene. I Am a Dolphin: The Life of a Bottlenose Dolphin. Ouren, Todd, illus. 2004. (I Live in the Ocean Ser.). 24p. (J). (gr. k-2). lib. bdg. 22.60 (978-1-4048-0596-5(6)) Picture Window Bks.

Sweeney, Diane & Reddy, Michelle. Dolphin Babies: Making a Splash. Smith, Jeff, photos by. 1998. (Illus.). 64p. (J). (gr. 3-7). pap. 14.95 (978-1-57098-194-4(9)) Rinehart, Roberts Pubs.

Taylor, L. R. Dolphins. Wu, Norbert, photos by. 1999. (Early Bird Nature Bks.). (Illus.). 48p. (J). (gr. 2-4). lib. bdg. 25.26 (978-0-8225-3033-6(3) , Lerner Pubns.) Lerner Publishing Group.

Thomson, Sarah L. Amazing Dolphins! (I Can Read Bks.). 32p. (J). 2008. 3.99 (*978-0-06-054455-3(4) , Harper Trophy); 2006. (Illus.). 15.99 (978-0-06-054453-9(8)); 2006. (Illus.). lib. bdg. 16.89 (978-0-06-054454-6(6)) HarperCollins Pubs.

Vogel, Julia. Dolphins. 2004. (Our Wild World Ser.). (Illus.). 48p. (J). (gr. 2-5). pap. 7.95 (978-1-55971-776-2(9) , NorthWord Bks. for Young Readers) T&N Children's Publishing.

—Dolphins. 2001. (gr. 3-6). lib. bdg. 16.40 (978-0-613-55822-8(7)) Tandem Library Bks.

Walker, Sally M. Dolphins. (Nature Watch Ser.). 48p. 2007. (J). (gr. 4-8). lib. bdg. 26.60 (*978-0-8225-6767-7(9) , Lerner Pubns.); 1999. (Illus.). (gr. 3-8). lib. bdg. 25.26 (978-1-57505-221-2(0)) Lerner Publishing Group.

Wallace, Karen. Diving Dolphin. 2001. (Readers Ser.). (Illus.). 32p. (J). (ps-k). pap. 3.99 (978-0-7894-7355-4(0)) Dorling Kindersley Publishing, Inc.

Waxman, Laura Hamilton. Diving Dolphins. 2005. (Pull Ahead Bks.). (Illus.). 32p. (gr. k-3). lib. bdg. 22.60 (978-0-8225-0684-3(X)) Lerner Publishing Group.

—Diving Dolphins. 2003. (gr. k-3). lib. bdg. 14.10 (978-0-613-52359-2(8)) Tandem Library Bks.

Whales & Dolphins. (Eyes on Nature Ser.). 32p. (J). (gr. 1). pap. (978-1-882210-56-5(5)) Action Publishing, Inc.

Whales & Dolphins. (Eyes on Nature Ser.). (Illus.). 32p. (J). (gr. 1 up). 7.95 (978-1-56156-423-1(0)) Kidsbooks, Inc.

Wicker, Jan Lee. Those Delightful Dolphins. 2007. (J). 14.95 (*978-1-56164-380-6(7)); pap. 8.95 (*978-1-56164-381-3(5)) Pineapple Pr., Inc.

Wildlife Education, Ltd Staff, contrib. by. Dolphins. (Critters Up Close Ser.). (Illus.). (J). 2006. bds. 5.95 (*978-1-932396-14-0(4)); 2005. 20p. (978-1-932396-09-6(8)) Wildlife Education, Ltd.

Wildlife Education, Ltd. Staff & Brust, Beth W. Dolphins - Porpoises. 1999. (Zoobooks Ser.). (Illus.). 18p. (J). pap. 2.95 (978-0-937934-62-3(3)) Wildlife Education, Ltd.

Wilson, Ben. Dolphins of the World. rev. ed. 2001. (World-Life Discovery Guide Ser.). (Illus.). 132p. (gr. 8 up). reprint ed. pap. 21.95 (978-0-89658-536-2(0)) Voyageur Pr., Inc.

Worth, Bonnie. A Whale of a Tale! All about Porpoises, Dolphins, & Whales. Ruiz, Aristides & Mathieu, Joseph, illus. 2006. (Cat in the Hat's Learning Library). 48p. (J). (gr. k-3). 8.99 (978-0-375-82279-7(8)); lib. bdg. 12.99 (978-0-375-92279-4(2)) Random Hse. Children's Bks. (Random Hse. Bks. for Young Readers).

DOLPHINS—FICTION

Andrews, McKenna. Riding the Storm Out. 2006. 73p. pap. 22.99 (978-1-4116-7216-1(X)) Lulu.com.

Asato, Dennis. A Dolphin Day in Hawaii. 2001. (Illus.). 50p. (J). (ps-1). pap. 9.95 (978-0-9702618-2-3(9)) Anoai Pr.

—A Dolphin Day in Hawaii. Asato, Dennis, illus. l.t. ed. 1999. (Illus.). 50p. (J). (ps-1). 12.00 (978-0-9653971-8-6(1)) Anoai Pr.

Baglio, Ben M. Dancing the Seas. 2003. (Dolphin Diaries). (Illus.). 160p. (J). (gr. 3-6). pap. 4.99 (978-0-439-44615-0(5)) Scholastic, Inc.

—Dolphin Diaries: Chasing the Dream. Lawton, Judith, illus. 2003. (Dolphin Diaries: No. 5). 160p. (J). (gr. 3-6). 4.99 (978-0-439-31951-5(X)) Scholastic, Inc.

—Dolphin Diaries: Chasing the Dream. 2003. (gr. 3-6). lib. bdg. 12.40 (978-0-613-72059-5(8)) Tandem Library Bks.

—Dolphin in the Deep. Gregory, Jenny, illus. 2001. (Animal Ark Ser.: Vol. 22). 144p. (J). (gr. 3-5). 3.99 (978-0-439-23021-6(7)) Scholastic, Inc.

—Dolphin in the Deep. 2001. (gr. 3-6). lib. bdg. 11.80 (978-0-613-36310-5(8)) Tandem Library Bks.

—Following the Rainbow. 2003. (Dolphin Diaries Ser.: No. 7). (Illus.). 160p. (J). (gr. 3-6). pap. 4.99 (978-0-439-44614-3(7) , Scholastic Paperbacks) Scholastic, Inc.

—Following the Rainbow. 2003. (gr. 3-6). lib. bdg. 12.40 (978-0-613-72206-3(X)) Tandem Library Bks.

—Into the Blue. 2002. (Dolphin Diaries Ser.: No. 1). (Illus.). 176p. (J). (gr. 3-6). pap. 4.99 (978-0-439-31947-8(1)) Scholastic, Inc.

—Into the Blue. 2002. (gr. 3-6). lib. bdg. 12.40 (978-0-613-70893-7(8)) Tandem Library Bks.

—Leaving the Shallows. 2004. (Dolphin Diaries). (Illus.). 160p. (J). pap. 4.99 (978-0-439-44616-7(3)) Scholastic, Inc.

—Racing the Wind. 2003. (Dolphin Diaries: No. 6). 160p. (J). pap. 4.99 (978-0-439-31952-2(8)) Scholastic, Inc.

—Racing the Wind. 2003. (gr. 3-6). lib. bdg. 12.40 (978-0-613-72053-3(9)) Tandem Library Bks.

—Riding the Storm. 2002. (Dolphin Diaries: No. 3). 176p. (J). pap. 4.99 (978-0-439-31949-2(8)) Scholastic, Inc.

—Riding the Storm. 2002. (gr. 3-6). lib. bdg. 12.40 (978-0-613-72055-7(5)) Tandem Library Bks.

—Touching the Waves. 2002. (Dolphin Diaries Ser.: No. 2). (Illus.). 176p. (J). (gr. 3-6). pap. 4.99 (978-0-439-31948-5(X)) Scholastic, Inc.

—Touching the Waves. 2002. (gr. 3-6). lib. bdg. 12.40 (978-0-613-70905-7(5)) Tandem Library Bks.

—Under the Stars. Lawton, Judith, illus. 2002. (Dolphin Diaries: No. 4). 176p. (J). 4.99 (978-0-439-31950-8(1)) Scholastic, Inc.

—Under the Stars. 2002. (gr. 3-6). lib. bdg. 12.40 (978-0-613-58139-4(3)) Tandem Library Bks.

Ballantyne, R. M. The World of Ice (Illustrated Edition) (2006. pap. (***978-1-4065-0533-7(1)***) Dodo Pr.

Bertagna, Julie. Dolphin Boy. 1999. (Illus.). 96p. (J). pap. 7.50 (978-0-7497-3730-6(1)) Egmont Bks., Ltd. GBR. *Dist:* Independent Pubs. Group.

Blake, Richard R. A Dolphin's Tale. Blake, Rachelle & Seratte, Rachel, illus. 2001. (J). per. 9.97 (978-0-9670242-3-3(4)) Thornton Publishing.

Boerner, Matthew. The Great Dolphin Door: The Adventures of Frostfin & Silverbeak. Cameron, Vinya, illus. 2006. 52p. (J). pap. 9.95 (978-0-9778525-5-0(5)) Peppertree Pr., The.

Bond, Linda. Retishella & the Dolphins. 2006. 50p. pap. 12.95 (978-1-4241-1868-7(9)) PublishAmerica, Inc.

Book Buddy: Dolphin with Story Book. Orig. Title: Child's Play. (Illus.). 10p. (J). (ps-3). reprint ed. (978-1-881469-49-0(2)) Safari, Ltd.

Book Company Staff. Moon Dance. Lassen, Christian R., illus. 2005. (Sparkle Bks.). (J). (gr. 4-11). bds. 14.95 (978-1-74047-355-2(8)) Book Co. Publishing Pty, Ltd., The AUS. *Dist:* Penton Overseas, Inc.

Bornemann, Elsa. Cuadernos de un Delfin. 2003. (SPA., Illus.). 125p. (J). (gr. 5-8). pap. 11.95 (978-950-511-724-6(8)) Santillana USA Publishing Co., Inc.

Caffrey-Kira, Albina. The Bear Who Loves Apples. 2006. 25.00 (978-0-8059-9128-4(X)) Dorrance Publishing Co., Inc.

Carris, Joan D. A Ghost of a Chance. 2003. (Legends of the Carolinas Ser.). 155p. (J). 8.95 (978-1-928556-40-4(X)) Coastal Carolina Pr.

Charlotte Latin School Staff. Ann & the Dolphin. Sher, illus. 2001. 32p. (J). per. 4.95 (978-0-9707920-1-3(8)) Charlotte's Storybooks.

Christie, Jean. Danny Dolphin: Inflatable Bath Book. Canals, Sonia, illus. 2003. 7p. (J). 6.95 (978-1-4027-0446-8(1)) Sterling Publishing Co., Inc.

Cordish, Janet Luckey. Dolly Dolphin. Cordish, Janet Luckey, illus. 2004. (Illus.). 32p. (J). (gr. k-3). 19.95 (978-0-9661315-6-7(8)) FreeStar Pr.

Crouse, Donna J. The Ruby Ring: The Whispering Cove Kids Club. 2005. 114p. pap. 12.99 (978-0-9765339-0-0(1)) Crouse, Donna J.

Damitz, Charlie. Diving for el Corazon. Diefendorf, Cathy, illus. 2007. 100p. (J). pap. 7.95 (978-0-9744446-3-5(4)) All About Kids Publishing.

Daniels, Lucy. Animal Ark: Dolphin in the Deep. unabr. l.t. ed. 2001. (Read-Along Ser.). 160p. (J). 29.95 incl. audio (978-0-7540-6243-1(0) , RAO44, Chivers Children's Audio Bks.) BBC Audiobooks America.

—Dolphin Diaries: Touching the Waves. Lawton, Judith, illus. l.t. ed. 2002. 216p. (J). 16.95 (978-0-7540-7822-7(1) , Galaxy Children's Large Print) BBC Audiobooks America.

—Into the Blue. 2002. (J). pap. 29.95 incl. audio (978-0-7540-6245-5(7)) BBC Audiobooks America.

Daniels, Lucy. Oscar's Best Friends. 2005. 57p. (***978-0-439-68199-5(5)***) Scholastic, Inc.

Davis, Lambert. Swimming with Dolphins. Davis, Lambert, illus. 2004. (Illus.). 32p. (J). pap. 15.95 (978-0-439-47257-9(1) , Blue Sky Pr., The) Scholastic, Inc.

Dell, Scott O. L Isola Dei Delfini Blu. pap. 16.95 (978-88-09-02504-2(0)) Giunti, Gruppo Editoriale ITA. *Dist:* Distribooks, Inc.

Denver, John. Ancient Rhymes, a Dolphin Lullaby: With Audio CD & Score. Canyon, Christopher, illus. 2004. (Sharing Nature with Children Book Ser.). 36p. (J). (ps-6). 19.95 incl. audio compact disk (978-1-58469-064-1(X)) Dawn Pubns.

Dexter, Anthony. The Adventures of Manny the Manatee. 2004. 45p. pap. 19.95 (978-1-4137-2751-7(4)) PublishAmerica, Inc.

Doinet, Mymi, et al, illus. The Dolphin. 2000. (My Animal Library). 32p. (J). (ps-1). pap. 6.95 (978-0-7892-0661-9(7) , Abbeville Kids) Abbeville Pr., Inc.

The Dolphin Caller: Chapter Book, 6 Packs. Vol. 30. 32p. (gr. 5 up). 44.00 (978-0-7578-0983-5(9)) Rigby Education.

Dolphin Diaries. 2005. (J). (978-1-59564-639-2(6)) Steps To Literacy, LLC.

Dolphin Halloween & Elsie's Scrapbook. l.t. ed. 2004. (Illus.). 32p. (J). mass mkt. 4.99 (978-0-9760868-0-2(8)) Pluegl Bks.

The Dolphins, 6 Packs. 16p. (gr. 2 up). 35.00 (978-0-7635-9384-1(2)) Rigby Education.

The Dolphin's Gift: El Don Del Delfin. 2005. (J). per. 8.95 (978-0-9766572-0-0(1)) Tucu Pr.

Donovan, Stacey. Who I Am Keeps Happening. 2004. (YA). (978-0-7636-1988-6(4)) Candlewick Pr.

Douglas, Babette. Amazing Grace. 2004. (J). 9.99 (978-1-890343-33-0(1)) Kiss A Me Productions, Inc.

Douglas, Vincent & School Specialty Publishing Staff. Daphne Dolphin. 2006. (Bath Buddies Ser.). 7p. (J). 12.95 (978-0-7696-4598-8(4) , Brighter Child) School Specialty Publishing.

E. Baglio, Ben. Beyond the Sunrise. 2004. (Dolphin Diaries). 160p. (J). pap. 4.99 (978-0-439-44617-4(1) , Scholastic Paperbacks) Scholastic, Inc.

Emmer, E. R. The Dolphin Project. 2005. (Going to Ser.). (Illus.). 202p. (gr. 4-8). pap. 6.95 (978-1-893577-12-1(0)) Four Corners Publishing Co., Inc.

Fripp, Deborah & Fripp, Michael. Naya & the Haunted Shipwreck. Fripp, Jean, ed. Barbor, Carol, illus. 2004. 32p. (J). (gr. k-4). pap. 5.99 (978-0-9701008-7-0(6)) Bicast, Inc.

Gadboys, Pamela C. No Dolphins Today! 2001. (Illus.). 32p. (J). (gr. 3-7). pap. 14.95 (978-1-929727-04-9(6)) Bayshore Publishing Group.

George, Twig C. A Dolphin Named Bob. Merrill, Christine Herma, illus. 1998. (Trophy Chapter Bks.). 80p. (J). (gr. 2-5). pap. 4.99 (978-0-06-442079-2(5) , Harper Trophy) HarperCollins Pubs.

—A Dolphin Named Bob. 1999. (YA). pap. 22.50 incl. audio (978-0-7887-2997-3(7) , 46844) Recorded Bks., LLC.

—A Dolphin Named Bob. 1998. (Trophy Chapter Bks.). (J). 11.05 (978-0-606-13336-4(4)) Tandem Library Bks.

Globe-Fearon Staff. The Sea-Wolf. (YA). (gr. 5-12). pap. 6.50 (978-0-8359-0969-3(7)) Globe Fearon Educational Publishing.

Grooms, Molly. We Are Dolphins. Oda, Takashi, illus. 32p. (J). (ps-2). pap. 7.95 (978-1-55971-904-9(4) , NorthWord Bks. for Young Readers) T&N Children's Publishing.

Grover, Wayne. Dolphin Adventure. 2000. (gr. 3-6). lib. bdg. 13.00 (978-0-613-18589-9(7)) Tandem Library Bks.

—Dolphin Freedom. Fowler, Jim, illus. 1999. 112p. (J). (gr. 3-7). 15.00 (978-0-688-16010-4(7)) HarperCollins Pubs.

—Dolphin Freedom. 2000. (gr. 3-6). lib. bdg. 12.95 (978-0-613-24880-8(5)); (Illus.). (J). 11.75 (978-0-606-18900-2(9)) Tandem Library Bks.

Halfmann, Janet. Dolphin's Rescue: The Story of a Pacific White-Sided Dolphin. Petruccio, Steven James, illus. 2005. (Smithsoniah Oceanic Colection Ser.). 32p. (J). (gr. 1-3). 15.95 (978-1-59249-426-2(9) , B4028); (ps-2). 4.95 (978-1-59249-427-9(7) , B4078); (ps-2). pap. 6.95 (978-1-59249-428-6(5) , S4028) Soundprints.

Hesse, Karen. The Music of Dolphins. 244p. (J). pap. 4.50 (978-0-8072-1542-5(2) , YA113P); 2004. (gr. 5-9). pap. 29.00 incl. audio (978-0-8072-8135-2(2) , YA113SP) Random Hse. Audio Publishing Group. (Listening Library).

—The Music of Dolphins. 1998. (Apple Signature Edition Ser.). 192p. (J). (gr. 4-7). 5.99 (978-0-590-89798-3(5)) Scholastic, Inc.

—The Music of Dolphins. 1998. (Apple Signature Edition Ser.). (J). (978-0-606-13628-0(2)) Tandem Library Bks.

James, Larry W. Captain Petey: An Adventure at Sea. Ramos, Violet M., ed. James, Larry W. & Freshman, Floris R., illus. 2003. 28p. pap. 6.99 (978-0-9742154-0-2(6)) Cross Pointe Printing.

Kendall, Sarita H. Al Rescate de Omacha. (SPA.). (YA). (gr. 5-8). 8.95 (978-958-04-2930-2(8) , NR2139) Norma S.A. COL. *Dist:* Distribuidora Norma, Inc., Lectorum Pubns., Inc.

Leaney, Cindy. Desert Dream. Whitehouse, Patty, ed. King, Sue & Wilks, Peter, illus. 2004. (Friendly Phonics Ser.). 24p. (J). lib. bdg. 14.95 (978-1-59054-117-3(0)) Fitzgerald Bks.

L'Engle, Madeleine. A Ring of Endless Light. 2006. (Austin Family Ser.: No. 5). 21.75 (978-0-8446-7285-4(8)) Smith, Peter Pub., Inc.

Little Dolphin Learns. 2002. (Oceanic Mini Bks.). (Illus.). 32p. (J). (978-1-59069-001-7(X) , H1002) Studio Mouse LLC.

Lombardi, Kristine. Summer under the Sea. 2006. 12p. (J). pap. 12.99 (978-0-7944-1102-2(9)) Reader's Digest Assn., Inc., The.

Lumry, Amanda & Hurwitz, Laura. Adventures of Riley: Dolphins in Danger. McIntyre, Sarah, illus. 2005. 36p. 15.95 (978-0-9748411-1-3(0)) Eaglemont Pr.

Maden, Mary. A Dolphin Adventure: Touched by a Dolphin. Geib, Stephanie K., illus. 1999. (Earth/Ocean Adventures Ser.: Vol. 3). (J). (gr. 1-7). pap. 5.95 (978-1-890479-59-6(4)) Dog & Pony Publishing.

Marciano, John Bemelmans. There's a Dolphin in the Grand Canal! 2005. (Illus.). 40p. (J). (ps). 15.99 (978-0-670-05987-4(0) , Viking Juvenile) Penguin Group (USA) Inc.

Mohn, Eric A. Ocean Encounter. 2005. 56p. spiral bd. 15.75 (978-1-4116-6199-8(0)) Lulu.com.

Morpurgo, Michael & Foreman, Michael. Dolphin Boy. 2005. (Illus.). 32p. (J). pap. 8.99 (***978-1-84270-448-6(6)***); 14.99 (978-1-84270-320-5(X)) Andersen GBR. *Dist:* Independent Pubs. Group, Trafalgar Square Publishing.

Nahu. Dolphina's World: And Other Stories. 2006. 80p. pap. 12.95 (978-1-59800-178-5(7)) Outskirts Press, Inc.

Nyikos, Stacy Ann. Dizzy. Lee, Kary, illus. l.t. ed. 2007. 32p. (J). lib. bdg. 15.95 (***978-0-9764199-2-1(0)*** , 888-867-1927) Stonehorse Publishing, LLC.

O'Dell, Scott. Island of the Blue Dolphins. l.t. ed. 2005. pap. 10.95 (978-0-7862-7254-9(6) , Large Print Pr.) Thorndike Pr.

Osborne, Mary Pope. Dolphins at Daybreak. unabr. ed. 2004. (Magic Tree House Ser. : No. 9). 67p. (J). (gr. k-3). pap. 17.00 incl. audio (978-0-8072-0534-1(6) , Listening Library) Random Hse. Audio Publishing Group.

Parish, Steve, illus. Little Dolphin's Big Leap. 2005. 24p. (J). lib. bdg. 20.67 (978-0-8368-5973-7(1)) Stevens, Gareth Inc.

Rabley, Stephen. Maisie & the Dolphin. 2002. (Illus.). 16p. pap. (978-0-582-40283-6(2) , Putnam Juvenile) Penguin Group (USA) Inc.

Renne. Little Dolphin's Big Adventure. 2001. (Illus.). 28p. (J). 17.95 (978-0-86315-335-8(6)) Floris Bks. GBR. *Dist:* SteinerBooks, Inc.

Robison, Dan, Jr. Kimo's Escape: The Story of a Hawaiian Boy Who Learns to Believe in Himself. 2005. 100p. (J). per. 19.95 (978-0-922993-28-4(9)) Marquette Bks., LLC.

Rorby, Ginny. Dolphin Sky. 1998. (978-0-606-13338-8(0)) Tandem Library Bks.

Santillo, LuAnn. Flipper. Santillo, LuAnn, ed. 2003. (Half-Pint Kids Readers Ser.). (Illus.). 7p. (J). (ps-1). pap. (978-1-59256-095-0(4)) Half-Pint Kids, Inc.

Segal, Douglas. Dolphin's Day. 2007. 5p. 15.95 (***978-1-58117-555-4(8)*** , Intervisual/Piggy Toes) Dalmatian Pr.

Self, Timothy. Davy the Dolphin. l.t. ed. 2003. (Illus.). 22p. (J). per. 8.99 (978-1-932338-30-0(6)) Lifevest Publishing, Inc.

Seth, Vikram. Arion y el Delfin. Dieguez Dieguez, Remedios, tr. Ray, Jane, illus. 2004. (SPA.). 40p. 14.95 (978-84-95939-74-6(6)) Blume ESP. *Dist:* Independent Pubs. Group.

Simmons, Monica. Aster Ocean: Dolfina the Bottlenoze Dolf. Ward, Jon, illus. 1998. (Aster Planet Chronicles Ser.: Vol. 4). 32p. (J). (gr. k-4). 15.95 (978-0-9658128-5-6(5)) Long Wind Publishing.

Tate, Suzanne. Danny & Daisy: A Tale of a Dolphin Duo. Melvin, James, illus. 2004. (Suzanne Tate's Nature Ser.). 32p. (J). per. 10.95 (978-1-878405-44-9(6)) Nags Head Art, Inc.

Tekkel, Tatjana. Jessie & the Dolphins. 2001. (Illus.). 24p. bds. 12.95 (978-1-85149-711-9(0)) Antique Collectors' Club.

Tobias, Ann. Floaties! Dolphin Splash. Austin, Terri, illus. 2004. (Floaties Ser.). 12p. (J). bds. 7.95 (978-1-4027-2155-7(2)) Sterling Publishing Co., Inc.

Tramontozzi, Vanessa, ed. Dolphin Diaries. 2006. 496p. (J). pap. 9.99 (978-0-439-80844-6(8) , Scholastic) Scholastic, Inc.

Vornholt, John. Dolphin Watch. 2002. (gr. 5-8). lib. bdg. 11.80 (978-0-613-70888-3(1)) Tandem Library Bks.

Wallace & Bostock. Imagine You Are a Dolphin. (Illus.). 25p. (J). pap. (978-0-340-67833-6(X) , Hodder & Stoughton) Hodder General Publishing Division.

Wallace, Karen. Diving Dolphin. 2001. (gr. k-3). lib. bdg. 11.80 (978-0-613-35104-1(5)); (Illus.). (J). 10.79 (978-0-606-21152-9(7)) Tandem Library Bks.

Weidner Zoehfeld, Kathleen & Langeland, Deirdre. Smithsonian Oceanic Dolphin & Octopus Box. Petruccio, Steven James, illus. 2002. (Smithsonian Soundprints Ser.). 64p. (J). 19.95 (978-1-931465-58-8(4) , Silver Dolphin Bks.) Advantage Pubs. Group.

Weiss, Shelly. Dillin the Dolphin. 2003. 32p. (J). per. 15.00 (978-1-59196-454-4(7)) Instantpublisher.com.

West, Tracey & Artful Doodlers Limited Staff. Dolphin Rescue. 2006. (Totally Spies! Ser.). (Illus.). 16p. (J). pap. 5.99 (978-1-4169-1560-7(5) , Simon Spotlight) Simon & Schuster Children's Publishing.

Winton, Tim. The Deep. Louise, Karen, illus. 1998. 32p. (YA). 21.95 (978-1-86368-242-8(2)) Fremantle Pr. AUS. *Dist:* International Specialized Bk. Services.

—The Deep. Louise, Karen, illus. 2004. 32p. (ps-2). 14.95 (978-1-58246-024-6(8) , Tricycle Pr.) Ten Speed Pr.

Winton, Tim & Louise, Karen. The Deep. (Illus.). 32p. (YA). pap. 13.95 (978-1-86368-210-7(4)) Fremantle Pr. AUS. *Dist:* International Specialized Bk. Services.

Wlodarski, Loran. If A Dolphin Were A Fish. Klein, Laurie Allen, illus. 2006. 32p. (J). 15.95 (978-0-9768823-2-9(9)) Sylvan Dell Pubng.

Wlodarski, Loran. If a Dolphin Were a Fish. Klein, Laurie Allen, illus. 2007. 1p. (J). 8.95 (***978-1-934359-03-7(3)***) Sylvan Dell Pubng.

Wolfer, Dianne, et al. Dolphin Song. Gelsthorpe, Loraine & Rex, Sue, eds. 2002. 176p. (J). pap. 14.95 (978-1-86368-384-5(4)) Fremantle Pr. AUS. *Dist:* International Specialized Bk. Services.

Wood, Audrey. The Rainbow Bridge. 2000. (gr. 3-6). lib. bdg. 15.30 (978-0-613-28618-3(9)) Tandem Library Bks.

Wright, Mary H. Stranded: Stormy's Adventure. Morris, Kim, ed. Guire, Cindy A., illus. 2000. 44p. (J). lib. bdg. 16.95 (978-0-9645493-0-2(1)) Bluebonnets, Boots & Bks.

Zinsser, Anne. More Dolphin Magic: The Adventure Continues. Sohl, Lee Ellen, illus. 2001. viii, 120p. (J). per. 6.95 (978-0-933951-20-4(5)) Locust Hill Pr.

Zoehfeld, Kathleen Weidner. Dolphin's First Day: The Story of a Bottlenose Dolphin. 2005. (Illus.). 32p. (J). (ps-2). pap. 6.95 (978-1-59249-056-1(5) , S4001) Soundprints.

DOMESTIC ANIMALS

see also Animals—Treatment; Camels; Cats; Cattle; Cows; Dogs; Horses; Livestock; Pets; Reindeer; Sheep

Amery, Heather. La Oveja Rizos. Cartwright, Stephen, illus. 2004. (Titles in Spanish Ser.). (SPA.). 10p. (J). bds. 3.99 (978-0-7460-6104-6(8) , Usborne) EDC Publishing.

Auch, Alison. Tame & Wild. 2002. (Spyglass Books). (Illus.). 24p. (J). (gr. 1 up). lib. bdg. 18.60 (978-0-7565-0226-3(8)) Compass Point Bks.

Balfour, Sandy & Dorling Kindersley Publishing Staff. My First Farm Board Book. 2003. (My First Board Books (Bilingual) Ser.). (Illus.). 36p. (J). bds. 6.99 (978-0-7894-9522-8(8)) Dorling Kindersley Publishing, Inc.

Bampton, Bob, illus. Animals on the Farm. 2004. (Look & Learn about Ser.). 18p. (J). bds. 5.99 (978-1-85854-319-2(3)) Brimax Books Ltd. GBR. *Dist:* Byeway Bks.

Banek, Yvette Santiago, illus. Counting Farm. 2003. (J). (978-0-7853-7824-2(3)) Publications International, Ltd.

Barraclough, Sue. Animals on the Farm. 2005. (J). pap. (978-1-4109-1904-5(8)); (Illus.). 24p. (gr. 3-5). lib. bdg. 21.36 (978-1-4109-1899-4(8)) Steck-Vaughn.

Bell, Rachael. Chickens. (Farm Animals Ser.). (Illus.). 32p. (J). (gr. k-2). 2001. pap. 6.95 (978-1-58810-367-3(6) , 91087); 2000. lib. bdg. 21.36 (978-1-57572-530-7(4)) Heinemann Library.

—Farm Animals, 6 bks., Set. Incl. Chickens. lib. bdg. 21.36 (978-1-57572-530-7(4)); Cows. lib. bdg. 21.36 (978-1-57572-529-1(0)); Horses. lib. bdg. 21.36 (978-1-57572-531-4(2)); Pigs. pap. 21.36 (978-1-57572-532-1(0)); Sheep. lib. bdg. 21.36 (978-1-57572-533-8(9)); Turkeys. lib. bdg. 21.36 (978-1-57572-534-5(7)); (J). (gr. k-2). (Farm Animals Ser.). (Illus.). 32p. 2000. Set lib. bdg. 128.36 (978-1-57572-528-4(2)) Heinemann Library.

—Turkeys. (Farm Animals Ser.). 32p. 2003. pap. 6.95 (978-1-4034-4041-9(7)); 2000. (Illus.). (J). lib. bdg. 21.36 (978-1-57572-534-5(7)) Heinemann Library.

Bicknell, Joanna. Farm Animals. 2001. (Softies Ser.). (Illus.). 12p. (ps-k). per., bds. 6.95 (978-1-84610-084-0(4)) Make Believe Ideas GBR. *Dist:* Ingram Pub. Services.

—Funny Farm. 2007. (Googlies Ser.). (Illus.). 14p. (ps). per., bds. 6.95 (***978-1-84610-477-0(7)***) Make Believe Ideas GBR. *Dist:* Ingram Pub. Services.

Bicknell, Joanna. Googlies: Funny Farm. 2006. (Illus.). 12p. (ps). per. 6.95 (978-1-84610-295-0(2)) Make Believe Ideas GBR. *Dist:* Ingram Pub. Services.

Blevins, Wiley. Farm Animals. 2006. (Let's Find Out Ser.). (Illus.). 24p. (J). pap. 8.99 (978-0-439-72604-7(2) , Cartwheel Bks.) Scholastic, Inc.

Bolam, Emily. Chunky Farm Cow. 2000. (Chunky Farm Bks.). (Illus.). 14p. (J). (ps-k). bds. 5.99 (978-0-7641-5319-8(6)) Barron's Educational Series, Inc.

Borton, Paula & Goldsack, Gabby. Pets. 2003. (Busy Book of... Ser.). (Illus.). 32p. (J). 9.95 (978-1-57768-890-7(2) , Waterbird Bks.) School Specialty Publishing.

Bracken, Carolyn & Durk, Jim, illus. Early Learning Farm, 8 vols. 2001. (Fisher-Price Little People Ser.). (J). (978-0-7853-4959-4(6)) Publications International, Ltd.

Brady, Peter. Animales de la Granja (Farm Animals), 4 bks. Schon, Isabel, ed. Ferrer, Martín Luis Guzman, tr. Munoz, William, illus. Incl. Cerdos. lib. bdg. 18.60 (978-1-56065-789-7(8)); Ovejas. lib. bdg. 18.60 (978-1-56065-790-3(1) , CAP2405); Pollos. lib. bdg. 18.60 (978-1-56065-787-3(1) , CAP1683); Vacas. lib. bdg. 18.60 (978-1-56065-788-0(X)); 24p. (J). (gr. k-3). 1998. (SPA., Illus.). Set lib. bdg. 74.40 (978-0-7368-0145-4(6) , Bridgestone Bks.) Capstone Pr., Inc.

—Farm Animals, 4 bks. Incl. Chickens. lib. bdg. 18.60 (978-1-56065-347-9(7)); Cows. lib. bdg. 18.60 (978-1-56065-344-8(2)); Pigs. lib. bdg. 18.60 (978-1-56065-345-5(0)); Sheep. lib. bdg. 18.60 (978-1-56065-346-2(9)); 24p. (J). (gr. 1-2). 1996. (Illus.). Set lib. bdg. 74.40 (978-1-56065-632-6(8) , Bridgestone Bks.) Capstone Pr., Inc.

Brighter Vision Publishing Staff. About the Farm. 2000. (My Discovery Bks.). (Illus.). 20p. (J). (ps). pap. 2.95 (978-1-55254-202-6(5)) Brighter Vision Pubns.

Butterfield, Moira. Farm Animals. 2006. (Illus.). 24p. (YA). (gr. 1 up). lib. bdg. 22.80 (978-1-931983-61-7(5)) Chrysalis Education.

Cabat, Erni. Erni Cabat's Magical ABC: Animals Around the Farm. Date not set. (Illus.). 64p. (Orig.). (J). (ps-2). 23.00 (978-0-943173-73-3(6)) Cabat Studio Pubns.

Cambell, Rod & Wen, Dref. Anifeiliaid y Fferm. 2005. (WEL., Illus.). 13p. (978-1-85596-654-3(9)) Dref Wen.

Campbell, Rod. Farm Friends. 2003. (Illus.). 12p. (J). 3.99 (978-1-85292-225-2(7) , Campbell Bks.) Pan Macmillan GBR. *Dist:* Trafalgar Square Publishing.

Can Press Staff, ed. This Is Daniel Cook at the Farm. 2006. (Illus.). 28p. (J). (978-1-55453-078-6(4)); (978-1-55453-077-9(6)) Kids Can Pr., Ltd.

Casado, Alicia & Casado, Dami. Bebes de la Granja. 2005. (SPA.). 12p. 7.99 (978-84-272-6264-5(7)) Molino, Editorial ESP. *Dist:* Santillana USA Publishing Co., Inc.

—Los Ruidos de la Granja. 2005. (SPA.). 12p. 7.99 (978-84-272-8291-9(5)) Molino, Editorial ESP. *Dist:* Santillana USA Publishing Co., Inc.

Childrens Press Staff, ed. Farm Animals. 1998. (Rookie Read-About Science Ser.). pap. 29.85 (978-0-516-29983-9(2) , Children's Pr.) Scholastic Library Publishing.

Chronicle Books Staff, contrib. by. Baby Animals: Books in Box:18 Board Books Inside!, 18 vols. 2006. (Illus.). (J). bds. 19.95 (978-0-8118-5241-8(5)) Chronicle Bks. LLC.

Cooper, Wade. Schol Rdr Lvl2: Farm Animals: Farm Animals. 2008. 32p. pap. 3.99 (***978-0-545-00721-4(6)*** , Cartwheel Bks.) Scholastic, Inc.

Cousins, Lucy. Farm Animals. Cousins, Lucy, illus. 2004. (Illus.). 12p. (J). (gr. k-k). bds. 4.99 (978-0-7636-2303-6(2)) Candlewick Pr.

Curley, Andrea, ed. My First Farm Board Book. 2004. (Illus.). 36p. (J). bds. 5.99 (978-0-7894-9902-8(9)) Dorling Kindersley Publishing, Inc.

Dahl, Michael. Do Dogs Make Dessert? A Book about How Animals Help Humans. Yesh, Jeff, illus. 2004. (Animals All Around Ser.). 24p. (J). (gr. k-2). 22.60 (978-1-4048-0289-6(4)) Picture Window Bks.

Daynes, Katie. Farm Animals (Level 1) - Internet Referenced. 2006. 32p. (J). 4.99 (978-0-7945-1396-2(4) , Usborne) EDC Publishing.

DK Publishing. Farm. (J). (ps-k). 2008. 14p. bds. 5.99 (***978-0-7566-3467-4(9)***); 2007. 26p. 9.99 (***978-0-7566-3369-1(9)***) Dorling Kindersley Publishing, Inc.

—Toddler on the Move: Farm: Activity Pack. 2008. 75p. (J). (ps-k). 9.99 (***978-0-7566-3808-5(9)***) Dorling Kindersley Publishing, Inc.

Dorling Kindersley Publishing Staff. Farm ABC. 2006. (Illus.). 12p. (J). (ps-1). 8.99 (978-0-7566-2331-9(6)) Dorling Kindersley Publishing, Inc.

—Farm Animals. 2001. (Soft-to-Touch Bk.). (Illus.). 18p. (J). (ps-3). bds. 4.99 (978-0-7894-7403-2(4)) Dorling Kindersley Publishing, Inc.

Dorling Kindersley Publishing Staff, ed. La Granja / Farm. 2004. (Touch & Feel Ser.). (SPA.). 12p. (J). bds. 6.99 (978-0-7566-0629-9(2)) Dorling Kindersley Publishing, Inc.

Elliott, David. On the Farm. Meade, Holly, illus. 2008. (J). (***978-0-7636-3322-6(4)***) Candlewick Pr.

Everyday Animals Classroom Library. (gr. k-2). lib. bdg. 81.95 (978-0-7368-1821-6(9)) Red Brick Learning.

Everyday Animals Complete Unit. (gr. k-2). 468.95 (978-0-7368-1822-3(7)) Red Brick Learning.

Farm Animals. 2005. (Illus.). 32p. (gr. 2-4). pap. 138.00 (978-0-7910-8463-2(9) , Chelsea Hse.) Facts On File, Inc.

Farm Animals. 2003. (Illus.). 12p. (J). 2.98 (978-1-4054-1181-3(3)) Parragon, Inc.

Farm Animals. 2007. (My First Sticker Encyclopedia Ser.). (Illus.). 18p. (J). pap. 5.95 (***978-1-59496-150-2(6)***) Teora USA LLC.

Farm Animals: KinderFacts Individual Title, 6 packs. (Kinderstarters Ser.). 8p. (ps-1). 21.00 (978-0-7635-8752-9(4)) Rigby Education.

Farm Animals, Level 1, 6 bks., Set. Incl. Chickens. Green, Emily K. 18.50 (***978-0-531-17550-7(2)***); Cows. Green, Emily. 18.50 (***978-0-531-17551-4(0)***); Goats. Green, Emily. 18.50 (***978-0-531-17552-1(9)***); Horses. Green, Emily. 18.50 (***978-0-531-17553-8(7)***); Pigs. Green, Emily. 18.50 (***978-0-531-17554-5(5)***); Sheep. Green, Emily. 18.50 (***978-0-531-17555-2(3)***); 24p. (J). (gr. k-2). 2007. (Blastoff! Readers Ser.). 2007. 111.00 (***978-0-531-17579-8(0)***, Children's Pr.) Scholastic Library Publishing.

Farmyard Animals. 2003. 32p. 12.98 (978-1-4054-1929-1(6)) Parragon, Inc.

Friendly Animals. 2001. 12p. (J). bds. 11.95 (978-0-7525-5262-0(7)) Parragon, Inc.

Furfur, Christopher. Rebecca & the Great Goat Getaway. Artigas, Alexandra, illus. 2005. 40p. (J). (ps). per. 15.95 (978-0-9742845-7-6(2)) Mystic Ridge Bks.

Gillis, Jennifer Blizin. Farm Animals. 2004. (Let's See Library). (Illus.). 24p. (J). (gr. 1 up). lib. bdg. 19.93 (978-0-7565-0670-4(0)) Compass Point Bks.

Golden Books Staff. Baby Farm Animals. Williams, Garth, illus. 2003. (Little Golden Book Classics). 24p. (J). (gr. k-k). 2.99 (978-0-307-02175-5(0), Golden Bks.) Random Hse. Children's Bks.

Goldie, Sonia. My Favorite Nature Book: Animals on the Farm: Includes an Activity Kit with Posters & Stickers. 2007. (Illus.). 24p. (J). 9.95 (978-1-57990-922-2(1)) Lark Bks.

Group/McGraw-Hill, Wright. Animales Domesticos, 6 vols., Vol. 2. (First Explorers. Primeros Exploradores Nonfiction Sets Ser.). (SPA.). (gr. 1-2). 29.95 (978-0-7699-1483-1(7)) Shortland Pubns. (U. S. A.) Inc.

Hankin, Rosie. Cut & Paste Farm Animals. 2006. (Illus.). 32p. (J). lib. bdg. (***978-0-8368-7719-9(5)***) Stevens, Gareth Inc.

Harvey, Bob. The Farm. Elliot, Rebecca, illus. 2006. (Get Inside... Ser.). 48p. pap. 18.95 (978-1-904668-95-4(X)) Mercury Bks. Ltd. GBR. *Dist:* International Publishers Marketing.

Head, Honor. Kitten. Burton, Jane, photos by. 2000. (My Pet Ser.). (Illus.). 32p. (J). (gr. 3-5). lib. bdg. 25.69 (978-0-7398-2884-7(3)) Raintree.

—Kitten. 2000. (My Pet Ser.). (Illus.). 32p. (J). (gr. 3-5). pap. 8.95 (978-0-7398-3011-6(2)) Steck-Vaughn.

Hellen, Nancy. A Visit to the Farm: Pop-up. Hellen, Nancy, illus. 2004. (Illus.). 16p. (J). (gr. k-2). reprint ed. 7.00 (978-0-7567-7063-1(7)) DIANE Publishing Co.

Hess, Paul. Farmyard Animals. (Animals Ser.). (Illus.). (ps-k). 2001. 24p. (J). bds. (978-1-84089-164-5(5)); 1998. (YA). (978-1-84089-006-8(1), 868227) Evans Publishing Group. (Zero to Ten, Limited).

—Farmyard Animals. 2002. (ps-2). lib. bdg. 15.25 (978-0-613-80018-1(4)) Tandem Library Bks.

Hess, Paul, illus. Farm Animals. 2002. (Animal Worlds Ser.). 24p. (J). (ps up). lib. bdg. 20.67 (978-0-8368-3039-2(3)) Stevens, Gareth Inc.

—Farmyard Animals. 2002. (Animals Ser.). 24p. (J). pap. 6.95 (978-1-84089-170-6(X), Zero to Ten, Limited) Evans Publishing Group GBR. *Dist:* Independent Pubs. Group.

Hester, Elizabeth, ed. Farm Animals. 2003. (Lift-the-Flap Books Ser.). (Illus.). 16p. (J). bds. 6.99 (978-0-7894-9235-7(0)) Dorling Kindersley Publishing, Inc.

Hewitt, Sally. Local Wildlife: What's in My Garden? 2005. (Illus.). 32p. (J). (gr. 1-4). lib. bdg. 27.10 (978-1-59604-021-2(1)) Stargazer Bks.

Hinkler Books. At the Farm. rev. ed. 2007. (Illus.). 8p. (J). (gr. 2-5). 9.95 (***978-1-74181-321-0(2)***) Hinkler Bks. Pty, Ltd. AUS. *Dist:* Penton Overseas, Inc.

HOP, LLC. Hooked on Animals on the Farm Super Activity Kit. 2006. (J). (ps). 9.99 (978-1-933863-19-1(6)) HOP, LLC.

James, Diana. On the Farm. 2000. (gr. k-3). lib. bdg. 14.10 (978-0-613-43361-7(0)) Tandem Library Bks.

Kimble, Evan & Kimble, Lael. Farm Animals Dot-to-Dot. 2004. (Illus.). 80p. pap. 5.95 (978-1-4027-0993-7(5)) Sterling Publishing Co., Inc.

King-Smith, Dick. All Pigs Are Beautiful. 2001. (Read & Wonder Ser.). (J). 12.79 (978-0-606-20540-5(3)) Tandem Library Bks.

Kuhn, Dwight, illus. & photos by. Homes. Kuhn, Dwight, photos by. 2004. 24p. (J). (gr. 2-4). 22.45 (978-1-4103-0313-4(6), Blackbirch Pr., Inc.) Thomson Gale.

Kutner, Merrily. Down on the Farm. Hillenbrand, Will, illus. 2005. 32p. (J). pap. 6.95 (978-0-8234-1985-2(1)) Holiday Hse., Inc.

Lambilly-Bresson, Elisabeth de. Animals on the Farm. 2006. (Illus.). 14p. (J). lib. bdg. (***978-0-8368-7834-9(5)***) Stevens, Gareth Inc.

Lawlor, Elizabeth P. Discover Nature Around the House: Things to Know & Things to Do. 2003. (gr. 3-6). lib. bdg. 24.55 (978-0-613-76161-1(8)) Tandem Library Bks.

Leberer, Sigrid. Farm Animals. 2000. (Funny Fingers Ser.). (Illus.). 16p. (J). pap. 6.95 (978-0-7892-0670-1(6)) Abbeville Pr., Inc.

Longnecker, Theresa. Who Grows Up on the Farm? A Book about Farm Animals & Their Offspring. Carpenter, Melissa, illus. 2004. (Who Grows Up Here? Ser.). 24p. (C). (gr. k-4). 21.26 (978-1-4048-0029-8(8)) Picture Window Bks.

Look Who's Popping Up: On the Farm. 2003. (J). (ps-k). 4.98 (978-0-7525-8903-9(2)) Parragon, Inc.

Lorenz Books Staff & Tuxworth, Nicola. Farm Animals. 2000. (Very First Picture Bks.). (Illus.). 12p. 4.95 (978-0-7548-0062-0(8), Lorenz Bks.) Anness Publishing, Inc.

Macken, JoAnn Early. Animals That Live on theFarm. 24p. (YA). 115.98 (978-0-8368-4284-5(7)) Stevens, Gareth Inc.

McCurry, Kristen. Farm Babies. McCurry, Kristen, ed. 2006. (Illus.). 22p. (J). bds. 5.95 (978-1-55971-941-4(9), NorthWord Bks. for Young Readers) T&N Children's Publishing.

My TakeAlong Li, ed. Farm Animals. 2007. (My Take-along Library). 120p. (J). (ps-k). bds. 14.95 (***978-0-7696-5559-8(9)***) School Specialty Publishing.

Newman-D'Amico, Fran. Farm Animal Mazes. 2006. 32p. (J). pap. 2.95 (978-0-486-45184-8(4)) Dover Pubns., Inc.

Nicholson, Sue. A Day at Greenhill Farm. 1998. (Eyewitness Readers). (Illus.). 32p. (gr. 5-1). pap. 3.99 (978-0-7894-2957-5(8)) Dorling Kindersley Publishing, Inc.

Parker, Helen. Farm Animals. 2006. (Lift Stick & Learn Ser.). (Illus.). 12p. (J). (ps-k). pap. 4.95 (978-1-84610-281-3(2)) Make Believe Ideas GBR. *Dist:* Ingram Pub. Services.

Perols, Sylvaine. La Granja. (Coleccion Mundo Maravilloso). (SPA., Illus.). 40p. (J). (gr. 2-7). (978-84-348-3809-3(5), SM5478) SM Ediciones ESP. *Dist:* Lectorum Pubns., Inc.

Perols, Sylvaine & Gallimard Jeunesse Staff. Farm Animals. 1998. (First Discovery Book Ser.). (Illus.). 24p. (J). (ps-2). 12.95 (978-0-590-11618-3(5)) Scholastic, Inc.

Pets & Farm Animals Action Sticker Book. 2002. 12p. (J). pap. 3.98 (978-0-7525-8039-5(6)) Parragon, Inc.

Phillips, Dee. Find It on the Farm. 2006. (Can You Find It? Ser.). (Illus.). 24p. (J). lib. bdg. 22.00 (978-0-8368-6303-1(8)) Stevens, Gareth Inc.

Pipe, Jim. Farm Animals. 2006. (Read & Play Ser.). (Illus.). 24p. (J). (ps-k). lib. bdg. 22.80 (978-1-59604-112-7(9)) Stargazer Bks.

Play & Learn Fo, ed. Farm Animals. 2007. (Play & Learn Foam Puzzle Bks.). 10p. (J). bds. 16.95 (***978-0-7696-5389-1(8)***, Brighter Child) School Specialty Publishing.

Post, Hans. Creepy Crawlies. Goede, Irene, illus. 2006. 32p. (J). 16.95 (978-1-932425-65-9(9), Lemniscaat) Boyds Mills Pr.

Pountney, Beth. Farmyard Friends. 2007. (Lift & Count Ser.). (Illus.). 12p. (ps). per., bds. 5.95 (978-1-84610-458-9(0)) Make Believe Ideas GBR. *Dist:* Ingram Pub. Services.

Priddy, Roger. Baby Gund Cloth Book Barnyard Buddies. 2006. 10p. 9.95 (***978-0-312-49843-6(8)***, Priddy Bks.) St. Martin's Pr.

—Bright Baby Board Book Farm. 2007. (J). bds. 4.95 (***978-0-312-49777-4(6)***, Priddy Bks.) St. Martin's Pr.

—Bright Baby Touch & Feel on the Farm. 2006. 10p. (J). bds. 4.95 (978-0-312-49859-7(4), Priddy Bks.) St. Martin's Pr.

—Bunny & Friends. rev. ed. 2001. (Touch & Feel Ser.). (Illus.). 12p. (J). bds. 6.95 (978-0-312-49030-0(5), Priddy Bks.) St. Martin's Pr.

—Duckling & Friends: Bright Baby Touch Feel Listen Duckling. rev. ed. 2006. (Touch, Feel & Say Ser.). (Illus.). 10p. (J). bds. 8.95 (978-0-312-49673-9(7), Priddy Bks.) St. Martin's Pr.

—Farm. 2005. (Bright Baby Ser.). 12p. (J). bds. 0.97 (978-0-312-49618-0(4), Priddy Bks.) St. Martin's Pr.

—Farm: Picture Pops. 2006. (Illus.). 18p. (J). 12.95 (978-0-312-49677-7(X), Priddy Bks.) St. Martin's Pr.

Priddy, Roger. Pop up Farm IQ. 2007. 12p. (J). 5.95 (***978-0-312-50047-4(5)***, Priddy Bks.) St. Martin's Pr.

Professor Q's Chinese-English Language Books: Sh#275;ng Chu- Farm Animals. 2006. (J). (978-0-9743359-7-1(5)) Murdock Publishing Co.

Provensen, Alice. Year at Maple Hill Farm. 2001. (ps-2). lib. bdg. 15.30 (978-0-613-90198-7(3)) Tandem Library Bks.

Remson, Billie. A Mississippi Spring on Bluebird Hill. Garraway, Kym W., illus. 2004. per. 12.95 (978-1-59571-004-8(3)) Word Association Pubs.

—A Mississippi Winter on Bluebird Hill: A True Story about Our Little Farm in the Hills of Southern Mississippi. Garraway, Kym, illus. 2004. (J). per. 12.95 (978-1-59571-044-4(2)) Word Association Pubs.

Rettore, Kenny E. Farm Friends. Ferri, Francesca, illus. 2004. 6p. (J). 12.95 (978-0-7641-2809-7(4)) Barron's Educational Series, Inc.

Reyes, Blanca Matilde. Farm Animals. 2006. (Illus.). 16p. (J). act. bk. ed. 0.75 (978-1-933984-02-5(3)) Two Languages.

Ross, Kathy. Crafts for Kids Who are Learning about Farm Animals. Barger, Jan, illus. 2007. (Crafts for Kids Who Are Learning about Ser.). 48p. (J). (gr. k-3). lib. bdg. 25.26 (***978-0-8225-6366-2(5)***, Millbrook Pr.) Lerner Publishing Group.

Sanchez, Isidro. Mi Gato. Ruis, Maria, illus. (Coleccion Mis Animales Preferidos).Tr. of My Cat. (SPA.). 32p. (J). (gr. k-3). 6.36 (978-84-342-1128-0(0), PR0482) Parramon Ediciones S.A. ESP. *Dist:* Lectorum Pubns., Inc.

—Mi Hamster. Ruis, Maria, illus. (Coleccion Mis Animales Preferidos).Tr. of My Hamster. (SPA.). 32p. (J). (gr. k-3). 6.36 (978-84-342-1129-7(7), PR0485) Parramon Ediciones S.A. ESP. *Dist:* Lectorum Pubns., Inc.

—Mi Pajaro. Ruis, Maria, illus. (Coleccion Mis Animales Preferidos).Tr. of My Bird. (SPA.). 32p. (J). (gr. k-3). 6.36 (978-84-342-1127-3(9), PR0483) Parramon Ediciones S.A. ESP. *Dist:* Lectorum Pubns., Inc.

—Mi Perro. Ruis, Maria, illus. (Coleccion Mis Animales Preferidos).Tr. of My Dog. (SPA.). 32p. (J). (gr. k-3). (978-84-342-1126-1(2), PR0481) Parramon Ediciones S.A. ESP. *Dist:* Lectorum Pubns., Inc.

Schlepp, Tammy J. Farm Animals. 2001. 11.79 (978-0-606-22440-6(8)) Tandem Library Bks.

Scholastic, Inc. Staff. Petting Farm. 2007. (Little Scholastic Ser.). (J). (ps). bds. 12.99 incl. DVD (***978-0-439-88558-4(2)***, Cartwheel Bks.) Scholastic, Inc.

School Specialty Publishing. Farm Animals. 2004. (On-File Ser.). 4p. (J). (gr. k-k). ring bd. 4.99 (978-0-7424-2858-4(3), Instructional Fair) Schaffer, Frank Pubns.

Schwartz, David M. At the Farm. Kuhn, Dwight, photos by. 1998. (Springboards into Science Ser.). (Illus.). 24p. (J). (gr. 1 up). lib. bdg. 19.93 (978-0-8368-2221-2(8)) Stevens, Gareth Inc.

Scott, Janine. Farm Friends. 2002. (Spyglass Books). (Illus.). 24p. (J). (gr. 1 up). lib. bdg. 18.60 (978-0-7565-0232-4(2)) Compass Point Bks.

Sing & Learn, ed. Farm Animals. 2007. (Sing & Learn Padded Board Bks.). 53p. (J). bds. 16.95 (***978-0-7696-5429-4(0)***) School Specialty Publishing.

Southwater Staff. Farm Animals: Look & Learn. 2000. (Look & Learn Ser.). (Illus.). 32p. (ps). 7.95 (978-1-84215-091-7(X), Southwater) Anness Publishing GBR. *Dist:* National Bk. Network.

Sovak, Jan. Learning about Farm Animals. 2001. (Learning about Ser.). (Illus.). 16p. (J). (gr. 3-5). pap. 1.50 (978-0-486-41850-6(2)) Dover Pubns., Inc.

Stanley, Mandy. On the Farm. 2002. (All Aboard Ser.). (Illus.). 12p. (J). (gr. k-ps). bds. 3.95 (978-0-7534-5445-9(9), Kingfisher) Houghton Mifflin Co. Trade & Reference Div.

Stanos, Dimi. Taking Care of Farm Animals. 2002. (Windows on Literacy Ser.). (Illus.). 12p. (J). (978-0-7922-8482-6(8)) National Geographic Society.

Sterling Publishing Company Staff. Baby Animals. 1999. (Balloon Ser.). (Illus.). 6p. (ps-k). 2.95 (978-0-8069-1919-5(1)) Sterling Publishing Co., Inc.

—Farm Animals. 1999. (Balloon Ser.). (Illus.). 6p. (ps-k). 2.95 (978-0-8069-1917-1(5)) Sterling Publishing Co., Inc.

Stewart, Pat L. Old Macdonald's Farm Stickers. 2003. (Dover Little Activity Bks.). (Illus.). 4p. (J). pap. 1.50 (978-0-486-43010-2(3)) Dover Pubns., Inc.

Stone, Lynn M. Farm Animals. 2001. (Life on the Farm Ser.). (Illus.). 24p. (J). (gr. 1-4). lib. bdg. 20.64 (978-1-58952-090-5(4)) Rourke Publishing, LLC.

Tarbett, Debbie, illus. Farm Babies. 2006. 12p. (J). (ps). bds. 12.99 (978-0-7566-2721-8(4)) Dorling Kindersley Publishing, Inc.

Teora, ed. Hi Read Stick & Learn about Farm Animals. 2004. (Illus.). 20p. pap. 6.99 (978-1-59496-049-9(6)) Teora USA LLC.

Tiger Tales, Inc., creator. Farm Animals. 2006. (Illus.). 24p. (J). bds. 7.95 (978-1-58925-797-9(9), tiger tales) ME Media LLC.

Time for Dinner: Individual Title Six-Packs. (Chiquilibros Ser.). (gr. k-1). 23.00 (978-0-7635-0414-4(9)) Rigby Education.

Toms, Kate. Farm Animals. 2006. (Funny Faces Ser.). (Illus.). 10p. (ps-k). bds. 9.95 (978-1-84610-117-5(4)) Make Believe Ideas GBR. *Dist:* Ingram Pub. Services.

Tuxworth, Nicola. Farm Animals. 2005. (Illus.). 12p. (ps). bds. 6.99 (978-0-7548-1335-4(5), Lorenz Bks.) Anness Publishing GBR. *Dist:* National Bk. Network.

—Farm Animals: A Very First Picture Book. 1999. (Pictures & Words Ser.). (Illus.). 24p. (J). (ps up). lib. bdg. 22.00 (978-0-8368-2271-7(4)) Stevens, Gareth Inc.

Tuxworth, Nicola & Lorenz Editors. Farm Animals. 2001. (Very First Picture Bks.). (Illus.). 20p. 5.95 (978-0-7548-0941-8(2)) Anness Publishing GBR. *Dist:* National Bk. Network.

Van Eerbeek, Ton. The World of Farm Animals: An Early Encyclopedia for Beginning Readers. Balloon Books Staff, ed. 2002. (Animal Bring-Along Bks.). (Illus.). 24p. (J). (ps-1). 4.95 (978-0-8069-8461-2(9), Balloon Bks.) Sterling Publishing Co., Inc.

Wald, Christina, illus. The Barnyard Read-and-Play. 2006. 12p. pap. 7.95 (978-1-58017-640-8(2)) Storey Publishing, LLC.

Walker-Hodge, Judith. Animal Hospital. 1999. (Eyewitness Readers). (Illus.). 32p. (J). (gr. 5-4). pap. 3.99 (978-0-7894-3996-3(4), 0-7894-4752-5) Dorling Kindersley Publishing, Inc.

—Animal Hospital. 1999. (J). 10.79 (978-0-606-18988-0(2)) Tandem Library Bks.

Wallace, Bruce & Make Believe Ideas Staff. Farm Animals. 2005. (Touch & Sparkle Ser.). (Illus.). 12p. (ps-k). bds. 5.95 (978-1-905051-02-1(6)) Make Believe Ideas GBR. *Dist:* Ingram Pub. Services.

Watt, Fiona & Wells, Rachel. Anifeiliaid y Fferm. 2005. (WEL., Illus.). 8p. (978-1-84512-000-9(0)) Cymdeithas Lyfrau Ceredigion.

Weber, Vicky. Animal Babies on the Farm. Kingfisher Editors, ed. 2005. (Animal Babies Ser.). (Illus.). 24p. (J). (ps-k). bds. 6.95 (978-0-7534-5838-9(1), Kingfisher) Houghton Mifflin Co. Trade & Reference Div.

Who Grows up on the Farm? (Who Grows up Here? Ser.). 24p. (J). 7.95 (978-1-4048-0211-7(8)) Picture Window Bks.

Wildsmith, Brian. Los Animales de la Granja. 2005. (SPA., Illus.). 16p. (J). (ps-ps). per. 5.95 (978-1-59572-004-7(9)) Star Bright Bks., Inc.

Wildsmith, Brian, illus. Brian Wildsmith's Farm Animals (Korean) 2003. (KOR.). 16p. (J). bds. 4.95 (978-1-932065-19-0(9), 1-718-784-9112) Star Bright Bks., Inc.

—Brian Wildsmith's Farm Animals (Portugese) 2003. (POR.). 16p. (J). bds. 4.95 (978-1-932065-20-6(2), 1-718-784-9112) Star Bright Bks., Inc.

—Brian Wildsmith's Farm Animals (Simplified Chinese) 2003. (CHI.). 16p. (J). bds. 4.95 (978-1-932065-22-0(9), 1-718-784-9112) Star Bright Bks., Inc.

—Brian Wildsmith's Farm Animals (Tagalog) 2003. (TAG.). 16p. (J). bds. 4.95 (978-1-932065-29-9(6), 1-718-784-9112) Star Bright Bks., Inc.

—Brian Wildsmith's Farm Animals (Traditional Chinese) 2003. (CHI.). 16p. (J). bds. 4.95 (978-1-932065-23-7(7), 1-718-784-9112) Star Bright Bks., Inc.

—Brian Wildsmith's Farm Animals (Vietnamese) 2003. (VIE.). 16p. (J). bds. 4.95 (978-1-932065-21-3(0)) Star Bright Bks., Inc.

Wildsmith, Brian & Ayiilaa, Naaltsoos. Brian Wildsmith's Farm Animals (Navajo) 2004. Tr. of Farm Animals. (NAV., Illus.). 16p. (J). bds. 4.95 (978-1-932065-26-8(1)) Star Bright Bks., Inc.

Wilkinson, Doris J. Farm Animals. Wilkinson, Doris J., ed. Chipping, Oliver, illus. 2000. (Jacob's Magic Box Discovery Ser.). 20p. (J). (ps). pap. 4.95 (978-0-9700386-2-3(3)) Magic Box Pubns.

Yoon, Salina, illus. Peek-a-Boo Farm Animals. 2005. (Peek-a-Boo Guess Who Book Ser.: Vol. 2). 10p. (J). 7.95 (978-1-58117-158-7(7), Intervisual/Piggy Toes) Dalmatian Pr.

Yoyo Books Staff. Farm Animals: Animal Jigsaw Fun. 2004. 12p. bds. 9.95 (978-90-5843-549-1(0)) YoYo Bks. BEL. *Dist:* National Bk. Network.

DOMESTIC ANIMALS—DISEASES

see Veterinary Medicine

DOMESTIC ANIMALS—FICTION

Albee, Sarah. Where Is Pig? Velez, Walter, illus. 2006. (Step-By-Step Readers Ser.). (J). pap. (978-1-59939-056-7(6), Reader's Digest Young Families, Inc.) Reader's Digest Children's Publishing, Inc.

Alex Toys Staff. Farm Fun: Bath Book & Squirting Tub Toy. Silver-Thompson, Pattie, illus. 2007. (Little Squirts Ser.). 8p. (J). (ps-17). 7.99 (***978-0-316-06525-2(0)***) Little, Brown Bks. for Young Readers.

Allen, Nancy K. Once upon a Dime: A Math Adventure. Doyle, Adam, illus. 2004. (Math Adventures Ser.). 32p. (J). pap. 6.95 (978-1-57091-161-3(4)) Charlesbridge Publishing, Inc.

Amerel. The Summer Holidays: A Story for Childre. 2006. pap. (***978-1-4065-0808-6(X)***) Dodo Pr.

Amery, H. Where's Curly? Cartwright, Stephen, illus. 2004. (Treasury of Farmyard Tales Ser.). 16p. (J). (gr. 1 up). lib. bdg. 15.95 (978-1-58086-563-0(1)) EDC Publishing.

—Where's Woolly? Cartwright, Stephen, illus. 2004. (Treasury of Farmyard Tales Ser.). 16p. (J). (gr. 1 up). lib. bdg. 15.95 (978-1-58086-531-9(3)) EDC Publishing.

Amery, Heather. Farmyard Tales Treasury - Internet Referenced. Cartwright, Stephen, illus. 2007. 96p. (J). 19.99 (978-0-7945-1440-2(5), Usborne) EDC Publishing.

Anderson, Carolyn. Granny's Farm Friends. 2005. (J). per. 39.95 (978-1-59453-550-5(7), Airleaf Publishing) Airleaf Publishing & Bookselling.

Anderson, Peggy Perry. Chuck's Band. 2008. 32p. (J). 16.00 (***978-0-618-96506-9(8)***) Houghton Mifflin Co.

Anderson, Peggy Perry. Chuck's Truck. 2006. (Illus.). 32p. (J). (gr. k-3). 16.00 (978-0-618-66836-6(5)) Houghton Mifflin Co.

Annabelle Alpaca Plants a Garden. 2002. (J). 7.99 (978-0-9746409-0-7(5)) O'Neill, Jan.

Armstrong, Alan W. Whittington. Schindler, S. D., illus. 2005. 208p. (J). (gr. 3-7). 14.95 (978-0-375-82864-5(8)); lib. bdg. 16.99 (978-0-375-92864-2(2)) Random Hse. Children's Bks. (Random Hse. Bks. for Young Readers).

Arnold, Marsha Diane. Roar of a Snore. Pratt, Pierre, illus. 2006. (J). (ps). 32p. 16.99 (978-0-8037-2936-0(7)); (***978-1-4156-8271-5(2)***) Penguin Group (USA) Inc. (Dial).

Auch, Mary Jane. Poultrygeist. Jane, Mary & Auch, Herm, illus. 32p. (J). (gr. k-3). reprint ed. 6.95 (978-0-8234-1876-3(6)) Holiday Hse., Inc.

Auch, Mary Jane & Auch, Herm. Souperchicken. 2003. (Illus.). 32p. (J). (gr. k-3). reprint ed. pap. 6.95 (978-0-8234-1829-9(4)) Holiday Hse., Inc.

Baddiel, Ivor & Jubb, Sophie. Cock-A-Doodle Quack Quack. Busby, Ailie, illus. 2007. 40p. (J). (ps-3). 15.99 (978-0-385-75104-9(4)); lib. bdg. 18.99 (978-0-385-75105-6(2)) Random Hse. Children's Bks. (Fickling, David Bks.).

Bailey, Linda. The Farm Team. Slavin, Bill, illus. 2006. 32p. (J). (978-1-55337-850-1(4)) Kids Can Pr., Ltd.

Baker, Alan. Little Rabbits First Farm Book. 2001. (Little Rabbit Bks.). (Illus.). 32p. (J). (ps-k). tchr. ed. 11.95 (978-0-7534-5352-0(5), Kingfisher) Houghton Mifflin Co. Trade & Reference Div.

Balian, Lorna. Humbug Rabbit. 2004. (Illus.). 40p. (J). 15.95 (978-1-932065-40-4(7)) Star Bright Bks., Inc.

Barn Party: Level M, 6 vols. 128p. (gr. 2-3). 49.95 (978-0-7699-0983-7(3)) Shortland Pubns. (U. S. A.) Inc.

Beaumont, Karen. Duck, Duck, Goose! (A Coyote's on the Loose!) Aruego, Jose, illus. 2004. 32p. (J). (ps-2). 16.99 (978-0-06-050802-9(7)); lib. bdg. 17.89 (978-0-06-050804-3(3)) HarperCollins Pubs.

Benjamin, A. H. Baa! Moo! What Will We Do? Chapman, Jane, tr. Chapman, Jane, illus. 2003. 32p. (J). pap. 6.95 (978-1-58925-381-0(7), tiger tales) ME Media LLC.

Blackman, Malorie. Jessica Strange. (Illus.). (J). 2003. 32p. pap. 8.99 (978-0-340-77964-4(0)); 2002. 24p. 17.99 (978-0-340-77963-7(2)) Hodder General Publishing Division GBR. (Hodder & Stoughton). *Dist:* Trafalgar Square Publishing.

Bloom, Becky. Wolf. Biet, Pascal, illus. 1999. 32p. (J). (ps-3). pap. 16.95 (978-0-531-30155-9(5), Orchard Bks.) Scholastic, Inc.

Bock, Lee. Oh Crumps/ Ay, Caramba. de la Jusa, Eida, tr. Midgett, Morgan, illus. 2006. (SPA.). (J). 4.99 (978-0-9770906-3-1(9)) Raven Tree Pr.

—Oh, Crumps!/¡Ay, Caramba! de la Vega, Eida, tr. Midgett, Morgan, illus. 2003. Tr. of ¡Ay, Caramba!. (SPA & ENG.). 32p. (J). (gr. k-3). 16.95 (978-0-9720192-4-8(3) , 626999) Raven Tree Pr.

Bonnell, Kris. The Petting Farm. 2005. (J). 3.75 (978-1-933727-11-0(X)) Reading Reading Bks., LLC.

Boonen, Stefan. When Pigs Fly! Loufane, illus. 2004. 32p. (J). 6.95 (978-1-58925-384-1(1) , tiger tales) ME Media LLC.

Broekstra, Lorette. Baby Bbear Goes to the Farm. 2004. (Baby-Bear Ser.). (Illus.). 32p. (J). 5.99 (978-1-85854-488-5(2)) Brimax Books Ltd. GBR. *Dist:* Byeway Bks.

Brooks, Walter R. Freddy & the Bean Home News. Wiese, Kurt, illus. 2000. (Freddy Ser.). 230p. (J). (gr. 3-7). 23.95 (978-1-58567-081-9(2)) Overlook Pr., The.

—Freddy & the IgnormOus. Wiese, Kurt, illus. 2001. 288p. (J). pap. 6.99 (978-0-14-230043-5(8) , Puffin) Penguin Group (USA) Inc.

—Freddy & the Ignormus. 2001. (gr. 3-6). lib. bdg. 15.30 (978-0-613-43621-2(0)) Tandem Library Bks.

—Freddy & the Perilous Adventure. Wiese, Kurt, illus. 2001. 245p. (J). 23.95 (978-1-58567-178-6(9)) Overlook Pr., The.

—Freddy & the Pilot. Wiese, Kurt, illus. 1999. 288p. (J). (gr. 3-7). 23.95 (978-0-87951-941-4(X)) Overlook Pr., The.

—Freddy & the Politician. Wiese, Kurt, illus. 2000. (Freddy Ser.). 253p. (J). (gr. 3-7). 23.95 (978-1-58567-080-2(4)) Overlook Pr., The.

—Freddy & the Popinjay. Wiese, Kurt, illus. 2001. 244p. (J). (gr. 4-7). 23.95 (978-1-58567-134-2(7)) Overlook Pr., The.

—Freddy & the Space Ship. Wiese, Kurt, illus. 2001. 262p. (J). (gr. 3). 23.95 (978-1-58567-105-2(3)) Overlook Pr., The.

—Freddy Goes Camping. Wiese, Kurt, illus. 2001. 258p. (J). 23.95 (978-1-58567-177-9(0)) Overlook Pr., The.

—Freddy Goes Camping. 2003. (gr. 3-6). lib. bdg. 16.45 (978-0-613-61624-9(3)) Tandem Library Bks.

—Freddy Goes to Florida. Wiese, Kurt, illus. 2001. 208p. (J). (gr. 4-7). pap. 7.99 (978-0-14-131233-0(5) , Puffin) Penguin Group (USA) Inc.

—Freddy Goes to Florida. Wiese, Kurt, illus. 2001. 196p. (J). (gr. 4-7). per. 15.30 (978-0-613-36062-3(1)) Tandem Library Bks.

—Freddy Goes to the North Pole. Wiese, Kurt, illus. 2001. 306p. (J). 23.95 (978-1-58567-104-5(5)) Overlook Pr., The.

—Freddy the Pilot. 2000. (YA). pap. 67.95 incl. audio (978-0-7887-4167-8(5) , 41111) Recorded Bks., LLC.

—Freddy the Pilot. 2001. (978-0-606-22516-8(1)) Tandem Library Bks.

—Freddy's Cousin Weedly. Wiese, Kurt, illus. 2002. 220p. (J). 23.95 (978-1-58567-309-4(9)) Overlook Pr., The.

Brown, Craig. In the Spring. Brown, Craig, illus. 2004. (Illus.). 21p. (J). reprint ed. 14.00 (978-0-7567-8298-6(8)) DIANE Publishing Co.

Brown, Jo. Hoppity Skip Little Chick. 2005. (Illus.). 32p. (J). 15.95 (978-1-58925-045-1(1) , tiger tales) ME Media LLC.

Brown, Margaret Wise. Big Red Barn. 2002. (Illus.). (J). 25.11 (978-0-7587-2100-6(5)) Book Wholesalers, Inc.

—El Gran Granero Rojo. Bond, Felicia, illus. 2003. (SPA.). 34p. (J). (ps-1). bds. 7.99 (978-0-06-009107-1(X)) HarperCollins Pubs.

Bruss, Deborah. Book! Book! Book! Beeke, Tiphanie, illus. 2001. (J). (ps-1). 40p. pap. 16.95 (978-0-439-13525-2(7)); pap. (978-0-439-13526-9(5)) Scholastic, Inc.

Bunting, Eve. Hurry! Hurry! Mack, Jeff, illus. 2007. 40p. (J). (ps-1). 16.00 (978-0-15-205410-6(3)) Harcourt Trade Pubs.

Capucilli, Alyssa Satin. Biscuit's Day at the Farm. Schories, Pat, illus. (My First I Can Read Bks.). 32p. (J). 2008. pap. 3.99 (***978-0-06-074169-3(4)*** , Harper Trophy); 2007. 15.99 (978-0-06-074167-9(8)); 2007. lib. bdg. 16.89 (978-0-06-074168-6(6)) HarperCollins Pubs.

Carle, Eric. The Very Busy Spider. 2006. (World of Eric Carle Ser.). (Illus.). 24p. (J). (ps-1). pap. 5.99 (978-0-448-44421-5(6) , Grosset & Dunlap) Penguin Group (USA) Inc.

Carlstrom, Nancy White. The Way to Wyatt's House. Morgan, Mary, illus. 2000. 32p. (J). (gr. k-3). lib. bdg. 16.85 (978-0-8027-8742-2(8)); 15.95 (978-0-8027-8740-8(1)) Walker & Co.

Carpenter, Dimitrea. Together. 2006. 24p. (J). pap. 8.99 (978-0-439-80323-6(3) , Orchard Bks.) Scholastic, Inc.

Cazet, Denys. Minnie & Moo: The Attack of the Easter Bunnies. Cazet, Denys, illus. 2004. (I Can Read Bks.). (Illus.). 48p. (J). (gr. k-3). 15.99 (978-0-06-000506-1(8)); lib. bdg. 17.89 (978-0-06-000507-8(6)) HarperCollins Pubs.

—Minnie & Moo: The Case of the Missing Jelly Donut. Cazet, Denys, illus. (I Can Read Bks.). 48p. (J). 2006. pap. 3.99 (978-0-06-073009-3(9) , Harper Trophy); 2005. (Illus.). 15.99 (978-0-06-073007-9(2)) HarperCollins Pubs.

—Minnie & Moo: The Night of the Living Bed. Cazet, Denys, illus. (I Can Read Bks.). 48p. (J). (gr. k-3). 2004. pap. 3.99 (978-0-06-000505-4(X) , Harper Trophy); 2003. (Illus.). 16.99 (978-0-06-000503-0(3)); 2003. (Illus.). lib. bdg. 16.89 (978-0-06-000504-7(1)) HarperCollins Pubs.

—Minnie & Moo & the Seven Wonders of the World. Cazet, Denys, illus. 2003. (Illus.). 144p. (J). 16.95 (978-0-689-85330-2(0) , Atheneum/Richard Jackson Bks.) Simon & Schuster Children's Publishing.

—Minnie & Moo & the Thanksgiving Tree. Cazet, Denys, illus. 2002. (Minnie & Moo Ser.). (Illus.). (J). 11.45 (978-0-7587-6206-1(2)) Book Wholesalers, Inc.

—Minnie & Moo & the Thanksgiving Tree. Cazet, Denys, illus. 2002. (Live Oak Readalong Ser.). (Illus.). (J). pap. 16.95 incl. audio (978-0-87499-914-3(6)); 28.95 incl. audio compact disk (978-1-59112-587-7(1)) Live Oak Media.

—Minnie & Moo & the Thanksgiving Tree. 2000. (ps-2). lib. bdg. 11.80 (978-0-613-32839-5(6)) Tandem Library Bks.

—Minnie & Moo Meet Frankenswine. Cazet, Denys, illus. 2002. (Minnie & Moo Ser.). (Illus.). 12.34 (978-1-4046-1308-9(0)) Book Wholesalers, Inc.

—Minnie & Moo Meet Frankenswine. Cazet, Denys, illus. (I Can Read Bks.: Bk. 3). (Illus.). 48p. (J). 2002. pap. 3.99 (978-0-06-444311-1(6)); 2001. 15.89 (978-0-06-623749-7(1)); 2001. 14.95 (978-0-06-623748-0(3)) HarperCollins Pubs.

—Minnie & Moo Meet Frankenswine. Cazet, Denys, illus. (Readalongs for Beginning Readers Ser.). (Illus.). 2005. (J). pap. 16.95 incl. audio (978-1-59112-261-6(9)); 2005. (J). pap. 18.95 incl. audio compact disk (978-1-59112-875-5(7)); 2004. 28.95 incl. audio compact disk (978-1-59112-876-2(5)); 2004. (J). 25.95 incl. audio (978-1-59112-262-3(7)); 2004. (J). pap. 29.95 incl. audio (978-1-59112-263-0(5)); 2004. (J). pap. 31.95 incl. audio compact disk (978-1-59112-877-9(3)) Live Oak Media.

—Minnie & Moo Meet Frankenswine. 2002. (gr. k-3). lib. bdg. 11.80 (978-0-613-62183-0(2)) Tandem Library Bks.

—The Night of the Living Bed. Cazet, Denys, illus. unabr. ed. 2005. (Minnie & Moo Ser.). (J). (gr. k-4). (Illus.). 25.95 incl. audio (978-1-59519-389-6(8)); (Illus.). 28.95 incl. audio compact disk (978-1-59519-393-3(6)); (Illus.). pap. 16.95 incl. audio (978-1-59519-388-9(X)); (Illus.). pap. 18.95 incl. audio compact disk (978-1-59519-392-6(8)); Set. pap. 31.95 incl. audio compact disk (978-1-59519-394-0(4)); Set. (Illus.). pap. 29.95 incl. audio (978-1-59519-390-2(1)) Live Oak Media.

Cazet, Denys & Dorling Kindersley Publishing Staff. Minnie & Moo & the Thanksgiving Tree. Cazet, Denys, illus. 2000. (Illus.). 48p. (J). (gr. 1-3). 12.99 (978-0-7894-2654-3(4)); pap. 3.99 (978-0-7894-2655-0(2)) Dorling Kindersley Publishing, Inc.

Chaconas, Dori. Coriander the Contrary Hen. Carrington, Marsha Gray, illus. 2007. 32p. (J). (gr. k-4). spiral bd. 15.95 (978-1-57505-749-1(2) , Carolrhoda Bks.) Lerner Publishing Group.

Chapman, Keith. Itsy Bitsy Spider. Tickle, Jack, illus. 2006. 32p. (J). 15.95 (978-1-58925-055-0(9) , tiger tales) ME Media LLC.

Chitwood, Suzanne. Wake Up, Big Barn. Chitwood, Suzanne, illus. 2002. (Illus.). 40p. (J). (ps-2). pap. 15.95 (978-0-439-26627-7(0) , Cartwheel Bks.) Scholastic, Inc.

Christelow, Eileen. Where's the Big Bad Wolf? Christelow, Eileen, illus. 2002. (Illus.). 40p. (J). (gr. k-3). tchr. ed. 16.00 (978-0-618-18194-0(6) , Clarion Bks.) Houghton Mifflin Co. Trade & Reference Div.

Church, Caroline Jayne. Digby Takes Charge. 2007. 32p. (J). (ps-2). 14.99 (978-1-4169-3441-7(3) , McElderry, Margaret K.) Simon & Schuster Children's Publishing.

Church, Caroline Jayne, illus. Little Apple Goat. 2007. 28p. (J). (ps-2). 16.00 (***978-0-8028-5320-2(X)*** , Eerdmans Bks For Young Readers) Eerdmans, William B. Publishing Co.

Click Clack Moo Cows That Type Spanish. 2004. (J). pap. 32.75 incl. audio (978-1-55592-652-6(5)); (SPA.). pap. 14.95 incl. audio (978-1-55592-653-3(3)) Weston Woods Studios, Inc.

Cohen, Caron Lee. Digger Pig & the Turnip. Denise, Christopher, illus. 2003. (Green Light Readers Level 2 Ser.). 24p. (J). 11.95 (978-0-15-204869-3(3)); pap. 3.95 (978-0-15-204829-7(4)) Harcourt Children's Bks. (Green Light Readers).

Courtin, Thierry. Decouvre les petits de la Ferme. 15.95 (978-2-09-202273-3(3)) Nathan, Fernand FRA. *Dist:* Distribooks, Inc.

Cowley, Joy. Mr. Wishy Washy. Fuller, Elizabeth, illus. 2003. 18p. (J). (ps-1). bds. 5.99 (978-0-399-24200-7(7) , Philomel) Penguin Group (USA) Inc.

—Mrs. Wishy Washy Makes a Splash. Fuller, Elizabeth, illus. 2003. 18p. (J). (ps-1). bds. 5.99 (978-0-399-24201-4(5) , Philomel) Penguin Group (USA) Inc.

Coxe, Molly. Big Egg. Coxe, Molly, illus. 2002. (Illus.). (J). 11.91 (978-0-7587-6028-9(0)) Book Wholesalers, Inc.

Crebbin, June. Cows in the Kitchen. McEwen, Katharine, illus. 2003. 24p. (J). (gr. k-k). bds. 6.99 (978-0-7636-2129-2(3)) Candlewick Pr.

Crisp, Marty. Black & White. Neidigh, Sherry, illus. 2000. 24p. (ps-3). 12.95 (978-0-87358-756-3(1) , Rising Moon Bks. for Young Readers) Northland Publishing.

Cronin, Doreen. Click, Clack, Moo: Cows That Type. Lewin, Betsy, illus. 2000. 32p. (J). (ps-3). 15.95 (978-0-689-83213-0(3)) Simon & Schuster Children's Publishing.

—Click, Clack, Moo: Cows That Type. 2004. 29.95 incl. cd-rom (978-1-55592-104-0(3)); (J). pap. 18.95 incl. audio compact disk (978-1-55592-139-2(6)); (J). pap. 38.75 incl. audio compact disk (978-1-55592-630-4(4)); (J). pap. 32.75 incl. audio (978-1-55592-183-5(3)); (J). pap. 32.75 incl. audio (978-1-55592-347-1(X)); (J). pap. 14.95 incl. audio (978-1-55592-171-2(X)) Weston Woods Studios, Inc.

—Click, Clack, Moo: Cows That Type. Lewin, Betsy, illus. 2004. (J). 24.95 incl. audio (978-1-55592-077-7(2)) Weston Woods Studios, Inc.

—Click, Clack, Moo: Cows that Type. 2006. (Illus.). (J). (ps-3). 22.78 (978-1-59961-088-7(4)) Spotlight.

—Dooby Dooby Moo. Lewin, Betsy, illus. 2006. 40p. (J). (ps-2). 16.95 (978-0-689-84507-9(3)) Simon & Schuster Children's Publishing.

—Giggle, Giggle, Quack. 2006. (J). (ps-3). 22.78 (978-1-59961-092-4(2)) Spotlight.

—Jaja, Jijí, Cuac. Jimenez, Alberto, tr. from ENG. Lewin, Betsy, illus. 2003. Tr. of Giggle, Giggle, Quack. (SPA.). (J). 15.00 (978-1-930332-46-1(7)) Lectorum Pubns., Inc.

Cronin, Doreen & Lewin, Betsy. Giggle, Giggle, Quack. 2002. (Illus.). 32p. (J). (ps-3). 15.95 (978-0-689-84506-2(5)) Simon & Schuster Children's Publishing.

Cruickshank, Margrit. Down by the Pond: A Surprise Farmyard Book. Saunders, Dave, illus. 1999. 32p. (J). (ps-k). pap. 7.99 (978-0-7112-0978-7(2)) Lincoln, Frances Ltd. GBR. *Dist:* Transition Vendor.

Dalmatian Press Staff. Old Macdonald Had a Farm: Musical Book to Color. (Musical Book to Color Ser.). 32p. (J). pap. 3.99 (978-1-4037-0715-4(4)) Dalmatian Pr.

Davenier, Christine. Leon & Albertine. Barth, Dominic, tr. 1998. (Illus.). 32p. (J). (ps-1). pap. 15.95 (978-0-531-30072-5(2) , Orchard Bks.) Scholastic, Inc.

DePrisco, Dorothea. Mini Whos on the Farm. 2006. 10p. 4.95 (978-1-58117-508-0(6) , Intervisual/Piggy Toes) Dalmatian Pr.

Dipucchio, Kelly. What's the Magic Word? Winborn, Marsha, illus. 2005. 32p. (J). (ps-1). 15.99 (978-0-06-000578-8(5)) HarperCollins Pubs.

DK Publishing Staff. Fun on the Farm Activity Book. 2007. 28p. (J). (ps-1). pap. 19.99 (***978-0-7566-3212-0(9)***) Dorling Kindersley Publishing, Inc.

—Peekaboo Farm. 2007. 12p. (J). (ps-2). bds. 6.99 (***978-0-7566-3104-8(1)***) Dorling Kindersley Publishing, Inc.

Doepker, David. Funny Farm. Sterling Publishing Company Staff, ed. 2004. (Illus.). 16p. (J). bds. 4.95 (978-1-4027-1316-3(9) , 1233029) Sterling Publishing Co., Inc.

—Zany Zoo. Sterling Publishing Company Staff, ed. 2004. (Illus.). 16p. (J). bds. 4.95 (978-1-4027-1317-0(7) , 1233028) Sterling Publishing Co., Inc.

Doreen Cronin: Click-Clack & More. 2006. (J). (ps-3). 136.68 (978-1-59961-087-0(6)) Spotlight.

Dorling Kindersley Publishing Staff, ed. Old MacDonald Had a Farm. 2004. (Baby Fun Ser.). (Illus.). 16p. (J). bds. 5.99 (978-0-7566-0591-9(1)) Dorling Kindersley Publishing, Inc.

Dunbar, Joyce. A Chick Called Saturday. Granstrom, Brita, illus. 2004. 32p. (J). 16.00 (978-0-8028-5260-1(2)) Eerdmans, William B. Publishing Co.

Dunrea, Olivier. Boo Boo. 2008. (Illus.). 32p. (J). (gr. k-ps). bds. 6.95 (***978-0-618-75505-9(5)***) Houghton Mifflin Co. Trade & Reference Div.

Dunrea, Olivier. Gossie & Friends: A First Flap Book. 2006. (Illus.). 12p. (J). (ps-k). 11.99 (978-0-618-70786-7(7)) Houghton Mifflin Co.

Duvoisin, Roger. Donkey-Donkey. 2007. 56p. (J). (gr. k-1). 15.99 (978-0-375-84065-4(6)); lib. bdg. 18.99 (978-0-375-94065-1(0)) Random Hse. Children's Bks. (Knopf Bks. for Young Readers).

Edwards, Julie & Hamilton, Emma Walton. Dumpy's Extra-Busy Day. Walton, Tony & Boyd, Katherine H., illus. 2006. (I Can Read Bks.). 32p. (J). 15.99 (978-0-06-088576-2(9) , Julie Andrews Collection) HarperCollins Pubs.

Edwards, Julie Andrews. Dumpy's Extra-Busy Day. Walton, Tony, illus. 2006. (I Can Read Bks.). 32p. (J). pap. 3.99 (978-0-06-088578-6(5) , Harper Trophy) HarperCollins Pubs.

Edwards, Julie Andrews & Hamilton, Emma Walton. Dumpy to the Rescue! Walton, Tony, illus. 2004. (My First I Can Read Bks.). 32p. (J). (ps up). 14.99 (978-0-06-052689-4(0)); pap. 3.99 (978-0-06-052691-7(2)); lib. bdg. 15.89 (978-0-06-052690-0(4)) HarperCollins Pubs.

Edwards, Julie Andrews & Hamilton, Emma Walton. Dumpy to the Rescue. Walton, Tony, illus. 2004. 24p. (J). lib. bdg. 13.85 (***978-1-4242-0707-7(X)***) Fitzgerald Bks.

Edwards, Pamela Duncan. McGillycuddy Could! Porter, Sue, illus. 2005. 32p. (J). (ps-1). 14.99 (978-0-06-029001-6(3)); lib. bdg. 15.89 (978-0-06-029002-3(1)) HarperCollins Pubs.

Egan, Kate. Charlotte's Web: The Movie Storybook. 2006. (Charlotte's Web Ser.). 48p. (J). 8.99 (978-0-06-088625-7(0)) HarperCollins Pubs.

Egan, Tim. Serious Farm. 2006. (Illus.). 32p. (J). (gr. k-3). 6.95 (978-0-618-73745-1(6)) Houghton Mifflin Co. Trade & Reference Div.

—Serious Farm. Egan, Tim, illus. 2003. (Illus.). 32p. (J). (gr. k-3). 15.00 (978-0-618-22694-8(X)) Houghton Mifflin Co. Trade & Reference Div.

Ellis, Tacy. Goat Tales: Stories of Izzy & Her Friends. Collins, Don, illus. 2006. 128p. (J). 17.95 (978-1-931721-78-3(5)) Bright Sky Pr.

Ellmore, Melba C. U-Shaped Shoes. Roseberry, Susan, illus. 2001. 32p. (J). (ps-3). 14.95 (978-0-8249-5425-3(4) , Ideals Children's Bks.) Ideals Pubns.

Elschner, Geraldine. Mark's Messy Room. Myngheer, Charise, tr. from GER. Junge, Alexandra, illus. 2006. 32p. (J). (ps-3). 16.99 (978-0-698-40047-4(X) , Minedition) Penguin Group (USA) Inc.

Faulkner, Keith. Funny Farm. Lambert, Jonathan, illus. 2002. (Mixed-Up Pop-Up Bks.). 5p. (J). (ps-1). 7.95 (978-0-439-30904-2(2) , Cartwheel Bks.) Scholastic, Inc.

—Surprise on the Farm. Clucas, Philip, illus. 2000. (J). (978-0-439-21059-1(3)) Scholastic, Inc.

Fernandes, Eugenie. Busy Little Mouse. Fernandes, Kim, illus. 2006. 24p. 6.95 (978-1-55453-027-4(X)) Kids Can Pr., Ltd. CAN. *Dist:* Wybel Marketing Group.

—Busy Little Mouse. Fernandes, Kim, illus. 2004. 20p. (ps-ps). lib. bdg. 12.75 (978-0-606-31383-4(4)) Tandem Library Bks.

Fisher, Carolyn. A Twisted Tale. 2004. (Illus.). 33p. (J). (gr. k-4). reprint ed. 16.00 (978-0-7567-8412-6(3)) DIANE Publishing Co.

—A Twisted Tale. 2002. (Illus.). 40p. (J). (ps-3). 15.95 (978-0-375-81540-9(6) , Knopf Bks. for Young Readers) Random Hse. Children's Bks.

Foreman, Michael. Cat in the Manger. rev. ed. 2001. (Illus.). 32p. (J). (ps-3). 17.95 (978-0-8050-6677-7(2) , Holt, Henry & Co. Bks. For Young Readers) Holt, Henry & Co.

Fox, Mem. Hattie & the Fox. Mullins, Patricia, illus. 2005. (Stories to Go! Ser.). 32p. (J). 4.99 (978-1-4169-0308-6(9) , Aladdin) Simon & Schuster Children's Publishing.

Frantz, Jennifer. Charlotte's Web: Coloring & Activity Book & Stickers. Kirkland, Boyd, illus. 2006. (Charlotte's Web Ser.). 32p. (J). pap., act. bk. ed. 3.99 (978-0-06-088275-4(1)) HarperCollins Pubs.

—Wilbur Finds a Friend. Ivanov, Aleksey, illus. 2006. (Charlotte's Web Ser.). 32p. (J). 15.99 (978-0-06-088282-2(4)); pap. 3.99 (978-0-06-088281-5(6) , Harper Trophy) HarperCollins Pubs.

—Wilbur's Prize. Ivanov, Aleksey, illus. 2006. (Charlotte's Web Ser.). 32p. (J). pap. 3.99 (978-0-06-088283-9(2) , Harper Trophy) HarperCollins Pubs.

Friend, Catherine. The Perfect Nest. Manders, John, illus. 2007. (J). (ps-2). 40p. 16.99 (978-0-7636-2430-9(6)); (***978-1-4287-3697-9(2)***) Candlewick Pr.

A friend for Flash. 2006. (J). per. 3.99 (978-1-934004-14-2(6)) Byeway Bks.

Gernhart, Cyndi. Gertrude Sees... On the Farm. Gernhart, Cyndi et al, illus. l.t. ed. 2006. 20p. (J). 8.00 (978-0-9778240-0-7(4)) Prairie Winds Publishing.

Giggle, Giggle Quack. 2004. (J). 24.95 incl. audio (978-1-55592-691-5(6)); 29.95 incl. cd-rom (978-1-55592-701-1(7)) Weston Woods Studios, Inc.

Giggle, Giggle, Quack. 2004. (J). pap. 38.75 incl. audio compact disk (978-1-55592-686-1(X)) Weston Woods Studios, Inc.

Gilliland, Lucille. Kittycat Farm. 2006. (Illus.). 36p. (J). per. 8.95 (978-1-59453-647-2(3)) Airleaf Publishing & Bookselling.

Golden Books Staff. Farm Tales. 2007. (Little Golden Book Ser.). (Illus.). 224p. (J). (ps-k). 10.99 (978-0-375-83942-9(9) , Golden Bks.) Random Hse. Children's Bks.

Gondek, Heather J. Who's on the Farm? Lift-the-Flap 'n' Learn Book. Gilvan-Cartwright, Chris, illus. 2005. (Fun with Animals Ser.). 10p. (J). (ps-k). act. bk. ed. 9.95 (978-1-58117-143-3(9) , Intervisual/Piggy Toes) Dalmatian Pr.

Goodman, Susan E. What Do You Do... at the Farm? Pica, Steve, illus. 2002. (Silly Millies Ser.). 32p. (gr. k-2). lib. bdg. 17.90 (978-0-7613-2756-1(8) , Millbrook Pr.) Lerner Publishing Group.

—What Do You Do on a Farm? 2002. (gr. k-3). lib. bdg. 13.00 (978-0-613-55925-6(8)) Tandem Library Bks.

Goodspeed, J. Fun on the Farm. 2006. (J). pap. 4.99 (978-0-448-43882-5(8) , Grosset & Dunlap) Penguin Group (USA) Inc.

Gorbachev, Valeri. Dragon Is Coming! 2008. (J). (***978-0-15-205196-9(1)***) Harcourt Trade Pubs.

Grant, Nicola. Don't Be So Nosy, Posy! Warnes, Tim, illus. 2004. 32p. (J). tchr. ed. 15.95 (978-1-58925-036-9(2) , tiger tales) ME Media LLC.

Gray, Rita. Mama Mine, Mama Mine. Goembel, Ponder, illus. 2008. 32p. (J). (ps). 15.99 (***978-0-525-47206-3(1)*** , Dutton Juvenile) Penguin Group (USA) Inc.

Greene, Rhonda Gowler. Barnyard Song. Bender, Robert M., illus. 2001. 32p. (J). (ps-3). 7.99 (978-0-689-84054-8(3) , Aladdin) Simon & Schuster Children's Publishing.

—Barnyard Song. 2001. (ps-2). lib. bdg. 14.15 (978-0-613-34598-9(3)) Tandem Library Bks.

Gulbis, Stephen, illus. Old MacDonald Had a Barn. 2003. 22p. (YA). (978-1-85602-453-2(9)) Chrysalis Children's Bks.

Gutman, Anne. Penelope at the Farm. Hallensleben, Georg, illus. 2005. 12p. (J). (ps-ps). pap. 12.95 (978-0-439-67358-7(5) , Cartwheel Bks.) Scholastic, Inc.

Hall, Kristen. On the Farm. Gurney, John Steven, illus. 2005. (My First Reader Ser.). 32p. (J). (gr. k-1). pap. 3.95 (978-0-516-25115-8(5) , Children's Pr.) Scholastic Library Publishing.

—On the Farm. Gurney, John, illus. 2004. (My First Reader Ser.). 31p. (J). 18.50 (978-0-516-24680-2(1) , Children's Pr.) Scholastic Library Publishing.

Hamilton, Arlene. Only a Cow. Griffiths, Dean, illus. 2006. 32p. (J). (ps-2). (***978-1-55041-871-2(8)***) Fitzhenry & Whiteside, Ltd.

Hapka, Catherine. New in the Barn. 2006. (Charlotte's Web Ser.). 24p. (J). pap. 3.99 (978-0-06-088273-0(5)) HarperCollins Pubs.

—The Perfect Word. 2006. (Charlotte's Web Ser.). 24p. (J). pap. 3.99 (978-0-06-088274-7(3)) HarperCollins Pubs.

Harper, Jessica. A Place Called Kindergarten. Karas, G. Brian, illus. 2006. 32p. (J). (ps-3). 15.99 (978-0-399-24226-7(0) , Putnam Juvenile) Penguin Group (USA) Inc.

Harper, Piers, illus. Little Lamb. 2003. 32p. (J). 15.95 (978-0-439-54429-0(7)) Scholastic, Inc.

Harry, Rebecca, illus. Little Lamb. 2006. (Noisy Farm Babies Ser.). 8p. (J). bds. 5.99 (978-0-7641-5937-4(2)) Barron's Educational Series, Inc.

Hayward, Linda. The King's Chorus. Goldfinger, Jennifer P., illus. 2006. 32p. (J). (ps-k). 16.00 (978-0-618-51618-6(2) , Clarion Bks.) Houghton Mifflin Co. Trade & Reference Div.

Heinlein, Robert A. & Briggs, Anita. Hobart. Rayner, Mary, illus. 2002. 64p. (J). (gr. 3-7). 14.00 (978-0-689-84129-3(9)) Simon & Schuster Children's Publishing.

Hill, Eric. Spot Goes to the Farm. Hill, Eric, illus. 2003. (Illus.). 24p. (J). pap. 6.99 (978-0-14-250123-8(9) , Puffin) Penguin Group (USA) Inc.

—Spot Goes to the Farm. 2001. (Spot Ser.). (Illus.). 12p. (J). (ps-1). bds. 7.99 (978-0-399-23647-1(3) , Putnam Juvenile) Penguin Group (USA) Inc.

—Spot Goes to the Farm. 2003. (ps-2). lib. bdg. 15.30 (978-0-613-86708-5(4)) Tandem Library Bks.

C
D

Hillenbrand, Will. Cock-a-Doodle Christmas! Hillenbrand, Will, illus. 2007. (Illus.). 32p. (J). (ps-2). 16.99 ***(978-0-7614-5354-3(7))*** Cavendish, Marshall Corp.

Hills, Tad. My Fuzzy Farm Babies: A Book to Touch & Feel. Hills, Tad, illus. 2001. (My Fuzzy Friends Board Bks.). (Illus.). 12p. (J). bds. 6.99 (978-0-689-84165-1(5) , Little Simon) Simon & Schuster Children's Publishing.

Himmelman, John. Chickens to the Rescue. 2006. (Illus.). 32p. (J). (ps-3). 16.95 (978-0-8050-7951-7(3)) Holt, Henry & Co.

Holt, Rinehart and Winston Staff. Animal Farm with Connections. 1999. pap. 14.60 (978-0-03-055417-9(9)) Holt, Rinehart & Winston.

Huneck, Stephen. Sally Goes to the Farm. Huneck, Stephen, illus. 2002. (Illus.). 40p. (J). (ps-3). 17.95 (978-0-8109-4498-5(7)) Abrams, Harry N. , Inc.

Hutchins, Pat. Barn Dance! Hutchins, Pat, illus. 2007. (Illus.). 32p. (J). (ps-k). 16.99 ***(978-0-06-089120-6(3));*** lib. bdg. 17.89 ***(978-0-06-089122-0(X))*** HarperCollins Pubs. (Greenwillow Bks.).

—Don't Get Lost! Hutchins, Pat, illus. 2004. (Illus.). 32p. (J). 15.99 (978-0-06-055996-0(9)); lib. bdg. 16.89 (978-0-06-055997-7(7)) HarperCollins Pubs.

—Little Pink Pig. 2000. (Illus.). 32p. (J). (ps-3). pap. 5.95 (978-0-688-17516-0(3) , Harper Trophy) HarperCollins Pubs.

—Little Pink Pig. 2000. (Illus.). (J). (978-0-606-18703-9(0)) Tandem Library Bks.

Ipcar, Dahlov. Brown Cow Farm: A Counting Book. 2003. (Illus.). 42p. pap. 9.95 (978-0-89272-602-8(4)) Down East Bks.

—Brown Cow Farm: A Counting Book. 2003. (gr. k-3). lib. bdg. 18.75 (978-0-613-77417-8(5)) Tandem Library Bks.

Jacobs, Lana. Charlotte's Web: Paint Book. Farley, Rick, illus. 2006. (Charlotte's Web Ser.). 32p. (J). pap. 4.99 (978-0-06-088277-8(8)) HarperCollins Pubs.

—Charlotte's Web: The Reusable Sticker Book. 2006. (Charlotte's Web Ser.). 12p. (J). pap. 6.99 (978-0-06-088280-8(8)) HarperCollins Pubs.

Johnson, D. B., illus. Four Legs Bad, Two Legs Good! 2007. 32p. (J). (gr. 3-5). 16.00 ***(978-0-618-80909-7(0))*** Houghton Mifflin Co.

Johnson, Paul Brett. The Pig Who Ran a Red Light. 1999. (Illus.). 32p. (J). (ps-2). 16.99 (978-0-531-33136-1(9)); pap. 15.95 (978-0-531-30136-4(2)) Scholastic, Inc. (Orchard Bks.).

Jugran, Jan. Hello, Baby. Larranaga, Ana, illus. 2007. 10p. (J). (ps). bds. 9.99 (978-1-58476-557-8(7) , IKIDS) Innovative Kids.

Julian, Russell. My First Farm Books: Lost Calf/Busy Dog/Hungry Pig/Happy Cockerel, 4 vols. 2005. (Illus.). 12p. (J). per. 12.50 (978-1-4052-1667-8(0)) Egmont Bks., Ltd. GBR. *Dist:* Trafalgar Square Publishing.

Kelly, Mij. Where's My Darling Daughter? McEwen, Katharine, illus. 2006. 28p. (J). 16.00 (978-1-56148-537-6(3)) Good Bks.

King-Smith, Dick. Animal Stories. Terry, Michael, illus. 1998. 128p. (J). (gr. 4-7). pap. 18.95 (978-0-531-30099-2(4) , Orchard Bks.) Scholastic, Inc.

—Babe: The Gallant Pig. Kneen, Maggie, illus. 2005. 144p. (J). (gr. 4-7). 16.95 (978-0-375-82970-3(9) , Knopf Bks. for Young Readers) Random Hse. Children's Bks.

Klein, Adria F. Max Goes to the Farm. Gallagher-Cole, Mernie, illus. 2007. (J). lib. bdg. ***(978-1-4048-3678-5(0))*** Picture Window Bks.

Klise, Kate. Shall I Knit You A Hat? A Christmas Yarn. Klise, M. Sarah, illus. 2007. 32p. (J). pap. 6.99 ***(978-0-312-37139-5(X))*** Square Fish.

Krosoczka, Jarrett. Punk Farm on Tour. 2007. 40p. (J). (gr. k-3). 15.99 ***(978-0-375-83343-4(9));*** lib. bdg. 18.99 ***(978-0-375-93343-1(3))*** Random Hse. Children's Bks. (Knopf Bks. for Young Readers).

Krosoczka, Jarrett J. Punk Farm. 2005. (Illus.). 40p. (J). (gr. k-3). 15.95 (978-0-375-82429-6(4)); lib. bdg. 17.99 (978-0-375-92429-3(9)) Random Hse. Children's Bks. (Knopf Bks. for Young Readers).

Lamerton, Todd, illus. Wow! What a Cow- A Tale from Funky Farm. 2003. (J). (978-0-7575-0005-3(6)) Kendall/Hunt Publishing Co.

Lawrence, John. This Little Chick. Lawrence, John, illus. 2002. (Illus.). 32p. (J). (ps up). 15.99 (978-0-7636-1716-5(4)) Candlewick Pr.

Lee, Jeanie. Baby Farm Friends. 2006. (Flips & Flaps Book Ser.). (Illus.). 10p. (J). 12.95 (978-1-4169-0702-2(5) , Little Simon) Simon & Schuster Children's Publishing.

—Baby Snow Friends. 2006. (Flips & Flaps Book Ser.). 10p. (J). 12.95 (978-1-4169-0703-9(3) , Little Simon) Simon & Schuster Children's Publishing.

Lee, Taylor & Van Dijk, Peter. Winchell Cuts the Cheese. 2005. (Illus.). 32p. (J). 14.95 (978-1-58246-140-3(6) , Tricycle Pr.) Ten Speed Pr.

Lenski, Lois. The Easter Rabbit's Parade. 2004. (Illus.). 40p. (J). (ps-1). 12.95 (978-0-375-82748-8(X) , Random Hse. Bks. for Young Readers) Random Hse. Children's Bks.

Lesser, Carolyn. What a Wonderful Day to Be a Cow. 1999. (Illus.). (J). (978-0-606-16958-5(X)) Tandem Library Bks.

Lewis, Rob. Whats up Jac. 2005. (Illus.). 32p. pap. 12.95 (978-1-84323-428-9(9)) Beekman Bks., Inc.

Lewison, Wendy Cheyette. Buzz Said the Bee. Wilhelm, Hans, illus. 2004. 32p. (J). lib. bdg. 15.00 (978-1-59054-589-8(3)) Fitzgerald Bks.

Lodge, Bernard. Custard Surprise. Bowers, Tim, illus. 2007. (I Can Read Bks.). 48p. (J). (ps-3). lib. bdg. 16.89 ***(978-0-06-073688-0(7));*** 15.99 ***(978-0-06-073687-3(9))*** HarperCollins Pubs.

Ludmila's Way - Teaching Guide. 2003. (J). 17.95 (978-1-55942-192-8(4)) Marsh Media.

Ludmila's Way: Evaluation Guide. 2006. (J). (978-1-55942-415-8(X)) Marsh Media.

MacDonald, Alan. The Pig in a Wig. Hess, Paul, illus. 2003. 32p. (J). (gr. k-3). pap. 6.95 (978-1-56145-299-6(8) , Q32523) Peachtree Pubs., Ltd.

—Pig in a Wig. 1999. (gr. k-3). lib. bdg. 16.40 (978-0-613-68926-7(7)) Tandem Library Bks.

Mackinnon, Mairi. Gingerbread Man (Picture Book) 2007. (Picture Book Classics Ser.). 24p. (J). 9.99 ***(978-0-7945-1786-1(2)*** , Usborne) EDC Publishing.

Martin, Bill, Jr. Chicken Chuck. Salerno, Steven, illus. 40p. (J). (ps-3). 2001. pap. 7.95 (978-1-58837-017-4(8)); 2000. 16.95 (978-1-890817-31-2(7)) Winslow Pr.

Martin, Bill. Chicken Chuck. Salerno, Steven, illus. 2005. 32p. (J). pap. 5.95 (978-0-7614-5216-4(8)) Cavendish, Marshall Corp.

Massey, Jane, illus. Farm Animals. 2000. (Touch & Fit Ser.). 10p. (J). (ps-k). bds. 12.95 (978-1-57145-416-4(0) , Silver Dolphin Bks.) Advantage Pubs. Group.

Mayer, Mercer. My Trip to the Farm, Vol. 3. 2002. (Little Critter First Readers Ser.). (Illus.). 24p. (J). (gr. 1-2). pap. 3.95 (978-1-57768-817-4(1)) School Specialty Publishing.

—My Trip to the Farm. 2000. (gr. k-3). lib. bdg. 11.80 (978-0-613-67647-2(5)) Tandem Library Bks.

McDonnell, Flora. I Love Animals. McDonnell, Flora, illus. 2002. (Illus.). (J). 24.00 (978-0-7587-2805-0(0)) Book Wholesalers, Inc.

—I Love Animals. McDonnell, Flora, illus. 2001. (Illus.). 24p. (J). (gr. k-ps). bds. 6.99 (978-0-7636-1546-8(3)) Candlewick Pr.

McDonnell, Flora & Jones, Gordon. Rwy'n Hoffi Anifeiliaid. 2005. (WEL., Illus.). 26p. 11.99 (978-1-84323-316-9(9)) Gomer Pr. GBR. *Dist:* Gomer Pr.

McGuire, Leslie & Brunelle, Lynn. Animal Singalong. Voo, Rhonda, illus. 1999. 12p. (J). 5.95 (978-1-892374-16-5(1)) Weldon Owen, Inc.

McMahon, Kara. Raloo Rocket's Busy Week. Entara Ltd. Staff, photos by. 2007. (Jakers! Ser.). 10p. (J). bds. 5.99 (978-1-4169-3531-5(2) , Simon Spotlight) Simon & Schuster Children's Publishing.

McPhail, David M. The Day the Sheep Showed Up. 1998. (Hello Reader! Ser.). (Illus.). 32p. (J). (gr. k-2). pap. 3.99 (978-0-590-84910-4(7)) Scholastic, Inc.

—Dia Que el Perro Dijo Quiquiriqui. 1999. (SPA.). (ps-2). lib. bdg. 11.80 (978-0-613-16656-0(6)) Tandem Library Bks.

Meister, Cari. Tiny on the Farm. Davis, Rich, illus. 2008. 32p. (J). (ps). 15.99 ***(978-0-670-06246-1(4)*** , Viking Juvenile) Penguin Group (USA) Inc.

Milgrim, David. Young McDonald. Milgrim, David, illus. 2006. (Illus.). 32p. (J). (gr. k). 12.99 (978-0-525-47570-5(2) , Dutton Juvenile) Penguin Group (USA) Inc.

Minne, Brigitte. The Best Bottom. Pottie, Marjolein, illus. 2008. 32p. (978-1-59687-183-0(0) , Milk & Cookies) ibooks, Inc.

—The Best Bottom. Pottie, Marjolein, illus. 2004. 32p. (J). 15.95 (978-0-689-03595-1(0) , Milk & Cookies) ibooks, Inc.

Miranda, Anne. Neat Pete: A Pig's Tale. Callen, Liz, illus. 2002. 16p. (J). (978-0-439-35077-8(8)) Scholastic, Inc.

Moffatt, Julia. Buttercup, the Clumsy Cow. Williams, Lisa, illus. 2005. 32p. (J). (ps-k). lib. bdg. 11.15 (978-0-606-33581-2(1)) Tandem Library Bks.

Morpurgo, Michael. It's a Dog's Life. Allibone, Judith, illus. 2007. (J). ***(978-0-374-33620-2(2))*** Farrar, Straus & Giroux.

Mozelle, Shirley. The Pig Is in the Pantry, the Cat Is on the Shelf. Plecas, Jennifer, illus. 2000. 32p. (J). (gr. k-3). tchr. ed. 15.00 (978-0-395-78627-7(4) , Clarion Bks.) Houghton Mifflin Co. Trade & Reference Div.

Murphy, Bonnie. Can A Rooster Drive A Tractor? Richardson, Shelley, illus. 2001. 32p. (J). 14.95 (978-0-9714419-0-3(1)) Alabama Farmers Federation.

Murphy, Mary. How Kind! Murphy, Mary, illus. 2004. (Illus.). 24p. (J). (gr. k-k). bds. 6.99 (978-0-7636-2307-4(5)) Candlewick Pr.

Nash, Margaret. Hetty's New Hat. Impey, Martin, illus. 2005. (Reading Corner Ser.). 24p. (J). (gr. k-3). lib. bdg. 22.80 (978-1-59771-007-7(5)) Sea-To-Sea Pubns.

Newton, Jill. Gordon in Charge. Newton, Jill, illus. 2003. (Illus.). 32p. (J). 15.95 (978-1-58234-823-0(5) , Bloomsbury Children) Bloomsbury Publishing.

Nobisso, Josephine. In English, of Course. Ziborova, Dasha, illus. 2003. Tr. of En Ingles, Por Supuesto. 32p. (J). (SPA.). 16.95 (978-0-940112-07-0(8)); pap. 8.95 (978-0-940112-08-7(6)) Gingerbread Hse.

Novak, Matt. Rock-A-Bye Christmas. 2007. (Illus.). 16p. (J). (ps-1). 7.95 ***(978-1-59643-187-4(3))*** Roaring Brook Pr.

O'Brien, Claire. Barn Party. Archbold, Tim, illus. 2005. 46p. (J). (ps-ps). lib. bdg. 10.75 (978-0-606-33661-1(3)) Tandem Library Bks.

Packard, Mary & Mitter, Matt. 1, 2, 3: Counting Rymes. Cushman, Doug & Banta, Susan, illus. 2004. (Rhyme Time Learning Ser.). 16p. (J). (gr. 1 up). lib. bdg. 20.67 (978-0-8368-4094-0(1)) Stevens, Gareth Inc.

Palatini, Margie. Earthquack! Moser, Barry, illus. 2005. 32p. (J). (ps-ps). pap., pap. 6.99 (978-1-4169-0260-7(0) , Aladdin) Simon & Schuster Children's Publishing.

—Oink? Cole, Henry, illus. 2006. 40p. (J). (ps-3). 15.95 (978-0-689-86258-8(X)) Simon & Schuster Children's Publishing.

Palatini, Margie & Moser, Barry. Earthquack! 2002. (Illus.). 32p. (J). (ps-3). 15.95 (978-0-689-84280-1(5)) Simon & Schuster Children's Publishing.

Park, Barbara. Junie B. Jones Tiene un Pio, Pio en el Bolsillo. 2006. (SPA., Illus.). 80p. (J). pap. 3.99 (978-0-439-66122-5(6) , Scholastic en Espanol) Scholastic, Inc.

Pedersen, Janet. Millie Wants to Play! Pedersen, Janet, illus. 2004. (Illus.). 32p. (J). (ps-1). 15.99 (978-0-7636-1993-0(0)) Candlewick Pr.

Perl, Erica S. Chicken Bedtime Is Really Early. Bates, George, illus. 2005. 32p. (J). (ps-1). 14.95 (978-0-8109-4926-3(1)) Abrams, Harry N. , Inc.

Picotee: The Polka Dotted Llama. 1999. (Illus.). 24p. (J). (ps-5). pap. 8.00 (978-0-9669355-4-7(3)) Chiappini, Lydia .

Pierce, Chonda & Pierce, David. Tales from the Manger. LeBarre, Matt, illus. 2004. 96p. (J). pap. 9.99 (978-0-310-70849-0(4)) Zonderkidz.

Piers, Helen. Who's in My Bed? Saunders, Dave, illus. 1999. (Accelerated Reader Bks.). 24p. (J). (ps-k). 15.95 (978-0-7614-5046-7(7) , Cavendish Children's Bks.) Cavendish, Marshall Corp.

Piggy Toes Press Staff. Farm Faces. 1998. (Cuddly Cloth Book Ser.). (Illus.). 6p. (J). (ps-k). 14.95 (978-1-888443-51-6(0) , Intervisual/Piggy Toes) Dalmatian Pr.

Pingry, Patricia A. Sounds. Rose, Drew, illus. 2005. (J). (978-0-8249-6596-9(5) , Candy Cane Pr.) Ideals Pubns.

Pixton, Amy, creator. Farm Charm. 2006. (J). (978-0-9779631-0-2(1)) TyBook.

Pluta, K. There's a Yak in my Bed. Stallop, Christy, illus. 2007. 32p. (J). 16.95 (978-0-9769417-4-3(0)) Blooming Tree Pr.

Polacco, Patricia. Mommies Say Shh! Polacco, Patricia, illus. 2007. 32p. (J). (ps). 5.99 (978-0-399-24720-0(3) , Philomel) Penguin Group (USA) Inc.

—Mommies Say Shhh! Polacco, Patricia, illus. 2005. (Illus.). 40p. (J). (ps-1). 16.99 (978-0-399-24341-7(0) , Philomel) Penguin Group (USA) Inc.

Post, Jim & Post, Janet. Barnyard Boogie. Vasconsellos, Daniel, illus. gif. ed. 2003. 32p. (J). 15.99 (978-1-57939-130-0(3)) Accord Publishing, Ltd.

Potter, Beatrix. Jemima Puddle-Duck. 2008. (Potter Ser.). 12p. (J). (ps). bds. 7.99 ***(978-0-7232-5955-8(0)*** , Warne) Penguin Group (USA) Inc.

—The Tale of Jemima Puddle-Duck Board Bk. 2007. (Illus.). 24p. (J). bds. 6.99 (978-0-7232-5794-3(9) , Warne) Penguin Group (USA) Inc.

—The Tale of Jemima Puddle Duck Sticker Book. 2007. 24p. (J). pap. 5.99 (978-0-7232-5877-3(5) , Warne) Penguin Group (USA) Inc.

Prami, S. & Schmid, S. One Two Three Pull! Bb. 2006. (Illus.). 16p. (J). 7.95 (978-0-7358-2098-2(8)) North-South Bks., Inc.

Priddy, Roger. Bright Baby Chunky: Farm. rev. ed. 2005. 10p. (J). bds. 0.01 (978-0-312-49643-2(5) , Priddy Bks.) St. Martin's Pr.

Priddy, Roger. Millie Cow Large Format. 2007. 10p. (J). bds. 14.95 ***(978-0-312-50115-0(3)*** , Priddy Bks.) St. Martin's Pr.

Regan, Dian Curtis. Barnyard Slam. Meisel, Paul, illus. 2006. (J). (978-0-8234-1907-4(X)) Holiday Hse., Inc.

Reynolds, Aaron. Chicks & Salsa. Bogan, Paulette, illus. 2005. 32p. (J). (ps-3). 16.95 (978-1-58234-972-5(X)) Bloomsbury Publishing.

Richardson, Lans. A Calf Named Polly. Arndt, Charles T., illus. 2003. 38p. per. 11.95 (978-1-59405-022-0(8)) New Age World Publishing.

Rigamonti, Justin. The Pigs Went Marching Out! Thatch, Nancy R., ed. Rigamonti, Justin, illus. 1998. (Books for Students by Students). (Illus.). 29p. (J). (ps-3). lib. bdg. 15.95 (978-0-933849-70-9(2)) Landmark Editions, Inc.

Robinson, Sue. Bear in the Barnyard. Morris, Tony, illus. 2004. 28p. (J). 16.00 (978-1-56148-430-0(X)) Good Bks.

Roddie, Shen. You're Too Small! Lavis, Steve, illus. 2004. 32p. (J). 6.95 (978-1-58925-385-8(X)); tchr. ed. 15.95 (978-1-58925-038-3(9)) ME Media LLC. (tiger tales).

Rostoker-Gruber, Karen. Rooster Can't Cock-a-Doodle-Doo. Ratz de Tagyos, Paul, illus. 2004. 32p. (J). (ps). 15.99 (978-0-8037-2877-6(8) , Dial) Penguin Group (USA) Inc.

Roth, Carol. Who Will Tuck Me in Tonight? Gorbachev, Valeri, illus. 2003. 32p. (J). 15.95 (978-0-7358-1772-2(3)); 16.50 (978-0-7358-1773-9(1)) North-South Bks., Inc.

—Who Will Tuck Me in Tonight Sp. 2007. (J). 16.50 (978-0-7358-2108-8(9)); (Illus.). pap. 6.95 (978-0-7358-2107-1(0)) North-South Bks., Inc.

Ruffenach, Jessie, ed. Baby Learns about Animals. Thomas, Peter, tr. from NAV. Blacksheep, Beverly, illus. 2004. (ENG & NAV.). 16p. 7.95 (978-1-893354-49-4(0)) Salina Bookshelf.

Russell, Naomi. Guess Who's on the Farm. Russell, Naomi, illus. 2nd ed. 1999. (Flip-the-Flap Book Ser.). (Illus.). 32p. (J). (gr. k-ps). pap. 3.99 (978-0-7636-0689-3(8)) Candlewick Pr.

Ruurs, Margriet. Emma's Cold Day. 2003. (Illus.). 24p. (J). pap. (978-1-55005-076-9(1)) Fitzhenry & Whiteside, Ltd.

—Emma's Cold Day. Spurll, Barbara, illus. 2002. 24p. (J). (ps-3). 16.95 (978-0-7737-3314-5(0)) Stoddart Kids CAN. *Dist:* Fitzhenry & Whiteside, Ltd.

—Emma's Cold Day. 2004. (gr. k-3). lib. bdg. 16.40 (978-0-613-70722-0(2)) Tandem Library Bks.

Rylant, Cynthia. Henry & Mudge & the Wild Goose Chase. Bracken, Carolyn, illus. 2004. (Henry & Mudge Ser.). 40p. (J). pap. 3.99 (978-0-689-83450-9(0) , Aladdin) Simon & Schuster Children's Publishing.

—Henry & Mudge & the Wild Goose Chase. Bracken, Carolyn, illus. 2004. (Henry & Mudge Ser.). 40p. (J). (gr. k-2). lib. bdg. 12.10 (978-1-4176-4340-0(4)) Tandem Library Bks.

Rylant, Cynthia & Bracken, Carolyn. Henry & Mudge & the Wild Goose Chase. 2003. (Henry & Mudge Ser.). (Illus.). 40p. (J). (gr. k-3). 14.95 (978-0-689-81172-2(1)) Simon & Schuster Children's Publishing.

Sargent, Dave. Glenda Goose. Lenoir, Jane, illus. 2000. (J). lib. bdg. 19.95 (978-1-56763-461-7(3)) Ozark Publishing.

Scheffler, Axel. Muddle Farm: A Magnetic Play Book. 2007. 8p. (J). (ps-1). 9.99 (978-0-7641-6038-7(9)) Barron's Educational Series, Inc.

Scholastic, Inc. Staff. Old Macdonald Puppet Book. Berg, Michelle, illus. 2007. (Little Scholastic Ser.). 6p. (J). bds. 12.99 ***(978-0-545-02603-1(2))*** Scholastic, Inc.

Scott, Janine. Fun in the Sun. Forss, Ian, illus. 2006. (Farmer Claude & Farmer Maude Ser.). 32p. (J). (gr. k-2). 22.60 (978-1-4048-1697-8(6) , 1253180) Picture Window Bks.

—Rain on the Roof. Forss, Ian, illus. 2006. 32p. (J). (gr. k-2). 22.60 (978-1-4048-1698-5(4)) Picture Window Bks.

—The Rowdy Rooster. Forss, Ian, illus. 2006. 32p. (J). (gr. k-2). 22.60 (978-1-4048-1699-2(2)) Picture Window Bks.

—Sunny Sunday Drive. Forss, Ian, illus. 2006. 32p. (J). (gr. k-2). 22.60 (978-1-4048-1696-1(8)) Picture Window Bks.

Shannon, David. Duck on a Bike. Shannon, David, illus. 2002. (Illus.). 40p. (J). (ps up). pap. 15.95 (978-0-439-05023-4(5) , Blue Sky Pr., The) Scholastic, Inc.

Shannon, George. Wise Acres. Zemke, Deborah, illus. 2004. 40p. (J). 15.95 (978-1-59354-041-8(8)) Handprint Bks.

Sharratt, Nick. Muddlewitch on the Farm. 2007. (Illus.). 18p. (J). (ps-k). bds. 14.95 ***(978-1-4052-2651-6(X))*** Egmont Bks., Ltd. GBR. *Dist:* Independent Pubs. Group.

Shaw, Nancy. Sheep Trick or Treat. 2000. (J). (978-0-606-19428-0(2)) Tandem Library Bks.

Shepherd, Jodie. Farm Friends. Ovresat, Laura, illus. 2006. (Guess Who? Ser.). 12p. (J). pap. 7.99 (978-0-7944-1048-3(0)) Reader's Digest Assn., Inc., The.

Simmons, Jane. Daisy & the Beastie. Simmons, Jane, illus. 2002. (Illus.). (J). 19.11 (978-0-7587-2334-5(2)) Book Wholesalers, Inc.

Simmons, Lynn Sheffield. Sugar Lump, the Orphan Calf. 2004. (Illus.). 50p. (YA). pap. 8.95 (978-1-58980-216-2(0)) Pelican Publishing Co., Inc.

Simon-Kerr, Julia. Charlotte's Web: Coloring & Activity Book 3-in-1. Kirkland, Boyd, illus. 2006. (Charlotte's Web Ser.). 96p. (J). pap., act. bk. ed. 2.99 (978-0-06-088276-1(X)) HarperCollins Pubs.

—Charlotte's Web: Coloring & Activity Book & Crayons. Kirkland, Boyd, illus. 2006. (Charlotte's Web Ser.). 32p. (J). pap. 4.99 (978-0-06-088279-2(4)) HarperCollins Pubs.

Sio, Betsy Menson. Little Critters. Richter, Hank, illus. 2003. (Books for Young Learners). 16p. (J). pap. 5.00 net. (978-1-57274-532-2(0) , 2458) Owen, Richard C. Pubs., Inc.

Sloat, Teri. Farmer Brown Goes Round & Round. 2001. (978-0-606-22359-1(2)) Tandem Library Bks.

Sommer, Carl. Proud Rooster & Little Hen. 2003. (Another Sommer-Time Story Ser.). (Illus.). 48p. (J). (gr. 1-4). 16.95 incl. audio compact disk (978-1-57537-510-6(9)); 16.95 incl. audio (978-1-57537-559-5(1)) Advance Publishing, Inc.

—Proud Rooster & Little Hen. Budwine, Greg, illus. (Another Sommer-Time Story Ser.). 48p. (J). (gr. k-3). 2000. lib. bdg. 16.95 (978-1-57537-060-6(3)); 1999. 9.95 (978-1-57537-010-1(7)) Advance Publishing, Inc.

Stevens, Carla. Who's Knocking at the Door? Chapman, Lee, illus. 2004. 40p. (J). 16.95 (978-0-7614-5168-6(4)) Cavendish, Marshall Corp.

Stewart, Wilson N. Cock-a-Doodle-Who? 2007. (Illus.). 6p. (J). 15.99 (978-0-7868-0826-7(8)) Hyperion Bks. for Children.

Stiegemeyer, Julie. Hide & Sleep. Baicker-McKee, Carol, illus. 2009. 32p. (J). 15.95 ***(978-1-59990-008-7(4)*** , Bloomsbury Children) Bloomsbury Publishing.

Stock, Catherine. A Porc in New York. Stock, Catherine, illus. 2007. (Illus.). 32p. (J). (ps-3). 16.95 (978-0-8234-1994-4(0)) Holiday Hse., Inc.

Stoeke, Janet Morgan. Minerva Louise & Her Barnyard Friends. Stoeke, Janet Morgan, illus. 2nd ed. 2002. (Illus.). (978-0-525-46877-6(3) , Dutton Juvenile) Penguin Group (USA) Inc.

Studio Mouse. Sesame Street My First Trip to the Farm: Book & CD. rev. ed. 2007. 24p. 4.99 ***(978-1-59069-561-6(5))*** Studio Mouse LLC.

Sykes, Julie. Dora's Eggs. Chapman, Jane, illus. 2002. 32p. (J). 5.95 (978-1-58925-365-0(5) , tiger tales) ME Media LLC.

—Dora's Eggs. 2002. (gr. k-3). lib. bdg. 14.10 (978-0-613-56323-9(9)) Tandem Library Bks.

Sykes, Julie. That Pesky Dragon. Williamson, Melanie, illus. 2007. 32p. (J). (ps-2). 15.95 ***(978-1-58925-069-7(9)*** , tiger tales) ME Media LLC.

Talley, Linda. Ludmila's Way. Chase, Andra, illus. 2003. (J). 17.95 (978-1-55942-190-4(8)) Marsh Media.

Tate, Don, illus. The Hidden Feast: A Folktale from the American South. 2006. 32p. (J). 16.95 (978-0-87483-758-2(8)) August Hse. Pubs., Inc.

Tekavec, Heather. Storm Is Coming! Spengler, Margaret, illus. 32p. (J). (ps). 2002. 15.99 (978-0-8037-2626-0(0) , Dial); 2004. reprint ed. pap. 6.99 (978-0-14-240070-8(X) , Puffin) Penguin Group (USA) Inc.

Thompson, Lauren. Wee Little Chick. Butler, John, illus. 2008. (Wee Little Ser.). 32p. (J). 14.99 ***(978-1-4169-3468-4(5))*** Simon & Schuster Children's Publishing.

Thomson, Pat. It's So Unfair. Allen, Jonathan, illus. 2007. 32p. (J). pap. 9.95 ***(978-1-84270-594-0(6))*** Andersen GBR. *Dist:* Independent Pubs. Group.

Tokunbo, Dimitrea. Together. Oliver, Jennifer, illus. 2005. (J). pap. (978-0-439-79654-5(7)) Scholastic, Inc.

Turcotte, Elise. Puce, Mes Animaux. 2001. 3. (FRE., Illus.). 16p. (J). bds. (978-2-89021-488-0(5)) Diffusion du livre Mirabel.

Urdaneta, Josefina. Busca que te Busca. 7.95 (978-980-6437-06-7(3)) Baker & Taylor Bks.

Wallace, Barbara Brooks. Palmer Patch. 2000. (Illus.). 132p. (J). (gr. 4-7). pap. 9.95 (978-0-595-09573-5(9) , Backinprint.com) iUniverse, Inc.

Wallace, Karen. Clever Cat. Axworthy, Ann, illus. 2004. (Read-It! Readers Ser.). 32p. (C). (gr. k-3). 18.60 (978-1-4048-0560-6(5)) Picture Window Bks.

—Marvin, the Blue Pig. Williams, Lisa, illus. 2004. (Read-It! Readers Ser.). 32p. (C). (gr. k-3). 18.60 (978-1-4048-0564-4(8)) Picture Window Bks.

Weeks, Sarah. Baa-Choo! Manning, Jane, illus. (I Can Read Bks.). 32p. (J). (ps-3). 2006. pap. 3.99 (978-0-06-443740-0(X)); 2004. 15.99 (978-0-06-029236-2(9)); 2004. lib. bdg. 16.89 (978-0-06-029237-9(7)) HarperCollins Pubs.

Wheeler, Lisa. Farmer Dale's Red Pickup Truck. Bates, Ivan, illus. 2006. 40p. (J). pap. 6.00 (978-0-15-205912-5(1) , Voyager Bks./Libros Viajeros) Harcourt Children's Bks.

—Farmer Dale's Red Pickup Truck. Bates, Ivan, tr. Bates, Ivan, illus. 2004. 40p. (J). 16.00 (978-0-15-202319-5(4)) Harcourt Children's Bks.

White, E. B. Charlotte's Web. Williams, Garth, illus. 2006. 192p. (J). 15.99 (978-0-06-088261-7(1)); 8.99 (978-0-06-112495-2(8)); pap. 7.99 (978-0-06-112026-8(X)) HarperCollins Pubs.

—The Telarana of Carlota (LaTelarana de Carlota) Williams, Garth, illus. movie tie-in ed. 2006. (Charlotte's Web Ser.). (SPA.). 224p. (J). pap. 7.99 (978-0-06-112522-5(9) , Rayo) HarperCollins Pubs.

White, E. B. Wilbur's Adventure: A Charlotte's Web Picture Book. Kneen, Maggie, illus. 2008. (Charlotte's Web Ser.). 32p. (J). 17.89 ***(978-0-06-078165-1(3))*** HarperCollins Pubs.

Whybrow, Ian. The Noisy Way to Bed. Beeke, Tiphanie, tr. Beeke, Tiphanie, illus. 2004. (J). (978-0-439-55690-3(2) , Levine, Arthur A. Bks.) Scholastic, Inc.

—Noisy Way to Bed. Beeke, Tiphanie, tr. Beeke, Tiphanie, illus. 2004. 32p. (J). 16.95 (978-0-439-55689-7(9) , Levine, Arthur A. Bks.) Scholastic, Inc.

Wild, Margaret. Piglet & Mama. King, Stephen Michael, illus. 2005. 32p. (J). (ps-1). 14.95 (978-0-8109-5869-2(4)) Abrams, Harry N. , Inc.

—Piglet & Papa. King, Stephen Michael, illus. 2007. (J). (ps-3). 32p. 14.95 (978-0-8109-1476-6(X)); ***(978-1-4287-4648-0(X))*** Abrams, Harry N. , Inc. (Abrams Bks. for Young Readers).

Williams, Sue. Let's Go Visiting. Vivas, Julie, illus. 32p. (J). 2006. bds. 10.95 (978-0-15-205539-4(8) , Red Wagon Bks.); 2003. bds. 6.95 (978-0-15-204638-5(0) , Red Wagon Bks.); 2000. pap. 7.00 (978-0-15-202410-9(7) , Voyager Bks./Libros Viajeros) Harcourt Children's Bks.

—Let's Go Visiting. 1998. 90.00 (978-0-15-202036-1(5) , Gulliver Bks.) Harcourt Children's Bks.

—Let's Go Visiting. Vivas, Julie, illus. 1998. 32p. (J). (ps). 16.00 (978-0-15-201823-8(9) , Gulliver Bks.) Harcourt Children's Bks.

—Let's Go Visiting. 2000. (978-0-606-20330-2(3)); (J). (978-0-606-20167-4(X)) Tandem Library Bks.

Willow Creek Press Staff, creator. Secret of the Pasture. 2005. (Illus.). 32p. (J). (ps-k). 12.95 (978-1-59543-237-7(X)) Willow Creek Pr., Inc.

Winthrop, Elizabeth. Dumpy la Rue. Lewin, Betsy, illus. rev. ed. 40p. (J). 2004. reprint ed. pap. 7.95 (978-0-8050-7535-9(6)); 2001. 16.95 (978-0-8050-6385-1(4)) Holt, Henry & Co. (Holt, Henry & Co. Bks. For Young Readers).

—Dumpy la Rue. Lewin, Betsy, illus. 2004. 48p. (J). (ps-4). lib. bdg. 14.15 (978-0-606-30292-0(1)) Tandem Library Bks.

Wiskur, Darrell. Really Big Barn on Noah's Farm. 2001. (Illus.). 40p. (J). 11.99 (978-0-89051-353-8(8)) Master Bks.

Wormell, Mary. Why Not? 2003. lib. bdg. 14.10 (978-0-613-59763-0(X)) Tandem Library Bks.

Wu, Liz. Rosa Farm. Phelan, Matt, illus. 2006. 144p. (J). (gr. 2-7). 15.95 (978-0-375-83681-7(0)); lib. bdg. 17.99 (978-0-375-93681-4(5)) Random Hse. Children's Bks. (Knopf Bks. for Young Readers).

Wyatt, Cherokee. The Adventures of Margaret Mouse: Hide 'n Seek. Redmon, Angela M., illus. l.t. ed. 2005. 32p. (J). (gr. k-5). 6.95 (978-0-9761326-4-6(8)) www.margaretmouse.com publishing co.

Yee, Wong Herbert. Mrs. Brown Went to Town. 2003. (Illus.). 32p. (J). (ps-3). pap. 5.95 (978-0-618-36918-8(X)) Houghton Mifflin Co. Trade & Reference Div.

—Mrs Brown Went to Town. 2003. (gr. k-3). lib. bdg. 14.10 (978-0-613-91047-7(8)) Tandem Library Bks.

Yocum, Randi. Cowpie Corgi: A Dog's Tale. Yocum, Sam, 2nd, photos by. 2007. 32p. (J). lib. bdg. 16.98 (978-0-9663629-3-0(4)) By Grace Enterprises.

Young, Pippa, illus. On the Farm. (Match & Twist Ser.). (J). 11.99 (978-0-525-47054-0(9) , Dutton Juvenile) Penguin Group (USA) Inc.

Ziefert, Harriet & Taback, Simms. Where Is My Baby? 2002. (Lift-the-Flap Bks.). (Illus.). 8p. bds. 7.95 (978-1-929766-46-8(7)) Blue Apple Bks.

DOMESTIC ANIMALS—PICTORIAL WORKS

Blathwayt, Benedict. One Farm. (Illus.). 32p. (J). 2001. pap. 9.99 (978-0-09-940759-1(0)); 2000. 17.99 (978-0-09-176966-6(3)) Random Hse. GBR. *Dist:* Trafalgar Square Publishing, Independent Pubs. Group.

Chicks. 2003. (Three Minute Tales Ser.). 32p. (J). 5.98 (978-0-7525-8915-2(6)); 7.95 (978-0-7525-4759-6(3)) Parragon, Inc.

Dorling Kindersley Publishing Staff. Farm Animals. 2004. (Dk Readers Ser.). 32p. (J). 12.99 (978-0-7566-0534-6(2)); (Illus.). pap. 3.99 (978-0-7566-0536-0(9)) Dorling Kindersley Publishing, Inc.

Farm Animals, 4 bks., Set. (J). (gr. 2-6). lib. bdg. 145.26 (978-1-56766-339-6(7) , PR0086-B1162) Child's World, Inc.

Farm Animals. Date not set. (Illus.). 16p. (J). 5.98 (978-0-7525-7697-8(6)); 2.98 (978-0-7525-9761-4(2)) Parragon, Inc.

Farm Animals. (Puppet Board Books Ser.). (J). 2.50 Penguin Group (USA) Inc.

Farm Animals. (Illus.). 12p. (J). (978-2-7643-0148-7(0)) Phidal Publishing, Inc./Editions Phidal, Inc.

Farm Animals. 2005. (Illus.). 10p. bds. (978-0-7853-6789-5(6) , 7166800) Publications International, Ltd.

Farm Animals. (Little Tot Dot-to-Dots Ser.). 32p. (gr. k-2). 4.29 (978-0-7647-0384-3(6) , FS30304) Schaffer, Frank Pubns.

Farm Animals. 2001. (Early Learning Ser.). (J). (gr. k-12). vinyl bd. 4.95 (978-1-58845-044-9(9)) School Specialty Publishing.

Hansen, Ann L. Farm Animals, Set. Incl. Cattle. lib. bdg. 22.78 (978-1-56239-603-9(X)); Chickens. lib. bdg. 22.78 (978-1-56239-602-2(1)); Goats. lib. bdg. 22.78 (978-1-56239-604-6(8)); Pigs. lib. bdg. 22.78 (978-1-56239-605-3(6)); Sheep. lib. bdg. 22.78 (978-1-56239-606-0(4)); Uncommon Farm Animals. lib. bdg. 22.78 (978-1-56239-607-7(2)); 32p. (J). (gr. k-6). 1998. (Illus.). 1998. Set lib. bdg. 136.68 (978-1-56239-930-6(6) , Checkerboard Library) ABDO Publishing Co.

Holmes, Stephen. Number Farm. 2003. (J). bds. 5.98 (978-0-7525-8920-6(2)) Parragon, Inc.

Llewellyn, Claire. Farm Animals. 2005. (Illus.). 24p. (YA). (gr. 1 up). lib. bdg. 22.80 (978-1-932889-33-8(7)) Sea-To-Sea Pubns.

Magloff, Lisa & Dorling Kindersley Publishing Staff. Farm Animals. 2005. (Watch me Grow Ser.). (Illus.). 24p. (J). 7.99 (978-0-7566-1272-6(1)) Dorling Kindersley Publishing, Inc.

Sladen, Louisa. Farm Animals. Rinaldo, Luana, illus. 2004. (Magic Color Bks.). 10p. (J). 3.95 (978-1-4027-1207-4(3)) Sterling Publishing Co., Inc.

Sterling/Balloon. Balloon. 1998. (Peek-a-Boo Bks.). (Illus.). 20p. (J). bds. 3.95 (978-0-8069-3763-2(7) , Balloon Bks.) Sterling Publishing Co., Inc.

DOMESTIC APPLIANCES

see Household Appliances, Electric; Household Equipment and Supplies

DOMESTIC ARCHITECTURE

see Architecture, Domestic

DOMESTIC ARTS

see Home Economics

DOMESTIC RELATIONS

see also Divorce; Marriage; Parent and Child

Armitage, Ronda. Family Violence. 1999. (Talking Points Ser.). (Illus.). 64p. (J). (gr. 4-7). lib. bdg. 27.12 (978-0-7398-1371-3(4)) Raintree.

Bartel, Blaine. Little Black Book on How to Get Along with Your Parents. 2004. (Illus.). 80p. (J). pap. 4.99 (978-1-57794-626-7(X)) Harrison Hse., Inc.

Bianchi, Anne. Everything You Need to Know about Family Court. 2005. (Need to Know Library). (Illus.). 64p. (YA). (gr. 7-12). lib. bdg. 25.25 (978-0-8239-3163-7(3) , NTFACO) Rosen Publishing Group, Inc., The.

Braida, Dolly. What Holds the Family Together. Vaughan, Christina, ed. Cook, Scott, illus. 2002. 42p. (J). lib. bdg. 15.95 (978-0-9658113-6-1(0)) Jo-Eric Pubns.

Brown, Isobel. Domestic Crime. 2003. (Crime & Detection Ser.). (Illus.). 96p. (J). (gr. 7 up). lib. bdg. (978-1-59084-370-3(3)) Mason Crest Pubs.

Crowe, Carole. Waiting for Dolphins. 2003. 144p. (YA). (gr. 4-6). pap. 9.95 (978-1-59078-073-2(6)); (Illus.). pap. 16.95 (978-1-56397-847-0(4)) Boyds Mills Pr.

—Waiting for Dolphins. 2003. (gr. 3-6). lib. bdg. 18.75 (978-0-613-59368-7(5)) Tandem Library Bks.

Haughton, Emma & Clarke, Penny. Rights in the Home. 2005. (What Do We Mean by Human Rights? Ser.). (Illus.). 46p. (J). (gr. 5-9). lib. bdg. 29.95 (978-1-932889-65-9(5)) Sea-To-Sea Pubns.

Jaworski, Anna M. My Brother Needs an Operation. Ball, Linda, illus. 1998. 57p. (J). (ps-5). 20.00 (978-0-9652508-2-5(2)) Baby Hearts Pr.

McGraw-Hill Staff. Skills for Life. 2nd ed. 2001. stu. ed. 73.32 (978-0-538-42956-6(9) , 9780538429566) Glencoe/McGraw-Hill.

Richmond, Marianne. I Love You Because... 2004. (Illus.). 40p. (YA). 7.95 (978-0-9741465-5-3(2)) Marianne Richmond Studios, Inc.

Smith, Michael. Questions for Kids: A Book to Discover a Child's Imagination & Knowledge. Smith, Crystal & Lin, Albert, illus. 2003. 209p. (J). (gr. k-4). 13.95 (978-0-9669437-3-3(2)) East West Discovery Pr.

—Questions for Kids: A Book to Discover a Child's Imagination & Knowledge. Lin, Albert & Smith, Crystal, illus. 2003. 208p. (J). (gr. k-4). pap. 9.95 (978-0-9669437-1-9(6)) East West Discovery Pr.

DOMESTIC RELATIONS—FICTION

Brennan, Herbie. Faerie Wars. 2003. (Illus.). 370p. (J). 17.95 (978-1-58234-810-0(3) , Bloomsbury Children) Bloomsbury Publishing.

Brooks, Kevin. Martyn Pig. 240p. (J). 2003. pap. 6.99 (978-0-439-50752-3(9)); 2002. (gr. 5 up). pap. 16.95 (978-0-439-29595-6(5) , Chicken Hse., The) Scholastic, Inc.

—Martyn Pig. 2003. (gr. 7-12). lib. bdg. 15.30 (978-0-613-64813-4(7)) Tandem Library Bks.

Cross, Gillian. Tightrope. 1999. 224p. (J). (gr. 7 up). 16.95 (978-0-8234-1512-0(0)) Holiday Hse., Inc.

—Tightrope. 1999. 210p. (YA). (978-0-19-271804-4(5)) Oxford Univ. Pr., Inc.

Dean, Carolee. Comfort. (J). (gr. 7 up). 2004. 256p. pap. 6.99 (978-0-618-43912-6(9) , Graphia); 2002. 240p. 15.00 (978-0-618-13846-3(3)) Houghton Mifflin Co. Trade & Reference Div.

Dewey, Jennifer Owings. Borderlands. 2002. 192p. (YA). 14.95 (978-0-7614-5114-3(5) , Cavendish Children's Bks.) Cavendish, Marshall Corp.

Fisk, Pauline. Midnight Blue. (J). 2003. 250p. 16.95 (978-1-58234-829-2(4) , Bloomsbury Children); 2005. 218p. reprint ed. pap. 6.95 (978-1-58234-998-5(3)) Bloomsbury Publishing.

—Telling the Sea. 2002. 252p. (J). pap. 9.99 (978-0-7459-4740-2(9) , Lion) Lion Hudson plc GBR. *Dist:* Independent Pubs. Group.

Frank, E. R. Life Is Funny. 2002. 272p. (YA). pap. 7.99 (978-0-14-230083-1(7) , Puffin) Penguin Group (USA) Inc.

Lisle, Janet Taylor. How I Became a Writer & Oggie Learned to Drive. 2003. (Illus.). 160p. (YA). (ps-17). pap. 5.99 (978-0-14-250167-2(0) , Puffin) Penguin Group (USA) Inc.

Matthews, Kezi. Scorpio's Child. 2001. 160p. (YA). (gr. 6-8). 16.95 (978-0-8126-2890-6(X)) Cricket Bks.

Montes, Marisa. A Circle of Time. 2002. (Time Travel Mystery Ser.). 272p. (YA). (gr. 6-10). 17.00 (978-0-15-202626-4(6)) Harcourt Children's Bks.

Rinaldi, Ann. Millicent's Gift. 2002. (Illus.). 224p. (J). (ps-3). 15.95 (978-0-06-029636-0(4)) HarperCollins Pubs.

Saksena, Kate. Hang on in There, Shelley. 2003. 219p. (J). 16.95 (978-1-58234-822-3(7) , Bloomsbury Children) Bloomsbury Publishing.

Taylor, Kim. Cissy Funk. 2001. 224p. (J). (gr. 5 up). 15.95 (978-0-06-029041-2(2)); 15.89 (978-0-06-029042-9(0)) HarperCollins Pubs.

DOMINICA

Staub, Frank. Children of Dominica. 1998. (World's Children Ser.). (Illus.). 48p. (J). (gr. 3-6). 23.93 (978-1-57505-217-5(2) , Carolrhoda Bks.) Lerner Publishing Group.

DOMINICAN REPUBLIC

Armentrout, David & Armentrout, Patricia, trs. Alex Rodriguez. 2003. (Discover the Life of a Sports Star Ser.). (Illus.). 24p. (J). 20.64 (978-1-58952-654-9(6)) Rourke Publishing, LLC.

Augustin, Byron. The Dominican Republic. 2005. (to Z Ser.). (Illus.). 40p. (J). (gr. ps-ps). 24.50 (978-0-516-23663-6(6) , Children's Pr.) Scholastic Library Publishing.

—Dominican Republic. 2006. (to Z Ser.). (Illus.). 40p. (J). (gr. 2-4). pap. 6.95 (978-0-516-24951-3(7) , Children's Pr.) Scholastic Library Publishing.

Dubois, Muriel L. Dominican Republic. 2001. (Countries of the World Ser.). (Illus.). 126p. (J). (gr. 2-3). 18.60 (978-0-7368-0812-5(4) , Bridgestone Bks.) Capstone Pr., Inc.

Englar, Mary. The Dominican Republic. 2004. (Many Cultures, One World Ser.). (Illus.). 32p. (J). (gr. 2-3). lib. bdg. 23.93 (978-0-7368-2453-8(7) , Bridgestone Bks.) Capstone Pr., Inc.

Foley, Erin & Jermyn, Leslie. Dominican Republic. 2nd ed. 2005. (Cultures of the World Ser.). (Illus.). 144p. (J). (gr. 6-10). lib. bdg. (978-0-7614-1966-2(7) , Benchmark Bks.) Cavendish, Marshall Corp.

Furlong, Kate A. Dominican Republic. 2000. (Countries Ser.). (Illus.). 40p. (J). (gr. k-6). lib. bdg. 22.78 (978-1-57765-391-2(2) , Checkerboard Library) ABDO Publishing Co.

Haberle, Susan E. The Dominican Republic. 2003. (Countries & Cultures Ser.). (Illus.). 64p. (J). lib. bdg. 25.26 (978-0-7368-2177-3(5) , Bridgestone Bks.) Capstone Pr., Inc.

Khoo, Eileen. Welcome to the Dominican Republic. 2005. (Welcome to My Country Ser.). (Illus.). 48p. (J). lib. bdg. 26.00 (978-0-8368-3128-3(4)) Stevens, Gareth Inc.

Landau, Elaine. The Dominican Republic. 2000. (True Bks.). (Illus.). 48p. (J). (gr. 3-5). pap. 6.95 (978-0-516-27022-7(2)); 25.00 (978-0-516-21171-8(4)) Scholastic Library Publishing. (Children's Pr.).

Marcus, Amy. Exploring the Dominican Republic with the Five Themes of Geography. 2004. (Library of the Western Hemisphere). (J). pap. (978-0-8239-4643-3(6)); (Illus.). 24p. lib. bdg. (978-0-8239-4631-0(2)); (Illus.). 24p. lib. bdg. 19.95 (978-1-4042-2671-5(0)) Rosen Publishing Group, Inc., The.

McCarthy, Pat. The Dominican Republic: A MyReportLinks.com Book. 2004. (Top Ten Countries of Recent Immigrants Ser.). (Illus.). 48p. (J). lib. bdg. 25.26 (978-0-7660-5179-9(X) , MyReportLinks.com Bks.) Enslow Pubs., Inc.

Morris, Kerry-Ann & Ismail, Nafisah. Dominican Republic. 2004. (Countries of the World Ser.). (Illus.). 96p. (J). (gr. 6 up). lib. bdg. 30.00 (978-0-8368-3110-8(1)) Stevens, Gareth Inc.

Price Hossell, Karen. Dominican Americans. 2004. (We Are America Ser.). (Illus.). 32p. (J). lib. bdg. 24.22 (978-1-4034-5020-3(X)) Heinemann Library.

Rinker, Kimberly. Immigration from the Dominican Republic. 2003. (Changing Face of North America Ser.). (Illus.). 112p. (J). lib. bdg. (978-1-59084-689-6(3)) Mason Crest Pubs.

Rodriguez Marcos, Julian. Republica Dominicana. 2002. (ENG & SPA.). 64p. 9.95 (978-84-241-0364-4(5) , EV13504) Everest de Ediciones y Distribucion, S.L. ESP. *Dist:* Lectorum Pubns., Inc.

Spengler, Kremena. The Dominican Republic: A Question & Answer Book. 2006. (Fact Finders Ser.). (Illus.). 32p. (J). (978-0-7368-4353-9(1) , Fact Finders) Capstone Pr., Inc.

Temple, Bob. Dominican Republic. 2003. (Discovering Latin America Ser.). (Illus.). 64p. (J). (gr. 5 up). lib. bdg. (978-1-59084-301-7(0)) Mason Crest Pubs.

Zuchora-Walske, Christine. Dominican Republic in Pictures. 2008. (J). lib. bdg. ***(978-0-8225-8569-5(3))*** Twenty First Century Bks.

DOMINICAN REPUBLIC—FICTION

Alvarez, Julia. Antes de Ser Libre. Valenzuela, Liliana, tr. 2004. (SPA.). 192p. (YA). (gr. 7). mass mkt. 5.99 (978-0-375-81545-4(7) , Laurel Leaf) Random Hse. Children's Bks.

—Antes de Ser Libre. 2004. (SPA.). (gr. 7-12). lib. bdg. 14.15 (978-0-613-71931-5(X)) Tandem Library Bks.

—Before We Were Free. 2004. 192p. (J). (gr. 7 up). pap. 38.00 incl. audio (978-1-4000-9017-4(2) , Listening Library) Random Hse. Audio Publishing Group.

—Before We Were Free. (gr. 7-10). 2002. (Illus.). 176p. (J). lib. bdg. 17.99 (978-0-375-91544-4(3) , Knopf Bks. for Young Readers); 2002. (Illus.). 176p. (YA). 15.95 (978-0-375-81544-7(9) , Knopf Bks. for Young Readers); 2004. 192p. (YA). reprint ed. mass mkt. 5.99 (978-0-440-23784-6(X) , Laurel Leaf) Random Hse. Children's Bks.

—Before We Were Free. 2004. (gr. 7-12). lib. bdg. 14.15 (978-0-613-72269-8(8)) Tandem Library Bks.

—A Gift of Gracias: The Legend of Altagracia. Vidal, Beatriz, illus. 2005. 40p. (J). (gr. k-3). 15.95 (978-0-375-82425-8(1)); lib. bdg. 17.99 (978-0-375-92425-5(6)) Random Hse. Children's Bks. (Knopf Bks. for Young Readers).

Joseph, Lynn. El Color de Mis Palabras. Rioja, Alberto Jiménez, tr. 2004. (SPA., Illus.). (YA). (gr. 5 up). ring bd. 15.95 (978-1-930332-22-5(X) , LC7235) Lectorum Pubns., Inc.

—Color of My Words. 2002. (gr. 3-6). lib. bdg. 12.95 (978-0-613-44515-3(5)) Tandem Library Bks.

Mi Abuelita. 2001. (SPA.). (J). pap. 14.95 (978-0-9630310-5-1(8)) Will Hall Bks.

Moore, Robin. The Man with the Silver Oar. 2002. 192p. (J). (gr. 5 up). 15.89 (978-0-06-000048-6(1)) HarperCollins Pubs.

DOMINION OF THE SEA

see Sea Power

DON QUIXOTE (FICTITIOUS CHARACTER)—FICTION

Cervantes Saavedra, Miguel de. Don Quijote. Svetlin, illus. 2005. 159p. (J). (gr. 6-8). pap. 14.99 (978-84-316-7637-7(X)) Vicens-Vives, Editorial, S.A. ESP. *Dist:* Lectorum Pubns., Inc.

—Don Quixote. Marshall, Michael J., ed. abr. ed. 1999. (Core Classics Ser.: Vol. 6). (Illus.). 264p. (J). (gr. 4-6). pap. 7.95 (978-1-890517-10-6(0)) Core Knowledge Foundation.

—Don Quixote of the Mancha. 1999. (Everyman's Library Children's Classics). (Illus.). 256p. (gr. 8-12). 14.95 (978-0-375-40659-1(X) , Everyman's Library) Knopf Publishing Group.

—Tales of Don Quixote, Bk. 2. 2006. 224p. (J). (gr. 5). 18.95 (978-0-88776-744-9(3)) Tundra Bks., Inc./Livres Toundra, Inc. CAN. *Dist:* Random Hse., Inc.

Coté, Denis. La Forêt aux Mille et un Périls, Tome 2. Poulin, Stephane, illus. 2004. (Roman Jeunesse Ser.). (FRE.). 96p. (J). (gr. 4-7). pap. (978-2-89021-696-9(9)) Diffusion du livre Mirabel.

Kimmel, Eric A. Don Quixote & the Windmills. Fisher, Leonard Everett, illus. 2004. 32p. (J). 16.00 (978-0-374-31825-3(5) , Farrar, Straus & Giroux (BYR)) Farrar, Straus & Giroux.

Nichol, Barbara, retold by. Tales of Don Quixote, 2 vols. 2004. 216p. (J). (gr. 5). 15.95 (978-0-88776-674-9(9)) Tundra Bks., Inc./Livres Toundra, Inc. CAN. *Dist:* Random Hse., Inc.

DONALD DUCK (FICTITIOUS CHARACTER)—FICTION

Amano, Shiro. Kingdom Hearts: Chain of Memories, Vol. 2. 2nd rev. ed. 2007. 232p. (gr. 4-7). pap. 9.99 (978-1-59816-638-5(7) , Tokyopop Kids) TOKYOPOP, Inc.

Barks, Carl & Rosa, Don. Donald Duck Adventures: Donald Duck's Atom Bomb/the Duck Who Fell to Earth. 2007. 64p. pap. 8.99 ***(978-1-60360-006-4(X))*** Gemstone Publishing, Inc.

Barks, Carl, et al. Uncle Scrooge #372. 2007. 64p. pap. 7.99 ***(978-1-60360-002-6(7))*** Gemstone Publishing, Inc.

—Walt Disney's Christmas Parade #5. 2007. 80p. pap. 10.50 ***(978-1-60360-005-7(1))*** Gemstone Publishing, Inc.

—Walt Disney's Comics & Stories #684. 2007. 64p. pap. 7.99 ***(978-1-888472-95-0(2))*** Gemstone Publishing, Inc.

—Walt Disney's Comics & Stories #685. 2007. 64p. pap. 7.99 ***(978-1-888472-96-7(0))*** Gemstone Publishing, Inc.

—Walt Disney's Comics & Stories #686. 2007. 64p. pap. 7.99 ***(978-1-888472-97-4(9))*** Gemstone Publishing, Inc.

Clark, John, ed. Donald Duck Adventures, Vol. 15. 2005. 128p. (YA). pap. 7.95 (978-0-911903-99-7(2)) Gemstone Publishing, Inc.

Disney Staff. The Story of Donald Duck. 2004. (Illus.). 96p. (J). (ps-3). 35.00 incl. audio compact disk (978-1-55709-354-7(7)) Applewood Bks.

Donald Duck Adventures, Vol. 2. 2003. (Illus.). 128p. pap. 7.95 (978-0-911903-11-9(9)) Diamond Bk. Distributors.

Donald Duck Adventures, Vol. 17. 2006. 128p. (YA). pap. 7.95 (978-1-888472-12-7(X)) Gemstone Publishing, Inc.

Erickson, Byron, et al. Walt Disney's Comics & Stories #687. 2007. 64p. pap. 7.99 ***(978-1-888472-98-1(7))*** Gemstone Publishing, Inc.

Figuerola, Maite. Los Deportes. 2003. (Disney Collection). (SPA., Illus.). 32p. (J). 5.95 (978-84-670-0301-7(4)) Espasa Calpe, S.A. ESP. *Dist:* Planeta Publishing Corp.

Gemstone Publishing, creator. Donald Duck Adventures, Vol. 14. 2005. (Illus.). 128p. (YA). (gr. 4-7). pap. 7.95 (978-0-911903-94-2(1)) Gemstone Publishing, Inc.

Higginson, Sheila Sweeny. Donald's Christmas Gift. rev. ed. 2007. 24p. (ps-1). pap. 3.99 (*978-1-4231-0745-3(4)) Disney Pr.

—5+1 Makes More Fun. rev. ed. 2007. 10p. (J). (ps-1). 12.99 (*978-1-4231-0744-6(6)) Disney Pr.

Jensen, Lars, et al. Donald Duck Adventures, Vol. 18. 2006. (Illus.). 128p. (YA). pap. 7.95 (978-1-888472-30-1(8)) Gemstone Publishing, Inc.

Lustig, John & Barks, Carl. Donald Duck & Uncle Scrooge: Somewhere in Nowhere. Block, Pat & Rockwell, Scott, illus. 2005. 64p. (YA). pap. 6.95 (978-1-888472-05-9(7)) Gemstone Publishing, Inc.

McGreal, Pat, et al. Donald Duck Adventures, Vol. 19. 2006. (Illus.). 128p. (YA). pap. 7.95 (978-1-888472-31-8(6)) Gemstone Publishing, Inc.

Mouse Works Staff. Donald Duck. 1998. (Friendly Tales Ser.). (Illus.). 10p. (J). (ps). 6.99 (978-1-57082-927-7(6)) Mouse Works.

O'Connor, Eddie, et al. Donald Duck Adventures, Vol. 16. 2006. 128p. (YA). pap. 7.95 (978-1-888472-11-0(1)) Gemstone Publishing, Inc.

Shiro Amano. Kingdom Hearts, 4 vols., Vol. 4. 4th rev. ed. 2006. (Disney Squaresoft Ser.). (Illus.). pap. 5.99 (978-1-59816-220-2(9), Tokyopop Kids) TOKYOPOP, Inc.

Soundprints. Old Macdonald: And Other Favorites. 2002. (Illus.). 36p. (J). bds. 8.95 (978-1-931465-24-3(X), Little Soundprints) Soundprints.

—Old MacDonald: And Other Favorites. 2005. (Meet Mother Goose Ser.). (Illus.). 36p. (J). bds. 10.95 incl. audio compact disk (978-1-931465-30-4(4)) Soundprints.

DONATIONS

see Gifts

DONKEYS

Chottin, Ariane. Little Donkeys. 2006. (Born to Be Wild Ser.). (Illus.). 23p. (J). lib. bdg. 22.00 (978-0-8368-6165-5(5)) Stevens, Gareth Inc.

Donkey Work: Level J, 6 vols. (Wonder Worldtm Ser.). 16p. 29.95 (978-0-7802-4569-3(5)) Wright Group, The.

Ziefert, Harriet. Buzzy's Booboo. 2004. (Illus.). 24p. 9.95 (978-1-59354-023-4(X)) Blue Apple Bks.

DONKEYS—FICTION

Aboff, Marcie. Shrek: Classic Shrek Holiday. 2005. (Shrek Ser.). 49p. (J). pap. 3.99 (978-0-439-80586-5(4)) Scholastic, Inc.

Adams, Michelle Medlock. Little Colt's Palm Sunday. Parmenter, Wayne, illus. 2005. 28p. (J). 14.95 (978-0-8249-5503-8(X)) Ideals Pubns.

Aesop. The Miller & the Donkey: A Tale about Thinking for Yourself. Branch, Beverly, illus. 2006. (J). (978-1-59939-087-1(6), Reader's Digest Young Families, Inc.) Reader's Digest Children's Publishing, Inc.

Amery, Heather. Hungry Donkey. Tyler, Jenny, ed. Cartwright, Stephen, illus. rev. ed. 2004. (Farmyard Tales Readers Ser.). 16p. (J). pap. 5.95 (978-0-7945-0752-7(2), Usborne) EDC Publishing.

Anderson, James O. Poggy, the Stuffed Donkey. 2005. 16p. pap. 4.95 (*978-1-57258-395-5(9)) TEACH Services, Inc.

Barnes, Laura T. Teeny Tiny Ernest. Camburn, Carol A., illus. 2002. (Ernest Ser.: Vol. 2). 32p. (J). (ps-3). 15.95 (978-0-9674681-1-2(6)) Barnesyard Bks.

Bezek, Lyn. Daisy: The Cripple Creek Donkey. 2004. (J). pap. 7.95 (978-1-932738-09-4(6)) Western Reflections Publishing Co.

A Boy & His Donkey: Individual Title Six-Packs. (Literatura 2000 Ser.). (gr. 2-3). 33.00 (978-0-7635-0193-8(X)) Rigby Education.

Brabham, Barbara. Donkey Tales — Color with Paco! [English/Spanish Versions]. 2006. (J). 2.95 (*978-1-882185-86-3(2)) Cornerstone Publishing, Inc.

Broome, Errol. The Judas Donkey. Thompson, Sharon, illus. 2003. 144p. pap. 13.50 (978-1-920731-18-2(0)) Fremantle Pr. AUS. *Dist:* International Specialized Bk. Services.

Cahill, Doris. Nina. Blackwell, Anne, illus. John, Chirs, photos by. 2001. 80p. (J). 15.95 (978-0-9713224-0-0(6)) Johnson, J LLC.

Capucilli, Alyssa Satin. Pedro's Burro. Estrada, Pau, illus. 2007. (My First I Can Read Bks.). 32p. (J). lib. bdg. 16.89 (*978-0-06-056032-4(0)) HarperCollins Pubs.

De Segur, Comtesse & Willard, J. H. The Story of a Donkey. 2004. reprint ed. pap. 20.95 (978-1-4179-4273-2(8)) Kessinger Publishing, LLC.

De Segur, Condesa. Memorias de un Asno. (Torre de Papel Ser.). (SPA.). (YA). (gr. 6 up). 7.95 (978-958-04-4144-1(8)) Norma S.A. COL. *Dist:* Distribuidora Norma, Inc.

Delval, Marie-Helene. Burrito escucha los Ruidos. Courtin, Thierry, illus. 2004. (Palabras menudas Ser.). (SPA.). 14p. 5.95 (978-84-7864-710-1(4)) Combel Editorial, S.A. ESP. *Dist:* Independent Pubs. Group.

Doherty, Berlie. Coconutomes to School. 2003. (Illus.). 32p. (J). pap. 9.99 (978-0-00-710434-5(0)) HarperCollins Pubs. Ltd. GBR. *Dist:* Independent Pubs. Group.

Dowley, Tim. El Viaje Especial del Burrito - Donkey's Special Ride. (Serie Libros de Carton - Board Bks.). pap. (978-1-56063-956-5(3)) Editorial Unilit.

Duvoisin, Roger. Donkey-Donkey. 2007. 56p. (J). (gr. k-1). 15.99 (978-0-375-84065-4(6)); lib. bdg. 18.99 (978-0-375-94065-1(0)) Random Hse. Children's Bks. (Knopf Bks. for Young Readers).

Estrada, Pau, illus. Pedro's Burro. 2007. (My First I Can Read Bks.). 32p. (J). 15.99 (*978-0-06-056031-7(2)) HarperCollins Pubs.

Ferrell, Annie K. Benny the Burro Bears His Burden. 2004. 24p. pap. 14.95 (978-1-4137-2495-0(7)) PublishAmerica, Inc.

Foreman, Michael. Rock-a-Doodle-Do! 2001. (Illus.). 32p. (J). (gr. k-3). 16.99 (978-0-86264-951-7(9)) Andersen GBR. *Dist:* Independent Pubs. Group.

Griffin, Lydia. Prunes & Rupe. Hunt, Judith, illus. 2007. (J). (*978-0-86541-086-2(0)); pap. (*978-0-86541-087-9(9)) Filter Pr., LLC.

Grindley, Sally, et al. Pam Mae'r Awyr Yn Las? Stori Gan Sally Grindley. 2005. (WEL., Illus.). 25p. (978-1-85596-265-1(9)) Dref Wen.

Hamilton, Elizabeth L. Dorrie Donkey's Cooperation Camp. l.t. ed. 2005. (Character Critters Ser.: No. 12). (Illus.). 32p. (J). per. 5.95 (978-0-9754629-9-7(7), Character-in-Action) Quiet Impact, Inc.

Hamilton, Tisha & Primeau, Chuck. Shrek the Third Storybook & Viewer. Laguna, Fabio, illus. 2007. (RD Innovative Book & Player Format Ser.). 40p. (J). (ps-3). 24.99 (978-0-7944-1279-1(3)) Reader's Digest Assn., Inc., The.

Harcourt School Publishers Staff. The Burro's Land Below Level. 3rd ed. 2002. (Trophies Reading Program Ser.). (Illus.). pap. 5.10 (978-0-15-323157-5(2)) Harcourt Schl. Pubs.

Holder, Mig. All Safe in the Stable: A Donkey's Tale. Smallman, Steve, illus. 2005. (J). 12.99 (978-0-8254-7305-0(5)) Kregel Pubns.

Howard, Annabelle. A Father, His Son, & Their Donkey: An Aesop's Fable. 2006. spiral bd. 42.00 (*978-1-4108-7154-1(1)) Benchmark Education Co.

Ippolito, Eva Marie. The Donkey's Tale. Ippolito, Eva Marie, illus. 2003. (Illus.). III, 15p. (J). (ps-3). pap. 1.95 (978-0-9705350-3-0(1)) Ippolito, Eva Marie.

Jaffrey, Saeed. The Four Friends - The Musical Donkey. 1998. (Karadi Tales Ser.). (Illus.). 24p. (YA). (gr. 1 up). 15.99 incl. audio (978-81-86838-08-2(2)) APG Sales and Fulfillment.

—The Musical Donkey. 1998. (Karadi Tales Ser.). (Illus.). 24p. (YA). (gr. 1 up). 9.99 incl. audio (978-81-86838-37-2(6)) APG Sales and Fulfillment.

Jiménez, Juan Ramon. Platero & I. 2000. (Illus.). 196p. (YA). pap. 12.95 (978-0-595-00345-7(1)) iUniverse, Inc.

—Platero y Yo. (SPA.). 192p. (J). 13.95 (978-84-206-1851-7(9), AZ1851); (Illus.). 159p. 15.95 (978-84-206-3408-1(5)) Alianza Editorial, S. A. ESP. *Dist:* Continental Bk. Co., Inc., Distribooks, Inc., Distribooks, Inc.

—Platero y Yo. (SPA.). (J). pap. 9.95 (978-968-432-357-5(3), PM223) Editorial Porrua MEX. *Dist:* Continental Bk. Co., Inc.

—Platero y Yo. annot. ed. (SPA., Illus.). 232p. (J). 15.95 (978-84-207-2636-6(2), ANY010) Grupo Anaya, S.A. ESP. *Dist:* Continental Bk. Co., Inc.

—Platero y Yo. (SPA.). 240p. (YA). (gr. 5-8). (978-958-30-0744-6(7), PV0560) Panamericana Editorial COL. *Dist:* Lectorum Pubns., Inc.

—Platero y Yo (Platero & I) (SPA.). (J). pap. 9.95 (978-968-416-022-4(4), AOR01) Fernandez USA Publishing.

—Platero y Yo/Platero & I. Frasconi, Antonio, illus. 2003. 64p. (J). (gr. 4-6). pap. 5.95 (978-0-618-37838-8(3), Clarion Bks.) Houghton Mifflin Co. Trade & Reference Div.

Johnson, Veronica E. The Donkey Ride. 2006. per. 9.95 (978-0-9779600-0-2(5)) Euphema Press.

Jumbo & the Lost Tail. 2004. (J). per. 15.99 (978-0-9744205-0-9(6)) Golden Eagle Publishing Hse., Inc.

Kilimo, R. Donkey Who Wanted to Be a Lion. 2004. (Illus.). 11p. 13.95 (978-9966-25-169-5(3)) Heinemann Kenya, Limited (East African Educational Publishers Ltd E.A.E.P.) KEN. *Dist:* Michigan State Univ. Pr.

King, Emily. Clopper the Christmas Donkey. Olson, Ed, illus. 2004. 32p. 12.99 (978-0-8254-3069-5(0)) Kregel Pubns.

Koshkin, Alexander, illus. The Angel & the Donkey. 2004. 40p. (J). (ps-ps). lib. bdg. 13.15 (978-0-606-30510-5(6)) Tandem Library Bks.

Kouyama, Yoshiko. The Giving Chair. Kakimoto, Kozo, illus. 2006. 32p. (J). 14.95 (978-1-74126-432-6(4)) R.I.C. Pubns. AUS. *Dist:* SCB Distributors.

Kromhout, Rindert. Little Donkey & the Babysitter. Martens, Marianne, tr. from DUT. Van Haeringen, Annemarie, illus. 2006. 32p. (J). 15.95 (978-0-7358-2057-9(0)) North-South Bks., Inc.

Kromhout, Rindert. Little Donkey & the Birthday Present. Martens, Marianne, tr. from DUT. Van Haeringen, Annemarie, illus. 2007. 32p. (J). (ps-2). 15.95 (*978-0-7358-2132-3(1)) North-South Bks., Inc.

Long, Jonathan & Paul, K. The Wonky Donkey. 1999. (Illus.). 25p. (J). 19.99 (978-0-370-32466-1(8)) Random Hse. GBR. *Dist:* Independent Pubs. Group.

Mackall, Dandi Daley. Little Lost Donkey. 2007. 26p. (J). bds. 6.99 (*978-1-4003-1009-8(1)) Nelson, Thomas Inc.

Manchado & His Friends. 2000. Tr. of Manchado y Sus Amigos. 18.95 (978-0-9711930-1-7(0)) Barbed Wire Publishing.

Memorias de un Burrito. (SPA., Illus.). (YA). 11.95 (978-84-7281-087-7(9), AF1087) Auriga, Ediciones S.A. ESP. *Dist:* Continental Bk. Co., Inc.

Monks, Lydia. No More Eee-orrh! 2005. (Illus.). 32p. (J). (ps). 19.99 (978-1-4052-1739-2(1)); pap. 9.99 (978-1-4052-1740-8(5)) Egmont Bks., Ltd. GBR. *Dist:* Independent Pubs. Group, Independent Pubs. Group, Trafalgar Square Publishing.

Monks, Lydia. No More Eee-Orrhh. 2007. (Illus.). 24p. (J). 8.99 (*978-1-4052-2919-7(5)) Egmont Bks., Ltd. GBR. *Dist:* Independent Pubs. Group.

Morpurgo, Michael. Jo-Jo the Melon Donkey. 2002. (gr. 3-6). lib. bdg. 12.95 (978-0-613-52863-4(8)) Tandem Library Bks.

Un nino y su Burro: Individual Title Six-Packs. (Literatura 2000 Ser.). (SPA.). (gr. 2-3). 33.00 (978-0-7635-1097-8(1)) Rigby Education.

Oldfield, Jenny. Bright Eyes 3. 2007. (Illus.). 144p. pap. 6.95 (*978-0-340-91075-7(5)) Hodder Children's Division GBR. *Dist:* Independent Pubs. Group.

Once Enemies Now Friends: Manchado y Sus Amigos. 2001. per. 14.95 (978-0-9711930-0-0(2)) Barbed Wire Publishing.

Orme, David. El Burro Que Fue Muy Rapido, Level 3: Basado en un Cuento Folclorico Filipino. Rivers, Ruth, illus. 2005. (Lightning Readers Ser.). 32p. (J). (gr. 1-2). pap., pap. 3.95 (978-0-7696-4231-4(4), Gingham Dog Pr.) School Specialty Publishing.

—The Donkey That Went Too Fast, Level 3 Level 3: A Philippine Folktale. Rivers, Ruth, illus. 2005. (Lightning Readers Ser.). 32p. (J). (gr. 1-2). pap., pap. 3.95 (978-0-7696-4211-6(X), Gingham Dog Pr.) School Specialty Publishing.

Orme/Rivers, David/Ruth. The Donkey That Went Too Fast. 2005. (Illus.). 32p. (J). lib. bdg. 9.00 (*978-1-4242-0890-6(4)) Fitzgerald Bks.

Paterson, Katherine. The Angel & the Donkey. 2003. (gr. k-3). lib. bdg. 14.10 (978-0-613-70991-0(8)) Tandem Library Bks.

Paulk, Earl. Fir for a King: The Story of Obed, the Ugly Donkey. (J). pap. 9.95 (978-0-917595-63-9(7)) Cathedral of the Holy Spirit.

Pequeña the Burro: Evaluation Guide. 2006. (J). (978-1-55942-420-2(6)) Marsh Media.

Perera, Hilda. El Burrito Que Quería Ser Azul. 2000. (SPA., Illus.). 28p. (J). 13.99 (978-84-241-3334-4(X)) Everest de Ediciones y Distribucion, S.L. ESP. *Dist:* Lectorum Pubns., Inc.

Phillips, Rachelle. Dinkey the Donkey. Randolph, Carolyn, illus. l.t. ed. 2004. 24p. (J). 7.50 (978-0-9748591-5-6(X), MSP) Main St Publishing, Inc.

Pulley, Kelly, illus. The Donkey's Big Find. 2007. (Beginner's Bible' Ser.). 20p. (J). 6.99 (978-0-310-71388-3(9)) Zondervan.

Puttock, Simon. Goat & Donkey in Strawberry Sunglasses. Julian, Russell, illus. 2007. 28p. (J). (ps-2). 16.00 (*978-1-56148-572-7(1)) Good Bks.

—Goat & Donkey in the Great Outdoors. Julian, Russell, illus. 2007. 28p. (J). (ps-2). 16.00 (*978-1-56148-573-4(X)) Good Bks.

Reviejo, Carlos. Platero y Juan Ramon. Wensell, Ulises, illus. 2005. (SPA.). 29p. (J). 12.99 (978-1-933032-10-8(3)) Lectorum Pubns., Inc.

Schloesser, Natalie, illus. The Donkey's Ear. 2005. 34p. (J). 10.00 (978-0-9743850-1-3(8)) O'Brien, Gerard.

Schoberl, Elisabeth. When Donkeys Fly. 2007. (Illus.). 32p. (J). 15.95 (978-0-7358-2121-7(6)) North-South Bks., Inc.

Scholastic, Inc. Staff & Steele, Michael Anthony. Snowgre, Vol. 2. 2004. (Shark Tale Ser.: No. 2). (Illus.). 64p. (J). (gr. 2-5). pap. 3.99 (978-0-439-59717-3(X)) Scholastic, Inc.

Sehlin, Gunhild. Mary's Little Donkey: And the Flight to Egypt. Latham, Hugh & Maclean, Donald, trs. from SWE. Verheijen, Jan, illus. 2004. 160p. (J). (gr. 3-6). pap. 12.00 (978-0-86315-064-7(0)) Floris Bks. GBR. *Dist:* SteinerBooks, Inc.

Speirs, Gill & Speirs, John. The Donkey & the Golden Light: Peace, Goodwill & a New Beginning for All. 2004. (Illus.). 32p. (J). (ps-3). 16.95 (978-0-8109-4812-9(5)) Abrams, Harry N., Inc.

Steig, William. Sylvester & the Magic Pebble. Steig, William, illus. (Stories to Go! Ser.). (J). 2006. 32p. 4.99 (978-1-4169-1857-8(4), Aladdin); 2005. (Illus.). 42p. 17.99 (978-1-4169-0206-5(6)) Simon & Schuster Children's Publishing.

Tafuri, Nancy. Donkey's Christmas Song. 2006. (Illus.). 32p. (J). bds. 7.99 (978-0-439-74618-2(3), Scholastic Pr.) Scholastic, Inc.

Tarlow, Ellen. Pinwheel Days. Parker, Gretel, illus. 2007. 56p. (J). pap. 6.95 (978-1-59572-059-7(6)) Star Bright Bks., Inc.

Taylor, Dan & Taylor, Damon J. Duncan Carries a King: A Donkey's Tale. Taylor, Damon J., illus. 2005. (Illus.). (YA). 10.99 (978-0-8254-3869-1(1)) Kregel Pubns.

Toledo, Leila J. Little Peter & Sela. Davis, Chad L., illus. l.t. ed. 2004. 17p. (J). pap. 8.95 (978-0-9753118-0-6(8)) Bimini Bks.

Tomkinson, Raymond. Bravo the Donkey & Other Stories for Christmas. 2006. 72p. pap. (*978-1-84549-151-2(3)) arima publishing.

The Trouble with Patrick: Individual Title Six-Packs. (Action Packs Ser.). 120p. (gr. 3-5). 44.00 (978-0-7635-8431-3(2)) Rigby Education.

Ure, Jean. Daffy down Donkey. 1999. (We Love Animals Bks.). (Illus.). 144p. (J). (gr. 4-7). pap. 3.95 (978-0-7641-0969-0(3)) Barron's Educational Series, Inc.

Varley, Susan & Grindley, Sally. Why Is the Sky Blue? 2007. (Illus.). 32p. (J). pap. 9.95 (*978-1-84270-589-6(X)) Andersen GBR. *Dist:* Independent Pubs. Group.

Williams, Carol. Dickey. 2005. 16.00 (978-0-8059-9830-6(6)) Dorrance Publishing Co., Inc.

Wolf, Jackie. Picture Me Peek-A-Boo Farm. 2002. (Peek-a-Boo Ser.). (Illus.). 10p. (J). (ps up). bds. 4.99 (978-1-57151-595-7(X)) Playhouse Publishing.

Woods, Denise & McKelvain, Dana. The Legend of the Donkey's Cross. 2004. (Illus.). 32p. (J). per. 12.99 (978-1-58930-112-2(9)) Selah Publishing Group, LLC.

Wright, Boyd. Donkey Tales. 2006. 74p. pap. 14.95 (978-1-4241-1900-4(6)) PublishAmerica, Inc.

Young, Ed. Donkey Trouble. 1998. (J). (978-0-606-13342-5(9)) Tandem Library Bks.

Ziefert, Harriet. Buzzy's Balloon. Bolam, Emily, illus. 2007. 28p. (J). 9.95 (978-1-59354-603-8(3)) Blue Apple Bks.

DORA THE EXPLORER (FICTITIOUS CHARACTER)—FICTION

A&J Studios Staff. Dora Climbs Star Mountain. 2007. (Dora the Explorer Ser.). 24p. (J). pap. 3.99 (978-1-4169-4059-3(6), Simon Spotlight/Nickelodeon) Simon & Schuster Children's Publishing.

—Dora's Three Little Fairy Tales. 2005. (Dora the Explorer Ser.). (Illus.). 36p. (J). bds. 8.99 (978-1-4169-0640-7(1), Simon Spotlight/Nickelodeon) Simon & Schuster Children's Publishing.

Aikins, Dave. I Love My Mami! Dora the Explorer. 2006. (Illus.). 24p. (J). lib. bdg. 9.00 (*978-1-4242-0967-5(6)) Fitzgerald Bks.

Aikins, Dave, illus. At the Carnival. 2005. (J). (*978-1-4156-0769-5(9), Simon Spotlight/Nickelodeon) Simon & Schuster Children's Publishing.

—Big Sister Dora! 2005. (Dora the Explorer Ser.). 24p. (J). pap. 3.99 (978-0-689-87846-6(X), Simon Spotlight/Nickelodeon) Simon & Schuster Children's Publishing.

—Dora's Pirate Adventure. 2005. (Dora the Explorer Ser.). 24p. (J). pap. 3.99 (978-0-689-87583-0(5), Simon Spotlight/Nickelodeon) Simon & Schuster Children's Publishing.

Artful Doodlers. Dora Salva a las Sirenas (Dora Saves Mermaid Kingdom!) 2007. (Dora la Exploradora Ser.). (SPA., Illus.). 24p. (J). (ps-2). pap. 3.99 (*978-1-4169-4725-7(6), Libros Para Ninos) Simon & Schuster Children's Publishing.

—Dora Saves Mermaid Kingdom! 2007. (Dora the Explorer Ser.). 24p. (J). pap. 3.99 (*978-1-4169-3841-5(9), Simon Spotlight/Nickelodeon) Simon & Schuster Children's Publishing.

Beinstein, Phoebe. Count with Dora! A Counting Book in Both English & Spanish. Thompson Brothers Staff, illus. 2002. (Dora the Explorer Ser.). 14p. (J). bds. 4.99 (978-0-689-84818-6(8), Simon Spotlight/Nickelodeon) Simon & Schuster Children's Publishing.

—Dora. Mangano, Tom, illus. 2003. (Dora the Explorer Ser.). (ENG & SPA.). 12p. (J). bds. 7.99 (978-0-689-85484-2(6), Simon Spotlight/Nickelodeon) Simon & Schuster Children's Publishing.

—Dora Explora Los Colores/Dora Explores Colors. Hall, Susan, illus. 2007. (Dora la Exploradora Ser.). (SPA.). 14p. (J). (ps). bds. 4.99 (*978-1-4169-4726-4(4), Libros Para Ninos) Simon & Schuster Children's Publishing.

—Dora Goes for a Ride. Fruchter, Jason, illus. 2004. (Dora the Explorer Ser.). 22p. (J). bds. 4.99 (978-0-689-86372-1(1), Simon Spotlight/Nickelodeon) Simon & Schuster Children's Publishing.

—Meet Dora! Mangano, Tom, illus. 2005. (Dora the Explorer Ser.). 12p. (J). bds. 5.99 (978-1-4169-0998-9(2), Simon Spotlight/Nickelodeon) Simon & Schuster Children's Publishing.

—¿Qué voy a ser? / What Will I Be? Saunders, Zina, illus. 2007. (Dora la Exploradora Ser.). 14p. (J). bds. 4.99 (978-1-4169-3366-3(2), Libros Para Ninos) Simon & Schuster Children's Publishing.

—¡Vamonos! / Let's Go! Ziegler, Argentina Palacios, tr. Fruchter, Jason, illus. 2007. (Dora la Exploradora Ser.). 14p. (J). bds. 4.99 (978-1-4169-3367-0(0), Libros Para Ninos) Simon & Schuster Children's Publishing.

Bergen, Lara. Dora's I Love You Book. Roper, Robert, illus. 2007. (Dora the Explorer Ser.). 12p. (J). bds. 7.99 (*978-1-4169-4716-5(7), Simon Spotlight/Nickelodeon) Simon & Schuster Children's Publishing.

Bergen, Lara. Dora's Sleepover. Miller, Victoria, illus. 2006. (Dora the Explorer Ser.). 24p. (J). pap. 3.99 (978-1-4169-1508-9(7), Simon Spotlight/Nickelodeon) Simon & Schuster Children's Publishing.

Dora & Diego's Adventures! 2007. (Dora the Explorer Ser.). 80p. (J). 6.99 (*978-1-4169-3532-2(0), Simon Spotlight/Nickelodeon) Simon & Schuster Children's Publishing.

Dora the Explorer. 2006. (J). (ps-2). 128.10 (978-1-59961-066-5(3)) Spotlight.

Dora's Bedtime Adventures. 2005. (Dora the Explorer Ser.). (Illus.). 36p. (J). bds. 8.99 (978-1-4169-0628-5(2), Simon Spotlight/Nickelodeon) Simon & Schuster Children's Publishing.

Dora's Ready-to-Read Adventures. 2005. (Dora the Explorer Ser.). (Illus.). 128p. (J). pap. 7.99 (978-0-689-87815-2(X), Simon Spotlight/Nickelodeon) Simon & Schuster Children's Publishing.

Dora's Stories: A Boxed Set. 2005. (Dora the Explorer Ser.). 56p. (J). bds. 9.99 (978-1-4169-0035-1(7), Simon Spotlight/Nickelodeon) Simon & Schuster Children's Publishing.

Dora's Storytime Collection. 2003. (Dora the Explorer Ser.). (Illus.). 160p. (J). 10.95 (978-0-689-86623-4(2), Simon Spotlight/Nickelodeon) Simon & Schuster Children's Publishing.

Dorling Kindersley Publishing Staff. Dora the Explorer Essential Guide. 2006. (Dora the Explorer Ser.). (Illus.). 24p. (J). 8.99 (978-0-7566-2027-1(9)) Dorling Kindersley Publishing, Inc.

Driscoll, Laura. Dance to the Rescue. Aikins, Dave, illus. 2005. 24p. (J). lib. bdg. 9.00 (*978-1-4242-0981-1(1)) Fitzgerald Bks.

—Dora Helps Diego! Mangano, Tom, illus. 2007. (Ready-To-Read Ser.). 24p. (J). pap. 3.99 (978-1-4169-1509-6(5), Simon Spotlight/Nickelodeon) Simon & Schuster Children's Publishing.

—Eggs for Everyone! A & J Studio, illus. ed. 2005. 22p. (J). lib. bdg. 15.00 (978-1-59054-973-5(2)) Fitzgerald Bks.

Fruchter, Jason, illus. Dora's Favorite Fairy Tales. 2004. (Dora the Explorer Ser.). 80p. (J). 15.95 (978-0-689-86583-1(X), Simon Spotlight/Nickelodeon) Simon & Schuster Children's Publishing.

Gifford, Christopher. Swiper, No Swiping! Fruchter, Jason, illus. 2003. (Dora the Explorer Ser.). 14p. (J). bds. 12.95 (978-0-689-84773-8(4), Simon Spotlight/Nickelodeon) Simon & Schuster Children's Publishing.

Gilbert, Laura & Dorling Kindersley Publishing Staff. Dora the Explorer. 2005. (Ultimate sticker Bks.). (Illus.). 16p. (J). (ps-12). pap. 6.99 (978-0-7566-1560-4(7)) Dorling Kindersley Publishing, Inc.

Golden Books Staff. All My Friends! 2007. (Color Plus Puzzles to Color Ser.). (Illus.). 32p. (J). (ps-2). pap. 6.99 ***(978-0-375-84189-7(X)***, Golden Bks.) Random Hse. Children's Bks.

—Dora the Explorer - Dora Place Mats. 2001. (Illus.). 64p. (J). (ps-2). pap. 4.99 (978-0-307-23420-9(7), Golden Bks.) Random Hse. Children's Bks.

—Journey to Fairytale Land. 2007. (Book & CD Ser.). (Illus.). 24p. (J). (ps-2). 9.99 (978-0-375-84025-8(7), Golden Bks.) Random Hse. Children's Bks.

—Super Friends! Fruchter, Jason, illus. 2004. (Dora the Explorer Ser.). 48p. (J). (ps-2). pap. 2.99 (978-0-375-82651-1(3), Golden Bks.) Random Hse. Children's Bks.

Golden Books Staff. World of Colors. 2008. (Deluxe Paint Box Book Ser.). (Illus.). 128p. (J). (ps-2). pap. 7.99 ***(978-0-375-84293-1(4)***, Golden Bks.) Random Hse., Inc.

Hall, Susan, illus. Dora's Fairy-Tale Adventure. 2004. (Dora the Explorer Ser.). 24p. (J). pap. 3.99 (978-0-689-87012-5(4), Simon Spotlight/Nickelodeon) Simon & Schuster Children's Publishing.

Hazen, Barbara Shook & Golden Books Staff. The Circus Lion/Bouncy Ball. Gergely, Tibor & Roper, Bob, illus. 2003. (Super Coloring Book Ser.). 64p. (J). (ps-2). pap. 2.99 (978-0-307-10482-3(6), Golden Bks.) Random Hse. Children's Bks.

Inches, Alison. Big Sister Dora. 2006. (Illus.). (J). (ps-2). 21.35 (978-1-59961-067-2(1)) Spotlight.

—Big Sister Dora! Aikins, Dave, illus. ed. 2005. (Dora the Explorer Ser.: 13). 32p. (J). lib. bdg. 15.00 (978-1-59054-790-8(X)) Fitzgerald Bks.

—Dora Loves Boots. Saunders, Zina, illus. 2003. (Dora the Explorer Ser.). 24p. (J). pap. 3.99 (978-0-689-86373-8(X), Simon Spotlight/Nickelodeon) Simon & Schuster Children's Publishing.

—Dora's Big Dig. Roper, Robert, illus. 2006. 24p. (J). lib. bdg. 9.00 ***(978-1-4242-0983-5(8))*** Fitzgerald Bks.

—Dora's Big Dig. Roper, Robert, illus. 2006. (Dora the Explorer Ser.). 24p. (J). pap. 5.99 (978-1-4169-0806-7(4), Simon Spotlight/Nickelodeon) Simon & Schuster Children's Publishing.

—Learn with Dora!/¡A aprender con Dora! A Bilingual Adventure with Pull-tabs, Wheels, & Flaps! Ziegler, Argentina Palacios, tr. Aikins, Dave, illus. 2006. (Dora the Explorer Ser.). 12p. (J). 7.99 (978-1-4169-1210-1(X), Simon Spotlight/Nickelodeon) Simon & Schuster Children's Publishing.

Inches, Alison. Let's Play Sports! A Lift-the-Flap Story. Aikins, Dave, illus. 2007. (Dora the Explorer Ser.). 16p. (J). pap. 6.99 ***(978-1-4169-3350-2(6)***, Simon Spotlight/Nickelodeon) Simon & Schuster Children's Publishing.

John Brown Publishing Ltd. & Murphy, Harriet. Dora's Enchanted Adventure: Follow the Reader Level II. 2007. (Dora the Explorer Ser.). 24p. (J). 24.99 ***(978-1-4169-4992-3(5)***, Simon Scribbles) Simon & Schuster Children's Publishing.

Koeppel, Ruth. Nick Jr. Dora & Friends Movie Theater Storybook & Movie Projector. 2005. (Nick Jr. Movie Theater Ser.). (Illus.). 48p. (J). 24.99 (978-0-7944-0783-4(8)) Reader's Digest Assn., Inc., The.

Koeppel, Ruth & Reader's Digest Editors. Exploring with Dora. 2007. (Readers Book & DVD Ser.). 32p. (J). 17.99 (978-0-7944-1280-7(7)) Reader's Digest Assn., Inc., The.

Koeppel, Ruth & Reader's Digest Staff. Dora's Special Memories: Storybook & Toy Camera. 2007. (RD Innovative Book & Player Format Ser.). 10p. (J). 21.99 ***(978-0-7944-1294-4(7))*** Reader's Digest Assn., Inc., The.

Larsen, Kirsten. Dora's Perfect Pumpkin. Miller, Victoria, illus. 2007. (Dora the Explorer Ser.). 24p. (J). pap. 3.99 ***(978-1-4169-3438-7(3)***, Simon Spotlight/Nickelodeon) Simon & Schuster Children's Publishing.

Larsen, Kirsten. It's Sharing Day. Zalme, Ron, illus. 2007. (Dora the Explorer Ser.). 24p. (J). pap. 3.99 (978-1-4169-1575-1(3), Simon Spotlight/Nickelodeon) Simon & Schuster Children's Publishing.

Lee, Quinlan B. Dora the Explorer Phonics Box, 12 bks. Fruchter, Jason, illus. 2004. 16p. (J). (ps-3). 12.99 (978-0-439-67753-0(X)) Scholastic, Inc.

—Let's Explore!, Bks. 1-6. 2007. (Dora the Explorer Ser.: Bks. 1-6). 112p. (J). pap. 5.99 (978-0-439-90237-3(1)) Scholastic, Inc.

—On the Go! 2007. (Dora the Explorer Ser.: Bks. 7-12). 112p. (J). pap. 5.99 (978-0-439-90238-0(X)) Scholastic, Inc.

Lee, Quinlan B. Sail Away. 2005. (Illus.). (J). ***(978-0-439-77933-3(2))*** Scholastic, Inc.

Lindner, Brooke. Dora's Sweet Adventure: A Scratch & Sniff Board Book. Mangano, Tom, illus. 2007. (Dora the Explorer Ser.). 14p. (J). bds. 7.99 (978-1-4169-2747-1(6), Simon Spotlight/Nickelodeon) Simon & Schuster Children's Publishing.

Lou Weber. Dora the Explorer My First Look & Find. 18p. 7.98 (978-1-4127-3909-2(8), PIL Kids) Publications International, Ltd.

Maher, Alex, illus. El safari de Diego (Diego's Safari Rescue) 2007. (Go, Diego, Go! Ser.). 24p. (J). pap. 3.99 ***(978-1-4169-5998-4(X)***, Libros Para Ninos) Simon & Schuster Children's Publishing.

Mangano, Tom, illus. Dora explora el mundo. 2006. (Dora la Exploradora Ser.). (SPA.). 24p. (J). pap. 3.99 (978-1-4169-2448-7(5), Libros Para Ninos) Simon & Schuster Children's Publishing.

—Dora's Outer Space Adventure. 2004. (Dora the Explorer Ser.). 12p. (J). bds. 6.99 (978-0-689-86794-1(8), Simon Spotlight/Nickelodeon) Simon & Schuster Children's Publishing.

—Dora's World Adventure! 2006. (Dora the Explorer Ser.). 24p. (J). pap. 3.99 (978-1-4169-2447-0(7), Simon Spotlight/Nickelodeon) Simon & Schuster Children's Publishing.

McMahon, Kara. Dora Rides to Bike Park. Aikins, Dave, illus. 2007. (Dora the Explorer Ser.). 12p. (J). bds. 8.99 (978-1-4169-3539-1(8), Simon Spotlight/Nickelodeon) Simon & Schuster Children's Publishing.

Miller, Sara Swan & Koeppel, Ruth. Adventures with Dora Storybook & Electronic Picture Dictionary. 2007. (RD Innovative Book & Player Format Ser.). 40p. (J). (ps-3). bds. 24.99 (978-0-7944-1210-4(6)) Reader's Digest Assn., Inc., The.

Miller, Victoria, illus. Super Babies! 2006. (Dora the Explorer Ser.). 24p. (J). pap. 3.99 (978-1-4169-1485-3(4), Simon Spotlight/Nickelodeon) Simon & Schuster Children's Publishing.

Murphy, Harriet. Hello, Dora! Follow the Reader Level 1. 2007. (Dora the Explorer Ser.). 24p. (J). 24.99 ***(978-1-4169-4990-9(9)***, Simon Scribbles) Simon & Schuster Children's Publishing.

Nickelodeon Staff, illus. Dora's Big Book of Stories. 2005. (Dora the Explorer Ser.). 192p. (J). 10.95 (978-1-4169-0708-4(4), Simon Spotlight/Nickelodeon) Simon & Schuster Children's Publishing.

La Princesa Dora: Magic Wand Adventure. 2005. (Illus.). 10p. (J). bds. 15.98 (978-1-4127-3536-0(X), 7263400) Publications International, Ltd.

Ricci, Christine. Los Buenos Modales de Dora. Hall, Susan, illus. 2005. (Dora the Explorer Ser.).Tr. of Dora's Book of Manners. (SPA.). 24p. pap. 3.99 (978-1-4169-0069-6(1), Libros Para Ninos) Simon & Schuster Children's Publishing.

—Dora & the Rainbow Kite Festival. Roper, Robert, illus. 2008. (Dora the Explorer Ser.). 24p. (J). pap. 3.99 ***(978-1-4169-4777-6(9)***, Simon Spotlight/Nickelodeon) Simon & Schuster Children's Publishing.

—Dora in the Deep Sea. Roper, Robert, illus. 2003. (Dora the Explorer Ser.: Vol. 3). 24p. (J). pap. 3.99 (978-0-689-85845-1(0), Simon Spotlight/Nickelodeon) Simon & Schuster Children's Publishing.

—Dora in the Deep Sea. 2003. (ps-2). lib. bdg. 11.80 (978-0-613-73392-2(4)) Tandem Library Bks.

—Dora's Book of Manners. Hall, Susan', illus. ed. 2005. (Dora the Explorer Ser.: No. 7). 22p. (J). lib. bdg. 15.00 (978-1-59054-793-9(4)) Fitzgerald Bks.

—Dora's Christmas Adventure. Piluso, Piero, illus. 2006. (Dora the Explorer Ser.). 14p. (J). bds. 6.99 (978-1-4169-1755-7(1), Simon Spotlight/Nickelodeon) Simon & Schuster Children's Publishing.

—Dora's Costume Party! Saunders, Zina, illus. 2005. 24p. (J). lib. bdg. 9.00 ***(978-1-4242-0978-1(1))*** Fitzgerald Bks.

—Dora's Costume Party! Saunders, Zina, illus. 2005. (Dora the Explorer Ser.). 24p. (J). (ps-ps). pap. 3.99 (978-1-4169-0010-8(1), Simon Spotlight/Nickelodeon) Simon & Schuster Children's Publishing.

—Dora's Costume Party. 2006. (J). (ps-2). 21.35 (978-1-59961-071-9(X)) Spotlight.

—Dora's Fairy-Tale Adventure. Hall, Susan', illus. ed. 2005. (Dora the Explorer Ser.: No. 9). 22p. (J). lib. bdg. 15.00 (978-1-59054-795-3(0)) Fitzgerald Bks.

—Dora's Favorite Adventures! Miller, Victoria, illus. 2007. (Dora the Explorer Ser.). 14p. (J). bds. 7.99 ***(978-1-4169-3802-6(8)***, Simon Spotlight/Nickelodeon) Simon & Schuster Children's Publishing.

—Dora's Mystery of the Missing Shoes. Savitsky, Steven, illus. 2007. (Dora the Explorer Ser.). 24p. (J). pap. 3.99 ***(978-1-4169-3824-8(9)***, Simon Spotlight/Nickelodeon) Simon & Schuster Children's Publishing.

—Dora's Rainbow Surprise. Hall, Susan T., illus. 2002. (Dora the Explorer Ser.). 14p. (J). bds. 9.99 (978-0-689-85038-7(7), Simon Spotlight/Nickelodeon) Simon & Schuster Children's Publishing.

—Dora's River Race. Roper, Robert, illus. 2006. (Dora the Explorer Ser.). 16p. (J). pap. 5.99 (978-1-4169-1208-8(8), Simon Spotlight/Nickelodeon) Simon & Schuster Children's Publishing.

—Dora's Starry Christmas. Studios, A&J, illus. 2005. 24p. (J). lib. bdg. 9.00 ***(978-1-4242-0980-4(3))*** Fitzgerald Bks.

—Dora's Starry Christmas. Ziegler, Argentina Palacios, tr. A&J Studios Staff, illus. 2005. (Dora the Explorer Ser.). (SPA.). 24p. (J). pap. 3.99 (978-1-4169-1183-8(9), Libros Para Ninos) Simon & Schuster Children's Publishing.

—Good Night, Dora! A Lift-the-Flap Story. Hall, Susan, illus. 2002. (Dora the Explorer Ser.).Tr. of Good Night, Dora!. 16p. (J). (ps-1). pap. 5.99 (978-0-689-84774-5(2), Simon Spotlight/Nickelodeon) Simon & Schuster Children's Publishing.

—Music Player Storybook. 2006. (Nick Jr. Dora the Explorer Ser.). (Illus.). 40p. (J). DVD 24.99 (978-0-7944-1004-9(9)) Reader's Digest Assn., Inc., The.

—Say Cheese! Savitsky, Steven, illus. ed. 2005. 22p. (J). lib. bdg. 15.00 (978-1-59054-975-9(9)) Fitzgerald Bks.

—Show Me Your Smile! Roper, Robert, illus. ed. 2005. (Dora the Explorer Ser.: 11). 22p. (J). lib. bdg. 15.00 (978-1-59054-800-4(0)) Fitzgerald Bks.

—Show Me Your Smile! A Visit to the Dentist. Roper, Robert, illus. 2005. (Dora the Explorer Ser.). 24p. (J). pap. 3.99 (978-0-689-87169-6(4), Simon Spotlight/Nickelodeon) Simon & Schuster Children's Publishing.

Ricci, Christine & A&J Studios Staff. Dora's Lunch Box. 2006. (Dora the Explorer Ser.). (Illus.). 10p. (J). bds. 5.99 (978-1-4169-0845-6(5)) Simon & Schuster Children's Publishing.

—Dora's Starry Christmas, Vol. 17. 2005. (Dora the Explorer Ser.). (Illus.). 24p. (J). pap. 3.99 (978-1-4169-0249-2(X), Simon Spotlight/Nickelodeon) Simon & Schuster Children's Publishing.

—Dora's Valentine Adventure. 2006. (Dora the Explorer Ser.). 14p. (J). bds. 6.99 (978-1-4169-1754-0(3), Simon Spotlight/Nickelodeon) Simon & Schuster Children's Publishing.

Saunders, Zina. Dora Loves Boots. Saunders, Zina, illus. ed. 2005. (Dora the Explorer Ser.: No. 6). (Illus.). 22p. (J). lib. bdg. 15.00 (978-1-59054-792-2(6)) Fitzgerald Bks.

—Dora Loves Boots. 2004. (ps-2). lib. bdg. 11.80 (978-0-613-73435-6(1)) Tandem Library Bks.

Saunders, Zina, illus. Splish, Splash, Dora! 2007. (Dora the Explorer Ser.). 8p. (J). 7.99 ***(978-1-4169-3875-0(3)***, Simon Spotlight/Nickelodeon) Simon & Schuster Children's Publishing.

Savitsky, Steven, illus. Dora Had a Little Lamb. 2007. (Dora the Explorer Ser.). 24p. (J). pap. 3.99 ***(978-1-4169-3368-7(9)***, Simon Spotlight/Nickelodeon) Simon & Schuster Children's Publishing.

Silverhardt, Lauryn. Best Friends. Style Guide Staff, illus. 2005. (Dora the Explorer Ser.). 8p. (J). 6.99 (978-0-689-87694-3(7), Simon Spotlight/Nickelodeon) Simon & Schuster Children's Publishing.

—A Day at the Beach. Fruchter, Jason, illus. 2003. (Dora the Explorer Ser.). 22p. (J). bds. 4.99 (978-0-689-85482-8(X), Simon Spotlight/Nickelodeon) Simon & Schuster Children's Publishing.

—Un Dia en la Playa. Ziegler, Argentina Palacios, tr. Fruchter, Jason, illus. 2004. (Dora the Explorer Ser.).Tr. of Day at the Beach. (SPA.). 22p. (J). bds. 4.99 (978-0-689-86976-1(2), Libros Para Ninos) Simon & Schuster Children's Publishing.

—Dora Discovers. Aikins, Dave, illus. 2004. (Dora the Explorer Ser.). 12p. (J). bds. 12.95 (978-0-689-86871-9(5), Simon Spotlight/Nickelodeon) Simon & Schuster Children's Publishing.

—A Surprise Party. Yee, Josie, illus. 2003. (Dora the Explorer Ser.). 22p. (J). bds. 4.99 (978-0-689-85483-5(8), Simon Spotlight/Nickelodeon) Simon & Schuster Children's Publishing.

Silverhardt, Lauryn & Thompson Bros. Staff. Meet Boots! 2005. (Dora the Explorer Ser.). 12p. (J). bds. 5.99 (978-1-4169-0999-6(0), Simon Spotlight/Nickelodeon) Simon & Schuster Children's Publishing.

Simon and Schuster Staff, ed. Cuentos de Dora y sus amigos. 2006. (Dora la Exploradora Ser.).Tr. of Dora's Storytime Collection. (SPA.). 160p. (J). 10.95 (978-1-4169-1564-5(8), Libros Para Ninos) Simon & Schuster Children's Publishing.

Sollinger, Emily. Dora's School Day! Mangano, Tom, illus. 2005. (Dora the Explorer Ser.). 12p. (J). bds. 4.99 (978-0-689-87786-5(2), Simon Spotlight/Nickelodeon) Simon & Schuster Children's Publishing.

Sollinger, Emily & Leigh, Emma. Dora's Special Delivery. Aikins, Dave, illus. 2007. (Dora the Explorer Ser.). 12p. (J). 7.99 (978-1-4169-4128-6(2), Simon Spotlight/Nickelodeon) Simon & Schuster Children's Publishing.

Storytime with Dora & Blue! 2006. (Nick Jr. Carry-along Boxed Set Ser.). (Illus.). 144p. (J). 9.99 (978-1-4169-1302-3(5), Simon Spotlight/Nickelodeon) Simon & Schuster Children's Publishing.

Thorpe, Kiki. Dora's Chilly Day. Savitsky, Steven, illus. ed. 2005. (Dora the Explorer Ser.: No. 10). 22p. (J). lib. bdg. 15.00 (978-1-59054-794-6(2)) Fitzgerald Bks.

—Dora's Chilly Day. Savitsky, Steven, illus. 2004. (Dora the Explorer Ser.). 24p. (J). pap. 3.99 (978-0-689-86795-8(6), Simon Spotlight/Nickelodeon) Simon & Schuster Children's Publishing.

—Where Is Boots? A Lift-the-Flap Story. Savitsky, Steve, illus. 2002. (Dora the Explorer Ser.). 16p. (J). (ps-1). pap. 5.99 (978-0-689-84775-2(0), Simon Spotlight/Nickelodeon) Simon & Schuster Children's Publishing.

Torres, Melissa & A&J Studios Staff. Dora's Potty Book. 2005. (Dora the Explorer Ser.). 14p. (J). bds. 8.99 (978-1-4169-0059-7(4), Simon Spotlight/Nickelodeon) Simon & Schuster Children's Publishing.

—El entrenamiento de Dora (Dora's Potty Book) 2006. (Dora la Exploradora Ser.). (SPA.). 14p. (J). bds. 8.99 (978-1-4169-1565-2(6), Libros Para Ninos) Simon & Schuster Children's Publishing.

Valdes, Leslie. At the Carnival. Roper, Robert, illus. 2005. 24p. (J). lib. bdg. 9.00 ***(978-1-4242-0982-8(X))*** Fitzgerald Bks.

—At the Carnival. 2006. (J). (ps-2). 21.35 (978-1-59961-069-6(8)) Spotlight.

—Dora Goes to School. Roper, Robert, illus. ed. 2005. (Dora the Explorer Ser.: 8). 22p. (J). lib. bdg. 15.00 (978-1-59054-791-5(8)) Fitzgerald Bks.

—Dora Goes to School. 2006. (Dora the Explorer Ser.). (Illus.). (J). (ps-2). 21.35 (978-1-59961-068-9(X)) Spotlight.

—Dora's Christmas Parade. Aikins, Dave, illus. 2003. (Dora the Explorer Ser.). 32p. (J). 5.99 (978-0-689-85843-7(4), Simon Spotlight/Nickelodeon) Simon & Schuster Children's Publishing.

—Dora's Christmas Parade. 2003. (gr. k-3). lib. bdg. 14.15 (978-0-613-73391-5(6)) Tandem Library Bks.

—Dora's Pirate Adventure. Aikins, Dave, illus. ed. 2005. (Dora the Explorer Ser.: No. 12). 22p. (J). lib. bdg. 15.00 (978-1-59054-796-0(9)) Fitzgerald Bks.

—Dora's Pirate Adventure. 2006. (Illus.). (J). (ps-2). 21.35 (978-1-59961-072-6(8)) Spotlight.

—Happy Mother's Day, Mami! Fruchter, Jason, illus. ed. 2005. (Dora the Explorer Ser.: No. 3). 22p. (J). lib. bdg. 15.00 (978-1-59054-798-4(5)) Fitzgerald Bks.

—Meet Diego! Hall, Susan', illus. ed. 2005. (Dora the Explorer Ser.: No. 4). 22p. (J). lib. bdg. 15.00 (978-1-59054-799-1(3)) Fitzgerald Bks.

—Meet Diego! Hall, Susan T., illus. 2003. (Dora the Explorer Ser.). 24p. (J). pap. 3.50 (978-0-689-85993-9(7), Simon Spotlight/Nickelodeon) Simon & Schuster Children's Publishing.

—Meet Diego! 2003. (ps-2). lib. bdg. 11.25 (978-0-613-73344-1(4)) Tandem Library Bks.

Wax, Wendy & A&J Studios. Dora's Camping Trip. 2007. (Dora the Explorer Ser.). 26p. (J). bds. 5.99 ***(978-1-4169-3434-9(0)***, Simon Spotlight/Nickelodeon) Simon & Schuster Children's Publishing.

Wax, Wendy & A&J Studios Staff. Five Stars for Abuela! 2006. (Dora the Explorer Ser.). 14p. (J). 6.99 (978-1-4169-1301-6(7), Simon Spotlight/Nickelodeon) Simon & Schuster Children's Publishing.

Weber, Lou, ed. Dora the Explorer Look & Find. 2005. (Illus.). 24p. (J). 7.98 (978-1-4127-3318-2(9), 7241500) Publications International, Ltd.

—Dora the Explorer Musical Treasury. 2005. 40p. (J). bds. 12.98 (978-1-4127-3314-4(6), 7241900) Publications International, Ltd.

—Dora's Number Adventure Sight & Sound Activity. 2005. (Active Minds Ser.). (Illus.). 64p. (J). 16.98 (978-1-4127-3534-6(3), 7258200) Publications International, Ltd.

Willson. Dora's Thanksgiving. Roper, Robert, illus. ed. 2005. (Dora the Explorer Ser.: No. 5). 22p. (J). lib. bdg. 15.00 (978-1-59054-797-7(7)) Fitzgerald Bks.

Willson, Sarah. Dora's Backpack. 2006. (Dora the Explorer Ser.). (Illus.). (J). (ps-2). 21.35 (978-1-59961-070-2(1)) Spotlight.

—Dora's Easter Basket. Hall, Susan T., illus. 2003. (Dora the Explorer Ser.). 32p. (J). 5.99 (978-0-689-85240-4(1), Simon Spotlight/Nickelodeon) Simon & Schuster Children's Publishing.

—Dora's Easter Basket. 2003. (ps-2). lib. bdg. 14.15 (978-0-613-73354-0(1)) Tandem Library Bks.

—Dora's Halloween Adventure. Savitsky, Steven, illus. 2003. (Dora the Explorer Ser.). 14p. (J). bds. 5.99 (978-0-689-85844-4(2), Simon Spotlight/Nickelodeon) Simon & Schuster Children's Publishing.

—Dora's Thanksgiving. Roper, Robert, illus. 2003. (Dora the Explorer Ser.). 24p. (J). pap. 3.99 (978-0-689-85842-0(6), Simon Spotlight/Nickelodeon) Simon & Schuster Children's Publishing.

Zalme, Ron, illus. Around the World! 2006. (Dora the Explorer Ser.). 24p. (J). pap. 3.99 (978-1-4169-2478-4(7), Simon Spotlight/Nickelodeon) Simon & Schuster Children's Publishing.

Ziegler, Argentina Palacios, tr. Aventura magica de Dora (Dora's Fairy-Tale Adventure) Hall, Susan', illus. 2006. (Dora la Exploradora Ser.). (SPA.). 24p. (J). pap. 3.99 (978-1-4169-1184-5(7), Libros Para Ninos) Simon & Schuster Children's Publishing.

DOUBLE STARS

see Stars

DOUBLEDAY, ABNER, 1819-1893

Dunham, Montrew. Abner Doubleday: Boy Baseball Pioneer, 11 vols. Underdown, Harold, ed. Morrison, Cathy, illus. 2nd ed. 2005. (Young Patriots Ser.: 11). 118p. (J). 15.95 (978-1-882859-49-8(9)); pap. 9.95 (978-1-882859-50-4(2)) Patria Pr., Inc. (Young Patriots Series).

DOUBT

see Belief and Doubt

DOUG (FICTITIOUS CHARACTER)—FICTION

Campbell, Daniel. Bad to the Bone. 2000. (gr. 3-6). lib. bdg. 13.00 (978-0-613-30975-2(8)) Tandem Library Bks.

Campbell, Danny & Campbell, Kimberly. Bad to the Bone. 2000. (Doug: No. 6). (Illus.). 112p. (gr. 2-7). pap. 4.99 (978-0-7868-4412-8(4)) Disney Pr.

—True Graffiti. 2nd ed. 2000. (Doug: No. 2). (Illus.). 80p. (gr. 3-7). pap. 4.99 (978-0-7868-4383-1(7)) Disney Pr.

Campbell, Kim, et al. Invasion of the Judy Snatchers. 2000. (Doug: 1). (Illus.). 96p. (gr. 2-5). pap. 4.99 (978-0-7868-4382-4(9)) Disney Pr.

Carr, Jan. Doug's Secret Christmas. 1999. (Doug Ser.). (Illus.). 32p. (J). (gr. k-4). pap. 4.99 (978-0-7868-4351-0(9)) Disney Pr.

Garvey, Dennis. Haunted House Hysteria. 2000. (gr. 3-6). lib. bdg. 13.00 (978-0-613-31295-0(3)) Tandem Library Bks.

Garvey, Dennis & Nichols, Tommy. Haunted House Hysteria. 2000. (Doug: No. 5). (Illus.). 112p. (gr. 2-5). pap. 4.99 (978-0-7868-4411-1(6)) Disney Pr.

Garvey, Linda K. Doug's Twelve Days of Christmas. 1998. (Doug Ser.). (Illus.). 32p. (J). (ps-2). 8.95 (978-0-7868-3197-5(9)) Disney Pr.

Krulik, Nancy E. Doug Makes the Team. 1999. (Doug Ser.). (Illus.). 32p. (J). (gr. k-4). 8.99 (978-0-7868-3193-7(6)) Disney Pr.

—Untitled. 176p. (J). 2001. pap. 4.99 (978-0-7868-1578-4(7)); No. 7. 2002. pap. 4.99 (978-0-7868-1577-7(9)) Disney Pr.

Pollack, Pamela. The Curse of the Beetenkaumun. 2000. (Funnie Mysteries Ser.: No. 4). (Illus.). 80p. (gr. 2-7). pap. 4.99 (978-0-7868-4410-4(8)) Disney Pr.

Ryan, Pam Muñoz. Doug Counts Down. 1998. (Doug Ser.). (Illus.). 32p. (J). (gr. k-4). 8.95 (978-0-7868-3141-8(3)) Disney Pr.

DOUGLAS, STEPHEN ARNOLD, 1813-1861

Bonner, Mike. Stephen A. Douglas: Champion of the Union. 2001. (Famous Figures of the Civil War Era Ser.). (Illus.). 80p. (gr. 5 up). (J). pap. 25.00 (978-0-7910-6403-0(4)); (YA). 25.00 (978-0-7910-6402-3(6)) Facts On File, Inc. (Chelsea Hse.).

—Stephen a Douglas: Champion of the Union. 2002. (gr. 5-8). lib. bdg. 17.60 (978-0-613-52728-6(3)) Tandem Library Bks.

Burgan, Michael. The Lincoln-Douglas Debates. 2006. (Illus.). 48p. (J). (gr. 4-6). 23.93 (978-0-7565-1632-1(3)) Compass Point Bks.

January, Brendan. The Lincoln-Douglas Debates. 1998. (Illus.). 32p. (J). (gr. 4-7). lib. bdg. 14.10 (978-0-613-37439-2(8)) Tandem Library Bks.

DOUGLASS, FREDERICK, 1818-1895

Adler, David A. A Picture Book of Frederick Douglass. Byrd, Samuel, illus. 2005. (Picture Book Readalongs Ser.). (J). (ps-3). pap. 16.95 incl. audio (978-1-59519-372-8(3)); 30p. audio compact disk 18.95 (978-1-59519-376-6(6)); 25.95 incl. audio (978-1-59519-373-5(1)); pap. 28.95 incl. audio compact disk (978-1-59519-377-3(4)); Set. pap. 37.95 incl. audio (978-1-59519-374-2(X)); Set. pap. 39.95 incl. audio compact disk (978-1-59519-378-0(2)) Live Oak Media.

Burchard, Peter. Frederick Douglass. 2003. (Illus.). 240p. (YA). (gr. 7 up). 18.95 (978-0-689-83240-6(0) , Atheneum) Simon & Schuster Children's Publishing.

Collier, James Lincoln. The Frederick Douglass. 2004. (You Never Knew Ser.). (J). (gr. 4-6). pap. 6.95 (978-0-516-25837-9(0) , Children's Pr.) Scholastic Library Publishing.

Douglass, Frederick. Narrative of the Life of Frederick Douglass, an American Slave. 2006. (Illus.). cd-rom (978-1-892824-44-8(2)) AFCHRON.

Fleming, Alice Mulcahey. Frederick Douglass: From Slave to Statesman. 2005. (Library of American Lives & Times). (Illus.). 112p. (J). (gr. 4-8). lib. bdg. 31.95 (978-0-8239-6624-0(0)) Rosen Publishing Group, Inc., The.

Frederick Douglass. (Photo Illustrated Biographies Ser.). 24p. (J). 6.95 (978-0-7368-8427-3(0)) Capstone Pr., Inc.

Frederick Douglass. (Compass Point Early Biographies Ser.). 32p. (J). 7.95 (978-0-7565-1168-5(2)) Compass Point Bks.

Frederick Douglass, 6 vols. (gr. k-2). 28.95 (978-0-7368-9371-8(7)); (gr. 2-5). 36.95 (978-0-7368-8438-9(6)) Red Brick Learning.

Group/McGraw-Hill, Wright. Frederick Douglass: A Voice for Civil Rights, 6 vols. (Book2WebTM Ser.). (gr. 4-8). 36.50 (978-0-322-04464-7(2)) Wright Group, The.

Haugen, Brenda. Frederick Douglass: Slave, Writer, Abolitionist. 2004. (Signature Lives Ser.). (Illus.). 112p. (J). 30.60 (978-0-7565-0818-0(5) , 1240139) Compass Point Bks.

Kerby, Mona. Frederick Douglass & Samuel Morse. 2001. (Illus.). 132p. (gr. 4-7). pap. 10.95 (978-0-595-18574-0(6)) iUniverse, Inc.

Kiely Miller, Barbara. Frederick Douglass. 2007. (J). pap. (*978-0-8368-8322-0(5)* , Weekly Reader Early Learning Library) Stevens, Gareth Inc.

Lantier, Patricia. Frederick Douglass. 2002. (Raintree Biographies Ser.). (Illus.). 32p. (J). lib. bdg. 25.69 (978-0-7398-5674-1(X)) Raintree.

Lilley, Stephen R. Fighters Against American Slavery. 1998. (History Makers Ser.). (Illus.). 128p. (YA). (gr. 7-10). 27.45 (978-1-56006-036-9(0) , Lucent Bks.) Thomson Gale.

Lutz, Norma Jean. Frederick Douglass: Abolitionist & Author. (Famous Figures of the Civil War Era Ser.). (Illus.). 80p. (J). (gr. 4-7). 2001. 25.00 (978-0-7910-6003-2(9)); 2000. pap. 8.95 (978-0-7910-6141-1(8)) Facts On File, Inc. (Chelsea Hse.).

—Frederick Douglass: Aboloitionist & Author. 2001. (Famous Figures of the Civil War Era Ser.). (J). 15.75 (978-0-606-20665-5(5)) Tandem Library Bks.

Major, Devorah. Frederick Douglass: A Hero for All Times. Stemach, Jerry, ed. Nichols, Jack, illus. l.t. ed. 2000. (J). 50.00 (978-1-58702-451-1(9)) Johnston, Don Inc.

Marlowe, Sam. Learning about Dedication from the Life of Frederick Douglass. 2004. (Character Building Book Ser.). (Illus.). 24p. (J). lib. bdg. 18.75 (978-0-8239-6928-9(2) , PowerKids Pr.) Rosen Publishing Group, Inc., The.

Mayer, Cassie. Frederick Douglass. 2007. (J). (*978-1-4034-9974-5(8)); pap. (*978-1-4034-9983-7(7))* Heinemann Library.

McKissack, Patricia C. & McKissack, Fredrick L. Frederick Douglass: Leader Against Slavery. rev. ed. 2002. (Great African Americans Ser.). (Illus.). 32p. (J). (gr. 1-4). lib. bdg. 18.60 (978-0-7660-1696-5(X)) Enslow Pubs., Inc.

Miller, Barbara Kiely. Frederick Douglass. 2007. (Great Americans Ser.). 24p. (J). (gr. 2-4). lib. bdg. 19.93 (*978-0-8368-8315-2(2)* , Weekly Reader Early Learning Library) Stevens, Gareth Inc.

Miller, Douglas T. Frederick Douglass & the Fight for Freedom. 1999. (Illus.). 160p. (J). lib. bdg. 24.95 (978-0-7351-0217-0(1)) Replica Bks.

Myers, Elisabeth. Frederick Douglass: Young Defender of Human Rights. Underdown, Harold, ed. Morrison, Cathy, illus. 2nd rev. ed. 2007. (Young Patriots Ser.). Orig. Title: Frederick Douglass Boy Champion of Human Rights. 120p. (J). 15.95 (978-1-882859-57-3(X) , Young Patriots Series) Patria Pr., Inc.

—Frederick Douglass: Young Defender of Human Rights. Underdown, Harold, ed. Morrison, Cathy, illus. 2nd rev. ed. 2007. (Young Patriots Ser.). Orig. Title: Frederick Douglass, Boy Champion of Human Rights. 120p. (J). pap. 9.95 (978-1-882859-58-0(8) , Young Patriots Series) Patria Pr., Inc.

Narrative of Frederick Douglass: Prestwick House Literary Touchstone Edition. 2004. 96p. (YA). per. (978-1-58049-576-9(1) , PWH5761) Prestwick Hse., Inc.

Rau, Dana Meachen. Frederick Douglass. 2003. (Compass Point Early Biographies Ser.). (Illus.). 32p. (J). (gr. 2 up). lib. bdg. 21.26 (978-0-7565-0418-2(X)) Compass Point Bks.

Ruffin, Frances E. Frederick Douglass: Rising up from Slavery. 2008. (Sterling Biographies Ser.). (Illus.). 128p. (J). pap. 5.95 (*978-1-4027-4118-0(9))* Sterling Publishing Co., Inc.

Russell, Sharman Apt. Frederick Douglass: Abolitionist Editor. (Black Americans of Achievement Ser.). (Illus.). 112p. (gr. 6-12). 2005. pap. 13.25 (978-0-7910-8331-4(4)); 2004. 30.00 (978-0-7910-8157-0(5)) Facts On File, Inc. (Chelsea Hse.).

Schaefer, Lola M. Frederick Douglass. Saunders-Smith, Gail, ed. 2002. (First Biographies Ser.). (Illus.). 24p. (J). (gr. k-1). lib. bdg. 15.93 (978-0-7368-1174-3(5) , Pebble Bks.) Capstone Pr., Inc.

Schraff, Anne. Frederick Douglass: Speaking Out Against Slavery. 2002. (African-American Biographies Ser.). (Illus.). 128p. (YA). (gr. 6-12). lib. bdg. 26.60 (978-0-7660-1773-3(7)) Enslow Pubs., Inc.

Scott, James. Narrative of the Life of Frederick Douglass: Reproducible Teaching Unit. 1999. 43p. (YA). (gr. 7-12). ring bd. 29.50 (978-1-58049-140-2(5) , TU103) Prestwick Hse., Inc.

Slade, Suzanne. Frederick Douglass: Writer, Speaker, & Opponent of Slavery. McGuire, Robert, illus. 2006. (Biographies Ser.). 24p. (J). (gr. k-3). lib. bdg. 23.93 (*978-1-4048-3102-5(9))* Picture Window Bks.

Spengler, Kremena. Frederick Douglass: Voice for Freedom. 2006. (Fact Finders Ser.). (Illus.). 32p. (J). 22.60 (978-0-7368-5434-4(7) , Fact Finders) Capstone Pr., Inc.

Weidt, Maryann N. Voice of Freedom: A Story about Frederick Douglass. Reeves, Jeni, illus. (Creative Minds Biographies Ser.). 64p. (J). (gr. 3-6). 2003. 6.95 (978-1-57505-553-4(8)); 2001. lib. bdg. 22.60 (978-1-57505-459-9(0) , Carolrhoda Bks.) Lerner Publishing Group.

—Voice of Freedom: A Story about Frederick Douglass. Reeves, Jeni, illus. 2001. 64p. (J). (ps-3). lib. bdg. 15.25 (978-0-613-68475-0(3)) Tandem Library Bks.

Welch, Catherine A. Frederick Douglass. 2003. (History Maker Bios Ser.). (Illus.). 48p. (J). (gr. 4-7). pap. 6.95 (978-0-8225-4802-7(X)); (gr. 3-5). lib. bdg. 26.60 (978-0-8225-4672-6(8)) Lerner Publishing Group.

Wilson, Camilla. Frederick Douglass: A Voice for Freedom in the 1800s. 2003. (Scholastic Biography Ser.). (Illus.). 90p. (J). pap. (978-0-439-38082-9(0)) Scholastic, Inc.

Yancey, Diane. Frederick Douglass. 2002. (Heroes & Villains Ser.). (Illus.). 112p. (J). 28.70 (978-1-56006-950-8(3) , Lucent Bks.) Thomson Gale.

DOWN SYNDROME

Bowman-Kruhm, Mary. Everything You Need to Know about Down Syndrome. rev. ed. 2005. (Need to Know Library). (Illus.). 64p. (YA). (gr. 4-6). lib. bdg. 25.25 (978-0-8239-3767-7(4)) Rosen Publishing Group, Inc., The.

Bowman-Kruhm, Mary, ed. Everything You Need to Know about Down Syndrome. 1999. (Need to Know Library). (Illus.). 64p. (YA). (gr. 4-6). lib. bdg. 25.25 (978-0-8239-2949-8(3) , NTDOSY) Rosen Publishing Group, Inc., The.

Brill, Marlene Targ. Down Syndrome. 2006. (Health Alert Ser.). (Illus.). 64p. (J). lib. bdg. 31.36 (978-0-7614-2207-5(2) , Benchmark Bks.) Cavendish, Marshall Corp.

Bryan, Jenny. Living with Down Syndrome. 1999. 32 p. (J). lib. bdg. 27.12 (978-0-8172-5569-5(9)) Raintree.

de Fatima Campos, Maria. Victoria's Day. 2007. (Illus.). 32p. (J). (ps-k). 16.95 (*978-1-84507-571-2(4))* Lincoln, Frances Ltd. GBR. *Dist:* Perseus Distribution.

Glatzer, Jenna. Taking Down Syndrome to School. Dineen, Tom, illus. 2002. (Special Kids in School Ser.: Vol. 12). 32p. (J). pap. 11.95 (978-1-891383-19-9(1)) JayJo Bks., LLC.

Gordon, Melanie Apel. Let's Talk about Down Syndrome. 1999. (Let's Talk Library). (Illus.). 24p. (J). (gr. 3). lib. bdg. 18.75 (978-0-8239-5197-0(9) , PowerKids Pr.) Rosen Publishing Group, Inc., The.

Junot, Dan. Jackie, The Heart-Warming, Inspirational True Story of a Remarkable Down Syndrome Girl: Plus, Parables for Parents of Down Syndrome Children. Orgeron, Randy, ed. 2002. (Illus.). v, 113p. pap. 23.00 (978-0-9717246-0-0(1)) Ctr. For Special Services.

Margulies, Phillip. Down Syndrome. 2006. (Genetic Diseases & Disorders Ser.). (Illus.). 64p. (YA). (gr. 6-8). lib. bdg. 26.50 (978-1-4042-0695-3(7)) Rosen Publishing Group, Inc., The.

Routh, Kristina. Down's Syndrome. 2004. (Just the Facts Ser.). (Illus.). 56p. (J). lib. bdg. 27.07 (978-1-4034-5145-3(1)) Heinemann Library.

Royston, Angela. Down's Syndrome. 2005. (What's It Like? Ser.). (Illus.). 32p. (J). (gr. k-2). lib. bdg. 24.21 (978-1-4034-5851-3(0)) Heinemann Library.

DOWN SYNDROME—FICTION

Butler, Geoff. The Hangashore. Butler, Geoff, illus. 1998. (Illus.). 32p. (J). (gr. 3-7). 15.95 (978-0-88776-444-8(4)) Tundra Bks., Inc./Livres Toundra, Inc. CAN. *Dist:* Random Hse., Inc.

Cairo, Shelly, et al. Our Brother Has Down's Syndrome. McNeil, Irene, photos by. 2003. (Illus.). 24p. (J). (ps-3). pap. 5.95 (978-0-920303-31-3(5)); lib. bdg. 15.95 (978-0-920303-30-6(7)) Annick Pr., Ltd. CAN. *Dist:* Firefly Bks., Ltd.

Carter, Alden R. Dustin's Big School Day. Young, Dan & Carter, Carol S., illus. 1999. (Concept Book Ser.). 32p. (J). (gr. k-3). lib. bdg. 14.95 (978-0-8075-1741-3(0)) Whitman, Albert & Co.

Dodds, Bill. My Sister Annie. Hunt, Judith, illus. 2003. 96p. (YA). (gr. 4-6). pap. 10.95 (978-1-56397-554-7(8)) Boyds Mills Pr.

Flinn, Alex. Fade to Black. 2006. 208p. (J). pap. 7.99 (978-0-06-056842-9(9) , HarperTeen) HarperCollins Pubs.

Fox, Paula. Radiance Descending. 1999. (978-0-606-17838-9(4)) Tandem Library Bks.

Goodhart, Pippa. Ginny's Egg. Brouwer, Aafke, illus. 142p. (J). pap. 7.50 (978-0-7497-4557-8(6)) Egmont Bks., Ltd. GBR. *Dist:* Trafalgar Square Publishing.

Hubler, Marsha. Skye's Final Test, Vol. 6. 2005. (Keystone Stables Ser.). (Illus.). 112p. (J). pap. 4.99 (978-0-310-70799-8(4)) Zonderkidz.

Kneeland, Linda. Cookie. Fargo, Todd, illus. rev. l.t. ed. 1999. 32p. (J). pap. 9.95 (978-0-944727-38-6(7)); lib. bdg. 14.95 (978-0-944727-39-3(5)) Jason & Nordic Pubs. (Turtle Bks.).

Plucker, Sheri. Me, Hailey. Fargo, Todd, illus. 2005. (Turtle Books). 32p. (J). (gr. k-3). pap. 9.95 (978-0-944727-49-2(2)); lib. bdg. 15.95 (978-0-944727-50-8(6) , Turtle Bks.) Jason & Nordic Pubs.

Rottman, S. L. Head above Water. 192p. (YA). 2003. pap. 6.95 (978-1-56145-238-5(6) , Q21186); 1999. (gr. 7-11). 14.95 (978-1-56145-185-2(1) , Q21186) Peachtree Pubs., Ltd.

—Head above Water. 2003. (gr. 7-12). lib. bdg. 15.25 (978-0-613-60386-7(9)) Tandem Library Bks.

Rue, Nancy. Sophie's Encore, Vol. 12. 2006. (Faithgirlz! Ser.). (Illus.). 144p. (J). pap. 6.99 (978-0-310-71027-1(8)) Zonderkidz.

Stuve-Bodeen, Stephanie. We'll Paint the Octopus Red. DeVito, Pamela, illus. 1998. 25p. (J). (ps-2). 15.95 (978-1-890627-06-5(2)) Woodbine Hse.

Woloson, Eliza. My Friend Isabelle. Gough, Bryan, tr. Gough, Bryan, illus. 2003. 28p. (J). 14.95 (978-1-890627-50-8(X)) Woodbine Hse.

Wood, June Rae. The Man Who Loved Clowns. 2005. 224p. (J). (gr. 4-7). pap. 5.99 (978-0-14-240422-5(5) , Puffin) Penguin Group (USA) Inc.

DOWN'S SYNDROME

see Down Syndrome

DOYLE, ARTHUR CONAN, SIR, 1859-1930

Adams, Cynthia. The Mysterious Case of Sir Arthur Conan Doyle. 2004. (World Writers Ser.). (Illus.). 112p. (gr. 5-13). 21.95 (978-1-883846-34-3(X)) Reynolds, Morgan Inc.

DRACULA, COUNT (FICTITIOUS CHARACTER)—FICTION

Dadey, Debbie & Jones, Marcia Thornton. Dracula Doesn't Rock & Roll. Gurney, John Steven, illus. 2000. (Adventures of the Bailey School Kids Ser.: No. 39). 80p. (J). (gr. 2-4). mass mkt. 3.99 (978-0-439-04399-1(9) , Scholastic Paperbacks) Scholastic, Inc.

—Dracula Doesn't Rock & Roll. 2000. (Adventures of the Bailey School Kids Ser.: No. 39). (Illus.). (J). (gr. 2-4). 10.79 (978-0-606-18537-0(2)); 1999. (gr. 3-6). lib. bdg. 11.80 (978-0-613-21464-3(1)) Tandem Library Bks.

Dracula. (J). 9.95 (978-1-56156-373-9(0)) Kidsbooks, Inc.

Dracula: Picture Book. 2002. (Illus.). 32p. (J). 16.99 (978-0-7868-0799-4(7)) Disney Pr.

Dracula's Den: Make Hundreds of Funny Faces with Re-Usable Stickers! 1999. (Funny Faces Ser.). (Illus.). 10p. (J). (ps-7). 1.99 (978-1-86091-124-8(2) , 84) Trident Pr. International.

Fearon Staff. Dracula. (YA). (gr. 5-12). pap., stu. ed. 6.50 (978-0-8359-0958-7(1)) Globe Fearon Educational Publishing.

Greenburg, Dan. Don't Count on Dracula. Davis, Jack E., illus. 2000. (Zack Files Ser.: No. 21). 64p. (J). (gr. 2-5). pap. 4.99 (978-0-448-42175-9(5) , Grosset & Dunlap) Penguin Group (USA) Inc.

—Don't Count on Dracula. 2000. (gr. 3-6). lib. bdg. 13.00 (978-0-613-31134-2(5)); (Zack Files Ser.: No. 21). (J). (gr. 2-5). 10.79 (978-0-606-20270-1(6)) Tandem Library Bks.

Hoffman, Mary & Riddell, Chris. Dracula's Daughter. 2006. (Yellow Bananas Ser.). (Illus.). (J). 48p. pap. (978-0-7787-1000-4(9)); 43p. (978-0-7787-0954-1(X)) Crabtree Publishing Co.

Jones, Marcia Thornton & Dadey, Debbie. Dracula Doesn't Play Kickball. 2004. (Baily School Kids Ser.). 80p. (J). pap. 3.99 (978-0-439-56000-9(4) , Scholastic Paperbacks) Scholastic, Inc.

Labatt, Mary. Spying on Dracula. Jackson, Troy, illus. 1999. (Sam Ser.). 120p. (J). (gr. 4-6). (978-1-55074-632-7(4)) Kids Can Pr., Ltd.

—Spying on Dracula. Hill-Jackson, Troy, illus. 1999. (Sam Ser.). 120p. (J). (gr. 4-6). (978-1-55074-634-1(0)) Kids Can Pr., Ltd.

—Spying on Dracula. 1999. (J). (978-0-606-19023-7(6)) Tandem Library Bks.

Lutzen, Hanna. Vlad the Undead. 2001. (gr. 7-12). lib. bdg. 14.10 (978-0-613-88930-8(4)) Tandem Library Bks.

Ratnett, Michael. Dracula Steps Out. Goulding, June & Smyth, Iain, illus. 2005. 12p. (J). (gr. k-4). reprint ed. 16.00 (978-0-7567-8585-7(5)) DIANE Publishing Co.

—Dracula Steps Out. Goulding, June, illus. 1998. 12p. (J). (ps-1). pap. 15.95 (978-0-531-30100-5(1) , Orchard Bks.) Scholastic, Inc.

Sierra, Judy. The House That Drac Built. Hillenbrand, Will, illus. 1998. 32p. (J). (ps-2). pap. 7.00 (978-0-15-201879-5(4) , Harcourt Paperbacks) Harcourt Children's Bks.

Stoker, Bram. Count Dracula. 2004. (Fast Track Classics Ser.). (Illus.). 48p. (J). pap. 8.99 (978-0-237-52401-2(5) , Evans Brothers, Limited) Evans Publishing Group GBR. *Dist:* Independent Pubs. Group.

—Dracula. Redondo, Nestor, illus. 1998. (Illustrated Classic Book Ser.). 61p. (J). (gr. 3 up). pap. 4.95 (978-1-56767-261-9(2)) Educational Insights, Inc.

—Dracula. Moser, Barry, illus. 2000. (Books of Wonder). 430p. (J). (gr. 7-12). 21.95 (978-0-688-13921-6(3)) HarperCollins Pubs.

—Dracula. 2002. (ENG.). 368p. 27.99 (*978-1-4043-3654-4(0))* IndyPublish.com.

—Dracula. Becky, Cloonan, illus. 2006. (Puffin Graphics Ser.). 176p. (J). (gr. 3). pap. 10.99 (978-0-14-240572-7(8) , Puffin) Penguin Group (USA) Inc.

—Dracula. 2000. 502p. (gr. 4-7). pap. 4.99 (978-0-439-15411-6(1)) Scholastic, Inc.

—Dracula. 1999. (Saddleback Classics). (Illus.). (J). 13.75 (978-0-606-21550-3(6)) Tandem Library Bks.

DRAFTING, MECHANICAL

see Mechanical Drawing

DRAG RACING

see Automobile Racing

DRAGONFLIES

Allen, Judy. Are You a Dragonfly? Humphries, Tudor, illus. 2001. (Backyard Bks.). 32p. (J). (gr. k-3). tchr. ed. 9.95 (978-0-7534-5346-9(0) , Kingfisher) Houghton Mifflin Co. Trade & Reference Div.

Armstrong, Robert H., et al. Dragons in the Pond. 2007. pap. (*978-1-57833-362-2(8))* Todd Communications.

Borchelt, Kelly L. Dragonfly. 2004. (Bugs! Ser.). (Illus.). 32p. (J). (gr. 4-7). 24.95 (978-0-7377-1770-9(X) , Greenhaven Pr., Inc.) Thomson Gale.

Cooper, Jason. Dragonflies. (Insects Ser.). 24p. (gr. k-2). 2006. (Illus.). 14.95 (978-1-59515-426-2(4)); 2005. pap. 5.45 (978-1-59515-740-9(9)) Rourke Publishing, LLC.

Coughlan, Cheryl. Dragonflies. 2005. (Bugs, Bugs, Bugs Ser.). 24p. (YA). (gr. k-3). pap. (978-0-7368-8209-5(X) , Pebble Bks.) Capstone Pr., Inc.

Dragonflies, 6 vols. (gr. k-2). 28.95 (978-0-7368-8249-1(9)) Red Brick Learning.

Dragonflies: Early Level Satellite Individual Title Six-Packs. (Sails Literacy Ser.). 16p. (gr. 1-2). 27.00 (978-0-7578-6518-3(6)) Rigby Education.

Dragonflies World of Insects. 2006. (Illus.). 24p. (J). (gr. k-2). 18.50 (*978-0-531-17862-1(5))* Scholastic Library Publishing.

Dragonfly. 2004. per. 18.00 (978-0-9749492-2-2(1)) Giant Robot Bks.

Dragonfly: Big Book. 2003. (J). 38.95 (978-0-8136-4156-0(X)) Modern Curriculum Pr.

Glaser, Linda. Dazzling Dragonflies: A Life Cycle Story. Posada, Mia, illus. 2008. (Linda Glaser's Classic Creatures Ser.). (J). lib. bdg. 22.60 (*978-0-8225-6753-0(9)* , Millbrook Pr.) Lerner Publishing Group.

Green, Emily K. Dragonflies. 2006. (Blastoff! Readers Ser.). (Illus.). 24p. (J). lib. bdg. 16.95 (978-1-60014-012-9(2)) Bellwether Media.

Halfmann, Janet. Dragonflies. 1998. (Bugs Ser.). (Illus.). 32p. (YA). (gr. 3-12). lib. bdg. 16.95 (978-1-887068-32-1(5)) Smart Apple Media.

Hall, Margaret. Dragonflies. 2006. (Bugs, Bugs, Bugs! Ser.). (Illus.). 24p. (J). (978-0-7368-4252-5(7)) Capstone Pr., Inc.

Helget, Nicole Lea. Dragonflies. 2007. (J). (978-1-58341-541-2(6) , Creative Education) Creative Co., The.

Jacobs, Liza. Dragonflies. 2003. (Wild Wild World Ser.). (Illus.). 24p. (J). 22.45 (978-1-4103-0042-3(0) , Blackbirch Pr., Inc.) Thomson Gale.

Kirkland, Jane. Take a Walk with Butterflies & Dragonflies, 1. Kirkland, Rob et al, eds. 2005. (Take a Walk Book Ser.). (Illus.). 32p. (J). pap. 9.95 (978-0-9709754-2-3(2) , Take a Walk Bk.) Stillwater Publishing.

Lockwood, Sophie. Dragonflies. 2007. (World of Insects Ser.). 40p. (J). (gr. 2-6). 29.93 (*978-1-59296-821-3(X))* Child's World, Inc.

Loewen, Nancy. Dancing Dragons: Dragonflies in Your Backyard. Peterson, Rick, illus. 2005. (Backyard Bugs Ser.). 24p. (J). (ps). lib. bdg. 22.60 (978-1-4048-1142-3(7)) Picture Window Bks.

Macken, JoAnn Early. The Life Cycle of a Dragonfly. 2006. (Illus.). 24p. (J). pap. (978-0-8368-6388-8(7)); lib. bdg. 19.33 (978-0-8368-6381-9(X)) Stevens, Gareth Inc.

McEvey, Shane F. Dragonflies. 2001. (Insects & Spiders Ser.). (Illus.). 32p. (J). (gr. 4 up). 28.00 (978-0-7910-6597-6(9) , 010553, Chelsea Hse.) Facts On File, Inc.

McLaughlin, Kari Massie. My Adventure with Dragonflies. 2007. 44p. (J). 8.99 (978-1-59092-452-5(5) , Orchard Academy Pr.) Windstorm Creative.

Meister, Cari. Dragonflies. 2001. (Insects Ser.). (Illus.). 24p. (J). (gr. k-6). lib. bdg. 21.35 (978-1-57765-461-2(7) , Checkerboard Library) ABDO Publishing Co.

Merrick, Patrick. Dragonflies. 2006. (New Naturebooks). (Illus.). 32p. (J). (gr. 1-5). 27.07 (978-1-59296-635-6(7)) Child's World, Inc.

Morris, Neil & Morris, Ting. Dragonfly. 2003. (Illus.). 32p. (J). lib. bdg. 27.10 (978-1-58340-380-8(9)) Smart Apple Media.

Pierre, Stephanie S. Dragonfly. 2002. (Bug Bks.). (Illus.). 32p. (J). (gr. k-2). pap. 6.95 (978-1-58810-924-8(0) , 91522) Heinemann Library.

Pringle, Laurence P. A Dragon in the Sky: The Story of a Green Darner Dragonfly. Marstall, Bob, illus. 2001. 64p. (J). (gr. 3-7). pap. 18.95 (978-0-531-30315-3(2) , Orchard Bks.) Scholastic, Inc.

Pringle, Laurence P. & Marstall, Bob. A Dragon in the Sky: The Story of a Green Darner Dragonfly. 2001. (Illus.). 64p. (J). lib. bdg. (978-0-531-33315-0(9) , Orchard Bks.) Scholastic, Inc.

Prischmann, Deirdre A. Dragonflies. 2005. (World of Insects Ser.). (Illus.). 24p. (J). (ps-7). lib. bdg. 21.26 (978-0-7368-4337-9(X)) Capstone Pr., Inc.

Shaffer, Christy. Shiny Dragonflies Stickers. 2006. (Dover Little Activity Bks.). 2p. (J). 1.50 (978-0-486-44926-5(2)) Dover Pubns., Inc.

St. Pierre, Stephanie. Dragonfly. 2002. (Heinemann First Library). (Illus.). 32p. (J). (gr. k-2). lib. bdg. 21.36 (978-1-58810-171-6(1)) Heinemann Library.

—Dragonfly. 2002. (gr. k-3). lib. bdg. 14.75 (978-0-613-61416-0(X)) Tandem Library Bks.

DRAGONS

Awaken the Dragon. 1999. (Dragon Ball Z Giant Coloring & Activity Bks.). (Illus.). 96p. (J). (gr. 1-2). pap. (978-0-7666-0539-8(6)) Modern Publishing.

Barnett, Paul & Grant, John. Life-Size Dragons. Gambino, Fred, illus. 2006. (Life-Size Ser.). 28p. (J). 9.95 (978-1-4027-2536-4(1)) Sterling Publishing Co., Inc.

Brucken, Kelli M. Dragons. 2006. (Mysterious Encounters Ser.). (Illus.). 48p. (J). (gr. 4-8). 26.20 (978-0-7377-3548-2(1) , Kidhaven) Thomson Gale.

Carr, Roger. Dragon. 2000. (gr. k-3). lib. bdg. 11.80 (978-0-613-29599-4(4)) Tandem Library Bks.

Cosgrove, Stephen. Muffin Dragon. 2001. (gr. k-3). lib. bdg. 13.00 (978-0-613-64550-8(2)) Tandem Library Bks.

Doeden, Matt. Dragon Life. 2008. (J). (***978-1-4296-1297-5(5)***) Capstone Pr., Inc.

—Dragonatomy. 2008. (J). (***978-1-4296-1295-1(9)***) Capstone Pr., Inc.

—Real-Life Dragons. 2008. (J). (***978-1-4296-1296-8(7)***) Capstone Pr., Inc.

Dragons: Coloring Book. 2007. (Illus.). 20p. (J). 10.00 (***978-0-9795206-5-5(7)***) Unseen Gallery.

Drake, Ernest. Dragonology: Field Guide to Dragons. Steer, Dugald A., ed. 2007. (Ologies Ser.). (Illus.). 32p. (J). (gr. 3). 24.99 (***978-0-7636-3686-9(X)***) Candlewick Pr.

—Dragonology: The Complete Book of Dragons. Steer, Dugald, ed. 2003. (Ologies Ser.). (Illus.). 32p. (J). (gr. 3 up). 19.99 (978-0-7636-2329-6(6)) Candlewick Pr.

—The Dragonology Handbook: A Practical Course in Dragons. Steer, Dugald, ed. Anderson, Wayne et al, illus. ed. 2005. 80p. (J). (gr. 4 up). 12.99 (978-0-7636-2814-7(X)) Candlewick Pr.

Drake, Ernest. The Dragonology Tracking & Taming Dragons Volume 2: A Deluxe Book & Model Set: Frost Dragon. Steer, Dugald A., ed. 2007. (Ologies Ser.: Vol. 2). (Illus.). 24p. (J). (gr. 3). 14.99 (***978-0-7636-3426-1(3)***) Candlewick Pr.

Eckart, Edana. Komodo Dragon. 2003. (Animals of the World Ser.). (Illus.). 24p. (J). 18.00 (978-0-516-24295-8(4)); pap. 4.95 (978-0-516-27893-3(2)) Scholastic Library Publishing. (Children's Pr.).

—Komodo Dragon. 2003. (gr. k-3). lib. bdg. 12.95 (978-0-613-67737-0(4)) Tandem Library Bks.

Hallmark, Darla, illus. More Dragons: Coloring Book by Darla Hallmark. 2007. 20p. (YA). 10.00 (***978-0-9795206-8-6(1)***) Unseen Gallery.

Hamilton, John. Dragons. 2005. (Fantasy & Folklore Ser.). (Illus.). 32p. (J). (gr. 4-8). lib. bdg. 24.21 (978-1-59197-711-7(8)) ABDO Publishing Co.

Krensky, Stephen. Dragons. 2007. (Monster Chronicles Ser.). (Illus.). 48p. (J). (gr. 4-8). lib. bdg. 26.60 (978-0-8225-6543-7(9) , Lerner Pubns.) Lerner Publishing Group.

Lehner, Ernst & Lehner, Johanna. Big Book of Dragons, Monsters, & Other Mythical Creatures. 2004. (Pictorial Archive Ser.). (Illus.). 192p. pap. 16.95 (978-0-486-43512-1(1)) Dover Pubns., Inc.

Levin, Freddie. 1-2-3 Draw Knights, Castles & Dragons: A Step-by-Step Guide. 2001. (One-Two-Three Draw Ser.). (Illus.). 64p. (J). (gr. 1-7). pap. 8.99 (978-0-939217-43-4(0) , 32064) Peel Productions, Inc.

Marsico, Katie. A Komodo Dragon Hatchling Grows Up. 2007. (Scholastic News Nonfiction Readers: Life Cycles Ser.). 24p. (J). 6.95 (***978-0-531-18696-1(2)*** , Children's Pr.) Scholastic Library Publishing.

Maynard, Thane. Komodo Dragons. 2006. (New Naturebooks). (Illus.). 32p. (J). (gr. 1-5). 27.07 (978-1-59296-642-4(X)) Child's World, Inc.

Meredith Books Staff, ed. Dragons. 2007. 32p. pap. 6.99 (***978-0-696-23693-8(1)***) Meredith Bks.

Nigg, Joe. The Book of Dragons & Other Mythical Beasts. 2002. (Illus.). 128p. 18.99 (978-0-7641-5510-9(5)) Barron's Educational Series, Inc.

Nigg, Joe & Topsell, John. How to Raise & Keep a Dragon. 2006. (Illus.). 128p. (J). 18.99 (978-0-7641-5920-6(8)) Barron's Educational Series, Inc.

Passes, David. Dragons: Truth, Myth & Legend. Anderson, Wayne, illus. 2007. 46p. (J). pap. 9.99 (***978-1-84458-476-5(3)***) Anova Bks. GBR. *Dist:* Independent Pubs. Group.

Penner, Lucille Recht. Dragons. Scott, Peter David, tr. Scott, Peter David, illus. ed. 2004. (Stepping Stones Ser.). 48p. (J). (gr. 5). pap. 3.99 (978-0-307-26417-6(3) , Random Hse. Bks. for Young Readers) Random Hse. Children's Bks.

Petrini, Catherine. Dragons. 2006. (Kidhaven Science Library). (Illus.). 48p. (J). (gr. 4-8). 26.20 (978-0-7377-3163-7(X) , 1256753, Kidhaven) Thomson Gale.

Priddy, Roger. Funny Faces Dizzy Dragon. 2007. 24p. (J). bds. 14.95 (***978-0-312-49894-8(2)*** , Priddy Bks.) St. Martin's Pr.

Pringle, Laurence P. Imagine a Dragon. Neilan, Eujin Kim, illus. 2008. (J). (***978-1-56397-328-4(6)***) Boyds Mills Pr.

Tatchell, Judy. Dragons Lift-the-flap. Scott, Peter, illus. 2005. 16p. (J). (gr. 1 up). 11.95 (978-0-7945-0968-2(1) , Usborne) EDC Publishing.

Truscott, Julia. Your Safari: In Search of the Real Komodo Dragon. White, Daniel, photos by. 2005. (Illus.). 48p. (J). 11.95 (978-1-59594-014-8(6) , Wingspan Pr.) WingSpan Publishing.

Wyly, Michael J. Dragons. 2001. (Mystery Library). (Illus.). 96p. (J). (gr. 4-12). 29.95 (978-1-56006-972-0(4) , Lucent Bks.) Thomson Gale.

Yates, Gene. The Dragon Opposites Book. 2005. (Illus.). 14p. (J). (***978-1-58865-283-6(1)***) Kidsbooks, Inc.

DRAGONS—FICTION

Abbott, Tony. The Moon Dragon. 2006. (Secrets of Droon Ser.: No. 26). (Illus.). 112p. (J). pap. 3.99 (978-0-439-67174-3(4) , Scholastic Paperbacks) Scholastic, Inc.

—The Moon Dragon. Merrell, David, illus. 2006. (Little Apple Ser.). 121p. (J). (978-1-4156-4703-5(8)) Scholastic, Inc.

—Moon Dragon. Merrell, David, illus. 2006. 121p. (J). lib. bdg. 15.38 (***978-1-4242-0309-3(0)***) Fitzgerald Bks.

Abbott, Tony. Sleeping Giant of Goll. 2000. (gr. 3-6). lib. bdg. 11.80 (978-0-613-22389-8(6)) Tandem Library Bks.

Aiken, Joan. The Wooden Dragon. 2005. (Illus.). 32p. (J). 14.99 (978-0-224-06480-4(0) , Jonathan Cape) Random Hse. Children's Bks. GBR. *Dist:* Trafalgar Square Publishing.

—The Wooden Dragon. 2004. (Illus.). 32p. (J). pap. 10.99 (978-0-09-943958-5(1) , Arrow Bks., Ltd.) Random Hse. GBR. *Dist:* Independent Pubs. Group.

Albee, Sarah. The Dragon's Scales. Manders, John, illus. 1998. 48p. (J). (gr. 1-3). (Step into Reading & Math Step 2 Bks.). lib. bdg. 11.99 (978-0-679-98381-1(3)); (Step Into Reading & Math Ser.: Vol. 3). pap. 3.99 (978-0-679-88381-4(9)) Random Hse. Children's Bks. (Random Hse. Bks. for Young Readers).

—The Dragon's Scales. 1998. (Step into Reading & Math Step 2 Bks.). (J). (gr. 1-3). 10.79 (978-0-606-13960-1(5)) Tandem Library Bks.

Algozin, Bruce. Claw of the Dragon. 2008. (Endless Quest Ser.). 192p. (J). (gr. 3-7). 5.99 (***978-0-7869-4719-5(5)*** , Mirrorstone) Wizards of the Coast.

Allaire, Mj. Prisoner Denicalis Dragon Chronicles. 2006. pap. 16.59 (***978-1-4259-6680-5(2)***) AuthorHouse.

Allende, Isabel. El Reino del Dragon de Oro. 2003. (SPA.). 432p. 19.99 (978-0-06-059170-0(6)) HarperCollins Pubs.

Alonso, Fernando. Ennia. 2002. Tr. of Ennia. (SPA.). (gr. 3-6). lib. bdg. 17.05 (978-0-613-80660-2(3)) Tandem Library Bks.

Anna, Jennifer. Year of the Dragon. 2nd ed. 2007. (Illus.). 56p. (J). pap. 24.99 (***978-1-59092-155-5(0)*** , Blue Works) Windstorm Creative.

—Year of the Dragon. Brandon, Theresa, illus. 2nd ed. 2001. 120p. (YA). reprint ed. pap. 10.99 (978-1-883573-17-1(3) , Little Blue Works) Windstorm Creative.

Ashburn, Boni. Hush, Little Dragon. Murphy, Kelly, illus. 2008. 32p. (J). 15.95 (***978-0-8109-9491-1(7)*** , Abrams Bks. for Young Readers) Abrams, Harry N. , Inc.

Asprin, Robert. M. Y. T. H. Inc. Link. 2006. 176p. (gr. 12). mass mkt. 6.99 (978-0-441-01449-1(6) , Ace Bks.) Penguin Group (USA) Inc.

Auxier, Bryan. Where Have All the Dragons Gone? Daniels, Regina, illus. l.t. ed. 2002. 32p. (J). (gr. 3-7). pap. 7.95 (978-0-9719144-0-7(0)) Where? Pr., Inc.

Avalon, Dawn. Bubbels. Een Vochtig Draakje. 2006. 60p. pap. 8.23 (978-1-4116-1193-1(4)) Lulu.com.

—Bubbles. A Wet Dragon. 2006. 59p. pap. 8.21 (978-1-4116-1177-1(2)) Lulu.com.

Awdry, Wilbert V. Thomas & Percy & the Dragon. 2003. (ps-2). lib. bdg. 11.80 (978-0-613-89791-4(9)) Tandem Library Bks.

Baker, E. D. Dragon's Breath. 2005. (Tales of the Frog Princess Ser.: Bk. 2). (Illus.). 304p. (J). (gr. 3-7). reprint ed. pap. 6.95 (978-1-58234-666-3(6) , Bloomsbury Children) Bloomsbury Publishing.

Balaban, Mariah, ed. Dragonfire. 2006. (Duel Masters Ser.). (Illus.). 32p. (J). pap. 3.99 (978-0-439-78956-1(7) , Scholastic) Scholastic, Inc.

Ballou, Kathy. The Tracks Out Back. l.t. ed. 2005. (Illus.). 24p. (J). per. 10.00 (978-1-932338-50-8(0)) Lifevest Publishing, Inc.

Banerjee, Anjali. The Silver Spell, Bk. 8. 2005. (Dungeons & Dragons Ser.: Bk. 8). (Illus.). 192p. (J). pap. 5.99 (978-0-7869-3750-9(5)) Wizards of the Coast.

Banks, Kate. Max's Dragon. Kulikov, Boris, illus. 2008. 32p. (J). 16.95 (***978-0-374-39921-4(2)***) Farrar, Straus & Giroux.

Banks, Steven & Artifact Group. Lost in Time: A Medieval Adventure. 2006. (SpongeBob SquarePants Ser.). (Illus.). 24p. (J). pap. 3.99 (978-1-4169-1464-8(1) , Simon Spotlight/Nickelodeon) Simon & Schuster Children's Publishing.

—Perdidos en el tiempo (Lost in Time) Una aventura Medieval. 2006. (SpongeBob SquarePants Ser.). (SPA.). 24p. (J). pap. 3.99 (978-1-4169-1505-8(2) , Libros Para Ninos) Simon & Schuster Children's Publishing.

Banta, Sandra F. Fancy the Beautiful Little Dragon: Book Number Two Little One's Series. Hecker, Vera, illus. l.t. ed. 2006. 45p. per. 11.99 (978-1-59879-157-0(5)) Lifevest Publishing, Inc.

—Muffy the Dragon. Hecker, Vera, illus. l.t. ed. 2005. 19p. (J). per. 9.99 (978-1-59879 060-3(9)) Lifevest Publishing, Inc.

Base, Graeme. Discovery of Dragons: New Research Revealed. 2007. 42p. (J). (gr. k-17). 19.95 (***978-0-8109-5967-5(4)***) Abrams, Harry N. , Inc.

Bass, Jules. Herb, the Vegetarian Dragon. Harter, Debbie, illus. 2005. 32p. (J). (gr. 1-5). pap. 6.99 (978-1-905236-47-3(6)); reprint ed. pap. 6.99 (978-1-84148-127-2(0)) Barefoot Bks., Inc.

—Herb, the Vegetarian Dragon. Harter, Debbie, illus. 2001. 32p. (J). (gr. 1-5). lib. bdg. 13.79 (978-0-606-19750-2(8)) Tandem Library Bks.

—Herb, the Vegetarian Dragon. 2000. (gr. 3-6). lib. bdg. 14.15 (978-0-613-33702-1(6)) Tandem Library Bks.

—Herb, the Vegetarian Dragon: Book & Bendo Gift Set. Harter, Debbie, illus. 2005. 32p. (J). pap. 14.99 (978-1-905236-43-5(3)) Barefoot Bks., Inc.

Batten, Ralph & McCafferty, Jan. In the Kingdom of the Carpet Dragon. 2001. (Illus.). 128p. (J). pap. 7.99 (978-0-7459-4566-8(X) , Lion) Lion Hudson plc GBR. *Dist:* Independent Pubs. Group.

Baynton, Martin. Jane & the Dragon. Baynton, Martin, illus. 2007. (Illus.). 32p. (J). (ps-3). pap. 4.99 (***978-0-7636-3570-1(7)***) Candlewick Pr.

—Jane & the Magician. Baynton, Martin, illus. 2007. (Illus.). 32p. (J). (ps-3). pap. 4.99 (***978-0-7636-3571-8(5)***) Candlewick Pr.

Beagle, Peter S. I'm Afraid You've Got Dragons. 2007. 192p. (YA). pap. 11.99 (978-0-14-240875-9(1) , Puffin) Penguin Group (USA) Inc.

Beekman, Kelley Lee. Sir Eli & the Halloween Dragon: The Legend of the Toasted Marshmallow. 2006. 55p. pap. 12.95 (***978-1-4241-4047-3(1)***) PublishAmerica, Inc.

Bell, Hilari. The Prophecy. 208p. (J). 2007. pap. 6.50 (***978-0-06-059945-4(6)*** , Eos); 2006. lib. bdg. 16.89 (978-0-06-059944-7(8)); 2006. (Illus.). 15.99 (978-0-06-059943-0(X)) HarperCollins Pubs.

Bergsma, Jody Lynn. The Little Wizard. Bergsma, Jody Lynn, illus. l.t. ed. 2000. (Illus.). 32p. (J). (ps-7). 15.95 (978-0-935699-19-7(8)) Illumination Arts Publishing Co., Inc.

Bergsma, Jody Lynn, et al. Dragon. Bergsma, Jody Lynn, illus. 1999. (Illus.). 32p. (ps-7). 15.95 (978-0-935699-17-3(1)) Illumination Arts Publishing Co., Inc.

Berkeley, Jon. Chopsticks. 2005. (Illus.). 32p. (J). (ps-3). 16.95 (978-0-375-83309-0(9) , Random Hse. Bks. for Young Readers) Random Hse. Children's Bks.

Bernhardt, William. Princess Alice & the Dreadful Dragon. McGhee, Kerry, illus. 2007. 36p. (J). 19.95 (***978-1-930709-65-2(X)***) HAWK Publishing Group.

Black, Robyn Hood. Sir Mike. Murphy, David, illus. (J). (gr. k-2). 2006. 32p. pap. 4.95 (978-0-516-25020-5(5)); 2005. 31p. 19.50 (978-0-516-24862-2(6)) Scholastic Library Publishing. (Children's Pr.).

Blackford, Ami. Quest for the Dragon Stone: A Duncan Family Adventure. Blackford, Ami, illus. 2006. (Illus.). 48p. (J). (gr. 3-7). 16.95 (978-0-60108-008-0(5)) Red Cygnet Pr.

Blackman, Malorie. The Monster Crisp-Guzzler. Sweeten, Sami, illus. 2002. (Corgi Pups Ser.). 64p. (J). pap. 7.99 (978-0-552-54783-3(2) , Corgi) Transworld Publishers Ltd. GBR. *Dist:* Independent Pubs. Group.

Blake-Brekke, Carri. Panuk, Princess & Prince. Melton, Jodi, illus. 2002. (J). pap. (978-0-9720549-1-1(X)) Mom's Pride Enterprises.

Blishen, Edward & Blishen, Nancy. The Kingfisher Treasury of Stories for Four Year Olds. Dinan, Carolyn, illus. 2005. (Kingfisher Treasury of Stories Ser.). 160p. (J). (gr. k-3). pap. 5.95 (978-0-7534-5891-4(8) , Kingfisher) Houghton Mifflin Co. Trade & Reference Div.

Branson, Terri. Brother Dragon. Taylor, Chet, illus. 2004. (J). 18.99 (978-0-9755888-5-7(0)) Dragonfly Publishing, Inc.

Bremer, Michael. Ronald Dragon: An Electronic Storybook. Dowlen, James, illus. 2000. 32p. (J). (ps up). cd-rom 9.95 (978-0-9669949-7-1(3)) UnTechnical Pr.

Broger, Achim. Historia de Dragolina (Story of Little Dragon) 4th ed. (SPA., Illus.). 32p. (J). 14.95 (978-84-261-1924-7(7)) Juventud, Editorial ESP. *Dist:* AIMS International Bks., Inc.

Brooks, Felicity. Jason & the Argonauts. Humphreys, Graham, illus. 2005. 144p. (J). pap. 4.95 (978-0-7945-0275-1(X) , Usborne) EDC Publishing.

Brooks, Stephen J. Alexander Asenby's Great Adventure. Rajesh, illus. 2006. 32p. (J). 16.96 (978-0-9769017-2-3(2)) Purple Sky Publishing.

Brouillet, Chrystine. Mon Frere, le Dragon. Dion, Nathalie, illus. 2001. (Premier Roman Ser.: 115). (FRE.). 64p. (J). pap. (978-2-89021-543-6(1)) Diffusion du livre Mirabel.

Brouillet, Chrystine & Dion, Nathalie. Mon Frere, le Dragon. 2001. (FRE., Illus.). 64p. (J). pap. (978-2-89021-531-3(8)) Diffusion du livre Mirabel.

Brovelli, Tito Alberto. Kiko, el Dragon Desobediente: Cuentos Bilingues. Anderson, Kirk, tr. Munoz, Rafael Sanchez, illus. 2000. Tr. of Kiko, the Disobedient Dragon: Bilingual Stories. (SPA & ENG.). 24p. (YA). (gr. k up). 14.95 (978-0-9673032-2-2(2)) Sweet Dreams Bilingual Pubs.

Brown, Kevin. In a Field of Sunflowers. 2006. pap. 9.00 (978-0-8059-6921-4(7)) Dorrance Publishing Co., Inc.

Brown, Tricia, ed. Sled Dog Wisdom. 2005. 64p. pap. 4.95 (978-0-9745014-5-1(X)) Epicenter Pr., Inc.

Browne, N. M. Basilisk. 2006. 320p. (YA). pap. 7.95 (978-1-58234-910-7(X) , Bloomsbury Children) Bloomsbury Publishing.

Bryan, Jennifer. The Different Dragon. Hosler, Danamarie, illus. 2006. (J). pap. 10.95 (978-0-9674468-6-8(4)) Two Lives Publishing.

Bucher, Heatherly & Menking, Amanda. The Happy Dragon, 1 vol. Menking, Amanda & Fisher, Sean, illus. 2006. 32p. (J). (***978-0-9790920-1-5(9)***) MoonRattles.

Bulla, Lynda. Freedom Rings: An American Parable. 2005. (Illus.). 32p. (J). lib. bdg. 14.99 (978-0-9724272-3-4(6)) Katydid Publishing LLC.

Bullock, Harold B. The Dragon of Raldan. Dumas, Barbara, ed. 1999. (Tarlian Adventures Ser.: Vol. 3). 120p. (J). (gr. 2-5). pap. (978-1-929248-04-9(0)) Golden Oak Pubs.

Burnham, Janet Hayward. The Dragoness Mess. 2003. (Illus.). 32p. (J). (gr. k-1). pap. 12.95 (978-0-9740743-1-3(4)) My Little Jessie Pr.

Cadnum, Michael. The Dragon Throne. 2005. 224p. (YA). (gr. 7). 16.99 (978-0-670-03631-8(5) , Viking Juvenile) Penguin Group (USA) Inc.

Carey, Janet Lee. Dragon's Keep. (Illus.). 320p. (YA). 2008. pap. 7.95 (***978-0-15-206401-3(X)*** , Magic Carpet Bks.); 2007. (gr. 6-10). 17.00 (978-0-15-205926-2(1)) Harcourt Children's Bks.

—Dragon's Keep. 2007. 302p. (J). (***978-1-4287-3929-1(7)***) Harcourt Trade Pubs.

Carus, Marianne, ed. Fire & Wings: Dragon Tales from East & West. Mistry, Nilesh, illus. 2002. ix, 146p. (J). (gr. 4-7). 17.95 (978-0-8126-2664-3(8)) Cricket Bks.

Casey, C. A. Dragon Drool. 2005. (J). 21.95 (978-0-9759555-0-5(0)); per. 9.95 (978-0-9759555-1-2(9)) Bedazzled Ink Publishing Co.

Cason, Sue. Dragon Trouble. Grimwood, Tracie, illus. 1999. (Supa Doopers Ser.). 64p. (J). (978-0-7608-3289-9(7)) Sundance/Newbridge Educational Publishing.

—Dragon Trouble. 1999. (gr. 3-6). lib. bdg. 12.60 (978-0-613-30364-4(4)) Tandem Library Bks.

Cassidy, Anne. The Queen's Dragon. Williamson, Gwyneth, illus. 2004. (Read-It! Readers Ser.). 32p. (C). (gr. k-3). 18.60 (978-1-4048-0553-8(2)) Picture Window Bks.

Cattanach, Ann. Malpas the Dragon. Renouf, Michael, illus. 2007. 24p. (***978-1-84310-572-5(1)***) Kingsley, Jessica Ltd.

Cave, Kathryn. You've Got Dragons. Maland, Nick, illus. 2003. 32p. (J). (gr. 1-5). 16.95 (978-1-56145-284-2(X)) Peachtree Pubs., Ltd.

Charlotte Latin School Staff. Ann & the Dragon. Sher, illus. 2001. 32p. (J). per. 4.95 (978-0-9707920-0-6(X)) Charlotte's Storybooks.

Cherry, Lynne. The Dragon & the Unicorn. 2001. (J). (gr. 1-5). pap. 17.95 incl. audio Spoken Arts, Inc.

—The Dragon & the Unicorn. 1998. 13.80 (978-0-606-13347-0(X)) Tandem Library Bks.

Childress, Jenna Lynn. Dragon Soul: Book One of the Triune Jewels. 2003. 262p. (YA). per. 8.00 (978-0-9704006-2-8(4)) Bound & Determined Pubs.

Chipman, Laura. Dragonspeaker. 2005. 76p. pap. 14.95 (978-1-4241-0136-8(0)) PublishAmerica, Inc.

Christian, Peggy. The Bookstore Mouse. Lippincott, Gary A., illus. 2002. 144p. (YA). (gr. 3-7). pap. 6.95 (978-0-15-204564-7(3) , Harcourt Paperbacks) Harcourt Children's Bks.

—Bookstore Mouse. 2002. (gr. 3-6). lib. bdg. 14.10 (978-0-613-56250-8(X)) Tandem Library Bks.

Clark, Hamish. Mara's Flame. 2006. 191p. spiral bd. 9.26 (978-1-4116-2768-0(7)) Lulu.com.

Clark, John T. & Clark, Nicole K. Adventures in Dreamtime. l.t. ed. 1998. (Illus.). 32p. (J). (gr. k-2). 15.95 (978-1-892176-12-7(2)) PremaNations Publishing.

Clarke, Jane. G. E. M. 2008. (Illus.). 32p. (J). pap. 9.95 (***978-0-09-948012-9(3)***) Transworld Publishers Ltd. GBR. *Dist:* Independent Pubs. Group.

Cohen, Warren Lee. Dragon Baked Bread. Ssebulime, John, illus. 2005. 32p. (J). (978-1-902636-70-2(8)) Clairview Bks.

Collier, Kevin Scott. Diligence the Dragon Vol. 1: A Prebiblical Fable. l.t. ed. 2005. (Illus.). 22p. (J). E-Book 9.95 incl. cd-rom (978-1-933090-25-2(1)) Guardian Angel Publishing, Inc.

Coombs, Kate. The Runaway Princess. 2006. 288p. (J). 17.00 (978-0-374-35546-3(0)) Farrar, Straus & Giroux.

Cosgrove, Stephen. The Muffin Dragon. James, Robin, illus. ed. 2001. (Serendipity Bks.). 32p. (J). pap. 4.99 (978-0-8431-7687-2(3) , Price Stern Sloan) Penguin Group (USA) Inc.

Coughlin, Denise. Dragon in My Pocket. Kastan, Bill, illus. 2005. (J). (***978-0-9765905-0-7(6)***) Rose Valley Publishing.

Coville, Bruce. The Dragon of Doom. Coville, Katherine, illus. (Moongobble & Me Ser.). 80p. (J). 2005. pap. 3.99 (978-0-689-85757-7(8) , Aladdin); 2003. (gr. 1-5). 14.95 (978-0-689-85754-6(3)) Simon & Schuster Children's Publishing.

—The Dragon of Doom. Coville, Katherine, illus. 2005. 69p. (J). (ps-k). lib. bdg. 10.64 (978-0-606-33373-3(8)) Tandem Library Bks.

—The Dragonslayers. unabr. ed. 2004. (Words Take Wingtm Ser.). 119p. (J). (gr. 3-6). pap. 29.00 incl. audio (978-0-8072-7988-5(9) , S YA 958 SP, Listening Library) Random Hse. Audio Publishing Group.

—Jeremy Thatcher, Dragon Hatcher. Lippincott, Gary A., illus. 2002. (Magic Shop Bks.). 168p. (YA). (gr. 3-7). 17.00 (978-0-15-204614-9(3)) Harcourt Children's Bks.

—Jeremy Thatcher, Dragon Hatcher. 148p. (J). (gr. 4-6). pap. 4.50 (978-0-8072-1471-8(X) , Listening Library) Random Hse. Audio Publishing Group.

Coville, Bruce. Jeremy Thatcher, Dragon Hatcher: A Magic Shop Book. Lippincott, Gary A., illus. 2007. (Magic Shop Book Ser.). 168p. (J). (gr. 3-7). pap. 5.95 (***978-0-15-206252-1(1)*** , Magic Carpet Bks.) Harcourt Children's Bks.

Cowell, Cressida. Heroic Misadventures of Hiccup the Viking, the: the First Collection Boxed Set. 2007. (gr. 3-7). 28.99 (***978-0-316-00592-0(4)***) Little, Brown Bks. for Young Readers.

—How to Be a Pirate. 2005. (Illus.). 224p. (J). (gr. 3-7). 10.99 (978-0-316-15598-4(5)) Little Brown & Co.

—How to Cheat a Dragon's Curse. 2007. (Heroic Misadventures of Hiccup the Viking Ser.). 256p. (J). (gr. 3-7). 10.99 (***978-0-316-11425-7(1)***) Little, Brown Bks. for Young Readers.

—How to Speak Dragonese. 2006. (Illus.). 240p. (J). (gr. 3-7). 10.99 (978-0-316-15600-4(0)) Little Brown & Co.

—How to Train Your Dragon. 2004. (Illus.). 224p. (J). (gr. 3-7). 10.99 (978-0-316-73737-1(2)) Little Brown & Co.

Cowsert, Sami. Tammi & Her Dragon. 2006. 48p. pap. 12.95 (***978-1-4241-5211-7(9)***) PublishAmerica, Inc.

Crowley, Suzanne Carlisle. The Very Ordered Existence of Merilee Marvelous. 2007. (J). (gr. 5 up). 256p. 16.99 (***978-0-06-123197-1(5)***); 384p. lib. bdg. 17.89 (***978-0-06-123198-8(3)***) HarperCollins Pubs. (Greenwillow Bks.).

Crump, Fred, Jr. Marigold & the Dragon. 2007. 32p. (J). 12.95 (***978-1-934056-73-8(1)***) UMI (Urban Ministries, Inc.).

Cuentos de Dragones para Ninos. 1999. (Stories for Children Ser.). (SPA.). 125p. pap. 7.95 (978-970-643-223-0(X)) Selector, S.A. de C.V. MEX. *Dist:* Libros Sin Fronteras.

Curry, Kenneth. The Return of Gamalok: The Return of Gamalok. 2007. (Illus.). 83p. (J). per. 12.95 (***978-0-9798364-2-8(5)***) Curry Brothers Publishing.

D' Lacey, Chris. The Fire Within. 2005. 352p. (YA). 15.99 (978-0-439-67243-6(0)) Scholastic, Inc.

Dadey, Debbie & Jones, Marcia Thornton. Dragons Don't Throw Snowballs. 2006. (Little Apple Ser.). (Illus.). 80p. (J). pap. 3.99 (978-0-439-79337-7(8) , Scholastic Paperbacks) Scholastic, Inc.

—Dragons Don't Throw Snowballs. Gurney, John Steven, illus. 2006. (Little Apple Ser.). 75p. (J). (978-1-4156-4913-8(8)) Scholastic, Inc.

C
D

Dahl, Michael. The Princess & the Tower. Zhurkina, Svetlana A., illus. 2005. (Read-It! Readers Ser.). 32p. (J). (ps). lib. bdg. 18.60 (978-1-4048-1184-3(2)) Picture Window Bks.

Daisy, April. The Lonely Dragon. Daisy, April, illus. 2005. (J). per. 7.95 (978-1-59466-074-0(3) , Little Ones) Port Town Publishing.

Davidson, Mary Janice & Alongi, Anthony. Jennifer Scales & the Ancient Furnace. 2007. 224p. (gr. 12). mass mkt. 6.99 (978-0-441-01474-3(7) , Ace Bks.) Penguin Group (USA) Inc.

—Jennifer Scales & the Messenger of Light. (gr. 12). 2007. 288p. mass mkt. 6.99 (***978-0-441-01510-8(7)*** , Ace Bks.); 2006. 336p. (YA). pap. 9.99 (978-0-425-21011-6(1) , Berkley Trade) Penguin Group (USA) Inc.

Davis, Mike. Pirates, Bats, & Dragons. Simpson, William, illus. 2004. 174p. (J). 15.95 (978-0-9747078-2-2(1)) Perceval Pr.

Dawson, Janine, illus. Lily Quench 6 Hand of Manuelo, Vol. 6. 2004. 176p. (J). pap. 4.99 (978-0-14-240222-1(2) , Puffin) Penguin Group (USA) Inc.

de Bruno, Oanna. Cuentos de Dragones para Ninos. (Stories for Children Ser.).Tr. of Children's Dragon Stories. (SPA.). (J). 7.95 (978-970-643-264-3(7)) Selector, S.A. de C.V. MEX. *Dist:* Libros Sin Fronteras.

De Mari, Silvana. The Last Dragon. Whiteside, Shaun, tr. rev. ed. 2007. 361p. (J). (gr. 5-7). per. 6.99 (***978-1-4231-0405-6(6)***) Miramax Bks.

de Paola, Tomie. The Knight & the Dragon. de Paola, Tomie, illus. 2002. (Illus.). 32p. (J). pap. 6.95 (978-1-931016-05-6(4) , MHC-05-4) Minnesota Humanities Commission.

DeFalco, Tom. Spider-Girl Battles the Deadly Dragon King. 2006. (Illus.). (J). (gr. 2-6). 21.35 (978-1-59961-025-2(6)) Spotlight.

Demi. The Boy Who Painted Dragons. Demi, illus. 2007. 52p. (J). (gr. 2-5). 21.99 (978-1-4169-2469-2(8) , McElderry, Margaret K.) Simon & Schuster Children's Publishing.

Dennis, Anne. Taming the Diabetes Dragon. Mitchell, Barb, ed. Buttner, Thom, illus. 1998. 24p. (J). (gr. 3-7). pap. 14.95 (978-1-891383-03-8(5)) JayJo Bks., LLC.

Diagram Visual Staff & Robertson, Michael. Super Little Giant Book of Dragons. 2007. (Illus.). 288p. (J). pap. 6.95 (978-1-4027-3903-3(6)) Sterling Publishing Co., Inc.

Dickins, Rosie. Dragon Painter. Nez, John, illus. 2006. 48p. (J). 8.99 (978-0-7945-1275-0(5) , Usborne) EDC Publishing.

Diggs, Linda. Gwynepe Slew the Dragon Almost. Hanna, Ellen & Steier, John, eds. Morris, Samuel L., illus. 2004. 49p. (J). (gr. k-6). 17.99 (978-0-9754126-0-2(4)) Willie & Willie.

Dixon, Andy. Dragon Quest. Brooks, Felicity, ed. Harris, Nick, illus. rev. ed. 2005. 32p. (J). (ps-7). pap. 7.99 (978-0-7945-1098-5(1) , Usborne) EDC Publishing.

DK Publishing. The Wise Dragon. 2008. 12p. (J). (ps-k). 12.99 (***978-0-7566-3811-5(9)***) Dorling Kindersley Publishing, Inc.

D'Lacey, Chris. Fire Star. 560p. (J). 2008. pap. 7.99 (978-0-439-90185-7(5)); 2007. (gr. 4-7). pap. 15.99 (978-0-439-84582-3(3)) Scholastic, Inc. (Orchard Bks.).

—The Fire Within. 2007. 352p. (J). pap. 7.99 (978-0-439-67244-3(9) , Orchard Bks.) Scholastic, Inc.

—Icefire. 432p. (J). 2007. pap. 7.99 (978-0-439-67246-7(5)); 2006. pap. 14.99 (978-0-439-67245-0(7)) Scholastic, Inc. (Orchard Bks.).

Doherty, Gillian. Stories of Dragons. Edwards, Linda, illus. 2007. 96p. (J). 16.99 (978-0-7945-1465-5(0) , Usborne) EDC Publishing.

Dolby, Karen. Dragon in the Cupboard. 2004. (Young Puzzle Adventures Ser.). 32p. (J). (gr. 2 up). pap. 4.95 (978-0-7945-0232-4(6)); lib. bdg. 12.95 (978-1-58086-461-9(9)) EDC Publishing.

Dominguez, Xan Lopez. Teodomiro Suena con Dragones. 2002. (SPA., Illus.). 45p. pap. 6.95 (978-84-241-8016-4(X) , EV31120) Everest de Ediciones y Distribucion, S.L. ESP. *Dist:* Lectorum Pubns., Inc.

Donaldson, Julia. Room on the Broom. Scheffler, Axel, illus. 32p. (J). (gr. k-3). 2003. pap. 6.99 (978-0-14-250112-2(3) , Puffin); 2001. 16.99 (978-0-8037-2657-4(0) , Dial) Penguin Group (USA) Inc.

—Room on the Broom. 2003. (gr. k-3). lib. bdg. 15.30 (978-0-613-83001-0(6)) Tandem Library Bks.

Dongweck, James. The Dragon Cant. Baker, Joe, illus. 2004. 32p. (J). per. 16.95 (978-0-9719632-0-7(7)) Golden Monkey Publishing, LLC.

Downer, Ann. The Dragon of Never-Was. Rayyan, Omar, illus. 2006. 320p. (J). (gr. 3-6). 16.95 (978-0-689-85571-9(0) , Atheneum) Simon & Schuster Children's Publishing.

—Hatching Magic. 256p. (J). 2006. pap. 2.99 (978-1-4169-2497-5(3) , Aladdin); 2005. pap. 2.99 (978-1-4169-0535-6(9) , Aladdin); 2003. (Illus.). (gr. 3-7). 17.95 (978-0-689-83400-4(4) , Atheneum); 2004. reprint ed. pap. 5.99 (978-0-689-87057-6(4) , Aladdin) Simon & Schuster Children's Publishing.

Dozier, Kim. Where's Dwight Dragon. Dozier, Ashlyn McCauley, illus. l.t. ed. 2004. (ENG.). 32p. (J). 10.00 (978-0-9745839-2-1(8) , Fun to Read Bks. with Royally Good Morals) MKADesigns.

Dragon: Enter the Realm. 2007. (YA). per. (***978-1-934345-43-6(1)***) SouthWest Pubns.

Dragon: The Fantasy Continues. 2007. (YA). per. (***978-1-934345-44-3(X)***) SouthWest Pubns.

Dragon Slayer's Academy. 2006. (J). (gr. 1-6). 145.26 (978-1-59961-121-1(X)) Spotlight.

Dragon Tales. 2005. (Thrillogy Ser.). (Illus.). 48p. (gr. 4-8). 17.50 (978-0-7910-8887-6(1)) Facts On File, Inc.

Dragons, Phantoms, & Secrets: The Best New Fantasy from Arrow Writers. 2005. 63p. (J). (***978-0-439-74432-4(6)***) Scholastic, Inc.

Dragon's Tears. 2004. (J). cd-rom (978-1-84444-458-8(9)) Mantra Publishing, Ltd.

Drake, Salamanda. Dragonsdale. Marklew, Gilly, illus. 2007. 288p. (J). (gr. 4-7). pap. 16.99 (***978-0-439-87173-0(5)*** , Chicken Hse., The) Scholastic, Inc.

Draper, Rochelle, illus. The Stone Wall Dragon. 2007. 32p. 15.95 (***978-0-89272-690-5(3)***) Down East Bks.

Duckett, Brenda. The Giggling Purple Dragon. 2006. 84p. pap. 9.99 (978-1-4116-3826-6(3)) Lulu.com.

Durant, Sybrina, et al. Blue Unicorn II: Return of the Dragons, 3 vols. Johnson, Britt, ed. l.t. ed. 2003. (Illus.). 25p. (J). (gr. k-5). spiral bd. 8.99 (978-1-929063-93-2(8) , 331) Moons & Stars Publishing For Children.

Eastwood, J. G. Dragon the Fantasy Continues. 2006. pap. 33.49 (***978-1-4259-7068-0(0)***) AuthorHouse.

Edwards, Stuart. Dragon Jack. 2006. 42p. 15.99 (978-1-4116-7499-8(5)) Lulu.com.

Ellery, Amanda. If I Had a Dragon. Ellery, Tom, illus. 2006. 40p. (J). (ps-2). 14.95 (978-1-4169-0924-8(9) , Simon & Schuster Children's Publishing) Simon & Schuster Children's Publishing.

Ellery, Tom, et al. If I Had a Dragon. Ellery, Tom & Ellery, Amanda, illus. 2006. (ENG & SPA.). (J). 12.99 (978-1-933032-16-0(2)); pap. 3.99 (978-1-933032-17-7(0)) Lectorum Pubns., Inc.

Ende, Michael. El Dragon y la Mariposa. De Horna, Luis, illus. 2003. (SPA.). 48p. (J). (gr. k-3). pap. 8.95 (978-84-204-3710-1(7)) Santillana USA Publishing Co., Inc.

Erickson, Byron. World of the Dragon Lords. 2005. 176p. (YA). pap. 12.99 (978-0-911903-98-0(4)) Gemstone Publishing, Inc.

Estes, Rose. Dragon of Doom. 2008. (Endless Quest Ser.). 192p. (J). (gr. 3-7). 5.99 (***978-0-7869-4717-1(9)*** , Mirrorstone) Wizards of the Coast.

Ferrone, John M. Gus & the Golden Dragon. Ferrone, John M., illus. Date not set. (Illus.). 36p. (ps-5). pap. 16.95 (978-1-928811-02-2(7)) Story Stuff, Inc.

Fienberg, Anna & Fienberg, Barbara. The Big Big Big Book of Tashi. Gamble, Kim, illus. 2002. (Tashi Ser.). 448p. (J). (gr. 1-5). pap. 15.95 (978-1-86508-563-0(4)) Allen & Unwin AUS. *Dist:* Independent Pubs. Group.

Fletcher, Charlie. Stoneheart. 2007. (Stoneheart Trilogy Ser.: Bk. 1). 464p. (gr. 5-9). 16.99 (***978-1-4231-0175-8(8)***) Hyperion Pr.

Flether, Ralph. The Sand Man. rev. ed. 2008. (Illus.). 32p. (J). 16.95 (***978-0-8050-7726-1(X)***) Holt, Henry & Co.

Forbeck, Matt. The Dragons Revealed, Pt. 2. ed. 2006. (Illus.). 192p. (YA). pap. 5.99 (978-0-7869-4032-5(8) , Mirrorstone) Wizards of the Coast.

Forbes, Anne. Dragonfire. 2006. 256p. (YA). pap. 11.95 (978-0-86315-552-9(9)) Floris Bks. GBR. *Dist:* Steiner-Books, Inc.

French, Jackie. My Dad the Dragon. King, Stephen Michael, illus. 2007. (Funny Families Ser.). (J). (gr. 2-4). 107p. pap. 7.95 (***978-1-59889-436-3(6)***); 112p. lib. bdg. 22.60 (***978-1-59889-343-4(2)***) Stone Arch Bks.

Friedman, Jim. The Mysterious Misadventures of Foy Rin Jin: A Decidedly Dysfunctional Dragon. 1999. (Illus.). 32p. (J). (ps-3). 15.89 (978-0-06-028551-7(6)) HarperCollins Pubs.

—The Mysterious Misadventures of Foy Rin Jin: A Decidedly Dysfunctional Dragon. Stren, Patti, illus. 1999. 32p. (J). (ps-3). 15.95 (978-0-06-028000-0(X)) HarperCollins Pubs.

Funke, Cornelia. Dragon Rider. Bell, Anthea, tr. from GER. 2004. Orig. Title: Drachenreiter. 528p. (J). (gr. 3-6). pap. 14.99 (978-0-439-45695-1(9) , Chicken Hse., The) Scholastic, Inc.

—Dragon Rider. collector's ed. 2004. Orig. Title: Drachenreiter. 528p. (J). 100.00 (978-0-439-74336-5(2)) Scholastic, Inc.

—Dragon Rider. Bell, Anthea, tr. l.t. ed. 2005. Orig. Title: Drachenreiter. 542p. 23.95 (978-0-7862-7263-1(5) , Large Print Pr.) Thorndike Pr.

Funkhouser, Allison. Zealk & the Humans. 2005. 60p. 16.99 (978-1-58752-111-9(3)) Timberwolf Pr., Inc.

Gabriel. Dragonheart, Level 2. 2000. 48p. (C). pap. 9.00 (978-0-582-36401-1(9)) Longman Publishing Group.

Gannett, Ruth Stiles. The Dragons of Blueland. 2007. (My Father's Dragon Ser.). 112p. (J). (gr. 4-7). 6.50 (978-0-440-42137-5(3) , Yearling) Random Hse. Children's Bks.

—Elmer & the Dragon. Gannett, Ruth Chrisman, illus. 2002. (J). 14.47 (978-0-7587-9151-1(8)) Book Wholesalers, Inc.

—Elmer & the Dragon. Gannett, Ruth Chrisman, illus. (Tales of My Father's Dragon Ser.: Bk. 2). 87p. (J). (gr. 3-6). pap. 4.99 incl. audio (978-0-8072-1288-2(1) , Listening Library) Random Hse. Audio Publishing Group.

—Elmer & the Dragon. 2007. (My Father's Dragon Ser.). (Illus.). 96p. (J). (gr. 4-7). 6.50 (978-0-440-42136-8(5) , Yearling) Random Hse. Children's Bks.

—My Father's Dragon: Books 1 & 2: #1 My Father's Dragon #2 Elmer & the Dragon. Gannett, Ruth Chrisman, illus. 2002. (J). 14.47 (978-0-7587-0296-8(5)) Book Wholesalers, Inc.

—My Father's Dragon: Books 1 & 2: #1 My Father's Dragon #2 Elmer & the Dragon. 2005. (Illus.). 96p. (J). (gr. 5). 6.50 (978-0-440-42121-4(7) , Yearling) Random Hse. Children's Bks.

Garrison, Terie. AutumnQuest. 2006. 192p. (YA). (gr. 7-9). pap. 8.95 (978-0-7387-0926-0(3) , Flux) Llewellyn Pubns.

Gelber, Peter Frost. The Dragon Who Lived Next Door. Tucker, Lewis R. & Mosher, Scott, illus. l.t. ed. 2003. 64p. (J). (ps-6). pap. 12.00 (978-0-9658920-4-9(2)) Fore Angels Pr.

Gelsey, James. The Ultimate Dragon Booster Scrapbook. 2005. (Illus.). 32p. (gr. 2-5). pap. 4.99 (978-0-7868-3770-0(5) , Volo) Hyperion Bks. for Children.

George, Jessica Day. Dragon Slippers. 2007. 336p. (J). 16.95 (***978-1-59990-057-5(2)*** , Bloomsbury Children) Bloomsbury Publishing.

George Ramey. The Friendly Dragon. 2006. (ENG.). 28p. per. 13.99 (***978-1-4259-7967-6(X)***) AuthorHouse.

Givens, Terryl L. Escamas de Dragon y Hojas de Sauce. Portwood, Andrew, illus. (SPA.). (J). pap. 7.95 (978-958-04-4168-7(5)) Norma S.A. COL. *Dist:* Distribuidora Norma, Inc., Lectorum Pubns., Inc.

Golden, Christopher & Sniegoski, Thomas E. Dragon Secrets. 2004. (Outcasts Ser.: Bk. 02). 240p. (J). pap. 5.99 (978-0-689-86662-3(3) , Aladdin) Simon & Schuster Children's Publishing.

Goldwell, Bruce. Dragon Keepers. 2006. (YA). pap. (978-1-894936-47-7(7)) Saga Bks.

Goldwell, Bruce. Dragon Keepers II. 2006. per. (***978-1-894936-59-0(0)***) Saga Bks.

Goodhart, Pippa. Dragon Boy. Ursell, Martin, illus. 2005. (Red Bananas Ser.). 48p. (J). (978-0-7787-1071-4(8)) Crabtree Publishing Co.

—Dragon Boy. 2005. (Red Bananas Ser.). (Illus.). 48p. (J). (ps). pap. (978-0-7787-1087-5(4)) Crabtree Publishing Co.

Goodhart, Pippa & Paine, Colin. Arthur's Tractor: A Fairy Tale with Mechanical Parts. 2003. (Illus.). 32p. (J). (ps-3). 15.95 (978-1-58234-847-6(2) , Bloomsbury Children) Bloomsbury Publishing.

Gouveia, Keith. Children of the Dragon. 2005. (ENG.). 174p. pap. (***978-1-897217-03-0(X)***) Coscom Entertainment.

Graham, L. B. Father of Dragons. 2007. (Binding of the Blade Ser.). (YA). pap. 16.99 (***978-0-87552-723-9(X)***) P & R Publishing.

Grahame, Kenneth. The Reluctant Dragon. Moore, Inga, illus. 2004. 64p. (J). (ps-3). 17.99 (978-0-7636-2199-5(4)) Candlewick Pr.

—The Reluctant Dragon Me. 2003. (J). cd-rom (978-0-9724995-6-9(3)) Alcazar AudioWorks.

Gray, Luli. Falcon & the Charles Street Witch. 2002. 144p. (J). (gr. 5-9). 16.00 (978-0-618-16410-3(3)) Houghton Mifflin Co. Trade & Reference Div.

Gregory, Manju. Dragon's Tears. Le, Guo, illus. 2004. (CHI & ENG.). 24p. (J). pap. (978-1-84444-477-9(5)) Mantra Publishing, Ltd.

Gregory, Manju & Le, Guo, illus. The Dragon's Tears: Lotet e Kucedres. 2004. (TAM, CZE, VIE, SPA & GUJ.). 24p. (J). pap. (978-1-85269-685-6(0)) Mantra Publishing, Ltd.

Gregory, Philippa. Draco, Mi Pequeno Dragon. (Raton de Biblioteca Coleccion). (SPA.). 128p. (J). (gr. 3). 7.95 (978-84-88061-72-0(2)) Serres, Ediciones, S. L. ESP. *Dist:* Lectorum Pubns., Inc.

Gregory, the Mean Dragon. (Early Intervention Levels Ser.). 28.38 (978-0-7362-0409-5(1)) Hampton-Brown Bks.

Grochowski, Brad. The Secret Weakness of Dragons: And Other Tales a Fairy Whispered in My Ear. 2004. (Illus.). 105p. (YA). per. 12.50 (978-0-9755606-0-0(3)) Eepie Pr.

Grosset, Juvenile. Dragon Slayers. pap. (978-0-448-41915-2(7) , Putnam Juvenile) Penguin Group (USA) Inc.

Haggarty, Holly. Summer Dragons. 2007. 144p. (J). (gr. 3 up). pap. 7.98 (***978-1-894917-52-0(9)***) Napoleon Publishing/Rendezvous Pr. CAN. *Dist:* AtlasBooks Distribution.

Hamel, Mike. Dragon's Lair: Matterhorn, the Brave Series, 5. 2007. 192p. (J). pap. 12.99 (***978-0-89957-837-8(3)***) AMG Pubs.

Hart, Derek. Secret of the Dragon's Eye. 2007. 264p. per. 16.95 (***978-0-595-42967-7(X)***) iUniverse, Inc.

Harvey, Ken. Brothers of the Storm: A Tale of Boys Born to Fight. 2007. per. 10.99 (***978-1-59886-676-6(1)***) Tate Publishing & Enterprises, L.L.C.

Hébert, Marie-Francine. La Drole de Vie de Meli-Melo. 2000. (Premier Roman Ser.). (FRE.). 192p. (J). (gr. 2-5). pap. (978-2-89021-384-5(6)) Diffusion du livre Mirabel.

Henham, R. D. Red Dragon Codex. 2008. 256p. (J). bds. (***978-0-7869-4925-0(2)***); (YA). (gr. 3-7). 9.95 (***978-0-7869-4780-5(2)*** , Mirrorstone) Wizards of the Coast.

Herman, George & Seaton, Kristen. Nine Dragons: A Contemporary Fable. 2003. (Illus.). 48p. 15.95 (978-0-8048-3481-0(4)) Tuttle Publishing.

Hess, Brian F. Lynquest & the Search for Greatness. 2006. (ENG.). 116p. per. 16.95 (978-1-4241-4503-4(1)) PublishAmerica, Inc.

Hicks, Bob. Cornelius, the Little Dragon Book. Hicks, Bob, illus. 2004. (J). ring bd. incl. audio compact disk (978-0-9722036-5-4(6)) T. E. Publishing, Inc.

Hiebert, Elfrieda H. & Juel, Connie. Dragon's Lunch. (Little Book Practice Reader). (J). (gr. k-6). (978-0-8136-2072-5(4)) Modern Curriculum Pr.

Hightman, Jason. The Saint of Dragons. (gr. 7 up). 2004. (J). 16.99 (978-0-06-054011-7(7)); 2004. 304p. (J). lib. bdg. 17.89 (978-0-06-054012-8(5)); 2005. 340p. (YA). reprint ed. pap. 6.99 (978-0-06-054013-5(3)) HarperCollins Pubs.

Hightman, Jason. Samurai. (J). 2007. 416p. pap. 6.99 (***978-0-06-054016-6(8)*** , Eos); 2006. 320p. 15.99 (978-0-06-054014-2(1)); 2006. 320p. lib. bdg. 16.89 (978-0-06-054015-9(X)) HarperCollins Pubs.

Hill, Douglas. The Dragon Charmer. Melnyczuk, Peter, illus. 2005. 151p. (J). (ps-k). pap. 4.95 (978-1-903015-36-0(7)) Barn Owl Bks, London GBR. *Dist:* Independent Pubs. Group.

Hill, William. Dragon Pawns: Jules & the Runt Dragon. 2005. 358p. (J). 24.95 (978-1-890611-37-8(9)) Atlas-Books Distribution.

—Dragon Pawns: Jules & the Runt Dragon. 2005. 358p. (J). pap. 15.95 (978-1-890611-38-5(7)) Otter Creek Pr., Inc.

Hillert, Margaret. Come to School, Dear Dragon. 2002. (Illus.). (J). 15.00 (978-0-7587-9456-7(8)) Book Wholesalers, Inc.

—Come to School, Dear Dragon. Helton, David, illus. rev. ed. 2006. (Beginning to Read Ser.). 32p. (J). lib. bdg. 18.60 (978-1-59953-017-8(1)) Norwood Hse. Pr.

—Dragon Goes to the Farm. 2005. (J). (978-1-59577-034-9(8)); (978-1-59577-032-5(1)) Starfall Education.

—A Friend for Dear Dragon. Helton, David, illus. rev. ed. 2006. (Beginning to Read Ser.). 32p. (J). lib. bdg. 18.60 (978-1-59953-016-1(3)) Norwood Hse. Pr.

—Go to Sleep, Dear Dragon. Helton, David, illus. rev. ed. 2006. (Beginning to Read Ser.). 32p. (J). lib. bdg. 18.60 (978-1-59953-018-5(X)) Norwood Hse. Pr.

—Happy Birthday, Dear Dragon. 2002. (Illus.). (J). 15.00 (978-0-7587-9477-2(0)) Book Wholesalers, Inc.

—Happy Birthday, Dear Dragon. Kock, Carl, illus. rev. exp. ed. 2007. (Beginning to Read Ser.). 32p. (J). lib. bdg. (978-1-59953-037-6(6)) Norwood Hse. Pr.

—Happy Easter, Dear Dragon. Kock, Carl, illus. rev. exp. ed. 2007. (Beginning to Read Ser.). 32p. (J). lib. bdg. 18.60 (978-1-59953-038-3(4)) Norwood Hse. Pr.

—Happy Mother's Day, Dear Dragon, 5 bks. (Illus.). 32p. (J). 2005. 6.95 (978-1-59577-022-6(4)); 2004. (978-1-59577-023-3(2)) Starfall Education.

—Help for Dear Dragon. Helton, David, illus. rev. ed. 2006. (Beginning to Read Ser.). 32p. (J). lib. bdg. 18.60 (978-1-59953-019-2(8)) Norwood Hse. Pr.

—I Love You, Dear Dragon. Kock, Carl, illus. rev. ed. 2006. (Beginning to Read Ser.). 32p. (J). lib. bdg. 18.60 (978-1-59953-020-8(1)) Norwood Hse. Pr.

—I Need You, Dear Dragon. Helton, David, illus. rev. exp. ed. 2007. (Beginning to Read Ser.). 32p. (J). lib. bdg. (978-1-59953-039-0(2)) Norwood Hse. Pr.

—It's Circus Time, Dear Dragon. Helton, David, illus. rev. exp. ed. 2007. (Beginning to Read Ser.). (J). lib. bdg. (978-1-59953-040-6(6)) Norwood Hse. Pr.

—It's Earth Day, Dear Dragon: For the Earliest Reader. 2005. (Illus.). 32p. (J). (978-1-59577-042-4(9)); (978-1-59577-041-7(0)) Starfall Education.

—It's Halloween, Dear Dragon. Kock, Carl, illus. rev. exp. ed. 2007. (Beginning to Read Ser.). 32p. (J). lib. bdg. (978-1-59953-041-3(4)) Norwood Hse. Pr.

—Let's Go, Dear Dragon. Kock, Carl, illus. rev. ed. 2006. (Beginning to Read Ser.). 32p. (J). lib. bdg. 18.60 (978-1-59953-021-5(X)) Norwood Hse. Pr.

—Little Red Riding Hood. Connelly, Gwen, illus. rev. ed. 2006. (Beginning to Read Ser.). 32p. (J). lib. bdg. 18.60 (978-1-59953-022-2(8)) Norwood Hse. Pr.

—Merry Christmas, Dear Dragon. Kock, Carl, illus. rev. exp. ed. 2007. (Beginning to Read Ser.). 32p. (J). lib. bdg. (978-1-59953-042-0(2)) Norwood Hse. Pr.

Hitchcock, Alfred. Misterio del Dragon. (Alfred Hitchcock y los Tres Investigadores Ser.). (SPA.). 176p. (YA). 8.95 (978-84-272-4914-1(4) , MO66) Molino, Editorial ESP. *Dist:* Continental Bk. Co., Inc.

Hodges, Margaret. Saint George & the Dragon. Hyman, Trina Schart, illus. 2002. (J). 13.79 (978-0-7587-0070-4(9)) Book Wholesalers, Inc.

—Saint George & the Dragon. braille ed. 2004. (Illus.). (J). (gr. 2-4). spiral bd. (978-0-616-01675-6(1)) Canadian National Institute for the Blind/Institut National Canadien pour les Aveugles.

Hodgson, Louise & Jones, Eric. Delyth y Ddraig. 2005. (WEL., Illus.). 20p. pap. (978-1-85596-220-0(9)) Dref Wen.

Hoel, Charlotte. The Magical Mischief Maker. 2004. (J). spiral bd. (978-0-9754004-0-1(1)) Magical Mischief Maker.

Holder, Nancy. Long Way Home. 2001. (gr. 7-12). lib. bdg. 15.30 (978-0-613-63316-1(4)) Tandem Library Bks.

Hook, Jason. Where's the Dragon? Hook, Richard, illus. 2004. 26p. (J). 14.95 (978-1-4027-1624-9(9)) Sterling Publishing Co., Inc.

Horns, Scales, Claws, & Tails: Individual Title Six-Packs. (Story Steps Ser.). (gr. k-2). 32.00 (978-0-7635-9830-3(5)) Rigby Education.

Howard, Arthur. Serious Trouble. (Illus.). 32p. (J). 2007. pap. 6.00 (978-0-15-205853-1(2) , Voyager Bks./Libros Viajeros); 2003. 16.00 (978-0-15-202664-6(9)) Harcourt Children's Bks.

Howe, John. Beowulf: A Tale of Blood, Heat, & Ashes. 2007. (Illus.). 96p. (J). (gr. 5). 18.99 (***978-0-7636-3647-0(9)***) Candlewick Pr.

Huxman, K. D. Dragon Talk. Farrington, Teresa, illus. l.t. ed. 2006. 24p. (J). pap. 14.99 (978-0-9765786-7-3(0)) Dragonfly Publishing, Inc.

Huxman, Karin (K. D.). Dragon Talk. 2006. (Illus.). 24p. (J). lib. bdg. 24.95 (978-0-9778651-7-8(7)) Dragonfly Publishing, Inc.

Impey, Rose. Wanda Witch & the Stray Dragon. 2006. (Scholastic Reader Ser.). (Illus.). 32p. (J). pap. 3.99 (978-0-439-78452-8(2) , Cartwheel Bks.) Scholastic, Inc.

Inches, Alison. In the Mushroom Meadow. 2002. (gr. k-3). lib. bdg. 10.95 (978-0-613-86241-7(4)) Tandem Library Bks.

The Jade Emperor & the Four Dragons: Individual Title Six-Pack Pouch - Level L. (Lighthouse Ser.). 16p. (gr. 2 up). 28.00 (978-0-7578-0878-4(6)) Rigby Education.

Jenkins, Jerry B. & Fabry, Chris. The Book of the King. 2007. (Wormling Ser.). 288p. (J). (gr. 5-9). pap. 7.99 (***978-1-4143-0155-6(3)***) Tyndale Hse. Pubs.

—The Changeling. 2007. (Wormling Ser.). 336p. (J). (gr. 5-9). pap. 7.99 (***978-1-4143-0157-0(X)***) Tyndale Hse. Pubs.

—The Sword of the Wormling. 2007. (Wormling Ser.). 336p. (J). (gr. 5-9). pap. 7.99 (***978-1-4143-0156-3(1)***) Tyndale Hse. Pubs.

Jeremy Thatcher, Dragon Hatcher. 2001. (J). pap., stu. ed., wbk. ed. (978-1-56137-878-4(X)) Novel Units, Inc.

Johnson, Bob. The Squatland Chronicles: Book 5 - the Dreaded Swamp of the Bubble Dragon. 2005. (Illus.). 56p. (J). per. 11.00 (978-1-59453-853-7(0) , Airleaf Publishing) Airleaf Publishing & Bookselling.

Johnson, Sandi. Dorp the Scottish Dragon: Conquest City. Johnson, Britt, ed. Praker, Jon, illus. 1999. (Conquest City Ser.: Vol. 7). 35p. (J). (ps-6). 10.99 (978-1-929063-06-2(7) , 142) Moons & Stars Publishing For Children.

—Dorp the Scottish Dragon Bk. 1: Lost in Scotland, 7 vols. Brundige, Britt, ed. Trevino, Juan, illus. 3rd rev. ed. 1999. (Little Choo-Choo Bks.). 35p. (J). (ps-6). spiral bd. 5.99 (978-1-929063-10-9(5) , 110) Moons & Stars Publishing For Children.

—Jim Elephant: The Nasty Bug, 2 vols. l.t. ed. 2003. (Illus.). 10p. (J). (gr. k-5). spiral bd. 5.99 (978-1-929063-33-8(4) , 330) Moons & Stars Publishing For Children.

Jordan, Sherryl. The Hunting of the Last Dragon. 2002. 192p. (J). (gr. 7 up). 15.99 (978-0-06-028902-7(3)); 15.89 (978-0-06-028903-4(1)) HarperCollins Pubs.

—Hunting of the Last Dragon. 2002. (gr. 7-12). lib. bdg. 14.15 (978-0-613-68349-4(8)) Tandem Library Bks.

Kaaberbol, Lene. The Shamer's War. 4th rev. ed. 2006. (Shamer Chronicles Ser.). 368p. (J). (gr. 6-10). 17.95 (978-0-8050-7771-1(5)) Holt, Henry & Co.

Katz, Welwyn Wilton. Beowulf. Gal, Laszlo, illus. 2nd ed. 2007. 96p. (J). (gr. 5 up). 17.95 (978-0-88899-807-1(4)) Groundwood Bks. CAN. *Dist:* Perseus Distribution.

Keller, Bill. Beowulf. McLean, J., illus. 2007. (Kingfisher Epics Ser.). 176p. (J). (gr. 5-9). pap. 7.95 (***978-0-7534-6134-1(X)*** , Kingfisher) Houghton Mifflin Co. Trade & Reference Div.

Kemp, Moira. Tell Me a Story, Daddy. 2006. (Illus.). 32p. (J). pap. (978-0-340-87560-5(7) , Hodder Children's Books) Hodder Children's Division.

Kent, Jack. There's No Such Thing As a Dragon. Kent, Jack, illus. 2005. (Illus.). 40p. (J). (gr. k-k). 12.95 (978-0-375-83208-6(4) , Golden Bks.) Random Hse. Children's Bks.

King, Steve. The Stone Dragon. 2005. 80p. pap. 14.95 (978-1-4137-9628-5(1)) PublishAmerica, Inc.

Kingsley, Kaza. Erec Rex: The Monsters of Otherness. Payne, John, ed. 2007. 350p. (J). 18.99 (***978-0-9786555-7-0(5)***) Firelight Press, Inc.

K.M. Mohr, John Kelley and. Waking Dalifi. 2005. 72p. pap. 9.95 (978-1-4116-6364-0(0)) Lulu.com.

Knappman, Timothy. Guess What I Found in Dragon Wood? Millward, Gwen, illus. 2007. 32p. (J). 16.95 (***978-1-59990-190-9(0)***) Bloomsbury Publishing.

Koller, Jackie French. The Dragonling, 3 bks., Vol. 1. collector's ed. 2000. (Dragonling Ser.). 224p. (J). (gr. 2-5). pap. 11.95 (978-0-7434-1019-9(X) , Aladdin) Simon & Schuster Children's Publishing.

—The Dragonling. 2000. (J). 12.64 (978-0-606-19872-1(5)) Tandem Library Bks.

Kroner, David. Seasons. 2007. 72p. pap. 6.95 (***978-1-882190-54-6(8)***) Polar Bear & Co.

Lake, A. J. The Book of the Sword: The Darkest Age II. 2007. 240p. (J). 16.95 (***978-1-59990-039-1(4)*** , Bloomsbury Children) Bloomsbury Publishing.

—The Coming of Dragons. 2006. (Darkest Age Ser.: Bk. 1). (Illus.). 250p. (J). 16.95 (978-1-58234-965-7(7) , Bloomsbury Children) Bloomsbury Publishing.

—The Coming of Dragons Bk. 1: Darkest Age I. 2007. (Illus.). 240p. (YA). pap. 6.95 (978-1-58234-902-2(9) , Bloomsbury Children) Bloomsbury Publishing.

Lang, Andrew. The Violet Fairy Book. 2005. 404p. pap. 16.95 (978-1-4218-0107-0(8) , 1st World Library - Literary Society) 1st World Publishing, Inc.

Lang, Andrew & Ford, H. J. The Tale of the Cid: And Other Stories of Knights & Chivalry. Ford, H. J., illus. 2007. (Illus.). 208p. pap. 9.95 (***978-0-486-45470-2(3)***) Dover Pubns., Inc.

Larochelle, David. The Best Pet of All. Wakiyama, Hanako, illus. 2004. 32p. (J). (ps). 16.99 (978-0-525-47129-5(4) , Dutton Juvenile) Penguin Group (USA) Inc.

Law, Felicia. Rumble Meets Buddy Beaver. 2005. (Read-It! Readers Ser.). (Illus.). 32p. (J). (ps-k). lib. bdg. 18.60 (978-1-4048-1287-1(3)) Picture Window Bks.

—Rumble Meets Chester the Chef. Pak, Yoon Mi, illus. 2006. (Read-It! Readers Ser.). 32p. (J). (gr. 2-4). 18.60 (978-1-4048-1335-9(7)) Picture Window Bks.

—Rumble Meets Eli Elephant. 2005. (Read-It! Readers Ser.). (Illus.). 32p. (J). (ps-k). lib. bdg. 18.60 (978-1-4048-1332-8(2)) Picture Window Bks.

—Rumble Meets Keesha Kangaroo. 2005. (Read-It! Readers Ser.). (Illus.). 32p. (J). (ps-k). lib. bdg. 18.60 (978-1-4048-1290-1(3)) Picture Window Bks.

—Rumble Meets Lucas Lizard. Pak, Yoon Mi, illus. 2006. (Read-It! Readers Ser.). 32p. (J). (gr. 2-4). 18.60 (978-1-4048-1334-2(9)) Picture Window Bks.

—Rumble Meets Milly the Maid. Pak, Yoon Mi, illus. 2007. (Read-It! Readers Ser.). (J). 19.93 (978-1-4048-1341-0(1)) Picture Window Bks.

—Rumble Meets Penny Panther. 2005. (Read-It! Readers Ser.). (Illus.). 32p. (J). (ps-k). lib. bdg. 18.60 (978-1-4048-1331-1(4)) Picture Window Bks.

—Rumble Meets Randy Rabbit. Pak, Yoon Mi, illus. 2006. (Read-It! Readers Ser.). 32p. (J). (gr. 2-4). 18.60 (978-1-4048-1337-3(3)) Picture Window Bks.

—Rumble Meets Shelby Spider. 2005. (Read-It! Readers Ser.). (Illus.). 32p. (J). (ps-k). lib. bdg. 18.60 (978-1-4048-1286-4(5)) Picture Window Bks.

—Rumble Meets Sylvia & Sally Swan. 2005. (Read-It! Readers Ser.). (Illus.). 32p. (J). (ps-k). lib. bdg. 18.60 (978-1-4048-1541-4(4)) Picture Window Bks.

—Rumble Meets Todd Toad. Pak, Yoon Mi, illus. 2006. (Read-It! Readers Ser.). 32p. (J). (gr. 2-4). 18.60 (978-1-4048-1340-3(3)) Picture Window Bks.

—Rumble Meets Vikki Viper. Pak, Yoon Mi, illus. 2006. (Read-It! Readers Ser.). 32p. (J). (gr. 2-4). 18.60 (978-1-4048-1342-7(X)) Picture Window Bks.

—Rumble Meets Wally Warthog. 2005. (Read-It! Readers Ser.). (Illus.). 32p. (J). (ps-k). lib. bdg. 18.60 (978-1-4048-1289-5(X)) Picture Window Bks.

—Rumble Meets Wilson Wolf. Pak, Yoon Mi, illus. 2006. (Read-It! Readers: Rumble's Cave Hotel Ser.). 32p. (J). (gr. k-3). (978-1-4048-1288-8(1)) Picture Window Bks.

—Rumble the Dragon's Cave. 2005. (Read-It! Readers Ser.). (Illus.). 32p. (J). (ps-k). lib. bdg. 18.60 (978-1-4048-1353-3(5)) Picture Window Bks.

—Rumble's Famous Granny. Pak, Yoon Mi, illus. 2006. (Read-It! Readers Ser.). 32p. (J). (gr. 2-4). 18.60 (978-1-4048-1336-6(5)) Picture Window Bks.

Lemmens, Riske. Little Dragon. 2004. (POR, VIE, CHI, ARA & BEN., Illus.). 24p. (J). (978-1-85269-482-1(3)); (978-1-85269-537-8(4)); (978-1-85269-575-0(7)); (978-1-85269-576-7(5)); (978-1-85269-577-4(3)) Mantra Publishing, Ltd.

Lisle, Holly. Vengeance of Dragons. 2000. (gr. 7-12). lib. bdg. 15.30 (978-0-613-29378-5(9)) Tandem Library Bks.

Little Dragon Boats: Second Grade Guided Reading Level I. (On Our Way to English Ser.). (gr. 2 up). 34.50 (978-0-7578-7086-6(4)) Rigby Education.

Loehr, Mallory. Dragon Egg. Wittwer, Hala, illus. 2007. (Step into Reading Ser.). 32p. (J). (ps-k). 3.99 (***978-0-375-84350-1(7));*** lib. bdg. 11.99 (***978-0-375-94350-8(1))*** Random Hse. Children's Bks. (Random Hse. Bks. for Young Readers).

Lore, Erin, illus. Timmy the Dragon. l.t. ed. 2007. 32p. (J). 8.95 (***978-0-9741562-7-9(2)***) Yarrow Pr.

Lowenstein, Sallie, illus. Sir Kyle & Lady Madeline. Lowenstein, Sallie, . 2007. 32p. (J). 18.95 (978-0-9658486-6-4(3)) Lion Stone Bks.

Luberto, Bradley. Clide & Druce: A Repulsive Tale of Trolls & Tax Money. 2006. (ENG.). 48p. per. 12.95 (***978-1-4241-5012-0(4)***) PublishAmerica, Inc.

Lucia encuentra un Dragon: Individual Title, 6 packs. (Literatura 2000 Ser.). (SPA.). (gr. 2-3). 33.00 (978-0-7635-1095-4(5)) Rigby Education.

Luckett, Dave. Girl Dragon, & the Wild Magic. 2003. (gr. 3-6). lib. bdg. 13.00 (978-0-613-72141-7(1)) Tandem Library Bks.

Lucy Meets a Dragon, 6 Packs. (Literatura 2000 Ser.). (gr. 2-3). 33.00 (978-0-7635-0177-8(8)) Rigby Education.

Lukas, Sarah. Dragon Dance. 2003. (Illus.). (J). bds. 6.99 (978-0-375-82340-4(9)) Random Hse. Children's Bks.

Maelor, Gwawr, et al. Tan Yn y Jyngl. 2005. (WEL., Illus.). 16p. (978-1-85644-842-0(8)) Univ. of Wales, Aberystwyth, Centre for Educational Studies.

Magee, Wes. Little Dragon. Warburton, Sarah, illus. 2004. 24p. (J). lib. bdg. 22.65 (***978-1-59646-690-6(1)***) Dingles & Co.

Martin, George R. R. The Ice Dragon. 2007. 112p. (J). 5.99 (***978-0-7653-5539-3(6)*** , Starscape) Doherty, Tom Assocs., LLC.

—The Ice Dragon. Gilbert, Yvonne, illus. 2006. 112p. (J). (gr. 3-5). 12.95 (978-0-7653-1631-8(5) , Starscape) Doherty, Tom Assocs., LLC.

Mayher, Lauren. The Legend of Darien: A Hero Rises. 2007. pap. 12.95 (***978-0-9794545-0-9(6)***) Blue Eyed Mayhem Publishing.

Mayhew, James. The Knight Who Took All Day. Mayhew, James, illus. 2005. (Illus.). 32p. (J). (ps-3). pap. 15.99 (978-0-439-74829-2(1) , Chicken Hse., The) Scholastic, Inc.

—Who Wants a Dragon? Gardiner, Lindsey, illus. 2004. 32p. (J). (gr. k-ps). pap. 15.95 (978-0-439-67237-5(6) , Orchard Bks.) Scholastic, Inc.

McAffee, Diane. Kaylee, Clean Your Room. Francis, Guy, illus. 1999. 24p. (J). (978-1-57008-688-5(5)) Scribbulations LLC.

McAllister, Angela. Digory & the Lost King. Beck, Ian, illus. 2007. 128p. (J). (gr. 3-5). 14.95 (***978-1-59990-088-9(2));*** pap. 5.95 (***978-1-59990-089-6(0))*** Bloomsbury Publishing.

—Digory the Dragon Slayer. Beck, Ian, illus. 2006. 128p. (J). 14.95 (978-1-58234-722-6(0)); pap. 5.95 (978-1-58234-912-1(6)) Bloomsbury Publishing. (Bloomsbury Children).

—Felix & the Blue Dragon. Smith, Mary Claire, illus. 2005. 32p. (J). (ps). 16.99 (978-1-84255-182-0(5)) Orion Children's Bks. GBR. *Dist:* Independent Pubs. Group.

McCaffrey, Anne. Dragondrums. 2003. (Harper Hall Trilogy: Vol. 3). (J). (gr. 5-8). lib. bdg. 14.15 (978-0-613-91041-5(9)); (gr. 7-12). lib. bdg. 15.30 (978-0-613-66493-6(0)) Tandem Library Bks.

—Dragonsinger. 2003. (Harper Hall Trilogy: Vol. 2). (gr. 5-8). lib. bdg. 14.15 (978-0-613-73345-8(2)); (gr. 7-12). lib. bdg. 15.30 (978-0-613-66494-3(9)) Tandem Library Bks.

—The Masterharper of Pern. 1999. (Pern Ser.). (gr. 7-12). lib. bdg. 15.30 (978-0-613-37699-0(4)) Tandem Library Bks.

—The Skies of Pern. 2002. (Pern Ser.). (gr. 7-12). lib. bdg. 16.45 (978-0-613-62648-4(6)) Tandem Library Bks.

McClanahan, Teel, 3rd. Dragons' Truth. 2007. 208p. (YA). per. 12.99 (***978-1-934516-02-7(3)***) Modern Evil Pr.

McDonald, Ann-Eve. The Dragon's Lair, a Counterpane Story. 2004. (J). (978-0-9770158-3-2(1)) BeachWalk Bks. Inc.

McKinley, Robin. Dragonhaven. 2007. 342p. (J). (gr. 5 up). 17.99 (***978-0-399-24675-3(4)*** , Putnam Juvenile) Penguin Group (USA) Inc.

McLerran, Alice. Dragonfly. 2000. (gr. 3-6). lib. bdg. 21.05 (978-0-613-61417-7(8)) Tandem Library Bks.

McMahon, P. J. The Case of the Singing Sea Dragons. Manders, John, illus. 2005. (Freaky Joe Club Ser.: No. 6). 160p. (J). pap. 4.99 (978-1-4169-0050-4(0) , Aladdin) Simon & Schuster Children's Publishing.

McMullan, Kate. Beware! It's Friday the 13th. Basso, Bill, illus. 2005. (Dragon Slayers' Academy Ser.: No. 13). 112p. (J). (gr. 2-5). pap. 4.99 (978-0-448-43531-2(4) , Grosset & Dunlap) Penguin Group (USA) Inc.

—Beware! It's Friday the 13th. 2006. (Dragon Slayers' Academy Ser.: No. 13). (Illus.). 107p. (J). (gr. 1-6). 24.21 (978-1-59961-122-8(8)) Spotlight.

—Class Trip to the Cave of Doom. Basso, Bill, illus. 2003. (Dragon Slayers' Academy Ser.: No. 3). 112p. (J). (gr. 1-4). pap. 4.99 (978-0-448-43110-9(6) , Grosset & Dunlap) Penguin Group (USA) Inc.

—Class Trip to the Cave of Doom. 2006. (Dragon Slayers' Academy Ser.: No. 3). (J). (gr. 1-6). 24.21 (978-1-59961-123-5(6)) Spotlight.

—Class Trip to the Cave of Doom. 2003. (Dragon Slayers' Academy Ser.: No. 3). (gr. 3-6). lib. bdg. 13.00 (978-0-613-72615-3(4)) Tandem Library Bks.

—Countdown to the Year 1000. Basso, Bill, illus. 2003. (Dragon Slayers' Academy Ser.: No. 8). 112p. (J). pap. 4.99 (978-0-448-43508-4(X) , Grosset & Dunlap) Penguin Group (USA) Inc.

—Countdown to the Year 1000. 2007. (Dragon Slayers' Academy Ser.: No. 8). 112p. (J). (gr. 1-6). 24.21 (***978-1-59961-376-5(X)***) Spotlight.

—Countdown to the Year 1000. 2003. (Dragon Slayers' Academy Ser.: No. 8). (gr. 3-6). lib. bdg. 13.00 (978-0-613-72562-0(X)) Tandem Library Bks.

—Double Dragon Trouble. Basso, Bill, illus. 2005. (Dragon Slayers' Academy Ser.: No. 15). 112p. (J). (gr. 2-5). pap. 4.99 (978-0-448-43821-4(6) , Grosset & Dunlap) Penguin Group (USA) Inc.

—Dragon Slayers' Academy. Basso, Bill, illus. 2005. (Dragon Slayers' Academy Ser.). 112p. (J). lthr. 19.96 (978-0-448-43976-1(X) , Grosset & Dunlap) Penguin Group (USA) Inc.

—Help! It's Parent's Day at DSA, No. 10. Basso, Bill, illus. 2004. (Dragon Slayers' Academy Ser.: No. 10). 112p. (J). (gr. 2-5). pap. 4.99 (978-0-448-43220-5(X) , Grosset & Dunlap) Penguin Group (USA) Inc.

—Help! It's Parent's Day at DSA. 2006. (Dragon Slayers' Academy Ser.: No. 10). (J). (gr. 1-6). 24.21 (978-1-59961-125-9(2)) Spotlight.

—The New Kid at School. 2006. (Dragon Slayers' Academy Ser.: No. 1). (J). (gr. 1-6). 24.21 (978-1-59961-126-6(0)) Spotlight.

—The New Kid at School. 2003. (Dragon Slayers' Academy Ser.: No. 1). (gr. 3-6). lib. bdg. 13.00 (978-0-613-72614-6(6)) Tandem Library Bks.

—Wheel of Misfortune. Basso, Bill, illus. 2003. (Dragon Slayers' Academy Ser.: No. 7). 112p. (J). pap. 4.99 (978-0-448-43507-7(1) , Grosset & Dunlap) Penguin Group (USA) Inc.

—Wheel of Misfortune. 2007. (Dragon Slayers' Academy Ser.: No. 7). 112p. (J). (gr. 1-6). 24.21 (***978-1-59961-381-9(6)***) Spotlight.

—World's Oldest Living Dragon. Basso, Bill, illus. 2006. (Dragon Slayers' Academy Ser.: No. 16). 112p. (J). (gr. 2-5). pap. 4.99 (978-0-448-44112-2(8) , Grosset & Dunlap) Penguin Group (USA) Inc.

—97 Ways to Train a Dragon. Basso, Bill, illus. 2003. (Dragon Slayers' Academy Ser.: No. 9). 112p. (J). (gr. 2-5). pap. 4.99 (978-0-448-43177-2(7) , Grosset & Dunlap) Penguin Group (USA) Inc.

—97 Ways to Train a Dragon. 2003. (Dragon Slayers' Academy Ser.: No. 9). (gr. 3-6). lib. bdg. 13.00 (978-0-613-72474-6(7)) Tandem Library Bks.

McMullan, Kate & Basso, Bill, illus. The New Kid at School. 2003. (Dragon Slayers' Academy Ser.: No. 1). 112p. (J). (gr. 1-4). mass mkt. 4.99 (978-0-448-43108-6(4) , Grosset & Dunlap) Penguin Group (USA) Inc.

McShane, Pol. Return to Animal Land: The Adventures of Johnny & Joey. 2007. 132p. (J). per. 10.95 (***978-0-595-45804-2(1)***) iUniverse, Inc.

Meddaugh, Susan. Harry on the Rocks. 2007. (Illus.). 32p. (J). (gr. k-3). 6.95 (***978-0-618-84068-7(0)*** , Walter Lorraine) Houghton Mifflin Co. Trade & Reference Div.

—Harry on the Rocks. Meddaugh, Susan, illus. 2003. (Illus.). 32p. (J). (gr. k-3). tchr. ed. 15.00 (978-0-618-27603-5(3) , Walter Lorraine) Houghton Mifflin Co. Trade & Reference Div.

Meeks, Elizbiff. Without Millard's Wings. 2006. 58p. pap. 12.95 (978-1-4241-2199-1(X)) PublishAmerica, Inc.

Memoirs of Gulis: Growing Up. l.t. ed. 2005. (Illus.). 28p. (J). pap. 14.95 (978-0-9768752-1-5(7)) Open Spaces Publishing (Rupen), LLC.

Metz, Diana. Talon & the Dragons of Crinnelia. Metz, Dave, illus. 2002. 280p. (J). per. 6.95 (978-0-9718431-1-0(2)) M.O.T.H.E.R. Publishing Co., Inc., The.

Miller, James K. Leviathon the Dragon. 2007. 32p. per. 21.99 (***978-1-59886-298-0(7)***) Tate Publishing & Enterprises, L.L.C.

The Missing Man & the Twenty Dragons. 2005. (Illus.). 204p. (J). per. (978-0-9760045-1-6(8) , Reluctant Reader Bks.) e-Pluribus Unum Publishing Co.

Mitchell, N. J. W. Saraly & the Dragons. 2003. 124p. pap. 10.95 (978-0-595-30264-2(5)) iUniverse, Inc.

Moeller, Christopher. A League of One. rev. ed. 2002. (Justice League Adventures Ser.). (Illus.). 112p. pap. 14.95 (978-1-56389-923-2(X)) DC Comics.

Molnar, Cheri Eplin. Dee Diddly Dragon Is Not a Wimp. Gutwein, Gwendolyn, illus. 2004. 32p. (J). per. 17.95 (978-0-9746330-3-9(8)) Anton Berkshire Publishing.

Moredun, P. R. The World of Eldaterra Vol. 1: The Dragon Conspiracy. 2005. (World of Eldaterra Ser.). (Illus.). 304p. (J). (gr. 7 up). lib. bdg. 17.89 (978-0-06-076664-1(6)) HarperCollins Pubs.

Moredun, P.R. The World of Eldaterra: The Dragon Conspiracy, Vol. 1. 2005. (World of Eldaterra Ser.). 304p. (J). (gr. 7 up). 16.99 (978-0-06-076663-4(8)) HarperCollins Pubs.

Morgan, Mary. Dragon Pizzeria. 2008. (J). (***978-0-375-82309-1(3));*** lib. bdg. (***978-0-375-92309-8(8))*** Knopf, Alfred A. Inc.

Morgan, Michaela. The Thing in the Basement. Weir, Doffy, illus. 2006. 48p. (J). (***978-1-4048-3133-9(9)***) Picture Window Bks.

Morningforest, Chris & Raymond, Rebecca. Princess Underdrawers & the Dragon. 2006. 37p. (J). pap. 15.58 (978-1-4116-8837-7(6)) Lulu.com.

Mortenson, R. K. Landon Snow & the Auctors Kingdom # 5. 2007. (Landon Snow Ser.). 224p. (J). 9.97 (***978-1-59789-297-1(1)***) Barbour Publishing, Inc.

Mortenson, R. K. Landon Snow & the Igneus Forest. 2007. 224p. (J). 9.97 (978-1-59789-296-4(3) , Barbour Bks.) Barbour Publishing, Inc.

Moseley, Keith. Dragons: A Pop-up Book of Fantastic Adventures. Robertson, M. P., illus. 2006. 10p. (J). (ps-7). 15.95 (978-0-8109-4900-3(8)) Abrams, Harry N. , Inc.

Moseley, Keith, et al. Dragon World: A Pop-up Guide to These Scaled Beasts. 2007. 12p. (J). (ps-17). 15.95 (***978-0-8109-9456-0(9)***) Abrams, Harry N. , Inc.

Mulligan, Glori. The Challenge of the Dragons: Book Two of the Trilogy of the Dragons. 2007. (Illus.). 48p. (J). per. 19.95 (***978-1-933324-73-9(2)***) Cedar Hill Publishing.

Mulligan, Glori. A Dragon's Tail. 2005. (Illus.). 51p. (J). pap. 19.95 (978-1-933324-24-1(4)) Cedar Hill Publishing.

Murakami, Jon & Yeh, Phil. The Winged Tiger & the Dragons of Hawaii. 2005. 48p. pap. 11.95 (978-0-9755635-0-2(5)) Eastland Studios.

Myers, Walter Dean. The Dragon Takes a Wife. French, Fiona, illus. rev. ed. 2000. 32p. (ps-3). pap. 5.99 (978-0-590-46694-3(1)) Scholastic, Inc.

—The Dragon Takes a Wife. 2000. (Illus.). (J). (978-0-606-18871-5(1)) Tandem Library Bks.

Nash, Ogden. Custard the Dragon & the Wicked Knight. Munsinger, Lynn, illus. 1999. 32p. (J). (ps-3). pap. 6.99 (978-0-316-59905-4(0)) Little Brown & Co.

—Custard the Dragon & the Wicked Knight. 1999. (J). (gr. k up). pap., stu. ed. 25.20 incl. audio (978-0-7887-2986-7(1) , 40868); Class set. pap. 91.30 incl. audio (978-0-7887-3016-0(9) , 46833) Recorded Bks., LLC.

—The Tale of Custard the Dragon. Munsinger, Lynn, illus. 1998. 32p. (J). (ps-3). pap. 6.99 (978-0-316-59031-0(2)) Little Brown & Co.

—The Tale of Custard the Dragon. 1998. (J). (978-0-606-13833-8(1)) Tandem Library Bks.

Nelson, Bruce. Ibakon,Gretl & the Stinky,Sticky Dragon, 1 book, Vol.1. 2nd ed. 2007. (Illus.). 45p. (J). 10.95 (***978-0-9721410-2-4(2)***) Vinland Pr.

Nesbit, E. The Book of Dragons. Millar, H. R., illus. 2001. 180p. (J). (ps-7). per. 18.75 (978-0-613-37138-4(0)) Tandem Library Bks.

—Book of Dragons. Millar, H. R. & Zelinsky, Paul O., illus. 2001. (Peter Glassman Bk.). 256p. (J). (gr. 3-7). pap. 9.95 (978-1-58717-106-2(6) , SeaStar Bks.) Chronicle Bks. LLC.

—The Book of Dragons. Fell, H. Granville & Millar, H. R., illus. unabr. ed. 2004. (Thrift Edition Ser.). 176p. pap. 7.95 (978-0-486-43648-7(9)) Dover Pubns., Inc.

—Lionel & the Book of Beasts. Hague, Michael, illus. 2006. 48p. (J). (gr. 2-4). lib. bdg. 17.89 (978-0-06-084272-7(5)); 16.99 (978-0-688-14006-9(8)) HarperCollins Pubs.

Nettrour, Nelani. Banshees Bk. 2: Dragon Lands. Nettrour, Heather, illus. l.t. ed. 2003. 114p. (J). pap. 11.95 (978-1-932657-03-6(7)) Third Millennium Pubns.

—Meeshu's Keep Bk. 1: Dragon Guardians. Nettrour, Heather, illus. 2005. 113p. pap. 14.95 (978-1-932657-37-1(1)) Third Millennium Pubns.

Neuhaus, Eve. Journey to Mythaca. 2006. 347p. (YA). per. 16.95 (***978-1-59594-101-5(0)*** , Wingspan Pr.) Wingspan Publishing.

Newhouse, Mark H. Dragons in the Neighborhood. Blair, June H., illus. 2001. 32p. (J). (ps-6). 14.95 (978-0-9704629-1-6(3)); pap. 8.95 (978-0-9704629-2-3(1)) Earthkids Publishing.

Neyer, Daniel. Bulkington. Wilmot, Anita, illus. 2004. 136p. (YA). pap. 9.95 (978-0-9666701-1-0(6)) One Faithful Harp Publishing Co.

Norton, Andre. Dragon Magic. 2006. (Magic Bks.: No. 4). 224p. (J). 5.99 (978-0-7653-5300-9(8) , Starscape) Doherty, Tom Assocs., LLC.

Nortung, Sandra. Voice from the Forest. Wimmet, Greg, illus. 1999. 32p. (J). (gr. k-6). 11.95 (978-1-892885-50-0(6)) Daring Child Pr.

Nunez, Alonso. El Invencible y Malvado Dragon Curiambro. (SPA.). (J). (gr. 2-4). 18.95 (978-968-494-096-3(3) , CI30452) Centro de Informacion y Desarrollo de la Comunicacion y la Literatura MEX. *Dist:* AIMS International Bks., Inc., Continental Bk. Co., Inc., Lectorum Pubns., Inc.

Nyikos, Stacy. Dragon Wishes. 2008. (J). 16.95 (***978-1-933831-11-4(1)***) Blooming Tree Pr.

Offen, Hilda. There Might Be Giants. (Illus.). 25p. (J). pap. (978-0-340-68149-7(7) , Hodder & Stoughton) Hodder General Publishing Division.

Ogilvy, Ian. Measle & the Dragodon. 352p. (J). 2006. pap. 6.99 (978-0-06-058690-4(7)); 2005. lib. bdg. 16.89 (978-0-06-058689-8(3)) HarperCollins Pubs. (Harper Trophy).

Ohkami, Mineko. Dragon Knights, Vol. 24. 24th rev. ed. 2007. 192p. pap. 9.99 (978-1-59816-797-9(9) , Tokyopop Adult) TOKYOPOP, Inc.

C
D

O'Mahony, Carol. A Dee Dee & Clark Delay Magical Mystery. 2006. 73p. pap. 14.95 (***978-1-4241-5119-6(8)***) PublishAmerica, Inc.

Owen, James A. Here, There Be Dragons. Owen, James A., illus. (Chronicles of the Imaginarium Geographica Ser.). (YA). 2007. 352p. pap. 9.99 (***978-1-4169-1228-6(2)***, Simon Pulse); 2006. 336p. 17.95 (978-1-4169-1227-9(4)) Simon & Schuster Children's Publishing.

Palmer, Slim. The Albert Tales. 2005. (Illus.). 240p. (J). per. (978-1-905363-35-3(4), Exposure Publishing) Meadow Bks.

Paolini, Christopher. Eldest: Inheritance. 2005. (Inheritance Trilogy: Bk. 2). (Illus.). 704p. (YA). (gr. 7 up). 21.00 (978-0-375-82670-2(X), Knopf Bks. for Young Readers) Random Hse. Children's Bks.

—Eragon. 2006. (Inheritance Trilogy: Bk. 1). (YA). cd-rom 39.99 (978-1-59895-406-7(7)) Findaway World, LLC.

—Eragon. 2006. (Inheritance Trilogy: Bk. 1). (Illus.). 503p. (YA). (gr. 7 up). (***978-1-4287-0954-6(1)***) Knopf, Alfred A. Inc.

—Eragon. (Inheritance Trilogy: Bk. 1). (gr. 7 up). 2007. 768p. (YA). mass mkt. 6.99 (***978-0-440-24073-0(5)***, Laurel Leaf); 2006. 768p. (YA). mass mkt. 6.99 (978-0-440-23848-5(X), Laurel Leaf); 2003. (Illus.). 544p. (J). lib. bdg. 20.99 (978-0-375-92668-6(2), Knopf Bks. for Young Readers); 2003. (Illus.). 544p. (YA). 18.95 (978-0-375-82668-9(8), Knopf Bks. for Young Readers); 2005. 528p. (J). reprint ed. pap. 10.95 (978-0-375-82669-6(6), Knopf Bks. for Young Readers) Random Hse. Children's Bks.

—Eragon. (Inheritance Trilogy: Bk. 1). (SPA.). (YA). pap. (978-84-96284-44-9(1)) Roca Editorial De Libros.

—Eragon. 2005. (Inheritance Trilogy: Bk. 1). 503p. (YA). (gr. 7 up). per. 16.60 (978-0-606-33728-1(8)) Tandem Library Bks.

Peel, John. Double Disaster! 2002. (gr. 3-6). lib. bdg. 13.00 (978-0-613-70890-6(3)) Tandem Library Bks.

Peet, Bill. How Droofus the Dragon Lost His Head. Peet, Bill, illus. 2002. (Illus.). (J). 16.66 (978-0-7587-2761-9(5)) Book Wholesalers, Inc.

—How Droofus the Dragon Lost His Head. 1999. (Illus.). (J). (ps-2). lib. bdg. 17.60 (978-0-8085-3078-7(X)) Tandem Library Bks.

Pendziwol, Jean. Once upon a Dragon: Stranger Safety for Kids (And Dragons) Gourbault, Martine, illus. 2006. 32p. (J). (978-1-55337-722-1(2)) Kids Can Pr., Ltd.

—Once upon a Dragon: Stranger Safety for Kids (And Dragons) Gourbault, Martine, illus. 2006. 32p. 6.95 (978-1-55337-969-0(1)) Kids Can Pr., Ltd. CAN. *Dist:* Wybel Marketing Group.

Pepper, Sly. Dugan Peckles & the Keepers of the Crystal Flame. 2006. 232p. pap. 5.99 (978-0-9747668-1-2(X)) MindMaze Publishing Co.

Peretti, Frank E. The Door in the Dragon's Throat. 2005. (Cooper Kids Adventure Ser.: Vol. 1). 128p. (gr. 3-6). pap. 5.99 (978-1-58134-618-3(2), Crossway Bibles) Crossway Bks.

Philippa & the Dragon, Pk. 6. (Literatura 2000 Ser.). (gr. 1-2). 28.00 (978-0-7635-0148-8(4)) Rigby Education.

Picard, Anne M. Peace & Pancakes. 2006. 48p. bds. 25.00 (978-1-59298-149-6(6)) Beaver's Pond Pr., Inc.

Pilkey, Dav. Un Amigo para Dragon. 1999. (Dragon's Tales Ser.: Bk. 1). (SPA., Illus.). 48p. (J). (gr. 1-3). pap. 7.99 (978-980-257-216-8(0)) Ekare, Ediciones VEN. *Dist:* Kane/Miller Bk. Pubs., Inc., Lectorum Pubns., Inc.

—Dragon Gets By. Pilkey, Dav, illus. 2002. (Dragon's Tales Ser.: Bk. 2). (Illus.). (J). 13.79 (978-0-7587-4536-1(2)) Book Wholesalers, Inc.

—Dragon y el Gato Panzon. 1999. (Dragon's Tales Ser.: Bk. 4). (SPA., Illus.). 48p. (J). (gr. 1-3). pap. 7.50 (978-980-257-218-2(7)) Ekare, Ediciones VEN. *Dist:* Kane/Miller Bk. Pubs., Inc., Lectorum Pubns., Inc.

—Dragon y el Gato Panzon. 2000. (Dragon's Tales Ser.: Bk. 4). (Illus.). (J). 14.75 (978-0-606-20639-6(6)) Tandem Library Bks.

—Dragon's Merry Christmas. 2003. (Dragon's Tales Ser.: Bk. 3). (gr. k-3). lib. bdg. 14.10 (978-0-613-72145-5(4)) Tandem Library Bks.

Pitcher, Caroline. The Winter Dragon. Williams, Sophy, illus. 36p. (J). (ps-7). 2005. pap. 7.95 (978-1-84507-445-6(9)); 2004. 15.95 (978-1-84507-322-0(3)) Lincoln, Frances Ltd. GBR. *Dist:* Perseus Distribution.

Polacco, Patricia. The Graves Family Goes Camping. Polacco, Patricia, illus. 2005. (Illus.). 48p. (J). (ps-5). 16.99 (978-0-399-24369-1(0), Philomel) Penguin Group (USA) Inc.

Pratchett, Terry. Guards! Guards! 2001. (gr. 5-8). lib. bdg. 15.30 (978-0-613-57217-0(3)) Tandem Library Bks.

Prior, Natalie. Lily Quench & the Dragon of Ashby. Janine, Dawson, illus. 2004. 160p. (J). (gr. 3 up). pap. 5.99 (978-0-14-240020-3(3), Puffin) Penguin Group (USA) Inc.

Prior, Natalie Jane. Lily Quench & the Treasure of Mote Ely, Vol. 3. 2004. (Illus.). 160p. (J). (gr. 3-7). pap. 4.99 (978-0-14-240022-7(X), Puffin) Penguin Group (USA) Inc.

—The Search for King Dragon. Dawson, Janine, illus. 2005. (Lily Quench Ser.: Vol. 7). 192p. (J). (gr. 3). pap. 4.99 (978-0-14-240267-2(2), Puffin) Penguin Group (USA) Inc.

Prior, Natalie Jane, contrib. by. Lily Quench & the Black Mountains, Vol. 2. 2004. (Illus.). 160p. (YA). (gr. 3 up). pap. 4.99 (978-0-14-240021-0(1), Puffin) Penguin Group (USA) Inc.

Rash, Brett. The Dragon Lords. 2007. 160p. per. 12.95 (***978-0-595-43842-6(3)***) iUniverse, Inc.

Rawson, Christopher. Dragons, Stories Of. Cartwright, Stephen, illus. 2004. (Young Reading Series One Ser.). 48p. (J). (gr. 2 up). pap. 5.95 (978-0-7945-0446-5(9), Usborne) EDC Publishing.

Reyes, Yolanda. A Bed for Three. Coll, Ivar Da, illus. 2004. (SPA.). 36p. (J). (gr. k-3). 14.95 (978-958-704-055-5(4)) Santillana USA Publishing Co., Inc.

Richards, Maxwell J. George & the Dragon. 2000. 268p. (J). pap. 13.95 (978-1-891929-36-6(4)) Four Seasons Pubs.

Riddell, Chris. The Emperor of Absurdia. 2006. (Illus.). 32p. (J). (***978-1-4050-5061-6(6)***, Macmillan Children's Bks.) Pan Macmillan.

Roberts, Esyllt Nest & Owen, Carys Eurwen. Dinas Emrys. 2005. (WEL., Illus.). 34p. (978-0-86381-439-6(5)) Gwasg Carreg Gwalch.

Robertson, M. P. The Dragon Snatcher. 2005. (Illus.). 32p. (J). (ps-3). 16.99 (978-0-8037-3103-5(5), Dial) Penguin Group (USA) Inc.

—The Egg. 2004. (Illus.). 32p. (J). pap. 6.99 (978-0-14-240038-8(6), Puffin) Penguin Group (USA) Inc.

—The Egg. 2004. (gr. k-3). lib. bdg. 15.30 (978-0-613-87827-2(2)) Tandem Library Bks.

—The Great Dragon Rescue. 2004. (Illus.). 32p. (J). (ps-2). 16.99 (978-0-8037-2973-5(1), Dial) Penguin Group (USA) Inc.

Robertson, M. P., illus. The Egg. 2001. 32p. (J). (ps-3). 15.99 (978-0-8037-2546-1(9), Dial) Penguin Group (USA) Inc.

Robertson, Mark. Dragon Snatcher. 2005. (Illus.). 32p. (J). (***978-1-84507-398-5(3)***) Lincoln, Frances Ltd.

Robertson, Mark, illus. Kingfisher Treasury of Dragon Stories. 2005. (Kingfisher Treasury of Stories Ser.: Vol. 14). 160p. (J). (gr. k-3). pap. 5.95 (978-0-7534-5889-1(6), Kingfisher) Houghton Mifflin Co. Trade & Reference Div.

Robinson, Marcus. Samurai Baby the Adventure Begins. 2007. 87p. pap. 11.98 (***978-1-4303-0350-3(6)***) Lulu.com.

Rodda, Emily. Dragon's Nest. McBride, Marc, illus. 2004. (Deltora Quest, Dragons Of Ser.: No. 1). 192p. (J). pap. 4.99 (978-0-439-63373-4(7), Scholastic Paperbacks) Scholastic, Inc.

—Isle of the Dead. 2004. 195p. (J). lib. bdg. 16.92 (***978-1-4242-0273-7(6)***) Fitzgerald Bks.

—Shadowgate. 2004. 195p. (J). lib. bdg. 16.92 (***978-1-4242-0274-4(4)***) Fitzgerald Bks.

—Shadowgate. McBride, Marc, illus. 2004. (Dragons of Deltora Ser.: No. 2). 208p. (J). (gr. 4-7). pap. 4.99 (978-0-439-63374-1(5), Scholastic Paperbacks) Scholastic, Inc.

Rodda, Emily. Sister of the South. 2004. 205p. (J). lib. bdg. 16.92 (***978-1-4242-0275-1(2)***) Fitzgerald Bks.

Rodgers, Frank. Little T & the Dragon's Tooth. 2007. (Read-It! Chapter Books). (J). 21.26 (978-1-4048-2727-1(7)) Picture Window Bks.

Romey, Elizabeth A. Dragon Magic. (YA). pap. 9.99 (978-0-88092-625-6(2)) Royal Fireworks Publishing Co.

Rovetch, Lissa & Whitman, Emily. Sir Henry, the Polite Knight. Barnard, Bryn, illus. 2006. (J). (***978-1-58987-204-2(5)***) Kindermusik International.

Rudkin, Nancy. A Dragon at School. 2005. 28p. (J). 9.95 (978-1-4116-3877-8(8)) Lulu.com.

Rupp, Rebecca. The Dragon of Lonely Island. 2004. 160p. (J). (gr. 4-8). reprint ed. (978-0-7567-7861-3(1)) DIANE Publishing Co.

—The Return of the Dragon. 160p. (J). 2006. (gr. 3-6). pap. 5.99 (978-0-7636-2804-8(2)); 2005. (gr. 5-6). 15.99 (978-0-7636-2377-7(6)) Candlewick Pr.

Ruttle, Keith. The Lord Mount Dragon. 2005. (Cambridge Storybooks Ser.). (Illus.). 32p. pap. 7.00 (978-0-521-67487-4(5)) Cambridge Univ. Pr.

Ryan, Margaret. Littlest Dragon. 2002. (Roaring Good Reads Ser.). (Illus.). 64p. (J). pap. 7.99 (978-0-00-714163-0(7)) HarperCollins Pubs. Ltd. GBR. *Dist:* Independent Pubs. Group.

Salvatore, R. A. Road of the Patriarch. 2007. (Forgotten Realms Ser.: No. 3). 384p. pap. 7.99 (***978-0-7869-4277-0(0)***) Wizards of the Coast.

Sampson, Jeff. Dragon Spell. 2005. (Dragonlance Ser.: Vol. 8). (Illus.). 256p. (J). (gr. k-17). pap. 5.99 (978-0-7869-3744-8(0)) Wizards of the Coast.

San Souci, Daniel. Rabbit & the Dragon King. 2006. 32p. pap. 9.95 (978-1-59078-418-1(9)) Boyds Mills Pr.

San Souci, Robert D. & Grahame, Kenneth. The Reluctant Dragon. Segal, John, illus. 2004. 40p. (J). pap. 16.95 (978-0-439-45581-7(2), Orchard Bks.) Scholastic, Inc.

Sanami, Matoh. Tenryu: The Dragon Cycle, Vol. 3. 2005. (Illus.). 200p. (gr. 8-12). pap. 9.99 (978-1-4012-0671-0(9)) DC Comics.

Sansone, Adele. Pequeno Ganso Verde. 2001. (SPA.). (gr. k-3). lib. bdg. 15.25 (978-0-613-36002-9(8)) Tandem Library Bks.

Schaefer, Carole Lexa. Dragon Dancing. Morgan, Pierr, illus. 2006. 40p. (J). (ps-1). 16.99 (978-0-670-06084-9(4), Viking Juvenile) Penguin Group (USA) Inc.

Scharf, J. L. Grace & the Ice Prince. 2007. 262p. pap. 15.95 (***978-1-897235-09-6(7)***) Thistledown Pr., Ltd. CAN. *Dist:* Fitzhenry & Whiteside, Ltd.

Sellier, Marie. Legend of the Chinese Dragon. Louis, Catherine, illus. 2008. 40p. (J). (ps). 15.95 (***978-0-7358-2152-1(6)***) North-South Bks., Inc.

Seock Seo, Hong. Dragon Hunter. (Illus.). 192p. Vol. 3. rev. ed. 2003. pap. 9.99 (978-1-59182-163-2(0)); Vol. 4. rev. ed. 2004. pap. 9.99 (978-1-59182-434-3(6)); Vol. 5. 5th rev. ed. 2004. pap. 9.99 (978-1-59182-435-0(4)); Vol. 6. 6th rev. ed. 2004. pap. 9.99 (978-1-59182-436-7(2)); Vol. 7. 7th rev. ed. 2004. pap. 9.99 (978-1-59182-437-4(0)) TOKYOPOP, Inc. (Tokyopop Adult).

Service, Pamela F. Yesterday's Magic. 2008. (J). (gr. 3-7). 224p. 16.99 (***978-0-375-85577-1(7)***); 320p. lib. bdg. 19.99 (***978-0-375-95577-8(1)***) Random Hse. Children's Bks. (Random Hse. Bks. for Young Readers).

Shaver, Brianna. A Diamond in the Rough. 2005. 160p. pap. 19.95 (978-1-4137-6601-1(3)) PublishAmerica, Inc.

Shrestha, Sophie & Shrestha, Romio, illus. In Search of the Thunder Dragon. 2007. 32p. (J). 16.95 (978-1-60109-100-0(1)) Mandala Publishing.

Silver, Rita. Best Friends. 2006. 17.00 (978-0-8059-9932-7(9)) Dorrance Publishing Co., Inc.

Skudera, George. The Adventures of Freddie the Little Fir. 2006. pap. 10.49 (***978-1-4259-5950-0(4)***) AuthorHouse.

Smith, Jeff. The Dragonslayer. 2006. (Bone Ser.: No. 4). (Illus.). 176p. (J). (gr. 4 up). pap. 18.99 (978-0-439-70626-1(2)); pap. 9.99 (978-0-439-70637-7(8)) Scholastic, Inc. (Graphix).

—Eyes of the Storm. 2006. (Bone Ser.: No. 3). (Illus.). 192p. (J). pap. 9.99 (978-0-439-70638-4(6)); (gr. 4-7). pap. 18.99 (978-0-439-70625-4(4)) Scholastic, Inc. (Graphix).

Spaulding, Mar. Kate Lynn's Fantastic Dream. 1999. (Illus.). 64p. (J). pap. 15.00 (978-0-9674281-0-9(6)) Allen & Douglas Pubs.

Springett, Martin, illus. Jousting with Jesters: An ABC for the Younger Dragon. 2006. 32p. (J). 17.95 (978-1-55143-327-1(3)) Orca Bk. Pubs. USA.

Stanek, Robert. In the Service of Dragons. 2005. 220p. (YA). (gr. 4-9). pap. 14.00 (978-1-57545-089-6(5)) Reagent Pr.

—In the Service of Dragons II. 2005. (Illus.). 220p. (YA). (gr. 4-9). pap. 14.00 (978-1-57545-090-2(9)) Reagent Pr.

Steer, Dugald A. Dragonology Tracking & Taming Dragons Book & Model Set Vol. I: European Dragon. Carrel, Douglas, illus. deluxe ed. 2006. (Dragonology Ser.: Vol. 1). 24p. (J). (gr. 3). 14.99 (978-0-7636-3233-5(3)) Candlewick Pr.

—The Dragon's Eye: The Dragonology Chronicles, Vol 1. Carrel, Douglas, illus. 2006. (Dragonology Chronicles ; 01 Ser.). 256p. (J). (gr. 4). 15.99 (978-0-7636-2810-9(7)) Candlewick Pr.

Sterling Publishing Co., Inc. & Fernleigh Books Staff. Step Inside ... Dragons: A Magic 3-Dimensional World of Dragons. Harris, Nick, illus. 2006. (Step Inside Ser.). 12p. (J). 9.95 (978-1-4027-3990-3(7)) Sterling Publishing Co., Inc.

Stewart, Jennifer. If That Breathes Fire, We're Toast! 1999. 128p. (J). (gr. 4-6). tchr. ed. 15.95 (978-0-8234-1430-7(2)) Holiday Hse., Inc.

—If That Breathes Fire, We're Toast! 2001. (978-0-606-22151-1(4)); 2000. (gr. 3-6). lib. bdg. 12.40 (978-0-613-35730-2(2)) Tandem Library Bks.

Stewart, Paul & Riddell, Chris. Dragon's Hoard. 2005. (Knight's Story Ser.). (Illus.). 144p. (J). 9.95 (978-0-689-87241-9(0), Atheneum) Simon & Schuster Children's Publishing.

Stone, Jeff. Eagle. 2008. (Five Ancestors Ser.). 224p. (J). (gr. 5). 15.99 (***978-0-375-83083-9(9)***); lib. bdg. 18.99 (***978-0-375-93083-6(3)***) Random Hse. Children's Bks. (Random Hse. Bks. for Young Readers).

Strickland, Brad. Dragon's Plunder. 2006. (Illus.). 160p. pap. 9.95 (978-1-59687-391-9(4)) ibooks, Inc.

Stroud, Jonathan. Buried Fire. 2004. 332p. (J). pap. (978-0-7818-5794-9(5)) Hippocrene Bks., Inc.

—Buried Fire. 2004. 336p. (gr. 5-17). pap. 6.95 (978-0-7868-5194-2(5)) Miramax Bks.

Swallow, Su. Matt's Sand & Sea Dragon. Raga, Silvia, illus. 2006. (Lightning Readers Ser.). 32p. (J). pap. 3.95 (978-0-7696-4196-6(2), Gingham Dog Pr.) School Specialty Publishing.

Swindells, Robert. Room 13 & Inside the Worm. 2008. 352p. (YA). pap. 9.95 (***978-0-552-55591-3(6)***) Transworld Publishers Ltd. GBR. *Dist:* Independent Pubs. Group.

Sykes, Julie. That Pesky Dragon. Williamson, Melanie, illus. 2007. 32p. (J). (ps-2). 15.95 (***978-1-58925-069-7(9)***, tiger tales) ME Media LLC.

Tania, Kim. Yeti & the Dragon. 2005. pap. (978-0-8048-3649-4(3), PeriplusEdition) Tuttle Publishing.

Tatchell, Judy. Dragones. Scott, Peter, illus. 2006. 16p. (J). 11.99 (978-0-7460-7382-7(8), Usborne) EDC Publishing.

Taylor, Jennifer. Dragon Sitter. 2005. 36p. (J). 14.99 (978-1-4116-6449-4(3)) Lulu.com.

Taylor, Keith. Dragon Tales. 2000. (gr. 7-12). lib. bdg. 12.10 (978-0-613-28824-8(6)) Tandem Library Bks.

Terri, Branson. Brother Dragon. l.t. ed. 2007. (Illus.). 24p. (J). 9.99 (***978-0-9787421-9-5(2)***) Dragonfly Publishing, Inc.

Thomas, Shelley Moore. Get Well, Good Knight. Plecas, Jennifer, illus. 48p. (J). 2004. pap. 3.99 (978-0-14-240050-0(5), Puffin); 2002. 13.99 (978-0-525-46914-8(1), Dutton Juvenile) Penguin Group (USA) Inc.

—Good Night, Good Knight. Plecas, Jennifer, illus. 2002. 11.49 (978-1-4046-1571-7(7)) Book Wholesalers, Inc.

—Good Night, Good Knight. Plecas, Jennifer, illus. 2000. 48p. (J). (ps-2). 13.99 (978-0-525-46326-9(7), Dutton Juvenile) Penguin Group (USA) Inc.

—Take Care, Good Knight. Meisel, Paul, illus. 2006. 36p. (J). (ps). 15.99 (978-0-525-47695-5(4), Dutton Juvenile) Penguin Group (USA) Inc.

Thomas, Shelley Moore & Plecas, Jennifer. Good Night, Good Knight. 2002. (Easy-to-Read Ser.). (Illus.). 48p. (J). pap. 3.99 (978-0-14-230201-9(5), Puffin) Penguin Group (USA) Inc.

Thomson, Sarah L. Dragon's Egg. 2007. 272p. (J). (gr. 3-7). 16.99 (***978-0-06-128848-7(9)***); lib. bdg. 17.89 (***978-0-06-128847-0(0)***) HarperCollins Pubs. (Greenwillow Bks.).

Tolkien, J. R. R. Farmer Giles of Ham. Hammond, Wayne G., ed. 50th anniv. ed. 1999. (Illus.). 128p. 18.00 (978-0-618-00936-7(1)) Houghton Mifflin Co. Trade & Reference Div.

—Roverandom. Scull, Christina & Hammond, Wayne G., eds. (Illus.). 1999. 106p. pap. 12.00 (978-0-395-95799-8(0)); 1998. 128p. (gr. 3-5). 17.00 (978-0-395-89871-0(4)) Houghton Mifflin Co. Trade & Reference Div.

Tolkien, J. R. R., et al. Roverandom. Scull, Christina & Hammond, Wayne G., eds. 783rd l.t. ed. 1998. (Illus.). 191p. (J). 25.95 (978-0-7838-0299-2(4)) Thorndike Pr.

Tomasso, Phillip. King Gauthier & the Little Dragon Slayer. l.t. ed. 2003. (Illus.). 61p. (J). per. (978-0-9740833-5-3(6)) Port Town Publishing.

Townsend, Tom. The Dragon Trader, 8 vols., Vol. 3. Lewis, Jason, illus. 2000. (Fairie Ring Ser.: No. 3). 158p. (YA). (gr. 6-12). 9.99 (978-0-88092-527-3(2), 5272) Royal Fireworks Publishing Co.

Travalino, Rob & Gelsey, James. The Choosing. 2005. (Illus.). 96p. (gr. 2-5). pap. 4.99 (978-0-7868-3771-7(3), Volo) Hyperion Bks. for Children.

Trewellard, J. M. Butterfingers. Beck, Ian, illus. 2007. 208p. (J). (gr. 3-7). 15.99 (***978-0-385-75123-0(0)***); lib. bdg. 18.99 (***978-0-385-75124-7(9)***) Random Hse. Children's Bks. (Fickling, David Bks.).

Trumbauer, Lisa. The Hidden Dragon. Fiegenschuh, Emily, illus. 2005. (Dungeons & Dragons Ser.: Bk. 7). 192p. (J). (ps-7). pap. 5.99 (978-0-7869-3748-6(3)) Wizards of the Coast.

—The Hidden Dragon. Fiegenshuh, Emily, illus. 2005. (Knights of the Silver Dragon Ser.: Bk. 7). 178p. (J). (***978-1-4156-0424-3(X)***, Mirrorstone) Wizards of the Coast.

Trumbauer, Lisa & Suncatcher, Sindri. A Practical Guide to Dragons. 2006. (Illus.). 80p. (J). (gr. 3-7). pap. 12.95 (978-0-7869-4164-3(2), Mirrorstone) Wizards of the Coast.

Tucker, Kathy. The Seven Chinese Sisters. Lin, Grace, illus. 2003. 32p. (J). (gr. k-3). 16.95 (978-0-8075-7309-9(4)) Whitman, Albert & Co.

Turner, Jessie E. Moon in the Day Sky. 2006. 19p. (YA). pap. 19.95 (***978-1-59299-238-6(2)***) Inkwater Pr.

Ulmer, Mari P. Adventures of the Little Green Dragon. Maass, Mary K., illus. 1998. (Weewisdom Bks.). 64p. (J). (ps-3). 17.95 (978-0-87159-228-6(2)) Unity Schl. of Christianity.

Umansky, Kaye. Big Iggy. l.t. ed. 2005. (J). pap. (978-0-7540-7944-6(9)) BBC Audio.

Urrea, Lourdes, et al. El Dragon Jines. 2005. (Ediciones Castillo Castillo Del Terror Ser.). (SPA.). (J). (gr. 2-6). pap. 7.95 (978-970-20-0357-1(1)) Castillo, Ediciones, S. A. de C. V. MEX. *Dist:* Iaconi, Mariuccia Bk. Imports.

Valle-Inclan, Ramon del. La Cabeza del Dragon. 1998. Tr. of Head of the Dragon. (SPA.). (gr. 5-8). lib. bdg. 17.60 (978-0-613-86339-1(9)) Tandem Library Bks.

Vande Velde, Vivian. Dragon's Bait. 2003. (gr. 7-12). lib. bdg. 14.10 (978-0-613-59892-7(X)) Tandem Library Bks.

Vrombart, An. Dear Dragon. 2006. (Illus.). 32p. (J). (ps). 19.99 (978-0-340-88149-1(6)); pap. 9.99 (978-0-340-88150-7(X)) Hodder General Publishing Division GBR. (Hodder & Stoughton). *Dist:* Trafalgar Square Publishing.

Ward, Helen. The Dragon Machine. Anderson, Wayne, illus. 2005. 32p. (J). pap. 6.99 (978-0-14-240364-8(4), Puffin) Penguin Group (USA) Inc.

Watson, T. E. Mom, Can I Have a Dragon? Patterson, Dave, illus. 2nd l.t. ed. 2004. 32p. (J). (gr. 1-6). lib. bdg. 16.95 (978-1-58478-020-5(7), Paw Prints Pr.) Heather & Highlands Publishing.

Watt, Fiona. Hide-and-Seek Dragons. 2007. (Touchy-Feely Flap Bks). 10p. (J). bds. 16.99 (978-0-7945-1590-4(8), Usborne) EDC Publishing.

—That's Not My Dragon. 2006. 10p. (J). bds. 7.99 (978-0-7945-1285-9(2), Usborne) EDC Publishing.

Wealth, Viktoria. Aadorn Kingdom of the Dragons' Light: Book-I. 2003. 214p. (YA). pap. 14.95 (978-0-595-28175-6(3)) iUniverse, Inc.

Webb. Wanted One Dragon. 1999. (Illus.). 128p. (J). pap. 8.99 (978-0-7459-4069-4(2), Lion) Lion Hudson plc GBR. *Dist:* Independent Pubs. Group.

Weis, Margaret. Dragons of Autumn Twilight. 2000. (gr. 7-12). lib. bdg. 16.45 (978-0-8335-3164-3(6)) Tandem Library Bks.

Weis, Margaret & Hickman, Tracy. Dragons of Spring Dawning. 1999. (gr. 7-12). lib. bdg. 16.45 (978-0-8335-3165-0(4)) Tandem Library Bks.

—Dragons of Winter Night. 2000. (gr. 7-12). lib. bdg. 16.45 (978-0-8335-3166-7(2)) Tandem Library Bks.

Weiss, Bobbi. Hiro: Dragon Warrior. Short, Robbie, illus. 2007. 24p. (J). (gr. 1). pap. 3.99 (***978-1-58476-616-2(6)***, IKIDS) Innovative Kids.

Whyte, John. Buddy's Adventures in Reading. 2007. pap. 8.95 (***978-0-533-15641-2(6)***) Vantage Pr., Inc.

Wiesner, David, illus. & retold by. The Loathsome Dragon. Wiesner, David, retold by. 2005. 32p. (J). (gr. k-3). 16.00 (978-0-618-54359-5(7), Clarion Bks.) Houghton Mifflin Co. Trade & Reference Div.

Wilkinson, Carole. Garden of the Purple Dragon. 2007. 368p. (gr. 3-7). 16.99 (***978-1-4231-0338-7(6)***) Hyperion Pr.

Willis, Dan. The Dragon Well. 2004. (Dragonlance Ser.). (Illus.). 256p. (YA). pap. 5.99 (978-0-7869-3354-9(2)) Wizards of the Coast.

Wills, David. Fern's Dragon. 2005. 55p. pap. 12.95 (978-1-4137-7017-9(7)) PublishAmerica, Inc.

Wilson, Gina. Ignis. Lynch, P. J., illus. 2003. 40p. (J). (ps). pap. 6.99 (978-0-7636-2192-6(7)) Candlewick Pr.

Wilson, Sarah. Dragon Tooth Trouble. 2006. (Illus.). 64p. (J). 15.95 (978-0-8050-7830-5(4), Holt, Henry & Co. Bks. For Young Readers) Holt, Henry & Co.

Wilson, Wendy. The First Book of Red. 2005. 99p. pap. 14.95 (978-1-4137-5570-1(4)) PublishAmerica, Inc.

Wisbauer, Cortney. Rodney, the Ice Dragon. Wisbauer, Cortney, illus. 2006. (Illus.). 48p. (J). 22.95 (*978-1-59879-215-7(6)) Lifevest Publishing, Inc.

Witschen, Kay. Clinker's Dragon. 2006. (J). 6.95 (978-0-9741352-2-9(4)) Dwitt Publishing.

Wong, Benedict Norbert. Lo & Behold. Wong, Benedict Norbert, illus. l.t. ed. 2003. (Illus.). 38p. (gr. 1 up). 16.95 (978-0-9728192-0-6(7) , LOBE) Taiji Arts Publishing.

—Lo & Behold: A Boy & His Dragon. 2004. (Illus.). 44p. (J). (gr. 1-12). 8.95 (978-0-9728192-4-4(X)) Taiji Arts Publishing.

—Lo & Behold: Good Enough to Eat. Wong, Benedict Norbert, illus. l.t. ed. 2003. (Illus.). 40p. (J). (gr. 1-12). 16.95 (978-0-9728192-1-3(5) , 1002LB) Taiji Arts Publishing.

—Lo & Behold: The Millennia Just Roll By. 2004. (Illus.). 40p. (J). (gr. 1-12). 16.95 (978-0-9728192-3-7(1)) Taiji Arts Publishing.

Wood, Audrey. The Princess & the Dragon. 2002. (Illus.). 32p. (J). 7.99 (978-0-85953-716-2(1)) Child's Play-International.

—The Princess & the Dragon. 2003. (gr. k-3). lib. bdg. 16.45 (978-0-613-77050-7(1)) Tandem Library Bks.

—The Princess & the Dragon Storysack. (J). 65.00 (978-0-85953-199-3(6)) Child's Play-International.

—Princess, the Dragon & Scaredy Cats. (J). audio 10.97 (978-0-85953-375-1(1)) Child's Play-International.

Woodberry, Gareth. Gakeva Gluntok's New School. 2005. 65p. pap. 12.95 (978-1-4137-9894-4(2)) PublishAmerica, Inc.

Woods, Tonita. Mystical Forest of Wise. 2001. 120p. pap. 10.95 (978-0-595-19147-5(9) , Writers Club Pr.) iUniverse, Inc.

Wormell, Christopher. George & the Dragon. 2006. (Illus.). 32p. (J). (gr. k-3). 16.95 (978-0-375-83315-1(3) , Knopf Bks. for Young Readers) Random Hse. Children's Bks.

Wormell, Christopher. George, the Dragon & the Princess: 2008. (Illus.). 32p. (J). 16.95 (*978-0-224-07072-0(X)) Transworld Publishers Ltd. GBR. *Dist:* Independent Pubs. Group.

Wrede, Patricia C. Dealing with Dragons. 2002. (Enchanted Forest Chronicles: Bk. 1). (Illus.). 240p. (YA). (gr. 5 up). pap. 5.95 (978-0-15-204566-1(X) , Magic Carpet Bks.) Harcourt Children's Bks.

—Dealing with Dragons. 2002. (gr. 7-12). lib. bdg. 14.10 (978-0-613-56300-0(X)) Tandem Library Bks.

—Searching for Dragons. 2002. (Enchanted Forest Chronicles: Bk. 2). (Illus.). 272p. (YA). (gr. 5 up). pap. 5.95 (978-0-15-204565-4(1) , Magic Carpet Bks.) Harcourt Children's Bks.

—Searching for Dragons. unabr. ed. 2004. (Enchanted Forest Chronicles Ser.). 242p. (J). (gr. 5 up). pap. 38.00 incl. audio (978-0-8072-0670-6(9) , Listening Library) Random Hse. Audio Publishing Group.

—Searching for Dragons. 2002. 242p. (J). (ps-ps). per. 14.10 (978-0-613-55189-2(3)) Tandem Library Bks.

Wynn, Thad & Wynn, Juliette. The Tale of a Dragon. 2004. (Illus.). 85p. (gr. k-4). 15.95 (978-1-57197-140-1(8)) Pentland Pr., Inc.

Yep, Laurence. Tiger's Blood. 2005. (Tiger's Apprentice Ser.: Bk. 2). 240p. (J). (gr. 5 up). 15.99 (978-0-06-001016-4(9)) HarperCollins Pubs.

—Tiger's Blood. 2006. (Tiger's Apprentice Ser.: Bk. 2). 240p. (J). pap. 5.99 (978-0-06-001018-8(5) , Harper Trophy) HarperCollins Pubs.

Yolen, Jane. Dragon's Blood. 2004. (Pit Dragon Chronicles: Vol. 1). (Illus.). 320p. (YA). pap. 6.95 (978-0-15-205126-6(0) , Magic Carpet Bks.) Harcourt Children's Bks.

—Dragon's Boy. 2001. (gr. 3-6). lib. bdg. 13.00 (978-0-613-34680-1(7)) Tandem Library Bks.

—Heart's Blood. 2004. (Pit Dragon Chronicles: Vol. 2). (Illus.). 368p. (YA). pap. 6.95 (978-0-15-205118-1(X) , Magic Carpet Bks.) Harcourt Children's Bks.

—A Sending of Dragons. 2004. (Pit Dragon Chronicles: Vol. 3). (Illus.). 312p. (YA). pap. 6.95 (978-0-15-205128-0(7) , Magic Carpet Bks.) Harcourt Children's Bks.

Zahn, Timothy. Dragon & Herdsman. (Dragonback Ser.). 304p. (J). 2007. mass mkt. 5.99 (*978-0-7653-5276-7(1)); 2006. 17.95 (978-0-7653-1417-8(7)) Doherty, Tom Assocs., LLC. (Starscape).

—Dragon & Judge. 2007. (Dragonback Ser.). 320p. (J). 17.95 (*978-0-7653-1418-5(5) , Starscape) Doherty, Tom Assocs., LLC.

—Dragon & Slave: The Third Dragonback Adventure. rev. ed. 2005. (Dragonback Ser.). 304p. (J). 17.95 (978-0-7653-0126-0(1) , Tor Bks.) Doherty, Tom Assocs., LLC.

—Dragon & Soldier. 2005. (Dragonback Ser.). 304p. (J). 5.99 (978-0-7653-5017-6(3) , Starscape) Doherty, Tom Assocs., LLC.

—Dragon & Soldier: The Second Dragonback Adventure. rev. ed. 2004. (Dragonback Ser.). 304p. (J). 17.95 (978-0-7653-0125-3(3) , Tor Bks.) Doherty, Tom Assocs., LLC.

Zhang, Song Nan. A Time of Golden Dragons. ed. 2004. (J). (gr. 3-5). spiral bd. (978-0-616-07258-5(9)) Canadian National Institute for the Blind/Institut National Canadien pour les Aveugles.

Ziefert, Harriet. William & the Dragon. Brown, Richard, illus. 2005. 36p. (ps-ps). 15.95 (978-1-59354-089-0(2)) Blue Apple Bks.

Zinnen, Linda. The Dragons of Spratt, Ohio. 2004. 240p. (J). 15.99 (978-0-06-000021-9(X)) ; lib. bdg. 17.89 (978-0-06-000022-6(8)) HarperCollins Pubs.

DRAKE, FRANCIS, SIR, 1540?-1596

Champion, Neil. Sir Francis Drake. (Groundbreakers Ser.). (Illus.). 48p. (J). (gr. 5-7). 2002. pap. 8.50 (978-1-58810-372-7(2) , 91098); 2001. lib. bdg. 25.64 (978-1-58810-048-1(0)) Heinemann Library.

Crompton, Samuel Willard. Francis Drake & the Oceans of the World. 2005. (Explorers of New Worlds Ser.). (Illus.). 160p. (J). (gr. 4-8). 30.00 (978-0-7910-8615-5(1) , Chelsea Hse.) Facts On File, Inc.

Gallagher, Jim. Sir Francis Drake & the Foundation of a World Empire. 2000. (Explorers of the New World Ser.). (Illus.). 63p. (J). (gr. 4-7). pap. 25.00 (978-0-7910-6160-2(4)); (gr. 8-12). 31.00 (978-0-7910-5950-0(2)) Facts On File, Inc. (Chelsea Hse.).

—Sir Francis Drake & the Foundation of a World Empire. 2001. (gr. 3-6). lib. bdg. 17.60 (978-0-613-33057-2(9)) Tandem Library Bks.

Henty, G. A. Under Drake's Flag: A Tale of the Spanish Main. Browne, Gordon, illus. 1998. 298p. (J). lib. bdg. 20.99 (978-1-887159-15-9(0)) Preston-Speed Pubns.

Hoogenboom, Lynn. Sir Francis Drake: A Primary Source Portrait. 2006. (J). lib. bdg. (978-1-4042-3035-4(1) , PowerKids Pr.) Rosen Publishing Group, Inc., The.

Kline, Trish. Sir Francis Drake. (Rourke Discovery Library). 2003. (Illus.). 24p. (gr. 2-5). 14.95 (978-1-58952-295-4(8)); 2002. (J). lib. bdg. 19.27 (978-1-58952-429-3(2)) Rourke Publishing, LLC.

Larkin, Tanya. Sir Francis Drake. 2001. (Famous Explorers Ser.). (Illus.). 24p. (J). (gr. 3). lib. bdg. 18.75 (978-0-8239-5556-5(7) , PowerKids Pr.) Rosen Publishing Group, Inc., The.

Petrie, Kristin. Sir Francis Drake. 2004. (Explorers Ser.). (Illus.). 32p. (J). (gr. k-6). lib. bdg. 22.78 (978-1-59197-601-1(4) , Checkerboard Library) ABDO Publishing Co.

Rice, Earle. Sir Francis Drake, Navigator & Pirate. 2002. (Great Explorations Ser.). (Illus.). 76p. (J). 29.93 (978-0-7614-1483-4(5) , Benchmark Bks.) Cavendish, Marshall Corp.

Stewart, David. You Wouldn't Want to Explore with Sir Francis Drake! A Pirate You'd Rather Not Know. Antram, David, illus. 2005. (You Wouldn't Want to... Ser.). 32p. (J). (gr. 2-5). 28.50 (978-0-531-12413-0(4)); pap. 9.95 (978-0-531-12393-5(6)) Scholastic Library Publishing. (Watts, Franklin).

DRAKE, FRANCIS, SIR, 1540?-1596—FICTION

Cadnum, Michael. Ship of Fire. 2003. 208p. (J). (gr. 7). 16.99 (978-0-670-89907-4(0) , Viking Juvenile) Penguin Group (USA) Inc.

Henty, A. G. Under Drakes Flag A Tale of the Spanish. 2007. 97.99 (*978-1-4280-5259-8(3)); pap. 91.99 (*978-1-4280-5245-1(3)) IndyPublish.com.

Lawlor, Laurie. Dead Reckoning: A Pirate Voyage with Captain Drake. 2007. 336p. (J). pap. 5.99 (978-0-689-86578-7(3) , Aladdin) Simon & Schuster Children's Publishing.

Lawlor, Laurie & Barkat, Jonathan. Dead Reckoning: A Pirate Voyage with Captain Drake. 2005. (Illus.). 272p. (J). 15.95 (978-0-689-86577-0(5) , Simon & Schuster Children's Publishing) Simon & Schuster Children's Publishing.

DRAMA—COLLECTIONS

see also American Drama—Collections; Christmas Plays

Foxton, David. Sepia & Song. 2003. (Drama Anthologies Ser.). (Illus.). 148p. (Orig.). (YA). (gr. 6-12). pap. 15.00 (978-0-333-40923-7(X)) Macmillan Education, Ltd. GBR. *Dist:* Players Pr., Inc.

Garrett, Dan, ed. Friends & Neighbors. 2003. (Drama Workshop Plays Ser.). (Illus.). 96p. (Orig.). (YA). (gr. 6-12). pap. 15.00 (978-0-333-36054-5(0)) Macmillan Education, Ltd. GBR. *Dist:* Players Pr., Inc.

—Girls. 2003. (Drama Anthologies Ser.). (Illus.). 86p. (Orig.). (YA). pap. 15.00 (978-0-333-46708-4(6)) Macmillan Education, Ltd. GBR. *Dist:* Players Pr., Inc.

—Masks & Faces. 5th ed. 2003. (Drama Workshop Plays Ser.). (Illus.). 96p. (Orig.). (YA). (gr. 6-12). pap. 15.00 (978-0-333-36056-9(7)) Macmillan Education, Ltd. GBR. *Dist:* Players Pr., Inc.

—Scapegoats. 3rd ed. 2003. (Drama Workshop Plays Ser.). (Illus.). 96p. (Orig.). (YA). (gr. 6-12). pap. 15.00 (978-0 333 36055-2(9)) Macmillan Education, Ltd. GBR. *Dist:* Players Pr., Inc.

Hezlep, William, ed. Trouble in the Mountains. 2003. (Players Press Classic Plays Ser.). 20p. (J). (gr. 3-8). pap. 7.50 (978-0-88734-862-4(9)) Players Pr., Inc.

Kamerman, Sylvia E., ed. The Big Book of Holiday Plays. 2001. 335p. (J). (ps-12). 16.95 (978-0-8238-0291-3(4)) Kalmbach Publishing Co., Bks. Div.

Lambert, Alan & Scott-Hughes, Brian. Junior Drama Workshop. 2003. (Drama Anthologies Ser.). (Illus.). 96p. (Orig.). (YA). (gr. 4-12). pap. 15.00 (978-0-333-43459-8(5)) Macmillan Education, Ltd. GBR. *Dist:* Players Pr., Inc.

Pugliano, Carol. Just Right Plays: 25 Emergent Reader Plays Around the Year. 1999. 64p. pap. 10.95 (978-0-439-10564-4(1)) Scholastic, Inc.

DRAMA—HISTORY AND CRITICISM

see also American Drama—History and Criticism

Dramentexte Analysieren. (Duden Abiturhilfen Ser.). (GER.). 112p. (YA). (gr. 12-13). (978-3-411-70131-5(5)) Bibliographisches Institut & F. A. Brockhaus AG DEU. *Dist:* International Bk. Import Service, Inc.

Harcourt School Publishers Staff. The Birth of the Drama Advanced Level. 3rd ed. 2002. (Trophies Reading Program Ser.). (Illus.). pap. 5.10 (978-0-15-323474-3(1)) Harcourt Schl. Pubs.

Kamerman, Sylvia E., ed. Plays of Great Achievers. 2001. 364p. (gr. 4-9). 16.95 (978-0-8238-0297-5(3)) Kalmbach Publishing Co., Bks. Div.

McDonnell, Kathleen. Putting on a Show: Theater for Young People. 2005. (Illus.). 199p. (J). pap. 11.95 (978-1-896764-89-4(4)) Second Story Pr. CAN. *Dist:* Orca Bk. Pubs. USA, Univ. of Toronto Pr.

Pickering, Kenneth. Drama in the Cathedral: The Twentieth Century Encounter of Church & Stage. 2nd ed. 2003. (Illus.). 384p. (J). pap. 25.00 (978-0-85343-627-0(4)) Miller, J. Garnet Ltd. GBR. *Dist:* Empire Publishing Service.

DRAMA—STUDY AND TEACHING

Antigone. 1998. 40p. (YA). 11.95 (978-1-56137-745-9(7) , NU7457SP) Novel Units, Inc.

McCaslin, Nellie. Children & Drama. Landes, William Alan, ed. 3rd rev. ed. 2003. (Illus.). 288p. (YA). (gr. 8-12). pap. 40.00 (978-0-88734-662-0(6)) Players Pr., Inc.

O'Neill, Eugene. Long Day's Journey into Night. 1998. 40p. (YA). 11.95 (978-1-58130-565-4(6) , NU5656SP) Novel Units, Inc.

Tanner, Fran A. Basic Drama Projects. 7th ed. 1999. (Illus.). (YA). (gr. 9-12). pap. 30.00 (978-0-931054-56-3(7)); 50.00 (978-0-931054-52-5(4)) Clark Publishing, Inc.

DRAMA—TECHNIQUE

Burkholder, Kelly. Plays. 2000. (Artistic Adventures Ser.). (Illus.). 24p. (J). (gr. 2-6). lib. bdg. 23.93 (978-1-57103-357-4(2)) Rourke Publishing, LLC.

Cobb, Lisa Kaniut. Literary Ideas & Scripts for Young Playwrights. 2004. (Illus.). 192p. (J). pap. 30.00 (978-1-59158-071-3(4) , LU0714, Teacher Ideas Pr.) Libraries Unlimited, Inc.

Korty, Carol. Writing Your Own Plays: Creating, Adapting, Improvising. 2nd ed. 2003. (Writing & Publishing Ser.). 192p. (YA). (gr. 6-12). pap. 17.00 (978-0-88734-668-2(5)) Players Pr., Inc.

Peterson, Debra A. Playwriting: A Manual for Beginners. 1999. 51p. (gr. 10 up). pap. 9.95 (978-0-87129-822-5(8) , P85) Dramatic Publishing Co.

Poets & Playwrights, 5 vols., Set. Incl. Carl Sandburg. Murcia, Rebecca Thatcher. lib. bdg. 37.10 (978-1-58415-430-3(6)); Emily Dickinson. Griskey, Michele. lib. bdg. 37.10 (978-1-58415-429-7(2)); Langston Hughes. Gibson, Karen Bush. lib. bdg. 37.10 (978-1-58415-431-0(4)); Tennessee Williams. Tracy, Kathleen. lib. bdg. 37.10 (978-1-58415-427-3(6)); William Shakespeare. Whiting, Jim. lib. bdg. 37.10 (978-1-58415-426-6(8)); (Illus.). 112p. (YA). (gr. 6-12). 2006. 2007. Set lib. bdg. 185.50 (*978-1-58415-284-2(2)) Mitchell Lane Pubs., Inc.

DRAMATIC MUSIC

see Opera; Operetta

DRAMATISTS

Allison, Amy. John Leguizamo. 2001. (Latinos in the Limelight Ser.). (Illus.). 64p. (J). (gr. 6-9). 27.50 (978-0-7910-6477-1(8) , Chelsea Hse.) Facts On File, Inc.

Ashworth, Leon. William Shakespeare. 2004. (British History Makers Ser.). (Illus.). 32p. (YA). pap. 11.99 (978-1-84234-284-8(3) , Cherrytree Books) Evans Publishing Group GBR. *Dist:* Independent Pubs. Group.

Bloom, Harold, ed. Tony Kushner. 2005. (Bloom's Modern Critical Views Ser.). (Illus.). 300p. (gr. 9-13). 45.00 (978-0-7910-8139-6(7) , Chelsea Hse.) Facts On File, Inc.

Bloom, Harold, et al. Bloom's Major Dramatists. 2005. (Illus.). 80-144p. (J). pap. 830.70 (978-0-7910-7376-6(9)) Facts On File, Inc.

Bloom's Major Dramatists Series, 24 vols., Set. Incl. Aeschylus. Bloom, Harold, ed. & intro. 120p. (YA). (gr. 8 up). 2001. 31.95 (978-0-7910-6355-2(0) , 040011, Chelsea Hse.); Anton Chekhov. Bloom, Harold. 120p. (YA). (gr. 8 up). 1999. 31.95 (978-0-7910-5243-3(5) , 040007, Chelsea Hse.); Aristophanes. Bloom, Harold. 120p. (YA). (gr. 8 up). 2002. 31.95 (978-0-7910-6358-3(5) , 040012, Chelsea Hse.); Arthur Miller. Bloom, Harold. 120p. (YA). (gr. 8 up). 1999. 31.95 (978-0-7910-5246-4(X) , 040010, Chelsea Hse.); Ben Jonson. Bloom, Harold, ed. & intro. 120p. (YA). (gr. 8 up). 2001. 31.95 (978-0-7910-6359-0(3) , 040015, Chelsea Hse.); Berthold Brecht. Bloom, Harold, ed. & intro. 120p. (YA). (gr. 8 up). 2002. 31.95 (978-0-7910-6363-7(1) , 040013, Chelsea Hse.); Christopher Marlowe. Bloom, Harold, ed. & intro. 120p. (YA). (gr. 8 up). 2001. 31.95 (978-0-7910-6357-6(7) , 040016, Chelsea Hse.); Eugene Ionesco. Erskine, Robb. Bloom, Harold, ed. (Illus.). 120p. (gr. 9-13). 2002. 31.95 (978-0-7910-7037-6(9) , 040021, Chelsea Hse.); Eugene O'Neill. Bloom, Harold. (Illus.). 80;144p. (YA). (gr. 9-13). 1999. 31.95 (978-0-7910-5245-7(1) , 040009); Euripides. Albertazzi, Anne Marie. Bloom, Harold, ed. (Illus.). 120p. (gr. 9-13). 2002. 31.95 (978-0-7910-6356-9(9) , 040014, Chelsea Hse.); George Bernard Shaw. Bloom, Harold. 120p. (YA). (gr. 8 up). 1999. 31.95 (978-0-7910-5237-2(0) , 040001, Chelsea Hse.); Henrik Ibsen. Bloom, Harold. (Illus.). 120p. (YA). (gr. 8 up). 1999. 31.95 (978-0-7910-5239-6(7) , 040003, Chelsea Hse.); Luigi Pirandello. Griffin, Patsy. Bloom, Harold, ed. (Illus.). 120p. (gr. 9-13). 2003. 31.95 (978-0-7910-7036-9(0) , 040023, Chelsea Hse.); Neil Simon. Bloom, Harold, ed. & intro. 120p. (YA). (gr. 8 up). 2001. 31.95 (978-0-7910-6360-6(7) , 040017, Chelsea Hse.); Oscar Wilde. Bloom, Harold, ed. & intro. 120p. (YA). (gr. 8 up). 2001. 31.95 (978-0-7910-6361-3(5) , 040020, Chelsea Hse.); Sam Shepard. Bloom, Harold & Albertazzi, Anne Marie, eds. (Illus.). 120p. (gr. 9-13). 2002. 31.95 (978-0-7910-7035-2(2) , 040024, Chelsea Hse.); Shakespeare's Comedies. Bloom, Harold. 120p. (YA). (gr. 8 up). 1999. 31.95 (978-0-7910-5238-9(9) , 040002, Chelsea Hse.); Shakespeare's Histories. Bloom, Harold. (Illus.). 120p. (YA). (gr. 8 up). 1999. 31.95 (978-0-7910-5241-9(9) , 040005, Chelsea Hse.); Shakespeare's Romances. Bloom, Harold. 120p. (YA). (gr. 8 up). 1999. 31.95 (978-0-7910-5244-0(3) , 040008, Chelsea Hse.); Shakespeare's Tragedies. Bloom, Harold. 120p. (YA). (gr. 8 up). 1999. 31.95 (978-0-7910-5242-6(7) , 040006, Chelsea Hse.); Sophocles. Marson, Janyce. Bloom, Harold, ed. (Illus.). 120p. (gr. 9-13). 2002. 31.95 (978-0-7910-6354-5(2) , 040018, Chelsea Hse.); Tennessee Williams. Bloom, Harold. (Illus.). 120p. (YA). (gr. 8 up). 1999. 31.95 (978-0-7910-5240-2(0) , 040004, Chelsea Hse.); Thornton Wilder. Bloom, Harold & Weiskel, Portia Williams, eds. (Illus.). 120p. (gr. 9-13). 2002. 31.95 (978-0-7910-7033-8(6) , 040026, Chelsea Hse.); Set lib. bdg. 550.80 (978-0-7910-7198-4(7) , 040000S, Chelsea Hse.) Facts On File, Inc.

Dommermuth-Costa, Carol. William Shakespeare. 2001. (Biography Ser.). (Illus.). 112p. (J). (gr. 6-12). lib. bdg. 27.93 (978-0-8225-4996-3(4) , Lerner Pubns.) Lerner Publishing Group.

Greenhill, Wendy & Wignall, Paul. Shakespeare: A Life. 2006. (Illus.). 32p. (978-1-4034-8609-7(3)) Heinemann Library.

—Shakespeare: Man of the Theater. 2000. (Illus.). 196p. (J). (gr. 8 up). lib. bdg. 28.50 (978-1-57572-282-5(8)) Heinemann Library.

Greenhill, Wendy & Wignall, Paul, contrib. by. Shakespeare: A Life. 2000. (Shakespeare Library). (Illus.). 32p. (J). lib. bdg. 21.36 (978-1-57572-287-0(9)) Heinemann Library.

Mannis, Celeste & Davidson, Mannis. Who Was William Shakespeare? John, Obrien, illus. 2006. (Who Was... ? Ser.). 112p. (J). (gr. 2-5). pap. 4.99 (978-0-448-43904-4(2) , Grosset & Dunlap) Penguin Group (USA) Inc.

Mittelstaedt, Walt. A Student's Guide to William Shakespeare. 2005. (Understanding Literature Ser.). (Illus.). 192p. (J). lib. bdg. 27.93 (978-0-7660-2284-3(6)) Enslow Pubs., Inc.

Nardo, Don. Great Elizabethan Playwrights. 2002. (Lucent Library of Historical Eras). (Illus.). 112p. (J). 32.45 (978-1-59018-017-4(8) , Lucent Bks.) Thomson Gale.

Perrin, Pat & Coleman, Wim. The Mystery of the Murdered Playwright. 2004. (Cover-To-Cover Books). (Illus.). 56p. pap. (*978-0-7891-6001-0(3)); (gr. 4-7). lib. bdg. 17.95 (*978-0-7569-1353-3(5)) Perfection Learning Corp.

Rocamore, Carol. Acts of Courage: Vaclav Havel's Life in the Theater. 2005. (Ultimate Audition Book for Middle School Actors Ser.: Vol. 1). (Illus.). xx, 490p. 35.00 (978-1-57525-344-2(5)) Smith and Kraus Publishers, Incorporated.

Rosen, Michael. Shakespeare: His Work & His World. Ingpen, Robert R., illus. 2006. 96p. (J). (gr. 7-11). pap. 9.99 (978-0-7636-3201-4(5)) Candlewick Pr.

Ross, Stewart. William Shakespeare. 2004. (Illus.). 48p. (J). lib. bdg. 28.56 (978-0-7398-6630-6(3)) Raintree.

Rostand, Edmond. Cyrano Bergerac: School Edition. 2001. (Illus.). (J). pap. 4.13 (978-0-03-001905-0(2)) Holt, Rinehart & Winston.

Scheader, Catherine. Lorraine Hansberry: Playwright & Voice of Justice. 1998. (African-American Biographies Ser.). (Illus.). 128p. (YA). (gr. 6-12). lib. bdg. 26.60 (978-0-89490-945-0(2)) Enslow Pubs., Inc.

Sinnott, Susan. Lorraine Hansberry: Award-Winning Playwright & Civil Rights Activist. 1999. (J). (978-0-606-19366-5(9)) Tandem Library Bks.

Smith-Howard, Alycia & Heintzelman, Greta. Critical Companion to Tennessee Williams: A Literary Reference to His Life & Work. (Critical Companion To Ser.). (Illus.). 448p. (gr. 9). pap. 19.95 (978-0-8160-6429-8(6) , Checkmark Bks.) Facts On File, Inc.

Stanley, Diane & Vennema, Peter. Bard of Avon: The Story of William Shakespeare. Stanley, Diane, illus. 1998. (Illus.). (J). (ps-ps). lib. bdg. 15.30 (978-0-613-09937-0(0)) Tandem Library Bks.

Summers, Ann. The George Bernard Shaw Papers. 2005. (British Library - Catalogue of Additions to the Manuscripts). (Illus.). 330p. 100.00 (*978-0-7123-4887-4(5)) British Library, The GBR. *Dist:* Chicago Distribution Ctr.

DRAUGHTS

see Checkers

DRAWING

see also Anatomy, Artistic; Crayon Drawing; Design, Decorative; Drawings; Figure Drawing; Geometrical Drawing; Graphic Methods; Illustration of Books; Mechanical Drawing; Pastel Drawing; Pencil Drawing; Perspective; Shadows

Abraham, Philip. How to Draw the Life & Times of George Washington. 2005. (Kid's Guide to Drawing the Presidents of the United States of America Ser.). (J). lib. bdg. 31.95 (978-1-4042-0364-8(8) , PowerKids Pr.) Rosen Publishing Group, Inc., The.

Accord Publishing, Ltd. Staff, ed. African Safari Drawing Book. 2004. (Illus.). 48p. (J). spiral bd. 12.99 (978-1-57939-133-1(8)) Accord Publishing, Ltd.

—Eyeball Animation Drawing Book: Creatures Edition. 2004. (Illus.). 48p. (J). spiral bd. 12.99 (978-1-57939-134-8(6)) Accord Publishing, Ltd.

—Eyeball Animation Drawing Book: People Edition. 2004. (Illus.). 48p. (J). spiral bd. 12.99 (978-1-57939-131-7(1)) Accord Publishing, Ltd.

—Eyeball Animation Drawing Book: Under the Sea Edition. 2004. (Illus.). 48p. (J). spiral bd. 12.99 (978-1-57939-132-4(X)) Accord Publishing, Ltd.

Ames, Lee J. Draw 50 Baby Animals: The Step-by-Step Way to Draw Kittens, Lambs, Chicks & Other Adorable Offspring. Zak, Murray, illus. 2003. 64p. pap. 8.95 (978-0-7679-1284-6(5) , Broadway) Broadway Bks.

Ames, Lee J. & Estrada, Ric. Draw 50 Aliens: UFOS, Galaxy Ghouls, Milky Way Marauders, & Other Extraterrestrial Creatures. 1998. (Illus.). 64p. pap. 8.95 (978-0-385-49145-7(X) , Broadway) Broadway Bks.

The Art of Drawing the Male Form: Artistic Anatomy Drawing Series. 2003. (Illus.). 60p. 20.00 (978-0-9747389-4-9(8)); 35.00 (978-0-9747389-5-6(6)) Hensley, Michael.

Artell, Mike. Cartooning for Kids. 2002. (Illus.). 128p. pap. 9.95 (978-1-4027-0111-5(X)) Sterling Publishing Co., Inc.

—Cartooning for Kids. 2002. (gr. 3-6). lib. bdg. 18.75 (978-0-613-84767-4(9)) Tandem Library Bks.

—Oodles of Doodles. 2003. (Illus.). 256p. pap. 5.95 (978-0-8069-9366-9(9)) Sterling Publishing Co., Inc.

Baker, Michael. Thinker Doodles: Think, Draw, & Color: Beginning Clues & Choose. 2005. (J). pap. 8.99 (978-0-89455-869-6(2)) Critical Thinking Bks. & Software.

—Thinker Doodles Clues & Choose A1: Think, Draw, & Color. 2005. (J). pap. 8.99 (978-0-89455-870-2(6)) Critical Thinking Bks. & Software.

Barlowe, Dot. Birds to Paint or Color. 2006. 48p. (J). pap. 4.95 (978-0-486-45171-8(2)) Dover Pubns., Inc.

Barr, Steve. 1-2-3 Draw Cartoon Aliens & Space Stuff: A Step-by-Step Guide. 2003. (One-Two-Three Draw Ser.). (Illus.). 64p. (J). pap. 8.99 (978-0-939217-71-7(6)) Peel Productions, Inc.

—1-2-3 Draw Cartoon Aliens & Space Stuff: A Step-by-Step Guide. 2003. (gr. k-3). lib. bdg. 17.60 (978-0-613-87983-5(X)) Tandem Library Bks.

—1-2-3 Draw Cartoon Animals: A Step-by-Step Guide. 2002. (One-Two-Three Draw Ser.). (Illus.). 64p. (J). (gr. 1). pap. 8.99 (978-0-939217-48-9(1)) Peel Productions, Inc.

—1-2-3 Draw Cartoon Animals: A Step-by-Step Guide. 2002. (gr. k-3). lib. bdg. 17.60 (978-0-613-86905-8(2)) Tandem Library Bks.

—1-2-3 Draw Cartoon Cars: A Step-By-Step Guide. 2005. (Illus.). 64p. (J). pap. 8.99 (978-0-939217-75-5(9)) Peel Productions, Inc.

—1-2-3 Draw Cartoon Faces: A Step-by-Step Guide. 2002. (One-Two-Three Draw Ser.). (Illus.). 64p. (J). (gr. 1). pap. 8.99 (978-0-939217-47-2(3)) Peel Productions, Inc.

—1-2-3 Draw Cartoon People: A Step-by-Step Guide. 2002. (One-Two-Three Draw Ser.). (Illus.). 64p. (J). (gr. 1). pap. 8.99 (978-0-939217-46-5(5)) Peel Productions, Inc.

—1-2-3 Draw Cartoon People: A Step-by-Step Guide. 2002. (gr. k-3). lib. bdg. 17.60 (978-0-613-89960-4(1)) Tandem Library Bks.

Baugh, Bryan. Draw Future Worlds. 1998. (Illus.). 64p. (J). (gr. 4-7). pap. 7.95 (978-1-56565-925-4(2) , 09252W) Lowell Hse. Juvenile.

—Predators. Pederson, Jason, illus. 2001. (Draw Science Ser.). 64p. (J). (gr. 2-6). pap. 7.95 (978-0-7373-0504-3(5)) Lowell Hse. Juvenile.

—50 Nifty Dinosaurs to Draw. 1999. (Fifty Nifty Ser.). (Illus.). 96p. (J). (gr. 2-6). pap. 6.95 (978-0-7373-0198-4(8) , 01988W) McGraw-Hill/Contemporary.

Beilenson, Suzanne. Rain Forest Scratch & Sketch: An Art Activity Book for Adventurous Artists & Explorers of All Ages. 2007. (Illus.). 64p. (YA). 12.99 ***978-1-59359-862-4(9)*** Peter Pauper Pr. Inc.

Bernard, Robin. Quickart Crayon Projects: 25 Instant Activities That Bring Out the Creativity in Every Child. 1999. (Illus.). 64p. pap. 10.95 (978-0-590-98339-6(3)) Scholastic, Inc.

The Best Workbook of Drawing Practice for Very Young Children. 2006. (Illus.). (J). (ps-3). pap. 14.95 (978-0-9773205-0-9(2)) Godinez-Hammermaster Design.

The Big Yellow Drawing Book, Newsprint Edition. 2005. wbk. ed. (978-0-9675919-4-0(5)) O'Neill, Hugh & Associates.

Billman, Hilary Barton. How to Draw the Life & Times of William Henry Harrison. 2006. (Kid's Guide to Drawing the Presidents of the United States of America Ser.). (Illus.). 32p. (J). 25.25 (978-1-4042-2986-0(8) , PowerKids Pr.) Rosen Publishing Group, Inc., The.

Blake, Quentin & Cassidy, John. Drawing for the Artistically Undiscovered. Blake, Quentin, illus. 1999. (Illus.). 106p. (J). (gr. 4-7). spiral bd. 19.95 (978-1-57054-320-3(8)) Klutz.

Booth, Scott, illus. How to Draw Superheroes & Super Villains. 2003. 64p. (J). (978-0-439-55133-5(1)) Scholastic, Inc.

Bramich, Melvin, illus. Create Your Own Masterpiece: On a Journey Through Art. 2005. 48p. (J). (ps). pap. 7.95 (978-1-84507-450-0(5)) Lincoln, Frances Ltd. GBR. *Dist:* Perseus Distribution.

Bratun, Katy. Drawing Cats. Bratun, Katy, illus. 2002. (Books & Stuff Ser.). (Illus.). 64p. (J). pap. 7.99 (978-0-448-42595-5(5) , Grosset & Dunlap) Penguin Group (USA) Inc.

—Drawing Cats. 2002. (gr. 3-6). lib. bdg. 15.30 (978-0-613-72440-1(2)) Tandem Library Bks.

—The Drawing Dogs. 2003. (Illus.). 64p. (J). (gr. 2). pap. 6.99 (978-0-448-43173-4(4) , Grosset & Dunlap) Penguin Group (USA) Inc.

—Drawing Dogs. 2003. (gr. 3-6). lib. bdg. 15.30 (978-0-613-72475-3(5)) Tandem Library Bks.

Buster's Adventures Activity Workbook. 2001. (J). (978-0-9653871-6-3(X)) Frederick Pr.

Butkus, Mike. Drawing, Bk. 1. Foster, Walter T., ed. 2003. (How to Draw & Paint Ser.). Orig. Title: Starting Out Drawing. (Illus.). 32p. (J). (gr. k-6). pap. 7.95 (978-1-56010-484-1(8)) Foster, Walter Publishing, Inc.

Canfield, Judy. How to Draw a Dinosaur. 2000. (gr. k-3). lib. bdg. 11.80 (978-0-613-29644-1(3)) Tandem Library Bks.

Catlow, Nikalas. Do You Doodle? 2007. 256p. (J). pap. 12.95 ***978-0-7624-2927-1(5)*** , Running Pr. Kids) Running Pr. Bk. Pubs.

Celia, Shannon Casey. Nature's Music, 2003. (Illus.). 12p. (J). spiral bd. 10.95 (978-1-931844-07-9(0) , PP1019) Piano Pr.

Conor, William. Titan a E How to Draw. 2000. (gr. 3-6). lib. bdg. 15.30 (978-0-613-82378-4(8)) Tandem Library Bks.

Conroy, Don. Spooks. 2000. (Draw with Don Ser.: No. 1). 31p. (J). (gr. 1-4). pap. (978-1-84210-027-1(0)) Mentor Bks.

—Wildlife. 2000. (Draw with Don Ser.: No. 5). 31p. pap. (978-1-84210-029-5(7)) Mentor Bks.

Coope, Katy. How to Draw More Manga. Coope, Katy, illus. 2004. 64p. (J). (gr. 2-5). pap. 6.99 (978-0-439-58560-6(0)) Scholastic, Inc.

Coupe, Peter. A Beginner's Guide to Drawing Comics, Caricatures & Cartoon Strips. Coupe, Peter, illus. 2004. (Illus.). 80p. (YA). (gr. 5-10). reprint ed. pap. 15.00 (978-0-7567-7306-9(7)) DIANE Publishing Co.

Court, Rob. How to Draw Action Sports Figures. 2005. (Scribbles Institute). (Illus.). 32p. (J). (gr. 1-5). 24.21 (978-1-59296-147-4(9)) Child's World, Inc.

—How to Draw Cars & Trucks. 2005. (Scribbles Institute). (Illus.). 32p. (J). (gr. 1-5). 24.21 (978-1-59296-148-1(7)) Child's World, Inc.

—How to Draw Cartoons. 2005. (Scribbles Institute). (Illus.). 32p. (J). (gr. 1-5). 24.21 (978-1-59296-149-8(5)) Child's World, Inc.

—How to Draw Dinosaurs. 2005. (Scribbles Institute). (Illus.). 32p. (J). (gr. 1-5). 24.21 (978-1-59296-150-4(9)) Child's World, Inc.

—How to Draw Faces. 2005. (Scribbles Institute). (Illus.). 32p. (J). (gr. 1-5). 24.21 (978-1-59296-151-1(7)) Child's World, Inc.

—How to Draw Things in Nature. 2005. (Scribbles Institute). (Illus.). 32p. (J). (gr. 1-5). 24.21 (978-1-59296-152-8(5)) Child's World, Inc.

Cranium Inc. Staff & Baseman. Cranium: the Creative Cat Book of Outrageous Fun! Draw it, Sculpt it, Build It! 2006. (Illus.). 38p. (J). (gr. 2-17). 14.99 (978-0-316-05760-8(6)) Little, Brown Bks. for Young Readers.

Dalmatian Press Staff. Drawing & Writing: Practice Tablet. 2002. (Home Learning Tools Ser.). (Illus.). 32p. (J). (gr. k-1). 2.99 (978-1-57759-232-7(8)) Dalmatian Pr.

Davies, Carolyn. Josef Herman in Wales. 2004. (Illus.). 31p. pap. 15.95 (978-1-85902-999-2(X)) Beekman Bks., Inc.

Davis, Billy. Design My Ride. 2006. (J). 9.99 (978-0-439-77764-3(X) , Tangerine Pr.) Scholastic, Inc.

de Rosamel, Godeleine. Drawing Is Easy, 5 bks. de Rosamel, Godeleine, illus. Incl. Drawing with Circles. lib. bdg. 22.00 (978-0-8368-3625-7(1)); Drawing with Nature. lib. bdg. 22.00 (978-0-8368-3626-4(X)); Drawing with Objects. lib. bdg. 22.00 (978-0-8368-3627-1(8)); Drawing with Your Fingerprints. lib. bdg. 22.00 (978-0-8368-3628-8(6)); Drawing with Your Hands. lib. bdg. 22.00 (978-0-8368-3629-5(4)); 24p. (J). (ps up). 2003. (Illus.). 2002. Set lib. bdg. 110.00 (978-0-8368-3624-0(3)) Stevens, Gareth Inc.

—Drawing with Circles. de Rosamel, Godeleine, illus. 2003. (Drawing Is Easy Ser.). (Illus.). 24p. (J). (ps up). lib. bdg. 22.00 (978-0-8368-3625-7(1)) Stevens, Gareth Inc.

—Drawing with Nature. de Rosamel, Godeleine, illus. 2003. (Drawing Is Easy Ser.). (Illus.). 24p. (J). (ps up). lib. bdg. 22.00 (978-0-8368-3626-4(X)) Stevens, Gareth Inc.

—Drawing with Objects. de Rosamel, Godeleine, illus. 2003. (Drawing Is Easy Ser.). (Illus.). 24p. (J). (ps up). lib. bdg. 22.00 (978-0-8368-3627-1(8)) Stevens, Gareth Inc.

—Drawing with Your Fingerprints. de Rosamel, Godeleine, illus. 2003. (Drawing Is Easy Ser.). (Illus.). 24p. (J). (ps up). lib. bdg. 22.00 (978-0-8368-3628-8(6)) Stevens, Gareth Inc.

—Drawing with Your Hands. de Rosamel, Godeleine, illus. 2003. (Drawing Is Easy Ser.). (Illus.). 24p. (J). (ps up). lib. bdg. 22.00 (978-0-8368-3629-5(4)) Stevens, Gareth Inc.

Deinard, Jenny. How to Draw Indianas Sights & Symbols. 2002. (Kids Guide to Drawing America Ser.). 32p. (J). lib. bdg. 25.25 (978-0-8239-6070-5(6) , PowerKids Pr.) Rosen Publishing Group, Inc., The.

—How to Draw Iowas Sights & Symbols. 2002. (Kids Guide to Drawing America Ser.). 32p. (J). lib. bdg. 25.25 (978-0-8239-6071-2(4) , PowerKids Pr.) Rosen Publishing Group, Inc., The.

—How to Draw Kansas Sights & Symbols. 2002. (Kids Guide to Drawing America Ser.). 32p. (J). lib. bdg. 25.25 (978-0-8239-6072-9(2) , PowerKids Pr.) Rosen Publishing Group, Inc., The.

—How to Draw Kentuckys Sights & Symbols. 2002. (Kids Guide to Drawing America Ser.). 32p. (J). lib. bdg. 25.25 (978-0-8239-6073-6(0) , PowerKids Pr.) Rosen Publishing Group, Inc., The.

—How to Draw Louisianas Sights & Symbols. 2002. (Kids Guide to Drawing America Ser.). 32p. (J). lib. bdg. 25.25 (978-0-8239-6074-3(9) , PowerKids Pr.) Rosen Publishing Group, Inc., The.

—How to Draw Maines Sights & Symbols. 2002. (Kids Guide to Drawing America Ser.). 32p. (J). lib. bdg. 25.25 (978-0-8239-6075-0(7) , PowerKids Pr.) Rosen Publishing Group, Inc., The.

—How to Draw Marylands Sights & Symbols. 2002. (Kids Guide to Drawing America Ser.). 32p. (J). lib. bdg. 25.25 (978-0-8239-6076-7(5) , PowerKids Pr.) Rosen Publishing Group, Inc., The.

—How to Draw Michigans Sights & Symbols. 2002. (Kids Guide to Drawing America Ser.). 32p. (J). lib. bdg. 25.25 (978-0-8239-6078-1(1) , PowerKids Pr.) Rosen Publishing Group, Inc., The.

DeLong, Ron. Crayola (R) Dream-Makers (R) 11: Drawing on Character. DeLong, Ron, ed. 2004. per. 6.00 (978-0-86696-317-6(0)) Binney & Smith, Inc.

Le Dessin Anime. 2002. (How to Draw & Paint Ser.). Orig. Title: Animation 1 with Preston Blair. (FRE.). pap. 7.95 (978-1-56010-670-8(0)) Foster, Walter Publishing, Inc.

Le Dessin Au Crayon de Couleur. 2002. (How to Draw & Paint Ser.). Orig. Title: Drawing - Colored Pencil. (FRE., Illus.). pap. 7.95 (978-1-56010-674-6(3)) Foster, Walter Publishing, Inc.

Dessiner les Animaux. 2002. (How to Draw & Paint Ser.). Orig. Title: Drawing - Animals. (FRE.). pap. 7.95 (978-1-56010-669-2(7)) Foster, Walter Publishing, Inc.

Dickins, Rosie. Drawing Faces. 2002. (gr. 5-8). lib. bdg. 17.60 (978-0-613-75314-2(3)) Tandem Library Bks.

Dickins, Rosie & McCafferty, Jan. Drawing Faces. 2004. (Art Ideas Ser.). (Illus.). 64p. (J). pap. 8.99 (978-0-7945-0097-9(8) , Usborne); lib. bdg. 16.99 (978-1-58086-382-7(5)) EDC Publishing.

Disney. Disney Fairies: Learn to Draw the Fairies of Pixie Hollow. 2006. (Disney Magic Artist Learn to Draw Bks.). 32p. (J). pap. 5.95 (978-1-56010-958-7(0)) Foster, Walter Publishing, Inc.

Disney-Pixar Creative Development Team. Pixar. Foster, Walter, ed. Disney-Pixar Creative Development Team, illus. 2005. (DMA Learn to Draw Ser.). 32p. (J). pap. 5.95 (978-1-56010-886-3(X)) Foster, Walter Publishing, Inc.

Doodle: Drawing Faces, Cartooning & Caricatures. 2000. 21p. (J). pap., wbk. ed. 19.95 incl. VHS (978-0-9674428-1-5(8)) Interlight Studios, Inc.

Douglas, Vincent & School Specialty Publishing Staff. Let's Make Funny Faces. 2002. (Edu-Slates Ser.). (Illus.). 1p. (J). 2.99 (978-1-57768-999-7(2) , Brighter Child) School Specialty Publishing.

Dover Staff. Design Discovery Coloring Book. 2006. (Illus.). 32p. pap. 3.95 (978-0-486-45109-1(7)) Dover Pubns., Inc.

DPWW. Draw Mickey Kit. 1999. (J). 12.95 (978-0-7868-3222-4(3)) Disney Pr.

Draw 50 Airplanes, Aircraft & Spacecraft. 2002. (Draw 50 Ser.). (Illus.). (J). 17.60 (978-0-7587-4700-6(4)) Book Wholesalers, Inc.

Draw 50 Aliens: Ufos, Galaxy Ghouls, Milky Way Mauraunders, & Other Extraterrestrial Creatures. 2002. (Draw 50 Ser.). (Illus.). (J). 17.60 (978-0-7587-4132-5(4)) Book Wholesalers, Inc.

Draw 50 Animals. 2002. (Draw 50 Ser.). (Illus.). (J). 17.60 (978-0-7587-5314-4(4)) Book Wholesalers, Inc.

Draw 50 Athletes. 2002. (Draw 50 Ser.). (Illus.). (J). 17.60 (978-0-7587-4160-8(X)) Book Wholesalers, Inc.

Draw 50 Beasties & Yugglies & Turnover Uglies & Things That Go Bump in the Night. 2002. (Draw 50 Ser.). (Illus.). (J). 17.60 (978-0-7587-4704-4(7)) Book Wholesalers, Inc.

Draw 50 Boats, Ships, Trucks & Trains. 2002. (Draw 50 Ser.). (Illus.). (J). 17.60 (978-0-7587-6968-8(7)) Book Wholesalers, Inc.

Draw 50 Cars, Trucks, & Motorcycles. 2002. (Draw 50 Ser.). (Illus.). (J). 17.60 (978-0-7587-0011-7(3)) Book Wholesalers, Inc.

Draw 50 Cats. 2002. (Draw 50 Ser.). (J). 17.60 (978-0-7587-4162-2(6)) Book Wholesalers, Inc.

Draw 50 Creepy Crawlies. 2002. (Draw 50 Ser.). (Illus.). (J). 17.60 (978-0-7587-4561-3(3)) Book Wholesalers, Inc.

Draw 50 Dinosaurs & Other Prehistoric Animals. 2002. (Draw 50 Ser.). (Illus.). (J). 17.60 (978-0-7587-4163-9(4)) Book Wholesalers, Inc.

Draw 50 Dogs. 2002. (Draw 50 Ser.). (Illus.). (J). 17.60 (978-0-7587-4164-6(2)) Book Wholesalers, Inc.

Draw 50 Endangered Animals. 2002. (Draw 50 Ser.). (Illus.). (J). 17.60 (978-0-7587-4707-5(1)) Book Wholesalers, Inc.

Draw 50 Holiday Decorations. 2002. (Draw 50 Ser.). (Illus.). (J). 17.60 (978-0-7587-4703-7(9)) Book Wholesalers, Inc.

Draw 50 Horses. 2002. (Illus.). (J). 17.60 (978-0-7587-4165-3(0)) Book Wholesalers, Inc.

Draw 50 Monsters, Creeps, Superheroes, Demons, Dragons, Nerds, Dirts, Ghouls, Giants, Vampires, Zombies, & Other Curiosa. 2002. (Draw 50 Ser.). (Illus.). (J). 17.60 (978-0-7587-4166-0(9)) Book Wholesalers, Inc.

Draw 50 People from the Bible. 2002. (Draw 50 Ser.). (Illus.). (J). 17.60 (978-0-7587-6506-2(1)) Book Wholesalers, Inc.

Draw 50 Sharks, Whales, & Other Sea Creatures. 2002. (Draw 50 Ser.). (Illus.). (J). 17.60 (978-0-7587-6970-1(9)) Book Wholesalers, Inc.

Draw 50 Trees, Flowers, & Other Plants. 2002. (Draw 50 Ser.). (Illus.). (J). 17.60 (978-0-7587-6969-5(5)) Book Wholesalers, Inc.

Draw 50 Vehicles: Selections from Draw 50 Boats, Ships, Trucks, And Trains, & Draw 50 Airplanes, Aircraft, And Spacecraft. 2002. (Draw 50 Ser.). (Illus.). (J). 17.60 (978-0-7587-6971-8(7)) Book Wholesalers, Inc.

Draw It!, 10 vols., Set. 2003. (Illus.). (J). (gr. 3-5). lib. bdg. 242.20 (978-1-4034-0215-8(9)) Heinemann Library.

Drawing Animals Kid Kit. 2004. (Illus.). 64p. (J). 17.95 (978-1-58086-527-2(5)) EDC Publishing.

Drawing Cartoons. 2004. (I-Quest Ser.). (J). (978-1-84229-756-8(2)) Top That! Publishing PLC.

Drawing on the Go! (Learning Ser.). 22p. (J). bds. (978-2-7643-0165-4(0)) Phidal Publishing, Inc./Editions Phidal, Inc.

DuBosque, Doug. Draw 3-D: A Step-by-Step Guide to Perspective Drawing. 1999. (gr. 5-8). lib. bdg. 17.60 (978-0-613-87985-9(6)) Tandem Library Bks.

—Draw 3-D Vol. 2: A Step-by-Step Guide to Perspective Drawing. DuBosque, Doug, illus. rev. ed. 2000. (Learn to Draw Ser.). (Illus.). 64p. (J). (gr. 6-9). pap. 8.99 (978-0-939217-14-4(7)) Peel Productions, Inc.

—Draw Cars, Vol. 12. rev. ed. 2000. (Learn to Draw Ser.). (Illus.). 64p. (J). (gr. 6-9). pap. 8.99 (978-0-939217-29-8(5)) Peel Productions, Inc.

—Draw Insects. 2000. (Learn to Draw Ser.). (Illus.). 64p. (J). (gr. 6-9). pap. 8.99 (978-0-939217-28-1(7)) Peel Productions, Inc.

—Learn to Draw Now. DuBosque, Doug, illus. 2000. (Learn to Draw Ser.). (Illus.). 64p. (J). (gr. 6-9). pap. 8.99 (978-0-939217-16-8(3)) Peel Productions, Inc.

Dunn, Ben. How to Draw Manga. 2004. (Illus.). 344p. (YA). pap. 3.25 (978-1-59412-063-3(3)) Mud Puddle, Inc.

Emberley, Ed. Ed Emberley's Complete Funprint Drawing Book. 2002. (gr. k-3). lib. bdg. 21.05 (978-0-613-71783-0(X)) Tandem Library Bks.

—Ed Emberley's Drawing Book of Trucks & Trains. Emberley, Ed, illus. 2005. (Illus.). 32p. (J). (gr. 2-17). pap. 6.99 (978-0-316-78967-7(4)) Little, Brown Bks. for Young Readers.

—Ed Emberley's Drawing Book of Weirdos. 2005. (Illus.). 32p. (J). (gr. 2-17). pap. 6.99 (978-0-316-78971-4(2)) Little, Brown Bks. for Young Readers.

—Ed Emberley's Drawing Book of Weirdos. 2002. (gr. 3-6). lib. bdg. 16.40 (978-0-613-52750-7(X)) Tandem Library Bks.

—Ed Emberley's Fingerprint Drawing Book. Emberley, Ed, illus. 2005. (Illus.). 48p. (J). (gr. 2-17). pap., pap. 7.99 (978-0-316-78969-1(0)) Little Brown & Co.

—Ed Emberley's Fingerprint Drawing Book. 2001. (Illus.). (J). 14.50 (978-0-606-21169-7(1)) Tandem Library Bks.

—Ed Emberley's Great Thumbprint Drawing Book. Emberley, Ed, illus. 2005. (Illus.). 48p. (J). (gr. 2-17). pap. 7.99 (978-0-316-78968-4(2)) Little Brown & Co.

Fashion Designs. 2004. (Art Rom Create Your Own... Ser.). (Illus.). 24p. (J). pap. incl. audio compact disk (978-1-84229-769-8(4)) Top That! Publishing PLC.

Fazzi, Cindy. How to Draw Ireland's Sights & Symbols. 2005. (Kid's Guide to Drawing the Countries of the World Ser.). (Illus.). 48p. (J). (ps-k). lib. bdg. 26.50 (978-1-4042-2738-5(5) , PowerKids Pr.) Rosen Publishing Group, Inc., The.

—How to Draw Pakistan's Sights & Symbols. 2005. (Kid's Guide to Drawing the Countries of the World Ser.). (J). 26.50 (978-1-4042-2739-2(3) , PowerKids Pr.) Rosen Publishing Group, Inc., The.

—How to Draw Peru's Sights & Symbols. 2005. (Kid's Guide to Drawing the Countries of the World Ser.). (J). 26.50 (978-1-4042-2740-8(7) , PowerKids Pr.) Rosen Publishing Group, Inc., The.

—How to Draw the Philippines's Sights & Symbols. 2005. (Kid's Guide to Drawing the Countries of the World Ser.). (J). 26.50 (978-1-4042-2742-2(3) , PowerKids Pr.) Rosen Publishing Group, Inc., The.

Fedhar. Como Dibujar Personajes Magicos. Fedhar, illus. 2003. (SPA., Illus.). 160p. (J). (gr. 4-8). pap. (978-987-550-281-9(2)) Longseller S.A. ARG. *Dist:* Bilingual Pubns. Co., The.

Fein, E. How to Draw Nevadas Sights & Symbols. 2002. (Kids Guide to Drawing America Ser.). 32p. (J). lib. bdg. 25.25 (978-0-8239-6084-2(6) , PowerKids Pr.) Rosen Publishing Group, Inc., The.

—How to Draw New Yorks Sights & Symbols. 2002. (Kids Guide to Drawing America Ser.). 32p. (J). lib. bdg. 25.25 (978-0-8239-6088-0(9) , PowerKids Pr.) Rosen Publishing Group, Inc., The.

—How to Draw Oklahomas Sights & Symbols. 2002. (Kids Guide to Drawing America Ser.). 32p. (J). lib. bdg. 25.25 (978-0-8239-6092-7(7) , PowerKids Pr.) Rosen Publishing Group, Inc., The.

—How to Draw Utahs Sights & Symbols. 2002. (Kids Guide to Drawing America Ser.). 32p. (J). lib. bdg. 25.25 (978-0-8239-6101-6(X) , PowerKids Pr.) Rosen Publishing Group, Inc., The.

—How to Draw West Virginias Sights & Symbols. 2002. (Kids Guide to Drawing America Ser.). 32p. (J). lib. bdg. 25.25 (978-0-8239-6105-4(2) , PowerKids Pr.) Rosen Publishing Group, Inc., The.

Fein, Eric & Muschinske, Emily. How to Draw Puerto Rico's Sights & Symbols. 2002. (Kid's Guide to Drawing America Ser.). (Illus.). 32p. (J). lib. bdg. 25.25 (978-0-8239-6095-8(1) , PowerKids Pr.) Rosen Publishing Group, Inc., The.

A First Look at Art. (Illus.). (gr. 3-5). lib. bdg. 59.80 (978-0-7910-7944-7(9) , Chelsea Hse.) Facts On File, Inc.

Flux, Paul. Line & Tone. (How Artists Use Ser.). (Illus.). 32p. (J). (gr. 1-4). 2002. pap. 6.95 (978-1-58810-437-3(0) , 91165); 2001. lib. bdg. 22.79 (978-1-58810-079-5(0)) Heinemann Library.

—Perspective. 2001. (Seeing & Feeling Art Ser.). (Illus.). 32p. (J). (gr. 1-3). lib. bdg. 22.79 (978-1-58810-080-1(4)) Heinemann Library.

Fogle, Robin. The First Easter Dot-to-Dot Activity Book. 2007. (Illus.). 16p. (J). pap. 1.89 ***978-1-59317-192-6(7)*** Warner Pr. Pubs.

Foster, Walter, ed. Best of Nickelodeon. Crespo, Steve et al, illus. 2004. (Nick How to Draw Ser.). 32p. (J). pap. 5.95 (978-1-56010-848-1(7)) Foster, Walter Publishing, Inc.

—Drawing Animals. Fisher, Diana, illus. 2005. 32p. (J). pap. 12.95 (978-1-56010-937-2(8)) Foster, Walter Publishing, Inc.

—Drawing Pets. Fisher, Diana, illus. 2005. 32p. (J). pap. 12.95 (978-1-56010-938-9(6)) Foster, Walter Publishing, Inc.

—Drawing Techniques. 2004. (WF /Color & Co. Art for Kids Ser.). (Illus.). 40p. (J). pap. 4.95 (978-1-56010-853-5(3)) Foster, Walter Publishing, Inc.

—Finding Nemo. 2003. (Disney's How to Draw Classic Character Ser.). (Illus.). 32p. (J). pap. 5.95 (978-1-56010-689-0(1)) Foster, Walter Publishing, Inc.

—My Little Pony. Edwards, Ken, illus. 2004. (How to Draw Ser.). 32p. (J). pap. 5.95 (978-1-56010-804-7(5)) Foster, Walter Publishing, Inc.

—Scooby-Doo! Step by Step. Musacchia, Vince, illus. 2002. (How to Draw Ser.). 32p. (J). pap. 5.95 (978-1-56010-715-6(4)) Foster, Walter Publishing, Inc.

—Spongebob: 5 Splashy Styles. Dress, Robert, illus. 2005. (Nick How to Draw Ser.). 32p. (J). pap. 5.95 (978-1-56010-928-0(9)) Foster, Walter Publishing, Inc.

Freed, Shirley Ann & Morelan, Bill. I Can Draw. Evans, Cassie & Harrell, Rob, illus. l.t. ed. 2002. 16p. (J). (gr. 5). pap. 3.99 (978-1-58938-014-1(2)) Concerned Communications.

Gair, Angela. How to Draw Anything: A Complete Guide. 2003. (Essential Art Ser.). 160p. (YA). 19.95 (978-0-7525-8773-8(0)) Parragon, Inc.

Gamble, Kim. You Can Draw Anything. 1999. (Illus.). 48p. (J). (gr. 3-7). pap. 7.95 (978-1-86373-680-0(8)) Allen & Unwin AUS. *Dist:* Independent Pubs. Group.

Gibson, R. What Shall I Draw? 2004. (What Shall I Do Today? Ser.). 32p. (J). pap. 7.95 (978-0-7945-0375-8(6)); lib. bdg. 15.95 (978-1-58086-504-3(6)) EDC Publishing.

Gibson, Ray. Drawing Animals Pack. 2004. (Activity Kits Ser.). 24p. (J). act. bk. ed. 14.95 (978-0-7945-0456-4(6)) EDC Publishing.

—I Can Draw People. Watt, Fiona, ed. Barlow, Amanda, illus. 2004. (Playtime Ser.). (SPA.). 32p. (J). (ps-3). pap., act. bk. ed. 4.95 (978-0-7460-3704-1(X)); lib. bdg., act. bk. ed. 12.95 (978-1-58086-223-3(3)) EDC Publishing.

—I Can Draw People. Watt, Fiona, ed. Barlow, Amanda, illus. 2000. (J). 11.75 (978-0-606-18130-3(X)) Tandem Library Bks.

Gilpin, Rebecca. How to Draw Trucks & Tractors. 2005. 34p. (J). pap. 8.95 (978-0-7945-1134-0(1), Usborne) EDC Publishing.

Gluck, Larry. The Art of Drawing Pt. 1: Creating Accurate Lines & Shapes. 2003. (YA). spiral bd. (978-1-929473-51-9(6)) Renaissance Pubns.

Go Office Staff. How to Draw Manga: Official More How to Draw Manga Illustration Kit, 1. 2004. (Illus.). 126p. 29.99 (978-1-59396-121-3(9)) Diamond Bk. Distributors.

Griffin, Georgene. Dinosaurs. 2001. (How to Draw Ser.). (Illus.). 32p. (J). (gr. 2-5). lib. bdg. 25.27 (978-1-58952-153-7(6)) Rourke Publishing, LLC.

—Monster Trucks. 2001. (How to Draw Ser.). (Illus.). 32p. (J). (gr. 2-5). lib. bdg. 25.27 (978-1-58952-155-1(2)) Rourke Publishing, LLC.

Griffin, Georgene, illus. Dinosaurs, Meat-Eaters. 2004. (J). (978-1-59203-086-6(6)) Learning Challenge, Inc.

—Endangered Mammals. 2004. (J). (978-1-59203-089-7(0)) Learning Challenge, Inc.

Griffin, Georgene & Jael, illus. Cool Wheels. 2004. (J). (978-1-59203-087-3(4)) Learning Challenge, Inc.

Griffin, Georgene & Walker, Karen, illus. How to Draw Funny Faces. 1999. 123p. (J). (978-1-56156-791-1(4)) Kidsbooks, Inc.

Gross, Miriam. How to Draw the Life & Times of James Monroe. 2006. (Kid's Guide to Drawing the Presidents of the United States of America Ser.). (J). 25.25 (978-1-4042-2982-2(5), PowerKids Pr.) Rosen Publishing Group, Inc., The.

Hablitzel, Marie & Stitzer, Kim H. Draw Write Now, 8 bks.; set. Incl. Animals of the World : Forest Animals. Hablitzel, Marie & Stitzer, Kim H., illus. 2000. pap. 10.95 (978-0-9639307-7-4(X)); Draw Write Now Bk. 1 : On the Farm, Kids & Critters, Storybook Characters. Hablitzel, Marie & Stitzer, Kim H., illus. 1994. pap. 10.95 (978-0-9639307-1-2(0)); Draw Write Now Bk. 2 : Christopher Columbus, Autumn Harvest, the Weather. Hablitzel, Marie & Stitzer, Kim H., illus. 1995. pap. 10.95 (978-0-9639307-2-9(9)); Draw Write Now Bk. 3 : Native Americans, North America, the Pilgrims. Hablitzel, Marie & Stitzer, Kim H., illus. 1996. pap. 10.95 (978-0-9639307-3-6(7)); Draw Write Now Bk. 4 : The Polar Regions, Arctic, Antarctic. Hablitzel, Marie & Stitzer, Kim H., illus. 1997. pap. 10.95 (978-0-9639307-4-3(5)); Draw Write Now Bk. 5 : The United States, from Sea to Sea, Moving Forward. 1998. pap. 10.95 (978-0-9639307-5-0(3)); Draw Write Now Bk. 6 : Animal Habitats - On Land, Ponds & Rivers, Oceans. Hablitzel, Marie & Stitzer, Kim H., illus. 1999. pap. 10.95 (978-0-9639307-6-7(1)); Draw Write Now Bk. 8 : Animals of the World: Grassland & Desert Animals. Hablitzel, Marie & Stitzer, Kim H., illus. 2001. pap. 10.95 (978-0-9639307-8-1(8)); 64p. (J). (gr. k-5). (Draw Write Now Ser.). 2001. Set pap. 79.95 (978-0-9639307-9-8(6)) Barker Creek Publishing, Inc.

—Draw Write Now Bk. 6: Animal Habitats - On Land, Ponds & Rivers, Oceans. Hablitzel, Marie & Stitzer, Kim H., illus. 1999. (Draw Write Now Ser.). (Illus.). 64p. (J). (gr. k-5). pap. 10.95 (978-0-9639307-6-7(1)) Barker Creek Publishing, Inc.

—Draw Write Now Bk. 8: Animals of the World: Grassland & Desert Animals. Hablitzel, Marie & Stitzer, Kim H., illus. 2001. (Draw Write Now Ser.). (Illus.). 64p. (J). (gr. k-5). pap. 10.95 (978-0-9639307-8-1(8)) Barker Creek Publishing, Inc.

Hagen, Kathryn. Illustration for Designers. 2nd rev. ed. 2000. (Illus.). 275p. (Orig.). (YA). (gr. 10-13). pap. 59.95 (978-0-9704303-5-9(3)) Hagen Publishing.

Harcourt School Publishers Staff. You Are an Artist. 3rd ed. 2002. (Trophies English Language Learners Ser.). (Illus.). pap. 5.10 (978-0-15-327827-3(7)) Harcourt Schl. Pubs.

Harpster, Steve. Horses. 2006. (Pencil, Paper, Draw! Ser.). (Illus.). 64p. (J). pap., spiral bd. 5.95 (978-1-4027-2977-5(4)) Sterling Publishing Co., Inc.

Hart, Christopher. How to Draw Fast Cars, Monster Trucks & Fighter Jets. 2000. (Illus.). 64p. pap. 10.95 (978-0-8230-2395-0(8)) Watson-Guptill Pubns., Inc.

—Kids Draw Animals. 2003. (Kids Draw Ser.). (Illus.). 64p. (J). pap. 11.95 (978-0-8230-2631-9(0)) Watson-Guptill Pubns., Inc.

—Kids Draw Anime. 2003. (gr. 3-6). lib. bdg. 19.90 (978-0-613-88815-8(4)) Tandem Library Bks.

—Kids Draw Anime. 2002. (Kids Draw Ser.). (Illus.). 64p. (J). (gr. 3-6). pap. 11.95 (978-0-8230-2690-6(6)) Watson-Guptill Pubns., Inc.

—Kids Draw Manga. 2004. (Kids Draw Ser.). (Illus.). 64p. (J). pap. 11.95 (978-0-8230-2623-4(X)) Watson-Guptill Pubns., Inc.

—Manga Mania: How to Draw Japanese Comics. 2003. (Illus.). 144p. (gr. 5-8). lib. bdg. 30.35 (978-0-613-49336-9(2)) Tandem Library Bks.

—Mecha Mania: How to Draw Warrior Robots, Cool Spaceships, & Military Vehicles. 2002. (gr. 7-12). lib. bdg. 30.35 (978-0-613-60579-3(9)) Tandem Library Bks.

—Xtreme Art: Draw Manga Villains! 2004. (Xtreme Art Ser.). (Illus.). 64p. (J). pap. 7.95 (978-0-8230-0370-9(1)) Watson-Guptill Pubns., Inc.

Hastings, John. The Drawing Breakthrough Kit: Taking the Mystery Out of Learning to Draw. 2004. (Illus.). spiral bd. 49.95 (978-0-9749418-0-6(8)) Draw Three Lines Publishing.

Heins, Edward. Drawing Dinosaurs. 2001. (gr. k-3). lib. bdg. 15.30 (978-0-613-72458-6(5)) Tandem Library Bks.

Henley, Claire, illus. Draw with Bear, Here, There & Everywhere! 2001. 20p. (J). (ps-3). 10.95 (978-0-7641-7433-9(9)) Barron's Educational Series, Inc.

—Draw with Cat, in, Out & All About! 2001. 20p. (J). (ps-3). 10.95 (978-0-7641-7434-6(7)) Barron's Educational Series, Inc.

Henson, Paige. Drawing with Markers. 1999. (How to Paint & Draw Ser.). (Illus.). 32p. (J). (gr. 3-6). lib. bdg. 26.60 (978-1-57103-309-3(2)) Rourke Publishing, LLC.

—Drawing with Pencils. 1999. (How to Paint & Draw Ser.). (Illus.). 32p. (J). (gr. 3-6). lib. bdg. 26.60 (978-1-57103-310-9(6)) Rourke Publishing, LLC.

Henwood, Debby. You Can Draw: Puppies & Dogs. 1998. (Illus.). 32p. reprint ed. pap. 3.99 (978-0-87406-880-1(0), Willowisp Pr.) Darby Creek Publishing.

Hill, Eric. Drawing Fun with Spot. 2005. bds. 7.99 (978-0-399-24337-0(2), Putnam Juvenile) Penguin Group (USA) Inc.

Hodge, Anthony. Drawing. 2004. 32p. (J). lib. bdg. (978-1-932799-01-9(X)) Stargazer Bks.

Holub, Joan. Cars & Trucks. 2002. (gr. k-3). lib. bdg. 14.15 (978-0-613-82376-0(1)) Tandem Library Bks.

—I Can Draw Animals. Holub, Joan & Regan, Dana, illus. 2002. (Easy-to-Read! Easy-to-Draw! Ser.). 48p. (J). (ps-2). pap. 6.99 (978-0-8431-4548-9(X), Price Stern Sloan) Penguin Group (USA) Inc.

Holub, Joan & Regan, Dana, illus. Magical Creatures. 2003. (Easy-to-Read! Easy-to-Draw! Ser.). 48p. (J). pap. 5.99 (978-0-8431-0436-3(8), Price Stern Sloan) Penguin Group (USA) Inc.

How to Draw 101 Animals. 2004. (How to Draw... Ser.). (Illus.). 48p. (J). pap. (978-1-84229-740-7(6)) Top That! Publishing PLC.

How to Draw 101 Funny People. 2004. (How to Draw... Ser.). (Illus.). 48p. (J). pap. (978-1-84229-739-1(2)) Top That! Publishing PLC.

How to Draw 101 Monsters. 2004. (How to Draw... Ser.). (Illus.). 48p. (J). pap. (978-1-84229-742-1(2)) Top That! Publishing PLC.

How to Draw 101 Things That Go. 2004. (How to Draw... Ser.). (Illus.). 48p. (J). pap. (978-1-84229-741-4(4)) Top That! Publishing PLC.

How to Draw Cartoon Animals Adventure Pack. 2001. (978-1-883772-64-2(8)) Flying Rhinoceros, Inc.

How to Draw Cartoons Adventure Pack. 2001. (978-1-883772-63-5(X)) Flying Rhinoceros, Inc.

How to Draw Shojo Supersize, Vol. 1. 2003. (Illus.). 144p. (YA). pap. 19.95 (978-0-9728978-4-6(4)) Antarctic Pr., Inc.

How to Draw Wings & Wheels. (Illus.). 128p. (J). (gr. 1 up). 14.95 (978-1-56156-223-7(8)) Kidsbooks, Inc.

Hutnick, Liz. Doodle Cats. 2004. (Illus.). 56p. (J). (gr. 1 up). spiral bd. 9.95 (978-1-57054-835-2(8)) Klutz.

Hutnick, Liz, ed. Doodle Faces. 2004. (Klutz Ser.). (Illus.). 58p. (J). 9.95 (978-1-57054-837-6(4)) Klutz.

I Can Draw: Cartoons. 2002. 256p. pap. 12.98 (978-0-7525-8723-3(4)) Parragon, Inc.

I Can Draw Animals. (My Wipe-off Book Ser.). 16p. (J). spiral bd., bds. (978-1-4127-0523-3(1), 7222000) Publications International, Ltd.

I Can Draw Cartoons. Date not set. (I Can Draw Ser.). (Illus.). 128p. (J). 7.98 (978-1-4054-0542-3(2)) Parragon, Inc.

I Can Draw Dinosaurs. (My Wipe-off Book Ser.). 16p. (J). spiral bd., bds. (978-1-4127-0524-0(X), 7221900) Publications International, Ltd.

Jael, illus. How to Draw Tanks & Other Fighting Machines. 2002. 96p. (J). (978-1-58865-036-8(7)) Kidsbooks, Inc.

Jael, tr. & illus. Superheroes: [includes Drawing & Tracing Paper]. Jael, illus. 2002. (Ready, Set, Draw Ser.). (J). (978-1-58865-073-3(1)) Kidsbooks, Inc.

Jeffus, Richard & Jeffus, Sharon. Master Drawing. 1999. (Illus.). 100p. (YA). (gr. 5-12). pap. 14.95 (978-0-9677386-2-8(8)) Visual Manna.

Khu, Jannell. Drawing Fire Trucks. 2005. (Let's Draw with Shapes Ser.). (Illus.). 24p. (J). 17.25 (978-1-4042-2794-1(6), PowerKids Pr.) Rosen Publishing Group, Inc., The.

Kidd, Nina. Draw Science: Strange & Weird Animals. 1999. (Illus.). 63p. (YA). (gr. 3 up). pap. 7.95 (978-0-7373-0235-6(6), 02356W) McGraw-Hill/Contemporary.

—Reptiles & Amphibians. Kidd, Nina, illus. 1998. (Draw Science Ser.). (Illus.). 64p. (J). (gr. 3-7). pap. 7.95 (978-1-56565-936-0(8), 09368W) Lowell Hse. Juvenile.

—Whales, Sharks & Other Sea Creatures. 2nd rev. ed. 1998. (Draw Science Ser.). (Illus.). 64p. (J). (gr. 4-7). pap. 7.95 (978-1-56565-975-9(9), 09759W) Lowell Hse. Juvenile.

Kistler, Mark. Monster Mania. 2002. (Dare to Draw in 3-D Ser.: No. 1). (Illus.). 40p. (J). pap. 4.99 (978-0-439-38073-7(1)) Scholastic, Inc.

—Monster Mania. 2002. (gr. 3-6). lib. bdg. 13.00 (978-0-613-72049-6(0)) Tandem Library Bks.

Klutz Press Staff. Draw Thumb Animals. 2002. (Illus.). 44p. (J). spiral bd. 6.95 (978-1-57054-981-6(8)) Klutz.

Klutz Press Staff, creator. Hand Art. 2005. (Illus.). 24p. (J). spiral bd. 9.95 (978-1-59174-163-3(7)) Klutz.

Kohl, MaryAnn F. & Potter, Jean. Storybook Art: Hands-on Art for Children in the Styles of 100 Great Picture Book Illustrators. Davis, Katheryn & Van Slyke, Rebecca, illus. 2003. (Bright Ideas for Learning Ser.). 144p. (J). pap. 18.95 (978-0-935607-03-1(X)) Bright Ring Publishing, Inc.

Kuedee, Jaycee. How to Draw Minnesotas Sights & Symbols. 2002. (Kids Guide to Drawing America Ser.). 32p. (J). lib. bdg. 25.25 (978-0-8239-6079-8(X), PowerKids Pr.) Rosen Publishing Group, Inc., The.

—How to Draw Mississippis Sights & Symbols. 2002. (Kids Guide to Drawing America Ser.). 32p. (J). lib. bdg. 25.25 (978-0-8239-6080-4(3), PowerKids Pr.) Rosen Publishing Group, Inc., The.

—How to Draw Missouris Sights & Symbols. 2002. (Kids Guide to Drawing America Ser.). 32p. (J). lib. bdg. 25.25 (978-0-8239-6081-1(1), PowerKids Pr.) Rosen Publishing Group, Inc., The.

—How to Draw Montanas Sights & Symbols. 2002. (Kids Guide to Drawing America Ser.). 32p. (J). lib. bdg. 25.25 (978-0-8239-6082-8(X), PowerKids Pr.) Rosen Publishing Group, Inc., The.

LaPlaca, Michael. How to Draw Cars & Trucks. 1999. (J). (gr. 4-7). 10.05 (978-0-88103-749-4(4), Plume) Penguin Group (USA) Inc.

Last, Ian & Smith, Diana, illus. How to Draw. 2005. 48p. (J). (gr. 4-7). (978-1-84510-676-8(8)) Top That! Publishing PLC.

Learn to Draw. (Learning Ser.). 22p. (J). bds. (978-2-7643-0000-8(X)) Phidal Publishing, Inc./Editions Phidal, Inc.

Lee, Justin. How to Draw African Animals. 2002. (Kid's Guide to Drawing Ser.). (Illus.). 24p. (J). lib. bdg. 21.25 (978-0-8239-5790-3(X), PowerKids Pr.) Rosen Publishing Group, Inc., The.

—How to Draw Animals of the Rain Forest. 2002. (Kid's Guide to Drawing Ser.). (Illus.). 24p. (J). lib. bdg. 21.25 (978-0-8239-5793-4(4), PowerKids Pr.) Rosen Publishing Group, Inc., The.

—How to Draw Fish. 2002. (Kid's Guide to Drawing Ser.). (Illus.). 24p. (J). lib. bdg. 21.25 (978-0-8239-5792-7(6), PowerKids Pr.) Rosen Publishing Group, Inc., The.

—How to Draw Insects. 2002. (Kid's Guide to Drawing Ser.). (Illus.). 24p. (J). lib. bdg. 21.25 (978-0-8239-5791-0(8), PowerKids Pr.) Rosen Publishing Group, Inc., The.

—How to Draw Sharks. 2002. (Kid's Guide to Drawing Ser.). (Illus.). 24p. (J). lib. bdg. 21.25 (978-0-8239-5788-0(8), PowerKids Pr.) Rosen Publishing Group, Inc., The.

—How to Draw Whales. 2002. (Kid's Guide to Drawing Ser.). (Illus.). 24p. (J). lib. bdg. 21.25 (978-0-8239-5789-7(6), PowerKids Pr.) Rosen Publishing Group, Inc., The.

Legendre, Philippe, illus. Kids Can Draw Ancient Egypt. 2002. (Kids Can Draw Ser.). 24p. (J). pap. 3.95 (978-1-56010-656-2(5)) Foster, Walter Publishing, Inc.

—Kids Can Draw Monsters. 2002. (Kids Can Draw Ser.). 24p. (J). pap. 3.95 (978-1-56010-653-1(0)) Foster, Walter Publishing, Inc.

—Kids Can Draw Pirates. 2002. (Kids Can Draw Ser.). 24p. (J). pap. 3.95 (978-1-56010-654-8(9)) Foster, Walter Publishing, Inc.

Leroux-Hugon, Helene. I Can Draw Country Animals. Leroux-Hugon, Helene, illus. 2001. (I Can Draw Animals! Ser.). (Illus.). 40p. (J). (gr. 1 up). lib. bdg. 24.67 (978-0-8368-2838-2(0)) Stevens, Gareth Inc.

—I Can Draw Forest Animals. Leroux-Hugon, Helene, illus. 2001. (I Can Draw Animals! Ser.). (Illus.). 40p. (J). (gr. 1 up). lib. bdg. 24.67 (978-0-8368-2839-9(9)) Stevens, Gareth Inc.

—I Can Draw Polar Animals. Leroux-Hugon, Helene, illus. 2001. (I Can Draw Animals! Ser.). (Illus.). 40p. (J). (gr. 1 up). lib. bdg. 24.67 (978-0-8368-2840-5(2)) Stevens, Gareth Inc.

—I Can Draw Wild Animals. Leroux-Hugon, Helene, illus. 2001. (I Can Draw Animals! Ser.). (Illus.). 40p. (J). (gr. 1 up). lib. bdg. 24.67 (978-0-8368-2841-2(0)) Stevens, Gareth Inc.

Less, Emma. Little Scribbles: Outer Space Fun. Harpster, Steve, illus. 2007. (Little Scribbles Ser.). 12p. (J). bds. 5.95 (***978-1-4027-4666-6(0)***) Sterling Publishing Co., Inc.

Levin, Freddie. 1-2-3 Draw Cars, Trucks, & Other Vehicles: A Step-by-Step Guide. 2001. (1-2-3 Draw Ser.). (Illus.). 64p. (J). (gr. 1-7). pap. 8.99 (978-0-939217-44-1(9), 32065) Peel Productions, Inc.

—1-2-3 Draw Cars, Trucks & Other Vehicles: A Step-by-Step Guide. 2001. (gr. 3-6). lib. bdg. 17.60 (978-0-613-88581-2(3)) Tandem Library Bks.

—1-2-3 Draw Dinosaurs: And Other Prehistoric Animals. 2000. (gr. k-3). lib. bdg. 17.60 (978-0-613-86904-1(4)) Tandem Library Bks.

—1-2-3 Draw Dinosaurs & Other Prehistoric Animals: Step-by-Step Guide. 2000. (One-Two-Three Draw Ser.). (Illus.). 64p. (J). (gr. 1-5). pap. 8.99 (978-0-939217-41-0(4)) Peel Productions, Inc.

—1-2-3 Draw Horses. Levin, Freddie, illus. 2004. (Illus.). 64p. pap. 8.99 (978-0-939217-61-8(9)) Peel Productions, Inc.

—1-2-3 Draw Knights, Castles & Dragons: A Step-by-Step Guide. 2001. (One-Two-Three Draw Ser.). (Illus.). 64p. (J). (gr. 1-7). pap. 8.99 (978-0-939217-43-4(0), 32064) Peel Productions, Inc.

—1-2-3 Draw Knights, Castles & Dragons: A Step by Step Guide. 2001. (gr. 3-6). lib. bdg. 17.60 (978-0-613-87987-3(2)) Tandem Library Bks.

—1-2-3 Draw Mythical Creatures: A Step-by-Step Guide. 2003. (One-Two-Three Draw Ser.). (Illus.). 64p. pap. 8.99 (978-0-939217-49-6(X)) Peel Productions, Inc.

—1-2-3 Draw Pets & Farm Animals. 2000. (gr. k-3). lib. bdg. 17.60 (978-0-613-87986-6(4)) Tandem Library Bks.

—1-2-3 Draw Pets & Farm Animals: A Step by Step Guide. Levin, Freddie, illus. 2000. (One-Two-Three Draw Ser.). (Illus.). 64p. (J). (gr. 1-5). pap. 8.99 (978-0-939217-40-3(6)) Peel Productions, Inc.

—1-2-3 Draw Wild Animals: A Step-by-Step Guide. 2001. (One-Two-Three Draw Ser.). (Illus.). 64p. (J). (gr. 1-5). pap. 8.95 (978-0-939217-42-7(2)) Peel Productions, Inc.

Levy, Barbara Soloff. How to Draw Christmas Pictures. 2005. (Illus.). 32p. (J). (ps-3). pap. 2.95 (978-0-486-44008-8(7)) Dover Pubns., Inc.

—How to Draw Flowers. 2001. (Illus.). 32p. (J). (gr. k-5). pap. 2.95 (978-0-486-41337-2(3)) Dover Pubns., Inc.

—How to Draw Flowers. 2001. (gr. 3-6). lib. bdg. 10.60 (978-0-613-88092-3(7)) Tandem Library Bks.

—How to Draw Funny Monsters. 2004. (Illus.). 32p. pap. 2.95 (978-0-486-43838-2(4)) Dover Pubns., Inc.

—How to Draw Insects. 1999. (gr. k-3). lib. bdg. 10.60 (978-0-613-90822-1(8)) Tandem Library Bks.

—How to Draw Planes, Trains & Boats. 2004. lib. bdg. 10.60 (978-0-613-87586-8(9)) Tandem Library Bks.

—How to Draw Storybook Characters. 2005. 32p. (J). pap. 2.95 (978-0-486-43989-1(5)) Dover Pubns., Inc.

—How to Draw Wild Animals. 1999. (Illus.). 32p. (J). (gr. k-5). pap. 2.95 (978-0-486-40821-7(3)) Dover Pubns., Inc.

—How to Draw Wizards, Dragons & Other Magical Creatures. 2004. lib. bdg. 10.60 (978-0-613-85389-7(X)) Tandem Library Bks.

—Pets Follow the Dots. 2006. 64p. (J). pap. 1.50 (978-0-486-44890-9(8)) Dover Pubns., Inc.

—You Can Draw Animals. 2003. (Dover Super Value Editions Ser.). (Illus.). 128p. (J). pap. 7.95 (978-0-486-42899-4(0)) Dover Pubns., Inc.

Levy, Janey. Renaissance Paintings: Using Perspective to Represent Three-Dimensional Objects. 2005. (PowerMath Ser.). (Illus.). 32p. (J). 22.50 (978-1-4042-2926-6(4), PowerKids Pr.); (978-1-4042-5116-8(2), PowerKids Pr.); pap. (978-1-4042-5115-1(4)) Rosen Publishing Group, Inc., The.

Lewis & Clark Hands on Art And. 2004. pap. 12.95 (978-0-9715970-5-1(7)) Visual Manna.

Lipe, Riki. Wonder What Would Happen If... Don't Know but I'm Gonna Try! Spears-Stewart, Reta, ed. Lipe, Riki, illus. 2001. (Illus.). 48p. (YA). (gr. 3 up). spiral bd. 12.00 (978-0-9659381-5-0(8)) Hoot N' Cackle Pr.

Lipsey, Jennifer. I Love to Draw! 2005. (My Very Favorite Art Bks.). (Illus.). 48p. (J). (gr. k-3). 9.95 (978-1-57990-629-0(X)) Lark Bks.

Lockman, Vic. Father Time: Biblical Science Fiction. 2001. (Illus.). 75p. (YA). (gr. 4-12). per. (978-0-936175-40-9(0)) Lockman, Vic.

—Trace & Learn Drawing Book: The 3-Step Method. Lockman, Vic, illus. 2000. (Illus.). 24p. (J). 6.00 (978-0-936175-39-3(7)) Lockman, Vic.

Longhurst, Terry. I Can Draw Sharks, Whales & Dolphins. 2002. (I Can Draw Ser.). 32p. (J). 9.95 (978-0-7525-7279-6(2)) Parragon, Inc.

Longhurst, Terry, illus. I Can Draw. 2002. 256p. (J). 12.98 (978-0-7525-8434-8(0)) Parragon, Inc.

Makowski, Robin. Drawing Anything You Like. 2005. 32p. pap. 6.45 (978-1-59515-784-3(0)) Rourke Publishing, LLC.

—Fish Drawing Made Fun. 2005. 32p. pap. 6.45 (978-1-59515-785-0(9)) Rourke Publishing, LLC.

Makowski, Robin Lee. Dogs. 2001. (How to Draw Ser.). (Illus.). 32p. (J). (gr. 2-5). lib. bdg. 25.27 (978-1-58952-154-4(4)) Rourke Publishing, LLC.

—Draw Anything You Like. 2006. (Drawing Made Fun Ser.). (Illus.). 32p. (gr. 2-5). 20.95 (978-1-59515-470-5(1), 1244420) Rourke Publishing, LLC.

—Sea Creatures. 2001. (How to Draw Ser.). (Illus.). 32p. (J). (gr. 2-5). lib. bdg. 25.27 (978-1-58952-156-8(0)) Rourke Publishing, LLC.

Makowski, Robin Lee, illus. Dogs. 2004. (J). (978-1-59203-088-0(2)) Learning Challenge, Inc.

—How to Draw Cats & Dogs. 1999. 128p. (J). (978-1-56156-790-4(6)) Kidsbooks, Inc.

—Sea Creatures. 2004. (J). (978-1-59203-090-3(4)) Learning Challenge, Inc.

Masiello, Ralph. Bug Drawing Book: Simple Steps to Make Anyone an Artist. Masiello, Ralph, illus. 2004. (Illus.). 32p. (J). 16.95 (978-1-57091-525-3(3)); pap. 6.95 (978-1-57091-526-0(1)) Charlesbridge Publishing, Inc.

—Ralph Masiello's Dinosaur Drawing Book. 2005. (Illus.). 32p. (J). (ps-k). pap. 6.95 (978-1-57091-528-4(8)); 16.95 (978-1-57091-527-7(X)) Charlesbridge Publishing, Inc.

Mayne, Don. Draw Your Own Cartoons! 2000. (Quick Starts for Kids! Ser.). (Illus.). 64p. (J). (gr. 3 up). pap. 8.95 (978-1-885593-76-4(7), Williamson Bks.) Ideals Pubns.

—Draw Your Own Cartoons! 2000. (gr. 3-6). lib. bdg. 17.60 (978-0-613-57600-0(4)) Tandem Library Bks.

—Drawing Horses (That Look Real) 2002. (Quick Starts for Kids! Ser.). (Illus.). 64p. (J). (gr. 3 up). pap. 8.95 (978-1-885593-74-0(0), Williamson Bks.) Ideals Pubns.

McBride, Susan. The Don't-Get-Caught Doodle Notebook. 2005. (Illus.). 128p. (gr. k-17). 7.95 (978-1-57990-702-0(4)) Lark Bks.

—Stick It Notes: 100 Doodles to Draw & Leave Behind. 2007. (Illus.). 208p. (J). pap. 4.95 (978-1-60059-073-3(X)) Lark Bks.

McKee, Karen & Griffin, Georgene. Airplanes. 2001. (How to Draw Ser.). (Illus.). 32p. (J). (gr. 2-5). lib. bdg. 25.27 (978-1-58952-151-3(X)) Rourke Publishing, LLC.

McKee, Karen & Griffin, Georgene, illus. Hot Wings. 2004. (J). (978-1-59203-091-0(2)) Learning Challenge, Inc.

Milbourne, Anna. Drawing Animals. 2004. (Art School Ser.). (Illus.). 64p. (J). pap. 8.95 (978-0-7945-0109-9(5), Usborne); lib. bdg. 16.95 (978-1-58086-381-0(7)) EDC Publishing.

C
D

—Drawing Animals. 2002. (gr. 5-8). lib. bdg. 17.60 (978-0-613-75316-6(X)) Tandem Library Bks.

Mis, Melody S. How to Draw Australia's Sights & Symbols. 2005. (Kid's Guide to Drawing the Countries of the World Ser.). (J). 26.50 (978-1-4042-2731-6(8) , PowerKids Pr.) Rosen Publishing Group, Inc., The.

—How to Draw Brazil's Sights & Symbols. 2004. (Kid's Guide to Drawing the Countries of the World Ser.). (Illus.). 48p. (J). lib. bdg. 26.50 (978-0-8239-6667-7(4) , PowerKids Pr.) Rosen Publishing Group, Inc., The.

—How to Draw China's Sights & Symbols. 2004. (Kid's Guide to Drawing the Countries of the World Ser.). (Illus.). 48p. (J). lib. bdg. 26.50 (978-0-8239-6664-6(X) , PowerKids Pr.) Rosen Publishing Group, Inc., The.

—How to Draw India's Sights & Symbols. 2005. (Kid's Guide to Drawing the Countries of the World Ser.). (Illus.). 48p. (J). (ps-k). lib. bdg. 26.50 (978-1-4042-2732-3(6) , PowerKids Pr.) Rosen Publishing Group, Inc., The.

—How to Draw Kenya's Sights & Symbols. 2005. (Kid's Guide to Drawing the Countries of the World Ser.). (Illus.). 48p. (J). (ps-k). lib. bdg. 26.50 (978-1-4042-2733-0(4) , PowerKids Pr.) Rosen Publishing Group, Inc., The.

—How to Draw Mexico's Sights & Symbols. 2004. (Kid's Guide to Drawing the Countries of the World Ser.). (Illus.). 48p. (J). lib. bdg. 26.50 (978-0-8239-6668-4(2) , PowerKids Pr.) Rosen Publishing Group, Inc., The.

—How to Draw New Jersey's Sights & Symbols. 2002. (Kids Guide to Drawing America Ser.). 32p. (J). lib. bdg. 25.25 (978-0-8239-6086-6(2) , PowerKids Pr.) Rosen Publishing Group, Inc., The.

—How to Draw North Dakota's Sights & Symbols. 2002. (Kids Guide to Drawing America Ser.). 32p. (J). lib. bdg. 25.25 (978-0-8239-6090-3(0) , PowerKids Pr.) Rosen Publishing Group, Inc., The.

—How to Draw Norway's Sights & Symbols. 2005. (Kid's Guide to Drawing the Countries of the World Ser.). (Illus.). 48p. (J). (ps-k). lib. bdg. 26.50 (978-1-4042-2734-7(2) , PowerKids Pr.) Rosen Publishing Group, Inc., The.

—How to Draw Pennsylvania's Sights & Symbols. 2002. (Kids Guide to Drawing America Ser.). 32p. (J). lib. bdg. 25.25 (978-0-8239-6094-1(3) , PowerKids Pr.) Rosen Publishing Group, Inc., The.

—How to Draw Poland's Sights & Symbols. 2004. (Kid's Guide to Drawing the Countries of the World Ser.). (Illus.). 48p. (J). lib. bdg. 26.50 (978-0-8239-6669-1(0) , PowerKids Pr.) Rosen Publishing Group, Inc., The.

—How to Draw Portugal's Sights & Symbols. 2005. (Kid's Guide to Drawing the Countries of the World Ser.). (J). 26.50 (978-1-4042-2735-4(0) , PowerKids Pr.) Rosen Publishing Group, Inc., The.

—How to Draw Russia's Sights & Symbols. 2004. (Kid's Guide to Drawing the Countries of the World Ser.). (Illus.). 48p. (J). lib. bdg. 26.50 (978-0-8239-6666-0(6) , PowerKids Pr.) Rosen Publishing Group, Inc., The.

—How to Draw South Africa's Sights & Symbols. 2004. (Kid's Guide to Drawing the Countries of the World Ser.). (Illus.). 48p. (J). lib. bdg. 26.50 (978-0-8239-6665-3(8) , PowerKids Pr.) Rosen Publishing Group, Inc., The.

—How to Draw South Korea's Sights & Symbols. 2005. (Kid's Guide to Drawing the Countries of the World Ser.). (J). 26.50 (978-1-4042-2736-1(9) , PowerKids Pr.) Rosen Publishing Group, Inc., The.

—How to Draw Tennessee's Sights & Symbols. 2002. (Kids Guide to Drawing America Ser.). 32p. (J). lib. bdg. 25.25 (978-0-8239-6099-6(4) , PowerKids Pr.) Rosen Publishing Group, Inc., The.

—How to Draw the Life & Times of Andrew Jackson. 2006. (Kid's Guide to Drawing the Presidents of the United States of America Ser.). (J). 25.25 (978-1-4042-2984-6(1) , PowerKids Pr.) Rosen Publishing Group, Inc., The.

—How to Draw the Life & Times of Thomas Jefferson. 2006. (Kid's Guide to Drawing the Presidents of the United States of America Ser.). (J). 25.25 (978-1-4042-2980-8(9) , PowerKids Pr.) Rosen Publishing Group, Inc., The.

—How to Draw Virginia's Sights & Symbols. 2002. (Kids Guide to Drawing America Ser.). 32p. (J). lib. bdg. 25.25 (978-0-8239-6103-0(6) , PowerKids Pr.) Rosen Publishing Group, Inc., The.

—How to Draw Wyoming's Sights & Symbols. 2002. (Kids Guide to Drawing America Ser.). 32p. (J). lib. bdg. 25.25 (978-0-8239-6107-8(9) , PowerKids Pr.) Rosen Publishing Group, Inc., The.

—A Kid's Guide to Drawing the Countries of the World: Set 2, 6 bks., Set 2003. (Illus.). (J). (gr. k-5). (978-0-8239-8486-2(9) , PowerKids Pr.) Rosen Publishing Group, Inc., The.

Mottashed, Susie. Who Lives in Your Backyard? Creating a journal that opens your eyes & heart to nature's nearby Wonders. Mottashed, Susie, illus. 2005. (Illus.). 96p. 24.95 (978-0-9759300-0-7(1)) Sketches From The Heart Publishing.

Mravec, James. Animals. 2005. (Illus.). 96p. spiral bd. (978-0-7853-8378-9(6) , 3439101) Publications International, Ltd.

—You Can Draw Planes, Trains & Boats. 2005. (Illus.). 96p. spiral bd. (978-0-7853-8303-1(4) , 3460900) Publications International, Ltd.

Muehlenhardt, Amy Bailey. Drawing & Learning about Bugs: Using Shapes & Lines. 2004. (Sketch It! Ser.). (Illus.). 24p. (J). (gr. k-4). 22.60 (978-1-4048-0270-4(3)) Picture Window Bks.

—Drawing & Learning about Cars: Using Shapes & Lines. 2004. (Sketch It! Ser.). (Illus.). 24p. (J). (gr. k-4). 22.60 (978-1-4048-0269-8(X)) Picture Window Bks.

—Drawing & Learning about Dinosaurs: Using Shapes & Lines. 2004. (Sketch It! Ser.). (Illus.). 24p. (J). (gr. k-4). 22.60 (978-1-4048-0268-1(1) , 1229555) Picture Window Bks.

—Drawing & Learning about Dogs: Using Shapes & Lines. 2004. (Sketch It! Ser.). (Illus.). 24p. (J). (gr. k-4). 22.60 (978-1-4048-0266-7(5) , 1229556) Picture Window Bks.

—Drawing & Learning about Faces: Using Shapes & Lines. 2004. (Sketch It! Ser.). (Illus.). 24p. (J). (gr. k-4). 22.60 (978-1-4048-0271-1(1) , 1229557) Picture Window Bks.

—Drawing & Learning about Horses: Using Shapes & Lines. Muehlenhardt, Amy Bailey, illus. 2004. (Sketch It! Ser.). (Illus.). 24p. (J). (gr. k-4). 22.60 (978-1-4048-0267-4(3) , 1229558) Picture Window Bks.

—Sketch It!, 6 bks. Incl. Drawing & Learning about Bugs : Using Shapes & Lines. 22.60 (978-1-4048-0270-4(3)); Drawing & Learning about Cars : Using Shapes & Lines. 22.60 (978-1-4048-0269-8(X)); Drawing & Learning about Dinosaurs : Using Shapes & Lines. 22.60 (978-1-4048-0268-1(1) , 1229555); Drawing & Learning about Dogs : Using Shapes & Lines. 22.60 (978-1-4048-0266-7(5) , 1229556); Drawing & Learning about Faces : Using Shapes & Lines. 22.60 (978-1-4048-0271-1(1) , 1229557); Drawing & Learning about Horses : Using Shapes & Lines. Muehlenhardt, Amy Bailey, illus. 22.60 (978-1-4048-0267-4(3) , 1229558); 24p. (J). (gr. k-4). 2004. 2004. 127.56 (978-1-4048-0265-0(7)) Picture Window Bks.

Murawski, Laura. How to Draw Airplanes. 2001. (Kid's Guide to Drawing Ser.). (Illus.). 24p. (J). (gr. 3). lib. bdg. 21.25 (978-0-8239-5547-3(8) , PowerKids Pr.) Rosen Publishing Group, Inc., The.

—How to Draw Cars. 2001. (Kid's Guide to Drawing Ser.). (Illus.). 24p. (J). (gr. 3). lib. bdg. 21.25 (978-0-8239-5548-0(6) , PowerKids Pr.) Rosen Publishing Group, Inc., The.

—How to Draw Cats. 2001. (Kid's Guide to Drawing Ser.). (Illus.). 24p. (J). (gr. 3). lib. bdg. 21.25 (978-0-8239-5549-7(4) , PowerKids Pr.) Rosen Publishing Group, Inc., The.

—How to Draw Dinosaurs. 2001. (Kid's Guide to Drawing Ser.). (Illus.). 24p. (J). (gr. 3). lib. bdg. 21.25 (978-0-8239-5550-3(8) , PowerKids Pr.) Rosen Publishing Group, Inc., The.

—How to Draw Dogs. 2001. (Kid's Guide to Drawing Ser.). (Illus.). 24p. (J). (gr. 3). lib. bdg. 21.25 (978-0-8239-5551-0(6) , PowerKids Pr.) Rosen Publishing Group, Inc., The.

—A Kid's Guide to Drawing, 6 bks. Incl. How to Draw Airplanes. lib. bdg. 21.25 (978-0-8239-5547-3(8)); How to Draw Cars. lib. bdg. 21.25 (978-0-8239-5548-0(6)); How to Draw Cats. lib. bdg. 21.25 (978-0-8239-5549-7(4)); How to Draw Dinosaurs. lib. bdg. 21.25 (978-0-8239-5550-3(8)); How to Draw Dogs. lib. bdg. 21.25 (978-0-8239-5551-0(6)); How to Draw Horses. lib. bdg. 21.25 (978-0-8239-5552-7(4)); 24p. (J). (gr. 3). (Illus.). 2001. Set lib. bdg. 127.50 (978-0-8239-7058-2(2) , PowerKids Pr.) Rosen Publishing Group, Inc., The.

Nemmers, Tom. Pirates Scratch & Sketch: An Art Activity Book for Adventurous Artists & Explorers of All Ages. 2007. (Illus.). 64p. (YA). 12.99 ***978-1-59359-871-6(8))** Peter Pauper Pr. Inc.

Nicholson, Sue. Drawing, 6 vols. 2005. (QEB Let's Start! Art Ser.). (Illus.). 24p. (J). (gr. 2-5). lib. bdg. 16.95 (978-1-59566-083-1(6)) QEB Publishing Inc.

Nick Jr. Staff. Watch Me Draw Dora's Favorite Adventures. Aikins, David, illus. 2006. (Nick Jr. Watch Me Draw Ser.). 24p. (J). pap. 5.95 (978-1-56010-780-4(4)) Foster, Walter Publishing, Inc.

Nickelodeon. Spongebob Squarepants Underwater Escapades. Goldberg, Barry, illus. 2006. (Nickelodeon Watch Me Draw Ser.). 24p. (J). pap. 5.95 (978-1-56010-781-1(2)) Foster, Walter Publishing, Inc.

Nuages et Ciels. 2002. (How to Draw & Paint Ser.). Orig. Title: Oil - Clouds & Skies. (FRE.). pap. 7.95 (978-1-56010-671-5(9)) Foster, Walter Publishing, Inc.

Oka, Joseph J. Rosary Reflections for Kids. 2003. (Illus.). 30p. (J). (ps-8). 9.95 (978-0-9729800-0-5(8)) Joseph's Labor.

Panik, Alison Saeger. Painting with Pencils. 2002. (I Am an Artist Club Ser.). (Illus.). 32p. (J). (978-0-439-33625-3(2)) Scholastic, Inc.

Papel, Dibujos y Pinturas. (One Hundred One Things to Do Ser.).Tr. of Paper, Drawing & Painting. (SPA.). (J). (gr. 3-5). pap. 4.76 (978-950-724-204-5(X)) Lumen ARG. *Dist:* Lectorum Pubns., Inc.

Pearce, Querida L. The Land Before Time: How to Draw Dinosaurs. 1999. (Illus.). 64p. (YA). (gr. 2 up). pap. 6.95 (978-0-7373-0237-0(2) , 02372W) McGraw-Hill/ Contemporary.

Penton Overseas, Inc. Staff & Bater, Lucy. Dinosaur Stenciling Book: Learn to Draw Dinosaurs & Discover Dinosaur Facts. Robbins, Jim, illus. 2007. (J). (gr. 3-7). bds. 12.95 (978-1-59125-563-5(5) , Penton Kids) Penton Overseas, Inc.

Perry, Fred. Gold Digger Pocket Manga, Vol. 10. 2003. (Illus.). 124p. (gr. 11 up). pap. 12.95 (978-0-9728978-7-7(9)) Antarctic Pr., Inc.

Peters, S. True. How to Draw New Hampshires Sights & Symbols. 2002. (Kids Guide to Drawing America Ser.). 32p. (J). lib. bdg. 25.25 (978-0-8239-6085-9(4) , PowerKids Pr.) Rosen Publishing Group, Inc., The.

—How to Draw North Carolinas Sights & Symbols. 2002. (Kids Guide to Drawing America Ser.). 32p. (J). lib. bdg. 25.25 (978-0-8239-6089-7(7) , PowerKids Pr.) Rosen Publishing Group, Inc., The.

—How to Draw Oregons Sights & Symbols. 2002. (Kids Guide to Drawing America Ser.). 32p. (J). lib. bdg. 25.25 (978-0-8239-6093-4(5) , PowerKids Pr.) Rosen Publishing Group, Inc., The.

—How to Draw South Dakotas Sights & Symbols. 2002. (Kids Guide to Drawing America Ser.). 32p. (J). lib. bdg. 25.25 (978-0-8239-6098-9(6) , PowerKids Pr.) Rosen Publishing Group, Inc., The.

—How to Draw Vermonts Sights & Symbols. 2002. (Kids Guide to Drawing America Ser.). 32p. (J). lib. bdg. 25.25 (978-0-8239-6102-3(8) , PowerKids Pr.) Rosen Publishing Group, Inc., The.

—How to Draw Wisconsins Sights & Symbols. 2002. (Kids Guide to Drawing America Ser.). 32p. (J). lib. bdg. 25.25 (978-0-8239-6106-1(0) , PowerKids Pr.) Rosen Publishing Group, Inc., The.

Peterson, Tiffany. Draw It!, 2 vols., Set. Westerfield, David, illus. 2003. (J). (gr. 3-5). lib. bdg. 91.16 (978-1-4034-0216-5(7)) Heinemann Library.

—Fashion Design. Westerfield, David, illus. 2003. (Draw It! Ser.). 32p. (J). (gr. 3-5). lib. bdg. 24.22 (978-1-4034-0211-0(6)); pap. 7.50 (978-1-4034-4030-3(1)) Heinemann Library.

—Sports Stars. Westerfield, David, illus. 2003. (Draw It! Ser.). 32p. (J). (gr. 3-5). lib. bdg. 24.22 (978-1-4034-0213-4(2)); pap. 7.50 (978-1-4034-4032-7(8)) Heinemann Library.

—Sports Stars. 2003. (gr. 3-6). lib. bdg. 15.25 (978-0-613-60988-3(3)) Tandem Library Bks.

—Watercraft. Westerfield, David, illus. 2003. (Draw It! Ser.). 32p. (J). (gr. 3-5). lib. bdg. 24.22 (978-1-4034-0214-1(0)); pap. 7.50 (978-1-4034-4033-4(6)) Heinemann Library.

—Watercraft. 2003. (gr. 3-6). lib. bdg. 15.25 (978-0-613-61000-1(8)) Tandem Library Bks.

Phelps, Earl R. How to Draw Muticultural Supercharacters. 2000. (Coleccion Mujeres de Palabra Ser.). (SPA., Illus.). 96p. (gr. 3-7). pap. 18.95 (978-1-887627-04-7(9)) Phelps Publishing.

—How to Draw Muticultural Supercharacters. 2000. (gr. 5-8). lib. bdg. 29.20 (978-0-613-85835-9(2)) Tandem Library Bks.

—How to Draw Spectacular Reptiles. Phelps, Earl R., illus. 2002. (Illus.). 112p. (YA). (gr. 4-12). pap. 19.95 (978-1-887627-05-4(7)) Phelps Publishing.

Pocket Artist Kid Kit. (Illus.). 288p. (YA). (gr. 2). 18.95 (978-1-58086-450-3(3)); 17.95 (978-1-58086-443-5(0)) EDC Publishing.

Powell, William F. Drawing - Wild Animals with William F. Powell. Foster, Walter, ed. 2004. (How to Draw & Paint/Art Instruction Program Ser.). (Illus.). 32p. pap. 7.95 (978-1-56010-815-3(0)) Foster, Walter Publishing, Inc.

Princenthal, Nancy. Heide Fasnacht. 2004. (Illus.). 80p. (978-1-878607-54-6(5) , 50) Kent Gallery.

Princess & Butterflies Sketchbook. 2005. (J). pap. (978-1-59461-068-4(1)) eeBoo Corp.

QEB Learn Art National Book Stores Edition: Drawing & Sketching. 2006. (J). per. (978-1-59566-280-4(4)) QEB Publishing Inc.

QEB Let's Start! Art National Book Stores Edition: Drawing. 2006. (J). per. (978-1-59566-304-7(5)) QEB Publishing Inc.

Quasha, Jennifer. California's Sights & Symbols. 2004. 48p. pap. 8.95 (978-1-4042-8500-2(8)) Rosen Publishing Group, Inc., The.

—How to Draw Alaskas Sights & Symbols. 2002. (Kids Guide to Drawing America Ser.). 32p. (J). lib. bdg. 25.25 (978-0-8239-6056-9(0) , PowerKids Pr.) Rosen Publishing Group, Inc., The.

—How to Draw Colorados Sights & Symbols. 2002. (Kids Guide to Drawing America Ser.). 32p. (J). lib. bdg. 25.25 (978-0-8239-6060-6(9) , PowerKids Pr.) Rosen Publishing Group, Inc., The.

—How to Draw Connecticuts Sights & Symbols. 2002. (Kids Guide to Drawing America Ser.). 32p. (J). lib. bdg. 25.25 (978-0-8239-6061-3(7) , PowerKids Pr.) Rosen Publishing Group, Inc., The.

—How to Draw Delawares Sights & Symbols. 2002. (Kids Guide to Drawing America Ser.). 32p. (J). lib. bdg. 25.25 (978-0-8239-6062-0(5) , PowerKids Pr.) Rosen Publishing Group, Inc., The.

—How to Draw Floridas Sights & Symbols. 2002. (Kids Guide to Drawing America Ser.). 32p. (J). lib. bdg. 25.25 (978-0-8239-6064-4(1) , PowerKids Pr.) Rosen Publishing Group, Inc., The.

—How to Draw Georgias Sights & Symbols. 2002. (Kids Guide to Drawing America Ser.). 32p. (J). lib. bdg. 25.25 (978-0-8239-6065-1(X) , PowerKids Pr.) Rosen Publishing Group, Inc., The.

—How to Draw Hawaiis Sights & Symbols. 2002. (Kids Guide to Drawing America Ser.). 32p. (J). lib. bdg. 25.25 (978-0-8239-6067-5(6) , PowerKids Pr.) Rosen Publishing Group, Inc., The.

—How to Draw Idahos Sights & Symbols. 2002. (Kids Guide to Drawing America Ser.). 32p. (J). lib. bdg. 25.25 (978-0-8239-6068-2(4) , PowerKids Pr.) Rosen Publishing Group, Inc., The.

—A Kid's Guide to Drawing America. 2002. (Kids Guide to Drawing America Ser.). (Illus.). 32p. (J). lib. bdg. 25.25 (978-0-8239-6057-6(9)); lib. bdg. 25.25 (978-0-8239-6058-3(7)); lib. bdg. 25.25 (978-0-8239-6091-0(9)); lib. bdg. 25.25 (978-0-8239-6055-2(2)) Rosen Publishing Group, Inc., The. (PowerKids Pr.).

Randolph, Joanne. Drawing Birds. 2005. (Let's Draw with Shapes Ser.). (Illus.). 24p. (J). 17.25 (978-1-4042-2792-7(X) , PowerKids Pr.) Rosen Publishing Group, Inc., The.

—Drawing Dinosaurs. 2005. (Let's Draw with Shapes Ser.). (J). 17.25 (978-1-4042-2793-4(8) , PowerKids Pr.) Rosen Publishing Group, Inc., The.

—Drawing Houses. 2005. (Let's Draw with Shapes Ser.). (Illus.). 24p. (J). 17.25 (978-1-4042-2795-8(4) , PowerKids Pr.) Rosen Publishing Group, Inc., The.

—Drawing School Buses. 2005. (Let's Draw with Shapes Ser.). (Illus.). 24p. (J). 17.25 (978-1-4042-2791-0(1) , PowerKids Pr.) Rosen Publishing Group, Inc., The.

—Drawing Trucks. 2005. (Let's Draw with Shapes Ser.). (J). 17.25 (978-1-4042-2796-5(2) , PowerKids Pr.) Rosen Publishing Group, Inc., The.

—Let's Draw a Bird with Shapes: Vamos a Dibujar un Ave Usando Figuras. Muschinske, Emily, illus. 2005. (Let's Draw with Shapes/ Vamos a dibujar con Figuras Ser.). (J). 17.25 (978-1-4042-7555-3(X) , PowerKids Pr.) Rosen Publishing Group, Inc., The.

—Let's Draw a Dinosaur with Shapes: Vamos a Dibujar un Dinosaurio Usando Figuras. 2005. (Let's Draw with Shapes/ Vamos a dibujar con Figuras Ser.). (ENG & SPA.). (J). 17.25 (978-1-4042-7553-9(3) , PowerKids Pr.) Rosen Publishing Group, Inc., The.

—Let's Draw a Fire Truck with Shapes: Vamos a Dibujar un Camion de Bomberos Usando Figuras. Muschinske, Emily, illus. 2005. (Let's Draw with Shapes/ Vamos a dibujar con Figuras Ser.). (ENG & SPA.). (J). 17.25 (978-1-4042-7556-0(8) , PowerKids Pr.) Rosen Publishing Group, Inc., The.

—Let's Draw a House with Shapes: Vamos a Dibujar una Casa Usando Figuras. Muschinske, Emily, illus. 2005. (Let's Draw with Shapes/ Vamos a dibujar con Figuras Ser.). (ENG & SPA.). (J). 17.25 (978-1-4042-7558-4(4) , PowerKids Pr.) Rosen Publishing Group, Inc., The.

—Let's Draw a School Bus with Shapes: Vamos a Dibujar un Autobus Escolar Usando Figuras. Muschinske, Emily, illus. 2005. (Let's Draw with Shapes/ Vamos a dibujar con Figuras Ser.). (ENG & SPA.). (J). 17.25 (978-1-4042-7557-7(6) , PowerKids Pr.) Rosen Publishing Group, Inc., The.

—Let's Draw a Truck with Shapes: Vamos a Dibujar un Camion Usando Figuras. Muschinske, Emily, illus. 2005. (Let's Draw with Shapes/ Vamos a dibujar con Figuras Ser.). (ENG & SPA.). (J). 17.25 (978-1-4042-7554-6(1) , PowerKids Pr.) Rosen Publishing Group, Inc., The.

—Let's Draw a Turtle with Half Circles: Vamos a Dibujar una Tortuga Usando Medios Circulos. Muschinske, Emily, tr. Muschinske, Emily, illus. 2004. (Let's Draw with Shapes Ser.). (ENG & SPA.). 24p. (J). lib. bdg. 17.25 (978-1-4042-7504-1(5) , PowerKids Pr.) Rosen Publishing Group, Inc., The.

Randolph, Ryan P. How to Draw the Life & Times of John Adams. 2006. (Kid's Guide to Drawing the Presidents of the United States of America Ser.). (J). 25.25 (978-1-4042-2979-2(5) , PowerKids Pr.) Rosen Publishing Group, Inc., The.

Raynes, John & Raynes, Jody. How to Draw a Human Figure. 2003. (Essential Art Ser.). 160p. (YA). 19.95 (978-0-7525-8772-1(2)) Parragon, Inc.

Reagan, Dawn. Duck Pad: Toon Takes Artist Pad & Pencil. 1999. (Illus.). 50p. (J). (gr. 1-7). pap. 7.95 (978-1-929456-11-6(5)) Myrtle-Seal Publishing.

Realtime Associates and Mazer Corporation Staff & LeapFrog Staff, compiled by. Understand Diagrams, Charts, & Pictures. 2002. (J). (gr. 2). 66.75 (978-1-58605-295-9(0) , LeapFrog Schl. Hse.) LeapFrog Enterprises, Inc.

—Understand Diagrams, Charts, Graphs, & Pictures. 2002. (J). (gr. 3). 66.75 (978-1-58605-357-4(4) , LeapFrog Schl. Hse.) LeapFrog Enterprises, Inc.

—Understand Diagrams, Charts, Graphs, Pictures. 2002. (J). (gr. 4). 66.75 (978-1-58605-413-7(9) , LeapFrog Schl. Hse.) LeapFrog Enterprises, Inc.

Regan, Lisa & Williams, Beckie. Born Free How to Draw Wild Horses. Forder, Nicholas, illus. 2005. 48p. (J). pap. (978-1-84510-746-8(2)) Top That! Publishing PLC.

Reinagle, Damon J. Draw: A Step-by-Step Guide. 2005. (Illus.). 64p. pap. 8.99 (978-0-939217-34-2(1)) Peel Productions, Inc.

—Draw Alien Fantasies. 2000. (Learn to Draw Ser.). (Illus.). 64p. (J). (gr. 6-9). pap. 8.99 (978-0-939217-31-1(7)) Peel Productions, Inc.

—Draw Magical Fantasies: A Step-by-Step Guide. 2001. (Learn to Draw Ser.). (Illus.). 64p. (J). (gr. 3-9). pap. 8.99 (978-0-939217-33-5(3) , 32069) Peel Productions, Inc.

—Draw Magical Fantasies: A Step-by-Step Guide. 2002. (gr. 5-8). lib. bdg. 17.60 (978-0-613-86903-4(6)) Tandem Library Bks.

—Draw Medieval Fantasies. Reinagle, Damon J., illus. 2000. (Learn to Draw Ser.). (Illus.). 64p. (J). (gr. 6-9). pap. 8.99 (978-0-939217-30-4(9)) Peel Productions, Inc.

Reynolds, Virginia. Fine Art Scratch & Sketch: A Cool Art Activity Book for Budding Fine Artists of All Ages. 2005. (Activity Journal Ser.). (Illus.). (J). 12.99 (978-0-88088-596-6(3)) Peter Pauper Pr. Inc.

Robertson, Scott. How to Draw Cars the Hot Wheels Way. rev. ed. 2004. (Illus.). 144p. (J). pap., pap. 21.95 (978-0-7603-1480-7(2)) MBI Distribution Services.

Rubin, Judith. My Mom & Dad Don't Live Together Anymore: A Drawing Book for Children of Separated or Divorced Parents. Matthews, Bonnie, illus. 2002. 80p. (J). (ps-6). pap. 14.95 (978-1-55798-835-5(8) , Magination Pr.) American Psychological Assn.

Santos, Dina. I Can Draw: Learning the DR Sound. (Power-Phonics Ser.). (Illus.). (J). 2002. 24p. (gr. 1). lib. bdg. 18.50 (978-0-8239-5946-4(5)); 2001. 23p. pap. 26.40 (978-0-8239-8291-2(2)) Rosen Publishing Group, Inc., The. (PowerKids Pr.).

Saxon, Victoria. The Rescuers. 1998. 48p. (J). 3.50 (978-0-7364-0129-6(6)) Mouse Works.

Schmidt, Roderic. How to Draw the Life & Times of James Madison. 2006. (Kid's Guide to Drawing the Presidents of the United States of America Ser.). (J). 25.25 (978-1-4042-2981-5(7) , PowerKids Pr.) Rosen Publishing Group, Inc., The.

—How to Draw the Life & Times of Martin Van Buren. 2006. (Kid's Guide to Drawing the Presidents of the United States of America Ser.). (J). 25.25 (978-1-4042-2985-3(X) , PowerKids Pr.) Rosen Publishing Group, Inc., The.

—How to Draw the Life & Times of Zachary Taylor. 2006. (Kid's Guide to Drawing the Presidents of the United States of America Ser.). (J). 25.25 (978-1-4042-2989-1(2) , PowerKids Pr.) Rosen Publishing Group, Inc., The.

Scholastic, Inc. Staff. Clifford Bones & Dots. 2004. pap. 3.50 (978-0-439-56811-1(0)) Scholastic, Inc.

Schwartz, Linda. California Geodoodles, Grades 4-6: Learning about California Through Step-by-Step Drawings. Armstrong, Beverly, illus. 2000. 64p. (J). pap., tchr. ed. 9.99 (978-0-88160-355-2(4) , LW-394, Learning Works, The) Creative Teaching Pr., Inc.

—Jewish Superdoubles: Step by Step Drawing Fun for Kids 6-12. Clark Editorial and Design Staff, ed. Armstrong, Beverly, illus. 1999. 32p. (J). (gr. 1-7). pap. 4.95 (978-0-88160-322-4(8) , LW385) Creative Teaching Pr., Inc.

—Texas Geodoodles, Grades 4-6: Learning about Texas Through Step-by-Step Drawings. Smith, Stephanie W. & Clark, Kim, eds. Armstrong, Beverly, illus. 2000. 64p. pap., tchr. ed. 9.99 (978-0-88160-352-1(X) , LW-391, Learning Works, The) Creative Teaching Pr., Inc.

Sebastiani, Laura, creator. Penny & Drew's Penciltips, Vols. 1-4. 2006. (J). 19.95 (978-0-9766793-4-9(5)) ThoughtRockets, Inc.

—Penny & Drew's Penciltips: Animal Alliteration. 2006. 80p. (J). 4.95 (978-0-9766793-1-8(0)) ThoughtRockets, Inc.

—Penny & Drew's Penciltips: Draw THIS! 2006. 80p. (J). 4.95 (978-0-9766793-0-1(2)) ThoughtRockets, Inc.

—Penny & Drew's Penciltips: Idioms. 2006. 80p. (J). 4.95 (978-0-9766793-2-5(9)) ThoughtRockets, Inc.

—Penny & Drew's Penciltips: Transportation. 2006. 80p. (J). 4.95 (978-0-9766793-3-2(7)) ThoughtRockets, Inc.

Seif, Adam. Adam & Jeremy's Artistic Adventure: The World Isn't Flat... Learn to Draw Pictures That Jump Out at You. Cutcliff, Linda & Havenga, Marilyn, eds. Seif, Adam, illus. 2001. (Illus.). (J). (gr. 1-8). pap. 19.95 (978-0-9678810-8-9(0)) DreamCatcherPress, Inc.

Silver Dolphin en Español Editors. Serie aprendizaje: Aprende con tus Amigas: Learning Series: Learn with Your Friends. 2007. (Illus.). 8p. (J). bds. 16.95 (***978-970-718-467-1(1)*** , Silver Dolphin en Español) Advanced Marketing, S. de R. L. de C. V. MEX. *Dist:* Perseus Distribution.

Smith, A. & Tatchell, J. Complete Book of Drawing. 2004. (Art Ideas Ser.). (Illus.). 128p. (J). pap. 17.95 (978-0-7945-0015-3(3) , Usborne); lib. bdg. 25.95 (978-1-58086-353-7(1)) EDC Publishing.

Smith, Theron. Draw Science Fiction No. II: Mutant Aliens, Far-Out Spaceships & Other Outer Space Wonders. 2000. (Draw Science Fiction Ser.: Vol. II). (Illus.). 64p. (J). (gr. 2 up). pap. 7.95 (978-0-7373-0477-0(4) , 04774W, Roxbury Park Juvenile) Lowell Hse. Juvenile.

Soltero, Emilio, illus. & text. Draw the Line. Soltero, Emilio, text. 2003. 128p. (YA). per. 15.95 (978-0-9741332-0-1(5)) Pearl Pr.

Songhurst, B. & Breed. Activators Drawing. (Illus.). 128p. (J). pap. 8.99 (978-0-340-71521-5(9) , Hodder & Stoughton) Hodder General Publishing Division GBR. *Dist:* Trafalgar Square Publishing.

Staiano, Andrew. Draw the Titanic. Pederson, Jason, illus. 1999. 64p. (J). (gr. 1-4). pap. 6.99 (978-0-439-07670-8(6)) Scholastic, Inc.

Stillinger, Doug. Espirales de Colores. 2004. (SPA., Illus.). 56p. (J). spiral bd. 23.95 (978-987-1078-24-0(2)) Klutz Latino MEX. *Dist:* Independent Pubs. Group.

—The Spiral Draw Book. 2003. (Illus.). 38p. (J). (gr. 3 up). spiral bd. 19.95 (978-1-57054-960-1(5)) Klutz.

Striker, Susan, et al. The Second Anti-Coloring Book: Creative Activites for Ages 6 & Up. 2nd rev. ed. 2001. (Illus.). 96p. pap. 11.95 (978-0-8050-6843-6(0) , Owl Bks.) Holt, Henry & Co.

Sundby, Scott. Cut down to Size at High Noon: A Math Adventure. Geehan, Wayne, illus. 2004. (Math Adventures Ser.). 32p. (J). (gr. 3-11). pap. 6.95 (978-1-57091-168-2(1)) Charlesbridge Publishing, Inc.

Tallarico, Tony. I Can Draw Spaceships, Aliens & Robots. 1998. (I Can Draw Ser.). (J). (978-0-606-12967-1(7)) Tandem Library Bks.

—I Can Draw Sports. 2000. (J). 4.99 (978-0-689-81451-8(8) , Simon & Schuster Children's Publishing) Simon & Schuster Children's Publishing.

—I Can Draw the Bible: The Old Testament. 1998. (I Can Draw Ser.). (978-0-606-13501-6(4)) Tandem Library Bks.

Tecco, Betsy Dru. How to Draw Egypt's Sights & Symbols. 2004. (Kid's Guide to Drawing the Countries of the World Ser.). (Illus.). 48p. (J). lib. bdg. 26.50 (978-0-8239-6682-0(8) , PowerKids Pr.) Rosen Publishing Group, Inc., The.

—How to Draw France's Sights & Symbols. 2004. (Kid's Guide to Drawing the Countries of the World Ser.). (Illus.). 48p. (J). lib. bdg. 26.50 (978-0-8239-6683-7(6) , PowerKids Pr.) Rosen Publishing Group, Inc., The.

—How to Draw Germany's Sights & Symbols. 2004. (Kid's Guide to Drawing the Countries of the World Ser.). (Illus.). 48p. (J). lib. bdg. 26.50 (978-0-8239-6685-1(2) , PowerKids Pr.) Rosen Publishing Group, Inc., The.

—How to Draw Hungary's Sights & Symbols. 2005. (Kid's Guide to Drawing the Countries of the World Ser.). (Illus.). 48p. (J). (ps-k). lib. bdg. 26.50 (978-1-4042-2737-8(7) , PowerKids Pr.) Rosen Publishing Group, Inc., The.

—How to Draw Italy's Sights & Symbols. 2004. (Kid's Guide to Drawing the Countries of the World Ser.). (Illus.). 48p. (J). lib. bdg. 26.50 (978-0-8239-6686-8(0) , PowerKids Pr.) Rosen Publishing Group, Inc., The.

—How to Draw Japan's Sights & Symbols. 2004. (Kid's Guide to Drawing the Countries of the World Ser.). 48p. (J). lib. bdg. 26.50 (978-0-8239-6681-3(X) , PowerKids Pr.) Rosen Publishing Group, Inc., The.

—How to Draw Thailand's Sights & Symbols. 2005. (Kid's Guide to Drawing the Countries of the World Ser.). (J). 26.50 (978-1-4042-2741-5(5) , PowerKids Pr.) Rosen Publishing Group, Inc., The.

—How to Draw the Life & Times of John Quincy Adams. 2006. (Kid's Guide to Drawing the Presidents of the United States of America Ser.). (J). 25.25 (978-1-4042-2983-9(3) , PowerKids Pr.) Rosen Publishing Group, Inc., The.

—How to Draw the Life & Times of Ulysses S. Grant. 2006. (Kid's Guide to Drawing the Presidents of the United States of America Ser.). (J). 25.25 (978-1-4042-2995-2(7) , PowerKids Pr.) Rosen Publishing Group, Inc., The.

—How to Draw the United Kingdom's Sights & Symbols. 2004. (Kid's Guide to Drawing the Countries of the World Ser.). (Illus.). 48p. (J). lib. bdg. 26.50 (978-0-8239-6684-4(4) , PowerKids Pr.) Rosen Publishing Group, Inc., The.

—A Kid's Guide to Drawing the Countries of the World: Set 1, 6 bks., Set 2003. (Illus.). (J). (gr. k-5). (978-0-8239-8485-5(0) , PowerKids Pr.) Rosen Publishing Group, Inc., The.

Teitelbaum, Michael. How to Draw Nintendo Heroes & Villians. Zalme, Ron, illus. 2004. 32p. (J). 4.99 (978-0-439-63579-0(9)) Scholastic, Inc.

—How to Draw the Legend of Zelda. Zalme, Ron, illus. 2004. 32p. (J). pap. 4.99 (978-0-439-63581-3(0)) Scholastic, Inc.

Tell It to a Friend, 6 Packs. (gr. k-1). 23.00 (978-0-7635-8827-4(X)) Rigby Education.

Temple, Kathryn. Drawing: The Only Drawing Book You'll Ever Need to Be the Artist You've Always Wanted to Be. 2005. (Art Skills for Kids Ser.). (Illus.). 112p. 17.95 (978-1-57990-587-3(0)) Lark Bks.

Tezuka Productions. Tezuka School of Animation 1: Learning the Basics. 2003. (Illus.). 108p. pap. 13.95 (978-1-56970-995-5(5)) Macmillan.

Thomson, Ruth. Creatures. 2003. (First Look at Art Ser.). (Illus.). 32p. (gr. 3-5). 23.00 (978-0-7910-7945-4(7) , Chelsea Hse.) Facts On File, Inc.

Timms, Diann. Hare & Bear Draw, 5 vols., Set. Date not set. (Illus.). 22p. (J). (978-0-89577-548-1(4)) Reader's Digest Assn., Inc., The.

Top That, ed. How to Draw 101 Fantasy Characters. Green, Dan, illus. 2005. 48p. (J). pap. (978-1-84510-736-9(5)) Top That! Publishing PLC.

—How to Draw 101 Manga Characters. Fish, Custard, illus. 2005. 48p. (J). pap. (978-1-84510-737-6(3)) Top That! Publishing PLC.

—How to Draw 101 Super Heroes. Griffin, Hedley, illus. 2005. 48p. (J). pap. (978-1-84510-738-3(1)) Top That! Publishing PLC.

Top That Publishing Editors, ed. Silly Scribbles. Dahl, Roald, illus. 2005. 24p. (J). pap. (978-1-905359-52-3(7)) Top That! Publishing PLC.

Top That Publishing Staff, ed. Drawing with Pastels. 2005. (Illus.). 48p. (978-1-84510-677-5(6)) Top That! Publishing PLC.

—How to Draw Monster Reptiles. 2005. (Illus.). 48p. pap. (978-1-84510-745-1(4)) Top That! Publishing PLC.

—Sketching with Pencils. 2004. (Art Tricks Ser.). (Illus.). 48p. (978-1-84510-320-0(3)) Top That! Publishing PLC.

Top That!, creator. How to Draw Managa Fantasy Fighters. 2005. (Illus.). 48p. (J). (gr. 4-7). pap. (978-1-84510-972-1(4)) Top That! Publishing PLC.

—How to Draw Manga Transforming Robots. 2005. (Illus.). 48p. (J). (gr. 4-7). pap. (978-1-84510-973-8(2)) Top That! Publishing PLC.

—How to Draw Manga Urban Crew. 2005. (Illus.). 48p. (J). (gr. 4-7). pap. (978-1-84510-974-5(0)) Top That! Publishing PLC.

Tracing & Cutting. 2003. (Right Start for Early Learners Ser.). 48p. (J). (ps-1). pap. 7.99 (978-0-7439-3228-8(5)) Teacher Created Materials, Inc.

Usborne Publishing Staff, ed. Pintar Personajes. 2004. Tr. of I Can Draw People. (SPA., Illus.). 32p. (J). (ps-3). lib. bdg. 12.95 (978-1-58086-285-1(3)) EDC Publishing.

Usworth, Jean Morman. Drawing Is Basic: Grade 2. 2000. (Illus.). 96p. (J). (gr. 2). pap. 13.95 (978-0-7690-2510-0(2)) Seymour, Dale Pubns.

—Drawing Is Basic: Grade 4. 2000. (Illus.). 96p. (J). (gr. 4). pap. 13.95 (978-0-7690-2500-1(5)) Seymour, Dale Pubns.

—Drawing Is Basic: Grade 5. 2000. (Illus.). 96p. (J). (gr. 5). pap. 13.95 (978-0-7690-2501-8(3)) Seymour, Dale Pubns.

Valdivia, Manny & Valdivia, Rochelle. Big Machines: Let's Draw. Valdivia, Manny & Valdivia, Rochelle, illus. 2000. (Let's Draw Ser.). (Illus.). 32p. (J). (gr. 1-7). mass mkt. 2.99 (978-0-7681-0223-9(5) , 67301, McClanahan Bk.) Learning Horizons, Inc.

—Dogs & Cats: Let's Draw. Valdivia, Manny & Valdivia, Rochelle, illus. 2000. (Let's Draw Ser.). (Illus.). 32p. (J). (gr. 1-7). mass mkt. 2.99 (978-0-7681-0222-2(7) , 67303, McClanahan Bk.) Learning Horizons, Inc.

Very Very van Gogh. 2004. (J). (978-0-9765917-0-2(7)) EDUKIT, L.L.C.

Visca, Curt & Visca, Kelley. How to Draw Cartoon Careers. 2004. (Kid's Guide to Drawing Ser.). (Illus.). 24p. (J). lib. bdg. 21.25 (978-0-8239-6725-4(5) , PowerKids Pr.) Rosen Publishing Group, Inc., The.

—How to Draw Cartoon Holiday Symbols. 2004. (Kid's Guide to Drawing Ser.). (Illus.). 24p. (J). lib. bdg. 21.25 (978-0-8239-6726-1(3) , PowerKids Pr.) Rosen Publishing Group, Inc., The.

—How to Draw Cartoon Spacecraft & Astronauts in Action. 2004. (Kid's Guide to Drawing Ser.). (Illus.). 24p. (J). lib. bdg. 21.25 (978-0-8239-6729-2(8) , PowerKids Pr.) Rosen Publishing Group, Inc., The.

—How to Draw Cartoon Symbols of the United States. 2004. (Kid's Guide to Drawing Ser.). (Illus.). 24p. (J). lib. bdg. 21.25 (978-0-8239-6727-8(1) , PowerKids Pr.) Rosen Publishing Group, Inc., The.

—How to Draw Cartoon Symbols of the Wild West. 2004. (Kid's Guide to Drawing Ser.). (Illus.). 24p. (J). lib. bdg. 21.25 (978-0-8239-6728-5(X) , PowerKids Pr.) Rosen Publishing Group, Inc., The.

—How to Draw Cartoon Vehicles. 2004. (Kid's Guide to Drawing Ser.). (Illus.). 24p. (J). lib. bdg. 21.25 (978-0-8239-6724-7(7) , PowerKids Pr.) Rosen Publishing Group, Inc., The.

Walsh, Patricia. Aircraft. 2002. (Draw It! Ser.). (Illus.). 32p. (J). (gr. 3-6). pap. 7.50 (978-1-58810-291-1(2) , 91041) Heinemann Library.

—Cars. 2002. (Draw It! Ser.). (Illus.). 32p. (J). (gr. 3-6). pap. 7.50 (978-1-58810-292-8(0) , 91042) Heinemann Library.

—Dinosaurs. 2002. (Draw It! Ser.). (Illus.). 32p. (J). (gr. 3-6). pap. 7.50 (978-1-58810-293-5(9) , 91043) Heinemann Library.

—Space Vehicles. 2002. (Draw It! Ser.). (Illus.). 32p. (J). (gr. 3-6). pap. 7.50 (978-1-58810-294-2(7) , 91044) Heinemann Library.

—Wild Animals. 2002. (Draw It! Ser.). (Illus.). 32p. (J). (gr. 3-6). pap. 7.50 (978-1-58810-295-9(5) , 91045) Heinemann Library.

—Wild Animals. Westerfield, David, illus. 2000. (Draw It! Ser.). 32p. (J). (gr. 3-5). lib. bdg. 22.79 (978-1-57572-351-8(4)) Heinemann Library.

—Woodland Animals. 2002. (Illus.). 32p. (J). (gr. 3-6). pap. 7.50 (978-1-58810-296-6(3) , 91046) Heinemann Library.

Walsh, Patricia & Adamic, Marc. Aircraft. 2000. (Draw It! Ser.). (Illus.). 32p. (J). (gr. 3-5). lib. bdg. 22.79 (978-1-57572-347-1(6)) Heinemann Library.

—Space Vehicles. 2000. (Draw It! Ser.). (Illus.). 32p. (J). (gr. 3-5). lib. bdg. 22.79 (978-1-57572-350-1(6)) Heinemann Library.

Walsh, Patricia & Westerfield, David. Cars. 2000. (Draw It! Ser.). (Illus.). 32p. (J). (gr. 3-5). lib. bdg. 22.79 (978-1-57572-348-8(4)) Heinemann Library.

—Dinosaurs. 2000. (Draw It! Ser.). (Illus.). 32p. (J). (gr. 3-5). lib. bdg. 22.79 (978-1-57572-349-5(2)) Heinemann Library.

—Woodlands Animals. 2000. (Draw It! Ser.). (Illus.). 32p. (J). (gr. 3-5). lib. bdg. 22.79 (978-1-57572-352-5(2)) Heinemann Library.

Walter Foster Editors, ed. Dora the Explore. 2003. (Art for Children Ser.). (Illus.). 32p. (J). pap. 5.95 (978-1-56010-759-0(6)) Foster, Walter Publishing, Inc.

—Fairly Oddparents. 2004. (Nickelodeon How to Draw Ser.). (Illus.). 32p. (J). pap. 5.95 (978-1-56010-803-0(7)) Foster, Walter Publishing, Inc.

—How to Animate SpongeBob SquarePants. 2004. (Art for Children Ser.). (Illus.). 32p. (J). pap. 5.95 (978-1-56010-758-3(8)) Foster, Walter Publishing, Inc.

—How to Draw Disney-Pixar's Toy Story. 2003. (Disney's Classic Character Ser.). (Illus.). 40p. (J). (gr. 3 up). pap. 8.95 (978-1-56010-462-9(7)) Foster, Walter Publishing, Inc.

—Learn to Draw Looney Tunes. 2000. (Looney Tunes Collection). (Illus.). 96p. (J). (gr. 3). pap. 14.95 (978-1-56010-552-7(6)) Foster, Walter Publishing, Inc.

Watson, B. S. How to Draw Dragonball Z. 2001. 11.79 (978-0-606-22180-1(8)) Tandem Library Bks.

Watt, Fiona. Art Ideas Drawing Pack: Internet-Linked. 2004. (Activity Kits Ser.). 32p. (J). act. bk. ed. 16.95 (978-0-7945-0539-4(2)) EDC Publishing.

—How to Draw Ballerinas & Princesses. 2005. (Illus.). 32p. (J). pap. 8.95 (978-0-7945-0956-9(8) , Usborne) EDC Publishing.

—How to Draw Dinosaurs. Figg, Non et al, illus. 2005. 31p. (J). (ps-ps). pap. 8.95 (978-0-7945-1056-5(6) , Usborne) EDC Publishing.

—How to Draw Fairies & Mermaids. 2005. (Activity Books Ser.). 34p. (J). pap. 8.95 (978-0-7945-0919-4(3) , Usborne) EDC Publishing.

—50 Things to Draw & Paint. 2006. 50p. (J). 9.99 (978-0-7945-1215-6(1) , Usborne) EDC Publishing.

Webster, Christine. How to Draw Christmas Symbols. 2005. (Kid's Guide to Drawing Ser.). (Illus.). 24p. (J). (ps-k). lib. bdg. 21.25 (978-1-4042-2725-5(3) , PowerKids Pr.) Rosen Publishing Group, Inc., The.

—How to Draw Easter Symbols. 2005. (Kid's Guide to Drawing Ser.). (Illus.). 24p. (J). (ps-k). lib. bdg. 21.25 (978-1-4042-2726-2(1) , PowerKids Pr.) Rosen Publishing Group, Inc., The.

—How to Draw Hanukkah Symbols. 2005. (Kid's Guide to Drawing Ser.). (Illus.). 24p. (J). (ps). lib. bdg. 21.25 (978-1-4042-2727-9(X) , PowerKids Pr.) Rosen Publishing Group, Inc., The.

—How to Draw Kwanzaa Symbols. 2005. (Kid's Guide to Drawing Ser.). (Illus.). 24p. (J). (ps). lib. bdg. 21.25 (978-1-4042-2728-6(8) , PowerKids Pr.) Rosen Publishing Group, Inc., The.

—How to Draw Passover Symbols. 2005. (Kid's Guide to Drawing Ser.). (Illus.). 24p. (J). (ps). lib. bdg. 21.25 (978-1-4042-2729-3(6) , PowerKids Pr.) Rosen Publishing Group, Inc., The.

—How to Draw Thanksgiving Symbols. 2005. (Kid's Guide to Drawing Ser.). (Illus.). 24p. (J). (ps). lib. bdg. 21.25 (978-1-4042-2730-9(X) , PowerKids Pr.) Rosen Publishing Group, Inc., The.

Weintraub, A. How to Draw District of Columbias Sights & Symbols. 2002. (Kids Guide to Drawing America Ser.). 32p. (J). lib. bdg. 25.25 (978-0-8239-6063-7(3) , PowerKids Pr.) Rosen Publishing Group, Inc., The.

—How to Draw Nebraskas Sights & Symbols. 2002. (Kids Guide to Drawing America Ser.). 32p. (J). lib. bdg. 25.25 (978-0-8239-6083-5(8) , PowerKids Pr.) Rosen Publishing Group, Inc., The.

—How to Draw New Mexicos Sights & Symbols. 2002. (Kids Guide to Drawing America Ser.). 32p. (J). lib. bdg. 25.25 (978-0-8239-6087-3(0) , PowerKids Pr.) Rosen Publishing Group, Inc., The.

—How to Draw Rhode Islands Sights & Symbols. 2002. (Kids Guide to Drawing America Ser.). 32p. (J). lib. bdg. 25.25 (978-0-8239-6096-5(X) , PowerKids Pr.) Rosen Publishing Group, Inc., The.

—How to Draw South Carolinas Sights & Symbols. 2002. (Kids Guide to Drawing America Ser.). 32p. (J). lib. bdg. 25.25 (978-0-8239-6097-2(8) , PowerKids Pr.) Rosen Publishing Group, Inc., The.

—How to Draw Texass Sights & Symbols. 2002. (Kids Guide to Drawing America Ser.). 32p. (J). lib. bdg. 25.25 (978-0-8239-6100-9(1) , PowerKids Pr.) Rosen Publishing Group, Inc., The.

—How to Draw Washingtons Sights & Symbols. 2002. (Kids Guide to Drawing America Ser.). 32p. (J). lib. bdg. 25.25 (978-0-8239-6104-7(4) , PowerKids Pr.) Rosen Publishing Group, Inc., The.

Weintraub, Aileen. Texas's Sights & Symbols. 2005. 48p. pap. 8.95 (978-1-4042-8503-3(2)) Rosen Publishing Group, Inc., The.

West, Tracey. How to Draw Pokemon. 2003. (Pokemon Ser.). (Illus.). 32p. (J). pap. 4.99 (978-0-439-43440-9(8)) Scholastic, Inc.

—How to Draw Pokemon. 2003. (gr. k-3). lib. bdg. 13.00 (978-0-613-72110-3(1)) Tandem Library Bks.

Wheeler, Jill C. Children's Illustrators Set I. 2005. (Children's Illustrators Set I Ser.). (J). (gr. k-6). lib. bdg. 128.10 (978-1-59197-717-9(7) , Checkerboard Library) ABDO Publishing Co.

White, Kimberly. Mood Music, 2003. (Musical Colors Rhyming Story Coloring Book Ser.). 16p. (J). spiral bd. 10.95 (978-1-931844-06-2(2) , PP1018) Piano Pr.

Wild Animals. 1998. (Illus.). 8p. (J). pap. 2.00 (978-0-9703548-2-2(7)) Belle River Readers, Inc.

Wild Animals. (J). Date not set. (Illus.). 16p. 5.98 (978-0-7525-7699-2(2)); Date not set. (Illus.). 16p. 2.98 (978-0-7525-9763-8(9)); 2002. bds. 7.98 (978-0-7525-8732-5(3)); 2001. 12p. bds. 11.95 (978-0-7525-5261-3(9)) Parragon, Inc.

Wild Animals. 2001. (Early Learning Ser.). (J). (gr. k-12). vinyl bd. 4.95 (978-1-58845-043-2(0)) School Specialty Publishing.

Williams, Ted & Williams, Amy E., illus. Construction. 2005. 96p. spiral bd. (978-0-7853-8302-4(6) , 3461000) Publications International, Ltd.

Winterberg, Jenna. Outer Space: A Step-by-Step Drawing & Story Book for Kids As Young As Four Years Old. Fisher, Diana, illus. 2006. (Watch Me Draw Ser.). 24p. (J). pap. 4.95 (978-1-56010-797-2(9)) Foster, Walter Publishing, Inc.

—Rainforest: A Step-by-Step Drawing & Story Book. Fisher, Diana, illus. 2006. (Watch Me Draw Ser.). 24p. (J). pap. 4.95 (978-1-56010-785-9(5)) Foster, Walter Publishing, Inc.

—Zoo: A Step-by-Step Drawing & Story Book for Kids as Young as Four Years Old. Fisher, Diana, illus. 2006. (Watch Me Draw Ser.). 24p. (J). pap. 4.95 (978-1-56010-798-9(7)) Foster, Walter Publishing, Inc.

Wipe It Off... And Start Again: Drawing Fun. 2002. 24p. (J). spiral bd. 4.98 (978-0-7525-8354-9(9)) Parragon, Inc.

The Wonderful Art of Drawing Horses. 2001. 14.95 (978-0-9717874-0-7(9)) How Great Thou Art Pubns.

Yamamoto, Neal, illus. Funny Faces to Draw. 2000. (Fifty Nifty Ser.). 80p. (J). (gr. 3-7). pap. 6.95 (978-0-7373-0479-4(0) , 04790W, Roxbury Park Juvenile) Lowell Hse. Juvenile.

—50 Nifty Space Aliens to Draw. 1999. (Fifty Nifty Ser.). 79p. (J). (gr. 2-7). pap. 6.95 (978-0-7373-0163-2(5) , 01635W) McGraw-Hill/Contemporary.

Young, Eddie. How to Draw Scooby-Doo. 1998. (gr. 3-6). lib. bdg. 16.40 (978-0-613-81783-7(4)) Tandem Library Bks.

Zalme, Ron. World's Best Pokemon Drawing Book. 2000. (J). (978-0-606-19675-8(7)) Tandem Library Bks.

Zamora, Dulce. How to Draw the Life & Times of Franklin Pierce. 2006. (Kid's Guide to Drawing the Presidents of the United States of America Ser.). (J). 25.25 (978-1-4042-2991-4(4) , PowerKids Pr.) Rosen Publishing Group, Inc., The.

—How to Draw the Life & Times of John Tyler. 2006. (Kid's Guide to Drawing the Presidents of the United States of America Ser.). (J). 25.25 (978-1-4042-2987-7(6) , PowerKids Pr.) Rosen Publishing Group, Inc., The.

Zemke, Deborah. D Is for Doodle: Doodles from A. 2004. (Illus.). 64p. pap. 12.95 (978-1-59354-029-6(9)) Blue Apple Bks.

—Doodle a Zoodle: Oodles of Animal Doodles. 2006. (Illus.). 64p. spiral bd. 12.95 (978-1-59354-140-8(6)) Blue Apple Bks.

Zschock, Heather. Under the Sea Scratch & Sketch: An Art Activity Book for Imaginative Artists of All Ages. 2005. (Activity Book Ser.). (Illus.). 64p. (J). 12.99 (978-1-59359-905-8(6)) Peter Pauper Pr. Inc.

DRAWING—FICTION

Alexander, Martha. I'll Never Share You, Blackboard Bear. Alexander, Martha, illus. 2003. (Illus.). 32p. (J). (ps-1). 13.99 (978-0-7636-1590-1(0)) Candlewick Pr.

Baker, Liza. Harold & the Purple CrayonTM: Dinosaur Days. Chiang, Andy, illus. 2002. (Harold & the Purple Crayon Ser.). 40p. (J). (ps-1). 12.99 (978-0-06-000541-2(6)) HarperCollins Pubs.

The Big Toe Robbery: Individual Chapter Book Title Six-Packs. Vol. 28. 32p. (gr. 4 up). 44.00 (978-0-7578-0602-5(3)) Rigby Education.

Browne, Anthony. Bear Goes to Town. (Illus.). 32p. (J). 17.95 (978-0-241-10817-8(9) , Hamilton, Hamish) Penguin Bks., Ltd. GBR. *Dist:* Trafalgar Square Publishing.

Carle, Eric. Draw Me a Star. Carle, Eric, illus. 2002. (Illus.). (J). 14.04 (978-0-7587-2416-8(0)) Book Wholesalers, Inc.

—Draw Me a Star. 1998. (Illus.). 40p. (J). (ps-3). pap. 6.99 (978-0-698-11632-0(1) , Putnam Juvenile) Penguin Group (USA) Inc.

Coll, Ivar Da. Garabato. 2001. (SPA.). 32p. (J). (gr. k-2). (978-958-30-0521-3(5)) Panamericana Editorial COL. *Dist:* Lectorum Pubns., Inc.

Cotten, Cynthia. Fair Has Nothing to Do with It. 2007. 160p. (J). (gr. 4-7). 16.00 (978-0-374-39935-1(2)) Farrar, Straus & Giroux.

Coville, Bruce. Jeremy Thatcher, Dragon Hatcher: A Magic Shop Book. Lippincott, Gary A., illus. 2007. (Magic Shop Book Ser.). 168p. (J). (gr. 3-7). pap. 5.95 (***978-0-15-206252-1(1)*** , Magic Carpet Bks.) Harcourt Children's Bks.

Cowen-Fletcher, Jane. Nell's Elf. Cowen-Fletcher, Jane, illus. 2006. (Illus.). 32p. (J). (ps-2). 14.99 (978-0-7636-2391-3(1)) Candlewick Pr.

Crockett, Johns. Dessin pour Harold. (FRE.). pap. 13.95 (978-2-266-09597-6(8)) Presses Pocket FRA. *Dist:* Distribooks, Inc.

Demi. The Girl Who Drew a Phoenix. 2008. (J). (***978-1-4169-5347-0(7)*** , McElderry, Margaret K.) Simon & Schuster Children's Publishing.

Dougherty, Terri. Emily's Pictures. Rooney, Ronnie, illus. 2006. (Read-It! Readers Ser.). (J). 19.93 (978-1-4048-2409-6(X)) Picture Window Bks.

Drescher, Henrik. Simon's Book. Drescher, Henrik, illus. 2006. (Illus.). 32p. (J). 14.95 (978-1-59692-135-1(8)) MacAdam/Cage Publishing, Inc.

Ericsson, Jennifer A. A Piece of Chalk. Shapiro, Michelle, illus. rev. ed. 2007. 32p. (J). (ps-3). 16.95 (***978-1-59643-057-0(5)***) Roaring Brook Pr.

Falwell, Cathryn. David's Drawings. 2001. (Illus.). 32p. (J). (ps-3). 16.00 (978-1-58430-031-1(0)) Lee & Low Bks., Inc.

Falwell, Cathryn, illus. & text. David's Drawings. Falwell, Cathryn, text. 2005. 32p. (J). (ps-ps). pap. 7.95 (978-1-58430-261-2(5)) Lee & Low Bks., Inc.

Freedman, Deborah. Scribble. 2007. (Illus.). 40p. (J). (ps-1). 15.99 (978-0-375-83966-5(6)); lib. bdg. 18.99 (978-0-375-93966-2(0)) Random Hse. Children's Bks. (Knopf Bks. for Young Readers).

Fulmer, Jeffrey. My Imagination Kit. Pickering, Jimmy, tr. Pickering, Jimmy, illus. 2003. (J). 24p. 15.95 (978-1-59336-008-5(8)); 23p. pap. (978-1-59336-009-2(6)) Mondo Publishing.

Golden Books Staff. Stick Together! 2007. (Illus.). 32p. (J). (ps-3). 2.99 (978-0-375-83485-1(0) , Golden Bks.) Random Hse. Children's Bks.

Grosgebauer, Clare Ham. My Snickerdoodle Doodle Book: Creative Writing & Drawing Adventures. 2004. (Illus.). 72p. (J). spiral bd. 3.00 (978-0-9741888-1-2(6)) Small Wonders Enterprises.

Gurnick, Isabella Grace & Beals, Stephen Naayvek. Girls Have Eyelashes. 2004. 39p. pap. 11.63 (978-1-4116-1696-7(0)) Lulu.com.

Hamsa, Bobbie. Fast-Draw Freddie. Miller, Susan, illus. rev. ed. 2001. (Rookie Reader Skill Set Ser.). 32p. (J). (gr. k-2). pap. 4.95 (978-0-516-27150-7(4) , Children's Pr.) Scholastic Library Publishing.

—Fast-Draw Freddie. rev. ed. 2000. (gr. k-3). lib. bdg. 12.95 (978-0-613-54482-5(X)) Tandem Library Bks.

Hands on Crafts for Kids Staff. Invisible Magic Coloring Book. 2002. (Fun House Paperbacks Ser.). (Illus.). 72p. pap. 2.95 (978-0-8069-8955-6(6)) Sterling Publishing Co., Inc.

Johnson, D. B. Eddie's Kingdom. 2005. (Illus.). 32p. (J). (gr. k-3). 16.00 (978-0-618-56299-2(0)) Houghton Mifflin Co. Trade & Reference Div.

Jules, Jacqueline. No English. Huntington, Amy, illus. 2007. 32p. (J). 17.95 (***978-1-58726-474-0(9)*** , Mitten Pr.) Ann Arbor Media Group, LLC.

Kleven, Elisa. The Paper Princess Finds Her Way. Kleven, Elisa, illus. 2003. (Illus.). 32p. (J). (gr. k). 16.99 (978-0-525-46911-7(7) , Dutton Juvenile) Penguin Group (USA) Inc.

Korelitz, Jean Hanff. Interference Powder. 2006. 144p. (J). pap. 5.95 (978-0-7614-5275-1(3)) Cavendish, Marshall Corp.

Kroll, Steven. Patches Lost & Found. Gott, Barry, illus. 2005. 32p. (J). pap. 5.95 (978-0-7614-5217-1(6)) Cavendish, Marshall Corp.

—Patches Lost & Found. Gott, Barry, illus. 2001. 40p. (J). (gr. k-3). 15.95 (978-1-890817-53-4(8)) Winslow Pr.

—Patches Lost & Found. Gott, Barry, illus. 2005. 32p. (J). (gr. k-4). lib. bdg. 13.15 (978-0-606-33744-1(X)) Tandem Library Bks.

Lloyd, Gita & Binder, Eric, illus. Clifford's Doodle Pad: Scribble Pad. 2004. (Clifford Ser.). (J). bds. 2.49 (978-0-439-55671-2(6)) Scholastic, Inc.

Look What I Found! Individual Title Six-Pack Pouch - Level B. (Lighthouse Ser.). 12p. (gr. k-1). 24.00 (978-0-7578-0817-3(4)) Rigby Education.

Lying as Still as I Can: Six-Pack. (Greetings Ser.: Vol. 3). (gr. 2-3). 31.00 (978-0-7635-9433-6(4)) Rigby Education.

Martinez, Rocio. Matias Dibuja el Sol. 2002. (SPA.). 28p. (J). (978-980-257-261-8(6)) Ekare, Ediciones.

—Matias Pintor Famoso. 2002. (SPA.). 28p. (J). pap. (978-980-257-263-2(2)) Ekare, Ediciones.

McCallum, C. Dawn. The Caretaker of Tree Palace. Doxey, Morgan, illus. l.t. ed. 2006. 120p. (J). lib. bdg. 16.95 (978-0-9764026-3-3(7) , 3300) Longhorn Creek Pr.

McDonnell, Patrick. Art. 2006. (Illus.). 44p. (J). (ps-1). 14.99 (978-0-316-11491-2(X)) Little Brown & Co.

McNeal, Laura & McNeal, Tom. The Decoding of Lana Morris. 2007. 304p. (J). (gr. 7). lib. bdg. 18.99 (978-0-375-93106-2(6)); 15.99 (978-0-375-83106-5(1)) Random Hse. Children's Bks. (Knopf Bks. for Young Readers).

Mielcarek, David. Time for your Mind. Mielcarek, David, ed. 2006. (Illus.). 38p. (J). (978-0-9785480-0-1(0)) Mielcarek, David.

Mills, Claudia. Ziggy's Blue-Ribbon Day. Alley, R. W. & Alley, Robert W., illus. 2005. 32p. (J). (ps-ps). 16.00 (978-0-374-32352-3(6) , Farrar, Straus & Giroux (BYR)) Farrar, Straus & Giroux.

Newell, Jeff. Skimper-Scamper. Hranilovich, Barbara J., illus. 2005. (Green Light Readers Level 2 Ser.). 24p. (J). 12.95 (978-0-15-205166-2(X)); pap. 3.95 (978-0-15-205165-5(1)) Harcourt Children's Bks. (Green Light Readers).

Nikola-Lisa, W. Can You Top That? Lee, Hector Viveros, illus. 2000. 32p. (J). (ps-2). 15.95 (978-1-880000-99-1(7)) Lee & Low Bks., Inc.

Pearce, Jacqueline. Discovering Emily. 2004. (Orca Young Readers Ser.). (Illus.). 144p. (J). (gr. 3-6). pap. 4.99 (978-1-55143-295-3(1)) Orca Bk. Pubs. USA.

Prestine, Joan Singleton. It's Hard to Share My Teacher. Kylberg, Virginia, illus. 2002. 32p. (J). pap. 6.95 (978-1-57768-657-6(8)) School Specialty Publishing.

—It's Hard to Share My Teacher: Picture Book & Resource Guide, 2 bks., Set. 2001. (Kids Have Feelings, Too Ser.). (J). (ps-3). 14.99 (978-1-56417-773-5(4) , FE0061, Fearon Teacher Aids) Schaffer, Frank Pubns.

Priest, Robert. Pirate's Eye. 2005. (Illus.). 32p. (J). (gr. k-3). 16.00 (978-0-618-43990-4(0)) Houghton Mifflin Co. Trade & Reference Div.

Prosek, James. The Day My Mother Left. Prosek, James, illus. 2007. (Illus.). 304p. (J). 15.99 (978-1-4169-0770-1(X)) Simon & Schuster Children's Publishing.

Rex, Michael. Pals, Level 1. Rex, Michael, illus. 2003. (Word-by-Word First Reader Ser.). (Illus.). 32p. (J). pap. 3.99 (978-0-439-49310-9(2) , Cartwheel Bks.) Scholastic, Inc.

Rey, H. A. & Rey, Margret. Billy's Picture. 2004. (Illus.). 24p. (J). (gr. k-3). 15.00 (978-0-618-49422-4(7)); pap. 5.95 (978-0-618-49420-0(0)) Houghton Mifflin Co. Trade & Reference Div.

Reynolds, Peter. Ish. Reynolds, Peter, illus. 2004. (Illus.). 32p. (J). (gr. k up). 14.00 (978-0-7636-2344-9(X)) Candlewick Pr.

Reynolds, Peter H. Ish. Reynolds, Peter H., illus. 2005. (Illus.). (J). (ps-4). 29.95 incl. audio compact disk (978-0-439-80429-5(9) , WHCD676); 24.95 incl. audio (978-0-439-80428-8(0) , WHRA676) Scholastic, Inc.

Say, Allen. Emma's Rug. Say, Allen, illus. 2002. (Illus.). (J). 24.30 (978-0-7587-2457-1(8)) Book Wholesalers, Inc.

—Emma's Rug. 2003. (Illus.). 32p. (J). pap. 6.95 (978-0-618-33523-7(4) , Walter Lorraine) Houghton Mifflin Co. Trade & Reference Div.

Scholastic, Inc. Staff. Clifford the Big Red Dog Art Kit. 1999. (Clifford Ser.). (J). 16.99 (978-0-590-63453-3(4) , Sidekicks TM) Scholastic, Inc.

Stairs-Oberlick, Anita Ruth. Helen the Transartist. 2004. (Illus.). 256p. (J). per. 15.95 (978-0-9759738-0-6(0)) Carleton Bks.

Wang, Gabrielle. El Jardin de la Emperatriz Casia. Holguin, Magdalena, tr. Cuellar, Olga, illus. 2004. (SPA.). 108p. (YA). 8.95 (978-958-04-7346-6(3)) Norma S.A. COL. *Dist:* Distribuidora Norma, Inc., Lectorum Pubns., Inc.

Wing, Natasha. Go to Bed, Monster! Kantorovitz, Sylvie, illus. 2007. 40p. (J). (ps-2). 16.00 (978-0-15-205775-6(7)) Harcourt Trade Pubs.

Zemach, Kaethe. Ms. Mccaw Learns To Draw. (J). 2008. 32p. pap. 16.99 (978-0-439-82914-4(3)); 2006. (978-0-439-82915-1(1)) Scholastic, Inc. (Levine, Arthur A. Bks.).

DRAWING—TECHNIQUE

Ahmed, Kazi & Ahmed, Cindy. RainbowBrush Alphabet Edition. 2007. (Illus.). 48p. pap. 24.95 (***978-0-9734981-0-3(2)***) RainbowBrush, LLC CAN. *Dist:* Biblio Distribution.

—RainbowBrush Land & Seascapes. 2007. (Illus.). 48p. pap. 24.95 (***978-0-9734981-1-0(0)***) RainbowBrush, LLC CAN. *Dist:* Biblio Distribution.

Alfano, Maria B. How to Draw. Choi Sung Hwan, Aragon Noel, illus. 2005. (Trollz Ser.). 32p. (J). pap. 4.99 (978-0-439-75311-2(0)) Scholastic, Inc.

AOL. Princess Natasha. 2007. (How to Draw Ser.). (Illus.). 32p. (J). (gr. k-1). pap. 5.95 (978-1-60058-028-4(9)) Foster, Walter Publishing, Inc.

Auerbach, Annie & Heiss, Lori. Lilo & Stitch. 2003. (DMA Learn to Draw Ser.). (Illus.). 32p. (J). pap. 5.95 (978-1-56010-045-4(1)) Foster, Walter Publishing, Inc.

Beasant, Pam. Ht Draw Buildings. Ashman, Iain, illus. 2006. 32p. (J). pap. 5.99 (978-0-7945-1371-9(9) , Usborne) EDC Publishing.

Bellen-Berthel[81]zel(UNKNOWN CHARACTER)ne, Cyndie. Flipping Out! How to Draw Flip Animation. Steck, Jim, illus. 2005. 48p. (J). (***978-0-439-81335-8(2)***) Scholastic, Inc.

Bontinck, Helga. All Around Town. 2006. (Illus.). 24p. (J). 22.00 (978-0-8368-6310-9(0)) Stevens, Gareth Inc.

—At the Circus. 2006. (Illus.). 24p. (J). 22.00 (978-0-8368-6312-3(7)) Stevens, Gareth Inc.

Bontinck, Helga, illus. At the Seashore. 2006. (Simple Steps to Drawing Ser.). 24p. (J). 22.00 (978-0-8368-6313-0(5)) Stevens, Gareth Inc.

Burton, Bonnie. You Can Draw Star Wars Characters. 2007. (You Can Draw Ser.). (Illus.). 96p. (J). 19.99 (978-0-7566-2343-2(X)) Dorling Kindersley Publishing, Inc.

Cardaci, Diane. Realistic Textures: Discover Your Inner Artist As You Explore the Basic Theories & Techniques of Pencil Drawing. 2007. (Drawing Made Easy Ser.). (Illus.). 64p. pap. 9.95 (978-1-56010-997-6(1)) Foster, Walter Publishing, Inc.

Carle, Eric. Little Cloud: A Draw-with-Chalk Book. 2006. (World of Eric Carle Ser.). 10p. (J). (ps-1). bds. 6.99 (978-0-448-44418-5(6) , Grosset & Dunlap) Penguin Group (USA) Inc.

Claridge, Marit. Ht Draw Dinosaurs & Prehistoric Life. PRINGLE MIKE ET AL, illus. 2006. 32p. (J). pap. 5.99 (978-0-7945-1372-6(7) , Usborne) EDC Publishing.

Cook, Janet. Ht Draw Robots & Aliens. FORSTER MARY ET AL, illus. 2006. 32p. (J). pap. 5.99 (978-0-7945-1370-2(0) , Usborne) EDC Publishing.

Court, Rob. How to Draw Airplanes. 2007. (Doodle Bks.). 32p. (J). 21.36 (***978-1-59296-803-9(1)***) Child's World, Inc.

—How to Draw Cars & Trucks. 2007. (Doodle Bks.). 32p. (J). 21.36 (***978-1-59296-804-6(X)***) Child's World, Inc.

—How to Draw Christmas Things. 2007. (Doodle Bks.). 32p. (J). 21.36 (***978-1-59296-805-3(8)***) Child's World, Inc.

—How to Draw Dinosaurs. 2007. (Doodle Bks.). 32p. (J). 21.36 (***978-1-59296-806-0(6)***) Child's World, Inc.

—How to Draw Food. 2008. (Doodle Bks.). 32p. (J). 21.36 (***978-1-59296-953-1(4)***) Child's World, Inc.

—How to Draw Halloween Things. 2007. (Doodle Bks.). 32p. (J). 21.36 (***978-1-59296-808-4(2)***) Child's World, Inc.

—How to Draw Independence Day Things. 2008. (Doodle Bks.). 32p. (J). 21.36 (***978-1-59296-954-8(2)***) Child's World, Inc.

—How to Draw Jungle Animals. 2008. (Doodle Bks.). 32p. (J). 21.36 (***978-1-59296-955-5(0)***) Child's World, Inc.

—How to Draw Sports Things. 2008. (Doodle Bks.). 32p. (J). 21.36 (***978-1-59296-956-2(9)***) Child's World, Inc.

—How to Draw Thanksgiving Things. 2008. (Doodle Bks.). 32p. (J). 21.36 (***978-1-59296-957-9(7)***) Child's World, Inc.

—How to Draw Things in Nature. 2007. (Doodle Bks.). 32p. (J). 21.36 (***978-1-59296-807-7(4)***) Child's World, Inc.

—How to Draw Underwater Animals. 2007. (Doodle Bks.). 32p. (J). 21.36 (***978-1-59296-810-7(4)***) Child's World, Inc.

—How to Draw Watercraft. 2008. (Doodle Bks.). 32p. (J). 21.36 (***978-1-59296-958-6(5)***) Child's World, Inc.

Cranium Inc. Staff. The Cranium Ultimate Book of Fantastic Fun & Games. 2007. 54p. (J). (ps-3). 19.99 (***978-0-316-01208-9(4)***) Little, Brown Bks. for Young Readers.

Criscione, Rachel. How to Draw the Life & Times of Chester A. Arthur. 2006. (Kid's Guide to Drawing the Presidents of the United States of America Ser.). (J). 25.25 (978-1-4042-2998-3(1) , PowerKids Pr.) Rosen Publishing Group, Inc., The.

Daronco, Mickey. Now We Draw. 2003. (BuildUp Ser.). (J). pap. 22.00 (978-1-4108-0772-4(X)) Benchmark Education Co.

Deinard, Jenny. How to Draw Illinois' Sights & Symbols. 2002. (Kid's Guide to Drawing America Ser.). (Illus.). 32p. (J). (gr. 3-5). lib. bdg. 25.25 (978-0-8239-6069-9(2) , PowerKids Pr.) Rosen Publishing Group, Inc., The.

—Illinois's Sights & Sounds. 2004. 48p. pap. 8.95 (978-1-4042-8502-6(4)) Rosen Publishing Group, Inc., The.

Disney, ed. Disney's Little Einsteins' Amazing Missions. 2007. (Watch Me Draw Ser.). (Illus.). 24p. (J). pap. 5.95 (978-1-60058-033-8(5)) Foster, Walter Publishing, Inc.

—Disney's Mickey Mouse Clubhouse. 2007. (Watch Me Draw Ser.). (Illus.). 24p. (J). pap. 5.95 (978-1-60058-043-7(2)) Foster, Walter Publishing, Inc.

Disney Pixar Staff, ed. Disney Pixar's Ratatouille. 2007. (Learn to Draw Ser.). (Illus.). 32p. (J). (gr. 3-5). pap. 5.95 (978-1-60058-029-1(7)) Foster, Walter Publishing, Inc.

Dogs & Puppies. 2006. (Illus.). (J). cd-rom 9.99 (***978-0-9795190-0-0(4)***) Color & Learn.

Dorling Kindersley Publishing Staff. I Can Draw Animals. 2006. (I can Draw Ser.). (Illus.). 48p. (J). pap. 7.99 (978-0-7566-1987-9(4)) Dorling Kindersley Publishing, Inc.

—I Can Draw Machines. 2006. (I can Draw Ser.). (Illus.). 48p. (J). pap. 7.99 (978-0-7566-1988-6(2)) Dorling Kindersley Publishing, Inc.

—I Can Draw Magical Creatures. 2006. (I can Draw Ser.). (Illus.). 48p. (J). (gr. 5). 7.99 (978-0-7566-1986-2(6)) Dorling Kindersley Publishing, Inc.

Dorling Kindersley Publishing Staff & Furman, Simon. You Can Draw Transformers. 2007. (You Can Draw Ser.). 96p. (J). 19.99 (978-0-7566-2746-1(X)) Dorling Kindersley Publishing, Inc.

Douglas, Vincent & School Specialty Publishing Staff. Let's Make Animals. EduSlate, ed. 2006. (Edu-Slates Ser.). (Illus.). 1p. (J). 2.99 (978-0-7696-4889-7(4) , Brighter Child) School Specialty Publishing.

—Practice Drawing Shapes. EduSlate, ed. 2006. (Edu-Slates Ser.). (Illus.). 1p. (J). 2.99 (978-0-7696-4899-6(1) , Brighter Child) School Specialty Publishing.

DreamWorks Staff. DreamWorks Shrek the Third: Step-by-Step Instructions for Drawing All Your Favorite Characters. 2007. (Learn to Draw Ser.). (Illus.). 32p. (J). (gr. 3-5). pap. 5.95 (978-1-56010-784-2(7)) Foster, Walter Publishing, Inc.

DuBosque, Doug. Draw 3-D Vol. 2: A Step-by-Step Guide to Perspective Drawing. DuBosque, Doug, illus. rev. ed. 2000. (Learn to Draw Ser.). (Illus.). 64p. (J). (gr. 6-9). pap. 8.99 (978-0-939217-14-4(7)) Peel Productions, Inc.

—Draw Desert Animals. 2000. (Learn to Draw Ser.). (Illus.). 64p. (J). (gr. 6-9). pap. 8.99 (978-0-939217-26-7(0)) Peel Productions, Inc.

—Draw Dinosaurs. rev. ed. 2000. (Learn to Draw Ser.). (Illus.). 64p. (J). (gr. 6-9). pap. 8.99 (978-0-939217-22-9(8)) Peel Productions, Inc.

—Draw Grassland Animals. 2000. (Learn to Draw Ser.). (Illus.). 64p. (J). (gr. 6-9). pap. 8.99 (978-0-939217-25-0(2)) Peel Productions, Inc.

—Draw Ocean Animals. 2000. (Learn to Draw Ser.). (Illus.). 64p. (J). (gr. 6-9). pap. 8.99 (978-0-939217-24-3(4)) Peel Productions, Inc.

—Draw Rainforest Animals. 2000. (Learn to Draw Ser.). (Illus.). 64p. (J). (gr. 6-9). pap. 8.99 (978-0-939217-23-6(6)) Peel Productions, Inc.

Duhig, Lee. Draw Dinosaurs! 2006. (Illus.). 64p. (J). pap. (***978-1-59412-158-6(3)***) Mud Puddle, Inc.

Eding, June. Napoleon Dynamite Sketchbook. 2006. 32p. (J). (gr. 3). 4.99 (978-0-8431-2182-7(3) , Price Stern Sloan) Penguin Group (USA) Inc.

Elliott, Craig. Craig Elliott Sketchbook. 2006. (Illus.). 24p. per. (978-0-9754912-4-9(5)) Aristata Publishing.

Elliott, Ruth. See What You're Looking At. Elliott, Ruth, illus. 2007. (J). 27.00 (***978-0-9795017-0-8(9)***) Edu Designs.

Emberley, Ed. Ed Emberley's Big Green Drawing Book. Emberley, Ed, illus. 2005. (Illus.). 96p. (J). (gr. 2-17). pap. 10.99 (978-0-316-78976-9(3)) Little Brown & Co.

—Ed Emberley's Big Orange Drawing Book. Emberley, Ed, illus. 2005. (Illus.). 96p. (J). (gr. 2-17). pap. 10.99 (978-0-316-78975-2(5)) Little Brown & Co.

—Ed Emberley's Big Purple Drawing Book. Emberley, Ed, illus. 2005. (Illus.). 96p. (J). (gr. 2-17). pap. 10.99 (978-0-316-78973-8(9)) Little Brown & Co.

—Ed Emberley's Big Red Drawing Book. Emberley, Ed, illus. 2005. (Illus.). 96p. (J). (gr. 2-17). pap. 10.99 (978-0-316-78974-5(7)) Little Brown & Co.

—Ed Emberley's Big Red, White & Blue Drawing Book. 2005. (Illus.). 95p. (J). (978-1-4156-2968-0(4)) Little Brown & Co.

—Ed Emberley's Drawing Book: Make a World. 2006. (Illus.). 32p. (J). (978-1-4156-6706-4(3)) Little Brown & Co.

—Ed Emberley's Drawing Book of Animals. Emberley, Ed, illus. 2006. (Illus.). 32p. (J). (gr. 2-17). pap. 6.99 (978-0-316-78979-0(8)) Little Brown & Co.

—Ed Emberley's Drawing Book of Faces. Emberley, Ed, illus. 2006. (Illus.). 30p. (J). (gr. 2-17). pap. 6.99 (978-0-316-78970-7(4)) Little Brown & Co.

—Ed Emberley's Drawing Book of Halloween. Emberley, Ed, illus. 2006. (Illus.). 32p. (J). (gr. 2-17). pap. 6.99 (978-0-316-78977-6(1)) Little Brown & Co.

—Ed Emberley's Picture Pie: A Circle Drawing Book. Emberley, Ed, illus. 2006. 48p. (J). (gr. 2-17). pap. 9.99 (978-0-316-78982-0(8)) Little Brown & Co.

—Make a World. Emberley, Ed, illus. 2006. (Ed Emberley Drawing Book Ser.). (Illus.). 32p. (J). (gr. 2-17). pap. 6.99 (978-0-316-78972-1(0)) Little Brown & Co.

Fein, Eric. New York's Sights & Symbols. 2004. 48p. pap. 8.95 (978-1-4042-8505-7(9)) Rosen Publishing Group, Inc., The.

First Drawings. 2007. (J). 128.10 (***978-1-59679-798-7(3)*** , Buddy Bks.) ABDO Publishing Co.

Fisher, Diana. Insects: Step-by-Step Instructions for 26 Creepy Crawlies. 2007. (Draw & Color Ser.). (Illus.). 40p. (J). (gr. k-1). pap. 4.95 (978-1-60058-507-4(8)) Foster, Walter Publishing, Inc.

—Reptiles & Amphibians: Step by Step Intsructions for 29 Reptiles & Amphibians. 2006. (Draw & Color Ser.). (Illus.). 40p. (J). pap. 4.95 (978-1-56010-994-5(7)) Foster, Walter Publishing, Inc.

Flanagan, Jennifer. Fun with Gel Markers. 2002. (Illus.). 32p. (J). (978-0-439-33624-6(4)) Scholastic, Inc.

Flux, Paul. Line & Tone. 2007. (Illus.). 32p. (J). (***978-1-4034-9630-0(7)***) Heinemann Library.

—Line & Tone (2nd Edition) 2007. (Illus.). 32p. (J). (***978-1-4034-9636-2(6)***) Heinemann Library.

—Perspective. 2007. (Illus.). 32p. (J). (***978-1-4034-9632-4(3)***) Heinemann Library.

—Perspective (2nd Edition) 2007. (Illus.). 32p. (J). (***978-1-4034-9638-6(2)***) Heinemann Library.

Foster, Walter, ed. Cars. 2006. (DMA Learn to Draw Ser.). (Illus.). 32p. (J). pap. 5.95 (978-1-56010-918-1(1)) Foster, Walter Publishing, Inc.

—Dinosaurs. Fisher, Diana, illus. 2006. (Watch Me Draw Ser.). 24p. (J). pap. 4.95 (978-1-56010-951-8(3)) Foster, Walter Publishing, Inc.

—Favorite Pets. Fisher, Diana, illus. 2006. (Watch Me Draw Ser.). 24p. (J). pap. 4.95 (978-1-56010-948-8(3)) Foster, Walter Publishing, Inc.

—Spongebob Squarepants. Martinez, Heather, illus. 2002. (Nick How to Draw Ser.). 32p. (J). pap. 5.95 (978-1-56010-662-3(X)) Foster, Walter Publishing, Inc.

—Things Girls Love. Fisher, Diana, illus. 2006. (Watch Me Draw Ser.). 24p. (J). pap. 4.95 (978-1-56010-950-1(5)) Foster, Walter Publishing, Inc.

—Whales, Dolphins, Fish & More. Fisher, Diana, illus. 2006. (Watch Me Draw Ser.). 24p. (J). pap. 4.95 (978-1-56010-949-5(1)) Foster, Walter Publishing, Inc.

Gandolfi, Claudine. Dragons & Mythical Creatures Scratch & Sketch. Gandolfi, Claudine, illus. 2006. (Illus.). 68p. (J). ring bd. 12.99 (978-1-59359-937-9(4)) Peter Pauper Pr. Inc.

Ganeri, Anita & Tatchell, Judy. Ht Draw Animals. rev. ed. 2006. 32p. (J). pap. 5.99 (978-0-7945-1373-3(5) , Usborne) EDC Publishing.

C D

Geller, Kristin. Follow-the-Directions Draw & Write Activities: Step-by-Step Directions & Writing Prompts That Guide Children to Draw Pictures & Write Stories about Them. 2005. (Illus.). 48p. (ps-ps). pap. 10.99 (978-0-439-47122-0(2) , Teaching Resources) Scholastic, Inc.

Getha, Patricia & Maltseff, Michele. Drawing Horses Kit: A Complete Drawing Kit for Beginners. 2008. (Walter Foster Drawing Kits Ser.). (Illus.). 32p. pap. 19.95 ***978-1-60058-056-7(4))** Foster, Walter Publishing, Inc.

Goldman, Ken. Understanding Values: Discover Your Inner Artist As You Explore the Basic Theories & Techniques of Pencil Drawing. 2007. (Drawing Made Easy Ser.). (Illus.). 64p. pap. 9.95 (978-1-56010-996-9(3)) Foster, Walter Publishing, Inc.

Gressman, Carylee Anne. Draw & Write Through History: Creation Through Jonah. Wolf, Aaron D., ed. Dick, Peggy, illus. 2006. (J). per. 12.95 (978-0-9778597-0-2(3)) CPR Pubng.

Gross, Miriam J. How to Draw the Life & Times of William Jefferson Clinton. 2007. (Kid's Guide to Drawing the Presidents of the United States of America Ser.). (Illus.). 32p. (J). 25.25 (978-1-4042-3018-7(1) , PowerKids Pr.) Rosen Publishing Group, Inc., The.

Halligan, James. USA Dot-to-Dot. 2006. (Illus.). 80p. pap. 5.95 (978-1-4027-2797-9(6)) Sterling Publishing Co., Inc.

Hamsters. 2007. (Illus.). (J). cd-rom 9.99 ***978-0-9795190-3-1(9))** Color & Learn.

Harpster, Steve. Animals. 2006. (Pencil, Paper, Draw! Ser.). (Illus.). 64p. (J). pap., pap., spiral bd. 5.95 (978-1-4027-2972-0(3)) Sterling Publishing Co., Inc.

—Cars & Trucks. 2006. (Pencil, Paper, Draw! Ser.). (Illus.). 64p. (J). pap., pap., spiral bd. 5.95 (978-1-4027-2975-1(8)) Sterling Publishing Co., Inc.

—Dinosaurs. 2006. (Pencil, Paper, Draw! Ser.). (Illus.). 64p. (J). pap., pap., spiral bd. 5.95 (978-1-4027-2974-4(X)) Sterling Publishing Co., Inc.

—Dogs. 2006. (Pencil, Paper, Draw! Ser.). (Illus.). 64p. (J). pap., pap., spiral bd. 5.95 (978-1-4027-2973-7(1)) Sterling Publishing Co., Inc.

—Fantasy Creatures. 2006. (Pencil, Paper, Draw! Ser.). (Illus.). 64p. (J). pap., pap., spiral bd. 5.95 (978-1-4027-2976-8(6)) Sterling Publishing Co., Inc.

—Pencil, Paper, Draw!: Baby Animals. 2007. (Pencil, Paper, Draw! Ser.). (Illus.). 64p. (J). pap. 5.95 ***978-1-4027-4678-9(4))** Sterling Publishing Co., Inc.

—Pencil, Paper, Draw!: Pirates. 2007. (Pencil, Paper, Draw! Ser.). (Illus.). 64p. (J). pap. 5.95 ***978-1-4027-4677-2(6))** Sterling Publishing Co., Inc.

Hart, Christopher. Draw Mini Manga! 2006. (XTreme Art Ser.). (Illus.). 64p. (J). (gr. 4-6). pap. 7.95 (978-0-8230-0373-0(6)) Watson-Guptill Pubns., Inc.

—How to Draw Chic Fashions. 2006. 25p. (gr. 8). pap. 16.99 (978-0-9776925-7-6(4)) Loew-Cornell, Inc.

—Kids Draw Manga Fantasy. 2004. (Kids Draw Ser.). (Illus.). 64p. (J). (gr. 4-6). pap. 11.95 (978-0-8230-2639-5(6)) Watson-Guptill Pubns., Inc.

Horvath, David & Kim, Sun. Uglydoll: Ugly Drawings in a Few Easy Steps. 2006. (Uglydoll Ser.). 32p. pap. 5.95 (978-1-56010-991-4(2)) Foster, Walter Publishing, Inc.

Hosley, Maria. Airplanes. 2007. (Illus.). 24p. (J). 21.35 ***978-1-59679-799-4(1))** ABDO Publishing Co.

—Cars. 2007. (Illus.). 24p. (J). 21.35 ***978-1-59679-800-7(9))** ABDO Publishing Co.

—Cats. 2007. (Illus.). 24p. (J). 21.35 ***978-1-59679-801-4(7))** ABDO Publishing Co.

—Dogs. 2007. (Illus.). 24p. (J). 21.35 ***978-1-59679-803-8(3))** ABDO Publishing Co.

—People. 2007. (Illus.). 24p. (J). 21.35 ***978-1-59679-812-0(2))** ABDO Publishing Co.

How to Draw a Horse. 2006. (J). (978-1-933343-13-6(3)) Stabenfeldt Inc.

How to Draw Cartoon Animals. 2002. 48p. lib. bdg. (978-1-59168-011-6(5)) Flying Rhinoceros, Inc.

Hutnick, Liz. Doodle Dogs. 2004. (Klutz Ser.). (Illus.). 58p. (J). spiral bd. 9.95 (978-1-57054-836-9(6)) Klutz.

I Can Draw Creepy Crawlies. 2002. 32p. (J). 9.95 (978-0-7525-7281-9(4)) Parragon, Inc.

Iguanas & Reptiles. 2007. (Illus.). (J). cd-rom 9.99 ***978-0-9795190-5-5(5))** Color & Learn.

Johansen, Heidi Leigh. How to Draw the Life & Times of Calvin Coolidge. 2007. (Kid's Guide to Drawing the Presidents of the United States of America Ser.). (Illus.). 32p. (J). 25.25 (978-1-4042-3006-4(8) , PowerKids Pr.) Rosen Publishing Group, Inc., The.

Johnson, Shane L. Avatar: The Last Airbender Drawing Book & Kit: Complete Kit Includes Everything You Need to Draw Your Favorite Characters. 2007. (Nickelodeon Drawing Books & Kits Ser.). (Illus.). 32p. (J). (gr. 3-5). pap. 16.95 ***978-1-60058-060-4(2))** Foster, Walter Publishing, Inc.

Johnson, Shane L., illus. Nickelodeon Avatar: The Last Airbender. 2007. (How to Draw Ser.). 32p. (J). (gr. 3-5). pap. 5.95 (978-1-56010-783-5(9)) Foster, Walter Publishing, Inc.

A Kid's Guide to Drawing: Set 5. (Illus.). (J). (gr. k-5). 127.50 (978-1-4042-2957-0(4)) Rosen Publishing Group, Inc., The.

A Kid's Guide to Drawing the Countries of the World: Set 3. (Illus.). (J). (gr. k-5). 159.00 (978-1-4042-2958-7(2)) Rosen Publishing Group, Inc., The.

A Kid's Guide to Drawing the Countries of the World: Set 4. (Illus.). (J). (gr. k-5). 159.00 (978-1-4042-2959-4(0)) Rosen Publishing Group, Inc., The.

A Kid's Guide to Drawing the Presidents of the United States of America Set 1. 530.25 (978-1-4042-3020-0(3)) Rosen Publishing Group, Inc., The.

Kinkade, Thomas, contrib. by. Lifepac Elective Drawing Basics, Bk. 5. 2006. pap. 3.49 (978-0-7403-0712-6(6)) Alpha Omega Pubns., Inc.

Klutz Press Staff. Draw Thumb People. 2002. (Illus.). 44p. (J). 6.95 (978-1-57054-984-7(2)) Klutz.

—Draw Thumb Things. 2002. (Illus.). 46p. (J). spiral bd. 6.95 (978-1-57054-987-8(7)) Klutz.

Knowles, Jon. Drawing with Doodle, Bk. 1. Knowles, Jon, illus. 1999. (Illus.). 32p. (J). (gr. 1-7). pap. 3.95 (978-0-9674428-0-8(X) , Fly by Night Productions) Interlight Studios, Inc.

LBCL & Emberley, Ed. Ed Emberley's Picture Pie 2: A Drawing Book & Stencil. Emberley, Ed, illus. 2005. 32p. (J). (gr. 2-17). pap. 9.99 (978-0-316-78980-6(1)) Little Brown & Co.

Lepp, Royden. How to Draw Big Bad Bible Beasts. 2007. (2:52 Ser.). (Illus.). 48p. (J). pap. 6.99 (978-0-310-71336-4(6)) Zonderkidz.

—How to Draw Good, Bad & Ugly Bible Guys. 2007. (2:52 Ser.). (Illus.). 48p. (J). pap. 6.99 (978-0-310-71337-1(4)) Zonderkidz.

Less, Emma. Little Scribbles: Princess Fun. Harpster, Steve, illus. 2006. (Little Scribbles Ser.). 12p. (J). bds. 5.95 (978-1-4027-3806-7(4)) Sterling Publishing Co., Inc.

Let's Draw with Shapes: Set 2.Tr. of Vamos a dibujar con figuras Set 2. (Illus.). (J). (gr. k-1). 103.50 (978-1-4042-2947-1(7) , Powerstart Pr.); (ENG & SPA., 103.50 (978-1-4042-7560-7(6) , Buenas Letra) Rosen Publishing Group, Inc., The.

Levin, Freddie. 1-2-3 Draw Ocean Life: A Step-By-Step Guide. 2005. (Illus.). 64p. (J). pap. 8.99 (978-0-939217-62-5(7)) Peel Productions, Inc.

Levy, Barbara Soloff. How to Draw Circus Pictures. 2007. 32p. (J). pap. 2.95 ***978-0-486-45647-8(1))** Dover Pubns., Inc.

—How to Draw Dogs. 2000. (Illus.). 32p. (J). (gr. k-5). pap. 2.95 (978-0-486-41058-6(7)) Dover Pubns., Inc.

—How to Draw Farm Animals. 2006. (Illus.). 32p. (J). pap. 2.95 (978-0-486-45168-8(2)) Dover Pubns., Inc.

—How to Draw for All Seasons. 2007. 32p. (J). pap. 3.95 ***978-0-486-46219-6(6))** Dover Pubns., Inc.

—How to Draw Forest Animals. 2006. 32p. (J). pap. 2.95 (978-0-486-45231-9(X)) Dover Pubns., Inc.

—How to Draw Holiday Pictures. 2007. 32p. (J). pap. 2.95 ***978-0-486-45662-1(5))** Dover Pubns., Inc.

—How to Draw Mother Goose Characters. 2006. 32p. (J). pap. 2.95 (978-0-486-44769-8(3)) Dover Pubns., Inc.

—How to Draw Pets. 2006. 32p. (J). pap. 2.95 (978-0-486-44710-0(3)) Dover Pubns., Inc.

—I Can Draw Animals. 2007. (Boxed Sets/Bindups Ser.). 64p. 5.95 ***978-0-486-46384-1(2))** Dover Pubns., Inc.

—I Can Draw Dinosaurs. 2007. (Boxed Sets/Bindups Ser.). 64p. 5.95 ***978-0-486-46386-5(9))** Dover Pubns., Inc.

—I Can Draw Insects. 2007. (Boxed Sets/Bindups Ser.). 64p. 5.95 ***978-0-486-46388-9(5))** Dover Pubns., Inc.

—I Can Draw People. 2007. (Boxed Sets/Bindups Ser.). 64p. 5.95 ***978-0-486-46387-2(7))** Dover Pubns., Inc.

—I Can Draw Wizards, Dragons & other Magical Creatures. 2007. (Boxed Sets/Bindups Ser.). 64p. 5.95 ***978-0-486-46389-6(3))** Dover Pubns., Inc.

Levy, Barbara Soloff & Dover. I Can Draw Dogs. 2007. (Boxed Sets/Bindups Ser.). 64p. 5.95 ***978-0-486-46385-8(0))** Dover Pubns., Inc.

Lewis K., Parker. How to Draw the Life & Times of Richard M. Nixon. 2007. (Kid's Guide to Drawing the Presidents of the United States of America Ser.). (Illus.). 32p. (J). 25.25 (978-1-4042-3013-2(0) , PowerKids Pr.) Rosen Publishing Group, Inc., The.

Lifepac Elective Drawing Basics. 2006. Bk. 1. pap. 3.90 (978-0-7403-0708-9(8)); Bk. 2. 3.50 (978-0-7403-0709-6(6)); Bk. 2. 3.99 (978-0-7403-0710-2(X)); Bk. 4. pap. 3.90 (978-0-7403-0711-9(8)) Alpha Omega Pubns., Inc.

Longhurst, Terry. I Can Draw Cars & Trucks. 2002. (I Can Draw Ser.). 32p. (J). 9.95 (978-0-7525-7282-6(2)) Parragon, Inc.

—I Can Draw Dinosaurs. 2002. (I Can Draw Ser.). 32p. (J). 9.95 (978-0-7525-7277-2(6)) Parragon, Inc.

—I Can Draw on the Farm. 2002. (I Can Draw Ser.). 32p. (J). 9.95 (978-0-7525-7278-9(4)) Parragon, Inc.

—I Can Draw Wild Animals. 2002. (I Can Draw Ser.). 32p. (J). pap. 9.95 (978-0-7525-7280-2(6)) Parragon, Inc.

Luxbacher, Irene. 123 I Can Draw! 2008. 24p. pap. ***978-1-55453-152-3(7))** Kids Can Pr., Ltd.

Makowski, Robin Lee. Cats. (Drawing Made Fun Ser.). (Illus.). 32p. (gr. 2-5). 2006. 20.95 (978-1-59515-468-2(X) , 1244418); 2001. (J). lib. bdg. 25.27 (978-1-58952-152-0(8)) Rourke Publishing, LLC.

—Dogs. 2006. (Drawing Made Fun Ser.). (Illus.). 32p. (gr. 2-5). 20.95 (978-1-59515-469-9(8) , 1244419) Rourke Publishing, LLC.

—Fish. 2005. (Drawing Made Fun Ser.). (Illus.). 32p. (J). (ps-k). lib. bdg. 6.45 (978-1-59515-471-2(X) , 1244421) Rourke Publishing, LLC.

—Marine Mammals. 2006. (Drawing Made Fun Ser.). (Illus.). 32p. (gr. 2-5). 20.95 (978-1-59515-472-9(8) , 1244423) Rourke Publishing, LLC.

Makowski, Robin Lee, illus. Reptiles. 2006. (Drawing Made Fun Ser.). 32p. (gr. 2-5). 20.95 (978-1-59515-473-6(6) , 1244424) Rourke Publishing, LLC.

Masiello, Ralph. Ralph Masiello's Dragon Drawing Book. Masiello, Ralph, illus. 2007. 64p. (J). (gr. 3-6). pap. 7.95 ***978-1-57091-532-1(6));** (Illus.). 16.95 (978-1-57091-531-4(8)) Charlesbridge Publishing, Inc.

Masiello, Ralph. Ralph Masiello's Ocean Drawing Book. Masiello, Ralph, illus. 2006. (Illus.). (J). 16.95 (978-1-57091-529-1(6) , 1258410); pap. 6.95 (978-1-57091-530-7(X) , 1258410) Charlesbridge Publishing, Inc.

Miller, Steve & Baugh, Bryan. Scared! How to Draw Fantastic Horror Comic Characters. 2004. (Illus.). 144p. pap. 19.95 (978-0-8230-1664-8(1)) Watson-Guptill Pubns., Inc.

Millidge, Gary Spencer & McKay, James. Draw Fantasy Figures: Basic Drawing Techniques*Develop Characters from Elves to Dragons*Create Fantasy Worlds. 2007. (Illus.). 96p. pap. 14.95 ***978-1-84537-753-3(2))** New Holland Pubs., Ltd. GBR. *Dist:* Sterling Publishing Co., Inc.

Mis, Melody S. How to Draw the Life & Times of Benjamin Harrison. 2007. (Kid's Guide to Drawing the Presidents of the United States of America Ser.). (Illus.). 32p. (J). 25.25 (978-1-4042-3000-2(9) , PowerKids Pr.) Rosen Publishing Group, Inc., The.

—How to Draw the Life & Times of Franklin Delano Roosevelt. 2007. (Kid's Guide to Drawing the Presidents of the United States of America Ser.). (Illus.). 32p. (J). 25.25 (978-1-4042-3008-8(4) , PowerKids Pr.) Rosen Publishing Group, Inc., The.

—How to Draw the Life & Times of James Buchanan. 2006. (Kid's Guide to Drawing the Presidents of the United States of America Ser.). (J). 25.25 (978-1-4042-2992-1(2) , PowerKids Pr.) Rosen Publishing Group, Inc., The.

—How to Draw the Life & Times of James K. Polk. 2006. (Kid's Guide to Drawing the Presidents of the United States of America Ser.). (J). 25.25 (978-1-4042-2988-4(4) , PowerKids Pr.) Rosen Publishing Group, Inc., The.

—How to Draw the Life & Times of Lyndon B. Johnson. 2007. (Kid's Guide to Drawing the Presidents of the United States of America Ser.). (Illus.). 32p. (J). 25.25 (978-1-4042-3012-5(2) , PowerKids Pr.) Rosen Publishing Group, Inc., The.

—How to Draw the Life & Times of Ronald Reagan. 2007. (Kid's Guide to Drawing the Presidents of the United States of America Ser.). (Illus.). 32p. (J). 25.25 (978-1-4042-3016-3(5) , PowerKids Pr.) Rosen Publishing Group, Inc., The.

—How to Draw the Life & Times of Rutherford B. Hayes. 2006. (Kid's Guide to Drawing the Presidents of the United States of America Ser.). (J). 25.25 (978-1-4042-2996-9(5) , PowerKids Pr.) Rosen Publishing Group, Inc., The.

—How to Draw the Life & Times of Woodrow Wilson. 2007. (Kid's Guide to Drawing the Presidents of the United States of America Ser.). (Illus.). 32p. (J). 25.25 (978-1-4042-3004-0(1) , PowerKids Pr.) Rosen Publishing Group, Inc., The.

Monroe, Colleen. The Wonders of Nature Sketchbook: Learn about Nature & How to Draw It. Monroe, Michael Glenn, illus. 2005. (J). 15.00 (978-0-9754942-1-9(X)) Storytime Pr., Inc.

Mouse Works Staff. Learn & Draw Shapes with Mickey. 1999. (Disney's Ser.). 22p. (J). (ps-3). 12.99 (978-0-7364-0101-2(6)) Mouse Works.

Mravec, James. Boats, Planes & Trains. 2004. (Illus.). 96p. spiral bd. (978-1-4127-0564-6(9) , 3460901) Publications International, Ltd.

Muehlenhardt, Amy Bailey. Drawing & Learning about Cats: Using Shapes & Lines. Muehlenhardt, Amy Bailey, illus. 2005. (Sketch It! Ser.). (Illus.). 24p. (J). (ps-k). lib. bdg. 22.60 (978-1-4048-1190-4(7) , 1243854) Picture Window Bks.

—Drawing & Learning about Fish: Using Shapes & Lines. Muehlenhardt, Amy Bailey, illus. 2005. (Sketch It! Ser.). (Illus.). 24p. (J). (ps-k). lib. bdg. 22.60 (978-1-4048-1192-8(3) , 1243856) Picture Window Bks.

—Drawing & Learning about Jungle Animals: Using Shapes & Lines. Muehlenhardt, Amy Bailey, illus. 2005. (Sketch It! Ser.). (Illus.). 24p. (J). (ps-k). lib. bdg. 22.60 (978-1-4048-1193-5(1) , 1243857) Picture Window Bks.

—Drawing & Learning about Monster Trucks: Using Shapes & Lines. Muehlenhardt, Amy Bailey, illus. 2005. (Sketch It! Ser.). (Illus.). 24p. (J). (ps-k). lib. bdg. 22.60 (978-1-4048-1194-2(X) , 1243858) Picture Window Bks.

—Drawing & Learning about Monsters: Using Shapes & Lines. Muehlenhardt, Amy Bailey, illus. 2005. (Sketch It! Ser.). (Illus.). 24p. (J). (ps-k). lib. bdg. 22.60 (978-1-4048-1195-9(8) , 1243859) Picture Window Bks.

Murawski, Laura. How to Draw Horses. 2001. (Kid's Guide to Drawing Ser.). (Illus.). 24p. (J). (gr. 3). lib. bdg. 21.25 (978-0-8239-5552-7(4) , PowerKids Pr.) Rosen Publishing Group, Inc., The.

—A Kid's Guide to Drawing, 6 bks. Incl. How to Draw Airplanes. lib. bdg. 21.25 (978-0-8239-5547-3(8)); How to Draw Cars. lib. bdg. 21.25 (978-0-8239-5548-0(6)); How to Draw Cats. lib. bdg. 21.25 (978-0-8239-5549-7(4)); How to Draw Dinosaurs. lib. bdg. 21.25 (978-0-8239-5550-3(8)); How to Draw Dogs. lib. bdg. 21.25 (978-0-8239-5551-0(6)); How to Draw Horses. lib. bdg. 21.25 (978-0-8239-5552-7(4)); 24p. (J). (gr. 3). (Illus.). 2001. Set lib. bdg. 127.50 (978-0-8239-7058-2(2) , PowerKids Pr.) Rosen Publishing Group, Inc., The.

NASCAR. NASCAR Learn to Draw Race Cars. 2006. (NASCAR Ser.). 32p. (J). (gr. 3-5). pap. 5.95 (978-1-56010-782-8(0)) Foster, Walter Publishing, Inc.

Nick Jr. Staff, ed. Nick Jr's. Diego's Animal Adventures. 2007. (Watch Me Draw Ser.). (Illus.). 24p. (J). pap. 5.95 (978-1-56010-892-4(4)) Foster, Walter Publishing, Inc.

Obrero, Rudy. Watch Me Draw Curious George's Everyday Adventures. 2008. (Watch Me Draw Ser.). (Illus.). 24p. (J). pap. 5.95 ***978-1-60058-059-8(9))** Foster, Walter Publishing, Inc.

Pallotta, Jerry. How to Draw Icky Bugs. Gee, Bonnie, illus. 2003. (J). mass mkt. (978-0-439-38916-7(X)) Scholastic, Inc.

Parker, Lewis K. How to Draw the Life & Times of George H. W. Bush. 2007. (Kid's Guide to Drawing the Presidents of the United States of America Ser.). (Illus.). 32p. (J). 25.25 (978-1-4042-3017-0(3) , PowerKids Pr.) Rosen Publishing Group, Inc., The.

—How to Draw the Life & Times of Harry S. Truman. 2007. (Kid's Guide to Drawing the Presidents of the United States of America Ser.). (Illus.). 32p. (J). 25.25 (978-1-4042-3009-5(2) , PowerKids Pr.) Rosen Publishing Group, Inc., The.

—How to Draw the Life & Times of James A. Garfield. 2006. (Kid's Guide to Drawing the Presidents of the United States of America Ser.). (J). 25.25 (978-1-4042-2997-6(3) , PowerKids Pr.) Rosen Publishing Group, Inc., The.

—How to Draw the Life & Times of Warren G. Harding. 2007. (Kid's Guide to Drawing the Presidents of the United States of America Ser.). (Illus.). 32p. (J). 25.25 (978-1-4042-3005-7(X) , PowerKids Pr.) Rosen Publishing Group, Inc., The.

—How to Draw the Life & Times of William McKinley. 2007. (Kid's Guide to Drawing the Presidents of the United States of America Ser.). (Illus.). 32p. (J). 25.25 (978-1-4042-3001-9(7) , PowerKids Pr.) Rosen Publishing Group, Inc., The.

Peffer, J. Neondragon. Dragonart Fantasy Characters. 2007. (Illus.). 128p. pap. 19.99 (978-1-58180-852-0(6) , Impact) F & W Pubns., Inc.

Pericoli, Matteo. See the City: The Journey of Manhattan Unfurled. 2004. (Illus.). 64p. (J). (gr. 1-5). 15.95 (978-0-375-82469-2(3) , Knopf Bks. for Young Readers) Random Hse. Children's Bks.

Peters, Stephanie True. North Carolina's Sights & Symbols. 2004. 48p. pap. 8.95 (978-1-4042-8504-0(0)) Rosen Publishing Group, Inc., The.

Plaut, Michael F. How to Draw the Life & Times of Gerald R. Ford. 2007. (Kid's Guide to Drawing the Presidents of the United States of America Ser.). (Illus.). 32p. (J). 25.25 (978-1-4042-3014-9(9) , PowerKids Pr.) Rosen Publishing Group, Inc., The.

Powell, William F. Dynamic Composition: Discover Your Inner Artist As You Explore the Basic Theories & Techniques of Pencil Drawing. 2007. (Drawing Made Easy Ser.). (Illus.). 64p. pap. 9.95 (978-1-56010-998-3(X)) Foster, Walter Publishing, Inc.

Pratt, Leonie & Stowell, Louie. Ht Draw Animals. 2006. 32p. (J). pap. 8.99 (978-0-7945-1241-5(0) , Usborne) EDC Publishing.

Quasha, Jennifer. Florida's Sights & Symbols. 2004. 48p. pap. 8.95 (978-1-4042-8501-9(6)) Rosen Publishing Group, Inc., The.

Randolph, Ryan P. How to Draw the Life & Times of Andrew Johnson. 2006. (Kid's Guide to Drawing the Presidents of the United States of America Ser.). (J). 25.25 (978-1-4042-2994-5(9) , PowerKids Pr.) Rosen Publishing Group, Inc., The.

—How to Draw the Life & Times of Dwight D. Eisenhower. (Kid's Guide to Drawing the Presidents of the United States of America Ser.). (Illus.). 32p. (J). 2007. 25.25 (978-1-4042-3010-1(6)); 2006. lib. bdg. ***978-1-4042-30106-6(1))** Rosen Publishing Group, Inc., The. (PowerKids Pr.).

—How to Draw the Life & Times of Millard Fillmore. 2006. (Kid's Guide to Drawing the Presidents of the United States of America Ser.). (J). 25.25 (978-1-4042-2990-7(6) , PowerKids Pr.) Rosen Publishing Group, Inc., The.

—How to Draw the Life & Times of William Howard Taft. 2007. (Kid's Guide to Drawing the Presidents of the United States of America Ser.). (Illus.). 32p. (J). 25.25 (978-1-4042-3003-3(3) , PowerKids Pr.) Rosen Publishing Group, Inc., The.

Revoir, Katherine Q. Create! A Sketchbook & Journal. Carluccio, Maria, illus. 2001. 96p. (gr. 4-7). 14.95 (978-0-8118-2784-3(4)) Chronicle Bks. LLC.

Robins, Deri. Drawing & Sketching. 2004. (QEB Learn Art Ser.). (Illus.). 32p. (J). lib. bdg. 18.95 (978-1-59566-045-9(3)) QEB Publishing Inc.

—Drawing & Sketching. 2006. (Illus.). 32p. (J). 9.95 (978-1-58728-543-1(6) , Two Can Publishing) T&N Children's Publishing.

Roche, Art. Art for Kids: Comic Strips: Create Your Own Comic Strips from Start to Finish. 2007. (Illus.). 112p. 17.95 (978-1-57990-788-4(1)) Lark Bks.

Rosinski, Carol. Getting Started: Discover Your Inner Artist As You Explore the Basic Theories & Techniques of Pencil Drawing. 2007. (Drawing Made Easy Ser.). (Illus.). 64p. pap. 9.95 (978-1-56010-995-2(5)) Foster, Walter Publishing, Inc.

Ruffin, Frances E. How to Draw the Life & Times of Theodore Roosevelt. 2007. (Kid's Guide to Drawing the Presidents of the United States of America Ser.). (Illus.). 32p. (J). 25.25 (978-1-4042-3002-6(5) , PowerKids Pr.) Rosen Publishing Group, Inc., The.

Salvador Alcaide, Ana. Draw Your Own Picasso. 2008. (Illus.). 48p. (J). pap. 12.95 ***978-1-84507-819-5(5))** Lincoln, Frances Ltd. GBR. *Dist:* Perseus Distribution.

Sautter, Aaron. How to Draw Amazing Motorcycles. Smith, Tod, illus. 2008. (J). ***978-1-4296-0073-6(X))** Capstone Pr., Inc.

—How to Draw Crazy Fighter Planes. Whigham, Rod, illus. 2008. (J). ***978-1-4296-1298-2(3))** Capstone Pr., Inc.

—How to Draw Disgusting Aliens. Lentz, Bob, illus. 2008. (J). ***978-1-4296-0075-0(6))** Capstone Pr., Inc.

—How to Draw Ferocious Animals. Stiles, Tim, illus. 2008. (J). ***978-1-4296-1299-9(1))** Capstone Pr., Inc.

—How to Draw Ferocious Dinosaurs. Martin, Cynthia, illus. 2008. (J). ***978-1-4296-0076-7(4))** Capstone Pr., Inc.

—How to Draw Grotesque Monsters. Bascle, Brian, illus. 2008. (J). ***978-1-4296-1300-2(9))** Capstone Pr., Inc.

—How to Draw Incredible Cars. Bascle, Brian, illus. 2008. (J). ***978-1-4296-0077-4(2))** Capstone Pr., Inc.

—How to Draw Indestructible Tanks. Whigham, Rod, illus. 2008. (J). ***978-1-4296-1301-9(7))** Capstone Pr., Inc.

—How to Draw Monster Trucks. Bascle, Brian, illus. 2008. (J). ***978-1-4296-0079-8(9))** Capstone Pr., Inc.

C
D

—How to Draw Terrifying Robots. Knudson, Jason, illus. 2008. (J). (***978-1-4296-0080-4(2)**) Capstone Pr., Inc.

—How to Draw Unreal Spaceships. Bascle, Brian, illus. 2008. (J). (***978-1-4296-1302-6(5)**) Capstone Pr., Inc.

Schmidt, Roderic. How to Draw the Life & Times of Abraham Lincoln. 2006. (Kid's Guide to Drawing the Presidents of the United States of America Ser.). (J). 25.25 (978-1-4042-2993-8(0) , PowerKids Pr.) Rosen Publishing Group, Inc., The.

—How to Draw the Life & Times of George W. Bush. 2007. (Kid's Guide to Drawing the Presidents of the United States of America Ser.). (Illus.). 32p. (J). 25.25 (978-1-4042-3019-4(X) , PowerKids Pr.) Rosen Publishing Group, Inc., The.

Silver Dolphin en Español Editors. Serie Aprendizaje: Drawing with Fairies. 2006. (SPA., Illus.). 22p. (J). bds. 16.95 (978-970-718-331-5(4)) Advantage Pubs. Group.

—Serie Aprendizaje: Let's Draw with Pixar. 2006. (SPA., Illus.). 22p. (J). bds. 16.95 (978-970-718-320-9(9)) Advantage Pubs. Group.

Sketch It. (C). 271.20 (978-1-4048-1518-6(X)) Picture Window Bks.

Smith, Andrea Helen. A Catholic How-to-Draw. 2006. (Illus.). 102p. (J). spiral bd. 14.95 (978-0-9764691-3-1(8)) Little Way Pr.

Smith, Lucy. Ht Draw Horses. Chapman, Chris, illus. 2006. 32p. (J). pap. 5.99 (978-0-7945-1368-9(9) , Usborne) EDC Publishing.

Soloff-Levy, Barbara. How to Draw Sea Creatures. 2002. (gr. 3-6). lib. bdg. 11.80 (978-0-613-89988-8(1)) Tandem Library Bks.

Speakman, Christopher. Street Scenes Drawing: Learn to Draw Step by Step. 2007. (How to... Ser.). 32p. pap. 8.95 (978-1-56010-989-1(0)) Foster, Walter Publishing, Inc.

Stegenga, Wil. Pinwheel Designs. 2007. 32p. pap., pap. 3.95 (***978-0-486-46227-1(7)**) Dover Pubns., Inc.

Stephens, Jay. Heroes! Draw Your Own Superheroes, Gadget Geeks & Other Do-Gooders. 2007. (Illus.). 64p. (J). pap. 5.95 (***978-1-60059-179-2(5)**) Lark Bks.

—Monsters! Draw Your Own Mutants, Freaks & Creeps. 2007. (Illus.). 64p. (J). pap. 5.95 (***978-1-60059-178-5(7)**); (gr. 4-6). 12.95 (978-1-57990-935-2(3)) Lark Bks.

—Robots! Draw Your Own Androids, Cyborgs & Battle Bots. 2008. (Illus.). 64p. (J). 12.95 (***978-1-57990-937-6(X)**) Lark Bks.

Strevens-Marzo, Bridget. Big Book for Little Hands. 2007. (Illus.). 58p. (J). (ps-1). 15.95 (***978-1-85437-753-1(1)**) Tate Gallery Publishing, Ltd. GBR. *Dist:* Hachette Bk. Group.

Sutton, Scott E. How to Draw Stuff. Sutton, Scott E., illus. 2002. (Illus.). 32p. pap. 7.95 (978-1-888045-15-4(9)) Action Publishing, LLC.

Tatchell, Judy & Varley, Carol. Ht Draw Lettering. 2006. 32p. (J). pap. 5.99 (978-0-7945-1379-5(4) , Usborne) EDC Publishing.

Tecco, Betsy Dru. How to Draw the Life & Times of Grover Cleveland. 2006. (Kid's Guide to Drawing the Presidents of the United States of America Ser.). (J). 25.25 (978-1-4042-2999-0(X) , PowerKids Pr.) Rosen Publishing Group, Inc., The.

Thomas, Isabel. Action Art: Drawing. 2005. (Heinemann Read & Learn Ser.). (Illus.). 24p. (J). pap. (978-1-4034-6924-3(5)) Heinemann Library.

—Drawing. 2005. (Heinemann Read & Learn Ser.). (Illus.). 24p. (J). (ps-1). lib. bdg. 21.36 (978-1-4034-6918-2(0)) Heinemann Library.

Top That, ed. How to Draw 101 Cartoon Characters. 2005. (Illus.). 48p. (J). pap. (978-1-84510-735-2(7)) Top That! Publishing PLC.

Top That!, creator. How to Draw Manga Ninja Warriors. 2005. (Illus.). 48p. (J). (gr. 4-7). pap. (978-1-84510-971-4(6)) Top That! Publishing PLC.

Walsh, Patricia. Aircraft. Adamic, Mark, illus. 2006. 32p. (J). (***978-1-4034-8921-0(1)**) Heinemann Library.

—Cars. Westerfield, David, illus. 2006. 32p. (J). (***978-1-4034-8922-7(X)**) Heinemann Library.

—Dinosaurs. Westerfield, David, illus. 2006. (Draw It! Ser.). 32p. (J). (***978-1-4034-8923-4(8)**) Heinemann Library.

—Dinosaurs. 2nd ed. 2006. (Draw It! Ser.). (Illus.). 32p. (J). pap. (***978-1-4034-8930-2(0)**) Heinemann Library.

—Space Vehicles. Adamic, Mark, illus. 2006. (Draw It! Ser.). 32p. (J). (***978-1-4034-8924-1(6)**) Heinemann Library.

—Wild Animals. Westerfield, David, illus. 2006. 32p. (***978-1-4034-8925-8(4)**) Heinemann Library.

—Wild Animals. 2nd ed. 2006. (Illus.). 32p. pap. (***978-1-4034-8932-6(7)**) Heinemann Library.

—Woodland Animals. Westerfield, David, illus. 2006. 32p. (J). (***978-1-4034-8926-5(2)**) Heinemann Library.

—Woodland Animals. 2nd ed. 2006. (Illus.). 32p. (J). pap. (***978-1-4034-8933-3(5)**) Heinemann Library.

Walter Foster. Watch Me Draw the Playful World of My Little Pony. 2008. (Watch Me Draw Ser.). (Illus.). 24p. (J). pap. 5.95 (***978-1-60058-030-7(0)**) Foster, Walter Publishing, Inc.

Walter Foster Editors, ed. Brother Bear. 2004. (Disney Classic Character Ser.). (Illus.). 32p. (J). pap. 5.95 (978-1-56010-799-6(5)) Foster, Walter Publishing, Inc.

—Winnie the Pooh Snap Pack. 2002. (Snap Pack Ser.). (Illus.). 32p. (J). (gr. 1 up). pap. 12.95 (978-1-56010-307-3(8)) Foster, Walter Publishing, Inc.

Watson, B. S. & Teitelbaum, Michael. How to Draw Dragonball Z. 2001. (Dragonball Z Ser.). (Illus.). 32p. (J). 4.99 (978-0-439-31348-3(1)) Scholastic, Inc.

Watt, Fiona & Milbourne, Anna. Big Bk of Things to Draw. 2007. 96p. (J). pap. 15.99 (978-0-7945-1328-3(X) , Usborne) EDC Publishing.

Williams, Ted & Williams, Amy E., illus. Construction. 2004. 96p. (978-1-4127-1123-4(1) , 3461002) Publications International, Ltd.

Wilson, Natashya. How to Draw the Life & Times of Herbert Hoover. 2007. (Kid's Guide to Drawing the Presidents of the United States of America Ser.). (Illus.). 32p. (J). 25.25 (978-1-4042-3007-1(6) , PowerKids Pr.) Rosen Publishing Group, Inc., The.

Wilson, Natashya & Natashya, Wilson. How to Draw the Life & Times of James Earl Carter Jr. 2007. (Kid's Guide to Drawing the Presidents of the United States of America Ser.). (Illus.). 32p. (J). 25.25 (978-1-4042-3015-6(7) , PowerKids Pr.) Rosen Publishing Group, Inc., The.

Winterberg, Jenna. A Boy's Adventure: A Step-by-Step Drawing & Story Book for Kids As Young As Four Years Old. Fisher, Diana, illus. 2006. (Watch Me Draw Ser.). 24p. (J). pap. 4.95 (978-1-56010-788-0(X)) Foster, Walter Publishing, Inc.

Yaun, Debra. People with Debra Yaun Drawing: Learn to Draw Step by Step. 2007. (How to... Ser.). 32p. pap. 8.95 (978-1-56010-795-8(2)) Foster, Walter Publishing, Inc.

Zamora, Dulce. How to Draw the Life & Times of John Fitzgerald Kennedy. 2007. (Kid's Guide to Drawing the Presidents of the United States of America Ser.). (Illus.). 32p. (J). 25.25 (978-1-4042-3011-8(4) , PowerKids Pr.) Rosen Publishing Group, Inc., The.

Zemke, Deborah. Doodles to Go: Oodles of Step-by-Step Doodles. 2007. (Illus.). 64p. 12.95 (978-1-59354-604-5(1)) Blue Apple Bks.

Zschock, Heather. Merry Christmas Scratch & Sketch. 2006. (Illus.). 64p. (J). 12.99 (978-1-59359-943-0(9)) Peter Pauper Pr. Inc.

DRAWING MATERIALS

see Artists' Materials

DRAWINGS

Barry, Bill. How to Draw a Comic Book for Fun or Profit! Barry, O. H., ed. Barry, Bill, illus. 2002. (Illus.). 96p. (YA). pap. 16.95 (978-0-944099-26-1(2)) Bill Barry's Compass Bks.

Conroy, Don. Birds. 2000. (Draw with Don Ser.: No. 6). 31p. (J). (gr. 1-4). pap. (978-1-84210-031-8(9)) Mentor Bks.

—Cartoon Birds. 2000. (Draw with Don Ser.: No. 4). (Illus.). 31p. (J). (gr. 1-4). pap. (978-1-84210-032-5(7)) Mentor Bks.

—Cartoon People. 2000. (Draw with Don Ser.: No. 2). 31p. (J). (gr. 1-4). pap. (978-1-84210-028-8(9)) Mentor Bks.

Greenaway, Kate. Kate Greenaway Illustrations CD-ROM & Book. 2008. (Illus.). 48p. pap. 19.95 incl. cd-rom (***978-0-486-99871-8(1)**) Dover Pubns., Inc.

Hart, Christopher. Kids Draw Dinosaurs. 2003. (gr. k-3). lib. bdg. 19.90 (978-0-613-90863-4(5)) Tandem Library Bks.

Klutz Editors. Draw Christmas Thumb Prints. 2005. (Illus.). 46p. (J). spiral bd. 7.95 (978-1-57054-003-5(9)) Klutz.

Kunkel, Jeff, ed. What Scares Me & What I Do about It: Stories & Pictures by Sunday School Kids. 2004. (Illus.). 48p. 12.99 (978-0-8066-4558-2(X) , Augsburg Bks.) Augsburg Fortress, Pubs.

DREAMS

see also Nightmares

Apel, Melanie Ann. Let's Talk about Nightmares. 2002. (Let's Talk Library). (Illus.). 24p. (J). lib. bdg. 18.75 (978-0-8239-5860-3(4) , PowerKids Pr.) Rosen Publishing Group, Inc., The.

Blum, Renon. Explore Your Dream. 2003. (Musicals for Young Audiences Ser.). 55p. (Orig.). (YA). (gr. k-12). pap. 8.00 (978-0-88734-528-9(X)) Players Pr., Inc.

Cheung, Theresa. Dreams: What Are Your Dreams Trying to Tell You? 2004. (Illus.). 128p. (J). pap. 7.99 (978-0-340-88236-8(0) , Hodder & Stoughton) Hodder General Publishing Division GBR. *Dist:* Trafalgar Square Publishing.

Collier-Thompson, Kristi. The Girls' Guide to Dreams. Turchyn, Sandie, illus. 2006. 128p. (YA). (gr. 8-11). reprint ed. pap. 13.00 (978-0-7567-9899-4(X)) DIANE Publishing Co.

Crispin, Gerald W. God Speaks Through Dreams: But Who's Listening?, No. 1. Crispin, Gerald W. & Crispin, Vera G., eds. unabr. ed. 2003. (Illus.). 160p. (gr. 10 up). reprint ed. pap. 19.95 (978-0-9744015-1-5(X)) Benchmark Book Craft.

Cron, Mary Herd. Dreams: Mind Movies of the Night. Ning, Amy, illus. 2000. 6. 64p. (gr. 4-6). lib. bdg. (978-0-7613-1512-4(8) , Millbrook Pr.) Lerner Publishing Group.

DeLong, Ron. Crayola Dream-Makers: Dreams You Can Count On. DeLong, Ron, ed. 14th ed. 2004. (Illus.). 48p. per. 6.00 (978-0-86696-316-9(2)) Binney & Smith, Inc.

Eaton, William S., Sr. The Money Book of Dreams. 2001. (Illus.). 12p. (YA). (gr. 7-12). 12.95 (978-0-9713693-0-6(5)) Eaton, William.

Garfield, Patricia. Dream Book: A Young Person's Guide to Understanding Dreams. 2002. (gr. 5-8). lib. bdg. 18.75 (978-0-613-57038-1(3)) Tandem Library Bks.

—Dream Catcher: A Young Person's Journal for Exploring Dreams. 2003. (Illus.). 96p. (J). (gr. 5 up). 11.95 (978-0-88776-661-9(7)) Tundra Bks., Inc./Livres Toundra, Inc. CAN. *Dist:* Random Hse., Inc.

Garfield, Patricia L. The Dream Book: A Young Person's Guide to Understanding Dreams. 2002. 128p. (J). (gr. 7 up). pap. 9.95 (978-0-88776-594-0(7)) Tundra Bks., Inc./Livres Toundra, Inc. CAN. *Dist:* Random Hse., Inc.

Gibson, Clare. The Secret Life of Dreams: Decoding the Messages from Your Subconscious. 2003. (Illus.). 400p. 29.98 (978-1-59223-101-0(2)) Advantage Pubs. Group.

Jaskolka, Anna. Teen Dreams & What They Mean. (Illus.). 1p. 10.95 (978-0-572-02877-0(6)) Foulsham, W. Co., Ltd. GBR. *Dist:* APG Sales and Fulfillment.

Kallen, Stuart A. Dreams. 2003. (Illus.). 112p. (J). 29.95 (978-1-59018-288-8(X) , Lucent Bks.) Thomson Gale.

MacGregor, Rob. Dream Power for Teens. 2005. 192p. (J). pap. 8.95 (978-1-59337-024-4(5)) Adams Media Corp.

McPhee, Andrew T. Sleep & Dreams. 2001. (Single Title - Science Ser.). (Illus.). 112p. (J). (gr. 9-12). 26.00 (978-0-531-11735-4(9) , Watts, Franklin) Scholastic Library Publishing.

Moonchild, Karen Davies. Moon Dreams. 2003. 184p. 25.95 (978-0-595-74890-7(2)); pap. 15.95 (978-0-595-28343-9(8)) iUniverse, Inc.

Morina, Barbara. Dream: A Dream Journal. 2000. (Write It down Ser.). (Illus.). 202p. (YA). (gr. 6 up). 19.95 (978-1-892033-22-2(4)) Journals Unlimited, Inc.

Muhammad, Renay. Dreams Do Come True. 2004. (Illus.). (J). cd-rom (978-0-9754024-0-5(4)) Sharif, Mboya.

Page, Jason. The Secret Side of You: A Fun Guide to Your Star Signs, Dreams, Lucky Numbers & More! 1999. (Illus.). 128p. (YA). (gr. 4-7). pap. 5.95 (978-1-902618-21-0(1)) Element Children's Bks.

Reid, Lori. Naked at the Prom: The Secret Language of Dreams. 2003. (gr. 7-12). lib. bdg. 18.75 (978-0-613-79096-3(0)) Tandem Library Bks.

Reid, Lori, et al. Naked at the Prom. 2003. 128p. pap. 9.95 (978-1-56975-356-9(3)) Ulysses Pr.

Rosen, Marvin. Demystifying Dreams. 2004. 64p. (YA). pap. 9.95 (978-0-595-30290-1(4)) iUniverse, Inc.

Sonandres, Thomas William & Peterson, Marilyn A. DreamLady.com: Guidance from Your Dreams. 2003. 224p. per. 12.95 (978-0-9728531-0-1(3)) Spica Bks.

Trudi, Strain Trueit. Dreams & Sleep. 2004. (Life Balance Ser.). 80p. (YA). (gr. 5-8). pap. 6.95 (978-0-531-15579-0(X) , Watts, Franklin) Scholastic Library Publishing.

Trueit, Trudi Strain, tr. Dreams & Sleep. 2004. (Life Balance Ser.). (Illus.). 80p. (J). 20.50 (978-0-531-12260-0(3) , Watts, Franklin) Scholastic Library Publishing.

DREAMS—FICTION

Abbott, Tony. Dream Thief. Merrell, David, illus. 2003. (Secrets of Droon Ser.: No. 17). 128p. (J). (gr. 2-5). pap. 4.99 (978-0-439-42078-5(4) , Scholastic Paperbacks) Scholastic, Inc.

—Dream Thief. 2003. (gr. k-3). lib. bdg. 11.80 (978-0-613-58148-6(2)) Tandem Library Bks.

Abshire, Lisa D. Sam's Magical Day. 2006. 48p. pap. 12.95 (978-1-4241-1484-9(5)) PublishAmerica, Inc.

Aigner-Clark, Julie. Sweet Dreams, Mimi. Zaidi, Nadeem, illus. 2004. (Baby Einstein Ser.). 16p. (J). (ps-17). bds. 5.99 (978-0-7868-5115-7(5)) Hyperion Bks. for Children.

Albee, Sarah. Blue's Bad Dream. Chernichaw, Ian, illus. 2006. (Blue's Clues Ser.). 24p. (J). pap. 3.99 (978-1-4169-1553-9(2) , Simon Spotlight/Nickelodeon) Simon & Schuster Children's Publishing.

Alonso, Fernando. El Arbol de los Suenos. Urberuaga, Emilio, illus. 2003. Tr. of Dream Trees. (SPA.). 124p. (J). (gr. 5-8). pap. 10.95 (978-968-19-0978-9(X)) Santillana USA Publishing Co., Inc.

—El Arbol de los Suenos. 1998. Tr. of Dream Trees. (SPA., Illus.). 128p. (J). (gr. 4-7). 15.95 (978-84-204-4802-2(8)) Santillana USA Publishing Co., Inc.

—Las Fantasias de la Lechera. (Superbks./Superlibros).Tr. of Milkmaid's Daydreams. (J). (gr. k-1). (SPA.). pap. 6.95 (978-0-88272-473-7(8)); (Illus.). 16p. pap. 6.95 (978-0-88272-474-4(6)); Big Book. (SPA.). 21.95 (978-0-88272-463-8(0)); Big Book. 21.95 (978-0-88272-464-5(9)) Santillana USA Publishing Co., Inc.

Anfousse, Ginette. Le Grand Reve de Rosalie. 2002. (Roman Jeunesse Ser.). (FRE.). 96p. (YA). (gr. 4-7). pap. (978-2-89021-182-7(7)) Diffusion du livre Mirabel.

Applegate, Katherine. Survival. 2003. (Remnants Ser.: No. 13). (gr. 3-6). lib. bdg. 13.00 (978-0-613-66387-8(X)) Tandem Library Bks.

Argiento, Cindy. Doris in Dreamland. 2007. pap. 8.00 (***978-0-8059-7461-4(X)**) Dorrance Publishing Co., Inc.

Asch, Frank. Moonbear's Dream. Asch, Frank, illus. 2002. (Illus.). 32p. (J). (ps-1). pap. 6.99 (978-0-689-85310-4(6) , Aladdin) Simon & Schuster Children's Publishing.

Ashworth, Sherry. Dream Travellers. 2004. 336p. (YA). pap. 9.99 (978-0-689-83756-2(9)) Simon & Schuster, Ltd. GBR. *Dist:* Independent Pubs. Group.

Atnip, Linda. Miranda's Magic Garden. 2004. cd-rom 15.98 (978-1-885394-25-5(X)) Amber Lotus Publishing.

—Miranda's Magic Garden. Rothan, Ann, illus. 2004. 32p. (ps-7). 19.95 (978-1-885394-21-7(7)) Amber Lotus Publishing.

Baicker, Karen. Snuggle Me Snuggly! 2004. (Illus.). 5p. (J). bds. 6.95 (978-1-59354-038-8(8)) Handprint Bks.

Balzola, Asun. Munia y el Cocolilo Naranja. (SPA.). 32p. (J). (978-84-233-1335-8(2)) Ediciones Destino ESP. *Dist:* Lectorum Pubns., Inc.

Banks, Kate. And If the Moon Could Talk. Hallensleben, Georg, illus. 2002. (J). 24.36 (978-0-7587-1943-0(4)) Book Wholesalers, Inc.

—And If the Moon Could Talk. Hallensleben, Georg, illus. 2001. (J). (gr. k-2). 25.95 incl. audio (978-0-8045-6867-8(7) , 6867) Spoken Arts, Inc.

—Close Your Eyes. Hallensleben, Georg, illus. 2002. 40p. (J). (ps-1). 16.95 (978-0-374-31382-1(2) , Farrar, Straus & Giroux (BYR)) Farrar, Straus & Giroux.

Barbey, Beatrice. Meow Said the Mouse. Ames, Philippe, illus. 2005. 40p. (J). 15.00 (978-1-888375-49-7(3)) Parallax Pr.

Beard, Robert. Lovenia Little & Her Big Dreams. 2005. 60p. (J). pap. (978-1-886098-16-9(6)) Gye Nyame Hse.

Beaumont, Karen. Baby Danced the Polka. Plecas, Jennifer, illus. 2004. 32p. (J). (ps). 12.99 (978-0-8037-2587-4(6) , Dial) Penguin Group (USA) Inc.

Beletic, Kittie/N. What Color Is Your Dream. 2007. (J). 16.95 (***978-1-933285-56-6(7)**) Brown Bks. Publishing Group.

Belinsky, Ruth. I Dream Before I Sleep. 2002. (Illus.). 32p. pap. 9.95 (978-0-9740012-0-3(1)) Idee, LLC.

Benevenia, Rose. Dolly & Babe. Benevenia, Rose, illus. l.t. ed. 2004. (Illus.). 9p. (J). (gr. k-2). pap. 9.00 (978-0-9729044-0-7(9)) Cabbage Patch Pr.

Bennett, John Roy. Jason Mason Middleton-Tapp. Pavanel, Jane, ed. Charbonneau, Isabelle, illus. 2000. 32p. (J). (ps-k). pap. 8.95 (978-1-894222-12-9(1)) Lobster Pr. CAN. *Dist:* Univ. of Toronto Pr.

Bentley, Dawn. Fuzzy Bear's Bedtime. Nagy, Krisztina, illus. 2005. (Fuzzy Bear Ser.). 10p. (J). (ps-k). act. bk. ed. 10.95 (978-1-58117-055-9(6) , Intervisual/Piggy Toes) Dalmatian Pr.

Berenstain, Stan & Berenstain, Jan. The Berenstain Bears & the Bad Dream. Berenstain, Stan & Berenstain, Jan, illus. 2002. (Berenstain Bears First Time Bks.). (Illus.). (J). 11.19 (978-0-7587-0957-8(9)) Book Wholesalers, Inc.

—The Berenstain Bears & the Bad Dream. ed. 2004. (Berenstain Bears First Time Bks.). (J). (ps-2). spiral bd. (978-0-616-01555-1(0)); spiral bd. (978-0-616-01556-8(9)) Canadian National Institute for the Blind/Institut National Canadien pour les Aveugles.

Black, Robert A. Lunar Pioneers. 2008. 280p. (YA). pap. 14.99 (978-1-59092-397-9(9) , Blue Works) Windstorm Creative.

Blackstone, Stella. I Dreamt I Was a Dinosaur. Beaton, Clare, illus. 2005. 32p. (J). (ps-3). 15.99 (978-1-84148-238-5(2)) Barefoot Bks., Inc.

Bosak, Susan V. Dream: A Tale of Wonder, Wisdom & Wishes. Dillon, Leo and Diane et al, illus. 2004. 40p. (J). (978-1-896232-04-1(3) , TCP Pr.) Communication Project, The.

Bosworth, Richard. The Box Seat Dream. Cioffi, Joseph, illus. 2000. 126p. (YA). (gr. 3-10). pap. 6.95 (978-0-9679395-0-6(X) , 33) Boz Imagineering.

Braganza, Sheraleen. Butterfly Kisses. 2006. (Illus.). 68p. pap. (***978-1-84401-812-3(1)**) Athena Pr.

Brami, Elisabeth. Sweet Dreams, Scary Monsters. McGowan, Siobhan, tr. from FRE. Bertrand, Philippe, illus. 1999. 32p. (J). (ps-3). 14.95 (978-1-55670-945-6(5)) Stewart, Tabori & Chang.

Breslin, Theresa. The Dream Master. unabr. ed. 2000. (Read-Along Ser.). 184p. (J). pap. 29.95 incl. audio (978-0-7540-6222-6(8) , RA023, Chivers Children's Audio Bks.) BBC Audiobooks America.

—Dream Master: Nightmare! unabr. l.t. ed. 2003. (Read-Along Ser.). 176p. (J). pap. 29.95 incl. audio (978-0-7540-6236-3(8) , RAO37, Galaxy Children's Large Print) BBC Audiobooks America.

Bronzan, William M., Sr. A Time to Dream. 2006. 41p. (J). pap. 8.95 (978-0-7414-3158-5(0)) Infinity Publishing.

Brooks, Martha. Bone Dance. 2005. 184p. (J). (gr. 7-16). pap. 6.95 (978-0-88899-336-6(6)) Groundwood Bks. CAN. *Dist:* Perseus Distribution.

—The Bone Dance. 1999. (J). (978-0-606-16716-1(1)) Tandem Library Bks.

Brown, Alan. Dreaming Tree. Fletcher, Claire, illus. 2000. 29p. (J). (gr. k-3). 17.95 (978-0-00-198321-2(0)) Zondervan.

Brown, Margaret Wise. The Dream Book. 2005. 32p. (J). (978-0-7868-2097-9(7)) Hyperion Bks. for Children.

—The Dream Book. 2000. 32p. (J). (978-0-7868-0124-4(7)) Hyperion Pr.

Brown, Margaret Wise & Wiggins, Beth Foster. Buenas noches Oso. 2006. 24p. (J). 12.95 (978-1-882077-61-8(X)) Sweetwater Pr.

Browne, Anthony. Willy the Dreamer. 1998. (J). 16.99 (978-0-7636-0617-6(0)) Candlewick Pr.

Browne, N. M. Basilisk. 2006. 320p. (YA). pap. 7.95 (978-1-58234-910-7(X) , Bloomsbury Children) Bloomsbury Publishing.

Bullock, Thomas. Siwash, the Biggest Little Indian Brave. 2004. 50p. pap. 12.95 (978-1-4137-5070-6(2)) PublishAmerica, Inc.

Burrows, Terry. Chiquitines Cuentos de las Bunas Noches. 2002. (Toddler's Ser.).Tr. of Stories for Bedtime. (SPA., Illus.). 78p. (J). (978-968-5308-38-0(1) , Silver Dolphin en Español) Advanced Marketing, S. de R. L. de C. V.

Butcher, A. J. Conexion Caos Vol. 2: Spy High, Episodio 2. Morales, Andrea & Yver, Camila, trs. 2004. (SPA., Illus.). 272p. (978-84-95618-58-0(3) , Umbriel) Ediciones Urano S. A.

Cabrera, Jane. Bear's Good Night. Cabrera, Jane, illus. 2002. (J). (gr. k-k). (Illus.). 12p. bds. 4.99 (978-0-7636-1796-7(2)); bds. 4.99 Candlewick Pr.

Campbell, Joanna. Good-Bye, Midnight Wanderer. 1999. (gr. 3-6). lib. bdg. 12.40 (978-0-613-15804-6(0)) Tandem Library Bks.

Carpenter, Suzanne, illus. So Hungry. 2004. 32p. pap. 29.95 (978-1-84323-455-5(6)) Beekman Bks., Inc.

Carruth, George. The Boy Who Loved Birds. Carruth Krock, Libby, illus. 2007. (ENG.). 32p. (J). 15.95 (***978-0-9773167-1-7(8)**) Too Much Fun, LLC.

Caruso, Tina Silvio. The Magical Dream. Larsson, Rod, illus. 2000. 32p. (J). (ps-5). pap. 6.95 (978-0-9706745-0-0(3)) Caruso, Tina Silvio.

Catalano, Dominic. Hush! Catalano, Dominic, illus. 2003. (Illus.). 32p. (J). (gr. k-3). 14.95 (978-1-57768-679-8(9) , Gingham Dog Pr.) School Specialty Publishing.

Cazet, Denys. Minnie & Moo: The Night of the Living Bed. Cazet, Denys, illus. (I Can Read Bks.). 48p. (J). (gr. k-3). 2004. pap. 3.99 (978-0-06-000505-4(X) , Harper Trophy); 2003. (Illus.). 16.99 (978-0-06-000503-0(3)); 2003. (Illus.). lib. bdg. 16.89 (978-0-06-000504-7(1)) HarperCollins Pubs.

—The Night of the Living Bed. Cazet, Denys, illus. unabr. ed. 2005. (Minnie & Moo Ser.). (J). (gr. k-4). (Illus.). 25.95 incl. audio (978-1-59519-389-6(8)); (Illus.). 28.95 incl. audio compact disk (978-1-59519-393-3(6)); (Illus.). pap. 16.95 incl. audio (978-1-59519-388-9(X)); (Illus.). pap. 18.95 incl. audio compact disk (978-1-59519-392-6(8)); Set. pap. 31.95 incl. audio compact disk (978-1-59519-394-0(4)); Set. (Illus.). pap. 29.95 incl. audio (978-1-59519-390-2(1)) Live Oak Media.

Child, Lauren. My Dream Bed. 2002. (Illus.). 18p. (J). (ps-2). pap. 15.95 (978-0-439-30912-7(3) , Levine, Arthur A. Bks.) Scholastic, Inc.

Chronicle Books LLC Staff. Paul Frank Picturebook 1. 2008. (J). 12.95 (978-0-8118-6024-6(8)) Chronicle Bks. LLC.

—Winter Dreams. 2008. (J). 12.95 (978-0-8118-4672-1(5)) Chronicle Bks. LLC.

Clark, John T. & Clark, Nicole K. Adventures in Dreamtime. l.t. ed. 1998. (Illus.). 32p. (J). (gr. k-2). 15.95 (978-1-892176-12-7(2)) PremaNations Publishing.

Clark, Matthew. SongrrrLines: A Beastie Bedtime Dreaming & Coloring Book. 2005. 26p. (J). pap. 8.95 net. (978-1-59975-106-1(2)) Independent Pub.

Clayton, A. J. An Egg-Citing Dream. 2006. 17.00 (*978-0-8059-9127-7(1)) Dorrance Publishing Co., Inc.

Coburn, Ann. Mission 1: Flying Solo. Horne, Sarah, illus. 2006. (Dream Team Ser.: Vol. 1). 80p. (J). pap. (*978-1-84428-118-3(3)) Walker & Co.

—Showtime. Horne, Sarah, illus. 2006. (Dream Team Mission Ser.: Vol. 2). 80p. (J). pap. (*978-1-84428-071-1(3)) Walker Bks., Ltd.

Cohen, Edythe. The Ghetto Garden. 2005. 51p. pap. 12.95 (978-1-4137-9539-4(0)) PublishAmerica, Inc.

Cohen, Miriam. Eddy's Dream. Cohen, Adam, photos by. l.t. ed. 2000. (Illus.). 32p. (J). (gr. k-2). 16.95 (978-1-887734-57-8(0)) Star Bright Bks., Inc.

Colbert, Norman. Norman Okay, Not Today. 2001. 109p. pap. 10.95 (978-0-7414-0674-3(8)) Infinity Publishing.

Cole, Brock. Fair Monaco. 2004. (Illus.). 32p. (J). 16.95 (978-1-932425-07-9(1) , Lemniscaat) Boyds Mills Pr.

Collins, Terry. Spongebob NaturePants, Vol. 7. 2004. 64p. (J). (gr. 2-5). pap. 17.00 incl. audio (978-1-4000-8630-6(2) , Listening Library) Random Hse. Audio Publishing Group.

Conover, David & Conover, Patricia. Humphrey the Hugganite. Acker, I. M., illus. 2000. 32p. (J). (ps-3). pap. 7.99 (978-0-9677987-0-7(1)) Hugganite Publishing.

Constantin, Pascale, illus. Dan's Bad Dream. 2006. (I'm Going to Read Ser.). 32p. (J). pap. 3.95 (978-1-4027-3342-0(9)) Sterling Publishing Co., Inc.

Cordell, Greg. Digging to Reach the Top. Hyun, Jinsun, illus. 2004. (J). (978-0-9759699-0-8(0)) Greenville Family Partnership.

Costantino, Eric. Beeboo Bear Dreamed A Dream. 2004. 31p. pap. 17.95 (978-1-4137-3649-6(1)) PublishAmerica, Inc.

Cousins, Lucy. Maisy's Rainbow Dream. Cousins, Lucy, illus. 2003. (Maisy Ser.). (Illus.). 32p. (J). (ps up). 16.99 (978-0-7636-2195-7(1)) Candlewick Pr.

Craven, Tracy Leininger. Life of Faith/Kathleens Dreams. 2006. (Life of Faith': Kathleen Mckenzie Ser.). 160p. (YA). pap. 6.99 (978-1-928749-25-7(9)) Mission City Pr., Inc.

Curry, Don, ed. Ella's Fairy Dream. 2006. 22p. (J). 14.95 (978-0-696-23406-4(8)) Meredith Bks.

Cyr, Joe. Two Tales of That Very First Christmas: An Angel Named Etoile & the Straw Girl, Owen, Ramon E., illus. l.t. ed. 2002. 24p. 5.95 (978-0-9713768-1-6(6)) Cyr, Joe.

Dalmatian Press Staff. Fairy Dreams. 2004. 12p. (J). bds. 3.99 (978-1-4037-0742-0(1)) Dalmatian Pr.

Dalmatian Press Staff, ed. Bedtime Bear: Sweet Dreams. (Care Bearstm Ser.). 6p. (J). bds. 9.99 (978-1-4037-0556-3(9)) Dalmatian Pr.

Dalrymple, Farel. Pop Gun War. 2003. (Illus.). 136p. (gr. 11 up). pap. 13.95 (978-1-56971-934-3(9)) Dark Horse Comics.

Davis, Maggie Steincrohn. A Garden of Whales. O'Connell, Jennifer Barrett, illus. 2000. 32p. (J). (ps-2). reprint ed. pap. 6.95 (978-0-944475-35-5(3)) Camden Hse. Publishing CAN. *Dist:* Firefly Bks., Ltd.

De Lint, Charles. The Blue Girl. 2006. 384p. (YA). (gr. 7). reprint ed. pap. 7.99 (978-0-14-240545-1(0) , Puffin) Penguin Group (USA) Inc.

Dealey, Erin. Little Bo Peep Can't Get to Sleep. Wakiyama, Hanako, illus. 2005. 40p. (J). 15.95 (978-0-689-84099-9(3) , Atheneum) Simon & Schuster Children's Publishing.

DeMascio, William. Don't Forget to Visit the Moon. 2005. 31p. (J). 13.01 (978-1-4116-1239-6(6)) Lulu.com.

Demi, illus. The Magic Pillow. 2008. (J). (*978-1-4169-2470-8(1) , McElderry, Margaret K.) Simon & Schuster Children's Publishing.

DeVore, Maggie. White Crow. Barron, Lynn, ed. DeVore, Jeffrey, illus. 2002. (J). 17.00 (978-0-9708940-3-8(1)) Gently Worded Bks., LLC.

Dexter, Catherine. I Dream of Murder. 1999. 160p. (YA). (gr. 5-9). pap. 5.95 (978-0-688-16668-7(7)) HarperCollins Pubs.

—I Dream of Murder. 1999. (J). (978-0-606-16805-2(2)) Tandem Library Bks.

Dobkin, Bonnie. Dream Spinner. 2006. 288p. pap. 8.95 (978-0-7387-0919-2(0) , Flux) Llewellyn Pubns.

Docan, Cristina C. A Secret Promise. 2007. (Illus.). 24p. (J). 16.95 (*978-1-905636-01-3(6)) Beautiful Bks. GBR. *Dist:* International Publishers Marketing.

Docheff, Dennis. The Not-So-Average Chester P. Mcadams. 2004. 76p. pap. 14.95 (978-1-4137-1059-5(X)) PublishAmerica, Inc.

Doherty, Berlie. Jinnie Ghost. Ray, Jane, illus. 2005. 40p. (J). (ps-7). 16.95 (978-1-84507-292-6(8)) Lincoln, Frances Ltd. GBR. *Dist:* Perseus Distribution.

Dream Catchers - Evaluation Guide: Evaluation Guide. 2006. (J). (978-1-55942-403-5(6)) Marsh Media.

Dream Catchers - Teaching Guide. 2001. (J). 17.95 (978-1-55942-183-6(5)) Marsh Media.

Dreaming: Set D Individual Title Six-Packs. (Smart Start Ser.). (gr. k-1). 23.00 (978-0-7635-0451-9(3)) Rigby Education.

Dreams. Date not set. 5.95 (978-0-89868-309-7(2)) ARO Publishing Co.

Dulaney, Kim L. My Lost Dream. 1999. (Fuzzy-Feeling Bks.). (J). pap. 8.25 (978-1-891636-07-3(3)) Unique Expression.

Dunbar, Joyce. Tell Me Something Happy Before I Go to Sleep, Set. Gliori, Debi, illus. gif. ed. 2003. (Lullaby Lights Ser.). 32p. (J). 16.95 (978-0-15-204756-6(5) , Red Wagon Bks.) Harcourt Children's Bks.

Duncan, Lois. I Walk at Night. Johnson, Steve & Fancher, Lou, illus. 2002. 32p. (J). (gr. k-3). pap. 6.99 (978-0-14-230090-9(X) , Puffin) Penguin Group (USA) Inc.

Dunmore, Helen. Amina's Blanket. Dainton, Paul, illus. 2002. (Yellow Bananas Ser.). 48p. (J). (gr. 3-4). pap. (978-0-7787-0984-8(1)); lib. bdg. (978-0-7787-0938-1(6)) Crabtree Publishing Co.

—Amina's Blanket. 2002. (gr. 3-6). lib. bdg. 12.95 (978-0-613-52802-3(6)) Tandem Library Bks.

Dunn, Hunter S. A Winter's Dream. Ellis, Joey, illus. 2004. 65p. (J). 19.95 (978-0-9761732-0-5(4)) Dunn, Hunter.

Dunnick, Regan. Sweet Dreams Douglas. Dunnick, Regan, illus. 2002. (Illus.). (J). (ps-2). 16.95 (978-0-9632421-3-6(X)) Junior League of Houston, Inc.

Durango, Julia. Dream Hop. Lee, Jared D., illus. 2005. 32p. (J). (gr. k-2). 15.95 (978-0-689-87163-4(5)) Simon & Schuster Children's Publishing.

Dwyer, Mindy. Sweet Dreams, Polar Bear. 2005. (Illus.). 32p. (J). 15.95 (978-0-88240-554-4(3)); pap. 8.95 (978-0-88240-555-1(1)) Graphic Arts Ctr. Publishing Co.

Dychtwald, Ken, et al. Gideons Dream. Zaboski, Dave, illus. 2008. 40p. (J). (ps-3). 16.99 (*978-0-06-143497-6(3)) HarperCollins Pubs.

Eduar, Gilles. Dream Journey. Eduar, Gilles, illus. 1999. (Illus.). 32p. (J). (ps-2). pap. 15.95 (978-0-531-30202-6(4) , Orchard Bks.) Scholastic, Inc.

Edwards, Frank B. The Zookeeper's Sleepers. 1999. (New Reader Ser.). (Illus.). (J). (978-0-606-22040-8(2)) Tandem Library Bks.

Emberley, Rebecca. My Mother's Secret Life. Emberley, Rebecca, illus. 1998. (Illus.). 28p. (J). (ps-3). 15.95 (978-0-316-23496-2(6)) Little Brown & Co.

Emmons, Katherine M. & Roman, Claire. Oh, Brother! Disney Storybook Artists Staff, illus. 2007. 24p. (J). (ps-2). pap. 3.99 (978-0-7364-2432-5(6) , RH/Disney) Random Hse. Children's Bks.

Erne, Monica. Fantazzzmia: Where Dreams Come From. 2004. 26p. pap. 7.99 (978-0-9745746-0-8(0)) Four Dolphins Pr.

Evans, Margaret. The Tale of Rainbow's End. 2007. pap. 11.00 (*978-0-8059-8716-4(9)) Dorrance Publishing Co., Inc.

Fant, Donna. Scotty's Dream. McKeown, David, illus. 2004. 16p. (J). 14.99 (*978-1-931844-17-8(8) , PP1034) Piano Pr.

Farmer, Bonnie. Isaac's Dreamcatcher. Bell, Anouk Perusse, illus. 2001. 32p. (J). (gr. 1-3). 14.95 (978-1-894222-46-4(6)) Lobster Pr. CAN. *Dist:* Univ. of Toronto Pr.

Fernandes, Eugenie. Baby Dreams. 1999. (Illus.). 11p. (J). (ps-3). 13.95 (978-0-7737-3139-4(3)) Stoddart Kids CAN. *Dist:* Fitzhenry & Whiteside, Ltd.

Fletcher, Ralph. Marshfield Dreams: When I Was a Kid. rev. ed. 2005. (Illus.). 192p. (J). (gr. k-10). 17.95 (978-0-8050-7242-6(X) , Holt, Henry & Co. Bks. For Young Readers) Holt, Henry & Co.

Fletcher, Susan. Alphabet of Dreams. 2008. 432p. (YA). mass mkt. 6.99 (*978-0-689-85152-0(9) , Simon Pulse) Simon & Schuster Children's Publishing.

Geringer & Czernecki, Stefan. Silverpoint. 1999. 160p. (J). (gr. 5 up). pap. (978-0-06-440432-7(3) , Harper Trophy) HarperCollins Pubs.

Gil, Alejandra & Magnasco, Carlos. Mystery in the Depth of My Bed. 2005. (Illus.). 28p. (J). (ps-ps). 12.95 (978-9974-7896-2-3(1)) Hardenville SA URY. *Dist:* Independent Pubs. Group.

Girard, Jeremy Marc. A Dreamer's Story: The Tales of Slumber. 2004. 207p. (J). pap. 19.95 (978-1-4137-1530-9(3)) PublishAmerica, Inc.

Gorbachev, Valeri. Nico Y Los Lobos Feroces. 2000. (SPA.). (gr. k-3). lib. bdg. 15.25 (978-0-613-32887-6(6)) Tandem Library Bks.

Gordon, Jeffie Ross. Two Badd Babies. Demarest, Chris L., illus. 2003. 32p. (J). (gr. k-2). pap. 8.95 (978-1-56397-895-1(4)) Boyds Mills Pr.

Gottfried, Maya. Last Night I Dreamed a Circus. Zakanitch, Robert Rahway, illus. 2003. 32p. (J). (ps-1). 15.95 (978-0-375-82388-6(3) , Knopf Bks. for Young Readers) Random Hse. Children's Bks.

Greene, Thomas. Whacked Out Wrestling: Memorial - A tale of Headlocks, Hurricanranas, & High School. 2007. 228p. pap. 14.95 (*978-1-60145-175-0(X)) Booklocker-.com, Inc.

Grimes, Terri & Timmons, Jasmine. A Pony Named Penny. 2007. 16p. 11.95 (*978-0-615-15990-4(7)) Dm Productions.

Hacke, Alex. Bear Called Sunday. 2004. (Illus.). 32p. (J). 14.95 (978-1-58234-929-9(0) , Bloomsbury Children) Bloomsbury Publishing.

Haile, Carol J. A Dream Vacation. Miller, Robert, illus. 2003. 32p. (J). per. 19.95 (978-0-9724699-0-6(7)) Panda Bear Pr.

Hamilton, Leo. Leo Hamilton Presents: Children's Dream Adventures, Larkin, Jessica, illus. l.t. ed. 2002. 40p. (J). (ps-5). pap. 8.99 (978-0-9671660-2-5(0)) Story Place, The.

Handelsman, Valerie J. Lobster Monica: Dream, Dream, Dream - Monica Was Always Dreaming. Handelsman, Valerie J., illus. 2004. (Illus.). 31p. (J). 7.95 (978-0-9748884-0-8(0)) Little Thoughts For Little Ones Publishing, Inc.

Hannan, Peter. Super Goofballs, Book 5: Doomed in Dreamland. Hannan, Peter, illus. 2008. (Super Goofballs Ser.). 144p. (J). pap. 4.99 (*978-0-06-085219-1(4) , Harper Trophy) HarperCollins Pubs.

Harcourt School Publishers Staff. A Drummer's Dream: Take-Home Book. 2001. (Collections Ser.). (Illus.). (J). pap. 1.90 (978-0-15-319535-8(5)) Harcourt Schl. Pubs.

—A Drummer's Dream Below Level. 3rd ed. 2002. (Trophies Reading Program Ser.). (Illus.). pap. 5.10 (978-0-15-323333-3(8)) Harcourt Schl. Pubs.

—Julian, Dream Doctor: Library Edition. 1999. (Collections Ser.). (Illus.). (J). 5.30 (978-0-15-314310-6(X)) Harcourt Schl. Pubs.

—Julia's Dreams Come True: Take-Home Book. 1999. (Signatures Ser.). (Illus.). (J). pap. 1.90 (978-0-15-313882-9(3)) Harcourt Schl. Pubs.

—Len's Democracy Report Advanced Level. 3rd ed. 2002. (Trophies Reading Program Ser.). (Illus.). pap. 5.10 (978-0-15-323465-1(2)) Harcourt Schl. Pubs.

—Mae Jamison & Her Dream Advanced Level. 3rd ed. 2002. (Trophies Reading Program Ser.). (Illus.). pap. 5.10 (978-0-15-323130-8(0)) Harcourt Schl. Pubs.

—Roberto's Dream - 5 Pack - Grade 3, On Level. 3rd ed. 2002. pap. 25.60 (978-0-15-327029-1(2)) Harcourt Schl. Pubs.

—What Jason's Mom Didn't See Advanced Level. 3rd ed. 2002. (Trophies Reading Program Ser.). (Illus.). pap. 5.10 (978-0-15-323117-9(3)) Harcourt Schl. Pubs.

Hargreaves, Roger. Little Miss Lucky. 1999. (Little Miss Bks.). 32p. (J). pap. 3.99 (978-0-8431-7504-2(4) , Price Stern Sloan) Penguin Group (USA) Inc.

—Little Miss Lucky. 1999. (ps-2). lib. bdg. 10.65 (978-0-613-21914-3(7)) Tandem Library Bks.

Haroula, Paroni. The Sorrowful Look of Hero. 2001. 108p. pap. 9.95 (978-0-595-17805-6(7) , Writers Club Pr.) iUniverse, Inc.

Harris, Dorthy. Taylor's Dream Ends Summer School Nightm. 2006. 95p. pap. 14.95 (978-1-4241-3574-5(5)) PublishAmerica, Inc.

Harrison, Paul. El gran partido de Guille, Level P. RAGA, Silvia, illus. 2006. (Lightning Readers Ser.). 32p. (J). pap. 3.95 (978-0-7696-4207-9(1) , Gingham Dog Pr.) School Specialty Publishing.

Harrison, Troon. The Dream Collector. Daniel, Alan & Daniel, Lea, illus. 2001. 32p. (J). (gr. k-3). (978-1-55074-915-1(3)) Kids Can Pr., Ltd.

—Dream Collector. 2001. (gr. k-3). lib. bdg. 14.10 (978-0-613-83950-1(1)) Tandem Library Bks.

—The Dream Collector. ed. 2004. (Illus.). (J). (gr. k-3). spiral bd. (978-0-616-01671-8(9)) Canadian National Institute for the Blind/Institut National Canadien pour les Aveugles.

—The Dream Collector. Daniel, Alan & Daniel, Lea, illus. unabr. ed. 1999. 32p. (J). (gr. k-3). (978-1-55074-437-8(2)) Kids Can Pr., Ltd.

Harrison/Raga, Paul/Silvia. Billy's Big Game. 2005. (Illus.). 32p. (J). lib. bdg. 9.00 (*978-1-4242-0878-4(5)) Fitzgerald Bks.

Hartinger, Brent. Dreamquest: Tales of Slumberia. 2007. 160p. (J). (gr. 8 up). 16.95 (*978-0-7653-1397-3(9) , Starscape) Doherty, Tom Assocs., LLC.

Harvey, Gill. Orphan of the Sun. 2006. (Illus.). 320p. (J). (gr. 5-8). 16.95 (978-1-58234-685-4(2) , Bloomsbury Children) Bloomsbury Publishing.

Hasler, Eveline. En Suenos Puedo Volar. (Barril Sin Fondo Ser.).Tr. of In Dreams I Can Fly. (SPA.). (J). (gr. 3-5). pap. 8.76 (978-968-6465-04-4(9)) Casa de Estudios de Literatura y Talleres Artisticos Amaquemecan A.C. MEX. *Dist:* Lectorum Pubns., Inc.

Hebert, Marie-Francine. John's Day. Hamel, Caroline, illus. 2005. (Read-It! Readers Ser.). 32p. (C). (gr. k-3). 18.60 (978-1-4048-1071-6(4)) Picture Window Bks.

Heine, Helme. Wunderbare Reise Durch Die Na. 12.95 (978-3-7876-9528-7(1)) Middelhauve Verlags GmbH DEU. *Dist:* Distribooks, Inc.

Heo, Yumi. One Sunday Morning. 1999. (Illus.). 32p. (J). (ps-1). 16.99 (978-0-531-33156-9(3) , Orchard Bks.) Scholastic, Inc.

Hicks, Ingrid M. E. Dare to Dream Ambrosia. 2000. (Illus.). 23p. (J). (ps-7). pap. 12.95 (978-0-9678295-0-0(X)) Nu-VISIONS & Assocs., Inc.

—Dare to Dream Ambrosia: The Adventures of Ambrosia Nittie. Hicks, Ingrid M. E., illus. 2nd rev. l.t. ed. 2002. (CHI.). 56p. (J). per. 14.95 (978-0-9678295-7-9(7)) Nu-VISIONS & Assocs., Inc.

Hillard, Shirley. One Big Hug. 2005. (Illus.). 32p. (J). 13.95 (978-1-933014-20-3(2)) Mamoo Hse.

Hobbs, Will. Beardream. 2000. (gr. k-3). lib. bdg. 15.30 (978-0-613-28414-1(3)) Tandem Library Bks.

Hobbs, William. Beardream. Kastner, Jill, illus. 2000. 32p. (J). (ps-3). 6.99 (978-0-689-83536-0(1) , Aladdin) Simon & Schuster Children's Publishing.

—Beardream. 2000. (Illus.). (J). 13.79 (978-0-606-20495-8(4)) Tandem Library Bks.

Hondo. Dream World Tales. 2005. pap. 9.99 (978-0-9773016-0-7(5)) Capital Publishing.

Honigsberg, Peter Jan. Pillow of Dreams. Morse, Tony, illus. 2004. 32p. (gr. k-4). 17.95 (978-1-57143-076-2(8)) RDR Bks.

Hopes & Dreams Series II. 64p. (gr. 6-12). pap., tchr.'s training gde. ed. 32.50 (978-0-8224-3817-5(8)) Globe Fearon Educational Publishing.

Hopton, Stan. To Dance Beneath a Diamond Sky. 2005. 118p. pap. 16.95 (978-1-4241-0032-3(1)) PublishAmerica, Inc.

Hoving, Isabel. The Dream Merchant. Velmans, Hester, tr. from DUT. 2005. 640p. (YA). (gr. 7 up). 19.99 (978-0-7636-2880-2(8)) Candlewick Pr.

Howard-Hess, Susan. Harriet Higby. Learner, Vickie, illus. 2006. (J). pap. 4.95 (978-1-57874-093-2(2)) Kaeden Corp.

Huelin, Jodi. My Little Pony: Pinkie Pie's Spooky Dream. Edwards, Ken, illus. 2003. (My Little Pony Ser.). 24p. (J). (ps-1). pap. 3.99 (978-0-06-054949-7(1)) HarperCollins Pubs.

Hurd, Thacher. Sleepy Cadillac: A Bedtime Drive. Hurd, Thacher, illus. 2005. (Illus.). 32p. (J). 15.99 (978-0-06-073020-8(X)) HarperCollins Pubs.

I Dream of Sleeping Dogs. 2006. (J). 24.95 (978-0-9789633-0-9(X)) Village Monkey LLC, The.

I Love Dreaming. 2005. (J). bds. (978-0-9759086-0-0(X)) Twinbrook Publishing.

Ingpen, Robert R. The Dreamkeeper. Ingpen, Robert R., illus. 1998. (Illus.). 40p. (J). (ps-3). 14.95 (978-1-887734-41-7(4)) Star Bright Bks., Inc.

Irwin, Esther. White Cloud: A Little Boy's Dream. Puett, Gayle, ed. Roberson, Ron, illus. 2006. 61p. (J). spiral bd. 10.00 (978-0-9778462-0-7(2)) Irwin, Esther L.

Irwin, Maia. Isabel's Dream: The Light from Within. 1998. (Illus.). 32p. (J). (gr. k-5). 16.95 (978-1-891569-21-0(X)) Pura Vida Publishing Co.

Isadora, Rachel. Caribbean Dream. Isadora, Rachel, illus. 2002. (Illus.). 32p. (J). pap. 6.99 (978-0-698-11944-4(4) , Putnam Juvenile) Penguin Group (USA) Inc.

—Caribbean Dream. 2002. (ps-2). lib. bdg. 15.30 (978-0-613-51441-5(6)) Tandem Library Bks.

Jacko, the Dreamer: Early Level Satellite Individual Title Six-Packs. (Sails Literacy Ser.). 16p. (gr. 1-2). 27.00 (978-0-7578-3159-1(1)) Rigby Education.

Janer Manila, Gabriel. Esto Que Ves Es el Mar. 3rd ed. (SPA., Illus.). 88p. (YA). (gr. 5-8). (978-84-246-8627-7(6) , GL2774) La Galera, S.A. Editorial ESP. *Dist:* Lectorum Pubns., Inc.

Jantti, Mariana. Christopher Has a Dream. 2006. (Illus.). 28p. (J). 12.95 (978-9974-7960-0-3(8)) Hardenville SA URY. *Dist:* Independent Pubs. Group.

Johnson, Lindan Lee. The Dream Jar. Curmi, Serena, illus. 2005. 32p. (J). (gr. k-3). 16.00 (978-0-618-17698-4(5)) Houghton Mifflin Co. Trade & Reference Div.

Johnson, Vickey L. The Monster Mix-Up. 2003. (Illus.). (J). pap. 9.00 (978-0-8059-6125-6(9)) Dorrance Publishing Co., Inc.

Jones, H. Lena. Trapped on Planet Liska. 2006. 180p. pap. 19.95 (978-1-4241-0989-0(2)) PublishAmerica, Inc.

Jonsberg, Barry. Dreamrider. 2008. 256p. (J). (gr. 9). lib. bdg. 18.99 (*978-0-375-94457-4(5) , Knopf Bks. for Young Readers) Random Hse. Children's Bks.

Joseph, Elaine. Dreamstealer. (Illus.). 32p. (J). 2002. (TUR & ENG.). 19.95 (978-1-85269-156-1(5)); 2000. (BEN, ENG & GUJ., 19.95 (978-1-85269-153-0(0)); 2000. (GUJ, ENG & BEN., 19.95 (978-1-85269-155-4(7)); 2000. (SOM & ENG., 18.95 (978-1-85269-159-2(X)); 2000. (URD & ENG., 19.95 (978-1-85269-157-8(3)) Mantra Publishing, Ltd. GBR. *Dist:* AIMS International Bks., Inc.

—Dreamstealer. 2000. (CHI & ENG., Illus.). 32p. (J). 15.95 (978-1-85269-154-7(9)) Yuan-liou Publishing Co., Ltd. TWN. *Dist:* AIMS International Bks., Inc.

Jossa, Isabelle. Ned Goes to Bed. 2005. (Illus.). 32p. (J). (ps-7). 16.95 (978-1-894965-17-0(5)) Simply Read Bks. CAN. *Dist:* Perseus Distribution.

Kaaberbol, Lene. The Serpent Gift. 3rd ed. 2007. (Shamer Chronicles Ser.). Orig. Title: Slangens Gave. 377p. (J). pap. 9.95 (*978-0-8050-8655-3(2) , Holt, Henry & Co. Bks. For Young Readers) Holt, Henry & Co.

Kelly, Jack. Keoni's Dream. 1999. (J). 17.95 (978-0-9662777-1-5(6)) Pleiades Publishing.

Kelman, Marcy. Disney's Little Einsteins: Quincy's Dream. rev. ed. 2007. 24p. (ps-1). pap. 3.99 (*978-1-4231-0216-8(9)) Disney Pr.

Kenah, Katharine. The Dream Shop. Catalanotto, Peter, illus. 2002. 32p. (J). (gr. 1 up). 16.95 (978-0-688-17900-7(2)) HarperCollins Pubs.

Kimmel, Elizabeth Cody. What Do You Dream? Kim, Joung Un, illus. 2003. 32p. (J). (ps-1). 14.99 (978-0-7636-1338-9(X)) Candlewick Pr.

Knox, Elizabeth. Dreamhunter. 2006. (Dreamhunter Duet Ser.: Bk. 1). (Illus.). 384p. (YA). (gr. 7 up). 19.00 (978-0-374-31853-6(0)) Farrar, Straus & Giroux.

—Dreamquake. 2007. (Dreamhunter Duet Ser.: Bk. 2). (Illus.). 464p. (YA). (gr. 7 up). 19.00 (978-0-374-31854-3(9)) Farrar, Straus & Giroux.

Knox, Elizabeth. Dreamquake: Book Two of the Dreamhunter Duet. 2007. (Illus.). 449p. (J). (*978-1-4287-3321-3(3)) Farrar, Straus & Giroux.

Lacoursiere, Patrick. Dream Songs Night Songs—China to Senegal. 2006. 16.95 (978-2-923163-24-6(9)) La Montagne Secrete CAN. *Dist:* National Bk. Network.

Lagonegro, Melissa & Random House Disney Staff. Ballerina Princess. 2007. (Step into Reading Ser.). (Illus.). 32p. (J). (ps-2). lib. bdg. 11.99 (978-0-7364-8051-2(X) , RH/Disney) Random Hse. Children's Bks.

—Ballerina Princess. Harding, Niall, illus. 2007. (Step into Reading Ser.). 32p. (J). (ps-2). pap. 3.99 (978-0-7364-2428-8(8) , RH/Disney) Random Hse. Children's Bks.

Lalich, Nadine. The Dream of Becoming. 2001. 32p. per. 5.95 (978-0-9711776-0-4(0)) Hug Bandit & Co., LLC.

Lambert, Janet. A Dream for Susan. 2001. (Jordon Ser.: Vol. 4). (YA). pap. 12.95 (978-1-930009-35-6(6)) Image Cascade Publishing.

Lampl, Patricia Ryan. My Blankie: A Book to Touch & Feel. Petrone, Valeria, illus. 2005. 16p. (J). 8.99 (978-0-689-85589-4(3) , Little Simon) Simon & Schuster Children's Publishing.

Lancett, Peter. The Dark Never Hides. Pedroietta, Jan, illus. 2008. (J). pap. (*978-1-59889-925-2(2)); (gr. 3-8). lib. bdg. 15.95 (*978-1-59889-865-1(5)) Stone Arch Bks.

Larsen, Beverly Jean. Bessy Bear's Winter Dreams. McWaters, Karen, illus. 2000. 34p. (Orig.). (J). (gr. 3-8). pap. 13.95 (978-1-58275-053-8(X)) Black Forest Pr.

Larsen, Wendy. After Dark. Larsen, Wendy, illus. 1999. (Illus.). 19p. (J). (ps-3). pap. 10.99 (978-0-9665699-0-2(3)) Chase Pubns.

Layne, Steven L. Thomas' Sheep & the Great Geography Test. Board, Perry, illus. 1998. 32p. (J). (ps-3). 15.95 (978-1-56554-274-7(6)) Pelican Publishing Co., Inc.

Layton, Dan. Adventures in the Kingdom, the Dreamer. 2004. 64p. pap. 5.99 (978-0-9707919-4-8(1)) Mercy Place, Inc.

Lee, Hyun Se. Armageddon 1, Vol. 1. 2004. (Illus.). 184p. pap. 9.99 (978-1-58664-909-8(4) , CMX 65401G, CPM Manhwa) Central Park Media Corp.

Lee, Quinlan B. Care Bears: Sweet Dreams. Johnson, Jay, illus. 2005. (Care Bears Ser.). 5p. (J). bds. 7.99 (978-0-439-69162-8(1)) Scholastic, Inc.

Live Your Dream. 2007. (J). lib. bdg. (*978-0-9793492-1-8(4)) Rising Lyons Pr.

Lloyd-Jones, Sally. Sweet Dreams. 2004. (Illus.). (J). bds. 8.99 (978-0-8423-7740-9(9)) Tyndale Hse. Pubs.

Lopez, C. Pellicer. Juan y Sus Zapatos. (SPA., Illus.). (J). (gr. k-2). pap. 5.95 (978-970-629-132-5(6) , SI6616) Sistemas Tecnicos de Edicion, S.A. de C.V. MEX. *Dist:* AIMS International Bks., Inc., Lectorum Pubns., Inc.

Lore, Erin, illus. Timmy the Dragon. l.t. ed. 2007. 32p. (J). 8.95 (*978-0-9741562-7-9(2)) Yarrow Pr.

Lowry, Lois. Gossamer. 2006. 144p. (J). (gr. 5). 16.00 (978-0-618-68550-9(2)) Houghton Mifflin Co.

—Gossamer. 2008. 160p. (J). (gr. 4-7). pap. 6.99 (*978-0-385-73416-5(6) , Delacorte Bks. for Young Readers) Random Hse. Children's Bks.

—Gossamer. l.t. ed. 2006. 151p. (YA). 23.95 (978-0-7862-8947-9(3)) Thorndike Pr.

Lutz, Norma Jean. Meg Follows a Dream: The Fight for Freedom. 2004. (Sisters in Time Ser.). 144p. (J). pap. 4.97 (978-1-59310-205-0(4)) Barbour Publishing, Inc.

Lyon, George Ella. Dreamplace. Catalanotto, Peter, illus. 1998. 32p. (J). (ps-2). pap. 6.95 (978-0-531-07101-4(4) , Orchard Bks.) Scholastic, Inc.

MacHado, Ana Maria. Delantal Que el Viento Lleva. (SPA.). pap. 12.95 (978-950-07-2220-9(8)) Editorial Sudamericana S.A. ARG. *Dist:* Distribooks, Inc.

Mahy, Margaret. Alchemy. 2004. 207p. (YA). (gr. 7-12). per. 16.75 (978-1-4176-3556-6(8)) Tandem Library Bks.

Malik, S. A. Omari's Flight: The Mercy of Love. 2007. (Illus.). 81p. (YA). per. 7.98 (*978-0-9794615-0-7(2)) EDR.

Manners, Richard T. Girl Child Saturday, Bk. 3. 2002. 172p. (J). (gr. 4-7). pap. 12.95 (978-0-595-22421-0(0) , Writer's Showcase Pr.) iUniverse, Inc.

Martins, Miller Susan. Rosa Takes a Chance: Mexican Immigrants in the Dust Bowl Years. 2006. (Sisters in Time Ser.). 144p. (J). pap. 4.97 (978-1-59789-065-6(0)) Barbour Publishing, Inc.

Matott, J. P. & Baker, Margaret. When I Was a Girl ... I Dreamed. Ludy, Mark, illus. 2005. 32p. (J). 16.95 (978-0-9664276-3-9(7)) Green Pastures Publishing, Inc.

Mayer, Mercer. Una Pesadilla en Mi Armario. 2003. (SPA., Illus.). 32p. (J). (gr. k-3). 7.95 (978-84-372-1754-3(7) , SAN7547) Altea, Ediciones, S.A. - Grupo Santillana ESP. *Dist:* Santillana USA Publishing Co., Inc.

—Una Pesadilla en Mi Armario. (SPA.). 48p. (J). (gr. k-1). 15.20 (978-84-8464-102-5(3) , KA31669) Kalandraka Editora, S.L. ESP. *Dist:* Lectorum Pubns., Inc.

—What a Bad Dream. Mayer, Mercer, illus. 1999. (Little Critter Ser.). (Illus.). 24p. (J). (gr. k-k). pap. 3.99 (978-0-307-12685-6(4) , 12685, Random Hse. Bks. for Young Readers) Random Hse. Children's Bks.

McAllister, Margaret. Life Shop. 2004. 160p. (J). pap. 8.99 (978-0-7459-4906-2(1) , Lion) Lion Hudson plc GBR. *Dist:* Trafalgar Square Publishing.

McAuley, Amy. Over & over You. rev. ed. 2005. 192p. (J). 16.95 (978-1-59643-017-4(6)) Roaring Brook Pr.

McCain, Becky Ray. Grandmother's Dreamcatcher. 2001. (Illus.). (J). (978-0-606-21858-0(0)) Tandem Library Bks.

—Grandmother's Dreamcatcher. Schuett, Stacey, illus. 32p. (J). (gr. k-3). 2004. pap. 6.95 (978-0-8075-3032-0(8)); 1998. 15.95 (978-0-8075-3031-3(X)) Whitman, Albert & Co.

McCullagh, Sheila. Griffin. 2007. (Three Pirates Ser.). (Illus.). 48p. 15.95 (*978-1-84560-044-0(4)) Mercury Bks. Ltd. GBR. *Dist:* International Publishers Marketing.

McCullough, Pierce. Bunbun at Bedtime. 2002. (Bunbun Ser.). (Illus.). 24p. (J). (gr. k-2). bds. 6.99 (978-1-84148-379-5(6)) Barefoot Bks., Inc.

McEwan, Ian. The Daydreamer. 2003. (gr. 3-6). lib. bdg. 14.15 (978-0-613-58678-8(6)) Tandem Library Bks.

McKechnie, Edward. Sweet Dreams for Scotty. Blanding, Allison, illus. 2007. 14p. (J). spiral bd. 14.95 (*978-0-9785302-0-4(9)) Beanstalk Pubns.

McMullan, Kate. Fluffy Saves Christmas. Smith, Mavis, illus. 2004. 40p. (J). lib. bdg. 15.00 (978-1-59054-462-4(5)) Fitzgerald Bks.

—Fluffy Saves Christmas, Level 3. Smith, Mavis, illus. 1999. (Hello Reader! Ser.). 40p. (J). (gr. 1-3). pap. 3.99 (978-0-590-52308-0(2) , Cartwheel Bks.) Scholastic, Inc.

McPhail, David. Boy on the Brink. 2006. (Illus.). (J). (*978-1-4156-7145-0(1)); 32p. 15.95 (978-0-8050-7618-9(2)) Holt, Henry & Co.

Melmed, Laura Krauss. Jumbo's Lullaby. Sorensen, Henri, illus. 1999. 24p. (J). (ps-k). lib. bdg. 15.89 (978-0-688-16996-1(1)) HarperCollins Pubs.

Merberg, Julie & Bober, Suzanne. Dreaming with Rousseau. 2007. (Illus.). 22p. (J). (ps). bds. 6.95 (978-0-8118-5712-3(3)) Chronicle Bks. LLC.

Milgrim, David. Another Day in the Milky Way. Milgrim, David, illus. 2007. (Illus.). 32p. (J). (ps-1). 15.99 (978-0-399-24548-0(0) , Putnam Juvenile) Penguin Group (USA) Inc.

Min, Willemien, illus. Peter's Patchwork Dream. 1999. (Barefoot Beginner Ser.). 32p. (J). (ps-1). 15.95 (978-1-902283-45-6(7)) Barefoot Bks., Inc.

Mitchell, Malinda. Kon-Reah's Dream Guy. 2005. 50p. pap. 12.95 (978-1-4137-5317-2(5)) PublishAmerica, Inc.

Moffett, Rodney. The Eighth Crest. 2006. (ENG.). 228p. per. 19.95 (*978-1-4241-3907-1(4)) PublishAmerica, Inc.

Moore, Raina. Tweet Dreams. Style Guide Staff, illus. 2006. (Baby Looney Tunes Ser.). 96p. (J). act. bk. ed. 2.99 (978-1-4169-1842-4(6) , Simon Scribbles) Simon & Schuster Children's Publishing.

Morgan, Allen. Matthew & the Midnight Hospital. ed. 2004. (Illus.). (J). (gr. k-3). spiral bd. (978-0-616-01529-2(1)) Canadian National Institute for the Blind/Institut National Canadien pour les Aveugles.

Morgan, Allen & Martchenko, Michael. Matthew & the Midnight Hospital. 1999. (Matthew's Midnight Adventures Ser.). (Illus.). 32p. (J). (ps-3). 6.99 (978-0-7737-6014-1(8)) Stoddart Kids CAN. *Dist:* Fitzhenry & Whiteside, Ltd.

Morgan, Michaela & Carroll, Sara. Sleepy Dreams. Wilbur, Leanne Louise, illus. 1998. 4p. (J). bds. 14.98 (978-1-58048-040-6(3)) Sandvik Publishing.

Moverley, Richard. The Reluctant Rajput. Dean, David, illus. 2005. (Yellow Go Bananas Ser.). 48p. (J). lib. bdg. (978-0-7787-2723-1(8)) Crabtree Publishing Co.

Musgrave, Susan. Dreams Are More Real Than Bathtubs. braille ed. 2004. (Illus.). (J). (gr. k-3). spiral bd. (978-0-616-01748-7(0)) Canadian National Institute for the Blind/Institut National Canadien pour les Aveugles.

—Dreams Are More Real Than Bathtubs. Gay, Marie-Louise, illus. 1999. 32p. (J). (ps-2). 14.95 (978-1-55143-107-9(6)) Orca Bk. Pubs. USA.

Myers, Walter Dean. The Dream Bearer. 2004. 192p. (J). (gr. 5 up). reprint ed. pap. 5.99 (978-0-06-447289-0(2) , Amistad) HarperCollins Pubs.

Neuschwander, Cindy, et al. Amanda Bean's Amazing Dream: A Mathematical Story. Litzinger, Rosanne, illus. 1998. 40p. (J). (gr. 1-4). pap. 16.95 (978-0-590-30012-4(1)) Scholastic, Inc.

Newby, John. Summer Dreams. 2005. 16.95 (978-1-55278-419-8(3)) McArthur & Co. CAN. *Dist:* National Bk. Network.

Newsome, Jill. Dream Dancer. 2002. (Illus.). 32p. (J). (ps-3). 15.89 (978-0-06-001322-6(2)) HarperCollins Pubs.

Nicely, Adam. Naptime for Thaddeus. 2005. (Illus.). 32p. (J). 16.95 (978-1-894965-28-6(0)) Simply Read Bks. CAN. *Dist:* Perseus Distribution.

Nielsen, Gwyn English. Serendipity & the Dream Catcher. Nielsen, Gwyn English, ed. Colby, Devon English, illus. 2003. 176p. (gr. 3-7). pap. 5.95 (978-0-9660726-2-4(6)) C.G.S. Pr.

Oldfield, Jenny. Dream on, Daisy! Child, Lauren, illus. 144p. (J). pap. 7.99 (978-0-340-85078-7(7)) Hodder Children's Division GBR. *Dist:* Independent Pubs. Group.

Oliver, Mark Herren. Trish & the Wishing Star. 2006. (ENG.). 32p. per. 18.65 (*978-1-4134-9402-0(1)) Xlibris Corp.

Olvera, Jillann. Christian's Lullaby. 2006. 29p. pap. 14.95 (978-1-4241-1909-7(X)) PublishAmerica, Inc.

Once upon My Summer Camp Dream. 2003. spiral bd. 14.95 (978-0-9744437-1-3(9)) Imagination Workshop, The.

Orgel, Doris. Sarah's Room. Sendak, Maurice, illus. 2003. (Sendak Reissues Ser.). 48p. (J). (gr. 5 up). 14.95 (978-0-06-029727-5(1)) HarperCollins Pubs.

Osofsky, Audrey. Dreamcatcher. 1999. (J). lib. bdg. (978-0-606-16921-9(0)) Tandem Library Bks.

Owens, Mary Beth. Panda Whispers. 2007. (Illus.). 32p. (J). (ps-2). 16.99 (978-0-525-47171-4(5) , Dutton Juvenile) Penguin Group (USA) Inc.

Page, Philip & Pettit, Marilyn. Livewire Shakespeare: A Midsummer Night's Dream. 2003. (Livewires Ser.). 64p. pap. (978-0-340-84936-1(3)) Cambridge Univ. Pr.

Paladin, Frank. Hole in My Stocking. Amber, Holly & Lin, Melanie, illus. 2005. 24p. (J). per. 16.95 (978-0-9763635-4-5(2)) Beyond the Stars Pubns.

Pardoe, David. Jasper Tippett's Amazing Journey to Page 42. 2006. (Illus.). 132p. pap. (*978-1-84401-785-0(0)) Athena Pr.

Parr, Todd. Otto Goes to Bed. 2003. (Illus.). 24p. (J). (ps-3). 9.95 (978-0-316-73873-6(5) , Tingley, Megan Bks.) Little, Brown Bks. for Young Readers.

Parry, Alan. Mouse Can't Sleep. Parry, Linda, illus. 2004. (Oaktree Wood Ser.). (ps-3). 5.00 (978-0-687-09711-1(8)) Abingdon Pr.

Patneaude, David. Framed in Fire. 2001. (gr. 5-8). lib. bdg. 14.10 (978-0-613-35946-7(1)) Tandem Library Bks.

—Framed in Fire. 224p. (J). (gr. 6-9). 2004. pap. 5.95 (978-0-8075-9096-6(7)); 1999. (Illus.). 15.95 (978-0-8075-9098-0(3)) Whitman, Albert & Co.

Pearson, Kit. Awake & Dreaming. 1999. (J). (978-0-606-21048-5(2)) Tandem Library Bks.

Peck, Richard. The Great Interactive Dream Machine. 1998. (Puffin Novel Ser.). 160p. (J). (gr. 5-9). pap. 6.99 (978-0-14-038264-8(X) , Puffin) Penguin Group (USA) Inc.

Peel, John. Book of Nightmares, Vol. 6. 2005. (Diadem: World Magic Ser.: Book 6). 192p. pap. 4.99 (978-0-7387-0612-2(4)) Llewellyn Pubns.

—Book of Nightmares. 1998. (Diadem Ser.). (978-0-606-13329-6(1)) Tandem Library Bks.

Pelham, P.J. Hanna Searches for "Me!" 2004. 24p. (J). pap. (978-1-4120-3208-7(3)) Trafford Publishing.

Picard, Barbara Leonie. One Is One. 2006. 321p. pap. 9.95 (978-1-58988-027-6(7)) Consortium Bk. Sales & Distribution.

Pippenger, Jack G. The Young Rebel. 2007. 292p. 27.95 (*978-0-595-86314-3(0)); per. 17.95 (*978-0-595-41077-4(4)) iUniverse, Inc.

Polacco, Patricia. Appelemando's Dreams. pap. 6.99 (978-0-14-240003-6(3) , Puffin) Penguin Group (USA) Inc.

Postgate, Daniel. Engelbert Sneem & His Dream Vacuum Machine. Postgate, Daniel, illus. 2007. (Illus.). 32p. (J). (ps). 16.95 (*978-0-7358-2151-4(8)) North-South Bks., Inc.

Pottle, Bill T. DreamQuest. 2003. (gr. 7-12). lib. bdg. 26.85 (978-0-613-86659-0(2)) Tandem Library Bks.

Preble, Laura. Lica's Angel. 2003. 142p. (YA). 21.95 (978-0-595-74914-0(3)); pap. 11.95 (978-0-595-28253-1(9)) iUniverse, Inc.

Price, Mary Ellizabeth. Wallbaby Bumblebees. 2004. (Illus.). 40p. (J). per. 15.75 (978-0-9715402-2-4(5) , 410-707-6686) Barnhardt & Ashe Publishing, Inc.

Priest, Christopher. Dream Archipelago. 264p. (978-0-671-03388-0(3) , Free Pr.) Simon & Schuster.

Rader, Jared. Sandy's Dream. 2007. (J). per. 10.99 (*978-1-59879-398-7(5)) Lifevest Publishing, Inc.

Random House Disney Staff. My Best Friend Is a Princess: A Princess Friendship Treasury. 2007. (Toddler Board Bks.). 30p. (J). (gr. k-k). bds. 11.99 (*978-0-7364-2505-6(5) , RH/Disney) Random Hse. Children's Bks.

Random House Disney Staff, illus. Off to the Ball. 2005. (Disney Princess Ser.). 10p. (J). (gr. k-k). bds. 3.99 (978-0-7364-2300-7(1) , RH/Disney) Random Hse. Children's Bks.

Rassmus, Jens. Farmer Enno & His Cow. 1998. (Illus.). 32p. (J). (gr. k-4). pap. 14.95 (978-0-531-30081-7(1) , Orchard Bks.) Scholastic, Inc.

Rawady, Ed. Everywhere & Everything: A Spiritual Story about the First Dream. Cordaro, Joseph, illus. 1998. 48p. (YA). (gr. 3 up). 18.95 (978-0-9662194-0-1(6)) Table 12 Publishing.

Ray, Mary Lyn. My Carousel Horse. Taxali, Gary, illus. 2000. (J). 13.95 (978-0-15-200023-3(2)) Harcourt Trade Pubs.

RealBuzz Studios Staff. Let There Be Lighten Up! 2007. (Goofyfoot Gurl Ser.: No. 1). 96p. (YA). pap. 4.97 (978-1-59789-573-6(3) , Barbour Bks.) Barbour Publishing, Inc.

Reetz, Kurt & Schure, Kimberley. Kasey & the Dream Forest: The First Dream. Voelker, Marty, illus. 2000. 24p. (J). (gr. 1-3). pap. (978-0-9701450-0-0(4)) Long Hill Productions, Inc.

Reetz, Kurt & Schure, Kimberly. Kasey & the Dream Forest: The First Dream. 2000. mass mkt. 8.95 incl. audio compact disk (978-1-931179-05-8(0)) Long Hill Productions, Inc.

Rey, Margret & Rey, H. A. Curious George's Dream. 1998. (Curious George Ser.). (Illus.). 24p. (J). (gr. k-3). tchr. ed. 12.95 (978-0-395-91905-7(3)) Houghton Mifflin Co. Trade & Reference Div.

—Curious George's Dream. Vipah Interactive Staff, illus. 1998. (Curious George Ser.). 24p. (J). (gr. k-3). pap. 3.95 (978-0-395-91911-8(8)) Houghton Mifflin Co. Trade & Reference Div.

Richards, Kitty. SpongeBob AirPants: The Lost Episode, Vol. 8. 2004. 64p. (J). (gr. 2-5). pap. 17.00 incl. audio (978-1-4000-8631-3(0) , Listening Library) Random Hse. Audio Publishing Group.

Richardson, Bill. But If They Do. Mongeau, Marc, illus. 2003. 24p. (J). (ps-1). pap. 6.95 (978-1-55037-786-6(8)); lib. bdg. 18.95 (978-1-55037-787-3(6)) Annick Pr., Ltd. CAN. *Dist:* Firefly Bks., Ltd.

Riley, Christine. Chester's Field, O'Brien, Laurel, illus. 2004. 296p. (J). per. 17.50 (978-0-9740683-6-7(5)) Authors & Artists Publishers of New York, Inc.

—Chester's Field. 2002. 103p. per. 10.00 (978-0-9724680-3-9(X)) Lifevest Publishing, Inc.

Ritsema van Eck, Patricia. The Dreaming of Paradise. 2005. 62p. (J). pap. 24.70 (978-1-4116-6097-7(8)) Lulu.com.

ROBERTSON, M. P. The Sandcastle. 2008. (Illus.). 32p. (J). pap. 7.95 (*978-1-84507-800-3(4)) Lincoln, Frances Ltd. GBR. *Dist:* Perseus Distribution.

Robleda, Margarita. Suenos. Suarez, Maribel, illus. (Rana, Rema, Rimas Ser.). (SPA.). 16p. (J). (gr. k-3). 7.95 (978-1-59437-821-8(5)) Santillana USA Publishing Co., Inc.

Robson, Jenny. Savannah 2116 Ad. 2005. 144p. pap. (*978-0-624-04230-3(8)) Tafelberg Pubs., Ltd.

Rock, Lois. I Wish Tonight. Wilson, Anne, illus. 28p. (J). 2003. 6.95 (978-1-56148-404-1(0)); 2001. 16.00 (978-1-56148-315-0(X)) Good Bks.

Rockhill, Dennis. Ocean Whisper/Susurro del Océano. de la Vega, Eida, tr. Rockhill, Dennis, illus. 2005. Tr. of Susurro del Océano. (SPA & ENG., Illus.). 32p. (J). 16.95 (978-0-9741992-4-5(9) , 626999) Raven Tree Pr.

—Polar Slumber. Rockhill, Dennis, illus. 2006. 32p. (J). (gr. k-3). pap. 16.95 (978-0-9741992-8-3(1)) Raven Tree Pr.

Rodriguez, Elizabeth. Jumping Jack. 2006. pap. 14.99 (*978-1-4259-8197-6(6)) AuthorHouse.

Rodriguez-Nora, Tere. En busca de la Paz. Gordo, Alex, illus. 2005. (SPA.). 32p. (J). 13.95 (978-84-96046-51-1(6)) Ediciones Norte, Inc.

Russell, Barbara Timberlake. The Remembering Stone. Peck, Beth, illus. 1999. (J). (978-0-7894-2583-6(1)) Dorling Kindersley Publishing, Inc.

—The Remembering Stone. Cotts, Claire B., illus. 2004. 32p. (J). 16.00 (978-0-374-36242-3(4) , Farrar, Straus & Giroux (BYR)) Farrar, Straus & Giroux.

Saenz, Benjamin Alire. A Perfect Season for Dreaming. 2007. (SPA & ENG.). 32p. (J). 15.95 (*978-1-933693-01-9(0)) Cinco Puntos Pr.

Salton, Liz. Eelfish, a Rock & Roll King. Hathaway, Karen, illus. 2004. 38p. pap. 17.95 (978-1-4137-1847-8(7)) PublishAmerica, Inc.

Sargent, Dave, et al. Dream Catcher Vol. 5: (Lakota Sioux) Be Strong, 20 vols., Vol. 5. Lenoir, Jane, illus. l.t. ed. 2003. (Story Keeper Ser.: 5). 42p. (J). pap. 6.95 (978-1-56763-912-4(7)); lib. bdg. 22.60 (978-1-56763-911-7(9)) Ozark Publishing.

Sayles, Elizabeth. The Goldfish Yawned. Sayles, Elizabeth, illus. rev. ed. 2005. (Illus.). 40p. (J). (ps-1). 16.95 (978-0-8050-7624-0(7)) Holt, Henry & Co.

Schneider, Antonie. Leo's Dream. Cole, Alison, tr. from GER. Bansch, Helga, illus. 2006. 32p. 22.95 (978-0-7475-8184-0(3) , Bloomsbury Children) Bloomsbury Publishing Plc GBR. *Dist:* Independent Pubs. Group.

Schreck, Karen. Dream Journal. 2006. 256p. (gr. 7-17). 15.99 (978-1-4231-0105-5(7)) Hyperion Pr.

Schuch, Steve. A Symphony of Whales. Sylvada, Peter, illus. 2002. 32p. (J). (gr. 1-4). pap. 7.00 (978-0-15-216548-2(7) , Voyager Bks./Libros Viajeros) Harcourt Children's Bks.

—Symphony of Whales. 2002. (gr. k-3). lib. bdg. 14.15 (978-0-613-56636-0(X)) Tandem Library Bks.

Schwartz, Howard. Before You Were Born. Swarner, Kristina, illus. rev. ed. 2005. 32p. (J). 16.95 (978-1-59643-028-0(1)) Roaring Brook Pr.

Scotton, Rob. Go to Sleep, Russell the Sheep. Scotton, Rob, illus. 2007. 16p. (J). 9.99 (*978-0-06-128434-2(3)) HarperCollins Pubs.

Seibold, J. Otto. Penguin Dreams. Walsh, V. L., illus. 2005. 36p. (J). (ps-3). reprint ed. pap. 6.95 (978-0-8118-5100-8(1)) Chronicle Bks. LLC.

Sendak, Maurice. Kenny's Window. Sendak, Maurice, illus. 2004. (Illus.). 54p. (J). (gr. k-4). reprint ed. 14.00 (978-0-7567-7767-8(4)) DIANE Publishing Co.

—Kenny's Window. 2002. (Sendak Reissues Ser.). (Illus.). 64p. (J). 13.89 (978-0-06-028790-0(X)) HarperCollins Pubs.

—Kenny's Window. Sendak, Maurice, illus. 2002. (Sendak Reissues Ser.). (Illus.). 64p. (J). reprint ed. 18.95 (978-0-06-028789-4(6)) HarperCollins Pubs.

Severe, Beth. I Wanna Fly! The Dream. Whitewolf, Brad, illus. 2000. 35p. (J). per. 14.95 (978-0-9656957-1-8(9)) Lighthouse Productions, Inc.

Sharpe, Gerald. What Lies Beneath the Bed: Tommy's Tales. 2006. 304p. (YA). pap. 7.00 (978-1-933894-00-3(8)) IJN Publishing, Inc.

Shields, Gillian. Angel Baby. 2006. (Illus.). 24p. (J). (ps). pap. 9.99 (978-0-00-718006-6(3) , HarperCollins Children's Bks.) HarperCollins Pubs. Ltd. GBR. *Dist:* Independent Pubs. Group.

Shinn, Sharon. The Dream-Maker's Magic. 2008. 272p. (YA). (gr. 7). pap. 7.99 (*978-0-14-241096-7(9) , Puffin) Penguin Group (USA) Inc.

Shulevitz, Uri. The Treasure. Shulevitz, Uri, illus. 2001. (Illus.). 25.95 incl. audio (978-0-87499-755-2(0)); 28.95 incl. audio compact disk (978-1-59112-553-2(7)); pap. 33.95 incl. audio (978-0-87499-756-9(9)); pap. 35.95 incl. audio compact disk (978-1-59112-552-5(9)) Live Oak Media.

Simson, Dana & Book Company Staff. Dreamland. Simson, Dana, illus. 2003. (Pop-up Bks.). (Illus.). 14p. (J). 15.95 (978-1-74047-211-1(X)) Book Co. Publishing Pty, Ltd., The AUS. *Dist:* Penton Overseas, Inc.

Sinclair, Nicholas, et al. The Cookie Story. Wall, Randy Hugh, ed. Varela, Juan D., tr. Varela, Juan D., illus. l.t. ed. 2005. Tr. of Cuent de Galletas. (SPA.). 33p. (J). 14.95 (978-0-9764798-1-9(8)) Story Store Collection Publishing.

Singleton, Clayton. Dream an Awesome Dream. 2007. (J). per. 10.99 (*978-1-59872-828-6(8)) Instantpublisher.com.

Singleton, Glynn. Buddy Boy Brooks Takes the Wheel: A Mile Wide Tale from the Mighty Mississippi. 2007. 32p. (J). 12.95 (*978-1-57072-320-9(6)) Overmountain Pr.

Skye, Obert. Leven Thumps & the Gateway to Foo. 2005. (Leven Thumps Ser.: Bk. 1). (Illus.). 384p. (J). 17.95 (978-1-59038-369-8(9) , Shadow Mountain) Deseret Bk. Co.

—Leven Thumps & the Gateway to Foo. Sowards, Ben, illus. 2006. (Leven Thumps Ser.: Bk. 1). 400p. (J). (gr. 4 up). pap. 7.99 (978-1-4169-2806-5(5) , Aladdin) Simon & Schuster Children's Publishing.

Sleator, William. Into the Dream. Sanderson, Ruth, illus. 2000. 144p. (J). (gr. 5-9). pap. 5.99 (978-0-14-130814-2(1) , Puffin) Penguin Group (USA) Inc.

—Into the Dream. 2001. (YA). 21.00 (978-0-8446-7188-8(6)) Smith, Peter Pub., Inc.

—Into the Dream. 2000. (gr. 3-6). lib. bdg. 14.15 (978-0-8335-6871-7(X)); (Illus.). (J). 12.64 (978-0-606-18839-5(8)) Tandem Library Bks.

Sleepytime Monsters Pop-up Boggle Eyes. 2001. (Illus.). 10p. (J). (ps-k). 2.99 (978-0-307-20042-6(6) , Golden Bks.) Random Hse. Children's Bks.

Smith, Bryon. Night Visions Bk. 5: The Adventures of Megan Martin. 2003. 524p. (YA). pap. 20.00 (978-0-9745434-1-3(1)) Sweetgrass Pr., L.L.C.

Sonney, Dale N. Dog, Duck & Dade: May the Country in Them, Tease the Youth in You. 2001. 276p. (YA). pap. 15.95 (978-0-595-19233-5(5)) iUniverse, Inc.

Sorenson, Margo. Ambrose & the Cathedral Dream. Szegedi, Katalin, illus. 2006. 30p. (J). (978-0-8146-3004-4(9)) Liturgical Pr.

Sosa, Joe. The Lonely Little World. 2006. 48p. pap. 9.95 (978-1-59800-419-9(0)) Outskirts Press, Inc.

Spaulding, Mar. Kate Lynn's Fantastic Dream. 1999. (Illus.). 64p. (J). pap. 15.00 (978-0-9674281-0-9(6)) Allen & Douglas Pubs.

Sperring, Mark. Mermaid Dreams. 2006. (Illus.). 32p. (J). pap. 16.99 (978-0-439-79610-1(5) , Chicken Hse., The) Scholastic, Inc.

Stanley's Great Adventures: Stanley Dreams. 2001. (J). spiral bd. 15.95 net. (978-0-9705225-2-8(5)) Harvest Inspirational Publishing, Inc.

Starke, Ruth. Stella by the Sea: Stella's Not Just an Ordinary Girl in an Ordinary World! 2006. (Chomps Ser.). (Illus.). 96p. (J). (gr. 3-7). pap. 3.95 (978-0-7624-2625-6(X) , Running Pr. Kids) Running Pr. Bk. Pubs.

Steinberg, Laya. All Around Me, I See. Arbo, Cris, illus. 2005. (Sharing Nature with Children Book Ser.). 32p. (J). 16.95 (978-1-58469-068-9(2)); pap. 8.95 (978-1-58469-069-6(0)) Dawn Pubns.

Steiner, Barbara. 23 Shadow Street: Deadly Dreams. 2006. 304p. pap. 8.95 (978-1-59687-329-2(9)) ibooks, Inc.

Stewart, Paul. Wakening. 2000. (Yearling Book Ser.). (Illus.). 197p. (J). pap. 8.99 (978-0-440-86347-2(3)) Transworld Publishers Ltd. GBR. *Dist:* Trafalgar Square Publishing.

Stolarz, Laurie Faria. Blue Is for Nightmares. Zins, Rebecca, ed. 2nd rev. ed. 2003. (Blue Is for Nightmares Ser.: Vol. 1). 288p. pap. 9.95 (978-0-7387-0391-6(5)) Llewellyn Pubns.

—Silver Is for Secrets. 2005. (Blue Is for Nightmares Ser.: Vol. 3). 288p. pap. 8.95 (978-0-7387-0631-3(0)) Llewellyn Pubns.

Stone, Kazuko G. & Keido, Ippo. The Butterfly's Dream: Children's Stories from China. 2003. (Illus.). 32p. 15.95 (978-0-8048-3480-3(6)) Tuttle Publishing.

Strickland, Brad & MacHale, D. J. The Storm, No. 4. 2006. (Flight 29 Down Ser.: Vol. 4). 224p. (J). (gr. 4-7). pap. 5.99 (978-0-448-44130-6(6) , Grosset & Dunlap) Penguin Group (USA) Inc.

Strickler, Ashley. Once upon A Time. 2007. 212p. pap. 12.95 (***978-1-4327-0207-6(6)***) Outskirts Press, Inc.

Strong, Beverly Jean. Gypsy the Circus Dog: A Story for Children. Strong, Beverly Jean, illus. 1999. (Illus.). 48p. (J). (ps-3). 24.95 (978-0-86534-300-9(4)) Sunstone Pr.

Stroud, Jonathan. The Leap. 2004. 240p. (gr. 5-17). pap. 6.95 (978-0-7868-5195-9(3)) Miramax Bks.

Stussy, Virginia. Wishes & Wonder. 2007. (ENG.). 52p. per. 12.95 (***978-1-4241-6086-0(3)***) PublishAmerica, Inc.

Suarez, Maribel, illus. Dreams. (Rowing Frog's Rhymes Ser.). 16p. (J). (gr. k-3). 7.95 (978-1-59437-842-3(8)) Santillana USA Publishing Co., Inc.

Sunderland, Margot & Hancock, Nicky. A Pea Called Mildred: A Story to Help Children Pursue Their Hopes & Dreams. Armstrong, Nicky, tr. Armstrong, Nicky, illus. 36p. pap. (978-0-86388-497-9(0) , 002-5062) Speechmark Publishing Ltd.

Sunkuli, O. Hero & the Dream. 2004. (Illus.). 24p. 13.95 (978-9966-25-161-9(8)) Heinemann Kenya, Limited (East African Educational Publishers Ltd E.A.E.P.) KEN. *Dist:* Michigan State Univ. Pr.

Sutherland, Marc. The Waiting Place. Sutherland, Marc, illus. 2004. (Illus.). 24p. (J). (gr. k-4). reprint ed. 15.00 (978-0-7567-8382-2(8)) DIANE Publishing Co.

Swaim, Jessica. Nate by Night. Carpenter, Christina, ed. O'Dea, Helen, illus. 2000. 32p. (J). (ps-3). 15.95 (978-1-886440-02-9(6)) Portunus Publishing Co.

Sweet Dreams. 2003. (J). per. (978-1-57657-876-6(3)) Paradise Pr., Inc.

Sweet Dreams. Date not set. 88p. (J). 7.98 (978-0-7525-9846-8(5)) Parragon, Inc.

Swimpson, Alayne. Murphy's Big Dream. 2006. (ENG.). 36p. per. 19.49 (***978-1-4259-5188-7(0)***) AuthorHouse.

Taylor, S. G. Books of Merlin I. 2006. pap. 10.49 (***978-1-4259-6740-6(X)***) AuthorHouse.

Thomas, John Ira. Zoo Force: Dear Eniko. Smith, Jeremy, illus. 2003. 68p. per. 6.95 (978-0-9743147-1-6(4)) Candle Light Pr.

Thompson, D. R. My New Town: A Flying Naptime Adventure. Thompson, D. R. & Thompson, Dave, illus. 2003. (Naptime Adventure Ser.: Vol. 1). 32p. 14.95 (978-0-9723252-0-2(4)) This New World Publishing, LLC.

Tibo, Gilles. Le Gardien du Sommeil. Jorisch, Stephane, illus. 2004. (Mon Roman Ser.). (FRE.). 64p. (J). (gr. 2). pap. (978-2-89021 691-4(8)) Diffusion du livre Mirabel.

—Simon Says: Seasons. 2006. (Illus.). 48p. (J). (ps-3). 17.95 (978-0-88776-793-7(1)) Tundra Bks., Inc./Livres Toundra, Inc. CAN. *Dist:* Random Hse., Inc.

Tiernan, Cate. Calling. 2001. (gr. 7-12). lib. bdg. 13.00 (978-0-613-64029-9(2)) Tandem Library Bks.

Timmers, Leo. Happy with Me. 2002. (Illus.). 32p. (J). 16.95 (978-1-931290-08-1(3)) Tallfellow Pr.

Townley, Roderick. The Great Good Thing. unabr. ed. 2004. (Middle Grade Cassette Librariestm Ser.). 176p. (J). (gr. 4-6). pap. 29.00 incl. audio (978-0-8072-1001-7(3) , S YA 302 SP, Listening Library) Random Hse. Audio Publishing Group.

—The Great Good Thing. Anderson, Stephanie, illus. 2002. 240p. (J). (gr. 5-9). pap. 4.99 (978-0-689-85328-9(9) , Aladdin) Simon & Schuster Children's Publishing.

—The Great Good Thing. 2001. (Illus.). 232p. (J). (gr. 5-9). 17.00 (978-0-689-84324-2(0) , Atheneum/Richard Jackson Bks.) Simon & Schuster Children's Publishing.

Trevelyan, Kathryn. El Sueno del Rey Ivan. Cornner, Haydn, illus. 2001. Tr. of King Ivan's Dream. (SPA.). (J). (gr. 3). 15.96 (978-84-88342-21-8(7)) S.A. Kokinos ESP. *Dist:* Lectorum Pubns., Inc.

Trottier, Maxine. Dreamstones. East, Stella, illus. 2000. 22p. (J). (ps-3). 8.95 (978-0-7737-6141-4(1)) Stoddart Kids CAN. *Dist:* Fitzhenry & Whiteside, Ltd.

Tukan, Jaytoe Anthony, Sr. Kitty cat had a Dream: Kingdom without a King. 2005. (J). per. 19.95 (978-0-9665909-7-5(X)) Kalawantis Publishing Services, Inc.

Van Allsburg, Chris. Just a Dream. Van Allsburg, Chris, illus. 2002. (Illus.). (J). 25.28 (978-0-7587-2914-9(6)) Book Wholesalers, Inc.

Van Zant, Dawn. No More Night Mares: A Dream of Freedom. McElroy, Kim, illus. 2005. (J). pap. 9.99 (978-0-9761768-1-7(5)) Wild Heart Ranch, Inc.

Vande Velde, Vivian. Witch Dreams. 2005. 128p. (J). (gr. 5-9). 15.95 (978-0-7614-5235-5(4)) Cavendish, Marshall Corp.

Voll, Donna G. Tell Me, Could a Bad Thing Happen to Me? Voll, Donna G. & Voll, Dudley J., eds. 2002. (Illus.). 26p. (J). (ps-3). 12.95 (978-0-9726662-0-6(6)) Golden Words Publishing.

Von, Cristina. Diego y el Monstruo. 2003. (ENG & SPA., Illus.). 24p. pap. 6.95 (978-85-7416-189-1(6)) Callis Editora Ltda BRA. *Dist:* Independent Pubs. Group.

Waddell, Martin. Mimi & the Dream House. 2002. (Illus.). (J). 12.34 (978-0-7587-3136-4(1)) Book Wholesalers, Inc.

Wahl, Jan. Elf Night. Weevers, Peter, illus. 2005. (Picture Bks.). 32p. (gr. k-2). 15.25 (978-1-57505-512-1(0)) Lerner Publishing Group.

Weatherby, Brenda & Weatherby, Mark Alan. The Trucker. 2004. (Illus.). 32p. (J). pap. 15.95 (978-0-439-39877-0(0)) Scholastic, Inc.

Weber, Lenora Mattingly. Pick a New Dream. 1999. (Beany Malone Ser.). 301p. (J). reprint ed. pap. 12.95 (978-1-930009-03-5(8)) Image Cascade Publishing.

Weinberg, Moshe. The Unforgettable Journey. 142p. 12.95 (978-1-56871-306-9(1)) Targum Pr., Inc.

Weninger, Brigitte. Good Night, Nori. Bishop, Kathryn, tr. from GER. Yonezu, Yusuke, illus. 2007. 32p. (J). (ps-2). 15.99 (***978-0-698-40065-8(8)*** , Minedition) Penguin Group (USA) Inc.

Whatley, Bruce. Clinton Gregory's Secret. 2008. 32p. (J). 15.95 (***978-0-8109-9364-8(3)*** , Abrams Bks. for Young Readers) Abrams, Harry N. , Inc.

When Kids Dream & Trucks Fly. 2007. per. 14.99 (***978-0-9792258-6-4(8)***) Bezalel Bks.

Wiede, Edie. Pinky & Bluey Explore the Sky. 1999. (J). (gr. k-3). pap. 6.95 (978-0-533-13148-8(0)) Vantage Pr., Inc.

Wiesner, David. Free Fall. Wiesner, David, illus. 2008. 32p. (J). 17.99 (***978-0-06-156741-4(8)***) HarperCollins Pubs.

Wilde, Terry Lee. The Vampire ... in My Dreams. 2007. (YA). pap. (978-1-932815-38-2(4) , Bronze Medallion) Medallion Pr., Inc.

Williams, Harland. The Kid with Too Many Nightmares. 2006. (Illus.). 32p. (J). (ps-2). pap. 3.99 (978-0-448-44365-2(1) , Grosset & Dunlap) Penguin Group (USA) Inc.

Williams, Harland, illus. The Kid with Too Many Nightmares. 2004. (J). (978-0-8431-1582-6(3) , Price Stern Sloan) Penguin Group (USA) Inc.

Williams, Regina. What If... Keith, Doug, illus. l.t. ed. 2001. 32p. (J). (ps up). 15.95 (978-0-935699-22-7(8)) Illumination Arts Publishing Co., Inc.

Willson, Sarah. Dora's Backpack. Roper, Robert, illus. 2002. (Dora the Explorer Ser.). 24p. (J). pap. 3.50 (978-0-689-84720-2(3) , Simon Spotlight/Nickelodeon) Simon & Schuster Children's Publishing.

—Dora's Backpack. 2002. (ps-2). lib. bdg. 11.25 (978-0-613-73315-1(0)) Tandem Library Bks.

Winerip, Michael. Adam Canfield Watch Your Back! 2007. (Adam Canfield of the Slash Ser.). (Illus.). 256p. (J). (gr. 3-7). 15.99 (***978-0-7636-2341-8(5)***) Candlewick Pr.

Wood, Audrey. Sweet Dream Pie. Teague, Mark, illus. 2002. 32p. (J). (ps-4). pap. 5.99 (978-0-439-39472-7(4)) Scholastic, Inc.

—Sweet Dream Pie. 2002. (ps-2). lib. bdg. 14.15 (978-0-613-46233-4(5)) Tandem Library Bks.

The Wrong Side of the Bed. 2003. (J). lib. bdg. 16.95 (978-1-931650-20-5(9)) Coastal Publishing Carolina, Inc.

Wyss, Tyan. Night Flyer. Immelman, Sarita, illus. 2006. 40p. (J). per. 14.95 (***978-1-58939-916-7(1)***) Virtualbookworm.com Publishing, Inc.

Yoshizuki, Kumichi. Someday's Dreamers. 2006. (Illus.). pap. 9.99 (978-1-59816-178-6(4) , Tokyopop Kids) TOKYOPOP, Inc.

Yueh, Tung. The Tower of Myriad Mirrors. Schulz, Larry J. & Lin, Shuen-Fu, trs. from CHI. 2nd ed. 2000. (Michigan Classics in Chinese Studies: No. 1). (Illus.). 150p. pap. 20.00 (978-0-89264-142-0(8)) Ctr. for Chinese Studies Pubns.

Zoehfeld, Kathleen Weidner. Pooh's Bad Dream. 2000. (My Very First Winnie the Pooh Ser.). (Illus.). 32p. (J). (ps-k). pap. 4.99 (978-0-7868-4377-0(2)) Disney Pr.

—Pooh's Bad Dream. Cuddy, Robbin, illus. 1998. (My Very First Winnie the Pooh Ser.). 32p. (J). (ps-k). 11.95 (978-0-7868-3137-1(5)) Disney Pr.

DRESS

see Clothing and Dress

DRESSMAKING

see also Sewing

Hughes, Sarah. My Grandmother Works in a Dress Shop. (Welcome Bks.). (Illus.). 24p. (J). (ps-2). 2001. pap. 4.95 (978-0-516-29576-3(4)); 2000. lib. bdg. (978-0-516-23283-6(5)) Scholastic Library Publishing. (Children's Pr.).

—My Grandmother Works in a Dress Shop. 2001. (gr. k-3). lib. bdg. 12.95 (978-0-613-58865-2(7)) Tandem Library Bks.

Patterns: Individual Title Six-Packs. (Story Steps Ser.). (gr. k-2). 29.00 (978-0-7635-9569-2(1)) Rigby Education.

Patterns Are Fun!, 6 Packs. (Story Steps Ser.). (gr. k-2). 29.00 (978-0-7635-9576-0(4)) Rigby Education.

DRESSMAKING—FICTION

Brightwood, Laura, illus. King's New Suit. Brightwood, Laura, . 2007. (J). DVD (***978-1-934409-05-3(7)***) 3-C Institute for Social Development.

Chessa, Francesca. A Button Muddle. Chessa, Francesca, illus. 2003. (Illus.). 32p. (YA). pap. (978-1-85602-461-7(X)) Chrysalis Children's Bks.

FLCL T-Shirt - Turn Around - Extra Large: Fooly Cooly. 2004. (YA). mass mkt. 17.99 (978-1-932480-99-3(4)) Broccoli International USA, Inc.

Floca, Brian, illus. The Hinky Pink. 2008. 48p. (J). (***978-0-689-87588-5(6)***) Simon & Schuster Children's Publishing.

Gay, Marie-Louise. Buenos Dias Samuel. 2004. (SPA.). (J). (gr. k up). pap. 7.99 (978-980-257-293-9(4)) Ekare, Ediciones VEN. *Dist:* Lectorum Pubns., Inc., Iaconi, Mariuccia Bk. Imports.

Markowitz-Meredith, Susan. Frances & the Fairy Dressmaker. ed. 2003. (Early Connections Ser.). (J). pap. 35.00 (978-1-4108-1557-6(9)) Benchmark Education Co.

Noland, Charles. The Adventures of Drew & Ellie: The Magical Dress. Baker, Sherri, illus. 2006. (J). (978-0-9789297-1-8(3)); 2nd rev. ed. per. 7.95 (978-0-9789297-0-1(5)) TMD Enterprises.

Off to School: Individual Title Six-Packs. (Story Steps Ser.). (gr. k-2). 29.00 (978-0-7635-9577-7(2)) Rigby Education.

Stop Knitting, Nina!, 6 Packs. (gr. k-1). 23.00 (978-0-7635-9028-4(2)) Rigby Education.

DREW, CHARLES RICHARD, 1904-1950

Salas, Laura Purdie. Charles Drew: Pioneer in Medicine. 2006. (Fact Finders Ser.). (Illus.). 32p. (J). (978-0-7368-5433-7(9)) Capstone Pr., Inc.

Schraff, Anne. Charles Drew: Pioneer in Medicine. 2003. (Famous Inventors Ser.). (Illus.). 32p. (J). (gr. 1-4). lib. bdg. 22.60 (978-0-7660-2008-5(8)) Enslow Pubs., Inc.

—Dr. Charles Drew: Blood Bank Innovator. 2003. (African-American Biographies Ser.). (Illus.). 128p. (J). (gr. 6-12). lib. bdg. 26.60 (978-0-7660-2117-4(3)) Enslow Pubs., Inc.

Trice, Linda. Charles Drew. 2000. (Ideas on Trial Ser.). (Illus.). 121p. (C). (gr. 8-12). pap. 8.95 (978-0-07-135317-5(8)) McGraw-Hill Cos., The.

DREW, NANCY (FICTITIOUS CHARACTER)—FICTION

Alexander, Fern. Hello, Hollywood. 2007. (Nancy Drew Movie Ser.). 32p. (J). pap. 3.99 (978-1-4169-3900-9(8) , Simon Spotlight) Simon & Schuster Children's Publishing.

Burr, Daniela. Murder in Hollywood Hills. 2007. (Nancy Drew Movie Ser.). 128p. (J). pap. 5.99 (978-1-4169-3899-6(0) , Simon Spotlight) Simon & Schuster Children's Publishing.

Keene, Carolyn. Alien in the Classroom. 1998. (Nancy Drew Notebooks: No. 23). (Illus.). 80p. (J). (gr. k-3). pap. 3.99 (978-0-671-00818-5(8) , Aladdin) Simon & Schuster Children's Publishing.

—Alien in the Classroom. 1998. (Nancy Drew Notebooks: No. 23). (J). (gr. k-3). 10.79 (978-0-606-13653-2(3)) Tandem Library Bks.

—The Apple Bandit. Jones, Jan Naimo, illus. 2005. 74p. (J). lib. bdg. 15.00 (***978-1-4242-0917-0(X)***) Fitzgerald Bks.

—The Apple Bandit. Jones, Jan Naimo, illus. 2005. 74p. (J). (978-1-4156-2882-9(3) , Aladdin) Simon & Schuster Children's Publishing.

—Bad Times, Big Crimes. 2005. 139p. (J). lib. bdg. 15.00 (***978-1-4242-0242-3(6)***) Fitzgerald Bks.

—Bad Times, Big Crimes. 2005. (Nancy Drew Ser.: Vol. 14). 160p. (J). (gr. 3-7). pap. 4.99 (978-0-689-87883-1(4) , Aladdin) Simon & Schuster Children's Publishing.

—The Black Velvet Mystery. 1999. (Nancy Drew Notebooks: No. 32). (J). (gr. k-3). (978-0-606-19059-6(7)) Tandem Library Bks.

—The Bungalow Mystery, No. 3. Tandy, Russell H., illus. fac. ed. 2004. (Nancy Drew Mystery Stories: No. 3). 204p. (J). (gr. 4-7). reprint ed. 17.95 (978-1-55709-157-4(9)) Applewood Bks.

—The Bunny-Hop Hoax. Jones, Jan Naimo, illus. 2005. 70p. (J). lib. bdg. 15.00 (***978-1-4242-0921-7(8)***) Fitzgerald Bks.

—The Bunny-Hop Hoax. Jones, Jan Naimo, illus. Frost, Michael, photos by. 2005. (Nancy Drew Notebooks). 80p. (J). pap. 3.99 (978-0-689-87754-4(4) , Aladdin) Simon & Schuster Children's Publishing.

—Captive Witness. 2005. (Nancy Drew Mystery Stories: No. 64). (Illus.). 192p. (J). (gr. 3-8). 6.99 (978-0-448-43695-1(7) , Grosset & Dunlap) Penguin Group (USA) Inc.

—The Case of Capital Intrigue. 1998. (Nancy Drew Mystery Stories: No. 142). (J). (gr. 3-6). 11.64 (978-0-606-13644-0(4)) Tandem Library Bks.

—The Case of the Creative Crime. 2002. (Nancy Drew Mystery Stories: Vol. 166). (Illus.). 160p. (J). (gr. 3-6). pap. 4.99 (978-0-7434-3748-6(9) , Aladdin) Simon & Schuster Children's Publishing.

—The Case of the Creative Crime. 2002. (gr. 5-8). lib. bdg. 13.00 (978-0-613-45020-1(5)) Tandem Library Bks.

—The Case of the Lost Song. 2001. (Nancy Drew Mystery Stories: Vol. 162). (Illus.). 160p. (J). (gr. 3-6). pap. 4.99 (978-0-7434-0688-8(5) , Aladdin) Simon & Schuster Children's Publishing.

—The Case of the Lost Song. 2001. (gr. 5-8). lib. bdg. 13.00 (978-0-613-63388-8(1)) Tandem Library Bks.

—The Case of the Vanishing Veil. 2001. (gr. 5-8). lib. bdg. 13.00 (978-0-613-63390-1(3)) Tandem Library Bks.

—The Chocolate-Covered Contest. 1999. (Nancy Drew Mystery Stories: No. 151). 160p. (J). (gr. 3-6). pap. 4.99 (978-0-671-03443-6(X) , Aladdin) Simon & Schuster Children's Publishing.

—The Chocolate-Covered Contest. 1999. (gr. 5-8). lib. bdg. 13.00 (978-0-613-21340-0(8)); (Nancy Drew Mystery Stories: No. 151). (J). (gr. 3-6). 11.64 (978-0-606-19058-9(9)) Tandem Library Bks.

—The Cinderella Ballet Mystery. 2007. (Nancy Drew & the Clue Crew Ser.). 96p. (J). (gr. 2-4). 24.21 (***978-1-59961-345-1(X)***) Spotlight.

—Close Encounters. 2006. (Nancy Drew Ser.: No. 21). 176p. (J). pap. 4.99 (978-1-4169-1245-3(2) , Aladdin) Simon & Schuster Children's Publishing.

—The Clue in the Diary. Tandy, Russell H., illus. fac. ed. 2004. (Nancy Drew Mystery Stories: No. 7). 228p. (J). (gr. 4-7). reprint ed. 17.95 (978-1-55709-161-1(7)) Applewood Bks.

—The Clue of the Broken Locket. Tandy, Russell H., illus. fac. ed. 2004. (Nancy Drew Mystery Stories: No. 11). 228p. (J). (gr. 4-7). reprint ed. 14.95 (978-1-55709-165-9(X)) Applewood Bks.

—Clues to Good Sleuthing. 2007. (Nancy Drew Mystery Stories). 160p. (J). (gr. 3-8). 7.99 (978-0-448-44568-7(9) , Grosset & Dunlap) Penguin Group (USA) Inc.

—The Crime Lab Case. 2002. (gr. 5-8). lib. bdg. 13.00 (978-0-613-45025-6(6)) Tandem Library Bks.

—Danger on the Great Lakes. 2003. (gr. 5-8). lib. bdg. 13.00 (978-0-613-66491-2(4)) Tandem Library Bks.

—Dangerous Plays. 2006. 146p. (J). (978-1-4156-5040-0(3) , Aladdin) Simon & Schuster Children's Publishing.

—Dare at the Fair. 1998. (Nancy Drew Notebooks: No. 25). (J). (gr. 2-4). (978-0-606-13655-6(X)) Tandem Library Bks.

—Double Horror of Fenley Place. 2001. (gr. 5-8). lib. bdg. 13.00 (978-0-613-63401-4(2)) Tandem Library Bks.

—The Double Horror of Fenley Place. 2001. (Nancy Drew on Campus Ser.: Vol. 79). (Illus.). 160p. (J). (gr. 3-6). reprint ed. pap. 4.99 (978-0-7434-2343-4(7) , Aladdin) Simon & Schuster Children's Publishing.

—Dressed to Steal. 2007. (Nancy Drew Ser.: No. 22). 160p. (J). pap. 4.99 (978-1-4169-3385-4(9) , Aladdin) Simon & Schuster Children's Publishing.

—The E-Mail Mystery, Vol. 144. 1998. (Nancy Drew Mystery Stories: No. 144). 160p. (gr. 3-6). pap. 4.99 (978-0-671-00121-6(3) , Aladdin) Simon & Schuster Children's Publishing.

—The E-Mail Mystery. 1998. (Nancy Drew Mystery Stories: No. 144). (J). (gr. 3-6). 11.64 (978-0-606-13646-4(0)) Tandem Library Bks.

—En Garde. 2006. (Nancy Drew Ser.: No. 17). 160p. (J). pap. 4.99 (978-1-4169-0603-2(7)) Simon & Schuster Children's Publishing.

—The Fashion Disaster. Pamintuan, Macky, illus. 2007. (Nancy Drew & the Clue Crew Ser.: No. 6). 96p. (J). pap. 3.99 (978-1-4169-3485-1(5) , Aladdin) Simon & Schuster Children's Publishing.

—Fishing for Clues. 2007. (Nancy Drew Ser.: No. 26). 144p. (J). pap. 4.99 (***978-1-4169-3525-4(8)*** , Aladdin) Simon & Schuster Children's Publishing.

—Framed. 2006. 149p. (J). (978-1-4156-4605-2(8) , Aladdin) Simon & Schuster Children's Publishing.

—Getting Burned. 2006. (Nancy Drew Ser.: No. 21). 160p. (J). pap. 4.99 (978-0-689-87703-2(X) , Aladdin) Simon & Schuster Children's Publishing.

—The Gumdrop Ghost. 1999. (Nancy Drew Notebooks: No. 33). (J). (gr. k-3). (978-0-606-19060-2(0)) Tandem Library Bks.

—The Hidden Staircase, No. 2. Tandy, Russell H., illus. fac. ed. 2004. (Nancy Drew Mystery Stories: No. 2). 206p. (J). (gr. 4-7). reprint ed. 17.95 (978-1-55709-156-7(0)) Applewood Bks.

—The Hidden Treasures. Accardo, Anthony, illus. 1998. (Nancy Drew Notebooks: No. 24). 80p. (J). (gr. k-3). pap. 3.99 (978-0-671-00819-2(6) , Aladdin) Simon & Schuster Children's Publishing.

—The Hidden Treasures. 1998. (Nancy Drew Notebooks: No. 24). (J). (gr. k-3). 10.79 (978-0-606-13654-9(1)) Tandem Library Bks.

—High Risk. 2004. (Nancy Drew Ser.). 160p. mass mkt. 4.99 (978-0-689-86569-5(4) , Aladdin) Simon & Schuster Children's Publishing.

—Intruder. 2007. (Nancy Drew Ser.: No. 27). 160p. (J). pap. 4.99 (***978-1-4169-3526-1(6)*** , Aladdin) Simon & Schuster Children's Publishing.

—The Kachina Doll Mystery, Vol. 62. 2005. (Nancy Drew Mystery Stories). (Illus.). 192p. (J). (gr. 3-8). 6.99 (978-0-448-43693-7(0) , Grosset & Dunlap) Penguin Group (USA) Inc.

—The Key in the Satin Pocket. 2000. (gr. 5-8). lib. bdg. 13.00 (978-0-613-21851-1(5)) Tandem Library Bks.

—The Kitten Caper. Jones, Jan Naimo, illus. 2005. 72p. (J). lib. bdg. 15.00 (***978-1-4242-0916-3(1)***) Fitzgerald Bks.

—Legend of the Emerald Lady. 2000. (gr. 5-8). lib. bdg. 13.00 (978-0-613-27933-8(6)) Tandem Library Bks.

—Lights, Camera ... ed. 2005. (Nancy Drew Ser.: 5). 154p. (J). lib. bdg. 15.00 (978-1-59054-812-7(4)) Fitzgerald Bks.

—Lights, Camera ... Cats! Pamintuan, Macky, illus. 2007. (Nancy Drew & the Clue Crew Ser.: No. 8). 96p. (J). pap. 3.99 (978-1-4169-3957-3(1) , Aladdin) Simon & Schuster Children's Publishing.

—The Message in the Haunted Mansion. 2001. 154p. (J). (gr. 4-7). per. 13.00 (978-0-613-63431-1(4)) Tandem Library Bks.

—The Message in the Hollow Oak. Tandy, Russell H., illus. fac. ed. 2004. (Nancy Drew Mystery Stories: No. 12). 210p. (J). (gr. 4-7). 17.95 (978-1-55709-258-8(3)) Applewood Bks.

—Mistletoe Mystery. 2002. (Nancy Drew Mystery Stories). 160p. (J). pap. 4.99 (978-0-7434-3765-3(9) , Aladdin) Simon & Schuster Children's Publishing.

—Mistletoe Mystery. 2002. (gr. 5-8). lib. bdg. 13.00 (978-0-613-63432-8(2)) Tandem Library Bks.

—Murder on the Set. 2007. (Nancy Drew Ser.: No. 24). 176p. (J). pap. 4.99 (978-1-4169-3397-7(2) , Aladdin) Simon & Schuster Children's Publishing.

—Mystery at Moorsea Manor. 1999. (Nancy Drew Mystery Stories: No. 150). (J). (gr. 3-6). (978-0-606-19038-1(4)) Tandem Library Bks.

—Mystery by Moonlight. 2002. (Nancy Drew Mystery Stories: Vol. 167). 160p. (J). (gr. 3-7). pap. 4.99 (978-0-7434-3762-2(4) , Aladdin) Simon & Schuster Children's Publishing.

—Mystery by Moonlight. 2002. (gr. 5-8). lib. bdg. 13.00 (978-0-613-45083-6(3)) Tandem Library Bks.

—The Mystery of Mother Wolf. 2002. (Nancy Drew Mystery Stories: Vol. 164). 160p. (J). pap. 4.99 (978-0-7434-3743-1(8) , Aladdin) Simon & Schuster Children's Publishing.

—The Mystery of the Moss-Covered Mansion. Tandy, Russell H., illus. 2003. (Nancy Drew Mystery Stories). 215p. (J). (gr. 4-7). per. 14.95 (978-1-55709-264-9(8)) Applewood Bks.

—Mystery on Maui. 1998. (Nancy Drew Mystery Stories: No. 143). 160p. (gr. 3-6). mass mkt. 4.99 (978-0-671-00753-9(X) , Aladdin) Simon & Schuster Children's Publishing.

—Mystery on Maui. 1998. (Nancy Drew Mystery Stories: No. 143). (J). (gr. 3-6). (978-0-606-13645-7(2)) Tandem Library Bks.

—Nancy Drew, Set. 75th anniv. ed. 2005. 1250p. (J). (gr. 3-7). 75.00 (978-1-55709-154-3(4)) Applewood Bks.

—Nancy Drew, Vols. 1-6. 1998. (J). 22.98 (978-0-448-41673-1(5) , Grosset & Dunlap) Penguin Group (USA) Inc.

—Nancy Drew: The Scarlet Macaw Scandal. Frost, Michael, illus. 2004. (Nancy Drew Ser.). 160p. (J). pap. 4.99 (978-0-689-86844-3(8) , Aladdin) Simon & Schuster Children's Publishing.

—Nancy Drew Girl Detective (Boxed Set) Sleuth Set: Without a Trace; A Race Against Time; False Notes; High Risk. 2004. (Nancy Drew Ser.). (Illus.). 640p. (J). pap. 19.99 (978-0-689-03691-0(4) , Aladdin) Simon & Schuster Children's Publishing.

—The Nancy Drew Pocketbook Mysteries. 2007. (Nancy Drew Mystery Stories). 192p. (J). (gr. 3-8). 19.99 (978-0-448-44544-1(1) , Grosset & Dunlap) Penguin Group (USA) Inc.

—Nancy's Mysterious Letter. Tandy, Russell H., illus. fac. ed. 2004. (Nancy Drew Mystery Stories Ser.: No. 8). 210p. (J). (gr. 4-7). reprint ed. 14.95 (978-1-55709-162-8(5)) Applewood Bks.

—Natural Enemies. 2000. (Nancy Drew Files: No. 121). (YA). (gr. 6 up). per. (978-0-671-50396-3(0) , Simon Pulse) Simon & Schuster Children's Publishing.

—Once upon a Crime. 2006. 185p. (J). (978-1-4156-7698-1(4) , Aladdin) Simon & Schuster Children's Publishing.

—Operation Titanic. 1998. (Nancy Drew & Hardy Boys Super Mystery Ser.: No. 35). (YA). (gr. 6 up). (978-0-606-13650-1(9)) Tandem Library Bks.

—The Orchid Thief. 2006. (Nancy Drew Ser.: No. 19). 144p. (J). pap. 4.99 (978-1-4169-0980-4(X) , Aladdin) Simon & Schuster Children's Publishing.

—The Password to Larkspur Lane, No. 10. Tandy, Russell H., illus. fac. ed. 2004. (Nancy Drew Mystery Stories: No. 10). 210p. (J). (gr. 4-7). 17.95 (978-1-55709-164-2(1)) Applewood Bks.

—Pony Problems. Pamintuan, Macky, illus. 2006. (Nancy Drew & the Clue Crew Ser.: No. 3). 96p. (J). pap. 3.99 (978-1-4169-1815-8(9) , Aladdin) Simon & Schuster Children's Publishing.

—Pony Problems. 2007. (Nancy Drew & the Clue Crew Ser.). 96p. (J). (gr. 2-4). 24.21 (***978-1-59961-346-8(8)***) Spotlight.

—The Puppy Problem. Accardo, Anthony, illus. 2005. 69p. (J). lib. bdg. 15.00 (***978-1-4242-0373-4(2)***) Fitzgerald Bks.

—The Quest of the Missing Map. 2004. (Nancy Drew Mystery Stories: No. 19). 228p. (J). (gr. 4-7). 17.95 (978-1-55709-265-6(6)) Applewood Bks.

—Real Fake. 2007. (Nancy Drew Ser.). 224p. (J). pap. 5.99 (978-1-4169-3881-1(8) , Aladdin) Simon & Schuster Children's Publishing.

—Riverboat Ruse. ed. 2005. (Nancy Drew Ser.: 11). 154p. (J). lib. bdg. 15.00 (978-1-59054-813-4(2)) Fitzgerald Bks.

—The Scarlet Macaw Scandal. ed. 2005. (Nancy Drew Ser.: 8). 154p. (J). lib. bdg. 15.00 (978-1-59054-816-5(7)) Fitzgerald Bks.

—Scream for Ice Cream. Pamintuan, Macky, illus. 2006. (Nancy Drew & the Clue Crew Ser.: No. 2). 96p. (J). pap. 3.99 (978-1-4169-1253-8(3) , Aladdin) Simon & Schuster Children's Publishing.

—Scream for Ice Cream. 2007. (Nancy Drew & the Clue Crew Ser.). 96p. (J). (gr. 2-4). 24.21 (***978-1-59961-347-5(6)***) Spotlight.

—The Secret in the Old Attic. 2005. (Nancy Drew Mystery Stories). (Illus.). 210p. (J). (gr. 4-7). 17.95 (978-1-55709-278-6(8)) Applewood Bks.

—The Secret of Red Gate Farm, No. 6. Tandy, Russell H., illus. fac. ed. 2004. (Nancy Drew Mystery Stories: No. 6). 228p. (J). (gr. 4-7). reprint ed. 17.95 (978-1-55709-160-4(9)) Applewood Bks.

—The Secret of Shadow Ranch, No. 5. Tandy, Russell H., illus. fac. ed. 2004. (Nancy Drew Mystery Stories: No. 5). 224p. (J). (gr. 4-7). reprint ed. 17.95 (978-1-55709-159-8(5)) Applewood Bks.

—The Secret of Shady Glen. 2001. (Nancy Drew Mystery Stories: Vol. 85). 160p. (J). (gr. 3-6). reprint ed. pap. 4.99 (978-0-7434-1936-9(7) , Aladdin) Simon & Schuster Children's Publishing.

—The Secret of Shady Glen. 2001. (gr. 5-8). lib. bdg. 13.00 (978-0-613-63460-1(8)) Tandem Library Bks.

—The Secret of the Old Clock. Tandy, Russell H., illus. fac. ed. 2004. (Nancy Drew Mystery Stories: No. 1). 210p. (J). (gr. 4-7). reprint ed. 17.95 (978-1-55709-155-0(2)) Applewood Bks.

—Secret of the Spa. ed. 2005. (Nancy Drew Ser.: 9). 154p. (J). lib. bdg. 15.00 (978-1-59054-814-1(0)) Fitzgerald Bks.

—The Sign of the Twisted Candles, No. 9. Tandy, Russell H., illus. fac. ed. 2004. (Nancy Drew Mystery Stories: No. 9). 210p. (J). (gr. 4-7). reprint ed. 17.95 (978-1-55709-163-5(3)) Applewood Bks.

—The Singing Suspects. Jones, Jan, illus. 2005. 69p. (J). lib. bdg. 15.00 (***978-1-4242-0918-7(8)***) Fitzgerald Bks.

—Ski School Sneak. Pamintuan, Macky, illus. 2007. (Nancy Drew & the Clue Crew Ser.: No. 11). 96p. (J). (gr. 1-4). pap. 3.99 (***978-1-4169-4936-7(4)*** , Aladdin) Simon & Schuster Children's Publishing.

—Sleepover Sleuths. 2007. (Nancy Drew & the Clue Crew Ser.). 96p. (J). (gr. 2-4). 24.21 (***978-1-59961-348-2(4)***) Spotlight.

—Snowman Surprise. Casale, Paul, illus. Frost, Michael, photos by. 2004. (Nancy Drew Notebooks: No. 63). 80p. (J). pap. 3.99 (978-0-689-87411-6(1) , Aladdin) Simon & Schuster Children's Publishing.

—Space Case. Jones, Jan, illus. 2004. 68p. (J). lib. bdg. 15.00 (***978-1-4242-0924-8(2)***) Fitzgerald Bks.

—The Stolen Relic. ed. 2005. (Nancy Drew Ser.: 7). 152p. (J). lib. bdg. 15.00 (978-1-59054-817-2(5)) Fitzgerald Bks.

—The Stolen Relic. 2004. (Nancy Drew Ser.: #7). 160p. mass mkt. 4.99 (978-0-689-86843-6(X) , Aladdin) Simon & Schuster Children's Publishing.

—Stop the Clock. ed. 2005. (Nancy Drew Ser.: 12). 160p. (J). lib. bdg. 15.00 (978-1-59054-815-8(9)) Fitzgerald Bks.

—Strange Memories. 2000. (Nancy Drew Files: No. 122). (YA). (gr. 6 up). per. (978-0-671-50397-0(9) , Simon Pulse) Simon & Schuster Children's Publishing.

—Strike-Out Scare. Jones, Jan Naimo, illus. 2005. 70p. (J). (978-1-4155-7741-7(2) , Aladdin) Simon & Schuster Children's Publishing.

—The Swami's Ring. 2005. (Nancy Drew Mystery Stories Ser.: Vol. 61). (Illus.). 192p. (J). (gr. 3-8). 6.99 (978-0-448-43692-0(2) , Grosset & Dunlap) Penguin Group (USA) Inc.

—A Taste of Danger. 2003. (Nancy Drew Mystery Stories: No. 174). 176p. (J). pap. 4.99 (978-0-689-86154-3(0) , Aladdin) Simon & Schuster Children's Publishing.

—Ticket Trouble. Pamintuan, Macky, illus. 2007. (Nancy Drew & the Clue Crew Ser.: No. 10). 87p. (J). (gr. 1-4). per. 3.99 (***978-1-4169-4733-2(7)*** , Aladdin) Simon & Schuster Children's Publishing.

—Trade Wind Danger. 2005. 148p. (J). lib. bdg. 15.00 (***978-1-4242-0243-0(4)***) Fitzgerald Bks.

—Trails of Treachery. 2007. (Nancy Drew Ser.). 144p. (J). pap. 4.99 (***978-1-4169-3524-7(X)*** , Aladdin) Simon & Schuster Children's Publishing.

—Troubled Waters. 2007. (Nancy Drew Ser.). 160p. (J). pap. 4.99 (978-1-4169-2513-2(9) , Aladdin) Simon & Schuster Children's Publishing.

—The Twin Dilemma. 2005. (Nancy Drew Mystery Stories: Vol. 63). (Illus.). 196p. (J). (gr. 3-8). pap. 6.99 (978-0-448-43694-4(9) , Grosset & Dunlap) Penguin Group (USA) Inc.

—Uncivil Acts. ed. 2005. (Nancy Drew Ser.: 10). 152p. (J). lib. bdg. 15.00 (978-1-59054-818-9(3)) Fitzgerald Bks.

—Valentine's Day Secret. 2007. (Nancy Drew & the Clue Crew Ser.). 96p. (J). pap. 3.99 (***978-1-4169-4944-2(5)*** , Aladdin) Simon & Schuster Children's Publishing.

—The Walkie-Talkie Mystery. 2002. (gr. 3-6). lib. bdg. 11.80 (978-0-613-53893-0(0)) Tandem Library Bks.

—Werewolf in a Winter Wonderland. 2003. (Nancy Drew Mystery Stories). 160p. (J). pap. 4.99 (978-0-689-86182-6(6) , Aladdin) Simon & Schuster Children's Publishing.

—The Whispering Statue, No. 14. 2000. (Nancy Drew Mystery Stories Ser.: No. 14). (Illus.). 228p. (J). (gr. 4-7). 17.95 (978-1-55709-260-1(5)) Applewood Bks.

—Without a Trace. ed. 2005. (Nancy Drew Ser.: 1). (Illus.). 154p. (J). lib. bdg. 15.00 (978-1-59054-819-6(1)) Fitzgerald Bks.

—Without a Trace. 2004. (Nancy Drew Ser.: No. 1). 160p. (J). pap. 4.99 (978-0-689-86566-4(X) , Aladdin) Simon & Schuster Children's Publishing.

Keene, Carolyn. Zoo Clue. Jones, Jan, illus. 2005. 74p. (J). lib. bdg. 15.00 (***978-1-4242-0919-4(6)***) Fitzgerald Bks.

Keene, Carolyn & Benson, Mildred Wirt. The Mystery at Lilac Inn. Tandy, Russell H., illus. fac. ed. 2004. (Nancy Drew Mystery Stories Ser.: No. 4). 224p. (J). (gr. 4-7). reprint ed. 17.95 (978-1-55709-158-1(7)) Applewood Bks.

Keene, Carolyn & Dixon, Franklin W. Terror on Tour. 2007. (Nancy Drew & the Hardy Boys Ser.: No. 1). 224p. (J). pap. 5.99 (***978-1-4169-2726-6(3)*** , Aladdin) Simon & Schuster Children's Publishing.

Keene, Carolyn & Greene, James. The Missing Horse Mystery. 1998. (Nancy Drew Mystery Stories: No. 145). 160p. (J). (gr. 3-6). pap. 4.99 (978-0-671-00754-6(8) , Aladdin) Simon & Schuster Children's Publishing.

Keene, Carolyn & Whelan, Patrick. Danger on the Great Lakes. 2003. (Nancy Drew Mystery Stories). (Illus.). 160p. (J). pap. 4.99 (978-0-689-86146-8(X) , 53545777, Aladdin) Simon & Schuster Children's Publishing.

Kilpatrick, Irene. The Movie Star Mystery. 2007. (Nancy Drew Movie Ser.). 24p. (J). pap. 3.99 (978-1-4169-3901-6(6) , Simon Spotlight) Simon & Schuster Children's Publishing.

Murase, Sho & Petrucha, Stefan. The Haunted Dollhouse. 3rd rev. ed. 2005. (Nancy Drew Ser.: No. 3). (Illus.). 96p. (J). (gr. 3-7). 12.95 (978-1-59707-009-6(2)) Papercutz.

Nancy Drew. 2006. (J). (gr. 3-8). 72.63 (978-1-59961-056-6(6)) Spotlight.

Petrucha, Stefan. The Charmed Bracelet. Ross, Vaughn, illus. 2006. (Nancy Drew Ser.). 96p. (J). rev. ed. 12.95 (978-1-59707-037-9(8)); 7th rev. ed. pap. 7.95 (978-1-59707-036-2(X)) Papercutz.

—Demon of River Heights. 2006. (J). (gr. 3-8). 24.21 (978-1-59961-057-3(4)) Spotlight.

—The Disoriented Express. Murase, Sho, illus. 10th rev. ed. 2007. (Nancy Drew Ser.: No. 10). 112p. (J). pap. 7.95 (***978-1-59707-066-9(1)***) Papercutz.

—Disoriented Express. Murase, Sho, illus. 10th rev. ed. 2007. (Nancy Drew Ser.: No. 10). 112p. (J). 12.95 (***978-1-59707-067-6(X)***) Papercutz.

—Ghost in the Machinery. Murase, Sho, illus. 9th rev. ed. 2007. (Nancy Drew Ser.: No. 9). 112p. (J). 12.95 (***978-1-59707-061-4(0))***; pap. 7.95 (***978-1-59707-058-4(0)***) Papercutz.

—The Girl Who Wasn't There. Murase, Sho, illus. 4th rev. ed. 2006. (Nancy Drew Ser.: No. 4). 96p. (J). 12.95 (978-1-59707-013-3(0)); pap. 7.95 (978-1-59707-012-6(2)) Papercutz.

—Global Warning. Murase, Sho, illus. 8th rev. ed. 2007. (Nancy Drew Ser.: No. 8). 112p. (J). 12.95 (978-1-59707-052-2(1)); pap. 7.95 (978-1-59707-051-5(3)) Papercutz.

Petrucha, Stefan & Murase, Sho. The Haunted Dollhouse. 3rd rev. ed. 2005. (Nancy Drew Ser.: No. 3). (Illus.). 96p. (J). (gr. 3-7). pap., pap. 7.95 (978-1-59707-008-9(4)) Papercutz.

—Mr. Cheeters Is Missing. 6th rev. ed. 2006. (Nancy Drew Ser.: No. 6). (Illus.). 96p. (J). pap. 7.95 (978-1-59707-030-0(0)) Papercutz.

—Writ in Stone. 2nd rev. ed. 2005. (Nancy Drew Ser.: No. 2). (Illus.). 96p. (J). (gr. 3-9). 12.95 (978-1-59707-006-5(8)); pap., pap. 7.95 (978-1-59707-002-7(5)) Papercutz.

Weber, Jen Funk. Hollywood Head Scratchers. 2007. (Nancy Drew Movie Ser.). 64p. (J). pap. 5.99 (978-1-4169-3380-9(8) , Simon Scribbles) Simon & Schuster Children's Publishing.

—Still Sleuthing! 2007. (Nancy Drew Movie Ser.). 64p. (J). pap. 5.99 (978-1-4169-3381-6(6) , Simon Scribbles) Simon & Schuster Children's Publishing.

DREXEL, KATHARINE, 1858-1955

Jablonski, Patricia Edward. Kate from Philadelphia: The Life of Saint Katharine Drexel for Children. Hausmann, Mary J., illus. 2001. 40p. (J). pap. 6.95 (978-0-8198-4207-7(9) , 332-161) Pauline Bks. & Media.

Wallace, Susan Helen. Saint Katharine Drexel: The Total Gift. Kiwak, Barbara, illus. 2003. (Encounter the Saints Ser.: Vol. 15). 144p. (J). pap. 5.95 (978-0-8198-7068-1(4) , 332-365) Pauline Bks. & Media.

DREYFUS, ALFRED, 1859-1935

Finkelstein, Norman H. Captain of Innocence: France & the Dreyfus Affair. 2000. (gr. 7-12). lib. bdg. 23.40 (978-0-613-81391-4(X)) Tandem Library Bks.

—Captain of Innocence: France & the Dreyfus Affair. 2001. (Illus.). 160p. (YA). (gr. 7-12). pap. 13.95 (978-0-595-15651-1(7) , Backinprint.com) iUniverse, Inc.

DRINKS

see Beverages

DRIVERS, AUTOMOBILE

see Automobile Drivers

DROMEDARIES

see Camels

DROON (IMAGINARY PLACE)—FICTION

Abbott, Tony. Chariot of Queen Zara. Merrell, David, illus. 2006. 124p. (J). lib. bdg. 15.38 (***978-1-4242-0308-6(2)***) Fitzgerald Bks.

—The Coiled Viper. Jessell, Tim, illus. 2003. (Secrets of Droon Ser.: Vol. 19). 128p. (J). (gr. 2-5). pap. 4.99 (978-0-439-42080-8(6)) Scholastic, Inc.

—Dream Thief. Merrell, David, illus. 2003. (Secrets of Droon Ser.: No. 17). 128p. (J). (gr. 2-5). pap. 4.99 (978-0-439-42078-5(4) , Scholastic Paperbacks) Scholastic, Inc.

—Dream Thief. 2003. (gr. k-3). lib. bdg. 11.80 (978-0-613-58148-6(2)) Tandem Library Bks.

—Flight of the Genie. Jessell, Tim, illus. 2004. 122p. (J). lib. bdg. 15.38 (***978-1-4242-0314-7(7)***) Fitzgerald Bks.

—Fortress of the Treasure Queen. Merrell, David, illus. 2004. (Secrets of Droon Ser.). 112p. (J). (gr. 2-5). 3.99 (978-0-439-66157-7(9) , Scholastic Paperbacks) Scholastic, Inc.

—Fortress of the Treasure Queen. Merrell, David, illus. 2004. 115p. (J). lib. bdg. 15.38 (***978-1-4242-0312-3(0)***) Fitzgerald Bks.

—Golden Wasp. Jessell, Tim, illus. 2000. (Secrets of Droon Ser.: No. 8). 112p. (J). (gr. 2-5). pap. 4.99 (978-0-439-18298-0(0)) Scholastic, Inc.

—Golden Wasp. 2000. (gr. 3-6). lib. bdg. 11.80 (978-0-613-25348-2(5)) Tandem Library Bks.

—The Great Ice Battle. 1999. (gr. 3-6). lib. bdg. 11.80 (978-0-613-21639-5(3)) Tandem Library Bks.

—The Hidden Stairs & the Magic Carpet. 2007. (Secrets of Droon Ser.: No. 1). 96p. (J). pap. 2.99 (***978-0-545-01038-2(1)***) Scholastic, Inc.

—The Moon Dragon. Merrell, David, illus. 2006. (Little Apple Ser.). 121p. (J). (978-1-4156-4703-5(8)) Scholastic, Inc.

—Moon Dragon. Merrell, David, illus. 2006. 121p. (J). lib. bdg. 15.38 (***978-1-4242-0309-3(0)***) Fitzgerald Bks.

—The Moon Scroll. 2002. (gr. 3-6). lib. bdg. 11.80 (978-0-613-50472-0(0)) Tandem Library Bks.

—The Riddle of Zorfendorf Castle. Merrell, David, illus. 2005. 124p. (J). (ps-k). lib. bdg. 10.79 (978-0-606-33298-9(7)) Tandem Library Bks.

—Riddle of Zorfendorf Castle. Merrell, David, illus. 2005. 124p. (J). lib. bdg. 15.38 (***978-1-4242-0310-9(4)***) Fitzgerald Bks.

—Search for the Dragon Ship. Jessell, Tim, illus. 2003. (Secrets of Droon Ser.: Vol. 18). 128p. (J). (gr. 2-5). pap. 3.99 (978-0-439-42079-2(2) , Scholastic Paperbacks) Scholastic, Inc.

—Search for the Dragon Ship. 2003. (gr. 3-6). lib. bdg. 11.80 (978-0-613-66379-3(9)) Tandem Library Bks.

—Secrets Droon Spec Ed #5 Moon Magic. 2008. 176p. pap. 5.99 (***978-0-439-90255-7(X)*** , Scholastic Paperbacks) Scholastic, Inc.

—Secrets of Droon: Voyagers of the Silver Sand. Merrell, David, illus. 3rd ed. 2005. (Secrets of Droon Special Edition Ser.). 192p. (ps-k). 5.99 (978-0-439-67177-4(9) , Scholastic Paperbacks) Scholastic, Inc.

—The Voyage of the Jaffa Wind. 2002. (gr. 3-6). lib. bdg. 11.80 (978-0-613-50522-2(0)) Tandem Library Bks.

Abbott, Tony & Jessell, Tim. The Moon Scroll. 2002. (Secrets of Droon Ser.: No. 15). (Illus.). 144p. (J). (gr. 2-5). pap. 3.99 (978-0-439-30608-9(6)) Scholastic, Inc.

DROPOUTS—FICTION

McDonald, Janet. Spellbound. 2003. 144p. (YA). pap. 5.99 (978-0-14-250193-1(X) , Puffin) Penguin Group (USA) Inc.

—Spellbound. 2003. (gr. 7-12). lib. bdg. 14.15 (978-0-613-86523-4(5)) Tandem Library Bks.

Velasquez, Gloria. Tyrone's Betrayal. 144p. (J). pap. 9.95 (978-1-55885-465-9(7) , Piñata Books) Arte Publico Pr.

DRUG ABUSE

see also Drug Addiction

Amos, Janine. Alex Does Drugs. 2002. (Body Matters Ser.). (Illus.). 32p. (YA). 22.00 (978-1-84234-110-0(3) , Cherrytree Books) Evans Publishing Group GBR. *Dist:* Independent Pubs. Group.

Apel, Melanie Ann. Cocaine & Your Nose: The Incredibly Disgusting Story. 2005. (Incredibly Disgusting Drugs Ser.). (Illus.). 48p. (YA). (gr. 5-8). lib. bdg. 25.25 (978-0-8239-3251-1(6) , DDCONO) Rosen Publishing Group, Inc., The.

—Cocaine & Your Nose (Rev) The Incredibly Disgusting Story. rev. ed. 2005. (Illus.). 48p. (J). (ps-ps). lib. bdg. 25.25 (978-1-4042-0632-8(9) , Rosen Central) Rosen Publishing Group, Inc., The.

Aue, Pamela Willwerth. Teen Drug Abuse. 2006. 244p. (gr. 10-12). (J). pap. 36.20 (978-0-7377-3335-8(7)); 24.95 (978-0-7377-3336-5(5)) Thomson Gale. (Greenhaven Pr., Inc.).

Aware, Earl E. Drug Awareness. 2000. (Illus.). 72p. (J). pap. 9.95 (978-1-58597-050-6(6)) Leathers Publishing.

Axelrod-Contrada, Joan. The Facts about Drugs & Society. 2007. (Drugs Ser.). (J). lib. bdg. 39.93 (***978-0-7614-2674-5(4)*** , Benchmark Bks.) Cavendish, Marshall Corp.

Bankston, John. Ecstasy = Busted! 2005. (Busted! Ser.). (Illus.). 104p. (J). (gr. 6-13). lib. bdg. 31.93 (978-0-7660-2387-1(7)) Enslow Pubs., Inc.

Barth, Kelly. Drug Abuse. 2007. (History of Issues Ser.). 240p. (gr. 10-12). 34.95 (***978-0-7377-2007-5(7)*** , Greenhaven Pr., Inc.) Thomson Gale.

Being Me & Drug-Free. (J). 29.50 (978-1-56230-034-0(2)); (SPA.). 29.50 (978-1-56230-211-5(6)) Syndistar, Inc.

Berne, Emma Carlson. Methamphetamine. 2007. (Compact Research Ser.). 112p. (YA). lib. bdg. (***978-1-60152-004-3(2)***) ReferencePoint Pr., Inc.

Bigelow, Barbara C. & Edgar, Kathleen J. The UXL Encyclopedia of Drugs & Addictive Substances, 5 vols. 2005. (Illus.). (J). (978-1-4144-0445-5(X)); (978-1-4144-0446-2(8)); (978-1-4144-0447-9(6)); (978-1-4144-0448-6(4)); (978-1-4144-0449-3(2)) Thomson Gale.

Biggers, Jeff. Chemical Dependency. rev. ed. 2005. (Drug Abuse Prevention Library). (Illus.). 64p. (YA). (gr. 7-12). lib. bdg. 25.25 (978-0-8239-3269-6(9)) Rosen Publishing Group, Inc., The.

—Transgenerational Addiction. 1998. (Drug Abuse Prevention Library). 64p. pap. 6.95 (978-1-56838-247-0(2)) Hazelden Publishing & Educational Services.

Bingham, Jane. Marijuana. 2005. (What's the Deal? Ser.). (Illus.). 56p. (J). (978-1-4034-7023-2(5)) Heinemann Library.

Carroll, Marilyn. Cocaine & Crack. 2001. (Drug Library). (Illus.). 128p. (YA). (gr. 6-12). pap. 13.26 (978-0-7660-1919-5(5)) Enslow Pubs., Inc.

Carson-DeWitt, Rosalyn, ed. Drugs, Alcohol, & Tobacco: Learning about Addictive Behavior, 3 vols. 2002. (Illus.). (J). Vol. 1. (978-0-02-865757-8(8)); Vol. 2. (978-0-02-865758-5(6)); Vol. 3. (978-0-02-865759-2(4)) Thomson Gale. (Macmillan Reference USA).

Cefrey, Holly. Hallucinogens & Your Neurons: The Incredibly Disgusting Story. 2005. (Illus.). 48p. (J). (gr. k-3). lib. bdg. 25.25 (978-1-4042-0633-5(7) , Rosen Central); (YA). (gr. 5-8). lib. bdg. 25.25 (978-0-8239-3391-4(1)) Rosen Publishing Group, Inc., The.

Chastain, Zachary. Cocaine: The Rush to Destruction. 2008. (J). (***978-1-4222-0154-1(6)***) Mason Crest Pubs.

Clayton, Lawrence. Alcohol Drug Dangers. 2000. (Drug Dangers Ser.). (Illus.). 64p. (YA). (gr. 4-10). pap. 13.26 (978-0-7660-1735-1(4)) Enslow Pubs., Inc.

—Amphetamines & Other Stimulants. rev. ed. 2005. (Drug Abuse Prevention Library). (Illus.). 64p. (YA). (gr. 7-12). lib. bdg. 25.25 (978-0-8239-3444-7(6)) Rosen Publishing Group, Inc., The.

—Barbiturates & Other Depressants. rev. ed. 2005. (Drug Abuse Prevention Library). (Illus.). 64p. (YA). (gr. 7-12). lib. bdg. 25.25 (978-0-8239-3442-3(X)) Rosen Publishing Group, Inc., The.

—Coping with a Drug-Abusing Parent. 2003. (C). per. 34.95 (978-0-9709523-6-3(8)) Clayro Corp.

—Diet Pill Drug Dangers. 2000. (Drug Dangers Ser.). (Illus.). 64p. (YA). (gr. 4-10). pap. 13.26 (978-0-7660-1737-5(0)) Enslow Pubs., Inc.

Clued in! on Street Drugs. 2005. (J). 4.95 (978-1-55548-148-3(5) , 672) Human Relations Media.

Cobb, Allan B. Heroin & Your Veins: The Incredibly Disgusting Story. 2005. (Incredibly Disgusting Drugs Ser.). (Illus.). 48p. (YA). (gr. 5-8). lib. bdg. 25.25 (978-0-8239-3249-8(4) , DDHEVE) Rosen Publishing Group, Inc., The.

—Speed & Your Brain. rev. ed. 2005. (Incredibly Disgusting Drugs Ser.). (Illus.). 48p. (YA). (gr. 5-8). lib. bdg. 25.25 (978-0-8239-4091-2(8)) Rosen Publishing Group, Inc., The.

—Speed & Your Brain: The Incredibly Disgusting Story. 2000. (Incredibly Disgusting Drugs Ser.). (Illus.). 48p. (YA). (gr. 5-8). lib. bdg. 25.25 (978-0-8239-3253-5(2) , DDSPBR, Rosen Central) Rosen Publishing Group, Inc., The.

Cohen, Julian. Drugs. rev. ed. 2000. (Life Files Ser.). (Illus.). 62p. (J). 24.99 (978-0-237-52185-1(7)); pap. 15.99 (978-0-237-52181-3(4)) Evans Publishing Group GBR. (Evans Brothers, Limited). *Dist:* Independent Pubs. Group.

Connelly, Elizabeth Russell. Predatory Drugs = Busted! 2006. (Busted! Ser.). (Illus.). 104p. (J). lib. bdg. 31.93 (978-0-7660-2474-8(1)) Enslow Pubs., Inc.

Connolly, Sean. Amphetamines. 2000. (Just the Facts Ser.). (Illus.). 56p. (YA). (gr. 6-8). lib. bdg. 24.22 (978-1-57572-254-2(2)) Heinemann Library.

—Cocaine. 2000. (Just the Facts Ser.). (Illus.). 56p. (YA). (gr. 6-8). lib. bdg. 24.22 (978-1-57572-255-9(0)) Heinemann Library.

—Ecstasy. 2000. (Just the Facts Ser.). (Illus.). 56p. (YA). (gr. 6-8). lib. bdg. 24.22 (978-1-57572-256-6(9)) Heinemann Library.

—Heroin. 2000. (Just the Facts Ser.). (Illus.). 56p. (YA). (gr. 6-8). lib. bdg. 24.22 (978-1-57572-257-3(7)) Heinemann Library.

—Inhalants. 2002. (Just the Facts Ser.). (Illus.). 56p. (J). (gr. 6-8). lib. bdg. 25.64 (978-1-58810-679-7(9)) Heinemann Library.

—LSD. 2000. (Just the Facts Ser.). (Illus.). 56p. (YA). (gr. 6-8). lib. bdg. 24.22 (978-1-57572-258-0(5)) Heinemann Library.

—Marijuana. 2002. (Just the Facts Ser.). (Illus.). 56p. (J). (gr. 6-8). lib. bdg. 25.64 (978-1-58810-680-3(2)) Heinemann Library.

—Steroids. 2000. (Just the Facts Ser.). (Illus.). 56p. (YA). (gr. 6-8). lib. bdg. 24.22 (978-1-57572-259-7(3)) Heinemann Library.

David C. Cook. Substance Abuse, Communicating with Others, Who Is Jesus? 2003. (Domain 456 Ser.). 128p. (J). (gr. 4-6). pap., pap. 15.99 (978-0-7814-5519-0(7) , 0781455197) Cook, David C. Publishing Co.

Deboo, Ana. Drugs. 2007. (J). ***(978-1-4034-9736-9(2));*** pap. ***(978-1-4034-9741-3(9))*** Heinemann Library.

Derkins, Susie. Barbiturates & Your Central Nervous System: The Incredibly Disgusting Story. 2005. (Incredibly Disgusting Drugs Ser.). (Illus.). 48p. (YA). (gr. 5-8). lib. bdg. 25.25 (978-0-8239-3388-4(1)) Rosen Publishing Group, Inc., The.

DiConsiglio, John. True Confessions: Real stories about drinking & Drugs. 2008. (Scholastic Choices Ser.). 112p. (J). pap. 8.95 (***978-0-531-14773-3(8)*** , Watts, Franklin) Scholastic Library Publishing.

Dinan, Robert S. Drug Free Teen: The Ultimate Guide for Parents, Teens, Teachers & Friends. 2004. (Illus.). 64p. (YA). per. 12.95 (978-0-9744682-0-4(7)) Red Men Interprises.

Drug Abuse & Society, 6 bks., Set. Incl. GHB & Analogs : High Risk Club Drugs. Wolf, Marie. (J). 27.95 (978-1-4042-0910-7(7)); Ketamine. Lockwood, Brad. (J). lib. bdg. 27.95 (978-1-4042-0911-4(5)); Methamphetamine : The Dangers of Crystal Meth. Spalding, Frank. (YA). lib. bdg. 27.95 (978-1-4042-0912-1(3)); Oxycontin : From Pain Relief to Addiction. Lockwood, Brad. (YA). lib. bdg. 27.95 (978-1-4042-0913-8(1)); Prescription Drugs. Ramen, Fred. (YA). lib. bdg. 27.95 (978-1-4042-0915-2(8)); Rohypnol : Roofies, the Date Rape Drug. Adams, Colleen. (YA). lib. bdg. 27.95 (978-1-4042-0914-5(X)); (Illus.). 64p. (gr. 7-12). 2006. 2006. 167.70 (978-1-4042-1016-5(4)) Rosen Publishing Group, Inc., The.

Drug Dangers, 14 bks., Set. (Illus.). (YA). (gr. 4-10). lib. bdg. 279.30 (978-0-7660-1405-3(3)) Enslow Pubs., Inc.

Drug Dangers, 14 bks., Set. Incl. Alcohol Drug Dangers. Clayton, Lawrence. 64p. (YA). 2000. pap. 13.26 (978-0-7660-1735-1(4)); Alcohol Drug Dangers. Clayton, Lawrence. 64p. (YA). 1999. lib. bdg. 27.93 (978-0-7660-1159-5(3)); Amphetamine Drug Dangers. Pellowski, Michael J. 64p. (YA). 2000. lib. bdg. 27.93 (978-0-7660-1321-6(9)); Amphetamine Drug Dangers. Pellowski, Michael J. 64p. (YA). 2001. pap. 13.26 (978-0-7660-1962-1(4)); Crack & Cocaine Drug Dangers. Robbins, Paul R. 64p. (YA). 2000. pap. 13.26 (978-0-7660-1736-8(2)); Crack & Cocaine Drug Dangers. Robbins, Paul R. 64p. (YA). 1999. lib. bdg. 27.93 (978-0-7660-1155-7(0)); Diet Pill Drug Dangers. Clayton, Lawrence. 64p. (YA). 2000. pap. 13.26 (978-0-7660-1737-5(0)); Diet Pill Drug Dangers. Clayton, Lawrence. 64p. (YA). 1999. lib. bdg. 19.95 (978-0-7660-1158-8(5)); Ecstasy & Other Designer Drug Dangers. Weatherly, Myra. 64p. (J). 2000. lib. bdg. 27.93 (978-0-7660-1322-3(7)); Ecstasy & Other Designer Drug Dangers. Weatherly, Myra. 64p. (YA). 2001. pap. 10.95 (978-0-7660-1963-8(2)); Herbal Drug Dangers. Monroe, Judy. 64p. (YA). 2000. lib. bdg. 27.93 (978-0-7660-1319-3(7)); Herbal Drug Dangers. Monroe, Judy. 64p. (YA). 2001. pap. 13.26 (978-0-7660-1964-5(0)); Heroin Drug Dangers. Littell, Mary Ann. 64p. (YA). 2000. pap. 13.26 (978-0-7660-1738-2(9)); Heroin Drug Dangers. Littell, Mary Ann. 64p. (YA). 1999. lib. bdg. 27.93 (978-0-7660-1156-4(9)); Inhalant Drug Dangers. Monroe, Judy. 64p. (YA). 2000. pap. 13.26 (978-0-7660-1739-9(7)); Inhalant Drug Dangers. Monroe, Judy. 64p. (YA). 1999. lib. bdg. 27.93 (978-0-7660-1153-3(4)); LSD, PCP & Hallucinogen Drug Dangers. Monroe, Judy. 64p. (YA). 2001. pap. 13.26 (978-0-7660-1965-2(9)); LSD, PCP & Hallucinogen Drug Dangers. Monroe, Judy. 64p. (YA). 2000. lib. bdg. 27.93 (978-0-7660-1318-6(9)); Marijuana Drug Dangers. Somdahl, Gary L. 64p. (YA). 2000. pap. 13.26 (978-0-7660-1740-5(0)); Marijuana Drug Dangers. Somdahl, Gary L. 64p. (YA). 1999. lib. bdg. 27.93 (978-0-7660-1214-1(X)); Speed & Methamphetamine Drug Dangers. Littell, Mary Ann. 64p. (YA). 2000. pap. 13.26 (978-0-7660-1741-2(9)); Speed & Methamphetamine Drug Dangers. Littell, Mary Ann. 64p. (YA). 1999. lib. bdg. 27.93 (978-0-7660-1157-1(7)); Steroid Drug Dangers. Monroe, Judy. 64p. (YA). 2000. pap. 13.26 (978-0-7660-1742-9(7)); Steroid Drug Dangers. Monroe, Judy. 64p. (YA). 1999. lib. bdg. 27.93 (978-0-7660-1154-0(2)); Tobacco & Nicotine Drug Dangers. MacDonald, Joan Vos. 64p. (YA). 2000. lib. bdg. 27.93 (978-0-7660-1317-9(0)); Tobacco & Nicotine Drug Dangers. MacDonald, Joan Vos. 64p. (YA). 2001. pap. 13.26 (978-0-7660-1966-9(7)); Tranquilizer, Barbiturate & Downer Drug Dangers. Houle, Michelle M. 64p. (YA). 2001. pap. 13.26 (978-0-7660-1967-6(5)); Tranquilizer, Barbiturate & Downer Drug Dangers. Houle, Michelle M. 64p. (YA). 2000. lib. bdg. 27.93 (978-0-7660-1320-9(0)); Set. (YA). lib. bdg. 279.30 (978-0-7660-1405-3(3)); (gr. 4-10). (Illus.). Set pap. 153.30 (978-0-7660-1794-8(X)) Enslow Pubs., Inc.

Egendorf, Laura K. Chemical Dependency. 2003. (Opposing Viewpoints Ser.). (Illus.). (YA). 224p. pap. 24.95 (978-0-7377-1221-6(X)); 208p. lib. bdg. 36.20 (978-0-7377-1222-3(8)) Thomson Gale. (Greenhaven Pr., Inc.).

Elliot-Wright, Susan. Amphetamines. 2004. (Health Issues Ser.). (Illus.). 64p. (J). (978-0-7398-6895-9(0)) Harcourt Schl. Pubs.

—Heroin. 2004. (Health Issues Ser.). (Illus.). 64p. (J). 32.79 (978-0-7398-6894-2(2)) Harcourt Schl. Pubs.

Etingoff, Kim. Abusing Over-The-Counter Drugs: Illicit Uses for Everyday Drugs. 2008. (J). ***(978-1-4222-0150-3(3))*** Mason Crest Pubs.

Etingoff, Kim. Methamphetamines: Unsafe Speed. 2008. (978-1-4222-0159-6(7)) Mason Crest Pubs.

Ferreiro, Carmen. Heroin. 2003. (Drugs, the Straight Facts Ser.). (Illus.). 112p. (J). (gr. 9-13). 30.00 (978-0-7910-7262-2(2) , Chelsea Hse.) Facts On File, Inc.

Fitzhugh, Karla. Prescription Drug Abuse. 2005. (What's the Deal? Ser.). (Illus.). 56p. (J). (978-1-4034-7024-9(3)) Heinemann Library.

Frisch, Carlienne A. When a Friend Has a Drug Problem. 2005. (Drug Abuse Prevention Library). (Illus.). 64p. (YA). (gr. 7-12). lib. bdg. 25.25 (978-0-8239-3120-0(X) , DRFRPR) Rosen Publishing Group, Inc., The.

Gale Research Staff. Drugs & Controlled Substances for Students. 2002. (Illus.). 1000p. (YA). 177.00 (978-0-7876-6264-6(X) , GML00502-180467) Thomson Gale.

Gifford, Clive. Drugs & Sports. 2003. (Face the Facts Ser.). (Illus.). 56p. pap. 8.95 (978-1-4109-0339-6(7)); (J). lib. bdg. 28.56 (978-0-7398-6849-2(7)) Raintree.

—Drugs & Sports. 2003. (gr. 5-8). lib. bdg. 17.60 (978-0-613-78304-0(2)) Tandem Library Bks.

Gordon, Melanie Apel. Drug Interactions: Protecting Yourself from Dangerous Drug, Medication & Food Combinations. 1999. (Drug Abuse Prevention Library). (Illus.). 64p. (YA). (gr. 7-12). lib. bdg. 25.25 (978-0-8239-2825-5(X) , DRINTE) Rosen Publishing Group, Inc., The.

Green, Jen. Alcohol. 1999. (Talking about Ser.). (Illus.). 32p. (J). (gr. k-4). lib. bdg. 25.69 (978-0-8172-5888-7(4)) Raintree.

Haughton, Emma. Drinking, Smoking & Other Drugs. 1999. (Health & Fitness Ser.). (Illus.). 48p. (J). (gr. 4-6). lib. bdg. 27.12 (978-0-7398-1345-4(5)) Raintree.

—Drug Abuse? 2005. (Illus.). 32p. (YA). (gr. 5 up). lib. bdg. 27.10 (978-1-932889-60-4(4)) Sea-To-Sea Pubns.

Herscovitch, Arthur. Everything You Need to Know about Drug Abuse. rev. ed. 2005. (Need to Know Library). (Illus.). 64p. (YA). (gr. 7-12). lib. bdg. 25.25 (978-0-8239-3036-4(X) , NTGUGU) Rosen Publishing Group, Inc., The.

Houle, Michelle M. Tranquilizer, Barbiturate & Downer Drug Dangers. (Drug Dangers Ser.). (Illus.). 64p. (YA). (gr. 4-10). 2001. pap. 13.26 (978-0-7660-1967-6(5)); 2000. lib. bdg. 27.93 (978-0-7660-1320-9(0)) Enslow Pubs., Inc.

Howard, Todd. Heroin. 2002. (Drug Education Library). (Illus.). 112p. (J). 32.45 (978-1-59018-018-1(6) , Lucent Bks.) Thomson Gale.

Hurwitz, Ann Ricki & Hurwitz, Sue. Hallucinogens. rev. ed. 1999. (Drug Abuse Prevention Library). (Illus.). 64p. (J). (gr. 7-12). lib. bdg. 25.25 (978-0-8239-3006-7(8) , DRHALL) Rosen Publishing Group, Inc., The.

Hyde, Margaret O. Mind Drugs, Vol. VI. 6th ed. 1998. (Mind Drugs Ser.: up). (Illus.). 144p. (gr. 7 up). lib. bdg. 24.90 (978-0-7613-0970-3(5) , Twenty-First Century Bks.) Lerner Publishing Group.

Hyde, Margaret O. & Setaro, John F. Drugs 101: An Overview for Teens. 2003. (Single Titles Ser.). (Illus.). 160p. (gr. 7 up). lib. bdg. 25.90 (978-0-7613-2608-3(1) , Twenty-First Century Bks.) Lerner Publishing Group.

Jaffe, Steven L., ed. Ecstasy & Other Designer Drugs. 1999. (Junior Drug Awareness Ser.). (Illus.). 80p. (J). (gr. 4-8). 27.50 (978-0-7910-5201-3(X) , Chelsea Hse.) Facts On File, Inc.

—How to Say No. 1999. (Junior Drug Awareness Ser.). (Illus.). 80p. (J). (gr. 4-8). 27.50 (978-0-7910-5202-0(8) , Chelsea Hse.) Facts On File, Inc.

—Junior Drug Awareness, 15 bks. 1999. (Illus.). 64p. (J). (gr. 4-8). 299.25 (978-0-7910-5173-3(0) , Chelsea Hse.) Facts On File, Inc.

—LSD, PCP & Other Hallucinogens. 1999. (Junior Drug Awareness Ser.). (Illus.). 80p. (J). (gr. 4-8). 32.00 (978-0-7910-5183-2(8) , Chelsea Hse.) Facts On File, Inc.

—Marijuana. 1999. (Junior Drug Awareness Ser.). (Illus.). 80p. (J). (gr. 4-8). 27.50 (978-0-7910-5176-4(5) , Chelsea Hse.) Facts On File, Inc.

—Steroids. 1999. (Junior Drug Awareness Ser.). (Illus.). 80p. (J). (gr. 4-8). 27.50 (978-0-7910-5179-5(X) , Chelsea Hse.) Facts On File, Inc.

Jamuna Carroll. Drug Abuse. 2007. (Writing the Critical Essay Ser.). 128p. (gr. 6-10). 29.95 (978-0-7377-3461-4(2) , Greenhaven Pr., Inc.) Thomson Gale.

Jeffrey, Laura S. Marijuana = Busted! 2006. (Busted! Ser.). (Illus.). 104p. (J). lib. bdg. 31.93 (978-0-7660-2796-1(1)) Enslow Pubs., Inc.

Junior Drug Awareness. 2005. pap. 247.50 (978-0-7910-9165-4(1) , Chelsea Hse.) Facts On File, Inc.

Kallen, Stuart A. Heroin. 2006. (Illus.). 128p. (gr. 10-12). 21.20 (978-0-7377-2716-6(0)); pap. 29.95 (978-0-7377-2715-9(2)) Thomson Gale. (Greenhaven Pr., Inc.).

Karson, Jill. Club Drugs. 2007. (J). lib. bdg. ***(978-1-60152-005-0(0))*** ReferencePoint Pr., Inc.

Kerrigan, Michael. The War Against Drugs. 2002. (Crime & Detection Ser.). (Illus.). 96p. (J). (gr. 7 up). lib. bdg. (978-1-59084-368-0(1)) Mason Crest Pubs.

Knight, S. Black Magic. 2007. (ENG.). 156p. per. ***(978-1-84747-007-2(6))*** Chipmunkapublishing.

Koellhoffer, Tara. Ecstasy & Other Club Drugs. 2008. (Junior Drug Awareness Ser.). 112p. (J). (gr. 5-8). 30.00 (***978-0-7910-9697-0(1)*** , Chelsea Hse.) Facts On File, Inc.

Konieczko, Craig. Intervention: Putting Yourself Between a Friend & Addiction. 2005. (Drug Abuse Prevention Library). (Illus.). 64p. (YA). (gr. 7-12). lib. bdg. 25.25 (978-0-8239-3156-9(0) , DRINVE) Rosen Publishing Group, Inc., The.

Kreiner, Anna. Let's Talk about Drug Abuse. 1998. (PowerKids Ser.). 24p. (J). (gr. k-3). reprint ed. pap. 6.95 (978-1-56838-219-7(7)) Hazelden Publishing & Educational Services.

Kutz-Mellem, Sharon. Honest Talk about Eating Disorders. 2000. 28p. (YA). (978-1-57895-096-6(1)) Bridge Resources.

Laliberte, Michelle. Marijuana: A MyReportLinks. com Book. 2005. (Drugs Ser.). (Illus.). 48p. (J). lib. bdg. 25.26 (978-0-7660-5281-9(8) , MyReportLinks.com Bks.) Enslow Pubs., Inc.

Landau, Elaine. Cocaine. 2003. (Watts Library). (Illus.). 64p. (J). 25.50 (978-0-531-12026-2(0) , Watts, Franklin) Scholastic Library Publishing.

Landau, Elaine. Methamphetamines: An American Epidemic. 2007. (J). lib. bdg. ***(978-0-8225-6808-7(X))*** Twenty First Century Bks.

Lawler, Jennifer. Drug Testing in Schools: A Pro/Con Issue. 2000. (Hot Pro/Con Issues Ser.). (Illus.). 64p. (YA). (gr. 6-12). lib. bdg. 27.93 (978-0-7660-1367-4(7)) Enslow Pubs., Inc.

Lennard-Brown, Sarah. Cocaine. 2004. (Health Issues Ser.). (Illus.). 64p. (J). 30.00 (978-0-7398-6893-5(4)) Harcourt Schl. Pubs.

—Drugs. 2002. (Health Issues Ser.). (Illus.). 64p. (YA). (gr. 6-8). lib. bdg. 28.54 (978-0-7398-4773-2(2)) Raintree.

—Marijuana. 2004. (Health Issues Ser.). (Illus.). 84p. (J). 28.56 (978-0-7398-6896-6(9)) Harcourt Schl. Pubs.

Leshkevich, Jackie. Drug Abuse. Langwith, Jacqueline, ed. 2006. (Illus.). 244p. (gr. 7-10). 33.70 (978-0-7377-3566-6(X) , Greenhaven Pr., Inc.) Thomson Gale.

Levete, Sarah. Drugs. 2007. (Let's Talk about Ser.). (Illus.). 32p. (J). (gr. 3-5). lib. bdg. 27.10 ***(978-1-59604-090-8(4))*** Stargazer Bks.

Lishak, Antony. Drugs. 2007. (J). ***(978-1-59920-035-4(X))*** Smart Apple Media.

Littell, Mary Ann. Heroin Drug Dangers. 2000. (Drug Dangers Ser.). (Illus.). 64p. (YA). (gr. 4-10). pap. 13.26 (978-0-7660-1738-2(9)) Enslow Pubs., Inc.

—Speed & Methamphetamine Drug Dangers. 2000. (Drug Dangers Ser.). (Illus.). 64p. (YA). (gr. 4-10). pap. 13.26 (978-0-7660-1741-2(9)) Enslow Pubs., Inc.

Lynette, Rachel. Drugs. 2007. (J). ***(978-1-4034-9693-5(5));*** pap. ***(978-1-4034-9700-0(1))*** Heinemann Library.

—The Real Deal: Drugs Hardback. 2007. (Illus.). 32p. (J). ***(978-0-431-90729-1(3))*** Steck-Vaughn.

—The Real Deal: Drugs Paperback. 2007. (Illus.). 32p. (J). ***(978-0-431-90736-9(6))*** Steck-Vaughn.

MacDonald, Joan Vos. Tobacco & Nicotine Drug Dangers. 2000. (Drug Dangers Ser.). (Illus.). 64p. (YA). (gr. 4-10). lib. bdg. 27.93 (978-0-7660-1317-9(0)) Enslow Pubs., Inc.

MacGregor, Cynthia. Refuse to Use. 2002. (Reading Room Collection). (Illus.). 24p. (J). lib. bdg. 18.75 (978-0-8239-3747-9(X)) Rosen Publishing Group, Inc., The.

Manley, Claudia B. Crack & Your Circulatory System: The Incredibly Disgusting Story. 2005. (Incredibly Disgusting Drugs Ser.). (Illus.). 48p. (YA). (gr. 5-8). lib. bdg. 25.25 (978-0-8239-3389-1(X)) Rosen Publishing Group, Inc., The.

Marcovitz, Hal. Club Drugs. 2006. (Drug Education Library). 112p. (J). (gr. 7-10). 32.45 (978-1-59018-517-9(X) , Lucent Bks.) Thomson Gale.

—Drugs & Alcohol. 2006. (Gallup Major Trends & Events Ser.). (Illus.). 112p. (J). (gr. 7 up). lib. bdg. (978-1-59084-963-7(9)) Mason Crest Pubs.

Masline, Shelagh Ryan. Drug Abuse & Teens. 2000. (Illus.). 64p. (YA). (gr. 6-12). lib. bdg. 27.93 (978-0-7660-1372-8(3)) Enslow Pubs., Inc.

McCage, Crystal. Hallucinogens. 2007. (YA). lib. bdg. ***(978-1-60152-014-2(X))*** ReferencePoint Pr., Inc.

—Inhalants. 2007. (YA). lib. bdg. ***(978-1-60152-015-9(8))*** ReferencePoint Pr., Inc.

McGraw-Hill Staff. Teen Health Course 2, Modules, Tobacco, Alcohol, & Other Drugs. 5th ed. 2002. (Three-Level Middle School Health Ser.). (C). (gr. 7 up). 15.32 (978-0-07-826183-1(X) , 9780078261831) Glencoe/ McGraw-Hill.

McGuigan, Jim. The Drug Trade. 2004. (Face the Facts Ser.). (Illus.). 56p. (J). 28.56 (978-1-4109-1072-1(5)) Harcourt Schl. Pubs.

McIntosh, Kenneth & Livingston, Phyllis. Youth with Alcohol & Drug Addiction: Escape from Bondage. 2008. (J). (978-1-4222-0143-5(0)) Mason Crest Pubs.

Mehling, Randi. Marijuana. 2003. (Drugs, the Straight Facts Ser.). (Illus.). 112p. (gr. 9-13). 30.00 (978-0-7910-7263-9(0) , Chelsea Hse.) Facts On File, Inc.

Mehling, Randi. Methamphetamine. 2007. (Drugs: the Straight Facts Ser.). 128p. (J). (gr. 9). 30.00 (***978-0-7910-9532-4(0)*** , Chelsea Hse.) Facts On File, Inc.

Menhard, Francha Roffe. The Facts about Amphetamines. 2005. (Drugs Ser.). (Illus.). 96p. (J). (978-0-7614-1972-3(1) , Benchmark Bks.) Cavendish, Marshall Corp.

Miller, Maia. Drugs & Mental Illness. 2005. (Drug Abuse Prevention Library). (Illus.). 64p. (YA). (gr. 7-12). lib. bdg. 25.25 (978-0-8239-3155-2(2) , DRMEIL) Rosen Publishing Group, Inc., The.

Miller, Steve & Papa, Susan. Addiction. 2001. (Amazing Brain Ser.). (Illus.). 64p. (J). (gr. 6-10). 24.95 (978-1-56711-421-8(0) , Blackbirch Pr., Inc.) Thomson Gale.

Mintzer, Rich. Meth & Speed = Busted! 2005. (Busted! Ser.). (Illus.). 104p. (J). (gr. 6-13). lib. bdg. 31.93 (978-0-7660-2551-6(9)) Enslow Pubs., Inc.

Mintzer, Richard. Steroids=Busted! 2006. (Busted! Ser.). (Illus.). 112p. (J). lib. bdg. 31.93 (978-0-7660-2471-7(7)) Enslow Pubs., Inc.

Mirman, Heather Moehn. Issues in Drug Abuse. 2005. (Contemporary Issues Ser.). (Illus.). 112p. (YA). (gr. 7-10). 29.95 (978-1-59018-035-8(6) , Lucent Bks.) Thomson Gale.

Moe, Barbara. Drug Abuse Relapse: Helping Teens to Get Clean Again. 2005. (Drug Abuse Prevention Library). (Illus.). 64p. (YA). (gr. 7-12). lib. bdg. 25.25 (978-0-8239-3157-6(9) , DRRELA) Rosen Publishing Group, Inc., The.

Monroe, Judy. Herbal Drug Dangers. (Drug Dangers Ser.). (Illus.). 64p. (YA). (gr. 4-10). 2001. pap. 13.26 (978-0-7660-1964-5(0)); 2000. lib. bdg. 27.93 (978-0-7660-1319-3(7)) Enslow Pubs., Inc.

—Inhalant Drug Dangers. 2000. (Drug Dangers Ser.). (Illus.). 64p. (YA). (gr. 4-10). pap. 13.26 (978-0-7660-1739-9(7)) Enslow Pubs., Inc.

—LSD, PCP & Hallucinogen Drug Dangers. (Drug Dangers Ser.). (Illus.). 64p. (YA). (gr. 4-10). 2001. pap. 13.26 (978-0-7660-1965-2(9)); 2000. lib. bdg. 27.93 (978-0-7660-1318-6(9)) Enslow Pubs., Inc.

—Steroid Drug Dangers. (Drug Dangers Ser.). (Illus.). 64p. (YA). (gr. 4-10). 2000. pap. 13.26 (978-0-7660-1742-9(7)); 1999. lib. bdg. 27.93 (978-0-7660-1154-0(2)) Enslow Pubs., Inc.

—Steroids, Sports, & Body Image: The Risks of Performance-Enhancing Drugs. 2004. (Issues in Focus Ser.). (Illus.). 128p. (J). lib. bdg. 26.60 (978-0-7660-2160-0(2)) Enslow Pubs., Inc.

Murphy, Patricia J. Avoiding Drugs. 2006. (Illus.). 32p. (J). pap. 5.95 (978-0-8225-2779-4(0)); (gr. 3-7). 22.60 (978-0-8225-2867-8(3)) Lerner Publishing Group. (Lerner Pubns.).

—Evitar las Drogas. 2005. (Libros para Avanzar (Pull Ahead Bks.)). (SPA., Illus.). 32p. (J). (gr. 3-7). lib. bdg. 22.60 (978-0-8225-3172-2(0) , Ediciones Lerner) Lerner Publishing Group.

Murphy, Patrick & Shlafer, Marshal. Over-the-counter Drugs of Abuse. 2006. 112p. 30.00 (978-0-7910-8549-3(X) , Chelsea Hse.) Facts On File, Inc.

Naden, Corinne J. The A-Z of Drugs. 2007. (Drugs Ser.). (J). lib. bdg. 39.93 (***978-0-7614-2673-8(6)*** , Benchmark Bks.) Cavendish, Marshall Corp.

Nagle, Jeanne M. Polysubstance Abuse. 2005. (Drug Abuse Prevention Library). (Illus.). 64p. (YA). (gr. 7-12). lib. bdg. 25.25 (978-0-8239-3154-5(4) , DRPOLY) Rosen Publishing Group, Inc., The.

Nelson, Sheila. Hallucinogens: Unreal Visions. 2008. ***(978-1-4222-0155-8(4))*** Mason Crest Pubs.

No Thanks, Not for Me. 1999. (SmartReader Ser.). (J). Level 1. pap., tchr. ed. 19.95 incl. audio (978-0-7887-1158-9(X) , 79419T3); Level 2. pap., tchr. ed. 19.95 incl. audio (978-0-7887-0124-5(X) , 79312T3) Recorded Bks., LLC.

O'Donnell, Kerri. Inhalants & Your Nasal Passages: The Incredibly Disgusting Story. 2005. (Incredibly Disgusting Drugs Ser.). (Illus.). 48p. (YA). (gr. 5-8). lib. bdg. 25.25 (978-0-8239-3392-1(X)) Rosen Publishing Group, Inc., The.

Olive, M. Foster. Designer Drugs. 2003. (Drugs, the Straight Facts Ser.). (Illus.). 112p. (gr. 9-13). 30.00 (978-0-7910-7638-5(5) , Chelsea Hse.) Facts On File, Inc.

O'Neill, Eugene. Long Day's Journey into Night. 2002. (gr. 7-12). lib. bdg. 22.20 (978-0-613-58331-2(0)) Tandem Library Bks.

Outsmarting Gateway Drugs with Dr. Craniac Workbook. 2006. (J). 4.95 (978-1-55548-001-1(2) , 4201) Human Relations Media.

Pellowski, Michael J. Amphetamine Drug Dangers. (Drug Dangers Ser.). (Illus.). 64p. (YA). (gr. 4-10). 2001. pap. 13.26 (978-0-7660-1962-1(4)); 2000. lib. bdg. 27.93 (978-0-7660-1321-6(9)) Enslow Pubs., Inc.

Persico, Deborah A. Vernonia School District vs. Acton: Drug Testing in Schools. 1999. (Landmark Supreme Court Cases Ser.). (Illus.). 128p. (YA). (gr. 6-12). lib. bdg. 26.60 (978-0-7660-1087-1(2)) Enslow Pubs., Inc.

Polish, Daniel F. Drugs, Sex, & Integrity: What Does Judaism Say? 1998. (gr. 7-12). lib. bdg. 21.10 (978-0-613-90995-2(X)) Tandem Library Bks.

Rees, Jonathan. Drugs. 2002. (World Issues Ser.). (Illus.). 57p. (J). lib. bdg. 28.50 (978-1-931983-29-7(1)) Chrysalis Education.

—Drugs. 2005. (It's Your Health Ser.). (Illus.). 45p. (J). (gr. 6-9). lib. bdg. 29.95 (978-1-58340-586-4(0)) Smart Apple Media.

—Drugs. 2006. (Global Issues Ser.). (Illus.). 64p. (J). (gr. 4-12). pap. 12.95 (978-1-55285-743-4(3) , Walrus Bks.) Whitecap Bks., Ltd. CAN. *Dist:* Firefly Bks., Ltd.

Robbins, Paul R. Crack & Cocaine Drug Dangers. 2000. (Drug Dangers Ser.). (Illus.). 64p. (YA). (gr. 4-10). pap. 13.26 (978-0-7660-1736-8(2)) Enslow Pubs., Inc.

Roberts, Jeremy. Prescription Drug Abuse. 2005. (Drug Abuse Prevention Library). (Illus.). 64p. (YA). (gr. 7-12). lib. bdg. 25.25 (978-0-8239-3158-3(7) , DRPRES) Rosen Publishing Group, Inc., The.

Roleff, Tamara L. Cocaine & Crack. 2007. (YA). lib. bdg. ***(978-1-60152-001-2(8))*** ReferencePoint Pr., Inc.

Rooney, Anne. Drugs on the Street. 2007. (Illus.). 48p. (J). ***(978-1-58340-986-2(6))*** Smart Apple Media.

Royston, Angela. Inhalents. 2000. (Learn to Say No! Ser.). (Illus.). 32p. (J). (gr. 4-6). lib. bdg. 22.79 (978-1-57572-237-5(2)) Heinemann Library.

Sanders, Pete & Myers, Steve. Taking Drugs. 2005. (Choices & Decisions Ser.). (Illus.). 32p. (J). (gr. 4-7). lib. bdg. 27.10 (978-1-59604-077-9(7)) Stargazer Bks.

Sanna, E. J. Heroin & Other Opiates: Poppies' Perilous Children. 2008. (J). ***(978-1-4222-0156-5(2))*** Mason Crest Pubs.

Sanna, E. J. Marijuana: Mind-Altering Weed. 2008. (J). (978-1-4222-0158-9(9)) Mason Crest Pubs.

Santella, Thomas. Opium. 2007. (Drugs Ser.). (Illus.). 120p. (J). (gr. 9-12). 30.00 (978-0-7910-8547-9(3)) Facts On File, Inc.

Saying No & Feeling Fine. (J). 29.50 (978-1-56230-078-4(4)) Syndistar, Inc.

Schroeder, Brock E. Ecstasy. 2003. (Drugs, the Straight Facts Ser.). (Illus.). 112p. (gr. 9-13). 30.00 (978-0-7910-7633-0(4) , Chelsea Hse.) Facts On File, Inc.

Schwartzenberger, Tina. Substance Use & Abuse. 2004. (Understanding Global Issues Ser.). (J). lib. bdg. (978-1-59036-232-7(2)) Weigl Pubs., Inc.

Sherry, Clifford. Inhalants. rev. ed. 2005. (Drug Abuse Prevention Library). (Illus.). 64p. (YA). (gr. 7-12). lib. bdg. 25.25 (978-0-8239-3443-0(8)) Rosen Publishing Group, Inc., The.

Slade, Suzanne. OxyContin Abuse. 2007. (J). ***(978-1-4042-1954-0(4))*** Rosen Publishing Group, Inc., The.

Smith, Sandra Lee. Marijuana. rev. ed. 1999. (Drug Abuse Prevention Library). (Illus.). 64p. (J). (gr. 7-12). 25.25 (978-0-8239-3007-4(6) , DRMARI) Rosen Publishing Group, Inc., The.

Somdahl, Gary L. Marijuana Drug Dangers. 2000. (Drug Dangers Ser.). (Illus.). 64p. (YA). (gr. 4-10). pap. 13.26 (978-0-7660-1740-5(0)) Enslow Pubs., Inc.

Sonder, Ben. All about Heroin. 2002. (Watts Reference Ser.). (Illus.). 128p. (YA). (gr. 9-12). 26.00 (978-0-531-11541-1(0) , Watts, Franklin) Scholastic Library Publishing.

Spring, Albert. Steroids & Your Muscles: The Incredibly Disgusting Story. 2005. (Incredibly Disgusting Drugs Ser.). (Illus.). 48p. (YA). (gr. 5-8). lib. bdg. 25.25 (978-0-8239-3393-8(8)) Rosen Publishing Group, Inc., The.

Stanley, Debbie. Marijuana & Your Lungs: The Incredibly Disgusting Story. rev. ed. 2005. (Incredibly Disgusting Drugs Ser.). (Illus.). 48p. (YA). (gr. 5-8). lib. bdg. 25.25 (978-0-8239-3252-8(4) , DDMALU) Rosen Publishing Group, Inc., The.

Stewart, Gail B. Drugs. 2001. (Understanding Issues Ser.). (Illus.). 48p. (J). (gr. 3-5). 23.70 (978-0-7377-0951-3(0) , LML00902-178585, Kidhaven) Thomson Gale.

Tattersall, Clare. Date Rape Drugs. 2000. (Drug Abuse Prevention Library). (Illus.). 64p. (YA). (gr. 7-12). lib. bdg. 25.25 (978-0-8239-3119-4(6) , DRDATE) Rosen Publishing Group, Inc., The.

Triggle, David J., ed. Drugs: The Straight Facts. (Illus.). (gr. 9-13). lib. bdg. 275.40 (978-0-7910-7632-3(6)); lib. bdg. (978-0-7910-8397-0(7)) Facts On File, Inc. (Chelsea Hse.).

Tubbs, Janet. Substance Abuse. 2000. (Spud Packs Ser.). (Illus.). 16p. (J). (ps-4). pap. 19.95 (978-1-881185-26-0(5)) Arcadia Pr.

Wagner, Heather Lehr. Alcohol. 2003. (Drugs, the Straight Facts Ser.). (Illus.). 112p. (gr. 9-13). 30.00 (978-0-7910-7259-2(2) , Chelsea Hse.) Facts On File, Inc.

—Cocaine. 2003. (Drugs, the Straight Facts Ser.). (Illus.). 112p. (J). (gr. 9-13). 30.00 (978-0-7910-7260-8(6) , Chelsea Hse.) Facts On File, Inc.

Walker, Ida. Natural & Everyday Drugs: A False Sense of Security. 2008. ***(978-1-4222-0160-2(0))*** Mason Crest Pubs.

Walker, Pam & Wood, Elaine. Stimulants. 2004. (Drug Education Library). (Illus.). 112p. lib. bdg. 32.45 (978-1-59018-044-0(5) , Lucent Bks.) Thomson Gale.

Warburton, Lianne, et al. Amphetamines & Other Stimulants. 2008. (Junior Drug Awareness Ser.). 112p. (J). (gr. 5-8). 30.00 ***(978-0-7910-9712-0(9)*** , Chelsea Hse.) Facts On File, Inc.

Weatherly, Myra. Ecstasy & Other Designer Drug Dangers. (Drug Dangers Ser.). (Illus.). 64p. (gr. 4-10). 2001. (YA). pap. 10.95 (978-0-7660-1963-8(2)); 2000. (J). lib. bdg. 27.93 (978-0-7660-1322-3(7)) Enslow Pubs., Inc.

—Inhalants. 2001. (Drug Library). (Illus.). 112p. (YA). (gr. 6-12). pap. 13.26 (978-0-7660-1923-2(3)) Enslow Pubs., Inc.

Weaver, David J. Only Mortals Can Be Heroes: A True Story about Drug Addiction. 2005. 200p. 23.95 (978-0-9770916-0-7(0)) Cambria Creations, LLC.

Werther, Scott P. Ecstasy & Your Heart: The Incredibly Disgusting Story. 2005. (Incredibly Disgusting Drugs Ser.). (Illus.). 48p. (YA). (gr. 5-8). lib. bdg. 25.25 (978-0-8239-3390-7(3)) Rosen Publishing Group, Inc., The.

West, Krista & Brogan, Ronald J. Cocaine & Crack. 2008. (Junior Drug Awareness Ser.). 112p. (J). (gr. 5-8). 30.00 ***(978-0-7910-9704-5(8)*** , Chelsea Hse.) Facts On File, Inc.

Westcott, Patsy. Why Do People Take Drugs? 2001. (Exploring Tough Issues Ser.). (Illus.). 48p. (J). (gr. 4-7). lib. bdg. 25.69 (978-0-7398-3231-8(X)) Raintree.

Wolny, Philip. Abusing Prescription Drugs. 2007. (J). ***(978-1-4042-1955-7(2))*** Rosen Publishing Group, Inc., The.

Woods, Geraldine. Heroin. 2001. (Drug Library). (Illus.). 104p. (YA). (gr. 6-12). pap. 13.26 (978-0-7660-1922-5(5)) Enslow Pubs., Inc.

Youngs, Bettie B. Teen's Guide to Living Drug-Free. 2003. (gr. 7-12). lib. bdg. 22.20 (978-0-613-90161-1(4)) Tandem Library Bks.

Ziemer, Maryann. Quaaludes. 2001. (Drug Library). (Illus.). 112p. (YA). (gr. 6-12). pap. 13.26 (978-0-7660-1929-4(2)) Enslow Pubs., Inc.

DRUG ABUSE—FICTION

Alki Zei Staff. Tina's Web. 2007. 300p. pap. 18.95 ***(978-0-9551566-1-8(0))*** Aurora Metro Pubns. Ltd. GBR. *Dist:* Consortium Bk. Sales & Distribution.

Anaya, Rudolfo. Curse of the ChupaCabra. 2006. 174p. (YA). 24.95 (978-0-8263-4114-3(4)) Univ. of New Mexico Pr.

Anonymous. Go Ask Alice. 1998. 11.64 (978-0-606-13431-6(X)) Tandem Library Bks.

—Go Ask Alice: A Real Diary. 2005. 224p. (YA). pap. 8.99 (978-1-4169-1463-1(3) , Simon Pulse) Simon & Schuster Children's Publishing.

Brooks, Kevin. Candy. 2006. 384p. (J). pap. 7.99 (978-0-439-68328-9(9) , PUSH); 2005. 368p. pap. 16.95 (978-0-439-68327-2(0) , Chicken Hse., The) Scholastic, Inc.

Burgess, Melvin. Smack. 2003. 384p. pap. 7.99 (978-0-06-052187-5(2)); 1999. 304p. (J). (gr. 7-12). pap. 6.99 (978-0-380-73223-4(8)) HarperCollins Pubs.

—Smack. 1998. 288p. (YA). (gr. 9-13). 17.95 (978-0-8050-5801-7(X) , Holt, Henry & Co. Bks. For Young Readers) Holt, Henry & Co.

—Smack. 2003. (gr. 7-12). lib. bdg. 15.30 (978-0-613-65712-9(8)); 1999. (978-0-606-16355-2(7)) Tandem Library Bks.

Callahan, Billy. Muckraker. 1999. 224p. (gr. 7-12). pap. 12.75 (978-1-892657-06-0(6)) Town Bk. Pr. The.

Carlson, Melody. Road Trip, No. 7. 2003. (Diary of a Teenage Girl Ser.). 304p. pap. 12.99 (978-1-59052-142-7(0) , Multnomah) WaterBrook Pr.

Childress, Alice. A Hero Ain't Nothin' but a Sandwich. 2000. 128p. (J). (gr. 7-12). pap. 5.99 (978-0-698-11854-6(5) , Putnam Juvenile) Penguin Group (USA) Inc.

—A Hero Ain't Nothin' but a Sandwich. 2000. 12.64 (978-0-606-17821-1(X)) Tandem Library Bks.

Choyce, Lesley. Roid Rage. unabr. ed. 1999. 112p. (978-1-55017-206-5(9)) Harbour Publishing Co., Ltd.

—Roid Rage. 1999. (gr. 7-12). lib. bdg. 15.25 (978-0-613-83360-8(0)) Tandem Library Bks.

Coy, John. Crackback. (J). 2007. 224p. pap. 6.99 ***(978-0-439-69734-7(4)*** , Scholastic Paperbacks); 2005. 208p. (gr. 7 up). pap. 16.99 (978-0-439-69733-0(6) , Scholastic Pr.) Scholastic, Inc.

Douglas, Lola. True Confessions of a Hollywood Starlet. (YA). (gr. 7-12). 2007. 272p. 6.99 (978-1-59514-153-8(7)); 2006. 288p. pap. 6.99 (978-1-59514-093-7(X)) Penguin Group (USA) Inc. (Razorbill).

Fletcher, Ralph J. Uncle Daddy. rev. ed. 2001. (Illus.). 144p. (J). (gr. 4-6). 16.95 (978-0-8050-6663-0(2) , Holt, Henry & Co. Bks. For Young Readers) Holt, Henry & Co.

Frye, Tom. Scratchin' on the Eight Ball. 2000. 240p. (YA). pap. 12.95 (978-0-595-12971-3(4) , Writer's Showcase Pr.) iUniverse, Inc.

Gaetz, Dayle Campbell. No Problem. 2006. (Orca Soundings Ser.). 112p. (YA). lib. bdg. 14.95 (978-1-55143-556-5(X)) Orca Bk. Pubs. USA.

Garsee, Jeannine. Before, after, & Somebody in Between. 2007. 352p. (YA). (gr. 9 up). 16.95 ***(978-1-59990-022-3(X))*** Bloomsbury Publishing.

Going, K. L. Fat Kid Rules the World. (YA). 2004. (gr. 8-12). 17.99 (978-0-8037-2948-3(0) , Dial); 2003. 224p. (gr. 4 up). 17.99 (978-0-399-23990-8(1) , Putnam Juvenile); 2004. 192p. (gr. 6). reprint ed. pap. 6.99 (978-0-14-240208-5(7) , Puffin) Penguin Group (USA) Inc.

—Saint Iggy. 2006. (Illus.). 272p. (YA). 17.00 (978-0-15-205795-4(1)) Harcourt Children's Bks.

Hardrick, Jackie. Imani in Never Say Goodbye. 2004. 272p. (YA). per. 15.00 (978-0-9706226-2-4(7)) Enlighten Pubns.

Harrison, Mette Ivie. The Monster in Me. 2003. 160p. (J). (gr. 7 up). tchr. ed. 16.95 (978-0-8234-1713-1(1)) Holiday Hse., Inc.

Hernandez, David. Suckerpunch. 2008. 224p. (J). 16.99 ***(978-0-06-117330-1(4));*** lib. bdg. 17.89 ***(978-0-06-117331-8(2))*** HarperCollins Pubs. (HarperTeen).

Koertge, Ronald. Stoner & Spaz. 176p. (YA). (gr. 9-12). 2002. 15.99 (978-0-7636-1608-3(7)); 2004. reprint ed. pap. 6.99 (978-0-7636-2150-6(1)) Candlewick Pr.

Lipsyte, Robert. Raiders Night. 2007. 256p. (J). (gr. 9 up). pap. 6.99 ***(978-0-06-059948-5(0));*** 2006. 240p. (YA). 15.99 (978-0-06-059946-1(4)); 2006. 240p. (YA). lib. bdg. 16.89 (978-0-06-059947-8(2)) HarperCollins Pubs. (HarperTeen).

Lynn, Tracy. Rx. 2005. 272p. (YA). pap. 7.99 (978-1-4169-1155-5(3) , Simon Pulse) Simon & Schuster Children's Publishing.

MacKall, Dandi Daley. Kyra's Story. 2003. (Degrees of Guilt Ser.). (YA). pap. 9.99 (978-0-8423-8284-7(4)) Tyndale Hse. Pubs.

Madison, Ron. Ned Learns to Say No: A Lesson about Drugs. l.t. ed. 2003. (Health & Safety Ser.). (Illus.). 24p. 4.95 (978-1-887206-23-5(X)) Ned's Head Productions.

—Ned Learns to Say No: A Lesson about Drugs. 2002. (gr. k-3). lib. bdg. 12.95 (978-0-613-80300-7(0)) Tandem Library Bks.

McCormick, Patricia. My Brother's Keeper. 2005. 192p. (gr. 5-17). 15.99 (978-0-7868-5173-7(2)) Hyperion Bks. for Children.

Mowry, Jess. Babylon Boyz. Gore, Leonid, illus. 1999. 192p. (YA). (gr. 8-12). mass mkt. 10.95 (978-0-689-82592-7(7) , 076714008007, Simon Pulse) Simon & Schuster Children's Publishing.

—Babylon Boyz. 1999. (J). (978-0-606-16318-7(2)) Tandem Library Bks.

Murray, Jaye. Bottled Up. 2004. 224p. (YA). (gr. 6-12). reprint ed. pap. 6.99 (978-0-14-240240-5(0) , Puffin) Penguin Group (USA) Inc.

—Bottled Up. 2004. 220p. (J). (gr. 2-13). lib. bdg. 13.04 (978-0-606-32733-6(9)) Tandem Library Bks.

Myers, Walter Dean. The Beast. 2005. 192p. (YA). (gr. 7-12). 6.99 (978-0-439-36842-1(1) , Scholastic Paperbacks) Scholastic, Inc.

—Motown & Didi: A Love Story. 2002. (Illus.). (J). 13.40 (978-0-7587-0384-2(8)) Book Wholesalers, Inc.

Oates, Joyce Carol. After the Wreck, I Picked Myself up, Spread My Wings, & Flew Away. 2007. 320p. (J). (gr. 9 up). pap. 7.99 ***(978-0-06-073527-2(9));*** 2006. 304p. (YA). lib. bdg. 17.89 (978-0-06-073526-5(0)) HarperCollins Pubs. (HarperTeen).

Oates, Joyce Carol. After the Wreck, I Picked Myself Up, Spread My Wings, & Flew Away. 2006. 304p. (YA). 16.99 (978-0-06-073525-8(2) , HarperTeen) HarperCollins Pubs.

Rapp, Adam. Under the Wolf, under the Dog. 320p. (YA). (gr. 9). 2007. pap. 8.99 (978-0-7636-3365-3(8)); 2004. 16.99 (978-0-7636-1818-6(7)) Candlewick Pr.

Ratcliffe, Jane. The Free Fall. rev. ed. 2001. (Illus.). 192p. (YA). (gr. 9-12). 16.95 (978-0-8050-6667-8(5) , Holt, Henry & Co. Bks. For Young Readers) Holt, Henry & Co.

Reynolds, Marilyn. If You Loved Me. 1999. (True-to-Life Series from Hamilton High: Vol. 7). 32p. (J). pap., tchr. ed. 2.50 (978-1-885356-59-8(5)) Morning Glory Pr., Inc.

—If You Loved Me: True-to-Life Stories from Hamilton High. 1999. (True-to-Life Series from Hamilton High: Vol. 7). 224p. (J). (gr. 7-12). pap. 8.95 (978-1-885356-55-0(2)) Morning Glory Pr., Inc.

Schweser, Jamie. S. K. A. M. #7: Super Kick-Ass Magazine. 2002. (J). (gr. 9 up). 4.00 (978-0-9666469-4-8(0)) New Mouth from the Dirty South.

Stoehr, Shelley. Crosses. 2003. (gr. 7-12). lib. bdg. 23.40 (978-0-613-86660-6(6)) Tandem Library Bks.

—Crosses. 2003. 161p. (YA). pap. 13.95 (978-0-595-26952-5(4) , Backinprint.com) iUniverse, Inc.

Toten, Teresa. The Game. 2004. (Illus.). 160p. (YA). (gr. 9 up). pap. 7.95 (978-0-88995-232-4(9)) Red Deer Pr. CAN. *Dist:* Fitzhenry & Whiteside, Ltd.

van Diepen, Allison. Street Pharm. 2006. 304p. (YA). (gr. 8 up). pap. 6.99 (978-1-4169-1154-8(5) , Simon Pulse) Simon & Schuster Children's Publishing.

Volponi, Paul. Rooftop. (gr. 7). 2007. 224p. (J). pap. 6.99 (978-0-14-240844-5(1) , Puffin); 2006. 208p. (YA). 15.99 (978-0-670-06069-6(0) , Viking Adult) Penguin Group (USA) Inc.

Wert, Debra L. Caterfly: Mac's Back Struggling to Stay Drug-Free. 1998. (J). (978-0-944576-27-4(3)) Rocky River Pubs., LLC.

Whitmore, Benette. Shelter. 2006. 304p. (YA). 16.95 (978-0-8027-8884-9(X)) Walker & Co.

Wilhelm, Doug. Falling. 2007. 256p. (YA). (gr. 9 up). 17.00 (978-0-374-32251-9(1)) Farrar, Straus & Giroux.

Wilson, Eric G. Vancouver Nightmare: A Tom Austin Mystery. Row, Richard, illus. 2000. (Tom Austin Mysteries Ser.). 112p. (J). pap. 4.99 (978-1-55143-149-9(1)) Orca Bk. Pubs. USA.

DRUG ADDICTION

Beal, Eileen J. Ritalin. 1998. (Drug Abuse Prevention Library). 64p. (J). (gr. 7-12). pap. 6.95 (978-1-56838-248-7(0)) Hazelden Publishing & Educational Services.

—Ritalin. 2005. (Drug Abuse Prevention Library). (Illus.). 64p. (YA). (gr. 7-12). lib. bdg. 25.25 (978-0-8239-3759-2(3)) Rosen Publishing Group, Inc., The.

Benton, John. New Hope Series, 10 bks., Set. 2004p. (J). (gr. 3-12). 35.00 (978-0-9635411-1-6(0)) Benton, John Bks.

Biggers, Jeff. Chemical Dependency & the Dysfunctional Family. rev. ed. 1998. (Drug Abuse Prevention Library). (Illus.). 64p. (YA). (gr. 7-12). lib. bdg. 17.95 (978-0-8239-2749-4(0) , DRDYFA) Rosen Publishing Group, Inc., The.

Buckalew, M. Walter. Drugs & Stress. 1998. (Drug Abuse Prevention Library). 64p. (YA). (gr. 7 up). reprint ed. pap. 6.95 (978-1-56838-213-5(8)) Hazelden Publishing & Educational Services.

Clayton, Lawrence. Designer Drugs. 1998. (Drug Abuse Prevention Library). 64p. (YA). (gr. 7 up). reprint ed. pap. 6.95 (978-1-56838-209-8(X)) Hazelden Publishing & Educational Services.

—Diet Pill Drug Dangers. 1999. (Drug Dangers Ser.). (Illus.). 64p. (YA). (gr. 4-10). lib. bdg. 19.95 (978-0-7660-1158-8(5)) Enslow Pubs., Inc.

Drug & Alcohol Prevention. (J). (gr. 2-3). 3.80 (978-0-8374-1262-7(5) , 211); (gr. 3). 3.80 (978-0-8374-0120-1(8) , 212); (gr. 4). 3.80 (978-0-8374-0121-8(6) , 213); (gr. 5-6). 5.95 (978-0-8374-1266-5(8) , 267); (gr. 7-9). 3.80 (978-0-8374-0080-8(5) , 411) Weekly Reader Corp.

Ferreiro, Carmen. Heroin. 2003. (Drugs, the Straight Facts Ser.). (Illus.). 112p. (J). (gr. 9-13). 30.00 (978-0-7910-7262-2(2) , Chelsea Hse.) Facts On File, Inc.

Graves, Bonnie. Drug Use & Abuse. 2000. (Perspectives on Physical Health Ser.). (Illus.). 64p. (J). (gr. 4-6). lib. bdg. 23.93 (978-0-7368-0416-5(1) , LifeMatters Bks.) Capstone Pr., Inc.

Greenwood, Carmel & Taylor, Chris. Wake up Mum: A Mother & Son's True Crisis Story of Overcoming Drug Addiction with Love, Laughter & Miraculous Insights. (Illus.). (Orig.). (YA). 16.95 (978-0-9646285-0-2(3)); pap. 12.95 (978-0-9646285-1-9(1)) Carmel Concepts, Ltd.

Hanan, Jessica. When Someone You Love Is Addicted. 1999. (Drug Abuse Prevention Library). (Illus.). 64p. (YA). (gr. 7-12). 25.25 (978-0-8239-2831-6(4) , DRSOLO) Rosen Publishing Group, Inc., The.

Haughton, Emma. Drug Abuse. 1998. (Viewpoints Ser.). (Illus.). 32p. (J). (gr. 5-8). 23.00 (978-0-531-14444-2(5) , Watts, Franklin) Scholastic Library Publishing.

Houle, Michelle M. Tranquilizer, Barbiturate & Downer Drug Dangers. 2000. (Drug Dangers Ser.). (Illus.). 64p. (YA). (gr. 4-10). lib. bdg. 27.93 (978-0-7660-1320-9(0)) Enslow Pubs., Inc.

Huard, Donald V. Teen-Agers: What Will Cigarettes, Booze & Drugs Do for/to You? 1998. 50p. (J). (gr. 7-12). mass mkt. 3.95 (978-0-9661606-1-1(4)) Huard Pubns.

Jaffe, Steven L., ed. Amphetamines & Other Uppers. 1999. (Junior Drug Awareness Ser.). (Illus.). 80p. (J). (gr. 4-8). lib. bdg. 21.95 (978-0-7910-5200-6(1) , Chelsea Hse.) Facts On File, Inc.

—Crack & Cocaine. 1999. (Junior Drug Awareness Ser.). (Illus.). 80p. (J). (gr. 4-8). 32.00 (978-0-7910-5177-1(3) , Chelsea Hse.) Facts On File, Inc.

—Heroin. 1999. (Junior Drug Awareness Ser.). (Illus.). 80p. (J). (gr. 4-8). 27.50 (978-0-7910-5181-8(1) , Chelsea Hse.) Facts On File, Inc.

—Inhalants & Solvents. 1999. (Junior Drug Awareness Ser.). (Illus.). 80p. (J). (gr. 4-8). 27.50 (978-0-7910-5178-8(1) , Chelsea Hse.) Facts On File, Inc.

—Valium & Other Downers. 1999. (Junior Drug Awareness Ser.). (Illus.). 80p. (J). (gr. 4-8). 27.50 (978-0-7910-5206-8(0) , Chelsea Hse.) Facts On File, Inc.

Johnson, Marlys. Cross-Addiction. 1998. (Drug Abuse Prevention Library). 64p. (J). (gr. 7-12). pap. 6.95 (978-1-56838-251-7(0)) Hazelden Publishing & Educational Services.

—Cross-Addiction: The Hidden Risk of Multiple Addictions. 1999. (Drug Abuse Prevention Library). (Illus.). 64p. (YA). (gr. 7-12). lib. bdg. 25.25 (978-0-8239-2776-0(8) , DRCRAD) Rosen Publishing Group, Inc., The.

Kaplan, Sheldon A. Cold Turkey Before You Become One! Stop Smoking, Drinking, Gambling & or Abusing Drugs. Resseguie, Douglas, ed. deluxe ed. 1999. (YA). 5.95 (978-0-9677993-1-5(7)) Kaplan, Sheldon A. & Associates.

Keegan, Kyle, et al. Chasing the High: A Firsthand Account of One Young Person's Experience with Substance Abuse. 2008. (Illus.). 192p. 30.00 ***(978-0-19-531471-7(9));*** pap. 9.95 ***(978-0-19-531472-4(7))*** Oxford Univ. Pr., Inc.

Klosterman, Lorrie. The Facts about Dependence to Treatment. 2007. (Drugs Ser.). (J). lib. bdg. 39.93 ***(978-0-7614-2676-9(0)*** , Benchmark Bks.) Cavendish, Marshall Corp.

Konieczko, Craig. Recovery from Drug Addiction. 2005. (Drug Abuse Prevention Library). (Illus.). 64p. (YA). (gr. 7-12). lib. bdg. 25.25 (978-0-8239-3284-9(2) , DRRECO) Rosen Publishing Group, Inc., The.

Lawler, Jennifer. Drug Legalization. 1999. (Hot Pro/Con Issues Ser.). (Illus.). 64p. (YA). (gr. 6-12). lib. bdg. 27.93 (978-0-7660-1197-7(6)) Enslow Pubs., Inc.

Lee, Mary P. & Lee, Richard S. Drugs & Codependency. 1998. (Drug Abuse Prevention Library). 64p. (J). (gr. 7 up). pap. 6.95 (978-1-56838-252-4(9)) Hazelden Publishing & Educational Services.

Littell, Mary Ann. Heroin Drug Dangers. 1999. (Drug Dangers Ser.). (Illus.). 64p. (YA). (gr. 4-10). lib. bdg. 27.93 (978-0-7660-1156-4(9)) Enslow Pubs., Inc.

—Speed & Methamphetamine Drug Dangers. 1999. (Drug Dangers Ser.). (Illus.). 64p. (YA). (gr. 4-10). lib. bdg. 27.93 (978-0-7660-1157-1(7)) Enslow Pubs., Inc.

Moe, Barbara. Drug Abuse Relapse: Helping Teens to Get Clean Again. 2005. (Drug Abuse Prevention Library). (Illus.). 64p. (YA). (gr. 7-12). lib. bdg. 25.25 (978-0-8239-3157-6(9) , DRRELA) Rosen Publishing Group, Inc., The.

Monroe, Judy. Inhalant Drug Dangers. 1999. (Drug Dangers Ser.). (Illus.). 64p. (YA). (gr. 4-10). lib. bdg. 27.93 (978-0-7660-1153-3(4)) Enslow Pubs., Inc.

Murdico, Suzanne J. Drug Abuse. 1998. (Preteen Pressures Ser.). (Illus.). 48p. (J). (gr. 4-8). lib. bdg. 25.69 (978-0-8172-5027-0(1)) Raintree.

Robbins, Paul R. Crack & Cocaine Drug Dangers. 1999. (Drug Dangers Ser.). (Illus.). 64p. (YA). (gr. 4-10). lib. bdg. 27.93 (978-0-7660-1155-7(0)) Enslow Pubs., Inc.

Rundquist, Thomas J., ed. The Drug Addict Trials Before the US Supreme Court: An Educational Prevention Game. 2003. (Illus.). 66p. (gr. 9-12). pap. 29.95 (978-1-884239-65-6(X)) Nova Media, Inc.

Schleifer, Jay. Methamphetamines. 1998. (Drug Abuse Prevention Library). 64p. (J). (gr. 7-12). pap. 6.95 (978-1-56838-250-0(2)) Hazelden Publishing & Educational Services.

Schliefer, Jay. Methamphetamines: Speed Kills. 1999. (Drug Abuse Prevention Library). (Illus.). 64p. (YA). (gr. 7-12). lib. bdg. 25.25 (978-0-8239-2512-4(9) , DRMEAM) Rosen Publishing Group, Inc., The.

Shepherd, Kenneth R. Drugs & Low Self-Esteem. 1999. (Drug Abuse Prevention Library). (Illus.). 64p. (YA). (gr. 7-12). lib. bdg. 25.25 (978-0-8239-2826-2(8) , DRSEES) Rosen Publishing Group, Inc., The.

Sheva, Marie, mem. The Year of the Dogs: A Chronicle of Redemption, a Story of Love. 2003. (Illus.). 247p. (YA). per. 15.95 (978-0-9741736-0-3(6) , 9900) Sheva, Marie.

Sonder, Ben. All about Heroin. 2002. (Watts Reference Ser.). (Illus.). 128p. (YA). (gr. 9-12). 26.00 (978-0-531-11541-1(0) , Watts, Franklin) Scholastic Library Publishing.

Tattersall, Clare. Drugs, Runaways & Teen Prostitution. 1999. (Drug Abuse Prevention Library). (Illus.). 64p. (YA). (gr. 7-12). lib. bdg. 25.25 (978-0-8239-2827-9(6) , DRTEPR) Rosen Publishing Group, Inc., The.

Torr, James D. & Barbour, Scott. Drug Use. 1999. (Opposing Viewpoints Ser.). (Illus.). 176p. (YA). (gr. 10-12). pap. 21.20 (978-0-7377-0050-3(5) , Greenhaven Pr., Inc.) Thomson Gale.

Walker, Ida. Addiction Treatment: Escaping the Trap. 2008. (J). (***978-1-4222-0152-7(X)***) Mason Crest Pubs.

Westcott, Patsy. Why Do People Take Drugs? 2001. (Exploring Tough Issues Ser.). (Illus.). 48p. (J). (gr. 4-7). lib. bdg. 25.69 (978-0-7398-3231-8(X)) Raintree.

Wise, Francis H. Youth & Drugs. Wise, Joyce M., illus. (YA). (gr. 10 up). 4.95 (978-0-8096-1781-4(1)) Wise Publishing Co.

DRUG ADDICTION—FICTION

Berenstain, Stan & Berenstain, Jan. The Berenstain Bears & the Drug Free Zone. Berenstain, Stan & Berenstain, Jan, illus. 2002. (Berenstain Bears Big Chapter Bks.). (Illus.). (J). (gr. 2-6). 11.91 (978-0-7587-0941-7(2)) Book Wholesalers, Inc.

Gibbons, Alan. Blood Pressure. 2006. 208p. (J). pap. 11.99 (***978-1-84255-199-8(X)***) Orion Publishing Group, Ltd. GBR. *Dist:* Independent Pubs. Group.

Javier's Sister - A Family's Struggle with Drug Addiction: One Day the Sun Will Shine Again Series. 2005. (J). pap. 16.95 (978-0-9768827-8-7(7)) Prevention Through Puppetry, Inc.

Kendal, Penny. Broken. 2003. (Illus.). 192p. (YA). pap. 9.99 (978-1-84270-174-4(6)) Andersen GBR. *Dist:* Independent Pubs. Group.

Orme, Helen. Who Cares? 2004. (Shades Ser.). 64p. (J). pap. 7.99 (978-0-237-52625-2(5) , Evans Brothers, Limited) Evans Publishing Group GBR. *Dist:* Independent Pubs. Group.

Voigt, Cynthia. Orfe. 2002. (Illus.). 160p. (YA). pap. 4.99 (978-0-689-84868-1(4) , Simon Pulse) Simon & Schuster Children's Publishing.

DRUG HABIT

see Drug Addiction

DRUGS

see also Materia Medica; Pharmacy; Poisons

also names of individual drugs, and groups of drugs, e.g. Narcotics

Amos, Janine. Alex Does Drugs. 2002. (Body Matters Ser.). (Illus.). 32p. (YA). 22.00 (978-1-84234-110-0(3) , Cherrytree Books) Evans Publishing Group GBR. *Dist:* Independent Pubs. Group.

Apel, Melanie Ann. Cocaine & Your Nose (Rev) The Incredibly Disgusting Story. rev. ed. 2005. (Illus.). 48p. (J). (ps-ps). lib. bdg. 25.25 (978-1-4042-0632-8(9) , Rosen Central) Rosen Publishing Group, Inc., The.

Aretha, David. Cocaine & Crack: A MyReportLinks. com Book. 2005. (Drugs Ser.). (Illus.). 48p. (J). lib. bdg. 25.26 (978-0-7660-5276-5(1) , MyReportLinks.com Bks.) Enslow Pubs., Inc.

—Ecstasy & Other Party Drugs: A MyReportLinks. com Book. 2005. (Drugs Ser.). (Illus.). 48p. (J). lib. bdg. 25.26 (978-0-7660-5278-9(8) , MyReportLinks.com Bks.) Enslow Pubs., Inc.

—Methamphetamine & Amphetamines: A MyReportLinks. com Book. 2005. (Drugs Ser.). (Illus.). 48p. (J). lib. bdg. 25.26 (978-0-7660-5279-6(6) , MyReportLinks.com Bks.) Enslow Pubs., Inc.

Ballard, Carol. From Cowpox to Antibiotics: Discovering Vaccines & Medicines. 2006. (Chain Reactions Ser.). (Illus.). 62p. (YA). (gr. 6-9). lib. bdg. 34.29 (978-1-4034-8839-8(8)) Heinemann Library.

Barter, James. Opium. 2004. (Drug Education Library). (Illus.). 112p. (J). (gr. 7-10). 32.45 (978-1-59018-419-6(X) , Lucent Bks.) Thomson Gale.

Beal, Eileen J. Ritalin: Its Use & Abuse. 1999. (Drug Abuse Prevention Library). (Illus.). 64p. (YA). (gr. 7-12). lib. bdg. 17.95 (978-0-8239-2775-3(X) , DRRITA) Rosen Publishing Group, Inc., The.

Bell, Suzanne. Drugs, Poisons, & Chemistry. 2008. (Essentials of Forensic Science Ser.). 176p. (gr. 6-12). 35.00 (978-0-8160-5510-4(6)) Facts On File, Inc.

Bryant-Mole, Karen. Drugs. 1999. (Talking about Ser.). (Illus.). 32p. (J). (gr. k-4). lib. bdg. 25.69 (978-0-8172-5887-0(6)) Raintree.

Carroll, Marilyn. Cocaine & Crack. 2001. (Drug Library). (Illus.). 128p. (YA). (gr. 6-12). pap. 13.26 (978-0-7660-1919-5(5)) Enslow Pubs., Inc.

Chastain, Zachary. Cocaine: The Rush to Destruction. 2008. (J). (***978-1-4222-0154-1(6)***) Mason Crest Pubs.

Clayton, Lawrence. Steroids. (Drug Abuse Prevention Library). (Illus.). 64p. (YA). (gr. 7-12). 1998. lib. bdg. 16.95 (978-0-8239-2063-1(1)); 1999. 25.25 (978-0-8239-2888-0(8) , DRSTER) Rosen Publishing Group, Inc., The.

—Tranquilizers. 2001. (Drug Library). (Illus.). 104p. (YA). (gr. 6-12). pap. 13.26 (978-0-7660-1931-7(4)) Enslow Pubs., Inc.

Cobb, Allan B. Heroin & Your Veins: The Incredibly Disgusting Story. 2005. (Incredibly Disgusting Drugs Ser.). (Illus.). 48p. (YA). (gr. 5-8). lib. bdg. 25.25 (978-0-8239-3249-8(4) , DDHEVE) Rosen Publishing Group, Inc., The.

Cohen, Julian. Drugs. rev. ed. 2000. (Life Files Ser.). (Illus.). 62p. (J). 24.99 (978-0-237-52185-1(7)); pap. 15.99 (978-0-237-52181-3(4)) Evans Publishing Group GBR. (Evans Brothers, Limited). *Dist:* Independent Pubs. Group.

Constant. Drugs. 2004, (Teen Issues Ser.). (J). 28.56 (978-1-4109-0611-3(6)); (Illus.). pap. 8.95 (978-1-4109-0882-7(8)) Harcourt Schl. Pubs.

—Drugs 6-Pack. 2004. (Teen Issues Ser.). (Illus.). (YA). pap. 48.30 (978-1-4109-0889-6(5)) Harcourt Schl. Pubs.

—Tobacco. 2004. (Teen Issues Ser.). (Illus.). 56p. (J). pap. 8.95 (978-1-4109-0885-8(2)) Harcourt Schl. Pubs.

—Tobacco 6-Pack. 2004. (Teen Issues Ser.). (Illus.). (YA). pap. 48.30 (978-1-4109-0892-6(5)) Harcourt Schl. Pubs.

Croft, Jennifer. PCP: High Risk on the Streets. 1998. (Drug Abuse Prevention Library). (Illus.). 64p. (YA). (gr. 7-12). 25.25 (978-0-8239-2774-6(1) , DRPCP) Rosen Publishing Group, Inc., The.

Custom Curricul Staff. What about Sex, Drugs, And... ? 2004. (Custom Curriculum Ser.). 256p. pap., pap. 19.99 (978-0-7814-4093-6(9) , 0781440939) Cook, David C. Publishing Co.

DeBenedette, Valerie. Caffeine. 2001. (Drug Library). (Illus.). 104p. (YA). (gr. 6-12). pap. 13.26 (978-0-7660-1918-8(7)) Enslow Pubs., Inc.

Docalavich, Heather. Antidepressants & Psychology: Talk Therapy vs. Medication. 2006. (Antidepressants Ser.). (Illus.). 120p. (J). (gr. 7 up). (978-1-4222-0096-4(5)) Mason Crest Pubs.

Drugs, 5 bks., Group 2. Incl. Facts about Amphetamines. Menhard, Francha Roffe. 96p. (978-0-7614-1972-3(1)); Facts about Cocaine. LeVert, Suzanne. 96p. (978-0-7614-1973-0(X)); Facts about Depressants. Klosterman, Lorrie. 96p. (978-0-7614-1976-1(4)); Facts about Heroin. LeVert, Suzanne. 95p. (978-0-7614-1975-4(6)); Facts about LSD. LeVert, Suzanne. 96p. (978-0-7614-1974-7(8)); (Illus.). (J). 2005. 2005. (978-0-7614-1971-6(3) , Benchmark Bks.) Cavendish, Marshall Corp.

Drugs: The Straight Facts. 2005. 480.00 (978-0-7910-9167-8(8) , Chelsea Hse.) Facts On File, Inc.

Drugs Group 3, 5 bks., Set. Incl. Facts about Antidepressants. LeVert, Suzanne. lib. bdg. 39.93 (978-0-7614-2241-9(2)); Facts about Caffeine. Klosterman, Lorrie. lib. bdg. 39.95 (978-0-7614-2242-6(0)); Facts about Nicotine. LeVert, Suzanne. lib. bdg. 39.93 (978-0-7614-2244-0(7)); (Illus.). 112p. (J). 2006. 2007. Set lib. bdg. 199.64 (***978-0-7614-2240-2(4)*** , Benchmark Bks.) Cavendish, Marshall Corp.

Drugs Series, 5 Bks, Set. 2004. (J). 185.35 (978-0-7614-1804-7(0)) Cavendish, Marshall Corp.

Durham, Michael. Painkillers & Tranquilizers. 2003. (Just the Facts Ser.). (Illus.). 56p. (YA). lib. bdg. 25.64 (978-1-4034-0821-1(1)) Heinemann Library.

Egendorf, Laura K. Performance Enhancing Drugs. 2007. (Compact Research Ser.). 112p. (YA). (gr. 7-10). lib. bdg. (***978-1-60152-003-6(4)***) ReferencePoint Pr., Inc.

Esherick, Joan. Dying for Acceptance: A Teen's Guide to Drug- & Alcohol-Related Health Issues. 2005. (Science of Health Ser.). (Illus.). 128p. (J). lib. bdg. 24.95 (978-1-59084-847-0(0)) Mason Crest Pubs.

—The FDA & Psychiatric Drugs: How a Drug Is Approved. 2003. (Encyclopedia of Psychiatric Drugs & Their Disorders Ser.). (Illus.). 128p. (J). lib. bdg. (978-1-59084-578-3(1)) Mason Crest Pubs.

—Natural Alternatives to Antidepressants: St. John's Wort, Kava Kava, & Others. 2006. (Antidepressants Ser.). (Illus.). 120p. (J). (gr. 7 up). (978-1-4222-0105-3(8)) Mason Crest Pubs.

Esherick, Joan. Prozac: North American Culture & the Wonder Drug. 2007. (Antidepressants Ser.). (Illus.). 120p. (YA). (gr. 7 up). 24.95 (***978-1-4222-0106-0(6)***) Mason Crest Pubs.

Etingoff, Kim. Abusing Over-The-Counter Drugs: Illicit Uses for Everyday Drugs. 2008. (J). (***978-1-4222-0150-3(3)***) Mason Crest Pubs.

Etingoff, Kim. Methamphetamines: Unsafe Speed. 2008. (978-1-4222-0159-6(7)) Mason Crest Pubs.

Fitzhugh, Karla. Crack & Cocaine. 2005. (What's the Deal? Ser.). (Illus.). 56p. (J). (978-1-4034-7028-7(6)) Heinemann Library.

—Ecstasy. 2005. (What's the Deal? Ser.). (Illus.). 56p. (J). (978-1-4034-7027-0(8)) Heinemann.

—Inhalants. 2003. (Health Issues Ser.). (Illus.). 64p. (J). lib. bdg. 28.56 (978-0-7398-6425-8(4)) Raintree.

Fooks, Louie. The Drugs Trade. 2003. (21st Century Debates Ser.). (Illus.). 64p. (J). lib. bdg. 28.56 (978-0-7398-6033-5(X)) Raintree.

Gale Research Staff. Drugs & Controlled Substances for Students. 2002. (Illus.). 1000p. (YA). 177.00 (978-0-7876-6264-6(X) , GML00502-180467) Thomson Gale.

Gold, Susan Dudley. Vernonia School District v. Acton: Drug Testing in the Schools. 2005. (Supreme Court Milestones Ser.). (Illus.). 141p. (J). (978-0-7614-1941-9(1) , Benchmark Bks.) Cavendish, Marshall Corp.

Hager, Holly. Heroin = Busted! 2005. (Busted! Ser.). (Illus.). 104p. (J). (gr. 6-12). lib. bdg. 31.93 (978-0-7660-2386-4(9)) Enslow Pubs., Inc.

Haughton, Emma. Drinking, Smoking & Other Drugs. 1999. (Health & Fitness Ser.). (Illus.). 48p. (J). (gr. 4-6). lib. bdg. 27.12 (978-0-7398-1345-4(5)) Raintree.

Holt, Rinehart and Winston Staff. Decisions for Health Blue, Chptr. 16: Medicine & Illegal Drugs. 4th ed. 2004. pap. 11.20 (978-0-03-068051-9(4)) Holt, Rinehart & Winston.

—Decisions for Health Green Chptr. 13: Understanding Drugs. 4th ed. 2004. pap. 11.20 (978-0-03-068034-2(4)) Holt, Rinehart & Winston.

—Decisions for Health Red Chptr. 13: Teens & Drugs. 4th ed. 2004. pap. 11.20 (978-0-03-068039-7(5)) Holt, Rinehart & Winston.

—A Lifetime of Health Chptr. 12: Illegal Drugs. 4th ed. Date not set. pap. 11.20 (978-0-03-068104-2(9)) Holt, Rinehart & Winston.

Houle, Michelle M. Tranquilizer, Barbiturate & Downer Drug Dangers. 2001. (Drug Dangers Ser.). (Illus.). 64p. (YA). (gr. 4-10). pap. 13.26 (978-0-7660-1967-6(5)) Enslow Pubs., Inc.

Howard, Todd. Heroin. 2002. (Drug Education Library). (Illus.). 112p. (J). 32.45 (978-1-59018-018-1(6) , Lucent Bks.) Thomson Gale.

Hunter, David. Antidepressants & Advertising: Marketing Happiness. 2007. (Antidepressants Ser.). (Illus.). 112p. (J). (gr. 7 up). 24.95 (978-1-4222-0095-7(7)) Mason Crest Pubs.

—Antidepressants & the Pharmaceutical Companies: Corporate Responsibilities. 2007. (Antidepressants Ser.). (Illus.). 112p. (J). (gr. 7 up). 24.95 (978-1-4222-0101-5(5)) Mason Crest Pubs.

Hyde, Margaret O. Mind Drugs, Vol. VI. 6th ed. 1998. (Mind Drugs Ser.: up). (Illus.). 144p. (gr. 7 up). lib. bdg. 24.90 (978-0-7613-0970-3(5) , Twenty-First Century Bks.) Lerner Publishing Group.

Hyde, Margaret O. & Setaro, John F. Drugs 101: An Overview for Teens. 2003. (Single Titles Ser.). (Illus.). 160p. (gr. 7 up). lib. bdg. 25.90 (978-0-7613-2608-3(1) , Twenty-First Century Bks.) Lerner Publishing Group.

Incredibly Disgusting Drugs. 2005. (Illus.). 48p. (gr. 5-8). lib. bdg. 227.40 (978-0-8239-3918-3(9)) Rosen Publishing Group, Inc., The.

Incredibly Disgusting Drugs: Set 2, 6 bks. Incl. Barbiturates & Your Central Nervous System : The Incredibly Disgusting Story. Derkins, Susie. lib. bdg. 25.25 (978-0-8239-3388-4(1)); Crack & Your Circulatory System : The Incredibly Disgusting Story. Manley, Claudia B. lib. bdg. 25.25 (978-0-8239-3389-1(X)); Ecstasy & Your Heart : The Incredibly Disgusting Story. Werther, Scott P. lib. bdg. 25.25 (978-0-8239-3390-7(3)); Hallucinogens & Your Neurons : The Incredibly Disgusting Story. Cefrey, Holly. lib. bdg. 25.25 (978-0-8239-3391-4(1)); Inhalants & Your Nasal Passages : The Incredibly Disgusting Story. O'Donnell, Kerri. lib. bdg. 25.25 (978-0-8239-3392-1(X)); Steroids & Your Muscles : The Incredibly Disgusting Story. Spring, Albert. lib. bdg. 25.25 (978-0-8239-3393-8(8)); 48p. (YA). (gr. 5-8). 2005. (Illus.). 2000. Set lib. bdg. 151.50 (978-0-8239-9425-0(2) , Rosen Central) Rosen Publishing Group, Inc., The.

Jaffe, Steven L., ed. Ecstasy & Other Designer Drugs. 1999. (Junior Drug Awareness Ser.). (Illus.). 80p. (J). (gr. 4-8). 27.50 (978-0-7910-5201-3(X) , Chelsea Hse.) Facts On File, Inc.

—How to Get Help. 1999. (Junior Drug Awareness Ser.). (Illus.). 80p. (J). (gr. 4-8). 27.50 (978-0-7910-5180-1(3) , Chelsea Hse.) Facts On File, Inc.

—Pain Relievers, Diet Pills & Other Over-the-Counter Drugs. 1999. (Junior Drug Awareness Ser.). (Illus.). 80p. (J). (gr. 4-8). 27.50 (978-0-7910-5203-7(6) , Chelsea Hse.) Facts On File, Inc.

Kirby-Payne, Ann. Refuse to Use: A Girl's Guide to Drugs & Alcohol. 1999. (Girls' Guides). (Illus.). 48p. (YA). (gr. 5-8). lib. bdg. 23.95 (978-0-8239-2982-5(5) , GGREUS) Rosen Publishing Group, Inc., The.

Klosterman, Lorrie. The Facts about Caffeine. 2006. (Drugs Ser.). (Illus.). 112p. (J). lib. bdg. 39.95 (978-0-7614-2242-6(0) , Benchmark Bks.) Cavendish, Marshall Corp.

Klosterman, Lorrie. The Facts about Drugs & the Body. 2007. (Drugs Ser.). (J). lib. bdg. 39.93 (***978-0-7614-2675-2(2)*** , Benchmark Bks.) Cavendish, Marshall Corp.

Koellhoffer, Tara. Ecstasy & Other Club Drugs. 2008. (Junior Drug Awareness Ser.). 112p. (J). (gr. 5-8). 30.00 (***978-0-7910-9697-0(1)*** , Chelsea Hse.) Facts On File, Inc.

Laliberte, Michelle. Marijuana: A MyReportLinks. com Book. 2005. (Drugs Ser.). (Illus.). 48p. (J). lib. bdg. 25.26 (978-0-7660-5281-9(8) , MyReportLinks.com Bks.) Enslow Pubs., Inc.

Landau, Elaine. Cocaine. 2003. (gr. 5-8). lib. bdg. 17.60 (978-0-613-67605-2(X)) Tandem Library Bks.

Lane, Stephanie. Ecstasy. 2005. (Drug Education Library). (Illus.). 112p. (YA). (gr. 7-10). lib. bdg. 32.45 (978-1-59018-415-8(7) , Lucent Bks.) Thomson Gale.

Lennard-Brown, Sarah. Cocaine. 2004. (Health Issues Ser.). (Illus.). 64p. (J). 30.00 (978-0-7398-6893-5(4)) Harcourt Schl. Pubs.

—Drugs. 2002. (Health Issues Ser.). (Illus.). 64p. (YA). (gr. 6-8). lib. bdg. 28.54 (978-0-7398-4773-2(2)) Raintree.

LeVert, Suzanne. The Facts about Antidepressants. 2006. (Drugs Ser.). (Illus.). 112p. (J). lib. bdg. 39.93 (978-0-7614-2241-9(2) , Benchmark Bks.) Cavendish, Marshall Corp.

—The Facts about Ecstasy. 2004. (J). 37.07 (978-0-7614-1807-8(5) , Benchmark Bks.) Cavendish, Marshall Corp.

—The Facts about Steroids. 2004. (J). 37.07 (978-0-7614-1808-5(3)) Benchmark Investigative Group.

Levete, Sarah. Drugs. 2007. (Let's Talk about Ser.). (Illus.). 32p. (J). (gr. 3-5). lib. bdg. 27.10 (***978-1-59604-090-8(4)***) Stargazer Bks.

Libal, Joyce. Antidepressants & Social Anxiety: A Pill for Shyness? 2006. (Antidepressants Ser.). (Illus.). 120p. (J). (gr. 7 up). (978-1-4222-0098-8(1)) Mason Crest Pubs.

Llewellyn, Claire. Me Hace Bien o Mal? Aprender Sobre Medicamentos, Drogas y Salud. Gordon, Mike, illus. (SPA.). (J). (gr. k-2). pap. (978-950-24-0946-7(9)) Albatros ARG. *Dist:* Lectorum Pubns., Inc.

Lockwood, Brad. Ketamine. 2006. (Drug Abuse & Society Ser.). (Illus.). 64p. (J). (gr. 7-12). lib. bdg. 27.95 (978-1-4042-0911-4(5)) Rosen Publishing Group, Inc., The.

Louise I. Gerdes. Marijuana. 2006. (Illus.). 244p. (gr. 6-10). 29.95 (978-0-7377-3583-3(X) , Greenhaven Pr., Inc.) Thomson Gale.

Marcovitz, Hal. Marijuana. 2006. (Drug Education Library). (Illus.). 112p. (J). (gr. 7-10). 32.45 (978-1-59018-959-7(0) , Lucent Bks.) Thomson Gale.

—Methamphetamine. 2005. (Drug Educatrion Library). (Illus.). 112p. (YA). (gr. 7-10). lib. bdg. 32.45 (978-1-59018-418-9(1) , Lucent Bks.) Thomson Gale.

—Pcp. 2005. (Drug Educatrion Library). (Illus.). 112p. (J). (gr. 7-10). lib. bdg. 32.45 (978-1-59018-420-2(3) , Lucent Bks.) Thomson Gale.

Mayo Clinic Staff, contrib. by. Getting the Most from Your Medications. 2002. (Mayo Clinic on Health Ser.). (Illus.). 36,52p. (YA). (gr. 8 up). lib. bdg. (978-1-59084-251-5(0)) Mason Crest Pubs.

McGuigan, Jim. The Drug Trade. 2004. (Face the Facts Ser.). (Illus.). 56p. (J). 28.56 (978-1-4109-1072-1(5)) Harcourt Schl. Pubs.

Mitchell, E. Siobhan. Anti-Depressants. 2003. (Drugs, the Straight Facts Ser.). (Illus.). 112p. (gr. 9-13). 30.00 (978-0-7910-7635-4(0) , Chelsea Hse.) Facts On File, Inc.

Monroe, Judy. Antidepressants. 2001. (Drug Library). (Illus.). 128p. (YA). (gr. 6-12). pap. 13.26 (978-0-7660-1917-1(9)) Enslow Pubs., Inc.

—LSD, PCP & Hallucinogen Drug Dangers. 2000. (Drug Dangers Ser.). (Illus.). 64p. (YA). (gr. 4-10). lib. bdg. 27.93 (978-0-7660-1318-6(9)) Enslow Pubs., Inc.

Mur, Cindy. Drug Testing. 2006. 80-244*p. (gr. 10-12). 29.95 (978-0-7377-3093-7(5)); pap. 21.20 (978-0-7377-3094-4(3)) Thomson Gale. (Greenhaven Pr., Inc.).

Murphy, Patricia J. Avoiding Drugs. 2006. (Illus.). 32p. (J). pap. 5.95 (978-0-8225-2779-4(0) , Lerner Pubns.) Lerner Publishing Group.

—Evitar las Drogas. 2005. (Libros para Avanzar (Pull Ahead Bks.)). (SPA., Illus.). 32p. (J). (gr. 3-7). lib. bdg. 22.60 (978-0-8225-3172-2(0) , Ediciones Lerner) Lerner Publishing Group.

Nadelson, Carol C. & Reinburg, Claire E., eds. Psychological Disorders Related to Designer Drugs. 1999. (Encyclopedia of Psychological Disorders Ser.). (Illus.). 88p. (YA). (gr. 6 up). 35.00 (978-0-7910-4957-0(4) , Chelsea Hse.) Facts On File, Inc.

Naik, Anita. Drugs. 2nd ed. 2005. (Illus.). 144p. (YA). pap. 12.00 (978-0-340-88392-1(8) , Hodder & Stoughton) Hodder General Publishing Division GBR. *Dist:* Trafalgar Square Publishing.

Newman, Gerald & Layfield, Eleanor Newman. PCP (The Drug Library) 2001. (Drug Library). (Illus.). 128p. (YA). (gr. 6-12). pap. 13.26 (978-0-7660-1927-0(6)) Enslow Pubs., Inc.

Newton, David E. Chemistry of Drugs. 2007. (New Chemistry Ser.). 192p. (J). (gr. 6-12). 35.00 (978-0-8160-5276-9(X)) Facts On File, Inc.

—Drug Testing: An Issue for School, Sports, & Work. 1999. (Issues in Focus Ser.). (Illus.). 128p. (YA). (gr. 6-12). lib. bdg. 26.60 (978-0-89490-954-2(1)) Enslow Pubs., Inc.

Olive, M. Foster. Designer Drugs. 2003. (Drugs, the Straight Facts Ser.). (Illus.). 112p. (gr. 9-13). 30.00 (978-0-7910-7638-5(5) , Chelsea Hse.) Facts On File, Inc.

—Sleep AIDS. Triggle, David J., ed. 2005. (Drugs: the Straight Facts Ser.). (Illus.). 106p. (YA). (gr. 9-12). 30.00 (978-0-7910-8200-3(8) , Chelsea Hse.) Facts On File, Inc.

Palenque, Stephanie Maher. Crack & Cocaine = Busted! 2005. (Busted! Ser.). (Illus.). 104p. (J). (gr. 6-12). lib. bdg. 31.93 (978-0-7660-2169-3(6)) Enslow Pubs., Inc.

Parker, Jim. DrugWise: A Handbook for Young People. rev. ed. 1999. (YA). pap. 3.50 (978-0-89230-229-1(1)) Do It Now Foundation.

Pollard, Jim & Kent, Chloe. Tobacco. 2004. (Teen Issues Ser.). (Illus.). 56p. (J). (gr. 6-8). lib. bdg. 28.56 (978-1-4109-0614-4(0)) Harcourt Schl. Pubs.

Pomere, Jonas. Frequently Asked Questions about Drug Testing. 2006. (FAQ Ser.). (Illus.). 64p. (J). (gr. 7-12). lib. bdg. 27.95 (***978-1-4042-1973-1(0)*** , 1267045) Rosen Publishing Group, Inc., The.

Porterfield, Jason. Downers: Depressant Abuse. 2007. (J). lib. bdg. (***978-1-4042-1957-1(9)***) Rosen Publishing Group, Inc., The.

Rees, Jonathan. Drugs. 2002. (World Issues Ser.). (Illus.). 57p. (J). lib. bdg. 28.50 (978-1-931983-29-7(1)) Chrysalis Education.

—Drugs. 2005. (It's Your Health Ser.). (Illus.). 45p. (J). (gr. 6-9). lib. bdg. 29.95 (978-1-58340-586-4(0)) Smart Apple Media.

—Drugs. 2006. (Global Issues Ser.). (Illus.). 64p. (J). (gr. 4-12). pap. 12.95 (978-1-55285-743-4(3) , Walrus Bks.) Whitecap Bks., Ltd. CAN. *Dist:* Firefly Bks., Ltd.

Robbins, Paul R. Designer Drugs. 2001. (Drug Library). (Illus.). 104p. (YA). (gr. 6-12). pap. 13.26 (978-0-7660-1920-1(9)) Enslow Pubs., Inc.

Roberts, Jeremy. Prescription Drug Abuse. 2005. (Drug Abuse Prevention Library). (Illus.). 64p. (YA). (gr. 7-12). lib. bdg. 25.25 (978-0-8239-3158-3(7) , DRPRES) Rosen Publishing Group, Inc., The.

Rooney, Anne. Drugs on the Street. 2007. (Illus.). 48p. (J). (***978-1-58340-986-2(6)***) Smart Apple Media.

Royston, Angela. Marijuana. 2000. (Learn to Say No! Ser.). (Illus.). (J). (gr. 4-6). lib. bdg. 22.79 (978-1-57572-238-2(0)) Heinemann Library.

Russell, Craig. Antidepressants & Their Side Effects: Managing the Risks. 2006. (Antidepressants Ser.). (Illus.). 120p. (J). (gr. 7 up). (978-1-4222-0097-1(3)) Mason Crest Pubs.

—Psychostimulants As Antidepressants: Worth the Risk? 2007. (Antidepressants Ser.). (Illus.). 112p. (J). (gr. 7 up). 24.95 (978-1-4222-0107-7(4)) Mason Crest Pubs.

Sanders, Pete & Myers, Steve. Taking Drugs. 2005. (Choices & Decisions Ser.). (Illus.). 32p. (J). (gr. 4-7). lib. bdg. 27.10 (978-1-59604-077-9(7)) Stargazer Bks.

Sanna, E. J. Heroin & Other Opiates: Poppies' Perilous Children. 2008. (J). (***978-1-4222-0156-5(2)***) Mason Crest Pubs.

Schleichert, Elizabeth. Marijuana. 2001. (Drug Library). (Illus.). 104p. (YA). (gr. 6-12). pap. 13.26 (978-0-7660-1925-6(X)) Enslow Pubs., Inc.

C D

Schroeder, Brock E. Ecstasy. 2003. (Drugs, the Straight Facts Ser.). (Illus.). 112p. (gr. 9-13). 30.00 (978-0-7910-7633-0(4) , Chelsea Hse.) Facts On File, Inc.

Sheff, Nic. Tweak: Growing up on Methamphetamines. 2008. 336p. (YA). (gr. 9 up). 16.99 ***978-1-4169-1362-7(9)** , Ginne Seo Bks) Simon & Schuster Children's Publishing.

Sherry, Clifford J. Drugs & Eating Disorders. rev. ed. 1999. (Drug Abuse Prevention Library). (Illus.). 64p. (J). (gr. 7-12). lib. bdg. 25.25 (978-0-8239-3005-0(X) , DREADI) Rosen Publishing Group, Inc., The.

Slade, Suzanne. OxyContin Abuse. 2007. (J). ***978-1-4042-1954-0(4))** Rosen Publishing Group, Inc., The.

Somerville, Clive. The Drug Enforcement Administration. 2002. (Rescue & Prevention Ser.). (Illus.). 96p. (J). (gr. 7 up). lib. bdg. (978-1-59084-413-7(0)) Mason Crest Pubs.

Stewart, Jan. Stars How Drugs & Alcohol Affect Us. 2004. (Illus.). 32p. (J). pap. 9.95 (978-0-89793-314-8(1)) Hunter Hse., Inc.

Toufexis, Donna & Hammack, Sayamwong. Anti-anxiety Drugs. 2006. (Drugs Ser.). (Illus.). 128p. (J). (gr. 9-12). 30.00 (978-0-7910-8556-1(2) , Chelsea Hse.) Facts On File, Inc.

Triggle, David J., ed. The Straight Facts. (Drugs, the Straight Facts Ser.). (Illus.). (J). 137.70 (978-0-7910-7258-5(4) , Chelsea Hse.) Facts On File, Inc.

The Truth about Drugs. 1998. 144p. (YA). pap. 9.95 (978-0-7894-3515-6(2)) Dorling Kindersley Publishing, Inc.

Walker, Ida J. Sedatives & Hypnotics: Deadly Downers. 2008. (J). ***978-1-4222-0163-3(5))** Mason Crest Pubs.

Warburton, Lianne, et al. Amphetamines & Other Stimulants. 2008. (Junior Drug Awareness Ser.). 112p. (J). (gr. 5-8). 30.00 ***978-0-7910-9712-0(9)** , Chelsea Hse.) Facts On File, Inc.

Weatherly, Myra. Ecstasy & Other Designer Drug Dangers. (Drug Dangers Ser.). (Illus.). 64p. (gr. 4-10). 2001. (YA). pap. 10.95 (978-0-7660-1963-8(2)); 2000. (J). lib. bdg. 27.93 (978-0-7660-1322-3(7)) Enslow Pubs., Inc.

Wilkinson, Beth. Drugs & Depression. rev. ed. 1999. (Drug Abuse Prevention Library). (Illus.). 64p. (YA). (gr. 7-12). 25.25 (978-0-8239-3004-3(1) , DRDEPR) Rosen Publishing Group, Inc., The.

Winters, Adam & Sommers, Michael A. Tobacco & Your Mouth: The Incredibly Disgusting Story. 2005. (Incredibly Disgusting Drugs Ser.). (Illus.). 48p. (YA). (gr. 5-8). lib. bdg. 25.25 (978-0-8239-3250-4(8) , DDTOMO) Rosen Publishing Group, Inc., The.

Wolf, Marie. GHB & Analogs: High Risk Club Drugs. 2006. (Drug Abuse & Society Ser.). (Illus.). 64p. (J). (gr. 7-12). 27.95 (978-1-4042-0910-7(7)) Rosen Publishing Group, Inc., The.

Ziemer, Maryann. Quaaludes. 2001. (Drug Library). (Illus.). 112p. (YA). (gr. 6-12). pap. 13.26 (978-0-7660-1929-4(2)) Enslow Pubs., Inc.

DRUGS—FICTION

Anderson, J. A. Dragon Fire No.1: The Starriders Saga. 2002. (gr. 7-12). lib. bdg. 16.40 (978-0-613-84083-5(6)) Tandem Library Bks.

Cooper, Patrick. I Is Someone Else. 304p. (YA). 2007. (gr. 7-11). mass mkt. 6.50 (978-0-440-23919-2(2) , Laurel Leaf); 2006. (Illus.). (gr. 9). 16.95 (978-0-385-73269-7(4) , Delacorte Bks. for Young Readers); 2006. (Illus.). (gr. 9). lib. bdg. 18.99 (978-0-385-90286-1(7) , Delacorte Bks. for Young Readers) Random Hse. Children's Bks.

DeFelice, Cynthia C. Death at Devil's Bridge. 2000. 192p. (J). (gr. 3-7). 16.00 (978-0-374-31723-2(2) , Farrar, Straus & Giroux (BYR)) Farrar, Straus & Giroux.

—Death at Devil's Bridge. 2002. 192p. (J). (gr. 3-7). pap. 5.99 (978-0-06-441037-3(4) , Harper Trophy) HarperCollins Pubs.

—Death at Devil's Bridge. 2002. (gr. 3-6). lib. bdg. 14.10 (978-0-613-82528-3(4)) Tandem Library Bks.

Gaetz, Dayle Campbell. No Problem. 2003. (Orca Soundings Ser.). 96p. (J). (gr. 7-12). pap. 7.95 (978-1-55143-231-1(5)) Orca Bk. Pubs. USA.

—No Problem. 2003. (gr. 7-12). lib. bdg. 16.40 (978-0-613-62976-8(0)) Tandem Library Bks.

Halvorson, Marilyn. Let It Go. 2004. 224p. (YA). (gr. 7-9). (978-1-55005-105-6(9)) Fitzhenry & Whiteside, Ltd.

Hinton, S. E. Esto Ya Es Otra Historia. (SPA.). (J). 6.95 (978-84-204-4121-4(X)) Santillana USA Publishing Co., Inc.

—That Was Then, This Is Now. 1998. 160p. (YA). (gr. 7-12). pap. 7.99 (978-0-14-038966-1(0) , Puffin) Penguin Group (USA) Inc.

—That Was Then, This Is Now. 1998. (Puffin Book Ser.). (YA). (978-0-606-12861-2(1)) Tandem Library Bks.

Hopkins, Ellen. Glass. 2007. 688p. (YA). (gr. 9 up). 16.99 (978-1-4169-4090-6(1) , McElderry, Margaret K.) Simon & Schuster Children's Publishing.

Kennedy, John Wayne. To Slay a Demon. Kennedy, John Wayne, illus. 2001. (Illus.). 224p. (gr. k-2). pap. 14.95 (978-1-880090-97-8(X)) Galde Pr., Inc.

Ketchedjian, Armen G. & Ketch. Golden Apples. 2007. 12.95 (978-0-9778274-0-4(2)) Parental Interventional Tools, Inc.

Mac, Carrie. Charmed. 2006. 112p. (YA). lib. bdg. 14.95 (978-1-55143-578-7(0)) Orca Bk. Pubs. USA.

McCormick, Patricia. My Brother's Keeper. 2006. 192p. (gr. 5-17). reprint ed. pap. 5.99 (978-0-7868-5174-4(0)) Hyperion Pr.

McNab, Andy & Rigby, Robert. Meltdown. 2008. 276p. (YA). (gr. 7). 16.99 ***978-0-399-24686-9(X)** , Putnam Juvenile) Penguin Group (USA) Inc.

McRae, David. Blood of the Donnellys. 2008. 152p. (YA). pap. 9.99 ***978-1-55002-754-9(9)** , Sandcastle Bks.) Dundurn Group, The CAN. *Dist:* Univ. of Toronto Pr.

Nixon-Weaver, Elizabeth. Rooster. 2001. (Illus.). 320p. (J). (gr. 7 up). 16.95 (978-1-58837-001-3(1)) Winslow Pr.

Rodriguez, Paul. Don't Do Drugs! Do Dance! Character Education/Prevention. Rodriguez, Paul, illus. 2003. (Illus.). 32p. (J). lib. bdg. 15.99 (978-0-9744770-1-5(X)) Rodro.

Runaway-A Survivor, 1. 2004. 365p. 14.99 (978-0-9753252-0-9(5)) IndieArtz, Inc.

Thunder Brook: Escape from the Land of Huffra, Adam & the Valley of the Weedgrass. 2005. (Illus.). 136p. (J). 14.95 (978-0-9768152-0-4(6)) Buttercup Media.

Vaval, Fisepe. The Blueprint. Bubsy, Nancy, ed. 2003. 270p. (YA). pap. 15.00 (978-0-9743207-0-0(6)) Tayes Bks.

Wert, Debra L. Caterfly: Mac's Back Struggling to Stay Drug-Free. Wert, Debra L., illus. 1998. (Illus.). (J). (gr. 4-6). pap. 16.00 (978-0-944576-11-3(7)) Rocky River Pubs., LLC.

DRUGS—HISTORY

Facklam, Margery, et al. Modern Medicines: The Discovery & Development of Healing Drugs. 2nd ed. 2004. (Science & Technology in Focus Ser.). (Illus.). 240p. (YA). (gr. 6-12). 35.00 (978-0-8160-4706-2(5)) Facts On File, Inc.

Fuller, Robert C. Stairways to Heaven: Drugs in American Religious History. 2000. 237p. (YA). reprint ed. 27.00 (978-0-7567-6120-2(4)) DIANE Publishing Co.

Rose, Susannah & Shearing, Colin. Opium, a Journey Through Time. 2005. (Illus.). 128p. 19.95 (978-1-904668-50-3(X)) Mercury Bks. Ltd. GBR. *Dist:* International Publishers Marketing.

Townsend, John. Medication: Pills, Powders & Potions. 2005. (Raintree Freestyle Ser.). (Illus.). 56p. (J). pap. (978-1-4109-1340-1(6)) Steck-Vaughn.

—Pills, Powders & Potions: A History of Medication. (Freestyle Express Ser.). 2006. 56p. (978-1-4109-2540-4(4)); 2006. 48p. pap. (978-1-4109-2545-9(5)); 2005. (Illus.). 56p. (YA). (gr. 8-12). lib. bdg. 32.86 (978-1-4109-1335-7(X)) Steck-Vaughn.

Weintraub, Aileen. Heroin: A MyReportLinks. com Book. 2005. (Drugs Ser.). (Illus.). 48p. (J). lib. bdg. 25.26 (978-0-7660-5275-8(3) , MyReportLinks.com Bks.) Enslow Pubs., Inc.

DRUGS—LAW AND LEGISLATION

Croft, Jennifer. Drugs & the Legalization Debate. rev. ed. (Drug Abuse Prevention Library). (Illus.). 64p. (YA). (gr. 7-12). 2005. lib. bdg. 25.25 (978-0-8239-3206-1(0) , DRLEDE); 2000. lib. bdg. 17.95 (978-0-8239-2509-4(9) , 2509-9) Rosen Publishing Group, Inc., The.

Harmon, Daniel E. The Food & Drug Administration. 2002. (Your Government Ser.). 64p. (J). (gr. 4-7). 25.00 (978-0-7910-6791-8(2) , Chelsea Hse.) Facts On File, Inc.

Marvis, B. Drugs, Crime & Criminal Justice. 2001. (Crime, Justice & Punishment Ser.). (Illus.). 80p. (YA). (gr. 8 up). 30.00 (978-0-7910-4262-5(6) , Chelsea Hse.) Facts On File, Inc.

Ruschmann, Paul. Legalizing Marijuana/By Paul Ruschmann. 2003. (Point/Counterpoint Ser.). (Illus.). 112p. (gr. 9-13). 32.95 (978-0-7910-7483-1(8) , Chelsea Hse.) Facts On File, Inc.

Ruschmann, Paul. Prescription & Non-prescription Drugs. 2007. (Point/Counterpoint Ser.). 136p. (gr. 9). 32.95 ***978-0-7910-9552-2(5)** , Chelsea Hse.) Facts On File, Inc.

Tardiff, Joe. Marijuana. 2007. (Contemporary Issues Companion Ser.). (Illus.). 240p. (YA). (gr. 10-12). pap. 24.95 ***978-0-7377-2776-0(4)** , Greenhaven Pr., Inc.) Thomson Gale.

DRUIDS AND DRUIDISM

Hamilton, John. Witches. 2007. (ENG., Illus.). 32p. (J). lib. bdg. 24.21 ***978-1-59928-776-8(5)** , ABDO & Daughters) ABDO Publishing Co.

DRUIDS AND DRUIDISM—FICTION

Boyes, Vivien. The Druid's Head. 1998. (J). (gr. 4-8). pap. 19.95 (978-0-8464-4596-8(4)) Beekman Bks., Inc.

Brooks, Terry. Morgawr. 2003. (Voyage of the Jerle Shannara Ser.: Bk. 3). lib. bdg. 16.45 (978-0-613-66596-4(1)) Tandem Library Bks.

Farmer, Nancy. The Land of the Silver Apples. Sardinha, Rick, illus. 2007. 512p. (J). (gr. 5-9). 18.99 ***978-1-4169-0735-0(1)** , Atheneum/Richard Jackson Bks.) Simon & Schuster Children's Publishing.

Farmer, Nancy. The Sea of Trolls. 480p. (J). (gr. 5-8). 2004. (Illus.). 17.95 (978-0-689-86744-6(1) , Atheneum); 2006. reprint ed. pap. 9.99 (978-0-689-86746-0(8) , Simon Pulse) Simon & Schuster Children's Publishing.

—The Sea of Trolls, l.t. ed. 2005. 554p. 23.95 (978-0-7862-7151-1(5)) Thorndike Pr.

Fisher, Catherine. Darkhenge. (J). 2007. 432p. pap. 7.99 (978-0-06-078584-0(5)); 2006. 352p. 15.99 (978-0-06-078582-6(9)) HarperCollins Pubs.

Freeman, Martha. The Spy Wore Shades. Date not set. 160p. (YA). (gr. 3 up). pap. 4.99 (978-0-06-440957-5(0)) HarperCollins Pubs.

—The Spy Wore Shades. Cigliano, Bill, illus. 2001. 240p. (J). (gr. 3 up). 15.89 (978-0-06-029270-6(9)) HarperCollins Pubs.

L'Engle, Madeleine. An Acceptable Time. 2007. 224p. (J). 6.99 (978-0-312-36862-3(3)); pap. 6.99 (978-0-312-36858-6(5)) Square Fish.

Pope, Elizabeth Marie. The Perilous Gard. Cuffari, Richard, illus. 2001. 280p. (J). (ps-7). per. 14.10 (978-0-613-35551-3(2)) Tandem Library Bks.

DRUM

Crask, Tom. Should I Play the Drums? 2006. (Learning Musical Instruments Ser.). (Illus.). 32p. (J). (gr. 3-5). lib. bdg. 28.21 (978-1-4034-8186-3(5)) Heinemann Library.

Davis, Billy, illus. Beat the Drum! This Old Man. 2000. (Rockin' Rhythm Band Board Books Ser.). 12p. (J). (ps-1). bds. 7.95 (978-0-439-19262-0(5)) Scholastic, Inc.

Feldstein, Sandy & Clark, Larry. Barcarolle - Snare Drum Solo with Piano Acc. 2005. (YA). pap. 10.95 (978-1-932895-96-4(5)) PlayinTime Productions, Inc.

Harcourt School Publishers Staff. Drums On Level: The Beat Goes On. 3rd ed. 2002. (Trophies Reading Program Ser.). (Illus.). pap. 5.10 (978-0-15-323093-6(2)) Harcourt Schl. Pubs.

Klingel, Cynthia Fitterer & Noyed, Robert B. Drums. 2002. (Wonder Books Level 1: Musical Instuments Ser.). (Illus.). 24p. (J). (ps-3). 22.79 (978-1-56766-946-6(8)) Child's World, Inc.

Riley, Peter D. Xtreme Drums. 2005. (Illus.). 80p. audio compact disk 14.95 (978-1-84492-019-8(4)) Sanctuary Publishing, Ltd. GBR. *Dist:* Warner Bros. Pubns.

Tischitanissohen. The Drum: A Training Aid for Ceremonial Teams. Tischitanissohen, illus. 10th rev. ed. 2002. (Illus.). 40p. (YA). (gr. 7 up). pap. 5.00 (978-0-9677560-0-4(6)) Dunbar, Doctor Jay.

Weber, Lou, ed. Elmo's Monster Music Drum Book. 2004. 12p. 15.98 (978-1-4127-3325-0(1) , PIL Kids) Publications International, Ltd.

Zubraski, Dave & Jenner, Clive. Fast Forward: Hip Hop Drum Patterns. 2004. (Illus.). 64p. audio compact disk 15.95 (978-0-7119-8398-4(4) , AM966493) Music Sales Corp.

DRUM—FICTION

Bynum, Eboni & Jackson, Roland. Jamari's Drum. Wagué Diakité, Baba, illus. 2004. 32p. (J). 16.95 (978-0-88899-531-5(8)) Groundwood Bks. CAN. *Dist:* Perseus Distribution.

Carrigan, Nancy J., et al. Rabbinia Hopinska's Magic Music. Carrigan, Nancy J., illus. 1998. 32p. (J). (gr. 2-5). pap. 6.95 (978-1-890156-01-5(9)) Arbor Hill Pr.

Coleman, Evelyn. To Be a Drum. Robinson, Aminah B., illus. 2004. 32p. (J). (gr. k up). pap. 6.95 (978-0-8075-8007-3(4)) Whitman, Albert & Co.

Darden, Floyd. Drumdee makes a Drum. 2007. 15.95 ***978-1-59526-711-5(5))** Media Creations, Inc.

Davol, Marguerite W. The Loudest, Fastest, Best Drummer in Kansas. Smith, Cat Bowman, illus. 2000. 32p. (J). (gr. k-4). 16.99 (978-0-531-33191-0(1)); pap. 15.95 (978-0-531-30191-3(5)) Scholastic, Inc. (Orchard Bks.).

Donnelly, Michael. Awakening Curry Buckle. 2005. (ALB.). 380p. (YA). pap. 14.99 (978-1-59092-226-2(3) , Blue Works) Windstorm Creative.

Francis, Panama, et al. David Gets His Drum. Velasquez, Eric, illus. 2002. 32p. (J). (gr. k-3). 16.95 (978-0-7614-5088-7(2)) Cavendish, Marshall Corp.

Pinkney, Brian. Max Found Two Sticks. Pinkney, Brian, illus. 2002. (Illus.). (J). 15.53 (978-0-7587-3106-7(X)) Book Wholesalers, Inc.

Protopopescu, Orel Odinov. Two Sticks. Wilsdorf, Anne, illus. 2007. 32p. (J). (ps-1). 16.00 (978-0-374-38022-9(8)) Farrar, Straus & Giroux.

Rodowsky, Colby. Jason Rat-A-Tat. Peck, Beth, illus. 2002. 80p. (J). (gr. 2-4). 15.00 (978-0-374-33671-4(7) , Farrar, Straus & Giroux (BYR)) Farrar, Straus & Giroux.

Todd, Traci N. The Drum Circle. Reisch, Jesse, illus. 2006. (J). (978-1-58987-023-9(9)) Kindermusik International.

DRUNKENNESS

see Alcoholism

DRY GOODS

see Textile Industry

DUBLIN (IRELAND)—FICTION

Doyle, Roddy. The Meanwhile Adventures. Ajhar, Brian, illus. 176p. (J). 2006. pap. 5.99 (978-0-439-66211-6(7)); 2004. (gr. 4-7). pap. 16.95 (978-0-439-66210-9(9)) Scholastic, Inc. (Levine, Arthur A. Bks.).

Gibson, Maggie. Alice Little & the Big Girls' Blouse. 2nd ed. 2001. 266p. (J). pap. 9.99 (978-0-575-40330-7(6) , Weidenfeld & Nicolson) Orion Publishing Group, Ltd. GBR. *Dist:* Independent Pubs. Group.

McDonnell, Vincent. The Knock Airport Mystery. 2006. (Illus.). 203p. (J). pap. 9.95 (978-1-903464-87-8(0)) Collins Pr., The IRL. *Dist:* Dufour Editions, Inc.

Regan, Peter. Riverside: The Curse. Myler, Terry, illus. 2004. 127p. (J). pap. 9.95 (978-1-901737-46-2(2)) Anvil Bks., Ltd. IRL. *Dist:* Dufour Editions, Inc.

Reilly, Tina. The Onion Girl. 2001. 520p. pap. (978-1-84223-013-8(1)) Poolbeg Pr. IRL. *Dist:* Dufour Editions, Inc.

Thompson, Kate. Switchers. 220p. (J). (gr. 4-7). pap. 5.99 (978-0-8072-1553-1(8)); 2004. (Switchers Ser.; Vol. 1). (gr. 5-9). pap. 38.00 incl. audio (978-0-8072-8138-3(7) , YA115SP) Random Hse. Audio Publishing Group. (Listening Library).

—Switchers. 1999. (978-0-606-17387-2(0)); (gr. 5-8). lib. bdg. 14.15 (978-0-613-20224-4(4)) Tandem Library Bks.

DU BOIS, W. E. B. (WILLIAM EDWARD BURGHARDT), 1868-1963

Gillis, Jennifer Blizin. W.E.B. Dubois. 2005. (Illus.). 32p. (J). (978-1-4034-6982-3(2)); pap. (978-1-4034-6989-2(X)) Heinemann Library.

Hinman, Bonnie. A Stranger in My Own House: The Story of W. E. B. du Bois. 2005. (Civil Rights Leaders Ser.). (Illus.). 176p. (J). (gr. 6-12). 26.95 (978-1-931798-45-7(1)) Reynolds, Morgan Inc.

Rowh, Mark. W. E. B. Du Bois: Champion of Civil Rights. 1999. (African-American Biographies Ser.). (Illus.). 128p. (J). (gr. 6-12). lib. bdg. 26.60 (978-0-7660-1209-7(3)) Enslow Pubs., Inc.

Stafford, Mark & Davenport, John, texts. W. E. B. Du Bois: Scholar & Activist. 2004. (Black Americans of Achievement Ser.). (Illus.). 112p. (J). (gr. 6-12). 30.00 (978-0-7910-8158-7(3) , Chelsea Hse.) Facts On File, Inc.

Williams, Horace Randall. W. E. B. Du Bois: A Scholar's Courageous Life. 2001. (J). (gr. 4-7). pap. 7.95 (978-1-58838-024-1(6) , Junebug Bks.) NewSouth, Inc.

DUCKS

Arnosky, Jim. All Night near the Water. 1999. (J). lib. bdg. (978-0-606-16846-5(X)) Tandem Library Bks.

Baker, Keith. Quack & Count! 1999. (Illus.). 24p. (J). (ps-2). 15.00 (978-0-15-292858-2(8)) Harcourt Children's Bks.

Barry, Frances. Duckie's Rainbow. Barry, Frances, illus. 2004. (Illus.). 14p. (J). (gr. k-ps). 7.99 (978-0-7636-2066-0(1)) Candlewick Pr.

Brenner, Barbara & Takaya, Julia. Chibi: A True Story from Japan. Otani, June, illus. 1999. 63p. (J). (ps-ps). lib. bdg. 14.10 (978-0-613-17774-0(6)) Tandem Library Bks.

Brenner, Barbara, et al. Chibi: A True Story from Japan. Otani, June, illus. 1999. 64p. (J). (gr. k-3). pap. 7.95 (978-0-395-72088-2(5) , Clarion Bks.) Houghton Mifflin Co. Trade & Reference Div.

Bygrave, Linda. Duck. (Illus.). 24p. (YA). (gr. 1 up). lib. bdg. 22.80 (978-1-931983-48-8(8)) Chrysalis Education.

Cox, Phil Roxbee, ed. Find the Duck. Cartwright, Stephen, illus. 2004. (Find It Board Bks.). 10p. (J). (ps up). 3.95 (978-0-7460-3821-5(6)) EDC Publishing.

Davie, Helen K. Ducks Don't Get Wet. 1999. (Let's-Read-and-Find-Out Ser.). (J). 11.79 (978-0-606-16695-9(5)) Tandem Library Bks.

DK Publishing Staff. Duck. 2007. (See How They Grow Ser.). 24p. (J). pap. 3.99 ***978-0-7566-3263-2(3))** Dorling Kindersley Publishing, Inc.

Do Ducks Live in the Desert? (Animals All Around Ser.). 24p. (J). 7.95 (978-1-4048-0379-4(3)) Picture Window Bks.

Dorling Kindersley Publishing Staff. Duck. 2005. 8p. (J). 5.99 (978-0-7566-1710-3(3)) Dorling Kindersley Publishing, Inc.

—Duckling. 2006. (Watch Me Grow Ser.). 24p. (J). pap. 4.99 (978-0-7566-2212-1(3)) Dorling Kindersley Publishing, Inc.

—Duckpond Dip. 2006. (Dk Readers Ser.). (Illus.). 32p. (J). 14.99 (978-0-7566-1958-9(0)); pap. 3.99 (978-0-7566-1957-2(2)) Dorling Kindersley Publishing, Inc.

Duck. 2004. (J). per. (978-1-57657-354-9(0)) Paradise Pr., Inc.

Ducks. Date not set. (Old MacDonald Stickers Ser.). (Illus.). 16p. (J). 2.98 (978-0-7525-7061-7(7)); 5.98 (978-0-7525-9967-0(4)) Parragon, Inc.

Ducks Have Ducklings. (Animals & Their Young Ser.). 24p. (J). 7.95 (978-0-7565-1241-5(7)) Compass Point Bks.

Endres, Hollie. Ducks. 2007. (Illus.). 24p. (J). lib. bdg. 19.95 (978-1-60014-112-6(9)) Bellwether Media.

Frahm, Randy. Duck Hunting. 2008. (J). ***978-1-4296-0818-3(8))** Capstone Pr., Inc.

Ganeri, Anita. Ducks & Ducklings. 2007. (J). ***978-1-58340-810-0(X))** Smart Apple Media.

Giguere, Sarah. Ducks: Includes Fact Sheets, Bulletin Board Ideas, Songs & Finger Plays, Games, Journal Ideas, Activity Sheets & More! Bachand, Stephen, illus. 2000. 29p. (J). ring bd. 18.95 (978-1-928972-06-8(3)) Critter Pubns.

Goldin, Augusta. Ducks Don't Get Wet. Davie, Helen K., illus. 1999. (Let's-Read-and-Find-Out Science Ser.). 32p. (J). (ps-1). 15.95 (978-0-06-027881-6(1)); 15.89 (978-0-06-027882-3(X)); pap. 4.99 (978-0-06-445187-1(9) , Harper Trophy) HarperCollins Pubs.

—Ducks Don't Get Wet. 1999. (gr. k-3). lib. bdg. 13.00 (978-0-8335-4636-4(8)) Tandem Library Bks.

Hall, Margaret. Ducks & Their Ducklings. 2003. (Animal Offspring Ser.). (Illus.). 24p. (J). lib. bdg. 17.26 (978-0-7368-2106-3(6) , Pebble Bks.) Capstone Pr., Inc.

—Mallards. Saunders-Smith, Gail, ed. 2004. (Wetland Animals Ser.). (Illus.). 24p. (J). (gr. k-1). lib. bdg. 15.93 (978-0-7368-2065-3(5) , Pebble Bks.) Capstone Pr., Inc.

Hedelin, Pascale. Face-to-Face with the Duck. 2005. (Illus.). 28p. (J). 9.95 (978-1-57091-457-7(5)) Charlesbridge Publishing, Inc.

Hickman, Pamela & Collins, Heather. A New Duck: My First Look at the Life Cycle of a Bird. 1999. (My First Look at Nature Ser.). (Illus.). 20p. (J). (gr. k-3). (978-1-55074-613-6(8)) Kids Can Pr., Ltd.

Hills, Tad. What's up Duck? Hills, Tad, illus. 2008. (Illus.). 22p. (J). bds. ***978-0-375-84738-7(3)** , Schwartz & Wade Bks.) Random Hse. Children's Bks.

Hipp, Andrew. The Life Cycle of a Duck. 2002. (Life Cycles Library). (Illus.). 24p. (J). lib. bdg. 18.75 (978-0-8239-5868-9(X) , PowerKids Pr.) Rosen Publishing Group, Inc., The.

Hudak, Heather C. Ducks. 2006. (J). (978-1-59036-504-5(6)); (978-1-59036-505-2(4)) Weigl Pubs., Inc.

Ibsen, Henrik. The Wild Duck. 2000. 96p. (gr. 9). pap. 2.00 (978-0-486-41116-3(8)) Dover Pubns., Inc.

Jaffe, Elizabeth Dana. Ducks Have Ducklings. 2002. (Animals & Their Young Ser.). (Illus.). 24p. (J). (gr. 1 up). lib. bdg. 18.60 (978-0-7565-0170-9(9)) Compass Point Bks.

Kavanagh, James. Ducks Nature Activity Book. 2004. (Pocket Naturalist Ser.). (Illus.). 32p. pap. 6.95 (978-1-58355-258-2(8)) Waterford Pr., Ltd.

Ling, Mary, ed. Duck. 2001. (See How They Grow Ser.). (Illus.). 24p. (J). (ps-3). pap. 4.99 (978-0-7894-7655-5(X)) Dorling Kindersley Publishing, Inc.

Little Ducks Don't Fly. (Illus.). 32p. (J). (ps-3). (978-0-914082-27-9(2)) Syentek, Inc.

Llewellyn, Claire. Duck. Mendez, Simon, tr. Mendez, Simon, illus. 2004. (Starting Life Ser.). 24p. (J). (ps-3). ring bd. 16.95 (978-1-55971-878-3(1) , NorthWord Bks. for Young Readers) T&N Children's Publishing.

Love, Maryann Cusimano. Alphaducks. 2007. (Lucky Ducks Ser.). 14p. (J). (ps-k). pap. 6.99 (978-0-8431-2495-8(4) , Price Stern Sloan) Penguin Group (USA) Inc.

Mara, Wil. Ducks. 2008. (J). ***978-0-7614-2927-2(1))** Cavendish, Marshall Bks., Ltd.

McMillan, Bruce. Days of the Ducklings. (Illus.). 32p. (J). (gr. k-3). 2007. 6.95 ***(978-0-618-86270-2(6));*** 2001. tchr. ed. 16.00 (978-0-618-04878-6(2)) Houghton Mifflin Co. Trade & Reference Div. (Walter Lorraine).

Miller, Sara Swan. Waterfowl: From Swans to Screamers. 1999. (Animals in Order Ser.). (Illus.). 48p. (J). (gr. 4-6). 26.50 (978-0-531-11584-8(4) , Watts, Franklin) Scholastic Library Publishing.

Mitchell, Melanie S. Ducks. (First Step Nonfiction Ser.). (Illus.). (gr. k-2). 2005. 24p. lib. bdg. 17.27 (978-0-8225-4602-3(7)); 2002. 23p. (J). pap. 3.95 (978-0-8225-4603-0(5) , Lerner Pubns.) Lerner Publishing Group.

Morgan, Sally. Ducks & Other Birds. 2001. (Illus.). 32p. (J). lib. bdg. 24.25 (978-1-930643-44-4(6)) Chrysalis Education.

—From Egg to Duck. 2002. (How Things Grow Ser.). (Illus.). 32p. (J). lib. bdg. (978-1-930643-86-4(1)) Chrysalis Education.

Petty, Kate. Ducklings. 2005. (Illus.). 24p. (J). (ps-3). lib. bdg. 22.80 (978-1-59604-034-2(3)) Stargazer Bks.

Royer, Anne. Little Ducks. 2006. (Born to Be Wild Ser.). (Illus.). 23p. (J). lib. bdg. ***(978-0-8368-6697-1(5))*** Stevens, Gareth Inc.

Royston, Angela. The Duck. 2001. (978-0-606-22323-2(1)) Tandem Library Bks.

Savage, Stephen. Duck. 2005. (Illus.). 32p. (J). (978-0-7502-4660-6(X) , Hodder Wayland) Hodder Children's Division.

Schuh, Mari C. Ducks on the Farm. 2003. (On the Farm Ser.). (Illus.). 24p. (J). (gr. k-1). lib. bdg. 15.93 (978-0-7368-1661-8(5) , Pebble Bks.) Capstone Pr., Inc.

—Ducks on the Farm. (On the Farm Ser.). 24p. (J). pap. 5.95 (978-0-7368-3423-0(0)) Capstone Pr., Inc.

Sherman, Rose. Danielle the Duck. 2006. 17.00 (978-0-8059-9890-0(X)) Dorrance Publishing Co., Inc.

Spilsbury, Louise. Duck. 2005. (Heinemann Read & Learn Ser.). (Illus.). 24p. (J). (ps-1). lib. bdg. 20.64 (978-1-4034-6771-3(4)); pap. (978-1-4034-6776-8(5)) Heinemann Library.

Stockland, Patricia M. On the Duck Pond. Ouren, Todd, illus. 2007. (Barnyard Buddies Ser.). 24p. (J). (ps-2). lib. bdg. 25.65 ***(978-1-60270-027-7(3)*** , Looking Glass Library) Magic Wagon.

Swecker, Theodocia. Ducks, Ducks. Swecker, Theodocia, illus. 1998. (Illus.). 32p. (J). (ps-2). 14.95 (978-0-9666537-0-0(X)) Ducks Publishing.

Top That Publishing Staff, ed. Wacky Duck. 2004. (Wacky Animals Ser.). (Illus.). 10p. (J). pap. (978-1-84510-086-5(7)) Top That! Publishing PLC.

Twine, Alice. Ducks. 2008. (J). lib. bdg. ***(978-1-4042-3771-1(2)*** , PowerKids Pr.) Rosen Publishing Group, Inc., The.

Walker-Hodge, Judith. Animal Hospital. 1999. (Eyewitness Readers). (Illus.). 32p. (J). (gr. 5-4). pap. 3.99 (978-0-7894-3996-3(4) , 0-7894-4752-5) Dorling Kindersley Publishing, Inc.

—Animal Hospital. 1999. (J). 10.79 (978-0-606-18988-0(2)) Tandem Library Bks.

Wallace, Karen. Duckling Days. 1999. (Eyewitness Readers). (Illus.). 32p. (J). (ps-4). 12.99 (978-0-7894-3995-6(6)); pap. 3.99 (978-0-7894-3994-9(8)) Dorling Kindersley Publishing, Inc.

—Duckling Days. 1999. (Eyewitness Readers Ser.). (J). 10.75 (978-0-606-16984-4(9)) Tandem Library Bks.

Watts, Barrie. Duck. 2002. 32p. (J). lib. bdg. 24.25 (978-1-58340-197-2(0)) Smart Apple Media.

Wilsdon, Christina. Ducks. 2007. (J). ***(978-1-59939-119-9(8)*** , Reader's Digest Young Families, Inc.) Reader's Digest Children's Publishing, Inc.

Zemlicka, Shannon. Mallard Ducks. (Pull Ahead Books Ser.). 32p. (J). 2004. 22.60 (978-0-8225-3773-1(7) , Carolrhoda Bks.); 2003. pap. 5.95 (978-0-8225-9888-6(4)) Lerner Publishing Group.

DUCKS—FICTION

Abedi & Neuendorf. No Quiero Verte Mas! 2004. (SPA., Illus.). 196p. (J). 17.99 (978-84-261-3303-8(7)) Juventud, Editorial ESP. *Dist:* Lectorum Pubns., Inc.

Aggs, Patrice. Ooh la Booga Bomp. Aggs, Patrice, illus. 2002. (Panda Ser.). (Illus.). 64p. (YA). (gr. k up). pap. 4.95 (978-0-86278-753-0(X)) O'Brien Pr., Ltd., The IRL. *Dist:* Independent Pubs. Group.

Alborough, Jez. Duck in the Truck. Alborough, Jez, illus. 2002. (Illus.). (J). 25.04 (978-0-7587-4201-8(0)) Book Wholesalers, Inc.

—Duck in the Truck. Alborough, Jez, illus. (Illus.). 40p. (J). (ps-1). 2002. pap. 6.99 (978-0-06-443833-9(3) , Harper Trophy); 2000. 16.99 (978-0-06-028685-9(7)) HarperCollins Pubs.

—Duck in the Truck. 1999. (Illus.). 16p. (J). (ps-3). pap. 10.98 (978-1-58048-064-2(0)) Sandvik Publishing.

—Duck in the Truck. Alborough, Jez, illus. 2005. (Illus.). 16p. (J). (ps-ps). per. 7.99 (978-1-929132-83-6(2)) Kane/Miller Bk. Pubs., Inc.

—Duck's Key: Where Can It Be? Alborough, Jez, illus. 2005. (Illus.). 18p. (J). 14.95 (978-1-929132-72-0(7)) Kane/Miller Bk. Pubs., Inc.

—Fix-It Duck. Alborough, Jez, illus. 2002. (Illus.). 40p. (J). (ps-1). 16.99 (978-0-06-000699-0(4)) HarperCollins Pubs.

—Fix-It Duck. Alborough, Jez, illus. 2007. (Illus.). 16p. (J). (ps-1). bds. 7.99 (978-1-933605-30-2(8) , 05302) Kane/Miller Bk. Pubs., Inc.

—Hit the Ball Duck! Alborough, Jez, illus. 2006. (Illus.). 32p. (J). 15.95 (978-1-929132-96-6(4)) Kane/Miller Bk. Pubs., Inc.

Allan, Jayne. PC Polly to the Rescue. Mercer, Lynn, illus. 2003. 32p. (YA). (gr. 1 up). pap. 10.95 (978-0-9535413-8-6(X)) iynx publishing GBR. *Dist:* Dufour Editions, Inc.

Andersen, Hans Christian. The Ugly Duckling. Andersen, Hans Christian, illus. (Fairy Tale Fun Ser.). (J). 3.95 (978-0-7214-5432-0(1) , Dutton Juvenile) Penguin Group (USA) Inc.

—The Ugly Duckling. Tatar, Maria, ed. Galeron, Henri, illus. 2006. 32p. (J). (ps). 85.00 (978-0-670-06177-8(8) , Viking Juvenile) Penguin Group (USA) Inc.

—The Ugly Duckling. Angaramo, Roberta, illus. 2006. 32p. (J). 16.50 (978-1-933327-10-5(3)) Purple Bear Bks., Inc.

—The Ugly Duckling. Angeldorff, W., tr. from DAN. Angaramo, Roberta, illus. 2006. 32p. (J). 15.95 (978-1-933327-09-9(X)) Purple Bear Bks., Inc.

—The Ugly Duckling. Andersen, Hans Christian & Hanff, Margitta, illus. 1998. (Froggy's Country Storybook Ser.: Vol. 3). 16p. (J). (gr. k-3). pap. 12.98 incl. audio (978-1-890818-28-9(3)) Virginia Records, Inc.

—The Ugly Duckling. Johnson, Steve & Fancher, Lou, illus. 2008. 40p. (J). (ps-3). 16.99 ***(978-0-7636-2159-9(5))*** Candlewick Pr.

—The Ugly Duckling. Bell, Anthea, tr. from DAN. Andersen, Hans Christian & Ingpen, Robert R., illus. anniv. ed. 2005. 36p. (J). (ps). 16.99 (978-0-698-40010-8(0) , Minedition) Penguin Group (USA) Inc.

—The Ugly Duckling Signed Edition. Tatar, Maria, ed. Galeron, Henri, illus. 2007. 32p. (J). (gr. k). 250.00 ***(978-0-670-01104-9(5)*** , Viking Juvenile) Penguin Group (USA) Inc.

Andersen, Hans Christian. Le Vilain Petit Canard. Barrington, Lara, illus. adapted ed. 2000. (Best-Sellers Ser.).Tr. of Ugly Duckling. (FRE.). (J). (ps-2). audio, audio compact disk 9.95 (978-2-921997-05-8(3)) Coffragants CAN. *Dist:* Penton Overseas, Inc.

Andersen, Hans Christian & Davidson, Susanna. Ugly Duckling. 2006. 48p. (J). 8.99 (978-0-7945-1274-3(7) , Usborne) EDC Publishing.

Angus & the Ducks. 2004. (J). pap. 18.95 incl. audio compact disk (978-1-55592-369-3(0)); pap. 38.75 incl. audio compact disk (978-1-55592-370-9(4)); pap. 32.75 incl. audio (978-1-55592-187-3(6)) Weston Woods Studios, Inc.

Apperley, Dawn. Hello Little Ducklings. Apperley, Dawn, illus. 2000. (Hello Bks.). (Illus.). 12p. (J). bds. 3.95 (978-1-86233-176-1(6)) David & Charles Children's Bks. GBR. *Dist:* Sterling Publishing Co., Inc.

Arengo, Sue. The Ugly Duckling: Beginner Level 2. 2001. (Illus.). 24p. (J). 5.50 (978-0-19-422058-3(3)) Oxford Univ. Pr., Inc.

Arnold, Katya R., illus. & retold by. Me Too! Two Small Stories about Small Animals. Arnold, Katya R., retold by. 2000. 32p. (J). (gr. k-3). tchr. ed. 15.95 (978-0-8234-1483-3(3)) Holiday Hse., Inc.

Aston, Dianna Hutts. Loony Little. Murphy, Kelly, illus. 2003. 40p. (J). (ps-3). 15.99 (978-0-7636-1682-3(6)) Candlewick Pr.

Bailey, Elinor Peace. Ducks in a Row. Bailey, Elinor Peace, illus. 2002. (J). 9.50 (978-0-9716586-2-2(5)) Fairfield Processing Corp.

Baker, Harriet Lila. Boyduck Goose: His Life & Times, Bk. II. 2005. (J). pap. 9.00 (978-0-8059-6694-7(3)) Dorrance Publishing Co., Inc.

Bampton, Bob. Animal Friends Little Duck Board Book. 1999. (Illus.). 14p. (ps-k). 7.95 (978-1-58185-223-3(1)) Quadrillion Media LLC.

Barry, Frances. Duckie's Ducklings: A One-to-Ten Counting Book. Barry, Frances, illus. 2005. (Illus.). 32p. (J). (gr. k-ps). 7.99 (978-0-7636-2514-6(0)) Candlewick Pr.

—Duckie's Splash. Barry, Frances, illus. 2006. (Illus.). 14p. (J). (gr. k-ps). bds. 5.99 (978-0-7636-2897-0(2)) Candlewick Pr.

Batson, Susann. A Duck at the Dog Pound. 2007. (Illus.). 32p. (J). E-Book 5.00 incl. cd-rom ***(978-1-933090-23-8(5))*** Guardian Angel Publishing, Inc.

Bedard, Michael. Sitting Ducks. Bedard, Michael, illus. 2001. (Illus.). 40p. (J). (ps-3). pap. 6.99 (978-0-698-11897-3(9) , Putnam Juvenile) Penguin Group (USA) Inc.

Behn, Rosa & Graham, Dora. The Adventures of Jenny Duck. 2006. 109p. pap. 16.95 (978-1-4137-9450-2(5)) PublishAmerica, Inc.

Belch, Cheryl Renee. The Heroic Adventures of Dizzy Jr. 2007. 20.00 ***(978-0-8059-8977-9(3))*** Dorrance Publishing Co., Inc.

Benjamin, A. H. & Holstien, Elisabeth. A Duck So Small. 1998. (Illus.). 32p. (J). (ps-3). 14.95 (978-1-888444-30-8(4) , 21028) Little Tiger Pr.

Bentley, Dawn. Little Lost Duck. Tom-Nellis, Susan, illus. 1998. (Baby Buddy Bks.). 12p. (YA). (ps up). bds. 4.95 (978-1-888443-72-1(3) , Intervisual/Piggy Toes) Dalmatian Pr.

Berg, Ray. Sailing Duck. 2005. 15p. (J). 9.33 (978-1-4116-3554-8(X)) Lulu.com.

Berry, Lynne. Duck Dunks. Nakata, Hiroe, illus. 2008. 32p. (J). 16.95 ***(978-0-8050-8128-2(3))*** Holt, Henry & Co.

Berry, Lynne & Nakata, Hiroe. Duck Skates. rev. ed. 2005. (Illus.). 32p. (J). 15.95 (978-0-8050-7219-8(5) , Holt, Henry & Co. Bks. For Young Readers) Holt, Henry & Co.

The Big Rain. 2003. (Illus.). 32p. (J). mass mkt. (978-0-9740599-2-1(7) , 3) Omnibus Publishing.

Blackaby, Susan. El Patito Feo: Version del Cuento de Hans Christian Andersen. Delage, Charlene, illus. 2006. (Read-It! Readers en Espanol Ser.).Tr. of Ugly Duckling: A Retelling of the Hans Christian Andersen Fairy Tale. (SPA.). 32p. (J). (ps-3). 19.95 (978-1-4048-1644-2(5)) Picture Window Bks.

Blazek, Frank. Phil & His Fabulous Feathers. Thomas, Wes, illus. 2005. 32p. (J). (gr. 4-7). 15.95 (978-1-58980-280-3(2)) Pelican Publishing Co., Inc.

Bordoy, Irene, illus. El Patito Feo / the Ugly Duckling. 2006. (Bilingual Tales Ser.). 24p. (J). pap. 3.50 (978-0-439-77376-8(8) , Scholastic en Espanol) Scholastic, Inc.

Brennan, Herbie. Eddie the Duck. (Illus.). 64p. (J). 7.95 (978-0-14-038632-5(7)) Penguin Bks., Ltd. GBR. *Dist:* Trafalgar Square Publishing.

Broome, Errol. Drusilla the Lucky Duck. Thompson, Sharon, illus. 2003. (Annick Chapter Bks.). 72p. (J). (gr. 2-4). 16.95 (978-1-55037-799-6(X)); pap. 4.95 (978-1-55037-798-9(1)) Annick Pr., Ltd. CAN. *Dist:* Firefly Bks., Ltd.

Brown, J. A. Scaredy Duck. Knight, Paula, illus. 2004. (Funny Faces Ser.). 10p. (J). 3.95 (978-1-58925-716-0(2) , tiger tales) ME Media LLC.

Brown, Margaret Wise. The Golden Egg Book. Weisgard, Leonard, illus. 2004. (Big Little Golden Book Ser.). 32p. (J). (gr. k-k). 8.99 (978-0-375-82717-4(X) , Golden Bks.) Random Hse. Children's Bks.

Il Brutto Anatroccolo. 1999. Tr. of Ugly Duckling. (ITA., Illus.). 24p. (J). (ps-5). pap. 7.95 (978-88-8148-256-6(8)) European Language Institute ITA. *Dist:* Distribooks, Inc., Midwest European Pubns.

Bunting, Eve. Ducky. Wisniewski, David, illus. 2004. 32p. (J). (gr. k-ps). 4.95 (978-0-618-43240-0(X) , Clarion Bks.) Houghton Mifflin Co. Trade & Reference Div.

Burgess, Thornton W. Adventures of Poor Mrs. Quack. 2004. reprint ed. pap. 15.95 (978-1-4191-5160-6(6)); pap. 1.99 (978-1-4192-5160-3(0)) Kessinger Publishing, LLC.

Buzzeo, Toni. Dawdle Duckling. Spengler, Margaret, illus. 2003. 32p. (J). (ps). 15.99 (978-0-8037-2731-1(3) , Dial) Penguin Group (USA) Inc.

—Dawdle Duckling. Spengler, Margaret, illus. 2005. 32p. (J). (ps-k). reprint ed. pap. 5.99 (978-0-14-240277-1(X) , Puffin) Penguin Group (USA) Inc.

—Ready or Not, Dawdle Duckling. Spengler, Margaret, illus. 2005. 32p. (J). (ps). 15.99 (978-0-8037-2959-9(6) , Dial) Penguin Group (USA) Inc.

Byers, Carla Rae. Lucky Little Duck Lessons! The Adventures of Snowflake & Astar. l.t. ed. 2000. Vol. 8. 18p. (gr. 1 up). 7.95 (978-1-930910-05-8(3)) Heyokah Publishing Co.

The Can Do Duck: A Story about Believing in Yourself. 2005. (J). pap. (978-0-9768384-1-8(9)) Can Do Duck Publishing.

Candlewick Press Staff. Bordrs Baby Duck Stories. 2001. (J). 2.80 (978-0-7636-1647-2(8)) Candlewick Pr.

Caple, Kathy. Duck & Company. 2007. (Illus.). 32p. (J). (gr. k-3). 14.95 (978-0-8234-1993-7(2)); pap. 4.95 ***(978-0-8234-2125-1(2))*** Holiday Hse., Inc.

Capucilli, Alyssa Satin. Katy Duck. Cole, Henry, illus. 2007. 16p. (J). (ps-k). bds. 7.99 ***(978-1-4169-1901-8(5)*** , Little Simon) Simon & Schuster Children's Publishing.

—Katy Duck, Big Sister. Cole, Henry, illus. 2007. 14p. (J). (ps-k). 7.99 ***(978-1-4169-4209-2(2)*** , Little Simon) Simon & Schuster Children's Publishing.

Carle, Eric. 10 Little Rubber Ducks. Carle, Eric, illus. 2005. (Illus.). 36p. (J). (ps-1). 19.99 (978-0-06-074075-7(2)) HarperCollins Pubs.

—10 Little Rubber Ducks (Spanish Edition) 10 patitos de Goma. Carle, Eric, illus. 2007. (SPA.). 36p. (J). 19.99 (978-0-06-112623-9(3) , Rayo) HarperCollins Pubs.

Carr, Roger. Duckling. 2000. (gr. k-3). lib. bdg. 11.80 (978-0-613-29603-8(6)) Tandem Library Bks.

Carter, D. J. The Singing Lesson. 2007. (J). per. 6.99 ***(978-1-59886-914-9(0))*** Tate Publishing & Enterprises, L.L.C.

Carter, Maureen, illus. The Tale of Jemima Puddle-Duck: A Story about Trust. 2006. (J). 6.99 (978-1-59939-000-0(0)) Reader's Digest Young Families, Inc.

Catherine, Rose. Fido the Duck: A Short Tale. 2006. (J). 9.43 (978-0-9786276-5-2(2)) Mentzer Printing Ink.

Chaconas, Dori. Cork & Fuzz: The Collectors. McCue, Lisa, illus. 2008. 32p. (J). (ps-1). 13.99 ***(978-0-670-06286-7(3)*** , Viking Adult) Penguin Group (USA) Inc.

Chae, In-Son. How Do You Count a Dozen Ducklings? Yu, Sung-Ha, illus. 2006. 32p. (J). 16.95 (978-0-8075-1718-5(6)) Whitman, Albert & Co.

Chambers, Sally. The Duck. 1999. (Zippy Animal Bks.). (Illus.). 24p. (J). (ps-k). 6.95 (978-1-86233-030-6(1)) David & Charles Children's Bks. GBR. *Dist:* Sterling Publishing Co., Inc.

Chambers, Sally, et al. Waldo'n Ennill y Dydd. 2005. (WEL., Illus.). 32p. pap. (978-1-85596-658-1(1)) Dref Wen.

Chen, Chih-Yuan. Guji Guji. Chen, Chih-Yuan, illus. (Illus.). (J). 2007. (SPA.). 36p. pap. 7.95 (978-1-933605-34-0(0) , 05340); 2004. 32p. 15.95 (978-1-929132-67-6(0)) Kane/Miller Bk. Pubs., Inc.

Churchill, Jill. Five Little Ducks. Yaccarino, Dan, illus. 2005. 26p. (J). (ps up). pap. 5.99 (978-0-06-073465-7(5) , Harper Festival) HarperCollins Pubs.

Comella, Angels, illus. & retold by. El Patito Feo. Comella, Angels, retold by. 2001. Tr. of Ugly Duckling. (SPA.). 36p. (J). (978-84-348-7874-7(7)) SM Ediciones ESP. *Dist:* AIMS International Bks., Inc.

Conlon, Mara, adapted by. Bill Hatches an Egg. 2005. (Sitting Ducks Ser.). (J). (978-0-8431-1343-3(X) , Price Stern Sloan) Penguin Group (USA) Inc.

Cooper, Helen. Delicious! A Pumpkin Soup Story. 2007. (Illus.). 32p. (J). (ps-3). 16.00 ***(978-0-374-31756-0(9)*** , Farrar, Straus & Giroux (BYR)) Farrar, Straus & Giroux.

—A Pipkin of Pepper. 2005. (Illus.). 32p. (J). (ps-ps). 16.00 (978-0-374-35953-9(9)) Farrar, Straus & Giroux.

—Pumpkin Soup. Cooper, Helen, illus. 1999. (Illus.). 32p. (J). (ps-3). 16.00 (978-0-374-36164-8(9) , Farrar, Straus & Giroux (BYR)) Farrar, Straus & Giroux.

Costello, Emily. Ducks in Danger, No. 2. 1999. (Animal Emergency Ser.: No. 2). (Illus.). 128p. (J). (gr. 3-7). pap. 3.99 (978-0-380-79754-7(2)) HarperCollins Pubs.

Cowley, Joy. Mrs. Wishy-Washy's Farm. Fuller, Elizabeth, illus. 32p. (J). (ps). 2006. pap. 5.99 (978-0-14-240299-3(0) , Puffin); 2003. 15.99 (978-0-399-23872-7(7) , Philomel) Penguin Group (USA) Inc.

Cox, Phil Roxbee & Cartwright, S. Ted in a Red Bed. 2004. (Phonics Board Bks.). 10p. (J). 4.95 (978-0-7945-0061-0(7) , Usborne) EDC Publishing.

—Toad Makes a Road. 2004. (Phonics Board Bks.). 10p. (J). 4.99 (978-0-7945-0062-7(5) , Usborne) EDC Publishing.

Cronin, Doreen. Duck for President. Lewin, Betsy, illus. 2004. 40p. (J). 15.95 (978-0-689-86377-6(2)) Simon & Schuster Children's Publishing.

—Duck for President. 2006. (J). (ps-3). 22.78 (978-1-59961-091-7(4)) Spotlight.

—Giggle, Giggle, Quack. 2006. (J). (ps-3). 22.78 (978-1-59961-092-4(2)) Spotlight.

—Jaja, Jijí, Cuac. Jimenez, Alberto, tr. from ENG. Lewin, Betsy, illus. 2003. Tr. of Giggle, Giggle, Quack. (SPA.). (J). 15.00 (978-1-930332-46-1(7)) Lectorum Pubns., Inc.

Cronin, Doreen & Lewin, Betsy. Giggle, Giggle, Quack. 2002. (Illus.). 32p. (J). (ps-3). 15.95 (978-0-689-84506-2(5)) Simon & Schuster Children's Publishing.

Cruickshank, Margrit. We're Going to Feed the Ducks. Reeve, Rosie, illus. 2004. 24p. (J). (gr. 1 up). lib. bdg. 23.33 (978-0-8368-4027-8(5)) Stevens, Gareth Inc.

Cuentecitos- El Patito Feo. 2003. (SPA.). 1.75 (978-970-607-787-5(1)) Larousse, Ediciones, S. A. de C. V. MEX. *Dist:* Giron Bks.

Curtis, Susan. Five Little Ducklings. Smith, Eric, illus. 2007. 24p. (J). 14.99 (978-1-4169-3835-4(4) , Little Simon) Simon & Schuster Children's Publishing.

Cuthand, Beth. The Little Duck. Longman, Mary, illus. 28p. 2003. 14.95 (978-1-894778-10-7(3)); 1999. (CRE & ENG.). (J). pap. 7.95 (978-0-919441-74-3(2)) Theytus Bks., Ltd. CAN. *Dist:* Orca Bk. Pubs. USA.

Dalmatian Press Staff. Disney Vintage Donald Duck. rev. ed. 2006. 16p. (J). pap. 3.99 (978-1-4037-2339-0(7)) Dalmatian Pr.

—The Lovable Ugly Duckling. 2002. (Illus.). 24p. (J). (gr. k-5). pap. 2.99 (978-1-57759-473-4(8)) Dalmatian Pr.

Daniels, Lucy & Baglio, Ben M. Duckling Diary. Howard, Paul, illus. 2000. (Animal Ark Pets Ser.: No. 10). 128p. (J). (gr. 2-5). pap. 3.99 (978-0-439-05167-5(3)) Scholastic, Inc.

Dann, Penny. Five Little Ducks. 2003. (Illus.). 16p. (J). bds. 3.95 (978-0-7641-5663-2(2)) Barron's Educational Series, Inc.

Danny the Duck. (Chunky Animal Shaped Boards Ser.). (J). 2003. 10p. bds. 9.95 (978-0-7525-7853-8(7)); 2003. (Illus.). bds. 1.98 (978-0-7525-7774-6(3)); 2002. bds. 4.98 (978-0-7525-4631-5(7)) Parragon, Inc.

Das, Christina. Coo Coo Duckling. l.t. ed. 2005. (Illus.). 32p. (J). 15.95 (978-0-9763082-4-9(X) , A JuneOne Production) JuneOne Publishing Hub.

Demas, Corinne. Yuck! Stuck in the Muck. 2006. (Illus.). 32p. (J). lib. bdg. 9.00 ***(978-1-4242-0985-9(4))*** Fitzgerald Bks.

—Yuck! Stuck in the Muck. Rader, Laura, illus. 2006. (Scholastic Reader Ser.). 32p. (J). pap. 3.99 (978-0-439-79431-2(5) , Cartwheel Bks.) Scholastic, Inc.

Dewey, Ariane & Aruego, Jose. The Last Laugh. 2006. (Illus.). 32p. (J). (ps). 12.99 (978-0-8037-3093-9(4) , Dial) Penguin Group (USA) Inc.

Dexter Rescues Matt the Duckling. 2004. (J). per. 15.99 (978-0-9753533-3-2(0)) Golden Eagle Publishing Hse., Inc.

Dodd, Lynley. Hairy Maclary & Zachary Quack. Dodd, Lynley, illus. 2000. (Gold Star First Readers Ser.). (Illus.). 32p. (J). (gr. 1 up). lib. bdg. 22.00 (978-0-8368-2676-0(0)) Stevens, Gareth Inc.

—Hairy Maclary & Zachary Quack. 2005. (Illus.). 32p. (J). reprint ed. 5.95 (978-1-58246-147-2(3) , Tricycle Pr.) Ten Speed Pr.

—Zachary Quack Minimonster. 2006. (Gold Star First Readers Ser.). (Illus.). 31p. (J). 22.00 (978-0-8368-6187-7(6)) Stevens, Gareth Inc.

Dolan, Penny. Flora McQuack. Widdowson, Kay, illus. 2004. (Read-It! Readers Ser.). 32p. (C). (gr. k-3). 18.60 (978-1-4048-0561-3(3)) Picture Window Bks.

Donahoe, Susan. The Magic of the Duck Pond. 1999. (J). (gr. k-3). pap. 6.95 (978-0-533-12747-4(5)) Vantage Pr., Inc.

Dorling Kindersley Publishing Staff. Duckling. Deschamps, Nicola, ed. 2002. (Jumbo Shaped Board Bks.). (Illus.). 12p. (J). (ps-k). bds. 6.99 (978-0-7894-7856-6(0)) Dorling Kindersley Publishing, Inc.

—Quack, Quack! 2004. (Baby's World Board Books Ser.). (Illus.). 12p. (J). bds. 6.99 (978-0-7894-9282-1(2)) Dorling Kindersley Publishing, Inc.

Dow, Jill. Webster's Walk. 2001. (Windy Edge Farm Ser.). (Illus.). 32p. (J). (ps-3). pap. 7.99 (978-0-7112-1777-5(7)) Lincoln, Frances Ltd. GBR. *Dist:* Transition Vendor.

—Windy Edge: Webster's Walk. 2004. (Windy Edge Farm Ser.). (Illus.). 26p. (J). pap. 7.95 (978-1-84507-252-0(9)) Lincoln, Frances Ltd. GBR. *Dist:* Perseus Distribution.

The Duck: Duck Learns to Make Friends. 2004. (J). per. 17.00 (978-0-9758861-0-6(X)) Zest Publishing.

Duck & Pig: Early Level Satellite Individual Title Six-Packs. (Sails Literacy Ser.). 16p. (gr. 1-2). 27.00 (978-0-7578-2908-6(2)) Rigby Education.

Duck for President. 2004. 29.95 incl. cd-rom (978-0-7882-0540-8(4)); 24.95 incl. audio (978-0-7882-0539-2(0)) Weston Woods Studios, Inc.

Duck Grows Up. 2002. (Backyard Mini Bks.). (Illus.). 32p. (J). (978-1-59069-023-9(0) , H2012) Studio Mouse LLC.

C D

Duck Wants to Swim. 2002. (J). 4.98 (978-0-7525-7218-5(0)) Parragon, Inc.

Ducklings. 2002. (Three Minute Tales Ser.). 32p. (J). 5.98 (978-0-7525-3832-7(2)) Parragon, Inc.

Dupasquier, Philippe. Quack, Quack! 2001. (Illus.). 32p. (J). 17.99 (978-1-84270-015-0(4)) Andersen GBR. *Dist:* Independent Pubs. Group.

—Quack Quack! 2002. (Illus.). 32p. (J). (gr. k-3). pap. 8.99 (978-1-84270-112-6(6)) Andersen GBR. *Dist:* Trafalgar Square Publishing.

Dussling, Jennifer. Picky Peggy. Adams, Lynn, illus. 2004. 32p. (J). lib. bdg. 20.00 (***978-1-4242-1099-2(2)***) Fitzgerald Bks.

—Picky Peggy. Adams, Lynn, tr. Adams, Lynn, illus. 2004. (Science Solves It! Ser.). 32p. (J). 4.99 (978-1-57565-138-5(6)) Kane Pr., The.

East, Jacqueline, illus. Duckling. 2007. (Wiggle-Waggles Ser.). 8p. (J). (ps). bds. 4.99 (***978-0-7641-6072-1(9)***) Barron's Educational Series, Inc.

Edwards, Hazel & Wilson, Rosemary. Stickybeak. 2005. (Illus.). 32p. (J). pap. 10.00 (978-0-14-054114-4(4) , Penguin Global) Penguin Group (USA) Inc.

Egan, Tim. Dodsworth in New York. 2007. (Illus.). 48p. (J). (gr. 3-5). 15.00 (***978-0-618-77708-2(3)***) Houghton Mifflin Co.

Ehrlich, F. M. Does a Duck Have a Daddy? 2004. (Early Experiences Ser.). (Illus.). 32p. 10.95 (978-1-59354-032-6(9)) Blue Apple Bks.

Ehrlich, H. M. Dr. Duck & the New Babies. Rader, Laura, illus. 2005. 36p. (J). 15.95 (978-1-59354-073-9(6)) Blue Apple Bks.

Ehrlich, H. M., et al. Dr. Duck. Rader, Laura, illus. 2000. 36p. (J). (ps-1). pap. 14.95 (978-0-531-30254-5(7) , Orchard Bks.) Scholastic, Inc.

Emmett, Jonathan. This Way, Ruby! Harry, Rebecca, illus. 2007. 32p. (J). (ps-k). 16.99 (978-0-439-87992-7(2) , Scholastic Pr.) Scholastic, Inc.

Erickson, Byron. World of the Dragon Lords. 2005. 176p. (YA). pap. 12.99 (978-0-911903-98-0(4)) Gemstone Publishing, Inc.

Farrell, Melissa. One Little Duck. Style Guide Staff, illus. 2004. (Blue's Clues Ser.). 10p. (J). bds. 5.99 (978-0-689-85806-2(X) , Simon Spotlight/Nickelodeon) Simon & Schuster Children's Publishing.

Fierstein, Harvey. The Sissy Duckling. Cole, Henry, illus. 2005. 40p. (J). reprint ed. 6.99 (978-1-4169-0313-0(5) , Aladdin) Simon & Schuster Children's Publishing.

Fierstein, Harvey & Cole, Henry. The Sissy Duckling. 2002. (Illus.). 40p. (J). (ps-3). 16.00 (978-0-689-83566-7(3)) Simon & Schuster Children's Publishing.

Filipowich, Bob & Hoe, Susan. My Ducky. 2004. (Soft Shapestm Ser.). (Illus.). 8p. (J). (ps-ps). 8.99 (978-1-58476-215-7(2)) Innovative Kids.

Flack, Marjorie. Angus & the Ducks. Flack, Marjorie, illus. 2002. (Illus.). (J). 14.43 (978-0-7587-9219-8(0)) Book Wholesalers, Inc.

—Angus & the Ducks. unabr. ed. 1998. (J). (ps-2). pap. 14.95 incl. audio (978-0-7882-0694-8(X) , PRA039) Weston Woods Studios, Inc.

—The Story about Ping. Flack, Marjorie, illus. 2002. (Illus.). (J). 11.06 (978-0-7587-3710-6(6)) Book Wholesalers, Inc.

—The Story of Ping. Wiese, Kurt, illus. 2000. (Reading Railroad Bks.). 32p. (J). (ps-3). pap. 3.99 (978-0-448-42165-0(8) , Grosset & Dunlap) Penguin Group (USA) Inc.

Ford, Bernette. No More Bottles for Bunny! Williams, Sam, illus. 2007. 32p. (J). (ps). 12.95 (978-1-905417-34-6(9)) Boxer Bks., Ltd. GBR. *Dist:* Sterling Publishing Co., Inc.

—No More Diapers for Ducky! Williams, Sam, illus. (J). 2007. 26p. bds. 6.95 (***978-1-905417-38-4(1)***); 2006. 32p. 12.95 (978-1-905417-08-7(X)) Boxer Bks., Ltd. GBR. *Dist:* Sterling Publishing Co., Inc.

Galvin, Kim. RJ's Farm. 2000. 208p. (J). (gr. 4-7). pap. 12.95 (978-0-595-13989-7(2) , Writers Club Pr.) iUniverse, Inc.

Garis, Howard Roger. Lulu Alice & Jimmie Wibblewobble. 2006. 77.99 (***978-1-4280-3866-0(3)***); pap. 71.99 (***978-1-4280-3854-7(X)***) IndyPublish.com.

George, Jean Craighead. Goose & Duck. Lamont, Priscilla, illus. 2008. (I Can Read Bks.). 48p. (J). 16.99 (***978-0-06-117076-8(3)***); lib. bdg. 17.89 (***978-0-06-117077-5(1)***) HarperCollins Pubs. (Geringer, Laura Book).

Gibson, Betty & Denton, Kady MacDonald. Couac, la Petite Cane (Little Quack) (FRE., Illus.). (J). pap. 7.99 (978-0-590-73575-9(6)) Scholastic, Inc.

Giggle, Giggle Quack. 2004. (J). 24.95 incl. audio (978-1-55592-691-5(6)); 29.95 incl. cd-rom (978-1-55592-701-1(7)) Weston Woods Studios, Inc.

Giggle, Giggle, Quack. 2004. (J). pap. 18.95 incl. audio compact disk (978-1-55592-684-7(3)); pap. 38.75 incl. audio compact disk (978-1-55592-686-1(X)); pap. 32.75 incl. audio (978-1-55592-685-4(1)); pap. 14.95 incl. audio (978-1-55592-683-0(5)) Weston Woods Studios, Inc.

Ginsburg, Mirra. The Chick & the Duckling. 2002. (Illus.). (J). 14.47 (978-0-7587-2221-8(4)) Book Wholesalers, Inc.

Goodspeed, Judy. Perky Turkey Finds a Friend. Taylor, Chet, illus. l.t. ed. 2006. 24p. (J). pap. 14.99 (978-0-9765786-6-6(2)) Dragonfly Publishing, Inc.

The Goose, the Chick & the Duck. 1998. (Fisher-Price Phonics Storybooks Ser.: Vol. 4). (Illus.). (J). pap. (978-0-7666-0173-4(0) , Honey Bear Bks.) Modern Publishing.

Graff, Nancy Price. Taking Wing. Minor, Wendell, illus. 2005. 224p. (YA). (gr. 5-9). 15.00 (978-0-618-53591-0(8) , Clarion Bks.) Houghton Mifflin Co. Trade & Reference Div.

Grandreams Staff. Deborah the Dozy Duckling: A Squeaky Storybook. (Illus.). 16p. (J). bds. (978-0-7554-1170-2(6)) Grandreams Bks., Inc.

Gray, Kes. You Do! A Daisy Book. Sharratt, Nick, illus. 2006. (Daisy Book Ser.: Vol. 3). 32p. (J). (ps-1). 10.95 (978-0-8109-5973-6(9)) Abrams, Harry N. , Inc.

Greenhalgh, Miranda. Rapid Duck. 2007. (Illus.). 38p. (J). per. 14.99 (***978-1-59879-348-2(9)*** , Lifevest) Lifevest Publishing, Inc.

Grimes, Cookie. A New Year's Family. 2007. 36p. (J). 11.99 (***978-1-60247-154-2(1)***) Tate Publishing & Enterprises, L.L.C.

Grindley, Sally. Mucky Duck. Layton, Neal, illus. 2003. 32p. (J). (ps-1). 15.95 (978-1-58234-821-6(9) , Bloomsbury Children) Bloomsbury Publishing.

—Silly Goose & Dizzy Duck & the Colorful Day. Reynolds, Adrian, illus. 2001. (Toddlers Ser.). 24p. (J). (ps). pap. 5.95 (978-0-7894-7860-3(9) , D K Ink) Dorling Kindersley Publishing, Inc.

Groves. Duck in the Box, Bk. 4A. Date not set. (Illus.). 16p. (J). pap. 129.15 (978-0-582-18795-5(8)) Addison-Wesley Longman, Ltd. GBR. *Dist:* Trans-Atlantic Pubns., Inc.

Gruetzke, Mary, ed. Duck Book & Purse. McDonald, Jill, illus. 2006. 8p. (J). bds. 5.99 (978-0-439-73339-7(1) , Cartwheel Bks.) Scholastic, Inc.

Gus the Duck. 2004. (Illus.). (J). (978-1-59577-005-9(4)) Starfall Education.

Hahn, Phil. Henrietta: The Homely Duckling. Coker, Paul, Jr., illus. 2004. (Weewisdom Bks.). 47p. (J). 16.95 (978-0-87159-293-4(2) , 168, Unity Hse.) Unity Schl. of Christianity.

Hall, Kirsten. Duck, Duck, Goose! 2004. (My First Reader Ser.). (Illus.). 31p. (J). (gr. k-1). pap. 3.95 (978-0-516-24627-7(5) , Children's Pr.) Scholastic Library Publishing.

Hammond, Franklin. Dix Petits Canards. (FRE., Illus.). (J). pap. 5.99 (978-0-590-74161-3(6)) Scholastic, Inc.

Happy Quacky Lucky Duck. 2005. (J). per. 4.95 (978-0-9761763-1-2(9)) Banana Bunch Publishing.

Harcourt School Publishers Staff. The Best Food: On Level. 3rd ed. 2002. (Trophies Reading Program Ser.). (Illus.). (J). pap. 4.10 (978-0-15-322990-9(X)) Harcourt Schl. Pubs.

—Collections: Five Little Ducks: Grade Level Library. 1999. (Illus.). (J). pap. 4.70 (978-0-15-315201-6(X)) Harcourt Schl. Pubs.

—Tickle My Feet: Take-Home Book. rev. ed. 2001. (Collections Ser.: Bk. 13). (Illus.). (J). pap. 1.90 (978-0-15-319071-1(X)) Harcourt Schl. Pubs.

—5 Little Ducks: Little Book. 2000. (Collections Ser.). (Illus.). pap. 12.10 (978-0-15-314498-1(X)) Harcourt Schl. Pubs.

Harmen vonStraaten. Duck's Tale. 2007. (Illus.). 32p. (J). 16.95 (***978-0-7358-2133-0(X)***) North-South Bks., Inc.

Harris, Polly. Peep Peep, You're a Duck, Not a People! 2nd ed. 2004. Orig. Title: Peep Peep. . You're a Duck! Not a Peeple!. (Illus.). 43p. (J). 10.95 (978-0-9749375-0-2(9) , 73032) Harris, Polly.

Harry, Rebecca, illus. Little Duckling. 2006. (Noisy Farm Babies Ser.). 8p. (J). bds. 5.99 (978-0-7641-5936-7(4)) Barron's Educational Series, Inc.

Haskins, Lori. Ducks in Muck. Petrone, Valeria, illus. 2007. (For Baby Board Bks.). 24p. (J). (gr. k-ps). bds. 4.99 (978-0-375-84028-9(1) , Random Hse. Bks. for Young Readers) Random Hse. Children's Bks.

—Ducks in Muck. Petrone, Valeria, illus. 2000. 32p. (J). (ps-ps). lib. bdg. 11.80 (978-0-613-21470-4(6)) Tandem Library Bks.

Hayes, Sarah. Nine Ducks Nine. Hayes, Sarah, illus. 2000. (Big Books! Ser.). (Illus.). 32p. (J). (ps-2). pap. 19.99 (978-0-7636-1284-9(7)) Candlewick Pr.

Hazelton, Jack W. Charlie Duck. Hazelton, Jack W., illus. l.t. ed. 2003. (Illus.). 24p. (J). 12.95 (978-1-928907-54-1(7)) Jack's Bookshelf, Inc.

Hello, Duck! (Early Intervention Levels Ser.). 21.30 (978-0-7362-2118-4(2)) Hampton-Brown Bks.

Hest, Amy. Baby Duck & the Bad Eyeglasses. Barton, Jill, illus. 2002. (J). 13.83 (978-0-7587-2019-1(X)) Book Wholesalers, Inc.

—Baby Duck & the Bad Eyeglasses. 1999. (J). 12.79 (978-0-606-19309-2(X)) Tandem Library Bks.

—Baby Duck & the Cozy Blanket. Barton, Jill, illus. 2002. (Baby Duck Books! Ser.). 14p. (J). (gr. k-k). 10.99 (978-0-7636-1582-6(X)) Candlewick Pr.

—Guess Who, Baby Duck! Barton, Jill, illus. 2004. 32p. (J). (gr. k-k). 15.99 (978-0-7636-1981-7(7)) Candlewick Pr.

—In the Rain with Baby Duck. Barton, Jill, illus. 2002. (J). 13.83 (978-0-7587-2842-5(5)) Book Wholesalers, Inc.

—In the Rain with Baby Duck. Barton, Jill, illus. 1999. (Baby Duck Books! Ser.). 32p. (J). (ps-1). pap. 5.99 (978-0-7636-0697-8(9)) Candlewick Pr.

—In the Rain with Baby Duck. 1999. (Illus.). (J). 12.79 (978-0-606-16398-9(0)) Tandem Library Bks.

—In the Rain with Baby Duck. Barton, Jill, illus. 1999. (J). (ps-ps). lib. bdg. 14.15 (978-0-613-18256-0(1)) Tandem Library Bks.

—Make the Team, Baby Duck! Barton, Jill, illus. 2002. (Baby Duck Books! Ser.). 32p. (J). (ps-1). 16.99 (978-0-7636-1541-3(2)) Candlewick Pr.

—Off to School, Baby Duck! Barton, Jill, illus. 2002. (J). 26.15 (978-0-7587-3294-1(5)) Book Wholesalers, Inc.

—Off to School, Baby Duck! Barton, Jill, illus. 2007. 32p. (J). (ps-1). pap. 6.99 (***978-0-7636-3438-4(7)***) Candlewick Pr.

—You Can Swim, Baby Duck! Barton, Jill, illus. 2005. 32p. (J). (ps-1). pap. 6.99 (978-0-7636-2732-4(1)) Candlewick Pr.

—You're the Boss, Baby Duck! 2001. (978-0-606-22536-6(6)) Tandem Library Bks.

Hiebert, Elfrieda H. & Juel, Connie. The Lucky Duck. (Little Book Practice Reader). (J). (gr. k-6). 9.90 (978-0-8136-2012-1(0)) Modern Curriculum Pr.

Hilbert, Richard A. The Duck King. Peck, Christopher Scott, illus. 2000. (J). 9.95 (978-0-8362-5254-5(3)) Andrews McMeel Publishing.

Hill, Becky. The Duck That Stayed Behind. 2007. (J). per. 8.99 (***978-1-60247-417-8(6)***) Tate Publishing & Enterprises, L.L.C.

Hillert, Margaret & Andersen. The Funny Baby: The Ugly Duckling Retold. Depper, Hertha, illus. rev. exp. ed. 2007. (Beginning to Read Ser.). 32p. (J). lib. bdg. (978-1-59953-048-2(1)) Norwood Hse. Pr.

Hills, Tad. Duck & Goose. Hills, Tad, illus. 2006. 40p. (J). (ps-2). lib. bdg. 16.99 (978-0-375-93611-1(4)); (Illus.). 14.95 (978-0-375-83611-4(X)) Random Hse. Children's Bks. (Schwartz & Wade Bks.).

—Duck, Duck, Goose. 2007. (Illus.). 40p. (J). (ps-2). 15.99 (978-0-375-84068-5(0)); lib. bdg. 18.99 (978-0-375-94068-2(5)) Random Hse. Children's Bks. (Schwartz & Wade Bks.).

Hindley, Judy. Do Like a Duck Does! Bates, Ivan, illus. 40p. (J). (ps-k). 2007. pap. 4.99 (978-0-7636-3284-7(8)); 2002. 14.99 (978-0-7636-1668-7(0)) Candlewick Pr.

Hoff, Syd. Duncan the Dancing Duck. Hoff, Syd, illus. 1999. (Illus.). 32p. (J). (gr. k-3). pap. 5.95 (978-0-395-96889-5(5) , Clarion Bks.) Houghton Mifflin Co. Trade & Reference Div.

Hurwitz, Andy Blackman. Duck Ellington Swings Through the Zoo: Baby Loves Jazz. Cunningham, Andrew, illus. 2006. 18p. (J). (ps-1). 7.99 (978-0-8431-2083-7(5) , Price Stern Sloan) Penguin Group (USA) Inc.

Hutchins, Hazel J. One Duck. Ohi, Ruth, illus. 1999. 32p. (J). (ps-2). pap. 6.95 (978-1-55037-560-2(1)); lib. bdg. 18.95 (978-1-55037-561-9(X)) Annick Pr., Ltd. CAN. *Dist:* Firefly Bks., Ltd.

—One Duck. 1999. (978-0-606-18142-6(3)); lib. bdg. 15.25 (978-0-613-26478-5(9)) Tandem Library Bks.

Hutchins, Pat. We're Going on a Picnic! Hutchins, Pat, illus. 2002. (Illus.). 32p. (J). 16.99 (978-0-688-16799-8(3)) HarperCollins Pubs.

I Can Hear S/s -Duck. 2005. (J). bds. (978-1-4194-0057-5(6)) Paradise Pr., Inc.

ImageBooks Staff. Finger Puppet Friends: Little Duck, Little Ladybug, Little Lamb, & Little Bee. 2007. (Illus.). 48p. (J). (ps). bds. 22.95 (978-0-8118-5805-2(7)) Chronicle Bks. LLC.

Irvin-Marston, Hope. My Little Book of Wood Ducks. Magdalena-Brown, Maria, illus. 2nd ed. 2004. 32p. (J). pap. 7.95 (978-0-89317-053-0(4) , WW-0534, Windward Publishing) Finney Co., Inc.

Ives, Penny. Five Little Ducks. 2002. (Illus.). 16p. (J). 19.99 (978-0-85953-124-5(4)) Child's Play-International.

Ives, Penny, illus. Five Little Ducks. (J). 2005. bds. 12.99 (978-0-85953-204-4(6)); 2002. 16p. 6.99 (978-0-85953-935-7(0)); 2002. 16p. bds. 5.99 (978-0-85953-141-2(4)) Child's Play-International.

Jackson, Chris. The Gaggle Sisters River Tour. Pavanel, Jane, ed. Jackson, Chris, illus. 2002. (Illus.). 32p. (J). (ps-1). 15.95 (978-1-894222-58-7(X)) Lobster Pr. CAN. *Dist:* Univ. of Toronto Pr.

—The Gaggle Sisters Sing Again. Jackson, Chris, illus. 2005. (Gaggle Sisters Trilogy Ser.). (Illus.). 32p. (J). 15.95 (978-1-894222-56-3(3)) Lobster Pr. CAN. *Dist:* Univ. of Toronto Pr.

James, Simon. Little One Step. James, Simon, illus. (Illus.). (J). (gr. k-ps). 2007. 24p. bds. 6.99 (***978-0-7636-3520-6(0)***); 2003. 32p. 15.99 (978-0-7636-2070-7(X)) Candlewick Pr.

Janet Wannet Quack! Quack! l.t. ed. 2001. 65p. (J). 14.95 (978-0-9709119-1-9(2)) Limpid Butterfly Productions, The.

Jasmine's Duck: Individual Title Six-Pack Pouch - Level I. (Lighthouse Ser.). 16p. (gr. 1 up). 26.00 (978-0-7578-0853-1(0)) Rigby Education.

Jennings, Sharon, et al. Franklin & the Duckling. Jeffrey, Sean et al, illus. 2007. 32p. pap. (***978-1-55337-889-1(X)***) Kids Can Pr., Ltd.

Jeram, Anita. All Together Now. Jeram, Anita, illus. 2005. (Illus.). 40p. (J). (gr. k-1). reprint ed. pap. 5.99 (978-0-7636-2690-7(2)) Candlewick Pr.

Johansen, Hanna & Barrett, John S. The Duck & the Owl. Bhend, Kathi, illus. 2005. 80p. (J). 17.95 (978-1-56792-285-1(6)) Godine, David R. Pub.

John Philip Duck. 2004. (J). 27.95 incl. audio (978-0-8045-6932-3(0)); 29.95 incl. audio compact disk (978-0-8045-4127-5(2)) Spoken Arts, Inc.

Kaldor, Connie. A Duck in New York City. 2005. (Illus.). 36p. (J). (ps-3). 16.95 incl. audio compact disk (978-2-923163-02-4(8)) La Montagne Secrete CAN. *Dist:* National Bk. Network.

Kaminsky, Jeff & Atwater, Martha. Duck. Kaminsky, Jeff, illus. 2002. (Stickamajigs Ser.: Vol. 2). (Illus.). 8p. (ps-1). 5.99 (978-0-7868-0711-6(3)) Hyperion Bks. for Children.

Kanninen, Barbara J. A Story with Pictures. Reed, Lynn Rowe, illus. 2007. 32p. (J). (ps-3). 16.95 (***978-0-8234-2049-0(3)***) Holiday Hse., Inc.

Keller, John G. The Rubber-Legged Duck. Cole, Henry, illus. 2008. (J). (***978-0-15-205289-8(5)***) Harcourt Trade Pubs.

Kenney, Cindy. King George & His Duckies. 2004. (Illus.). 22p. 4.99 (978-0-310-70781-3(1)) Zonderkidz.

King-Smith, Dick. Funny Frank. Eastwood, John, illus. 2003. 112p. (gr. 2-5). pap. 5.50 (978-0-440-41880-1(1) , Yearling) Random Hse. Children's Bks.

—Funny Frank. Roth, Roger & Eastwood, John, illus. 2002. 112p. (J). (gr. 2-5). 14.95 (978-0-375-81460-0(4) , Knopf Bks. for Young Readers) Random Hse. Children's Bks.

—Funny Frank. 2003. (gr. 3-6). lib. bdg. 13.00 (978-0-613-72193-6(4)) Tandem Library Bks.

Kitamura, Satoshi. Hello, Who's There? 2008. (Illus.). 16p. (J). 12.95 (***978-1-84270-587-2(3)***) Andersen GBR. *Dist:* Independent Pubs. Group.

—Pato Esta Sucio. 2001. (Los Especiales de A la Orilla Del Viento Ser.). (SPA.). 16p. (J). bds. 6.99 (978-968-16-5538-9(9)) Fondo de Cultura Economica USA.

Kitamura, Satoshi. Play with Me! 2008. (Illus.). 12p. (J). 12.95 (***978-1-84270-639-8(X)***) Andersen GBR. *Dist:* Independent Pubs. Group.

Klingel, Cynthia Fitterer. Quack! The Sound of Q. 1999. (Wonder Books Phonics: Consonants Ser.). (Illus.). 24p. (J). (ps-3). 21.36 (978-1-56766-724-0(4)) Child's World, Inc.

Kompelien, Tracy. Duck Bills. Nobens, C. A., illus. 2006. (Fact & Fiction Ser.). 24p. (J). 21.35 (978-1-59679-933-2(1) , SandCastle) ABDO Publishing Co.

—Duck Bills. Haberstroh, Anne, illus. 2006. (Fact & Fiction Ser.). 24p. (J). pap. (***978-1-59679-934-9(X)***) ABDO Publishing Co.

Kreschner, Bill & Kreschner, Phyllis. Plucky-lucky duck's amazing Adventures. 2007. 16.95 (***978-0-533-15647-4(5)***) Vantage Pr., Inc.

Lachenmeyer, Nathaniel. The Decoy. Slade, Christian, illus. 2007. 32p. (J). 17.95 (***978-1-58726-319-4(X)*** , Mitten Pr.) Ann Arbor Media Group, LLC.

Ladybird Books Staff. Downy Duckling. (Rhyming Stories Ser.: No. 401-5). (Illus.). 52p. (J). (ps). 3.50 (978-0-7214-0210-9(0) , Dutton Juvenile) Penguin Group (USA) Inc.

Lakeshore Learning Materials Staff, contrib. by. Make Way for Duckling. 2000. (J). pap. 19.95 (978-1-929255-42-9(X)) Lakeshore Learning Materials.

Leonard, Barry, ed. The Ugly Duckling. 2003. (Illus.). 12p. (J). (gr. k-4). reprint ed. 17.00 (978-0-7567-6858-4(6)) DIANE Publishing Co.

Long, Ethan. Stop Kissing Me! 2007. 24p. bds. 7.99 (***978-0-316-01921-7(6)***) Little, Brown Bks. for Young Readers.

Long, Ethan. Tickle the Duck: Don't You Dare. 2005. (Illus.). 24p. (J). (ps-ps). 10.99 (978-0-316-00102-1(3)) Little Brown & Co.

Long, Jonathan & Paul, Korky. The Duck That Had No Luck. 1999. (Illus.). 25p. (J). pap. 9.95 (978-0-09-952961-3(0)) Random Hse. GBR. *Dist:* Trafalgar Square Publishing.

Losey, Tori. The Ducks of Congress Park. Liguori, Kathy, illus. 2004. 36p. (J). (978-0-925168-97-9(1)) North Country Bks., Inc.

The Lovable Ugly Duckling. 2002. (Puppy Tales Ser.). (Illus.). 24p. (J). (gr. k-3). 1.49 (978-1-57759-492-5(4)) Dalmatian Pr.

Luthardt, Kevin. Peep! Luthardt, Kevin, illus. 2003. (Illus.). 36p. (J). 15.95 (978-1-56145-046-6(4)) Peachtree Pubs., Ltd.

Macieiski, Ellen. The Nest. Baumgartner, Mary Beth, illus. 2004. 31p. pap. 17.95 (978-1-4137-1463-0(3)) PublishAmerica, Inc.

Make Way for Ducklings. 2004. 24.95 incl. audio (978-0-89719-892-9(1)); pap. 32.75 incl. audio (978-1-55592-262-7(7)); pap. 32.75 incl. audio (978-1-55592-263-4(5)); pap. 14.95 incl. audio (978-1-56008-065-7(5)); pap. 14.95 incl. audio (978-0-7882-0507-1(2)) Weston Woods Studios, Inc.

Mallat, Kathy. Just Ducky. Mallat, Kathy, illus. 2004. (Illus.). 32p. (J). (ps-k). 15.95 (978-0-8027-8824-5(6)) Walker & Co.

—Just Ducky. 2004. (Illus.). 24p. (J). (ps-1). 16.85 (978-0-8027-8825-2(4)) Walker & Co.

Mandrake the Wild Mallard Duck. 2000. (Illus.). 133p. (YA). (gr. 10 up). pap. 13.95 (978-0-9616701-0-8(X)) Oak Hill Bks.

Manning, Mick. Snap! Granstrom, Brita, illus. 2006. 24p. 14.95 (978-1-84507-408-1(4)) Lincoln, Frances Ltd. GBR. *Dist:* Perseus Distribution.

Martin, Ann M. Ducky. 1998. (California Diaries Ser.: Bk 5). 10p. (YA). (gr. 6-8). pap. 4.50 (978-0-590-29839-1(9)) Scholastic, Inc.

Mathers, Petra. A Cake for Herbie. 2000. Orig. Title: A Poem for Lottie. (J). 15.00 (978-0-689-01506-9(2) , Atheneum) Simon & Schuster Children's Publishing.

Mathews-Danzer, R. & Mathews, Rinaldo. Murder at Fort Christmas: The Duck Did It. Kipnis, Libby, ed. 2002. (Provost Files Ser.). 200p. 14.95 (978-1-888417-50-0(1)) Dimefast, Ltd.

Maxwell, Wayne F., Jr. The Miracle of Sandy Duck. Samples, M. David, ed. McCabe, Jane M., illus. 34p. (J). (gr. k-4). 15.00 (978-0-9747023-0-8(7)) Pegasus Pubns.

Mayberry, Stephanie. Douglas the Duck & the Meeting Place. 2006. 30p. (J). 10.00 (978-0-9777290-9-8(5) , 349-025) High-Pitched Hum Inc.

McBratney, Sam. Yes We Can! Fuge, Charles, illus. 2007. 32p. (J). (ps-1). 16.99 (***978-0-06-121515-5(5)***) HarperCollins Pubs.

McCloskey, Robert. Abran Paso a los Patitos. 2000. (SPA., Illus.). (J). (gr. k-3). 25.95 incl. audio (978-0-87499-660-9(0)); pap. 16.95 incl. audio (978-0-87499-659-3(7)); pap., tchr. ed. 37.95 incl. audio (978-0-87499-661-6(9)) Live Oak Media.

—Abran Paso a los Patitos. McCloskey, Robert, illus. 2000. (Illus.). 28.95 incl. audio compact disk (978-1-59519-122-9(4)); pap. 39.95 incl. audio compact disk (978-1-59519-121-2(6)); (SPA., (J). pap. 18.95 incl. audio compact disk (978-1-59519-120-5(8)) Live Oak Media.

—Abran Paso a los Patitos. Blanco, Osvaldo, tr. from ENG. 2005. (SPA., Illus.). 62p. (J). (gr. k-4). reprint ed. 15.00 (978-0-7567-8841-4(2)) DIANE Publishing Co.

—Make Way for Ducklings. McCloskey, Robert, illus. 2002. (Illus.). (J). 13.60 (978-0-7587-0056-8(3)) Book Wholesalers, Inc.

—Make Way for Ducklings. 2000. (J). pap. 19.97 incl. audio (978-0-7366-9196-3(0)) Books on Tape, Inc.

—Make Way for Ducklings. 1999. (Illus.). 76p. (J). (ps-3). pap. 7.99 (978-0-14-056434-1(9) , Puffin) Penguin Group (USA) Inc.

—Make Way for Ducklings. 2000. (J). (ps-k). pap. 12.95 incl. audio Weston Woods Studios, Inc.

—Make Way for Ducklings. McCloskey, Robert, illus. 2005. (Illus.). (J). pap. 18.95 incl. audio compact disk (978-1-59112-731-4(9)) Live Oak Media.

—Make Way for Ducklings: Abran Paso a los Patitos, 2 bks., Set. McCloskey, Robert, illus. unabr. ed. 2000. (ENG & SPA., Illus.). (J). (gr. k-3). pap. 33.95 incl. audio (978-0-87499-667-8(8)) Live Oak Media.

McNeil, Niki, et al. HOCPP 1079 All about Ping. 2006. spiral bd. 15.00 ***(978-1-60308-079-8(1))*** In the Hands of a Child.

McQueen, Lucinda & Shaw, Gina. Little Duck's Easter Surprise. 1999. (Illus.). 10p. (J). (ps-1). pap. 3.50 (978-0-590-68130-8(3)) Scholastic, Inc.

Melinda, Braun. Luella. 2007. (Illus.). 32p. (J). lib. bdg. 14.95 ***(978-1-886028-85-2(0))*** Savage Pr.

Merer, Laura, illus. Fuzzy Ducky's Birthday: A Touch-and-Feel Pop-up Book. 2005. 10p. (J). 8.95 (978-1-58117-324-6(5) , Intervisual/Piggy Toes) Dalmatian Pr.

Metrobooks Staff. Hello, Baby Duck: A Tub Time Book. 2000. (Illus.). 8p. (J). (ps-k). 9.99 (978-1-58663-106-2(3)) Friedman, Michael Publishing Group, Inc.

Metzenthen, David. Rodney, the Surfing Duck. Axelsen, Stephen, illus. 1999. (Supa Doopers Ser.). 64p. (J). (978-0-7608-1929-6(7)) Sundance/Newbridge Educational Publishing.

Meyrick, Judith. Gracie, the Public Garden's Duck. Rudnicki, Richard, illus. 2007. 32p. (J). (ps-3). ***(978-1-55109-605-6(6))*** Nimbus Publishing, Ltd.

Miller, David. Refugees. 2005. (Illus.). 32p. (J). (978-0-7344-0633-0(9) , Lothian Bks.) Hachette Livre Australia.

Mitchard, Jacquelyn. Rosalie, My Rosalie: The Tale of a Duckling. Bendall-Brunello, John, illus. 2005. 128p. (J). (ps-7). 15.99 (978-0-06-072219-7(3)) HarperCollins Pubs.

Moeckel, Christine. Dick the Duck. Moeckel, Christine, illus. l.t. ed. 2004. (Illus.). 31p. (J). spiral bd. 9.98 (978-0-9720350-2-6(8)) Duckpond Publishing, Inc.

Moloney, James. Quack! Quack! Help Jack Save the Ducks! King, Stephen Michael, illus. 2007. 80p. (J). pap. 3.95 ***(978-0-7624-2933-2(X)*** , Running Pr. Kids) Running Pr. Bk. Pubs.

Montgomery, R. A. Lost on the Amazon. 1999. (Illus.). 114p. mass mkt. (978-0-553-23733-7(0)) Random Hse., Inc.

Morgan, Allen. Quackadack Duck. Beder, John, illus. 2003. 32p. (J). (ps-2). pap. 5.95 (978-1-55037-760-6(4)) Annick Pr., Ltd. CAN. *Dist:* Firefly Bks., Ltd.

Morrison, Marianne. The Saddleshoe Quackers Present Lucky's Adventure. 2004. 17p. (J). 5.95 (978-0-9709575-3-5(X)) Singing River Pubns.

Morton, Jane & Dreier, Ted. Moozie's Cow Wisdom for Loving to the "Uddermost" Royse, Jane, illus. 2003. (J). pap. 4.95 (978-0-9662268-3-6(6)) Best Friends Bks.

Mother Duck's Walk: First Grade Big Books. (On Our Way to English Ser.). (gr. 1 up). 29.95 (978-0-7578-1509-6(X)) Rigby Education.

Mother Duck's Walk: Small Versions of Big Books. (On Our Way to English Ser.). (gr. 1 up). 29.00 (978-0-7578-7229-7(8)) Rigby Education.

Mouse Works Staff. Donald Duck. 1998. (Friendly Tales Ser.). (Illus.). 10p. (J). (ps). 6.99 (978-1-57082-927-7(6)) Mouse Works.

Mudd, Missy. Candy Bar Caper. 2007. (J). per. 7.99 ***(978-1-59886-843-2(8))*** Tate Publishing & Enterprises, L.L.C.

Muller, Lisa M. Master smokey & mr. Duck. 2006. 15p. (J). 9.99 (978-1-4276-0027-1(9)) Aardvark Global Publishing.

Murphy, Mary. I Kissed the Baby! Murphy, Mary, illus. 2003. (Illus.). 24p. (J). (gr. k-k). 14.99 (978-0-7636-2122-3(6)) Candlewick Pr.

Murphy, Mary Elizabeth. I Kissed the Baby! Murphy, Mary Elizabeth, illus. 2004. (Illus.). 24p. (J). (gr. k-ps). bds. 6.99 (978-0-7636-2443-9(8)) Candlewick Pr.

Nancy, Tafuri. Goodnight, My Duckling. 2006. (J). bds. 7.99 (978-0-439-79660-6(1) , Scholastic Pr.) Scholastic, Inc.

Nedwidek, John. Ducks Don't Wear Socks. 2008. 32p. (J). (ps). 15.99 ***(978-0-670-06136-5(0)*** , Viking Juvenile) Penguin Group (USA) Inc.

Nellis, Micki. Jacop & the Duck Patrol / Pepe y la Patrulla de Patos. Uhl, Anton, illus. 2001. (SPA.). (J). cd-rom 14.95 (978-1-885534-16-3(7)) Buffalo Creek Pr.

—Logan & the Duck Patrol. Uhl, Anton, illus. 2001. (SPA.). (J). cd-rom 14.95 (978-1-885534-12-5(4)) Buffalo Creek Pr.

—Matthew & the Duck Patrol / Juanito y la Patrulla de Patos. Uhl, Anton, illus. 2001. (SPA.). (J). cd-rom 14.95 (978-1-885534-17-0(5)) Buffalo Creek Pr.

—Michael & the Duck Patrol / Miguel y la Patrulla de Patos. Uhl, Anton, illus. 2001. (SPA.). (J). cd-rom 1495.00 (978-1-885534-15-6(9)) Buffalo Creek Pr.

Nethery, Mary. Mary Veronica's Egg. Yalowitz, Paul, illus. 1999. 32p. (J). (ps-2). 16.99 (978-0-531-33134-7(2) , Orchard Bks.) Scholastic, Inc.

Newth, Rebecca. Tinkum's Dog. Primm, Thomas, illus. 2005. 32p. (J). 15.00 ***(978-0-9630310-7-5(4))*** Will Hall Bks.

Noel, Delia & Galloway, Ruth. Quack, Quack Who's That? 2002. 12p. (J). (ps). bds. 4.95 (978-0-7641-5478-2(8)) Barron's Educational Series, Inc.

Nolan, J. & Moffatt, J. Floaties: Five Little Ducks. 2003. (J). 9.95 (978-1-929766-59-8(9)) Handprint Bks.

Nolan, Lucy. Jack Quack. Wesson, Andrea, illus. 32p. (J). 2005. pap. 5.95 (978-0-7614-5153-2(6)); 2001. 15.95 (978-0-7614-5091-7(2) , Cavendish Children's Bks.) Cavendish, Marshall Corp.

Oke, Janette. Ducktails. Munger, Nancy, illus. 2001. (Animal Friends Ser.: Vol. 6). 80p. (J). (ps-3). pap. 6.99 (978-0-7642-2450-8(6)) Bethany Hse. Pubs.

—Ducktails. 2001. (gr. k-3). lib. bdg. 14.15 (978-0-613-82430-9(X)) Tandem Library Bks.

Oram, Hiawyn. Rubbaduck & Ruby Roo. Lucas, David, illus. 2004. 28p. (J). 15.95 (978-1-59078-356-6(5)) Boyds Mills Pr.

Otto, Carolyn B., et al. Big Box of Backyard Animals, 4 bks., Set. Sherrow, Victoria et al, illus. 2002. (Big Box of Board Bks.). 10p. (J). (ps-k). bds. (978-1-59069-177-9(6)) Studio Mouse LLC.

Palatini, Margie. Shelly. Francis, Guy, illus. 2006. 32p. (J). (ps). 15.99 (978-0-525-47565-1(6) , Dutton Juvenile) Penguin Group (USA) Inc.

—The Web Files. Egielski, Richard, illus. 2001. 32p. 15.99 (978-0-7868-0419-1(X) , Volo) Hyperion Bks. for Children.

Parker, Marjorie. Mama's Little Duckling. Wohnoutka, Mike, illus. 2008. 32p. (J). (ps). 15.99 ***(978-0-525-47950-5(3)*** , Dutton Juvenile) Penguin Group (USA) Inc.

Parks, Charlsie Austin. The Beautiful Duckling. Moisan, Elizabeth, illus. 2001. 64p. (J). 20.95 (978-1-57736-210-4(1) , Hillsboro Pr.) Providence Hse Pubs.

Paterson, Katherine. The Tale of the Mandarin Ducks. Dillon, Leo & Dillon, Diane, illus. 2004. 32p. (J). (gr. k-4). reprint ed. 15.00 (978-0-7567-7698-5(8)) DIANE Publishing Co.

—The Tale of the Mandarin Ducks. Dillon, Leo & Dillon, Diane, illus. unabr. ed. 1998. (J). (gr. k-4). 24.95 incl. audio (978-0-7882-0679-5(6) , HRA376) Weston Woods Studios, Inc.

PC Treasures, prod. The Ugly Duckling. 2007. (J). ***(978-1-60072-018-5(8))*** PC Treasures, Inc.

Perry, Shelly. Duckling's First Adventure. Loebel, Bonnie, illus. 2006. (ENG.). 56p. (J). per. 9.95 (978-0-9787740-3-5(5)) Peppertree Pr., The.

Peters, Lisa. Cold Little Duck, Duck, Duck. Williams, Sam, illus. 2005. 32p. (J). (ps up). 6.99 (978-0-06-072223-4(1) , Harper Festival) HarperCollins Pubs.

Peters, Lisa Westberg. Cold Little Duck, Duck, Duck. Williams, Sam, illus. 2000. 32p. (J). (ps-3). 16.99 (978-0-688-16178-1(2)) HarperCollins Pubs.

Petsch, Maggie, photos by & text. Dora the A-Dora-ble Duck. Petsch, Maggie, text. 2004. (J). per. 9.95 (978-0-9715860-4-8(7)) From the Asylum Bks. & Pr.

Pfeffer, Wendy. Mallard Duck at Meadow View Pond. Oughton, Taylor, illus. (Smithsonian's Backyard Ser.). 32p. (J). (ps-2). 2005. 9.95 (978-1-56899-961-6(5) , PB5071); 2005. 19.95 incl. reel tape (978-1-56899-958-6(5) , BC5021); 2001. 32.95 (978-1-56899-960-9(7)); 2001. pap. 6.95 (978-1-931465-92-2(4) , S5021) Soundprints.

—Mallard Duck at Mountain View Pond. Oughton, Taylor, illus. 2005. (Smithsonian's Backyard Ser.). 32p. (J). (ps-2). 4.95 (978-1-56899-957-9(7) , B5071); 15.95 (978-1-56899-956-2(9) , B5021) Soundprints.

Pfister, Marcus. Charlie at the Zoo. James, J. Alison, tr. from GER. Pfister, Marcus, illus. 2007. (Illus.). 32p. (J). (ps). 17.95 ***(978-0-7358-2144-6(5))*** North-South Bks., Inc.

Pinkney, Jerry, et al. The Ugly Duckling (Spanish Version) El Patito Feo. Pinkney, Jerry, illus. 2007. (SPA.). 40p. (J). pap. 6.99 ***(978-0-06-111727-5(7)*** , Rayo) HarperCollins Pubs.

Polacco, Patricia. John Philip Duck. Polacco, Patricia, illus. 2004. (Illus.). 48p. (J). (ps-5). 16.99 (978-0-399-24262-5(7) , Philomel) Penguin Group (USA) Inc.

Pomerantz, Charlotte. One Duck, Another Duck. 2000. pap. (978-0-688-17719-5(0)) HarperCollins Pubs.

Potter, Beatrix. Conte de Sophie Canetang. pap. 18.95 (978-2-07-054701-2(9)) Gallimard, Editions FRA. *Dist:* Distribooks, Inc.

—Jemima Puddle-Duck. 2007. 12p. (J). bds. 3.99 (978-0-7232-5856-8(2) , Warne) Penguin Group (USA) Inc.

—Quack Quack with Peter Rabbit. 2006. (Potter Ser.). 10p. (J). 6.99 (978-0-7232-5718-9(3) , Warne) Penguin Group (USA) Inc.

—The Tale of Jemima Puddle-Duck Board Bk. 2007. (Illus.). 24p. (J). bds. 6.99 (978-0-7232-5794-3(9) , Warne) Penguin Group (USA) Inc.

—The Tale of Jemima Puddle Duck Sticker Book. 2007. 24p. (J). pap. 5.99 (978-0-7232-5877-3(5) , Warne) Penguin Group (USA) Inc.

Potter, Beatrix, text. Jemima Puddle-Duck. 2003. (Play-A-Sound Ser.). (Illus.). (J). (978-0-7853-7970-6(3)); (978-0-7853-7969-0(X)) Publications International, Ltd.

Puzzle Track Staff, ed. Adv with Little Duck. 2007. (Puzzle Track Ser.). 20p. (J). bds. 18.95 ***(978-0-7696-5619-9(6))*** School Specialty Publishing.

Quack! Quack! 2002. (Little Board Books Ser.). 24p. (J). bds. 3.95 (978-0-7894-8465-9(X)) Dorling Kindersley Publishing, Inc.

Quack, Quack, Goodmorning Ducks. 2005. (J). 9.95 (978-1-59352-177-6(4)) Christian Services Publishing.

Quackenbush, Robert. Flamenco to Mischief: A Miss Mallard Mystery. 2000. (Miss Mallard Mystery Ser.: Vol. 16). (Illus.). 48p. (J). (gr. 2-4). pap. 5.95 (978-0-9612518-2-6(4)) Quackenbush, Robert Studios.

—Henry's Awful Mistake. Quackenbush, Robert, illus. rev. deluxe ed. 2005. (Illus.). 40p. (J). (gr. k-2). reprint ed. 12.95 (978-0-9712757-0-6(X)) Quackenbush, Robert Studios.

—Miss Mallard's Case Book. 2000. (Miss Mallard Mystery Ser.: Vol. 17). (Illus.). 48p. (J). (ps-4). pap. 5.95 (978-0-9612518-3-3(2)) Quackenbush, Robert Studios.

Quacky Duck Touch-and-Squeak. 2002. (Bath Books Ser.). 10p. (J). 5.95 (978-0-7894-8462-8(5)) Dorling Kindersley Publishing, Inc.

Quadrillion Media Staff. Duckling Swims with the Animals. 1999. 5.95 (978-1-58185-219-6(3)) Quadrillion Media LLC.

—Show Me the Duck! 1999. bds. 3.95 (978-1-58185-215-8(0)) Quadrillion Media LLC.

Raffi. Five Little Ducks. Aruego, Jose & Dewey, Ariane, illus. 1999. (Raffi Songs to Read Ser.). 32p. (J). (gr. k-ps). bds. 6.99 (978-0-517-80057-7(8) , Crown Books For Young Readers) Random Hse. Children's Bks.

The Rainy Day: Individual Title Two-Packs. (Chiquilibros Ser.). (ps-1). 12.00 (978-0-7635-8532-7(7)) Rigby Education.

Rankin, Joan. Wow! It's Great Being a Duck. 2001. (Illus.). (J). (978-0-606-21003-4(2)) Tandem Library Bks.

Rankin, Laura. Fluffy & Baron. 2006. (Illus.). 32p. (J). (ps). 16.99 (978-0-8037-2953-7(7) , Dial) Penguin Group (USA) Inc.

Reinoso, Carlos. Little Ducky Jr. & the Whirlwind Storm: A Tale of Loss, Hope,and Renewal. Reinoso, Carlos, illus. l.t. ed. 2005. (Illus.). 50p. (J). 8.99 (978-0-9777672-0-5(5)) Behavioral Health & Human Development Ctr.

Reynolds, Adrian. Pete & Polo's Farmyard Adventure. Reynolds, Adrian, illus. 2002. (Illus.). 32p. (J). (ps-1). pap 16.95 (978-0-439-30913-4(1) , Orchard Bks.) Scholastic, Inc.

Ricci, Christine. The Little Duck. Hall, Susan T., illus. 2004. 24p. (J). 15.98 (978-0-7853-9959-9(3) , 7209800) Publications International, Ltd.

Rigby Education Staff. Fat Ducks. (Sails Literacy Ser.). (Illus.). 16p. (gr. 1-2). 27.00 (978-0-7635-9917-1(4) , 699174C99) Rigby Education.

—The Robbers. (Sails Literacy Ser.). (Illus.). 16p. (gr. 1-2). 27.00 (978-0-7635-9913-3(1) , 699131C99) Rigby Education.

Roddie, Shen. Not Now, Mrs. Wolf. 2000. (J). (978-0-606-19386-3(3)) Tandem Library Bks.

—Simon Says. Lambert, Sally Anne, illus. 32p. (J). (ps-3). 2001. pap. 8.99 (978-0-7112-1532-0(4)); 2000. 19.99 (978-0-7112-1529-0(4)) Lincoln, Frances Ltd. GBR. *Dist:* Transition Vendor, Antique Collectors' Club.

Roddie, Shen & Lambert, Sally Ann. Simon Says. 2004. (Illus.). 32p. (J). pap. 7.95 (978-1-84507-233-9(2)) Lincoln, Frances Ltd. GBR. *Dist:* Perseus Distribution.

Roitman, Tanya, illus. I'm Going to Boston to Visit the Ducks. 2006. (I'm Going to Read Ser.). 24p. (J). pap. 3.95 (978-1-4027-3092-4(6)) Sterling Publishing Co., Inc.

Root, Phyllis. One Duck Stuck. Chapman, Jane, illus. 2001. 32p. (J). (gr. k-ps). bds. 6.99 (978-0-7636-1104-0(2)) Candlewick Pr.

—One Duck Stuck. 2003. (gr. k-3). lib. bdg. 14.15 (978-0-613-60361-4(3)) Tandem Library Bks.

—One Duck Stuck: A Mucky Ducky Counting Book. Chapman, Jane, illus. (J). (gr. k-k). 2003. 40p. pap. 5.99 (978-0-7636-1566-6(8)); 1998. 32p. 15.99 (978-0-7636-0334-2(1)) Candlewick Pr.

—Quack! Meade, Holly, illus. 2005. 16p. (J). (gr. k-ps). bds. 6.99 (978-0-7636-1793-6(8)) Candlewick Pr.

Ross, Tony. Silly Silly. 1999. (Illus.). 29p. (J). pap. 9.99 (978-0-86264-904-3(8)) Andersen GBR. *Dist:* Independent Pubs. Group.

Roxbee-Cox, Phil. Find the Duck. 2007. (Find-its Board Bks). 12p. (J). bds. 6.99 ***(978-0-7945-1804-2(4)*** , Usborne) EDC Publishing.

Roy, Ron. The Quicksand Question. Gurney, John Steven, illus. 2002. (A to Z Mysteries Ser.: No. 17). (J). (gr. k-3). lib. bdg. 11.80 (978-0-613-50491-1(7)) Tandem Library Bks.

Santa Elena, Antonio E. Babba Has Golden Feathers. (Illus.). (J). (gr. 4-6). (978-0-89626-019-1(4)) Alchemy Bks.

Santillo, LuAnn. The Duck. Santillo, LuAnn, ed. 2003. (Half-Pint Kids Readers Ser.). (Illus.). 7p. (J). (ps-1). pap. (978-1-59256-069-1(5)) Half-Pint Kids, Inc.

Sargent, Dave. Dinky Duck. Lenoir, Jane, illus. 2000. (Feather Tales Ser.). ix, 36p. (J). lib. bdg. 19.95 (978-1-56763-473-0(7)) Ozark Publishing.

Sargent, Dave & Sargent, David M., Jr. Dinky Duck: Be Prompt, 19 vols., Vol. 7. Lenoir, Jane, illus. 2003. (Feather Tales Ser.: 7). 42p. (J). pap. 6.95 (978-1-56763-732-8(9)) Ozark Publishing.

Sargent, Dave & Sargent, David M. Dinky Duck: Be Prompt, 20 vols., Vol. 7. Lenoir, Jane, illus. 2nd ed. 2003. (Feather Tales Ser.: 7). 42p. (J). lib. bdg. 19.95 (978-1-56763-731-1(0)) Ozark Publishing.

Sargent, Dave & Sargent, Pat. Do All Ducks Quack?, 10, 14. Robinson, Laura, illus. 2004. (Learn to Read Ser.: 10). 18p. (J). lib. bdg. 19.95 (978-1-56763-823-3(6)); lib. bdg. 9.95 (978-1-56763-824-0(4)) Ozark Publishing.

—Do All Ducks Quack?/¿Granznan todos los Patos?, 10, 14. Robinson, Laura, illus. 2004. (Learn to Read Ser.: 10). (ENG & SPA.). 18p. (J). pap. 9.95 (978-1-56763-988-9(7)); lib. bdg. 19.95 (978-1-56763-987-2(9)) Ozark Publishing.

Sattler, Jennifer Gordon. Bella's Saratoga Summer. 2002. (Illus.). (J). (978-0-9713069-4-3(X)); 32p. pap. 10.95 (978-0-9713069-3-6(1)) Burns, Nicholas K. Publishing.

Scholastic, Inc. Staff. What's the Weather? 2008. (Little Secrets Ser.). 28p. (J). 9.99 ***(978-0-545-02599-7(0)*** , Cartwheel Bks.) Scholastic, Inc.

Screech! Individual Title Six-Packs. (Literatura 2000 Ser.). (gr. 1-2). 28.00 (978-0-7635-0109-9(3)) Rigby Education.

Shannon, David. Duck on a Bike. Shannon, David, illus. 2002. (Illus.). 40p. (J). (ps up). pap. 15.95 (978-0-439-05023-4(5) , Blue Sky Pr., The) Scholastic, Inc.

Shelton, Ricky V. Quacker Meets His Dad the Squirrel: Tales from a Duck Named Quacker. Williams, Shan, illus. Date not set. (J). (ps-1). pap. 7.00 (978-0-9634257-3-7(0)) RVS Bks., Inc.

Silverman, Erica. Don't Fidget a Feather. Schindler, S. D., illus. 1998. 32p. (J). (ps-2). 6.99 (978-0-689-81967-4(6) , Aladdin) Simon & Schuster Children's Publishing.

—Don't Fidget a Feather. 1998. 12.79 (978-0-606-13340-1(2)) Tandem Library Bks.

Simmons, Jane. Come along, Daisy! Simmons, Jane, illus. 2002. (Illus.). (J). 19.96 (978-0-7587-2263-8(X)) Book Wholesalers, Inc.

—Come along, Daisy! Simmons, Jane, illus. 1998. (Illus.). 32p. (J). (ps-2). 15.99 (978-0-316-79790-0(1)) Little Brown & Co.

—Come along, Daisy! Simmons, Jane, illus. (Illus.). (J). (ps-1). 2003. 32p. pap. 6.99 (978-0-316-16878-6(5)); 2001. 20p. 5.95 (978-0-316-79603-3(4)) Little, Brown Bks. for Young Readers.

—Come on, Daisy! (Illus.). (Orig.). 2005. (ARA, ENG, VIE, CHI & BEN.). 32p. 11.95 (978-1-84059-217-6(8)); 2005. (URD, ENG, VIE, CHI & ARA., 32p. 11.95 (978-1-84059-182-8(X)); 2005. (VIE, ENG, CHI, ARA & BEN., 32p. 11.95 (978-1-84059-183-5(8)); 2000. (BEN, ENG, VIE, CHI & ARA., 36p. (J). pap. 11.95 (978-1-84059-177-4(3)); 2000. (GUJ, ENG, VIE, CHI & ARA., 36p. (J). pap. 11.95 (978-1-84059-179-8(X)); 2000. (TUR, ENG, VIE, CHI & ARA., 36p. (J). pap. 11.95 (978-1-84059-181-1(1)) Milet Publishing.

—Daisy & the Beastie. Simmons, Jane, illus. 2002. (Illus.). (J). 19.11 (978-0-7587-2334-5(2)) Book Wholesalers, Inc.

—Daisy & the Egg. Simmons, Jane, illus. 2002. (Illus.). (J). 19.96 (978-0-7587-2335-2(0)) Book Wholesalers, Inc.

—Daisy & the Egg. (Illus.). (ps-1). 2005. (ARA, ENG, VIE, CHI & BEN.). 32p. 11.95 (978-1-84059-216-0(8)); 2005. (VIE, ENG, CHI, ARA & BEN., 32p. pap. 11.95 (978-1-84059-176-7(5)); 2000. (CHI, ENG, VIE, ARA & BEN., 36p. (J). pap. 11.95 (978-1-84059-171-2(4)); 2000. (GUJ, ENG, VIE, CHI & ARA., 36p. (J). pap. 11.95 (978-1-84059-173-6(0)); 2000. (TUR, ENG, VIE, CHI & ARA., 36p. (J). pap. 11.95 (978-1-84059-174-3(9)); 2000. (ALB, ENG, VIE, CHI & ARA., 36p. (J). pap. 11.95 (978-1-84059-172-9(2)) Milet Publishing.

—Daisy & the Egg. Datta, Kanai, tr. 2000. (Daisy Ser.). (BEN, ENG, VIE, CHI & ARA., Illus.). 36p. (J). (ps-1). pap. 11.95 (978-1-84059-170-5(6)) Milet Publishing.

—Daisy & the Egg. Iqbal, Gulshan, tr. 2000. (Daisy Ser.). (ENG, URD, VIE, CHI & ARA., Illus.). 36p. (J). (ps-1). pap. 11.95 (978-1-84059-175-0(7)) Milet Publishing.

—Daisy & the Egg. 2003. (ps-2). lib. bdg. 15.30 (978-0-613-71811-0(9)) Tandem Library Bks.

—Daisy Says Here We Go Round the Mulberry Bush. Simmons, Jane, illus. 2002. (Daisy Bks.). (Illus.). 7p. (J). (ps-17). 7.95 (978-0-316-79811-2(8)) Little, Brown Bks. for Young Readers.

—Daisy's Day Out. 2000. (Illus.). 10p. (J). bds. 5.95 (978-0-316-79763-4(4)) Little Brown & Co.

—Ven Aqui, Daisy! (SPA., Illus.). 32p. (J). (ps). (978-84-488-0849-5(5) , BS5842) Beascoa, Ediciones S.A. ESP. *Dist:* Lectorum Pubns., Inc.

Simmons, Martha. Grandma Perkido & Sidney. 2007. (Illus.). 24p. (J). 14.95 ***(978-0-9777041-4-9(9))*** Third Dimension Publishing.

Simon, Mary Manz. Duckling Is Patient. Clearwater, Linda, illus. 2006. (First Virtues for Toddlers Ser.). 20p. (J). 5.99 (978-0-7847-1410-2(X) , 04038) Standard Publishing.

Skalak, Barbara Anne. Waddle, Waddle, Quack, Quack, Quack. Long, Sylvia, illus. 2005. 36p. (J). 14.95 (978-0-8118-4342-3(4)) Chronicle Bks. LLC.

Sklansky, Amy E. The Duck Who Played the Kazoo. Beeke, Tiphanie, illus. 2008. 32p. (J). (ps-1). 16.00 ***(978-0-618-42854-0(2)*** , Clarion Bks.) Houghton Mifflin Co. Trade & Reference Div.

Sloat, Teri. I'm a Duck! 2008. 32p. (J). (ps). pap. 6.99 ***(978-0-14-241062-2(4)*** , Puffin) Penguin Group (USA) Inc.

—I'm a Duck! Sloat, Teri, illus. 2006. (Illus.). 32p. (J). (ps-2). 15.99 (978-0-399-24274-8(0) , Putnam Juvenile) Penguin Group (USA) Inc.

Smith, Sherrie B. Lonely Hearts. 2004. 49p. pap. 12.95 (978-1-4137-3108-8(2)) PublishAmerica, Inc.

Spafford, Suzy. Little Suzy Witzy to the Rescue. 2001. 32p. (J). pap. 10.95 (978-0-439-36554-3(6)) Scholastic, Inc.

—Little Suzy Witzy's Friends Forever. 2001. (J). 8.95 (978-0-439-36553-6(8)) Scholastic, Inc.

—Tales from Duckport: Helping Out Day Hooray. Spafford, Suzy, illus. 2003. (Tales from Duckport Ser.). (Illus.). 40p. (J). (gr. k-3). pap. 3.99 (978-0-439-38358-5(7)) Scholastic, Inc.

—Tales from Duckport: Stick Together! 2003. (Suzy's Zoo Ser.). (Illus.). 40p. (J). (gr. k-3). pap. 3.99 (978-0-439-38357-8(9)) Scholastic, Inc.

—Tales from Duckport: Stick Together! 2003. (gr. k-3). lib. bdg. 11.80 (978-0-613-63568-4(X)) Tandem Library Bks.

—Witzy Wonders. 2001. (Little Suzy's Zoo Ser.). (Illus.). 18p. (J). pap. 5.99 (978-0-439-36555-0(4)) Scholastic, Inc.

—Witzy's Block Party. 2001. (Little Suzy's Zoo Ser.). (Illus.). 16p. (J). (ps). pap. 9.99 (978-0-439-34356-5(9)) Scholastic, Inc.

Spikes, James L. The Adventures of LemonHead & Mudd Duck: What to do if Someone Tries to Grab You. 2005. 36p. (J). lib. bdg. 19.95 net. (978-0-9749202-7-6(4)) Excel Digital Pr., Inc.

Stephenson, Nancy Ann. The Ducks' New Friends. Coffin, Marilyn, illus. l.t. ed. 2006. 34p. (J). per. 9.99 (978-1-59879-164-8(8)) Lifevest Publishing, Inc.

C
D

The Story about Ping. 2004. 24.95 incl. audio (978-0-89719-688-8(0)); pap. 32.75 incl. audio (978-1-55592-313-6(5)); pap. 32.75 incl. audio (978-1-55592-314-3(3)); pap. 14.95 incl. audio (978-1-56008-076-3(0)) Weston Woods Studios, Inc.

A Story about Ping. 2004. (J). pap. 14.95 incl. audio (978-1-55592-857-5(9)) Weston Woods Studios, Inc.

Stuart, Karen A. Perfect. Senesi, Susan, illus. 2000. 24p. (J). (gr. 2-6). pap. 9.95 (978-1-56167-618-7(7) , Shooting Star Edition) American Literary Pr.

Swarta, Donna. At the Beach. Ferri, Francesca, illus. 2006. 6p. (J). 15.99 (978-0-7641-7923-5(3)) Barron's Educational Series, Inc.

Sweeney, Jacqueline. Lou Goes Too! Hart, G. K. & Empey, Mark, illus. 1999. (We Can Read! Ser.). 32p. (J). (gr. 1-2). lib. bdg. 21.36 (978-0-7614-0921-2(1) , Benchmark Bks.) Cavendish, Marshall Corp.

—Meadow Magic. 2001. (We Can Read! Ser.). (Illus.). 32p. (J). (gr. 1-2). lib. bdg. 21.36 (978-0-7614-1124-6(0) , Benchmark Bks.) Cavendish, Marshall Corp.

—What about Bettie? Hart, G. K. & Empey, Mark, illus. 2000. (We Can Read! Ser.). 32p. (J). (gr. 1-2). lib. bdg. 21.36 (978-0-7614-1118-5(6) , Benchmark Bks.) Cavendish, Marshall Corp.

Swimming Lessons with Stewie the Duck. 2005. (J). 9.95 (978-0-9668611-3-6(2)) Kimberly Pr., LLC.

Swoboda, Annette. El Chupete de Dudu. 2005. (SPA.). (J). bds. 7.99 (978-84-261-3247-5(2)) Juventud, Editorial ESP. *Dist:* Lectorum Pubns., Inc., Iaconi, Mariuccia Bk. Imports.

—Dudu Se Viste. 2005. (SPA.). (J). bds. 8.50 (978-84-261-3243-7(X)) Juventud, Editorial ESP. *Dist:* Lectorum Pubns., Inc.

—Dudu y el Orinal. 2005. (SPA.). (J). bds. 8.50 (978-84-261-3245-1(6)) Juventud, Editorial ESP. *Dist:* Lectorum Pubns., Inc.

Tafuri, Nancy. Goodnight, My Duckling. 2005. (Illus.). 32p. (J). pap. 16.95 (978-0-439-39881-7(9)) Scholastic, Inc.

—Have You Seen My Duckling? Tafuri, Nancy, illus. 2002. (Illus.). (J). 14.47 (978-0-7587-5475-2(2)) Book Wholesalers, Inc.

The Tale of the Mandarin Duck. 2004. pap. 14.95 incl. audio (978-0-7882-0505-7(6)) Weston Woods Studios, Inc.

The Tale of the Mandarin Ducks. 2004. 29.95 incl. cd-rom (978-1-55592-736-3(X)); pap. 18.95 incl. audio compact disk (978-1-55592-742-4(4)); pap. 18.95 incl. audio compact disk (978-1-55592-743-1(2)); pap. 38.75 incl. audio compact disk (978-1-55592-750-9(5)); pap. 38.75 incl. audio compact disk (978-1-55592-751-6(3)); pap. 32.75 incl. audio (978-1-55592-320-4(8)); pap. 32.75 incl. audio (978-1-55592-321-1(6)); pap. 14.95 incl. audio (978-1-55592-049-4(7)) Weston Woods Studios, Inc.

Talley, Linda. Thank You, Meiling. Maeno, Itoko, illus. 1999. (Key Concepts in Personal Development Ser.). 32p. (J). (gr. k-4). 16.95 (978-1-55942-118-8(5) , 7666) Marsh Media.

Tarbett, Debbie. Five Little Ducks. Penton Overseas, Inc. Staff, ed. Tarbett, Debbie, illus. 2006. (Illus.). 16p. (J). (gr. 3-5). bds. 10.95 (978-1-59125-747-9(6) , Penton Kids) Penton Overseas, Inc.

Taylor, Douglas. Downtown Ducks. Taylor, Catherine, illus. 2005. 62p. (J). pap. 22.99 (978-1-4134-3803-1(2)) Xlibris Corp.

Teddy Bear-Duck. 2003. (J). per. (978-1-57657-160-6(2)) Paradise Pr., Inc.

Ten Little Ducks & Other Stories: Individual Title Six-Pack. (Story Steps Ser.). (gr. k-2). 48.00 (978-0-7635-9798-6(8)) Rigby Education.

Thank You, Meiling: Evaluation Guide. 2006. (J). (978-1-55942-423-3(0)) Marsh Media.

Thomas, Kate. Mother Duck Knows the Way. Larkins, Mona, illus. 2005. 32p. (J). 8.95 (978-1-58374-122-1(4)) Chicago Spectrum Pr.

Thompson, Lauren. Little Quack. Anderson, Derek, illus. 2005. (Classic Board Bks.). 32p. (J). bds. 7.99 (978-0-689-87645-5(9) , Little Simon) Simon & Schuster Children's Publishing.

—Little Quack's Bath Book. Anderson, Derek, illus. 2006. 8p. (J). pap. 6.99 (978-1-4169-0803-6(X) , Little Simon) Simon & Schuster Children's Publishing.

—Little Quack's Bedtime. Anderson, Derek, illus. 2005. 32p. (J). 14.95 (978-0-689-86894-8(4)) Simon & Schuster Children's Publishing.

—Little Quack's Hide & Seek. Anderson, Derek, illus. (Classic Board Bks.). (J). 2007. 34p. 7.99 (978-1-4169-0325-3(9) , Little Simon); 2004. 32p. 14.95 (978-0-689-85722-5(5)) Simon & Schuster Children's Publishing.

Thompson, Lauren. Little Quack's New Friend. Anderson, Derek, illus. (Classic Board Bks.). (J). 2008. 34p. bds. 7.99 (***978-1-4169-4923-7(2)*** , Little Simon); 2006. 32p. 14.95 (978-0-689-86893-1(6)) Simon & Schuster Children's Publishing.

Thompson, Lauren & Anderson, Derek. Little Quack. 2003. (Illus.). 32p. (J). (ps-1). 14.95 (978-0-689-84723-3(8)) Simon & Schuster Children's Publishing.

Tiger Tales Staff. Little Ducky. Finn, Rebecca, illus. 2005. (Cuddly Cuffs Ser.). 6p. (J). 6.95 (978-1-58925-762-7(6) , tiger tales) ME Media LLC.

Tischler, Helene & Lockwood, Charlotte. Jamie & the Ducks of August: A Tale of Decoys. Lockwood, Charlotte, illus. 2001. (Illus.). 32p. (J). (ps-2). 6.95 (978-0-9679350-0-3(8)) Parkstone Publishing.

Tripp, Valerie. Lindy's Happy Ending. Allen, Joy, illus. 2005. 48p. (J). (ps-ps). lib. bdg. 10.79 (978-0-606-33674-1(5)) Tandem Library Bks.

Truax, Doug. A Good Day for Ducks. Smith, Jack K., illus. 2003. 32p. (gr. k-4). 16.95 (978-1-932052-12-1(7)) Ducks Unlimited, Inc.

Tryon, Leslie. Albert's Christmas. 2000. (J). (978-0-606-19247-7(6)) Tandem Library Bks.

—Albert's Field Trip. 2001. (gr. 3-6). lib. bdg. 15.30 (978-0-613-49708-4(2)); (Illus.). (J). 13.79 (978-0-606-21018-8(0)) Tandem Library Bks.

—Albert's Halloween: The Case of the Stolen Pumpkins. 2001. 13.79 (978-0-606-22101-6(8)) Tandem Library Bks.

Tyler, Jenny & Cartwright, S. Duck by the Sea. 2004. (SPA.). 6p. (J). vinyl bd. 7.95 (978-0-7945-0569-1(4)) EDC Publishing.

Udry, Janice May. Thump & Plunk. 2000. (Illus.). (gr. k-3). lib. bdg. 11.80 (978-0-613-31814-3(5)) Tandem Library Bks.

Ugly Duckling. 2004. (My First Fairy Tales Ser.). (Illus.). 24p. (J). pap. 3.99 (978-1-85854-685-8(0)) Brimax Books Ltd. GBR. *Dist:* Byeway Bks.

Urbanovic, Jackie. Duck at the Door. Urbanovic, Jackie, illus. 2007. (Illus.). 32p. (J). (gr. k-3). 16.99 (978-0-06-121438-7(8)); lib. bdg. 17.89 (978-0-06-121439-4(6)) HarperCollins Pubs.

Urbanovic, Jackie. Duck Soup. 2008. 32p. (J). 17.89 (***978-0-06-121442-4(6)***) HarperCollins Pubs.

—Duck Soup. Urbanovic, Jackie, illus. 2008. 32p. (J). 16.99 (***978-0-06-121441-7(8)***) HarperCollins Pubs.

van der Put, Klaartje. Little Duck: Finger Puppet Book. 2005. (Illus.). 12p. (J). 6.95 (978-0-8118-4847-3(7)) Chronicle Bks. LLC.

Van Scoyoc, Pam. The Ballerina with Webbed Feet/la Bailarina Palmipeda. Teichman, Diane E., tr. Lewis, R. J., illus. l.t. ed. 2004. (ENG & SPA.). 40p. (J). (gr. k-2). lib. bdg. 16.98 (978-0-9663629-2-3(6)) By Grace Enterprises.

Victoria & the Baby Tree. 2005. pap. 14.95 (***978-1-59526-525-8(2)***) Media Creations, Inc.

Volker, Kerstin. Lilly's Birthday Party. 2003. (Funny Friends Lift-and-Learn Bks.). (Illus.). 14p. (J). 5.99 (978-1-59384-022-8(5)) Parklane Publishing.

Waddell, Martin. Farmer Duck. 2002. (Illus.). (J). 13.83 (978-0-7587-2481-6(0)) Book Wholesalers, Inc.

—Farmer Duck. Oxenbury, Helen, illus. 2002. 26p. (J). (ps). bds. 6.99 (978-0-7636-2167-4(6)) Candlewick Pr.

—It's Quacking Time! Barton, Jill, illus. 2005. 32p. (J). (ps-1). 15.99 (978-0-7636-2738-6(0)) Candlewick Pr.

—Webster J. Duck. Parkins, David & Firth, Barbara, illus. 2004. 32p. (J). (gr. k-ps). pap. 6.99 (978-0-7636-2431-6(4)) Candlewick Pr.

—Webster J. Duck. Parkins, David, illus. 2001. 32p. (J). (gr. k-ps). 13.99 (978-0-7636-1506-2(4)) Candlewick Pr.

Wallen, Virginia. Amanda: Duck or Chicken? 2007. 17.00 (***978-0-8059-8828-4(9)***) Dorrance Publishing Co., Inc.

Ward, Nick. Come on, Baby Duck! 2004. (Illus.). 30p. (J). (ps up). 16.00 (978-1-56148-447-8(4)) Good Bks.

Watson, Jane Werner. The Fuzzy Duckling. Provensen, Alice & Provensen, Martin, illus. 2003. (Big Little Golden Bks.). 32p. (J). (gr. k). 8.99 (978-0-307-10325-3(0) , Golden Bks.) Random Hse. Children's Bks.

Watts, Bernadette. Ugly Duckling. Watts, Bernadette, illus. 2008. 0032p. pap. 6.95 (***978-0-7358-2146-0(1)***) North-South Bks., Inc.

Weiss, Ellen. Lucky Duck. Lies, Brian, illus. 2004. (Ready-to-Reads Ser.). 32p. (J). pap. 3.99 (978-0-689-86029-4(3) , Aladdin) Simon & Schuster Children's Publishing.

—Lucky Duck. Lies, Brian, illus. ed. 2005. 32p. (J). lib. bdg. 15.00 (978-1-59054-976-6(7)) Fitzgerald Bks.

Whippo, Walt. Little White Duck. Paley, Joan, illus. 2002. (J). 20.81 (978-0-7587-3019-0(5)) Book Wholesalers, Inc.

Whippo, Walt & Zaritzky, Bernard. Little White Duck. Paley, Joan, illus. 2005. 22p. (J). (ps-k). bds. 6.99 (978-0-316-73397-7(0)) Little, Brown Bks. for Young Readers.

Wildsmith, Brian. The Little Wood Duck. Wildsmith, Brian, illus. 2006. (Illus.). 32p. (J). 16.95 (978-1-59572-042-9(1)); pap. 6.95 (978-1-59572-049-8(9)) Star Bright Bks., Inc.

Wilhelm, Hans. Quacky Ducky's Easter Egg. Wilhelm, Hans, illus. 2004. (Illus.). 14p. (J). (ps up). 5.99 (978-0-06-053430-1(3) , Harper Festival) HarperCollins Pubs.

—Quacky Ducky's Easter Fun. Wilhelm, Hans, illus. 2004. (Illus.). 14p. (J). (ps up). 5.99 (978-0-06-053431-8(1) , Harper Festival) HarperCollins Pubs.

Willems, Mo. The Pigeon Finds a Hot Dog! 2004. (Illus.). 40p. (ps-1). 12.99 (978-0-7868-1869-3(7)) Hyperion Bks. for Children.

Williamgoldenpen. Quacker's Bedtime Stories. 2006. 49p. pap. 12.95 (978-1-4241-2236-3(8)) PublishAmerica, Inc.

Williamgoldenpen. Quacker's Bedtime Stories... Continued. 2007. (ENG.). 68p. per. 12.95 (***978-1-4241-7448-5(1)***) PublishAmerica, Inc.

Williams, Rozanne Lanczak. Look at Della Duck. Yakovetic Productions Staff, illus. 12p. (J). (gr. k-2). (978-1-58605-014-6(1)) LeapFrog Enterprises, Inc.

Winburn, William B., photos by. 10 Rubber Duckies. 2005. (Illus.). 24p. (J). (ps). 9.95 (978-1-4027-1943-1(4)) Sterling Publishing Co., Inc.

Windsor, Jo. Lazy Duck. Webb, Philip, illus. (Sails Literacy Ser.). 24p. (gr. k up). 27.00 (978-0-7635-6989-1(5)) Rigby Education.

—Lazy Duck: 3-in-1 Package. Webb, Philip, illus. (Sails Literacy Ser.). 24p. (gr. k up). 57.00 (978-0-7578-3199-7(0)) Rigby Education.

—Lazy Duck: 6 Small Books. Webb, Philip, illus. (Sails Literacy Ser.). 24p. (gr. k up). 25.00 (978-0-7578-3175-1(3)) Rigby Education.

Wood, Ellen. Hundreds of Fish. Felix, Monique, illus. 2000. (Notebooks Ser.). 40p. (gr. 4 up). 17.95 (978-1-56846-162-5(3) , Creative Editions) Creative Co., The.

Yamamura, Anji. Hannah Duck. Yamamura, Anji, illus. 2008. (Illus.). 24p. (J). 15.95 (***978-1-933605-74-6(X)***) Kane/Miller Bk. Pubs., Inc.

Yarborough, N. Patricia. The Duck Wedding. Diaz, Rolando, illus. 2002. 24p. (J). (978-1-57864-167-3(5)) Donning Co. Pubs.

Yolen, Jane. Dimity Duck. Braun, Sebastien, illus. 2008. 30p. (J). (ps). bds. 6.99 (***978-0-399-25060-6(3)*** , Philomel) Penguin Group (USA) Inc.

—Dimity Duck. Braun, Sebastian, illus. 2006. 32p. (J). (ps). 15.99 (978-0-399-24632-6(0) , Philomel) Penguin Group (USA) Inc.

Yoon, Salina. Duckling's First Spring. 2006. (Illus.). 10p. (J). (ps-1). bds. 5.99 (978-0-8431-1792-9(3) , Price Stern Sloan) Penguin Group (USA) Inc.

Yorinks, Arthur. Quack! Written in the International Language of Ducks! Yorinks, Adrienne, illus. 2003. 24p. (J). (ps-1). 12.95 (978-0-8109-3548-8(1)) Abrams, Harry N. , Inc.

Yorinks, Arthur & Yorinks, Adrienne, illus. Quack! There's a Duck on the Moon! 2002. 40p. (J). 9.95 (978-1-58837-021-1(6)) Winslow Pr.

Ziefert, Harriet. A Dozen Ducklings Lost & Found: A Counting Story. Dreifuss, Donald, illus. 2003. 32p. (J). (gr. k-3). tchr. ed. 15.00 (978-0-618-14175-3(8) , Walter Lorraine) Houghton Mifflin Co. Trade & Reference Div.

Zoller, Jayson D. The Laziest Duck. l.t. ed. 2004. (Illus.). 13p. (J). lib. bdg. 12.95 (978-1-932338-55-3(1)); per. 7.99 (978-1-932338-52-2(7)) Lifevest Publishing, Inc.

DUMB (DEAF MUTES)

see Deaf

DUNBAR, PAUL LAURENCE, 1872-1906

Reef, Catherine. Paul Laurence Dunbar: Portrait of a Poet. 2000. (African-American Biographies Ser.). (Illus.). 128p. (J). (gr. 6-12). lib. bdg. 26.60 (978-0-7660-1350-6(2)) Enslow Pubs., Inc.

DUNES

see Sand Dunes

DUNGEONS

see Prisons

DUNHAM, KATHERINE, 1910-

O'Connor, Barbara. Katherine Dunham: Pioneer of Black Dance. 2005. (Trailblazers Biographies Ser.). (Illus.). 112p. (gr. 5-9). 27.93 (978-1-57505-353-0(5)) Lerner Publishing Group.

DURER, ALBRECHT, 1471-1528

Adams, Colleen. Magic Squares. 2006. (Rosen Publishing Group's Reading Room Collection). (Illus.). 16p. (J). lib. bdg. (978-1-4042-3335-5(0) , PowerKids Pr.) Rosen Publishing Group, Inc., The.

Kerr, Kathleen. 7th Knot. 2007. 192p. (J). pap. 5.99 (***978-0-7614-5368-0(7)***) Cavendish, Marshall Corp.

DUST

Dust. braille ed. 2001. (gr. 2). spiral bd. (978-0-616-08850-0(7)) Canadian National Institute for the Blind/Institut National Canadien pour les Aveugles.

Dust Bunnies. 2007. 13.95 (***978-1-4218-9932-9(9)***) 1st World Publishing, Inc.

Sayre, April Pulley. Stars Beneath Your Bed: The Surprising Story of Dust. Jonas, Ann, illus. 2005. 32p. (J). 16.99 (978-0-06-057188-7(8)); lib. bdg. 17.89 (978-0-06-057189-4(6)) HarperCollins Pubs.

DUSTLAND (IMAGINARY PLACE)—FICTION

Hamilton, Virginia. Dustland. 1998. (Justice Cycle Ser.: Bk. 2). 214p. (YA). (gr. 6-12). pap. 4.50 (978-0-590-36217-7(8)) Scholastic, Inc.

—Dustland. 1998. (Justice Cycle Ser.). (978-0-606-12927-5(8)) Tandem Library Bks.

—The Gathering. 1998. (Justice Cycle Ser.: Bk. 3). 214p. (J). (gr. 6-12). mass mkt. 4.50 (978-0-590-36216-0(X)) Scholastic, Inc.

—The Gathering. 1998. (Justice Cycle Ser.). (978-0-606-13414-9(X)) Tandem Library Bks.

DUTCH—UNITED STATES

Gibson, Karen Bush. New Netherland: The Dutch Settle the Hudson Valley. 2006. (Building America Ser.). (Illus.). 48p. (J). (gr. 4-8). lib. bdg. 20.95 (978-1-58415-461-7(6)) Mitchell Lane Pubs., Inc.

DUTCH—UNITED STATES—FICTION

The Little Dutch Boy: 6 Small Books. (gr. k-2). 23.00 (978-0-7635-8509-9(2)) Rigby Education.

DWARFS

Krensky, Stephen. Watchers in the Woods. 2007. (Monster Chronicles Ser.). 48p. (J). (gr. 4-8). lib. bdg. 26.60 (***978-0-8225-6763-9(6)*** , Lerner Pubns.) Lerner Publishing Group.

Riggs, Stephanie. Never Sell Yourself Short. Youmans, Bill, illus. Youmans, Bill, photos by. 2001. 32p. (J). (gr. 1-5). 15.95 (978-0-8075-5563-7(0)) Whitman, Albert & Co.

DWARFS—FICTION

Alfaro Sifontes, Manuel Guillermo. Alboroto en un Lugar Remoto. 2005. (Illus.). 32p. (J). (978-1-58018-052-8(3)) Versal Editorial Group.

Black, Holly & DiTerlizzi, Tony. Spiderwick Chronicles Set: The Field Guide, the Seeing Stone, Lucinda's Secret, the Ironwood Tree, the Wrath of Mulgarath. DiTerlizzi, Tony, illus. movie tie-in ed. 2008. (Spiderwick Chronicles). 672p. (J). 49.99 (***978-1-4169-5016-5(8)***) Simon & Schuster Children's Publishing.

Blair, Eric. Blanca Nieves: Version del Cuento de los Hermanos Grimm. Wolf, Claudia, illus. 2006. (Read-It! Readers en Espanol Ser.).Tr. of Snow White: A Retelling of the Grimm's Fairy Tale. (SPA.). 32p. (J). (ps-3). 19.95 (978-1-4048-1640-4(2)) Picture Window Bks.

Blanca Nieves y los Siete Enanitos. 2001. Tr. of Snow White & the Seven Dwarfs. (SPA.). (978-968-6347-31-9(3)) Larousse, Ediciones, S. A. de C. V.

Combel Editorial Staff. Blancanieves. 2004. (Caballo alado clasicos-Al Trote Ser.). (SPA., Illus.). 24p. 6.95 (978-84-7864-778-1(3)) Combel Editorial, S.A. ESP. *Dist:* Independent Pubs. Group.

Crump, Fred, Jr. Ebonita & the Seven Boyz. 2007. 32p. (J). 12.95 (***978-1-934056-71-4(5)***) UMI (Urban Ministries, Inc.).

DiTerlizzi, Tony & Black, Holly. The Ironwood Tree. (Spiderwick Chronicles: Bk. 4). 128p. (J). 2004. (Illus.). (gr. 1-5). 10.99 (978-0-689-85939-7(2)); 2008. 10.99 (***978-1-4169-5020-2(6)***) Simon & Schuster Children's Publishing.

—The Ironwood Tree. l.t. ed. 2006. (Spiderwick Chronicles: Bk. 4). 90p. (YA). (gr. 2 up). 23.95 (978-0-7862-8583-9(4)) Thorndike Pr.

Fairy Tales - Snow White. 2005. (J). bds. (978-1-4194-0102-2(5)) Paradise Pr., Inc.

Fairy Tales- Snow White. 2005. (J). bds. (978-1-4194-0043-8(6)) Paradise Pr., Inc.

Fairy tales s/s - SNow White. 2005. (J). bds. (978-1-4194-0068-1(1)) Paradise Pr., Inc.

Frabetti, Carlo. La Magia Mas Poderosa. 11th ed. 2003. (SPA., Illus.). 120p. (J). 15.95 (978-84-204-4844-2(3)) Alfaguara, Ediciones, S.A.- Grupo Santillana ESP. *Dist:* Santillana USA Publishing Co., Inc.

—La Magia Mas Poderosa. 2000. (SPA.). (gr. 5-8). lib. bdg. 18.75 (978-0-613-82085-1(1)) Tandem Library Bks.

Graff, Lisa. The Thing about Georgie. 2007. 224p. (J). (gr. 3-6). 15.99 (978-0-06-087589-3(5)); lib. bdg. 16.89 (978-0-06-087590-9(9)) HarperCollins Pubs. (Geringer, Laura Book).

Hargreaves, Martin, illus. Rumpelstiltskin. 2008. (J). (***978-1-4027-3066-5(7)***) Sterling Publishing Co., Inc.

Hassinger, Peter W. The Book of Alfar: A Tale of the Hudson Highlands. 2002. (Illus.). 272p. (J). (gr. 4 up). 15.89 (978-0-06-028470-1(6) , Geringer, Laura Book) HarperCollins Pubs.

Jocelyn, Marthe. Earthly Astonishments. 2003. (gr. 3-6). lib. bdg. 16.40 (978-0-613-77300-3(4)) Tandem Library Bks.

Lagonegro, Melissa. Friends for a Princess. Harchy, Atelier Philippe, illus. 2004. (Disney Princess Ser.). 32p. (J). (ps-1). pap. 3.99 (978-0-7364-2208-6(0) , RH/Disney) Random Hse. Children's Bks.

—Friends for a Princess. 2004. (Disney Princess Ser.). (ps-2). lib. bdg. 11.80 (978-0-613-73713-5(X)) Tandem Library Bks.

Mendo, Miguel Angel, tr. Blancanieves. Barrett, Angela, illus. 2007. (SPA.). (J). (gr. 2-5). 24.95 (***978-84-96629-17-2(1)***) S.A. Kokinos ESP. *Dist:* Lectorum Pubns., Inc.

Morgan, C. M. Silver Doorway #1: A Gnome Away from Home. 2003. 104p. (J). pap. 6.99 (978-0-9702189-2-6(3)) Sabledrake Enterprises.

—Silver Doorway #2: Dwarves in the Dark. 2003. 104p. (J). pap. (978-0-9702189-3-3(1)) Sabledrake Enterprises.

Page, Nick & Claire. Snow White. 2006. (Read with Me (Make Believe Ideas) Ser.). (Illus.). 32p. (J). (gr. k-2). 3.95 (978-1-84610-163-2(8)) Make Believe Ideas GBR. *Dist:* Ingram Pub. Services.

PC Treasures, prod. Snow White & the Seven Dwarfs. 2007. (J). (***978-1-60072-033-8(1)***) PC Treasures, Inc.

Peterson, John. The Littles Have a Wedding. Clark, Roberta C., illus. 2007. (Littles Ser.). 96p. (J). (gr. 1-5). pap. 3.99 (978-0-590-46224-2(5)) Scholastic, Inc.

Random House Disney Staff. Snow White & the Seven Dwarfs. 2006. (Illus.). 24p. (J). (gr. k-k). bds. 4.99 (978-0-7364-2426-4(1) , RH/Disney) Random Hse. Children's Bks.

Ruzzier, Sergio. The Little Giant. 2004. (Illus.). 32p. (J). (ps-2). 16.89 (978-0-06-052952-9(0) , Geringer, Laura Book) HarperCollins Pubs.

Snow White & the Seven Dwarfs: Individual Title Six-Packs. 32p. (gr. 2 up). 37.00 (978-0-7635-9401-5(6)) Rigby Education.

Walt Disney's Snow White & the Seven Dwarfs. 2002. (J). spiral bd. (978-0-9720651-6-0(4)) Story Reader, Inc.

Worrall, Linda, illus. Snow White & the Seven Dwarfs: A Story about Vanity. 2006. (J). 6.99 (978-1-59939-025-3(6) , Reader's Digest Young Families, Inc.) Reader's Digest Children's Publishing, Inc.

DWELLINGS

see Architecture, Domestic; Houses

DYES AND DYEING

Charlie Needs a Cloak. 2004. 24.95 incl. audio (978-1-56008-023-7(X)); pap. 18.95 incl. audio compact disk (978-1-55592-382-2(8)); pap. 18.95 incl. audio compact disk (978-1-55592-384-6(4)); pap. 38.75 incl. audio compact disk (978-1-55592-383-9(6)); pap. 38.75 incl. audio compact disk (978-1-55592-385-3(2)); pap. 32.75 incl. audio (978-1-55592-200-9(7)); pap. 32.75 incl. audio (978-1-55592-201-6(5)); pap. 14.95 incl. audio (978-1-55592-719-6(X)) Weston Woods Studios, Inc.

de Paola, Tomie. Charlie Needs a Cloak. 2002. (J). (ps-2). lib. bdg. 14.15 (978-0-8335-0342-8(1)) Tandem Library Bks.

Kassinger, Ruth. Dyes: From Sea Snails to Synthetics. 2003. (Material World Ser.). (Illus.). 80p. (gr. 6-8). lib. bdg. 25.90 (978-0-7613-2112-5(8) , Twenty-First Century Bks.) Lerner Publishing Group.

Senisi, Ellen B. Berry Smudges & Leaf Prints: Finding & Making Colors from Nature. Senisi, Ellen B., photos by. 2005. (Illus.). 40p. (J). (gr. 4-8). reprint ed. 17.00 (978-0-7567-9707-2(1)) DIANE Publishing Co.

DYLAN, BOB, 1941-

Dylan, Bob. Bob Dylan Concise. 2004. 850p. pap. 39.95 (978-0-8256-1774-4(X) , Schirmer Trade Bks.) Music Sales Corp.

Horn, Geoffrey M. Bob Dylan. 2002. (Trailblazers of the Modern World Ser.). (Illus.). 48p. (J). (gr. 5 up). pap. 14.95 (978-0-8368-5236-3(2)); lib. bdg. 30.00 (978-0-8368-5076-5(9)) Stevens, Gareth Inc. (World Almanac Library).

Mazur, Kevin, photos by. Bob Dylan "Love & Theft" 2004. (Illus.). 56p. 17.95 (978-0-8256-1918-2(1) , AM972323) Music Sales Corp.

Play Guitar with... Bob Dylan. 2004. (Illus.). 48p. audio compact disk 21.95 (978-0-7119-8217-8(1) , AM955944) Music Sales Corp.

Roberts, Jeremy. Bob Dylan: Voice of a Generation. 128p. (J). (gr. 6 up). 18.95 (978-1-58013-155-1(7)) Kar-Ben Publishing.

—Bob Dylan: Voice of a Generation. 2005. (Lerner Biographies Ser.). (Illus.). 112p. (J). 27.93 (978-0-8225-1368-1(4) , Lerner Pubns.) Lerner Publishing Group.

Schuman, Michael A. Bob Dylan: The Life & Times of an American Icon. 2003. (People to Know Ser.). (Illus.). 112p. (J). lib. bdg. 26.60 (978-0-7660-2108-2(4)) Enslow Pubs., Inc.

Trailblazers of the Modern World: Neil Armstrong; Bob Dylan; Bill Gates; Nelson Mandela; Eleanor Roosevelt; Steven Spielberg, 6 bks. 2002. (Illus.). (J). (gr. 5 up). pap. 87.60 (978-0-8368-5234-9(6) , World Almanac Library) Stevens, Gareth Inc.

DYNAMICS

see also Aerodynamics; Force and Energy; Matter; Motion; Physics; Quantum Theory; Thermodynamics

Hewitt, Sally. Forces: Tractors. 2005. (Illus.). 32p. (J). (gr. 1-4). lib. bdg. 27.10 (978-1-59604-008-3(4)) Stargazer Bks.

Holt, Rinehart and Winston Staff. Holt Science & Technology Chapter 6: Physical Science: Forces in Motion. 5th ed. 2004. (Illus.). pap. 12.86 (978-0-03-030381-4(8)) Holt, Rinehart & Winston.

Roberts, Jeremy. How Do We Know the Laws of Motion? 2001. (Great Scientific Questions & the Scientists Who Answered Them Ser.). (Illus.). 112p. (YA). (gr. 4-6). lib. bdg. 26.50 (978-0-8239-3383-9(0)) Rosen Publishing Group, Inc., The.

Thomas, Isabel. Search & Rescue. 2007. (J). pap. ***(978-1-4109-2867-2(5));*** lib. bdg. ***(978-1-4109-2850-4(0))*** Steck-Vaughn.

Viegas, Jennifer. Kinetic & Potential Energy: Understanding Changes Within Physical Systems. 2004. (Library of Physics). (Illus.). 48p. (J). (gr. 7 up). lib. bdg. 25.25 (978-1-4042-0333-4(8)) Rosen Publishing Group, Inc., The.

DYSLEXIA

Clark, Arda Darakjian. Dyslexia. 2005. (Diseases & Disorders Ser.). (Illus.). 112p. (J). (gr. 7-10). 32.45 (978-1-59018-040-2(2) , Lucent Bks.) Thomson Gale.

Donnelly, Karen J. Coping with Dyslexia. 2005. (Coping Ser.). (Illus.). 192p. (YA). (gr. 7-12). lib. bdg. 26.50 (978-0-8239-2850-7(0) , CODYSL) Rosen Publishing Group, Inc., The.

Goldish, Meish. Everything You Need to Know about Dyslexia. 2001. (Need to Know Library). (Illus.). 64p. (YA). (gr. 4-6). lib. bdg. 25.25 (978-0-8239-3462-1(4)) Rosen Publishing Group, Inc., The.

Gordon, Melanie Apel. Let's Talk about Dyslexia. 1999. (Let's Talk Library). 24p. (YA). (gr. 3 up). pap. 6.95 (978-1-56838-275-3(8)) Hazelden Publishing & Educational Services.

—Let's Talk about Dyslexia. 1999. (Let's Talk Library). (Illus.). 24p. (J). (gr. 3). lib. bdg. 18.75 (978-0-8239-5199-4(5) , PowerKids Pr.) Rosen Publishing Group, Inc., The.

Landau, Elaine. Dyslexia. 2004. (Life Balance Ser.). 80p. (YA). (gr. 5-8). pap. 6.95 (978-0-531-16612-3(0)); (J). 20.50 (978-0-531-12217-4(4)) Scholastic Library Publishing. (Watts, Franklin).

Moody, Sylvia. Dyslexia: A Teenager's Guide. 2004. (Illus.). 176p. pap. 15.95 (978-0-09-190001-4(8)) Random Hse. GBR. *Dist:* Independent Pubs. Group.

Moore-Malinos, Jennifer & Roca, Nuria. Se Llama Dislexia: It's Called Dyslexia (Spanish Edition) Fabrega, Marta, illus. 2007. (Vive y Aprende Ser.). (SPA.). 32p. (J). (ps-2). pap. 6.99 ***(978-0-7641-3795-2(6))*** Barron's Educational Series, Inc.

Moynihan, Lauren E. Taking Dyslexia to School. Dineen, Tom, illus. 2002. (Special Kids in School Ser.: Vol. 11). 32p. (J). pap. 11.95 (978-1-891383-17-5(5)) JayJo Bks., LLC.

Silverstein, Alvin. Dyslexia. 2001. (gr. 3-6). lib. bdg. 15.25 (978-0-613-51635-8(4)) Tandem Library Bks.

Wiltshire, Paula. Dyslexia. 2002. (Health Issues Ser.). (Illus.). 64p. (J). (gr. 6-8). lib. bdg. 28.54 (978-0-7398-5221-7(3)) Raintree.

DYSLEXIA—FICTION

Beckhorn, Susan Williams. Sarey by Lantern Light. 2003. (Illus.). 150p. pap. 9.95 (978-0-89272-612-7(1)) Down East Bks.

—Sarey by Lantern Light. 2003. (gr. 7-12). lib. bdg. 18.75 (978-0-613-77418-5(3)) Tandem Library Bks.

Goodhart, Pippa. Rescued by a Dog Called Flow. 2006. (Illus.). 128p. (J). pap. 6.95 (978-1-903015-47-6(2)) Barn Owl Bks, London GBR. *Dist:* Independent Pubs. Group.

Hodge, Deborah. Lily & the Mixed-Up Letters. Brassard, France, illus. 2007. 32p. (J). (gr. 1-3). 18.95 (978-0-88776-757-9(5)) Tundra Bks., Inc./Livres Toundra, Inc. CAN. *Dist:* Random Hse., Inc.

Janover, Caroline D. The Worst Speller in Jr. High. 2001. 208p. (YA). (gr. 4-7). pap. 13.95 (978-0-595-15328-2(3) , Backinprint.com) iUniverse, Inc.

Joyce, Mildred. Why Cody Can't Learn. Kirk, Jacqueline, illus. 2007. 42p. (J). per. 18.95 (978-0-9788985-1-9(6)) A Better Be Write Pub.

Lester, Tyler. Welcome to Dyslexic Park. Russell, Diane & Eskola, Toby Alice, illus. l.t. ed. 1999. 25p. (J). 15.00 (978-0-938911-16-6(3)) Individualized Education Systems/Poppy Lane Publishing.

Per, Sharon Mills. Double Dutch. 2004. (gr. 5-8). lib. bdg. 13.00 (978-0-613-88160-9(5)) Tandem Library Bks.

Robb, Diane Burton. The Alphabet War: A Story about Dyslexia. Piazza, Gail, illus. 2004. 32p. (J). (gr. 2-5). 15.95 (978-0-8075-0302-7(9)) Whitman, Albert & Co.

Winkler, Henry & Oliver, Lin. Day of the Iguana. Heyer, Carol, illus. 2003. (Hank Zipzer Ser.: No. 3). 160p. (J). 13.99 (978-0-448-43288-5(9)); (gr. 3-8). mass mkt. 4.99 (978-0-448-43212-0(9)) Penguin Group (USA) Inc. (Grosset & Dunlap).

—Holy Enchilada! Heyer, Carol & Watson, Jesse Joshua, illus. 2004. (Hank Zipzer Ser.: No. 6). 160p. (J). (gr. 3-8). pap. 4.99 (978-0-448-43353-0(2) , Grosset & Dunlap) Penguin Group (USA) Inc.

—Holy Enchilada!, No. 6. Watson, Jesse Joshua, illus. 2004. (Hank Zipzer Ser.: No. 6). 160p. (J). (gr. 3-7). 13.99 (978-0-448-43554-1(3) , Grosset & Dunlap) Penguin Group (USA) Inc.

—Holy Enchilada! 2003. (Hank Zipzer Ser.: No. 6). (gr. 3-6). lib. bdg. 13.00 (978-0-613-72546-0(8)) Tandem Library Bks.

—The Zippity Zinger. 2003. (Hank Zipzer Ser.: No. 4). (Illus.). 160p. (J). (gr. 3-8). mass mkt. 4.99 (978-0-448-43193-2(9) , Grosset & Dunlap) Penguin Group (USA) Inc.

—The Zippity Zinger. Heyer, Carol, illus. 2003. (Hank Zipzer Ser.: No. 4). 160p. (J). 13.99 (978-0-448-43287-8(0) , Grosset & Dunlap) Penguin Group (USA) Inc.

E

EAGLES

America's Bald Eagle. (J). pap. (978-0-02-507955-7(7) , Scribner) Simon & Schuster.

Animal Lives: Eagles. 2006. pap. 4.99 (978-1-4206-8154-3(0)) Teacher Created Materials, Inc.

The Bald Eagle. (Wildlife of North America Ser.). 48p. (YA). 7.95 (978-0-7368-8493-9(1)) Capstone Pr., Inc.

Bald Eagles: Individual Title Six-Packs. (Action Packs Ser.). 120p. (gr. 3-5). 44.00 (978-0-7635-8422-1(3)) Rigby Education.

Bardhan-Quallen, Sudipta. Flying Eagle. Ray, Deborah Kogan, illus. 2008. (J). ***(978-1-57091-671-7(3))*** Charlesbridge Publishing, Inc.

Barghusen, Joan D. The Bald Eagle. 1998. (Endangered Animals & Habitats Ser.). (Illus.). 96p. (YA). (gr. 4-12). 28.70 (978-1-56006-254-7(1) , Lucent Bks.) Thomson Gale.

Barnes, Julia. 101 Facts about Eagles. 2004. (One Hundred One Facts about Predators Ser.). (Illus.). 32p. (J). (gr. 3 up). lib. bdg. 23.33 (978-0-8368-4036-0(4)) Stevens, Gareth Inc.

Bechtold, Phyliss. Seymour Bluffs & the Legend of the Piasa Bird. 2007. 26p. 9.95 ***(978-0-9728532-8-6(6))*** New Horizons Christian Ctr.

Binns, Tristan Boyer. The Bald Eagle. (Symbols of Freedom Ser.). (Illus.). 32p. (J). (gr. k-2). 2002. pap. 6.95 (978-1-58810-402-1(8) , 91144); 2001. lib. bdg. 21.36 (978-1-58810-118-1(5)) Heinemann Library.

—The Bald Eagle. 2001. (J). 13.79 (978-0-606-22573-1(0)); (gr. 3-6). lib. bdg. 14.75 (978-0-613-43300-6(9)) Tandem Library Bks.

Butterfield, Moira. Golden Eagle. (Who Am I? Ser.). (Illus.). 32p. (J). lib. bdg. 24.25 (978-1-930643-90-1(X)) Chrysalis Education.

Colman, C. H. The Bald Eagle's View of American History. Friar, Joanne H., illus. 2006. (J). (gr. 1-4). 48p. 12.95 (978-1-58089-300-8(7)); pap. 5.95 (978-1-58089-301-5(5)) Charlesbridge Publishing, Inc.

Cooper, Ann C. Eagles: Hunters of the Sky. 1999. (Wonder Ser.). (Illus.). 64p. (ps-3). pap. 7.95 (978-1-879373-11-2(4)) Rinehart, Roberts Pubs.

DeFries, Cheryl L. The Bald Eagle: A MyReportLinks. com Book. 2003. (Endangered & Threatened Animals Ser.). (Illus.). 48p. (J). (gr. 4-10). lib. bdg. 25.26 (978-0-7660-5057-0(2) , MyReportLinks.com Bks.) Enslow Pubs., Inc.

Dell, Pamela. The Bald Eagle. 2004. (Let's See Library). (Illus.). 24p. (J). (gr. 1 up). lib. bdg. 19.93 (978-0-7565-0616-2(6)) Compass Point Bks.

Donovan. Harpy Eagles. 2002. pap. 7.20 (978-0-7398-5810-3(6)) Steck-Vaughn.

Donovan, Sandy. Harpy Eagles. 2002. (Animals of the Rain Forest Ser.). (Illus.). 32p. (YA). lib. bdg. 22.83 (978-0-7398-5371-9(6)) Raintree.

Dornhoffer, Mary K. & Scherrer, Robert F. Eagles. 2004. (First Reports). (Illus.). 48p. (J). (gr. 3 up). lib. bdg. 22.60 (978-0-7565-0577-6(1)) Compass Point Bks.

Douglas, Lloyd G. The Bald Eagle. 2003. (Welcome Book Ser.). (J). 24p. 18.00 (978-0-516-25851-5(6)); pap. 4.95 (978-0-516-27874-2(6)) Scholastic Library Publishing. (Children's Pr.).

—The Bald Eagle. 2003. (gr. k-3). lib. bdg. 12.95 (978-0-613-67690-8(4)) Tandem Library Bks.

Dudley, Karen. Bald Eagles. 2000. (Untamed World Ser.). (Illus.). 64p. (J). (gr. 5-9). pap. 10.95 (978-0-7398-1681-3(0)) Steck-Vaughn.

Evert, Laura. Eagles. 2004. (Our Wild World Ser.). (Illus.). 48p. (J). (gr. 2-5). pap. 7.95 (978-1-55971-777-9(7) , NorthWord Bks. for Young Readers) T&N Children's Publishing.

—Eagles. 2001. (gr. 3-6). lib. bdg. 16.40 (978-0-613-55825-9(1)) Tandem Library Bks.

Furgang, Kathy. ¡Salvemos al aguila cabeza blanca! & Saving the Bald Eagles. 2005. spiral bd. 66.00 ***(978-1-4108-5652-4(6))*** Benchmark Education Co.

Furgang, Kathy. Saving the Bald Eagles. 2003. (Early Connections Ser.). (J). pap. 33.00 (978-1-4108-1089-2(5)) Benchmark Education Co.

Gibbons, Gail. Soaring with the Wind: The Bald Eagle. Gibbons, Gail, illus. 1998. (Illus.). 32p. (J). (gr. k-3). 16.99 (978-0-688-13730-4(X)); lib. bdg. 17.89 (978-0-688-13731-1(8)) HarperCollins Pubs.

Gilkerson, Patricia. My Adventure with Eagles. 2006. 44p. (J). 8.99 (978-1-59092-453-2(3) , Orchard Academy Pr.) Windstorm Creative.

Goldish, Meish. Bald Eagles: A Chemical Nightmare. 2008. (America's Animal Comebacks Ser.). (J). lib. bdg. 25.27 ***(978-1-59716-505-1(0))*** Bearport Publishing Co., Inc.

Grambo, Rebecca L. Eagles. 2003. (WorldLife Library). (Illus.). 72p. pap. 17.95 (978-0-89658-363-4(5)) Voyageur Pr., Inc.

Harcourt School Publishers Staff. The Bald Eagle Advanced Level. 3rd ed. 2002. (Trophies Reading Program Ser.). (Illus.). pap. 5.10 (978-0-15-323219-0(6)) Harcourt Schl. Pubs.

Hodge, Deborah. Eagles. Ogle, Nancy Gray, illus. 2004. (Kids Can Press Wildlife Ser.). 32p. (J). (gr. k-3). (978-1-55074-717-1(7)) Kids Can Pr., Ltd.

—Eagles. Gray, Nancy, illus. 2004. (Kids Can Press Wildlife Ser.). 32p. (J). (gr. k-3). (978-1-55074-715-7(0)) Kids Can Pr., Ltd.

—Eagles. 2000. (gr. 3-6). lib. bdg. 14.10 (978-0-613-30372-9(5)) Tandem Library Bks.

Jango-Cohen, Judith. The Bald Eagle. (Pull Ahead Bks.). 32p. (J). (gr. k-3). 2004. (Illus.). lib. bdg. 22.60 (978-0-8225-3645-1(5)); 2003. pap. 5.95 (978-0-8225-4750-1(3)) Lerner Publishing Group.

Kalz, Jill. Eagles. 2003. (Birds Ser.). (Illus.). 23p. (J). 21.35 (978-1-58340-129-3(6)) Smart Apple Media.

Landau, Elaine. The Bald Eagle. 2008. (True Booktrade;: American History Ser.). 48p. (J). pap. 6.95 ***(978-0-531-14776-4(2)*** , Children's Pr.) Scholastic Library Publishing.

Macken, JoAnn Early. Golden Eagles. 2006. (Illus.). 24p. (J). pap. 5.95 (978-0-8368-6326-0(7)); lib. bdg. 19.33 (978-0-8368-6319-2(4)) Stevens, Gareth Inc.

—Golden Eagles: Aguila Real. 2006. (ENG & SPA., Illus.). 24p. (J). pap. (978-0-8368-6457-1(3)); lib. bdg. 19.33 (978-0-8368-6450-2(6)) Stevens, Gareth Inc.

Marcovitz, Hal. The Bald Eagle. 2002. (American Symbols & Their Meanings Ser.). (Illus.). 48p. (YA). (gr. 4 up). lib. bdg. (978-1-59084-032-0(1)) Mason Crest Pubs.

Martin-James, Kathleen. Soaring Bald Eagles. (Pull Ahead Bks.). (Illus.). 32p. (J). (gr. k-2). 2003. pap. 5.95 (978-0-8225-3640-6(4)); 2001. lib. bdg. 22.60 (978-0-8225-3636-9(6) , Lerner Pubns.) Lerner Publishing Group.

—Soaring Bald Eagles. 2001. (gr. k-3). lib. bdg. 14.10 (978-0-613-58876-8(2)) Tandem Library Bks.

Merrick, Patrick. Eagles. 2006. (New Naturebooks). (Illus.). 32p. (J). (gr. 1-5). 27.07 (978-1-59296-636-3(5)) Child's World, Inc.

Miller, Sara Swan. Eagles. 2008. (J). lib. bdg. ***(978-1-4042-4163-3(9)*** , PowerKids Pr.) Rosen Publishing Group, Inc., The.

Morrison, Gordon. Bald Eagle. 2003. (Illus.). 32p. (J). (gr. k-3). pap. 5.95 (978-0-618-38626-0(2) , Walter Lorraine) Houghton Mifflin Co. Trade & Reference Div.

—Bald Eagle. 2003. (gr. k-3). lib. bdg. 14.10 (978-0-613-86972-0(9)) Tandem Library Bks.

Murray, Julie. Eagles. 2002. (Buddy Book Ser.). (Illus.). 24p. (J). (gr. k-4). lib. bdg. 21.35 (978-1-57765-703-3(9)) ABDO Publishing Co.

Nobleman, Marc Tyler. Eagles. 2006. (Animals Animals Ser.). (Illus.). 48p. (J). lib. bdg. 28.50 (978-0-7614-2236-5(6) , Benchmark Bks.) Cavendish, Marshall Corp.

Parry-Jones, Jemima. Eagle & Birds of Prey. 2000. (Eyewitness Bks.). (Illus.). 64p. (J). (gr. 4-7). 15.99 (978-0-7894-5860-5(8)) Dorling Kindersley Publishing, Inc.

Parry-Jones, Jemima & Dorling Kindersley Publishing Staff. Eagle & Birds of Prey. 2000. (Eyewitness Bks.). (Illus.). 64p. (J). (gr. 4-7). lib. bdg. 19.99 (978-0-7894-6618-1(X)) Dorling Kindersley Publishing, Inc.

Patent, Dorothy Hinshaw. The Bald Eagle Returns. Munoz, William, illus. 2000. 80p. (J). (gr. 4-6). tchr. ed. 16.00 (978-0-395-91416-8(7) , Clarion Bks.) Houghton Mifflin Co. Trade & Reference Div.

Pearl, Norman. The Bald Eagle. Skeens, Matthew, illus. 2006. 24p. (J). ***(978-1-4048-2642-7(4))*** Picture Window Bks.

Penny, Malcolm. Golden Eagle: Habitats, Life Cycles, Food Chains, Threats. 2001. (Illus.). 48p. (J). lib. bdg. 27.12 (978-0-7398-4437-3(7)) Raintree.

Potts, Steve. The Bald Eagle, 6 vols. (gr. 4 up). 39.95 (978-0-7368-8495-2(5)) Red Brick Learning.

Priebe, Mac. The Bald Eagle: Endangered No More. Priebe, Jennifer, illus. 2000. (Wildlife Winners). 32p. (J). (gr. 2-6). 15.95 (978-0-9669551-8-7(8)) Mindfull Publishing.

—EagleQuest CD-ROM + the Bald Eagle Book, 2003. (Illus.). (J). 29.95 incl. cd-rom (978-0-9669551-6-3(1) , 1) Mindfull Publishing.

Quiri, Patricia Ryon. The Bald Eagle. Joffe, Shari, ed. 1998. (True Bks.). (Illus.). 48p. (J). (gr. 3-5). pap. 6.95 (978-0-516-26373-1(0) , Children's Pr.) Scholastic Library Publishing.

Rauzon, Mark J. Golden Eagles of Devil Mountain. (Wildlife Conservation Society Bks.). (Illus.). 48p. (J). (gr. 4-6). 2001. pap. 6.95 (978-0-531-16525-6(6)); 2000. 24.50 (978-0-531-11787-3(1)) Scholastic Library Publishing. (Watts, Franklin).

—Golden Eagles of Devil Mountain. 2000. (gr. 3-6). lib. bdg. 15.25 (978-0-613-34238-4(0)) Tandem Library Bks.

Richardson, Adele D. Eagles: Birds of Prey. 2002. (Wild World of Animals Ser.). (Illus.). 24p. (J). (gr. 1-2). lib. bdg. 18.60 (978-0-7368-1136-1(2) , Bridgestone Bks.) Capstone Pr., Inc.

Silate, Jennifer. The Bald Eagle. 2005. (Illus.). 24p. (J). lib. bdg. (978-1-4042-2697-5(4)) Rosen Publishing Group, Inc., The.

Solway, Andrew. Eagles & Other Birds. 2006. (Illus.). 48p. (J). (978-1-4034-8222-8(5)); pap. (978-1-4034-8229-7(2)) Heinemann Library.

Stone, Lynn M. Bald Eagle. 2003. (Animals in U.S. History Ser.). (Illus.). 24p. (J). 25.64 (978-1-58952-699-0(6)) Rourke Publishing, LLC.

Stone, Lynn M., photos by. Bald Eagles. 2004. (Early Bird Nature Bks.). (Illus.). 48p. (J). (gr. 2-4). lib. bdg. 25.26 (978-0-8225-3034-3(1)) Lerner Publishing Group.

Swanson, Diane. Eagles. 2003. (Welcome to the World of Animals Ser.). (Illus.). 32p. (J). (gr. 3 up). lib. bdg. 23.33 (978-0-8368-3561-8(1)) Stevens, Gareth Inc.

Wechsler, Doug. Bald Eagles. 2001. (Really Wild Life of Birds of Prey Ser.). (Illus.). 24p. (J). lib. bdg. 18.75 (978-0-8239-5595-4(8) , PowerKids Pr.) Rosen Publishing Group, Inc., The.

Wexo, John Bonnett. Eagles. (Zoobooks Ser.). (Illus.). 24p. (J). (gr. 1-6). 2001. 15.95 (978-1-888153-41-5(5)); 2003. 10.95 (978-1-888153-98-9(9) , Zoo Bks.) Wildlife Education, Ltd.

Wicker, Jan Lee. Those Excellent Eagles. 2006. (Illus.). 55p. (J). 14.95 (978-1-56164-360-8(2)); pap. 8.95 (978-1-56164-355-4(6)) Pineapple Pr., Inc.

Wilcox, Charlotte. Bald Eagles. Boucher, Jerry, illus. Boucher, Jerry, photos by. 2005. (Nature Watch Ser.). 48p. (gr. 3-8). lib. bdg. 25.26 (978-1-57505-170-3(2)) Lerner Publishing Group.

Worsley, Arlene. Bald Eagles. 2006. (Amazing Animals Ser.). (J). (978-1-59036-388-1(4)); (978-1-59036-394-2(9)) Weigl Pubs., Inc.

Yanuck, Debbie L. The Bald Eagle. 2003. (American Symbols Ser.). (Illus.). 24p. (J). (gr. 1-2). lib. bdg. 23.93 (978-0-7368-1629-8(1) , Bridgestone Bks.) Capstone Pr., Inc.

EAGLES—FICTION

Andrews, Ted. Dreamsong of the Eagle. Hayner, Deborah, illus. 2002. 48p. (J). 16.95 (978-1-57174-294-0(8)) Hampton Roads Publishing Co., Inc.

Anrias, Donnan. Targ - the King of Eagles. 2005. 138p. (YA). per. 23.00 (978-1-4116-1923-4(4)) Lulu.com.

Barnwell, Dan. The Fire in Thunder Hollow. 2006. pap. 10.99 ***(978-1-4259-6741-3(8))*** AuthorHouse.

—Tree in Thunder Hollow. 2006. pap. 10.99 ***(978-1-4259-6742-0(6))*** AuthorHouse.

Beckwith, Agnes. Zar Meets Rahbue: From the Land of Senga. 1998. (Illus.). 16p. (J). (gr. 3-6). pap. 6.00 (978-0-8059-4263-7(7)) Dorrance Publishing Co., Inc.

Bugmann, Marlies. Golden Wings. 2005. (Green Heart Ser.). 216p. (J). pap. 12.99 (978-1-55410-283-9(9) , PO 00132) Zumaya Pubns. LLC.

Burns, Joanne. How & Why Eagles Fly. 2005. 27p. (J). 9.99 (978-1-4116-3387-2(3)) Lulu.com.

Echols, Larry. When the Eagles Fly. 2004. (YA). per. 11.95 (978-1-932496-11-6(4)) Penman Publishing, Inc.

Edwards, Carol. Jacy's Search for Jesus, Frey, Daniel J., illus. 2005. 32p. (J). 15.95 (978-0-9755314-0-2(9)) Majestic Publishing, LLC.

Farber, Erica. Golden Eagle. Mayer, Mercer, illus. 2006. (Critter Kids Adventure Ser.). 32p. (J). (gr. 2-5). pap. 4.95 (978-0-7696-4764-7(2) , Gingham Dog Pr.) School Specialty Publishing.

Ferer, Whitney H. The Owl Who Thinks He Is an Eagle. McCaslin, Anna, illus. 2003. 20p. (J). 14.95 (978-0-9729975-0-8(4) , OWL1) Graphically Speaking, Inc.

Hoover, T. A. The Last Eagle. Kaths, Kathy, illus. 2004. 38p. (J). 16.00 (978-0-9702216-3-6(0)) Sport Story Publishing.

Johnson, Brian. Ellie, the West Coast Eagle. Peet, Linda, illus. l.t. ed. 1999. 24p. (J). (ps-5). pap. (978-1-894303-25-5(3)) Raven Rock Publishing.

Korman, Gordon. Liar, Liar, Pants on Fire. 1999. (gr. 3-6). lib. bdg. 11.80 (978-0-613-11773-9(5)) Tandem Library Bks.

Losness, Howard. Little Eagle & the Sacred Waterfall. 2002. (ENG.). 208p. 24.95 ***(978-0-595-65510-6(6));*** 206p. pap. 14.95 (978-0-595-26053-9(5)) iUniverse, Inc. (Writers Club Pr.).

Mark, Hoog. Your Song: The First Growing Field Adventure. 2007. (Illus.). 48p. (J). 16.95 ***(978-0-9770391-2-8(9))*** Growing Field Bks.

McAuliffe, Nichola. Attila, Loolagax & the Eagle. Collins, Ross, tr. Collins, Ross, illus. 2003. 126p. pap. 10.99 (978-0-7475-6499-7(X)) Bloomsbury Publishing Plc GBR. *Dist:* Independent Pubs. Group.

McDonald, Megan. Julie & the Eagles, Bk. 4. McAliley, Susan, illus. 2007. 88p. (YA). (gr. 3 up). 12.95 ***(978-1-59369-351-0(6))*** American Girl Publishing, Inc.

—Julie & the Eagles, Bk. 4. McAliley, Susan & Hunt, Robert, illus. 2007. 88p. (YA). (gr. 3 up). pap. 6.95 ***(978-1-59369-350-3(8))*** American Girl Publishing, Inc.

Minshull, Evelyn. Eaglet's World. Gabriel, Andrea, illus. 2002. 32p. (J). (ps-3). 16.95 (978-0-8075-8929-8(2)) Whitman, Albert & Co.

Mirhady, Irandought. Thorn-Bush Boy: Pesare Tigh. Mirhady, Irandought, illus. 2004. Orig. Title: Pesare Tigh. (PEO., Illus.). 63p. (YA). per. (978-0-9760323-0-4(9)) Mirhady, Farhad.

Nesin, Aziz, et al. The Dance of the Eagle & the Fish. Christie, Ruth, tr. from TUR. 2001. (Illus.). 24p. (J). pap. 7.95 (978-1-84059-316-7(4)) Milet Publishing.

O'Kane, George & Weikert, Dana, illus. Baldwin's Colorful Campus Tour - Boston College A-Z. 2004. (J). 9.99 (978-1-933069-00-5(7)) Odd Duck Ink, Inc.

Porter, Cassyashton. Colin's Eagle. 2003. 134p. pap. 19.95 (978-1-59286-517-8(8)) PublishAmerica, Inc.

Rexroth, Sharon. America from the Sky. 2006. (J). 9.95 ***(978-1-57166-429-7(7));*** per. 22.95 ***(978-1-57166-430-3(0))*** Quixote Pr.

—Ohio. 2006. (J). per. 19.95 ***(978-1-57166-421-1(1))*** Quixote Pr.

Rylant, Cynthia. The Eagle. McDaniels, Preston, illus. 2004. (Lighthouse Family Ser.). 64p. (J). 14.95 (978-0-689-86243-4(1)) Simon & Schuster Children's Publishing.

Sargent, Dave. Baldy Eagle: Honor. 2003. (Feather Tales Ser.: 1). (Illus.). 42p. (J). lib. bdg. 19.95 (978-1-56763-719-9(1)) Ozark Publishing.

—Baldy Eagle: Honor. Lenoir, Jane, illus. 2003. (Feather Tales Ser.: 1). 42p. (J). pap. 6.95 (978-1-56763-720-5(5)) Ozark Publishing.

Sinclair, Carl R. The Way of the Eagle. 3rd l.t. rev. ed. 1998. Orig. Title: Elvis A. Eagle: A Magical Adventure. (Illus.). 220p. reprint ed. 17.95 (978-1-882833-01-6(5)) Scribe Pr.

Sobol, Donald J. Encyclopedia Brown & the Case of the Dead Eagles. 2008. (Encyclopedia Brown Ser.). 96p. (J). (gr. 1-3). pap. 4.99 ***(978-0-14-241135-3(3)*** , Puffin) Penguin Group (USA) Inc.

Stearns, Carolyn. Quiet Please—Eaglets Growing. Aiken, David, illus. 2002. 30p. (J). 11.95 (978-0-87033-541-9(3) , Tidewater Pubs.) Cornell Maritime Pr., Inc.

Thiele, Colin. Brahminy: The Story of a Boy & a Sea Eagle. (Illus.). 196p. pap. (978-0-7344-0402-2(6) , Lothian Bks.) Hachette Livre Australia.

Vaughan, Richard Lee. Eagle Boy: A Pacific Northwest Native Tale. Christiansen, Lee, illus. 2002. 32p. (J). (gr. 1-5). 16.95 (978-1-57061-171-1(8)) Sasquatch Bks.

Walters, Eric. War of the Eagles. 1998. 160p. (YA). (gr. 7-12). 14.00 (978-1-55143-118-5(1)) Orca Bk. Pubs. USA.

Wargin, Kathy-Jo. The Legend of Old Abe: A Civil War Eagle. Caple, Laurie, illus. 2006. 40p. (J). (gr. k-5). 17.95 (978-1-58536-232-5(8)) Sleeping Bear Pr.

EAR

see also Hearing

Ballard, Carol. Ears. 2003. (Body Focus Ser.). (Illus.). 48p. (J). lib. bdg. 27.07 (978-1-4034-0749-8(5)); pap. (978-1-4034-3297-1(X)) Heinemann Library.

Douglas, Lloyd G. My Ears. 2004. (Wel-My Body Ser.). (J). 18.00 (978-0-516-24062-6(5)); 24p. pap. 4.95 (978-0-516-22126-7(4)) Scholastic Library Publishing. (Children's Pr.).

Ear. 2001. (Human Anatomy Ser.). (J). (gr. k-12). vinyl bd. 4.95 (978-1-58845-082-1(1)) School Specialty Publishing.

Ears. (Early Intervention Levels Ser.). 23.10 (978-0-7362-0026-4(6)) Hampton-Brown Bks.

Equipo Staff. El Oido. (Coleccion Mundo Maravilloso). (SPA., Illus.). 22p. (J). (gr. 2-4). (978-84-348-5096-5(6) , SM7493) SM Ediciones ESP. *Dist:* Lectorum Pubns., Inc.

Eyes & Ears Sets: 1 Each of 3 Big Books. (Sunshinetm Science Ser.). (gr. 1-2). 111.50 (978-0-7802-1445-3(5)) Wright Group, The.

Eyes & Ears Sets: 1 Each of 3 Student Books. (Sunshinetm Science Ser.). (gr. 1-2). 20.95 (978-0-7802-1747-8(0)) Wright Group, The.

Fernandez, A. & Fernandez, Q. Hooray for My Ears. (Hooray for My Senses Ser.). (Illus.). (J). 19.27 (978-1-58952-373-9(3)) Rourke Publishing, LLC.

Furgang, Kathy, et al, contrib. by. My Ears. 2001. (My Body Ser.). (Illus.). 24p. (J). lib. bdg. 19.95 (978-0-8239-5572-5(9) , PowerKids Pr.) Rosen Publishing Group, Inc., The.

Glaser, Jason. Ear Infections. 2007. (First Facts Ser.). (Illus.). 24p. (J). 21.26 (978-0-7368-6390-2(7)) Capstone Pr., Inc.

Gordon, Sharon. Earaches. 2003. (Rookie Read-About Health Ser.). (Illus.). (J). (gr. k-2). 31p. pap. 5.95 (978-0-516-27397-6(3)); 32p. 20.50 (978-0-516-22584-5(7)) Scholastic Library Publishing. (Children's Pr.).

—Earaches. 2003. (gr. k-3). lib. bdg. 14.10 (978-0-613-67882-7(6)) Tandem Library Bks.

—Hearing. 2002. (Rookie Read-About Health Ser.). (Illus.). 32p. (J). (gr. k-2). pap. 5.95 (978-0-516-25989-5(X) , Children's Pr.) Scholastic Library Publishing.

—Hearing. 2001. (gr. k-3). lib. bdg. 14.10 (978-0-613-50700-4(2)) Tandem Library Bks.

Gray, Susan Heinrichs. The Ears. 2005. (Human Body Ser.). (Illus.). 32p. (J). (gr. 2-6). 27.07 (978-1-59296-425-3(7)) Child's World, Inc.

Hall, John. Mickey Mcguffin's Ear. Gilpin, Stephen, illus. 2005. 48p. (J). (ps-7). lib. bdg. 12.99 (978-1-59379-068-4(6)) White Stone Bks.

Hall, Peg. Whose Ears Are These? A Look at Animal Ears - Short, Flat, & Floppy. Landmark, Ken, illus. 2004. (Whose Is It? Ser.). 24p. (C). (gr. k-2). 22.60 (978-1-4048-0004-5(2)) Picture Window Bks.

Hidalgo, Maria. Hearing. 2003. 24p. (J). lib. bdg. 21.35 (978-1-58340-304-4(3)) Smart Apple Media.

Klingel, Cynthia Fitterer & Noyed, Robert B. Ears/Orejas. Acosta, Tatiana & Gutiérrez, Guillermo, trs. Andersen, Gregg, photos by. 2002. (Weekly Reader Early Learning Library). (Illus.). 24p. (J). (ps up). (SPA & ENG.). pap. (978-0-8368-3320-1(1)); (ENG & SPA., lib. bdg. 19.33 (978-0-8368-3071-2(7)) Stevens, Gareth Inc. (Weekly Reader Early Learning Library).

Labella, Susan. Bats & Other Animals with Amazing Ears. 2005. (Scholastic News Nonfiction Readers Ser.). (Illus.). 24p. (J). (gr. 1-2). 19.00 (978-0-516-24926-1(6) , Children's Pr.) Scholastic Library Publishing.

Lansky, Vicki. Koko Bear's Big Earache: Preparing Your Child for Ear Tube Surgery. 2nd ed. 2004. (Lansky, Vicki Ser.). (Illus.). 32p. (J). pap. 8.95 (978-1-931863-42-1(3)) Book Peddlers.

Libra, Anna. Why Does Loud Music Hurt My Ears? An Inside Look at the Ear. 2003. (J). pap. (978-1-58417-072-3(7)); lib. bdg. (978-1-58417-009-9(3)) Lake Street Pubs.

Miles, Elizabeth. Ears. (Animal Parts Ser.). (Illus.). 32p. (J). (gr. k-2). 2003. pap. 6.95 (978-1-4034-0423-7(2)); 2002. lib. bdg. 21.36 (978-1-4034-0014-7(8)) Heinemann Library.

—Ears. 2003. (gr. k-3). lib. bdg. 14.75 (978-0-613-45744-6(7)) Tandem Library Bks.

Miller, Sara Swan. All Kinds of Ears. 2007. (All Kinds Of Ser.). (Illus.). 48p. (J). (ps-3). lib. bdg. 28.50 (978-0-7614-2518-2(7) , Benchmark Bks.) Cavendish, Marshall Corp.

Mitchell, Melanie S. Ears. 2003. (First Step Nonfiction Ser.). (Illus.). 8p. (J). pap. 3.95 (978-0-8225-3910-0(1) , Lerner Pubns.) Lerner Publishing Group.

Murphy, Patricia J. Hearing. 2003. (True Bks.). (gr. 3-5). pap. 6.95 (978-0-516-26970-2(4) , Children's Pr.) Scholastic Library Publishing.

—Hearing. 2003. (gr. 3-6). lib. bdg. 15.25 (978-0-613-67968-8(7)) Tandem Library Bks.

Nelson, Robin. Hearing. 2005. (First Step Nonfiction Ser.). (Illus.). 24p. (gr. k-2). lib. bdg. 17.27 (978-0-8225-1264-6(5)) Lerner Publishing Group.

—Seeing & Hearing Well. 2006. (Pull Ahead Bks.). (J). 22.60 (978-0-8225-3488-4(6) , Lerner Pubns.) Lerner Publishing Group.

Nunn, Daniel. Ears. 2006. (Illus.). 24p. (J). pap. (978-1-4034-8478-9(3)); lib. bdg. 20.71 (978-1-4034-8473-4(2)) Heinemann Library.

Olson, Karen W. Eyes, Ears, Nose & Mouth. George, Leonard, Jr., illus. 2006. 20p. (J). pap. 10.95 (978-1-894778-34-3(0)) Theytus Bks., Ltd. CAN. *Dist:* Orca Bk. Pubs. USA.

Pringle, Laurence P. Hearing. 2000. (Explore Your Senses Ser.). (Illus.). 32p. (J). (gr. 4-8). lib. bdg. 25.64 (978-0-7614-0735-5(9) , Benchmark Bks.) Cavendish, Marshall Corp.

Pryor, Kimberley Jane. Hearing. 2003. (Senses Ser.). (Illus.). 32p. (gr. 2-4). 23.00 (978-0-7910-7554-8(0) , Chelsea Hse.) Facts On File, Inc.

Rau, Dana Meachen. Shhhh...listen! A Book about Your Sense of Hearing. Peterson, Rick, illus. 2005. (Amazing Body Ser.). 24p. (C). (gr. k-3). 22.60 (978-1-4048-1018-1(8)) Picture Window Bks.

Royston, Angela. Healthy Eyes & Ears. 2003. (Illus.). 32p. (J). pap. 6.95 (978-1-4034-4455-4(2)); lib. bdg. (978-1-4034-4446-2(3)) Heinemann Library.

Schuette, Sarah L. Como Cuidar MIS Oídos: Taking Care of My Ears. 2007. (SPA.). ***(978-0-7368-7652-0(9))*** Capstone Pr., Inc.

Schuette, Sarah L. Taking Care of My Ears. 2006. (Pebble Plus Ser.). (Illus.). 24p. (J). (978-0-7368-4259-4(4)) Capstone Pr., Inc.

Sherman, Josepha. The Ear: Learning How We Hear. 2002. (3-D Library of the Human Body). (Illus.). 48p. (YA). (gr. 5-8). lib. bdg. 26.50 (978-0-8239-3529-1(9) , Rosen Central) Rosen Publishing Group, Inc., The.

Silverstein, Alvin. Earaches. 2002. (gr. 3-6). lib. bdg. 15.25 (978-0-613-54181-7(2)) Tandem Library Bks.

Silverstein, Alvin, et al. Earaches. 2002. (My Health Ser.). (Illus.). 48p. (J). (gr. 3-5). pap. 6.95 (978-0-531-15562-2(5) , Watts, Franklin) Scholastic Library Publishing.

—Hearing. 2001. (Senses & Sensors Ser.). (Illus.). 64p. (gr. 5-8). lib. bdg. 25.90 (978-0-7613-1666-4(3) , Millbrook Pr.) Lerner Publishing Group.

Simon, Seymour. Eyes & Ears. (Illus.). (J). 2005. 32p. pap. 6.99 (978-0-06-073302-5(0) , Harper Trophy); 2003. 15.99 (978-0-688-15303-8(8)) HarperCollins Pubs.

Sirret, Dawn. Winking, Blinking, Wiggling, & Waggling. 2000. (Eyewitness Readers Ser.). (978-0-606-18121-1(0)); lib. bdg. 11.80 (978-0-613-27596-5(9)) Tandem Library Bks.

Stone, Lynn M. How Do Animals Use Their Ears? 2008. (J). ***(978-1-60044-503-3(9))*** Rourke Publishing, LLC.

Take Care of Your Ears! With Annie Funelli & the Funsters. 2002. (Lessons for a Healthy Childhood Ser.). (J). (gr. k-3). instr.'s gde. ed. 69.95 (978-1-55942-188-1(6) , 9234V9) Marsh Media.

Trumbauer, Lisa. Animal Ears. 2000. (Yellow Umbrella Books). (Illus.). 16p. (J). (gr. 1). lib. bdg. 14.60 (978-0-7368-0723-4(3) , Pebble Bks.) Capstone Pr., Inc.

Windsor, Jo. Big Ears: Emergent Level Satellite Individual Title Six-Packs. (Sails Literacy Ser.). (gr. k-1). 27.00 (978-0-7578-7927-2(6)) Rigby Education.

EARHART, AMELIA, 1898-1937

Abraham, Philip. Amelia Earhart. 2002. (Wel-Real People Ser.). (Illus.). 24p. (J). (ps-2). 18.00 (978-0-516-23952-1(X)); pap. 4.95 (978-0-516-23600-1(8)) Scholastic Library Publishing. (Children's Pr.).

—Amelia Earhart. 2002. (gr. k-3). lib. bdg. 12.95 (978-0-613-58823-2(1)) Tandem Library Bks.

Amelia Earhart. (Photo Illustrated Biographies Ser.). 24p. (J). 6.95 (978-0-7368-8421-1(1)) Capstone Pr., Inc.

Amelia Earhart: Individual Title Six-Packs. (Action Packs Ser.). 120p. (gr. 3-5). 44.00 (978-0-7635-8395-8(2)) Rigby Education.

Anderson, Jameson. Amelia Earhart: Legendary Aviator. Whigham, Rod & Barnett, Charles, illus. 2007. (Graphic Library). 32p. (J). 25.26 (978-0-7368-6496-1(2)); pap. ***(978-0-7368-7532-5(8))*** Capstone Pr., Inc.

Brown, Jonatha A. Amelia Earhart. 19.33 (978-0-8368-4581-5(1)) Stevens, Gareth Inc.

Bull, Angela. Flying Ace: The Story of Amelia Earhart. 2000. (gr. k-3). lib. bdg. 11.80 (978-0-613-25210-2(1)) Tandem Library Bks.

Bull, Angela & Dorling Kindersley Publishing Staff. Flying Ace: The Story of Amelia Earhart. 2000. (Eyewitness Bks.). (Illus.). 48p. (J). (gr. 2-4). 14.99 (978-0-7894-5436-2(X)); pap. 3.99 (978-0-7894-5435-5(1)) Dorling Kindersley Publishing, Inc.

Burke, John. Sterling Point Books: Amelia Earhart: Flying Solo. 2007. (Sterling Point Bks.). (Illus.). 208p. (J). 12.95 (978-1-4027-4520-1(6)); pap. 6.95 (978-1-4027-4140-1(5)) Sterling Publishing Co., Inc.

Burleigh, Robert. Amelia Earhart: Free in the Skies. Wylie, Bill, illus. 2003. (American Heroes Ser.). 48p. (J). 16.00 (978-0-15-202498-7(0) , Silver Whistle) Harcourt Trade Pubs.

—Amelia Earhart: Free in the Skies. 2003. (gr. 3-6). lib. bdg. 14.10 (978-0-613-70522-6(X)) Tandem Library Bks.

—Amelia Earhart Free in the Skies. Wylie, Bill, illus. 2003. (American Heroes Ser.). 48p. (J). pap. 5.95 (978-0-15-216810-0(9) , Silver Whistle) Harcourt Trade Pubs.

Canizares, Susan & Chanko, Pamela. Up, up & Away: The Story of Amelia Earhart. 1999. (Social Studies Emergent Readers). (J). 2.50 (978-0-439-04578-0(9)) Scholastic, Inc.

—Up, up, & Away: The Story of Amelia Earhart. 1999. (ps-2). lib. bdg. 10.10 (978-0-613-22557-1(0)) Tandem Library Bks.

Connolly, Sean. Amelia Earhart. 2000. (Profiles Ser.). (Illus.). 56p. (J). (gr. 4-6). lib. bdg. 24.22 (978-1-57572-223-8(2)) Heinemann Library.

Devillier, Christy. Amelia Earhart. 2001. (First Biographies Ser.). (Illus.). 32p. (J). (gr. k-4). lib. bdg. 22.78 (978-1-57765-596-1(6) , Buddy Bks.) ABDO Publishing Co.

Feinstein, Stephen. Read about Amelia Earhart. 2006. (I Like Biographies! Ser.). (Illus.). 24p. (J). lib. bdg. 21.26 (978-0-7660-2582-0(9) , Enslow Elementary) Enslow Pubs., Inc.

Ford, Carin T. Amelia Earhart: Meet the Pilot. 2002. (Meeting Famous People Ser.). (Illus.). 32p. (J). (gr. 1-4). lib. bdg. 22.60 (978-0-7660-2003-0(7)) Enslow Pubs., Inc.

Ganeri, Anita. Amelia Earhart. 1999. (What Would You Ask...? Ser.). (Illus.). 32p. (J). (gr. 2-6). lib. bdg. 16.95 (978-1-929298-01-3(3)) Chrysalis Education.

Gormley, Beatrice. Amelia Earhart: Young Aviator. Henderson, Meryl, illus. 2000. (Childhood of Famous Americans Ser.). 272p. (J). (gr. 3-7). pap. 5.99 (978-0-689-83188-1(9) , Aladdin) Simon & Schuster Children's Publishing.

—Amelia Earhart: Young Aviator. 2000. (gr. 3-6). lib. bdg. 13.00 (978-0-613-21095-9(6)); (Illus.). (J). 11.64 (978-0-606-17901-0(1)) Tandem Library Bks.

Harcourt School Publishers Staff. Amelia Earhart. 3rd ed. 2002. (Horizons Ser.). (Illus.). (J). (gr. 2). pap. 3.70 (978-0-15-333194-7(1)) Harcourt Schl. Pubs.

—Amelia Earhart Below Level. 3rd ed. 2002. (Trophies Reading Program Ser.). (Illus.). pap. 5.10 (978-0-15-323225-1(0)); (SPA., pap. 6.80 (978-0-15-324136-9(5)) Harcourt Schl. Pubs.

—Conoce a Amelia Earhart On Level. 3rd ed. 2002. (Trofeos Ser.). (SPA., Illus.). pap. 6.80 (978-0-15-324165-9(9)) Harcourt Schl. Pubs.

—Meet Amelia Earhart On Level. 3rd ed. 2002. (Trophies Reading Program Ser.). (Illus.). pap. 5.10 (978-0-15-323255-8(2)) Harcourt Schl. Pubs.

—Sky Pioneer Level D: Library Edition. 2001. (Collections Ser.). (Illus.). (J). 6.90 (978-0-15-314437-0(8)) Harcourt Schl. Pubs.

Haugen, Brenda. Amelia Earhart: Legendary Aviator. 2006. (J). (978-0-7565-1880-6(6)) Compass Point Bks.

Howe, Jane Moore. Amelia Earhart: Young Air Pioneer. Underdown, Harold, ed. Morrison, Cathy, illus. 2nd rev. ed. 2000. (Young Patriots Ser.). 111p. (J). (gr. 5 up). 15.95 (978-1-882859-02-3(2)); pap. 9.95 (978-1-882859-04-7(9)) Patria Pr., Inc.

—Amelia Earhart: Young Air Pioneer. 2000. (gr. 3-6). lib. bdg. 18.75 (978-0-613-80158-4(X)) Tandem Library Bks.

Jerome, Kate Boehm. Who Was Amelia Earhart? Cain, David & Harrison, Nancy, illus. 2002. (Who Was...? Ser.). 112p. (J). mass mkt. 4.99 (978-0-448-42856-7(3) , Grosset & Dunlap) Penguin Group (USA) Inc.

—Who Was Amelia Earhart? 2002. (gr. 3-6). lib. bdg. 13.00 (978-0-613-61667-6(7)) Tandem Library Bks.

Klingel, Cynthia Fitterer. Amelia Earhart: Aviation Pioneer. 2003. (Spirit of America: Our People Ser.). (Illus.). 32p. (J). (gr. 2-6). 27.07 (978-1-59296-000-2(6)) Child's World, Inc.

Lakin, Patricia. Amelia Earhart: More Than A Flier. 2003. (gr. k-3). lib. bdg. 11.80 (978-0-613-66447-9(7)) Tandem Library Bks.

Lakin, Patricia, et al. Amelia Earhart: More Than a Flier. 2003. (Ready-to-Read Stories of Famous Americans Ser.). (Illus.). 48p. (J). pap. 3.99 (978-0-689-85575-7(3) , Aladdin) Simon & Schuster Children's Publishing.

Leavitt, Amie. Amelia Earhart. 2007. (What's So Great About... ? Ser.). (J). lib. bdg. 25.70 ***(978-1-58415-576-8(0))*** Mitchell Lane Pubs., Inc.

Mara, Wil. Amelia Earhart. (Rookie Biographies Ser.). (Illus.). 32p. (J). (gr. 1-2). 2003. pap. 4.95 (978-0-516-27338-9(8)); 2002. 20.50 (978-0-516-22522-7(7)) Scholastic Library Publishing. (Children's Pr.).

—Amelia Earhart. 2002. (gr. k-3). lib. bdg. 12.95 (978-0-613-59445-5(2)) Tandem Library Bks.

McLeese, Don. Amelia Earhart. 2003. (Discover the Life of an American Legend Ser.). (gr. 2-5). 14.95 (978-1-58952-301-2(6)) Rourke Publishing, LLC.

Micklos, John. Unsolved: What Really Happened to Amelia Earhart? 2006. (Prime Ser.). (Illus.). 128p. (J). (gr. 5 up). lib. bdg. 33.27 (978-0-7660-2365-9(6)) Enslow Pubs., Inc.

Mortensen, Lori. Amelia Earhart: Female Pioneer in Flight. McGuire, Robert, illus. 2007. (J). lib. bdg. ***(978-1-4048-3728-7(0))*** Picture Window Bks.

Netzley, Patricia D. The Disappearance of Amelia Earhart. 2005. (Mystery Library). (Illus.). 112p. (YA). (gr. 7-10). lib. bdg. 29.95 (978-1-59018-629-9(X) , Lucent Bks.) Thomson Gale.

Patricia, Torres. Amelia Earhart. 2005. 136p. pap. (978-958-30-1680-6(2)) Panamericana Editorial.

Patrick, Jean L. S. & Sutcliffe, Jane. Amelia Earhart. 2002. (History Maker Bios Ser.). (Illus.). 48p. (J). pap. 6.95 (978-0-8225-1561-6(X)) Lerner Publishing Group.

Pflueger, Lynda. Amelia Earhart: Legend of Flight. 2003. (Historical American Biographies Ser.). (Illus.). 128p. (J). lib. bdg. 26.60 (978-0-7660-1976-8(4)) Enslow Pubs., Inc.

Raatma, Lucia. Amelia Earhart. 2001. (Trailblazers of the Modern World Ser.). (Illus.). 48p. (J). (gr. 5 up). pap. 14.95 (978-0-8368-5223-3(0)); lib. bdg. 30.00 (978-0-8368-5063-5(7)) Stevens, Gareth Inc. (World Almanac Library).

Reyburn, Susan. Women Who Dare: Amelia Earhart. 2006. (Illus.). 64p. 12.95 (978-0-7649-3545-9(3) , A111) Pomegranate Communications, Inc.

Rinaldo, Denise. Amelia Earhart: With a Discussion of Courage. 2004. (Values in Action Ser.). (J). (978-1-59203-068-2(8)) Learning Challenge, Inc.

Rosenthal, Marilyn S. & Freeman, Daniel. Amelia Earhart. 1999. (Photo-Illustrated Biographies Ser.). (Illus.). 24p. (J). (gr. 2-3). lib. bdg. 18.60 (978-0-7368-0203-1(7) , Bridgestone Bks.) Capstone Pr., Inc.

Sabin, Francene & Mattern, Joanne. Amelia Earhart: Adventure in the Sky. Dugan, Karen, illus. 2006. 50p. (J). pap. ***(978-0-439-66041-9(6))*** Scholastic, Inc.

Schaefer, Lola M. Amelia Earhart. Saunders-Smith, Gail, ed. 2002. (First Biographies Ser.). (Illus.). 24p. (J). (gr. k-1). lib. bdg. 15.93 (978-0-7368-1433-1(7) , Pebble Bks.) Capstone Pr., Inc.

Sutcliffe, Jane. Amelia Earhart. 2003. (History Maker Bios Ser.). (Illus.). 48p. (J). (gr. 3-5). lib. bdg. 26.60 (978-0-8225-0396-5(4)) Lerner Publishing Group.

Szabo, Corinne. Sky Pioneer: A Photobiography of Amelia Earhart. 2007. (Illus.). 64p. (J). (gr. 5). 7.95 (978-1-4263-0044-8(1) , National Geographic Children's Bks.) National Geographic Society.

Theisen, Gordon. The Disappearance of Amelia Earhart. 2001. (Natural History Guides Ser.). (Illus.). 40p. pap. 9.99 (978-0-86730-844-0(3)) Lebhar-Friedman Bks.

Wagner, Heather Lehr. Amelia Earhart. 2003. (Famous Flyers Ser.). (Illus.). 112p. (gr. 6-12). 30.00 (978-0-7910-7213-4(4)); pap. 30.00 (978-0-7910-7498-5(6)) Facts On File, Inc. (Chelsea Hse.).

—Amelia Earhart. 2003. (gr. 5-8). lib. bdg. 18.75 (978-0-613-65152-3(9)) Tandem Library Bks.

Wheeler, Jill C. Amelia Earhart. 2002. (Breaking Barriers Ser.). (Illus.). 64p. (J). (gr. 3-8). lib. bdg. 25.65 (978-1-57765-318-9(1) , ABDO & Daughters) ABDO Publishing Co.

EARHART, AMELIA, 1898-1937—FICTION

Lakin, Patricia. Amelia Earhart: Amelia Earhart: More Than A Flier. Daniel, Alan & Daniel, Lea, illus. ed. 2005. 48p. (J). lib. bdg. 15.00 (978-1-59054-957-5(0)) Fitzgerald Bks.

Ryan, Pam Muñoz. Amelia & Eleanor Go for a Ride. Selznick, Brian, illus. 1999. 40p. (J). (gr. k-4). pap. 16.95 (978-0-590-96075-5(X)) Scholastic, Inc.

EARP, WYATT, 1848-1929

Alagna, Magdalena. Wyatt Earp: Lawman of the American West. (Famous People in American History Ser.). (Illus.). 32p. (J). (ps-7). 2004. 21.25 (978-0-8239-4123-0(X) , Rosen Central); 2003. pap. (978-0-8239-4195-7(7)) Rosen Publishing Group, Inc., The.

Goodman, Michael E. Wyatt Earp. 2005. (Legends of the West Ser.). (Illus.). 48p. (gr. 5-9). 21.95 (978-1-58341-339-5(1) , Creative Education) Creative Co., The.

Landau, Elaine. Wyatt Earp: Wild West Lawman. 2004. (Best of the West Biographies Ser.). (Illus.). 48p. (YA). lib. bdg. 23.93 (978-0-7660-2217-1(X)) Enslow Pubs., Inc.

Staeger, Rob. Wyatt Earp. 2001. (Famous Figures of the American Frontier Ser.). (Illus.). 64p. (J). (gr. 5 up). pap. 8.95 (978-0-7910-6486-3(7)); 25.00 (978-0-7910-6485-6(9)) Facts On File, Inc. (Chelsea Hse.).

—Wyatt Earp. 2002. (gr. 5-8). lib. bdg. 17.60 (978-0-613-51040-0(2)) Tandem Library Bks.

Urban, William. Wyatt Earp: The OK Corral & the Law of the American West. 2005. (Library of American Lives & Times). (Illus.). 112p. (YA). (gr. 4-8). lib. bdg. 31.95 (978-0-8239-5740-8(3)) Rosen Publishing Group, Inc., The.

Winter, Jonah. Wyatt Earp. 1999. (J). pap. 3.50 (978-0-7868-4030-4(7)) Disney Pr.

EARP, WYATT, 1848-1929—FICTION

Breault, Christie Merriman. Logan West, Printer's Devil. Archembault, Matthew, illus. 2006. 142p. (J). pap. (978-1-59336-762-6(7)) Mondo Publishing.

EARTH

see also Antarctica; Arctic Regions; Atmosphere; Creation; Earthquakes; Geography; Geology; Geophysics; Glacial Epoch; Meteorology; Ocean; Oceanography; Physical Geography; Universe

Adamson, Heather. In My World. 2005. (Illus.). 24p. (J). (978-0-7368-4242-6(X)) Capstone Pr., Inc.

Adamson, Thomas K. Earth. (J). 2008. ***(978-1-4296-0731-5(9));*** 2003. (Illus.). 24p. lib. bdg. 17.26 (978-0-7368-2111-7(2) , Pebble Bks.) Capstone Pr., Inc.

Adamson, Thomas K. La Tierra: Earth. 2006. (ENG & SPA., Illus.). 24p. (J). (978-0-7368-5878-6(4)) Capstone Pr., Inc.

Ashby, Ruth. The Earth & Its Moon. 2003. (New Solar System Ser.). (J). lib. bdg. 28.50 (978-1-58340-287-0(X)) Smart Apple Media.

Asimov, Isaac. The Solar System: Earth. 2004. (Illus.). 32p. 14.00 (978-1-59102-177-3(4)) Prometheus Bks., Pubs.

Asimov, Isaac & Hantula, Richard. Earth. (Isaac Asimov's 21st Century Library of the Universe). (Illus.). 32p. (gr. 3 up). 2003. (J). pap. (978-0-8368-3938-8(2) , Weekly Reader Early Learning Library); 2002. (YA). lib. bdg. 24.67 (978-0-8368-3234-1(5)) Stevens, Gareth Inc.

—La Tierra. Porras, Carlos & D'Andrea, Patricia, trs. 2003. (Isaac Asimov's Biblioteca del Universo del Siglo XXI). (SPA., Illus.). 32p. (J). (gr. 3 up). lib. bdg. 24.67 (978-0-8368-3862-6(9)); pap. 8.95 (978-0-8368-3875-6(0) , Weekly Reader Early Learning Library) Stevens, Gareth Inc.

Atkinson, Mary. The Earth Is Flat! Science Facts & Fictions. 2007. (Shockwave: Science in Practice Ser.). (Illus.). 36p. (J). (gr. 4-6). lib. bdg. 25.00 (*978-0-531-17580-4(4) , Children's Pr.) Scholastic Library Publishing.

Bailey, Jacqui. Sun Up, Sun Down: The Story of Day & Night. Lilly, Matthew, illus. 2004. (Science Works Ser.). 32p. (J). (gr. 3-6). 23.93 (978-1-4048-0567-5(2)) Picture Window Bks.

Ball, Jackie. Earth's History. 2004. (Discovery Channel School Science Ser.). (Illus.). 32p. (J). (gr. 5 up). lib. bdg. 24.67 (978-0-8368-3379-9(1)) Stevens, Gareth Inc.

Banquieri, Eduardo. Secrets of Earth. 2005. (Our Planet Ser.). (Illus.). 32p. (J). (gr. 4-8). lib. bdg. 28.00 (978-0-7910-9011-4(6) , Chelsea Clubhouse) Facts On File, Inc.

Baquedano, Elizabeth & Van Rose, Susanna. La Tierra. 2004. (Dk Eyewitness Books Ser.). (SPA.). 64p. (J). 15.99 (978-0-7566-0416-5(8)) Dorling Kindersley Publishing, Inc.

Baxter, Nicola. Nuestra Fantastica Tierra. 2004. (Discovery Guides Ser.). (SPA., Illus.). 32p. (gr. 2-5). (J). pap. 6.95 (978-1-58728-706-0(4)); 11.95 (978-1-58728-649-0(1)) T&N Children's Publishing. (Two Can Publishing).

—Our Wonderful World. 2004. (Discovery Guides Ser.). (SPA., Illus.). 32p. (J). (gr. 2-5). 11.95 (978-1-58728-219-5(4)); pap. 6.95 (978-1-58728-213-3(5)) T&N Children's Publishing. (Two Can Publishing).

Baxter, Nicole. Our Wonderful World. 2001. (gr. 3-6). lib. bdg. 14.10 (978-0-613-43488-1(9)) Tandem Library Bks.

Bell, Trudy E. Earth's Journey Through Space. 2007. (Scientific American Ser.). 72p. (gr. 5-8). 30.00 (*978-0-7910-9050-3(7) , Chelsea Hse.) Facts On File, Inc.

Benchmark Education Staff, compiled by. Earth the Inside Story & Earth Systems. 2005. spiral bd. 225.00 (*978-1-4108-5823-8(5)) Benchmark Education Co.

—Earth the Inside Story & Earth's HIST. 2005. spiral bd. 225.00 (*978-1-4108-5822-1(7)) Benchmark Education Co.

—Our Changing Earth. 2006. spiral bd. 135.00 (*978-1-4108-7081-0(2)) Benchmark Education Co.

Berger, Melvin & Berger, Gilda. Do Bears Sleep All Winter? Questions & Answers about Bears. Osti, Roberto, illus. 2002. (Question & Answer Ser.). 48p. (J). pap. 5.95 (978-0-439-26671-0(8) , Scholastic Reference) Scholastic, Inc.

Bevan, Finn & Mayo, Diana. Beneath the Earth: The Facts & the Fables. 1999. (Landscapes of Legend Ser.). (Illus.). 32p. (J). (gr. 4). pap. 6.95 (978-0-516-26302-1(1) , Children's Pr.) Scholastic Library Publishing.

BHB International Staff. Earth. 1998. (Our World in Pictures Ser.). (J). (ps). (978-2-215-06162-5(6)) Editions Fleurus.

Billings. True Tales of Burning Earth. 1999. (J). pap. 13.00 (978-0-7398-2390-3(6)) Steck-Vaughn.

—True Tales of Shifting Ground. 1999. (Illus.). (J). pap. 13.00 (978-0-7398-2392-7(2)) Steck-Vaughn.

Birch, Robin. Earth. 2004. (Solar System Ser.). (Illus.). 32p. (gr. 3-5). 23.00 (978-0-7910-7925-6(2) , Chelsea Hse.) Facts On File, Inc.

—Earth, Sun, & Moon. 2002. (Space Ser.). (Illus.). 32p. (gr. k-2). 23.00 (978-0-7910-6970-7(2) , Chelsea Hse.) Facts On File, Inc.

Blashfield, Jean F. & Jacobs, Richard P. When Land, Sea, & Life Began: The Precambrian. 2005. (Illus.). 80p. (J). 37.14 (978-1-4034-7657-9(8)) Heinemann Library.

—When Land, Sea, & Life Began: The Precambrian. 2004. (J). 35.64 (978-1-4109-1288-6(4)) Raintree.

—When Life Flourished in Ancient Seas: The Paleozoic Era. 2005. (Illus.). 80p. (J). 37.14 (978-1-4034-7658-6(6)) Heinemann Library.

—When Life Flourished in Ancient Seas: The Paleozoic Era. 2004. (J). 35.64 (978-1-4109-1289-3(2)) Raintree.

The Blue Planet, Earth: Alien Technical Research. 2004. (YA). cd-rom 15.00 (978-0-934269-60-5(2)) UFO Photo Archives.

Boehm, Richard G., et al. Assessment Programs: The World. 1999. (Harcourt Brace Social Studies). (gr. k-7). pap. 100.60 (978-0-15-312123-4(8)) Harcourt Schl. Pubs.

Bredeson, Carmen. What Do You Know about Earth? 2008. (I Like Space! Ser.). (Illus.). 32p. (J). (gr. 1-3). lib. bdg. 22.60 (*978-0-7660-2945-3(X) , Enslow Elementary) Enslow Pubs., Inc.

The Bridgestone Science Library: Exploring the Earth, 6 bks. Incl. Changing Earth. Olien, Rebecca. lib. bdg. 18.60 (978-0-7368-0949-8(X)); Erosion. Olien, Rebecca. lib. bdg. 18.60 (978-0-7368-0950-4(3)); Fossils. Olien, Rebecca. lib. bdg. 18.60 (978-0-7368-0951-1(1)); Minerals. Richardson, Adele D. lib. bdg. 18.60 (978-0-7368-0952-8(X)); Rocks. Richardson, Adele D. lib. bdg. 18.60 (978-0-7368-0953-5(8)); Soil. Richardson, Adele G. lib. bdg. 18.60 (978-0-7368-0954-2(6)); 24p. (J). (gr. 2-3). 2001. (Illus.). 2001. Set lib. bdg. 111.60 (978-0-7368-1010-4(2) , Bridgestone Bks.) Capstone Pr., Inc.

Brighter Vision Publishing Staff. Our Earth. 1999. (Learning Adventures Kindergarten Ser.). (Illus.). (J). (gr. k-1). pap. 2.25 (978-1-55254-061-9(8) , BV12023) Brighter Vision Pubns.

Brinkman, Patricia. Discover Earth. 2006. pap. 39.00 (*978-1-4108-6479-6(0)) Benchmark Education Co.

—Earth. 2006. pap. 42.00 (*978-1-4108-6476-5(6)) Benchmark Education Co.

Caes, Charles J. How Do We Know the Age of the Earth? 2001. (Great Scientific Questions & the Scientists Who Answered Them Ser.). (Illus.). 112p. (YA). (gr. 4-6). lib. bdg. 26.50 (978-0-8239-3381-5(4)) Rosen Publishing Group, Inc., The.

Carroll, Colleen. Elements: Earth, Air, Fire & Water. 1998. (How Artists See Ser.). (Illus.). 48p. (gr. 3 up). 12.95 (978-0-7892-0476-9(2)) Abbeville Pr., Inc.

Caviezel, Giovanni. Our Planet Earth. Pagnoni, Roberta, illus. 2004. 40p. (J). bds. 8.95 (978-0-7641-5750-9(7)) Barron's Educational Series, Inc.

Chancellor, Deborah. Planet Earth. 2006. (Kingfisher Young Knowledge Ser.). (Illus.). 48p. (J). (gr. k-3). 9.95 (978-0-7534-5934-8(5) , Kingfisher) Houghton Mifflin Co. Trade & Reference Div.

Charman, Andrew, et al. The Living World. 1998. (Fact Finders Ser.). (Illus.). 144p. (J). (gr. 3-7). (978-0-563-37620-0(1)) BBC Worldwide.

Cheshire, Gerard. The Solar System & Beyond. 2006. (Fundamental Physics Ser.). (Illus.). 48p. (978-1-58340-998-5(X)) Smart Apple Media.

Clark, Stuart. Earth. 2003. (Universe Ser.). (Illus.). 32p. (J). (gr. 3-5). lib. bdg. 22.79 (978-1-58810-910-1(0)) Heinemann Library.

—The Earth. 2002. (Universe Ser.). (Illus.). 32p. (J). pap. (978-1-4034-0611-8(1)) Heinemann Library.

Clarke, Phillip. Planet Earth Facts & Lists: Internet-Linked. 2004. (Facts & Lists Internet-Linked Ser.). 64p. (J). lib. bdg. 15.95 (978-1-58086-637-8(9) , Usborne) EDC Publishing.

Claybourne, A. Encyclopedia of Planet Earth. 2004. (Geography Ser.). (Illus.). 160p. (J). lib. bdg. 27.95 (978-1-58086-573-9(9)) EDC Publishing.

Claybourne, Anna. Enciclopedia del Planeta Tierra. 2004. (SPA.). 160p. (J). 19.95 (978-0-7460-4526-8(3)) EDC Publishing.

Coble, Charles. Earth Science. 3rd ed. (J). 33.47 (978-0-13-982109-7(0)) Prentice Hall (Schl. Div.).

Cole, Joanna. The Magic School Bus Inside the Earth. 2001. (Early Readers Ser.: Vol. 1). (J). lib. bdg. (978-1-59054-523-2(0)) Fitzgerald Bks.

Cole, Michael D. Earth: The Third Planet. 2001. (Countdown to Space Ser.). (Illus.). 48p. (YA). (gr. 4-10). lib. bdg. 23.93 (978-0-7660-1507-4(6)) Enslow Pubs., Inc.

Colson, Mary. Shaky Ground: Earthquakes. 2005. (Turbulent Planet Ser.). (J). (978-1-4109-1736-2(3)); pap. (978-1-4109-1746-1(0)) Steck-Vaughn.

Coote, Roger. Earth. 2003. (Knowledge Masters Ser.). (Illus.). 32p. (YA). pap. incl. cd-rom (978-1-903954-11-9(8)) Chrysalis Children's Bks.

Dalmatian Press Staff. God's Wonderful World: Bright Idea Book to Color. 2003. (Bright Idea Book to Color Ser.). (Illus.). 32p. (J). pap. 3.99 (978-1-57759-893-0(8)) Dalmatian Pr.

Daniels, Patricia. Earth. 1998. (Nature Library). (J). (978-0-7922-7046-1(0)) National Geographic Society.

Davies, Francis. Earth. 2002. (Nature's Record-Breakers Ser.). (Illus.). 32p. (J). (gr. 3 up). lib. bdg. 23.33 (978-0-8368-2907-5(7)) Stevens, Gareth Inc.

Davis, Barbara J. Earth's Core & Crust. 2006. (J). pap. (*978-0-8368-7873-8(6)) Stevens, Gareth Inc.

Davis, Kenneth C. Don't Know Much about Planet Earth. Bloom, Tom, illus. 2001. (Don't Know Much About Ser.). (J). (gr. 2-6). 144p. pap. 7.99 (978-0-06-440834-9(5) , Harper Trophy); 160p. 19.89 (978-0-06-028600-2(8)) HarperCollins Pubs.

—Don't Know Much about Planet Earth. unabr. ed. 2004. (Don't Know Much about Ser.). 144p. (J). (gr. 4-7). pap. 29.00 incl. audio (978-0-8072-0660-7(1) , Listening Library) Random Hse. Audio Publishing Group.

—Don't Know Much about Planet Earth. 2001. (J). 13.60 (978-0-606-22303-4(7)) Tandem Library Bks.

Day, Trevor. DK Guide to Savage Earth. Parsons, Jayne, ed. 2001. (Illus.). 64p. (J). (gr. 3-12). 15.95 (978-0-7894-7919-8(2)) Dorling Kindersley Publishing, Inc.

—DK Guide to Savage Earth. 2001. (Illus.). 64p. (J). 25.98 (978-0-7513-3075-5(2)) Dorling Kindersley Publishing, Inc.

De Munn, Michael. The Earth Is Good: A Chant in Praise of Nature. McMullan, Jim, illus. 1999. 32p. (J). (gr. k-4). pap. 15.95 (978-0-590-35010-5(2)) Scholastic, Inc.

¿De Que Esta Hecha la Tierra? (Coleccion Primeros Pasos en la Ciencia). (SPA., Illus.). (J). (gr. 1-3). pap. (978-950-724-689-0(4) , LMA8230) Lumen ARG. *Dist:* Lectorum Pubns., Inc.

Dobeck, Maryann. Circling the Sun. 2004. (Illus.). 16p. (J). (978-0-7608-8917-6(1)) Sundance/Newbridge Educational Publishing.

Dorling Kindersley Publishing Staff. Compact Atlas of the World. 2005. 192p. pap. 15.00 (978-0-7566-0965-8(8)) Dorling Kindersley Publishing, Inc.

—Concise Atlas of the World. 2005. 384p. 34.95 (978-0-7566-0966-5(6)) Dorling Kindersley Publishing, Inc.

—Earth. 2005. (Eyewitness Books). 72p. (J). (ps-12). 15.99 (978-0-7566-1069-2(9)) Dorling Kindersley Publishing, Inc.

—Essential Atlas of the World. 2005. 256p. pap. 15.00 (978-0-7566-0964-1(X)) Dorling Kindersley Publishing, Inc.

Dorling Kindersley Publishing Staff & Turner, Matt. Earth. 2004. (Google E Guides Ser.). (Illus.). 96p. (J). 17.99 (978-0-7566-0539-1(3)) Dorling Kindersley Publishing, Inc.

Downs, Sandra. The Earth's Hidden Treasures. 1999. (Exploring Planet Earth Ser.). (Illus.). 64p. (gr. 5-8). lib. bdg. 24.90 (978-0-7613-1411-0(3) , Twenty-First Century Bks.) Lerner Publishing Group.

—When the Earth Moves. 2000. (Exploring Planet Earth Ser.). (Illus.). 64p. (gr. 5-8). lib. bdg. 24.90 (978-0-7613-1412-7(1) , Twenty-First Century Bks.) Lerner Publishing Group.

Draper, Allison Stark. Earth. 2004. (Library of the Nine Planets). (Illus.). 48p. (J). lib. bdg. 26.50 (978-1-4042-0167-5(X)) Rosen Publishing Group, Inc., The.

Dunn, Mary R. A Look at Earth. 2008. (J). lib. bdg. (*978-1-4042-3827-5(1) , PowerKids Pr.) Rosen Publishing Group, Inc., The.

The Earth. 2001. (Our World Ser.). (J). (gr. k-12). vinyl bd. 4.95 (978-1-58845-072-2(4)) School Specialty Publishing.

Earth. (Make it Work Ser.). 42p. (J). (gr. 4-8). pap. (978-1-882210-44-2(1)) Action Publishing, Inc.

Earth, Module C. 2003. (gr. 3 up). suppl. ed. 15.50 (978-0-328-03437-6(1)); (gr. 4 up). suppl. ed. 15.50 (978-0-328-03441-3(X)); (gr. 5 up). suppl. ed. 16.00 (978-0-328-03445-1(2)); (gr. 6 up). suppl. ed. 16.00 (978-0-328-03449-9(5)) Addison-Wesley Educational Pubs., Inc.

Earth. (Dk Eyewitness Books Ser.). (J). pap. 8.95 (978-0-7894-6168-1(4)) Dorling Kindersley Publishing, Inc.

Earth. 2002. (Questions & Answers Ser.). 48p. (J). pap. 5.98 (978-0-7525-7888-0(X)) Parragon, Inc.

The Earth: First Grade Newcomer Books. (On Our Way to English Ser.). (gr. 1 up). 23.50 (978-0-7578-7201-3(8)) Rigby Education.

Earth & Space. Date not set. (Illus.). 48p. (J). 5.98 (978-1-4054-0206-4(7)); 2003. (Illus.). 256p. (J). 12.98 (978-1-4054-1543-9(6)); 2000. 40p. (YA). 8.33 (978-0-7525-4530-1(2)) Parragon, Inc.

Earth Features Set. (gr. k-2). 230.95 (978-0-7368-3282-3(3)) Red Brick Learning.

Earth's Water Assessment Book: Unit 6: Earth's Water. 2000. (McGraw-Hill Science Ser.). (gr. 4 up). (978-0-02-277761-6(X)) Macmillan/McGraw-Hill Schl. Div.

Essential Atlas of the World. (Illus.). 159p. reprint ed. pap. (978-0-681-50234-5(7)) Borders Pr.

Exploring Earth's Treasures. (Eyes on Adventure Ser.). (Illus.). 32p. (J). (gr. 1 up). 7.95 (978-1-56156-485-9(0)) Kidsbooks, Inc.

Exploring Wonders of the World. (Eyes on Adventure Ser.). (Illus.). 32p. (J). (gr. 1 up). 7.95 (978-1-56156-486-6(9)) Kidsbooks, Inc.

Farndon, John. Planet Earth: Informative Tips & Practical Projects Unravel the Mysteries of Our World. 2000. (Investigations Ser.). (Illus.). 64p. (gr. 3-7). 12.95 (978-0-7548-0475-8(5) , Lorenz Bks.) Anness Publishing GBR. *Dist:* National Bk. Network.

Farndon, John & Walshaw, Rodney. Planet Earth. 2002. (All about Ser.). (Illus.). 64p. (gr. 3-7). pap. 7.95 (978-1-84215-614-8(4) , Southwater) Anness Publishing GBR. *Dist:* National Bk. Network.

Farndon, John, et al. Planet Earth. 2003. (Illustrated Science Encyclopedia Ser.). (Illus.). 264p. (gr. 3-7). pap. 19.99 (978-0-7548-1207-4(3)) Anness Publishing GBR. *Dist:* National Bk. Network.

Feinstein, Stephen. Earth: A MyReportLinks. com Book. 2005. (Solar System Ser.). (Illus.). 48p. (J). lib. bdg. 25.26 (978-0-7660-5301-4(6) , MyReportLinks.com Bks.) Enslow Pubs., Inc.

Fitzgerald, Michael. Hooray for the Planet. Burns, John, illus. 2001. 64p. (J). pap. 8.95 (978-1-888547-05-4(7)) Special Ideas.

Fleurus. Earth. 1999. (ps-3). (978-2-215-06242-4(8)) Editions Fleurus.

Frasier, Debra. On the Day You Were Born. 2005. (Illus.). 40p. (J). (ps-ps). 18.95 (978-0-15-205567-7(3)) Harcourt Children's Bks.

—On the Day You Were Born: A Photo Journal. 2001. (Illus.). 16p. (J). spiral bd. 9.95 (978-0-15-202172-6(8)) Harcourt Trade Pubs.

Frisch, Aaron. Earth. 2001. (Elements Ser.). (Illus.). 24p. (J). 21.35 (978-1-58340-074-6(5)) Smart Apple Media.

Frith, Alex. See Inside under the Ground. 2007. 16p. (J). bds. 12.99 (978-0-7945-1600-0(9) , Usborne) EDC Publishing.

Fry, Erin. Earth: Fast Changes. 2005. (Navigators Ser.). (J). pap. 42.00 (*978-1-4108-5078-2(1)) Benchmark Education Co.

Furniss, Tim. The Earth. 2000. (Spinning Through Space Ser.). (Illus.). 32p. (J). (gr. 2-4). lib. bdg. (978-0-7398-2737-6(5)) Raintree.

—The Earth. 2000. (Spinning Through Space Ser.). (Illus.). 32p. (J). (gr. 2-4). pap. 10.34 (978-0-7398-3089-5(9)) Steck-Vaughn.

Gaff, Jackie. Looking at Earth: How Does It Change? 2008. (Looking at Science: How Things Change Ser.). 32p. (J). (gr. 1-3). lib. bdg. 22.60 (*978-0-7660-3088-6(1)) Enslow Pubs., Inc.

Gall, Steve J. Professor Gall's Explorer Ball. 2002. (J). cd-rom 12.00 (978-1-931457-13-2(1)) Stargate Electronic Library, Inc.

Gallant, Roy A. Earth's Place in Space. 2000. (Story of Science Ser.). (Illus.). 80p. (J). (gr. 5 up). lib. bdg. 28.50 (978-0-7614-0963-2(7) , Benchmark Bks.) Cavendish, Marshall Corp.

—Structure: Exploring Earth's Interior. 2002. (Earthworks Ser.). (Illus.). 80p. (J). 29.93 (978-0-7614-1368-4(5) , Benchmark Bks.) Cavendish, Marshall Corp.

Gallant, Roy A. & Schuberth, Christopher J. Earth: The Making of a Planet. 1998. (Accelerated Reader Bks.). (Illus.). 160p. (YA). (gr. 5-9). 14.95 (978-0-7614-5012-2(2) , Cavendish Children's Bks.) Cavendish, Marshall Corp.

Ganeri, Anita. I Wonder Why the Wind Blows: And Other Questions about Our Planet. 2003. (I Wonder Why Ser.). 32p. (J). (gr. k-3). pap. 6.95 (978-0-7534-5664-4(8) , Kingfisher) Houghton Mifflin Co. Trade & Reference Div.

—I Wonder Why the Wind Blows: And Other Questions about Our Planet. 2003. (gr. k-3). lib. bdg. 14.10 (978-0-613-90899-3(6)) Tandem Library Bks.

—Shaky Ground. 2004. (Turbulent Planet Ser.). (Illus.). pap. 8.50 (978-1-4109-1027-1(X)) Raintree.

—Turbulent Planet, 4 vols., Set 1. 2004. (Illus.). 114.24 (978-1-4109-0591-8(8)); pap. 30.60 (978-1-4109-1028-8(8)) Raintree.

Gardner, Robert. Earth-Shaking Science Projects about Planet Earth. LaBaff, Tom, illus. 2007. (Rockin' Earth Science Experiments Ser.). 48p. (J). (gr. 3-4). lib. bdg. 23.93 (*978-0-7660-2733-6(3) , Enslow Elementary) Enslow Pubs., Inc.

George, Jean Craighead. La Tierra Que Habla.Tr. of Talking Earth. (SPA.). 136p. (J). 9.95 (978-84-204-3699-9(2)) Santillana USA Publishing Co., Inc.

Giant Sticker Book: Our World. 2002. 48p. pap. 5.98 (978-0-7525-8195-8(3)) Parragon, Inc.

Gibbons, Gail. Planet Earth/Inside Out. 1998. (J). (978-0-606-13712-6(2)) Tandem Library Bks.

Goldstein, Margaret J. Earth. 2005. (Pull Ahead Bks.). (Illus.). 32p. (gr. 2-4). lib. bdg. 22.60 (978-0-8225-4650-4(5)) Lerner Publishing Group.

Gottlieb. The Earth & Beyond. 2004. (Illus.). pap. 15.60 incl. cd-rom (978-0-7398-9181-0(2)) Steck-Vaughn.

—Earth & Beyond. 2004. pap., tchr. ed. 17.60 incl. cd-rom (978-0-7398-9187-2(1)) Steck-Vaughn.

Graun, Ken. Our Earth & the Solar System. Niwa, Debra K., illus. 2001. (Twenty-First Century Astronomy Ser.: Vol. 1). 36p. (J). (gr. 4-6). 15.95 (978-1-928771-02-9(5)) Ken Pr.

Grenier, Christian. Our Planet Earth. 1999. (Megascope Ser.). (Illus.). 61p. (J). (gr. 5-9). 6.95 (978-0-7641-5181-1(9)) Barron's Educational Series, Inc.

Group/McGraw-Hill, Wright. Dreams of Flight, 6 vols. (Book2WebTM Ser.). (gr. 4-8). 36.50 (978-0-322-04433-3(2)) Wright Group, The.

—La Erosion de la Tierra, 6 vols., Vol. 2. (First Explorers. Primeros Exploradores Nonfiction Sets Ser.). (SPA.). (gr. 1-2). 34.95 (978-0-7699-1481-7(0)) Shortland Pubns. (U. S. A.) Inc.

—Rocks & Minerals Tell Earth's Story, 6 vols. (Book2WebTM Ser.). (gr. 4-8). 36.50 (978-0-322-04426-5(X)) Wright Group, The.

Hall, Cally, et al. Earth Facts. 2nd ed. 2004. (Pocket Guides Ser.). (Illus.). 160p. (J). pap. 6.99 (978-0-7566-0202-4(5)) Dorling Kindersley Publishing, Inc.

Hall, Margaret. Day & Night. 2007. (Pebble Plus Ser.). (Illus.). 24p. (J). 19.93 (978-0-7368-6338-4(9)) Capstone Pr., Inc.

Handwerker, Mark J. Ready-to-Use Earth & Astronomical Activities for Grades 5-12. 2000. (Secondary Science Curriculum Activities Library: Vol. 4). (Illus.). 256p. (J). pap. 27.50 (978-0-13-029100-4(5) , Addison Wesley) Benjamin-Cummings Publishing Co.

Harcourt School Publishers Staff. Earth: Our Planet: Library Edition. 1999. (Collections Ser.). (Illus.). (J). 5.30 (978-0-15-314327-4(4)) Harcourt Schl. Pubs.

—Horizons Unit 3: Looking at the Earth. 3rd ed. 2001. (Illus.). pap. 169.80 (978-0-15-322578-9(5)) Harcourt Schl. Pubs.

—Looking at the Earth, Unit 3. 3rd ed. 2003. (Horizons Ser.). (Illus.). pap. 166.70 (978-0-15-340229-6(6)) Harcourt Schl. Pubs.

—Looking at the Earth Big Book No. 3. 2nd ed. 2003. (Illus.). pap. 139.70 (978-0-15-337568-2(X)) Harcourt Schl. Pubs.

Haslam, Andrew. Earth. 2001. (gr. 3-6). lib. bdg. 15.25 (978-0-613-43317-4(3)) Tandem Library Bks.

Haslam, Andrew, et al. Earth. (Make It Work! Ser.). (Illus.). 48p. (J). pap. 7.99 (978-0-590-24617-0(8)) Scholastic, Inc.

Haswell, Arthur. Earth Strikes Back: How We Use & Abuse Our Planet, 4 vols. Incl. Air & Energy. Grant, Pamela. (gr. 2-6). lib. bdg. 16.95 (978-1-929298-58-7(7)); Land. (gr. 2-6). lib. bdg. 16.95 (978-1-929298-59-4(5)); Water. (gr. 4-7). lib. bdg. 16.95 (978-1-929298-60-0(9)); Wildlife. (gr. 2-6). lib. bdg. 16.95 (978-1-929298-61-7(7)); 48p. (J). (Illus.). 2000. Set lib. bdg. 67.80 (978-1-929298-62-4(5)) Chrysalis Education.

Helbrough, Emma. Great Planet Earth Search. Jackson, Ian, illus. 2006. 32p. (J). (*978-0-439-83402-5(3)) Scholastic, Inc.

Hil, Mcgraw. Gr 5 Earth & It's Resc S. 2000. (McGraw-Hill Science Ser.). (gr. 5 up). (978-0-02-278227-6(3)) Macmillan/McGraw-Hill Schl. Div.

—Sciasmtbk Lrng Abt Earth. 2000. (McGraw-Hill Science Ser.). (gr. 4 up). (978-0-02-277757-9(1)) Macmillan/McGraw-Hill Schl. Div.

Hill, E. C. Earth: The Water Planet. 2005. (Navigators Ser.). (J). pap. 42.00 (*978-1-4108-5083-6(8)) Benchmark Education Co.

Historia de la Tierra: Cuaderno de Evaluacion: Unit 3: Historia de la Tierra (Learning about Earth's History) 2000. (McGraw-Hill Ciencias Ser.). (ENG & SPA.). (gr. 4 up). (978-0-02-278662-5(7)) Macmillan/McGraw-Hill Schl. Div.

Historia de la Tierra: Recursos para el maestro con clave de Respuestas: Unit 3: Historia de la Tierra (Learning about Earth's History) 2000. (McGraw-Hill Ciencias Ser.). (ENG & SPA.). (gr. 4 up). (978-0-02-278702-8(X)) Macmillan/McGraw-Hill Schl. Div.

Holt, Rinehart and Winston Staff. Holt Science & Technology: Earth. 2000. pap., stu. ed. 17.13 (978-0-03-054389-0(4)) Holt, Rinehart & Winston.

—Holt Science & Technology Level F: Inside the Restless Earth. 5th ed. 2004. tchr. ed. 46.66 (978-0-03-025571-7(6)) Holt, Rinehart & Winston.

—Holt Science Spectrum Chptr. 21: Planet Earth. 4th ed. Date not set. pap. 11.20 (978-0-03-068059-5(X)) Holt, Rinehart & Winston.

Howard, Fran. Earth. 2007. (Planets Ser.). (ENG., Illus.). 32p. (J). (gr. k-4). lib. bdg. 24.21 (*978-1-59928-825-3(7) , Buddy Bks.) ABDO Publishing Co.

Howell, Laura & Rogers, Kirsteen. Earth & Space. 2004. (Library of Science Ser.). 64p. (J). lib. bdg. 17.95 (978-1-58086-373-5(6)) EDC Publishing.

In the World. (J). (gr. 6). 3.80 (978-0-8374-1455-3(5) , 406) Weekly Reader Corp.

Jackson, Ellen B. The Spring Equinox: The Greening of the Earth. 2003. (Illus.). 32p. (J). (gr. 3-6). pap. 7.95 (978-0-7613-1983-2(2) , Millbrook Pr.) Lerner Publishing Group.

—The Spring Equinox: The Greening of the Earth. Ellis, Jan Davey, illus. 2001. 4. 32p. (gr. 2). 14.95 (978-0-7613-1644-2(2) , Millbrook Pr.) Lerner Publishing Group.

Jefferis, David. Planet Earth. 2002. (Young Library). (Illus.). 32p. (J). lib. bdg. 25.69 (978-0-7398-6325-1(8)) Raintree.

Kalman, Bobbie. Earth from a to Z. 1999. (gr. k-3). lib. bdg. 16.40 (978-0-613-11502-5(3)) Tandem Library Bks.

Kalman, Bobbie & Crossingham, John. The Earth from A to Z. 1999. (AlphaBasiCs Ser.). (Illus.). 32p. (J). (gr. 2-3). lib. bdg. (978-0-86505-383-0(9)) Crabtree Publishing Co.

Karas, G. Brian. On Earth. 2008. 32p. (J). (ps). pap. 6.99 (*978-0-14-241063-9(2) , Puffin) Penguin Group (USA) Inc.

—On Earth. Karas, G. Brian, illus. 2005. (Illus.). 32p. (J). (ps-3). 16.99 (978-0-399-24025-6(X) , Putnam Juvenile) Penguin Group (USA) Inc.

Kerrod, Robin. Planet Earth. (Planet Library). 2005. (Illus.). 32p. (gr. 3-8). lib. bdg. 21.27 (978-0-8225-3902-5(0)); 1999. (J). (978-1-57505-381-3(0)) Lerner Publishing Group.

Khanduri, K. The Great World Search. rev. ed. 2004. (Great Searches Ser.). (SPA., Illus.). 48p. (J). lib. bdg. 17.95 (978-1-58086-596-8(8)) EDC Publishing.

Kipp, Steven L. Earth. 2000. (Galaxy Ser.). (Illus.). 24p. (J). (gr. 2-3). lib. bdg. 18.60 (978-0-7368-0521-6(4) , Bridgestone Bks.) Capstone Pr., Inc.

—Earth, 6 vols. (gr. 2-5). 36.95 (978-0-7368-8967-4(1)) Red Brick Learning.

Knapp, Brian J., et al. Earth Science: Discovering the Secrets of the Earth, 8 vols., Set. 2000. (Illus.). 576p. (J). (gr. 5-12). lib. bdg. 269.00 (978-0-7172-7499-4(3) , Grolier) Scholastic Library Publishing.

Kosek, Jane Kelly. What's Inside Earth? 1999. (What's Inside Library). 24p. (J). (gr. k-4). lib. bdg. 18.75 (978-0-8239-5277-9(0) , PowerKids Pr.) Rosen Publishing Group, Inc., The.

Kraft, Maurice. Planet Earth. 2000. (Creative Discoveries Ser.). Orig. Title: Our Planet Earth. (Illus.). 75p. (J). (gr. 4 up). lib. bdg. 25.30 (978-0-88682-953-7(4) , Creative Education) Creative Co., The.

Landau, Elaine. Earth. (True Booktrade;: Space Ser.). 48p. (J). 2008. pap. 6.95 (*978-0-531-14788-7(6)); 2007. (Illus.). (gr. 3-5). lib. bdg. 26.00 (*978-0-531-12558-8(0)) Scholastic Library Publishing. (Children's Pr.).

Lauber, Patricia. How We Learned the Earth Is Round. 2002. (Let's-Read-and-Find-Out Science Ser.). 32p. (gr. k-4). lib. bdg. 15.89 (978-0-06-000174-2(7)) HarperCollins Pubs.

—How We Learned the Earth Is Round. Lloyd, Megan, illus. 2002. (Trophy Let's-Read-and-Find-Out Bk.). 32p. (J). (gr. k-4). pap. 4.95 (978-0-06-445109-3(7) , Harper Trophy) HarperCollins Pubs.

Lauw, Darlene. Earth & the Solar System. 2003. (gr. 3-6). lib. bdg. 16.40 (978-0-613-52834-4(4)) Tandem Library Bks.

Lauw, Darlene & Puay, Lim Cheng. Earth & the Solar System. 2002. (Science Alive! Ser.). (Illus.). 32p. (J). (gr. 4-5). lib. bdg. (978-0-7787-0569-7(2)) Crabtree Publishing Co.

—The Earth & the Solar System. 2002. (Science Alive! Ser.). (Illus.). 32p. (J). (gr. 4-5). pap. (978-0-7787-0615-1(X)) Crabtree Publishing Co.

Learning about the Earth, 8 vols., Set. 2006. (Blastoff! Readers Ser.). (Illus.). (J). (gr. k-2). 148.00 (*978-0-531-16880-6(8)) Scholastic Library Publishing.

Lewis, J. Patrick. Earth & Us-Continuous: Earth's Past & Future. Canyon, Christopher, illus. 2004. (Sharing Nature with Children Book Ser.). 36p. (J). 16.95 (978-1-58469-024-5(0)); pap. 7.95 (978-1-58469-023-8(2)) Dawn Pubns.

Linde, Barbara M. Earth: Measuring Its Changes. 2005. (Navigators Ser.). (J). pap. 42.00 (*978-1-4108-5080-5(3)) Benchmark Education Co.

Lindsay, Elizabeth, ed. Investigating Science - the Earth. 2000. 48p. 9.95 (978-1-56234-412-2(9) , Mailbox Bks., The) Education Ctr., Inc.

Look at the World! Third Grade Newcomer Books. (On Our Way to English Ser.). (gr. 3 up). 29.50 (978-0-7578-7253-2(0)) Rigby Education.

Lowery, Linda. Earth Day. Bergherr, Mary, illus. rev. ed. 2004. (On My Own Holidays Ser.). 48p. (J). (gr. 2-4). lib. bdg. 25.26 (978-1-57505-700-2(X)) Lerner Publishing Group.

Luenn, Nancy. Mother Earth. 1998. (J). pap. 4.95 (978-0-87628-942-6(1)) Ctr. for Applied Research in Education, The.

Luhr, James F., ed. Earth. 2007. (Illus.). 520p. (gr. 12). pap. 24.95 (*978-0-7566-3332-5(X)) Dorling Kindersley Publishing, Inc.

Lunn, Martin, et al. Earth & Beyond. 1998. (Fact Finders Ser.). (Illus.). 48p. (J). (gr. 3-7). (978-0-563-37622-4(8)) BBC Worldwide.

Maddern, Eric. Earth Story. (Illus.). 32p. (J). 2004. 19.95 (978-1-84507-184-4(0)); 1998. pap. 7.95 (978-1-84507-185-1(9)) Lincoln, Frances Ltd. GBR. *Dist:* Perseus Distribution.

Maddern, Eric, et al. Earth Story. 2001. (Big Bks.). (Illus.). 32p. (J). (ps-3). pap. 22.95 (978-0-7112-1443-9(3)) Lincoln, Frances Ltd. GBR. *Dist:* Transition Vendor.

Maisner, Heather. Amazing Earth. 2006. (Amazing World). 28p. (J). (gr. 3-8). 17.95 (978-0-7696-4832-3(0)) School Specialty Publishing.

Malam, John. Earth. 2001. (Popular Science Mini Guides). (Illus.). 128p. (J). (gr. 4-7). pap. 7.95 (978-1-58663-216-8(7) , Friedman-Fairfax) Friedman, Michael Publishing Group, Inc.

Mariner, Tom, ed. The Land. (Illus.). 32p. (J). (978-0-7451-5316-2(X) , Cherrytree Books) Evans Publishing Group.

Martin, Bill & Sampson, Michael R. I Love Our Earth. Sampson, Michael R. & Lipow, Dan, illus. Lipow, Dan, photos by. 2006. 32p. (J). 14.95 (978-1-58089-106-6(3)) Charlesbridge Publishing, Inc.

Martin, Theresa. Flat Earth? Round Earth? Martin, Theresa, illus. 2004. (Young Readers Ser.). (Illus.). 54p. pap. 14.00 (978-1-57392-988-2(3)) Prometheus Bks., Pubs.

Marzollo, Jean. I Am Planet Earth. Moffatt, Judith, illus. 2001. (Hello Reader! Science Ser.). 32p. (J). (ps-1). pap. 3.99 (978-0-439-11321-2(0) , Cartwheel Bks.) Scholastic, Inc.

—I Am Planet Earth. 2001. (978-0-606-22156-6(5)) Tandem Library Bks.

McClanahan Book Company Staff. The World Sticker Book, 8 vols. 1998. (Active Learning Bks.). (Illus.). 24p. (J). (gr. 1-7). pap. 8.99 (978-1-56293-941-0(6) , McClanahan Bk.) Learning Horizons, Inc.

McDaniel, Melissa. Earth: Slow Changes. 2005. (Navigators Ser.). (J). pap. 42.00 (*978-1-4108-5079-9(X)) Benchmark Education Co.

McMorrow, Annalisa. Exciting Earth. 1999. (Illus.). 80p. (J). pap. 9.95 (978-1-57612-111-5(9)) Monday Morning Bks., Inc.

Miles Kelly Staff. Our Planet. 2003. (Ask Me a Question Ser.). (Illus.). 20p. (J). spiral bd. 7.95 (978-1-84236-128-3(7)) Miles Kelly Publishing, Ltd. GBR. *Dist:* Independent Pubs. Group.

Miller, Joe. If the Earth... Were a Few Feet in Diameter. McLean, Wilson, illus. 1999. 36p. (J). (ps-3). tchr. ed. 16.95 (978-0-86713-054-6(7) , 85131) Greenwich Workshop Pr.

Miller, Ron. Earth & the Moon. 2003. (Worlds Beyond Ser.). (Illus.). 96p. (gr. 7 up). lib. bdg. (978-0-7613-2358-7(9) , Twenty-First Century Bks.) Lerner Publishing Group.

Mist, Rosalind. Will the Sun Ever Burn Out? Earth, Sun, & Moon. 2006. (Stargazers Guides Ser.). (Illus.). 48p. (J). (978-1-4034-7707-1(8)); pap. (978-1-4034-7714-9(0)) Heinemann Library.

Mitchell, Melanie S. Earth. 2004. (First Step Nonfiction Ser.). (Illus.). 24p. (J). (gr. k-2). lib. bdg. 18.60 (978-0-8225-5137-9(3)) Lerner Publishing Group.

—The Earth. 2003. (First Step Nonfiction Ser.). (Illus.). 22p. (J). pap. 3.95 (978-0-8225-3590-4(4) , Lerner Pubns.) Lerner Publishing Group.

Mitchell, Nancy. Earth Rising. Christensen, Edie et al, illus. 1999. (Changing Earth Trilogy Ser.: Bk. 1). 191p. (Orig.). (J). (ps-12). mass mkt. 5.95 (978-1-892713-00-1(4)) Lightstream Pubns.

Morgan, Jennifer. From Lava to Life: The Universe Tells Our Earth Story. Andersen, Dana Lynne, illus. (Sharing Nature with Children Book Ser.: Vol. 2). (YA). 2004. 48p. 19.95 (978-1-58469-043-6(7)); 2003. 47p. pap. 9.95 (978-1-58469-042-9(9)) Dawn Pubns.

—From Lava to Life: The Universe Tells Our Earth Story. 2003. (gr. 3-6). lib. bdg. 18.75 (978-0-613-79612-5(8)) Tandem Library Bks.

Morris. Earth's Changing Continents. 2003. (Illus.). pap. 40.50 (978-1-4109-0405-8(9)) Raintree.

Murphy, Patricia J. Why Is Earth Round? 2004. (Library of Why). (Illus.). 24p. (J). lib. bdg. 18.75 (978-0-8239-6236-5(9) , PowerKids Pr.) Rosen Publishing Group, Inc., The.

Murrie, Steve & Murrie, Matthew. Every Minute on Earth. Lloyd, Mary Anne, illus. 2007. 224p. (J). (gr. 4-7). pap. 9.99 (*978-0-439-90887-0(6) , Scholastic Reference) Scholastic, Inc.

My World. 2004. 80p. (YA). per. 15.00 (978-0-9754834-6-6(3)) Standing For Christ, Inc.

My World, 6 vols., Set. 1999. 192p. (J). (gr. 2-7). (978-0-7166-9418-2(2)) World Bk., Inc.

Nicolson, Cynthia Pratt. The Earth. Slavin, Bill, illus. unabr. ed. 1999. (Starting with Space Ser.). 40p. (J). (gr. 4-6). (978-1-55074-327-2(9)) Kids Can Pr., Ltd.

Nicolson, Cynthia Pratt & Slavin, Bill. Starting with Space: The Earth.Tr. of Destination Univers: La Terre. (FRE., Illus.). 40p. (J). pap. 8.99 (978-0-590-16009-4(5)) Scholastic, Inc.

Niz, Ellen Sturm. Peninsulas. 2005. (Earthforms Ser.). (Illus.). 24p. (J). (ps-7). lib. bdg. 21.26 (978-0-7368-4308-9(6)) Capstone Pr., Inc.

Nuestro Planeta: La Tierra. (SPA.). (J). 10.00 (978-84-342-1813-0(5)) Parramon Ediciones S.A. ESP. *Dist:* Distribuidora Norma, Inc.

Olien, Rebecca. Exploring Earth. 2007. (Objects in the Sky Ser.). (Illus.). 24p. (J). (gr. 4-6). lib. bdg. 21.25 (978-1-4042-3465-9(9)) Rosen Publishing Group, Inc., The.

—Physical Characteristics of the Earth. 2007. (Objects in the Sky Ser.). (Illus.). 24p. (J). (978-1-4042-2364-6(9)); pap. (978-1-4042-2178-9(6)) Rosen Publishing Group, Inc., The.

Orme, Helen & Orme, David. Let's Explore Earth. 2006. (J). pap. (*978-0-8368-8124-0(9)); lib. bdg. (*978-0-8368-7939-1(2)) Stevens, Gareth Inc.

O'Shaughnessy, Tam E. The Inside Story of Earth. 2006. (J). 7.80 (978-1-933798-09-7(2)) Sally Ride Science.

Our Changing Earth: Fourth Grade Class Collection Books. (On Our Way to English Ser.). (gr. 4 up). 29.95 (978-0-7578-4339-6(5)) Rigby Education.

Our Changing Earth: Small Versions of Class Collection Books. (On Our Way to English Ser.). (gr. 4 up). 34.50 (978-0-7578-7268-6(9)) Rigby Education.

Our Changing Planet, 6, Pack. (Rigby Infoquest Ser.). 24p. (gr. 3 up). 34.00 (978-0-7578-5774-4(4)) Rigby Education.

Our Enchanting World, Vol. 3. 2004. 983.00 (978-0-516-22088-8(8)) Scholastic Library Publishing.

Our World-Flip Chart. 2003. (J). (gr. k-12). spiral bd. 12.95 (978-1-58845-177-4(1)) School Specialty Publishing.

Oxlade, Chris. The Earth & Beyond. 2003. (Science Topics Ser.). (Illus.). 32p. (J). (gr. 4-7). lib. bdg. 24.22 (978-1-57572-770-7(6)) Heinemann Library.

Oxlade, Chris. The Earth & Its Moon. 2007. (J). lib. bdg. (*978-1-4042-3734-6(8) , Rosen Central) Rosen Publishing Group, Inc., The.

Page, Alan. The Garden Earth. 2003. 29p. pap. 11.95 (978-1-59286-839-1(8)) PublishAmerica, Inc.

Parker, Gary. Exploring the World Around You: From the Ice of Abtarctuca to the Heat of the Sahara. 2002. (Illus.). 160p. (YA). pap. 13.99 (978-0-89051-377-4(5)) Master Bks.

Parker, Steve. The Earth's Resources. 2001. (Science Fact Files Ser.). (Illus.). 48p. (J). (gr. 4-7). lib. bdg. 27.12 (978-0-7398-1009-5(X)) Raintree.

Parks, Peggy. The Earth. 2007. (KidHaven Science Library Ser.). (Illus.). 48p. (J). (gr. 4-8). 23.70 (*978-0-7377-3776-9(X) , Kidhaven) Thomson Gale.

Paula, Manzanero, ed. Scholastic Atlas of Earth. 2005. (Illus.). 80p. (J). pap. 17.99 (978-0-439-67270-2(8) , Scholastic Reference) Scholastic, Inc.

Peel, John. Book of Earth, Vol. 5. 2005. 208p. pap. 4.99 (978-0-7387-0613-9(2)) Llewellyn Pubns.

—Book of Earth. 1998. (Diadem Ser.: Vol. 5). (gr. 4-7). pap. 3.99 (978-0-590-14965-5(2)) Scholastic, Inc.

—Book of Earth, 5. 1998. (Diadem Ser.). (J). (978-0-606-12913-8(8)) Tandem Library Bks.

Perez, Miguel. The Earth & the Universe. Rius, María, illus. 1998. (Universe Ser.). 36p. (J). (ps-3). pap. 6.95 (978-0-7641-0687-3(2)) Barron's Educational Series, Inc.

—The Universe: The Solar System; Stars & Galaxies; The Earth & the Universe, 3 bks., Set. Rius, María, illus. 1998. 36p. (J). (ps-2). pap. 17.95 (978-0-7641-7203-8(4)) Barron's Educational Series, Inc.

Pettigrew, Mark. Planet Earth. 2004. (J). lib. bdg. 27.10 (978-1-932799-28-6(1)) Stargazer Bks.

PH Inc. Staff. PH Science Ecology Earth. (J). pap., act. bk. ed. (978-0-13-225582-0(0)) Prentice Hall (Schl. Div.).

Phelan, Glen. Earth, Sun, Moon. 2004. (National Geographic Reading Expeditions Ser.). (Illus.). 32p. (J). pap. (978-0-7922-4573-5(3)) National Geographic Society.

Pifer, Joanne. EarthWise: Environmental Learning Series, Vol. II. (Illus.). 192p. (J). (gr. 5-8). 24.95 (978-0-9633019-6-3(9)) WP Pr., Inc.

Planet Earth. 2002. (Blackbirch Visual Encyclopedia Ser.). (Illus.). 64p. (J). 37.44 (978-1-56711-514-7(4) , Blackbirch Pr., Inc.) Thomson Gale.

Planet Earth: Individual Title Six-Packs. (Rigby Focus Ser.). 24p. (gr. 2 up). 28.00 (978-0-7578-5340-1(4)); 30.00 (978-0-7578-5570-2(9)) Rigby Education.

Planet Earth/Inside Out. (Lexile Levels Ser.). 9.09 (978-1-56334-748-1(2)) Hampton-Brown Bks.

Pluckrose, Henry. Earth. 2001. (Let's Explore Ser.). (Illus.). 32p. (J). (gr. 1 up). lib. bdg. 23.33 (978-0-8368-2960-0(3)) Stevens, Gareth Inc.

Pluckrose, Henry Arthur. Earth. 2006. (Illus.). 32p. (J). (978-1-59771-036-7(9)) Sea-To-Sea Pubns.

Potts, Steve. Earth. 2001. (Illus.). 24p. (J). 21.35 (978-1-58340-096-8(6)) Smart Apple Media.

Prentice-Hall Staff. Exploring Planet Earth. (J). tchr. ed. (978-0-13-400607-9(0)); pap., act. bk. ed. (978-0-13-400615-4(1)); 2nd ed. stu. ed. (978-0-13-400599-7(6)) Prentice Hall (Schl. Div.).

Priddy, Roger. Earth IQ. 2007. 24p. (J). bds. 14.95 (*978-0-312-50011-5(4) , Priddy Bks.) St. Martin's Pr.

Priddy, Roger. 3 in 1: My Big Animal,World,Dinosaur. 2005. (J). bds. 16.95 (978-0-312-49562-6(5) , Priddy Bks.) St. Martin's Pr.

Pringle, Laurence P. Taking Care of the Earth Vol. 1: Kids in Action. Moore, Bobbie, illus. 2003. 64p. (J). (gr. 2-4). pap. 9.95 (978-1-56397-634-6(X)) Boyds Mills Pr.

Quadrillion Media Staff. The Earth (Unsere Erde) 1998. (Start Me Up Ser.: Vol. 1). 48p. (J). (gr. 4-7). pap. 12.95 (978-1-58185-000-0(X) , Tessloff Publishing) Quadrillion Media LLC.

¿Que Hay Debajo de la Tierra? (Coleccion Primeros Pasos en la Ciencia). (SPA., Illus.). (J). (gr. 1-3). pap. (978-950-724-015-7(2) , LMA8214) Lumen ARG. *Dist:* Lectorum Pubns., Inc.

Raintree Steck-Vaughn Staff. Restless Planet, 4 bks., Set. 1999. (Illus.). (J). lib. bdg. 108.48 (978-0-7398-1331-7(5)) Raintree.

Rau, Dana Meachen. Earth. 2002. (Illus.). 32p. (J). (gr. 3 up). lib. bdg. 21.26 (978-0-7565-0295-9(0)) Compass Point Bks.

Redfern, Martin. The Kingfisher Young People's Book of Planet Earth. 1999. (Kingfisher Book of Ser.). (Illus.). 96p. (J). (gr. 4-8). trch. ed. 21.95 (978-0-7534-5180-9(8) , Kingfisher) Houghton Mifflin Co. Trade & Reference Div.

Reed, W. Maxwell. The Earth for Sam the Story of Mountains. 2005. reprint ed. pap. 34.95 (978-0-7661-9449-6(3)) Kessinger Publishing, LLC.

Richardson, Adele. Earth. 2008. (J). (*978-1-4296-0720-9(3)) Capstone Pr., Inc.

Richardson, Adele D. Earth. 2005. (Illus.). 24p. (J). 21.26 (978-0-7368-3695-1(0)) Capstone Pr., Inc.

Ride, Sally K. & O'Shaughnessy, Tam E. The Third Planet: Exploring the Earth from Space. 2nd rev. ed. 2004. (J). per. 20.00 (978-0-9753920-0-3(X)) Sally Ride Science.

Riley, Peter D. Earth. 1998. (Cycles in Science Ser.). (Illus.). 32p. (J). (gr. 4-7). lib. bdg. 22.79 (978-1-57572-620-5(3)) Heinemann.

Riley, Peter D. Earth, Moon & Sun. 2007. (J). (*978-1-59920-025-5(2)) Smart Apple Media.

Riley, Peter D. & Snedden, Robert. Earth & Beyond. 1999. (Smart Science Ser.). (Illus.). 32p. (YA). (gr. 4-7). lib. bdg. 22.79 (978-1-57572-867-4(2)) Heinemann Library.

Ring, Susan. The Earth. 2002. (Exploring Planets Ser.). (Illus.). 24p. (J). lib. bdg. 15.95 (978-1-59036-104-7(0)) Weigl Pubs., Inc.

Robson, Pam. Our Planet. 2004. (Earthwise Ser.). (J). lib. bdg. 27.10 (978-1-932799-51-4(6)) Stargazer Bks.

Roca, Nuria. Aprendamos sobre los 4 Elementos: The 4 Elements (Spanish Edition) Curto, Rosa M., illus. 2006. (Let's Learn About Ser.). (SPA.). 36p. (J). pap. 6.99 (978-0-7641-3315-2(2)) Barron's Educational Series, Inc.

—Let's Learn about the 4 Elements. Curto, Rosa M., illus. 2006. (Let's Learn About Ser.). 36p. (J). pap. 6.99 (978-0-7641-3314-5(4)) Barron's Educational Series, Inc.

Rushworth, Gary. Our Solar System: The Earth. 2006. (Navigators Ser.). (J). pap. 38.00 (*978-1-4108-6222-8(4)) Benchmark Education Co.

Schimmel, Schim, illus. Magic Planet: Pop-Up Fun. 2003. 12p. (J). (gr. k-5). 20.00 (978-0-7567-6651-1(6)) DIANE Publishing Co.

Schofield and Sims Staff. Around the World: An Infant Atlas. 1999. (Illus.). (J). (gr. 1-3). pap. 35.00 (978-0-7217-1080-8(8)) Schofield & Sims Ltd. GBR. *Dist:* State Mutual Bk. & Periodical Service, Ltd.

Senior, Kathryn. Planet Earth. 2000. (Fast Forward Ser.). (Illus.). 32p. (J). (gr. 4-8). pap. 9.95 (978-0-531-16445-7(4)); 29.00 (978-0-531-11879-5(7)) Scholastic Library Publishing. (Watts, Franklin).

—Planet Earth. 2000. (J). (978-0-606-19787-8(7)); (gr. 3-6). lib. bdg. 18.75 (978-0-613-34899-7(0)) Tandem Library Bks.

Shaping the Earth: Individual Title Six-Packs. (Rigby Focus Ser.). 24p. (gr. 2 up). 28.00 (978-0-7578-5349-4(8)); 30.00 (978-0-7578-5579-5(2)) Rigby Education.

Shepherd, Donna Walsh. Earth. 2003. (Watts Library). (Illus.). 64p. (J). (gr. 5-7). pap. 8.95 (978-0-531-15559-2(5) , Watts, Franklin) Scholastic Library Publishing.

Sian revision our changing Earth. 2004. (Science in A Nutshell(R) Ser.). (J). (978-1-59242-053-7(2)) Delta Education, LLC.

Simon, Seymour. Earth: Our Planet in Space. rev. ed. 2003. (Illus.). 32p. (J). 17.95 (978-0-689-83562-9(0)) Simon & Schuster Children's Publishing.

Sneider, Cary I. Earth, Moon & Stars. Bergman, Lincoln & Fairwell, Kay, eds. Baker, Lisa H. et al, illus. Sneider, Cary I., photos by. rev. ed. 1998. (Great Explorations in Math & Science Ser.). 100p. (YA). (gr. 5-8). pap. 13.50 (978-0-924886-05-8(6) , GEMS) Univ. of California, Berkeley, Lawrence Hall of Science.

Sovak, Jan. Before the Dinosaurs. 1999. (Illus.). 48p. (J). pap. 3.95 (978-0-486-40568-1(0)) Dover Pubns., Inc.

Stace, Alexa. Atlas of Earth. 1999. (Illus.). 96p. (J). (gr. 5 up). lib. bdg. 34.00 (978-0-8368-2505-3(5)) Stevens, Gareth Inc.

Stace, Alexa & Dixon, Dougal. Earth: The Living Planet. 2000. lib. bdg. (978-0-8368-2490-2(3)) Stevens, Gareth Inc.

Stefoff, Rebecca. Earth & the Moon. 2001. (Blastoff! Ser.). (Illus.). 64p. (J). (gr. 5 up). lib. bdg. 28.50 (978-0-7614-1235-9(2) , Benchmark Bks.) Cavendish, Marshall Corp.

Stewart, Kathy D. Earth Facts for Earthlings Bk. 1: The World. Cameau, Martine et al, illus. 2005. 64p. (J). per. 12.95 (978-0-9773583-0-4(5) , EFFE01) EFFE Bks.

Stille, Darlene R. Earth. 2003. (Planets Ser.). (Illus.). 32p. (J). (gr. 2-6). 27.07 (978-1-59296-048-4(0)) Child's World, Inc.

Stone, Lynn M. Day & Night. 2007. (Illus.). 24p. (J). (978-1-60044-176-9(9)) Rourke Publishing, LLC.

Storad, Conrad J. The Earth's Crust. 2007. (Early Bird Earth Science Ser.). (Illus.). 48p. (J). (gr. 2-4). 25.26 (978-0-8225-5944-3(7) , Lerner Pubns.) Lerner Publishing Group.

Superlibro de Conoce tu Mundo: Unit 1: Conoce tu mundo (Learn about Your World) 2000. (McGraw-Hill Ciencias Ser.). (ENG & SPA.). (gr. k up). (978-0-02-277157-7(3)) Macmillan/McGraw-Hill Schl. Div.

Sussman, Art. Dr Art's Guide to Planet Earth: For Earthlings Age 12 & Up. 2000. (gr. 5-8). lib. bdg. 24.55 (978-0-613-35380-9(3)) Tandem Library Bks.

Taylor, Barbara. Earth. 2004. (Picture Reference Ser.). (SPA., Illus.). 32p. (J). (gr. 3-6). 13.95 (978-1-58728-652-0(1) , Two Can Publishing) T&N Children's Publishing.

—Earth, 5 vols., Set. 1999. (Picture Reference Ser.). (Illus.). 48p. (J). (gr. 2-6). (978-0-7166-9904-0(4)) World Bk., Inc.

—Earth: The Geography of Our World. 2001. (gr. k-3). lib. bdg. 19.90 (978-0-613-90369-1(2)) Tandem Library Bks.

Taylor-Butler, Christine. Earth. (Scholastic News Nonfiction Readers: Space Science Ser.). 24p. (J). 2008. pap. 6.95 (*978-0-531-14760-3(6)); 2007. (Illus.). (gr. 1-2). lib. bdg. 20.00 (*978-0-531-14695-8(2)) Scholastic Library Publishing. (Children's Pr.).

Thompson, Luke. Earth. Thompson, Luke, illus. 2001. (Library of the Planets). (Illus.). 24p. (J). lib. bdg. 21.25 (978-0-8239-5644-9(X) , PowerKids Pr.) Rosen Publishing Group, Inc., The.

Top That Publishing Staff, ed. Our Planet. 2004. (Know How Know Why Ser.). (Illus.). 48p. (J). pap. (978-1-84510-028-5(X)) Top That! Publishing PLC.

Trumbauer, Lisa. To the Core: Earth's Structure. 2006. (Illus.). 32p. (J). (978-1-4109-2577-0(3)); pap. (978-1-4109-2606-7(0)) Steck-Vaughn.

Turner, Matt. Earth. 2006. (Dk Online Ser.). (Illus.). 96p. (J). pap. 9.99 (978-0-7566-2292-3(1)) Dorling Kindersley Publishing, Inc.

Twist, Clint. The Earth. 2006. (Stories of the Sun). 28p. (J). (gr. 3-8). 14.95 (978-0-7696-4489-9(9)) School Specialty Publishing.

Two Can. Planet Earth. 2000. (Life In... Ser.). (J). (gr. 3-6). pap. 19.95 (978-1-58728-284-3(4) , Two Can Publishing) T&N Children's Publishing.

Two-Can Publishing Ltd. Staff, contrib. by. Planet Earth. 2004. (Illus.). 192p. (J). (gr. 3-6). 24.95 (978-1-58728-049-8(3) , Two Can Publishing) T&N Children's Publishing.

Two-Can Publishing Ltd. Staff, ed. Planetearth. 2004. (Interfact Reference Ser.). (Illus.). 48p. (J). (gr. 3-6). 19.95 incl. cd-rom (978-1-58728-421-2(9) , Two Can Publishing) T&N Children's Publishing.

Van Rose, Susanna & Dorling Kindersley Publishing Staff. Earth. 2005. (Eyewitness Books). (Illus.). 72p. (J). (ps-7). lib. bdg. 19.99 (978-0-7566-1070-8(2)) Dorling Kindersley Publishing, Inc.

Vogt, Gregory L. Earth's Core & Mantle: Heavy Metal, Moving Rock. 2007. (Earth's Spheres Ser.). (Illus.). 80p. (J). (gr. 6-8). 29.27 (978-0-7613-2837-7(8)) , Twenty-First Century Bks.) Lerner Publishing Group.

—Earth's Spheres, 6 bks., Set. Incl. Atmosphere : Planetary Heat Engine. 29.27 (978-0-7613-2841-4(6)); Biosphere : Realm of Life. 29.27 (978-0-7613-2840-7(8)); Earth's Core & Mantle : Heavy Metal, Moving Rock. 29.27 (978-0-7613-2837-7(8)); Earth's Outer Atmosphere : Bordering Space. 29.27 (978-0-7613-2842-1(4)); Hydrosphere : Agent of Change. 29.27 (978-0-7613-2839-1(4)); Lithosphere : Earth's Crust. 29.27 (978-0-7613-2838-4(6)); (Illus.). 80p. (J). (gr. 6-8). 2007. 2007. Set lib. bdg. 175.62 (*978-0-8225-8058-4(6) , Twenty-First Century Bks.) Lerner Publishing Group.

—The Lithosphere: Earth's Crust. 2007. (Earth's Spheres Ser.). (Illus.). 80p. (J). (gr. 6-8). 29.27 (978-0-7613-2838-4(6) , Twenty-First Century Bks.) Lerner Publishing Group.

—Mercury, Venus, Earth & Mars. 2000. (Our Universe Ser.). (Illus.). 48p. (J). (gr. 4-7). lib. bdg. 22.83 (978-0-7398-3110-6(0)) Raintree.

Volke, Gordon. Our Planet. 2007. (Illus.). 48p. (J). (*978-1-60044-261-2(7)) Rourke Publishing, LLC.

Walsh Shepherd, Donna. Earth. 2003. (Illus.). 63p. (J). (gr. 4-7). lib. bdg. 17.60 (978-0-613-59465-3(7)) Tandem Library Bks.

West, Krista. Hands-On Projects about Earth & Space. 2002. (Great Earth Science Projects Ser.). (Illus.). 24p. (J). lib. bdg. 19.95 (978-0-8239-5843-6(4)) Rosen Publishing Group, Inc., The.

Wharfe, William. Earth: The Book & Disk That Work Together. 2000. (Interfact Reference Ser.). (Illus.). 48p. (J). (gr. 3-6). spiral bd. 19.95 incl. cd-rom (978-1-58728-472-4(3) , Two Can Publishing) T&N Children's Publishing.

What Does the Earth Have? Third Grade Newcomer Books. (On Our Way to English Ser.). (gr. 3 up). 29.50 (978-0-7578-7256-3(5)) Rigby Education.

What on Earth?, 10 bks., Set. Incl. Set. What on Earth? - It's Alive! 127.50 (978-0-516-25223-0(2)); Set. What on Earth? - Wild Weather. 127.50 (978-0-516-25224-7(0)); (J). (gr. 2-4). 2005. 255.00 (978-0-516-24599-7(6) , Children's Pr.) Scholastic Library Publishing.

What on Earth? - It's Alive!, 5 bks., Set. Incl. Life in a Rain Forest. Senior, Kathryn. 25.50 (978-0-516-25315-2(8)); Life in the Desert. Legg, Gerald. 25.50 (978-0-516-25317-6(4)); Life in the Grasslands. Chambers, Catherine. 25.50 (978-0-516-25319-0(0)); Life in the Tundra. Clarke, Penny. 25.50 (978-0-516-25316-9(6)); Life in the Wetlands. Scrace, Carolyn. (gr. 2-4). 25.50 (978-0-516-25318-3(2)); (Illus.). 32p. (J). 2005. (What on Earth? Ser.). 2005. 127.50 (978-0-516-25223-0(2) , Children's Pr.) Scholastic Library Publishing.

What on Earth? - Wild Weather, 5 bks., Set. Incl. Hurricanes. Chambers, Catherine. 25.50 (978-0-516-25320-6(4)); Lightning. Williams, Brian. 25.50 (978-0-516-25322-0(0)); Tornadoes. Orme, David & Orme, Helen. 25.50 (978-0-516-25321-3(2)); Tsunamis. Orme, David. 25.50 (978-0-516-25323-7(9)); Volcanoes. Senior, Kathryn. 25.50 (978-0-516-25324-4(7)); (Illus.). 32p. (J). (What on Earth? Ser.). 2005. 127.50 (978-0-516-25224-7(0) , Children's Pr.) Scholastic Library Publishing.

Whitehouse, Patricia. Earth. 2004. (J). lib. bdg. 24.21 (978-1-4034-5150-7(8)) Heinemann Library.

—The Earth. 2004. (J). pap. 7.25 (978-1-4034-5654-0(2)) Heinemann Library.

—Plains. 2004. (My World of Geography Ser.). (J). 22.79 (978-1-4034-5684-7(4)) Heinemann Library.

Williams, Zella. Experiments about Planet Earth. 2007. (Do-It-Yourself Science Ser.). (Illus.). 24p. (J). (gr. 2-5). lib. bdg. 23.95 (978-1-4042-3662-2(7) , PowerKids Pr.) Rosen Publishing Group, Inc., The.

Wimmer, Teresa. Earth. 2007. (J). (978-1-58341-516-0(5) , Creative Education) Creative Co., The.

Wollard, Kathy. How Come? Planet Earth. 1999. (gr. 3-6). lib. bdg. 22.20 (978-0-613-88984-1(3)) Tandem Library Bks.

—How Come Planet Earth? Every Kid's Science Questions Explained. Solomon, Debra, illus. 1999. 332p. (J). (gr. 4-7). pap. 12.95 (978-0-7611-1239-6(1) , 11239) Workman Publishing Co., Inc.

World Book, contrib. by. Earth & Earth's Moon. 2nd ed. 2007. (World Book's Solar System & Space Exploration Library). (Illus.). 64p. (J). (*978-0-7166-9512-7(X)) World Bk., Inc.

World Book, Inc Staff, contrib. by. Earth & Earth's Moon. 2006. (World Book's Solar System & Space Exploration Library). 63p. (J). (978-0-7166-9503-5(0)) World Bk., Inc.

York, Penelope. Earth. 2002. (Eye Wonder Ser.). (Illus.). 48p. (gr. k-3). 9.99 (978-0-7894-8867-1(1)) Dorling Kindersley Publishing, Inc.

York, Penelope & Dorling Kindersley Publishing Staff. Earth. 2002. (Eye Wonder Ser.). (Illus.). 48p. (J). (gr. k-3). lib. bdg. 17.99 (978-0-7894-8868-8(X)) Dorling Kindersley Publishing, Inc.

EARTH—DICTIONARIES

Brooks, Felicity. First Encyclopedia of Our World. (First Encyclopedias Ser.). (Illus.). 64p. (J). 2004. (SPA.). (gr. 3 up). lib. bdg. 17.95 (978-1-58086-427-5(9)); 2000. (ps-3). lib. bdg. 17.95 (978-1-58086-265-3(9)) EDC Publishing.

—First Encyclopedia of Our World. 2002. (gr. k-3). lib. bdg. 18.75 (978-0-613-75301-2(1)) Tandem Library Bks.

Disney Press Staff & Feldman, Thea. My Very First Encyclopedia with Winnie the Pooh & Friends: Earth. 2006. 192p. (ps-2). 19.99 (978-0-7868-3407-5(2)) Disney Pr.

Dorling Kindersley Publishing Staff. The Concise Encyclopedia of the Earth. 2000. (978-0-606-17806-8(6)) Tandem Library Bks.

Malam, John & Hincks, Gary. Extraordinary World: Highest, Longest, Deepest - An Exploration of the World's Most Fantastic Features. (Illus.). 44p. (J). pap. 19.99 (978-0-590-24956-0(8)) Scholastic, Inc.

EARTH, EFFECT OF HUMAN BEINGS ON

see Nature—Effect of Human Beings on

EARTH—ROTATION

Dolan, Graham. The Greenwich Guide to Day & Night. 2001. (Illus.). 32p. (J). (gr. 2-4). lib. bdg. 22.79 (978-1-58810-042-9(1)) Heinemann Library.

Guidoux, Valerie. By Day & by Night. Faller, Regis et al, illus. 2006. (Explore Your World Ser.). (ENG & FRE.). 28p. (J). (ps-1). 15.95 (978-1-55407-003-9(1)) Firefly Bks., Ltd.

Hall, Margaret. El Día y la Noche: Day & Night. 2008. (ENG & SPA.). (J). (*978-1-4296-0012-5(8)) Capstone Pr., Inc.

Llewellyn, Claire. Day & Night. 2007. (Illus.). 24p. (J). (*978-1-59771-018-3(0)) Sea-To-Sea Pubns.

Pluckrose, Henry. Day & Night. 2001. (Let's Explore Ser.). (Illus.). 32p. (J). (gr. 1 up). lib. bdg. 23.33 (978-0-8368-2958-7(1)) Stevens, Gareth Inc.

Slade, Suzanne. Seasonal Cycles. 2007. (Illus.). 24p. (J). (978-1-4042-2388-2(6)); pap. (978-1-4042-2198-7(0)) Rosen Publishing Group, Inc., The. (PowerKids Pr.).

Stewart, Melissa. Why Do the Seasons Change? 2006. (Tell Me Why, Tell Me How Ser.). (Illus.). 32p. (J). lib. bdg. 28.50 (978-0-7614-2112-2(2) , Benchmark Bks.) Cavendish, Marshall Corp.

Stone, Lynn M. Season to Season. 2007. (Illus.). 24p. (J). (978-1-60044-181-3(5)) Rourke Publishing, LLC.

Thomas, Isabel. The Day the Earth Stood Still. 2005. (Illus.). 32p. (J). lib. bdg. (978-1-4109-1930-4(7)) Steck-Vaughn.

—The Day the Earth Stood Still: The Earth's Movement in Space. 2005. (Illus.). 32p. (J). (gr. 3-5). pap. 7.85 (978-1-4109-1961-8(7)) Steck-Vaughn.

Upgrade kit dsm-3 earth Movement. (J). 2004. (978-1-59242-529-7(1)); 2003. (978-1-59242-412-2(0)) Delta Education, LLC.

EARTH SCIENCES

Achieve Now Institute Staff. ESR Anthology, Band 6-8. 2004. pap. 12.32 (978-0-7398-9891-4(2)) Steck-Vaughn.

—ESR Student Resource Book. 2004. pap. 8.12 (978-0-7398-9881-9(7)); pap. 12.32 (978-0-7398-9886-4(8)) Steck-Vaughn.

Allison, Carol J. Mighty Earth. 2007. (Shockwave: Earth & Physical Science Ser.). (Illus.). 36p. (J). (gr. 4-6). lib. bdg. 25.00 (*978-0-531-17794-5(7) , Children's Pr.) Scholastic Library Publishing.

Arthus, Yann B. Tierra explicada a los ninos. 2005. 34p. (978-970-651-910-8(6)) Editorial Oceano De Mexico, S.A. DE C.V.

Benchmark Education Staff, compiled by. Earth & Space Science. 2006. spiral bd. 365.00 (*978-1-4108-6946-3(6)); 2006. spiral bd. 695.00 (*978-1-4108-6942-5(3)); 2006. spiral bd. 365.00 (*978-1-4108-6939-5(3)); 2006. spiral bd. 365.00 (*978-1-4108-6925-8(3)); 2006. spiral bd. 80.00 (*978-1-4108-6927-2(X)); 2006. spiral bd. 235.00 (*978-1-4108-6934-0(2)); 2005. spiral bd. 220.00 (*978-1-4108-3851-3(X)); 2005. spiral bd. 370.00 (*978-1-4108-3858-2(7)); 2005. spiral bd. 220.00 (*978-1-4108-3859-9(5)); 2005. spiral bd. 75.00 (*978-1-4108-3870-4(6)); 2005. spiral bd. 55.00 (*978-1-4108-3874-2(9)); 2005. spiral bd. 870.00 (*978-1-4108-4518-4(4)); 2005. spiral bd. 305.00 (*978-1-4108-3850-6(1)); 2005. spiral bd. 950.00 (*978-1-4108-5441-4(8)); 2005. spiral bd. 675.00 (*978-1-4108-5851-1(0)); 2005. spiral bd. 405.00 (*978-1-4108-5852-8(9)); 2005. spiral bd. 335.00 (*978-1-4108-3829-2(3)); 2005. spiral bd. 580.00 (*978-1-4108-3826-1(9)); 2005. spiral bd. 1025.00 (*978-1-4108-5440-7(X)) Benchmark Education Co.

—Learning about Earth's Past. 2006. spiral bd. 189.00 (*978-1-4108-7059-9(6)) Benchmark Education Co.

—Life on Earth. 2006. spiral bd. 239.00 (*978-1-4108-7119-0(3)) Benchmark Education Co.

—Science Theme: Earth & Space Science. 2005. spiral bd. 340.00 (*978-1-4108-5314-1(4)) Benchmark Education Co.

—Science Theme: Life on Earth. 2005. spiral bd. 115.00 (*978-1-4108-5320-2(9)) Benchmark Education Co.

—Science Theme: What Changes Our Earth. 2005. spiral bd. 115.00 (*978-1-4108-5315-8(2)) Benchmark Education Co.

—What Changes Our Earth. 2006. spiral bd. 330.00 (*978-1-4108-7017-9(0)); 2005. (J). spiral bd. 265.00 (*978-1-4108-5762-0(X)) Benchmark Education Co.

Brimner, Larry Dane. Geysers. 2001. (True Bks.). (Illus.). 48p. (J). (gr. 3-5). pap. 6.95 (978-0-516-27190-3(3) , Children's Pr.) Scholastic Library Publishing.

—Geysers. 2001. 13.75 (978-0-606-22877-0(2)) Tandem Library Bks.

—Valleys & Canyons. 2001. (True Bks.). (Illus.). 48p. (gr. 3-5). pap. 6.95 (978-0-516-27193-4(8) , Children's Pr.) Scholastic Library Publishing.

Calhoun, Yael. Earth Science Fair Projects: Using Rocks, Minerals, Magnets, Mud, & More. 2005. (Earth Science! Best Science Projects Ser.). (Illus.). 128p. (J). (gr. 6-12). lib. bdg. 26.60 (978-0-7660-2363-5(X)) Enslow Pubs., Inc.

Campbell, Ann-Jeanette. Tierra Increible. 1999. (978-0-606-22715-5(6)) Tandem Library Bks.

—La Tierra Increible. 1999. Tr. of New York Public Library Incredible Earth. (SPA.). (gr. 3-6). lib. bdg. 26.85 (978-0-613-83731-6(2)) Tandem Library Bks.

Cannon, William, Jr. Earth Science. 2008. (Twentieth-Century Science Ser.). 272p. (gr. 6-12). 49.50 (978-0-8160-5533-3(5)) Facts On File, Inc.

Carnibucci, Patricia. Our Physical World: Over 15 Complete Printable Unit Studies with Interactive Links. 2002. 160p. (gr. k-12). cd-rom 15.95 (978-1-891400-72-8(X)) Champion Pr., Ltd.

Chancellor, Deborah. Planet Earth. 2006. (Kingfisher Young Knowledge Ser.). (Illus.). 48p. (J). (gr. k-3). 9.95 (978-0-7534-5934-8(5) , Kingfisher) Houghton Mifflin Co. Trade & Reference Div.

Chrisp, Peter. La Grace Antique. 2000. (Come & Discover My World Ser.). (Illus.). 32p. (J). (gr. 2-5). pap. 7.95 (978-1-58728-193-8(7) , Two Can Publishing) T&N Children's Publishing.

Clarke, Phillip. Planet Earth Facts & Lists - Internet Linked. 2004. (Facts & Lists Internet-Linked Ser.). (Illus.). 64p. (J). pap. 7.95 (978-0-7945-0644-5(5) , Usborne) EDC Publishing.

Claybourne, Anna, et al, eds. Encyclopedia of Planet Earth. 2000. (Usborne Encyclopedia Ser.). (Illus.). 160p. (YA). (gr. 4 up). 21.95 (978-0-7460-3405-7(9)) EDC Publishing.

Claybourne, Anna, et al. Encyclopedia of Planet Earth. 2000. (Usborne Encyclopedia Ser.). (Illus.). 160p. (YA). (gr. 4 up). lib. bdg. 29.95 (978-1-58086-260-8(8)) EDC Publishing.

Cooper, John. Planet Earth & Art Activities. 2002. (Arty Facts Ser.). (Illus.). 48p. (J). (gr. 3-4). pap. (978-0-7787-1139-1(0)); lib. bdg. (978-0-7787-1111-7(0)) Crabtree Publishing Co.

Cox, Reg. The Seven Wonders of the Natural World. 2000. (Wonders of the World Ser.). (Illus.). 32p. (J). (gr. 4-7). 25.50 (978-0-7910-6049-0(7) , Chelsea Hse.) Facts On File, Inc.

Crawford, Gerald. The Magic in the Mud. Date not set. (Illus.). 48p. (J). (gr. 1-4). 14.95 (978-0-9672996-0-0(8)) Red Mud Pr.

Cullen, Katherine. Earth Science. 2006. (Science News for Kids Ser.). (Illus.). 64p. (J). 30.00 (978-0-7910-9124-1(4) , Chelsea Clubhouse) Facts On File, Inc.

—Earth Science: The People Behind the Science. 2005. (Pioneers in Science Ser.). (Illus.). 192p. (gr. 6-12). 29.95 (978-0-8160-5464-0(9)) Facts On File, Inc.

Diagram Group. Earth Science. 2006. (Science Visual Resources Ser.). 208p. (YA). (gr. 6-12). 49.50 (978-0-8160-6164-8(5)) Facts On File, Inc.

—The Facts on File Earth Science Handbook. 2nd rev. ed. 2006. (Science Handbook Ser.). 272p. (gr. 6-12). 35.00 (978-0-8160-5879-2(2)) Facts On File, Inc.

Dicks, Ian & Watton, Nick, illus. God's Earth Forces. 1999. (Zoomers Ser.). 4p. (J). (gr. 3-7). 2.99 (978-0-7847-1123-1(2) , 03533, Bean Sprouts) Standard Publishing.

DK Publishing Staff. Earth. 2007. (Eyewitness Workbks.). 48p. (J). (gr. 2-8). pap., wbk. ed. 9.99 (978-0-7566-3009-6(6)) Dorling Kindersley Publishing, Inc.

Douglas, Vincent & School Specialty Publishing Staff. Earth Science at School- Grades 3-5. 2003. (Illus.). 48p. (J) (gr. 3-5). pap. 6.99 (978-0-7682-2502-0(7) , FS99028, Schaffer, Frank) Schaffer, Frank Pubns.

—Earth Science at School- Grades K-2. 2003. (Basic Skills Ser.). (Illus.). 48p. (J). (gr. k-2). pap. 6.99 (978-0-7682-2503-7(5) , FS99027, Schaffer, Frank) Schaffer, Frank Pubns.

—Life Science at School: Grades 3-5. 2003. (It's Everyplace You Are! Ser.). (Illus.). 48p. (J). (gr. 3-5). pap. 6.99 (978-0-7682-2505-1(1) , FS99030, Schaffer, Frank) Schaffer, Frank Pubns.

Earth Day Fun. 2003. (Holiday Fun Bks.). 32p. (J). 2.99 (978-0-88724-924-2(8)) Carson-Dellosa Publishing Co., Inc.

Earth Features. 2005. (Earth & Outer Space Ser.). (YA). (gr. k-3). 237.60 (978-0-7368-4212-9(8) , Pebble Bks.) Capstone Pr., Inc.

Earth Science: Earth Science PE. l.t. ed. 2005. (YA). (gr. 6-8). 79.08 (978-0-618-30368-7(5) , 2-01003) McDougal Littell Inc.

Earth Science: Visualizations. 2003. (gr. 6-12). cd-rom (978-0-618-16400-4(6) , 2-01601) McDougal Littell Inc.

Earth Science, Physics, Chemistry for 21st Century Kit. 2000. bds. (978-1-58591-121-9(6)) It's About Time, Herff Jones Education Diiv.

Earth Science, Physics, Chemistry for the 21st Century. 2002. tchr. ed., per. (978-1-58591-120-2(8)); stu. ed., bds. (978-1-58591-119-6(4)) It's About Time, Herff Jones Education Diiv.

Earth Science Sets: 1 Each of 3 Big Books. (Sunshinetm Science Ser.). (gr. 1-2). 111.50 (978-0-7802-2810-8(3)) Wright Group, The.

Earth Science Sets: 1 Each of 3 Student Books. (Sunshinetm Science Ser.). (gr. 1-2). 20.95 (978-0-7802-2811-5(1)) Wright Group, The.

Earth Watch: Tracks. (J). (gr. 4-6). (978-0-669-15884-7(4)) Houghton Mifflin Co. (Schl. Div.).

EarthComm, 5 vols., Set. 2001. stu. ed., bds. (978-1-58591-070-0(8)) It's About Time, Herff Jones Education Diiv.

EarthComm Cryosphere. 2001. cd-rom (978-1-58591-099-1(6)) It's About Time, Herff Jones Education Diiv.

EarthComm Earth System Evolution. 2001. stu. ed., bds. (978-1-58591-059-5(7)) It's About Time, Herff Jones Education Diiv.

EarthComm Earth System Evolution Material Kit: Chapter One. 2002. bds. (978-1-58591-198-1(4)) It's About Time, Herff Jones Education Diiv.

EarthComm Earth System Evolution Material Kit: Chapter Three. 2002. bds. (978-1-58591-200-1(X)) It's About Time, Herff Jones Education Diiv.

EarthComm Earth System Evolution Material Kit: Chapter Two. 2002. bds. (978-1-58591-199-8(2)) It's About Time, Herff Jones Education Diiv.

Earthforms. 2005. (Illus.). (J). (gr. 2-3). lib. bdg. 212.60 (978-0-7368-4416-1(3)) Capstone Pr., Inc.

Enderle, Dotti. Storytime Discoveries: Earth Science. 2003. (Illus.). 64p. (J). pap. 9.95 (978-1-57310-412-8(4)) Teaching & Learning Co.

Englehart, Deirdre. Write about Earth Science: The Test Connection. 2003. (Write about Science Ser.). 64p. (J). (gr. 3-5). pap. 9.99 (978-0-7424-1914-8(2) , FS99239, Schaffer, Frank) Schaffer, Frank Pubns.

—Write about Life Science: The Test Connection. 2003. (Write about Science Ser.). 64p. (J). (gr. 3-5). pap. 9.99 (978-0-7424-1916-2(9) , FS99241, Schaffer, Frank) Schaffer, Frank Pubns.

Exploring Planet Earth, 5 bks. Incl. Earth's Fiery Fury. Downs, Sandra. (gr. 5-8). 2000. lib. bdg. (978-0-7613-1413-4(X)); Earth's Hidden Treasures. Downs, Sandra. (gr. 5-8). 1999. lib. bdg. 24.90 (978-0-7613-1411-0(3)); Earth's Wild Winds. Friend, Sandra. (gr. 5-8). 2002. lib. bdg. 24.90 (978-0-7613-2673-1(1)); Shaping the Earth : Erosion. Downs, Sandra. (gr. 6-8). 2000. lib. bdg. (978-0-7613-1414-1(8)); When the Earth Moves. Downs, Sandra. (gr. 5-8). 2000. lib. bdg. 24.90 (978-0-7613-1412-7(1)); (Illus.). 64p. Set lib. bdg. 124.50 (978-0-7613-3021-9(6) , Twenty-First Century Bks.) Lerner Publishing Group.

Farndon, John. Amazing Planet Earth: The Story of Our World & the Forces That Shaped It With. 2001. (gr. 3-6). lib. bdg. 30.35 (978-0-613-84237-2(5)) Tandem Library Bks.

Fishman, Cathy Goldberg. Soup. Rooney, Ronnie, illus. 2002. (Rookie Reader Espanol Ser.). 32p. (J). (gr. k-2). pap. 4.95 (978-0-516-26981-8(X) , Children's Pr.) Scholastic Library Publishing.

—Soup. 2002. (gr. k-3). lib. bdg. 12.95 (978-0-613-53866-4(8)) Tandem Library Bks.

Flaechen und Ihre Berechnung I. 2nd ed. (Duden-Schuelerhilfen Ser.). (GER.). 112p. (YA). (gr. 5-8). (978-3-411-04412-2(8)) Bibliographisches Institut & F. A. Brockhaus AG DEU. *Dist:* International Bk. Import Service, Inc.

Flaechen und Ihre Berechnung II. (Duden-Schuelerhilfen Ser.). (GER.). 96p. (YA). (gr. 9-10). (978-3-411-04711-6(9)) Bibliographisches Institut & F. A. Brockhaus AG DEU. *Dist:* International Bk. Import Service, Inc.

Forbes, Claire. Our Wonderful World. 2000. (Illus.). (J). (978-0-606-20408-8(3)) Tandem Library Bks.

Fowler, Allan. Science, Rookie Read-About Science: Earth Science. 2004. (Illus.). 247.00 (978-0-516-29320-2(6)) Scholastic Library Publishing.

Frank, Marjorie Slavick, et al. Science Instant Readers: Earth Science Collection. 1999. (Harcourt Science Ser.). (gr. 1 up). pap. 12.40 (978-0-15-316229-9(5)); (gr. 2 up). pap. 12.40 (978-0-15-316232-9(5)) Harcourt Schl. Pubs.

Franklin, Kent. Exploring Earth & Space Systems. 2006. 96p. pap. 9.95 (978-1-4116-3469-5(1)) Lulu.com.

Gallant, Roy A. Earth Science: Grades 9-12, 4 bks., Set. Incl. Fossils. 2000. lib. bdg. 25.64 (978-0-7614-1041-6(4)); Minerals. 2000. lib. bdg. 25.64 (978-0-7614-1039-3(2)); Rocks. 2000. lib. bdg. 25.64 (978-0-7614-1042-3(2)); Water. 2001. lib. bdg. 25.64 (978-0-7614-1040-9(6)); 48p. (J). (gr. 3 up). (Kaleidoscope Ser.). (Illus.). 2001. Set lib. bdg. 102.57 (978-0-7614-1038-6(4) , Benchmark Bks.) Cavendish, Marshall Corp.

Gallavotti, Barbara. La Vida en la Tierra. (SPA.). 88p. (YA). (gr. 5-8). (978-84-7131-936-4(5)) Editex, Editorial S.A. ESP. *Dist:* Lectorum Pubns., Inc.

Ganeri, Anita. La Lluvia. 2004. 24p. 19.33 (978-0-8368-4367-5(3)); pap. 5.95 (978-0-8368-4372-9(X)) Stevens, Gareth Inc. (Weekly Reader Early Learning Library).

—La Nieve. 2004. 24p. 19.33 (978-0-8368-4368-2(1)); pap. 5.95 (978-0-8368-4373-6(8)) Stevens, Gareth Inc. (Weekly Reader Early Learning Library).

—El Viento. 2004. 24p. 19.33 (978-0-8368-4366-8(5)); pap. 5.95 (978-0-8368-4371-2(1)) Stevens, Gareth Inc. (Weekly Reader Early Learning Library).

Garnsey, Wayne & Page, Virginia. Earth Science: STARReview. 2000. (ENG., Illus.). 282p. (YA). (gr. 7-12). per. 15.95 (978-0-935487-74-9(3) , STARReviews) N&N Publishing Co., Inc.

Griffith, Dave. Earth Science. 1999. (Illus.). (YA). pap., stu. ed., wbk. ed. 35.00 (978-1-886998-13-1(2)) Pasco Scientific.

Group/McGraw-Hill, Wright. Earth & Physical Science: Exploring Electricity, 6 vols. (Book2WebTM Ser.). (gr. 4-8). 36.50 (978-0-322-04428-9(9)) Wright Group, The.

Harcourt School Publishers Staff. Earth Science: Instant Reader Standard Package. 2000. (Harcourt Ciencias Ser.). (SPA., Illus.). (gr. 1 up). pap. 17.70 (978-0-15-316953-3(2)); (gr. 2 up). pap. 17.70 (978-0-15-316956-4(7)) Harcourt Schl. Pubs.

—Harcourt Ciencias, Grade 3 Unit C&D: Earth Science. 2003. (Harcourt Ciencias Ser.). (SPA.). (gr. 3 up). tchr. ed. 67.40 (978-0-15-314809-5(8)) Harcourt Schl. Pubs.

—Harcourt Ciencias, Grade 4 Unit C&D: Earth Science. 2003. (Harcourt Ciencias Ser.). (SPA.). (gr. 4 up). tchr. ed. 67.40 (978-0-15-314812-5(8)) Harcourt Schl. Pubs.

—Harcourt Ciencias, Grade 5 Unit C&D: Earth Science. 2003. (Harcourt Ciencias Ser.). (SPA.). (gr. 5 up). tchr. ed. 70.00 (978-0-15-314815-6(2)) Harcourt Schl. Pubs.

—Harcourt Science: Earth Instant Reader CD-ROM Teacher's Guide. 2nd ed. 2003. (Harcourt Science Ser.). (gr. k up). tchr. ed. 8.00 incl. cd-rom (978-0-15-324956-3(0)) Harcourt Schl. Pubs.

—Harcourt Science; My Earth Reader. 1999. (Illus.). pap. 2.90 (978-0-15-314844-6(6)) Harcourt Schl. Pubs.

—Harcourt Science Unit C: Processes That Change the Earth. 2000. (Illus.). pap. 17.10 (978-0-15-315700-4(3)) Harcourt Schl. Pubs.

—Harcourt Science, Grade 1 Vol. 2: Earth Science: Tennessee Edition. 2nd ed. 2002. tchr. ed. 106.70 (978-0-15-328335-2(1)) Harcourt Schl. Pubs.

—Harcourt Science, Grade 2 Vol. 2: Earth Science: Tennessee Edition. 2nd ed. 2002. tchr. ed. 106.70 (978-0-15-328338-3(6)) Harcourt Schl. Pubs.

—Harcourt Science, Grade 3 Vol. 2: Earth Science: Louisiana Edition. 2nd ed. 2002. tchr. ed. 104.30 (978-0-15-328360-4(2)) Harcourt Schl. Pubs.

—Harcourt Science, Grade 3 Vol. 2: Earth Science: Tennessee Edition. 2nd ed. 2002. tchr. ed. 110.60 (978-0-15-328341-3(6)) Harcourt Schl. Pubs.

—Harcourt Science, Grade 4 Vol. 2: Earth Science: Tennessee Edition. 2nd ed. 2002. tchr. ed. 110.60 (978-0-15-328344-4(0)) Harcourt Schl. Pubs.

—Harcourt Science, Grade 5 Vol. 2: Earth Science: Louisiana Edition. 2nd ed. 2002. tchr. ed. 107.90 (978-0-15-328366-6(1)) Harcourt Schl. Pubs.

—Harcourt Science, Grade 5 Vol. 2: Earth Science: Tennessee Edition. 2nd ed. 2002. tchr. ed. 114.50 (978-0-15-328347-5(5)) Harcourt Schl. Pubs.

—Harcourt Science, Grade 6 Vol. 2: Earth Science: Louisiana Edition. 2nd ed. 2002. tchr. ed. 113.50 (978-0-15-328369-7(6)) Harcourt Schl. Pubs.

—Harcourt Science, Grade 6 Vol. 2: Earth Science: Tennessee Edition. 2nd ed. 2002. tchr. ed. 120.30 (978-0-15-328350-5(5)) Harcourt Schl. Pubs.

Harman, Rebecca. Earth's Changing Crust. 2005. (Heinemann Infosearch Ser.). (Illus.). 32p. (J). lib. bdg. (978-1-4034-7056-0(1)) Heinemann Library.

—Earth's Changing Crust: Plate Tectonics & Extreme Events. 2005. (Heinemann Infosearch Ser.). (Illus.). 32p. (J). (gr. 3-5). pap. 7.85 (978-1-4034-7063-8(4)) Heinemann Library.

Harris, Nicholas. Our Planet Earth. 2006. (First Library of Knowledge). 32p. (J). (gr. 2-4). 23.70 (978-1-4103-0345-5(4) , Blackbirch Pr., Inc.) Thomson Gale.

Haslam, Andrew. Earth. 2004. (Make It Work! Science Ser.). (Illus.). 48p. (J). (gr. 3-6). 12.95 (978-1-58728-376-5(X) , Two Can Publishing) T&N Children's Publishing.

Head, Heno, Jr. God Made the Earth. Derico, Laura, ed. Fletcher, Rusty, illus. 2000. (Happy Day Bks.). 24p. (J). (ps-2). 2.49 (978-0-7847-1060-9(0) , 04332, Bean Sprouts) Standard Publishing.

Hewitt, Sally. Earth & Space. (Illus.). 32p. (YA). (gr. 2 up). lib. bdg. 27.10 (978-1-932333-31-2(2)) Chrysalis Education.

Hil, Mcgraw. Gr 4 Lrng Abt Earth Hist. 2000. (McGraw-Hill Science Ser.). (gr. 4 up). (978-0-02-278217-7(6)) Macmillan/McGraw-Hill Schl. Div.

—Sciasmtbk Earth & It's Re. 2000. (McGraw-Hill Science Ser.). (gr. 5 up). (978-0-02-277767-8(9)) Macmillan/McGraw-Hill Schl. Div.

—Trfpaswak Earth & Its Res. 2000. (McGraw-Hill Science Ser.). (gr. 5 up). (978-0-02-277648-0(6)) Macmillan/McGraw-Hill Schl. Div.

—Trfpaswak Lrng Abt Easths. 2000. (McGraw-Hill Science Ser.). (gr. 4 up). (978-0-02-277638-1(9)) Macmillan/McGraw-Hill Schl. Div.

Hodge, Judith. Riches from Earth. 2004. (Navigators Ser.). (J). pap. 42.00 (978-1-4108-0429-7(1)) Benchmark Education Co.

Holt, Rinehart and Winston Staff. Correlation Earth: Holt Science & Technology: California Edition. 2001. pap. 4.20 (978-0-03-067226-2(0)) Holt, Rinehart & Winston.

—Earth: Middle Science Test Preparation - Alabama Edition. 2001. (Holt Science & Technology Ser.). pap. 13.73 (978-0-03-067802-8(1)) Holt, Rinehart & Winston.

—Earth: Science Test Preparation - Georgia Edition. 2002. (Holt Science & Technology Ser.). pap. 13.73 (978-0-03-068122-6(7)) Holt, Rinehart & Winston.

—Earth Science. 5th ed. 2004. (Holt Science & Technology Ser.). (SPA., Illus.). 75.80 (978-0-03-021213-0(8)) Holt, Rinehart & Winston.

—Earth Science: Chapter Resources. 5th ed. 2004. (Holt Science & Technology Ser.). (Illus.). pap. 277.93 (978-0-03-030121-6(1)) Holt, Rinehart & Winston.

—Earth Science: Critical Thinking Worksheets. 2nd ed. 2002. pap. 4.00 (978-0-03-064311-8(2)) Holt, Rinehart & Winston.

—Earth Science: Directed Reading & Vocabulary Workbook. 5th ed. 2004. (Holt Science & Technology Ser.). (SPA., Illus.). pap., wbk. ed. 17.13 (978-0-03-036058-9(7)) Holt, Rinehart & Winston.

—Earth Science: Study Guide. 5th ed. 2004. (Holt Science & Technology Ser.). (SPA., Illus.). pap., stu. ed. 17.13 (978-0-03-030156-8(4)) Holt, Rinehart & Winston.

—Earth Science No. 2: Earth & It's Systems. 6th ed. 2006. pap. 11.73 incl. cd-rom (978-0-03-036892-9(8)) Harcourt Schl. Pubs.

—Earth Science No. 3: Models of Earth. 6th ed. 2006. pap. 11.73 incl. cd-rom (978-0-03-036893-6(6)) Harcourt Schl. Pubs.

—Earth Science No. 4: Earth Chemistry. 6th ed. 2006. pap. 11.73 incl. cd-rom (978-0-03-036894-3(4)) Harcourt Schl. Pubs.

—Earth Science No. 5: Minerals & Earth's Crust. 6th ed. 2006. pap. 11.73 incl. cd-rom (978-0-03-036896-7(0)) Harcourt Schl. Pubs.

—Earth Science No. 7: Resources & Energy. 6th ed. 2006. pap. 11.73 incl. cd-rom (978-0-03-036898-1(7)) Harcourt Schl. Pubs.

—Earth Science No. 8: The Rock Record. 6th ed. 2006. pap. 11.73 incl. cd-rom (978-0-03-036899-8(5)) Harcourt Schl. Pubs.

—Holt Ciencias y Technologia: Earth. 2000. 75.80 (978-0-03-064756-7(8)); 2001. 140.40 (978-0-03-064757-4(6)) Holt, Rinehart & Winston.

—Holt Ciencias y Technologia 2001: Earth. 2001. pap., stu. ed. 17.33 (978-0-03-064758-1(4)) Holt, Rinehart & Winston.

—Holt Science & Technology. 4th ed. 2004. (Illus.). 75.80 (978-0-03-073167-9(4)) Holt, Rinehart & Winston.

—Holt Science & Technology: Earth: California Edition. 2001. 75.86 (978-0-03-055667-8(8)); 2000. pap., stu. ed. 16.00 (978-0-03-055669-2(4)); 2001. tchr. ed. 136.53 (978-0-03-055668-5(6)) Holt, Rinehart & Winston.

—Holt Science & Technology: Earth: Creative Thinking & Problem Worksheet - California Edition. 2001. pap. 10.93 (978-0-03-055698-2(8)) Holt, Rinehart & Winston.

—Holt Science & Technology: Earth: Directed Reading Worksheets - California Edition. 2001. pap. 15.13 (978-0-03-055697-5(X)) Holt, Rinehart & Winston.

—Holt Science & Technology: Earth: Georgia Edition. annot. ed. 2001. tchr. ed. 133.80 (978-0-03-066894-4(8)) Holt, Rinehart & Winston.

—Holt Science & Technology: Earth: Reinforcement & Vocational Worksheets. 2000. pap. 15.20 (978-0-03-055414-8(4)) Holt, Rinehart & Winston.

—Holt Science & Technology: Earth: Reinforcement & Vocational Worksheets - California Edition. 2001. pap. 14.33 (978-0-03-055693-7(7)) Holt, Rinehart & Winston.

—Holt Science & Technology: Earth Science. 5th ed. 2004. tchr. ed. 128.80 (978-0-03-066479-3(9)) Holt, Rinehart & Winston.

—Holt Science & Technology: Earth Science: Enhanced Online Edition. 2002. 74.53 (978-0-03-072491-6(0)); 4th ed. 2004. 17.26 (978-0-03-037151-6(1)) Holt, Rinehart & Winston.

—Holt Science & Technology: Earth Science: Online Edition Upgrade. 4th ed. 2004. 31.93 (978-0-03-037171-4(6)); 7.93 (978-0-03-037213-1(5)) Holt, Rinehart & Winston.

—Holt Science & Technology: Earth Science: Reading & Comprehension Guide. 5th ed. 2004. pap. 17.13 (978-0-03-036062-6(5)) Holt, Rinehart & Winston.

—Holt Science & Technology: Earth Science: Special Needs Workbook. 5th ed. 2004. pap., wbk. ed. 17.13 (978-0-03-036054-1(4)) Holt, Rinehart & Winston.

—Holt Science & Technology: Earth Science Study Guide. 5th ed. 2004. (Illus.). pap., stu. ed. 17.13 (978-0-03-030159-9(9)) Holt, Rinehart & Winston.

—Holt Science & Technology: Earth Science: Tutorial Site License. 2nd ed. 2002. 864.00 (978-0-03-070399-7(9)) Holt, Rinehart & Winston.

—Holt Science & Technology: Earth Science with Answer Key. 2000. pap., stu. ed. 12.20 (978-0-03-051767-9(2)) Holt, Rinehart & Winston.

—Holt Science & Technology: Earth: Study Guide with Answer Key - California Edition. 2000. pap., stu. ed. 10.80 (978-0-03-055689-0(9)) Holt, Rinehart & Winston.

—Holt Science & Technology: Life Science: Tutorial Site License. 2nd ed. 2002. 861.84 (978-0-03-070397-3(2)) Holt, Rinehart & Winston.

—Holt Science & Technology Chapter 1: Earth Science: The World of Earth Science. 5th ed. 2004. (Illus.). pap. 12.86 (978-0-03-030266-4(8)) Holt, Rinehart & Winston.

—Holt Science & Technology Chapter 20: Life Science: Earth's Ecosystems. 5th ed. 2004. (Illus.). pap. 12.86 (978-0-03-030231-2(5)) Holt, Rinehart & Winston.

—Holt Science & Technology Chptr. 5: Earth's Econsystem: Chapter Resources - Tennessee Edition. 3rd ed. 2003. (YA). pap. 11.40 (978-0-03-069163-8(X)) Holt, Rinehart & Winston.

—Holt Science & Technology No. 6: Dynamic Earth Resources: Texas Edition. 2nd ed. 2001. pap. 26.00 (978-0-03-064864-9(5)) Holt, Rinehart & Winston.

—Holt Science & Technology No. 7: Earth & Beyond Resources: Texas Edition - Grade 7. 2nd ed. 2001. pap. 26.00 (978-0-03-064866-3(1)) Holt, Rinehart & Winston.

—Holt Science & Technology 2001: Earth: Directed Reading Worksheets with Answer Key. 2000. pap. 12.00 (978-0-03-055413-1(6)) Holt, Rinehart & Winston.

Investigating Earth Systems Dynamic Earth. 2002. stu. ed. (978-1-58591-081-6(3)) It's About Time, Herff Jones Education Diiv.

Investigating Earth Systems Dynamic Planet. 2002. stu. ed., bds. (978-1-58591-104-2(6)) It's About Time, Herff Jones Education Diiv.

Investigating Earth Systems Energy Resources. 2002. stu. ed., per. (978-1-58591-082-3(1)); stu. ed., bds. (978-1-58591-106-6(2)) It's About Time, Herff Jones Education Diiv.

Investigating Earth Systems Fossils. 2002. stu. ed., per. (978-1-58591-083-0(X)); stu. ed., bds. (978-1-58591-107-3(0)) It's About Time, Herff Jones Education Diiv.

Investigating Earth Systems Materials & Minerals. 2002. stu. ed., per. (978-1-58591-075-5(9)); stu. ed., bds. (978-1-58591-105-9(4)) It's About Time, Herff Jones Education Diiv.

Jennings, Terry. Wood. 2006. (Illus.). 32p. (YA). (gr. 1 up). lib. bdg. 27.10 (978-1-932333-00-8(2)) Chrysalis Education.

Lambert, David & Redfern, Martin. The Kingfisher Young People's Book of the Universe. 2001. (Kingfisher Book of Ser.). (Illus.). 224p. (J). (gr. 5-8). tchr. ed. 24.95 (978-0-7534-5327-8(4) , Kingfisher) Houghton Mifflin Co. Trade & Reference Div.

LeapFrog Staff, compiled by. Leap into Geography: The Seven Continents. 2001. (J). (ps-2). spiral bd. 14.99 (978-1-58605-033-7(8)) LeapFrog Enterprises, Inc.

Loeschnig, Louis V. No-Sweat Science: Earth Science Experiments. Gallagher, Jack, illus. 2006. 128p. (J). pap. 5.95 (978-1-4027-2333-9(4)) Sterling Publishing Co., Inc.

El Mar Es Salado. (Enciclopedia Me Pregunto Por Que). (SPA., Illus.). 32p. (J). (gr. 3-5). (978-84-241-2176-1(7) , EV2038) Everest de Ediciones y Distribucion, S.L. ESP. *Dist:* Lectorum Pubns., Inc.

McClish, Bruce. Earth & Its Continents. 2003. (Continents Ser.). (Illus.). 32p. pap. 7.50 (978-1-4034-4244-4(4)) Heinemann Library.

McGraw-Hill Staff. The Changing Surface of Earth. 2nd ed. 2004. (Glencoe Science Ser.). stu. ed. 20.64 (978-0-07-861752-2(9) , 9780078617522) Glencoe/McGraw-Hill.

—Earth Science: Geology, the Environment, & the Universe. 2001. (C). stu. ed. 88.00 (978-0-07-821591-9(9) , 9780078215919); 2nd ed. 2004. stu. ed. 88.64 (978-0-07-866423-6(3) , 9780078664236) Glencoe/McGraw-Hill.

—Earth Science, Reinforcement. 2004. (C). pap., stu. ed. 11.96 (978-0-07-866972-9(3) , 9780078669729) Glencoe/McGraw-Hill.

—Glencoe Science: Earth Science Modules. 2004. pap., stu. ed. 8.64 (978-0-07-866936-1(7) , 9780078669361) Glencoe/McGraw-Hill.

—Glencoe Science: Earth's Materials & Processes. 2nd ed. 2004. stu. ed. 20.64 (978-0-07-861749-2(9) , 9780078617492) Glencoe/McGraw-Hill.

—Glencoe Science: The Water Planet. 2nd ed. 2004. stu. ed. 20.64 (978-0-07-861755-3(3) , 9780078617553) Glencoe/McGraw-Hill.

McGuire, Thomas. Earth Science Reviewing the Essentials. 2001. (gr. 8-10). pap. 8.25 (978-0-87720-182-3(X) , R704P) AMSCO Schl. Pubns., Inc.

Medina, Phil. Homework Helpers: Earth Science. 2005. (Homework Helpers Ser.). (Illus.). 352p. (gr. 9-12). pap. 14.99 (978-1-56414-767-7(3)) Career Pr., Inc.

Menetrez, Marc Yves, et al. Encyclopedia of Environmental Studies. 3rd rev. ed. 2008. (Science Encyclopedia Ser.). 800p. (gr. 9). 150.00 (***978-0-8160-6511-0(X)***) Facts On File, Inc.

Milbourne, Anna. Under the Ground. Riglietti, Serena, illus. 2006. 24p. (J). 9.99 (978-0-7945-1264-4(X) , Usborne) EDC Publishing.

Miles Kelly Staff. Larger Than Life: Gigantic Views of the Microscopic. 2003. (Illus.). 48p. (J). 12.95 (978-1-84236-020-0(5)) Miles Kelly Publishing, Ltd. GBR. *Dist:* Independent Pubs. Group.

Modules: Earth Science; Earth's Atmosphere PE. 2005. (gr. 6-12). (978-0-618-33415-5(7) , 2-01005) McDougal Littell Inc.

Modules: Earth Science; Earth's Waters PE. 2005. (gr. 6-12). (978-0-618-33417-9(3) , 2-01007) McDougal Littell Inc.

Modules: Earth Science; Space Science PE. 2005. (gr. 6-12). (978-0-618-33421-6(1) , 2-01011) McDougal Littell Inc.

Modules: Earth Science; the Changing Earth PE. 2005. (gr. 6-12). (978-0-618-33424-7(6) , 2-01013) McDougal Littell Inc.

Modules: Physical Science. 2005. (gr. 6-12). cd-rom (978-0-618-42030-8(4) , 2-01144) McDougal Littell Inc.

Modules: Physical Science; Content Review CD-ROM: Earth Science. 2005. (gr. 6-12). cd-rom (978-0-618-42024-7(X) , 2-01138) McDougal Littell Inc.

Modules: Physical Science; Earth's Atmosphere. 2005. (gr. 6-12). lab manual ed. (978-0-618-43725-2(8) , 2-01218) McDougal Littell Inc.

Modules: Physical Science; Earth's Surface Lab Manual, PE. 2005. (gr. 6-12). lab manual ed. (978-0-618-43726-9(6) , 2-01219) McDougal Littell Inc.

Modules: Physical Science; Earth's Waters. 2005. (gr. 6-12). lab manual ed. (978-0-618-43727-6(4) , 2-01220) McDougal Littell Inc.

Modules: Physical Science; the Changing Earth Lab Manual, PE. 2005. (gr. 6-12). (978-0-618-43735-1(5) , 2-01228) McDougal Littell Inc.

Navarro, Jose & Navarro, Amparo. El Enorme Pequenoz de la Abuela Tierra.Tr. of Enormous Smallness of Grandmother Earth. (SPA.). 142p. (J). 10.95 (978-84-7960-107-2(8)) Ediciones de la Torre ESP. *Dist:* Libros Sin Fronteras.

Ohanesian, Diane. Rocks, Rocks, Rocks. 2nd rev. ed. 2003. (BuildUp Ser.). (J). pap. 22.00 (978-1-4108-0756-4(8)) Benchmark Education Co.

O'Shaughnessy, Tam E. Totally Amazing Careers in Earth Science. 2006. (J). 7.80 (978-1-933798-02-8(5)) Sally Ride Science.

Our Changing Earth: an Encyclopedia of Landforms: Fifth Grade Guided Comprehension Level M. (On Our Way to English Ser.). (gr. 5 up). 34.50 (978-0-7578-6596-1(8)) Rigby Education.

Our Planet. 2005. (Illus.). 32p. (gr. 4-8). pap. 112.00 (978-0-7910-9087-9(6) , Chelsea Clubhouse) Facts On File, Inc.

Parramon Staff. Secretos de la Tierra. 2006. (SPA.). 31p. (J). (gr. 6-8). 10.40 (978-84-342-2692-0(8) , PR33937) Parramon Ediciones S.A. ESP. *Dist:* Lectorum Pubns., Inc.

Parratore, Phil. Hands-On Earth Science. 2001. (Cool, Awesome, Simple Science Ser.). (Illus.). 64p. (J). pap. 9.99 (978-0-88724-649-4(4) , CD-7320) Carson-Dellosa Publishing Co., Inc.

Pebble Books: Earth & Outer Space. 2005. (YA). (gr. k-3). 594.00 (978-0-7368-4222-8(5) , Pebble Bks.) Capstone Pr., Inc.

Pentland, Peter & Stoyles, Pennie. Earth Science. 2002. (Science & Scientists Ser.). (Illus.). 32p. (gr. 4-8). 28.00 (978-0-7910-7012-3(3) , Chelsea Hse.) Facts On File, Inc.

Pratt, Leonie. Planet Earth (Level 2) - Internet Referenced. 2007. (Beginners Nature Ser.). 32p. (J). 4.99 (***978-0-7945-1707-6(2)*** , Usborne) EDC Publishing.

Raintree Steck-Vaughn Staff. True Tales of Shifting Ground. 2003. (gr. 5-8). lib. bdg. 22.25 (978-0-613-73998-6(1)) Tandem Library Bks.

Redmond, Stephanie L. Christian Kids Explore Earth Science. 2006. (J). pap. (978-1-892427-19-9(2)) Bright Ideas! Educational Resources.

Rohrer, Lesa. Write about Earth Science: The Test Connection. 2003. (Write about Science Ser.). 64p. (J). (gr. 6-8). pap. 9.99 (978-0-7424-1915-5(0) , FS99240, Schaffer, Frank) Schaffer, Frank Pubns.

Roza, Greg. Beneath Earth's Surface. 2002. (Reading Room Collection). (Illus.). 24p. (J). lib. bdg. 18.75 (978-0-8239-3718-9(6)) Rosen Publishing Group, Inc., The.

Sally Ride Science Editors, Sally Ride Science. What Do You Want to Be? Explore Earth Sciences. 2004. (J). 6.00 (978-0-9753920-2-7(6)) Sally Ride Science.

Saunders-Smith, Gail, ed. Earth Features, 8 bks. Incl. What Are Caves? Schuh, Mari C. 2002. lib. bdg. 15.93 (978-0-7368-1169-9(9)); What Are Deserts? Trumbauer, Lisa. 2001. lib. bdg. 15.93 (978-0-7368-0987-0(2)); What Are Forests? Trumbauer, Lisa. 2001. lib. bdg. 15.93 (978-0-7368-0988-7(0)); What Are Lakes? Schuh, Mari C. 2002. lib. bdg. 15.93 (978-0-7368-1170-5(2)); What Are Mountains? Trumbauer, Lisa. 2001. lib. bdg. 15.93 (978-0-7368-0989-4(9)); What Are Oceans? Trumbauer, Lisa. 2001. lib. bdg. 15.93 (978-0-7368-0990-0(2)); What Are Rivers? Schuh, Mari C. 2002. lib. bdg. 15.93 (978-0-7368-1171-2(0)); What Are Volcanoes? Schuh, Mari C. 2002. lib. bdg. 15.93 (978-0-7368-1172-9(9)); 24p. (J). (gr. k-1). (Illus.). 2001. Set lib. bdg. 127.44 (978-0-7368-1198-9(2) , Pebble Bks.) Capstone Pr., Inc.

Schmid, Eleonore. Living Earth. 2000. (gr. k-3). lib. bdg. 15.25 (978-0-613-26040-4(6)) Tandem Library Bks.

School Specialty Publishing. Write about Life Science: The Test Connection. 2003. (Write about Science Ser.). 64p. (J). (gr. 6-8). pap. 9.99 (978-0-7424-1917-9(7) , FS99242, Schaffer, Frank) Schaffer, Frank Pubns.

Schwartz, David M. El Arce. Kuhn, Dwight, photos by. 2001. (Springboards into Science Ser.). (SPA., Illus.). 24p. (J). (gr. 1 up). lib. bdg. 20.67 (978-0-8368-2990-7(5)) Stevens, Gareth Inc.

Science & Technology for Books, Life & Earth Sciences Library, 6 vols. 2004. (Illus.). 64p. (J). (978-1-933008-25-7(3)) National Science Resources Ctr.

Science Files - Set II - Earth: Deserts; Forests; Islands; Mountains; Oceans; Rivers & Lakes, 6 bks. 2002. (Illus.). (J). (gr. 3 up). lib. bdg. 148.02 (978-0-8368-3565-6(4)) Stevens, Gareth Inc.

Seuling, Barbara. Earth Is Like a Giant Magnet & Other Freaky Facts about Planets, Oceans, & Volcanoes. Skeens, Matthew, illus. 2007. (J). lib. bdg. (***978-1-4048-3752-2(3)***) Picture Window Bks.

Sian student journal break'n earth Holdp/5. 2000. (Science in A Nutshell(R) Ser.). (J). (978-1-59242-007-0(9)) Delta Education, LLC.

Skelton, Renee. Forecast Earth: The Story of Climate Scientist Inez Fung. 2006. (Women's Adventures in Science Ser.). (Illus.). 128p. pap. 9.95 (978-0-309-09554-9(9) , Joseph Henry Pr.) National Academies Pr.

Sloan, Frank, ed. Biomes, 5 bks., Set. Incl. Deserts. Steele, Christy. lib. bdg. 22.83 (978-0-7398-3560-9(2)); Forests. Nelson, Julie. lib. bdg. 22.83 (978-0-7398-3561-6(0)); Grasslands. Nelson, Julie. lib. bdg. 22.83 (978-0-7398-3562-3(9)); Oceans. Steele, Christy. lib. bdg. 22.83 (978-0-7398-3564-7(5)); Tundra. Nelson, Julie. lib. bdg. 22.83 (978-0-7398-3565-4(3)); (Illus.). (J). (gr. 4-7). 32p. 2001. Set lib. bdg. 114.15 (978-0-7398-3566-1(1)) Raintree.

Spaulding & Namowitz. Earth Science. 2003. (gr. 6-12). (SPA.). (978-0-618-19220-5(4) , 2-01615); (978-0-618-19221-2(2) , 2-01616); (978-0-618-20354-3(0) , 2-01624); stu. ed. (978-0-618-11550-1(1) , 2-01600); stu. ed., lab manual ed. (978-0-618-19215-1(8) , 2-01610) McDougal Littell Inc.

Spyglass Books-Earth Science Complete Set. (Spyglass Books-Earth Science Ser.). (gr. 1-2). 219.23 (978-0-7565-0784-8(7)) Compass Point Bks.

Staub, Frank. The Kids' Book of Clouds & Sky. 2005. (Illus.). 80p. (J). pap. 9.95 (978-1-4027-2806-8(9)) Sterling Publishing Co., Inc.

Steck-Vaughn Staff. Earth & Space Science. 1999. (J). (gr. 3). pap. (978-0-8172-3768-4(2)); (gr. 5). pap. (978-0-8172-3770-7(4)); (Illus.). (gr. 6). pap. (978-0-8172-3771-4(2)) Steck-Vaughn.

—Earth Forces & Formations: 10 Lab Classroom. 1998. pap. 748.30 (978-0-8172-8294-3(7)) Steck-Vaughn.

—Earth Forces & Formations: 3 Lab Classroom. 1998. pap. 415.70 (978-0-8172-8292-9(0)) Steck-Vaughn.

—Earth Forces & Formations: 5 Lab Classroom. 1998. pap. 582.00 (978-0-8172-8293-6(9)) Steck-Vaughn.

—Science: Earth & Space Science, Physical Science. 2002. (Illus.). pap. (978-0-7398-5425-9(9)) Steck-Vaughn.

Stein, Sara. The Evolution Book. Stein, Sara, illus. 1999. (Illus.). 400p. (YA). (gr. 7-12). pap. 12.95 (978-0-89480-927-9(X) , 927) Workman Publishing Co., Inc.

Stewart, Melissa. Rocks & Minerals, 7 bks., Set. 2002. (J). (gr. 4-6). lib. bdg. 159.53 (978-1-58810-191-4(6)) Heinemann Library.

Stradling, Jan. Earth Materials: Level I, 6 vols. (First Explorers Ser.). 24p. (gr. 1-2). 29.95 (978-0-7699-1444-2(6)) Shortland Pubns. (U. S. A.) Inc.

Superlibro de Mi hogar: la Tierra: Unit 4: Mi hogar: la Tierra (A Home Called Earth) 2000. (McGraw-Hill Ciencias Ser.). (ENG & SPA.). (gr. k up). (978-0-02-277161-4(1)) Macmillan/McGraw-Hill Schl. Div.

Thompson, Gare. Kids Care for the Earth. 2002. (Kids Make a Difference Ser.). 32p. (J). (gr. 3-6). 49.35 (978-0-7922-8675-2(8)) National Geographic Society.

La Tierra Increible. (SPA.). (YA). (gr. 5-8). pap. 13.56 (978-950-04-1967-3(X)) Emecé Editores S.A. ARG. *Dist:* Lectorum Pubns., Inc.

Time Tunnel Play Pack. 2000. (Illus.). 12p. (J). (ps up). pap. 7.99 (978-0-85953-001-9(9)) Child's Play-International.

Trueit, Trudi Strain & Vriesenga, Daryl. Earth Science. 1999. (100+ Ser.). 128p. (J). (gr. 5-8). pap. 12.99 (978-0-88012-853-7(4) , IF8755) School Specialty Publishing.

Two-Can Publishing Ltd. Staff, contrib. by. Planet Earth. 2004. (Illus.). 192p. (J). (gr. 3-6). 24.95 (978-1-58728-049-8(3) , Two Can Publishing) T&N Children's Publishing.

Understanding Forces of Nature. 2000. (Primary Source Science Collection). (J). (gr. 5-8). pap. incl. VHS (978-0-7398-3216-5(6)) Raintree.

Van Rose, Susanna. La Tierra. 2004. (DK Guides Ser.). 64p. (J). lib. bdg. 19.99 (978-0-7566-0417-2(6)) Dorling Kindersley Publishing, Inc.

VanCleave, Janice Pratt. Janice VanCleave's A+ Projects in Earth Science: Winning Experiments for Science Fairs & Extra Credit. 1998. (Illus.). 234p. (YA). (gr. 7-12). lib. bdg. 22.20 (978-0-613-16516-7(0)) Tandem Library Bks.

Warhol, Tom. Earth's Biomes, 6 bks., Set. Incl. Chaparral & Scrub. (YA). (gr. 5-8). lib. bdg. 32.79 (978-0-7614-2195-5(5)); Desert. (YA). (gr. 5-8). lib. bdg. 32.79 (978-0-7614-2194-8(7)); Forest. (J). lib. bdg. 32.79 (978-0-7614-2189-4(0)); Grassland. (J). lib. bdg. 32.79 (978-0-7614-2196-2(3)); Tundra. (YA). (gr. 5-8). lib. bdg. 32.79 (978-0-7614-2193-1(9)); Water. (J). lib. bdg. 32.79 (978-0-7614-2192-4(0)); (Illus.). 80p. 2006. 2007. Set lib. bdg. 196.71 (*978-0-7614-2188-7(2) , Benchmark Bks.) Cavendish, Marshall Corp.

Wilkes, Angela. The Little Encyclopedia of Our World. 2002. (Kingfisher Little Encyclopedias Ser.). (Illus.). 128p. (J). (gr. k-3). pap. 11.95 (978-0-7534-5570-8(6) , Kingfisher) Houghton Mifflin Co. Trade & Reference Div.

Williams, Brian. Planet Earth: Biggest & Best. 2004. (Biggest & Best Ser.). (Illus.). 40p. (J). pap. 7.95 (978-1-84236-029-3(9)) Miles Kelly Publishing, Ltd. GBR. *Dist:* Independent Pubs. Group.

Williams, Zella. Experiments about Planet Earth. 2007. (Do-It-Yourself Science Ser.). (Illus.). 24p. (J). (gr. 2-5). lib. bdg. 23.95 (978-1-4042-3662-2(7) , PowerKids Pr.) Rosen Publishing Group, Inc., The.

Wolf, Aline D. Pledge to the Earth. Servello, Joe, illus. 2000. 24p. (J). spiral bd. 6.00 (978-0-939195-21-3(6) , 310) Parent Child Pr., Inc.

EARTHQUAKES

see also San Francisco Earthquake, Calif., 1906; Volcanoes

Armentrout, David & Armentrout, Patricia. Earthquakes. 2007. (Illus.). 32p. (J). (978-1-60044-230-8(7)) Rourke Publishing, LLC.

Ball, Jackie. Earthquakes. 2004. (Discovery Channel School Science Ser.). (Illus.). 32p. (J). (gr. 5 up). lib. bdg. 24.67 (978-0-8368-3378-2(3)) Stevens, Gareth Inc.

Benchmark Education Staff. Earthquake! 2005. 2.00 (*978-1-4108-4641-9(5)) Benchmark Education Co.

Bennett, Paul. Earthquake. 1999. (World Reacts Ser.). (Illus.). 32p. (J). (gr. 2-5). lib. bdg. 16.95 (978-1-887068-44-4(9)) Smart Apple Media.

Berger, Melvin. Why Do Volcanoes Blow Their Tops? Questions & Answers about Volcanoes & Earthquakes. 2000. (Question & Answer Ser.). (J). (978-0-606-19623-9(4)) Tandem Library Bks.

Berger, Melvin & Berger, Gilda. Why Do Volcanoes Blow Their Tops? Questions & Answers about Volcanoes & Earthquakes. Bond, Barbara Higgins, illus. 2000. (Question & Answer Ser.). 48p. (J). (gr. 2-5). pap. 14.95 (978-0-439-09580-8(8)) Scholastic, Inc.

Berger, Melvin, et al. Why Do Volcanoes Blow Their Tops? Questions & Answers about Volcanoes & Earthquakes. 1999. (Question & Answer Ser.). (J). (978-0-439-09581-5(6)) Scholastic, Inc.

Bowen, Mary & Ruth, Monty. Estar a Salvo Durante un Terremoto y Otras Emergencias. Jepsen, Mark, illus. Reyes, Rico J., photos by. l.t. ed. 2000. (SPA.). 96p. (J). (gr. 4-7). 28.95 (978-0-9702765-1-3(6)) Global Vision, LLC.

Bowen, Mary, et al. To Be Safe During an Earthquake & Other Emergencies: With Lucy & Her Emergency Buddies. Jepsen, Ricki & Jepsen, Mark, illus. Reyes, Rico J., photos by. deluxe l.t. ed. 2000. (To Be Safe Ser.: Vol. 1). 9696p. (J). (ps-3). 28.95 (978-0-9702765-0-6(8)) Global Vision, LLC.

Branley, Franklyn M. Earthquakes. Lloyd, Megan, illus. 2005. (Let's-Read-and-Find-Out Science Ser.). 40p. (J). (gr. k-4). pap. 5.99 (978-0-06-445188-8(7) , Harper Trophy); 15.99 (978-0-06-028008-6(5)); lib. bdg. 16.89 (978-0-06-028009-3(3)) HarperCollins Pubs.

Branley, Franklyn Mansfield. Earthquakes. Lloyd, Megan, illus. 2005. 33p. (J). (ps-ps). lib. bdg. 11.64 (978-0-606-33314-6(2)) Tandem Library Bks.

Brannon, Barbara. Discover Earthquakes. 2005. 39.00 (*978-1-4108-5132-1(X)) Benchmark Education Co.

Brunelle, Lynn. Earthquake! The 1906 San Francisco Nightmare. 2005. (X-Treme Disasters That Changed America Ser.). (J). lib. bdg. 25.27 (978-1-59716-008-7(3)) Bearport Publishing Co., Inc.

Bulletpoints Volcanoes & Earthquakes. 2005. (Illus.). (J). per. 4.99 (978-1-933581-06-4(9)) Byeway Bks.

Challen, Paul C. Volcano Alert! 2004. (Disaster Alert! Ser.). (Illus.). 32p. (J). pap. (978-0-7787-1602-0(3)); (978-0-7787-1570-2(1)) Crabtree Publishing Co.

Chippendale, Lisa. San Francisco Earthquake of 1906. 2000. (Great Disasters Ser.). (Illus.). 112p. (J). (gr. 5-9). 30.00 (978-0-7910-5270-9(2) , Chelsea Hse.) Facts On File, Inc.

Collier, Barbara. Earthquakes! 2006. 32p. (J). lib. bdg. 15.00 (*978-1-4242-0694-0(4)) Fitzgerald Bks.

Colson, Mary. Shaky Ground: Earthquakes. 2005. 48p. (J). pap. 8.50 (978-1-4109-1912-0(9)) Raintree.

—Shaky Ground: Earthquakes. 2005. (Turbulent Planet Ser.). (J). (978-1-4109-1736-2(3)); pap. (978-1-4109-1746-1(0)) Steck-Vaughn.

—Shaky Ground: Earthquakes. 2005. 48p. (J). lib. bdg. 29.93 (978-1-4109-1911-3(0)) Raintree.

Connolly, Sean. Earthquakes. 2003. (Illus.). 32p. (J). lib. bdg. 27.10 (978-1-58340-388-4(4)) Smart Apple Media.

Cooke, Tim. 1906 San Francisco Earthquake. 2005. (Illus.). 32p. (J). lib. bdg. 24.67 (978-0-8368-4494-8(7)) Stevens, Gareth Inc.

Dahlstrom, Kathryn. Trapped by an Earthquake. Date not set. (Good News Club Ser.). (J). (gr. 4-11). pap. 4.99 (978-1-55976-827-6(4)) CEF Pr.

Dalgleish, Sharon. Earthquakes. 2002. (Junior Adventure Ser.). (Illus.). 32p. (J). (gr. 3 up). lib. bdg. (978-1-59084-187-7(5)) Mason Crest Pubs.

Day, Trevor. Savage Earth. 2006. (DK Guides Ser.). 64p. (J). pap. 7.99 (978-0-7566-1791-2(X)) Dorling Kindersley Publishing, Inc.

Deedrick, Tami. Earthquakes. 2000. (Nature on the Rampage Ser.). (Illus.). 32p. (J). (gr. 4-7). lib. bdg. 22.83 (978-0-7398-1795-7(7)) Raintree.

Dorling Kindersley Publishing Staff, ed. Volcanoes & Earthquakes. 2004. (Dk Eyewitness Books Ser.). (Illus.). 72p. (J). 15.99 (978-0-7566-0735-7(3)) Dorling Kindersley Publishing, Inc.

Drohan, Michele Ingber. Earthquakes. 1999. (High Interest Bks.). (Illus.). 24p. (J). (gr. k-4). lib. bdg. 19.95 (978-0-8239-5285-4(1) , PowerKids Pr.) Rosen Publishing Group, Inc., The.

Dussling, Jennifer. Earthquakes: All Aboard Science Reader Station Stop 2. Osiecki, Lori, illus. 2004. (All Aboard Science Reader Ser.). 48p. (J). (gr. 1-3). pap. 3.99 (978-0-448-43203-8(X)); 13.89 (978-0-448-43327-1(3)) Penguin Group (USA) Inc. (Grosset & Dunlap).

Earthquake!, Level 2. 1999. (SmartReader Ser.). (J). pap., tchr. ed. 19.95 incl. audio (978-0-7887-0114-6(2) , 79302T3) Recorded Bks., LLC.

Earthquake! Individual Title Six-Packs. (Bookweb Ser.). 32p. (gr. 5 up). 34.00 (978-0-7635-3785-2(3)) Rigby Education.

Earthquake Experts: 6 Small Books. (Greetings Ser.: Vol. 2). 32p. (gr. 3-5). 31.00 (978-0-7635-2060-1(8)) Rigby Education.

Earthquake Experts: Big Book. (Greetings Ser.: Vol. 2). 32p. (gr. 3-5). 31.00 (978-0-7635-3236-9(3)) Rigby Education.

Earthquakes. 2000. (Pathfinders Ser.). (Illus.). (J). (gr. 1-5). pap. (978-1-57584-708-5(6)) Reader's Digest Children's Publishing, Inc.

Earthquakes: Level Q, 6 vols., Vol. 3. (Explorers Ser.). 32p. (gr. 3-6). 44.95 (978-0-7699-0622-5(2)) Shortland Pubns. (U. S. A.) Inc.

Expertas en Terremotos: 6 Small Books. (Saludos Ser.: Vol. 2). (SPA.). (gr. 3-5). 31.00 (978-0-7635-2066-3(7)) Rigby Education.

Farndon, John & Riley, Peter D. Volcanoes & Earthquakes & Other Facts about Planet Earth: Bulletpoints. 2003. (Bulletpoints Ser.). (Illus.). 40p. (J). pap. 6.95 (978-1-84236-238-9(0)) Miles Kelly Publishing, Ltd. GBR. *Dist:* Independent Pubs. Group.

Frisch, Aaron. Earthquakes. 2001. (Natural Disasters Ser.). (Illus.). 24p. (J). 21.35 (978-1-58340-123-1(7)) Smart Apple Media.

Gallant, Roy A. Plates: Restless Earth. 2002. (Earthworks Ser.). (Illus.). 80p. (J). 29.93 (978-0-7614-1370-7(7) , Benchmark Bks.) Cavendish, Marshall Corp.

Ganeri, Anita. Shaky Ground. 2004. (Turbulent Planet Ser.). (Illus.). 48p. (J). 28.56 (978-1-4109-0589-5(6)); pap. 8.50 (978-1-4109-1027-1(X)) Raintree.

—Shaky Ground 6-Pack. 2004. (Turbulent Planet Ser.). (Illus.). pap. 45.90 (978-1-4109-1032-5(6)) Raintree.

Gates, Alexander E. & Ritchie, David. Encyclopedia of Earthquakes & Volcanoes. 3rd rev. ed. (Science Encyclopedia Ser.). 368p. pap. 21.95 (*978-0-8160-7120-3(9) , Checkmark Bks.) Facts On File, Inc.

Gentle, Victor & Perry, Janet. Earthquakes. 2001. (Natural Disasters Ser.). (Illus.). 24p. (J). (gr. 2 up). lib. bdg. 22.00 (978-0-8368-2832-0(1)) Stevens, Gareth Inc.

George, Linda. Plate Tectonics. 2002. (Kidhaven Science Library). (Illus.). 48p. (J). (gr. 3-5). 23.70 (978-0-7377-1405-0(0) , Greenhaven Pr., Inc.) Thomson Gale.

Givon, Hannah Gelman. We Shake in a Quake. Uttal, David, illus. 2004. 32p. (J). (ps-3). reprint ed. 7.95 (978-1-58246-022-2(1) , Tricycle Pr.) Ten Speed Pr.

Group/McGraw-Hill, Wright. Forces of Nature: Level K, 6 vols., Vol. 2. (First Explorers Ser.). 24p. (gr. 1-2). 34.95 (978-0-7699-1458-9(6)) Shortland Pubns. (U. S. A.) Inc.

Gullard, Pamela & Lund, Nancy. Life on the San Andreas Fault: A History of Portola Valley. 2003. (Illus.). 288p. 60.00 (978-0-942087-19-2(4)) Scottwall Assocs.

Harcourt School Publishers Staff. The Day the Stadium Shook: Take-Home Book. 2001. (Collections Ser.). (Illus.). (J). pap. 1.90 (978-0-15-319523-5(1)) Harcourt Schl. Pubs.

—Making Mountains On Level. 3rd ed. 2002. (Trophies Reading Program Ser.). (Illus.). pap. 5.10 (978-0-15-323446-0(6)) Harcourt Schl. Pubs.

—Ring of Fire. 3rd ed. 2002. (Trophies English Language Learners Ser.). (Illus.). pap. 5.10 (978-0-15-327821-1(8)) Harcourt Schl. Pubs.

—Ring of Fire: Take-Home Book. 1999. (Collections Ser.). (Illus.). (J). pap. 1.90 (978-0-15-317318-9(1)) Harcourt Schl. Pubs.

—Ring of Fire Below Level. 3rd ed. 2002. (Trophies Reading Program Ser.). (Illus.). pap. 5.10 (978-0-15-323158-2(0)) Harcourt Schl. Pubs.

Harkins, Susan Sales & Harkins, William. Earthquake in Loma Prieta, CA 1989. 2005. (Natural Disasters Ser.). (Illus.). 32p. (J). (gr. 1-4). lib. bdg. (978-1-58415-417-4(9)) Mitchell Lane Pubs., Inc.

Harper, D. Volcanoes & Earthquakes. (Information Ser.). (Illus.). 32p. (J). (gr. 2-6). 3.50 (978-0-7214-1744-8(2) , Dutton Juvenile) Penguin Group (USA) Inc.

Harrison, David L. Earthquakes: Earth's Mightiest Moments. Nathan, Cheryl, illus. 2004. (Earthworks Ser.). 32p. (J). (gr. k-2). 15.95 (978-1-59078-243-9(7)) Boyds Mills Pr.

Heiligman, Deborah. Earthquakes. 2002. (Scholastic Science Readers Ser.). (Illus.). 48p. (J). (978-0-439-26992-6(X)) Scholastic, Inc.

Herman, Gail & Cole, Joanna. Earthquake. Gangloff, Hope, tr. Gangloff, Hope, illus. 2003. 90p. (J). (978-0-439-42938-2(2)) Scholastic, Inc.

Holt, Rinehart and Winston Staff. Holt Science & Technology Chapter 8: Earth Science: Earthquakes. 5th ed. 2004. (Illus.). pap. 12.86 (978-0-03-030301-2(X)) Holt, Rinehart & Winston.

—Holt Science & Technology Chptr. 12: Earthquakes: Chapter Resources - Tennessee Edition. 3rd ed. 2003. (YA). pap. 11.40 (978-0-03-069172-0(9)) Holt, Rinehart & Winston.

Hort, Leonard. Ring of Fire. 2003. (Science Links Ser.). (Illus.). 32p. (gr. 3-5). 23.00 (978-0-7910-7431-2(5) , Chelsea Hse.) Facts On File, Inc.

Hunter, Rebecca M. Volcanoes & Earthquakes. 2001. (Discovering Science Ser.). (Illus.). 32p. (J). (gr. 4-7). lib. bdg. 25.69 (978-0-7398-3249-3(2)) Raintree.

Jennings, Terry. Volcanoes & Earthquakes. 2002. (Restless Earth Ser.). (Illus.). 32p. (J). lib. bdg. 24.25 (978-1-931983-21-1(6)) Chrysalis Education.

Jerome, Kate Boehm. Volcanoes & Earthquakes. 2003. (National Geographic Reading Expeditions Ser.). (Illus.). 32p. (J). (978-0-7922-8874-9(2)) National Geographic Society.

Kerrod, Robin. Shaking Earth: Volcanoes, Earthquakes, Hurricanes Etc. 2005. (Illus.). 128p. pap. 17.99 (978-1-84476-097-8(9) , Southwater) Anness Publishing GBR. *Dist:* National Bk. Network.

Krohn, Katherine E. The Earth-Shaking Facts about Earthquakes with Max Axiom, Super Scientist. Smith, Tod, illus. 2008. (J). (*978-1-4296-1328-6(9)) Capstone Pr., Inc.

Lassieur, Allison. Earthquakes. 2000. (Natural Disasters Ser.). (Illus.). 48p. (J). (gr. 3-4). lib. bdg. 21.26 (978-0-7368-0586-5(9) , Capstone High-Interest Bks.) Capstone Pr., Inc.

Levithan, David. In the Heart of the Earthquake. 1998. (Disaster Zone Ser.: Vol. 2). (J). pap. 3.99 (978-0-590-12916-9(3) , Scholastic Paperbacks) Scholastic, Inc.

Los Terremotos, 6 vols., Vol. 3. (Explorers. Exploradores Nonfiction Sets Ser.). (SPA.). (gr. 3-6). (978-0-7699-0658-4(3)) Shortland Pubns. (U. S. A.) Inc.

Markle, Sandra. Amazing Earth: Earthquakes. Bosson, Jo-Ellen, illus. 2002. 48p. (J). (978-0-439-35614-5(8)) Scholastic, Inc.

Maslin, Mark. Earthquakes. 1999. (Restless Planet Ser.). (Illus.). 48p. (J). (gr. 4-6). lib. bdg. 27.12 (978-0-7398-1328-7(5)) Raintree.

McCay, William. After the Earthquake/Después del Terremoto: English/Spanish Pair, 12 texts, 2 titles, Vol. 2. ed. 2004. (Navigators Ser.). (J). pap., instr.'s gde. ed. 84.00 (978-1-4108-1776-1(8) , 17768) Benchmark Education Co.

McMorrow, Catherine. Quakes! Kilgras, Heidi, ed. Marchesi, Stephen, illus. 2000. (Step into Reading Step 4 Bks.). 48p. (J). (gr. 2-5). pap. 3.99 (978-0-679-86945-0(X) , Random Hse. Bks. for Young Readers) Random Hse. Children's Bks.

—Quakes! 2000. (gr. 3-6). lib. bdg. 11.80 (978-0-613-28352-6(X)) Tandem Library Bks.

—Quakes! Marchesi, Stephen, illus. 2000. (Step into Reading Ser.). (J). (978-0-606-19905-6(5)) Tandem Library Bks.

Mehta-Jones, Shilpa. Earthquake Alert! 2004. (Disaster Alert! Ser.). (Illus.). 32p. (J). pap. (978-0-7787-1604-4(X)); (978-0-7787-1572-6(8)) Crabtree Publishing Co.

Meister, Cari. Earthquakes. 1999. (Nature's Fury Ser.). (Illus.). 32p. (J). (gr. 3-8). lib. bdg. 24.21 (978-1-57765-083-6(2) , ABDO & Daughters) ABDO Publishing Co.

Morris, Neil. Earthquakes. 1999. (Natural Disasters Ser.). (Illus.). 31p. (J). (gr. 5 up). pap. 5.95 (978-0-7641-1059-7(4)) Barron's Educational Series, Inc.

—Earthquakes. 1998. (Wonders of Our World Ser.). (Illus.). 32p. (J). (gr. 3-4). lib. bdg. (978-0-86505-832-3(6)); pap. (978-0-86505-844-6(X)) Crabtree Publishing Co.

—Inside Earthquakes. 2006. (Inside Nature's Disasters Ser.). (Illus.). 36p. (J). lib. bdg. (978-0-8368-7247-7(9)) Stevens, Gareth Inc.

Murdico, Suzanne J. & Roza, Greg. Earthquakes: A Practical Survival Guide. 2005. (Library of Emergency Preparedness). (Illus.). 64p. (J). (978-1-4042-0531-4(4)) Rosen Publishing Group, Inc., The.

Nault, Jennifer. Earthquakes. 2004. (Science Matters Ser.). (Illus.). 24p. (J). lib. bdg. 24.45 (978-1-59036-212-9(8)) Weigl Pubs., Inc.

Nicolson, Cynthia Pratt. Earthquake. unabr. ed. 2002. (Disaster Ser.). (Illus.). 32p. (J). (gr. 4-6). (978-1-55074-968-7(4)); (978-1-55074-949-6(8)) Kids Can Pr., Ltd.

Nuttall, Gina. Volcanoes & Earthquakes. 2004. (QEB Start Writing Ser.). (Illus.). 24p. (J). lib. bdg. 15.95 (978-1-59566-018-3(6)) QEB Publishing Inc.

Olien, Rebecca. The Changing Earth. 2001. (Bridgestone Science Library). (Illus.). 24p. (J). (gr. 2-3). lib. bdg. 18.60 (978-0-7368-0949-8(X) , Bridgestone Bks.) Capstone Pr., Inc.

Oxlade, Chris. Earthquakes & Volcanoes. 2004. (Earth's Changing Landscape Ser.). (Illus.). 46p. (J). lib. bdg. 28.50 (978-1-58340-479-9(1)) Smart Apple Media.

Park, Louise. Earthquakes. 2007. (J). (*978-1-59920-111-5(9)) Smart Apple Media.

Parks, Peggy J. Predicting Earthquakes. 2006. (Kidhaven Science Library). (Illus.). 48p. (J). (gr. 4-8). 26.20 (978-0-7377-3602-1(X) , 1256754, Kidhaven) Thomson Gale.

Penny, Sam. Broken River: Book 2 of the 7. 9 Scenario. 2004. (Illus.). 238p. (YA). pap. 16.99 (978-0-9755671-1-1(X)) TwoPenny Pubns.

Ponzio, Richard, ed. Earthquake! Beyond Duck, Cover, & Hold. 2006. (Illus.). 115p. (J). (gr. 3-6). reprint ed. pap. 35.00 (978-1-4223-0756-4(5)) DIANE Publishing Co.

Prager, Ellen J. Earthquakes. Greenstein, Susan, illus. 2007. (Jump into Science Ser.). 32p. (J). (ps-3). 6.95 (978-1-4263-0090-5(5) , National Geographic Children's Bks.) National Geographic Society.

—Earthquakes. Prager, Ellen J. & Greenstein, Susan, illus. 2002. (Jump into Science Ser.). 32p. (J). (ps-3). 16.95 (978-0-7922-8202-0(7) , National Geographic Children's Bks.) National Geographic Society.

Putnam, James & Van Rose, Sussanna. Volcano & Earthquake. (Dk Eyewitness Books Ser.). (J). pap. 8.95 (978-0-7894-5781-3(4)) Dorling Kindersley Publishing, Inc.

QEB Start Reading & Writing National Book Stores Edition: Volcanoes & Earthquakes. 2006. (J). per. (978-1-59566-265-1(0)) QEB Publishing Inc.

Rae, Alison. Earthquakes & Volcanoes. 2005. (Looking at Landscapes Ser.). (Illus.). 47p. (J). (gr. 6-9). lib. bdg. 29.95 (978-1-58340-729-5(4)) Smart Apple Media.

Reed, Jennifer. Earthquakes: Disaster & Survival. 2005. (Deadly Disasters Ser.). (Illus.). 48p. (J). lib. bdg. 23.93 (978-0-7660-2381-9(8)) Enslow Pubs., Inc.

Richards, Julie. Quivering Quakes. 2001. (Natural Disasters Ser.). (Illus.). 32p. (J). (gr. 5 up). 28.00 (978-0-7910-6582-2(0) , 010453, Chelsea Hse.) Facts On File, Inc.

Riley, Joelle. Earthquakes. 2008. (Pull Ahead Books-Forces of Nature Ser.). (J). lib. bdg. 22.60 (*978-0-8225-7905-2(7) , Lerner Pubns.) Lerner Publishing Group.

Rogers, Daniel. Earthquakes. 1999. (Geography Starts Here Ser.). (Illus.). 32p. (J). lib. bdg. 25.69 (978-0-8172-5546-6(X)) Raintree.

Rooney, Anne. Earthquake! 2007. (Illus.). 32p. (J). (978-1-84193-565-2(4)) Arcturus Pubs., Inc.

Roza, Greg. The Indian Ocean Tsunami. 2006. (Nature in the News Ser.). (Illus.). 32p. (J). lib. bdg. (978-1-4042-3538-0(8) , PowerKids Pr.) Rosen Publishing Group, Inc., The.

Rubin, Ken. Volcanoes & Earthquakes. 2007. (Insiders Ser.). 64p. (J). (gr. 3-7). 16.99 (*978-1-4169-3862-0(1)) Simon & Schuster Children's Publishing.

Sengupta, Monalisa. Volcanoes & Earthquakes. 2008. (J). lib. bdg. (*978-1-4042-3901-2(4) , PowerKids Pr.) Rosen Publishing Group, Inc., The.

Sherrow, Victoria. San Francisco Earthquake, 1989: Death & Destruction. 1998. (American Disasters Ser.). (Illus.). 48p. (YA). (gr. 4-10). lib. bdg. 23.93 (978-0-7660-1060-4(0)) Enslow Pubs., Inc.

Sillet, Helen. The Awesome Power of Volcanoes & Earthquakes. 2005. (YA). pap. 12.95 (978-1-4105-0421-0(2)); cd-rom (978-1-4105-0423-4(9)) Johnston, Don Inc.

—Understanding Volcanoes & Earthquakes. 2005. (YA). pap. 12.95 (978-1-4105-0417-3(4)); cd-rom (978-1-4105-0419-7(0)) Johnston, Don Inc.

Silverstein, Alvin, et al. Plate Tectonics. 1998. (Science Concepts Ser.. 8). (Illus.). 64p. (gr. 5-8). lib. bdg. 26.90 (978-0-7613-3225-1(1) , Twenty-First Century Bks.) Lerner Publishing Group.

Simon, Seymour. Danger! Earthquake. 2002. (See More Readers Ser.). (Illus.). 32p. (J). (gr. k-4). 13.95 (978-1-58717-139-0(2)); Vol. 2. pap. 3.95 (978-1-58717-140-6(6)) Chronicle Bks. LLC. (SeaStar Bks.).

—Danger! Earthquake. 2002. (gr. 3-6). lib. bdg. 11.80 (978-0-613-58408-1(2)) Tandem Library Bks.

—Earthquakes. 2006. 32p. (J). 16.99 (978-0-06-087714-9(6)); (Illus.). pap. 6.99 (978-0-06-087715-6(4)) HarperCollins Pubs.

Sipiera, Paul P. Earthquakes. 1998. (True Bks.). (Illus.). 48p. (J). (gr. 3-5). 25.00 (978-0-516-20665-3(6) , Children's Pr.) Scholastic Library Publishing.

Sipiera, Paul P. & Sipiera, Diane M. Earthquakes. 1999. (True Bks.). (Illus.). 48p. (J). (gr. 3-5). pap. 6.95 (978-0-516-26432-5(X) , Children's Pr.) Scholastic Library Publishing.

Spilsbury, Louise & Spilsbury, Richard. Shattering Earthquakes. 2004. (Heinemann Infosearch Ser.). (Illus.). 32p. (J). pap. 7.50 (978-1-4034-5446-1(9)); lib. bdg. (978-1-4034-4784-5(5)) Heinemann Library.

Stewart, Melissa. Earthquakes & Volcanoes. 2008. 80p. (J). 16.99 (*978-0-06-089951-6(4)); pap. 7.99 (*978-0-06-089950-9(6)) HarperCollins Pubs.

Tanaka, Shelley. Earthquake! A Day That Changed America. Craig, David, illus. 2006. 48p. (J). (gr. 4-8). reprint ed. 17.00 (978-1-4223-5635-7(3)) DIANE Publishing Co.

Thompson, Luke. Earthquakes. 2000. (High Interest Bks.). (Illus.). 48p. (YA). (gr. 7-12). pap. 6.95 (978-0-516-23566-0(4) , Children's Pr.) Scholastic Library Publishing.

—Earthquakes. 2000. (gr. 3-6). lib. bdg. 15.25 (978-0-613-89018-2(3)) Tandem Library Bks.

Thoron, Joe. Earthquakes. 2006. (Kaleidoscope Natural Disasters Ser.). (Illus.). 48p. (J). lib. bdg. 28.50 (978-0-7614-2102-3(5) , Benchmark Bks.) Cavendish, Marshall Corp.

Time for Kids Editors. Almanac 2007. 2006. (Time for Kids Ser.). 360p. 24.95 (978-1-933405-08-7(2)); (Illus.). (J). pap. 12.99 (978-1-933405-33-9(3)) Time, Inc. Home Entertainment.

—Earthquakes! 2006. (Time for Kids Science Scoops Ser.). (Illus.). 32p. (J). 14.99 (978-0-06-078212-2(9)); pap. 3.99 (978-0-06-078211-5(0)) HarperCollins Pubs.

Townsend, John. Earthquakes & Volcanoes: A Survival Guide. 2005. (Illus.). 32p. (J). (978-1-4109-1927-4(7)) Steck-Vaughn.

—Earthquakes & Volcanoes: A Survival Guide; Earth's Physical Processes. 2005. (Illus.). 32p. (J). (gr. 6-9). 7.85 (978-1-4109-1958-8(7)) Steck-Vaughn.

Trueit, Trudi Strain. Earthquakes. 2003. (Watts Library). (Illus.). 64p. (J). (gr. 5-7). pap. 8.95 (978-0-531-16243-9(5)); 25.50 (978-0-531-12197-9(6)) Scholastic Library Publishing. (Watts, Franklin).

—Earthquakes. 2003. (gr. 5-8). lib. bdg. 17.60 (978-0-613-67614-4(9)) Tandem Library Bks.

Trumbauer, Lisa. Earthquake! 2005. 39.00 (***978-1-4108-4593-1(1)***) Benchmark Education Co.

Tubbs, Janet. Earthquakes. 2000. (Spud Packs Ser.). 16p. (J). pap. 19.95 (978-1-881185-16-1(8)) Arcadia Pr.

van Rose, Susanna. Volcano & Earthquake. 2008. (DK Eyewitness Bks.). 72p. (J). (gr. 3-8). 15.99 (***978-0-7566-3780-4(5)***) Dorling Kindersley Publishing, Inc.

Van Rose, Susanna & Dorling Kindersley Publishing Staff. Volcanoes & Earthquakes. Stevenson, James, illus. 2004. (Eyewitness Books). 72p. (J). lib. bdg. 19.99 (978-0-7566-0734-0(5)) Dorling Kindersley Publishing, Inc.

Walker, Jane. Earthquakes. 2004. (Natural Disasters Ser.). (J). lib. bdg. 27.10 (978-1-932799-07-1(9)) Stargazer Bks.

Walker, Sally M. Earthquakes. 2007. (Early Bird Earth Science Ser.). (J). 26.60 (978-0-8225-6735-6(0) , Lerner Pubns.) Lerner Publishing Group.

Watt, Fiona. Earthquakes & Volcanoes. rev. ed. 2007. (Geography Ser.). 32p. (J). pap. 7.99 (***978-0-7945-1531-7(2)*** , Usborne) EDC Publishing.

Weil, Ann. Earthquakes. 2003. (Illus.). 64p. (YA). per. 3.95 (978-1-56254-652-6(X) , SP652X) Saddleback Educational Publishing.

Woods, Michael & Woods, Mary B. Earthquakes. 2007. (Disasters up Close Ser.). (Illus.). 64p. (J). 27.93 (978-0-8225-4711-2(2) , Lerner Pubns.) Lerner Publishing Group.

World Book, Inc Staff, contrib. by. Earthquakes. 2007. (J). (***978-0-7166-9804-3(8)***) World Bk., Inc.

Worth, Richard. The San Francisco Earthquake. 2005. (Environmental Disasters Ser.). (Illus.). 112p. (J). (gr. 6-12). 35.00 (978-0-8160-5756-6(7)) Facts On File, Inc.

EARTHQUAKES—FICTION

Baum, L. Frank. Dorothy & the Wizard in Oz. 2006. pap. 26.99 (***978-1-4219-7695-2(1)***) IndyPublish.com.

Carman, Patrick. Atherton: The House of Power. 2007. (Illus.). 330p. (J). (***978-1-4287-4140-9(2)***) Little Brown & Co.

Cook, Sherry & Johnson, Terri. Quincy Quake, 26. Kuhn, Jesse, illus. l.t. ed. 2006. (Quirkles—Exploring Phonics through Science Ser.: 17). 32p. (J). 7.99 (978-1-933815-16-9(7) , Quirkles, The) Creative 3, LLC.

Crofford, Emily. When the River Ran Backward. (Adventures in Time Ser.). (gr. 4-8). 2005. (Illus.). 84p. 15.95 (978-1-57505-305-9(5)); 2003. 80p. (J). pap. 6.95 (978-1-57505-488-9(4)) Lerner Publishing Group.

Dell, Pamela. A Song for Sung Li: A Story of the 1906 San Francisco Earthquake. 2002. (Scrapbooks of America Ser.). (Illus.). 48p. (J). (gr. 2-6). 28.50 (978-1-59187-015-9(1)) Child's World, Inc.

Duey, K. & Bale, K. A. Salvados! Terremoto. 2003. (Survival Ser.).Tr. of Survival! Earthquake. (SPA.). (J). pap. 9.95 (978-0-9715256-5-8(X)) Planeta Publishing Corp.

Duey, Kathleen. San Francisco Earthquake, 1906. 1999. (978-0-606-17951-5(8)) Tandem Library Bks.

Earthquake! 1999. (SmartReader Ser.). (J). Level 1. pap., tchr. ed. 19.95 incl. audio (978-0-7887-0766-7(3) , 79351T3); Level 2. pap., tchr. ed. 19.95 incl. audio (978-0-7887-0114-6(2) , 79302T3) Recorded Bks., LLC.

Gregory, Kristiana. Earthquake at Dawn. 2003. (gr. 5-8). lib. bdg. 14.10 (978-0-613-64493-8(X)) Tandem Library Bks.

Gregory, Kristiana & Campbell, Mary Exa Atkins. Earthquake at Dawn. 2003. (Great Episodes Ser.). (Illus.). 224p. (J). pap. 5.95 (978-0-15-204681-1(X)) Harcourt Children's Bks.

Harcourt School Publishers Staff. The Autumn of the Earthquake Below Level. 3rd ed. 2002. (Trophies Reading Program Ser.). (Illus.). pap. 5.10 (978-0-15-323407-1(5)) Harcourt Schl. Pubs.

—Earthquake! 3rd ed. 2002. (Horizons Ser.). (Illus.). (J). pap. 5.50 (978-0-15-333390-3(1)) Harcourt Schl. Pubs.

—Earthquake Terror: Reader's Choice Book. 2001. (Collections Ser.). (Illus.). pap. 12.10 (978-0-15-314393-9(2)) Harcourt Schl. Pubs.

—The Golden Atlas On Level. 3rd ed. 2002. (Trophies Reading Program Ser.). (Illus.). pap. 5.10 (978-0-15-323456-9(3)) Harcourt Schl. Pubs.

—Hazanas para Gigantes Below Level. 3rd ed. 2002. (Trofeos Ser.). (SPA., Illus.). pap. 6.80 (978-0-15-324159-8(4)) Harcourt Schl. Pubs.

—October 17: Take-Home Book. 2001. (Collections Ser.). (Illus.). (J). pap. 1.90 (978-0-15-319549-5(5)) Harcourt Schl. Pubs.

—The Perfect Ending On Level. 3rd ed. 2002. (Trophies Reading Program Ser.). (Illus.). pap. 5.10 (978-0-15-323188-9(2)) Harcourt Schl. Pubs.

—Tall Tales, Big Numbers: Take-Home Book. 2001. (Collections Ser.). (Illus.). (J). pap. 1.90 (978-0-15-319509-9(6)) Harcourt Schl. Pubs.

—Tall Tales, Big Numbers Below Level. 3rd ed. 2002. (Trophies Reading Program Ser.). (Illus.). pap. 5.10 (978-0-15-323248-0(X)) Harcourt Schl. Pubs.

Herbert, James. The Fog. 2003. (Illus.). vi, 345p. (J). pap. 13.99 (978-0-330-37615-0(2) , Pan) Pan Macmillan GBR. *Dist:* Trafalgar Square Publishing.

Herzog, Arthur. Earthsound. 2003. 192p. pap. 13.95 (978-0-595-27073-6(5) , Authors Choice Pr.) iUniverse, Inc.

Hinman, Bonnie. Earthquake in Cincinnati: Disaster Changes Life Forever, 1999. (American Adventure Ser.: No. 14). 144p. (J). (gr. 3-7). lib. bdg. 15.95 (978-0-7910-5589-2(2) , Chelsea Hse.) Facts On File, Inc.

—San Francisco Earthquake. 32nd ed. 1998. (American Adventure Ser.: No. 32). (Illus.). (J). (gr. 3-7). pap. 3.97 (978-1-57748-393-9(6)) Barbour Publishing, Inc.

Holt, Rinehart and Winston Staff. Earthquake at Dawn. 2nd ed. 2002. (J). 4.80 (978-0-03-073523-3(8)) Holt, Rinehart & Winston.

Hopkinson, Deborah. Into the Firestorm: A Novel of San Francisco, 1906. 2006. 208p. (J). (gr. 3-7). 15.95 (978-0-375-83652-7(7)); lib. bdg. 17.99 (978-0-375-93652-4(1)) Random Hse. Children's Bks. (Knopf Bks. for Young Readers).

Hopkinson, Deborah. Into the Firestorm: A Novel of San Francisco 1906. 2008. 208p. (J). (gr. 4-7). 5.99 (***978-0-440-42129-0(2)*** , Yearling) Random Hse. Children's Bks.

Kehret, Peg. Earthquake Terror. 1998. (Puffin Novel Ser.). 144p. (J). (gr. 3-7). pap. 5.99 (978-0-14-038343-0(3) , Puffin) Penguin Group (USA) Inc.

—Earthquake Terror. 1998. (Puffin Novel Ser.). (J). 11.64 (978-0-606-13073-8(X)) Tandem Library Bks.

—Escaping the Giant Wave. (Illus.). 160p. (J). 2004. pap. 5.99 (978-0-689-85273-2(8) , Aladdin); 2003. 16.99 (978-0-689-85272-5(X)) Simon & Schuster Children's Publishing.

—Escaping the Giant Wave. l.t. ed. 2003. 152p. (J). 21.95 (978-0-7862-5985-4(X)) Thorndike Pr.

King, Susan. Amy & the Real April Fool; Amy & the Easter Basket. King, Susan, illus. 2002. (Illus.). 81p. (J). (ps-6). 7.00 (978-0-9714446-3-8(3)) King RIT - ACKS Pubs.

Klaassen, Mike. Cracks. 2006. 142p. (YA). pap. 14.99 (978-1-59092-171-5(2) , Blue Works) Windstorm Creative.

Lavender, William. Aftershocks. 2006. (Illus.). 352p. (YA). 17.00 (978-0-15-205882-1(6)) Harcourt Children's Bks.

Lazewnik, Libby. Forever & a Day. 2002. 300p. 18.95 (978-1-56871-265-9(0)) Targum Pr., Inc.

Lee, Milly. Earthquake. Choi, Yangsook, illus. 2006. 32p. (J). reprint ed. pap. 6.95 (978-0-374-41946-2(9)) Macmillan.

Levithan, David. In the Heart of the Quake, 2. 1998. (Disaster Zone Ser.). (978-0-606-13335-7(6)) Tandem Library Bks.

Lowell, Susan. I Am Lavina Cumming. 2005. (Historical Fiction for Young Readers Ser.). (Illus.). 200p. (J). pap. 6.95 (978-1-57131-655-4(8)) Milkweed Editions.

MacDonald, George. A Rough Shaking. 2006. 66.99 (***978-1-4280-3048-0(4)***) IndyPublish.com.

Mein eigenes Auto. 2005. (GER.). 4.95 net. (978-0-929724-89-8(5)) Command Performance Language Institute.

Moonshower, Candie. The Legend of Zoey. 224p. (J). (gr. 4-7). 2007. 5.99 (***978-0-440-23924-6(9)*** , Yearling); 2006. 15.95 (978-0-385-73280-2(5) , Delacorte Bks. for Young Readers); 2006. lib. bdg. 17.99 (978-0-385-90298-4(0) , Delacorte Bks. for Young Readers) Random Hse. Children's Bks.

Mother Earth Quake's. 2004. (Illus.). 33p. (J). per. 11.95 (978-0-9716721-0-9(5) , 2000) Marker, Margaret Penfield.

Osborne, Mary Pope. Earthquake in the Early Morning, Vol. 24. unabr. ed. 2004. (Magic Tree House Ser. : No. 24). 71p. (J). (gr. k-3). pap. 17.00 incl. audio (978-0-8072-0933-2(3) , S FTR 256 SP, Listening Library) Random Hse. Audio Publishing Group.

—Earthquake in the Early Morning. Murdocca, Sal, illus. 2001. (Magic Tree House Ser.: No. 24). 96p. (J). (gr. k-3). 11.99 (978-0-679-99070-3(4)); mass mkt. 3.99 (978-0-679-89070-6(X)) Random Hse. Children's Bks. (Random Hse. Bks. for Young Readers).

—Earthquake in the Early Morning. 2001. (Magic Tree House Ser. : No. 24). (J). (gr. k-3). lib. bdg. 11.80 (978-0-613-35684-8(5)); (Illus.). 10.79 (978-0-606-21166-6(7)) Tandem Library Bks.

Osorio, Rick. The Great Adventure of Sally Rock & the Cretaceous Chicken. 2006. 65p. pap. 12.95 (978-1-4241-0971-5(X)) PublishAmerica, Inc.

Reiss, Kathryn. PaperQuake: A Puzzle. 2002. 288p. (YA). pap. 6.00 (978-0-15-216782-0(X) , Harcourt Paperbacks) Harcourt Children's Bks.

—Paperquake: A Puzzle. 2002. (gr. 5-8). lib. bdg. 14.15 (978-0-613-53851-0(X)) Tandem Library Bks.

Richter, Danny. The Big Gozonga. 2006. 16.95 (978-0-9786107-0-8(9)) Arbor Bks.

Rucker, Mike. Terry & the Earthquake. 2006. (Terry the Tractor Ser.: Vol. 14). 72p. (J). (gr. k-4). pap. 4.95 (978-0-9711659-5-3(5)) Univ. Editions.

Salisbury, Graham. Night of the Howling Dogs. 2007. 208p. (J). (gr. 3-7). 16.99 (***978-0-385-73122-5(1)***); lib. bdg. 19.99 (***978-0-385-90146-8(1)***) Random Hse. Children's Bks. (Lamb, Wendy).

San Francisco Shake-Up, 6 Packs. (Greetings Ser.: Vol. 3). (gr. 3-5). 31.00 (978-0-7635-2075-5(6)) Rigby Education.

Sanders, Evelin. Janine. 1999. 221p. (YA). (gr. 7-17). pap. 9.99 (978-0-88092-444-3(6)) Royal Fireworks Publishing Co.

Sargent, Dave & Sargent, Pat. Hank: (Black Sabino) Be Responsible, 25, 33. Lenoir, Jane, illus. 2001. (Saddle Up Ser.). 36p. (J). pap. 6.95 (978-1-56763-656-7(X)); lib. bdg. 22.60 (978-1-56763-655-0(1)) Ozark Publishing.

Torres, J. Birthquake. 2003. (Jason & the Argobots Ser.: Vol. 1). (Illus.). 112p. pap. 11.95 (978-1-929998-55-5(4)) Oni Pr., Inc.

Veldkamp, Debby. Quake! Six Point Five: The Cat Survived. Van Den Berg, Helen, illus. 2004. (J). lib. bdg. 16.95 (978-1-930401-25-9(6)) Central Coast Pr.

Williams, Carol Lynch. Victoria's Courage. 1998. (Latter-Day Daughters Ser.). (J). 5.95 (978-1-57345-434-6(6)) Deseret Bk. Co.

Yep, Laurence. The Earth Dragon Awakes: The San Francisco Earthquake Of 1906. 2006. (Illus.). 128p. (J). (gr. 3-7). 14.99 (978-0-06-027524-2(3)); lib. bdg. 15.89 (978-0-06-027525-9(1)) HarperCollins Pubs.

Yep, Laurence. The Earth Dragon Awakes: The San Francisco Earthquake Of 1906. 2008. 128p. (J). pap. 5.99 (***978-0-06-000846-8(6)*** , Harper Trophy) HarperCollins Pubs.

EARTHWORKS (ARCHEOLOGY)

see Excavations (Archaeology)

EARTHWORMS

Appelhof, Mary, et al. Worms Eat Our Garbage: Classroom Activities for a Better Environment. Fenton, Mary Frances & Kostecke, Nancy, illus. 2004. 232p. (Orig.). (gr. 4 up). pap., stu. ed. 22.95 (978-0-942256-05-5(0)) Flowerfield Enterprises.

Barraclough, Sue. Earthworms. 2005. (Raintree Sprouts Ser.). (Illus.). 24p. (J). (ps-ps). lib. bdg. 21.36 (978-1-4109-1506-1(9)); pap. (978-1-4109-1511-5(5)) Steck-Vaughn.

Costain, Meredith. How to Make an Earthworm Farm. 2000. (gr. k-3). lib. bdg. 11.80 (978-0-613-30481-8(0)) Tandem Library Bks.

Dell'Oro, Suzanne Paul. Tunneling Earthworms. (Pull Ahead Bks.). (Illus.). 32p. (J). (gr. k-2). 2003. pap. 5.95 (978-0-8225-3768-7(0)); 2000. lib. bdg. 22.60 (978-0-8225-3762-5(1) , Lerner Pubns.) Lerner Publishing Group.

—Tunneling Earthworms. 2001. (gr. k-3). lib. bdg. 14.10 (978-0-613-58880-5(0)) Tandem Library Bks.

Dixon, Norma. Low-Down on Earthworms. Holdcroft, Tina, illus. 2002. 32p. (J). (gr. 2-7). pap. (978-0-7737-6270-1(1)) Stoddart Kids.

—The Lowdown on Earthworms. 2004. (Illus.). 32p. (J). (gr. 2-5). (978-1-55005-114-8(8)) Fitzhenry & Whiteside, Ltd.

—The Lowdown on Earthworms. 2006. (Illus.). 32p. (J). pap. 9.95 (978-1-55005-119-3(9)) Fitzhenry & Whiteside, Ltd. CAN. *Dist:* F & W Pubns., Inc.

Earthworm. 2001. (Zoology Ser.). (J). (gr. k-12). vinyl bd. 4.95 (978-1-58845-153-8(4)) School Specialty Publishing.

Earthworms, 6 vols. (gr. 2-5). 36.95 (978-0-7368-8175-3(1)) Red Brick Learning.

Earthworms: Individual Title Six-Packs. (Rigby Focus Ser.). 24p. (gr. 2 up). 30.00 (978-0-7578-5567-2(9)); 28.00 (978-0-7578-5337-1(4)) Rigby Education.

Earthworms & their Food: 6 Each of 1 Student Book, 6 vols. (Sunshinetm Science Ser.). 24p. (gr. 1-2). 41.95 (978-0-7802-2708-8(5)) Wright Group, The.

Earthworms & their Food: Big Book. (Sunshinetm Science Ser.). 24p. (gr. 1-2). 37.50 (978-0-7802-2788-0(3)) Wright Group, The.

Earthworms Sets: 1 Each of 3 Big Books. (Sunshinetm Science Ser.). (gr. 1-2). 111.50 (978-0-7802-2812-2(X)) Wright Group, The.

Earthworms Sets: 1 Each of 3 Student Books. (Sunshinetm Science Ser.). (gr. 1-2). 20.95 (978-0-7802-2813-9(8)) Wright Group, The.

Greenaway, Theresa. Worms. 1999. (Minipets Ser.). (Illus.). 32p. (gr. 1-5). pap. 7.95 (978-0-8172-4208-4(2)) Steck-Vaughn.

Group/McGraw-Hill, Wright. Earthworms: Level E, 6 vols. (Take Twostm Ser.). 16p. 29.95 (978-0-322-08959-4(X)) Wright Group, The.

Heinrichs, Ann. Worms. 2004. (Illus.). 32p. (J). (gr. 2 up). lib. bdg. 21.26 (978-0-7565-0589-9(5)) Compass Point Bks.

Himmelman, John. An Earthworm's Life. Himmelman, John, illus. (Nature Upclose Ser.). (Illus.). 32p. (J). (gr. k-2). 2001. pap. 6.95 (978-0-516-26535-3(0)); 2000. 25.00 (978-0-516-21164-0(1)) Scholastic Library Publishing. (Children's Pr.).

—An Earthworm's Life. 2000. (gr. k-3). lib. bdg. 15.25 (978-0-613-54185-5(5)) Tandem Library Bks.

Hipp, Andrew. The Life Cycle of an Earthworm. 2002. (Life Cycles Library). (Illus.). 24p. (J). lib. bdg. 18.75 (978-0-8239-5870-2(1) , PowerKids Pr.) Rosen Publishing Group, Inc., The.

Hovanec, Erin M. I Wonder What It's Like to Be an Earthworm. 2000. (Life Science Wonder Bks.). (Illus.). 24p. (J). (gr. k-4). lib. bdg. 18.75 (978-0-8239-5454-4(4) , PowerKids Pr.) Rosen Publishing Group, Inc., The.

How Earthworms Grow: 6 Each of 1 Student Book, 6 vols. (Sunshinetm Science Ser.). 24p. (gr. 1-2). 41.95 (978-0-7802-2706-4(9)) Wright Group, The.

How Earthworms Grow: Big Book. (Sunshinetm Science Ser.). 24p. (gr. 1-2). 37.50 (978-0-7802-2787-3(5)) Wright Group, The.

How Earthworms Life: 6 Each of 1 Student Book, 6 vols. (Sunshinetm Science Ser.). 24p. (gr. 1-2). 41.95 (978-0-7802-2710-1(7)) Wright Group, The.

How Earthworms Life: Big Book. (Sunshinetm Science Ser.). 24p. (gr. 1-2). 37.50 (978-0-7802-2789-7(1)) Wright Group, The.

Jacobs, Lee. Earthworm. 2003. (Wild America Ser.). (Illus.). 24p. (J). 22.45 (978-1-56711-568-0(3) , Blackbirch Pr., Inc.) Thomson Gale.

Kalman, Bobbie. El Ciclo de vida de la Lombriz de Tierra. 2006. (SPA., Illus.). 32p. (gr. 2-3). pap. (978-0-7787-8716-7(8)) Crabtree Publishing Co.

—The Lifecycle of an Earthworm. 2003. (Life Cycle Ser.). (Illus.). 32p. (J). (978-0-7787-0666-3(4)); pap. (978-0-7787-0696-0(6)) Crabtree Publishing Co.

Lackner, Michelle Myers & Powers, Daniel. Toil in the Soil. 2001. (All about Animals Ser.). (Illus.). 32p. (gr. k-3). lib. bdg. 22.90 (978-0-7613-1807-1(0) , Millbrook Pr.) Lerner Publishing Group.

Llewellyn, Claire. Earthworms. 2000. (gr. k-3). lib. bdg. 12.95 (978-0-613-54184-8(7)) Tandem Library Bks.

Loewen, Nancy. Garden Wigglers: Earthworms in Your Backyard. Peterson, Rick, illus. 2005. 24p. (J). (ps-ps). lib. bdg. 22.60 (978-1-4048-1144-7(3)) Picture Window Bks.

Pfeffer, Wendy. Wiggling Worms at Work. Jenkins, Steve, illus. 2004. (Let's-Read-and-Find-Out Science Ser.). 40p. (J). (gr. k-4). 15.99 (978-0-06-028448-0(X)); pap. 5.99 (978-0-06-445199-4(2)); lib. bdg. 16.89 (978-0-06-028449-7(8)) HarperCollins Pubs.

Rau, Dana Meachen. ¡Serpentea Lombriz, Serpentea! 2007. (¡Vamos Criaturita, Vamos! Ser.). (SPA.). 24p. (J). lib. bdg. 22.79 (***978-0-7614-2791-9(0)*** , Benchmark Bks.) Cavendish, Marshall Corp.

—Squirm, Earthworm, Squirm! 2007. (Go, Critter, Go! Ser.). (Illus.). 23p. (J). (ps-3). lib. bdg. 22.79 (***978-0-7614-2650-9(7)*** , Benchmark Bks.) Cavendish, Marshall Corp.

—Squirm, Earthworm, Squirm!/¡Serpentea Lombriz, Serpentea! 2007. (Go, Critter, Go!/¡Vamos Criaturita, Vamos! Ser.). (SPA & ENG.). 24p. (J). lib. bdg. 22.79 (***978-0-7614-2815-2(1)*** , Benchmark Bks.) Cavendish, Marshall Corp.

Schaefer, Lola M. Earthworms. 2002. (Ooey-Gooey Animals Ser.). (Illus.). 24p. (J). (ps-1). pap. 5.25 (978-1-58810-713-8(2) , 91366); lib. bdg. (978-1-58810-504-2(0)) Heinemann Library.

—Earthworms: Underground Burrowers. 2001. (Wild World of Animals Ser.). (Illus.). 24p. (J). (gr. 1-2). lib. bdg. 18.60 (978-0-7368-0826-2(4) , Bridgestone Bks.) Capstone Pr., Inc.

Watts, Barrie. Earthworms. (Illus.). 32p. (YA). (gr. 2 up). lib. bdg. 27.10 (978-1-932889-20-8(5)) Sea-To-Sea Pubns.

EAST (FAR EAST)

see East Asia

EAST AFRICA

see Africa, East

EAST AND WEST

Here are entered works on both acculturation and cultural conflict between Oriental and Western civilizations.

Harvey, Miles. Look What Came from Japan. 1999. (J). (978-0-606-20146-9(7)) Tandem Library Bks.

EAST ASIA

Here are entered works dealing collectively with China, Japan, Korea, Taiwan, and Macao.

Ashcroft, Minnie. East Asia. 2003. (National Geographic Reading Expeditions Ser.). (Illus.). 64p. (J). (978-0-7922-4376-2(5)); (978-0-7922-4377-9(3)) National Geographic Society.

Courtot, Marilyn, ed. Far Eastern Cultures: East of the Urals. 1998. (Illus.). 48p. (Orig.). (J). pap. 14.99 (978-1-890920-09-8(6)) Children's Literature.

Kort, Michael. The Handbook of East Asia. 2006. (Single Titles Ser.). (Illus.). 272p. (J). (gr. 7-17). 39.93 (978-0-7613-2672-4(3) , Twenty-First Century Bks.) Lerner Publishing Group.

Morris, Neil. North & East Asia. 2007. (J). (***978-1-4034-9898-4(9)***); pap. (***978-1-4034-9907-3(1)***) Heinemann Library.

Phillips, Douglas A. East Asia. 2005. (Modern World Cultures Ser.). (Illus.). 136p. (J). (gr. 6-12). 30.00 (978-0-7910-8148-8(6) , Chelsea Hse.) Facts On File, Inc.

EAST INDIANS

Thomson, Ruth. India. 2006. (Living In- Ser.). (Illus.). 32p. (J). (978-1-59771-046-6(6)) Sea-To-Sea Pubns.

EAST INDIANS—UNITED STATES

Aalgaard, Wendy. East Indians in America. 2005. (In America Ser.). (Illus.). 72p. (J). (ps-7). 27.93 (978-0-8225-4871-3(2) , Lerner Pubns.) Lerner Publishing Group.

Doak, Robin S. Indian Americans. 2008. (J). (***978-1-60044-612-2(4)***) Rourke Publishing, LLC.

McDaniel, Jan. Indian Immigration. 2004. (Changing Face of North America Ser.). (Illus.). 112p. (YA). lib. bdg. (978-1-59084-683-4(4)) Mason Crest Pubs.

Yoder, Carolyn. Asian American Indians. 2003. (We Are America Ser.). (Illus.). 32p. (J). (gr. 2-4). lib. bdg. 24.22 (978-1-4034-0167-0(5)) Heinemann Library.

—Asian Indian Americans. 2002. (We Are America Ser.). (Illus.). 32p. (J). pap. 6.95 (978-1-4034-0422-0(4)) Heinemann Library.

—Asian Indian Americans. 2003. (gr. k-3). lib. bdg. 15.25 (978-0-613-60849-7(6)) Tandem Library Bks.

EASTER

Adams, Michelle Medlock. What Is Easter? Wummer, Amy, illus. 26p. (J). 2007. bds. 12.99 (***978-0-8249-6691-1(0)***); 2006. bds. 6.95 (978-0-8249-6639-3(2) , Candy Cane Pr.) Ideals Pubns.

Anders, Isabel. Easter ABCs. Rasche, Shelly, illus. 2004. (ENG.). 32p. (J). tchr. ed. 7.99 (978-0-570-07020-7(1) , 56-2040) Concordia Publishing Hse.

Arbelbide, C. L. The White House Easter Egg Roll. Gibson, Barbara Leonard, illus. 2005. 29p. (J). (gr. k-4). reprint ed. 17.00 (978-0-7567-4772-5(4)) DIANE Publishing Co.

Barnett, Michelle Noble, et al. Theme Pockets - April: Easter; Animals That Lay Eggs; Celebrate Earth Day. Evans, Marilyn, ed. Larsen, Jo, illus. 1999. (Making Books with Pockets). 96p. (J). pap., tchr. ed. 12.99 (978-1-55799-701-2(2) , EMC 587) Evan-Moor Educational Pubs.

Barsness, Todd. God's Easter Promise. Hehenberger, Shelly, illus. 2006. (ENG.). 32p. (J). 9.99 (978-0-7586-0817-8(9)) Concordia Publishing Hse.

Barth, Edna. Lilies, Rabbits, & Painted Eggs: The Story of the Easter Symbols. Arndt, Ursula, illus. 2001. 64p. (YA). (gr. 4-6). pap. 7.95 (978-0-618-09648-0(5) , Clarion Bks.) Houghton Mifflin Co. Trade & Reference Div.

—Lilies, Rabbits, & Painted Eggs: The Story of the Easter Symbols. 2001. (Illus.). (J). (978-0-606-21297-7(3)) Tandem Library Bks.

—Lilies, Rabbits & Painted Eggs: The Story of the Easter Symbols. Arndt, Ursula, illus. 2001. 63p. (J). (ps-6). lib. bdg. 16.40 (978-0-613-35532-2(6)) Tandem Library Bks.

Beveridge, Amy. Let's Celebrate Jesus on Easter. 2006. 24p. (J). bds. 6.99 (978-0-7847-1506-2(8) , 04385) Standard Publishing.

Bickico Enterprises, concept. BabyKids: Easter Book. 2005. 16p. (J). pap. 2.95 (978-0-9746508-8-3(9)) Bickico Enterprises, Inc.

Blue Lantern Studio Staff, compiled by. The Truth about Easter Rabbits. 2005. (Illus.). 36p. (J). (ps-3). pap. 17.95 (978-1-59583-011-1(1) , Green Tiger Pr.) Laughing Elephant.

Bohlmann, Katherine. Grandma, What Is Prayer? 2003. 32p. (J). 14.99 (978-0-7586-0043-1(7)) Concordia Publishing Hse.

Bostrom, Kathleen Long. Easter, Easter Almost Here! Larranaga, Ana Martin, illus. 2005. 24p. (J). bds. 6.99 (978-0-310-70800-1(1)) Zonderkidz.

Brighter Child Publishing Staff. The Story of Easter. 1999. (J). cd-rom (978-5-550-17737-2(4)) Nairi.

Brighter Vision Publishing Staff. Easter Bunny. 2000. (Illus.). (J). (ps-3). pap., act. bk. ed. 1.59 (978-1-55254-076-3(6)) Brighter Vision Pubns.

Broslavick, Chris & Pichler, Tony. Totally Lent! A Teen's Journey to Easter 2004. Cannizzo, Karen, ed. Jones, Doug, illus. 2003. 64p. (J). 5.95 (978-0-89837-233-5(X) , 3564) Pflaum Publishing Group.

—Totally Lent: A Teen's Journey to Easter 2006. Cannizzo, Karen A., ed. 2005. (Illus.). 64p. (J). 5.95 (978-1-933178-24-0(8) , 3566) Pflaum Publishing Group.

Brown, Marc. Arthur's Easter Activity Book. Brown, Marc, illus. 2002. (Arthur Ser.). (Illus.). 16p. (J). (ps-3). act. bk. ed. 7.99 (978-0-316-11850-7(8)) Little, Brown Bks. for Young Readers.

Brunner, Sharon. Christmas Came for Easter. 2007. (J). per. 8.99 (***978-1-60247-242-6(4)***) Tate Publishing & Enterprises, L.L.C.

Carter, David A. Easter Bugs: A Springtime Pop-up by David A Carter. Carter, David A., illus. 2001. (Bugs in a Box Bks.). (Illus.). 14p. (J). (ps-2). 10.95 (978-0-689-81862-2(9) , Little Simon) Simon & Schuster Children's Publishing.

Catholic Baby's First Easter. 2000. (Illus.). (J). (ps-k). bds. 8.99 (978-0-88271-017-4(6)) Regina Pr., Malhame & Co.

Chambers, Catherine. Easter. 1999. (World of Holidays Ser.). (Illus.). 32p. (gr. 2-5). pap. 8.95 (978-0-8172-3886-5(7)) Steck-Vaughn.

Chapman, Gillian. Easter Make & Do. 2004. 32p. (J). 7.99 (978-0-7586-0583-2(8)) Concordia Publishing Hse.

Coffey, Kathy. Children & Christian Initiation: Journal for Children (Ages 7-10) 2001. (Children & Christian Initiation Ser.). (Illus.). 40p. (J). (gr. 1-4). 5.95 (978-1-889108-35-3(9)) Living the Good News.

Cosgrove, Stephen. Easter Bunnies. Edelson, Wendy, illus. 32p. (J). pap. 4.95 (978-0-8249-5371-3(1) , Ideals) Ideals Pubns.

Croll, Carolyn, illus. The Great Easter Egg Hunt. (Muppets Ser.). (J). 11.70 (978-0-7611-1036-1(4) , 21036) Workman Publishing Co., Inc.

Dandi. Easter Colors Sticker Book: Over 50 stickers Inside! Fyffe, Brian, illus. 2004. 10p. (J). (ps up). bds. 4.99 (978-1-57151-723-4(5)) Playhouse Publishing.

Daning, Tom, ed. Fun-to-Make Crafts for Easter. 2004. (Illus.). 64p. (J). 15.95 (978-1-59078-340-5(9)); 7.95 (978-1-59078-365-8(4)) Boyds Mills Pr.

De Jonge, Joanne. Precious Moments Easter. 2000. (Precious Moments for Children Ser.). 32p. (J). 9.99 (978-0-8010-4418-2(9)) Baker Bks.

Deboer, Miller. Hosanna! 1999. (SPA.). 12p. (J). (ps up). 2.99 (978-0-8297-2147-8(9)) Vida Pubs.

Dingles, Molly. On Easter Morning. Wallis, Rebecca, illus. 2005. (Holiday Happenings Ser.). 32p. (J). per. 9.95 (978-1-59646-193-2(4)) Dingles & Co.

Dowley, Tim. My First Story of Easter. Langton, Roger, illus. 2005. 24p. (J). 7.99 (978-0-8024-1767-1(1)) Moody Pubs.

Doyle, Christopher. The Story of Easter. Haysom, John, illus. 2005. (ENG.). 32p. (J). 12.99 (978-0-7586-0837-6(3)) Concordia Publishing Hse.

Easter. (Illus.). (gr. 1-4). 3.00 (978-0-570-05524-2(5) , 54-1034) Concordia Publishing Hse.

Easter Activities. 32p. (J). (ps). pap., act. bk. ed. 6.95 (978-0-7945-0161-7(3)) EDC Publishing.

Easter Fun. 2003. (Holiday Fun Bks.). 32p. (J). 2.99 (978-0-88724-926-6(4)) Carson-Dellosa Publishing Co., Inc.

Easter/Lent Fun. 2005. 32p. (J). per. 4.99 (978-1-59441-078-9(X) , CD-204004) Carson-Dellosa Publishing Co., Inc.

Elliot, Julie. Easter Stories. Kyle, Margaret, illus. 2001. 32p. (J). (ps-5). incl. VHS (978-1-55145-434-4(3)) Wood Lake Bks., Inc.

Fisher, Aileen. The Story of Easter. Vitale, Stefano, illus. 1998. (Trophy Picture Bk.). 32p. (J). (ps-2). pap. 6.99 (978-0-06-443490-4(7) , Harper Trophy) HarperCollins Pubs.

—The Story of Easter. 1998. (Trophy Picture Bks.). (978-0-606-13043-1(8)) Tandem Library Bks.

Fogle, Robin. The Easter Story Coloring Book. 2007. (Illus.). 16p. (J). pap. 1.89 (***978-1-59317-190-2(0)***) Warner Pr. Pubs.

—The First Easter Dot-to-Dot Activity Book. 2007. (Illus.). 16p. (J). pap. 1.89 (***978-1-59317-192-6(7)***) Warner Pr. Pubs.

Frisch, Aaron. Easter. 2005. (My First Look at Holidays Ser.). (Illus.). 24p. (gr. k-3). 15.95 (978-1-58341-367-8(7) , Creative Education) Creative Co., The.

Galvin, Jennifer. My Catholic Lent & Easter. 2003. 32p. act. bk. ed. 6.95 (978-0-8091-6706-7(9) , 6706-9) Paulist Pr.

Ganeri, Anita. The Easter Story. Phillips, Rachael, illus. 2003. (Festival Stories Ser.). 24p. (J). (978-0-237-52531-6(3)); pap. (978-0-237-52475-3(9)) Evans Publishing Group. (Evans Brothers, Limited).

—The Easter Story. Phillips, Rachael, tr. Phillips, Rachael, illus. 2004. 23p. (J). lib. bdg. (978-1-58340-488-1(0)) Smart Apple Media.

Gibbons, Gail. Easter. Gibbons, Gail, illus. (Illus.). (J). (gr. k-3). 32p. 6.95 (978-0-8234-0866-5(3)); 36p. tchr. ed. 17.95 (978-0-8234-0737-8(3)) Holiday Hse., Inc.

Gibson, C. R., Company Staff. Story of Easter. (Illus.). (J). 9.95 (978-0-8378-2838-1(4)) Gibson, C. R. Co.

Gibson, Ray. Easter Activities. (Activity Bks.). (Illus.). 32p. (J). pap. 6.95 (978-0-7460-4234-2(5)) EDC Publishing.

Gillis. My Easter. 2004. (Festivals Ser.). (Illus.). 24p. (J). pap. 5.50 (978-1-4109-0785-1(6)) Raintree.

—My Easter 6-Pack. 2004. (Illus.). pap. 29.70 (978-1-4109-0790-5(2)) Raintree.

Gillis, Jennifer Blizin. My Easter. 2005. (Festivals Ser.). (Illus.). 24p. (J). (gr. 2-4). lib. bdg. 18.56 (978-1-4109-0780-6(5)) Raintree.

Golden Books Staff. A Hoppy Ending! Baker, Darrell & Vakofsky, Pattie, illus. 2004. (Winnie the Pooh Ser.). 32p. (J). (ps-2). pap. 2.99 (978-0-7364-2189-8(0) , Golden/Disney) Random Hse. Children's Bks.

Hall, Katy, pseud & Eisenberg, Lisa. Easter Yolks Egg-Dyeing Kit. Alley, R. W., illus. 2000. 20p. (J). (gr. k-3). 9.95 (978-0-694-01294-7(7)) HarperCollins Pubs.

Hardesty, Susan. Child's Story of Easter. Stephenson, Christina & Julien, Terry, illus. 2006. 16p. (J). pap. 1.99 (978-0-7847-1805-6(9) , 04187) Standard Publishing.

Harrast, Tracy. Easter. Workman, Terry, illus. 2001. (Peek-a-Bible Ser.). 18p. (J). 6.99 (978-0-310-97972-2(2)) Zonderkidz.

Haugen, Brenda. Easter. Boyd, Sheree, illus. 2004. (Holidays & Celebrations Ser.). 24p. (gr. k-3). 22.60 (978-1-4048-0194-3(4)) Picture Window Bks.

Hayes, Don, illus. The Easter. 24p. (Orig.). (J). pap., act. bk. ed. 4.95 (978-0-8249-5368-3(1) , Ideals) Ideals Pubns.

Heiligman, Deborah. Celebrate Easter: With Colored Eggs, Flowers, & Prayer. 2007. (Holidays Around the World Ser.). (Illus.). 32p. (J). (gr. 1-4). 23.90 (978-1-4263-0021-9(2)); 15.95 (978-1-4263-0020-2(4)) National Geographic Society. (National Geographic Children's Bks.).

He's Alive! The Story of Easter. (Illus.). 16p. (J). pap. 1.50 (978-0-87162-859-6(7) , E4572) Warner Pr. Pubs.

Heyer, Carol, illus. The First Easter. 2003. 32p. (J). 14.95 (978-0-8249-5463-5(7)) Ideals Pubns.

Heyer, Carol, illus. & retold by. The Easter Story. Heyer, Carol, retold by. 32p. (J). 12.95 (978-0-8249-5363-8(0) , Ideals) Ideals Pubns.

La Historia de Semana Santa. 2001. (Libros Arco Ser.). (SPA.). 24p. (J). (gr. k-4). 2.49 (978-0-570-05182-4(7)) Concordia Publishing Hse.

Howie, Vicki. Someone Very Special. Bishop, Roma, illus. 2004. 24p. (ps-k). 6.99 (978-0-8066-4154-6(1) , Augsburg Bks.) Augsburg Fortress, Pubs.

ICB. The Easter Story. 2004. (Illus.). 20p. (J). bds. 6.99 (978-1-4003-0378-6(8)) Nelson, Thomas Inc.

Jesus Lives! the Easter Story. 2006. 16p. (J). pap. 1.99 (978-0-7847-1720-2(6) , 04181) Standard Publishing.

Kennedy, Pamela. An Easter Celebration: Traditions & Customs from Around the World. 10.95 (978-0-8249-5364-5(9)) Ideals Pubns.

—Prayers at Eastertime. Britt, Stephanie McFetridge, illus. 2001. 32p. (J). 7.95 (978-0-8249-5366-9(5)); 5.95 (978-0-8249-5367-6(3)) Ideals Pubns.

Kershner, Jan, ed. Peter Tells the Easter Story. 2004. (Bible Big Bks.). (Illus.). 8p. (ps-k). pap. 15.99 (978-1-55945-426-1(1) , Flagship Church Resources) Group Publishing, Inc.

Kittleson, Gail. Celebrate Easter. 2004. (ps-6). pap. 6.00 (978-0-687-02694-4(6)) Abingdon Pr.

Knudsen, Michelle. Easter Fun. Starace, Tom, illus. 2006. 12p. (J). bds. 4.99 (978-0-689-87894-7(X) , Little Simon) Simon & Schuster Children's Publishing.

Knudsen, Michelle & Yoon, Salina. Happy Easter! 2003. (Sparkle 'n' Shimmer Book Ser.). (Illus.). 14p. (J). 5.99 (978-0-689-85311-1(4) , Little Simon) Simon & Schuster Children's Publishing.

Knudsen Shannon. La Pascua en todo el mundo (Easter around the World) Erickson, David L., illus. 2007. (Yo solo Festividades (on My Own Holidays) Ser.). (J). pap. 6.95 (***978-0-8225-7794-2(1)*** , Ediciones Lerner) Lerner Publishing Group.

Knudsen, Shannon. La Pascua en Todo el Mundo (Easter Around the World) Erickson, David L., illus. 2007. (Yo Solo Festividades (On My Own Holidays) Ser.). (SPA.). 48p. (J). (gr. 2-4). lib. bdg. 25.26 (***978-0-8225-7791-1(7)*** , Ediciones Lerner) Lerner Publishing Group.

Kupperstein, Joel. Celebrating Easter: The Easter Egg Hunt. 1999. (ps-2). lib. bdg. 10.65 (978-0-613-34119-6(8)) Tandem Library Bks.

—Celebrating Easter No. 4526: The Easter Egg Hunt. O'Malia, Carol, illus. 1999. 16p. (J). (ps-2). pap. 2.99 (978-1-57471-571-2(2)) Creative Teaching Pr., Inc.

Landau, Elaine. Easter: Parades, Chocolates, & Celebration. 2004. (Finding Out about Holidays Ser.). (Illus.). 48p. (J). lib. bdg. 23.93 (978-0-7660-2172-3(6)) Enslow Pubs., Inc.

Larrison, Joanne. Week That Led to Easter. 2001. (gr. k-3). lib. bdg. 9.85 (978-0-613-71027-5(4)) Tandem Library Bks.

Let's Celebrate Jesus on Easter. (J). 2006. 16p. pap. 1.99 (978-0-7847-1721-9(4) , 04182); 2006. 16p. pap. 1.99 (978-0-7847-1537-6(8) , 22141); 2004. 24p. 2.49 (978-0-7847-1582-6(3)) Standard Publishing.

Loesch, Joe. He Is Risen: The True Meaning of Easter. Hutchinson, Cheryl J., ed. Cox, Brian T., illus. 2000. (Bible Stories for Kids Ser.). (J). (ps-3). pap. 14.95 incl. audio (978-1-887729-74-1(7)); pap. 16.95 incl. audio compact disk (978-1-887729-75-8(5)) Toy Box Productions.

Maier, Paul L. The Very First Easter. Ordaz, Francisco, illus. (ENG.). (J). 2005. 20p. bds. 6.99 (978-0-7586-0717-1(2)); 2004. 32p. 12.99 (978-0-570-07053-5(8)) Concordia Publishing Hse.

Manz Simon, Mary. My Easter Basket: And the True Story of Easter. Clearwater, Linda, illus. 2006. 14p. (J). bds. 10.99 (978-0-7847-1356-3(1) , 04017) Standard Publishing.

McGrath, Barbara Barbieri. The M & M's' Brand Easter Egg Hunt. Tagel, Peggy, illus. 2004. 12p. (J). (ps-3). bds. 6.95 (978-1-57091-423-2(0)) Charlesbridge Publishing, Inc.

Murphy, Elspeth Campbell. Happy Easter, God. Lewis, Jim, illus. 2001. (Prayer-Poems Ser.). 32p. (J). (ps-3). 7.99 (978-0-7642-2386-0(0)) Bethany Hse. Pubs.

Neusner, Dena Wallenstein. Colorful Easter. Swendsen, Silje, ed. 2004. (Barney Ser.). 32p. (J). pap. 3.99 (978-0-439-45873-3(0)) Scholastic, Inc.

O'Neal, Debbie Trafton. Before & after Easter: Activities & Ideas for Lent to Pentecost. 2nd ed. 2001. (Illus.). 64p. (gr. 3-7). 11.99 (978-0-8066-4157-7(6) , Augsburg Bks.) Augsburg Fortress, Pubs.

—J Is for Jesus: An Easter Alphabet & Activity Book. Bryan-Hunt, Jan, illus. 2005. 32p. (J). pap., act. bk. ed. 10.99 (978-0-8066-5123-1(7) , Augsburg Bks.) Augsburg Fortress, Pubs.

Oursler, Fulton. A Child's Story of Easter. Caswell, Helen Rayburn, illus. 1998. 24p. (J). (gr. k-3). 5.00 (978-0-687-02190-1(1)) Abingdon Pr.

Pfeifer, Alice Ann. Totally Lent! My Journey to Easter 2005! Larkin, Jean K., ed. 2004. (Illus.). 64p. (J). 5.95 (978-0-89837-248-9(8) , 3575) Pflaum Publishing Group.

Pingry, Patricia A. The Easter Story. 2006. (Illus.). 32p. pap. 3.95 (978-0-8249-5531-1(5) , Ideals Children's Bks.) Ideals Pubns.

—The Easter Story. Utt, Mary Ann, illus. 2003. 26p. (J). bds. 6.95 (978-0-8249-4231-1(0)) Ideals Pubns.

—La Historia de la Pascua. Wells, Lorraine Schreiner, illus. 1999. Tr. of Story of Easter. (SPA.). 22p. (J). (gr. 2-4). reprint ed. 15.00 (978-0-7567-5863-9(7)) DIANE Publishing Co.

—La Historia de la Pascua. Wells, Lorraine Schreiner, illus. 2000. Tr. of Story of Easter. (SPA.). 26p. (J). (ps-k). 6.95 (978-0-8249-4185-7(3)) Ideals Pubns.

—On Easter Sunday. Johnson, Meredith, illus. 2007. 26p. (J). bds. 6.99 (***978-0-8249-6692-8(9)*** , Candy Cane Pr.) Ideals Pubns.

Pingry, Patricia A. The Story of Easter. Wells, Lorraine Schreiner, illus. (J). 2002. (ENG & SPA.). 32p. 3.95 (978-0-8249-4204-5(3)); 1998. 26p. bds. 6.95 (978-0-8249-4090-4(3)) Ideals Pubns.

Pirotta, Saviour. Christian Cookbook. Sloan, Frank, ed. 2001. (Holiday Cookbooks from Around the World). (Illus.). 32p. (J). (gr. 4-7). lib. bdg. 25.69 (978-0-7398-3263-9(8)) Raintree.

Pirotta, Saviour. Easter. 2007. (J). lib. bdg. (***978-1-4042-3705-6(4)*** , PowerKids Pr.) Rosen Publishing Group, Inc., The.

Pomaska, Anna. Easter. 2002. (Illus.). 64p. (J). pap., act. bk. ed. 1.50 (978-0-486-28329-6(1)) Dover Pubns., Inc.

—Invisible Easter Magic Picture Book. 1998. 16p. (J). pap. 1.50 (978-0-486-40331-1(9)) Dover Pubns., Inc.

Potts, Steve. Easter. 2001. (Holiday Ser.). (Illus.). 24p. (J). 21.35 (978-1-58340-118-7(0)) Smart Apple Media.

Press, Running. The Story of Easter. 2007. 128p. (J). 4.95 (978-0-7624-2937-0(2) , Running Pr. Minature Editions) Running Pr. Bk. Pubs.

Raabe, Emily. An Easter Holiday Cookbook. 2002. (Festive Foods for the Holidays Ser.). (Illus.). 24p. (J). (gr. 2-5). lib. bdg. 19.50 (978-0-8239-5624-1(5) , PowerKids Pr.) Rosen Publishing Group, Inc., The.

Radtke, Becky. Easter Spot-the-Differences. 2004. (Illus.). 64p. (J). pap. 1.50 (978-0-486-43852-8(X)) Dover Pubns., Inc.

Resurrection Eggs. 2006. pap. 6.99 (978-1-57229-790-6(5)) FamilyLife.

Robertson, Brynn, compiled by. Standard Easter Program Book. annual 2005. (Illus.). 48p. pap. 5.99 (978-0-7847-1618-2(8) , 08716) Standard Publishing.

Rock. Easter: Fun & Festive Things To Make. 1999. (Illus.). 24p. (J). pap. 4.95 (978-0-7459-4050-2(1) , Lion) Lion Hudson plc GBR. *Dist:* Trafalgar Square Publishing.

Ross, Kathy. All New Crafts for Easter. Holm, Sharon Lane, tr. Holm, Sharon Lane, illus. 2004. (All New Holiday Crafts for Kids Ser.). 48p. lib. bdg. (978-0-7613-2921-3(8) , Millbrook Pr.) Lerner Publishing Group.

Rottmann, Erik. The Easter Victory: The Story of Easter: Matthew 26-28 for Children. Billin-Frye, Paige, illus. 2006. (ENG.). (J). 1.99 (978-0-7586-0869-7(1)) Concordia Publishing Hse.

Rudel-Tessier, Melanie. Caillou Happy Easter! Rudel-Tessier, Melanie & Tipeo, illus. 2003. (Confetti Ser.). 24p. (J). (ps up). pap. 12.95 (978-2-89450-386-7(5)) Chouette Publishing CAN. *Dist:* Perseus Distribution.

Sanders, Nancy I. Easter. 2003. (True Book Ser.). (Illus.). 48p. (J). 25.00 (978-0-516-22763-4(7) , Children's Pr.) Scholastic Library Publishing.

—Easter, March. 2003. Tr. of April. (gr. 3-6). lib. bdg. 15.25 (978-0-613-89014-4(0)) Tandem Library Bks.

Savitskas, Margaret. Totally Lent! A Kid's Journey to Easter 2006. Larkin, Jean K., ed. 2005. (Illus.). 64p. (J). 5.95 (978-1-933178-25-7(6) , 3576) Pflaum Publishing Group.

Savitskas, Margaret & Behe, Mary. Totally Lent! A Child's Journey to Easter 2006. Larkin, Jean K., ed. 2005. (Illus.). 64p. (J). 5.95 (978-1-933178-26-4(4) , 3586) Pflaum Publishing Group.

Schroeder, Doug. Does the Bunny Lay Easter Eggs. 2004. pap. 4.99 (978-0-570-04953-1(9)) Concordia Publishing Hse.

Schuh, Mari C. Easter. (Holidays & Celebrations Ser.). (Illus.). 24p. (gr. k-1). 2002. (J). lib. bdg. 15.93 (978-0-7368-1445-4(0)); Vol. 2. 2005. (YA). (978-0-7368-9398-5(9)) Capstone Pr., Inc. (Pebble Bks.).

Spear, Kevin. Itty-bitty Bible Activity Book, Easter. 2007. (Illus.). 48p. (J). pap. 1.49 (***978-1-59317-196-4(X)***) Warner Pr. Pubs.

Spieler, Cathy M. My More-Than-Coloring Book about Easter. 2000. (My More-Than-Coloring Bks.). (Illus.). 64p. (J). (ps-2). pap. 4.99 (978-0-570-07028-3(7)) Concordia Publishing Hse.

Spirin, Gennady, illus. The Easter Story: According to the Gospels of Matthew, Luke & John from the King James Bible. rev. ed. 1999. 32p. (J). 19.95 (978-0-8050-6333-2(1) , Holt, Henry & Co. Bks. For Young Readers) Holt, Henry & Co.

Stewart, Jennifer. The Easter Story Sticker & Activity Book. 2000. (Illus.). 28p. (J). (ps-2). pap., act. bk. ed. 3.49 (978-0-7847-1130-9(5) , 22082) Standard Publishing.

Stiegemeyer, Julie. Things I See at Easter. Mitter, Kathy, illus. 2005. (ENG.). 20p. (J). bds. 4.99 (978-0-7586-0797-3(0)) Concordia Publishing Hse.

Stohs, Anita R. A Very Blessed Easter. 1998. (Illus.). 32p. (J). (ps-2). act. bk. ed. 3.99 (978-0-570-05491-7(5)) Concordia Publishing Hse.

Tangvald, Christine. The Best Thing about Easter (board Book) Couri, Kathy, illus. 2007. (J). 6.99 (***978-0-7847-2000-4(2)***) Standard Publishing.

Tangvald, Christine. Easter Is... for Me! 2000. (for Me! Bks.). (Illus.). 24p. (J). (ps-3). pap. 3.99 (978-0-7642-2333-4(X)) Bethany Hse. Pubs.

Tebo, Mary Elizabeth & Jablonski, Patricia E. The Very First Easter. Winek-Leliwa, Anna, illus. 2002. 32p. (J). pap. 6.95 (978-0-8198-8032-1(9) , 332-400) Pauline Bks. & Media.

Totally Lent! A Child's Journey to Easter 2007. 2006. (J). 5.95 (978-1-933178-46-2(9)) Pflaum Publishing Group.

Totally Lent! A Child's Journey to Easter 2008. 2007. (J). 5.95 (***978-1-933178-70-7(1)***) Pflaum Publishing Group.

Totally Lent! A Kid's Journey to Easter 2007. 2006. (J). 5.95 (978-1-933178-45-5(0)) Pflaum Publishing Group.

Totally Lent! A Kid's Journey to Easter 2008. 2007. (J). 5.95 (***978-1-933178-71-4(X)***) Pflaum Publishing Group.

Totally Lent! A Teen's Journey to Easter 2007. 2006. (J). 5.95 (978-1-933178-44-8(2)) Pflaum Publishing Group.

Totally Lent! A Teen's Journey to Easter 2008. 2007. (YA). 5.95 (***978-1-933178-72-1(8)***) Pflaum Publishing Group.

Trafton-O'Neal, Debbie. Family Countdown to Easter: A Day-by-Day Celebration. Woodworth, Viki, illus. 1999. 48p. (gr. k-6). 10.99 (978-0-8066-3827-0(3) , 9-3827, Augsburg Bks.) Augsburg Fortress, Pubs.

Trueit, Trudi Strain. Easter. 2007. (Holidays, Festivals, & Celebrations Ser.). 32p. (J). (gr. k-4). 22.79 (***978-1-59296-812-1(0)***) Child's World, Inc.

Tuttle, Emily. Baby's First Easter. 2006. (First Bible Collection). (Illus.). 10p. (J). (ps-k). 9.99 (978-0-7847-1206-1(9) , 04393) Standard Publishing.

Vidrine, Beverly Barras. Easter Day Alphabet. Lyne, Alison Davis, illus. 2003. 32p. (J). (gr. k-3). pap. 7.95 (978-1-58980-076-2(1)) Pelican Publishing Co., Inc.

Walker, Joni, illus. & contrib. by. Tell Me the Easter Story. Walker, Joni, contrib. by. 2004. 14p. (J). bds. 4.99 (978-0-7586-0629-7(X)) Concordia Publishing Hse.

Watt, Fiona. Easter Activities. 2004. (Activity Bks.). (Illus.). 32p. (J). pap., act. bk. ed. 6.95 (978-0-7945-0344-4(6) , Usborne) EDC Publishing.

Wedeven, Carol. The Easter Cave. Ebert, Len, illus. 2004. (ENG.). 32p. (J). (ps-2). 9.99 (978-0-570-07135-8(6)) Concordia Publishing Hse.

Wildsmith, Brian. The Easter Story. Wildsmith, Brian, illus. 2004. (Illus.). 24p. (ps-7). 18.00 (978-0-8028-5189-5(4)) Eerdmans, William B. Publishing Co.

Williams, Colleen Madonna Flood. My Adventure on Easter. 2007. 44p. (J). 8.99 (978-1-59092-546-1(7) , Orchard Academy Pr.) Windstorm Creative.

Willoughby, Robert. Three Easter Journeys. 2004. (Illus.). 24p. (ps-3). pap. 5.00 (978-0-687-04851-9(6)) Abingdon Pr.

Wilson, Etta. A Child's Story of Easter. Utt, Mary Ann, illus. 2001. 32p. (J). 7.95 (978-0-8249-5365-2(7)) Ideals Pubns.

Winne, Joanne. Let's Get Ready for Easter. 2001. (gr. k-3). lib. bdg. 12.95 (978-0-613-51081-3(X)) Tandem Library Bks.

Wolf, Jackie. Sparkle Basket. 2003. (Illus.). 10p. (J). (ps up). bds. 6.99 (978-1-57151-713-5(8)) Playhouse Publishing.

Youd, Pauline. Thomas Becomes a Believer: An Easter Story. Sandland, Reg, illus. 2000. 13p. (J). (gr. 2-5). pap. 3.95 (978-0-8198-7403-0(5)) Pauline Bks. & Media.

Zemlicka, Shannon. Easter Around the World. Erickson, David, illus. 2005. (On My Own Holidays Ser.). 48p. (J). (gr. k-3). 5.95 (978-1-57505-765-1(4)); (gr. 2-4). 25.26 (978-1-57505-655-5(0)) Lerner Publishing Group.

Zobel-Nolan, Allia. Librito para Jugar: Un día muy Especial. 2001. (Play along Ser.).Tr. of Play along book: A Very Special Day. bds. 4.99 (978-0-7899-0999-2(5)) Editorial Unilit.

Zocchi, Judy. On Easter Morning. Wallis, Rebecca, illus. 2005. (Holiday Happenings Ser.). 32p. (J). pap. 9.95 (978-1-59646-192-5(6)); (ENM.). lib. bdg. 20.65 (978-1-891997-41-9(6)) Dingles & Co.

—On Easter Morning/la mañana de Pascua. Wallis, Rebecca, illus. 2005. (Holiday Happenings Ser.).Tr. of mañana de Pascua. (ENG & SPA.). 32p. (J). pap. 9.95 (978-1-59646-194-9(2)); lib. bdg. 20.65 (978-1-891997-42-6(4)); per. 9.95 (978-1-59646-195-6(0)) Dingles & Co.

EASTER—FICTION

Ada, Alma Flor. A Surprise for Mother Rabbit. 2000. (gr. k-3). lib. bdg. 17.60 (978-0-613-79391-9(9)) Tandem Library Bks.

Adams, Adrienne. The Easter Egg Artists. Adams, Adrienne, illus. 2002. (Illus.). (J). 14.47 (978-0-7587-2429-8(2)) Book Wholesalers, Inc.

Adams, Michelle Medlock. The Sparrow's Easter Song. Eldridge, Marion, illus. 2003. 32p. (J). 14.95 (978-0-8249-5470-3(X)) Ideals Pubns.

Albee, Sarah. The Bunny Hop. Swanson, Maggie, illus. 2004. 24p. (J). (gr. k-ps). bds. 4.99 (978-0-375-82693-1(9) , Random Hse. Bks. for Young Readers) Random Hse. Children's Bks.

Alex Toys. Bunny's Easter Basket. Silver-Thompson, Pattie, illus. rev. ed. 2008. 10p. (J). (ps-1). 5.99 (*978-0-316-15404-8(0)) Little, Brown Bks. for Young Readers.

Alexander, Heather. The Case of the Easter Egg Race. 2004. 84p. (J). (ps-17). 11.79 (978-0-606-32976-7(5)) Tandem Library Bks.

Amery, Heather. The Easter Story. 2004. (Bible Tales Readers Ser.). (Illus.). 6p. (J). pap. 4.95 (978-0-7945-0254-6(7) , Usborne); lib. bdg. 12.95 (978-1-58086-456-5(2)) EDC Publishing.

—Easter Story. 1999. (gr. k-3). lib. bdg. 12.95 (978-0-613-67542-0(8)) Tandem Library Bks.

Amery, Heather, ed. The Easter Story. 1999. (Bible Tales Readers Ser.). (Illus.). 16p. (J). (ps-k). pap. 4.50 (978-0-7460-3358-6(3)); lib. bdg. 12.95 (978-1-58086-170-0(9)) EDC Publishing.

Auch, Mary Jane. The Easter Egg Farm. Auch, Mary Jane, illus. (Illus.). (J). (gr. k-3). 32p. pap. 6.95 (978-0-8234-1076-7(5)); 36p. tchr. ed. 17.95 (978-0-8234-0917-4(1)) Holiday Hse., Inc.

Auer, Chris. The Legend of the Sand Dollar: An Inspirational Story of Hope for Easter. Johnson, Rick, illus. 2005. 32p. (J). 15.99 (978-0-310-70780-6(3)) Zonderkidz.

Augustine, Peggy. It Looks A Lot Like Easter. 2008. pap. 1.59 (*978-0-687-49158-2(4)) Abingdon Pr.

Baby Strawberry's First Easter. 2007. (Strawberry Shortcake Baby Ser.). 10p. (J). bds. 4.99 (978-0-448-44453-6(4) , Grosset & Dunlap) Penguin Group (USA) Inc.

Backstein, Karen. Little Chick's Easter Surprise. McQueen, Lucinda, illus. 2005. 8p. (J). bds. 1.99 (978-0-439-69728-6(X) , Cartwheel Bks.) Scholastic, Inc.

Baker, Stacy. Sammy's Secret. 2005. (J). lib. bdg. 19.95 (*978-1-933732-03-9(2) , Bear Hug Bks.) MidAmerica Publishing Co.

Balian, Lorna. Humbug Rabbit. 2004. (Illus.). 40p. (J). 15.95 (978-1-932065-40-4(7)) Star Bright Bks., Inc.

Banks, Steven. Show Me the Bunny! 2004. (gr. k-3). lib. bdg. 11.80 (978-0-613-73446-2(7)) Tandem Library Bks.

—SpongeBob's Easter Parade. Goldberg, Barry, illus. 2005. (Spongebob Squarepants Ser.). 24p. (J). pap. 3.99 (978-0-689-87314-0(X) , Simon Spotlight/Nickelodeon) Simon & Schuster Children's Publishing.

Banks, Steven & Hillenburg, Stephen. Show Me the Bunny! Greenblatt, C. H. & Reiss, William, illus. 2004. (SpongeBob SquarePants Ready-To-Read Ser.: Vol. 3). 32p. (J). pap. 3.99 (978-0-689-86485-8(X) , Simon Spotlight/Nickelodeon) Simon & Schuster Children's Publishing.

Benoit, Gschwind. My First Little Easter Book. 2001. 52p. 2.95 (978-1-58595-202-1(8)) Twenty-Third Pubns./Bayard.

Berenstain, Stan & Berenstain, Jan. The Berenstain Bears & the Real Easter Eggs. Berenstain, Stan & Berenstain, Jan, illus. 2002. (Berenstain Bears Ser.). (Illus.). (J). 11.19 (978-0-7587-8978-5(5)) Book Wholesalers, Inc.

—The Berenstain Bears & the Real Easter Eggs. 2002. (Berenstain Bears Ser.). (Illus.). 32p. (J). (gr. k-3). pap. 3.99 (978-0-375-81133-3(8) , Random Hse. Bks. for Young Readers) Random Hse. Children's Bks.

—The Berenstain Bears & the Real Easter Eggs. 2002. (gr. k-3). lib. bdg. 10.95 (978-0-613-64153-1(1)) Tandem Library Bks.

—The Berenstain Bears' Easter Surprise. l.t. ed. 1998. (Berenstain Bears Ser.). (Illus.). 48p. (J). (ps-3). pap. 10.95 (978-0-590-94730-5(3)) Scholastic, Inc.

The Best Thing about Easter. 2006. 16p. (J). pap. 1.99 (978-0-7847-1724-0(9) , 04185) Standard Publishing.

Beuschlein, Marti & Hoffman, Patricia A. Early Easter Morning. Siegfried, Jim, illus. 1999. 32p. (J). (ps-k). 4.99 (978-0-570-05473-3(7) , 56-1936GJ) Concordia Publishing Hse.

Bickel, Karla. Easter Lights. Bickel, Karla, illus. l.t. ed. 2004. (Illus.). 16p. (J). (ps-6). pap. 5.00 (978-1-891452-14-7(2) , 7) Heart Arbor Bks.

Boniface, William. Easter Bunnies Everywhere. Rooney, Ronnie, illus. 2003. 12p. (J). (ps-2). bds. 9.99 (978-0-8431-0257-4(8) , Price Stern Sloan) Penguin Group (USA) Inc.

—Five Little Easter Eggs. Adams, Lynn, illus. 2003. 12p. (J). (ps). 5.99 (978-0-8431-0233-8(0) , Price Stern Sloan) Penguin Group (USA) Inc.

Bostrom, Kathleen Long. Sunrise Hill. Johnson, Rick, illus. 2004. 32p. (J). 14.99 (978-0-310-70508-6(8)) Zonderkidz.

Bowman, Crystal. An Easter Gift for Me. Gèvry, Claudine, illus. 2007. 14p. (J). 6.99 (978-0-310-71159-9(2)) Zonderkidz.

Bridwell, Norman. The Big Red Reader: The Egg Hunt. Bridwell, Norman, illus. 2002. (Big Red Readers Ser.). (Illus.). (J). 11.91 (978-0-7587-9315-7(4)) Book Wholesalers, Inc.

Bridwell, Norman. Clifford's Happy Easter - Library Edition. 2007. (J). 18.95 (*978-0-439-02329-0(7)) Scholastic, Inc.

Bryant, Ann. The Easter Egg Hunt: Paas. Artful Doodlers Limited Staff, illus. 2007. 32p. (J). pap. 3.99 (978-0-448-44488-8(7) , Grosset & Dunlap) Penguin Group (USA) Inc.

Bryant, Megan E. Paas: The Friendship Egg. 2006. 24p. (J). (ps-1). pap. 3.99 (978-0-448-44137-5(3) , Grosset & Dunlap) Penguin Group (USA) Inc.

Burg, Sara Emmanuelle. One More Egg. 2005. (Illus.). 32p. (J). (ps up). 16.50 (978-0-7358-2002-9(3)) North-South Bks., Inc.

Burg, Sarah Emmanuelle. One More Egg. 2005. (Illus.). 32p. (J). (ps up). 15.95 (978-0-7358-2001-2(5)) North-South Bks., Inc.

Burling, Marlene L. Grandma Tell Me the Easter Story. 1998. (Illus.). 45p. (J). (gr. k-4). pap. 7.25 (978-1-55630-889-5(2)) Brentwood Communications Group.

Butcher, Sam. The Wonder of Easter. 2000. 24p. pap. 1.95 (978-0-307-59650-5(8)) Random Hse., Inc.

Capucilli, Alyssa Satin. Biscuit's Pet & Play Easter. Berlin, Rose Mary, illus. 2008. (Biscuit Ser.). 12p. (J). 6.99 (*978-0-06-112839-4(2) , Harper Festival) HarperCollins Pubs.

Capucilli, Alyssa Satin. Happy Easter, Biscuit! Schories, Pat, illus. 2000. (Biscuit Ser.). 20p. (J). (ps-1). pap. 6.99 (978-0-694-01223-7(8) , Harper Festival) HarperCollins Pubs.

—Happy Easter, Biscuit! 2000. (gr. k-3). lib. bdg. 15.25 (978-0-613-70589-9(0)) Tandem Library Bks.

Carling, Amelia Lau. Alfombras de Aserrín. 2005. (SPA., Illus.). 32p. (J). pap. 6.95 (978-0-88899-730-2(2)) Groundwood Bks. CAN. *Dist:* Perseus Distribution.

—Sawdust Carpets. 2005. (Illus.). 32p. (J). 16.95 (978-0-88899-625-1(X)) Groundwood Bks. CAN. *Dist:* Perseus Distribution.

Carlson, Melody, et al. Benjamin's Box: A Resurrection Story. Stockman, Jack, illus. 2000. 40p. (J). (gr. k-5). 10.99 (978-0-310-70044-9(2)) Zonderkidz.

Carlsox, Melody. The Easterville Miracle. Reagan, Susan Joy, illus. 2004. 32p. (J). (ps-4). 12.99 (978-0-8054-2680-9(9)) B&H Publishing Grp.

Caviezel, Giovanni. Bunny's Egg Hunt. Pagnoni, Roberta, illus. 2003. 12p. (J). bds. 4.99 (978-0-689-85246-6(0) , Little Simon) Simon & Schuster Children's Publishing.

Cazet, Denys. Minnie & Moo: The Attack of the Easter Bunnies. Cazet, Denys, illus. 2004. (I Can Read Bks.). (Illus.). 48p. (J). (gr. k-3). 15.99 (978-0-06-000506-1(8)); lib. bdg. 17.89 (978-0-06-000507-8(6)) HarperCollins Pubs.

Chardiet, Bernice. The Easter Rabbit. Micucci, Charles, illus. 1998. (Read with Me Cartwheel Bks.). 32p. (J). (ps-3). pap. 3.50 (978-0-590-10072-4(6)) Scholastic, Inc.

—The Easter Ribbit. 1998. (Read with Me Ser.). (J). (978-0-606-13350-0(X)) Tandem Library Bks.

Chesterfield, Sadie. My Little Pony: Easter Surprise Coloring Book: Easter Surprise Coloring Book. Edwards, Ken, illus. 2007. (My Little Pony Ser.). 32p. (J). pap. 3.99 (978-0-06-121526-1(0) , Harper Festival) HarperCollins Pubs.

Chisholm, Sarah Reid. An Easter Hunt: A Hide-and-Seek Story. 2004. (Illus.). 32p. (ps-3). 6.99 (978-0-8066-2740-3(9) , 9-2740, Augsburg Bks.) Augsburg Fortress, Pubs.

Ciminera, Siobhan. Paas: Egg-Tivities for Easter! 2006. 32p. (J). (ps-1). 2.99 (978-0-448-44135-1(7) , Grosset & Dunlap) Penguin Group (USA) Inc.

Conlon, Mara. One Hungry Bunny. Wittwer, Hala, illus. 2003. (Reading Railroad Bks.). 14p. (J). (ps-1). bds. 5.99 (978-0-448-43121-5(1) , Grosset & Dunlap) Penguin Group (USA) Inc.

Cooner, Donna D. & Scholastic, Inc. Staff. Barney's Easter Basket. Valentine-Ruppe, June, illus. 2001. (Barney Ser.). 14p. (J). (ps-k). bds. 5.99 (978-1-58668-045-9(5)) Scholastic, Inc.

Coudriet, Dawn M. & Black, Jodi. El Conejo de Resurrección. 1999. 28p. pap. 4.99 (978-1-930442-01-6(7)) Nathanael Publishing.

—The Resurrection Rabbit. 1999. 28p. pap. 4.99 (978-1-930442-00-9(9)) Nathanael Publishing.

Cousins, Lucy. Happy Easter, Maisy! Cousins, Lucy, illus. 2007. 14p. (J). (gr. k-k). bds. 4.99 (978-0-7636-3230-4(9)) Candlewick Pr.

Dadey, Debbie & Jones, Marcia Thornton. Ogres Don't Hunt Easter Eggs. 2004. (Adventures of the Bailey School Kids Ser.). 96p. (J). pap. 3.99 (978-0-439-40834-9(2) , Scholastic Paperbacks) Scholastic, Inc.

Dalmatian Press Staff. Sesame Street Happy Easter. 2007. 24p. (J). pap. 3.50 (*978-1-4037-3198-2(5)) Dalmatian Pr.

Davidson, Alice Joyce. My Day with Jesus. Clar, David Austin, illus. 2005. (Easter Board Bks.). 16p. (J). bds. 3.99 (978-0-310-70843-8(5)) Zonderkidz.

—My Good Shepherd. Clar, David Austin, illus. 2005. (Easter Board Bks.). 16p. (J). bds. 3.99 (978-0-310-70844-5(3)) Zonderkidz.

DeBoer, Jesslyn. The First Easter. Clar, David Austin, illus. 2005. (Easter Board Bks.). 12p. (J). bds. 3.99 (978-0-310-70842-1(7)) Zonderkidz.

—Jesus Is Coming! Clar, David Austin, illus. 2005. (Easter Board Bks.). 12p. (J). bds. 3.99 (978-0-310-70841-4(9)) Zonderkidz.

deGroat, Diane. Last One in Is a Rotten Egg! deGroat, Diane, illus. 2007. (Illus.). 32p. (J). (ps-3). 15.99 (978-0-06-089294-4(3)); lib. bdg. 16.89 (978-0-06-089295-1(1)) HarperCollins Pubs.

Denim, Sue & Pilkey, Dav. The Dumb Bunnies' Easter. Pilkey, Dav, illus. 1998. (Dumb Bunnies Ser.). (Illus.). 32p. (J). (ps-3). pap. 4.99 (978-0-590-20242-8(1)) Scholastic, Inc.

dePaola, Tomie. My First Easter. 2008. 12p. (J). (ps-k). bds. 5.99 (*978-0-448-44790-2(8)) Penguin Group (USA) Inc.

Derico, Laura. Easter Surprises. Harris, Phyllis, illus. 2007. (Happy Day Bks.). (J). 1.99 (*978-0-7847-2085-1(1)) Standard Publishing.

Dillard, Sarah, illus. Follow the Bunny. 2006. 10p. (J). (ps-1). bds. 5.99 (978-0-8431-1813-1(X) , Price Stern Sloan) Penguin Group (USA) Inc.

Disney Press Staff. Easter Bear? 2003. (gr. k-3). lib. bdg. 10.95 (978-0-613-73671-8(0)) Tandem Library Bks.

—Pooh's Easter Egg Hunt. 2002. (ps-2). lib. bdg. 11.80 (978-0-613-73601-5(X)) Tandem Library Bks.

DK Publishing. Hop A Long Bunny: Fiberoptic Light. 2007. 16p. (J). pap. 4.99 (*978-0-7566-3447-6(4)) Dorling Kindersley Publishing, Inc.

Doyle, Alfreda C. Easter Story Rhymes. unabr. ed. 1998. (Alfreda's Radio Ser.: Vol. 8). (J). (gr. 5-9). 16.95 incl. audio (978-1-56820-312-6(8)) Story Time Stories That Rhyme.

Doyle, Tara. Little Bunny's Easter Surprise. McQueen, Lucinda, illus. 2005. 8p. (J). bds. 1.99 (978-0-439-69682-1(8) , Cartwheel Bks.) Scholastic, Inc.

Dunrea, Olivier. Ollie's Eggs. 2006. (J). (978-0-618-53243-8(9)) Houghton Mifflin Co.

Easter Dreams. 1999. (Easter Mini Storybooks Ser.: Vol. 6). (Illus.). 32p. (J). (978-0-7666-0252-6(4) , Honey Bear Bks.) Modern Publishing.

Easter Egg Mystery. 1999. (Easter Mini Storybooks Ser.: Vol. 5). (Illus.). 32p. (J). (978-0-7666-0251-9(6) , Honey Bear Bks.) Modern Publishing.

Eding, June. Easter Showers. Chauhan, Manhar, illus. 2007. (Puppy Scooby-Doo Ser.). 32p. (J). pap. 3.99 (978-0-448-44485-7(2) , Grosset & Dunlap) Penguin Group (USA) Inc.

Elkins, Stephen. I've Just Seen Jesus: A Very Special Story for Children. Colton, Ellie, illus. 2003. (Dove Award Signature Ser.). 32p. (J). 14.99 incl. audio compact disk (978-0-8054-2665-6(5)) B&H Publishing Grp.

Elliott, Ann. GypsyBridge Friends: The Surprise. 2003. 40p. pap. 12.95 (978-0-9721825-2-2(7)) Open Vision Entertainment Corp.

Elschner, Geraldine. The Easter Chick. Junge, Alexandra, illus. 2006. 32p. (J). reprint ed. 6.95 (978-0-7358-2076-0(7)) North-South Bks., Inc.

Ende, Michael. Tragasuenos. 5th ed. (SPA., Illus.). 32p. (J). 15.95 (978-84-261-1740-3(6)) Juventud, Editorial ESP. *Dist:* AIMS International Bks., Inc.

Engelbreit, Mary. Queen of Easter. Engelbreit, Mary, illus. 2006. (Ann Estelle Stories Ser.). (Illus.). 32p. (J). 15.99 (978-0-06-008184-3(8)); lib. bdg. 16.89 (978-0-06-008185-0(6)) HarperCollins Pubs.

Faye, Charlet. The Feather-Dusted Easter. Letterman, Kimberlee, illus. 1999. 48p. (J). (gr. k-3). 16.95 (978-0-9655222-0-5(2)) FayeHouse. Pr. International.

First Easter Story. Date not set. (Illus.). (J). bds. 9.98 (978-0-7525-9172-8(X)) Parragon, Inc.

Fleming, Maria. Hippity Skippity Easter. Bratun, Katy, illus. 2004. 32p. (J). pap. 3.50 (978-0-439-56417-5(4) , Cartwheel Bks.) Scholastic, Inc.

Fontes, Justine. The Easter Cub. McQueen, Lucinda, illus. 2003. (Hello Reader! Ser.). 32p. (J). (gr. k-2). pap. 3.99 (978-0-439-44340-1(7) , Cartwheel Bks.) Scholastic, Inc.

Forte, Lauren & S. I. International Staff. Hello, Rainbow! 2007. (Peeps Ser.). 224p. (J). 4.99 (978-1-4169-3373-1(5) , Simon Scribbles) Simon & Schuster Children's Publishing.

Franklin's Easter: A Sticker Activity Book. 2004. (Franklin Sticker & Activity Bks.). (Illus.). 16p. (J). (gr. k-3). (978-1-55337-690-3(0)) Kids Can Pr., Ltd.

Freeman, Don. Corduroy's Easter. McCue, Lisa, illus. 1999. (Corduroy Ser.). 8p. (J). (gr. k-1). 11.99 (978-0-670-88101-7(5) , Viking Juvenile) Penguin Group (USA) Inc.

—Corduroy's Easter Party. McCue, Lisa, illus. 2000. (Corduroy Ser.). 32p. (J). (gr. k-1). pap. 3.49 (978-0-448-42154-4(2) , Grosset & Dunlap) Penguin Group (USA) Inc.

—Corduroy's Easter Party. 2000. (ps-2). lib. bdg. 11.25 (978-0-613-24691-0(8)) Tandem Library Bks.

—Happy Easter, Corduroy. McCue, Lisa, illus. 2004. 16p. (J). (ps-ps). bds. 5.99 (978-0-670-03677-6(3) , Viking Juvenile) Penguin Group (USA) Inc.

Friedrich, Priscilla & Friedrich, Otto. The Easter Bunny That Overslept. Saaf, Donald, illus. 2002. 32p. (J). (ps-3). 16.99 (978-0-06-029645-2(3)); lib. bdg. 17.89 (978-0-06-029646-9(1)) HarperCollins Pubs.

Fry, Sonali. Happy Easter, Holly! Berry, Bob, illus. 2008. (Holly Hobbie & Friends Ser.). 24p. (J). pap. 3.99 (*978-1-4169-4926-8(7) , Little Simon) Simon & Schuster Children's Publishing.

Fry, Sonali. Make Your Own Easter Treats! Moffatt, Judith, illus. 2002. 12p. (J). (ps-k). bds. 6.99 (978-0-439-34202-5(3)) Scholastic, Inc.

Gaines, Isabel. Pooh's Easter Egg Hunt. 1999. (Winnie the Pooh First Readers Ser.: No. 10). (Illus.). 40p. (J). (gr. k-3). pap. 3.99 (978-0-7868-4268-1(7)) Disney Pr.

Gaines, Isabel, et al. Pooh's Easter Egg Hunt. 2002. (Step into Reading Ser.). (Illus.). 32p. (J). (ps-1). pap. 3.99 (978-0-7364-1208-7(5) , RH/Disney) Random Hse. Children's Bks.

Garfield, Valerie. Sergeant Sniff's Easter Egg Mystery. Durrell, Julie, illus. 2001. (Sergeant Sniff Scratch-and-Sniff Mystery Ser.). 16p. (J). (ps-k). 6.95 (978-0-694-01508-5(3) , Harper Festival) HarperCollins Pubs.

Garland, Michael. The Great Easter Egg Hunt. Garland, Michael, illus. 2007. 32p. (J). pap. 6.99 (978-0-14-240753-0(4) , Puffin) Penguin Group (USA) Inc.

Golden Books Staff. Peter Cottontail: A Colorful Easter. 2001. 32p. (J). (ps-2). pap. 3.99 (978-0-307-09225-0(9) , Golden Bks.) Random Hse. Children's Bks.

—Spring into Action! 2007. (Illus.). 48p. (J). (ps-2). pap. 3.99 (978-0-375-83482-0(6) , Golden Bks.) Random Hse. Children's Bks.

Gomez, Rebecca. Happy Easter, Hello Kitty! 2005. (Illus.). 32p. (*978-0-439-67637-3(1)) Scholastic, Inc.

Grambling, Lois G. Here Comes T. Rex Cottontail. Davis, Jack E., illus. 2007. 32p. (J). lib. bdg. 16.89 (978-0-06-053131-7(2)); 15.99 (978-0-06-053129-4(0)) HarperCollins Pubs.

The Great Mix Up. 2005. (Illus.). 40p. (J). lib. bdg. 15.95 (978-0-9772282-0-1(7)) B. T. Brooks.

Green, Shirley. A Fairy Good Easter Hunt. 1998. (Illus.). 16p. (J). (gr. 2-4). pap. 7.00 (978-0-8059-4457-0(5)) Dorrance Publishing Co., Inc.

Hallinan, P. K. Easter at Our House. Hallinan, P. K., illus. 2007. 28p. 8.99 (*978-0-8249-5552-6(8) , Ideals Children's Bks.) Ideals Pubns.

Hallinan, P. K. Today Is Easter! Hallinan, P. K., illus. 2001. (Illus.). 24p. (J). 7.95 (978-0-8249-5361-4(4)); 5.95 (978-0-8249-5362-1(2)) Ideals Pubns.

Harwood, Beth. The Easter Basket. Ronchi, Susanna, illus. 2007. 10p. (J). (ps). 15.99 (978-0-525-47846-1(9) , Dutton Juvenile) Penguin Group (USA) Inc.

Hermes, Patricia. Hoppy Easter. 1998. (Little Apple Ser.). (J). (gr. 1-4). pap. 3.50 (978-0-590-38365-3(5) , Scholastic Paperbacks) Scholastic, Inc.

—Hoppy Easter. 1998. (J). (978-0-606-13489-7(1)) Tandem Library Bks.

High, Linda. Lap Talks with Granny at Easter. 2003. (J). pap. 9.95 (978-0-9661186-9-8(3)) Books for Children of the World.

Hill, Eric. Spot's Easter Surprise. Hill, Eric, illus. 2007. 10p. (J). (ps-k). bds. 5.99 (978-0-399-24743-9(2) , Putnam Juvenile) Penguin Group (USA) Inc.

—Spot's First Easter: A Lift-the-flap Book. Hill, Eric, illus. 2004. (Illus.). 12p. (J). (ps-1). bds. 7.99 (978-0-399-24245-8(7) , Putnam Juvenile) Penguin Group (USA) Inc.

—Spot's First Easter: A Lift-the-flap Book. 2004. (Illus.). 24p. (J). pap. 6.99 (978-0-14-240084-5(X) , Puffin) Penguin Group (USA) Inc.

Hillert, Margaret. Happy Easter, Dear Dragon. Kock, Carl, illus. rev. exp. ed. 2007. (Beginning to Read Ser.). 32p. (J). lib. bdg. 18.60 (978-1-59953-038-3(4)) Norwood Hse. Pr.

Holcomb, Nan. Of Easter Eggs & Things. Yoder, Dot, illus. l.t. ed. 2000. 32p. (J). (ps-2). lib. bdg. 5.95 (978-0-944727-42-3(5)) Jason & Nordic Pubs.

Holmes, Andy. Bible for Me: Easter. Voltz, Ralph, illus. 2006. 48p. (J). 9.99 (978-1-4003-0698-5(1)) Nelson, Thomas Inc.

Holub, Joan. Happy Easter Eggs. Holub, Joan, illus. 2005. (Illus.). 12p. (J). bds. 5.99 (978-0-689-86476-6(0) , Little Simon) Simon & Schuster Children's Publishing.

Hooray It's Easter! 1999. (Easter Mini Storybooks Ser.: Vol. 1). (Illus.). 32p. (J). (978-0-7666-0247-2(8) , Honey Bear Bks.) Modern Publishing.

Hope, Laura Lee. Freddie & Flossie & the Easter Egg Hunt. Downer, Maggie, illus. 2006. 32p. (J). lib. bdg. 15.00 (*978-1-4242-0966-8(8)) Fitzgerald Bks.

—Freddie & Flossie & the Easter Egg Hunt. Downer, Maggie, illus. 2006. (Bobbsey Twins Ser.). 32p. (J). pap. 3.99 (978-1-4169-1029-9(8) , Aladdin) Simon & Schuster Children's Publishing.

—Freddie & Flossie & the Easter Egg Hunt. 2006. (Ready-To-Read Ser.). (Illus.). 32p. (J). (ps-2). 21.35 (978-1-59961-100-6(7)) Spotlight.

Innovative Kids Staff. My Easter Basket. Filipowich, Bob, illus. 2006. (Soft Shapes Ser.). 6p. (J). (ps). 9.99 (978-1-58476-469-4(4) , IKIDS) Innovative Kids.

James, Brian. Easter Bunny's on His Way! 2005. pap. (*978-0-439-74530-7(6)) Scholastic, Inc.

Jenisch, Betty. Rennie. 2007. 9.00 (*978-0-8059-8947-2(1)) Dorrance Publishing Co., Inc.

Joyce, William. The True Story of E. Astor Bunnyman. 2004. (J). 15.99 (978-0-06-050831-9(0)); (Illus.). lib. bdg. 16.89 (978-0-06-050832-6(9)) HarperCollins Pubs. (Geringer, Laura Book).

Kafarakis, Katherine & Kouzes, Nicholas. Esther's Easter Dress: A Young Girl's Adventure Through Holy Week. 1999. (J). (gr. 3-6). pap. 8.95 (978-1-880971-49-9(6)) Light & Life Publishing Co.

Katz, Danny. Big Bad Bunnies. 2007. (Bites Ser.). 72p. (Orig.). (J). pap. 3.95 (978-0-7624-2924-0(0) , Running Pr. Kids) Running Pr. Bk. Pubs.

Katz, Karen. Where Are Baby's Easter Eggs? Katz, Karen, illus. 2008. 14p. (J). bds. 6.99 (*978-1-4169-4924-4(0) , Little Simon) Simon & Schuster Children's Publishing.

Kempf, Molly. Easter Egg Hunt. MJ Illustrations Staff & Huxtable, T., illus. 2008. (Strawberry Shortcake Ser.). 16p. (J). (ps-1). 4.99 (*978-0-448-44713-1(4) , Grosset & Dunlap) Penguin Group (USA) Inc.

Kenney, Cindy. An Easter Carol. 2004. (Illus.). 48p. 12.99 (978-0-310-70673-1(4)) Zonderkidz.

Kinnear, Kay. Deedee's Easter Surprise. Park, Julie, illus. 2003. 32p. (J). pap. 9.99 (978-0-7459-4443-2(4) , Lion) Lion Hudson plc GBR. *Dist:* Trafalgar Square Publishing.

Knudsen, Michelle & Apperley, Dawn. Easter Basket. 2002. (Easter Weave Ser.). (Illus.). 14p. (J). 4.99 (978-0-689-84725-7(4) , Little Simon) Simon & Schuster Children's Publishing.

—Easter Egg. 2002. (Easter Weave Ser.). (Illus.). 14p. (J). 4.99 (978-0-689-84726-4(2) , Little Simon) Simon & Schuster Children's Publishing.

Korman, Justine. The Grumpy Easter Bunny. McQueen, Lucinda, illus. 2004. 32p. (J). 3.50 (978-0-439-63595-0(0)) Scholastic, Inc.

Krensky, Stephen. Milo the Really Big Bunny. Suber, Melissa, illus. 2006. 32p. (J). (ps-1). 14.95 (978-0-689-87345-4(X)) Simon & Schuster Children's Publishing.

Kroll, Steven. The Biggest Easter Basket Ever. 2008. 32p. pap. 4.99 (***978-0-545-01702-2(5)*** , Cartwheel Bks.) Scholastic, Inc.

Kroll, Virginia. Easter Eggs for Anya: A Ukrainian Celebration of New Life in Christ. Comport, Sally Wern, illus. 2007. (Traditions of Faith Ser.). 40p. (J). 15.99 (978-0-310-71079-0(0)) Zonderkidz.

Kroll, Virginia L. Easter Eggs for Anya: A Ukrainian Celebration of New Life in Christ. Comport, Sally Wern, illus. 2007. (Traditions of Faith from Around the World Ser.). (J). (***978-1-4287-2360-3(9)***) Zonderkidz.

Landolf, Diane Wright. Here Comes Peter Cottontail: The Movie. Kapow Pictures Pty Ltd, illus. movie tie-in ed. 2006. 24p. (J). (gr. k-ps). pap. 3.99 (978-0-375-83491-2(5) , Golden Bks.) Random Hse. Children's Bks.

Lanza, Barbara, illus. The Great Golden Easter Egg Hunt. 2000. 12p. (J). (ps-1). bds. 10.95 (978-0-439-14262-5(8) , Cartwheel Bks.) Scholastic, Inc.

Larsen, Kirsten. Dora's Rainbow Egg Hunt. Savitsky, Steven, illus. 2006. (Dora the Explorer Ser.). 14p. (J). bds. 6.99 (978-1-4169-0798-5(X) , Simon Spotlight/Nickelodeon) Simon & Schuster Children's Publishing.

Lee, Quinlan B. Care Bears: Easter Egg Hunt. Johnson, Jay, illus. 2005. (Care Bears Ser.). 24p. (J). 3.50 (978-0-439-69161-1(3)) Scholastic, Inc.

Lenski, Lois. The Easter Rabbit's Parade. 2004. (Illus.). 40p. (J). (ps-1). 12.95 (978-0-375-82748-8(X) , Random Hse. Bks. for Young Readers) Random Hse. Children's Bks.

Lewandowski, Frrich. The First Easter Bunny. 1999. (Illus.). 24p. (J). (ps-3). 9.50 (978-0-9646439-2-5(8)) Ambassador Bks., Inc.

Lewison, Wendy Cheyette. Easter Bunny's Amazing Egg Machine. 2002. (ps-2). lib. bdg. 10.95 (978-0-613-83538-1(7)) Tandem Library Bks.

Little Fish Easter Merchandiser. (J). 128.16 (978-0-8307-2908-1(9) , Gospel Light) Gospel Light Pubns.

Loesch, Joe. He Is Risen: The True Meaning of Easter As Told by God's Animals. Hutchinson, Cheryl, ed. Cox, Brian T., illus. unabr. ed. 1999. (Bible Stories for Kids Ser.). 56p. (gr. k-5). reprint ed. 16.95 incl. audio compact disk (978-1-932332-09-4(X)) Toy Box Productions.

Maccarone, Grace. Peter Rabbit's Happy Easter. 2008. 11p. bds. 5.99 (***978-0-545-03784-6(0)*** , Cartwheel Bks.) Scholastic, Inc.

—Peter Rabbit's Happy Easter. McPhail, David, illus. 2006. 32p. (J). pap. 5.99 (978-0-439-79139-7(1)) Scholastic, Inc.

Machle, Rick. Ester's Easter Tale: How the Easter Bunny Came to Be. Nervig, Sandy, illus. 1999. 36p. (J). pap. 7.99 (978-0-9670375-0-9(6)) Growing Ideas, L.L.C.

MacKall, Dandi Daley. Easter Adventure. 1998. (Illus.). (J). (ps-2). (Puzzle Club Mysteries Ser.). 32p. 7.00 (978-0-570-05474-0(5) , 56-1937GJ); (Puzzle Club Ser.: Vol. 6). 80p. pap. 4.99 (978-0-570-05479-5(6) , 56-1942GJ) Concordia Publishing Hse.

—My Happy Easter Morning. O'Neill, Rachael, illus. 2006. (Carry Me Along Ser.). 24p. (J). 6.99 (978-0-310-70940-4(7)) Zonderkidz.

Man-Kong, Mary. Eggstra-Special Easter! Nowell, Christopher, illus. 2007. 12p. (J). (ps-1). pap. 6.99 (978-0-375-84012-8(5) , Golden Bks.) Random Hse. Children's Bks.

Marchesani, Laura. My Little Pony: Easter Celebration Reusable Sticker Book. 2008. (My Little Pony Ser.). 12p. (J). 6.99 (***978-0-06-123467-5(2)*** , Harper Festival) HarperCollins Pubs.

Marzollo, Jean. Ten Little Eggs. Marzollo, Jean, illus. 2004. (Illus.). 24p. (J). (ps-1). 10.99 (978-0-06-053052-5(9) , Harper Festival) HarperCollins Pubs.

Masino, Brian. Easter Bunny's on His Way. 2007. 24p. (J). pap. 3.99 (978-0-439-87389-5(4) , Cartwheel Bks.) Scholastic, Inc.

Matthews, Derek. Happy Snappy Easter Egg Hunt. 2006. (Happy Snappy Bks.). (Illus.). 10p. (J). 4.95 (978-1-59223-565-0(4) , Silver Dolphin Bks.) Advantage Pubs. Group.

Mayer, Mercer. Happy Easter, Little Critter. Mayer, Mercer, illus. 2000. (Little Critter Ser.). (Illus.). 24p. (J). (gr. k-k). pap. 3.99 (978-0-307-11723-6(5) , 11723, Random Hse. Bks. for Young Readers) Random Hse. Children's Bks.

—It's Easter. Mayer, Mercer, illus. 2007. (Little Critter Ser.). 20p. (J). pap. 6.99 (978-0-06-053974-0(7) , Harper Festival) HarperCollins Pubs.

McCafferty, Catherine, et al. Tigger's Bouncy Easter. Kleven, Dean, illus. 2002. (Disney's Winnie the Pooh Ser.). (J). (978-0-7853-6672-0(5)) Publications International, Ltd.

McQueen, Lucinda. Little Chick's Easter Surprise. 1999. (Illus.). 10p. (J). (ps-1). pap. 3.50 (978-0-590-64985-8(X)) Scholastic, Inc.

—Little Lamb's Easter Surprise. 1999. (Illus.). 10p. (J). (ps-1). pap. 3.50 (978-0-590-41968-0(4)) Scholastic, Inc.

McQueen, Lucinda & Shaw, Gina. Little Bunny's Easter Surprise. 1999. (Illus.). 10p. (J). (ps-1). pap. 3.50 (978-0-590-65029-8(7)) Scholastic, Inc.

—Little Duck's Easter Surprise. 1999. (Illus.). 10p. (J). (ps-1). pap. 3.50 (978-0-590-68130-8(3)) Scholastic, Inc.

Medearis, Deanna. Bunny's Easter Hunt. Bratun, Katy, illus. 2006. (Cuddle & Read Ser.). 24p. (J). (ps-ps). 6.95 (978-1-4027-2019-2(X)) Sterling Publishing Co., Inc.

Mickey, Mouse Clubhouse. Mickeys Easter Hunt. rev. ed. 2007. 16p. pap. 4.99 (***978-1-4231-0747-7(0)***) Disney Pr.

Modesitt, Jeanne. Little Bunny's Easter Surprise. Spowart, Robin, illus. 2002. 32p. (J). pap. 5.99 (978-0-689-84895-7(1) , Aladdin) Simon & Schuster Children's Publishing.

Mody, Monica. Barney's Easter Party! Baker, Darrell, illus. 2000. (Barney Ser.). 22p. (J). (ps-k). pap. 5.99 (978-1-57064-714-7(3)) Scholastic, Inc.

Moore, Raina. Easter Basket Surprise! Dillard, Sarah, illus. 2008. 16p. (J). 6.99 (***978-0-06-117105-5(0)*** , Harper Festival) HarperCollins Pubs.

Morgan, Ruth. The Funny Easter Bunny. 2003. (Illus.). 22p. per. 1.95 (978-1-932338-10-2(1)) Lifevest Publishing, Inc.

Mouse Works Staff. Happy Easter, Pooh! Friendly Tales. 2000. (Winnie the Pooh Ser.). (Illus.). 10p. (J). (ps-k). bds. 6.99 (978-0-7364-1056-4(2)) Hyperion Pr.

Mussenbrock, Anne. Easter Notes. 2004. 12p. (J). (ps-k). 5.99 (978-1-59384-037-2(3)); bds, 5.99 (978-1-59384-038-9(1)) Parklane Publishing.

Myra, Harold Lawrence. Easter Bunny, Are You for Real? Kurisu, Jane, illus. 2006. 18p. (J). bds. 6.99 (978-1-4003-0632-9(9)) Nelson, Thomas Inc.

Nelson, Steve & Rollins, Jack. Here Comes Peter Cottontail. Levy, Pamela R., illus. 2007. 26p. bds. 12.99 (***978-0-8249-6690-4(2)***); Set. pap. 16.99 (***978-0-8249-6689-8(9)***) Ideals Pubns. (Candy Cane Pr.).

Nye, Ann Marie, ed. Biggest Easter Egg. 2006. (Clifford the Big Red Dog Ser.). (Illus.). 32p. (J). pap. 3.99 (978-0-439-78954-7(0)) Scholastic, Inc.

Ostby, Kristin. Very Special Easter Baskets: Paas. Artful Doodlers Limited Staff, illus. 2007. 16p. (J). 3.99 (978-0-448-44486-4(0) , Grosset & Dunlap) Penguin Group (USA) Inc.

Parent, Nancy. Clifford's Big Red Easter. Cuddy, Robin, illus. 2003. (Clifford, the Big Red Dog Ser.). 7p. (J). (ps up). bds. 4.99 (978-0-439-43428-7(9)) Scholastic, Inc.

Park, Barbara. Junie B., First Grader: Dumb Bunny. Brunkus, Denise, illus. 2007. (Junie B. Jones Ser.: No. 27). 128p. (J). (gr. 1-4). 11.99 (978-0-375-83809-5(0) , Random Hse. Bks. for Young Readers) Random Hse. Children's Bks.

Parry, Alan. Badger's Easter Surprise. Parry, Linda, illus. 2004. (Oaktree Wood Ser.). 16p. (ps-3). 15.00 (978-0-687-04813-7(3)) Abingdon Pr.

Pfister, Marcus. Henri Egg Artiste. Pfister, Marcus, illus. 2008. 32p. (J). (ps). 15.95 (***978-0-7358-2130-9(5)***) North-South Bks., Inc.

Pingry, Patricia A. A Child's Easter. Britt, Stephanie McFetridge, illus. 2001. 32p. (J). (ps-3). 12.95 (978-0-8249-4197-0(7) , Ideals Children's Bks.) Ideals Pubns.

Piper, Sophie. Little Bunnys Easter. 2008. (Illus.). 32p. (J). pap. 10.95 (***978-0-7459-4961-1(4)***) Lion Hudson plc GBR. *Dist:* Independent Pubs. Group.

Random House Disney Staff. Pooh's Easter Basket. 2005. (Illus.). 10p. (J). (gr. k-k). bds. 3.99 (978-0-7364-2301-4(X) , RH/Disney) Random Hse. Children's Bks.

Random House Disney Staff & Braybrooks, Ann. The Easter Bear? Yee, Josie, illus. 2003. 24p. (J). (gr. k-3). pap. 3.99 (978-0-7364-1298-8(0) , RH/Disney) Random Hse. Children's Bks.

La Reina Ester. (Libros Arco (Spanish Arch(R) Books) Ser.).Tr. of Just in Time Esther. (SPA.). 24p. (J). 2.49 (978-0-7586-0497-2(1)) Concordia Publishing Hse.

Reitze, Glenn Logan. Ernie the Easter Hippopotamus: A Comic Adventure for Anytime. Reitze, Glenn Logan, illus. 2007. (Illus.). 50p. (J). lib. bdg. 19.95 (***978-0-88265-040-1(8)*** , Fine Art Editions) North American International.

Reitze, Glenn Logan, illus. & text. Ernie the Easter Hippotamus: A Comic Adventure for Anytime. Reitze, Glenn Logan, text. 2007. (J). pap. (***978-0-88265-041-8(6)***) North American International.

Ritchie, Joseph R. An Easter Basket Peek a Boo! Halverson, Lydia, illus. 2007. 14p. bds. 7.99 (***978-0-8249-6688-1(0)*** , Candy Cane Pr.) Ideals Pubns.

—Peter Cottontail's Easter Egg Hunt. Thornburgh, Rebecca McKillip, illus. 2004. 12p. (J). (ps-k). bds. 9.95 (978-0-8249-6522-8(1)) Ideals Pubns.

—Peter Cottontail's Easter Surprise. Rasmussen, Wendy, illus. 2006. 18p. (J). bds. 9.95 (978-0-8249-6627-0(9) , Candy Cane Pr.) Ideals Pubns.

Roberts, Bethany. Easter Mice! Cushman, Doug, illus. 2003. 32p. (J). (gr. k-ps). tchr. ed. 13.00 (978-0-618-16455-4(3) , Clarion Bks.) Houghton Mifflin Co. Trade & Reference Div.

Ruelle, Karen Gray. Easter Egg Disaster: A Harry & Emily Adventure. Ruelle, Karen Gray, illus. (Holiday House Readers Ser.). (Illus.). 32p. (J). (gr. k-3). pap. 4.95 (978-0-8234-1823-7(5)) Holiday Hse., Inc.

—Easter Egg Disaster: A Harry & Emily Adventure. (Illus.). 32p. (J). (gr. k-3). tchr. ed. 14.95 (978-0-8234-1806-0(5)) Holiday Hse., Inc.

Running Press Staff. Easter Bunny's Peek-a-Boo Party. 2009. (Illus.). 8p. (J). pap. 9.95 (978-0-7624-2928-8(3) , Running Pr. Kids) Running Pr. Bk. Pubs.

—Silly Goose's Lost Easter Eggs. 2006. (Illus.). 8p. (J). 4.95 (978-0-7624-2632-4(2) , Running Pr. Kids) Running Pr. Bk. Pubs.

Running Press Staff & Studio Books Staff. Easter Bunny's Egg Hunt. 2006. (Illus.). 8p. (J). 4.95 (978-0-7624-2633-1(0) , Running Pr. Kids) Running Pr. Bk. Pubs.

Samuel, Catherine. Timmy's Eggs-Ray Vision. Saunders, Zina, illus. 2005. (Fairly OddParents Ser.). 16p. (J). pap. 5.99 (978-0-689-87229-7(1) , Simon Spotlight/Nickelodeon) Simon & Schuster Children's Publishing.

Samuel, Catherine & Hartman, Butch. Timmy's Eggs-Ray Vision. Saunders, Zina, illus. 2005. (J). (***978-1-4155-8053-0(7)*** , Simon Spotlight/Nickelodeon) Simon & Schuster Children's Publishing.

Sasso, Sandy Eisenberg. Abuelita's Secret Matzahs. Bryer, Diana, illus. 2005. 32p. (J). pap. 9.99 (978-1-57860-177-6(0)) Emmis Bks.

Schiller, Rachel & S. I. International Staff. Marshmallow Love. 2007. (Peeps Ser.). 32p. (J). 4.99 (978-1-4169-3372-4(7) , Simon Scribbles) Simon & Schuster Children's Publishing.

Scholastic, Inc. Staff. Barney's Favorite Easter Stories, 2 vols., Set. Amaral, Gayla, ed. Sharp, Chris & Valentine-Ruppe, June, illus. 2001. (Barney Ser.). 48p. (J). (ps-k). pap. 4.99 (978-1-58668-072-5(2)) Scholastic, Inc.

—Hop to It! A Scholastic Treasury of Easter Tales. Torres, Melissa, ed. McPhail, David M., illus. 2003. 224p. (J). (ps-3). pap. 10.99 (978-0-439-44267-1(2) , Cartwheel Bks.) Scholastic, Inc.

Schultz, Charles M. It's the Easter Beagle, Charlie Brown. 2006. (Illus.). 128p. 4.95 (978-0-7624-2695-9(0) , Running Pr. Minature Editions) Running Pr. Bk. Pubs.

Schulz, Charles M. It's the Easter Beagle, Charlie Brown. 2002. lib. bdg. 14.15 (978-0-613-61781-9(9)) Tandem Library Bks.

Shulman, Mark. Storytime Stickers: Easter Bunny. Swanson, Maggie, illus. 2007. (Storytime Stickers Ser.). 16p. (J). pap. 4.95 (978-1-4027-3363-5(1)) Sterling Publishing Co., Inc.

Shulman, Mark & Less, Emma. Little Scribbles: Easter Fun. Harpster, Steve, illus. 2005. (Little Scribbles Ser.). 128p. bds. 5.95 (978-1-4027-2256-1(7)) Sterling Publishing Co., Inc.

—My Easter Basket. Ledger, Bill, illus. 2006. 14p. bds. 5.95 (978-1-4027-2178-6(1)) Sterling Publishing Co., Inc.

Silverhardt, Lauryn. Happy Easter, Sprinkles! Kanemoto, Dan, illus. 2008. (Blue's Clues Ser.). 12p. (J). bds. 5.99 (***978-1-4169-4775-2(2)*** , Simon Spotlight/Nickelodeon) Simon & Schuster Children's Publishing.

Smath, Jerry. Best Easter Eggs Ever! 2003. (gr. k-3). lib. bdg. 11.25 (978-0-613-66616-9(X)) Tandem Library Bks.

Snyder, Bethany. Herbie's Easter Bunny. Campbell, Jenny, illus. 2001. 24p. (J). (ps-3). 7.95 (978-1-57102-145-8(0)) Warehousing & Fulfillment Specialists, LLC (WFS, LLC).

Spafford, Suzy. Witzy's Backyard Easter Hunt. 2002. (Little Suzy's Zoo Ser.). (Illus.). 15p. (J). bds. 5.99 (978-0-439-36778-3(6)) Scholastic, Inc.

Stephens, Monique Z. The Easter Bonnet Parade: All Aboard Reading Station Stop 1. S. I. Artists Staff, illus. 2004. (All Aboard Reading Ser.). 32p. (J). (ps-2). mass mkt. 3.99 (978-0-448-43486-5(5) , Grosset & Dunlap) Penguin Group (USA) Inc.

Stoeke, Janet Morgan. Minerva Louise & the Colorful Eggs. 2006. (Illus.). 24p. (J). (ps). 15.99 (978-0-525-47633-7(4) , Dutton Juvenile) Penguin Group (USA) Inc.

Sypolt, Carl W. Fibber Lygood at Christmas, Easter, & St. Patrick's Day. 2006. 108p. (J). pap. 10.95 (978-0-7414-2982-7(9)) Infinity Publishing.

Talkington, Bruce. Disney's: Winnie the Pooh's - Easter. 1998. 32p. (J). 5.95 (978-0-7868-3202-6(9)) Hyperion Bks. for Children.

Tangvald, Christine Harder. The Best Thing about Easter. Nobens, Cheryl A., illus. 2006. 28p. (J). (ps-2). 7.99 (978-0-7847-1285-6(9) , 04039) Standard Publishing.

Taylor-Butler, Christine. Lamb's Easter Surprise. Johnson, Cathy Ann, illus. 2006. 24p. (J). (ps-ps). 6.95 (978-1-4027-2020-8(3)) Sterling Publishing Co., Inc.

Taylor, Shirley A. The Cross in the Egg. Hall, Wendell E., illus. 1999. 32p. (J). (ps-2). 15.95 (978-0-87483-549-6(6)) August Hse. Pubs., Inc.

Tegen, Katherine. The Story of the Easter Bunny. Lambert, Sally Anne, illus. 40p. (J). 2007. pap. 6.99 (978-0-06-058781-9(4) , Harper Trophy); 2005. 12.99 (978-0-06-050711-4(X)); 2005. lib. bdg. 14.89 (978-0-06-050712-1(8)) HarperCollins Pubs.

Tudor, Tasha. Tale for Easter. 2004. lib. bdg. 14.15 (978-0-613-88066-4(8)) Tandem Library Bks.

—A Tale for Easter. Tudor, Tasha, illus. 2004. (Illus.). 32p. (J). pap. 5.99 (978-0-689-86694-4(1) , Aladdin) Simon & Schuster Children's Publishing.

Verschuren, Ineke. The Easter Story Book. 2001. (Illus.). 240p. (J). pap. 19.95 (978-0-86315-146-0(9)) Floris Bks. GBR. *Dist:* Gryphon Hse., Inc., SteinerBooks, Inc.

Walburg, Lori. The Legend of the Easter Egg. 2004. (Illus.). 26p. (J). bds. 6.99 (978-0-310-70785-1(4)) Zonderkidz.

—The Legend of the Easter Egg. Bernardin, James, illus. 1999. 32p. (J). 15.99 (978-0-310-22447-1(0)) Zonderkidz.

Wang, Margaret. Easter Egg Hunt. Johnson, Richard, illus. 2005. 10p. (J). bds. 9.95 (978-1-58117-375-8(X) , Intervisual/Piggy Toes) Dalmatian Pr.

Wangerin, Walter, Jr. & Ladwig, Tim. Peter's First Easter. 2000. (Illus.). 48p. (J). 14.99 (978-0-310-22217-0(6)) Zonderkidz.

Warne, Frederick. Peter Rabbit's Easter. 2004. (Peter Rabbit Seedlings Ser.). (Illus.). 12p. (J). (ps). bds. 6.99 (978-0-7232-4953-5(9) , Warne) Penguin Group (USA) Inc.

Wasserman, Veronica. The Egg-Painting Party: Paas. Artful Doodlers Limited Staff, illus. 2007. 24p. (J). 4.99 (978-0-448-44487-1(9) , Grosset & Dunlap) Penguin Group (USA) Inc.

Wax, Wendy. It's Easter, Eliza! 2004. (gr. k-3). lib. bdg. 11.80 (978-0-613-73447-9(5)) Tandem Library Bks.

Weaver, Alexis Rae. Hunter Bunny Saves Easter. Kohnke, Jennifer M., illus. 2002. (Hunter Bunny: Vol. 1). 42p. (J). (ps-2). per. (978-0-9712473-6-9(6)) Golden Bunny Publishing.

Weigelt, U. & Kadmon, C. Hide, Easter Bunny, Hide! 2006. (Illus.). 32p. (J). 16.95 (978-0-7358-2054-8(6)) North-South Bks., Inc.

Weiss, Ellen, et al. Hello Kitty's Easter Bonnet Surprise. Hirashima, Jean, illus. 2004. 22p. (J). (ps-3). 12.95 (978-0-8109-4819-8(2)) Abrams, Harry N., Inc.

Wells, Rosemary. Max's Chocolate Chicken. Wells, Rosemary, illus. 2002. (Max the Bunny Ser.). (Illus.). (J). 13.19 (978-0-7587-3110-4(8)) Book Wholesalers, Inc.

—Max's Chocolate Chicken. Wells, Rosemary, illus. 2000. (Max & Ruby Ser.). (Illus.). 32p. (J). (gr. k-2). pap. 5.99 (978-0-14-056672-7(4) , Puffin) Penguin Group (USA) Inc.

—Max's Chocolate Chicken. 1999. (Max & Ruby Ser.). (Illus.). 32p. (J). (gr. k-2). 16.99 (978-0-670-88713-2(7) , Viking Juvenile) Penguin Group (USA) Inc.

—Max's Chocolate Chicken. 2000. (Max & Ruby Ser.). (J). (gr. k-2). (978-0-606-18431-1(7)) Tandem Library Bks.

Wells, Rosemary. Max's Easter Surprise. 2008. (Max & Ruby Ser.). 24p. (J). (ps-k). pap. 3.99 (***978-0-448-44783-4(5)*** , Grosset & Dunlap) Penguin Group (USA) Inc.

Wilhelm, Hans. Quacky Ducky's Easter Egg. Wilhelm, Hans, illus. 2004. (Illus.). 14p. (J). (ps up). 5.99 (978-0-06-053430-1(3) , Harper Festival) HarperCollins Pubs.

—Quacky Ducky's Easter Fun. Wilhelm, Hans, illus. 2004. (Illus.). 14p. (J). (ps up). 5.99 (978-0-06-053431-8(1) , Harper Festival) HarperCollins Pubs.

Willson, Sarah. La Canasta Pascual de Dora. Hall, Susan T., illus. 2004. (Dora the Explorer Ser.).Tr. of Dora's Easter Basket. (SPA.). 32p. (J). 5.99 (978-0-689-86649-4(6) , Libros Para Ninos) Simon & Schuster Children's Publishing.

—Chuckie Meets the Beastie Bunny. 2000. (gr. k-3). lib. bdg. 11.25 (978-0-613-21347-9(5)) Tandem Library Bks.

—Dora's Easter Basket. Hall, Susan T., illus. 2003. (Dora the Explorer Ser.). 32p. (J). 5.99 (978-0-689-85240-4(1) , Simon Spotlight/Nickelodeon) Simon & Schuster Children's Publishing.

—Dora's Easter Basket. 2003. (ps-2). lib. bdg. 14.15 (978-0-613-73354-0(1)) Tandem Library Bks.

—Rugrats' Easter Surprise. 2002. (gr. k-3). lib. bdg. 14.15 (978-0-613-51321-0(5)) Tandem Library Bks.

Willson, Sarah & Hot Animation Staff, Animation. Bob's Spring Parade. Giles, Mike, illus. 2005. (Bob the Builder Ser.). 16p. (J). pap. 5.99 (978-0-689-87475-8(8) , Simon Spotlight) Simon & Schuster Children's Publishing.

Wing, Natasha. The Night Before Easter. Couri, Kathy, illus. 1999. (All Aboard Bks.). 32p. (J). (ps-3). pap. 3.99 (978-0-448-41873-5(8) , Grosset & Dunlap) Penguin Group (USA) Inc.

Winters, Kay. How Will the Easter Bunny Know? 1999. (978-0-606-17670-5(5)); (gr. 3-6). lib. bdg. 12.40 (978-0-613-16128-2(9)) Tandem Library Bks.

Witt, Rici. God, Santa & the Easter Bunny. 2006. 32p. (J). pap. 12.95 (978-1-4116-8014-2(6)) Lulu.com.

Wolf, Jackie, et al. My Sparkle Egg Book. 2005. (Illus.). (J). (***978-1-57151-750-0(2)***) Playhouse Publishing.

Wolif, T. Hal & His Pal Al: The Easter Bunny's Helpers. 2007. (Illus.). 36p. per. 12.97 (***978-1-932344-93-6(4)***) Thornton Publishing.

Woods, Denise & McKelvain, Dana. The Legend of the Donkey's Cross. 2004. (Illus.). 32p. (J). per. 12.99 (978-1-58930-112-2(9)) Selah Publishing Group, LLC.

Yoon, Salina. Easter Egg Surprise. Yoon, Salina, illus. 2005. (Illus.). 12p. (J). (ps-1). bds. 5.99 (978-0-8431-1364-8(2) , Price Stern Sloan) Penguin Group (USA) Inc.

Zabrosky, Joseph. Sunny & Hunny, 2 vols., 4 bks. l.t. ed. 2005. (Illus.). 32p. (J). per. (978-0-9768831-1-1(2)) Elohim Bks.

Ziefert, Harriet. I Need an Easter Egg! Rader, Laura, illus. 1999. (Holiday Lift-the-Flap Ser.). 16p. (J). (ps-1). 5.99 (978-0-689-81994-0(3) , Little Simon) Simon & Schuster Children's Publishing.

—Ready for Easter: A Rosie Rabbit Book. Rader, Laura, illus. 2005. 14p. (J). bds. 7.95 (978-1-4027-2296-7(6)) Sterling Publishing Co., Inc.

—Where's Nicky's Easter Egg? Brown, Richard, illus. 2003. 7p. bds. 6.95 (978-1-929766-80-2(7)) Blue Apple Bks.

—Where's the Easter Bunny? Schumacher, Claire, illus. 2006. 16p. (J). (ps-ps). pap. 5.95 (978-1-4027-2017-8(3)) Sterling Publishing Co., Inc.

Zolotow, Charlotte. The Bunny Who Found Easter. Craig, Helen, illus. 1998. 32p. (J). (gr. k-3). tchr. ed. 16.00 (978-0-395-86265-0(5)) Houghton Mifflin Co. Trade & Reference Div.

—The Bunny Who Found Easter. Craig, Helen, illus. 2001. (J). (ps-3). lib. bdg. 14.10 (978-0-613-35493-6(1)) Tandem Library Bks.

—The Bunny Who Found Easter. 2001. (Illus.). (J). 12.75 (978-0-606-21091-1(1)) Tandem Library Bks.

EASTER—POETRY

Grimes, Nikki. At Jerusalem's Gate: Poems of Easter. Frampton, David, illus. 2005. 48p. 20.00 (978-0-8028-5183-3(5)) Eerdmans, William B. Publishing Co.

Lawrie, Robin, illus. Song of the Morning: Easter Stories & Poems for Children: A Special Collection. 192p. (J). pap. 13.99 (978-0-7459-3951-3(1) , Lion) Lion Hudson plc GBR. *Dist:* Trafalgar Square Publishing.

Stiegemeyer, Julie. Bright Easter Day. Spellman, Susan, illus. 2005. (ENG.). 32p. (J). 9.99 (978-0-7586-0818-5(7)) Concordia Publishing Hse.

EASTER ISLAND

Arnold, Caroline. Easter Island: Giant Stone Statues Tell of a Rich & Tragic Past. (Illus.). 48p. (J). (gr. 4-6). 2004. pap. 5.95 (978-0-618-48605-2(4)); 2000. tchr. ed. 15.00 (978-0-395-87609-1(5)) Houghton Mifflin Co. Trade & Reference Div. (Clarion Bks.).

Jackson, Kay. The Ancient Mystery of Easter Island. 2006. (Robbie Reader Ser.). (Illus.). 32p. (J). (gr. 1-4). lib. bdg. (978-1-58415-495-2(0)) Mitchell Lane Pubs., Inc.

Pelta, Kathy. Rediscovering Easter Island. 2005. (How History Is Invented Ser.). (Illus.). 112p. (gr. 6-12). lib. bdg. 23.93 (978-0-8225-4890-4(9)) Lerner Publishing Group.

Pfeil, Susan. Professor Kiwi, Explorer of the Seven Seas: The Eye of Easter Island. 2005. (J). per. 6.95 (978-1-59094-062-4(8)) Jawbone Publishing Corp.

Simmons, Alex. Mysteries of the Past: A Chapter Book. 48p. (J). 2006. (gr. 2-4). pap. 4.95 (978-0-516-25451-7(0)); 2005. (Illus.). (ps-ps). 22.50 (978-0-516-25184-4(8)) Scholastic Library Publishing. (Children's Pr.).

Underwood, Deborah. The Easter Island Statues. 2004. (Illus.). 48p. (J). 26.20 (978-0-7377-3065-4(X), Greenhaven Pr., Inc.) Thomson Gale.

EASTERN EUROPE

see Europe, Eastern

EASTERN SEABOARD

see Atlantic States

EASTMAN, GEORGE, 1854-1932

Aller, Susan Bivin. George Eastman. 2004. (History Maker Bios Ser.). (Illus.). 48p. (J). (gr. 3-5). lib. bdg. 26.60 (978-0-8225-0200-5(3)) Lerner Publishing Group.

Fandel, Jennifer. George Eastman & the Kodak Camera. 2007. 32p. (J). (***978-0-7368-6848-8(8)***) Capstone Pr., Inc.

Ford, Carin T. George Eastman: The Kodak Camera Man. 2004. (Famous Inventors Ser.). (Illus.). 32p. (J). lib. bdg. 22.60 (978-0-7660-2247-8(1)) Enslow Pubs., Inc.

Gillis, Jennifer Blizin. George Eastman. 2004. (Illus.). 32p. (J). pap. 6.50 (978-1-4034-5334-1(9)); lib. bdg. 22.79 (978-1-4034-5326-6(8)) Heinemann Library.

Mattern, Joanne. George Eastman & Photographic Film. 2004. (Uncharted, Unexplored, & Unexplained Ser.). (Illus.). 48p. (J). (gr. 4-8). lib. bdg. 29.95 (978-1-58415-258-3(3)) Mitchell Lane Pubs., Inc.

Pflueger, Lynda. George Eastman: Bringing Photography to the People. 2002. (Historical American Biographies Ser.). (Illus.). 128p. (YA). (gr. 6-12). lib. bdg. 26.60 (978-0-7660-1617-0(X)) Enslow Pubs., Inc.

Rausch, Monica. George Eastman & the Camera. 2006. (Illus.). 24p. (J). pap. (***978-0-8368-7730-4(6)***); lib. bdg. (***978-0-8368-7499-0(4)***) Stevens, Gareth Inc. (Weekly Reader Early Learning Library).

—George Eastman y la Camara. 2006. (ENG & SPA.). (J). pap. (***978-0-8368-7999-5(6)***); lib. bdg. (***978-0-8368-7994-0(5)***) Stevens, Gareth Inc. (Weekly Reader Early Learning Library).

EATING DISORDERS

Here are entered works on gross disturbances in eating behavior as a subclass of mental disorders. .

Amos, Janine. Kim Won't Eat. 2002. (Body Matters Ser.). (Illus.). 32p. (YA). 19.99 (978-0-84234-109-4(X), Cherrytree Books) Evans Publishing Group GBR. *Dist:* Independent Pubs. Group.

Barrett, Cece. The Dangers of Diet Drugs & Other Weight-Loss Products. 1999. (Teen Health Library of Eating Disorder Prevention). (Illus.). 64p. (J). (gr. 7-12). lib. bdg. 26.50 (978-0-8239-2768-5(7), EDDIDR) Rosen Publishing Group, Inc., The.

Berry, Joy Wilt. Eating Disorders: Good Answers to Tough Questions. Bartholomew, illus. rev. ed. 2000. (Good Answers to Tough Questions Ser.: Vol. 7). 48p. (J). (gr. 4-7). pap. 4.95 (978-1-58634-217-3(7), 01-0901-07) Goldstar Publishing, Inc.

Bjorklund, Ruth. Eating Disorders. 2005. (Health Alert Ser.). (Illus.). 64p. (J). (978-0-7614-1914-3(4), Benchmark Bks.) Cavendish, Marshall Corp.

Brinkerhoff, Shirley. Drug Therapy & Eating Disorders. 2003. (Encyclopedia of Psychiatric Drugs & Their Disorders Ser.). (Illus.). 128p. (J). lib. bdg. (978-1-59084-565-3(X)) Mason Crest Pubs.

Chiu, Christina. Eating Disorder Survivors Tell Their Stories. 1999. (Teen Eating Disorder Prevention Library). 64p. (YA). (gr. 3-10). pap. 6.95 (978-1-56838-259-3(6)) Hazelden Publishing & Educational Services.

Clarke, Julie & Kirby-Payne, Ann. Understanding Weight & Depression. 2005. (Teen Eating Disorder Prevention Book Ser.). (Illus.). 192p. (J). (gr. 7-12). lib. bdg. 25.25 (978-0-8239-2994-8(9), E2WEDE) Rosen Publishing Group, Inc., The.

Cotter, Alison. Anorexia & Bulimia. 2001. (Diseases & Disorders Ser.). (Illus.). 120p. (J). (gr. 6-9). 32.45 (978-1-56006-725-2(X), GML12001-178076, Lucent Bks.) Thomson Gale.

Danger Zone: Dieting & Eating Disorders, 6 bks., Set. Incl. Anorexia. Watson, Stephanie. lib. bdg. 27.95 (***978-1-4042-1996-0(X)***); Binge Eating. Watson, Stephanie. lib. bdg. 27.95 (***978-1-4042-1998-4(6)***); Bulimia. Watson, Stephanie. lib. bdg. 27.95 (***978-1-4042-1997-7(8)***); Diet Drugs. Williams, Kara. lib. bdg. 27.95 (***978-1-4042-1994-6(3)***); Diet Fads. Zahensky, Barbara A. lib. bdg. 27.95 (***978-1-4042-1999-1(4)***); Negative Body Image. Willett, Edward. lib. bdg. 27.95 (***978-1-4042-1995-3(1)***); (Illus.). 64p. (J). (gr. 7-12). 2006. 2007. Set lib. bdg. 167.70 (***978-1-4042-1061-5(X)***) Rosen Publishing Group, Inc., The.

Davis, Brangien. What's Real, What's Ideal: Overcoming a Negative Body Image. 1999. (Teen Eating Disorder Prevention Library). 64p. (YA). (gr. 3-10). pap. 6.95 (978-1-56838-258-6(8)) Hazelden Publishing & Educational Services.

A Deadly Secret Set. 1999. (Illus.). (J). 10.00 (978-1-892421-87-6(9), 119SET) Boulden Publishing.

Esherick, Joan. Diet & Your Emotions: The Comfort Food Falsehood. 2004. (Obesity Ser.). (Illus.). 104p. (J). (ps-7). lib. bdg. 23.95 (978-1-59084-950-7(7)) Mason Crest Pubs.

Gay, Kathlyn. Am I Fat? The Obesity Issue for Teens. 2006. (Issues in Focus Today Ser.). (Illus.). 112p. (YA). (gr. 8-12). lib. bdg. 31.93 (978-0-7660-2527-1(6)) Enslow Pubs., Inc.

—Eating Disorders: Anorexia, Bulimia & Binge Eating. 2003. (Diseases & People Ser.). (Illus.). 112p. (YA). (gr. 6-12). lib. bdg. 26.60 (978-0-7660-1894-5(6)) Enslow Pubs., Inc.

Goodnough, David. Eating Disorders. 1999. (Hot Issues Ser.). (Illus.). 64p. (YA). (gr. 6-12). lib. bdg. 27.93 (978-0-7660-1336-0(7)) Enslow Pubs., Inc.

Gottlieb, Lori. Stick Figure: A Diary of My Former Self. 2001. (Illus.). (J). (978-0-606-21465-0(8)) Tandem Library Bks.

Graves, Bonnie. Anorexia. 2000. (Perspectives on Mental Health Ser.). (Illus.). 64p. (J). (gr. 4-6). lib. bdg. 23.93 (978-0-7368-0431-8(5), LifeMatters Bks.) Capstone Pr., Inc.

—Bulimia. 2000. (Perspectives on Mental Health Ser.). (Illus.). 64p. (J). (gr. 4-6). lib. bdg. 23.93 (978-0-7368-0430-1(7), LifeMatters Bks.) Capstone Pr., Inc.

Hubble, Joan. Understanding Anorexia Nervosa. 1999. (Teen Eating Disorder Prevention Library). 144p. (gr. 7-12). pap. 6.95 (978-1-56838-260-9(X)) Hazelden Publishing & Educational Services.

Kalodner, Cynthia R. Too Fat or Too Thin? A Reference Guide to Eating Disorders. 2003. (Illus.). 240p. 56.95 (978-0-313-31581-7(7), GR1581, Greenwood Pr.) Greenwood Publishing Group, Inc.

Kolodny, Nancy. The Beginner's Guide to Eating Disorders Recovery. 2004. (Illus.). 224p. pap. 14.95 (978-0-936077-45-1(X)) Gurze Bks.

Kubersky, Rachel. Everything You Need to Know about Eating Disorders. rev. ed. 1999. (Need to Know Library). (Illus.). 64p. (YA). (gr. 7-12). lib. bdg. 25.25 (978-0-8239-3078-4(5), NTEADI) Rosen Publishing Group, Inc., The.

Kutz-Mellem, Sharon. Honest Talk about Eating Disorders. 2000. 28p. (YA). (978-1-57895-096-6(1)) Bridge Resources.

Lauri S. Friedman. Eating Disorders. 2006. (Writing the Critical Essay Ser.). (Illus.). 244p. (J). 29.95 (978-0-7377-3641-0(0), Greenhaven Pr., Inc.) Thomson Gale.

Lawton, Sandra Augustyn, ed. Eating Disorders Information for Teens: Health Tips about Anorexia, Bulimia, Binge Eating, & Other Eating Disorders. 2005. (Teen Health Ser.). (Illus.). 337p. (J). (gr. 7 up). 65.00 (978-0-7808-0783-9(9)) Omnigraphics, Inc.

Levete, Sarah. Eating & Health. 2005. (Illus.). 32p. (J). (gr. 3-7). lib. bdg. 27.10 (978-1-59604-049-6(1)) Stargazer Bks.

Lynette, Rachel. Anorexia. 2005. (Understanding Diseases & Disorders Ser.). (Illus.). 48p. (J). (gr. 3-8). lib. bdg. 26.20 (978-0-7377-3176-7(1), Greenhaven Pr., Inc.) Thomson Gale.

McGraw, Jay. The Ultimate Weight Solution for Teens: The 7 Keys to Weight Freedom. 2004. 291p. reprint ed. pap. 16.00 (978-0-7567-8159-0(0)) DIANE Publishing Co.

Moehn, Heather. Understanding Eating Disorder Support Groups. 2005. (Teen Eating Disorder Prevention Book Ser.). (Illus.). 192p. (YA). (gr. 7-12). lib. bdg. 25.25 (978-0-8239-2992-4(2), E2UGR) Rosen Publishing Group, Inc., The.

Normandi, Carol Emery. Over It: A Teen's Guide to Getting Beyond Obsessions with Food & Weight. 2001. (gr. 7-12). lib. bdg. 23.40 (978-0-613-79250-9(5)) Tandem Library Bks.

Normandi, Carol Emery & Roark, Laurelee. Over It: A Teen's Guide to Getting Beyond Obsessions with Food & Weight. 2001. (Illus.). 224p. (gr. 8-12). pap. 13.95 (978-1-57731-148-5(5)) New World Library.

O'Brien, Eileen. Starving to Win: Athletes & Eating Disorders. 1998. (Teen Health Library of Eating Disorder Prevention). (Illus.). 64p. (J). (gr. 4-6). lib. bdg. 26.50 (978-0-8239-2764-7(4), EDATEA) Rosen Publishing Group, Inc., The.

Ojeda, Auriana. Dieting. 2003. (Teen Decisions Ser.). (Illus.). 152p. (J). (gr. 10 up). pap. 24.95 (978-0-7377-1257-5(0), Greenhaven Pr., Inc.) Thomson Gale.

Orr, Tamra B. When the Mirror Lies: Anorexia, Bulimia, & Other Eating Disorders. 2006. (Illus.). 144p. (J). (gr. 9-12). 30.50 (978-0-531-16791-5(7)); pap. 17.95 (***978-0-531-17977-2(X)***) Scholastic Library Publishing. (Watts, Franklin).

Owens, Peter. Teens Health & Obesity. 2005. (Gallup Youth Survey, Major Issues & Trends Ser.). (Illus.). 112p. (J). (ps-7). lib. bdg. 22.95 (978-1-59084-872-2(1)) Mason Crest Pubs.

Peacock, Judith. Compulsive Overeating. 2000. (Perspectives on Mental Health Ser.). (Illus.). 64p. (J). (gr. 4-6). lib. bdg. 23.93 (978-0-7368-0437-0(4), LifeMatters Bks.) Capstone Pr., Inc.

Robbins, Paul R. Anorexia & Bulimia. 1998. (Diseases & People Ser.). (Illus.). 128p. (YA). (gr. 6-12). lib. bdg. 26.60 (978-0-7660-1047-5(3)) Enslow Pubs., Inc.

Sherry, Clifford J. Drugs & Eating Disorders. rev. ed. 1999. (Drug Abuse Prevention Library). (Illus.). 64p. (J). (gr. 7-12). lib. bdg. 25.25 (978-0-8239-3005-0(X), DREADI) Rosen Publishing Group, Inc., The.

Silverstein, Alvin, et al. The Eating Disorders Update: Understanding Anorexia, Bulimia, & Binge Eating. 2008. (J). (***978-0-7660-2802-9(X)***) Enslow Pubs., Inc.

Simpson, Carolyn. Understanding Compulsive Eating. 2005. (Teen Eating Disorder Prevention Book Ser.). (Illus.). 192p. (YA). (gr. 7-12). lib. bdg. 25.25 (978-0-8239-2989-4(2), E2COEA) Rosen Publishing Group, Inc., The.

Smith, Erica. Anorexia Nervosa: When Food Is the Enemy. 1999. (Teen Eating Disorder Prevention Library). 64p. (YA). (gr. 3-10). pap. 6.95 (978-1-56838-256-2(1)) Hazelden Publishing & Educational Services.

Smolin, Lori A. & Grosvenor, Mary B. Nutrition & Eating Disorders. 2004. (Eating Right Ser.). (J). pap. (978-0-7910-8016-0(1)); (Illus.). 160p. (gr. 9-13). 35.00 (978-0-7910-7851-8(5)) Facts On File, Inc. (Chelsea Hse.).

Strada, Jennifer L. Eating Disorders. rev. ed. 2001. (Overview Ser.). (Illus.). 96p. (YA). (gr. 6-9). lib. bdg. 29.95 (978-1-56006-659-0(8), LML00902-178012, Lucent Bks.) Thomson Gale.

A Teen Eating Disorder Prevention Book. 2005. (Illus.). 192p. (gr. 7-12). lib. bdg. 227.40 (978-0-8239-3904-6(9)) Rosen Publishing Group, Inc., The.

A Teen Eating Disorder Prevention Book: Set 1: Finding Answers, 6 bks. Incl. Understanding Compulsive Eating. Simpson, Carolyn. (YA). lib. bdg. 25.25 (978-0-8239-2989-4(2), E2COEA); Understanding Eating Disorder Support Groups. Moehn, Heather. (YA). lib. bdg. 25.25 (978-0-8239-2992-4(2), E2UGR); Understanding Exercise Addiction. Johnson, Marlys. (YA). lib. bdg. 25.25 (978-0-8239-2990-0(6), E2EXAD); Understanding Sports & Eating Disorders. Stanley, Debbie. (YA). lib. bdg. 25.25 (978-0-8239-2993-1(0), E2SPEA); Understanding the Risks of Diet Drugs. Walker, Pamela. (YA). lib. bdg. 25.25 (978-0-8239-2991-7(4), E2DIDR); Understanding Weight & Depression. Clarke, Julie & Kirby-Payne, Ann. (J). lib. bdg. 25.25 (978-0-8239-2994-8(9), E2WEDE); 192p. (gr. 7-12). (Illus.). 2005. Set lib. bdg. 151.50 (978-0-8239-9052-8(4), E2FIAN) Rosen Publishing Group, Inc., The.

A Teen Eating Disorder Prevention Book: Set 2: Seeking Support, 6 bks. Incl. Understanding Anorexia Nervosa. Stanley, Debbie. lib. bdg. 25.25 (978-0-8239-2877-4(2), E2ANNE); Understanding Bulimia Nervosa. Stanley, Debbie. lib. bdg. 25.25 (978-0-8239-2878-1(0), E2BULI); Understanding Food & Your Family. Tattersall, Clare. lib. bdg. 25.25 (978-0-8239-2860-6(8), E2FOFA); Understanding Negative Body Image. Moe, Barbara. lib. bdg. 25.25 (978-0-8239-2865-1(9), E2BOIM); Understanding Recovery from Eating Disorders. Rocha, Toni L. lib. bdg. 25.25 (978-0-8239-2884-2(5), E2UNRE); Understanding Weight-Loss Programs. Monroe, Judy. lib. bdg. 25.25 (978-0-8239-2866-8(7), E2WEPR); 192p. (YA). (gr. 7-12). (Illus.). 1999. Set lib. bdg. 151.50 (978-0-8239-9323-9(X)) Rosen Publishing Group, Inc., The.

The Teen Health Library of Eating Disorder Prevention. 2005. (Illus.). 64p. (gr. 7-12). lib. bdg. 219.45 (978-0-8239-3905-3(7)) Rosen Publishing Group, Inc., The.

Trueit, Trudi Strain. Eating Disorders. (Life Balance Ser.). 2004. (YA). (gr. 5-8). pap. 6.95 (978-0-531-16610-9(4)); 2003. (Illus.). 80p. (J). 20.50 (978-0-531-12218-1(2)) Scholastic Library Publishing. (Watts, Franklin).

Turck, Mary. Food & Emotions. 2000. (Nutrition & Fitness Ser.). (Illus.). 64p. (J). (gr. 4-6). lib. bdg. 23.93 (978-0-7368-0711-1(X), LifeMatters Bks.) Capstone Pr., Inc.

Vander Hook, Sue. Eating Disorders. 2000. (Understanding Illness Ser.). (Illus.). 32p. (YA). (gr. 4-10). lib. bdg. 16.95 (978-1-58340-024-1(9)) Smart Apple Media.

Vollstadt, Elizabeth Weiss. Teen Eating Disorders. 1999. (Teen Issues Ser.). (Illus.). 112p. (YA). (gr. 4-12). lib. bdg. 27.45 (978-1-56006-516-6(8), LML00902-177874, Lucent Bks.) Thomson Gale.

Wagner, Viqi. Eating Disorders 2007. 2007. (Opposing Viewpoints Ser.). 240p. (J). (gr. 10-12). 34.95 (***978-0-7377-3348-8(9)***); pap. 23.70 (***978-0-7377-3349-5(7)***) Thomson Gale. (Greenhaven Pr., Inc.).

Walker, Ida. Youth with Eating Disorders: When Food Is an Enemy. 2008. (J). (***978-1-4222-0144-2(9)***) Mason Crest Pubs.

Walker, Pamela. Understanding the Risks of Diet Drugs. 2005. (Teen Eating Disorder Prevention Book Ser.). (Illus.). 192p. (YA). (gr. 7-12). lib. bdg. 25.25 (978-0-8239-2991-7(4), E2DIDR) Rosen Publishing Group, Inc., The.

Warbrick, Caroline. Eating Disorders. 2002. (Just the Facts Ser.). (Illus.). 56p. (J). (gr. 6-8). lib. bdg. 25.64 (978-1-58810-678-0(0)) Heinemann Library.

Watson, Stephanie. Anorexia. 2006. (Danger Zone Ser.). (Illus.). 64p. (J). (gr. 7-12). lib. bdg. 27.95 (***978-1-4042-1996-0(X)***) Rosen Publishing Group, Inc., The.

—Binge Eating. 2006. (Danger Zone Ser.). (Illus.). 64p. (J). (gr. 7-12). lib. bdg. 27.95 (***978-1-4042-1998-4(6)***) Rosen Publishing Group, Inc., The.

—Bulimia. 2006. (Danger Zone Ser.). (Illus.). 64p. (J). (gr. 7-12). lib. bdg. 27.95 (***978-1-4042-1997-7(8)***) Rosen Publishing Group, Inc., The.

Whelan, Jo. Eating Disorders. 2001. (Health Issues Ser.). (Illus.). 64p. (YA). (gr. 6-8). lib. bdg. 28.54 (978-0-7398-4421-2(0)) Raintree.

Willett, Edward. Negative Body Image. 2006. (Danger Zone Ser.). (Illus.). 64p. (J). (gr. 7-12). lib. bdg. 27.95 (***978-1-4042-1995-3(1)***) Rosen Publishing Group, Inc., The.

Yancey, Diane. Eating Disorders. 1999. (Medical Library: up). (Illus.). 144p. (gr. 4-7). lib. bdg. 26.90 (978-0-7613-0950-5(0), Twenty-First Century Bks.) Lerner Publishing Group.

Zeckhausen, Dina. Full Mouse, Empty Mouse: A Tale of Food & Feelings. Boyd, Brian, illus. 2007. 40p. (J). (gr. 2-7). 14.95 (***978-1-4338-0132-7(9)***, 4418003); pap. 8.95 (***978-1-4338-0133-4(7)***, 4418004) American Psychological Assn. (Magination Pr.).

EATING DISORDERS—FICTION

Antieau, Kim. Mercy, Unbound. 2006. (Illus.). 176p. (YA). pap. 6.99 (978-1-4169-0893-7(5), Simon Pulse) Simon & Schuster Children's Publishing.

Bennett, Cherie. Life in the Fat Lane. 1999. 272p. (YA). (gr. 7-12). pap. 5.99 (978-0-440-22029-9(7), Laurel Leaf) Random Hse. Children's Bks.

—Life in the Fat Lane. 1999. (YA). (gr. 7 up). pap., stu. ed. 57.24 incl. audio (978-0-7887-2665-1(X), 40825) Recorded Bks., LLC.

—Life in the Fat Lane. 1999. (YA). (978-0-606-16720-8(X)); (gr. 7-12). lib. bdg. 13.00 (978-0-613-16143-5(2)) Tandem Library Bks.

—Life in the Fat Lane. l.t. ed. 2000. 351p. (YA). (gr. 8-12). 21.95 (978-0-7862-2887-4(3)) Thorndike Pr.

Brinkerhoff, Shirley. Balancing Act. 1998. (Nikki Sheridan Ser.: Vol. 4). 208p. (J). (gr. 9-12). pap. 5.99 (978-1-56179-559-8(3)) Bethany Hse. Pubs.

Brooks, Bruce. Vanishing. 2000. (J). pap. 4.95 (978-0-06-440754-0(3)); 1999. 112p. (YA). (gr. 5 up). 14.89 (978-0-06-028237-0(1), Geringer, Laura Book) HarperCollins Pubs.

Burton, Rebecca. Leaving Jetty Road. (YA). (gr. 7). 2008. 272p. mass mkt. 6.50 (***978-0-553-49505-8(4)***, Laurel Leaf); 2006. 256p. 15.95 (978-0-375-83488-2(5), Knopf Bks. for Young Readers); 2006. 256p. lib. bdg. 17.99 (978-0-375-93488-9(X), Knopf Bks. for Young Readers) Random Hse. Children's Bks.

Carlson, Melody. Faded Denim. 2006. 224p. (YA). pap. 12.99 (978-1-57683-537-1(5), Think Bks.) NavPress Publishing Group.

Davenport, Jennifer. Anna Begins. 2007. 21.95 (***978-0-930773-83-0(7)***) Black Heron Pr.

Friend, Natasha. Perfect. 2004. 232p. (J). 16.95 (978-1-57131-652-3(3)); pap. 6.95 (978-1-57131-651-6(5)) Milkweed Editions.

Hanson, Ann. Thin Veils. 1999. 105p. (YA). (gr. 5-9). 14.95 (978-1-881636-99-1(2)); 207p. (J). (gr. 6-10). pap. 8.95 (978-1-881636-87-8(9)) Windsor Hse. Publishing Group, The.

Hautzig, Deborah. Second Star to the Right. 1999. (978-0-606-17428-2(1)) Tandem Library Bks.

Hautzig, Deborah, frwd. Second Star to the Right. 1999. (Illus.). 176p. (YA). (gr. 5-9). reprint ed. pap. 5.99 (978-0-14-130580-6(0), Puffin) Penguin Group (USA) Inc.

Hoekstra, Molly. Upstream: A Novel. 2001. 221p. (YA). (gr. 6-12). pap. 15.95 (978-0-936389-86-8(9)) Tudor Pubs., Inc.

Kaslik, Ibi. Skinny. 2006. (YA). 256p. 16.95 (978-0-8027-9608-0(7)); viii, 244p. (***978-1-4287-0474-9(4)***) Walker & Co.

LeMieux, Anne Connelly. Dare to Be, M. E.! 1998. (J). (gr. 3-7). pap. 3.99 (978-0-380-72889-3(3)) HarperCollins Pubs.

Martin, Ann M. Amalia: Diary Two. 1998. (California Diaries: Bk. 9). (Illus.). 10p. (YA). (gr. 6-8). pap. 4.50 (978-0-590-02385-6(3)) Scholastic, Inc.

—Maggie: Diary Two. 1998. (California Diaries: Bk. 8). (YA). (gr. 6-8). pap. 3.99 (978-0-590-02383-2(7)) Scholastic, Inc.

—Maggie: Diary Two. 1998. (California Diaries: Bk. 8). (YA). (gr. 6-8). (978-0-606-13239-8(2)) Tandem Library Bks.

McGowan, Sharlene. Macaroni Monday. 2007. 112p. (YA). per. 10.95 (***978-0-595-45984-1(6)***) iUniverse, Inc.

Rodriguez Vidal, Andrea. Who Is Devouring Me? 2006. (Little Books for Big Kids Ser.). (Illus.). 32p. (J). pap. 9.95 (978-9974-7896-4-7(8)) Hardenville SA URY. *Dist:* Independent Pubs. Group.

Rosoff, Meg. How I Live Now. 2006. 250p. (YA). 23.95 (978-0-7862-8878-6(7)) Thorndike Pr.

Shapiro, Lawrence E. Freddy Fights Fat: An Emotional Literacy Book. Harpster, Steve, illus. 2004. (Emotional Literacy Ser.). 54p. (J). (gr. 2 up). 14.95 (978-0-9747789-5-2(8), 67873) CTC Publishing.

Sparks, Beatrice, ed. Kim: Empty Inside: The Diary of an Anonymous Teenager. 2002. 176p. (YA). (gr. 7 up). pap. 5.99 (978-0-380-81460-2(9)) HarperCollins Pubs.

A Story in the Life of the Shapette Family. 2004. (J). 17.95 (978-0-9747509-0-3(5)) Del Gatto, Maria.

Tokio, Marnelle. More Than You Can Chew. 2003. (gr. 7-12). lib. bdg. 18.75 (978-0-613-77305-8(5)) Tandem Library Bks.

—More Than You Can Chew. 2003. (Illus.). 240p. (J). (gr. 9 up). pap. 9.95 (978-0-88776-639-8(0)) Tundra Bks., Inc./Livres Toundra, Inc. CAN. *Dist:* Random Hse., Inc.

Vrettos, Adrienne Maria. Skin. 2007. 272p. (YA). pap. 6.99 (***978-1-4169-0656-8(8)***, Simon Pulse) Simon & Schuster Children's Publishing.

Wasserman, Robin. Gluttony. 2007. (Seven Deadly Sins Ser.). 256p. (YA). pap. 8.99 (978-1-4169-0719-0(X), Simon Pulse) Simon & Schuster Children's Publishing.

Weyland, Jack. Ashley & Jen. 2000. (Illus.). 287p. (YA). 16.95 (978-1-57345-803-0(1)) Deseret Bk. Co.

Willey, Margaret. The Bigger Book of Lydia. 2001. 228p. (YA). pap. 16.95 (978-0-595-17700-4(X), Backinprint.com) iUniverse, Inc.

ECCLESIASTICAL ARCHITECTURE

see Church Architecture

ECCLESIASTICAL ART

see Christian Art and Symbolism

ECCLESIASTICAL BIOGRAPHY

see Christian Biography

ECCLESIASTICAL FASTS AND FEASTS

see Fasts and Feasts

ECCLESIASTICAL HISTORY

see Church History

ECCLESIASTICAL RITES AND CEREMONIES

see Funeral Rites and Ceremonies; Rites and Ceremonies

ECOLOGY

see also Adaptation (Biology); Forest Ecology; Geographical Distribution of Animals and Plants; Human Ecology; Marine Ecology; Plant Ecology; Wetland Ecology

El Agua en Peligro. (Coleccion Operacion Tierra). (SPA.). 46p. (YA). (gr. 5 up). pap. 12.95 (978-950-11-0976-4(3) , SGM799) Sigmar ARG. *Dist:* Continental Bk. Co., Inc.

El Aire Contaminado. (Coleccion Operacion Tierra). (SPA.). 46p. (YA). (gr. 5 up). pap. 12.95 (978-950-11-0975-7(5) , SGM801) Sigmar ARG. *Dist:* Continental Bk. Co., Inc.

Allaby, Michael. Biomes of the World, 9 vols. 1999. (Illus.). 576p. (YA). (gr. 5-8). lib. bdg. 259.00 (978-0-7172-9341-4(6) , Grolier) Scholastic Library Publishing.

—Deserts & Semideserts. 2003. (gr. 5-8). lib. bdg. 18.20 (978-0-613-78194-7(5)) Tandem Library Bks.

—The Environment. 2000. (Inside Look Ser.). (Illus.). 48p. (J). (gr. 4 up). lib. bdg. 26.00 (978-0-8368-2725-5(2)) Stevens, Gareth Inc.

Allaby, Michael, et al. Biomes of the Earth Set. 2006. (Biomes of the Earth Ser.). 144-144p. (gr. 6-12). 395.00 (978-0-8160-5319-3(7)) Facts On File, Inc.

—Deserts & Semideserts. 2002. (Biomes Atlases Ser.). (Illus.). 64p. (J). lib. bdg. 31.40 (978-0-7398-5247-7(7)) Raintree.

Allred, Sylvester. The DesertAlphabet Encyclopedia. Iverson, Diane, illus. 2006. 48p. (YA). pap. 7.95 (***978-0-88045-168-0(8)*** , NaturEncyclopedia) Stemmer Hse. Pubs., Inc.

Aloian, Molly. El Habitat de la Antartida. 2007. (SPA & ENG.). 32p. (J). (gr. 1-2). (***978-0-7787-8332-9(4)***) Crabtree Publishing Co.

—El Habitat del Artico. 2007. (SPA & ENG.). 32p. (J). (gr. 1-2). (***978-0-7787-8330-5(8)***) Crabtree Publishing Co.

—Habitats Subterraneos. 2007. (SPA.). 32p. (J). (gr. 1-2). (***978-0-7787-8331-2(6)***) Crabtree Publishing Co.

Aloian, Molly. Underground Habitats. 2006. (Illus.). 32p. (J). (gr. 2). (978-0-7787-2954-9(0)) Crabtree Publishing Co.

Aloian, Molly & Kalman, Bobbie. The Antarctic Habitat. 2006. (Introducing Habitats Ser.). (Illus.). 32p. (J). (gr. 2-4). lib. bdg. (978-0-7787-2956-3(7)) Crabtree Publishing Co.

—The Arctic Habitat. 2006. (Introducing Habitats Ser.). (Illus.). 32p. (J). (gr. 2-4). lib. bdg. (978-0-7787-2953-2(2)) Crabtree Publishing Co.

—El Habitat de la Antartida. rev. ed. 2007. (SPA & ENG.). 32p. (J). (gr. 1-2). pap. (***978-0-7787-8356-5(1)***) Crabtree Publishing Co.

—El Habitat del Artico. rev. ed. 2007. (SPA & ENG.). 32p. (J). (gr. 1-2). pap. (***978-0-7787-8354-1(5)***) Crabtree Publishing Co.

—Habitats Subterraneos. rev. ed. 2007. (SPA.). 32p. (J). (gr. 1-2). pap. (***978-0-7787-8355-8(3)***) Crabtree Publishing Co.

Amato, Carol A. Backyard Pets: Activities for Exploring Wildlife Close to Home. 2002. (gr. 3-6). lib. bdg. 22.20 (978-0-613-61361-3(9)) Tandem Library Bks.

—Backyard Pets: Activities for Exploring Wildlife Close to Home. Noll, Cheryl Kirk, illus. 2002. 128p. (gr. 3-7). pap. 12.95 (978-0-471-41693-7(2) , Wiley) Wiley, John & Sons, Inc.

Amsel, Sheri. The Everything Kids' Environment Book: Learn How You Can Help the Environment—by Getting Involved at School, at Home, or at Play. 2007. (Everything Kids' Ser.). (Illus.). 129p. (J). (gr. 4-7). per. 7.95 (***978-1-59869-670-7(X)***) Adams Media Corp.

Anderson, Sheila. Coast. 2008. (First Step Nonfiction - Landforms Ser.). (J). lib. bdg. 18.60 (***978-0-8225-8595-4(2)*** , Lerner Pubns.) Lerner Publishing Group.

Arms. Environmental Science: Enhanced Online Edition. 4th ed. 2004. 17.26 (978-0-03-037156-1(2)) Holt, Rinehart & Winston.

—Holt Environmental Science: Online Edition Upgrade. 4th ed. 2004. 31.93 (978-0-03-037176-9(7)); 7.93 (978-0-03-037218-6(6)) Holt, Rinehart & Winston.

Bailey, Jacqui. Staying Alive: The Story of a Food Chain. Lilly, Matthew, illus. 2006. (Science Works). 32p. (J). (gr. 3-6). 23.93 (978-1-4048-1595-7(3)) Picture Window Bks.

Baker, Lucy. Vida en las Desiertos. 2000. Tr. of Life in the Deserts. (Illus.). (J). (978-0-606-20970-0(0)) Tandem Library Bks.

—Vida en las Montanas. 2000. Tr. of Life in the Mountains. (Illus.). (J). (978-0-606-20971-7(9)) Tandem Library Bks.

Baldwin, Carol. Living by a River. 2003. (Living Habitats Ser.). (Illus.). 32p. (J). lib. bdg. 24.22 (978-1-4034-0842-6(4)); pap. 6.95 (978-1-4034-3226-1(0)) Heinemann Library.

—Living in a Desert. 2003. (Living Habitats Ser.). (Illus.). 32p. (J). lib. bdg. 24.22 (978-1-4034-0840-2(8)); pap. 6.95 (978-1-4034-3224-7(4)) Heinemann Library.

—Living in a Prairie. 2003. (Living Habitats Ser.). 32p. (J). lib. bdg. 24.22 (978-1-4034-0841-9(6)); (Illus.). pap. 6.95 (978-1-4034-3225-4(2)) Heinemann Library.

—Living in a Taiga. 2003. (Heinemann Infosearch Ser.). (Illus.). 32p. (J). lib. bdg. 24.22 (978-1-4034-2994-0(4)) Heinemann Library.

—Living in the Taiga. 2003. (Living Habitats Ser.). (Illus.). 32p. (J). pap. (978-1-4034-3236-0(8)) Heinemann Library.

—Living in the Tundra. 2003. (Heinemann Infosearch Ser.). (Illus.). 32p. (J). pap. 6.95 (978-1-4034-3235-3(X)); lib. bdg. 24.22 (978-1-4034-2991-9(X)) Heinemann Library.

—Living on a Mountain. 2003. (Living Habitats Ser.). (Illus.). 32p. (J). pap. (978-1-4034-3233-9(3)); lib. bdg. 24.22 (978-1-4034-2993-3(6)) Heinemann Library.

Ballance, Alison. Habitats of the World, 6 vols. 2000. (Illus.). (J). (978-0-7685-0544-3(5)); (978-0-7685-0546-7(1)); (978-0-7685-0547-4(X)); (978-0-7685-0549-8(6)); (978-0-7685-0548-1(8)); (978-0-7685-0545-0(3)) Dominie Pr., Inc.

Banting, Erinn. Tundras. 2005. (Illus.). 32p. (J). (gr. 4-6). lib. bdg. 24.45 (978-1-59036-347-8(7)); (ps-7). pap. 7.95 (978-1-59036-353-9(1)) Weigl Pubs., Inc.

Barnes, Julia. 101 Facts about Lakes. 2003. (One Hundred One Facts about Our World Ser.). (Illus.). 32p. (J). (gr. 3 up). lib. bdg. 23.33 (978-0-8368-3707-0(X)) Stevens, Gareth Inc.

—101 Facts about Rivers. 2003. (One Hundred One Facts about Our World Ser.). (Illus.). 32p. (J). (gr. 3 up). lib. bdg. 23.33 (978-0-8368-3711-7(8)) Stevens, Gareth Inc.

Barnett, Michelle Noble, et al. Theme Pockets - November: The First Thanksgiving; Native Americans; the Food Pyramid. Evans, Marilyn, ed. Larsen, Jo, illus. 1999. (Making Books with Pockets). 96p. (J). pap., tchr. ed. 12.99 (978-1-55799-708-1(X) , EMC 594) Evan-Moor Educational Pubs.

Barrett, Katharine, et al. Aquatic Habitats: Exploring Desktop Ponds. Bergman, Lincoln et al, eds. Klofkorn, Lisa et al, illus. 1998. (Great Explorations in Math & Science Ser.). 136p. (J). (gr. 2-6). pap. 16.00 (978-0-924886-01-0(3) , GEMS) Univ. of California, Berkeley, Lawrence Hall of Science.

Barron's Educational Editorial Staff. Amazing Nature. 1998. (Megascope Ser.). (Illus.). 64p. (J). (gr. 5). 6.95 (978-0-7641-5090-6(1)) Barron's Educational Series, Inc.

Bash, Barbara. Ancient Ones: The World of the Old-Growth Douglas Fir. Bash, Barbara, illus. 2nd ed. 2002. (Illus.). 32p. (J). (ps-6). reprint ed. pap., pap. 6.95 (978-1-57805-081-9(2)) Gibbs Smith, Publisher.

—Ancient Ones: The World of the Old-Growth Douglas Fir. 2002. (gr. 3-6). lib. bdg. 15.25 (978-0-613-79299-8(8)) Tandem Library Bks.

Beatty, Richard. Wetlands. 2002. (Biomes Atlases Ser.). (Illus.). 64p. (J). lib. bdg. 31.40 (978-0-7398-5251-4(5)) Raintree.

Beil, Karen Magnuson. Fire in Their Eyes: Wildfires & the People Who Fight Them. Beil, Karen Magnuson, photos by. 1999. (Illus.). 64p. (YA). (gr. 5-9). pap. 11.00 (978-0-15-201042-3(4) , Harcourt Paperbacks) Harcourt Children's Bks.

—Fire in Their Eyes: Wildfires & the People Who Fight Them. 1999. (gr. 5-8). lib. bdg. 19.95 (978-0-613-15785-8(0)) Tandem Library Bks.

Bell, Mary. Oceans. 2001. (Water Worlds Ser.). (Illus.). 32p. (J). (gr. 4 up). 28.00 (978-0-7910-6570-9(7) , 010355, Chelsea Hse.) Facts On File, Inc.

Benchmark Education Staff, compiled by. Cactus & Canyons & Ecosystems. 2005. spiral bd. 225.00 (***978-1-4108-5806-1(5)***) Benchmark Education Co.

—The Environment. 2006. spiral bd. 330.00 (***978-1-4108-7019-3(7));*** 2006. spiral bd. 209.00 (***978-1-4108-7147-3(9));*** 2005. (J). spiral bd. 265.00 (***978-1-4108-5764-4(6)***) Benchmark Education Co.

—Habitats. 2006. spiral bd. 330.00 (***978-1-4108-7015-5(4)***) Benchmark Education Co.

—Our Environment. 2006. spiral bd. 279.00 (***978-1-4108-7058-2(8)***) Benchmark Education Co.

—Science Theme: Habitats. 2005. spiral bd. 115.00 (***978-1-4108-5319-6(5)***) Benchmark Education Co.

—Science Theme: The Environment. 2005. spiral bd. 115.00 (***978-1-4108-5317-2(9)***) Benchmark Education Co.

—Watery World & Ecosystems. 2005. spiral bd. 225.00 (***978-1-4108-5815-3(4)***) Benchmark Education Co.

Bertolucci, Cristiano, et al. Night & Day. Cucchiariani, Fer, illus. 2003. (Contrasts Ser.). 32p. (J). (gr. 1-4). 14.95 (978-1-57768-523-4(7) , Waterbird Bks.) School Specialty Publishing.

Bi;;, Schuyler. Crocodile Crossing. 2005. (Soundprints' Amazing Animal Adventures! Ser.). (Illus.). 36p. (J). (ps-2). 8.95 incl. audio (978-1-59249-391-3(2) , SC7104) Soundprints.

Biomes & Habitats, 4 bks., Set. 2005. (Illus.). (J). (gr. 5-7). 98.00 (978-0-531-18755-5(1) , Watts, Franklin) Scholastic Library Publishing.

Biomes Atlases, 72 bks. (Illus.). 6 Pack. 2004. pap. 615.60 (978-1-4109-1246-6(9)); Set. 2003. pap. 107.40 (978-1-4109-0024-1(X)) Raintree.

Biomes Atlases Series, 12 bks., Set. 2003. 377.04 (978-0-7398-5518-8(2)); (Illus.). 251.36 (978-0-7398-5517-1(4)) Raintree.

Biomes of North America. 2004. (Illus.). lib. bdg. 7.95 (978-0-8225-4518-7(7)); Set. 2006. (J). (gr. 3-6). 84.95 (***978-0-8225-5304-5(X)***) Lerner Publishing Group.

Biomes, Science, & Animals of Biomes Collection. 2002. (Illus.). (J). pap. (978-0-7398-6948-2(5)) Steck-Vaughn.

Biomes Series: Complete Set. 2001. (Illus.). (J). pap. (978-0-7398-4671-1(X)) Steck-Vaughn.

Biomes/Science of the Biomes Collection. 2002. (Illus.). pap. (978-0-7398-6029-8(1)) Steck-Vaughn.

Biskup, Agnieszka. Exploring Ecosystems with Max Axiom, Super Scientist. Smith, Tod, illus. 2007. (J). (***978-0-7368-6842-6(9)***) Capstone Pr., Inc.

Bograd, Larry. The Rocky Mountains. 2001. (Ecosystems of North America Ser.). (Illus.). 64p. (J). (gr. 6 up). lib. bdg. 27.07 (978-0-7614-0925-0(4) , Benchmark Bks.) Cavendish, Marshall Corp.

Bosques en Extincion. (Coleccion Operacion Tierra). (SPA.). 46p. (YA). (gr. 5 up). pap. 12.95 (978-950-11-0977-1(1) , SGM800) Sigmar ARG. *Dist:* Continental Bk. Co., Inc.

Bradley, Catherine. Life in the Mountains: Animals, People, Plants. 2000. (gr. 3-6). lib. bdg. 15.25 (978-0-613-43344-0(0)) Tandem Library Bks.

—Life in the Plains: Animals, People, Plants. 2000. (gr. 3-6). lib. bdg. 15.25 (978-0-613-43346-4(7)) Tandem Library Bks.

—Life on the Plains. 2001. (World Book Ecology Ser.). (Illus.). 32p. (J). (978-0-7166-5230-4(7)) World Bk., Inc.

—Las Montanas. 2004. (Ecologia Ser.). (SPA., Illus.). 32p. (gr. 3-6). 12.95 (978-1-58728-979-8(2) , Two Can Publishing) T&N Children's Publishing.

Bredeson, Carmen. Tide Pools. 1999. (First Bks.). (Illus.). 64p. (J). (gr. 5-7). 22.00 (978-0-531-20368-2(9) , Watts, Franklin) Scholastic Library Publishing.

Brenner, Barbara. One Small Place by the Sea. Leonard, Tom, illus. 2004. (One Small Place Ser.). 32p. (J). (gr. k-3). 15.99 (978-0-688-17182-7(6)) HarperCollins Pubs.

Bull, Schuyler. Crocodile Crossing. Male, Alan, illus. 2005. (Amazing Animal Adventures Ser.). 36p. (J). (ps-2). 15.95 (978-1-59249-051-6(4) , B7104); pap. 6.95 (978-1-59249-052-3(2) , S7104) Soundprints.

—Crocodile Crossing. Male, Alan, illus. 2005. (Soundprints' Amazing Animal Adventures! Ser.). 36p. (J). (ps-2). 9.95 (978-1-59249-060-8(3) , PS7154) Soundprints.

Buller, Laura & Pollock, Steve. Ecology. 2005. (Dk eyewitness Bks.). (Illus.). 72p. (J). (gr. 4-7). lib. bdg. 19.99 (978-0-7566-1396-9(5)) Dorling Kindersley Publishing, Inc.

Burine. Shrublands. 2003. (Illus.). 64p. pap. 9.50 (978-1-4109-0015-9(0)) Raintree.

Burnie, David. Shrublands. 2003. (Biomes Atlases Ser.). (Illus.). 64p. (J). lib. bdg. 31.42 (978-0-7398-5514-0(X)) Raintree.

—Shrublands. 2003. (gr. 5-8). lib. bdg. 18.20 (978-0-613-78188-6(0)) Tandem Library Bks.

Burton, Lawrence D. Fish & Wildlife: Principles of Zoology & Ecology. 2nd rev. ed. 2001. (Illus.). 480p. (C). 100.95 (978-0-7668-3260-2(0)) Thomson Delmar Learning.

Butterworth, Nick & Inkpen, Mick. Wonderful Earth. 2003. (Illus.). 32p. 14.99 (978-1-85608-005-7(6)) Hunt, John Publishing Ltd. GBR. *Dist:* STL Distribution North America.

Byles, Monica. Los Polos. (Coleccion Tierra Viva).Tr. of Polar Lands. (SPA.). 32p. (YA). (gr. 5-8). (978-84-348-3372-2(7)) SM Ediciones.

Campbell, Andrew. Who Eats Who in Rivers & Lakes? 2006. (Food Chains in Action Ser.). (Illus.). 32p. (J). (978-1-58340-966-4(1)) Smart Apple Media.

—Who Eats Who in the Desert? 2006. (Food Chains in Action Ser.). (Illus.). 32p. (J). (978-1-58340-962-6(9)) Smart Apple Media.

Capeci, Anne. Food Chain Frenzy. Speirs, John, illus. 2004. (Magic School Bus Ser.). 96p. (J). pap. 4.99 (978-0-439-56050-4(0)) Scholastic, Inc.

Carole Telford and Rod Theodorou. Inside a Coral Reef. 2nd ed. 2006. (Illus.). 32p. (J). pap. (***978-1-4034-8797-1(9)***) Heinemann Library.

—Up a Rainforest Tree. 2nd ed. 2006. (Illus.). 32p. (J). pap. (***978-1-4034-8800-8(2)***) Heinemann Library.

Castaldo, Nancy F. Deserts: An Activity Guide for Ages 6-9. 2004. (Illus.). 128p. (J). pap. 14.95 (978-1-55652-524-7(9)) Chicago Review Pr., Inc.

Castner, James L. Surviving in the Rain Forest: Deep in the Amazon. 2002. (Deep in the Amazon Ser.). (Illus.). 32p. (J). (gr. 5 up). lib. bdg. 28.50 (978-0-7614-1126-0(7) , Benchmark Bks.) Cavendish, Marshall Corp.

Cefrey, Holly. Coniferous Forests. 2003. (Reading Power Ser.). (Illus.). 24p. (J). lib. bdg. 17.25 (978-0-8239-6455-0(8) , PowerKids Pr.) Rosen Publishing Group, Inc., The.

—Deciduous Forests. 2003. (Reading Power Ser.). (Illus.). 24p. (J). lib. bdg. 17.25 (978-0-8239-6454-3(X) , PowerKids Pr.) Rosen Publishing Group, Inc., The.

—Deserts. 2003. (Reading Power Ser.). (Illus.). 24p. (J). lib. bdg. 17.25 (978-0-8239-6456-7(6) , PowerKids Pr.) Rosen Publishing Group, Inc., The.

—Grasslands. 2003. (Reading Power Ser.). (Illus.). 24p. (J). lib. bdg. 17.25 (978-0-8239-6457-4(4) , PowerKids Pr.) Rosen Publishing Group, Inc., The.

—Oceans. 2003. (Reading Power Ser.). (Illus.). 24p. (J). lib. bdg. 17.25 (978-0-8239-6453-6(1) , PowerKids Pr.) Rosen Publishing Group, Inc., The.

Cerfolli, Fulvio. Adapting to the Environment. Stalio, Ivan, illus. 1999. (Everyday Life of Animals Ser.). 64p. (J). (gr. 4-6). 19.98 (978-0-8172-4196-4(5)) Raintree.

Chancellor, Deborah. The Kingfisher First Animal Picture Atlas. Lewis, Anthony, illus. 2006. (Kingfisher First Ser.). 48p. (J). (gr. k-3). 10.95 (978-0-7534-5988-1(4) , Kingfisher) Houghton Mifflin Co. Trade & Reference Div.

Chapman, Jenny & Reiss, Michael J. Environmental Biology. 2nd rev. ed. 2000. (Cambridge Advanced Sciences Ser.). (Illus.). 104p. pap. 15.00 (978-0-521-78727-7(0)) Cambridge Univ. Pr.

Childrens Press Staff. Earth Science & Ecology: Classroom Theme Set. 1998. (Rookie Read-About Science Ser.). (J). pap. 43.11 (978-0-516-29987-7(5) , Children's Pr.) Scholastic Library Publishing.

Claybourne, Anna. Mountains. 2004. (Geography Fact Files Ser.). (Illus.). (J). lib. bdg. 28.50 (978-1-58340-426-3(0)) Smart Apple Media.

Cobb, Allan B. Looking at the Interdependence of Plants, Animals, & the Environment with Graphic Organizers. 2005. (Using Graphic Organizers to Study the Living Environment Ser.). (Illus.). 48p. (J). (978-1-4042-0615-1(9)) Rosen Publishing Group, Inc., The.

Cole, Joanna. The Magic School Bus Explores the World of Animals. 2000. (Magic School Bus Ser.). (J). (gr. 1-4). (978-0-606-20063-9(0)) Tandem Library Bks.

—The Magic School Bus in the Rain Forest: A Book about Rainforest Ecology. 1998. (Magic School Bus Ser.). (Illus.). 32p. (J). (gr. 1-4). pap. 3.50 (978-0-590-81837-7(6)) Scholastic, Inc.

—The Magic School Bus in the Rain Forest: A Book about Rainforest Ecology. 2000. (Magic School Bus Ser.). (J). (gr. 1-4). (978-0-606-20064-6(9)) Tandem Library Bks.

Cole, Melissa S. Desert. 2003. (Wild America Habitats Ser.). (Illus.). 24p. (J). 24.94 (978-1-56711-799-8(6) , Blackbirch Pr., Inc.) Thomson Gale.

—Mountain. 2003. (Wild America Habitats Ser.). (Illus.). 24p. (J). 21.20 (978-1-56711-806-3(2) , Blackbirch Pr., Inc.) Thomson Gale.

—Prairies. 2003. (Wild America Habitats Ser.). (Illus.). 24p. (J). 22.45 (978-1-56711-807-0(0) , Blackbirch Pr., Inc.) Thomson Gale.

—Sand Bottoms. 2004. (Illus.). 24p. (J). 22.45 (978-1-56711-910-7(7) , Blackbirch Pr., Inc.) Thomson Gale.

—Tide Pools. 2004. (Illus.). 24p. (J). (978-1-56711-907-7(7) , Blackbirch Pr., Inc.) Thomson Gale.

Collard, Sneed B., III. Forest in the Clouds. Rothman, Michael, illus. 2000. 32p. (J). (ps-3). 16.95 (978-0-88106-985-3(X)); pap. 6.95 (978-0-88106-986-0(8)) Charlesbridge Publishing, Inc.

—Our Wet World. Needham, James M., illus. 1998. 32p. (J). (gr. 8-12). 16.95 (978-0-88106-267-0(7)); (gr. k-5). pap. 6.95 (978-0-88106-268-7(5)) Charlesbridge Publishing, Inc.

Como? (Coleccion Mil Preguntas). (SPA., Illus.). 24p. (J). pap. 5.50 (978-950-11-0612-1(8) , SGM128) Sigmar ARG. *Dist:* Continental Bk. Co., Inc.

Costain, Meredith. African Grasslands. 2000. (gr. k-3). lib. bdg. 11.80 (978-0-613-30211-1(7)) Tandem Library Bks.

Craighead, Shirley A. Bugling Elk & Sleeping Grizzlies: The Who, What, & When of Yellowstone & Grand Teton National Parks. 2004. (Illus.). 48p. pap. 9.95 (978-0-7627-2864-0(7) , Falcon) Globe Pequot Pr., The.

Crenson, Victoria. Horseshoe Crabs & Shorebirds: The Story of a Food Web. Cannon, Annie, illus. 2003. 32p. (J). 16.95 (978-0-7614-5115-0(3)) Cavendish, Marshall Corp.

Crossingham, John & Kalman, Bobbie. Seashore Food Chains. 2005. (Food Chains Ser.). (Illus.). 32p. (J). (978-0-7787-1949-6(9)); pap. (978-0-7787-1995-3(2)) Crabtree Publishing Co.

Cuando? (Coleccion Mil Preguntas). (SPA., Illus.). 24p. (J). pap. 5.50 (978-950-11-0610-7(1) , SGM101) Sigmar ARG. *Dist:* Continental Bk. Co., Inc.

Dahl, Michael. Do Ducks Live in the Desert? A Book about Where Animals Live. Haberstroh, Anne, illus. 2004. (Animals All Around Ser.). 24p. (J). (gr. k-2). 22.60 (978-1-4048-0290-2(8) , 1229500) Picture Window Bks.

—High, Higher, Highest: Animals That Go to Great Heights. Jensen, Brian, illus. 2005. (Animal Extremes Ser.). 24p. (J). (ps). lib. bdg. 22.60 (978-1-4048-1016-7(1)) Picture Window Bks.

Davidson, Avelyn. Beach Biology. 2007. (Shockwave: Life Science & Medicine Ser.). (Illus.). 36p. (J). (gr. 4-6). lib. bdg. 25.00 (***978-0-531-17764-8(5)*** , Children's Pr.) Scholastic Library Publishing.

Davis, Barbara J. Biomes & Ecosystems. 2006. (J). pap. (***978-0-8368-7872-1(8));*** lib. bdg. (***978-0-8368-7761-8(6)***) Stevens, Gareth Inc.

Davis, Wendy. City Park. 1998. (Habitats Ser.). (Illus.). 32p. (J). (gr. 2-3). pap. 6.95 (978-0-516-20370-6(3) , Children's Pr.) Scholastic Library Publishing.

Day. Taiga. 2003. (Biomes Atlas Ser.). (Illus.). 64p. pap. 9.50 (978-1-4109-0016-6(9)); pap. 48.30 (978-1-4109-0251-1(X)) Raintree.

Day, Trevor. Taiga. 2003. (Biomes Atlases Ser.). (Illus.). 64p. (J). lib. bdg. 31.42 (978-0-7398-5515-7(8)) Raintree.

—Taiga. 2003. (gr. 5-8). lib. bdg. 18.20 (978-0-613-78191-6(0)) Tandem Library Bks.

Delano, Marfe Ferguson. Deserts. 1999. (Nature Library). (Illus.). (J). (978-0-7922-7544-2(6)) National Geographic Society.

Dewin, Howard & Corwin, Jeff. Habitat Is Where It's At! A Sticker Book Experience. 2003. (Illus.). 31p. (J). (978-0-439-43595-6(1)) Scholastic, Inc.

Diagram Group Staff. Environment: An Illustrated Guide to Science. 2006. (Science Visual Resources Ser.). 208p. (YA). (gr. 6-12). 49.50 (978-0-8160-6165-5(3)) Facts On File, Inc.

Ditchfield, Christin. Soil. 2002. (True Book Ser.). (Illus.). 48p. (J). (gr. 3-5). pap. 25.00 (978-0-516-22344-5(5) , Children's Pr.) Scholastic Library Publishing.

Doeden. Grasslands. 2000. (Biomes Ser.). (Illus.). (J). pap. (978-0-7398-4159-4(9)) Steck-Vaughn.

Donde? (Coleccion Mil Preguntas). (SPA., Illus.). 24p. (J). pap. 5.50 (978-950-11-0609-1(8) , SGM098) Sigmar ARG. *Dist:* Continental Bk. Co., Inc.

Dorling Kindersley Publishing Staff. Rivers & Lakes. (Eye Wonder Ser.). (Illus.). 48p. (J). (gr. k-3). 2003. 9.99 (978-0-7894-9046-9(3)); 2002. lib. bdg. 17.99 (978-0-7894-9047-6(1)) Dorling Kindersley Publishing, Inc.

Drake, Jane & Love, Ann. Cool Woods: A Trip Around the World's Boreal Forest. Kiss, Andrew, illus. 2003. 80p. (J). (gr. 4). 19.95 (978-0-88776-608-4(0)) Tundra Bks., Inc./Livres Toundra, Inc. CAN. *Dist:* Random Hse., Inc.

Dunphy, Madeleine. Here Is the Coral Reef. Leonard, Tom, illus. 2006. (Web of Life Ser.). 32p. (J). 16.95 (978-0-9773795-5-2(8)); pap. 9.95 (978-0-9773795-4-5(X)) Web of Life Children's Bks.

—Here Is the Southwestern Desert. Coe, Anne, illus. 2006. (Web of Life Ser.). 32p. (J). 16.95 (978-0-9773795-7-6(4)); pap. 9.95 (978-0-9773795-6-9(6)) Web of Life Children's Bks.

Dunphy, Madeline. Here Is the Coral Reef. Leonard, Tom, illus. 1998. 32p. (J). (ps-3). 14.95 (978-0-7868-0163-3(8)) Hyperion Bks. for Children.

—Here Is the Coral Reef. Leonard, Tom, illus. 1998. 32p. (J). (ps-3). 15.49 (978-0-7868-2135-8(3)) Hyperion Bks. for Children.

La Ecologia: Las Mil Caras de la Vida. (Coleccion Bravo). (SPA., Illus.). (YA). (gr. 5-8). pap. (978-84-7131-911-1(X) , EDI30263) Editex, Editorial S.A. ESP. *Dist:* Lectorum Pubns., Inc.

Ecology, 6 vols. , Set. 1999. (J). (gr. 3-8). 32p. 32.00 (978-0-7166-5218-2(8)); (Illus.). 192p. 54.00 (978-0-7166-5219-9(6)) World Bk., Inc.

Ecology Alert, 4 bks. 2003. (Illus.). (J). 102.80 (978-1-4109-0233-7(1)) Raintree.

Ecology & Evolution Complete Materials Package W/Teacher's Guide. 2001. (Illus.). (YA). ring bd. (978-1-887725-40-8(7)) Lab-Aids, Inc.

Ecology & Evolution Complete Materials Package W/Teacher's Guide & Student Books. 2001. (Illus.). (YA). ring bd. (978-1-887725-57-6(1)) Lab-Aids, Inc.

Ecosistemas del mundo: Cuaderno de Evaluacion: Unit 6: Ecosistemas del mundo (Ecosystems Around the World) 2000. (McGraw-Hill Ciencias Ser.). (ENG & SPA.). (gr. 5 up). (978-0-02-278676-2(7)) Macmillan/McGraw-Hill Schl. Div.

Ecosistemas del mundo: Recursos para el maestro con clave de Respuestas: Unit 6: Ecosistemas del mundo (Ecosystems Around the World) 2000. (McGraw-Hill Ciencias Ser.). (ENG & SPA.). (gr. 5 up). (978-0-02-278713-4(5)) Macmillan/McGraw-Hill Schl. Div.

Ecosystems Around the World Assessment Book: Unit 6: Ecosystems around the World. 2000. (McGraw-Hill Science Ser.). (gr. 5 up). (978-0-02-277768-5(7)) Macmillan/McGraw-Hill Schl. Div.

Ecosystems Around the World Pupil Edition: Unit 6: Ecosystems around the World. 2000. (McGraw-Hill Science Ser.). (gr. 5 up). (978-0-02-278228-3(1)) Macmillan/McGraw-Hill Schl. Div.

Ecosystems Classroom Library. (gr. 2-5). lib. bdg. 34.95 (978-0-7368-9268-1(0)) Red Brick Learning.

Ecosystems Complete Unit. (gr. 2-5). 198.95 (978-0-7368-9269-8(9)) Red Brick Learning.

Exploring the Environment. (J). (gr. 2). (978-0-8374-1461-4(X) , 387); (gr. 3). (978-0-8374-1462-1(8) , 388); (gr. 4). (978-0-8374-1463-8(6) , 389); (gr. 5). (978-0-8374-1464-5(4) , 390); (gr. 6). (978-0-8374-1465-2(2) , 391) Weekly Reader Corp.

Farndon, John. Wildlife Atlas: A Complete Guide to Animals & Their Habitats. 2002. (Illus.). 176p. 29.95 (978-0-7621-0354-6(X)) Reader's Digest Assn., Inc., The.

Fisher, Enid Broderick. The Great Dinosaur Record Book. Grant, Richard, illus. 1998. 32p. (J). (gr. 4 up). lib. bdg. 22.60 (978-0-8368-2176-5(9)) Stevens, Gareth Inc.

Fleisher, Paul. Alpine Meadow. 1998. (Webs of Life Ser.). (Illus.). 40p. (J). (gr. 2-5). lib. bdg. 22.79 (978-0-7614-0836-9(3) , Benchmark Bks.) Cavendish, Marshall Corp.

—Desert Food Webs. 2007. (Early Bird Food Webs Ser.). 48p. (J). (gr. 2-5). lib. bdg. 26.60 (***978-0-8225-6728-8(8)*** , Lerner Pubns.) Lerner Publishing Group.

—Lake & Pond Food Webs. 2007. (Early Bird Food Webs Ser.). 48p. (J). (gr. 2-5). 26.60 (***978-0-8225-6731-8(8)*** , Lerner Pubns.) Lerner Publishing Group.

—Mountain Stream. 1998. (Webs of Life Ser.). (Illus.). 40p. (J). (gr. 2-5). lib. bdg. 22.79 (978-0-7614-0838-3(X) , Benchmark Bks.) Cavendish, Marshall Corp.

—Pond. 1998. (Webs of Life Ser.). (Illus.). 40p. (J). (gr. 2-5). lib. bdg. 22.79 (978-0-7614-0835-2(5) , Benchmark Bks.) Cavendish, Marshall Corp.

—Salt Marsh. Cassels, Jean, illus. 1998. (Webs of Life Ser.). 40p. (J). (gr. 2-5). lib. bdg. 22.79 (978-0-7614-0834-5(7) , Benchmark Bks.) Cavendish, Marshall Corp.

—Tundra Food Webs. 2007. (Early Bird Food Webs Ser.). 48p. (J). (gr. 2-5). 26.60 (***978-0-8225-6727-1(X)*** , Lerner Pubns.) Lerner Publishing Group.

Fleisher, Paul. Webs of Life - Group 2, 4 bks., Set. Incl. Alpine Meadow. lib. bdg. 22.79 (978-0-7614-0836-9(3)); Mountain Stream. lib. bdg. 22.79 (978-0-7614-0838-3(X)); Pond. lib. bdg. 22.79 (978-0-7614-0835-2(5)); Salt Marsh. Cassels, Jean, illus. lib. bdg. 22.79 (978-0-7614-0834-5(7)); 40p. (J). (gr. 2-5). 1998. Set lib. bdg. 91.14 (978-0-7614-0833-8(9) , Benchmark Bks.) Cavendish, Marshall Corp.

Foster, Leila Merrell. Antarctica. 2001. (Continents Ser.). (Illus.). 32p. (J). (gr. k-2). lib. bdg. 21.36 (978-1-57572-447-8(2)) Heinemann Library.

Foster, Leila Merrell & Fox, Mary Virginia. Antarctica. 2002. (Continents Ser.). (Illus.). 32p. (J). (gr. k-2). pap. 6.95 (978-1-58810-946-0(1) , 91436) Heinemann Library.

Fowler, Allan. Living in a Desert. 2000. (Rookie Read-About Geography Ser.). (Illus.). 32p. (J). (gr. 1-2). pap. 5.95 (978-0-516-27049-4(4) , Children's Pr.) Scholastic Library Publishing.

—Living in a Desert. 2000. (gr. k-3). lib. bdg. 14.10 (978-0-613-54731-4(4)) Tandem Library Bks.

Frahm, Randy. Lakes. 2002. (LifeViews Ser.). (J). (978-0-89812-371-5(2) , Creative Paperbacks) Creative Co., The.

—Lakes: Timeless Reserviors. 2002. (LifeViews Ser.). (Illus.). 32p. (J). lib. bdg. (978-1-58341-244-2(1) , Creative Education) Creative Co., The.

—Rivers. 2002. (LifeViews Ser.). (J). (978-0-89812-374-6(7) , Creative Paperbacks) Creative Co., The.

—Rivers: Sculpters of the Land. 2002. (LifeViews Ser.). (Illus.). 32p. (J). lib. bdg. (978-1-58341-124-7(0) , Creative Education) Creative Co., The.

Frisch, Aaron. Tundra. 2008. (J). (***978-1-58341-574-0(2)*** , Creative Education) Creative Co., The.

Furgang, Kathy. Let's Take a Field Trip to a Tide Pool. 2000. (Neighborhoods in Nature Ser.). (Illus.). 24p. (J). (gr. k-4). lib. bdg. 18.75 (978-0-8239-5446-9(3) , PowerKids Pr.) Rosen Publishing Group, Inc., The.

Galko, Francine. Cave Animals. 2003. (Animals in Their Habitats Ser.). (Illus.). 32p. (J). (gr. k-2). lib. bdg. 21.36 (978-1-4034-0176-2(4)); pap. 6.95 (978-1-4034-0433-6(X)) Heinemann Library.

—Cave Animals. 2003. (gr. k-3). lib. bdg. 14.75 (978-0-613-45720-0(X)) Tandem Library Bks.

—Coral Reef Animals. 2003. (Animals in Their Habitats Ser.). (Illus.). 32p. (J). (gr. k-2). lib. bdg. 21.36 (978-1-4034-0177-9(2)); pap. 6.95 (978-1-4034-0434-3(8)) Heinemann Library.

—Desert Animals. 2003. (Animals in Their Habitats Ser.). (Illus.). 32p. (J). (gr. k-2). lib. bdg. 21.36 (978-1-4034-0178-6(0)); pap. 6.95 (978-1-4034-0435-0(6)) Heinemann Library.

—Desert Animals. 2003. (gr. k-3). lib. bdg. 14.75 (978-0-613-45737-8(4)) Tandem Library Bks.

Ganeri, Anita. Deserts. 2003. (Science Files Ser.). (Illus.). 32p. (J). (gr. 3 up). lib. bdg. 24.67 (978-0-8368-3566-3(2)) Stevens, Gareth Inc.

—Food Chains. 2004. (Nature's Patterns Ser.). (Illus.). 32p. (J). 22.79 (978-1-4034-5878-0(2)); pap. 7.25 (978-1-4034-5884-1(7)) Heinemann Library.

Gardner, Robert. Science Projects about the Environment & Ecology. 1999. (Science Projects Ser.). (Illus.). 112p. (YA). (gr. 6-12). lib. bdg. 26.60 (978-0-89490-951-1(7)) Enslow Pubs., Inc.

George, Michael. Tundra: The Barren Wilderness. 2001. (Life on Earth Ser.). (Illus.). 32p. (J). lib. bdg. (978-1-58341-023-3(6) , Creative Education) Creative Co., The.

Geozonen und Landschaftsoekologie. (Duden Abiturhilfen Ser.). (GER.). 96p. (YA). (gr. 12-13). (978-3-411-04471-9(3)) Bibliographisches Institut & F. A. Brockhaus AG DEU. *Dist:* International Bk. Import Service, Inc.

Gerber, Carole. Tundra Food Chains. 2003. (What Eats What? Ser.). (J). pap. (978-1-58417-221-5(5)); lib. bdg. (978-1-58417-220-8(7)) Lake Street Pubs.

Gifford, Clive & Cadle, Jerry. The Kingfisher Young People's Book of Living Worlds. 2002. (Kingfisher Book of Ser.). (Illus.). 80p. (J). (gr. 4-8). tchr. ed. 21.95 (978-0-7534-5390-2(8) , Kingfisher) Houghton Mifflin Co. Trade & Reference Div.

Gray, Shirley W. Rain Forests. 2000. (First Reports). (Illus.). 48p. (J). (gr. 3 up). lib. bdg. 21.26 (978-0-7565-0023-8(0)) Compass Point Bks.

—Wetlands. 2000. (First Reports). (Illus.). 48p. (J). (gr. 3 up). lib. bdg. 21.26 (978-0-7565-0025-2(7)) Compass Point Bks.

Gray, Susan Heinrichs. Coral Reefs. 2000. (First Reports). (Illus.). 48p. (J). (gr. 3 up). lib. bdg. 21.26 (978-0-7565-0018-4(4)) Compass Point Bks.

—Deserts. 2000. (First Reports). (Illus.). 48p. (J). (gr. 3 up). lib. bdg. 21.26 (978-0-7565-0019-1(2)) Compass Point Bks.

—Mountains. 2000. (First Reports). (Illus.). 48p. (J). (gr. 3 up). lib. bdg. 21.26 (978-0-7565-0021-4(4)) Compass Point Bks.

—Tundra. 2000. (First Reports). (Illus.). 48p. (J). (gr. 3 up). lib. bdg. 21.26 (978-0-7565-0024-5(9)) Compass Point Bks.

Green, Jen. Feeding the People. 2004. (J). lib. bdg. (978-1-59389-138-1(5)) Chrysalis Education.

—On the Tundra. 2002. (Small Worlds Ser.). (Illus.). 32p. (J). (gr. 3-4). pap. (978-0-7787-0153-8(0)); lib. bdg. (978-0-7787-0139-2(5)) Crabtree Publishing Co.

—On the Tundra. 2002. (gr. 3-6). lib. bdg. 17.60 (978-0-613-52986-0(3)) Tandem Library Bks.

—People of the Polar Regions. 1998. (Wide World Ser.). (Illus.). 48p. (J). (gr. 3-7). 18.98 (978-0-8172-5065-2(4)) Raintree.

Green, Mary. Rivers in Action. 2004. (Earth's Changing Landscape Ser.). (Illus.). 46p. (J). lib. bdg. 28.50 (978-1-58340-477-5(5)) Smart Apple Media.

Green, Tamara. Cretaceous Dinosaur World. Grant, Richard, illus. 1998. 32p. (J). (gr. 4 up). lib. bdg. 22.60 (978-0-8368-2173-4(4)) Stevens, Gareth Inc.

—Jurassic Dinosaur World. Grant, Richard, illus. 1998. 32p. (J). (gr. 4 up). lib. bdg. 22.60 (978-0-8368-2174-1(2)) Stevens, Gareth Inc.

Guiberson, Brenda Z. Cactus Hotel. 2007. (Illus.). 32p. (J). 23.95 (***978-0-8050-8228-9(X)*** , Holt, Henry & Co. Bks. For Young Readers) Holt, Henry & Co.

Harcourt School Publishers Staff. What Is a Food Chain: Science Reader. 2000. (SPA., Illus.). (J). pap. 3.70 (978-0-15-316118-6(3)) Harcourt Schl. Pubs.

Harlow, Rosie. Nature in Danger. 2002. (Young Discoverers Ser.). (Illus.). 32p. (J). (gr. k-3). pap. 7.95 (978-0-7534-5504-3(8) , Kingfisher) Houghton Mifflin Co. Trade & Reference Div.

—Nature in Danger: Environmental Facts & Experiments. 2002. (gr. k-3). lib. bdg. 16.40 (978-0-613-90902-0(X)) Tandem Library Bks.

Harper, Judith E. Unique Places. 2005. (Real Deal Ser.). (Illus.). 32p. (J). pap. (978-0-7608-9635-8(6)) Sundance/Newbridge Educational Publishing.

Harris, Nicholas. The Living World. 2006. 32p. (gr. 2-4). 23.70 (978-1-4103-0349-3(7) , Blackbirch Pr., Inc.) Thomson Gale.

Harris, Tim. Mountains & Highlands. 2002. (Biomes Atlases Ser.). (Illus.). 64p. (J). lib. bdg. 31.42 (978-0-7398-5511-9(5)) Raintree.

—Mountains & Highlands. 2003. (gr. 5-8). lib. bdg. 18.20 (978-0-613-78181-7(3)) Tandem Library Bks.

Haus, Robyn. Create a Year-Round Wildlife Habitat: For Urban & Suburban Small Spaces. 2004. (Quick Starts for Kids! Ser.). (Illus.). 64p. (J). pap. 8.95 (978-1-885593-97-9(X) , Williamson Bks.) Ideals Pubns.

Heinz, Brian J. & Marstall, Bob, illus. Butternut Hollow Pond. 2000. 6. 32p. (gr. 2-6). (978-0-7613-1325-0(7) , Millbrook Pr.) Lerner Publishing Group.

Helbrough, Emma. Great Planet Earth Search. Jackson, Ian, illus. 2006. 32p. (J). (***978-0-439-83402-5(3)***) Scholastic, Inc.

Hess, Paul. Animal Worlds. 2006. (Animal Verse Ser.). (Illus.). 96p. (J). pap. 10.95 (978-1-84089-408-0(3) , Zero to Ten, Limited) Evans Publishing Group GBR. *Dist:* Independent Pubs. Group.

Hewitt, Sally. All Kinds of Habitats. 1999. (It's Science! Ser.). (Illus.). 32p. (J). (gr. k-3). 23.50 (978-0-516-21181-7(1) , Children's Pr.) Scholastic Library Publishing.

—All Kinds of Habitats. 1999. (gr. k-3). lib. bdg. 15.25 (978-0-613-37261-9(1)) Tandem Library Bks.

Hill, Mary K. The Environment. 2006. 224p. (gr. 10-12). 29.95 (978-0-7377-2907-8(4) , Greenhaven Pr., Inc.) Thomson Gale.

Himmelman, John. Frog in a Bog. Himmelman, John, illus. 2004. (Illus.). 32p. (J). 15.95 (978-1-57091-517-8(2)) Charlesbridge Publishing, Inc.

—Frog in a Bog. 2004. (Illus.). 32p. (J). pap. 6.95 (978-1-57091-518-5(0)) Charlesbridge Publishing, Inc.

—Mouse in a Meadow. Himmelman, John, illus. 2005. (Illus.). 32p. (J). 15.95 (978-1-57091-520-8(2)); pap. 6.95 (978-1-57091-521-5(0)) Charlesbridge Publishing, Inc.

Hoare, Ben. Temperate Grasslands. 2002. (Biomes Atlases Ser.). (Illus.). 64p. (J). lib. bdg. 31.42 (978-0-7398-5249-1(3)) Raintree.

—Temperate Grasslands. 2003. (gr. 5-8). lib. bdg. 18.20 (978-0-613-78189-3(9)) Tandem Library Bks.

Holly Wallace. Food Chains & Webs. 2nd ed. 2006. (Life Processes Ser.). (Illus.). 32p. (J). pap. (***978-1-4034-8853-4(3)***) Heinemann Library.

Holt, Rinehart and Winston Staff. Environmental Science. 4th ed. Date not set. pap., stu. ed. 11.20 (978-0-03-066602-5(3)); Vol. E. 3rd ed. 2003. (SPA.). 18.60 (978-0-03-069244-4(X)) Holt, Rinehart & Winston.

—Environmental Science Chptr. 21: Economics, Policy & the Future. 4th ed. Date not set. (YA). pap. 11.20 (978-0-03-068083-0(2)) Holt, Rinehart & Winston.

—Holt Science & Technology: Ecolabs & Field Activities. 5th ed. 2004. (Illus.). pap. 11.60 (978-0-03-035189-1(8)) Holt, Rinehart & Winston.

—Holt Science & Technology Chapter 18: Life Science: Interactions with Living Things. 5th ed. 2004. (Illus.). pap. 12.86 (978-0-03-030228-2(5)) Holt, Rinehart & Winston.

—Holt Science & Technology Chptr. 4: Environmental Problems & Solutions: Chapter Resources - Tennessee Edition. 3rd ed. 2003. (J). pap. 11.40 (978-0-03-069109-6(5)) Holt, Rinehart & Winston.

—Holt Science & Technology Chptr. 12: Earth's Ecosystem: Chapter Resources - Tennessee Edition. 3rd ed. 2003. (YA). pap. 11.40 (978-0-03-069143-0(5)) Holt, Rinehart & Winston.

—West Virginia Environmental Science Resources. 2nd ed. 2002. pap. 205.80 (978-0-03-064279-1(5)) Holt, Rinehart & Winston.

Hooper, Roseanne. Coastlines. 2004. (Life In... Ser.). (SPA., Illus.). (gr. 3-6). 32p. (J). pap. 6.95 (978-1-58728-566-0(5)); 31p. 12.95 (978-1-58728-551-6(7)) T&N Children's Publishing. (Two Can Publishing).

—Life on the Islands. 2001. (World Book Ecology Ser.). (Illus.). 32p. (J). (978-0-7166-5227-4(7)) World Bk., Inc.

Howard, Fran. Grasslands. 2007. (Habitats Ser.). (Illus.). 32p. (J). (gr. k-4). lib. bdg. 22.78 (978-1-59679-778-9(9)) ABDO Publishing Co.

Huggins-Cooper, Lynn. Seashore. McNicholas, Shelagh & Burroughs, Dave, trs. McNicholas, Shelagh & Burroughs, Dave, illus. 2004. 30p. (J). lib. bdg. (978-1-58340-446-1(5)) Smart Apple Media.

Hunter, Anne. What's in the Tide Pool? 2000. (Illus.). 32p. (J). (gr. k-3). tchr. ed. 4.95 (978-0-618-01510-8(8)) Houghton Mifflin Co. Trade & Reference Div.

Hunter, Rebecca. The Facts about Habitats. 2004. (Illus.). 32p. (J). lib. bdg. (978-1-58340-455-3(4)) Smart Apple Media.

Invasion de la Basura. (Coleccion Operacion Tierra). (SPA.). 46p. (YA). (gr. 5 up). pap. 12.95 (978-950-11-0979-5(8) , SGM798) Sigmar ARG. *Dist:* Continental Bk. Co., Inc.

El Investigador Verde. (SPA.). 25p. (J). pap. 7.95 (978-950-11-0934-4(8) , SGM348) Sigmar ARG. *Dist:* Continental Bk. Co., Inc.

J. G. Ferguson Publishing Company Staff. Careers in Focus: Environment. 2nd ed. 1999. (Careers in Focus Ser.). (Illus.). 176-192p. (YA). (gr. 8-12). 22.95 (978-0-89434-288-2(6) , F614, Ferguson Publishing Co.) Facts On File, Inc.

Jackson, Kay. Explore the Grasslands. 2007. (Fact Finders Ser.). (Illus.). 32p. (J). 22.60 (978-0-7368-6405-3(9)) Capstone Pr., Inc.

Jakab, Cheryl. The Food Cycle. 2007. (J). (***978-1-59920-149-8(6)***) Smart Apple Media.

Jenkins, Steve & Page, Robin. I See a Kookaburra! Discovering Animal Habitats Around the World. 2005. (Illus.). 32p. (J). (gr. k-3). 16.00 (978-0-618-50764-1(7)) Houghton Mifflin Co. Trade & Reference Div.

Jennings, Terry J. Ecology: The Study of Living Things. 2002. (Investigating Science Ser.). (Illus.). 36p. (J). (gr. 4 up). lib. bdg. 24.67 (978-0-8368-3230-3(2)) Stevens, Gareth Inc.

Jerome, Kate Boehm. Science at the Aquarium. 2004. (National Geographic Reading Expeditions Ser.). (Illus.). 24p. (J). pap. (978-0-7922-8625-7(1)) National Geographic Society.

Johansson, Philip. The Coral Reef: A Colorful Web of Life. 2007. (Wonderful Water Biomes Ser.). (Illus.). 48p. (J). (gr. 3-4). lib. bdg. 23.93 (978-0-7660-2813-5(5) , Enslow Elementary) Enslow Pubs., Inc.

—The Dry Desert: A Web of Life. 2004. (World of Biomes Ser.). (Illus.). 48p. (J). lib. bdg. 23.93 (978-0-7660-2200-3(5)) Enslow Pubs., Inc.

—The Forested Taiga: A Web of Life. 2004. (World of Biomes Ser.). (Illus.). 48p. (J). lib. bdg. 23.93 (978-0-7660-2197-6(1)) Enslow Pubs., Inc.

—The Frozen Tundra: A Web of Life. 2004. (World of Biomes Ser.). (Illus.). 48p. (J). lib. bdg. 23.93 (978-0-7660-2176-1(9)) Enslow Pubs., Inc.

—Lakes & Rivers: A Freshwater Web of Life. 2007. (Wonderful Water Biomes Ser.). (Illus.). 48p. (J). (gr. 3-4). lib. bdg. 23.93 (***978-0-7660-2812-8(7)*** , Enslow Elementary) Enslow Pubs., Inc.

—The Temperate Forest: A Web of Life. 2004. (World of Biomes Ser.). (Illus.). 48p. (J). lib. bdg. 23.93 (978-0-7660-2198-3(X)) Enslow Pubs., Inc.

—The Wide Open Grasslands: A Web of Life. 2004. (World of Biomes Ser.). (Illus.). 48p. (J). lib. bdg. 23.93 (978-0-7660-2201-0(3)) Enslow Pubs., Inc.

John Farndon. Life in the Soil. 2004. (J). 23.70 (978-1-4103-0124-6(9) , Blackbirch Pr., Inc.) Thomson Gale.

Johnson, Linda Carlson. Rain Forests: A Pro/Con Issue. 1999. (Hot Pro/Con Issues Ser.). (Illus.). 64p. (YA). (gr. 6-12). lib. bdg. 21.95 (978-0-7660-1202-8(6)) Enslow Pubs., Inc.

Johnson, Rebecca L. A Journey into a Lake. Saroff, Phyllis V., illus. 2004. (Biomes of North America Ser.). (J). pap. 6.95 (978-0-8225-2043-6(5)); 48p. (gr. 3-6). lib. bdg. 23.93 (978-1-57505-594-7(5)) Lerner Publishing Group.

—A Journey into a River. Saroff, Phyllis V., illus. 2004. (Biomes of North America Ser.). (J). pap. 6.95 (978-0-8225-2044-3(3)); 48p. (gr. 3-6). 23.93 (978-1-57505-595-4(3)) Lerner Publishing Group.

—A Journey into a Wetland. Saroff, Phyllis V., illus. 2004. (Biomes of North America Ser.). (J). pap. 6.95 (978-0-8225-2047-4(8)) Lerner Publishing Group.

—A Journey into a Wetlands. Saroff, Phyllis V., illus. 2004. (Biomes of North America Ser.). 48p. (J). (gr. 3-6). lib. bdg. 23.93 (978-1-57505-593-0(7)) Lerner Publishing Group.

—A Journey into an Estuary. Saroff, Phyllis V., illus. 2004. (Biomes of North America Ser.). (J). pap. 6.95 (978-0-8225-2045-0(1)); 48p. (gr. 3-6). lib. bdg. 23.93 (978-1-57505-592-3(9)) Lerner Publishing Group.

—A Journey into the Ocean. Saroff, Phyllis V., illus. 2004. (J). pap. 6.95 (978-0-8225-2046-7(X) , 1); 48p. (gr. 3-6). lib. bdg. 23.93 (978-1-57505-591-6(0)) Lerner Publishing Group.

Josephs, David. Lakes, Ponds, & Temporary Pools. 2000. (gr. 7-12). lib. bdg. 15.25 (978-0-613-34319-0(0)) Tandem Library Bks.

Kalman, Bobbie. The ABCs of Habitats. 2007. 32p. (J). (gr. 6-10). pap. (***978-0-7787-3431-4(5)***) Crabtree Publishing Co.

—Las Cadenas Alimentarias y Tu. (Cadenas Alimentarias Ser.). (SPA., Illus.). 32p. (J). pap. (978-0-7787-8528-6(9)); 2006. pap. (978-0-7787-8544-6(0)) Crabtree Publishing Co.

—La Chaine Alimentaire. 2002. (FRE., Illus.). 32p. (J). pap. (978-2-920660-82-3(9)) Crabtree Publishing Co.

—Food Chains & You. 2004. (Food Chains Ser.). (Illus.). 32p. (J). pap. (978-0-7787-1988-5(X)) Crabtree Publishing Co.

—Un Habitat de Sabana. 2007. (SPA.). 32p. (J). (gr. 1-2). (***978-0-7787-8329-9(4)***) Crabtree Publishing Co.

—Habitats Terrestres. 2007. (SPA & ENG.). 32p. (J). (gr. 1-2). (***978-0-7787-8324-4(3)***) Crabtree Publishing Co.

—Land Habitats. 2006. (Illus.). 32p. (J). (gr. 2). pap. (978-0-7787-2976-1(1)) Crabtree Publishing Co.

—Que Son las Redes y Cadenas Alimentarias? 2005. (Ciencia de los Seres Vivos Ser.). (SPA., Illus.). 32p. (J). (978-0-7787-8756-3(7)) Crabtree Publishing Co.

—Qué Son los Biomas? 2005. (Ciencia de los Seres Vivos Ser.). (SPA., Illus.). 32p. (J). (978-0-7787-8755-6(9)) Crabtree Publishing Co.

—Underground Habitats. 2006. (Illus.). 32p. (J). pap. (978-0-7787-2982-2(6)) Crabtree Publishing Co.

—What Are Wetlands? 2002. (Science of Living Things Ser.). (Illus.). 32p. (J). (gr. 2-3). (978-0-86505-993-1(4)); pap. (978-0-86505-970-2(5)) Crabtree Publishing Co.

—What Are Wetlands? 2003. (gr. 3-6). lib. bdg. 14.10 (978-0-613-52930-3(8)) Tandem Library Bks.

—What Is a Biome? 1999. (Science of Living Things Ser.). (Illus.). 32p. (J). (gr. 2-3). (978-0-86505-875-0(X)) Crabtree Publishing Co.

Kalman, Bobbie & Burns, Kylie. Wetland Food Chains. 2006. (Food Chains Ser.). (Illus.). 32p. (J). (gr. 3-5). (978-0-7787-1953-3(7)) Crabtree Publishing Co.

Kalman, Bobbie & Crossingham, John. Habitats Terrestres. rev. ed. 2007. (SPA & ENG.). 32p. (J). (gr. 1-2). pap. (***978-0-7787-8348-0(0)***) Crabtree Publishing Co.

Kalman, Bobbie & Crossingham, John. Land Habitats. 2006. (Illus.). 32p. (J). (978-0-7787-2948-8(6)) Crabtree Publishing Co.

Kalman, Bobbie & Dyer, Hadley. Australian Outback Food Chains. 2006. (Food Chains Ser.). (Illus.). 32p. (J). (gr. 3-5). pap. (978-0-7787-1996-0(0)); lib. bdg. (978-0-7787-1950-2(2)) Crabtree Publishing Co.

Kalman, Bobbie & Langille, Jacqueline. What Are Food Chains & Webs? 1998. (Illus.). 32p. (J). (ps-ps). lib. bdg. 14.10 (978-0-613-09047-6(0)) Tandem Library Bks.

Kalman, Bobbie & MacAulay, Kelley. Cadenas Alimentarias del Desierto. (Cadenas Alimentarias Ser.). (SPA., Illus.). 32p. (J). pap. (***978-0-7787-8530-9(0)***) Crabtree Publishing Co.

Kalman, Bobbie & MacAulay, Kelley. Meadow Food Chains. 2004. (Food Chains Ser.). (Illus.). 32p. (J). (978-0-7787-1945-8(6)); pap. (978-0-7787-1991-5(X)) Crabtree Publishing Co.

Kalman, Bobbie & Sjonger, Rebecca. Un Habitat de Sabana. rev. ed. 2007. (SPA.). 32p. (J). (gr. 1-2). pap. (***978-0-7787-8353-4(7)***) Crabtree Publishing Co.

Kalman, Bobbie & Sjonger, Rebecca. A Savanna Habitat. 2006. (Illus.). 32p. (J). (978-0-7787-2952-5(4)) Crabtree Publishing Co.

Katz, Sharon. The Great Lakes. 1999. (Ecosystems of North America Ser.). (Illus.). 64p. (YA). (gr. 6 up). lib. bdg. 28.50 (978-0-7614-0898-7(3) , Benchmark Bks.) Cavendish, Marshall Corp.

Kidd, J. S. & Kidd, Renee A. Agricultural Versus Environmental Science: A Green Revolution. 2005. (Science & Society Ser.). 224p. (YA). (gr. 6-12). 35.00 (978-0-8160-5608-8(0)) Facts On File, Inc.

The Kid's Book of Awesome Stuff. 2004. (J). spiral bd. (978-0-9762568-0-9(0)) Brotman-Marshfield Curriculums.

Klingel, Cynthia Fitterer & Noyed, Robert B. Underground. 2001. (Wonder Books Level 2: Habitats Ser.). (Illus.). 24p. (J). (ps-3). 22.79 (978-1-56766-975-6(1)) Child's World, Inc.

Knight, Tim. Fantastic Feeders. 2003. (Amazing Nature Ser.). (Illus.). 32p. (J). pap. 6.95 (978-1-4034-3256-8(2)); (gr. 2-4). lib. bdg. 24.22 (978-1-4034-1146-4(8)) Heinemann Library.

—Handmade Cards. 2003. (Step-by-Step Ser.). 32p. (J). pap. 7.95 (978-1-4034-0717-7(7)) Heinemann Library.

Knowlton, Laurie Lazzaro. Come on Down. Brown, Kevin, illus. 2005. (J). (978-1-933248-07-3(6)) World Quest Learning.

Kosek, Jane Kelly. What's Inside Lakes? 1999. (What's Inside Library). 24p. (J). (gr. k-4). lib. bdg. 18.75 (978-0-8239-5280-9(0) , PowerKids Pr.) Rosen Publishing Group, Inc., The.

Kudlinski, Kathleen V. The Seaside Switch. Burnett, Lindy, illus. 2007. 32p. (gr. k-3). 16.95 (978-1-55971-964-3(8) , NorthWord Bks. for Young Readers) T&N Children's Publishing.

LaBella, Susan. A Home in the Savannah. 2006. (Scholastic News Nonfiction Readers Ser.). (Illus.). 24p. (J). 19.00 (978-0-516-25348-0(4) , Children's Pr.) Scholastic Library Publishing.

Lakeshore Learning Materials Staff, contrib. by. Food Chain Activity Kit. 2000. (J). pap. 24.95 (978-1-929255-73-3(X)) Lakeshore Learning Materials.

Lane, Brian & Buller, Laura. Ecology. 2005. (Dk eyewitness Bks.). (Illus.). 72p. (J). (gr. 4-7). 15.99 (978-0-7566-1387-7(6)) Dorling Kindersley Publishing, Inc.

Langeland, Deirdre. Kangaroo Island: A Story of An Australian Mallee Forest. Ordaz, Frank, illus. 1998. (Habitat Ser.). (J). (gr. 1-4). 32p. 19.95 incl. reel tape (978-1-56899-545-8(8) , BC7007); 36p. pap. 10.95 incl. audio (978-1-56899-546-5(6)); Incl. toy. 36p. pap. 19.95 incl. audio (978-1-56899-550-2(4)) Soundprints.

Lauber, Patricia. Who Eats What? Food Chains & Food Webs. 2001. 24.75 (978-0-06-000332-6(4)) HarperCollins Pubs.

Leeson, Cole. Arctic. 2003. (Wild America Habitats Ser.). (Illus.). 24p. (J). 21.20 (978-1-56711-798-1(8) , Blackbirch Pr., Inc.) Thomson Gale.

—Tidal Flat/Coastal. 2003. (Wild America Habitats Ser.). (Illus.). 24p. (J). 24.94 (978-1-56711-809-4(7) , Blackbirch Pr., Inc.) Thomson Gale.

Lerner Publishing Group Staff. Habitats: Classroom Set. 2005. (Illus.). (J). (gr. k-2). 16.95 (978-0-8225-5369-4(4)) Lerner Publishing Group.

Levy, Janey. Discovering Mountains. 2008. (J). lib. bdg. (***978-1-4042-3785-8(2)*** , PowerKids Pr.) Rosen Publishing Group, Inc., The.

—Discovering the Arctic Tundra. 2008. (J). lib. bdg. (***978-1-4042-3787-2(9)*** , PowerKids Pr.) Rosen Publishing Group, Inc., The.

Lewis, J. Earth & You, a Closer View: Nature's Features. 2000. (gr. 3-6). lib. bdg. 16.40 (978-0-613-49730-5(9)) Tandem Library Bks.

Lewis, J. Patrick. Earth & You - A Closer View: Nature's Features. Canyon, Christopher, illus. 2004. (Sharing Nature with Children Book Ser.). 36p. (J). (gr. 4-7). pap. 7.95 (978-1-58469-015-3(1)); (ps-3). 16.95 (978-1-58469-016-0(X)) Dawn Pubns.

L'Hommedieu, Arthur John. Ocean Tidepool. 1998. (Habitats Ser.). (Illus.). 32p. (J). (gr. 2-3). pap. 6.95 (978-0-516-20373-7(8) , Children's Pr.) Scholastic Library Publishing.

Llewellyn, Claire. Asi Nace un Arbol. Mendez, Simon, illus. (Coleccion Asi Nace... Ser.). (SPA.). T/Ap. (J). (gr. 3-5). pap. 7.95 (978-1-59437-838-6(X)) Santillana USA Publishing Co., Inc.

Lorbiecki, Marybeth. Planet Patrol: A Kids' Action Guide to Earth Care. Meyers, Nancy, illus. 2005. 48p. (J). (gr. 4-7). 8.95 (978-1-58728-518-9(5)); 15.95 (978-1-58728-514-1(2)) T&N Children's Publishing. (Two Can Publishing).

Lovell, Scarlett, et al. Exploring Mountain Habitats. Noreika, Robert & Katin, Miriam, illus. 1999. (Mondo's Exploring Ser.). 24p. (J). (gr. 1-5). pap. 4.95 (978-1-57255-164-0(X)) Mondo Publishing.

Lynch, Emma. Ocean Food Chains. 2004. (Food Webs Ser.). (Illus.). 32p. (J). pap. 7.50 (978-1-4034-5864-3(2)) Heinemann Library.

—Rainforest Food Chains. 2004. (Food Webs Ser.). (Illus.). 32p. (J). pap. 7.50 (978-1-4034-5865-0(0)) Heinemann Library.

—River Food Chains. 2004. (Food Webs Ser.). (Illus.). 32p. (J). (ps-7). pap. 7.50 (978-1-4034-5866-7(9)); lib. bdg. 24.22 (978-1-4034-5859-9(6)) Heinemann Library.

Lynch, Wayne. Arctic Alphabet: Exploring the North from A to Z. Lynch, Wayne, photos by. 2006. (Illus.). 32p. (J). (gr. k-4). reprint ed. 20.00 (978-1-4223-5190-1(4)) DIANE Publishing Co.

—Arctic Alphabet: Exploring the North from A to Z. 1999. (Illus.). 32p. (J). (gr. k-5). lib. bdg. 19.95 (978-1-55209-336-8(0)) Firefly Bks., Ltd.

MacAulay, Kelley & Kalman, Bobbie. Backyard Habitats. 2006. (Illus.). 32p. (J). (978-0-7787-2957-0(5)) Crabtree Publishing Co.

—Coral Reef Food Chains. 2005. (Food Chains Ser.). (Illus.). 32p. (J). (978-0-7787-1948-9(0)); pap. (978-0-7787-1994-6(4)) Crabtree Publishing Co.

—Prairie Food Chains. 2005. (Food Chains Ser.). (Illus.). 32p. (J). (978-0-7787-1947-2(2)); pap. (978-0-7787-1993-9(6)) Crabtree Publishing Co.

—Tundra Food Chains. 2005. (Food Chains Ser.). (Illus.). 32p. (J). (978-0-7787-1946-5(4)); pap. (978-0-7787-1992-2(8)) Crabtree Publishing Co.

MacAuley, Kelley. A Backyard Habitat. 2006. (Illus.). 32p. (J). (gr. 2). pap. (978-0-7787-2985-3(0)) Crabtree Publishing Co.

Macken, JoAnn Early. Coral Reefs. 2005. (Illus.). 24p. (J). pap. (978-0-8368-4890-8(X)); lib. bdg. 19.33 (978-0-8368-4883-0(7)) Stevens, Gareth Inc.

—Rivers. 2005. (Illus.). 24p. (J). pap. (978-0-8368-4893-9(4)); lib. bdg. 19.33 (978-0-8368-4886-1(1)) Stevens, Gareth Inc.

Martin, Patricia A. Fink. Prairies, Fields, & Meadows. (Exploring Ecosystems Ser.). (Illus.). 144p. (YA). (gr. 8-12). pap. 6.95 (978-0-531-16604-8(X) , Watts, Franklin) Scholastic Library Publishing.

—Rivers & Streams. 1999. (Exploring Ecosystems Ser.). (Illus.). 144p. (YA). (gr. 8-12). 24.50 (978-0-531-11523-7(2) , Watts, Franklin) Scholastic Library Publishing.

Mattern, Joanne. What Desert Animals Eat. 2006. (Illus.). 24p. (J). pap. (978-0-8368-6877-7(3)); lib. bdg. (978-0-8368-6870-8(6)) Stevens, Gareth Inc.

—What Desert Animals Eat: Qué Comen Los Animales Del Desierto? 2006. (ENG & SPA., Illus.). 24p. (J). pap. (978-0-8368-7378-8(5)); lib. bdg. (978-0-8368-7371-9(8)) Stevens, Gareth Inc. (Weekly Reader Early Learning Library).

—What Forest Animals Eat: Qué Comen Los Animales Del Bosque? 2006. (ENG & SPA., Illus.). 24p. (J). pap. (978-0-8368-7379-5(3)); lib. bdg. (978-0-8368-7372-6(6)) Stevens, Gareth Inc. (Weekly Reader Early Learning Library).

—What Forest Animals Eat/By Joanne Mattern. 2006. (Illus.). 24p. (J). pap. (978-0-8368-6878-4(1)); lib. bdg. (978-0-8368-6871-5(4)) Stevens, Gareth Inc.

—What Grassland Animals Eat. 2006. (Nature's Food Chains Ser.). (Illus.). 24p. (J). (gr. 1-2). pap. 5.95 (978-0-8368-6879-1(X)); lib. bdg. 19.93 (978-0-8368-6872-2(2)) Stevens, Gareth Inc.

—What Grassland Animals Eat: Qué Comen Los Animales de Las Praderas? 2006. (ENG & SPA., Illus.). 24p. (J). pap. (978-0-8368-7380-1(7)); lib. bdg. (978-0-8368-7373-3(4)) Stevens, Gareth Inc. (Weekly Reader Early Learning Library).

—What Polar Animals Eat: Qué Comen Los Animales de Los Polos? 2006. (ENG & SPA., Illus.). 24p. (J). pap. (978-0-8368-7381-8(5)); lib. bdg. (978-0-8368-7374-0(2)) Stevens, Gareth Inc. (Weekly Reader Early Learning Library).

—What River Animals Eat: Qué Comen Los Animales de Los Ríos? 2006. (ENG & SPA., Illus.). 24p. (J). pap. (978-0-8368-7382-5(3)); lib. bdg. (978-0-8368-7375-7(0)) Stevens, Gareth Inc. (Weekly Reader Early Learning Library).

—What Sea Animals Eat: Qué Comen Los Animales Del Mar? 2006. (ENG & SPA., Illus.). 24p. (J). pap. (978-0-8368-7383-2(1)); lib. bdg. (978-0-8368-7376-4(9)) Stevens, Gareth Inc. (Weekly Reader Early Learning Library).

Mayer, Cassie. Polar Region. 2007. (J). (***978-1-4034-9426-9(6)); pap. (*978-1-4034-9432-0(0))*** Heinemann Library.

Mazur, Ivan & Mazur, Elena. Children of the Galaxy: Ecology for Children. Pyatikop, Alexander, illus. 2001. 146p. (YA). (gr. 4-10). 14.95 (978-0-9707034-0-8(6)) Bks. To Enjoy.com, Inc.

—Neptune's Kingdom. Freedman, Stella, ed. Piatikop, Alexander, illus. 1998. (Ecology for Children Ser.: Vol. 1). 48p. (J). (gr. 2-6). 11.95 (978-1-892316-03-5(X)) Rama Pr., Inc.

—Treasures of the North. Freedman, Stella, ed. Piatikop, Alexander, illus. 1998. (Ecology for Children Ser.: Vol. 2). 48p. (J). (gr. 2-6). 11.95 (978-1-892316-04-2(8)) Rama Pr., Inc.

McGinty, Alice B. Carnivores in the Food Chain. 2002. (Library of Food Chains & Food Webs). (Illus.). 24p. (J). lib. bdg. 18.75 (978-0-8239-5754-5(3) , PowerKids Pr.) Rosen Publishing Group, Inc., The.

—Decomposers in the Food Chain. Kuhn, Dwight, photos by. 2002. (Library of Food Chains & Food Webs). (Illus.). 24p. (J). lib. bdg. 18.75 (978-0-8239-5757-6(8) , PowerKids Pr.) Rosen Publishing Group, Inc., The.

—Herbivores in the Food Chain. Kuhn, Dwight, photos by. 2002. (Library of Food Chains & Food Webs). (Illus.). 24p. (J). lib. bdg. 18.75 (978-0-8239-5753-8(5) , PowerKids Pr.) Rosen Publishing Group, Inc., The.

—Omnivores in the Food Chain. Kuhn, Dwight, photos by. 2002. (Library of Food Chains & Food Webs). (Illus.). 24p. (J). lib. bdg. 18.75 (978-0-8239-5756-9(X) , PowerKids Pr.) Rosen Publishing Group, Inc., The.

—Producers in the Food Chain. 2002. (Library of Food Chains & Food Webs). (Illus.). 24p. (J). lib. bdg. 18.75 (978-0-8239-5752-1(7) , PowerKids Pr.) Rosen Publishing Group, Inc., The.

—Scavengers & Parasites in the Food Chain. 2002. (Library of Food Chains & Food Webs). (Illus.). 24p. (J). lib. bdg. 18.75 (978-0-8239-5755-2(1) , PowerKids Pr.) Rosen Publishing Group, Inc., The.

McGraw-Hill Staff. Ecology. 2nd ed. 2004. (Glencoe Science Ser.). stu. ed. 20.64 (978-0-07-861746-1(4) , 9780078617461) Glencoe/McGraw-Hill.

—Glencoe Science: Ecology Standardized Test Practice. 2004. (C). pap., stu. ed. 8.64 (978-0-07-866974-3(X) , 9780078669743) Glencoe/McGraw-Hill.

McKissack, Fredrick, Jr. & McKissack, Lisa Beringer. Counting in the Desert. 2008. (Counting in the Biomes Ser.). 32p. (J). (gr. 1-3). lib. bdg. 22.60 (***978-0-7660-2988-0(3)***) Enslow Pubs., Inc.

McLaurin, Thad, ed. Investigating Science - Environment. 2000. 48p. 9.95 (978-1-56234-366-8(1) , Mailbox Bks., The) Education Ctr., Inc.

McLeish, Ewan. Sustainable Homes. 2006. (Sustainable Futures Ser.). (Illus.). 48p. (J). (978-1-58340-982-4(3) , 1262624) Smart Apple Media.

Metabolic Processes & Energy Transfers: An Anthology of Current Thought. 2005. (Contemporary Discourse in the Field of Biology Ser.). (Illus.). 192p. (J). (ps-7). lib. bdg. 30.60 (978-1-4042-0399-0(0)) Rosen Publishing Group, Inc., The.

Meucci, Antonella. Seas & Oceans. Chesi, Matteo, illus. 2000. (Nature's Record-Breakers Ser.). 32p. (J). (gr. 3 up). lib. bdg. 23.33 (978-0-8368-2475-9(X)) Stevens, Gareth Inc.

Microhabitats, 6 books. 2003. (Illus.). 145.68 (978-0-7398-6807-2(1)); 2003. (Illus.). 291.36 (978-0-7398-6808-9(X)); Set. 2001. 32p. lib. bdg. 154.14 (978-0-7398-4335-2(4)); Set 1. 2003. (Illus.). pap. 40.50 (978-1-4109-0435-5(0)) Raintree.

Miller. Forest Scientists. 2001. (Scientists of the Biomes Ser.). (Illus.). (J). pap. (978-0-7398-4936-1(0)) Steck-Vaughn.

—The Tundra Scientists. 2001. (Scientists of the Biomes Ser.). (Illus.). (J). pap. (978-0-7398-4940-8(9)) Steck-Vaughn.

Miller, Chuck. Tundra Scientists. 2001. (Scientists of the Biomes Ser.). (Illus.). 48p. (J). (gr. 4-7). lib. bdg. 24.26 (978-0-7398-4752-7(X)) Raintree.

Miller-Schroeder, Patricia. The Science of the Environment. 2001. (Living Science Ser.). (Illus.). 32p. (J). (gr. 2 up). lib. bdg. 24.67 (978-0-8368-2788-0(0)) Stevens, Gareth Inc.

—The Science of the Environment. 2003. (Living Science Ser.). (Illus.). 32p. (J). (gr. 1-3). pap. 7.95 (978-1-930954-21-2(2)) Weigl Pubs., Inc.

Modules: Life Science; Ecology PE. 2005. (gr. 6-12). (978-0-618-33429-2(7) , 2-01017) McDougal Littell Inc.

Moor, Jo Ellen. Habitats. Evans, Marilyn, ed. Robison, Don, illus. 1998. (ScienceWorks for Kids Ser.: Vol. 7). 80p. (J). (gr. 1-3). pap., tchr. ed. 9.95 (978-1-55799-688-6(1) , EMC 859) Evan-Moor Educational Pubs.

Moore & Peter, D. Tundra. 2007. (Ecosystem Ser.). 280p. (J). (gr. 9). 70.00 (***978-0-8160-5933-1(0)***) Facts On File, Inc.

Morgan, Ben. Tropical Grasslands. 2002. (Biomes Atlases Ser.). (Illus.). 64p. (J). lib. bdg. 31.42 (978-0-7398-5516-4(6)) Raintree.

Morgan, Sally. Cities. 2004. (Life In... Ser.). (SPA., Illus.). (gr. 3-6). 32p. (J). pap. 6.95 (978-1-58728-565-3(7)); 31p. 12.95 (978-1-58728-550-9(9)) T&N Children's Publishing. (Two Can Publishing).

—Cities, 1 vols. 2001. (World Book Ecology Ser.). (Illus.). 32p. (J). (978-0-7166-5228-1(5)) World Bk., Inc.

—Under a Stone & Other Rocky Places. 2006. (Hidden Habitats Ser.). (J). (978-1-59389-285-2(3)) Chrysalis Education.

Morris. Landscapes & People, Bks. 36, 6 Packs., Set. 2004. (Illus.). pap. 243.00 (978-1-4109-1259-6(0)) Raintree.

Morris, Neil. Earth's Changing Continents. 2003. (Illus.). (J). pap. 7.50 (978-1-4109-0342-6(7)); 32p. lib. bdg. 25.70 (978-1-4109-0179-8(3)) Raintree.

—Earth's Changing Continents. 2003. (gr. 3-6). lib. bdg. 15.90 (978-0-613-78236-4(4)) Tandem Library Bks.

—Earth's Changing Islands. 2003. (Illus.). 32p. (J). 7.50 (978-1-4109-0344-0(3)); lib. bdg. 25.70 (978-1-4109-0177-4(7)) Raintree.

—Earth's Changing Islands. 2003. (gr. 3-6). lib. bdg. 15.90 (978-0-613-78237-1(2)) Tandem Library Bks.

—Earth's Changing Mountains. 2003. (Illus.). (J). pap. 7.50 (978-1-4109-0345-7(1)); 32p. lib. bdg. 25.70 (978-1-4109-0174-3(2)) Raintree.

—Earth's Changing Mountains. 2003. (gr. 3-6). lib. bdg. 15.90 (978-0-613-78239-5(9)) Tandem Library Bks.

—Earth's Changing Rivers. 2003. (Illus.). (J). 7.50 (978-1-4109-0346-4(X)); 32p. lib. bdg. 25.70 (978-1-4109-0175-0(0)) Raintree.

—Earth's Changing Rivers. 2003. (gr. 3-6). lib. bdg. 15.90 (978-0-613-78240-1(2)) Tandem Library Bks.

—Living at the Coast. 2004. (J). lib. bdg. 27.10 (978-1-58340-486-7(4)) Smart Apple Media.

—Living by Lakes. 2004. (J). lib. bdg. (978-1-58340-485-0(6)) Smart Apple Media.

—Living by Rivers. 2004. (J). lib. bdg. (978-1-58340-482-9(1)) Smart Apple Media.

—Living in Cities. 2004. (J). lib. bdg. (978-1-58340-483-6(X)) Smart Apple Media.

—Living in the Mountains. 2004. (J). lib. bdg. (978-1-58340-484-3(8)) Smart Apple Media.

—Living on Islands. 2004. (J). lib. bdg. 27.10 (978-1-58340-487-4(2)) Smart Apple Media.

Morrison, Gordon. Drop of Water. 2006. (Illus.). 32p. (J). (gr. k-3). 16.00 (978-0-618-58557-1(5)) Houghton Mifflin Co.

—Oak Tree. 2005. (Illus.). 32p. (J). (gr. k-3). 6.95 (978-0-618-60918-5(0) , Walter Lorraine) Houghton Mifflin Co. Trade & Reference Div.

Morrison, Yvonne. Earth Matters. 2007. (Shockwave: People & Communities Ser.). (Illus.). 36p. (J). (gr. 4-6). lib. bdg. 25.00 (***978-0-531-17747-1(5)*** , Children's Pr.) Scholastic Library Publishing.

Mudd-Ruth, Maria. The Mississippi River. 2001. (Ecosystems of North America Ser.). (Illus.). 64p. (J). (gr. 6 up). lib. bdg. 28.50 (978-0-7614-0934-2(3) , Benchmark Bks.) Cavendish, Marshall Corp.

—The Pacific Coast. 2001. (Ecosystems of North America Ser.). (Illus.). 64p. (J). (gr. 6 up). lib. bdg. 28.50 (978-0-7614-0935-9(1) , Benchmark Bks.) Cavendish, Marshall Corp.

Nadeau, Isaac. Food Chains in a Desert Habitat. Kuhn, Dwight, photos by. 2002. (Library of Food Chains & Food Webs). (Illus.). 24p. (J). lib. bdg. 18.75 (978-0-8239-5760-6(8) , PowerKids Pr.) Rosen Publishing Group, Inc., The.

—Food Chains in a Meadow Habitat. Kuhn, Dwight, photos by. 2002. (Library of Food Chains & Food Webs). (Illus.). 24p. (J). lib. bdg. 18.75 (978-0-8239-5762-0(4) , PowerKids Pr.) Rosen Publishing Group, Inc., The.

—Food Chains in a Pond Habitat. Kuhn, Dwight, photos by. 2002. (Library of Food Chains & Food Webs). (Illus.). 24p. (J). (gr. 2-4). lib. bdg. 18.75 (978-0-8239-5763-7(2) , PowerKids Pr.) Rosen Publishing Group, Inc., The.

—Interdependence of Organisms & Environments. 2006. (Life Science Library). (Illus.). 24p. (J). 21.25 (978-1-4042-2819-1(5) , PowerKids Pr.) Rosen Publishing Group, Inc., The.

Nadeau, Issac. Food Chains in a Backyard Habitat. 2002. (Library of Food Chains & Food Webs). (Illus.). 24p. (J). lib. bdg. 18.75 (978-0-8239-5759-0(4)) Rosen Publishing Group, Inc., The.

—Food Chains in a Tide Pool Habitat. Kuhn, Dwight, photos by. 2002. (Library of Food Chains & Food Webs). (Illus.). 24p. (J). (gr. 2-4). lib. bdg. 18.75 (978-0-8239-5761-3(6) , PowerKids Pr.) Rosen Publishing Group, Inc., The.

Nelson, Julie. Tundra. Sloan, Frank, ed. 2001. (Biomes Ser.). (Illus.). 32p. (J). (gr. 4-7). lib. bdg. 22.83 (978-0-7398-3565-4(3)) Raintree.

Nichols, Catherine. A Dry Place. 2002. (We Can Read about Nature! Ser.). (Illus.). 32p. (J). 21.36 (978-0-7614-1431-5(2) , Benchmark Bks.) Cavendish, Marshall Corp.

—Grassy Lands. 2002. (We Can Read about Nature! Ser.). (Illus.). 32p. (J). 21.36 (978-0-7614-1435-3(5) , Benchmark Bks.) Cavendish, Marshall Corp.

—Wetlands. 2002. (We Can Read about Nature! Ser.). (Illus.). 32p. (J). 21.36 (978-0-7614-1434-6(7) , Benchmark Bks.) Cavendish, Marshall Corp.

Nsrc. Science & Technology for Children Books, Land & Water: Land & Water. 2004. (Illus.). 64p. (J). (978-1-933008-01-1(6)) National Science Resources Ctr.

Oceanor Staff. Ecologia - Atlas Visual. 1999. (SPA.). (gr. 3-6). lib. bdg. 20.00 (978-0-613-80885-9(1)) Tandem Library Bks.

O'Donnell, Kerri. Denali National Park, an Alaskan Ecosystem: Creating Graphical Representations of Data. 2006. (Math for the Real World Ser.). (Illus.). 32p. (J). pap. (978-1-4042-6083-2(8)); lib. bdg. (978-1-4042-3365-2(2)) Rosen Publishing Group, Inc., The.

Die Oekologie. (Duden-Schuelerduden Ser.). (GER., Illus.). 368p. (YA). 27.95 (978-3-411-02240-3(X)) Bibliographisches Institut & F. A. Brockhaus AG DEU. *Dist:* Continental Bk. Co., Inc., International Bk. Import Service, Inc.

Oliver, Clare. Life in a Flowerbed. 2002. (Microhabitats Ser.). (Illus.). 32p. (J). lib. bdg. 25.69 (978-0-7398-4329-1(X)) Raintree.

—Life in a House. 2002. (Microhabitats Ser.). (Illus.). 31p. (J). lib. bdg. 25.69 (978-0-7398-4333-8(8)) Raintree.

Ormsby, Alison. The Prairie. 1999. (Ecosystems of North America Ser.). (Illus.). 64p. (YA). (gr. 6 up). lib. bdg. 28.50 (978-0-7614-0897-0(5) , Benchmark Bks.) Cavendish, Marshall Corp.

Osborne, Mary Pope & Osborne, Will. Rain Forests. Murdocca, Sal, illus. 2001. (Magic Tree House Research Guide Ser.: No. 5). 128p. (J). (gr. k-3). 4.99 (978-0-375-81355-9(1) , Random Hse. Bks. for Young Readers) Random Hse. Children's Bks.

—Rain Forests: A Nonfiction Companion to Afternoon on the Amazon. Murdocca, Sal, illus. 2001. (Magic Tree House Research Guide Ser.: No. 5). 128p. (J). (gr. k-3). lib. bdg. 11.99 (978-0-375-91355-6(6) , Random Hse. Bks. for Young Readers) Random Hse. Children's Bks.

Oxlade, Chris. Mountains. 2003. (Science Files Ser.). (Illus.). 32p. (J). (gr. 3 up). lib. bdg. 24.67 (978-0-8368-3569-4(7)) Stevens, Gareth Inc.

—Rivers & Lakes. 2003. (Science Files Ser.). (Illus.). 32p. (J). (gr. 3 up). lib. bdg. 24.67 (978-0-8368-3571-7(9)) Stevens, Gareth Inc.

Parasites & Partners, 6 vols. 2003. (Illus.). (978-0-7398-6992-5(2)) Raintree.

Parker, Steve. Survival & Change. (Life Processes Ser.). 32p. pap. 7.50 (978-1-4034-4076-1(X)); 2006. (Illus.). (J). (***978-1-4034-8848-0(7)***); 2000. (Illus.). (J). (gr. 4-6). lib. bdg. 21.36 (978-1-57572-340-2(9)) Heinemann Library.

Pascoe, Elaine. The Ecosystem of a Fallen Tree. Kuhn, Dwight, illus. 2003. (Library of Small Ecosystems Ser.). 24p. (J). lib. bdg. 21.25 (978-0-8239-6308-9(X) , PowerKids Pr.) Rosen Publishing Group, Inc., The.

—The Ecosystem of a Garden. 2003. (Library of Small Ecosystems Ser.). (Illus.). 24p. (J). lib. bdg. 21.25 (978-0-8239-6306-5(3) , PowerKids Pr.) Rosen Publishing Group, Inc., The.

—The Ecosystem of a Grassy Field. 2003. (Library of Small Ecosystems Ser.). (Illus.). 24p. (J). lib. bdg. 21.25 (978-0-8239-6305-8(5) , PowerKids Pr.) Rosen Publishing Group, Inc., The.

—The Ecosystem of a Milkweed Patch. 2003. (Library of Small Ecosystems Ser.). (Illus.). 24p. (J). lib. bdg. 21.25 (978-0-8239-6309-6(8)) Rosen Publishing Group, Inc., The.

—The Ecosystem of a Stream. 2003. (Library of Small Ecosystems Ser.). (Illus.). 24p. (J). lib. bdg. 21.25 (978-0-8239-6307-2(1)) Rosen Publishing Group, Inc., The.

E F G

—The Ecosystem of an Apple Tree. 2003. (Library of Small Ecosystems Ser.). (Illus.). 24p. (J). lib. bdg. 21.25 (978-0-8239-6304-1(7) , PowerKids Pr.) Rosen Publishing Group, Inc., The.

—How & Why Insects Visit Flowers. Kupperstein, Joel, ed. Kuhn, Dwight, photos by. 2000. (How & Why Ser.). (Illus.). 16p. (J). (gr. 1-3). pap. 2.99 (978-1-57471-657-3(3) , 2964) Creative Teaching Pr., Inc.

Patent, Dorothy Hinshaw. Colorful, Captivating Coral Reefs. Jubb, Kendahl Jan, tr. Jubb, Kendahl Jan, illus. 2003. 40p. (J). 17.95 (978-0-8027-8862-7(9)) Walker & Co.

—Life in a Desert. Munoz, William, illus. Munoz, William, photos by. 2003. (Ecosystems in Action Ser.). 72p. (J). (gr. 6-12). 26.60 (978-0-8225-2140-2(7)) Lerner Publishing Group.

—Life in a Grassland. Munoz, William, illus. 2003. (Ecosystems in Action Ser.). 72p. (J). (gr. 6-12). 26.60 (978-0-8225-2139-6(3)) Lerner Publishing Group.

Penguin Books Staff, ed. Ecology. (Learners Ser.). (Illus.). 48p. (J). 3.50 (978-0-7214-1710-3(8) , Dutton Juvenile) Penguin Group (USA) Inc.

Penny, Malcolm. Life in a Rotten Log. 2003. (Microhabitats Ser.). (Illus.). 32p. (J). lib. bdg. 24.28 (978-0-7398-6804-1(7)) Raintree.

—Life in a Rotten Log. 2003. (gr. k-3). lib. bdg. 15.90 (978-0-613-78244-9(5)) Tandem Library Bks.

—Life in a Sand Dune. 2003. (Microhabitats Ser.). (Illus.). 32p. (J). pap. (978-1-4109-0350-1(8)); lib. bdg. 24.28 (978-0-7398-6805-8(5)) Raintree.

—Life in a Sand Dune. 2003. (gr. k-3). lib. bdg. 15.90 (978-0-613-78243-2(7)) Tandem Library Bks.

—Life under a Stone. 2003. (Illus.). 32p. (J). pap. (978-1-4109-0352-5(4)); lib. bdg. 24.28 (978-0-7398-6806-5(3)) Raintree.

—Our Environment. 1999. (Talking about Ser.). (Illus.). 32p. (J). (gr. k-4). lib. bdg. 25.69 (978-0-8172-5889-4(2)) Raintree.

Pfeffer, Wendy. Hot Deserts. 2002. (Living on the Edge Ser.). (J). 25.64 (978-0-7614-1440-7(1) , Benchmark Bks.) Cavendish, Marshall Corp.

PH Inc. Staff. PH Science Ecology Earth. (J). pap., act. bk. ed. (978-0-13-225582-0(0)) Prentice Hall (Schl. Div.).

Pifer, Joanne. EarthWise: Environmental Learning Series, Vol. II. (Illus.). 192p. (J). (gr. 5-8). 24.95 (978-0-9633019-6-3(9)) WP Pr., Inc.

Pipe, Jim. Habitats: Where Wildlife Lives. Hewitt, Sally, ed. 2005. (Science Starters Ser.). (Illus.). 32p. (J). (gr. 3-7). lib. bdg. 27.10 (978-1-59604-013-7(0)) Stargazer Bks.

Pirotta, Saviour. Trees & Plants in the Rain Forest. 1999. (Deep in the Rain Forest Ser.). (Illus.). 32p. (J). (978-0-7502-2198-6(4)) Steck-Vaughn.

Pratt, Kristin Joy. Salamander Rain: A Lake & Pond Journal. 2000. (gr. 3-6). lib. bdg. 16.40 (978-0-613-49355-0(9)) Tandem Library Bks.

Pratt-Serafini, Kristin Joy. Saguaro Moon: A Desert Journal. 2002. (gr. 3-6). lib. bdg. 16.40 (978-0-613-52786-6(0)) Tandem Library Bks.

—Salamander Rain: A Lake & Pond Journal. 2004. (Sharing Nature with Children Book Ser.). (Illus.). 32p. (YA). (gr. 4-7). 16.95 (978-1-58469-018-4(6)) Dawn Pubns.

Pratt-Serafini, Kristin Joy, illus. Saguaro Moon: A Desert Journal. 2004. (Sharing Nature with Children Book Ser.). 32p. (YA). 16.95 (978-1-58469-037-5(2)); pap. 7.95 (978-1-58469-036-8(4)) Dawn Pubns.

Pratt-Serafini, Kristin Joy & Pratt, Kristin Joy. Salamander Rain: A Lake & Pond Journal. 2004. (Sharing Nature with Children Book Ser.). (Illus.). 32p. (YA). (gr. 4-7). pap. 7.95 (978-1-58469-017-7(8)) Dawn Pubns.

Pressnall, Deb, ed. Inquiry Investigations: Food Chains & Webs: Backyard & Pond. 2005. 48p. (J). per. 6.99 (978-1-59441-056-7(9) , CD-104029) Carson-Dellosa Publishing Co., Inc.

Price, Martin F. Mountains: Geology, Natural History, & Ecosystems. rev. ed. 2002. (WorldLife Library Ser.). (Illus.). 72p. (J). pap. 17.95 (978-0-89658-251-4(5)) Voyageur Pr., Inc.

Pryor, Kimberley Jane. Coral Reefs. 2007. (J). (***978-1-59920-140-5(2)**) Smart Apple Media.

—Mangrove Swamps. 2007. (J). (***978-1-59920-138-2(0)**) Smart Apple Media.

—Rocky Shores. 2007. (J). (***978-1-59920-139-9(9)**) Smart Apple Media.

Pupeza, Lori K. Eco-Gardens. 2002. (J). lib. bdg. 19.92 (978-1-57765-033-1(6)) ABDO Publishing Co.

Pyers. Coral Reef Explorer, 6 Pack. 2004. (Habitat Explorer Ser.). (Illus.). pap. 40.50 (978-1-4109-0914-5(X)) Raintree.

—Habitat Explorer, 5 bks., Set 2. 2004. (Illus.). (J). 25.70 (978-1-4109-1216-9(7)) Harcourt Schl. Pubs.

—Habitat Explorer. 2004. (Illus.). (J). pap. 33.75 (978-1-4109-0843-8(7)); Set 1. pap. 27.00 (978-1-4109-0910-7(7)) Raintree.

—River Explorer. 2004. (Habitat Explorer Ser.). (Illus.). pap. 7.50 (978-1-4109-0908-4(5)) Raintree.

Pyers, Greg. Mountain Explorer. 2004. (Habitat Explorer Ser.). (Illus.). 32p. (J). (ps). lib. bdg. 25.70 (978-1-4109-0509-3(8)) Raintree.

—Ocean Explorer. 2004. (Habitat Explorer Ser.). (Illus.). 32p. (J). (ps-ps). lib. bdg. 25.70 (978-1-4109-0510-9(1)) Raintree.

Quigley, Mary. Prairie Explorer. 2004. (Habitat Explorer Ser.). (Illus.). 32p. (J). (ps-ps). lib. bdg. 25.70 (978-1-4109-0513-0(6)) Raintree.

Rapp, Valerie. Life in a River: The Columbia River Basin. 2003. (American Ecosystems Ser.). (Illus.). 72p. (J). (gr. 6-12). 26.60 (978-0-8225-2136-5(9)) Lerner Publishing Group.

Rau, Dana Meachen. Deserts. 2007. (Wonders of Nature Ser.). 32p. (J). lib. bdg. 22.79 (***978-0-7614-2667-7(1)** , Benchmark Bks.) Cavendish, Marshall Corp.

Reid, Greg. Deserts. 2004. (Ecosystems Ser.). (Illus.). 32p. (J). (gr. 3-5). 23.00 (978-0-7910-7938-6(4) , Chelsea Hse.) Facts On File, Inc.

—Ecosystems. 2005. (Illus.). 32p. (J). (gr. 4-7). lib. bdg. 27.10 (978-1-58340-764-6(2)) Smart Apple Media.

—Grasslands. 2004. (Ecosystems Ser.). (Illus.). 32p. (J). (gr. 3-5). 23.00 (978-0-7910-7939-3(2) , Chelsea Hse.) Facts On File, Inc.

—Human Impacts. 2005. (Illus.). 32p. (J). (gr. 4-7). lib. bdg. 27.10 (978-1-58340-763-9(4)) Smart Apple Media.

—Rain Forests. 2004. (Ecosystems Ser.). (Illus.). 32p. (J). (gr. 3-5). 23.00 (978-0-7910-7941-6(4) , Chelsea Hse.) Facts On File, Inc.

—Temperate Forests. 2004. (Ecosystems Ser.). (Illus.). 32p. (J). (gr. 3-5). 23.00 (978-0-7910-7942-3(2) , Chelsea Hse.) Facts On File, Inc.

—Wetlands. 2004. (Ecosystems Ser.). (Illus.). 32p. (J). (gr. 3-5). 23.00 (978-0-7910-7943-0(0) , Chelsea Hse.) Facts On File, Inc.

Richardson, Gillian. The Science of Ecosystems: Species, Spaces, & Relationships. 2003. (J). lib. bdg. 27.14 (978-0-7398-6994-9(9)) Raintree.

Riley, Peter D. Food. 1998. (Cycles in Science Ser.). (Illus.). 32p. (J). (gr. 4-7). lib. bdg. (978-1-57572-618-2(1)) Heinemann Library.

—Habitats. Moller, Ray, photos by. 2003. (Everyday Science Ser.). (Illus.). 32p. (J). (gr. 1 up). lib. bdg. 23.33 (978-0-8368-3714-8(2)) Stevens, Gareth Inc.

—The Ocean. 2004. (Survivor's Science Ser.). 28.56 (978-1-4109-0229-0(3)) Harcourt Schl. Pubs.

—The Polar Regions. 2004. (Survivor's Science Ser.). 28.56 (978-1-4109-0228-3(5)) Harcourt Schl. Pubs.

—Survivor's Science on an Island. 2004. (Survivor's Science Ser.). (Illus.). 48p. (J). (gr. 6-8). lib. bdg. 28.56 (978-1-4109-0226-9(9)) Harcourt Schl. Pubs.

Ring, Elizabeth. Drylands. 2005. (Communities in Nature Ser.). (Illus.). 48p. (J). (gr. 2-5). 24.95 (978-1-4103-0320-2(9) , Blackbirch Pr., Inc.) Thomson Gale.

—Shorelands. 2004. (Illus.). 48p. (J). (gr. 2-4). 24.95 (978-1-4103-0316-5(0) , Blackbirch Pr., Inc.) Thomson Gale.

—Wetlands. 2004. (Illus.). 48p. (J). (gr. 2-4). 24.95 (978-1-4103-0315-8(2) , Blackbirch Pr., Inc.) Thomson Gale.

Ring, Susan. The Ocean. 2003. (Yellow Umbrella Books for Early Readers). (Illus.). 17p. (J). 15.93 (978-0-7368-2920-5(2)); pap. (978-0-7368-2879-6(6)) Yellow Umbrella Pr.

—Wildfires. 2003. (Science Links Ser.). (Illus.). 32p. (gr. 3-5). 23.00 (978-0-7910-7432-9(3) , Chelsea Hse.) Facts On File, Inc.

Rockwell, Anne F. Alligators. 2000. (Let's-Read-and-Find-Out Science Ser.). (Illus.). 40p. (J). (gr. k-4). lib. bdg. 15.89 (978-0-06-028531-9(1)) HarperCollins Pubs.

Rompella, Natalie. Ecosystems. 2007. (J). (***978-1-4034-7915-0(1)**) Heinemann Library.

Rosenberg, Pam. Underground. 2007. (Icky, Sticky, Gross-Out Bks.). 24p. (J). (gr. 2-6). 22.79 (***978-1-59296-900-5(3)**) Child's World, Inc.

Ross, Mandy. Rivers. 2004. (Geography Fact Files Ser.). (J). lib. bdg. 28.50 (978-1-58340-429-4(5)) Smart Apple Media.

Rotter, Charles. Mountains. 2002. (LifeViews Ser.). (J). (978-0-89812-375-3(5) , Creative Paperbacks) Creative Co., The.

—Mountains: The Towering Sentinels. 2002. (LifeViews Ser.). (Illus.). 32p. (J). lib. bdg. (978-1-58341-123-0(2) , Creative Education) Creative Co., The.

—The Prairie: An Enduring Spirit. 2001. (Life on Earth Ser.). (Illus.). 32p. (J). lib. bdg. (978-1-58341-029-5(5) , Creative Education) Creative Co., The.

Ruth, Maria M. The Deserts of the Southwest. 1999. (Ecosystems of North America Ser.). (Illus.). 64p. (YA). (gr. 6 up). lib. bdg. 28.50 (978-0-7614-0899-4(1) , Benchmark Bks.) Cavendish, Marshall Corp.

Rybolt, Thomas R. & Mebane, Robert C. Science Experiments for Young People, 5 bks., Set. (Illus.). (YA). (gr. 4-9). lib. bdg. 99.75 (978-0-89490-448-6(5)) Enslow Pubs., Inc.

Sachidhanandam, Uma. Threatened Habitats. 2004. (Green Alert Ser.). (Illus.). 48p. (J). lib. bdg. 28.56 (978-0-7398-7015-0(7)) Raintree.

Sasman, Irene D. H. Ecology & the Environment Children's Library, Set. 1998. (Illus.). (J). (ps-6). pap. 99.95 (978-1-56831-955-1(X)) Learning Connection, The.

Sayre, April Pulley. Exploring Earth's Biomes, 7 vols. Incl. Coral Reef. 80p. lib. bdg. 25.90 (978-0-8050-4087-6(0)); Desert. 64p. lib. bdg. (978-0-8050-2825-6(0)); Grassland. 64p. lib. bdg. (978-0-8050-2827-0(7)); Lake & Pond. 64p. lib. bdg. 25.90 (978-0-8050-4089-0(7)); Ocean. 80p. lib. bdg. 25.90 (978-0-8050-4084-5(6)); River & Stream. 64p. lib. bdg. (978-0-8050-4088-3(9)); Seashore. 64p. lib. bdg. 25.90 (978-0-8050-4085-2(4)); Taiga. 64p. lib. bdg. (978-0-8050-2830-0(7)); Temperate Deciduous Forest. 64p. lib. bdg. (978-0-8050-2828-7(5)); Tropical Rainforest. 64p. lib. bdg. (978-0-8050-2826-3(9)); Tundra. 64p. lib. bdg. (978-0-8050-2829-4(3)); Wetland. 80p. lib. bdg. 25.90 (978-0-8050-4086-9(2)); (gr. 5 up). 1997. (Illus.). 2004. 310.80 (978-0-7613-3020-2(8) , Twenty-First Century Bks.) Lerner Publishing Group.

—Good Morning, Africa! 2003. 32p. (J). (gr. 2-5). pap. 7.95 (978-0-7613-1993-1(X)); (Celebrate the Continents Ser.: 4). (Illus.). lib. bdg. 21.90 (978-0-7613-2121-7(7)) Lerner Publishing Group. (Millbrook Pr.).

—Good Morning, Africa! 2003. (gr. k-3). lib. bdg. 16.40 (978-0-613-90691-3(8)) Tandem Library Bks.

—El Nino & la Nina: Weather in the Headlines. 2000. (Science & Technology Ser.). (Illus.). 80p. (gr. 7 up). lib. bdg. (978-0-7613-1405-9(9) , Millbrook Pr.) Lerner Publishing Group.

Sayre, April Pulley. Trout Are Made of Trees. Endle, Kate, illus. 2008. (J). (***978-1-58089-137-0(3)**) Charlesbridge Publishing, Inc.

Sayres, Meghan Nuttall. The Shape of Betts Meadow: A Wetlands Story. Friar, Joanne, illus. 2002. 32p. (ps-3). lib. bdg. 22.90 (978-0-7613-2115-6(2) , Millbrook Pr.) Lerner Publishing Group.

Schmid, Eleonore. Living Earth. 2000. (Illus.). 32p. (J). (gr. k-3). pap. 6.95 (978-0-7358-1315-1(9)) North-South Bks., Inc.

—Living Earth. 2000. (gr. k-3). lib. bdg. 15.25 (978-0-613-26040-4(6)) Tandem Library Bks.

Schwartz, David M. In the Garden. Kuhn, Dwight, photos by. 1999. (Springboards into Science Ser.). (Illus.). 24p. (J). (gr. 1 up). lib. bdg. 19.93 (978-0-8368-2242-7(0)) Stevens, Gareth Inc.

Science & Technology for Children Books, Land & Water Set, 8 vols. 2004. (Illus.). 64p. (J). (978-1-933008-13-4(X)) National Science Resources Ctr.

Science Files - Set II - Earth: Deserts; Forests; Islands; Mountains; Oceans; Rivers & Lakes, 6 bks. 2002. (Illus.). (J). (gr. 3 up). lib. bdg. 148.02 (978-0-8368-3565-6(4)) Stevens, Gareth Inc.

Science Stories Foss Spanish Environments EA CR05. 2005. (J). (978-1-59242-593-8(3)) Delta Education, LLC.

Scott, Janine. Food Found All Around. 2002. (Spyglass Books). (Illus.). 24p. (J). (gr. 1 up). lib. bdg. 18.60 (978-0-7565-0234-8(9)) Compass Point Bks.

Sheppard, Charles. Coral Reefs: Ecology, Threats, & Conservation. 2002. (World Life Library). (Illus.). 72p. pap. 17.95 (978-0-89658-220-0(5)) Voyageur Pr., Inc.

Shevick, Edward. Environment: Explorations in Environmental Science. Mitchell, Judy, ed. Abbett, Leo, illus. 1998. (Science Action Labs Ser.). (Illus.). 64p. (gr. 4-8). pap., tchr. ed. 8.95 (978-1-57310-137-0(0)) Teaching & Learning Co.

Shrublands. 2003. (Biomes Atlas Ser.). (Illus.). pap. 48.30 (978-1-4109-0250-4(1)) Raintree.

Silverstein, Alvin & Silverstein, Virginia. Life in a Tidal Pool. Carroll, Walter & Carroll, Pamela, illus. 2005. 64p. (gr. 3). pap. 6.95 (978-0-486-44592-2(5)) Dover Pubns., Inc.

Silverstein, Alvin, et al. Food Chains. (Illus.). 2007. (Science Concepts, Second Ser.). 96p. (YA). (gr. 6-8). lib. bdg. 31.93 (***978-0-8225-6797-4(0)**); 1998. (Science Concepts Ser.: 8). 64p. (gr. 5-8). lib. bdg. 26.90 (978-0-7613-3002-8(X)) Lerner Publishing Group. (Twenty-First Century Bks.).

Smith, Andrea Claire Harte. The Effects of Farming. 2004. (Earth's Changing Landscape Ser.). (Illus.). 45p. (J). lib. bdg. 28.50 (978-1-58340-475-1(9)) Smart Apple Media.

Snedden, Robert. Around the Poles. 2003. (Illus.). 32p. (J). lib. bdg. (978-1-58340-383-9(3)) Smart Apple Media.

—Mountains. 2004. (Illus.). 32p. (J). lib. bdg. (978-1-58340-384-6(1)) Smart Apple Media.

—Tropical Grasslands. 2004. (Illus.). 32p. (J). lib. bdg. (978-1-58340-386-0(8)) Smart Apple Media.

—Who Eats Who in City Habitats? 2006. (Food Chains in Action Ser.). (Illus.). 32p. (J). (978-1-58340-965-7(3) , 1262626) Smart Apple Media.

Sohn, Emily, et al. The Environment. 2006. (Science News for Kids Ser.). (Illus.). 64p. (J). 30.00 (978-0-7910-9123-4(6) , Chelsea Clubhouse) Facts On File, Inc.

Soltis, Nicki. We Need More Trees! 2001. (gr. k-3). lib. bdg. 11.95 (978-0-613-33453-2(1)) Tandem Library Bks.

Solway, Andrew. Food Chains & Webs: The Struggle to Survive. 2008. (J). (***978-1-60044-601-6(9)**) Rourke Publishing, LLC.

Somervill, Barbara A. Our Living World: Earth's Biomes, 7 vols., Set. 2005. (Illus.). (J). (gr. 4-8). 350.00 (978-1-59187-052-4(6)) Tradition Publishing Co.

Souza, Dorothy M. Plant Invaders. 2003. (Watts Library). (Illus.). 64p. (J). 25.50 (978-0-531-12211-2(5) , Watts, Franklin) Scholastic Library Publishing.

Spilsbury, Louise & Spilsbury, Richard. Desert Food Chains. 2004. (Food Webs Ser.). (Illus.). 32p. (J). 24.22 (978-1-4034-5855-1(3)); pap. (978-1-4034-5862-9(6)) Heinemann Library.

—Food Chains & Webs: From Producers to Decomposers. 2004. (Science Answers Ser.). (Illus.). 32p. (J). pap. 7.50 (978-1-4034-5510-9(4)); lib. bdg. 24.22 (978-1-4034-4764-7(0)) Heinemann Library.

—Grassland Food Chains. 2004. (Food Webs Ser.). (Illus.). 32p. (J). pap. 7.50 (978-1-4034-5867-4(7)) Heinemann Library.

—Mountain Food Chains. 2004. (Food Webs Ser.). (Illus.). 32p. (J). (ps-k). lib. bdg. 24.22 (978-1-4034-5856-8(1)) Heinemann Library.

—Shark Snacks: Food Chains & Webs. 2005. (Illus.). 32p. (J). (978-1-4034-5510-9(4)); lib. bdg. (978-1-4109-1942-7(0)) Steck-Vaughn.

—The War in Your Backyard: Life in an Ecosystem. 2005. (Illus.). 32p. (J). lib. bdg. (978-1-4109-1939-7(0)) Steck-Vaughn.

Spilsbury, Richard. The Great Outdoors: Saving Habitats. 2005. (Where Are Wild Places? — How Do Wild Places Work? — Why Are Wild Places under Threat? — How Can We Look after Woodlands & Forests? — How Can We Help Protect Mountains & Hills? — How Can We Look after Rivers & Lakes? — How Can We Keep Coasts Clean? — Where Are the Wild Places in Towns & Cities? — Is Your School Wildlife-Friendly? Ser.). (Illus.). 32p. (J). (gr. 3-7). pap. 7.85 (978-1-4034-6853-6(2)); lib. bdg. 28.21 (978-1-4034-6847-5(8)) Heinemann Library.

Spilsbury, Richard & Spilsbury, Louise. Mountain Food Chains. 2004. (Food Webs Ser.). (Illus.). 32p. (J). (ps-7). pap. 7.50 (978-1-4034-5863-6(4)) Heinemann Library.

—The War in Your Backyard: Life in an Ecosystem. 2005. (Illus.). 32p. (J). (gr. 3-5). 7.85 (978-1-4109-1970-0(6)) Steck-Vaughn.

Staub, Frank. America's Forests. 1998. (Earth Watch Ser.). (Illus.). 56p. (gr. 4-6). lib. bdg. 21.27 (978-1-57505-265-6(2)) Lerner Publishing Group.

—The Food Chain. 2003. (Illus.). 32p. (J). lib. bdg. (978-1-58341-269-5(7) , Creative Education) Creative Co., The.

Steele, Christy. Desert Animals. 2002. (Animals of the Biomes Ser.). (Illus.). 48p. (J). lib. bdg. 24.26 (978-0-7398-5686-4(3)) Raintree.

—Desert Animals. 2003. (Animals of the Biomes Ser.). (Illus.). 48p. (J). pap. 6.95 (978-0-7398-6406-7(8)) Steck-Vaughn.

Steele, Philip. A Tidal Pool. 1999. (Illus.). 32p. (J). (ps-7). lib. bdg. 17.60 (978-0-613-19533-1(7)) Tandem Library Bks.

Stetson, Emily. Create a Wildlife Habitat for Urban & Suburban Small Spaces. 2004. (Quick Starts for Kids! Ser.). (Illus.). 128p. (J). pap. 12.95 (978-0-8249-8665-0(2)) Ideals Pubns.

Stewart, Melissa. Down to Earth. 2004. (Investigate Science Ser.). (Illus.). 32p. (J). (gr. 1 up). lib. bdg. 21.26 (978-0-7565-0595-0(X)) Compass Point Bks.

—Life in a Lake: Lake Superior. 2003. (Ecosystems in Action Ser.). (Illus.). 72p. (J). (gr. 6-12). 26.60 (978-0-8225-2138-9(5)) Lerner Publishing Group.

—Plants. 2003. (Simply Science Ser.). (Illus.). 32p. (J). (gr. 3 up). lib. bdg. 19.93 (978-0-7565-0444-1(9)) Compass Point Bks.

—Soil. 2002. (Rocks & Minerals Ser.). (Illus.). 32p. (J). (gr. 4-6). lib. bdg. 24.22 (978-1-58810-260-7(2)); pap. 7.50 (978-1-4034-0096-3(2) , 91663) Heinemann Library.

Stockland, Patricia M. Sand, Leaf, or Coral Reef: A Book about Animal Habitats. Ouren, Todd, illus. 2005. (Animal Wise Ser.). 24p. (C). (gr. k-2). 22.60 (978-1-4048-0932-1(5)) Picture Window Bks.

Stone, Lynn M. Deserts. 2003. (Rourke Discovery Library). (Illus.). 24p. (J). 20.64 (978-1-58952-683-9(X)) Rourke Publishing, LLC.

—The Food Chain. 2001. (Under the Sea Ser.). (Illus.). 24p. (J). (gr. 1-4). lib. bdg. 20.64 (978-1-58952-113-1(7)) Rourke Publishing, LLC.

—Forests. 2003. (Rourke Discovery Library). (Illus.). 24p. (J). 20.64 (978-1-58952-684-6(8)) Rourke Publishing, LLC.

—Grasslands. 2003. (Rourke Discovery Library). (Illus.). 24p. (J). 20.64 (978-1-58952-685-3(6)) Rourke Publishing, LLC.

—Partners. 2001. (Under the Sea Ser.). (Illus.). 24p. (J). (gr. 1-4). lib. bdg. 20.64 (978-1-58952-114-8(5)) Rourke Publishing, LLC.

—Tundra. 2003. (Rourke Discovery Library). (Illus.). 24p. (J). 20.64 (978-1-58952-687-7(2)) Rourke Publishing, LLC.

Stonehouse, Bernard. Nature Unfolds the Poles. 2001. (Nature Unfolds Ser.). (Illus.). 40p. (J). (gr. 4). pap. (978-0-7787-0321-1(5)); lib. bdg. (978-0-7787-0309-9(6)) Crabtree Publishing Co.

—Poles. 2001. (gr. 5-8). lib. bdg. 18.75 (978-0-613-89192-9(9)) Tandem Library Bks.

Stronach, Neil. Mountains. 2001. (People & Places in Peril Ser.). (Illus.). 48p. 19.99 (978-0-7451-5216-5(3) , Cherrytree Books) Evans Publishing Group GBR. *Dist:* Independent Pubs. Group.

Suzuki, David & Vanderlinden, Kathy. Eco-Fun: Great Projects, Games & Experiments for a Greener Earth. Kurisu, Jane, illus. 2003. (David Suzuki Children's Titles Ser.). 128p. (J). (gr. 3-6). pap. 12.95 (978-1-55054-823-5(9)) Douglas & McIntyre, Ltd. CAN. *Dist:* Transition Vendor.

Tagliaferro, Linda. Explore the Tundra. 2007. (Fact Finders Ser.). (Illus.). 32p. (J). 22.60 (978-0-7368-6408-4(3)) Capstone Pr., Inc.

Talmadge, Ellen. Unearthing Garden Mysteries Vol. 1: Experiments for Kids. Curtis, Bruce, photos by. 2004. (Illus.). 96p. (gr. 4-7). 17.95 (978-1-55591-993-1(6)) Fulcrum Publishing.

Tarbox, A. D. The Arctic Tundra. 2008. (J). (***978-1-58341-596-2(3)** , Creative Education) Creative Co., The.

—The Mountains. 2008. (J). (***978-1-58341-599-3(8)** , Creative Education) Creative Co., The.

—The Prairie. 2008. (J). (***978-1-58341-600-6(5)** , Creative Education) Creative Co., The.

—The Rainforest. 2008. (J). (***978-1-58341-601-3(3)** , Creative Education) Creative Co., The.

Telford, Carole & Theodorou, Rod. Inside a Coral Reef. (Illus.). 32p. (J). 2006. (***978-1-4034-8790-2(1)**); 1998. (gr. 2-4). lib. bdg. 22.79 (978-1-57572-154-5(6)) Heinemann Library.

—Up a Rainforest Tree. 2006. (Illus.). 32p. (J). (***978-1-4034-8793-3(6)**) Heinemann Library.

Tocci, Salvatore. The Chaparral: Life on the Scrubby Coast. (Watts Library Ser.). (J). 2005. (Illus.). 64p. (gr. 5-7). pap. 8.95 (978-0-531-16671-0(6)); 2004. 25.50 (978-0-531-12303-4(0)) Scholastic Library Publishing. (Watts, Franklin).

—Coral Reefs: Life below the Sea. (Watts Library). (J). 2005. (Illus.). 64p. (gr. 5-7). pap. 8.95 (978-0-531-16669-7(4)); 2004. 25.50 (978-0-531-12304-1(9)) Scholastic Library Publishing. (Watts, Franklin).

Toft, Kim Michelle. The World That We Want. 2005. (Illus.). 32p. (J). (ps-ps). pap. 6.95 (978-1-58089-115-8(2)); bds. 16.95 (978-1-58089-114-1(4)) Charlesbridge Publishing, Inc.

—The World That We Want. Toft, Kim Michelle, illus. 2005. (Illus.). 32p. (J). pap. 17.95 (978-0-7022-3482-8(6)) Univ. of Queensland Pr. AUS. *Dist:* International Specialized Bk. Services.

Toupin, Laurie Peach. Freshwater Habitats: Life in Freshwater Ecosystems. 2004. (Watts Library Ser.). (J). 25.50 (978-0-531-12305-8(7) , Watts, Franklin) Scholastic Library Publishing.

—Savannas: Life in the Tropical Grasslands. 2005. (Biomes & Habitats Ser.). (Illus.). 64p. (J). (gr. 5-7). 24.50 (978-0-531-12386-7(3) , Watts, Franklin) Scholastic Library Publishing.

Two-Can Publishing Ltd. Staff. Las Praderas. 2000. (Ecologia Ser.). (SPA., Illus.). 32p. (J). (gr. 3-6). mass mkt. 4.95 (978-1-58728-973-6(3) , Two Can Publishing) T&N Children's Publishing.

Viendo. (Coleccion Mil Preguntas). (SPA., Illus.). 24p. (J). pap. 5.50 (978-950-11-0658-9(6) , SGM626) Sigmar ARG. *Dist:* Continental Bk. Co., Inc.

Wadsworth, Pamela. Cynefinoedd. 2005. (WEL., Illus.). 24p. pap. (978-1-85596-229-3(2)) Dref Wen.

—Golwg Gyntaf Ar Ble Mae Pethau'n Byw. 2005. (WEL., Illus.). 24p. pap. (978-1-85596-256-9(X)) Dref Wen.

—Pethau Byw Ar Waith. 2005. (WEL., Illus.). 24p. pap. (978-1-85596-233-0(0)) Dref Wen.

—Rhagor Am Gynefinoedd. 2005. (WEL., Illus.). 24p. pap. (978-1-85596-230-9(6)) Dref Wen.

Walker, Jane. La Costa. 2001. (SPA., Illus.). 32p. (J). (ps-3). 10.95 (978-84-263-3171-7(8)) Lectorum Pubns., Inc.

Walker, Pam & Wood, Elaine. Ecosystem Science Fair Projects Using Worms, Leaves, Crickets, & Other Stuff. 2005. (Biology! Best Science Projects Ser.). (Illus.). 128p. (J). lib. bdg. 26.60 (978-0-7660-2367-3(2) , 1238537) Enslow Pubs., Inc.

Walker, Sally M. Life in an Estuary. 2003. (American Ecosystems Ser.). (Illus.). 72p. (J). (gr. 6-12). 26.60 (978-0-8225-2137-2(7)) Lerner Publishing Group.

Wallace, Holly. Food Chains & Webs. (Life Processes Ser.). 32p. pap. 7.50 (978-1-4034-4074-7(3)); 2006. (Illus.). (J). (***978-1-4034-8846-6(0));*** 2000. (Illus.). (J). (gr. 4-6). lib. bdg. 21.36 (978-1-57572-338-9(7)) Heinemann Library.

Wallace, Marianne D. America's Prairies & Grasslands: Guide to Plants & Animals. 2004. (America's EcoSystem Ser.: Vol. 3). (Illus.). 48p. (J). (gr. 3-6). pap. 11.95 (978-1-55591-992-4(8)) Fulcrum Publishing.

—Americas Prairies & Grasslands: Guide to Plants & Animals. 2001. (gr. 5-8). lib. bdg. 26.85 (978-0-613-87963-7(5)) Tandem Library Bks.

Ward, Brian R. Microscopic Life in the Garden. 2004. (Illus.). 32p. (J). lib. bdg. (978-1-58340-473-7(2)) Smart Apple Media.

—Microscopic Life in Your Home. 2004. (Illus.). 32p. (J). lib. bdg. (978-1-58340-472-0(4)) Smart Apple Media.

Warhol, Tom. Desert. 2006. (Earth's Biomes Ser.). (Illus.). 80p. (YA). (gr. 5-8). lib. bdg. 32.79 (978-0-7614-2194-8(7) , Benchmark Bks.) Cavendish, Marshall Corp.

—Tundra. 2006. (Earth's Biomes Ser.). (Illus.). 80p. (YA). (gr. 5-8). lib. bdg. 32.79 (978-0-7614-2193-1(9) , Benchmark Bks.) Cavendish, Marshall Corp.

—Water. 2006. (Earth's Biomes Ser.). (Illus.). 80p. (J). lib. bdg. 32.79 (978-0-7614-2192-4(0) , Benchmark Bks.) Cavendish, Marshall Corp.

Waters, Jo. A Walk in the City. 2006. (Illus.). 24p. (J). (978-1-4109-2293-9(6)); pap. (978-1-4109-2298-4(7)) Steck-Vaughn.

Watson, Stephanie. The Tundra. 2003. (Biomes Around the World Ser.). (J). pap. (978-1-58417-305-2(X)); lib. bdg. (978-1-58417-304-5(1)) Lake Street Pubs.

Watson, Susan. Living Sustainably. 2003. 32p. (J). lib. bdg. 24.25 (978-1-58340-404-1(X)) Smart Apple Media.

Weigel, Marlene. U-X-L Encyclopedia of Biomes, 3 vols., Set. Carnagie, Julie L., ed. 2000. (Illus.). 520p. (J). (gr. 4-7). 181.00 (978-0-7876-3732-3(7) , GML00502-113380, UXL) Thomson Gale.

Whitcraft, Melissa. Hudson River. 1999. (gr. 3-6). lib. bdg. 17.60 (978-0-613-29447-8(5)) Tandem Library Bks.

Whitehouse, Patricia. Living in the Arctic. 2007. (Illus.). 24p. (J). (978-1-60044-188-2(2)) Rourke Publishing, LLC.

Wickings, Ruth. Round the Garden. 2006. (World at Your Feet Ser.). (Illus.). 10p. 9.95 (978-1-84560-025-9(8)) Mercury Bks. Ltd. GBR. *Dist:* International Publishers Marketing.

Wiley, G. D. Tropical Rain Forests. 2003. (Biomes Around the World Ser.). (J). pap. (978-1-58417-301-4(7)); lib. bdg. (978-1-58417-300-7(9)) Lake Street Pubs.

Wilson, Brenda. Totally Amazing Careers in Environmental Sciences. 2006. (J). 7.80 (978-1-933798-01-1(7)) Sally Ride Science.

Winner, Cherie. Life in the Tundra. 2003. (Ecosystems in Action Ser.). (Illus.). 72p. (J). (gr. 6-12). lib. bdg. 26.60 (978-0-8225-4686-3(8)) Lerner Publishing Group.

Wood, Jenny. Los Desiertos. (Coleccion Tierra Viva).Tr. of Deserts. (SPA.). 32p. (YA). (gr. 5-8). (978-84-348-3266-4(6)) SM Ediciones.

Woodford, Chris. Arctic Tundra & Polar Deserts. 2002. (Biomes Atlases Ser.). (Illus.). 64p. (J). lib. bdg. 31.40 (978-0-7398-5246-0(9)) Raintree.

—Arctic Tundra & Polar Deserts. 2003. (gr. 5-8). lib. bdg. 18.20 (978-0-613-78192-3(9)) Tandem Library Bks.

Woodward. Temperate Forests. 2003. (Biomes Atlas Ser.). (Illus.). 64p. pap. 9.50 (978-1-4109-0022-7(3)) Raintree.

Woodward, John. Midnight Zone. 2004. (Illus.). 48p. (J). lib. bdg. (978-1-4034-5125-5(7)) Heinemann Library.

—The Midnight Zone. 2004. (Illus.). 48p. (J). pap. 8.50 (978-1-4034-5131-6(1)) Heinemann Library.

—The Seafloor. 2004. (Illus.). 48p. (J). pap. 8.50 (978-1-4034-5132-3(X)); lib. bdg. 27.07 (978-1-4034-5126-2(5)) Heinemann Library.

—The Sunlit Zone. 2004. (Illus.). 48p. (J). pap. 8.50 (978-1-4034-5133-0(8)); lib. bdg. (978-1-4034-5127-9(3)) Heinemann Library.

—The Tidal Zone. 2004. (Illus.). 48p. (J). pap. 8.50 (978-1-4034-5134-7(6)); lib. bdg. (978-1-4034-5128-6(1)) Heinemann Library.

—The Twilight Zone. 2004. (Illus.). 48p. (J). pap. 8.50 (978-1-4034-5135-4(4)); lib. bdg. (978-1-4034-5129-3(X)) Heinemann Library.

Wright, Alexandra. At Home in the Tide Pool. 1999. (gr. k-3). lib. bdg. 15.25 (978-0-613-16322-4(2)) Tandem Library Bks.

Wright, David. Environment Atlas. rev. ed. (Atlas Ser.). (Illus.). 96p. (YA). (gr. 4-9). 18.95 (978-0-8160-3715-5(9)) Facts On File, Inc.

Wright, Rachel & Baines, Francesca. Ocean Worlds. 2004. (Discovery Guides Ser.). (SPA., Illus.). 32p. (gr. 2-5). 11.95 (978-1-58728-221-8(6) , Two Can Publishing) T&N Children's Publishing.

ECOLOGY—FICTION

Arnosky, Jim. Crinkleroot's Visit to Crinkle Cove. 1999. (J). (978-0-606-18948-4(3)) Tandem Library Bks.

Atkins, Jeannine. Aani & the Tree Huggers. Pinto, Venantius J., illus. 2000. 32p. (J). (ps-5). 6.95 (978-1-58430-004-5(3)); 15.95 (978-1-880000-24-3(5)) Lee & Low Bks., Inc.

—Aani & the Tree Huggers. 2000. (Illus.). (J). 13.75 (978-0-606-18245-4(4)) Tandem Library Bks.

Baer, Julie. Love Me Later. 2005. (Illus.). 28p. (J). (ps-ps). 16.99 (978-1-932188-03-5(7)) Bollix Bks.

Baldwin, Robert F. This Is the Sea That Feeds Us. Dyen, Don, illus. 1998. 32p. (YA). (ps-3). 16.95 (978-1-883220-69-3(6)); pap. 7.95 (978-1-883220-70-9(X)) Dawn Pubns.

Brooks, John. Balloons, Sea Creatures, & Me. 2006. 34p. (J). 14.58 (978-0-9661789-3-7(9)) Lulu.com.

Carmody, Isobelle. The Legend Begins. 2006. (Illus.). 208p. (J). (gr. 1-7). 12.95 (978-0-375-83854-5(6)); (gr. 3-7). lib. bdg. 14.99 (978-0-375-93854-2(0)) Random Hse. Children's Bks. (Random Hse. Bks. for Young Readers).

—Little Fur: The Legend Begins. 2006. (Illus.). 272p. (J). (978-0-375-83855-2(4)) Random Hse., Inc.

Carmody, Isobelle. A Mystery of Wolves: Little Fur #3. 2008. (J). pap. (***978-0-375-83859-0(7));*** (Little Fur: 3). 12.99 (***978-0-375-83858-3(9));*** (Little Fur: 3). lib. bdg. 15.99 (***978-0-375-93858-0(3))*** Random Hse., Inc.

Cherry, Lynne. Great Kapok Tree. 2000. (gr. k-3). lib. bdg. 15.30 (978-0-613-28507-0(7)) Tandem Library Bks.

—Great Kapok Tree: A Tale of the Amazon Rain Forest. 2000. (Illus.). 33p. lib. bdg. 13.80 (978-0-606-17843-3(0)) Tandem Library Bks.

—The Sea, the Storm, & the Mangrove Tangle. 2004. (Illus.). 40p. (J). 17.00 (978-0-374-36482-3(6) , Farrar, Straus & Giroux (BYR)) Farrar, Straus & Giroux.

Choyce, Lesley. Big Burn. 2004. 215p. mass mkt. (978-1-895449-43-3(X)) Thistledown Pr., Ltd.

Collard, Sneed. Flash Point. 2006. 256p. (J). 15.95 (978-1-56145-385-6(4) , Peachtree Junior) Peachtree Pubs., Ltd.

Crocker, Carter & Snyder, Carrie A. The Tale of the Swamp Rat. 2005. 176p. (J). (gr. 4). reprint ed. pap. 6.99 (978-0-14-240314-3(8) , Puffin) Penguin Group (USA) Inc.

Day, Robert O. & Day, Linda S. There's a Frog on a Log in the Bog. Day, Linda S., illus. 2003. (Just So Wild Ser.: Vol. 1). (Illus.). (J). (gr. 3-6). 212p. pap. 8.95 (978-1-890905-50-7(X)); 14.95 (978-1-890905-51-4(8)) Day to Day Enterprises. (Eco Fiction Bks.).

Dennard, Deborah. Hedgehog Haven: A Story of a British Hedgerow Community. 2005. (Soundprints' Wild Habitats Ser.). (Illus.). 32p. (J). (gr. 1-4). 8.95 incl. audio (978-1-59249-108-7(1) , SC7020) Soundprints.

—Hedgehog Haven: The Story of an English Hedgerow Community. Hynes, Robert, illus. (Wild Habitats Ser.). (J). (gr. 1-4). 2005. 32p. 15.95 (978-1-56899-987-6(9) , B7020); 2005. 32p. 19.95 incl. audio (978-1-56899-989-0(5) , BC7020); 2005. 32p. pap. 6.95 (978-1-56899-988-3(7) , S7020); 2001. 36p. 26.95 (978-1-56899-991-3(7)) Soundprints.

D'Lacey, Chris. A Break in the Chain. Carey, Joanna, illus. 2002. (Yellow Bananas Ser.). 48p. (J). (gr. 3-4). pap. (978-0-7787-0977-0(9)); lib. bdg. (978-0-7787-0931-2(0)) Crabtree Publishing Co.

Domm, Kristin & Domm, Jeff. Ahmed & the Nest of Sand. Domm, Jeffrey, illus. 2000. 32p. (ps-3). pap. 8.95 (978-1-55109-338-3(3)) Nimbus Publishing, Ltd. CAN. *Dist:* National Bk. Network.

Douglas, Babette. Amazing Grace. 2004. (J). 9.99 (978-1-890343-33-0(1)) Kiss A Me Productions, Inc.

Dowd, John. Hogsty Reef. 1999. 192p. (YA). (gr. 6-10). pap. 5.95 (978-1-56145-187-6(8) , Q19223) Peachtree Pubs., Ltd.

—Hogsty Reef. 1999. (gr. 7-12). lib. bdg. 14.10 (978-0-613-29258-0(8)) Tandem Library Bks.

Ellis, Brian. The Web at Dragonfly Pond. Maydak, Michael S., illus. 2006. (Sharing Nature with Children Book Ser.). 32p. (J). 16.95 (978-1-58469-078-8(X)); pap. 8.95 (978-1-58469-079-5(8)) Dawn Pubns.

Foreman, Michael. One World. 2004. (Illus.). 32p. (J). pap. 11.00 (978-1-84270-334-2(X)) Andersen GBR. *Dist:* Independent Pubs. Group.

George, Jean Craighead. The Case of the Missing Cutthroats. Duranceau, Suzanne, illus. 1999. (Eco Mystery Ser.). 160p. (J). (gr. 3-7). pap. 5.99 (978-0-06-440647-5(4) , Harper Trophy) HarperCollins Pubs.

—The Case of the Missing Cutthroats. 1999. (J). 12.64 (978-0-606-16703-1(X)); (gr. 3-6). lib. bdg. 14.15 (978-0-613-18242-3(1)) Tandem Library Bks.

Grooms, Molly. We Are Wolves. 2002. (Illus.). 32p. (J). (ps-2). pap. 7.95 (978-1-55971-835-6(8) , NorthWord Bks. for Young Readers) T&N Children's Publishing.

Hallinan, P. K., illus. For the Love of Our Earth. 2001. 24p. (J). (ps-3). 7.95 (978-0-8249-5384-3(3)); pap. 5.95 (978-0-8249-5385-0(1)) Ideals Pubns. (Ideals).

Harms, John, II. The Saving of Sly Manatee. Belizar, Denise H., ed. Makowski, Robin Lee, illus. 2001. (J). 32p. lib. bdg. 18.95 (978-1-931329-02-6(8)); (gr. 2-7). pap. 6.95 (978-0-9653871-9-4(4)) Frederick Pr.

—The Saving of Valiant Blue Heron. Belizar, Denise H., ed. Makowski, Robin Lee, illus. 2001. 32p. (J). (gr. 2-7). pap. 6.95 (978-0-9653871-8-7(6)) Frederick Pr.

Harms, John, II & Nelson, Brian. The Saving of Arma Armadillo. 2001. (Illus.). (J). (gr. 2-7). pap. 6.95 (978-0-9653871-2-5(7)) Frederick Pr.

Harris, Monica. Animal Therapy. 2001. (Illus.). 18p. (J). (ps-5). 4.70 (978-0-9712923-0-7(2)) Taylor-Dth Publishing.

Julietta, Melinda. We Are Wolves. Guamotta, Lucia, illus. 1999. 32p. (ps-3). 12.95 (978-1-55971-713-7(0) , NorthWord Bks. for Young Readers) T&N Children's Publishing.

Klass, David. Firestorm. 2006. (Caretaker Trilogy Ser.: Bk. 1). 304p. (YA). 17.00 (978-0-374-32307-3(0) , Frances Foster Bks.) Farrar, Straus & Giroux.

—Firestorm: The Caretaker Trilogy: Book 1. 2008. (Caretaker Trilogy Ser.). 320p. (YA). pap. 8.99 (***978-0-312-38018-2(6))*** Square Fish.

—Whirlwind. 2008. (Caretaker Trilogy Ser.). 304p. (YA). 17.95 (***978-0-374-32308-0(9))*** Farrar, Straus & Giroux.

Langeland, Deirdre. Kangaroo Island: A Story of an Australian Mallee Forest. 2005. (Soundprints' Wild Habitats Ser.). (Illus.). 32p. (J). (gr. 1-4). pap. 8.95 incl. reel tape (978-1-59249-095-0(6)) Soundprints.

Loehr, Mallory. Fire Dreams. 2001. (Stepping Stone Book Ser.: Vol. 4). (Illus.). 128p. (J). (gr. 3-5). pap. 3.99 (978-0-679-89219-9(2) , Random Hse. Bks. for Young Readers) Random Hse. Children's Bks.

—Wind Spell. 2000. (Magic Elements Quartet Ser.: No. 3). (Illus.). 128p. (J). (gr. 3-5). pap. 3.99 (978-0-679-89217-5(6) , Random Hse. Bks. for Young Readers) Random Hse. Children's Bks.

—Wind Spell. 2000. (gr. 3-6). lib. bdg. 11.80 (978-0-613-27595-8(0)); (Illus.). (J). (978-0-606-20993-9(X)) Tandem Library Bks.

Logsdon, Gene. The Man Who Created Paradise: A Fable. 2001. (Illus.). 68p. 20.00 (978-0-8214-1407-1(0)) Ohio Univ. Pr.

Mason, Cherie. Everybody's Somebody's Lunch. Moore, Gustav, illus. 2005. 40p. (J). (gr. 3-6). 7.95 (978-0-88448-200-0(6)) Tilbury Hse. Pubs.

Mills, J. C. Carew. rev. ed. 2007. (Illus.). 248p. pap. 7.95 (***978-1-55263-788-3(3))*** Key Porter Bks. CAN. *Dist:* Perseus Distribution.

Morpurgo, Michael, ed. Beyond the Rainbow Warrior: A Collection of Stories to Celebrate 25 Years of Greenpeace. 1998. (Illus.). 144p. (J). (gr. 5-9). pap. 17.95 (978-1-86205-035-8(X) , Pavilion Bks., Ltd.) Anova Bks. GBR. *Dist:* Trafalgar Square Publishing.

Oliver, Narelle. The Best Beak in Boonaroo Bay. Oliver, Narelle, illus. (Illus.). 48p. (YA). pap. (978-0-85091-671-3(2) , Lothian Bks.) Hachette Livre Australia.

Pandell, Karen. I Love You, Sun I Love You, Moon: Te amo, sol Te amo, Luna. dePaola, Tomie, illus. 2007. 20p. (J). (gr. k-3). bds. 6.99 (***978-0-448-44800-8(9)*** , Grosset & Dunlap) Penguin Group (USA) Inc.

Pandell, Karen. Te Amo Sol, Te Amo Luna/I Love You Sun, I Love You Moon. de Paola, Tomie, illus. 2003. (SPA & ENG.). 18p. (J). (ps-1). bds. 6.99 (978-0-399-24165-9(5) , Putnam Juvenile) Penguin Group (USA) Inc.

Pauli, Gunter. Shiitake Love Caffeine. Salazar, Pamela, illus. 2007. 33p. pap. 9.95 (***978-958-692-833-5(0))*** Marion Institute.

Raphael, Morris. Ti-Nute, the Angel of Devil's Pond. Ferry, Kate, illus. 2000. 47p. (J). (978-0-8187-0332-4(6)) Harlo Pr.

Robinson, Tim. Tobias, the Quig & the Rumplenut Tree. Robinson, Tim, illus. 2000. (Illus.). 40p. (J). (ps-3). 16.95 (978-1-890817-20-6(1)) Winslow Pr.

Saltzman, Ruth E. Poppy Bear: The Garden That Overslept. Deeter, Catherine, illus. 2001. 32p. (J). (gr. k-2). 16.95 (978-1-58270-042-7(7)) Beyond Words Publishing, Inc.

Sidjanski, Brigitte. The River. Watts, Bernadette, illus. 2008. 32p. (J). (ps). 16.99 (***978-0-698-40077-1(1)*** , Minedition) Penguin Group (USA) Inc.

Sleator, William. The Beasties, Vol. 1. 1999. (Illus.). 208p. (J). (gr. 3-7). pap. 6.99 (978-0-14-130639-1(4) , Puffin) Penguin Group (USA) Inc.

—The Beasties. 1999. (J). 12.64 (978-0-606-17410-7(9)); (gr. 5-8). lib. bdg. 14.15 (978-0-613-22820-6(0)) Tandem Library Bks.

Smith, Tim. Who Stole the Animal Poop? 2006. (Buck Wilder's Adventure Ser.). 60p. (J). pap. (978-1-934133-05-7(1)) Mackinac Island Pr., Inc.

Smith, Timothy R. The Owls Don't Give a Hoot. 2007. (Buck Wilder's Adventure Ser.: 4). (Illus.). 96p. (J). pap. 5.95 (***978-1-934133-11-8(6))*** Mackinac Island Pr., Inc.

Sommer, Carl. King of the Pond. 2003. (Another Sommer-Time Story Ser.). (Illus.). 48p. (J). (gr. k-4). lib. bdg. 23.95 incl. audio (978-1-57537-766-7(7)); (gr. k-4). lib. bdg. 23.95 incl. audio compact disk (978-1-57537-716-2(0)); (gr. 1-4). 16.95 incl. audio (978-1-57537-565-6(6)); (gr. 1-4). 16.95 incl. audio compact disk (978-1-57537-516-8(8)) Advance Publishing, Inc.

—King of the Pond. Budwine, Greg, illus. 2000. (Another Sommer-Time Story Ser.). 48p. (J). (gr. k-3). lib. bdg. 16.95 (978-1-57537-065-1(4)); 9.95 (978-1-57537-016-3(6)) Advance Publishing, Inc.

Suzuki, David & Ellis, Sarah. The Salmon Forest. Lott, Sheena, illus. 2003. (David Suzuki Children's Titles Ser.). (gr. k-2). 15.95 (978-1-55054-937-9(5)) Douglas & McIntyre, Ltd. CAN. *Dist:* Transition Vendor.

—Salmon Forest. Lott, Sheena, illus. 2006. 32p. (J). pap. 8.95 (978-1-55365-163-5(4) , Greystone Bks.) Douglas & McIntyre, Ltd. CAN. *Dist:* Transition Vendor.

Tennyson, Michael. Morpha: A Rain Forest Story. Yoswa, Jennifer H., illus. 2002. (CMC Wilderness Kids Ser.). 40p. 14.95 (978-0-9671466-8-3(2)) Colorado Mountain Club Pr., The.

Terry & the Ecological Disaster. pap. (978-1-56002-792-8(4)) Univ. Editions.

Trout, Richard. Sign of the Dragon. 2007. (J). 15.95 (***978-1-58980-476-0(7))*** Pelican Publishing Co., Inc.

Ward, Jennifer. The Seed & the Giant Saguaro. Rangner, Mike, illus. 2003. 32p. (gr. 4-8). 15.95 (978-0-87358-845-4(2) , Rising Moon Bks. for Young Readers) Northland Publishing.

White, Carolyn. Snowff & the Rowdy-Cloudy Bunch. 2006. (Snowff the Snowflake Kid Adventure Ser.). (J). 24.95 (978-1-893563-05-6(7)) AARO Publishing.

—Snowff Visits Razorteeth Village. 2006. (J). 24.95 (978-1-893563-10-0(3)) AARO Publishing.

—Snowff's MIST.erious Journey (Snowff the Snowflake Kid Adventure, 1) 2006. (J). 24.95 (978-1-893563-00-1(6)) AARO Publishing.

Wolfson, Jill. Home, & Other Big, Fat Lies. 2006. (Illus.). 224p. (J). 16.95 (978-0-8050-7670-7(0) , Holt, Henry & Co. Bks. For Young Readers) Holt, Henry & Co.

ECOLOGY, MARINE

see Marine Ecology

ECONOMIC ASSISTANCE

Garlake, Teresa. Global Debt. 2003. (21st Century Debates Ser.). (Illus.). 64p. (J). lib. bdg. 28.56 (978-0-7398-6035-9(6)) Raintree.

Katella-Cofrancesco, Kathy. Economic Causes. 1998. (Celebrity Activists Ser.). (Illus.). 64p. (gr. 5-8). lib. bdg. 25.90 (978-0-7613-3014-1(3) , Twenty-First Century Bks.) Lerner Publishing Group.

Morgan, John. Development, Globalisation & Sustainability. 2001. (Epics Ser.). (Illus.). 96p. (YA). (gr. 11 up). pap. 23.50 (978-0-7487-5822-7(4)) Nelson Thornes Ltd. GBR. *Dist:* Trans-Atlantic Pubns., Inc.

ECONOMIC BOTANY

see Botany, Economic

ECONOMIC CONDITIONS

see Economic History

ECONOMIC DEPRESSIONS

see Depressions

ECONOMIC DEVELOPMENT

see Economic History

ECONOMIC ENTOMOLOGY

see Insects, Injurious and Beneficial

ECONOMIC GEOGRAPHY

see also Commercial Geography

Sheppard, Paul. Access to Geography: Economic Activity & Change. 2004. (Illus.). 144p. pap. 27.50 (***978-0-340-81500-7(0)*** , Hodder Murray) Hodder Education GBR. *Dist:* Trans-Atlantic Pubns., Inc.

ECONOMIC HISTORY

Davidson, Avelyn. Dollars & Sense: Economics & Science. (Shockwave: Economics & Geography Ser.). (J). 2008. 32p. pap. 6.95 (***978-0-531-18836-1(1));*** 2007. (Illus.). 36p. (gr. 4-6). lib. bdg. 25.00 (***978-0-531-17750-1(5))*** Scholastic Library Publishing. (Children's Pr.).

Downing, David. The Great Depression. (20th Century Perspectives Ser.). (Illus.). 48p. (J). 2001. (gr. 4-7). lib. bdg. 25.64 (978-1-57572-435-5(9)); Set 1. 2002. (gr. 5-7). pap. 7.95 (978-1-58810-374-1(9) , 91126) Heinemann Library.

—The Great Depression. 2001. (YA). 15.30 (978-0-606-22492-5(0)) Tandem Library Bks.

Gifford, Clive. Sustainable Development. 2003. (Face the Facts Ser.). (Illus.). 56p. (J). lib. bdg. 28.56 (978-0-7398-6851-5(9)) Raintree.

Grant, R. G. The Great Depression. 2005. (How Did It Happen? Ser.). (Illus.). 48p. (YA). (gr. 7-10). lib. bdg. 29.95 (978-1-59018-606-0(0) , Lucent Bks.) Thomson Gale.

Harmon, Daniel E. Turkey. 2003. (Modern Middle East Nations & Their Strategic Place in the World Ser.). (Illus.). 112,128p. (YA). (gr. 7 up). lib. bdg. (978-1-59084-524-0(2)) Mason Crest Pubs.

Heinemann Library Staff. The Great Depression. 2003. (Illus.). 56p. (J). pap. 8.95 (978-1-4034-4576-6(1)) Heinemann Library.

Moriarty, J. T. The Birth of American Capitalism: The Rise of the American Bank. 2003. (America's Industrial Society in the 19th Century Ser.). (Illus.). 32p. (J). pap. (978-0-8239-4280-0(5)) Rosen Publishing Group, Inc., The.

Murray, Meredith A. To Live & Die Amongst the Monongahela Hills: The Story of Albert Gallatin & Friendship Hill. 1999. (Illus.). 48p. (YA). (gr. 6-12). pap. 4.95 (978-1-888213-34-8(5)) Eastern National.

The New Global Society. 2005. (Illus.). 112p. (gr. 9-12). pap. 180.00 (978-0-7910-9094-7(9) , Chelsea Hse.) Facts On File, Inc.

Poggio, Pier Paolo & Simoni, Carlo. The Global Community, 1975-2000. Bacchin, Giorgio, illus. 2002. (Road to Globalization Ser.). 32p. (YA). 22.95 (978-0-7910-7096-3(4)) Facts On File, Inc.

Winters, Adam. Sustainable Development. 2006. (Extreme Environmental Threats Ser.). (Illus.). 64p. (YA). lib. bdg. (978-1-4042-0746-2(5)) Rosen Publishing Group, Inc., The.

ECONOMIC PLANNING

see Economic Policy

ECONOMIC POLICY

see also International Economic Relations

Pratten, J. & Proctor, Nigel. Business, Government & Economics. 1999. (Illus.). 160p. (J). pap. 24.95 (978-1-872807-58-4(5)) Liverpool Academic Pr. GBR. *Dist:* International Specialized Bk. Services.

ECONOMIC RELATIONS, FOREIGN

see International Economic Relations

ECONOMIC ZOOLOGY

see Zoology, Economic

ECONOMICS

see also Business; Capitalism; Commerce; Consumption (Economics); Credit; Depressions; Economic History; Economic Policy; Finance; Industry; Labor and Laboring Classes; Land Use; Money; Population; Socialism; Waste (Economics)

Adil, Janeen R. Supply & Demand. 2006. (First Facts Ser.). (Illus.). 24p. (J). (978-0-7368-5397-2(9)) Capstone Pr., Inc.

Andrews, Matthew, et al. HIGCSE Economics Module 3, Nicholson, Jillian, ed. 2nd rev. ed. 2000. (Cambridge Open Learning Project in South Africa Ser.). (Illus.). v, 104p. pap. 9.40 (978-0-521-64777-9(0)) Cambridge Univ. Pr.

Ayllon Torres, Maria Teresa. Geografia Economica para las Escuelas Preparatorias. 9th ed. 1999. (SPA., Illus.). 268p. (C). (978-968-18-5867-4(0) , Limusa) Noriega Editores.

Benchmark Education Staff, compiled by. Economics. 2006. spiral bd. 95.00 (***978-1-4108-7070-4(7)***); spiral bd. 99.00 (***978-1-4108-7086-5(3)***) Benchmark Education Co.

—Production, Distribution, & Consumption. 2005. spiral bd. 345.00 (***978-1-4108-3749-3(1)***); spiral bd. 180.00 (***978-1-4108-3940-4(0)***); spiral bd. 90.00 (***978-1-4108-3941-1(9)***); spiral bd. 165.00 (***978-1-4108-3965-7(6)***); spiral bd. 110.00 (***978-1-4108-3966-4(4)***); spiral bd. 230.00 (***978-1-4108-4498-9(6)***); spiral bd. 375.00 (***978-1-4108-5422-3(1)***); spiral bd. 225.00 (***978-1-4108-5838-2(3)***) Benchmark Education Co.

Berry, Rob & Duey, Kathleen. The Smart Kids Allowance System: Step-by-Step Money Management Guidebook. Bartholomew, illus. Date not set. (Family Skill Builders Ser.). (J). (gr. k-6). pap. 9.95 (978-1-883761-34-9(4)) Family Life Productions.

Boyes. Boyes, Fundamentals of Economics, with Life Handbook, 3rd Edition. 3rd ed. 2005. (YA). pap., pap. 110.36 (978-0-618-64101-7(7) , 396078) Houghton Mifflin College Div.

—Boyes Macroeconomics with Student Support Package Sixth Edition Plus Eduspace Two. 6th ed. 2004. (YA). pap., pap. 115.96 incl. cd-rom (978-0-618-53451-7(2) , 389567) Houghton Mifflin College Div.

—Study Guide: Used with ... Boyes-Economics; Boyes-Microeconomics. 6th ed. 2004. (YA). stu. ed. 36.76 (978-0-618-37255-3(5) , 305003) Houghton Mifflin College Div.

Boyes, William. Study Guide: Macroeconomics: Used with ... Boyes-Economics; Boyes-Macroeconomics. 6th ed. 2004. (YA). stu. ed. 36.76 (978-0-618-37256-0(3) , 305004) Houghton Mifflin College Div.

Callella, Trisha. Integrating Maps & Money with Reading Instruction, 2830. Walter, LaDawn, ed. Campbell, Jenny, illus. 2002. 72p. (J). (gr. 3-4). pap. 10.99 (978-1-57471-905-5(X) , 2830) Creative Teaching Pr., Inc.

Condon, Daniel & Giesecke, Ernestine. Everyday Economics, Set 2. 2003. (J). (gr. 3-5). lib. bdg. 81.21 (978-1-4034-0713-9(4)) Heinemann Library.

Cost Benefit Jr. Stories in Microeconomics. 2003. (J). spiral bd. 29.95 (978-0-9746242-2-8(5)) Consilient Pubns.

de Garis, Nina. Cambridge Checkpoints VCE Economics 2004-2005. 2003. (Cambridge Checkpoints Ser.). 176p. pap. 11.95 (978-0-521-54075-9(5)) Cambridge Univ. Pr.

Economics: Student Technology Package. 4th ed. 2004. (gr. 6-12). (978-0-618-38192-0(9) , 3-52024) McDougal Littell Inc.

Economics: Student Tutorial. 4th ed. 2004. (gr. 6-12). cd-rom (978-0-618-23010-5(6) , 3-52019) McDougal Littell Inc.

Economics: Test Bank, Macroeconomics. 4th ed. 2004. (gr. 6-12). (978-0-618-23007-5(6) , 3-52016) McDougal Littell Inc.

Everyday Economics, 7 vols., Set. 2003. 48p. (J). (gr. 3-5). lib. bdg. 189.49 (978-1-4034-0712-2(6)) Heinemann Library.

Facts on File, Inc. Staff. Top Careers for Economics Graduates. 2004. (Top Careers Ser.). (Illus.). 384p. (gr. 9). pap. 14.95 (978-0-8160-5566-1(1) , Checkmark Bks.) Facts On File, Inc.

Gall, Timothy L. & Gall, Susan B., eds. Junior Worldmark Encyclopedia of the Nations, 9 vols. 2nd ed. 1999. (Illus.). (J). (978-0-7876-3804-7(8)); (978-0-7876-3805-4(6)) Thomson Gale.

Garey, Marita. Kids Are Consumers. 2002. (Illus.). 32p. (J). (978-0-7922-8700-1(2)) National Geographic Society.

Giesecke, Ernestine. Everyday Economics, Set 1. 2003. (J). (gr. 3-5). lib. bdg. 108.28 (978-1-58810-419-9(2)) Heinemann Library.

Gillette, David D. Economics. 3rd ed. 2002. (Illus.). vii, 463p. (YA). pap. (978-0-393-97780-6(3)) Norton, W. W. & Co., Inc.

Gilman, Laura Anne. Economics. 2006. (How Economics Works). (Illus.). 48p. (J). (gr. 3-7). 25.26 (978-0-8225-2662-9(X) , Lerner Pubns.) Lerner Publishing Group.

Going Global: Teaching How Nation. 2001. spiral bd. 15.95 (978-1-56004-107-8(2)) Social Studies Schl. Service.

Grant, R. G. Protesting Capitalism. 2003. (Ideas of the Modern World Ser.). (Illus.). 64p. (J). lib. bdg. 28.56 (978-0-7398-6414-2(9)) Raintree.

Grolier Educational Staff. Economics, 6. 2000. (Illus.). (YA). (978-0-7172-9571-5(0) , Grolier) Scholastic Library Publishing.

—Economics., 6 vols. 2000. (Illus.). (YA). (978-0-7172-9482-4(X)); (978-0-7172-9483-1(8)); (978-0-7172-9484-8(6)); (978-0-7172-9485-5(4)); (978-0-7172-9570-8(2)) Scholastic Library Publishing. (Grolier).

Harcourt School Publishers Staff. Baseball Cards & the Ultimate Value of Everything Advanced Level. 3rd ed. 2002. (Trophies Reading Program Ser.). (Illus.). (gr. 6). pap. 5.10 (978-0-15-323463-7(6)) Harcourt Schl. Pubs.

Here's the Scoop. 1998. (Neale Godfrey Money Program Ser.). (J). incl. cd-rom (978-0-8136-4214-7(0)) Modern Curriculum Pr.

Herman, Stephanie. Cost Benefit Jr Bk. 1: Bound Text with Looseleaf Q & A - Answer Key: How Free Markets Work. 2003. spiral bd. 29.95 (978-0-9746242-0-4(9)) Consilient Pubns.

—Cost Benefit Jr Bk. 1: Self-Contained: How Free Markets Work. 2003. spiral bd., wbk. ed. 29.95 (978-0-9746242-1-1(7)) Consilient Pubns.

Hibbert, Adam. Globalization. 2004. (Face the Facts Ser.). (Illus.). 56p. (J). 28.56 (978-1-4109-1071-4(7)) Harcourt Schl. Pubs.

Holt, Rinehart and Winston Staff. Holt Researcher: Economics & Government: User Guide for CD-ROM. 1999. pap. 6.73 (978-0-03-051714-3(1)) Holt, Rinehart & Winston.

How Economics Works, 6 bks., Set. Incl. Banking. Allman, Barbara. (ps-7). 25.26 (978-0-8225-2148-8(2)); Budgeting. Donovan, Sandy. (gr. 3-7). 25.26 (978-0-8225-2665-0(4)); Earning Money. Murphy, Patricia J. (ps-7). 25.26 (978-0-8225-2149-5(0)); Economics. Gilman, Laura Anne. (gr. 3-7). 25.26 (978-0-8225-2662-9(X)); Saving Money. Heckman, Philip. (gr. 3-7). 25.26 (978-0-8225-2664-3(6)); Stock Market. Fuller, Donna Jo. (ps-7). 25.26 (978-0-8225-2635-3(2)); (Illus.). 48p. (J). 2006. 2005. Set lib. bdg. 151.56 (978-0-8225-0034-6(5) , Lerner Pubns.) Lerner Publishing Group.

Hyclak, Thomas, et al. Fundamentals of Labor Economics. 2004. (Illus.). 523p. (YA). 143.96 (978-0-395-92362-7(X) , 326940) Houghton Mifflin College Div.

Katella-Cofrancesco, Kathy. Economic Causes. 1998. (Celebrity Activists Ser.). (Illus.). 64p. (gr. 5-8). lib. bdg. 25.90 (978-0-7613-3014-1(3) , Twenty-First Century Bks.) Lerner Publishing Group.

Landau, Elaine. All-American Companies. 2003. (Single Titles Ser.). 112p. (J). lib. bdg. 32.90 (978-0-7613-2350-1(3) , Twenty-First Century Bks.) Lerner Publishing Group.

Let's See Library-Economics Complete Set. (Let's See Library-Economics Ser.). (gr. 1-3). 79.72 (978-0-7565-0496-0(1)) Compass Point Bks.

Marsh, Carole. Pass the Test! Civics & Economics. (Virginia Experience! Ser.). lab manual ed. 195.00 incl. cd-rom (978-0-635-01593-8(5) , 15935); cd-rom 395.00 (978-0-635-01594-5(3) , 15943); 2004. cd-rom 24.95 (978-0-635-01592-1(7) , 15927) Gallopade International.

—Virginia Civics & Economics: Student Workbook. 2004. (Virginia Experience! Ser.). (Illus.). 160p. pap., wbk. ed. 12.95 (978-0-635-01590-7(0) , 15900) Gallopade International.

Maybury, Richard J. Uncle Eric Talks about Personal, Career, & Financial Security. Williams, Jane A. & Daniels, Kathryn, eds. 2nd ed. 2004. ("Uncle Eric" Bk.). (Illus.). 187p. (YA). pap. 14.95 (978-0-942617-38-2(X)) Bluestocking Pr.

McGraw-Hill Staff. Economics. 2001. stu. ed. 92.23 (978-0-538-43036-4(2) , 9780538430364) Glencoe/McGraw-Hill.

—Economics: Principles & Practices. 2007. stu. ed. 92.64 (***978-0-07-874764-9(3)*** , 9780078747649); 2002. (gr. 6-12). stu. ed. 91.33 (978-0-07-825977-7(0) , 9780078259777); 2001. (gr. 6-12). stu. ed. 91.33 (978-0-07-828093-1(1) , 9780078280931); 3rd ed. 2004. stu. ed. 92.64 (978-0-07-860693-9(4) , 9780078606939) Glencoe/McGraw-Hill.

—Economics: Principles & Practices, Interactive Tutor: Self-Assessment, CD-ROM. 2007. (C). cd-rom 93.32 (***978-0-07-878602-0(9)*** , 9780078786020) Glencoe/McGraw-Hill.

—Economics: Principles & Practices, Reading Essentials. 2004. (C). pap., stu. ed., wbk. ed. 22.00 (978-0-07-865040-6(2) , 9780078650406) Glencoe/McGraw-Hill.

—Economics: Principles & Practices, Reading Essentials & Note-Taking Guide. 2007. pap. 18.00 (***978-0-07-878593-1(6)*** , 9780078785931) Glencoe/McGraw-Hill.

—Economics: Principles & Practices, Spanish Reading Essentials & Note-Taking Guide. 2007. (C). pap. 18.00 (***978-0-07-878595-5(2)*** , 9780078785955) Glencoe/McGraw-Hill.

—Economics: Today & Tomorrow. (C). 2002. (gr. 6-12). stu. ed. 91.33 (978-0-07-825980-7(0) , 9780078259807); 3rd ed. 2004. stu. ed. 92.64 (978-0-07-860696-0(9) , 9780078606960) Glencoe/McGraw-Hill.

—Economics: Today & Tomorrow, Interactive Tutor: Self Assessment. 2007. (C). cd-rom 93.32 (***978-0-07-878359-3(3)*** , 9780078783593) Glencoe/McGraw-Hill.

—Economics: Today & Tomorrow, Reading Essentials & Study Guide. 2007. (C). pap. 18.00 (***978-0-07-878351-7(8)*** , 9780078783517) Glencoe/McGraw-Hill.

—Economics: Today & Tomorrow, Spanish Reading Essentials & Study Guide. 2007. (C). pap. 18.00 (***978-0-07-878590-0(1)*** , 9780078785900) Glencoe/McGraw-Hill.

—Economics: Today & Tomorrow, StudentWorks with Audio. 2007. (C). cd-rom 116.64 (***978-0-07-878355-5(0)*** , 9780078783555) Glencoe/McGraw-Hill.

—Economics, Principles & Practices, StudentWorks. 5th ed. 2004. (C). 104.64 (978-0-07-865056-7(9) , 9780078650567) Glencoe/McGraw-Hill.

—Economics Today & Tomorrow. 2001. (C). (gr. 6-12). stu. ed. 91.33 (978-0-07-828095-5(8) , 9780078280955) Glencoe/McGraw-Hill.

—Economics Today & Tomorrow: Reading Essentials. 3rd ed. 2004. pap., stu. ed., wbk. ed. 18.00 (978-0-07-865063-5(1) , 9780078650635) Glencoe/McGraw-Hill.

—Economics, Today & Tomorrow: StudentWorks. 3rd ed. 2004. (C). stu. ed. 104.64 incl. cd-rom (978-0-07-865073-4(9) , 9780078650734) Glencoe/McGraw-Hill.

—Economics Today & Tomorrow, Spanish Reading Essentials. 3rd ed. 2004. (SPA.). (C). stu. ed., wbk. ed. 18.00 (978-0-07-864044-5(X) , 9780078640445) Glencoe/McGraw-Hill.

Probert, Jason, et al. HIGCSE Economics Module 2, Nicholson, Jillian, ed. 2nd rev. ed. 2000. (Cambridge Open Learning Project in South Africa Ser.). (Illus.). 124p. pap. 9.40 (978-0-521-64778-6(9)) Cambridge Univ. Pr.

Rancic, Bill. Beyond the Lemonade Stand: Starting Small to Make It Big! 2005. (Illus.). 160p. (YA). (gr. 3-7). 12.99 (978-1-59514-103-3(0) , Razorbill) Penguin Group (USA) Inc.

Seidman, David L. The Young Zillionaire's Guide to Supply & Demand. 2000. (Be a Zillionaire Ser.). (Illus.). 48p. (YA). (gr. 5-8). lib. bdg. 23.95 (978-0-8239-3264-1(8) , ZISUDE, Rosen Central) Rosen Publishing Group, Inc., The.

Shafer, Jean & Clark, Susan P. Easy Economics. 1998. (Illus.). 48p. (J). (gr. 4-8). pap., wbk. ed. 15.95 (978-0-938682-47-9(4) , 682-47-4) River Road Pubns., Inc.

Student Courseware: Applying the Principles. wbk. ed. 12.95 (978-0-8219-3404-3(X)) EMC/Paradigm Publishing.

Student Courseware: Textbook. 54.95 (978-0-8219-3401-2(5)) EMC/Paradigm Publishing.

Taylor. Economics: AP Version. 4th ed. 2003. (YA). (gr. 6-12). 147.96 (978-0-618-38191-3(0) , 352023) Houghton Mifflin College Div.

—Economics Ap Version Plus Student Technology Package 4th Edition. 4th ed. 2003. (YA). (gr. 6-12). 147.06 incl. cd-rom (978-0-618-39397-8(8) , 384997) Houghton Mifflin College Div.

—Study Guide: Used with ... Taylor-Economics. 4th ed. 2003. (YA). (gr. 6-12). stu. ed. 36.76 (978-0-618-23004-4(1) , 352013) Houghton Mifflin College Div.

Understanding Money in Business Made Easy. 2002. per. 14.99 (978-0-9657083-4-0(9)) ANUP Research & Multimedia LP.

Unidad 4 Superlibro: Economia: Superlibros. 2003. (MacMillan/McGraw-Hill. Estudios Sociales Ser.). (ENG & SPA.). (gr. 1 up). (978-0-02-149437-8(1)) Macmillan/McGraw-Hill Schl. Div.

Unidad 4 Superlibro: Economia: Vivimos Juntos: Superlibros (Big Books) 2003. (MacMillan/McGraw-Hill. Estudios Sociales Ser.). (ENG & SPA.). (gr. 2 up). (978-0-02-149444-6(4)) Macmillan/McGraw-Hill Schl. Div.

University of Cambridge Local Examinations Syndication Staff. HIGCSE Economics Module 4, 2nd rev. ed. 2000. (Cambridge Open Learning Project in South Africa Ser.). (Illus.). 108p. pap. 9.20 (978-0-521-64776-2(2)) Cambridge Univ. Pr.

Walton, Stephen, et al. Economics for AS OCR. Bamford, Colin, ed. 2nd rev. ed. 2003. (Illus.). 270p. pap. 22.00 (978-0-521-54166-4(2)) Cambridge Univ. Pr.

Williams, Jane A. A Bluestocking Guide - Economics: Based on Richard J. Maybury's Book Whatever Happened to Penny Candy? 3rd ed. 1998. (Bluestocking Guide Ser.). 124p. (J). pap. 12.95 (978-0-942617-30-6(4)) Bluestocking Pr.

Williams, Jane A. & Daniels, Kathryn, eds. Economics - A Free Market Reader. 2004. 127p. (YA). pap. 12.95 (978-0-942617-44-3(4)) Bluestocking Pr.

Wirtschaft. (Duden-Schuelerduden Ser.). (GER., Illus.). 428p. (YA). 27.95 (978-3-411-04892-2(1) , B4892E) Bibliographisches Institut & F. A. Brockhaus AG DEU. *Dist:* Continental Bk. Co., Inc., International Bk. Import Service, Inc.

ECONOMICS—DICTIONARIES

Bookbinder, Steve & Einleger, Lynne. The Dictionary of the Global Economy. 2001. (Reference Watts Dictionary of Ser.). (Illus.). 160p. (YA). (gr. 8 up). 39.00 (978-0-531-11975-4(0) , Watts, Franklin) Scholastic Library Publishing.

Gall, Timothy L. & Gall, Susan B. Junior Worldmark Encyclopedia of the Nations, 10 vols., Set. 5th rev. ed. 2007. 520.00 (978-1-4144-1095-1(6) , UXL) Thomson Gale.

—Junior Worldmark Encyclopedia of the Nations, 9 vols. 3rd ed. Incl. Junior Worldmark Encyclopedia of the Nations Vol. 1 : Afghanistan to Brunei Darussalam. (978-0-7876-5367-5(5)); Junior Worldmark Encyclopedia of the Nations Vol. 2 : Bulgaria to Czech Republic. (978-0-7876-5368-2(3)); Junior Worldmark Encyclopedia of the Nations Vol. 3 : Denmark to Guyana. (978-0-7876-5369-9(1)); Junior Worldmark Encyclopedia of the Nations Vol. 4 : Haiti to Kyrgyzstan. (978-0-7876-5370-5(5)); Junior Worldmark Encyclopedia of the Nations Vol. 5 : Laos to Myanmar. (978-0-7876-5371-2(3)); Junior Worldmark Encyclopedia of the Nations Vol. 6 : Nambia to Portugal. (978-0-7876-5372-9(1)); Junior Worldmark Encyclopedia of the Nations Vol. 7 : Qatar to South Africa. (978-0-7876-5373-6(X)); Junior Worldmark Encyclopedia of the Nations Vol. 8 : Spain to Tuvalu. (978-0-7876-5374-3(8)); Junior Worldmark Encyclopedia of the Nations Vol. 9 : Uganda to Zimbabwe. (978-0-7876-5375-0(6)); (J). (Illus.). 2200p. 2001. lib. bdg. (978-0-7876-5366-8(7) , GML00502-173512, UXL) Thomson Gale.

—Junior Worldmark Encyclopedia of the Nations Vol. 1: Afghanistan to Brunei Darussalam, 9 vols. 3rd ed. 2001. (Illus.). (J). (978-0-7876-5367-5(5) , UXL) Thomson Gale.

—Junior Worldmark Encyclopedia of the Nations Vol. 2: Bulgaria to Czech Republic, 9 vols. 3rd ed. 2001. (Illus.). (J). (978-0-7876-5368-2(3) , UXL) Thomson Gale.

—Junior Worldmark Encyclopedia of the Nations Vol. 3: Denmark to Guyana, 9 vols. 3rd ed. 2001. (Illus.). (J). (978-0-7876-5369-9(1) , UXL) Thomson Gale.

—Junior Worldmark Encyclopedia of the Nations Vol. 4: Haiti to Kyrgyzstan, 9 vols. 3rd ed. 2001. (Illus.). (J). (978-0-7876-5370-5(5) , UXL) Thomson Gale.

—Junior Worldmark Encyclopedia of the Nations Vol. 5: Laos to Myanmar, 9 vols. 3rd ed. 2001. (Illus.). (J). (978-0-7876-5371-2(3) , UXL) Thomson Gale.

—Junior Worldmark Encyclopedia of the Nations Vol. 6: Nambia to Portugal, 9 vols. 3rd ed. 2001. (Illus.). (J). (978-0-7876-5372-9(1) , UXL) Thomson Gale.

—Junior Worldmark Encyclopedia of the Nations Vol. 7: Qatar to South Africa, 9 vols. 3rd ed. 2001. (Illus.). (J). (978-0-7876-5373-6(X) , UXL) Thomson Gale.

—Junior Worldmark Encyclopedia of the Nations Vol. 8: Spain to Tuvalu, 9 vols. 3rd ed. 2001. (Illus.). (J). (978-0-7876-5374-3(8) , UXL) Thomson Gale.

—Junior Worldmark Encyclopedia of the Nations Vol. 9: Uganda to Zimbabwe, 9 vols. 3rd ed. 2001. (Illus.). (J). (978-0-7876-5375-0(6) , UXL) Thomson Gale.

ECONOMISTS

Bussing-Burks, Marie. Influential Economists. 2003. (Illus.). 160p. (gr. 5 up). lib. bdg. 19.95 (978-1-881508-72-4(2)) Oliver Pr., Inc.

ECUADOR

Alexander, Vimala & Daniels, Amy S. Welcome to Ecuador. 2003. (Welcome to My Country Ser.). (Illus.). 48p. (J). (gr. 2 up). lib. bdg. 26.00 (978-0-8368-2543-5(8)) Stevens, Gareth Inc.

Crespi, Jess. Exploring Ecuador with the Five Themes of Geography. 2005. (Library of the Western Hemisphere). (J). (Illus.). 24p. 19.95 (978-1-4042-2675-3(3) , PowerKids Pr.); pap. (978-0-8239-4647-1(9)); (Illus.). 24p. pap. (978-0-8239-4635-8(5)) Rosen Publishing Group, Inc., The.

Daniels, Amy S. Ecuador. 2002. (Countries of the World Ser.). (Illus.). 96p. (J). (gr. 6 up). lib. bdg. 30.00 (978-0-8368-2343-1(5)) Stevens, Gareth Inc.

Foley, Erin & Jermyn, Leslie. Ecuador. 2nd ed. 2006. (Illus.). 144p. (J). (978-0-7614-2050-7(9) , Benchmark Bks.) Cavendish, Marshall Corp.

Heller, Ruth. Galapagos Means Tortoises! 2003. (gr. k-3). lib. bdg. 15.25 (978-0-613-79301-8(3)) Tandem Library Bks.

Kendall, Sarita H. Ecuador. 1999. (Major World Nations Ser.). (Illus.). 144p. (YA). (ps up). lib. bdg. 19.95 (978-0-7910-4970-9(1) , Chelsea Hse.) Facts On File, Inc.

Lourie, Peter. Lost Treasure of the Inca. 2003. (Illus.). 48p. (J). (gr. 4-6). 18.95 (978-1-56397-743-5(5)); pap. 10.95 (978-1-56397-983-5(7)) Boyds Mills Pr.

—Lost Treasure of the Inca. 2001. (gr. 3-6). lib. bdg. 18.75 (978-0-613-53831-2(5)) Tandem Library Bks.

Morrison, Marion. Ecuador. 2000. (Enchantment of the World, Second Ser.). (Illus.). 144p. (YA). (gr. 5-9). 36.00 (978-0-516-21544-0(2) , Children's Pr.) Scholastic Library Publishing.

Williams, Colleen Madonna Flood. Ecuador. 2003. (Discovering Latin America Ser.). (Illus.). 64p. (J). (gr. 5 up). lib. bdg. (978-1-59084-293-5(6)) Mason Crest Pubs.

ECUADOR—FICTION

Elkington, Sandra. The Adventures of Pedro in Ecuador. 2003. (YA). per. 9.95 (978-1-59453-005-0(X) , 1113) Airleaf Publishing & Bookselling.

Iturralde, Edna. Verde fue mi Selva. Cornejo, Eulalia et al, illus. (SPA.). 154p. (J). (gr. 5-8). pap. 9.95 (978-9978-07-421-3(X)) Santillana USA Publishing Co., Inc.

—Y Su Corazon Escapo para Convertirse en Pajaro. Gonzalez, Santiago, illus. (SPA.). 177p. (J). (gr. 8-12). pap. 10.95 (978-9978-07-331-5(0)) Santillana USA Publishing Co., Inc.

EDDY, MARY BAKER, 1821-1910

Ferguson, Isabel. Come & See: The Life of Mary Baker Eddy. Wolcott, Joan, illus. 2001. (J). viii, 95p. (gr. 5 up). 18.00 (978-0-9655317-3-3(2) , 2); 98p. pap. (978-0-9655317-2-6(4)) Small Rain Pr.

Koestler-Grack, Rachel A. Mary Baker Eddy. 2004. (Spiritual Leaders & Thinkers Ser.). (Illus.). 120p. (gr. 9-13). 30.00 (978-0-7910-7866-2(3) , Chelsea Hse.) Facts On File, Inc.

Parsons, Cynthia. The Discoverer, Mary Baker Eddy. Longyear Museum Staff, photos by. 2000. (Illus.). 132p. (J). (gr. 4-8). 20.00 (978-1-892286-00-0(9)) Vermont Schoolhouse Pr., The.

EDIBLE PLANTS

see Plants, Edible

EDINBURGH (SCOTLAND)

Orme, Helen. Edinburgh Castle: Scotland's Haunted Fortress. 2006. (Castles, Palaces, & Tombs Ser.). (Illus.). 32p. (J). lib. bdg. 25.27 (978-1-59716-248-7(5)) Bearport Publishing Co., Inc.

Sasek, Miroslav. This Is Edinburgh. 2006. (Illus.). 64p. (J). (gr. k). 17.95 (978-0-7893-1387-4(1)) Random Hse. Value Publishing.

EDINBURGH (SCOTLAND)—FICTION

Dunlop, Eileen. A Flute in Mayferry Street. 2000. 256p. (YA). (gr. 5 up). pap. (978-0-86315-328-0(3)) Floris Bks. GBR. *Dist:* SteinerBooks, Inc.

Forbes, Anne. Dragonfire. 2006. 256p. (YA). pap. 11.95 (978-0-86315-552-9(9)) Floris Bks. GBR. *Dist:* SteinerBooks, Inc.

Hendry, Frances. Quest for a Queen: The Falcon. 2006. pap. (***978-1-905665-06-8(7)***) Pollinger In Print.

Lightwood, Donald. The Long Revenge. 128p. pap. 7.95 (978-1-899827-94-7(3)) Scottish Children's Pr. GBR. *Dist:* Wilson & Assocs.

Lingard, J. Odd Girl Out. 187p. (J). pap. (978-0-340-75735-2(3) , Hodder & Stoughton) Hodder General Publishing Division.

Lingard, Joan. Tortoise Trouble. 2002. (Illus.). 112p. (J). pap. 8.99 (978-0-340-80578-7(1) , Hodder & Stoughton) Hodder General Publishing Division GBR. *Dist:* Trafalgar Square Publishing.

Spirn, Michele Sobel. The Bridges in Edinburgh. 2004. (Going to Ser.). 144p. pap. 6.95 (978-1-893577-11-4(2)) Four Corners Publishing Co., Inc.

EDISON, THOMAS A. (THOMAS ALVA), 1847-1931

Auch, Allison. Personalidades electrizantes & Electrifying Personalities. 2005. spiral bd. 84.00 (***978-1-4108-5713-2(1)***) Benchmark Education Co.

Benge, Janet & Benge, Geoff. Thomas Edison: Inspiration & Hard Work. 2007. (J). pap. (***978-1-932096-37-8(X)***) Emerald Bks.

Berger, Melvin & Berger, Gilda. What Makes the Light Bright, Mr. Edison? Dorman, Brandon, illus. 2007. (Scholastic Science Supergiants Ser.). 48p. (J). pap. 4.99 (978-0-439-83380-6(9)) Scholastic, Inc.

Bryant, Tamera. Thomas Alva Edison. 2003. (World Was Never the Same Ser.). (J). (978-1-58417-260-4(6)); pap. (978-1-58417-261-1(4)) Lake Street Pubs.

Burgan, Michael. Thomas Alva Edison: Great American Inventor. 2006. (J). (978-0-7565-1884-4(9)) Compass Point Bks.

Carlson, Laurie. Thomas Edison for Kids: His Life & Ideas, 21 Activities. 2006. (For Kids Ser.). (Illus.). 160p. (J). pap. 14.95 (978-1-55652-584-1(2) , 1248637) Chicago Review Pr., Inc.

Cefrey, Holly. The Inventions of Thomas Alva Edison. 2003. (19th Century American Inventors Ser.). (Illus.). 24p. (J). lib. bdg. 17.25 (978-0-8239-6440-6(X) , PowerKids Pr.) Rosen Publishing Group, Inc., The.

Davis, Lucile. Thomas Edison, 6 vols. (gr. 2-5). 36.95 (978-0-7368-8430-3(0)) Red Brick Learning.

Delano, Marfe Ferguson. Inventing the Future: A Photobiography of Thomas Alva Edison. 2006. 64p. (J). (gr. 5). pap. 7.95 (978-0-7922-5934-3(3) , National Geographic Children's Bks.) National Geographic Society.

Dolan, Ellen M. Thomas Alva Edison: Inventor. 1998. (Historical American Biographies Ser.). (Illus.). 128p. (YA). (gr. 6-12). lib. bdg. 26.60 (978-0-7660-1014-7(7)) Enslow Pubs., Inc.

Dooling, Michael. Young Thomas Edison. 2005. (Illus.). 40p. (J). (ps-3). 16.95 (978-0-8234-1868-8(5)) Holiday Hse., Inc.

Fandel, Jennifer. The Light Bulb. 2004. (What in the World? Ser.). (Illus.). 48p. 19.95 (978-1-58341-271-8(9) , Creative Education) Creative Co., The.

Ford, Carin T. Thomas Edison: Inventor. 2002. (Famous Inventors Ser.). (Illus.). 32p. (J). (gr. 1-4). lib. bdg. 22.60 (978-0-7660-1860-0(1)) Enslow Pubs., Inc.

Frith, Margaret. Who Was Thomas Alva Edison? O'Brien, John & Harrison, Nancy, illus. 2005. (Who Was... ? Ser.). 112p. (J). (gr. 2-5). pap. 4.99 (978-0-448-43765-1(1) , Grosset & Dunlap) Penguin Group (USA) Inc.

Gaines, Ann Graham. Thomas Edison. 2001. (Inventores Famosos Ser.). (Illus.). 24p. (J). (gr. 1-4). (SPA & ENG.). lib. bdg. 19.27 (978-1-58952-174-2(9) , RK2159); lib. bdg. 20.64 (978-1-58952-122-3(6)) Rourke Publishing, LLC.

Ganeri, Anita. Thomas Edison. 2000. (What Would You Ask...? Ser.). (Illus.). 32p. (J). (gr. 2-6). pap. 16.95 (978-1-929298-10-5(2)) Chrysalis Education.

Goldsmith, Howard. Thomas Edison to the Rescue! DiVito, Anna, illus. 2003. (Ready-to-Read Cofa Ser.). 32p. (J). pap. 3.99 (978-0-689-85331-9(9) , Aladdin) Simon & Schuster Children's Publishing.

—Thomas Edison to the Rescue! 2003. (gr. k-3). lib. bdg. 11.80 (978-0-613-61591-4(3)) Tandem Library Bks.

—Thomas Edison to the Rescue. DiVito, Anna, illus. ed. 2005. 32p. (J). lib. bdg. 15.00 (978-1-59054-956-8(2)) Fitzgerald Bks.

Gomez, Rebecca. Thomas Edison. 2003. (First Biographies Ser.). (Illus.). 32p. (J). (gr. k-4). lib. bdg. 22.78 (978-1-57765-945-7(7)) ABDO Publishing Co.

Graham, Amy. Thomas Edison: Wizard of Light & Sound. 2007. (Inventors Who Changed the World Ser.). (Illus.). 128p. (J). lib. bdg. 33.27 (978-1-59845-052-1(2) , MyReportLinks.com Bks.) Enslow Pubs., Inc.

Hantula, Richard. Thomas Edison. 2004. (Trailblazers of the Modern World Ser.). (Illus.). 48p. (J). pap. 11.95 (978-0-8368-5265-3(6)); lib. bdg. 30.00 (978-0-8368-5496-1(9)) Stevens, Gareth Inc. (World Almanac Library).

Harcourt School Publishers Staff. Tom Edison, Inventor: Take-Home Book. 1999. (Signatures Ser.). (Illus.). (J). pap. 1.90 (978-0-15-313883-6(1)) Harcourt Schl. Pubs.

Jenner, Caryn. Thomas Edison. 2007. 48p. (J). (gr. 3-4). 14.99 (978-0-7566-2947-2(0)); pap. 3.99 (978-0-7566-2946-5(2)) Dorling Kindersley Publishing, Inc.

Klingel/Noyed. Thomas Edison. Inventor. 2003. (Spirit of America: Our People Ser.). (Illus.). 32p. (J). (gr. 2-6). 27.07 (978-1-56766-449-2(0)) Child's World, Inc.

Linder, Greg. Thomas Edison. 1999. (Photo-Illustrated Biographies Ser.). (Illus.). 24p. (J). (gr. 2-3). lib. bdg. 18.60 (978-0-7368-0207-9(X) , Bridgestone Bks.) Capstone Pr., Inc.

Mara, Wil. Thomas Alva Edison. 2004. (Rookie Biographies Ser.). (J). 32p. (gr. 1-2). pap. 4.95 (978-0-516-25822-5(2)); (Illus.). 31p. 20.50 (978-0-516-21843-4(3)) Scholastic Library Publishing. (Children's Pr.).

Marsh, Carole. Thomas Edison. 2002. (One Thousand Readers Ser.). (Illus.). 12p. (J). (gr. k-4). 2.95 (978-0-635-01562-4(5) , 15625) Gallopade International.

—Thomas Edison: An Ohio Experience Reader. 2001. (J). (gr. k-5). pap. 1.95 (978-0-635-00432-1(1)) Gallopade International.

Mason, Paul. Thomas A. Edison. 2001. (Scientists Who Made History Ser.). (Illus.). 48p. (J). (gr. 4-6). lib. bdg. 27.12 (978-0-7398-4414-4(8)) Raintree.

McLaughlin, Kari Massie. My Adventure with Thomas Edison. 2007. 44p. (J). 8.99 (978-1-59092-472-3(X) , Orchard Academy Pr.) Windstorm Creative.

Miller, Francis Trevel. Thomas A Edison an Inspiring Story for B. 2006. pap. 31.95 (***978-1-4286-5329-0(5)***) Kessinger Publishing, LLC.

Mortensen, Lori. Thomas Edison: Inventor, Scientist, & Genius. Thompson, Jeffrey, illus. 2006. (Biographies Ser.). 24p. (J). (gr. k-3). lib. bdg. 23.93 (978-1-4048-3105-6(3)) Picture Window Bks.

Pederson, Charles E. Thomas Edison. 2007. (Essential Lives Ser.). (ENG., Illus.). 112p. (YA). (gr. 8-12). lib. bdg. 32.79 (***978-1-59928-845-1(1)*** , Essential Library) ABDO Publishing Co.

Price-Groff, Claire. Thomas Alva Edison: Inventor & Entrepreneur. 2003. (Great Life Stories Ser.). 128p. (J). 30.50 (978-0-531-12275-4(1) , Watts, Franklin) Scholastic Library Publishing.

Raatma, Lucia. Thomas Edison. 2004. (Compass Point Early Biographies Ser.). (Illus.). 32p. (J). (gr. 2 up). lib. bdg. 21.26 (978-0-7565-0567-7(4)) Compass Point Bks.

Rausch, Monica. Thomas Edison & the Light Bulb. 2006. (Illus.). 24p. (J). pap. (***978-0-8368-7732-8(2)***); lib. bdg. (***978-0-8368-7501-0(X)***) Stevens, Gareth Inc. (Weekly Reader Early Learning Library).

—Thomas Edison y la Bombilla Eléctrica. 2006. (J). pap. (***978-0-8368-8002-1(1)***); lib. bdg. (***978-0-8368-7997-1(X)***) Stevens, Gareth Inc. (Weekly Reader Early Learning Library).

Sabin, Louis & Macken, JoAnn Early. Thomas Edison: Incredible Inventor. 2006. (Illus.). 52p. (J). (***978-0-439-88006-0(8)***) Scholastic, Inc.

Saunders-Smith, Gail, ed. Thomas Edison. 2002. (First Biographies Ser.). (Illus.). 24p. (J). (gr. k-1). lib. bdg. 15.93 (978-0-7368-1436-2(1) , Pebble Bks.) Capstone Pr., Inc.

Shuter, Jane. Thomas Edison. (Lives & Times Ser.). (Illus.). 24p. (J). 2000. lib. bdg. 19.92 (978-1-57572-230-6(5)); Set 1. 2002. pap. 6.50 (978-1-58810-347-5(1) , 91107) Heinemann Library.

Sonneborn, Liz. The Electric Light: Thomas Edison's Illuminating Invention. 2007. (Milestones in American History Ser.). 128p. (J). (gr. 6-12). 35.00 (***978-0-7910-9350-4(6)*** , Chelsea Hse.) Facts On File, Inc.

Sullivan, George. Thomas Edison. 2001. (gr. 3-6). lib. bdg. 12.40 (978-0-613-50839-1(4)) Tandem Library Bks.

Sullivan, George E. Thomas Edison. 2002. (In Their Own Words Ser.). (Illus.). 128p. (J). (gr. 3-5). 4.99 (978-0-439-26319-1(0) , Scholastic Reference) Scholastic, Inc.

Tagliaferro, Linda. Thomas Edison: Inventor of the Age of Electricity. 2003. (Lerner Biographies Ser.). (Illus.). 128p. (J). 27.93 (978-0-8225-4689-4(2) , Lerner Pubns.) Lerner Publishing Group.

Thatcher Murcia, Rebecca. Thomas Edison: Great Inventor. 2004. (Uncharted, Unexplored, & Unexplained Ser.). (Illus.). 48p. (J). (gr. 4-8). lib. bdg. 29.95 (978-1-58415-306-1(7)) Mitchell Lane Pubs., Inc.

Thomas Alva Edison. (Guided Reading Levels Ser.). 8.48 (978-0-7362-1773-6(8)); 50.88 (978-0-7362-2174-0(3)) Hampton-Brown Bks.

Thomas Alva Edison. 2000. (McGraw-Hill Ciencias Ser.). (ENG & SPA.). (gr. 2 up). (978-0-02-279622-8(3)) Macmillan/McGraw-Hill Schl. Div.

Thomas Alva Edison: Libros Aventuras (Adventure Books) 2000. (MacMillan/McGraw-Hill. Estudios Sociales Ser.). (ENG & SPA.). (gr. 2 up). (978-0-02-148683-0(2)) Macmillan/McGraw-Hill Schl. Div.

Thomas Edison. (Photo Illustrated Biographies Ser.). 24p. (J). 6.95 (978-0-7368-8419-8(X)); 2005. (YA). (978-0-7368-9414-2(4) , Pebble Bks.) Capstone Pr., Inc.

Thomas Edison. (Compass Point Early Biographies Ser.). 32p. (J). 7.95 (978-0-7565-1182-1(8)) Compass Point Bks.

Thomas Edison, 6 vols. (gr. k-2). 28.95 (978-0-7368-9415-9(2)) Red Brick Learning.

Time for Kids Editors. Thomas Edison: A Brilliant Inventor. 2005. (Time for Kids Ser.). (Illus.). 48p. (J). 14.99 (978-0-06-057612-7(X)); pap. 3.99 (978-0-06-057611-0(1)) HarperCollins Pubs.

Welvaert, Scott R. Thomas Edison & the Lightbulb. 2007. (Graphic Library). (Illus.). 32p. 25.26 (978-0-7368-6489-3(X)) Capstone Pr., Inc.

Williams, Brian. Thomas Alva Edison. 2002. (Groundbreakers Ser.). (Illus.). 48p. (J). (gr. 5-7). pap. 8.50 (978-1-58810-996-5(8) , 91471) Heinemann Library.

Williams, Brian, contrib. by. Thomas Alva Edison. 2000. (Groundbreakers Ser.). (Illus.). 48p. (J). (gr. 5-7). lib. bdg. 25.64 (978-1-57572-377-8(8)) Heinemann Library.

Woodside, Martin. Sterling Biographies: Thomas Edison: The Man Who Lit up the World. 2007. (Sterling Biographies Ser.). (Illus.). 128p. (J). 12.95 (***978-1-4027-4955-1(4)***); pap. 5.95 (***978-1-4027-3229-4(5)***) Sterling Publishing Co., Inc.

Young, Robert. A Personal Tour of Edison's Lab. 2000. (How It Was Ser.). (Illus.). 64p. (J). (gr. 4-6). lib. bdg. 25.26 (978-0-8225-3581-2(5) , Lerner Pubns.) Lerner Publishing Group.

Zemlicka, Shannon. Thomas Edison. 2003. (History Maker Bios Ser.). (Illus.). 48p. (J). lib. bdg. 25.26 (978-0-8225-0239-5(9) , Lerner Pubns.) Lerner Publishing Group.

EDISON, THOMAS A. (THOMAS ALVA), 1847-1931—FICTION

Gutman, Dan. The Edison Mystery: Back in Time. 2002. (Illus.). 201p. lib. bdg. 13.00 (978-0-613-62098-7(4)) Tandem Library Bks.

Roop, Peter & Roop, Connie. Turn on the Light, Thomas Edison! 2003. (Illus.). 58p. (J). (978-0-439-43927-5(2)) Scholastic, Inc.

Sargent, Dave & Sargent, Pat. Ginger: (Lilac Roan) Be Likeable, 30 vols., Vol. 27. Lenoir, Jane, illus. 2003. (Saddle Up Ser.: Vol. 27). 42p. (J). pap. 6.95 (978-1-56763-812-7(0)); lib. bdg. 22.60 (978-1-56763-811-0(2)) Ozark Publishing.

Shafer, Susan. Thomas Edison Invents the Light Bulb. 2005. 22.00 (***978-1-4108-4188-9(X)***) Benchmark Education Co.

EDITORS AND EDITING

see Journalism; Journalists; Publishers and Publishing

EDMONDS, S. EMMA E. (SARAH EMMA EVELYN), 1841-1898

Reit, Seymour V. Behind Rebel Lines: The Incredible Story of Emma Edmonds, Civil War Spy. 2001. (Great Episodes Ser.). 144p. (YA). (gr. 5-9). pap. 6.95 (978-0-15-216427-0(8) , Gulliver Bks.) Harcourt Children's Bks.

—Behind Rebel Lines: The Incredible Story of Emma Edmonds, Civil War Spy. 2001. (gr. 5-8). lib. bdg. 14.15 (978-0-613-37187-2(9)) Tandem Library Bks.

EDUCATION

see also Audio-Visual Education; Books and Reading; Business Education; Culture; Educators; Learning and Scholarship; Libraries; Literacy; Military Education; Moral Education; Physical Education and Training; Religious Education; Scholarships; Schools; Self-Culture; Study Skills; Teachers; Teaching; Technical Education; Universities and Colleges

also names of classes of people and social and ethnic groups with the subdivision Education, (e.g. African Americans—Education); subjects with the subdivision Study and Teaching (e.g. Science—Study and Teaching); and headings beginning with the words Education and Educational

Actividades de Cuatro Grado. 2004. (Home Workbooks Ser.). 64p. (J). pap. 2.99 (978-0-88724-264-9(2) , CD-4553) Carson-Dellosa Publishing Co., Inc.

Actividades de Jardin de Ninos. 2004. (Home Workbooks Ser.). 64p. (J). pap. 2.99 (978-0-88724-512-1(9) , CD-4499) Carson-Dellosa Publishing Co., Inc.

Actividades de Preescolar. 2004. (Home Workbooks Ser.). 64p. (J). pap. 2.99 (978-0-88724-984-6(1) , CD-4498) Carson-Dellosa Publishing Co., Inc.

Actividades de Primer Grado. 2004. (Home Workbooks Ser.). 64p. (J). pap. 2.99 (978-0-88724-261-8(8) , CD-4550) Carson-Dellosa Publishing Co., Inc.

Actividades de Segundo Grado. 2004. (Home Workbooks Ser.). 64p. (J). pap. 2.99 (978-0-88724-262-5(6) , CD-4551) Carson-Dellosa Publishing Co., Inc.

Actividades de Tercer Grado. 2004. (Home Workbooks Ser.). 64p. (J). pap. 2.99 (978-0-88724-263-2(4) , CD-4552) Carson-Dellosa Publishing Co., Inc.

Ajmera, Maya. Back to School. 2001. (ps-2). lib. bdg. 15.25 (978-0-613-45461-2(8)) Tandem Library Bks.

Ajmera, Maya & Ivanko, John D. Back to School. 2004. (It's a Kid's World Ser.). (Illus.). 32p. (J). (ps-2). 15.95 (978-1-57091-383-9(8)) Charlesbridge Publishing, Inc.

Ajmera, Maya, et al. Back to School. 2004. (It's a Kid's World Ser.). (Illus.). 32p. (J). (ps-2). pap. 6.95 (978-1-57091-384-6(6)) Charlesbridge Publishing, Inc.

American Education Publishing Staff. Something Special for Christopher Robin with Sticker & Other. 2000. (I Can Learn with Pooh Ser.). 32p. (J). (ps-3). pap. 2.99 (978-1-56189-532-8(6) , 31225, American Education Publishing) School Specialty Publishing.

—Winnie the Pooh: Rabbit's Garden. 2000. (I Can Learn with Pooh Ser.). (Illus.). 32p. (J). (ps-3). pap. 2.99 (978-1-56189-533-5(4) , 31226, American Education Publishing) School Specialty Publishing.

—Winnie the Pooh: Rumbly in My Tummy. 2000. (I Can Learn with Pooh Ser.). (Illus.). 32p. (J). (ps-3). pap., wbk. ed. 2.99 (978-1-56189-529-8(6) , American Education Publishing) School Specialty Publishing.

—Winnie the Pooh Treasure Hunt. 2000. (I Can Learn with Pooh Ser.). (Illus.). 32p. (J). (ps-3). pap. 2.99 (978-1-56189-530-4(X) , 31223, American Education Publishing) School Specialty Publishing.

Bickico Enterprises Staff, concept. BabyKids: The Shapes Book. 2003. 16p. (J). pap. 2.95 (978-0-9746508-3-8(8)) Bickico Enterprises, Inc.

Black, Donald F. The Woman in Your Wife's Body. 1999. 60p. (J). pap. 12.50 (978-1-885631-37-4(5) , 37-5, Family Of Man Pr., The) Hutchison, G.F. Pr.

Blue Sky Ink Staff. Congratulations Graduate You Did It! 2004. (Illus.). 128p. 9.99 (978-1-59475-010-6(6)) Blue Sky Ink.

Boyd, Anne A. Help Me Decide! 2004. (Illus.). 192p. pap. (978-0-673-58663-6(4)) Good Year Bks.

Brams, Jolie S., contrib. by. Show What You Know on the 6th Grade FCAT. 2002. (J). 2.00 (978-1-884183-81-2(6) , FL1603); (J). stu. ed., per., wbk. ed. 9.95 (978-1-884183-80-5(8) , FL1602); (gr. 6). tchr. ed., per. 14.95 (978-1-884183-79-9(4) , FL1601) Englefield & Assocs., Inc.

Brighter Vision Publishing Staff. Cars & Trains, Ships & Planes. 1998. (Learning Adventures Preschool Ser.). 32p. (J). (ps-k). pap. 2.25 (978-1-55254-008-4(1) , BV12004) Brighter Vision Pubns.

—First Grade Skills Review. 1998. (Skills Review Workbks.). (J). (gr. 1). pap. 5.99 (978-1-55254-010-7(3)); 48p. pap. 5.95 (978-1-55254-048-0(0)) Brighter Vision Pubns.

—Kindergarten Skills Review. 1998. (J). (gr. k-1). 48p. pap. (978-1-55254-047-3(2)); 96p. pap. 5.99 (978-1-55254-009-1(X)) Brighter Vision Pubns.

—Second Grade Skills Review. 1998. (Skills Review Workbks.). (J). (gr. 2). pap. (978-1-55254-011-4(1)); pap. 5.95 (978-1-55254-049-7(9)) Brighter Vision Pubns.

—Third Grade Skills Review. 1998. (Skills Review Workbks.). (J). (gr. 3). pap. (978-1-55254-012-1(X)); 48p. pap. 5.95 (978-1-55254-050-3(2)) Brighter Vision Pubns.

Brookes, Kate. Exam Skills. (Illus.). 2002. 123p. pap. 9.99 (978-0-340-80498-8(X)); 2nd ed. 2005. 128p. (YA). pap. 12.00 (978-0-340-88396-9(0)) Hodder General Publishing Division GBR. (Hodder & Stoughton). *Dist:* Trafalgar Square Publishing.

—Homework Sorted! 2002. (Illus.). 160p. pap. (978-0-7502-4172-4(1) , Hodder Wayland) Hodder Children's Division.

Brooks, Susan Leigh. TV & Me: A Beginning Book of Activities to Help Middle School Students Take a Look at the Influence of Television on Their Lives. 2000. 96p. (YA). (gr. 7-10). per., act. bk. ed. 18.95 (978-1-877673-40-5(4) , TV-BWK03) Cottonwood Pr., Inc.

Bumcrot, Curt & Bumcrot, Jenny. Achieving Peak Performance New Edition. Krischke, Nikki, ed. 2nd rev. ed. 2003. 21p. (gr. 3 up). pap. 5.00 (978-1-888786-42-2(6)) Basic Skills Assessment & Educational Services.

Bumcrot, Curt, et al. ELO Quick Assessment: Grade 1. (Illus.). (J). 2000. 63p. wbk. ed. 18.00 (978-1-888786-17-0(5)); 2nd ed. 2002. 21p. (gr. 1). pap., wbk. ed. 9.00 (978-1-888786-24-8(8)) Basic Skills Assessment & Educational Services.

—ELO Quick Assessment: Grade 2. (Illus.). (J). 2000. 97p. wbk. ed. 18.00 (978-1-888786-19-4(1)); 2nd ed. 2002. 36p. (gr. 2). pap., wbk. ed. 9.00 (978-1-888786-26-2(4)) Basic Skills Assessment & Educational Services.

—ELO Quick Assessment: Grade 3. (Illus.). (J). 2000. 85p. wbk. ed. 18.00 (978-1-888786-18-7(3)); 2nd ed. 2002. 31p. (gr. 3). pap., wbk. ed. 9.00 (978-1-888786-28-6(0)) Basic Skills Assessment & Educational Services.

—ELO Quick Assessment: Grade 4. (Illus.). (J). 2000. 101p. wbk. ed. 18.00 (978-1-888786-20-0(5)); 2nd ed. 2002. 39p. (gr. 4). pap., wbk. ed. 9.00 (978-1-888786-30-9(2)) Basic Skills Assessment & Educational Services.

Challenge Your Child. 2003. (Homework Booklets Ser.). 80p. (gr. k up). 2.99 (978-0-7424-0037-5(9) , IF0291); (gr. 1 up). 2.99 (978-0-7424-0038-2(7) , IF0292); (gr. 2 up). 2.99 (978-0-7424-0039-9(5) , IF0293); (gr. 3 up). 2.99 (978-0-7424-0040-5(9) , IF0294); (gr. 4 up). 2.99 (978-0-7424-0041-2(7) , IF0295); (gr. 5 up). 2.99 (978-0-7424-0042-9(5) , IF0296); (gr. 6 up). 2.99 (978-0-7424-0043-6(3) , IF0297) School Specialty Publishing.

Clarke, Jacqueline. April. 2001. (Fresh & Fun Ser.). 32p. (J). pap. 8.95 (978-0-439-21608-1(7)) Scholastic, Inc.

Clausen, Andrew. Holes Study Guide. 2002. 84p. (YA). ring bd. 12.99 (978-1-58609-183-5(2)) Progeny Pr.

Cleland, JoAnn. I Listen. 2007. (J). (978-1-59515-937-3(1)) Rourke Publishing, LLC.

Coats, Lynda. Far above Rubies. Gleaton, Terry, ed. 4th exp. ed. 2001. 632p. (YA). ring bd. 59.95 (978-1-930165-00-7(5)) Small Ventures.

Color, Cut, Paste, & Trace: Getting Ready for School. (ps-k). 2.99 (978-0-7424-0170-9(7) , IF0403) School Specialty Publishing.

Cookson, Paul. Crazy Classrooms & Secret Staffrooms. Baines, Nigel, illus. 2001. 96p. (J). pap. 8.99 (978-0-7459-4590-3(2) , Lion) Lion Hudson plc GBR. *Dist:* Independent Pubs. Group.

Cordes, Helen. Girl Power in the Classroom. 1999. (Girl Power Ser.). (Illus.). 96p. (YA). (gr. 6-9). lib. bdg. (978-0-8225-2693-3(X) , Lerner Pubns.) Lerner Publishing Group.

Cotter, Joan A. RightStart Mathematics: Level C Worksheets. 2001. (J). spiral bd., wbk. ed. 10.00 (978-1-931980-07-4(1) , W-C) Activities for Learning.

—RightStart Mathematics: Level D Worksheets. 2001. spiral bd., wbk. ed. 10.00 (978-1-931980-08-1(X) , W-D); spiral bd., wbk. ed. 10.00 (978-1-931980-09-8(8) , W-E) Activities for Learning.

Cullum, Albert, ed. Geranium on the Windowsill Just Died, but Teacher You Went Right On. 2003. (Illus.). 40p. (YA). (gr. 4-7). 15.95 (978-0-8252-0500-2(X)) Quist, Harlin Bks.

Dahl, Michael. Teacher Says: A Book of Teacher Jokes. Haugen, Ryan, illus. 2004. (Read-It! Joke Books). 24p. (C). (gr. k-3). 18.60 (978-1-4048-0301-5(7)) Picture Window Bks.

Daily Core Curriculum, Grade 1. 2003. (J). pap. 19.95 (978-1-56911-123-9(5)) Learning Resources, Inc.

Daily Core Curriculum, Grade 2. 2003. (J). pap. 19.95 (978-1-56911-124-6(3)) Learning Resources, Inc.

Daily Core Curriculum, Grade 3. 2003. (J). pap. 19.95 (978-1-56911-125-3(1)) Learning Resources, Inc.

Daily Core Curriculum, Grade 4. 2003. (J). pap. 19.95 (978-1-56911-126-0(X)) Learning Resources, Inc.

Daily Core Curriculum, Grade 5. 2003. (J). pap. 19.95 (978-1-56911-127-7(8)) Learning Resources, Inc.

Degelman, Charles, et al. Active Citizenship Today Field Guide. 2nd ed. 2005. (J). pap. (978-1-886253-31-5(5)) Constitutional Rights Foundation.

Dooley, Virginia. Quick Reference Guides: 10 Indispensable, Reproducible Guides for Students to Use for Reference, Research, & Review. 2004. 64p. pap. 11.99 (978-0-590-76994-5(4) , Teaching Resources) Scholastic, Inc.

Douglas, Vincent. Everything for Early Learning: Grade 1. 2004. (Everything for Early Learning Ser.). (Illus.). 320p. (J). (gr. 1-1). pap. 7.95 (978-0-7696-3348-0(X) , American Education Publishing) School Specialty Publishing.

Douglas, Vincent & School Specialty Publishing Staff. Here & There. 2004. (Kindergarten Bound Ser.). (Illus.). 80p. (J). (ps up). pap. 5.95 (978-0-7696-3440-1(0) , American Education Publishing) School Specialty Publishing.

—Summer Link Basic Learning Skills, Grades 4-5. 2004. (Summer Link Ser.). (Illus.). 96p. (J). (ps-6). pap. 6.95 (978-0-7696-3564-4(4) , American Education Publishing) School Specialty Publishing.

—Summer Link Basic Learning Skills, Grades 5-6. 2004. (Summer Link Ser.). (Illus.). 96p. (J). (ps-6). pap. 6.95 (978-0-7696-3565-1(2) , American Education Publishing) School Specialty Publishing.

Duckworth, Katie. Education. 2004. (Children's Rights Ser.). (J). lib. bdg. 27.10 (978-1-58340-419-5(8)) Smart Apple Media.

Early Learning Centers. 2005. (Take It to Your Seat Learning Centers). (Illus.). 192p. (ps-k). suppl. ed. 19.99 (978-1-55799-838-5(8) , EMC 2401) Evan-Moor Educational Pubs.

Emigh, Karen. Herman's Hiding Places. 2004. (J). (ps-3). per. 9.95 (978-1-932565-01-0(9)) Future Horizons, Inc.

Emmer, Rae. Periodico Escolar. 2004. (Actividades Escolares Ser.). (SPA & ENG., Illus.). 24p. (J). lib. bdg. 17.25 (978-0-8239-6901-2(0) , Buenas Letra) Rosen Publishing Group, Inc., The.

E F G

Esparza, Thomas, Jr., prod. Esther's Playhouse, Disk B. 2004. (Illus.). (J). cd-rom (978-1-879817-43-2(8), Children) Star Light Pr.

—Esther's Playhouse, Disk F. 2004. (Illus.). (J). cd-rom (978-1-879817-47-0(0), Children) Star Light Pr.

Espeland, Pamela & Verdick, Elizabeth. Loving to Learn: The Commitment to Learning Assets. 2005. (Adding Assets Series for Kids). (Illus.). 80p. (J). (gr. 3-7). pap. 9.95 (978-1-57542-183-4(6)) Free Spirit Publishing, Inc.

Farish, Leah. Lemon vs. Kurtzman: The Religion & Public Funds Case. 2000. (Landmark Supreme Court Cases Ser.). (Illus.). 128p. (YA). (gr. 6-12). lib. bdg. 26.60 (978-0-7660-1339-1(1)) Enslow Pubs., Inc.

Fetty, Margaret & Jasinski, Diane, eds. Three Cheers for December: PreK-K. 2004. (Illus.). 96p. (ps-k). pap. 12.99 (978-0-7398-9311-1(4)) Steck-Vaughn.

—Three Cheers for February: PreK-K. 2004. (Illus.). 96p. pap. 12.99 (978-0-7398-9313-5(0)) Steck-Vaughn.

—Three Cheers for January: PreK-K. 2004. (Illus.). 96p. pap. 12.99 (978-0-7398-9312-8(2)) Steck-Vaughn.

First Grade Skills. 2000. (Kelley Wingate Ser.). 80p. (J). (gr. k-2). pap. 9.99 (978-0-88724-594-7(3)) Carson-Dellosa Publishing Co., Inc.

Fisher, Ann Richmond. Seasons to Celebrate: January to Summer. 2003. (Illus.). 320p. (J). pap. 29.95 (978-1-57310-408-1(6)) Teaching & Learning Co.

Fisher-Price Kindergarten Educational Box Set. 2004. (J). (978-0-7666-1352-2(6), 64068) Modern Publishing.

Fisher-Price Preschool Educational Box Set. 2004. (J). (978-0-7666-1351-5(8), 64067) Modern Publishing.

Fisher-Price Preschool Practice Books. 2004. (J). (978-0-7666-0267-0(2), 39425); (978-0-7666-0268-7(0), 39425); (978-0-7666-0269-4(9), 39425); (978-0-7666-0270-0(2), 39425) Modern Publishing.

Fisk, Sally. First Grade in Review. 1999. (100+ Seriestm Ser.). (Illus.). 128p. (J). (gr. k-6). pap. 12.99 (978-1-56822-192-2(4), IF8783) School Specialty Publishing.

Fridell, Ron. Education for All: Floating Schools, Cave Classrooms, & Backpacking Teachers. 2003. (In a Perfect World Ser.). (Illus.). 80p. (gr. 5-8). lib. bdg. 26.90 (978-0-7613-2624-3(3), Twenty-First Century Bks.) Lerner Publishing Group.

Fun with Foster Kids Educational Curriculum Student Edition. 2004. (J). 29.95 (978-1-59210-327-0(8)); spiral bd. 29.95 (978-1-59210-328-7(6)) Whispering Pine Pr., Inc.

Gareis, Elisabeth. A Novel Approach: The Color Purple. (Illus.). (C). pap., stu. ed. (978-0-472-08543-9(3)) Univ. of Michigan Pr.

Ginn, Janel D. Bilingual Education. 2007. (At Issue Ser.). (Illus.). 128p. (gr. 10-12). 29.95 (***978-0-7377-3912-1(6)***); pap. 21.20 (***978-0-7377-3913-8(4)***) Thomson Gale. (Greenhaven Pr., Inc.).

Good, Janet. Homework, Homework, & More Homework. 1998. (Illus.). 24p. (J). (ps-2). pap. 5.95 (978-0-9661602-6-0(6)) Hadassah Investments, Inc.

Gordon, Sharon. Escuchamos. 2006. (Bookworms Ser.). (SPA & ENG.). 24p. (J). lib. bdg. 22.79 (978-0-7614-2359-1(1), Benchmark Bks.) Cavendish, Marshall Corp.

—We Listen. 2005. (Bookworms Ser.). (ENG & SPA., Illus.). 24p. (J). (gr. 3-7). lib. bdg. (978-0-7614-1991-4(8), Benchmark Bks.) Cavendish, Marshall Corp.

—We Listen (Esuchamos) 2006. (Bookworms Ser.). (ENG & SPA.). 24p. (J). lib. bdg. 22.79 (978-0-7614-2439-0(3)) Cavendish, Marshall Corp.

Groves, Penny. Strengthening Visual Discrimination Skills. 2001. (Modified Basic Skills Ser.). 48p. (J). (gr. k-4). pap. 6.99 (978-0-7424-0163-1(4), LL80021) School Specialty Publishing.

Harcourt School Publishers Staff. Materials Kit, Unit A. 1999. (gr. 6). 349.50 (978-0-15-314797-5(0)) Harcourt Schl. Pubs.

Hauser, Jill Frankel. Kindergarten Success. Hauser, Salvan, illus. 2005. (Little Hands! Ser.). 128p. (J). (gr. k up). pap. 12.95 (978-0-8249-6751-2(8), Williamson Bks.) Ideals Pubns.

Hazouri, Sandra Peyser & Smith, Miriam Frey. Peer Listening in the Middle School: Training Activities for Students. Brown, Christine M., illus. 1998. 215p. (J). (gr. 6-8). pap. 8.95 (978-0-932796-34-9(6)) Educational Media Corp.

Hill, Lee Sullivan. Schools Help Us Learn. 1998. (Building Block Bks.). (Illus.). 32p. (J). (gr. k-3). lib. bdg. (978-1-57505-092-8(7), Carolrhoda Bks.) Lerner Publishing Group.

Hood, Karen Jean Matsko. Girls Can Do Activity & Coloring Book. 2005. (Educational Activity & Coloring Book Ser.).Tr. of Japanese. (J). spiral bd. 15.95 (978-1-59649-361-2(5)); cd-rom 13.95 (978-1-59649-363-6(1)) Whispering Pine Pr., Inc.

Hudson, David L. Educational Standards. 2007. (Point/Counterpoint Ser.). 112p. (J). (gr. 9). 32.95 (***978-0-7910-9278-1(X)***, Chelsea Hse.) Facts On File, Inc.

I Love Educational, 4 vols. 2000. (YA). 49.95 (978-1-58209-555-4(8)) Books Are Fun, Ltd.

Israel, Elaine. Best Ever Back-to-School Activities: 50 Winning & Welcoming Activities, Strategies, & Tips That Save You Time & Get Your School Year off to a Sensational Start. 2001. 64p. pap. 10.95 (978-0-439-30462-7(8)) Scholastic, Inc.

Issues, Evidence & You - Energy Mega Module Complete Materials Package. 2003. (Illus.). (YA). tchr. ed., ring bd. (978-1-887725-48-4(2)) Lab-Aids, Inc.

Issues, Evidence & You - Material Science Mega Module Complete Materials Package. 2003. (Illus.). (YA). tchr. ed., stu. ed., per. (978-1-887725-61-3(X)); tchr. ed., ring bd. (978-1-887725-45-3(8)) Lab-Aids, Inc.

It's Circle Time: Themes to Enrich Shared Learning. 2003. 80p. (J). per. 9.99 (978-0-88724-915-0(9)) Carson-Dellosa Publishing Co., Inc.

Jackson, Ellen B. It's Back to School We Go! First Day Stories Fro Around the World. Ellis, Jan Davey, illus. 2003. 32p. lib. bdg. 23.90 (978-0-7613-2562-8(X), Millbrook Pr.) Lerner Publishing Group.

—It's Back to School We Go! First Day Stories from Around the World. Ellis, Jan Davey, illus. 2003. 32p. (J). 15.95 (978-0-7613-1948-1(4), Millbrook Pr.) Lerner Publishing Group.

JIST Publishing Staff. Instructor's Guide for Creating Your High School Portfolio & Creating Your High School Resume. 2nd ed. 2003. 112p. (YA). pap. 14.95 (978-1-56370-908-1(2)) JIST Publishing.

Kilgore, James. Pedagogic Logic. 2005. 224p. (J). pap. 12.00 (978-0-9770405-4-4(2)) Infinite Visions Forum.

King, Jennifer, illus. Show What You Know on the 4th Grade FCAT. 2001. (Show What You Know on the FCAT). 96p. (J). (gr. 4). stu. ed., per., wbk. ed. 9.95 (978-1-884183-75-1(1), FL1402) Englefield & Assocs., Inc.

LeapFrog Staff, compiled by & des. Smart Guide to Fourth Grade. LeapFrog Staff, des. 2002. (J). spiral bd. 14.99 (978-1-58605-736-7(7)) LeapFrog Enterprises, Inc.

—Smart Guide to Third Grade. LeapFrog Staff, des. 2002. (J). spiral bd. 14.99 (978-1-58605-735-0(9)) LeapFrog Enterprises, Inc.

Lillard Jessen, Lynn & Lillard, Paula Polk. Montessori from the Start: The Child at Home, from Birth to Age Three. 2003. (Illus.). 304p. pap. 13.95 (978-0-8052-1112-2(8), Schocken) Knopf Publishing Group.

Lindsay, Norene. Dream Catchers. 3rd ed. 2003. 88p. pap., tchr. ed. 19.95 (978-1-59357-004-0(X), JIST Works) JIST Publishing.

Literature Pockets: Caldecott Winners. 2001. (Illus.). 96p. (J). (gr. 1-3). suppl. ed. 12.99 (978-1-55799-820-0(5), EMC 2701); (gr. 4-6). suppl. ed. 12.99 (978-1-55799-821-7(3), EMC 2702) Evan-Moor Educational Pubs.

Lou Weber Staff, ed. Rubbadubber Back to the Bath Sound Book. 2004. 24p. 15.98 (978-1-4127-3124-9(0)) Publications International, Ltd.

Lovell, Nadine. Children Around the World: Passport to Adventure. (Illus.). 89p. (J). (gr. 1-6). pap. 9.95 (978-1-56861-058-0(0)) Swift Learning Resources.

McPherson, Stephanie Sammartino. Lau vs. Nichols: Bilingual Education in Public Schools. 2000. (Landmark Supreme Court Cases Ser.). (Illus.). 128p. (YA). (gr. 6-12). lib. bdg. 26.60 (978-0-7660-1472-5(X)) Enslow Pubs., Inc.

Middle School Excelerator (Ages 13-16), 5 CDs. 2003. cd-rom 29.99 (978-1-59150-270-8(5)) TOPICS Entertainment.

Miller, Heather. Maestro. (Esto es lo Que Quiero Ser (This Is What I Want to Be) Ser.). 24p. pap. 5.25 (978-1-4034-0604-0(9)) Heinemann Library.

Modoc Press Editors. Directory of Distance Learning Opportunities: K-12. 2003. 432p. (gr. k-12). 81.95 (978-1-57356-515-8(6), OXDLK-12) Greenwood Publishing Group, Inc.

Moore, Jo Ellen. Literacy Centers. Larsen, Jo, illus. 2005. (Take It to Your Seat Learning Centers). 192p. (gr. 1-3). tchr. ed. 19.99 (978-1-55799-798-2(5), EMC 788) Evan-Moor Educational Pubs.

Murdoch, Bernard Constantine. A Revolutionary View of Education & Teaching for the Third Millenium. 2002. 142p. pap. 20.00 (978-0-9664283-4-6(X), 145193) For-e(In)Sight Foundation.

My First Learning-Flip Chart. 2003. 10p. (J). (gr. k-12). pap. 14.95 (978-1-58845-176-7(3)) School Specialty Publishing.

Nathan, Amy. Surviving Homework: Tips That Really Work! Green, Anne Canevari, illus. 1998. (Single Titles Ser.: 8). 80p. (gr. 4-8). pap. 8.95 (978-0-7613-0137-0(2), Millbrook Pr.) Lerner Publishing Group.

NJMUSST 2004 Anthology. 2004. 112p. (J). per. 10.00 (978-0-9744744-4-1(4), 0-9744744-4-4) Cloonfad Pr.

Norris, Jill. Bulletin Boards Every Classroom Needs, Grades K-6. Larsen, Jo, illus. 2001. 304p. (J). (gr. k-6). pap., tchr. ed. 29.99 (978-1-55799-797-5(7), EMC 787) Evan-Moor Educational Pubs.

—Seasonal Bulletin Boards. Davis, Cindy, illus. 2001. 304p. (J). (gr. k-6). pap., tchr. ed. 29.99 (978-1-55799-796-8(9), EMC 786) Evan-Moor Educational Pubs.

Numbers & Letters Excelerator (Ages 2-5) 2003. cd-rom 29.99 (978-1-59150-260-9(8)) TOPICS Entertainment.

O'Connell, Lisa B. C. Miracle Max... Missing in Maryland!, Vol. 1. O'Connell, Lisa B. C., illus. 2000. (Illus.). 88p. (J). (gr. 2-7). per. 15.95 (978-1-56167-642-2(X), Shooting Star Edition) American Literary Pr.

Painter, Carol. Friends Helping Friends: A Handbook for Helpers. 2nd ed. 2003. (Illus.). 224p. (J). pap. 10.95 (978-1-930572-21-8(2)) Educational Media Corp.

Parker, Harvey C. Listen, Look & Think: A Self-Regulation Program for Children. 2003. 8p. (J). pap., tchr. ed. 22.00 incl. audio (978-1-886941-12-0(2), 0955) Specialty Pr., Inc.

Phillips, Vivian A. Education: Show & Tell. Date not set. (Illus.). 10p. (Orig.). (J). pap. (978-1-888413-05-2(0)) Seasoning Quilting (Arts & Crafts).

Plan Your Education, Prepare for Your Future, Because You Can. 2000. xi, 29p. (YA). (gr. 8 up). pap. 5.00 (978-0-9705677-0-3(7)) Max-A-Million Guidance Pubns.

Preschool Skills. 2000. (Kelley Wingate Ser.). 80p. (J). (ps-k). pap. 9.99 (978-0-88724-592-3(7)) Carson-Dellosa Publishing Co., Inc.

Read, Marya & Jana, P. Lynn, contrib. by. An Educated Choice Journal. 2003. 133p. (YA). (978-1-929931-11-8(5)) Intrepid Films, LLC.

Riera, Mike. Surviving High School: Making the Most of the High School Years. 2004. (Illus.). 160p. (gr. 8-12). pap. 12.95 (978-0-89087-825-5(0), Celestial Arts Publishing Company) Ten Speed Pr.

Rookie Books. 2004. 722.00 (978-0-516-27719-6(7)) Scholastic Library Publishing.

Rosengarten, Johannes & Arena Verlag. Kids' Seasonal Mandalas. 2005. (Illus.). 64p. (ps-ps). pap. 4.95 (978-1-4027-1802-1(0)) Sterling Publishing Co., Inc.

Scholastic, Inc. Staff, contrib. by. Entering Kindergarten. 2004. (Jumpstart Ser.). (Illus.). 96p. (J). (gr. k up). pap. 6.99 (978-0-439-38233-5(5)) Scholastic, Inc.

School Specialty Publishing. Look & Learn-Flip Chart. 2001. 10p. (J). (gr. k-12). spiral bd. 12.95 (978-1-58845-183-5(6)) School Specialty Publishing.

Schumacher, Bev. Play Action: Juego en Accion. st. John-Lagenaur, Elaine, tr. 2005. Tr. of Juego en Accion. (SPA.). 20p. lib. bdg. 9.95 net. (978-0-9741549-5-4(4)) Learning Props.

—Which Way? St. John-Lagenaur, Elaine, tr. 2005. (SPA.). 20p. lib. bdg. 9.95 net. (978-0-9741549-3-0(8)) Learning Props.

Shagoury, Teri. A Wrinkle in Time. 2002. (J). stu. ed., ring bd. 12.99 (978-1-58609-184-2(0)) Progeny Pr.

Slater, Judith J., et al, eds. The Freirean Legacy: Educating for Social Justice. 2002. (Counterpoints Ser.). 226p. (J). pap. 29.95 (978-0-8204-5671-3(3)) Lang, Peter Publishing, Inc.

Sorenson, Don L. & Nord, David A., texts. Discussion-Provoking Scripts for Teens. 2002. 80p. (YA). per. 12.95 (978-1-930572-16-4(6)) Educational Media Corp.

Steck-Vaughn Staff. Skateboard City. 2002. (Illus.). pap. 41.60 incl. audio compact disk (978-0-7398-6955-0(8)) Steck-Vaughn.

Stewart, Faith. Teens & Rural Education: Opportunities & Challenges. 2008. (Youth in Rural North America Ser.). (Illus.). (J). (978-1-4222-0015-5(9)) Mason Crest Pubs.

Stewart, Tobi Stanton. Colonial Teachers. 2006. (J). lib. bdg. (978-1-4042-3351-5(2), PowerKids Pr.) Rosen Publishing Group, Inc., The.

Stradling, Jan. Handle with Care: Level I, 6 vols., Vol. 2. (First Explorers Ser.). 24p. (gr. 1-2). 29.95 (978-0-7699-1459-6(4)) Shortland Pubns. (U. S. A.) Inc.

Suzuki, David T. & Hehner, Barbara. Descubre los Insectos. 2004. (Juego de la Ciencia Ser.). (SPA., Illus.). 96p. 14.99 (978-84-9754-051-3(4), 87816) Ediciones Oniro S.A. ESP. *Dist:* Bilingual Pubns. Co., The, Lectorum Pubns., Inc.

Tanner, Dawn Leasman. A Kitty Named Indra/Una Gata Llamada Indra. Leasman, Nancy Packard, illus. l.t. ed. 2003. (SPA & ENG.). 36p. (J). per. 6.95 (978-0-9741725-0-7(2)) Leatherwood Publishing.

Teaching Character Education Using Children's Literature. 2001. 72p. 18.00 (978-1-57337-099-8(1)) Wisconsin Dept. of Public Instruction.

Teal, Joyce Willard. Clifford's War & A. E. P. 2004. 152p. (YA). per. 13.95 (978-1-932196-32-0(3)) WordWright-.biz, Inc.

Thiessen, Karen J. World Landmark Books, A Homeschoolers' Guide: Select, Find, & Use World Landmarks in Homeschool Curriculum. 2004. (Illus.). 216p. per. 24.95 (978-0-9749578-5-2(2)) Pure Joy Pubns.

Thomas, Marian. The Brush Off. 2002. (Wizard Study Guides Ser.). 48p. pap., stu. ed. 6.00 (978-1-876367-16-9(4)) Cambridge Univ. Pr.

Thompson, Karen & Mitzo Thompson, Kim. Preschool: Songs That Teach Preschool. 2006. (Sing along Activity Books with CDs Ser.). (Illus.). 32p. (J). pap. 4.99 (978-0-7696-4574-2(7)) School Specialty Publishing.

Thurston, Cheryl M., ed. Everything but the Kitchen Sink: Activities from 16 Cottonwood Press Books. 2001. 106p. (YA). per. 18.95 (978-1-877673-47-4(1), KS-BWK03) Cottonwood Pr., Inc.

Top That Publishing Staff, ed. My First Library. 2005. 180p. (978-1-84510-658-4(X)) Top That! Publishing PLC.

Trumbauer, Lisa. Lighthouses of North America! Kline, Michael, illus. 2007. 96p. (J). (gr. 3-9). 16.99 (***978-0-8249-6791-8(7)***); pap. 12.99 (***978-0-8249-6790-1(9)***) Ideals Pubns. (Williamson Bks.).

Twin Sisters Productions Staff, prod. Kindergarten: Songs That Teach. 2005. (J). per. 12.99 (978-1-57583-818-2(4)) Twin Sisters Productions, LLC.

Uhlig, Susan. Things Little Kids Need to Know. Wharton, Jennifer Heyd, illus. 2000. 32p. (J). (ps-3). 16.00 (978-0-9611872-9-3(8)) Our Child Pr.

Understein, Adam L. Learn2study Student Pocket Guide. 2003. 72p. (C). per. 6.99 (978-0-9729557-1-3(2)) Learn2study.

User Manual. 2003. ring bd. (978-1-932166-07-1(6)) Achieve3000.

Verdick, Elizabeth & Romain, Trevor. True or False? Tests Stink! 2004. (Laugh & Learn Ser.). (Illus.). 88p. (YA). (gr. 3-8). pap. 8.95 (978-1-57542-073-8(2)) Free Spirit Publishing, Inc.

Viverito, Philip J., et al. Classical Hack Second Edition: Ancient Warfare 600 B. C. to 600 A. D. Cholewa, Thomas H., ed. Connolly, Peter, illus. 2nd exp. ed. 2002. 38p. 24.00 (978-1-889584-07-2(X), 011802) LMW Works.

Weber, Lou, ed. My 1st Library Tonka. 2004. 72p. (J). bds. 10.98 (978-1-4127-0516-5(9), 7219100) Publications International, Ltd.

World Almanac Editors, ed. World Almanac for Kids 2006. 2005. (Illus.). 336p. (J). 21.95 (978-0-88687-961-7(2)) World Almanac Bks.

Young, Jay, creator. The Amazing Magic Fact Machine. 2004. (Illus.). 30p. (978-1-903174-16-6(3)) Chrysalis Children's Bks.

Zeng, Sunny. Student Workbook: To Accompany Videos 1 & 2. 2003. (CHI & ENG.). stu. ed., wbk. ed. 14.95 (978-0-9707332-9-0(1), NIHALIWO) Chinasprout, Inc.

Ziegler, Mark. School Kidders: A Book of School Jokes. Haberstroh, Anne, illus. 2005. (Read-It! Readers Ser.). 24p. (C). (gr. 1-3). 18.60 (978-1-4048-0964-2(3)) Picture Window Bks.

500 Palabras (500 Words) (SPA., Illus.). (J). pap. 6.95 (978-950-11-0122-5(3), SGM122) Sigmar ARG. *Dist:* Continental Bk. Co., Inc.

EDUCATION—AIMS AND OBJECTIVES

Advancing Student Achievement Schools & Actuary Partners Preparing Students for Tomorrow's Possibilities Count Yourself In! 1999. (Illus.). (J). pap. (978-0-938959-57-1(3)) Society of Actuaries.

EDUCATION, BUSINESS

see Business Education

EDUCATION, CHARACTER

see Moral Education

EDUCATION, CHRISTIAN

see Religious Education

EDUCATION—DATA PROCESSING

Blocksom, Jonathon T. Golly Gee Blocks. 2000. (J). (gr. 3-8). ring bd. 25.00 incl. cd-rom (978-0-9701391-0-8(1)) GollyGee Software, Inc.

Kidspiration 2 US 10-Pack License. 2004. (J). cd-rom (978-1-932463-33-0(X)) Inspiration Software, Inc.

Kidspiration 2 US 20-Pack License. 2004. (J). cd-rom (978-1-932463-34-7(8)) Inspiration Software, Inc.

Kidspiration 2 US 5-Pack License. 2004. (J). cd-rom (978-1-932463-32-3(1)) Inspiration Software, Inc.

Kidspiration 2 US Exploring CD. 2004. (J). cd-rom 24.95 (978-1-932463-36-1(4)) Inspiration Software, Inc.

Kidspiration 2 US Personal Edition. 2004. (J). cd-rom (978-1-932463-29-3(1)) Inspiration Software, Inc.

Kidspiration 2 US Upgrade Single. 2004. (J). cd-rom 39.95 (978-1-932463-31-6(3)) Inspiration Software, Inc.

Kidspiration in the Classroom. 2004. (J). per. 29.95 (978-1-932463-51-4(8)) Inspiration Software, Inc.

Kidspiration in the Classroom School License. 2004. (J). per. 199.00 (978-1-932463-52-1(6)) Inspiration Software, Inc.

Lesson Express, Minimum Of 10. 2005. cd-rom (978-0-9740533-1-8(7)) Maestro Learning.

Lesson Express, Minimum Of 100. 2005. cd-rom (978-0-9740533-2-5(5)) Maestro Learning.

Lesson Express, Single User. 2005. cd-rom (978-0-9740533-0-1(9)) Maestro Learning.

OpenBook to Literacy Student Workbooks, 3 vols. 2002. (Illus.). 28p. (J). (gr. k-3). pap., wbk. ed. 7.00 (978-1-893586-36-9(7)) OpenBook Learning, Inc.

Read & Write 7 Standard. 2002. (YA). cd-rom 295.00 (978-0-9712893-5-2(2)) Texthelp Systems, Inc.

Read & Write for Mac. 2002. (YA). cd-rom 605.00 (978-1-932625-02-8(X)) Texthelp Systems, Inc.

Read & Write for Mac K-12. 2002. (YA). cd-rom (978-1-932625-10-3(0)) Texthelp Systems, Inc.

Read & Write GOLD K-12. 2002. (YA). cd-rom 625.00 (978-1-932625-01-1(1)) Texthelp Systems, Inc.

EDUCATION, DISCRIMINATION IN

see Discrimination in Education

EDUCATION, ELEMENTARY

Ajmera, Maya. Back to School. 2001. (978-0-606-22636-3(2)) Tandem Library Bks.

Angela's Ashes: Response Journal. 2003. 40p. (YA). (978-1-58049-991-0(0), RJ91) Prestwick Hse., Inc.

Around the World in Eighty Days: Response Journal. 2003. 40p. (YA). (978-1-58049-987-3(2), RJ87) Prestwick Hse., Inc.

The Arts. (Britannica Learning Library). (Illus.). (gr. 2-5). 14.95 (978-1-59339-004-4(1), 049905-EN-REF) Encyclopaedia Britannica, Inc.

Atkinson, Sue. Supermaths: Age 4-5. 2003. (Illus.). 32p. pap. (978-0-340-80559-6(5), Hodder Children's Books) Hodder Children's Division.

—Supermaths 3: Age 3-6. 2003. (Illus.). 32p. pap. (978-0-340-80561-9(7), Hodder Children's Books) Hodder Children's Division.

Blevins, Wiley, ed. Grade K. 2006. (SmartSquares Ser.). 16p. 14.99 (978-0-439-83831-3(2), Teaching Resources) Scholastic, Inc.

—Grade PreK. 2006. (SmartSquares Ser.). 16p. spiral bd. 14.99 (978-0-439-83829-0(0), Teaching Resources) Scholastic, Inc.

—Smart Squares: Grade 1. 2006. (SmartSquares Ser.). 16p. 14.99 (978-0-439-83833-7(9), Teaching Resources) Scholastic, Inc.

Bowman, Susan. The Adventures of Dakota: A Friendly Wolf Who Teaches Children (Grades K-4) Lessons about Life. 2004. (Illus.). 56p. (J). (978-1-889636-60-3(6)) Youthlight, Inc.

Boyd, Kassandra, et al. Kids on the Move: Creative Movement for Children of All Ages, 1. 2003. (Illus.). 29.95 (978-0-9744833-0-6(3)) Creative Publishing.

Bradford-Vernon, Jennifer R. How to Be Your Child's First Teacher: Insights for Parent Involvement. 2003. (Illus.). 176p. (gr. k-1). 14.99 (978-1-56822-998-0(4), IF27018) School Specialty Publishing.

Brent, Lynnette R. At School: Long Ago & Today. 2003. (Times Change Ser.). (Illus.). 32p. (J). lib. bdg. 24.22 (978-1-4034-4533-9(8)) Heinemann Library.

Brown, Robin. Practice Papers: Advanced Maths. 2nd ed. (Illus.). 32p. (YA). pap. (978-0-340-72690-7(3), Hodder & Stoughton) Hodder General Publishing Division.

—Practice Papers: Advanced Non-Verbal Reasoning. 2nd ed. (Illus.). 32p. (YA). pap. 6.99 (978-0-340-72686-0(5), Hodder & Stoughton) Hodder General Publishing Division GBR. *Dist:* Trafalgar Square Publishing.

—Practice Papers: English. 2nd ed. (Illus.). 32p. (YA). pap. 6.99 (978-0-340-72687-7(3), Hodder & Stoughton) Hodder General Publishing Division GBR. *Dist:* Trafalgar Square Publishing.

—Practice Papers: Maths. 2nd ed. (Illus.). 32p. (YA). pap. (978-0-340-72689-1(X), Hodder & Stoughton) Hodder General Publishing Division.

Castellano, Marie. Simply Super Storytimes: Programming Ideas. 2003. (Illus.). 104p. (J). pap. 16.95 (978-1-57950-005-4(6), Upstart Bks.) Highsmith Inc.

Cleland, JoAnn. At School. 2007. (J). (978-1-59515-936-6(3)) Rourke Publishing, LLC.

Cooper, Terry, ed. Learning Early Concepts. 2006. (Kindergarten Ser.). 48p. pap. 5.99 (978-0-439-81955-8(5) , Teaching Resources) Scholastic, Inc.

Cryer, Debby, et al. Active Learning for Fives. 2003. (Active Learning Ser.). (Illus.). 450p. (Orig.). (ps). 26.50 (978-0-201-49401-3(9)) Seymour, Dale Pubns.

Dalmatian Press Staff. ABC's, 123's & Shapes: Chalkboard Book. 2003. (Home Learning Tools Ser.). 10p. (J). (ps-k). pap. 3.99 (978-1-4037-0329-3(9)) Dalmatian Pr.

—First Grade Workbook: Complete Curriculum of Basic Skills. 2002. (Home Learning Tools Ser.). (Illus.). 384p. (J). (gr. 1 up). pap., wbk. ed. 12.99 (978-1-57759-623-3(4)) Dalmatian Pr.

del Sur, Duendes, illus. Jumbo Jumpstart: 1st Grade. 2001. (Jumpstart Ser.). 320p. (J). (gr. 1). mass mkt., wbk. ed. 14.99 (978-0-439-16409-2(5)) Scholastic, Inc.

Discover New Skills. 1998. (Captain Kangaroo Fun-to-Learn Activity Bks.: Vol. 2). (J). pap. (978-0-7666-0216-8(8) , Honey Bear Bks.) Modern Publishing.

Doherty, Edith J. S. & Evans, Louise C. Primary Independent Study. 2003. 60p. (J). pap. 14.95 (978-0-945984-05-4(7) , Zephyr Pr.) Chicago Review Pr., Inc.

Douglas, Vincent. Math, Time, & Money. 2004. (Flash Card Collection). 324p. (C). 16.95 (978-1-58845-663-2(3)) School Specialty Publishing.

Douglas, Vincent & School Specialty Publishing Staff. Comprehensive Curriculum of Basic Skills, Grade 2. 2001. (Comprehensive Curriculum of Basic Skills Ser.). (Illus.). 544p. (J). (ps-6). pap., wbk. ed. 19.95 (978-1-56189-369-0(2) , 60012, American Education Publishing) School Specialty Publishing.

—Comprehensive Curriculum of Basic Skills, Grade 3. 2001. (Comprehensive Curriculum of Basic Skills Ser.). (Illus.). 544p. (J). (ps-6). pap., wbk. ed. 19.95 (978-1-56189-370-6(6) , 60013, American Education Publishing) School Specialty Publishing.

—Comprehensive Curriculum of Basic Skills, Grade 4. 2001. (Comprehensive Curriculum of Basic Skills Ser.). (Illus.). 544p. (J). (ps-6). pap., wbk. ed. 19.95 (978-1-56189-371-3(4) , 60014, American Education Publishing) School Specialty Publishing.

—Comprehensive Curriculum of Basic Skills, Grade 5. 2001. (Comprehensive Curriculum of Basic Skills Ser.). (Illus.). 544p. (J). (ps-6). pap., wbk. ed. 19.95 (978-1-56189-372-0(2) , 60015, American Education Publishing) School Specialty Publishing.

—Comprehensive Curriculum of Basic Skills, Grade 6. 2001. (Comprehensive Curriculum of Basic Skills Ser.). (Illus.). 544p. (J). (ps-6). pap., wbk. ed. 19.95 (978-1-56189-373-7(0) , 60016, American Education Publishing) School Specialty Publishing.

Fences. 2003. 44p. (YA). tchr. ed., ring bd. (978-1-58049-468-7(4) , TU224) Prestwick Hse., Inc.

Fletcher, Terri. Scrumpy's Educational Kid Songs. 2003. (Illus.). 16p. (J). (ps-1). pap. 12.95 incl. audio compact disk (978-0-9672279-1-7(7)) Scrumps Entertainment, Inc.

Fulk, Virginia. Learning to Listen - Listening to Learn. Harvey, Gayle S., illus. 1999. (Kids' Stuff Ser.). 80p. (J). (ps-3). pap. 9.95 (978-0-86530-413-0(0) , IP 413-0) Incentive Pubns., Inc.

Gilbert, LaBritta. 50 Great Make-It, Take-It Projects. 2002. 80p. (J). (gr. k-5). pap. 18.95 (978-1-57950-070-2(6) , Upstart Bks.) Highsmith Inc.

Gillham, Bill, et al. Essential Skills, 4 bks. (Illus.). 128p. (YA). pap. 15.99 (978-0-340-71583-3(9) , Hodder & Stoughton) Hodder General Publishing Division GBR. *Dist:* Trafalgar Square Publishing.

Hall, M. C. First Grade Scholar. Boyer, Robin, illus. 2004. 32p. (J). pap. 2.49 (978-1-58947-456-7(2)) School Zone Publishing Co.

—Second Grade Scholar. Boyer, Robin, illus. 2004. 32p. (J). pap. 2.49 (978-1-58947-457-4(0)) School Zone Publishing Co.

Haugen, Brenda. The 100th Day of School. Boyd, Sheree, illus. 2004. (Holidays & Celebrations Ser.). 24p. (C). (gr. k-3). 22.60 (978-1-4048-0196-7(0)) Picture Window Bks.

Hoena, B. A. Weather ABC: An Alphabet Book. 2005. (A+ Alphabet Books). (Illus.). 32p. (J). 22.60 (978-0-7368-3666-1(7)); 22.60 (978-0-7368-3667-8(5)) Capstone Pr., Inc.

Hughes, Monica. First Day at School. 2003. (Raintree Sprouts Ser.). (Illus.). 24p. (J). pap. 5.50 (978-1-4109-0669-4(8)) Raintree.

—First Day at School. 2003. (ps-2). lib. bdg. 13.55 (978-0-613-78205-0(4)) Tandem Library Bks.

Kalman, Bobbie. School from A to Z. 1999. (gr. 3-6). lib. bdg. 16.40 (978-0-613-19531-7(0)) Tandem Library Bks.

Laugh & Learn. 1998. (Captain Kangaroo Fun-to-Learn Activity Bks.: Vol. 4). (J). pap. (978-0-7666-0218-2(4) , Honey Bear Bks.) Modern Publishing.

Learning Co Bks Staff. Reader Rabbit Comprehensive Workbook: First Grade. 2005. (J). (gr. 1). pap., wbk. ed. 19.99 (978-0-7630-8150-8(7)) Riverdeep, Inc.

—Reader Rabbit Comprehensive Workbook: Kindergarten. 2005. (J). (gr. k). pap., wbk. ed. 19.99 (978-0-7630-8151-5(5)) Riverdeep, Inc.

—Reader Rabbit Comprehensive Workbook: Preschool. 2005. (J). (ps). pap., wbk. ed. 19.99 (978-0-7630-8149-2(3)) Riverdeep, Inc.

Let's Find Out Early Learning Books, 8 bks., Set. Incl. Set. Five Senses/Opposites & Position Words. 72.00 (*978-0-531-17574-3(X)); Set. Letters/Numbers. 72.00 (*978-0-531-17599-6(5)); (J). (ps-k). 2007. 2007. 144.00 (*978-0-531-17734-1(3) , Children's Pr.) Scholastic Library Publishing.

Listening, Understanding, Remembering, Verbalizing! 1999. 90p. per. 28.50 (978-1-886143-46-3(3)) Great Ideas for Teaching, Inc.

Make Way for Learning. 1998. (Captain Kangaroo Fun-to-Learn Activity Bks.: Vol. 3). (J). pap. (978-0-7666-0217-5(6) , Honey Bear Bks.) Modern Publishing.

Mcgraw-Hill Editorial Staff, ed. Everything for Early Learning: Grade K. 2004. (Everything for Early Learning Ser.). (Illus.). 320p. (J). (gr. k-k). pap. 7.95 (978-0-7696-3362-6(5) , American Education Publishing) School Specialty Publishing.

Modoc Press Editors. Directory of Distance Learning Opportunities: K-12. 2003. 432p. (gr. k-12). 81.95 (978-1-57356-515-8(6) , OXDLK-12) Greenwood Publishing Group, Inc.

NCPTA Staff. Home Learning 11 Sats Practical Science. (Illus.). 32p. pap. 6.99 (978-0-340-71046-3(2) , Coronet) Hodder General Publishing Division GBR. *Dist:* Trafalgar Square Publishing.

—Home Learning 5-7 Mathematics. (Illus.). 24p. pap. 6.99 (978-0-340-71680-9(0) , Coronet) Hodder General Publishing Division GBR. *Dist:* Trafalgar Square Publishing.

Penton Overseas, Inc. Staff. Your Baby Can Read!, Vol. 2. rev. ed. 2006. (J). (gr. k-5). 16.95 (978-1-59125-750-9(6) , Smart Kids) Penton Overseas, Inc.

The Prince & the Pauper: Response Journal. 2003. 36p. (YA). (978-1-58049-986-6(4) , RJ86) Prestwick Hse., Inc.

Rainbow Bridge Publishing Staff. Deep Space Division Fission. 2004. (Ready, Set... Flashcards! Ser.). 8.95 (978-1-932210-90-3(3)) Rainbow Bridge Publishing.

—World Vacation Multiplication. 2004. (Ready, Set... Flashcards! Ser.). 8.95 (978-1-932210-89-7(X)) Rainbow Bridge Publishing.

Rayner, Amanda. Going to School. 2005. (Illus.). 30p. (J). (gr. 3-7). lib. bdg. 27.10 (978-1-58340-697-7(2)) Smart Apple Media.

Rozakis, Laurie. Be a Super Test Taker! 2007. 128p. (J). pap. 6.99 (978-0-439-87879-1(9) , Scholastic Reference) Scholastic, Inc.

Rudman, Jack. Education in the Elementary School. 2002. (National Teacher Examination Ser.: NT-1). 49.95 (978-0-8373-8511-2(3)) National Learning Corp.

Schiller, Pam. Start Smart: How to Build Brain Power in the Early Years. 2004. (Illus.). 192p. (ps-1). pap. 14.95 (978-0-87659-201-4(9) , 19378) Gryphon Hse., Inc.

School Specialty Publishing. Total Toddler Learning Kit. 2007. (Total Learning Kits Ser.). 78p. (J). 49.95 (*978-0-7696-5333-4(2)) School Specialty Publishing.

School Zone Interactive Staff. Preschool. (J). 2005. cd-rom 24.99 (978-1-58947-681-3(6)); 2002. 320p. pap. 19.99 (978-1-58947-851-0(7)) School Zone Publishing Co.

Sheldon, Ken. Sing along & Learn: Around the Year Kit. 2006. 32p. (J). 9.99 (978-0-439-80211-6(3) , Teaching Resources) Scholastic, Inc.

—Sing along & Learn: Early Skills Kit. 2006. 32p. (J). 9.99 (978-0-439-80208-6(3) , Teaching Resources) Scholastic, Inc.

—Sing along & Learn: Follow Directions Kit. 2006. 32p. (J). 9.99 (978-0-439-80217-8(2) , Teaching Resources) Scholastic, Inc.

—Sing along & Learn Follow Directions: 10 Lively Learning Songs with Reproducibles That Teach Key Listening Skills. 2004. 32p. pap. 11.99 (978-0-439-37080-6(9) , Teaching Resources) Scholastic, Inc.

The Story of My Life: Response Journal. 2003. 40p. (YA). (978-1-58049-990-3(2) , RJ90) Prestwick Hse., Inc.

Thomas, Pat. Do I Have to Go to School? A First Look at Starting School. Harker, Lesley, illus. 2006. (First Look At... Ser.). 32p. (J). pap. 6.99 (978-0-7641-3216-2(4)) Barron's Educational Series, Inc.

Through the Looking Glass: Response Journal. 2003. 32p. (YA). (978-1-58049-989-7(9) , RJ89) Prestwick Hse., Inc.

Trumbauer, Lisa. At School. 2000. (Yellow Umbrella Books). (Illus.). 16p. (J). (gr. 1). lib. bdg. 14.60 (978-0-7368-0741-8(1) , Pebble Bks.) Capstone Pr., Inc.

Turkington, Carol & Maack, Molly. Get Ready! for Standardized Tests: Reading Grade 1. 2001. (Get Ready for Standardized Tests Ser.). (Illus.). 168p. (gr. 1). pap. 14.95 (978-0-07-137405-7(1)) McGraw-Hill Cos., The.

Whiteford, Rhona. Complete English, 3 bks. in 1. (Illus.). 96p. (YA). pap. 15.99 (978-0-340-71582-6(0) , Hodder & Stoughton) Hodder General Publishing Division GBR. *Dist:* Trafalgar Square Publishing.

Whiteford, Rhona & Fitzsimmons, Jim. Complete English, 4 bks. in 1. (Illus.). 96p. (YA). pap. 15.99 (978-0-340-71580-2(4) , Hodder & Stoughton) Hodder General Publishing Division GBR. *Dist:* Trafalgar Square Publishing.

—Complete Math, 4 bks. in 1. (Illus.). 96p. (YA). pap. 15.99 (978-0-340-71581-9(2) , Hodder & Stoughton) Hodder General Publishing Division GBR. *Dist:* Trafalgar Square Publishing.

The Witch of Blackbird Pond: Response Journal. 2003. 36p. (YA). (978-1-58049-993-4(7) , RJ93) Prestwick Hse., Inc.

Wolf, Tony. On the Farm. 2005. (Illus.). 10p. (J). (ps-ps). pap. 9.98 (978-0-7624-2031-5(6) , Courage Bks.) Running Pr. Bk. Pubs.

Yoshinori, Kano. Graded Go Problems for Beginners, Vol. 1. 1998. (Beginner & Elementary Go Bks.). (Illus.). (J). pap. 15.00 (978-4-906574-46-9(7)) KISEIDO.

EDUCATION, ETHICAL

see Moral Education; Religious Education

EDUCATION—FICTION

Adams, Chanelle. Myra. 2006. 22p. 12.16 (978-1-4116-9426-2(0)) Lulu.com.

Bickico Enterprises Staff, concept. BabyKids Bk. 1: El Libro Para Contar. 2003. (SPA.). 16p. (J). pap. 2.95 (978-0-9746508-4-5(6)) Bickico Enterprises, Inc.

—BabyKids Bk. 2: El Libro de los Colores. 2003. (SPA.). 16p. (J). pap. (978-0-9746508-5-2(4)) Bickico Enterprises, Inc.

Black, Jessica L. Why Have Rules? Gillen, Lisa P., illus. l.t. ed. 2003. (Hrl Little Book Ser.). 8p. (J). (ps). pap. 10.95 (978-1-57332-271-3(7)); pap. 10.95 (978-1-57332-270-6(9)) HighReach Learning, Inc.

Bognomo, Joel Ebouerne. Madoulina: A Girl Who Wanted to Go to School. 2003. (Illus.). 32p. (J). (gr. 2-4). 14.95 (978-1-56397-769-5(9)); pap. 8.95 (978-1-56397-822-7(9)) Boyds Mills Pr.

—Madoulina: A Girl Who Wanted to Go to School. 1999. (978-0-606-17704-7(3)); lib. bdg. 17.60 (978-0-613-23339-2(5)) Tandem Library Bks.

Bowen, Anne. The Great Math Tattle Battle. Zollars, Jaime, illus. 2006. 32p. (J). 15.95 (978-0-8075-3163-1(4)) Whitman, Albert & Co.

Carr, Jan. Greedy Apostrophe: A Cautionary Tale. Long, Ethan, illus. 2007. 32p. (J). (gr. 1-3). 16.95 (978-0-8234-2006-3(X)) Holiday Hse., Inc.

Carroll, Michelle. Surviving Chauncy High: Adventures in Education in the 90's. 2001. (gr. 7-12). lib. bdg. 21.60 (978-0-613-74567-3(1)) Tandem Library Bks.

Chouette, ed. Caillou Count with Me! rev. ed. 2006. (Caillou Board Bks.). (ENG & FRE., Illus.). 24p. (J). pap. 7.95 (*978-2-89450-591-5(4)) Chouette Publishing CAN. *Dist:* Independent Pubs. Group.

Cook, Barbara L. Families. Cress, Michelle H., illus. l.t. ed. 2004. (Hrl Board Book Ser.). 8p. (J). (ps-1). pap. 10.95 (978-1-57332-280-5(6)) HighReach Learning, Inc.

Cooper, Barbara. Hannah Hyphen-Hyphen. Raynor, Maggie, illus. 2004. 32p. (J). lib. bdg. 23.33 (978-0-8368-4226-5(X)) Stevens, Gareth Inc.

Cosgrove, Stephen. Shimmeree. 2003. (gr. k-3). lib. bdg. 13.00 (978-0-613-64593-5(6)) Tandem Library Bks.

—Trafalgar True. James, Robin, illus. rev. ed. 2002. (Serendipity Bks.). 32p. (J). pap. 4.99 (978-0-8431-4890-9(X) , Price Stern Sloan) Penguin Group (USA) Inc.

—Trafalgar True. 2002. (gr. k-3). lib. bdg. 13.00 (978-0-613-64606-2(1)) Tandem Library Bks.

Courtin, Thierry. Decouvre les nombres Avec. (FRE.). pap. (978-2-09-202149-1(4)) Editions Rouge et Or.

Delval, Marie-Helene. Lili y Minino Juegan al Escondite. Courtin, Thierry, illus. 2002. (Palabras Menudas Ser.). (SPA.). 14p. (ps). 4.95 (978-84-7864-515-2(2)) Combel Editorial, S.A. ESP. *Dist:* Independent Pubs. Group.

Donahue, Moira Rose. Alfie the Apostrophe. Adinolfi, JoAnn, illus. 2006. 32p. (J). 16.95 (978-0-8075-0255-6(3)) Whitman, Albert & Co.

Driscoll, Laura. Super Specs. Gott, Barry, illus. 2005. 32p. (J). lib. bdg. 20.00 (*978-1-4242-1074-9(7)) Fitzgerald Bks.

Ellis, Kathryn. Joey Jeremiah. 2006. (Degrassi Junior High Ser.). 184p. (YA). (gr. 5-10). 7.95 (978-1-55028-924-4(1)) Lorimer, James & Co., Ltd., Pubs. CAN. *Dist:* Casemate Pubs. & Bk. Distributors, LLC.

Elvgren, Jennifer Riesmeyer. Josias, Hold the Book. Tadgell, Nicole, illus. 2006. 32p. (J). 15.95 (978-1-59078-318-4(2)) Boyds Mills Pr.

Epstein, Brad, ed. Auburn University 101. l.t. ed. 2003. (My First Text Board Bks.). (Illus.). 20p. (J). bds. 9.95 (978-0-9727702-7-9(5)) Michaelson Entertainment.

—Dartmouth College 101. l.t. ed. 2003. (My First Text Board Bks.). (Illus.). 20p. (J). bds. 9.95 (978-0-9727702-5-5(9)) Michaelson Entertainment.

—University of Alabama 101. l.t. ed. 2003. (My First Text Board Bks.). (Illus.). 20p. (J). bds. 9.95 (978-0-9727702-6-2(7)) Michaelson Entertainment.

—University of Tennessee 101. l.t. ed. 2003. (My First Text Board Bks.). (Illus.). 20p. (J). bds. 9.95 (978-0-9727702-8-6(3)) Michaelson Entertainment.

—University of Washington 101. l.t. ed. 2003. (My First Text Board Bks.). (Illus.). 20p. (J). bds. 9.95 (978-0-9727702-9-3(1) , 101 Bk.) Michaelson Entertainment.

Fine, Edith Hope & Josephson, Judith Pinkerton. Armando & the Blue Tarp School. Sosa, Hernan, illus. 2007. 32p. (J). (gr. k-4). 16.95 (*978-1-58430-278-0(X)) Lee & Low Bks., Inc.

Franco, Betsy. 20 Marvelous Math Tales. 2000. (J). pap. 3.99 (978-0-439-15393-5(X)) Scholastic, Inc.

Gershon, Dann. The Spelling Bee. Robinson, David, illus. 1998. (Hangin' with the Hombeez Ser.: Vol. 1). 40p. (J). (gr. k-6). 14.95 (978-0-9656985-3-5(X)) Noware Bks.

Gershon, Dann & Gershon, Gina. Hollyhive Hunnie. Robinson, David, illus. 2000. (Hangin' with the Hombeez Ser.: Vol. 5). 40p. (J). (gr. k-6). 9.95 (978-0-9656985-7-3(2)) Noware Bks.

Gomes, Julie. ABC Exercise with Me. Dungan, Julia, illus. 2005. (J). per. 7.50 (978-0-9770207-0-6(3)) JCCJ Pr.

Goodson, Daphnie. Without the Alphabet. 2006. (Illus.). 98p. (J). per. 19.95 (978-1-59453-565-9(5) , Airleaf Publishing) Airleaf Publishing & Bookselling.

Green, John. An Abundance of Katherines. 2006. 256p. (YA). (gr. 9). 16.99 (978-0-525-47688-7(1) , Dutton Juvenile) Penguin Group (USA) Inc.

Grejniec, Michael. Good Morning Good Night Biling. 2007. (J). 16.50 (978-0-7358-2109-5(7)); (ENG & SPA.). pap. 6.95 (978-0-7358-2110-1(0)) North-South Bks., Inc.

Harris, Ruth Elwin. Sarah's Story. 2002. (Quantock's Quartet Ser.). (Illus.). 288p. (YA). (gr. 7 up). pap. 5.99 (978-0-7636-1707-3(5)) Candlewick Pr.

—Sarah's Story. 2002. (gr. 7-12). lib. bdg. 14.15 (978-0-613-74779-0(8)) Tandem Library Bks.

Hayes, Larry E. My Name Starts with K. Anderson, Airlie, illus. Hayes, Larry E., photos by. 2005. (My Name Starts With Ser.). 32p. (J). 12.95 (978-0-9725292-6-6(8)) Inspire Pubns.

Hensley, Sarah M. I Want to Ride. Gray, Stacy A., illus. l.t. ed. 2004. (Hrl Board Book Ser.). 10p. (J). (ps-1). pap. 10.95 (978-1-57332-282-9(2)) HighReach Learning, Inc.

Herman, Gail. Lucky Goes to School. Gorbaty, Norman, illus. 2001. (All Aboard Reading Ser.). 1p. (J). (ps-1). pap. 3.99 (978-0-448-42498-9(3) , Grosset & Dunlap) Penguin Group (USA) Inc.

—Lucky Goes to School. 2001. (gr. k-3). lib. bdg. 11.80 (978-0-613-35616-9(0)); (Illus.). (J). (978-0-606-21309-7(0)) Tandem Library Bks.

Hide & Seek. (Illus.). (J). pap. 2.95 (978-1-55254-020-6(0) , BV26002) Brighter Vision Pubns.

Hide & Seek. Date not set. (Magic Windows Ser.). (Illus.). (J). Vol. 1. (978-0-7624-1983-8(0)); Vol. 2. (978-0-7624-1984-5(9)) Running Pr. Bk. Pubs. (Running Pr. Kids).

Higashi/Glaser Design Inc. Staff, illus. Hello Kitty, Hello World! 2000. 32p. (J). (ps-3). 12.95 (978-0-8109-3443-6(4)) Abrams, Harry N. , Inc.

Hutchins, Hazel J. Robyn Makes the News. Cathcart, Yvonne, illus. 2003. (First Novel Ser.). 64p. (J). (gr. 1-5). 4.95 (978-0-88780-593-6(0)); (*978-0-88780-594-3(9)) Formac Publishing Co., Ltd. CAN. *Dist:* Casemate Pubs. & Bk. Distributors, LLC.

Isdell, Wendy. The Chemy Called Al by Wendy Isdell. 2nd ed. 2004. 150p. (YA). per. 9.99 (978-1-4116-1095-8(4)) Lulu.com.

Jarrell, Pamela R. Caillou Finds a Caterpillar. Storch, Ellen N., illus. l.t. ed. 2005. (Hrl Board Book Ser.). (J). (ps-1). pap. 10.95 (978-1-57332-292-8(X)) HighReach Learning, Inc.

Jones, Marcia Thornton & Dadey, Debbie. Hide-and-Spook, No. 7. Tugeau, Jeremy, illus. 2004. (Ghostville Elementary Ser.: No. 7). 96p. (J). (gr. 2-5). 3.99 (978-0-439-56003-0(9) , Scholastic Paperbacks) Scholastic, Inc.

Klingel, Cynthia Fitterer & Noyed, Robert B. Quentin's Quiz & the Letter Q. 2003. (Alphaphonics Ser.). (Illus.). 24p. (J). (ps-2). 21.36 (978-1-59296-107-8(X)) Child's World, Inc.

Konigsburg, E. L. Throwing Shadows. 1998. 160p. (J). (gr. 5-9). pap. 5.99 (978-0-689-82120-2(4) , Aladdin) Simon & Schuster Children's Publishing.

—The View from Saturday. Konigsburg, E. L., illus. 2002. (Illus.). (J). 25.11 (978-0-7587-0221-0(3)) Book Wholesalers, Inc.

—The View from Saturday. 2000. (J). 11.95 (978-1-56137-936-1(0)) Novel Units, Inc.

—The View from Saturday. 280p. (YA). (gr. 5 up). pap. 4.95 (978-0-8072-1511-1(2) , Listening Library) Random Hse. Audio Publishing Group.

—The View from Saturday. 1998. (Jean Karl Bks.). 176p. (J). (gr. 3-7). reprint ed. pap. 5.99 (978-0-689-81721-2(5) , Aladdin) Simon & Schuster Children's Publishing.

—The View from Saturday. 1998. (J). (978-0-606-13063-9(2)) Tandem Library Bks.

Leblanc, Louise. Maddie's Big Test. Cummins, Sarah, tr. from FRE. Gay, Marie-Louise, illus. 2006. (First Novel Ser.). 64p. (J). (gr. 2-5). (*978-0-88780-718-3(6)); 4.95 (*978-0-88780-714-5(3)) Formac Publishing Co., Ltd. CAN. *Dist:* Casemate Pubs. & Bk. Distributors, LLC.

Lee, Karen. ABC Safari. Lee, Karen, illus. 2007. (Illus.). (J). (ps-2). 1p. 8.95 (*978-0-9777423-6-3(9)); 32p. 15.95 (978-0-9777423-0-1(X)) Sylvan Dell Pubng.

Leedy, Loreen, illus. Missing Math. 2008. (J). (*978-0-7614-5385-7(7)) Cavendish, Marshall Corp.

Lewis, Caryl & Lolfa, Y. Iawn Boi? 2005. (WEL.). 80p. pap. (978-0-86243-699-5(0)) Y Lolfa.

Lipp, Frederick. Running Shoes. Gaillard, Jason, illus. 2008. (J). (*978-1-58089-175-2(6)) Charlesbridge Publishing, Inc.

MacHado, Ana Maria. De carta en Carta. Basulto, Rita, illus. (SPA.). 44p. (J). (gr. 3-5). pap. 7.95 (978-968-19-1483-7(X)) Santillana USA Publishing Co., Inc.

Masterson, Carla & Druckman, Mike. Memory Emory & His Hiding Places. 2005. (J). per. 16.95 (978-1-59858-052-5(3)) Dog Ear Publishing, LLC.

McKee, Ruby. The Land of Phonicia: An Enchanted Tale to Learn Phonics. Allen, Timothy, illus. l.t. ed. 2003. 52p. (J). per. 39.95 (978-0-9744944-0-1(2)) Jewel Publishing.

Mota, Michael. Mikey Has a Problem, a Math Problem. Soares, Michael, illus. 2003. 34p. lib. bdg. 16.99 (978-1-932338-05-8(5)) Lifevest Publishing, Inc.

Muench-Williams, Heather. At the Circus. Storch, Ellen N., illus. l.t. ed. 2005. (Hrl Board Book Ser.). 10p. (J). (ps-1). bds. 10.95 (978-1-57332-285-0(7)) HighReach Learning, Inc.

Mullican, Judy. A Big Mess. Gray, Stacy A., illus. l.t. ed. 2003. (Hrl Little Book Ser.). 8p. (J). (ps). pap. 10.95 (978-1-57332-273-7(3)) HighReach Learning, Inc.

—Caillou Is Healthy. Gray, Stacy A., illus. l.t. ed. 2004. (Hrl Board Book Ser.). (J). (ps-1). pap. 10.95 (978-1-57332-287-4(3)) HighReach Learning, Inc.

Mullican, Judy & Williams, Heather L. Building a Sand Castle. Storch, Ellen N., illus. l.t. ed. 2004. (Hrl Big Book Ser.). (J). (ps). pap. 10.95 (978-1-57332-297-3(0)); pap. 10.95 (978-1-57332-298-0(9)) HighReach Learning, Inc.

Olker, Constance. The Punctuation Pals Go to the Beach. 2005. (Illus.). (J). 36p. per. 18.95 (978-1-933449-12-8(8)); 22p. per. 17.95 (978-0-9761289-5-3(0)) Nightengale Pr.

—The Punctuation Pals Go to the Moon. 2005. (Illus.). (J). 64p. per. 24.95 (978-1-933449-13-5(6)); per. 19.95 (978-0-9761289-6-0(9)) Nightengale Pr.

—The Punctuation Pals Meet at School. 2005. (Illus.). (J). 40p. per. 18.95 (978-1-933449-07-4(1)); 18p. per. 16.95 (978-0-9761289-4-6(2)) Nightengale Pr.

Park, Frances. Royal Bee. 2000. (gr. 3-6). lib. bdg. 17.60 (978-0-613-29043-2(7)) Tandem Library Bks.

E F G

Peck, Richard. The Teacher's Funeral: A Comedy in Three Parts. 2004. 208p. (J). (gr. 5). 16.99 (978-0-8037-2736-6(4) , Dial); 2006. 224p. (YA). (gr. 3). reprint ed. pap. 6.99 (978-0-14-240507-9(8) , Puffin) Penguin Group (USA) Inc.

—The Teacher's Funeral: A Comedy in Three Parts. l.t. ed. 2005. 226p. 22.95 (978-0-7862-7750-6(5) , Large Print Pr.) Thorndike Pr.

Ponti, Claude & Desarthe, Agnes. El Principito Puf. 2003. (SPA.). 102p. (978-84-8470-063-0(1)) Corimbo, Editorial S.L.

Rowen, Amy & Rowen, Tyla Marie. Waggin' Tails. 2003. 182p. 23.95 (978-0-595-65740-7(0)); pap. 13.95 (978-0-595-28171-8(0)) iUniverse, Inc.

Scaglione, Joanne & Small, Gail. The Big Squeal: A Wild, True, & Twisted Tail. Endelman, David, illus. 2005. 56p. pap. 19.95 (978-1-57886-256-6(6)) Rowman & Littlefield Education.

Scieszka, Jon. Math Curse. Smith, Lane, illus. 2007. 32p. (J). (ps). pap. 9.99 ***(978-0-670-06299-7(5)*** , Viking Juvenile) Penguin Group (USA) Inc.

Selway, Martina. So Many Babies. 2003. (Illus.). 32p. (J). pap. 9.99 (978-0-09-940769-0(8)) Random Hse. GBR. *Dist:* Independent Pubs. Group.

Sempe & Goscinny. Los Recreos del Pequeno Nicolas. 2003. (SPA., Illus.). 116p. (J). (gr. 3-5). pap. 9.95 (978-84-204-4814-5(1)) Santillana USA Publishing Co., Inc.

Turcotte, Elise. La Legon d'Annette. 1999. (La Courte Echelle Premier Roman Ser.). (FRE., Illus.). 64p. (J). (gr. 2-5). pap. (978-2-89021-338-8(2)) Diffusion du livre Mirabel.

Villoro, Juan. El Profesor Ziper y la Fabulosa Guitarra Electrica. 1998. (SPA., Illus.). 96p. (gr. 4-7). pap. 9.95 (978-968-29-4003-3(6)) Libros Sin Fronteras.

—El Profesor Ziper y la Fabulosa Guitarra Electrica. El Fisgon, illus. 2003. (SPA.). 96p. (J). (gr. 5-8). pap. 11.95 (978-968-19-0206-3(8)) Santillana USA Publishing Co., Inc.

Weber, Lou, ed. Barney ABC: Sound Activity Pad. 2004. 48p. (J). 12.98 (978-1-4127-0167-9(8) , 7217200) Publications International, Ltd.

—Barney Numbers: Sound Activity Pad. 2004. 48p. (J). 12.98 (978-1-4127-0168-6(6) , 7217300) Publications International, Ltd.

White, Andrea. Surviving Antarctica: Reality TV 2083. (J). 2006. 448p. pap. 6.99 (978-0-06-055456-9(8)); 2005. 336p. (gr. 7 up). 16.99 (978-0-06-055454-5(1) , Harper-Collins); 2005. 336p. (gr. 7 up). lib. bdg. 16.89 (978-0-06-055455-2(X)) HarperCollins Pubs.

Williams, Heather L. Andy & Jerome. Crowell, Knox, illus. l.t. ed. 2004. (Hrl Big Book Ser.). 8p. (J). (ps-1). pap. 10.95 (978-1-57332-276-8(8)); pap. 10.95 (978-1-57332-277-5(6)) HighReach Learning, Inc.

—Brians Garden. Gillen, Lisa P., illus. l.t. ed. 2004. (Hrl Little Book Ser.). (J). (ps-1). pap. 10.95 (978-1-57332-300-0(4)); pap. 10.95 (978-1-57332-299-7(7)) High-Reach Learning, Inc.

Williams, Rozanne Lanczak. I Love to Write! Maio, Barbara & Faulkner, Stacey, eds. Schuett, Stacey, illus. 2006. (J). 8p. pap. 1.99 (978-1-59198-283-8(9) , 6177); per. 4.99 ***(978-1-59198-334-7(7))*** Creative Teaching Pr., Inc.

—This Is My Story. Maio, Barbara & Faulkner, Stacey, eds. Burris, Priscilla, illus. 2006. (Learn to Write Ser.). 8p. (J). pap. 1.99 (978-1-59198-280-7(4) , 6174) Creative Teaching Pr., Inc.

—Writing about Books. Maio, Barbara & Faulkner, Stacey, eds. Schneider, Christine, illus. 2006. (Learn to Write Ser.). 8p. (J). pap. 1.99 (978-1-59198-289-0(8) , 6183) Creative Teaching Pr., Inc.

Winfield, Arthur M. Putnam Hall Rivals. 2006. pap. 27.95 ***(978-1-4286-1948-7(8))*** Kessinger Publishing, LLC.

—The Rover Boys in the Mountains: Or, A Hunt for Fun & Fortune. 2007. 170p. pap. 11.99 ***(978-1-4264-7052-3(5));*** 188p. pap. 14.99 ***(978-1-4264-7128-5(9))*** BiblioBazaar.

Wood, Audrey & Wood, Bruce. Alphabet Rescue. 2006. (Illus.). 40p. (J). pap. 15.99 (978-0-439-85316-3(8) , Blue Sky Pr., The) Scholastic, Inc.

Yim, Shirin. Ruby's Wish. Blackall, Sophie, illus. 2002. 36p. (J). (gr. k-3). 15.95 (978-0-8118-3490-2(5)) Chronicle Bks. LLC.

Yoon, Salina. Hoppy Graduation! 2006. (Illus.). 10p. (J). (ps-1). bds. 5.99 (978-0-8431-2002-8(9) , Price Stern Sloan) Penguin Group (USA) Inc.

EDUCATION, HIGHER

see also Technical Education

Jordan, Keith. Don't Stress the Process: The College Plan. 2005. (J). lib. bdg. 18.95 (978-0-9761218-0-0(8)) Knowledge College Planning.

Maynigo, Traci. A Girl's Guide to College. (Illus.). 96p. pap. 10.95 (978-1-58786-012-6(0) , Blue Mountain Pr.) Blue Mountain Arts Inc.

Schneider, Robyn. The Social Climber's Guide to High School. Hess, Kerrie, illus. 2007. 272p. (YA). (gr. 7-10). pap. 8.99 ***(978-1-4169-3427-1(8)*** , Simon Pulse) Simon & Schuster Children's Publishing.

Watkins, Boyce. Everything You Ever Wanted to Know about College: A Guide for Minority Students. 2004. xiii, 330p. (YA). per. 25.00 (978-0-9742632-0-5(6)) Blue Boy Publishing Co.

Watkins, Dewhite. Quick & Dirty Secrets of College Success: A Professor Tells It All. 2004. 128p. (YA). per. 14.95 (978-0-9742632-1-2(4)) Blue Boy Publishing Co.

Williams, Rozalia. College FAQ Book: Over 5,000 Not Frequently Asked Questions about College! 2005. (Illus.). 494p. (YA). per. 24.95 (978-0-9755103-0-8(4)) Hidden Curriculum Education.

EDUCATION—HISTORY

Brent, Lynnette R. At School. 2003. (Times Change Ser.). (Illus.). 32p. (J). (978-1-4034-4539-1(7)) Heinemann Library.

—At School: Long Ago & Today. 2003. (Times Change Ser.). (Illus.). 32p. (J). lib. bdg. 24.22 (978-1-4034-4533-9(8)) Heinemann Library.

Feldman, Ruth Tenzer. Don't Whistle in School: The History of America's Public Schools. 2005. (People's History Ser.). (Illus.). 96p. (gr. 6-12). lib. bdg. 26.60 (978-0-8225-1745-0(0)) Lerner Publishing Group.

Graves, Kerry A. Going to School During the Civil War: The Confederacy. 2001. (Blue Earth Books). (Illus.). 32p. (J). (gr. 3-4). lib. bdg. 22.60 (978-0-7368-0802-6(7) , Bridgestone Bks.) Capstone Pr., Inc.

—Going to School During the Civil War: The Union. 2001. (Blue Earth Books). (Illus.). 32p. (J). (gr. 3-4). lib. bdg. 22.60 (978-0-7368-0801-9(9) , Bridgestone Bks.) Capstone Pr., Inc.

Harcourt School Publishers Staff. School in the 50s On Level. 3rd ed. 2002. (Trophies Reading Program Ser.). (Illus.). pap. 5.10 (978-0-15-323365-4(6)) Harcourt Schl. Pubs.

Randolph, Ryan P. Frontier Schools & Schoolteachers. 2003. (Library of the Westward Expansion). (Illus.). 24p. (J). lib. bdg. 19.95 (978-0-8239-6295-2(4) , PowerKids Pr.) Rosen Publishing Group, Inc., The.

Rau, Dana Meachen. Going to School in American History. 2006. (J). pap. (978-0-8368-7214-9(2)); lib. bdg. (978-0-8368-7207-1(X)) Stevens, Gareth Inc.

Sateren, Shelley Swanson. Going to School in Colonial America. 2001. (Blue Earth Books). (Illus.). 32p. (J). (gr. 3-4). lib. bdg. 22.60 (978-0-7368-0803-3(5) , Bridgestone Bks.) Capstone Pr., Inc.

Thomas, Mark. School in Colonial America. 2002. (Wel-Colonial America Ser.). (Illus.). 24p. (J). (ps-2). 18.00 (978-0-516-23931-6(7)); pap. 4.95 (978-0-516-23494-6(3)) Scholastic Library Publishing. (Children's Pr.).

—School in Colonial America. 2002. (gr. k-3). lib. bdg. 12.95 (978-0-613-58799-0(5)) Tandem Library Bks.

Townsend, John. Scary Schools & Horrid Homework. 2006. (Illus.). 48p. (J). (978-1-4109-1871-0(8)) Steck-Vaughn.

Woolf, Alex. Education. 2004. (Medieval Realms Ser.). (J). (gr. 7-10). 29.95 (978-1-59018-532-2(3) , Lucent Bks.) Thomson Gale.

EDUCATION, INDUSTRIAL

see Technical Education

EDUCATION, INTERCULTURAL

see Multicultural Education

EDUCATION, MILITARY

see Military Education

EDUCATION, MORAL

see Moral Education

EDUCATION, MUSICAL

see Music—Study and Teaching

EDUCATION—PERSONNEL SERVICE

see Educational Counseling

EDUCATION, PHYSICAL

see Physical Education and Training

EDUCATION, PRESCHOOL

see Nursery Schools

EDUCATION, PRIMARY

see Education, Elementary

EDUCATION, RELIGIOUS

see Religious Education

EDUCATION, SCIENTIFIC

see Science—Study and Teaching

EDUCATION, SECONDARY

Gumm, Merry L. Help! I'm in Middle School... How Will I Survive? 2005. (Illus.). 80p. (J). per. 9.95 (978-0-9761724-5-1(3) , B-HMS) NSR Pubns.

I'm Going to High School: A Guide to the Private High School Admissions Process. 2001. 108p. (J). per. 19.95 (978-0-9670338-2-2(9)) Necessity Breeds Invention.

Modoc Press Editors. Directory of Distance Learning Opportunities: K-12. 2003. 432p. (gr. k-12). 81.95 (978-1-57356-515-8(6) , OXDLK-12) Greenwood Publishing Group, Inc.

Silverthorne, Sandy. Surviving Middle School: How to Manage the Maze. 2006. (Illus.). 96p. (YA). (gr. 3-6). pap. 5.99 (978-0-7847-1433-1(9) , 42175) Standard Publishing.

Zaroulis, Christina. Tackling Your High School Term Paper. 2003. (Students Helping Students Ser.). 80p. (gr. 9-12). pap. 8.95 (978-0-9719392-1-9(7)) Natavi Guides.

EDUCATION, SEGREGATION IN

see Segregation in Education

EDUCATION—STUDY AND TEACHING

see also Teachers—Training of

The Chocolate War: Response Journal. 2003. 36p. (YA). (978-1-58049-995-8(3) , RJ95) Prestwick Hse., Inc.

Monster. 2003. 38p. (YA). tchr. ed., ring bd. (978-1-58049-469-4(2) , TU225) Prestwick Hse., Inc.

School Zone Interactive Staff. Preschool. 2003. (On-Track Software Ser.). (J). (ps up). cd-rom 24.99 (978-1-58947-539-7(9)) School Zone Publishing Co.

Thompson, Karen. Preschool. (ps up). 2004. 54.99 (978-0-7644-0389-7(3)); 2004. 54.99 (978-0-7644-0401-6(6)); 2004. tchr. ed. 19.99 (978-0-7644-0381-1(8)); 2004. tchr. ed. 19.99 (978-0-7644-0395-8(8)); 2004. 54.99 (978-0-7644-0374-3(5)); 2004. tchr. ed. 19.99 (978-0-7644-0368-2(0)); 2003. 54.99 (978-0-7644-0362-0(1)); 2003. tchr. ed. 19.99 (978-0-7644-0356-9(7)) Group Publishing, Inc. (Flagship Church Resources).

—Preschool. 2003. (Software Ser.). (J). 29.99 (978-1-58947-534-2(8)) School Zone Publishing Co.

—Preschool. 2004. (J). stu. ed. 2.69 (978-0-7847-7200-3(2) , 09430) Standard Publishing.

Wolf, Jonathan S. How to Prepare for the AP Physics B. 3rd ed. 2003. (Illus.). 480p. pap. 16.95 (978-0-7641-2359-7(9)) Barron's Educational Series, Inc.

EDUCATION, TECHNICAL

see Technical Education

EDUCATION, THEOLOGICAL

see Religious Education

EDUCATION—VOCATIONAL GUIDANCE

Drury, James H. Dear Willy, Who Needs School? You Do, Fool! 25 Questions & Answers about Education & Your Future. 2002. (Illus.). vii, 153p. (YA). (gr. 7-12). pap. 15.00 (978-0-9725238-0-6(4)) Edsemco, Inc.

Reeves, Diane Lindsey & Karlitz, Gail. Career Ideas for Teens in Education & Training. (Career Ideas for Teens Ser.). 192p. (gr. 6-12). pap. 16.95 (978-0-8160-6919-4(0) , Checkmark Bks.); 2005. (Illus.). (J). 40.00 (978-0-8160-5295-0(6) , Ferguson Publishing Co.) Facts On File, Inc.

Zannos, Susan. Careers in Education. 2001. (Latinos at Work Ser.). (Illus.). 96p. (gr. 5-12). lib. bdg. 22.95 (978-1-58415-081-7(5)) Mitchell Lane Pubs., Inc.

EDUCATION AND STATE

see also Scholarships

Kowalski, Kathiann M. Lemon V. Kurtzman & the Separation of Church & State Debate. 2005. (Debating Supreme Court Decisions Ser.). (Illus.). 128p. (YA). (gr. 7-12). lib. bdg. 26.60 (978-0-7660-2391-8(5)) Enslow Pubs., Inc.

EDUCATION OF CHILDREN

see Education, Elementary

EDUCATION OF GIRLS

see Women—Education

EDUCATION OF THE BLIND

see Blind—Education

EDUCATION OF THE DEAF

see Deaf—Education

EDUCATIONAL ADMINISTRATION

see School Management And Organization

EDUCATIONAL COUNSELING

see also Counseling; Vocational Guidance

Meggie, Mary, et al. Conflict Resolution: A Blueprint for Preventing School Violence. 2001. 121p. (YA). 19.95 (978-0-934623-74-2(0)) Solomon Pr., The.

Who Is Your School Counselor? A Two-Session Program to Familiarize Young Students with the Counselor & the Counselor's Roles. 2002. 24p. 17.95 (978-1-57543-111-6(4)) MAR*CO Products, Inc.

EDUCATIONAL GUIDANCE

see Educational Counseling

EDUCATIONAL MEASUREMENTS

see Educational Tests and Measurements

EDUCATIONAL PSYCHOLOGY

see also Imagination; Perception; Thought and Thinking

Teele, Sue. Rainbows of Intelligence: Exploring How Students Learn. 2000. (Illus.). 184p. pap. 27.95 (978-0-7619-7630-1(2) , 86334) Corwin Pr.

EDUCATIONAL TESTS AND MEASUREMENTS

ACT Reading Victory Student Textbook. 2nd ed. 2005. per. (978-1-58894-033-9(0)) Cambridge Educational Services, Inc.

ACT Science Reasoning Victory Student Textbook. 2nd ed. 2005. per. (978-1-58894-034-6(9)) Cambridge Educational Services, Inc.

Avenues Language & Literacy Tests: Level C Posttest Booklet (10-Pack) 30.00 (978-0-7362-2514-4(5)) Hampton-Brown Bks.

Avenues Language & Literacy Tests: Level D Posttest Booklet (10-Pack) 30.00 (978-0-7362-2516-8(1)) Hampton-Brown Bks.

Avenues Language & Literacy Tests: Level E Posttest Booklet (10-Pack) 30.00 (978-0-7362-2518-2(8)) Hampton-Brown Bks.

Avenues Language & Literacy Tests: Level F Posttest Booklet (10-Pack) 30.00 (978-0-7362-2520-5(X)) Hampton-Brown Bks.

Avenues Unit Progress Tests: Level A Progress Test Booklets (10-Pack) (gr. k up). 40.00 (978-0-7362-2227-3(8)) Hampton-Brown Bks.

Avenues Unit Progress Tests: Level B Progress Test Booklets (10-Pack) (gr. 1 up). 60.00 (978-0-7362-2230-3(8)) Hampton-Brown Bks.

Avenues Unit Progress Tests: Level C Progress Test Booklets - Advanced (10-Pack) (gr. 2 up). 80.00 (978-0-7362-2241-9(3)) Hampton-Brown Bks.

Avenues Unit Progress Tests: Level C Progress Test Booklets - Beginning (10-Pack) (gr. 2 up). 80.00 (978-0-7362-2235-8(9)) Hampton-Brown Bks.

Avenues Unit Progress Tests: Level C Progress Test Booklets - Intermediate (10-Pack) (gr. 2 up). 80.00 (978-0-7362-2238-9(3)) Hampton-Brown Bks.

Avenues Unit Progress Tests: Level D Progress Test Booklets - Advanced (10-Pack) (gr. 3 up). 80.00 (978-0-7362-2252-5(9)) Hampton-Brown Bks.

Avenues Unit Progress Tests: Level D Progress Test Booklets - Beginning (10-Pack) (gr. 3 up). 80.00 (978-0-7362-2246-4(4)) Hampton-Brown Bks.

Avenues Unit Progress Tests: Level D Progress Test Booklets - Intermediate (10-Pack) (gr. 3 up). 80.00 (978-0-7362-2249-5(9)) Hampton-Brown Bks.

Avenues Unit Progress Tests: Level E Progress Test Booklets - Advanced (10-Pack) (gr. 4 up). 80.00 (978-0-7362-2263-1(4)) Hampton-Brown Bks.

Avenues Unit Progress Tests: Level E Progress Test Booklets - Beginning (10-Pack) (gr. 4 up). 80.00 (978-0-7362-2257-0(X)) Hampton-Brown Bks.

Avenues Unit Progress Tests: Level E Progress Test Booklets - Intermediate (10-Pack) (gr. 4 up). 80.00 (978-0-7362-2260-0(X)) Hampton-Brown Bks.

Avenues Unit Progress Tests: Level F Progress Test Booklets - Advanced (10-Pack) (gr. 5 up). 80.00 (978-0-7362-2284-6(7)) Hampton-Brown Bks.

Avenues Unit Progress Tests: Level F Progress Test Booklets - Beginning (10-Pack) (gr. 5 up). 80.00 (978-0-7362-2278-5(2)) Hampton-Brown Bks.

Avenues Unit Progress Tests: Level F Progress Test Booklets - Intermediate (10-Pack) (gr. 5 up). 80.00 (978-0-7362-2281-5(2)) Hampton-Brown Bks.

Bender, Janet. Tyler Tames the Testing Tiger. 2004. (Illus.). 70p. (J). per. 19.95 (978-1-931636-27-8(3)) National Center For Youth Issues.

Book Builders, Inc. Staff & Chin, Beverly. How to Ace Any Test. 2004. (Illus.). 120p. pap. 12.95 (978-0-471-43156-5(7) , Wiley) Wiley, John & Sons, Inc.

Brams, Jolie S. How to Do Your Best on Every Test: Test-Taking Skills for Elementary Students. 2003. 172p. per. 12.95 (978-1-59230-027-3(8)) Englefield & Assocs., Inc.

Brams, Jolie S., contrib. by. Show What You Know on the 6th Grade FCAT. 2002. (J). 2.00 (978-1-884183-81-2(6) , FL1603); (J). stu. ed., per., wbk. ed. 9.95 (978-1-884183-80-5(8) , FL1602); (gr. 6). tchr. ed., per. 14.95 (978-1-884183-79-9(4) , FL1601) Englefield & Assocs., Inc.

—Show What You Know on the 7th Grade FCAT. 2002. (Show What You Know on the FCAT). (YA). 2.00 (978-1-884183-91-1(3) , FL1703); (YA). stu. ed., per., wbk. ed. 9.95 (978-1-884183-90-4(5) , FL1702); (gr. 7). tchr. ed., per. 14.95 (978-1-884183-89-8(1) , FL1701) Englefield & Assocs., Inc.

Brookes, Kate. Revision Sorted! 2003. (Illus.). 160p. (J). pap. (978-0-7502-4173-1(X) , Hodder Wayland) Hodder Children's Division.

Bumcrot, Curt, et al. Achieving Peak Performance Practice Test: Grade 10. 2003. 23p. (YA). (gr. 10 up). pap. 5.00 (978-1-888786-37-8(X)) Basic Skills Assessment & Educational Services.

—Achieving Peak Performance Practice Test New Edition. 2nd rev. ed. 2003. 20p. (J). (gr. 2 up). pap. 5.00 (978-1-888786-40-8(X)) Basic Skills Assessment & Educational Services.

—Achieving Peak Performance Practice Test New Edition. Finley, Mavion, ed. 2nd rev. ed. 2003. 30p. (J). (gr. 3 up). pap. 5.00 (978-1-888786-41-5(8)) Basic Skills Assessment & Educational Services.

Douglas, Vincent. California Test Practice, Grade 5. Spectrum Staff, ed. 2003. (Illus.). 168p. (C). (gr. 5). pap. 15.95 (978-0-7696-3035-9(9) , Spectrum) School Specialty Publishing.

—California Test Practice, Grade 6. Spectrum Staff, ed. 2003. (Illus.). 200p. (C). (gr. 6). pap. 15.95 (978-0-7696-3036-6(7) , Spectrum) School Specialty Publishing.

—Comprehensive Curriculum Plus Test Practice: Grade 6. 2003. (Comprehensive Curriculum Plus Test Practice Ser.). (Illus.). 616p. (J). (ps-6). pap. 24.95 (978-0-7696-2906-3(7) , American Education Publishing) School Specialty Publishing.

—Spectrum California Test Practice, Grade 3. Spectrum Staff, ed. 2003. (Illus.). 176p. (C). (gr. 3). pap. 15.95 (978-0-7696-3033-5(2) , Spectrum) School Specialty Publishing.

—Spectrum California Test Practice, Grade 4. Spectrum Staff, ed. 2003. (Illus.). 192p. (C). (gr. 4). pap. 15.95 (978-0-7696-3034-2(0) , Spectrum) School Specialty Publishing.

—Spectrum Test Prep: Grade 3. 2001. (Spectrum Test Prep Ser.). (Illus.). 160p. (J). (gr. 1-8). pap., wbk. ed. 9.95 (978-1-57768-663-7(2) , Learning Materials) School Specialty Publishing.

—Spectrum Test Prep: Grade 4. 2001. (Spectrum Test Prep Ser.). (Illus.). 160p. (J). (gr. 1-8). pap. 9.95 (978-1-57768-664-4(0) , Learning Materials) School Specialty Publishing.

—Spectrum Test Prep: Grade 5. 2001. (Spectrum Test Prep Ser.). (Illus.). 160p. (J). (gr. 1-8). pap. 9.95 (978-1-57768-665-1(9) , Learning Materials) School Specialty Publishing.

—Spectrum Test Prep: Grade 6. 2001. (Spectrum Test Prep Ser.). (Illus.). 160p. (J). (gr. 1-8). pap. 9.95 (978-1-57768-666-8(7) , Learning Materials) School Specialty Publishing.

—Spectrum Test Prep: Grade 7. Sibbing, Phyllis, ed. 2001. (Spectrum Test Prep Ser.). (Illus.). 160p. (YA). (gr. 1-8). pap. 9.95 (978-1-57768-667-5(5) , Learning Materials) School Specialty Publishing.

—Spectrum Test Prep: Grades 1-2. 2001. (Spectrum Test Prep Ser.). (Illus.). 160p. (J). (gr. 1-8). pap. 9.95 (978-1-57768-662-0(4) , Learning Materials) School Specialty Publishing.

—Spectrum Texas Test Prep: Grade 3. Spectrum Staff, ed. 2003. (Illus.). 200p. (J). (gr. 3). pap. 15.95 (978-0-7696-3073-1(1) , Learning Materials) School Specialty Publishing.

—Spectrum Texas Test Prep: Grade 4. Spectrum Staff, ed. 2003. (Illus.). 200p. (J). (gr. 4). pap. 15.95 (978-0-7696-3074-8(X) , Learning Materials) School Specialty Publishing.

—Spectrum Texas Test Prep: Grade 5. Spectrum Staff, ed. 2003. (Illus.). 200p. (J). (gr. 5). pap. 15.95 (978-0-7696-3075-5(8) , Learning Materials) School Specialty Publishing.

—Spectrum Texas Test Prep: Grade 6. Spectrum Staff, ed. 2003. (Illus.). 200p. (J). (gr. 6). pap. 15.95 (978-0-7696-3076-2(6) , Learning Materials) School Specialty Publishing.

Douglas, Vincent & School Specialty Publishing Staff. Spectrum California Test Practice, Grade 3. 2003. (Spectrum California Test Practice Ser.). (Illus.). 176p. (J). (gr. 3-3). pap. 15.95 (978-0-7696-3003-8(0) , Spectrum) School Specialty Publishing.

—Spectrum California Test Practice, Grade 4. 2003. (Spectrum California Test Practice Ser.). (Illus.). 192p. (J). (gr. 4-4). pap. 15.95 (978-0-7696-3004-5(9) , Spectrum) School Specialty Publishing.

—Spectrum California Test Practice, Grade 5. 2003. (Spectrum California Test Practice Ser.). (Illus.). 168p. (J). (gr. 5-5). pap. 15.95 (978-0-7696-3005-2(7) , Spectrum) School Specialty Publishing.

—Spectrum California Test Practice, Grade 6. 2003. (Spectrum California Test Practice Ser.). (Illus.). 200p. (J). (gr. 6-6). pap. 15.95 (978-0-7696-3006-9(5) , Spectrum) School Specialty Publishing.

—Spectrum Florida Test Prep, Grade 3. 2003. (Spectrum Florida Test Prep Ser.). (Illus.). 160p. (J). (gr. 3-3). pap. 15.95 (978-0-7696-3013-7(8) , Spectrum) School Specialty Publishing.

—Spectrum Florida Test Prep, Grade 4. 2003. (Spectrum Florida Test Prep Ser.). (Illus.). 160p. (J). (gr. 4-4). pap. 15.95 (978-0-7696-3014-4(6) , Spectrum) School Specialty Publishing.

—Spectrum Florida Test Prep, Grade 5. 2003. (Spectrum Florida Test Prep Ser.). (Illus.). 160p. (J). (gr. 5-5). pap. 15.95 (978-0-7696-3015-1(4) , Spectrum) School Specialty Publishing.

—Spectrum Florida Test Prep, Grade 6. 2003. (Spectrum Florida Test Prep Ser.). (Illus.). 160p. (J). (gr. 6-6). pap. 15.95 (978-0-7696-3016-8(2) , Spectrum) School Specialty Publishing.

—Spectrum Georgia Test Prep, Grade 3. 2004. (Spectrum Georgia Ser.). (Illus.). 208p. (J). (gr. 3-3). pap. 15.95 (978-0-7696-3473-9(7) , Spectrum) School Specialty Publishing.

—Spectrum Georgia Test Prep, Grade 4. 2004. (Spectrum Georgia Ser.). (Illus.). 208p. (J). (gr. 4-4). pap. 15.95 (978-0-7696-3474-6(5) , Spectrum) School Specialty Publishing.

—Spectrum Georgia Test Prep, Grade 5. 2004. (Spectrum Georgia Ser.). (Illus.). 224p. (J). (gr. 5-5). pap. 15.95 (978-0-7696-3475-3(3) , Spectrum) School Specialty Publishing.

—Spectrum Georgia Test Prep, Grade 6. 2004. (Spectrum Georgia Ser.). (Illus.). 208p. (J). (gr. 6-6). pap. 15.95 (978-0-7696-3476-0(1) , Spectrum) School Specialty Publishing.

—Spectrum Illinois Test Prep, Grade 3. 2004. (Illinois State Specific Test Prep Ser.). (Illus.). 208p. (J). (gr. 3-3). pap. 15.95 (978-0-7696-3483-8(4) , Spectrum) School Specialty Publishing.

—Spectrum Illinois Test Prep, Grade 4. 2004. (Illinois State Specific Test Prep Ser.). (Illus.). 272p. (J). (gr. 4-4). pap. 15.95 (978-0-7696-3484-5(2) , Spectrum) School Specialty Publishing.

—Spectrum Illinois Test Prep, Grade 5. 2004. (Illinois State Specific Test Prep Ser.). (Illus.). 216p. (J). (gr. 5-5). pap. 15.95 (978-0-7696-3485-2(0) , Spectrum) School Specialty Publishing.

—Spectrum Illinois Test Prep, Grade 6. 2004. (Illinois State Specific Test Prep Ser.). (Illus.). 200p. (J). (gr. 6-6). pap. 15.95 (978-0-7696-3486-9(9) , Spectrum) School Specialty Publishing.

—Spectrum New York Test Prep, Grade 3. 2004. (Spectrum New York Ser.). (Illus.). 160p. (J). (gr. 3-3). pap. 15.95 (978-0-7696-3493-7(1) , Spectrum) School Specialty Publishing.

—Spectrum New York Test Prep, Grade 4. 2004. (Spectrum New York Ser.). (Illus.). 224p. (J). (gr. 4-4). pap. 15.95 (978-0-7696-3494-4(X) , Spectrum) School Specialty Publishing.

—Spectrum New York Test Prep, Grade 5. 2004. (Spectrum New York Ser.). (Illus.). 232p. (J). (gr. 5-5). pap. 15.95 (978-0-7696-3495-1(8) , Spectrum) School Specialty Publishing.

—Spectrum New York Test Prep, Grade 6. 2004. (Spectrum New York Ser.). (Illus.). 184p. (J). (gr. 6-6). pap. 15.95 (978-0-7696-3496-8(6) , Spectrum) School Specialty Publishing.

—Spectrum Pennsylvania Test Prep, Grade 3. 2004. (Pennsylvania State Specific Test Prep Ser.). (Illus.). 184p. (J). (gr. 3-3). pap. 15.95 (978-0-7696-3503-3(2) , Spectrum) School Specialty Publishing.

—Spectrum Pennsylvania Test Prep, Grade 4. 2004. (Pennsylvania State Specific Test Prep Ser.). (Illus.). 160p. (J). (gr. 4-4). pap. 15.95 (978-0-7696-3504-0(0) , Spectrum) School Specialty Publishing.

—Spectrum Pennsylvania Test Prep, Grade 5. 2004. (Pennsylvania State Specific Test Prep Ser.). (Illus.). 168p. (J). (gr. 5-5). pap. 15.95 (978-0-7696-3505-7(9) , Spectrum) School Specialty Publishing.

—Spectrum Pennsylvania Test Prep, Grade 6. 2004. (Pennsylvania State Specific Test Prep Ser.). (Illus.). 168p. (J). (gr. 6-6). pap. 15.95 (978-0-7696-3506-4(7) , Spectrum) School Specialty Publishing.

—Spectrum Test Prep, Grade 8. 2001. (Spectrum Test Prep Ser.). (Illus.). 160p. (YA). (gr. 1-8). pap. 9.95 (978-1-57768-668-2(3) , Learning Materials) School Specialty Publishing.

—Spectrum Texas Test Prep, Grade 3. 2003. (Spectrum Texas Test Prep Ser.). (Illus.). 168p. (J). (gr. 3 up). pap. 15.95 (978-0-7696-3023-6(5) , Spectrum) School Specialty Publishing.

—Spectrum Texas Test Prep, Grade 4. 2003. (Spectrum Texas Test Prep Ser.). (Illus.). 168p. (J). (gr. 4 up). pap. 15.95 (978-0-7696-3024-3(3) , Spectrum) School Specialty Publishing.

—Spectrum Texas Test Prep, Grade 5. 2003. (Spectrum Texas Test Prep Ser.). (Illus.). 200p. (J). (gr. 5 up). pap. 15.95 (978-0-7696-3025-0(1) , Spectrum) School Specialty Publishing.

—Spectrum Texas Test Prep, Grade 6. 2003. (Spectrum Texas Test Prep Ser.). (Illus.). 160p. (J). (gr. 6 up). pap. 15.95 (978-0-7696-3026-7(X) , Spectrum) School Specialty Publishing.

DynaNotes Test Taking Tips. 2006. (J). pap. (978-1-933854-37-3(5)) DynaStudy, Inc.

DynaNotes Test Taking Tips Transparency Set. 2006. (J). trans. (978-1-933854-38-0(3)) DynaStudy, Inc.

Evans, Lesli. Open-Ended Questions, Grade 3. 2005. (Test Connection Ser.). (Illus.). 80p. (J). pap. 10.99 (978-0-7682-3083-3(7) , Schaffer, Frank) Schaffer, Frank Pubns.

—Open-Ended Questions, Grade 4. 2005. (Test Connection Ser.). (Illus.). 80p. (J). pap. 10.99 (978-0-7682-3084-0(5) , Schaffer, Frank) Schaffer, Frank Pubns.

—Open-Ended Questions, Grade 5. 2005. (Test Connection Ser.). (Illus.). 80p. (J). pap. 10.99 (978-0-7682-3085-7(3) , Schaffer, Frank) Schaffer, Frank Pubns.

Farr. Think along to a Better Test. 2002. (J). (gr. 6). pap., tchr. ed. (978-0-7398-6532-3(3)) Steck-Vaughn.

—Think along to Better Test Paper. 2002. (J). pap., tchr. ed. (978-0-7398-6527-9(7)); (gr. 2). pap., tchr. ed. (978-0-7398-6528-6(5)); (gr. 3). pap., tchr. ed. (978-0-7398-6529-3(3)); (gr. 4). pap., tchr. ed. (978-0-7398-6530-9(7)); (gr. 5). pap., tchr. ed. (978-0-7398-6531-6(5)) Steck-Vaughn.

Foreman, Dale, et al. Spectrum Test Prep, Grade 1. 2002. (Starburst Spectrum Ser.). (Illus.). 160p. (J). (gr. 1 up). pap. 9.95 (978-0-7696-3051-9(0) , Spectrum) School Specialty Publishing.

—Spectrum Test Prep, Grade 2. 2002. (Starburst Spectrum Ser.). (Illus.). 160p. (J). (gr. 2 up). pap. 9.95 (978-0-7696-3052-6(9) , Spectrum) School Specialty Publishing.

—Spectrum Test Prep, Grade 3. 2002. (Starburst Spectrum Ser.). (Illus.). 160p. (J). (gr. 3 up). pap. 9.95 (978-0-7696-3053-3(7) , Spectrum) School Specialty Publishing.

—Spectrum Test Prep, Grade 4. 2002. (Starburst Spectrum Ser.). (Illus.). 160p. (J). (gr. 4 up). pap. 9.95 (978-0-7696-3054-0(5) , Spectrum) School Specialty Publishing.

—Spectrum Test Prep, Grade 5. 2002. (Starburst Spectrum Ser.). (Illus.). 160p. (J). (gr. 5 up). pap. 9.95 (978-0-7696-3055-7(3) , Spectrum) School Specialty Publishing.

—Spectrum Test Prep, Grade 8. 2002. (Starburst Spectrum Ser.). (Illus.). 160p. (YA). (gr. 8 up). pap. 9.95 (978-0-7696-3058-8(8) , Spectrum) School Specialty Publishing.

Gilbert, Sara Dulaney. How to Do Your Best on Tests. rev. ed. 1998. (Illus.). 128p. (J). (ps-7). lib. bdg. 12.95 (978-0-613-11649-7(6)) Tandem Library Bks.

Harcourt School Publishers Staff. Harcourt Language Arts: Standardized Test Preparation. 2nd ed. 2003. (Harcourt Language Ser.). (Illus.). (gr. 2 up). 7.60 (978-0-15-321223-9(3)); (gr. 3 up). 7.60 (978-0-15-321224-6(1)); (gr. 4 up). 7.60 (978-0-15-321225-3(X)); (gr. 5 up). 7.60 (978-0-15-321226-0(8)) Harcourt Schl. Pubs.

—Harcourt Science: Standardized Test Preparation. 2001. (Illus.). (gr. 1). pap. 9.20 (978-0-15-320582-8(2)); (gr. 2). pap. 9.20 (978-0-15-320583-5(0)); (gr. 3). pap. 9.20 (978-0-15-320584-2(9)); (gr. 4). pap. 9.60 (978-0-15-320585-9(7)); (gr. 5). pap. 9.60 (978-0-15-320586-6(5)); (gr. 6). pap. 9.60 (978-0-15-320587-3(3)); 2nd ed. (gr. 4 up). pap. 9.10 (978-0-15-334073-4(8)) Harcourt Schl. Pubs.

Holt, Rinehart and Winston Staff. Are You Ready? Intervention. 4th ed. 2003. (Illus.). (J). 73.60 incl. cd-rom (978-0-03-073076-4(7)) Holt, Rinehart & Winston.

—Holt Handbook: Activities & Tests. 3rd ed. 2003. cd-rom 38.53 (978-0-03-073133-4(X)) Holt, Rinehart & Winston.

—Holt Handbook: Activities & Tests Online. 3rd ed. 2003. cd-rom 38.53 (978-0-03-073132-7(1)) Holt, Rinehart & Winston.

—Holt Preparation Workbook: Texas Edition. 3rd ed. 2002. (J). pap. 14.00 (978-0-03-069058-7(7)) Holt, Rinehart & Winston.

Powell, Karen & Hardwick, Georgia. Passing the Georgia High School Social Studies Test. 2nd ed. 1999. (Illus.). 200p. (YA). (gr. 11-12). pap. 12.00 (978-0-89892-193-9(7)) Contemporary Publishing Co. of Raleigh, Inc.

Practice for Standardized Tests. 2000. (gr. 4 up). 52.10 (978-0-673-28950-6(8)) Addison-Wesley Educational Pubs., Inc.

Preparing Your 3rd Grader to Succeed on the MEAP. 2005. (978-0-9789612-0-6(X)) Excellence Student Incentives.

Preparing Your 4th Grader to Succeed on the MEAP. 2005. (978-0-9789612-1-3(8)) Excellence Student Incentives.

Preparing Your 5th Grader to Succeed on the MEAP. 2005. (978-0-9789612-2-0(6)) Excellence Student Incentives.

Ready, Set, Show What You Know: Building Skills for Florida's Comprehensive Assessment Test. 2002. (J). (gr. k-1). stu. ed., per. 10.95 (978-1-884183-96-6(4)); (gr. 2). stu. ed., per. 10.95 (978-1-884183-98-0(0)) Englefield & Assocs., Inc.

Rozakis, Laurie. Be a Super Test Taker! 2007. 128p. (J). pap. 6.99 (978-0-439-87879-1(9) , Scholastic Reference) Scholastic, Inc.

School Specialty Publishing. AEP Test Prep, Grade 3. 2004. (AEP Test Prep Ser.). 80p. (J). (gr. 3-3). pap. 5.95 (978-0-7696-3653-5(5) , American Education Publishing) School Specialty Publishing.

—AEP Test Prep, Grade 4. 2004. (AEP Test Prep Ser.). 80p. (J). (gr. 4-4). pap. 5.95 (978-0-7696-3654-2(3) , American Education Publishing) School Specialty Publishing.

—AEP Test Prep, Grade 5. 2004. (AEP Test Prep Ser.). 80p. (J). (gr. 5-5). pap. 5.95 (978-0-7696-3655-9(1) , American Education Publishing) School Specialty Publishing.

—AEP Test Prep, Grade 6. 2004. (AEP Test Prep Ser.). 80p. (J). (gr. 6-6). pap. 5.95 (978-0-7696-3656-6(X) , American Education Publishing) School Specialty Publishing.

—AEP Test Prep, High School. 2004. (AEP Test Prep Ser.). 80p. (YA). (gr. 9-12). pap. 5.95 (978-0-7696-3657-3(8) , American Education Publishing) School Specialty Publishing.

—Is the Answer Reasonable? The Test Connection. 2004. 48p. (J). (gr. 3 up). pap. 6.99 (978-0-7682-2973-8(1) , FS99325); (J). (gr. 4 up). pap. 6.99 (978-0-7682-2974-5(X) , FS99326); (J). (gr. 5 up). pap. 6.99 (978-0-7682-2975-2(8) , FS99327); (J). (gr. 6 up). pap. 6.99 (978-0-7682-2976-9(6) , FS99328); (YA). (gr. 7 up). pap. 6.99 (978-0-7682-2977-6(4) , FS99329); (YA). (gr. 8 up). pap. 6.99 (978-0-7682-2978-3(2) , FS99330) Schaffer, Frank Pubns.

—Spectrum Science Test Practice, Grade 3. 2006. (Spectrum Science Test Practice Ser.). 96p. (J). pap. 9.95 (978-0-7696-8063-7(1) , Schaffer, Frank) Schaffer, Frank Pubns.

—Spectrum Science Test Practice, Grade 4. 2006. (Spectrum Science Test Practice Ser.). 96p. (J). pap. 9.95 (978-0-7696-8064-4(X) , Schaffer, Frank) Schaffer, Frank Pubns.

—Spectrum Science Test Practice, Grade 5. 2006. (Spectrum Science Test Practice Ser.). 96p. (J). pap. 9.95 (978-0-7696-8065-1(8) , Schaffer, Frank) Schaffer, Frank Pubns.

—Spectrum Science Test Practice, Grade 6. 2006. (Spectrum Science Test Practice Ser.). 96p. (J). pap. 9.95 (978-0-7696-8066-8(6) , Schaffer, Frank) Schaffer, Frank Pubns.

—Spectrum Science Test Practice, Grade 7. 2006. (Spectrum Science Test Practice Ser.). 96p. (J). pap. 9.95 (978-0-7696-8067-5(4) , Schaffer, Frank) Schaffer, Frank Pubns.

—Spectrum Science Test Practice, Grade 8. 2006. (Spectrum Science Test Practice Ser.). 96p. (J). pap. 9.95 (978-0-7696-8068-2(2) , Schaffer, Frank) Schaffer, Frank Pubns.

—The Test Connection Reading, Grade 2. 2004. 144p. (C). pap. 15.99 (***978-0-7682-2812-0(3)*** , Schaffer, Frank) Schaffer, Frank Pubns.

—The Test Connection Reading, Grade 3. 2004. 144p. (C). pap. 15.99 (***978-0-7682-2813-7(1)*** , Schaffer, Frank) Schaffer, Frank Pubns.

—The Test Connection Reading, Grade 4. 2004. 144p. (C). pap. 15.99 (***978-0-7682-2814-4(X)*** , Schaffer, Frank) Schaffer, Frank Pubns.

—The Test Connection Reading, Grade 5. 2004. 144p. (C). pap. 15.99 (***978-0-7682-2815-1(8)*** , Schaffer, Frank) Schaffer, Frank Pubns.

—The Test Connection Reading, Grade 6. 2004. 144p. (C). pap. 15.99 (***978-0-7682-2816-8(6)*** , Schaffer, Frank) Schaffer, Frank Pubns.

Shostak, Jerome & Peters, Max. SSAT/ISEE: How to Prepare for the High School Entrance Examinations. 9th ed. 2001. (Illus.). viii, 626p. (YA). mass mkt. 14.95 (978-0-7641-1380-2(1)) Barron's Educational Series, Inc.

Show What You Know on the 4th Grade FCAT. 2001. (Show What You Know on the FCAT). (J). (gr. 4). 2.00 (978-1-884183-76-8(X) , Fl1403) Englefield & Assocs., Inc.

Show What You Know on the FCAT 8, New English Language Arts Student Self Study Workbook. 2006. (YA). per. 16.95 (978-1-59230-179-9(7)) Englefield & Assocs., Inc.

Show What You Know on the FCAT, Grade 8 Math Student Self Study Workbook. 2006. (YA). per. 16.95 (978-1-59230-177-5(0)) Englefield & Assocs., Inc.

Show What You Know on the OAT for Grade 7, Math Student Workbook. 2006. (J). per. 16.95 (978-1-59230-174-4(6)) Englefield & Assocs., Inc.

Show What You Know on the OAT for Grade 7, Reading/Writing Student Workbook. 2006. (J). per. 16.95 (978-1-59230-172-0(X)) Englefield & Assocs., Inc.

Show What You Know on the OAT for Grade 8, Social Studies, Student Self Study Workbook. 2006. (YA). per. 16.95 (978-1-59230-176-8(2)) Englefield & Assocs., Inc.

Show What You Know on the TAKS for Grade 4, Spanish Student Workbook. 2006. (J). per. 12.95 (978-1-59230-207-9(6)) Englefield & Assocs., Inc.

Show What You Know on the TAKS for Grade 5, Student Workbook, Second Edition. 2006. (J). per. 16.95 (978-1-59230-197-3(5)) Englefield & Assocs., Inc.

Show What You Know on the TAKS, Grade 3. 2004. (SPA.). (J). 14.95 (978-1-59230-102-7(9)); 14.95 (978-1-59230-103-4(7)) Englefield & Assocs., Inc.

Show What You Know on the WASL, 3 Grade Student Workbook (2nd Edition) 2006. (J). per. 13.95 (978-1-59230-183-6(5)) Englefield & Assocs., Inc.

Show What You Know on the WASL Grade 7, 2nd Edition Student Workbook. 2006. (J). per. 13.95 (978-1-59230-185-0(1)) Englefield & Assocs., Inc.

Show What You Know Publishing, creator. Show What You Know on the OAT for Grade 4 Practice Test Workbook. 2007. (J). per. (***978-1-59230-271-0(8)***) Englefield & Assocs., Inc.

Sico, John J., Jr. Pre-ESPA Success Work-a-Text in Mathematics. 2002. (J). 25p. pap. (978-1-56749-532-4(X)); 120p. pap. (978-1-56749-531-7(1)) Instructivision, Inc.

Standardized Test Preparation Binder 1. 2002. (Illus.). 100p. (YA). ring bd. 29.95 (978-1-56254-595-6(7) , SP5957) Saddleback Educational Publishing.

Standardized Test Preparation Binder 2. 2002. (Illus.). 100p. (YA). ring bd. 29.95 (978-1-56254-594-9(9) , SP5949) Saddleback Educational Publishing.

Steck-Vaughn Staff. GED 2001: Hardware with Site Life: Macintosh Edition. 1998. (YA). cd-rom (978-0-8114-9866-1(2)) Steck-Vaughn.

—Half-Length Practice Test. 2002. (Illus.). pap. (978-0-7398-5433-4(X)); (J). pap. (978-0-7398-5434-1(8)) Steck-Vaughn.

—Half-Length Practice Test PC. 2002. (J). pap. (978-0-7398-5435-8(6)) Steck-Vaughn.

—Pre-GED Complete Preparation. 2004. (Illus.). pap. 13.95 (978-0-7398-8785-1(8)) Steck-Vaughn.

Terkel, Marni & Terkel, Susan Neiburg. What's an "A" Anyway? How Important Are Grades? 2001. (Single Titles Social Studies Ser.). (Illus.). 144p. (YA). (gr. 7-9). 26.00 (978-0-531-11417-9(1) , Watts, Franklin) Scholastic Library Publishing.

Timeless Voices, Timeless Themes. 2001. (YA). Gold Level (gr. 9). pap. 24.47 (978-0-13-436131-4(8)); Platinum Level (gr. 10). pap. 24.47 (978-0-13-436132-1(6)) Prentice Hall PTR.

Timeless Voices, Timeless Themes: Copper, Standardized Test Preparation Blackline Masters. 2001. (J). (gr. 6). pap. 19.97 (978-0-13-043575-0(9)) Prentice-Hall.

Timeless Voices, Timeless Themes: Copper, Standardized Test Preparation Workbook. 2001. (J). (gr. 6). pap., wbk. ed. 6.97 (978-0-13-050608-5(7)) Prentice Hall PTR.

Timeless Voices, Timeless Themes: Gold, Standardized Test Preparation Answers & Explanations. 2001. (YA). (gr. 9). trans. 129.97 (978-0-13-050822-5(5)) Prentice Hall PTR.

Timeless Voices, Timeless Themes: Gold, Standardized Test Preparation Notes. 2001. (YA). (gr. 9). trans. 109.97 (978-0-13-052186-6(8)) Prentice Hall PTR.

Timeless Voices, Timeless Themes: Standardized Test Preparation Answers & Explanations, Platinum. 2001. (YA). (gr. 10). trans. 129.97 (978-0-13-050823-2(3)) Prentice Hall PTR.

Turkington, Carol & Maack, Molly. Get Ready! for Standardized Tests: Reading Grade 1. 2001. (Get Ready for Standardized Tests Ser.). (Illus.). 168p. (gr. 1). pap. 14.95 (978-0-07-137405-7(1)) McGraw-Hill Cos., The.

Ty-Mc Productions Staff, prod. Thinking Caps for the MAP. 2002. (Illus.). 62p. (J). (gr. 3-4). pap., stu. ed. 19.99 (978-0-9723982-2-0(8)) Ty-Mc Productions, Inc.

Ulrich, Louise & Turkington, Carol. Get Ready! for Standardized Tests: Reading Grade 2. 2001. (Get Ready for Standardized Tests Ser.). (Illus.). 216p. (gr. 2). pap. 14.95 (978-0-07-137406-4(X) , 9780071374064) McGraw-Hill Cos., The.

Ulrich, Louise, et al. Get Ready! for Standardized Tests: Reading Grade 3. 2001. (Get Ready for Standardized Tests Ser.). (Illus.). 216p. (gr. 3). pap. 14.95 (978-0-07-137407-1(8) , 9780071374071) McGraw-Hill Cos., The.

Vanderveen, Pam. Acing the State Reading Assessment: Grade 10. 2003. 128p. pap. 9.95 (978-1-58049-326-0(2) , PWH3262A) Prestwick Hse., Inc.

Verdick, Elizabeth & Romain, Trevor. True or False? Tests Stink! 2004. (Laugh & Learn Ser.). (Illus.). 88p. (YA). (gr. 3-8). pap. 8.95 (978-1-57542-073-8(2)) Free Spirit Publishing, Inc.

You Rock... the SATs. (Illus.). (J). pap. 14.95 (978-0-439-40867-7(9)) Scholastic, Inc.

EDUCATORS

see also Teachers

Amper, Thomas. Booker T. Washington. Reeves, Jeni, illus. (On My Own Biographies Ser.). 48p. 2003. (J). (gr. 1-3). pap. 5.95 (978-0-87614-534-0(9) , Carolrhoda Bks.); 1998. (gr. 2-5). lib. bdg. 23.93 (978-1-57505-094-2(3)) Lerner Publishing Group.

Booker T Washington. (Photo Illustrated Biographies Ser.). 24p. (J). 6.95 (978-1-56065-942-6(4)); 32p. (YA). 7.95 (978-0-7368 6190 8(4)); Vol. 2. 2005. (YA). (978-0-7368-3379-0(X) , Pebble Bks.) Capstone Pr., Inc.

Braun, Eric. Booker T. Washington: Great American Educator. Martin, Cynthia, illus. 2005. (Graphic Library). 32p. (J). (gr. 3-7). lib. bdg. 25.26 (978-0-7368-4630-1(1)) Capstone Pr., Inc.

Durden, Robert F. Carter G. Woodson: Father of African-American History. 1998. (African-American Biographies Ser.). (Illus.). 128p. (YA). (gr. 6-12). lib. bdg. 26.60 (978-0-89490-946-7(0)) Enslow Pubs., Inc.

Ferris, Jeri Chase. Demanding Justice: A Story about Mary Ann Shadd Cary. Smith, Kimanne, illus. 2003. 64p. (J). 6.95 (978-0-87614-928-7(X) , Carolrhoda Bks.); (gr. 4-8). 22.60 (978-1-57505-177-2(X)) Lerner Publishing Group.

—Demanding Justice: A Story about Mary Ann Shadd Cary. 2003. (gr. 3-6). lib. bdg. 14.10 (978-0-613-58898-0(3)) Tandem Library Bks.

Frost, Helen. Let's Meet Booker T. Washington. 2003. (Let's Meet Biographies Ser.). (Illus.). 32p. (gr. 2-4). 23.00 (978-0-7910-7318-6(1) , Chelsea Hse.) Facts On File, Inc.

Gonzales Bertrand, Diane. Ricardo's Race: La Carrera de Ricardo. (SPA.). (J). 15.95 (***978-1-55885-481-9(9)***) Arte Publico Pr.

Gosda, Randy T. Booker T. Washington. 2002. (First Biographies Ser.). (Illus.). 32p. (J). (gr. k-4). lib. bdg. 22.78 (978-1-57765-734-7(9) , Buddy Bks.) ABDO Publishing Co.

Harcourt School Publishers Staff. Booker T. Washington: Library Edition. 1999. (Collections Ser.). (Illus.). (J). 5.30 (978-0-15-314344-1(4)) Harcourt Schl. Pubs.

Marsh, Carole. Booker T. Washington. 2002. (One Thousand Readers Ser.). (Illus.). 12p. (J). (gr. k-4). 2.95 (978-0-635-01479-5(3) , 14793) Gallopade International.

E
F
G

McKissack, Patricia C. & McKissack, Fredrick L. Booker T. Washington: Leader & Educator. rev. ed. 2001. (Great African Americans Ser.). (Illus.). 32p. (J). (gr. 1-4). lib. bdg. 18.60 (978-0-7660-1679-8(X)) Enslow Pubs., Inc.

Mitchell, Melanie. Principals. 2005. (Pull Ahead Bks.). (Illus.). 32p. (J). lib. bdg. 22.60 (978-0-8225-1694-1(2)) Lerner Publishing Group.

Naden, Corinne J. & Blue, Rose. Condoleeza Rice. 2004. (African-American Biographies Ser.). (Illus.). 64p. (J). 28.56 (978-1-4109-1039-4(3)) Raintree.

Nava, Julian. Julian Nava: My Mexican-American Journey. 2002. (Hispanic Civil Rights Ser.). 248p. (YA). 16.95 (978-1-55885-364-5(2) , Piñata Books) Arte Publico Pr.

—Julian Nava: My Mexican-American Journey. 2002. (gr. 7-12). lib. bdg. 18.75 (978-0-613-82668-6(X)) Tandem Library Bks.

Nicholson, Lois P. Booker T. Washington - Educator/Activist: A Modern Moses. 1998. (Junior Black Americans of Achievement Ser.). (Illus.). 80p. (J). (gr. 3-6). pap. 10.20 (978-0-7910-4461-2(0) , Chelsea Hse.) Facts On File, Inc.

Schaefer, Lola M. Booker T. Washington. Saunders-Smith, Gail, ed. 2003. (First Biographies Ser.). (Illus.). 24p. (J). (gr. k-1). lib. bdg. 15.93 (978-0-7368-1647-2(X) , Pebble Bks.) Capstone Pr., Inc.

Schraff, Anne E. Booker T. Washington: Character Is Power. 2006. (African-American Biography Library). (Illus.). 128p. (J). lib. bdg. 31.93 (978-0-7660-2535-6(7)) Enslow Pubs., Inc.

Schroeder, Alan. Booker T. Washington: Educator & Racial Spokesman. (Black Americans of Achievement Ser.). (Illus.). 112p. (J). (gr. 6-12). 2005. pap. 13.25 (978-0-7910-8374-1(8)); 2004. 30.00 (978-0-7910-8253-9(9)) Facts On File, Inc. (Chelsea Hse.).

Spielman, Gloria. Janusz Korczak's Children. 2007. (Kar-Ben for Older Readers Ser.). (Illus.). (J). (gr. 2-5). 17.95 (978-1-58013-255-8(3)) Kar-Ben Publishing.

—Janusz Korczak's Children. Archambault, Matthew, illus. 2007. (Kar-Ben for Older Readers Ser.). (J). (gr. 2-5). pap. 7.95 (***978-0-8225-7050-9(5)***) Kar-Ben Publishing.

Swain, Gwenyth. A Hunger for Learning: A Story about Booker T. Washington. Johnson, Larry, illus. (Creative Minds Biography Ser.). 64p. (J). 2006. (gr. 3-7). lib. bdg. 22.60 (978-1-57505-754-5(9)); 2005. (gr. 4-8). pap. 6.95 (978-0-8225-3090-9(2)) Lerner Publishing Group.

Taylor-Butler, Christine. Booker T. Washington. 2006. (Illus.). 31p. (J). (978-0-516-29842-9(9)) Children's Pr., Ltd.

Thoennes Keller, Kristin. Booker T. Washington. 2005. (Fact Finders Ser.). (Illus.). 32p. (J). (978-0-7368-4343-0(4)) Capstone Pr., Inc.

—Booker T. Washington: Innovative Educator. 2006. (J). (978-0-7565-1881-3(4)) Compass Point Bks.

Wilds, Mary. I Dare Not Fail: Notable African American Women Educators. 2004. (Avisson Young Adult Ser.). 139p. (J). pap. 19.95 (978-1-888105-64-3(X)) Avisson Pr., Inc.

EDWARD VI, KING OF ENGLAND, 1537-1553—FICTION

Olmstead, Kathleen & Twain, Mark. The Prince & the Pauper. Akib, Jamel, illus. 2007. (Classic Starts Ser.). 152p. (J). (***978-1-4287-4214-7(X)***) Sterling Publishing Co., Inc.

Twain, Mark. The Prince & the Pauper. Lynch, Brendan, illus. 2002. (Great Illustrated Classics Ser.). 240p. (J). (gr. 3-8). 21.35 (978-1-57765-698-2(9) , ABDO & Daughters) ABDO Publishing Co.

—The Prince & the Pauper. (J). 19.95 (978-0-8488-0849-5(5)) Amereon LTD.

—The Prince & the Pauper. 2007. (Bantam Classics Ser.). 224p. (J). (gr. 4-11). pap. 3.95 (978-0-553-21256-3(7) , Bantam Classics) Bantam Bks.

—The Prince & the Pauper. 1999. reprint ed. pap. 28.00 (978-1-4047-1120-4(1)) Classic Textbooks.

—The Prince & the Pauper. 2000. (Thrift Edition Ser.). 176p. (gr. 6). pap. 2.50 (978-0-486-41110-1(9)) Dover Pubns., Inc.

—The Prince & the Pauper. (YA). (gr. 5-12). pap. 6.50 (978-0-8224-9344-0(6)) Globe Fearon Educational Publishing.

—The Prince & the Pauper. (J). 9.95 (978-1-56156-311-1(0)) Kidsbooks, Inc.

—The Prince & the Pauper. l.t. ed. 2000. (Large Print Heritage Ser.). 364p. (J). lib. bdg. 33.95 (978-1-58118-068-8(3) , 23662) LRS.

—The Prince & the Pauper. 2003. (Modern Library Classics). (Illus.). 240p. pap. 8.95 (978-0-375-76112-6(8) , Modern Library) Random House Publishing Group.

—The Prince & the Pauper. Akib, Jamel, illus. 2007. (Classic Starts Ser.). 160p. (J). 4.95 (978-1-4027-3687-2(8)) Sterling Publishing Co., Inc.

—The Prince & the Pauper. l.t. ed. 2000. (Perennial Bestsellers Ser.). 307p. (J). 26.95 (978-0-7838-9061-6(3)) Thorndike Pr.

—The Prince & the Pauper. 1998. (Children's Library). 288p. (J). pap. 3.95 (978-1-85326-147-3(5) , 1475WW) Wordsworth Editions, Ltd. GBR. *Dist:* Combined Publishing.

—The Prince & the Pauper: With a Discussion of Respect. 2003. (Values in Action Illustrated Classics Ser.). (J). (978-1-59203-052-1(1)) Learning Challenge, Inc.

EDWARDS, JONATHAN, 1703-1758

Crompton, Samuel Willard. Jonathan Edwards. 2004. (Spiritual Leaders & Thinkers Ser.). (Illus.). 120p. (gr. 9-13). 30.00 (978-0-7910-8103-7(6) , Chelsea Hse.) Facts On File, Inc.

EEYORE (FICTITIOUS CHARACTER)—FICTION

Kennedy, Marge. The Book of Boo! 2002. (Illus.). 32p. (ps-1). 5.99 (978-0-7868-3364-1(5)) Disney Pr.

Krensky, Stephen. Eeyore Has a Birthday. 2001. 10.79 (978-0-606-22514-4(5)) Tandem Library Bks.

Milne, A. A. Where Is Eeyore: Slide & Find Books. Shepard, Ernest H., illus. 2001. 8p. (J). (ps-k). bds. 6.99 (978-0-525-46540-9(5) , Dutton Juvenile) Penguin Group (USA) Inc.

EGGS

see also Birds—Eggs and Nests

Amazing Eggs: Individual Title Six-Packs. (Discovery World Ser.). 16p. (gr. 1-2). 28.00 (978-0-7635-8455-9(X)) Rigby Education.

Aston, Dianna Hutts. An Egg Is Quiet. Long, Sylvia, illus. 2006. (J). 16.95 (978-0-8118-5554-9(6)); 36p. 16.95 (978-0-8118-4428-4(5)) Chronicle Bks. LLC.

Bentley, Joyce. Eggs. 2005. (Illus.). 32p. (J). (gr. 2 up). lib. bdg. 27.10 (978-1-59389-219-7(5)) Chrysalis Education.

Burton, Jane. Egg: A Photographic Story of Hatching. 2000. (978-0-606-17807-5(4)) Tandem Library Bks.

Burton, Jane & Taylor, Kim. The Nature & Science of Eggs. Burton, Jane & Taylor, Kim, photos by. 1998. (Exploring the Science of Nature Ser.). (Illus.). 32p. (J). (gr. 3 up). lib. bdg. 23.93 (978-0-8368-2105-5(X)) Stevens, Gareth Inc.

Chicken & Egg. 2003. (J). 36.95 (978-0-8136-9274-6(1)) Modern Curriculum Pr.

Curry, Don L. What Hatches? 2000. (Yellow Umbrella Books). (Illus.). 16p. (J). (gr. 1). lib. bdg. 14.60 (978-0-7368-0721-0(7) , Pebble Bks.) Capstone Pr., Inc.

Egg Incubators: MainSails Individual Title Six-Packs. (Sails Literacy Ser.). (gr. 5 up). 37.00 (978-0-7578-8040-7(1)) Rigby Education.

Eggs! (Little Book Practice Reader). (J). (978-0-8136-5350-1(9)) Modern Curriculum Pr.

Eggs, Eggs, Eggs, 6 Pks. (Sails Literacy Ser.). (gr. 1-2). 36.00 (978-0-7578-6732-3(4)) Rigby Education.

Eggs, Eggs, Eggs: 3-in-1 Package. (Sails Literacy Ser.). 24p. (gr. 1 up). 57.00 (978-0-7578-3206-2(7)) Rigby Education.

Eggs, Eggs, Eggs: 6 Small Books. (Sails Literacy Ser.). 24p. (gr. 1 up). 25.00 (978-0-7578-3182-9(6)) Rigby Education.

Eggs, Eggs, Eggs: Big Book Only. (Sails Literacy Ser.). 24p. (gr. 1 up). 27.00 (978-0-7635-5930-4(X)) Rigby Education.

Eggs, Eggs, Eggs: Level L, 6 vols. (Wonder Worldtm Ser.). 16p. 34.95 (978-0-7802-1990-8(2)) Wright Group, The.

Eggs in the Sun, 6 Pks. (Sails Literacy Ser.). (gr. 1-2). 36.00 (978-0-7578-6709-5(X)) Rigby Education.

Equipo Staff. Crea con Huevos. (Coleccion Manualidades Divertidas).Tr. of Making Things with Eggs. (SPA.). 76p. (J). (gr. k-3). 10.00 (978-84-342-1899-4(2)) Parramon Ediciones S.A. ESP. *Dist:* Distribuidora Norma, Inc., Lectorum Pubns., Inc.

Frank, Marjorie Slavick, et al. Science Leveled Libraries: Eggs. 3rd ed. 2003. (Harcourt Science Ser.). (gr. 3 up). pap. 25.60 (978-0-15-326940-0(5)) Harcourt Schl. Pubs.

Ganeri, Anita. From Egg to Chicken. 2006. (Heinemann First Library). (Illus.). 32p. (J). (978-1-4034-7867-2(8)); (978-1-4034-7858-0(9)) Heinemann Library.

Gill, Shelley R. The Egg. Bosson, Jo-Ellen, illus. 2001. 32p. (J). (ps-5). 16.95 (978-1-57091-377-8(3)); pap. 6.95 (978-1-57091-378-5(1)) Charlesbridge Publishing, Inc.

Harcourt School Publishers Staff. Animal Babies That Hatch. 3rd ed. 2002. (Trophies English Language Learners Ser.). (Illus.). pap. 5.10 (978-0-15-327649-1(5)) Harcourt Schl. Pubs.

—Eggs On Level. 3rd ed. 2002. (Trophies Reading Program Ser.). (Illus.). pap. 5.10 (978-0-15-323266-4(8)); pap. 5.10 (978-0-15-323090-5(8)) Harcourt Schl. Pubs.

Heller, Ruth. Chickens Aren't the Only Ones. 1999. (Ruth Heller's World of Nature Ser.). (Illus.). 48p. (J). (ps-3). pap. 7.99 (978-0-698-11778-5(6) , Putnam Juvenile) Penguin Group (USA) Inc.

—Chickens Aren't the Only Ones. 1999. (gr. k-3). lib. bdg. 16.45 (978-0-613-73469-1(6)); (J). 14.79 (978-0-606-16792-5(7)) Tandem Library Bks.

—Chickens Aren't the Only Ones: Big Book. l.t. ed. (FRE., Illus.). (J). bds. 29.95 (978-0-590-73732-6(5)) Scholastic, Inc.

James, Susan. The Amazing Egg. 2002. (Spyglass Books). (Illus.). 24p. (J). (gr. 1 up). lib. bdg. 18.60 (978-0-7565-0225-6(X)) Compass Point Bks.

Lakeshore Learning Materials Staff, contrib. by. Egg Hatching Activity Kit. 2000. (J). pap. 24.95 (978-1-929255-72-6(1)) Lakeshore Learning Materials.

Legg, Gerald & Salariya, David. From Egg to Chicken. Scrace, Carolyn, illus. 1998. (Life Cycles Ser.). 32p. (J). (gr. k-2). 25.50 (978-0-531-14490-9(9) , Watts, Franklin) Scholastic Library Publishing.

Martineau, Susan. Healthy Eating. 2006. (Illus.). 32p. (J). (978-1-58340-893-3(2) , 1262657) Smart Apple Media.

Mettler, Ren'e. El Huevo. (Coleccion Mundo Maravilloso). (SPA., Illus.). 40p. (J). (gr. 2-4). (978-84-348-3468-2(5) , SM5468) SM Ediciones ESP. *Dist:* Lectorum Pubns., Inc.

Metz, Lynn. Every Egg: Learning the Short E Sound. (PowerPhonics Ser.). (Illus.). (J). 2002. 24p. (gr. 1). lib. bdg. 18.50 (978-0-8239-5909-9(0)); 2001. 23p. pap. 26.40 (978-0-8239-8254-7(8)) Rosen Publishing Group, Inc., The. (PowerKids Pr.).

Pascoe, Elaine. Animals Hatch from Eggs. Kuhn, Dwight, photos by. 2002. (Springboards into Science Ser.). (Illus.). 24p. (J). (gr. 1 up). lib. bdg. 20.67 (978-0-8368-3004-0(0)) Stevens, Gareth Inc.

—How & Why Animals Hatch from Eggs. Kupperstein, Joel, ed. Kuhn, Dwight, photos by. 2000. (How & Why Ser.). (Illus.). 16p. (J). (gr. 1-3). pap. 2.99 (978-1-57471-660-3(3) , 2967) Creative Teaching Pr., Inc.

Patchett, Fiona. Eggs & Chicks. 2004. (Beginners Ser.). (Illus.). 32p. (J). (gr. 1 up). pap. 4.95 (978-0-7945-0166-2(4) , Usborne); lib. bdg. 12.95 (978-1-58086-482-4(1)) EDC Publishing.

Patchett, Fiona. Eggs & Chicks - Internet Referenced (Level 1) 2007. 32p. (J). 4.99 (***978-0-7945-1342-9(5)*** , Usborne) EDC Publishing.

Posada, Mia. Guess What Is Growing Inside This Egg. 2007. 32p. (J). (gr. k-4). spiral bd. 15.95 (978-0-8225-6192-7(1) , Millbrook Pr.) Lerner Publishing Group.

Raintree Steck-Vaughn Staff. Quiénes Ponen Huevos? 1999. (Coleccion en Parejas). (SPA.). (J). pap., stu. ed. 21.50 (978-0-7398-0835-1(4)) Steck-Vaughn.

Renne. Animals & Their Eggs. Taurel, Alison, tr. from DUT. Renne, illus. 2000. (Animals Up Close Ser.). (Illus.). 38p. (J). (gr. 3 up). lib. bdg. 24.67 (978-0-8368-2714-9(7)) Stevens, Gareth Inc.

Rigby Education Staff. Discovery World Org Amazing Egg Big Book. (Discovery World Ser.). (Illus.). 12p. (gr. 1-2). 27.00 (978-0-7635-2699-3(1)) Rigby Education.

—What's in an Egg? (Illus.). 16p. (J). pap. 3.95 (978-0-7635-6459-9(1) , 764591C99) Rigby Education.

Shelley, Gil. The Egg. 2001. 13.75 (978-0-606-22633-2(8)) Tandem Library Bks.

Singer, Marilyn. Eggs. Kratter, Paul, illus. 2003. (J). (978-0-8234-1727-8(1)) Holiday Hse., Inc.

Sklansky, Amy E. Where Do Chicks Come From? Paparone, Pam, illus. 2005. (Let's-Read-and-Find-Out Science Ser.). 40p. (J). (ps-1). 15.99 (978-0-06-028892-1(2)) HarperCollins Pubs.

—Where Do Chicks Come From? Paparone, Pamela, illus. 2005. (I Can Read Bks.). 40p. (J). (ps-1). pap. 5.99 (978-0-06-445212-0(3)) HarperCollins Pubs.

—Where Do Chicks Come From? Paparone, Pam, illus. 2005. (I Can Read Science Bks.). 40p. (J). (ps-1). lib. bdg. 16.89 (978-0-06-028893-8(0)) HarperCollins Pubs.

Spilsbury, Louise. Eggs. 2001. (Food Ser.). (Illus.). 32p. (J). (gr. k-2). lib. bdg. 21.36 (978-1-58810-144-0(4)) Heinemann Library.

Stone, Lynn M. Eggs. 2002. (Harvest to Home Ser.). (Illus.). 24p. (gr. 2-5). 14.95 (978-1-58952-126-1(9)) Rourke Publishing, LLC.

—From an Egg. 2007. (Illus.). 24p. (J). (978-1-60044-172-1(6)) Rourke Publishing, LLC.

The Swamp Eggs: 3-in-1 Package. (Sails Literacy Ser.). 24p. (gr. k up). 57.00 (978-0-7578-3202-4(4)) Rigby Education.

The Swamp Eggs: 6 Small Books. (Sails Literacy Ser.). 24p. (gr. k up). 25.00 (978-0-7578-3178-2(8)) Rigby Education.

The Swamp Eggs: Big Book Only. (Sails Literacy Ser.). 24p. (gr. k up). 27.00 (978-0-7635-6991-4(7)) Rigby Education.

Warren, Jean. Eggs. Cubley, Kathleen, ed. 1998. (Sticker Book Ser.). (Illus.). 32p. (J). (ps). pap. 3.95 (978-1-57029-217-0(5) , WPH 3707, Totline Pubns.) Schaffer, Frank Pubns.

Windsor, Jo. Eggs: Early Level Satellite Individual Title Six-Packs. (Sails Literacy Ser.). 16p. (gr. 1-2). 27.00 (978-0-7578-2914-7(7)) Rigby Education.

EGGS—FICTION

Ada, Alma Flor. Daniel's Mystery Egg. Karas, G. Brian, illus. 2003. (Green Light Readers Level 2 Ser.). 24p. (J). 11.95 (978-0-15-204885-3(5)); pap. 3.95 (978-0-15-204845-7(6)) Harcourt Children's Bks. (Green Light Readers).

—Daniel's Mystery Egg. 2001. (978-0-606-22612-7(5)); lib. bdg. 11.80 (978-0-613-64169-2(8)) Tandem Library Bks.

—Daniel's Mystery Egg: La Sorpresa de Daniel. Ada, Alma Flor & Campoy, F. Isabel, trs. from EST. Karas, G. Brian, illus. 2007. (Green Light Readers Level 2 Ser.). (ENG & SPA.). 28p. (J). 12.95 (978-0-15-205966-8(0)); pap. 3.95 (978-0-15-205971-2(7)) Harcourt Trade Pubs.

—A Surprise for Mother Rabbit. 2000. (gr. k-3). lib. bdg. 17.60 (978-0-613-79391-9(9)) Tandem Library Bks.

Alexander, Heather. The Case of the Easter Egg Race. 2004. 84p. (J). (ps-17). 11.79 (978-0-606-32976-7(5)) Tandem Library Bks.

Artifact Group. Follow That Egg! 2008. (Backyardigans Ser.). 24p. (J). pap. 3.99 (***978-1-4169-5040-0(0)*** , Simon Spotlight/Nickelodeon) Simon & Schuster Children's Publishing.

Auch, Mary Jane. The Easter Egg Farm. Auch, Mary Jane, illus. (Illus.). 36p. (J). (gr. k-3). tchr. ed. 17.95 (978-0-8234-0917-4(1)) Holiday Hse., Inc.

—Egg Series, 2 bks., Set. Auch, Mary Jane, illus. 2000. (Illus.). (J). (gr. k-3). pap. 29.95 incl. audio (978-0-87499-572-5(8)) Live Oak Media.

Balaban, Mariah, ed. Easter Egg Hunt. 2007. (Care Bears Ser.). (J). bds. 5.99 (978-0-439-89465-4(4)) Scholastic, Inc.

Black, Andy. Little Joe's Big Race. Archbold, Tim, illus. 2004. (Read-It! Readers Ser.). 32p. (C). (gr. k-3). 18.60 (978-1-4048-0063-2(8)) Picture Window Bks.

Blackaby, Susan. Hatching Chicks. Muehlenhardt, Amy Bailey, illus. 2004. (Read-It! Readers Classroom Tales Ser.). 32p. (C). (gr. k-3). 18.60 (978-1-4048-0585-9(0)) Picture Window Bks.

Bloch, Chana. Mrs. Dumpty. 1998. 80p. (J). 26.95 (978-0-299-16000-5(9)); pap. 11.95 (978-0-299-16004-3(1)) Univ. of Wisconsin Pr.

Boniface, William. Five Little Easter Eggs. Adams, Lynn, illus. 2003. 12p. (J). (ps). 5.99 (978-0-8431-0233-8(0) , Price Stern Sloan) Penguin Group (USA) Inc.

Bonnell, Kris. Robins in the Spring. 2007. (J). 3.95 (***978-1-933727-53-0(5)***) Reading Reading Bks., LLC.

Branson, Terri. Brother Dragon. Taylor, Chet, illus. 2004. (J). 18.99 (978-0-9755888-5-7(0)) Dragonfly Publishing, Inc.

Brett, Jan. Hedgie's Surprise. Brett, Jan, illus. 2004. (Illus.). 30p. (J). (gr. k-4). reprint ed. 17.00 (978-0-7567-7704-3(6)) DIANE Publishing Co.

—Hedgie's Surprise. 2001. (J). (gr. k-3). incl. audio (978-0-8045-6883-8(9) , 6883) Spoken Arts, Inc.

Brown, Margaret Wise. The Golden Egg Book. Weisgard, Leonard, illus. 2004. (Big Little Golden Book Ser.). 32p. (J). (gr. k-k). 8.99 (978-0-375-82717-4(X) , Golden Bks.) Random Hse. Children's Bks.

Bryant, Ann. The Easter Egg Hunt: Paas. Artful Doodlers Limited Staff, illus. 2007. 32p. (J). pap. 3.99 (978-0-448-44488-8(7) , Grosset & Dunlap) Penguin Group (USA) Inc.

Bunting, Eve. Hurry! Hurry! Mack, Jeff, illus. 2007. 40p. (J). (ps-1). 16.00 (978-0-15-205410-6(3)) Harcourt Trade Pubs.

Butterworth, Oliver. The Enormous Egg. 188p. (J). (gr. 3-5). pap. 4.95 (978-0-8072-1393-3(4) , Listening Library) Random Hse. Audio Publishing Group.

Caviezel, Giovanni. Bunny's Egg Hunt. Pagnoni, Roberta, illus. 2003. 12p. (J). bds. 4.99 (978-0-689-85246-6(0) , Little Simon) Simon & Schuster Children's Publishing.

Ciminera, Siiobhan & Ostby, Kristin. Paas: The Great Egg Show! 2006. 32p. (J). (ps-1). act. bk. ed. 2.99 (978-0-448-44136-8(5)) Penguin Group (USA) Inc.

Clayton, A. J. An Egg-Citing Dream. 2006. 17.00 (***978-0-8059-9127-7(1)***) Dorrance Publishing Co., Inc.

Cohen, Caron Lee. Digger Pig & the Turnip: Marranita Poco Rabo y el Nabo. Denise, Christopher, illus. 2008. (Green Light Readers Level 2 Ser.). (SPA & ENG.). 28p. (J). 12.95 (***978-0-15-206249-1(1)***) Harcourt Trade Pubs.

Cohen, Caron Lee & Douglas, Erin. Digger Pig & the Turnip: Marranita Poco Rabo y el Nabo. Denise, Christopher, illus. 2008. (Green Light Readers Level 2 Ser.). (SPA & ENG.). 28p. (J). 12.95 (***978-0-15-206263-7(7)***) Harcourt Trade Pubs.

Cohen, Miriam. Eggy, Meggy & Peggy. Cohen, Miriam, illus. Date not set. (Illus.). 16p. (J). bds. 5.95 (978-1-932065-09-1(1)) Star Bright Bks., Inc.

Conlon, Mara, adapted by. Bill Hatches an Egg. 2005. (Sitting Ducks Ser.). (J). (978-0-8431-1343-3(X) , Price Stern Sloan) Penguin Group (USA) Inc.

Coxe, Molly. Big Egg. Coxe, Molly, illus. 2002. (Illus.). (J). 11.91 (978-0-7587-6028-9(0)) Book Wholesalers, Inc.

Cutbill, Andy. The Cow That Laid an Egg. Ayto, Russell, illus. 2008. 32p. (J). 16.99 (***978-0-06-137295-7(1)***) HarperCollins Pubs.

Daniel, Claire. The Chick That Wouldn't Hatch. Ernst, Lisa Campbell, illus. 2003. (Green Light Readers Level 2 Ser.). 24p. (J). 11.95 (978-0-15-204871-6(5)); pap. 3.95 (978-0-15-204831-0(6)) Harcourt Children's Bks. (Green Light Readers).

—Chick That Wouldn't Hatch. 1999. (gr. k-3). lib. bdg. 11.80 (978-0-613-63269-0(9)) Tandem Library Bks.

de Brunhoff, Laurent & Weiss, Ellen. Babar & the Runaway Egg. Gibert, Jean Claude & Gray, Judith, illus. 2004. 24p. (J). (ps-1). 9.95 (978-0-8109-4838-9(9)) Abrams, Harry N. , Inc.

Disney Press Staff. Pooh's Easter Egg Hunt. 2002. (ps-2). lib. bdg. 11.80 (978-0-613-73601-5(X)) Tandem Library Bks.

Dolan, Penny. Flora McQuack. Widdowson, Kay, illus. 2004. (Read-It! Readers Ser.). 32p. (C). (gr. k-3). 18.60 (978-1-4048-0561-3(3)) Picture Window Bks.

Douglas, Erin. Get That Pest! 2000. (gr. k-3). lib. bdg. 11.80 (978-0-613-63287-4(7)); (Illus.). (J). (978-0-606-18174-7(1)) Tandem Library Bks.

—Get That Pest! Yee, Wong Herbert, illus. 2003. (Green Light Readers Level 2 Ser.). 24p. (J). 11.95 (978-0-15-204873-0(1)); pap. 3.95 (978-0-15-204833-4(2)) Harcourt Children's Bks. (Green Light Readers).

Douglas, Erin. Get That Pest! Agarren a ése! Yee, Wong Herbert, illus. 2008. (Green Light Readers Level 2 Ser.). (SPA & ENG.). 28p. (J). pap. 3.95 (***978-0-15-206269-9(6)***) Harcourt Trade Pubs.

Dow, Jill. Bridget's Secret. 2004. (Windy Edge Farm Ser.). (Illus.). 26p. (J). pap. 7.95 (978-1-84507-253-7(7)) Lincoln, Frances Ltd. GBR. *Dist:* Perseus Distribution.

Driscoll, Laura. Eggs for Everyone! A & J Studio, illus. ed. 2005. 22p. (J). lib. bdg. 15.00 (978-1-59054-973-5(2)) Fitzgerald Bks.

—Eggs for Everyone! A&J Studios Staff, illus. 2005. (Dora the Explorer Ser.). 24p. (J). pap. 3.99 (978-0-689-87176-4(7) , Simon Spotlight/Nickelodeon) Simon & Schuster Children's Publishing.

—Eggs for Everyone! A&J Studios Staff, illus. 2005. 32p. (J). (ps-ps). lib. bdg. 10.79 (978-0-606-33392-4(4)) Tandem Library Bks.

Dunbar, Joyce. Eggday. Cabrera, Jane, illus. 1999. 32p. (J). (ps-3). 15.95 (978-0-8234-1510-6(4)) Holiday Hse., Inc.

Dunrea, Olivier. Ollie. 2007. (Illus.). 16p. (J). bds. 6.95 (***978-0-618-75503-5(9)***) Houghton Mifflin Co. Trade & Reference Div.

—Ollie. Dunrea, Olivier, illus. 2003. (Illus.). 32p. (J). (gr. k-ps). tchr. ed. 9.95 (978-0-618-33928-0(0)) Houghton Mifflin Co. Trade & Reference Div.

—Ollie's Eggs. 2006. (J). (978-0-618-53243-8(9)) Houghton Mifflin Co.

Dyreson, Patricia A. A Very Special Egg. Blair, Guy A., illus. 1999. 22p. (J). (ps-2). pap. 8.95 (978-0-9676135-0-5(7)) Dyreson, Patricia A.

Eagle, Kin. Humpty Dumpty. Gilbert, Rob, illus. 2004. (Nursery Rhyme Ser.). 32p. (J). (ps-3). 15.95 (978-1-58089-019-9(9)) Charlesbridge Publishing, Inc.

Elschner, Geraldine. The Easter Chick. Junge, Alexandra, illus. 2006. 32p. (J). reprint ed. 6.95 (978-0-7358-2076-0(7)) North-South Bks., Inc.

The Enormous Egg. 2004. (Literature Units Ser.). (Illus.). 48p. 7.99 (978-1-57690-632-3(9)) Teacher Created Materials, Inc.

Entara Ltd., photos by. What's Hatching? 2008. (Jakers! Ser.). 24p. (J). pap. 3.99 (*978-0-689-87861-9(3), Simon Spotlight) Simon & Schuster Children's Publishing.

Fitzgerald, Kevin. The EGG-Cellent Adventure. Fitzgerald, Anita, illus. 2005. (J). (978-0-9765987-3-2(6)) Foundation, Pr. The.

Fleming, Maria. Hippity Skippity Easter. Bratun, Katy, illus. 2004. 32p. (J). pap. 3.50 (978-0-439-56417-5(4), Cartwheel Bks.) Scholastic, Inc.

Fox, Mem. Hunwick's Egg. Lofts, Pamela, tr. Lofts, Pamela, illus. 2005. 32p. (J). 16.00 (978-0-15-216318-1(2)) Harcourt Children's Bks.

Fry, Sonali. Make Your Own Easter Treats! Moffatt, Judith, illus. 2002. 12p. (J). (ps-k). bds. 6.99 (978-0-439-34202-5(3)) Scholastic, Inc.

Garland, Michael. The Great Easter Egg Hunt. Garland, Michael, illus. 2007. 32p. (J). pap. 6.99 (978-0-14-240753-0(4), Puffin) Penguin Group (USA) Inc.

Gernhart, Cyndi. The Adventures of Gertrude Mccluck, Chicken in Charge Vol. 1: The Missing Eggs, 4 vols. Gernhart, Carlie, illus. l.t. ed. 2005. 32p. (J). 8.00 (978-0-9778240-1-4(2)) Prairie Winds Publishing.

Golden Books Staff. Egg Surprise. Roper, Bob, illus. 2003. (Dora the Explorer Ser.). 32p. (J). (ps-2). pap. 3.99 (978-0-307-10043-6(X), Golden Bks.) Random Hse. Children's Bks.

Graham, Bob. Dimity Dumpty: The Story of Humpty's Little Sister. 2007. (Illus.). 40p. (J). (ps). 15.99 (978-0-7636-3078-2(0)) Candlewick Pr.

The Great Bird Adventure. 2003. (J). lib. bdg. 18.95 (978-0-9725485-1-9(3)) Waterfall Ridge.

The Great Egg Problem: Individual Title Six-Packs. (Bookweb Ser.). 32p. (gr. 5 up). 34.00 (978-0-7635-3789-0(6)) Rigby Education.

Grey, Mini. Egg Drop. 2002. (Illus.). 32p. (J). (978-0-224-06458-3(4), Jonathan Cape) Random Hse. Children's Bks.

Grimes, Janice D. Before You Were Born - Our Wish for A Baby: Version 3: Egg Donation. 2004. (Illus.). 18p. (J). 14.97 (978-0-9755028-2-2(4)) X, Y, & Me LLC.

Harcourt School Publishers Staff. My Eggs: A Reader. 1999. (Collections Ser.). (Illus.). (J). pap. 2.10 (978-0-15-313449-4(6)) Harcourt Schl. Pubs.

—Next Time: Take-Home Book. rev. ed. 2001. (Collections Ser.: Bk. 12). (Illus.). (J). pap. 1.90 (978-0-15-319070-4(1)) Harcourt Schl. Pubs.

—Watch the Eggs: Take-Home Book. rev. ed. 2001. (Collections Ser.: Bk. 14). (Illus.). (J). pap. 1.90 (978-0-15-319072-8(8)) Harcourt Schl. Pubs.

Hardy, Cindy & Masterman, Lorrine A. Egg Island Reader. 2003. (Math in A Cultural Context Ser.). (Illus.). 74p. pap. 14.95 (978-1-55059-246-7(7)) Temeron Bks., Inc.

Harvey, Ken. Life in the Fridge: The Eggsters Story. Hermes, Mary Sue, illus. 2002. 32p. (J). (ps-k). 12.95 (978-1-930093-17-1(9)) Brookfield Reader, Inc., The.

Hayes, Sarah. True Story of Humpty Dumpty. Voake, Charlotte, illus. 1999. (Reading Together Ser.). 32p. (J). (ps). pap. 3.99 (978-0-7636-0864-4(5)) Candlewick Pr.

Head, Honor. Size & Shape. Stower, Adam, illus. 1998. (Ed Mouse Finds Out about Ser.). 32p. (J). (ps-2). 19.98 (978-0-8172-5201-4(0)) Raintree.

Holub, Joan. Happy Easter Eggs. Holub, Joan, illus. 2005. (Illus.). 12p. (J). bds. 5.99 (978-0-689-86476-6(0), Little Simon) Simon & Schuster Children's Publishing.

Hope, Laura Lee. Freddie & Flossie & the Easter Egg Hunt. Downer, Maggie, illus. 2006. 32p. (J). lib. bdg. 15.00 (*978-1-4242-0966-8(8)) Fitzgerald Bks.

—Freddie & Flossie & the Easter Egg Hunt. 2006. (Ready-To-Read Ser.). (Illus.). 32p. (J). (ps-2). 21.35 (978-1-59961-100-6(7)) Spotlight.

Howard, Reginald. Big, Big Wall. 2001. (gr. k-3). lib. bdg. 11.80 (978-0-613-66350-2(0)) Tandem Library Bks.

Jenkin-Pearce, Susie. A Pal for Pugwug. Macnaughton, Tina, illus. 2005. 32p. (J). 14.95 (978-0-7696-4433-2(3), Gingham Dog Pr.) School Specialty Publishing.

Jocson, Antonio & Christian, J. E. The Egg Thief. Swanson, John, illus. 1998. (Muddy Tom's Wacky Adventures Ser.: Vol. 4). 31p. (J). (gr. 1-3). 14.95 (978-1-890963-03-3(8), LB Bks.) Liberty Bell Productions.

Katz, Karen. Where Are Baby's Easter Eggs? Katz, Karen, illus. 2008. 14p. (J). bds. 6.99 (*978-1-4169-4924-4(0), Little Simon) Simon & Schuster Children's Publishing.

Kellogg, Steven. A Penguin Pup for Pinkerton. 2003. (Picture Puffin Ser.). (Illus.). 32p. (J). (gr. k-3). pap. 6.99 (978-0-14-250170-2(0), Puffin) Penguin Group (USA) Inc.

—Penguin Pup for Pinkerton. 2003. (gr. k-3). lib. bdg. 15.30 (978-0-613-87825-8(6)) Tandem Library Bks.

Kempf, Molly. Easter Egg Hunt. MJ Illustrations Staff & Huxtabel, T., illus. 2008. (Strawberry Shortcake Ser.). 16p. (J). (ps-1). 4.99 (*978-0-448-44713-1(4), Grosset & Dunlap) Penguin Group (USA) Inc.

Kimura, Ken. 999 Tadpoles. Murakami, Yasunari, illus. 2006. 40p. (J). 14.95 (978-1-74126-433-3(2)) R.I.C. Pubns. AUS. *Dist:* SCB Distributors.

Kirk, David & Scholastic, Inc. Staff. Miss Spider's Sunny Patch Kids. Rees, Jenifer, ed. 2004. (Illus.). 40p. (J). pap. 14.95 (978-0-439-40870-7(9), Scholastic Pr.) Scholastic, Inc.

Krauss, Ruth. The Happy Egg. Johnson, Crockett, illus. 2005. (J). (ps-3). 32p. 12.99 (978-0-06-076005-2(2)); 40p. lib. bdg. 15.89 (978-0-06-076006-9(0)) HarperCollins Pubs.

Kroll, Virginia. Easter Eggs for Anya: A Ukrainian Celebration of New Life in Christ. Comport, Sally Wern, illus. 2007. (Traditions of Faith Ser.). 40p. (J). 15.99 (978-0-310-71079-0(0)) Zonderkidz.

Kroll, Virginia L. Easter Eggs for Anya: A Ukrainian Celebration of New Life in Christ. Comport, Sally Wern, illus. 2007. (Traditions of Faith from Around the World Ser.). (J). (*978-1-4287-2360-3(9)) Zonderkidz.

Larson, Helen C. Kia Kayanguqau? Larson, Helen C. & Shantz, Joy, illus. 1998. Tr. of Whose Egg is This?. (ESK.). 8p. (J). (gr. k-3). pap. 6.00 (978-1-58084-040-8(X)) Lower Kuskokwim Schl. District.

Levine, Gail Carson. Fairy Dust & the Quest for the Egg. Christiana, David, illus. 2005. 208p. (gr. 1-5). 16.99 (978-0-7868-3491-4(9)) Disney Pr.

Lewison, Wendy Cheyette. Easter Bunny's Amazing Egg Machine. 2002. (ps-2). lib. bdg. 10.95 (978-0-613-83538-1(7)) Tandem Library Bks.

Little Spring Eggs. 2003. per. 8.99 (978-0-89610-792-2(2)) Island Heritage Publishing.

Loehr, Mallory. Dragon Egg. Wittwer, Hala, illus. 2007. (Step into Reading Ser.). 32p. (J). (ps-k). 3.99 (*978-0-375-84350-1(7)); lib. bdg. 11.99 (*978-0-375-94350-8(1)) Random Hse. Children's Bks. (Random Hse. Bks. for Young Readers).

Maccarone, Grace. Peter Rabbit's Happy Easter. McPhail, David, illus. 2006. 32p. (J). pap. 5.99 (978-0-439-79139-7(1)) Scholastic, Inc.

Mackinnon, Mairi. Goose That Laid the Golden Eggs. Howarth, Daniel, illus. 2006. 48p. (J). 8.99 (978-0-7945-1378-8(6), Usborne) EDC Publishing.

Maguire, Gregory. Three Rotten Eggs. Clayton, Elaine, illus. 2002. 192p. (J). (gr. 4-6). 16.00 (978-0-618-09655-8(8), Clarion Bks.) Houghton Mifflin Co. Trade & Reference Div.

—Three Rotten Eggs. l.t. ed. 2005. 281p. 20.95 (978-0-7862-7276-1(7), Large Print Pr.) Thorndike Pr.

Marvin's Egg: Early Level Satellite Individual Title Six-Packs. (Sails Literacy Ser.). 16p. (gr. 1-2). 27.00 (978-0-7578-3155-3(9)) Rigby Education.

Marzollo, Jean. Ten Little Eggs. Marzollo, Jean, illus. 2004. (Illus.). 24p. (J). (ps-1). 10.99 (978-0-06-053052-5(9), Harper Festival) HarperCollins Pubs.

McBratney, Sam. When I'm Big. Jeram, Anita, illus. 2007. (Guess How Much I Love You Ser.). 24p. (J). (gr. k-ps). bds. 7.99 (*978-0-7636-3546-6(4)) Candlewick Pr.

Meddaugh, Susan. Harry on the Rocks. 2007. (Illus.). 32p. (J). (gr. k-3). 6.95 (*978-0-618-84068-7(0), Walter Lorraine) Houghton Mifflin Co. Trade & Reference Div.

—Harry on the Rocks. Meddaugh, Susan, illus. 2003. (Illus.). 32p. (J). (gr. k-3). tchr. ed. 15.00 (978-0-618-27603-5(3), Walter Lorraine) Houghton Mifflin Co. Trade & Reference Div.

Michael & the Chicks. 2005. (J). (978-1-58453-295-8(5)) Pioneer Valley Educational Pr., Inc.

Montes, Marisa. Egg-Napped! Winborn, Marsha, illus. 2002. 32p. (J). (ps-2). 15.95 (978-0-06-028950-8(3)) HarperCollins Pubs.

—Egg-Napped! 1999. (Illus.). 32p. (J). (ps-2). 5.95 (978-0-06-443676-2(4)) HarperCollins Pubs.

Morse, Scott. Magic Pickle vs. the Egg Poacher. 2008. 144p. (J). pap. 5.99 (*978-0-439-87997-2(3), Graphix) Scholastic, Inc.

My hard-boiled Egg: Individual Title Six-Packs. (gr. 1-2). 22.00 (978-0-7635-9186-1(6)) Rigby Education.

Nakagawa, Rieko. Guri & Gura. Howlett, Peter & McNamara, Richard B., trs. from JPN. Yamawaki, Yuriko, illus. 2003. (Guri & Gura Ser.). 32p. (gr. k-3). 10.95 (978-0-8048-3352-3(4)) Tuttle Publishing.

Nethery, Mary. Mary Veronica's Egg. Yalowitz, Paul, illus. 1999. 32p. (J). (ps-2). 16.99 (978-0-531-33134-7(2), Orchard Bks.) Scholastic, Inc.

Nicholls, Judith. The Noisy Egg. 2007. (Little Scholastic Ser.). (J). (ps). bds. 7.99 (*978-0-439-02151-7(0)) Scholastic, Inc.

O'Malley, Kevin. Humpty Dumpty Egg-Splodes. O'Malley, Kevin, illus. 2002. (Illus.). 32p. (J). (gr. 1-5). 15.95 (978-0-8027-8756-9(8)) Walker & Co.

Park, Barbara. Junie B., First Grader: Dumb Bunny. Brunkus, Denise, illus. 2007. (Junie B. Jones Ser.: No. 27). 128p. (J). (gr. 1-4). 11.99 (978-0-375-83809-5(0), Random Hse. Bks. for Young Readers) Random Hse. Children's Bks.

Pfister, Marcus. Henri Egg Artiste. Pfister, Marcus, illus. 2008. 32p. (J). (ps). 15.95 (*978-0-7358-2130-9(5)) North-South Bks., Inc.

Piper, Sophie. Little Bunnys Easter. 2008. (Illus.). 32p. (J). pap. 10.95 (*978-0-7459-4961-1(4)) Lion Hudson plc GBR. *Dist:* Independent Pubs. Group.

Polacco, Patricia. Rechenka's Eggs. Polacco, Patricia, illus. 2002. (Illus.). (J). 14.04 (978-0-7587-3502-7(2)) Book Wholesalers, Inc.

Polhemus, Coleman. The Crocodile Blues. Polhemus, Coleman, illus. 2007. (Illus.). 48p. (J). (ps-1). 16.99 (*978-0-7636-3543-5(X)) Candlewick Pr.

Pujol, Carlos. Emma's Eggs. 1999. (Illus.). (J). (978-0-606-16547-1(9)) Tandem Library Bks.

Rawlinson, Julia. Fred & the Little Egg. Massey, Jane, illus. 2005. 28p. (J). 16.00 (978-1-56148-468-3(7)) Good Bks.

Reber, Deborah. Blue en Busca de Huevos. Norden, Carolyn, illus. 2004. (Blue's Clues Ser.).Tr. of Blue's Egg Hunt. (SPA.). 24p. (J). pap. 3.99 (978-0-689-86650-0(X), Libros Para Ninos) Simon & Schuster Children's Publishing.

Reitze, Glenn Logan. Ernie the Easter Hippopotamus: A Comic Adventure for Anytime. Reitze, Glenn Logan, illus. 2007. (Illus.). 50p. (J). lib. bdg. 19.95 (*978-0-88265-040-1(8), Fine Art Editions) North American International.

Reitze, Glenn Logan, illus. & text. Ernie the Easter Hippopotamus: A Comic Adventure for Anytime. Reitze, Glenn Logan, text. 2007. (J). pap. (*978-0-88265-041-8(6)) North American International.

Rigby Education Staff. The Egg Saga. (Sails Literacy Ser.). (Illus.). 16p. (gr. 2-3). 27.00 (978-0-7635-9935-5(2), 699352C99) Rigby Education.

—Look at My Eggs. (Sails Literacy Ser.). (Illus.). 16p. (gr. k-1). 27.00 (978-0-7635-9870-9(4), 698704C99) Rigby Education.

Roberts, Bethany. Easter Mice! Cushman, Doug, illus. 2003. 32p. (J). (gr. k-ps). tchr. ed. 13.00 (978-0-618-16455-4(3), Clarion Bks.) Houghton Mifflin Co. Trade & Reference Div.

Robertson, M. P. The Dragon Snatcher. 2005. (Illus.). 32p. (J). (ps-3). 16.99 (978-0-8037-3103-5(5), Dial) Penguin Group (USA) Inc.

Robertson, M. P., illus. The Egg. 2001. 32p. (J). (ps-3). 15.99 (978-0-8037-2546-1(9), Dial) Penguin Group (USA) Inc.

Running Press Staff. Silly Goose's Lost Easter Eggs. 2006. (Illus.). 8p. (J). 4.95 (978-0-7624-2632-4(2), Running Pr. Kids) Running Pr. Bk. Pubs.

Running Press Staff & Studio Books Staff. Easter Bunny's Egg Hunt. 2006. (Illus.). 8p. (J). 4.95 (978-0-7624-2633-1(0), Running Pr. Kids) Running Pr. Bk. Pubs.

Samuel, Catherine & Hartman, Butch. Timmy's Eggs-Ray Vision. Saunders, Zina, illus. 2005. (J). (*978-1-4155-8053-0(7), Simon Spotlight/Nickelodeon) Simon & Schuster Children's Publishing.

Santillo, LuAnn. The Eggs. Santillo, LuAnn, ed. 2003. (Half-Pint Kids Readers Ser.). (Illus.). 7p. (J). (ps-1). pap. (978-1-59256-061-5(X)) Half-Pint Kids, Inc.

Sargent, Dave & Sargent, David M., Jr. Glenda Goose: Sharing, 19. Lenoir, Jane, illus. 2003. (Feather Tales Ser.: 8). 42p. (J). 8. pap. 6.95 (978-1-56763-734-2(5)); Vol. 8. 2nd ed. lib. bdg. 19.95 (978-1-56763-733-5(7)) Ozark Publishing.

Schertle, Alice. Down the Road. Lewis, Earl, illus. 2000. 40p. (J). (gr. k-3). pap. 7.00 (978-0-15-202471-0(9), Harcourt Paperbacks) Harcourt Children's Bks.

—Down the Road. Lewis, E. B., illus. 2000. (J). (ps-17). lib. bdg. 14.15 (978-0-613-29935-0(3)) Tandem Library Bks.

—Down the Road. 2000. 12.80 (978-0-606-20324-1(9)) Tandem Library Bks.

Schmauss, Judy Kentor. Ted Saw an Egg. 2006. (Reader's Clubhouse Set A Ser.). (Illus.). 24p. (J). pap. 3.99 (978-0-7641-3283-4(0)) Barron's Educational Series, Inc.

Schulz, Charles M. Baby Woodstock's Easter Eggs. Schulz, Charles M., illus. 2004. (Baby Snoopy Ser.). (Illus.). 12p. (J). bds. 5.99 (978-0-689-85782-9(9), Little Simon) Simon & Schuster Children's Publishing.

Schwartz, Roslyn. The Mole Sisters & the Blue Egg. Schwartz, Roslyn, illus. 2001. (Mole Sisters Ser.). (Illus.). 32p. (J). (ps-k). pap. 4.95 (978-1-55037-704-0(3)); lib. bdg. 14.95 (978-1-55037-705-7(1)) Annick Pr., Ltd. CAN. *Dist:* Firefly Bks., Ltd.

Seuss, Dr. Green Eggs & Ham Book & CD. 2005. (Illus.). 64p. (J). (ps-2). audio compact disk 9.95 (978-0-375-83495-0(8), Random Hse. Bks. for Young Readers) Random Hse. Children's Bks.

—Tonho Choca o Ovo. pap. 23.95 (978-85-7406-098-9(4)) Schwarcz, Editora Ltda, Companhia das Letrinhas BRA. *Dist:* Distribooks, Inc.

Simmons, Jane. Daisy & the Egg. Simmons, Jane, illus. 2002. (Illus.). (J). 19.96 (978-0-7587-2335-2(0)) Book Wholesalers, Inc.

—Daisy & the Egg. (Illus.). (ps-1). 2005. (ARA, ENG, VIE, CHI & BEN.). 32p. 11.95 (978-1-84059-216-0(8)); 2005. (VIE, ENG, CHI, ARA & BEN., 32p. pap. 11.95 (978-1-84059-176-7(5)); 2000. (CHI, ENG, VIE, ARA & BEN., 36p. (J). pap. 11.95 (978-1-84059-171-2(4)); 2000. (GUJ, ENG, VIE, CHI & ARA., 36p. (J). pap. 11.95 (978-1-84059-173-6(0)); 2000. (TUR, ENG, VIE, CHI & ARA., 36p. (J). pap. 11.95 (978-1-84059-174-3(9)); 2000. (ALB, ENG, VIE, CHI & ARA., 36p. (J). pap. 11.95 (978-1-84059-172-9(2)) Milet Publishing.

—Daisy & the Egg. Datta, Kanai, tr. 2000. (Daisy Ser.). (BEN, ENG, VIE, CHI & ARA., Illus.). 36p. (J). (ps-1). pap. 11.95 (978-1-84059-170-5(6)) Milet Publishing.

—Daisy & the Egg. Iqbal, Gulshan, tr. 2000. (Daisy Ser.). (ENG, URD, VIE, CHI & ARA., Illus.). 36p. (J). (ps-1). pap. 11.95 (978-1-84059-175-0(7)) Milet Publishing.

—Daisy & the Egg. 2003. (ps-2). lib. bdg. 15.30 (978-0-613-71811-0(9)) Tandem Library Bks.

Smath, Jerry. The Best Easter Egg Ever! Smath, Jerry, illus. 2003. (Illus.). 32p. (J). (ps-3). 3.50 (978-0-439-44321-0(0), Cartwheel Bks.) Scholastic, Inc.

—Best Easter Eggs Ever! 2003. (gr. k-3). lib. bdg. 11.25 (978-0-613-66616-9(X)) Tandem Library Bks.

Speceal, Edetha. The Lost Egg & Other Stories. 2006. 144p. pap. (*978-1-84401-644-0(7)) Athena Pr.

Stoeke, Janet Morgan. Minerva Louise & the Colorful Eggs. 2006. (Illus.). 24p. (J). (ps). 15.99 (978-0-525-47633-7(4), Dutton Juvenile) Penguin Group (USA) Inc.

Sykes, Julie. Dora's Eggs. Chapman, Jane, illus. (J). 2007. bds. 6.95 (978-1-58925-801-3(0)); 2002. 32p. 5.95 (978-1-58925-365-0(5)) ME Media LLC. (tiger tales).

—Dora's Eggs. 2002. (gr. k-3). lib. bdg. 14.10 (978-0-613-56323-9(9)) Tandem Library Bks.

Tafuri, Nancy. Whose Chick Are You? Tafuri, Nancy, illus. 2007. (Illus.). 40p. (J). (ps-k). 16.99 (978-0-06-082514-0(6)); lib. bdg. 17.89 (978-0-06-082515-7(4)) HarperCollins Pubs.

Thiele, Colin. Danny's Egg. (Illus.). 160p. pap. (978-0-7344-0403-9(4), Lothian Bks.) Hachette Livre Australia.

Thomson, Sarah L. Dragon's Egg. 2007. 272p. (J). (gr. 3-7). 16.99 (*978-0-06-128848-7(9)); lib. bdg. 17.89 (*978-0-06-128847-0(0)) HarperCollins Pubs. (Greenwillow Bks.).

Waddell, Martin. It's Quacking Time! Barton, Jill, illus. 2005. 32p. (J). (ps-1). 15.99 (978-0-7636-2738-6(0)) Candlewick Pr.

Wallace. Flash Harriet & Ostrich Eggs Mys. (Illus.). 64p. (J). pap. (978-0-340-61961-2(9), Hodder & Stoughton) Hodder General Publishing Division.

Wallace, Carol. Turkeys Together. Rogers, Jaqueline, illus. 40p. (J). (ps). 15.95 (978-0-8234-1895-4(2)) Holiday Hse., Inc.

Wang, Margaret. Easter Egg Hunt. Johnson, Richard, illus. 2005. 10p. (J). bds. 9.95 (978-1-58117-375-8(X), Intervisual/Piggy Toes) Dalmatian Pr.

Washington, LaVonne and LaShawn. The Life of Humpty Dumpty Volume 1. 2005. 33p. 11.35 (978-1-4116-2497-9(1)) Lulu.com.

Weeks, Sarah & Lewin, Betsy. Two Eggs, Please. (Illus.). 32p. (J). 2003. 15.95 (978-0-689-83196-6(X), Atheneum); 2007. reprint ed. pap. 6.99 (978-1-4169-2714-3(X), Aladdin) Simon & Schuster Children's Publishing.

Wells, Rosemary. Max's Chocolate Chicken. Wells, Rosemary, illus. 2000. (Illus.). (J). (ps-ps). lib. bdg. 14.15 (978-0-613-28571-1(9)) Tandem Library Bks.

Whose Egg Is This? Individual Title Six-Packs. (Story Steps Ser.). (gr. k-2). 32.00 (978-0-7635-9607-1(8)) Rigby Education.

Wolf, Jackie, et al. My Sparkle Egg Book. 2005. (Illus.). (J). (*978-1-57151-750-0(2)) Playhouse Publishing.

Wood, A. J. Golden Egg. Hunt, Janie Louise & Kneen, Maggie, illus. 2000. 20p. (J). (ps-1). 15.95 (978-0-8118-2837-6(9)) Chronicle Bks. LLC.

EGYPT

Aykroyd, Clarissa. Egypt. 2003. (Modern Middle East Nations & Their Strategic Place in the World Ser.). (Illus.). 112,128p. (YA). (gr. 7 up). lib. bdg. (978-1-59084-505-9(6)) Mason Crest Pubs.

Benge, Janet & Benge, Geoff. Lillian Trasher: The Greatest Wonder in Egypt. 2003. (Christian Heroes, Then & Now Ser.). 190p. (J). pap. 8.99 (978-1-57658-305-0(8)) YWAM Publishing.

Bingham, Caroline & Dorling Kindersley Publishing Staff. Pyramid. 2004. (Eye Wonder Ser.). (Illus.). 48p. (J). lib. bdg. 17.99 (978-0-7566-0286-4(6)) Dorling Kindersley Publishing, Inc.

Blevins, Wiley. Egypt. 2002. (Steadwell Books World Tour). (Illus.). 48p. (J). lib. bdg. 24.26 (978-0-7398-5752-6(5)) Raintree.

Broida, Marian. The Ancient Egyptians & Their Neighbors. 1999. (Illus.). 208p. (J). (gr. 4-7). pap., act. bk. ed. 16.95 (978-1-55652-360-1(2)) Chicago Review Pr., Inc.

Broyles, Janell. Egyptian Mythology. 2005. (Mythology Around the World Ser.). (Illus.). 64p. (J). (978-1-4042-0770-7(8)) Rosen Publishing Group, Inc., The.

Burgan, Michael. The Valley of the Kings: Egypt's Greatest Mummies. 2005. (Mummies Ser.). (Illus.). 32p. (J). 22.60 (978-0-7368-3772-9(8)) Capstone Pr., Inc.

Chelsea House Publishing Staff & Harmon, Daniel E. Egypt: 1880 to the Present. 2001. (Exploration of Africa). (Illus.). 112p. (J). (gr. 7-12). 35.00 (978-0-7910-5744-5(5), Chelsea Hse.) Facts On File, Inc.

Clements, Andrew. Temple Cat. Kiesler, Kate A., illus. 2001. 32p. (J). (gr. k-3). pap. 6.95 (978-0-618-11139-8(5), Clarion Bks.) Houghton Mifflin Co. Trade & Reference Div.

Costain, Meredith & Collins, Paul, eds. Welcome to Egypt. 2001. (Countries of the World Ser.). (Illus.). 32p. (J). 28.00 (978-0-7910-6874-8(9), Chelsea Hse.) Facts On File, Inc.

Delafosse, Claude. Egyptian Tomb. 1999. (Hidden World Ser.). (Illus.). 26p. (J). (ps-2). 12.95 (978-0-439-06776-8(6)) Scholastic, Inc.

Egypt - Kush & Axum. (Ancient Civilizations Ser.). 48p. (gr. 5 up). 6.99 (978-0-7647-0148-1(7), FS10502) Schaffer, Frank Pubns.

Frank, Nicole & Wilson, Susan S. Welcome to Egypt. 1999. (Welcome to My Country Ser.). (Illus.). 48p. (J). (gr. 2 up). lib. bdg. 26.00 (978-0-8368-2494-0(6)) Stevens, Gareth Inc.

Frost, Helen. A Look at Egypt. 2005. (One World, Many Cultures Ser.). (Illus.). 24p. (J). (gr. k-3). 15.93 (978-0-7368-9390-9(3), Pebble Bks.) Capstone Pr., Inc.

—A Look at Egypt. Saunders-Smith, Gail, ed. 2002. (Our World Ser.). (Illus.). 24p. (J). (gr. k-1). lib. bdg. 15.93 (978-0-7368-1429-4(9), Pebble Bks.) Capstone Pr., Inc.

—A Look at Egypt, 6 vols. Saunders-Smith, Gail, ed. (gr. k-2). 28.95 (978-0-7368-9391-6(1)) Red Brick Learning.

Furstinger, Nancy. Cairo. 2005. (Cities Ser.). (Illus.). 32p. (J). (gr. k-6). lib. bdg. 22.78 (978-1-59197-856-5(4)) ABDO Publishing Co.

Gray, Susan Heinrichs. Egypt. 2001. (First Reports). (Illus.). 48p. (J). (gr. 3 up). lib. bdg. 22.60 (978-0-7565-0126-6(1)) Compass Point Bks.

Green, Jen. Focus on Egypt. 2006. (Illus.). 64p. (J). pap. (*978-0-8368-6741-1(6)); lib. bdg. (*978-0-8368-6734-3(3)) Stevens, Gareth Inc. (World Almanac Library).

Hardwick, Susan, ed. Egypt. 2005. (World-Wise Kids Project Guides). (Illus.). 96p. (978-1-59258-078-1(5)) Hylas Publishing.

Haskins, James & Benson, Kathleen. Count Your Way Through Egypt. Rama, Sue, illus. 2007. (Count Your Way Ser.). 24p. (J). 19.93 (978-1-57505-882-5(0), Millbrook Pr.) Lerner Publishing Group.

Heinrichs, Ann. Egypt. 2006. (Enchantment of the World, Second Ser.). (Illus.). 144p. (J). 36.00 (978-0-516-24866-0(9), Children's Pr.) Scholastic Library Publishing.

Hiemen, Sara. Egypt ABCs: A Book about the People & Places of Egypt. Ouren, Todd, illus. 2004. (Country ABCs Ser.). 32p. (gr. k-5). 23.93 (978-1-4048-0019-9(0)) Picture Window Bks.

Hinds, Kathryn. The City. 2006. (Life in Ancient Egypt Ser.). (Illus.). 80p. (J). lib. bdg. 32.79 (978-0-7614-2184-9(X), Benchmark Bks.) Cavendish, Marshall Corp.

E F G

Hobbs, Joseph J. Egypt. (Modern World Nations Ser.). (Illus.). (gr. 6-12). 2003. 200p. pap. 30.00 (978-0-7910-7178-6(2)); 2002. 150p. 30.00 (978-0-7910-6931-8(1)) Facts On File, Inc. (Chelsea Hse.).

Italia, Bob. Egypt. 2001. (Countries Ser.). (Illus.). 40p. (J). (gr. k-6). lib. bdg. 22.78 (978-1-57765-493-3(5) , Checkerboard Library) ABDO Publishing Co.

Jackson, Elaine. Egypt. 2004. (QEB Travel Through Ser.). (Illus.). 32p. (J). lib. bdg. 18.95 (978-1-59566-059-6(3)) QEB Publishing Inc.

Jankowski, Susan. Egypt in the News: Past, Present, & Future. 2006. (Middle East Nations in the News Ser.). (Illus.). 128p. (J). lib. bdg. 33.27 (978-1-59845-031-6(X) , MyReportLinks.com Bks.) Enslow Pubs., Inc.

Kallen, Stuart A. Pyramids. 2002. (Mystery Library). (Illus.). 112p. (YA). (gr. 4-12). 29.95 (978-1-56006-773-3(X) , Lucent Bks.) Thomson Gale.

Kaplan, Leslie C. Home Life in Ancient Egypt. 2004. (Primary Sources of Ancient Civilizations Ser.). (Illus.). 24p. (J). lib. bdg. (978-0-8239-8935-5(6)); lib. bdg. 19.95 (978-0-8239-6784-1(0)) Rosen Publishing Group, Inc., The. (PowerKids Pr.).

—Politics & Government in Ancient Egypt. 2004. (Primary Sources of Ancient Civilizations Ser.). (Illus.). 24p. (J). lib. bdg. (978-0-8239-8933-1(X)); lib. bdg. 19.95 (978-0-8239-6783-4(2)) Rosen Publishing Group, Inc., The. (PowerKids Pr.).

Kaplan, Sarah Pitt. The Great Pyramid at Giza: Tomb of Wonders. 2005. (Illus.). 48p. (J). (ps-7). 24.00 (978-0-516-25131-8(7)); (YA). (gr. 7-12). pap. 6.95 (978-0-516-25095-3(7)) Scholastic Library Publishing. (Children's Pr.).

A Kid's Guide to Drawing the Countries of the World: Set 3. (Illus.). (J). (gr. k-5). 159.00 (978-1-4042-2958-7(2)) Rosen Publishing Group, Inc., The.

A Kid's Guide to Drawing the Countries of the World: Set 4. (Illus.). (J). (gr. k-5). 159.00 (978-1-4042-2959-4(0)) Rosen Publishing Group, Inc., The.

Kras, Sarah Louise. Anwar Sadat. 2002. (Major World Leaders Ser.). (Illus.). 112p. (gr. 6-12). 30.00 (978-0-7910-6949-3(4) , Chelsea Hse.) Facts On File, Inc.

Kudalis, Eric. The Royal Mummies: Remains from Ancient Egypt. 2002. (Mummies Ser.). (Illus.). 32p. (J). (gr. 3-4). lib. bdg. 21.26 (978-0-7368-1308-2(X) , Capstone High-Interest Bks.) Capstone Pr., Inc.

LaFontaine, Bruce. Gods of Ancient Egypt. 2002. (Illus.). 32p. (J). pap. 3.95 (978-0-486-42088-2(4)) Dover Pubns., Inc.

Levy, Janey. The Great Pyramid of Giza: Measuring Length, Area, Volume, & Angles. 2006. (Math for the Real World Ser.). (Illus.). 32p. (J). pap. (978-1-4042-6059-7(5)); lib. bdg. (978-1-4042-3353-9(9)) Rosen Publishing Group, Inc., The.

Malam, John. Ancient Egyptian Jobs. (People in the Past Ser.). (Illus.). 48p. (J). 2003. (gr. 4-6). lib. bdg. 27.07 (978-1-4034-0311-7(2)); 2002. pap. 8.50 (978-1-4034-0515-9(8)) Heinemann Library.

—Ancient Egyptian Jobs. 2002. (gr. 3-6). lib. bdg. 17.05 (978-0-613-86431-2(X)) Tandem Library Bks.

March, Michael. Guide to Egypt. 1999. (World Guides Ser.). (Illus.). 32p. (J). (gr. 2-6). lib. bdg. 21.27 (978-1-884756-42-9(5)) Davidson Titles, Inc.

McLaughlin, Kari Massie. My Adventure in Ancient Egypt. 2007. 44p. (J). 8.99 (978-1-59092-421-1(5) , Orchard Academy Pr.) Windstorm Creative.

Millard, Anne. The Great Pyramid of Giza. 2005. (Places in History Ser.). (Illus.). 48p. (J). pap. (978-0-8368-5818-1(2)); lib. bdg. 30.00 (978-0-8368-5811-2(5)) Stevens, Gareth Inc. (World Almanac Library).

Millard, Anne. Pyramids. 2007. (Hallmarks of History Ser.). (Illus.). 32p. (J). (***978-1-59604-122-6(6)***) Stargazer Bks.

Minnis. You Are in Ancient Egypt. 2004. (Illus.). 32p. (J). pap. 7.50 (978-1-4109-1008-0(3)) Harcourt Schl. Pubs.

Morris, Ann. Grandma Hekmat Remembers: An Egyptian - American Family Story. Linenthal, Peter, illus. 2003. (What Was It Like, Grandma? Ser.). 32p. lib. bdg. 22.90 (978-0-7613-2864-3(5) , Millbrook Pr.) Lerner Publishing Group.

—Grandma Hekmat Remembers: An Egyptian - American Family Story. Linenthal, Peter, photos by. 2003. (Illus.). 32p. (J). (gr. 5 up). pap. 7.95 (978-0-7613-1944-3(1) , Millbrook Pr.) Lerner Publishing Group.

Moscovitch, Arlene. Egypt - The Culture. 1999. (Lands, Peoples & Cultures Ser.). (Illus.). 32p. (J). (gr. 4-5). (978-0-86505-234-5(4)); pap. (978-0-86505-314-4(6)) Crabtree Publishing Co.

—Egypt - The Land. 1999. (Lands, Peoples & Cultures Ser.). (Illus.). 32p. (J). (gr. 4-5). (978-0-86505-232-1(8)); pap. (978-0-86505-312-0(X)) Crabtree Publishing Co.

—Egypt - The People. 1999. (Lands, Peoples & Cultures Ser.). (Illus.). 32p. (J). (gr. 4-5). (978-0-86505-233-8(6)); pap. (978-0-86505-313-7(8)) Crabtree Publishing Co.

—Egypt the Culture. 2000. (gr. 3-6). lib. bdg. 16.40 (978-0-613-21478-0(1)) Tandem Library Bks.

—Egypt the Land. 2000. (gr. 3-6). lib. bdg. 16.40 (978-0-613-21479-7(X)) Tandem Library Bks.

Moses, Brian. An Egyptian Tomb. Hook, Adam, illus. 2000. (Look Inside Ser.). 32p. (J). (gr. 4-6). lib. bdg. 25.69 (978-0-7398-2378-1(7)) Raintree.

Nardo, Don. Ancient Egypt. 2002. (History of Weapons & Warfare Ser.). (Illus.). 112p. (J). 27.45 (978-1-59018-066-2(6) , Lucent Bks.) Thomson Gale.

—People of the Nile: Rhythms of Daily Life. 2005. (Lucent Library of Historical Eras Ser.). (Illus.). 112p. (YA). (gr. 7-10). lib. bdg. 32.45 (978-1-59018-705-0(9) , Lucent Bks.) Thomson Gale.

Nations of the World: Includes: Brazil, Egypt, Germany, Israel, 4 bks., Set. 2001. (Illus.). (YA). (gr. 5-9). lib. bdg. 95.92 (978-0-7398-4289-8(7)) Raintree.

Nicolotti, Muriel. Madhi: A Child of Egypt. 2005. (Children of the World Ser.). (Illus.). 24p. (J). (gr. 2-4). 22.45 (978-1-4103-0288-5(1) , Blackbirch Pr., Inc.) Thomson Gale.

O'Connor, Jane & Heller, Ruth. Ancient Egypt. 1999. (Designs for Coloring Ser.). (Illus.). 64p. (J). (gr. 4-7). pap. 5.99 (978-0-448-41994-7(7) , Grosset & Dunlap) Penguin Group (USA) Inc.

Pallister, John. Egypt. 2004. (Countries of the World (Facts on File, Inc.) Ser.). (Illus.). 64p. (J). (gr. 6-12). 30.00 (978-0-8160-5504-3(1)) Facts On File, Inc.

Park, Ted. Taking Your Camera To... Includes: Australia, Brazil, Canada, Egypt, France, Israel, Italy, Japan, Mexico, Panama, Russia, Spain, 12 bks., Set. 2000. (Taking Your Camera to Ser.). (Illus.). (J). (gr. 4-7). 273.96 (978-0-7398-3096-3(1)) Raintree.

—Taking Your Camera to Egypt. 2001. (Illus.). pap. (978-0-7398-3333-9(2)) Steck-Vaughn.

Parker, Lewis K. Egypt. 2003. (Discovering Cultures Ser.). (Illus.). 48p. (J). 25.64 (978-0-7614-1519-0(X) , Benchmark Bks.) Cavendish, Marshall Corp.

Parker, Victoria. We're from Egypt. 2005. (Heinemann First Library). (Illus.). 32p. (J). pap. 7.25 (978-1-4034-5790-5(5)); lib. bdg. 24.21 (978-1-4034-5783-7(2)) Heinemann.

Popper, Garry. Ali in Egypt. Johnson, Andi, illus. 2004. 36p. (ps-7). 4.00 (978-1-84161-078-8(X)) Ravette Publishing, Ltd. GBR. *Dist:* Parkwest Pubns., Inc.

Putnam, James. Make Your Own Egyptian Pyramid. 1999. 24p. pap. 9.95 (978-0-688-17019-6(6)) HarperCollins Pubs.

Ragsdale, Ron. Egypt. 2003. (Changing Face Of... Ser.). (Illus.). 48p. (J). lib. bdg. 28.56 (978-0-7398-5488-4(7)) Raintree.

Reynolds, Jeff. Egypt. Reynolds, Jeff E., ed. 2005. (to Z Ser.). (Illus.). 40p. (J). (gr. 2-4). pap. 6.95 (978-0-516-25070-0(1) , Children's Pr.) Scholastic Library Publishing.

Reynolds, Jeff E. Egypt. 2004. (to Z Ser.). (Illus.). 40p. (J). 24.50 (978-0-516-23652-0(0) , Children's Pr.) Scholastic Library Publishing.

Roop, Peter & Roop, Connie. Egypt. 2005. (Visit to Ser.). (Illus.). 32p. (J). (ps-ps). pap. 6.50 (978-1-4034-4148-5(0)) Heinemann Library.

Rumford, James. Seeker of Knowledge: The Man Who Deciphered Egyptian Hieroglyphs. (Illus.). 32p. (J). (gr. k-3). 2003. pap. 6.95 (978-0-618-33345-5(2)); 2000. tchr. ed. 16.00 (978-0-395-97934-1(X)) Houghton Mifflin Co. Trade & Reference Div.

—Seeker of Knowledge: The Man Who Deciphered Egyptian Hieroglyphs. 2000. (gr. k-3). lib. bdg. 15.25 (978-0-613-60835-0(6)) Tandem Library Bks.

Ruth, Angie. My Adventure in Egypt. 2007. 44p. (J). 8.99 (978-1-59092-426-6(6) , Orchard Academy Pr.) Windstorm Creative.

Ryan, Patrick. Welcome to Egypt. 2008. (Welcome to the World Ser.). 32p. (J). (gr. 1-5). 27.07 (***978-1-59296-969-2(0)***) Child's World, Inc.

Salas, Laura Purdie. China. 2001. (Countries & Cultures Ser.). (Illus.). 64p. (J). (gr. 3-4). lib. bdg. 23.93 (978-0-7368-0767-8(5) , Bridgestone Bks.) Capstone Pr., Inc.

Shuter, Jane. Ancient Egypt. Hook, Christa, illus. 2000. (People Who Made History Ser.). 48p. (J). (gr. 4-6). lib. bdg. 27.12 (978-0-7398-2748-2(0)) Raintree.

—Life along the River Nile. 2004. (Picture the Past Ser.). (Illus.). 32p. (J). 24.22 (978-1-4034-5827-8(8)) Heinemann Library.

—Life in an Egyptian Town. 2004. (Picture the Past Ser.). (Illus.). 32p. (J). 24.22 (978-1-4034-5831-5(6)) Heinemann Library.

—Life in an Egyptian Workers' Village. 2004. (Picture the Past Ser.). (Illus.). 32p. (J). 24.22 (978-1-4034-5832-2(4)) Heinemann Library.

Somervill, Barbara A. Teens in Egypt. 2007. (J). lib. bdg. (***978-0-7565-3294-9(9)***) Compass Point Bks.

Streissguth, Thomas. Egypt. (Country Explorers Ser.). (J). 2008. lib. bdg. 27.93 (***978-0-8225-8660-9(6)*** , Lerner Pubns.); 1999. (Illus.). 48p. (gr. 3-5). lib. bdg. 22.60 (978-1-57505-110-9(9) , Carolrhoda Bks.); 1999. (Illus.). 48p. (gr. k-2). lib. bdg. 22.60 (978-1-57505-135-2(4) , Carolrhoda Bks.) Lerner Publishing Group.

Subanthore, Aswin & Hobbs, Joseph J. Egypt. 2nd rev. ed. 2007. (Modern World Nations Ser.). 120p. (J). (gr. 6-12). 30.00 (***978-0-7910-9515-7(0)*** , Chelsea Hse.) Facts On File, Inc.

Tanaka, Shelley. Secrets of the Mummies: Uncovering the Bodies of Ancient Egyptians. 2001. (I Was There Bk.). (Illus.). (J). (978-0-606-20900-7(X)) Tandem Library Bks.

Thomson, Ruth. The Egyptians. 1998. (Footsteps in Time Ser.). 24p. (J). (gr. 2-5). pap. 3.95 (978-0-516-26232-1(7) , Children's Pr.) Scholastic Library Publishing.

Time-Life Audiobooks Staff, contrib. by. Egypt. (J). tchr. ed. 41.95 (978-0-382-40665-2(6)) Cobblestone Publishing Co.

—Egypt, 5 bks., Set 3. 2003. (People in the Past Ser.). (J). (gr. 4-6). lib. bdg. 135.35 (978-1-58810-711-4(6)) Heinemann Library.

Trumble, Kelly. Cat Mummies. Kubinyi, Laszlo, illus. 1999. 64p. (J). (gr. 4-6). pap. 7.95 (978-0-395-96891-8(7) , Clarion Bks.) Houghton Mifflin Co. Trade & Reference Div.

Webster, Christine. Egypt: A Question & Answer Book. 2004. (Fact Finders Ser.). (Illus.). 32p. (J). lib. bdg. 22.60 (978-0-7368-2688-4(2)) Capstone Pr., Inc.

White, Graham. Los Secretos de las Piramides. 2003. (SPA.). 30p. 14.95 (978-84-89396-94-4(9)) Blume ESP. *Dist:* Independent Pubs. Group.

Wilkens, Frances. Egypt. 1999. (Major World Nations Ser.). (Illus.). 144p. (J). (gr. 4-7). lib. bdg. 21.95 (978-0-7910-4989-1(2) , Chelsea Hse.) Facts On File, Inc.

Williams, Colleen Madonna Flood. My Adventure in Ancient Egypt: Advanced My Adventure. 2007. 44p. (J). pap. 8.99 (978-1-59092-422-8(3) , Orchard Academy Pr.) Windstorm Creative.

Wilson, Neil. Egypt. 2001. (Nations of the World Ser.). (Illus.). 128p. (J). (gr. 6-8). lib. bdg. 34.26 (978-0-7398-1283-9(1)) Raintree.

Wilson, Susan L. Egypt. 1999. (Countries of the World Ser.). (Illus.). 96p. (J). (gr. 6 up). lib. bdg. 30.00 (978-0-8368-2259-5(5)) Stevens, Gareth Inc.

Wood, Selina. Egypt. 2007. (National Geographic Countries of the World Ser.). (Illus.). 64p. (J). (gr. 3-5). 27.90 (978-1-4263-0027-1(1) , National Geographic Children's Bks.) National Geographic Society.

Zuehlke, Jeffrey. Egypt in Pictures. 2nd rev. ed. 2003. (Visual Geography Ser.). (Illus.). 80p. (J). (gr. 5-12). 27.93 (978-0-8225-0367-5(0)) Lerner Publishing Group.

EGYPT—ANTIQUITIES

Armentrout, David & Armentrout, Patricia. Treasures from Egypt. 2000. (Treasures from the Past Ser.). (Illus.). 48p. (J). (gr. 4-8). lib. bdg. 29.93 (978-1-55916-289-0(9)) Rourke Publishing, LLC.

Briscoe, Diana. King Tut: Tales from the Tomb. 2002. (High Five Reading Ser.). (Illus.). 48p. (J). (gr. 3-4). lib. bdg. 22.60 (978-0-7368-9553-8(1) , Capstone High-Interest Bks.); pap. (978-0-7368-9531-6(0)) Capstone Pr., Inc.

Burgan, Michael. The Curse of King Tut's Tomb. (Graphic History Ser.). 32p. (YA). pap. 7.95 (978-0-7368-5244-9(1)) Capstone Pr., Inc.

—The Curse of King Tut's Tomb. Lohse, Otha Zackariah Edward, illus. 2005. (Graphic Library). 32p. (J). 22.60 (978-0-7368-3833-7(3)) Capstone Pr., Inc.

—King Tut's Tomb: Ancient Treasures Uncovered. 2005. (Mummies Ser.). (Illus.). 31p. (J). (ps-4). lib. bdg. 22.60 (978-0-7368-3770-5(1)) Capstone Pr., Inc.

Chapman, Gillian. Egyptian Crafts from the Past. 2000. (Crafts from the Past Ser.). (Illus.). 37p. (J). (gr. 4-7). pap. 9.95 (978-0-688-17746-1(8)) HarperCollins Pubs.

Gaff, Jackie. Ancient Egypt. 2004. (Excavating the Past Ser.). (J). pap. 8.50 (978-1-4034-5456-0(6)); lib. bdg. (978-1-4034-4836-1(1)) Heinemann Library.

Giblin, James Cross. Secrets of the Sphinx. Ibatoulline, Bagram, illus. 2004. (J). 47p. pap. (978-0-590-09852-6(7)); 48p. (gr. 4-7). pap. 17.95 (978-0-590-09847-2(0)) Scholastic, Inc.

Gogerly, Liz. Look Around an Egyptian Tomb: By Liz Gogerly. 2007. (J). (***978-1-84193-719-9(3)***) Smart Apple Media.

Green, Jen. Tutankhamen's Tomb: Uncover the Secrets & Treasures of Ancient Egypt. Slater, Gary, illus. 2006. 32p. (J). (gr. 4 up). 18.99 (978-0-7641-5999-2(2)) Barron's Educational Series, Inc.

Harris, Geraldine, et al. Illustrated Encyclopedia of Ancient Egypt. 2001. (Illus.). 160p. (J). (gr. 3 up). 29.95 (978-0-87226-606-3(0) , 66060B, Bedrick, Peter Bks.) School Specialty Publishing.

Harvey, Gill. Tutankhamun. Tomlins, Karen, illus. 2006. 64p. (J). 8.99 (978-0-7945-1271-2(2) , Usborne) EDC Publishing.

Hawass, Zahi. The Curse of the Pharaohs: My Adventures with Mummies. 2004. (Illus.). 160p. (J). (gr. 5). 19.95 (978-0-7922-6665-5(X)); 29.90 (978-0-7922-6963-2(2)) National Geographic Society. (National Geographic Children's Bks.).

Hinds, Kathryn. Life in Ancient Egypt, 4 bks., Set. Incl. City. lib. bdg. 32.79 (978-0-7614-2184-9(X)); Countryside. lib. bdg. 32.79 (978-0-7614-2185-6(8)); Pharaoh's Court. lib. bdg. 32.79 (978-0-7614-2183-2(1)); (Illus.). 80p. (J). 2006. 2007. Set lib. bdg. 131.14 (***978-0-7614-2182-5(3)*** , Benchmark Bks.) Cavendish, Marshall Corp.

Hooper, Meredith. Who Built the Pyramid? Heighway-Bury, Robin, illus. 2006. 40p. (J). (gr. 2-5). pap. 6.99 (978-0-7636-3046-1(2)) Candlewick Pr.

Hyman, Teresa L. The Pyramids of Giza. 2005. (Great Structures in History Ser.). (Illus.). 48p. (J). (gr. 4-8). 26.20 (978-0-7377-1560-6(X) , Greenhaven Pr., Inc.) Thomson Gale.

Kunhardt, Edith. Mummies. 2000. (Road to Reading Ser.). (Illus.). (J). (978-0-606-20445-3(8)) Tandem Library Bks.

Lace, William W. The Curse of King Tut. 2007. (YA). lib. bdg. (***978-1-60152-024-1(7)***) ReferencePoint Pr., Inc.

MacDonald, Fiona. Mysterious Mummies. 2003. (History Hunters Ser.). (Illus.). 32p. (J). (gr. 3 up). lib. bdg. 24.67 (978-0-8368-3742-1(8)) Stevens, Gareth Inc.

—Pyramids. 2001. (Topic Bks.). (Illus.). 32p. (J). (gr. 2-5). 23.50 (978-0-531-14552-4(2) , Watts, Franklin) Scholastic Library Publishing.

—Pyramids. 2000. (gr. 3-6). lib. bdg. 15.25 (978-0-613-34424-1(3)); (Illus.). (J). (978-0-606-20869-7(0)) Tandem Library Bks.

Malam, John. See-Through Mummies. Malam, John, illus. 2000. (See-Through Ser.). (Illus.). 32p. (J). 15.95 (978-0-7624-1586-1(X) , Running Pr. Kids) Running Pr. Bk. Pubs.

Millard, Anne. The Great Pyramid of Giza. 2005. (Places in History Ser.). (Illus.). 48p. (J). pap. (978-0-8368-5818-1(2)); lib. bdg. 30.00 (978-0-8368-5811-2(5)) Stevens, Gareth Inc. (World Almanac Library).

Morely, Jacqueline. Inside the Tomb of Tutankhamun. James, John, illus. 2005. 48p. (J). (gr. 3-7). 19.95 (978-1-59270-042-4(X)) Enchanted Lion Bks., LLC.

Naden, Corinne J. & Blue, Rose. Ancient Egyptians & the Pyramids. 2003. (J). (978-1-58417-310-6(6)); pap. (978-1-58417-311-3(4)) Lake Street Pubs.

Nardo, Don. Ancient Egypt. 2002. (History of Weapons & Warfare Ser.). (Illus.). 112p. (J). 27.45 (978-1-59018-066-2(6) , Lucent Bks.) Thomson Gale.

—King Tut's Tomb. 2004. (Illus.). (J). (gr. 4-7). 26.20 (978-0-7377-2352-6(1) , Greenhaven Pr., Inc.) Thomson Gale.

—Pyramids of Egypt. 2002. (Watts Library). (Illus.). (J). (gr. 5-7). 63p. pap. 8.95 (978-0-531-16226-2(5)); 64p. 25.50 (978-0-531-20359-0(X)) Scholastic Library Publishing. (Watts, Franklin).

—Pyramids of Egypt. 2002. (gr. 3-6). lib. bdg. 17.60 (978-0-613-53855-8(2)) Tandem Library Bks.

National Geographic Society Staff. Rediscovering Ancient Egypt. 1999. (Cultural & Geographical Exploration Ser.). (Illus.). 144p. (YA). 21.95 (978-0-7910-5445-1(4) , Chelsea Hse.) Facts On File, Inc.

O'Donnell, Kerri. The Pyramids of Egypt. 2002. (Places Around the World Ser.). (Illus.). 24p. (J). lib. bdg. 18.75 (978-0-8239-3739-4(9)) Rosen Publishing Group, Inc., The.

Pace, Mildred M. Pyramids: Tombs for Eternity. Vero, Radu & Zisu, Mirela, illus. 1998. 192p. (J). (gr. 7-12). pap. 10.95 (978-0-87226-548-6(X) , 6548XB, Bedrick, Peter Bks.) School Specialty Publishing.

Platt, Richard. Hieroglyphics Vol. 9: The Secrets of Ancient Eqyptian Writing to Unlock & Discover. 2003. (Treasure Chest Ser.). (Illus.). 32p. (J). pap. 22.95 (978-0-7624-1593-9(2) , Running Pr. Kids) Running Pr. Bk. Pubs.

Rau, Dana Meachen. Pyramid. 2006. (Bookworms Ser.). (Illus.). 32p. (J). (gr. k-2). lib. bdg. 22.79 (***978-0-7614-2275-4(7)*** , Benchmark Bks.) Cavendish, Marshall Corp.

Roberts, Russell. Rulers of Ancient Egypt. 1998. (History Makers Ser.). (Illus.). 96p. (YA). (gr. 7-10). 28.70 (978-1-56006-438-1(2) , Lucent Bks.) Thomson Gale.

Rosati, A. & Morris, Neil. The Atlas of Ancient Egypt. 2000. (Atlas Ser.). (Illus.). 64p. (J). (gr. 5 up). 19.95 (978-0-87226-610-0(9) , 66109B, Bedrick, Peter Bks.) School Specialty Publishing.

Sands, Emily. The Egyptology Handbook: A Course in the Wonders of Egypt. 2005. (Illus.). 80p. (J). (gr. 4 up). 12.99 (978-0-7636-2932-8(4)) Candlewick Pr.

Shuter, Jane. Pharaohs & Priests. 1999. (Ancient Egypt Ser.). 32p. (J). (gr. 3-5). lib. bdg. 22.79 (978-1-57572-731-8(5)) Heinemann Library.

Shuter, Jane, contrib. by. Ancient Egypt. 1999. (History Beneath Your Feet Ser.). 48p. (J). (gr. 3-7). lib. bdg. 27.12 (978-0-8172-5751-4(9)) Raintree.

Smith, Stuart Tyson & Bernard, Nancy S. The Valley of the Kings. 2002. (Digging for the Past Ser.). (Illus.). 48p. (YA). 22.95 (978-0-19-514770-4(7)) Oxford Univ. Pr., Inc.

Stewart, David. You Wouldn't Want to Be an Egyptian Mummy! Disgusting Things You'd Rather Not Know. Antram, David & Salariya, David, illus. 2001. (You Wouldn't Want to Ser.). 32p. (J). (gr. 2-5). 28.50 (978-0-531-14597-5(2) , Watts, Franklin) Scholastic Library Publishing.

—You Wouldn't Want to Be an Egyptian Mummy! Disgusting Things You'd Rather Not Know. Antram, David, illus. 2001. (You Wouldn't Want to Ser.). 32p. (J). (gr. 2-5). pap. 9.95 (978-0-531-16206-4(0) , Watts, Franklin) Scholastic Library Publishing.

Strom, Laura Layton. The Egyptian Science Gazette. 2007. (Shockwave: Science in Practice Ser.). (Illus.). 36p. (J). (gr. 4-6). lib. bdg. 25.00 (***978-0-531-17582-8(0)*** , Children's Pr.) Scholastic Library Publishing.

The Treasures of Tutankhamun. (Butterfly Bks.). (ARA.). 48p. (YA). (gr. 5-8). 9.95 (978-0-86685-485-6(1)) International Bk. Ctr., Inc.

Whiting, Jim. Threat to Ancient Egyptian Treasures. 2007. (On the Verge of Extinction Ser.). (Illus.). 32p. (J). (gr. 1-4). lib. bdg. 25.70 (***978-1-58415-588-1(4)***) Mitchell Lane Pubs., Inc.

Woods, Michael & Woods, Mary B. The Tomb of King Tutankhamun. 2008. (J). lib. bdg. (***978-0-8225-7506-1(X)***) Twenty First Century Bks.

Zoehfeld, Kathleen Weidner. The Curse of King Tut's Mummy. Nelson, James, illus. 2007. (Stepping Stones Ser.). 112p. (J). (gr. 1-4). 3.99 (978-0-375-83862-0(7) , Random Hse. Bks. for Young Readers) Random Hse. Children's Bks.

—Curse of King Tut's Mummy. Nelson, James, illus. 2007. (Stepping Stones Ser.). 112p. (J). (gr. 2-4). lib. bdg. 11.99 (978-0-375-93862-7(1) , Random Hse. Bks. for Young Readers) Random Hse. Children's Bks.

EGYPT—CIVILIZATION

Adams, Simon. Ancient Egypt. 2006. (Kingfisher Voyages Ser.). (Illus.). 60p. (J). (gr. 4-6). 15.95 (978-0-7534-6027-6(0) , Kingfisher) Houghton Mifflin Co. Trade & Reference Div.

Alcraft, Rob. Valley of the Kings. 2002. (Visiting the Past Ser.). (Illus.). 32p. (J). (gr. 5-7). pap. 6.95 (978-1-58810-421-2(4) , 91185) Heinemann Library.

—Valley of the Kings. 2001. (gr. 5-8). lib. bdg. 15.90 (978-0-613-89423-4(5)) Tandem Library Bks.

The Ancient Egyptians. 2002. (History Makers Ser.). 32p. (J). 9.95 (978-0-7525-7825-5(1)) Parragon, Inc.

Armentrout, David & Armentrout, Patricia. Egypt. 2003. (Illus.). 32p. (J). 28.50 (978-1-58952-720-1(8)) Rourke Publishing, LLC.

Benduhn, Tea. Ancient Egypt. 2006. (Illus.). 24p. (J). pap. (***978-0-8368-7786-1(1)***); lib. bdg. (***978-0-8368-7781-6(0)***) Stevens, Gareth Inc. (Weekly Reader Early Learning Library).

Bramwell, Neil D. Ancient Egypt: A MyReportLinks. com Book. 2004. (Civilizations of the Ancient World Ser.). (Illus.). 48p. (J). lib. bdg. 25.26 (978-0-7660-5252-9(4) , MyReportLinks.com Bks.) Enslow Pubs., Inc.

Briscoe, Diana. King Tut: Tales from the Tomb. 2002. (High Five Reading Ser.). (Illus.). 48p. (J). (gr. 3-4). lib. bdg. 22.60 (978-0-7368-9553-8(1) , Capstone High-Interest Bks.); pap. (978-0-7368-9531-6(0)) Capstone Pr., Inc.

Broida, Marian. The Ancient Egyptians & Their Neighbors. 1999. (Illus.). 208p. (J). (gr. 4-7). pap., act. bk. ed. 16.95 (978-1-55652-360-1(2)) Chicago Review Pr., Inc.

—Ancient Egyptians & Their Neighbors: An Activity Guide. 1999. (gr. 3-6). lib. bdg. 26.85 (978-0-613-83344-8(9)) Tandem Library Bks.

Challen, Paul C. Life in Ancient Egypt. 2004. (Peoples of the Ancient World Ser.). (Illus.). 32p. (J). (978-0-7787-2038-6(1)); pap. (978-0-7787-2068-3(3)) Crabtree Publishing Co.

Chapman, Gillian. Egyptian Crafts from the Past. 2000. (Crafts from the Past Ser.). (Illus.). 37p. (J). (gr. 4-7). pap. 9.95 (978-0-688-17746-1(8)) HarperCollins Pubs.

Cole, Joanna. Ancient Egypt. 2003. (gr. k-3). lib. bdg. 15.30 (978-0-613-72892-8(0)) Tandem Library Bks.

Deady, Kathleen W. Ancient Egypt. 2004. (Illus.). 48p. (J). 17.95 (978-0-7368-2467-5(7) , Bridgestone Bks.) Capstone Pr., Inc.

Dickinson, Clive. Mummies, Temples & Tombs. 2003. (TV tie-in Edition Ser.). (Illus.). 96p. (YA). pap. 7.99 (978-0-00-715378-7(3)) HarperCollins Pubs. Ltd. GBR. *Dist:* Independent Pubs. Group.

Dorling Kindersley Publishing Staff, et al. Ancient Egypt. 2002. (Dk Revealed Ser.). (Illus.). 48p. (J). (gr. 3-12). 12.99 (978-0-7894-8883-1(3)) Dorling Kindersley Publishing, Inc.

Eddy, Jim R. Ancient Egypt. 2005. (Life During the Great Civilizations Ser.). (Illus.). 48p. (J). (gr. 5-7). 23.70 (978-1-4103-0528-2(7) , Blackbirch Pr., Inc.) Thomson Gale.

Egyptian Life. 2006. (YA). per. (978-1-59905-052-2(8)) Saddleback Educational Publishing.

Fine, Jil. Writing in Ancient Egypt. 2003. (Writing in the Ancient World Ser.). (Illus.). 24p. (J). lib. bdg. 17.25 (978-0-8239-6506-9(6) , PowerKids Pr.) Rosen Publishing Group, Inc., The.

Fix, Alexandra. History & Activities of Ancient Egypt. 2006. (Hands-On Ancient History Ser.). (Illus.). 32p. (J). (978-1-4034-7923-5(2)); pap. (978-1-4034-7931-0(3)) Heinemann Library.

Gaff, Jackie. Ancient Egypt. 2004. (Excavating the Past Ser.). (J). pap. 8.50 (978-1-4034-5456-0(6)); lib. bdg. (978-1-4034-4836-1(1)) Heinemann Library.

Ganeri, Anita. Ancient Egypt. 2004. (Historic Civilizations Ser.). (Illus.). 32p. (J). lib. bdg. 24.67 (978-0-8368-4197-8(2)) Stevens, Gareth Inc.

—Ancient Egyptians. 2006. (Illus.). 32p. (J). (978-0-7565-1645-1(5)) Compass Point Bks.

—Mummies & Ancient Egypt. 2005. (First Look at History Ser.). (Illus.). 24p. (J). lib. bdg. 22.00 (978-0-8368-4527-3(7)) Stevens, Gareth Inc.

—Pharaohs, Heros & Thieves. 2003. (TV tie-in Edition Ser.). (Illus.). 120p. (YA). pap. 8.99 (978-0-00-715377-0(5)) HarperCollins Pubs. Ltd. GBR. *Dist:* Independent Pubs. Group.

Gibbons, Gail. Mummies, Pyramids, & Pharaohs: A Book about Ancient Egypt. 2004. (Illus.). 32p. (J). 16.99 (978-0-316-30928-8(1)) Little Brown & Co.

Gifford, Clive. Tomb Hunters: Discover the Incredible Lost World of Egypt. 2007. (Illus.). 32p. 19.95 (**978-0-7624-3018-5(4)*) Running Pr. Bk. Pubs.

Gleason, Katherine. Ancient Egyptian Culture. 2006. (Discovering the Arts Ser.). (Illus.). 48p. (J). (gr. 4-8). 20.95 (978-1-59515-519-1(8)) Rourke Publishing, LLC.

Glencoe McGraw-Hill Staff & McGraw-Hill - Jamestown Education Staff. Jamestown's Early Civilizations: Egyptian Life. 2001. (gr. 5-12). pap. 11.96 (978-0-8092-9594-4(6) , 9780809295944) Jamestown.

Gogerly, Liz. Ancient Egypt. 2007. (Illus.). 64p. (J). (**978-1-4109-2735-4(0)); (*978-1-4109-2728-6(8)*) Steck-Vaughn.

Harris, Nathaniel. Everyday Life in Ancient Egypt. 2005. (Clues to the Past Ser.). (Illus.). 32p. (J). (gr. 4-7). lib. bdg. 27.10 (978-1-932889-78-9(7)) Sea-To-Sea Pubns.

Hewitt, Sally. The Egyptians. 2007. (J). (**978-1-59920-044-6(9)*) Smart Apple Media.

Hibbert, Clare. Ancient Egypt. 2005. (Rich & Poor in Ser.). (Illus.). 32p. (J). (gr. 4-7). lib. bdg. 27.10 (978-1-58340-720-2(0)) Smart Apple Media.

Hinds, Kathryn. Life in Ancient Egypt, 4 bks., Set. Incl. City. lib. bdg. 32.79 (978-0-7614-2184-9(X)); Countryside. lib. bdg. 32.79 (978-0-7614-2185-6(8)); Pharaoh's Court. lib. bdg. 32.79 (978-0-7614-2183-2(1)); (Illus.). 80p. (J). 2006. 2007. Set lib. bdg. 131.14 (**978-0-7614-2182-5(3)* , Benchmark Bks.) Cavendish, Marshall Corp.

Hossell, Karen Price. Hieroglyphics. 2003. (Communicating Ser.). 48p. (J). (gr. 3-5). pap. 8.50 (978-1-58810-941-5(0) , 91580) Heinemann Library.

HSP. First-Place Reading for Title I: Growing up in Ancient Egypt. 2nd ed. 2002. (Harcourt Title I Reading Programs Ser.). (gr. 6 up). pap. 58.40 (978-0-15-338168-3(X)) Harcourt Schl. Pubs.

Jane Shuter. Ancient Egypt. 2nd ed. 2007. (Illus.). 32p. (J). pap. (**978-1-4034-8817-6(7)*) Heinemann Library.

Jovinelly, Joann & Netelkos, Jason. The Crafts & Culture of the Ancient Egyptians. 2002. (Crafts of the Ancient World Ser.). (Illus.). 48p. (YA). (gr. 5-8). lib. bdg. 29.25 (978-0-8239-3509-3(4) , Rosen Central) Rosen Publishing Group, Inc., The.

Kaplan, Leslie C. Art & Religion in Ancient Egypt. 2004. (Primary Sources of Ancient Civilizations Ser.). (J). lib. bdg. (978-0-8239-8932-4(1)); (Illus.). 24p. lib. bdg. 19.95 (978-0-8239-6782-7(4)) Rosen Publishing Group, Inc., The. (PowerKids Pr.).

—Land & Resources in Ancient Egypt. 2004. (Primary Sources of Ancient Civilizations Ser.). (Illus.). 24p. (J). lib. bdg. 19.95 (978-0-8239-6781-0(6) , PowerKids Pr.) Rosen Publishing Group, Inc., The.

—Land & Resources of Ancient Egypt. 2004. (Primary Sources of Ancient Civilizations Ser.). (Illus.). 24p. (J). lib. bdg. (978-0-8239-8931-7(3) , PowerKids Pr.) Rosen Publishing Group, Inc., The.

—Technology of Ancient Egypt. 2004. (Primary Sources of Ancient Civilizations Ser.). (Illus.). 24p. (J). lib. bdg. (978-0-8239-8934-8(8)); lib. bdg. 19.95 (978-0-8239-6785-8(9)) Rosen Publishing Group, Inc., The. (PowerKids Pr.).

King, David C. Projects about Ancient Egypt. 2006. (Hands-On History Ser.). (Illus.). 48p. (J). lib. bdg. 29.93 (978-0-7614-2258-7(7) , Benchmark Bks.) Cavendish, Marshall Corp.

Klingel, Cynthia Fitterer & Noyed, Robert B. Ancient Egypt. 2002. (Let's See Library). (Illus.). 24p. (J). (gr. 1 up). lib. bdg. 19.93 (978-0-7565-0291-1(8)) Compass Point Bks.

Landau, Elaine. Exploring Ancient Egypt with Elaine Landau. 2005. (Exploring Ancient Civilizations with Elaine Landau Ser.). (Illus.). 48p. (J). (ps-7). lib. bdg. 23.93 (978-0-7660-2339-0(7) , Enslow Elementary) Enslow Pubs., Inc.

Langley, Andrew. Ancient Egypt. 2002. (History in Stone Ser.). 64p. (J). (gr. 3-7). 16.95 (978-1-57145-552-9(3) , Silver Dolphin Bks.) Advantage Pubs. Group.

—Ancient Egypt. 2005. (History in Art Ser.). (Illus.). 48p. (J). lib. bdg. 29.93 (978-1-4109-0518-5(7)) Steck-Vaughn.

MacDonald, Fiona. Ancient Egypt. 2004. (Illus.). 64p. (J). 17.99 (978-0-00-715376-3(7)) HarperCollins Pubs. Ltd. GBR. *Dist:* Independent Pubs. Group.

—The Ancient Egyptians. 2007. (J). lib. bdg. 19.95 (**978-1-59566-352-8(5)*) QEB Publishing Inc.

MacDonald, Fiona. Ancient Egyptians Ancient Egypt. (Illus.). 64p. (J). pap. 9.99 (978-0-00-717797-4(6)) Zondervan.

Malam, John. Ancient Egypt. rev. ed. 1998. (Remains to Be Seen Ser.). (Illus.). 48p. (J). (gr. 5-8). (978-0-237-51839-4(2) , Evans Brothers, Limited) Evans Publishing Group.

—Ancient Egyptian Children. 2003. (People in the Past Ser.). (Illus.). 48p. (J). (gr. 4-6). lib. bdg. 27.07 (978-1-4034-0309-4(0)) Heinemann Library.

—Ancient Egyptian Homes. 2003. (People in the Past Ser.). (Illus.). 48p. (J). (gr. 4-6). lib. bdg. 27.07 (978-1-4034-0310-0(4)) Heinemann Library.

—Ancient Egyptian Jobs. (People in the Past Ser.). (Illus.). 48p. (J). 2003. (gr. 4-6). lib. bdg. 27.07 (978-1-4034-0311-7(2)); 2002. pap. 8.50 (978-1-4034-0515-9(8)) Heinemann Library.

—Ancient Egyptian Jobs. 2002. (gr. 3-6). lib. bdg. 17.05 (978-0-613-86431-2(X)) Tandem Library Bks.

—Ancient Egyptian Women. (People in the Past Ser.). (Illus.). 48p. (J). 2003. (gr. 4-6). lib. bdg. 27.07 (978-1-4034-0313-1(9)); 2002. pap. 8.50 (978-1-4034-0517-3(4)) Heinemann Library.

—Homes. 2002. (People in the Past Ser.). (Illus.). 48p. (J). pap. (978-1-4034-0514-2(X)) Heinemann Library.

Martin, Amanda. Ancient Egypt. 2000. (My World Ser.). (Illus.). (J). 14.75 (978-0-606-21903-7(X)) Tandem Library Bks.

McRae, Anne & Agosta, Loredana. Who Were the Ancient Egyptians? 2007. (J). (**978-88-6098-053-3(4)*) McRae Bks. Srl.

Millard, Anne. The Great Pyramid of Giza. 2005. (Places in History Ser.). (Illus.). 48p. (J). pap. (978-0-8368-5818-1(2)); lib. bdg. 30.00 (978-0-8368-5811-2(5)) Stevens, Gareth Inc. (World Almanac Library).

—Pyramids. 2007. (Hallmarks of History Ser.). (Illus.). 32p. (J). (**978-1-59604-122-6(6)*) Stargazer Bks.

Millard, Anne. The World of Pyramids. 2004. (World Of Ser.). (Illus.). 64p. (J). (gr. 4-6). pap. 8.95 (978-0-7534-5787-0(3) , Kingfisher) Houghton Mifflin Co. Trade & Reference Div.

Minnis. Ancient Egypt. 2004. (Illus.). 32p. (J). 26.36 (978-1-4109-0616-8(7)) Harcourt Schl. Pubs.

Morely, Jacqueline. Inside the Tomb of Tutankhamun. James, John, illus. 2005. 48p. (J). (gr. 3-7). 19.95 (978-1-59270-042-4(X)) Enchanted Lion Bks., LLC.

Morin, Jacqueline. So You Want to Be an Egyptian Princess. Hewetson, Nicholas, illus. 1999. (So You Want to Be... Ser.). 32p. (gr. 3-6). lib. bdg. 21.90 (978-0-7613-1422-6(9) , Twenty-First Century Bks.) Lerner Publishing Group.

Morley, Jacqueline. You Wouldn't Want to Be a Pyramid Builder! 2004. (You Wouldn't Want To Ser.). (Illus.). 32p. (J). 28.50 (978-0-531-12351-5(0)); (gr. 2-5). pap. 9.95 (978-0-531-16396-2(2)) Scholastic Library Publishing. (Watts, Franklin).

Morris, Neil. Ancient Egypt. 2003. (Uncovering History Ser.). (Illus.). 46p. (J). lib. bdg. 28.50 (978-1-58340-247-4(0)) Smart Apple Media.

Moscovitch, Arlene. Egypt the People. 2000. (gr. 3-6). lib. bdg. 16.40 (978-0-613-21480-3(3)) Tandem Library Bks.

Naden, Corinne J. & Blue, Rose. Ancient Egyptians & the Pyramids. 2003. (J). (978-1-58417-310-6(6)); pap. (978-1-58417-311-3(4)) Lake Street Pubs.

Nardo, Don. Ancient Alexandria. 2002. (Traveler's Guide to Ser.). (Illus.). 112p. (J). 29.95 (978-1-59018-142-3(5) , Lucent Bks.) Thomson Gale.

—Ancient Egypt. (World History Ser.). (Illus.). (J). 2006. 112p. (gr. 7-10). 32.45 (978-1-59018-857-6(8) , 1256847, Lucent Bks.); 2002. 48p. (gr. 3-5). 23.70 (978-0-7377-0955-1(3) , LML00902-178589, Kidhaven) Thomson Gale.

National Geographic Society Staff. Rediscovering Ancient Egypt. 1999. (Cultural & Geographical Exploration Ser.). (Illus.). 144p. (YA). 21.95 (978-0-7910-5445-1(4) , Chelsea Hse.) Facts On File, Inc.

Netzley, Patricia D. Ancient Egypt. 2003. (A to Z Encyclopedias Ser.). (Illus.). 336p. (J). 77.45 (978-0-7377-1150-9(7) , Greenhaven Pr., Inc.) Thomson Gale.

Nicholson, Robert. Egyptians. 2000. (Collectafact Ser.: Vol. 3). (Illus.). 48p. (J). (gr. 1-5). 4.95 (978-1-58728-754-1(4) , Two Can Publishing) T&N Children's Publishing.

Nobleman, Marc Tyler. History Pockets: Ancient Egypt. Davis, Cindy, illus. 2003. (History Pockets Ser.). 96p. (J). (gr. 4-6). suppl. ed. (978-1-55799-904-7(X) , EMC 3706) Evan-Moor Educational Pubs.

Osborne, Mary Pope & Osborne, Will. Mummies & Pyramids: A Nonfiction Companion to Mummies in the Morning. Murdocca, Sal, illus. 2001. (Magic Tree House Research Guide Ser.: No. 3). 128p. (J). (gr. k-3). lib. bdg. 11.99 (978-0-375-90298-7(8) , Random Hse. Bks. for Young Readers) Random Hse. Children's Bks.

Osborne, Will & Osborne, Mary Pope. Mummies & Pyramids: A Nonfiction Companion to Mummies in the Morning. Murdocca, Sal, illus. 2001. (Magic Tree House Research Guide Ser.: No. 3). 128p. (J). (gr. k-3). pap. 4.99 (978-0-375-80298-0(3) , Random Hse. Bks. for Young Readers) Random Hse. Children's Bks.

Pancella, Peggy. Hatshepsut. 2003. (Historical Biographies Ser.). (Illus.). 32p. (J). pap. 6.95 (978-1-4034-3709-9(2)); lib. bdg. 22.79 (978-1-4034-3701-3(7)) Heinemann Library.

Pavan, Toni. Egypt, Nubia, & Kush. 2005. (Navigators Ser.). (J). pap. 44.00 (**978-1-4108-5113-0(3)*) Benchmark Education Co.

Perl, Lila. The Ancient Egyptians. (People of the Ancient World Ser.). (Illus.). 112p. (J). 2005. (gr. 6-8). pap. 9.95 (978-0-531-16738-0(0)); 2004. 30.50 (978-0-531-12345-4(6)) Scholastic Library Publishing. (Watts, Franklin).

Price Hossell, Karen. Hieroglyphics. 2003. (Communicating Ser.). (Illus.). 48p. (J). (gr. 3-5). lib. bdg. 27.07 (978-1-58810-485-4(0)) Heinemann Library.

Reece, Katherine E. The Egyptians: Builders of the Pyramids. 2005. (Ancient Civilizations Ser.). (Illus.). 48p. (gr. 4-8). 20.95 (978-1-59515-505-4(8)) Rourke Publishing, LLC.

Rees, Rosemary. The Ancient Egyptians. (Illus.). 64p. (J). 2006. (**978-1-4034-8746-9(4)*); 2002. (gr. 4-6). pap. 8.95 (978-1-58810-314-7(5) , 91069) Heinemann Library.

Rosati, A. & Morris, Neil. The Atlas of Ancient Egypt. 2000. (Atlas Ser.). (Illus.). 64p. (J). (gr. 5 up). 19.95 (978-0-87226-610-0(9) , 66109B, Bedrick, Peter Bks.) School Specialty Publishing.

Rosemary Rees. The Ancient Egyptians. 2nd ed. 2006. (Illus.). 64p. (J). pap. (**978-1-4034-8752-0(9)*) Heinemann Library.

Ross, Stewart. Ancient Egyptians. 2006. (Illus.). 48p. (J). pap. (978-0-8368-6241-6(4)); lib. bdg. 30.00 (978-0-8368-6189-1(2)) Stevens, Gareth Inc. (World Almanac Library).

—Egypt in Spectacular Cross-Section. Biesty, Stephen, illus. 2005. (Egypt Ser.). 32p. (J). 18.99 (978-0-439-74537-6(3) , Scholastic Nonfiction) Scholastic, Inc.

Sharp, Anne Wallace. Women of Ancient Egypt. 2005. (Women in History Ser.). (Illus.). 112p. (YA). (gr. 7-10). lib. bdg. 32.45 (978-1-59018-361-8(4) , Lucent Bks.) Thomson Gale.

Shuter, Jane. The Ancient Egyptians. 2007. (Illus.). 32p. (J). (**978-1-4034-8810-7(X)*) Heinemann Library.

—The Ancient Egyptians. 1999. (History Starts Here Ser.). (Illus.). 32p. (J). (ps-3). lib. bdg. 25.69 (978-0-7398-1351-5(X)) Raintree.

—Builders & Craftsmen. 1999. (Ancient Egypt Ser.). 32p. (J). (gr. 3-5). lib. bdg. 22.79 (978-1-57572-728-8(5)) Heinemann Library.

—Discoveries & Inventions. 1999. (Ancient Egypt Ser.). 32p. (J). (gr. 3-5). lib. bdg. 22.79 (978-1-57572-729-5(3)) Heinemann Library.

—The Egyptians. 2003. (Strange Histories Ser.). (Illus.). 32p. (J). lib. bdg. 25.70 (978-0-7398-6440-1(8)) Raintree.

—Food & Farming. 1999. (Ancient Egypt Ser.). 32p. (J). (gr. 3-5). lib. bdg. 22.79 (978-1-57572-730-1(7)) Heinemann Library.

—Pharaohs & Priests. 1999. (Ancient Egypt Ser.). 32p. (J). (gr. 3-5). lib. bdg. 22.79 (978-1-57572-731-8(5)) Heinemann Library.

—The Pyramids. 2003. (Visiting the Past Ser.). (Illus.). 32p. (J). pap. 7.50 (978-1-4034-0622-4(7)); (gr. 5-7). lib. bdg. 25.64 (978-1-58810-706-0(X)) Heinemann Library.

Shuter, Jane, contrib. by. Ancient Egypt. 1999. (History Beneath Your Feet Ser.). 48p. (J). (gr. 3-7). lib. bdg. 27.12 (978-0-8172-5751-4(9)) Raintree.

Shuter, Jane & Taylor, Pat. The Ancient Egyptians. 1999. (History Opens Windows Ser.). 32p. (J). (gr. 2-4). pap. (978-1-57572-590-1(8)) Heinemann Library.

Simon, Seymour. Pyramids & Mummies. 2004. (See More Readers). (Illus.). 40p. (J). 14.50 (978-1-58717-240-3(2)); Vol. 3. pap. 3.95 (978-1-58717-241-0(0)) Chronicle Bks. LLC. (SeaStar Bks.).

Solodky, M. The Technology of Ancient Egypt. 2005. (Technology of the Ancient World Ser.). (Illus.). 48p. (J). (978-1-4042-0557-4(8)) Rosen Publishing Group, Inc., The.

Steedman, Scott. The Egyptian News. 2000. (History News Ser.). (Illus.). 32p. (J). (gr. 3 up). lib. bdg. 24.67 (978-0-8368-2719-4(8)) Stevens, Gareth Inc.

—Egyptian News. 2000. (News Ser.). (J). (978-0-606-19313-9(8)); (gr. 3-6). lib. bdg. 15.30 (978-0-613-28473-8(9)) Tandem Library Bks.

Steele, Christy. Egypt. Sloan, Frank, ed. 2001. (Ancient Civilizations Ser.). (Illus.). 48p. (J). (gr. 4-7). lib. bdg. 22.83 (978-0-7398-3576-0(9)) Raintree.

Steele, Philip. Ancient Egypt. 2000. (Illus.). 256p. pap. 7.95 (978-1-84215-040-5(5) , Southwater) Anness Publishing GBR. *Dist:* National Bk. Network.

—Ancient Egypt. 1998. (Step into Ser.). (Illus.). 64p. (gr. 3-7). 14.95 (978-1-85967-525-0(5) , Lorenz Bks.) Anness Publishing, Inc.

—Ancient Egypt. 2002. (Curious Kids Guides). (Illus.). 32p. (J). tchr. ed. 6.95 (978-0-7534-5475-6(0) , Kingfisher) Houghton Mifflin Co. Trade & Reference Div.

Streissguth, Thomas. Life in Ancient Egypt. 2000. (Way People Live Ser.). (Illus.). 96p. (YA). (gr. 7-10). 29.95 (978-1-56006-643-9(1) , LML00902-177997, Lucent Bks.) Thomson Gale.

Strom, Laura Layton. Tombs & Treasure: Ancient Egypt. 2007. (Shockwave: Arts & Culture Ser.). (Illus.). 36p. (J). (gr. 4-6). lib. bdg. 25.00 (**978-0-531-17787-7(4)* , Children's Pr.) Scholastic Library Publishing.

Tames, Richard. Children. 2002. (People in the Past Ser.). (Illus.). 48p. (J). pap. (978-1-4034-0513-5(1)) Heinemann Library.

Theisen, Gordon. The Secrets of Tutankhamen. 2001. (Natural History Guides Ser.). (Illus.). 40p. (J). pap. 9.99 (978-0-86730-843-3(5)) Lebhar-Friedman Bks.

Turnbull, Stephanie. Egyptians. (Beginners Social Studies). 32p. (J). (gr. 1 up). lib. bdg. 12.99 (978-1-58086-656-9(5) , Usborne) EDC Publishing.

—Egyptians - Internet Referenced (Level 2) 2007. 32p. (J). 4.99 (978-0-7945-1344-3(1) , Usborne) EDC Publishing.

Van Vleet, Carmella. Explore Ancient Egypt! 25 Great Projects, Activities, & Experiments. 2008. (Explore Your World Ser.). 96p. (J). (gr. 1-4). pap. 12.95 (**978-0-9792268-3-0(X)*) Nomad Pr.

Weatherill, Sue & Weatherill, Steve. Egyptian Activity Book. 2006. (Creative Fun Ser.). (Illus.). 24p. (J). pap., act. bk. ed. 5.99 (978-0-7641-3414-2(0)) Barron's Educational Series, Inc.

Williams, Brenda & Williams, Brian. Reach for the Stars: Ancient Egyptian Pyramids. 2007. (J). (**978-1-4109-2888-7(8)); pap. (*978-1-4109-2895-5(0)*) Steck-Vaughn.

Williams, Brian. Tutankhamen. 2002. (Historical Biographies Ser.). (Illus.). 32p. (J). (gr. 2-4). lib. bdg. 22.79 (978-1-58810-568-4(7)) Heinemann Library.

Winters, Kay. Voices of Ancient Egypt. Moser, Barry, illus. 2003. 32p. (J). (gr. 3-7). 16.95 (978-0-7922-7560-2(8) , National Geographic Children's Bks.) National Geographic Society.

Wood, Tim. Maravillas de la Antig Edad. Colella, Elida Marta, tr. Adams, Jonathan, illus. 2002. (SPA.). 48p. (J). 24.95 (978-950-11-1566-6(6)) Sigmar ARG. *Dist:* Lectorum Pubns., Inc.

Wright, Rachel. The Egyptians. (Illus.). 32p. (YA). (gr. 3 up). lib. bdg. 27.10 (978-1-932889-00-0(0)) Sea-To-Sea Pubns.

Wroble, Lisa A. Kids in Ancient Egypt. 1999. (Kids Throughout History Ser.). (Illus.). 24p. (J). (gr. 3). lib. bdg. 18.75 (978-0-8239-5256-4(8) , PowerKids Pr.) Rosen Publishing Group, Inc., The.

EGYPT—FICTION

Abuan, Natalye, adapted by. The Emperor's New Groove. 2000. (Read-Aloud Book Ser.). (Illus.). 64p. (J). (ps-2). 6.99 (978-0-7364-0196-8(2)) Mouse Works.

Adler, David A. Brothers in Egypt. abr. ed. (Prince of Egypt Ser.). 64p. pap. (978-0-582-36482-0(5)) Addison-Wesley Longman, Inc.

Al Kalifa & the Nile, 6, Pack. (Bookweb Ser.). 32p. (gr. 5 up). 34.00 (978-0-7635-3788-3(8)) Rigby Education.

Arnold, Edward Ronny. Rashida. 2003. 110p. (YA). pap. 7.99 (978-0-9721216-6-8(8) , 0972121668) Computer Classics (R).

Bastet - Evaluation Guide: Evaluation Guide. 2006. (J). (978-1-55942-400-4(1)) Marsh Media.

Bastet - Teaching Guide. 2000. (J). 17.95 (978-1-55942-175-1(4)) Marsh Media.

Beechen, Adam. Cat's Meow. 2001. (gr. k-3). lib. bdg. 11.25 (978-0-613-43922-0(8)) Tandem Library Bks.

Bott, Elizabeth. Vinnie in Egypt. Frosini, Guido & Cecchetti, Alessandra, illus. Lt. ed. 2000. (Laugh & Learn Travel Ser.: No. 1). 54p. (J). (gr. k-8). 15.95 (978-0-9704678-0-5(X)) Pageturner Bks.

Bradman, Tony & Chatterton, Martin. The Mummy Family Finds Fame. 2006. (Illus.). 46p. (J). (978-0-7787-1076-9(9)) Crabtree Publishing Co.

Chananie, Gloria. Fearful Frannie Flies to Egypt. 2005. 81p. pap. 14.95 (978-1-4137-7701-7(5)) PublishAmerica, Inc.

Clements, Andrew. Temple Cat. 2001. (J). (978-0-606-21484-1(4)); lib. bdg. 14.10 (978-0-613-35581-0(4)) Tandem Library Bks.

Cooney, Caroline B. For All Time. 2003. 272p. (YA). (gr. 7). pap. 5.99 (978-0-440-22931-5(6) , Laurel Leaf) Random Hse. Children's Bks.

—For All Time. 2003. (gr. 7-12). lib. bdg. 13.00 (978-0-613-72328-2(7)) Tandem Library Bks.

Corwin, Susan Simon. The Cryptic Cat. Corwin, Stuart, illus. 2006. 99p. (YA). (**978-0-9790632-0-6(5)*) Lucky Duck Designs.

Cuentos Egipcios. (SPA., Illus.). (YA). 11.95 (978-84-7281-068-6(2) , AF1068) Auriga, Ediciones S.A. ESP. *Dist:* Continental Bk. Co., Inc.

Curry, Jane Louise. The Egyptian Box. 2002. (Illus.). 192p. (J). (gr. 4-7). 16.95 (978-0-689-84273-3(2) , McElderry, Margaret K.) Simon & Schuster Children's Publishing.

—The Egyptian Box. Lt. ed. 2002. 216p. (J). 21.95 (978-0-7862-4896-4(3)) Thorndike Pr.

Davie, Jan. Stairway to the Stars. 2005. 76p. pap. (**978-1-84401-569-6(6)*) Athena Pr.

Deary, Terry. The Magic & the Mummy. Flook, Helen, illus. 2005. (Read-It! Chapter Bks.). 64p. (J). (ps-k). lib. bdg. 19.95 (978-1-4048-1271-0(7)) Picture Window Bks.

Doyle, Bill. Betrayed! The 1977 Journal of Zeke Moorie. Hoskins, Brian, illus. 2006. 139p. (J). lib. bdg. 18.46 (**978-1-4242-1733-5(4)*) Fitzgerald Bks.

E F G

—Betrayed! The 1977 Journal of Zeke Moorie. 4th ed. 2006. (Crime Through Time Ser.: No. 4). 144p. (J). (gr. 3-7). pap. 5.99 (978-0-316-05741-7(X)) Little Brown & Co.

—ICED: The 2007 Journal of Nick Fitzmorgan. 5th ed. 2006. (Crime Through Time Ser.: No. 5). (Illus.). 144p. (J). (gr. 3-7). pap. 5.99 (978-0-316-05753-0(3)) Little Brown & Co.

—Trapped: The 2031 Journal of Otis Fitzmorgan. 6th ed. 2006. (Crime Through Time Ser.: No. 6). 144p. (J). (gr. 3-7). pap. 5.99 (978-0-316-05754-7(1)) Little Brown & Co.

Duey, Kathleen. Mummy. 2007. (Illus.). 96p. (J). 24.21 (978-1-59961-225-6(9)) Spotlight.

Gantos, Jack. Rotten Ralph Helps Out: A Rotten Ralph Rotten Reader. Rubel, Nicole, illus. (Rotten Ralph Rotten Readers Ser.). 48p. (J). 2004. pap. 5.95 (978-0-374-46355-7(7) , Sunburst); 2001. (gr. 1-3). 15.00 (978-0-374-36355-0(2) , Farrar, Straus & Giroux (BYR)) Farrar, Straus & Giroux.

Hall, Margaret & Jones, Dawn L. Sebastian in Egypt. Wenzel, David, illus. 2001. (Suitcase Bear Adventures Ser.). (J). (978-0-9713174-2-0(9) , Bear & Co.) Bear & Co.

Harcourt School Publishers Staff. Egyptian Adventure Advanced Level. 3rd ed. 2002. (Trophies Reading Program Ser.). (Illus.). pap. 5.10 (978-0-15-323473-6(3)) Harcourt Schl. Pubs.

—How Will I Get There? 3rd ed. 2002. (Trophies English Language Learners Ser.). (Illus.). pap. 5.10 (978-0-15-327882-2(X)) Harcourt Schl. Pubs.

Harp, O. J. Across Time: Love Eternal. 2002. pap. 19.95 (978-1-885778-97-0(X)) Seaburn Pubs.

Harris, Whittney N., et al. Chocolate Covered Adventures: Tyco's Search for the Ark of the Covenant. 1999. (Illus.). 32p. (J). pap. 6.00 (978-0-9677469-4-4(9)) Van Buren California Publishing.

Harvey, M. A. The Scorpion Secret: Dare to Take the Test. 2004. (Illus.). 128p. (J). pap. (978-1-84458-050-7(4)) Chrysalis Children's Bks.

Hawes, Louise. Muti's Necklace: The Oldest Story in the World. Guay, Rebecca, illus. 2006. 32p. (J). (gr. k-3). 16.00 (978-0-618-53583-5(7)) Houghton Mifflin Co.

Hergé. Les Cigares du Pharaon. 1999. (Tintin Ser.).Tr. of Cigars of the Pharaoh. (FRE., Illus.). 62p. (J). (gr. 4-7). 21.95 (978-2-203-00103-9(8)) Casterman, Editions FRA. *Dist:* Distribooks, Inc.

—Cigars of the Pharaoh.Tr. of Cigares du Pharoan. (Illus.). 62p. (J). 19.95 (978-0-8288-5021-6(6)) French & European Pubns., Inc.

Howe, James. Screaming Mummies of the Pharaoh's Tomb II. Helquist, Brett, illus. 2003. (Tales from the House of Bunnicula Ser.). 112p. (J). pap. 3.99 (978-0-689-83954-2(5) , Aladdin) Simon & Schuster Children's Publishing.

Irbinskas, Heather & King, Andra. Morgan the Dog: An Egyptian Adventure. 2002. 33p. 14.95 (978-0-9711970-2-2(4)) Morgan Hse. Publishing.

Jarman, Julia. The Time-Travelling Cat & the Tudor Treasure. 2007. 144p. (J). (gr. 4-7). 7.95 (*978-1-84270-616-9(0)) Andersen GBR. *Dist:* Independent Pubs. Group.

Jones, Allan Frewin. Legend of the Pharaoh's Tomb. 2005. 191p. pap. (*978-0-439-80373-1(X)) Scholastic, Inc.

Kanaan, Hanan S. The Jewel of Love. 2003. (Illus.). 114p. (J). per. 11.95 (978-1-59405-000-8(7) , New Age World Pr.) New Age World Publishing.

Karr, Kathleen. Bone Dry. 2002. (Illus.). 240p. (gr. 5-9). 15.99 (978-0-7868-0776-5(8)) Hyperion Bks. for Children.

—Bone Dry. 2002. lib. bdg. 14.15 (978-0-613-68195-7(9)) Tandem Library Bks.

Kendrick, Rosalyn. Bride of the Nile. 1998. 176p. (YA). (gr. 9 up). pap. 6.95 (978-0-86327-622-4(9)) Wolfhound Pr. IRL. *Dist:* Irish American Bk. Co.

Kerr, P. B. The Akhenaten Adventure. 2004. (Children of the Lamp Ser.: Bk. 1). 368p. (J). (gr. 4-7). pap. 16.95 (978-0-439-67019-7(5) , Orchard Bks.) Scholastic, Inc.

—The Akhenaten Adventure No. 1: Children of the Lamp. l.t. ed. 2005. 430p. 23.95 (978-0-7862-7299-0(6) , Large Print Pr.) Thorndike Pr.

Knife and Packer Staff. Egyptian Adventure. 4th rev. ed. 2005. (Captain Fact Ser.: Bk. 4). (Illus.). 112p. (gr. 2-5). pap. 4.99 (978-0-7868-5574-2(6) , Volo) Hyperion Bks. for Children.

Krebs, Laurie. We're Sailing down the Nile: A Journey Through Egypt. Wilson, Anne, illus. 2007. 32p. (J). (ps-3). 16.99 (*978-1-84686-040-9(7)) Barefoot Bks., Inc.

LaFevers, R. L. Theodosia & the Serpents of Chaos. Tanaka, Yoko, illus. 2007. 368p. (J). (gr. 5-7). 16.00 (*978-0-618-75638-4(8)) Houghton Mifflin Co. Trade & Reference Div.

Lardone, Lilia. Papiros. (SPA.). (YA). 9.95 (978-958-04-6874-5(5)) Norma S.A. COL. *Dist:* Distribuidora Norma, Inc.

Lattimore, Deborah Nourse. Winged Cat: And Other Tales of Ancient Civilization. 2002. (Illus.). 80p. (J). pap. 4.25 (978-0-06-442154-6(6) , Harper Trophy) HarperCollins Pubs.

Levithan, David. The Mummy, Level 2. 2001. 48p. (C). pap. 9.00 (978-0-582-45193-3(0)) Longman Publishing Group.

Lewin, Betsy. What's the Matter, Habibi? 2004. (Illus.). 32p. (J). (gr. k-3). pap. 6.95 (978-0-618-43242-4(6) , Clarion Bks.) Houghton Mifflin Co. Trade & Reference Div.

Limke Jeff. Isis y Osiris (Isis & Osiris) Hasta el fin del mundo (to the Ends of the Earth) Witt, David, illus. 2007. (Mitos y leyendas en viñetas (Graphic Myths & Legends) Ser.). (SPA & ENG.). (J). pap. 8.95 (*978-0-8225-7971-7(5) , Ediciones Lerner) Lerner Publishing Group.

Logan, Claudia. The 5,000-Year-Old Puzzle: Solving a Mystery at Giza. Sweet, Melissa, illus. 2001. (J). (978-0-7894-2635-2(8)) Dorling Kindersley Publishing, Inc.

—The 5,000-Year-Old Puzzle: Solving a Mystery of Ancient Egypt. Sweet, Melissa, illus. 2002. 48p. (J). 17.00 (978-0-374-32335-6(6) , Farrar, Straus & Giroux (BYR)) Farrar, Straus & Giroux.

London, Victoria. Lucy & the Beauty Queen. 2002. (Gifted Girls Ser.). 64p. (J). (gr. 2-7). per. 6.95 (978-0-9714776-1-2(2)) Sparklesoup Studios, Inc.

Lopez, David Mark. Walk Like an Egyptian. 2006. (J). (gr. 3-7). (*978-0-9744097-0-2(7)) Lopez, David.

Lukas, Catherine. Say Please. 2007. 24p. (J). 21.35 (*978-1-59961-160-0(0)) Spotlight.

Marcellino, Fred. I, Crocodile. Marcellino, Fred, illus. (Illus.). (J). (ps-3). 2002. 32p. pap. 7.99 (978-0-06-008859-0(1) , Harper Trophy); 1999. 40p. 19.99 (978-0-06-205168-4(7)) HarperCollins Pubs.

Marsh, Carole. The Mystery at the Ancient Pyramid. 2006. 144p. (gr. 3-5). 14.95 (*978-0-635-03473-1(5)) Gallopade International.

Marston, Elsa. The Ugly Goddess. 2002. 218p. (J). (gr. 5-8). 16.95 (978-0-8126-2667-4(2)) Cricket Bks.

Mary, Foster & Kenrick, John. Ancient Egypt under the Pharaohs: Viking Tales. 2001. 450p. im. lthr. 65.00 (978-1-57179-109-2(4)) Scientists of New Atlantis.

Matthews, Mary. Magid Fasts for Ramadan. Lewis, E. B., illus. 2000. 48p. (J). (gr. 4-6). 6.95 (978-0-618-04035-3(8) , Clarion Bks.) Houghton Mifflin Co. Trade & Reference Div.

Matze, Claire Sidhom. The Stars in My Geddoh's Sky. Farnsworth, Bill, illus. 1999. (Concept Book Ser.). 32p. (J). (gr. k-3). pap. 14.95 (978-0-8075-5332-9(8)) Whitman, Albert & Co.

May, Scott. Sten Gizzle, Time Traveler: The Egyptian Adventure. Farkas, Josh, illus. 2000. 24p. (J). (gr. 1-3). pap. (978-0-9701450-4-8(7)) Long Hill Productions, Inc.

McCaughrean, Geraldine. Casting the Gods Adrift: A Tale of Ancient Egypt. Ludlow, Patricia D., illus. 2003. 112p. (J). (gr. 4-7). 15.95 (978-0-8126-2684-1(2)) Cricket Bks.

Mercer, Gary. Justin Flowers & the Orb of Time. 2003. 147p. pap. 16.95 (978-1-59286-530-7(5)) PublishAmerica, Inc.

Moore, Ishbel. Xanthe's Pyramid. 1998. 120p. (YA). (gr. 7-12). pap. 6.95 (978-1-896184-34-0(0)) Roussan Pubs., Inc./Roussan Editeur, Inc. CAN. *Dist:* Orca Bk. Pubs. USA.

Obi Shaaim Maa. Kheru Nefer (Beautiful Night) A Khamitic (Ancient Egyptian) Lullaby. 2006. (Illus.). (J). 21.95 incl. audio compact disk (978-0-9770967-0-1(X)) Spirit Publishing LLC.

O'Connell, Tyne. True Love, the Sphinx, & Other Unsolvable Riddles: A Comedy in Four Voices. 2007. 256p. (YA). (gr. 7 up). 16.95 (*978-1-59990-050-6(5)) Bloomsbury Publishing.

Oppenheim, Shulamith Levey. The Hundredth Name. Hays, Michael, illus. 2003. 32p. (J). (gr. k-2). pap. 9.95 (978-1-56397-694-0(3)) Boyds Mills Pr.

Paulsen, Gary & Roberts, Esyllt Nest. Plygu Amser. 2005. (WEL.). 77p. (978-0-86381-683-3(5)) Gwasg Carreg Gwalch.

Perkins, TJ. Trade Secret: A Kim & Kelly Mystery. 2004. (Illus.). 175p. (YA). 10.99 (978-0-9777538-2-6(4)) GumShoe Press.

Peters, Elizabeth, pseud. The Falcon at the Portal. 2000. 450p. (gr. 7-12). per. 15.90 (978-0-613-25117-4(2)) Tandem Library Bks.

Pirotta, Saviour & Marks, Alan. The Golden Slipper. 2007. (J). (*978-1-59771-077-0(6)) Sea-To-Sea Pubns.

Richards, Jane. Tombs, Temples, & Thrones. 2005. 125p. pap. 17.95 (978-1-4137-9084-9(4)) PublishAmerica, Inc.

Riggs, Sandy. Three Ancient Communities. 2005. (Navigators Ser.). (J). pap. 38.00 (*978-1-4108-5093-5(5)) Benchmark Education Co.

Rockwell, Anne F. Boy Who Became an Egyptian Scribe. 2003. (J). 15.99 (978-0-06-029507-3(4)); 16.89 (978-0-06-029508-0(2)) HarperCollins Pubs.

Rubalcaba, Jill. Place in the Sun. 1998. (Puffin Novel Ser.). 96p. (J). (gr. 3-7). pap. 4.99 (978-0-14-130123-5(6) , Puffin) Penguin Group (USA) Inc.

Schaenen, Inda. All the Cats of Cairo. 2007. 232p. (J). (gr. 5-10). pap. 8.95 (*978-0-9768126-5-4(7)) Brown Barn Bks.

Scherer, Catherine W. Simon & Barklee in Egypt. Richardson, Kara, illus. 2006. (Another Country Calling Ser.). 65p. (J). per. 15.00 (978-0-9714502-3-3(4) , Explorer Media) Simon & Barklee, Inc./ExplorerMedia.

Scieszka, Jon. Tu Mama Era Neanderthal. Smith, Lane, illus. (SPA.). (J). (gr. 5-8). 7.95 (978-958-04-5045-0(5) , NR3076) Norma S.A. COL. *Dist:* Distribuidora Norma, Inc., Lectorum Pubns., Inc.

Snyder, Zilpha Keatley. The Egypt Game. 2002. (Illus.). (J). 14.47 (978-0-7587-0259-3(0)) Book Wholesalers, Inc.

Sommers, Stephen. The Mummy. novel ed. 1999. (Illus.). 172p. (J). pap. 3.99 (978-0-439-05015-9(4)) Scholastic, Inc.

Stilton, Geronimo. The Curse of the Cheese Pyramid. Wolf, Matt, illus. 2004. (Geronimo Stilton Ser.: No. 2). 113p. (J). lib. bdg. 10.00 (*978-1-4242-0696-4(0)) Fitzgerald Bks.

—The Curse of the Cheese Pyramid. Wolf, Matt & Keys, Larry, illus. 2004. (Geronimo Stilton Ser.: No. 2). 128p. (J). pap. 5.99 (978-0-439-55964-5(2)) Scholastic, Inc.

Surget, Alain. Tirya y el Complot del Nilo. 2004. Tr. of Tirya & the Conspiracy in the Nile. (SPA.). 208p. (978-84-95618-50-4(8) , Umbriel) Ediciones Urano S. A.

Talley, Linda. Bastet. Maeno, Itoko, illus. (Key Concepts in Personal Development Ser.). 2001. 32p. pap., tchr. ed. 89.95 incl. VHS (978-1-55942-176-8(2) , 9390K3); 2000. 30p. (J). 89.95 incl. VHS (978-1-55942-161-4(4)) Marsh Media.

Thomas Nelson Publishing Staff. Miriam's Gift Book & Keepsake: Prince of Egypt. 1998. (Prince of Egypt Ser.). (Illus.). 32p. (J). (gr. 1-4). 9.99 (978-0-8499-5895-3(4)) Nelson, Thomas Inc.

Thompson, Bart A. Mummy. Miroglio, Brian, illus. 2007. (Graphic Horror Ser.). 32p. (YA). (gr. 5-8). lib. bdg. 27.07 (*978-1-60270-061-1(3) , Graphic Planet) Magic Wagon.

Travis, Alva. Secret of the Hidden Chamber. 2006. pap. 12.95 (978-1-4241-2071-0(3)) PublishAmerica, Inc.

Trout, Richard E. Falcon of Abydos: Oracle of the Nile. 2005. 288p. (J). 15.95 (978-1-58980-327-5(2)) Pelican Publishing Co., Inc.

—Falcon of Abydos Vol. 3: Oracle of the Nile. 2002. (Harbor Lights Ser.: No. 3). 220p. (J). (gr. 5-12). pap. 11.95 (978-1-880292-73-0(4)) LangMarc Publishing.

Turner, Ann. Maia of Thebes, 1463 B. C. 2005. (Life & Times Ser.). 176p. (J). pap. 10.95 (978-0-439-65223-0(5)) Scholastic, Inc.

Wallace, Karen. Freaky Families- Cousin Cedric Goes. (Illus.). 64p. (J). 7.95 (978-0-14-038500-7(2)) Penguin Bks., Ltd. GBR. *Dist:* Trafalgar Square Publishing.

Walsh, Paton Jill. Pepi & the Secret Names. French, Fiona, illus. 2004. 32p. (J). pap. 8.95 (978-1-84507-351-0(7)) Lincoln, Frances Ltd. GBR. *Dist:* Perseus Distribution.

Wilding. Secret Diaries 4 - Egyptian. 2008. (Illus.). 160p. (J). pap. 7.95 (*978-1-4052-1840-5(1)) Egmont Bks., Ltd. GBR. *Dist:* Independent Pubs. Group.

Williams, Jeff E. The Unknown Priestess. 1998. (Illus.). (J). pap. 8.80 (978-1-56763-343-6(9)); lib. bdg. 25.25 (978-1-56763-342-9(0)) Ozark Publishing.

Yates, Philip. Ten Little Mummies: An Egyptian Counting Book. Karas, G. Brian, illus. 2005. 40p. (J). pap. 6.99 (978-0-14-240367-9(9) , Puffin) Penguin Group (USA) Inc.

Zick, Bruce, illus. The Anubis Tapestry: Between Twilights. 2006. 152p. (J). 12.95 (978-0-9742803-8-7(0) , Actionopolis) Komikwerks, LLC.

Zindel, Paul. Egyptian Mystery. 192p. (YA). (gr. 6 up). Date not set. lib. bdg. 16.89 (978-0-06-028509-8(5)); 2002. 15.95 (978-0-06-028508-1(7)) HarperCollins Pubs.

Zoehfeld, Kathleen Weidner, adapted by. The Emperor's New Groove: Junior Novel. 2000. (Illus.). 96p. (J). (gr. 3-7). pap. 4.99 (978-0-7868-4429-6(9)) Disney Pr.

EGYPT—HISTORY

Ackroyd, Peter. Kingdom of the Dead. 2005. (Voyages Through Time Ser.). (Illus.). 144p. (J). 19.99 (978-0-7566-0846-0(5) , 1241635) Dorling Kindersley Publishing, Inc.

—Kingdom of the Dead. 2006. (Voyages through Time Ser.). 144p. (J). pap. 9.99 (978-0-7566-1476-8(7)) Dorling Kindersley Publishing, Inc.

Adam, Winky. Invisible Egyptian Magic Picture Book. 2000. (Dover Little Activity Bks.). (Illus.). 16p. (J). pap. 1.50 (978-0-486-41006-7(4)) Dover Pubns., Inc.

Adams, Michelle Medlock. The Life & Times of Cleopatra. 2005. (Biography from Ancient Civilizations Ser.). (Illus.). 48p. (J). (gr. 4-8). lib. bdg. 29.95 (978-1-58415-335-1(0)) Mitchell Lane Pubs., Inc.

Ancient Egypt DBA. 2003. spiral bd. 16.95 (978-1-56004-151-1(X)) Social Studies Schl. Service.

Bailey, Linda. Adventures in Ancient Egypt. Slavin, Bill, illus. 2004. (Good Times Travel Agency Ser.). 48p. (J). (gr. 4-6). (978-1-55074-548-1(4)); (978-1-55074-546-7(8)) Kids Can Pr., Ltd.

—Adventures in Ancient Egypt. 2000. (gr. 3-6). lib. bdg. 16.40 (978-0-613-30208-1(7)) Tandem Library Bks.

Balkwill, Richard. Clothes & Crafts in Ancient Egypt. 2000. (Clothes & Crafts in History Ser.). (Illus.). 32p. (J). (gr. 4-6). lib. bdg. 24.67 (978-0-8368-2733-0(3)) Stevens, Gareth Inc.

Barber, Nicola & Sheehan, Sean. Egypt: Listen Up! 2006. (Destination Detectives Ser.). (Illus.). 48p. (J). (978-1-4109-2334-9(7)); pap. (978-1-4109-2345-5(2)) Steck-Vaughn.

Bargallo I Chaves, Eva. Egypt. 2005. (Ancient Civilizations Ser.). (Illus.). 32p. (J). (gr. 4-8). lib. bdg. 28.00 (978-0-7910-8603-2(8) , Chelsea Clubhouse) Facts On File, Inc.

Barron's Educational Editorial Staff. The Pharaohs of Ancient Egypt. 1998. (Megascope Ser.). (Illus.). 64p. (J). (gr. 3-7). 6.95 (978-0-7641-5096-8(0)) Barron's Educational Series, Inc.

Barron's Educational Editorial Staff & Rossi, Renzo. The Egyptians: History, Society, Religion. 1999. (Bravo Ser.). (Illus.). 120p. (J). (gr. 6 up). 8.95 (978-0-7641-0942-3(1)) Barron's Educational Series, Inc.

Benchmark Education Staff. The Empire of Egypt. 2005. 2.00 (*978-1-4108-4647-1(4)) Benchmark Education Co.

Berger, Melvin & Berger, Gilda. Mummies of the Pharaohs: Exploring the Valley of the Kings. 2001. (Illus.). 64p. (J). (gr. 3-7). 17.95 (978-0-7922-7223-6(4) , National Geographic Children's Bks.) National Geographic Society.

Bowden, Rob & Maconachie, Roy. Cairo. 2004. (Great Cities of the World Ser.). (Illus.). 48p. (J). pap. 11.95 (978-0-8368-5195-3(1)); lib. bdg. 30.00 (978-0-8368-5035-2(1)) Stevens, Gareth Inc. (World Almanac Library).

Brannon, Barbara. Discover the Empire of Egypt. 2005. 39.00 (*978-1-4108-5159-8(1)) Benchmark Education Co.

Brucken, Kelli M. The Great Sphinx. 2006. (J). (978-0-7377-3444-7(2) , Greenhaven Pr., Inc.) Thomson Gale.

Charman, Andrew. Life & Times in Ancient Egypt. 2007. (Life & Times Ser.). (Illus.). 32p. (J). pap. 9.95 (*978-0-7534-6149-5(8) , Kingfisher) Houghton Mifflin Co. Trade & Reference Div.

Christensen, Wendy. Empire of Ancient Egypt. 2004. (Great Empires of the Past Ser.). (Illus.). 128p. (J). (gr. 6-12). 35.00 (978-0-8160-5558-6(0)) Facts On File, Inc.

Cole, Joanna. Ancient Egypt. 2003. (gr. k-3). lib. bdg. 15.30 (978-0-613-72892-8(0)) Tandem Library Bks.

Cumming, David. Egypt. Davies, Howard, photos by. 2005. (Letters from Around the World Ser.). (Illus.). 32p. (J). (gr. 3-7). lib. bdg. (978-1-84234-351-7(3) , Cherrytree Books) Evans Publishing Group.

Dawson, Ian. Prehistoric & Egyptian Medicine. 2005. (Illus.). 64p. (J). 19.95 (978-1-59270-035-6(7)) Enchanted Lion Bks., LLC.

Day, Nancy. Your Travel Guide to Ancient Egypt. 2005. (Passport to History Ser.). (Illus.). 96p. (gr. 5-8). lib. bdg. 26.50 (978-0-8225-3075-6(9)) Lerner Publishing Group.

Deady, Kathleen W. Egypt. 2000. (Countries of the World Ser.). (Illus.). 126p. (J). (gr. 2-3). 18.60 (978-0-7368-0626-8(1) , Bridgestone Bks.) Capstone Pr., Inc.

Dickinson, Clive. Mummies, Temples & Tombs. 2003. (TV tie-in Edition Ser.). (Illus.). 96p. (YA). pap. 7.99 (978-0-00-715378-7(3)) HarperCollins Pubs. Ltd. GBR. *Dist:* Independent Pubs. Group.

DK Publishing. Ancient Egypt. 2008. (DK Eyewitness Bks.). 48p. (J). (gr. 2-8). pap. 9.99 (*978-0-7566-3781-1(3)) Dorling Kindersley Publishing, Inc.

—Egyptorium. 2008. 20p. (J). (gr. 5-8). 24.99 (*978-0-7566-3754-5(6)) Dorling Kindersley Publishing, Inc.

DK Publishing Staff & Cando, Rich. Ancient Egyptian Dudes. Cando, Rich, illus. 2007. 64p. (J). (gr. 5-8). 12.99 (978-0-7566-2941-0(1)) Dorling Kindersley Publishing, Inc.

Dorling Kindersley Publishing Staff. Ancient Egypt. 2nd rev. ed. 2003. (DK Pockets Ser.). (Illus.). 160p. (J). pap. 6.99 (978-0-7894-9597-6(X)) Dorling Kindersley Publishing, Inc.

Egipto. 2005. (Coleccion Las Grandes Aventuras Ser.). (SPA.). (J). (978-968-7381-53-4(1)); pap. 17.95 (978-968-7381-49-7(3)) Tecolote, Ediciones, S.A. de C.V. MEX. *Dist:* Iaconi, Mariuccia Bk. Imports.

Egyptian Life. 2006. (YA). per. (978-1-59905-052-2(8)) Saddleback Educational Publishing.

Eldash, Khaled & Khattab, Dalia. In an Egyptian City. 2002. (Child's Day Ser.). (Illus.). 32p. (J). 25.64 (978-0-7614-1410-0(X) , Benchmark Bks.) Cavendish, Marshall Corp.

Filer, Joyce. Pyramids. 2nd ed. 2005. (Illus.). 48p. (YA). 16.95 (978-0-19-530521-0(3)); 18.95 (978-0-19-530525-8(6)) Oxford Univ. Pr., Inc.

Fister, Nancy & Olexiewicz, Charlene. Make History: Ancient Egypt. Stubbs, Elizabeth, illus. Bogart, Ann, photos by. 1999. 32p. (J). (gr. 3-7). pap. 9.95 (978-0-7373-0153-3(8) , 01538W) McGraw-Hill/Contemporary.

Fix, Alexandra. History & Activities of Ancient Egypt. 2006. (Hands-On Ancient History Ser.). (Illus.). 32p. (J). (978-1-4034-7923-5(2)); pap. (978-1-4034-7931-0(3)) Heinemann Library.

Galford, Ellen. Hatshepsut: The Princess Who Became King. 2005. (World History Biographies Ser.). (Illus.). 64p. (J). (gr. 3-7). 17.95 (978-0-7922-3645-0(9) , National Geographic Children's Bks.) National Geographic Society.

—Hatshepsut: The Princess Who Became King. 2005. (World History Biographies Ser.). (Illus.). 64p. (J). (gr. 3-7). 27.90 (978-0-7922-3646-7(7) , National Geographic Children's Bks.) National Geographic Society.

Galford, Ellen. World History Biographies: Hatshepsut: The Princess Who Became King. 2007. (NG World History Biographies Ser.). (Illus.). 64p. (J). (gr. 3-7). pap. 6.95 (*978-1-4263-0133-9(2) , National Geographic Children's Bks.) National Geographic Society.

Ganeri, Anita. Legacies from Ancient Egypt. 1999. (Legacies Ser.). (Illus.). 32p. (J). (gr. 4-7). lib. bdg. 16.95 (978-1-929298-52-5(8)) Chrysalis Education.

—Pharaohs, Heros & Thieves. 2003. (TV tie-in Edition Ser.). (Illus.). 120p. (YA). pap. 8.99 (978-0-00-715377-0(5)) HarperCollins Pubs. Ltd. GBR. *Dist:* Independent Pubs. Group.

Geras, Adèle. Cleopatra. 2009. (Illus.). 64p. (J). (gr. 1-5). 16.95 (*978-0-7534-6025-2(4) , Kingfisher) Houghton Mifflin Co. Trade & Reference Div.

Giblin, James Cross. Secrets of the Sphinx. Ibatoulline, Bagram, illus. 2004. (J). 47p. pap. (978-0-590-09852-6(7)); 48p. (gr. 4-7). pap. 17.95 (978-0-590-09847-2(0)) Scholastic, Inc.

Green, Jen. Tutankhamen's Tomb: Uncover the Secrets & Treasures of Ancient Egypt. Slater, Gary, illus. 2006. 32p. (J). (gr. 4 up). 18.99 (978-0-7641-5999-2(2)) Barron's Educational Series, Inc.

Greenblatt, Miriam. Hatshepsut & Ancient Egypt. 1999. (Rulers & Their Times Ser.). (Illus.). 80p. (YA). (gr. 6 up). lib. bdg. 29.93 (978-0-7614-0911-3(4) , Benchmark Bks.) Cavendish, Marshall Corp.

Greene, Jacqueline Dembar. Slavery in Ancient Egypt & Mesopotamia. 2000. (History of Slavery Library). (Illus.). 64p. (J). (gr. 5-7). 25.50 (978-0-531-11692-0(1) , Watts, Franklin) Scholastic Library Publishing.

—Slavery in Ancient Egypt & Mesopotamia. 2000. (gr. 3-6). lib. bdg. 17.60 (978-0-613-34472-2(3)) Tandem Library Bks.

Group/McGraw-Hill, Wright. Ancient Egypt: The Realm of Pharaohs, 6 vols. (Book2WebTM Ser.). (gr. 4-8). 36.50 (978-0-322-04451-7(0)) Wright Group, The.

Harcourt School Publishers Staff. Ancient Egypt. 3rd ed. 2002. (Horizons Ser.). (Illus.). (J). pap. 5.50 (978-0-15-333308-8(1)) Harcourt Schl. Pubs.

—Cleopatra's Lost City. 3rd ed. 2002. (Horizons Ser.). (Illus.). (J). pap. 7.30 (978-0-15-333628-7(5)) Harcourt Schl. Pubs.

—The Riddle of the Rosetta Stone. 2001. (Reader's Choice Bks.). (Illus.). (J). pap. 8.40 (978-0-15-314424-0(6)) Harcourt Schl. Pubs.

Harris, Geraldine. Ancient Egypt. (Cultural Atlas for Young People Ser.). (Illus.). 96p. 2nd rev. ed. 2003. (J). (gr. 4-9). 35.00 (978-0-8160-5148-9(8)); 3rd rev. ed. 2007. (YA). (gr. 5-8). 35.00 (*978-0-8160-6823-4(2) , Chelsea Hse.) Facts On File, Inc.

Harris, Nathaniel. Everyday Life in Ancient Egypt. 2005. (Clues to the Past Ser.). (Illus.). 32p. (J). (gr. 4-7). lib. bdg. 27.10 (978-1-932889-78-9(7)) Sea-To-Sea Pubns.

Harrison, James. A Magic Skeleton Book: Discovering Ancient Egypt. Smith, Jan & Bull, Peter, illus. 2004. (Magic Color Bks.). 12p. (J). 9.95 (978-1-4027-1596-9(X) , Sterling/Pinwheel) Sterling Publishing Co., Inc.

Hart, George. Ancient Egypt. 2008. (DK Eyewitness Bks.). 72p. (J). (gr. 3-8). 15.99 (*978-0-7566-3765-1(1)) Dorling Kindersley Publishing, Inc.

Hart, George & Dorling Kindersley Publishing Staff. Ancient Egpyt. 2004. (Eyewitness Books). 72p. (J). lib. bdg. 19.99 (978-0-7566-0652-7(7)) Dorling Kindersley Publishing, Inc.

Harvey, Gill. Tutankhamun. Tomlins, Karen, illus. 2006. 64p. (J). 8.99 (978-0-7945-1271-2(2) , Usborne) EDC Publishing.

Harvey, Gill & Reid, Struan. Encyclopedia of Ancient Egypt. 2004. (History Encyclopedias Ser.). (Illus.). 144p. (J). 19.95 (978-0-7945-0118-1(4) , Usborne); (gr. 4 up). lib. bdg. 27.95 (978-1-58086-387-2(6)) EDC Publishing.

Harvey, Miles. Look What Came from Egypt. 1999. (Look What Came from Ser.). (Illus.). 32p. (J). (gr. 2-4). pap. 6.95 (978-0-531-15937-8(X) , Watts, Franklin) Scholastic Library Publishing.

Haslam, Andrew. Ancient Egypt. 2004. (Make It Work! History Ser.). (Illus.). 64p. (gr. 3-6). 14.95 (978-1-58728-307-9(7) , Two Can Publishing) T&N Children's Publishing.

Hinds, Kathryn. The Countryside. 2006. (Life in Ancient Egypt Ser.). (Illus.). 80p. (J). lib. bdg. 32.79 (978-0-7614-2185-6(8) , Benchmark Bks.) Cavendish, Marshall Corp.

—The Pharaoh's Court. 2006. (Life in Ancient Egypt Ser.). (Illus.). 80p. (J). lib. bdg. 32.79 (978-0-7614-2183-2(1) , Benchmark Bks.) Cavendish, Marshall Corp.

—Religion. 2006. (Life in Ancient Egypt Ser.). (Illus.). 80p. (J). lib. bdg. 32.79 (978-0-7614-2186-3(6) , Benchmark Bks.) Cavendish, Marshall Corp.

Hirsch, E. D., ed. Ancient Egypt. 2003. tchr. ed. 9.95 (978-0-7690-5037-9(9)); stu. ed. 49.95 (978-0-7690-2942-9(6)) Pearson Learning.

Hodge, Susie. Ancient Egyptian Art. 2003. (Art in History Ser.). 32p. 6.95 (978-1-4034-4016-7(6)) Heinemann Library.

—Ancient Egyptian Art. 2003. (gr. 5-8). lib. bdg. 15.25 (978-0-613-87161-7(8)) Tandem Library Bks.

Hollingsworth, Patricia L., et al. Ancient Egypt. 1999. (Students' Active Interdisciplinary Learning Ser.). (Illus.). 104p. (YA). (gr. 1-12). pap. 20.00 (978-1-893413-06-1(3)) Univ. Schl. at the Univ. of Tulsa.

Holmes, Burton. Egypt. Schlesinger, Arthur M., Jr. & Isreal, Fred L., eds. 1999. (World 100 Years Ago Ser.). (Illus.). 144p. (YA). (ps up). 29.95 (978-0-7910-4670-8(2) , Chelsea Hse.) Facts On File, Inc.

Honan, Linda. Spend the Day in Ancient Egypt: Projects & Activities That Bring the Past to Life. Kosmer, Ellen, illus. 1999. (Spend the Day Ser.: Vol. 2). 128p. (gr. 3-7). pap. 12.95 (978-0-471-29006-3(8) , Wiley) Wiley, John & Sons, Inc.

Hunt, Norman Bancroft. Living in Ancient Egypt. 2007. (Living in the Ancient World Ser.). 96p. (gr. 6-12). 35.00 (978-0-8160-6338-3(9)) Facts On File, Inc.

Hynson, Colin. You Wouldn't Want to Be an Inca Mummy! A One-Way Journey You'd Rather Not Make. Antram, David, illus. 2007. (You Wouldn't Want to...: Ancient Civilization Ser.). 32p. (J). 29.00 (*978-0-531-18744-9(6)); (gr. 2-5). pap. 9.95 (*978-0-531-13926-4(3)) Scholastic Library Publishing. (Watts, Franklin).

Israel, Fred L., intro. Egyptian Kings & Queens & Classical Deities. 1999. (Looking into the Past). (Illus.). 64p. (YA). (gr. 5 up). 28.00 (978-0-7910-4677-7(X) , Chelsea Hse.) Facts On File, Inc.

Jeffrey, Gary & Ganeri, Anita. Cleopatra: The Life of an Egyptian Queen. 2005. (Graphic Nonfiction Ser.). (Illus.). 48p. (J). lib. bdg. 26.50 (978-1-4042-0242-9(0)) Rosen Publishing Group, Inc., The.

Joachim, Jean. Ancient Egypt Dot-to-Dot. 2006. (Illus.). 80p. (J). pap. 5.95 (978-1-4027-2880-8(8)) Sterling Publishing Co., Inc.

Jordan, Shirley. Ancient Egypt: Moments in History. 1999. (Cover-to-Cover Informational Bks.). (Illus.). 56p. (J). (gr. 4-7). lib. bdg. 17.95 (978-0-7807-8999-9(7) , Covercraft); (YA). (gr. 5-8). pap. 8.95 (978-0-7891-2840-9(3)) Perfection Learning Corp.

Kramer, Ann. Egyptian Myth: A Treasury of Legends, Art, & History. 2007. (World of Mythology Ser.). (Illus.). 96p. (YA). (gr. 6 up). 35.95 (*978-0-7656-8105-8(6)) Sharpe, M.E. Inc.

Kunhardt, Edith. Mummies. 2000. (Road to Reading Ser.). (Illus.). (J). (978-0-606-20445-3(8)) Tandem Library Bks.

Landau, Elaine. Egypt. 2000. (True Bks.). (Illus.). 48p. (J). (gr. 3-5). pap. 6.95 (978-0-516-27018-0(4) , Children's Pr.) Scholastic Library Publishing.

Leaders of Ancient Egypt, 6 bks. Incl. Ahmose : Liberator of Egypt. Thomas, Susanna. (YA). lib. bdg. 31.95 (978-0-8239-3599-4(X)); Akhenaten & Tutankhamen : The Religious Revolution. Thomas, Susanna. (YA). lib. bdg. 31.95 (978-0-8239-3589-5(2)); Cleopatra : Ruling in the Shadow of Rome. Morgan, Julian. (YA). lib. bdg. 31.95 (978-0-8239-3591-8(4)); Hatsheput : The First Woman Pharaoh. Thomas, Susanna. (J). lib. bdg. 31.95 (978-0-8239-3594-9(9)); Rameses II : Pharaoh of the New Kingdom. Thomas, Susanna. (J). lib. bdg. 31.95 (978-0-8239-3597-0(3)); Snefru : The Pyramid Builder. Thomas, Susanna. (J). lib. bdg. 31.95 (978-0-8239-3598-7(1)); 112p. (gr. 5-8). 2003. (Illus.). 2002. Set lib. bdg. 191.70 (978-0-8239-4051-6(9) , Rosen Central) Rosen Publishing Group, Inc., The.

Leonard, Barry, ed. Treasure Trove of an Ancient Egyptian Child. 2005. (Illus.). 24p. (J). (gr. 4-8). 27.00 (978-0-7567-8939-8(7)) DIANE Publishing Co.

MacDonald, Fiona. Ancient Egypt. 2004. (Illus.). 64p. (J). 17.99 (978-0-00-715376-3(7)) HarperCollins Pubs. Ltd. GBR. *Dist:* Independent Pubs. Group.

—Ancient Egyptians Ancient Egypt. (Illus.). 64p. (J). pap. 9.99 (978-0-00-717797-4(6)) Zondervan.

—Cleopatra. 2006. (DK Discoveries Ser.). 48p. (J). pap. 6.99 (978-0-7566-1964-0(5)) Dorling Kindersley Publishing, Inc.

—Tutankhamen. 2000. (World in the Time of... Ser.). (Illus.). (J). (gr. 4-7). 17.95 (978-0-7910-6035-3(7) , Chelsea Hse.) Facts On File, Inc.

Malam, John. Ancient Egypt. Malam, John, illus. 2004. (Picturing the Past Ser.). (Illus.). 32p. (J). 15.95 (978-1-59270-021-9(7)) Enchanted Lion Bks., LLC.

—Ancient Egypt. rev. ed. 1998. (Remains to Be Seen Ser.). (Illus.). 48p. (J). (gr. 5-8). (978-0-237-51839-4(2) , Evans Brothers, Limited) Evans Publishing Group.

—Ancient Egyptian Children. 2003. (People in the Past Ser.). (Illus.). 48p. (J). (gr. 4-6). lib. bdg. 27.07 (978-1-4034-0309-4(0)) Heinemann Library.

—Ancient Egyptian Homes. 2003. (People in the Past Ser.). (Illus.). 48p. (J). (gr. 4-6). lib. bdg. 27.07 (978-1-4034-0310-0(4)) Heinemann Library.

—Ancient Egyptian War & Weapons. 2003. (People in the Past Ser.). (Illus.). 48p. (J). (gr. 4-6). lib. bdg. 27.07 (978-1-4034-0312-4(0)) Heinemann Library.

—Ancient Egyptian War & Weapons. 2002. (gr. 3-6). lib. bdg. 17.05 (978-0-613-85908-0(1)) Tandem Library Bks.

Manning, Mick. Pharaoh's Egypt. Granstrom, Brita, illus. 2005. (Fly on the Wall Ser.). 36p. (J). 15.95 (978-1-84507-100-4(X)) Lincoln, Frances Ltd. GBR. *Dist:* Perseus Distribution.

Martin, Amanda. Ancient Egypt. rev. ed. 2004. (Come & Discover My World Ser.). (Illus.). 32p. (gr. 2-5). (J). pap. 7.95 (978-1-58728-067-2(1)); 14.95 (978-1-58728-061-0(2)) T&N Children's Publishing. (Two Can Publishing).

—L' Egypte Ancienne. 2000. (Come & Discover My World Ser.). (FRE., Illus.). 32p. (J). (gr. 2-5). pap. 7.95 (978-1-58728-192-1(9) , Two Can Publishing) T&N Children's Publishing.

Mason. Mummies. 2003. (Mysteries of the Past Ser.). (Illus.). 32p. pap. 7.95 (978-1-4109-0064-7(9)) Raintree.

Metropolitan Museum of Art Staff, contrib. by. Write Like an Ancient Egyptian! 2003. (Illus.). 69p. (J). (978-1-58839-036-3(5)) Metropolitan Museum of Art, The.

Millard, Anne. Going to War in Ancient Egypt. Bergin, Mark, illus. 2001. (Armies of the Past Ser.). 32p. (J). (gr. 3-6). 25.50 (978-0-531-14589-0(1)); pap. 6.95 (978-0-531-16350-4(4)) Scholastic Library Publishing. (Watts, Franklin).

—Going to War in Ancient Egypt. 2001. (gr. 3-6). lib. bdg. 15.25 (978-0-613-54517-4(6)) Tandem Library Bks.

—The World of Pyramids. 2004. (World Of Ser.). (Illus.). 64p. (J). (gr. 4-6). pap. 8.95 (978-0-7534-5787-0(3) , Kingfisher) Houghton Mifflin Co. Trade & Reference Div.

Minnis. You Are in Ancient Egypt, 6 Packs. 2004. (Illus.). pap. 40.50 (978-1-4109-1013-4(X)) Harcourt Schl. Pubs.

Morin, Jacqueline. So You Want to Be an Egyptian Princess. Hewetson, Nicholas, illus. 1999. (So You Want to Be... Ser.). 32p. (gr. 3-6). lib. bdg. 21.90 (978-0-7613-1422-6(9) , Twenty-First Century Bks.) Lerner Publishing Group.

Morley, Jacqueline. How to Be an Eqyptian Princess. 2006. (Illus.). 32p. (J). (gr. 3-7). 14.95 (978-0-7922-7494-0(6)); 21.90 (978-0-7922-7548-0(9)) National Geographic Society. (National Geographic Children's Bks.).

Murphy, Michaela. Egypt. Mitchell, Judy, ed. Freeman, Joel, photos by. 2002. (Exploring Ancient Civilizations Ser.). (Illus.). 48p. (J). (gr. 3-6). pap., tchr. ed. 7.95 (978-1-57310-306-0(3)) Teaching & Learning Co.

Naden, Corinne J. & Blue, Rose. Cleopatra. 2001. (Women of Achievement Ser.). (J). 32.00 (978-0-7910-6320-0(8) , Chelsea Hse.) Facts On File, Inc.

Nardo, Don. Arts. Leisure & Sport in Ancient Egypt. 2005. (Lucent Library of Historical Eras Ser.). (Illus.). 112p. (YA). (gr. 7-10). lib. bdg. 32.45 (978-1-59018-706-7(7) , Lucent Bks.) Thomson Gale.

—Ramesses II: Ruler of Ancient Egypt. 2006. (Rulers of the Ancient World Ser.). (Illus.). 160p. (J). lib. bdg. 27.93 (978-0-7660-2562-2(4)) Enslow Pubs., Inc.

Nicholson, Robert. Egyptians. 2000. (Collectafact Ser.: Vol. 3). (Illus.). 48p. (J). (gr. 1-5). 4.95 (978-1-58728-754-1(4) , Two Can Publishing) T&N Children's Publishing.

Nicholson, Robert & Watts, Claire. Egyptians. 2004. (Interfact Ser.). (SPA., Illus.). 48p. (J). (gr. 3-6). 14.95 incl. cd-rom (978-1-58728-458-8(8) , Two Can Publishing) T&N Children's Publishing.

Osborne, Will & Osborne, Mary Pope. Mummies & Pyramids: A Nonfiction Companion to Mummies in the Morning. Murdocca, Salvatore, illus. 2001. (Magic Tree House Research Guide Ser.: No. 3). 119p. (J). (gr. k-3). per. 13.00 (978-0-613-33837-0(5)) Tandem Library Bks.

Owens, L. L. Eye on Ancient Egypt. 1999. (Cover-to-Cover Bks.). (Illus.). 56p. (J). pap. (978-0-7891-2855-3(1)); (gr. 1-4). lib. bdg. 16.95 (978-0-7807-7836-8(7) , Covercraft) Perfection Learning Corp.

Park, Ted. Egypt. 2000. (Taking Your Camera to Ser.). (Illus.). 32p. (J). (gr. 4-7). lib. bdg. 22.83 (978-0-7398-1812-1(0)) Raintree.

Parks, Peggy J. Aswan High Dam. (Building World Landmarks Ser.). (J). 2004. 26.19 (978-1-4103-0204-5(0)); 2003. (Illus.). 48p. 24.95 (978-1-56711-329-7(X)) Thomson Gale. (Blackbirch Pr., Inc.).

Parsons, Alexandra. Ancient Egypt. Haslam, Andrew, illus. 2004. (Make It Work! History Ser.). 64p. (J). (gr. 3-6). pap. 7.95 (978-1-58728-300-0(X) , Two Can Publishing) T&N Children's Publishing.

Patton, Geoff. Mummies. 2005. (X-Zone Ser.). (Illus.). 30p. (gr. 4-8). 23.00 (978-0-7910-8993-4(2)) Facts On File, Inc.

Pemberton, Delia. Atlas of Ancient Egypt: With Artworks & Photographs from the British Museum. 2005. (Illus.). 96p. (J). (gr. 3-7). 19.95 (978-0-8109-5796-1(5) , Abrams Bks. for Young Readers) Abrams, Harry N., Inc.

Pipe, Jim. You Wouldn't Want to Be Cleopatra! An Egyptian Ruler You'd Rather Not Be. Antram, David, illus. 2007. (You Wouldn't Want to... Ser.). 32p. (J). (gr. 2-5). 28.50 (*978-0-531-18726-5(8)); pap. 9.95 (*978-0-531-18923-8(6)) Scholastic Library Publishing. (Watts, Franklin).

Reid, S. & Chisholm, J. Who Built the Pyramids? 2004. (Starting Point History Ser.). 32p. (J). lib. bdg. 12.95 (978-1-58086-629-3(8)); (Illus.). pap. 4.95 (978-0-7945-0343-7(8)) EDC Publishing. (Usborne).

Reid, Struan. Cleopatra. 2002. (Historical Biographies Ser.). (Illus.). 32p. (J). (gr. 2-4). lib. bdg. 22.79 (978-1-58810-565-3(2)) Heinemann Library.

—Cleopatra. 2002. (gr. 3-6). lib. bdg. 15.25 (978-0-613-45727-9(7)) Tandem Library Bks.

Riddles of the Pharaohs: Exploring Ancient Egypt. 1999. (Middle Grades Interdisciplinary Units Ser.). (J). stu. ed. 84.47 (978-0-13-419680-0(5)) Prentice Hall PTR.

Ridgley, Sara & Mole, Gavin. Sing It & Say - Ancient Egypt. (J). 10.95 incl. audio (978-1-85909-391-7(4) , Warner Bros. Pubns.) Alfred Publishing Co., Inc.

Roberts, Russell. Rulers of Ancient Egypt. 1998. (History Makers Ser.). (Illus.). 96p. (YA). (gr. 7-10). 28.70 (978-1-56006-438-1(2) , Lucent Bks.) Thomson Gale.

Ross, Stewart. Clever Cleo. Shields, Sue, illus. 32p. pap. 9.99 (978-0-7502-2853-4(9) , Hodder & Stoughton) Hodder General Publishing Division GBR. *Dist:* Trafalgar Square Publishing.

—The Finest Pharaoh of All! Princess Hatshepsut Takes over Egypt. Shields, Susan, illus. 1999. (Coming Alive Ser.). 62p. (J). pap. 8.99 (978-0-237-51960-5(7) , Evans Brothers, Limited) Evans Publishing Group GBR. *Dist:* Independent Pubs. Group.

Rubalcaba, Jill & Walsh, Kieran. Ancient Egypt: Archaeology Unlocks the Secrets of Egypt's Past. 2006. (National Geographic Investigates Ser.). (Illus.). 64p. (J). (gr. 3-7). 17.95 (978-0-7922-7784-2(8)); lib. bdg. 27.90 (978-0-7922-7857-3(7)) National Geographic Society. (National Geographic Children's Bks.).

Ryall, Michael. The Empire of Egypt. 2005. 39.00 (*978-1-4108-4599-3(0)) Benchmark Education Co.

Sands, Emily. Egyptology: Search for the Tomb of Osiris. Andrew, Ian et al, illus. 2004. (Ologies Ser.). 32p. (J). (gr. 3). 19.99 (978-0-7636-2638-9(4)) Candlewick Pr.

Sheen, Martin, contrib. by. Ancient Egypt. 2007. 16p. (J). (gr. 3-8). pap. 29.99 (*978-0-7566-3134-5(3)) Dorling Kindersley Publishing, Inc.

Shuter, Jane. The Ancient Egyptians. 2000. (History Starts Here Ser.). (Illus.). 32p. (J). (ps-3). pap. 8.95 (978-0-7398-2030-8(3)) Steck-Vaughn.

—Life along the River Nile. 2004. (Picture the Past Ser.). (Illus.). 32p. (J). pap. (978-1-4034-5835-3(9)) Heinemann Library.

—Life in an Egyptian Town. 2004. (Picture the Past Ser.). (Illus.). 32p. (J). pap. (978-1-4034-5839-1(1)) Heinemann Library.

—Life in an Egyptian Workers' Village. 2004. (Picture the Past Ser.). (Illus.). 32p. (J). pap. (978-1-4034-5840-7(5)) Heinemann Library.

Solbiati, Romano. Ancient Egypt. 2001. (Journey to the Past Ser.). (Illus.). 56p. (J). (gr. 6-8). lib. bdg. 27.12 (978-0-7398-1954-8(2)) Raintree.

Steele. Ancient Egypt. 2000. (Ancient Civilizations Ser.). (Illus.). (J). pap. (978-0-7398-4148-8(3)) Steck-Vaughn.

Steele, Philip. Step Into: Ancient Egypt. 2008. (Illus.). 64p. pap. 10.99 (*978-1-84476-347-4(1) , Southwater) Anness Publishing GBR. *Dist:* National Bk. Network.

Stewart, David. You Wouldn't Want to Be Tutankhamen! A Mummy Who Really Got Meddled With. Antram, David, illus. 2007. (You Wouldn't Want to Ser.). 32p. (J). (gr. 2-5). 28.50 (*978-0-531-18725-8(X)); pap. 9.95 (*978-0-531-18924-5(4)) Scholastic Library Publishing. (Watts, Franklin).

Strachan, Bruce. Wonders of Ancient Egypt. rev. ed. Date not set. 32p. (J). 17.95 (978-0-8050-7432-1(5) , Holt, Henry & Co. Bks. For Young Readers) Holt, Henry & Co.

Suzanne Beilenson. Ancient Egypt Scratch & Sketch. 2006. (Activity Book Ser.). 64p. (J). 12.99 (978-1-59359-915-7(3)) Peter Pauper Pr. Inc.

Sylvester, Diane. Ancient Egypt. VanBlaricum, Pam, ed. Hillam, Corbin & Ciccarelli, Gary, illus. 2006. (Museum Ser.). 64p. pap. 13.99 (978-0-88160-386-6(4) , LW442, Learning Works, The) Creative Teaching Pr., Inc.

Thomas, Susanna. Ahmose: Liberator of Egypt. 2003. (Leaders of Ancient Egypt Ser.). (Illus.). 112p. (YA). (gr. 5-8). lib. bdg. 31.95 (978-0-8239-3599-4(X) , Rosen Central) Rosen Publishing Group, Inc., The.

—Snefru: The Pyramid Builder. 2003. (Leaders of Ancient Egypt Ser.). (Illus.). 112p. (J). (gr. 5-8). lib. bdg. 31.95 (978-0-8239-3598-7(1) , Rosen Central) Rosen Publishing Group, Inc., The.

Tiano, Olivier. Dioses de Egipto. Gonzalez Batlle, Jorge, tr. Heinrich, Christian, illus. 2004. (Tras los pasos de ... Ser.). (SPA.). 128p. pap. 14.95 (978-84-95939-66-1(5)) Blume ESP. *Dist:* Independent Pubs. Group.

Trumble, Kelly. The Library of Alexandria. Marshall, Robina MacIntyre, illus. 2003. 80p. (J). (gr. 4-6). tchr. ed. 17.00 (978-0-395-75832-8(7) , Clarion Bks.) Houghton Mifflin Co. Trade & Reference Div.

Turnbull, Stephanie. Egyptians. (Beginners Social Studies). 32p. (J). (gr. 1 up). lib. bdg. 12.99 (978-1-58086-656-9(5) , Usborne) EDC Publishing.

—Egyptians - Internet Referenced. King, Colin, illus. 2004. (Beginners Ser.). 32p. (J). (gr. 1 up). pap. 4.99 (978-0-7945-0681-0(X) , Usborne) EDC Publishing.

—Egyptians Kid Kit. King, Colin, illus. 2005. 32p. (J). 9.99 (978-1-58086-844-0(4) , Usborne) EDC Publishing.

Tyldesley, Joyce. Egypt. 2007. (Insiders Ser.). 64p. (J). 16.99 (*978-1-4169-3858-3(3)) Simon & Schuster Children's Publishing.

Van Vleet, Carmella. Explore Ancient Egypt! 25 Great Projects, Activities, & Experiments. 2008. (Explore Your World Ser.). 96p. (J). (gr. 1-4). pap. 12.95 (*978-0-9792268-3-0(X)) Nomad Pr.

Van Vleet, Carmella. Great Ancient Egypt Projects You Can Build Yourself. 2006. (Build It Yourself Ser.). (Illus.). 128p. (J). (gr. 4-6). pap. 14.95 (978-0-9771294-5-4(4)) Nomad Pr.

Waryncia, Lou, et al. If I Were a Kid in Ancient Egypt: Children of the Ancient World. 2007. (Children of the Ancient World Ser.). (Illus.). 32p. (J). 17.95 (978-0-8126-7932-8(6)) Cricket Bks.

Whiting, Jim. The Life & Times of Rameses the Great. 2005. (Biography from Ancient Civilizations Ser.). (Illus.). 48p. (J). (gr. 5-8). lib. bdg. 29.95 (978-1-58415-341-2(5)) Mitchell Lane Pubs., Inc.

Williams, Brian. Tutankhamen. 2003. (Historical Biographies Ser.). 32p. pap. 7.50 (978-1-4034-0102-1(0)) Heinemann Library.

Worth, Richard. Cleopatra: Queen of Ancient Egypt. 2006. (Rulers of the Ancient World Ser.). (Illus.). 160p. (J). lib. bdg. 27.93 (978-0-7660-2559-2(4)) Enslow Pubs., Inc.

Writing in Ancient Egypt, 6 Packs. (On Deck Ser.: Vol. 2). 24p. (gr. 4-5). 35.00 (978-0-7578-5867-3(8)) Rigby Education.

EGYPT—HISTORY—FICTION

Adams, Anne Tyra. Songbird of the Nile: The Diary of Miriam's Best Friend, Egypt, 1527 B. C. -1526 B. C. 2004. (Promised Land Diaries). (Illus.). 192p. (J). 10.99 (978-0-8010-4525-7(8)) Baker Bks.

Banks, Lynne Reid. Moses in Egypt: A Novel Inspired by The Prince of Egypt & The Book of Exodus. 1998. (Prince of Egypt Ser.). (Illus.). 128p. (J). (gr. 5-9). pap. 4.99 (978-0-8499-5898-4(9)) Nelson, Thomas Inc.

Booth, Bradley. Plagues in the Palace. 2006. 159p. (J). (978-0-8163-2143-8(4)) Pacific Pr. Publishing Assn.

Bunting, Eve. I Am the Mummy Heb-Nefert. Christiana, David, illus. 2000. 32p. (J). (ps-3). pap. 7.00 (978-0-15-202464-2(6) , Harcourt Paperbacks) Harcourt Children's Bks.

Deary, Terry. The Gold in the Grave. Flook, Helen, illus. 2005. (Read-It! Chapter Bks.). 64p. (J). (ps-k). lib. bdg. 19.95 (978-1-4048-1270-3(9)) Picture Window Bks.

—The Phantom & the Fisherman. Flook, Helen, illus. 2005. (Read-It! Chapter Bks.). 64p. (J). (ps-k). lib. bdg. 19.95 (978-1-4048-1272-7(5)) Picture Window Bks.

—The Plot on the Pyramid. Flook, Helen, illus. 2005. (Read-It! Chapter Bks.). 64p. (J). (ps-k). lib. bdg. 19.95 (978-1-4048-1273-4(3)) Picture Window Bks.

Farmer, Nancy. Clever Ali. De Marcken, Gail, illus. 2006. 40p. (J). pap. 17.99 (978-0-439-37014-1(0) , Orchard Bks.) Scholastic, Inc.

Gantos, Jack. Rotten Ralph Helps Out. Rubel, Nicole, illus. unabr. ed. 2006. (Readalongs for Beginning Readers Ser.). (J). (gr. k-3). 24.95 incl. audio (978-1-59519-678-1(1)); 28.95 incl. audio compact disk (978-1-59519-679-8(X)); pap. 16.00 incl. audio (978-1-59519-674-3(9)); pap. 18.95 incl. audio compact disk (978-1-59519-675-0(7)); Set. pap. 29.95 incl. audio (978-1-59519-676-7(5)); Set. pap. 31.95 incl. audio compact disk (978-1-59519-677-4(3)) Live Oak Media.

Gregory, Kristiana. Cleopatra VII: Daughter of the Nile, Egypt, 57 B. C. 1999. (Royal Diaries Ser.). (Illus.). 224p. (J). (gr. 4-8). pap. 10.95 (978-0-590-81975-6(5) , Scholastic Pr.) Scholastic, Inc.

Harvey, Gill. Orphan of the Sun. 2006. (Illus.). 320p. (J). (gr. 5-8). 16.95 (978-1-58234-685-4(2) , Bloomsbury Children) Bloomsbury Publishing.

Henty, G. A. The Cat of Bubastes: A Tale of Ancient Egypt. 2002. 370p. 29.95 (978-1-59087-113-3(8) , GAH113); per. 19.95 (978-1-59087-112-6(X) , GAH112) Althouse Pr.

—The Cat of Bubastes: A Tale of Ancient Egypt. 2002. 320p. (J). (gr. 4-7). pap. 6.95 (978-0-486-42363-0(8)) Dover Pubns., Inc.

—The Cat of Bubastes: A Tale of Ancient Egypt. 2006. (ENG.). pap. 33.95 (*978-1-4286-0382-0(4)) Kessinger Publishing, LLC.

—The Cat of Bubastes: A Tale of Ancient Egypt. collector's ed. 2002. (Illus.). im. lthr. 38.85 (978-1-4115-1348-7(7)); pap. 19.95 (978-1-4115-0588-9(3)); 25.95 (978-1-4115-0918-4(8)); pap. 17.95 (978-1-4115-0097-6(0)) Polyglot Pr., Inc.

—The Cat of Bubastes: A Tale of Ancient Egypt. 2000. 294p. (YA). 7.99 (978-1-887159-68-5(1)) Preston-Speed Pubns.

—The Cat of Bubastes: A Tale of Ancient Egypt. Preston Speed Publications Staff, ed. Weguelin, J. R., illus. 1998. 339p. (YA). pap. 14.99 (978-1-887159-23-4(1)) Preston-Speed Pubns.

—The Cat of Bubastes: A Tale of Ancient Egypt. 1998. (Illus.). 339p. (J). lib. bdg. 20.99 (978-1-887159-16-6(9)) Preston-Speed Pubns.

E F G

Hernandez, David. Land of the Pharaohs. 2003. (Adventures of Toby Digz Ser.). (Illus.). 96p. (J). pap. 5.99 (978-1-4003-0195-9(5)) Nelson, Thomas Inc.

Jacq, Christian. Paneb the Ardent. 2001. (gr. 7-12). lib. bdg. 25.75 (978-0-613-49452-6(0)) Tandem Library Bks.

—Wise Woman. 2000. (gr. 7-12). lib. bdg. 25.75 (978-0-613-49466-3(0)) Tandem Library Bks.

Joyce, Tyldesley. Stories from Ancient Egypt. Julian, Heath, illus. 107p. pap. 9.95 (978-0-9547622-1-6(5)) Rutherford Pr. GBR. *Dist:* Brown, David Bk. Co., The.

Kramer, Alan. Ramses & Nefertari. 2005. 40.00 (***978-1-4108-4224-4(X)***) Benchmark Education Co.

Lester, Julius. Pharaoh's Daughter: A Novel of Ancient Egypt. 2002. 192p. (J). (gr. 5 up). pap. 5.99 (978-0-06-440969-8(4) , Harper Trophy) HarperCollins Pubs.

—Pharaoh's Daughter: A Novel of Ancient Egypt. 2002. (gr. 5-8). lib. bdg. 14.15 (978-0-613-87835-7(3)) Tandem Library Bks.

McGraw, Eloise Jarvis. Mara, Daughter of the Nile. 1999. (J). (gr. 5-8). lib. bdg. 14.15 (978-0-613-03326-8(4)) Tandem Library Bks.

McIntosh, C. Ruth Bay & the Minotaur. 2004. 91p. pap. 14.95 (978-1-4137-4811-6(2)) PublishAmerica, Inc.

Moore, Ulysses. The Long-Lost Map. Bruno, Iacopo, illus. 2006. (Ulysses Moore Ser.: No. 2). 272p. (J). pap. 12.99 (978-0-439-77439-0(X) , Scholastic) Scholastic, Inc.

Moss, Marissa. Max's Mystical Logbook. 2004. (J). 12.95 (978-0-439-46663-9(6)) Scholastic, Inc.

O'Neill, Katrina & Thompson, Lisa. In Search of the Egyptian Queen. Cantell, Brenda, illus. 2005. (Treasure Trackers Ser.). 80p. (gr. 5-9). 19.00 (978-0-7910-8874-6(X)) Facts On File, Inc.

Platt, Richard. Egyptian Diary: The Journal of Nakht. Parkins, David, illus. 2005. 64p. (J). (gr. 4 up). 17.99 (978-0-7636-2756-0(9)) Candlewick Pr.

Roberts, Katherine. The Cleopatra Curse. 2006. (Seven Fabulous Wonders Ser.). (Illus.). 288p. (J). pap. 11.99 (978-0-00-711284-5(X) , HarperCollins Children's Bks.) HarperCollins Pubs. Ltd. GBR. *Dist:* Independent Pubs. Group.

Rose, Russell. Egyptians. 2003. (Know it All! Ser.). (Illus.). 16p. (J). pap. 6.99 (978-0-7498-5814-8(1)) Egmont Bks., Ltd. GBR. *Dist:* Independent Pubs. Group.

Rubalcaba, Jill. The Wadjet Eye. 2006. 160p. (J). (gr. 4-6). pap. 5.95 (978-0-618-68927-9(3) , Clarion Bks.) Houghton Mifflin Co. Trade & Reference Div.

Scholastic, Inc. Staff. Long-lost Map. 2007. (Ulysses Moore Ser.). 272p. (J). pap. 5.99 (***978-0-439-77673-8(2)***) Scholastic, Inc.

Scieszka, Jon. Tut, Tut. Smith, Lane, illus. (SPA.). (J). (gr. 5-8). 7.95 (978-958-04-5046-7(3) , NR7010) Norma S.A. COL. *Dist:* Distribuidora Norma, Inc., Lectorum Pubns., Inc.

—Tut, Tut. Smith, Lane, illus. 2004. (Time Warp Trio Ser.: No. 6). 80p. (J). (gr. 2-6). pap. 4.99 (978-0-14-240047-0(5) , Puffin) Penguin Group (USA) Inc.

—Tut, Tut. Smith, Lane, illus. 2004. (Time Warp Trio Ser.: No. 6). 74p. (J). (ps-7). lib. bdg. 11.79 (978-0-606-30136-7(4)) Tandem Library Bks.

—Tut, Tut. 1998. (Time Warp Trio Ser.: No. 6). (978-0-606-13879-6(X)) Tandem Library Bks.

Sturges, Philemon. Crocky Dilly. Miglio, Paige, illus. 1998. 32p. (J). (ps-3). 14.95 (978-0-87846-458-6(1)) Museum of Fine Arts, Boston.

Thompson, James. The Amarna Experiment. 2003. 128p. (YA). 21.95 (978-0-595-65753-7(2)); pap. 11.95 (978-0-595-28296-8(2)) iUniverse, Inc.

Williams, Maiya. The Hour of the Cobra. (YA). 2007. 320p. (gr. 2-7). pap. 5.95 (***978-0-8109-9362-4(7));*** 2006. 312p. (gr. 4-9). 16.95 (978-0-8109-5970-5(4) , Amulet Bks.) Abrams, Harry N. , Inc.

Williams, Mark London. Ancient Fire. 2004. (Danger Boy Ser.: No. 1). (Illus.). 224p. (J). (gr. 4-8). 12.99 (978-0-7636-2152-0(8)) Candlewick Pr.

—Ancient Fire: Danger Boy Episode 1. 2006. 232p. (J). (gr. 4-8). pap. 4.99 (978-0-7636-3092-8(6)) Candlewick Pr.

Would, Nick. The Scarab's Secret. Balit, Christina, illus. 2006. 32p. (J). 16.95 (978-0-8027-9561-8(7)) Walker & Co.

EGYPT—KINGS AND RULERS

Barron's Educational Editorial Staff. The Pharaohs of Ancient Egypt. 1998. (Megascope Ser.). (Illus.). 64p. (J). (gr. 3-7). 6.95 (978-0-7641-5096-8(0)) Barron's Educational Series, Inc.

Berger, Melvin & Berger, Gilda. Mummies of the Pharaohs: Exploring the Valley of the Kings. 2001. (Illus.). 64p. (J). (gr. 3-7). 17.95 (978-0-7922-7223-6(4) , National Geographic Children's Bks.) National Geographic Society.

Geyer, Flora. Saladin: The Muslim Warrior Who Defended His People. 2006. (World History Biographies Ser.). (Illus.). 64p. (J). (gr. 3-7). 17.95 (978-0-7922-5535-2(6)); 27.90 (978-0-7922-5536-9(4)) National Geographic Society. (National Geographic Children's Bks.).

Harvey, Gill. Tutankhamun. Tomlins, Karen, illus. 2006. 64p. (J). 8.99 (978-0-7945-1271-2(2) , Usborne) EDC Publishing.

Kennett, David. Pharaoh: Life & Afterlife of a God. Kennett, David, illus. 2008. (Illus.). 48p. (J). 19.85 (***978-0-8027-9568-7(4));*** 18.95 (***978-0-8027-9567-0(6)***) Walker & Co.

Leaders of Ancient Egypt, 6 bks. Incl. Ahmose : Liberator of Egypt. Thomas, Susanna. (YA). lib. bdg. 31.95 (978-0-8239-3599-4(X)); Akhenaten & Tutankhamen : The Religious Revolution. Thomas, Susanna. (YA). lib. bdg. 31.95 (978-0-8239-3589-5(2)); Cleopatra : Ruling in the Shadow of Rome. Morgan, Julian. (YA). lib. bdg. 31.95 (978-0-8239-3591-8(4)); Hatsheput : The First Woman Pharaoh. Thomas, Susanna. (J). lib. bdg. 31.95 (978-0-8239-3594-9(9)); Rameses II : Pharaoh of the New Kingdom. Thomas, Susanna. (J). lib. bdg. 31.95 (978-0-8239-3597-0(3)); Snefru : The Pyramid Builder. Thomas, Susanna. (J). lib. bdg. 31.95 (978-0-8239-3598-7(1)); 112p. (gr. 5-8). 2003. (Illus.). 2002. Set lib. bdg. 191.70 (978-0-8239-4051-6(9) , Rosen Central) Rosen Publishing Group, Inc., The.

Nardo, Don. Ramesses II: Ruler of Ancient Egypt. 2006. (Rulers of the Ancient World Ser.). (Illus.). 160p. (J). lib. bdg. 27.93 (978-0-7660-2562-2(4)) Enslow Pubs., Inc.

Pancella, Peggy. Hatshepsut. 2003. (Historical Biographies Ser.). (Illus.). 32p. (J). pap. 6.95 (978-1-4034-3709-9(2)); lib. bdg. 22.79 (978-1-4034-3701-3(7)) Heinemann Library.

Reid, Struan. Cleopatra. 2002. (Historical Biographies Ser.). (Illus.). 32p. (J). (gr. 2-4). lib. bdg. 22.79 (978-1-58810-565-3(2)) Heinemann Library.

—Cleopatra. 2002. (gr. 3-6). lib. bdg. 15.25 (978-0-613-45727-9(7)) Tandem Library Bks.

Ross, Stewart. Clever Cleo. Shields, Sue, illus. 32p. pap. 9.99 (978-0-7502-2853-4(9) , Hodder & Stoughton) Hodder General Publishing Division GBR. *Dist:* Trafalgar Square Publishing.

Solbiati, Romano. Ancient Egypt. 2001. (Journey to the Past Ser.). (Illus.). 56p. (J). (gr. 6-8). lib. bdg. 27.12 (978-0-7398-1954-8(2)) Raintree.

Stanley, Diane. Saladin: Noble Prince of Islam. Stanley, Diane, illus. 2002. (Illus.). 48p. (J). (gr. 5-8). 16.99 (978-0-688-17135-3(4)); lib. bdg. 18.89 (978-0-688-17136-0(2)) HarperCollins Pubs.

Thomas, Susanna. Ahmose: Liberator of Egypt. 2003. (Leaders of Ancient Egypt Ser.). (Illus.). 112p. (YA). (gr. 5-8). lib. bdg. 31.95 (978-0-8239-3599-4(X) , Rosen Central) Rosen Publishing Group, Inc., The.

Whiting, Jim. The Life & Times of Rameses the Great. 2005. (Biography from Ancient Civilizations Ser.). (Illus.). 48p. (J). (gr. 5-8). lib. bdg. 29.95 (978-1-58415-341-2(5)) Mitchell Lane Pubs., Inc.

Worth, Richard. Saladin: Sultan of Egypt & Syria. 2007. (Rulers of the Middle Ages Ser.). (Illus.). 160p. (J). (gr. 6 up). lib. bdg. 34.60 (978-0-7660-2712-1(0)) Enslow Pubs., Inc.

EGYPTOLOGY

see Egypt—Antiquities

EINSTEIN, ALBERT, 1879-1955

Albert Einstein. (Compass Point Early Biographies Ser.). 32p. (J). 7.95 (978-0-7565-1050-3(3)) Compass Point Bks.

Bankston, John. Albert Einstein & the Theory of Relativity. l.t. ed. 2002. (Unlocking the Secrets of Science Ser.). (Illus.). 56p. (gr. 4-10). lib. bdg. 25.70 (978-1-58415-137-1(4)) Mitchell Lane Pubs., Inc.

Barasch, Lynne. Ask Albert Einstein. 2005. (Illus.). 40p. (J). (gr. k-3). 16.00 (978-0-374-30435-5(1)) Farrar, Straus & Giroux.

Berger, Melvin & Berger, Gilda. Did It Take Creativity to Find Relativity, Albert Einstein? 2007. (Scholastic Science Supergiants Ser.). 48p. (J). pap. 4.99 (978-0-439-83384-4(1) , Scholastic Nonfiction) Scholastic, Inc.

Brallier, Jess M. Who Was Albert Einstein? 2002. (gr. 3-6). lib. bdg. 13.00 (978-0-613-43652-6(0)) Tandem Library Bks.

Brallier, Jess M. & Parker, Robert Andrew. Who Was Albert Einstein? Harrison, Nancy & Parker, Robert, illus. 2002. (Who Was...? Ser.). 112p. (J). (gr. 3-5). pap. 4.99 (978-0-448-42496-5(7) , Grosset & Dunlap) Penguin Group (USA) Inc.

Brown, Don. Odd Boy Out: Young Albert Einstein. 2004. (Illus.). 32p. (J). (gr. k-3). 16.00 (978-0-618-49298-5(4)) Houghton Mifflin Co. Trade & Reference Div.

—Teedie: The Boyhood Adventures of Teddy Roosevelt. 2008. 32p. (J). (gr. k-3). 16.00 (978-0-618-17999-2(2)) Houghton Mifflin Co. Trade & Reference Div.

Clark, Ronald. Einstein: The Life & Times. 1999. (Illus.). 878p. (gr. 7-12). lib. bdg. 16.45 (978-0-613-21483-4(8)) Tandem Library Bks.

Cugota, Lluis. Albert Einstein. 2006. (SPA.). 66p. (J). (gr. 4-5). 7.60 (978-84-342-2603-6(0) , PR33293) Parramon Ediciones S.A. ESP. *Dist:* Lectorum Pubns., Inc.

Cugota, Lluís. My Name Is Albert Einstein. Roldan, Gustavo, illus. 2006. (My Name Is ... Ser.). 64p. (J). pap. 7.99 (978-0-7641-3391-6(8)) Barron's Educational Series, Inc.

Dorling Kindersley Publishing Staff, ed. Albert Einstein: A Photographic Story of a Life. 2005. (Biography Ser.). (Illus.). 128p. (J). 14.99 (978-0-7566-1248-1(9)) Dorling Kindersley Publishing, Inc.

—Albert Einstein Vol. 2: A Photographic Story of a Life. 2005. (First Biographies Ser.). 24p. (YA). (gr. k-3). (978-0-7368-3382-0(X) , Pebble Bks.) Capstone Pr., Inc.

Einstein, el matematico Imaginativo 15: Leveled Books. 2001. (McGraw-Hill. Lectura Ser.). (ENG & SPA.). (gr. 4 up). (978-0-02-188215-1(0)) Macmillan/McGraw-Hill Schl. Div.

Fiona Macdonald. Albert Einstein. 2005. (Gigantes de Ciencia Ser.). (ENG & SPA., Illus.). 64p. (J). (gr. 5-7). 28.70 (978-1-4103-0504-6(X) , Blackbirch Pr., Inc.) Thomson Gale.

Frisch, Aaron. Albert Einstein. 2005. (Illus.). 48p. (J). (gr. 5-9). 21.95 (978-1-58341-328-9(6) , Creative Education) Creative Co., The.

Goldenstern, Joyce. Albert Einstein: Physicist & Genius. (Great Minds of Science Ser.). (Illus.). 128p. (gr. 4-10). 2001. (YA). pap. 13.26 (978-0-7660-1864-8(4)); 2007. (J). lib. bdg. 31.93 (***978-0-7660-2838-8(0)***) Enslow Pubs., Inc.

Gomez, Rebecca. Albert Einstein. 2003. (First Biographies Ser.). (Illus.). 32p. (J). (gr. k-4). lib. bdg. 22.78 (978-1-57765-946-4(5)) ABDO Publishing Co.

Hasday, Judy L. Albert Einstein: The Giant of 20th Century Science. 2004. (Nobel Prize-Winning Scientists Ser.). (Illus.). 128p. (J). lib. bdg. 26.60 (978-0-7660-2185-3(8)) Enslow Pubs., Inc.

Heinrichs, Ann. Albert Einstein. 2002. (Trailblazers of the Modern World Ser.). (Illus.). 48p. (J). (gr. 5 up). lib. bdg. 30.00 (978-0-8368-5069-7(6)); (ps-7). pap., lib. bdg. 14.95 (978-0-8368-5229-5(X)) Stevens, Gareth Inc. (World Almanac Library).

—Albert Einstein. 2002. (gr. 3-6). lib. bdg. 16.40 (978-0-613-76811-5(6)) Tandem Library Bks.

Lakin, Patricia. Albert Einstein: Genius of the Twentieth Century. Daniel, Alan & Daniel, Lea, illus. 2005. (Ready-To-Read Ser.). 48p. (J). (ps). pap. 3.99 (978-0-689-87034-7(5)); lib. bdg. 11.89 (978-0-689-87035-4(3)) Simon & Schuster Children's Publishing. (Aladdin).

Lassieur, Allison. Albert Einstein: Genius of the Twentieth Century. 2005. (Great Life Stories Ser.). (Illus.). 127p. (J). (gr. 6-8). 30.50 (978-0-531-12401-7(0) , Watts, Franklin) Scholastic Library Publishing.

MacDonald, Fiona. Albert Einstein: Genius Beyond the Theory of Relativity. 2000. (Giants of Science Ser.). (Illus.). 64p. (J). (gr. 5-8). 27.44 (978-1-56711-330-3(3) , Blackbirch Pr., Inc.) Thomson Gale.

—Einstein. 2000. (World in the Time of... Ser.). (Illus.). 48p. (J). (gr. 4-7). 22.95 (978-0-7910-6031-5(4) , Chelsea Hse.) Facts On File, Inc.

MacLeod, Elizabeth. Albert Einstein: A Life of Genius. 2004. (Snapshots Ser.). (Illus.). 32p. (J). (gr. 4-6). (978-1-55337-397-1(9)) Kids Can Pr., Ltd.

—Albert Einstein: A Life of Genius. 2003. (gr. 3-6). lib. bdg. 15.25 (978-0-613-84411-6(4)) Tandem Library Bks.

—Albert Einstein: A Questioning Life. 2004. (Snapshots Ser.). (Illus.). 32p. (J). (gr. 4-6). (978-1-55337-396-4(0)) Kids Can Pr., Ltd.

Mattern, Joanne & Santrey, Laurence. Albert Einstein, Creative Genius. Beier, Ellen, illus. 2005. 45p. (J). pap. (978-0-439-80152-2(4)) Scholastic, Inc.

McLeese, Don. Albert Einstein. (Rourke Discovery Library). (Illus.). 24p. 2006. (gr. 2-5). 14.95 (978-1-59515-433-0(7)); 2005. (SPA & ENG., (J). (978-1-59515-673-0(9)) Rourke Publishing, LLC.

McPherson, Stephanie Sammartino. Albert Einstein. 48p. (J). (gr. 2-5). 18.95 (978-1-58013-094-3(1)) Kar-Ben Publishing.

—Albert Einstein. 2004. (History Maker Bios Ser.). (Illus.). 48p. (J). (gr. 3-5). lib. bdg. 26.60 (978-0-8225-0350-7(6)) Lerner Publishing Group.

Meltzer, Milton. Albert Einstein: A Biography. 2007. (Illus.). 48p. (J). (gr. 1-5). 16.95 (978-0-8234-1966-1(5)) Holiday Hse., Inc.

Morton, Alan. Einstein's Theories of Relativity. 2005. (Milestones in Modern Science Ser.). (J). pap. (978-0-8368-5860-0(3)); (Illus.). 48p. lib. bdg. 30.00 (978-0-8368-5853-2(0)) Stevens, Gareth Inc. (World Almanac Library).

Oxlade, Chris. Albert Einstein. 2003. (20th Century History Makers Ser.). (Illus.). 112p. (J). lib. bdg. 32.85 (978-0-7398-5259-0(0)) Raintree.

Pirotta, Saviour. Albert Einstein. 2002. (Scientists Who Made History Ser.). (Illus.). 48p. (J). lib. bdg. 27.12 (978-0-7398-4844-9(5)) Raintree.

Rau, Dana Meachen. Albert Einstein. 2003. (Compass Point Early Biographies Ser.). (Illus.). 32p. (J). (gr. 2 up). lib. bdg. 21.26 (978-0-7565-0416-8(3)) Compass Point Bks.

Reid, Struan. Albert Einstein. 2002. (Groundbreakers Ser.). (Illus.). 48p. (J). (gr. 5-7). pap. 8.50 (978-1-58810-988-0(7) , 91463) Heinemann Library.

—Albert Einstein. 2002. (gr. 5-8). lib. bdg. 17.05 (978-0-613-89417-3(0)) Tandem Library Bks.

Reid, Struan & Einstein, Albert. Albert Einstein. 2000. (Groundbreakers Ser.). (Illus.). 48p. (J). (gr. 5-7). lib. bdg. 25.64 (978-1-57572-365-5(4)) Heinemann Library.

Renn, Jurgen, ed. Einstein's Annalen Papers: The Complete Collection 1901 - 1922. 2005. (ENG & GER., Illus.). 590p. 155.00 (978-3-527-40564-0(X)) Wiley, John & Sons, Inc.

Santrey, Laurence. Albert Einstein. 2007. 48p. (J). pap. 3.99 (***978-0-439-87479-3(3)*** , Scholastic en Espanol) Scholastic, Inc.

Schaefer, Lola M. & Schaefer, Wyatt S. Albert Einstein. Saunders-Smith, Gail, ed. 2003. (First Biographies Ser.). (Illus.). 24p. (J). (gr. k-1). lib. bdg. 15.93 (978-0-7368-2079-0(5) , Pebble Bks.) Capstone Pr., Inc.

Slade, Suzanne. Albert Einstein: Scientist & Genius. Schultz, Jolene, illus. 2007. (J). lib. bdg. (***978-1-4048-3730-0(2)***) Picture Window Bks.

Sullivan, Anne Marie. Albert Einstein: Scientist Theory of Relativity. 2002. (Great Names Ser.). (Illus.). 32p. (J). (gr. 3 up). lib. bdg. (978-1-59084-140-2(9)) Mason Crest Pubs.

Wishinsky, Frieda. What's the Matter with Albert? A Story of Albert Einstein. 2004. (Illus.). 32p. (J). pap. 6.95 (978-1-897066-15-7(5)) Maple Tree Pr. CAN. *Dist:* Perseus Distribution.

—What's the Matter with Albert? A Story of Albert Einstein. Lamontagne, Jacques, illus. 2002. 32p. (J). (gr. 2-5). 19.95 (978-1-894379-31-1(4)) Maple Tree Pr. CAN. *Dist:* Firefly Bks., Ltd.

Wyborny, Sheila. Albert Einstein. 2002. (Inventors & Creators Ser.). (Illus.). 48p. (J). (gr. 3-5). 23.70 (978-0-7377-1278-0(3) , Kidhaven) Thomson Gale.

Yeatts, Tabatha. Sterling Biographies: Albert Einstein: The Miracle Mind. 2007. (Sterling Biographies Ser.). (Illus.). 128p. (J). 12.95 (***978-1-4027-4950-6(3));*** pap. 5.95 (***978-1-4027-3228-7(7)***) Sterling Publishing Co., Inc.

YKids Staff. Albert Einstein. 2007. (Great Figures in History Ser.). 148p. (J). (gr. 4-7). pap. 14.95 (***978-981-05-4944-2(X)***) Youngjin (Singapore) Pte Ltd. SGP. *Dist:* Independent Pubs. Group.

EISENHOWER, DWIGHT D. (DWIGHT DAVID), 1890-1969

Adler, David A. A Picture Book of Dwight David Eisenhower. 2002. (Illus.). 32p. (J). (gr. k-3). 6.95 (978-0-8234-1830-5(8)); tchr. ed. 16.95 (978-0-8234-1702-5(6)) Holiday Hse., Inc.

Alphin, Elaine Marie & Alphin, Arthur B. Dwight D. Eisenhower. 2005. (History Maker Bios Ser.). (Illus.). 48p. (J). (gr. 3-5). lib. bdg. 26.60 (978-0-8225-1544-9(X)) Lerner Publishing Group.

Birkner, Michael. Dwight D. Eisenhower. 2005. (Encyc of Presidents, 2ND Ser.). (Illus.). 112p. (J). (gr. 6-8). 34.00 (978-0-516-22969-0(9) , Watts, Franklin) Scholastic Library Publishing.

Brenner, Samuel. Dwight D. Eisenhower. 2002. (Presidents & Their Decisions Ser.). (Illus.). 186p. (J). 36.20 (978-0-7377-1110-3(8)); pap. 24.95 (978-0-7377-1109-7(4)) Thomson Gale. (Greenhaven Pr., Inc.).

Brown, D. Clayton. Dwight D. Eisenhower. 1998. (United States Presidents Ser.). (Illus.). 128p. (YA). (gr. 5-12). lib. bdg. 26.60 (978-0-89490-940-5(1)) Enslow Pubs., Inc.

Darby, Jean. Dwight D. Eisenhower. 2004. (Presidential Leaders Ser.). (Illus.). 112p. (J). (gr. 6-12). lib. bdg. 29.27 (978-0-8225-0813-7(3)) Lerner Publishing Group.

Joseph, Paul. Dwight D. Eisenhower. 1999. (United States Presidents Ser.). (Illus.). 32p. (J). (gr. k-6). lib. bdg. 22.78 (978-1-56239-744-9(3) , Checkerboard Library) ABDO Publishing Co.

Karr, Kathleen. Dwight D. Eisenhower: Letters from a New Jersey Schoolgirl. 2002. (Dear Mr. President Ser.). (Illus.). 128p. (YA). 9.95 (978-1-58837-007-5(0)) Winslow Pr.

Marsh, Carole. Dwight D. Eisenhower. 2002. (One Thousand Readers Ser.). (Illus.). 12p. (J). (gr. k-4). 2.95 (978-0-635-01569-3(2) , 15692) Gallopade International.

Raatma, Lucia. Dwight D. Eisenhower. 2002. (Profiles of the Presidents Ser.). (Illus.). 64p. (J). (gr. 4 up). lib. bdg. 23.93 (978-0-7565-0279-9(9)) Compass Point Bks.

Randolph, Ryan P. How to Draw the Life & Times of Dwight D. Eisenhower. (Kid's Guide to Drawing the Presidents of the United States of America Ser.). (Illus.). 32p. (J). 2007. 25.25 (978-1-4042-3010-1(6)); 2006. lib. bdg. (***978-4-04-230106-6(1)***) Rosen Publishing Group, Inc., The. (PowerKids Pr.).

Schultz, Randy. Dwight D. Eisenhower: A MyReportLinks. Com Book. 2003. (Presidents Ser.). (Illus.). 48p. (J). (gr. 5-10). lib. bdg. 25.26 (978-0-7660-5102-7(1) , MyReportLinks.com Bks.) Enslow Pubs., Inc.

Stanley, George Edward. Dwight D. Eisenhower: Young Military Leader. 2006. (Illus.). 117p. (J). (***978-1-4156-7635-6(6)*** , Aladdin) Simon & Schuster Children's Publishing.

Venezia, Mike. Dwight D. Eisenhower. Venezia, Mike, illus. 2007. (Getting to Know the U. S. Presidents Ser.). 32p. (J). 7.95 (***978-0-531-17944-4(3));*** (Illus.). (gr. 3-4). 27.00 (978-0-516-22638-5(X)) Scholastic Library Publishing. (Children's Pr.).

Young, Jeff C. Dwight D. Eisenhower: Soldier & President. 2004. (Notable Americans Ser.). (Illus.). 128p. (YA). (gr. 6-12). 23.95 (978-1-883846-76-3(5) , First Biographies) Reynolds, Morgan Inc.

EL NINO CURRENT

Alatorre, Antonio. El Apogeo del Castellano. 2000. 11.80 (978-0-606-17642-2(X)) Tandem Library Bks.

Arnold, Caroline. El Nino: Stormy Weather for People & Wildlife. 1998. (Illus.). 48p. (J). (gr. 4-6). tchr. ed. 16.00 (978-0-395-77602-5(3) , Clarion Bks.) Houghton Mifflin Co. Trade & Reference Div.

Bredeson, Carmen. El Niano & La Niana: Deadly Weather. 2002. (American Disasters Ser.). (Illus.). 48p. (J). (gr. 4-10). lib. bdg. 23.93 (978-0-7660-1551-7(3)) Enslow Pubs., Inc.

Gold, Susan Dudley. Blame It on El Nino. 1999. (Illus.). 96p. (YA). (gr. 5-9). lib. bdg. 28.54 (978-0-7398-1376-8(5)) Raintree.

Seibert, Patricia. Discovering El Nino: How Fable & Fact Together Help Explain the Weather. Ellis, Jan Davey, illus. 1999. (Our World Ser.). 32p. (gr. 2-5). lib. bdg. 22.90 (978-0-7613-1273-4(0) , Millbrook Pr.) Lerner Publishing Group.

EL SALVADOR

Deady, Kathleen W. El Salvador. 2001. (Countries of the World Ser.). (Illus.). 24p. (J). (gr. 2-3). lib. bdg. 18.60 (978-0-7368-0941-2(4) , Bridgestone Bks.) Capstone Pr., Inc.

—El Salvador. 2005. (Fact Finders Ser.). (Illus.). 32p. (J). 22.60 (978-0-7368-3750-7(7)) Capstone Pr., Inc.

Deem, James M. El Salvador: A MyReportLinks. com Book. 2004. (Top Ten Countries of Recent Immigrants Ser.). (Illus.). 48p. (J). lib. bdg. 25.26 (978-0-7660-5241-3(9) , MyReportLinks.com Bks.) Enslow Pubs., Inc.

DiPiazza, Francesca. El Salvador in Pictures. 2007. (J). lib. bdg. (***978-0-8225-7145-2(5)***) Twenty First Century Bks.

Foley, Erin & Hapipi, Rafiz. El Salvador. 2nd ed. 2005. (Cultures of the World Ser.). (Illus.). 144p. (J). (gr. 6-10). lib. bdg. (978-0-7614-1967-9(5) , Benchmark Bks.) Cavendish, Marshall Corp.

Morrison, Marion. El Salvador. 2001. (Enchantment of the World, Second Ser.). (Illus.). 144p. (J). (gr. 5-9). 36.00 (978-0-516-21118-3(8) , Children's Pr.) Scholastic Library Publishing.

Nickles, Greg. El Salvador: The Land. 2002. (SPA.). (gr. 3-6). lib. bdg. 16.40 (978-0-613-52948-8(0)) Tandem Library Bks.

—El Salvador: The People & Culture. 2002. (gr. 3-6). lib. bdg. 16.40 (978-0-613-52949-5(9)) Tandem Library Bks.

—El Salvador — The People & Culture. 2001. (Lands, Peoples & Cultures Ser.). (Illus.). 32p. (J). (gr. 4-5). pap. (978-0-7787-9736-4(8)) Crabtree Publishing Co.

—El Salvador - The Land. 2001. (Lands, Peoples & Cultures Ser.). (Illus.). 32p. (J). (gr. 4-5). (978-0-7787-9367-0(2)); pap. (978-0-7787-9735-7(X)) Crabtree Publishing Co.

—El Salvador - The People & Culture. 2001. (Lands, Peoples & Cultures Ser.). (Illus.). 32p. (J). (gr. 4-5). (978-0-7787-9368-7(0)) Crabtree Publishing Co.

Sanders, Renfield. El Salvador. 1999. (Major World Nations Ser.). (Illus.). 144p. (YA). (gr. 4-7). 29.95 (978-0-7910-4737-8(7) , Chelsea Hse.) Facts On File, Inc.

Shields, Charles J. El Salvador. 2002. (Let's Discover Central America Ser.). (Illus.). 63p. (YA). (gr. 5 up). lib. bdg. (978-1-59084-094-8(1)) Mason Crest Pubs.

EL SALVADOR—FICTION

Argueta, Jorge. Alfredito Flies Home. Amado, Elisa, tr. from SPA. Garay, Luis, illus. 2007. 40p. (J). (ps-3). 17.95 ***(978-0-88899-585-8(7))*** Groundwood Bks. CAN. *Dist:* Perseus Distribution.

Argueta, Jorge. Zipitio. Amado, Elisa, tr. from SPA. Calderon, Gloria, illus. 2003. 32p. (J). 16.95 (978-0-88899-487-5(7)) Groundwood Bks. CAN. *Dist:* Perseus Distribution.

Argueta, Jorge & Alvarez, María Jesus. La Fiesta de Las Tortillas. Alvarez, María Jesus, illus. 2005. (ENG & SPA., Illus.). 32p. (J). 14.95 (978-1-59820-094-2(1) , Alfaguara) Santillana USA Publishing Co., Inc.

Bencastro, Mario. A Promise to Keep. Giersbach-Rascon, Susan, tr. from SPA. 2005. 134p. (J). (gr. 3-7). pap. 9.95 (978-1-55885-457-4(6) , Piñata Books) Arte Publico Pr.

Contreras-Rosado, Rosalina. Adventures of Two Little Sisters in El Salvador: Tatiana & Irene Visit for the First Time Their Mother's Homeland. 2002. 46p. 15.40 (978-0-9726541-0-4(0)) Adventures In Books.

Harrell, Deborah A. Pintos Hope. 2003. 124p. (YA). pap. 10.95 (978-0-595-26514-5(6)) iUniverse, Inc.

Jorge, Argueta. Alfredito Regresa Volando a Su Casa. Garay, Luis, illus. 2007. (SPA.). 40p. (J). (ps-4). 17.95 ***(978-0-88899-586-5(5))*** Groundwood Bks. CAN. *Dist:* Perseus Distribution.

ELECTIONEERING

see Politics, Practical

ELECTIONS

see also Presidents—United States—Election; Suffrage

Ansary, Mir Tamim. Election Day. (Holiday Histories Ser.). (Illus.). 32p. (J). (gr. k-2). 2001. lib. bdg. 21.36 (978-1-58810-221-8(1)); 2nd ed. 2006. ***(978-1-4034-8885-5(1))*** Heinemann Library.

Ansary, Tamim. Election Day. 2002. (Holiday Histories Ser.). (Illus.). 32p. (J). (gr. k-2). pap. 6.95 (978-1-58810-571-4(7) , 91686) Heinemann Library.

Baicker, Karen. The Election Activity Book: Dozens of Activities That Help Kids Learn about Voting, Campaigns, Our Government, Presidents, & More. 2004. (Illus.). 32p. pap., tchr. ed. 9.99 (978-0-439-66826-2(3)) Scholastic, Inc.

Boyers, Sara Jane. Teen Power Politics: Make Yourself Heard. 2000. (Single Titles Ser.). (Illus.). 128p. (gr. 9 up). lib. bdg. 24.90 (978-0-7613-1307-6(9) , Twenty-First Century Bks.) Lerner Publishing Group.

Buehler, Stephanie & Kremer, Kelly Dos Santos. Elections: Primary. 2000. (Illus.). 48p. (Orig.). (J). pap., tchr. ed. 7.99 (978-1-57690-618-7(3) , TCA2618) Teacher Created Materials, Inc.

California 2003-2004 Recall Election Calendar. l.t. ed. 2003. (Illus.). 40p. 14.95 (978-0-9745991-0-6(7)) Princess Ring, LLC.

Christelow, Eileen. Vote! Christelow, Eileen, illus. (Illus.). 48p. (J). 2004. (gr. 1-5). 47.60 (978-0-618-51723-7(5)); 2003. (gr. 3-5). 16.00 (978-0-618-24754-7(8)) Houghton Mifflin Co. Trade & Reference Div. (Clarion Bks.).

De Capua, Sarah. Voting. 2002. (True Bks.). (Illus.). 48p. (J). (gr. 3-5). pap. 6.95 (978-0-516-27365-5(5) , Children's Pr.) Scholastic Library Publishing.

Decapua, Sarah. Running for Public Office. 2002. (gr. 3-6). lib. bdg. 15.25 (978-0-613-54330-9(0)) Tandem Library Bks.

DeGezelle, Terri. Voting in Elections. 2005. (First Facts Ser.). (Illus.). 24p. (J). 21.26 (978-0-7368-3687-6(X)) Capstone Pr., Inc.

Deitch, JoAnne Weisman, ed. Voting in America. 2003. (Researching American History Ser.). (Illus.). 52p. (J). pap. 7.95 (978-1-57960-092-1(1)) History Compass, LLC.

DK Publishing & Steele, Phillip. Vote. 2008. (DK Eyewitness Bks.). 72p. (J). (gr. 3-8). 15.99 ***(978-0-7566-3382-0(6));*** lib. bdg. 19.99 ***(978-0-7566-3381-3(8))*** Dorling Kindersley Publishing, Inc.

Doherty, Edith J. S. & Evans, Louise C. Electing the President: Simulation Similes. 2000. 66p. (J). spiral bd. 8.99 (978-0-945984-65-8(0) , Zephyr Pr.) Chicago Review Pr., Inc.

Donovan, Sandy. Running for Office: A Look at Political Campaigns. 2004. (How Government Works Ser.). (Illus.). 56p. (J). (gr. 4-8). lib. bdg. 25.26 (978-0-8225-4700-6(7)) Lerner Publishing Group.

Egan, Tracie. Voting. 2004. (Primary Source Library of American Citizenship). (Illus.). 32p. (YA). lib. bdg. (978-1-4042-5093-2(X)) Rosen Publishing Group, Inc., The.

Elections. 2000. (Illus.). (YA). (gr. 6-9). pap. 4.95 (978-1-55708-625-9(7) , MCR554) McDonald Publishing Co.

Elections in the United States, 6 vols. (gr. 2-5). 39.95 (978-0-7368-8926-1(4)) Red Brick Learning.

Giddens-White, Bryon. Our Government: National Elections & the Political Process. 2005. (J). 28.21 (978-1-4034-6604-4(1)); pap. (978-1-4034-6609-9(2)) Heinemann Library.

Gottfried, Ted. The 2000 Election. 2002. (Headliners Ser.). (Illus.). 64p. (gr. 5-8). lib. bdg. 25.90 (978-0-7613-2406-5(2) , Millbrook Pr.) Lerner Publishing Group.

Gutman, Dan. Landslide! A Kid's Guide to the U. S. Elections. 2000. (gr. 3-6). lib. bdg. 11.80 (978-0-613-25923-1(8)) Tandem Library Bks.

Hamilton, John. Voting in an Election. 2005. (Government in Action! Ser.). (J). (gr. k-6). lib. bdg. 22.78 (978-1-59197-647-9(2)) ABDO Publishing Co.

Harcourt School Publishers Staff. Election 2000. 3rd ed. 2002. (Horizons Ser.). (Illus.). (J). pap. 7.30 (978-0-15-333595-2(5)) Harcourt Schl. Pubs.

—We Elect a President. 3rd ed. 2002. (Horizons Ser.). (Illus.). (J). pap. 3.70 (978-0-15-333198-5(4)) Harcourt Schl. Pubs.

Harris, Nancy. What Are Elections? 2007. (J). ***(978-1-4034-9469-6(X));*** pap. ***(978-1-4034-9475-7(4))*** Heinemann Library.

Heath, David. Elections in the United States. 1998. (American Civics Ser.). (Illus.). 48p. (J). (gr. 3-4). lib. bdg. 22.60 (978-0-7368-0000-6(X) , Bridgestone Bks.) Capstone Pr., Inc.

—Elections in the United States. (American Civics Ser.). 48p. (YA). pap. 6.95 (978-0-7368-8857-8(8)) Capstone Pr., Inc.

Holt, Rinehart and Winston Staff. Call to Freedom: 1865-Present: Election Update 2001. 2001. 81.06 (978-0-03-066427-4(6)) Holt, Rinehart & Winston.

—Call to Freedom: Election Update 2000. 2001. 82.40 (978-0-03-066426-7(8)) Holt, Rinehart & Winston.

Hudak, Heather C. Election Day. 2006. (J). (978-1-59036-404-8(X)); (978-1-59036-407-9(4)) Weigl Pubs., Inc.

Isler, Claudia. The Right to Vote. 2001. (Individual Rights & Civic Responsibility Ser.). (Illus.). 64p. (YA). (gr. 7-12). lib. bdg. 26.50 (978-0-8239-3235-1(4)) Rosen Publishing Group, Inc., The.

Jennett, Pamela & Marchant, Sherry. Electing Our President: The Process to Elect the Nation's Leader. Jennett, Pamela, ed. Hillam, Corbin & Grayson, Rick, illus. 2004. 48p. pap. 8.99 (978-0-88160-379-8(1) , LW-436) Creative Teaching Pr., Inc.

Kowalski, Kathiann M. Campaign Politics: What's Fair, What's Foul? 2005. (Pro/Con Ser.). (Illus.). 144p. (gr. 6-12). lib. bdg. 25.26 (978-0-8225-2630-8(1)) Lerner Publishing Group.

Lankford, Ronnie D. Should the Voting Age Be Lowered? 2007. (At Issue Ser.). (Illus.). 128p. (gr. 10-12). 29.95 ***(978-0-7377-3936-7(3));*** pap. 21.20 ***(978-0-7377-3937-4(1))*** Thomson Gale. (Greenhaven Pr., Inc.).

Liljeblad, Fredrik. Voting. 2008. (J). lib. bdg. 25.26 ***(978-1-60279-062-9(0))*** Cherry Lake Publishing.

Lishak, Antony. Elections & Voting. 2007. (J). ***(978-1-59920-036-1(8))*** Smart Apple Media.

Marzilli, Alan. Election Reform. 2003. (Point/Counterpoint Ser.). (Illus.). 112p. (gr. 9-13). 32.95 (978-0-7910-7698-9(9) , Chelsea Hse.) Facts On File, Inc.

McNamara, Margaret. Election Day. Gordon, Mike, illus. 2004. (Robin Hill School Ser.). 32p. (J). lib. bdg. 11.89 (978-0-689-86426-1(4) , Aladdin Library) Simon & Schuster Children's Publishing.

McNamara, Margaret & Gordon, Mike. Election Day. 2004. (Robin Hill School Ser.). (Illus.). 32p. (J). pap. 3.99 (978-0-689-86425-4(6) , Aladdin) Simon & Schuster Children's Publishing.

Murphy, Patricia. Election Day. 2002. (gr. k-3). lib. bdg. 14.10 (978-0-613-54196-1(0)) Tandem Library Bks.

Murphy, Patricia J. Election Day. 2002. (Rookie Read-About Holidays Ser.). (Illus.). 32p. (J). (gr. 1-2). pap. 5.95 (978-0-516-27488-1(0) , Children's Pr.) Scholastic Library Publishing.

—Voting & Elections. 2001. (Let's See Library). (Illus.). 24p. (J). (gr. 1 up). lib. bdg. 19.93 (978-0-7565-0144-0(X)) Compass Point Bks.

Nobleman, Marc Tyler. Election Day. 2004. (Let's See Ser.). (Illus.). 24p. (J). (gr. 1 up). lib. bdg. 19.93 (978-0-7565-0644-5(1)) Compass Point Bks.

Orr, Tamra. Electing Leaders. 2008. (J). lib. bdg. 25.26 ***(978-1-60279-063-6(9))*** Cherry Lake Publishing.

Ring, Susan. Election Connection: The Official Nick Guide to Electing the President. 2004. (Illus.). 72p. (J). pap. 7.95 (978-0-8118-4175-7(8)) Chronicle Bks. LLC.

Sandak, Cass R. Your Right to Vote. 1999. (American Government Today Ser.). (Illus.). 48p. (J). lib. bdg. 22.83 (978-0-7398-1790-2(6)) Raintree.

Sanders. Your Right to Vote. 1999. (American Government Today Ser.). (Illus.). pap. 7.20 (978-0-7398-2132-9(6)) Steck-Vaughn.

Schlesinger, Arthur M., Sr., et al, eds. The Election of 1800. 2003. (Major Presidential Elections & the Administrations That Followed Ser.). (Illus.). 154p. (J). (gr. 7 up). lib. bdg. (978-1-59084-352-9(5)) Mason Crest Pubs.

—The Election of 1840 & the Harrison/Tyler Administrations. 2003. (Major Presidential Elections & the Administrations That Followed Ser.). (Illus.). 154p. (YA). (gr. 7 up). lib. bdg. (978-1-59084-354-3(1)) Mason Crest Pubs.

—The Election of 1860 & the Administration of Abraham Lincoln. 2003. (Major Presidential Elections & the Administrations That Followed Ser.). (Illus.). 154p. (YA). (gr. 7 up). lib. bdg. (978-1-59084-355-0(X)) Mason Crest Pubs.

Schlesinger, Arthur M., Jr. & Israel, Fred L., eds. Major Presidential Elections, 15 bks., Set. (Illus.). (YA). (gr. 7 up). lib. bdg. (978-1-59084-350-5(9)) Mason Crest Pubs.

See, Betty. Electing President: The Electoral Process in Action. 2005. 48p. 10.95 (978-1-59363-067-6(0)) Prufrock Pr.

Shea, Therese. America's Electoral College: Choosing the President Comparing & Analyzing Charts, Graphs, & Tables. 2006. (Math for the Real World Ser.). (Illus.). 32p. pap. (978-1-4042-6069-6(2)); (J). (gr. 4-8). lib. bdg. 23.95 (978-1-4042-3358-4(X)) Rosen Publishing Group, Inc., The.

Sobel, Syl. Presidential Elections. 2001. (United States & Its Flag Ser.). (Illus.). (J). lib. bdg. 14.95 (978-1-56674-305-1(2)) Forest Hse. Publishing Co., Inc.

—Presidential Elections. 2000. (978-0-606-18005-4(2)) Tandem Library Bks.

Wingate, Katherine. Political Reforms: American Citizens Gain More Control over Their Government. 2006. (Progressive Movement, 1900-1920—Efforts to Reform America's New Industrial Society Ser.). (Illus.). 32p. (J). (978-1-4042-0853-7(4)) Rosen Publishing Group, Inc., The.

ELECTIONS—FICTION

Alberto, Daisy. Pete for President! Sims, Blanche, illus. 2004. 32p. (J). lib. bdg. 20.00 ***(978-1-4242-1115-9(8))*** Fitzgerald Bks.

—Pete for President! Sims, Blanche, illus. 2004. (Social Studies Connects). 32p. (J). (gr. 1-3). pap. 4.99 (978-1-57565-142-2(4)) Kane Pr., The.

Barnes, Peter W. Woodrow for President: A Tail of Voting, Campaigns & Elections. Barnes, Cheryl Shaw, illus. 1999. 32p. (J). (gr. 3-6). 16.95 (978-1-893622-01-2(0) , VSP Bks.) Vacation Spot Publishing.

Buchanan, Paul. Hail to the Chump, Vol. 9. 1998. (Misadventures of Willie Plummett Ser.: Vol. 9). 128p. (J). (gr. 3-7). 5.99 (978-0-570-05088-9(X)) Concordia Publishing Hse.

Carr, Richard Wallace. Dolly & Ike at the Willard Hotel: Abraham Lincoln's Slippers. Parrish, Mary, illus. 2005. (J). 15.95 (978-0-933165-08-3(0)) Dicmar Publishing Co.

Cronin, Doreen. Duck for President. Lewin, Betsy, illus. 2004. 40p. (J). 15.95 (978-0-689-86377-6(2)) Simon & Schuster Children's Publishing.

—Duck for President. 2006. (J). (ps-3). 22.78 (978-1-59961-091-7(4)) Spotlight.

Dahl, Elizabeth. Vote for Me. 2001. (gr. k-3). lib. bdg. 11.65 (978-0-613-33452-5(3)) Tandem Library Bks.

de Brunhoff, Laurent. Babar & the Circus Star. 2005. (J). (978-0-8109-5774-9(4)) Abrams, Harry N. , Inc.

Dilly for President. 2005. (Illus.). 64p. (J). (ps-k). pap. 6.95 (978-0-7613-2442-3(9) , First Avenue Editions) Lerner Publishing Group.

Dowell, Frances O'Roark. Phineas L. MacGuire... Gets Slimed! The Second Experiment. McDaniels, Preston L., illus. 2007. (From the Highly Scientific Notebooks of Phineas L. MacGuire Ser.). 208p. (J). (gr. 3-7). 16.99 (978-1-4169-0196-9(5)) Simon & Schuster Children's Publishing.

Driscoll, Laura. Stuart Little Bk. 2: Think Big, Vote Little! Perkins, Thomas, illus. 2003. (Festival Reader Ser.). 32p. (J). (ps-2). pap. 3.99 (978-0-06-000748-5(6) , Harper Festival) HarperCollins Pubs.

Duck for President. 2004. 29.95 incl. cd-rom (978-0-7882-0540-8(4)); 24.95 incl. audio (978-0-7882-0539-2(0)) Weston Woods Studios, Inc.

Edwards, Nancy. Mom for Mayor. Chesworth, Michael, illus. 2006. 96p. (J). 16.95 (978-0-8126-2743-5(1)) Cricket Bks.

Ellerbee, Linda. Girl Reporter Rocks Polls! 2000. (Get Real Ser.: No. 6). 224p. (J). (gr. 3-7). 14.89 (978-0-06-028250-9(9)) HarperCollins Pubs.

Gephart, Donna. As If Being 12 3/4 Isn't Bad Enough, My Mother Is Running for President! 2008. (J). (gr. 3-7). 240p. 15.99 ***(978-0-385-73481-3(6));*** 192p. lib. bdg. 18.99 ***(978-0-385-90479-7(7))*** Random Hse. Children's Bks. (Delacorte Bks. for Young Readers).

Gorman, Carol. Dork on the Run. 192p. (J). 2003. (Illus.). pap. 5.99 (978-0-06-440970-4(8) , Harper Trophy); 2002. (gr. 3-6). 15.99 (978-0-06-029409-0(4)) HarperCollins Pubs.

—Dork on the Run. 2003. (gr. 3-6). lib. bdg. 14.15 (978-0-613-61371-2(6)) Tandem Library Bks.

Harcourt School Publishers Staff. Who's Running for President? Advanced Level. 3rd ed. 2002. (Trophies Reading Program Ser.). (Illus.). pap. 5.10 (978-0-15-323391-3(5)) Harcourt Schl. Pubs.

Howe, James. The Misfits. 2002. lib. bdg. 24.00 incl. audio (978-1-932076-12-7(3) , 02010A) Full Cast Audio.

—The Misfits. 2003. 288p. (YA). mass mkt. 5.99 (978-0-689-83956-6(1) , Aladdin) Simon & Schuster Children's Publishing.

—The Misfits. Slota, Gerald, illus. 2001. 288p. (gr. 5-9). 16.95 (978-0-689-83955-9(3) , Atheneum) Simon & Schuster Children's Publishing.

Katschke, Judy. If I Were President. 1999. (gr. 3-6). lib. bdg. 11.80 (978-0-613-21748-4(9)) Tandem Library Bks.

Krosoczka, Jarrett J. Max for President. 2004. (Illus.). 40p. (J). (ps-3). 15.95 (978-0-375-82428-9(6)); lib. bdg. 17.99 (978-0-375-92428-6(0)) Random Hse. Children's Bks. (Knopf Bks. for Young Readers).

Levithan, David. Wide Awake. 2006. 240p. (YA). (gr. 9). 16.95 (978-0-375-83466-0(4)); lib. bdg. 18.99 (978-0-375-93466-7(9)) Random Hse. Children's Bks. (Knopf Bks. for Young Readers).

Mason, Jane & Stephens, Sarah Hines. Zoey 101: Girls vs. Boys. 2007. (Teenick Ser.: No. 8). 112p. (J). pap. 4.99 (978-0-439-88258-3(3)) Scholastic, Inc.

McNamara, Margaret. Election Day. Gordon, Mike, illus. 2004. 32p. (J). (ps-ps). lib. bdg. 10.79 (978-0-606-32652-0(9)) Tandem Library Bks.

—A Tooth Story. Gordon, Mike, tr. Gordon, Mike, illus. 2004. (Read-to-Read Ser.). 32p. (J). lib. bdg. 11.89 (978-0-689-86424-7(8) , Aladdin Library) Simon & Schuster Children's Publishing.

McNamara, Margaret & Gordon, Mike. A Tooth Story. 2004. (Read-to-Read Ser.). (Illus.). 32p. (J). pap. 3.99 (978-0-689-86423-0(X) , Aladdin) Simon & Schuster Children's Publishing.

McVeigh, Mark. Clifford for President. LaPadula, Tom, illus. 2004. (Big Red Reader Ser.). 32p. (J). pap. 3.99 (978-0-439-69391-2(8)) Scholastic, Inc.

Moss, Marissa. Vote 4 Amelia. Moss, Marissa, illus. 2007. (Amelia's Notebooks). 80p. (J). (gr. 5-8). 9.99 ***(978-1-4169-2789-1(1) ,*** Simon & Schuster/Paula Wiseman Bks.) Simon & Schuster Children's Publishing.

Muldrow, Diane. Winner Takes the Cake. Pollack, Barbara, illus. 2007. (Dish Ser.: No. 11). 160p. (J). (gr. 4-7). pap. 4.99 ***(978-0-448-44666-0(9) ,*** Grosset & Dunlap) Penguin Group (USA) Inc.

Murphy, Stuart J. Grizzly Gazette. 2003. (gr. k-3). lib. bdg. 13.00 (978-0-613-59243-7(3)) Tandem Library Bks.

Nagy, Gloria & Chwast, Seymour. The Wizard Who Wanted to Be Santa. 2000. (Illus.). (J). (ps-3). 16.95 (978-0-9679436-0-2(4)) Sheer Bliss Communications, LLC.

Nigro, D. M. The Wolfman, the Shrink & the Eighth-Grade Election. 2006. 116p. (J). pap. 13.50 (978-1-931201-66-7(8)) Twilight Times Bks.

Pratts, Christine. Tabby Wise for School Secretary. 2005. 61p. pap. 8.99 (978-1-4116-4935-4(4)) Lulu.com.

Rallison, Janette. All's Fair in Love, War, & High School. 2005. 192p. (J). pap. 6.95 (978-0-8027-7725-6(2)) Walker & Co.

—How to Take the Ex Out of Ex-Boyfriend. 2007. 272p. (YA). (gr. 7 up). 15.99 (978-0-399-24617-3(7) , Putnam Juvenile) Penguin Group (USA) Inc.

Schmidt, Gary. First Boy. 2007. 224p. (YA). pap. 6.99 ***(978-0-312-37149-4(7))*** Square Fish.

Schmidt, Gary D. First Boy. rev. ed. 2005. 208p. (YA). (gr. 6). 17.95 (978-0-8050-7859-6(2)) Holt, Henry & Co.

Sheldon, Dyan. My Perfect Life. 2002. (Illus.). 224p. (YA). (gr. 7 up). 16.99 (978-0-7636-1839-1(X)) Candlewick Pr.

Tashjian, Janet. Vote for Larry. rev. ed. 2004. (Illus.). 240p. (J). 16.95 (978-0-8050-7201-3(2) , Holt, Henry & Co. Bks. For Young Readers) Holt, Henry & Co.

Tayleur, Karen. Promises! David Mortimore Baxter. Garvey, Brann, illus. 2007. 87p. (J). pap. ***(978-1-59889-208-6(8))*** Stone Arch Bks.

Thaler, Mike. The Class Election from the Black Lagoon. Lee, Jared D., illus. 2004. (Black Lagoon Adventures Ser.). 64p. (J). (gr. 2-5). pap. 3.99 (978-0-439-55716-0(X) , Scholastic Paperbacks) Scholastic, Inc.

Vote for Us! Individual Title Six-Packs. (Bookweb Ser.). 32p. (gr. 6 up). 34.00 (978-0-7578-0907-1(3)) Rigby Education.

Walters, Eric. Laggan Lard Butts. 2006. 112p. (gr. 5-10). pap. 7.95 (978-1-55143-518-3(7)); lib. bdg. 14.95 (978-1-55143-531-2(4)) Orca Bk. Pubs. USA.

ELECTORAL COLLEGE

see Presidents—United States—Election

ELECTRIC APPLIANCES

see Electric Apparatus and Appliances; Household Appliances, Electric

ELECTRIC APPARATUS AND APPLIANCES

see also Electric Batteries; Electric Lamps; Electric Motors; Electromagnets; Household Appliances, Electric

Alphin, Elaine Marie. Toasters. 1998. (Household History Ser.). (Illus.). 48p. (J). (gr. 2-5). lib. bdg. (978-1-57505-243-4(1) , Carolrhoda Bks.) Lerner Publishing Group.

Bartholomew, Alan. Electric Gadgets & Gizmos: Battery-Powered Buildable Gadgets That Go! annual Bartholomew, Lynn, illus. 1998. (Kids Can Do It Ser.). 156p. (J). (gr. 4-6). (978-1-55074-439-2(9)) Kids Can Pr., Ltd.

—Electric Gadgets & Gizmos: Battery-Powered Buildable Gadgets That Go! Bartholomew, Lynn, illus. 1998. 47p. (J). (ps-7). lib. bdg. 14.10 (978-0-613-16348-4(6)) Tandem Library Bks.

—Electric Mischief: Battery-Powered Gadgets Kids Can Build. Bartholomew, Lynn, illus. 2004. (Kids Can Do It Ser.). 48p. (J). (gr. 4-6). (978-1-55074-925-0(0)); (978-1-55074-923-6(4)) Kids Can Pr., Ltd.

—Electric Mischief: Battery-Powered Gadgets Kids Can Build. 2002. (gr. 3-6). lib. bdg. 14.10 (978-0-613-67883-4(4)) Tandem Library Bks.

Brimner, Larry Dane. Geysers. 2000. (gr. 3-6). lib. bdg. 15.25 (978-0-613-54506-8(0)) Tandem Library Bks.

Lytle, Elizabeth Stewart. Exploring Careers As an Electrician. rev. ed. 1999. (Careers). (Illus.). 192p. (YA). (gr. 7-12). lib. bdg. 26.50 (978-0-8239-2885-9(3) , CAE-LEC) Rosen Publishing Group, Inc., The.

Mawson, Dave, et al. Design & Make It! Electronic Products. 1998. (Illus.). 144p. pap. 30.00 (978-0-7487-2473-4(7)) State Mutual Bk. & Periodical Service, Ltd.

Sloan, Peter. Machines in the School. 1999. (gr. k-3). lib. bdg. 11.65 (978-0-613-30575-4(2)) Tandem Library Bks.

ELECTRIC BATTERIES

Flaherty, Michael. Electricity & Batteries. 2008. (J). lib. bdg. ***(978-1-4042-3905-0(7) ,*** PowerKids Pr.) Rosen Publishing Group, Inc., The.

Sloan, Peter. Car That Stopped. 2000. (gr. k-3). lib. bdg. 11.80 (978-0-613-30305-7(9)) Tandem Library Bks.

Tiner, John Hudson. Water, Acid, & a Metal Make Battery Power. 2003. (From Resource to Energy Source Ser.). (J). (978-1-58417-290-1(8)); pap. (978-1-58417-291-8(6)) Lake Street Pubs.

ELECTRIC CURRENTS

Bergethon, Peter R. The Electric World: An Introduction to Electricity, Student Science Journal. 1999. (Illus.). 84p. (J). (gr. 4-6). pap. (978-1-58447-013-7(5)) Symmetry Learning Systems.

EFG

ELECTRIC ENGINEERING

see also Electric Apparatus and Appliances; Radio; Telegraph; Telephone

Bailey, Jacqui. How Do We Use Electricity? 2006. (J). (978-1-58340-928-2(9)) Smart Apple Media.

Benge, Janet & Benge, Geoff. Thomas Edison: Inspiration & Hard Work. 2007. (J). pap. (***978-1-932096-37-8(X)***) Emerald Bks.

Donnelley, Karen J. Electrician. 2000. (Career Exploration Ser.). (Illus.). 48p. (J). (gr. 3-4). lib. bdg. 21.26 (978-0-7368-0594-0(X) , LifeMatters Bks.) Capstone Pr., Inc.

Electricity/Electron Srs Lab P. (YA). cd-rom 699.87 (978-0-7365-6721-3(6)) Films Media Group.

Firestone, Mary. Electricians. 2001. (Community Helpers Ser.). (Illus.). 24p. (J). (gr. 1-2). lib. bdg. 18.60 (978-0-7368-0956-6(2) , Bridgestone Bks.) Capstone Pr., Inc.

Fitzpatrick, Anne. Electricity. 2003. 24p. (J). lib. bdg. 21.35 (978-1-58340-320-4(5)) Smart Apple Media.

Gaines, Ann Graham. Thomas Edison. 2001. (Inventores Famosos Ser.). (Illus.). 24p. (J). (gr. 1-4). (SPA & ENG.). lib. bdg. 19.27 (978-1-58952-174-2(9) , RK2159); lib. bdg. 20.64 (978-1-58952-122-3(6)) Rourke Publishing, LLC.

Minden, Cecilia. Electricians. 2006. (Neighborhood Helpers Ser.). (Illus.). 32p. (J). (gr. k-4). 22.79 (978-1-59296-563-2(6)) Child's World, Inc.

Nsrc. Science & Technology for Children Books, Electric Circuits: Electric Circuits. 2004. (Illus.). 64p. (J). (978-1-933008-02-8(4)) National Science Resources Ctr.

O'Shei, Tim. Marconi & Tesla: Pioneers of Radio Communication. 2008. (Inventors Who Changed the World Ser.). (Illus.). 128p. (J). (gr. 6 up). lib. bdg. 33.27 (***978-1-59845-076-7(X)*** , MyReportLinks.com Bks.) Enslow Pubs., Inc.

Overcamp, David. Electrician. 2004. (Great Jobs Ser.). (Illus.). 48p. (J). 24.00 (978-0-516-24086-2(2)); (gr. 7-12). pap. 6.95 (978-0-516-25924-6(5)) Scholastic Library Publishing. (Children's Pr.).

Parker, Steve. Fully Charged: Electricity. (Illus.). 56p. (J). 2005. pap. (978-1-4034-6419-4(7)); 2004. lib. bdg. (978-1-4034-4813-2(2)) Heinemann Library.

Schiffer, Michael B., et al. Draw the Lightning Down - Benjamin Franklin & Electrical Technology in the Age of Enlightenment. 2003. (Illus.). 380p. 50.00 (978-0-520-23802-2(8)) Univ. of California Pr.

Science & Technology for Children Books, Electric Circuits Set, 8 vols. 2004. (Illus.). 64p. (J). (978-1-933008-14-1(8)) National Science Resources Ctr.

Tagliaferro, Linda. Thomas Edison: Inventor of the Age of Electricity. 2003. (Lerner Biographies Ser.). (Illus.). 128p. (J). 27.93 (978-0-8225-4689-4(2) , Lerner Pubns.) Lerner Publishing Group.

Thatcher Murcia, Rebecca. Thomas Edison: Great Inventor. 2004. (Uncharted, Unexplored, & Unexplained Ser.). (Illus.). 48p. (J). (gr. 4-8). lib. bdg. 29.95 (978-1-58415-306-1(7)) Mitchell Lane Pubs., Inc.

Thomas, Mark. A Day with an Electrician. 2001. (Welcome Bks.). (Illus.). 24p. (J). (ps-2). pap. 4.95 (978-0-516-23065-8(4)); 17.00 (978-0-516-23140-2(5)) Scholastic Library Publishing. (Children's Pr.).

Time for Kids Editors. Thomas Edison: A Brilliant Inventor. 2005. (Time for Kids Ser.). (Illus.). 48p. (J). 14.99 (978-0-06-057612-7(X)); pap. 3.99 (978-0-06-057611-0(1)) HarperCollins Pubs.

Welvaert, Scott R. Thomas Edison & the Lightbulb. 2007. (Graphic Library). (Illus.). 32p. 25.26 (978-0-7368-6489-3(X)) Capstone Pr., Inc.

ELECTRIC HOUSEHOLD APPLIANCES

see Household Appliances, Electric

ELECTRIC LAMPS

Flashlights, 6 vols. (Sunshinetm Science Ser.). 24p. (gr. 1-2). 31.50 (978-0-7802-0306-8(2)); 36.95 (978-0-7802-0557-4(X)) Wright Group, The.

Matthews, John R. The Light Bulb. 2005. (Inventions That Shaped the World Ser.). (Illus.). 80p. (J). (gr. 5-8). pap. 9.95 (978-0-531-16721-2(6)); 30.50 (978-0-531-12334-8(0)) Scholastic Library Publishing. (Watts, Franklin).

O'Neil, Sarah. Making a Flashlight. 2001. (gr. k-3). lib. bdg. 11.65 (978-0-613-33395-5(0)) Tandem Library Bks.

ELECTRIC MOTORS

Hannon, Robert A. J. L. Cowen's Postwar Lionel Trains: O-Gauge Reference Manual II, Motorized Units, Rolling Stock & Accessories. 2003. (Illus.). 160p. per. 29.95 (978-0-9710225-2-2(6) , 0-9710225-2-6) CrowsNest Publishing.

Sloan, Peter. Electric Motors. 1999. (gr. k-3). lib. bdg. 11.80 (978-0-613-30381-1(4)) Tandem Library Bks.

ELECTRIC POWER

Byers, Ann. Blackouts. 2005. (Library of Emergency Preparedness). (Illus.). 64p. (J). (978-1-4042-0535-2(7)) Rosen Publishing Group, Inc., The.

Claybourne, Anna. Blackout. 2005. (Illus.). 32p. (J). (978-1-4109-1947-2(1)); (978-1-4109-1916-8(1)) Steck-Vaughn.

Cole, Joanna. The Magic School Bus & the Electric Field Trip. Degen, Bruce, illus. 1999. (Magic School Bus Ser.). 48p. (J). (gr. 1-4). pap. 5.99 (978-0-590-44683-9(5)) Scholastic, Inc.

Degen, Bruce, illus. The Magic School Bus & the Electric Field Trip. 1999. (Magic School Bus Ser.). (J). (gr. 1-4). 39.92 (978-0-439-04356-4(5)) Scholastic, Inc.

Mahaney, Ian F. Electricity. 2007. (Energy's Many Forms Ser.). 24p. (J). pap. (978-1-4042-2187-1(5)); (Illus.). (gr. 4-6). lib. bdg. 21.25 (978-1-4042-3478-9(0)) Rosen Publishing Group, Inc., The. (PowerKids Pr.).

Prokos, Anna. Flick the Switch. 2003. (Step Back Science Ser.). (Illus.). 48p. (J). 24.95 (978-1-56711-676-2(0) , Blackbirch Pr., Inc.) Thomson Gale.

Riley, Peter D. Electricity & Power. 2005. (Illus.). 32p. (J). (gr. 4-7). lib. bdg. 27.10 (978-1-58340-719-6(7)) Smart Apple Media.

Royston, Angela. Energy of the Future. 2007. (J). pap. (***978-1-4329-0134-9(6)***); lib. bdg. (***978-1-4329-0129-5(X)***) Heinemann Library.

Suen, Anastasia. Wired. Carrick, Paul, illus. 2007. 32p. (J). (gr. 1-4). 16.95 (978-1-57091-599-4(7)); pap. 6.95 (978-1-57091-494-2(X)) Charlesbridge Publishing, Inc.

Wyborny, Sheila. Electricity. 2003. (Kidhaven Science Library). (Illus.). 48p. (J). (gr. 3-5). 23.70 (978-0-7377-1535-4(9) , Kidhaven) Thomson Gale.

ELECTRIC UTILITIES

see Public Utilities

ELECTRIC WIRING

see also Telegraph; Telephone

Residential Wiring: Special Purpose Circuits. 1998. (YA). (gr. 10 up). pap., wbk. ed. 7.00 (978-0-8064-1286-3(0) , E46, Delmar Learning) Thomson Delmar Learning.

ELECTRICITY

see also Lightning; Magnetism; Radioactivity; Telegraph; Telephone; X-Rays

Angliss, Sarah. Electricity & Magnets. Le Jars, David, illus. 2001. (Hands-On Science Ser.). 40p. (J). (gr. 3-5). pap. 6.95 (978-0-7534-5349-0(5) , Kingfisher) Houghton Mifflin Co. Trade & Reference Div.

—Electricity & Magnets. 2001. (Hands-On Science Ser.). (Illus.). (J). 13.75 (978-0-606-21172-7(1)) Tandem Library Bks.

Ardley, Neil. Electricity. 1999. (Way It Works Ser.). (Illus.). 48p. (J). (gr. 8-9). 22.00 (978-0-02-705665-5(1) , Simon & Schuster Children's Publishing) Simon & Schuster Children's Publishing.

Ardley, Neil & Challoner, Jack. Electricity. 2000. (J). (gr. 4-6). 11.00 (978-0-8172-9798-5(7)) Steck-Vaughn.

Bailey, Jacqui. Charged Up: The Story of Electricity. Lilly, Matthew, illus. 2004. (Science Works Ser.). 32p. (J). (gr. 3-6). 23.93 (978-1-4048-0568-2(0)) Picture Window Bks.

—How Do We Use Electricity? 2006. (J). (978-1-58340-928-2(9)) Smart Apple Media.

Baker, Wendy & Haslam, Andrew. Electricity. (Make It Work! Ser.). (Illus.). 48p. (J). 15.95 (978-0-590-74521-5(2)) Scholastic, Inc.

Baker, Wendy, et al. Electricity. (Make It Work! (Eureka!) Ser.). (FRE., Illus.). (J). pap. 9.99 (978-0-590-74806-3(8)) Scholastic, Inc.

Bartholomew, Alan. Electric Mischief: Battery-Powered Gadgets Kids Can Build. Bartholomew, Lynn, illus. 2004. (Kids Can Do It Ser.). 48p. (J). (gr. 4-6). (978-1-55074-925-0(0)); (978-1-55074-923-6(4)) Kids Can Pr., Ltd.

—Electric Mischief: Battery-Powered Gadgets Kids Can Build. 2002. (gr. 3-6). lib. bdg. 14.10 (978-0-613-67883-4(4)) Tandem Library Bks.

Ben Franklin's Big Shock. 2007. (J). pap. 5.95 (***978-0-8225-6450-8(5)*** , First Avenue Editions) Lerner Publishing Group.

Benchmark Education Staff, compiled by. Electricity & Magnetism. 2006. spiral bd. 85.00 (***978-1-4108-7035-3(9)***); spiral bd. 119.00 (***978-1-4108-7136-7(3)***) Benchmark Education Co.

Berger, Samantha. Electricity. 1999. (J). pap. 2.50 (978-0-439-08122-1(X)) Scholastic, Inc.

Bergethon, Peter R. Sparks to Circuits - Electricity: Models & Mechanisms, Student Science Journal. 1999. (Illus.). 80p. (YA). (gr. 6-8). pap. (978-1-58447-019-9(4)) Symmetry Learning Systems.

Bliss, Pamela. The Mystery of Magnets. 2004. (National Geographic Reading Expeditions Ser.). (Illus.). 32p. (J). pap. (978-0-7922-4581-0(4)) National Geographic Society.

The Bridgestone Science Library: Our Physical World, 4 bks. Incl. Electricity. Olien, Rebecca. lib. bdg. 18.60 (978-0-7368-1404-1(3)); Light. Olien, Rebecca. lib. bdg. 18.60 (978-0-7368-1405-8(1)); Magnets. Olien, Rebecca. lib. bdg. 18.60 (978-0-7368-1406-5(X)); Sound. Olien, Becky. lib. bdg. 18.60 (978-0-7368-1407-2(8)); 24p. (J). (gr. 1-2). 2002. (Illus.). 2002. Set lib. bdg. 74.40 (978-0-7368-1408-9(6) , Bridgestone Bks.) Capstone Pr., Inc.

Bryant-Mole, Karen & Dineen, Jacqueline. Death. 1999. (Talking about Ser.). (Illus.). 32p. (J). (gr. k-4). lib. bdg. 25.69 (978-0-8172-5536-7(2)) Raintree.

Buban, et al. Electricity & Electronics Technology. 7th ed. (Illus.). (gr. 6-12). 1999. (YA). stu. ed., wbk. ed. 6.99 (978-0-02-683429-2(4)); 1998. stu. ed. 60.64 (978-0-02-683427-8(8) , 9780026834278) Glencoe/McGraw-Hill.

Charged Up. (Science Works). 32p. (YA). 8.95 (978-1-4048-1129-4(X)) Picture Window Bks.

Cheshire, Gerard. Electricity & Magnetism. 2006. (Illus.). 48p. (J). (978-1-58340-994-7(7) , 1262672) Smart Apple Media.

Claybourne, Anna. Shocking Story of Electricity - Internet Referenced. Hopgood, Kevin, illus. 2006. 64p. (J). pap. 5.99 (978-0-7945-1248-4(8) , Usborne) EDC Publishing.

Clemmet, Mike. Electricity & Magnetism. 1998. (Fact Finders Ser.). (Illus.). 48p. (J). (gr. 3-7). pap. (978-0-563-37308-7(3)) BBC Worldwide.

Cole, Joanna. The Magic School Bus & the Electric Field Trip. Degen, Bruce, illus. 1999. (Magic School Bus Ser.). 48p. (J). (gr. 1-4). pap. 5.99 (978-0-590-44683-9(5)) Scholastic, Inc.

Cook, Sherry & Johnson, Terri. Ellie Electricity, 26 vols. Kuhn, Jesse, illus. l.t. ed. 2006. (Quirkles—Exploring Phonics through Science Ser.: 5). 32p. (J). 7.99 (978-1-933815-04-6(3) , Quirkles, The) Creative 3, LLC.

Cooper, Christopher. Electricity: From Amps to Volts. 2003. (Science Answers Ser.). (Illus.). 32p. (J). pap. 7.50 (978-1-4034-3547-7(2)); lib. bdg. 24.22 (978-1-4034-0950-8(1)) Heinemann Library.

Cooper, Jason. Electricity. 2003. (Science Secrets Discovery Library). (Illus.). 24p. (gr. 1-4). 14.95 (978-1-58952-410-1(1)) Rourke Publishing, LLC.

Dalton, Cindy Devine. Electricity. 2001. (How Can I Experiment With? Ser.). (Illus.). 32p. (gr. 1-4). 19.95 (978-1-58952-011-0(4)) Rourke Publishing, LLC.

Davis, Beth. Electricity & Magnetism. 2000. (Inquiry Science Ser.). 32p. (J). (gr. 4-5). pap. 4.99 (978-1-56822-950-8(X) , IF20857) School Specialty Publishing.

¿De Donde Viene la Electricidad? (Coleccion Primeros Pasos en la Ciencia). (SPA., Illus.). (J). (gr. 1-3). pap. (978-950-724-016-4(0) , LMA8213) Lumen ARG. *Dist:* Lectorum Pubns., Inc.

Degen, Bruce, illus. The Magic School Bus & the Electric Field Trip. 1999. (Magic School Bus Ser.). (J). (gr. 1-4). 39.92 (978-0-439-04356-4(5)) Scholastic, Inc.

Dixon, Malcolm & Smith, Karen. Electricity. 1998. (Young Scientists Ser.). (Illus.). 32p. (J). (ps-3). lib. bdg. 16.95 (978-1-887068-67-3(8)) Smart Apple Media.

Dreier, David Louis & Schultz, Ashlee. Electrical Circuits: Harnessing Electricity. 2007. (J). lib. bdg. (***978-0-7565-3267-3(1)***) Compass Point Bks.

Dussling, Jennifer. Lightning: It's Electrifying. Osiecki, Lori, illus. 2002. (All Aboard Science Reader Ser.). 48p. (J). pap. 3.99 (978-0-448-42860-4(1) , Grosset & Dunlap) Penguin Group (USA) Inc.

—Lightning: It's Electrifying. 2002. (gr. k-3). lib. bdg. 11.80 (978-0-613-64414-3(X)) Tandem Library Bks.

Electricidad e Imanes. (Coleccion Jugando Con la Ciencia). (SPA., Illus.). 39p. (J). pap. 9.95 (978-950-11-0828-6(7) , SGM309) Sigmar ARG. *Dist:* Continental Bk. Co., Inc.

Electricidad y magnetismo: Cuaderno de Evaluacion: Unit 5: Electricidad y magnetismo (Electricity & Magnetism) 2000. (McGraw-Hill Ciencias Ser.). (ENG & SPA.). (gr. 4 up). (978-0-02-278664-9(3)) Macmillan/McGraw-Hill Schl. Div.

Electricidad y magnetismo: Recursos para el maestro con clave de Respuestas: Unit 5: Electricidad y magnetismo (Electricity & Magnetism) 2000. (McGraw-Hill Ciencias Ser.). (ENG & SPA.). (gr. 4 up). (978-0-02-278704-2(6)) Macmillan/McGraw-Hill Schl. Div.

Electricity. (Make it Work Ser.). 42p. (J). (gr. 4-8). pap. (978-1-882210-38-1(7)) Action Publishing, Inc.

Electricity/Electron Srs Lab P. (YA). cd-rom 699.87 (978-0-7365-6721-3(6)) Films Media Group.

Elektrizitaetslehre I: Felder. (Duden Abiturhilfen Ser.). (GER.). 96p. (YA). (gr. 12-13). (978-3-411-04461-0(6)) Bibliographisches Institut & F. A. Brockhaus AG DEU. *Dist:* International Bk. Import Service, Inc.

Ellse, Mark, et al. Electricity & Thermal Physics. 2nd rev. ed. 2004. (Nelson Advanced Science Ser.). (Illus.). 146p. (YA). pap. 39.50 (978-0-7487-7663-4(X)) Nelson Thornes Ltd. GBR. *Dist:* Trans-Atlantic Pubns., Inc.

Evans, Neville. The Science of a Light Bulb. 1999. (Science World Ser.). (Illus.). 32p. (J). (gr. 2-4). lib. bdg. 25.69 (978-0-7398-1325-6(0)) Raintree.

Fairley, Peter. Electricity & Magnetism. 2007. (J). lib. bdg. (***978-0-8225-6605-2(2)***) Twenty First Century Bks.

Farndon, John. Electricity. 2000. (Science Experiments Ser.). (Illus.). 32p. (J). (gr. 3-5). lib. bdg. 25.64 (978-0-7614-1086-7(4) , Benchmark Bks.) Cavendish, Marshall Corp.

Fitzpatrick, Anne. Electricity. 2003. 24p. (J). lib. bdg. 21.35 (978-1-58340-320-4(5)) Smart Apple Media.

Fowler, Richard J. Electricity: Principles & Applications, Student Text with MultiSIM CD-ROM. 6th rev. ed. 2002. (C). (gr. 6-12). 110.00 incl. cd-rom (978-0-07-830973-1(5) , 9780078309731) Glencoe/McGraw-Hill.

French, Cathy. Chasquea, cruje y fluye & Snap, Crackle, & Flow. 2005. spiral bd. 84.00 (***978-1-4108-5697-5(6)***) Benchmark Education Co.

Furgang, Kathy. Trabajar con la electricidad y el magnetismo & Working with Electricity & Magnetism. 2005. spiral bd. 84.00 (***978-1-4108-5719-4(0)***) Benchmark Education Co.

Gardner, Robert. Electricity & Magnetism Science Fair Projects Using Batteries, Balloons, & Other Hair-Raising Stuff. 2004. (Physics! Best Science Projects Ser.). (Illus.). 128p. (J). lib. bdg. 26.60 (978-0-7660-2127-3(0)) Enslow Pubs., Inc.

—Shocking Science Projects with Electricity & Magnetism. LaBaff, Tom, illus. 2006. (Fantastic Physical Science Experiments Ser.). 48p. (J). lib. bdg. 23.93 (978-0-7660-2584-4(5) , Enslow Elementary) Enslow Pubs., Inc.

Gareth Stevens Publishing Staff, contrib. by. Electricity. 2003. (Discovery Channel School Science Ser.). (Illus.). 32p. (J). (gr. 5 up). lib. bdg. 24.67 (978-0-8368-3356-0(2)) Stevens, Gareth Inc.

Glover, David. Batteries, Bulbs, & Wires. 2002. (Young Discoverers Ser.). (Illus.). 32p. (J). (gr. k-3). pap. 7.95 (978-0-7534-5510-4(2) , Kingfisher) Houghton Mifflin Co. Trade & Reference Div.

—Electricity: American Edition. 2001. (Experiments in Science Ser.). (Illus.). (J). (978-0-7894-7462-9(X)) Dorling Kindersley Publishing, Inc.

Godwin, Sam. Which Switch Is Which? 2002. (Little Bees Ser.). 31p. (J). lib. bdg. 24.25 (978-1-58340-224-5(1)) Smart Apple Media.

Hands on Science: Electricity & Magnetism. 1999. (Illus.). (J). 74.20 (978-0-7398-1679-0(9)) Raintree.

Hantula, Richard. Electricity & Forces. 2006. (Real World Science Ser.). (Illus.). 32p. (J). 24.67 (978-0-8368-6305-5(4)) Stevens, Gareth Inc.

Haslam, Andrew. Electricity. 2004. (Make It Work! Science Ser.). (Illus.). 48p. (J). (gr. 3-6). (J). pap. 6.95 (978-1-58728-354-3(9)); 12.95 (978-1-58728-369-7(7)) T&N Children's Publishing. (Two Can Publishing).

—Electricity: The Hands-on Approach to Science. 2001. (gr. 3-6). lib. bdg. 15.25 (978-0-613-43318-1(1)) Tandem Library Bks.

Hewitt, Sally. Amazing Electricity. 2007. 32p. pap. (***978-0-7787-3624-0(5)***) Crabtree Publishing Co.

Holt, Rinehart and Winston Staff. Holt Science & Technology Chapter 17: Physical Science: Introduction to Electricity. 5th ed. 2004. (Illus.). pap. 12.86 (978-0-03-030416-3(4)) Holt, Rinehart & Winston.

—Holt Science & Technology Pt. N: Electricity & Magnetism. 3rd ed. 2003. (SPA.). 18.60 (978-0-03-069329-8(2)) Holt, Rinehart & Winston.

—Holt Science & Technology 2002 Pt. N: Electricity. 2nd ed. 2002. 18.60 (978-0-03-064804-5(1)); tchr. ed. 46.66 (978-0-03-064806-9(8)) Holt, Rinehart & Winston.

Hunter, Rebecca. The Facts about Electricity. 2004. (Illus.). 32p. (J). lib. bdg. 27.10 (978-1-58340-453-9(8)) Smart Apple Media.

Hunter, Rebecca M. Electricity & Magnetism. 2000. (Discovering Science Ser.). (Illus.). 32p. (J). (gr. 3-5). lib. bdg. 25.69 (978-0-7398-2970-7(X)) Raintree.

—Electricity & Magnetism. 2000. (Discovering Science Ser.). (Illus.). 32p. (J). (gr. 3-5). pap. 8.95 (978-0-7398-3015-4(5)) Steck-Vaughn.

Jango-Cohen, Judith. Ben Franklin's Big Shock. Lepp, Kevin, illus. 2006. (On My Own Science Ser.). 48p. (J). (gr. 2-4). 25.26 (978-1-57505-873-3(1) , Millbrook Pr.) Lerner Publishing Group.

Jennings, Terry. Electricidad y Magnetismo (Electricity & Magnetism) (SPA.). 32p. (J). 6.95 (978-84-348-1741-8(1)) SM Ediciones ESP. *Dist:* AIMS International Bks., Inc.

Kids Publishing Science Staff. Amazing Force Fields: The Story of Electricity & Magnetism. 1999. pap. 6.95 (978-1-891418-18-1(1)) Science Kids.

Larousse Mexico Staff, ed. Imanes y Electricidad. 2005. (40 Fantasticos Experimentos Ser.). (SPA.). 40p. (gr. 3-5). pap. 5.95 (978-970-22-0864-8(5)) Larousse, Ediciones, S. A. de C. V. MEX. *Dist:* Houghton Mifflin Co. Trade & Reference Div.

Lauw, Darlene. Electricity. 2002. (gr. 3-6). lib. bdg. 16.40 (978-0-613-52838-2(7)) Tandem Library Bks.

Lauw, Darlene & Puay, Lim Cheng. Electricity. 2001. (Science Alive! Ser.). (Illus.). 32p. (J). (gr. 4-5). pap. (978-0-7787-0607-6(9)); lib. bdg. (978-0-7787-0561-1(7)) Crabtree Publishing Co.

Llewellyn, Claire. Electricity. 2005. (Illus.). 24p. (J). (gr. 1-4). lib. bdg. (978-1-84234-334-0(3) , Cherrytree Books) Evans Publishing Group.

—Electricity. 2005. (Illus.). 24p. (YA). (gr. 1 up). lib. bdg. 22.80 (978-1-932889-35-2(3)) Sea-To-Sea Pubns.

Lyons, Suzanne. Electricidad logica & Electricity Adds Up. 2005. spiral bd. 84.00 (***978-1-4108-5711-8(5)***) Benchmark Education Co.

Lyons, Suzanne. Electricity Adds Up. 2004. (Navigators Ser.). (J). pap. 42.00 (978-1-4108-0439-6(9)) Benchmark Education Co.

Magnetism & Electricity. (Jump Ser.). (Illus.). 32p. (J). (gr. 2-7). pap. (978-1-882210-27-5(1)) Action Publishing, Inc.

Magnets & Electricity. 2002. (Super Science Activities Ser.). 48p. (J). (gr. 2-5). 7.99 (978-0-7439-3664-4(7) , 3664) Teacher Created Materials, Inc.

Mahaney, Ian F. Electricity. 2007. (Energy's Many Forms Ser.). 24p. (J). pap. (978-1-4042-2187-1(5)); (Illus.). (gr. 4-6). lib. bdg. 21.25 (978-1-4042-3478-9(0)) Rosen Publishing Group, Inc., The. (PowerKids Pr.).

Mayes, Susan. Where Does Electricity Come From? 2006. 24p. (J). pap. 4.99 (978-0-7945-1411-2(1) , Usborne) EDC Publishing.

McGraw-Hill Staff. Glencoe Science: Electricy & Magnetism. 2nd ed. 2004. stu. ed. 20.64 (978-0-07-861773-7(1) , 9780078617737) Glencoe/McGraw-Hill.

McNeil, Niki, et al. HOCPP 1087 Electricity. 2006. spiral bd. 24.50 (***978-1-60308-087-3(2)***) In the Hands of a Child.

Morgan, Sally. Electricity & Electrical Circuits. 2007. (J). (***978-1-4034-9926-4(8)***); pap. (***978-1-4034-9934-9(9)***) Heinemann Library.

Multimedia Electrical Safety. (Shop Safety Ser.). (YA). cd-rom 69.95 (978-0-7365-9987-0(8)) Films Media Group.

Murray, Julie. Electricity. 2007. (Illus.). 24p. (J). 21.35 (978-1-59679-822-9(X) , Buddy Bks.) ABDO Publishing Co.

Nankivell-Aston, Sally. Science Experiments with Electricity. 2000. (J). (978-0-606-19790-8(7)); (gr. 3-6). lib. bdg. 15.25 (978-0-613-50728-8(2)) Tandem Library Bks.

Nankivell-Aston, Sally & Jackson, Dorothy. Science Experiments with Electricity. 2000. (Science Experiments Ser.). (Illus.). 32p. (YA). (gr. 3-6). pap. 6.95 (978-0-531-15443-4(2) , Watts, Franklin) Scholastic Library Publishing.

Nemzer, Marilyn, ed. Energy for Keeps: An Illustrated Guide for Everyone Who Uses Electricity. 2005. (Illus.). 176p. 24.95 (978-0-9744765-3-7(6)) Energy Education Group.

Newell, Ella. Turn on the Light: How Electricity Works. 2008. (J). (***978-1-60044-608-5(6)***) Rourke Publishing, LLC.

Newson, Lesley & Wadsworth, Pamela. Trydan a Magnetedd. 2005. (WEL., Illus.). 24p. pap. (978-1-85596-225-5(X)) Dref Wen.

Norman, Penny. Science One Two Three Electricity. Einstein, Ann, ed. 2005. 31p. 15.95 (978-1-886978-65-2(4)) Norman & Globus, Inc.

O'Donnell, Liam. The Shocking World of Electricity with Max Axiom, Super Scientist. 2007. (J). (***978-0-7368-6839-6(9)***); (***978-0-7368-6835-8(6)***) Capstone Pr., Inc.

Olien, Rebecca. Electricity. 2002. (Bridgestone Science Library). (Illus.). 24p. (J). (gr. 1-2). lib. bdg. 18.60 (978-0-7368-1404-1(3) , Bridgestone Bks.) Capstone Pr., Inc.

Parker, Steve. Electricity & Magnetism. 2004. (Science View Ser.). (Illus.). 32p. (J). (gr. 4-8). 28.00 (978-0-7910-8208-9(3) , Chelsea Hse.) Facts On File, Inc.

—Electricity & Magnetism. 2000. (Science Fact Files Ser.). (Illus.). 48p. (J). (gr. 4-7). lib. bdg. 27.12 (978-0-7398-1010-1(3)) Raintree.

—Fully Charged: Electricity. (Illus.). 56p. (J). 2005. pap. (978-1-4034-6419-4(7)); 2004. lib. bdg. (978-1-4034-4813-2(2)) Heinemann Library.

—The Science of Electricity & Magnetism: Projects & Experiments with Electricity & Magnets. 2005. (Illus.). 32p. (J). (ps-6). lib. bdg. 29.29 (978-1-4034-7283-0(1)); pap. 7.95 (978-1-4034-7290-8(4)) Heinemann Library.

Parker, Steve & Buller, Laura. Electricity. 2005. (Dk eyewitness Bks.). (Illus.). 72p. (J). (gr. 4-7). 15.99 (978-0-7566-1388-4(4)); lib. bdg. 19.99 (978-0-7566-1397-6(3)) Dorling Kindersley Publishing, Inc.

Peters, Celeste A. Circuits, Shocks & Lightning: The Science of Electricity. 1999. (Science @ Work Ser.). (Illus.). 48p. (J). (gr. 4-6). pap. 27.12 (978-0-7398-0143-7(0)) Raintree.

Pipe, Jim. Using Electricity: Switch It On. 2005. (Illus.). 32p. (J). (gr. 1-4). lib. bdg. 27.10 (978-1-59604-022-9(X)) Stargazer Bks.

Randolph, Joanne. Electricity in My World. 2006. (My World of Science Ser.). (J). 16.00 (978-1-4042-3288-4(5) , PowerKids Pr.) Rosen Publishing Group, Inc., The.

—Electricity in My World: La Electricidad en Mi Mundo. 2006. (My World of Science/ Mi mundo y la Ciencia Ser.). (ENG & SPA.). (J). 16.00 (978-1-4042-3319-5(9) , PowerKids Pr.) Rosen Publishing Group, Inc., The.

Richardson, Adele. Electricity: A Question & Answer Book. 2006. (Fact Finders Ser.). (Illus.). 32p. (J). (978-0-7368-5444-3(4)) Capstone Pr., Inc.

Riley, Gail Blasser. Benjamin Franklin & Electricity. 2004. (Cornerstones of Freedom Ser.). (Illus.). 48p. (J). 26.00 (978-0-516-24240-8(7) , Children's Pr.) Scholastic Library Publishing.

Riley, Peter D. Circuits & Conductors. 2007. (J). (***978-1-59920-024-8(4)***) Smart Apple Media.

—Electricity. 1999. (Straightforward Science Ser.). (Illus.). 32p. (J). (gr. 3-5). pap. 6.95 (978-0-531-15366-6(5) , Watts, Franklin) Scholastic Library Publishing.

—Electricity. 1999. (Illus.). (J). 32p. (gr. 3-5). lib. bdg. 15.25 (978-0-613-31153-3(1)); 13.75 (978-0-606-18147-1(4)) Tandem Library Bks.

—Electricity. Moller, Ray, photos by. 2002. (Everyday Science Ser.). (Illus.). 32p. (J). (gr. 1 up). lib. bdg. 23.33 (978-0-8368-3247-1(7)) Stevens, Gareth Inc.

—Electricity & Power. 2005. (Illus.). 32p. (J). (gr. 4-7). lib. bdg. 27.10 (978-1-58340-719-6(7)) Smart Apple Media.

Riley, Peter D. & Snedden, Robert. Electricity & Magnetism. 1999. (Smart Science Ser.). (Illus.). 32p. (YA). (gr. 4-7). lib. bdg. 22.79 (978-1-57572-868-1(0)) Heinemann Library.

Rogers, K. Light, Sound & Electricity. 2004. (Library of Science Ser.). 64p. (J). lib. bdg. 17.95 (978-1-58086-376-6(0)) EDC Publishing.

Royston, Angela. Conductors & Insulators. 2003. (My World of Science Ser.). (Illus.). 32p. pap. 6.95 (978-1-4034-3164-6(7)); (J). lib. bdg. 22.79 (978-1-4034-0851-8(3)) Heinemann Library.

—Using Electricity. (My World of Science Ser.). (Illus.). 32p. (J). (gr. k-2). 2002. pap. 6.95 (978-1-4034-0046-8(6) , 91490); 2001. lib. bdg. 21.36 (978-1-58810-239-3(4)) Heinemann Library.

—Using Electricity. 2002. (gr. k-3). lib. bdg. 15.25 (978-0-613-88701-4(8)) Tandem Library Bks.

Roza, Greg. It's Electric! 2003. (Reading Room Collection). (Illus.). 24p. (J). lib. bdg. 18.75 (978-0-8239-3708-0(9)) Rosen Publishing Group, Inc., The.

Sadler, Wendy. Electricity: Turn It On! 2005. (Raintree Perspectives Ser.). (Illus.). 32p. (J). pap. (978-1-4109-1557-3(3)); lib. bdg. (978-1-4109-1549-8(2)) Steck-Vaughn.

Saunders, N. Electricity & Magnetism. 2007. (J). lib. bdg. (***978-1-4042-3749-0(6)*** , PowerKids Pr.) Rosen Publishing Group, Inc., The.

Schiffer, Michael B., et al. Draw the Lightning Down - Benjamin Franklin & Electrical Technology in the Age of Enlightenment. 2003. (Illus.). 380p. 50.00 (978-0-520-23802-2(8)) Univ. of California Pr.

Schuh, Mari. Electricity. 2007. (Illus.). 24p. (J). lib. bdg. 19.95 (978-1-60014-095-2(5)) Bellwether Media.

Sganga, Francis. Essentials of Electricity for Gifted Students: Preparation for High School Physics, Grades 4 ¿ 8. 2003. (Illus.). 70p. (978-0-910609-46-3(2)) Gifted Education Pr.

Sloan, Peter. Electricity at Work. 1999. (gr. k-3). lib. bdg. 11.80 (978-0-613-30383-5(0)) Tandem Library Bks.

—Making Electricity. 1999. (gr. k-3). lib. bdg. 11.80 (978-0-613-30589-1(2)) Tandem Library Bks.

Sources of Forces: Science Fun with Force Fields. 2007. (J). pap. 7.95 (***978-0-8225-7023-3(8)*** , First Avenue Editions) Lerner Publishing Group.

Spilsbury, Richard & Spilsbury, Louise. What Is Electricity & Magnetism? Exploring Science with Hands-On Activities. 2008. (In Touch with Basic Science Ser.). 32p. (J). (gr. 3-4). lib. bdg. 22.60 (***978-0-7660-3096-1(2)***) Enslow Pubs., Inc.

Stille, Darlene R. Electricity. 2004. (Science Around Us Ser.). 32p. (J). (gr. 2-6). 27.07 (978-1-59296-219-8(X)) Child's World, Inc.

—Electricity. 2001. (Simply Science Ser.). (Illus.). 32p. (J). (gr. 3 up). lib. bdg. 19.93 (978-0-7565-0089-4(3)) Compass Point Bks.

—Electricity: Bulbs, Batteries, & Sparks. Boyd, Sheree, illus. 2004. (Amazing Science Ser.). 24p. (C). (gr. k-4). 22.60 (978-1-4048-0245-2(2)) Picture Window Bks.

Suen, Anastasia. Wired. Carrick, Paul, illus. 2007. 32p. (J). (gr. 1-4). 16.95 (978-1-57091-599-4(7)); pap. 6.95 (978-1-57091-494-2(X)) Charlesbridge Publishing, Inc.

Tocci, Salvatore. Experiments with Electricity. 2001. (True Science Experiments Bks.). (Illus.). 48p. (J). (gr. 3-5). 25.00 (978-0-516-22247-9(3) , Children's Pr.) Scholastic Library Publishing.

Trumbauer, Lisa. What Is Electricity? 2004. (Rookie Read-About Science Ser.). (J). 32p. (gr. 1-2). pap. 4.95 (978-0-516-25845-4(1)); (Illus.). 31p. 20.50 (978-0-516-23449-6(8)) Scholastic Library Publishing. (Watts, Franklin).

Twist, Clint. Electricity. 2005. (Check It Out! Ser.). (Illus.). 24p. (J). (gr. 3-7). lib. bdg. 19.96 (978-1-59716-062-9(8)) Bearport Publishing Co., Inc.

Valkenburgh. Electricidad Basica. 2006. 160p. Vol. 1. 10.95 (978-968-26-0378-5(1)); Vol. 2. (SPA.). pap. 10.95 (978-968-26-0382-2(X)); Vol. 3. (SPA.). pap. 10.95 (978-968-26-0383-9(8)); Vol. 4. (SPA.). 10.95 (978-968-26-0395-2(1)); Vol. 5. (SPA.). pap. 10.95 (978-968-26-0433-1(8)) Compania Editorial Continental MEX. *Dist:* Fondo de Cultura Economica USA.

Wadsworth, Pamela. Golwg Gyntaf Ar Drydan a Magnetau. 2005. (WEL., Illus.). 24p. pap. (978-1-85596-255-2(1)) Dref Wen.

Walker, Sally M. La Electricidad (Electricity) 2007. (Libros de Energía para madrugadores (Early Bird Energy) Ser.). (SPA.). 48p. (J). (gr. 2-5). lib. bdg. 26.60 (***978-0-8225-7717-1(8)*** , Ediciones Lerner) Lerner Publishing Group.

Walker, Sally M. Electricity. 2006. (Early Bird Energy Ser.). (Illus.). 48p. (J). (gr. 3-7). 25.26 (978-0-8225-2919-4(X) , Lerner Pubns.) Lerner Publishing Group.

Whalley, Margaret. Electricity & Magnetism. (Illus.). 48p. (J). 2004. (Interfact Ser.). (SPA.). (gr. 3-6). 14.95 incl. cd-rom (978-1-58728-451-9(0)); 2000. (Collectafact Ser.: Vol. 4). (gr. 1-5). 4.95 (978-1-58728-751-0(X)) T&N Children's Publishing. (Two Can Publishing).

Whyman, Kathryn. Electricity & Magnetism. 2004. (J). lib. bdg. (978-1-932799-19-4(2)) Stargazer Bks.

Wood, Robert W. Electricity & Magnetism Fundamentals. 1999. (Funtastic Science Activities for Kids Ser.). (Illus.). 160p. (YA). (gr. 4-7). lib. bdg. 25.25 (978-0-7910-4841-2(1) , Chelsea Hse.) Facts On File, Inc.

Wright, Russell G. Blackout! Investigations in Electricity. (Event-Based Science Ser.). (YA). (gr. 5-9). 66p. pap., stu. ed. 11.50 (978-0-7690-2346-5(0)); 56p. pap., tchr.'s training gde. ed. 25.95 incl. VHS (978-0-7690-2347-2(9)) Seymour, Dale Pubns.

Wyborny, Sheila. Electricity. 2003. (Kidhaven Science Library). (Illus.). 48p. (J). (gr. 3-5). 23.70 (978-0-7377-1535-4(9) , Kidhaven) Thomson Gale.

ELECTRICITY—FICTION

Baum, L. Frank. Master Key. 2006. 18.99 (***978-1-4280-2748-0(3)***) IndyPublish.com.

Baum, L. Frank. The Master Key. 2004. reprint ed. pap. 15.95 (978-1-4191-7199-4(2)); pap. 1.99 (978-1-4192-7199-1(7)) Kessinger Publishing, LLC.

Capeci, Anne. Electric Storm. 2002. (gr. 3-6). lib. bdg. 11.80 (978-0-613-63280-5(X)) Tandem Library Bks.

Capeci, Anne & Moore, Eva. Electric Storm. Gangloff, Hope, illus. 2003. (Magic School Bus Chapter Bks.: No. 14). 96p. (J). pap. 4.99 (978-0-439-31434-3(8)) Scholastic, Inc.

Collins, Suzanne. When Charlie McButton Lost Power. Lester, Mike, illus. 2005. 32p. (J). (ps-3). 15.99 (978-0-399-24000-3(4) , Putnam Juvenile) Penguin Group (USA) Inc.

Collins, Suzanne. When Charlie Mcbutton Lost Power. Lester, Mike, illus. 2007. 32p. (J). (ps). pap. 5.99 (***978-0-14-240857-5(3)*** , Puffin) Penguin Group (USA) Inc.

Deubreau, Sharon. Heather & Avery & the Magic Kite. Pileggi, Steve, illus. l.t. ed. 2006. 23p. (J). per. 11.99 (978-1-59879-143-3(5)) Lifevest Publishing, Inc.

D'Lacey, Chris. Franklin's Bear. Taylor, Thomas, illus. 2005. (Red Go Bananas Ser.). 42p. (J). lib. bdg. (978-0-7787-2674-6(6)) Crabtree Publishing Co.

Jennings, Patrick. Faith & the Electric Dogs. 1998. 11.64 (978-0-606-13373-9(9)) Tandem Library Bks.

Santolaya Ruiz-Clavijo, Adoracion. Las Damas de la Luz. 2000. Tr. of Ladies of the Light. (SPA., Illus.). (J). (ps-2). 14.95 (978-84-233-3208-3(X)) Ediciones Destino ESP. *Dist:* Baker & Taylor Bks.

Sargent, Dave & Sargent, Pat. Sugar: (Cream) Curiosity Is Good, 25, 57. Lenoir, Jane, illus. 2001. (Saddle Up Ser.: 57). 36p. (J). pap. 6.95 (978-1-56763-668-0(3)); lib. bdg. 22.60 (978-1-56763-667-3(5)) Ozark Publishing.

ELECTRICITY IN THE HOME

see Household Appliances, Electric

ELECTROCHEMISTRY

see also Electric Batteries

Bergethon, Peter R. The Mystery of the Electric Lemon: An Introduction to Electrochemistry, Student Science Journal. 1999. (Illus.). 47p. (YA). (gr. 6-9). pap. (978-1-58447-059-5(3)) Symmetry Learning Systems.

ELECTROMAGNETISM

Fleisher, Paul. Waves: Principles of Light, Electricity, & Magnetism. 2005. (Secrets of the Universe Ser.). (Illus.). 80p. (gr. 6-12). 25.26 (978-0-8225-2987-3(4)) Lerner Publishing Group.

Hil, Mcgraw. Trfpaswak Elctrcty & Magn. 2000. (McGraw-Hill Science Ser.). (gr. 4 up). (978-0-02-277641-1(9)) Macmillan/McGraw-Hill Schl. Div.

Holt, Rinehart and Winston Staff. Holt Science & Technology Chapter 18: Physical Science: Electromagnetism. 5th ed. 2004. (Illus.). pap. 12.86 (978-0-03-030421-7(0)) Holt, Rinehart & Winston.

—Holt Science & Technology Chptr. 14: Electromagnetics: Chapter Resources - Tennessee Edition. 3rd ed. 2003. (J). pap. 11.40 (978-0-03-069122-5(2)) Holt, Rinehart & Winston.

Jedicke, Peter. Electromagnetism, & How It Works. 2007. (Scientific American Ser.). 80p. (J). (gr. 5-8). 30.00 (***978-0-7910-9052-7(3)*** , Chelsea Hse.) Facts On File, Inc.

Kids Publishing Science Staff. Amazing Force Fields: The Story of Electricity & Magnetism. 1999. pap. 6.95 (978-1-891418-18-1(1)) Science Kids.

Matthews, Stuart. Electromagnetics. 2001. (How Does It Work? Ser.). (Illus.). 24p. (J). (gr. 2-7). lib. bdg. 21.30 (978-1-58340-066-1(4)) Smart Apple Media.

Pompea, Stephen, et al. Invisible Universe: The Electromagnetic Spectrum from Radio Waves to Gamma Rays. Gould, Alan et al, illus. Pompea, Stephen & Willard, Sam, photos by. 2002. (Great Explorations in Math & Science Ser.). 116p. (gr. 6-9). pap. 21.00 (978-0-924886-69-0(2) , GEMS) Univ. of California, Berkeley, Lawrence Hall of Science.

Reader dsm-3 electromagnetism Ea. 2004. (J). (978-1-59242-522-8(4)) Delta Education, LLC.

Smuskiewicz, Alfred J. Magnets & Electromagnetism. 2007. (J). (***978-1-4034-9927-1(6)***); pap. (***978-1-4034-9935-6(7)***) Heinemann Library.

Zannos, Susan. Michael Faraday & the Discovery of Electromagnetism. 2004. (Uncharted, Unexplored, & Unexplained Ser.). (Illus.). 48p. (J). (gr. 4-8). lib. bdg. 29.95 (978-1-58415-307-8(5)) Mitchell Lane Pubs., Inc.

ELECTROMAGNETS

Bliss, Pamela. The Mystery of Magnets. 2004. (National Geographic Reading Expeditions Ser.). (Illus.). 32p. (J). pap. (978-0-7922-4581-0(4)) National Geographic Society.

O'Daley, Anne. Magnetism. 2003. (Illus.). 24p. (J). 22.45 (978-1-4103-0080-5(3) , Blackbirch Pr., Inc.) Thomson Gale.

ELECTRONIC CIRCUITS

Basic Introduction to PLCs: Student Kit. (Dvd Training Ser.). 138.00 net. (978-0-8269-9208-6(0)) American Technical Pubs., Inc.

ELECTRONIC COMPUTERS

see Computers

ELECTRONIC DATA PROCESSING

Burstein, John. Usar Computadoras: Una Maquina con Raton: Basado en la Serie de Television Publica Math Monsters(Tm), Desarrollada en Colaboracion con el Consejo Nacional de Maestros de Matematicas (NCTM) 2006. (ENG & SPA., Illus.). 24p. (J). pap. (978-0-8368-6694-0(0)); lib. bdg. 19.33 (978-0-8368-6679-7(7)) Stevens, Gareth Inc.

—Using Computers: Machine with a Mouse. 2003. (Weekly Reader Early Learning Library). (Illus.). 24p. (J). (gr. 1 up). pap. 7.93 (978-0-8368-3832-9(7) , Weekly Reader Early Learning Library) Stevens, Gareth Inc.

McAlpine, Margaret. Working with Computers. 2004. (My Future Career Ser.). (Illus.). 64p. (J). lib. bdg. 26.00 (978-0-8368-4242-5(1)) Stevens, Gareth Inc.

Patrice Cassedy. Computer Technology. 2004. (Careers for the Twenty-First Century Ser.). (Illus.). 112p. (J). 29.95 (978-1-56006-896-9(5)) Thomson Gale.

ELECTRONIC DATA PROCESSING—KEYBOARDING

McGraw-Hill Staff. Glencoe Keyboarding Connections: Projects & Applications with Office 2000. 2nd ed. 2003. (gr. 6-12). stu. ed. 61.32 (978-0-07-861074-5(5) , 9780078610745) Glencoe/McGraw-Hill.

—Glencoe Keyboarding Connections: Projects & Applications with Office XP. 2nd ed. 2003. (gr. 6-12). stu. ed. 61.32 (978-0-07-861073-8(7) , 9780078610738) Glencoe/McGraw-Hill.

—Glencoe Keyboarding with Computer Applications: Complete Course, Lessons 1-150. 1999. 554p. (C). stu. ed. 73.32 (978-0-02-804171-1(2) , 9780028041711) Glencoe/McGraw-Hill.

—Glencoe Keyboarding with Computer Applications, Lessons 1-150 with Office XP. 2nd ed. 2003. (gr. 6-12). stu. ed. 83.96 (978-0-07-861075-2(3) , 9780078610752) Glencoe/McGraw-Hill.

—Glencoe Keyboarding with Computer Applications, Lessons 1-80 with Office 2000. 2nd ed. 2003. (gr. 6-12). stu. ed. 71.28 (978-0-07-861167-4(9) , 9780078611674) Glencoe/McGraw-Hill.

—Glencoe Keyboarding with Computer Applications, Lessons 1-80 with Office XP. 2nd ed. 2003. (gr. 6-12). stu. ed. 71.28 (978-0-07-861168-1(7) , 9780078611681) Glencoe/McGraw-Hill.

McGraw-Hill Staff & Johnson, Jack E. Glencoe Keyboarding with Computer Applications, Lessons 1-150. 2003. 596p. (gr. 9-12). stu. ed. 75.32 (978-0-07-860256-6(4) , 9780078602566) Glencoe/McGraw-Hill.

Shimp, Emily. ABC Play Book. Dorn, Dave, ed. 1998. (Illus.). 28p. (Orig.). (J). (ps-1). pap., wbk. ed. (978-0-9658251-0-8(8)) KidBoard, Inc.

ELECTRONIC SPREADSHEETS

Johnson, Rebecca L. Crunching Numbers. 2004. (Math Behind the Science Ser.). (Illus.). 24p. (J). pap. (978-0-7922-4592-6(X)) National Geographic Society.

Patchett, Fiona. An Introduction to Spreadsheets: Using Microsoft Excel 2000 or Microsoft Office 2000. 2004. (Computer Guides Ser.). (Illus.). 64p. (YA). (gr. 5 up). pap. 10.95 (978-0-7460-4146-8(2)); lib. bdg. 18.95 (978-1-58086-323-0(X)) EDC Publishing.

Rodriguez, Albert F. An Honors Thesis: "An Electronic Spreadsheet: Function & Application" 1999. (Illus.). 23p. (YA). (gr. 9-12). pap. 25.00 (978-0-9642829-5-7(X)) A.F.R. Software.

ELECTRONICS

see also Cybernetics; Electronic Circuits; Microelectronics

The Boy Mechanic, Bk. 1. 470p. (J). (gr. 5 up). reprint ed. pap. 18.95 (978-0-917914-88-1(0)) Lindsay Pubns., Inc.

Bridgman, Roger & Challoner, Jack. Electronics. 2000. (Eyewitness Bks.). (Illus.). 64p. (J). (gr. 3-7). 15.99 (978-0-7894-5598-7(6)) Dorling Kindersley Publishing, Inc.

Bridgman, Roger & Dorling Kindersley Publishing Staff. Electronics. Bull, Stephen & Woodcock, John, illus. 2000. (Eyewitness Bks.). 64p. (J). (gr. 4-7). lib. bdg. 19.99 (978-0-7894-6724-9(0)) Dorling Kindersley Publishing, Inc.

Bruce, Linda & Bruce, Ian. Household Technology. 2006. (How Does It Work? Ser.). (Illus.). 32p. (J). (978-1-58340-797-4(9)) Smart Apple Media.

Buban, et al. Electricity & Electronics Technology. 7th ed. (Illus.). (gr. 6-12). 1999. (YA). stu. ed., wbk. ed. 6.99 (978-0-02-683429-2(4)); 1998. stu. ed. 60.64 (978-0-02-683427-8(8) , 9780026834278) Glencoe/McGraw-Hill.

Butterfield, Moira. Electronics. 2004. (Illus.). 44p. (J). lib. bdg. 28.50 (978-1-58340-506-2(2)) Smart Apple Media.

Dalgleish, Sharon. How Things Work. 1999. (Explorers Ser.). (Illus.). 32p. (J). (978-0-7699-0496-2(3)) Shortland Pubns. (U. S. A.) Inc.

Fonetica: Aventuras con Pepe Antenas Network: Technology. 2001. (McGraw-Hill. Lectura Ser.). (ENG & SPA.). (gr. 2-3). (978-0-02-186194-1(3)) Macmillan/McGraw-Hill Schl. Div.

Frisch, Aaron. The Story of Sony. 2003. (Built for Success Ser.). (Illus.). 48p. (J). 28.50 (978-1-58340-296-2(9)) Smart Apple Media.

Good, Keith. Zap It! Exciting Electricity Activities. 1999. (Design It! Ser.). (Illus.). 30p. (gr. 4-8). lib. bdg. 21.27 (978-0-8225-3565-2(3)) Lerner Publishing Group.

Graham, Ian. Going Digital. 2001. (Technoworld Ser.). (Illus.). 32p. (J). lib. bdg. 25.69 (978-0-7398-3254-7(9)) Raintree.

Hoare, Stephen. Digital Revolution. 1999. (20th Century Inventions Ser.). (Illus.). 48p. (J). (gr. 4-9). lib. bdg. 27.12 (978-0-8172-4897-0(8)) Raintree.

Holt, Rinehart and Winston Staff. Holt Science & Technology Chapter 19: Physical Science: Electronic Technology. 5th ed. 2004. (Illus.). x, 262p. pap. 12.86 (978-0-03-030426-2(1)) Holt, Rinehart & Winston.

Jugendhandbuch Naturwissen: Bausteine des Lebens, 6 vols., Vol. 1. (GER.). (YA). pap. 750.00 (978-3-499-16203-9(2) , M-7486) French & European Pubns., Inc.

Markle, Sandra. Build a Room Alarm & 16 More Electrifying Projects! Brace, Eric, illus. 2003. (Science Dares You! Ser.). 64p. (J). (978-0-439-44432-3(2)) Scholastic, Inc.

Mawson, Dave, et al. Design & Make It! Electronic Products. 1998. (Illus.). 144p. pap. 30.00 (978-0-7487-2473-4(7)) State Mutual Bk. & Periodical Service, Ltd.

—Electronic Products. 2nd rev. ed. 2001. (Design & Make It Ser.). (Illus.). 152p. (YA). pap. 27.50 (978-0-7487-6079-4(2)) Nelson Thornes Ltd. GBR. *Dist:* Trans-Atlantic Pubns., Inc.

La Revolucion Digital. 2003. (Essential Science Ser.). (SPA.). (J). pap. (978-970-690-598-7(7)) Planeta Mexicana Editorial S. A. de C. V.

Rooney, Anne. Electronics. 2006. (Illus.). 56p. (J). pap. (978-1-4034-7433-9(8)) Heinemann.

Schuler, Charles A. Electronics: Principles & Applications, Experiments Manual. 5th ed. 1998. (Illus.). (C). (gr. 6-12). pap., stu. ed. 58.33 (978-0-02-804245-9(X) , 9780028042459, McGraw-Hill Science, Engineering & Mathematics) McGraw-Hill Higher Education.

—Electronics: Principles & Applications, Student Text with Multisim. 6th ed. 2002. (C). (gr. 6-12). stu. ed. 107.67 incl. cd-rom (978-0-07-830977-9(8) , 9780078309779) Glencoe/McGraw-Hill.

Stillinger, Doug. Klutz Battery Science. 2003. (Illus.). 56p. (J). spiral bd. 19.95 (978-1-59174-251-7(X) , 53643124) Klutz.

TBC Staff. Cutting Edge Electronics: Watching, Listening, Talking & Playing. 2006. (Illus.). 56p. (J). (978-0-431-13268-6(2)) Heinemann.

Time-Life Books Editors. How Things Work in Your Home. 1999. (Illus.). 88p. (J). (gr. 1-4). 14.95 (978-0-8094-4873-9(4)) Time-Life, Inc.

Tokheim, Roger L. Digital Electronics: Principles & Applications, Experiments Manual. 5th ed. 1998. (Illus.). (C). (gr. 6-12). pap., stu. ed. 60.33 (978-0-02-804162-9(3) , 9780028041629, McGraw-Hill Science, Engineering & Mathematics) McGraw-Hill Higher Education.

Woodford, Chris. Digital Technology. 2006. (Science in Focus Ser.). 48p. (J). 27.00 (978-0-7910-8861-6(8) , Chelsea Hse.) Facts On File, Inc.

ELECTROSTATICS

Mahaney, Ian F. Electricity. 2007. (Energy's Many Forms Ser.). 24p. (J). pap. (978-1-4042-2187-1(5)); (Illus.). (gr. 4-6). lib. bdg. 21.25 (978-1-4042-3478-9(0)) Rosen Publishing Group, Inc., The. (PowerKids Pr.).

ELEMENTARY EDUCATION

see Education, Elementary

ELEMENTS, CHEMICAL

see Chemical Elements

ELEPHANTS

Albee, Sarah. Elephants. 2006. (All about Animals Ser.). (J). (978-1-59939-063-5(9) , Reader's Digest Young Families, Inc.) Reader's Digest Children's Publishing, Inc.

Anderson, Jill. Elephants. 2006. (Illus.). 24p. (J). 6.95 (978-1-55971-951-3(6)); 12.95 (978-1-55971-950-6(8)) T&N Children's Publishing. (NorthWord Bks. for Young Readers).

Animal Lives: Elephants. 2006. pap. 4.99 (978-1-4206-8158-1(3)) Teacher Created Materials, Inc.

Arnold, Katya R. Elephants Can Paint Too! Arnold, Katya R., photos by. 2005. (Illus.). 40p. (J). 16.95 (978-0-689-86985-3(1) , Atheneum) Simon & Schuster Children's Publishing.

Aygun, Aysegul. The Brave Elephant. 2002. (Our Dear Prophet in the Words of the Creation Ser.: 1). (Illus.). 24p. (J). pap. 4.99 (978-1-932099-01-0(8)) Light, Inc., The.

Barnes, Julia. Elephants at Work. 2006. (Illus.). 32p. (J). lib. bdg. (*978-0-8368-6224-9(4)) Stevens, Gareth Inc.

—The Secret Lives of Elephants. 2006. (Illus.). 32p. (J). lib. bdg. (*978-0-8368-7657-4(1)) Stevens, Gareth Inc.

Beeler, Selby B. How Many Elephants? A Lift-the-Flap Counting Book. Saltzberg, Barney, illus. 2004. 20p. (J). (gr. k-k). 9.99 (978-0-7636-1583-3(8)) Candlewick Pr.

The Biggest Land Animal: Individual Title Six-Packs. (Sails Literacy Ser.). (gr. 1-2). 36.00 (978-0-7578-4018-0(3)) Rigby Education.

Bloom, Steve. Elephant. 2006. (Illus.). 224p. 45.00 (978-0-8118-5727-7(1)) Chronicle Bks. LLC.

Bloom, Steve & Wilson, David Henry. Elephants: A Book for Children. 2008. (Illus.). 64p. 19.95 (*978-0-500-54344-3(5)) Thames & Hudson.

Books Are Fun 8 Title Animal Lives Set: Elephants. 2006. (J). (978-1-59566-309-2(6)) QEB Publishing Inc.

Buckley, Carol. Just for Elephants. 2006. (Illus.). 32p. (J). (gr. 3-6). 16.95 (978-0-88448-283-3(9)) Tilbury Hse. Pubs.

—Travels with Tarra. 2005. (Illus.). 40p. (J). (gr. 3-7). 16.95 (978-0-88448-241-3(3)) Tilbury Hse. Pubs.

Bull, Schuyler. Through Tsavo: A Story of an East African Savanna. Kratter, Paul, illus. 1998. (Soundprints' Wild Habitats Ser.). 32p. (J). (gr. 1-4). pap. 6.95 (978-1-56899-553-3(9) , S7008) Soundprints.

Burroughs, Elizabeth. Elephant: South African Edition. 1998. (Cambridge Reading Routes Ser.). (Illus.). 16p. pap. 5.00 (978-0-521-63668-1(X)) Cambridge Univ. Pr.

Crossingham, John. What Is an Elephant? 2002. (gr. 3-6). lib. bdg. 14.10 (978-0-613-50847-6(5)) Tandem Library Bks.

Crossingham, John & Kalman, Bobbie. Les Elephants. 2004. (FRE., Illus.). 32p. (J). pap. (978-2-89579-015-0(9)) Crabtree Publishing Co.

Darling, Kathy. The Elephant Hospital. Darling, Tara, illus. 2000. 40p. (gr. 4-6). lib. bdg. 23.90 (978-0-7613-1723-4(6) , Millbrook Pr.) Lerner Publishing Group.

Dineen, Jacqueline. Elephants. 2003. (Amazing Animals Ser.). (Illus.). 24p. (J). lib. bdg. 21.35 (978-1-58340-227-6(6)) Weigl Pubs., Inc.

Dorling Kindersley Publishing Staff. Are Elephants Tiny? 2003. (DK See Through Ser.). (Illus.). 21p. (J). 6.99 (978-0-7894-9852-6(9)) Dorling Kindersley Publishing, Inc.

Eckart, Edana. African Elephant. 2003. (Welcome Book Ser.). (Illus.). 24p. (J). 17.00 (978-0-516-24301-6(2) , Children's Pr.) Scholastic Library Publishing.

Elephants. (Early Intervention Levels Ser.). 21.30 (978-0-7362-0379-1(6)) Hampton-Brown Bks.

Elephants. 2002. 21.95 (978-1-57572-462-1(6)) Heinemann Library.

Elephants. 2003. (J). per. (978-1-57657-943-5(3)) Paradise Pr., Inc.

Elephants. 2006. (Zootles Ser.). (J). 4.95 (*978-1-932396-21-8(7)) Wildlife Education, Ltd.

Elephant's Trunk. Date not set. (Touch & Feel Ser.). (Illus.). (J). 4.98 (978-0-7525-9568-9(7)) Parragon, Inc.

En Donde Marchan los Elefantes? (Pebble Soup Exploraciones Ser.). (SPA.). 16p. (ps up). 31.00 (978-0-7578-1679-6(7)) Rigby Education.

En donde marchan los Elefantes? Small Book. (Pebble Soup Exploraciones Ser.). (SPA.). 16p. (ps up). 5.00 (978-0-7578-1719-9(X)) Rigby Education.

Feeney, Kathy, et al. Wild Animals: Explore the Fascinating Worlds Of. . . McGee, John F., illus. 2000. 192p. (J). pap. (978-1-55971-741-0(6) , NorthWord Bks. for Young Readers) T&N Children's Publishing.

Fredericks, Anthony D. Elephant Magic for Kids. McGee, John F., illus. 1999. (Animal Magic for Kids Ser.). 48p. (J). (gr. 3 up). lib. bdg. 26.00 (978-0-8368-2632-6(9)) Stevens, Gareth Inc.

—Elephants for Kids. 1999. (Wildlife for Kids Ser.). (Illus.). 48p. (J). (ps-3). pap. 6.95 (978-1-55971-678-9(9) , Creative Publishing International) Quayside.

—Elephants for Kids. 1999. (Illus.). (J). (978-0-606-18077-1(X)) Tandem Library Bks.

Galvin, Laura Gates. Elephant & Mommy. Cohen, Jessie, photos by. 2005. (Let's Go to the Zoo! Ser.: Vol. 7). (Illus.). 16p. (J). (ps-k). bds. 5.95 (978-1-56899-911-1(9) , B9007) Soundprints.

Gareth Stevens Publishing Staff, contrib. by. Elephants. 2004. (All about Wild Animals Ser.). (Illus.). 32p. (J). lib. bdg. 23.33 (978-0-8368-4183-1(2)) Stevens, Gareth Inc.

Hall, Kirsten. African Elephant: The World's Biggest Land Mammal. 2007. (SuperSized! Ser.). (Illus.). 24p. (J). (gr. k-2). lib. bdg. 21.28 (978-1-59716-387-3(2) , 1265929) Bearport Publishing Co., Inc.

Hall, Margaret. Elephants & Their Calves. 2003. (Animal Offspring Ser.). (Illus.). 24p. (J). lib. bdg. 17.26 (978-0-7368-2107-0(4) , Pebble Bks.) Capstone Pr., Inc.

Harcourt School Publishers Staff. The Raja's Elephant Below Level. 3rd ed. 2002. (Trophies Reading Program Ser.). (Illus.). pap. 5.10 (978-0-15-323240-4(4)) Harcourt Schl. Pubs.

—The Raja's Elephants: Take-Home Book. 2001. (Collections Ser.). (Illus.). (J). pap. 1.90 (978-0-15-319502-0(9)) Harcourt Schl. Pubs.

Head, Honor. What's It Like to Be a Baby Elephant? Nichols, Matthew, illus. 1998. (Baby Animals Ser.). 32p. (gr. k-3). lib. bdg. 20.90 (978-0-7613-1252-9(8) , Millbrook Pr.) Lerner Publishing Group.

Helfer, Ralph. The World's Greatest Elephant. Lewin, Ted, illus. 2006. 48p. (J). (gr. 5). 16.99 (978-0-399-24190-1(6) , Philomel) Penguin Group (USA) Inc.

Hirschmann, Kris. Elephants. 2005. (Animals Attack! Ser.). (Illus.). 48p. (J). lib. bdg. 26.20 (978-0-7377-3238-2(5) , Greenhaven Pr., Inc.) Thomson Gale.

Holmes, Kevin J. Elephants. 2000. (Animals Ser.). (Illus.). 24p. (J). (gr. 2-3). lib. bdg. 18.60 (978-0-7368-0495-0(1) , Bridgestone Bks.) Capstone Pr., Inc.

I Like Elephants: Individual Title, 6 Packs. (Sails Literacy Ser.). 16p. (gr. k up). 27.00 (978-0-7635-4403-4(5)) Rigby Education.

Johnson, Jinny. Elephant. Rosewarne, Graham, illus. 2005. 32p. (J). (gr. 2-5). lib. bdg. 27.10 (978-1-58340-643-4(3)) Smart Apple Media.

—Elephant. Ch'en-Ling, illus. 2001. (Busy Baby Animals Ser.). 16p. (J). (ps up). lib. bdg. 19.33 (978-0-8368-2923-5(9)) Stevens, Gareth Inc.

Johnston, Marianne. Mastodons, Mammoths, & Modern-Day Elephants. 2000. (Prehistoric Animals & Their Modern-Day Relatives Ser.). 24p. (J). (gr. k-4). lib. bdg. 18.75 (978-0-8239-5202-1(9) , PowerKids Pr.) Rosen Publishing Group, Inc., The.

Jonas, Anne. Little Elephants. 2005. (Born to Be Wild Ser.). (Illus.). 23p. (J). lib. bdg. 22.00 (978-0-8368-4434-4(3)) Stevens, Gareth Inc.

Kalman, Bobbie. Endangered Elephants. 2005. (Earth's Endangered Animals Ser.). (Illus.). 32p. (J). (978-0-7787-1860-4(3)); (gr. 3-5). pap. (978-0-7787-1906-9(5)) Crabtree Publishing Co.

Kalman, Bobbie & Crossingham, John. What Is an Elephant? 2001. (Science of Living Things Ser.). (Illus.). 32p. (J). (gr. 2-3). (978-0-86505-989-4(6)); pap. (978-0-86505-966-5(7)) Crabtree Publishing Co.

Kendell, Patricia. Elephants. 2002. (In the Wild Ser.). (Illus.). 32p. (J). lib. bdg. 25.69 (978-0-7398-4906-4(9)) Raintree.

Kimiko, Mitsuko. El Elefante. (SPA.). 24p. (978-84-95150-55-4(7)) Corimbo, Editorial S.L.

Knapik, Michael Don. Everything Elephants: A Collector's Pictorial Encyclopedia. 2002. (Schiffer Book for Collectors Ser.). (Illus.). 144p. (gr. 10-13). pap. 29.95 (978-0-7643-1494-0(7)) Schiffer Publishing, Ltd.

Knudsen, Shannon. African Elephants. 2006. (Pull Ahead Books). (Illus.). 32p. (J). 22.60 (978-0-8225-3483-9(5) , Lerner Pubns.) Lerner Publishing Group.

Kulling, Monica. Elephants: Life in the Wild. 2000. (Road to Reading Ser.). (J). 10.79 (978-0-606-18925-5(4)); (gr. 3-6). lib. bdg. 11.80 (978-0-613-32502-8(8)) Tandem Library Bks.

Lang, Aubrey. Baby Elephant. Lynch, Wayne, photos by. 2002. (Nature Babies Ser.). (Illus.). 36p. (J). (gr. k-3). (978-1-55041-715-9(0)) Fitzhenry & Whiteside, Ltd.

Lang, Aubrey & Lynch, Wayne. Baby Elephant. 2003. (Nature Babies Ser.). (Illus.). 36p. (J). (gr. k-3). pap. (978-1-55041-717-3(7)) Fitzhenry & Whiteside, Ltd.

Lantier-Sampon, Patricia & Fredericks, Anthony D. The Wonder of Elephants. McGee, John F., illus. 2001. (Animal Wonders Ser.). 48p. (J). (gr. 1 up). lib. bdg. 26.00 (978-0-8368-2764-4(3)) Stevens, Gareth Inc.

Latta, Jan. Ella the Elephant. 2006. (Illus.). 24p. (J). pap. (*978-0-8368-7775-5(6)); lib. bdg. (*978-0-8368-7768-7(3)) Stevens, Gareth Inc.

Lockwood, Sophie. Elephants. 2008. (World of Mammals Ser.). 40p. (J). (gr. 2-6). 29.93 (*978-1-59296-928-9(3)) Child's World, Inc.

Louie the Miracle Elephant. 2006. (J). 9.37 (978-0-9776974-0-3(1)) Toledo Zoo, The.

Macken, JoAnn Early. Elephants. 2002. (Animals I See at the Zoo Ser.). (Illus.). (J). (ps up). 24p. lib. bdg. 19.33 (978-0-8368-3268-6(X)); 48p. pap. 5.95 (978-0-8368-3281-5(7)) Stevens, Gareth Inc. (Weekly Reader Early Learning Library).

—Elephants/Los Elefantes. Coffey, Colleen & Carrillo, Consuelo, trs. from ENG. 2003. (Weekly Reader Early Learning Library). (SPA & ENG., Illus.). 24p. (J). (ps up). 19.33 (978-0-8368-3999-9(4) , Weekly Reader Early Learning Library) Stevens, Gareth Inc.

—Elephants/Los Elefantes. 2003. (Weekly Reader Early Learning Library). (SPA & ENG., Illus.). 24p. (J). (ps up). pap. 5.95 (978-0-8368-4004-9(6) , Weekly Reader Early Learning Library) Stevens, Gareth Inc.

Magloff, Lisa & Dorling Kindersley Publishing Staff. Elephant. 2005. (Watch me Grow Ser.). (Illus.). 24p. (J). (ps-ps). 7.99 (978-0-7566-1155-2(5)) Dorling Kindersley Publishing, Inc.

Markert, Jenny. Elephants. 2006. (New Naturebooks). (Illus.). 32p. (J). (gr. 1-5). 27.07 (978-1-59296-637-0(3)) Child's World, Inc.

McClanahan. Elephant. 1999. (Wild Baby Animals Ser.). (Illus.). (J). (ps-k). 4.99 (978-0-7681-0188-1(3) , McClanahan Bk.) Learning Horizons, Inc.

Meeker, Clare Hodgson. Hansa, the True Story of an Asian Elephant Baby. Feltner, Linda M., illus. 2002. 48p. (J). pap. 12.95 (978-1-57061-370-8(2)); (gr. 1-5). 16.95 (978-1-57061-344-9(3)) Sasquatch Bks.

Moller, Jonathan R. Bath Time: Picture Book. l.t. ed. 2003. (Illus.). 71p. pap. 19.95 (978-0-9740169-0-0(X)) Lemonflavor Productions.

Molter, Carey. Elephants. l.t. ed. 2001. (Zoo Animals Ser.). (Illus.). 24p. (J). (ps-3). lib. bdg. 19.93 (978-1-57765-560-2(5) , SandCastle) ABDO Publishing Co.

Morgan, Jody. Elephant Rescue: Changing the Future for Endangered Wildlife. 2004. (Firefly Animal Rescue Ser.). (Illus.). 64p. (J). (gr. 5-8). 19.95 (978-1-55297-595-4(9)); pap. 9.95 (978-1-55297-594-7(0)) Firefly Bks., Ltd.

—Elephant Rescue: Changing the Future for Endangered Wildlife. 2004. (gr. 5-8). lib. bdg. 18.75 (978-0-613-78600-3(9)) Tandem Library Bks.

Morgan, Sally. Elephants. 2004. (QEB Animal Lives Ser.). (Illus.). 32p. (J). lib. bdg. 18.95 (978-1-59566-032-9(1)) QEB Publishing Inc.

Murray, Julie. Elephants. 2005. (Animal Kingdom Set Ii Ser.). (Illus.). 24p. (J). (gr. k-4). lib. bdg. 21.35 (978-1-59197-314-0(7)) ABDO Publishing Co.

Nichol, Barbara. Trunks All Aboard: An Elephant ABC. Van Horne, William C., illus. 2001. 24p. (J). (gr. 1-3). 14.95 (978-0-88776-536-0(X)) Tundra Bks., Inc./Livres Toundra, Inc. CAN. *Dist:* Random Hse., Inc.

Nieson, Marc. Elephants. 2001. (Let's Investigate Ser.). (Illus.). 32p. (J). 18.95 (978-1-58341-194-0(1) , Creative Education) Creative Co., The.

Niz, Xavier. Elephants. 2005. (Illus.). 24p. (J). 21.26 (978-0-7368-3717-0(5)) Capstone Pr., Inc.

Orme, Helen. Elephants in Danger. 2007. (Wildlife Survival Ser.). (Illus.). 32p. (J). (gr. 2-4). lib. bdg. 25.27 (978-1-59716-260-9(4)) Bearport Publishing Co., Inc.

Petty, Kate. Elephants. 2004. (J). lib. bdg. 22.80 (978-1-932799-42-2(7)) Stargazer Bks.

Prudom, Sharla. Jambo! Elephants. Prudom, Sharla, photos by. 2002. (Jambo! Ser.). (SWA & ENG., Illus.). 11p. (J). cd-rom 12.50 (978-1-931792-23-3(2)) E-Digital Bks., LLC.

Redmond, Ian. Elephant. 2000. (Eyewitness Bks.). (Illus.). 64p. (J). (gr. 4-7). 15.99 (978-0-7894-5872-8(1)) Dorling Kindersley Publishing, Inc.

Redmond, Ian & Dorling Kindersley Publishing Staff. Elephant. 2000. (Eyewitness Bks.). (Illus.). 64p. (J). (gr. 4-7). lib. bdg. 19.99 (978-0-7894-6591-7(4)) Dorling Kindersley Publishing, Inc.

Richardson, Adele D. Elephants: Trunks & Tusks. 2001. (Wild World of Animals Ser.). (Illus.). 24p. (J). (gr. 1-2). lib. bdg. 18.60 (978-0-7368-0962-7(7) , Bridgestone Bks.) Capstone Pr., Inc.

Rigby Education Staff. Where Do Elephants Stomp? (Pebble Soup Explorations Ser.). (Illus.). 16p. (ps up). 31.00 (978-0-7635-6462-9(1) , 764621C99) Rigby Education.

Ring, Susan. Project Elephant. 2003. (gr. 3-6). lib. bdg. 15.25 (978-0-613-79813-6(9)) Tandem Library Bks.

—Project Elephant. Kissock, Heather & Marshall, Diana, eds. 2003. (Zoo Life Ser.). 24p. (J). pap. 6.95 (978-1-59036-056-9(7)) Weigl Pubs., Inc.

—Project Elephant. 2002. (Zoo Babies Ser.). (Illus.). 24p. (J). lib. bdg. 15.15 (978-1-59036-016-3(8)) Weigl Pubs., Inc.

Salem, Lynn & Stewart, Josie. The Elephant's Trunk. Gerner, Kristian, illus. 2000. 8p. (J). (gr. k-2). pap. 3.75 (978-1-58323-031-2(9) , Seedling Pubns.) Continental Pr., Inc.

Sally & the Elephant: Level B, 6 vols. (Wonder Worldtm Ser.). 16p. 24.95 (978-0-7802-1047-9(6)) Wright Group, The.

Schlaepfer, Gloria G. Elephants. 2002. (Animalways Ser.). (Illus.). 112p. (J). 31.36 (978-0-7614-1390-5(1) , Benchmark Bks.) Cavendish, Marshall Corp.

Schwabacher, Martin. Elephants. 2000. (Animals Animals Ser.). (Illus.). 48p. (J). (gr. 3-5). lib. bdg. 25.64 (978-0-7614-1168-0(2) , Benchmark Bks.) Cavendish, Marshall Corp.

Searl, Duncan. Elephants. 2006. (Smart Animals! Ser.). (Illus.). 32p. (J). lib. bdg. 25.27 (978-1-59716-162-6(4)) Bearport Publishing Co., Inc.

Shively, Julie. Baby Elephant. Johnson, Meredith, illus. 2005. (San Diego Zoo Animal Library: Vol. 11). 24p. (J). bds. 6.95 (978-0-8249-6577-8(9)) Ideals Pubns.

Sobol, Richard. An Elephant in the Backyard. 2004. (Illus.). 32p. (J). (gr. 1). 17.99 (978-0-525-47288-9(6) , Dutton Juvenile) Penguin Group (USA) Inc.

Sobol, Richard, photos by. An Elephant in the Backyard. 2004. (Illus.). (J). (978-0-525-46970-4(2) , Dutton Juvenile) Penguin Group (USA) Inc.

Spilsbury, Louise & Spilsbury, Richard. A Herd of Elephants. 2004. 32p. (J). pap. 6.95 (978-1-4034-5416-4(7)); (Illus.). lib. bdg. 24.22 (978-1-4034-4689-3(X)) Heinemann Library.

—Save the Asian Elephant. 2006. (Illus.). 32p. (J). (978-1-4034-7802-3(3)); pap. (978-1-4034-7810-8(4)) Heinemann Library.

Steck-Vaughn Staff. Early Reader Program Level B: How the Elephant Got His Trunk, 6 Pack. 2004. (Illus.). pap. 33.00 (978-0-7398-8253-5(8)) Steck-Vaughn.

Stewart, Melissa. Elephants. 2002. (True Bks.). (Illus.). 48p. (J). (gr. 3-5). pap. 6.95 (978-0-516-26990-0(9)); 25.00 (978-0-516-22199-1(X)) Scholastic Library Publishing. (Children's Pr.).

—Elephants. 2002. (gr. 3-6). lib. bdg. 15.25 (978-0-613-54197-8(9)) Tandem Library Bks.

Stone, Lynn M. Elephants. 2001. (Wildlife in Danger Ser.). (Illus.). 24p. (J). (gr. 1-4). lib. bdg. 20.64 (978-1-58952-019-6(X)) Rourke Publishing, LLC.

Stone, Tanya Lee. Elephants. 2003. (Wild Wild World Ser.). 24p. (YA). 24.94 (978-1-56711-825-4(9) , Blackbirch Pr., Inc.) Thomson Gale.

Suen, Anastasia. An Elephant Grows Up. Denman, Michael L. & Huiett, William J., illus. 2005. (Wild Animals Ser.). 24p. (J). (ps). lib. bdg. 23.93 (978-1-4048-0984-0(8)) Picture Window Bks.

Swanson, Diane. Elephants. 2004. (Welcome to the World of Animals Ser.). (Illus.). 32p. (J). (gr. 3 up). lib. bdg. 23.33 (978-0-8368-4022-3(4)) Stevens, Gareth Inc.

—Elephants. 2003. (gr. k-3). lib. bdg. 14.10 (978-0-613-78586-0(X)) Tandem Library Bks.

—Welcome to the World of Elephants. 2003. (Welcome to the World Ser.). (Illus.). 32p. (J). (ps-2). pap. 5.95 (978-1-55285-451-8(5)) Whitecap Bks., Ltd. CAN. *Dist:* Firefly Bks., Ltd.

Taylor. Nature Fact File: Elephants. 2000. (Nature Fact Files Ser.). (Illus.). 64p. (J). (gr. 3-7). pap. 7.95 (978-1-84215-234-8(3) , Southwater) Anness Publishing GBR. *Dist:* National Bk. Network.

Taylor, Barbara. Why Don't Elephants Live in the City? 2002. (Animal Puzzlers Ser.). (Illus.). 32p. (J). 12.95 (978-1-57768-948-5(8) , Waterbird Bks.) School Specialty Publishing.

Thomas, Isabel. Elephant vs. Rhino. 2006. (Illus.). 32p. (J). (978-1-4109-2393-6(2)); pap. (978-1-4109-2400-1(9)) Steck-Vaughn.

Three Elephants: Big Book. (Pebble Soup Explorations Ser.). 16p. (ps up). 31.00 (978-0-7578-1657-4(6)) Rigby Education.

Three Elephants: Small Book. (Pebble Soup Explorations Ser.). 16p. (ps up). 5.00 (978-0-7578-1697-0(5)) Rigby Education.

Torres, John Albert. The African Elephant: A MyReportLinks. com Book. 2004. (Endangered & Threatened Animals Ser.). (Illus.). 48p. (J). lib. bdg. 25.26 (978-0-7660-5174-4(9) , MyReportLinks.com Bks.) Enslow Pubs., Inc.

Travers, Will. Elephant. 1999. (Natural World Ser.). (Illus.). 48p. (J). (gr. 4-7). pap. 7.95 (978-0-7398-0947-1(4)) Steck-Vaughn.

—Elephant: Habitats, Life Cycles, Food Chains, Threats. 1999. (Natural World Ser.). (Illus.). 48p. (J). (gr. 3-7). lib. bdg. 27.12 (978-0-7398-1056-9(1)) Raintree.

Tres Elefantes: Big Book. (Pebble Soup Exploraciones Ser.). (SPA.). 16p. (ps up). 31.00 (978-0-7578-1676-5(2)) Rigby Education.

Tres Elefantes: Small Book. (Pebble Soup Exploraciones Ser.). (SPA.). 16p. (ps up). 5.00 (978-0-7578-1716-8(5)) Rigby Education.

Turner, Matt. Asian Elephant. 2004. (Animals under Threat Ser.). (Illus.). 48p. (J). 29.93 (978-1-4034-5581-9(3)) Heinemann Library.

—The Asian Elephant. 2004. (Animals under Threat Ser.). (Illus.). 48p. (J). pap. 8.50 (978-1-4034-5688-5(7)) Heinemann Library.

Twine, Alice. Baby Elephants. 2008. (J). lib. bdg. (*978-1-4042-4148-0(5) , PowerKids Pr.) Rosen Publishing Group, Inc., The.

Twinn, Michael. Elephant. Adams, Pam, illus. 2000. (Pocket Pals Ser.). 12p. (J). (ps-1). bds. 1.99 (978-0-85953-875-6(7)) Child's Play-International.

Wexo, John Bonnett. Elefantes. Rountree, Monica, tr. 2003. (Zoobooks). Orig. Title: Elephants. (SPA., Illus.). 24p. (J). (gr. k-6). lib. bdg. 15.95 (978-1-888153-76-7(8)) Wildlife Education, Ltd.

—Elephants. (Zoobooks Ser.). (Illus.). 24p. 2001. (J). (gr. 1-6). 15.95 (978-1-888153-42-2(3)); 2003. 10.95 (978-1-888153-95-8(4) , Zoo Bks.) Wildlife Education, Ltd.

Where Do Elephants Stomp? Small Book. (Pebble Soup Explorations Ser.). 16p. (ps up). 5.00 (978-0-7635-7046-0(X)) Rigby Education.

White Elephants & Yellow Jackets: Individual Title Six-Packs. (Action Packs Ser.). 120p. (gr. 3-5). 44.00 (978-0-7635-8428-3(2)) Rigby Education.

Whitehouse, Patricia. El Elefante. 2003. (Animales del Zoologico (Zoo Animals) Ser.). (SPA., Illus.). 24p. (ps-1). (J). lib. bdg. 17.08 (978-1-4034-0403-9(8)); pap. 5.25 (978-1-4034-0651-4(0)) Heinemann Library.

—Elephant. 2003. (Zoo Animals Ser.). (Illus.). 24p. (ps-1). (J). lib. bdg. 17.08 (978-1-58810-897-5(X)); pap. 5.25 (978-1-4034-0643-9(X)) Heinemann Library.

Wildlife Education, Ltd. Staff. Elephants: Wildlife in Danger Discovery Library. Hoopes, Barbara et al, illus. 2002. (Zoobooks Ser.). 18p. (Orig.). (YA). (gr. 5 up). pap. 2.95 (978-0-937934-00-5(3)) Wildlife Education, Ltd.

Worth, Bonnie. Jumbo: The Most Famous Elephant in the World. 2001. (Step into Reading Ser.). (Illus.). (J). 10.79 (978-0-606-21272-4(8)) Tandem Library Bks.

Wrinkles: Individual Title Six-Packs. (Literatura 2000 Ser.). (gr. 1-2). 28.00 (978-0-7635-0119-8(0)) Rigby Education.

Zumbusch, Amelie von. Elephants. 2007. (Safari Animals Ser.). (Illus.). 24p. (J). (gr. k-3). lib. bdg. 21.25 (978-1-4042-3616-5(3) , PowerKids Pr.) Rosen Publishing Group, Inc., The.

ELEPHANTS—FICTION

Adams, Pam. Elephant. 2005. (Illus.). 8p. (J). (ps). bds. 5.99 (978-1-904550-27-3(4)) Child's Play-International.

Alexander, Harry. Baby Hang-Ons: Hang on Elephant. 2001. (Pinwheel Ser.). (Illus.). 12p. (J). bds. 5.95 (978-0-8069-2801-2(8)) Sterling Publishing Co., Inc.

Allan, Nicholas. Que Animales! Mayobre, Maria Francisca, tr. from ENG. Allan, Nicholas, illus. 2001. (Coleccion Primeras Lecturas). (SPA., Illus.). 28p. (J). pap. 7.50 (978-980-257-264-9(0)) Ekare, Ediciones VEN. *Dist:* AIMS International Bks., Inc., Lectorum Pubns., Inc.

Allende, Isabel. El Bosque de los Pigmeos. 2005. Tr. of Forest of the Pygmies. (SPA.). 304p. pap. 7.99 (978-0-06-081619-3(8) , Rayo) HarperCollins Pubs.

—Forest of the Pygmies. Peden, Margaret Sayers, tr. from SPA. 2005. 304p. (J). (gr. 5 up). 19.99 (978-0-06-076196-7(2) , Rayo) HarperCollins Pubs.

—Forest of the Pygmies. l.t. ed. 2005. 304p. (J). (gr. 5 up). pap. 19.99 (978-0-06-076200-1(4) , Rayo) HarperCollins Pubs.

Alsenas, Linas. Peanut. 2007. 32p. (J). (ps-k). pap. 16.99 (*978-0-439-77980-7(4)) Scholastic, Inc.

Archer, Mike. Looking after Little Ellie. Archer, Dosh, illus. 2005. 300p. (J). 15.95 (978-1-58234-971-8(1)) Bloomsbury Publishing.

Artful Doodlers, illus. Ice Age 2: Join the Pack. 2006. 32p. (J). lib. bdg. 13.85 (*978-1-4242-0692-6(8)) Fitzgerald Bks.

Ashley, Elana. Splunkunio Splunkey Detective & Peacemaker: Case One: The Missing Friendship Bracelet. 2003. (ENG & SPA., Illus.). 32p. (J). 17.95 (978-0-9744812-0-3(3)) Dream Image Pr., LLC.

—Splunkunio Splunkey Detective & Peacemaker Detective y Pacificador: Case One: The Missing Friendship Bracelet Caso Primero: El Brazalete de la Amistad Desaparecido.

Nikolov, Stefan V., tr. Ashley, Elana, photos by. 2005. (SPA & ENG., Illus.). 32p. (J). (gr. k-3). 17.95 (978-0-9744812-1-0(1)) Dream Image Pr., LLC.

Awdry, Wilbert V. Thomas & Friends: Henry & the Elephant. Courtney, Richard, illus. 2007. 32p. (J). (ps-1). pap. 3.99 (978-0-375-83976-4(3)); lib. bdg. 11.99 (978-0-375-93976-1(8)) Random Hse. Children's Bks. (Random Hse. Bks. for Young Readers).

Bachelet, Gilles. When the Silliest Cat Was Small. Bachelet, Gilles, illus. 2007. (FRE & ENG., Illus.). 32p. (J). (ps-3). 16.95 (***978-0-8109-9415-7(1)*** , Abrams Bks. for Young Readers) Abrams, Harry N. , Inc.

Backstein, Karen. Los Seis Ciegos y el Elefante. Mitra, Annie, illus. 1999. (Coleccion "Hola, Lector" Ser.). (SPA.). 48p. (J). (gr. 1-3). pap. 3.99 (978-0-439-06338-8(8) , SO0352, Scholastic en Espanol) Scholastic, Inc.

Bailey, Elinor Peace. Effie Longnostril. 2002. (J). 9.50 (978-0-9716586-5-3(X)) Fairfield Processing Corp.

BAKER, E. D. Story of kitten Cuckoo. 2007. 32p. 15.95 (***978-1-933572-04-8(3)***) Centro Bks., LLC.

Ballesta, Juan. Tommy y el Elefante. (SPA., Illus.). 28p. (J). (gr. k-3). (978-84-264-3578-1(5) , LM1605) Editorial Lumen ESP. *Dist:* Lectorum Pubns., Inc.

Bates, Ivan. All by Myself. Bates, Ivan, illus. 2000. (Illus.). 32p. (J). (ps-2). 14.95 (978-0-06-028585-2(0)) HarperCollins Pubs.

—All by Myself. 1999. 32p. (J). (ps-2). pap. 4.95 (978-0-06-443608-3(X)) HarperCollins Pubs.

Baxter Staff. Long Tusk. 2000. 23.00 (978-0-06-105133-3(0)) HarperCollins Pubs.

Beake, Lesley. Home Now. Littlewood, Karin, illus. 2007. 32p. (J). (gr. k-3). 16.95 (978-1-58089-162-2(4)); pap. 6.95 (***978-1-58089-163-9(2)***) Charlesbridge Publishing, Inc.

Bergen, Lara Rice. An Elephant Never Forgets. 2003. (ps-2). lib. bdg. 11.25 (978-0-613-75015-8(2)) Tandem Library Bks.

Bildner, Phil. Twenty-One Elephants. Pham, LeUyen, illus. 2004. 40p. (J). 16.95 (978-0-689-87011-8(6)) Simon & Schuster Children's Publishing.

Biro, Val. Gumdrops & the Elephant. (Illus.). 32p. (J). (978-0-340-71442-3(5) , Hodder & Stoughton) Hodder General Publishing Division.

Bolam, Emily, illus. Chunky Safari Elephant. 2001. (Chunky Farm Ser.). 14p. (J). (ps-k). bds. 5.99 (978-0-7641-5331-0(5)) Barron's Educational Series, Inc.

Bornemann, Elsa. Un Elefante Ocupa Mucho Espacio. (SPA.). (YA). (gr. 5-8). pap. 7.95 (978-958-04-3453-5(0) , NR7780) Norma S.A. COL. *Dist:* Distribuidora Norma, Inc., Lectorum Pubns., Inc.

Bowdish, Lynea. Preguntas Tontitas. 2002. (SPA.). lib. bdg. 12.95 (978-0-613-54300-2(9)) Tandem Library Bks.

Brandon, Taylor. The Elephant Who Couldn't Remember! Sandow, Paris, illus. 1999. (World's Greatest Children's Bks.). 48p. (J). (gr. k-5). 14.99 (978-1-889945-53-8(6)) Imperius.

Bridges, Margaret Park. Edna Elephant. Bynum, Janie, illus. 2002. (Brand New Readers Ser.). 32p. (J). (ps-2). pap. 5.99 (978-0-7636-1556-7(0)) Candlewick Pr.

Brown, J. A. Hurray for Elephant. 2003. (Funny Faces Ser.). (Illus.). (J). 3.95 (978-1-58925-717-7(0) , tiger tales) ME Media LLC.

Buchanan, Sue & Hodges, Lynn. Dear God, It's Me: A Song of God's Love. Bendall-Brunello, John, illus. 2005. (Song of God's Love Ser.). 32p. (J). 14.99 (978-0-310-70645-8(9)) Zonderkidz.

Caletti, Deb. The Nature of Jade. 2007. (YA). 304p. (gr. 7 up). 16.99 (978-1-4169-1005-3(0)); 288p. (***978-1-4287-2344-3(7)***) Simon & Schuster Children's Publishing. (Simon & Schuster Children's Publishing).

Carr, Jon & Carr, Debra. Sammy the Elephant in a Lesson on Personal Differences. 2000. 13p. 6.00 (978-1-885072-39-9(2)) Creflo Dollar Ministries Pubns.

Chamber, Catherine. The Elephants' Ears. Mockford, Caroline, illus. 2004. 32p. (J). pap. 6.99 (978-1-84148-249-1(8)) Barefoot Bks., Inc.

Chambers, Catherine. The Elephants' Ears. Mockford, Caroline, illus. 2000. 32p. (J). (ps-1). 15.95 (978-1-84148-052-7(5)) Barefoot Bks., Inc.

Christie, Jean. Sylvia the Sleepy Elephant. 2000. (Felt Lift the Flap Bks.). (Illus.). (J). (ps-k). 4.95 (978-1-58646-006-8(4)) Polka Dot Pr.

Cipolletti, George. Once upon an Elephant. Cipolletti, Suzanne, illus. 2006. (ENG.). 40p. (J). per. 16.99 (***978-1-4259-6441-2(9)***) AuthorHouse.

Clark, Patricia Nikolina. In the Shadow of the Mammoth. LeTourneau, Anthony Alex, illus. 2003. 190p. (J). pap. 6.99 (978-0-9674602-4-6(7)) Blue Marlin Pubns.

Clish, Marian L. I Wonder... What Would Happen If I Took an Elephant to School? Anderson, Jan, illus. unabr. ed. 1999. (J). (gr. k-3). 22.95 incl. cd-rom (978-1-928632-37-5(8)); 18.95 incl. audio (978-1-928632-36-8(X)); 15.95 (978-1-928632-35-1(1)); pap. 14.95 incl. cd-rom (978-1-928632-34-4(3)); pap. 7.95 (978-1-928632-32-0(7)); pap. 10.95 incl. audio (978-1-928632-33-7(5)) Writers Marketplace:Consulting, Critiquing & Publishing.

Cock, Nicole de. The Girl & the Elephant. 2004. (Illus.). 48p. (J). 15.95 (978-1-58246-133-5(3) , Tricycle Pr.) Ten Speed Pr.

Corke, Estelle. Little Elephant Tale. 2001. (Bendy Tales Ser.). (Illus.). 8p. (J). (ps). bds. 4.95 (978-0-7641-5369-3(2)) Barron's Educational Series, Inc.

Corman, Clifford L. & Trevino, Esther. Eukee the Jumpy Jumpy Elephant. DiMatteo, Richard A., illus. 2003. 24p. (J). (gr. 1-4). 15.00 (978-0-9621629-8-5(1)) Specialty Pr., Inc.

Coté, Geneviève. What Elephant? 2006. (Illus.). 32p. (978-1-55337-875-4(X)) Kids Can Pr., Ltd.

Cousins, Lucy. Maisy Makes Lemonade. 2002. (Maisy Ser.). (Illus.). 24p. (J). (ps-k). pap. 3.99 (978-0-7636-1729-5(6)) Candlewick Pr.

—Maisy Makes Lemonade. 2002. (ps-2). lib. bdg. 11.00 (978-0-613-51316-6(9)) Tandem Library Bks.

—La Nochebuena de Maisy. 2004. (SPA., Illus.). 32p. (J). 16.99 (978-84-8488-106-3(7)) Serres, Ediciones, S. L. ESP. *Dist:* Lectorum Pubns., Inc.

Cowan, Charlotte. The Little Elephant with the Big Earache. 2007. (Dr. Hippo Ser.). (Illus.). 32p. 17.95 (978-0-9753516-0-4(5)) Hippocratic Pr., The.

Crazy Elephants' First Number Fun. 2002. (J). bds. 4.98 (978-0-7525-8862-9(1)) Parragon, Inc.

Cross, Frances. Mystery of the Green Elephant. 2007. (Blobber Trilogy Ser.). 96p. pap. 7.95 (***978-1-84167-559-6(8)***) Ransom Publishing Ltd. GBR. *Dist:* International Publishers Marketing.

Cushman, Doug. Mystery at the Club Sandwich. 2004. (Illus.). 32p. (J). (gr. k-3). tchr. ed. 15.00 (978-0-618-41969-2(1) , Clarion Bks.) Houghton Mifflin Co. Trade & Reference Div.

Dalmatian Press Staff. Disney's Dumbo. rev. ed. 2007. 24p. 3.50 (***978-1-4037-3315-3(5)***) Dalmatian Pr.

Daly, Niki. Welcome to Zanzibar Road. 2006. (Illus.). 40p. (J). (gr. k-3). 16.00 (978-0-618-64926-6(3) , Clarion Bks.) Houghton Mifflin Co. Trade & Reference Div.

D'Amico, Carmela. Ella Sets the Stage. D'Amico, Steven, illus. 2006. 41p. (J). pap. 16.99 (978-0-439-83153-6(9) , Levine, Arthur A. Bks.) Scholastic, Inc.

—Ella Takes the Cake. D'Amico, Steven, illus. 2005. 48p. (J). pap. 16.99 (978-0-439-62794-8(X) , Levine, Arthur A. Bks.) Scholastic, Inc.

D'Amico, Carmela & D'Amica, Steve. Ella the Elegant Elephant. 2005. (J). (gr. k-3). 29.95 incl. audio compact disk (978-0-8045-4128-2(0) , SACD4128) Spoken Arts, Inc.

D'amico, Carmela & D'amico, Steve. Ella the Elegant Elephant. unabr. ed. 2006. (J). 9.95 (978-0-439-87589-9(7)) Scholastic, Inc.

D'Amico, Carmela & D'Amico, Steven. Ella Sets Sail. 2008. (J). (***978-0-439-83156-7(3));*** pap. (***978-0-439-83155-0(5)***) Scholastic, Inc. (Levine, Arthur A. Bks.).

D'Amico, Carmela & D'Amico, Steven. Ella the Elegant Elephant. 2004. (Illus.). (J). (ps-3). 56p. pap. 16.95 (978-0-439-62792-4(3)); (978-0-439-62793-1(1)) Scholastic, Inc. (Levine, Arthur A. Bks.).

—Ella the Elegant Elephant. 2005. (J). (gr. k-3). 27.95 incl. audio (978-0-8045-6933-0(9) , SAC6933) Spoken Arts, Inc.

D'Amico, Carmela & D'Amico, Steven, illus. Ella Takes the Cake. 2005. (J). (978-0-439-62795-5(8) , Levine, Arthur A. Bks.) Scholastic, Inc.

Davies, Timothy, Sr. The Polka-Dotted Elephant. 2007. (J). per. 12.00 (***978-0-9793207-0-5(4)***) Wildlife Tales Publishing.

de Brunhoff, Jean. Babar & Father Christmas. Haas, Merle, tr. from FRE. 2001. Tr. of Babar et le Pere Noel. (Illus.). 48p. (J). (ps-2). 15.95 (978-0-375-81444-0(2) , Random Hse. Bks. for Young Readers) Random Hse. Children's Bks.

—Bonjour, Babar! The Six Unabridged Classics by the Creator of Babar. Schulman, Janet, ed. Haas, Merle, tr. unabr. ed. 2000. (Babar Ser.). (Illus.). 280p. (J). (gr. k-3). 29.95 (978-0-375-81060-2(9) , Random Hse. Bks. for Young Readers) Random Hse. Children's Bks.

—Les Vacances de Zephir. 2000. (Babar Ser.). (FRE., Illus.). (J). 13.95 (978-2-01-003571-5(2)) Istra FRA. *Dist:* Distribooks, Inc.

—Le Voyage de Babar. 1999. (Babar Ser.). (FRE., Illus.). (J). (ps-3). 13.95 (978-2-01-002518-1(0)) Istra FRA. *Dist:* Distribooks, Inc.

de Brunhoff, Jean & de Brunhoff, Laurent. Babar en Famille. 1999. (Babar Ser.).Tr. of Babar & His Children. (FRE., Illus.). (J). (ps-3). 15.95 (978-2-01-002516-7(4)) Distribooks, Inc.

de Brunhoff, Jean, et al. Isabelle the Flower Girl. 2004. (Babar Ser.). (Illus.). 24p. (J). (ps-3). 9.95 (978-0-8109-5039-9(1)) Abrams, Harry N. , Inc.

de Brunhoff, Laurent. L' Anniversaire de Babar. (Babar Ser.). (FRE., Illus.). (J). (ps-3). pap. (978-2-01-002551-8(2)) Hachette Groupe Livre.

—Babar a New York. 1999. (Babar Ser.). (FRE., Illus.). (J). (ps-3). (978-2-01-002552-5(0)) Istra.

—Babar & the Ghost. 2001. (Babar Ser.). (Illus.). 40p. (J). (ps-3). 16.95 (978-0-8109-4398-8(0)) Abrams, Harry N. , Inc.

—Babar & the Ghost. de Brunhoff, Laurent, illus. 2002. (Babar Ser.). (Illus.). (J). 26.13 (978-0-7587-6816-2(8)) Book Wholesalers, Inc.

—Babar & the Ghost. ed. 2004. (Illus.). (J). (gr. k-3). spiral bd. (978-0-616-14570-8(5)); spiral bd. (978-0-616-14571-5(3)) Canadian National Institute for the Blind/ Institut National Canadien pour les Aveugles.

—Babar & the Succotash Bird. 2000. (Babar Ser.). (Illus.). 38p. (J). (ps-3). 16.95 (978-0-8109-5700-8(0)) Abrams, Harry N. , Inc.

—Babar & the Wully-Wully. 2001. (Illus.). 40p. (J). (ps-3). 16.95 (978-0-8109-4397-1(2)) Abrams, Harry N. , Inc.

—Babar dans l'Ile aux Oiseaux.Tr. of Babar in the Jungle. (FRE., Illus.). (J). pap. 16.95 (***978-2-211-09806-9(1)***) Archimede Editions FRA. *Dist:* Distribooks, Inc.

—Babar dans l'Ile aux Oiseaux. (Babar Ser.).Tr. of Babar in the Jungle. (FRE., Illus.). 29p. (J). (ps-3). 15.95 (978-0-7859-0681-0(9) , F2002) French & European Pubns., Inc.

—Babar dans l'Ile aux Oiseaux. 1999. (Babar Ser.).Tr. of Babar in the Jungle. (FRE., Illus.). (J). (ps-3). (978-2-01-002547-1(4)) Istra.

—Babar en Amerique. 1999. (Babar Ser.).Tr. of Babar in America. (FRE., Illus.). (J). (ps-3). 13.95 (978-2-01-002553-2(9)) Istra FRA. *Dist:* Distribooks, Inc.

—Babar et la Vieille Dame. (Babar Ser.). (FRE., Illus.). (J). (ps-3). pap. 15.95 (978-0-7859-0614-8(2) , FC254) French & European Pubns., Inc.

—Babar et le Pere Noel. 1999. (Babar Ser.).Tr. of Babar & Father Christmas. (FRE., Illus.). (J). (ps-3). (978-2-01-002549-5(0)) Istra.

—Babar et le Professeur Grifaton. 1999. (Babar Ser.). (FRE., Illus.). (J). (ps-3). (978-2-01-002550-1(4)) Istra.

—Babar et le Wouly-Wouly. (Babar Ser.).Tr. of Babar & the Wully-Wully. (FRE., Illus.). 26p. (J). (ps-3). 15.95 (978-0-7859-0682-7(7) , M11805) French & European Pubns., Inc.

—Babar et le Wouly-Wouly. 1999. (Babar Ser.).Tr. of Babar & the Wully-Wully. (FRE., Illus.). (J). (ps-3). (978-2-01-004209-6(3)) Istra.

—Babar et ses Amis a la Ferme. (Babar Ser.). (FRE., Illus.). 48p. (J). (ps-3). 19.95 (978-0-7859-8805-2(X)) French & European Pubns., Inc.

—Babar et ses Amis a la Fete. (Babar Ser.). (FRE., Illus.). 48p. (J). (ps-3). 19.95 (978-0-7859-8806-9(8)) French & European Pubns., Inc.

—Babar et ses Amis a la Maison. (Babar Ser.). (FRE., Illus.). 48p. (J). (ps-3). 19.95 (978-0-7859-8804-5(1)) French & European Pubns., Inc.

—Babar et ses Amis a la Ville. (Babar Ser.). (FRE., Illus.). 48p. (J). (ps-3). 19.95 (978-0-7859-8809-0(2)) French & European Pubns., Inc.

—Babar et ses Amis a L'Ecole. (Babar Ser.). (FRE., Illus.). 48p. (J). (ps-3). 19.95 (978-0-7859-8802-1(5)) French & European Pubns., Inc.

—Babar et ses Amis au Spectacle. (Babar Ser.). (FRE., Illus.). 48p. (J). (ps-3). 19.95 (978-0-7859-8803-8(3)) French & European Pubns., Inc.

—Babar et ses Amis en Foret. (Babar Ser.). (FRE., Illus.). 48p. (J). (ps-3). 19.95 (978-0-7859-8811-3(4)) French & European Pubns., Inc.

—Babar et ses Amis en Vacances. (Babar Ser.). (FRE., Illus.). 48p. (J). (ps-3). 19.95 (978-0-7859-8808-3(4)) French & European Pubns., Inc.

—Babar et ses Amis Font les Courses. (Babar Ser.). (FRE., Illus.). 48p. (J). (ps-3). 19.95 (978-0-7859-8810-6(6)) French & European Pubns., Inc.

—Babar et ses Amis Visitent le Royaume. (Babar Ser.). (FRE., Illus.). 48p. (J). (ps-3). 19.95 (978-0-7859-8807-6(6)) French & European Pubns., Inc.

—Babar in Famiglia. pap. 12.95 (978-88-04-46271-2(X)) Mondadori ITA. *Dist:* Distribooks, Inc.

—Babar les 500 Premiers Mots. (Babar Ser.). (FRE., Illus.). 48p. (J). (ps-3). 19.95 (978-0-7859-8812-0(2)) French & European Pubns., Inc.

—Babar Raconte Flore Reporter. (Babar Ser.). (FRE., Illus.). 48p. (J). (ps-3). 19.95 (978-0-7859-8813-7(0)) French & European Pubns., Inc.

—Babar Raconte Halte a la Pollution. (Babar Ser.). (FRE., Illus.). 48p. (J). (ps-3). 19.95 (978-0-7859-8816-8(5)) French & European Pubns., Inc.

—Babar Raconte la Course a la Lune. (Babar Ser.). (FRE., Illus.). 48p. (J). (ps-3). 19.95 (978-0-7859-8820-5(3)) French & European Pubns., Inc.

—Babar Raconte l'Affaire de la Couronne. (Babar Ser.). (FRE., Illus.). 48p. (J). (ps-3). 19.95 (978-0-7859-8818-2(1)) French & European Pubns., Inc.

—Babar Raconte l'Arrivee du Bebe Elephant. (Babar Ser.). (FRE., Illus.). 48p. (J). (ps-3). 19.95 (978-0-7859-8815-1(7)) French & European Pubns., Inc.

—Babar Raconte le Fantome. (Babar Ser.). (FRE., Illus.). 48p. (J). (ps-3). 19.95 (978-0-7859-8819-9(X)) French & European Pubns., Inc.

—Babar Raconte le Meilleur Ami des Elephants. (Babar Ser.). (FRE., Illus.). 48p. (J). (ps-3). 19.95 (978-0-7859-8823-6(8)) French & European Pubns., Inc.

—Babar Raconte le Pianiste. (Babar Ser.). (FRE., Illus.). 48p. (J). (ps-3). 19.95 (978-0-7859-8822-9(X)) French & European Pubns., Inc.

—Babar Raconte le Plus Beau Cadeau du Monde. (Babar Ser.). (FRE., Illus.). 48p. (J). (ps-3). 19.95 (978-0-7859-8821-2(1)) French & European Pubns., Inc.

—Babar Raconte Que la Fete Continue. (Babar Ser.). (FRE., Illus.). 48p. (J). (ps-3). 19.95 (978-0-7859-8824-3(6)) French & European Pubns., Inc.

—Babar Raconte un Diner Chez Rataxes. (Babar Ser.). (FRE., Illus.). 48p. (J). (ps-3). 19.95 (978-0-7859-8817-5(3)) French & European Pubns., Inc.

—Babar Raconte Zephir Fait le Singe. (Babar Ser.). (FRE., Illus.). 48p. (J). (ps-3). 19.95 (978-0-7859-8814-4(9)) French & European Pubns., Inc.

—Babar sur la Planete Molle. 2000. (Babar Ser.). (FRE., Illus.). (J). (ps-3). 13.95 (978-2-01-006867-6(X)) Istra FRA. *Dist:* Distribooks, Inc.

—Babar the King. de Brunhoff, Laurent, illus. 2002. (Babar Ser.). (Illus.). (J). 23.36 (978-0-7587-2011-5(4)) Book Wholesalers, Inc.

—Babar the Magician. 2005. (Illus.). 24p. (J). (ps-1). 9.95 (978-0-8109-5863-0(5)) Abrams, Harry N. , Inc.

—Babar Visits Another Planet. 2003. (Illus.). 32p. (J). (ps-3). 16.95 (978-0-8109-4244-8(5)) Abrams, Harry N. , Inc.

—Babar's Battle. 2002. (Babar Ser.). (Illus.). 38p. (J). (ps-3). 16.95 (978-0-8109-5714-5(0)) Abrams, Harry N. , Inc.

—Babar's Book of Color. 2004. (Illus.). 32p. (J). (ps-1). 17.95 (978-0-8109-4840-2(0)) Abrams, Harry N. , Inc.

—Babar's Busy Year. 2005. (Illus.). 24p. (J). (ps-1). 9.95 (978-0-8109-5864-7(3)) Abrams, Harry N. , Inc.

—Babar's Counting Book. 2003. (Illus.). 32p. (J). (ps-k). 16.95 (978-0-8109-4243-1(7)) Abrams, Harry N. , Inc.

—Babar's Little Girl. 2001. (Babar Ser.). (Illus.). 38p. (J). (ps-3). 16.95 (978-0-8109-5703-9(5)) Abrams, Harry N. , Inc.

—Babar's Little Girl Makes a Friend. 2002. (Babar Ser.). (Illus.). 30p. (J). (ps-3). 9.95 (978-0-8109-0556-6(6)) Abrams, Harry N. , Inc.

—Babar's Museum of Art. 2003. (Illus.). 48p. (J). (ps-17). 17.95 (978-0-8109-4597-5(5)) Abrams, Harry N. , Inc.

—Babar's Mystery. ed. 2004. (Illus.). 30p. (J). (ps-3). 16.95 (978-0-8109-5033-7(2)) Abrams, Harry N. , Inc.

—Babar's Rescue. 2004. (Illus.). 32p. (J). (ps-3). 16.95 (978-0-8109-4839-6(7)) Abrams, Harry N. , Inc.

—Babar's World Tour. 2005. (Illus.). 48p. (J). (ps-3). 16.95 (978-0-8109-5780-0(9) , Abrams Bks. for Young Readers); (978-0-8109-5982-8(8)) Abrams, Harry N. , Inc.

—Le Chateau de Babar. 1999. (Babar Ser.).Tr. of Babar's House. (FRE., Illus.). (J). (ps-3). pap. (978-2-01-002515-0(6)) Hachette Groupe Livre.

—Meet Babar & His Family. 2002. (Babar Ser.). (Illus.). 30p. (J). (ps-3). 9.95 (978-0-8109-0555-9(8)) Abrams, Harry N. , Inc.

—Meet Babar & His Family. (Babar Ser.). (Illus.). 32p. (J). (ps-3). Random Hse. Children's Bks.

—Il Re Babar. pap. 12.95 (978-88-04-44195-3(X)) Mondadori ITA. *Dist:* Distribooks, Inc.

—Le Roi Babar.Tr. of Babar the King. (FRE.). (J). pap. 14.95 (978-2-211-06483-5(3)) Archimede Editions FRA. *Dist:* Distribooks, Inc.

—Le Roi Babar. 1999. (Babar Ser.).Tr. of Babar the King. (FRE., Illus.). (J). (ps up). pap. 19.95 (978-2-01-002517-4(2)) Hachette Groupe Livre FRA. *Dist:* Distribooks, Inc.

de Brunhoff, Laurent & de Brunhoff, Jean. Babar Goes to School. 2003. (Illus.). 32p. (J). (ps-1). 9.95 (978-0-8109-4582-1(7)) Abrams, Harry N. , Inc.

de Brunhoff, Laurent & Weiss, Ellen. Babar & the Runaway Egg. Gibert, Jean Claude & Gray, Judith, illus. 2004. 24p. (J). (ps-1). 9.95 (978-0-8109-4838-9(9)) Abrams, Harry N. , Inc.

Delittle, Cathy. If You See Some Elephants. Delittle, Cathy, illus. 1998. (Illus.). 8p. (J). (ps-1). spiral bd. 7.95 (978-1-892633-01-9(9) , OOCD202) Delittle Storyteller Co.

Delval, Marie He. Elephants est toujours Conten. (FRE.). pap. 14.95 (978-2-227-75601-4(2)) Bayard Editions FRA. *Dist:* Distribooks, Inc.

Derrick, Patricia. Riley the Rhinoceros. 2007. 32p. 18.95 (978-1-933818-15-3(8)) Animalations.

Disney Staff. Dumbo. (FRE.). 96p. (J). (gr. k-5). pap. 9.95 (978-0-7859-8849-6(1)) French & European Pubns., Inc.

—Dumbo. 2002. (Illus.). (J). pap. 2.99 (978-0-7364-1287-2(5)) Mouse Works.

Dodd, Emma. No Matter What. 2008. 24p. (J). (ps). 10.99 (***978-0-525-47932-1(5)*** , Dutton Juvenile) Penguin Group (USA) Inc.

Doinet, Mymi, et al, illus. The Elephant. 2000. (My Animal Library). 32p. (J). (ps-1). pap. 6.95 (978-0-7892-0662-6(5) , Abbeville Kids) Abbeville Pr., Inc.

Dolan, Penny. Eight Enormous Elephants. Bradley, Leo, illus. 2004. (Read-It! Readers Ser.). 32p. (C). (gr. k-3). 18.60 (978-1-4048-0054-0(9)) Picture Window Bks.

Donald, Margaret. Eli the Elephant: A Tsunami Story. 2007. 25p. 7.95 (978-81-8386-024-6(9)) India Research Pr. IND. *Dist:* Independent Pubs. Group.

Dowling, James. Suzy Saves Elysha, the Baby Elephant, Vol. 2. 1999. (J). pap. (978-0-9666535-1-9(3)) Animal Ark, Inc.

Drachman, Eric. Ellison the Elephant. Muscarello, James, illus. 2004. 32p. 18.95 (978-0-9703809-1-3(7)) Kidwick Bks.

Dubowski, Cathy East. Wild Thornberrys Movie. 2002. (gr. 3-6). lib. bdg. 13.00 (978-0-613-58171-4(7)) Tandem Library Bks.

Duey, Kathleen & Bale, Karen. Trainwreck: Kansas, 1892. 1999. (Survival! Ser.: No. 8). (J). (gr. 4-7). (978-0-606-16279-1(8)) Tandem Library Bks.

Eggleton, Jill. Elephant Is Stuck! 3-in-1 Package. (Sails Literacy Ser.). 24p. (gr. k up). 57.00 (978-0-7578-8616-4(7)) Rigby Education.

—Elephant Is Stuck! 6 Small Books. (Sails Literacy Ser.). 24p. (gr. k up). 25.00 (978-0-7578-7729-2(X)) Rigby Education.

—Elephant Is Stuck! Big Book Only. (Sails Literacy Ser.). 24p. (gr. k up). 27.00 (978-0-7578-6199-4(7)) Rigby Education.

Ehrlich, Fred. Does an Elephant Take a Bath? Bolam, Emily, illus. 2005. (Early Experiences Ser.). 32p. (J). (ps-k). 13.50 (978-1-59354-111-8(2)) Blue Apple Bks.

—Does & Elephant Take a Bath? Bolam, Emily, illus. 2005. (Early Experiences Ser.). 32p. (J). (ps-k). pap. 5.95 (978-1-59354-123-1(6)) Blue Apple Bks.

Ehrlich, Fred. You Can't Lay an Egg If You're an Elephant: A Book about How Animals are Born. Haley, Amanda, illus. 2007. 40p. (J). (gr. 2-4). 15.95 (***978-1-59354-606-9(8)***) Blue Apple Bks.

Eide, Scott M. Chicago Bob & the Case of the Missing Elephant. 2006. 20p. pap. 3.99 net. (978-1-59975-649-3(8)) Independent Pub.

El Elefante. 2002. Tr. of Elephant. (SPA.). (J). 6.50 (978-84-246-1729-5(0)) La Galera, S.A. Editorial ESP. *Dist:* AIMS International Bks., Inc.

An Elephant in the House: Individual Title Six-Pack. (Story Steps Ser.). (gr. k-2). 23.00 (978-0-7635-9852-5(6)) Rigby Education.

Elephant Trick: First Wave Satellite Individual Title Six-Packs. (Sails Literacy Ser.). 16p. (gr. k up). 27.00 (978-0-7578-6871-9(1)) Rigby Education.

Ellis, Mary. Elephant Child. 2003. (Illus.). 128p. (J). pap. 7.99 (978-0-00-712820-4(7)) HarperCollins Pubs. Ltd. GBR. *Dist:* Independent Pubs. Group.

Elly the Elephant. 1999. (Illus.). 6p. (J). 12.98 (978-1-58048-092-5(6)) Sandvik Publishing.

Elsie Elephant's Jungle Shower. 2002. (My First Tab Story Ser.). (J). bds. 3.98 (978-0-7525-8955-8(5)) Parragon, Inc.

Elwell, Telva & Kelley, Barbara. Ellasense Misses the Train. Elwell, Telva, illus. 2004. (Illus.). 48p. (J). per. 12.95 (978-0-9754591-0-2(4)) Cubby Hole Tales.

E
F
G

Enormous Elephant Show. 2001. (ps-2). lib. bdg. 9.80 (978-0-613-32505-9(2)) Tandem Library Bks.

Eschberger, Beverly. The Elephants Tour England: An Elephant Family Adventure. Gower, Jim, illus. 2008. (J). per. 3.99 (978-1-932926-29-3(1) , Kinkajou Pr.) Artemesia Publishing, LLC.

—The Elephants Visit London: An Elephant Family Adventure. Gower, Jim, illus. Lt. ed. 2007. 96p. (J). per. 3.99 (978-1-932926-30-9(5) , Kinkajou Pr.) Artemesia Publishing, LLC.

—The Elephants Visit Paris: An Elephant Family Adventure. Gower, Jim, illus. 2009. (J). per. 3.99 (978-1-932926-28-6(3) , Kinkajou Pr.) Artemesia Publishing, LLC.

Ferrier, Nathalie. I Am Zelephant! Weissglass, Jeannie, illus. 2001. (J). 24.00 (978-0-9707002-0-9(2)) Born To Be Wild, LLC.

Fleischman, Sid. The White Elephant. McGuire, Robert, illus. 2006. 112p. (J). (gr. 3-6). 15.99 (978-0-06-113136-3(9) , Greenwillow Bks.); lib. bdg. 16.89 (978-0-06-113137-0(7)) HarperCollins Pubs.

Francis, Davy. Jim the Elephant. Brundige, Britt, ed. Francis, Davy, illus. 2001. (Illus.). 10p. (J). (gr. k-5). spiral bd. 5.99 (978-1-929063-78-9(4) , 251) Moons & Stars Publishing For Children.

Frankel, Alona. The Family of Tiny White Elephants. Frankel, Alona, illus. rev. ed. 1999. (Illus.). 48p. (J). (ps-6). 5.95 (978-1-888509-09-0(0)) Baby Matters, Inc.

French, Vivian. Ellie & Elvis. Terry, Michael, illus. 2007. 32p. (J). pap. 9.99 (***978-0-7475-8403-2(6)***) Bloomsbury Publishing Plc GBR. *Dist:* Independent Pubs. Group.

French, Vivian. Meet the Mammoth! Level P. Williams, Lisa, illus. 2006. (Lightning Readers Ser.). 32p. (J). pap. 3.95 (978-0-7696-4187-4(3) , Gingham Dog Pr.) School Specialty Publishing.

French/Williams, Vivian/Lisa. Meet the Mammoth! 2005. (Illus.). 32p. (J). lib. bdg. 9.00 (***978-1-4242-0881-4(5)***) Fitzgerald Bks.

Furlong, Marguerite, text. Alexander Goes Out to Eat. 2002. (Alexander, the Elephant Who Couldn't Eat Peanuts Ser.). pap. 5.00 (978-1-882541-31-7(6)) Food Allergy & Anaphylaxis Network.

Gallo, Sofia & Cillario, Simona. El Elefantito en el Polo Norte. Brignole, Giancarla, tr. rev. ed. 2002. (Fabulas De Familia Ser.). (SPA.). 32p. (J). pap. 6.95 (978-970-20-0265-9(6)) Castillo, Ediciones, S. A. de C. V. MEX. *Dist:* Macmillan.

—El Elefantito y el Mar. Brignole, Giancarla, tr. rev. ed. 2002. (Fabulas De Familia Ser.). (SPA.). 32p. (J). pap. 6.95 (978-970-20-0254-3(0)) Castillo, Ediciones, S. A. de C. V. MEX. *Dist:* Macmillan.

Galvin, Laura Gates. Judy the Elephant. Denman, Michael & Huiett, William, illus. 2005. (African Wildlife Foundation(R) Ser.). 32p. (J). (ps-2). 8.95 incl. cd-rom (978-1-59249-198-8(7) , SD6502); 2.95 incl. cd-rom (978-1-59249-171-1(5) , S6552); 9.95 (978-1-59249-172-8(3) , PS6552) Soundprints.

—Judy the Elephant. Denman, Michael L. & Huiett, William J., trs. Denman, Michael L. & Huiett, William J., illus. 2005. (African Wildlife Foundation(R) Ser.). 36p. (J). (ps-2). 6.95 (978-1-59249-170-4(7) , S6502); 14.95 incl. cd-rom (978-1-59249-169-8(3) , H6502) Soundprints.

Garcia, Lionel. El Elefante y la Hormiga. 2000. 28p. 16.99 (978-0-9678364-1-6(7)) Wisdom Pr.

—The Elephant & the Ant. 2000. 28p. 16.99 (978-0-9678364-0-9(9)) Wisdom Pr.

Garis, Howard Roger. Umboo the Elephant. 2004. reprint ed. pap. 15.95 (978-1-4191-9168-8(3)); pap. 1.99 (978-1-4192-9168-5(8)) Kessinger Publishing, LLC.

Garis, Howard Roger. Umboo the Elephant Circus Animal Stories. 2006. 62.99 (***978-1-4280-2342-0(9)***) IndyPublish.com.

Gatehouse, John. Eric's Elephant on Holiday. (Illus.). 32p. (J). pap. 7.95 (978-0-14-038612-7(2)) Penguin Bks., Ltd. GBR. *Dist:* Trafalgar Square Publishing.

Geraghty, Paul. Yamina. 2nd ed. 2001. (SPA., Illus.). 32p. (J). (gr. 2-4). (978-84-89675-77-3(5)) Zendrera Zariquiey, Editorial ESP. *Dist:* Lectorum Pubns., Inc.

Geras, Adele. Little Elephant's Moon. (Illus.). 32p. (J). 13.95 (978-0-241-11729-3(1) , Hamilton, Hamish) Penguin Bks., Ltd. GBR. *Dist:* Trafalgar Square Publishing.

Getting Ready for the Ball: Individual Title Six-Packs. (Literatura 2000 Ser.). (ps-1). 28.00 (978-0-7635-0005-4(4)) Rigby Education.

Ginkel, Anne. I've Got an Elephant. Bynum, Janie, illus. 2006. 32p. (J). 16.95 (978-1-56145-373-3(0) , Peachtree Junior) Peachtree Pubs., Ltd.

Glassman, Sandra. The Sloppy, Floppy, Tales of Charlee the Elephant. Frances, Dee, ed. 1999. (Illus.). 50p. (J). pap. 10.00 (978-1-885519-34-4(6)) DDDD Pubns.

Golden Books Staff. The Saggy Baggy Elephant. 1999. (Little Golden Bks.). 24p. (J). (gr. k-k). 2.99 (978-0-307-02110-6(6) , 98092, Golden Bks.) Random Hse. Children's Bks.

Goodman, Joan Elizabeth. Bernard Goes to School. Catalano, Dominic, illus. 2003. 32p. (J). (ps up). 15.95 (978-1-56397-958-3(6)) Boyds Mills Pr.

—Bernard's Bath. Catalano, Dominic, illus. 2003. 32p. (J). (ps up). reprint ed. pap. 8.95 (978-1-56397-854-8(7)) Boyds Mills Pr.

—Bernard's Bath. 2000. (gr. k-3). lib. bdg. 16.40 (978-0-613-28754-8(1)); (Illus.). (J). (978-0-606-18011-5(7)) Tandem Library Bks.

Gorbachev, Valeri. Big Little Elephant. 2005. (Illus.). 32p. (J). (ps-ps). 16.00 (978-0-15-205195-2(3) , Harcourt Children's Bks) Harcourt Children's Bks.

Greban, Quentin. Nestor. 2001. (Illus.). 27p. (J). pap. 15.95 (978-1-59034-012-7(4)) Mondo Publishing.

—Nestor. Greban, Quentin, illus. 2001. (Illus.). 27p. (J). (ps-4). 15.95 (978-1-58653-855-2(1)) Mondo Publishing.

—Nestor. (Buenas Noches Coleccion). (SPA., Illus.). (J). (gr. k-3). 8.95 (978-958-04-6032-9(9)) Norma S.A. COL. *Dist:* Distribuidora Norma, Inc., Lectorum Pubns., Inc.

Gregar, Steve. The Littlest Elephant. 2004. 13p. pap. 9.98 (978-1-4116-1148-1(9)) Lulu.com.

Grindley, Sally. Elephant Small Goes to a Party. 1999. (Toddler Bks.). (Illus.). 20p. (J). pap. 4.95 (978-0-7641-0870-9(0)) Barron's Educational Series, Inc.

—Little Elephant Thunderfoot. Butler, John, illus. 1999. 32p. (J). (ps-3). 15.95 (978-1-56145-180-7(0)) Peachtree Pubs., Ltd.

Grindley, Sally & Ellis, Andy. Elephant Small & the Splashy Bath. 1999. (Little Barron's Toddler Bks.). (Illus.). 20p. (J). (ps). pap. 4.95 (978-0-7641-0858-7(1)) Barron's Educational Series, Inc.

—Elephant Small Is Lost. 1999. (Little Barron's Toddler Bks.). (Illus.). 20p. (J). (ps). pap. 4.95 (978-0-7641-0860-0(3)) Barron's Educational Series, Inc.

Gusti. Half of an Elephant. Gusti, illus. 2006. (Illus.). 40p. (J). 15.95 (978-1-933605-09-8(X)) Kane/Miller Bk. Pubs., Inc.

Gwent (Wales), Staff Development Unit Staff & Acen Staff, contrib. by. Nos Da, Arthur. 2005. (WEL., Illus.). 8p. (978-1-874049-31-9(9)) Acen Limited.

Haile, Carol J. Elephant Overboard! Haile, Carol J., illus. 2007. (J). lib. bdg. 19.95 (978-0-9711236-3-2(2)) Firenze Pr.

Hamilton, Elizabeth L. Little Zoh's Submissive Trunk. 2003. (Character Critters Ser.: No. 3). (Illus.). 32p. (J). (gs-3). per. 5.95 (978-0-9713749-9-7(6) , Character-in-Action) Quiet Impact, Inc.

Harcourt School Publishers Staff. Elmer: Library Book. 1999. (Collections Ser.). (Illus.). pap. 14.90 (978-0-15-313410-4(0)) Harcourt Schl. Pubs.

—Elmer: Library Edition. 1999. (SPA., Illus.). pap. 19.10 (978-0-15-315873-5(5)) Harcourt Schl. Pubs.

—The Little Elephant: Little Book. 2000. (Collections Ser.). (Illus.). (J). pap. 10.20 (978-0-15-314500-1(5)) Harcourt Schl. Pubs.

Harris, Erin. Elephant on My Roof. Harris, Erin, illus. 2006. (Illus.). 32p. (J). 15.95 (978-1-60108-002-8(6)) Red Cygnet Pr.

Harry, Rebecca, illus. Little Elephant. 2007. (Noisy Jungle Babies Ser.). 8p. (J). bds. 5.99 (978-0-7641-6035-6(4)) Barron's Educational Series, Inc.

Hart, Christopher. Merwin: Master of Disguise. 2002. (Illus.). 32p. (ps-2). 14.95 (978-0-8230-3049-1(0)) Watson-Guptill Pubns., Inc.

Hawkins, Colin & Hawkins, Jacqui. Here's a Happy Elephant. 2004. (Illus.). 8p. (J). 3.95 (978-1-56148-442-3(3)) Good Bks.

Heaton, Caroline. Yi-Min & the Elephants: A Tale of Ancient China. Vyner, Tim, illus. 2004. 32p. (J). pap. 7.95 (978-1-84507-146-2(8)) Lincoln, Frances Ltd. GBR. *Dist:* Perseus Distribution.

Heaton, Caroline & Vyner, Tim. Yi-Min & the Elephants: A Story of Ancient China. 2004. (Illus.). 32p. (J). (978-0-7112-1852-9(8)) Lincoln, Frances Ltd. GBR. *Dist:* Transition Vendor.

Heide, Florence Parry & Clief, Sylvia Van. That's What Friends Are For. Meade, Holly, illus. 2007. 40p. (J). (ps-3). pap. 6.99 (978-0-7636-2646-4(5)) Candlewick Pr.

Heine, Theresa. Elephant Dance. Moxley, Sheila, illus. 2006. 0040p. pap. 6.99 (978-1-905236-79-4(4)) Barefoot Bks., Inc.

Heron Books Editors. The Elephant's Clock, 3 vols., Set. 2nd ed. Incl. Elephant's Clock Workbook. 103p. pap., wbk. ed. 15.00 (978-0-89739-007-1(5)); How to Tell Time. 2nd ed. 110p. pap., wbk. ed. 15.00 (978-0-89739-008-8(3)); Story about Learning to Tell Time. 95p. pap. 20.00 (978-0-89739-006-4(7)); (Illus.). (J). (gr. 1-2). 2000. Set pap. 50.00 (978-0-89739-010-1(5)) Heron Bks.

—The Elephant's Clock Workbook. 2000. (Elephant's Clock Ser.: Bk. 2). (Illus.). 103p. (J). (gr. 1-2). pap., wbk. ed. 15.00 (978-0-89739-007-1(5)) Heron Bks.

—How to Tell Time. 2nd ed. 2000. (Elephant's Clock Ser.: Bk. 3). (Illus.). 110p. (J). (gr. 1-2). pap., wbk. ed. 15.00 (978-0-89739-008-8(3)) Heron Bks.

—A Story about Learning to Tell Time. 2000. (Elephant's Clock Ser.: Bk. 1). (Illus.). 95p. (J). (gr. 1-2). pap. 20.00 (978-0-89739-006-4(7)) Heron Bks.

Hillenbrand, Will. My Book Box. 2006. (Illus.). 32p. (J). 16.00 (978-0-15-202029-3(2)) Harcourt Trade Pubs.

Hindley, Judy. Can You Move Like an Elephant? Stojic, Manya, illus. 2003. 32p. (J). pap. 5.95 (978-0-7641-2586-7(9)) Barron's Educational Series, Inc.

Hirshkowith, Sandra. Premlata & the Festival of Lights. Andrew, Ian, illus. 1999. (Chapter Bks.). 96p. (J). (gr. 2-5). pap. 4.25 (978-0-06-442091-4(4) , Harper Trophy) HarperCollins Pubs.

Hobson, Sally, illus. All Aboard! 2000. 24p. (J). (978-1-86233-079-5(4) , Gullane Children's Bks.) Pinwheel.

Hockerman, Dennis, illus. The Little Seed: A Tale about Integrity. 2006. (J). (***978-1-59939-094-9(9)***) , Reader's Digest Young Families, Inc.) Reader's Digest Children's Publishing, Inc.

Hoff, Syd. Oliver. Hoff, Syd, illus. 2002. (Illus.). (J). 12.34 (978-0-7587-4575-0(3)) Book Wholesalers, Inc.

—Oliver. 2000. (I Can Read Bks.). (978-0-606-18709-1(X)); lib. bdg. 11.80 (978-0-613-28307-6(4)) Tandem Library Bks.

—Oliver! Hoff, Syd, illus. 2002. (Illus.). pap. 18.95 incl. audio compact disk (978-1-59112-660-7(6)); pap. 31.95 incl. audio compact disk (978-1-59112-661-4(4)); (J). pap. 16.95 incl. audio (978-0-87499-902-0(2)) Live Oak Media.

—Oliver. Hoff, Syd, illus. rev. ed. 2000. (I Can Read Bks.). (Illus.). 64p. (J). (gr. k-3). pap. 3.99 (978-0-06-444272-5(1) , Harper Trophy); lib. bdg. 17.89 (978-0-06-028709-2(8)); 14.95 (978-0-06-028708-5(X)) HarperCollins Pubs.

Holub, Joan. Lost & Found in Jumpstart Town. del Sur, Duendes, illus. 2000. (Jumpstart Workbooks). 32p. (J). (ps-k). pap. 3.99 (978-0-439-08789-6(9)) Scholastic, Inc.

Hood, Susan. Little Elephant's Listening Ears. 2007. 12p. (J). bds. 12.99 (978-0-7944-1230-2(0)) Reader's Digest Assn., Inc., The.

Hope, Laura Lee. The Story of a Stuffed Elephant. 2007. (ENG.). 68p. per. 87.99 (***978-1-4280-7311-1(6)***) IndyPublish.com.

Horner, William. Snyder & Baldy, Wisconsin Circus Elephants. Schneider, Claude, illus. 2001. 32p. (J). (gr. 2-4). lib. bdg. 24.95 (978-1-931765-01-5(4) , BHC503) Badger Hse., LLC.

Howard, Arthur. The Hubbub Above. 2005. (Illus.). 32p. (J). 16.00 (978-0-15-204592-0(9)) Harcourt Trade Pubs.

Hudson, Marilyn A. Elephant Hips Are Expensive! A Tale of the Sooner State. Fulco, Haley, illus. 2007. 50p. (J). per. (***978-0-9778850-2-2(X)***) Hudson House Publishing & Productions.

Hughes, Monica. More Little Mouse Deer Tales. Clemenston, John, illus. 2005. 24p. (J). lib. bdg. 22.65 (***978-1-59646-730-9(4)***) Dingles & Co.

Hurwitz, Andy Blackman. Ella Elephant Scats Like That: Baby Loves Jazz. Cunningham, Andrew, illus. 2006. 18p. (J). (ps-1). 7.99 (978-0-8431-2085-1(1) , Price Stern Sloan) Penguin Group (USA) Inc.

Huskins, Suzanne Hallier, illus. No Matter What! 2004. (J). (978-1-887905-93-0(6)) Parkway Pubs., Inc.

Intercambio Cultural. 2001. (la Orilla Del Viento Ser.).Tr. of Cultural Exchange. (SPA., Illus.). 31p. (J). (ps-ps). pap. 6.99 (978-968-16-6261-5(X) , 136) Fondo de Cultura Economica USA.

Jackson, Byron & Jackson, Kathryn. The Saggy Baggy Elephant. Tenggren, Gustaf, illus. 2007. 26p. (J). (gr. k-ps). bds. 4.99 (978-0-375-83926-9(7) , Golden Bks.) Random Hse. Children's Bks.

Jackson, Kathryn & Jackson, B. The Saggy Baggy Elephant. Tenggren, Gustaf, illus. deluxe ed. Date not set. (J). (ps-2). reprint ed. (978-1-929566-60-0(3)) Cronies.

—The Saggy Baggy Elephant: Classic Edition. Tenggren, Gustaf, illus. Date not set. 23p. (J). (ps-1). (978-1-929566-54-9(9)) Cronies.

Jackson, Kathryn & Jackson, Byron. The Saggy Baggy Elephant. Tenggren, Gustaf, illus. enl. ed. 2003. 32p. (J). (gr. k-k). 8.99 (978-0-375-82590-3(8) , Golden Bks.) Random Hse. Children's Bks.

Jaffrey, Madhur. Robi Dobi: The Marvellous Adventures of an Indian Elephant. Hall, Amanda, illus. 2001. 64p. (YA). (gr. 1 up). pap. 13.00 (978-1-86205-160-7(7) , Pavilion Bks., Ltd.) Anova Bks. GBR. *Dist:* Trafalgar Square Publishing.

Johnson, Paul Brett. The Goose Who Had Blueberry Pie. 2001. (Illus.). (J). lib. bdg. (978-0-531-33317-4(5) , Orchard Bks.) Scholastic, Inc.

—The Goose Who Went off in a Huff. Johnson, Paul Brett, illus. 2001. (Illus.). 40p. (J). (ps-1). pap. 15.95 (978-0-531-30317-7(9) , Orchard Bks.) Scholastic, Inc.

Jomo & Mata: Evaluation Guide. 2006. (J). (978-1-55942-411-0(7)) Marsh Media.

Jumbo 3. 2004. (J). per. (978-1-57657-008-1(8)) Paradise Pr., Inc.

Jumbo 4. 2004. (J). per. (978-1-57657-009-8(6)) Paradise Pr., Inc.

Kaska, Keiko. Cuando el Elefante Camina. 2001. (SPA.). (J). (ps-3). pap. 7.95 (978-958-04-1425-4(4) , NR6444) Norma S.A. COL. *Dist:* Distribuidora Norma, Inc., Lectorum Pubns., Inc.

Kasza, Keiko. The Mightiest. 2003. (Picture Puffin Ser.). (Illus.). 32p. (J). pap. 5.99 (978-0-14-250185-6(9) , Puffin) Penguin Group (USA) Inc.

—The Mightiest. Kasza, Keiko, illus. 2001. (Illus.). 32p. (J). 16.99 (978-0-399-23586-3(8) , Putnam Juvenile) Penguin Group (USA) Inc.

—Mightiest. 2003. (ps-2). lib. bdg. 14.15 (978-0-613-89797-6(8)) Tandem Library Bks.

—When the Elephant Walks. Kasza, Keiko, illus. 2002. (Illus.). (J). 14.04 (978-0-7587-4946-8(5)) Book Wholesalers, Inc.

—When the Elephant Walks. Kasza, Keiko, illus. 2004. (Illus.). 30p. (J). (ps-1). bds. 6.99 (978-0-399-24261-8(9) , Putnam Juvenile) Penguin Group (USA) Inc.

Kavanagh, Peter. I Love My Mama. Chapman, Jane, illus. 2003. 32p. (J). (ps-1). 14.99 (978-0-689-85691-4(1)) Simon & Schuster Children's Publishing.

—I Love My Mama. Chapman, Jane, tr. Chapman, Jane, illus. 2003. 32p. (J). 12.95 (978-1-85430-806-1(8) , Simon & Schuster Children's Publishing) Simon & Schuster Children's Publishing.

Kehret, Peg. Saving Lilly. 160p. (J). 2002. pap. 4.99 (978-0-671-03423-8(5) , Aladdin); 2001. (gr. 3-6). 16.95 (978-0-671-03422-1(7)) Simon & Schuster Children's Publishing.

—Saving Lilly. 2002. (gr. 3-6). lib. bdg. 13.00 (978-0-613-64783-0(1)) Tandem Library Bks.

Keller, John E. The Emperor's Elephant. 2006. 127p. (YA). per. 12.95 (978-0-942566-45-1(9)) LinguaText, Ltd.

Kilaka, John. True Friends: A Tale from Tanzania. 2006. (Illus.). 32p. (J). 16.95 (978-0-88899-698-5(5)) Groundwood Bks. CAN. *Dist:* Perseus Distribution.

Kipling, Rudyard. The Elephant's Child. 1999. (Illus.). 36p. (J). (ps-5). 7.99 (978-0-85953-674-5(2)) Child's Play-International.

—The Elephant's Child. Mogensen, Jan, illus. 2000. 48p. (J). (ps-3). pap. 6.95 (978-0-940793-77-4(6) , Crocodile Bks.) Interlink Publishing Group, Inc.

—The Elephant's Child. Patterson, Geoffrey, illus. 2006. 36p. (J). (ps-2). 16.95 (978-1-84507-068-7(2)) Lincoln, Frances Ltd. GBR. *Dist:* Perseus Distribution.

—The Elephant's Child: From the Just So Stories. Raglin, Tim, illus. 2006. (J). (gr. 2-6). 25.65 (978-1-59679-343-9(0)) Spotlight.

—El Hijo del Elefante. Mogensen, Jan, illus. (Barril Sin Fondo Ser.).Tr. of Elephant's Child. (SPA.). (J). (gr. 3-5). pap. 8.76 (978-968-6465-06-8(5)) Casa de Estudios de Literatura y Talleres Artisticos Amaquemecan A.C. MEX. *Dist:* Lectorum Pubns., Inc.

Kitamura, Satoshi. Pablo the Artist. 2006. (Illus.). 32p. (J). 16.00 (978-0-374-35687-3(4)) Macmillan.

Kompelien, Tracy. Elephant Trunks. Nobens, C. A., illus. 2006. (Fact & Fiction Ser.). 24p. (J). 21.35 (978-1-59679-935-6(8) , SandCastle); pap. (978-1-59679-936-3(6)) ABDO Publishing Co.

Laiz, Jana. Elephants of the Tsunami. Cafiero, Tara, illus. 2005. (J). 10.00 (978-0-9771818-3-4(9)) EarthBound Bks.

Langton, Jane. The Mysterious Circus. 2005. (Hall Family Chronicles). 224p. (J). lib. bdg. 16.89 (978-0-06-009487-4(7)) HarperCollins Pubs.

Law, Felicia. Rumble Meets Eli Elephant. 2005. (Read-It! Readers Ser.). (Illus.). 32p. (J). (ps-k). lib. bdg. 18.60 (978-1-4048-1332-8(2)) Picture Window Bks.

—Rumble Meets Harry Hippo. Pak, Yoon Mi, illus. 2006. (Read-It! Readers Ser.). 32p. (J). (gr. 2-4). 18.60 (978-1-4048-1338-0(1)) Picture Window Bks.

Laxman, Kamala. The Thama Stories. Laxman, R. K., illus. 120p. (J). pap. (978-0-14-037812-2(X) , Puffin) Penguin Group (USA) Inc.

Layton, Neal. Oscar & Arabella. (Illus.). 32p. (J). (ps-k). 2003. 15.99 (978-0-340-79719-8(3)); 2002. mass mkt. 9.99 (978-0-340-79720-4(7)) Hodder General Publishing Division GBR. (Hodder & Stoughton). *Dist:* Trafalgar Square Publishing.

Lee, P. Janet. Ella Elephant: And Her Fear of Mice. 2007. (ENG., Illus.). 36p. (J). per. 15.95 (***978-1-59800-713-8(0)***) Outskirts Press, Inc.

The Legend of the Great Salt Mountain. 2005. (J). pap. (978-0-9771804-1-7(7)) Terra Tales.

Lester, Helen. Hurty Feelings. Munsinger, Lynn M., illus. 32p. (J). (gr. k-3). 2007. 6.95 (***978-0-618-84062-5(1)***); 2004. tchr. ed. 16.00 (978-0-618-41082-8(1)) Houghton Mifflin Co. Trade & Reference Div. (Walter Lorraine).

Lewis, Kim. Good Night Harry. Lewis, Kim, illus. 2004. (Illus.). 32p. (J). (ps-1). 15.99 (978-0-7636-2206-0(0)) Candlewick Pr.

—Here We Go, Harry. Lewis, Kim, illus. 2005. (Illus.). 32p. (J). (ps-1). 15.99 (978-0-7636-2549-8(3)) Candlewick Pr.

Lewis, Kim. Hooray for Harry. Lewis, Kim, illus. 2006. (Illus.). 32p. (J). (ps-1). 15.99 (978-0-7636-2962-5(6)) Candlewick Pr.

—Hooray for Harry. 2006. (Illus.). (J). (***978-1-4156-7111-5(7)***) Candlewick Pr.

Lincoln, Hazel. Little Elephant's Trunk. Lincoln, Hazel, illus. 2006. (Illus.). 32p. (J). 15.95 (978-0-8075-4591-1(0)) Whitman, Albert & Co.

Lindahl, Inger. Bertil & the Bathroom Elephants. Dysseg-aard, Elisabeth Kallick, tr. Lindstrom, Eva, illus. 2003. 28p. (J). 15.00 (978-91-29-65944-3(2)) R & S Bks. SWE. *Dist:* Macmillan.

Little Elephant's Journey. 2002. (Animal's Around the World Mini Bks.). (Illus.). 32p. (J). (978-1-59069-168-7(7) , H4004) Studio Mouse LLC.

Little Golden Books Staff. Dumbo. 1998. (J). (ps-2). bds. 2.99 (978-0-307-01040-7(6) , Golden Bks.) Random Hse. Children's Bks.

Lobel, Arnold. Uncle Elephant (Tio Elefante) (SPA.). 68p. (J). 9.95 (978-84-204-3716-3(6)) Santillana USA Publishing Co., Inc.

Long, Olivia. The Elephant Who Forgot. Long, Olivia, illus. Date not set. (Kaleidoscope Ser.). (Illus.). 32p. (J). (ps-4). (978-1-880042-05-2(3)) Shelf-Life Bks.

Louthain, J. A. Ame the Elephant: Terrorized by Evil Mice. Eberbach, Andrea, illus. 2nd l.t. ed. 2003. 48p. (J). 12.97 (978-0-9679416-2-2(8) , 0-9679416-2-8) Alexie Bks.

Ludwig, Charles. Rogue Elephant & Man-Eaters Don't Laugh. 2000. 164p. (YA). (gr. 5-8). reprint ed. pap. 7.95 (978-0-9673806-1-2(8)) King's Bookshelf Pubns.

MacDonald, Suse. Elephants on Board. 1999. (Illus.). 32p. (J). (ps-1). 14.00 (978-0-15-200951-9(5) , Gulliver Bks.) Harcourt Children's Bks.

MacMillan, Ian C. Khala Maninge - the Little Elephant That Cried a Lot: An African Fable. MacMillan, Eric G., illus. 2nd ed. 2003. lib. bdg. 5.00 (978-0-9729698-0-2(2)) Maninge Mali.

Magoon, Scott. Hugo & Miles In: I've Painted Everything! 2007. (Illus.). (J). (***978-1-4287-3565-1(8)***) Houghton Mifflin Co.

Magoon, Scott. Hugo & Miles in I've Painted Everything! 2007. (Illus.). 40p. (J). (gr. 3-5). 16.00 (978-0-618-64638-8(1)) Houghton Mifflin Co.

Malone, Geoffrey. Elephant Ben. 2nd ed. 2002. 160p. (J). pap. (978-0-340-86059-5(6) , Hodder & Stoughton) Hodder General Publishing Division.

Martin, John, ed. The Elephant in My Tree. Lyons, Matthew, illus. 2002. 24p. (J). pap. 7.99 (978-0-9719054-0-5(1) , E-022478) Buzzy's Bks.

Mary, Nanette. Ashby, the Happy Little Elephant. 2007. (Illus.). 40p. (J). per. 12.95 (***978-0-9787112-7-6(0)***) , 01002) New World Publishing.

McDonnell, Flora. Splash! 2003. (Illus.). 26p. (J). (gr. k-k). bds. 6.99 (978-0-7636-2035-6(1)) Candlewick Pr.

—Splash! 2004. (TAM, VIE, SPA, GUJ & PER., Illus.). 25p. (J). (978-1-85269-487-6(4)); (978-1-85269-488-3(2)); (978-1-85269-489-0(0)); (978-1-85269-492-0(0)); (978-1-85269-486-9(6)) Mantra Publishing, Ltd.

—Splash. 2004. (Illus.). (J). (TAM, VIE, SPA, GUJ & PER.). 28p. (978-1-85269-490-6(4)); (TAM, VIE, SPA, GUJ & PER., 28p. (978-1-85269-491-3(2)); (TAM, VIE, SPA, GUJ & PER., 28p. (978-1-85269-493-7(9)); (TAM, VIE, SPA, GUJ & PER., 28p. (978-1-85269-496-8(3)); (TAM, VIE, SPA, GUJ & PER., 28p. (978-1-85269-497-5(1)); (TAM, VIE, SPA, GUJ & PER., 28p. (978-1-85269-498-2(X)); (TAM, VIE, SPA, GUJ & PER., 28p. (978-1-85269-499-9(8)); (TAM, VIE, SPA, GUJ & PER., 28p. (978-1-85269-544-6(7)); (TAM, VIE, SPA, GUJ & PER., 28p. (978-1-85269-545-3(5)); (TAM, SPA, VIE, GUJ & PER., 28p. (978-1-85269-546-0(3)); (KOR & ENG., (978-1-85269-547-7(1)) Mantra Publishing, Ltd.

—Splash. 2004. (TAM, VIE, SPA, GUJ & PER., Illus.). 28p. (J). 13.50 (978-1-85269-494-4(7)); 13.50 (978-1-85269-495-1(5)) Mantra Publishing, Ltd. GBR. *Dist:* AIMS International Bks., Inc.

McDonnell, Flora & Habashi, Azza. Splash. 2004. (TAM, VIE, SPA, GUJ & PER., Illus.). 28p. (J). 13.50 (978-1-85269-485-2(8)) Mantra Publishing, Ltd. GBR. *Dist:* AIMS International Bks., Inc.

McGrory, Anik. Kidogo. 2005. (Illus.). 32p. (J). 15.95 (978-1-58234-974-9(6)) Bloomsbury Publishing.

McKee, David. Los Colores de Elmer. 2001. (Coleccion "Elmer" Ser.). (SPA.). (J). (978-968-16-6065-9(X)) Fondo de Cultura Economica MEX. *Dist:* Lectorum Pubns., Inc.

—El Dia de Elmer. 2000. (Adventures of Elmer the Patchwork Elephant Ser.). (SPA., Illus.). 14p. (J). 9.95 (978-84-207-8099-3(5)) Grupo Anaya, S.A. ESP. *Dist:* Distribooks, Inc.

—Elmer & Snake. 2004. (Illus.). 32p. (978-1-84270-303-8(X)) Andersen.

—Elmer & the Kangaroo. McKee, David, illus. 2000. (Elmer Bks.). (Illus.). 32p. (J). (ps up). 15.99 (978-0-688-17951-9(7)) HarperCollins Pubs.

—Elmer & the Lost Teddy. McKee, David, illus. (Elmer Bks.). 32p. (J). 2004. 9.99 (978-0-06-075243-9(2)); 1999. (Illus.). 15.99 (978-0-688-16912-1(0)) HarperCollins Pubs.

—Elmer & Wilbur. McKee, David, illus. 2004. (Elmer Bks.). 32p. (J). 9.99 (978-0-06-075239-2(4)) HarperCollins Pubs.

—Elmer et le Vent. 2000. (Adventures of Elmer the Patchwork Elephant Ser.).Tr. of Elmer & the Wind. (FRE.). (J). pap. 12.95 (978-2-211-05286-3(X)) Archimede Editions FRA. *Dist:* Distribooks, Inc.

—Elmer First Colouring Activity Book. 2006. 32p. (J). pap., act. bk. ed. 6.99 (978-1-84270-536-0(9)) Andersen GBR. *Dist:* Trafalgar Square Publishing.

—Elmer in the Snow. McKee, David, illus. 2004. (Elmer Bks.). (Illus.). 32p. (J). 9.99 (978-0-06-075240-8(8)) HarperCollins Pubs.

—Elmer Miniature. ed. 2004. (Illus.). 32p. (J). (978-1-84270-345-8(5)) Andersen GBR. *Dist:* Random Hse. of Canada, Ltd.

—Elmer sous la Neige. 2000. (Adventures of Elmer the Patchwork Elephant Ser.).Tr. of Elmer under the Snow. (FRE.). (J). pap. 12.95 (978-2-211-05262-7(2)) Archimede Editions FRA. *Dist:* Distribooks, Inc.

—Elmer Takes Off. McKee, David, illus. 2004. (Elmer Bks.). 32p. (J). 9.99 (978-0-06-075241-5(6)) HarperCollins Pubs.

—Elmer y el Tiempo. 2000. (Adventures of Elmer the Patchwork Elephant Ser.). (SPA., Illus.). 14p. (J). 9.95 (978-84-207-8101-3(0)) Grupo Anaya, S.A. ESP. *Dist:* Distribooks, Inc.

—Elmer's Baby Record Book. 2007. (Illus.). 32p. (J). 15.99 (***978-1-84270-534-6(2)***) Andersen GBR. *Dist:* Independent Pubs. Group.

—Elmer's Colours. 2004. (Elmer Ser.). (ENG & SOM., Illus.). 16p. (J). bds. 6.95 (978-1-84059-397-6(0)) Milet Publishing.

—Elmer's Day. 2004. (Elmer Ser.). (ENG & SOM., Illus.). 16p. (J). bds. 6.95 (978-1-84059-400-3(4)) Milet Publishing.

McKee, David. Tusk Tusk. 2007. (Illus.). 32p. (J). pap. 7.95 (***978-1-84270-579-7(2)***) Andersen GBR. *Dist:* Independent Pubs. Group.

McKinlay, Penny. Elephants Don't Do Ballet. (Illus.). 25p. (J). pap. (978-0-7112-1130-8(2)) Lincoln, Frances Ltd. GBR. *Dist:* Transition Vendor.

McPherson, Missie & O'Neill, Elizabeth. Alfred Visits Alaska. 2006. (Illus.). 24p. (J). pap. 12.00 (978-0-9771836-3-0(7)) Funny Bone Bks.

—Alfred Visits Washington D. C. 2006. 24p. (J). pap. 12.00 (978-0-9771836-1-6(0)) Funny Bone Bks.

MegRyan. A Hat for Markie. 2004. 45p. pap. 19.95 (978-1-4137-2027-3(7)) PublishAmerica, Inc.

Melmed, Laura Krauss. Jumbo's Lullaby. Sorensen, Henri, illus. 1999. 24p. (J). (ps-k). lib. bdg. 15.89 (978-0-688-16996-1(1)) HarperCollins Pubs.

Mills, Joyce C. & Crowley, Richard J. Sammy the Elephant & Mr. Camel: A Story to Help Children Overcome Bedwetting. Pillo, Cary, illus. 2nd ed. 2005. 32p. (J). 14.95 (978-1-59147-247-6(4)); pap. 8.95 (978-1-59147-248-3(2)) American Psychological Assn. (Magination Pr.).

Mohorkar, Anupama. Wild Elephant at Camp. 2005. (Illus.). 48p. pap. 8.95 (978-81-86211-73-1(X)) Tara Publishing IND. *Dist:* Consortium Bk. Sales & Distribution.

Montardre, Helene. Elephant & Mouse. 2004. (Turn & Learn Ser.). (Illus.). 8p. (J). (ps up). bds. 7.95 (978-1-58728-482-3(0) , Two Can Publishing) T&N Children's Publishing.

Moonbeam: The Little Elephant. 2005. (Illus.). 32p. (J). 16.95 (978-0-9763596-0-9(X)) Dream Pubns., I, Inc.

Morris, April. Eldon the Elephant. 2004. (J). lib. bdg. 25.95 (978-1-893595-49-1(8)) Four Seasons Bks., Inc.

Mouse Works Staff. Dumbo. 2000. (Read-Aloud Storybook Ser.). 64p. (J). 6.99 (978-0-7364-1052-6(X)) Hyperion Bks. for Children.

—Dumbo. 1999. (Disney's Friendly Tales Ser.). (Illus.). 10p. (J). (ps-k). 6.99 (978-0-7364-1012-0(0)) Mouse Works.

—Dumbo Classic Storybook. rev. ed. 1998. 96p. (J). 7.99 (978-0-7364-0022-0(2)) Mouse Works.

Mueller, Doris. Small One's Adventure. Guevara, Linda L., ed. Fulton, Parker, illus. 2004. 32p. (J). (gr. k-5). 16.95 (978-0-9710278-1-7(1)) All About Kids Publishing.

Mukluks for Annabelle. 2005. 14.95 (978-0-9673915-0-2(4)) Alaska Zoo, The.

Murphy, Jill. Mr. Large in Charge. Murphy, Jill, illus. 2007. (Illus.). 40p. (J). (ps-2). 16.99 (978-0-7636-3504-6(9)); pap. 6.99 (978-0-7636-2739-3(9)) Candlewick Pr.

Nelson Gets a Fright: Individual Title Six-Packs. 16p. (gr. 2 up). 35.00 (978-0-7635-9227-1(7)) Rigby Education.

Nelson Is Kidnapped: Individual Title Six-Packs. (gr. 3 up). 35.00 (978-0-7635-9657-6(4)) Rigby Education.

New Pet. l.t. ed. 2005. (Illus.). 32p. (J). lib. bdg. 14.95 (978-0-9658365-8-6(4)) Beetle Bug Bks.

O Neil, Elizabeth. Alfred Visits Tennessee. 2006. 24p. pap. 12.00 (978-0-9771836-5-4(3)) Funny Bone Bks.

Oneil, Elizabeth. Alfred Visits Massachusetts. 2006. 24p. (J). pap. 12.00 (***978-0-9771836-7-8(X)***) Funny Bone Bks.

Oneill, Elizabeth. Alfred Visits Arizona. 2006. 24p. pap. 12.00 (***978-0-9790240-0-9(5)***) Funny Bone Bks.

Oneill, Elizabeth. Alfred Visits Michigan. 2006. 24p. pap. 12.00 (978-0-9771836-6-1(1)) Funny Bone Bks.

O'Neill, Elizabeth. Alfred Visits Ohio. 2005. 26p. per. 12.50 (978-1-59453-408-9(X) , 2442) Airleaf Publishing & Bookselling.

Oneill, Elizabeth. Alfred Visits Ohio. 2006. 24p. pap. 12.00 (978-0-9771836-4-7(5)) Funny Bone Bks.

Ormerod, Jan. When an Elephant Comes to School. Ormerod, Jan, illus. 2005. (Illus.). 32p. (J). pap. 16.95 (978-0-439-73967-2(5) , Orchard Bks.) Scholastic, Inc.

Paterson, Andrew Barton 'Banjo'. Three Elephant Power & Other Stories. 2004. reprint ed. pap. 15.95 (978-1-4191-8979-1(4)); pap. 1.99 (978-1-4192-8979-8(9)) Kessinger Publishing, LLC.

Patz, Nancy. Pumpernickel Tickle & Mean Green Cheese. Patz, Nancy, photos by. 2000. (Illus.). 40p. (J). reprint ed. 16.95 (978-1-893116-17-7(4)) Baltimore Sun, The.

Pavlova, Elena. Adventures at Tall Oaks: New Friends. 2004. (Illus.). 80p. (J). 19.95 (978-0-9755839-0-6(5)) Read 2 Children.

Perera, Hilda. Mumu. (SPA.). (YA). (gr. 5-8). 128p. 8.95 (978-84-216-1207-1(7) , BU3780); 100p. (978-84-216-2557-6(8) , BU1696); 64p. 8.76 (978-84-216-1611-6(0) , BU4757) Bruño, Editorial ESP. *Dist:* Lectorum Pubns., Inc.

Phillippe, Esther. The Ants Will Carry the Elephant. 2000. (Illus.). 24p. (J). (gr. 1-3). pap. 3.99 (978-0-89827-211-6(4)) Wesleyan Publishing Hse.

Platt, Kin. Big Max & the Mystery of the Missing Giraffe. Cravath, Lynne, illus. 2006. (I Can Read Bks.). 64p. (J). pap. 3.99 (978-0-06-009920-6(8) , Harper Trophy) HarperCollins Pubs.

Polacco, Patricia. Emma Kate. Polacco, Patricia, illus. 2005. (Illus.). 40p. (J). (ps-1). 16.99 (978-0-399-24452-0(2) , Philomel) Penguin Group (USA) Inc.

Porque los elefantes tienen narices Largas: Individual Title Six-Packs. (Literatura 2000 Ser.). (SPA.). (gr. 1-2). 28.00 (978-0-7635-1073-2(4)) Rigby Education.

Preller, James. Elefante Tiene Hipo. 1999. Tr. of Hiccups for Elephant. (SPA.). (gr. k-3). lib. bdg. 11.80 (978-0-613-81949-7(7)) Tandem Library Bks.

—Hiccups for Elephants. Wilheml, Hans, illus. 2004. 32p. (J). lib. bdg. 15.00 (978-1-59054-396-2(3)) Fitzgerald Bks.

Price, Reynolds. A Perfect Friend. 2002. 176p. pap. 11.00 (978-0-7432-2521-2(X) , Scribner) Simon & Schuster.

—Perfect Friend. 2002. (gr. 3-6). lib. bdg. 19.95 (978-0-613-90179-6(7)) Tandem Library Bks.

—A Perfect Friend. l.t. ed. 2001. 150p. (J). (gr. 4-7). 21.95 (978-0-7862-3589-6(6)) Thorndike Pr.

Prince, April Jones. Twenty-One Elephants & Still Standing. Roca, Francois, illus. 2005. 32p. (J). (gr. k-3). 16.00 (978-0-618-44887-6(X)) Houghton Mifflin Co. Trade & Reference Div.

Pullman, Philip. The Firework-Maker's Daughter. 1999. 120p. (J). 16.95 (978-0-7540-6055-0(1) , Galaxy Children's Large Print) BBC Audiobooks America.

—The Firework-Maker's Daughter. Gallagher, Susan Saelig, illus. 1999. (J). pap. (978-0-590-12943-5(0) , Levine, Arthur A. Bks.) Scholastic, Inc.

—The Firework-Maker's Daughter. 2001. 11.64 (978-0-606-21186-4(1)) Tandem Library Bks.

Radunsky, Vladimir. I Love You Dude. 2005. (Illus.). 48p. (J). (gr. 2-5). 16.00 (978-0-15-205176-1(7) , Gulliver Bks.) Harcourt Children's Bks.

Rae, Nan, illus. Suma the Elephant. 2006. 80p. 18.00 (978-0-9762544-0-9(9)) Garden Fleetfoot Pr.

Randall, Ronne. A Hose of a Nose! Church, Caroline Jayne, illus. 2002. (Little Friends Ser.). 14p. (J). (ps-1). 12.95 (978-1-57145-773-8(9) , Silver Dolphin Bks.) Advantage Pubs. Group.

Random House Disney Staff. Dumbo. Disney Storybook Artists Staff, illus. 2004. (Little Golden Book Ser.). 24p. (J). (gr. k-k). 2.99 (978-0-7364-2309-0(5) , Golden/ Disney) Random Hse. Children's Bks.

Ravishankar, Anushka. Elephants Never Forget HC. Pieper, Christiane, illus. 2008. 48p. (J). (ps-3). 16.00 (***978-0-618-99784-8(9)***) Houghton Mifflin Co. Trade & Reference Div.

Rigby Education Staff. The Egg Saga. (Sails Literacy Ser.). (Illus.). 16p. (gr. 2-3). 27.00 (978-0-7635-9935-5(2) , 699352C99) Rigby Education.

—House for Mouse. (Sails Literacy Ser.). (Illus.). 16p. (gr. 1-2). 27.00 (978-0-7635-9893-8(3)) Rigby Education.

Rivers, Freya A. Easy Elephant. Brooks, Julian A. & Rivers, Shariba W., eds. Moore, La Mailede, illus. 2001. 41p. (J). (ps-2). pap. 20.00 (978-0-9667215-7-7(8)) Sankofa Publishing Co.

Rodda, Emily. Where Do You Hide Two Elephants? McLean, Andrew, illus. 2001. 32p. (J). (ps up). lib. bdg. 24.67 (978-0-8368-2898-6(4)) Stevens, Gareth Inc.

Rolt-Wheeler, Francis. TuskHunters. 2006. pap. 31.95 (***978-1-4286-5352-8(X)***) Kessinger Publishing, LLC.

Roome, Diana Reynolds & Daly, Jude. The Elephant's Pillow. 2007. (Illus.). 32p. pap. 7.95 (***978-1-84507-798-3(9)***) Lincoln, Frances Ltd. GBR. *Dist:* Perseus Distribution.

Rucker, Mike. Terry & the Elephant. pap. (978-1-56002-746-1(0)) Univ. Editions.

Safari Press Staff, ed. Book Buddy - Elephant with Story Book. (Illus.). 10p. (J). (ps-3). pap. (978-1-881469-83-4(2)) Safari, Ltd.

Salerno, Steven. Little Tumbo. 2003. (Illus.). 32p. (J). 14.95 (978-0-7614-5136-5(6)) Cavendish, Marshall Corp.

Sargent, Dave & Sargent, Pat. Ellie Elephant: Grudge, 56 vols., 45. Lenoir, Jane, illus. 2001. (Animal Pride Ser.: Vol. 45). 36p. (J). lib. bdg. 19.95 (978-1-56763-531-7(8)) Ozark Publishing.

Sargent, Dave, et al. Ellie Elephant: Grudge, 17 bks, 45. 2000. (Animal Pride Ser.: 45). (Illus.). 42p. (J). pap. 6.95 (978-1-56763-532-4(6)) Ozark Publishing.

Sattler, Jennifer Gordon. Bella's Saratoga Summer. 2002. (Illus.). (J). (978-0-9713069-4-3(X)); 32p. pap. 10.95 (978-0-9713069-3-6(1)) Burns, Nicholas K. Publishing.

Scheer, Ruth D. Elephant's Trunk. 2001. (Grandmother Ruth Stories Ser.: 3). (J). per. 15.95 (978-0-9671761-2-3(3)) Scheer Delight Publishing.

Schwartz, Amy & Dorling Kindersley Publishing Staff. How to Catch an Elephant. 2001. (Illus.). 40p. (J). (ps-1). pap. 6.95 (978-0-7894-8185-6(5)) Dorling Kindersley Publishing, Inc.

Schwartz, Corey Rosen & Klein, Tali. Hop! Plop! Dunrea, Olivier, illus. 2006. 32p. (J). 16.85 (978-0-8027-8057-7(1)); 15.95 (978-0-8027-8056-0(3)) Walker & Co.

Sefton, Catherine. First Young Puffin Pocket Elephant. (Illus.). 32p. (J). pap. 7.95 (978-0-14-038614-1(9)) Penguin Bks., Ltd. GBR. *Dist:* Trafalgar Square Publishing.

—Pocket Elephant. (Illus.). 32p. (J). 13.95 (978-0-241-00197-4(8) , Hamilton, Hamish) Penguin Bks., Ltd. GBR. *Dist:* Trafalgar Square Publishing.

Seuss, Dr. Tonho Choca o Ovo. pap. 23.95 (978-85-7406-098-9(4)) Schwarcz, Editora Ltda, Companhia das Letrinhas BRA. *Dist:* Distribooks, Inc.

Sexton, Brenda. Elephants in the Bathtub & Other Silly Riddles. Mills, Liz, ed. 2006. (Illus.). 12p. (J). pap. 5.99 (978-0-439-82312-8(9) , Cartwheel Bks.) Scholastic, Inc.

Shaky Elephant. alt. ed. 2002. (J). (978-1-931312-96-7(6)) SoftPlay, Inc.

Siete Ratones Ciegos. 1999. (SPA.). (J). mass mkt. 4.95 (978-0-590-48525-8(3) , SO5874) Scholastic, Inc.

Silver Dolphin en Español Editors. Caritas felices: Dumbo: Happy Faces: Dumbo, Spanish-Language Edition. 2007. (Illus.). 8p. (J). bds. 7.95 (***978-970-718-394-0(2)*** , Silver Dolphin en Español) Advanced Marketing, S. de R. L. de C. V. MEX. *Dist:* Perseus Distribution.

Smith, Alexander McCall. Akimbo & the Elephants. Pham, LeUyen, illus. 2007. (Akimbo Ser.). 80p. (J). (gr. 2-4). pap. 4.95 (978-1-59990-031-5(9) , Bloomsbury Children) Bloomsbury Publishing.

—Akimbo & the Elephants. Pham, LeUyen, illus. 2005. 80p. (J). (ps-7). 9.95 (978-1-58234-686-1(0)) Bloomsbury Publishing.

Smith, Nicole. Allie the Allergic Elephant: A Children's Story of Peanut Allergies. 2006. (J). 14.95 (978-1-58628-053-6(8)) Allergic Child Publishing Group.

Smith, Roland. Elephant Run. rev. ed. 2007. 336p. (gr. 3-7). 15.99 (***978-1-4231-0402-5(1)***) Hyperion Pr.

Soundprints. Pat-a-Cake: And Othe Favorites. 2005. (Meet Mother Goose Ser.). (Illus.). 36p. (J). bds. 14.95 incl. audio compact disk (978-1-931465-48-9(7) , MPD1104) Soundprints.

—Pat-a-Cake: And Other Favorites. 2005. (Meet Mother Goose Ser.). (Illus.). 36p. (J). bds. 10.95 incl. audio compact disk (978-1-931465-28-1(2) , MD1104) Soundprints.

Sparks, David. Marvin & Bailey's Junkyard Performance. 2004. (Illus.). 32p. (J). spiral bd. 19.95 (978-1-932373-61-5(6) , Cedar Hill Pr.) Cedar Hill Publishing.

Spooner, Joe. The Elephant Walk. Spooner, Joe, illus. 2004. (Illus.). (J). pap. 14.95 (978-0-9745686-3-8(5)) Arnica Publishing, Inc.

Stadler, John. Big & Little. 2007. (Illus.). 32p. (J). (ps-1). 9.99 (978-0-375-84175-0(X) , Robin Corey Bks.) Random Hse. Children's Bks.

Stamatis, Alexis. The Seventh Elephant. Connolly, David, tr. 2000. (Illus.). 208p. pap. 13.95 (978-1-900850-21-6(4)) Arcadia Bks. Ltd. GBR. *Dist:* Independent Pubs. Group.

Steck-Vaughn Staff. How the Elephant Got His Trunk Level B: Early Reader. 2003. (Illus.). pap. (978-0-7398-8222-1(8)) Steck-Vaughn.

Stevenson, Linda Walton. The Baby Elephant's Painted Face. Julich, Jennifer, illus. 2001. 16p. (J). (gr. k-3). 12.95 (978-0-9748725-0-6(4)) Bubbi's Touch Pr.

Sykes, Julie. Rainy Day Adventure. 2001. (gr. k-3). lib. bdg. 11.25 (978-0-613-53545-8(6)) Tandem Library Bks.

Tantor Friendly Tales. 1999. 10p. (J). 6.99 (978-0-7364-0189-0(X)) Mouse Works.

Tibo, Gilles. Forrest & Freddy the Elephant. Fanny, illus. 2005. (Read-It! Readers Ser.). 32p. (J). (gr. k-3). 18.60 (978-1-4048-1078-5(1)) Picture Window Bks.

Trease, Christine K. The Greedy Little Elephant. 1999. 30p. (J). (ps-7). cd-rom 14.95 (978-1-929450-07-7(9)) Lexico.

—The Greedy Little Elephant. Trease, Christine K., illus. 1999. (Illus.). 30p. (J). (ps-7). 14.95 (978-1-929450-06-0(0)) Lexico.

Tres Elefantes: Big Book. (Pebble Soup Exploraciones Ser.). (SPA.). 16p. (ps up). 31.00 (978-0-7578-1676-5(2)) Rigby Education.

Tres Elefantes: Small Book. (Pebble Soup Exploraciones Ser.). (SPA.). 16p. (ps up). 5.00 (978-0-7578-1716-8(5)) Rigby Education.

Tresh, Doreene. Elephants, Aren't They Great? 2003. (Illus.). 28p. (J). per. 9.95 (978-1-59405-028-2(7)) New Age World Publishing.

Turin, Adela. Rosa Caramelo. Bosnia, Nella, illus. (SPA.). 40p. (J). (gr. 2-4). (978-84-264-3800-3(8)) Editorial Lumen ESP. *Dist:* Lectorum Pubns., Inc.

Two Baby Elephants: Individual Title Six-Pack Pouch - Level J. (Lighthouse Ser.). 16p. (gr. 2 up). 28.00 (978-0-7578-0866-1(2)) Rigby Education.

Van Fleet, Mara. Mama Loves Me. Gévry, Claudine, illus. 2005. 12p. (J). bds. 12.99 (978-0-7944-0762-9(5)) Reader's Digest Assn., Inc., The.

Van Straaten, Harmen. Little trunk Late. 2008. 32p. 12.95 (***978-1-60136-004-5(5)***) Mars Media Pubs.

Velthuijs, Max. Crocodile's Masterpiece. 2001. (Illus.). 32p. pap. 9.95 (978-1-84270-002-0(2)) Andersen GBR. *Dist:* Trafalgar Square Publishing.

Velvin, Ellen. Rataplan. 2004. reprint ed. pap. 20.95 (978-1-4191-4398-4(0)); pap. 1.99 (978-1-4192-4398-1(5)) Kessinger Publishing, LLC.

Vere, Ed. Everyone's Little. 2003. (Illus.). 14p. (J). bds. 6.95 (978-0-333-78039-8(6)) Macmillan Publishers Ltd. GBR. *Dist:* Trafalgar Square Publishing.

—Everyone's Little. 2001. (Illus.). 12p. (J). (ps). 6.95 (978-0-531-30336-8(5) , Orchard Bks.) Scholastic, Inc.

Vere, Ed. The Getaway. Vere, Ed, illus. 2007. 34p. (J). (gr. k-2). 16.99 (***978-1-4169-4789-9(2)*** , McElderry, Margaret K.) Simon & Schuster Children's Publishing.

Viagem de Babar. pap. 19.95 (978-85-85466-78-7(2)) Companhia das Letras BRA. *Dist:* Distribooks, Inc.

Villalobos, Ligiah. Save the Elephants. Zalme, Ronald, illus. 2007. (Go, Diego, Go! Ser.). 24p. (J). pap. 3.99 (***978-1-4169-3821-7(4)*** , Simon Spotlight) Simon & Schuster Children's Publishing.

von Konigslow, Andrea Wayne. Bing & Chutney. von Konigslow, Andrea Wayne, illus. 1999. (Bing & Chutney Adventures Ser.). (Illus.). 32p. (J). (gr. k-ps). lib. bdg. 16.95 (978-1-55037-609-8(8)) Annick Pr., Ltd. CAN. *Dist:* Firefly Bks., Ltd.

—Bing & Chutney. 1999. (ps-2). lib. bdg. 14.10 (978-0-613-53145-0(0)) Tandem Library Bks.

Walsh, Maria Elena. Dailan Kifki. Lavandeira, Sandra, illus. 2003. (SPA.). 248p. (YA). (gr. 5-8). 18.95 (978-950-511-629-4(2)) Alfaguara S.A. de Ediciones ARG. *Dist:* Santillana USA Publishing Co., Inc.

Wayne, D. 1-2-3 Chubby Little Elephants. 2001. 32p. (J). 17.00 (978-0-8059-5414-2(7)) Dorrance Publishing Co., Inc.

Weber, Lou, ed. Little People Forgetful Elephant. 2004. 10p. (J). bds. 9.98 (978-1-4127-3337-3(5) , 7246900) Publications International, Ltd.

Weiss, Ellen. Babar: Four Stories to Read & Share. Gibert, Jean Claude & Gray, J. M. L., illus. 2006. (J). (***978-0-8109-9308-2(2)*** , Abrams Bks. for Young Readers) Abrams, Harry N. , Inc.

Weiss, Ellen, et al. Babar & the Christmas House. 2003. (Illus.). 28p. (J). (ps-1). 9.95 (978-0-8109-4583-8(5) , 53604968) Abrams, Harry N. , Inc.

—Babar & the Scary Day. Gibert, Jean Claude, illus. 2004. 24p. (J). (ps-3). 9.95 (978-0-8109-5019-1(7)) Abrams, Harry N. , Inc.

Widner, Rose. Limbo & the Talking Umbrella. 1998. (Illus.). 16p. (J). (gr. k-3). pap. 6.00 (978-0-8059-4338-2(2)) Dorrance Publishing Co., Inc.

Willems, Mo. I Am Invited to a Party! An Elephant & Piggie Book. Willems, Mo, illus. rev. ed. 2007. 64p. (J). (ps-3). 8.99 (***978-1-4231-0687-6(3)***) Hyperion Pr.

—My Friend Is Sad. 2007. 64p. (ps-3). 8.99 (978-1-4231-0297-7(5)) Hyperion Bks. for Children.

—There Is a Bird on Your Head! An Elephant & Piggie Book. Willems, Mo, illus. rev. ed. 2007. 64p. (J). (ps-3). 8.99 (***978-1-4231-0686-9(5)***) Hyperion Pr.

Willems, Mo. Today I Will Fly! 2007. 64p. (ps-3). 8.99 (978-1-4231-0295-3(9)) Hyperion Bks. for Children.

Wilson-Max, Ken. Max's Starry Night. 2001. (Illus.). 32p. (ps-k). 14.99 (978-0-7868-0553-2(6) , Jump at the Sun) Hyperion Bks. for Children.

Wolf, Jake. Daddy, Could I Have an Elephant? 1998. (Picture Puffin Ser.). (J). (978-0-606-13303-6(8)) Tandem Library Bks.

Yamada, Rikako. The Unordinary Elephant. States, Anna, illus. 2005. (JPN.). 26p. (J). per. 14.99 (978-0-9761606-0-1(9)) Wonder Toash Arts Inc.

Youcha, Geraldine. How Does an Elephant Say Hello? Date not set. (J). 15.95 (978-0-8050-7197-9(0) , Holt, Henry & Co. Bks. For Young Readers) Holt, Henry & Co.

Young, Ed. Seven Blind Mice. Young, Ed, illus. 2007. pap. 18.95 incl. audio compact disk (***978-0-439-02785-4(3)***); (Illus.). pap. 14.95 incl. audio (***978-0-439-02784-7(5)***) Scholastic, Inc.

Zaretsky, Evan. Ashley's Elephant. Spurll, Barbara, illus. 2005. (J). pap. 4.95 (978-1-57874-095-6(9)) Kaeden Corp.

Ziefert, Harriet. April Fool! Demarest, Chris L., illus. 2000. (Viking Easy-to-Read Ser.). 32p. (J). (ps-2). pap. 3.99 (978-0-14-130582-0(7) , Puffin) Penguin Group (USA) Inc.

—April Fool! 2000. (ps-2). lib. bdg. 11.80 (978-0-613-24229-5(7)); (Illus.). (J). 10.79 (978-0-606-18387-1(6)) Tandem Library Bks.

Zondervan. Elephant's Big Ride. Pulley, Kelly, illus. 2006. (Beginner's Bible' Ser.). 20p. (J). 6.99 (978-0-310-71340-1(4)) Zonderkidz.

ELEVATORS

Freeman, Marcia S. Going Up? 2006. (City Science Ser.). (Illus.). 24p. (gr. k-3). 14.95 (978-1-59515-409-5(4)) Rourke Publishing, LLC.

ELGAR, EDWARD WILLIAM, SIR, 1857-1934

Porte, John F. Sir Edward Elgar. 2001. 214p. (YA). reprint ed. 98.00 (978-0-7222-5407-3(5)) Library Reprints, Inc.

ELIJAH (BIBLICAL PROPHET)

Aderman, James A. Elijah: Fiery Prophet. 2003. (God's People Ser.). pap. 6.99 (978-0-8100-1339-1(8)) Northwestern Publishing Hse.

Chronicles of Faith - Elijah. 2007. 224p. (J). pap. 4.97 (***978-1-59789-923-9(2)***) Barbour Publishing, Inc.

Colburn, Rhonda. The Story of Elijah. Harrison, Susan J., illus. 2001. (J). (ps-3). pap. 3.95 (978-0-8249-5410-9(6), Ideals Children's Bks.) Ideals Pubns.

De Graaf, Anne. Elijah. Montero, Jose Perez, illus. 2001. (Little Children's Bible Bks.: No. 21). 38p. (J). (ps-1). 5.99 (978-0-8054-2192-7(0)) B&H Publishing Grp.

Miller, Susan Martins. Elijah. 1998. (Young Reader's Christian Library). (Illus.). 224p. (J). (gr. 4-7). pap. 1.39 (978-1-55748-189-4(X)) Barbour Publishing, Inc.

PowerXpress Elijah Unit. 2005. 115.00 (978-0-687-00579-6(5)) Abingdon Pr.

ELIOT, T. S. (THOMAS STEARNS), 1888-1965

Pasachoff, Naomi E. A Student's Guide to T.S. Eliot. 2008. (***978-0-7660-2881-4(X)***) Enslow Pubs., Inc.

ELIZABETH I, QUEEN OF ENGLAND, 1533-1603

Adams, Simon. Elizabeth I: The Outcast Who Became England's Queen. 2005. (World History Biographies Ser.). (Illus.). 64p. (J). (gr. 3-7). 27.90 (978-0-7922-3654-2(8)); 17.95 (978-0-7922-3649-8(1)) National Geographic Society. (National Geographic Children's Bks.).

Ashby, Ruth. Elizabethan England. 1998. (Cultures of the Past Ser.). (Illus.). 80p. (J). (gr. 5 up). lib. bdg. 29.93 (978-0-7614-0269-5(1), Benchmark Bks.) Cavendish, Marshall Corp.

Ashworth, Leon. Queen Elizabeth I. 2002. (Illus.). 32p. (J). (gr. 4-6). (978-1-84234-071-4(9), Evans Brothers, Limited) Evans Publishing Group.

Brassey, Richard. Queen Elizabeth 1. Brassey, Richard, illus. 2005. (Brilliant Brits Ser.). (Illus.). 24p. (J). pap. 8.99 (978-1-84255-233-9(3)) Orion Children's Bks. GBR. *Dist:* Independent Pubs. Group.

Crompton, Samuel Willard. Queen Elizabeth: And England's Golden Age. 2005. (Makers of the Middle Ages & Renaissance Ser.). (Illus.). 148p. (J). (gr. 4-8). lib. bdg. 30.00 (978-0-7910-8632-2(1), Chelsea Hse.) Facts On File, Inc.

Eding, June. Who Was Queen Elizabeth? Harrison, Nancy, illus. 2008. (Who Was... ? Ser.). 112p. (J). (gr. 2-5). 4.99 (***978-0-448-44839-8(4)***, Grosset & Dunlap) Penguin Group (USA) Inc.

Greenblatt, Miriam. Elizabeth I & Tudor England. 2001. (Rulers & Their Times Ser.). (Illus.). 80p. (J). (gr. 6 up). lib. bdg. 29.93 (978-0-7614-1028-7(7), Benchmark Bks.) Cavendish, Marshall Corp.

Guy, John. Elizabeth I & the Armada. 2004. (Illus.). 32p. (J). (gr. 4-7). pap. (978-1-86007-029-7(9)) Ticktock Media Ltd.

Havelin, Kate. Queen Elizabeth I. 2002. (Biography Ser.). (Illus.). 112p. (J). (gr. 6-12). lib. bdg. 27.93 (978-0-8225-0029-2(9), Lerner Pubns.) Lerner Publishing Group.

Hinds, Kathryn. Elizabeth & Her Court. 2007. (Life in Elizabethan England Ser.). 80p. (J). lib. bdg. 32.79 (***978-0-7614-2542-7(X)***, Benchmark Bks.) Cavendish, Marshall Corp.

Holub, Joan. Elizabeth & the Royal Pony: Based on a True Story of Elizabeth I of England. Aleshina, Nonna, illus. 2007. (Young Princesses Around the World Ser.). (J). 48p. (gr. 1-3). pap. 3.99 (978-0-689-87191-7(0)); 48p. (gr. 1-3). lib. bdg. 13.89 (978-0-689-87193-1(7)); (***978-1-4287-2005-3(7)***) Simon & Schuster Children's Publishing. (Aladdin).

Hynson, Colin. Elizabeth I & the Spanish Armada. 2006. (Stories from History Ser.). 48p. (J). 14.95 (978-0-7696-4703-6(0)); pap. 6.95 (978-0-7696-4629-9(8)) School Specialty Publishing.

Lace, William W. Elizabeth I & Her Court. 2002. (Lucent Library of Historical Eras. Elizabethan England Library). (Illus.). 112p. (J). 28.70 (978-1-59018-098-3(4), Lucent Bks.) Thomson Gale.

Lasky, Kathryn. Elizabeth I: Red Rose of the House of Tudor, England 1544. 1999. (Royal Diaries Ser.). (Illus.). 240p. (J). (gr. 4-8). 10.95 (978-0-590-68484-2(1), Scholastic Pr.) Scholastic, Inc.

Pascal, Francine. Principe para Elisabeth. Orig. Title: Princess Elizabeth. (SPA.). 112p. (J). 6.95 (978-84-272-3591-5(7)) Molino, Editorial ESP. *Dist:* AIMS International Bks., Inc.

Price-Groff, Claire. Queen Elizabeth I. 2000. (Importance of Ser.). (Illus.). 112p. (J). (gr. 7-10). 28.70 (978-1-56006-700-9(4), Lucent Bks.) Thomson Gale.

Shone, Rob & Ganeri, Anita. Elizabeth I: The Life of England's Renaissance Queen. 2005. (Graphic Nonfiction Ser.). (Illus.). 48p. lib. bdg. 26.50 (978-1-4042-0246-7(3)) Rosen Publishing Group, Inc., The.

Thomas, Jane Resh. Behind the Mask: The Life of Queen Elizabeth I. 1998. (Illus.). 208p. (J). (gr. 7-9). tchr. ed. 20.00 (978-0-395-69120-5(6), Clarion Bks.) Houghton Mifflin Co. Trade & Reference Div.

Turnbull, S. Elizabeth I. (Beginners Social Studies). 32p. (J). (gr. 1 up). lib. bdg. 12.95 (978-1-58086-741-2(3), Usborne) EDC Publishing.

Turnbull, Stephanie. Elizabeth I Internet Referenced. King, Colin, illus. 2004. 32p. (J). (gr. 1 up). pap. 4.95 (978-0-7945-0808-1(1), Usborne) EDC Publishing.

Vennema, Peter & Stanley, Diane. Good Queen Bess: The Story of Elizabeth I of England. Stanley, Diane, illus. 2001. (Illus.). 40p. (J). (gr. 2 up). 16.99 (978-0-688-17961-8(4)) HarperCollins Pubs.

Weatherly, Myra. Elizabeth I: Queen of Tudor England. 2005. (Signature Lives Ser.). (Illus.). 112p. (J). (gr. 5-7). (978-0-7565-0988-0(2)) Compass Point Bks.

ELIZABETH I, QUEEN OF ENGLAND, 1533-1603—FICTION

Armson, Michelle. A Pair of Snaphaunce Locks. 2002. 114p. pap. 9.95 (978-0-595-24641-0(9), Writers Club Pr.) iUniverse, Inc.

Deary, Terry. The Actor, the Rebel, & the Wrinkled Queen. Flook, Helen, illus. 2005. (Read-It! Chapter Bks.). 64p. (J). (ps-k). lib. bdg. 19.95 (978-1-4048-1297-0(0)) Picture Window Bks.

Faulkner, Matt. The Pirate Meets the Queen: Two Women of Consequence. Faulkner, Matt, illus. 2005. (Illus.). 32p. (J). (gr. 1-5). 15.99 (978-0-399-24038-6(1), Philomel) Penguin Group (USA) Inc.

King-Smith, Dick. Titus Rules! Eastwood, John, illus. 2003. 96p. (J). (gr. 2-4). lib. bdg. 17.99 (978-0-375-91461-4(7), Knopf Bks. for Young Readers) Random Hse. Children's Bks.

Meyer, Carolyn. Beware, Princess Elizabeth. (Young Royals Ser.). 2002. (Illus.). 240p. (YA). pap. 5.95 (978-0-15-204556-2(2)); 2001. (J). 17.00 (978-0-15-202639-4(8)) Harcourt Children's Bks. (Gulliver Bks.).

Rinaldi, Ann. The Redheaded Princess. 2008. 224p. (J). 15.99 (***978-0-06-073374-2(8)***); lib. bdg. 16.89 (***978-0-06-073375-9(6)***) HarperCollins Pubs.

Scholastic, Inc. Staff. Elizabeth I: Red Rose of the House of Tudor, England 1544. 2000. (Royal Diaries Ser.). (J). lthr. 9.95 (978-0-439-26654-3(8)) Scholastic, Inc.

Stainer, M. L. The Lyon's Throne. Melvin, James, illus. 1999. (Lyon Saga Ser.: Bk. 4). 153p. (YA). (gr. 5-9). pap. 6.95 (978-1-893337-02-2(2)) Chicken Soup Pr., Inc.

Thomas, Jane Resh. The Counterfeit Princess. 2005. (J). 208p. (gr. 5-9). 15.00 (978-0-395-93870-6(8)); 197p. (978-0-618-93780-6(3)) Houghton Mifflin Co. Trade & Reference Div. (Clarion Bks.).

ELIZABETH II, QUEEN OF GREAT BRITAIN, 1926-

Barton-Wood, Sara. Queen Elizabeth II: Monarch of Our Times. 2001. (Famous Lives Ser.). (Illus.). 48p. (J). (gr. 4-6). lib. bdg. 27.12 (978-0-7398-4430-4(X)) Raintree.

Malam, John. Queen Elizabeth II. 2002. (Illus.). 22p. pap. (978-0-237-52449-4(X), Evans Brothers, Limited) Evans Publishing Group.

ELK

Goecke, Michael P. Irish Elk. 2004. (Prehistoric Animals Set II Ser.). (Illus.). 24p. (J). (gr. k-4). lib. bdg. 21.35 (978-1-57765-975-4(9)) ABDO Publishing Co.

Hodge, Deborah. Deer, Moose, Elk & Caribou. 1999. (J). 12.75 (978-0-606-19013-8(9)) Tandem Library Bks.

—Deer, moose, elk & caribou. 2004. (Kids Can Press Wildlife Ser.). (Illus.). 32p. (J). (gr. k-3). (978-1-55074-667-9(7)) Kids Can Pr., Ltd.

—Deer, moose, elk & caribou. Stephens, Pat, illus. 1998. (Kids Can Press Wildlife Ser.). 32p. (J). (gr. k-3). (978-1-55074-435-4(6)) Kids Can Pr., Ltd.

Macken, JoAnn Early. Elk. 2006. (Illus.). 24p. (J). pap. 5.95 (978-0-8368-6325-3(9)); lib. bdg. 19.33 (978-0-8368-6318-5(6)) Stevens, Gareth Inc.

—Elk: Venado. 2006. (ENG & SPA., Illus.). 24p. (J). pap. (978-0-8368-6456-4(5)); lib. bdg. 19.33 (978-0-8368-6449-6(2)) Stevens, Gareth Inc.

Wrobel, Scott. Elk. 2000. (Northern Trek Ser.). (Illus.). 24p. (J). lib. bdg. 15.95 (978-1-58340-033-3(8)) Smart Apple Media.

ELK—FICTION

Black, Debra S. Bugling the Elk. 2005. 9.00 (978-0-8059-9882-5(9)) Dorrance Publishing Co., Inc.

Sargent, Dave & Sargent, Pat. Eli the Elk: I Can! You Can't!, 6 vols., 27. Huff, Jeane, illus. 2001. (Animal Pride Ser.: Vol. 27). 36p. (J). pap. 19.95 (978-1-56763-371-9(4)) Ozark Publishing.

Steinhofel, Andreas & Jaffa, Alisa. An Elk Dropped In. Meyer, Kerstin, illus. 80p. (J). 16.95 (978-1-932425-80-2(2), Lemniscaat) Boyds Mills Pr.

ELLINGTON, DUKE, 1899-1974

Bankston, John. The Life & Times of Duke Ellington. 2004. (Masters of Music Ser.). (Illus.). 48p. (gr. 4-8). lib. bdg. 20.95 (978-1-58415-248-4(6)) Mitchell Lane Pubs., Inc.

Brown, Gene. Duke Ellington: Jazz Master. 2001. (Giants of Art & Culture Ser.). (Illus.). 128p. (J). (gr. 5-8). 28.70 (978-1-56711-505-5(5), Blackbirch Pr., Inc.) Thomson Gale.

Duke Ellington. 2004. (J). 24.95 incl. audio (978-1-55592-057-9(8)); pap. 32.75 incl. audio (978-1-55592-212-2(0)); pap. 14.95 incl. audio (978-1-55592-090-6(X)) Weston Woods Studios, Inc.

Ford, Carin T. Duke Ellington: I Live with Music. 2007. (African-American Biography Library). (Illus.). 128p. (J). (gr. 6 up). lib. bdg. 31.93 (978-0-7660-2702-2(3)) Enslow Pubs., Inc.

Monroe, Judy. Duke Ellington. 2005. (Fact Finders Ser.). (Illus.). 32p. (J). 22.60 (978-0-7368-3741-5(8)) Capstone Pr., Inc.

Pinkney, Andrea Davis. Duke Ellington: The Piano Prince & His Orchestra. Pinkney, Brian, illus. 1999. 32p. (gr. k-4). 15.95 (978-0-7868-0178-7(6), Jump at the Sun) Hyperion Bks. for Children.

—Duke Ellington: The Piano Prince & His Orchestra. Pinkney, Brian, illus. 2007. 32p. (gr. k-4). pap. 5.99 (978-0-7868-1420-6(9)) Hyperion Pr.

Terrill, Richard. Duke Ellington. 2003. (African-American Biographies Ser.). 64p. pap. 8.95 (978-1-4109-0035-7(5)); (Illus.). (J). lib. bdg. 28.56 (978-0-7398-6869-0(1)) Raintree.

ELLIS ISLAND (N.J. AND N.Y.)

Anderson, Dale. Arriving at Ellis Island. 2002. (Landmark Events in American History Ser.). (Illus.). 48p. (J). (gr. 5 up). lib. bdg. 30.00 (978-0-8368-5337-7(7)); pap. 14.60 (978-0-8368-5351-3(2)) Stevens, Gareth Inc. (World Almanac Library).

Bierman, Carol. Journey to Ellis Island. McGaw, Laurie, illus. 1998. 48p. (gr. 3-17). 17.95 (978-0-7868-0377-4(0)) Hyperion Bks. for Children.

—Journey to Ellis Island: How My Father Came to America. 1999. 48p. (J). pap. 8.95 (978-0-7868-1411-4(X)) Disney Pr.

Bierman, Carol & Hehner, Barbara. Journey to Ellis Island: How My Father Came to America. McGaw, Laurie, illus. 2003. 48p. (gr. 4-8). 18.00 (978-0-7567-6844-7(6)) DIANE Publishing Co.

Binns, Tristan Boyer. Ellis Island. (Visiting the Past Ser.). (Illus.). 32p. (J). (gr. 5-7). 2002. pap. 6.95 (978-1-58810-412-0(5), 91180); 2001. lib. bdg. 24.22 (978-1-58810-270-6(X)) Heinemann Library.

—Ellis Island. 2001. (gr. 5-8). lib. bdg. 15.90 (978-0-613-82114-8(9)) Tandem Library Bks.

Boyer Binns, Tristan. Ellis Island. 2002. (978-0-606-22483-3(1)) Tandem Library Bks.

Britton, Tamara L. Ellis Island. 2005. (Symbols, Landmarks, & Monuments Set Ii Ser.). (Illus.). 32p. (J). (gr. k-6). lib. bdg. 22.78 (978-1-59197-519-9(0)) ABDO Publishing Co.

DeGezelle, Terri & Andrews, Melodie. Ellis Island. 2003. (First Facts Ser.). (Illus.). 24p. (J). lib. bdg. 19.93 (978-0-7368-2292-3(5)) Capstone Pr., Inc.

Doherty, Ellen. Ellis Island. ed. 2003. (Early Connections Ser.). (J). pap. 35.00 (978-1-4108-1546-0(3)) Benchmark Education Co.

Faria, Joseph D. The Statue of Liberty & Ellis Island: A MyReportLinks.com Book. 2005. (Virtual Field Trips Ser.). (Illus.). 48p. (J). (gr. 4-10). lib. bdg. 25.26 (978-0-7660-5226-0(5), MyReportLinks.com Bks.) Enslow Pubs., Inc.

Harcourt School Publishers Staff. Ellis Island. 3rd ed. 2002. (Horizons Ser.). (Illus.). (J). pap. 3.70 (978-0-15-333212-8(3)) Harcourt Schl. Pubs.

Isaacs, Sally Senzell. Life at Ellis Island. (Picture the Past Ser.). (Illus.). 32p. (J). 2002. (gr. k-3). pap. 7.50 (978-1-58810-417-5(6), 91190); 2001. (gr. 2-4). lib. bdg. (978-1-58810-252-2(1)) Heinemann Library.

Jango-Cohen, Judith. Ellis Island. 2005. (Cornerstones of Freedom Ser.). (Illus.). 48p. (J). (gr. 4-6). 26.00 (978-0-516-23625-4(3), Children's Pr.) Scholastic Library Publishing.

Landau, Elaine. Ellis Island. 2008. (True Booktrade;: American History Ser.). 48p. (J). pap. 6.95 (***978-0-531-14781-8(9)***, Children's Pr.) Scholastic Library Publishing.

Marcovitz, Hal. Ellis Island. 2002. (American Symbols & Their Meanings Ser.). (Illus.). 48p. (YA). (gr. 4 up). lib. bdg. (978-1-59084-031-3(3)) Mason Crest Pubs.

Nixon, Joan Lowery. Ellis Island Stories, 3 bks. l.t. ed. Incl. Land of Dreams. 153p. lib. bdg. 23.33 (978-0-8368-2810-8(0)); Land of Hope. 171p. lib. bdg. 23.33 (978-0-8368-2811-5(9)); Land of Promise. 169p. lib. bdg. 23.33 (978-0-8368-2812-2(7)); (J). (gr. 4 up). 2001. Set lib. bdg. 69.99 (978-0-8368-2809-2(7)) Stevens, Gareth Inc.

Peacock, Louise. At Ellis Island: A History in Many Voices. Krudop, Walter Lyon, illus. 2007. 48p. (J). (gr. 2-5). 18.99 (***978-0-689-83026-6(2)***, Atheneum) Simon & Schuster Children's Publishing.

Raatma, Lucia. Ellis Island. 2002. (We the People Ser.). (Illus.). 48p. (J). (gr. 4 up). lib. bdg. 22.60 (978-0-7565-0302-4(7)) Compass Point Bks.

Ruffin, Frances E. Ellis Island. 2006. (Illus.). 24p. (J). pap. 5.95 (978-0-8368-6415-1(8)); lib. bdg. 19.33 (978-0-8368-6408-3(5)) Stevens, Gareth Inc.

Sandler, Martin W. Island of Hope: The Story of Ellis Island & the Journey to America. 2004. (Illus.). 144p. (J). pap. 18.95 (978-0-439-53082-8(2)) Scholastic, Inc.

Townsend, Dana E. Ellis Island. (Illus.). 32p. (J). (***978-0-7367-2944-4(5)***) Zaner-Bloser, Inc.

We the People - Modern America, 6 bks. Incl. Ellis Island. Raatma, Lucia. 2002. lib. bdg. 22.60 (978-0-7565-0302-4(7)); Great Depression. Burgan, Michael. 2001. lib. bdg. 22.60 (978-0-7565-0152-5(0)); Navajo Code Talkers. Santella, Andrew. 2004. lib. bdg. 22.60 (978-0-7565-0611-7(5)); Persian Gulf War. Santella, Andrew. 2004. lib. bdg. 22.60 (978-0-7565-0612-4(3)); Statue of Liberty. Heinrichs, Ann. 2001. lib. bdg. 22.60 (978-0-7565-0100-6(8)); Titanic. Burgan, Michael. 2004. lib. bdg. 22.60 (978-0-7565-0614-8(X)); 48p. (J). (gr. 4 up). (Illus.). Set lib. bdg. 135.60 (978-0-7565-0779-4(0)) Compass Point Bks.

Weinberger, Kimberly. Journey to a New Land: An Oral History. Meers, Tony, illus. 2000. 32p. (J). (978-1-57255-813-7(X)); pap. (978-1-57255-812-0(1)) Mondo Publishing.

Young, Robert. A Personal Tour of Ellis Island. 64p. (J). (gr. 3-6). 6.95 (978-1-58013-154-4(9)); 2003. (Illus.). 18.95 (978-1-58013-079-0(8)) Kar-Ben Publishing.

—A Personal Tour of Ellis Island. 2001. (How It Was Ser.). (Illus.). 64p. (J). (gr. 4-6). lib. bdg. (978-0-8225-3579-9(3), Lerner Pubns.) Lerner Publishing Group.

ELLIS ISLAND (N.J. AND N.Y.)—FICTION

Goldish, Meish. On Their Way. Mohr, Mark, illus. 2002. 16p. (J). (978-0-439-35130-0(8)) Scholastic, Inc.

Holub, Joan. Tatiana Comes to America: An Ellis Island Story. 2002. (gr. 3-6). lib. bdg. 11.80 (978-0-613-70904-0(7)) Tandem Library Bks.

Leighton, Maxinne R. An Ellis Island Christmas. Nolan, Dennis, illus. 2005. 32p. (J). (gr. k-3). pap. 6.99 (978-0-14-240506-2(X), Puffin) Penguin Group (USA) Inc.

Rhema, Dan. One Tiny Twig, 1. Leonard, Michael, illus. 2003. 32p. (J). per. 19.95 (978-0-9729835-0-1(3)) Mesquite Tress Pr., LLC.

Woodruff, Elvira. The Memory Coat. Dooling, Michael, illus. 1999. 32p. (J). (gr. 2-5). pap. 16.95 (978-0-590-67717-2(9)) Scholastic, Inc.

—The Orphan of Ellis Island: A Time Travel Adventure. 2000. 192p. (J). pap. 4.99 (978-0-590-48246-2(7)) Scholastic, Inc.

ELMER (FICTITIOUS CHARACTER)—FICTION

McKee, David. Elmer's Colours. 2004. (Elmer Ser.). (Illus.). 16p. (J). (ENG & ITA.). bds. 6.95 (978-1-84059-396-9(2)); (ARA & ENG., bds. 6.95 (978-1-84059-395-2(4)); (ENG, URD, TUR, VIE & SPA., bds. 6.95 (978-1-84059-055-5(6)); (ENG, URD, TUR, VIE & SPA., bds. 6.95 (978-1-84059-056-2(4)); (ENG, URD, TUR, VIE & SPA., bds. 6.95 (978-1-84059-059-3(9)); (ENG, TUR, URD, VIE & SPA., bds. 6.95 (978-1-84059-060-9(2)); (ENG, URD, TUR, VIE & SPA., bds. 6.95 (978-1-84059-057-9(2)); (VIE, ENG, URD, TUR & SPA., bds. 6.95 (978-1-84059-061-6(0)) Milet Publishing.

—Elmer's Colours. Pullin, Beatriz, tr. 2004. (Elmers Ser.). (ENG, URD, TUR, VIE & CHI., Illus.). 16p. (J). bds. 6.95 (978-1-84059-058-6(0)) Milet Publishing.

—Elmer's Day. 2004. (Elmer Ser.). (Illus.). 16p. (J). (ARA & ENG.). bds. 6.95 (978-1-84059-398-3(9)); (ENG & ITA., bds. 6.95 (978-1-84059-399-0(7)); (ENG & SOM., bds. 6.95 (978-1-84059-400-3(4)); (ENG, URD, TUR, VIE & CHI., bds. 6.95 (978-1-84059-065-4(3)); (ENG, URD, TUR, VIE & SPA., bds. 6.95 (978-1-84059-066-1(1)) Milet Publishing.

—Elmer's Day. Wood, Kim Marie, tr. 2004. (Elmers Ser.). (ENG, URD, TUR, SPA & CHI., Illus.). 16p. (J). bds. 6.95 (978-1-84059-068-5(8)) Milet Publishing.

—Elmer's Day. French, Li Yen, tr. 2004. (Elmers Ser.). (CHI, ENG, URD, TUR & VIE., Illus.). 16p. (J). bds. 6.95 (978-1-84059-063-0(7)) Milet Publishing.

—Elmer's Day. 2nd ed. 2004. (Elmers Ser.). (ENG, TUR, URD, VIE & SPA., Illus.). 16p. (J). bds. 6.95 (978-1-84059-067-8(X)) Milet Publishing.

—Elmer's Day. Datta, Kanai, tr. 2nd ed. 2004. (Elmers Ser.). (ENG, URD, TUR, VIE & SPA., Illus.). 16p. (J). bds. 6.95 (978-1-84059-062-3(9)) Milet Publishing.

—Elmer's Day. Dave, Pratima, tr. 2nd ed. 2004. (Elmers Ser.). (ENG, URD, TUR, VIE & SPA., Illus.). 16p. (J). bds. 6.95 (978-1-84059-064-7(5)) Milet Publishing.

—Elmer's Friends. 2004. (Elmers Ser.).Tr. of Amigos de Elmer. (ENG, TUR, URD, VIE & SPA., Illus.). 16p. (J). bds. 6.95 (978-1-84059-074-6(2)) Milet Publishing.

ELMO (FICTITIOUS CHARACTER)—FICTION

Albee, Sarah. Elmo Loves You. Swanson, Maggie, illus. 2002. (Big Bird's Favorites Board Bks.). 24p. (J). (gr. k-ps). bds. 4.99 (978-0-375-81208-8(3), Random Hse. Bks. for Young Readers) Random Hse. Children's Bks.

—Elmo Loves You! Swanson, Maggie, illus. rev. ed. 2005. 24p. (J). (ps). pap. 3.50 (978-1-4037-1694-1(3)) Dalmatian Pr.

—Where Is Elmo? A Wiggle & Giggle Peekaboo Book. 2005. (Sesame Street Ser.). (Illus.). 10p. (J). (ps-k). bds. 12.99 (978-0-7944-0776-6(5)) Reader's Digest Assn., Inc., The.

Albee, Sarah & Mathieu, Joe. Sesame Street Field Trip! Book & Finger Puppets. 2007. 12p. (J). bds. 14.99 (978-0-7944-1233-3(5)) Reader's Digest Assn., Inc., The.

Allen, Constance. Come Play with Elmo! 2006. (Sesame Street). (Illus.). 10p. (J). bds. 12.99 (978-0-7944-0778-0(1)) Reader's Digest Assn., Inc., The.

Dalmatian Press Staff. Abby Cadabby's Rhyme BK. 2007. 24p. pap. 3.50 (***978-1-4037-3609-3(X)***) Dalmatian Pr.

—Elmo Visits the Dentist. 2007. 24p. pap. 3.50 (***978-1-4037-3430-3(5)***) Dalmatian Pr.

—Sesame Street Happy Easter. 2007. 24p. (J). pap. 3.50 (***978-1-4037-3198-2(5)***) Dalmatian Pr.

Dalmatian Press Staff, ed. Elmo & Friends Treasury. rev. ed. 2005. 158p. 10.99 (978-1-4037-1993-5(4)) Dalmatian Pr.

Elmo: The Ultimate Edition. 2007. 288p. 21.95 (***978-1-4037-3717-5(7)***) Dalmatian Pr.

Elmo & the Monsters. 2001. (J). (978-1-931312-39-4(7)) SoftPlay, Inc.

Elmo Head to Toe. 2005. (Illus.). 24p. (J). 15.98 (978-1-4127-3332-8(4), 7247200) Publications International, Ltd.

Elmo's Christmas. 2000. (J). 9.99 (978-1-931312-29-5(X)) SoftPlay, Inc.

Elmo's Jukebox. 2003. 24p. (J). bds. (978-1-4127-0298-0(4), 7189801) Publications International, Ltd.

Goodnight Elmo. 2002. (J). (978-1-931312-74-5(5)) SoftPlay, Inc.

Kleinberg, Naomi. Elmo's World: Teachers! Nelson, Mary Beth, illus. 2007. 12p. (J). (gr. k-ps). bds. 4.99 (***978-0-375-83788-3(4)***, Random Hse. Bks. for Young Readers) Random Hse. Children's Bks.

Monica, Carol. Elmo's Easy As 1 2 3. 2006. (Sesame Street Ser.). 10p. (J). 15.99 (978-0-7944-1018-6(9)) Reader's Digest Assn., Inc., The.

Monica, Carol & Mathieu, Joe. Sesame Street Elmo's Favorite Places. 2007. 10p. (J). 11.99 (***978-0-7944-1357-6(9)***) Reader's Digest Assn., Inc., The.

November, Deborah. Elmo's ABC Book. Nicklaus, Carol, illus. 2007. (Big Bird's Favorites Brd Bks.). 24p. (J). (gr. k). bds. 4.99 (***978-0-375-84037-1(0)***, Random Hse. Bks. for Young Readers) Random Hse. Children's Bks.

November, Deborah. Sesame Street Big Block Party! Story Cookbook & Recipe Cards. 2006. (Sesame Street Ser.). 32p. (J). pap. 10.99 (978-0-7944-1104-6(5)) Reader's Digest Assn., Inc., The.

Sesame Street Carry Along #2. 2007. pap. 9.99 (***978-1-4037-3615-4(4)***) Dalmatian Pr.

Sesame Street Staff. Sesame Street Elmo Loves You: Happy Tale Storybook. 2005. (Illus.). 24p. (J). pap. 2.99 (978-1-4037-1042-0(2)) Dalmatian Pr.

Sesame Street Storybook COLL 2. 2007. 10.99 (***978-1-4037-3614-7(6)***) Dalmatian Pr.

Shepherd, Jodie. Ready for School. 2006. (Sesame Street Ser.). 10p. (J). pap. 10.99 (978-0-7944-1103-9(7)) Reader's Digest Assn., Inc., The.

Shepherd, Jodie & Moroney, Christopher. Sesame Street Big, Bigger, Biggest. 2007. 10p. (J). bds. 14.99 (978-0-7944-1232-6(7)) Reader's Digest Assn., Inc., The.

Sing along Elmo: Story Reader. 2004. 26p. (J). spiral bd. (978-1-4127-3232-1(8) , 7237500) Publications International, Ltd.

Snyder, Margaret. Elmo's Favorite Things. 2006. (Sesame Street Ser.). (Illus.). 10p. (J). bds. 12.99 (978-0-7944-1140-4(1)) Reader's Digest Assn., Inc., The.

Studio Mouse. Sesame Street My First Trip to the Farm: Book & CD. rev. ed. 2007. 24p. 4.99 (***978-1-59069-561-6(5)***) Studio Mouse LLC.

Wax, Wendy & Kwiat, Ernie. Sesame Street Guess Who? Elmo. 2007. 10p. (J). bds. 10.99 (978-0-7944-1211-1(4)) Reader's Digest Assn., Inc., The.

Weber, Lou, ed. Elmo ABC: Sound Activity Pad. 2004. 48p. (J). 12.98 (978-1-4127-0169-3(4) , 7217400) Publications International, Ltd.

—Elmo Best Friends Sing a Long. 2005. 14p. (J). bds. 15.98 (978-1-4127-3373-1(1) , 7251300) Publications International, Ltd.

—Elmo Numbers: Sound Activity Pad. 2004. 48p. (J). 12.98 (978-1-4127-0170-9(8) , 7217500) Publications International, Ltd.

—Elmos Rainbow. 2005. 32p. (J). 7.98 (978-1-4127-3057-0(0) , 7226800) Publications International, Ltd.

Webster, Christy. Lots of Opposites: All about Opposites. Moroney, Christopher, illus. 2007. 22p. (J). (gr. k-ps). bds. 7.99 (978-0-375-83778-4(7) , Random Hse. Bks. for Young Readers) Random Hse. Children's Bks.

Where's Elmo? A Peekaboo Book. (J). 1999. (978-1-931312-08-0(7)); 2000. (978-1-931312-05-9(2)) SoftPlay, Inc.

Where's Elmo? (mini) 2003. (J). (978-1-59292-031-0(4)) SoftPlay, Inc.

ELOCUTION

see Public Speaking

ELOISE (FICTITIOUS CHARACTER)—FICTION

Cheshire, Marc. Eloise Dresses Up: 50 Reusable Stickers! Hahner, Chris, illus. 2004. (Eloise Ser.). 12p. (J). pap. 6.99 (978-0-689-87455-0(3) , Little Simon) Simon & Schuster Children's Publishing.

—Merry Christmas, Eloise! A Lift-the-Flap Book. Bracken, Carolyn, illus. 2006. 18p. (J). pap. 6.99 (978-0-689-87155-9(4) , Little Simon) Simon & Schuster Children's Publishing.

Knight, Hilary & McClatchy, Lisa. Eloise & the Big Parade. Lyon, Tammie, illus. 2007. (Eloise Ser.). 32p. (J). pap. 3.99 (978-1-4169-3523-0(1) , Aladdin) Simon & Schuster Children's Publishing.

McNamara, Margaret. Eloise Breaks Some Eggs. Lyon, Tammie, illus. 2004. (Ready-to-Read Ser.). 32p. (J). pap. 3.99 (978-0-689-87368-3(9) , Aladdin) Simon & Schuster Children's Publishing.

—Eloise Has a Lesson. Mitter, Kathryn, illus. 2004. (Eloise Ser.). 32p. (J). pap. 3.99 (978-0-689-87367-6(0) , Aladdin) Simon & Schuster Children's Publishing.

—Eloise Has A Lesson. Mitter, Kathryn, illus. ed. 2005. (Eloise Ser.). 30p. (J). lib. bdg. 15.00 (978-1-59054-977-3(5)) Fitzgerald Bks.

Telfeyan, Kate, adapted by. Eloise at Christmas. 2003. 32p. (J). 6.99 (978-0-689-86982-2(7) , Simon Spotlight) Simon & Schuster Children's Publishing.

Thompson, Kay. Eloise. Knight, Hilary, illus. 2002. (Eloise Ser.). (SPA.). 64p. (J). (gr. k-3). 17.00 (978-84-264-3735-8(4) , LM30420) Editorial Lumen ESP. *Dist:* Distribooks, Inc., Lectorum Pubns., Inc.

—Eloise. 5th ed. 1998. (Eloise Ser.). (FRE., Illus.). 5p. (J). (ps-3). pap. 13.95 (978-2-07-052125-8(7)) Gallimard, Editions FRA. *Dist:* Distribooks, Inc.

—Eloise. 2001. (Eloise Ser.). (Illus.). 64p. (J). (ps). 22.00 incl. audio compact disk (978-0-689-84311-2(9) , Simon & Schuster Children's Publishing) Simon & Schuster Children's Publishing.

—Eloise en Navidad. Knight, Hilary, illus. 2002. (SPA.). 56p. (J). (gr. k-3). 18.95 (978-84-264-3748-8(6) , LM4922) Editorial Lumen ESP. *Dist:* Distribooks, Inc., Lectorum Pubns., Inc.

—Eloise en Paris. Knight, Hilary, illus. 2002. (SPA.). 84p. (J). (gr. k-3). 17.00 (978-84-264-3739-6(7) , LM30421) Editorial Lumen ESP. *Dist:* Distribooks, Inc., Lectorum Pubns., Inc.

—Eloise Takes a Bawth. Knight, Hilary, illus. ltd. ed. 2002. (Eloise Ser.). 300.00 (978-0-689-84694-6(0) , Simon & Schuster Children's Publishing) Simon & Schuster Children's Publishing.

—Eloise the Absolutely Essential Edition. Knight, Hilary, illus. 1999. 80p. (J). (ps-3). 19.95 (978-0-689-82703-7(2)) Simon & Schuster Children's Publishing.

—Eloise the Ultimate Edition. Knight, Hilary, illus. 2000. 304p. (J). (ps-3). 39.99 (978-0-689-83990-0(1)) Simon & Schuster Children's Publishing.

—Eloise's Guide to Life: Or, How to Eat, Dress, Travel, Behave, & Stay Six Forever. Knight, Hilary, illus. 2000. (Eloise Ser.). 48p. (J). (ps-3). 9.95 (978-0-689-83310-6(5)) Simon & Schuster Children's Publishing.

—Eloise's What I Absolutely Love Love Love. Knight, Hilary, illus. 2004. 32p. (J). 9.95 (978-0-689-84965-7(6) , Simon & Schuster Children's Publishing) Simon & Schuster Children's Publishing.

—Love & Kisses, Eloise. Enik, Ted, illus. 2004. (Eloise Ser.). 24p. (J). pap. 3.99 (978-0-689-87156-6(2) , Little Simon) Simon & Schuster Children's Publishing.

Thompson, Kay & Cheshire, Marc. Here Comes Eloise! Bracken, Carolyn, illus. 2004. (Eloise Ser.). 16p. (J). (ps-1). pap. 6.99 (978-0-689-87154-2(6) , Little Simon) Simon & Schuster Children's Publishing.

Thompson, Kay & Crowley, Mart. Eloise Takes a Bawth. Knight, Hilary, illus. 2002. (Eloise Ser.). 80p. (J). (ps-3). 17.95 (978-0-689-84288-7(0)) Simon & Schuster Children's Publishing.

Thompson, Kay & Fry, Sonali. Eloise Goes to the Beach. Lyon, Tammie, illus. 2007. (Eloise Ser.). 12p. (J). 7.99 (978-1-4169-3344-1(1) , Little Simon) Simon & Schuster Children's Publishing.

Thompson, Kay & Knight, Hilary. Eloise at Christmastime. 1999. (Illus.). 56p. (J). (ps-3). 17.95 (978-0-689-83039-6(4)) Simon & Schuster Children's Publishing.

—Eloise in Moscow. 40th ed. 2000. (Illus.). 80p. (J). (ps-3). 17.00 (978-0-689-83211-6(7)) Simon & Schuster Children's Publishing.

—Eloise in Paris. 1999. (Eloise Ser.). (Illus.). 72p. (J). (ps-3). 18.00 (978-0-689-82704-4(0)) Simon & Schuster Children's Publishing.

Thompson, Kay & McClatchy, Lisa. Eloise's Summer Vacation. Lyon, Tammie, illus. 2007. (Eloise Ser.). 32p. (J). pap. 3.99 (978-0-689-87454-3(5) , Aladdin) Simon & Schuster Children's Publishing.

Thompson, Kay, et al. Eloise Takes a Trip. Bracken, Carolyn, illus. 2007. (Eloise Ser.). 16p. (J). pap. 4.99 (978-1-4169-3343-4(3) , Little Simon) Simon & Schuster Children's Publishing.

ELVES

see Fairies

EMANCIPATION OF SLAVES

see Slavery—United States

EMANCIPATION PROCLAMATION

Armentrout, David & Armentrout, Patricia. The Emancipation Proclamation. 2004. (Documents That Shaped the Nation Ser.). 48p. pap. 7.95 (978-1-59515-332-6(2)) Rourke Publishing, LLC.

The Emancipation Proclamation. 2000. (My Ancestors—My Heroes Ser.: Vol. 23). (J). (gr. 3-4). (978-1-893091-22-1(8)) Parker Publishing Co.

Heinrichs, Ann. The Emancipation Proclamation. 2002. (We the People Ser.). (Illus.). 48p. (J). (gr. 4 up). lib. bdg. 22.60 (978-0-7565-0209-6(8)) Compass Point Bks.

Holford, David M. Lincoln & the Emancipation Proclamation in American History. 2002. (In American History Ser.). (Illus.). 128p. (YA). (gr. 5-12). lib. bdg. 26.60 (978-0-7660-1456-5(8)) Enslow Pubs., Inc.

King, Wilma. Children of the Emancipation. 2005. (Picture the American Past Ser.). (Illus.). 48p. (gr. 2-5). 22.60 (978-1-57505-396-7(9)) Lerner Publishing Group.

Martin, Michael J. Emancipation Proclamation: Hope of Freedom for the Slaves. 2002. (Let Freedom Ring Ser.). (Illus.). 48p. (J). (gr. 3-4). lib. bdg. 22.60 (978-0-7368-1339-6(X) , Bridgestone Bks.) Capstone Pr., Inc.

Pinkney, Andrea Davis. Abraham Lincoln: Letters from a Young Slave Girl. 2001. (Dear Mr. President Ser.). (Illus.). 136p. (J). (gr. 4-7). 8.95 (978-1-890817-60-2(0)) Winslow Pr.

Riehecky, Janet. The Emancipation Proclamation: The Abolition of Slavery. 2002. (Point of Impact Ser.). (Illus.). 32p. (J). (gr. 5-7). lib. bdg. 25.64 (978-1-58810-556-1(3)) Heinemann Library.

—The Emancipation Proclamation Set: The Abolition of Slavery. 2002. (Point of Impact Ser.). (Illus.). 32p. (J). (gr. 5-7). pap. (978-1-4034-0071-0(7) , 91552) Heinemann Library.

EMBLEMS

see Heraldry; Symbolism

EMBROIDERY

see also Beadwork

Cha, Dia. Dia's Story Cloth: The Hmong People's Journey of Freedom. Cha, Chue & Cha, Nhia Thao, illus. 1998. 24p. (J). (gr. 1 up). 6.95 (978-1-880000-63-2(6)) Lee & Low Bks., Inc.

Cherry, Winky. My First Embroidery Book Level 2: A Name Sampler. Palmer, Pati, ed. Cherry, Winky, illus. 2003. (My First Sewing Book Ser.). (Illus.). 40p. (J). (ps-6). pap. 14.95 (978-0-935278-31-6(1)) Palmer-Pletsch Assocs.

Cobb, Mary. A Sampler View of Colonial Life: With Projects Kids Can Make. Ellis, Jan Davey, illus. 1998. 64p. (gr. 2-4). lib. bdg. 24.90 (978-0-7613-0372-5(3) , Millbrook Pr.) Lerner Publishing Group.

—Sampler View of Colonial Life: With Projects Kids Can Make. 1999. (gr. 3-6). lib. bdg. 17.60 (978-0-613-26821-9(0)) Tandem Library Bks.

Green, Marilyn, ed. Klutz Simple Embroidery. 2003. (Illus.). 50p. (J). 21.95 (978-1-57054-957-1(5) , 53477606) Klutz.

Marigolds for Dona Remedios, 6 vols. (Multicultural Programs Ser.). 16p. (gr. 1-6). 31.95 (978-0-7802-8310-7(4)) Wright Group, The.

Miles, L. Hair Braiding Kid Kit. rev. ed. 2005. 32p. (J). 10.99 (978-1-58086-858-7(4) , Usborne) EDC Publishing.

Nicholas, Kristin. Kids' Embroidery: Projects for Kids of All Ages. Gruen, John, photos by. 2004. (Illus.). 144p. 19.95 (978-1-58479-366-3(X)) Stewart, Tabori & Chang.

Sadler, Judy Ann. Embroidery. Bradford, June, tr. Bradford, June, illus. 2004. (Kids Can Do It Ser.). 40p. (J). (gr. 4-6). (978-1-55337-617-0(X)); (978-1-55337-616-3(1)) Kids Can Pr., Ltd.

Switzer, Chris. Projects for Alpaca & Llama. 2004. 16.00 (978-0-9642663-2-2(6)) Switzer Land Enterprises.

EMBRYOLOGY

see also Cells; Reproduction

Aston, Dianna Hutts. An Egg Is Quiet. Long, Sylvia, illus. 2006. (J). 16.95 (978-0-8118-5554-9(6)) Chronicle Bks. LLC.

Burton, Jane. Egg: A Photographic Story of Hatching. 2000. (978-0-606-17807-5(4)) Tandem Library Bks.

Burton, Jane & Taylor, Kim. The Nature & Science of Eggs. Burton, Jane & Taylor, Kim, photos by. 1998. (Exploring the Science of Nature Ser.). (Illus.). 32p. (J). (gr. 3 up). lib. bdg. 23.93 (978-0-8368-2105-5(X)) Stevens, Gareth Inc.

Curry, Don L. What Hatches? 2000. (Yellow Umbrella Books). (Illus.). 16p. (J). (gr. 1). lib. bdg. 14.60 (978-0-7368-0721-0(7) , Pebble Bks.) Capstone Pr., Inc.

Gaither, Page. Human Embryo Experimentation. 2007. (At Issue Ser.). (Illus.). 128p. (J). (gr. 10-12). pap. 21.20 (978-0-7377-3244-3(X) , Greenhaven Pr., Inc.) Thomson Gale.

Gaither, Page, et al. Human Embryo Experimentation. 2007. (At Issue Ser.). (Illus.). 128p. (J). (gr. 10-12). 29.95 (978-0-7377-3243-6(1) , Greenhaven Pr., Inc.) Thomson Gale.

Gill, Shelley R. The Egg. Bosson, Jo-Ellen, illus. 2001. 32p. (J). (ps-5). 16.95 (978-1-57091-377-8(3)); pap. 6.95 (978-1-57091-378-5(1)) Charlesbridge Publishing, Inc.

Green, Jen. Cells & Reproduction. 2005. (Illus.). 32p. (J). (gr. 3-7). lib. bdg. 27.10 (978-1-59604-052-6(1)) Stargazer Bks.

James, Susan. The Amazing Egg. 2002. (Spyglass Books). (Illus.). 24p. (J). (gr. 1 up). lib. bdg. 18.60 (978-0-7565-0225-6(X)) Compass Point Bks.

Kalman, Bobbie. La Metamorfosis: Cuerpos que Cambian. 2006. (SPA., Illus.). 32p. (J). 3. pap. (978-0-7787-8387-9(1)); (J). (978-0-7787-8373-2(1)) Crabtree Publishing Co.

Pascoe, Elaine. Animals Hatch from Eggs. Kuhn, Dwight, photos by. 2002. (Springboards into Science Ser.). (Illus.). 24p. (J). (gr. 1 up). lib. bdg. 20.67 (978-0-8368-3004-0(0)) Stevens, Gareth Inc.

—How & Why Animals Hatch from Eggs. Kupperstein, Joel, ed. Kuhn, Dwight, photos by. 2000. (How & Why Ser.). (Illus.). 16p. (J). (gr. 1-3). pap. 2.99 (978-1-57471-660-3(3) , 2967) Creative Teaching Pr., Inc.

Pringle, Laurence P. Everybody Has a Bellybutton: Your Life Before You Were Born. Wood, Clare, illus. 2003. 32p. (J). (gr. k-2). 14.95 (978-1-56397-009-2(0)) Boyds Mills Pr.

Renne. Animals & Their Eggs. Taurel, Alison, tr. from DUT. Renne, illus. 2000. (Animals Up Close Ser.). (Illus.). 38p. (J). (gr. 3 up). lib. bdg. 24.67 (978-0-8368-2714-9(7)) Stevens, Gareth Inc.

Singer, Marilyn. Eggs. Kratter, Paul, illus. 2003. (J). (978-0-8234-1727-8(1)) Holiday Hse., Inc.

Zerucha, Ted. Human Development. 2003. (Your Body, How It Works). (Illus.). 112p. (gr. 9-13). 31.95 (978-0-7910-7631-6(8) , Chelsea Hse.) Facts On File, Inc.

EMERSON, RALPH WALDO, 1803-1882

Emerson, Ralph Waldo. Emerson's Essays. 2006. (Bloom's Modern Critical Interpretations Ser.). 150p. 45.00 (978-0-7910-8118-1(4) , Chelsea Hse.) Facts On File, Inc.

EMIGRATION AND IMMIGRATION

Here are entered works on migration from one country to another. Works on the movement of population within a country for permanent settlements are entered under Migration, internal.

see also Human Geography; Refugees

also names of countries with the subdivision Emigration and Immigration; names of countries, cities, etc. with the subdivision Foreign Population; and names of nationalities

Adasiewicz, Sue. Your Papers, Please: Crossing Borders. (Shockwave: People & Communities Ser.). (J). 2008. 32p. pap. 6.95 (***978-0-531-18841-5(8)***); 2007. (Illus.). 36p. (gr. 4-6). lib. bdg. 25.00 (***978-0-531-17572-9(3)***) Scholastic Library Publishing. (Children's Pr.).

Agbabian, Alidz. Dzalabadig: A Photographic Journey into Diaspora's First Armenian Community. Deroumian, Vartan, photos by. 2002. 32p. (J). (gr. 3-6). pap. 15.00 (978-0-9655507-5-8(3)) Dziludzar.

Aldridge, Rebecca. Italian Americans. 2003. (Immigrants in America Ser.). (J). pap. 9.95 (978-0-7910-7509-8(5)); (Illus.). 112p. (gr. 6-12). 30.00 (978-0-7910-7129-8(4)) Facts On File, Inc. (Chelsea Hse.).

Allan, Tony. The Irish Famine: The Birth of Irish America. (Point of Impact Ser.). 32p. pap. 7.50 (978-1-4034-4113-3(8)); 2001. (Illus.). (J). (gr. 5-7). lib. bdg. 24.22 (978-1-58810-077-1(4)) Heinemann Library.

Ancona, George. Mis Abuelos/My Grandparents. 32p. (J). 2006. (SPA.). (gr. 1-3). pap. 8.95 (978-0-516-25495-1(2)); 2005. (ENG & SPA.). 21.00 (978-0-516-25294-0(1)) Scholastic Library Publishing. (Children's Pr.).

Anderson, Dale. Korean Americans. 2008. (J). (***978-1-60044-613-9(2)***) Rourke Publishing, LLC.

Ansary, Mir Tamim. People of California. 2003. (Heinemann State Studies). (Illus.). 48p. (J). (gr. 3-5). lib. bdg. (978-1-4034-0342-1(2)) Heinemann Library.

Asgedom, Mawi. Of Beetles & Angels: A Boy's Remarkable Journey from A Refugee Camp to Harvard. 2002. (gr. 5-8). lib. bdg. 18.45 (978-0-613-64198-2(1)) Tandem Library Bks.

Bandon, Alexandra. Dominican Americans. 1999. (Footsteps to America Ser.). (J). 22.00 (978-0-02-768152-9(1) , Simon & Schuster Children's Publishing) Simon & Schuster Children's Publishing.

Bartoletti, Susan Campbell. Growing up in Coal Country. 1999. (Illus.). 128p. (J). (gr. 4-6). pap. 7.95 (978-0-395-97914-3(5)) Houghton Mifflin Co. Trade & Reference Div.

Behnke, Alison. Chinese in America. 2005. (In America Ser.). (Illus.). 80p. (J). (gr. 5-8). lib. bdg. 27.93 (978-0-8225-4695-5(7)) Lerner Publishing Group.

—Mexicans in America. 2005. (In America Ser.). (Illus.). 80p. (J). (gr. 5-8). lib. bdg. 27.93 (978-0-8225-3955-1(1)) Lerner Publishing Group.

Belcher, Angie. To Our Shores. 2004. (Illus.). 84p. (J). pap. (978-1-86948-682-2(X)) Reed Publishing (NZ), Ltd.

Berger, Melvin & Berger, Gilda. Where Did Your Family Come From? A Book about Immigrants. Quackenbush, Robert, illus. 1999. (Discovery Readers Ser.). 48p. (J). (ps-3). lib. bdg. 15.95 (978-0-7910-5063-7(7) , Chelsea Hse.) Facts On File, Inc.

Bial, Raymond. Tenement: Immigrant Life on the Lower East Side. Bial, Raymond, illus. 2002. (Illus.). 48p. (J). (gr. 4-6). tchr. ed. 16.00 (978-0-618-13849-4(8)) Houghton Mifflin Co. Trade & Reference Div.

Bierman, Carol. Journey to Ellis Island. McGaw, Laurie, illus. 1998. 48p. (gr. 3-17). 17.95 (978-0-7868-0377-4(0)) Hyperion Bks. for Children.

—Journey to Ellis Island: How My Father Came to America. 1999. 48p. (J). pap. 8.95 (978-0-7868-1411-4(X)) Disney Pr.

Bierman, Carol & Hehner, Barbara. Journey to Ellis Island: How My Father Came to America. McGaw, Laurie, illus. 2003. 48p. (gr. 4-8). 18.00 (978-0-7567-6844-7(6)) DIANE Publishing Co.

Binns, Tristan Boyer. Ellis Island. (Visiting the Past Ser.). (Illus.). 32p. (J). (gr. 5-7). 2002. pap. 6.95 (978-1-58810-412-0(5) , 91180); 2001. lib. bdg. 24.22 (978-1-58810-270-6(X)) Heinemann Library.

—Ellis Island. 2001. (gr. 5-8). lib. bdg. 15.90 (978-0-613-82114-8(9)) Tandem Library Bks.

Blohm, Judith M. & Lipinsky, Terri. Kids Like Me: Voices of the Immigrant Experience. 2006. (Illus.). 208p. (J). pap. 22.95 (978-1-931930-21-5(X)) Intercultural Pr., Inc.

Boat People. (VIE.). 76p. (YA). (gr. 6-12). pap. 9.95 (978-0-8224-3685-0(X)) Globe Fearon Educational Publishing.

Braun, Eric. Colombians in America. 2005. (J). lib. bdg. (978-0-8225-2113-6(X) , Lerner Pubns.) Lerner Publishing Group.

Broida, Marian. Projects about American Immigrants from China. 2005. (Hands-On History Ser.). (Illus.). 48p. (J). (978-0-7614-1978-5(0) , Benchmark Bks.) Cavendish, Marshall Corp.

Brooks, Philip. Immigration. 2003. (20th-Century Perspectives Ser.). (Illus.). 48p. (J). pap. (978-1-4034-4181-2(2)); lib. bdg. 27.07 (978-1-4034-3807-2(2)) Heinemann Library.

Bryan, Nichol. Cuban Americans. 2004. (One Nation Ser.). (Illus.). 31p. (J). (gr. k-6). lib. bdg. 22.78 (978-1-57765-980-8(5)) ABDO Publishing Co.

—Dominican Americans. 2004. (One Nation Set Ii Ser.). (Illus.). 32p. (J). (gr. k-6). lib. bdg. 22.78 (978-1-59197-526-7(3)) ABDO Publishing Co.

—Filipino Americans. 2004. (One Nation Ser.). (Illus.). 32p. (J). (gr. k-6). lib. bdg. 22.78 (978-1-57765-988-4(0)) ABDO Publishing Co.

—German Americans. 2004. (One Nation Ser.). (Illus.). 32p. (J). (gr. k-6). lib. bdg. 22.78 (978-1-57765-981-5(3)) ABDO Publishing Co.

—Haitian Americans. 2004. (One Nation Ser.). (Illus.). 32p. (J). (gr. k-6). lib. bdg. 22.78 (978-1-57765-982-2(1)) ABDO Publishing Co.

—Hmong Americans. 2004. (One Nation Ser.). (Illus.). 32p. (J). (gr. k-6). lib. bdg. 22.78 (978-1-57765-983-9(X)) ABDO Publishing Co.

—Indian Americans. 2004. (One Nation Ser.). (Illus.). 32p. (J). (gr. k-6). lib. bdg. 22.78 (978-1-57765-984-6(8)) ABDO Publishing Co.

—Italian Americans. 2004. (One Nation Ser.). (Illus.). 32p. (J). (gr. k-6). lib. bdg. 22.78 (978-1-57765-985-3(6)) ABDO Publishing Co.

—Korean Americans. 2004. (One Nation Set Ii Ser.). (Illus.). 32p. (J). (gr. k-6). lib. bdg. 22.78 (978-1-59197-530-4(1)) ABDO Publishing Co.

—Mexican Americans. 2004. (One Nation Ser.). (Illus.). 32p. (J). (gr. k-6). lib. bdg. 22.78 (978-1-57765-987-7(2)) ABDO Publishing Co.

—Russian Americans. 2004. (One Nation Set Ii Ser.). (Illus.). 32p. (J). (gr. k-6). lib. bdg. 22.78 (978-1-59197-533-5(6)) ABDO Publishing Co.

—Somali Americans. 2004. (One Nation Ser.). (Illus.). 32p. (J). (gr. k-6). lib. bdg. 22.78 (978-1-57765-989-1(9)) ABDO Publishing Co.

Budhos, Marina. Remix: Conversations with Immigrant Teenagers. rev. ed. 1999. (Illus.). 160p. (gr. 9-12). 16.95 (978-0-8050-5113-1(9) , Holt, Henry & Co. Bks. For Young Readers) Holt, Henry & Co.

Burgan, Michael. Italian Immigrants. 2004. (Immigration to the United States Ser.). (Illus.). 96p. (J). (gr. 4-9). 35.00 (978-0-8160-5681-1(1)) Facts On File, Inc.

Collier, Christopher & Collier, James Lincoln. A Century of Immigration: 1820-1924. 1999. (Drama of American History Ser.). (Illus.). 96p. (J). (gr. 5-9). lib. bdg. 31.36 (978-0-7614-0821-5(5) , Benchmark Bks.) Cavendish, Marshall Corp.

Cruz, Barbara. Triumphs & Struggles for Latino Civil Rights. 2008. (From Many Cultures, One History Ser.). (Illus.). 128p. (J). (gr. 5 up). lib. bdg. 31.93 (***978-0-7660-2804-3(6)***) Enslow Pubs., Inc.

Dalton, Dave. Economic Migrants. 2005. (People on the Move Ser.). (Illus.). 56p. (J). pap. (978-1-4034-6964-9(4)); (gr. 6-9). lib. bdg. 31.36 (978-1-4034-6959-5(8)) Heinemann Library.

—Environmental Migrants. 2005. (People on the Move Ser.). (Illus.). 56p. (J). pap. (978-1-4034-6965-6(2)); (YA). (gr. 6-9). lib. bdg. 31.36 (978-1-4034-6960-1(1)) Heinemann Library.

—Refugees & Asylum Seekers. 2005. (People on the Move Ser.). (Illus.). 56p. (YA). (gr. 6-9). lib. bdg. 31.36 (978-1-4034-6961-8(X)) Heinemann Library.

Donovan, Sandra. Iranians in America. 2005. (J). lib. bdg. (978-0-8225-2680-3(8) , Lerner Pubns.) Lerner Publishing Group.

Flotz, Katherine Haeger. A Pebble in My Shoe: A Memoir. 2004. (Illus.). 185p. lib. bdg. 29.95 (978-0-9657793-2-6(7)) Pannonia Pr.

For Gold & Blood (Chinese) 76p. (YA). (gr. 6-12). pap. 9.95 (978-0-8224-3679-9(5)) Globe Fearon Educational Publishing.

Frank, Sarah. Greeks in America. 2006. (J). lib. bdg. (978-0-8225-2686-5(7) , Lerner Pubns.) Lerner Publishing Group.

French Migration to North America. 2001. Tr. of Emigration Francaise en Amerique Du Nord. (FRE.). 332p. per. 33.00 (978-0-9640475-2-5(7)) Editions Houde.

Friedman, Michael & Friedman, Brett. Settlement Houses: Improving the Social Welfare of America's Immigrants. 2006. (Progressive Movement, 1900-1920—Efforts to Reform America's New Industrial Society Ser.). (Illus.). 32p. (J). (978-1-4042-0859-9(3)) Rosen Publishing Group, Inc., The.

Frost, Helen. German Immigrants, 1820-1920. 2001. (Blue Earth Books). (Illus.). 32p. (J). (gr. 3-4). lib. bdg. 22.60 (978-0-7368-0794-4(2) , Bridgestone Bks.) Capstone Pr., Inc.

—Russian Immigrants, 1860-1915. 2002. (Blue Earth Books). (Illus.). 32p. (J). (gr. 4-6). lib. bdg. 22.60 (978-0-7368-1209-2(1) , Bridgestone Bks.) Capstone Pr., Inc.

Gaines, Jena. Haitian Immigration. 2003. (Changing Face of North America Ser.). (Illus.). 112p. (J). lib. bdg. (978-1-59084-691-9(5)) Mason Crest Pubs.

Girod, Christina M. Indian Americans. 2003. (Immigrants in America Ser.). (Illus.). 112p. (J). 29.95 (978-1-59018-270-3(7) , Lucent Bks.) Thomson Gale.

Goldstein, Margaret J. British in America. 2006. (In America Ser.). (Illus.). 80p. (J). 27.93 (978-0-8225-4875-1(5) , Lerner Pubns.) Lerner Publishing Group.

Granfield, Linda. Pier 21: Gateway to Hope. 2000. (978-0-606-22840-4(3)) Tandem Library Bks.

—Pier 21: Gateway to Hope. 2000. (Illus.). 48p. (J). (gr. 3-8). pap. 12.95 (978-0-88776-517-9(3)) Tundra Bks., Inc./Livres Toundra, Inc. CAN. *Dist:* Random Hse., Inc.

—Pier Twenty-One: Gateway to Hope. 2000. (gr. 3-6). lib. bdg. 22.25 (978-0-613-49399-4(0)) Tandem Library Bks.

Graves, Kerry A. Irish Americans. 2004. (Immigrants in America Ser.). 126p. (J). pap. 9.95 (978-0-7910-7511-1(7) , Chelsea Hse.) Facts On File, Inc.

Greene, Meg. The Russian-Americans. 2002. (Immigrants in America Ser.). (Illus.). 104p. (YA). (gr. 4-12). 29.95 (978-1-56006-963-8(5) , LML00902-179006, Lucent Bks.) Thomson Gale.

Haberle, Susan E. Jewish Immigrants, 1880-1924. 2002. (Blue Earth Books). (Illus.). 32p. (J). (gr. 4). lib. bdg. 22.60 (978-0-7368-1207-8(5) , Bridgestone Bks.) Capstone Pr., Inc.

Hall, Margaret. Irish Americans. 2003. (We Are America Ser.). (Illus.). 32p. (J). lib. bdg. 24.22 (978-1-4034-0734-4(7)) Heinemann Library.

—Irish Americans. 2003. (gr. 3-6). lib. bdg. 15.25 (978-0-613-67417-1(0)) Tandem Library Bks.

Hamilton, Janice. Canadians in America. 2006. (In America Ser.). (Illus.). 72p. (J). 27.93 (978-0-8225-2681-0(6) , Lerner Pubns.) Lerner Publishing Group.

Hamilton, John. Becoming a Citizen. 2005. (Government in Action! Ser.). (J). (gr. k-6). lib. bdg. 22.78 (978-1-59197-642-4(1)) ABDO Publishing Co.

Hammerschmidt, Peter. Land of Immigrants. 2002. (Welcome to America Ser.). (Illus.). 64p. (J). (gr. 5 up). lib. bdg. (978-1-59084-104-4(2)) Mason Crest Pubs.

Harcourt School Publishers Staff. Angel Island. 3rd ed. 2002. (Horizons Ser.). (Illus.). (J). pap. 5.50 (978-0-15-333419-1(3)) Harcourt Schl. Pubs.

Hasler, Brian. Casper & Catherine Move to America: An Immigrant Family's Adventures, 1849-1850. Gouge, Angela, tr. Gouge, Angela, illus. 2003. 32p. 17.95 (978-0-87195-168-7(1)) Indiana Historical Society.

Hazen, Walter A. Immigration. 2004. (Everyday Life Ser.). (Illus.). 96p. pap. (978-0-673-58665-0(0)) Good Year Bks.

Hernandez, Roger E. Cuban Immigration. 2003. (Changing Face of North America Ser.). (Illus.). 112p. (YA). lib. bdg. (978-1-59084-681-0(8)) Mason Crest Pubs.

—Immigration. 2006. (Gallup Major Trends & Events Ser.). (Illus.). 112p. (J). (gr. 7 up). lib. bdg. (978-1-59084-965-1(5)) Mason Crest Pubs.

Hirsch, E. D., ed. Immigration, Level 6. tchr. ed. 9.95 (978-0-7690-5091-1(3)); stu. ed. 49.95 (978-0-7690-2856-9(X)) Pearson Learning.

Honovich, Nancy. Immigration from the Former Yugoslavia. 2003. (Changing Face of North America Ser.). (Illus.). 112p. (YA). lib. bdg. (978-1-59084-690-2(7)) Mason Crest Pubs.

Hopkinson, Deborah. Shutting Out the Sky: Life in the Tenements of New York, 1880-1924. 2003. (Illus.). 144p. (J). pap. 17.95 (978-0-439-37590-0(8) , Orchard Bks.) Scholastic, Inc.

Horrell, Sarah. Eastern Europe. 1998. (Origins Ser.). (Illus.). 32p. (YA). (gr. 5-8). 21.00 (978-0-531-14449-7(6) , Watts, Franklin) Scholastic Library Publishing.

Hunter, Miranda. Latino Americans & Immigration Laws: Crossing the Border. 2005. (Illus.). 112p. (J). (ps-7). lib. bdg. (978-1-59084-939-2(6)) Mason Crest Pubs.

Huthmacher, J. Joseph. A Nation of Newcomers. (J). 17.95 (978-0-88411-651-6(4)) Amereon LTD.

Immigration. 2003. (Eye on History Ser.). 32p. (gr. 5-12). 5.99 (978-1-56822-449-7(4) , IF2661) School Specialty Publishing.

Ingram, Scott. Greek Immigrants. 2004. (Immigration to the United States Ser.). (Illus.). 96p. (J). (gr. 4-9). 35.00 (978-0-8160-5689-7(7)) Facts On File, Inc.

—Japanese Immigrants. 2004. (Immigration to the United States Ser.). (Illus.). 96p. (J). (gr. 4-9). 35.00 (978-0-8160-5688-0(9)) Facts On File, Inc.

Ingram, Scott & Asher, Robert. Polish Immigrants. 2004. (Immigration to the United States Ser.). (Illus.). 96p. (YA). (gr. 4-9). 35.00 (978-0-8160-5686-6(2)) Facts On File, Inc.

Isaacs, Sally Senzell. Life at Ellis Island. (Picture the Past Ser.). (Illus.). 32p. (J). 2002. (gr. k-3). pap. 7.50 (978-1-58810-417-5(6) , 91190); 2001. (gr. 2-4). lib. bdg. (978-1-58810-252-2(1)) Heinemann Library.

Janssen-Mathes, Mieke. The Secret of Otherland. Kwakkenbos, Frans, illus. 2007. 96p. pap. 34.95 (978-90-6832-587-4(6)) KIT (Koninklijk Instituut voor de Tropen) NLD. *Dist:* Stylus Publishing, LLC.

Kale, Shelly. A Suitcase of Dreams: Immigration Stories from the Skirball Cultural Center. 2002. (Illus.). 32p. (J). (gr. 3-5). pap. 12.95 (978-0-9704295-0-6(9)) Skirball Cultural Ctr.

Karecki, Jason, illus. The Adventures of Drake Montana Vol. 1: The Great Migration. 1998. 24p. (J). (gr. k-5). (978-1-890716-07-3(3)) K&M International.

Kenney, Karen. Illegal Immigration. 2007. (Essential Viewpoints Ser.). (Illus.). 112p. (YA). (gr. 7-9). lib. bdg. 32.79 ***(978-1-59928-861-1(3)*** , Essential Library) ABDO Publishing Co.

Kling, Andrew A. Life on a New World Voyage. 2004. (Way People Live Ser.). (J). (gr. 7-10). 29.95 (978-1-59018-163-8(8) , Lucent Bks.) Thomson Gale.

Kowalski, Kathiann M. Salvadorans in America. 2006. (In America Ser.). (Illus.). 80p. (J). (ps-7). 27.93 (978-0-8225-2424-3(4) , Lerner Pubns.) Lerner Publishing Group.

Kroll, Steven. Sweet America: An Immigrants Story. 2000. (gr. 5-8). lib. bdg. 14.95 (978-0-613-36883-4(5)) Tandem Library Bks.

Lacivita, Michael J. Rag Man, Rag Man. 2004. (Mahoning Valley Writers Ser.). (Illus.). 262p. (YA). 26.95 (978-0-917530-80-7(2)); pap. 15.95 (978-0-917530-81-4(0)) Pig Iron Pr.

Laurel Corona. Jewish Americans. 2004. (Immigrants in America Ser.). (Illus.). 112p. (J). 29.95 (978-1-59018-431-8(9)) Thomson Gale.

Levete, Sarah. Being an Immigrant. 2006. (Let's Talk about Ser.). (Illus.). 32p. (J). (gr. 3-5). lib. bdg. 27.10 (978-1-59604-084-7(X)) Stargazer Bks.

Libal, Autumn. Cuban Americans: Exiles from an Island Home. 2005. (Illus.). 112p. (J). (ps-7). lib. bdg. (978-1-59084-928-6(0)) Mason Crest Pubs.

Maestro, Betsy. Coming to America: The Story of Immigration. Ryan, Susannah, illus. unabr. ed. 2001. (J). (gr. k-6). 26.90 incl. audio (978-0-8045-6853-1(7) , 6853) Spoken Arts, Inc.

Marín-Guzman, Roberto & Zéraoui, Zidane. Arab Immigration in Mexico in the Nineteenth & Twentieth Centuries: Assimilation & Arab Heritage. 2003. (Illus.). 208p. per. 18.95 (978-0-9636882-2-4(7)) Augustine Pr.

Martin, Jennifer C. The Korean Americans. 2005. (Immigrants in America Ser.). (Illus.). 112p. (YA). (gr. 7-10). lib. bdg. 29.95 (978-1-59018-079-2(8) , Lucent Bks.) Thomson Gale.

Mattern, Joanne. Coming to America: The Story of Immigration. Sanfilippo, Margaret, illus. 2000. (Cover-to-Cover Informational Bks.). 64p. (J). (gr. 4-7). lib. bdg. 17.95 (978-0-7807-9715-4(9) , Covercraft); pap. 8.95 (978-0-7891-2851-5(9)) Perfection Learning Corp.

—Japanese Americans. 2003. (Immigrants in America Ser.). (Illus.). 112p. (gr. 6-12). 30.00 (978-0-7910-7130-4(8)); pap. 13.25 (978-0-7910-7510-4(9)) Facts On File, Inc. (Chelsea Hse.).

McHugh, Michael J., et al. A Child's Story of America. 2nd ed. 1998. (Illus.). 202p. (J). (gr. 3-5). pap. 8.95 (978-1-930092-93-8(8) , CLP79945) Christian Liberty Pr.

Meltzer, Milton, et al. Bound for America: The Story of the European Immigrants. 2001. (Great Journeys Ser.). (Illus.). 112p. (J). (gr. 5 up). lib. bdg. 32.79 (978-0-7614-1227-4(1) , Benchmark Bks.) Cavendish, Marshall Corp.

Moreno, Barry, ed. & intro. We Came to America, 16 vols., Set. Moreno, Barry, intro. 2003. (Illus.). 64p. (YA). lib. bdg. (978-1-59084-100-6(X)) Mason Crest Pubs.

Moynihan, Daniel Patrick, intro. Immigrants in America. (Illus.). (gr. 6-12). lib. bdg. 39.80 (978-0-7910-8470-0(1) , Chelsea Hse.) Facts On File, Inc.

Nichol, Bryan. Norwegian Americans. 2004. (One Nation Ser.). (Illus.). 32p. (J). (gr. k-6). lib. bdg. 22.78 (978-1-59197-531-1(X) , Checkerboard Library) ABDO Publishing Co.

—Puerto Rican Americans. 2004. (One Nation Ser.). (Illus.). 32p. (J). (gr. k-6). lib. bdg. 22.78 (978-1-59197-532-8(8) , Checkerboard Library) ABDO Publishing Co.

Noonan, Sheila Smith. Korean Immigration. 2003. (Changing Face of North America Ser.). (Illus.). 112p. (YA). lib. bdg. (978-1-59084-693-3(1)) Mason Crest Pubs.

Olson, Kay Melchisedech. Norwegian, Swedish, & Danish Immigrants, 1820-1920. 2001. (Blue Earth Books). (Illus.). 32p. (J). (gr. 3-4). lib. bdg. 22.60 (978-0-7368-0798-2(5) , Bridgestone Bks.) Capstone Pr., Inc.

Ouellette, Jeannine. A Day Without Immigrants: Rallying Behind America's Newcomers. 2007. (J). lib. bdg. ***(978-0-7565-2498-2(9))*** Compass Point Bks.

Parker, Lewis K. Why German Immigrants Came to America. 2003. (Reading Power Ser.). (Illus.). 24p. (J). lib. bdg. 17.25 (978-0-8239-6458-1(2) , PowerKids Pr.) Rosen Publishing Group, Inc., The.

—Why Irish Immigrants Came to America. 2003. (Reading Power Ser.). (Illus.). 24p. (J). lib. bdg. 17.25 (978-0-8239-6462-8(0) , PowerKids Pr.) Rosen Publishing Group, Inc., The.

—Why Italian Immigrants Came to America. 2003. (Reading Power Ser.). (Illus.). 24p. (J). lib. bdg. 17.25 (978-0-8239-6460-4(4) , PowerKids Pr.) Rosen Publishing Group, Inc., The.

—Why Japanese Immigrants Came to America. 2003. (Reading Power Ser.). (Illus.). 24p. (J). lib. bdg. 17.25 (978-0-8239-6463-5(9) , PowerKids Pr.) Rosen Publishing Group, Inc., The.

—Why Mexican Immigrants Came to America. 2003. (Reading Power Ser.). (Illus.). 24p. (J). lib. bdg. 17.25 (978-0-8239-6459-8(0) , PowerKids Pr.) Rosen Publishing Group, Inc., The.

—Why Vietnamese Immigrants Came to America. 2003. (Reading Power Ser.). (Illus.). 24p. (J). lib. bdg. 17.25 (978-0-8239-6461-1(2) , PowerKids Pr.) Rosen Publishing Group, Inc., The.

Paulson, Timothy J. Irish Immigrants. 2004. (Immigration to the United States Ser.). (Illus.). 96p. (J). (gr. 4-9). per. 35.00 (978-0-8160-5682-8(X)) Facts On File, Inc.

Peacock, Louise. At Ellis Island: A History in Many Voices. Krudop, Walter Lyon, illus. 2007. 48p. (J). (gr. 2-5). 18.99 ***(978-0-689-83026-6(2)*** , Atheneum) Simon & Schuster Children's Publishing.

Peoples of North America, 10 vols. 2003. (Illus.). (J). 359.00 (978-0-7172-5777-5(0) , Grolier) Scholastic Library Publishing.

Peterson, Tiffany. Japanese Americans. 2004. (We Are America Ser.). (Illus.). 32p. (J). lib. bdg. 24.22 (978-1-4034-5022-7(6)) Heinemann Library.

Petrini, Catherine M. The Italian-Americans. 2001. (Immigrants in America Ser.). (Illus.). 104p. (YA). (gr. 4-12). 29.95 (978-1-56006-882-2(5) , LML00902-178205, Lucent Bks.) Thomson Gale.

Pferdehirt, Julia. They Came to Wisconsin. 2002. (New Badger History Ser.). (Illus.). 144p. (J). pap. 15.95 (978-0-87020-328-2(2)) Wisconsin Historical Society.

Price Hossell, Karen. Dominican Americans. 2004. (We Are America Ser.). (Illus.). 32p. (J). lib. bdg. 24.22 (978-1-4034-5020-3(X)) Heinemann Library.

—The Irish. 2004. (Illus.). 207p. (gr. 10-12). 34.95 (978-0-7377-2154-6(5) , Greenhaven Pr., Inc.) Thomson Gale.

Price Hossell, Karen & Peterson, Tiffany. We Are America, 6 bks., Set 3. 2004. (J). (gr. 2-4). lib. bdg. 153.86 (978-1-4034-5026-5(9)) Heinemann Library.

Rael, Elsa Okon. Rivka's First Thanksgiving. Kovalski, Maryann, illus. 2004. 32p. (J). pap. 6.99 (978-0-689-84105-7(1) , Aladdin) Simon & Schuster Children's Publishing.

Roberts, Bethany. Gramps & the Fire Dragon. Iwai, Melissa, illus. 2000. 32p. (J). (gr. k-3). tchr. ed. 15.00 (978-0-395-69849-5(9) , Clarion Bks.) Houghton Mifflin Co. Trade & Reference Div.

Rossi, Ann. Immigrants Today. 2004. (National Geographic Reading Expeditions Ser.). (Illus.). 40p. (J). pap. (978-0-7922-4560-5(1)) National Geographic Society.

Schonberg, Marcia. People of Michigan. 2003. (Heinemann State Studies). (Illus.). 48p. (J). pap. 8.50 (978-1-4034-2680-2(5)); 27.07 (978-1-4034-0661-3(8)) Heinemann Library.

Schur, Joan Brodsky. The Arab Americans. 2004. (Immigrants in America Ser.). (Illus.). 112p. (J). 29.95 (978-1-59018-075-4(5) , Lucent Bks.) Thomson Gale.

Schwartz, Eric. Central American Immigrants to the United States: Refugees from Unrest. 2005. (Illus.). 112p. (J). (ps-7). lib. bdg. (978-1-59084-929-3(9)) Mason Crest Pubs.

Senker, Cath. Immigrants & Refugees. 2004. (21st Century Issues Ser.). (J). pap. 11.95 (978-0-8368-5661-3(9)); lib. bdg. 30.00 (978-0-8368-5644-6(9)) Stevens, Gareth Inc.

Senker, Cath. Immigration. 2007. (J). lib. bdg. ***(978-1-4042-3755-1(0)*** , Rosen Central) Rosen Publishing Group, Inc., The.

Sioux, Tracee. Immigrants in Colonial America. 2004. (Primary Sources of Immigration & Migration in America Ser.). (Illus.). 24p. (J). lib. bdg. (978-0-8239-8949-2(6) , PowerKids Pr.) Rosen Publishing Group, Inc., The.

Smith, Trevor. Migrants & Refugees. 2004. (Understanding Global Issues Ser.). (Illus.). 56p. (J). (gr. 10-12). (978-1-58340-360-0(4)) Smart Apple Media.

Sonneborn, Liz. German Americans. 2003. (Immigrants in America Ser.). (Illus.). 112p. (gr. 6-12). 30.00 (978-0-7910-7127-4(8)); pap. 30.00 (978-0-7910-7512-8(5)) Facts On File, Inc. (Chelsea Hse.).

Staeger, Rob. Deported Aliens. 2003. (Changing Face of North America Ser.). (Illus.). 112p. (J). lib. bdg. (978-1-59084-686-5(9)) Mason Crest Pubs.

Steele, Christy, et al. Fighting for American Values. 2007. (Latino-American History Ser.). 112p. (J). (gr. 5-8). 35.00 (978-0-8160-6444-1(X) , Chelsea Hse.) Facts On File, Inc.

Stein, Robert. Jewish Americans: Coming to America. 2006. (Illus.). 128p. (J). (gr. 4-8). reprint ed. 15.00 (978-1-4223-5576-3(4)) DIANE Publishing Co.

Steward, Mark. People of New York. 2003. (Heinemann State Studies). (Illus.). 48p. (J). (gr. 3-5). lib. bdg. (978-1-4034-0355-1(4)) Heinemann Library.

Stewart, Gail B. Defending the Borders: The Role of Border & Immigration Control. 2003. (Lucent Library of Homeland Security). (Illus.). 112p. (J). 29.95 (978-1-59018-376-2(2) , Lucent Bks.) Thomson Gale.

Students at Balboa High School, compiled by. I Might Get Somewhere: Oral Histories of Immigration & Migration. 2005. 333p. (J). pap. 16.00 (978-1-932416-43-5(9)) 826 Valencia.

Taus-Bolstad, Stacy. Pakistanis in America. 2006. (In America Ser.). (Illus.). 80p. (J). 27.93 (978-0-8225-4872-0(0) , Lerner Pubns.) Lerner Publishing Group.

Teichmann, Iris. Immigration & Asylum. 2003. (In the News Ser.). (J). lib. bdg. 16.95 (978-1-58340-396-9(5)) Smart Apple Media.

—Life As an Immigrant. 2006. (Understanding Immigration Ser.). (Illus.). 44p. (YA). (gr. 5-8). lib. bdg. 31.35 (978-1-58340-968-8(8)) Smart Apple Media.

—A Multicultural World. 2006. (Understanding Immigration Ser.). (Illus.). 44p. (YA). (gr. 5-8). lib. bdg. 31.35 (978-1-58340-969-5(6)) Smart Apple Media.

—One Country to Another. 2006. (Understanding Immigration Ser.). (Illus.). 44p. (YA). (gr. 5-8). lib. bdg. 31.35 (978-1-58340-967-1(X)) Smart Apple Media.

Teitlebaum, Michael. Chinese Immigrants. 2004. (Immigration to the United States Ser.). (Illus.). 96p. (J). (gr. 4-9). 35.00 (978-0-8160-5687-3(0)) Facts On File, Inc.

Thompson, Linda. Immigration. 2005. 48p. pap. 7.45 (978-1-59515-824-6(3)) Rourke Publishing, LLC.

—Spanish Migration. 2005. 48p. pap. 7.45 (978-1-59515-828-4(6)) Rourke Publishing, LLC.

Thornton, Jeremy. The Gold Rush: Chinese Immigrants Come to America (1848-1882) 2004. (Primary Sources of Immigration & Migration in America Ser.). (Illus.). 24p. (J). lib. bdg. 19.95 (978-0-8239-6833-6(2) , PowerKids Pr.) Rosen Publishing Group, Inc., The.

—The Gold Rush: Chinese Immigrants Come to America, 1848-1882. 2004. (Primary Sources of Immigration & Migration in America Ser.). (Illus.). 24p. (J). lib. bdg. (978-0-8239-8959-1(3) , PowerKids Pr.) Rosen Publishing Group, Inc., The.

—Hard Times in Ireland: The Scotch-Irish Come to America, 1603-1775. 2004. (Primary Sources of Immigration & Migration in America Ser.). (Illus.). 24p. (J). lib. bdg. (978-0-8239-8956-0(9) , PowerKids Pr.) Rosen Publishing Group, Inc., The.

Trumbauer, Lisa. German Immigrants. 2004. (Immigration to the United States Ser.). (Illus.). 96p. (J). (gr. 4-9). 35.00 (978-0-8160-5683-5(8)) Facts On File, Inc.

—Hopes Fulfilled: The Irish Immigrants in Boston. 2005. (Illus.). 32p. (J). pap. ***(978-0-7367-2881-2(3))*** Zaner-Bloser, Inc.

Trumbauer, Lisa. Russian Immigrants. 2004. (Immigration to the United States Ser.). (Illus.). 96p. (J). (gr. 4-9). 35.00 (978-0-8160-5685-9(4)) Facts On File, Inc.

Wallner, Rosemary. Japanese Immigrants, 1850-1950. 2001. (Blue Earth Books). (Illus.). 32p. (J). (gr. 3-4). lib. bdg. 22.60 (978-0-7368-0797-5(7) , Bridgestone Bks.) Capstone Pr., Inc.

Wallner, Rosemary & Radzilowski, John. Polish Immigrants, 1890-1920. 2002. (Blue Earth Books). (Illus.). 32p. (J). (gr. 4). lib. bdg. 22.60 (978-0-7368-1208-5(3) , Bridgestone Bks.) Capstone Pr., Inc.

Weinberger, Kimberly. Journey to a New Land: An Oral History. Meers, Tony, illus. 2000. 32p. (J). (978-1-57255-813-7(X)); pap. (978-1-57255-812-0(1)) Mondo Publishing.

Wells, Rosemary, et al. Streets of Gold. Fogelman, Phyllis J., ed. Andreasen, Dan, illus. 1999. 40p. (J). (gr. k-3). 16.99 (978-0-8037-2149-4(8) , Dial) Penguin Group (USA) Inc.

Williams, Jean Kinney. Asian Indian Americans. 2003. (Spirit of America). (Illus.). 32p. (J). (gr. 2-6). 27.07 (978-1-59296-015-6(4)) Child's World, Inc.

Wilson, Ruth. Immigration. 2007. (J). ***(978-1-59604-142-4(0))*** Stargazer Bks.

Wilson, Ruth. Immigration: A Look at the Way the World Is Today. 2005. (Issues of the World Ser.). (Illus.). 48p. (J). (gr. 6-9). lib. bdg. 29.95 (978-1-59604-071-7(8) , 1247746) Stargazer Bks.

Wolf, Bernard. Coming to America: A Muslim Family's Story. Wolf, Bernard, photos by. 2003. (Illus.). 48p. (J). (gr. k-8). 17.95 (978-1-58430-086-1(8)); pap. 7.95 (978-1-58430-177-6(5)) Lee & Low Bks., Inc.

—Coming to America: A Muslim Family's Story. 2003. (gr. 3-6). lib. bdg. 16.40 (978-0-613-67796-7(X)) Tandem Library Bks.

Worth, Richard. Mexican Immigrants. 2004. (Immigration to the United States Ser.). (Illus.). 96p. (J). (gr. 4-9). 35.00 (978-0-8160-5690-3(0)) Facts On File, Inc.

Yancey, Diane. The German Americans. 2005. (Immigrants in America Ser.). (Illus.). 112p. (J). (gr. 4-7). lib. bdg. 29.95 (978-1-56006-962-1(7) , Lucent Bks.) Thomson Gale.

Zurlo, Tony. The Japanese Americans. 2003. (Immigrants in America Ser.). (Illus.). 112p. (J). 29.95 (978-1-59018-001-3(1) , Lucent Bks.) Thomson Gale.

EMIGRATION AND IMMIGRATION—FICTION

Ada, Alma Flor. El Vuelo de los Colibries. Jacobson, Judith, illus. 32p. (J). (gr. 3-6). pap. 9.95 (978-1-56492-211-3(1)) Laredo Publishing Co., Inc.

Aksomitis, Linda. Adeline's Dream. 2006. (From Many Peoples Ser.). 272p. (J). pap. 7.95 (978-1-55050-323-4(5)) Coteau Bks. CAN. *Dist:* F & W Pubns., Inc.

Aliki. Marianthe's Story: Painted Words & Spoken Memories, 2 bks. in 1. Aliki, illus. 1998. (Illus.). 64p. (J). (gr. k-3). lib. bdg. 17.89 (978-0-688-15662-6(2)); 16.99 (978-0-688-15661-9(4)) HarperCollins Pubs.

Arkadina, Mina. Nesmotrya Mina Chto. Arkadina, Mina, ed. 2003. Tr. of No Matter What.... (RUS.). 178p. (YA). (978-0-9728301-0-2(3)) Publishing Hse. Gelany.

Armstrong, Jennifer. Theodore Roosevelt: Letters from a Young Coal Miner. 2001. (Dear Mr. President Ser.: Vol. 1). (Illus.). 118p. (J). (gr. 4-7). 8.95 (978-1-890817-27-5(9)) Winslow Pr.

Atwell, Debby. The Thanksgiving Door. 2006. (Illus.). 32p. (J). (gr. k-3). pap. 5.95 (978-0-618-77124-0(7) , Walter Lorraine) Houghton Mifflin Co. Trade & Reference Div.

Auch, Mary Jane. Ashes of Roses. rev. ed. 2002. 256p. (YA). (gr. 7-10). 16.95 (978-0-8050-6686-9(1) , Holt, Henry & Co. Bks. For Young Readers) Holt, Henry & Co.

—Ashes of Roses. 2004. 256p. (YA). (gr. 7). reprint ed. pap. 5.99 (978-0-440-23851-5(X) , Laurel Leaf) Random Hse. Children's Bks.

—Ashes of Roses. 2004. (gr. 7-12). lib. bdg. 14.15 (978-0-613-72252-0(3)) Tandem Library Bks.

Avi. Silent Movie. Mordan, C. B., illus. 2003. 48p. (J). (gr. k-3). 16.95 (978-0-689-84145-3(0) , Atheneum/Anne Schwartz Bks.) Simon & Schuster Children's Publishing.

Barth-Grozinger, Inge. Something Remains. Bell, Anthea, tr. from GER. 2006. 400p. (gr. 5-9). 16.99 (978-0-7868-3880-6(9)) Hyperion Pr.

Bitton-Jackson, Livia. Hello, America: A Refugee's Journey from Auschwitz to the New World. 2005. 240p. (YA). (gr. 6 up). 16.95 (978-0-689-86755-2(7) , Simon & Schuster Children's Publishing) Simon & Schuster Children's Publishing.

Black, Robert. Liberty Girl. (YA). pap. 9.99 (978-0-88092-488-7(8)) Royal Fireworks Publishing Co.

Blasi, Kathleen McAlpin. A Name of Honor. Bowman, Leslie W., illus. 2006. (J). (978-1-59336-692-6(2)) Mondo Publishing.

Bruce, Mary Grant. Back to Billabong. l.t. ed. 2006. 200p. pap. 15.99 (978-1-4264-2197-6(4)) BiblioBazaar.

Bunting, Eve. A Picnic in October. Carpenter, Nancy, illus. 2004. 32p. (J). (gr. 1-4). lib. bdg. 13.20 (978-0-606-30433-7(9)) Tandem Library Bks.

Castilla, Julia Mercedes. Emilio. 1999. 160p. (YA). (gr. 4-7). pap. 9.95 (978-1-55885-271-6(9) , Piñata Books) Arte Publico Pr.

—Emilio. (SPA.). (YA). (gr. 5-8). 8.95 (978-958-04-4149-6(9) , NR3970) Norma S.A. COL. *Dist:* Distribuidora Norma, Inc., Lectorum Pubns., Inc.

Chan, Gillian. An Ocean Apart: The Gold Mountain Diary of Chin Mei-Ling. 2004. (Dear Canada Ser.). (Illus.). 217p. (J). pap. (978-0-7791-1353-8(5)) Scholastic Canada, Ltd.

Cheng, Andrea. Honeysuckle House. 2004. 136p. (YA). 16.95 (978-1-886910-99-7(5) , Lemniscaat) Boyds Mills Pr.

Children of the River. 1999. (Assessment Packs Ser.). 15p. (J). pap., tchr.'s training gde. ed. 15.95 (978-1-58303-092-9(1)) Pathways Publishing.

Citra, Becky. Ellie's New Home. 1999. (Young Reader Ser.). (J). (978-0-606-19475-4(4)) Tandem Library Bks.

—The Freezing Moon. McCallum, Stephen, illus. 2001. (Young Reader Ser.). 112p. (J). (gr. 3-6). pap. 4.99 (978-1-55143-181-9(5)) Orca Bk. Pubs. USA.

Cohen, Barbara. Molly's Pilgrim. Duffy, Daniel M. & Deraney, Michael J., illus. rev. ed. 1998. 32p. (J). (ps-3). 16.99 (978-0-688-16279-5(7)) HarperCollins Pubs.

—Molly's Pilgrim. Duffy, Daniel Mark & Deraney, Michael J., illus. 97th rev. ed. 1998. 32p. (J). (gr. 1-4). pap. 3.99 (978-0-688-16280-1(0) , Harper Trophy) HarperCollins Pubs.

—Molly's Pilgrim. (Literature to Go Ser.). pap., tchr. ed. incl. VHS (978-0-7919-2685-7(0)) Phoenix Films & Video.

Cohen, Carol L. & Cohen, Ellen R. Dare to Dream: An Immigration Story. 2002. (J). pap. 12.00 (978-1-57960-096-9(4)) History Compass, LLC.

Colato Lainez, Rene. Waiting for Papa/Esperando a Papa. Accardo, Anthony, illus. Tr. of Esperando a Papa. (ENG & SPA.). 32p. (gr. 1-3). 15.95 (978-1-55885-403-1(7) , Piñata Books) Arte Publico Pr.

Corey, Shana. Milly & the Macy's Parade. Helquist, Brett, illus. 2006. 38p. (J). (gr. 4-8). reprint ed. 17.00 (978-1-4223-5174-1(2)) DIANE Publishing Co.

Currier, Katrina Saltonstall. Kai's Journey to Gold Mountain: An Angel Island Story. 2004. 40p. 16.95 (978-0-9667352-7-7(7)); (Illus.). 44p. (J). pap. 10.95 (978-0-9667352-4-6(2)) Angel Island Assoc.

Drake, Isabelle. La Cancion de Gabriela: Como Me Adapto a un Lugar Nuevo. Burris, Priscilla Garcia, illus. 2007. (SPA.). 32p. (J). (ps-3). 12.99 (***978-0-06-114102-7(X)*** , Rayo) HarperCollins Pubs.

Dueck, Adele. Nettie's Journey. 2006. (Illus.). 224p. (J). pap. 7.95 (978-1-55050-322-7(7)) Coteau Bks. CAN. *Dist:* F & W Pubns., Inc.

Durbin, William. Darkest Evening. 2004. 240p. (J). (gr. 7 up). pap. 15.95 (978-0-439-37307-4(7) , Orchard Bks.) Scholastic, Inc.

—Song of Sampo Lake. 2004. 224p. (J). (gr. 5). reprint ed. pap. 5.50 (978-0-440-22899-8(9) , Yearling) Random Hse. Children's Bks.

—Song of Sampo Lake. 2004. (gr. 5-8). lib. bdg. 13.55 (978-0-613-85112-1(9)) Tandem Library Bks.

Figueredo, D. H. Un Mundo Nuevo. de la Vega, Eida, tr. from ENG. Sanchez, Enrique O., illus. 2000. (SPA & ENG.). 32p. (J). (gr. k-2). 15.95 (978-1-58430-006-9(X) , LW2987); pap. 6.95 (978-1-58430-007-6(8) , LW3110) Lee & Low Bks., Inc.

—Un Mundo Nuevo. Sanchez, Enrique O., illus. 2000. (SPA.). (J). (978-0-606-19833-2(4)); (978-0-606-19834-9(2)) Tandem Library Bks.

—When This World Was New. Sanchez, Enrique O., illus. 2003. (J). pap. 6.95 (978-1-58430-173-8(2)); 1999. 32p. (YA). 12.76 (978-1-880000-86-1(5)) Lee & Low Bks., Inc.

—When This World Was New. 2003. (gr. k-3). lib. bdg. 15.25 (978-0-613-83688-3(X)) Tandem Library Bks.

Fitz-Gibbon, Sally. Lizzie's Storm. Wood, Muriel, illus. (J). 2004. 64p. pap. (978-1-55041-795-1(9)); 2003. 67p. (978-1-55041-793-7(2)) Fitzhenry & Whiteside, Ltd.

Flatharta, Antoine O. The Prairie Train. Rohmann, Eric, illus. 1999. 40p. (J). (gr. k-3). 16.95 (978-0-517-70988-7(0) , Crown Books For Young Readers) Random Hse. Children's Bks.

French, Simon. Where in the World. 2003. 208p. (J). (gr. 3-6). 14.95 (978-1-56145-292-7(0) , Q34443) Peachtree Pubs., Ltd.

Frost, Helen. The Braid. 2006. (Illus.). 112p. (YA). (gr. 7 up). 16.00 (978-0-374-30962-6(0) , Frances Foster Bks.) Farrar, Straus & Giroux.

Gaberman, Judith. One-Way to Ansonia. 2001. 196p. pap. 12.95 (978-0-595-15830-0(7) , Backinprint.com) iUniverse, Inc.

Gallo, Donald R. First Crossing: Stories about Teen Immigrants. 2004. (Illus.). 240p. (J). (gr. 7 up). 16.99 (978-0-7636-2249-7(4)) Candlewick Pr.

Gallo, Donald R., ed. First Crossing: Stories about Teen Immigrants. 2007. 240p. (YA). (gr. 7). pap. 8.99 (978-0-7636-3291-5(0)) Candlewick Pr.

Giff, Patricia Reilly. A House of Tailors. (gr. 4-7). 2006. 160p. (YA). 5.50 (978-0-440-23800-3(5) , Yearling); 2004. 176p. (J). 15.95 (978-0-385-73066-2(7) , Lamb, Wendy) Random Hse. Children's Bks.

—Maggie's Door. 2003. (Illus.). 176p. (YA). (gr. 3-7). lib. bdg. 17.99 (978-0-385-90095-9(3) , Lamb, Wendy) Random Hse. Children's Bks.

Glaser, Linda. Bridge to America: Based on a True Story. 2005. (Illus.). 208p. (J). (gr. 4-6). 16.00 (978-0-618-56301-2(6)) Houghton Mifflin Co. Trade & Reference Div.

Goldish, Meish. On Their Way. Mohr, Mark, illus. 2002. 16p. (J). (978-0-439-35130-0(8)) Scholastic, Inc.

Gomez Cerda, Alfredo. Luna's Braids. (SPA.). (J). pap. (978-84-241-7934-2(X)) Everest de Ediciones y Distribucion, S.L. ESP. *Dist:* Lectorum Pubns., Inc.

Gundisch, Karin. How I Became an American. Skofield, James, tr. from GER. 2001. (Illus.). 144p. (J). (gr. 3-7). 15.95 (978-0-8126-4875-1(7)) Cricket Bks.

Harcourt School Publishers Staff. Am I an American? On Level. 3rd ed. 2002. (Trophies Reading Program Ser.). (Illus.). pap. 5.10 (978-0-15-323272-5(2)) Harcourt Schl. Pubs.

—People of Our Nation. 3rd ed. 2002. (Trophies English Language Learners Ser.). (Illus.). pap. 5.10 (978-0-15-327880-8(3)) Harcourt Schl. Pubs.

Hest, Amy. When Jessie Came Across the Sea. Lynch, P. J., illus. 2003. 40p. (J). (gr. 1-7). pap. 6.99 (978-0-7636-1274-0(X)) Candlewick Pr.

Ho, Minfong. The Stone Goddess. 2003. (First Person Fiction Ser.). 208p. (J). (gr. 4-7). pap. 16.95 (978-0-439-38197-0(5) , Orchard Bks.) Scholastic, Inc.

Ho, Shirley. Time to Be. Date not set. (J). (978-1-879965-10-2(0)) Polychrome Publishing Corp.

Hoffman, Mary. The Color of Home. Littlewood, Karin, illus. 2002. 32p. (J). (gr. k). 17.99 (978-0-8037-2841-7(7) , Dial) Penguin Group (USA) Inc.

Holt, Rinehart and Winston Staff. Goodbye, Vietnam. 2nd ed. 2002. pap., stu. ed. 13.20 (978-0-03-066514-1(0)) Holt, Rinehart & Winston.

—Goodbye, Vietnam: With Connections. 2nd ed. 2001. 14.64 (978-0-03-066513-4(2)) Holt, Rinehart & Winston.

—A Paradise Called Texas: With Connections. 2001. 14.64 (978-0-03-064737-6(1)); pap., stu. ed. 13.16 (978-0-03-064736-9(3)) Holt, Rinehart & Winston.

Holub, Joan. Tatiana Comes to America: An Ellis Island Story. 2002. (gr. 3-6). lib. bdg. 11.80 (978-0-613-70904-0(7)) Tandem Library Bks.

Hood, Karen Jean Matsko. Anna Arrives from Yugoslavia. 2003. (J). pap. 15.95 (978-1-930948-50-1(6)) Whispering Pine Pr., Inc.

—Anna Arrives from Yugoslavia. Scripture-Smith, Mary, illus. 2000. 128p. (J). (gr. 2-7). pap. 9.95 (978-0-9679368-5-7(3)) Whispering Pine Pr., Inc.

Hubbard, Coleen. Christmas in Silver Lake. Rabinowitz, Sandy & Keiffer, Christa, illus. l.t. ed. 1999. (Treasured Horses Collection). 128p. (J). (gr. 4 up). lib. bdg. 23.33 (978-0-8368-2400-1(8)) Stevens, Gareth Inc.

Imlay, Gilbert. The Emigrants. Verhoeven, W. M. & Gilroy, Amanda, eds. 1998. (Classics Ser.). (Illus.). 368p. pap. 14.00 (978-0-14-043672-3(3) , Penguin Classics) Penguin Group (USA) Inc.

Jaramillo, Ann. La Linea. 2006. (SPA.). 144p. (J). 16.95 (978-1-59643-154-6(7)) Roaring Brook Pr.

—La Linea. 2008. 160p. (YA). pap. 7.99 (***978-0-312-37354-2(6)***) Square Fish.

Jaspersohn, William. The Two Brothers. Donato, Michael A., illus. 2005. (Family Heritage Ser.). 36p. (gr. 1-5). 15.95 (978-0-916718-16-9(6)) Vermont Folklife Ctr.

Jimenez, Francisco. Cajas de Carton: Relatos de la Vida Peregrina de un Nino Campesino. 2002. Tr. of Circuit. (SPA.). (gr. 5-8). lib. bdg. 15.25 (978-0-613-89004-5(3)) Tandem Library Bks.

—Cajas de Carton: The Circuit Spanish Edition. 2002. (SPA., Illus.). 144p. (J). (gr. 5 up). pap. 6.95 (978-0-618-22616-0(8)) Houghton Mifflin Co. Trade & Reference Div.

Jiménez, Francisco. Cajas de Carton: The Circuit Spanish Edition. 2002. (SPA., Illus.). 144p. (J). (gr. 5). tchr. ed. 16.00 (978-0-618-22615-3(X)) Houghton Mifflin Co. Trade & Reference Div.

Jimenez, Francisco. Senderos Fronterizos: Breaking Through Spanish Edition. 2002. (SPA., Illus.). 240p. (J). tchr. ed. 16.00 (978-0-618-22617-7(6)) Houghton Mifflin Co. Trade & Reference Div.

Jiménez, Francisco. Senderos Fronterizos: Breaking Through Spanish Edition. 2002. (SPA., Illus.). 240p. (J). (gr. 5 up). pap. 6.95 (978-0-618-22618-4(4)) Houghton Mifflin Co. Trade & Reference Div.

Jones, Verda Boyd. Maureen the Detective: The Age of Immigration. 2005. (Sisters in Time Ser.). 144p. (J). pap. 4.97 (978-1-59310-661-4(0)) Barbour Publishing, Inc.

Kalman, Esther. Tchaikovsky Discovers America. Fernandez, Laura & Jacobson, Rick, illus. 2000. 48p. (J). (gr. k-3). pap. 6.95 (978-0-531-07168-7(5) , Orchard Bks.) Scholastic, Inc.

Krishnaswami, Uma. Chachaji's Cup. Sitaraman, Soumya, illus. 2003. 32p. (J). (gr. 1 up). 16.95 (978-0-89239-178-3(2)) Children's Bk. Pr.

Lasky, Kathryn. Dreams in the Golden Country: The Diary of Zipporah Feldman, a Jewish Immigrant Girl, New York City, 1903. 1998. (Dear America Ser.). (Illus.). 192p. (J). (gr. 4-9). pap. 10.95 (978-0-590-02973-5(8)) Scholastic, Inc.

Lawlor, Laurie. American Sisters: A Titanic Journey Across the Sea. 2000. (J). (978-0-606-20220-6(X)) Tandem Library Bks.

Lawson, Robert. The Great Wheel. 2004. (Illus.). 192p. (J). pap. 6.95 (978-0-8027-7705-8(8)) Walker & Co.

Leighton, Maxinne R. An Ellis Island Christmas. Nolan, Dennis, illus. 2005. 32p. (J). (gr. k-3). pap. 6.99 (978-0-14-240506-2(X) , Puffin) Penguin Group (USA) Inc.

Lombard, Jenny. Drita, My Homegirl. (J). (gr. 4-6). 2008. 144p. pap. 5.99 (***978-0-14-240905-3(7)*** , Puffin); 2006. 176p. 15.99 (978-0-399-24380-6(1) , Putnam Juvenile) Penguin Group (USA) Inc.

Look, Lenore. Ruby Lu, Empress of Everything. Wilsdorf, Anne, illus. 2006. 176p. (J). (gr. 1-5). 15.95 (978-0-689-86460-5(4) , Atheneum) Simon & Schuster Children's Publishing.

Loughrey, Eithne. Annie Moore: The Golden Dollar Girl. l.t. ed. 2006. (Dales Ser.). 208p. (J). 23.99 (978-1-84262-447-0(4)) Magna Large Print Bks. GBR. *Dist:* Ulverscroft Large Print Bks., Ltd.

—Annie Moore First in Line for America. l.t. ed. 2006. (Dales Ser.). 224p. (J). 23.99 (978-1-84262-446-3(6)) Magna Large Print Bks. GBR. *Dist:* Ulverscroft Large Print Bks., Ltd.

Lutzeier, Elizabeth. Bound for America. 2001. 176p. pap. 7.95 (978-0-86327-843-3(4)) Interlink Publishing Group, Inc.

The Magic Paper (Mexicans) 76p. (YA). (gr. 6-12). pap. 9.95 (978-0-8224-3686-7(8)) Globe Fearon Educational Publishing.

Magrane, Mijares. Grandma Garcia: La Abuela Garcia - An Intimate Journey into the Past. 2004. (SPA & ENG., Illus.). 96p. pap. 13.95 (978-0-9741167-0-9(X)) Magrane, Etna International.

Mak, Kam. Chinatown. Date not set. 32p. (J). (gr. k-3). pap. 5.99 (978-0-06-443732-5(9)) HarperCollins Pubs.

—My Chinatown: One Year in Poems. Mak, Kam, illus. 2001. (Illus.). 32p. (J). (gr. k-3). 16.99 (978-0-06-029190-7(7)) HarperCollins Pubs.

Making Heaven (Koreans) 76p. (YA). (gr. 6-12). pap. 9.95 (978-0-8224-3801-4(1)) Globe Fearon Educational Publishing.

Michelson, Richard. Grandpa's Gamble. Moser, Barry, illus. 1999. (Accelerated Reader Bks.). 32p. (YA). (ps up). 15.95 (978-0-7614-5034-4(3) , Cavendish Children's Bks.) Cavendish, Marshall Corp.

Mikaelsen, Ben. Red Midnight. 2003. 224p. (J). (gr. 5 up). pap. 5.99 (978-0-380-80561-7(8)) HarperCollins Pubs.

—Red Midnight. 2003. (gr. 5-8). lib. bdg. 14.15 (978-0-613-57776-2(0)) Tandem Library Bks.

Miller, Elizabeth I. Just Like Home. Reisberg, Mira, illus. 2004. Tr. of Como en Mi Tierra. (ENG & SPA.). 32p. (J). (gr. 1-3). 15.95 (978-0-8075-4068-8(4)) Whitman, Albert & Co.

Moss, Marissa. Hannah's Journal: The Story of an Immigrant Girl. 2002. (Young American Voices Ser.). (Illus.). 56p. (YA). (gr. 3-7). pap. 7.00 (978-0-15-216329-7(8) , Silver Whistle) Harcourt Trade Pubs.

—Hannah's Journal: The Story of an Immigrant Girl. 2002. (gr. 3-6). lib. bdg. 15.30 (978-0-613-53818-3(8)) Tandem Library Bks.

Murphy, Barbara Beasley. Miguel Lost & Found in the Palace. Ancona, George, illus. 2002. (Guidebook Ser.). 136p. pap. 14.95 (978-0-89013-394-1(8)); 1p. pap. 9.95 (978-0-89013-395-8(6)) Museum of New Mexico Pr.

—Miguel Lost & Found in the Palace. 2002. (gr. 3-6). lib. bdg. 24.55 (978-0-613-77345-4(4)) Tandem Library Bks.

Na, An. A Step from Heaven. 2003. 160p. (YA). (gr. 7-11). pap. 7.99 (978-0-14-250027-9(5) , Puffin) Penguin Group (USA) Inc.

—A Step from Heaven. l.t. ed. 2002. 193p. (J). 22.95 (978-0-7862-4126-2(8)) Thomson Gale.

Napoli, Donna Jo. The King of Mulberry Street. 256p. (gr. 3-7). 2007. 6.50 (***978-0-553-49416-7(3)*** , Yearling); 2005. (J). 15.95 (978-0-385-74653-3(9) , Lamb, Wendy); 2005. (J). lib. bdg. 17.99 (978-0-385-90890-0(3) , Lamb, Wendy) Random Hse. Children's Bks.

Neale, Cynthia G. The Irish Dresser: A Story of Hope During the Great Hunger (an Gorta Mor, 1845-1850) 2003. 148p. (J). pap. 7.95 (978-1-57249-344-5(5) , White Mane Kids) White Mane Publishing Co., Inc.

Never So Good (Jamaicans) 76p. (YA). (gr. 6-12). pap. 9.95 (978-0-8224-3806-9(2)) Globe Fearon Educational Publishing.

Nickles, Greg. The Poles. 2001. (978-0-606-21383-7(X)) Tandem Library Bks.

Nislick, June Levitt. Zayda Was a Cowboy. 2005. 128p. (J). pap. 9.95 (978-0-8276-0817-7(9)) Jewish Pubn. Society.

Nixon, Joan Lowery. Land of Dreams. l.t. ed. 2001. (Ellis Island Stories Ser.). 153p. (J). (gr. 4 up). lib. bdg. 23.33 (978-0-8368-2810-8(0)) Stevens, Gareth Inc.

—Land of Hope. l.t. ed. 2001. (Ellis Island Stories Ser.). 171p. (J). (gr. 4 up). lib. bdg. 23.33 (978-0-8368-2811-5(9)) Stevens, Gareth Inc.

—Land of Promise. l.t. ed. 2001. (Ellis Island Stories Ser.). 169p. (J). (gr. 4 up). lib. bdg. 23.33 (978-0-8368-2812-2(7)) Stevens, Gareth Inc.

Nobisso, Josephine. En Ingles, por Supuesto. Ziborova, Dasha, illus. 2003. Orig. Title: In English, of Course. (SPA.). 32p. 16.95 (978-0-940112-14-8(0)) Gingerbread Hse.

—En ingles, por Supuesto. Ziborova, Dasha, illus. 2003. Orig. Title: In English, of Course. (SPA.). 32p. pap. 8.95 (978-0-940112-16-2(7)) Gingerbread Hse.

Nobody Knows (Africans) 76p. (YA). (gr. 6-12). pap. 9.95 (978-0-8224-3683-6(3)) Globe Fearon Educational Publishing.

Nolan, Janet. The St. Patrick's Day Shillelagh. Stahl, Ben, illus. 2002. 32p. (J). (gr. 2-5). 16.95 (978-0-8075-7344-0(2)) Whitman, Albert & Co.

—The St. Patrick's Day Shillelagh. Stahl, Ben F., illus. 2002. 32p. (J). (gr. 2-5). pap. 6.95 (978-0-8075-7345-7(0)) Whitman, Albert & Co.

Nye, Naomi. Habibi. 1999. (gr. 7-12). lib. bdg. 14.15 (978-0-613-18312-3(6)) Tandem Library Bks.

Nye, Naomi Shihab. Habibi. unabr. ed. 2000. (YA). pap. 49.24 incl. audio (978-0-7887-3642-1(6) , 41008X4) Recorded Bks., LLC.

—Habibi. 1999. 272p. (YA). (gr. 5 up). pap. 5.99 (978-0-689-82523-1(4) , Simon Pulse) Simon & Schuster Children's Publishing.

—Habibi. 1999. (J). 12.64 (978-0-606-16320-0(4)) Tandem Library Bks.

O Little Town (Germans) 76p. (YA). (gr. 6-12). pap. 9.95 (978-0-8224-3681-2(7)) Globe Fearon Educational Publishing.

Oberman, Sheldon. The Always Prayer Shawl. Lewin, Ted, illus. 2005. 40p. (J). (ps-17). pap. 10.95 (978-1-59078-332-0(8)) Boyds Mills Pr.

Oh, Jina, reader. A Step from Heaven. 2004. 160p. (J). (gr. 6 up). pap. 36.00 incl. audio (978-0-8072-2287-4(9) , Listening Library) Random Hse. Audio Publishing Group.

Old Ways, New Ways (Eastern European Jews) 76p. (YA). (gr. 6-12). pap. 9.95 (978-0-8224-3682-9(5)) Globe Fearon Educational Publishing.

Pak, Soyung. A Place to Grow. Truong, Marcellino, illus. 2002. (J). pap. (978-0-439-13017-2(4) , Levine, Arthur A. Bks.) Scholastic, Inc.

—A Place to Grow. Truong, Marcelino, illus. 2002. 32p. (J). (ps-5). pap. 16.95 (978-0-439-13015-8(8) , Levine, Arthur A. Bks.) Scholastic, Inc.

Partridge, Elizabeth. Oranges on Golden Mountain. Sogabe, Aki, illus. 2003. 36p. (J). pap. 6.99 (978-0-14-250033-0(X) , Puffin) Penguin Group (USA) Inc.

—Oranges on Golden Mountain. 2003. (gr. k-3). lib. bdg. 15.30 (978-0-613-61651-5(0)) Tandem Library Bks.

Paterson, Katherine. Bread & Roses, Too. 2006. 288p. (J). (gr. 5-9). 16.00 (978-0-618-65479-6(8) , Clarion Bks.) Houghton Mifflin Co. Trade & Reference Div.

Perez, Amada Irma. My Diary from Here to There / Mi Diario de Aqui Hasta Alla. Gonzalez, Maya Christina, illus. 2002. Tr. of Mi Diario de Aqui Hasta Alla. (ENG & SPA.). 32p. (J). (gr. 2-5). 16.95 (978-0-89239-175-2(8)) Children's Bk. Pr.

Polacco, Patricia. The Keeping Quilt. 2001. (J). (gr. k-3). 26.95 incl. audio (978-0-8045-6842-5(1) , 6842) Spoken Arts, Inc.

—Keeping Quilt. 2001. (gr. k-3). lib. bdg. 15.30 (978-0-613-37155-1(0)) Tandem Library Bks.

—The Keeping Quilt. 10th anniv. ed. 1998. (Illus.). 48p. (J). (ps-3). 17.95 (978-0-689-82090-8(9)) Simon & Schuster Children's Publishing.

Polacco, Patricia, illus. The Keeping Quilt. 2001. 32p. (J). (ps-3). pap. 6.99 (978-0-689-84447-8(6) , Aladdin) Simon & Schuster Children's Publishing.

Push to the West (Norwegians) 76p. (YA). (gr. 6-12). pap. 9.95 (978-0-8224-3678-2(7)) Globe Fearon Educational Publishing.

Pushker, Gloria Teles. Toby Belfer Visits Ellis Island. Hierstein, Judith, illus. 2003. 32p. pap. 15.95 (978-1-58980-117-2(2)) Pelican Publishing Co., Inc.

Rael, Elsa Okon. What Zeesie Saw on Delancey Street. 2000. (978-0-606-17943-0(7)) Tandem Library Bks.

Raphael, Marie. Streets of Gold. rev. ed. 2001. (Illus.). 224p. (J). (gr. 5 up). pap. 9.95 (978-0-89255-256-6(5)) Persea Bks., Inc.

Recorvits, Helen. My Name Is Yoon. Swiatkowska, Gabi, illus. 2003. 32p. (J). (gr. k-3). 16.00 (978-0-374-35114-4(7) , Farrar, Straus & Giroux (BYR)) Farrar, Straus & Giroux.

Rosenberg, Liz. The Silence in the Mountains. Soentpiet, Chris K., illus. 32p. (J). (gr. k-4). 1999. 16.99 (978-0-531-33084-5(2)); 1998. pap. 15.95 (978-0-531-30084-8(6)) Scholastic, Inc. (Orchard Bks.).

Ruby, Lois. Swindletop. 2000. (Illus.). 128p. (J). 15.95 (978-1-57168-393-9(3)) Eakin Pr.

Ryan, Pam Muñoz. Esperanza Renace. 2002. (SPA.). (gr. 3-6). lib. bdg. 13.00 (978-0-613-82250-3(1)) Tandem Library Bks.

—Esperanza Rising. 2001. (gr. 5-8). lib. bdg. 13.00 (978-0-613-53807-7(2)) Tandem Library Bks.

Saturen, Myra. Journey to a New World: Mystic River of the West. 2006. (J). pap. (***978-0-88092-495-5(0)***) Royal Fireworks Publishing Co.

Schneider, Mical. Annie Quinn in America. (Adventures in Time Ser.). (J). 2003. (Illus.). 252p. (gr. 4-7). 15.95 (978-1-57505-510-7(4)); 2001. 6.95 (978-1-57505-535-0(X)) Lerner Publishing Group. (Carolrhoda Bks.).

Schrecengost, Maity. Tasso of Tarpon Springs. Stock, Rose, illus. 1998. 118p. (J). (gr. 3-6). pap. 5.95 (978-0-929895-24-6(X) , Hoot Owl Bks.) Maupin Hse. Publishing.

Schuman, Burt E. Chanukah on the Prairie. Kaye, Rosalind Charney, illus. 2004. (gr. k-3). 13.95 (978-0-8074-0814-8(X) , 381780) URJ Pr.

E F G

Schwartz, Ellen. Jesse's Star. 2000. (Young Reader Ser.). (J). 11.64 (978-0-606-19476-1(2)) Tandem Library Bks.

Shefelman, Janice J. Peddler's Dream. 1999. (Illus.). 32p. (ps-3). 14.95 (978-1-57168-294-9(5)) Eakin Pr.

Spanish Omelette: Individual Title Six-Packs. (gr. 3 up). 35.00 (978-0-7635-9668-2(X)) Rigby Education.

Step from Heaven. 2002. (gr. 7-12). lib. bdg. 16.45 (978-0-613-60366-9(4)) Tandem Library Bks.

Tal, Eve. Double Crossing: A Jewish Immigration Story. 2005. 216p. (gr. 3-7). 16.95 (978-0-938317-94-4(6)) Cinco Puntos Pr.

Tan, Shaun. The Arrival. 2007. (J). 128p. (gr. 7 up). pap. 19.99 (978-0-439-89529-3(4)); (978-0-439-89530-9(8)) Scholastic, Inc. (Levine, Arthur A. Bks.).

Tarbescu, Edith. Annushka's Voyage. Dabcovich, Lydia & Degen, Bruce, illus. 1998. 32p. (J). (gr. k-3). tchr. ed. 16.00 (978-0-395-64366-2(X) , Clarion Bks.) Houghton Mifflin Co. Trade & Reference Div.

Ties to the Past (Poles) 76p. (YA). (gr. 6-12). pap. 9.95 (978-0-8224-3803-8(8)) Globe Fearon Educational Publishing.

Tolliver, Ruby C. Sarita, Be Brave. 1999. 144p. (gr. 3-6). 14.95 (978-1-57168-184-3(1)) Eakin Pr.

Veciana-Suarez, Ana. Flight to Freedom. 2002. (First Person Fiction Ser.). 224p. (J). (gr. 6-9). pap. 16.95 (978-0-439-38199-4(1) , Orchard Bks.) Scholastic, Inc.

—Flight to Freedom. 2004. 215p. (YA). (gr. 8-12). lib. bdg. 13.64 (978-0-606-30967-7(5)) Tandem Library Bks.

Wargin, Kathy-Jo. The Legend of Thanksgiving. Papp, Robert, illus. 2008. (J). (978-0-310-71179-7(7)) Zonderkidz.

Wilson, Laura. The Great Hunger. 2000. (Time Travellers Ser.). (Illus.). 36p. (J). (ps up). pap. 9.95 (978-0-688-17750-8(6) , Harper Trophy) HarperCollins Pubs.

Wishinsky, Frieda. Just Call Me Joe. 2003. (Orca Young Readers Ser.). (Illus.). 112p. (J). (gr. 3-6). pap. 4.99 (978-1-55143-249-6(8)) Orca Bk. Pubs. USA.

Woodruff, Elvira. The Memory Coat. Dooling, Michael, illus. 1999. 32p. (J). (gr. 2-5). pap. 16.95 (978-0-590-67717-2(9)) Scholastic, Inc.

—Orphan of Ellis Island. 2000. (gr. 5-8). lib. bdg. 12.40 (978-0-613-30079-7(3)) Tandem Library Bks.

—The Orphan of Ellis Island: A Time Travel Adventure. 2000. 192p. (J). pap. 4.99 (978-0-590-48246-2(7)) Scholastic, Inc.

—Small Beauties: The Journey of Darcy Heart O'Hara. Rex, Adam, illus. 2006. 40p. (J). (gr. 1-4). 15.95 (978-0-375-82686-3(6)); lib. bdg. 17.99 (978-0-375-92686-0(0)) Random Hse. Children's Bks. (Knopf Bks. for Young Readers).

Yee, Paul. The Jade Necklace. Lin, Grace, illus. 2006. 29p. (J). (gr. 4-8). reprint ed. 16.00 (978-1-4223-5135-2(1)) DIANE Publishing Co.

—The Jade Necklace. Lin, Grace, illus. 2002. 32p. (J). (ps-3). 15.95 (978-1-56656-455-7(7) , Crocodile Bks.) Interlink Publishing Group, Inc.

Yezerski, Thomas F. Together in Pinecone Patch. Date not set. (J). pap. (978-0-374-47579-6(2) , Farrar, Straus & Giroux (BYR)) Farrar, Straus & Giroux.

—Together in Pinecone Patch. Yezerski, Thomas F., illus. 1998. (Illus.). 32p. (J). (gr. k-3). 16.00 (978-0-374-37647-5(6) , Farrar, Straus & Giroux (BYR)) Farrar, Straus & Giroux.

Yin. Coolies. Soentpiet, Chris, illus. 2003. 40p. (J). (gr. k-3). pap. 7.99 (978-0-14-250055-2(0) , Puffin) Penguin Group (USA) Inc.

—Coolies. Soentpiet, Chris K., illus. 2001. 1p. (J). (ps-3). 16.99 (978-0-399-23227-5(3) , Philomel) Penguin Group (USA) Inc.

—Coolies. 2003. (gr. 3-6). lib. bdg. 16.45 (978-0-613-62936-2(1)) Tandem Library Bks.

EMILY (FICTITIOUS CHARACTER)—FICTION

Addis, Sandra. Flashlight One, Night Fright Off. 2005. 18.00 (978-0-8059-9782-8(2)) Dorrance Publishing Co., Inc.

Battleson, Mariella. Her Name Was Emaline. 2005. 60p. (J). pap. 25.99 (978-1-4141-0364-8(6)) Pleasant Word.

Blossom, F. Blossom Kingdom: The Adventures of Emily. 2005. 189p. pap. 19.95 (978-1-4241-1112-1(9)) PublishAmerica, Inc.

Cosmic Debris Staff. The Lost Issue. 2005. (Emily the Strange Ser.: Bk. 2). (Illus.). 48p. (YA). pap. 7.95 (978-1-59307-429-6(8)) Dark Horse Comics.

Friederich, Uve. The World of Bridgett & Emily. Fitzpatrick, Meg & Ravenhill, John A., illus. 2004. 41p. (J). mass mkt. 8.95 (978-0-9747532-4-9(6)) Taylor-Dth Publishing.

Jones, Claudia. Riding Out the Storm. 2006. 264p. pap. 8.95 (978-0-7387-0867-6(4)) Llewellyn Pubns.

Kane, James. Ellie's Magic Kingdom. 2005. 73p. pap. 14.95 (978-1-4137-6420-8(7)) PublishAmerica, Inc.

London, Victoria. Emily Cobbs Collection Bk. 1 & Bk. 2: A Gifted Girls Series. 2005. (Gifted Girls Ser.). (J). per. 12.95 (978-1-59748-859-4(3)) Sparklesoup Studios, Inc.

Phillips, Betty Lou. Emily Works Out. Watts, Sharon, illus. 2005. 12p. (J). (ps). bds. 6.95 (978-1-58685-458-4(5)) Gibbs Smith, Publisher.

—Emily's Manners. Watts, Sharon, illus. 2005. 12p. (J). (ps). bds. 6.95 (978-1-58685-457-7(7)) Gibbs Smith, Publisher.

Reger, Rob & Parker, Buzz. Emily the Strange, Vol. 1. 2006. (SPA., Illus.). 64p. 19.95 (978-1-59497-188-4(9)) Public Square Bks.

—Emily the Strange Vol. 2: El libro Secreto de Las Cosas Extrañas. 2006. (SPA., Illus.). 64p. reprint ed. 19.95 (978-1-59497-189-1(7)) Public Square Bks.

Roberts, Rachel. Song of the Unicorns. 2003. (Avalon Ser.). 175p. (J). (gr. 3-7). pap. 4.99 (978-1-59315-002-0(4)) Perseus Bks. Group.

Ruelle, Karen Gray. Easter Egg Disaster: A Harry & Emily Adventure. Ruelle, Karen Gray, illus. (Holiday House Readers Ser.). (Illus.). 32p. (J). (gr. k-3). pap. 4.95 (978-0-8234-1823-7(5)) Holiday Hse., Inc.

Scholastic, Inc. Staff. Emily Elizabeth Dress-up Doll. 2000. (Clifford Ser.). (J). 24.99 (978-0-439-19388-7(5) , Sidekicks TM) Scholastic, Inc.

—Emily Elizabeth Play Wear-Winter Outfit. 2001. (Clifford Ser.). (J). 12.99 (978-0-439-30483-2(0) , Sidekicks TM) Scholastic, Inc.

—Emily Elizabeth Rain Outfit. 2001. (Clifford Ser.). (J). 12.99 (978-0-439-29698-4(6) , Sidekicks TM) Scholastic, Inc.

—Emily Elizabeth Sailor Outfit. 2001. (Clifford Ser.). (J). 12.99 (978-0-439-29697-7(8) , Sidekicks TM) Scholastic, Inc.

EMOTIONALLY DISTURBED CHILDREN

see Problem Children

EMOTIONS

see also Attitude (Psychology); Belief and Doubt; Fear; Grief; Jealousy; Love; Prejudices; Self-confidence

Adams, Lisa K. Dealing with Hurt Feelings. 1999. (Conflict Resolution Library). 24p. (gr. k-4). pap. 6.95 (978-1-56838-268-5(5)) Hazelden Publishing & Educational Services.

Agassi, Martine. Hands Are Not for Hitting. Heinlen, Marieka, illus. 2006. (Best Behavior Ser.). 24p. (J). 7.95 (978-1-57542-200-8(X)) Free Spirit Publishing, Inc.

Aigner-Clark, Julie. Baby Einstein: See How I Feel, Spanish-Language Edition. Zaidi, Nadeem, illus. 2005. (Baby Einstein: Libros de Carton Ser.). (SPA.). 14p. (J). bds. 7.95 (978-970-718-308-7(X) , Silver Dolphin en Español) Advanced Marketing, S. de R. L. de C. V. MEX. *Dist:* Perseus Distribution.

Alpern, Michele. Overcoming Feelings of Hatred. 2002. (Focus on Family Matters Ser.). (Illus.). 64p. (J). 25.00 (978-0-7910-6953-0(2)) Facts On File, Inc.

American Heritage Dictionary Editors. How Do I Feel? (Como Me Siento?) Cote, Pamela & Zagarenski, Pamela, illus. 2001. (Good Beginnings/Un Buen Comienzo Ser.). (SPA & ENG.). 4p. (J). (gr. k-ps). bds. 3.95 (978-0-618-16931-3(8)) Houghton Mifflin Co. Trade & Reference Div.

Amos, Janine. Moody. 2007. (Good & Bad Ser.). (Illus.). 32p. (J). (ps-2). pap. 9.95 (***978-1-84234-394-4(7)*** , Evans Brothers, Limited) Evans Publishing Group GBR. *Dist:* Independent Pubs. Group.

Amos, Janine, et al. Why Be Bossy? 2007. (Problem Solvers Ser.). (Illus.). 32p. (J). pap. 12.95 (***978-1-84234-191-9(X)*** , Evans Brothers, Limited) Evans Publishing Group GBR. *Dist:* Independent Pubs. Group.

—Why Fight? 2007. (Problem Solvers Ser.). (Illus.). 32p. (J). pap. 12.95 (***978-1-84234-193-3(6)*** , Evans Brothers, Limited) Evans Publishing Group GBR. *Dist:* Independent Pubs. Group.

—Why Lose Your Temper? 2007. (Problem Solvers Ser.). (Illus.). 32p. (J). pap. 12.95 (***978-1-84234-194-0(4)*** , Evans Brothers, Limited) Evans Publishing Group GBR. *Dist:* Independent Pubs. Group.

—Why Not Share? 2007. (Problem Solvers Ser.). (Illus.). 32p. (J). pap. 12.95 (***978-1-84234-195-7(2)*** , Evans Brothers, Limited) Evans Publishing Group GBR. *Dist:* Independent Pubs. Group.

Anderson, George. Controlling Ourselves. 2003. (YA). 27.00 net. (978-0-9743682-5-2(3)) Anderson, George.

Andrews, Linda Wasmer. Emotional Intelligence. (Life Balance Ser.). (Illus.). 80p. (J). 2005. (gr. 5-8). pap. 6.95 (978-0-531-16688-8(0)); 2004. 20.50 (978-0-531-12335-5(9)) Scholastic Library Publishing. (Watts, Franklin).

Angry Book. (J). pap. (978-0-02-053585-0(6) , Scribner Paper Fiction) Simon & Schuster.

Apel, Melanie Ann. Let's Talk about Feeling Confused. 2001. (Let's Talk Library). (Illus.). 24p. (J). (gr. 3). lib. bdg. 18.75 (978-0-8239-5623-4(7) , PowerKids Pr.) Rosen Publishing Group, Inc., The.

—Let's Talk about Feeling Defeated. 2002. (Let's Talk Library). (Illus.). 24p. (J). lib. bdg. 18.75 (978-0-8239-5864-1(7) , PowerKids Pr.) Rosen Publishing Group, Inc., The.

—Let's Talk about Feeling Embarrassed. 2001. (Let's Talk Library). (Illus.). 24p. (J). (gr. 3). lib. bdg. 18.75 (978-0-8239-5618-0(0) , PowerKids Pr.) Rosen Publishing Group, Inc., The.

Avery, Charles E. Everybody Has Feelings: Todos Tenemos Sentimientos: The Moods of Children. 2004. (ENG & SPA., Illus.). 50p. (ps-1). pap. 8.95 (978-0-87659-197-0(7) , 12849) Gryphon Hse., Inc.

Bender, Janet. Don't Pop Your Balloon! Get a Grip on Anger. 2006. 32p. (J). per. 12.95 (978-1-931636-29-2(X)) National Center For Youth Issues.

Berendes, Mary. Feelings/Las Emociones. 2007. (WordBooks/Libros de Palabras Ser.). (SPA & ENG.). 24p. (J). 19.93 (***978-1-59296-797-1(3)***) Child's World, Inc.

Berry, Joy Wilt. A Book about Throwing Tantrums. 2005. (Illus.). (J). (978-0-7172-8586-0(3)) Scholastic, Inc.

—Feeling Disappointed. Smith, Maggie, illus. 2002. (J). (978-0-439-34159-2(0)) Scholastic, Inc.

—Let's Talk about Feeling Defeated: A Personal Feelings Book. Fitzpatrick, Roey, illus. rev. ed. 2000. (Let's Talk about Ser. : Vol. 4). 36p. (J). (ps-2). pap. 3.95 (978-1-58634-035-3(2)) Goldstar Publishing, Inc.

—Let's Talk about Feeling Disappointed: An Interpersonal Feelings Book. Fitzpatrick, Roey, illus. rev. ed. 1999. (Let's Talk about Ser.: Vol. 4). 36p. (J). (ps-2). pap. 3.95 (978-1-58634-043-8(3) , 01-0202-04) Goldstar Publishing, Inc.

—Let's Talk about Feeling Embarrassed: An Interpersonal Feelings Book. Fitzpatrick, Roey, illus. rev. ed. 2000. (Let's Talk about Ser.: Vol. 1). 36p. (J). (ps-2). pap. 3.95 (978-1-58634-040-7(9)) Goldstar Publishing, Inc.

—Let's Talk about Feeling Embarrassed: An Interpersonal Feelings Book. Smith, Maggie, tr. Smith, Maggie, illus. 2002. (J). (978-0-439-34164-6(7)) Scholastic, Inc.

—Let's Talk about Feeling Frustrated: A Personal Feelings Book. Fitzpatrick, Roey, illus. rev. ed. 1999. (Let's Talk about Ser. : Vol. 3). 36p. (J). (ps-2). pap. 3.95 (978-1-58634-034-6(4) , 01-0201-03) Goldstar Publishing, Inc.

—Let's Talk about Feeling Inferior: An Interpersonal Feelings Book. Fitzpatrick, Roey, illus. rev. ed. 2000. (Let's Talk about Ser.: Vol. 2). 36p. (J). (ps-3). pap. 3.95 (978-1-58634-041-4(7)) Goldstar Publishing, Inc.

—Let's Talk about Feeling Worried: A Personal Feelings Book. Fitzpatrick, Roey, illus. rev. ed. 2000. (Let's Talk about Ser. : Vol. 2). 36p. (J). (ps-3). pap. 3.95 (978-1-58634-033-9(6)) Goldstar Publishing, Inc.

—Let's Talk about Feeling Worried: A Personal Feelings Book. Smith, Maggie, illus. 2002. (J). (978-0-439-34158-5(2)) Scholastic, Inc.

—Stress: Get over It! Bartholomew, illus. rev. ed. 2000. (Winning Skills Ser.: Vol. 2). 48p. (YA). (gr. 4-7). pap. 2.95 (978-1-58634-161-9(8)) Goldstar Publishing, Inc.

—Teach Me about Crying: A Safe & Sound Book. Fitzpatrick, Roey, illus. rev. ed. 1999. (Teach Me about Ser.: Vol. 2). 32p. (J). (ps). bds. 5.95 (978-1-58634-009-4(3) , 01-0103-02) Goldstar Publishing, Inc.

—Trauma: Good Answers to Tough Questions. Bartholomew, illus. rev. ed. 2000. (Good Answers to Tough Questions Ser.: Vol. 12). 48p. (J). (gr. 4-7). pap. 4.95 (978-1-58634-222-7(3) , 01-0901-12) Goldstar Publishing, Inc.

Bicknell, Joanna, ed. Baby Fun Baby Faces. 2005. 12p. (978-1-905051-15-1(8)) Make Believe Ideas.

Bingham, Jane & Turner, Helen. Angry. 2007. (QEB Everybody Feels Ser.). (Illus.). 24p. (J). lib. bdg. 17.95 (978-1-59566-215-6(4)) QEB Publishing Inc.

—Happy. 2006. (QEB Everybody Feels Ser.). (Illus.). 24p. (J). lib. bdg. 17.95 (978-1-59566-213-2(8)) QEB Publishing Inc.

—Sad. 2006. (QEB Everybody Feels Ser.). (Illus.). 24p. (J). lib. bdg. 17.95 (978-1-59566-214-9(6)) QEB Publishing Inc.

Bligh, Deirdre. Perfect World: I Was Soooo Embarrassed! Martini, Angela, illus. 2005. 62p. (J). (***978-0-439-80069-3(2)***) Scholastic, Inc.

Block, Joel D. Staying Cool: How to Get a Grip on Anger. 2002. (gr. 7-12). lib. bdg. 22.20 (978-0-613-79731-3(0)) Tandem Library Bks.

Bohensky, Anita. Anger Management Workbook for Kids & Teens. 2001. 106p. 54.00 (978-1-893505-06-3(5)) Growth Publishing.

—Manejar el Enojo: Manual de Instrucciones para Nios y Adolescentes. 2004. (SPA.). (YA). 54.00 (978-1-893505-23-0(5)) Growth Publishing.

Borgman, Jim. Mood Swings: Show Em How You're Feeling. Borgman, Jim, illus. 2001. (Illus.). 1p. (J). (gr. 4-7). 8.99 (978-0-8431-7560-8(5) , Price Stern Sloan) Penguin Group (USA) Inc.

Bowman, Robert P. & Frank, Kim T. The Magic Coloring Book of Feelings. Daugherty, Tonya & Peterson, Justin, illus. 2001. 120p. (J). (gr. k-8). pap. 19.95 (978-1-889636-41-2(X)) Youthlight, Inc.

Boye, B. D. The Look Book. Boye, B. D., illus. l.t. ed. 2004. (Illus.). 20p. (J). per. 4.99 (978-0-9768078-1-0(5) , 100001) Innerchild Publishing, Inc.

Braithwaite, Althea. Being Friends. Jude, Conny, illus. Best, Charlie, photos by. 1998. (Exploring Emotions Ser.). 32p. (J). (gr. 3 up). lib. bdg. 19.93 (978-0-8368-2115-4(7)) Stevens, Gareth Inc.

—Exploring Emotions, 5 bks. Jude, Conny, illus. Best, Charlie, photos by. Incl. Feeling Angry. lib. bdg. 23.33 (978-0-8368-2116-1(5)); Feeling Jealous. lib. bdg. 23.33 (978-0-8368-2117-8(3)); Feeling Scared. lib. bdg. 23.33 (978-0-8368-2118-5(1)); Feeling Shy. lib. bdg. 23.33 (978-0-8368-2119-2(X)); Telling the Truth. lib. bdg. 22.60 (978-0-8368-2120-8(3)); 32p. (J). (gr. 3 up). (Illus.). 1998. Set lib. bdg. 93.32 (978-0-8368-2114-7(9)) Stevens, Gareth Inc.

—Feeling Angry. Jude, Conny, illus. Best, Charlie, photos by. 1998. (Exploring Emotions Ser.). 32p. (J). (gr. 3 up). lib. bdg. 23.33 (978-0-8368-2116-1(5)) Stevens, Gareth Inc.

—Feeling Jealous. Jude, Conny, illus. Best, Charlie, photos by. 1998. (Exploring Emotions Ser.). 32p. (J). (gr. 3 up). lib. bdg. 23.33 (978-0-8368-2117-8(3)) Stevens, Gareth Inc.

—Feeling Scared. Jude, Conny, illus. Best, Charlie, photos by. 1998. (Exploring Emotions Ser.). 32p. (J). (gr. 3 up). lib. bdg. 23.33 (978-0-8368-2118-5(1)) Stevens, Gareth Inc.

Bratton, Heidi. Celebrate Feelings. 2000. (Illus.). 32p. (J). (ps-2). 8.99 (978-0-570-07093-1(7)) Concordia Publishing Hse.

Brownjohn, Emma. All Kinds of Feelings. 2004. (Illus.). (J). (ENG & ARA.). (978-1-84444-302-4(7)); (ENG & BEN., (978-1-84444-303-1(5)); (ENG & CHI., (978-1-84444-304-8(3)); (ENG & PER., (978-1-84444-305-5(1)); (ENG & FRE., (978-1-84444-306-2(X)); (ENG & PAN., (978-1-84444-307-9(8)); (POR & ENG., (978-1-84444-308-6(6)); (ENG & SOM., (978-1-84444-309-3(4)); (ENG & SPA., (978-1-84444-310-9(8)); (ENG & TUR., 12p. (978-1-84444-311-6(6)); (ENG & URD., (978-1-84444-312-3(4)) Mantra Publishing, Ltd.

Bryant-Mole, Karen. I Feel Happy. 1999. (gr. k-3). lib. bdg. 14.45 (978-0-613-30493-1(4)) Tandem Library Bks.

Cahoon, Joanne & Puls, Ruth. Dealing with Emotions. Cannizzo, Karen A., ed. 2000. (Conversations with Teens Ser.). 16p. (YA). pap. 7.95 (978-0-937997-65-9(X)) Pflaum Publishing Group.

Cain, Barbara S. Double-Dip Feelings: Stories to Help Children Understand Emotions. Patterson, Anne, illus. 2nd ed. 2001. 32p. (J). (ps-3). 14.95 (978-1-55798-812-6(9)); pap. 8.95 (978-1-55798-811-9(0)) American Psychological Assn. (Magination Pr.).

—Double-Dip Feelings: Stories to Help Children Understand Emotions. 2001. (gr. k-3). lib. bdg. 17.60 (978-0-613-83947-1(1)) Tandem Library Bks.

Cain, Janan. The Way I Feel. 2005. (Illus.). bds. 7.95 (978-1-884734-72-4(3)) Parenting Pr., Inc.

Canizares, Susan. Feelings. 1999. (Social Studies Emergent Readers). (J). 2.50 (978-0-439-04555-1(X)) Scholastic, Inc.

—Feelings. 1999. (ps-2). lib. bdg. 10.10 (978-0-613-21528-2(1)) Tandem Library Bks.

Cavaciuti, Susan. Someone Hurt Me. Cavaciuti, Susan, illus. 2004. (Illus.). 222p. pap. 8.95 (978-1-890995-20-1(7) , Vital Health Publishing) Square One Publishers.

Clairday, Robynn. Tell Me This Isn't Happening!, 1 vol. 1999. 144p. (gr. 3-7). pap. 4.50 (978-0-439-09502-0(6)) Scholastic, Inc.

Clark, John T. & Clark, Nicole K. A Journey Through Your Heart. Clark, John T., illus. l.t. ed. 2000. (Illus.). 32p. (J). (ps-4). 17.95 (978-1-892176-14-1(9)) PremaNations Publishing.

Clark, Nicole K. & Clark, John T. The Oceans of Emotions-3D. Clark, John T., illus. l.t. ed. 1999. (Illus.). 32p. (J). (ps-4). 17.95 (978-1-892176-13-4(0)) PremaNations Publishing.

Clark, Travis & Ziff, Jane. A Guys' Guide to Stress; A Girls' Guide to Stress. 2008. (Flip-It-over Guides to Teen Emotions Ser.). (Illus.). 128p. (J). (gr. 5 up). lib. bdg. 31.93 (***978-0-7660-2857-9(7)***) Enslow Pubs., Inc.

Crist, James. What to Do When Youre Sad & Lonely: A Guide for Kids. 2005. (What to Do When Ser.). (Illus.). 128p. (J). (gr. 4-8). pap. 9.95 (978-1-57542-189-6(5)) Free Spirit Publishing, Inc.

Crist, James J. Como Superar los Miedos y Preocupaciones. Marti, Nuria, tr. Chesworth, Michael, illus. 2004. (SPA.). 128p. (978-84-9754-125-1(1) , 87443) Ediciones Oniro S.A.

Curriculum in a Box: Managing Emotions. 2004. (YA). 699.95 incl. DVD (978-1-55548-194-0(9) , 605) Human Relations Media.

Curtis, Jamie Lee. Hoy Me Siento Tonta y Otros Estados de Animo. Cornell, Laura, illus. 2002. (CAT.). 40p. (J). (gr. k-2). 19.95 (978-84-8488-041-7(9)) Serres, Ediciones, S. L. ESP. *Dist:* Lectorum Pubns., Inc.

—Hoy Me Siento Tonta y Otros Estados de Animo. Rubio, Esther & Mendo, Miguel Angel, trs. Cornell, Laura, illus. 2002. (SPA.). 32p. (J). (gr. k-2). 19.99 (978-84-8488-040-0(0) , RR30979) Serres, Ediciones, S. L. ESP. *Dist:* Lectorum Pubns., Inc.

Day, Roger. Being Mad, Being Glad. 2004. (Kids' Guides Ser.). (Illus.). 32p. (J). (gr. 1-4). lib. bdg. 25.64 (978-1-4109-0570-3(5)) Raintree.

Delis-Abrams, Alexandra. The Feelings Story Book: 26 Illustrated Feelings Stories. Scott, Shari & Sherman, Chris, illus. 1998. 32p. (J). (ps-k). pap. 9.95 (978-1-879889-23-1(4)) Adage Pubns.

Ditta-Donahue, Gina. Josh's Smiley Faces: A Story about Anger. Blake, Anne Catharine, illus. 2003. 32p. (J). 14.95 (978-1-59147-000-7(5)); pap. 8.95 (978-1-59147-001-4(3)) American Psychological Assn. (Magination Pr.).

Dixon, Thomas. From Passions to Emotions: The Creation of a Secular Psychological Category. 2003. 300p. 75.00 (978-0-521-82729-4(9)) Cambridge Univ. Pr.

Dombrower, Jan. Getting to Know Your Emotional Needs. Sorba, Richard, illus. Date not set. (J). (978-1-55864-021-4(5)) Kidsrights.

Doudna, Kelly. How Do You Feel?, Set. l.t. ed. Incl. I Feel Angry. lib. bdg. 19.93 (978-1-57765-187-1(1)); I Feel Brave. lib. bdg. 19.93 (978-1-57765-190-1(1)); I Feel Happy. lib. bdg. 19.93 (978-1-57765-188-8(X)); I Feel Sad. lib. bdg. 19.93 (978-1-57765-189-5(8)); I Feel Safe. lib. bdg. 19.93 (978-1-57765-191-8(X)); I Feel Scared. lib. bdg. 19.93 (978-1-57765-192-5(8)); 24p. (J). (ps-3). 1999. (Illus.). 1999. Set lib. bdg. 119.58 (978-1-57765-265-6(7) , SandCastle) ABDO Publishing Co.

—I Feel Angry. l.t. ed. 1999. (How Do You Feel? Ser.). (Illus.). 24p. (J). (ps-3). lib. bdg. 19.93 (978-1-57765-187-1(1) , SandCastle) ABDO Publishing Co.

—I Feel Sad. l.t. ed. 1999. (How Do You Feel? Ser.). (Illus.). 24p. (J). (ps-3). lib. bdg. 19.93 (978-1-57765-189-5(8) , SandCastle) ABDO Publishing Co.

Early, Norm & Young, Danelle. Step Ball: A Child's Book about Feelings & Differences. Naughton, Brent, illus. 2000. 20p. (J). (ps-3). 13.95 (978-0-9665319-8-5(1)) Greenleaf Book Group.

Edwards, Dianna. It's Not Easy Being Patou - Book One. 2004. (J). (978-0-9767756-1-4(1)) Patou Bks., LLC.

—Meet Patou. 2006. (J). pap. 29.95 (978-0-9767756-0-7(3)) Patou Bks., LLC.

—My Journal & Drawings. 2004. (J). spiral bd. (978-0-9767756-4-5(6)) Patou Bks., LLC.

—When Niki Got Sick, Bk. 2. 2004. (J). (978-0-9767756-2-1(X)) Patou Bks., LLC.

—Why Can't Everything Just Stay the Same? Book Three. 2004. (J). (978-0-9767756-3-8(8)) Patou Bks., LLC.

Emotions Set. (gr. k-2). 114.95 (978-0-7368-9034-2(3)) Red Brick Learning.

Equipo Staff. El Gusto. (Coleccion Mundo Maravilloso). (SPA., Illus.). 36p. (J). (gr. 2-4). (978-84-348-4779-8(5) , SM2722) SM Ediciones ESP. *Dist:* Lectorum Pubns., Inc.

Everthing Changes Interactive Packages: Feelings. (Pebble Soup Explorations Ser.). (ps up). 52.00 (978-0-7578-5242-8(4)) Rigby Education.

Feel Good. (Your Health Ser.). 24p. (J). 6.95 (978-0-7368-4450-5(3)) Capstone Pr., Inc.

Feeling Angry, 6 vols. (gr. k-2). 28.95 (978-0-7368-8820-2(9)) Red Brick Learning.

Feeling Happy, 6 vols. (gr. k-2). 28.95 (978-0-7368-8821-9(7)) Red Brick Learning.

EFG

Seaward, Brian Luke. Hot Stones & Funny Bones: Teens Helping Teens Cope with Stress & Anger. 2002. 300p. (YA). pap. 12.95 (978-0-7573-0036-3(7)) Health Communications, Inc.

Shapiro, Lawrence E. Learning to Control Your Anger: With the Stop, Think & Go Bears. Floersch, Gene, illus. 1999. 80p. (J). (gr. k-5). pap. 19.95 (978-1-882732-80-7(4) , 63802) Childswork/Childsplay.

Silver Dolphin en Español Editors. Qué? Como? Por Qué? Esa Eres Tu Y Este Soy Yo: What? How? Why? You Are That & I Am This. 2006. (SPA., Illus.). 16p. (J). 9.95 (978-970-718-346-9(2)) Advantage Pubs. Group.

Simpson, Amy. Feelings & Emotions. Powell, Kara Eckmann, ed. 2000. (Pulse Ser.: No. 12). 96p. (gr. 6-9). 14.99 (978-0-8307-2548-9(2) , Gospel Light) Gospel Light Pubns.

Smith, Carrie. Las emociones Humanas. Hanner, Albert, illus. ed. 2004. (SPA.). 32p. (J). pap. 6.00 (978-1-4108-2345-8(8) , A23458) Benchmark Education Co.

Snow, Todd & Snow, Peggy. Feelings to Share from A to Z. Hartman, Carrie, illus. 2007. 32p. (J). per. 8.95 (***978-1-934277-00-3(2)***) Marn Green Publishing, Inc.

Spelman, Cornelia Maude. When I Feel Angry. Cote, Nancy, illus. 2000. (Way I Feel Bks.). 24p. (J). (ps-1). 15.95 (978-0-8075-8888-8(1)); pap. 6.95 (978-0-8075-8897-0(0)) Whitman, Albert & Co.

Sportelli-Rehak, Angela. Uncle Sam's Kids: When Duty Calls. Hinlicky, Gregg, illus. 2004. (Uncle Sam's Kids Ser.: Bk. 1). 40p. (gr. k-6). 15.95 (978-0-9714515-1-3(6)) Abidenme Bks.

Stanley, Mandy. How Do You Feel? Stanley, Mandy, illus. 2006. 24p. (J). bds. 7.99 (978-1-4169-1782-3(9) , Little Simon) Simon & Schuster Children's Publishing.

Stewart, Jan. Stars Learning about Anger. 2004. (Illus.). 32p. (J). pap. 9.95 (978-0-89793-309-4(5)) Hunter Hse., Inc.

—Stars Learning More about Anger. 2004. (Illus.). 32p. (J). pap. 9.95 (978-0-89793-310-0(9)) Hunter Hse., Inc.

Straight Talk about Self-Image & Identity. 2002. (YA). (gr. 6-8). tchr. ed. 69.95 (978-1-55942-180-5(0) , 9231V9) Marsh Media.

Swain, Gwenyth. Smiling. 2003. (Small World Ser.). (Illus.). 24p. (J). (ps-2). pap. 6.95 (978-1-57505-371-4(3)) Lerner Publishing Group.

—Smiling. 2nd ed. 2000. (Small World Ser.). (ARA & ENG., Illus.). 24p. (J). pap. 9.95 (978-1-84059-114-9(5)) Milet Publishing.

—Smiling. 1999. (gr. k-3). lib. bdg. 15.25 (978-0-613-42557-5(X)) Tandem Library Bks.

Taylor, Damon J. Aprende de las Emociones con la Biblia. 2004. (Mis Calcetines Ser.). (SPA., Illus.). 24p. 5.99 (978-0-8254-0775-8(3) , Editorial Portavoz) Kregel Pubns.

That's Mine: Social/Emotional Lap Book. (Pebble Soup Explorations Ser.). (ps up). 16.00 (978-0-7635-7565-6(8)) Rigby Education.

Tildes, Phyllis L. Baby Face. Tildes, Phyllis L., illus. 2004. (Illus.). 10p. (J). bds. 5.95 (978-1-57091-399-0(4)) Charlesbridge Publishing, Inc.

Tubbs, Janet. Anger. 2000. (Spud Packs Ser.). 16p. (J). pap. 19.95 (978-1-881185-10-9(9)) Arcadia Pr.

Tym, Kate. Coping with Your Emotions. 2004. (Illus.). 48p. (J). 29.93 (978-1-4109-0575-8(6)) Harcourt Schl. Pubs.

A veces estamos felices, a veces estamos Tristes: Social/Emotional Lap Book. (Pebble Soup Exploraciones Ser.). (SPA.). (ps up). 16.00 (978-0-7578-1789-2(0)) Rigby Education.

Verdick, Elizabeth. Feet Are Not for Kicking. Heinlen, Marieka, illus. 2004. (Best Behavior Ser.). 24p. (J). 7.95 (978-1-57542-158-2(5)) Free Spirit Publishing, Inc.

—How to Take the Grrrr Out of Anger. 2002. (gr. 3-6). lib. bdg. 18.75 (978-0-613-84940-1(X)) Tandem Library Bks.

Verdick, Elizabeth & Lisovskis, Marjorie. How to Take the Grrrr Out of Anger. 2004. (Laugh & Learn Ser.). (Illus.). 128p. (YA). (gr. 3-8). pap. 8.95 (978-1-57542-117-9(8)) Free Spirit Publishing, Inc.

Weiss, Ellen. Feeling Happy: A Spin the Wheel Emotions Book. Jourdan, Jason, illus. 2006. (PBS Kids(R) Ser.). 14p. (J). 6.95 (***978-1-57791-311-5(6)***) Brighter Minds Children's Publishing.

Weiss, Stefanie Iris. Everything You Need to Know about Dealing with Losses. rev. ed. 2000. (Need to Know Library). (Illus.). 64p. (YA). (gr. 4-6). lib. bdg. 25.25 (978-0-8239-3302-0(4)) Rosen Publishing Group, Inc., The.

Weixl, Twyla. Twenty-Two Feelings from Nice to Nasty. Weixl, Twyla, illus. 2004. (Illus.). 45p. (J). (gr. k-3). pap. 11.95 (978-0-929141-70-1(9)) Napoleon Publishing/Rendezvous Pr. CAN. *Dist:* AtlasBooks Distribution.

What Is Scary?, 6 Packs. (gr. 1-2). 22.00 (978-0-7635-9105-2(X)) Rigby Education.

Who You are on the Inside. 2002. (Illus.). (J). pap. 5.43 (978-0-7398-5932-2(3)) Steck-Vaughn.

Wilde, Jerry. More Hot Stuff to Help Kids Chill Out: The Anger & Stress Management Book. 2001. (Illus.). 85p. (YA). (gr. 5-12). pap. 9.95 (978-0-9657610-3-1(7)) LGR Publishing, Inc.

Young, Ed. Voices of the Heart. gif. ed. 2003. 72p. (J). pap. 8.95 (978-0-439-45693-7(2) , Scholastic Pr.) Scholastic, Inc.

Zientek, Joan A. Mrs. Ruby's Life Lessons for Kids: Essential Skills for Increasing Emotional Quotient. Norcross, Harry, illus. 2001. 143p. (J). (gr. 3-5). pap. 19.95 (978-1-57543-094-2(0)) MAR*CO Products, Inc.

EMOTIONS—FICTION

Adams, Michael. The Little King & the Honeybee. 2005. (J). per. 9.95 (978-1-58597-327-9(0)) Leathers Publishing.

Aigner-Clark, Julie. See How I Feel. Zaidi, Nadeem, illus. 2004. (Baby Einstein Ser.). 14p. (ps-17). 7.99 (978-0-7868-5114-0(7)) Hyperion Bks. for Children.

Al-Chokhachy, Elissa. The Angel with the Golden Glow: A Family's Journey Through Loss & Healing. Graf, Ulrike, illus. 2001. 32p. (J). (ps up). 15.95 (978-1-893356-00-9(0) , Penny Bear Publishing) Penny Bear Co., Inc., The.

Alger, Horatio. Fancy of Hers. 2006. pap. (***978-1-4250-3505-1(1)***); pap. (***978-1-4250-3545-7(0)***); pap. (***978-1-4250-3583-9(3)***) Assistedreadingbooks.com Inc.

Alonso, Manuel L. Extrano, Muy Extrano. Schubert, Karin, illus. 2003. (SPA.). 124p. (J). (gr. 3-5). pap. 10.95 (978-84-204-4906-7(7)) Santillana USA Publishing Co., Inc.

Amazing Mallika - Evaluation Guide: Evaluation Guide. 2006. (J). (978-1-55942-398-4(6)) Marsh Media.

Anderson, Laurie. Speak. 2006. 23.75 (978-0-8446-7292-2(0)) Smith, Peter Pub., Inc.

Anderson, Laurie Halse. Habla! (SPA.). (YA). 9.95 (978-958-04-5909-5(6)) Norma S.A. COL. *Dist:* Distribuidora Norma, Inc.

Annunziata, Jane & Nemiroff, Marc A. Why Am I an Only Child? Scott, Margaret, illus. 1998. 36p. (J). (ps-3). 19.95 (978-1-55798-506-4(5) , 441-5065) American Psychological Assn.

Apostolina, M. Hazing Meri Sugarman. 2005. 272p. (YA). pap. 8.99 (978-1-4169-0610-0(X) , Simon Pulse) Simon & Schuster Children's Publishing.

—Meri Strikes Back. 2006. (Hazing Meri Sugarman Ser.). 288p. (YA). pap. 8.99 (978-1-4169-1163-0(4) , Simon Pulse) Simon & Schuster Children's Publishing.

Athena Smiles. 2005. (J). (978-0-9758714-1-6(2)) Eveready Letter & Advertising Inc.

Bajaj, Varsha. How Many Kisses Do You Want Tonight? Bates, Ivan, illus. 2007. 26p. (J). bds. 6.99 (***978-0-316-06735-5(0)***) Little, Brown Bks. for Young Readers.

Baker, Keith. Sometimes. 2003. (Green Light Readers Level 1 Ser.). (Illus.). 24p. (J). 11.95 (978-0-15-204807-5(3)); pap. 3.95 (978-0-15-204847-1(2)) Harcourt Children's Bks. (Green Light Readers).

—Sometimes. 1999. (Green Light Readers Ser.). (978-0-606-16510-5(X)); lib. bdg. 11.80 (978-0-613-64597-3(9)) Tandem Library Bks.

—Sometimes/Algunas Veces. Campoy, F. Isabel & Ada, Alma Flor, trs. from ENG. 2007. (Green Light Readers Level 1 Ser.). (ENG & SPA., Illus.). 28p. (J). 12.95 (978-0-15-205959-0(8)); pap. 3.95 (978-0-15-205961-3(X)) Harcourt Trade Pubs.

Bang, Molly. When Sophie Gets Angry—Really, Really Angry... 2004. (Scholastic Bookshelf Ser.). (Illus.). 40p. (J). (gr. 17-17). reprint ed. pap. 5.99 (978-0-439-59845-3(1) , Scholastic Paperbacks) Scholastic, Inc.

Bang, Molly Garrett. When Sophie Gets Angry - Really, Really Angry. Bang, Molly Garrett, illus. 2002. (Illus.). (J). 25.06 (978-0-7587-0165-7(9)) Book Wholesalers, Inc.

—When Sophie Gets Angry - Really, Really Angry. Bang, Molly Garrett, illus. 1999. (Illus.). 40p. (J). (ps-2). pap. 15.95 (978-0-590-18979-8(4) , Blue Sky Pr., The) Scholastic, Inc.

—When Sophie Gets Angry - Really, Really Angry. 2001. (J). (gr. k-2). 26.90 incl. audio (978-0-8045-6861-6(8) , 6861) Spoken Arts, Inc.

Barclift, Betty. Gypsy Summer: A Novel. 2003. 160p. (J). pap. 6.99 (978-0-8254-2038-2(5)) Kregel Pubns.

Bateson, Catherine. A Dangerous Girl. 2000. 136p. pap. 15.50 (978-0-7022-3168-1(1)) Univ. of Queensland Pr. AUS. *Dist:* International Specialized Bk. Services.

Bellingham, Brenda. Lilly Takes the Lead. MacDonald, Clarke, illus. 2006. (First Novels Ser.: Vol. 34). 64p. (gr. 2-5). (***978-0-88780-703-9(8)***); (J). 4.95 (978-0-88780-701-5(1)) Formac Publishing Co., Ltd. CAN. *Dist:* Casemate Pubs. & Bk. Distributors, LLC.

Berry, Ron. Charlie the Can-Do Choo-Choo! Sharp, Chris, illus. 2006. 7p. (J). (ps). bds. 12.95 (978-0-8249-6678-2(3) , Candy Cane Pr.) Ideals Pubns.

Birdseye, Tom. Attack of the Mutant Underwear. 2006. (Illus.). 208p. (J). (gr. 3). pap. 6.99 (978-0-14-240734-9(8) , Puffin) Penguin Group (USA) Inc.

Blackaby, Susan. The Missing Tooth. Haugen, Ryan, illus. 2006. (Read-It! Readers Ser.). 32p. (J). (ps-3). 18.60 (978-1-4048-1592-6(9)) Picture Window Bks.

Blume, Judy. Double Fudge. 2007. (Fudge Ser.). 224p. (J). (gr. 2). 5.99 (***978-0-14-240878-0(6)*** , Puffin) Penguin Group (USA) Inc.

—Double Fudge. 2004. (Fudge Ser.). 160p. (J). (gr. 3-7). pap. 36.00 incl. audio (978-0-8072-2036-8(1) , Listening Library) Random Hse. Audio Publishing Group.

Boulden, Jim & Boulden, Joan. From Mad to Worse Set: Anger Management: Includes Reproducible Pages. 2000. (J). (gr. 1-4). act. bk. ed. 19.95 (978-1-878076-59-5(0)) Boulden Publishing.

Boyd, David. Closer to Hamlet. 2003. 120p. (YA). pap. 4.95 (978-0-921156-93-2(6)) Rubicon Publishing, Inc. CAN. *Dist:* International Publishers Marketing.

—Closer to Hamlet. 2003. (gr. 7-12). lib. bdg. 12.95 (978-0-613-77672-1(0)) Tandem Library Bks.

Bramwell, Wendie, et al. The Friendship Alphabet. Ziegler, Michael, illus. Ziegler, Michael, photos by. 2003. 32p. (J). pap. (978-0-9741388-3-1(5)) Committee for Children.

Brown, Ilknur. Faces of Little Robert. l.t. ed. 2006. (Illus.). 31p. (J). per. 13.99 (978-1-59879-191-4(5)) Lifevest Publishing, Inc.

Bruna, Dick. Miffy Is Crying. 1998. (Miffy Ser.). (Illus.). 28p. (J). (ps-k). 4.95 (978-1-56836-263-2(3)) Kodansha America, Inc.

Buddy Bear's Feelings. 2000. (Illus.). (J). (978-1-56156-832-1(5)) Kidsbooks, Inc.

Burgess, Melvin. El Fantasma tras la Pared. (SPA.). (J). 8.95 (978-958-04-6483-9(9)) Norma S.A. COL. *Dist:* Distribuidora Norma, Inc.

Burk, Mark Simon. Saddy & Gladdy. 2003. (J). 26.00 (978-0-9743619-0-1(9)) Ivy Hill Bunch, LLC.

Bush, Don. Little Brook Series, 3 bks. (Illus.). (J). (gr. 3). lib. bdg. 16.50 (978-0-943978-03-1(3)) Rolling Hills Pr.

Caletti, Deb. The Nature of Jade. 2007. 288p. (YA). (***978-1-4287-2344-3(7)*** , Simon & Schuster Children's Publishing) Simon & Schuster Children's Publishing.

Callian, Richard L. A Fat Girl's Name. 2002. 115p. pap. 16.95 (978-1-59129-319-4(7)) PublishAmerica, Inc.

Cantillon, Eli A. Amadeus: Four Stories in One. Stanley, Mandy, photos by. 1998. (Illus.). 62p. (J). (ps-k). 12.98 (978-1-58048-056-7(X)) Sandvik Publishing.

Capdevila, Roser & Vendrell, Maria Martinez. Reir y Llorar. 2003. Tr. of Laugh & Cry. (SPA.). 24p. (J). 7.95 (978-84-233-1458-4(8)) Ediciones Destino ESP. *Dist:* Planeta Publishing Corp.

Carlson, Nancy. ¡Sonríe! (Smile a Lot!) Carlson, Nancy, illus. 2007. (Ediciones Lerner Single Titles Ser.). (SPA., Illus.). 32p. (J). (gr. k-2). 15.95 (***978-0-8225-7817-8(4)*** , Ediciones Lerner) Lerner Publishing Group.

Carney, Karen L. Together, We'll Get Through This! Learning to Cope with Loss & Transition. Carney, Karen L., illus. 1999. (Barklay & Eve Ser.: Bk. 1). (Illus.). (J). pap. 6.95 (978-0-9667820-0-4(3)) Dragonfly Publishing.

Chappell, Crissa-Jean. Total Constant Order. 2007. 288p. (YA). (gr. 7 up). 16.99 (***978-0-06-088605-9(6)***); lib. bdg. 17.89 (***978-0-06-088606-6(4)***) HarperCollins Pubs. (HarperTeen).

Chbosky, Stephen. The Perks of Being a Wallflower. 1999. 213p. (gr. 7-12). pap. 14.00 (978-0-671-02734-6(4) , MTV) Simon & Schuster.

—The Perks of Being a Wallflower. 1999. (978-0-606-18378-9(7)) Tandem Library Bks.

Chidvilasananda, Gurumayi & Chidvilasananda, Swami. The Frogs & Their Monster. Martinot, Claude, illus. 2000. 36p. (J). (gr. k-2). 14.00 (978-0-911307-83-2(4)); reprint ed. 14.00 (978-0-911307-91-7(5) , 205200, Siddha Yoga Pubn.) SYDA Foundation.

Child, Lauren. Clarice Bean, Don't Look Now. Child, Lauren, illus. 2007. (Illus.). 256p. (J). (gr. 3-6). 15.99 (***978-0-7636-3536-7(7)***) Candlewick Pr.

Chung, Jenny. A Subtler Shade: Poems in Prose. 2007. 60p. per. 8.95 (***978-0-595-45997-1(8)***) iUniverse, Inc.

Clarke, Judith. Night Train. 2007. (J). pap. 9.95 (***978-1-932425-92-5(6)*** , Front Street) Boyds Mills Pr.

Cole, Brock. The Facts Speak for Themselves. 2000. (Illus.). (J). (978-0-606-18403-8(1)) Tandem Library Bks.

Cole, Michelle. Lilla Belle the First Stages. 2002. 118p. per. 10.99 (978-0-9722173-0-9(4)) Write World, Inc.

Cook, Julia. My Mouth Is A Volcano. Hartman, Carrie, illus. 2005. 32p. (J). pap. 9.95 (978-0-9747789-7-6(4)) CTC Publishing.

Coomer, Gerald. Summer I Was Seventeen. 2002. (gr. 7-12). lib. bdg. 32.70 (978-0-613-77565-6(1)) Tandem Library Bks.

Cooper, Helen. Ha Sido el Pequeno Monstruo! 2000. (SPA., Illus.). 32p. (J). (ps-2). 12.76 net. (978-84-261-3109-6(3)) Lectorum Pubns., Inc.

Cooper, John. First Day. Roscetti, John, illus. l.t. ed. 2002. (Heroes Start As Kids!: Vol. 1). 97p. (J). (gr. 2-7). per. 5.95 (978-0-9711474-9-2(3)) A B C-123 Publishing.

Corrigan, Eireann. Splintering. 2005. 184p. (YA). (gr. 8-12). lib. bdg. 15.04 (978-0-606-33304-7(5)) Tandem Library Bks.

Cummings, Catherine M. A Flea's Lament. Conner, Wendy Simpson, illus. 2002. (Flea Books: Vol. 1). 24p. (J). (ps-2). pap. 7.95 (978-0-9725155-0-4(X)) Junibird Productions.

Curtis, Jamie Lee. Today I Feel Silly Activity Book. 1998. (Illus.). (J). pap. (978-0-06-028099-4(9)) HarperCollins Pubs.

—Today I Feel Silly & Other Moods That Make My Day. (J). (ps). 2001. 32p. 6.95 (978-0-694-01343-2(9)); 2000. (Illus.). 32p. 15.95 incl. audio (978-0-06-028257-8(6)); 2000. 19.95 (978-0-00-225528-8(6)) HarperCollins Pubs.

—Today I Feel Silly & Other Moods That Make My Day. Cornell, Laura, illus. 1999. 40p. (J). (ps-3). 16.99 (978-0-06-024560-3(3) , Cotler, Joanna Books) HarperCollins Pubs.

—Today I Feely Silly / Canadian Edition. Cornell, Laura, illus. 1999. (J). (ps-3). (978-0-06-028842-6(6)) HarperCollins Pubs.

Cutler, Dave. When I Wished I Was Alone. Cutler, Dave, illus. 2003. (Illus.). 36p. (J). 16.95 (978-0-9671851-0-1(6)) GreyCore Pr.

Cuyler, Margery. 100th Day Worries. Howard, Arthur, illus. 2005. 32p. (J). reprint ed. 6.99 (978-1-4169-0789-3(0) , Aladdin) Simon & Schuster Children's Publishing.

Dalmatian Press Staff. Sesame Street What Makes You Giggle? 2007. 24p. pap. 3.50 (***978-1-4037-3232-3(9)***) Dalmatian Pr.

Davies, Rocky. Harvey Happy Bee. 2005. (Bee Attitude Board Books). (Illus.). (J). (978-1-59156-775-2(0)) Covenant Communications.

Dessen, Sarah. How to Deal: Someone Like You; That Summer. movie tie-in ed. 2003. 496p. (YA). pap. 7.99 (978-0-14-250103-0(4) , Puffin) Penguin Group (USA) Inc.

—Lock & Key. 2008. 432p. (YA). (gr. 7). 18.99 (***978-0-670-01088-2(X)*** , Viking Juvenile) Penguin Group (USA) Inc.

Dessen, Sarah. Someone Like You. 2003. (gr. 7-12). lib. bdg. 16.45 (978-0-613-66709-8(3)) Tandem Library Bks.

Divine, Jill. Miles Smiles. 2006. pap. (***978-1-84685-513-9(6)*** , Exposure Publishing) Meadow Bks.

Donahue, Jill L. Urban. Wendell the Worrier. Spence, Tom, illus. 2006. (Read-It! Readers Ser.). (J). 19.93 (978-1-4048-2425-6(1)) Picture Window Bks.

Doney, Meryl. The Very Worried Sparrow. Hansen, Gaby, illus. 2008. (J). 12.95 (***978-0-8198-8038-3(8)***) Pauline Bks. & Media.

Drake, David. Cricket Gets the Monster & 9 More Short Stories. 2002. (Cricket of Dew Drop Dell Ser.). (Illus.). 32p. (J). 3.49 (978-1-885631-61-9(8) , 618, Family Of Man Pr., The) Hutchison, G.F. Pr.

Drum, Emily. Happy Trails Horse Ranch. 2007. 16.95 (***978-1-58117-639-1(2)*** , Intervisual/Piggy Toes) Dalmatian Pr.

Du Bist Spat Aufgewacht, Mein Schatz: Eine Abenteuergeschichte. 2003. (Illus.). 284p. (YA). 15.00 (978-0-9712545-0-3(8)) Privatgaeste Verlag.

Dunbar, Polly. Flyaway Katie. Dunbar, Polly, illus. 2004. (Illus.). 40p. (J). (gr. k-k). 14.99 (978-0-7636-2366-1(0)) Candlewick Pr.

Easton, Kelly. Walking on Air. 2004. (Illus.). 240p. (YA). 16.95 (978-0-689-84875-9(7) , McElderry, Margaret K.) Simon & Schuster Children's Publishing.

Eisenson, Adam. Hope. 2005. (Illus.). 35p. (J). 14.95 (978-0-9766157-0-5(3)) Lone Star Pubns.

Elffers, Joost & Freymann, Saxton. How Are You Peeling? Foods with Moods. 2004. (Scholastic Bookshelf Ser.). 48p. (J). reprint ed. pap. 6.99 (978-0-439-59841-5(9) , Scholastic Paperbacks) Scholastic, Inc.

Ernst, Kathleen. Highland Fling. 2006. 192p. (J). 15.95 (978-0-8126-2742-8(3)) Cricket Bks.

Evans, Lezlie. Sometimes I Feel Like a Storm Cloud. Carrington, Marsha G., illus. 1999. 32p. (J). (gr. 6-13). 15.95 (978-1-57255-621-8(8)) Mondo Publishing.

Flanery, Alicia & Stephenson, Caitlin. Wow: We Wrote a Book! 2003. 140p. (YA). pap. 13.95 (978-0-595-28056-8(0)) iUniverse, Inc.

Fleischman, Paul. Whirligig. rev. ed. 1998. 160p. (J). (gr. 7 up). 17.95 (978-0-8050-5582-5(7) , Holt, Henry & Co. Bks. For Young Readers) Holt, Henry & Co.

—Whirligig. 1999. (Laurel-Leaf Bks.). 144p. (YA). (gr. 7-12). reprint ed. pap. 5.99 (978-0-440-22835-6(2) , Laurel Leaf) Random Hse. Children's Bks.

—Whirligig. 1999. 133p. (YA). (gr. 7-12). lib. bdg. 13.55 (978-0-613-23052-0(3)); (978-0-606-17219-6(X)) Tandem Library Bks.

Fox, Helen. Eager's Nephew. 2006. 304p. (J). (gr. 3-7). 15.95 (978-0-385-74673-1(3) , Lamb, Wendy) Random Hse. Children's Bks.

Fox, Mem. Harriet, You'll Drive Me Wild! Frazee, Marla, illus. 2000. 32p. (J). (ps-2). 16.00 (978-0-15-201977-8(4)) Harcourt Children's Bks.

Fox, Mem & Frazee, Marla. Harriet, You'll Drive Me Wild! 2003. (Illus.). 32p. (J). pap. 6.00 (978-0-15-204598-2(8) , Voyager Bks./Libros Viajeros) Harcourt Children's Bks.

Frame, Jeron Ashford. Yesterday I Had the Blues. Christie, Gregory R., illus. 2004. 30p. (J). (gr. k-3). 14.95 (978-1-58246-084-0(1) , Tricycle Pr.) Ten Speed Pr.

Free & Sparks Taylor, Chandra. Spin It Like That. 2007. 256p. pap. 9.99 (***978-0-373-83080-0(7)***) Harlequin Enterprises, Ltd. CAN. *Dist:* Simon & Schuster, Inc.

Friday, Mary Ellen. It's a Bad Day. 2006. (Illus.). 32p. (J). 15.95 (978-0-87358-904-8(1) , Rising Moon Bks. for Young Readers) Northland Publishing.

Fullerton, Alma. Walking on Glass. 2007. 144p. (J). (gr. 9 up). 15.99 (978-0-06-077851-4(2)); lib. bdg. 16.89 (978-0-06-077852-1(0)) HarperCollins Pubs. (HarperTeen).

Gaia Smiles. l.t. ed. 2002. (Illus.). 14p. (978-0-9718600-0-1(9)) Lightwatcher Publishing.

Genechten, Guido van. The Cuddle Book. Genechten, Guido van, illus. 2004. (Illus.). 32p. (J). (ps-k). 14.99 (978-0-06-075306-1(4)) HarperCollins Pubs.

Geringer & Czernecki, Stefan. Silverpoint. 1999. 160p. (J). (gr. 5 up). pap. (978-0-06-440432-7(3) , Harper Trophy) HarperCollins Pubs.

Goldblatt, Rob, illus. The Boy Who Didn't Want to Be Sad. 2004. 32p. (J). 14.95 (978-1-59147-134-9(6) , Magination Pr.) American Psychological Assn.

Goldblatt, Robert. The Boy Who Didn't Want to Be Sad. 2004. (Illus.). 32p. (J). pap. 8.95 (978-1-59147-135-6(4) , Magination Pr.) American Psychological Assn.

Golding, Theresa Martin. The Truth about Twelve. 2004. (Illus.). 176p. (J). (gr. 4-6). pap. 16.95 (978-1-59078-291-0(7)) Boyds Mills Pr.

Golds, Cassandra. Clair de Lune. Blackall, Sophie, illus. 2006. 208p. (J). (gr. 5). 15.95 (978-0-375-83395-3(1)); lib. bdg. 17.99 (978-0-375-93395-0(6)) Random Hse. Children's Bks. (Knopf Bks. for Young Readers).

Gray, Susan. Tess. 2002. 88p. pap. 14.95 (978-1-59286-080-7(X)) PublishAmerica, Inc.

Gregori, Anthony, illus. Meet the ItsIts. l.t. ed. 2007. 40p. (J). lib. bdg. 9.99 (***978-0-9769360-1-5(1)***) Adam Hill Pubns.

Griffin, Adele. Amandine. 2003. 208p. (gr. 5-9). pap. 6.99 (978-0-7868-1441-1(1)) Disney Pr.

Gugler, Laurel Dee. Facing the Day. Betteridge, Deirdre, illus. 1999. 24p. (J). (gr. k-ps). pap. 5.95 (978-1-55037-576-3(8)) Annick Pr., Ltd. CAN. *Dist:* Firefly Bks., Ltd.

—Revoltijo Carinoso. van Kampen, Vlasta, illus. 2003. (Hablemos Ser.).Tr. of Muddle Cuddle. (SPA.). 24p. (J). (gr. k). pap. 6.95 (978-1-55037-506-0(7)) Annick Pr., Ltd. CAN. *Dist:* Firefly Bks., Ltd.

Halpin, Brendan. How Ya Like Me Now. 2007. 208p. (YA). (gr. 7 up). 16.00 (978-0-374-33495-6(1)) Farrar, Straus & Giroux.

Hamilton, Richard & McCord, Patricia. Pictures in the Dark. 2004. (Illus.). 225p. (J). (gr. 5 up). 16.95 (978-1-58234-848-3(0) , Bloomsbury Children) Bloomsbury Publishing.

Harper, Charise Mericle. Just Grace. 2007. (Illus.). 144p. (J). (gr. 1-5). 15.00 (978-0-618-64642-5(6)) Houghton Mifflin Co. Trade & Reference Div.

Harper, Jessica. Lizzy's Ups & Downs: NOT an Ordinary School Day. Dupont, Lindsay Harper, illus. 2004. 32p. (J). (ps-3). 15.99 (978-0-06-052063-2(9)); lib. bdg. 16.89 (978-0-06-052064-9(7)) HarperCollins Pubs.

Harper, Jo & Harper, Josephine. Como los Perros de la Pradera. Gutiérrez, Guillermo, tr. Spearing, Craig, illus. 2000. (SPA.). 48p. (J). (ps-3). pap. 8.95 (978-1-890515-24-9(8)) Turtle Bks.

Harpster, Steve, illus. Arnold Gets Angry: An Emotional Literacy Book. 2004. (Emotional Literacy Ser.). 45p. (J). (gr. 2 up). 14.95 (978-0-9747789-0-7(7) , 67312) CTC Publishing.

Harrison, Lisi. Revenge of the Wannabes. 2005. (Clique Ser.: No. 3). 304p. (YA). (gr. 5-8). pap. 9.99 (978-0-316-70133-4(5) , Poppy) Little, Brown Bks. for Young Readers.

Hastings, Suanne. Many Moods of Maddie. 2006. 24p. pap. 12.95 (978-0-9769348-0-6(9)) Tastica, Suanne Creations Inc.

Hegg, Tom. Peef & His Best Friend. Hanson, Warren, illus. 2001. 48p. (J). (ps up). 15.95 (978-0-931674-49-5(2)) Waldman Hse. Pr., Inc.

Helfenbein, DeWayne. The Treasure Hunt. 2006. pap. 9.99 (***978-1-60034-562-3(X)***) Xulon Pr., Inc.

Helmore, Jim. Letterbox Lil: A Cautionary Tale. 2006. (Illus.). (J). (***978-1-4156-4110-1(2)***) Barron's Educational Series, Inc.

Henkes, Kevin. Prudencia Se Preocupa. (SPA.). 32p. (J). (gr. k-1). 7.20 (978-84-241-8067-6(4) , EV31695) Everest de Ediciones y Distribucion, S.L. ESP. *Dist:* Lectorum Pubns., Inc.

—Prudencia Se Preocupa. 2002. (SPA.). (gr. k-3). lib. bdg. 16.40 (978-0-613-64581-2(2)) Tandem Library Bks.

Heurtelou, Maude. Anayiz Gen Lapenn. Louissaint, Louis, illus. 1999. Tr. of Anayil is Sad. (CRP.). 28p. (J). (gr. 3-5). pap. 19.00 incl. audio (978-1-881839-87-3(7)) Educa Vision.

Hollstein, Stephanie. Connections. 2001. 192p. (YA). pap. 13.95 (978-0-595-17152-1(4) , Writers Club Pr.) iUniverse, Inc.

Holmes, Margaret M. A Terrible Thing Happened. Pillo, Cary, illus. 2000. 31p. (J). (ps-3). (978-1-55798-642-9(8) , 441-6428); pap. (978-1-55798-701-3(7) , 441-7017) American Psychological Assn. (Magination Pr.).

hooks, bell. Grump Groan Growl. Raschka, Chris, photos by. 2008. 40p. 16.99 (***978-0-7868-0816-8(0)***) Hyperion Pr.

Hossack, Sylvie A. Green Mango Magic. 1998. (Avon Camelot Bks.). 128p. (J). (gr. 3-7). 14.00 (978-0-380-97613-3(7)) HarperCollins Pubs.

Huebner, Dawn. Sometimes I Worry Too Much: A Book to Help Children Who Worry When They Don't Need To. Schader, Karen, ed. Morris, Robin C., illus. 2003. (J). per. 17.95 (978-1-58815-060-8(7) , 63814) Childswork/Childsplay.

Hunter, Jana Novotny. I Have Feelings. Porter, Sue, illus. 2002. (J). 25p. pap. (978-1-59034-193-3(7)); 32p. 15.95 (978-1-59034-196-4(1)) Mondo Publishing.

Hyperion Staff & Wow Worldwide Limited Staff. Wow Babies: Feelings. 2007. 12p. (ps-ps). 6.99 (***978-1-4231-0246-5(0)***) Hyperion Pr.

Imes, Jarold. Ain't No Punk Christian. 2007. (YA). per. 10.99 (***978-1-934195-07-9(3)***) Abednego's Free.

Impey, Rose & Huws, Emily. Dymuniad Mewn Eiliad. 2005. (WEL., Illus.). 64p. (978-0-86381-912-4(5)) Gwasg Carreg Gwalch.

Inkpen, Mick. Wibbly Pig Is Happy. 2000. (Wibbly Pig Ser.). (Illus.). 16p. (J). (ps). bds. 5.99 (978-0-670-89263-1(7) , Viking Juvenile) Penguin Group (USA) Inc.

Jahn-Clough, Lisa. Alicia Has a Bad Day. Jahn-Clough, Lisa, illus. 2002. (Illus.). 32p. (J). (gr. k-3). pap. 5.95 (978-0-618-26011-9(0) , Walter Lorraine) Houghton Mifflin Co. Trade & Reference Div.

—Alicia Has a Bad Day. 2002. (gr. k-3). lib. bdg. 14.10 (978-0-613-72916-1(1)) Tandem Library Bks.

Jahn-Clough, Lisa. Me, Penelope. 2007. 208p. (YA). (gr. 7 up). 16.00 (***978-0-618-77366-4(5)*** , Walter Lorraine) Houghton Mifflin Co. Trade & Reference Div.

Jantti, Mariana. A Little Bit of Sunshine for You. 2006. (Little Books for Big Kids Ser.). (Illus.). 32p. (J). pap. 9.95 (978-9974-7896-5-4(6)) Hardenville SA URY. *Dist:* Independent Pubs. Group.

Jennings, Sharon, et al. Franklin & the Contest. Jeffrey, Sean et al, trs. Jeffrey, Sean et al, illus. 2004. (Kids Can Read Ser.). 32p. (J). (gr. k-3). (978-1-55337-492-3(4)); (978-1-55337-491-6(6)) Kids Can Pr., Ltd.

—Franklin & the Scooter. Nikolic, Violeta & McIntyre, Sasha, trs. Nikolic, Violeta & McIntyre, Sasha, illus. 2004. (Kids Can Read Ser.). 32p. (J). (gr. k-3). (978-1-55337-494-7(0)); (978-1-55337-493-0(2)) Kids Can Pr., Ltd.

Jolin, Dominique. A Friend for Washington. Jolin, Dominique, illus. 1999. (Tickle Ser.). (Illus.). 16p. (J). (ps). bds. (978-1-894363-14-3(0)) Dominique & Friends.

—Hey Deecee, How Are You? Perkes, Carolyn, tr. from FRE. Jolin, Dominique, illus. 2001. (Deecee Ser.). (Illus.). 14p. (J). bds. (978-1-894363-52-5(3)) Dominique & Friends.

—Washington Dresses Up. Jolin, Dominique, illus. 1999. (Tickle Ser.). (Illus.). 16p. (J). (ps). bds. (978-1-894363-12-9(4)) Dominique & Friends.

—Washington Goes for a Walk. Jolin, Dominique, illus. 2000. (Illus.). 16p. (J). (ps-k). bds. (978-1-894363-28-0(0)) Dominique & Friends.

—Washington Plays Hide-and-Seek. Jolin, Dominique, illus. 1999. (Tickle Ser.). (Illus.). 16p. (J). (ps). bds. (978-1-894363-13-6(2)) Dominique & Friends.

—Washington Tells a Story. Jolin, Dominique, illus. 2000. (Illus.). 16p. (J). (ps-k). bds. (978-1-894363-27-3(2)) Dominique & Friends.

Jones, Patrick. Things Change. (J). 2004. 216p. 16.95 (978-0-8027-8901-3(3)); 2006. 228p. reprint ed. pap. 7.95 (978-0-8027-7746-1(5)) Walker & Co.

Jongman, Mariken & Boeke, Wanda. Rits. 2008. (J). (***978-1-59078-545-4(2)*** , Front Street) Boyds Mills Pr.

Jonsberg, Barry. Dreamrider. 2008. 256p. (J). (gr. 9). lib. bdg. 18.99 (***978-0-375-94457-4(5)*** , Knopf Bks. for Young Readers) Random Hse. Children's Bks.

Kachenmeister, Cherryl. On Monday When It Rained. Berthiaume, Tom, illus. 2001. (Sandpiper Bks.). 40p. (J). (gr. k-3). pap. 5.95 (978-0-618-11124-4(7)) Houghton Mifflin Co. Trade & Reference Div.

—On Monday When It Rained. 2001. (978-0-606-20828-4(3)); lib. bdg. 14.10 (978-0-613-35545-2(8)) Tandem Library Bks.

Kaslik, Ibi. Skinny. 2006. 256p. (YA). 16.95 (978-0-8027-9608-0(7)) Walker & Co.

Katz, Karen. Mommy Hugs. Katz, Karen, illus. 2007. (Classic Board Bks.). 32p. (J). bds. 7.99 (978-1-4169-4121-7(5) , Little Simon) Simon & Schuster Children's Publishing.

Kingsley, Charles. Water Babies. 2004. 21.95 (978-0-8488-2728-1(7)) Amereon LTD.

Kirk, David. Captain Sunny Patch. 2006. (Miss Spider Ser.). (Illus.). 32p. (J). 6.99 (978-0-448-44366-9(X)) Callaway Editions, Inc.

Kline, Suzy. Song Lee & the "I Hate You" Notes. Remkiewicz, Frank, illus. 1999. (Song Lee Ser.). 64p. (J). (gr. 2-5). 13.99 (978-0-670-87887-1(1) , Viking Juvenile) Penguin Group (USA) Inc.

Klise, Kate. Why Do You Cry? Not a Sob Story. Klise, M. Sarah, illus. rev. ed. 2006. 32p. (J). 16.95 (978-0-8050-7319-5(1) , Holt, Henry & Co. Bks. For Young Readers) Holt, Henry & Co.

Knudsen, Michelle. Love. Haley, Amanda, illus. 2001. (Sparkle 'n' Shimmer Ser.). 14p. (J). (ps-k). bds. 5.99 (978-0-689-83783-8(6) , Little Simon) Simon & Schuster Children's Publishing.

Kooser, Diane S. Potter Pig in Control: Four Stories on Anger Management. Norcross, Harry, illus. 2000. 64p. (J). (gr. 1-3). pap. 12.95 (978-1-57543-084-3(3)) MAR*CO Products, Inc.

Kriesel, Mae. Aggi Pursued. 2007. per. 12.99 (***978-1-59886-534-9(X)***) Tate Publishing & Enterprises, L.L.C.

Krosoczka, Jarrett J. My Buddy, Slug. 2006. (Illus.). 40p. (J). (gr. k-3). 15.95 (978-0-375-83342-7(0)); lib. bdg. 17.99 (978-0-375-93342-4(5)) Random Hse. Children's Bks. (Knopf Bks. for Young Readers).

Kulling, Monica. Edgar Badger's Butterfly Day. Twinem, Nancy, illus. 1999. 48p. (J). (gr. 1-5). pap. 4.50 (978-1-57255-604-1(8)) Mondo Publishing.

Lagonegro, Melissa & Random House Disney Staff. Monsters Get Scared of School, Too. Harchy, Atelier Philippe, illus. 2004. (Random House Pictureback Book Ser.). 16p. (J). (ps-2). pap. 3.99 (978-0-7364-2245-1(5) , RH/Disney) Random Hse. Children's Bks.

Langston, Laura. A Taste of Perfection. 2002. (Illus.). 190p. (J). (gr. 5 up). pap. 6.95 (978-0-7737-6274-9(4)) Stoddart Kids CAN. *Dist:* Fitzhenry & Whiteside, Ltd.

Lawrence, Jennifer B. Sad Doggy. Ering, Tim, illus. 2001. 24p. (J). (ps-k). 13.95 (978-1-58117-066-5(1) , Intervisual/Piggy Toes) Dalmatian Pr.

Lawrinson, Julia. Obsession. 2001. 264p. pap. 13.95 (978-1-86368-324-1(0)) Fremantle Pr. AUS. *Dist:* International Specialized Bk. Services.

Lemieux, Jean. Toby Laughs Last. Cummins, Sarah, tr. from FRE. Casson, Sophie, illus. 2006. (First Novel Ser.). 64p. (J). (gr. 2-5). (***978-0-88780-720-6(8)***); 4.95 (***978-0-88780-716-9(X)***) Formac Publishing Co., Ltd. CAN. *Dist:* Casemate Pubs. & Bk. Distributors, LLC.

Lester, Helen. Hurty Feelings. Munsinger, Lynn M., illus. 32p. (J). (gr. k-3). 2007. 6.95 (***978-0-618-84062-5(1)***); 2004. tchr. ed. 16.00 (978-0-618-41082-8(1)) Houghton Mifflin Co. Trade & Reference Div. (Walter Lorraine).

Light, Steve. I Am Happy: A Touch & Feel Book of Feelings. Light, Steve, illus. 2003. (Illus.). 12p. (J). (ps-1). 12.99 (978-0-7636-1753-0(9)) Candlewick Pr.

Lloyd, Sam. Grumpy Gracie. 2006. (Illus.). 12p. (J). 8.95 (978-0-7624-2521-1(0) , Running Pr. Kids) Running Pr. Bk. Pubs.

Lombardi, Kristine. Girl Talk: Complete Guide to IM Lingo, Emoticons, & More! 2006. (Illus.). 48p. (J). bds. 12.99 (978-0-7944-1129-9(0)) Reader's Digest Assn., Inc., The.

Lyga, Barry. Boy Toy. 2007. 416p. (YA). (gr. 7). 16.95 (***978-0-618-72393-5(5)***) Houghton Mifflin Co.

Lyon, George Ella. No Dessert Forever! Catalanotto, Peter, illus. 2006. 40p. (J). (gr. k-4). 16.95 (978-1-4169-0385-7(2) , Atheneum/Richard Jackson Bks.) Simon & Schuster Children's Publishing.

Maccarone, Grace. Mother, May I? 2006. 28p. (J). bds. 8.99 (978-0-439-77015-6(7) , Cartwheel Bks.) Scholastic, Inc.

MacKall, Dandi Daley. Eager Star. 2002. (Winnie the Horse Gentler Ser.: Bk. 2). (Illus.). 208p. (J). (gr. 4-7). mass mkt. 5.99 (978-0-8423-5543-8(X)) Tyndale Hse. Pubs.

—Unhappy Appy. 2003. (Winnie the Horse Gentler Ser.). (Illus.). 192p. (J). mass mkt. 5.99 (978-0-8423-5546-9(4)) Tyndale Hse. Pubs.

—Wild Thing. 2002. (Winnie The Horse Gentler Ser.: 1). (Illus.). 192p. (J). mass mkt. 5.99 (978-0-8423-5542-1(1)) Tyndale Hse. Pubs.

Mackler, Carolyn. Guyaholic. 2007. (Illus.). 192p. (YA). (gr. 9 up). 16.99 (***978-0-7636-2537-5(X)***) Candlewick Pr.

MacLean, Kerry Lee. Peaceful Piggy Meditation. MacLean, Kerry Lee, illus. 2004. (Illus.). 32p. (J). (gr. k-4). 16.95 (978-0-8075-6380-9(3)) Whitman, Albert & Co.

Madison, Ron. Ned & the General. 2004. (Illus.). 24p. (J). 8.95 (978-1-887206-24-2(8)) Ned's Head Productions.

Madonna. Lotsa de Casha. Paes, Rui, illus. 2005. 48p. (J). 19.95 (978-0-670-05888-4(2)) Callaway Editions, Inc.

—Madonna Box Set. 2004. 144p. (ps-6). 39.95 (978-0-670-06014-6(3)) Penguin Group (USA) Inc.

Mallat, Kathy. Mama Love. Mallat, Kathy, illus. 2004. (Illus.). 24p. (J). 15.95 (978-0-8027-8902-0(1)) Walker & Co.

Marks, Lisa Rey. Joy Is the Greatest Gift. 2007. (Illus.). 32p. (J). 16.99 (***978-0-9786028-0-2(3)***) Focus Friends, LLC.

Mathison, Tarver. Rebel Fortunes. 2002. 130p. (YA). pap. 10.95 (978-0-595-25413-2(6) , Writers Club Pr.) iUniverse, Inc.

Mayer, Mercer. I Was So Mad. Mayer, Mercer, illus. rev. ed. 2000. (Little Critter Ser.). (Illus.). 24p. (J). (gr. k-k). reprint ed. pap. 3.99 (978-0-307-11939-1(4) , 11939, Random Hse. Bks. for Young Readers) Random Hse. Children's Bks.

McBratney, Sam. I Love It When You Smile. Fuge, Charles, illus. 2006. 32p. (J). 15.99 (978-0-06-084245-1(8)) HarperCollins Pubs.

McClulre, Brian D. The Sun & the Moon. 2006. (Illus.). 36p. (J). 14.95 (978-1-933426-09-9(8)) Universal Flag Publishing.

McDaniel, Lurlene. To Live Again. 2001. (Dawn Rochelle Ser.: No. 5). (gr. 5-8). lib. bdg. 13.00 (978-0-613-57927-8(5)) Tandem Library Bks.

McDonald, Megan. The Holly Joliday. Reynolds, Peter H., illus. 2007. (Judy Moody Ser.). 96p. (J). (gr. k-3). 14.99 (***978-0-7636-3237-3(6)***) Candlewick Pr.

—Judy Moody. Reynolds, Peter H., illus. (Judy Moody Ser.: No. 1). (J). (gr. 1-5). 2002. 160p. pap. 5.99 (978-0-7636-1231-3(6)); 2000. 196p. 15.99 (978-0-7636-0685-5(5)) Candlewick Pr.

—Judy Moody. Reynolds, Peter H., illus. 2002. (Judy Moody Ser.: No. 1). 160p. (J). (ps-7). per. 14.15 (978-0-613-56467-0(7)) Tandem Library Bks.

—Judy Moody Esta de Mal Humor, de Muy Mal Humor. Mendoza Garcia, Isabel, tr. Reynolds, Peter H., illus. (SPA.). 168p. (J). (gr. 3-5). pap. 7.95 (978-1-59437-816-4(9)) Santillana USA Publishing Co., Inc.

McKee, David. Who Is Mrs Green? 2005. (Illus.). 32p. (J). pap. 9.99 (978-1-84270-429-5(X)) Trafalgar Square Publishing.

McKinley, Cynthia. One Smile. Byrne, Mary Gregg, illus. l.t. ed. 2002. 32p. (ps up). 15.95 (978-0-935699-23-4(6) , 0935699236) Illumination Arts Publishing Co., Inc.

McNeal, Laura & McNeal, Tom. Zipped. 2004. 304p. (YA). (gr. 7). reprint ed. pap. 7.99 (978-0-375-83098-3(7) , Knopf Bks. for Young Readers) Random Hse. Children's Bks.

McVeity, Jen. Green with Red Spots Horrible. Hobbs, Leigh, illus. 1999. (Supa Doopers Ser.). 64p. (J). (978-0-7608-1937-1(8)) Sundance/Newbridge Educational Publishing.

—Green with Red Spots Horrible. 1999. (gr. 3-6). lib. bdg. 12.60 (978-0-613-19369-6(5)) Tandem Library Bks.

Menchin, Scott. Taking a Bath with the Dog & Other Things That Make Me Happy. Menchin, Scott, illus. 2007. (Illus.). 40p. (J). (ps-3). 15.99 (978-0-7636-2919-9(7)) Candlewick Pr.

Merchant, Peter. Sojourner Truth: Path to Glory. Denos, Julia, illus. 2007. (Ready-to-read SOFA Ser.). 48p. (J). pap. 3.99 (978-0-689-87207-5(0) , Aladdin) Simon & Schuster Children's Publishing.

Metzger, Steve. I'm Having a Bad Day! Wilhelm, Hans, illus. 1998. (Dinofours Ser.: No. 2). 32p. (J). (ps-1). pap. 3.25 (978-0-590-03551-4(7)) Scholastic, Inc.

Michael, Veronica & Caole, Frances. Ayuqucinka. Michael, Veronica & Shantz, Joy, illus. l.t. ed. 1999. Tr. of My Feelings. (ESK.). 8p. (J). (gr. k-3). pap. 6.00 (978-1-58084-055-2(8)); pap. 6.00 (978-1-58084-117-7(1)) Lower Kuskokwim Schl. District.

—Mihigimanitka. Michael, Veronica & Shantz, Joy, illus. l.t. ed. 1999. Tr. of My Feelings. (ESK.). 8p. (J). (gr. k-3). pap. 6.00 (978-1-58084-130-6(9)) Lower Kuskokwim Schl. District.

—My Feelings. Michael, Veronica & Shantz, Joy, illus. l.t. ed. 1999. 8p. (J). (gr. k-3). pap. 6.00 (978-1-58084-054-5(X)) Lower Kuskokwim Schl. District.

—Qanuqitipit. Shantz, Joy, illus. l.t. ed. 1999. Tr. of My Feelings. (ESK.). 8p. (J). (gr. k-3). pap. 6.00 (978-1-58084-123-8(6)) Lower Kuskokwim Schl. District.

—Qanuqitipit. Michael, Veronica & Shantz, Joy, illus. l.t. ed. 1999. Tr. of My Feelings. (ESK.). 8p. (J). (gr. k-3). pap. 6.00 (978-1-58084-138-2(4)) Lower Kuskokwim Schl. District.

Michot, Fabienne. Maki, I Am Happy. braille ed. 2004. (J). (gr. 1). spiral bd., bds. (978-0-616-07267-7(8)) Canadian National Institute for the Blind/Institut National Canadien pour les Aveugles.

Mikaelsen, Ben. Touching Spirit Bear. l.t. ed. 2004. 305p. pap. 10.95 (978-0-7862-6351-6(2)) Thorndike Pr.

Mlynowski, Sarah. Bras & Broomsticks. 2006. 320p. (YA). (gr. 7). reprint ed. pap. 8.95 (978-0-385-73184-3(1) , Delacorte Bks. for Young Readers) Random Hse. Children's Bks.

Moon, Nicola & Busby, Ailie. Slugs for Breakfast. 2005. (Illus.). (J). mass mkt. 9.99 (978-0-340-87771-5(5)) Headway GBR. *Dist:* Trafalgar Square Publishing.

Mooney, Bel & Chamberlain, Margaret. Mr Tubs Is Lost. 2006. (Blue Bananas Ser.). (Illus.). 48p. (J). pap. (978-0-7787-0904-6(3)) Crabtree Publishing Co.

Morales, Maximino. Juan & the Three Wise Men (Juan y los Tres Reyes Mogos) 2002. (ENG & SPA., Illus.). 28p. (J). (gr. k-3). pap. 6.95 (978-0-9740308-1-4(3)) Maximum Publishing Co.

Moran, Alex. Six Silly Foxes. Baker, Keith, illus. 2003. (Green Light Readers Level 1 Ser.). 24p. (J). 11.95 (978-0-15-204823-5(5)); pap. 3.95 (978-0-15-204863-1(4)) Harcourt Children's Bks. (Green Light Readers).

Morrison, Toni, et al. The Book of Mean People. 2002. (Illus.). 48p. (ps-3). 17.49 (978-0-7868-2471-7(9)) Disney Pr.

Moss, Marissa. Amelia's Guide to Gossip: The Good, the Bad, & the Ugly. Moss, Marissa, illus. 2006. (Amelia's Notebooks). (Illus.). 80p. (J). 9.95 (978-1-4169-1475-4(7) , Simon & Schuster/Paula Wiseman Bks.) Simon & Schuster Children's Publishing.

Moss, Miriam. Smudge's Grumpy Day. Chapman, Lynne, illus. 2002. 24p. (J). (ps-2). (978-1-86233-282-9(7) , Gullane Children's Bks.) Pinwheel.

Mouse Works Staff. Disney's Winnie the Pooh's Feelings: Learn & Grow. 2000. (Winnie the Pooh Ser.). (Illus.). 20p. (J). (ps). bds. 4.99 (978-0-7364-1008-3(2) , RH/Disney) Random Hse. Children's Bks.

Muldrow, Diane. The Happy Book. 1999. (Illus.). 18p. (J). pap. 13.95 (978-0-590-10993-2(6)) Scholastic, Inc.

Myers, Walter Dean. The Dream Bearer. 2004. 192p. (J). (gr. 5 up). reprint ed. pap. 5.99 (978-0-06-447289-0(2) , Amistad) HarperCollins Pubs.

—Shooter. 2004. (J). 224p. 15.99 (978-0-06-029519-6(8)); (Illus.). 240p. lib. bdg. 16.89 (978-0-06-029520-2(1)) HarperCollins Pubs. (HarperTeen).

Napoli, Donna Jo. April Flowers. Ben-Ami, Doren & Klementz-Harte, Lauren, illus. 2000. (Angelwings Ser.: No. 7). 80p. (J). (gr. 2-5). pap. 7.95 (978-0-689-83207-9(9) , Aladdin) Simon & Schuster Children's Publishing.

—April Flowers. 2000. (Angelwings Ser.: No. 7). (Illus.). (J). 10.79 (978-0-606-17910-2(0)) Tandem Library Bks.

—Ugly. Judge, Lita, illus. 2006. 192p. (gr. 2-5). 14.99 (978-0-7868-3753-3(5)) Hyperion Pr.

Natlie, Jeffrey Michael. Emily Gets Angry. 2006. (J). 9.95 (978-0-9779822-0-2(3)) ErieKIDS, Inc.

Nettrour, Nelani. The Imagnyairs of Jemmidar, Bk. A. l.t. ed. 2006. (Illus.). 73p. (J). pap. 11.95 (978-1-932657-53-1(3)) Third Millennium Pubns.

Newman, Leslea. The Boy Who Cried Fabulous. Ferguson, Peter, illus. 2007. 32p. (J). (ps-2). pap. 7.95 (***978-1-58246-224-0(0)*** , Tricycle Pr.) Ten Speed Pr.

Nolan, Han. When We Were Saints. (YA). 2005. 312p. pap. 6.95 (978-0-15-205322-2(0) , Harcourt Paperbacks); 2003. (Illus.). 304p. 17.00 (978-0-15-216371-6(9) , 53586153) Harcourt Children's Bks.

Oates, Joyce Carol. After the Wreck, I Picked Myself up, Spread My Wings, & Flew Away. 2007. 320p. (J). (gr. 9 up). pap. 7.99 (***978-0-06-073527-2(9)***); 2006. 304p. (YA). lib. bdg. 17.89 (978-0-06-073526-5(0)) HarperCollins Pubs. (HarperTeen).

Oates, Joyce Carol. After the Wreck, I Picked Myself Up, Spread My Wings, & Flew Away. 2006. 304p. (YA). 16.99 (978-0-06-073525-8(2) , HarperTeen) HarperCollins Pubs.

Orenstein, Denise Gosliner. The Secret Twin. McCarthy, Dan, illus. 2007. 400p. (J). lib. bdg. 17.89 (978-0-06-078565-9(9)); (gr. 7 up). 16.99 (978-0-06-078564-2(0)) HarperCollins Pubs.

Osborne, Mary Pope. Dragon of the Red Dawn. Murdocca, Sal, illus. 2007. (Magic Tree House Ser.: No. 37). 108p. (J). (gr. k-3). pap. (978-0-375-83728-9(0)) Random Hse., Inc.

Pagliarulo, Antonio. A Different Kind of Heat. 2006. 192p. (YA). (gr. 9). pap. 7.50 (978-0-385-73298-7(8)); lib. bdg. 9.99 (978-0-385-90319-6(7)) Random Hse. Children's Bks. (Delacorte Bks. for Young Readers).

Palatini, Margie. Goldie Is Mad. Palatini, Margie, illus. 2001. (Illus.). 32p. (ps-k). 15.49 (978-0-7868-2490-8(5)); 14.99 (978-0-7868-0565-5(X)) Hyperion Bks. for Children.

Pantelides, Sherry. Make A Choice to Rejoice! A Story about Being Cheerful. Perez, Debi, illus. 2007. 32p. (J). 12.99 (***978-0-9771076-2-9(0)***) Lacey Productions.

Parker, Vicki Sue. The Get Well Soon... Balloon. Beebe, Susan, illus. 2005. 16p. (J). 15.00 (978-1-931117-35-7(7) , BALL) Lash & Assocs. Publishing/Training, Inc.

Parr, Todd. The Feel Good Book. Parr, Todd, illus. 2002. (Illus.). 32p. (J). (ps-3). 15.99 (978-0-316-07206-9(0) , Tingley, Megan Bks.) Little, Brown Bks. for Young Readers.

—The Feelings Book. 2005. (Illus.). 24p. (J). (ps-ps). bds. 6.99 (978-0-316-01249-2(1) , Tingley, Megan Bks.) Little, Brown Bks. for Young Readers.

Paulsen, Gary. The Crossing. 2006. 128p. (J). pap. 6.99 (978-0-439-78661-4(4) , Scholastic Paperbacks) Scholastic, Inc.

Petz, Moritz. Bad Mood. 2006. (Illus.). 32p. (J). pap. 6.95 (978-0-7358-2035-7(X)) North-South Bks., Inc.

Pielichaty, Helena. Starring Alex ... 2006. (Girls of Avenue Z Ser.). 128p. (J). pap. 4.99 (978-1-4169-0063-4(2) , Aladdin) Simon & Schuster Children's Publishing.

Plum-Ucci, Carol. The Body of Christopher Creed. 2001. (gr. 7-12). lib. bdg. 15.00 (978-0-613-49392-5(3)) Tandem Library Bks.

Porter, Eleanor. Pollyanna. 2005. 104p. per. 4.95 (978-1-4209-2555-5(5)) Digireads.com.

Powers-Fish, Amy Rose. Buddy's Forever Home. l.t. ed. 2006. (Illus.). 42p. (J). per. 11.99 (***978-1-59879-192-1(3)***) Lifevest Publishing, Inc.

Prestine, Joan Singleton. Moving Is Hard. Kylberg, Virginia, illus. 2002. 32p. (J). pap. 6.95 (978-1-57768-654-5(3)) School Specialty Publishing.

—Sometimes I Feel Awful. Kylberg, Virginia, illus. 2002. 32p. (J). pap. 6.95 (978-1-57768-653-8(5)) School Specialty Publishing.

—Sometimes I Feel Awful: Picture Book & Resource Guide, 2 bks., Set. 2001. (Kids Have Feelings, Too Ser.). (J). (ps-3). 14.99 (978-1-56417-763-6(7) , FE0051, Fearon Teacher Aids) Schaffer, Frank Pubns.

Profilet, Cynthia. Maggie's Golden Moment. Barron, Ann, illus. 2005. (J). (***978-0-9637735-1-7(8)***) Sterling Pr., Inc.

Purdy, Jo. A Day in a Night. 2005. 352p. pap. 24.95 (978-1-4137-6263-1(8)) PublishAmerica, Inc.

Random House Beginners Books Staff. Thomas Is Happy, Thomas Is Sad. 2002. (J). bds. 4.99 (978-0-375-81592-8(9) , Random Hse. Bks. for Young Readers) Random Hse. Children's Bks.

Random House Disney Staff. Honesty. 2007. (Pictureback(R) Ser.). 24p. (J). (ps-2). pap. 3.99 (*978-0-7364-2503-2(9), RH/Disney) Random Hse. Children's Bks.

Random House Staff. Clap Your Hands. Ewers, Joseph, illus. 2002. (Puppet Book Ser.). 10p. (J). (gr. k-ps). bds. 9.95 (978-0-375-82226-1(7), Random Hse. Bks. for Young Readers) Random Hse. Children's Bks.

Rapp, Jennifer, illus. I Can Wait for the Bell to Rin. 2006. 48p. (J). 9.95 (978-1-59354-170-5(8)) Blue Apple Bks.

Rau, Dana Meachen. Mi Lugar Preferido. Kim, Julie J., illus. 2005. (Rookie Reader Espanol Ser.). (SPA & ESP.). 31p. (J). (gr. k-2). pap. 4.95 (978-0-516-25534-7(7), Children's Pr.) Scholastic Library Publishing.

Rayner, Catherine. Augustus & His Smile. 2006. (Illus.). 28p. (J). (ps-2). 16.00 (978-1-56148-510-9(1)) Good Bks.

Reetz, Kurt. Lenny's Neighborhood: Lenny's New Hairdo. 2000. mass mkt. 8.95 (978-1-931179-09-6(3)) Long Hill Productions, Inc.

—Lenny's Neighborhood: Lenny's New Hairdo. Farkas, Josh, illus. 2000. 32p. (J). (gr. 1-3). pap. (978-0-9701450-8-6(X)) Long Hill Productions, Inc.

Rex, Annmarie. Black's Adventure in the Big, Scary, Hairy World. 2007. 46p. (J). 19.99 (*978-1-59879-365-9(9)); per. 15.99 (*978-1-59879-364-2(0)) Lifevest Publishing, Inc. (Lifevest).

Rey, H. A. & Rey, Margret, illus. Curious George's Are You Curious? 2003. (J). bds. 9.95 (978-0-618-27710-0(2)) Houghton Mifflin Co. Trade & Reference Div.

Ring, Susan. Mission: Where's June? Etienne, Kirk Albert & Luzzi, Micheal James, illus. 2006. (Disney's Little Einsteins Ser.). 32p. (ps-17). 9.99 (978-0-7868-5539-1(8)) Disney Pr.

Rosa-Mendoza, Gladys. When I Am/Cuando Estoy. Regan, Dana, illus. 2004. (English-Spanish Foundations Ser.). (SPA & ENG.). 20p. (J). (ps). bds. 6.95 (978-1-931398-12-1(7)) Me+Mi Publishing.

Rosen, Michael. Michael Rosen's Sad Book. Blake, Quentin, illus. 2005. 32p. (J). 16.99 (978-0-7636-2597-9(3)) Candlewick Pr.

Ross, Dave. A Book of Hugs. Rader, Laura, illus. 2000. 40p. (J). pap. 6.99 (978-0-06-443514-7(8), Harper Trophy) HarperCollins Pubs.

Roth, Susan L. It's Still a Dogs New York: A Book of Healing. 2001. 32p. (J). (gr. k-7). 12.00 (978-0-7922-7050-8(9), National Geographic Children's Bks.) National Geographic Society.

—Mi Amor Por Ti/My Love for You. 2003. (ENG & SPA., Illus.). 24p. (J). (ps). bds. 5.99 (978-0-8037-2944-5(8), Dial) Penguin Group (USA) Inc.

Rowe, John A. I Want a Hug. 2007. (Illus.). 32p. (J). (ps-3). 16.99 (*978-0-698-40064-1(X), Minedition) Penguin Group (USA) Inc.

Rozek, Kathy. Rudy & the Magical Twin Balloons. 2002. 32p. (J). 15.95 (978-0-9720871-0-0(9)) Brookline Merrimac Pubs.

Saenz, Benjamin Alire. He Forgot to Say Good-Bye. 2008. 272p. (YA). (*978-1-4169-4963-3(1), Simon & Schuster Children's Publishing) Simon & Schuster Children's Publishing.

Saltzberg, Barney. Baby Animals Kisses. 2001. (Illus.). 14p. (J). (ps). bds. 8.95 (978-0-15-202635-6(5), Red Wagon Bks.) Harcourt Children's Bks.

SAMi. Smiles. 2006. (Illus.). 10p. (J). bds. 8.95 (978-1-59354-160-6(0)) Blue Apple Bks.

Sartori, Rosanne Sheritz. Tales of Temper. 2005. (Illus.). 128p. (J). per. 21.95 (978-1-931636-48-3(6)) National Center For Youth Issues.

Schaffer, Sandra. What's under Benjamin's Bed? 1998. (Kid Genesis Ser.). (Illus.). 34p. pap. 8.95 (978-1-885478-43-6(7)) Kensington Publishing Corp.

Schirado, William C. Creatures Journey Through Life. l.t. ed. 2002. (Illus.). v, 27p. (J). (978-0-9660166-2-8(9)) TW Publishing.

Seeger, Laura Vaccaro. Walter Was Worried. (Illus.). 40p. (J). 2006. pap. 6.95 (978-1-59643-196-6(2)); 2005. 15.95 (978-1-59643-068-6(0)) Roaring Brook Pr.

Seuss, Dr. My Many Colored Days. Johnson, Stephen T. & Fancher, Lou, illus. 1998. 16p. (J). (gr. k-ps). bds. 6.99 (978-0-679-89344-8(X), Knopf Bks. for Young Readers) Random Hse. Children's Bks.

Shapiro, Lawrence. Ethan Has Too Much Energy: An Emotional Literacy Book. Harpster, Steve, illus. 2005. (Emotional Literacy Ser.). 42p. (J). 14.95 (978-0-9747789-4-5(X), 36027) CTC Publishing.

Shea, Chris. My Heart Purse. Shea, Chris, illus. 2006. (Illus.). 24p. (J). 9.99 (978-0-06-083875-1(2), Harper Festival) HarperCollins Pubs.

Shreve, Susan. Kiss Me Tomorrow. 2006. 224p. (YA). (gr. 5-8). 16.99 (978-0-439-68047-9(6), Levine, Arthur A. Bks.) Scholastic, Inc.

Shull, Megan. Amazing Grace. 2005. (Illus.). 256p. (gr. 6-9). 15.99 (978-0-7868-5690-9(4)) Hyperion Pr.

Silverstein, Shel. The Giving Tree. (Illus.). 95.94 (978-0-06-056897-9(6)); anniv. ed. 2004. 64p. (J). 18.99 incl. audio compact disk (978-0-06-058675-1(3)); 35th anniv. ed. 1999. 64p. (J). 17.99 (978-0-06-028451-0(X)) HarperCollins Pubs.

Simon, Charnan. Jeremy Jones, Clumsy Guy. Pillo, Cary, illus. 2006. (Magic Door to Learning Ser.). 24p. (J). (gr. 1-3). 21.36 (978-1-59296-619-6(5)) Child's World, Inc.

Small, David. Imogene's Antlers. Small, David, illus. 2002. (Illus.). (J). 14.79 (978-0-7587-2836-4(0)) Book Wholesalers, Inc.

—Imogene's Antlers. 2000. (J). pap. 19.97 incl. audio (978-0-7366-9207-6(X)) Books on Tape, Inc.

—Imogene's Antlers. 2005. (Illus.). (J). pap. 18.95 incl. audio compact disk (978-1-59112-723-9(8)) Live Oak Media.

—Imogene's Antlers. Small, David, illus. 2005. (Illus.). (J). (gr. 1-6). pap. 16.95 incl. audio (978-0-87499-322-6(9)) Live Oak Media.

—Imogene's Antlers. Boughton, Simon, ed. Small, David, illus. 2000. (Illus.). 32p. (J). (ps-3). 15.95 (978-0-375-81048-0(X), Crown Books For Young Readers) Random Hse. Children's Bks.

Smee, Nicola. Funny Face. 2006. (Illus.). 24p. (J). 8.95 (978-1-58234-710-3(7), Bloomsbury Children) Bloomsbury Publishing.

Smith, Linda. Mrs. Biddlebox: Her Bad Day... And What She Did about It! Frazee, Marla, illus. 2007. 32p. (J). (ps-2). 15.00 (*978-0-15-206349-8(8)) Harcourt Trade Pubs.

Sobel, Marla. The Penguin Who Lost Her Cool: A Story About Controlling Your Anger. Gilgannon, Denise, illus. 2000. (Early Prevention Ser.). 59p. (J). pap. 11.50 (978-1-882732-98-2(7)) Childswork/Childsplay.

Sommer, Carl. Can You Help Me Find My Smile? 2003. (Another Sommer-Time Story Ser.). (Illus.). 48p. (J). (gr. k-4). lib. bdg. 23.95 incl. audio compact disk (978-1-57537-707-0(1)); (gr. k-4). lib. bdg. 23.95 incl. audio (978-1-57537-757-5(8)); (gr. 1-4). 16.95 incl. audio (978-1-57537-556-4(7)); (gr. 1-4). 16.95 incl. audio compact disk (978-1-57537-507-6(9)) Advance Publishing, Inc.

Spencer, Katherine. Saving Grace. 2007. (Saving Grace Ser.). (Illus.). 256p. (YA). pap. 6.95 (*978-0-15-206096-1(0), Harcourt Paperbacks) Harcourt Children's Bks.

Spinelli, Eileen. When You Are Happy. Valerio, Geraldo, illus. 2006. 40p. (J). (ps-1). 16.95 (978-0-689-86251-9(2)) Simon & Schuster Children's Publishing.

Spotlight (Firm) Staff, contrib. by. Laugh with a Test Case. 2007. (Illus.). 80p. (J). 24.21 (*978-1-59961-284-3(4)) Spotlight.

—Laugh with Mammoth Madness. 2007. (Illus.). 80p. (J). 24.21 (*978-1-59961-281-2(X)) Spotlight.

—Laugh with Snack Swap. 2007. (Illus.). 80p. (J). 24.21 (*978-1-59961-282-9(8)) Spotlight.

—Laugh with Stampede. 2007. (Illus.). 80p. (J). 24.21 (*978-1-59961-283-6(6)) Spotlight.

Staunton, Ted. Super Move, Morgan! Slavin, Bill, illus. 2006. (First Novels Ser.: Vol. 35). 64p. (J). (gr. 2-5). (*978-0-88780-704-6(6)); 4.95 (978-0-88780-702-2(X)) Formac Publishing Co., Ltd. CAN. *Dist:* Casemate Pubs. & Bk. Distributors, LLC.

Sunderland, Margot & Hancock, Nicky. A Nifflenoo Called Nevermind: A Story for Children Who Bottle up Their Feelings. Armstrong, Nicky, tr. Armstrong, Nicky, illus. 32p. pap. (978-0-86388-496-2(2), 002-5064) Speechmark Publishing Ltd.

Sweet Sesame. 2004. (J). (978-1-59292-052-5(7)) SoftPlay, Inc.

Tan, Shaun. The Red Tree. 2002. (Illus.). 32p. (978-0-7344-0172-4(8), Lothian Bks.) Hachette Livre Australia.

—The Red Tree. Tan, Shaun, illus. 2003. (Illus.). 32p. 16.95 (978-0-9688768-3-1(8)) Simply Read Bks. CAN. *Dist:* Perseus Distribution.

T'choupi Est en Colere. 2000. (FRE., Illus.). (J). bds. 11.95 (978-2-09-202023-4(4)) Nathan, Fernand FRA. *Dist:* Distribooks, Inc.

Thompson, Colin. The Short & Incredibly Happy Life of Riley. Lissiat, Amy, illus. 2006. 32p. (J). (*978-0-7344-0806-8(4), Lothian Bks.) Hachette Livre Australia.

—The Short & Incredibly Happy Life of Riley. Lissiat, Amy, illus. 2007. 32p. (J). 15.95 (*978-1-933605-50-0(2)) Kane/Miller Bk. Pubs., Inc.

Thompson, Joan. Lucy Russell: Stardom & Stinkwater. 2003. 129p. (YA). pap. 10.95 (978-0-595-26867-2(6), Authors Choice Pr.) iUniverse, Inc.

Thompson, Tolya LaShawn. Worry Wart Wes. Perez, Juan R., illus. 2002. (Smarties Ser.: Vol. 2). (J). (gr. 2-4). lib. bdg. 16.00 (978-0-9708296-1-0(2)) Savor Publishing Hse., Inc.

Throckmorton, Patricia. The Adventures of Ish & Parr: Land of Happiness. 2007. (J). per. 10.99 (*978-1-59886-910-1(8)) Tate Publishing & Enterprises, L.L.C.

Tildes, Phyllis L. Cara de BeBe. Tildes, Phyllis L., illus. 2004. (SPA., Illus.). 10p. (J). bds. 5.95 (978-1-57091-428-7(1)) Charlesbridge Publishing, Inc.

A Touch of Gray: A Great American Story. 2004. (Illus.). (YA). per. (978-0-9654140-3-6(5)) Upword Pr.

Trueman, Terry. Cruise Control. 2004. 160p. (J). 15.99 (978-0-06-623960-6(5)) HarperCollins Pubs.

—Stuck in Neutral. 128p. (J). (gr. 5 up). 2001. pap. 7.99 (978-0-06-447213-5(2), HarperTeen); 2000. (Illus.). lib. bdg. 16.89 (978-0-06-028518-0(4)) HarperCollins Pubs.

—Stuck in Neutral. 2001. (gr. 7-12). lib. bdg. 15.30 (978-0-613-44419-4(1)) Tandem Library Bks.

Tunsel, Darrell. The Little House That No One Wanted. 2004. 41p. pap. 19.95 (978-1-4137-1422-7(6)) PublishAmerica, Inc.

Tyler, Anne. Timothy Tugbottom Says No! Modaressi, Mitra, illus. 2005. 36p. (J). (ps-2). 15.99 (978-0-399-24255-7(4), Putnam Juvenile) Penguin Group (USA) Inc.

Urdahl, Cathy Nelson. Emma's Question. Dawson, Janine, illus. 2008. (J). (*978-1-58089-145-5(4)) Charlesbridge Publishing, Inc.

Ure, Jean. Fruit & Nutcase. 2002. (Diary Ser.). (Illus.). 160p. (J). pap. 9.99 (978-0-00-712153-3(9)) HarperCollins Pubs. Ltd. GBR. *Dist:* Independent Pubs. Group.

Vail, Rachel. Sometimes I'm Bombaloo. Heo, Yumi, illus. (Bookshelf Ser.). (J). 2005. 32p. pap. 6.99 (978-0-439-66941-2(3)); 2002. 32p. pap. 16.95 (978-0-439-08755-1(4), Scholastic Pr.); 2000. pap. (978-0-439-08756-8(2)) Scholastic, Inc.

Vili, Fane. Mano: The Awakening. Frakes, Clint, ed. 2006. (YA). per. 19.95 (978-0-9774074-0-8(3)) Plankton Pr.

Volponi, Paul. The Hand You're Dealt. 2008. 256p. (YA). (*978-1-4169-3989-4(X)) Simon & Schuster Children's Publishing.

Voss, Dawn. Avenging Aja. 2007. 50p. pap. 15.00 (*978-0-615-15324-7(0)) Voss, Dawn L.

Walters, Eric. Sketches. 2008. 232p. (YA). (gr. 6). 15.99 (*978-0-670-06294-2(4), Viking Juvenile) Penguin Group (USA) Inc.

Warner, Sally. It's Only Temporary. 2008. 160p. (J). (gr. 4). 15.99 (*978-0-670-06111-2(5), Viking Juvenile) Penguin Group (USA) Inc.

Weedn, Flavia M. & Weedn, Lisa. I Feel Happy: Bedtime Magic for Baby's Sweet Dreams. 1999. (Flavia Children's Board Bks.). (Illus.). 26p. (ps up). pap. 7.95 (978-0-7683-2065-7(8)) CEDCO Publishing.

Werlin, Nancy. The Rules of Survival. 2006. 276p. (J). (gr. 7). 16.99 (978-0-8037-3001-4(2), Dial) Penguin Group (USA) Inc.

Whitfield, Peter. Zen Tails No Presents Please. Bevington, Nancy, illus. 2005. (Zen Tails Ser.). 28p. (J). (gr. 2-17). 15.95 (978-1-894965-23-1(X)) Simply Read Bks. CAN. *Dist:* Perseus Distribution.

Wild, Robyn. Benjamin's Basket. Cullen, Elizabeth, illus. 1999. (J). (ps-4). 12.95 (978-0-944576-17-5(6)) Rocky River Pubs., LLC.

Willems, Mo. My Friend Is Sad. 2007. 64p. (ps-3). 8.99 (978-1-4231-0297-7(5)) Hyperion Bks. for Children.

—The Pigeon Has Feelings, Too! 2005. (Illus.). 10p. (J). (ps-ps). bds. 6.99 (978-0-7868-3650-5(4)) Hyperion Bks. for Children.

Wilson, Essdale. Growing up on the cul de Sac. 2003. 156p. (YA). pap. 11.95 (978-0-595-26945-7(1)) iUniverse, Inc.

Wilson, John. Adrift in Time. 2005. 134p. (J). pap. 9.95 (978-1-55380-007-1(9)) Ronsdale Pr. CAN. *Dist:* Literary Pr. Group of Canada.

Withrow, Sarah. The Black Sunshine of Goody Pryne. pap. 9.95 (978-0-88899-577-3(6)); 2003. 160p. (J). (gr. 3-6). 15.95 (978-0-88899-477-6(X)) Groundwood Bks. CAN. *Dist:* Transition Vendor, Perseus Distribution.

Wood, June Rae. Turtle on a Fence Post. 2001. 272p. (J). pap. 6.99 (978-0-698-11783-9(2), Putnam Juvenile) Penguin Group (USA) Inc.

Zanimo. I Am Happy. Zanimo & Brasset, Doris, illus. 2000. (Maki Ser.). 14p. (J). (ps up). bds. (978-1-894363-06-8(X)) Dominique & Friends.

Zanimo & Brasset, Doris. I Am Cute. Zanimo & Brasset, Doris, illus. 2000. (Maki Ser.). (Illus.). 14p. (J). (ps up). bds. (978-1-894363-04-4(3)) Dominique & Friends.

—I Love. Zanimo & Brasset, Doris, illus. 2000. (Maki Ser.). (Illus.). 14p. (J). (ps up). bds. (978-1-894363-07-5(8)) Dominique & Friends.

Zindel, Paul. The Pigman. 2005. (Illus.). 192p. (J). (gr. 7 up). pap. 6.99 (978-0-06-075735-9(3), Harper Trophy) HarperCollins Pubs.

—The Pigman. Date not set. (Scholastic Bookfiles Ser.). 64p. (J). pap. 4.99 (*978-0-439-53831-2(9)) Scholastic, Inc.

EMPERORS

see Kings, Queens, Rulers, etc.

see and names of emperors

EMPLOYEES AND OFFICIALS

see Civil Service

see and names of countries, cities, etc. and organizations with the subdivision officials and employees, e.g. U. S.—Officials and Employees

EMPLOYEES' REPRESENTATION IN MANAGEMENT

see Management—Employee Participation

EMPLOYMENT DISCRIMINATION

see Discrimination in Employment

EMPLOYMENT OF WOMEN

see Women—Employment

ENCHANTED FOREST (IMAGINARY PLACE : WREDE)—FICTION

Wrede, Patricia C. Calling on Dragons. 2003. (Enchanted Forest Chronicles: Bk. 3). (Illus.). 272p. (YA). pap. 5.95 (978-0-15-204692-7(5), Magic Carpet Bks.) Harcourt Children's Bks.

—Calling on Dragons. unabr. ed. 2004. (Enchanted Forest Ser.: Vol 3). 244p. (J). (gr. 6 up). pap. 38.00 incl. audio (978-0-8072-0792-5(6), LYA 347 SP, Listening Library) Random Hse. Audio Publishing Group.

—Calling on Dragons. 2003. (gr. 7-12). lib. bdg. 14.10 (978-0-613-59887-3(3)) Tandem Library Bks.

—Dealing with Dragons. 2002. (Enchanted Forest Chronicles: Bk. 1). (Illus.). 240p. (YA). (gr. 5 up). pap. 5.95 (978-0-15-204566-1(X), Magic Carpet Bks.) Harcourt Children's Bks.

—Dealing with Dragons. 2002. (gr. 7-12). lib. bdg. 14.10 (978-0-613-56300-0(X)) Tandem Library Bks.

—Talking to Dragons. 2003. (Enchanted Forest Chronicles: Bk. 4). (Illus.). 272p. (YA). pap. 5.95 (978-0-15-204691-0(7), Magic Carpet Bks.) Harcourt Children's Bks.

—Talking to Dragons. unabr. ed. 2004. (Enchanted Forest Chronicles Ser.). 255p. (J). (gr. 6 up). pap. 38.00 incl. audio (978-0-8072-0983-7(X), S YA 385 SP, Listening Library) Random Hse. Audio Publishing Group.

—Talking to Dragons. 2003. (gr. 7-12). lib. bdg. 14.10 (978-0-613-59931-3(4)) Tandem Library Bks.

ENCYCLOPEDIAS AND DICTIONARIES

Acker, Kerry. The Kids' Fun-Filled Encyclopedia, A to Z. Tallarico, Tony, illus. 2000. 189p. (J). (978-1-56156-755-3(8)) Kidsbooks, Inc.

Allen, Sarah & Kingfisher Editors, eds. The Concise Kingfisher Children's Encyclopedia. 2001. (Illus.). 320p. (J). (gr. 4-8). tchr. ed. 14.95 (978-0-7534-5395-7(9), Kingfisher) Houghton Mifflin Co. Trade & Reference Div.

Ashbe, Jeanne. What's Inside? Ashbe, Jeanne, illus. 2001. (Illus.). 12p. (J). (ps). 9.95 (978-0-916291-97-6(9)) Kane/Miller Bk. Pubs., Inc.

Ashley, Susan. I Can Use a Dictionary. 2004. (Illus.). 24p. (J). pap. (978-0-8368-4333-0(9)); lib. bdg. 19.33 (978-0-8368-4326-2(6)) Stevens, Gareth Inc.

Balloon Books Staff. Dictionary for 1-Year-Olds. 1999. (Tiny the Mouse Dictionaries Ser.). (Illus.). 11p. (J). (ps-k). 4.95 (978-0-8069-5932-0(0)) Sterling Publishing Co., Inc.

—Dictionary for 3-Year-Olds. 1999. (Tiny the Mouse Dictionaries Ser.). (Illus.). 10p. (ps-k). 4.95 (978-0-8069-5934-4(7)) Sterling Publishing Co., Inc.

—Dictionary for 4-Year-Olds. 1999. (Tiny the Mouse Dictionaries Ser.). (Illus.). 10p. (ps-k). 4.95 (978-0-8069-5935-1(5)) Sterling Publishing Co., Inc.

—Tiny the Mouse Dictionary for 2-Year-Olds. 1999. (Tiny the Mouse Dictionaries Ser.). (Illus.). 10p. (J). (ps-k). 4.95 (978-0-8069-5933-7(9)) Sterling Publishing Co., Inc.

Barbey, Dorine, et al. Creative Discoveries, 8 vols., Set. (Illus.). 640p. (J). lib. bdg. 191.60 (978-0-88682-942-1(9)) Creative Co., The.

Barnes, Julia. 101 Facts about Our World, 6 bks. Incl. 101 Facts about Deserts. lib. bdg. 23.33 (978-0-8368-3706-3(1)); 101 Facts about Lakes. lib. bdg. 23.33 (978-0-8368-3707-0(X)); 101 Facts about Mountains. lib. bdg. 23.33 (978-0-8368-3708-7(8)); 101 Facts about Oceans. lib. bdg. 23.33 (978-0-8368-3709-4(6)); 101 Facts about Rivers. lib. bdg. 23.33 (978-0-8368-3711-7(8)); 101 Facts about Tropical Rain Forests. lib. bdg. 23.33 (978-0-8368-3710-0(X)); 32p. (J). (gr. 3 up). (Illus.). 2003. Set lib. bdg. 139.98 (978-0-8368-3705-6(3)) Stevens, Gareth Inc.

Basic Dictionary. (J). (gr. 3-6). pap. (978-0-87548-626-0(6), 48-626) Open Court Publishing Co.

Beginner Dictionary. (gr. 3-5). mass mkt. (978-0-673-12387-9(1)) Addison-Wesley Educational Pubs., Inc.

Bolchazy, Marie Carducci. What Will I Eat? Quid Edam? Fraczak, Michelle Kathryn, illus. 2002. (I Am Reading Latin Ser.). (LAT & ENG.). 64p. (J). 12.00 (978-0-86516-542-7(4)) Bolchazy-Carducci Pubs.

Brimax, S. My First Dictionary. 1998. (Illus.). 48p. (J). 60.00 (978-81-86982-64-8(7)) Business Pubns. Inc. IND. *Dist:* State Mutual Bk. & Periodical Service, Ltd.

Brooks, F. & Litchfield, J. Picture Dictionary: A First Alphabetical Word Book. 2004. (Picture Dictionaries Ser.). (Illus.). 96p. (J). 16.95 (978-0-7945-0176-1(1), Usborne) EDC Publishing.

Brooks, Felicity. The Usborne Internet-Linked Children's Encyclopedia. 2004. (First Encyclopedias Ser.). (Illus.). 320p. (J). 29.95 (978-0-7945-0368-0(3), Usborne) EDC Publishing.

Buckley, James, Jr., James & Stremme, Robert. Scholastic Book of Lists New & Updated. 2006. (Illus.). 320p. (J). pap. 9.99 (978-0-439-83757-6(X), Scholastic Reference) Scholastic, Inc.

Buckley, James & Stremme, Robert. Scholastic Book of Lists II. 2007. 320p. (J). (gr. 4-7). pap. 8.99 (*978-0-439-83763-7(4), Scholastic Reference) Scholastic, Inc.

Bunting, Jane. My First Action Word Book: A Picture Dictionary of 1,000 First Words. (Illus.). 48p. (J). pap. 17.99 (978-0-590-24897-6(9)) Scholastic, Inc.

Buntus Foclora: A Children's Irish Picture Dictionary. 2004. (IRI.). pap. 9.95 (978-0-7171-3752-7(X)) Gill & MacMillan, Ltd. IRL. *Dist:* Irish Bks. & Media, Inc.

Burke, Melissa Blackwell & Hall, Peg. My First Encyclopedia. 2005. (My First Ser.). (Illus.). 160p. (978-0-7853-8370-3(0), 7183900) Publications International, Ltd.

Cabot, Paloma, ed. Larousse Chidren's Spanish Dictionary. 2005. (Larousse Chidren's Dictionary Ser.). (SPA & ENG., Illus.). 128p. (gr. 4-6). 12.95 (978-2-03-542099-2(7)) Larousse, Editions FRA. *Dist:* Houghton Mifflin Co. Trade & Reference Div.

Children's First Encyclopedia. 2002. 256p. (J). 25.95 (978-0-7525-8720-2(X)) Parragon, Inc.

Children's Illustrated Dictionary. 384p. (J). 2002. 9.98 (978-0-7525-8439-3(1)); 2000. (Illus.). 25.95 (978-0-7525-4104-4(8)) Parragon, Inc.

Choron, Harry & Choron, Sandra. The Book of Lists for Teens. 2002. (Illus.). 336p. (YA). (gr. 7-11). pap. 12.00 (978-0-618-17907-7(0)) Houghton Mifflin Co. Trade & Reference Div.

Choron, Sandra & Choron, Harry. The All-New Book of Lists for Kids. 2002. (Illus.). 416p. (J). (gr. 4-6). pap. 11.95 (978-0-618-19135-2(6)) Houghton Mifflin Co. Trade & Reference Div.

Colvin, Leslie. Living World Encyclopedia. 1999. (Encyclopedias Ser.). (Illus.). 128p. (J). (gr. 4-7). lib. bdg. 22.95 (978-1-58086-171-7(2)) EDC Publishing.

—Living World Encyclopedia. 1999. (gr. 3-6). lib. bdg. 24.55 (978-0-613-74482-9(9)) Tandem Library Bks.

The Concise Encyclopedia of the Future. 2002. 160p. (J). (gr. 3-9). (978-0-7534-5419-0(X)) Kingfisher Publications, plc.

Corréard, Marie-Hélène, et al. Larousse Children's French Dictionary. 2005. (Larousse Chidren's Dictionary Ser.). (FRE & ENG., Illus.). 128p. (gr. 4-6). per. 12.95 (978-2-03-542098-5(9)) Larousse, Editions FRA. *Dist:* Houghton Mifflin Co. Trade & Reference Div.

Crawley, Angela & Grisewood, John, eds. Kingfisher First Dictionary. 2004. (Kingfisher First Reference Ser.). (Illus.). 176p. (J). (gr. k-3). pap. 9.95 (978-0-7534-5807-5(1), Kingfisher) Houghton Mifflin Co. Trade & Reference Div.

Cultures of the Past, 4 bks., Set, Group 3. (J). (gr. 5 up). lib. bdg. 114.00 (978-0-7614-0268-8(3), Benchmark Bks.) Cavendish, Marshall Corp.

Cultures of the Past - Group 4, 4 bks., Set. (Illus.). 80p. (J). (gr. 5 up). lib. bdg. 119.71 (978-0-7614-0300-5(0), Benchmark Bks.) Cavendish, Marshall Corp.

Daly, Kathleen N. Greek & Roman Mythology A to Z: A Young Readers Companion. 2nd rev. ed. 2003. (Mythology A to Z Ser.). (Illus.). 160p. (J). (gr. 4-9). 40.00 (978-0-8160-5155-7(0)) Facts On File, Inc.

—Norse Mythology A to Z: A Young Reader's Companion. 2nd rev. ed. 2003. (Mythology A to Z Ser.). (Illus.). 144p. (J). (gr. 4-9). 40.00 (978-0-8160-5156-4(9)) Facts On File, Inc.

Diagram Group, contrib. by. In the Air. 2004. (Life on Earth Ser.). (Illus.). 112p. (J). (gr. 4-9). 35.00 (978-0-8160-5049-9(X)) Facts On File, Inc.

—In the Sea. 2004. (Life on Earth Ser.). (Illus.). 112p. (J). (gr. 4-9). 35.00 (978-0-8160-5048-2(1)) Facts On File, Inc.

Diccionario Escolar Infantil.Tr. of Young Student's Dictionary. (SPA., Illus.). 208p. (J). (gr. 3-5). (978-958-04-0704-1(5) , NR4073) Norma S.A. COL. *Dist:* Distribuidora Norma, Inc.

Disney Press Staff. Disney's Magic Spanish: Spanish Picture Dictionary. 2005. (Disney Learning Ser.). (ENG & SPA., Illus.). 144p. (gr. 1-4). 14.99 (978-0-7868-3612-3(1)) Disney Pr.

DK Publishing. Visual Encyclopedia of Everything. 2008. 304p. (J). (gr. 3-12). 24.99 ***(978-0-7566-3843-6(7))*** Dorling Kindersley Publishing, Inc.

Doolin, Janet Caruthers. The Kid's Book of Knowledge: An Illustrated Dictionary & More! Zembo, Marlene, illus. 2002. 96p. (J). per. 16.95 (978-0-9710432-6-8(4)) Children's Literacy Pubns.

Dorling Kindersley Publishing Staff. Children's Illustrated Encyclopedia. Parsons, Jayne, ed. 5th rev. ed. 2000. (Illus.). 800p. (J). (ps-3). 40.00 (978-0-7894-6498-9(5)) Dorling Kindersley Publishing, Inc.

—Children's Illustrated Encyclopedia. 6th ed. 2006. (Illus.). 800p. (J). 39.99 (978-0-7566-1892-6(4)) Dorling Kindersley Publishing, Inc.

—DK Dictionary. 1999. (gr. 3-6). lib. bdg. 18.80 (978-0-613-75059-2(4)) Tandem Library Bks.

—My Little Encyclopedia. 2006. 160p. (J). 8.99 (978-0-7566-2541-2(6)) Dorling Kindersley Publishing, Inc.

—Online Encyclopedia. Hallinan, Camilla, ed. 2006. (Illus.). 448p. (J). pap. 19.99 (978-0-7566-2108-7(9)) Dorling Kindersley Publishing, Inc.

Douglas, Vincent & School Specialty Publishing Staff. Dictionary. 2002. (Notebook Reference Ser.). (Illus.). 128p. (J). (gr. 4-8). pap. 4.95 (978-1-57768-340-7(4)) School Specialty Publishing.

Dowswell, Paul. Mi Primera Enciclopedia del Espacio. 2003. Tr. of First Encyclopedia of Space. (SPA.). (gr. 3-6). lib. bdg. 18.75 (978-0-613-74510-9(8)) Tandem Library Bks.

Drobot, Eve, tr. from FRE. Smart-Opedia: The Amazing Book about Everything. 2007. (Illus.). 216p. (J). (gr. 3-7). 29.95 ***(978-1-897349-03-8(3));*** pap. 22.95 ***(978-1-897349-09-0(2))*** Maple Tree Pr. CAN. *Dist:* Perseus Distribution.

Dumont, Deborah, intro. Hippocrene Children's Illustrated Dutch Dictionary: English-Dutch/Dutch-English. 2002. (Children's Illustrated Foreign Language Dictionaries Ser.). (ENG & DUT., Illus.). 94p. (gr. k-5). pap. 11.95 (978-0-7818-0888-0(X)) Hippocrene Bks., Inc.

Dunham, M. L. Disney's Junior Encyclopedia of Animated Characters: Including Characters from Your Favorite Disney Pixar Films. 2004. (Illus.). 192p. (gr. 2-6). 17.99 (978-0-7868-3434-1(X) , Disney Editions) Disney Pr.

Elliot, Jane & King, Colin. Children's Encyclopedia. 2004. (Encyclopedias Ser.). (Illus.). 135p. (J). 7.95 (978-0-7945-0006-1(4) , Usborne) EDC Publishing.

Elliot, Jane & King, Colin, eds. Children's Encyclopedia. 2004. (Usborne Encyclopedia Ser.). (Illus.). 135p. (J). (gr. 3-7). pap. 14.95 (978-0-7460-3922-9(0)) EDC Publishing.

Elliott, Jane. Children's Encyclopedia. 2000. (gr. 3-6). lib. bdg. 24.55 (978-0-613-86951-5(6)) Tandem Library Bks.

—Usborne Children's Encyclopedia. 2000. (978-0-606-18132-7(6)) Tandem Library Bks.

Elliott, Jane & King, Colin. Children's Encyclopedia. 2004. (Encyclopedias Ser.). (Illus.). 135p. (J). (gr. 4-7). lib. bdg. 22.95 (978-1-58086-258-5(6)) EDC Publishing.

Elliott, Jane & King, Colin, eds. Animated Children's Encyclopedia. 1999. (Usborne Encyclopedia Ser.). (Illus.). 128p. (J). (gr. 3-7). 39.95 incl. cd-rom (978-0-7460-3355-5(9)) EDC Publishing.

—Children's Encyclopedia. 1999. (978-1-58086-021-5(4)) EDC Publishing.

Encyclopaedia Britannica Publishers, contrib. by. My First Britannica: An Engaging 13-Volume Thematic Reference Set for Grades 2-5, 13 vols. 2004. (ENG., Illus.). 1p. (J). (gr. 2-5). 249.00 net. (978-1-59339-017-4(3) , 046501-EN-REF) Encyclopaedia Britannica, Inc.

Encyclopedia of People & Places, 6 vols., Set. 2001. (Illus.). 1579p. (YA). (gr. 4 up). 249.00 incl. cd-rom (978-0-7166-3799-8(5)) World Bk., Inc.

The Encyclopedia of World Facts. 2002. 352p. (YA). 29.95 (978-0-7525-8445-4(6)) Parragon, Inc.

The Encyclopedia of World History. 2002. 320p. (YA). 29.95 (978-0-7525-8446-1(4)) Parragon, Inc.

The Encyclopedia of World Mythology. 2002. 320p. (YA). 29.95 (978-0-7525-8447-8(2)) Parragon, Inc.

Equipo Staff. Tu Primer Diccionario Ilustrado. 2001. Tr. of Your First Ilustrated Dictionary. (SPA.). 176p. (978-84-305-1033-7(8)) Lectorum Pubns., Inc.

Farndon, John. A History of Civilization Illustrated History Encyclopedia: The Great Landmarks in the Development of Mankind. 2006. (Illus.). 256p. (gr. 7-10). reprint ed. pap. 22.00 (978-1-4223-5514-5(4)) DIANE Publishing Co.

Farndon, John & Dorling Kindersley Publishing Staff. Visual Encyclopedia. 2005. (Illus.). 456p. (J). (ps-7). pap. 12.99 (978-0-7566-0699-2(3)) Dorling Kindersley Publishing, Inc.

Fevrier, Gilles. Atlas of World Facts. 2000. (Atlas of World Facts Ser.: Vol. 4). (Illus.). 60p. (YA). (gr. 4-7). lib. bdg. 25.30 (978-0-88682-944-5(5) , Creative Education) Creative Co., The.

First Encyclopedia. (J). 2003. (Illus.). 128p. 7.98 (978-1-4054-0520-1(1)); 2000. 64p. 9.99 (978-0-7525-3812-9(8)) Parragon, Inc.

First Fun Reference Library, 5 vols. (Illus.). 128p. (J). (gr. 3 up). lib. bdg. (978-1-59084-553-0(6)) Mason Crest Pubs.

First Reference Library, 3 vols. 2002. (J). 29.95 (978-0-7525-3740-5(7)) Parragon, Inc.

Fleming, Denise. The Everything Book. rev. ed. 2004. (Illus.). 64p. (J). bds. 6.95 (978-0-8050-7709-4(X) , Holt, Henry & Co. Bks. For Young Readers) Holt, Henry & Co.

Foster, John. Barron's Junior Rhyming Dictionary. 2006. (Illus.). 160p. (J). pap. 12.99 (978-0-7641-3424-1(8)) Barron's Educational Series, Inc.

Gall, Susan B., ed. Junior Worldmark Encyclopedia of Physical Geography, 5 vols. 2003. (Illus.). (J). 850p. 290.00 (978-0-7876-6265-3(8)); (978-0-7876-6266-0(6)); (978-0-7876-6267-7(4)); (978-0-7876-6268-4(2)); (978-0-7876-6269-1(0)); (978-0-7876-6633-0(5)) Thomson Gale. (UXL).

Gall, Timothy L. & Gall, Susan B. Junior Worldmark Encyclopedia of the Nations , 2 vols. 2nd ed. 1998. (Illus.). (J). (978-0-7876-3803-0(X) , UXL) Thomson Gale.

—Junior Worldmark Encyclopedia of the Nations, 9 Vols., Set. 2nd ed. 1998. (Junior Worldmark Encyclopedia of the Nations Ser.). (Illus.). 2204p. (J). (gr. 4-7). 260.00 (978-0-7876-3801-6(3) , GML14099-113563) Thomson Gale.

Gall, Timothy L. & Gall, Susan B. Junior Worldmark Encyclopedia of the States. 5th ed. 2007. (J). ***(978-1-4144-1107-1(3)); (978-1-4144-1108-8(1)); (978-1-4144-1109-5(X)); (978-1-4144-1110-1(3))*** Thomson Gale.

Gall, Timothy L. & Gall, Susan B., eds. Junior Worldmark Encyclopedia of the Canadian Provinces. 3rd ed. 2001. (Illus.). 240p. (J). 55.00 (978-0-7876-5386-6(1) , GML00502-173575, UXL) Thomson Gale.

—Junior Worldmark Encyclopedia of the States, 4 vols., Set. 3rd ed. Incl. Junior Worldmark Encyclopedia of the States Vol. 1 : Alabama to Illinois. (978-0-7876-5377-4(2)); Junior Worldmark Encyclopedia of the States Vol. 2 : Indiana to Nebraska. (978-0-7876-5378-1(0)); Junior Worldmark Encyclopedia of the States Vol. 3 : Nevada to South Dakota. (978-0-7876-5379-8(9)); Junior Worldmark Encyclopedia of the States Vol. 4 : Tennessee to Wyoming. (978-0-7876-5380-4(2)); (J). (Illus.). 900p. 2001. lib. bdg. (978-0-7876-5376-7(4) , GML00502-173569, UXL) Thomson Gale.

—Junior Worldmark Encyclopedia of the States Vol. 1: Alabama to Illinois, 4 vols. 3rd ed. 2001. (Illus.). (J). (978-0-7876-5377-4(2) , UXL) Thomson Gale.

—Junior Worldmark Encyclopedia of the States Vol. 2: Indiana to Nebraska, 4 vols. 3rd ed. 2001. (Illus.). (J). (978-0-7876-5378-1(0) , UXL) Thomson Gale.

—Junior Worldmark Encyclopedia of the States Vol. 3: Nevada to South Dakota, 4 vols. 3rd ed. 2001. (Illus.). (J). (978-0-7876-5379-8(9) , UXL) Thomson Gale.

—Junior Worldmark Encyclopedia of the States Vol. 4: Tennessee to Wyoming, 4 vols. 3rd ed. 2001. (Illus.). (J). (978-0-7876-5380-4(2) , UXL) Thomson Gale.

Ganeri, Anita & Oxlade, Chris. First Encyclopedia: People, Plants, Animals. Ling, Mary, ed. 2002. (Junior Reference Ser.). (Illus.). 160p. (J). (gr. k-3). 15.99 (978-0-7894-8580-9(X)) Dorling Kindersley Publishing, Inc.

Golden Books Staff. Little Golden Picture Dictionary. 2002. (Illus.). 24p. (J). (gr. k-k). 2.99 (978-0-307-96035-1(8) , Golden Bks.) Random Hse. Children's Bks.

Goodman, Marlene. Let's Learn Hebrew Picture Dictionary. 2003. (ENG & HEB., Illus.). 80p. 11.95 (978-0-07-140825-7(8) , 9780071408257) McGraw-Hill Cos., The.

—Let's Learn Italian Picture Dictionary. 2003. (ENG & ITA., Illus.). 80p. 10.95 (978-0-07-140826-4(6) , 9780071408264) McGraw-Hill Cos., The.

—Let's Learn Japanese Picture Dictionary. 2003. (JPN & ENG., Illus.). 80p. 11.95 (978-0-07-140827-1(4) , 9780071408271) McGraw-Hill Cos., The.

Griffin, Andrew & Randall, Ronne. Stanley: The Great Big Book of Everything. 2004. (Illus.). 96p. (ps-2). 14.99 (978 0 7868-3384-9(X)) Hyperion Pr.

Griffin, Robert H. & Shurgin, Ann H. Buddha's Birthday, Carnival, Christmas, Vol. 1. 2000. (Illus.). (J). (978-0-7876-3928-0(1) , UXL) Thomson Gale.

—Hanukkah, Independence Day, Kwanzaa, Vol. 3. 2000. (Illus.). (J). (978-0-7876-3930-3(3) , UXL) Thomson Gale.

—New Year, Ramadan & Id Al-Fitr, Thanksgiving & Harvest Festivals, Vol. 4. 2000. (Illus.). (J). (978-0-7876-3931-0(1)) Thomson Gale.

Grolier Educational Staff, contrib. by. Grolier Student Encyclopedia, 17 vols. 2003. (Illus.). (J). (978-0-7172-5865-9(3) , Grolier) Scholastic Library Publishing.

—The New Book of Knowledge, 21 vols. (Illus.). (J). 2003. 699.00 (978-0-7172-0538-7(X)); 2003. 10,500p. (978-0-7172-0535-6(5)); 2002. (978-0-7172-0533-2(9)); 2001. (978-0-7172-0532-5(0)); Set. 2000. (gr. 3-12). lib. bdg. 699.00 (978-0-7172-0531-8(2)); Set. 1999. (gr. 3-12). lib. bdg. 659.00 (978-0-7172-0530-1(4)) Scholastic Library Publishing. (Grolier).

—The New Grolier Children's Encyclopedia. (Illus.). (J). 1999. (978-0-7172-9374-2(2)); 1999. (978-0-7172-9375-9(0)); Set. 1998. (gr. 2-6). lib. bdg. 225.00 (978-0-7172-9373-5(4)) Scholastic Library Publishing. (Grolier).

Hall, Cally, et al. Earth Facts. 2nd ed. 2004. (Pocket Guides Ser.). (Illus.). 160p. (J). pap. 6.99 (978-0-7566-0202-4(5)) Dorling Kindersley Publishing, Inc.

Hanly, Sheila. My Fun Picture Dictionary. Douglass, Jo, ed. Brown, Richard, illus. 2003. (Smart Kids Ser.). 80p. (J). bds. 14.95 (978-0-312-49106-2(9) , Priddy Bks.) St. Martin's Pr.

Harris, Nicholas. Questions & Answers. 2002. (Blackbirch Visual Encyclopedia Ser.). 64p. (J). 24.94 (978-1-56711-524-6(1) , Blackbirch Pr., Inc.) Thomson Gale.

Heinemann First Encyclopedia, 12 vols., Set. 2005. (Illus.). (J). lib. bdg. 520.00 (978-1-4034-7122-2(3)) Heinemann Library.

Heinemann Library (Firm) Staff, contrib. by. Heinemann First Encyclopedia. 2005. (J). (978-1-4034-7120-8(7)); (978-1-4034-7121-5(5)); (978-1-4034-7108-6(8)); (978-1-4034-7109-3(6)); (978-1-4034-7110-9(X)); (978-1-4034-7111-6(8)); (978-1-4034-7112-3(6)); (978-1-4034-7113-0(4)); (978-1-4034-7114-7(2)); (978-1-4034-7115-4(0)); (978-1-4034-7116-1(9)); (978-1-4034-7117-8(7)); (978-1-4034-7118-5(5)); (978-1-4034-7119-2(3)) Heinemann Library.

Heinemann Library Firm Staff. Heinemann First Encyclopedia, 10 vols., Set. 1998. (Illus.). 48p. (ps-3). lib. bdg. 384.50 (978-1-57572-741-7(2)) Heinemann Library.

Hippocrene Books, ed. Children's Illustrated Korean Dictionary: English-Korean/Korean-English. 2006. 104p. pap. 14.95 (978-0-7818-1132-3(5)) Hippocrene Bks., Inc.

—Children's Illustrated Vietnamese Dictionary: English-Vietnamese/Vietnamese-English. 2006. (ENG & VIE.). 112p. (J). pap. 14.95 (978-0-7818-1133-0(3)) Hippocrene Bks., Inc.

Hippocrene Books Staff. Children's Illustrated Czech Dictionary. 2003. (gr. 3-6). lib. bdg. 21.05 (978-0-613-74955-8(3)) Tandem Library Bks.

—Children's Illustrated Czech Dictionary: English-Czech/Czech-English. 2003. (Hippocrene Children's Illustrated Foreign Language Dictionaries Ser.). (Illus.). 96p. pap. 11.95 (978-0-7818-0987-0(8)) Hippocrene Bks., Inc.

—Hippocrene Children's Illustrated Chinese Dictionary: English-Chinese/Chinese-English. 2000. (CHI & ENG., Illus.). 94p. (J). (gr. k-5). 14.95 (978-0-7818-0834-7(0)) Hippocrene Bks., Inc.

Hirsch, E. D., Jr., et al, eds. The New First Dictionary of Cultural Literacy: What Your Child Needs to Know. 3rd ed. 2004. 306p. (J). (gr. 3-7). per. 22.95 (978-0-606-32792-3(4)) Tandem Library Bks.

Hirsch, E. D., et al. The New First Dictionary of Cultural Literacy: What Your Child Needs to Know. 3rd rev. ed. 2004. (Illus.). 320p. pap. 15.00 (978-0-618-40853-5(3)) Houghton Mifflin Co. Trade & Reference Div.

Hochstatter, Daniel J. Italian. 2003. (ENG & ITA., Illus.). 96p. 11.95 (978-0-07-140830-1(4) , 9780071408301) McGraw-Hill Cos., The.

A Hole Is to Dig. 2004. (J). 24.95 incl. audio (978-0-7882-0551-4(X)); pap. 14.95 incl. audio (978-0-7882-0616-0(8)) Weston Woods Studios, Inc.

Holt, Rinehart and Winston Staff. World Geography Today, 25 vols., Set. 3rd ed. 2003. cd-rom 342.00 (978-0-03-035903-3(1)) Holt, Rinehart & Winston.

Holtz, Thomas & Benton, Michael J., contrib. by. Dinosaurs of the World, 11 vols., Set. 1999. (Illus.). 700p. (gr. 4 up). 471.36 (978-0-7614-7072-4(7) , Cavendish, Marshall Reference Bks.) Cavendish, Marshall Corp.

Hook, Jason. In the Air. 2002. (Young Library). (Illus.). 32p. (J). lib. bdg. 25.69 (978-0-7398-6315-2(0)) Raintree.

Hubbard, L. Ron. How to Use a Dictionary: Picture Book for Children. 2000. (gr. 3-6). lib. bdg. 30.35 (978-0-613-82778-2(3)) Tandem Library Bks.

Illustrated Family Encyclopedia. 2004. (YA). 69.99 (978-0-9753127-0-4(7)) Family Bks. at Home.

Information Station, 12 vols., Set. 2002. (Junior Adventure Ser.). (Illus.). 32p. (J). (gr. 3 up). lib. bdg. (978-1-59084-242-3(1)) Mason Crest Pubs.

Italiano, Bob & Dowlatabadi, Tamia, illus. Kidbits. 3rd ed. 2004. 320p. (J). 52.45 (978-1-4103-0527-5(9) , Blackbirch Pr., Inc.) Thomson Gale.

Der Jugend Brockhaus, 3 vols., Set. 3rd rev. ed. (GER., Illus.). (YA). (gr. 5-11). (978-3-7653-2303-4(9)) Brockhaus, F. A., GmbH DEU. *Dist:* International Bk. Import Service, Inc.

Juventud Staff. Diccionario Portugues - Espanol. (SPA.). 524p. (J). 29.95 (978-84-261-2888-1(2)) Juventud, Editorial ESP. *Dist:* AIMS International Bks., Inc.

Kamous Janna Il Hawonat.Tr. of Dictionary of the Zoo. (ARA., Illus.). 37p. (J). pap. 5.50 (978-0-86685-355-2(3) , LDL2804) Librairie du Liban Pubns. FRA. *Dist:* International Bk. Ctr., Inc.

Keene, Ann T., ed. Aardvarks-Canals, 9 vols., Vol. 1. 2nd ed. 2002. (Illus.). (J). (978-0-19-515783-3(4)) Oxford Univ. Pr., Inc.

—Biography: Abraham-Zhou Enlai, 9 vols., Vol. 8. 2nd ed. 2002. (Illus.). (J). (978-0-19-515790-1(7)) Oxford Univ. Pr., Inc.

—Canary Islands-Elections, 9 vols., Vol. 2. 2nd ed. 2002. (Illus.). (J). (978-0-19-515784-0(2)) Oxford Univ. Pr., Inc.

—Electricity-Gymnastics, 9 vols., Vol. 3. 2nd ed. 2002. (Illus.). (J). (978-0-19-515785-7(0)) Oxford Univ. Pr., Inc.

—Gypsies-Materials, 9 vols., Vol. 4. 2nd ed. 2002. (Illus.). (J). (978-0-19-515786-4(9)) Oxford Univ. Pr., Inc.

—Index, Gazetteer, & Timeline of World History, 9 vols., Vol. 9. 2nd ed. 2002. (Illus.). (J). (978-0-19-515791-8(5)) Oxford Univ. Pr., Inc.

—Mathematics-Population, 9 vols., Vol. 5. 2nd ed. 2002. (Illus.). (J). (978-0-19-515787-1(7)) Oxford Univ. Pr., Inc.

—Oxford American Children's Encyclopedia, 9 vols., Set. 2nd rev. ed. Incl. Vol. 1. Aardvarks-Canals. (978-0-19-515783-3(4)); Vol. 2. Canary Islands-Elections. (978-0-19-515784-0(2)); Vol. 3. Electricity-Gymnastics. (978-0-19-515785-7(0)); Vol. 4. Gypsies-Materials. (978-0-19-515786-4(9)); Vol. 5. Mathematics-Population. (978-0-19-515787-1(7)); Vol. 6. Porcupines-Stock Market. (978-0-19-515788-8(5)); Vol. 7. Stomachs-Zoos. (978-0-19-515789-5(3)); Vol. 8. Biography : Abraham-Zhou Enlai. (978-0-19-515790-1(7)); Vol. 9. Index, Gazetteer, & Timeline of World History. (978-0-19-515791-8(5)); (J). 2002. (Illus.). 1712p. 2002. 350.00 o.p. (978-0-19-515568-6(8)) Oxford Univ. Pr., Inc.

—Porcupines-Stock Market, 9 vols., Vol. 6. 2nd ed. 2002. (Illus.). (J). (978-0-19-515788-8(5)) Oxford Univ. Pr., Inc.

—Stomachs-Zoos, 9 vols., Vol. 7. 2nd ed. 2002. (Illus.). (J). (978-0-19-515789-5(3)) Oxford Univ. Pr., Inc.

Keyes, Joan Ross. The Oxford Picture Dictionary for Kids. 1998. (Oxford Picture Dictionary for Kids Ser.). (Illus.). 144p. 21.95 (978-0-19-434996-3(9)); 14.25 (978-0-19-434997-0(7)) Oxford Univ. Pr., Inc.

Keyes, Joan Ross & Bukantz, Dorothy. The Oxford Picture Dictionary for Kids. 1998. (Oxford Picture Dictionary for Kids Ser.). (Illus.). 62p. wbk. ed. 8.75 (978-0-19-435218-5(8)) Oxford Univ. Pr., Inc.

Keyes, Joan Ross, et al. The Oxford Picture Dictionary for Kids. 1998. (Oxford Picture Dictionary for Kids Ser.). (Illus.). 288p. tchr. ed. 21.95 (978-0-19-434998-7(5)) Oxford Univ. Pr., Inc.

Khatib, Ahmed. Al Mousou'a al Ilmiya al Mouysarah: Illustrated Children's Encyclopedia. (ARA., Illus.). 484p. (J). 30.00 (978-0-86685-351-4(0) , LDL1333) International Bk. Ctr., Inc.

Kingfisher Editors, ed. The Kingfisher Children's Encyclopedia. 2004. (Illus.). 480p. (J). (gr. 4-6). tchr. ed. 24.95 (978-0-7534-5767-2(9) , Kingfisher) Houghton Mifflin Co. Trade & Reference Div.

—The Kingfisher Facts & Records Book: The Ultimate Information Database. 2000. (Illus.). 96p. (J). (gr. 4-6). tchr. ed. 14.95 (978-0-7534-5270-7(7) , Kingfisher) Houghton Mifflin Co. Trade & Reference Div.

—The Kingfisher History Encyclopedia. rev. ed. 2004. (Illus.). 480p. (J). (gr. 4-6). 24.95 (978-0-7534-5784-9(9) , Kingfisher) Houghton Mifflin Co. Trade & Reference Div.

Kingfisher Larousse Chambers Staff. Fun Finding Out: About Our World. 1999. (Fun Finding Out Ser.). (Illus.). 96p. (J). (ps-1). pap. (978-0-7534-5264-6(2)) Kingfisher Publications, plc.

Larousse Editors, ed. Larousse Pocket Student Dictionary French-English/ English-French. 2005. (Larousse Pocket Student Dictionary Ser.). (FRE & ENG.). 768p. (gr. 7). pap. 6.95 (978-2-03-542120-3(9)) Larousse, Editions FRA. *Dist:* Houghton Mifflin Co. Trade & Reference Div.

—Larousse Pocket Student Dictionary Spanish-English/ English-Spanish. 2005. (Larousse Pocket Student Dictionary Ser.). (SPA & ENG.). 768p. (gr. 7). pap. 6.95 (978-2-03-542121-0(7)) Larousse, Editions FRA. *Dist:* Houghton Mifflin Co. Trade & Reference Div.

Larousse Kingfisher Chambers Staff. The Kingfisher Young Discoverer's Encyclopedia of Facts & Experiments. Kingfisher Editors, ed. 2000. (Young Discoverers Ser.). (Illus.). 216p. (J). (gr. 3-5). pap. 15.95 (978-0-7534-5301-8(0) , Kingfisher) Houghton Mifflin Co. Trade & Reference Div.

—The Little Book of Knowledge. Kingfisher Editors, ed. 2000. (Time-Life Do-It-Yourself Factfiles Ser.). (Illus.). 320p. (J). (gr. k-3). pap. 11.95 (978-0-7534-5299-8(5) , Kingfisher) Houghton Mifflin Co. Trade & Reference Div.

Larousse Mexico Staff. Enciclopedia Mega: Naturaleza y Ecologia. 2003. (SPA.). (gr. 3-6). lib. bdg. 19.90 (978-0-613-89815-7(X)) Tandem Library Bks.

Lectorum Publications Staff. Enciclopedia de los Paises del Mundo, 10 vols., Set. 1999. (SPA., Illus.). 576p. (YA). (gr. 5-8). (978-84-241-1980-5(0) , EV0929) Everest de Ediciones y Distribucion, S.L. ESP. *Dist:* Lectorum Pubns., Inc.

Mackay, David. What in the World? Date not set. (Whizz Bang Bumper Bk.). (Illus.). 64p. (J). 129.15 (978-0-582-19329-1(X)) Addison-Wesley Longman, Ltd. GBR. *Dist:* Trans-Atlantic Pubns., Inc.

MacLachlan, Patricia. What You Know First. 1998. (Trophy Picture Bks.). (J). (978-0-606-13905-2(2)) Tandem Library Bks.

Masoff, Joy. Oh, Yikes: History's Grossest Moments. 2006. (Illus.). 308p. (J). pap. 14.95 (978-0-7611-3684-2(3)) Workman Publishing Co., Inc.

—Oh, Yuck! The Encyclopedia of Everything Nasty. 2000. (J). (978-0-606-20303-6(6)) Tandem Library Bks.

—Oh, Yuck! The Encyclopedia of Everything Nasty. (Illus.). (J). 119.60 (978-0-7611-2529-7(9) , 22529); 2000. 224p. (gr. 3-7). pap. 14.95 (978-0-7611-0771-2(1) , 10771) Workman Publishing Co., Inc.

Matthews, Betty, compiled by. My Picture Dictionary. 1999. (Illus.). 48p. (J). (ps-2). pap. 29.00 (978-0-7217-0390-9(9)) Schofield & Sims Ltd. GBR. *Dist:* State Mutual Bk. & Periodical Service, Ltd.

McGraw-Hill Staff, ed. Young Learner's Dictionary. 2000. (Young Learner's Ser.). (Illus.). 40p. (J). (gr. k-5). pap. 6.95 (978-1-57768-771-9(X)) School Specialty Publishing.

—Young Learner's Encyclopedia. 2000. (Young Learner's Ser.). (Illus.). 40p. (J). (gr. k-5). pap. 6.95 (978-1-57768-772-6(8)) School Specialty Publishing.

McPhaul, John. What Is Child Support? No. 3: 25 Definitions Your Children Want to Know About. McPhaul, Lisa, ed. Date not set. 25p. (YA). (gr. 4-9). pap. (978-0-9655777-0-0(8)) McPhaul Bks.

Merriam-Webster. Merriam-Webster's Elementary Dictionary. 2nd rev. ed. 2000. (Illus.). 608p. (J). (gr. 7-5). pap. 11.95 (978-0-87779-630-5(0) , MER-630) Merriam-Webster, Inc.

—Merriam-Webster's How to Use Your Dictionary. 2004. (Illus.). 80p. (J). (gr. 7-7). pap. 8.95 (978-0-87779-670-1(X) , MER-670) Merriam-Webster, Inc.

Merriam-Webster, contrib. by. Merriam-Webster's Intermediate Dictionary. 2004. (Illus.). 1024p. (J). (gr. 9-11). 17.95 (978-0-87779-579-7(7) , MER-79N) Merriam-Webster, Inc.

Merriam-Webster, ed. Merriam-Webster's Intermediate Thesaurus. 2004. 896p. (YA). (gr. 3-5). 17.95 (978-0-87779-076-1(0) , MER-76) Merriam-Webster, Inc.

E F G

—Merriam-Webster's Notebook Thesaurus. 2004. 96p. (gr. 4-7). pap. 4.95 (978-0-87779-671-8(8) , MER-671) Merriam-Webster, Inc.

Merriam-Webster, Inc. Staff. Merriam-Webster's Elementary Dictionary. 2000. (978-0-606-18276-8(4)) Tandem Library Bks.

Middleton, John, ed. Africa: An Encyclopedia for Students, 4 vols. 2001. (Illus.). (J). (978-0-684-80651-8(7)); (978-0-684-80652-5(5)); (978-0-684-80653-2(3)); (978-0-684-80654-9(1)) Simon & Schuster. (Scribner).

Mini My First Picture Dictiona. 2004. (Early Learning Ser.). 18p. (J). bds. 2.99 (978-1-85854-832-6(2)) Brimax Books Ltd. GBR. *Dist:* Byeway Bks.

Mio Primo Dizionario Illustrato de Italia. (ITA., Illus.). pap. 9.95 (978-88-8148-840-7(X)) European Language Institute ITA. *Dist:* Distribooks, Inc.

Mio Primo Dizionario Illustrato de Italiano. (ITA., Illus.). pap. 9.95 (978-88-8148-835-3(3)); pap. 9.95 (978-88-8148-830-8(2)); pap. 9.95 (978-88-8148-845-2(0)) European Language Institute ITA. *Dist:* Distribooks, Inc.

Molinsky, Steven J. Word by Word Primary Picture Dictionary. 1999. (Illus.). 240p. (J). 23.06 (978-0-13-022206-0(2)) Longman Publishing Group.

Moretti, Stephanie. The At Book: Window on Words. Wheeler, Dennis, illus. 1999. 30p. (J). (gr. k-1). reprint ed. 20.00 (978-0-7881-6733-1(2)) DIANE Publishing Co.

Morgan, Nicola. Two-Can First Encyclopedia. 2004. (Illus.). 64p. (ps up). 12.95 (978-1-58728-440-3(5) , Creative Publishing International) Quayside.

My First Dictionary. 2002. 80p. (J). (ps up). 11.95 (978-0-7525-7763-0(8)) Parragon, Inc.

My First Encyclopedia. 2003. (Illus.). 256p. (J). 12.98 (978-1-4054-1706-8(4)) Parragon, Inc.

My Second Pictionary. Incl. My Second Picture Dictionary. 448p. (J). (gr. 2-5). 1990. pap. 16.38 (978-0-673-28453-2(0) , Scott Foresman); pap. 15.95 (978-0-673-12490-6(8)) Addison-Wesley Educational Pubs., Inc.

Nakata, Ritsuko & Hoskins, Barbara. Let's Go Picture Dictionary. 1999. (Illus.). 110p. 14.25 (978-0-19-435865-1(8)) Oxford Univ. Pr., Inc.

Osofsky, Jill. Fast Facts. 2000. (Funtastic Frogs Ser.). 32p. (J). (gr. k-2). pap., act. bk. ed. 4.99 (978-1-56451-316-8(5) , ID43016) School Specialty Publishing.

Oxford. The Oxford Young Readers' Dictionary. l.t. ed. 1999. (Illus.). 256p. 32.50 (978-0-19-910427-7(1)) Ulverscroft Large Print Bks. GBR. *Dist:* Ulverscroft Large Print Bks., Ltd.

Peoples of North America, 10 vols. 2003. (Illus.). (J). 359.00 (978-0-7172-5777-5(0) , Grolier) Scholastic Library Publishing.

Phillips, Sarah. My First Encyclopedia. Metcalf, Paula, illus. 2007. 64p. (J). (gr. k-2). 6.99 (978-1-84610-445-9(9)) Make Believe Ideas GBR. *Dist:* Ingram Pub. Services.

Picture Dictionary. 2003. (J). per. (978-1-884907-28-9(8)) Paradise Pr., Inc.

Pinkham, Julia. The Rainforest Encyclopedia Coloring Book. Pinkham, Julia, illus. 1998. (Naturencyclopedia Ser.). (Illus.). 48p. (J). (gr. 3-6). pap. 6.95 (978-0-88045-142-0(4)) Stemmer Hse. Pubs., Inc.

Pons Juniorwoerterbuch Deutsch. (GER., Illus.). 192p. (YA). (gr. 3 up). 34.95 (978-3-12-517630-0(1) , KL517630E) Klett, Ernst, Verlag GmbH DEU. *Dist:* Continental Bk. Co., Inc., International Bk. Import Service, Inc.

Priddy, Roger. My Big Book of Everything. 2000. (Illus.). 64p. (J). (ps-3). 15.95 (978-0-7894-0998-0(4)) Dorling Kindersley Publishing, Inc.

—Palabras Words: Spanish/English Bilingual. rev. ed. 2004. (Happy Baby). (ENG & SPA., Illus.). 28p. (J). bds. 5.95 (978-0-312-49230-4(8) , Priddy Bks.) St. Martin's Pr.

Richmond Publishing Staff. Richmond Picture Dictionary: A Beginner's Bilingual Dictionary. (SPA & ENG.). 128p. (J). (gr. k-3). pap. 22.95 (978-1-58105-260-2(X)) Santillana USA Publishing Co., Inc.

Root, Betty & Langley, Jonathan. My First Dictionary. (Illus.). (J). pap. 23.95 (978-0-590-74595-6(6)) Scholastic, Inc.

Rosen, Michael J. The 60 Second Encyclopedia. 2005. (Illus.). 272p. (J). (ps-7). pap., pap. 11.95 (978-0-7611-2902-8(2) , 12902) Workman Publishing Co., Inc.

Russell, William F. How to Choose & How to Use a Dictionary. 2000. (Family Learning Guidebooks Ser.). 128p. pap. 8.95 (978-0-9657752-8-1(3)) First Word Learning Systems, Inc.

Scholastic, Inc. Staff. Scholastic Kid's Almanac for the 21st Century. 1999. (978-0-606-16850-2(8)) Tandem Library Bks.

Scholastic, Inc. Staff, ed. The Children's Visual Dictionary. (Illus.). 64p. (J). pap. 21.99 (978-0-590-24522-7(8)) Scholastic, Inc.

—Scholastic First Encyclopedia, 4 vols., Set. (Illus.). (J). (gr. k-3). 60.00 (978-0-590-24498-5(1)) Scholastic, Inc.

Scholastic Library Publishing Staff, contrib. by. The New Book of Knowledge, 23 vols. (Illus.). (J). 2005. 659.00 (978-0-7172-0539-4(8)); Set. 2007. (gr. 3-8). 729.00 (978-0-7172-0541-7(X)); Set. 2006. (gr. 3-8). 699.00 (978-0-7172-0540-0(1)) Scholastic Library Publishing. (Grolier).

Spooner, Alan & Oxford Staff. Oxford Young Readers' Thesaurus. l.t. ed. 1999. (Illus.). 297p. 32.50 (978-0-19-910534-2(0)) Ulverscroft Large Print Bks. GBR. *Dist:* Ulverscroft Large Print Bks., Ltd.

Steck-Vaughn Staff. Dictionary Skills. 1999. (Illus.). (J). (gr. 6). pap. (978-0-7398-2825-0(8)); (gr. 2). pap. 5.99 (978-0-7398-2721-5(9)); (gr. 3). pap. (978-0-7398-2722-2(7)); (gr. 4). pap. 5.99 (978-0-7398-2723-9(5)); (gr. 5). pap. 5.99 (978-0-7398-2724-6(3)) Steck-Vaughn.

Strauss, Bob. The Big Book of What, How, & Why. 2005. (Illus.). 288p. (J). (978-1-4027-2900-3(6) , Sterling/Main St.) Sterling Publishing Co., Inc.

Tames, Richard. Ancient World, the Illus Children. 2007. (Illus.). 512p. pap. 19.99 (***978-1-84476-406-8(0)*** , Southwater) Anness Publishing GBR. *Dist:* National Bk. Network.

Terban, Marvin. The Scholastic Dictionary of Spelling. Campbell, Harry, illus. 2000. (Core Reference Ser.). 224p. (J). (gr. 4 up). pap. 8.95 (978-0-439-14496-4(5) , Scholastic Reference) Scholastic, Inc.

Turhan, Sedat. Milet Mini Picture Dictionary: English-Farsi. Hagin, Sally, illus. 2005. (Milet Mini Picture Dictionary Ser.). (ENG, PER & FRI.). 28p. (J). (ps-ps). bds. 7.99 (978-1-84059-468-3(3)) Milet Publishing.

—Milet Mini Picture Dictionary: English-Japanese. Hagin, Sally, illus. 2005. (Milet Mini Picture Dictionary Ser.). (JPN & ENG.). 28p. (J). (ps-ps). bds. 7.99 (978-1-84059-469-0(1)) Milet Publishing.

—Milet Mini Picture Dictionary: English-Kurdish. Hagin, Sally, illus. 2005. (Milet Mini Picture Dictionary Ser.). (KUR & ENG.). 28p. (J). (ps-ps). bds. 7.99 (978-1-84059-471-3(3)) Milet Publishing.

—Milet Mini Picture Dictionary: English-Portuguese. Hagin, Sally, illus. 2005. (Milet Mini Picture Dictionary Ser.). (POR & ENG.). 28p. (J). (ps-ps). bds. 7.99 (978-1-84059-473-7(X)) Milet Publishing.

Turhan, Sedat & Hagin, Sally. Milet Mini Picture Dictionary: English-Korean. 2005. (Milet Mini Picture Dictionary Ser.). (ENG & KOR., Illus.). 28p. (J). (ps-ps). bds. 7.99 (978-1-84059-470-6(5)) Milet Publishing.

—Milet Mini Picture Dictionary: English-Polish. 2005. (Milet Mini Picture Dictionary Ser.). (ENG & POL., Illus.). 28p. (J). (ps-ps). bds. 7.99 (978-1-84059-472-0(1)) Milet Publishing.

—Milet Mini Picture Dictionary: English-Russian. 2005. (Milet Mini Picture Dictionary Ser.). (RUS & ENG., Illus.). 28p. (J). (ps-ps). bds. 7.99 (978-1-84059-474-4(8)) Milet Publishing.

—Milet Picture Dictionary: English/Dinka. 2005. (Milet Picture Dictionary Ser.). (ENG & DIN., Illus.). 48p. (J). (ps-ps). 14.95 (978-1-84059-464-5(0)) Milet Publishing.

Walker, Jane. First Fun Encyclopedia. 2003. (Illus.). 48p. (J). (gr. 3 up). lib. bdg. (978-1-59084-558-5(7)) Mason Crest Pubs.

Waters, Kate, ed. Scholastic Children's Encyclopedia. 2004. (Illus.). 720p. (J). pap. 19.95 (978-0-439-43816-2(0) , Scholastic Reference) Scholastic, Inc.

Weaver, Janice. The A to Z of Everyday Things. Blake, Francis, illus. 2004. 128p. (J). (gr. 5). pap. 8.95 (978-0-88776-671-8(4)) Tundra Bks., Inc./Livres Toundra, Inc. CAN. *Dist:* Random Hse., Inc.

Webster's II Dictionary Editors. Webster's II Children's Dictionary. 2003. (Illus.). 800p. (J). (gr. 4-6). pap. 15.95 (978-0-618-37410-6(8)) Houghton Mifflin Co. Trade & Reference Div.

Wells, Rosemary. McDuff's Favorite Things. Jeffers, Susan, illus. 2004. 16p. (J). (ps-k). 9.99 (978-0-7868-0893-9(4)) Hyperion Bks. for Children.

Wilkes, Angela. The Little Encyclopedia of Our World. 2002. (Kingfisher Little Encyclopedias Ser.). (Illus.). 128p. (J). (gr. k-3). pap. 11.95 (978-0-7534-5570-8(6) , Kingfisher) Houghton Mifflin Co. Trade & Reference Div.

Wilkes, Angela, ed. Your World. 1999. (Kingfisher First Encyclopedia Ser.). (Illus.). 320p. (J). (gr. k-3). tchr. ed. 24.95 (978-0-7534-5217-2(0) , Kingfisher) Houghton Mifflin Co. Trade & Reference Div.

Wittels, Harriet & Greisman, Joan. A First Dictionary. Biggs, Gene, illus. 2004. 239p. (J). (gr. 4-8). reprint ed. pap. 15.00 (978-0-7567-8422-5(0)) DIANE Publishing Co.

World Book, Inc. Staff. Childcraft: The How & Why Library, 15 vols. 1999. (Childcraft Ser.). (Illus.). (J). (gr. k-6). (978-0-7166-0196-8(6) , 6003) World Bk., Inc.

—My World, 4 vols., Set. 2001. 32p. (J). (gr. 2-7). pap. 15.40 (978-0-7166-9417-5(4) , 3889) World Bk., Inc.

—World Book Looks at. . . Set, 4 vols., Vol. 4. 2001. (World Book Looks at Ser.). 256p. (J). (gr. 3-8). (978-0-7166-1819-5(2) , 1292) World Bk., Inc.

—World Book Looks at Series, 7 vols., Set. 1999. 448p. (J). (gr. 3-8). (978-0-7166-1816-4(8)) World Bk., Inc.

World Book, Inc. Staff, contrib. by. Childcraft: The How & Why Library, 15 vols. 2005. (Illus.). (J). (gr. k-5). 349.00 (978-0-7166-2203-1(3)) World Bk., Inc.

World Book, Inc Staff, contrib. by. Childcraft: The How & Why Library, 15 vols. 2006. (Illus.). (J). (978-0-7166-5729-3(5)) World Bk., Inc.

World Book, Inc. Staff, contrib. by. Childcraft - the How & Why Library, 15 vols. 2003. (Illus.). 16&17p. (J). (978-0-7166-6030-9(X)) World Bk., Inc.

—The World Book Student Discovery Encyclopedia, 13 vols. (Illus.). (J). 2004. (978-0-7166-7410-8(6)); 2003. 2,464p. 359.00 (978-0-7166-7409-2(2)) World Bk., Inc.

—The World Book Student Discovery Science Encyclopedia, 13 vols. 2005. (Me & My Pet Ser.). (Illus.). 1p. (J). (gr. 1-5). (978-0-7166-7500-6(5) , SKU 20174) World Bk., Inc.

World Book, Inc. Staff, ed. Fact Factory: The How & Why Supplement. 1999. (Childcraft Supplement Ser.). (Illus.). 224p. (J). (gr. 1-6). 23.00 (978-0-7166-0699-4(2)) World Bk., Inc.

—Interfact, 20 vols., Set. 1999. (Illus.). 48p. (J). (gr. 2-8). cd-rom 265.00 (978-0-7166-7293-7(6) , 30023) World Bk., Inc.

—World Book Annual, 3 vols., Set. 1999. (Illus.). 1232p. (YA). (978-0-7166-0467-9(1)) World Bk., Inc.

—The World Book Encyclopedia 2001, 22 vols., Set. 2000. (Illus.). 14000p. (YA). (gr. 3 up). (978-0-7166-0101-2(X)) World Bk., Inc.

—The World Book Encyclopedia of People & Places. 1999. (Illus.). 1579p. (YA). (gr. 4 up). (978-0-7166-3797-4(9)) World Bk., Inc.

—World Book Encyclopedia of People & Places, 6 vols. (J). 2002. (Illus.). 1,632p. (978-0-7166-3752-3(9) , 20106); 2001. cd-rom (978-0-7166-3798-1(7)) World Bk., Inc.

—The World Book Encyclopedia of People & Places, 6 vols., Vol. 6. 2001. (Illus.). 1,579p. (J). (gr. 4 up). (978-0-7166-3750-9(2) , 20073) World Bk., Inc.

—World Book Encyclopedia of Science, 8 vols., Vol. 8. 2001. (Illus.). 12p. (J). (gr. 6 up). incl. cd-rom (978-0-7166-3358-7(2) , 60040) World Bk., Inc.

—The World Book Student Discovery Encyclopedia, 13 vols. (Illus.). (J). 1999. 2384p. (gr. 2-6). stu. ed. 349.00 (978-0-7166-7400-9(9)); Set. 2001. 2,464p. (gr. 3 up). stu. ed. (978-0-7166-7403-0(3) , 20074) World Bk., Inc.

The World Book Student Discovery Encyclopedia, 13 vols. 2,464p. 369.00 (978-0-7166-7413-9(0) , 20176) World Bk., Inc.

Young, Caroline & Brooks, Felicity. Very first Dictionary. 2005. 64p. (J). 11.95 (978-0-7945-1002-2(7) , Usborne) EDC Publishing.

ENCYCLOPEDIAS AND DICTIONARIES—YEARBOOKS

Griffin, Robert H. & Shurgin, Ann H. Easter, Halloween & Festivals of the Dead, Vol. 2. 2000. (Illus.). (J). (978-0-7876-3929-7(X) , UXL) Thomson Gale.

END OF THE WORLD

McIntosh, Kenneth. Prophecies & End-Time Speculations: The Shape of Things to Come. 2005. (Religion & Modern Culture Ser.). (Illus.). 112p. (J). (gr. 7 up). (978-1-59084-979-8(5) , 1248068) Mason Crest Pubs.

ENDANGERED PLANTS

Burton, John, ed. The Atlas of Endangered Species. 2nd ed. 1998. (Illus.). 276p. (YA). 135.00 (978-0-02-865034-0(4) , GML00502-166800, Macmillan Reference USA) Thomson Gale.

Fandel, Jennifer. Endangered Plants. 2003. (Endangered Plants & Animals of North America Ser.). (J). pap. (978-1-58417-217-8(7)); lib. bdg. (978-1-58417-216-1(9)) Lake Street Pubs.

—Endangered Trees & Shrubs. 2003. (Endangered Plants & Animals of North America Ser.). (J). pap. (978-1-58417-215-4(0)); lib. bdg. (978-1-58417-214-7(2)) Lake Street Pubs.

Irvine, Sarah. No Animals, No Plants: North American Species at Risk. 2007. (Shockwave: Life Science & Medicine Ser.). (Illus.). 36p. (J). (gr. 4-6). lib. bdg. 25.00 (***978-0-531-17766-2(1)*** , Children's Pr.) Scholastic Library Publishing.

Souza, Dorothy M. Endangered Plants. 2003. (Watts Library). (Illus.). 64p. (J). 25.50 (978-0-531-12212-9(3) , Watts, Franklin) Scholastic Library Publishing.

ENDANGERED SPECIES

see also Wildlife Conservation

Aaseng, Nathan. The Cheetah. 2000. (Endangered Animals & Habitats Ser.). (Illus.). 96p. (YA). (gr. 4-12). 27.45 (978-1-56006-680-4(6) , Lucent Bks.) Thomson Gale.

Aloian, Molly & Kalman, Bobbie. Endangered Frogs. 2006. (Illus.). 32p. (J). (gr. 2-8). pap. (978-0-7787-1918-2(9)); (978-0-7787-1872-7(7)) Crabtree Publishing Co.

Aloian, Molly & Kalman, Bobbie. Endangered Monkeys. 2007. (Earth's Endangered Animals Ser.). (Illus.). 32p. (J). (gr. 1-7). (***978-0-7787-1862-8(X)***); pap. (***978-0-7787-1908-3(1)***) Crabtree Publishing Co.

Bailey, Jill. Falcons. 2002. (Secret World Of... Ser.). (Illus.). 48p. (J). lib. bdg. 27.12 (978-0-7398-4985-9(9)) Raintree.

Bair, Diane & Wright, Pamela. Sea Turtle Watching. 1999. (Wildlife Watching Ser.). (Illus.). 48p. (J). (gr. 3-4). lib. bdg. 21.26 (978-0-7368-0323-6(8) , Capstone High-Interest Bks.) Capstone Pr., Inc.

—Sea Turtle Watching. 1999. (Illus.). (J). (gr. 3-7). pap. 19.93 (978-0-516-21898-4(0) , Children's Pr.) Scholastic Library Publishing.

Bannor, Brett. Bighorn Sheep. 2002. (Endangered Animals & Habitats Ser.). (Illus.). 112p. (J). 27.45 (978-1-56006-887-7(6) , Lucent Bks.) Thomson Gale.

Barnes, Simon. Planet Zoo: One Hundred Animals We Can't Afford to Lose. Marks, Alan, illus. 2001. 256p. (J). (gr. 3-7). 29.99 (978-1-85881-488-9(X)) Orion Bks. Ltd. GBR. *Dist:* Trafalgar Square Publishing.

Barraclough, Sue. Protecting Species & Habitats. 2006. (What's Your View? Ser.). (Illus.). 48p. (J). (978-1-58340-976-3(9)) Smart Apple Media.

Becker, John. Grizzly Bears. 2003. (Returning Wildlife Ser.). (Illus.). 48p. (J). (gr. 3-5). 23.70 (978-0-7377-1534-7(0) , Kidhaven) Thomson Gale.

—Manatees. 2002. (Returning Wildlife Ser.). (Illus.). 48p. (J). (gr. 3-5). 23.70 (978-0-7377-1010-6(1) , Kidhaven) Thomson Gale.

Becker, John E. The California Condor. 2004. (Returning Wildlife Ser.). (Illus.). 48p. (J). 26.20 (978-0-7377-2292-5(4) , Kidhaven) Thomson Gale.

—Green Sea Turtles. 2003. (Returning Wildlife Ser.). (Illus.). 48p. (J). 26.20 (978-0-7377-1831-7(5) , Greenhaven Pr., Inc.) Thomson Gale.

—The Northern Elephant Seal. 2004. (Returning Wildlife Ser.). (Illus.). 48p. (J). (gr. 4-7). 26.20 (978-0-7377-2291-8(6) , Greenhaven Pr., Inc.) Thomson Gale.

Benchmark Education Staff, compiled by. Bringing Back the Whooping Crane & ¡Vamos a rescatar a la grulla Blanca! 2005. 52.00 (***978-1-4108-4494-1(3)***) Benchmark Education Co.

Benson, Sonia, et al. Endangered Species, 3 vols. 2nd ed. 2003. (Illus.). (J). 640p. 181.00 (978-0-7876-7618-6(7)); xxxviii, 740p. (978-0-7876-7619-3(5)); xxxviii, 740p. (978-0-7876-7620-9(9)); xxxviii, 740p. (978-0-7876-7621-6(7)) Thomson Gale. (UXL).

Bily, Cindy. Endangered Species. 2007. (Introducing Issues with Opposing Viewpoints Ser.). (Illus.). 144p. (gr. 7-10). 32.45 (***978-0-7377-3849-0(9)*** , Greenhaven Pr., Inc.) Thomson Gale.

Blomquist, Christopher. Desert Turtles. 2004. (Library of Turtles & Tortoises). (Illus.). 24p. (J). lib. bdg. 18.75 (978-0-8239-6739-1(5) , PowerKids Pr.) Rosen Publishing Group, Inc., The.

—Green Sea Turtles. 2004. (Library of Turtles & Tortoises). (Illus.). 24p. (J). lib. bdg. 18.75 (978-0-8239-6738-4(7) , PowerKids Pr.) Rosen Publishing Group, Inc., The.

Bow, Patricia. Chimpanzee Rescue: Changing the Future for Endangered Wildlife. 2004. (Firefly Animal Rescue Ser.). (Illus.). 64p. (J). (gr. 5-8). 19.95 (978-1-55297-909-1(1)); pap. 9.95 (978-1-55297-908-2(3)) Firefly Bks., Ltd.

Burton, John, ed. The Atlas of Endangered Species. 2nd ed. 1998. (Illus.). 276p. (YA). 135.00 (978-0-02-865034-0(4) , GML00502-166800, Macmillan Reference USA) Thomson Gale.

Burton, Margie & French, Tammy, Cathy - Jones. Animales en peligro de extincion & Endangered Animals, 2005. spiral bd. 66.00 (***978-1-4108-5622-7(4)***) Benchmark Education Co.

Butz, Christopher. Lemurs. 2002. (Animals of the Rain Forest Ser.). (Illus.). 32p. (YA). lib. bdg. 22.83 (978-0-7398-5528-7(X)) Raintree.

Casterline, Linda. Rare Animals: A Chapter Book. 2003. (True Tales Ser.). (Illus.). 48p. (J). 22.50 (978-0-516-22914-0(1) , Children's Pr.) Scholastic Library Publishing.

Catala, Ellen. Animals in Danger. (Yellow Umbrella Books for Early Readers). (J). (gr. k-2). 2006. (Illus.). 16p. 15.93 (978-0-7368-5832-8(6) , Yellow Umbrella Bks.); 2005. (978-0-7368-5298-2(0)); 2005. (Illus.). 17p. (978-0-7368-5262-3(X)) Capstone Pr., Inc.

Cerullo, Mary M. Sea Turtles: Ocean Nomads. Rotman, Jeffrey L., illus. Rotman, Jeffrey L., photos by. 2003. 48p. (J). (gr. 2-6). 17.99 (978-0-525-46649-9(5) , Dutton Juvenile) Penguin Group (USA) Inc.

Chancellor, Deborah. Tiger Tales. 2000. (Eyewitness Readers Ser.). (J). (978-0-606-19391-7(X)) Tandem Library Bks.

Charman, Andrew. Dodo Is Dead & other questions about extinct & endangered Animals. 2007. (I Wonder Why Ser.). (Illus.). 32p. (J). pap. 6.95 (***978-0-7534-6095-5(5)*** , Kingfisher) Houghton Mifflin Co. Trade & Reference Div.

Cherry Lake Publishing, compiled by. Road to Recovery. 2008. lib. bdg. (***978-1-60279-106-0(6)***) Cherry Lake Publishing.

Chinery, Michael. Animals in Danger. 2004. (Wild Animal Planet Ser.). (Illus.). 64p. 14.99 (978-0-7548-1264-7(2)) Anness Publishing GBR. *Dist:* National Bk. Network.

Cooper, Jason. Cheetahs. 2002. (Rourke Discovery Library). (Illus.). 24p. (J). lib. bdg. 20.64 (978-1-58952-401-9(2)) Rourke Publishing, LLC.

—Jaguars. 2002. (Illus.). 24p. (J). lib. bdg. 20.64 (978-1-58952-403-3(9)) Rourke Publishing, LLC.

—Lions. 2002. (Illus.). 24p. (J). lib. bdg. 20.64 (978-1-58952-405-7(5)) Rourke Publishing, LLC.

—Tigers. 2002. (Illus.). 24p. (J). lib. bdg. 20.64 (978-1-58952-406-4(3)) Rourke Publishing, LLC.

Costain, Meredith. American Buffalo. 2000. (gr. k-3). lib. bdg. 11.80 (978-0-613-30217-3(6)) Tandem Library Bks.

—Animals at Risk. 2000. (gr. k-3). lib. bdg. 11.80 (978-0-613-30229-6(X)) Tandem Library Bks.

—Golden Lion Tamarin Monkeys. 2000. (gr. k-3). lib. bdg. 11.80 (978-0-613-30439-9(X)) Tandem Library Bks.

Craats, Rennay. Black-Footed Ferret. 2003. (Endangered Plants & Animals of North America Ser.). (J). pap. (978-1-58417-209-3(6)); lib. bdg. (978-1-58417-208-6(8)) Lake Street Pubs.

—Whooping Cranes. 2003. (Endangered Plants & Animals of the United States Ser.). (J). pap. (978-1-58417-211-6(8)); lib. bdg. (978-1-58417-210-9(X)) Lake Street Pubs.

Crossingham, John & Kalman, Bobbie. Endangered Pandas. 2005. (Earth's Endangered Animals Ser.). (Illus.). 32p. (J). (978-0-7787-1858-1(1)); (gr. 3-5). pap. (978-0-7787-1904-5(9)) Crabtree Publishing Co.

Czech, Jan M. The Rhino: A MyReportLinks. com Book. 2005. (Endangered & Threatened Animals Ser.). (Illus.). 48p. (J). lib. bdg. 25.26 (978-0-7660-5062-4(9) , MyReportLinks.com Bks.) Enslow Pubs., Inc.

De Koster, Katie. Endangered Species. 1998. (gr. 5-8). lib. bdg. 28.90 (978-0-613-78989-9(X)) Tandem Library Bks.

DeFries, Cheryl L. The Bald Eagle: A MyReportLinks. com Book. 2003. (Endangered & Threatened Animals Ser.). (Illus.). 48p. (J). (gr. 4-10). lib. bdg. 25.26 (978-0-7660-5057-0(2) , MyReportLinks.com Bks.) Enslow Pubs., Inc.

Diamond, Claudia C. Gorilla Families. 2002. (Reading Room Collection). (Illus.). 24p. (J). pap. (978-0-8239-8168-7(1)); lib. bdg. 18.75 (978-0-8239-3731-8(3)) Rosen Publishing Group, Inc., The.

Doherty, James G., contrib. by. Endangered!, 6 bks., Set, Group 1. Incl. Apes. Horton, Casey. lib. bdg. 25.64 (978-0-7614-0212-1(8)); Bears. Horton, Casey. lib. bdg. 25.64 (978-0-7614-0211-4(X)); Dolphins. Horton, Casey. lib. bdg. 22.79 (978-0-7614-0216-9(0)); Eagles. Horton, Casey. lib. bdg. 25.64 (978-0-7614-0214-5(4)); Tigers. Harman, Amanda. lib. bdg. 22.79 (978-0-7614-0215-2(2)); Wolves. Horton, Casey. lib. bdg. 25.64 (978-0-7614-0213-8(6)); 32p. (J). (gr. 3-5). 1995. (Illus.). Set lib. bdg. 136.71 (978-0-7614-0210-7(1) , Benchmark Bks.) Cavendish, Marshall Corp.

—Endangered - Group 4, 4 bks., Set. Incl. Butterflies. Green, Jen. lib. bdg. 25.64 (978-0-7614-0321-0(3)); Cheetahs. Grimbly, Shona. lib. bdg. 25.64 (978-0-7614-0319-7(1)); Crocodiles & Alligators. Woodward, John.

lib. bdg. 25.64 (978-0-7614-0322-7(1)); Zebras. Grimbly, Shona. lib. bdg. 25.64 (978-0-7614-0320-3(5)); 32p. (J). (gr. 3-5). (Illus.). 1999. Set lib. bdg. 102.57 (978-0-7614-0318-0(3) , Benchmark Bks.) Cavendish, Marshall Corp.

Dollar. Caimans. 2001. (Animals of the Rain Forest Ser.). (SPA., Illus.). (J). pap. (978-0-7398-3357-5(X)) Steck-Vaughn.

Dollar, Sam. Caimans. 2000. (Animals of the Rain Forest Ser.). (Illus.). 32p. (J). (gr. 4-7). lib. bdg. 22.83 (978-0-7398-3097-0(X)) Raintree.

Donald, Rhonda Lucas. Endangered Animals. 2001. (gr. 3-6). lib. bdg. 15.25 (978-0-613-51641-9(9)) Tandem Library Bks.

Donovan, Sandy. Amazon River Dolphins. 2002. (Animals of the Rain Forest Ser.). (Illus.). 32p. (YA). lib. bdg. 22.83 (978-0-7398-5367-2(8)) Raintree.

—Chimpanzees. 2002. (Animals of the Rain Forest Ser.). (Illus.). 32p. (YA). lib. bdg. 22.83 (978-0-7398-5370-2(8)) Raintree.

—Quetzals. 2002. (Animals of the Rain Forest Ser.). (Illus.). 32p. (YA). (gr. 4 up). lib. bdg. 22.83 (978-0-7398-5530-0(1)) Raintree.

Dowd, John. Rare & Endangered. 2000. 169p. (YA). (gr. 6-10). pap. 5.95 (978-1-56145-217-0(3) , Q22040) Peachtree Pubs., Ltd.

—Rare & Endangered. 2000. (gr. 5-8). lib. bdg. 14.10 (978-0-613-49593-6(4)); (Illus.). (J). (978-0-606-20878-9(X)) Tandem Library Bks.

Draw 50 Endangered Animals. 2002. (Draw 50 Ser.). (Illus.). (J). 17.60 (978-0-7587-4707-5(1)) Book Wholesalers, Inc.

Ehrlich, Fred. You Can't See a Dodo at the Zoo. Haley, Amanda, illus. 2007. 36p. pap. 6.95 (*978-1-59354-624-3(6)) Handprint Bks.

Endangered Animals. 2000. 32p. (YA). 9.95 (978-0-7525-4318-5(0)) Parragon, Inc.

Endangered Animals, 6 vols. (Book2WebTM Ser.). (gr. 4-8). 36.50 (978-0-322-02978-1(3)) Wright Group, The.

Endangered Animals, 6 bks. Incl. Great White Sharks : The Ocean's Most Deadly Killers. Martin, James. lib. bdg. 21.26 (978-1-56065-241-0(1)); Killer Whales : The Orcas of the Pacific Ocean. Nielsen, Nancy J. lib. bdg. 21.26 (978-1-56065-236-6(5)); Komodo Dragons : Giant Lizards of Indonesia. Martin, James. lib. bdg. 21.26 (978-1-56065-238-0(1)); Lemurs & Other Animals of the Madagascar Rain Forest. Martin, James. lib. bdg. 21.26 (978-1-56065-237-3(3)); Poisonous Lizards : Gila Monsters & Mexican Beaded Lizards. Martin, James. lib. bdg. 21.26 (978-1-56065-240-3(3)); Spitting Cobras of Africa. Martin, James. lib. bdg. 21.26 (978-1-56065-239-7(X)); 48p. (J). (gr. 3-4). 1995. (Illus.). Set lib. bdg. 127.56 (978-1-56065-644-9(1) , Capstone High-Interest Bks.) Capstone Pr., Inc.

Endangered Mammals - Asia & China: An Educational Coloring Book. (J). (gr. 3 up). pap. 1.99 (978-0-86545-214-5(8)) Spizzirri Pr., Inc.

Evert, Laura. Wolves. McGee, John F., illus. 2004. (Our Wild World Ser.). 48p. (J). (gr. 2-5). pap. 7.95 (978-1-55971-748-9(3) , NorthWord Bks. for Young Readers) T&N Children's Publishing.

—Wolves. 2000. (gr. 3-6). lib. bdg. 16.40 (978-0-613-27613-9(2)) Tandem Library Bks.

Feeney, Kathy, et al. Wild Animals: Explore the Fascinating Worlds Of. . . McGee, John F., illus. 2000. 192p. (J). pap. (978-1-55971-741-0(6) , NorthWord Bks. for Young Readers) T&N Children's Publishing.

Feinstein, Stephen. California Plants & Animals. (Heinemann State Studies). (Illus.). 48p. (J). 2003. (gr. 3-5). lib. bdg. (978-1-4034-0343-8(0)); 2002. pap. 8.50 (978-1-4034-0560-9(3)) Heinemann Library.

—California Plants & Animals. 2003. (gr. 3-6). lib. bdg. 17.05 (978-0-613-60856-5(9)) Tandem Library Bks.

Forier, Elise. We Both Read-Endangered Animals. 2006. (We Both Read Ser.). (J). 7.99 (978-1-891327-71-1(2)); (Illus.). 48p. pap. 3.99 (978-1-891327-72-8(0)) Treasure Bay, Inc.

Fowler, Allan. It Could Still Be Endangered. 2000. (gr. k-3). lib. bdg. 12.95 (978-0-613-54585-3(0)) Tandem Library Bks.

Friedman, Lauri S. Endangered Species. 2007. (Writing the Critical Essay Ser.). (Illus.). 128p. (gr. 6-10). 29.95 (*978-0-7377-3856-8(1) , Greenhaven Pr., Inc.) Thomson Gale.

Gentle, Victor & Perry, Janet. Cheetahs. 2002. (Big Cats Ser.). (Illus.). 24p. (J). (gr. 2 up). lib. bdg. 22.00 (978-0-8368-3024-8(5)) Stevens, Gareth Inc.

Gibbons, Gail. Giant Pandas. 2002. (Illus.). 32p. (J). (gr. k-3). pap. 6.95 (978-0-8234-1828-2(6)) Holiday Hse., Inc.

—Grizzly Bears. Gibbons, Gail, illus. 2003. (Illus.). 32p. (J). (gr. k-3). tchr. ed. 16.95 (978-0-8234-1793-3(X)) Holiday Hse., Inc.

Gilders, Michelle. Why Am I Rare? Gilders, Michelle, photos by. 2004. (Illus.). 32p. (J). (gr. 1-5). 17.95 (978-0-88995-274-4(4)) Red Deer Pr. CAN. *Dist:* Fitzhenry & Whiteside, Ltd.

Goodnough, David. Endangered Animals of North America. 2001. (Hot Issues Ser.). (Illus.). 64p. (YA). (gr. 6-12). lib. bdg. 27.93 (978-0-7660-1373-5(1)) Enslow Pubs., Inc.

Graham, Amy & Haslam, William. The Woodland Caribou: A MyReportLinks.com Book. 2003. (Endangered & Threatened Animals Ser.). (Illus.). 48p. (J). (gr. 4-10). lib. bdg. 25.26 (978-0-7660-5054-9(8) , MyReportLinks.com Bks.) Enslow Pubs., Inc.

Green, Carl R. The Giant Panda: A MyReportLinks. com Book. 2004. (Endangered & Threatened Animals Ser.). (Illus.). 48p. (J). lib. bdg. 25.26 (978-0-7660-5061-7(0) , MyReportLinks.com Bks.) Enslow Pubs., Inc.

—The Tiger: A MyReportLinks.com Book. 2003. (Endangered & Threatened Animals Ser.). (Illus.). 48p. (J). (gr. 4-10). lib. bdg. 25.26 (978-0-7660-5059-4(9) , MyReportLinks.com Bks.) Enslow Pubs., Inc.

Green, Jen. Butterflies. 1999. (Endangered! Ser.). (Illus.). 32p. (J). (gr. 3-5). lib. bdg. 25.64 (978-0-7614-0321-0(3) , Benchmark Bks.) Cavendish, Marshall Corp.

—Wildlife in Danger. 2006. (Illus.). 32p. (YA). (gr. 4 up). lib. bdg. 27.10 (978-1-59389-117-6(2)) Chrysalis Education.

—Wildlife in Danger. 2005. (Your Environment Ser.). (Illus.). 32p. (J). lib. bdg. 27.10 (978-1-59604-060-1(2)) Stargazer Bks.

Greenberg, Daniel A. Wolves. 2002. (Animals, Animals Ser.). (Illus.). 48p. (J). 25.64 (978-0-7614-1447-6(9) , Benchmark Bks.) Cavendish, Marshall Corp.

Grolier Educational Staff, contrib. by. Endangered Animals, 10 vols. Incl. Endangered Animals Vol. 1 : What Is an Endangered Animal? (978-0-7172-5585-6(9)); Endangered Animals Vol. 2 : Addax - Blackbuck. (978-0-7172-5586-3(7)); Endangered Animals Vol. 3 : Boa, Jamaican - Danio, Barred. (978-0-7172-5587-0(5)); Endangered Animals Vol. 4 : Darter, Watercress - Frog, Gastric-Brooding. (978-0-7172-5588-7(3)); Endangered Animals Vol. 5 : Frog, Green & Golden Bell - Kestrel, Lesser. (978-0-7172-5589-4(1)); Endangered Animals Vol. 6 : Kestrel, Mauritius - Mulgara. (978-0-7172-5590-0(5)); Endangered Animals Vol. 7 : Murrelet, Japanese - Pupfish, Devil's Hole. (978-0-7172-5591-7(3)); Endangered Animals Vol. 8 : Pygmy-Possum, Mountain - Siskin, Red. (978-0-7172-5592-4(1)); Endangered Animals Vol. 9 : Skink, Pygmy Blue-Tongued - Tragopan, Temminck's. (978-0-7172-5593-1(X)); Endangered Animals Vol. 10 : Tree-Kangaroo, Goodfellow's - Zebra, Mountain. (978-0-7172-5594-8(8)); (J). 640p. 2001. 409.00 (978-0-7172-5584-9(0) , Grolier) Scholastic Library Publishing.

—Endangered Animals Vol. 1: What Is an Endangered Animal? 2001. (J). (978-0-7172-5585-6(9) , Grolier) Scholastic Library Publishing.

—Endangered Animals Vol. 2: Addax - Blackbuck. 2001. (J). (978-0-7172-5586-3(7) , Grolier) Scholastic Library Publishing.

—Endangered Animals Vol. 3: Boa, Jamaican - Danio, Barred. 2001. (J). (978-0-7172-5587-0(5) , Grolier) Scholastic Library Publishing.

—Endangered Animals Vol. 4: Darter, Watercress - Frog, Gastric-Brooding. 2001. (J). (978-0-7172-5588-7(3) , Grolier) Scholastic Library Publishing.

—Endangered Animals Vol. 5: Frog, Green & Golden Bell - Kestrel, Lesser. 2001. (J). (978-0-7172-5589-4(1) , Grolier) Scholastic Library Publishing.

—Endangered Animals Vol. 6: Kestrel, Mauritius - Mulgara. 2001. (J). (978-0-7172-5590-0(5) , Grolier) Scholastic Library Publishing.

—Endangered Animals Vol. 7: Murrelet, Japanese - Pupfish, Devil's Hole. 2001. (J). (978-0-7172-5591-7(3) , Grolier) Scholastic Library Publishing.

—Endangered Animals Vol. 8: Pygmy-Possum, Mountain - Siskin, Red. 2001. (J). (978-0-7172-5592-4(1) , Grolier) Scholastic Library Publishing.

—Endangered Animals Vol. 9: Skink, Pygmy Blue-Tongued - Tragopan, Temminck's. 2001. (J). (978-0-7172-5593-1(X) , Grolier) Scholastic Library Publishing.

—Endangered Animals Vol. 10: Tree-Kangaroo, Goodfellow's - Zebra, Mountain. 2001. (J). (978-0-7172-5594-8(8) , Grolier) Scholastic Library Publishing.

Gunzi, Christiane. The Best Book of Endangered & Extinct Animals. 2004. (Best Book of... Ser.). (Illus.). 32p. (J). (gr. k-3). 12.95 (978-0-7534-5757-3(1) , Kingfisher) Houghton Mifflin Co. Trade & Reference Div.

Hamilton, Garry. Frog Rescue: Changing the Future for Endangered Wildlife. 2004. (Firefly Animal Rescue Ser.). (Illus.). 64p. (J). (gr. 5-8). pap. 9.95 (978-1-55297-596-1(7)) Firefly Bks., Ltd.

—Rhino Rescue: Changing the Future for Endangered Wildlife. 2006. (Firefly Animal Rescue Ser.). (Illus.). 64p. (J). (gr. 5-12). pap. 9.95 (978-1-55297-910-5(5)); lib. bdg. 19.95 (978-1-55297-912-9(1)) Firefly Bks., Ltd.

Harkrader, Lisa. The Cheetah: A MyReportLinks. com Book. 2005. (Endangered & Threatened Animals Ser.). (Illus.). 48p. (J). lib. bdg. 25.26 (978-0-7660-5065-5(3) , MyReportLinks.com Bks.) Enslow Pubs., Inc.

Haugen, David M. Endangered Species. 2007. (Opposing Viewpoints Ser.). 240p. (gr. 10-12). 36.20 (978-0-7377-2931-3(7)); pap. 24.95 (978-0-7377-2932-0(5)) Thomson Gale. (Greenhaven Pr., Inc.).

Hawxhurst, Joan C. Turtles & Tortoises. 2000. (Endangered Animals & Habitats Ser.). (Illus.). 96p. (J). (gr. 4-12). 28.70 (978-1-56006-731-3(4) , Lucent Bks.) Thomson Gale.

Hickman, Pamela. Birds of Prey Rescue: Changing the Future for Endangered Wildlife. 2006. (Firefly Animal Rescue Ser.). (Illus.). 64p. (J). (gr. 5-12). pap. 9.95 (978-1-55407-144-9(5)); lib. bdg. 19.95 (978-1-55407-145-6(3)) Firefly Bks., Ltd.

—Turtle Rescue: Changing the Future for Endangered Wildlife. 2005. (Firefly Animal Rescue Ser.). (Illus.). 64p. (J). (gr. 5-12). 19.95 (978-1-55297-916-7(4)); pap. 9.95 (978-1-55297-915-0(6)) Firefly Bks., Ltd.

Holden, Henry M. The American Alligator: A MyReportLinks. Com Book. 2003. (Endangered & Threatened Animals Ser.). (Illus.). 48p. (J). lib. bdg. 25.26 (978-0-7660-5117-1(X) , MyReportLinks.com Bks.) Enslow Pubs., Inc.

Holmes, Kevin J. Rhinos. 2000. (Animals Ser.). (Illus.). 24p. (J). (gr. 2-3). 18.60 (978-0-7368-0496-7(X) , Bridgestone Bks.) Capstone Pr., Inc.

Hook, Cheryl. Coral Reefs. 2001. (Water Worlds Ser.). (Illus.). 32p. (J). (gr. 4 up). 28.00 (978-0-7910-6567-9(7) , 010352, Chelsea Hse.) Facts On File, Inc.

Hoose, Phillip M. The Race to Save the Lord God Bird. 2004. (Illus.). 208p. (YA). 20.00 (978-0-374-36173-0(8) , Nelanie Kroupa Bks.) Farrar, Straus & Giroux.

Hoyt, Erich. Whale Rescue: Changing the Future for Endangered Wildlife. 2005. (Firefly Animal Rescue Ser.). (Illus.). 64p. (J). (gr. 5-8). pap. 9.95 (978-1-55297-600-5(9)); lib. bdg. 19.95 (978-1-55297-601-2(7)) Firefly Bks., Ltd.

—Whale Rescue: Changing the Future for Endangered Wildlife. 2004. (gr. 5-8). lib. bdg. 18.75 (978-0-613-78603-4(3)) Tandem Library Bks.

Imbriaco, Alison. The Otter: A MyReportLinks. com Book. 2005. (Endangered & Threatened Animals Ser.). (Illus.). 48p. (J). lib. bdg. 25.26 (978-0-7660-5067-9(X) , MyReportLinks.com Bks.) Enslow Pubs., Inc.

—The Red Wolf: Help Save This Endangered Species! 2007. (Saving Endangered Species Ser.). (Illus.). 128p. (J). lib. bdg. 33.27 (978-1-59845-038-5(7) , MyReportLinks.com Bks.) Enslow Pubs., Inc.

Irvine, Sarah. No Animals, No Plants: North American Species at Risk. 2007. (Shockwave: Life Science & Medicine Ser.). (Illus.). 36p. (J). (gr. 4-6). lib. bdg. 25.00 (*978-0-531-17766-2(1) , Children's Pr.) Scholastic Library Publishing.

Jackson, Donna. Wildlife Detectives. 2000. (gr. 3-6). lib. bdg. 12.95 (978-0-613-60739-1(2)) Tandem Library Bks.

Jackson, Donna M. The Wildlife Detectives: How Forensic Scientists Fight Crimes Against Nature. Shattil, Wendy & Rozinski, Bob, photos by. 2002. (Scientists in the Field Ser.). (Illus.). 48p. (J). (gr. 4-6). pap. 6.95 (978-0-618-19683-8(8)) Houghton Mifflin Co. Trade & Reference Div.

Jango-Cohen, Judith. Crocodiles. 2002. (Animals, Animals Ser.). (Illus.). 47p. (J). 25.64 (978-0-7614-1446-9(0) , Benchmark Bks.) Cavendish, Marshall Corp.

Jay, Lorraine A. Sea Turtles. McGee, John F., photos by. 2004. (Our Wild World Ser.). (Illus.). 48p. (J). (gr. 2-5). pap. 7.95 (978-1-55971-746-5(7) , NorthWord Bks. for Young Readers) T&N Children's Publishing.

Jenkins, Steve. Almost Gone. 2006. (Let's-Read-and-Find-Out Science Ser.). (Illus.). 33p. (J). lib. bdg. (978-0-06-053599-5(7)) HarperCollins Pubs.

—Almost Gone: The World's Rarest Animals. Jenkins, Steve, illus. 2006. (Let's-Read-and-Find-Out Science Ser.). (Illus.). 40p. (J). 16.99 (978-0-06-053598-8(9)); pap. 5.99 (978-0-06-053600-8(4)) HarperCollins Pubs.

Kallen, Stuart A. Dolphins & Porpoises. 2001. (Endangered Animals & Habitats Ser.). (Illus.). 112p. (YA). (gr. 4-12). 27.45 (978-1-56006-729-0(2) , Lucent Bks.) Thomson Gale.

Kalman, Bobbie. Endangered Elephants. 2005. (Earth's Endangered Animals Ser.). (Illus.). 32p. (J). (978-0-7787-1860-4(3)); (gr. 3-5). pap. (978-0-7787-1906-9(5)) Crabtree Publishing Co.

—Endangered Komodo Dragons. 2004. (Earth's Endangered Animals Ser.). (Illus.). 32p. (J). (978-0-7787-1857-4(3)); pap. (978-0-7787-1903-8(0)) Crabtree Publishing Co.

—Endangered Monk Seals. 2004. (Earth's Endangered Animals Ser.). (Illus.). 32p. (J). (978-0-7787-1851-2(4)); pap. (978-0-7787-1897-0(2)) Crabtree Publishing Co.

—Endangered Rhinoceros. 2003. (Earth's Endangered Animals Ser.). (Illus.). 32p. (J). (978-0-7787-1852-9(2)); pap. (978-0-7787-1898-7(0)) Crabtree Publishing Co.

—Endangered Sea Turtles. 2004. (Earth's Endangered Animals Ser.). (Illus.). 32p. (J). (978-0-7787-1853-6(0)); pap. (978-0-7787-1899-4(9)) Crabtree Publishing Co.

—Endangered Tigers. 2003. (Earth's Endangered Animals Ser.). (Illus.). 32p. (J). (978-0-7787-1850-5(6)); pap. (978-0-7787-1896-3(4)) Crabtree Publishing Co.

—Endangered Wolves. 2004. (Earth's Endangered Animals Ser.). (Illus.). 32p. (J). (978-0-7787-1854-3(9)); pap. (978-0-7787-1900-7(6)) Crabtree Publishing Co.

Kalman, Bobbie & Burns, Kylie. Endangered Bears. 2007. (Earth's Endangered Animals Ser.). (Illus.). 32p. (J). (gr. 1-7). (*978-0-7787-1861-1(1)); pap. (*978-0-7787-1907-6(3)) Crabtree Publishing Co.

Kalman, Bobbie & Dyer, Hadley. Les Chimpanzés. rev. ed. 2007. (FRE., Illus.). 32p. (J). (gr. 2-3). pap. (*978-2-89579-128-7(7)) Editions Banjo.

—Endangered Chimpanzees. 2005. (Earth's Endangered Animals Ser.). (Illus.). 32p. (J). (gr. 3-5). (978-0-7787-1859-8(X)); (ps-k). pap. (978-0-7787-1905-2(7)) Crabtree Publishing Co.

—Endangered Manatees. 2006. (Illus.). 32p. (J). (gr. 2-8). pap. (978-0-7787-1914-4(6)); (978-0-7787-1868-0(9)) Crabtree Publishing Co.

Kalman, Bobbie & Johnson, Robin. Endangered Butterflies. 2006. (Illus.). 32p. (J). (gr. 2-8). pap. (978-0-7787-1916-8(2)); (978-0-7787-1870-3(0)) Crabtree Publishing Co.

Kalman, Bobbie & Johnson, Robin. Endangered Penguins. 2007. (Earth's Endangered Animals Ser.). (Illus.). 32p. (J). (gr. 1-7). (*978-0-7787-1863-5(8)); pap. (*978-0-7787-1909-0(X)) Crabtree Publishing Co.

Kalman, Bobbie & Lundblad, Kristina. Endangered Bats. 2006. (Illus.). 32p. (J). (gr. 2-8). pap. (978-0-7787-1912-0(X)); (978-0-7787-1866-6(2)) Crabtree Publishing Co.

—Endangered Mountain Gorillas. 2004. (Earth's Endangered Animals Ser.). (Illus.). 32p. (J). (978-0-7787-1855-0(7)); pap. (978-0-7787-1901-4(4)) Crabtree Publishing Co.

Kalman, Bobbie & Thal, Karuna. The Life Cycle of a Whale. 2001. (Life Cycle Ser.). (Illus.). 32p. (J). (gr. 2-3). (978-0-7787-0653-3(2)); pap. (978-0-7787-0683-0(4)) Crabtree Publishing Co.

Kane, Karen. Mountain Gorillas. Ellis, Gerry, photos by. 2001. (Early Bird Nature Bks.). (Illus.). 48p. (J). (gr. 2-4). lib. bdg. 25.26 (978-0-8225-3040-4(6) , Lerner Pubns.) Lerner Publishing Group.

Kendell, Patricia. Tigers. 2002. (In the Wild Ser.). (Illus.). 32p. (J). lib. bdg. 25.69 (978-0-7398-4909-5(3)) Raintree.

Kenyon, Linda J. Rainforest Bird Rescue: Changing the Future for Endangered Wildlife. 2006. (Firefly Animal Rescue Ser.). (Illus.). 64p. (J). (gr. 5-12). pap. 9.95 (978-1-55407-152-4(6)); lib. bdg. 19.95 (978-1-55407-153-1(4)) Firefly Bks., Ltd.

Kinsner, Kathy. ¿Condenadas a desaparecer? Especies en peligro de extincion & Doomed to Disappear? Endangered Species. 2005. spiral bd. 84.00 (*978-1-4108-5698-2(4)) Benchmark Education Co.

Knowlton, Laurie Lazzaro. African Giants. Tusan, Stan, illus. Prebeg, Rick, photos by. 2005. (J). (978-1-933248-08-0(4)) World Quest Learning.

Kulling, Monica. Alligators: Life in the Wild. Roper, Marty, illus. 1999. (Road to Reading Ser.). (978-0-307-26307-0(X)) Whitman Publishing LLC.

Labella, Susan. Animal Survivors, 6 bks., Set. Incl. Bats & Other Animals with Amazing Ears. 19.00 (978-0-516-24926-1(6)); Beavers & Other Animals with Amazing Teeth. 19.00 (978-0-516-24930-8(4)); Chameleons & Other Animals with Amazing Skin. 19.00 (978-0-516-24925-4(8)); Octopuses & Other Animals with Amazing Senses. 19.00 (978-0-516-24928-5(2)); Owls & Other Animals with Amazing Eyes. 19.00 (978-0-516-24927-8(4)); Salamanders & Other Animals with Amazing Tails. 19.00 (978-0-516-24929-2(0)); (Illus.). 24p. (J). (gr. 1-2). (Scholastic News Nonfiction Readers Ser.). 2005. 108.00 (978-0-516-25390-9(5) , Children's Pr.) Scholastic Library Publishing.

Laskey, Elizabeth. Sea Turtles. 2003. (Sea Creatures Ser.). (Illus.). 32p. (J). pap. 6.95 (978-1-4034-3564-4(2)); lib. bdg. 22.79 (978-1-4034-0962-1(5)) Heinemann Library.

Lasky, Kathryn. Interrupted Journey: Saving Endangered Sea Turtles. Knight, Christopher G., photos by. 2006. 48p. (J). (gr. 1-5). pap. 6.99 (978-0-7636-2883-3(2)) Candlewick Pr.

Ledu-Frattini, Stephanie. The Tiger. Uhlig, Elizabeth, tr. from FRE. Sah, Anup, photos by. 2004. (Animal Close-Ups Ser.). (Illus.). 28p. (J). pap. 6.95 (978-1-57091-373-0(0)) Charlesbridge Publishing, Inc.

Levine, Stuart P. The Orangutan. 1999. (Endangered Animals & Habitats Ser.). (Illus.). 112p. (YA). (gr. 4-12). 27.45 (978-1-56006-560-9(5) , Lucent Bks.) Thomson Gale.

Lithgow, John & Blackaby, Susan. It Stinks to Be Extinct! Level 4. 2007. (Lithgow Palooza Readers Ser.). (Illus.). 32p. (J). (gr. 2-3). pap. 3.95 (978-0-7696-4254-3(3)) School Specialty Publishing.

Long, Matthew & Long, Thomas. Any Bear Can Wear Glasses: The Spectacled Bear & other Curious Creatures. Long, Sylvia, illus. 2005. 24p. (J). (gr. k-4). reprint ed. 17.00 (978-0-7567-9763-8(2)) DIANE Publishing Co.

MacAulay, Kelley & Kalman, Bobbie. Endangered Zebras. 2007. (Earth's Endangered Animals Ser.). (Illus.). 32p. (J). (gr. 1-7). (*978-0-7787-1864-2(6)); pap. (*978-0-7787-1910-6(3)) Crabtree Publishing Co.

Malaspina, Ann. The Jaguar. 2000. (Endangered Animals & Habitats Ser.). (Illus.). 96p. (YA). (gr. 4-12). 29.95 (978-1-56006-813-6(2) , Lucent Bks.) Thomson Gale.

—The Koala. 2001. (Endangered Animals & Habitats Ser.). (Illus.). 112p. (YA). (gr. 4-12). 28.70 (978-1-56006-876-1(0) , Lucent Bks.) Thomson Gale.

Martin, Patricia. California Condors. 2002. (gr. 3-6). lib. bdg. 15.25 (978-0-613-59455-4(X)) Tandem Library Bks.

—Gray Wolves. 2002. (gr. 3-6). lib. bdg. 15.25 (978-0-613-59494-3(0)) Tandem Library Bks.

Martin, Patricia A. Fink. California Condors. (True Bks.). (Illus.). 48p. (J). (gr. 3-5). 2003. pap. 6.95 (978-0-516-27470-6(8)); 2002. pap. 25.00 (978-0-516-22161-8(2)) Scholastic Library Publishing. (Children's Pr.).

—Gray Wolves. 2003. (True Bks.). (Illus.). 48p. (J). (gr. 3-5). pap. 6.95 (978-0-516-27472-0(4) , Children's Pr.) Scholastic Library Publishing.

—Lemurs, Lorises, & Other Lower Primates. 2000. (True Bks.). (Illus.). 48p. (J). (gr. 3-5). pap. 6.95 (978-0-516-27015-9(X) , Children's Pr.) Scholastic Library Publishing.

—Manatees. 2003. (True Bks.). (Illus.). 48p. (J). (gr. 3-5). pap. 6.95 (978-0-516-27473-7(2) , Children's Pr.) Scholastic Library Publishing.

Mattern, Joanne. Going, Going, Gone? Saving Animals in Danger. 2001. (Animal Adventures Ser.). (Illus.). 56p. (J). pap. (978-0-7891-5398-2(X)); (gr. 1-4). lib. bdg. 16.95 (978-0-7807-9850-2(3)) Perfection Learning Corp.

McLimans, David. Gone Wild: An Endangered Animal Alphabet. 2006. (Illus.). 40p. (J). (gr. 3 up). 17.85 (978-0-8027-9564-9(1)); 16.95 (978-0-8027-9563-2(3)) Walker & Co.

McMillan, Diane. Humpback Whales. 2004. (Nature Watch Ser.). (Illus.). 48p. (J). 25.26 (978-1-57505-347-9(0)) Lerner Publishing Group.

McNab, Chris. Endangered Reptiles. 2006. (Nature's Monsters Ser.). (Illus.). 32p. (J). lib. bdg. 23.33 (978-0-8368-6171-6(X)) Stevens, Gareth Inc.

Miles, Victoria. Wild Science: Amazing Encounters Between Animals & the People Who Study Them. 2004. (Illus.). 168p. (J). pap. 18.95 (978-1-55192-618-6(0)) Raincoast Bk. Distribution CAN. *Dist:* Perseus Distribution.

Miller, Chuck. Tortoises. 2002. (Animals of the Rain Forest Ser.). (Illus.). 32p. (YA). lib. bdg. 22.83 (978-0-7398-5531-7(X)) Raintree.

—Tree Kangaroos. 2002. (Animals of the Rain Forest Ser.). (Illus.). 32p. (YA). lib. bdg. 22.83 (978-0-7398-5532-4(8)) Raintree.

Moore, Jaedyn. Last One Left: Saving Endangered Animals. 2006. (Illus.). 32p. (J). per. 11.95 (*978-1-933324-51-7(1)) Cedar Hill Publishing.

Morgan, Jody. Elephant Rescue: Changing the Future for Endangered Wildlife. 2004. (Firefly Animal Rescue Ser.). (Illus.). 64p. (J). (gr. 5-8). 19.95 (978-1-55297-595-4(9)); pap. 9.95 (978-1-55297-594-7(0)) Firefly Bks., Ltd.

—Elephant Rescue: Changing the Future for Endangered Wildlife. 2004. (gr. 5-8). lib. bdg. 18.75 (978-0-613-78600-3(9)) Tandem Library Bks.

Morgan, Sally. Wildlife in Danger. 2006. (Illus.). 32p. (J). (978-1-59771-070-1(9)) Sea-To-Sea Pubns.

Murdoch, J. D., et al. The African Wild Dog. 2002. (Library of Wolves & Wild Dogs). (Illus.). 24p. (J). (gr. 2-4). lib. bdg. 18.75 (978-0-8239-5769-9(1) , PowerKids Pr.) Rosen Publishing Group, Inc., The.

Noonan, Diana. The Crocodile. 2002. (Life Cycle Ser.). (Illus.). 32p. (gr. k-2). 23.00 (978-0-7910-6964-6(8) , Chelsea Hse.) Facts On File, Inc.

—The Green Turtle. 2002. (Life Cycle Ser.). (Illus.). 32p. (gr. k-2). 23.00 (978-0-7910-6967-7(2) , Chelsea Hse.) Facts On File, Inc.

O'Connell, Kim A. The Galapagos Penguin: A MyReportLinks. com Book. 2005. (Endangered & Threatened Animals Ser.). (Illus.). 48p. (J). lib. bdg. 25.26 (978-0-7660-5063-1(7) , MyReportLinks.com Bks.) Enslow Pubs., Inc.

—The Wallaby: A MyReportLinks. com Book. 2005. (Endangered & Threatened Animals Ser.). (Illus.). 48p. (J). lib. bdg. 25.26 (978-0-7660-5064-8(5) , MyReportLinks.com Bks.) Enslow Pubs., Inc.

O'Connor, Rebecca K. Frogs & Toads. 2003. (Endangered Animals & Habitats Ser.). (Illus.). 112p. (J). 29.95 (978-1-56006-919-5(8) , Lucent Bks.) Thomson Gale.

Parker, Edward. Reptiles & Amphibians. 2002. (Rain Forest Pilot Ser.). (Illus.). 48p. (J). lib. bdg. 27.12 (978-0-7398-5243-9(4)) Raintree.

Patent, Dorothy Hinshaw. Saving the Prairie Bandit. (Wildlife Conservation Society Bks.). (Illus.). 48p. (J). (gr. 4-6). 2002. pap. 6.95 (978-0-531-16567-6(1)); 2001. 24.50 (978-0-531-11851-1(7)) Scholastic Library Publishing. (Watts, Franklin).

Penny, Malcolm. Endangered Species: Our Impact on the Planet. 2002. (Twenty-First Century Debates Ser.). (Illus.). 64p. (YA). (gr. 6-8). lib. bdg. 27.12 (978-0-7398-4873-9(9)) Raintree.

Petersen, Rafe. Endangered Species Deskbook. 2003. lib. bdg. 111.55 (978-0-613-92350-7(2)) Tandem Library Bks.

Podojil, Catherine. Saving Endangered Species. 2005. (Illus.). 24p. (J). (***978-0-328-13528-8(3)*** , Scott Foresman) Addison-Wesley Educational Pubs., Inc.

Povey, Karen D. The Leopard. 2002. (Endangered Animals & Habitats Ser.). (Illus.). 128p. (J). 29.95 (978-1-56006-921-8(X) , Lucent Bks.) Thomson Gale.

Powell, James. Manatees: Natural History & Conservation. rev. ed. 2002. (WorldLife Library Ser.). (Illus.). 72p. pap. 17.95 (978-0-89658-583-6(2)) Voyageur Pr., Inc.

Pratt-Serafini, Kristin Joy. A Walk in the Rainforest. Pratt-Serafini, Kristin Joy, illus. 2007. (Illus.). 26p. (J). (ps-ps). bds. 7.95 (***978-1-58469-088-7(7)***) Dawn Pubns.

Price-Goff, Claire. The Manatee. 1999. (Endangered Animals & Habitats Ser.). (Illus.). 112p. (YA). (gr. 4-12). 27.45 (978-1-56006-445-9(5) , Lucent Bks.) Thomson Gale.

QEB Start Reading Together National Book Stores Edition: Animals in Danger. 2006. (J). per. (978-1-59566-259-0(6)) QEB Publishing Inc.

Raatma, Lucia. Sharks. 2001. (First Reports). (Illus.). 48p. (J). (gr. 3 up). lib. bdg. 21.26 (978-0-7565-0056-6(7)) Compass Point Bks.

Radley, Gail. Forests & Jungles. Sherlock, Jean, illus. (Vanishing from Ser.). 2005. 32p. (gr. 6-12). lib. bdg. 22.60 (978-1-57505-405-6(1)); 2003. 32p. (J). (gr. 3-5). 6.95 (978-1-57505-567-1(8)); 1998. (J). lib. bdg. (978-0-8225-1937-9(2)) Lerner Publishing Group.

—Forests & Jungles. Sherlock, Jean, illus. 2001. 32p. (J). (ps-7). lib. bdg. 15.25 (978-0-613-64497-6(2)) Tandem Library Bks.

—Grasslands & Deserts. Sherlock, Jean, illus. (Vanishing from Ser.). 32p. 2005. (gr. 6-12). lib. bdg. 22.60 (978-1-57505-406-3(X)); 2003. (YA). (gr. 3-5). 6.95 (978-1-57505-568-8(6) , Carolrhoda Bks.) Lerner Publishing Group.

—Grasslands & Deserts. 2001. (gr. 3-6). lib. bdg. 15.25 (978-0-613-64517-1(0)) Tandem Library Bks.

—The Skies. Sherlock, Jean, illus. (Vanishing from Ser.). 32p. 2005. (gr. 6-12). lib. bdg. 22.60 (978-1-57505-407-0(8)); 2003. (J). (gr. 3-5). pap. 6.95 (978-1-57505-566-4(X)) Lerner Publishing Group.

—Waterways. Sherlock, Jean, illus. 2003. (Vanishing from Ser.). 32p. (J). (gr. 3-5). 6.95 (978-1-57505-569-5(4)) Lerner Publishing Group.

—Waterways. 2001. (gr. 3-6). lib. bdg. 15.25 (978-0-613-64614-7(2)) Tandem Library Bks.

Reiter, Chris. The Blue Whale: A MyReportLinks.com Book. 2003. (Endangered & Threatened Animals Ser.). (Illus.). 48p. (J). (gr. 4-10). lib. bdg. 25.26 (978-0-7660-5055-6(6) , MyReportLinks.com Bks.) Enslow Pubs., Inc.

—The Gray Wolf: A MyReportLinks.com Book. 2003. (Endangered & Threatened Animals Ser.). (Illus.). 48p. (J). (gr. 4-10). lib. bdg. 25.26 (978-0-7660-5056-3(4) , MyReportLinks.com Bks.) Enslow Pubs., Inc.

Richardson, Adele D. Manatees: Peaceful Plant-Eaters. 2002. (Wild World of Animals Ser.). (Illus.). 24p. (J). (gr. 1). lib. bdg. 18.60 (978-0-7368-1395-2(0) , Bridgestone Bks.) Capstone Pr., Inc.

Ring, Susan. Project Otter. 2003. (gr. 3-6). lib. bdg. 15.25 (978-0-613-79818-1(X)) Tandem Library Bks.

—Project Otter. Kissock, Heather & Marshall, Diana, eds. 2003. (Zoo Life Ser.). (Illus.). 24p. (J). pap. 6.95 (978-1-59036-059-0(1)) Weigl Pubs., Inc.

—Project Otter. 2002. (Zoo Life Ser.). (Illus.). 24p. (J). lib. bdg. 22.80 (978-1-59036-018-7(4)) Weigl Pubs., Inc.

Ring, Susan & Miller-Schroeder, Patricia, trs. California Condors. 2003. (Untamed World Ser.). (Illus.). 64p. (J). lib. bdg. 28.56 (978-0-7398-6843-0(8)) Raintree.

Robbins, Ken. Thunder on the Plains: The Story of the American Buffalo. Robbins, Ken, illus. 2001. (Illus.). 32p. (J). (gr. 2-5). 16.99 (978-0-689-83025-9(4) , Atheneum) Simon & Schuster Children's Publishing.

Roberts, Russell. Manatees. 2003. (Endangered Plants & Animals of the United States Ser.). (J). pap. (978-1-58417-207-9(X)); lib. bdg. (978-1-58417-206-2(1)) Lake Street Pubs.

Salmansohn, Pete & Kress, Stephen. Saving Birds: Heroes Around the World. 2005. (Illus.). 40p. (gr. 3-6). 16.95 (978-0-88448-237-6(5)) Tilbury Hse. Pubs.

Schafer, Susan. Tigers. 2000. (Animals Animals Ser.). (Illus.). 48p. (J). (gr. 3-5). lib. bdg. 25.64 (978-0-7614-1170-3(4)) Cavendish, Marshall Corp.

Scholastic, Inc. Staff. Endangered Animals. 2007. (Scholastic First Discovery Ser.). 24p. (J). (ps-k). pap. 5.99 (***978-0-545-00143-4(9)*** , Scholastic Reference) Scholastic, Inc.

Schonberg, Marcia. Michigan Plants & Animals. 2003. (Heinemann State Studies). (Illus.). 48p. (J). 27.07 (978-1-4034-0662-0(6)); pap. 8.50 (978-1-4034-2679-6(1)) Heinemann Library.

Schueler, Donald G. The Gopher Tortoise: A MyReportLinks.com Book. 2003. (Endangered & Threatened Animals Ser.). (Illus.). 48p. (J). (gr. 4-10). lib. bdg. 25.26 (978-0-7660-5053-2(X) , MyReportLinks.com Bks.) Enslow Pubs., Inc.

Scott, Karen. Endangered Species & Friends in the U. S. A. Seamans, Amanda, illus. unabr. ed. Date not set. (J). (ps-6). 16.95 (978-1-889667-00-3(5)) Second Ark Pubns.

Simmons, Randy T. Endangered Species. 2002. (Illus.). 112p. (J). 33.70 (978-0-7377-1266-7(X) , Greenhaven Pr., Inc.) Thomson Gale.

Slater, Patrick. Australian Rare & Endangered Wildlife. 2002. (Nature Kids Ser.). (Illus.). 52p. (J). (gr. 3 up). lib. bdg. (978-1-59084-212-6(X)) Mason Crest Pubs.

Snyder, Trish. Alligator & Crocodile Rescue: Changing the Future for Endangered Wildlife. 2006. (Firefly Animal Rescue Ser.). (Illus.). 64p. (J). (gr. 5-12). pap. 9.95 (978-1-55297-919-8(9)); lib. bdg. 19.95 (978-1-55297-920-4(2)) Firefly Bks., Ltd.

Sobol, Richard. An Elephant in the Backyard. 2004. (Illus.). 32p. (J). (gr. 1). 17.99 (978-0-525-47288-9(6) , Dutton Juvenile) Penguin Group (USA) Inc.

Sobol, Richard, photos by. An Elephant in the Backyard. 2004. (Illus.). (J). (978-0-525-46970-4(2) , Dutton Juvenile) Penguin Group (USA) Inc.

Somervill, Barbara A. American Bison. 2008. (J). lib. bdg. 25.26 (***978-1-60279-031-5(0)***) Cherry Lake Publishing.

—Animal Survivors of the Arctic. 2004. (Watts Library). (Illus.). 64p. (J). 25.50 (978-0-531-12204-4(2) , Watts, Franklin) Scholastic Library Publishing.

—Animal Survivors of the Wetlands. 2004. (Watts Library). (Illus.). 64p. (J). 25.50 (978-0-531-12203-7(4) , Watts, Franklin) Scholastic Library Publishing.

Spilsbury, Louise & Spilsbury, Richard. The Alligator. 2004. (Animals under Threat Ser.). (Illus.). 48p. (J). pap. 8.50 (978-1-4034-5431-7(0)) Heinemann Library.

—American Alligator. 2004. (Animals under Threat Ser.). (Illus.). 48p. (J). lib. bdg. (978-1-4034-4857-6(4)) Heinemann Library.

—Animals under Threat. 2006. (Planet under Pressure Ser.). (Illus.). 48p. (J). lib. bdg. (978-1-4034-8217-4(9)) Heinemann Library.

—Bengal Tiger. 2004. (Animals under Threat Ser.). (Illus.). 48p. (J). lib. bdg. 27.07 (978-1-4034-4858-3(2)) Heinemann Library.

—The Bengal Tiger. 2004. (Animals under Threat Ser.). (Illus.). 48p. (J). pap. 8.50 (978-1-4034-5432-4(9)) Heinemann Library.

—Black Rhino. 2004. (Animals under Threat Ser.). (Illus.). 48p. (J). lib. bdg. 27.07 (978-1-4034-4859-0(0)) Heinemann Library.

—The Black Rhino. 2004. (Animals under Threat Ser.). (Illus.). 48p. (J). pap. 8.50 (978-1-4034-5433-1(7)) Heinemann Library.

—Great White Shark. 2004. (Animals under Threat Ser.). (Illus.). 48p. (J). lib. bdg. (978-1-4034-4860-6(4)) Heinemann Library.

—The Great White Shark. 2004. (Animals under Threat Ser.). (Illus.). 48p. (J). pap. 8.50 (978-1-4034-5434-8(5)) Heinemann Library.

St. Pierre, Stephanie. Siberian Tigers. 2002. (In the Wild Ser.). (Illus.). 24p. (J). (gr. k-2). pap. 6.95 (978-1-58810-384-0(6) , 91104) Heinemann Library.

Steck-Vaughn Staff. Endangered Marine Animals. 2000. (Primary Source Science Collection). (J). pap. incl. VHS (978-0-7398-3212-7(3)) Raintree.

Steele, Christy. Bengal Tigers. 2002. (Animals of the Rain Forest Ser.). (Illus.). 32p. (J). lib. bdg. 22.83 (978-0-7398-5369-6(4)) Raintree.

—Malayan Sun Bears. 2003. (Animals of the Rain Forest Ser.). (Illus.). 32p. (J). lib. bdg. 24.28 (978-0-7398-6838-6(1)) Raintree.

Stephanie, St Pierre. Siberian Tigers. 2001. (In the Wild Ser.). (Illus.). 24p. (J). (ps-3). lib. bdg. 21.36 (978-1-58810-110-5(X)) Heinemann Library.

Steward, Mark. New York Plants & Animals. 2003. (Heinemann State Studies). (Illus.). 48p. (J). (gr. 3-5). lib. bdg. (978-1-4034-0356-8(2)) Heinemann Library.

Stewart, Mark. New York Plants & Animals. 2003. (Heinemann State Studies). (Illus.). 48p. (J). pap. 8.50 (978-1-4034-0578-4(6)) Heinemann Library.

—New York Plants & Animals. 2003. (gr. 3-6). lib. bdg. 17.05 (978-0-613-60976-0(X)) Tandem Library Bks.

Stewart, Melissa. Elephants. 2002. (True Bks.). (Illus.). 48p. (J). (gr. 3-5). pap. 6.95 (978-0-516-26990-0(9)); 25.00 (978-0-516-22199-1(X)) Scholastic Library Publishing. (Children's Pr.).

—Elephants. 2002. (gr. 3-6). lib. bdg. 15.25 (978-0-613-54197-8(9)) Tandem Library Bks.

Stewart, Pat. Invisible Endangered Animals Magic Picture Book. 2001. (Invisible Magic Picture Bks.). (Illus.). 16p. (J). (ps up). pap. 1.50 (978-0-486-41849-0(9)) Dover Pubns., Inc.

Stille, Darlene R. Cheetahs. 2004. (First Reports). (Illus.). 48p. (J). (gr. 3 up). lib. bdg. 22.60 (978-0-7565-0576-9(3)) Compass Point Bks.

—Jaguars. 2001. (First Reports). (Illus.). 48p. (J). (gr. 3 up). lib. bdg. 21.26 (978-0-7565-0055-9(9)) Compass Point Bks.

Stone, Lynn M. Elephants. 2001. (Wildlife in Danger Ser.). (Illus.). 24p. (J). (gr. 1-4). lib. bdg. 20.64 (978-1-58952-019-6(X)) Rourke Publishing, LLC.

—Panda. 2001. (Wildlife in Danger Ser.). (Illus.). 24p. (gr. 1-4). 14.95 (978-1-58952-020-2(3)) Rourke Publishing, LLC.

—Rhinoceros. 2001. (Wildlife in Danger Ser.). (Illus.). 24p. (gr. 1-4). 14.95 (978-1-58952-021-9(1)) Rourke Publishing, LLC.

—Seals. 2001. (Wildlife in Danger Ser.). (Illus.). 24p. (gr. 1-4). 14.95 (978-1-58952-022-6(X)) Rourke Publishing, LLC.

—Tigers. 2005. (Nature Watch Ser.). (J). 25.26 (978-1-57505-578-7(3) , Carolrhoda Bks.) Lerner Publishing Group.

—Tigers. 2001. (Wildlife in Danger Ser.). (Illus.). 24p. (gr. 1-4). 14.95 (978-1-58952-023-3(8)) Rourke Publishing, LLC.

Stone, Tanya Lee. Gorillas. 2003. (Wild Wild World Ser.). (Illus.). 24p. (J). 24.94 (978-1-56711-814-8(3) , Blackbirch Pr., Inc.) Thomson Gale.

Sullivan, Jody. Cheetahs: Spotted Speedsters. 2002. (Wild World of Animals Ser.). (Illus.). 24p. (J). (gr. 1-3). lib. bdg. 18.60 (978-0-7368-1393-8(4) , Bridgestone Bks.) Capstone Pr., Inc.

Sway, Marlene. Bats: Mammals That Fly. 1999. (Animals in Order Ser.). (Illus.). 48p. (J). (gr. 4-6). 26.50 (978-0-531-11449-0(X) , Watts, Franklin) Scholastic Library Publishing.

Taylor, Marianne. Mountain Gorilla. 2004. (Animals under Threat Ser.). (Illus.). 48p. (J). lib. bdg. 27.07 (978-1-4034-4861-3(2)) Heinemann Library.

—The Mountain Gorilla. 2004. (Animals under Threat Ser.). (Illus.). 48p. (J). pap. 8.50 (978-1-4034-5435-5(3)) Heinemann Library.

Theodorou, Rod. Animals in Danger: Accelerated Reader, 12 bks., Set. 2001. (Illus.). (J). (gr. k-2). lib. bdg. 256.32 (978-1-57572-299-3(2)) Heinemann Library.

—Animals in Danger: Accelerated Reader, 6 bks., Set 1. Incl. Bengal Tiger. lib. bdg. 21.36 (978-1-57572-267-2(4)); Black Rhino. lib. bdg. 21.36 (978-1-57572-262-7(3)); Blue Whale. lib. bdg. 21.36 (978-1-57572-263-4(1)); Florida Manatee. lib. bdg. 21.36 (978-1-57572-265-8(8)); Giant Panda. lib. bdg. 21.36 (978-1-57572-264-1(X)); Mountain Gorilla. lib. bdg. 21.36 (978-1-57572-266-5(6)); (J). (gr. k-2). 2000. (Illus.). 32p. 2001. Set lib. bdg. 128.16 (978-1-57572-268-9(2)); Set lib. bdg. 128.16 (978-1-57572-298-6(4)) Heinemann Library.

—Cheetah. (Animals in Danger Ser.). (Illus.). 32p. (J). (gr. k-2). 2002. pap. 6.95 (978-1-58810-363-5(3) , 91075); 2001. lib. bdg. 21.36 (978-1-57572-269-6(0)) Heinemann Library.

—Florida Manatee. (Animals in Danger Ser.). (Illus.). 32p. (J). (gr. k-2). 2002. pap. 6.95 (978-1-58810-331-4(5) , 91076); 2000. lib. bdg. 21.36 (978-1-57572-265-8(8)) Heinemann Library.

—Florida Manatee. 2001. (Animals in Danger Ser.). (Illus.). (J). 13.30 (978-0-606-21995-2(1)) Tandem Library Bks.

—Giant Panda. 2002. (Animals in Danger Ser.). (Illus.). 32p. (J). (gr. k-2). pap. 6.95 (978-1-58810-332-1(3) , 91077) Heinemann Library.

—Giant Panda. 2001. (Animals in Danger Ser.). (Illus.). (J). 13.30 (978-0-606-21997-6(8)) Tandem Library Bks.

—Gray Bat. (Animals in Danger Ser.). (Illus.). 32p. (J). (gr. k-2). 2002. pap. 6.95 (978-1-58810-445-8(1) , 91152); 2001. lib. bdg. 21.36 (978-1-57572-270-2(4)) Heinemann Library.

—Koala. 2001. (Animals in Danger Ser.). (Illus.). 32p. (J). (gr. k-2). lib. bdg. 21.36 (978-1-57572-271-9(2)) Heinemann Library.

—Leatherback Sea Turtle. (Animals in Danger Ser.). (Illus.). 32p. (J). (gr. k-2). 2002. pap. 6.95 (978-1-58810-447-2(8) , 91154); 2001. lib. bdg. 21.36 (978-1-57572-272-6(0)) Heinemann Library.

—Polar Bear. (Animals in Danger Ser.). (Illus.). 32p. (J). (gr. k-2). 2002. pap. 6.95 (978-1-58810-364-2(1) , 91078); 2001. lib. bdg. 21.36 (978-1-57572-273-3(9)) Heinemann Library.

—Whooping Crane. 2002. (Animals in Danger Ser.). (Illus.). 32p. (J). (gr. k-2). pap. 6.95 (978-1-58810-448-9(6) , 91156) Heinemann Library.

Thomas, Keltie. Bear Rescue: Changing the Future for Endangered Wildlife. 2006. (Firefly Animal Rescue Ser.). (Illus.). 64p. (J). (gr. 5-12). pap. 9.95 (978-1-55297-921-1(0)); lib. bdg. 19.95 (978-1-55297-922-8(9)) Firefly Bks., Ltd.

Thomas, Peggy. Marine Mammal Preservation. 2000. (Science of Saving Animals Ser.: 8). (Illus.). 64p. (gr. 5-8). lib. bdg. (978-0-7613-1458-5(X) , Twenty-First Century Bks.) Lerner Publishing Group.

Thomson, Sarah L. Amazing Tigers! 2004. (Illus.). 32p. (J). lib. bdg. 13.85 (***978-1-4242-0511-0(5)***) Fitzgerald Bks.

Torres, John Albert. The African Elephant: A MyReportLinks. com Book. 2004. (Endangered & Threatened Animals Ser.). (Illus.). 48p. (J). lib. bdg. 25.26 (978-0-7660-5174-4(9) , MyReportLinks.com Bks.) Enslow Pubs., Inc.

—The Manatee: A MyReportLinks. com Book. 2004. (Endangered & Threatened Animals Ser.). (Illus.). 48p. (J). lib. bdg. 25.26 (978-0-7660-5173-7(0) , MyReportLinks.com Bks.) Enslow Pubs., Inc.

Tracqui, Valerie. Panda: Wild about Bamboo. 1999. (Animal Close-Ups Ser.). (978-0-606-18028-3(1)) Tandem Library Bks.

—The Whale. 2004. (Animal Close-Ups Ser.). (Illus.). 28p. (J). pap. 6.95 (978-1-57091-625-0(X)) Charlesbridge Publishing, Inc.

Turner, Matt. Asian Elephant. 2004. (Animals under Threat Ser.). (Illus.). 48p. (J). 29.93 (978-1-4034-5581-9(3)) Heinemann Library.

—The Asian Elephant. 2004. (Animals under Threat Ser.). (Illus.). 48p. (J). pap. 8.50 (978-1-4034-5688-5(7)) Heinemann Library.

Twist, Clint. Endangered Animals A-Z. 2004. (Illus.). 64p. (J). 26.20 (978-1-4103-0488-9(4)) Thomson Gale.

—Endangered Animals Dictionary: An a to Z of Threatened Species. 2004. (Illus.). 64p. (J). (978-0-439-55094-9(7)) Scholastic, Inc.

Unwin, Mike. Peregrine Falcon. 2004. (Animals under Threat Ser.). (Illus.). 48p. (J). lib. bdg. (978-1-4034-4862-0(0)) Heinemann Library.

—The Peregrine Falcon. 2004. (Animals under Threat Ser.). (Illus.). 48p. (J). pap. 8.50 (978-1-4034-5436-2(1)) Heinemann Library.

Vanishing From. 2004. (Illus.). lib. bdg. 7.95 (978-0-8225-3344-3(8)) Lerner Publishing Group.

Vergoth, Karin & Lampton, Christopher. Endangered Species. rev. ed. 1999. (Impact Bks.). (Illus.). 112p. (YA). (gr. 8-12). 26.00 (978-0-531-11480-3(5) , Watts, Franklin) Scholastic Library Publishing.

Wade, Mary. Texas Plants & Animals. 2003. (Heinemann State Studies). (Illus.). 48p. (J). pap. 8.50 (978-1-4034-2698-7(8)) Heinemann Library.

Wade, Mary Dodson. Texas Plants & Animals. 2003. (Heinemann State Studies). (Illus.). 48p. (J). lib. bdg. 27.07 (978-1-4034-0690-3(1)) Heinemann Library.

—Texas Plants & Animals. 2003. (gr. 3-6). lib. bdg. 17.05 (978-0-613-88569-0(4)) Tandem Library Bks.

Walker, Sally M. Crocodiles. 2004. (Nature Watch Ser.). (Illus.). 48p. (J). (gr. 3-8). lib. bdg. 25.26 (978-1-57505-345-5(4)) Lerner Publishing Group.

—Rays. 2002. (Nature Watch Ser.). (Illus.). 48p. (J). lib. bdg. 25.26 (978-1-57505-172-7(9) , Carolrhoda Bks.) Lerner Publishing Group.

Watson, Susan. Protecting Global Environments. 2003. 32p. (J). lib. bdg. 24.25 (978-1-58340-399-0(X)) Smart Apple Media.

Watt, Melanie. Leatherback Turtles. 2001. (Untamed World Ser.). (Illus.). 64p. (J). lib. bdg. 28.54 (978-0-8172-4575-7(8)) Raintree.

Welsbacher, Anne. Crocodiles. 2002. (Predators in the Wild Ser.). (Illus.). 32p. (J). (gr. 3-4). lib. bdg. 21.26 (978-0-7368-1315-0(2) , Capstone High-Interest Bks.) Capstone Pr., Inc.

Wilkinson, Rick. Endangered! Working to Save Animals at Risk. 2002. (Illus.). 32p. (J). (978-1-86508-664-4(9)) Allen & Unwin.

Williams, Judith. Saving Endangered Animals with a Scientist. 2004. (I Like Science! Ser.). (Illus.). 24p. (J). (gr. 2-4). lib. bdg. 21.26 (978-0-7660-2276-8(5)) Enslow Pubs., Inc.

Williams, Kimberly Joan & Stoops, Erik Daniel. Bat Conservation, 6 vols., Set. 2001. (Young Explorer Ser.). (Illus.). 32p. (J). (gr. 3-7). lib. bdg. 4.85 net. (978-1-890475-13-0(0)) Faulkner's Publishing Group.

Wlodarski, Loran. The Story of Manatees: Siren's Song. 2nd rev. ed. 1998. (Education Department Animal Information Publications). (Illus.). 64p. (gr. 4-12). per. 7.99 (978-1-893698-00-0(9) , B07, SeaWorld Education Dept.) SeaWorld, Inc.

ENDANGERED SPECIES—FICTION

Amato, Carol A. On the Trail of the Grizzly, Vol. 9. O'Brien, Patrick & Wenzel, David, illus. 1998. (Young Reader Ser.: No. 9). 48p. (J). (gr. 3-6). lib. bdg. 13.45 (978-1-56674-240-5(4)) Forest Hse. Publishing Co., Inc.

Anderson, Laurie Halse. Manatee Blues. 2003. (Wild at Heart Ser.). (Illus.). 114p. (J). (gr. 4 up). lib. bdg. 23.33 (978-0-8368-3258-7(2)) Stevens, Gareth Inc.

—Manatee Blues. 2000. (American Girl Wild at Heart Ser.: Bk. 4). (Illus.). (YA). (978-0-606-20455-2(5)) Tandem Library Bks.

Bow, Patricia. Chimpanzee Rescue: Changing the Future for Endangered Wildlife. 2004. (Illus.). 64p. (J). (gr. k-9). lib. bdg. 16.60 (978-0-606-33844-8(6)) Tandem Library Bks.

Butler, John. Pi-shu the Little Panda. 2001. (Illus.). 32p. (J). (ps-2). 15.95 (978-1-56145-242-2(4) , Q30580) Peachtree Pubs., Ltd.

Cole, Sheila. The Canyon. 2002. 160p. (J). (gr. 3-7). 15.89 (978-0-06-029496-0(5)) HarperCollins Pubs.

Costain, Meredith. Polar Bears. 2000. (gr. k-3). lib. bdg. 11.80 (978-0-613-30680-5(5)) Tandem Library Bks.

Cowcher, Helen. Jaguar. 2000. (SPA.). 32p. (J). pap. (978-980-257-248-9(9)) Ekare, Ediciones.

—Jaguar. (Illus.). 40p. (CHI, ENG, URD, TUR & VIE.). (J). 16.95 (978-1-84059-009-8(2)); 2001. (VIE, ENG, URD, TUR & CHI., (J). 16.95 (978-1-84059-014-2(9)); 2001. (BEN, ENG, URD, TUR & VIE., (YA). 16.95 (978-1-84059-008-1(4)); 2001. (GRE, ENG, URD, TUR & VIE., (YA). 16.95 (978-1-84059-010-4(6)); 2001. (GUJ, ENG, URD, TUR & VIE., (YA). 16.95 (978-1-84059-011-1(4)); 2001. (TUR, ENG, URD, VIE

& CHI., (YA). 16.95 (978-1-84059-012-8(2)); 2001. (URD, ENG, TUR, VIE & CHI., (YA). 16.95 (978-1-84059-013-5(0)); 2001. (TUR., (YA). 16.95 (978-1-84059-015-9(7)) Milet Publishing.

—Jaguar. (J). (gr. 1-2). (978-0-590-36037-1(X)); (SPA., Illus.). (gr. 1-3). pap. 3.96 net. (978-0-590-87599-8(X) , SO30738, Scholastic Pr.); 2002. 32p. pap. 5.99 (978-0-439-39470-3(8)) Scholastic, Inc.

Doerr, Bonnie J. Kenzie's Key. Aberle, Xylena Apotheloz, illus. 2003. 211p. (J). 16.95 (978-0-9619155-6-8(0)) Laurel & Herbert, Inc.

Dowson, Nick. Tracks of a Panda. Rong, Yu, illus. 2007. 32p. (J). (gr. k-3). 16.99 (***978-0-7636-3146-8(9)***) Candlewick Pr.

Doyle, Bill. Silenced! The 1969 Journal of Malcolm. Kelleher, Kathie, illus. 2006. 141p. (J). lib. bdg. 18.46 (***978-1-4242-1736-6(9)***) Fitzgerald Bks.

Farber, Erica. Golden Eagle. Mayer, Mercer, illus. 2006. (Critter Kids Adventure Ser.). 32p. (J). (gr. 2-5). pap. 4.95 (978-0-7696-4764-7(2) , Gingham Dog Pr.) School Specialty Publishing.

George, Jean Craighead. The Case of the Missing Cutthroats. 1999. (J). 12.64 (978-0-606-16703-1(X)); (gr. 3-6). lib. bdg. 14.15 (978-0-613-18242-3(1)) Tandem Library Bks.

Gill, Shelley. Big Blue. Barrow, Ann, illus. 32p. (J). (ps-6). 2005. pap. 6.95 (978-1-57091-667-0(5)); 2004. 15.95 (978-1-57091-352-5(8)) Charlesbridge Publishing, Inc.

Gilmore, Kate. The Exchange Student. 2006. 222p. (J). (gr. 7). pap. 6.95 (978-0-618-68948-4(6)) Houghton Mifflin Co.

—The Exchange Student. 1999. 224p. (J). (gr. 5-9). tchr. ed. 15.00 (978-0-395-57511-6(7)) Houghton Mifflin Co. Trade & Reference Div.

Graham, Lisa Faire. Olly Oliver & Rap Jack: The Endangered Journey. 2004. 58p. pap. 12.95 (978-1-4137-2533-9(3)) PublishAmerica, Inc.

Grote, Rich. Megan & the Borealis Butterfly. 1999. (Magic Attic Club Ser.). (J). lib. bdg. (978-0-606-16953-0(9)) Tandem Library Bks.

Halam, Ann. Siberia: A Novel. 2006. 272p. (YA). (gr. 7). mass mkt. 5.99 (978-0-553-49414-3(7) , Laurel Leaf) Random Hse. Children's Bks.

Hamilton, Virginia. Jaguarundi. Cooper, Floyd, illus. 1998. 40p. (J). (ps-3). pap. 14.95 (978-0-590-47366-8(2) , Blue Sky Pr., The) Scholastic, Inc.

Hobbs, Will. The Maze. 1999. 248p. (J). (gr. k-9). lib. bdg. 14.15 (978-0-613-19524-9(8)) Tandem Library Bks.

Hobbs, William. The Maze. (J). (gr. 5 up). 1999. (Illus.). 256p. pap. 5.99 (978-0-380-72913-5(X) , Harper Trophy); 1998. 208p. 17.99 (978-0-688-15092-1(6)) HarperCollins Pubs.

—The Maze. unabr. ed. 1999. (YA). pap., stu. ed. 59.00 incl. audio (978-0-7887-3990-3(5) , 41062X4) Recorded Bks., LLC.

—The Maze. 1999. (J). (978-0-606-16369-9(7)) Tandem Library Bks.

Jackson, Melanie. The Summer of the Spotted Owl. 2005. (Orca Young Readers Ser.: Book 4). (Illus.). 176p. (J). (gr. 3-7). pap. 6.95 (978-1-55143-412-4(1)) Orca Bk. Pubs. USA.

King, Jamie R. Kodi's Heroic Journey. Lemmon, David, illus. 1999. (Zoooo Stories Ser.). (J). (978-1-893993-01-3(9)) Medias & Co., Inc.

Lee, Evelyn. Mountain Mists: A Story of the Virungas. Kratter, Paul, illus. 1999. (Habitat Ser.: No. 14). 36p. (J). (gr. 1-4). 26.95 (978-1-56899-789-6(2)); (ps-3). 15.95 (978-1-56899-785-8(X)); (ps-3). pap. 5.95 (978-1-56899-786-5(8)) Soundprints.

—Mountain Mists: A Story of the Virungas. 1999. (gr. k-3). lib. bdg. 15.25 (978-0-613-56927-9(X)) Tandem Library Bks.

Lee, Julia Elizabeth. Seahorses Down Under. Weiser, Robert, ed. (Defenders of Wildlife Ser.). (Illus.). 50+p. (J). (gr. k-3). lib. bdg. 9.95 (978-0-9666857-0-1(9)) Dawn of Day Childrens Publishing Co., Inc.

Lewis, Preston. Blanca Is My Name: Or, How I Saved the Buffalo on the Texas Plains. Eckhardt, Jason C., illus. 2002. (Animal Legends Ser.: Vol. 2). 188p. 15.95 (978-1-57168-699-2(1)); 9.95 (978-1-57168-700-5(9)) Eakin Pr.

Littleton, Mark. Tracks in the Sand. 2001. (Ally OConnor Adventures Ser.: Vol. 1). 128p. (J). (gr. 4-7). pap. 5.99 (978-0-8010-4490-8(1)) Baker Bks.

Marshall, Felicity. Sage's Ark. 2000. 32p. (J). (Illus.). pap. 12.95 (978-1-86368-253-4(8)); 21.95 (978-1-86368-290-9(2)) Fremantle Pr. AUS. *Dist:* International Specialized Bk. Services.

Martin, Bill. Panda Bear, Panda Bear, What Do You See? Carle, Eric, illus. 2007. 32p. (J). 22.95 (***978-0-8050-8102-2(X)*** , Holt, Henry & Co. Bks. For Young Readers) Holt, Henry & Co.

—Panda Bear, Panda Bear, What Do You See? Carlen, Eric, illus. 2006. 28p. (J). bds. 7.95 (978-0-8050-8078-0(3) , Holt, Henry & Co. Bks. For Young Readers) Holt, Henry & Co.

Mesta, Robert I. Condor: Spirit of the Canyon. Ormsby, Lawrence, illus. 2007. (J). (***978-0-938216-85-8(6)***) Grand Canyon Assn.

Montero, Mayra. In the Palm of Darkness: A Novel. 1998. 192p. pap. 13.95 (978-0-06-092906-0(5)) HarperCollins Pubs.

Nelson, Rosemary. Hubcaps & Puppies. 2004. 172p. (J). pap. 7.95 (978-0-929141-98-5(9)) Napoleon Publishing/ Rendezvous Pr. CAN. *Dist:* AtlasBooks Distribution.

—Hubcaps & Puppies. 2002. (gr. 3-6). lib. bdg. 16.40 (978-0-613-62519-7(6)) Tandem Library Bks.

Osborne, Mary Pope. Tigers at Twilight, Vol. 19. unabr. ed. 2004. (Magic Tree House Ser. : No. 19). 72p. (J). (gr. k-3). pap. 17.00 incl. audio (978-0-8072-0928-8(7) , S FTR 251 SP, Listening Library) Random Hse. Audio Publishing Group.

—Tigers at Twilight. Murdocca, Sal, illus. 1999. (Magic Tree House Ser.: No. 19). 96p. (J). (gr. k-3). lib. bdg. 11.99 (978-0-679-99065-9(8)); mass mkt. 3.99 (978-0-679-89065-2(3)) Random Hse. Children's Bks. (Random Hse. Bks. for Young Readers).

—Tigers at Twilight. 1999. (Magic Tree House Ser. : No. 19). (J). (gr. k-3). (Illus.). 71p. lib. bdg. 10.79 (978-0-606-16957-8(1)); lib. bdg. 11.80 (978-0-613-16224-1(2)) Tandem Library Bks.

Reiche, Dietlof. Freddy to the Rescue. Cepeda, Joe, illus. 2006. (Golden Hamster Saga Ser.: Bk. 3). 240p. (J). pap. 4.99 (978-0-439-53158-0(6) , Scholastic Paperbacks) Scholastic, Inc.

—Freddy to the Rescue. Brownjohn, John, tr. from GER. Cepeda, Joe, illus. 2005. (Golden Hamster Saga: Bk. 3). 240p. (J). pap. 16.95 (978-0-439-53157-3(8)) Scholastic, Inc.

Skurzynski, Gloria. Over the Edge. 2002. (gr. 3-6). lib. bdg. 14.10 (978-0-613-62819-8(5)) Tandem Library Bks.

Skurzynski, Gloria & Ferguson, Alane. Over the Edge. 2002. (Mysteries in Our National Parks Ser.: Vol. 7). 160p. (J). (gr. 3-7). pap. 5.95 (978-0-7922-6686-0(2)); Vol. 7. 15.95 (978-0-7922-6677-8(3)) National Geographic Society. (National Geographic Children's Bks.).

Sleator, William. The Beasties, Vol. 1. 1999. (Illus.). 208p. (J). (gr. 3-7). pap. 6.99 (978-0-14-130639-1(4) , Puffin) Penguin Group (USA) Inc.

—The Beasties. 1999. (J). 12.64 (978-0-606-17410-7(9)) Tandem Library Bks.

Smith, Dale. What the Orangutan Told Alice: A Rain Forest Adventure. Smith, Dale & Russon, Anne E., photos by. 2003. (Illus.). 192p. (gr. 6-12). pap. 15.95 (978-0-9651452-8-2(X)) Deer Creek Publishing.

Smith, Roland. The Last Lobo. 2001. 192p. (gr. 5-17). pap. 5.99 (978-0-7868-1564-7(7)) Hyperion Bks. for Children.

Storm, Hannah, frwd. Buddy Booby's Birthmark. 2006. (Illus.). 36p. (J). 15.99 (***978-0-9794413-0-1(7));*** per. 8.99 (***978-0-9794413-1-8(5)***) E & D Bks., Ltd.

Talbott, Hudson. Safari Journal. 2003. (Illus.). 64p. (J). 18.00 (978-0-15-216393-8(X)) Harcourt Children's Bks.

Van Draanen, Wendelin. Sammy Keyes & the Wild Things. 2007. (Sammy Keyes Ser.: Bk. 11). 304p. (J). (gr. 5-8). 15.99 (978-0-375-83525-4(3) , Knopf Bks. for Young Readers) Random Hse. Children's Bks.

—Sammy Keyes & the Wild Things. Biggs, Brian, illus. 2007. (Sammy Keyes Ser.: Bk. 11). 304p. (J). (gr. 5-8). lib. bdg. 18.99 (978-0-375-93525-1(8) , Knopf Bks. for Young Readers) Random Hse. Children's Bks.

Wall, Suzy. The Dodo's Last Stand. 2005. 40.00 (***978-1-4108-4221-3(5)***) Benchmark Education Co.

Warner, Gertrude Chandler. The Poison Frog Mystery. 2000. (Boxcar Children Ser.: No. 74). (J). (gr. 2-5). (978-0-606-18767-1(7)) Tandem Library Bks.

—Poison Frog Mystery. 2000. (gr. 3-6). lib. bdg. 11.80 (978-0-613-22192-4(3)) Tandem Library Bks.

Warner, Gertrude Chandler, creator. The Poison Frog Mystery, Vol. 74. 2004. (Boxcar Children Ser.: No. 74). (Illus.). 128p. (J). (gr. 2-5). pap. 3.95 (978-0-8075-6587-2(3)) Whitman, Albert & Co.

Williams, Dar. Lights, Camera, Amalee. 2006. (Amalee Ser.: No. 2). 192p. (J). pap. 16.99 (978-0-439-80352-6(7) , Scholastic Pr.) Scholastic, Inc.

ENDURANCE, PHYSICAL

see Physical Fitness

ENERGY

see Force and Energy

ENFORCEMENT OF LAW

see Law Enforcement

ENGINEERING

see also specific forms of engineering, e.g. Chemical Engineering

Adams, Richard C. & Goodwin, Peter. Engineering Projects for Young Scientists. rev. ed. (Projects for Young Scientists Ser.). 128p. 2002. (J). pap. (978-0-531-16145-6(5)); 2001. (Illus.) (YA). (gr. 9 12). 23.50 (978-0-531-11668-5(9)) Scholastic Library Publishing. (Watts, Franklin).

Allison, Carol. Made by Humans: Astonishing Achievements. 2007. (Shockwave: Arts & Culture Ser.). (Illus.). 36p. (J). (gr. 4-6). lib. bdg. 25.00 (***978-0-531-17789-1(0)*** , Children's Pr.) Scholastic Library Publishing.

Allman, Toney. From Penguin Wings to Boat Flippers. 2005. (Imitating Nature Ser.). (Illus.). 32p. (J). (gr. 4-8). lib. bdg. 24.95 (978-0-7377-3386-0(1) , Greenhaven Pr., Inc.) Thomson Gale.

Ford, Carin T. Henry Ford: The Car Man. 2003. (Famous Inventors Ser.). (Illus.). 32p. (J). (gr. 1-4). lib. bdg. 22.60 (978-0-7660-2179-2(3)) Enslow Pubs., Inc.

Gareth Stevens Publishing Staff, contrib. by. Structures. 2003. (Discovery Channel School Science Ser.). (Illus.). 32p. (J). (gr. 5 up). lib. bdg. 24.67 (978-0-8368-3364-5(3)) Stevens, Gareth Inc.

Goeken, Brook. My Mom's an Engineer. 2004. (Illus.). 32p. 9.99 (978-1-881018-93-3(8)) Great Lakes Press, Inc.

Gonzales, Doreen. Seven Wonders of the Modern World: A MyReportLinks. com Book. 2005. (Seven Wonders of the World Ser.). (Illus.). 48p. (J). lib. bdg. 25.26 (978-0-7660-5292-5(3) , MyReportLinks.com Bks.) Enslow Pubs., Inc.

Haslam, Andrew, et al. Building. (Make It Work! Ser.). (Illus.). 48p. (J). pap. 15.95 (978-0-590-24332-2(2)) Scholastic, Inc.

Kenah, Katharine. Amazing Creations: Level 2. 2006. (Extreme Readers Ser.). (Illus.). 32p. (J). (gr. k-1). pap. 3.95 (978-0-7696-4336-6(1)) School Specialty Publishing.

Macaulay, David. Building Big. 2004. (Illus.). 192p. (YA). (gr. 5 up). reprint ed. pap. 12.95 (978-0-618-46527-9(8) , Walter Lorraine) Houghton Mifflin Co. Trade & Reference Div.

—Building Big, 5 cass.; set. 2004. (Building Big Ser.). (gr. 4 up). pap., act. bk. ed. 69.95 incl. VHS (978-1-57807-544-7(0) , WG965) WGBH Boston Video.

Maddox, Dianne. Nanotechnology. 2005. (Science on the Edge Ser.). (Illus.). 47p. (J). (ps-7). lib. bdg. 24.95 (978-1-4103-0530-5(9) , Blackbirch Pr., Inc.) Thomson Gale.

Parker, Janice. The Science of Structures. 2001. (Living Science Ser.) (Illus.). 32p. (J). (gr. 2 up). lib. bdg. 24.67 (978-0-8368-2792-7(9)) Stevens, Gareth Inc.

—The Science of Structures. 2003. (Living Science Ser.). (Illus.). 32p. (J). (gr. 1-3). pap. 7.95 (978-1-930954-26-7(3)) Weigl Pubs., Inc.

Pascoe, Elaine, ed. Thinking Big: America's Greatest Constructions. 2003. (Super Structures of the World Ser.). (Illus.). 48p. (J). 24.95 (978-1-56711-870-4(4)); 11.20 (978-1-4103-0193-2(1)) Thomson Gale. (Blackbirch Pr., Inc.).

Popular Mechanics Press Editors, ed. Make Cool Gadgets for Your Room. 2nd ed. 2001. (Popular Mechanics for Kids Ser.). (Illus.). 64p. (J). 16.95 (978-0-688-17798-0(0)) HarperCollins Pubs.

Royston, Angela. Bendy & Rigid. 2003. (My World of Science Ser.). (Illus.). 32p. (J). (gr. k-2). (J). lib. bdg. 22.79 (978-1-4034-0858-7(0)); pap. 6.50 (978-1-4034-3171-4(X)) Heinemann Library.

Sally Ride Science Editors, Sally Ride Science. What Do You Want to Be? Explore Engineering. 2005. (J). 6.00 (978-0-9753920-6-5(9)) Sally Ride Science.

Schaefer, Lola M. Push & Pull. Saunders-Smith, Gail, ed. 1999. (Way Things Move Ser.). (Illus.). 24p. (J). (gr. k-1). lib. bdg. 15.93 (978-0-7368-0396-0(3) , Pebble Bks.) Capstone Pr., Inc.

—Push & Pull. 1999. pap. 13.25 (978-0-516-21923-5(5) , Children's Pr.) Scholastic Library Publishing.

VanCleave, Janice Pratt. Engineering for Every Kid: Easy Activities That Make Learning Science Fun. 2007. (Science for Every Kid Ser.). 224p. pap. 14.95 (978-0-471-47182-0(8) , Jossey-Bass) Wiley, John & Sons, Inc.

Wilkinson, Philip & Dorling Kindersley Publishing Staff. Building. 2000. (Eyewitness Bks.). (Illus.). 64p. (J). (gr. 4-7). lib. bdg. 19.99 (978-0-7894-6607-5(4)) Dorling Kindersley Publishing, Inc.

Wright, Susan. Engineering Science Experiment Log. Aycock, Daniel & Ward, Sam, illus. 2001. (Mad Science Ser.). 48p. (J). (978-0-439-23584-6(7)) Scholastic, Inc.

Yes Mag Editors. Fantastic Feats & Failures. Kurisu, Jane, illus. 2005. 52p. (YA). (gr. 3-7). (978-1-55337-634-7(X)); (978-1-55337-633-0(1)) Kids Can Pr., Ltd.

ENGINEERING—HISTORY

Cannarella, Deborah & Fournier, Jane. Engineering. 1999. (Into the Next Millennium Ser.). (Illus.). 32p. (J). (gr. 4-8). lib. bdg. 27.93 (978-1-57103-272-0(X)) Rourke Publishing, LLC.

ENGINEERING—VOCATIONAL GUIDANCE

Brezina, Corona. Careers in Nanotechnology. 2006. (Cutting Edge Careers Ser.). (Illus.). 64p. (J). (gr. 7-12). lib. bdg. 27.95 (978-1-4042-0955-8(7)) Rosen Publishing Group, Inc., The.

Ferguson. Careers in Focus: Engineering. 3rd rev. ed. 2007. (Careers in Focus Ser.). 208p. (J). (gr. 6-12). 29.95 (***978-0-8160-6571-4(3)*** , Ferguson Publishing Co.) Facts On File, Inc.

—Engineering. 2nd rev. ed. 2007. (What Can I Do Now Ser.). 224p. (J). (gr. 6-12). 29.95 (***978-0-8160-6026-9(6)*** , Ferguson Publishing Co.) Facts On File, Inc.

Forbes, Charlotte. Those Amazing Engineers. Pillion, Dean, illus. 2nd ed. 2005. (Those Amazing... Ser.). 32p. (J). pap. (978-0-9772799-0-6(1)) Trilogy Pubns. LLC.

Hutson, Matt. Totally Amazing Careers in Engineering. 2006. (J). 7.80 (978-1-933798-04-2(1)) Sally Ride Science.

J. G. Ferguson Publishing Company Staff, ed. Careers in Focus: Engineering. (Careers in Focus Ser.). (YA). 1999. 488p. (gr. 7 up). pap. 22.95 (978-0-89434-282-0(7) , F702); 2nd ed. 2002. 192p. (gr. 6-12). 22.95 (978-0-89434-473-2(0)) Facts On File, Inc. (Ferguson Publishing Co.).

Pasternak, Ceel & Thornburg, Linda. Cool Careers for Girls in Engineering. 1999. (Cool Careers for Girls Ser.). (Illus.). 134p. (YA). (gr. 5-8). 19.95 (978-1-57023-126-1(5)) Impact Pubns.

Slade, Suzanne. Cycles in Nature, 6 bks., Set. Incl. Carbon Cycle. lib. bdg. 21.25 (978-1-4042-3490-1(X) , PowerKids Pr.); Four Seasons. lib. bdg. 21.25 (978-1-4042-3489-5(6)); Nitrogen Cycle. lib. bdg. 21.25 (978-1-4042-3491-8(8) , PowerKids Pr.); Phases of the Moon. lib. bdg. 21.25 (978-1-4042-3488-8(8) , PowerKids Pr.); Rock Cycle. lib. bdg. 21.25 (978-1-4042-3493-2(4) , PowerKids Pr.); Water on the Move. lib. bdg. 21.25 (978-1-4042-3492-5(6) , PowerKids Pr.); (Illus.). 24p. (J). (gr. 4-6). 2007. 2007. Set lib. bdg. 127.50 (978-1-4042-3506-9(X) , PowerKids Pr.) Rosen Publishing Group, Inc., The.

ENGINEERING DRAWING

see Mechanical Drawing

ENGINEERING MATERIALS

see Materials

ENGINEERS

African-American Engineers. 2000. (My Ancestors—My Heroes Ser.: Vol. 15). (J). (gr. 3-4). (978-1-893091-14-6(7)) Parker Publishing Co.

Aldrich, Lisa J. Nikola Tesla & the Taming of Electricity. 2005. (Profiles in Science Ser.). (Illus.). 160p. (J). (ps-7). lib. bdg. 26.95 (978-1-931798-46-4(X)) Reynolds, Morgan Inc.

Bankston, John. Karl Benz & the Single Cylinder Engine. 2004. (Uncharted, Unexplored, & Unexplained Ser.). (Illus.). 48p. (J). (gr. 4-8). lib. bdg. 29.95 (978-1-58415-244-6(3)) Mitchell Lane Pubs., Inc.

Binns, Tristan Boyer. Alfred Nobel. 2004. (Great Life Stories Ser.). (Illus.). 111p. (J). 30.50 (978-0-531-12328-7(6) , Watts, Franklin) Scholastic Library Publishing.

Boothroyd, Jennifer. Robert Fulton: A Life of Innovation. 2007. (Pull Ahead Books-Biographies Ser.). (J). 22.60 (978-0-8225-6458-4(0) , Lerner Pubns.) Lerner Publishing Group.

Brackett, Virginia. Steve Jobs: Computer Genius of Apple. 2003. (Internet Biographies Ser.). (Illus.). 48p. (J). (gr. 4-10). lib. bdg. 23.93 (978-0-7660-1970-6(5)) Enslow Pubs., Inc.

Delano, Marfe Ferguson. Inventing the Future: A Photobiography of Thomas Alva Edison. 2006. 64p. (J). (gr. 5). pap. 7.95 (978-0-7922-5934-3(3) , National Geographic Children's Bks.) National Geographic Society.

Duffield, Katy. Ken Kutaragi: Playstation Developer. 2007. (Innovators Ser.). (Illus.). 64p. (J). (gr. 4-8). 24.95 (***978-0-7377-3862-9(6)*** , Kidhaven) Thomson Gale.

Gaines, Ann Graham. Tim Berners-Lee & the Development of the World Wide Web. 2002. (Unlocking the Secrets of Science Ser.). (Illus.). 56p. (gr. 4-10). lib. bdg. 25.70 (978-1-58415-096-1(3)) Mitchell Lane Pubs., Inc.

Gillis, Jennifer Blizin. Robert Fulton. 2004. (Illus.). 32p. (J). pap. 6.50 (978-1-4034-5336-5(5)); lib. bdg. 22.79 (978-1-4034-5328-0(4)) Heinemann Library.

Gravenhorst, Edna Campos. Ay, Mijo! Why Do You Want to Be an Engineer? 2007. 155p. (***978-0-9745346-3-3(3)***) Big River Distribution.

Hirschmann, Kris. Burt Rutan: Aircraft Designer. 2006. 64p. (J). (gr. 4-8). 27.45 (978-0-7377-3450-8(7) , Kidhaven) Thomson Gale.

Johns, Linda. A Rocket Boy Grows Up. 2005. (Illus.). 16p. (J). (***978-0-7367-2904-8(6)***) Zaner-Bloser, Inc.

Johnston, Marianne. Casey Jones. 2001. (American Legends Ser.). (Illus.). 24p. (J). (gr. 3). lib. bdg. 18.75 (978-0-8239-5582-4(6) , PowerKids Pr.) Rosen Publishing Group, Inc., The.

Kahn, Jetty. Women in Engineering Careers. 1998. (Short Biographies Ser.). (Illus.). 48p. (J). (gr. 3-4). lib. bdg. 22.60 (978-0-7368-0013-6(1) , Bridgestone Bks.) Capstone Pr., Inc.

Krensky, Stephen. Casey Jones. Schroder, Mark, illus. 2007. (On My Own Folklore Ser.). 48p. (J). (gr. 2-5). lib. bdg. 25.26 (978-1-57505-890-0(1) , Millbrook Pr.) Lerner Publishing Group.

Krensky Stephen. Casey Jones. Schroder, Mark, illus. 2007. (On My Own Folklore Ser.). (J). pap. 6.95 (***978-0-8225-6476-8(9)*** , First Avenue Editions) Lerner Publishing Group.

Kulling, Monica. Eat My Dust! Henry Ford's First Race. Walz, Richard, illus. 2004. (Step into Reading Ser.). 48p. (gr. 1-3). (J). pap. 3.99 (978-0-375-81510-2(4)); (YA). lib. bdg. 11.99 (978-0-375-91510-9(9)) Random Hse. Children's Bks. (Random Hse. Bks. for Young Readers).

Lemke, Donald B. Steve Jobs, Steve Wozniak & the Personal Computer. 2007. (Illus.). 32p. (J). (***978-0-7368-9650-4(3)***) Capstone Pr., Inc.

Manatt, Kathleen. Robot Scientist. 2008. (J). pap. 7.95 (***978-1-60279-083-4(3)***) Cherry Lake Publishing.

Manatt, Kathleen G. Robot Scientist. 2008. (J). lib. bdg. 25.26 (***978-1-60279-051-3(5)***) Cherry Lake Publishing.

Mara, Wil. Thomas Alva Edison. 2004. (Rookie Biographies Ser.). (Illus.). 31p. (J). 20.50 (978-0-516-21843-4(3) , Children's Pr.) Scholastic Library Publishing.

Mortensen, Lori. Thomas Edison: Inventor, Scientist, & Genius. Thompson, Jeffrey, illus. 2006. (Biographies Ser.). 24p. (J). (gr. k-3). lib. bdg. 23.93 (978-1-4048-3105-6(3)) Picture Window Bks.

Murphy, Patricia J. Grace Hopper: Computer Pioneer. 2004 (Famous Inventors Ser.). (Illus.). 32p. (J). lib. bdg. 22.60 (978-0-7660-2273-7(0)) Enslow Pubs., Inc.

Oleksy, Walter. Hispanic-American Scientists. 1998. (American Profiles Ser.). (Illus.). 160p. (YA). (gr. 5-12). 25.00 (978-0-8160-3704-9(3)) Facts On File, Inc.

O'Shei, Tim. Philo T. Farnsworth: Visionary Inventor of Television. 2008. (Inventors Who Changed the World Ser.). 128p. (J). (gr. 6 up). lib. bdg. 33.27 (***978-1-59845-075-0(1)*** , MyReportLinks.com Bks.) Enslow Pubs., Inc.

Pederson, Charles E. Thomas Edison. 2007. (Essential Lives Ser.). (ENG., Illus.). 112p. (YA). (gr. 8-12). lib. bdg. 32.79 (***978-1-59928-845-1(1)*** , Essential Library) ABDO Publishing Co.

Raatma, Lucia. Thomas Edison. 2004. (Compass Point Early Biographies Ser.). (Illus.). 32p. (J). (gr. 2 up). lib. bdg. 21.26 (978-0-7565-0567-7(4)) Compass Point Bks.

Rausch, Monica. Henry Ford & the Model T Car. 2006. (Illus.). 24p. (J). pap. (***978-0-8368-7731-1(4));*** lib. bdg. (***978-0-8368-7500-3(1)***) Stevens, Gareth Inc. (Weekly Reader Early Learning Library).

—Henry Ford y el Modelo T. 2006. (ENG & SPA.). (J). pap. (***978-0-8368-8000-7(5));*** lib. bdg. (***978-0-8368-7995-7(3)***) Stevens, Gareth Inc. (Weekly Reader Early Learning Library).

Richie, Jason. Space Flight: Crossing the Last Frontier. 2001. (Innovators Ser.: Vol. 10). (Illus.). 144p. (gr. 5 up). lib. bdg. 21.95 (978-1-881508-77-9(3)) Oliver Pr., Inc.

Rooney, Thomas L. Tobey Boland & the Blackstone Canal. Donovan, Patte, illus. 2005. 30p. (J). (978-1-929039-30-2(1)) Ambassador Bks., Inc.

Rose, Drew, illus. Casey Jones. 2004. (Imagination Ser.). 32p. (J). (gr. 3 up). 22.60 (978-0-7565-0602-5(6)) Compass Point Bks.

EFG

Sherman, Josepha. Jerry Yang & David Filo: Chief Yahoos of Yahoo! 2001. (Techies Ser.: up). (Illus.). 80p. (J). (gr. 5 up). lib. bdg. 23.90 (978-0-7613-1961-0(1) , Twenty-First Century Bks.) Lerner Publishing Group.

Sneed, Dani. Ferris Wheel! George Ferris & His Amazing Invention. 2008. (Genius at Work! Great Inventor Biographies Ser.). (Illus.). 32p. (J). (gr. 3-4). lib. bdg. 22.60 (*978-0-7660-2834-0(8) , Enslow Elementary) Enslow Pubs., Inc.

Sullivan, George E. Thomas Edison. 2002. (In Their Own Words Ser.). (Illus.). 128p. (J). (gr. 3-5). 4.99 (978-0-439-26319-1(0) , Scholastic Reference) Scholastic, Inc.

Tracy, Kathleen. Marc Andreessen & the Development of the Web Browser. 2002. (Unlocking the Secrets of Science Ser.). (Illus.). 56p. (gr. 4-10). lib. bdg. 25.70 (978-1-58415-092-3(0)) Mitchell Lane Pubs., Inc.

—William Hewlett: Pioneer of the Computer Age. 2002. (Unlocking the Secrets of Science Ser.). (J). (978-1-58415-178-4(1)); (Illus.). 56p. (gr. 4-10). lib. bdg. 25.70 (978-1-58415-142-5(0)) Mitchell Lane Pubs., Inc.

Whiting, Jim. James Watt & the Steam Engine. 2005. (Uncharted, Unexplored, & Unexplained Ser.). (Illus.). 48p. (J). (gr. 4-8). lib. bdg. 29.95 (978-1-58415-371-9(7)) Mitchell Lane Pubs., Inc.

Woodside, Martin. Sterling Biographies: Thomas Edison: The Man Who Lit up the World. 2007. (Sterling Biographies Ser.). (Illus.). 128p. (J). pap. 5.95 (*978-1-4027-3229-4(5)) Sterling Publishing Co., Inc.

Wyckoff, Edwin Brit. Laser Man: Theodore H. Maiman & His Brilliant Invention. 2007. (Genius at Work! Great Inventor Biographies Ser.). (Illus.). 32p. (J). (gr. 3-4). lib. bdg. 22.60 (*978-0-7660-2848-7(8) , Enslow Elementary) Enslow Pubs., Inc.

—The Teen Who Invented Television: Philo T. Farnsworth & His Awesome Invention. 2007. (Genius at Work! Great Inventor Biographies Ser.). (Illus.). 32p. (J). (gr. 3-4). lib. bdg. 22.60 (*978-0-7660-2845-6(3) , Enslow Elementary) Enslow Pubs., Inc.

Zannos, Susan. Edward Roberts & the Story of the Personal Computer. l.t. ed. 2002. (Unlocking the Secrets of Science Ser.). (Illus.). 56p. (gr. 4-10). lib. bdg. 25.70 (978-1-58415-118-0(8)) Mitchell Lane Pubs., Inc.

—Godfrey Hounsfield & the Invention of CAT Scans. 2002. (Unlocking the Secrets of Science Ser.). (Illus.). 56p. (gr. 4-10). lib. bdg. 17.95 (978-1-58415-119-7(6)) Mitchell Lane Pubs., Inc.

Zaunders, Bo. The Great Bridge-Building Contest. Munro, Roxie, illus. 2004. 32p. (J). (gr. k-4). 16.95 (978-0-8109-4929-4(6)) Abrams, Harry N. , Inc.

Zuehlke, Jeffrey. Henry Ford. 2007. (History Maker Bios Ser.). (J). 26.60 (978-0-8225-6583-3(8) , Lerner Pubns.) Lerner Publishing Group.

E F G

ENGINEERS—VOCATIONAL GUIDANCE

Maze, Stephanie. I Want to Be an Engineer. 1999. (I Want to Be Ser.). (Illus.). 48p. (YA). (gr. 4-9). lib. bdg. 18.98 (978-0-8172-4160-5(4)) Raintree.

—I Want to Be an Engineer. 1999. (Illus.). (J). 15.80 (978-0-606-18178-5(4)) Tandem Library Bks.

Pasternak, Ceel & Thornburg, Linda. Cool Careers for Girls in Engineering. 1999. (Cool Careers for Girls Ser.). (Illus.). 134p. (YA). (gr. 5-8). 19.95 (978-1-57023-126-1(5)) Impact Pubns.

ENGINES

see also Automobiles—Engines; Fire Engines; Fuel; Steam-Engines

Sundance, ed. What Has an Engine? 2000. (ps-2). lib. bdg. 11.65 (978-0-613-37636-5(6)) Tandem Library Bks.

ENGLAND

Allport, Alan. England. 2002. (Modern World Nations Ser.). (Illus.). 150p. (gr. 6-12). 30.00 (978-0-7910-7209-7(6) , Chelsea Hse.) Facts On File, Inc.

Augustin, Byron & Augustin, Rebecca. England. 40p. (J). 2006. (gr. 2-4). pap. 6.95 (978-0-516-24952-0(5)); 2005. (Illus.). (ps-ps). 24.50 (978-0-516-23653-7(9)) Scholastic Library Publishing. (Children's Pr.).

Banting, Erinn. England — The Land. 2004. (Lands, Peoples, & Cultures Ser.). (Illus.). 32p. (J). (978-0-7787-9321-2(4)); pap. (978-0-7787-9689-3(2)) Crabtree Publishing Co.

Blashfield, Jean F. England. rev. ed. 2006. (Enchantment of the World, Second Ser.). (Illus.). 144p. (J). 36.00 (978-0-516-24869-1(3) , Children's Pr.) Scholastic Library Publishing.

Boraas, Tracey. England. 2002. (Countries & Cultures Ser.). (Illus.). 64p. (J). (gr. 4). lib. bdg. 23.93 (978-0-7368-0937-5(6) , Bridgestone Bks.) Capstone Pr., Inc.

Britton, Tamara L. England. 2001. (Countries Ser.). (Illus.). 40p. (J). (gr. k-6). lib. bdg. 22.78 (978-1-57765-499-5(4) , Checkerboard Library) ABDO Publishing Co.

Burgan, Michael. England. 1999. (True Bks.). (Illus.). 48p. (J). (gr. 3-5). pap. 6.95 (978-0-516-26492-9(3) , Children's Pr.) Scholastic Library Publishing.

Dahl, Michael. England: A Question & Answer Book. 2004. (Fact Finders Ser.). (Illus.). 32p. (J). (gr. 3-4). lib. bdg. 22.60 (978-0-7368-2477-4(4)) Capstone Pr., Inc.

Daly-Weir, Catherine. Knights. Crosby, Jeff, illus. 1998. (All Aboard Reading Ser.). 48p. (J). (gr. 1-3). pap. 3.99 (978-0-448-41857-5(6) , Grosset & Dunlap) Penguin Group (USA) Inc.

Deady, Kathleen W. England. 2000. (Countries of the World Ser.). (Illus.). 126p. (J). (gr. 2-3). 18.60 (978-0-7368-0627-5(X) , Bridgestone Bks.) Capstone Pr., Inc.

Faiella, Graham. England: A Primary Source Cultural Guide. 2005. (Primary Sources of World Cultures Ser.). (Illus.). 128p. (J). (gr. 4-8). lib. bdg. 34.60 (978-1-4042-2911-2(6)) Rosen Publishing Group, Inc., The.

Ganeri, Anita & Oxlade, Chris. A Visit to England. 2003. (Visit to Ser.). (Illus.). 32p. (J). lib. bdg. 22.79 (978-1-4034-0965-2(X)) Heinemann Library.

Mass, Wendy. Stonehenge. 1998. (Building History Ser.). (Illus.). 96p. (YA). (gr. 6-9). 27.45 (978-1-56006-432-9(3) , Lucent Bks.) Thomson Gale.

Olson, Kay Melchisedech. England. 2003. (Many Cultures, One World Ser.). (Illus.). 32p. (J). (gr. 2-3). lib. bdg. 23.93 (978-0-7368-1532-1(5) , Bridgestone Bks.) Capstone Pr., Inc.

Ruth, Angie. My Adventure in England. 2007. 44p. (J). 8.99 (978-1-59092-427-3(4) , Orchard Academy Pr.) Windstorm Creative.

Schemenauer, Elma. Welcome to England. 2008. (Welcome to the World Ser.). 32p. (J). (gr. 1-5). 27.07 (*978-1-59296-970-8(4)) Child's World, Inc.

Sevier, Marti & Lister, Maree. England. 1998. (Countries of the World Ser.). (Illus.). 96p. (J). (gr. 6 up). lib. bdg. 30.00 (978-0-8368-2125-3(4)) Stevens, Gareth Inc.

Stone, Lynn M. Yorkshire Terriers. 2005. (Eye to Eye with Dogs Ser.). (Illus.). 24p. (gr. 2-5). 17.95 (978-1-59515-163-6(X)) Rourke Publishing, LLC.

Wingfield, George & Allport, Alan. England. 2nd rev. ed. 2007. (Modern World Nations Ser.). 128p. (gr. 6-12). 30.00 (*978-0-7910-9514-0(2) , Chelsea Hse.) Facts On File, Inc.

ENGLAND—FICTION

Abela, Deborah. Mission: Spy Force Revealed. O'Connor, George, illus. 2005. (Spy Force Ser.). 288p. (J). (gr. 4-7). 9.95 (978-0-689-87358-4(1) , Simon & Schuster Children's Publishing) Simon & Schuster Children's Publishing.

Aber, Linda Williams. The Clue in the Castle Wall. 2004. (Barbie Mystery Ser.: No. 6). 48p. (J). pap. 3.99 (978-0-439-55709-2(7) , Scholastic Paperbacks) Scholastic, Inc.

Adone, Claudio. My Grandfather Jack the Ripper. 2000. Tr. of Mio Nonno Jack Lo Squartatore. (Illus.). 304p. (J). (gr. 7-10). 19.00 (978-1-928746-16-4(0)) Herodias.

Ahlberg, Allan. My Brother's Ghost. l.t. ed. 2005. (Illus.). 64p. (J). pap. (978-0-7540-6181-6(7) , CLP 372) BBC Audio.

Aiken, Joan. The Cuckoo Tree. 2000. (Illus.). 304p. (J). (gr. 5-9). 16.00 (978-0-618-07024-4(9)); pap. 6.95 (978-0-618-07023-7(0)) Houghton Mifflin Co. Trade & Reference Div.

—Midnight Is a Place. 2002. (J). (gr. 5 up). reprint ed. 292p. 16.00 (978-0-618-19626-5(9)); 304p. pap. 5.95 (978-0-618-19625-8(0)) Houghton Mifflin Co. Trade & Reference Div.

—Midnight Is a Place. 2002. (gr. 5-8). lib. bdg. 14.10 (978-0-613-70768-8(0)) Tandem Library Bks.

—Midwinter Nightingale. 256p. (gr. 5). 2003. 15.95 (978-0-385-73081-5(0) , Delacorte Bks. for Young Readers); 2003. lib. bdg. 17.99 (978-0-385-90103-1(8) , Delacorte Bks. for Young Readers); 2005. reprint ed. 5.99 (978-0-440-41928-0(X) , Yearling) Random Hse. Children's Bks.

—The Witch of Clatteringshaws. 2005. 144p. (J). (gr. 5). lib. bdg. 17.99 (978-0-385-90252-6(2) , Delacorte Bks. for Young Readers) Random Hse. Children's Bks.

—The Witch of Clatteringshaws. 2006. 160p. (gr. 4-7). 5.99 (978-0-440-42037-8(7) , Yearling) Random Hse. Children's Bks.

Allen, M. E. Gotta Get Some Bish Bash Bosh. 2005. (Illus.). 208p. (J). 15.99 (978-0-06-073198-4(2) , HarperTeen); lib. bdg. 16.89 (978-0-06-073201-1(6)) HarperCollins Pubs.

Allison, Jennifer. Gilda Joyce: The Ghost Sonata. 2007. 288p. (J). (gr. 5-8). 15.99 (*978-0-525-47808-9(6) , Dutton Juvenile) Penguin Group (USA) Inc.

Almond, David. Kit's Wilderness. l.t. ed. 2000. 263p. (J). pap. 16.95 (978-0-7540-6115-1(9) , Galaxy Children's Large Print) BBC Audiobooks America.

—Kit's Wilderness. unabr. ed. 2004. 240p. (J). (gr. 7 up). pap. 36.00 incl. audio (978-0-8072-8216-8(2) , Listening Library) Random Hse. Audio Publishing Group.

—Kit's Wilderness. (YA). (gr. 7). 2001. (Illus.). 256p. mass mkt. 5.99 (978-0-440-41605-0(1) , Laurel Leaf); 2000. 240p. 15.95 (978-0-385-32665-0(3) , Delacorte Bks. for Young Readers) Random Hse. Children's Bks.

—Kit's Wilderness. 2001. 229p. (YA). (gr. 8-12). lib. bdg. 13.00 (978-0-613-36836-0(3)); (978-0-606-22406-2(8)) Tandem Library Bks.

—Kit's Wilderness. l.t. ed. 2001. (Illus.). 272p. (J). (gr. 4-7). 22.95 (978-0-7862-2772-3(9)) Thorndike Pr.

—My Dad's A Birdman. Dunbar, Polly, illus. 2008. (J). 15.99 (*978-0-7636-3667-8(3)) Candlewick Pr.

Almond, David. Skellig. 2001. (Illus.). 208p. (gr. 5). mass mkt. 6.50 (978-0-440-22908-7(1) , Laurel Leaf) Random Hse. Children's Bks.

—Skellig. Wojtyla, Karen, ed. 2000. (Illus.). 192p. (gr. 5-7). 6.50 (978-0-440-41602-9(7) , Yearling) Random Hse. Children's Bks.

—Skellig. 1999. 192p. (gr. 5 up). 16.95 (978-0-385-32653-7(X) , Delacorte Bks. for Young Readers) Random Hse. Children's Bks.

—Skellig. 2001. (gr. 5-8). lib. bdg. 14.15 (978-0-613-84565-6(X)); 2000. (J). (978-0-606-19192-0(5)); 2000. (gr. 5-8). lib. bdg. 13.00 (978-0-613-28330-4(9)) Tandem Library Bks.

Alton, Steve. The Firehills. 2005. 192p. (J). (gr. 7-13). 15.95 (978-1-57505-798-9(0) , Carolrhoda Bks.) Lerner Publishing Group.

—The Malifex. 2003. (Middle Readers Ser.). (Illus.). 182p. (J). (gr. 3-7). 14.95 (978-0-8225-0959-2(8)) Lerner Publishing Group.

Anderson, Julian. View Halloo. 2005. (ENG., Illus.). 48p. pap. (*978-1-84401-601-3(3)) Athena Pr.

Andrews, Julie. The Little Grey Men: A Story for the Young in Heart. Watkins-Pitchford, Denys, illus. 2004. 304p. (J). 17.89 (978-0-06-055449-1(5) , Julie Andrews Collection) HarperCollins Pubs.

Andrews, Julie & "BB". The Little Grey Men: A Story for the Young in Heart. Watkins-Pitchford, Denys, illus. ed. 2004. 304p. (J). 17.99 (978-0-06-055448-4(7) , Julie Andrews Collection) HarperCollins Pubs.

Anson-Weber, Joan. Snuffles Goes to Scotland Yard. Russell, Judith, illus. 2001. (J). 16.95 (978-0-87797-293-8(1)) Cherokee Publishing Co.

Arnold, Louise. Golden & Grey: An Unremarkable Boy & a Rather Remarkable Ghost. 2005. 272p. (J). 15.95 (978-0-689-87473-4(1) , McElderry, Margaret K.) Simon & Schuster Children's Publishing.

—Golden & Grey: (an Unremarkable Boy & a Rather Remarkable Ghost) l.t. ed. 2006. 317p. 22.95 (978-0-7862-8290-6(8)) Thorndike Pr.

—Golden & Grey: The Nightmares That Ghosts Have. 2006. 304p. (J). (gr. 3-7). 16.99 (978-0-689-87586-1(X) , McElderry, Margaret K.) Simon & Schuster Children's Publishing.

—Golden & Grey (an Unremarkable Boy & a Rather Remarkable Ghost) 2006. (Illus.). 272p. (J). reprint ed. pap. 5.99 (978-0-689-87585-4(1) , Aladdin) Simon & Schuster Children's Publishing.

Arnold, Louise. Golden & Grey: the Nightmares That Ghosts Have. 2007. 304p. (J). pap. 5.99 (*978-0-689-87587-8(8) , Aladdin) Simon & Schuster Children's Publishing.

Ashley, Bernard. Little Soldier: A Novel. 2002. (Illus.). 240p. (J). (gr. 9 up). pap. 16.95 (978-0-439-22424-6(1) , Scholastic Pr.) Scholastic, Inc.

Augarde, Steve. Celandine. 2008. 496p. (J). (gr. 5). 6.99 (*978-0-440-42216-7(7) , Yearling) Random Hse. Children's Bks.

Austen, Jane. Pride & Prejudice. 1999. (YA). 11.95 (978-1-56137-767-1(8)) Novel Units, Inc.

—Pride & Prejudice. 2002. (gr. 7-12). lib. bdg. 16.45 (978-0-613-64095-4(0)) Tandem Library Bks.

—Pride & Prejudice: Penguin Readers Level 5. 1998. (Illus.). 80p. pap. 7.00 (978-0-14-081507-8(4)) Penguin Group (USA) Inc.

Avi. The Book Without Words: A Fable of Medieval Magic. 2005. 208p. (gr. 5-9). 15.99 (978-0-7868-0829-8(2)) Hyperion Bks. for Children.

Awdry, Wilbert V. Down at the Docks. Courtney, Richard, illus. 2003. (Thomas & Friends Ser.). 24p. (J). (ps-2). pap. 3.25 (978-0-375-82592-7(4) , Random Hse. Bks. for Young Readers) Random Hse. Children's Bks.

Ballantyne, R. M. The Battle & the Breeze. 2004. reprint ed. pap. 15.95 (978-1-4191-5365-5(X)); pap. 1.99 (978-1-4192-5365-2(4)) Kessinger Publishing, LLC.

Ballou, Kathy. The Tracks Out Back. l.t. ed. 2005. (Illus.). 24p. (J). per. 10.00 (978-1-932338-50-8(0)) Lifevest Publishing, Inc.

Banks, Lynne Reid. Alice-by-Accident. 2000. (Avon Camelot Bks.). 144p. (J). (gr. 4-7). 14.95 (978-0-380-97865-6(2)) HarperCollins Pubs.

Barkan, Joanne. A Pup in King Arthur's Court. l.t. ed. 1999. (Adventures of Wishbone Ser.: No. 15). (Illus.). 164p. (J). (gr. 2-5). lib. bdg. 22.60 (978-0-8368-2593-0(4)) Stevens, Gareth Inc.

Barradel, Isabel. Toyshop Tales. 2006. 275p. pap. 21.95 (*978-1-4241-2798-6(X)) PublishAmerica, Inc.

Beardshaw, Rosalind. Grandpa's Surprise. 2004. (Illus.). 32p. (J). (ps-2). 15.95 (978-1-58234-934-3(7) , Bloomsbury Children) Bloomsbury Publishing.

Beere, Peter. At Gehenna's Door. l.t. ed. 2000. (Illus.). 304p. 18.99 (978-0-7089-9500-6(4)) Ulverscroft Large Print Bks. GBR. *Dist:* Ulverscroft Large Print Bks., Ltd.

Bell, Julia. Massive. 2005. (Illus.). 272p. (YA). (gr. 7 up). pap. 6.99 (978-1-4169-0207-2(4) , Simon Pulse) Simon & Schuster Children's Publishing.

Bemelmans, Ludwig. Madeline in London. Bemelmans, Ludwig, illus. 2002. (Madeline Ser.). (Illus.). (J). 14.04 (978-0-7587-5002-0(1)) Book Wholesalers, Inc.

—Madeline in London. Bemelmans, Ludwig, illus. deluxe ed. 2000. (Madeline Ser.). (Illus.). 64p. (J). (ps-3). pap. 7.99 (978-0-14-056649-9(X) , Viking Juvenile) Penguin Group (USA) Inc.

—Madeline in London. 2000. (gr. k-3). lib. bdg. 15.30 (978-0-8085-2353-6(8)) Tandem Library Bks.

—Madeline in London. Bemelmans, Ludwig, illus. 2000. (Madeline Ser.). (Illus.). (J). (ps-3). (978-0-606-18429-8(5)) Tandem Library Bks.

Berry, Liz. China Garden. 1999. (gr. 5-8). lib. bdg. 15.30 (978-0-613-22975-3(4)) Tandem Library Bks.

—The China Garden. 1999. (Illus.). 288p. (J). pap. 7.99 (978-0-380-73228-9(9)) HarperCollins Pubs.

Bingham, J. & Brontë, Emily. Wuthering Heights. 2004. (Paperback Classics Ser.). 144p. (J). pap. 4.95 (978-0-7945-0573-8(2)); lib. bdg. 12.95 (978-1-58086-604-0(2)) EDC Publishing.

Blacker, Terence. Parent Swap. 2006. 240p. (J). 16.00 (978-0-374-35752-8(8) , Farrar, Straus & Giroux (BYR)) Farrar, Straus & Giroux.

Blackmore, Richard D. Lorna Doone, Level 4. 2nd abr. ed. 2000. (Bookworms Ser.). (Illus.). 96p. pap. 6.50 (978-0-19-423038-4(4)) Oxford Univ. Pr., Inc.

Blyton, Enid. Mr Twiddle in Trouble Again. 2000. (Enid Blyton's Happy Days Ser.). (Illus.). 95p. (J). (ps-3). pap. 7.99 (978-0-7475-4355-8(0)) Bloomsbury Publishing Plc GBR. *Dist:* Trafalgar Square Publishing.

Bond, Michael. Paddington on Top. Fortnum, Peggy, illus. rev. ed. 2002. (Paddington Bear Ser.). 144p. (J). (gr. 4-6). pap. 4.95 (978-0-618-25072-1(7)) Houghton Mifflin Co. Trade & Reference Div.

—Paddington Treasury. Fortnum, Peggy & Nuttall-Smith, Caroline, illus. 1999. (Paddington Ser.). 384p. (J). (gr. 4-6). 29.95 (978-0-395-90507-4(9)) Houghton Mifflin Co. Trade & Reference Div.

Booth, Martin. Doctor Illuminatus. 2006. (Alchemist's Son Ser.: Pt. 1). 192p. (J). (gr. 4-9). pap. 6.99 (978-0-316-01285-0(8)) Little Brown & Co.

—Soul Stealer. 2006. (Alchemist's Son Ser.: Pt. 2). 256p. (J). (gr. 5-9). pap. 6.99 (978-0-316-05993-0(5)) Little Brown & Co.

Boston, Lucy M. Children of Green Knowe. 2002. (gr. 3-6). lib. bdg. 14.15 (978-0-613-54457-3(9)) Tandem Library Bks.

—The Children of Green Knowe. Boston, Peter, illus. 2002. (Green Knowe Ser.). 192p. (YA). reprint ed. (gr. 3 up). 17.00 (978-0-15-202462-8(X) , Harcourt Young Classics); (gr. 4-7). pap. 6.95 (978-0-15-202468-0(9) , Odyssey Classics) Harcourt Children's Bks.

—Enemy at Green Knowe. 2002. (gr. 3-6). lib. bdg. 14.15 (978-0-613-54436-8(6)) Tandem Library Bks.

—An Enemy at Green Knowe. Boston, Peter, illus. 2002. (Green Knowe Ser.). 192p. (YA). (gr. 4-7). reprint ed. pap. 6.00 (978-0-15-202481-9(6) , Odyssey Classics) Harcourt Children's Bks.

—River at Green Knowe. 2002. (gr. 3-6). lib. bdg. 14.15 (978-0-613-54444-3(7)) Tandem Library Bks.

—The River at Green Knowe. Boston, Peter, illus. 2002. (Green Knowe Ser.). 176p. (YA). (gr. 4-7). reprint ed. pap. 6.00 (978-0-15-202607-3(X) , Odyssey Classics) Harcourt Children's Bks.

—Stranger at Green Knowe. 2002. (gr. 3-6). lib. bdg. 14.15 (978-0-613-54691-1(1)) Tandem Library Bks.

—A Stranger at Green Knowe. Boston, Peter, illus. 2002. (Green Knowe Ser.). 208p. (YA). reprint ed. (gr. 3 up). 17.00 (978-0-15-202583-0(9) , Harcourt Young Classics); (gr. 4-7). pap. 6.95 (978-0-15-202589-2(8) , Odyssey Classics) Harcourt Children's Bks.

—Treasure of Green Knowe. 2002. (gr. 3-6). lib. bdg. 14.15 (978-0-613-54447-4(1)) Tandem Library Bks.

—The Treasure of Green Knowe. Boston, Peter, illus. 2002. (Green Knowe Ser.). 224p. (YA). (gr. 4-7). reprint ed. pap. 7.00 (978-0-15-202601-1(0) , Odyssey Classics) Harcourt Children's Bks.

Brassey, Richard. Great Britons. 2005. (Brilliant Brits Ser.). (Illus.). 24p. (J). pap. 8.99 (978-1-84255-235-3(X)) Orion Children's Bks. GBR. *Dist:* Independent Pubs. Group.

Bray, Libba. A Great & Terrible Beauty. (YA). (gr. 7). 2003. 416p. 16.95 (978-0-385-73028-0(4)); 2005. 432p. reprint ed. pap. 8.95 (978-0-385-73231-4(7)) Random Hse. Children's Bks. (Delacorte Bks. for Young Readers).

—A Great & Terrible Beauty. 2005. 403p. (YA). (gr. 8-12). per. 15.60 (978-0-606-33978-0(7)) Tandem Library Bks.

—A Great & Terrible Beauty. l.t. ed. 2005. 512p. (YA). (gr. 8-12). pap. 10.95 (978-0-7862-8082-7(4)); 2004. 507p. 23.95 (978-0-7862-6504-6(3) , Large Print Pr.) Thorndike Pr.

—Rebel Angels. 2006. 592p. (YA). (gr. 7). pap. 9.99 (978-0-385-73341-0(0) , Delacorte Bks. for Young Readers) Random Hse. Children's Bks.

—Rebel Angels. l.t. ed. 2006. (Thorndike Press Large Print the Literacy Bridge Ser.). 655p. (J). 23.95 (978-0-7862-8087-2(5)) Thorndike Pr.

Bray, Libba. The Sweet Far Thing. 2007. 448p. (YA). (gr. 7). 17.99 (*978-0-385-73030-3(6)); lib. bdg. 20.99 (*978-0-385-90295-3(6)) Random Hse. Children's Bks. (Delacorte Bks. for Young Readers).

Brazil, Angela. The Luckiest Girl in the School. 2006. pap. 13.99 (*978-1-4280-2027-6(6)) IndyPublish.com.

—Luckiest Girl in the School. 2006. 20.99 (*978-1-4280-2006-1(3)) IndyPublish.com.

Brennan, Herbie. Fairy Nuff: A Tale of Bluebell Ball. Collins, Ross, illus. 2002. 128p. (J). (gr. 2-4). 13.95 (978-1-58234-770-7(0) , Bloomsbury Children) Bloomsbury Publishing.

—Nuff Said: Another Tale of Bluebell Wood. Collins, Ross, illus. 2002. 128p. (J). (gr. 2-5). 13.95 (978-1-58234-771-4(9) , Bloomsbury Children) Bloomsbury Publishing.

Brewster, Hugh. Carnation, Lily, Lily, Rose: The Story of a Painting. Sargent, John Singer, illus. 2007. 48p. (J). (gr. 3-7). (*978-1-55453-137-0(3)) Kids Can Pr., Ltd.

Brontë, Charlotte. Jane Eyre. Harvey, Bob, illus. 2004. (Paperback Classics Ser.). 144p. (J). pap. 4.95 (978-0-7945-0658-2(5) , Usborne) EDC Publishing.

—Jane Eyre. 1999. (Saddleback Classics). (Illus.). (J). 13.75 (978-0-606-21557-2(3)) Tandem Library Bks.

—Jane Eyre. 2003. (Illus.). 48p. (978-0-7502-3668-3(X) , Hodder Wayland) Hodder Children's Division.

—Jane Eyre. 2004. (Fast Track Classics Ser.). (Illus.). 48p. (J). pap. 9.99 (978-0-237-52687-0(5) , Evans Brothers, Limited) Evans Publishing Group GBR. *Dist:* Independent Pubs. Group.

—Jane Eyre. Olimar, N., illus. 2nd ed. 1998. (Illustrated Classic Book Ser.). 61p. (J). (gr. 3 up). reprint ed. pap. 4.95 (978-1-56767-267-1(1)) Educational Insights, Inc.

—Jane Eyre. adapted ed. (YA). (gr. 5-12). pap. 8.50 (978-0-8359-0215-1(3)) Globe Fearon Educational Publishing.

—Jane Eyre. unabr. ed. 1998. (Wordsworth Classics Ser.). (YA). (gr. 6-12). 5.27 (978-0-89061-020-6(7) , R0207WW) Jamestown.

—Jane Eyre, Level 6. 2nd abr. ed. 2000. (Bookworms Ser.). (Illus.). 128p. 6.50 (978-0-19-423088-9(0)) Oxford Univ. Pr., Inc.

Brontë, Emily. Wuthering Heights. abr. ed. (Classics Illustrated Ser.). (Illus.). 52p. (YA). pap. 4.95 (978-1-57209-011-8(1)) Classics International Entertainment, Inc.

—Wuthering Heights: Abridged for Children. 1998. (Illus.). 48p. (YA). (gr. 4-7). pap. 6.95 (978-0-8114-6847-3(X)) Steck-Vaughn.

Brook, H. & Doyle, Arthur Conan. The Hound of the Baskervilles. 2004. (Paperback Classics Ser.). 144p. (J). lib. bdg. 12.95 (978-1-58086-605-7(0)) EDC Publishing.

Brooks, Kevin. Lucas. 2004. (Push Ser.). 384p. (YA). 6.99 (978-0-439-53063-7(6) , Scholastic Paperbacks) Scholastic, Inc.

—The Road of the Dead. (J). (gr. 7 up). 2007. 368p. pap. 7.99 (978-0-439-78624-9(X) , PUSH); 2006. 352p. pap. 16.99 (978-0-439-78623-2(1) , Chicken Hse., The) Scholastic, Inc.

Brooks, Kevin. Road of the Dead. rev. l.t. ed. 2007. 353p. (YA). 22.95 (***978-0-7862-9550-0(3)***) Thorndike Pr.

Burchill, Julie. Sugar Rush. 2005. 288p. (J). lib. bdg. 17.89 (978-0-06-077620-6(X) , HarperTeen) HarperCollins Pubs.

Burgess, Melvin. Doing It. 336p. (YA). 2006. reprint ed. pap. 6.95 (978-0-8050-8079-7(1)); 2004. 15.95 (978-0-8050-7565-6(8)) Holt, Henry & Co. (Holt, Henry & Co. Bks. For Young Readers).

—Lady: My Life As A Bitch. 2002. (gr. 7-12). lib. bdg. 15.30 (978-0-613-68355-5(2)) Tandem Library Bks.

—Sara's Face. 2007. 272p. (YA). (gr. 7 up). 16.99 (978-1-4169-3617-6(3)) Simon & Schuster Children's Publishing.

—Smack. 2003. 384p. pap. 7.99 (978-0-06-052187-5(2)); 1999. 304p. (J). (gr. 7-12). pap. 6.99 (978-0-380-73223-4(8)) HarperCollins Pubs.

—Smack. 1998. 288p. (YA). (gr. 9-13). 17.95 (978-0-8050-5801-7(X) , Holt, Henry & Co. Bks. For Young Readers) Holt, Henry & Co.

—Smack. 2003. (gr. 7-12). lib. bdg. 15.30 (978-0-613-65712-9(8)); 1999. (978-0-606-16355-2(7)) Tandem Library Bks.

Burnett, Frances Hodgson. Little Lord Fauntleroy. (J). 21.95 (978-0-8488-0792-4(8)) Amereon LTD.

—Little Lord Fauntleroy. unabr. ed. 2002. (Dover Evergreen Classics Ser.). (Illus.). 176p. (J). (gr. 4-7). pap. 2.50 (978-0-486-42368-5(9)) Dover Pubns., Inc.

—Little Lord Fauntleroy. Rust, Graham, illus. (J). pap. 21.95 (978-0-590-74607-6(3)) Scholastic, Inc.

—Little Lord Fauntleroy. 2004. (Aladdin Classics Ser.). 288p. (J). pap. 4.99 (978-0-689-86994-5(0) , Aladdin) Simon & Schuster Children's Publishing.

—Little Lord Fauntleroy Book & Charm. 2004. (Charming Classics). (Illus.). 240p. (J). pap. 6.99 (978-0-06-055990-8(X) , Harper Festival) HarperCollins Pubs.

—A Little Princess: The Story of Sara Crewe. (J). 16.95 (978-0-8488-1253-9(0)) Amereon LTD.

—A Little Princess: The Story of Sara Crewe. unabr. ed. 2000. (Dover Juvenile Classics Ser.). (Illus.). 240p. (J). (gr. 4-7). pap. 2.00 (978-0-486-41446-1(9)) Dover Pubns., Inc.

—A Little Princess: The Story of Sara Crewe. Rust, Graham, illus. 2000. 192p. (YA). (gr. 4-7). reprint ed. 18.95 (978-0-87923-784-4(8)) Godine, David R. Pub.

—A Little Princess: The Story of Sara Crewe. Collier, Mary & McClintock, Barbara, illus. 2000. 32p. (J). (ps-3). 18.99 (978-0-06-027891-5(9)) HarperCollins Pubs.

—A Little Princess: The Story of Sara Crewe. 2000. (Illus.). 32p. (J). (ps-3). 16.89 (978-0-06-029010-8(2)) HarperCollins Pubs.

—A Little Princess: The Story of Sara Crewe. Tudor, Tasha, illus. 1999. 336p. (J). (gr. 4 up). 17.99 (978-0-397-30693-0(8)) HarperCollins Pubs.

—A Little Princess: The Story of Sara Crewe. Lindskoog, Kathryn, ed. Chitouras, Barbara, illus. 2002. (Classics for Young Readers Ser.). 208p. (J). pap. 7.99 (978-0-87552-727-7(2)) P & R Publishing.

—A Little Princess: The Story of Sara Crewe. 2002. (Classics Ser.). (Illus.). 272p. pap. 10.00 (978-0-14-243701-8(8) , Penguin Classics) Penguin Group (USA) Inc.

—A Little Princess: The Story of Sara Crewe. Rust, Graham, illus. (J). pap. 22.95 (978-0-590-24079-6(X)) Scholastic, Inc.

—A Little Princess: The Story of Sara Crewe. l.t. ed. 2003. 342p. (J). 29.95 (978-0-7862-5842-0(X)) Thorndike Pr.

—A Little Princess Book & Charm. Tudor, Tasha, illus. 1999. (Charming Classics). 336p. (J). (gr. 4 up). pap. 6.99 (978-0-694-01236-7(X) , Harper Festival) HarperCollins Pubs.

—The Secret Garden. 2002. (Illustrated Children's Library Ser.). (Illus.). 288p. (J). 12.99 (978-0-517-22115-0(2) , Gramercy) Random Hse. Value Publishing.

—The Secret Garden. Corvino, Lucy, illus. 2005. (Classic Starts Ser.). 160p. 4.95 (978-1-4027-1319-4(3)) Sterling Publishing Co., Inc.

—The Secret Garden. Engelbreit, Mary, illus. 2007. (Mary Engelbreit's Classic Library). 368p. (J). (gr. 3-7). 9.99 (***978-0-06-008136-2(8)*** , Harper Festival) HarperCollins Pubs.

—The Secret Garden: A Young Reader's Edition of the Classic Story. Kaster, Shelley Austin, illus. 2002. (Great Illustrated Classics Ser.). 240p. (J). (gr. 3-8). 21.35 (978-1-57765-809-2(4) , ABDO & Daughters) ABDO Publishing Co.

—The Secret Garden: A Young Reader's Edition of the Classic Story. ed. 2004. (Illus.). (J). (gr. 1-4). spiral bd. (978-0-616-14565-4(9)); spiral bd. (978-0-616-14566-1(7)) Canadian National Institute for the Blind/Institut National Canadien pour les Aveugles.

—The Secret Garden: A Young Reader's Edition of the Classic Story. Moore, Inga, illus. 2008. 272p. (J). (gr. 1). 21.99 (***978-0-7636-3161-1(2)***) Candlewick Pr.

—The Secret Garden: A Young Reader's Edition of the Classic Story. 1999. (Illus.). 256p. (J). (gr. 4-7). pap. 3.00 (978-0-486-40784-5(5)) Dover Pubns., Inc.

—The Secret Garden: A Young Reader's Edition of the Classic Story. 288p. 2003. (gr. 12). mass mkt. 3.95 (978-0-451-52883-4(2) , Signet Classics); 2002. pap. 8.00 (978-0-14-243705-6(0) , Penguin Classics) Penguin Group (USA) Inc.

—The Secret Garden: A Young Reader's Edition of the Classic Story. 2003. (Modern Library Classics Ser.). 288p. pap. 7.95 (978-0-8129-6998-6(7) , Modern Library) Random House Publishing Group.

—The Secret Garden: A Young Reader's Edition of the Classic Story. Sauber, Robert G., illus. 2001. 56p. (J). (ps up). 9.98 (978-0-7624-0572-5(4) , Courage Bks.) Running Pr. Bk. Pubs.

—The Secret Garden: A Young Reader's Edition of the Classic Story. (gr. 3-6). 2003. lib. bdg. 11.80 (978-0-613-83894-8(7)); 1999. lib. bdg. 11.80 (978-0-613-63230-0(3)) Tandem Library Bks.

—The Secret Garden: With a Discussion of Compassion. Lauter, Richard, illus. 2003. (Values in Action Illustrated Classics Ser.). 191p. (J). (978-1-59203-037-8(8)) Learning Challenge, Inc.

—The Secret Garden Includes Charm. Tudor, Tasha, illus. adapted ed. 1998. (Charming Classics). 368p. (YA). (gr. 5 up). pap. 6.99 (978-0-694-01110-0(X)) HarperCollins Pubs.

—The Secret Garden Book & Charm. Tudor, Tasha, illus. deluxe ed. 2005. (Charming Classics). 368p. (J). 9.99 (978-0-06-075771-7(X) , Harper Festival) HarperCollins Pubs.

Burnett, Frances Hodgson & Cockcroft, Jason. The Secret Garden: A Young Reader's Edition of the Classic Story. 2002. (Kingfisher Classics Ser.). (Illus.). 384p. (J). (978-0-7534-0602-1(0) , Kingfisher) Houghton Mifflin Co. Trade & Reference Div.

Burns, Laura J. & Metz, Melinda. Apocalypse Memories. 2004. (Buffy the Vampire Slayer Ser.). 256p. (YA). pap. 6.99 (978-0-689-86700-2(X) , Simon Spotlight Entertainment) Simon & Schuster.

Butler, Charles. Timon's Tide. Smith, George, illus. 2000. 192p. (YA). (gr. 7-12). 16.00 (978-0-689-82593-4(5) , McElderry, Margaret K.) Simon & Schuster Children's Publishing.

Byng, Georgia. Molly Moon's Incredible Book of Hypnotism. 2003. (Illus.). 384p. (J). (gr. 3-7). 16.99 (978-0-06-051406-8(X)); 2003. 135.92 (978-0-06-057217-4(5)); 2004. (Illus.). 400p. (J). reprint ed. pap. 7.99 (978-0-06-051409-9(4) , Harper Trophy) HarperCollins Pubs.

—Molly Moon's Incredible Book of Hypnotism. 2002. (Molly Moon Ser.: Bk. 1). 330p. (J). (gr. 3-7). (978-0-333-98489-5(7) , Macmillan Children's Bks.) Pan Macmillan.

Cann, Kate. Diving In. 2007. 304p. (J). pap. 5.99 (978-0-06-088601-3(3) , HarperTeen) HarperCollins Pubs.

—Diving In. 2000. (Livewire Ser.). 238p. (J). (gr. 7-11). pap. 9.99 (978-0-7043-4937-7(X)) Women's Pr., Ltd., The GBR. *Dist:* Independent Pubs. Group.

—Go! 2001. (Love Trilogy). 240p. (YA). (gr. 7 up). pap. (978-0-06-440868-4(X) , HarperTeen) HarperCollins Pubs.

—Ready? 2001. (Love Trilogy). 256p. (YA). (gr. 9 up). pap. (978-0-06-440869-1(8) , HarperTeen) HarperCollins Pubs.

—Sex. 2001. (Love Trilogy). 240p. (YA). (gr. 7 up). pap. (978-0-06-440870-7(1) , HarperTeen) HarperCollins Pubs.

Cann, Kate. Sink or Swim. 2007. 320p. (J). (gr. 9 up). pap. 5.99 (***978-0-06-088603-5(X)*** , HarperTeen) HarperCollins Pubs.

Carpenter, Ann. The Slumber Girls & the Mystical Dollhouse. 2006. (J). per. 8.99 (978-0-9771030-0-3(5)) Kidz By Dezign Pr., Inc.

Cassidy, Anne. Looking for JJ. 2007. (Illus.). 336p. (YA). (gr. 9 up). 17.00 (***978-0-15-206190-6(8)***) Harcourt Children's Bks.

Cassidy, Cathy. Indigo Blue. 2006. 240p. (J). (gr. 5). pap. 5.99 (978-0-14-240703-5(8) , Puffin) Penguin Group (USA) Inc.

Cave, Patrick. Number 99. 2001. 176p. (978-0-19-271878-5(9)) Oxford Univ. Pr., Inc.

Chaucer, Geoffrey. The Canterbury Tales - Literary Touchstone Edition. 2005. 128p. (YA). per. 3.99 (978-1-58049-396-3(3) , PWH3963) Prestwick Hse., Inc.

Cheshire, Simon. Kissing Vanessa. 2004. 144p. (YA). (gr. 7). 15.95 (978-0-385-73212-3(0) , Delacorte Bks. for Young Readers) Random Hse. Children's Bks.

A Christmas Carol. 2004. (J). cd-rom 7.99 (978-0-9740847-9-4(4)) GiGi Bks.

A Christmas Carol. 2003. (Illus.). 32p. (J). 9.98 (978-1-4054-0997-1(5)); 4.98 (978-1-4054-0980-3(0)) Parragon, Inc.

Christopher, John. The White Mountains: The Tripods Trilogy. l.t. ed. 2000. 168p. (J). 25.95 (978-0-7838-9170-5(9)) Thorndike Pr.

Clarke, Judith. Starry Nights. 2004. 148p. (YA). 15.95 (978-1-886910-82-9(0) , Lemniscaat) Boyds Mills Pr.

Claybourne, Anna. Jane Eyre. rev. ed. 2007. (Usborne Classics Retold Ser.). 144p. (J). pap. 4.99 (***978-0-7945-1870-7(2)*** , Usborne) EDC Publishing.

Coles Notes Staff. Canterbury Tales. 1999. (YA). 9.95 (978-1-56137-919-4(0)); (J). 11.95 (978-1-56137-920-0(4)) Novel Units, Inc.

Colfer, Eoin. The Arctic Incident. l.t. ed. 2003. (Artemis Fowl Ser.: Bk. 2). 296p. (J). (gr. 3-6). 16.95 (978-0-7540-7839-5(6) , Galaxy Children's Large Print) BBC Audiobooks America.

—The Arctic Incident. (Artemis Fowl Ser.: Bk. 2). 288p. (ps-17). 2003. (J). pap. 7.99 (978-0-7868-1708-5(9)); 2002. 16.95 (978-0-7868-0855-7(1)) Hyperion Bks. for Children.

—The Arctic Incident. l.t. ed. 2003. (Artemis Fowl Ser.: Bk. 2). 313p. (J). (gr. 3-6). 25.95 (978-0-7862-4825-4(4)) Thorndike Pr.

—Artemis Fowl. (Artemis Fowl Ser.: Bk. 1). (FRE.). pap. 34.95 (978-2-07-054681-7(0)) Gallimard, Editions FRA. *Dist:* Distribooks, Inc.

—Artemis Fowl. 2003. (Artemis Fowl Ser.: Bk. 1). (Illus.). 416p. (ps-17). pap. 5.99 (978-0-7868-1787-0(9)) Hyperion Bks. for Children.

—Artemis Fowl. 2002. (Artemis Fowl Ser.: Bk. 1). 304p. (J). (ps-17). pap. 7.99 (978-0-7868-1707-8(0)) Hyperion Paperbacks for Children.

—Artemis Fowl. 2001. (Artemis Fowl Ser.: Bk. 1). 288p. (gr. 8-17). 16.95 (978-0-7868-0801-4(2)) Miramax Bks.

—Artemis Fowl. abr. ed. 2001. (Artemis Fowl Ser.: Bk. 1). (Illus.). 2p. (J). (gr. 3-6). cd-rom (978-0-14-180286-2(3) , Penguin AudioBooks) Penguin Group (USA) Inc.

—Artemis Fowl. (Artemis Fowl Ser.: Bk. 1). 2003. (J). (gr. 7-12). lib. bdg. 14.15 (978-0-613-75035-6(7)); 2002. 277p. (YA). (gr. 8-12). lib. bdg. 14.39 (978-0-606-24618-7(5)); 2002. (gr. 5-8). lib. bdg. 16.15 (978-0-613-60637-0(X)) Tandem Library Bks.

—Artemis Fowl. l.t. ed. 2001. (Artemis Fowl Ser.: Bk. 1). 312p. (J). (gr. 3-6). 28.95 (978-1-58724-092-8(0) , Wheeler Publishing, Inc.) Thomson Gale.

—Artemis Fowl: The Graphic Novel. Rigano, Giovanni & Lamanna, Paolo, illus. 2007. (Artemis Fowl Ser.). 112p. (gr. 5 up). 18.99 (***978-0-7868-4881-2(2)***) Miramax Bks.

—Artemis Fowl: The Graphic Novel. Lamanna, Paolo, illus. 2007. (Artemis Fowl Ser.). 112p. (gr. 5 up). pap. 9.99 (***978-0-7868-4882-9(0)***) Miramax Bks.

—Artemis Fowl Encuentro en el Artico: Encuentro en el Artico. 2005. (SPA., Illus.). 320p. (J). pap. 13.95 (978-0-307-34310-9(3) , Montena) Random House Mondadori ESP. *Dist:* Random Hse., Inc.

—The Artemis Fowl Files. 2004. (Artemis Fowl Ser.). (Illus.). 208p. (J). (gr. 7-17). 12.95 (978-0-7868-5639-8(4)) Hyperion Bks. for Children.

—El Cubo B. 2005. (Artemis Fowl Ser.: No. 3). (SPA., Illus.). 352p. (J). pap. 13.95 (978-0-307-34311-6(1) , Montena) Random House Mondadori ESP. *Dist:* Random Hse., Inc.

—The Eternity Code. (Artemis Fowl Ser.: Bk. 3). 2005. 446p. (YA). (gr. 5-17). mass mkt. 5.99 (978-0-7868-5628-2(9)); 2003. 320p. (ps-17). 16.95 (978-0-7868-1914-0(6)) Hyperion Bks. for Children.

—The Lost Colony. 2006. (Artemis Fowl Ser.: Bk. 5). 400p. (J). (gr. 5-17). 16.95 (978-0-7868-4956-7(8)) Miramax Bks.

—El Mundo Subterraneo. 2005. (Artemis Fowl Ser.). (SPA., Illus.). 288p. (J). pap. 13.95 (978-0-307-34309-3(X) , Montena) Random House Mondadori ESP. *Dist:* Random Hse., Inc.

—The Opal Deception. 2005. (Artemis Fowl Ser.: Bk. 4). 352p. (gr. 5-17). 16.95 (978-0-7868-5289-5(5)) Hyperion Bks. for Children.

—The Opal Deception. (Artemis Fowl Ser.: Bk. 4). (J). 2005. pap. 7.99 (978-0-7868-3640-6(7)); 2006. 352p. (gr. 5-17). reprint ed. pap. 7.99 (978-0-7868-5290-1(9)) Miramax Bks.

—The Opal Deception. l.t. ed. 2005. (Artemis Fowl Ser.: Bk. 4). 421p. (J). 23.95 (978-0-7862-7754-4(8) , Large Print Pr.) Thorndike Pr.

Collins, Sheila Hebert. Jacques et la Canne a Sucre: A Cajun Jack & the Beanstalk. Lyne, Alison Davis, illus. 2004. (FRE.). 32p. (J). pap. 15.95 (978-1-58980-191-2(1)) Pelican Publishing Co., Inc.

Cookson, Catherine. The Cultured Handmaiden. 2000. 319p. (J). mass mkt. 10.95 (978-0-552-12476-8(1) , Corgi) Transworld Publishers Ltd. GBR. *Dist:* Trafalgar Square Publishing.

Cooper, Susan. King of Shadows. Clapp, John, illus. 192p. (J). (gr. 5-9). 2001. mass mkt. 5.99 (978-0-689-84445-4(X) , Aladdin); 1999. 16.00 (978-0-689-82817-1(9) , McElderry, Margaret K.) Simon & Schuster Children's Publishing.

—King of Shadows. l.t. ed. 2000. (Thorndike Press Large Print Juvenile Ser.). (Illus.). 246p. (J). (gr. 8-12). 21.95 (978-0-7862-2706-8(0)) Thorndike Pr.

Crake, D. A. Edwy the Fair or the First Chronicle of. 2006. 79.99 (***978-1-4280-0132-9(8)***); pap. 73.99 (***978-1-4280-0131-2(X)***) IndyPublish.com.

Craze, Galaxy. By the Shore. 1999. (gr. 7-12). lib. bdg. 21.10 (978-0-613-28778-4(9)) Tandem Library Bks.

Creech, Sharon. Pleasing the Ghost. unabr. ed. 2000. (J). (gr. 3 up). pap., stu. ed. 25.20 incl. audio (978-0-7887-3852-4(6) , 41050X1) Recorded Bks., LLC.

Cross, Gillian. Pictures in the Dark. 1998. (978-0-606-13703-4(3)) Tandem Library Bks.

—Tightrope. 1999. 224p. (J). (gr. 7 up). 16.95 (978-0-8234-1512-0(0)) Holiday Hse., Inc.

—Tightrope. 1999. 210p. (YA). (978-0-19-271804-4(5)) Oxford Univ. Pr., Inc.

Culbertson, Jan E. The Legend of Dunsmoor Manor. 2006. 88p. pap. 13.95 (978-1-58909-348-5(8)) Bookstand Publishing.

Cunliffe, John. Postman Pat Has Too Many Parcels. (Illus.). 32p. (J). (978-0-340-67812-1(7) , Hodder & Stoughton) Hodder General Publishing Division.

Cushman, Karen. Aprendiz de Comadrona. 2003. (SPA.). 96p. (YA). (gr. 5-8). (978-84-236-4773-6(0) , ED3133) Edebé ESP. *Dist:* Lectorum Pubns., Inc.

—Catherine, Called Birdy. 2002. (Illus.). (J). 15.00 (978-0-7587-0246-3(9)) Book Wholesalers, Inc.

—Matilda Bone. 2002. 13.94 (978-1-4046-1906-7(2)) Book Wholesalers, Inc.

—Matilda Bone. 2000. (Illus.). 176p. (J). (gr. 5-9). tchr. ed. 15.00 (978-0-395-88156-9(0) , Clarion Bks.) Houghton Mifflin Co. Trade & Reference Div.

—Matilda Bone. unabr. ed. 2004. (Middle Grade Cassette Librariestm Ser.). 176p. (J). (gr. 5-9). pap. 36.00 incl. audio (978-0-8072-1725-2(5) , S YA 252 SP, Listening Library) Random Hse. Audio Publishing Group.

—Matilda Bone. 2002. 176p. (J). (gr. 5-7). reprint ed. 5.99 (978-0-440-41822-1(4) , Yearling) Random Hse. Children's Bks.

—Matilda Bone. 2002. 167p. (J). (gr. 4-7). lib. bdg. 13.55 (978-0-613-45343-1(3)) Tandem Library Bks.

Dahl, Roald. The Witches. 2002. (J). pap. 29.95 incl. audio (978-0-7540-6247-9(3)) BBC Audiobooks America.

—The Witches. Blake, Quentin, illus. 208p. (J). 2007. (gr. 2). 6.99 (***978-0-14-241011-0(X)*** , Puffin); 1999. (gr. 3-7). pap. 3.95 (978-0-14-031730-5(9) , Viking Juvenile) Penguin Group (USA) Inc.

—The Witches. 1999. (J). (gr. 3-6). lib. bdg. 14.15 (978-0-8085-7491-0(4)) Tandem Library Bks.

Dale, Anna. Dawn Undercover. 2006. 368p. (J). pap. 7.95 (978-1-59990-002-5(5) , Bloomsbury Children) Bloomsbury Publishing.

—Whispering to Witches. 304p. (J). 2004. 16.95 (978-1-58234-890-2(1) , Bloomsbury Children); 2005. reprint ed. pap. 7.95 (978-1-58234-699-1(2)) Bloomsbury Publishing.

Davoll, Barbara. To London to See the Queen. Hockerman, Dennis, illus. 1999. (New Christopher Churchmouse Adventures Ser.: Vol. 4). 24p. (J). (ps-3). 9.99 (978-0-8024-5399-0(6)) Moody Pubs.

De Angeli, Marguerite. The Door in the Wall. 1998. (Illus.). 128p. (J). (gr. 5-9). reprint ed. pap. 4.99 (978-0-440-22779-3(8) , Laurel Leaf) Random Hse. Children's Bks.

—The Door in the Wall. 1998. 11.64 (978-0-606-13344-9(5)) Tandem Library Bks.

de Troyes, Chretien. Perceval: King Arthur's Knight of the Holy Grail. Spirin, Gennadii, illus. 2007. 38p. (J). (gr. 4 up). 16.99 (978-0-7614-5339-0(3)) Cavendish, Marshall Corp.

Dennard, Deborah. Hedgehog Haven: The Story of an English Hedgerow Community. Hynes, Robert, illus. (Wild Habitats Ser.). (J). (gr. 1-4). 2005. 32p. 15.95 (978-1-56899-987-6(9) , B7020); 2005. 32p. 19.95 incl. audio (978-1-56899-989-0(5) , BC7020); 2005. 32p. pap. 6.95 (978-1-56899-988-3(7) , S7020); 2001. 36p. 26.95 (978-1-56899-991-3(7)) Soundprints.

Dent, Grace. LBD: It's a Girl Thing. 2004. 288p. (J). (gr. 7 up). reprint ed. pap. 6.99 (978-0-14-240182-8(X) , Puffin) Penguin Group (USA) Inc.

—LBD: Live & Fabulous! 2006. 288p. (YA). (gr. 5). pap. 6.99 (978-0-14-240662-5(7) , Puffin) Penguin Group (USA) Inc.

—LBD: Friends Forever! Friends Forever! 2007. 272p. (YA). pap. 6.99 (978-0-14-240831-5(X) , Puffin) Penguin Group (USA) Inc.

Dhami, Narinder. Bhangra Babes. 2007. 192p. (J). (gr. 4-7). 5.99 (***978-0-440-42106-1(3)*** , Yearling) Random Hse. Children's Bks.

—Bindi Babes. 2004. 192p. (J). (gr. 3-7). 14.95 (978-0-385-73177-5(9) , Delacorte Bks. for Young Readers) Random Hse. Children's Bks.

—Bollywood Babes. 224p. (J). 2006. (gr. 4-7). pap. 5.50 (978-0-440-42020-0(2) , Yearling); 2005. (gr. 3). 14.95 (978-0-385-73178-2(7) , Delacorte Bks. for Young Readers) Random Hse. Children's Bks.

Dickens, Charles. A Christmas Carol. Date not set. (C). pap. (978-0-7593-9886-3(0) , Thomson Learning) CENGAGE Learning.

—A Christmas Carol. Wheatcroft, Andrew, illus. 2006. (Read & Listen Bks.). 64p. (J). 9.99 (978-0-7566-1831-5(2)) Dorling Kindersley Publishing, Inc.

—A Christmas Carol. Morrissey, Dean, illus. 2001. 80p. (J). (gr. 2-5). 17.89 (978-0-06-028578-4(8)) HarperCollins Pubs.

—A Christmas Carol. 2000. (Illus.). 144p. (J). (gr. 4-7). pap. 5.99 (978-0-439-10133-2(6)) Scholastic, Inc.

—A Christmas Carol. 1998. (Children's Classics). (ENG., Illus.). 96p. (YA). (ps up). pap. (978-1-85326-121-3(1) , 1211WW) Wordsworth Editions, Ltd.

—A Christmas Carol. 2003. (Illus.). 48p. (978-0-7502-3666-9(3) , Hodder Wayland) Hodder Children's Division.

—A Christmas Carol. 2005. (Great Illustrated Classics Ser.). (Illus.). 238p. (J). (gr. 3-8). 21.35 (978-1-59679-237-1(X) , ABDO & Daughters) ABDO Publishing Co.

—A Christmas Carol. Lynch, P. J., illus. 2006. 160p. (J). (gr. 5). 19.99 (978-0-7636-3120-8(5)) Candlewick Pr.

—A Christmas Carol. Lo Famia, Jon, illus. 2nd ed. 1998. (Illustrated Classic Book Ser.: Vol. III). 61p. (J). reprint ed. pap. 4.95 (978-1-56767-241-1(8)) Educational Insights, Inc.

—David Copperfield. 2000. (SPA., Illus.). 48p. (J). 7.95 (978-84-406-8898-9(9)) Ediciones B ESP. *Dist:* Distribooks, Inc.

—Great Expectations. (Classics Illustrated Ser.). (Illus.). 52p. (YA). pap. 4.95 (978-1-57209-001-9(4)) Classics International Entertainment, Inc.

—Great Expectations. 1999. (Saddleback Classics). (Illus.). (J). 13.75 (978-0-606-21552-7(2)) Tandem Library Bks.

—Great Expectations. Hegarty, Carol, ed. 1998. (Classics Ser. II). (Illus.). 77p. (YA). (gr. 5-12). pap. 6.95 (978-1-56254-266-5(4) , SP2664) Saddleback Educational Publishing.

Dickens, Charles & Birmingham, Christian. A Christmas Carol. 2000. (Miniature Editionstm Ser.). (Illus.). 128p. (gr. 4-7). 4.95 (978-0-7624-0831-3(6) , Running Pr. Miniature Editions) Running Pr. Bk. Pubs.

Dickens, Charles & Moore, Clement C. A Christmas Carol & the Night Before Christmas. Rackham, Arthur, illus. deluxe ed. 2006. 192p. 14.99 (978-0-517-22927-9(7) , Gramercy) Random Hse. Value Publishing.

Dickens, Charles & Sims, L. A Christmas Carol. (Young Reading Ser.: Vol. 2). 64p. (J). (gr. 2 up). lib. bdg. 13.95 (978-1-58086-790-0(1) , Usborne) EDC Publishing.

Dickens, Charles & Skarmeas, Nancy J. A Christmas Carol. Flint, Russ, illus. abr. ed. 1998. 48p. (J). (gr. 4-7). 14.00 (978-0-8249-4096-6(2) , Candy Cane Pr.) Ideals Pubns.

Dickens, Charles & Wheatcroft, Andrew. A Christmas Carol. 2000. (Read & Listen Ser.). (Illus.). 64p. (J). pap. incl. cd-rom (978-0-7894-6363-0(6)) Dorling Kindersley Publishing, Inc.

Dickinson, Peter. Chuck & Danielle. 115p. (J). (gr. 3-5). pap. 3.99 (978-0-8072-1504-3(X) , Listening Library) Random Hse. Audio Publishing Group.

E F G

—Chuck & Danielle. 2001. (Illus.). 128p. (gr. 4-7). pap. 12.00 (978-0-375-89505-0(1) , Yearling) Random Hse. Children's Bks.

—Chuck & Danielle. 2001. lib. bdg. 21.10 (978-0-613-87813-5(2)) Tandem Library Bks.

Dixon, Andy. Los Caballeros del Rey Arturo. 2001. (SPA., Illus.). 32p. (YA). (gr. 3 up). lib. bdg. 16.95 (978-1-58086-318-6(3)) EDC Publishing.

Dogar, Sharon. Waves. 2007. 344p. (J). (gr. 7 up). pap. 16.99 (978-0-439-87180-8(8) , Chicken Hse., The) Scholastic, Inc.

Doherty, Berlie. Holly Starcross. 2002. 192p. (J). (gr. 7 up). 17.89 (978-0-06-001342-4(7)) HarperCollins Pubs.

Downham, Jenny. Before I Die. 2007. 326p. (YA). (gr. 9-12). 15.99 (*978-0-385-75155-1(9)); lib. bdg. 18.99 (*978-0-385-75158-2(3)) Random Hse. Children's Bks. (Fickling, David Bks.).

Doyle, Arthur Conan. The Adventures & the Memoirs of Sherlock Holmes. McKowen, Scott, illus. 2004. (Unabridged Classics Ser.). 576p. 9.95 (978-1-4027-1453-5(X)) Sterling Publishing Co., Inc.

—Adventures of Sherlock Holmes. 1998. (Wordsworth Classics Ser.). (YA). (gr. 6-12). 5.27 (978-0-89061-033-6(9) , R0339WW) Jamestown.

—The Hound of the Baskervilles: Another Adventure of Sherlock Holmes. 2002. (YA). (gr. 5-12). pap. 6.50 (978-0-8359-0963-1(8)) Globe Fearon Educational Publishing.

—The Hound of the Baskervilles: Another Adventure of Sherlock Holmes. 2000. (Aladdin Classics Ser.). 256p. (J). (gr. 4-11). pap. 5.99 (978-0-689-83571-1(X) , Aladdin) Simon & Schuster Children's Publishing.

—The Hound of the Baskervilles: Another Adventure of Sherlock Holmes. 2001. (gr. 7-12). lib. bdg. 16.45 (978-0-613-64290-3(2)); 2001. (gr. 7-12). lib. bdg. 12.95 (978-0-613-37148-3(8)); 2000. (gr. 3-6). lib. bdg. 11.80 (978-0-613-63203-4(6)) Tandem Library Bks.

—The Hounds of the Baskervilles. abr. ed. 2001. (gr. 7-12). lib. bdg. 15.25 (978-0-613-43833-9(7)) Tandem Library Bks.

—The Return of Sherlock Holmes. l.t. ed. 1998. (Large Print Heritage Ser.). 278p. (YA). (gr. 7-12). lib. bdg. 29.95 (978-1-58118-038-1(1)) LRS.

—Sherlock Holmes & the Case of the Hound of the Baskervilles. 2005. (Great Illustrated Classics Ser.). (Illus.). 237p. (J). (gr. 3-8). 21.35 (978-1-59679-250-0(7) , ABDO & Daughters) ABDO Publishing Co.

Edwards, Julie Andrews. Mandy. Westerman, Johanna, illus. 2nd ed. 2006. (Julie Andrews Collection). 320p. (J). 16.99 (978-0-06-113162-2(8)); pap. 6.99 (978-0-06-120707-5(1)) HarperCollins Pubs. (Julie Andrews Collection).

Eliot, George & West, Clare. Silas Marner: The Weaver of Raveloe, Level 4. 2nd ed. 2000. (Bookworms Ser.). (Illus.). 96p. 6.50 (978-0-19-423044-5(9)) Oxford Univ. Pr., Inc.

Eschberger, Beverly. The Elephants Tour England: An Elephant Family Adventure. Gower, Jim, illus. 2008. (J). per. 3.99 (978-1-932926-29-3(1) , Kinkajou Pr.) Artemesia Publishing, LLC.

Ewing, Juliana Horatia. Six to Sixteen. 2007. (ENG.). 192p. 13.99 (*978-1-4280-7181-0(4)); per. 19.99 (*978-1-4280-7175-9(X)) IndyPublish.com.

Farber, Erica. The Prince. Mayer, Mercer, illus. 2006. (Critter Kids Adventure Ser.). 32p. (J). (gr. 2-5). pap. 4.95 (978-0-7696-4767-8(7) , Gingham Dog Pr.) School Specialty Publishing.

Farrar, F. W. Eric: Little by Little. 2nd ed. 2004. 240p. (YA). per. 7.50 (978-1-932774-51-1(3)) Christian, Harvey Pubs. Inc.

Fearnley, Jan. Colin & the Curly Claw. Fearnley, Jan, illus. 2001. (Blue Bananas Ser.). (Illus.). 48p. (J). (gr. 1-2). (978-0-7787-0840-7(3)); pap. (978-0-7787-0886-5(1)) Crabtree Publishing Co.

—Colin & the Curly Claw. 2002. (gr. k-3). lib. bdg. 12.95 (978-0-613-52821-4(2)) Tandem Library Bks.

Fine, Anne. Up on Cloud Nine. l.t. ed. 2005. (Illus.). 232p. (J). pap. incl. audio (978-0-7540-7878-4(7) , CLP 455) BBC Audio.

—Up on Cloud Nine. 2003. 160p. (J). (gr. 5-17). 4.99 (978-0-440-41916-7(6) , Yearling) Random Hse. Children's Bks.

Fine, Anne & Glover, Jamie. Up on Cloud Nine. 2004. (J). pap. 29.95 incl. audio (978-0-7540-6276-9(7) , Chivers Children's Audio Bks.) BBC Audiobooks America.

Fisher, Catherine. Corbenic. 2006. 288p. (J). 16.99 (978-0-06-072470-2(6) , Greenwillow Bks.) HarperCollins Pubs.

—Darkhenge. 2007. 432p. (J). pap. 7.99 (978-0-06-078584-0(5)) HarperCollins Pubs.

Fisk, Pauline. The Red Judge. 2005. 208p. (YA). 16.95 (978-1-58234-942-8(8) , Bloomsbury Children) Bloomsbury Publishing.

—The Secret of Sabrina Fludde. 2002. 250p. (J). (gr. 5 up). 15.95 (978-1-58234-754-7(9) , Bloomsbury Children) Bloomsbury Publishing.

Forrest, Emma. Namedropper. 2000. 240p. pap. 12.00 (978-0-684-86538-6(6) , Touchstone) Simon & Schuster.

Francis, Pauline. Sam Stars at Shakespeare's Globe. Tattersfield, Jane, illus. 2006. 32p. (J). 15.95 (978-1-84507-406-7(8)) Lincoln, Frances Ltd. GBR. *Dist:* Perseus Distribution.

Francis, Pauline & Burnett, Frances Hodgson. The Secret Garden. 2003. (Fast Track Classics Ser.). (Illus.). 48p. (YA). pap. 9.99 (978-0-237-52535-4(6) , Evans Brothers, Limited) Evans Publishing Group GBR. *Dist:* Independent Pubs. Group.

Franklin, Rosalind. Clemo the Cornish Cat. Coomber, Eva, illus. 2006. 32p. (J). (978-1-905363-08-7(7) , Diggory Pr. Ltd.) Meadow Bks.

Freeman, Don. Will's Quill: Or How a Goose Saved Shakespeare. ed. 2004. (Illus.). 32p. (J). (ps-k). 16.99 (978-0-670-03686-8(2) , Viking Juvenile) Penguin Group (USA) Inc.

Gaiman, Neil. Stardust. movie tie-in ed. 2007. 368p. (J). (gr. 7 up). pap. 6.99 (978-0-06-124048-5(6) , Harper Entertainment) HarperCollins Pubs.

—Stardust. 2005. (Single Volume Ser.). (SPA., Illus.). 210p. pap. 16.95 (978-1-59497-097-9(1)) Public Square Bks.

Garfield, Leon. Black Jack. 2000. (J). (978-0-606-21673-9(1)) Tandem Library Bks.

Garner, Alan. Elidor. 192p. (YA). (gr. 5 up). pap. 6.00 (978-0-8072-1545-6(7) , Listening Library) Random Hse. Audio Publishing Group.

Gates, Susan. Bill's Baggy Pants. Axworthy, Anni, illus. 2004. (Read-It! Readers Ser.). 32p. (C). (gr. k-3). 18.60 (978-1-4048-0050-2(6)) Picture Window Bks.

Geras, Adele. Pictures of the Night. 2005. (Egerton Hall Novels: Vol. 3). 192p. (YA). (gr. 7-17). pap. 6.95 (978-0-15-205543-1(6) , Harcourt Paperbacks) Harcourt Children's Bks.

Gilbert, D. Hide & Seek: A Mystery Novel for Children. 2005. 187p. pap. 19.95 (978-1-4137-9748-0(2)) PublishAmerica, Inc.

Gleitzman, Morris. Misery Guts. l.t. ed. 2005. (Illus.). 184p. (J). pap. incl. audio (978-0-7540-7867-8(1) , CLP 456) BBC Audio.

Globe-Fearon Staff, ed. Jane Eyre, Grades 5-12. pap., tchr. ed. 4.95 (978-0-8359-0109-3(2)) Globe Fearon Educational Publishing.

Godden, Rumer. Gypsy Girl. 2002. Orig. Title: The Diddakoi. (Illus.). 176p. (J). 15.89 (978-0-06-029192-1(3)) HarperCollins Pubs.

—Miss Happiness & Miss Flower. 2002. (Illus.). 128p. (J). (gr. 3-7). 14.89 (978-0-06-029193-8(1)) HarperCollins Pubs.

Goudge, Elizabeth. Linnets & Valerians. 2001. 256p. (J). pap. 6.99 (978-0-14-230026-8(8) , Puffin) Penguin Group (USA) Inc.

—The Little White Horse. 2001. 240p. (YA). (gr. 3-6). pap. 5.99 (978-0-14-230027-5(6) , Puffin) Penguin Group (USA) Inc.

—Little White Horse. 2001. (gr. 5-8). lib. bdg. 14.15 (978-0-613-44399-9(3)) Tandem Library Bks.

Grahame, Kenneth. Dream Days. Shepard, Ernest H., illus. 2001. (Company of Books Ser.). 163p. (YA). 22.95 (978-1-58579-018-0(4) , Common Reader Editions) Akadine Pr., The.

—Golden Age. 2006. pap. (*978-1-4068-3332-4(0)) Echo Library.

—Mr. Toad, Vol. 2. Johnson, Joe, tr. from FRE. 2003. (Wind in the Willows Ser.: Vol. 2). (Illus.). 32p. (gr. 4-7). 15.95 (978-1-56163-218-3(X)) NBM Publishing Co.

—El Viento en los Sauces. (SPA.). 192p. (J). I. 9.50 (978-84-372-1882-3(9)); II. 9.50 (978-84-372-1883-0(7)) Santillana USA Publishing Co., Inc.

—The Wind in the Willows. Tomei, Lorna, illus. 2002. (Great Illustrated Classics Ser.). 240p. (J). (gr. 3-8). 21.35 (978-1-57765-808-5(6) , ABDO & Daughters) ABDO Publishing Co.

—The Wind in the Willows. Percy, Graham, illus. 1999. (Abbeville Classics Ser.). 192p. (J). 12.95 (978-0-7892-0559-9(9)); pap. 7.95 (978-0-7892-0549-0(1)) Abbeville Pr., Inc. (Abbeville Kids).

—The Wind in the Willows. Moss, Joanne, illus. 253p. (J). (gr. 5-6). reprint ed. lib. bdg. 22.95 (978-0-88411-877-0(0)) Amereon LTD.

—The Wind in the Willows. Perry, Graham, illus. 2000. 192p. (J). pap. 8.95 (978-1-85793-914-9(X) , Pavilion Bks., Ltd.) Anova Bks. GBR. *Dist:* Trafalgar Square Publishing.

—The Wind in the Willows. Moore, Inga, illus. abr. ed. 2000. 180p. (J). 4.50 (978-0-7445-7553-8(2)) Candlewick Pr.

—The Wind in the Willows. 2003. 192p. (J). 4.99 (978-1-57759-567-0(X)) Dalmatian Pr.

—The Wind in the Willows. 1999. (Illus.). 176p. (J). (gr. 4-7). pap. 3.00 (978-0-486-40785-2(3)) Dover Pubns., Inc.

—The Wind in the Willows. Kliros, Thea, illus. abr. ed. 1998. (Dover Children's Thrift Classics Ser.). 96p. (J). pap. 1.00 (978-0-486-28600-6(2)) Dover Pubns., Inc.

—The Wind in the Willows. Hague, Michael, illus. rev. ed. 2003. 224p. (J). (gr. 1 up). 26.95 (978-0-8050-7237-2(3) , Holt, Henry & Co. Bks. For Young Readers) Holt, Henry & Co.

—The Wind in the Willows. l.t. ed. 2000. (LRS Large Print Heritage Ser.). 271p. (J). (gr. 3-8). lib. bdg. 29.95 (978-1-58118-066-4(7) , 23661) LRS.

—The Wind in the Willows. 1998. (Twelve-Point Ser.). 185p. reprint ed. lib. bdg. 24.00 (978-1-58287-080-9(2)) North Bks.

—The Wind in the Willows. Green, Peter, ed. 1999. (Oxford World's Classics Ser.). 192p. 11.95 (978-0-19-283515-4(7)) Oxford Univ. Pr., Inc.

—The Wind in the Willows. 240p. (gr. 12). 2006. pap. 5.95 (978-0-451-53014-1(4) , Signet Classics); 2005. (YA). 12.00 (978-0-14-303909-9(1) , Penguin Classics) Penguin Group (USA) Inc.

—The Wind in the Willows. 1999. (Aladdin Classics Ser.). (Illus.). 304p. (J). (gr. 4-7). pap. 4.99 (978-0-689-83140-9(4) , Aladdin) Simon & Schuster Children's Publishing.

—The Wind in the Willows. Hanft, Joshua, ed. (Great Illustrated Classics Ser.: Vol. 39). (Illus.). 240p. (J). (gr. 3-6). 9.95 (978-0-86611-990-0(6)) Waldman Publishing Corp.

—The Wind in the Willows. 1998. (Children's Classics). (ENG., Illus.). 192p. (YA). (ps up). pap. (978-1-85326-122-0(X) , 122XWW); (J). (gr. 4-7). pap. (978-1-85326-017-9(7) , 0177WW) Wordsworth Editions, Ltd.

—The Wind in the Willows Vol. 3: The Gates of Dawn. Johnson, Joe, tr. Plessix, Michel, illus. 2003. 32p. (gr. 4-7). 15.95 (978-1-56163-245-9(7)) NBM Publishing Co.

Grahame, Kenneth & Basset, Jennifer. The Wind in the Willows, Level 3. 2nd abr. ed. 2000. (Bookworms Ser.). (Illus.). 74p. 6.50 (978-0-19-423022-3(8)) Oxford Univ. Pr., Inc.

Gray, Elizabeth Janet. Adam of the Road. Lawson, Robert, illus. 2006. (Puffin Modern Classics Ser.). 320p. (J). (gr. 3). pap. 6.99 (978-0-14-240659-5(7) , Puffin) Penguin Group (USA) Inc.

Gray, Nigel. Oliver Twist Finds a Home. McLean, Andrew, illus. 2002. 32p. (YA). pap. 11.95 (978-1-876268-88-6(3)) Univ. of Western Australia Pr. AUS. *Dist:* International Specialized Bk. Services.

Great Expectations. 2004. (Literature Connections Ser.). (Illus.). (gr. 6-12). (978-0-395-87484-4(X) , 2-70843) McDougal Littell Inc.

Greene, Janice. Jane Eyre. Hagerty, Carol, ed. 1998. (Classics Ser.: Set II). (Illus.). 77p. (YA). (gr. 5-12). pap. 7.95 (978-1-56254-268-9(0) , SP2680) Saddleback Educational Publishing.

Greene, Vivien. Laurel for Libby: A Facsimile Edition of a Small Story Book Written for Graham Greene by his Wife, Vivien. 2006. (Illus.). 40p. 12.00 (978-1-85124-350-1(X)) Bodleian Library GBR. *Dist:* Chicago Distribution Ctr.

Gregory, Kristiana. Eleanor: Crown Jewel of Aquitaine: France 1136. 2002. (Royal Diaries Ser.). (Illus.). 192p. (gr. 4-9). pap. 10.95 (978-0-439-16484-9(2) , Scholastic Pr.) Scholastic, Inc.

Grindley, Sally. Bravo, Max! Ross, Tony, illus. 2007. 160p. (J). (gr. 1-4). 15.99 (978-1-4169-0393-2(3) , McElderry, Margaret K.); pap. 4.99 (978-1-4169-3645-9(9) , Aladdin) Simon & Schuster Children's Publishing.

—Dear Max. Ross, Tony, illus. 144p. (J). 2007. pap. 4.99 (978-1-4169-3443-1(X) , Aladdin); 2006. (gr. 1-4). 14.95 (978-1-4169-0392-5(5) , McElderry, Margaret K.) Simon & Schuster Children's Publishing.

Hadcroft, Will. Anne Droyd & Century Lodge. 2004. 282p. (J). pap. (978-1-84310-282-3(X)) Kingsley, Jessica Ltd.

Harris, Ruth Elwin. Gwen's Story. 2002. (gr. 7-12). lib. bdg. 14.15 (978-0-613-74775-2(5)) Tandem Library Bks.

—Gwen's Story: Sisters of the Quantock Hills. 2002. (Quantock's Quartet Ser.). (Illus.). 288p. (YA). (gr. 7 up). pap. 5.99 (978-0-7636-1705-9(9)) Candlewick Pr.

—Julia's Story. 2002. (gr. 7-12). lib. bdg. 14.15 (978-0-613-74777-6(1)) Tandem Library Bks.

—Sarah's Story. 2002. (Quantock's Quartet Ser.). (Illus.). 288p. (YA). (gr. 7 up). pap. 5.99 (978-0-7636-1707-3(5)) Candlewick Pr.

—Sarah's Story. 2002. (gr. 7-12). lib. bdg. 14.15 (978-0-613-74779-0(8)) Tandem Library Bks.

Harry Potter & the Chamber of Secrets. 2002. (Harry Potter Ser.). (Illus.). (J). 15.23 (978-0-7587-4426-5(9)) Book Wholesalers, Inc.

Harry Potter & the Sorcerer's Stone. 2002. (Harry Potter Ser.). (Illus.). (J). 15.23 (978-0-7587-0016-2(4)) Book Wholesalers, Inc.

Hart, Derek. Secret of the Dragon's Eye. 2007. 264p. per. 16.95 (*978-0-595-42967-7(X)) iUniverse, Inc.

Hearn, Julie. The Minister's Daughter. 2006. 272p. (YA). pap. 7.99 (978-0-689-87691-2(2) , Simon Pulse) Simon & Schuster Children's Publishing.

Henry, Marguerite. King of the Wind. 2002. (Illus.). (J). 13.40 (978-0-7587-0197-8(7)) Book Wholesalers, Inc.

—King of the Wind. unabr. ed. 2004. 173p. (J). (gr. 4-7). pap. 38.00 incl. audio (978-0-8072-8697-5(4) , YA239SP, Listening Library) Random Hse. Audio Publishing Group.

—King of the Wind. l.t. ed. 2001. (Illus.). 216p. (J). (gr. 4-7). 21.95 (978-0-7862-2848-5(2)) Thorndike Pr.

—King of the Wind: The Story of the Godolphin Arabian. Dennis, Wesley, illus. 2006. 176p. (J). pap. 5.99 (978-1-4169-2786-0(7) , Aladdin) Simon & Schuster Children's Publishing.

Henty, A. G. Both Sides the Border A Tale of Hotspur. 2007. 22.99 (*978-1-4280-5127-0(9)); pap. 15.99 (*978-1-4280-5117-1(1)) IndyPublish.com.

Henty, G. A. Both Sides of the Border: A Tale of Hotspur & Glendower. 2000. 252p. (J). pap. 9.95 (978-0-594-01504-8(9)) 1873 Pr.

—In the Reign of Terror: The Adventures of a Westminster Boy. 2000. 252p. pap. 9.95 (978-0-594-01344-0(5)) 1873 Pr.

—In the Reign of Terror: The Adventures of a Westminster Boy. 2002. 370p. 29.95 (978-1-59087-077-8(8) , GAH077); per. 19.95 (978-1-59087-076-1(X) , GAH076) Althouse Pr.

—In the Reign of Terror: The Adventures of a Westminster Boy. collector's ed. 2002. (Illus.). im. lthr. 38.85 (978-1-4115-1378-5(9)); pap. 19.95 (978-1-4115-0618-3(9)); 25.95 (978-1-4115-0946-7(3)); pap. 17.95 (978-1-4115-0128-7(4)) Polyglot Pr., Inc.

Hill, Pamela Smith. The Last Grail Keeper. 2001. 240p. (J). (gr. 7 up). tchr. ed. 17.95 (978-0-8234-1574-8(0)) Holiday Hse., Inc.

Hillert, Margaret. Tom Thumb. Hockerman, Dennis, illus. rev. ed. 2006. (Beginning to Read Ser.). 32p. (J). lib. bdg. 18.60 (978-1-59953-028-4(7)) Norwood Hse. Pr.

Hilton, James. Goodbye, Mr. Chips. 2004. 144p. (J). (gr. 7-17). mass mkt. 5.99 (978-0-316-01013-9(8)) Little Brown & Co.

Hoffman, Mary. Women of Camelot: Queens & Enchantresses at the Court of King Arthur. Balit, Christina, illus. 2006. 69p. (YA). (gr. 5-9). 20.00 (978-1-4223-5260-1(9)) DIANE Publishing Co.

Holeman, Linda. Search of the Moon King's Daughter. 2003. (gr. 7-12). lib. bdg. 18.75 (978-0-613-77367-6(5)) Tandem Library Bks.

—Search of the Moon King's Daughter. 2003. 320p. (J). (gr. 6). pap. 9.95 (978-0-88776-609-1(9)) Tundra Bks., Inc./ Livres Toundra, Inc. CAN. *Dist:* Random Hse., Inc.

Holmes, Victoria. Rider in the Dark: An Epic Horse Story. 2004. (Illus.). 320p. (J). (gr. 5 up). 15.99 (978-0-06-052025-0(6)); lib. bdg. 16.89 (978-0-06-052026-7(4)) HarperCollins Pubs.

Hooper, Mary. Amy. 2004. 176p. (J). (gr. 5-10). reprint ed. pap. 6.95 (978-1-58234-915-2(0) , Bloomsbury Children) Bloomsbury Publishing.

Hornby, Nick. Slam. 2007. 304p. (J). (gr. 6). 19.99 (*978-0-399-25048-4(4) , Putnam Juvenile) Penguin Group (USA) Inc.

Horowitz, Anthony. The Devil & His Boy. 2000. 1p. (YA). (gr. 5-9). 17.99 (978-0-399-23432-3(2) , Philomel) Penguin Group (USA) Inc.

—The Devil & His Boy. 2001. (978-0-606-22508-3(0)); (gr. 5-8). lib. bdg. 14.15 (978-0-613-44387-6(X)) Tandem Library Bks.

—The Falcon's Malteser. 2004. (Diamond Brothers Ser.). 192p. (J). (gr. 5). 16.99 (978-0-399-24153-6(1) , Philomel) Penguin Group (USA) Inc.

—Point Blank. (Alex Rider Ser.: Bk. 2). 2006. 304p. (J). (gr. 7). pap. 7.99 (978-0-14-240612-0(0) , Puffin); 2002. 208p. (YA). (gr. 5 up). 17.99 (978-0-399-23621-1(X) , Philomel) Penguin Group (USA) Inc.

—Ravens Gate. (Power of Five Ser.: Vol. 1). 2006. 272p. (J). pap. 6.99 (978-0-439-68009-7(3) , Scholastic Paperbacks); 2005. 256p. (YA). pap. 17.95 (978-0-439-67995-4(8)) Scholastic, Inc.

—Ravens Gate. l.t. ed. 2006. (Power of Five Ser.: Vol. 1). (YA). 23.95 (978-0-7862-8584-6(2)) Thorndike Pr.

—Skeleton Key. (Alex Rider Ser.: Bk. 3). 2006. 352p. (J). (gr. 7). pap. 7.99 (978-0-14-240614-4(7) , Puffin); 2003. 240p. (YA). (gr. 5). 17.99 (978-0-399-23777-5(1) , Philomel) Penguin Group (USA) Inc.

—Stormbreaker. (Alex Rider Ser.: Bk. 1). 2006. 256p. (J). (gr. 7). pap. 7.99 (978-0-14-240611-3(2) , Puffin); 2002. (Illus.). (J). (gr. 4-7). 5.99 (978-0-698-11932-1(0) , Puffin); 2001. (Illus.). 1p. (YA). (gr. 5 up). 17.99 (978-0-399-23620-4(1) , Philomel); 2006. 264p. (J). (gr. 5). 7.99 (978-0-14-240656-4(2) , Puffin) Penguin Group (USA) Inc.

—Stormbreaker. 2004. (Alex Rider Ser.: Bk. 1). 208p. (J). (gr. 4-7). pap. 38.00 incl. audio (978-0-8072-2277-5(1) , Listening Library) Random Hse. Audio Publishing Group.

—Stormbreaker: The Graphic Novel. Kanako & Yuzuru, illus. 2006. (Alex Rider Ser.). 144p. (J). (gr. 4). pap. 14.99 (978-0-399-24633-3(9) , Philomel) Penguin Group (USA) Inc.

Hubbard, Coleen. A Horse for Hannah. Rabinowitz, Sandy & Keiffer, Christa, illus. l.t. ed. 1999. (Treasured Horses Collection). 128p. (J). (gr. 4 up). lib. bdg. 23.33 (978-0-8368-2402-5(4)) Stevens, Gareth Inc.

Hughes, Shirley. Ella's Big Chance. Hughes, Shirley, illus. 2004. (Illus.). 48p. (J). 16.95 (978-0-689-87399-7(9) , Simon & Schuster Children's Publishing) Simon & Schuster Children's Publishing.

Hughes, Thomas. Tom Brown's School Days. 1998. lib. bdg. 22.95 (978-1-56723-061-1(X)) Yestermorrow, Inc.

—Tom Brown's Schooldays. 2002. (Children's Classics). (ENG., Illus.). 352p. (J). (gr. 3-6). pap. (978-1-85326-108-4(4)) Wordsworth Editions, Ltd.

Hughes, Thomas. Tom Browns Schooldays. 2006. pap. (*978-1-4068-1407-1(5)) Echo Library.

Hussey, Charmian. The Valley of Secrets. Crump, Christopher, illus. 400p. 2006. (J). pap. 9.99 (978-1-4169-0015-3(2) , Simon Pulse); 2005. (YA). 17.95 (978-0-689-87862-6(1)) Simon & Schuster Children's Publishing.

Ibbotson, Eva. The Beasts of Clawstone Castle. Hawkes, Kevin, illus. (J). 2007. 256p. (gr. 3 up). 6.99 (*978-0-14-240931-2(6) , Puffin); 2006. 192p. (gr. 5). 16.99 (978-0-525-47719-8(5) , Dutton Juvenile) Penguin Group (USA) Inc.

—Dial-a-Ghost. Hawkes, Kevin, illus. 2003. 224p. (J). (gr. 3-6). pap. 5.99 (978-0-14-250018-7(6) , Puffin) Penguin Group (USA) Inc.

—Dial-a-Ghost. Hawkes, Kevin, illus. l.t. ed. 2002. 212p. (J). 22.95 (978-0-7862-3927-6(1)) Thomson Gale.

—The Great Ghost Rescue. 2002. (J). pap. 29.95 incl. audio (978-0-7540-6253-0(8)) BBC Audiobooks America.

—The Great Ghost Rescue. Hawkes, Kevin, illus. (J). (gr. 3-7). 2003. 192p. pap. 5.99 (978-0-14-250087-3(9) , Puffin); 2002. 144p. 15.99 (978-0-525-46769-4(6) , Dutton Juvenile) Penguin Group (USA) Inc.

Jacobs, Joseph, ed. English Fairy Tales. 2005. (Twelve-Point Ser.). lib. bdg. 24.00 (978-1-58287-370-1(4)); lib. bdg. 25.00 (978-1-58287-862-1(5)) North Bks.

Jarvis, Robin. The Whitby Witches. Petersen, Jeff, illus. 2006. 296p. (J). 17.95 (978-0-8118-5413-9(2)) Chronicle Bks. LLC.

Johnson, Catherine. Face Value. 2006. 256p. (YA). 16.95 (978-0-8027-8920-4(X)) Walker & Co.

Johnson, Gillian. Thora: A Half-Mermaid Tale. Johnson, Gillian, illus. 2005. (Illus.). 256p. (J). 15.99 (978-0-06-074378-9(6)); lib. bdg. 15.89 (978-0-06-074379-6(4)) HarperCollins Pubs.

Johnson, Jane. The Secret Country. Stower, Adam, illus. 336p. (J). 2007. (Eidolon Chronicles Ser.). pap. 5.99 (*978-1-4169-3815-6(X) , Aladdin); 2006. (Chronicles of Eidolon Ser.: Bk. 1). (gr. 3-7). 14.95 (978-1-4169-0712-1(2)) Simon & Schuster Children's Publishing.

Johnson, Vargie. Charles Darwin, the Discoverer: What Made Them Famous? 2006. (Illus.). 152p. (J). per. 15.00 (978-1-931195-91-1(9)) KiwE Publishing, Ltd.

Jones, Diana Wynne. Witch's Business. 2002. 208p. (J). (gr. 3 up). 15.99 (978-0-06-008782-1(X)); lib. bdg. 17.89 (978-0-06-008783-8(8)) HarperCollins Pubs.

Jordan, Sherryl. The Hunting of the Last Dragon. 2002. 192p. (J). (gr. 7 up). 15.99 (978-0-06-028902-7(3)); 15.89 (978-0-06-028903-4(1)) HarperCollins Pubs.

—Hunting of the Last Dragon. 2002. (gr. 7-12). lib. bdg. 14.15 (978-0-613-68349-4(8)) Tandem Library Bks.

Keeling, E. Annie. Andrew Golding (a Tale of the Great Plag. 2006. 40.99 (***978-1-4280-0516-7(1)***); pap. 34.99 (***978-1-4280-0515-0(3)***) IndyPublish.com.

Keene, Carolyn. Mystery at Moorsea Manor. 1999. (Nancy Drew Mystery Stories: No. 150). (J). (gr. 3-6). (978-0-606-19038-1(4)) Tandem Library Bks.

Kelly, Tom. Finn's Going. 2007. 288p. (J). (gr. 5-9). 16.99 (***978-0-06-121453-0(1)***); lib. bdg. 17.89 (***978-0-06-121454-7(X)***) HarperCollins Pubs. (Greenwillow Bks.).

Kennemore, Tim. Circle of Doom. 2003. 208p. (J). 16.00 (978-0-374-31284-8(2) , Farrar, Straus & Giroux (BYR)) Farrar, Straus & Giroux.

Kennemore, Tim & Archbold, Tim. Circle of Doom. 2006. (Illus.). 208p. (J). pap. 6.95 (978-0-374-41198-5(0)) Macmillan.

King, Laurie R. The Beekeeper's Apprentice. 2002. (Mary Russell Mystery Ser.: Vol. 1). (gr. 7-12). lib. bdg. 21.05 (978-0-613-57620-8(9)) Tandem Library Bks.

King-Smith, Dick. Babe: The Gallant Pig. Kneen, Maggie, illus. 2005. 144p. (J). (gr. 4-7). 16.95 (978-0-375-82970-3(9) , Knopf Bks. for Young Readers) Random Hse. Children's Bks.

—The Catlady. 80p. (J). 2007. (gr. 1-4). 5.50 (***978-0-440-42031-6(8)*** , Yearling); 2006. (Illus.). (gr. 2-5). lib. bdg. 17.99 (978-0-375-92985-4(1) , Knopf Bks. for Young Readers) Random Hse. Children's Bks.

—The Catlady. Eastwood, John, illus. 2006. 80p. (J). (gr. 2-5). 15.95 (978-0-375-82985-7(7) , Knopf Bks. for Young Readers) Random Hse. Children's Bks.

—The Crowstarver. l.t. ed. 2000. (J). (Illus.). 243p. pap. (978-0-7540-6095-6(0) , Galaxy Children's Large Print); 216p. pap. incl. audio (978-0-7540-6228-8(7) , RA029, Chivers Children's Audio Bks.) BBC Audiobooks America.

—Funny Frank. Eastwood, John, illus. 2003. 112p. (gr. 2-5). pap. 5.50 (978-0-440-41880-1(1) , Yearling) Random Hse. Children's Bks.

—Funny Frank. Roth, Roger & Eastwood, John, illus. 2002. 112p. (J). (gr. 2-5). 14.95 (978-0-375-81460-0(4) , Knopf Bks. for Young Readers) Random Hse. Children's Bks.

—Funny Frank. 2003. (gr. 3-6). lib. bdg. 13.00 (978-0-613-72193-6(4)) Tandem Library Bks.

—The Roundhill. Bailey, Sian, illus. 2002. 96p. (YA). (gr. 5-8). 4.99 (978-0-440-41844-3(5) , Yearling) Random Hse. Children's Bks.

—Roundhill. 2002. (gr. 5-8). lib. bdg. 13.00 (978-0-613-62501-2(3)) Tandem Library Bks.

—The Roundhill. l.t. ed. 2001. (Illus.). 112p. (J). 16.95 (978-0-7540-6168-7(X) , Galaxy Children's Large Print) BBC Audiobooks America.

—Sophie's Snail. 1999. (Sophie Bks.). (978-0-606-16402-3(2)) Tandem Library Bks.

—Titus Rules! Eastwood, John, illus. 2003. 96p. (J). (gr. 2-4). lib. bdg. 17.99 (978-0-375-91461-4(7) , Knopf Bks. for Young Readers) Random Hse. Children's Bks.

Kipfer, Roger. TimePortal. 2002. 157p. (J). (gr. 4-7). pap. 9.99 (978-0-88092-568-6(X) , 568X) Royal Fireworks Publishing Co.

Kirchel, Karen. Irrepressible Lucie Archer. 2006. 147p. pap. 19.95 (***978-1-4241-3400-7(5)***) PublishAmerica, Inc.

Knight, Eric. Lassie Come-Home. Kirmse, Marguerite, illus. 2007. 256p. (J). pap. 6.99 (***978-0-312-37131-9(4)***) Square Fish.

Koponen, Libby. Blow Out the Moon. 2006. 224p. (gr. 8-17). pap. 15.99 (978-0-316-01480-9(X) , Tingley, Megan Bks.) Little, Brown Bks. for Young Readers.

Lambert, Janet. Love Taps Gently. 2001. (Jordon Ser.: Vol. 5). (YA). pap. 12.95 (978-1-930009-36-3(4)) Image Cascade Publishing.

Lankester-Brisley, Joyce. Milly-Molly-Mandy Stories. 2002. (Kingfisher Modern Classics Ser.). (Illus.). 240p. (J). (gr. k-3). tchr. ed. 15.95 (978-0-7534-5559-3(5) , Kingfisher) Houghton Mifflin Co. Trade & Reference Div.

Lawrence, Iain. Lord of the Nutcracker Men. (gr. 5). 2003. (Illus.). 240p. (J). pap. 5.99 (978-0-440-41812-2(7) , Laurel Leaf); 2001. 224p. lib. bdg. 17.99 (978-0-385-90024-9(4) , Delacorte Bks. for Young Readers) Random Hse. Children's Bks.

—Lord of the Nutcracker Men. l.t. ed. 2002. 280p. (J). 24.95 (978-0-7862-4155-2(1)) Thomson Gale.

—The Smugglers. (Illus.). (J). (gr. 5-9). 2000. 208p. 5.99 (978-0-440-41596-1(9) , Yearling); 1999. 192p. 15.95 (978-0-385-32663-6(7) , Delacorte Bks. for Young Readers) Random Hse. Children's Bks.

—The Smugglers. 2000. 184p. (J). (ps-7). lib. bdg. 12.15 (978-0-606-19693-2(5)) Tandem Library Bks.

—Smugglers. 2000. (gr. 5-8). lib. bdg. 13.55 (978-0-613-30132-9(3)) Tandem Library Bks.

—The Smugglers. l.t. ed. 2001. (Illus.). 246p. (J). 22.95 (978-0-7862-3465-3(2)) Thorndike Pr.

—The Wreckers. 1999. (978-0-606-17565-4(2)) Tandem Library Bks.

—Wreckers. 1999. (gr. 5-8). lib. bdg. 13.55 (978-0-613-22807-7(3)) Tandem Library Bks.

—The Wreckers. 1999. (Dell Yearling Book Ser.). 224p. (J). (gr. 5-9). reprint ed. 5.99 (978-0-440-41545-9(4) , Yearling) Random Hse. Children's Bks.

—The Wreckers. unabr. ed. 2000. (YA). (gr. 7). pap., stu. ed. 59.95 incl. audio (978-0-7887-4195-1(0) , 41097) Recorded Bks., LLC.

Lawrence, Michael. A Crack in the Line. (Withern Rise Ser.). 2005. 352p. (J). pap. 7.99 (978-0-06-072479-5(X) , HarperTeen); 2004. 336p. (J). lib. bdg. 16.89 (978-0-06-072478-8(1)); 2004. 336p. (YA). 15.99 (978-0-06-072477-1(3)) HarperCollins Pubs.

—Small Eternities. (Withern Rise Ser.). 336p. 2006. (J). pap. 7.99 (978-0-06-072482-5(X) , HarperTeen); 2005. (J). 15.99 (978-0-06-072480-1(3)); 2005. (YA). 16.89 (978-0-06-072481-8(1)) HarperCollins Pubs.

Lawrence, Michael. The Underwood See. 2007. (Withern Rise Ser.). 384p. (J). pap. 7.99 (***978-0-06-072485-6(4)*** , HarperTeen); 16.99 (978-0-06-072483-2(8)); lib. bdg. 17.89 (978-0-06-072484-9(6)) HarperCollins Pubs.

Lawrence, Sara. Those Girls. 2007. 320p. (YA). (gr. 9). pap. 9.99 (***978-1-59514-169-9(3)*** , Razorbill) Penguin Group (USA) Inc.

Le Feuvre, Amy. Teddy's Button. 2002. (Golden Inheritance Ser.: Vol. 6). (Illus.). 93p. (J). (978-0-921100-83-6(3)) Inheritance Pubns.

—Teddy's Button. 2004. reprint ed. pap. 15.95 (978-1-4191-5094-4(4)); pap. 1.99 (978-1-4192-5094-1(9)) Kessinger Publishing, LLC.

Leavitt, Caroline. The Prince & the Pooch. l.t. ed. 1999. (Adventures of Wishbone Ser.: No. 3). (Illus.). 144p. (J). (gr. 4 up). lib. bdg. 22.60 (978-0-8368-2299-1(4)) Stevens, Gareth Inc.

Lefeuvre, Amy. Probable Sons. 2004. reprint ed. pap. 15.95 (978-1-4191-4306-9(9)); pap. 1.99 (978-1-4192-4306-6(3)) Kessinger Publishing, LLC.

Lightfoot, Freda. Polly's War. 2006. 320p. (J). pap. 9.95 (978-0-340-71535-2(9) , Hodder & Stoughton) Hodder General Publishing Division GBR. *Dist:* Trafalgar Square Publishing.

Limb, Sue. Girl, 15, Charming but Insane. 2004. (Girl, 15 Ser.). 214p. (J). (gr. 5). per. 16.00 (978-0-606-33729-8(6)) Tandem Library Bks.

—Girl 15, Charming but Insane. 2007. (Girl, 15 Ser.). 224p. (YA). (gr. 7-11). mass mkt. 5.99 (978-0-440-23896-6(X) , Laurel Leaf) Random Hse. Children's Bks.

—Girl, Barely 15: Flirting for England. 2008. (Girl, 15 Ser.). 256p. (YA). (gr. 5). 15.99 (***978-0-385-73538-4(3)***); lib. bdg. 18.99 (***978-0-385-90520-6(3)***) Random Hse. Children's Bks. (Delacorte Bks. for Young Readers).

—Girl, Going on 17: Pants on Fire. (Girl, 15 Ser.). (gr. 5 up). 2007. 256p. (YA). pap. 8.99 (***978-0-385-73219-2(8)***); 2006. 240p. (J). 14.95 (978-0-385-73218-5(X)); 2006. 240p. (YA). lib. bdg. 17.99 (978-0-385-90246-5(8)) Random Hse. Children's Bks. (Delacorte Bks. for Young Readers).

Limb, Sue. Girl, (Nearly) 16: Absolute Torture. (Girl, 15 Ser.). 224p. (YA). (gr. 5-11). 2008. mass mkt. 6.50 (***978-0-440-23897-3(8)*** , Laurel Leaf); 2006. pap. 8.95 (978-0-385-73217-8(1) , Delacorte Bks. for Young Readers) Random Hse. Children's Bks.

Limke, Jeff. King Arthur: Excalibur Unsheathed. Yeates, Thomas, illus. 2007. (Graphic Myths & Legends Ser.). 48p. (YA). (gr. 4-9). pap. 8.95 (***978-0-8225-6483-6(1)***) Lerner Publishing Group.

Limke Jeff. El rey Arturo (King Arthur) La espada Excalibur desenvainada (Excalibur Unsheathed) Yeates, Thomas, illus. 2007. (Mitos y leyendas en viñetas (Graphic Myths & Legends) Ser.). (J). pap. 8.95 (***978-0-8225-7968-7(5)*** , Ediciones Lerner) Lerner Publishing Group.

Literature Connections English: Jane Eyre. 2004. (gr. 6-12). (978-0-395-77557-8(4) , 2-80126) McDougal Littell Inc.

Literature Connections English: Pride & Prejudice. 2004. (gr. 6-12). (978-0-395-77556-1(6) , 2-80125) McDougal Littell Inc.

Lloyd-Jones, Robin. Moonfleet. 2007. (Young Reading Series 3 Gift Bks). 64p. (J). 8.99 (***978-0-7945-1906-3(7)*** , Usborne) EDC Publishing.

Lorenzo, Mike. Allison's Summer Of '53. 2005. 53p. pap. 12.95 (978-1-4241-1074-2(2)) PublishAmerica, Inc.

Love, D. Anne. The Puppeteer's Apprentice. 192p. (J). 2003. 16.95 (978-0-689-84424-9(7) , McElderry, Margaret K.); 2004. (Illus.). reprint ed. pap. 4.99 (978-0-689-84425-6(5) , Aladdin) Simon & Schuster Children's Publishing.

Lutzen, Hanna. Vlad the Undead. 2001. (gr. 7-12). lib. bdg. 14.10 (978-0-613-88930-8(4)) Tandem Library Bks.

Magrs, Paul. Strange Boy. 2003. 304p. (YA). pap. 8.99 (978-0-689-83712-8(7)) Simon & Schuster, Ltd. GBR. *Dist:* Independent Pubs. Group.

Malley, Gemma. The Declaration. 2007. 320p. (J). (gr. 5 up). 16.95 (***978-1-59990-119-0(6)***) Bloomsbury Publishing.

Manning, Sarra. Pretty Things (Splashproof Ed.) 2007. 1p. (YA). (gr. 7). pap. 6.99 (978-0-14-240859-9(X) , Puffin) Penguin Group (USA) Inc.

Marks, Graham. Missing in Tokyo. 2006. 256p. (YA). 16.95 (978-1-58234-907-7(X) , Bloomsbury Children) Bloomsbury Publishing.

Marr, Andrew. Born in the Darkest Time of Year: Stories for the Season of the Christ Child. 2004. 180p. (J). pap. 13.95 (978-0-595-32633-4(1)) iUniverse, Inc.

Masefield, John. The Box of Delights. 2007. (Illus.). 320p. (J). (gr. 4-9). 17.95 (***978-1-59017-251-3(5)*** , NYR Children's Collection) New York Review of Bks., Inc., The.

Mason, Simon. The Quigleys. Stephens, Helen, illus. 160p. (gr. k-7). 2003. 4.99 (978-0-440-41898-6(4) , Yearling); 2002. (J). 14.95 (978-0-385-75006-6(4) , Fickling, David Bks.) Random Hse. Children's Bks.

—Quigleys: Not for Sale. Stephens, Helen, illus. 2004. 176p. (J). (gr. k-7). 14.95 (978-0-385-75043-1(9) , Fickling, David Bks.) Random Hse. Children's Bks.

—The Quigleys: Not for Sale. Stephens, Helen, illus. 2006. 176p. (J). (gr. k-7). 5.50 (978-0-440-42084-2(9) , Yearling) Random Hse. Children's Bks.

—The Quigleys in a Spin. Stephens, Helen, illus. 2006. 192p. (J). (gr. k-7). lib. bdg. 16.99 (978-0-385-75099-8(4) , Fickling, David Bks.) Random Hse. Children's Bks.

Matthews, L. S. A Dog for Life. 2006. 176p. (J). (gr. 5). 16.99 (978-0-385-90381-3(2)); 14.95 (978-0-385-73366-3(6)) Random Hse. Children's Bks. (Delacorte Bks. for Young Readers).

Matthews, L. S. The Outcasts. 2007. 272p. (YA). (gr. 7). 15.99 (***978-0-385-73367-0(4)***); lib. bdg. 18.99 (***978-0-385-90382-0(0)***) Random Hse. Children's Bks. (Delacorte Bks. for Young Readers).

Maxwell, Katie. The Year My Life Went down the Loo. 2003. (YA). pap. 5.99 (978-0-8439-5313-8(6)) Dorchester Publishing Co., Inc.

McAllister, Margaret. The Octave of Angels. 2004. 128p. (J). pap. 8.00 (978-0-8028-5240-3(8)) Eerdmans, William B. Publishing Co.

McKay, Hilary. The Amber Cat. 1999. (YA). pap., stu. ed. 41.00 incl. audio (978-0-7887-3635-3(3) , 41000) Recorded Bks., LLC.

—The Amber Cat. 1999. 'p. (J). 11.64 (978-0-606-16326-2(3)) Tandem Library Bks.

—Caddy Ever After. 224p. (J). 2007. pap. 5.99 (***978-1-4169-0931-6(1)*** , Aladdin); 2006. (gr. 5-9). 15.95 (978-1-4169-0930-9(3) , McElderry, Margaret K.) Simon & Schuster Children's Publishing.

—Dolphin Luck. l.t. ed. 2005. (Illus.). 272p. (J). pap. incl. audio (978-0-7540-7865-4(5) , CLP 449) BBC Audio.

—Dolphin Luck. 2004. (J). pap. 29.95 incl. audio (978-0-7540-6273-8(2) , Chivers Children's Audio Bks.) BBC Audiobooks America.

—Dolphin Luck. 2000. (J). (978-0-606-20086-8(X)) Tandem Library Bks.

—Dolphin Luck. l.t. ed. 2001. (Illus.). 198p. (J). (gr. 4-7). 21.95 (978-0-7862-2703-7(6)) Thorndike Pr.

—The Exiles in Love. 1999. (J). 11.15 (978-0-606-17315-5(3)) Tandem Library Bks.

—Forever Rose. 2008. 304p. (J). 16.99 (***978-1-4169-5486-6(4)*** , McElderry, Margaret K.) Simon & Schuster Children's Publishing.

—Indigo's Star. 272p. (J). (gr. 3-7). 2004. (Illus.). 16.95 (978-0-689-86563-3(5) , McElderry, Margaret K.); 2006. reprint ed. pap. 5.99 (978-1-4169-1403-7(X) , Aladdin) Simon & Schuster Children's Publishing.

—Permanent Rose. (J). (gr. 3-7). 2005. 240p. 16.99 (978-1-4169-0372-7(0) , McElderry, Margaret K.); 2006. 256p. reprint ed. pap. 5.99 (978-1-4169-2804-1(9) , Aladdin) Simon & Schuster Children's Publishing.

—Saffy's Angel. 2004. 160p. (J). (gr. 4-7). pap. 36.00 incl. audio (978-0-8072-2098-6(1) , Listening Library) Random Hse. Audio Publishing Group.

—Saffy's Angel. 160p. (J). (gr. 3-7). 2003. (Illus.). pap. 4.99 (978-0-689-84934-3(6) , Aladdin); 2002. 16.99 (978-0-689-84933-6(8) , McElderry, Margaret K.) Simon & Schuster Children's Publishing.

—Saffy's Angel. l.t. ed. 2003. (Juvenile Ser.). 227p. (J). 21.95 (978-0-7862-5500-9(5)) Thorndike Pr.

McNab, Andy & Rigby, Robert. Traitor. 2006. 288p. (YA). (gr. 7). pap. 6.99 (978-0-14-240727-1(5) , Puffin) Penguin Group (USA) Inc.

McNish, Cliff. Breathe: A Ghost Story. 2006. 264p. (J). 15.95 (978-0-8225-6443-0(2) , Carolrhoda Bks.) Lerner Publishing Group.

Meade, T. L. Polly (a New-Fashioned Girl) 2006. 43.99 (***978-1-4280-4099-1(4)***); pap. 37.99 (***978-1-4280-4078-6(1)***) IndyPublish.com.

Mendes, Valerie. Girl in the Attic. 2002. 213p. (YA). pap. 8.99 (978-0-689-83680-0(5)) Simon & Schuster, Ltd. GBR. *Dist:* Independent Pubs. Group.

Meyer, Carolyn. Doomed Queen Anne. 2004. (Young Royals Ser.). (Illus.). 256p. (J). pap. 5.95 (978-0-15-205086-3(8) , Gulliver Bks.) Harcourt Children's Bks.

—Mary, Bloody Mary. 2001. (Young Royals Ser.). 240p. (YA). (gr. 7 up). pap. 6.00 (978-0-15-216456-0(1) , Gulliver Bks.) Harcourt Children's Bks.

Michael, Livi. The Whispering Road. 2006. 336p. (J). (gr. 5). pap. 6.99 (978-0-14-240724-0(0) , Puffin) Penguin Group (USA) Inc.

Miles, Patricia. The Gods in Winter. 2005. 147p. (J). (gr. 3-7). pap. 8.95 (978-1-932425-47-5(0) , Lemniscaat) Boyds Mills Pr.

Miller, Gary & Miller, Lynda. The Adventures of Bob & Betty. 2006. (J). spiral bd. (978-1-933594-92-7(6)) Faith Baptist Church Publns.

Milne, A. A. The Red House Mystery. 2001. 202p. (J). per. 6.49 (978-1-57924-702-7(4)) Jones, Bob Univ. Pr.

Molloy, Michael. The House on Falling Star Hill. 2004. (Illus.). 384p. (J). pap. 16.95 (978-0-439-57740-3(3) , Chicken Hse., The) Scholastic, Inc.

Moloney, James. Black Taxi. 2005. 272p. (J). (gr. 7 up). 15.99 (978-0-06-055937-3(3)); lib. bdg. 16.89 (978-0-06-055938-0(1)) HarperCollins Pubs.

Montgomery, R. A. Forecast from Stonehenge. 2007. (Choose Your Own Adventure Ser.: No. 19). (Illus.). 144p. (J). mass mkt. 6.99 (***978-1-933390-19-2(0)***) Chooseco LLC.

Morgan, Jennifer. A Wind from the Sea. 2003. 200p. pap. 12.95 (978-1-84323-209-4(X)) Beekman Bks., Inc.

Morgan, Nicola. Chicken Friend. 2005. 160p. (J). (gr. 4-7). 15.99 (978-0-7636-2735-5(6)) Candlewick Pr.

Morpurgo, Michael. Farm Boy. Foreman, Michael, illus. 1999. 74p. (YA). pap. 16.99 (978-1-86205-192-8(5) , Pavilion Bks., Ltd.) Anova Bks. GBR. *Dist:* Trafalgar Square Publishing.

Morris, Gerald. Parsifal's Page. (Squire's Tales Ser.). 240p. (J). (gr. 5-9). 2004. pap. 5.95 (978-0-618-43237-0(X)); 2001. (Illus.). tchr. ed. 16.00 (978-0-618-05509-8(6)) Houghton Mifflin Co. Trade & Reference Div.

—The Princess, the Crone, & the Dung-Cart Knight. (Squire's Tales Ser.). 320p. (YA). (gr. 5-9). 2006. pap. 6.95 (978-0-618-73748-2(0)); 2004. tchr. ed. 16.00 (978-0-618-37823-4(5)) Houghton Mifflin Co. Trade & Reference Div.

—The Savage Damsel & the Dwarf. (Squire's Tales Ser.). 224p. (gr. 5-9). 2004. (YA). pap. 5.95 (978-0-618-19681-4(1)); 2000. (J). tchr. ed. 16.00 (978-0-395-97126-0(8)) Houghton Mifflin Co. Trade & Reference Div.

—The Squire & His Knight. l.t. ed. 2001. (Illus.). 257p. (J). (gr. 4-7). 21.95 (978-0-7862-3039-6(8)) Thorndike Pr.

—The Squire, His Knight, & His Lady. 1999. (Squire's Tales Ser.). 240p. (J). (gr. 5-9). tchr. ed. 16.00 (978-0-395-91211-9(3)) Houghton Mifflin Co. Trade & Reference Div.

—The Squire's Tale. 1998. (Squire's Tales Ser.). 224p. (J). (gr. 5-9). tchr. ed. 16.00 (978-0-395-86959-8(5)) Houghton Mifflin Co. Trade & Reference Div.

—Squire's Tale. 2000. (978-0-606-17839-6(2)) Tandem Library Bks.

Morton-Shaw, Christine. The Riddles of Epsilon. 384p. 2006. (J). pap. 7.99 (978-0-06-072821-2(3)); Vol. 1. 2005. (gr. 7 up). 16.99 (978-0-06-072819-9(1)) HarperCollins Pubs.

Moss, Alexandra. Boys or Ballet? 2006. 142p. (J). (***978-1-4156-8361-3(1)*** , Grosset & Dunlap) Penguin Group (USA) Inc.

Mould, Wendy. Ants in My Pants. Mould, Wendy, illus. 2001. (Illus.). 32p. (J). (gr. k-3). tchr. ed. 15.00 (978-0-618-09640-4(X) , Clarion Bks.) Houghton Mifflin Co. Trade & Reference Div.

Mullin, Caryl Cude. A Riddle of Roses. 2000. (Illus.). 222p. (YA). (gr. 5-8). pap. 6.95 (978-1-896764-28-3(2)) Second Story Pr. CAN. *Dist:* Orca Bk. Pubs. USA, Univ. of Toronto Pr.

Murail, Marie-Aude. Sin Azucar, Gracias. 2003. (la Orilla Del Viento Ser.). (SPA.). 104p. (J). 4.99 (978-968-16-6725-2(5)) Fondo de Cultura Economica USA.

Mussi, Sarah. The Door of No Return. 2008. (YA). (***978-1-4169-1550-8(8)*** , McElderry, Margaret K.) Simon & Schuster Children's Publishing.

My Way Sally: Evaluation Guide. 2006. (J). (978-1-55942-418-9(4)) Marsh Media.

Naidoo, Beverley. The Other Side of Truth. 2003. (gr. 5-8). lib. bdg. 14.15 (978-0-613-59158-4(5)) Tandem Library Bks.

Napoli, Donna Jo. Crazy Jack. 2000. (YA). pap., stu. ed. 51.95 incl. audio (978-0-7887-4159-3(4) , 41099) Recorded Bks., LLC.

—Crazy Jack. l.t. ed. 2000. 183p. (YA). (gr. 8-12). 20.95 (978-0-7862-3047-1(9)) Thorndike Pr.

Naylor, Phyllis Reynolds. Footprints at the Window. 2002. (York Trilogy Ser.: Vol. 3). (Illus.). 173p. (J). pap. 4.99 (978-0-689-84963-3(X) , Aladdin) Simon & Schuster Children's Publishing.

—Footprints at the Window. 2002. (gr. 7-12). lib. bdg. 13.00 (978-0-613-45042-3(6)) Tandem Library Bks.

Nesbit, E. The Enchanted Castle. l.t. ed. 2005. 388p. pap. (978-1-84637-202-5(X)) Echo Library.

—Five Children & IT. 207p. 20.95 (978-0-8488-2523-2(3)) Amereon LTD.

—Five Children & IT. 2002. (Dover Evergreen Classics Ser.). (Illus.). 160p. (J). (gr. 4-7). pap. 2.50 (978-0-486-42366-1(2)) Dover Pubns., Inc.

—Five Children & IT. Zelinsky, Paul O., illus. 1999. (Books of Wonder). 256p. (gr. 4-7). 22.95 (978-0-688-13545-4(5)) HarperCollins Pubs.

—Five Children & IT. 2002. 192p. pap. 14.95 (978-1-59224-938-1(8)); lib. bdg. 24.95 (978-1-59224-942-8(6)) Wildside Pr.

—Five Children & It. l.t. ed. 2005. 296p. pap. (978-1-84637-200-1(3)) Echo Library.

—Jack & the Beanstalk. Tavares, Matt, illus. 2006. 48p. (J). (ps-1). 16.99 (978-0-7636-2124-7(2)) Candlewick Pr.

—The Railway Children. Dryhurst, Dinah, illus. 2000. 224p. (J). pap. 8.99 (978-1-86205-235-2(2) , Pavilion Bks., Ltd.) Anova Bks. GBR. *Dist:* Trafalgar Square Publishing.

—The Railway Children. Dryhurst, Dinah, tr. Dryhurst, Dinah, illus. 2004. 184p. 18.95 (978-1-56792-261-5(9)) Godine, David R. Pub.

—The Railway Children. 2002. (gr. 3-6). lib. bdg. 23.40 (978-0-613-86551-7(0)) Tandem Library Bks.

—The Railway Children. 1998. (Children's Classics). (ENG., Illus.). 208p. (J). (gr. 4-7). pap. (978-1-85326-107-7(6) , 1076WW) Wordsworth Editions, Ltd.

—Railway Children. Brock, C. E., illus. (YA). 14.95 (978-0-8118-4933-3(3)) Chronicle Bks. LLC.

—Railway Children. 2000. (Dover Juvenile Classics Ser.). (Illus.). 208p. (J). (gr. 4-7). pap. 2.50 (978-0-486-41022-7(6)) Dover Pubns., Inc.

—Railway Children. 2006. pap. (***978-1-4068-3505-2(6)***) Echo Library.

—Railway Children. (J). (978-0-340-71497-3(2) , Hodder & Stoughton) Hodder General Publishing Division.

—The Railway Children, Level 3. 2nd ed. 2000. (Bookworms Ser.). (Illus.). 74p. 6.50 (978-0-19-423013-1(9)) Oxford Univ. Pr., Inc.

—The Railway Children, Level 2. 2000. (Illus.). 48p. (C). pap. 9.00 (978-0-582-41790-8(2)) Pearson ESL.

Nesbit, E. The Story of the Amulet. 2006. pap. 46.99 (***978-1-4280-0877-9(2)***) IndyPublish.com.

Newbery, Linda. At the Firefly Gate. 2007. 160p. (J). (gr. 5). 15.99 (978-0-385-75113-1(3)); lib. bdg. 18.99 (978-0-385-75114-8(1)) Random Hse. Children's Bks. (Fickling, David Bks.).

—The Shell House. 2004. 352p. (YA). (gr. 7-11). reprint ed. mass mkt. 6.50 (978-0-440-23786-0(6) , Laurel Leaf) Random Hse. Children's Bks.

Newman, Robert. Lost Treasures Bk. 5: Merlin's Mistake. 2001. 240p. (J). 13.49 (978-0-7868-2600-1(2)) Hyperion Pr.

Nimmo, Jenny. Charlie Bone & the Hidden King. 2006. (Children of the Red King Ser.: Bk. 5). xx, 441p. (J). (***978-1-4156-7832-9(4)*** , Orchard Bks.) Scholastic, Inc.

Nimmo, Jenny. Midnight for Charlie Bone. 2003. (Children of the Red King Ser.: Bk. 1). 416p. (gr. 4-6). 9.95 (978-0-439-47429-0(9) , Orchard Bks.) Scholastic, Inc.

Norton, Andre. Red Hart Magic. 2007. (Magic Bks.: Bk. 6). 224p. (J). 5.99 (978-0-7653-5302-3(4) , Starscape) Doherty, Tom Assocs., LLC.

Norton, Mary. The Borrowers. Krush, Beth & Krush, Joe, illus. 2003. (Borrowers Ser.). 192p. (J). pap. 5.95 (978-0-15-204737-5(9) , Odyssey Classics) Harcourt Children's Bks.

—The Borrowers. Stanley, Diana, illus. 50th anniv. gif. ed. 2003. (Borrowers Ser.). 176p. (J). 19.95 (978-0-15-204928-7(2)) Harcourt Children's Bks.

—The Borrowers Afield. Krush, Beth & Krush, Joe, illus. 50th anniv. ed. 2003. (Borrowers Ser.). 224p. (J). pap. 5.95 (978-0-15-204732-0(8) , Odyssey Classics) Harcourt Children's Bks.

—The Borrowers Afloat. Krush, Beth & Krush, Joe, illus. 2003. (Borrowers Ser.). 192p. (J). pap. 5.95 (978-0-15-204733-7(6) , Odyssey Classics) Harcourt Children's Bks.

—The Borrowers Avenged. Krush, Joe & Krush, Beth, illus. 50th anniv. ed. 2003. (Borrowers Ser.). 304p. (J). pap. 5.95 (978-0-15-204731-3(X) , Odyssey Classics) Harcourt Children's Bks.

Noyes, Deborah. Angel & the Apsotle. 2006. 304p. pap. 14.95 (978-1-932961-29-4(1)) Unbridled Bks.

O'Brien, Patrick. The Making of a Knight: How Sir James Earned His Armor. 1998. (Illus.). 32p. (J). (gr. 1-4). 15.95 (978-0-88106-354-7(1)) Charlesbridge Publishing, Inc.

O'Connell, Tyne. Dueling Princes: The Calypso Chronicles, Book 3. 2006. 272p. (YA). pap. 7.95 (978-1-58234-900-8(2) , Bloomsbury Children) Bloomsbury Publishing.

—Dumping Princes. (YA). 2007. 256p. pap. 7.95 (****978-1-59990-150-3(1)*** , Bloomsbury Children); 2006. (Calypso Chronicles Ser.: Bk. 4). (Illus.). 304p. (gr. 7-10). 16.95 (978-1-58234-852-0(9)) Bloomsbury Publishing.

O'Connell, Tyne. Stealing Princes. (Calypso Chronicles : Bk. 2). (ps-7). 2005. (Illus.). 250p. (J). 16.95 (978-1-58234-992-3(4)); 2006. 304p. (YA). reprint ed. pap. 7.95 (978-1-58234-905-3(3)) Bloomsbury Publishing. (Bloomsbury Children).

Oldham, Mary. No Fire, No Candle. 2001. 217p. (YA). pap. 12.95 (978-1-85902-945-9(0)) Beekman Bks., Inc.

O'Neill, Katrina & Thompson, Lisa. Quest for the Cup. Cantell, Brenda, illus. 2005. (Treasure Trackers Ser.). 80p. (gr. 5-9). 19.00 (978-0-7910-8876-0(6)) Facts On File, Inc.

Osborne, Mary Pope. Stage Fright on a Summer Night. Murdocca, Sal, illus. 2002. (Magic Tree House Ser.: No. 25). 96p. (J). (gr. k-3). lib. bdg. 11.99 (978-0-375-90611-4(8)); 25. pap. 3.99 (978-0-375-80611-7(3)) Random Hse. Children's Bks. (Random Hse. Bks. for Young Readers).

—Stage Fright on a Summer Night. Murdocca, Salvatore, illus. 2002. (Magic Tree House Ser. : No. 25). 70p. (J). (gr. k-3). lib. bdg. 10.79 (978-0-606-24092-5(6)) Tandem Library Bks.

—Stage Fright on a Summer Night. 2002. (Magic Tree House Ser. : No. 25). (J). (gr. k-3). lib. bdg. 11.80 (978-0-613-50506-2(9)) Tandem Library Bks.

Paine, Penelope C. Time for Horatio. Maeno, Itoko, illus. 2001. 48p. (J). per. 17.95 (978-0-9707944-7-5(9)) Paper Posie.

Parra, B. A. Tyler Trio Adventure on a Quest for Knighthood. 2007. 145p. pap. 10.50 (****978-0-615-15090-1(X)***) Parra, Beverly.

Patterson-Wallace, S. Forkyped. 2005. 114p. pap. 16.95 (978-1-4137-5622-7(0)) PublishAmerica, Inc.

Peck, Richard. Amanda/Miranda. 2001. (J). 12.64 (978-0-606-21025-6(3)); (gr. 7-12). lib. bdg. 14.15 (978-0-613-36046-3(X)) Tandem Library Bks.

Pennington, Kate. Brief Candle. 2005. (J). pap. (978-0-340-87370-0(1) , Hodder Children's Books) Hodder Children's Division.

—Nightingale's Song. 2007. 284p. (YA). (gr. 7 up). pap. 9.95 (****978-0-340-87875-0(4)***) Hodder Children's Division GBR. *Dist:* Independent Pubs. Group.

Pennington, Kate. Tread Softly. 2003. (YA). 16.99 (978-0-340-87862-0(2) , Hodder & Stoughton) Hodder General Publishing Division GBR. *Dist:* Trafalgar Square Publishing.

Pennington, Kate & Oldfield, Jenny. Tread Softly. 2005. (J). pap. (978-0-340-87343-4(4) , Hodder Children's Books) Hodder Children's Division.

Picard, Barbara Leonie. One Is One. 2006. 321p. pap. 9.95 (978-1-58988-027-6(7)) Consortium Bk. Sales & Distribution.

Pirotta, Saviour & Marks, Alan. The Giant Oak Tree. 2007. (J). (****978-1-59771-080-0(6)***) Sea-To-Sea Pubns.

Pope, Elizabeth Marie. The Perilous Gard. Cuffari, Richard, illus. 2001. 280p. (J). (ps-7). per. 14.10 (978-0-613-35551-3(2)) Tandem Library Bks.

Pratchett, Terry. Johnny & the Bomb. 2007. 256p. (J). lib. bdg. 17.89 (978-0-06-054192-7(X)); (gr. 5-8). 16.99 (978-0-06-054191-0(1)) HarperCollins Pubs.

—Johnny & the Dead. 224p. (J). 2007. pap. 5.99 (978-0-06-054190-3(3) , Harper Trophy); 2006. 15.99 (978-0-06-054188-0(1)); 2006. (gr. 5-7). lib. bdg. 16.89 (978-0-06-054189-7(X)) HarperCollins Pubs.

Pride & Prejudice. 2002. (Illus.). (YA). 48p. stu. ed., per. 17.95 (978-1-56254-530-7(2) , SP5302); 80p. per. 6.95 (978-1-56254-529-1(9) , SP5299) Saddleback Educational Publishing.

Priestley, Chris. Redwulf's Curse: A Tom Marlowe Adventure. 2005. (Illus.). 176p. (YA). (gr. 6-10). 16.99 (978-0-385-60695-0(8) , Doubleday) Transworld Publishers Ltd. GBR. *Dist:* Trafalgar Square Publishing.

The Prince & the Pauper. 2000. (Illus.). 80p. (YA). per. 6.95 (978-1-56254-287-0(7) , SP2877) Saddleback Educational Publishing.

Pringle, Eric. Big George. 2001. (gr. 3-6). lib. bdg. 18.75 (978-0-613-62506-7(4)) Tandem Library Bks.

—Big George: A Novel. Paine, Colin, illus. 2001. 160p. (J). (gr. 3-7). 18.95 (978-1-55037-713-2(2)); pap. 9.95 (978-1-55037-712-5(4)) Annick Pr., Ltd. CAN. *Dist:* Firefly Bks., Ltd.

Prue, Sally. The Devil's Toenail. 2004. (Illus.). 208p. (J). 16.95 (978-0-439-48634-7(3)) Scholastic, Inc.

Pullman, Philip. Count Karlstein. 2000. (Corgi Yearling Ser.). (Illus.). 112p. (J). pap. 9.99 (978-0-440-86266-6(3)) Transworld Publishers Ltd. GBR. *Dist:* Trafalgar Square Publishing.

—I Was a Rat! 2000. (Illus.). 176p. (gr. 3-5). 15.95 (978-0-375-80176-1(6) , Knopf Bks. for Young Readers) Random Hse. Children's Bks.

—I Was a Rat! Or the Scarlet Slippers. l.t. ed. 2005. 256p. (J). pap. (978-0-7540-6132-8(9) , CLP 326) BBC Audio.

—I Was a Rat! Or the Scarlet Slippers. unabr. l.t. ed. 2001. (Read-Along Ser.). 224p. (J). 29.95 incl. audio (978-0-7540-6233-2(3) , RA034, Chivers Children's Audio Bks.) BBC Audiobooks America.

—I Was a Rat! Or the Scarlet Slippers. 2002. (gr. 7-12). lib. bdg. 13.00 (978-0-613-64439-6(5)) Tandem Library Bks.

—Lyra's Oxford. Lawrence, John, illus. 2007. 64p. (YA). (gr. 7-12). per. 6.99 (****978-0-375-84369-3(8)*** , Knopf Bks. for Young Readers) Random Hse. Children's Bks.

—Lyra's Oxford: A Novel. Lawrence, John, illus. 2006. 49p. (YA). reprint ed. 11.00 (978-1-4223-5410-0(5)) DIANE Publishing Co.

—Sally y la Sombra del Norte. Miguel, Isabel de, tr. 2002. Tr. of Shadow in the North. (SPA.). 347p. (J). pap. (978-84-95618-46-7(X) , Umbriel) Ediciones Urano S. A.

Ransome, Arthur. The Big Six. 1999. (Swallows & Amazons Ser.). (Illus.). 367p. (J). (gr. 5 up). reprint ed. pap. 14.95 (978-1-56792-119-9(1)) Godine, David R. Pub.

Reiche, Dietlof & Brownjohn, John. The Haunting of Freddy. Cepeda, Joe, illus. 2006. (Golden Hamster Saga Ser.: Bk. 4). 320p. (J). pap. 16.99 (978-0-439-53159-7(4) , Scholastic Pr.) Scholastic, Inc.

Reiss, Kathryn. Blackthorn Winter: A Murder Mystery. (YA). 2007. (Illus.). 348p. pap. 6.95 (****978-0-15-206109-8(6)*** , Harcourt Paperbacks); 2006. 352p. 17.00 (978-0-15-205479-3(0)) Harcourt Children's Bks.

Renninson, Lou. Frontalknutschen. pap. 17.95 (978-3-570-30008-4(0)) Bertelsman, Verlagsgruppe C. GmbH DEU. *Dist:* Distribooks, Inc.

Rennison, Louise. Angus, Thongs & Full-Frontal Snogging. 2000. (Confessions of Georgia Nicolson Ser.). (Illus.). 256p. (J). (gr. 7 up). lib. bdg. 17.89 (978-0-06-028871-6(X)) HarperCollins Pubs.

—Angus, Thongs & Full-Frontal Snogging: Confessions of Georgia Nicolson. (Confessions of Georgia Nicolson Ser.). (J). (gr. 7 up). 2001. 272p. pap. 7.99 (978-0-06-447227-2(2) , HarperTeen); 2000. 256p. 16.99 (978-0-06-028814-3(0)) HarperCollins Pubs.

—Angus, Thongs & Full-Frontal Snogging: Confessions of Georgia Nicolson. 2003. (gr. 7-12). lib. bdg. 15.30 (978-0-613-71444-0(X)) Tandem Library Bks.

—Angus, Thongs, & Full-Frontal Snogging: Confessions of Georgia Nicolson. 2001. (gr. 7-12). lib. bdg. 15.30 (978-0-613-35897-2(X)) Tandem Library Bks.

—Dancing in My Nuddy-Pants: Even Further Confessions of Georgia Nicolson. (Confessions of Georgia Nicolson Ser.). 2003. 224p. (J). 15.99 (978-0-06-009746-2(9)); 2004. 240p. (YA). reprint ed. pap. 7.99 (978-0-06-009748-6(5)) HarperCollins Pubs. (HarperTeen).

—Further Confessions of Georgia Nicolson. ed. 2004. (Confessions of Georgia Nicolson Ser.). 416p. (J). pap. 13.99 (978-0-06-059007-9(6)) HarperCollins Pubs.

—Knocked Out by My Nunga-Nungas: Further, Further Confessions of Georgia Nicolson. 2002. (Confessions of Georgia Nicolson Ser.). 192p. (J). (gr. 8-10). 15.99 (978-0-06-623656-8(8)) HarperCollins Pubs.

—Knocked Out by My Nunga-Nungas: Further, Further Confessions of Georgia Nicolson. 2003. (gr. 7-12). lib. bdg. 15.30 (978-0-613-67208-5(9)) Tandem Library Bks.

—On the Bright Side, I'm Now the Girlfriend of a Sex God: Further Confessions Of. 2002. (gr. 7-12). lib. bdg. 15.30 (978-0-613-49344-4(3)) Tandem Library Bks.

—On the Bright Side, I'm Now the Girlfriend of a Sex God: Further Confessions of Georgia Nicolson. (Confessions of Georgia Nicolson Ser.). 2003. 256p. (J). pap. 6.99 (978-0-06-052185-1(6)); 2002. 272p. (YA). pap. 7.99 (978-0-06-447226-5(4)); 2001. 256p. (J). (gr. 7 up). 17.99 (978-0-06-028813-6(2)) HarperCollins Pubs.

—Startled by His Furry Shorts. 2007. (Confessions of Georgia Nicolson Ser.). 304p. (J). pap. 7.99 (****978-0-06-085386-0(7)*** , HarperTeen) HarperCollins Pubs.

—Startled by His Furry Shorts! 2006. (Confessions of Georgia Nicolson Ser.). 288p. (J). 16.99 (978-0-06-085384-6(0)); lib. bdg. 17.89 (978-0-06-085385-3(9)) HarperCollins Pubs. (HarperTeen).

—Then He Ate My Boy Entrancers: More Mad, Marvy Confessions of Georgia Nicolson. (Confessions of Georgia Nicolson Ser.). 2006. 336p. (J). pap. 7.99 (978-0-06-058939-4(6)); 2005. 320p. (J). lib. bdg. 16.89 (978-0-06-058938-7(8)); No. 6. 2005. 320p. (YA). 15.99 (978-0-06-058937-0(X)) HarperCollins Pubs. (HarperTeen).

Resnick, Jane Parker. A Christmas Carol: A Young Reader's Edition of the Classic Holiday Tale. Birmingham, Christian, illus. 2000. (Courage Children's Ser.). 56p. (J). (gr. 4-7). 9.98 (978-0-7624-0848-1(0) , Courage Bks.) Running Pr. Bk. Pubs.

Richards, Justin. The Invisible Detective: Double Life. 2005. 160p. (J). (gr. 4). 10.99 (978-0-399-24313-4(5) , Putnam Juvenile) Penguin Group (USA) Inc.

Rosoff, Meg. How I Live Now. 2006. 224p. (YA). (gr. 7). reprint ed. pap. 7.99 (978-0-553-37605-0(5) , Lamb, Wendy) Random Hse. Children's Bks.

—How I Live Now. 2006. 250p. (YA). 23.95 (978-0-7862-8878-6(7)) Thorndike Pr.

—Just in Case. 2008. 256p. (gr. 12). 14.00 (****978-0-452-28937-6(8)*** , Plume) Penguin Group (USA) Inc.

—Just in Case. 2006. 256p. (YA). (gr. 9-11). 16.95 (978-0-385-74678-6(4)); lib. bdg. 18.99 (978-0-385-90909-9(8)) Random Hse. Children's Bks. (Lamb, Wendy).

Rowling, J. K. Harrius Potter et Camera Secretorum. Needham, Peter, tr. from ENG. 2006. Orig. Title: Harry Potter & the Chamber of Secrets. (LAT., Illus.). 300p. (J). 23.95 (978-1-59990-067-4(X) , Bloomsbury Children) Bloomsbury Publishing.

—Harry Potter & the Chamber of Secrets. braille ed. 1999. (Harry Potter Ser.: Year 2). 520p. (YA). (gr. 3 up). pap. 17.99 (978-0-939173-35-8(2)) National Braille Pr.

—Harry Potter & the Chamber of Secrets. 2003. 203p. 23.95 (978-7-02-003344-7(X) , HAP02) People's Literature Publishing Hse. CHN. *Dist:* China Bks. & Periodicals, Inc.

—Harry Potter & the Chamber of Secrets. unabr. ed. 2004. (Harry Potter Ser.: Year 2). 352p. (J). (gr. 3 up). pap. 46.00 incl. audio (978-0-8072-8207-6(3) , S YA 137 SP, Listening Library) Random Hse. Audio Publishing Group.

—Harry Potter & the Chamber of Secrets. (RUS., Illus.). 28.95 (978-5-8451-0947-7(7)) Rosmen-Izdat RUS. *Dist:* Distribooks, Inc.

—Harry Potter & the Chamber of Secrets. 2003. (Harry Potter Ser.: Year 2). 352p. (J). 24.95 (978-0-439-55489-3(6) , Levine, Arthur A. Bks.) Scholastic, Inc.

—Harry Potter & the Chamber of Secrets. GrandPré, Mary, illus. (Harry Potter Ser.: Year 2). (J). 2002. 448p. mass mkt. 6.99 (978-0-439-42010-5(5) , Levine, Arthur A. Bks.); 2000. 352p. (gr. 3 up). mass mkt. 8.99 (978-0-439-06487-3(2)); 1999. 352p. (gr. 3 up). 22.99 (978-0-439-06486-6(4) , Levine, Arthur A. Bks.); 2002. 352p. 75.00 (978-0-439-20353-1(8) , Levine, Arthur A. Bks.) Scholastic, Inc.

—Harry Potter & the Chamber of Secrets. GrandPré, Mary, illus. l.t. ed. 2000. (Harry Potter Ser.: Year 2). 464p. (gr. 3 up). 24.95 (978-0-7862-2273-5(5) , Large Print Pr.) Thorndike Pr.

—Harry Potter & the Deathly Hallows. braille ed. 2007. (Harry Potter Ser.: Year 7). 34.99 (****978-0-939173-57-0(3)***) National Braille Pr.

—Harry Potter & the Deathly Hallows. GrandPré, Mary, illus. 2007. (Harry Potter Ser.: Year 7). 784p. (J). (gr. 4-7). 34.99 (****978-0-545-01022-1(5));*** 784p. (YA). (gr. 6 up). 39.99 (****978-0-545-02936-0(8));*** 816p. (J). 65.00 (****978-0-545-02937-7(6)***) Scholastic, Inc. (Levine, Arthur A. Bks.).

—Harry Potter & the Deathly Hallows. l.t. ed. 2007. (Harry Potter Ser.: Year 7). (YA). 34.95 (****978-0-7862-9665-1(8)***) Thorndike Pr.

—Harry Potter & the Goblet of Fire. braille ed. 2000. (Harry Potter Ser.: Year 4). 650p. (YA). (gr. 3 up). pap. 25.95 (978-0-939173-37-2(9)) National Braille Pr.

—Harry Potter & the Goblet of Fire. 2003. (Harry Potter Ser.: Year 4). 752p. (J). 30.95 (978-0-439-55490-9(X) , Levine, Arthur A. Bks.) Scholastic, Inc.

—Harry Potter & the Goblet of Fire. GrandPré, Mary, illus. (Harry Potter Ser.: Year 4). 752p. (J). (gr. 3 up). 2002. mass mkt. 9.99 (978-0-439-13960-1(0)); 2000. 29.99 (978-0-439-13959-5(7)) Scholastic, Inc. (Levine, Arthur A. Bks.).

—Harry Potter & the Goblet of Fire. 2002. (gr. 3-6). lib. bdg. 17.60 (978-0-613-49674-2(4)) Tandem Library Bks.

—Harry Potter & the Goblet of Fire. GrandPré, Mary, illus. l.t. ed. 2000. (Harry Potter Ser.: Year 4). 936p. (gr. 3 up). 25.95 (978-0-7862-2927-7(6) , Large Print Pr.) Thorndike Pr.

—Harry Potter & the Half-Blood Prince, 9 vols. braille ed. 2005. (Harry Potter Ser.: 6). (YA). 29.99 (978-0-939173-39-6(5) , HALF) National Braille Pr.

—Harry Potter & the Half-Blood Prince. 2003. (Harry Potter Ser.). 496p. 24.95 (****978-7-02-005323-0(8)*** , HAP06) People's Literature Publishing Hse. CHN. *Dist:* China Bks. & Periodicals, Inc.

—Harry Potter & the Half-Blood Prince. GrandPré, Mary, illus. (J). 2005. (Harry Potter Ser.: Year 6). 672p. 34.99 (978-0-439-78677-5(0)); 2005. (Harry Potter Ser.: Year 6). 672p. 29.99 (978-0-439-78454-2(9)); 2005. (Harry Potter Ser.: Year 6). 704p. 60.00 (978-0-439-79132-8(4)); 2006. 672p. reprint ed. pap. 9.99 (978-0-439-78596-9(0)) Scholastic, Inc. (Levine, Arthur A. Bks.).

—Harry Potter & the Half-Blood Prince. 832p. 2007. pap. 14.95 (****978-1-59413-221-6(6));*** 2005. (Harry Potter Ser.: Year 6). 29.95 (978-0-7862-7745-2(9)) Thorndike Pr. (Large Print Pr.).

—Harry Potter & the Order of the Phoenix. 2003. (Harry Potter Ser.). 575p. 25.95 (978-7-02-004327-9(5) , HAP05) People's Literature Publishing Hse. CHN. *Dist:* China Bks. & Periodicals, Inc.

—Harry Potter & the Order of the Phoenix. GrandPré, Mary, illus. l.t. ed. 2003. 1232p. (J). (gr. 4-7). pap. 14.95 (978-1-59413-112-7(0) , Large Print Pr.) Thorndike Pr.

—Harry Potter & the Prisoner of Azkaban. 2002. (Harry Potter Ser.). (Illus.). (YA). 16.26 (978-0-7587-5662-6(3)) Book Wholesalers, Inc.

—Harry Potter & the Prisoner of Azkaban. braille ed. 1999. (Harry Potter Ser.: Year 3). (YA). (gr. 3 up). pap. 19.95 (978-0-939173-36-5(0)) National Braille Pr.

—Harry Potter & the Prisoner of Azkaban. 2000. (J). tchr. ed. 9.95 (978-1-58130-656-9(3)); stu. ed. 11.95 (978-1-58130-657-6(1)) Novel Units, Inc.

—Harry Potter & the Prisoner of Azkaban. 2004. (Harry Potter Ser.: Year 3). 560p. mass mkt. 7.99 (978-0-439-65548-4(X) , Scholastic Paperbacks) Scholastic, Inc.

—Harry Potter & the Prisoner of Azkaban. GrandPré, Mary, illus. (Harry Potter Ser.: Year 3). 448p. (gr. 3 up). 2001. (YA). mass mkt. 8.99 (978-0-439-13636-5(9) , Levine, Arthur A. Bks.); 1999. (J). 22.99 (978-0-439-13635-8(0)) Scholastic, Inc.

—Harry Potter & the Prisoner of Azkaban. 2001. (gr. 3-6). lib. bdg. 16.45 (978-0-613-37106-3(2)) Tandem Library Bks.

—Harry Potter & the Prisoner of Azkaban. GrandPré, Mary, illus. l.t. ed. 2000. (Harry Potter Ser.: Year 3). 592p. (gr. 3 up). 24.95 (978-0-7862-2274-2(3) , Large Print Pr.) Thorndike Pr.

—Harry Potter & the Sorcerer's Stone. unabr. ed. (Harry Potter Ser.: Year 1). 320p. (gr. 3 up). (YA). pap. 62.00 incl. audio (978-0-8072-1547-0(3)); 2004. (J). pap. 46.00 incl. audio (978-0-8072-8119-2(0) , S YA 108 SP) Random Hse. Audio Publishing Group. (Listening Library).

—Harry Potter & the Sorcerer's Stone. GrandPré, Mary, illus. (Harry Potter Ser.: Year 1). (gr. 3 up). 2001. 400p. (J). mass mkt. 6.99 (978-0-439-36213-9(X)); 1999. 320p. (YA). mass mkt. 8.99 (978-0-590-35342-7(X)); 1998. 320p. (J). pap. 22.99 (978-0-590-35340-3(3) , Levine, Arthur A. Bks.) Scholastic, Inc.

—Harry Potter & the Sorcerer's Stone. collector's ed. 2000. (Harry Potter Ser.: Year 1). 320p. (YA). (gr. 3 up). 75.00 (978-0-439-20352-4(X)) Scholastic, Inc.

—Harry Potter & the Sorcerer's Stone. GrandPré, Mary, illus. l.t. ed. 1999. (Harry Potter Ser.: Year 1). 422p. (gr. 3 up). 24.95 (978-0-7862-2272-8(7) , Large Print Pr.) Thorndike Pr.

—Harry Potter Boxed Set, Bks. 1-7. 2007. (Harry Potter Ser.: Years 1-7). (J). 195.00 (****978-0-545-04425-7(1)*** , Levine, Arthur A. Bks.) Scholastic, Inc.

—Harry Potter Boxed Set: Harry Potter & the Sorcerer's Stone; Harry Potter & the Chamber of Secrets; Harry Potter & the Prisoner of Azkaban, 3 vols. GrandPré, Mary, illus. (Harry Potter Ser.: Years 1-3). (YA). 2002. pap. 21.97 (978-0-439-32466-3(1)); 1999. (gr. 3 up). 55.85 (978-0-439-13316-6(5)) Scholastic, Inc. (Levine, Arthur A. Bks.).

—Harry Potter Boxed Set: Harry Potter & the Sorcerer's Stone; Harry Potter & the Chamber of Secrets; Harry Potter & the Prisoner of Azkaban; Harry Potter & the Goblet of Fire, 4 vols. GrandPré, Mary, illus. 2000. (Harry Potter Ser.: Years 1-4). (YA). (gr. 3 up). 85.80 (978-0-641-06631-3(7) , Levine, Arthur A. Bks.) Scholastic, Inc.

—Harry Potter Coffret: Harry Potter a l'Ecole des Sorciers; Harry Potter et la Chambre des Secrets; Harry Potter et le Prisonnier d'Azkaban. 1999. (Harry Potter Ser.: Years 1-3). Tr. of Harry Potter Boxed Set: Harry Potter & the Chamber of Secrets; Harry Potter & the Sorcerer's Stone; Harry Potter & the Prisoner of Azkaban. (FRE.). (YA). (gr. 3 up). pap. 43.95 (978-2-07-052929-2(0)) Gallimard, Editions FRA. *Dist:* Distribooks, Inc.

—Harry Potter Coffret: Harry Potter a l'Ecole des Sorciers; Harry Potter et la Chambre des Secrets; Harry Potter et le Prisonnier d'Azkaban; Harry Potter et la Coupe de Feu. 1999. (Harry Potter Ser.: Years 1-3). Tr. of Harry Potter Boxed Set: Harry Potter & the Chamber of Secrets; Harry Potter & the Sorcerer's Stone; Harry Potter & the Prisoner of Azkaban; Harry Potter et la COupe de Feu. (FRE.). 1400p. (YA). (gr. 3 up). pap. 34.95 (978-0-320-03843-3(2)) French & European Pubns., Inc.

—Harry Potter e a Camara Secreta. (POR.). pap. 28.95 (978-85-325-1166-9(X)) Rocco, Editora, Ltda BRA. *Dist:* Distribooks, Inc.

—Harry Potter e a Pedra Filosofal. (POR.). pap. 28.95 (978-85-325-1101-0(5)) Rocco, Editora, Ltda BRA. *Dist:* Distribooks, Inc.

—Harry Potter e a Prisioneiro de Azkaban. (POR.). pap. 29.95 (978-85-325-1206-2(2)) Rocco, Editora, Ltda BRA. *Dist:* Distribooks, Inc.

—Harry Potter e o Calice de Fogo. (POR.). pap. 38.95 (978-85-325-1252-9(6)) Rocco, Editora, Ltda BRA. *Dist:* Distribooks, Inc.

—Harry Potter et la Chambre des Secrets. 1999. (Harry Potter Ser.: Year 2). Tr. of Harry Potter & the Chamber of Secrets. (FRE.). (YA). (gr. 3 up). pap. 13.95 (978-0-320-03778-8(9)) French & European Pubns., Inc.

—Harry Potter et la Chambre des Secrets. 1999. (Harry Potter Ser.: Year 2). Tr. of Harry Potter & the Chamber of Secrets. (FRE., Illus.). 358p. (YA). (gr. 3 up). pap. 16.95 (978-2-07-052455-6(8)) Gallimard, Editions FRA. *Dist:* Distribooks, Inc.

—Harry Potter et le Prisonnier d'Azkaban. 1999. (Harry Potter Ser.: Year 3). Tr. of Harry Potter & the Prisoner of Azkaban. (FRE.). 465p. (YA). (gr. 3 up). pap. 16.95 (978-2-07-052818-9(9)) Gallimard, Editions FRA. *Dist:* Distribooks, Inc.

—Harry Potter et l'Ecole des Sorciers. 3rd ed. 1998. (Harry Potter Ser.: Year 1). Tr. of Harry Potter & the Sorcerer's Stone. (FRE., Illus.). (YA). (gr. 3 up). pap. 14.95 (978-2-07-050142-7(6)) Distribooks, Inc.

—Harry Potter et l'Ecole des Sorciers. 1999. (Harry Potter Ser.: Year 1). Tr. of Harry Potter & the Sorcerer's Stone. (FRE.). (YA). (gr. 3 up). pap. 16.95 (978-0-320-03780-1(0)) French & European Pubns., Inc.

—Harry Potter et l'Ecole des Sorciers. 2007. Tr. of Harry Potter & the Sorcerer's Stone. 311p. pap. 14.95 (****978-2-07-061236-9(8)***) Gallimard, Editions FRA. *Dist:* Distribooks, Inc.

—Harry Potter und der Gefangene von Azkaban. 1999. (Harry Potter Ser.: Year 3). Tr. of Harry Potter & the Prisoner of Azkaban. (GER.). (YA). (gr. 3 up). pap. 34.95 (978-3-551-55169-6(3)) Carlsen Verlag DEU. *Dist:* Distribooks, Inc.

—Harry Potter und der Stein der Weisen. 1999. (Harry Potter Ser.: Year 1). (GER.). 335p. (YA). (gr. 3 up). pap. 34.95 (978-3-551-55167-2(7)) Carlsen Verlag DEU. *Dist:* Distribooks, Inc.

—Harry Potter und die Kammer des Schreckens. 1999. (Harry Potter Ser.: Year 2). Tr. of Harry Potter & Chamber of Secrets. (GER.). (YA). (gr. 3 up). pap. 36.95 (978-3-551-55168-9(5)) Carlsen Verlag DEU. *Dist:* Distribooks, Inc.

—Harry Potter y el Prisionero de Azkaban. 2004. (Harry Potter Ser.: Year 3). (SPA., Illus.). 360p. (gr. 3 up). 17.95 (978-84-7888-519-0(6) , SAL1889) Emece Editores ESP. *Dist:* Lectorum Pubns., Inc.

—Harry Potter y el Prisionero de Azkaban. 2000. (Harry Potter Ser.: Year 3). (SPA.). (YA). (gr. 3 up). 16.95 (978-0-320-03783-2(5)) French & European Pubns., Inc.

—Harry Potter y la Camara Secreta. 2004. (Harry Potter Ser.: Year 2). (SPA., Illus.). 288p. (YA). (gr. 3 up). 15.95 (978-84-7888-495-7(5) , SAL4595) Emece Editores ESP. *Dist:* Lectorum Pubns., Inc.

—Harry Potter y la Camara Secreta. 1999. (Harry Potter Ser.: Year 2). (SPA.). (YA). (gr. 3 up). 14.95 (978-0-320-03781-8(9)) French & European Pubns., Inc.

—Harry Potter y la Piedra Filosofal. 2004. (Harry Potter Ser.: Bk. 1). (SPA., Illus.). 256p. (YA). (gr. 7 up). 15.95 (978-84-7888-445-2(9) , SAL2819) Emece Editores ESP. *Dist:* Lectorum Pubns., Inc.

—Harry Potter y la Piedra Filosofal. 1999. (Harry Potter Ser.: Year 1). (SPA.). (YA). (gr. 3 up). 14.95 (978-0-320-03782-5(7)) French & European Pubns., Inc.

Rowling, J. K. & Dale, Jim. Harry Potter & the Goblet of Fire. unabr. ed. 2004. (Harry Potter Ser.). 752p. (J). pap. 65.00 incl. audio (978-0-8072-1196-0(6) , S YA 270 SP, Listening Library) Random Hse. Audio Publishing Group.

Rucka, Greg. Operation Vol. 4: Blackwall, 4 vols. 2003. (Queen & Country Ser.: Vol. 4). (Illus.). 88p. pap. 8.95 (978-1-929998-68-5(6)) Oni Pr., Inc.

Rue, Nancy N. Lily's in London: It's a God Thing! 2003. (gr. 3-6). lib. bdg. 13.00 (978-0-613-71688-8(4)) Tandem Library Bks.

Rushton, Rosie. Friends, Enemies. 2004. 240p. (gr. 5-17). 15.99 (978-0-7868-5177-5(5)) Hyperion Paperbacks for Children.

—Friends, Enemies. 2006. 240p. (gr. 5-17). pap. 5.99 (978-0-7868-5178-2(3)) Hyperion Pr.

Sanderson, Jeanette. Robin Hood Shoots for the Queen: A Legend from England. 2006. spiral bd. 42.00 ***(978-1-4108-7167-1(3))*** Benchmark Education Co.

Scherer, Catherine W. Simon & Barklee in England - Fun-Book. Scherer, Catherine W., ed. 2001. (Another Country Calling Ser.). (Illus.). 32p. (J). (gr. 2-6). 7.50 (978-0-9704661-5-0(3) , Explorer Media) Simon & Barklee, Inc./ExplorerMedia.

Schott, Elizabeth, illus. Jake & Sam at the Empty Abbey. 2006. 96p. (J). per. 9.95 (978-0-9724421-1-4(1)) Fountain Square Publishing.

Scott, Deborah. The California Kid Fights Back. 1998. (J). (gr. 3-7). pap. 3.99 (978-0-380-72851-0(6)) HarperCollins Pubs.

Scrase, Leslie. An Evacuee. 2000. 206p. (J). (978-1-85200-087-5(2)) United Writers Pubns., Ltd.

Sebag-Montefiore, Mary. Railway Children. Marks, Alan, illus. 2007. (Young Reading Series 2 Gift Bks). 64p. (J). 8.99 ***(*978-0-7945-1615-4(7)*** , Usborne) EDC Publishing.

Sewell, Anna. Black Beauty. 2002. (Great Illustrated Classics Ser.). (Illus.). 240p. (J). (gr. 3-8). 21.35 (978-1-57765-681-4(4) , ABDO & Daughters) ABDO Publishing Co.

—Black Beauty. (J). 21.95 (978-0-88411-065-1(6)) Amereon LTD.

—Black Beauty. Dryhurst, Dinah, illus. 2000. 224p. (J). pap. 8.95 (978-1-86205-240-6(9) , Pavilion Bks., Ltd.) Anova Bks. GBR. *Dist:* Trafalgar Square Publishing.

—Black Beauty. (J). reprint ed. lib. bdg. 48.00 (978-0-7426-1042-2(X)); 2001. (Illus.). pap. 28.00 (978-0-7426-6042-7(7)) Classic Bks.

—Black Beauty. 1999. (Dover Evergreen Classics Ser.). (Illus.). 208p. (J). (gr. 4-7). pap. 2.50 (978-0-486-40788-3(8)) Dover Pubns., Inc.

—Black Beauty. 2nd ed. 1998. (Illustrated Classic Book Ser.). (Illus.). 61p. (J). (gr. 3 up). reprint ed. pap. 4.95 (978-1-56767-253-4(1)) Educational Insights, Inc.

—Black Beauty. 2001. (Fast Track Classics Ser.). (Illus.). 48p. pap. 9.99 (978-0-237-52284-1(5) , Evans Brothers, Limited) Evans Publishing Group GBR. *Dist:* Independent Pubs. Group.

—Black Beauty. (Charming Classics). 288p. (J). 1998. (gr. 3-7). pap. 6.99 (978-0-694-01243-5(2)); 2005. 9.99 (978-0-06-075770-0(1) , Harper Festival) HarperCollins Pubs.

—Black Beauty. Andrew, Ian P., illus. 2001. (Kingfisher Classics Ser.). 352p. (J). (gr. 4-6). tchr. ed. 15.95 (978-0-7534-5379-7(7) , Kingfisher) Houghton Mifflin Co. Trade & Reference Div.

—Black Beauty. 2001. (J). (gr. 4-7). 17.95 (978-0-8249-5400-0(9)) Ideals Pubns.

—Black Beauty. Stemach, Jerry, ed. Ham, Jeff, illus. (J). 2000. 65.00 incl. audio, cd-rom (978-1-58702-312-5(1)); 2002. 150.00 (978-1-58702-023-0(8)); 2000. 50.00 (978-1-58702-508-2(6)) Johnston, Don Inc.

—Black Beauty. (Illus.). 192p. (J). 9.95 (978-1-56156-310-4(2)) Kidsbooks, Inc.

—Black Beauty. l.t. ed. 1999. (Large Print Heritage Ser.). 260p. (YA). (gr. 7-12). lib. bdg. 29.95 (978-1-58118-042-8(X) , 22511) LRS.

—Black Beauty, 2 vols., Set. l.t. ed. (YA). (gr. 8 up). reprint ed. 10.00 (978-0-89064-017-3(3)) National Assn. for Visually Handicapped.

—Black Beauty. (Twelve-Point Ser.). 2001. (J). lib. bdg. 24.00 (978-1-58287-132-5(9)); 2004. 268p. 25.00 (978-1-58287-619-1(3)) North Bks.

—Black Beauty, Level 4. 2nd abr. ed. 2000. (Bookworms Ser.). (Illus.). 90p. 6.50 (978-0-19-423028-5(7)) Oxford Univ. Pr., Inc.

—Black Beauty. Chitouras, Barbara, illus. 2002. (Classics for Young Readers Ser.). 208p. (J). per. 7.99 (978-0-87552-728-4(0)) P & R Publishing.

—Black Beauty. 2002. 240p. mass mkt. 4.95 (978-0-451-52865-0(4) , Signet Classics) Penguin Group (USA) Inc.

—Black Beauty. (J). 8.97 (978-0-13-052329-7(1)) Prentice Hall PTR.

—Black Beauty. 2000. (Illus.). 240p. (gr. 5-7). 5.99 (978-0-440-41645-6(0) , Yearling) Random Hse. Children's Bks.

—Black Beauty. 1998. (Children's Classics Ser.). (Illus.). 240p. (J). 5.99 (978-0-517-18958-0(5) , Children's Classics) Random Hse. Value Publishing.

—Black Beauty. 2000. 256p. (J). (gr. 4-7). pap. 4.50 (978-0-590-42354-0(1) , Scholastic Paperbacks) Scholastic, Inc.

—Black Beauty. 2001. (Classics Ser.). (Illus.). 224p. (J). (gr. 4-7). pap. 4.99 (978-0-689-84255-9(4) , Aladdin) Simon & Schuster Children's Publishing.

—Black Beauty. l.t. ed. 2001. 240p. (J). 28.95 (978-0-7838-9522-2(4)) Thorndike Pr.

—Black Beauty. 1998. (Children's Classics). (ENG.). 208p. (YA). (ps up). pap. (978-1-85326-109-1(2) , 1092WW) Wordsworth Editions, Ltd.

Sewell, Anna & Dorling Kindersley Publishing Staff. Black Beauty. Ambrus, Victor G., illus. 2000. (Classic Readers Ser.). (J). (gr. 2-4). 32p. 12.99 (978-0-7894-5702-8(4)); Vol. 4. 48p. pap. 3.99 (978-0-7894-5388-4(6)) Dorling Kindersley Publishing, Inc.

Sewell, Anna, et al. Black Beauty. 2001. (Young Reader's Classics Ser.). (Illus.). 95p. (J). 16.95 (978-1-55263-322-9(5) , Key Porter kids) Key Porter Bks. CAN. *Dist:* Firefly Bks., Ltd.

Shearer, Alex. Canned. 2008. (J). 240p. 16.99 ***(*978-0-439-90309-7(2)); (*978-0-439-90310-3(6))*** Scholastic, Inc. (Scholastic Pr.).

Shields, Gillian. The Actual Real Reality of Jennifer James: A Reality TV Novel. 2006. 384p. (J). lib. bdg. 17.89 (978-0-06-082241-5(4) , Tegen, Katherine Bks) HarperCollins Pubs.

Shulevitz, Uri. The Treasure. Shulevitz, Uri, illus. 2001. (Illus.). 25.95 incl. audio (978-0-87499-755-2(0)); 28.95 incl. audio compact disk (978-1-59112-553-2(7)); pap. 33.95 incl. audio (978-0-87499-756-9(9)); pap. 35.95 incl. audio compact disk (978-1-59112-552-5(9)) Live Oak Media.

Simon & Barklee in England. 2001. (Another Country Calling Ser.). (Illus.). 64p. (J). (gr. 3-5). per. 15.00 (978-0-9704661-1-2(0) , Explorer Media) Simon & Barklee, Inc./ExplorerMedia.

Skelton, Matthew. Endymion Spring. 2006. (Illus.). 400p. (J). (gr. 7). 17.95 (978-0-385-73380-9(1)); lib. bdg. 19.99 (978-0-385-90397-4(9)) Random Hse. Children's Bks. (Delacorte Bks. for Young Readers).

Skurzynski, Gloria. Spider's Voice. 1999. (Illus.). (J). (978-0-606-21446-9(1)) Tandem Library Bks.

Slahor, Stephenie. Tales from Merrie England I & Tales from Merrie England II, Vol. 2. 119p. (J). (gr. 3-5). 9.99 (978-0-88092-262-3(1)) Royal Fireworks Publishing Co.

Spalding, Andrea. Phoebe & the Gypsy. 1999. (Young Reader Ser.). (Illus.). 128p. (J). (gr. 3-6). pap. 4.99 (978-1-55143-135-2(1)) Orca Bk. Pubs. USA.

—Phoebe & the Gypsy. 1999. (Young Reader Ser.). (J). (978-0-606-19478-5(9)); (gr. 3-6). lib. bdg. 13.00 (978-0-8085-8430-8(8)) Tandem Library Bks.

Spirin, Gennadii, illus. Perceval: King Arthur's Knight of the Holy Grail. 2007. 36p. (J). ***(*978-1-4287-3696-2(4)*** , Cavendish Children's Bks.) Cavendish, Marshall Corp.

Springer, Nancy. I Am Mordred: A Tale from Camelot. 2002. (Firebird Ser.). 192p. (J). (gr. 7 up). pap. 6.99 (978-0-698-11841-6(3) , Puffin) Penguin Group (USA) Inc.

—I Am Mordred: A Tale from Camelot. unabr. ed. 2000. (YA). pap. 68.99 incl. audio (978-0-7887-3006-1(1) , 40888X4) Recorded Bks., LLC.

—I Am Mordred: A Tale from Camelot. 2002. (gr. 5-8). lib. bdg. 14.15 (978-0-613-44457-6(4)) Tandem Library Bks.

—I Am Morgan le Fay: A Tale from Camelot. 2002. (Firebird Ser.). 240p. (YA). pap. 6.99 (978-0-698-11974-1(6) , Puffin) Penguin Group (USA) Inc.

—I Am Morgan le Fay: A Tale from Camelot. 2002. (gr. 7-12). lib. bdg. 14.15 (978-0-613-55214-1(8)) Tandem Library Bks.

St. John, Patricia. The Tanglewoods' Secret. Rees, Gary, illus. 2001. 224p. (J). pap. 6.99 (978-0-8024-6576-4(5)) Moody Pubs.

Standish, Burt L. Frank Merriwell in England. Rudman, Jack, ed. 2003. (Frank Merriwell Ser.). 29.95 (978-0-8373-9344-5(2)); pap. 9.95 (978-0-8373-9044-4(3)) Merriwell, Frank Inc.

Stanley, George Edward. The Spy Who Barked. Francis, Guy, illus. 2002. (Adam Sharp Ser.: No. 1). 48p. (J). (gr. 2-4). pap. 3.99 (978-0-307-26412-1(2) , Random Hse. Bks. for Young Readers) Random Hse. Children's Bks.

Stanton, Andy. You're a Bad Man, Mr. Gum! Dezern, Chad, illus. 2008. 144p. (J). 9.99 ***(*978-0-06-115240-5(4));*** lib. bdg. 14.89 ***(*978-0-06-115243-6(9))*** HarperCollins Pubs.

Stevenson, Robert Louis. Treasure Island. Gelev, Penko, illus. 2006. (Graphic Classics Ser.). 48p. (J). (gr. 2-6). pap. 8.99 (978-0-7641-3491-3(4)); 15.99 (978-0-7641-5976-3(3)) Barron's Educational Series, Inc.

Stretton, Hesba. Little Meg's Children. 2000. (Golden Inheritance Ser.: Vol. 5). (Illus.). 88p. (J). pap. (978-0-921100-92-8(2)) Inheritance Pubns.

—Little Meg's Children. (Early Children's Bks.). (J). reprint ed. 15.00 (978-0-384-56160-1(8)) Johnson Reprint Corp.

Stroud, Jonathan. The Buried Fire. 2004. 332p. (J). pap. (978-0-7818-5794-9(5)) Hippocrene Bks., Inc.

—Buried Fire. 2004. 336p. (gr. 5-17). pap. 6.95 (978-0-7868-5194-2(5)) Miramax Bks.

—The Leap. 2004. 240p. (gr. 5-17). pap. 6.95 (978-0-7868-5195-9(3)) Miramax Bks.

Sturt, M. The Canterbury Pilgrims (Being Chaucer's. 2006. 94.99 ***(*978-1-4280-0313-2(4));*** pap. 88.99 ***(*978-1-4280-0309-5(6))*** IndyPublish.com.

Talbot, Bryan. The Tale of One Bad Rat. Talbot, Bryan, illus. 2002. (Illus.). (YA). 23.19 (978-1-4046-2391-0(4)) Book Wholesalers, Inc.

Talley, Linda. Toad in Town. Maeno, Itoko, illus. 2001. (Key Concepts in Personal Development Ser.). (gr. k-4). 30p. (J). 89.95 incl. VHS (978-1-55942-165-2(7)); 32p. pap., tchr. ed. 89.95 incl. VHS (978-1-55942-168-3(1) , 9387K3) Marsh Media.

Tanner, Geoffrey. Window on the Past. 2000. 128p. (gr. 4-7). pap. 9.95 (978-0-595-09332-8(9) , Writers Club Pr.) iUniverse, Inc.

Thomson, Sarah L. The Dragon's Son. 2001. (Illus.). 148p. (J). (gr. 7 up). 17.95 (978-0-531-30333-7(0) , Orchard Bks.) Scholastic, Inc.

Toad in Town - Teaching Guide. 2000. 17.95 (978-1-55942-167-6(3)) Marsh Media.

Tomlinson, Jill. Cat Wanted to Go Home - Picture Boo. Howard, Paul, illus. 2004. 32p. (J). (ps). pap. 9.99 (978-1-4052-1873-3(8)) Egmont Bks., Ltd. GBR. *Dist:* Independent Pubs. Group.

Tracey, Rhian. When Isla Meets Luke Meets Isla. 2003. 160p. (YA). pap. 12.95 (978-0-7475-6344-0(6)) Bloomsbury Publishing Plc GBR. *Dist:* Independent Pubs. Group.

Travers, P. L. Mary Poppins Vintage Boxed Set: Three Enchanting Classics: Mary Poppins, Mary Poppins Comes Back, & Mary Poppins Opens the Door. 2007. (Illus.). (J). 38.85 (978-0-15-205858-6(3)) Harcourt Children's Bks.

Tytler, Sarah. Girlhood & Womanhood the Story of Some. 2007. 43.99 ***(*978-1-4280-5160-7(0));*** pap. 36.99 ***(*978-1-4280-5161-4(9))*** IndyPublish.com.

Ure, Jean. Muddy Four Paws. 1999. (We Love Animals Bks.). (Illus.). 128p. (J). (gr. 4-7). pap. 3.95 (978-0-7641-0968-3(5)) Barron's Educational Series, Inc.

Wade, Rebecca. The Theft & the Miracle. 2007. 368p. (J). (gr. 5-9). 16.99 (978-0-06-077493-6(2)); lib. bdg. 17.89 (978-0-06-077495-0(9)) HarperCollins Pubs.

Wallace, Karen. Climbing a Monkey Puzzle Tree. 2004. 208p. (YA). (gr. 7-9). pap. 9.99 (978-0-689-83763-0(1)) Simon & Schuster, Ltd. GBR. *Dist:* Independent Pubs. Group.

Walters, Jennie. Shelter from the Storm. 2007. (Swallowcliffe Hall Trilogy: Book 3 Ser.). (Illus.). 240p. (J). pap. 9.99 ***(*978-0-689-87528-1(2))*** Simon & Schuster, Ltd. GBR. *Dist:* Independent Pubs. Group.

—Standing in the Shadows 2. 2007. (Swallowcliffe Hall Trilogy: Book 2 Ser.). (Illus.). 256p. (J). pap. 9.99 ***(*978-0-689-87527-4(4)*** , Pocket Bks.) Simon & Schuster, Ltd. GBR. *Dist:* Independent Pubs. Group.

Walton, O. F. Christie's Old Organ or Home, Sweet Home. 2005. reprint ed. pap. 22.95 (978-0-7661-9430-4(2)) Kessinger Publishing, LLC.

Watson, Sally. Highland Rebel. 2002. (J). pap. 12.95 (978-1-930009-63-9(1) , 800-691-7779) Image Cascade Publishing.

Watts, Irene N. Finding Sophie. 2002. (gr. 5-8). lib. bdg. 15.25 (978-0-613-62903-4(5)) Tandem Library Bks.

—Finding Sophie. 2002. 144p. (J). (gr. 5). pap. 6.95 (978-0-88776-613-8(7)) Tundra Bks., Inc./Livres Toundra, Inc. CAN. *Dist:* Random Hse., Inc.

Waugh, Sylvia. Mennyms Alive. 1999. 224p. (J). (gr. 3-7). pap. 4.50 (978-0-380-72943-2(1) , Harper Trophy) HarperCollins Pubs.

—Mennyms Alone. 1998. 224p. (J). (gr. 3-7). pap. 4.50 (978-0-380-78867-5(5) , Harper Trophy) HarperCollins Pubs.

—Space Race. 2001. 256p. (gr. 5 up). 5.50 (978-0-440-41714-9(7) , Yearling) Random Hse. Children's Bks.

—Space Race. 2001. (gr. 5-8). lib. bdg. 13.00 (978-0-613-88327-6(6)) Tandem Library Bks.

—Space Race. l.t. ed. 2001. 300p. (J). 20.95 (978-0-7862-3606-0(X)) Thorndike Pr.

—Who Goes Home? 2005. 224p. (gr. 4-7). 5.99 (978-0-440-41839-9(9) , Yearling) Random Hse. Children's Bks.

Weatherly, Lee. Kat Got Your Tongue. 2007. 208p. (YA). (gr. 7-9). lib. bdg. 18.99 (978-0-385-75122-3(2)); 15.99 (978-0-385-75117-9(6)) Random Hse. Children's Bks. (Fickling, David Bks.).

Wells, H. G. & Geary, Rick. The Invisible Man. (Classics Illustrated Ser.). (Illus.). 52p. (YA). pap. 4.95 (978-1-57209-020-0(0)) Classics International Entertainment, Inc.

Wells, Rosemary. Lassie Come-Home. Jeffers, Susan, illus. rev. ed. 1998. 48p. (J). (ps up). reprint ed. pap. 8.95 (978-0-8050-5995-3(4) , Holt, Henry & Co. Bks. For Young Readers) Holt, Henry & Co.

Whybrow, Ian. The Unvisibles. 2005. 184p. (J). 16.95 (978-0-8234-1972-2(X)) Holiday Hse., Inc.

Whytock, Cherry. My Saucy Stuffed Ravioli: The Life of Angelica Cookson Potts. Whytock, Cherry, illus. 2005. (Illus.). 176p. (YA). 14.95 (978-0-689-86550-3(3)) Simon & Schuster Children's Publishing.

—My Scrumptious Scottish Dumplings: The Life of Angelica Cookson Potts. Whytock, Cherry, illus. 2006. 192p. (YA). mass mkt. 5.99 (978-0-689-86552-7(X) , Simon Pulse) Simon & Schuster Children's Publishing.

Whytock, Cherry, illus. My Scrumptious Scottish Dumplings: The Life of Angelica Cookson Potts. 2004. 176p. (YA). 14.95 (978-0-689-86549-7(X)) Simon & Schuster Children's Publishing.

Wiggin, Kate Douglas. The Diary of a Goose Girl. 2006. (ENG.). pap. ***(*978-1-4250-2104-7(2))*** Assistedreading-books.com Inc.

—The Diary of a Goose Girl. 2004. reprint ed. pap. 1.99 (978-1-4192-5922-7(9)) Kessinger Publishing, LLC.

—The Diary of a Goose Girl. Shepperson, Claude A., illus. 2004. reprint ed. pap. 20.95 (978-1-4179-1501-9(3)) Kessinger Publishing, LLC.

—Penelope's English Experiences. 2004. reprint ed. pap. 15.95 (978-1-4191-4070-9(1)); pap. 1.99 (978-1-4192-4070-6(6)) Kessinger Publishing, LLC.

Wilde, Oscar. The Canterville Ghost. Date not set. (Nelson Readers Ser.). (J). pap. (978-0-17-557035-5(3)) Addison-Wesley Longman, Inc.

—The Canterville Ghost. 2nd ed. 2000. (Reading & Training Ser.). 112p. (YA). pap. (978-1-57159-012-1(9)) Los Andes Publishing Co.

—El Fantasma de Canterville. 2005. (Clasicos de la literatura Ser.). (SPA., Illus.). 184p. pap. 5.95 (978-84-9764-458-7(1)) Edimat Libros, S. A. ESP. *Dist:* Independent Pubs. Group.

—El Fantasma de Canterville. 2000. (SPA.). 112p. (978-950-03-6274-0(0) , 1060) Losada.

—The Picture of Dorian Gray. Marcos, Pablo, illus. 2002. (Great Illustrated Classics Ser.). 240p. (J). (gr. 3-8). 21.35 (978-1-57765-821-4(3) , ABDO & Daughters) ABDO Publishing Co.

—The Picture of Dorian Gray, 2 vols. l.t. ed. (YA). (gr. 10 up). reprint ed. 10.00 (978-0-89064-049-4(1)) National Assn. for Visually Handicapped.

—The Picture of Dorian Gray, Level 3. abr. ed. 2000. (Bookworms Ser.). (Illus.). 77p. 6.50 (978-0-19-423011-7(2)) Oxford Univ. Pr., Inc.

—The Picture of Dorian Gray. Ross, Tony, illus. 2001. (Whole Story Ser.). 272p. (YA). (gr. 10 up). 25.99 (978-0-670-89494-9(X) , Viking Juvenile) Penguin Group (USA) Inc.

Wilkins, Rose. So Super Starry. 2006. 240p. (YA). (gr. 7). reprint ed. pap. 6.99 (978-0-14-240581-9(7) , Puffin) Penguin Group (USA) Inc.

Willis, Jeanne. The Wind in the Willows. Ross, Tony, illus. 1998. 32p. (J). (ps-1). 15.99 (978-0-86264-782-7(7)) Andersen GBR. *Dist:* Trafalgar Square Publishing.

Wilson, Jacqueline. Bad Girls. Sharratt, Nick, illus. 2002. 176p. (gr. 3-7). pap. 5.50 (978-0-440-41806-1(2) , Yearling) Random Hse. Children's Bks.

—Bad Girls. 2002. (gr. 3-6). lib. bdg. 12.40 (978-0-613-83529-9(8)) Tandem Library Bks.

—The Bed & Breakfast Star. Sharratt, Nick, illus. l.t. ed. 2000. 255p. (J). pap. (978-0-7540-6090-1(X) , CLP 292) BBC Audio.

—The Bed & Breakfast Star. Sharratt, Nick, illus. unabr. ed. 2000. (Read-Along Ser.). 242p. (J). pap. 29.95 incl. audio (978-0-7540-6231-8(7) , RA032, Chivers Children's Audio Bks.) BBC Audiobooks America.

—The Bed & Breakfast Star. Sharratt, Nick, illus. 2001. (Yearling Book Ser.). 32p. pap. 9.99 (978-0-440-86324-3(4) , Corgi) Transworld Publishers Ltd. GBR. *Dist:* Trafalgar Square Publishing.

—Best Friends. 2008. (J). ***(*978-1-59643-278-9(0))*** Roaring Brook Pr.

—Girls in Tears. 176p. (YA). (gr. 7). 2004. (Girls Quartet: Bk. 4). mass mkt. 4.99 (978-0-440-23807-2(2) , Laurel Leaf); 2003. lib. bdg. 11.99 (978-0-385-90104-8(6) , Delacorte Bks. for Young Readers) Random Hse. Children's Bks.

—Girls in Tears. 2004. (gr. 7-12). lib. bdg. 13.00 (978-0-613-72253-7(1)) Tandem Library Bks.

—The Illustrated Mum. 288p. 2005. (J). (gr. 5). lib. bdg. 17.99 (978-0-385-90263-2(8) , Delacorte Bks. for Young Readers); 2006. (gr. 4-7). reprint ed. 5.50 (978-0-440-42043-9(1) , Yearling) Random Hse. Children's Bks.

—Vicky Angel. l.t. ed. 2001. (Illus.). 232p. (J). 16.95 (978-0-7540-6165-6(5) , Galaxy Children's Large Print) BBC Audiobooks America.

—Vicky Angel. 2003. (Illus.). 176p. (gr. 3-7). reprint ed. 5.50 (978-0-440-41808-5(9) , Yearling) Random Hse. Children's Bks.

—Vicky Angel. 2003. (gr. 3-6). lib. bdg. 13.00 (978-0-613-88328-3(4)) Tandem Library Bks.

Wilson, Jacqueline & Sharratt, Nick. Candyfloss. 2007. (Illus.). 352p. (J). (gr. 4-7). 14.95 ***(*978-1-59643-241-3(1))*** Roaring Brook Pr.

Windsor, Patricia. The Blooding. 1999. 288p. (gr. 7-12). pap. 4.50 (978-0-590-43308-2(3)) Scholastic, Inc.

Wiseman, David. Jeremy Visick. 2005. 176p. (YA). (gr. 5 up). 21.25 (978-0-8446-7271-7(8) , 3594) Smith, Peter Pub., Inc.

Wodehouse, P. G. Mike at Wrykyn. reprint ed. (J). lib. bdg. 98.00 (978-0-7426-3265-3(2)); 2001. pap. 28.00 (978-0-7426-8265-8(X)) Classic Bks.

Wood, Valerie. Children of the Tide. l.t. ed. 2004. (Magna Large Print Ser.). (Illus.). 640p. (978-0-7505-2126-0(0)) Magna Large Print Bks.

Yamada, Shutaro. R. O. D, Vol. 3. Yamada, Shutaro, illus. 2006. (Read or Die Ser.). 208p. (YA). pap. 9.99 (978-1-4215-0508-4(8)) Viz Media.

Zephaniah, Benjamin. Gangsta Rap. 2004. 200p. (J). (gr. 9 up). pap. 7.95 (978-1-58234-886-5(3) , Bloomsbury Children) Bloomsbury Publishing.

Zindel, Paul. The Doom Stone. 2004. 192p. (gr. 6-10). pap. 5.99 (978-0-7868-5151-5(1)) Hyperion Bks. for Children.

ENGLAND—HISTORY

see Great Britain—History

ENGLISH AUTHORS

see Authors, English

ENGLISH COMPOSITION

see English Language—Composition and Exercises

ENGLISH DRAMA

see also Mysteries and Miracle Plays

E
F
G

Scott, James. Othello: The World's Great Drama: Drama Centered Language Arts Activities. abr. ed. 1999. 56p. (YA). (gr. 7-12). pap., wbk. ed. 3.50 (978-1-58049-373-4(4) , GD04A) Prestwick Hse., Inc.

Shakespeare, William. Hamlet. 1999. (Bloom's Reviews Comprehensive Research & Study Guides). 80p. (gr. 4-7). pap. 4.95 (978-0-7910-4126-0(3) , Chelsea Hse.) Facts On File, Inc.

—Tales of William Shakespeare: Retold Timeless Classics. Cornelison, Sue F., illus. 2000. (Cover-to-Cover Timeless Classics Ser.). 72p. (J). pap. (978-0-7891-5067-7(0)); (gr. 1-4). lib. bdg. 13.95 (978-0-7807-9038-4(3) , Covercraft) Perfection Learning Corp.

Shakespeare, William & SparkNotes Staff. Twelfth Night: Or, What You Will. Crowther, John, ed. 2003. (No Fear Shakespeare Ser.). (Illus.). 256p. pap. 5.95 (978-1-58663-851-1(3)) Spark Publishing Group.

ENGLISH FOR FOREIGNERS

see English Language—Textbooks for Foreign Speakers

ENGLISH HISTORY

see Great Britain—History

ENGLISH LANGUAGE

Across the United States: Fourth Grade Class Collection Books. (On Our Way to English Ser.). (gr. 4 up). 29.95 (978-0-7578-4338-9(7)) Rigby Education.

Across the United States: Small Versions of Class Collection Books. (On Our Way to English Ser.). (gr. 4 up). 34.50 (978-0-7578-7272-3(7)) Rigby Education.

ACT English Victory Student Textbook. 2nd ed. 2005. per. (978-1-58894-032-2(2)) Cambridge Educational Services, Inc.

Ada, Alma Flor & Campoy, F. Isabel. Actividades de Refuerzo Hojas Reproducibles: Reteach Activities Copying Masters. 2nd ed. 2002. (Harcourt Lenguaje Ser.). (SPA.). (gr. 2 up). pap. 53.00 (978-0-15-320304-6(8)); (gr. 3 up). pap. 53.00 (978-0-15-320305-3(6)) Harcourt Schl. Pubs.

—La Lectoescritura en los Medios de Comunicacion: Media Literacy & Communication Skills Packages. 2nd ed. 2002. (Trofeos Ser.). (SPA.). (gr. 2 up). pap., tchr. ed. 15.90 (978-0-15-320356-5(0)); (gr. 3 up). pap., tchr. ed. 15.90 (978-0-15-320357-2(9)); (gr. 4 up). pap., tchr. ed. 15.90 (978-0-15-320358-9(7)); (gr. 5 up). pap., tchr. ed. 15.90 (978-0-15-320359-6(5)) Harcourt Schl. Pubs.

Ada, Alma Flor & Campoy, F. Isabel, contrib. by. Voices. (Literature Collection of Gateways to the Sun Ser.). 32p. (J). (gr. k-6). pap. 13.95 (978-1-59437-719-8(7)) Santillana USA Publishing Co., Inc.

Adams, Colleen. Planes Go Places: Learning the Sound of PL. 2002. (PowerPhonics Ser.). (Illus.). 24p. (J). (gr. 1). lib. bdg. 18.50 (978-0-8239-5951-8(1) , PowerKids Pr.) Rosen Publishing Group, Inc., The.

Aigner-Clark, Julie. Wordsworth's Book of Words: A Bilingual Book of Words. Zaidi, Nadeem, illus. 2002. (Baby Einstein Ser.). 64p. (ps-ps). 15.99 (978-0-7868-0883-0(7)) Disney Pr.

Albright, Thomas B. World English: My Start. 2nd l.t. ed. 2000. (Languages). 56p. (978-1-888264-15-9(2)) Twenty-First Century Co., The.

Allen, Margaret. Dr. Maggie's Play & Discover, Grades Preschool-2: Language. Bruno, Janet, ed. Sopp Rae, Terri, illus. 1998. (Dr. Maggie's Play & Discover Early-Childhood Ser.). 72p. pap., tchr. ed. 12.98 (978-1-57471-361-9(2) , 2349) Creative Teaching Pr., Inc.

Allman, Barbara. Language Arts Puzzles & Games. 1999. (Gifted & Talented Ser.). (Illus.). 64p. (J). (ps-1). pap. 4.95 (978-0-7373-0206-6(2)) Lowell Hse.

American Education Publishing Staff. English: Grade 4. 2003. (Brighter Child Workbooks Ser.). (Illus.). 24p. (J). (gr. 4). pap. 2.25 (978-1-56189-128-3(2) , American Education Publishing) School Specialty Publishing.

Amery, Heather, ed. Cead Focal: The First Hundred Words. Cartwright, Stephen, illus. 2004. 32p. (J). pap. 10.95 (978-0-7171-3580-6(2)) Gill & MacMillan, Ltd. IRL. *Dist:* Irish Bks. & Media, Inc.

Analogies & Multiple Meanings (Gr. 4-5) 2004. (J). (978-1-58232-139-4(6)) Bryan Hse. Pubs., Inc.

Anderson, Dianne & Anderson, Ian. Cambridge Checkpoints VCE English 2004. 2003. (Cambridge Checkpoints Ser.). pap. 12.80 (978-0-521-54094-0(1)) Cambridge Univ. Pr.

Anderson, Dianne & Anderson, Ian. Cambridge Checkpoints VCE English 2006. 2005. (Cambridge Checkpoints Ser.). 198p. pap., stu. ed. 17.10 (978-0-521-67707-3(6)) Cambridge Univ. Pr.

Andrews. Andrews, Public Speaking Multimedia Edition Plus Toolbox: Video Workshop. 2nd ed. 2004. (YA). pap. 76.36 incl. cd-rom (978-0-618-57211-3(2) , 395292) Houghton Mifflin College Div.

Antarctica. (J). pap. 19.39 (978-0-8136-3619-1(1)) Modern Curriculum Pr.

Armstrong, Linda. Fast Ideas for Busy Teachers: Language Arts. 2004. (Illus.). 80p. (J). (gr. 2-2). pap. 10.99 (978-0-7682-2802-1(6) , FS99270); (gr. 3-3). pap. 10.99 (978-0-7682-2803-8(4) , FS99271) Schaffer, Frank Pubns. (Schaffer, Frank).

Arnold, Ellen. MI Strategies for Kids: Featuring Brilliant Brain & Magnificent Mind, 7 bks., Set. 2001. (Illus.). 263p. (J). (gr. k-6). pap. 50.00 (978-1-56976-128-1(0) , 1147, Zephyr Pr.) Chicago Review Pr., Inc.

Awdry, Wilbert V. Thomas & Friends ABC Wipe-Off Sound Activity Book. 2002. (Illus.). 16p. (J). spiral bd., bds. 12.98 (978-0-7853-6397-2(1) , 7160400) Publications International, Ltd.

Ball, Robyn. The Badhdad Blog. 2006. (Cambridge Wizard English Student Guides). 63p. pap. 7.95 (978-0-521-68353-1(X)) Cambridge Univ. Pr.

Barney Malloon's Balloon: 3-in-1 Package. (Sails Literacy Ser.). 24p. (gr. 2 up). 57.00 (978-0-7578-3212-3(1)) Rigby Education.

Barney Malloon's Balloon: 6 Small Books. (Sails Literacy Ser.). 24p. (gr. 2 up). 25.00 (978-0-7578-3188-1(5)) Rigby Education.

Barney Malloon's Balloon: Big Book Only. (Sails Literacy Ser.). 24p. (gr. 2 up). 27.00 (978-0-7635-6993-8(3)) Rigby Education.

Bass. Beyond Borders, Second Edition & Smarthinking. 2nd ed. 2002. (YA). pap. 42.76 (978-0-618-34996-8(0) , 386004) Houghton Mifflin College Div.

Battistoni, Ilse. At the Zoo: Learning the Z Sound. (PowerPhonics Ser.). (Illus.). (J). 2002. 24p. (gr. 1). lib. bdg. 18.50 (978-0-8239-5926-6(0)); 2001. 23p. pap. 26.40 (978-0-8239-8271-4(8)) Rosen Publishing Group, Inc., The. (PowerKids Pr.).

Baxter, Alison. The U. S. A., Level 4. 1999. (Bookworms Factfiles Ser.). (Illus.). 32p. 7.50 (978-0-19-422871-8(1)) Oxford Univ. Pr., Inc.

Beaton, Clare. Toys: English-French. 2003. (ps-2). lib. bdg. 12.95 (978-0-613-81896-4(2)) Tandem Library Bks.

Beck, Ray, et al. Practicing Basic Skills in Language Arts. 2005. (Illus.). 584p. per. (978-1-59318-271-7(6)) Sopris West Educational Services.

Beckwith, Carrie, et al. Editor in Chief' Beginning Book: Grammar Disasters & Punctuation Faux Pas. 2002. (J). (gr. 3-4). pap. 17.99 (978-0-89455-766-8(1)) Critical Thinking Bks. & Software.

—Editor in Chief' Book A2: Grammar Disasters & Punctuation Faux Pas. 2000. (Illus.). 72p. (J). (gr. 4-6). pap. 15.99 (978-0-89455-719-4(X) , MP9704) Critical Thinking Bks. & Software.

Beech. Comprehension Skills Complete Classroom. 2000. (J). pap. 241.40 (978-0-7398-2671-3(9)) Steck-Vaughn.

—Comprehension Skills Conclusion. 1999. (J). pap. 143.20 (978-0-7398-2668-3(9)) Steck-Vaughn.

—Comprehension Skills Conclusion Level C. 1999. (J). pap. 11.08 (978-0-7398-2638-6(7)) Steck-Vaughn.

—Comprehension Skills Conclusion Level D. 1999. (J). pap. 11.08 (978-0-7398-2644-7(1)) Steck-Vaughn.

—Comprehension Skills Conclusion Level E. 1999. (J). pap. 11.08 (978-0-7398-2650-8(6)) Steck-Vaughn.

—Comprehension Skills Conclusion Level F. 1999. (J). pap. 11.08 (978-0-7398-2656-0(5)) Steck-Vaughn.

—Comprehension Skills Context. 1999. (J). pap. 143.20 (978-0-7398-2670-6(0)) Steck-Vaughn.

—Comprehension Skills Context Level C. 1999. (J). pap. 11.08 (978-0-7398-2640-9(9)) Steck-Vaughn.

—Comprehension Skills Context Level D. 1999. (J). pap. 11.08 (978-0-7398-2646-1(8)) Steck-Vaughn.

—Comprehension Skills Context Level E. 1999. (J). pap. 11.08 (978-0-7398-2652-2(2)) Steck-Vaughn.

—Comprehension Skills Context Level F. 1999. (J). pap. 11.08 (978-0-7398-2658-4(1)) Steck-Vaughn.

—Comprehension Skills Facts Level D. 1999. (J). pap. 11.08 (978-0-7398-2641-6(7)) Steck-Vaughn.

—Comprehension Skills Facts Level E. 1999. (J). pap. 11.08 (978-0-7398-2647-8(6)) Steck-Vaughn.

—Comprehension Skills Facts Level F. 1999. (J). pap. 11.08 (978-0-7398-2653-9(0)) Steck-Vaughn.

—Comprehension Skills Facts Set. 1999. (J). pap. 143.20 (978-0-7398-2665-2(4)) Steck-Vaughn.

—Comprehension Skills Inference. 1999. (J). pap. 143.20 (978-0-7398-2669-0(7)) Steck-Vaughn.

—Comprehension Skills Inference Level C. 1999. (J). pap. 11.08 (978-0-7398-2639-3(5)) Steck-Vaughn.

—Comprehension Skills Inference Level D. 1999. (J). pap. 11.08 (978-0-7398-2645-4(X)) Steck-Vaughn.

—Comprehension Skills Inference Level E. 1999. (J). pap. 11.08 (978-0-7398-2651-5(4)) Steck-Vaughn.

—Comprehension Skills Inference Level F. 1999. (J). pap. 11.08 (978-0-7398-2657-7(3)) Steck-Vaughn.

—Comprehension Skills Level B. 2000. (J). pap. 172.00 (978-0-7398-2660-7(3)) Steck-Vaughn.

—Comprehension Skills Level C. 2000. (J). pap. 172.00 (978-0-7398-2661-4(1)) Steck-Vaughn.

—Comprehension Skills Level D. 2000. (J). pap. 172.00 (978-0-7398-2662-1(X)) Steck-Vaughn.

—Comprehension Skills Level E. 2000. (J). pap. 172.00 (978-0-7398-2663-8(8)) Steck-Vaughn.

—Comprehension Skills Level F. 2000. (J). pap. 172.00 (978-0-7398-2664-5(6)) Steck-Vaughn.

—Comprehension Skills Main Idea. 1999. (J). pap. 143.20 (978-0-7398-2667-6(0)) Steck-Vaughn.

—Comprehension Skills Main Idea Level D. 1999. (J). pap. 11.08 (978-0-7398-2643-0(3)) Steck-Vaughn.

—Comprehension Skills Main Idea Level E. 1999. (J). pap. 11.08 (978-0-7398-2649-2(2)) Steck-Vaughn.

—Comprehension Skills Main Idea Level F. 1999. (J). pap. 11.08 (978-0-7398-2655-3(7)) Steck-Vaughn.

—Comprehension Skills Sequence. 1999. (J). pap. 143.20 (978-0-7398-2666-9(2)) Steck-Vaughn.

—Comprehension Skills Sequence Level D. 1999. (J). pap. 11.08 (978-0-7398-2642-3(5)) Steck-Vaughn.

—Comprehension Skills Sequence Level E. 1999. (J). pap. 11.08 (978-0-7398-2648-5(4)) Steck-Vaughn.

—Comprehension Skills Sequence Level F. 1999. (J). pap. 11.08 (978-0-7398-2654-6(9)) Steck-Vaughn.

Belasco, Susan. Constructing Literacies. pap. 33.95 (978-0-8384-5267-7(1)); pap. 65.95 (978-0-8384-9227-7(4)) Thomson Heinle.

Bennett, Leonie & Buckton, Chris. Cornerstones for Writing Year 2. 2002. (Cornerstones Ser.). (Illus.). 64p. pap., stu. ed. 15.00 (978-0-521-75197-1(7)) Cambridge Univ. Pr.

Bernard-Johnston, Jean, et al. Collaborations Intermediate 2. pap., wbk. ed. 23.95 (978-0-8384-5714-6(2)) Thomson Heinle.

Big Book of English & Math. 2003. (Bumper Gold Stars Ser.). (Illus.). 240p. (J). 9.98 (978-1-4054-1719-8(6)); 9.98 (978-1-4054-1720-4(X)) Parragon, Inc.

Big Book Package, 6 bks., Set. 2004. (gr. 2 up). 218.30 (978-0-673-61067-6(5)) Addison-Wesley Educational Pubs., Inc.

Big Books Package 1.2, 6 bks., Set. 2004. (gr. 1 up). 218.30 (978-0-673-59062-6(3)) Addison-Wesley Educational Pubs., Inc.

Big Books Package 1.3-1.6, 4 bks., Set. 2004. (gr. 1 up). 145.55 (978-0-673-59063-3(1)) Addison-Wesley Educational Pubs., Inc.

Blachowicz, Camille L. Z. Reading Fluency: Reader, Level B. 2004. pap. 15.96 (978-0-07-861710-2(3) , 9780078617102) Jamestown.

—Reading Fluency: Reader's Record B. 2004. pap. 10.64 (978-0-07-861713-3(8) , 9780078617133) Jamestown.

Blevins, Wiley, ed. Grade K. 2006. (SmartSquares Ser.). 16p. 14.99 (978-0-439-83831-3(2) , Teaching Resources) Scholastic, Inc.

—Smart Squares: Grade 1. 2006. (SmartSquares Ser.). 16p. 14.99 (978-0-439-83833-7(9) , Teaching Resources) Scholastic, Inc.

Body, Wendy. Meeble's Magic Box. 2006. (J). lib. bdg. 15.95 (978-1-59566-221-7(9)) QEB Publishing Inc.

Bostwick, Roni. Teach Me Writing: Level A - Kindergarten, 6 vols. 1998. (J). (gr. k-1). 249.98 (978-0-9727748-0-2(7)) Sanron Educ. Enterprises, Inc.

—Teach Me Writing: Level B - First Grade, 6 vols. 1998. 180p. (J). (gr. 1-3). 249.98 (978-0-9727748-1-9(5)) Sanron Educ. Enterprises, Inc.

—Teach Me Writing: Level C - Second Grade, 6 vols. 1998. 180p. (J). (gr. 2-4). 249.98 (978-0-9727748-2-6(3)) Sanron Educ. Enterprises, Inc.

—Teach Me Writing: Level D - Third Grade, 6 vols. 1998. 230p. (J). (gr. 4-6). 249.98 (978-0-9727748-3-3(1)) Sanron Educ. Enterprises, Inc.

—Teach Me Writing: Level E - Fourth Grade, 6 vols. 1998. 250p. (J). (gr. 4-7). 249.98 (978-0-9727748-5-7(8)) Sanron Educ. Enterprises, Inc.

—Teach Me Writing: Level F - Fifth Grade, 6 vols. 1998. 250p. (J). (gr. 5-7). 249.98 (978-0-9727748-6-4(6)) Sanron Educ. Enterprises, Inc.

Bottino, Marlane. My Language Book for Spelling, Writing & Vocabulary: Level C. Bottino, Marlane, illus. 2000. (My Language Books for Spelling, Writing & Vocabulary Ser.: Vol. 3). (Illus.). (J). (gr. k-6). pap. 6.50 (978-1-893615-02-1(2)) Creative Enterprises.

Braidich, Shelby. Little Pigs, Big Pigs: Learning the Short I Sound. (PowerPhonics Ser.). (Illus.). (J). 2002. 24p. (gr. 1). lib. bdg. 18.50 (978-0-8239-5904-4(X)); 2001. 23p. pap. 26.40 (978-0-8239-8249-3(1)) Rosen Publishing Group, Inc., The. (PowerKids Pr.).

Breaking the Writing Barrier: Activities for Adolescents. 2001. 144p. pap. 19.00 (978-0-86647-104-6(9)) Pro Lingua Assocs., Inc.

Brimax, S. My First Word Book. 1998. (Illus.). 48p. (J). pap. 40.00 (978-81-86982-65-5(5)) Business Pubns. Inc. IND. *Dist:* State Mutual Bk. & Periodical Service, Ltd.

Brimner, Larry Dane. Silent Kay & the Dragon. McMahon, Bob, illus. 2007. (Rookie Reader Skill Set Ser.). 32p. (J). (gr. k-2). 19.50 (978-0-531-17546-0(4) , Children's Pr.) Scholastic Library Publishing.

Brock, Paula. Nudges. 2004. 113p. pap. 12.95 (978-1-888842-31-9(8)) Absey & Co.

Brooks, Felicity. Goodnight Baby. 2005. (Busy Baby Board Books Ser.). 10p. (J). 8.95 (978-0-7945-0874-6(X) , Usborne) EDC Publishing.

Bryant-Mole, Karen. Mortimer's ABC's. Mukhida, Zul, illus. 2000. (Mortimer's Fun with Words Ser.). 24p. (J). (ps up). lib. bdg. 22.00 (978-0-8368-2750-7(3)) Stevens, Gareth Inc.

Building Dreams, Grade 3: American Readers. (J). tchr. ed., wbk. ed. (978-0-669-05019-6(9)); wbk. ed. (978-0-669-05018-9(0)) Houghton Mifflin Co. (Schl. Div.).

Bulloch, Ivan & James, Diane. Learn with Me ABC. Pangbourne, Daniel, photos by. 2007. (J). pap. (***978-1-58728-599-8(1)*** , Two Can Publishing) T&N Children's Publishing.

Bunches of Sentence Fun - 2. 2004. (YA). ring bd. 59.95 (978-1-58804-376-4(2)) PCI Educational Publishing.

Burg, Ann. E Is for Empire: A New York State Alphabet. Brookfield, Maureen, illus. 2003. 40p. (J). 17.95 (978-1-58536-113-7(5)) Sleeping Bear Pr.

Burgess, Chris. Study Reading Modules: (E) Elephant. 1999. (Illus.). 24p. (J). pap. 19.95 (978-0-7217-0508-8(1)) Schofield & Sims Ltd. GBR. *Dist:* State Mutual Bk. & Periodical Service, Ltd.

Burke, David. BEAUTY & the BEAST (Japanese to English - Level 3) Learn ENGLISH Through Fairy Tales. 2007. (JPN & ENG.). (J). per. 14.95 incl. audio compact disk (***978-1-891888-05-2(6)***) Slangman Publishing.

—BEAUTY & the BEAST (Spanish to English - Level 3) Learn ENGLISH Through Fairy Tales. 2007. (SPA & ENG.). (J). per. 14.95 incl. audio compact disk (***978-1-891888-97-7(8)***) Slangman Publishing.

—CINDERELLA (Japanese to English - Level 1) Learn ENGLISH Through Fairy Tales. 2007. (JPN & ENG.). (J). per. 14.95 incl. audio compact disk (***978-1-891888-03-8(X)***) Slangman Publishing.

—CINDERELLA (Korean to English - Level 1) Learn ENGLISH Through Fairy Tales. 2007. (KOR & ENG.). (J). per. 14.95 incl. audio compact disk (***978-1-891888-07-6(2)***) Slangman Publishing.

—CINDERELLA (Spanish to English - Level 1) Learn ENGLISH Through Fairy Tales. 2007. (SPA & ENG.). (J). per. 14.95 incl. audio compact disk (***978-1-891888-95-3(1)***) Slangman Publishing.

Burke, Eileen & Putnam, Lillian. Tough Issues, Good Decisions: 20 Reproducible Stories & Writing Prompts That Get Kids Discussing, Writing & Making Good Choices in & Out of School. 2001. 72p. (gr. 4). pap. 11.95 (978-0-439-24117-5(0)) Scholastic, Inc.

Callaghan, Paul. Raw. 2001. (Wizard Study Guides Ser.). pap., stu. ed. 6.00 (978-1-876973-18-6(8)) Cambridge Univ. Pr.

—Snow Falling on Cedars. 2002. (Wizard Study Guides Ser.). 64p. (YA). pap., stu. ed. 6.00 (978-1-876367-08-4(3)) Cambridge Univ. Pr.

—Things Fall Apart. 2002. (Cambridge Wizard English Student Guides). 64p. (YA). pap., stu. ed. 6.00 (978-1-876973-21-6(8)) Cambridge Univ. Pr.

—Wizard Study Guide in Between. 2002. (Wizard Study Guides Ser.). 48p. pap., stu. ed. 6.00 (978-1-876367-51-0(2)) Cambridge Univ. Pr.

Cambridge Esol Staff. Cambridge Certificate in Advanced English: Examination Papers from the University of Cambridge ESOL Examinations. 6th ed. 2005. 118p. pap., stu. ed. 15.00 (978-0-521-61372-9(8)) Cambridge Univ. Pr.

Carlson, Lavelle. The Fable of Mable with a Ladle at the Table: A Phonemic Awareness Tale. 2003. (Illus.). 32p. (J). per. 16.95 (978-0-9725803-1-1(X)) Children's Publishing.

Carnibucci, Patricia. Language Arts & Literature: Over 15 Complete Printable Unit Studies with Interactive Links. 2002. 160p. (gr. k-12). cd-rom 15.95 (978-1-891400-81-0(9)) Champion Pr., Ltd.

Carroll, Joyce Armstrong, et al. Writing & Grammar: Communication in Action, Copper Level, 3 vols. 2004. 952p. (YA). (gr. 6 up). 476.00 (978-0-13-037483-7(0)) Prentice Hall Pr.

Cheney, Martha C. Language Arts Puzzles & Games: A Workbook for Ages 6-8. 2000. (Gifted & Talented Ser.). (Illus.). 64p. (J). (gr. 1-3). pap., wbk. ed. 4.95 (978-0-7373-0372-8(7) , 03727W) Lowell Hse.

Church, Ellen Booth. Best Ever Circletime Activity Language Building: 50 Instant & Irresistible Activities & Games That Build Phonemic Awareness, Expand Vocabulary & Strengthen Listening Skills. 2004. 64p. pap. 11.99 (978-0-439-43113-2(1) , Teaching Resources) Scholastic, Inc.

Claire, Elizabeth. Help Your Buddy Learn English, Bk. 1. Nichols, Dave, illus. l.t. ed. 2003. 64p. 15.00 (978-0-937630-04-4(7)) Eardley Pubns.

Clark, Raymond C. English Interplay: Surviving. 2002. (YA). pap. 16.50 (978-0-86647-155-8(3)) Pro Lingua Assocs., Inc.

Clausen, Andrew & Roso, Calvin. Frankenstein. 2002. 94p. (YA). stu. ed., ring bd. 14.99 (978-1-58609-187-3(5)) Progeny Pr.

Cleary, Brian P. Hairy, Scary, Ordinary: What Is an Adjective? Prosmitsky, Jenya, illus. (Words Are Categorical Ser.). (J). 2003. 32p. (gr. 2-5). pap. 5.95 (978-1-57505-554-1(6)); 1999. (978-0-8225-2108-2(3)) Lerner Publishing Group.

—Mink, a Fink, a Skating Rink: What Is A Noun? 1999. (gr. 3-6). lib. bdg. 14.10 (978-0-613-43850-6(7)) Tandem Library Bks.

—Nearly, Dearly, Insincerely: What Is an Adverb? Gable, Brian, illus. 2005. (Words Are Categorical Ser.). 32p. (gr. 2-5). 14.95 (978-0-87614-924-9(7)) Lerner Publishing Group.

—Seneca Chief, Army General. 2003. (Words Are Categorical Ser.). (Illus.). 64p. (J). (gr. 2-4). pap. 6.95 (978-1-57505-419-3(1)) Lerner Publishing Group.

—To Root, to Toot, to Parachute: What Is a Verb? Prosmitsky, Jenya, illus. 1999. (Words Are Categorical Ser.). (J). (gr. 2-5). 5.95 (978-0-8225-2110-5(5) , Lerner Pubns.) Lerner Publishing Group.

Cline, Mike & Yi-Cline, Nancy. Franky Fox's Fun with English Activity Book, Level A1. Yi-Cline, Nancy, ed. Cline, Mike, illus. 2007. 62p. pap. 7.99 (***978-0-9777419-1-5(5)*** , SIAB) Lingo Pr. LLC.

—Franky Fox's Fun with English Level A1. Yi-Cline, Nancy, ed. Cline, Mike, illus. 2007. (Illus.). 65p. 14.99 (***978-0-9777419-0-8(7)*** , SITB) Lingo Pr. LLC.

Clink! Clink! Clink!, 6 vols. 8p. (gr. k-1). 21.50 (978-0-322-02057-3(3)) Wright Group, The.

Clues to Comprehension. 2002. 144p. (J). (gr. 1-2). pap. 19.99 incl. cd-rom (978-1-55799-862-0(0) , EMC 2720); (Illus.). (gr. 3-4). pap., tchr. ed. 19.99 incl. cd-rom (978-1-55799-863-7(9) , EMC 2721); (Illus.). (gr. 5-6). pap. 19.99 incl. cd-rom (978-1-55799-864-4(7) , EMC 2722) Evan-Moor Educational Pubs.

Cole, John O. Plugged in to English: English & Language Arts Activities for the Computer Lab. Thurston Miller, Cheryl, ed. 2003. (Illus.). 144p. pap. 28.95 (978-1-877673-60-3(9) , PI-BWK03) Cottonwood Pr., Inc.

Cole, Kathleen A. Preschool Skills. 2000. (Step Ahead Workbooks Ser.). (Illus.). 64p. (J). (ps). pap. 3.99 (978-0-307-03667-4(7) , 03667, Golden Bks.) Random Hse. Children's Bks.

Collins, S. H. Food Signs: Early Sign Language. 2002. (Beginning Sign Language Ser.). (Illus.). 26p. (J). bds. 6.95 (978-1-930820-09-8(7) , GP-109) Garlic Pr.

Come on, Dot: Short Vowel o: Level A, 6 vols. (Wright Skills Ser.). 12p. (gr. k-1). 17.95 (978-0-322-03112-8(5)) Wright Group, The.

Complete English Big Books Set. (gr. k-2). 269.95 (978-0-7368-3243-4(2)) Red Brick Learning.

Composing Made Easy Videotape: Videotape Packages. 2003. (Share the Music Ser.). (gr. 5-8). (978-0-02-295493-2(7)) Macmillan/McGraw-Hill Schl. Div.

Composition Workshop: Student Text. (YA). (gr. 11-12). stu. ed. (978-0-8215-0711-7(7)); 2005. (gr. 6-8). stu. ed. 7.95 (978-0-8215-0707-0(9)); 2005. (gr. 6-8). stu. ed. 7.95 (978-0-8215-0708-7(7)) Sadlier, William H. Inc.

Compound Word Memory Match. 2003. (Language Arts Card Games Ser.). (Illus.). (gr. 1-2). 9.99 (978-0-7682-2088-9(2) , J801300) School Specialty Publishing.

Comprehensive Assessment Multiple Choice: Assessment. 2001. (Artes Del Lenguaje Ser.). (ENG & SPA.). (gr. 2 up). (978-0-02-245351-0(2)); (gr. 3 up). (978-0-02-

E F G

245352-7(0)); (gr. 4 up). (978-0-02-245353-4(9)); (gr. 5 up). (978-0-02-245354-1(7)); (gr. 6 up). (978-0-02-245355-8(5)) Macmillan/McGraw-Hill Schl. Div.

Concept Books: 1 Each of 8 Student Books. 16p. (gr. k-1). 28.50 (978-0-7802-3862-6(1)); Vol. 2. 38.95 (978-0-7802-6810-4(5)) Wright Group, The.

Coyote, Fox, & Wolf Tales: Level M, 6 vols. 128p. (gr. 2-3). 41.95 (978-0-7699-1022-2(X)) Shortland Pubns. (U. S. A.) Inc.

Crane, Carol. P Is for Peach: A Georgia Alphabet. Braught, Mark, illus. rev. ed. 2002. 40p. (J). 17.95 (978-1-58536-046-8(5)) Sleeping Bear Pr.

Creepy Creatures: Level O, 6 vols. (Explorers Ser.). 32p. (gr. 3-6). 44.95 (978-0-7699-0592-1(7)) Shortland Pubns. (U. S. A.) Inc.

Crowther, Terence G. Up & Away in English. 1999. (Illus.). 74p. (J). (978-0-19-434985-7(3)) Oxford Univ. Pr., Inc.

—Up & Away in Phonics 4. 1998. (Illus.). 48p. (J). 7.50 (978-0-19-434975-8(6)) Oxford Univ. Pr., Inc.

Cummings, Renee. Extra Help: Math & Language Arts. 2003. (Homework Booklets Ser.). (Illus.). 72p. (gr. 1 up). 2.99 (978-1-56822-412-1(5) , IF0285); (gr. 2 up). 2.99 (978-1-56822-413-8(3) , IF0286); (gr. 3 up). 2.99 (978-1-56822-414-5(1) , IF0287); (gr. 4 up). 2.99 (978-1-56822-415-2(X) , IF0288); (gr. 5 up). 2.99 (978-1-56822-416-9(8) , IF0289); (gr. 6 up). 2.99 (978-1-56822-417-6(6) , IF0290) School Specialty Publishing.

Cut & Paste: Language Arts. 2003. pap. 11.99 (978-0-7439-3707-8(4)) Teacher Created Materials, Inc.

Daily Editing Practice, Grade 1. 2004. pap. 14.99 (978-0-7439-3221-9(8)) Teacher Created Materials, Inc.

Daily Editing Practice, Grade 2. 2004. pap. 14.99 (978-0-7439-3222-6(6)) Teacher Created Materials, Inc.

Daily Paragraph Editing. 2004. (J). (gr. 2 up). per. 19.99 (978-1-55799-956-2(6) , EMC 2725); (gr. 3 up). per. 19.99 (978-1-55799-957-3(0) , EMC 2726); (gr. 4 up). per. 19.99 (978-1-55799-958-0(9) , EMC 2727); (gr. 5 up). per. 19.99 (978-1-55799-959-7(7) , EMC 2728); (gr. 6 up). per. 19.99 (978-1-55799-960-3(0) , EMC 2729) Evan-Moor Educational Pubs.

Daily Word Routine Flip Chart. 2004. (gr. 3 up). suppl. ed. 275.00 (978-0-673-63004-9(8)); (gr. 4 up). suppl. ed. 275.00 (978-0-673-63005-6(6)); (gr. 5 up). suppl. ed. 275.00 (978-0-673-63006-3(4)); (gr. 6 up). suppl. ed. 275.00 (978-0-673-63007-0(2)) Addison-Wesley Educational Pubs., Inc.

Daise, Debra. In Charge 2 Scott Foresman Proulex. 2nd ed. 2002. 128p. (C). pap., stu. ed. 17.66 (978-0-13-098694-8(1)) Longman Publishing Group.

Dance My Dance: Level M, 6 vols. (Take-Twostm Ser.). 32p. 36.95 (978-0-322-03401-3(9)) Wright Group, The.

Dancin' Down, 6 vols., Set B. 32p. (gr. 1-3). 31.50 (978-0-7802-8048-9(2)) Wright Group, The.

Dandelion Wine. 2001. stu. ed., wbk. ed. (978-1-56137-749-7(X)) Novel Units, Inc.

Daniel, Claire, et al. Great Big Book of Fun Phonics Activities. 1999. 352p. (J). pap. 23.95 (978-0-439-08247-1(1)) Scholastic, Inc.

Dartez, Cecilia Casrill. L Is for Louisiana. 2002. (Illus.). 32p. (J). (gr. k-3). pap. 7.95 (978-1-58980-022-9(2)) Pelican Publishing Co., Inc.

—L Is for Louisiana. 2002. (gr. k-3). lib. bdg. 16.40 (978-0-613-71062-6(2)) Tandem Library Bks.

De Vincentis-Hayes, Nan. Troublesome Grammar. 1999. (Straight Forward Advanced English Ser.). 120p. (YA). (gr. 9-12). pap. 9.95 (978-0-931993-19-0(9) , GP-019) Garlic Pr.

Delessert, Etienne. A Was an Apple Pie. 2005. (Creative Editions Ser.). (Illus.). 32p. (J). 18.95 (978-1-56846-196-0(8)) Creative Co., The.

Dennis, Mary L. Reviewing English Language Arts. 2003. pap. (978-1-56765-105-8(4) , R765W) AMSCO Schl. Pubns., Inc.

—Reviewing English Language Arts Preparing for the Eighth-Grade Test. 2002. pap. (978-1-56765-090-7(2) , R742W) AMSCO Schl. Pubns., Inc.

Diagnostic Tests: Student Testing Kit, Features Tests for Language Arts, Including Reading & Mathematics & Also Includes a Parents Cumulative, Set. 2004. (Illus.). (YA). (gr. 7-12). pap. 19.95 (978-0-7403-0097-4(0) , AS9923) Alpha Omega Pubns., Inc.

Dignen, Sheila, et al. Thesaurus. 2nd ed. 2003. (Pockets Ser.). 512p. (J). (gr. 3). pap. 6.99 (978-0-7894-9600-3(3)) Dorling Kindersley Publishing, Inc.

DK Publishing. Very Silly Sentences. 2008. (DK Toys & Games Ser.). (J). (ps-1). 12.99 (***978-0-7566-3747-7(3)***) Dorling Kindersley Publishing, Inc.

Dorling Kindersley Publishing Staff, contrib. by. C Is for Cat: A Touch-and-Say ABC Book. 2002. (DK Ladybird Ser.). 16p. (J). bds. 6.95 (978-0-7894-8471-0(4)) Dorling Kindersley Publishing, Inc.

Dorling Kindersley Publishing Staff, ed. Barbie Word Book / Libro Barbie de Las Palabras. 2004. (J). 12.99 (978-0-7566-0492-9(3)) Dorling Kindersley Publishing, Inc.

Doudna, Kelly. Emma & Eddie. 2005. (First Sounds Ser.). (Illus.). 23p. (J). pap. (978-1-59679-145-9(4)); 19.93 (978-1-59679-144-2(6)) ABDO Publishing Co.

—Eva & Ethan. 2005. (First Sounds Ser.). (Illus.). 23p. (J). pap. (978-1-59679-147-3(0)); 19.93 (978-1-59679-146-6(2)) ABDO Publishing Co.

—Fay & Felix. 2005. (First Sounds Ser.). (Illus.). 23p. (J). (ps-3). 19.93 (978-1-59679-148-0(9)) ABDO Publishing Co.

—Flora & Floyd. 2005. (First Sounds Ser.). (Illus.). 23p. (J). pap. (978-1-59679-151-0(9)); 19.93 (978-1-59679-150-3(0)) ABDO Publishing Co.

—Fran & Fred. 2005. (First Sounds Ser.). (Illus.). 23p. (J). pap. (978-1-59679-153-4(5)); 19.93 (978-1-59679-152-7(7)) ABDO Publishing Co.

—Gail & Gary. 2005. (First Sounds Ser.). 23p. (J). pap. (978-1-59679-155-8(1)); 19.93 (978-1-59679-154-1(3)) ABDO Publishing Co.

—Gina & George. 2005. (First Sounds Ser.). (Illus.). 23p. (J). pap. (978-1-59679-157-2(8)); 19.93 (978-1-59679-156-5(X)) ABDO Publishing Co.

—Gladys & Glen. 2005. (First Sounds Ser.). (Illus.). 23p. (J). pap. (978-1-59679-159-6(4)); 19.93 (978-1-59679-158-9(6)) ABDO Publishing Co.

—Grace & Grant. 2005. (First Sounds Ser.). (Illus.). 23p. (J). pap. (978-1-59679-161-9(6)); 19.93 (978-1-59679-160-2(8)) ABDO Publishing Co.

—Hannah & Henry. 2005. (First Sounds Ser.). (Illus.). 23p. (J). pap. (978-1-59679-163-3(2)); 19.93 (978-1-59679-162-6(4)) ABDO Publishing Co.

—India & Iggy. 2005. (First Sounds Ser.). (Illus.). 23p. (J). pap. (978-1-59679-167-1(5)); 19.93 (978-1-59679-166-4(7)) ABDO Publishing Co.

—Splish Splash. 2004. (Sound Words Ser.). (Illus.). 23p. (J). (ps-3). lib. bdg. 19.93 (978-1-59197-453-6(4)) ABDO Publishing Co.

Douglas, Kathy M. Simple Centers. 1999. 240p. (J). (gr. k up). pap. 16.99 (978-1-56822-305-6(6) , IF8666) School Specialty Publishing.

Douglas, Vincent. Comprehensive Curriculum Plus Test Practice: Grade 2. 2003. (Comprehensive Curriculum Plus Test Practice Ser.). (Illus.). 616p. (J). (ps-6). pap. 24.95 (978-0-7696-2902-5(4) , American Education Publishing) School Specialty Publishing.

—Comprehensive Curriculum Plus Test Practice: Grade K. 2003. (Comprehensive Curriculum Plus Test Practice Ser.). (Illus.). 616p. (J). (ps-6). pap. 24.95 (978-0-7696-2900-1(8) , American Education Publishing) School Specialty Publishing.

—Daily Learning Drills: Grade 4. 2003. (Daily Learning Drills Ser.). (Illus.). 416p. (J). (gr. 4-4). pap., wbk. ed. 10.95 (978-0-7696-3094-6(4) , American Education Publishing) School Specialty Publishing.

—Daily Learning Drills: Grade 5. 2003. (Daily Learning Drills Ser.). (Illus.). 416p. (J). (gr. 5-5). pap., wbk. ed. 10.95 (978-0-7696-3095-3(2) , American Education Publishing) School Specialty Publishing.

—Daily Learning Drills: Grade 6. 2003. (Daily Learning Drills Ser.). (Illus.). 416p. (J). (gr. 6-6). pap. 10.95 (978-0-7696-3096-0(0) , Brighter Child) School Specialty Publishing.

Douglas, Vincent & School Specialty Publishing Staff. The Complete Book of English & Language Arts. 2005. (Complete Book Ser.). (Illus.). 352p. (J). pap. 14.95 (978-0-7696-4331-1(0) , American Education Publishing) School Specialty Publishing.

—Comprehensive Curriculum Plus Test Practice, Grade 1. 2003. (Comprehensive Curriculum Plus Test Practice Ser.). (Illus.). 616p. (J). (ps-6). pap. 24.95 (978-0-7696-2901-8(6) , American Education Publishing) School Specialty Publishing.

—Comprehensive Curriculum Plus Test Practice, Grade 3. 2003. (Comprehensive Curriculum Plus Test Practice Ser.). (Illus.). 616p. (J). (ps-6). pap. 24.95 (978-0-7696-2903-2(2) , American Education Publishing) School Specialty Publishing.

—Comprehensive Curriculum Plus Test Practice, Grade 4. 2003. (Comprehensive Curriculum Plus Test Practice Ser.). (Illus.). 616p. (J). (ps-6). pap. 24.95 (978-0-7696-2904-9(0) , American Education Publishing) School Specialty Publishing.

—Language Arts & Math Skills. 2004. (My Little Heavenly Helpers Ser.). (Illus.). 64p. (J). (ps-k). pap. 3.99 (978-0-7696-3650-4(0) , Brighter Child) School Specialty Publishing.

—Spectrum Language Arts, Grade 2. 2002. (Starburst Spectrum Workbook Ser.). (Illus.). 180p. (J). (gr. 2-2). pap. 8.95 (978-1-56189-952-4(6) , American Education Publishing) School Specialty Publishing.

—Spectrum Language Arts, Grade 3. 2002. (Starburst Spectrum Workbook Ser.). (Illus.). 180p. (J). (gr. 3-3). pap. 8.95 (978-1-56189-953-1(4) , American Education Publishing) School Specialty Publishing.

—Spectrum Language Arts, Grade 4. 2002. (Starburst Spectrum Workbook Ser.). (Illus.). 180p. (J). (gr. 4-4). pap. 8.95 (978-1-56189-954-8(2) , American Education Publishing) School Specialty Publishing.

—Spectrum Language Arts, Grade 5. 2002. (Starburst Spectrum Workbook Ser.). (Illus.). 180p. (J). (gr. 5-5). pap. 8.95 (978-1-56189-955-5(0) , American Education Publishing) School Specialty Publishing.

—Spectrum Language Arts, Grade 6. 2002. (Starburst Spectrum Ser.). (Illus.). 180p. (J). (gr. 6-6). pap. 8.95 (978-1-56189-956-2(9) , American Education Publishing) School Specialty Publishing.

Downie, Mary Alice. A Pioneer ABC. Gerber, Mary Jane, illus. 2005. 32p. (J). (gr. k-2). 15.95 (978-0-88776-688-6(9)) Tundra Bks., Inc./Livres Toundra, Inc. CAN. *Dist:* Random Hse., Inc.

Dyck, Norma J. & Kaff, Marilyn. Essential Skills for Paras. 1999. 32p. spiral bd. 14.00 (978-1-893206-03-8(3)) Curriculum Solutions, Inc.

Dyer, Dorothy & Lloyd, Glynis. English Matters Grade 8. 2000. (English Matters Ser.). 108p. (gr. 8). pap., tchr. ed. 11.05 (978-0-521-78818-2(8)) Cambridge Univ. Pr.

—English Matters Grade 8 Learner's Book. 2000. (English Matters Ser.). pap., tchr. ed. (978-0-521-78819-9(6)) Cambridge Univ. Pr.

—English Matters Grade 8 Learner's Pack. 2nd rev. ed. 2006. 144p. pap. 15.90 (978-0-521-67884-1(6)) Cambridge Univ. Pr.

Early Emergent Skills Guide. (Sunshine Skills Guides). 15.50 (978-0-7802-9809-5(8)) Wright Group, The.

Edgecomb, T. C. & Farrar, Josh. Leaptrack Assessment Practice Book. 2002. (J). (gr. k-1). spiral bd. 1.50 (978-1-58605-637-7(9)); spiral bd. 1.50 (978-1-58605-638-4(7)) LeapFrog Enterprises, Inc. (LeapFrog Schl. Hse.).

Eisele. Hip Hip Hooray: Level 1 with Practice Pages. 2003. (Illus.). 112p. (C). pap., stu. ed. 22.67 (978-0-13-061190-1(5)) Pearson ESL.

Ellis, Sarah. From Reader to Writer: Teaching Writing Through Classic Children's Books. 2001. (J). (978-0-606-21205-2(1)) Tandem Library Bks.

Emberley, Rebecca. My Day. 2000. Tr. of Mi Dia. (SPA.). (ps-2). lib. bdg. 14.95 (978-0-613-26312-2(X)) Tandem Library Bks.

English: Grade 4. 2000. (Master Skills Ser.). (Illus.). 128p. (J). (gr. k-6). pap., wbk. ed. 6.95 (978-1-56189-024-8(3) , 12014, American Education Publishing) School Specialty Publishing.

English: Grade 6. 1999. (Master Skills Ser.). (Illus.). 128p. (J). (gr. k-6). pap., wbk. ed. 6.95 (978-1-56189-026-2(X) , 12016, American Education Publishing) School Specialty Publishing.

English: Grades 3 - 4. (Illus.). (J). pap., wbk. ed. 4.99 (978-0-88743-844-8(X)) School Zone Publishing Co.

English Ages 3-4. Date not set. (Gold Stars Workbook Ser.). (Illus.). 32p. (J). 2.98 (978-0-7525-9556-6(3)) Parragon, Inc.

English Ages 4-5. Date not set. (Gold Stars Workbook Ser.). (Illus.). 32p. (J). 2.98 (978-0-7525-9557-3(1)) Parragon, Inc.

English Ages 5-6. Date not set. (Gold Stars Workbook Ser.). (Illus.). 32p. (J). 2.98 (978-0-7525-9558-0(X)) Parragon, Inc.

English Ages 6-7. Date not set. (Gold Stars Workbook Ser.). (Illus.). 32p. (J). 2.98 (978-0-7525-9559-7(8)) Parragon, Inc.

English for Kids/ English for PreTeens Oral Exams: Student's Booklet. 2000. (Illus.). 20p. (J). spiral bd. (978-1-929310-37-1(4)) ALL Publishing Hse.

English for PreTeens Book 2 Student's Book: Elt. 2000. (Illus.). 124p. pap., stu. ed. (978-1-929310-12-8(9)) ALL Publishing Hse.

English I: Language Skills, Chapter 1 Activities. 2005. (Illus.). 44p. (YA). pap. 5.00 (978-1-59476-137-9(X)) Paradigm Accelerated Curriculum.

English I: Language Skills, Chapter 1 Text, 11 vols. 2005. (Illus.). 58p. (YA). pap. 7.00 (978-1-59476-132-4(9)) Paradigm Accelerated Curriculum.

English I: Language Skills, Chapter 3 Activities. 2005. (Illus.). 54p. (YA). pap. 5.00 (978-1-59476-139-3(6)) Paradigm Accelerated Curriculum.

English I: Language Skills Full Course Kit, 11 bks. 2005. (Illus.). 852p. (YA). 75.00 (978-1-59476-093-8(4)) Paradigm Accelerated Curriculum.

English II: Communication Skills, Chapter 2, Text. 2004. Orig. Title: English Communication Skills, Chapter 2, Text. (Illus.). 64p. (YA). pap. (978-1-59476-002-0(0)) Paradigm Accelerated Curriculum.

English II: Communication Skills, Chapter 3, Text. 2004. Orig. Title: English Communication Skills, Chapter 3, Text. (Illus.). 58p. (YA). pap. (978-1-59476-003-7(9)) Paradigm Accelerated Curriculum.

English II: Communication Skills, Chapter 4, Text. 2004. Orig. Title: English Communication Skills, Chapter 4, Text. (Illus.). 66p. (YA). pap. (978-1-59476-004-4(7)) Paradigm Accelerated Curriculum.

English III: Communication Skills, Chapter 5, Activities. 2004. Orig. Title: English Communication Skills, Chapter 5, Text. 72p. (YA). pap. 5.00 (978-1-59476-020-4(9)) Paradigm Accelerated Curriculum.

English Language Arts Core Assignments: Grade 9-10: Response to Literature. 1999. 343p. (J). (gr. 9-10). pap. 40.00 (978-1-889630-23-6(3)) National Ctr. on Education & The Economy.

English-Language Arts Skills & Strategies Level 3. 2005. 144p. (YA). per. 17.95 (978-1-56254-837-7(9) , SP8379) Saddleback Educational Publishing.

English-Language Arts Skills & Strategies Level 4. 2005. 144p. (YA). per. 17.95 (978-1-56254-838-4(7) , SP8387) Saddleback Educational Publishing.

English-Language Arts Skills & Strategies Level 5. 2005. 144p. (YA). per. 17.95 (978-1-56254-839-1(5) , SP8395) Saddleback Educational Publishing.

English-Language Arts Skills & Strategies Level 6. 2005. 144p. (YA). per. 17.95 (978-1-56254-840-7(9) , SP8409) Saddleback Educational Publishing.

English Skills for Today. (J). Bk. D. (gr. 5). wbk. ed. (978-0-8374-1211-5(0) , 234); Bk. A. (gr. 2). wbk. ed. (978-0-8374-1208-5(0) , 232); Bk. B. (gr. 3). wbk. ed. (978-0-8374-1209-2(9) , 268); Bk. E. (gr. 6). wbk. ed. (978-0-8374-1212-2(9) , 289) Weekly Reader Corp.

English/Math 3-4. 2003. (Illus.). 48p. (J). wbk. ed. 7.98 (978-1-4054-1264-3(X)) Parragon, Inc.

English/Math 4-5. 2003. (Illus.). 48p. (J). wbk. ed. 7.98 (978-1-4054-1265-0(8)) Parragon, Inc.

English/Math 5-6. 2003. (Illus.). 48p. (J). wbk. ed. 7.98 (978-1-4054-1266-7(6)) Parragon, Inc.

English/Math 6-7. 2003. (Illus.). 48p. (YA). wbk. ed. 7.98 (978-1-4054-1267-4(4)) Parragon, Inc.

Escott, John. Goodbye Mr. Hollywood, Level 1. 2000. (Bookworms Ser.). (Illus.). 64p. 6.50 (978-0-19-422942-5(4)) Oxford Univ. Pr., Inc.

Everyday Spelling. 2000. (gr. 2 up). cd-rom 30.00 (978-0-673-62855-8(8)) Addison-Wesley Educational Pubs., Inc.

Everyday Writing. 2004. (Middle School Ser.). (Illus.). 80p. 10.99 (978-0-7439-3615-6(9)) Teacher Created Materials, Inc.

F. W. Prep, 8 bks., Set. Incl. Extraordinary E-Mails, Letters, & Resumes. Nobleman, Marc Tyler. 128p. 30.50 (978-0-531-16759-5(3)); Extraordinary Essays. Orr, Tamra B. 127p. 30.50 (978-0-531-16761-8(5)); Extraordinary Oral Presentations. Ryan, Margaret. 128p. 30.50 (978-0-531-16758-6(5)); Extraordinary Short Story Writing. Otfinoski, Steven. 128p. 30.50 (978-0-531-16760-1(7)); (Illus.). (YA). (gr. 8-13). 2005. 2005. Set lib. bdg. 244.00 (978-0-531-16823-3(9) , Watts, Franklin) Scholastic Library Publishing.

Fiderer, Adele. Paragraph Power. 2002. 128p. (J). pap. 14.95 (978-0-439-20577-1(8)) Scholastic, Inc.

Fifth Grade Workbook. 2002. (English Made Easy Ser.). 200p. (J). pap. 12.95 (978-0-7894-8587-8(7)) Dorling Kindersley Publishing, Inc.

Final Consonants. (Self-Checks Ser.). (gr. k-2). 8.99 (978-0-7647-0343-0(9) , FS65023) Schaffer, Frank Pubns.

Find it, Write It, Read It: Paragraphs. 2004. (J). pap. 7.95 (978-1-56911-180-2(4)) Learning Resources, Inc.

First Grade Workbook. 2002. (English Made Easy Ser.). 200p. (J). pap. 12.95 (978-0-7894-8583-0(4)) Dorling Kindersley Publishing, Inc.

Fisher-Price Jumbo First Grade Workbook. 2004. (J). wbk. ed. (978-0-7666-0301-1(6) , 11822) Modern Publishing.

Fisher-Price Jumbo Kindergarten Workbook. 2004. (J). wbk. ed. (978-0-7666-0300-4(8) , 11820) Modern Publishing.

Fisher-Price Jumbo Preschool Workbook. 2004. (J). wbk. ed. (978-0-7666-0167-3(6) , 11815) Modern Publishing.

Fitzsimmons, Jim & Whiteford, Rhona. English Tests. (Illus.). 32p. (J). pap. 6.99 (978-0-340-68069-8(5) , Hodder & Stoughton) Hodder General Publishing Division GBR. *Dist:* Trafalgar Square Publishing.

Flanagan, Alice K. Ben's Pens: The Sound of Short E. 1999. (Wonder Books Phonics: Vowels Ser.). (Illus.). 24p. (J). (ps-3). 21.36 (978-1-56766-695-3(7)) Child's World, Inc.

—Hats Can Help: The Sound of H. 1999. (Wonder Books Phonics: Consonants Ser.). (Illus.). 24p. (J). (ps-3). 21.36 (978-1-56766-693-9(0)) Child's World, Inc.

—Hot Pot: The Sound of Short O. 1999. (Wonder Books Phonics: Vowels Ser.). (Illus.). 24p. (J). (ps-3). 21.36 (978-1-56766-708-0(2)) Child's World, Inc.

—I Like Bugs: The Sound of B. 1999. (Wonder Books Phonics: Consonants Ser.). (Illus.). 24p. (J). (ps-3). 21.36 (978-1-56766-688-5(4)) Child's World, Inc.

—Kids: The Sound of K. 1999. (Wonder Books Phonics: Consonants Ser.). (Illus.). 24p. (J). (ps-3). 21.36 (978-1-56766-709-7(0)) Child's World, Inc.

—Left: The Sound of L. 1999. (Wonder Books Phonics: Consonants Ser.). (Illus.). 24p. (J). (ps-3). 21.36 (978-1-56766-702-8(3)) Child's World, Inc.

—Wish & Win: The Sound of W. 1999. (Wonder Books Phonics: Consonants Ser.). (Illus.). 24p. (J). (ps-3). 21.36 (978-1-56766-704-2(X)) Child's World, Inc.

—Zigzag: The Sound of Z. 1999. (Wonder Books Phonics: Consonants Ser.). (Illus.). 24p. (J). (ps-3). 21.36 (978-1-56766-707-3(4)) Child's World, Inc.

Forster, Anne & Martin, Paul. Early Writing. 1999. (Illus.). 32p. (J). (ps-3). Bk. 2. pap., wbk. ed. 20.00 (978-0-7217-0468-5(9)); Bk. 3. pap., wbk. ed. 20.00 (978-0-7217-0469-2(7)); Bk. 4. pap., wbk. ed. 20.00 (978-0-7217-0470-8(0)) Schofield & Sims Ltd. GBR. *Dist:* State Mutual Bk. & Periodical Service, Ltd.

Forte, Imogene & Schurr, Sandra. Standards-Based Language Arts Graphic Organizers & Rubrics. 2004. 128p. (J). per. 13.95 (978-0-86530-627-1(3)) Incentive Pubns., Inc.

Fourth Grade Workbook. 2002. (English Made Easy Ser.). 200p. (J). pap. 12.95 (978-0-7894-8586-1(9)) Dorling Kindersley Publishing, Inc.

French, Karen Lea. Dr. Frenchy's Bible ABC's. Wheeler, Ron, illus. 2005. 32p. (J). pap. 9.95 (978-1-57921-792-1(3)) WinePress Publishing.

Froloff, Karen. Practice & Learn: What Every 2nd Grader Needs to Know to Ensure Success in School. Fullam, Sue et al, illus. 1999. 304p. (J). (gr. 2). pap., act. bk. ed. 14.95 (978-1-57690-712-2(0) , TCA2712) Teacher Created Materials, Inc.

From Heart to Page. 2004. (gr. 4-8). pap. 7.00 (978-1-886061-31-6(9)) Wordsmiths.

Fry. Blends & Digraphs. 2004. (Word Charts Ser.). 8.99 (978-0-7439-3504-3(7)) Teacher Created Materials, Inc.

Furlong Reynolds, Cynthia. M Is for Maple Syrup: A Vermont Alphabet. Joyner, Ginny, illus. 2002. 40p. (J). (ps-5). 17.95 (978-1-58536-030-7(9)) Sleeping Bear Pr.

Gage Educational Publishing Staff. Gage Canadian School Thesaurus. 2000. 144p. (J). (gr. 3-8). pap. 12.95 (978-0-7715-1961-1(3)) Gage Learning Corp. CAN. *Dist:* CDG Bks. Canada, Inc.

Gerber, Carole. English. (Master Skills Ser.). (Illus.). 128p. (gr. k-6). 2003. 6.95 (978-1-56189-020-0(0) , 12010); 2000. (J). pap. 6.95 (978-1-56189-023-1(5) , 12013); 1999. (J). pap., wbk. ed. 6.95 (978-1-56189-021-7(9) , 12011); 1999. (J). pap., wbk. ed. 6.95 (978-1-56189-022-4(7) , 12012) School Specialty Publishing. (American Education Publishing).

—Reading Comprehension: Grade 1. 2000. (Master Skills Ser.). (Illus.). 128p. (J). (gr. k-6). pap., wbk. ed. 6.95 (978-1-56189-041-5(3) , 14011, American Education Publishing) School Specialty Publishing.

Gerber, Carole, ed. English: Grade 1. 2003. (Brighter Child Workbooks Ser.). (Illus.). 24p. (J). (gr. 1). pap. 2.25 (978-1-56189-081-1(2) , 51011, American Education Publishing) School Specialty Publishing.

—English: Grade 2. 2nd ed. 2003. (Brighter Child Workbooks Ser.). (Illus.). 24p. (J). (gr. 2). pap. 2.25 (978-1-56189-082-8(0) , American Education Publishing) School Specialty Publishing.

—English: Grade 3. 2003. (Brighter Child Workbooks Ser.). (Illus.). 24p. (gr. 3). pap. 2.25 (978-1-56189-083-5(9) , American Education Publishing) School Specialty Publishing.

—English & Phonics: Grade K. 2003. (Brighter Child Workbooks Ser.). (Illus.). 24p. (J). pap. 2.25 (978-1-56189-080-4(4) , 51010, American Education Publishing) School Specialty Publishing.

Gerngross, Gunter & Puchta, Herbert. Playway to English, Bk. 1. (Playway to English Ser.). 1999. 51p. pap., act. bk. ed. 8.00 (978-0-521-65690-0(7)); 1998. 77p. pap., stu. ed. 14.00 (978-0-521-65694-8(X)) Cambridge Univ. Pr.

—Playway to English 2. 1999. (Playway to English Ser.). 81p. pap., stu. ed. 14.00 (978-0-521-65683-2(4)) Cambridge Univ. Pr.

—Playway to English 3. 1999. (Playway to English Ser.). (Illus.). 75p. pap., stu. ed. 14.00 (978-0-521-65673-3(7)) Cambridge Univ. Pr.

Get Ready to Print. 2003. 16p. (J). 3.79 (978-1-58792-046-2(8)) Trend Enterprises, Inc.

Gifford, Myrna. Meet the Lit Kids: A Read-and-Sing Book. Cooper, Frances, illus. 2003. 12p. (J). 9.95 (978-0-9720763-7-1(9)) Action Factor, Inc.

Gifted and Talented Staff, ed. Reading, Writing, & Math. 2003. (Gifted & Talented Ser.). 192p. (ps-4). 14.95 (978-0-7696-3060-1(X)); 14.95 (978-0-7696-3061-8(8)); 14.95 (978-0-7696-3062-5(6)); 14.95 (978-0-7696-3063-2(4)) School Specialty Publishing.

Giglio, Judy. English 2. 2000. (Teacher Edition Wkbks.). (Illus.). 32p. (J). pap., tchr. ed. 3.99 (978-0-88743-843-1(1) , 02853) School Zone Publishing Co.

Gilleland, Michael S. & Roso, Calvin. Lord of the Flies. 2001. 76p. (J). stu. ed., ring bd. 14.99 (978-1-58609-175-0(1)) Progeny Pr.

Gilleland, Rebecca. The Whipping Boy. 2001. 52p. (J). stu. ed., ring bd. 12.99 (978-1-58609-177-4(8)) Progeny Pr.

Glencoe McGraw-Hill Staff. Oral Interpretation: Bringing Literature to Life Through Performance. 3rd ed. 2001. (C). pap., stu. ed. 43.32 (978-0-8442-1740-6(9) , 9780844217406) Glencoe/McGraw-Hill.

Glencoe McGraw-Hill Staff & McGraw-Hill - Jamestown Education Staff. Six-Way Paragraphs in the Content Areas: Advanced Level. 2001. (gr. 6-12). pap. 17.32 (978-0-8092-0373-4(1) , 9780809203734) Jamestown.

Going Places - PowerPhonics Skill Set III, 6 bks. Incl. Boats That Float : Learning the OA Sound. Richter, Abigail. lib. bdg. 18.50 (978-0-8239-5935-8(X)); Go Far in the Car : Learning the AR Sound. Figorito, Christine. lib. bdg. 18.50 (978-0-8239-5938-9(4)); On My Sled : Learning the SL Sound. Adams, Colleen. lib. bdg. 18.50 (978-0-8239-5952-5(X)); Planes Go Places : Learning the Sound of PL. Adams, Colleen. lib. bdg. 18.50 (978-0-8239-5951-8(1)); They Crawl! Learning the CR Sound. Hogenkamp, Susan. lib. bdg. 18.50 (978-0-8239-5947-1(3)); Train on the Track : Learning the TR Sound. Sheffield, Sarah. lib. bdg. 18.50 (978-0-8239-5937-2(6)); 24p. (J). (gr. 1). 2002. (Illus.). 2001. Set lib. bdg. 108.00 (978-0-8239-7209-8(7) , PowerKids Pr.) Rosen Publishing Group, Inc., The.

Goodman, Burton. Goodman's Five-Star. 2001. (gr. 4-12). Level C. pap., act. bk. ed. 13.96 (978-0-8092-0447-2(9) , 9780809204472); Level A. pap., act. bk. ed. 13.96 (978-0-8092-0445-8(2) , 9780809204458); Level B. pap., act. bk. ed. 13.96 (978-0-8092-0446-5(0) , 9780809204465); Level E. pap., act. bk. ed. 13.96 (978-0-8092-0449-6(5) , 9780809204496) Jamestown.

Graham, Carolyn. Children's Jazz Chants Old & New. 2002. (Jazz Chants Ser.). (Illus.). 96p. pap., stu. ed. 17.75 (978-0-19-433721-2(9)) Oxford Univ. Pr., Inc.

Graphic Organizer Flip Chart. 2004. (gr. k up). suppl. ed. 92.65 (978-0-673-61440-7(9)) Addison-Wesley Educational Pubs., Inc.

Greene, Jane Fell. Language! Student Mastery, Bk. A. 2nd rev. ed. 2000. 87p. (YA). (gr. 1-12). stu. ed. 5.25 (978-1-57035-231-7(3) , 120 BKA) Sopris West Educational Services.

Groves, Penny. Correcting Reversals. 2001. (Modified Basic Skills Ser.). 48p. (J). (gr. k-4). pap. 6.99 (978-0-7424-0162-4(6) , LL80020) School Specialty Publishing.

A Guide to ELL Adaptations to Ramp-up: RUMGL A Guide to ELL Adaptations to Ramp-up. 2005. 50p. 17.00 (978-1-932976-94-6(9)) National Ctr. on Education & The Economy.

A Guide to Fluency & Comprehension: RUMGL A Guide to Fluency & Comprehension. 2005. 50p. 17.00 (978-1-932976-96-0(5)) National Ctr. on Education & The Economy.

Hamilton, Fran Santoro. Hands-on English. Hamilton, Michael, illus. 2nd l.t. ed. 2004. 192p. per. 14.95 (978-0-9664867-5-9(7)) Portico Bks.

Hanson, Anders. Jill & John. 2005. (First Sounds Ser.). (Illus.). 23p. (J). pap. (978-1-59679-169-5(1)); lib. bdg. 19.93 (978-1-59679-168-8(3)) ABDO Publishing Co.

—Kim & Ken. 2005. (First Sounds Ser.). (Illus.). 23p. (J). (978-1-59679-171-8(3)); lib. bdg. 19.93 (978-1-59679-170-1(5)) ABDO Publishing Co.

—Liz & Len. 2005. (First Sounds Ser.). (Illus.). 23p. (J). pap. (978-1-59679-173-2(X)); lib. bdg. 19.93 (978-1-59679-172-5(1)) ABDO Publishing Co.

—Meg & Mark. 2005. (First Sounds Ser.). (Illus.). 23p. (J). pap. (978-1-59679-175-6(6)); lib. bdg. 19.93 (978-1-59679-174-9(8)) ABDO Publishing Co.

—Nan & Nick. 2005. (First Sounds Ser.). (Illus.). 23p. (J). pap. (978-1-59679-177-0(2)); lib. bdg. 19.93 (978-1-59679-176-3(4)) ABDO Publishing Co.

—Olga & Olaf. 2005. (First Sounds Ser.). (Illus.). 23p. pap. (978-1-59679-179-4(9)); (J). lib. bdg. 19.93 (978-1-59679-178-7(0)) ABDO Publishing Co.

—Olive & Oscar. 2005. (First Sounds Ser.). (Illus.). 23p. pap. (978-1-59679-181-7(0)); (J). lib. bdg. 19.93 (978-1-59679-180-0(2)) ABDO Publishing Co.

—Pam & Pete. 2005. (First Sounds Ser.). (Illus.). 23p. (J). pap. (978-1-59679-183-1(7)); lib. bdg. 19.93 (978-1-59679-182-4(9)) ABDO Publishing Co.

—Quinn & Quenton. 2005. (First Sounds Ser.). (Illus.). 23p. (J). pap. (978-1-59679-185-5(3)); lib. bdg. 19.93 (978-1-59679-184-8(5)) ABDO Publishing Co.

—Ruth & Rob. 2005. (First Sounds Ser.). 23p. (J). pap. (978-1-59679-187-9(X)); lib. bdg. 19.93 (978-1-59679-186-2(1)) ABDO Publishing Co.

—Sara & Sam. 2005. (First Sounds Ser.). (Illus.). 23p. (J). pap. (978-1-59679-189-3(6)); lib. bdg. 19.93 (978-1-59679-188-6(8)) ABDO Publishing Co.

—Sharon & Shawn. 2005. (First Sounds Ser.). (Illus.). 23p. (J). pap. (978-1-59679-191-6(8)); lib. bdg. 19.93 (978-1-59679-190-9(X)) ABDO Publishing Co.

Harcourt School Publishers Staff. Blue Skies: Intervention Reader & Practice Book. 2001. (Collections Ser.). (Illus.). (gr. 2). pap. 6.00 (978-0-15-324945-7(5)) Harcourt Schl. Pubs.

—But I Can: Decodable Book. 3rd ed. 2002. (Trophies Reading Program Ser.). (Illus.). pap. 2.90 (978-0-15-325433-8(5)) Harcourt Schl. Pubs.

—El Calcetin... Advanced Level. 3rd ed. 2002. (Trofeos Ser.). (SPA., Illus.). pap. 6.80 (978-0-15-324024-9(5)) Harcourt Schl. Pubs.

—El Caso del Estudiante On Level. 3rd ed. 2002. (Trofeos Ser.).Tr. of Case of the Student. (SPA., Illus.). pap. 6.80 (978-0-15-324074-4(1)) Harcourt Schl. Pubs.

—Collections: Benchmark Books Manual. (Illus.). 2001. (gr. 4). pap. 9.50 (978-0-15-319211-1(9)); 2001. (gr. 5). pap. 9.50 (978-0-15-319212-8(7)); 2001. (gr. 6). pap. 9.50 (978-0-15-319213-5(5)); 2000. (gr. 1). pap. 9.50 (978-0-15-319208-1(9)); 2000. (gr. 2). pap. 9.50 (978-0-15-319209-8(7)); 2000. (gr. 3). pap. 9.50 (978-0-15-319210-4(0)) Harcourt Schl. Pubs.

—Collections: Guided Reading Manual Take-Home Book. (Illus.). 1999. (SPA.). pap. 15.70 (978-0-15-316025-7(X)); 1999. (gr. 2). pap. 15.70 (978-0-15-316026-4(8)); 1999. (gr. 3). pap. 15.70 (978-0-15-316027-1(6)); 1999. (gr. 4). pap. 16.70 (978-0-15-316028-8(4)); 1999. (gr. 5). pap. 16.70 (978-0-15-316029-5(2)); 1999. (gr. 6). pap. 16.70 (978-0-15-316030-1(6)); 2001. pap. 15.70 (978-0-15-317822-1(1)) Harcourt Schl. Pubs.

—Collections: Leveled Library Plus. (Illus.). (J). 2001. (gr. 4). pap. 1507.40 (978-0-15-321143-0(1)); 2001. (gr. 6). pap. 1722.00 (978-0-15-321145-4(8)); 2000. (gr. 5). pap. 1539.30 (978-0-15-321144-7(X)) Harcourt Schl. Pubs.

—Collections: Mid-Year/End-of-Year Reading & Language Skills Assessment. rev. ed. 2001. (Illus.). (gr. 1). pap. 40.90 (978-0-15-319457-3(X)) Harcourt Schl. Pubs.

—Collections: Take-Home Book Collection, 34 vols. rev. ed. 2001. (Illus.). (gr. 1). pap. 77.10 (978-0-15-317821-4(3)) Harcourt Schl. Pubs.

—Collections Vol. 1: Take-Home Book. rev. ed. 2001. (Illus.). (gr. 1). pap. 20.20 (978-0-15-317812-2(4)) Harcourt Schl. Pubs.

—Collections, Grade 1: Intervention Strategies Manual. rev. ed. 2001. pap. 62.70 (978-0-15-319820-5(6)) Harcourt Schl. Pubs.

—Collections, Grade 1: Practice Book. Vol. 1. 1999. pap., tchr. ed. 18.20 (978-0-15-312718-2(X)); Vol. 1. 2001. pap., tchr. ed. 18.20 (978-0-15-317809-2(4)); Vol. 2. 1999. pap., tchr. ed. 18.20 (978-0-15-312719-9(8)) Harcourt Schl. Pubs.

—Collections, Grade 1, Level 1. rev. ed. 2001. pap., tchr. ed. 133.30 (978-0-15-317801-6(9)) Harcourt Schl. Pubs.

—Collections, Grade 3: Stanford-9 Test Preparation: Alabama Edition. 2001. pap., tchr. ed. 22.50 (978-0-15-322339-6(1)) Harcourt Schl. Pubs.

—Collections, Grade 4: Guided Reading Library. 2001. pap., tchr. ed. 12.60 (978-0-15-319199-2(6)) Harcourt Schl. Pubs.

—Collections, Grade 4 Theme 1: TX Edition. 2002. tchr. ed. 80.50 (978-0-15-319876-2(1)) Harcourt Schl. Pubs.

—Collections, Grade 4 Theme 2: TX Edition. 2002. tchr. ed. 80.50 (978-0-15-319877-9(X)) Harcourt Schl. Pubs.

—Collections, Grade 4 Theme 3: TX Edition. 2002. tchr. ed. 80.50 (978-0-15-319878-6(8)) Harcourt Schl. Pubs.

—Collections, Grade 4 Theme 4: TX Edition. 2002. tchr. ed. 80.50 (978-0-15-319879-3(6)) Harcourt Schl. Pubs.

—Collections, Grade 4 Theme 5: TX Edition. 2002. tchr. ed. 80.50 (978-0-15-319880-9(X)) Harcourt Schl. Pubs.

—Collections, Grade 4 Theme 6: TX Edition. 2002. tchr. ed. 80.50 (978-0-15-319881-6(8)) Harcourt Schl. Pubs.

—Collections, Grade 5: Guided Reading Library. 2001. pap., tchr. ed. 12.60 (978-0-15-319200-5(3)) Harcourt Schl. Pubs.

—Collections, Grade 5 Theme 1: TX Edition. 2002. tchr. ed. 80.50 (978-0-15-319882-3(6)) Harcourt Schl. Pubs.

—Collections, Grade 5 Theme 2: TX Edition. 2002. tchr. ed. 80.50 (978-0-15-319883-0(4)) Harcourt Schl. Pubs.

—Collections, Grade 5 Theme 3: TX Edition. 2002. tchr. ed. 87.80 (978-0-15-319884-7(2)) Harcourt Schl. Pubs.

—Come along Daisy! 3rd ed. 2002. (Trophies Reading Program Ser.). (Illus.). pap., lib. bdg. 13.50 (978-0-15-326534-1(5)) Harcourt Schl. Pubs.

—El Cometa: Take-Home Book. 1999. (Vamos Ser.). (SPA., Illus.). (J). pap. 2.50 (978-0-15-318852-7(9)) Harcourt Schl. Pubs.

—Conchita: Phonics Practice Reader. 1999. (Vamos Ser.). (SPA., Illus.). pap. 5.00 (978-0-15-319000-1(0)) Harcourt Schl. Pubs.

—Cuantos/Cielo Advanced Level. 3rd ed. 2002. (Trofeos Ser.). (SPA., Illus.). pap. 6.80 (978-0-15-324131-4(4)) Harcourt Schl. Pubs.

—Cuento/Circulo On Level. 3rd ed. 2002. (Trofeos Ser.). (SPA., Illus.). pap. 6.80 (978-0-15-324098-0(9)) Harcourt Schl. Pubs.

—Cuentos Acerca de Lobos On Level. 3rd ed. 2002. (Trofeos Ser.). (SPA., Illus.). pap. 6.80 (978-0-15-324090-4(3)) Harcourt Schl. Pubs.

—Cuentos de Porcelana Advanced Level. 3rd ed. 2002. (Trofeos Ser.). (SPA., Illus.). pap. 6.80 (978-0-15-324214-4(0)) Harcourt Schl. Pubs.

—Cuidado, Tortugas Below Level. 3rd ed. 2002. (Trofeos Ser.). (SPA., Illus.). pap. 6.80 (978-0-15-324047-8(4)) Harcourt Schl. Pubs.

—Dame Tu Mano: Phonics Practice Reader. 1999. (Vamos Ser.). (SPA., Illus.). pap. 5.00 (978-0-15-318954-8(1)) Harcourt Schl. Pubs.

—Dancing Colors: Take-Home Book. 1999. (Signatures Ser.). (Illus.). (J). pap. 1.90 (978-0-15-313924-6(2)) Harcourt Schl. Pubs.

—Dancing on the Farm: Take-Home Book. 1999. (Signatures Ser.). (Illus.). (J). pap. 1.70 (978-0-15-313853-9(X)) Harcourt Schl. Pubs.

—Danger on Ice: Take-Home Book. 1999. (Signatures Ser.). (Illus.). (J). pap. 1.90 (978-0-15-313938-3(2)) Harcourt Schl. Pubs.

—Daniel En la Nueva Escuela: Take-Home Book. 1999. (Vamos Ser.). (SPA., Illus.). (J). (gr. 3). pap. 2.50 (978-0-15-318837-4(5)) Harcourt Schl. Pubs.

—Davey Joe's Music: Take-Home Book. 1999. (Signatures Ser.). (Illus.). (J). pap. 1.90 (978-0-15-313877-5(7)) Harcourt Schl. Pubs.

—De Aqui Alla Below Level. 3rd ed. 2002. (Trofeos Ser.). (SPA., Illus.). pap. 6.80 (978-0-15-324070-6(9)) Harcourt Schl. Pubs.

—Dear Anna: Take-Home Book. 1999. (Signatures Ser.). (Illus.). (J). pap. 1.70 (978-0-15-313847-8(5)) Harcourt Schl. Pubs.

—Dear Lucy: Take-Home Book. 1999. (Signatures Ser.). (Illus.). (J). pap. 1.90 (978-0-15-313940-6(4)) Harcourt Schl. Pubs.

—Deer & Frog Run a Race: Take-Home Book. 1999. (Signatures Ser.). (Illus.). (J). pap. 1.90 (978-0-15-313891-1(2)) Harcourt Schl. Pubs.

—El Desafio Advanced Level. 3rd ed. 2002. (Trofeos Ser.). (SPA., Illus.). pap. 6.80 (978-0-15-324031-7(8)) Harcourt Schl. Pubs.

—El Disfraz de Luisa: Take-Home Book. 1999. (Vamos Ser.). (SPA., Illus.). (J). (gr. 3). pap. 2.50 (978-0-15-318849-7(9)) Harcourt Schl. Pubs.

—Diversnes Alrededra Advanced Level. 3rd ed. 2002. (Trofeos Ser.). (SPA., Illus.). (gr. 2). pap. 6.80 (978-0-15-324025-6(3)) Harcourt Schl. Pubs.

—Donde Es Cerdito: Get Ready Book. 1999. (Vamos Ser.). (SPA., Illus.). (J). pap. 3.00 (978-0-15-315908-4(1)) Harcourt Schl. Pubs.

—Dos Mundos Advanced Level. 3rd ed. 2002. (Trofeos Ser.). (SPA., Illus.). pap. 6.80 (978-0-15-324103-1(9)) Harcourt Schl. Pubs.

—Dupi y Daniel: Phonics Practice Reader. 1999. (Vamos Ser.). (SPA., Illus.). pap. 5.00 (978-0-15-318993-7(2)) Harcourt Schl. Pubs.

—El Elefante de la Raja Below Level. 3rd ed. 2002. (Trofeos Ser.). (SPA., Illus.). pap. 6.80 (978-0-15-324151-2(9)) Harcourt Schl. Pubs.

—The Emerald Forest: Standard Anthology. 95th ed. 1998. (Treasury of Literature Ser.). (Illus.). (gr. 4). 77.30 (978-0-15-301234-1(X)) Harcourt Schl. Pubs.

—El Emperador Below Level. 3rd ed. 2002. (Trofeos Ser.). (SPA., Illus.). pap. 6.80 (978-0-15-324149-9(7)) Harcourt Schl. Pubs.

—The Future of Reading: Take-Home Book. 2001. (Collections Ser.). (Illus.). (J). pap. 1.90 (978-0-15-319671-3(8)) Harcourt Schl. Pubs.

—Go! - Grade 2. 3rd ed. 2002. (Trophies English Language Learners Ser.). pap. 5.10 (978-0-15-327657-6(6)) Harcourt Schl. Pubs.

—The Graceful Bull Is Full of Surprises: Take-Home Book. 2001. (Collections Ser.). (Illus.). (J). pap. 1.90 (978-0-15-319537-2(1)) Harcourt Schl. Pubs.

—Harcourt Language: TAAS Preparation Book. 2nd ed. 2001. (Illus.). (gr. 2). pap. 8.00 (978-0-15-322492-8(4)); (gr. 3). pap. 8.00 (978-0-15-322493-5(2)); (gr. 4). pap. 8.00 (978-0-15-322494-2(0)); (gr. 5). pap. 8.00 (978-0-15-322495-9(9)) Harcourt Schl. Pubs.

—Harcourt Language Arts: Practice/Reteaching Book. 2nd ed. 2002. (Harcourt Language Ser.). (Illus.). (gr. 1 up). pap. 10.70 (978-0-15-320244-5(0)) Harcourt Schl. Pubs.

—Harcourt Language Arts: Standardized Test Preparation. 2nd ed. 2003. (Harcourt Language Ser.). (Illus.). (gr. 2 up). 7.60 (978-0-15-321223-9(3)); (gr. 3 up). 7.60 (978-0-15-321224-6(1)); (gr. 4 up). 7.60 (978-0-15-321225-3(X)); (gr. 5 up). 7.60 (978-0-15-321226-0(8)) Harcourt Schl. Pubs.

—Harcourt Language Arts: Texas Edition. 2nd ed. 2002. (Illus.). (gr. 2). 52.30 (978-0-15-320240-7(8)); (gr. 4). 63.90 (978-0-15-320242-1(4)); (gr. 5). 69.70 (978-0-15-320243-8(2)) Harcourt Schl. Pubs.

—Harcourt Language Arts Big Book. 2nd ed. 2002. (Harcourt Language Ser.). (Illus.). (gr. k-6). pap. 99.70 (978-0-15-319156-5(2)) Harcourt Schl. Pubs.

—Harcourt Language Arts, Grade 2: Lesson Planner: Texas Edition. 2nd ed. 2000. pap. 19.20 (978-0-15-319149-7(X)) Harcourt Schl. Pubs.

—Harcourt Language Arts, Grade 2: TAAS Preparation. 2nd ed. 2000. pap., tchr. ed. 30.50 (978-0-15-319136-7(8)) Harcourt Schl. Pubs.

—Harcourt Language Arts, Grade 2: TX Edition. 2nd ed. 2002. tchr. ed. 143.80 (978-0-15-319095-7(7)) Harcourt Schl. Pubs.

—Harcourt Language Arts, Grade 3: Lesson Planner: Texas Edition. 2nd ed. 2000. pap. 19.20 (978-0-15-319150-3(3)) Harcourt Schl. Pubs.

—Harcourt Language Arts, Grade 3: Reteaching Activities Copy Masters. 2nd ed. 2002. (Harcourt Language Ser.). (gr. 3 up). pap. 46.00 (978-0-15-319111-4(2)) Harcourt Schl. Pubs.

—Harcourt Language Arts, Grade 3: TAAS Preparation. 2nd ed. 2000. pap., tchr. ed. 30.50 (978-0-15-319137-4(6)) Harcourt Schl. Pubs.

—Harcourt Language Arts, Grade 3: TX Edition. 2nd ed. 2002. pap., tchr. ed. 150.50 (978-0-15-319096-4(5)) Harcourt Schl. Pubs.

—Harcourt Language Arts, Grade 4: Lesson Planner: Texas Edition. 2nd ed. 2000. pap. 19.20 (978-0-15-319151-0(1)) Harcourt Schl. Pubs.

—Harcourt Language Arts, Grade 4: TAAS Preparation. 2nd ed. 2000. pap., tchr. ed. 30.50 (978-0-15-319138-1(4)) Harcourt Schl. Pubs.

—Harcourt Language Arts, Grade 4: TX Edition. 2nd ed. 2002. tchr. ed. 155.30 (978-0-15-319097-1(3)) Harcourt Schl. Pubs.

—Harcourt Language Arts, Grade 5: Lesson Planner: Texas Edition. 2nd ed. 2000. pap. 19.20 (978-0-15-319154-1(6)) Harcourt Schl. Pubs.

—Harcourt Language Arts, Grade 5: TAAS Preparation. 2nd ed. 2000. pap., tchr. ed. 30.50 (978-0-15-319140-4(6)) Harcourt Schl. Pubs.

—Harcourt Language Arts, Grade 5: TX Edition. 2nd ed. 2002. tchr. ed. 155.30 (978-0-15-319098-8(1)) Harcourt Schl. Pubs.

—Harcourt Language, Grade 3: Teachers Guide to Electronic Testing System CD-ROM. 2nd ed. 2000. (Harcourt Language Ser.). (gr. 3 up). pap., tchr. ed. 10.90 (978-0-15-323723-2(6)) Harcourt Schl. Pubs.

—Harcourt Language, Grade 4: Teachers Guide to Electronic Testing System CD-ROM. 2nd ed. 2000. (Harcourt Language Ser.). (gr. 4 up). pap., tchr. ed. 10.90 (978-0-15-323724-9(4)) Harcourt Schl. Pubs.

—Harcourt Language, Grade 4: Writing Express CD-ROM Teacher's Guide. 2nd ed. 2001. (Trophies Ser.). (gr. 4 up). pap., tchr. ed. 10.90 (978-0-15-322260-3(3)) Harcourt Schl. Pubs.

—Harcourt Language, Grade 5: Teachers Guide to Electronic Testing System CD-ROM. 2nd ed. 2000. (Harcourt Language Ser.). (gr. 5 up). pap., tchr. ed. 10.90 (978-0-15-323725-6(2)) Harcourt Schl. Pubs.

—Harcourt Language, Grade 5: Writing Express CD-ROM Teacher's Guide. 2nd ed. 2001. (Trophies Ser.). (gr. 5 up). pap., tchr. ed. 10.90 (978-0-15-322261-0(1)) Harcourt Schl. Pubs.

—Harcourt Lenguaje. 2nd ed. 2002. (Harcourt Lenguaje Ser.). (SPA., Illus.). (gr. 2 up). pupil's gde. ed. 57.80 (978-0-15-320284-1(X)); (gr. 3 up). pupil's gde. ed. 68.80 (978-0-15-320285-8(8)); (gr. 4 up). pupil's gde. ed. 69.30 (978-0-15-320286-5(6)); (gr. 5 up). pupil's gde. ed. 75.00 (978-0-15-320287-2(4)) Harcourt Schl. Pubs.

—Harcourt Lenguaje: Practice Book. 2nd ed. 2002. (Harcourt Lenguaje Ser.). (SPA., Illus.). (gr. 3 up). pap. 10.80 (978-0-15-320297-1(1)); (gr. 5 up). pap. 10.80 (978-0-15-320299-5(8)) Harcourt Schl. Pubs.

—Harcourt Lenguaje: Standardized Test Preparation. 2nd ed. 2002. (Harcourt Lenguaje Ser.). (SPA., Illus.). (gr. 2 up). pap. 12.00 (978-0-15-321219-2(5)); (gr. 3 up). pap. 12.00 (978-0-15-321220-8(9)); (gr. 4 up). pap. 12.00 (978-0-15-321221-5(7)); (gr. 5 up). pap. 12.00 (978-0-15-321222-2(5)) Harcourt Schl. Pubs.

—Harcourt Lenguaje: TAAS Preparation Book. 2001. (SPA., Illus.). (gr. 3). pap. 10.40 (978-0-15-322536-9(X)); 2nd ed. (gr. 2). pap. 10.40 (978-0-15-322535-2(1)); 2nd ed. (gr. 4). pap. 10.40 (978-0-15-322537-6(8)); 2nd ed. (gr. 5). pap. 10.40 (978-0-15-322538-3(6)) Harcourt Schl. Pubs.

—Harcourt Lenguaje, Grade 2: Language Skills & Writing Assessment. 2nd ed. 2002. (Harcourt Lenguaje Ser.). (SPA.). (gr. 2 up). pap., tchr. ed. 66.20 (978-0-15-320324-4(2)) Harcourt Schl. Pubs.

—Harcourt Lenguaje, Grade 2: National & Texas Edition. 2nd ed. 2002. (Harcourt Lenguaje Ser.). (SPA.). (gr. 2 up). tchr. ed. 149.20 (978-0-15-320292-6(0)) Harcourt Schl. Pubs.

—Harcourt Lenguaje, Grade 2: Practice Book. 2nd ed. 2002. (Harcourt Lenguaje Ser.). (SPA.). (gr. 2 up). pap., tchr. ed. 46.40 (978-0-15-320300-8(5)) Harcourt Schl. Pubs.

—Harcourt Lenguaje, Grade 2: Standardized Test Preparation. 2nd ed. 2002. (Harcourt Lenguaje Ser.). (SPA.). (gr. 2 up). pap., tchr. ed. 18.70 (978-0-15-320328-2(5)) Harcourt Schl. Pubs.

—Harcourt Lenguaje, Grade 2: Vocabulary Power: Teacher's Guide. 2nd ed. 2002. (Harcourt Lenguaje Ser.). (SPA.). (gr. 2 up). pap., tchr. ed. 46.40 (978-0-15-320332-9(3)) Harcourt Schl. Pubs.

—Harcourt Lenguaje, Grade 3: Language Skills & Writing Assessment. 2nd ed. 2002. (Harcourt Lenguaje Ser.). (SPA.). (gr. 3 up). pap., tchr. ed. 66.20 (978-0-15-320325-1(0)) Harcourt Schl. Pubs.

—Harcourt Lenguaje, Grade 3: National & Texas Edition. 2nd ed. 2002. (Harcourt Lenguaje Ser.). (SPA.). (gr. 3 up). tchr. ed. 153.90 (978-0-15-320293-3(9)) Harcourt Schl. Pubs.

—Harcourt Lenguaje, Grade 3: Practice Book. 2nd ed. 2002. (Harcourt Lenguaje Ser.). (SPA.). (gr. 3 up). pap., tchr. ed. 46.40 (978-0-15-320301-5(3)) Harcourt Schl. Pubs.

—Harcourt Lenguaje, Grade 3: Standardized Test Preparation. 2nd ed. 2002. (Harcourt Lenguaje Ser.). (SPA.). (gr. 3 up). pap., tchr. ed. 18.70 (978-0-15-320329-9(3)) Harcourt Schl. Pubs.

—Harcourt Lenguaje, Grade 3: Teachers Guide to Electronic Testing System CD-ROM. 2nd ed. 2001. (Harcourt Lenguaje Ser.). (SPA.). (gr. 3 up). pap., tchr. ed. 12.30 (978-0-15-323726-3(0)) Harcourt Schl. Pubs.

—Harcourt Lenguaje, Grade 3: Vocabulary Power: Teacher's Guide. 2nd ed. 2002. (Harcourt Lenguaje Ser.). (SPA.). (gr. 3 up). pap., tchr. ed. 46.40 (978-0-15-320333-6(1)) Harcourt Schl. Pubs.

—Harcourt Lenguaje, Grade 4: Language Skills & Writing Assessment. 2nd ed. 2002. (Harcourt Lenguaje Ser.). (SPA.). (gr. 4 up). pap., tchr. ed. 66.20 (978-0-15-320326-8(9)) Harcourt Schl. Pubs.

—Harcourt Lenguaje, Grade 4: National & Texas Edition. 2nd ed. 2002. (Harcourt Lenguaje Ser.). (SPA.). (gr. 4 up). tchr. ed. 160.00 (978-0-15-320294-0(7)) Harcourt Schl. Pubs.

—Harcourt Lenguaje, Grade 4: Practice Book. 2nd ed. 2002. (Harcourt Lenguaje Ser.). (SPA.). (gr. 4 up). pap., tchr. ed. 46.40 (978-0-15-320302-2(1)) Harcourt Schl. Pubs.

—Harcourt Lenguaje, Grade 4: Reteaching Activities Copy Masters. 2nd ed. 2002. (Harcourt Lenguaje Ser.). (SPA.). (gr. 4 up). pap. 53.00 (978-0-15-320306-0(4)) Harcourt Schl. Pubs.

—Harcourt Lenguaje, Grade 4: Standardized Test Preparation. 2nd ed. 2002. (Harcourt Lenguaje Ser.). (SPA.). (gr. 4 up). pap., tchr. ed. 18.70 (978-0-15-320330-5(7)) Harcourt Schl. Pubs.

—Harcourt Lenguaje, Grade 4: Teachers Guide to Electronic Testing System CD-ROM. 2nd ed. 2001. (Harcourt Lenguaje Ser.). (SPA.). (gr. 4 up). pap., tchr. ed. 12.30 (978-0-15-323727-0(9)) Harcourt Schl. Pubs.

—Harcourt Lenguaje, Grade 4: Vocabulary Power: Teacher's Guide. 2nd ed. 2002. (Harcourt Lenguaje Ser.). (SPA.). (gr. 4 up). pap., tchr. ed. 46.40 (978-0-15-320334-3(X)) Harcourt Schl. Pubs.

—Harcourt Lenguaje, Grade 5: Language Skills & Writing Assessment. 2nd ed. 2002. (Harcourt Lenguaje Ser.). (SPA.). (gr. 5 up). pap., tchr. ed. 66.20 (978-0-15-320327-5(7)) Harcourt Schl. Pubs.

—Harcourt Lenguaje, Grade 5: National & Texas Edition. 2nd ed. 2002. (Harcourt Lenguaje Ser.). (SPA.). (gr. 5 up). tchr. ed. 161.00 (978-0-15-320295-7(5)) Harcourt Schl. Pubs.

—Harcourt Lenguaje, Grade 5: Practice Book. 2nd ed. 2002. (Harcourt Lenguaje Ser.). (SPA.). (gr. 5 up). pap., tchr. ed. 46.40 (978-0-15-320303-9(X)) Harcourt Schl. Pubs.

—Harcourt Lenguaje, Grade 5: Reteaching Activities Copy Masters. 2nd ed. 2002. (Harcourt Lenguaje Ser.). (SPA.). (gr. 5 up). pap. 53.00 (978-0-15-320307-7(2)) Harcourt Schl. Pubs.

—Harcourt Lenguaje, Grade 5: Teachers Guide to Electronic Testing System CD-ROM. 2nd ed. 2001. (Harcourt Lenguaje Ser.). (SPA.). (gr. 5 up). pap., tchr. ed. 12.30 (978-0-15-323728-7(7)) Harcourt Schl. Pubs.

—Harcourt Lenguaje, Grade 5: Vocabulary Power: Teacher's Guide. 2nd ed. 2002. (Harcourt Lenguaje Ser.). (SPA.). (gr. 5 up). pap., tchr. ed. 46.40 (978-0-15-320335-0(8)) Harcourt Schl. Pubs.

—Hilo de la Amistad: Take-Home Book. 1999. (Vamos Ser.). (SPA., Illus.). (J). pap. 2.50 (978-0-15-318831-2(6)) Harcourt Schl. Pubs.

—Hola, Roberto: Take-Home Book. 1999. (Vamos Ser.). (SPA., Illus.). (J). pap. 2.50 (978-0-15-318810-7(3)) Harcourt Schl. Pubs.

—Hop on Top: Decodable Book. 3rd ed. 2002. (Trophies Reading Program Ser.). (Illus.). pap. 2.90 (978-0-15-325425-3(4)) Harcourt Schl. Pubs.

—El Jardin de Papa On Level. 3rd ed. 2002. (Trofeos Ser.). (SPA., Illus.). pap. 6.80 (978-0-15-324099-7(7)) Harcourt Schl. Pubs.

—Jobs at All Hours Advanced Level. 3rd ed. 2002. (Trophies Reading Program Ser.). (Illus.). pap. 5.10 (978-0-15-323039-4(8)) Harcourt Schl. Pubs.

—Josie's Journal On Level. 3rd ed. 2002. (Trophies Reading Program Ser.). (Illus.). pap. 5.10 (978-0-15-323452-1(0)) Harcourt Schl. Pubs.

—Let's Eat! 3rd ed. 2002. (Trophies English Language Learners Ser.). (Illus.). (J). pap. 3.20 (978-0-15-327567-8(7)) Harcourt Schl. Pubs.

—El Lugar Advanced Level. 3rd ed. 2002. (Trofeos Ser.). (SPA., Illus.). pap. 6.80 (978-0-15-324117-8(9)) Harcourt Schl. Pubs.

—Moving into English. 5th ed. 2002. (Illus.). (gr. k). pap. 20.20 (978-0-15-334271-4(4)); (gr. 1). 35.90 (978-0-15-334283-7(8)); (gr. 2). 42.90 (978-0-15-334261-5(7)); (gr. 3). 42.90 (978-0-15-334262-2(5)); (gr. 4). 42.90 (978-0-15-334263-9(3)); (gr. 5). 42.90 (978-0-15-334264-6(1)) Harcourt Schl. Pubs.

—The No-Name Band: Take-Home Book. 1999. (Signatures Ser.). (Illus.). (J). pap. 1.90 (978-0-15-313900-0(5)) Harcourt Schl. Pubs.

—The Orphan: Take-Home Book. 1999. (Signatures Ser.). (Illus.). (J). pap. 1.90 (978-0-15-313905-5(6)) Harcourt Schl. Pubs.

—Paul Bunyan: Take-Home Book. 1999. (Signatures Ser.). (Illus.). (J). pap. 1.90 (978-0-15-313896-6(3)) Harcourt Schl. Pubs.

—Peek-a-Boo, I See You: Take-Home Book. 1999. (Signatures Ser.). (Illus.). (J). pap. 1.70 (978-0-15-314547-6(1)) Harcourt Schl. Pubs.

—Pet Show: Theme Book. 1998. (Treasury of Literature Ser.). (Illus.). (J). 3.70 (978-0-15-303496-1(3)) Harcourt Schl. Pubs.

—The Rerun: Take-Home Book. 1999. (Signatures Ser.). (Illus.). (J). pap. 1.90 (978-0-15-313889-8(0)) Harcourt Schl. Pubs.

—The Run-Away Tire: Take-Home Book. 1999. (Signatures Ser.). (Illus.). (J). pap. 1.90 (978-0-15-313858-4(0)) Harcourt Schl. Pubs.

—The Sea: Take-Home Book. 1999. (Signatures Ser.). (Illus.). (J). pap. 1.90 (978-0-15-313897-3(1)) Harcourt Schl. Pubs.

—The Secret of the Cypress: Take-Home Book. 1999. (Signatures Ser.). (Illus.). (J). pap. 1.90 (978-0-15-313935-2(8)) Harcourt Schl. Pubs.

—See Me Play: Independent Reader. 3rd ed. 2002. (Trophies Reading Program Ser.). (Illus.). (J). pap. 2.90 (978-0-15-325489-5(0)) Harcourt Schl. Pubs.

—The Seven Cities: Take-Home Book. 1999. (Signatures Ser.). (Illus.). (J). pap. 1.90 (978-0-15-313948-2(X)) Harcourt Schl. Pubs.

—Shades of Gold: Standard Anthology. 95th ed. 1998. (Treasury of Literature Ser.). (Illus.). (gr. 6). 77.30 (978-0-15-301236-5(6)) Harcourt Schl. Pubs.

—The Silence of the Dogooder: Take-Home Book. 1999. (Signatures Ser.). (Illus.). (J). pap. 1.90 (978-0-15-313933-8(1)) Harcourt Schl. Pubs.

—Sisters Forever: Take-Home Book. 1999. (Signatures Ser.). (Illus.). (J). pap. 1.90 (978-0-15-313860-7(2)) Harcourt Schl. Pubs.

—Snack Attack: Take Home Book. 1999. (Signatures Ser.). (Illus.). (J). pap. 1.90 (978-0-15-313971-0(4)) Harcourt Schl. Pubs.

—Starting Over: Take-Home Book. 1999. (Signatures Ser.). (Illus.). (J). pap. 1.90 (978-0-15-313926-0(9)) Harcourt Schl. Pubs.

—Stokers & Sandhogs: Take-Home Book. 1999. (Signatures Ser.). (Illus.). (J). pap. 1.90 (978-0-15-313954-3(4)) Harcourt Schl. Pubs.

—Supersmart Shadow: Take-Home Book. 1999. (Signatures Ser.). (Illus.). (J). pap. 1.90 (978-0-15-313930-7(7)) Harcourt Schl. Pubs.

—Susan Butcher And... Take Home Book. 1999. (Signatures Ser.). (Illus.). (J). pap. 1.90 (978-0-15-313990-1(0)) Harcourt Schl. Pubs.

—Test Best Leap 21/Itbs Reading. 2002. pap. (978-0-7398-7254-3(0)); pap. (978-0-7398-7257-4(5)); pap., tchr. ed. 15.10 (978-0-7398-7256-7(7)); pap., tchr. ed. (978-0-7398-7259-8(1)) Steck-Vaughn.

—Test Best NMAAP Language Art. 2002. pap. (978-0-7398-7335-9(0)) Steck-Vaughn.

—Test Best NMAAP Language Art: Grade 1. 2002. pap., tchr. ed. (978-0-7398-7328-1(8)); pap. (978-0-7398-7326-7(1)) Steck-Vaughn.

—Test Best NMAAP Language Art: Grade 2. 2002. pap. (978-0-7398-7329-8(6)); pap., tchr. ed. (978-0-7398-7331-1(8)) Steck-Vaughn.

—Test Best NMAAP Language Art: Grade 3. 2002. pap. (978-0-7398-7332-8(6)); pap., tchr. ed. (978-0-7398-7334-2(2)) Steck-Vaughn.

—Test Best NMAAP Language Art: Grade 4. 2002. pap., tchr. ed. (978-0-7398-7337-3(7)) Steck-Vaughn.

—Test Best NMAAP Language Art: Grade 5. 2002. pap. (978-0-7398-7338-0(5)); pap., tchr. ed. (978-0-7398-7340-3(7)) Steck-Vaughn.

—Test Best NMAAP Language Art: Grade 6. 2002. pap. (978-0-7398-7341-0(5)); pap., tchr. ed. (978-0-7398-7343-4(1)) Steck-Vaughn.

—Test Best SOL for English: Grade 1. 2002. pap. (978-0-7398-7434-9(9)); pap., tchr. ed. (978-0-7398-7436-3(5)) Steck-Vaughn.

—Test Best SOL for English: Grade 2. 2002. pap. (978-0-7398-7437-0(3)); pap., tchr. ed. (978-0-7398-7439-4(X)) Steck-Vaughn.

—Test Best SOL for English: Grade 3. 2002. pap., tchr. ed. (978-0-7398-7442-4(X)); pap. (978-0-7398-7440-0(3)) Steck-Vaughn.

—Test Best SOL for English: Grade 4. 2002. pap. (978-0-7398-7443-1(8)); pap., tchr. ed. (978-0-7398-7445-5(4)) Steck-Vaughn.

—Test Best SOL for English: Grade 5. 2002. pap. (978-0-7398-7446-2(2)); pap., tchr. ed. (978-0-7398-7448-6(9)) Steck-Vaughn.

—That Cat: Take-Home Book. 1999. (Signatures Ser.). (Illus.). (J). pap. 1.70 (978-0-15-313834-8(3)) Harcourt Schl. Pubs.

—The Together Team: Take-Home Book. 1999. (Signatures Ser.). (Illus.). (J). pap. 1.90 (978-0-15-313910-9(2)) Harcourt Schl. Pubs.

—Two Eggs: Take-Home Book. 1999. (Collections Ser.). (Illus.). (J). pap. 1.90 (978-0-15-317189-5(8)) Harcourt Schl. Pubs.

—Vamos de Fiesta: Grammar Practice. (SPA., Illus.). 2001. (gr. 4). pap. 9.20 (978-0-15-316153-7(1)); 2001. (gr. 5). pap. 9.20 (978-0-15-316163-6(9)); 1999. pap. 9.20 (978-0-15-316137-7(X)); 1999. pap. 9.20 (978-0-15-316144-5(2)); 1999. (gr. 1). pap. 9.00 (978-0-15-315999-2(5)) Harcourt Schl. Pubs.

—Vamos de Fiesta, Grade 2: Grammar Practice. 1999. (SPA.). pap., tchr. ed. 19.30 (978-0-15-316138-4(8)) Harcourt Schl. Pubs.

—The Weaver & the Girl: Take-Home Book. 1999. (Signatures Ser.). (Illus.). (J). pap. 1.90 (978-0-15-313890-4(4)) Harcourt Schl. Pubs.

—Why Elephants... Take-Home Book. 1999. (Illus.). (J). pap. 1.90 (978-0-15-313865-2(3)) Harcourt Schl. Pubs.

—The Wild Frontier: Take-Home Book. 1999. (Collections Ser.). (Illus.). (J). pap. 1.90 (978-0-15-317228-1(2)) Harcourt Schl. Pubs.

—Willie's Not the Hugging Kind: Library Edition. 1999. (Collections Ser.). (Illus.). (J). 4.70 (978-0-15-314349-6(5)) Harcourt Schl. Pubs.

—Wings Anthology. 99th ed. 1999. (Signatures Ser.). (Illus.). (gr. 1-3). 54.30 (978-0-15-310108-3(3)) Harcourt Schl. Pubs.

—Wish I Had a Rabbit: Take-Home Book. 1999. (Collections Ser.). (Illus.). (J). pap. 1.90 (978-0-15-317198-7(7)) Harcourt Schl. Pubs.

—Writing Express Espanol, Grade 2. 2nd ed. 2002. (Trofeos Ser.). (SPA.). (gr. 2 up). pap., tchr. ed. 12.60 (978-0-15-322307-5(3)) Harcourt Schl. Pubs.

—Writing Express Espanol, Grade 3. 2nd ed. 2001. (Trofeos Ser.). (SPA.). (gr. 3 up). pap., tchr. ed. 12.60 (978-0-15-322308-2(1)) Harcourt Schl. Pubs.

—Writing Express Espanol, Grade 4. 2nd ed. 2001. (Trofeos Ser.). (SPA.). (gr. 4 up). pap., tchr. ed. 12.60 (978-0-15-322309-9(X)) Harcourt Schl. Pubs.

—Writing Express, Grade 1: Language. 2nd ed. 2001. (Trophies Ser.). (gr. 1 up). pap., tchr. ed. 11.40 (978-0-15-324590-9(5)) Harcourt Schl. Pubs.

—Writing Express, Grade 5. 2nd ed. 2001. (Trofeos Ser.). (SPA.). (gr. 5 up). pap., tchr. ed. 12.60 (978-0-15-322310-5(3)) Harcourt Schl. Pubs.

—Writing Express, Grade 6. 2nd ed. 2003. (Trofeos Ser.). (SPA.). (gr. 6 up). tchr. ed. 10.10 incl. cd-rom (978-0-15-324609-8(X)) Harcourt Schl. Pubs.

—You: Take-Home Book. 1999. (Signatures Ser.). (Illus.). (J). pap. 1.70 (978-0-15-314552-0(8)) Harcourt Schl. Pubs.

—You & Me. 1999. (Collections Ser.). (Illus.). 6.40 (978-0-15-314982-5(5)) Harcourt Schl. Pubs.

—You Can Believe It Happened: Take-Home Book. 1999. (Collections Ser.). (Illus.). (J). pap. 1.90 (978-0-15-317306-6(8)) Harcourt Schl. Pubs.

—You Can, Snowman: Take-Home Book. 1999. (Signatures Ser.). (Illus.). (J). pap. 1.70 (978-0-15-314553-7(6)) Harcourt Schl. Pubs.

—You're Never Bored on a Farm: Take-Home Book. 1999. (Collections Ser.). (Illus.). (J). pap. 1.90 (978-0-15-317233-5(9)) Harcourt Schl. Pubs.

Headway Level C: Blue Hill Skill. (J). (gr. 1-2). (978-0-89688-473-1(2) , 1678) Open Court Publishing Co.

Headway Level J: Close to Sun. (J). (gr. 6). tchr. ed. (978-0-89688-493-9(7) , 88-493) Open Court Publishing Co.

Heinle. 2003 English Catalog. 2002. pap. (978-0-8384-0548-2(7)) Thomson Heinle.

Heller, Ruth. Fantastic! Wow! And Unreal! A Book about Interjections & Conjunctions. Heller, Ruth, illus. 2000. (World of Language Ser.). (Illus.). 32p. (J). (gr. 1 up). pap. 6.99 (978-0-698-11875-1(8) , Putnam Juvenile) Penguin Group (USA) Inc.

—Fantastic! Wow! & Unreal! a Book about Interjections & Conjunctions. 2000. (gr. k-3). lib. bdg. 15.30 (978-0-613-33697-0(6)) Tandem Library Bks.

—Kites Sail High: A Book about Verbs. Heller, Ruth, illus. 1998. (Illus.). (J). (ps-ps). lib. bdg. 16.45 (978-0-8335-6025-4(5)) Tandem Library Bks.

Hello! I'm Paty: Second Grade Big Books. (On Our Way to English Ser.). (gr. 2 up). 29.95 (978-0-7578-1413-6(1)) Rigby Education.

Hello! I'm Paty: Small Versions of Big Books. (On Our Way to English Ser.). (gr. 2 up). 29.00 (978-0-7578-7235-8(2)) Rigby Education.

Hernandez, Jose Francisco. Ingles para Ninos-Un Metodo Facil y Efectivo para Sus Hijos.Tr. of English for Your Kids. (SPA.). 7.98 (978-970-643-104-2(7)) Selector, S.A. de C.V. MEX. *Dist:* AIMS International Bks., Inc., Giron Bks.

Herrera, Mario & Hojel, Barbara. Balloons: Mascot Puppet Funny Froggy. 2005. (J). (gr. 3 up). 17.50 (978-0-7652-6327-8(0)) Longman Publishing Group.

—Balloons: Mascot Puppet Lucky Ducky. 2005. (J). (gr. 2 up). 17.50 (978-0-7652-6326-1(2)) Longman Publishing Group.

—Balloons: Mascot Puppet Sunny Bunny. 2005. (J). (gr. 1 up). 17.50 (978-0-7652-6325-4(4)) Longman Publishing Group.

—Balloons: Picture Cards. 2005. (J). (gr. 1 up). 33.95 (978-0-7652-6302-5(5)); (gr. 2 up). 33.95 (978-0-7652-6322-3(X)); (gr. 3 up). 33.95 (978-0-7652-6323-0(8)) Longman Publishing Group.

—Balloons: Storybooks Package. 2005. (J). 66.50 (978-0-7652-6313-1(0)) Longman Publishing Group.

Herzog, Joyce. School in a Box: Mini-Book. 2004. 4.00 ***(978-1-887225-27-4(7))*** JoyceHerzog.com, Inc.

—Todder School in a Box: Mini Book. 2004. 4.00 ***(978-1-887225-35-9(8))*** JoyceHerzog.com, Inc.

Herzog, Joyce M. Great Rule Book of Letter Sounds. 2002. (Scaredy Cat Reading System Ser.). 41p. (J). (gr. 4-6). pap. (978-1-887225-24-3(2)) JoyceHerzog.com, Inc.

Hey, Kids! (10-lesson edition) Book 1 Student's Book: English Language Teaching. 2002. (Illus.). 112p. stu. ed., spiral bd. (978-0-7428-1281-9(2)) CCLS Publishing Hse.

Hey, Kids! (10-lesson edition) Book 1 Student's Book (with CD) English Language Teaching. 2003. (Illus.). 112p. spiral bd. incl. audio compact disk (978-0-7428-0913-0(7)) CCLS Publishing Hse.

Hey, Kids! (10-lesson edition) Book 2 Student's Book: English Language Teaching. 2002. (Illus.). 112p. stu. ed., spiral bd. (978-0-7428-1283-3(9)) CCLS Publishing Hse.

Hey, Kids! (10-lesson edition) Book 2 Student's Book (with CD) English Language Teaching. 2003. (Illus.). 112p. spiral bd. incl. audio compact disk (978-0-7428-0914-7(5)) CCLS Publishing Hse.

Hey, Kids! (10-lesson edition) Book 3 Student's Book: English Language Teaching. 2002. (Illus.). 112p. stu. ed., spiral bd. (978-0-7428-1285-7(5)) CCLS Publishing Hse.

Hey, Kids! (10-lesson edition) Book 3 Student's Book (with CD) English Language Teaching. 2003. (Illus.). 112p. spiral bd. incl. audio compact disk (978-0-7428-0915-4(3)) CCLS Publishing Hse.

Hey, Kids! (10-lesson edition) Book 4 Student's Book: English Language Teaching. 2002. (Illus.). 128p. stu. ed., spiral bd. (978-0-7428-1287-1(1)) CCLS Publishing Hse.

Hey, Kids! (10-lesson edition) Book 4 Student's Book (with CD) English Language Teaching. 2003. (Illus.). 128p. spiral bd. incl. audio compact disk (978-0-7428-0916-1(1)) CCLS Publishing Hse.

Hey, Kids! (8-lesson edition) Book 1 Student's Book (with CD) English Language Teaching. 2003. (Illus.). 96p. spiral bd. incl. audio compact disk (978-0-7428-0908-6(0)) CCLS Publishing Hse.

Hey, Kids! (8-lesson edition) Book 2 Student's Book (with CD) English Language Teaching. 2003. (Illus.). 96p. spiral bd. incl. audio compact disk (978-0-7428-0909-3(9)) CCLS Publishing Hse.

Hey, Kids! (8-lesson edition) Book 3 Student's Book (with CD) English Language Teaching. 2003. (Illus.). 96p. spiral bd. incl. audio compact disk (978-0-7428-0910-9(2)) CCLS Publishing Hse.

Hey, Kids! (8-lesson edition) Book 4 Student's Book: English Language Teaching. 2002. (Illus.). 112p. stu. ed., spiral bd. (978-0-7428-0585-9(9)) CCLS Publishing Hse.

Hey, Kids! (8-lesson edition) Book 4 Student's Book (with CD) English Language Teaching. 2003. (Illus.). 112p. spiral bd. incl. audio compact disk (978-0-7428-0911-6(0)) CCLS Publishing Hse.

Heywood, Peta & Heywood, Rob. English Steps 2. 1999. (Cambridge Primary Grammar Ser.). 80p. (gr. 2-6). pap. 5.00 (978-0-521-64691-8(X)) Cambridge Univ. Pr.

—English Steps 4. 2000. (Cambridge Primary Grammar Ser.). 96p. pap. 6.00 (978-0-521-64693-2(6)) Cambridge Univ. Pr.

—English Steps 5. 2000. (Cambridge Primary Grammar Ser.). 96p. pap. 6.00 (978-0-521-64694-9(4)) Cambridge Univ. Pr.

—English Steps 6. 2000. (Cambridge Primary Grammar Ser.). 96p. pap. 6.00 (978-0-521-64695-6(2)) Cambridge Univ. Pr.

Heywood, Rob & Heywood, Peta. English Steps 1. 1999. (Cambridge Primary Grammar Ser.). 80p. pap. 5.00 (978-0-521-64690-1(1)) Cambridge Univ. Pr.

Hip Hip Hooray Level 1. 2001. (C). stu. ed. (978-0-13-017907-4(8)) Prentice Hall PTR.

Hockett, M. A. Language Mechanic Level A Book 1: Tuning up English with Logic. 2003. (J). (gr. 3-5). pap. 19.99 (978-0-89455-761-3(0)) Critical Thinking Bks. & Software.

Hoena, B. A. & Saunders-Smith, Gail. Farm ABC: An Alphabet Book. 2005. (A+ Alphabet Books). 32p. (J). 22.60 (978-0-7368-3664-7(0)) Capstone Pr., Inc.

Hojel, Barbara & Guy, Ginger F. I Don't Like Bananas. 1999. Bk. 6. (Illus.). (C). pap. 7.66 (978-0-201-35148-4(X)) Longman Publishing Group.

Hojel, Barbara & Herrera, Mario. Pockets 2. 2005. (C). pap. 18.67 (978-0-13-124662-1(3)) Pearson ESL.

—Pockets 3. 2005. (C). pap. 18.67 (978-0-13-124670-6(4)) Pearson ESL.

Holt, Rinehart and Winston Staff. American Nation: Main Idea Activities for English Language Students. 3rd ed. 2001. pap. 25.80 (978-0-03-065336-0(3)) Holt, Rinehart & Winston.

—Call to Freedom: Beginning-1914: Sheltered English Chapter Tests. 1998. pap. 45.60 (978-0-03-054504-7(8)) Holt, Rinehart & Winston.

—Call to Freedom 2003: Beginning-1877: Chapter Tests for English Language Students. 3rd ed. 2001. pap. 45.13 (978-0-03-065228-8(6)) Holt, Rinehart & Winston.

—Elementos del Lenguaje: Texas Edition - Grade 6. annot. ed. 2003. (Elementos Del Lenguaje Ser.). (SPA.). tchr. ed. 108.20 (978-0-03-064346-0(5)) Holt, Rinehart & Winston.

—Elements of Language: Preparation for English II Exam. 2001. pap. 14.33 (978-0-03-057559-4(1)) Holt, Rinehart & Winston.

—Elements of Language: Preparation for English II Exam - Grade 10. 2001. pap. 14.33 (978-0-03-057561-7(3)) Holt, Rinehart & Winston.

—Elements of Language: Standardized Test Preparation - Texas Edition. 2000. pap. 271.13 (978-0-03-052389-2(3)) Holt, Rinehart & Winston.

—Elements of Language: Support & Practice. 2000. pap. 37.80 (978-0-03-056394-2(1)) Holt, Rinehart & Winston.

—Elements of Language: Support & Practice - Grade 7. 2000. pap. 37.80 (978-0-03-056396-6(8)) Holt, Rinehart & Winston.

—Elements of Language, Grade 11. annot. ed. (Elements of Language Ser.). 2003. tchr. ed. 108.20 (978-0-03-054793-5(8)); 2000. tchr. ed. 119.33 (978-0-03-052103-4(3)); Vol. 1. 2000. 65.53 (978-0-03-064923-3(4)) Holt, Rinehart & Winston.

—Elements of Literature: Language Handbook Worksheets. 5th ed. 2003. pap. 31.40 (978-0-03-073917-0(9)); pap. 31.40 (978-0-03-073918-7(7)); pap. 31.40 (978-0-03-073919-4(5)) Holt, Rinehart & Winston.

—Elements of Literature: Language Handbook, Worksheets & Answer Key. 5th ed. 2003. (Illus.). pap. 13.20 (978-0-03-073927-9(6)) Holt, Rinehart & Winston.

—Elements of Literature: Language Handbook Worksheets Answer Key. 5th ed. 2003. pap. 13.20 (978-0-03-073928-6(4)); pap. 13.20 (978-0-03-073929-3(2)) Holt, Rinehart & Winston.

—Elements of Literature: Middle School PASS Practice Test Workbook: Oklahoma Edition. 2001. pap., wbk. ed. 13.46 (978-0-03-067256-9(2)) Holt, Rinehart & Winston.

—English II End of Chapter Resources Prep Guide: Elements of Literature. 1999. pap. 33.20 (978-0-03-053252-8(3)); pap. 33.20 (978-0-03-053253-5(1)) Holt, Rinehart & Winston.

—Florida Preparation & Response in English/Language Arts/ FCAT. 3rd ed. 2003. (J). pap. 12.20 (978-0-03-070211-2(9)); pap. 12.20 (978-0-03-070212-9(7)); pap. 12.20 (978-0-03-070213-6(5)); pap. 12.16 (978-0-03-070214-3(3)); pap. 12.20 (978-0-03-070216-7(X)); pap. 12.20 (978-0-03-070217-4(8)) Holt, Rinehart & Winston of Canada, Ltd. CAN. *Dist:* Harcourt Canada, Ltd.

—Holt Handbook: Language Practice Answer Key - Grade 6. 3rd ed. 2001. pap. 18.73 (978-0-03-065306-3(1)) Holt, Rinehart & Winston.

—Holt Handbook: Language Practice Answer Key - Grade 7. 3rd ed. 2001. pap. 18.73 (978-0-03-065307-0(X)) Holt, Rinehart & Winston.

—Holt Handbook: Language Practice Answer Key - Grade 8. 3rd ed. 2001. pap. 18.73 (978-0-03-065308-7(8)) Holt, Rinehart & Winston.

—Holt Literature & Language Access, Grade 10: Universal Access Language Skills: California Version. 3rd ed. 2001. pap. 18.73 (978-0-03-066026-9(2)) Holt, Rinehart & Winston.

—Holt Literature & Language Arts, Grade 10: Language Skills Practice - California Edition. 3rd ed. 2001. pap. 30.40 (978-0-03-066509-7(4)) Holt, Rinehart & Winston.

—Holt Literature & Language Arts, Grade 10: Language Skills Practice Answer Key: California Edition. 3rd ed. 2001. pap. 18.73 (978-0-03-066501-1(9)) Holt, Rinehart & Winston.

—Holt Literature & Language Arts, Grade 6: Language Skills Practice - California Edition. 3rd ed. 2001. pap. 30.40 (978-0-03-066504-2(3)) Holt, Rinehart & Winston.

—Holt Literature & Language Arts, Grade 6: Language Skills Practice Answer Key: California Edition. 3rd ed. 2001. pap. 18.73 (978-0-03-066496-0(9)) Holt, Rinehart & Winston.

—Holt Literature & Language Arts, Grade 6: Universal Access Language Skills: California Edition. 3rd ed. 2001. pap., tchr. ed. 14.20 (978-0-03-066029-0(7)) Holt, Rinehart & Winston.

—Holt Literature & Language Arts, Grade 7: Language Skills Practice - California Edition. 3rd ed. 2001. pap. 30.40 (978-0-03-066506-6(X)) Holt, Rinehart & Winston.

—Holt Literature & Language Arts, Grade 7: Universal Access Language Skills: California Edition. 3rd ed. 2001. pap., tchr. ed. 14.20 (978-0-03-066031-3(9)) Holt, Rinehart & Winston.

—Holt Literature & Language Arts, Grade 7: Universal Access Language Skills: California Version. 3rd ed. 2001. pap. 18.73 (978-0-03-066022-1(X)) Holt, Rinehart & Winston.

—Holt Literature & Language Arts, Grade 8: Holt Handbook: California Edition. 3rd annot. ed. 2001. tchr. ed. 104.00 (978-0-03-065291-2(X)) Holt, Rinehart & Winston.

—Holt Literature & Language Arts, Grade 8: Language Skills Practice - California Edition. 3rd ed. 2001. pap. 30.40 (978-0-03-066507-3(8)) Holt, Rinehart & Winston.

—Holt Literature & Language Arts, Grade 8: Language Skills Practice Answer Key: California Edition. 3rd ed. 2001. pap. 18.73 (978-0-03-066498-4(5)) Holt, Rinehart & Winston.

—Holt Literature & Language Arts, Grade 8: Universal Access Language Skills: California Edition. 3rd ed. 2001. pap., tchr. ed. 14.20 (978-0-03-066032-0(7)) Holt, Rinehart & Winston.

—Holt Literature & Language Arts, Grade 8: Universal Access Language Skills: California Version. 3rd ed. 2001. pap. 18.73 (978-0-03-066023-8(8)) Holt, Rinehart & Winston.

—Holt Literature & Language Arts, Grade 9: Language Skills Practice - California Edition. 3rd ed. 2001. pap. 30.40 (978-0-03-066508-0(6)) Holt, Rinehart & Winston.

—Holt Literature & Language Arts, Grade 9: Language Skills Practice Answer Key: California Edition. 3rd ed. 2001. pap. 18.73 (978-0-03-066499-1(3)) Holt, Rinehart & Winston.

—Holt Literature & Language Arts, Grade 9: Universal Access Language Skills: California Version. 3rd ed. 2001. pap. 18.73 (978-0-03-066024-5(6)) Holt, Rinehart & Winston.

—Holt Texas! Answer Key for Guided Reading Strategies. 3rd ed. 2002. pap. 8.00 (978-0-03-066684-1(8)) Holt, Rinehart & Winston.

—Holt Texas! Chapter Tests for English Language. 3rd ed. 2002. pap. 45.60 (978-0-03-065693-4(1)) Holt, Rinehart & Winston.

—Holt Texas! Chapter Tutorials. 3rd ed. 2002. pap. 27.66 (978-0-03-065696-5(6)) Holt, Rinehart & Winston.

—Holt Texas! Daily Quizzes. 3rd ed. 2002. pap. 23.13 (978-0-03-065698-9(2)) Holt, Rinehart & Winston.

—Language Arts: Test Preparation: New York State Edition - Grade 6 - 8. 1999. pap. 8.20 (978-0-03-055394-3(6)) Holt, Rinehart & Winston.

—Language Arts Standard Test Practice: Grade 8. 2001. pap., wbk. ed. 10.73 (978-0-03-071251-7(3)) Holt, Rinehart & Winston.

—Workshop: Course 2. 95th ed. 1998. pap. 19.60 (978-0-03-097175-4(6)) Holt, Rinehart & Winston.

—Workshop: Course 3. 95th ed. 1998. pap. 19.60 (978-0-03-097176-1(4)) Holt, Rinehart & Winston.

Home-School Activities. 2000. (gr. 1 up). suppl. ed. 30.70 (978-0-673-28955-1(9)); (gr. 2 up). suppl. ed. 30.70 (978-0-673-61812-2(9)); (gr. 3 up). suppl. ed. 30.70 (978-0-673-28957-5(5)); (gr. 4 up). suppl. ed. 30.70 (978-0-673-28958-2(3)); (gr. 5 up). suppl. ed. 30.70 (978-0-673-28959-9(1) , Scott Foresman); (gr. 6 up). suppl. ed. 30.70 (978-0-673-28960-5(5)); (gr. 7 up). suppl. ed. 30.70 (978-0-673-28961-2(3)); (gr. 8 up). suppl. ed. 30.70 (978-0-673-28962-9(1)) Addison-Wesley Educational Pubs., Inc.

Home-School Package. 1999. (gr. 1 up). suppl. ed. 38.20 (978-0-673-28576-8(6)); (gr. 2 up). suppl. ed. 38.20 (978-0-673-28577-5(4)); (gr. 3 up). suppl. ed. 38.20 (978-0-673-28578-2(2)); (Illus.). (gr. k up). suppl. ed. 38.20 (978-0-673-28575-1(8)) Addison-Wesley Educational Pubs., Inc. (Scott Foresman).

Homework Student English: RUA Homework Student English. 2005. 150p. per. 4.25 (978-1-932976-77-9(9)) National Ctr. on Education & The Economy.

Homework Student English: RUPA Homework Student English. 2005. 95p. per. 7.50 (978-1-932976-54-0(X)) National Ctr. on Education & The Economy.

Horton, Elizabeth, ed. English 1 Syllabus. 1998. (Illus.). 45p. (YA). (gr. 10-12). pap. 4.95 (978-1-57896-025-5(8) , 2535) Hewitt Research Foundation, Inc.

—English 2 Syllabus. 1998. (Illus.). 24p. (YA). (gr. 10-12). pap., suppl. ed. 4.95 (978-1-57896-026-2(6) , 2536, Hewitt Homeschooling Resources) Hewitt Research Foundation, Inc.

—English 3 Syllabus. 1998. (Illus.). 42p. (YA). (gr. 10-12). pap., suppl. ed. 4.95 (978-1-57896-027-9(4) , 2537) Hewitt Research Foundation, Inc.

—English 4 Syllabus. 1998. (Illus.). 28p. (YA). (gr. 10-12). pap. 4.95 (978-1-57896-028-6(2) , 2538) Hewitt Research Foundation, Inc.

Horton, Elizabeth & Doucey, Elisabeth, eds. Nonfiction English 1 Syllabus. 2nd ed. 1998. Orig. Title: English Syllabus 1. (Illus.). 24p. (YA). (gr. 10-12). pap. 4.95 (978-1-57896-034-7(7) , 1908) Hewitt Research Foundation, Inc.

—Nonfiction English 2 Syllabus. 1998. Orig. Title: English 2 Syllabus. 22p. (YA). (gr. 10-12). pap. 4.95 (978-1-57896-035-4(5) , 1909) Hewitt Research Foundation, Inc.

Horton, Elizabeth & Dousey, Elisabeth, eds. Nonfiction English 3 Syllabus. 1998. Orig. Title: English 3 Syllabus. 44p. (YA). (gr. 10-12). pap. 4.95 (978-1-57896-036-1(3) , 1910) Hewitt Research Foundation, Inc.

—Nonfiction English 4 Syllabus. 1998. Orig. Title: English 4 Syllabus. 28p. (YA). (gr. 10-12). pap. 4.95 (978-1-57896-037-8(1) , 1911) Hewitt Research Foundation, Inc.

Housel, Debra J. Main Idea: Grade 5 (Practice Make Perfect) 2004. 48p. pap. 4.99 (978-0-7439-8645-8(8)) Teacher Created Materials, Inc.

Howell, Kathy & Webb, Alisa. Literacy Bags, 2264. Cernek, Kim, ed. Tom, Darcy, illus. 2002. 176p. pap. 17.99 (978-1-57471-935-2(1) , 2264) Creative Teaching Pr., Inc.

I'm Learning Spanish, Vol. 3. 2005. (J). 12.99 (978-1-894677-77-6(3)) Kidzup Productions.

Jeopardy Langauge Arts Grade 4. 2006. (J). 28.00 (978-1-933178-54-7(X)) Pflaum Publishing Group.

Jeopardy Langauge Arts Grade 5. 2006. (J). 28.00 (978-1-933178-55-4(8)) Pflaum Publishing Group.

Jeopardy Language Arts Grade 3. 2006. (J). 28.00 (978-1-933178-53-0(1)) Pflaum Publishing Group.

Kaplan Staff. Score! Mountian Challenge Language Arts Workbook, Grade K/1 (Ages 5-7) 2007. (Score Mountain Challenge Ser.). 160p. pap. 10.95 (978-1-4195-9459-5(1)) Kaplan Publishing.

Kaye, Cathryn Berger. A Kids' Guide to Helping Others Read & Succeed: How to Take Action. 2007. (Illus.). 48p. (J). pap. (*978-1-57542-241-1(7)) Free Spirit Publishing, Inc.

Keep Books Organization Staff. Mini-Sets Letters, Words & Phonics. (Illus.). 8p. (ps-5). pap. (978-1-893986-17-6(9)) Keep Bks.

Kellas. Our English 2: Integrated Course for the Caribbean. 2007. (Illus.). 296p. pap., stu. ed. 16.95 (978-0-521-69169-7(9)) Cambridge Univ. Pr.

Kelliher, Debra & McRoberts, Richard. King Lear. 2002. (Wizard Study Guides Ser.). 72p. pap., stu. ed. 6.00 (978-1-876367-85-5(7)) Cambridge Univ. Pr.

Kemper, Dave. All Write Skills Book. 2000. pap. 5.99 (978-0-669-45981-4(X)) Great Source Education Group, Inc.

Kidzup Productions Staff. I'm Learning Spanish. 2005. (J). Vol. 1. 12.99 (978-1-894677-75-2(7)); Vol. 2. 12.99 (978-1-894677-76-9(5)) Kidzup Productions.

Kindergarten Jumbo Workbook. 1998. (Step Ahead Ser.). (J). pap., wbk. ed. 4.99 (978-0-307-11251-4(9) , Golden Bks.) Random Hse. Children's Bks.

Kirszner, Laurie G. Brief Holt Handbook for UCF. 3rd ed. pap. 48.95 (978-0-8384-7081-7(5)) Thomson Heinle.

Kirszner, Laurie G. & Mandell, Stephen R. Brief Holt Handbook with APA Update Card. 3rd ed. pap. 43.95 (978-0-8384-7817-2(4)); pap. 49.95 (978-0-8384-8227-8(9)); 2002. 496p. pap. 43.95 (978-0-8384-0697-7(1)) Thomson Heinle.

Klingel, Cynthia. Ack! There's a Bug in My Ear! (and Other Sayings That Just Aren't True) 2007. (Sayings & Phrases Ser.). 24p. (J). (gr. 1-5). 22.79 (*978-1-59296-902-9(X)) Child's World, Inc.

—Go Fly a Kite! (and Other Sayings We Don't Really Mean) 2007. (Sayings & Phrases Ser.). 24p. (J). (gr. 1-5). 22.79 (*978-1-59296-904-3(6)) Child's World, Inc.

—You Let the Cat Out of the Bag! (and Other Crazy Animal Sayings) 2007. (Sayings & Phrases Ser.). 24p. (J). (gr. 1-5). 22.79 (*978-1-59296-903-6(8)) Child's World, Inc.

—You're Clean as a Whistle! (and Other Silly Sayings) 2007. (Sayings & Phrases Ser.). 24p. (J). (gr. 1-5). 22.79 (*978-1-59296-905-0(4)) Child's World, Inc.

Klingel, Cynthia Fitterer & Ballard, Peg. Malls: The Sound of M. 1999. (Wonder Books Phonics: Consonants Ser.). (Illus.). 24p. (J). (ps-3). 21.36 (978-1-56766-686-1(8)) Child's World, Inc.

—Task Time: The Sound of T. 1999. (Wonder Books Phonics: Consonants Ser.). (Illus.). 24p. (J). (ps-3). 21.36 (978-1-56766-690-8(6)) Child's World, Inc.

Klingel, Cynthia Fitterer & Noyed, Robert B. The Cabin: The Sound of C. 1999. (Wonder Books Phonics: Consonants Ser.). (Illus.). 24p. (J). (ps-3). 21.36 (978-1-56766-692-2(2)) Child's World, Inc.

—Jump! The Sound of J. 1999. (Wonder Books Phonics: Consonants Ser.). (Illus.). 24p. (J). (ps-3). 21.36 (978-1-56766-696-0(5)) Child's World, Inc.

Kopp, Kathleen, ed. Language Arts Journal Booklet. 1999. (J). (gr. 1-3). 4.95 (978-1-55708-664-8(8) , MCJ805) McDonald Publishing Co.

Kruss, Susan. The Handmaid's Tale. 2002. (Wizard Study Guides Ser.). 48p. (YA). pap., stu. ed. 6.00 (978-1-875739-44-8(0)) Cambridge Univ. Pr.

Lagunilla, Cheryl, told to. The ABC's of Tennis. 2003. (Illus.). (J). lib. bdg. 24.95 (978-0-9726419-0-6(4)) GHL Publishing LLC.

Langsam, Miriam. Velcro Interactive Phonics Instruction Book. (Illus.). (J). (gr. 2-4). pap. (978-0-9673268-1-8(8)) Learning Fasten-Ations, Inc.

Language Arts. (Switched on Schoolhouse Ser.). 2004. (YA). (gr. 7). cd-rom 69.95 (978-0-7403-0588-7(3)); 2000. (Illus.). (J). (gr. 3-7). pap. 66.95 incl. cd-rom (978-0-7403-0224-4(8) , SOS300L); Set. 2004. (Illus.). (gr. 11). tchr. ed., stu. ed. 66.95 (978-1-58095-706-9(4) , LAN1115, Lifepac); Set. 2004. (Illus.). (gr. 12). tchr. ed., stu. ed. 51.95 (978-1-58095-709-0(9) , LAN1215, Lifepac) Alpha Omega Pubns., Inc.

Language Arts. 2000. (Quick Start Masters Technology Ser.). (J). (gr. 1-2). (978-0-7725-2362-4(2)); (gr. 3-4). (978-0-7725-2366-2(5)); (gr. 5-6). (978-0-7725-2368-6(1)) Thomson Nelson.

Language Arts: Student Testing Kit. 2004. (gr. 7-12). pap., stu. ed. 5.00 (978-1-58095-816-5(8) , LD002, Lifepac) Alpha Omega Pubns., Inc.

Language Arts: Test Generator. 2001. (Technology: Language Arts Ser.). (ENG & SPA.). (gr. 3 up). (978-0-02-245249-0(4)) Macmillan/McGraw-Hill Schl. Div.

Language Arts at Work, High School. 2001. (At Work High School Ser.: Vol. 2). (YA). cd-rom 69.95 (978-1-929879-18-2(0)) Career Kids.

Language Arts Centers. 2005. (Take It to Your Seat Learning Centers). (Illus.). 192p. (gr. 4-6). suppl. ed. 19.99 (978-1-55799-851-4(5) , EMC 2719) Evan-Moor Educational Pubs.

Language Network. 2001. (gr. 12 up). cd-rom (978-0-618-24590-1(1) , 2-22618); (gr. 6 up). cd-rom (978-0-618-09562-9(4) , 2-22556) McDougal Littell Inc.

The Language of Literature: The InterActive Reader Plus for English Learners. 2002. (gr. 10 up). (978-0-618-31021-0(5) , 2-04443); (gr. 10 up). (978-0-618-08732-7(X) , 2-04396); (gr. 7 up). (978-0-618-37783-1(2) , 2-10430); (gr. 7 up). (978-0-618-31018-0(5) , 2-04440); (gr. 8 up). (978-0-618-31019-7(3) , 2-04441); (gr. 8 up). (978-0-618-37784-8(0) , 2-10431) McDougal Littell Inc.

Language Works: Cheese. (J). pap. 16.15 (978-0-8136-3630-6(2)) Modern Curriculum Pr.

Language Works Staff. Early Morning, Vol. 1. 16p. (J). pap. (978-0-8136-3539-2(X)) Modern Curriculum Pr.

—Language Works Vol. I: Crocodile. 8p. (J). pap. (978-0-8136-3531-6(4)) Modern Curriculum Pr.

—Peter & the Wolf. 32p. (J). pap. (978-0-8136-3592-7(6)) Modern Curriculum Pr.

—Red Hen. 24p. (J). pap. (978-0-8136-3577-4(2)) Modern Curriculum Pr.

—Red Jack. 24p. (J). pap. (978-0-8136-3591-0(8)) Modern Curriculum Pr.

—Rhyme Time. 8p. (J). pap. (978-0-8136-3562-0(4)) Modern Curriculum Pr.

—Stone Soup. 8p. (J). pap. (978-0-8136-3556-9(X)) Modern Curriculum Pr.

Lanza, Janet R. & Flahive, Lynn K. Blooming Speech & Language Activities. 2003. (J). spiral bd. 37.95 (978-0-7606-0509-7(2)) LinguiSystems, Inc.

Lapin, Gloria & Radtke, Becky. More Sight Word Stories: 57 Reproducible Books for Beginning Readers. 2001. (Illus.). 136p. (J). (gr. 1-3). pap. 15.99 (978-1-56417-969-2(9) , FE7954, Fearon Teacher Aids) Schaffer, Frank Pubns.

Lawrence. The Fox, Level 2. 2001. (C). pap. 9.00 (978-0-582-41676-5(0)) Longman Publishing Group.

Lda. Correcting Word Reversals. 2002. (Modified Basic Skills Ser.). 48p. (J). (gr. k-4). pap. 6.99 (978-0-7424-0269-0(X) , LL80023) School Specialty Publishing.

LeapFrog Staff. LeapPad Grade 1 Getting Starter Kit. 2003. (Illus.). (J). (gr. 1). spiral bd. 99.00 (978-1-59319-014-9(X) , LeapFrog Schl. Hse.) LeapFrog Enterprises, Inc.

—LeapPad Grade 2 Getting Starter Kit. 2003. (Illus.). (J). (gr. 2). spiral bd. 99.00 (978-1-59319-015-6(8) , LeapFrog Schl. Hse.) LeapFrog Enterprises, Inc.

—LeapPad Kindergarten Getting Starter Kit. 2003. (Illus.). (J). spiral bd. 99.00 (978-1-59319-013-2(1) , LeapFrog Schl. Hse.) LeapFrog Enterprises, Inc.

LeapFrog Staff, compiled by. I Spy in the Sky. 2001. (J). (ps-2). spiral bd. 13.95 (978-1-58605-054-2(0)) LeapFrog Enterprises, Inc.

LeapFrog Staff, compiled by & des. Smart Guide to Fifth Grade. LeapFrog Staff, des. 2002. (J). spiral bd. 14.99 (978-1-58605-737-4(5)) LeapFrog Enterprises, Inc.

Ledbetter, Darriel & Graham, Leland. Graduation Exit Exam Preparation for Writing & Language Arts. Reiner, Angela, ed. 2000. 96p. (J). (gr. 8-12). pap. 10.95 (978-0-86530-450-5(5) , IP 450-5) Incentive Pubns., Inc.

Legrand, Njeri, ed. Games Galore Language Arts. 2002. 96p. (gr. 1-3). 14.95 (978-1-56234-494-8(3) , Mailbox Bks., The) Education Ctr., Inc.

Let's Print (Modern) 2003. 16p. (J). 3.79 (978-1-58792-049-3(2)) Trend Enterprises, Inc.

Let's Print (Zaner-Bloser) 2003. 16p. (J). 3.79 (978-1-58792-048-6(4)) Trend Enterprises, Inc.

Letters & Numbers. (Early Learning Ser.). (J). incl. audio NewSound, LLC.

Levin, Amy. Astronauts. 2003. (Compass Point Phonics Readers Ser.). (Illus.). 16p. (J). (gr. 1 up). 13.26 (978-0-7565-0503-5(8)) Compass Point Bks.

Levitt, Paul M. & Guralnick, Elissa S. The Weighty Word Book. Stevens, Janet, illus. 2nd ed. 2000. 96p. (gr. 4-7). 17.95 (978-1-57098-313-9(5)) Rinehart, Roberts Pubs.

Lewis, Starin. Fluency E-Book. 2005. 80p. (J). per. 10.99 (978-1-59441-563-0(3) , CD-104016-EB) Carson-Dellosa Publishing Co., Inc.

Literacy & Math Centers. 2005. (J). pap. (*978-1-60015-019-7(5)) Steps To Literacy, LLC.

Literacy Centers. 2005. 192p. (gr. 2-3). 19.99 (978-1-55799-976-4(7) , EMC 2723); (gr. 4-5). 19.99 (978-1-55799-977-1(5) , EMC 2724) Evan-Moor Educational Pubs.

Literature Pockets: Aesop's Fables. 2002. (J). (gr. 2-3). suppl. ed. 12.99 (978-1-55799-874-3(4) , EMC 2733) Evan-Moor Educational Pubs.

Literature Pockets: Fiction. 2001. (Illus.). 96p. (J). (gr. 4-6). suppl. ed. 12.99 (978-1-55799-822-4(1) , EMC 2703) Evan-Moor Educational Pubs.

Literature Pockets: Folktales & Fairytales. 2002. (Illus.). (J). (gr. k-1). suppl. ed. 12.99 (978-1-55799-871-2(X) , EMC 2730); (gr. 2-3). suppl. ed. 12.99 (978-1-55799-872-9(8) , EMC 2731) Evan-Moor Educational Pubs.

Literature Pockets: Greek & Roman Myths. 2002. (J). (gr. 4-6). suppl. ed. 12.99 (978-1-55799-875-0(2) , EMC 2734) Evan-Moor Educational Pubs.

Literature Pockets: Nonfiction. 2001. (Illus.). 96p. (J). (gr. 4-6). suppl. ed. 12.99 (978-1-55799-823-1(X) , EMC 2704) Evan-Moor Educational Pubs.

Literature Pockets: Tall Tales. 2002. (Illus.). (J). (gr. 4-6). suppl. ed. 12.99 (978-1-55799-873-6(6) , EMC 2732) Evan-Moor Educational Pubs.

Lloyd, Sylvia & Montgomery, Karen. English Matters: Grade 4 Learner's Book. 2000. (English Matters Ser.). pap. (978-0-521-78860-1(9)) Cambridge Univ. Pr.

—English Matters Grade 4. 2000. (English Matters Ser.). pap. (978-0-521-78859-5(5)) Cambridge Univ. Pr.

Lord, Roberta. Reflections: Albanian Version. 2003. 200p. 9.95 net. (978-1-931934-24-4(X)) Back Yard Pub.

Lundquist, Joegil K. & Lundquist, Jeanne L. English from the Roots Up: Help for Reading, Writing, Spelling, & S. A. T. Scores. 2003. 39.95 (978-1-885942-30-2(3)); II. (Illus.). 125p. 29.95 (978-1-885942-31-9(1)) Cune Pr., LLC.

MacDonald, Ross. Achoo! Bang! Crash! The Noisy Alphabet. MacDonald, Ross, illus. rev. ed. 2003. (Illus.). 32p. (J). (ps-3). 23.90 (978-0-7613-2900-8(5)) Roaring Brook Pr.

MacKall, Dandi Daley. Made by God. Halsey, Megan, illus. 2002. (First Things First Ser.). 12p. (ps-k). 6.99 (978-0-8066-4379-3(X) , Augsburg Bks.) Augsburg Fortress, Pubs.

—Things I Do. Halsey, Megan, illus. 2002. (First Things First Ser.). 12p. (ps-k). 6.99 (978-0-8066-4380-9(3) , Augsburg Bks.) Augsburg Fortress, Pubs.

Madden, Caolan. Let's Count Critters, 1-20. Vangsgard, Amy, illus. 2007. (Let's Find Out Early Learning Bks.). 32p. (J). (ps-k). lib. bdg. 18.00 (978-0-531-14870-9(X) , Children's Pr.) Scholastic Library Publishing.

Madden, Kerry. Writing Smarts: A Girl's Guide to Great Poetry, Storytelling, School Reports & More! McGuinness, Tracy, illus. 2002. (American Girl Library). 104p. (J). pap. 8.95 (978-1-58485-505-7(3)) American Girl Publishing, Inc.

Magner, Laura. Researching Adventures: Challenging GLYPH-Making Activities. 2004. (J). pap. 12.95 (978-1-931334-43-3(9)) Pieces of Learning.

MagneTalk' Match-up Adventure Kit (without Barrier) 2006. (J). 34.95 (*978-1-58650-616-2(1)); 34.95 (*978-1-58650-653-7(6)) Super Duper Pubns.

MagneTalk' Match-up Around the World. 2006. (J). 34.95 (*978-1-58650-644-5(7)) Super Duper Pubns.

MagneTalk' Match-up Around the World (with Barrier) 2006. (J). 44.95 (*978-1-58650-610-0(2)) Super Duper Pubns.

Mahoney, Judy. Teach Me... Classroom Kit English/ESL. 2005. (Illus.). (J). 129.95 (978-0-934633-19-2(3)) Teach Me Tapes, Inc.

Main Idea & Details (Gr. 4-5) 2004. (J). (978-1-58232-132-5(9)) Bryan Hse. Pubs., Inc.

Make-a-Story Journal. 2004. (J). pap. 12.95 (978-1-56911-183-3(9)) Learning Resources, Inc.

Mara, Wil. Quite Enough Hot Dogs. Whitehead, Peter, illus. 2007. (Rookie Reader Skill Set Ser.). 32p. (J). (gr. k-2). 19.50 (978-0-531-17548-4(0) , Children's Pr.) Scholastic Library Publishing.

Martin, Debrah J. Stars in Life: Coaching Kids to Success. 2nd ed. 2000. (Illus.). 96p. (YA). mass mkt. (978-0-9687920-0-1(6)) International Coaching Centre, Inc.

Marty, Lisa. Fast Ideas for Busy Teachers: Language Arts. 2004. (Illus.). 80p. (J). (gr. k-k). pap. 10.99 (978-0-7682-2800-7(X) , FS99274, Schaffer, Frank) Schaffer, Frank Pubns.

Maurer, Jay & Schoenberg, Irene E. True Voices Video Workbook: True Colors. Saslow, Joan, ed. 2002. (Illus.). 44p. (J). (gr. 4). per., suppl. ed. 22.05 (978-0-201-61989-8(X)) Longman Publishing Group.

Mayer, Mercer, illus. Language Arts: Grade 1. 2001. (Spectrum Language Arts Ser.). 160p. (J). (gr. 1-1). pap., wbk. ed. 8.95 (978-1-57768-841-9(4) , Spectrum) School Specialty Publishing.

—Language Arts: Grade K. 2001. (Spectrum Language Arts Ser.). 160p. (J). (gr. k-k). pap., wbk. ed. 8.95 (978-1-57768-840-2(6) , Spectrum) School Specialty Publishing.

McFadden, Patric. Fast Ideas for Busy Teachers: Language Arts. 2004. (Illus.). 80p. (J). (gr. 4-4). pap. 10.99 (978-0-7682-2804-5(2) , FS99272); (gr. 1-1). pap. 10.99 (978-0-7682-2801-4(8) , FS99269) Schaffer, Frank Pubns. (Schaffer, Frank).

—Fast Ideas for Busy Teachers: Language Arts, Grade 5. 2004. (Illus.). 80p. (J). (gr. 5-5). pap. 10.99 (978-0-7682-2805-2(0) , FS99273, Schaffer, Frank) Schaffer, Frank Pubns.

McGraw-Hill - Jamestown Education Staff. Complete Set (Introductory), 10 bks., Set. 3rd ed. 2000. (Comprehension Skills Ser.). (gr. 6-12). 100.64 (978-0-8092-0243-0(3) , 9780809202430) Jamestown.

—Comprehension Skills: Complete Set (Advanced), 10 bks., Set. 2nd ed. 2000. (Comprehension Skills Ser.). (gr. 9-12). 100.64 (978-0-8092-0164-8(X) , 9780809201648) Jamestown.

McGraw-Hill Staff. Glencoe Language Arts Vocabulary Power. 2nd ed. 2001. Grade 7. pap., wbk. ed. 18.00 (978-0-07-826226-5(7) , 9780078262265); Grade 10. pap., wbk. ed. 18.00 (978-0-07-826232-6(1) , 9780078262326) Glencoe/McGraw-Hill.

—Glencoe Language Arts, Vocabulary Power. 2nd ed. 2001. Grade 11. (C). pap., wbk. ed. 18.00 (978-0-07-826234-0(8) , 9780078262340); Grade 12. pap., wbk. ed. 18.00 (978-0-07-826236-4(4) , 9780078262364) Glencoe/ McGraw-Hill.

—Glencoe Language Arts Vocabulary Power Grade 6. 2nd ed. 2001. (C). pap., wbk. ed. 18.00 (978-0-07-826224-1(0) , 9780078262241) Glencoe/McGraw-Hill.

—Glencoe Language Arts, Vocabulary Power Grade 8. 2nd ed. 2001. pap., wbk. ed. 18.00 (978-0-07-826228-9(3) , 9780078262289) Glencoe/McGraw-Hill.

—Glencoe Language Arts Vocabulary Power Grade 9. 2nd ed. 2001. (C). pap., wbk. ed. 18.00 (978-0-07-826230-2(5) , 9780078262302) Glencoe/McGraw-Hill.

—Glencoe Literature: Florida Edition 2003. 2002. Grade 8. (C). stu. ed. 75.32 (978-0-07-828592-9(5) , 9780078285929); Grade 9. stu. ed. 79.32 (978-0-07-828593-6(3) , 9780078285936); Grade 10. stu. ed. 79.32 (978-0-07-828594-3(1) , 9780078285943) Glencoe/McGraw-Hill.

—Glencoe Literature: Grade 12 Florida Edition 2003. 2002. (C). stu. ed. 80.64 (978-0-07-828596-7(8) , 9780078285967) Glencoe/McGraw-Hill.

—Glencoe Literature: Grade 7 Florida Edition 2003. 2002. (C). stu. ed. 75.32 (978-0-07-828591-2(7) , 9780078285912) Glencoe/McGraw-Hill.

—Glencoe Literature: The Reader's Choice, Grade 12, British Literature. 1999. (C). stu. ed. 97.32 (978-0-02-635434-9(9) , 9780026354349) Glencoe/McGraw-Hill.

—Glencoe Literature, Grade 11, Florida. 2002. (C). stu. ed. 80.64 (978-0-07-828595-0(X) , 9780078285950) Glencoe/McGraw-Hill.

—Glencoe Literature Grade 6, Course 1 Interactive Reading Workbook. 2001. pap. 18.00 (978-0-07-825174-0(5) , 9780078251740) Glencoe/McGraw-Hill.

—Glencoe Literature, Grade 6, Florida. 2002. (C). stu. ed. 75.32 (978-0-07-828590-5(9) , 9780078285905) Glencoe/McGraw-Hill.

—Glencoe Literature World Literature Florida Edition 2003. 2002. (C). stu. ed. 80.64 (978-0-07-828597-4(6) , 9780078285974) Glencoe/McGraw-Hill.

McIntosh, Mary. Disaster!, Level 4. 1999. (Bookworms Factfiles Ser.). (Illus.). 48p. pap. 7.50 (978-0-19-422851-0(7)) Oxford Univ. Pr., Inc.

McRoberts, Richard. The Divine Wind. 2002. (Wizard Study Guides Ser.). 48p. pap., stu. ed. 6.00 (978-1-876367-44-2(X)) Cambridge Univ. Pr.

—Wizard Study Guide Great Expectations. 2002. (Cambridge Wizard English Student Guides). 80p. (YA). pap. 6.00 (978-1-876367-10-7(5)) Cambridge Univ. Pr.

McRoberts, Richard & Lyons Press Staff. Fly Away Peter. 2002. (Wizard Study Guides Ser.). 64p. pap., stu. ed. 6.00 (978-1-875739-95-0(5)) Cambridge Univ. Pr.

McRoberts, Richard & Pope, Marcia. Blade Runner - 'In the Wild' 2002. (Wizard Study Guides Ser.). 64p. pap., stu. ed. 6.00 (978-1-876367-94-7(6)) Cambridge Univ. Pr.

McTavish, Sandra. Ready... Set... English! 225 Ready-to-Use Starter Activities for Grades 6-12. 2004. 288p. pap. 29.95 (978-0-7879-7885-3(X)) Wiley, John & Sons, Inc.

Meador, Karen. Tiered Activities for Learning Centers. 2004. (J). pap. 15.95 (978-1-931334-29-7(3)) Pieces of Learning.

Meisinger, Amy L. First Words: A Little Husker Book. 1998. (Illus.). 16p. (J). pap. 6.99 (978-0-9665572-0-6(4)) U Lead, LLC.

Melling, David, illus. My First French Words. 1999. (My First Words to See & Learn Ser.). (FRE.). 48p. (ps-3). 11.95 (978-0-8442-2406-0(5) , 24065, Passport Bks.) McGraw-Hill Trade.

Miller, Amanda. Let's Add to Ten, Again & Again! Michael, Joan J., illus. Levin, James, photos by. 2007. (Let's Find Out Early Learning Bks.). 32p. (J). (ps-k). lib. bdg. 18.00 (978-0-531-14869-3(6) , Children's Pr.) Scholastic Library Publishing.

Miller Molengraft, Lisa. Simple Centers. 1999. 240p. (J). (gr. 1 up). pap. 16.99 (978-1-56822-306-3(4) , IF8667); (gr. 2 up). pap. 16.99 (978-1-56822-307-0(2) , IF8668) School Specialty Publishing.

Minden, Cecilia. Celine & Cedric Go to the Circus: The Sound of Soft C. 2004. (Phonics Friends Ser.). 24p. (J). (ps). 21.36 (978-1-59296-291-4(2)) Child's World, Inc.

Modern Beginning Cursive. 2002. (Home Workbooks Ser.). 64p. pap. 2.49 (978-0-88724-744-6(X) , CD-4546) Carson-Dellosa Publishing Co., Inc.

Modern Manuscript. 2002. (Home Workbooks Ser.). 64p. pap. 2.49 (978-0-88724-738-5(5) , CD-4540) Carson-Dellosa Publishing Co., Inc.

Molter, Carey. Sh: See It Say It Hear It. l.t. ed. 2000. (Blends Ser.). (Illus.). 24p. (J). (ps-3). lib. bdg. 19.93 (978-1-57765-412-4(9) , SandCastle) ABDO Publishing Co.

—Silent B As in Lamb. 2004. (Silent Letters Ser.). (Illus.). 23p. (J). (ps-3). lib. bdg. 19.93 (978-1-59197-443-7(7) , SandCastle) ABDO Publishing Co.

—Silent Gh As in Light. 2004. (Silent Letters Ser.). (Illus.). 23p. (J). (ps-3). lib. bdg. 19.93 (978-1-59197-444-4(5) , SandCastle) ABDO Publishing Co.

—Silent H As in Ghost. 2004. (Silent Letters Ser.). (Illus.). 23p. (J). (ps-3). lib. bdg. 19.93 (978-1-59197-445-1(3) , SandCastle) ABDO Publishing Co.

—Silent K As in Knot. 2004. (Silent Letters Ser.). (Illus.). 23p. (J). (ps-3). lib. bdg. 19.93 (978-1-59197-446-8(1) , SandCastle) ABDO Publishing Co.

—Silent L As in Chalk. 2004. (Silent Letters Ser.). (Illus.). 23p. (J). (ps-3). lib. bdg. 19.93 (978-1-59197-447-5(X) , SandCastle) ABDO Publishing Co.

—Silent W As in Wreath. 2004. (Silent Letters Ser.). (Illus.). 23p. (J). (ps-3). lib. bdg. 19.93 (978-1-59197-448-2(8) , SandCastle) ABDO Publishing Co.

—Tr: See It Say It Hear It. l.t. ed. 2000. (Blends Ser.). (Illus.). 24p. (J). (ps-3). lib. bdg. 19.93 (978-1-57765-411-7(0) , SandCastle) ABDO Publishing Co.

Mondello, Cindy, ed. Games Galore Language Arts. 2002. 96p. (gr. 4-6). 14.95 (978-1-56234-486-3(2) , Mailbox Bks., The) Education Ctr., Inc.

Montgomary, Beverly. Mommy where Is Heaven. 2004. (J). (978-0-9763093-3-8(5)) Creative Bk. Pubs.

—Mommy Why Don't I Look Good in the Mirror. 2004. (J). (978-0-9763093-4-5(3)) Creative Bk. Pubs.

Montgomery, Karen & Lloyd, Glynis. English Matters Grade 4. 2000. (English Matters Ser.). 128p. (gr. 4). pap., tchr. ed. 9.20 (978-0-521-78861-8(7)) Cambridge Univ. Pr.

—English Matters Grade 6 Learner's Book. 2002. (English Matters Ser.). pap. (978-0-521-00378-0(4)) Cambridge Univ. Pr.

Montgomery, Karen, et al. English Matters Grade 4 Learner's Pack. 2nd rev. ed. 2004. 192p. pap. 11.05 (978-0-521-54466-5(1)) Cambridge Univ. Pr.

—English Matters Grade 5 Learner's Pack. 2nd rev. ed. 2004. 192p. pap. 11.60 (978-0-521-54605-8(2)) Cambridge Univ. Pr.

—English Matters Grade 6 Learner's Pack. 2nd rev. ed. 2004. 208p. pap. 11.95 (978-0-521-54607-2(9)) Cambridge Univ. Pr.

Moore, Sheila. Abadaba Alphabet: Learning Letter Sounds. Holsinger, Carol, illus. 2006. (J). ***978-0-9789473-0-9(4))** Abadaba Reading LLC.

Morning Bath: Big Book: Level M. Group 1. (Sunshinetm Ser.). 24p. 36.50 (978-0-7802-5795-5(2)) Wright Group, The.

Moskal, Greg. Family Fun: Learning the F Sound. (Power-Phonics Ser.). (Illus.). (J). 2002. 24p. (gr. 1). lib. bdg. 18.00 (978-0-8239-5901-3(5)); 2001. 23p. lib. bdg. 26.40 (978-0-8239-8246-2(7)) Rosen Publishing Group, Inc., The. (PowerKids Pr.).

Murphy, Brenda K. The Mate's Log. (Sail Away Ser.). (J). (gr. k-5). Level A, Bk. 1. 1999. 104p. pap. 16.95 (978-1-58504-004-9(5)); Level A, Bk. 2. 2000. 124p. pap. 16.95 (978-1-58504-005-6(3)); Level A, Bk. 3. 2000. 124p. pap. 16.95 (978-1-58504-006-3(1)) UTW Resources, Inc.

—The Practice Pack. Jensen, Pamela G., illus. 1999. (Sail Away Ser.). 86p. (J). (ps-5). pap., wbk. ed. 15.95 (978-1-58504-002-5(9)) UTW Resources, Inc.

My First Phonics. (J). bds. 6.99 (978-0-7894-9767-3(0)) Dorling Kindersley Publishing, Inc.

Myers, R. E. Language Fundamentals. Mitchell, Judith, ed. Smith, Bron, illus. 2005. 96p. (J). Bk. 1. pap. 11.95 (978-1-57310-450-0(7)); Bk. 2. pap. 11.95 (978-1-57310-451-7(5)) Teaching & Learning Co.

Naidoo, Mathevan & Lague, Peter. Study & Master English Grade 11 Learner's Book. 2006. 288p. pap. 13.00 (978-0-521-68256-5(8)) Cambridge Univ. Pr.

Nama, Michael D., et al. Stay Tuned Student's Book For 3 ème. 2004. 160p. pap., stu. ed. 5.65 (978-0-521-60503-8(2)) Cambridge Univ. Pr.

—Stay Tuned Student's Book For 5 ème. Tamla, Berthe Kamga & Nijbamum, John Suh, eds. 2nd rev. ed. 2004. 144p. pap. 4.55 (978-0-521-60574-8(1)) Cambridge Univ. Pr.

—Stay Tuned Student's Book For 6 ème. 2nd rev. ed. 2004. 128p. pap. 4.10 (978-0-521-60572-4(5)) Cambridge Univ. Pr.

—Stay Tuned Workbook 3 éme. 2004. 96p. pap. 2.75 (978-0-521-60862-6(7)) Cambridge Univ. Pr.

—Stay Tuned Workbook For 5 éme. 2nd rev. ed. 2005. 88p. pap. 3.70 (978-0-521-67578-9(2)) Cambridge Univ. Pr.

—Stay Tuned Workbook For 6 éme. 2nd rev. ed. 2005. 64p. pap. 3.70 (978-0-521-67579-6(0)) Cambridge Univ. Pr.

Novelli, Joan. Phonics Make-&-Take Manipulatives: Dozens of Reproducible Patterns & Activities That Make Le. 1999. 64p. (J). (gr. k-2). pap. 9.95 (978-0-590-86716-0(4)) Scholastic, Inc.

Nunan, David. Expressions. pap., stu. ed. 16.95 (978-0-8384-2278-6(0)); Level 2. pap., stu. ed. 16.95 (978-0-8384-2245-8(4)) Thomson Heinle.

O'Connor, John. Literacy in Context for AQA A. 2003. (Literacy in Context Ser.). (Illus.). 208p. pap. 19.35 (978-0-521-53528-1(X)) Cambridge Univ. Pr.

O'Dell. Elements of Language. (Elements of Language Ser.). 2003. (gr. 6) pap. pupil's gde. ed. 64.73 (978-0-03-052662-6(0)); 2000. (gr. 11). 73.33 (978-0-03-052668-8(X)); 2000. (gr. 12). 73.33 (978-0-03-052669-5(8)); 2000. (gr. 7). 67.46 (978-0-03-052663-3(9)); 2000. (gr. 8). 67.46 (978-0-03-052664-0(7)) Holt, Rinehart & Winston.

Olien, Rebecca. Kids Write: Fantasy & Sci Fi, Mystery, Autobiography, Adventure & More! Kline, Michael, illus. 2005. (Little Hands! Ser.). 128p. (YA). (gr. 7-14). pap. 12.95 (978-0-8249-6771-0(2) , Williamson Bks.) Ideals Pubns.

Open Court Staff. Breaking Code Sentence Strips. (J). pap. (978-0-87548-958-2(3) , 8513) Open Court Publishing Co.

Orange & Turquoise Levels Certificate Only. (gr. k-5). 89.00 (978-0-7578-6543-5(7)) Rigby Education.

Orange Level Certificate Only. (Sails Literacy Ser.). (gr. 1-6). 89.00 (978-0-7578-6554-1(2)) Rigby Education.

Ortega, Vincente. Inglés para Sus Niños. 2002. (SPA.). 12.95 (978-968-7968-36-0(2) , LQ13627) Encuadernacion Geminis, S.A. de C.V. MEX. *Dist:* Lectorum Pubns., Inc.

Oxford Staff, ed. Benny & Sue. 1998. (Illus.). 16.95 (978-0-19-435374-8(5)) Oxford Univ. Pr., Inc.

Pallotta, Jerry. The Ocean Alphabet Board Book. Mazzola, Frank, Jr., illus. 2004. 28p. (J). bds. 6.95 (978-1-57091-524-6(5)) Charlesbridge Publishing, Inc.

Panman, Sandra & Panman, Richard. Writing Guides. 2000. (Illus.). 373p. (YA). (gr. 6 up). reprint ed. pap. 26.00 (978-0-912813-27-1(X)) Active Learning Corp.

Parker, Andrew & Stamford, Jane. Basic Skills - An Early Language Programme, Bk. 1. 1999. (Illus.). 31p. (J). (gr. k-3). pap. 20.00 (978-0-7217-0608-5(8)) Schofield & Sims Ltd. GBR. *Dist:* State Mutual Bk. & Periodical Service, Ltd.

Parr, Helen. Cloudstreet. 2002. (Wizard Study Guides Ser.). 48p. pap., stu. ed. 6.00 (978-1-876367-15-2(6)) Cambridge Univ. Pr.

Patrizzi, Barbara. O Is for Oystercatcher: A Book of Seaside ABCs. Patrizzi, Barbara, illus. 2005. (Illus.). 55p. (978-1-59322-008-2(1)) Down The Shore Publishing.

Pebble Soup Explorations: Complete Pebble Soup Explorations Package. 1650.00 (978-0-7578-3313-7(6)) Rigby Education.

Pebble Soup Explorations: Pebble Soup Explorations Extra Ingredients. 239.00 (978-0-7578-3341-0(1)) Rigby Education.

Pebble Soup Explorations: SAVE when you purchase the Complete Pebble Soup Exploration/Exploraciones Program! 3100.00 (978-0-7578-5226-8(2)) Rigby Education.

Petter, Constance & Bomberg, Hyman. Funics Vol. 1: A Fun Way to Improve Reading, Writing, Spelling & Thinking: Short Vowels. unabr. ed. 1999. (J). (gr. k-12). pap., wbk. ed. 8.33 (978-1-930676-01-5(8)) Funics Publishing.

Phillips, Heather. Habitats. Tom, Darcy et al, eds. Tom, Darcy, illus. 2003. (Stepping into Standards Theme Ser.). 64p. (J). (gr. 2-4). pap. 10.99 (978-1-59198-007-0(0) , CTP2489) Creative Teaching Pr., Inc.

Phonics Ad Libs: Blends & Digraphs. 2003. (J). pap. 9.95 (978-1-56911-105-5(7)) Learning Resources, Inc.

Pinnell, Gay Su & Fountas, Irene C. Phonics Lessons: Letters, Words, & How They Work. (Phonics Lessons Ser.). (J). Grade 1. 2002. 1152p. (gr. 1). pap. 82.00 (978-0-325-00408-2(0) , E00408); Grade 2. 2003. 496p. (gr. 2). pap. 82.00 (978-0-325-00409-9(9) , E00409) Heinemann.

Pitambar Publ. Staff. Bharat Junior English Dictionary. 1998. 104p. pap. 75.00 (978-81-86378-07-6(3)) Pitambar Publishing IND. *Dist:* State Mutual Bk. & Periodical Service, Ltd.

Playing with Words, 6 Packs. (Action Packs Ser.). 104p. (gr. 3-5). 44.00 (978-0-7635-2988-8(5)) Rigby Education.

Pope, Marcia & McRoberts, Richard. Witness. 2002. (Wizard Study Guides Ser.). 64p. pap., stu. ed. 6.00 (978-1-876367-87-9(3)) Cambridge Univ. Pr.

Poteet, Michael. Tuck Everlasting. 2002. 66p. (YA). stu. ed., ring bd. 12.99 (978-1-58609-189-7(1)) Progeny Pr.

Powell, Sara Davis. Super Strategies for Succeeding on the Standardized Tests: Reading / Language Arts. 2000. (Scholastic Teaching Strategies Ser.). 128p. pap. 14.95 (978-0-439-04249-9(6)) Scholastic, Inc.

Practice Masters. 2000. (gr. 1 up). suppl. ed. 48.90 (978-0-673-28988-9(5)); 2000. (gr. 2 up). suppl. ed. 48.90 (978-0-673-61809-2(9)); 2000. (gr. 3 up). suppl. ed. 48.90 (978-0-673-28990-2(7)); 2000. 45p. (gr. 4 up). suppl. ed. 48.90 (978-0-673-28991-9(5)); 2000. (gr. 5 up). suppl. ed. 48.90 (978-0-673-28992-6(3)); 2000. (gr. 6 up). suppl. ed. 48.90 (978-0-673-28993-3(1)); 2000. (gr. 7 up). suppl. ed. 48.90 (978-0-673-28994-0(X)); 2000. (gr. 8 up). suppl. ed. 48.90 (978-0-673-28995-7(8)); 1999. (gr. 1 up). suppl. ed. 31.60 (978-0-673-28763-2(7) , Scott Foresman); 1999. (gr. 2 up). suppl. ed. 31.60 (978-0-673-28764-9(5) , Scott Foresman); 1999. (gr. 3 up). suppl. ed. 31.60 (978-0-673-28765-6(3) , Scott Foresman); 1999. (gr. 4 up). suppl. ed. 31.60 (978-0-673-28766-3(1) , Scott Foresman); 1999. (gr. 5 up). 31.60 (978-0-673-28767-0(X) , Scott Foresman); 1999. (gr. 6 up). suppl. ed. 31.60 (978-0-673-28768-7(8) , Scott Foresman) Addison-Wesley Educational Pubs., Inc.

Practice Power School Bus Book: First Grade Language Arts. 2003. (Illus.). 24p. (J). (gr. k-1). spiral bd. (978-1-930355-43-9(2)) Greenbrier/Scentex.

Premium Education Bindup Grade 1. 2006. (J). per. 14.95 ***978-1-59545-026-5(2))** Learning Horizons, Inc.

Premium Education Bindup Grade 2. 2006. (J). per. 14.95 ***978-1-59545-027-2(0))** Learning Horizons, Inc.

Premium Education Bindup Grade 3. 2006. (J). per. 14.95 ***978-1-59545-028-9(9))** Learning Horizons, Inc.

Premium Education Bindup Grade K. 2006. (J). per. 14.95 ***978-1-59545-025-8(4))** Learning Horizons, Inc.

Premium Education Bindup Pre-K. 2006. (J). per. 14.95 ***978-1-59545-024-1(6))** Learning Horizons, Inc.

Preschool Jumbo Workbook. 1998. (Step Ahead Ser.). (J). (ps). pap., wbk. ed. 4.99 (978-0-307-11250-7(0) , Golden Bks.) Random Hse. Children's Bks.

Princeton Review Publishing Staff. Roadmap to 5th Grade Reading, Virginia Edition. 2002. (Princeton Review Ser.). 224p. pap. 14.95 (978-0-375-75600-9(0) , Princeton Review) Random Hse. Information Group.

—Roadmap to the Grade 10 FCAT Reading. 2002. (Princeton Review Ser.). 272p. pap. 14.95 (978-0-375-75573-6(X) , Princeton Review) Random Hse. Information Group.

Progressive Langauge Staff, prod. Bluw Wolf & Friends, Units 1-4. l.t. ed. 2004. (Illus.). 53p. act. bk. ed. (978-0-9758759-3-3(0)) Progressive Language, Inc.

Purslow, Frances & Hudak, Heather C. Descriptive Paragraphs. 2007. (J). ***978-1-59036-737-7(5)); (*978-1-59036-738-4(3))** Weigl Pubs., Inc.

—Expository Paragraphs. 2007. (J). ***978-1-59036-735-3(9)); (*978-1-59036-736-0(7))** Weigl Pubs., Inc.

—Narrative Paragraphs: Learning to Write. 2007. (J). **(*978-1-59036-733-9(2)); (*978-1-59036-734-6(0))** Weigl Pubs., Inc.

—Persuasive Paragraphs. 2007. (J). ***978-1-59036-731-5(6)); (*978-1-59036-732-2(4))** Weigl Pubs., Inc.

Rainbow Bridge Publishing Staff. Listening Skills First Grade: Mastering Basic Skills. 2002. (Mastering Basic Skills Ser.). (Illus.). 32p. (gr. 1 up). 4.95 (978-1-887923-69-9(1)) Rainbow Bridge Publishing.

—Listening Skills Second Grade: Mastering Basic Skills. 2002. (Mastering Basic Skills Ser.). (Illus.). 32p. (gr. 2 up). 4.95 (978-1-887923-70-5(5)) Rainbow Bridge Publishing.

Raintree Steck-Vaughn Staff. HCPS II Read & Write. 2002. (Soaring Scores Ser.). Level E. pap. (978-0-7398-6100-4(X)); Level H. pap. (978-0-7398-6106-6(9)) Steck-Vaughn.

Reader's Clubhouse Staff. How Can You Tell How People Feel? 2007. (Reader's Clubhouse Ser.). 24p. (J). (gr. k-2). pap. 3.99 (978-0-7641-3726-6(3)) Barron's Educational Series, Inc.

—Kirby's Circus. 2007. (Reader's Clubhouse Ser.). 24p. (J). (gr. k-2). pap. 3.99 (978-0-7641-3722-8(0)) Barron's Educational Series, Inc.

—Sweet Dreams. 2007. (Reader's Clubhouse Ser.). 24p. (J). (gr. k-2). pap. 3.99 (978-0-7641-3721-1(2)) Barron's Educational Series, Inc.

Reading Rods Word Families Double-Sided Activity Cards. 2001. (J). 12.95 (978-1-56911-071-3(9)) Learning Resources, Inc.

Realtime Associates and Mazer Corporation Staff & LeapFrog Staff, compiled by. Differentiate Fact from Opinion. 2002. (J). (gr. 3). 66.75 (978-1-58605-374-1(4)); (gr. 4). 66.75 (978-1-58605-432-8(5)); (gr. 5). 66.75 (978-1-58605-494-6(5)) LeapFrog Enterprises, Inc. (LeapFrog Schl. Hse.).

—Differentiate Fiction from Nonfiction. 2002. (J). (gr. 3). 66.75 (978-1-58605-373-4(6)); (gr. 4). 66.75 (978-1-58605-431-1(7)); (gr. 5). 66.75 (978-1-58605-493-9(7)) LeapFrog Enterprises, Inc. (LeapFrog Schl. Hse.).

—Differentiate Reality from Fantasy. 2002. (J). (gr. 2). 66.75 (978-1-58605-306-2(X)); (gr. 3). 66.75 (978-1-58605-372-7(8)); (gr. 4). 66.75 (978-1-58605-430-4(9)) LeapFrog Enterprises, Inc. (LeapFrog Schl. Hse.).

—Evaluate an Author's Assertion. 2002. (J). (gr. 5). 66.75 (978-1-58605-482-3(1) , LeapFrog Schl. Hse.) LeapFrog Enterprises, Inc.

—LeapTrack Cards - Language Arts 2. 2002. (J). (978-1-58605-126-6(1)) LeapFrog Enterprises, Inc.

—LeapTrack Cards - Language Arts 3. 2002. (J). (978-1-58605-181-5(4)) LeapFrog Enterprises, Inc.

—LeapTrack Cards - Language Arts 4. 2002. (J). (978-1-58605-184-6(9)) LeapFrog Enterprises, Inc.

—LeapTrack Cards - Language Arts 5. 2002. (J). (978-1-58605-226-3(8)) LeapFrog Enterprises, Inc.

—Make Inferences. 2002. (J). (gr. 2). 66.75 (978-1-58605-300-0(0)); (gr. 3). 66.75 (978-1-58605-362-8(0)); (gr. 4). 66.75 (978-1-58605-418-2(X)); (gr. 5). 66.75 (978-1-58605-477-9(5)) LeapFrog Enterprises, Inc. (LeapFrog Schl. Hse.).

—Use One or More Resources & References. 2002. (J). (gr. 2). 66.75 (978-1-58605-313-0(2)); (gr. 3). 66.75 (978-1-58605-380-2(9)); (gr. 4). 66.75 (978-1-58605-438-0(4)); (gr. 5). 66.75 (978-1-58605-501-1(1)) LeapFrog Enterprises, Inc. (LeapFrog Schl. Hse.).

Reilly, Geoff. Skills in Grammar & Style, Bk. 1. 2004. (Illus.). (J). pap., stu. ed. 19.95 (978-0-7487-7793-8(8)) Nelson Thornes Ltd. GBR. *Dist:* Trans-Atlantic Pubns., Inc.

Reilly, Mary A. GEPA Companion: Achieving Language Arts Literacy. 1999. (Illus.). 208p. (YA). (gr. 7-8). 39.95 (978-1-886292-33-8(7)) CEO Software Solutions.

Repetitive Text, 47 vols., Set. 2004. (Beastieville Ser.). (J). 605.15 (978-0-516-25143-1(0) , Children's Pr.) Scholastic Library Publishing.

Ring, Susan. Where? 2003. (Yellow Umbrella Books). (Illus.). 16p. (J). (gr. 1). lib. bdg. 14.60 (978-0-7368-2016-5(7) , Pebble Bks.) Capstone Pr., Inc.

—Where? 2003. (Math Ser.). (J). (978-0-7368-1700-4(X)) Yellow Umbrella Pr.

Rivers, Susan & Graham, Carolyn. Tiny Talk ABC Songbook, 2 vols. 1999. cd-rom, audio compact disk 35.95 (978-0-19-435360-1(5)) Oxford Univ. Pr., Inc.

Rondeau, Amanda. Cat + Fish = Catfish. 2004. (Compound Words Ser.). (Illus.). 23p. (J). (ps-3). lib. bdg. 19.93 (978-1-59197-432-1(1)) ABDO Publishing Co.

—Rain + Bow = Rainbow. 2004. (Compound Words Ser.). (Illus.). 23p. (J). (ps-3). lib. bdg. 19.93 (978-1-59197-436-9(4)) ABDO Publishing Co.

—Rattle + Snake = Rattlesnake. 2004. (Compound Words Ser.). (Illus.). 23p. (J). (ps-3). lib. bdg. 19.93 (978-1-59197-437-6(2)) ABDO Publishing Co.

—Skate + Board = Skateboard. 2004. (Compound Words Ser.). (Illus.). 23p. (J). (ps-3). lib. bdg. 19.93 (978-1-59197-438-3(0)) ABDO Publishing Co.

—Snow + Shoe = Snowshoe. 2004. (Compound Words Ser.). (Illus.). 23p. (J). (ps-3). lib. bdg. 19.93 (978-1-59197-439-0(9)) ABDO Publishing Co.

—Tea + Pot = Teapot. 2004. (Compound Words Ser.). (Illus.). 23p. (J). (ps-3). lib. bdg. 19.93 (978-1-59197-441-3(0)) ABDO Publishing Co.

Rose, Mary. Week-by-Week Homework for Building Reading Comprehension & Fluency. 2002. 96p. (J). (gr. 4-6). 13.95 (978-0-439-27164-6(9)) Scholastic, Inc.

Rovetch, Lissa. Ook the Book: And Other Silly Rhymes. McNeill, Shannon, illus. 2001. 36p. (J). (ps-1). 13.95 (978-0-8118-2660-0(0)) Chronicle Bks. LLC.

Rubenstein, J. & Gubbay, J. Essentials of Reading & Writing English Bk. 3: A Basic English Literacy Program. 2001. 181p. (J). pap. 18.95 (978-0-8442-7400-3(3) , NT4003) McGraw-Hill/Contemporary.

Rucco, Alison. If This Is a Man. 2005. (Cambridge Wizard English Student Guides). (Illus.). 63p. pap., stu. ed. 5.90 (978-0-521-60896-1(1)) Cambridge Univ. Pr.

E F G

—No Great Mischief. 2002. (Wizard Study Guides Ser.). 64p. pap., stu. ed. 6.00 (978-1-876973-12-4(9)) Cambridge Univ. Pr.

Salzmann, Mary Elizabeth. Aa: See It Say It Hear It. l.t. ed. 2000. (Long Vowels Ser.). (Illus.). 24p. (J). (ps-3). lib. bdg. 19.93 (978-1-57765-413-1(7) , SandCastle) ABDO Publishing Co.

—Alex & Max. 2005. (First Sounds Ser.). (Illus.). 23p. (J). pap. (978-1-59679-123-7(3)); 19.93 (978-1-59679-122-0(5)) ABDO Publishing Co.

—Amy & Abe. 2005. (First Sounds Ser.). (Illus.). 23p. (J). pap. (978-1-59679-125-1(X)); 19.93 (978-1-59679-124-4(1)) ABDO Publishing Co.

—Ann & Alan. 2005. (First Sounds Ser.). (Illus.). 23p. (J). pap. (978-1-59679-127-5(6)); 19.93 (978-1-59679-126-8(8)) ABDO Publishing Co.

—Bess & Bill. 2005. (First Sounds Ser.). (Illus.). 23p. (J). pap. (978-1-59679-217-3(5)); 19.93 (978-1-59679-216-6(7)) ABDO Publishing Co.

—Blair & Blaine. 2005. (First Sounds Ser.). (Illus.). 23p. (J). pap. (978-1-59679-129-9(2)); 19.93 (978-1-59679-128-2(4)) ABDO Publishing Co.

—Brandi & Brent. 2005. (First Sounds Ser.). (Illus.). 23p. (J). pap. (978-1-59679-131-2(4)); 19.93 (978-1-59679-130-5(6)) ABDO Publishing Co.

—Cassie & Carl. 2005. (First Sounds Ser.). (Illus.). 23p. (J). pap. (978-1-59679-133-6(0)); 19.93 (978-1-59679-132-9(2)) ABDO Publishing Co.

—Chelsey & Chad. 2005. (First Sounds Ser.). 23p. (J). pap. (978-1-59679-135-0(7)); 19.93 (978-1-59679-134-3(9)) ABDO Publishing Co.

—Cindy & Cecil. 2005. (First Sounds Ser.). (Illus.). 23p. (J). pap. (978-1-59679-137-4(3)); 19.93 (978-1-59679-136-7(5)) ABDO Publishing Co.

—Cristy & Craig. 2005. (First Sounds Ser.). (Illus.). 23p. (J). pap. (978-1-59679-139-8(X)); 19.93 (978-1-59679-138-1(1)) ABDO Publishing Co.

—Deb & Dan. 2005. (First Sounds Ser.). (Illus.). 23p. (J). pap. (978-1-59679-141-1(1)); 19.93 (978-1-59679-140-4(3)) ABDO Publishing Co.

—Drew & Drake. 2005. (First Sounds Ser.). (Illus.). 23p. (J). pap. (978-1-59679-143-5(8)); 19.93 (978-1-59679-142-8(X)) ABDO Publishing Co.

—Ii: See It Say It Hear It. l.t. ed. 2000. (Long Vowels Ser.). (Illus.). 24p. (J). (ps-3). lib. bdg. 19.93 (978-1-57765-415-5(3) , SandCastle) ABDO Publishing Co.

—Sometimes Yy: See It Say It Hear It. l.t. ed. 2000. (Long Vowels Ser.). (Illus.). 24p. (J). (ps-3). lib. bdg. 19.93 (978-1-57765-418-6(8) , SandCastle) ABDO Publishing Co.

—Uu: See It Say It Hear It. l.t. ed. 2000. (Long Vowels Ser.). (Illus.). 24p. (J). (ps-3). lib. bdg. 19.93 (978-1-57765-417-9(X) , SandCastle) ABDO Publishing Co.

Same & Different. 2002. (Home Workbooks Ser.). 64p. pap. 2.49 (978-0-88724-707-1(5) , CD-4509) Carson-Dellosa Publishing Co., Inc.

Santillo, LuAnn. Blends & Ends - Level B, 36 vols. Santillo, LuAnn, ed. 2003. (Half-Pint Kids Readers Ser.). (Illus.). 7p. (J). (ps-1). pap. 39.99 (978-1-59256-127-6(8)) Half-Pint Kids, Inc.

—Moving A-Long Level C, 36 vols. Santillo, LuAnn, ed. 2003. (Half-Pint Kids Readers Ser.). (Illus.). 7p. (J). (ps-1). pap. 39.99 (978-1-59256-128-5(4)) Half-Pint Kids, Inc.

Scheunemann, Pam. Ch: See It Say It Hear It. l.t. ed. 2000. (Blends Ser.). (Illus.). 24p. (J). (ps-3). lib. bdg. 19.93 (978-1-57765-409-4(9) , SandCastle) ABDO Publishing Co.

—Skye & Skip. 2005. (First Sounds Ser.). (Illus.). 23p. (J). pap. (978-1-59679-193-0(4)); lib. bdg. 19.93 (978-1-59679-192-3(6)) ABDO Publishing Co.

—Sloane & Sly. 2005. (First Sounds Ser.). (Illus.). 23p. (J). pap. (978-1-59679-195-4(0)); lib. bdg. 19.93 (978-1-59679-194-7(2)) ABDO Publishing Co.

—St: See It Say It Hear It. l.t. ed. 2000. (Blends Ser.). (Illus.). 24p. (J). (ps-3). lib. bdg. 19.93 (978-1-57765-407-0(2) , SandCastle) ABDO Publishing Co.

—Stacy & Steve. 2005. (First Sounds Ser.). (Illus.). 23p. (J). pap. (978-1-59679-197-8(7)); lib. bdg. 19.93 (978-1-59679-196-1(9)) ABDO Publishing Co.

—Tam & Tom. 2005. (First Sounds Ser.). (Illus.). 23p. (J). pap. (978-1-59679-199-2(3)); lib. bdg. 19.93 (978-1-59679-198-5(5)) ABDO Publishing Co.

—Th: See It Say It Hear It. l.t. ed. 2000. (Blends Ser.). (Illus.). 24p. (J). (ps-3). lib. bdg. 19.93 (978-1-57765-408-7(0) , SandCastle) ABDO Publishing Co.

—Tracy & Treavor. 2005. (First Sounds Ser.). (Illus.). 23p. (J). pap. (978-1-59679-201-2(9)); lib. bdg. 19.93 (978-1-59679-200-5(0)) ABDO Publishing Co.

—Ulma & Umberto. 2005. (First Sounds Ser.). 23p. pap. (978-1-59679-203-6(5)); (J). lib. bdg. 19.93 (978-1-59679-202-9(7)) ABDO Publishing Co.

—Unity & Uri. 2005. (First Sounds Ser.). 23p. pap. (978-1-59679-205-0(1)); (J). lib. bdg. 19.93 (978-1-59679-204-3(3)) ABDO Publishing Co.

—Val & Vince. 2005. (First Sounds Ser.). (Illus.). 23p. (J). pap. (978-1-59679-207-4(8)); lib. bdg. 19.93 (978-1-59679-206-7(X)) ABDO Publishing Co.

—Wendy & Wally. 2005. (First Sounds Ser.). (Illus.). 23p. (J). pap. (978-1-59679-209-8(4)); lib. bdg. 19.93 (978-1-59679-208-1(6)) ABDO Publishing Co.

—Whitney & Wheeler. 2005. (First Sounds Ser.). (Illus.). 23p. (J). pap. (978-1-59679-211-1(6)); lib. bdg. 19.93 (978-1-59679-210-4(8)) ABDO Publishing Co.

—Yana & Yosef. 2005. (First Sounds Ser.). (Illus.). 23p. (J). pap. (978-1-59679-213-5(2)); lib. bdg. 19.93 (978-1-59679-212-8(4)) ABDO Publishing Co.

—Zoe & Zach. 2005. (First Sounds Ser.). (Illus.). 23p. (J). pap. (978-1-59679-215-9(9)); lib. bdg. 19.93 (978-1-59679-214-2(0)) ABDO Publishing Co.

Schiller, Pam. Uniquely Me! 2006. (NOODLEBUG Activities for Hands-on Learning Ser.). 32p. (J). pap. 4.99 (978-0-7696-4238-3(1)) School Specialty Publishing.

Scholastic, Inc. Staff. 26 Interactive Alphabet Wheels. 2000. (Illus.). (J). 26.95 (978-0-439-15542-7(8)) Scholastic, Inc.

School Specialty Publishing. Buying, Selling, & Making Change. 2003. (Modified Basic Skills Ser.). 48p. (J). (gr. k-4). pap. 6.99 (978-0-7424-1925-4(8) , LL90002) School Specialty Publishing.

—English & Grammar, Grade 3. 2006. (Skills for Scholars Ser.). 80p. (C). pap. 4.99 (***978-0-7696-4983-2(1)*** , Schaffer, Frank) Schaffer, Frank Pubns.

—English & Grammar, Grade 4. 2006. (Skills for Scholars Ser.). 80p. (C). pap. 4.99 (***978-0-7696-4984-9(X)*** , Schaffer, Frank) Schaffer, Frank Pubns.

—English & Grammar, Grade 5. 2006. (Skills for Scholars Ser.). 80p. (C). pap. 4.99 (***978-0-7696-4985-6(8)*** , Schaffer, Frank) Schaffer, Frank Pubns.

—English & Grammar, Grade 6. 2006. (Skills for Scholars Ser.). 80p. (C). pap. 4.99 (***978-0-7696-4986-3(6)*** , Schaffer, Frank) Schaffer, Frank Pubns.

—I Can Learn Spanish & English. 2006. (Brighter Child I Can... Ser.). 128p. (J). pap. 3.95 (978-0-7696-4897-2(5) , Brighter Child) School Specialty Publishing.

—Oral Language for Daily Use, Grade 1. 2006. (Oral Language for Daily Use Ser.). 80p. (C). pap. 10.99 (978-0-7682-3361-2(5) , Schaffer, Frank) Schaffer, Frank Pubns.

—Oral Language for Daily Use, Grade 2. 2006. (Oral Language for Daily Use Ser.). 80p. (C). pap. 10.99 (978-0-7682-3362-9(3) , Schaffer, Frank) Schaffer, Frank Pubns.

—Oral Language for Daily Use, Grade 3. 2006. (Oral Language for Daily Use Ser.). 80p. (C). pap. 10.99 (978-0-7682-3363-6(1) , Schaffer, Frank) Schaffer, Frank Pubns.

—Oral Language for Daily Use, Grade 4. 2006. (Oral Language for Daily Use Ser.). 80p. (C). pap. 10.99 (978-0-7682-3364-3(X) , Schaffer, Frank) Schaffer, Frank Pubns.

—Oral Language for Daily Use, Grade 5. 2006. (Oral Language for Daily Use Ser.). 80p. (C). pap. 10.99 (978-0-7682-3365-0(8) , Schaffer, Frank) Schaffer, Frank Pubns.

—Oral Language for Daily Use, Grade 6. 2006. (Oral Language for Daily Use Ser.). 80p. (C). pap. 10.99 (978-0-7682-3366-7(6) , Schaffer, Frank) Schaffer, Frank Pubns.

—The Test Connection Reading, Grade 2. 2004. 144p. (C). pap. 15.99 (***978-0-7682-2812-0(3)*** , Schaffer, Frank) Schaffer, Frank Pubns.

—The Test Connection Reading, Grade 3. 2004. 144p. (C). pap. 15.99 (***978-0-7682-2813-7(1)*** , Schaffer, Frank) Schaffer, Frank Pubns.

—The Test Connection Reading, Grade 4. 2004. 144p. (C). pap. 15.99 (***978-0-7682-2814-4(X)*** , Schaffer, Frank) Schaffer, Frank Pubns.

—The Test Connection Reading, Grade 5. 2004. 144p. (C). pap. 15.99 (***978-0-7682-2815-1(8)*** , Schaffer, Frank) Schaffer, Frank Pubns.

—The Test Connection Reading, Grade 6. 2004. 144p. (C). pap. 15.99 (***978-0-7682-2816-8(6)*** , Schaffer, Frank) Schaffer, Frank Pubns.

School Zone Publishing Company Staff. English: Grades 1 & 2. (Illus.). (J). 19.99 incl. audio compact disk (978-0-88743-971-1(3)) School Zone Publishing Co.

—English: Grades 3 & 4. (Illus.). (J). 19.99 incl. audio compact disk (978-0-88743-943-8(8)) School Zone Publishing Co.

—Language Arts 1. (Illus.). (J). 19.99 incl. audio compact disk (978-0-88743-969-8(1)) School Zone Publishing Co.

—Language Arts 2. (Illus.). (J). 19.99 incl. audio compact disk (978-0-88743-970-4(5)) School Zone Publishing Co.

School Zone Publishing Company Staff & Giglio, Judith. Summer Scholar Grade 1. deluxe ed. 2000. (Deluxe Wkbks.). (Illus.). 64p. (J). (gr. 1). pap., wbk. ed. 3.79 (978-0-88743-832-5(6) , 02232) School Zone Publishing Co.

School Zone Publishing Company Staff & Hall, M. C. Summer Scholar Grade 3. deluxe ed. 2000. (Deluxe Wkbks.). (Illus.). 64p. (J). (gr. 3). pap., wbk. ed. 3.79 (978-0-88743-834-9(2) , 02234) School Zone Publishing Co.

School Zone Publishing Company Staff & Kupecky, Jere M. Summer Scholar Grade 2. Carmona, Lisa, ed. Sandford, John, illus. deluxe ed. 2000. (Deluxe Wkbks.). 64p. (J). (gr. 2). pap., wbk. ed. 3.79 (978-0-88743-833-2(4) , 02233) School Zone Publishing Co.

Schwartz, Linda. Language Arts Quiz Whiz 3-5, Vol. 430. VanBlaricum, Pam, ed. Armstrong, Beverly, illus. 2004. 128p. (J). (gr. 3-5). pap. 14.99 (978-0-88160-373-6(2) , LW-430) Creative Teaching Pr., Inc.

—Primary Language Quiz Whiz. VanBlaricum, Pam, ed. Mason, Mark, illus. 2004. 128p. (J). pap. (978-0-88160-370-5(8) , LW-428) Creative Teaching Pr., Inc.

Scissor Skills. 2002. (Home Workbooks Ser.). 64p. pap. 2.49 (978-0-88724-709-5(1) , CD-4511) Carson-Dellosa Publishing Co., Inc.

Scott, James. The Inferno: Reproducible Training Unit. 2001. 85p. (YA). (gr. 7-12). ring bd. 29.50 (978-1-58049-298-0(3) , TU183) Prestwick Hse., Inc.

—Lord of the Flies: Activity Pack. 2001. 148p. (YA). (gr. 7-12). pap., act. bk. ed. 34.95 (978-1-58049-605-6(9) , PA0110) Prestwick Hse., Inc.

—Outsiders: Activity Pack. 2001. 101p. (YA). (gr. 7-12). pap., act. bk. ed. 34.95 (978-1-58049-607-0(5) , PA0107) Prestwick Hse., Inc.

—1984: A Student Response Journal. 2002. 40p. (YA). (gr. 7-12). wbk. ed. 19.95 (978-1-58049-932-3(5) , RJ58) Prestwick Hse., Inc.

Senn, J. A. & Skinner, Carol Ann. BK English: Communication Skills in the New Millennium. 2001. 1213p. (J). (gr. 6). stu. ed. (978-1-58079-107-6(7)); 648p. (gr. 7). tchr. ed. (978-1-58079-115-1(8)); 648p. (gr. 10). tchr. ed. (978-1-58079-118-2(2)); 648p. (gr. 11). tchr. ed. (978-1-58079-119-9(0)); 648p. (gr. 12). stu. ed. (978-1-58079-120-5(4)); 648p. (gr. 6). tchr. ed. (978-1-58079-114-4(X)); 648p. (gr. 8). tchr. ed. (978-1-58079-116-8(6)); 648p. (gr. 9). tchr. ed. (978-1-58079-117-5(4)); 1408p. (YA). (gr. 10). stu. ed. (978-1-58079-111-3(5)); 1472p. (YA). (gr. 11). stu. ed. (978-1-58079-112-0(3)); 1504p. (YA). (gr. 12). stu. ed. (978-1-58079-113-7(1)); 1336p. (YA). (gr. 7). stu. ed. (978-1-58079-108-3(5)); 1335p. (YA). (gr. 8). stu. ed. (978-1-58079-109-0(3)); 1471p. (YA). (gr. 9). stu. ed. (978-1-58079-110-6(7)) Barrett Kendall Publishing, Ltd.

Sensational Me. 2000. (Learning Fun for Little Ones Ser.). (Illus.). 64p. (ps-1). pap. 8.99 (978-0-88724-574-9(9) , CD-6406) Carson-Dellosa Publishing Co., Inc.

Sesame Street Learn about Language with Big Bird. 2007. (J). pap. 3.95 (***978-1-59545-146-0(3)***) Learning Horizons, Inc.

Shake & Learn Language Arts. 2000. spiral bd. 119.95 incl. audio compact disk (978-0-9746001-0-9(5)) Salt Productions, Inc.

Shields, Charles J. Standardized Test Practice for 6th Grade. 1999. 96p. (J). (gr. 6). pap., tchr. ed. 11.99 (978-1-57690-681-1(7) , TCA2681) Teacher Created Materials, Inc.

Shiotsu, Vicky. First Grade Language Arts. 1998. (Grade Boosters Ser.). (Illus.). 64p. (J). (ps-3). pap., wbk. ed. 4.95 (978-1-56565-843-1(4) , 08434W) Lowell Hse. Juvenile.

—Monster Phonics: Consonants for Grades K-1. Helle, Lucy, illus. 1999. 48p. (J). (gr. 1-3). pap. 5.95 (978-0-7373-0141-0(4) , 01414W) McGraw-Hill/Contemporary.

—Monster Phonics: Short Vowels for Grades K-1. 1999. (Illus.). 48p. (J). (gr. 1-3). pap. 5.95 (978-0-7373-0143-4(0) , 01430W) McGraw-Hill/Contemporary.

Show What You Know on the FCAT 8, New English Language Arts Student Self Study Workbook. 2006. (YA). per. 16.95 (978-1-59230-179-9(7)) Englefield & Assocs., Inc.

Shulman, Mark. Flip-O-Matic: Instant Language Arts for Ages 9-12. 2006. (G - Reference,Information & Interdisciplinary Subjects Ser.). 256p. pap. 10.00 (978-1-4195-4179-7(X)) Kaplan Publishing.

Siebert, Anne. Celebrating American Heroes: Plays for Students of English. 2000. 80p. (YA). (gr. 7 up). pap., stu. ed. 14.00 (978-0-86647-127-5(8)) Pro Lingua Assocs., Inc.

—Celebrating American Heroes Teachers Guide: Plays for Students of English. 2000. 72p. pap., tchr. ed. 12.00 (978-0-86647-128-2(6)) Pro Lingua Assocs., Inc.

Siede Preis Photography (Firm) Staff & Brian Warling Photography (Firm) Staff, contrib. by. Phonics for Fun. 2003. (Lift-A-Flap Ser.). (Illus.). 12p. (J). bds. (978-0-7853-8623-0(8) , 7188300) Publications International, Ltd.

Simpson, Matt, creator. Happy Heart: English Book 1. l.t. ed. 2003. (Illus.). 44p. (J). per. (978-0-9727660-0-5(6)) Bks. by Matt.

Simpson, Ron. Quick Revision KS3 English. 2007. 46p. pap. 9.95 (***978-0-340-94307-6(6)*** , Hodder Murray) Hodder Education GBR. *Dist:* Trans-Atlantic Pubns., Inc.

Smith, Robert. How to Solve Word Problems: Grades 3-4. 2000. (Illus.). 48p. (J). (gr. 3-4). pap., tchr. ed. 7.99 (978-1-57690-483-1(0) , TCA2483) Teacher Created Materials, Inc.

Spanish & English Vocabulary Development. 2005. 123p. (J). spiral bd. 14.99 (978-1-59441-470-1(X) , K04021) Carson-Dellosa Publishing Co., Inc.

Spanish/English Desk Cards. 2004. (J). 8.95 (978-1-56911-177-2(4)) Learning Resources, Inc.

Spectacular Spring. 2000. (Learning Fun for Little Ones Ser.). 64p. (ps-1). pap. 8.99 (978-0-88724-576-3(5) , CD-6408) Carson-Dellosa Publishing Co., Inc.

Splat! Spelling Software. 2000. (gr. 1 up). 20.76 (978-0-673-28917-9(6)); (gr. 1 up). 20.76 (978-0-673-28923-0(0)); (gr. 2 up). 20.76 (978-0-673-62853-4(1)); (gr. 2 up). 20.76 (978-0-673-61828-3(5)); (gr. 3 up). 20.76 (978-0-673-28919-3(2)); (gr. 3 up). 20.76 (978-0-673-28925-4(7)); (gr. 4 up). 20.76 (978-0-673-28920-9(6)); (gr. 4 up). 20.76 (978-0-673-28926-1(5)); (gr. 5 up). 20.76 (978-0-673-28921-6(4)); (gr. 5 up). 20.76 (978-0-673-28927-8(3)); (gr. 6 up). 20.76 (978-0-673-28922-3(2)) Addison-Wesley Educational Pubs., Inc.

Spooky House: MainSails Individual Title Six-Packs. (Sails Literacy Ser.). (gr. 5 up). 37.00 (978-0-7578-8056-8(8)) Rigby Education.

Spring Fun. 2002. (Holiday Fun Bks.). 32p. (J). per. 2.99 (978-0-88724-923-5(X) , CD-0191) Carson-Dellosa Publishing Co., Inc.

Steck-Vaughn Staff. Answer Key Soaring Score CRCT Reading/Language Arts Level F. 2002. (J). pap. (978-0-7398-5556-0(5)) Steck-Vaughn.

—Answer Key Soaring Score CRCT Reading/Language Arts Level H. 2002. (J). pap. (978-0-7398-5560-7(3)) Steck-Vaughn.

—Capitalization & Punctuation Core Skills. 2001. pap. (978-0-7398-4901-9(8)) Steck-Vaughn.

—Complete Classroom Collection. 1999. (Take Me Home Ser.). (J). pap. (978-0-7398-2601-0(8)) Steck-Vaughn.

—Core Skills: Language Arts. 2003. (J). (gr. 1). pap. (978-0-7398-7088-4(2)); (gr. 2). pap. (978-0-7398-7089-1(0)); (gr. 3). pap. (978-0-7398-7090-7(4)); (gr. 4). pap. 9.99 (978-0-7398-7091-4(2)) Steck-Vaughn.

—Core Skills Language Arts. 2003. (J). (gr. 5). pap. (978-0-7398-7092-1(0)); (gr. 6). pap. (978-0-7398-7093-8(9)); (gr. 7). pap. (978-0-7398-7094-5(7)); (gr. 8). pap. (978-0-7398-7095-2(5)) Steck-Vaughn.

—English ASAP: Placement & Program Test. 2001. (J). pap. (978-0-7398-3386-5(3)) Steck-Vaughn.

—Figurative Language. 2000. (Illus.). (J). (gr. 2). pap. (978-0-7398-2716-1(2)); (gr. 3). pap. (978-0-7398-2717-8(0)); (gr. 4). pap. (978-0-7398-2718-5(9)); (gr. 5). pap. (978-0-7398-2719-2(7)); (gr. 6). pap. (978-0-7398-2720-8(0)) Steck-Vaughn.

—Foundation. 2000. (Pair-It Bks.). (J). pap., tchr. ed. (978-0-7398-4514-1(4)) Steck-Vaughn.

—Language Arts Handbook. 1999. (Illus.). (J). (gr. 1). pap. (978-0-8172-3887-2(5)); (gr. 6). pap. (978-0-8172-3892-6(1)) Steck-Vaughn.

—Learning Skills-Start Smart. 2002. (J). pap. (978-0-7398-6009-0(7)) Steck-Vaughn.

—Second Grade Leveled Reader Package 100. 2002. (Illus.). pap. (978-0-7398-7610-7(4)) Steck-Vaughn.

—Test Best Success Pack: High School, 10. rev. ed. 2002. (YA). (gr. 9-12). pap. (978-0-7398-6716-7(4)) Steck-Vaughn.

—Weekly Language Practice. 2002. (Illus.). (J). (gr. 2). pap. (978-0-7398-5360-3(0)); (gr. 6). pap. (978-0-7398-5361-0(9)) Steck-Vaughn.

Stevenson, Nancy. Basic Blue Level Core Manual. Gallager, Ann & Stevenson, William, eds. Semple, Janice, illus. 1998. (Language Skills Program Ser.). 406p. (J). pap. 26.95 (978-0-941112-44-4(6)) Stevenson Learning Skills, Inc.

Stuart, Samantha L., ed. Sentence & Paragraph Construction. 2000. (Illus.). (YA). (gr. 6-9). pap. 4.95 (978-1-55708-667-9(2) , MCR244) McDonald Publishing Co.

Super Summer. 2000. (Learning Fun for Little Ones Ser.). (Illus.). 64p. (ps-1). pap. 8.99 (978-0-88724-585-5(4) , CD-6412) Carson-Dellosa Publishing Co., Inc.

Test Best for Success, 10 Packs. 2002. pap. (978-0-7398-6742-6(3)); pap. (978-0-7398-6743-3(1)); pap. (978-0-7398-6744-0(X)); pap. (978-0-7398-6745-7(8)) Steck-Vaughn.

Test Best For Success, 10 Packs. 2002. pap. (978-0-7398-6746-4(6)) Steck-Vaughn.

Test Best for Success Level A, 10 Packs. 2002. pap. (978-0-7398-6740-2(7)) Steck-Vaughn.

Test Best for Success Level B, 10 Packs. 2002. pap. (978-0-7398-6741-9(5)) Steck-Vaughn.

Theme Packs for ELL: Theme Packs Complete Set. 2995.00 (978-0-7635-2870-6(6)) Rigby Education.

ThemeMaker Student Tool. 2005. 3.95 (***978-0-9769527-9-4(3)***) Mindwing Concepts, Inc.

Thewlis, Stephen, contrib. by. Topic Words: An Illustrated Workbook for Key State 1. 1999. (Illus.). 48p. (J). (ps-3). pap., wbk. ed. 29.00 (978-0-7217-0665-8(7)) Schofield & Sims Ltd. GBR. *Dist:* State Mutual Bk. & Periodical Service, Ltd.

Tiernon, Carol. Short & Long Vowels. 2001. (Self-Checks Ser.). (Illus.). 28p. (J). (gr. 1-3). pap. 8.99 (978-0-7647-0345-4(5) , FS65025, Schaffer, Frank) Schaffer, Frank Pubns.

Timeless Voices, Timeless Themes: Gold, Literary Analysis Activity Book. 2000. (YA). (gr. 9). pap. 6.97 (978-0-13-437571-7(8)) Prentice Hall PTR.

Timeless Voices, Timeless Themes: Platinum, Literary Analysis Activity Book. 2000. (YA). (gr. 10). pap. 6.97 (978-0-13-437574-8(2)) Prentice Hall PTR.

Timeless Voices, Timeless Themes: Platinum, Standardized Test Preparation. 2000. (YA). (gr. 10). pap., wbk. ed. 6.97 (978-0-13-050613-9(3)) Prentice Hall PTR.

Timeless Voices, Timeless Themes: The American Experience. 2000. (YA). (gr. 11). pap. 15.97 (978-0-13-050925-3(6)) Prentice Hall PTR.

Timeless Voices, Timeless Themes: The American Experience, Assessment Success Planning Guide. 2000. (YA). (gr. 11). pap. 4.97 (978-0-13-051094-5(7)) Prentice Hall PTR.

Timeless Voices, Timeless Themes: The American Experience, Literary Analysis Activity Book. 2000. (YA). (gr. 11). pap. 6.97 (978-0-13-050879-9(9)) Prentice Hall PTR.

Timeless Voices, Timeless Themes: The American Experience, Standardized Test Preparation Workbook. 2000. (YA). (gr. 11). pap., wbk. ed. 6.97 (978-0-13-050614-6(1)) Prentice Hall PTR.

Timeless Voices, Timeless Themes: The British Tradition. 2000. (YA). (gr. 12). pap. 7.47 (978-0-13-434645-8(9)) Prentice Hall PTR.

Timeless Voices, Timeless Themes: The British Tradition, Assessment Success Planning Guide. 2000. (YA). (gr. 12). pap. 4.97 (978-0-13-051096-9(3)) Prentice Hall PTR.

Timeless Voices, Timeless Themes: The British Tradition, Literary Analysis Activity Book. 2000. (YA). (gr. 12). pap. 6.97 (978-0-13-437581-6(5)) Prentice Hall PTR.

Timeless Voices, Timeless Themes: The British Tradition, Standardized Test Preparation Workbook. 2000. (YA). (gr. 12). pap., wbk. ed. 6.97 (978-0-13-050615-3(X)) Prentice Hall PTR.

Timeless Voices, Timeless Themes, Grade 12: The British Tradition, Teacher's Guidebook for Speaking, Listening, Viewing & Representing. 2000. pap., tchr. ed. 4.97 (978-0-13-051424-0(1)) Prentice Hall PTR.

Trattles, Patricia. Flying Butter. Swift, Gary, illus. 2005. (Rookie Reader Skill Set Ser.). (J). (gr. k-2). 23p. pap. 4.95 (978-0-516-25280-3(1)); 24p. 19.50 (978-0-516-25150-9(3)) Scholastic Library Publishing. (Children's Pr.).

Traynor, Tracy. Jump, Jog, Leapfrog: Fun with Action Words. Hambleton, Laura, illus. 2007. 28p. (J). (gr. k-2). pap. 6.95 (***978-1-84059-501-7(9)***) Milet Publishing.

Turner, Priscilla. The War Between the Vowels & the Consonants. Turner, Whitney, illus. 1999. 32p. (J). (ps-3). pap. 6.95 (978-0-374-48217-6(9) , Sunburst) Farrar, Straus & Giroux.

Usage (Gr. 1-3) 2003. (J). (978-1-58232-049-6(7)) Bryan Hse. Pubs., Inc.

Vestri Solomon, Elena & Shelley, John. Key Concepts 1: Listening, Note-Taking & Speaking Across the Disciplines, 2 vols. 2005. (Illus.). 143p. (YA). pap. 31.16 (978-0-618-38240-8(2) , 357616) Houghton Mifflin College Div.

—Key Concepts 2: Listening, Note-Taking & Speaking Across the Disciplines. 2005. 146p. (YA). pap. 31.16 (978-0-618-38241-5(0) , 357617) Houghton Mifflin College Div.

Viewpoints. 2003. instr.'s gde. ed. (978-0-618-04260-9(1)) McDougal Littell Inc.

Vocabulary Builders: Level A. 2003. 128p. (C). pap. 13.99 (978-0-7424-1858-5(8) , LL90018) School Specialty Publishing.

Vowel Pictures. (gr. k-3). 34.99 (978-1-56451-639-8(3) , ID2741) School Specialty Publishing.

Wade, Angela. New York City. 2006. (Illus.). 8p. (J). pap. (***978-0-439-74035-7(5)**) Scholastic, Inc.

Wagner, Better Jane. Language Arts: Grade 6. 2001. (Spectrum Language Arts Ser.). (Illus.). 203p. (J). (gr. 6-6). pap., wbk. ed. 8.95 (978-1-57768-486-2(9) , Spectrum) School Specialty Publishing.

Wagner, Betty Jane. Language Arts: Grade 4. 2001. (Spectrum Workbooks Ser.). (Illus.). 203p. (J). (gr. 4-4). pap., wbk. ed. 8.95 (978-1-57768-484-8(2) , Spectrum) School Specialty Publishing.

—Language Arts: Grade 5. 2001. (Spectrum Workbooks Ser.). (Illus.). 203p. (J). (gr. 5-5). pap., wbk. ed. 8.95 (978-1-57768-485-5(0) , Spectrum) School Specialty Publishing.

Watt, Fiona. Este No Es Mi Tren. rev. ed. 2004. (Titles in Spanish Ser.).Tr. of That's Not My Train. 32p. (J). 12.99 (978-1-58086-585-2(2)) EDC Publishing.

Wernham, Sara & Lloyd, Sue. The Grammar Handbook 1: U. S. English. 2000. 218p. (J). spiral bd. 32.50 (978-1-870946-86-5(3) , JL863) Jolly Learning, Ltd. GBR. *Dist:* American International Distribution Corp.

—The Grammar Handbook 2: U. S. English. 2001. 218p. (J). spiral bd. 32.50 (978-1-903619-08-7(4) , JL084) Jolly Learning, Ltd. GBR. *Dist:* American International Distribution Corp.

West, Kipling. A Rattle of Bones: A Halloween Book of Collective Nouns. West, Kipling, illus. 1999. (Illus.). 32p. (J). (ps-1). 16.99 (978-0-531-33196-5(2) , Orchard Bks.) Scholastic, Inc.

West, Tori. A Look at Opposites. West, Tori, illus. 1998. (Illus.). (J). (gr. k-2). (978-1-892800-10-7(1)) Tattoo Manufacturing.

What Follows Next? Sequence Picture Cards. (gr. k up). 9.99 (978-1-56451-632-9(6) , ID2683) School Specialty Publishing.

Whiteford, Rhona. Reading & Writing: Brand New Activities for Key Stage 2. 2003. (Hodder Home Learning Ser.). (Illus.). 32p. (J). pap. 6.99 (978-0-340-79183-7(7) , Hodder & Stoughton) Hodder General Publishing Division GBR. *Dist:* Trafalgar Square Publishing.

Wilber, Peggy M. & Hering, Marianne. Five Alive: Level 2, 5 vols. Pillo, Cary, illus. 2003. (Rocket Reader Ser.). (J). (gr. 2 up). pap. 8.99 (978-0-7814-3862-9(4) , 0781438624) Cook, David C. Publishing Co.

Williams, Robert. Language Arts. 2000. (gr. 7-12). lib. bdg. 41.95 (978-0-613-84821-3(7)) Tandem Library Bks.

Williams, Wendy. English for PreTeens Book 1 Student's Book: Elt. 2000. (Illus.). 120p. pap., stu. ed. (978-1-929310-10-4(2)) ALL Publishing Hse.

Words Cards for Prefixes Amd Suffixes: Systematic Sequential Phonics & Spelling Word Card Set. 2002. (J). pap. 39.99 (978-0-88724-808-5(X) , CD-2811) Carson-Dellosa Publishing Co., Inc.

Writing Grade 2. 2000. (Practice Makes Perfect Ser.). 80p. (J). (gr. 2). pap., wbk. ed. 2.99 (978-0-88724-621-0(4) , CD-3631) Carson-Dellosa Publishing Co., Inc.

Writing Grade 4. 2000. (Practice Makes Perfect Ser.). 80p. (J). (gr. 4). pap., wbk. ed. 2.99 (978-0-88724-623-4(0) , CD-3633) Carson-Dellosa Publishing Co., Inc.

Wyrick, Jean. Companion to the Practical Writer with Readings. 2002. pap. 13.95 (978 0 8384 7471-6(3)) Thomson Heinle.

Yong, Tohmoh J., et al. Tune in CM1 Pupil's Book. 2007. pap., stu. ed. 2.72 (***978-0-521-69595-4(3)**) Cambridge Univ. Pr.

YoYo Books. ABC: Mini Baby's First Library. 2005. 42p. bds. 4.95 (978-90-5843-806-5(6)) YoYo Bks. BEL. *Dist:* National Bk. Network.

Zuckerman, Rory. Alphabetical Sleepy Sheep. Roos, Maryn, illus. 2004. (J). bds. 12.95 (978-0-9749305-3-4(9)) Castle Pacific Publishing.

3rd & 4th Grade Excelerator, 2 CDs. 2002. cd-rom 9.99 (978-1-59150-014-8(1)) TOPICS Entertainment.

The 5W's & H (Gr. 4-5) 2004. (J). (978-1-58232-130-1(2)) Bryan Hse. Pubs., Inc.

ENGLISH LANGUAGE—AMERICANISMS

see Americanisms

ENGLISH LANGUAGE—BUSINESS ENGLISH

see also Business Letters

E. Taylor, Marcia. Orientation Business English Lev 1. (J). (gr. 7-12). (978-0-8325-0684-0(2)) McGraw-Hill/Contemporary.

Grant, David & McLarty, Robert. Business Basics. 2002. (Illus.). 16.50 (978-0-19-457340-5(0)) Oxford Univ. Pr., Inc.

1,001 Essential Letters, 2002. cd-rom 4.99 (978-1-59150-098-8(2)) TOPICS Entertainment.

ENGLISH LANGUAGE—COMPOSITION AND EXERCISES

Al-Marwani, Amatullah. Star Writers. 2006. (Illus.). vii, 167p. (J). (978-0-9767861-2-2(5)) Muslim Writers Publishing.

American Education Publishing, Inc. Staff & Barr, Linda. Spelling & Writing: Grade 6. 2003. (Brighter Child Workbooks Ser.). (Illus.). 24p. (J). (gr. 6). pap. 2.25 (978-1-56189-136-8(3) , American Education Publishing) School Specialty Publishing.

American Guidance Service Staff, contrib. by. AGS Preparing for Writing Tests: Student Activity Book: Grades 6-8. 2001. (Illus.). 96p. (978-0-7854-2472-7(5)) American Guidance Service, Inc.

Arco Staff. High Stakes: Writing. 2003. (High-Stakes Test Ser.). 288p. pap. 16.95 (978-0-7689-1073-5(0)) Peterson's.

Arois, Marcia M. Family Literacy: Easy Ways for Families to Read & Write Together. Johnson, Linda, illus. l.t. ed. 1999. 96p. (J). (ps-3). pap. 9.95 (978-0-9667936-1-1(7) , 123) Literacy Links.

Ashley, Susan. I Can Write a Letter. 2004. (Illus.). (J). 23p. pap. (978-0-8368-4335-4(5)); 24p. lib. bdg. 19.33 (978-0-8368-4328-6(2)) Stevens, Gareth Inc.

Babsky, Irene. Playing with Words. 2003. (Early Learner Ser.). (Illus.). 64p. 14.99 (978-0-7548-1053-7(4) , Lorenz Bks.) Anness Publishing GBR. *Dist:* National Bk. Network.

Bell, Nanci. Seeing Stars Decoding Workbook Vol. 1: Who Is Fip? 1999. 42p. (J). pap., wbk. ed. 3.95 (978-0-945856-14-6(8)) Gander Publishing.

—Seeing Stars Decoding Workbook Vol. 2: Who Is Bib? 1999. 42p. (J). pap., wbk. ed. 3.95 (978-0-945856-15-3(6)) Gander Publishing.

—Seeing Stars Decoding Workbook Vol. 3: Who Is Gus? 1999. 42p. (J). pap., wbk. ed. 3.95 (978-0-945856-16-0(4)) Gander Publishing.

—Seeing Stars Decoding Workbook Vol. 4: Who Is Poe? 1999. 42p. (J). pap., wbk. ed. 3.95 (978-0-945856-17-7(2)) Gander Publishing.

Benchmark Education Staff, compiled by. Comprehension Strategy Poster Set Levels A-E (1-8) Emergent. ed. 2004. (Comprehension Ser.). (J). spiral bd., instr.'s gde. ed. 70.00 (978-1-4108-1521-7(8)) Benchmark Education Co.

—Comprehension Strategy Poster Set Levels J-M (18-28) Fluent. ed. 2004. (Comprehension Ser.). (J). spiral bd., instr.'s gde. ed. 90.00 (978-1-4108-1523-1(4)) Benchmark Education Co.

—Comprehension Strategy Posters Set levels F-I (9-16) Early. ed. 2004. (Comprehension Ser.). (J). spiral bd., instr.'s gde. ed. 85.00 (978-1-4108-1522-4(6)) Benchmark Education Co.

Brantley, C. L. Writing Smart Junior. 2nd ed. 2002. (Smart Junior Guides). 320p. (J). (gr. 6-8). pap. 12.00 (978-0-375-76261-1(2) , Princeton Review) Random Hse. Information Group.

Broadwater, Deborah. English Skills Practice & Apply: Grade 4. 2000. (Illus.). 128p. (J). (gr. 4). pap. 10.95 (978-1-58037-119-3(1)) Twain, Mark Media, Inc. Pubs.

—English Skills Practice & Apply: Grade 5. 2000. (Illus.). 128p. (J). (gr. 5). pap. 10.95 (978-1-58037-120-9(5)) Twain, Mark Media, Inc. Pubs.

—English Skills Practice & Apply: Grade 6. 2000. (Illus.). 128p. (YA). (gr. 6). pap. 10.95 (978-1-58037-121-6(3)) Twain, Mark Media, Inc. Pubs.

—English Skills Practice & Apply: Grade 7. 2000. (Illus.). 128p. (YA). (gr. 7). pap. 10.95 (978-1-58037-122-3(1)) Twain, Mark Media, Inc. Pubs.

Bullard, Lisa. You Can Write a Story! A Story-Writing Recipe for Kids. Melmon, Deborah, illus. 2007. 48p. (J). (gr. 1-4). 16.95 (978-1-58728-587-5(8) , Two Can Publishing) T&N Children's Publishing.

Bumgardner, Joyce C. The New My Writing Book. LaRochelle, David, illus. 1998. 72p. (J). (gr. 2-6). pap. 5.95 (978-0-9624260-1-8(6)) Froggie Pr.

Burke, Sandra & Flebotte, Morrigan. The Crusading Communicator. Flebotte, Morrigan, ed. 2004. (Illus.). 2p. (J). per. (978-0-9735303-8-4(3)) Black Castle Industries, Inc.

Carroll, Joyce Armstrong, et al. Writing & Grammar: Communication in Action, Copper Level. 2001. (J). (gr. 6). 114.47 (978-0-13-052664-9(9)) Prentice Hall PTR.

—Writing & Grammar, Communication in Action Gold Level: Basic Skills Intervention Kit. 2001. (YA). (gr. 10). 499.97 (978-0-13-053997-7(X)) Prentice Hall PTR.

—Writing & Grammar, Grade 9: Communication in Action. 2001. (YA). Platinum Level. (gr. 10). pap., act. bk. ed. 8.47 (978-0-13-043917-8(7)); Ruby Level. (gr. 11). 114.47 (978-0-13-052669-4(X)); Ruby Level. (gr. 11). pap., act. bk. ed. 7.47 (978-0-13-043925-3(8)) Prentice Hall PTR.

Center for Learning Network Staff. Advanced Composition: Curriculum Unit. 2001. (English Ser.). 231p. (YA). (gr. 9-12). stu. ed., per., wbk. ed. 8.95 (978-1-56077-689-5(7)); 3rd rev. ed. tchr. ed., spiral bd. 39.95 (978-1-56077-688-8(9)) Ctr. for Learning, The.

—Basic Composition. 2001. (English Ser.). 218p. (YA). (gr. 7-9). tchr. ed., spiral bd. 397.95 (978-1-56077-664-2(1)) Ctr. for Learning, The.

—Basic Composition, Student Workbook: Curriculum Unit. 2001. (English Ser.). 202p. (YA). stu. ed., per., wbk. ed. 8.95 (978-1-56077-665-9(X)) Ctr. for Learning, The.

—Ceremony: Curriculum Unit. 2003. (Novel Ser.). 60p. (YA). tchr. ed., spiral bd. 19.95 (978-1-56077-731-1(1)) Ctr. for Learning, The.

Chasin, Rachel. Cut, Paste, & Write a School Story, Grades 1-3. Rogers, Kathy, ed. 2000. (Illus.). 32p. (J). pap., tchr. ed. 4.95 (978-1-56472-184-6(1) , EP184) Edupress, Inc.

—Cut, Paste, & Write a Seasonal Story, Grades 1-3. Rogers, Kathy, ed. 2000. (Illus.). 32p. (J). pap., tchr. ed. 4.95 (978-1-56472-181-5(7) , EP181) Edupress, Inc.

—Cut, Paste, & Write an Alphabet Story, Grades 1-3. Rogers, Kathy, ed. 2000. (Illus.). 32p. (J). pap., tchr. ed. 4.95 (978-1-56472-183-9(3) , EP183) Edupress, Inc.

—Cut, Paste, & Write an Animal Story, Grades 1-3. Rogers, Kathy, ed. 2000. (Illus.). 32p. (J). pap., tchr. ed. 4.95 (978-1-56472-182-2(5) , EP182) Edupress, Inc.

Cheyney, Arnold. Write Away. 2006. 176p. (J). pap. (978-1-59647-087-3(9)) Good Year Bks.

Dalmatian Press Staff. My Writing Tablet. 1998. (J). (ps-3). pap. 2.29 (978-1-888567-10-6(4)) Dalmatian Pr.

Daly, Mary. Elementary Diagramming Worktext. 2nd ed. 2002. 110p. per. 15.00 (978-0-9723239-0-1(2)) Ye Hedge Schl.

Dollard, Linda L. Writing Set, 3 bks., Set. 2003. (J). (gr. k-1). 25.99 (978-1-56417-728-5(9) , FE0004, Fearon Teacher Aids) Schaffer, Frank Pubns.

Donaldson. Gage Canadian Student Writer's Guide. 2000. 184p. (YA). (gr. 7-10). pap. 12.95 (978-0-7715-1319-0(4)) Gage Learning Corp. CAN. *Dist:* CDG Bks. Canada, Inc.

Donegan, Patricia. Haiku. 2004. (Asian Arts & Crafts for Creative Kids Ser.). (Illus.). 64p. (gr. 2-7). 12.95 (978-0-8048-3501-5(2)) Tuttle Publishing.

Eames, Jackie & Wainwright, Judith. Your Own Words. 2nd ed. 1999. (Illus.). 352p. (YA). (gr. 11-13). pap. 33.00 (978-0-17-490053-5(8)) Nelson Thornes Ltd. GBR. *Dist:* Trans-Atlantic Pubns., Inc.

English II: Composition Skills, Full Course Kit with CD-ROM. 2005. (Illus.). 910p. (YA). pap. 75.00 (978-1-59476-147-8(7)) Paradigm Accelerated Curriculum.

English III: Writing Skills, Chapter 1, Activities. 2005. (Illus.). 44p. (YA). pap. 7.00 (978-1-59476-016-7(0)) Paradigm Accelerated Curriculum.

English III: Writing Skills, Chapter 1, Text. 2005. (Illus.). 52p. (YA). 7.00 (978-1-59476-006-8(3)) Paradigm Accelerated Curriculum.

English III: Writing Skills, Chapter 2, Activities. 2005. (Illus.). 78p. (YA). pap. 5.00 (978-1-59476-017-4(9)) Paradigm Accelerated Curriculum.

English III: Writing Skills, Chapter 2, Text. 2005. (Illus.). 86p. (YA). pap. 7.00 (978-1-59476-007-5(1)) Paradigm Accelerated Curriculum.

English III: Writing Skills, Chapter 3, Activities. 2005. (Illus.). 76p. (YA). pap. 5.00 (978-1-59476-018-1(7)) Paradigm Accelerated Curriculum.

English III: Writing Skills, Chapter 3, Text. 2005. 72p. (YA). pap. 7.00 (978-1-59476-008-2(X)) Paradigm Accelerated Curriculum.

English III: Writing Skills, Chapter 4, Activities. 2005. (Illus.). 68p. (YA). pap. 5.00 (978-1-59476-019-8(5)) Paradigm Accelerated Curriculum.

English III: Writing Skills, Chapter 4, Text. 2005. (Illus.). 60p. (YA). pap. 7.00 (978-1-59476-009-9(8)) Paradigm Accelerated Curriculum.

English III: Writing Skills, Chapter 5, Text. 2005. (Illus.). 96p. (YA). pap. 7.00 (978-1-59476-010-5(1)) Paradigm Accelerated Curriculum.

English III: Writing Skills, Full Course Kit. 2005. (Illus.). 982p. (YA). 75.00 (978-1-59476-149-2(3)) Paradigm Accelerated Curriculum.

Francis, Barbara. Other People's Words: What Plagiarism Is & How to Avoid It. 2005. (Issues in Focus Today Ser.). (Illus.). 112p. (J). (gr. 6 up). lib. bdg. 31.93 (978-0-7660-2525-7(X)) Enslow Pubs., Inc.

Get in Shape to Write. 1998. (J). spiral bd. 14.00 (978-0-939564-22-4(X)) Pen Notes, Inc.

Glencoe McGraw-Hill Staff. Writer's Choice: Grammar & Composition, Grade 7. 3rd ed. 2000. stu. ed. 75.96 (978-0-02-818148-6(4) , 9780028181486) Glencoe/McGraw-Hill.

—Writer's Choice: Grammar & Composition, Grade 10. 3rd ed. 2000. stu. ed. 80.64 (978-0-02-818149-3(2) , 9780028181493) Glencoe/McGraw-Hill.

—Writer's Choice: Grammar & Composition, Grade 11. 2000. stu. ed. 82.64 (978-0-07-822660-1(0) , 9780078226601) Glencoe/McGraw-Hill.

—Writer's Choice: Grammar & Composition, Grade 12. 2000. stu. ed. 82.64 (978-0-07-822662-5(7) , 9780078226625) Glencoe/McGraw-Hill.

—Writer's Choice: Grammar & Composition, Grade 6. 2000. stu. ed. 73.32 (978-0-07-822652-6(X) , 9780078226526) Glencoe/McGraw-Hill.

—Writer's Choice: Grammar & Composition, Grade 8. 2000. stu. ed. 75.96 (978-0-07-822655-7(4) , 9780078226557) Glencoe/McGraw-Hill.

—Writer's Choice: Grammar & Composition, Grade 9. 2000. stu. ed. 80.64 (978-0-07-822657-1(0) , 9780078226571) Glencoe/McGraw-Hill.

Hedley, John. Springboard. 1999. (Illus.). (J). (gr. 1-6). Bk. 1. 32p. pap., wbk. ed. 20.00 (978-0-7217-0333-6(X)); Bk. 2. 32p. pap., wbk. ed. 20.00 (978-0-7217-0334-3(8)); Bk. 3. 32p. pap., wbk. ed. 20.00 (978-0-7217-0335-0(6)); Bk. 4. 32p. pap., wbk. ed. 20.00 (978-0-7217-0336-7(4)); Bk. 5. 32p. pap., wbk. ed. 20.00 (978-0-7217-0337-4(2)); Bk. 6. 32p. pap., wbk. ed. 20.00 (978-0-7217-0338-1(0)); Bk. 7. 48p. pap., wbk. ed. 20.00 (978-0-7217-0339-8(9)); Bk. 8. 48p. pap., wbk. ed. 20.00 (978-0-7217-0340-4(2)) Schofield & Sims Ltd. GBR. *Dist:* State Mutual Bk. & Periodical Service, Ltd.

—Springboard Introductory Book. 1999. (Illus.). 29p. (J). (gr. 1-6). pap., wbk. ed. 20.00 (978-0-7217-0724-2(6)) Schofield & Sims Ltd. GBR. *Dist:* State Mutual Bk. & Periodical Service, Ltd.

Horton, Elizabeth. Creative Writing Syllabus. 1998. 38p. (YA). (gr. 10-12). pap. 4.95 (978-1-57896-029-3(0) , 2539) Hewitt Research Foundation, Inc.

Hutson-Nechkash, Peg. Help Me Write: Frames & Rubrics for Classroom Writing Success. 2003. (Illus.). vii, 295p. (J). (978-1-932054-12-5(X)) Super Duper Pubns.

Janeczko, Paul B., et al. Writing Winning Reports & Essays. 2003. 224p. (J). pap. 7.95 (978-0-439-28718-0(9)) Scholastic, Inc.

Jarnow, Jill. Writing to Correspond. 2006. (Write Now Ser.). (J). 17.25 (978-1-4042-2831-3(4) , PowerKids Pr.) Rosen Publishing Group, Inc., The.

—Writing to Describe. 2006. (Write Now Ser.). 24p. (J). 17.25 (978-1-4042-2832-0(2) , PowerKids Pr.) Rosen Publishing Group, Inc., The.

—Writing to Explain. 2006. (Write Now Ser.). (J). 17.25 (978-1-4042-2833-7(0) , PowerKids Pr.) Rosen Publishing Group, Inc., The.

Jones. Language Exercises. 2004. Level C. pap., tchr. ed. 10.00 incl. cd-rom (978-0-7398-9124-7(3)); Level C. (Illus.). pap. 14.40 incl. cd-rom (978-0-7398-9115-5(4)); Level D. pap., tchr. ed. 10.00 incl. cd-rom (978-0-7398-9125-4(1)); Level D. (Illus.). pap. 14.40 incl. cd-rom (978-0-7398-9116-2(2)); Level A. pap., tchr. ed. 10.00 incl. cd-rom (978-0-7398-9122-3(7)); Level A. (Illus.). pap. 14.40 incl. cd-rom (978-0-7398-9113-1(8)); Level B. pap., tchr. ed. 10.00 incl. cd-rom (978-0-7398-9123-0(5)); Level B. (Illus.). pap. 14.40 incl. cd-rom (978-0-7398-9114-8(6)); Level E. pap., tchr. ed. 10.00 incl. cd-rom (978-0-7398-9126-1(X)); Level E. (Illus.). pap. 14.40 incl. cd-rom (978-0-7398-9117-9(0)); Level F. pap., tchr. ed. 10.00 incl. cd-rom (978-0-7398-9127-8(8)); Level F. (Illus.). pap. 14.40 incl. cd-rom (978-0-7398-9118-6(9)); Level G. pap., tchr. ed. 10.00 incl. cd-rom (978-0-7398-9236-7(3)); Level G. (Illus.). pap. 14.40 incl. cd-rom (978-0-7398-9119-3(7)); Level H. pap., tchr. ed. 10.00 incl. cd-rom (978-0-7398-9128-5(6)); Level H. (Illus.). pap. 14.40 incl. cd-rom (978-0-7398-9120-9(0)) Steck-Vaughn.

—Language Exercises Review. 2004. pap. 14.40 incl. cd-rom (978-0-7398-9121-6(9)); pap., tchr. ed. 10.00 incl. cd-rom (978-0-7398-9129-2(4)) Steck-Vaughn.

Kellaher, Karen. Writing Skills Made Fun: Parts of Speech. 2001. 48p. pap. 10.95 (978-0-439-22268-6(0)) Scholastic, Inc.

—Writing Skills Made Fun: Sentences & Paragraphs. 2001. 48p. (J). (gr. 2). pap. 10.95 (978-0-439-22266-2(4)) Scholastic, Inc.

Kerr, Bob. Grammar & Writing Skills Practice & Apply: Grade 4. 2000. (Illus.). 128p. (J). (gr. 4). pap. 10.95 (978-1-58037-123-0(X)) Twain, Mark Media, Inc. Pubs.

—Grammar & Writing Skills Practice & Apply: Grade 6. 2000. (Illus.). 128p. (J). (gr. 6). pap. 10.95 (978-1-58037-125-4(6)) Twain, Mark Media, Inc. Pubs.

—Grammar & Writing Skills Practice & Apply: Grade 7+ 2000. (Illus.). 128p. (YA). (gr. 7). pap. 10.95 (978-1-58037-126-1(4)) Twain, Mark Media, Inc. Pubs.

Krensky, Stephen. Write Away ! One Author's Favorite Activities That Help Ordinary Writers Become Extraordinary Writers. 1998. (Illus.). 96p. (J). 12.95 (978-0-590-38208-3(X)) Scholastic, Inc.

—50 Great Reproducible Writing Workouts: Awesome Activity Sheets to Build Skills in Grammar Usage. 1999. 64p. pap. 9.95 (978-0-590-98408-9(X)) Scholastic, Inc.

Language Network. 2001. (gr. 10 up). tchr. ed. (978-0-395-96747-8(3) , 2-22042); (gr. 10 up). tchr. ed. (978-0-618-05269-1(0) , 2-22376); (gr. 10 up). tchr. ed. (978-0-618-05333-9(6) , 2-22426); (gr. 10 up). stu. ed. (978-0-395-96740-9(6) , 2-22035); (gr. 10 up). stu. ed., wbk. ed. (978-0-618-05262-2(3) , 2-22369); (gr. 10 up). pap. incl. cd-rom (978-0-618-21274-3(4) , 2-19251); (gr. 10 up). tchr. ed. incl. cd-rom (978-0-618-05380-3(8) , 2-22445); (gr. 10 up). cd-rom (978-0-618-24588-8(X) , 2-22616); (gr. 11 up). tchr. ed. (978-0-618-05270-7(4) , 2-22377); (gr. 11 up). tchr. ed. (978-0-618-05334-6(4) , 2-22427); (gr. 11 up). tchr. ed. (978-0-395-96748-5(1) , 2-22043); (gr. 11 up). stu. ed. (978-0-395-96741-6(4) , 2-22036); (gr. 11 up). stu. ed., wbk. ed. (978-0-618-05263-9(1) , 2-22370); (gr. 11 up). pap. incl. cd-rom (978-0-618-21276-7(0) , 2-19253); (gr. 11 up). tchr. ed. incl. cd-rom (978-0-618-05379-7(4) , 2-22444); (gr. 11 up). cd-rom (978-0-618-24589-5(8) , 2-22617); (gr. 12 up). tchr. ed. (978-0-395-96749-2(X) , 2-22044); (gr. 12 up). tchr. ed. (978-0-618-05271-4(2) , 2-22378); (gr. 12 up). tchr. ed. (978-0-618-05335-3(2) , 2-22428); (gr. 12 up). stu. ed. (978-0-395-96742-3(2) , 2-22037); (gr. 12 up). stu. ed., wbk. ed. (978-0-618-05264-6(X) , 2-22371); (gr. 12 up). pap. incl. cd-rom (978-0-618-21278-1(7) , 2-19255); (gr. 12 up). tchr. ed. incl. cd-rom (978-0-618-05378-0(6) , 2-22443); (gr. 6 up). tchr. ed. (978-0-618-05268-4(2) , 2-22375); (gr. 6 up). tchr. ed. (978-0-618-05332-2(8) , 2-22425); (gr. 6 up). tchr. ed. (978-0-395-96746-1(5) , 2-22041); (gr. 6 up). tchr. ed. (978-0-395-96743-0(0) , 2-22038); (gr. 6 up). tchr. ed. (978-0-618-11894-6(2) , 2-80960); (gr. 6 up). stu. ed. (978-0-395-96739-3(2) , 2-22034); (gr. 6 up). stu. ed. (978-0-395-96736-2(8) , 2-22031); (gr. 6 up). stu. ed., wbk. ed. (978-0-618-05261-5(5) , 2-22368); (gr. 6 up). pap. incl. cd-rom (978-0-618-18242-8(X) , 2-22027); (gr. 6 up). pap. incl. cd-rom (978-0-618-21272-9(8) , 2-19249); (gr. 6 up). tchr. ed. incl. cd-rom (978-0-618-05381-0(6) , 2-22446); (gr. 6 up). tchr. ed. incl. cd-rom (978-0-618-16654-1(8) , 2-80954); (gr. 6 up). cd-rom (978-0-618-24587-1(1) , 2-22615); (gr. 6 up). cd-rom (978-0-618-24584-0(7) , 2-22612); (gr. 7 up). tchr. ed. (978-0-618-11895-3(0) , 2-80961); (gr. 7 up). tchr. ed. (978-0-395-96744-7(9) , 2-22039); (gr. 7 up). stu. ed. (978-0-395-96737-9(6) , 2-22032); (gr. 7 up). pap. incl. cd-rom (978-0-618-18251-0(9) , 2-22028); (gr. 7 up). tchr. ed. incl. cd-rom (978-0-618-16655-8(6) , 2-80955); (gr. 7 up). cd-rom (978-0-618-24585-7(5) , 2-22613); (gr. 8 up). tchr. ed. (978-0-395-96745-4(7) , 2-22040); (gr. 8 up). tchr. ed. (978-0-618-16814-9(1) , 2-80962); (gr. 8 up). stu. ed. (978-0-395-96738-6(4) , 2-22033); (gr. 8 up). pap. incl. cd-rom (978-0-618-18252-7(7) , 2-22029); (gr. 8 up). tchr. ed. incl. cd-rom (978-0-618-16656-5(4) , 2-80956); (gr. 8 up). cd-rom (978-0-618-24586-4(3) , 2-22614) McDougal Littell Inc.

Learn to Write. (Learning Ser.). 22p. (J). bds. (978-2-7643-0038-1(7)) Phidal Publishing, Inc./Editions Phidal, Inc.

The Library of Writing Skills. 2005. (Illus.). 48p. (gr. 5-8). lib. bdg. 159.00 (978-1-4042-0349-5(4)) Rosen Publishing Group, Inc., The.

Linaker, Kathryn. Nursery Writing Book. 1999. (Illus.). 23p. (J). (ps). Bk. 1. pap., wbk. ed. 19.00 (978-0-7217-6512-9(2)); Bk. 2. pap., wbk. ed. 19.00 (978-0-7217-6513-6(0)); Bk. 3. pap., wbk. ed. 19.00 (978-0-7217-6514-3(9)); Bk. 4. pap., wbk. ed. 19.00 (978-0-7217-6515-0(7)); Bk. 5. pap., wbk. ed. 19.00 (978-0-7217-6516-7(5)); Bk. 6. pap., wbk. ed. 19.00 (978-0-7217-6517-4(3)) Schofield & Sims Ltd. GBR. *Dist:* State Mutual Bk. & Periodical Service, Ltd.

MacGregor, Cynthia. When I Grow up, I Want to Be a Writer. Flook, Helen, illus. 2001. (Millennium Generation). 100p. (J). pap. 9.95 (978-1-894222-42-6(3)) Lobster Pr. CAN. *Dist:* Univ. of Toronto Pr.

Madden, Kerry. Writing Smarts: A Girl's Guide to Great Poetry, Storytelling, School Reports & More! McGuinness, Tracy, illus. 2002. (American Girl Library). 104p. (J). pap. 8.95 (978-1-58485-505-7(3)) American Girl Publishing, Inc.

Marzollo, Jean & Widmer, Katherine M. Think! Draw! Write! 48p. (J). Level 1. 2001. (gr. 1-3). pap. 8.99 (978-0-8224-6946-9(4) , FE6946); Level 2. 2003. (gr. 4-6). 8.99 (978-0-8224-6947-6(2) , FE-6947) Schaffer, Frank Pubns. (Fearon Teacher Aids).

Mason, Adrienne & Cupples, Pat. Lu & Clancy's Secret Codes. 1999. (Lu & Clancy Ser.). (Illus.). 40p. (J). (gr. k-3). (978-1-55074-553-5(0)) Kids Can Pr., Ltd.

Mayer, Mercer. Mercer Mayer - Writing: Preschool. 2003. (Little Critter Preschool Workbook Ser.). (Illus.). 128p. (J). (ps-2). pap., wbk. ed. 8.95 (978-1-57768-549-4(0) , Spectrum) School Specialty Publishing.

—Writing: Grade 2. 2001. (Spectrum Writing Ser.). (Illus.). 160p. (J). (gr. 2-2). pap., wbk. ed. 8.95 (978-1-57768-852-5(X) , Spectrum) School Specialty Publishing.

Mayer, Mercer, ed. Spectrum Writing: Grade 1. 2001. (Spectrum Writing Ser.). (Illus.). 160p. (J). (gr. 1-1). pap., wbk. ed. 8.95 (978-1-57768-851-8(1) , Spectrum) School Specialty Publishing.

McGraw-Hill Staff. Glencoe Language Arts, Grade 6, Grammar & Composition Handbook. 2001. 39.96 (978-0-07-825113-9(3) , 9780078251139) Glencoe/McGraw-Hill.

—Writer's Choice: Grammar & Composition, Grade 11, Interactive Student Edition. 2001. (C). stu. ed. 82.64 incl. cd-rom (978-0-07-827070-3(7) , 9780078270703) Glencoe/McGraw-Hill.

—Writer's Choice: Grammar & Composition, Grade 12, Interactive Student Edition. 2001. (C). stu. ed. 82.64 incl. cd-rom (978-0-07-827071-0(5) , 9780078270710) Glencoe/McGraw-Hill.

—Writer's Choice: Grammar & Composition, Grade 7, Interactive Student Edition. 2001. (C). stu. ed. 75.96 incl. cd-rom (978-0-07-827066-6(9) , 9780078270666) Glencoe/McGraw-Hill.

—Writer's Choice: Grammar & Composition, Grade 8, Interactive Student Edition. 2001. (C). stu. ed. 75.96 incl. cd-rom (978-0-07-827067-3(7) , 9780078270673) Glencoe/McGraw-Hill.

—Writer's Choice: Grammar & Composition, Grade 9, Interactive Student Edition. 2001. (C). stu. ed. 80.64 incl. cd-rom (978-0-07-827068-0(5) , 9780078270680) Glencoe/McGraw-Hill.

—Writer's Choice: Grammar & Composition, Grade 6. 2001. stu. ed. 73.32 incl. cd-rom (978-0-07-827065-9(0) , 9780078270659) Glencoe/McGraw-Hill.

—Writer's Choice Grade 6: Grammar & Composition, Grade 6. 2004. stu. ed. 74.60 (978-0-07-829814-1(8) , 9780078298141) Glencoe/McGraw-Hill.

—Writer's Choice Grade 8: Grammar & Composition, Grade 8. 2004. stu. ed. 74.60 (978-0-07-829816-5(4) , 9780078298165) Glencoe/McGraw-Hill.

—Writer's Choice Grade 9: Grammar & Composition. 2004. stu. ed. 78.00 (978-0-07-829817-2(2) , 9780078298172) Glencoe/McGraw-Hill.

McGraw-Hill Staff & School Specialty Publishing Staff. Beginning Writing. 2001. (Homework Helpers Activity Bks.). (Illus.). 56p. (J). (gr. k-1). pap., act. bk. ed. 2.99 (978-0-7682-0682-1(0) , FS109011, Schaffer, Frank) Schaffer, Frank Pubns.

Milliken, Linda. Fun & Fancy Alphabet Lined Writing Paper, Grades 1-3. 1999. (Illus.). 32p. (J). pap., tchr. ed. 4.95 (978-1-56472-177-8(9) , EP177) Edupress, Inc.

—Fun & Fancy Animal Lined Writing Paper, Grades 1-3. 1999. (Illus.). 32p. (J). pap., tchr. ed. 4.95 (978-1-56472-176-1(0) , EP176) Edupress, Inc.

—Fun & Fancy School Lined Writing Paper, Grades 1-3. 2000. (Illus.). 32p. (J). pap., tchr. ed. 4.95 (978-1-56472-178-5(7) , EP178) Edupress, Inc.

Montgomery, Karen & Lloyd, Glynis. English Matters Grade 6 Learner's Book. 2002. (English Matters Ser.). pap. (978-0-521-00378-0(4)) Cambridge Univ. Pr.

Nash, Kimberley. How to Write Essays & Research Reports - Level B: An Intermediate-Advanced One-Year Workbook Format Course. 2007. (ENG., Illus.). 168p. spiral bd., wbk. ed. 25.00 (978-0-9710950-2-1(7) , 12020) Resurrection Resources LLC.

Nobisso, Josephine. Show; Don't Tell! Secrets of Writing. Montanari, Eva, illus. 2004. 40p. (J). (gr. 2-6). 24.95 (978-0-940112-13-1(2)) Gingerbread Hse.

Nobleman, Marc Tyler. Writing. 2003. (5-Minute Daily Practice Ser.). (Illus.). 64p. pap., tchr. ed. 11.95 (978-0-439-26244-6(5) , Teaching Resources) Scholastic, Inc.

Novelli, Joan. Teaching Story Writing: Quick & Easy Literature-Based Lessons & Activities That Help Students Write Super Stories. 2001. (Illus.). 72p. (gr. 3-6). pap. 10.95 (978-0-439-05006-7(5)) Scholastic, Inc.

Null, Kathleen Christopher. How to Write a Paragraph. Wally, Barbara M., ed. 1999. (How to Ser.). (Illus.). 48p. (J). (gr. 5-8). pap., act. bk. ed. 7.99 (978-1-57690-490-9(3) , TCA2490); (gr. k-3). pap., act. bk. ed. 7.99 (978-1-57690-494-7(6) , TCA2494) Teacher Created Materials, Inc.

—How to Write a Sentence. Cook, David Fuller, ed. 1999. (How to Ser.). (Illus.). 48p. (J). (gr. k-3). pap., act. bk. ed. 7.99 (978-1-57690-498-5(9) , TCA2498) Teacher Created Materials, Inc.

—How to Write a Story. Guckian, Mary Ellen, ed. Apodaca-LaBounty, Blanca, illus. 1999. (How to Ser.). 48p. (J). (gr. k-3). pap., act. bk. ed. 7.99 (978-1-57690-495-4(4) , TCA2495) Teacher Created Materials, Inc.

Orehovec, Barbara & Alley, Marybeth. Revisiting the Writing Workshop. 2007. 160p. pap. 19.99 (*978-0-439-92643-0(2)) Scholastic, Inc.

Oseye, Ebele & Southerland, Ellease. Opening Line: The Creative Writer. 2000. 39p. (YA). pap. 10.00 (978-1-929454-01-3(5) , 917 863-6528) Eneke Pubns.

Parker, Andrew & Stamford, Jane. English Practice: Year 6. 1999. (Illus.). (J). (gr. 2-7). pap. 45.00 (978-0-7217-0664-1(9)) Schofield & Sims Ltd. GBR. *Dist:* State Mutual Bk. & Periodical Service, Ltd.

Peterson. Mastering Writing Skills. 2002. (Get Wise! Ser.). (Illus.). 216p. (YA). pap. 12.95 (978-0-7689-1078-0(1)) Peterson's.

Phillips, Wanda C. Easy Grammar Grade 3 Student Workbook. 2006. pap. 13.95 (*978-0-936981-48-2(2)) Isha Enterprises, Inc.

—Easy Grammar Grade 4 Student Test Booklet. 2006. pap. 4.95 (*978-0-936981-50-5(4)) Isha Enterprises, Inc.

—Easy Grammar Grade 5 Student Test Booklet. 2006. pap. 4.95 (*978-0-936981-51-2(2)) Isha Enterprises, Inc.

—Easy Grammar Grade 5 Student Workbook. 2006. pap. 13.95 (*978-0-936981-45-1(8)) Isha Enterprises, Inc.

—Easy Grammar Grade 6 Student Test Booklet. 2006. pap. 4.95 (*978-0-936981-52-9(0)) Isha Enterprises, Inc.

—Easy Grammar Grade 6 Student Workbook. 2006. pap. 13.95 (*978-0-936981-46-8(6)) Isha Enterprises, Inc.

—Easy Grammar Plus Student Test Booklet. 2006. pap. 4.95 (*978-0-936981-53-6(9)) Isha Enterprises, Inc.

Polon, Linda Beth. Storywriting: Grades 1-3. 2004. (Illus.). 88p. (gr. 1-3). pap. (978-0-673-57580-7(2)) Good Year Bks.

—Storywriting: Grades 4-6. 2004. (Illus.). 88p. (gr. 4-6). pap. (978-0-673-57726-9(0)) Good Year Bks.

Prentice-Hall Staff. PH Grammar & Composition. 3rd ed. (J). (978-0-13-708926-0(0)); (978-0-13-708934-5(1)); (978-0-13-708942-0(2)); (978-0-13-708868-3(X)) Prentice Hall (Schl. Div.).

Prior, Jennifer Overend. How to Write a Simple Report. Guckian, Mary Ellen, ed. Tanner, Andi, illus. 1999. (How to Ser.). 48p. (J). (gr. k-3). pap., act. bk. ed. 7.99 (978-1-57690-502-9(0) , TCA2502) Teacher Created Materials, Inc.

Raintree Steck-Vaughn Staff, contrib. by. Think Alongs: Level A. 1999. (J). (ps-3). pap. 13.26 (978-0-7398-0083-6(3)) Steck-Vaughn.

—Think Alongs: Level B. 1999. (J). (ps-3). pap. 13.26 (978-0-7398-0084-3(1)); pap. 12.10 (978-0-7398-0090-4(6)) Steck-Vaughn.

—Think Alongs: Level C. 1999. (J). (ps-3). pap. 13.26 (978-0-7398-0085-0(X)); pap. 12.10 (978-0-7398-0091-1(4)) Steck-Vaughn.

—Think Alongs: Level D. 1999. (J). (ps-3). pap. 13.26 (978-0-7398-0086-7(8)); pap. 12.10 (978-0-7398-0092-8(2)) Steck-Vaughn.

—Think Alongs: Level E. 1999. (J). (ps-3). pap. 13.26 (978-0-7398-0087-4(6)); pap. 12.10 (978-0-7398-0093-5(0)) Steck-Vaughn.

—Think Alongs: Level F. 1999. (J). (ps-3). pap. 13.26 (978-0-7398-0088-1(4)); pap. 12.10 (978-0-7398-0094-2(9)) Steck-Vaughn.

Rasmussen, Greta & Rasmussen, Ted. Just Write! Strategies to Build Writing Skill & Confidence. 1999. (Illus.). 112p. (J). (gr. 2-6). pap. 12.95 (978-0-936110-22-6(8)) Tin Man Pr.

Rawlings Miller, Carol. Overhead Writing Lessons: Exceptional Essays. 2005. (Overhead Writing Lessons Ser.). (Illus.). 48p. (gr. 5 up). pap. 12.99 (978-0-439-22258-7(3) , Teaching Resources) Scholastic, Inc.

Reilly, Geoff & Wren, Wendy. Skills in Fiction, Bk. 1. 2002. 112p. pap. (978-0-7487-6541-6(7)) Nelson Thornes Ltd.

—Skills in Non-Fiction, Bk. 1. 2002. 112p. pap. (978-0-7487-6542-3(5)) Nelson Thornes Ltd.

Rief, Linda, et al. 100 Quickwrites. 2003. (Illus.). 128p. pap. 17.99 (978-0-439-45877-1(3) , Teaching Resources) Scholastic, Inc.

Rol 'N' Write Handwriting Activity Worksheets. 48p. spiral bd. 19.99 (978-0-7424-1583-6(X) , LL00977) School Specialty Publishing.

Rondeau, Amanda. Base + Ball = Baseball. 2004. (Compound Words Ser.). (Illus.). 23p. (J). (ps-3). lib. bdg. 19.93 (978-1-59197-430-7(5)) ABDO Publishing Co.

—Bed + Time = Bedtime. 2004. (Compound Words Ser.). (Illus.). 23p. (J). (ps-3). lib. bdg. 19.93 (978-1-59197-431-4(3)) ABDO Publishing Co.

—Key + Board = Keyboard. 2004. (Compound Words Ser.). (Illus.). 23p. (J). (ps-3). lib. bdg. 19.93 (978-1-59197-434-5(8)) ABDO Publishing Co.

—Pan + Cake = Pancake. 2004. (Compound Words Ser.). (Illus.). 23p. (J). (ps-3). lib. bdg. 19.93 (978-1-59197-435-2(6)) ABDO Publishing Co.

—Sun + Screen = Sunscreen. 2004. (Compound Words Ser.). (Illus.). 23p. (J). (ps-3). lib. bdg. 19.93 (978-1-59197-440-6(2)) ABDO Publishing Co.

Roy, Jennifer Rozines. You Can Write Using Good Grammar. 2004. (You Can Write Ser.). (Illus.). 64p. (J). lib. bdg. 22.60 (978-0-7660-2084-9(3)) Enslow Pubs., Inc.

Roy, Jennifer Rozines & Haney, Johannah. You Can Write an Essay. 2004. (You Can Write Ser.). (Illus.). 64p. (J). lib. bdg. 22.60 (978-0-7660-2091-7(6)) Enslow Pubs., Inc.

Russell, Hilary. The Portable Writer. 2nd ed. 1998. 128p. (YA). (gr. 9-12). pap. 10.60 (978-1-877653-47-6(0)) Wayside Publishing.

Schofield, Tracey Ann. 101 Creative Writing Activities for Aspiring Authors. Mitchell, Judy, ed. Glikin, Alex, illus. 2000. 96p. (J). (gr. 3-6). pap., tchr. ed. 10.95 (978-1-57310-240-7(7)) Teaching & Learning Co.

Scholastic, Inc. Staff. Scholastic Explains Writing Homework: Everything Children (& Parents) Need to Survive 2nd & 3rd Grade. 1998. (Scholastic Explains Ser.). (Illus.). 64p. (J). (gr. 2-4). 14.95 (978-0-590-39756-8(7)) Scholastic, Inc.

—Thematic Writing Paper. 1999. pap. 9.95 (978-0-590-66697-8(5)) Scholastic, Inc.

School Specialty Publishing. Book Reports, Grades 2-3. 2006. (Frank Schaffer Classic Reproducibles Ser.). 48p. (J). (gr. 2-3). pap. 6.99 (978-0-7682-3512-8(X) , Schaffer, Frank) Schaffer, Frank Pubns.

Sevaly, Karen & Sevaly, Richard. Word Wall Workbook - Contractions & Compound Words! Skill Based Worksheets & Reproducible Word Cards for Each Group of Words! Sevaly, Karen, illus. l.t. ed. 1999. (Illus.). 80p. (J). (gr. 1-3). pap., wbk. ed. 9.95 (978-1-57882-029-0(4) , TF-2431) Teacher's Friend Pubns., Inc.

Simonson, Leslie. The Expository Writing Handbook: How to Write an Expository Composition. 1998. (Writing in Narrative). 48p. (YA). (gr. 6-12). pap. 5.95 (978-1-884098-14-7(2)) Elijah Co.

Smith, Susan C. & Shiras, Rosemary. Paragraph Writing Made Easy: 8 Classroom-Tested Lessons & Motivating Practice Pages That Teach Kids to Write Organized, Detailed, & Powerful Paragraphs. 2001. 80p. pap. 11.95 (978-0-439-20764-5(9)) Scholastic, Inc.

Spencer, Lauren. A Step-By-Step Guide to Descriptive Writing. 2005. (Illus.). 48p. (J). (gr. 5-8). lib. bdg. 26.50 (978-1-4042-0212-2(9)) Rosen Publishing Group, Inc., The.

Steck-Vaughn Staff. Core Skills Reading Comprehension. 2002. (Illus.). (J). (gr. 1). pap. (978-0-7398-5729-8(0)); (gr. 2). pap. (978-0-7398-5730-4(4)); (gr. 3). pap. (978-0-7398-5731-1(2)); (gr. 4). pap. (978-0-7398-5732-8(0)); (gr. 5). pap. 9.99 (978-0-7398-5733-5(9)); (gr. 6). pap. (978-0-7398-5734-2(7)) Steck-Vaughn.

—Middle School Sentences. 1999. (Illus.). (J). pap. (978-0-7398-1303-4(X)) Steck-Vaughn.

—Summarizing to Improve Comprehension. 1999. (Illus.). (J). (gr. 2). pap. (978-0-7398-2051-3(6)); (gr. 3). pap. (978-0-7398-2052-0(4)); (gr. 4). pap. (978-0-7398-2053-7(2)); (gr. 5). pap. 7.99 (978-0-7398-2054-4(0)); (gr. 6). pap. (978-0-7398-2055-1(9)) Steck-Vaughn.

—Weekly Language Practice. (Illus.). (J). 2002. (gr. 1). pap. (978-0-7398-5359-7(7)); 2000. (gr. 3). pap. (978-0-7398-3435-0(5)); 2000. (gr. 4). pap. 12.99 (978-0-7398-3436-7(3)); 2000. (gr. 5). pap. (978-0-7398-3437-4(1)) Steck-Vaughn.

—Write to the Top. 2002. (YA). (gr. 7). tchr. ed. 23.70 (978-0-7398-6489-0(0)) Harcourt Trade Pubs.

—Write to the Top. 2002. (J). (gr. 3). tchr. ed. (978-0-7398-6485-2(8)); (J). (gr. 4). tchr. ed. (978-0-7398-6486-9(6)); (J). (gr. 5). tchr. ed. (978-0-7398-6487-6(4)); (J). (gr. 6). tchr. ed. (978-0-7398-6488-3(2)); (YA). (gr. 8). tchr. ed. (978-0-7398-6475-3(0)); (Illus.). (J). (gr. 3). (978-0-7398-6480-7(7)); (Illus.). (J). (gr. 4). (978-0-7398-6481-4(5)); (Illus.). (J). (gr. 5). (978-0-7398-6482-1(3)); (Illus.). (J). (gr. 6). (978-0-7398-6483-8(1)); (Illus.). (YA). (gr. 7). (978-0-7398-6484-5(X)); (Illus.). (YA). (gr. 8). (978-0-7398-6473-9(4)) Steck-Vaughn.

Storm, Wilda. Write up A Storm! ¿ Practice for Proficiency: Student Handbook 3rd Grade. 2007. ring bd. (*978-0-9772935-8-2(0)) DoveTail Hse., Inc.

—Write up A Storm! ¿ Practice for Proficiency: Student Handbook 4th Grade. 2007. ring bd. (*978-0-9772935-9-9(9)) DoveTail Hse., Inc.

—Write up A Storm! ¿ Writing Tools: A Student Guide ¿ Grade 2-3. 2007. ring bd. (*978-0-9772935-5-1(6)) DoveTail Hse., Inc.

—Write up A Storm! Take Rewarding Revisions by Storm. 2007. ring bd. (*978-0-9772935-2-0(1)) DoveTail Hse., Inc.

Story Frames: Creative Writing Quickies for Building Grammar & Vocabulary Skills. (Basic Skills Ser.). 48p. (gr. 2-3). 5.99 (978-0-7424-0239-3(8) , IF5608); (gr. 4-5). 5.99 (978-0-7424-0240-9(1) , IF5609) School Specialty Publishing.

Strausser, Jeffrey. Painless Writing. Gilgannon, Denise, illus. 2001. (Barron's Painless Ser.). 256p. pap. 8.99 (978-0-7641-1810-4(2)) Barron's Educational Series, Inc.

—Painless Writing. 2001. (gr. 5-8). lib. bdg. 17.60 (978-0-613-52781-1(X)) Tandem Library Bks.

Tannenbaum, Judith. Running Records: A Self-Tutoring Guide. Stratton, Philippa, ed. 2000. 64p. (J). (gr. k-8). 22.50 (978-1-57110-321-5(X)) Stenhouse Pubs.

Thomson, Ruth. Go Further with Grammar. 2002. (Adventures in Literacy Ser.). (Illus.). 32p. (J). lib. bdg. 24.25 (978-1-931983-07-5(0)) Chrysalis Education.

—Grammar Is Great! 2002. (Adventures in Literacy Ser.). (Illus.). 32p. (J). lib. bdg. 24.25 (978-1-931983-06-8(2)) Chrysalis Education.

Thurston, Cheryl Miller & DiPrince, Dawn. Un-Journaling: Daily Writing Exercises That Are Not Personal, Not Introspective, Not Boring! 2006. 128p. (J). pap. 12.95 (978-1-877673-70-2(6)) Cottonwood Pr., Inc.

Tyler, Jenny & Gee, R. Ready for Writing. 2004. (First Learning Ser.). (Illus.). 24p. (J). (ps up). pap., act. bk. ed. 4.99 (978-0-7460-3520-7(9)) EDC Publishing.

Warriner. Holt Middle School Handbook Holt Science. 1998. (YA). 36.60 (978-0-03-094637-0(9)) Holt, Rinehart & Winston.

Weeks, Stephanie. I Like Writing! Weeks, Stephanie, illus. 2001. (Chalk It up to Learning Ser.). (Illus.). 10p. (J). (ps-3). bds. 8.95 (978-1-57091-366-2(8)) Charlesbridge Publishing, Inc.

Windsor, Laura. Term Papers - The Honest Way: A Guide to Help Students Research & Write Term Papers—On Their Own! Scherer, Daniel, ed. 1998. (Illus.). 16p. (YA). (gr. 7-12). pap. 3.95 (978-0-918734-98-3(3)) Reymont Assocs.

Writing to Explain. 2003. 64p. (J). (gr. 3-6). pap. 9.99 (978-0-7424-1837-0(5) , IFG99069) School Specialty Publishing.

Writing to Persuade. 2003. 64p. (J). (gr. 3-6). pap. 9.99 (978-0-7424-1839-4(1) , IFG99071) School Specialty Publishing.

Writing Works with NC Wordcrafter & Joey: Grade 3+ 2004. 28.00 (*978-0-9790796-0-3(8)) PJR Assocs., Ltd.

Writing Works with NC Wordcrafter & Joey: Grade 4+ 2004. 28.00 (*978-0-9790796-1-0(6)) PJR Assocs., Ltd.

Writing Works with NC Wordcrafter & Joey: Grade 5+ 2004. 28.00 (*978-0-9790796-2-7(4)) PJR Assocs., Ltd.

Young, Sue K. Writing with Style. 1999. (Scholastic Guides Ser.). 144p. (J). (gr. 3-7). pap. 8.95 (978-0-590-25424-3(3)) Scholastic, Inc.

ENGLISH LANGUAGE—CONVERSATION AND PHRASE BOOKS

see English Language—Textbooks for Foreign Speakers
see use subdivision conversation and phrase books for languages other than english

ENGLISH LANGUAGE—DICTIONARIES

Addison-Wesley Publishing Staff. Thorndike Barnhart Children's Dictionary. 1998. (Illus.). 770p. (J). (gr. 3-5). 17.95 (978-0-673-12450-0(9) , Scott Foresman) Addison Wesley Schl.

Allen, Robert. Oxford School Thesaurus. rev. ed. 592p. (978-0-19-911125-1(1)) Oxford Univ. Pr., Inc.

American Heritage Dictionary. 2001. (gr. 7-12). lib. bdg. 14.15 (978-0-613-36174-3(1)); lib. bdg. 22.20 (978-0-613-45356-1(5)) Tandem Library Bks.

American Heritage Dictionary Editors, ed. The American Heritage Children's Dictionary. 2006. (Illus.). 864p. (J). (gr. 3-5). 17.95 (978-0-618-70140-7(0)) Houghton Mifflin Co. Trade & Reference Div.

American Heritage Publishing Staff. American Heritage Dictionary. 4th ed. 2001. (Illus.). (J). 12.64 (978-0-606-21028-7(8)) Tandem Library Bks.

Anderson, Alasdair & MacLeod, Isabail, eds. Early Word Skills: Exercises. 1999. (Illus.). 20p. (J). (gr. 1-2). 29.00 (978-0-7217-0674-0(6)) Schofield & Sims Ltd. GBR. *Dist:* State Mutual Bk. & Periodical Service, Ltd.

—Early Words Dictionary. 1999. (Illus.). 172p. (J). (gr. 1-2). 29.00 (978-0-7217-0672-6(X)) Schofield & Sims Ltd. GBR. *Dist:* State Mutual Bk. & Periodical Service, Ltd.

—A Keyword Dictionary. 1999. (Illus.). 252p. (J). (gr. 2-3). pap. 39.00 (978-0-7217-0677-1(0)) Schofield & Sims Ltd. GBR. *Dist:* State Mutual Bk. & Periodical Service, Ltd.

—A Keyword Dictionary: Exercises. 1999. (Illus.). 40p. (J). (gr. 2-3). pap. 39.00 (978-0-7217-0678-8(9)) Schofield & Sims Ltd. GBR. *Dist:* State Mutual Bk. & Periodical Service, Ltd.

Ashley, Susan. I Can Use a Dictionary. 2004. (Illus.). 24p. (J). pap. (978-0-8368-4333-0(9)); lib. bdg. 19.33 (978-0-8368-4326-2(6)) Stevens, Gareth Inc.

Berlitz Publishing Staff, ed. Italian. Demarest, Chris L., illus. 2nd ed. 2004. (Berlitz Kids Ser.). (ITA & ENG.). 128p. (ps-4). pap. 12.95 (978-981-246-390-6(9) , 463909) Berlitz Publishing.

Berner, Beth Engelman & Heaven, Sarah. The Nick Dictionary. 2005. (Illus.). 160p. (J). (ps-7). 14.95 (978-0-8118-4953-1(8)) Chronicle Bks. LLC.

Bliss, Bill & Molinsky, Steven J. Phonics Picture Dictionary, Paperback, Word by Word Phonics. 1999. (Illus.). 236p. (C). pap. 23.67 (978-0-13-022171-1(6)) Pearson ESL.

Bollard, John. Scholastic Pocket Thesaurus. 2005. 272p. (J). (ps-7). pap. 6.95 (978-0-439-62037-6(6) , Scholastic Reference) Scholastic, Inc.

Bollard, John K. Scholastic Children's Thesaurus. Reed, Mike, illus. rev. ed. 2006. 240p. (J). pap. 16.99 (978-0-439-79831-0(0) , Scholastic Reference) Scholastic, Inc.

Brooks, F. & Litchfield, J. Picture Dictionary: A First Alphabetical Word Book. 2004. (Picture Dictionaries Ser.). 96p. (J). lib. bdg. 24.95 (978-1-58086-437-4(6)) EDC Publishing.

Burchers, Sam, III, et al. The Unofficial SAT Word Dictionary: The Book the College Board Didn't Want You to See. 2002. 456p. (YA). (gr. 7-12). pap. 9.95 (978-0-9652422-5-7(0)) New Monic Bks.

Burnie, David. Dictionary of Nature: Concise Encylcopedia of Nature. 2003. (Illus.). 192p. (YA). (gr. 8-10). reprint ed. pap. 10.00 (978-0-7567-5571-3(9)) DIANE Publishing Co.

Cartwright, Stephen, illus. First Thousand Words in English. 2004. (First Thousand Words Ser.). 64p. (J). lib. bdg. 20.95 (978-1-58086-474-9(0)) EDC Publishing.

Caso, Adolph. The KaSO English to Italian Dictionary: With a Proposed One-to-One Relationship of Italian Graphemes (Letters) & Phonemes (Sounds) 2003. 525p. pap. 19.95 (978-0-8283-2082-5(9)) Branden Bks.

COBUILD Staff, contrib. by. Collins COBUILD New Student's Dictionary. 2nd ed. 2002. (Illus.). 1088p. pap., stu. ed. 24.00 (978-0-00-712034-5(6)) Zondervan.

Collin, Peter Hodgson. Children's English Dictionary. 2001. 280p. (978-1-901659-86-3(0) , T&AD Poyser) A & C Black.

Corbeil, Jean-Claude & Archambault, Adrienne. Scholastic Visual Dictionary. 2000. (Core Reference Ser.). (Illus.). 224p. (J). (ps-3). pap. 21.95 (978-0-439-05940-4(2) , Scholastic Reference) Scholastic, Inc.

Corbeil, Jean-Claude & Archambault, Ariane. The Firefly Junior Visual Dictionary. 2006. (Illus.). 344p. (J). (gr. 5-12). 19.95 (978-1-55407-189-0(5)) Firefly Bks., Ltd.

Costello, Robert B. & Simon and Schuster Staff. Macmillan Dictionary for Children. 2nd rev. ed. 2001. (Illus.). 912p. (J). pap. 17.95 (978-0-689-84323-5(2)) Simon & Schuster Children's Publishing.

Cox, Steve, illus. Barron's First Thesaurus. 2005. 128p. (J). pap. 12.95 (978-0-7641-3159-2(1)) Barron's Educational Series, Inc.

Darley, W. L. An Easy Dictionary. 1999. 144p. (J). (gr. 2-4). 35.00 (978-0-7217-0035-9(7)) Schofield & Sims Ltd. GBR. *Dist:* State Mutual Bk. & Periodical Service, Ltd.

—An Easy Dictionary: Look It Up (Exercises) 1999. 48p. (J). (gr. 2-4). 35.00 (978-0-7217-0081-6(0)) Schofield & Sims Ltd. GBR. *Dist:* State Mutual Bk. & Periodical Service, Ltd.

—An Illustrated Dictionary. 1999. (Illus.). 192p. (J). (gr. 1-3). pap. 39.00 (978-0-7217-0455-5(7)) Schofield & Sims Ltd. GBR. *Dist:* State Mutual Bk. & Periodical Service, Ltd.

—An Illustrated Dictionary: Exercises. 1999. (Illus.). 46p. (J). (gr. 1-3). pap. 39.00 (978-0-7217-0676-4(2)) Schofield & Sims Ltd. GBR. *Dist:* State Mutual Bk. & Periodical Service, Ltd.

Delahunty, Andrew. Oxford School Dictionary. 4th rev. ed. 832p. (978-0-19-911301-9(7)) Oxford Univ. Pr., Inc.

Demarest, Chris L. Berlitz Kids English Picture Dictionary. Demarest, L. & Chris, L., eds. 2005. (Berlitz Picture Dictionaries Ser.). (Illus.). 128p. (J). pap. 12.95 (978-981-246-654-9(1) , 466541) Berlitz Publishing.

DK Publishing. Merriam-Webster Children's Dictionary. 2008. 1000p. (J). (gr. 1-4). 21.99 (***978-0-7566-3758-3(9)***) Dorling Kindersley Publishing, Inc.

Dorling Kindersley Publishing Staff. Barbie My Picture Dictionary. 2005. (Illus.). 48p. (J). 12.99 (978-0-7566-1007-4(9)) Dorling Kindersley Publishing, Inc.

—DK Concise Dictionary/Thesaurus: Over 70,000 Definitions & Synonyms. 1999. 512p. (J). (gr. 4-7). pap. 11.99 (978-0-7894-3949-9(2)) Dorling Kindersley Publishing, Inc.

—DK Dictionary Thesaurus: Over 100,000 Definitions & Synonyms. 1999. (Illus.). (978-0-606-20632-7(9)) Tandem Library Bks.

—English Dictionary. 2003. (gr. 3-6). lib. bdg. 15.30 (978-0-613-75188-9(4)) Tandem Library Bks.

Dorling Kindersley Publishing Staff, contrib. by. English Dictionary. 2nd ed. 2003. (Pockets Ser.). 512p. (J). (gr. 3). pap. 6.99 (978-0-7894-9598-3(8)) Dorling Kindersley Publishing, Inc.

Dorling Kindersley Publishing Staff, creator. Merriam-Webster Children's Dictionary. 2005. (Illus.). 912p. (J). (gr. 8-7). 19.99 (978-0-7566-1143-9(1)) Dorling Kindersley Publishing, Inc.

Douglas, Vincent & School Specialty Publishing Staff. The AEP Children's Dictionary. 2002. (Wordsmyth Reference Ser.). (Illus.). 960p. (J). (gr. 3 up). 24.95 (978-1-57768-298-1(X)) School Specialty Publishing.

—Spanish-English Picture Dictionary. 2004. (ENG & SPA., Illus.). 48p. (J). 9.95 (978-0-7696-3526-2(1) , Waterbird Bks.) School Specialty Publishing.

—Thesaurus. Notebk Referenc, ed. 2nd rev. ed. 2006. (Notebook Reference Ser.). 144p. (J). pap. 3.95 (978-0-7696-4344-1(2) , American Education Publishing) School Specialty Publishing.

—Webster's Dictionary. Notebk Referenc, ed. 2nd rev. ed. 2006. (Notebook Reference Ser.). 144p. (J). pap. 3.95 (978-0-7696-4341-0(8) , American Education Publishing) School Specialty Publishing.

Dumont, Deborah, intro. Hippocrene Children's Illustrated Arabic Dictionary: English-Arabic/Arabic-English. 2002. (Children's Illustrated Foreign Language Dictionaries Ser.). (ARA & ENG., Illus.). 122p. (gr. k-5). pap. 11.95 (978-0-7818-0891-0(X)) Hippocrene Bks., Inc.

Eason, Cassandra. Bamboo's Super Dictionary. 1998. (Illus.). 20p. (J). (ps-1). 7.95 (978-0-8069-9510-6(6)) Sterling Publishing Co., Inc.

Edmonds, David. Oxford Reverse Dictionary. 2002. (gr. 7-12). lib. bdg. 25.70 (978-0-613-64992-6(3)) Tandem Library Bks.

Feldman, Thea & Benjamin, Alan. Disney Picture Dictionary. 2003. (Illus.). 144p. (ps-2). 14.99 (978-0-7868-3385-6(8)) Disney Pr.

First Dictionary. (J). 2003. (Illus.). 96p. 7.98 (978-1-4054-0519-5(8)); 2000. 64p. 9.98 (978-0-7525-3811-2(X)) Parragon, Inc.

First Dictionary. (gr. k-3). 52p. 22.95 (978-0-322-01559-3(6)); 42p. act. bk. ed. 20.95 (978-0-322-01560-9(X)) Wright Group, The.

Gage Canadian Junior Dictionary. 2000. (Canadian Reference Ser.). (Illus.). 800p. (J). (gr. 3-8). 24.95 (978-0-7715-1997-0(4)) Gage Learning Corp. CAN. *Dist:* CDG Bks. Canada, Inc.

Gage Educational Publishing Staff. Gage Canadian School Dictionary. 2000. 384p. (J). (gr. 3-7). pap. 16.95 (978-0-7715-2005-1(0)) Gage Learning Corp. CAN. *Dist:* CDG Bks. Canada, Inc.

Goodman, Marlene. Let's Learn English Picture Dictionary. 2003. (Illus.). 80p. 10.95 (978-0-07-140822-6(3) , 9780071408226) McGraw-Hill Cos., The.

—Let's Learn Italian Picture Dictionary. 2003. (ENG & ITA., Illus.). 80p. 10.95 (978-0-07-140826-4(6) , 9780071408264) McGraw-Hill Cos., The.

—Let's Learn Japanese Picture Dictionary. 2003. (JPN & ENG., Illus.). 80p. 11.95 (978-0-07-140827-1(4) , 9780071408271) McGraw-Hill Cos., The.

Gould, Vera Dobson & Hughes, Patricia J. The Dominie Thesaurus for Young Writers. 2003. 393p. (J). 18.95 (978-0-7685-2298-3(6)) Dominie Pr., Inc.

Grapham, Jock & Lister, Marie. First School Dictionary. Strickland, S. & Quigley, S., illus. 2001. 184p. (J). 13.95 (978-0-7641-5434-8(6)) Barron's Educational Series, Inc.

Greenwood, Elinor, ed. DK First Dictionary & Thesaurus: Grammar, Definitions, Sentences, Pronunciations, Spelling Tips, Words Games. 2002. (Illus.). 256p. (J). (gr. k-3). 15.99 (978-0-7894-8579-3(6)) Dorling Kindersley Publishing, Inc.

Griesewood, John. The Kingfisher First Dictionary. 2001. (Illus.). (J). (978-0-606-21282-3(5)) Tandem Library Bks.

Grisewood, John. Little Dictionary. 2003. lib. bdg. 18.75 (978-0-613-65582-8(6)) Tandem Library Bks.

Hagin, Sally, tr. & illus. Milet Mini Picture Dictionary. Hagin, Sally, illus. 2003. (Milet Mini Picture Dictionary Ser.). (ENG & BEN.). 28p. (J). bds. 7.99 (978-1-84059-370-9(9)) Milet Publishing.

Harrap. French Student's Dictionary. (ENG & FRE., Illus.). 800p. (978-0-245-60676-2(9)) Harrap, Larousse Pubs.

Hayward, Linda. The Sesame Street Dictionary. Mathieu, Joe, illus. 2004. 256p. (J). (ps-3). 24.99 (978-0-375-82810-2(9) , Random Hse. Bks. for Young Readers) Random Hse. Children's Bks.

Hippocrene Books, ed. Chinese Children's Picture Dictionary: English-Chinese/Chinese-English. 2006. (Illus.). 114p. pap. 14.95 (978-0-7818-1161-3(9)) Hippocrene Bks., Inc.

—Hebrew Children's Picture Dictionary: English-Hebrew/Hebrew-English. 2006. (Illus.). 114p. pap. 14.95 (978-0-7818-1163-7(5)) Hippocrene Bks., Inc.

—Norwegian Children's Picture Dictionary: English-Norwegian/Norwegian-English. 2006. (Illus.). 114p. pap. 14.95 (978-0-7818-1164-4(3)) Hippocrene Bks., Inc.

Hippocrene Children's Illustrated Norwegian Dictionary: English-Norwegian/Norwegian-English. 2002. (Children's Illustrated Foreign Language Dictionaries Ser.). (ENG & NOR., Illus.). 94p. (gr. k-5). pap. 11.95 (978-0-7818-0887-3(1)) Hippocrene Bks., Inc.

Hippocrene Children's Illustrated Polish Dictionary: English-Polish/Polish-English. 2002. (Children's Illustrated Foreign Language Dictionaries Ser.). (ENG & POL., Illus.). 94p. (gr. k-5). pap. 11.95 (978-0-7818-0890-3(1)) Hippocrene Bks., Inc.

Hippocrene Children's Illustrated Portuguese Dictionary: English-Portuguese/Portuguese-English. 2002. (Children's Illustrated Foreign Language Dictionaries Ser.). (ENG & POR., Illus.). 94p. (gr. k-5). pap. 11.95 (978-0-7818-0886-6(3)) Hippocrene Bks., Inc.

Hippocrene Children's Illustrated Russian Dictionary: English-Russian/Russian-English. 2002. (Children's Illustrated Foreign Language Dictionaries Ser.). (ENG & RUS., Illus.). 96p. (gr. k-5). pap. 11.95 (978-0-7818-0892-7(8)) Hippocrene Bks., Inc.

Hobson, E. W., compiled by. A Basic Dictionary. 1999. 187p. (J). (gr. 3-6). pap. 35.00 (978-0-7217-0375-6(5)) Schofield & Sims Ltd. GBR. *Dist:* State Mutual Bk. & Periodical Service, Ltd.

—A Basic Dictionary: Exercises. 1999. (Illus.). 56p. (J). (gr. 3-8). pap. 35.00 (978-0-7217-0376-3(3)) Schofield & Sims Ltd. GBR. *Dist:* State Mutual Bk. & Periodical Service, Ltd.

Hochstatter, Daniel J. Italian. 2003. (ENG & ITA., Illus.). 96p. 11.95 (978-0-07-140830-1(4) , 9780071408301) McGraw-Hill Cos., The.

—Just Look 'n Learn English Picture Dictionary. 2003. (Illus.). 96p. 11.95 (978-0-07-140833-2(9) , 9780071408332) McGraw-Hill Cos., The.

Hochstatter, Daniel J., contrib. by. Just Look 'n Learn English Picture Dictionary. 2003. (Just Look 'n Learn Picture Dictionary Ser.). (Illus.). 96p. (J). (gr. 4-7). 11.95 (978-0-8442-5022-9(8) , 50228, Passport Bks.) McGraw-Hill Trade.

Hubbard, L. Ron. How to Use a Dictionary: Picture Book for Children. 2000. (gr. 3-6). lib. bdg. 30.35 (978-0-613-82778-2(3)) Tandem Library Bks.

Hubbard, L.Ron. How to Use a Dictionary: Picture Book for Children. 2000. (CHI., Illus.). 296p. (gr. 3-7). per. 19.95 (978-1-58460-007-7(1)) Effective Education Publishing.

IDEA Picture Dictionary: An IDEA Language Development Resource. 2004. (Illus.). (J). 152p. (978-1-55501-523-7(9)); 200p. (978-1-55501-522-0(0)) Ballard & Tighe Pubs.

Johnson, JoAnne, et al. Picture Perfect Dictionary 1. 1999. (Illus.). 128p. (J). (gr. 1-4). 17.91 (978-0-7362-0181-0(5)) Hampton-Brown Bks.

Jolivet, Joelle. Almost Everything. Siegel, Alexis, tr. from FRE. Jolivet, Joelle, illus. 2005. (Illus.). 40p. (J). (ps-3). 19.95 (978-1-59643-090-7(7)) Roaring Brook Pr.

Karapetian, Marjam. Bilingual Content Dictionary: English to Armenian. 2004. (ARM & ENG.). 4.95 (978-0-9767958-2-7(5)); 9.95 (978-0-9767958-4-1(1)); 4.95 (978-0-9767958-3-4(3)); 13.95 (978-0-9767958-6-5(8)); 15.95 (978-0-9767958-7-2(6)) WizdomInc.

—Bilingual Content Dictionary: English to Armenian: Social Studies - American History Through 1776. 2004. (ARM & ENG.). 14.95 (978-0-9767958-5-8(X)) WizdomInc.

—Bilingual Content Dictionary: English to Korean. 2004. (KOR & ENG.). 4.95 (978-0-9764829-7-0(5)); 4.95 (978-0-9764829-6-3(7)); 13.95 (978-0-9767958-0-3(9)); 9.95 (978-0-9764829-8-7(3)); 15.95 (978-0-9767958-1-0(7)) WizdomInc.

—Bilingual Content Dictionary: English to Korean: Social Studies - American History Through 1776. 2004. (KOR & ENG.). 14.95 (978-0-9764829-9-4(1)) WizdomInc.

—Bilingual Content Dictionary: English to Mandarin Chinese. 2004. (CHI & ENG.). 4.95 (978-0-9768053-0-4(8)); 4.95 (978-0-9768053-1-1(6)); 9.95 (978-0-9768053-2-8(4)); 13.95 (978-0-9768053-4-2(0)); 15.95 (978-0-9768053-5-9(9)) WizdomInc.

—Bilingual Content Dictionary: English to Mandarin Chinese: Social Studies - American History Through 1776. 2004. (CHI & ENG.). 14.95 (978-0-9768053-3-5(2)) WizdomInc.

Kauffman, Dorothy. Overhead Transparencies: Workbook. 2000. (Illus.). (J). (978-0-606-20845-1(3)) Tandem Library Bks.

Kauffman, Dorothy & Apple, Gary. Content Areas. 2000. (Oxford Picture Dictionary for the Content Areas Ser.). (Illus.). 144p. 15.25 (978-0-19-434338-1(3)); 290p. tchr. ed., wbk. ed. 21.95 (978-0-19-434340-4(5)) Oxford Univ. Pr., Inc.

—Overhead Transparencies: Workbook. 2000. (Oxford Picture Dictionary for the Content Areas Ser.). (Illus.). 146p. 24.25 (978-0-19-434336-7(7)) Oxford Univ. Pr., Inc.

—The Oxford Picture Dictionary for the Content Areas: Reproducibles Collection, 4 vols. 2000. (Oxford Picture Dictionary for the Content Areas Ser.). (Illus.). 115.95 (978-0-19-434999-4(3)) Oxford Univ. Pr., Inc.

Kauffman, Dorothy, et al. Overhead Transparencies. 2000. (Oxford Picture Dictionary for the Content Areas Ser.). (Illus.). 64p. wbk. ed. 8.75 (978-0-19-434337-4(5)) Oxford Univ. Pr., Inc.

Keyes, Joan Ross. The Oxford Picture Dictionary for Kids: English-Japanese. Springer, Sally, illus. 1999. (Oxford Picture Dictionary for Kids Ser.). (JPN & ENG.). 153p. 14.25 (978-0-19-436664-9(2)) Oxford Univ. Pr., Inc.

Kingfisher Editors, ed. Kingfisher Illustrated Pocket Dictionary. 2007. (Illus.). 240p. (J). (gr. 5-9). pap. 10.95 (978-0-7534-6116-7(1) , Kingfisher) Houghton Mifflin Co. Trade & Reference Div.

Kipfer, Barbara Ann. Roget's International Thesaurus. 2001. (gr. 7-12). lib. bdg. 26.85 (978-0-613-53551-9(0)) Tandem Library Bks.

La Bretesche, Genevieve de. Scholastic First Picture Dictionary. Manzanero, Paula, ed. Voake, Charlotte, illus. 2005. 112p. (J). pap. 14.95 (978-0-439-71993-3(3) , Scholastic Reference) Scholastic, Inc.

Larousse Staff, et al. Larousse Active Dictionary for Beginners — English-French/ French-English. Rivera, Enrique, illus. 2001. (FRE & ENG.). 64p. (J). (gr. 3-5). tchr. ed. 15.95 (978-2-03-542091-6(1)) Larousse, Editions FRA. *Dist:* Houghton Mifflin Co. Trade & Reference Div.

Law, Felicia. Picture Dictionary: A First See-and-Say Book. Knight, Paula, illus. (Patchwork First Poem Bks.). 24p. (J). (ps-7). 8.95 (978-1-904668-86-2(0)) Mercury Bks. Ltd. GBR. *Dist:* International Publishers Marketing.

Levey, Judith S. Scholastic First Dictionary. rev. ed. 2006. 256p. (J). pap. 16.99 (978-0-439-79834-1(5) , Scholastic Reference) Scholastic, Inc.

Levey, Judith S. & Scholastic, Inc. Staff. Scholastic First Dictionary. 1998. (Scholastic First Dictionary Ser.). (Illus.). 224p. (J). (gr. 1-4). pap. 14.95 (978-0-590-96786-0(X) , Scholastic Reference) Scholastic, Inc.

Lilly, Cordelia. Student's Dictionary. 2004. 1024p. pap. (978-0-00-716228-4(6)) Zondervan.

Longman Publishing Staff & Longman, Joshua. Zak's Activity Dictionary: English for Earthkids, Activity Dictionary. 1999. (Illus.). (C). (gr. 1-7). pap. 17.00 (978-0-582-32793-1(8)) Pearson ESL.

MacLeod, Isabail, et al, eds. A Compact Dictionary. 1999. 236p. (J). (gr. 4-8). 45.00 (978-0-7217-0653-5(3)) Schofield & Sims Ltd. GBR. *Dist:* State Mutual Bk. & Periodical Service, Ltd.

—A Concise Junior Dictionary. 1999. 144p. (J). (gr. 2-4). 35.00 (978-0-7217-0646-7(0)) Schofield & Sims Ltd. GBR. *Dist:* State Mutual Bk. & Periodical Service, Ltd.

—A Concise Junior Dictionary: Exercises. 1999. (Illus.). 40p. (J). (gr. 2-4). 35.00 (978-0-7217-0647-4(9)) Schofield & Sims Ltd. GBR. *Dist:* State Mutual Bk. & Periodical Service, Ltd.

Marshall, George W. The Kingfisher Children's Illustrated Dictionary & Thesaurus. 2003. (Illus.). 320p. (J). (gr. 2-5). tchr. ed. 12.95 (978-0-7534-5653-8(2) , Kingfisher) Houghton Mifflin Co. Trade & Reference Div.

Martin, Robert Stanly, ed. Hippocrene Hindi Children's Picture Dictionary. 2006. 112p. (J). pap. (978-0-7818-1129-3(5)) Hippocrene Bks., Inc.

Marzel, Pepi, illus. My First Hebrew Word Book. 2005. 32p. (J). (ps-2). lib. bdg. 17.95 (978-1-58013-126-1(3)) Kar-Ben Publishing.

Mayer, Mercer. Little Critter's. 2001. (ps-2). lib. bdg. 17.60 (978-0-613-88741-0(7)) Tandem Library Bks.

—Little Critter's. Picture Dictionary. Mayer, Mercer, illus. 2003. (Little Critter's(R) Picture Dictionary Ser.). (Illus.). 144p. (J). (ps up). pap. 8.95 (978-1-57768-839-6(2)) School Specialty Publishing.

McLaughlin, Patrick & MacLeod, Iseaball. In Other Words - A School Thesaurus. 1999. (Illus.). 192p. (J). (gr. 3-7). 45.00 (978-0-7217-0721-1(1)) Schofield & Sims Ltd. GBR. *Dist:* State Mutual Bk. & Periodical Service, Ltd.

McLlwine, John. Collins Shorter School Dictionary. 2nd ed. 2001. (Collins Children's Dictionaries Ser.). 448p. pap. 19.99 (978-0-00-316160-1(9)) HarperCollins Pubs. Ltd. GBR. *Dist:* Independent Pubs. Group.

Merriam-Webster. Merriam-Webster's Elementary Dictionary. 2000. (Illus.). 624p. (J). (gr. 2-5). 15.95 (978-0-87779-575-9(4)) Merriam-Webster, Inc.

—Merriam-Webster's Primary Dictionary. Heller, Ruth, illus. 2005. 448p. (J). (ps-2). 16.95 (978-0-87779-174-4(0) , MER-74) Merriam-Webster, Inc.

Merriam-Webster & Garfield Dictionary. 1999. (gr. 3-6). lib. bdg. 22.20 (978-0-613-23807-6(9)) Tandem Library Bks.

Merriam-Webster, Inc. Staff. Webster's Dictionary for Students. 2003. (Illus.). 480p. 2.49 (978-1-892859-55-6(6)) Federal Street Pr.

Merriam-Webster's Elementary Dictionary. rev. ed. 2000. (gr. 3-6). lib. bdg. 21.05 (978-0-613-23808-3(7)) Tandem Library Bks.

The Merriam-Webster's High School Dictionary. 1998. (YA). (gr. 9-12). 25.60 (978-0-03-096484-8(9)) Holt, Rinehart & Winston.

Miller, Susan A. My First Dictionary. Williams, Ted, illus. 2005. (My First Ser.). 160p. 7.98 (978-0-7853-8369-7(7) , 7183800) Publications International, Ltd.

Molinsky, Steven J. & Bliss, Bill. Word by Word Primary Phonics Picture Dictionary. 2003. (J). (gr. 1-2). wbk. ed. 16.06 (978-0-13-022167-4(8)) Longman Publishing Group.

Morehead, Philip D. New American Roget's College Thesaurus in Dictionary Form. 2002. (gr. 7-12). lib. bdg. 15.30 (978-0-613-52455-1(1)) Tandem Library Bks.

Morgan, Nicola. Two-Can First Dictionary. 2004. (Illus.). 64p. (ps up). 12.95 (978-1-58728-439-7(1) , Creative Publishing International) Quayside.

Morrow, David, ed. Spelling Dictionary. 2nd ed. 2003. (Pockets Ser.). 432p. (J). (gr. 3). pap. 6.99 (978-0-7894-9601-0(1)) Dorling Kindersley Publishing, Inc.

My First Words. 2004. 64p. (J). 9.95 (978-1-59496-000-0(3)) Teora USA LLC.

Nakata, Ritsuko. Let's Go Picture Dictionary: English-Chinese Edition. 1999. (CHI & ENG., Illus.). 139p. (J). 14.25 (978-0-19-435930-6(1)) Oxford Univ. Pr., Inc.

—Let's Go Picture Dictionary: English-Japanese Edition. 1999. (ENG & JPN., Illus.). (J). 14.25 (978-0-19-435929-0(8)) Oxford Univ. Pr., Inc.

Oliver, Archie. First Picture Dictionary. 2004. (Illus.). 96p. (J). (978-1-74121-401-7(7)) Hinkler Bks. Pty. Ltd.

Oxford American Desk Dictionary & Thesaurus. 2001. (gr. 7-12). lib. bdg. 15.30 (978-0-613-36859-9(2)) Tandem Library Bks.

Oxford Essential Business & Office Dictionary. 2002. (gr. 7-12). lib. bdg. 17.60 (978-0-613-64903-2(6)) Tandem Library Bks.

Passport Books Staff, ed. Let's Learn American English. Goodman, Marlene, illus. 2003. (Let's Learn... Picture Dictionary Ser.). 72p. (J). (gr. 4-7). 9.95 (978-0-8442-5453-1(3) , 54533, Passport Bks.) McGraw-Hill Trade.

Picture Dictionary/Thematic Dictionary. 68p. (gr. k-3). 25.50 (978-0-322-01562-3(6)) Wright Group, The.

Random House Staff. English Learner's Dictionary. 2001. (978-0-606-22333-1(9)) Tandem Library Bks.

Riverside Editors. Webster's II Children's Dictionary. 2001. (978-0-606-22397-3(5)) Tandem Library Bks.

Sabato, Nancy, contrib. by. Scholastic Pocket Dictionary. 2005. (Scholastic Reference Ser.). 624p. pap. 7.95 (978-0-439-62039-0(2) , Scholastic Reference) Scholastic, Inc.

Scholastic, Inc. Staff. Picture Dictionary: More Than 35 Real-Life Scenes; More Than 650 Every-Day Words. 1999. (Hello Reader! Ser.). (Illus.). (J). (978-0-606-18558-5(5)) Tandem Library Bks.

—Scholastic Dictionary of Synonyms, Antonyms, Homonyms. 2001. (Core Reference Ser.). (Illus.). 224p. (J). (gr. 5-9). pap. 4.95 (978-0-439-25415-1(9) , Scholastic Reference) Scholastic, Inc.

Scholastic Reference (Firm) Staff, contrib. by. Scholastic Children's Dictionary. rev. ed. 2007. 672p. (J). pap. 18.99 (***978-0-439-70258-4(5)*** , Scholastic Reference) Scholastic, Inc.

School Specialty Publishing. The AEP Dictionary: New Encyclopedic Edition. 2003. (Paperback Dictionary Ser.). 448p. (YA). (gr. 6-12). pap. 2.99 (978-0-7696-3308-4(0) , American Education Publishing) School Specialty Publishing.

Scott, Foresman and Company Staff. Thorndike Barnhart Children's Dictionary. 2000. 36.99 (978-0-673-60338-8(5)) Addison-Wesley Educational Pubs., Inc.

—Thorndike Barnhart Children's Dictionary: Medallion Edition. 1999. (Illus.). 864p. (J). (gr. 3-5). 17.95 (978-0-673-58933-0(1) , Scott Foresman) Addison Wesley Schl.

Shank, Cathy, et al. Collaborations Literacy: Newbury Dictionary. pap., stu. ed. 37.95 (978-0-8384-9487-5(0)) Thomson Heinle.

Shannon, Rosemarie. Franklin's Picture Dictionary. Southern, Shelley, illus. 2005. 112p. (J). (gr. k-3). (978-1-55337-711-5(7)) Kids Can Pr., Ltd.

Shapiro. Oxford Picture Dictionary English. 1999. Tr. of Arabic. (gr. k-3). lib. bdg. 24.55 (978-0-613-83266-3(3)) Tandem Library Bks.

Shapiro, Norma & Adelson-Goldstein, Jayme. The Oxford Picture Dictionary. 1999. (Oxford Picture Dictionary Program Ser.). (CAM & ENG., Illus.). 240p. 15.95 (978-0-19-435194-2(7)) Oxford Univ. Pr., Inc.

—The Oxford Picture Dictionary: American Edition. Kaewsanchai, Nisai, tr. 2002. (Oxford Picture Dictionary Program Ser.). (ENG & THA., Illus.). 216p. 15.95 (978-0-19-435720-3(1)) Oxford Univ. Pr., Inc.

Simon & Schuster. Macmillan Dictionary for Children. 2007. 848p. (J). 19.99 (***978-1-4169-3959-7(8)***) Simon & Schuster Children's Publishing.

—Macmillan Dictionary for Children: 4th Revised Edition. rev. ed. 2005. 896p. (J). 9.95 (978-0-689-86656-2(9)) Simon & Schuster Children's Publishing.

—Macmillan Dictionary for Children: Non Returnable. 2005. 912p. (J). 17.95 (978-0-689-04990-3(0)) Simon & Schuster Children's Publishing.

SunshineTM My First Dictionary. 64p. (gr. k-3). 15.50 (978-0-7802-6168-6(2)) Wright Group, The.

Terban, Marvin. Scholastic Dictionary of Idioms. rev. ed. 2006. 304p. (J). pap. 9.99 (978-0-439-77083-5(1) , Scholastic Reference) Scholastic, Inc.

Thorndike, Edward Lee. Thorndike Barnhart Junior Dictionary. 1998. (Illus.). 1024p. (J). (gr. 3-7). 19.00 (978-0-673-12449-4(5) , Scott Foresman) Addison Wesley Schl.

—Thorndike Barnhart Student Dictionary. 1998. (Illus.). 1328p. (YA). (gr. 7 up). 26.67 (978-0-673-12447-0(9) , Scott Foresman) Addison Wesley Schl.

E
F
G

Turhan, Sedat. Milet Mini Picture Dictionary. Hagin, Sally, tr. Hagin, Sally, illus. 2003. (Milet Mini Picture Dictionary Ser.). 28p. (J). bds. 6.99 (978-1-84059-367-9(9)); (ENG & ALB.). bds. 7.99 (978-1-84059-368-6(7)); (ENG & CHI.). bds. 7.99 (978-1-84059-371-6(7)); (ENG & GER.). bds. 7.99 (978-1-84059-373-0(3)); (ENG & SOM.). bds. 7.99 (978-1-84059-375-4(X)); (ENG & SPA.). bds. 7.99 (978-1-84059-376-1(8)) Milet Publishing.

—Milet Picture Dictionary. 2005. (SIT & ENG., Illus.). 48p. pap. 14.95 (978-1-84059-465-2(9)) Milet Publishing.

—Milet Picture Dictionary. Hagin, Sally, illus. 2003. (Milet Picture Dictionary Ser.). 48p. (J). (ARA & ENG.). 14.95 (978-1-84059-348-8(2)); (BEN, ENG, VIE, SPA & PER.). 14.95 (978-1-84059-349-5(0)); (CHI, ENG, VIE, SPA & PER.). 14.95 (978-1-84059-350-1(4)); (ENG & ITA.). 14.95 (978-1-84059-354-9(7)); (POR & ENG.). 14.95 (978-1-84059-357-0(1)); (SOM, ENG, VIE, SPA & PER.). 14.95 (978-1-84059-359-4(8)); (ALB & ENG.). 14.95 (978-1-84059-347-1(4)); (ENG, TUR, VIE, SPA & PER.). 14.95 (978-1-84059-361-7(X)); (URD & ENG.). 14.95 (978-1-84059-362-4(8)); (ENG & VIE.). 14.95 (978-1-84059-363-1(6)); (KUR, ENG, VIE, SPA & PER.). 14.95 (978-1-84059-365-5(2)); (ENG & SPA.). 14.95 (978-1-84059-360-0(1)); 18th ed. 13.95 (978-1-84059-346-4(6)) Milet Publishing.

—Milet Picture Dictionary: English/Tamil. Hagin, Sally, illus. 2003. (Milet Picture Dictionary Ser.). (TAM & ENG.). 48p. (J). (ps-ps). 14.95 (978-1-84059-467-6(5)) Milet Publishing.

Turhan, Sedat & Hagin, Sally. Milet Mini Picture Dictionary. 2003. (Milet Mini Picture Dictionary Ser.). (ENG & ARA., Illus.). 28p. (J). bds. 7.99 (978-1-84059-369-3(5)); bds. 7.99 (978-1-84059-372-3(5)); bds. 7.99 (978-1-84059-377-8(6)); bds. 7.99 (978-1-84059-378-5(4)); bds. 7.99 (978-1-84059-379-2(2)); bds. 7.99 (978-1-84059-385-3(7)) Milet Publishing.

—Milet Mini Picture Dictionary: English-Tamil. 2005. (Milet Mini Picture Dictionary Ser.). (TAM & ENG., Illus.). 28p. (J). (ps-ps). bds. 7.99 (978-1-84059-475-1(6)) Milet Publishing.

—Milet Picture Dictionary. 2003. (Milet Picture Dictionary Ser.). (Illus.). 48p. (J). (ENG, PER & FAR.). 14.95 (978-1-84059-351-8(2)); (ENG & FRE., 14.95 (978-1-84059-352-5(0)); (ENG & GER., 14.95 (978-1-84059-353-2(9)); (ENG & JPN., 14.95 (978-1-84059-355-6(5)); (KOR & ENG., 14.95 (978-1-84059-356-3(3)); (RUS & ENG., 14.95 (978-1-84059-358-7(X)) Milet Publishing.

Turner, Tracey. Disgusting Dictionary. 2004. (Illus.). (J). (978-0-340-88399-0(5) , Hodder Children's Books) Hodder Children's Division.

The Ultimate Picture Dictionary Workbook. 2002. (Home Learning Tools Ser.). (Illus.). 158p. (J). (gr. 3-4). pap. 4.97 (978-1-57759-124-5(0)) Dalmatian Pr.

Wardley, R. & Bingham, J. First Dictionary. 2004. (Illus.). 144p. (J). (gr. k up). 15.95 (978-0-7945-0145-7(1) , Usborne); lib. bdg. 23.95 (978-1-58086-436-7(8)) EDC Publishing.

Waters, Alison & Wehmeier, Sally, eds. Oxford Student's Dictionary of English. 2003. (Illus.). 17.95 (978-0-19-431517-3(7)) Oxford Univ. Pr., Inc.

Webster's Dictionary & Thesaurus for Students with Full-Color World Atlas. 2006. (Illus.). 880p. pap. 9.98 (978-1-59695-017-7(X)) Federal Street Pr.

Webster's Dictionary for Students. 2003. (gr. 3-6). lib. bdg. 10.10 (978-0-613-68548-1(2)) Tandem Library Bks.

Webster's Dictionary for Students: Special Encyclopedic Edition. 2003. (gr. 3-6). lib. bdg. 10.65 (978-0-613-68549-8(0)) Tandem Library Bks.

Webster's Dictionary New Encyclopedic Edition. 2003. 448p. pap. 2.99 (978-0-7696-1592-9(9)) School Specialty Publishing.

Webster's II Children's Dictionary. 2003. (gr. 3-6). lib. bdg. 25.70 (978-0-613-66556-8(2)) Tandem Library Bks.

Webster's New World Dictionary. 2003. (gr. 7-12). lib. bdg. 13.55 (978-0-613-67593-2(2)) Tandem Library Bks.

Webster's New World Staff. Websters New World College Dictionary: Webster's New World Roget's A-Z Thesaurus, 2 vols. 4th ed. 1999. (Illus.). (J). 39.95 (978-0-02-863559-0(0)) Wiley, John & Sons, Inc.

Wernham, Sara & Lloyd, Sue. Jolly Dictionary (US Ed) North American Edition. 2003. (Jolly Grammar Ser.: DICTIONARY). (Illus.). 300p. per. 9.95 (978-1-84414-001-5(6) , JL016) Jolly Learning, Ltd. GBR. *Dist:* American International Distribution Corp.

Wilkes, Ian. London Rabbit: A Guide to Cockney Rhyming Slang. 2004. (Illus.). 64p. (YA). (gr. 6-12). pap. (978-0-86025-538-3(7)) Henry, Ian Pubns.

Williams, Carol. What's the World for - ? Beth Yw'r Gair Am - ? 2004. (WEL & ENG., Illus.). 160p. (J). pap. (978-0-7083-1736-5(7)) Univ. of Wales Pr.

Windridge, C. Better Words - A First Thesaurus. 1999. 128p. (J). (gr. 2-4). 39.00 (978-0-7217-0501-9(4)) Schofield & Sims Ltd. GBR. *Dist:* State Mutual Bk. & Periodical Service, Ltd.

—Choose Your Words: A School Thesaurus. 1999. 143p. (J). (gr. 4-8). 35.00 (978-0-7217-0377-0(1)) Schofield & Sims Ltd. GBR. *Dist:* State Mutual Bk. & Periodical Service, Ltd.

World Book, Inc. Staff. The World Book Student Dictionary. 1999. (Illus.). 900p. (J). (gr. 2-8). (978-0-7166-1596-5(7) , 6070) World Bk., Inc.

World Book, Inc. Staff, contrib. by. The World Book Student Dictionary. 2001. (Illus.). 43p. (J). (gr. 2-8). 31.00 (978-0-7166-1599-6(1)) World Bk., Inc.

—World Book Student Dictionary. 2003rd ed. 2002. (Illus.). 944p. (J). (978-0-7166-1551-4(7) , 20111) World Bk., Inc.

World Book, Inc. Staff, ed. The World Book Student Dictionary. 2001. (Illus.). 944p. (J). (gr. 2-7). stu. ed. (978-0-7166-1550-7(9) , 20064) World Bk., Inc.

Worth, Bonnie. Oh, Say Can You say Di-No-Saur? 1999. (Cat in the Hat's Learning Library). (Illus.). 48p. (gr. k-3). lib. bdg. 11.99 (978-0-679-99114-4(X) , Random Hse. Bks. for Young Readers) Random Hse. Children's Bks.

Wright. Collins Picture Dictionary for Young Learners. Date not set. (Illus.). (J). pap. (978-0-17-556761-4(1)) Addison-Wesley Longman, Inc.

ENGLISH LANGUAGE—DICTIONARIES—FRENCH

Brooks, Felicity & Mackinnon, Mairi. Picture Dictionary in French. 2004. (Picture Dictionaries Ser.). (FRE & ENG., Illus.). 112p. (J). lib. bdg. 24.95 (978-1-58086-476-3(7)) EDC Publishing.

Demarest, Chris L., illus. French. 2nd ed. 2004. (Berlitz Kids Ser.). (ENG & FRE.). 128p. pap. 12.95 (978-981-246-387-6(9) , 463879) Berlitz Publishing.

Larousse Staff, ed. Larousse Student Dictionary: French-English / English-French. l.t. ed. 2003. (FRE & ENG., Illus.). 732p. (gr. 5). pap. 10.95 (978-2-03-542055-8(5)) Larousse, Editions FRA. *Dist:* Houghton Mifflin Co. Trade & Reference Div.

Lipton, Gladys C. French Bilingual Dictionary: A Beginner's Guide in Words & Pictures. 3rd rev. ed. 1998. (Barron's Bilingual Dictionaries Ser.). (ENG & FRE., Illus.). 180p. (gr. 3 up). pap. 8.99 (978-0-7641-0279-0(6)) Barron's Educational Series, Inc.

McGraw-Hill Staff. McGraw-Hill's French Picture Dictionary. 2004. (ENG & FRE.). 96p. 10.95 (978-0-07-142813-2(5) , 9780071428132) McGraw-Hill Cos., The.

Morton, Lone & Bougard, Marie-Therese. Space Postman/Le Facteur Spatial: English-French Edition. Ursell, Martin, illus. 2005. (I Can Read French Ser.). (FRE & ENG.). 28p. (J). (ps). 7.99 (978-0-7641-5876-6(7)) Barron's Educational Series, Inc.

ENGLISH LANGUAGE—DICTIONARIES—GERMAN

Berlitz Publishing Staff. German: Picture Dictionary. Demarest, Chris L., illus. 2nd ed. 2004. (Berlitz Picture Dictionaries Ser.). (ENG, GER & GRE.). 128p. (ps-4). pap. 12.95 (978-981-246-388-3(7) , 463887) Berlitz Publishing.

Goodman, Marlene. Let's Learn German Dictionary. 2003. (ENG & GER., Illus.). 80p. 10.95 (978-0-07-140824-0(X) , 9780071408240) McGraw-Hill Cos., The.

Hippocrene Books Staff. Children's Illustrated German Dictionary: English-German, German-English. 2003. (Hippocrene Children's Illustrated Foreign Language Dictionaries Ser.). (ENG & GER., Illus.). 122p. pap. 11.95 (978-0-7818-0986-3(X)) Hippocrene Bks., Inc.

Hippocrene Books Staff, ed. Children's Illustrated German Dictionary: English-German, German-English. 1998. (Children's Illustrated Foreign Language Dictionaries Ser.). (ENG & GER., Illus.). 122p. (gr. k-5). 14.95 (978-0-7818-0722-7(0)) Hippocrene Bks., Inc.

Hochstatter, Daniel J. Just Look 'n Learn German Picture Dictionary. 2003. (ENG & GER., Illus.). 96p. 11.95 (978-0-07-140831-8(2) , 9780071408318) McGraw-Hill Cos., The.

Lipton, Gladys C. & Losoncy, Renata. German Bilingual Dictionary. 1998. (Barron's Bilingual Dictionaries Ser.). (ENG & GER., Illus.). 180p. (gr. 4-7). pap. 10.99 (978-0-7641-0340-7(7)) Barron's Educational Series, Inc.

ENGLISH LANGUAGE—DICTIONARIES—POLISH

Hippocrene Books, ed. Polish Childrens Picture Dict. 2006. (ENG & POL., Illus.). 108p. (J). pap. 14.95 (978-0-7818-1127-9(9)) Hippocrene Bks., Inc.

Hippocrene Books Staff, ed. Children's Illustrated Polish Dictionary: English-Polish, Polish-English. 1998. (Children's Illustrated Foreign Language Dictionaries Ser.). (ENG & POL., Illus.). 94p. (gr. k-5). 14.95 (978-0-7818-0711-1(5)) Hippocrene Bks., Inc.

Turhan, Sedat. Milet Picture Dictionary: English/Polish. Hagin, Sally, illus. 2005. (Milet Picture Dictionary Ser.). (ENG & POL.). 48p. (J). (ps-ps). 14.95 (978-1-84059-466-9(7)) Milet Publishing.

ENGLISH LANGUAGE—DICTIONARIES—SPANISH

Bennet, Archie & Gutiérrez Bello, Marta. Beginner's English/Spanish Dictionary & Guide to Usage. 2004. (Back to School Basics Ser.).Tr. of Diccionario Espanol/Ingles para principiantes Y Guia de Uso. (ENG & SPA., Illus.). 512p. (J). 12.95 (978-1-58279-360-3(3)) Trident Pr. International.

Brooks, Felicity & Mackinnon, Mairi. Picture Dictionary in Spanish. 2004. (Picture Dictionaries Ser.). (ENG & SPA., Illus.). 112p. (J). lib. bdg. 24.95 (978-1-58086-477-0(5)) EDC Publishing.

Castillo, Carlos. University of Chicago Spanish & English Dictionary. 2003. (gr. 7-12). lib. bdg. 14.15 (978-0-613-66473-8(6)) Tandem Library Bks.

Corbeil, Jean-Claude & Archambault, Ariane. The Firefly Spanish/English Junior Visual Dictionary. 2006. (SPA & ENG., Illus.). 368p. (J). (gr. 5-12). 19.95 (978-1-55407-190-6(9)) Firefly Bks., Ltd.

—My First Spanish/English Visual Dictionary. 2006. (ENG & SPA., Illus.). 80p. (J). (gr. k-4). 14.95 (978-1-55407-194-4(1)) Firefly Bks., Ltd.

Dalmatian Press Staff. My First Spanish Word Book: Mis primeras palabras en espanol e Ingles. 2007. 12p. bds. 7.99 (***978-1-4037-3055-8(5)***) Dalmatian Pr.

Demarest, Chris L. & Berlitz Publishing Staff. Ingles Diccionario Ilustrado. 2nd ed. 2004. (Berlitz Kids Ser.). (SPA., Illus.). 128p. (ps-4). pap. 12.95 (978-981-246-389-0(5) , 463895) Berlitz Publishing.

Gareth Stevens Publishing Staff, contrib. by. My First Visual Dictionary/Mi Primer Diccionario Visual. 2001. (ENG & SPA., Illus.). 48p. (J). (gr. 3 up). lib. bdg. 26.00 (978-0-8368-2897-9(6)) Stevens, Gareth Inc.

Hippocrene Books, ed. Spanish Childrens Picture Dict: English-Spanish/Spanish-English. 2006. (ENG & SPA.). 104p. (J). pap. 14.95 (978-0-7818-1130-9(9)) Hippocrene Bks., Inc.

Hippocrene Children's Illustrated Spanish Dictionary: English-Spanish/Spanish-English. 2002. (Children's Illustrated Foreign Language Dictionaries Ser.). (ENG & SPA., Illus.). 96p. (gr. k-5). pap. 11.95 (978-0-7818-0889-7(8)) Hippocrene Bks., Inc.

Jordan, Sara. Bilingual Kids Vol. I: English - Spanish. 2005. 64p. (J). pap. (978-1-55386-024-2(1)) Crabtree Publishing Co.

—English - Spanish. 2005. 64p. (J). (978-1-55386-036-5(5)); 4. pap. (978-1-55386-041-9(1)) Crabtree Publishing Co.

Karapetian, Marjam. Bilingual Content Dictionary: English to Spanish. 2004. (SPA & ENG.). 9.95 (978-0-9764829-2-5(4)) WizdomInc.

Keyes, Joan Ross. The Oxford Picture Dictionary for Kids. Springer, Sally, illus. 1998. (Oxford Picture Dictionary for Kids Ser.). (SPA & ENG.). 152p. 14.25 (978-0-19-436662-5(6)) Oxford Univ. Pr., Inc.

Larousse Diccionario School Plus Espanol (Larousse School Plus Dictionary) 1999. (ENG & SPA.). 526p. (YA). (gr. 8 up). (978-970-22-0001-7(6)) Larousse.

Laud, Valerie. The Picture Book Dictionary: The Essential Source for Bilingual Families, English-Spanish Edition. Latushkin, Valentin, illus. l.t. ed. 2005. (ENG & SPA.). 96p. (J). (978-0-9747387-0-3(0)) EKADOO Publishing Group.

Lea, Christine. Oxford New Spanish Dictionary. 1999. (SPA.). (gr. 7-12). lib. bdg. 14.15 (978-0-613-16407-8(5)) Tandem Library Bks.

Longman. Longman Diccionario Pocket, Ingles-Espanol, Espanol-Ingles:Para Estudiantes Mexicanos. 2004. (ENG & SPA.). 832p. (C). pap. 19.93 (978-0-582-51157-6(7)) Pearson ESL.

Mabileau, Christine, et al. My First Spanish Picture Dictionary. 2001. (Children's First Picture Dictionaries Ser.). (ENG & SPA., Illus.). 48p. (J). 16.99 (978-0-7641-5437-9(0)) Barron's Educational Series, Inc.

Nakata, Ritsuko, et al. Let's Go Picture Dictionary: English-Spanish Edition. 1999. (ENG & SPA., Illus.). 140p. (J). 14.25 (978-0-19-435932-0(8)) Oxford Univ. Pr., Inc.

Spanish-English Picture Dictionary. 2003. (SPA & ENG.). (J). per. (978-1-884907-30-2(X)) Paradise Pr., Inc.

Vv. Richmond Advanced Dictionary: Spanish/English, English/Spanish. (ENG & SPA.). 720p. (J). (gr. 9-12). 30.95 (978-84-294-9861-5(3) , Richmond) Santillana USA Publishing Co., Inc.

—Richmond Pocket Dictionary: Spanish-English, English-Spanish. (SPA & ENG.). 806p. (J). (gr. 6-12). pap. 10.95 (978-84-294-9860-8(5)) Santillana USA Publishing Co., Inc.

Webster's Spanish-English Dictionary for Students. 2003. (gr. 3-6). lib. bdg. 10.65 (978-0-613-68550-4(4)) Tandem Library Bks.

Williams, Edwin B. The New College Spanish & English Dictionary. 3rd ed. 2003. (SPA & ENG.). 720p. (YA). (gr. 7-12). pap. (978-0-87720-538-8(8) , R760P) AMSCO Schl. Pubns., Inc.

ENGLISH LANGUAGE—ETYMOLOGY

Amery, H. & Cartwright, S. Pairs. 2004. (Pairs Ser.). (Illus.). (J). 8.95 (978-0-7945-0327-7(6) , Usborne) EDC Publishing.

Baker, Rosalie. In a Word: 750 Words & Their Origins. Lopes, Tom, illus. 2003. 250p. (J). 17.95 (978-0-8126-2710-7(5)) Cricket Bks.

Doudna, Kelly. Tick Tock. 2004. (Sound Words Ser.). (Illus.). 23p. (J). (ps-3). lib. bdg. 19.93 (978-1-59197-455-0(0) , SandCastle) ABDO Publishing Co.

Realtime Associates and Mazer Corporation Staff, compiled by. Understand Word Origins & Derivations. 2002. (J). (gr. 3). 66.75 (978-1-58605-382-6(5) , LeapFrog Schl. Hse.) LeapFrog Enterprises, Inc.

Realtime Associates and Mazer Corporation Staff & LeapFrog Staff, compiled by. Understand Word Origins & Derivations. 2002. (J). (gr. 4). 66.75 (978-1-58605-440-3(6)); (gr. 5). 66.75 (978-1-58605-503-5(8)) LeapFrog Enterprises, Inc. (LeapFrog Schl. Hse.).

Sikorski, Lorna D. The Consonant Variations of American English, 1 BK. 4th ed. 2004. (Mastering Effective English Communication Ser.). (Illus.). 119p. (gr. 7 up). spiral bd. 29.95 (978-1-883574-04-8(8) , 3603) LDS & Assocs., LLC.

Wulffson, Don L. & Wulffson, Pam. Abracadabra to Zombie: More Than 500 Wacky Word Origins. Lee, Jared D., illus. 2003. 160p. (J). (gr. 4). 15.99 (978-0-525-47100-4(6) , Dutton Juvenile) Penguin Group (USA) Inc.

ENGLISH LANGUAGE—GRAMMAR

Abraham, Philip. Language Development Grammer Usage. 2004. 48p. pap. 6.95 (978-1-4042-8519-4(9)) Rosen Publishing Group, Inc., The.

—Language Development Writing Process. 2004. 48p. pap. 6.95 (978-1-4042-8520-0(2)) Rosen Publishing Group, Inc., The.

Abrams, Majella. Reading Pals: Short & Long Vowels Gr. K-1. Taylor, Jennifer, ed. Sexton, Brenda, illus. 2007. (J). per. 6.99 (***978-1-59198-436-8(X)***) Creative Teaching Pr., Inc.

Accelerated Grammar & Spelling. 2004. cd-rom 2995.00 (978-1-59455-196-3(0)) Renaissance Learning, Inc.

Accelerated Grammar & Spelling High School Edition. 2004. cd-rom 2995.00 (978-1-59455-197-0(9)) Renaissance Learning, Inc.

Adams, Colleen. Planes Go Places: Learning the Sound of PL. 2001. (PowerPhonics Ser.). (Illus.). 23p. (J). pap. 26.40 (978-0-8239-8296-7(3) , PowerKids Pr.) Rosen Publishing Group, Inc., The.

All Aboard! Fifth Grade Guided Comprehension Level R. (On Our Way to English Ser.). (gr. 5 up). 34.50 (978-0-7578-6622-7(0)) Rigby Education.

All Charged Up! Fifth Grade Guided Comprehension Level Q. (On Our Way to English Ser.). (gr. 5 up). 34.50 (978-0-7578-6616-6(6)) Rigby Education.

All Kinds of Babies: Kindergarten Guided Reading Level B. (On Our Way to English Ser.). (gr. k up). 27.75 (978-0-7578-7013-2(9)) Rigby Education.

Analogies 1 Grd 7-8. 2004. pap. 7.25 (978-0-8388-2225-8(8)) Educators Publishing Service, Inc.

Analogies 2 Grd 9-10. 2004. pap. 7.25 (978-0-8388-2227-2(4)) Educators Publishing Service, Inc.

Analogies 3 Grd 11-12. 2004. pap. 7.25 (978-0-8388-2229-6(0)) Educators Publishing Service, Inc.

Analogies 3 Grd 11-12 Quiz Boo. 2004. pap. 8.20 (978-0-8388-2230-2(4)) Educators Publishing Service, Inc.

Andrews, Becky, ed. Grammar Plus! - Capitalization & Punctuation. 2000. 48p. 9.95 (978-1-56234-389-7(0) , Mailbox Bks., The) Education Ctr., Inc.

—Grammar Plus! - Parts of Speech. 2000. 48p. 9.95 (978-1-56234-434-4(X) , Mailbox Bks., The) Education Ctr., Inc.

Atlee, Nancy. The Absolutely Essential Grammar Guide. 2004. (J). per. 13.95 (978-1-883055-69-1(5)) Dandy Lion Pubns.

Bailey, LaWanda. Miss Myrtle Frag, the Grammar Nag. Strassburg, Brian, illus. 2000. 84p. (YA). (gr. 5 up). pap. 13.95 (978-1-888842-19-7(9)) Absey & Co.

Barden, Cindy. Using Standards Grammar Gr 6. 2003. (100+ Seriestm Ser.). 128p. (J). (gr. 6 up). pap. 12.99 (978-0-7424-1806-6(5) , IFG99055) School Specialty Publishing.

Barker, Ray & Moorcroft, Christine. Grammar First. (Illus.). 64p. Bk. 1. 2002. (YA). pap., stu. ed. 13.50 (978-0-7487-6535-5(2)); Bk. 2. 2002. (YA). pap., stu. ed. 13.50 (978-0-7487-6536-2(0)); Bk. 3. 2003. (J). (gr. 6-9). pap., stu. ed. 13.95 (978-0-7487-6537-9(9)) Nelson Thornes Ltd. GBR. *Dist:* Trans-Atlantic Pubns., Inc.

Battistoni, Ilse. The Red Rose: Learning the R Sound. (PowerPhonics Ser.). (Illus.). (J). 23p. pap. (978-0-8239-8257-8(2)); 2002. 24p. (gr. 1). lib. bdg. 18.50 (978-0-8239-5912-9(0)) Rosen Publishing Group, Inc., The. (PowerKids Pr.).

Beckwith, Carrie, et al. Editor in Chief' Book C2: Grammar Disasters & Punctuation Faux Pas. 2001. (Illus.). 140p. (J). (gr. 8 up). pap. 17.99 (978-0-89455-721-7(1) , MP9706) Critical Thinking Bks. & Software.

Becky, Andrews & Andrews, Becky, eds. Grammar Plus! - Sentence Structure & Usage. 2000. 48p. 9.95 (978-1-56234-413-9(7) , Mailbox Bks., The) Education Ctr., Inc.

Beginning Consonant Sounds. (Basic Skills Ser.). 48p. (ps-2). 5.99 (978-0-513-02334-5(8) , TSD23348) Denison, T. S. & Co., Inc.

Bell & Wheeler. Learning Grammar Through Writi. 2004. pap. 10.35 (978-0-8388-1493-2(X)) Educators Publishing Service, Inc.

Bentley, Linda. Big Book of Quick & Easy Art Activities: More Than 75 Creative Activities with Curriculum Connections That Keep Kids Creating & Learning All Year Long! 2007. 208p. pap. 26.99 (***978-0-439-58060-1(9)*** , Teaching Resources) Scholastic, Inc.

Bergman, Carol Ann. Heath Grammar & Composition: Level 5. (J). (gr. 11). (978-0-669-15978-3(6)) Houghton Mifflin Co. (Schl. Div.).

BJU Staff. Writing Grammar Tests Ak Grd 8. 2004. pap. 5.50 (978-1-57924-370-8(3)) Jones, Bob Univ. Pr.

—Writing Grammar Tests Grd 8. 2004. pap. 9.00 (978-1-57924-369-2(X)) Jones, Bob Univ. Pr.

—Writing Grammar Worktext Grd 2. 2004. pap. 13.50 (978-1-57924-820-8(9)) Jones, Bob Univ. Pr.

—Writing Grammar Worktext Grd 3. 2004. pap. 13.50 (978-1-57924-827-7(6)) Jones, Bob Univ. Pr.

—Writing Grammar Worktext Grd 4. 2004. pap. 13.50 (978-1-57924-839-0(X)) Jones, Bob Univ. Pr.

—Writing Grammar Worktext Grd 7. 2004. pap. 15.50 (978-1-57924-261-9(8)) Jones, Bob Univ. Pr.

—Writing Grammar Worktext Grd 8. 2004. pap. 15.50 (978-1-57924-338-8(X)) Jones, Bob Univ. Pr.

Bladon, Rachel. Improve Your Grammar. (Better English Ser.). 32p. (YA). (gr. 5 up). 2004. lib. bdg. 14.95 (978-1-58086-325-4(6)); 2001. (Illus.). pap. 6.95 (978-0-7460-4240-3(X)) EDC Publishing.

—Improve Your Grammar - Internet Linked. 2004. (Better English Ser.). 32p. (J). pap. 6.95 (978-0-7945-0880-7(4) , Usborne) EDC Publishing.

—Test Your Grammar. 1999. (Test Yourself Ser.). (Illus.). 32p. (J). (gr. 5 up). lib. bdg. 13.95 (978-0-88110-740-1(9)) EDC Publishing.

Bloom, Susan, et al. English Made Easy. Colby, Garry & Simard, Rémy, illus. 2005. (Learning Made Easy Ser.). 128p. per. (978-0-7853-8841-8(9) , 7191800) Publications International, Ltd.

Bones: Long Vowel o, CVCe Pattern: Level B, 6 vols. (Wright Skills Ser.). 16p. (gr. k-3). 17.95 (978-0-322-01466-4(2)) Wright Group, The.

Bonnie Pearson Education staff. Spin! Level C. 2003. 112p. (C). pap., stu. ed. 20.00 (978-0-13-041980-4(X)) Pearson ESL.

Bottino, Marlane. My Language Book for Spelling, Writing & Vocabulary: Level D. Bottino, Marlane, illus. 2000. (My Language Books for Spelling, Writing & Vocabulary Ser.: Vol. 4). (Illus.). (J). (gr. k-6). pap. 6.50 (978-1-893615-05-2(7)) Creative Enterprises.

Bridgman, Beth, contrib. by. Adjectives & Adverbs. rev. ed. 1998. (Horizons Ser.). (Illus.). 24p. (J). (gr. 4-6). pap. 5.95 (978-1-58086-062-8(1)) EDC Publishing.

—Capital Letters. rev. ed. 1998. (Horizons Ser.). (Illus.). 24p. (J). (gr. 4-6). pap. 5.95 (978-1-58086-070-3(2)) EDC Publishing.

—Context Clues. rev. ed. 1998. (Horizons Ser.). (Illus.). 24p. (J). (gr. 4-6). pap. 5.95 (978-1-58086-068-0(0)) EDC Publishing.

—Dictionary Skills. rev. ed. 1998. (Horizons Ser.). (Illus.). 24p. (J). (gr. 4-6). pap. 5.95 (978-1-58086-071-0(0)) EDC Publishing.

—Horizons Grammar Set: Incl. 15 Booklets, Slipcase, Answer Keys & Teacher Guide. rev. ed. Incl. Adjectives & Adverbs. (J). (gr. 4-6). pap. 5.95 (978-1-58086-062-8(1)); Apostrophe, Colon, Hyphen. (J). (gr. 4-6). pap. 5.95 (978-1-58086-059-8(1)); Capital Letters. (J). (gr. 4-6). pap. 5.95 (978-1-58086-070-3(2)); Comma. (J). (gr. 4-6). pap. 5.95 (978-1-58086-061-1(3)); Context Clues. (J). (gr. 4-6). pap. 5.95 (978-1-58086-068-0(0)); Dictionary Skills. (J). (gr. 4-6). pap. 5.95 (978-1-58086-071-0(0)); Figures of Speech. (J). (gr. 4-6). pap. 5.95 (978-1-58086-067-3(2)); Nouns & Pronouns. (J). (gr. 4-6). pap. 5.95 (978-1-58086-065-9(6)); Paragraph & Topic Sentence. (J). (gr. 4-6). pap. 5.95 (978-1-58086-072-7(9)); Period, Question Mark, Exclamation Mark. (J). (gr. 4-6). pap. 5.95 (978-1-58086-058-1(3)); Prefixes, Bases, Suffixes. (J). (gr. 4-6). pap. 5.95 (978-1-58086-066-6(4)); Prepositions & Conjunctions. (J). (gr. 4-6). pap. 5.95 (978-1-58086-063-5(X)); Quotation Marks, Underlining. (J). (gr. 4-6). pap. 5.95 (978-1-58086-060-4(5)); Synonyms, Antonyms, Homonyms. (J). (gr. 4-6). pap. 5.95 (978-1-58086-069-7(9)); Teacher's Guide. pap. 5.95 (978-1-58086-113-7(X)); Verbs. (J). (gr. 4-6). pap. 5.95 (978-1-58086-064-2(8)); (Illus.). 24p. 1998. Set pap. 5.95 (978-1-58086-075-8(3)) EDC Publishing.

—Nouns & Pronouns. rev. ed. 1998. (Horizons Ser.). (Illus.). 24p. (J). (gr. 4-6). pap. 5.95 (978-1-58086-065-9(6)) EDC Publishing.

—Paragraph & Topic Sentence. rev. ed. 1998. (Horizons Ser.). (Illus.). 24p. (J). (gr. 4-6). pap. 5.95 (978-1-58086-072-7(9)) EDC Publishing.

—Prefixes, Bases, Suffixes. rev. ed. 1998. (Horizons Ser.). (Illus.). 24p. (J). (gr. 4-6). pap. 5.95 (978-1-58086-066-6(4)) EDC Publishing.

—Prepositions & Conjunctions. rev. ed. 1998. (Horizons Ser.). (Illus.). 24p. (J). (gr. 4-6). pap. 5.95 (978-1-58086-063-5(X)) EDC Publishing.

—Synonyms, Antonyms, Homonyms. rev. ed. 1998. (Horizons Ser.). (Illus.). 24p. (J). (gr. 4-6). pap. 5.95 (978-1-58086-069-7(9)) EDC Publishing.

—Teacher's Guide. rev. ed. 1998. (Horizons Ser.). (Illus.). 24p. pap. 5.95 (978-1-58086-113-7(X)) EDC Publishing.

—Verbs. rev. ed. 1998. (Horizons Ser.). (Illus.). 24p. (J). (gr. 4-6). pap. 5.95 (978-1-58086-064-2(8)) EDC Publishing.

Bridgman, Beth, rev. Horizons Concepts Level 1 Set (3.5-4.5 Readability) Incl. 10 Booklets, Slipcase, Answer Keys & Teacher's Guide. rev. ed. Incl. Distinguishing Between Fact & Opinion. pap. 5.95 (978-1-58086-042-0(7)); Drawing Conclusions. pap. 5.95 (978-1-58086-043-7(5)); Establishing Sequence. pap. 5.95 (978-1-58086-040-6(0)); Following Directions. pap. 5.95 (978-1-58086-041-3(9)); Making Judgments. pap. 5.95 (978-1-58086-047-5(8)); Predicting Outcomes. pap. 5.95 (978-1-58086-045-1(1)); Recognizing Cause & Effect. pap. 5.95 (978-1-58086-044-4(3)); Recognizing Plot, Character, Mood. pap. 5.95 (978-1-58086-046-8(X)); Level 1. Finding the Main Idea. pap. 5.95 (978-1-58086-039-0(7)); Level 1. Recalling Details. pap. 5.95 (978-1-58086-038-3(9)); (J). (gr. 4-9). (Illus.). 24p. 1998. Set pap. 5.95 (978-1-58086-073-4(7)) EDC Publishing.

—Horizons Concepts Level 2 (4.5-5.5 Readability) Incl. 10 Booklets, Slipcase, Answer Keys & Teacher's Guide. rev. ed. Incl. Distinguishing Between Fact & Opinion. (J). (gr. 4-9). pap. 5.95 (978-1-58086-052-9(4)); Drawing Conclusions. (J). (gr. 4-9). pap. 5.95 (978-1-58086-053-6(2)); Establishing Sequence. (J). (gr. 4-9). pap. 5.95 (978-1-58086-050-5(8)); Finding the Main Idea. (J). (gr. 4-9). pap. 5.95 (978-1-58086-049-9(4)); Following Directions. (J). (gr. 4-9). pap. 5.95 (978-1-58086-051-2(6)); Making Judgments. (J). (gr. 4-9). pap. 5.95 (978-1-58086-057-4(5)); Predicting Outcomes. (J). (gr. 4-9). pap. 5.95 (978-1-58086-055-0(9)); Recognizing Cause & Effect. (J). (gr. 4-9). pap. 5.95 (978-1-58086-054-3(0)); Recognizing Plot, Character, Mood. (J). (gr. 4-9). pap. 5.95 (978-1-58086-056-7(7)); Teacher's Guide. pap. 5.95 (978-1-58086-112-0(1)); Level 2. Recalling Details. (J). (gr. 4-9). pap. 5.95 (978-1-58086-048-2(6)); (Horizons Ser.). (Illus.). 24p. 1998. Set pap. 5.95 (978-1-58086-074-1(5)) EDC Publishing.

—Teacher's Guide. rev. ed. 1998. (Horizons Ser.). (Illus.). 24p. pap. 5.95 (978-1-58086-112-0(1)) EDC Publishing.

Brimner, Larry Dane. A Bit Is a Bite. Kono, Erin Eitter, illus. 2007. (Rookie Reader': Silent Letters Ser.). 32p. (J). pap. 4.95 (***978-0-531-17780-8(7)**); 19.50 (***978-0-531-17547-7(2)**) Scholastic Library Publishing. (Children's Pr.).

—Silent Kay & the Dragon. McMahon, Bob, illus. 2007. (Rookie Reader Skill Set Ser.). 32p. (J). (gr. k-2). pap. 4.95 (***978-0-531-17783-9(1)**, Children's Pr.) Scholastic Library Publishing.

British Literature: Grammar, Usage, & Mechanics Book. 2004. (gr. 12 up). (978-0-618-30395-3(2) , 2-04300) McDougal Littell Inc.

British Literature: Grammar, Usage, & Mechanics Book Answer Key. 2004. (gr. 12 up). (978-0-618-30801-9(6) , 2-04416) McDougal Littell Inc.

Bromwell, L. Anne. English Grammar Basics. 2005. 42p. spiral bd. 14.95 (978-1-59196-932-7(8)) Instantpublisher.com.

Buffa, Liz. Grammar Smart Junior. 2nd ed. 2002. (Smart Junior Guides). 208p. pap. 12.00 (978-0-375-76259-8(0) , Princeton Review) Random Hse. Information Group.

Burg, Ann. Kate's Surprise. Harris, Phyllis, illus. 2007. (Rookie Reader Skill Set Ser.). 32p. (J). (gr. k-2). pap. 4.95 (***978-0-531-17781-5(5)**); 19.50 (***978-0-531-17549-1(9)**) Scholastic Library Publishing. (Children's Pr.).

Can Jo Fly? Open Vowel Words Ending in y with Long i Sound, Ending in o, Ending in e: Level B, 6 vols. (Wright Skills Ser.). 16p. (gr. k-3). 26.50 (978-0-322-03098-5(6)) Wright Group, The.

Capitalization & Punctuation: English in Context. 2000. (Illus.). 112p. per., wbk. ed. 8.95 (978-1-56254-350-1(4) , SP 3504) Saddleback Educational Publishing.

Capitalization & Punctuation (Gr. 1-3) 2003. (J). (978-1-58232-050-2(0)) Bryan Hse. Pubs., Inc.

Carbo Recorded Books: Easy Primary. 2003. (Illus.). (J). (ps-2). pap. 895.00 incl. audio (978-1-883186-28-9(5) , NAPS16) National Reading Styles Institute, Inc.

Carbo Recorded Books: High Intermediate. 2002. (Illus.). (YA). (gr. 4-8). pap. 1031.00 incl. audio (978-1-883186-31-9(5) , NHIS12) National Reading Styles Institute, Inc.

Carbo Recorded Books: Primary. 2003. (Illus.). (J). (gr. 2-4). pap. 1007.00 incl. audio (978-1-883186-29-6(3) , NAPS13) National Reading Styles Institute, Inc.

Carlson, Kim. Reading 1st Grade: Skill Builders. 2002. (Skill Builders Ser.). 64p. (gr. 1 up). pap. 2.95 (978-1-887923-94-1(2)) Rainbow Bridge Publishing.

—Reading 2nd Grade: Skill Builders. 2002. (Skill Builders Ser.). (gr. 2 up). pap. 2.95 (978-1-887923-95-8(0)) Rainbow Bridge Publishing.

—Reading 3rd Grade: Skill Builders. 2002. (Skill Builders Ser.). (gr. 3 up). pap. 2.95 (978-1-887923-96-5(9)) Rainbow Bridge Publishing.

Carroll, Joyce Armstrong, et al. Literature: Timeless Voices, Timeless Themes. 2001. Bronze Level. (YA). (gr. 7). pap., stu. ed., wbk. ed. 7.47 (978-0-13-043487-6(6)); Bronze Level. (YA). (gr. 7). trans. 33.47 (978-0-13-043945-1(2)); Copper Level. (J). (gr. 6). pap., stu. ed., wbk. ed. 7.47 (978-0-13-043486-9(8)); Copper Level (J). (gr. 6). trans. 33.47 (978-0-13-043944-4(4)); Diamond Level. (YA). (gr. 12). pap., stu. ed., wbk. ed. 7.47 (978-0-13-043492-0(2)); Diamond Level. (YA). (gr. 12). trans. 33.47 (978-0-13-043951-2(7)); Diamond Level. (YA). (gr. 12). cd-rom 29.97 (978-0-13-437184-9(4)); Gold Level. (YA). (gr. 9). pap., stu. ed., wbk. ed. 7.47 (978-0-13-043489-0(2)); Gold Level. (YA). (gr. 9). trans. 33.47 (978-0-13-043947-5(9)); Platinum Level. (YA). (gr. 10). pap., stu. ed., wbk. ed. 7.47 (978-0-13-043490-6(6)); Platinum Level. (YA). (gr. 10). trans. 33.47 (978-0-13-043948-2(7)); Ruby Level. (YA). (gr. 11). pap., stu. ed., wbk. ed. 7.47 (978-0-13-043491-3(4)); Ruby Level. (YA). (gr. 11). trans. 33.47 (978-0-13-043949-9(5)); Silver Level. (YA). (gr. 8). pap., stu. ed., wbk. ed. 7.47 (978-0-13-043488-3(4)); Silver Level. (YA). (gr. 8). trans. 33.47 (978-0-13-043946-8(0)) Prentice Hall PTR.

—Writiing & Grammar: Communication in Action, Platinum Level. 2001. (YA). (gr. 10). pap., wbk. ed. 16.47 (978-0-13-043475-3(2)) Prentice Hall PTR.

—Writing & Grammar: Communiation in Action, Gold Level. 2001. (YA). (gr. 9). pap., wbk. ed., act. bk. ed. 7.47 (978-0-13-043923-9(1)) Prentice Hall PTR.

—Writing & Grammar: Communicatin in Action. 2001. (YA). Diamond Level. (gr. 12). pap., wbk. ed. 7.47 (978-0-13-043521-7(X)); Diamond Level. (gr. 12). pap., act. bk. ed. 7.47 (978-0-13-043898-0(7)); Platinum Level. (gr. 10). pap. 7.47 (978-0-13-053217-6(7)) Prentice Hall PTR.

—Writing & Grammar: Communication in Action, Copper Level. 2001. (J). (gr. 6). 114.47 (978-0-13-052664-9(9)) Prentice Hall PTR.

—Writing & Grammar: Communication in Action, Bronze Level, 3 vols. 2004. 812p. (YA). (gr. 7 up). 406.00 (978-0-13-037492-9(X)) Prentice Hall Pr.

—Writing & Grammar: Communication in Action, Gold Level, 3 vols. 2004. 988p. (YA). (gr. 9 up). 494.00 (978-0-13-037494-3(6)) Prentice Hall Pr.

—Writing & Grammar: Communication in Action, Platinum Level, 3 vols. 2004. 992p. (YA). (gr. 10 up). 496.00 (978-0-13-116634-9(4)) Prentice Hall Pr.

—Writing & Grammar, Communication in Action Diamond Level: Writing in the Content Areas & in the Workplace. 2001. (YA). (gr. 12). pap. 6.97 (978-0-13-052662-5(2)); (J). (gr. 6). 6.97 (978-0-13-052656-4(8)); (YA). (gr. 7). pap. 6.97 (978-0-13-052657-1(6)); (YA). (gr. 8). pap. 6.97 (978-0-13-052658-8(4)) Prentice Hall PTR.

—Writing & Grammar, Communication in Action Gold Level: Basic Skills Intervention Kit. 2001. (YA). (gr. 10). 499.97 (978-0-13-053997-7(X)); (YA). (gr. 11). 499.97 (978-0-13-053998-4(8)); (YA). (gr. 12). 499.97 (978-0-13-053999-1(6)); (J). (gr. 6). 499.97 (978-0-13-053993-9(7)); (YA). (gr. 7). 499.97 (978-0-13-053994-6(5)); (YA). (gr. 8). 499.97 (978-0-13-053995-3(3)); (YA). (gr. 9). 499.97 incl. audio compact disk (978-0-13-053996-0(1)) Prentice Hall PTR.

—Writing & Grammar, Communication in Action Gold Level: Writing in Content Areas & Workplace. 2001. (YA). (gr. 9). pap. 6.97 (978-0-13-052659-5(2)) Prentice Hall PTR.

—Writing & Grammar, Communication in Action Platinum Level: Writing in Content Areas & in the Workplace. 2001. (YA). (gr. 10). pap. 6.97 (978-0-13-052660-1(6)) Prentice Hall PTR.

—Writing & Grammar, Communication in Action Ruby Level: Writing in the Content Areas & in the Workplace. 2001. (YA). (gr. 11). pap. 6.97 (978-0-13-052661-8(4)) Prentice Hall PTR.

—Writing & Grammar, Grade 9: Communication in Action. 2001. Bronze Level. (YA). (gr. 7). 114.47 (978-0-13-052665-6(7)); Bronze Level. (YA). (gr. 7). stu. ed. 45.47 (978-0-13-436963-1(7)); Bronze Level. (SPA.). (YA). (gr. 7). pap. 30.47 (978-0-13-054196-3(6)); Bronze Level. (YA). (gr. 7). pap. 7.47 (978-0-13-053213-8(4)); Bronze Level. (YA). (gr. 7). pap., wbk. ed. 16.47 (978-0-13-043472-2(8)); Bronze Level. (YA). (gr. 7). pap., wbk. ed. 7.47 (978-0-13-043516-3(3)); Bronze Level. (YA). (gr. 7). pap., act. bk. ed. 7.47 (978-0-13-043892-8(8)); Bronze Level. (YA). (gr. 7). pap., act. bk. ed. 8.47 (978-0-13-043914-7(2)); Bronze Level. (YA). (gr. 7). pap., act. bk. ed. 7.47 (978-0-13-043921-5(5)); Bronze Level. (YA). (gr. 7). trans. 114.47 (978-0-13-043884-3(7)); Bronze Level. (YA). (gr. 7). trans. 275.47 (978-0-13-043953-6(3)); Bronze Level. (YA). (gr. 7). trans. 20.97 (978-0-13-043960-4(6)); Copper Level. (SPA.). (J). (gr. 6). 30.47 (978-0-13-054195-6(8)); Copper Level. (J). (gr. 6). stu. ed. 42.97 (978-0-13-436962-4(9)); Copper Level. (J). (gr. 6). wbk. ed. 16.47 (978-0-13-043470-8(1)); Copper Level. (J). (gr. 6). act. bk. ed. 7.47 (978-0-13-043891-1(X)); Copper Level. (J). (gr. 6). act. bk. ed. 8.47 (978-0-13-043913-0(4)); Copper Level. (J). (gr. 6). pap. 7.47 (978-0-13-053212-1(6)); Copper Level. (J). (gr. 6). pap., act. bk. ed. 7.47 (978-0-13-043920-8(7)); Copper Level. (J). (gr. 6). trans. 275.47 (978-0-13-043952-9(5)); Copper Level. (J). (gr. 6). trans. 20.97 (978-0-13-043959-8(2)); Diamond Level. (YA). (gr. 12). 114.47 (978-0-13-052670-0(3)); Diamond Level. (YA). (gr. 12). stu. ed. 50.47 (978-0-13-436971-6(8)); Diamond Level. (YA). (gr. 12). pap. 30.47 (978-0-13-054202-1(4)); Diamond Level. (YA). (gr. 12). pap. 7.47 (978-0-13-053219-0(3)); Diamond Level. (YA). (gr. 12). pap., wbk. ed. 16.47 (978-0-13-043477-7(9)); Diamond Level. (YA). (gr. 12). pap., act. bk. ed. 8.47 (978-0-13-043919-2(3)); Diamond Level. (YA). (gr. 12). pap., act. bk. ed. 7.47 (978-0-13-043926-0(6)); Diamond Level. (YA). (gr. 12). trans. 275.47 (978-0-13-043958-1(4)); Diamond Level. (YA). (gr. 12). trans. 114.47 (978-0-13-043890-4(1)); Gold Level. (YA). (gr. 8). pap., act. bk. ed. 7.47 (978-0-13-043895-9(2)); Gold Level. (YA). (gr. 9). 114.47 (978-0-13-052667-0(3)); Gold Level. (YA). (gr. 9). stu. ed. 47.47 (978-0-13-436966-2(1)); Gold Level. (YA). (gr. 9). pap. 7.47 (978-0-13-053216-9(9)); Gold Level. (YA). (gr. 9). pap. 30.47 (978-0-13-054199-4(0)); Gold Level. (YA). (gr. 9). pap., wbk. ed. 7.47 (978-0-13-043518-7(X)); Gold Level. (YA). (gr. 9). pap., wbk. ed. 16.47 (978-0-13-043474-6(4)); Gold Level. (YA). (gr. 9). pap., act. bk. ed. 8.47 (978-0-13-043916-1(9)); Gold Level. (YA). (gr. 9). trans. 20.97 (978-0-13-043962-8(2)); Gold Level. (YA). (gr. 9). trans. 275.47 (978-0-13-043955-0(X)); Gold Level. (YA). (gr. 9). trans. 114.47 (978-0-13-043887-4(1)); Platinum Level. (YA). (gr. 10). 114.47 (978-0-13-052668-7(1)); Platinum Level. (YA). (gr. 10). 30.47 (978-0-13-054200-7(8)); Platinum Level. (YA). (gr. 10). stu. ed. 48.47 (978-0-13-436968-6(8)); Platinum Level. (YA). (gr. 10). pap., wbk. ed. 7.47 (978-0-13-043519-4(8)); Platinum Level. (YA). (gr. 10). pap., act. bk. ed. 7.47 (978-0-13-043896-6(0)); Platinum Level. (YA). (gr. 10). pap., act. bk. ed. 8.47 (978-0-13-043917-8(7)); Platinum Level. (YA). (gr. 10). pap., act. bk. ed. 7.47 (978-0-13-043924-6(X)); Platinum Level. (YA). (gr. 10). trans. 20.97 (978-0-13-043963-5(0)); Platinum Level. (YA). (gr. 10). trans. 275.47 (978-0-13-043956-7(8)); Ruby Level. (YA). (gr. 11). 114.47 (978-0-13-052669-4(X)); Ruby Level. (YA). (gr. 11). stu. ed. 49.47 (978-0-13-436969-3(6)); Ruby Level. (YA). (gr. 11). pap. 7.47 (978-0-13-053218-3(5)); Ruby Level. (YA). (gr. 11). pap. 30.47 (978-0-13-054201-4(6)); Ruby Level. (YA). (gr. 11). pap., wbk. ed. 7.47 (978-0-13-043520-0(1)); Ruby Level. (YA). (gr. 11). pap., wbk. ed. 16.47 (978-0-13-043476-0(0)); Ruby Level. (YA). (gr. 11). pap., act. bk. ed. 7.47 (978-0-13-043897-3(9)); Ruby Level. (YA). (gr. 11). pap., act. bk. ed. 8.47 (978-0-13-043918-5(5)); Ruby Level. (YA). (gr. 11). pap., act. bk. ed. 7.47 (978-0-13-043925-3(8)); Ruby Level. (YA). (gr. 11). trans. 114.47 (978-0-13-043889-8(8)); Ruby Level. (YA). (gr. 11). trans. 20.97 (978-0-13-043964-2(9)); Ruby Level. (YA). (gr. 11). trans. 275.47 (978-0-13-043957-4(6)); Silver Level. (YA). (gr. 8). 30.47 (978-0-13-054197-0(4)); Silver Level. (YA). (gr. 8). 114.47 (978-0-13-052666-3(5)); Silver Level. (YA). (gr. 8). stu. ed. 45.47 (978-0-13-436964-8(5)); Silver Level. (YA). (gr. 8). pap. 7.47 (978-0-13-053214-5(2)); Silver Level. (YA). (gr. 8). pap., wbk. ed. 16.47 (978-0-13-043473-9(6)); Silver Level. (YA). (gr. 8). pap., wbk. ed. 7.47 (978-0-13-043517-0(1)); Silver Level. (YA). (gr. 8). pap., act. bk. ed. 8.47 (978-0-13-043915-4(0)); Silver Level. (YA). (gr. 8). pap., act. bk. ed. 7.47 (978-0-13-043922-2(3)); Silver Level. (YA). (gr. 8). trans. 114.47 (978-0-13-043885-0(5)); Silver Level. (YA). (gr. 8). trans. 275.47 (978-0-13-043954-3(1)); Silver Level. (YA). (gr. 8). trans. 20.97 (978-0-13-043961-1(4)) Prentice Hall PTR.

—Writing & Grammer: Communication in Action, Platinum Level. 2001. (YA). (gr. 10). trans. 114.47 (978-0-13-043888-1(X)) Prentice Hall PTR.

Celia's Gift: Fourth Grade Guided Comprehension Level N. (On Our Way to English Ser.). (gr. 4 up). 34.50 (978-0-7578-7163-4(1)) Rigby Education.

Center for Learning Network Staff. Grammar Mastery: Curriculum Unit. 2nd ed. 2000. (English Ser.). 135p. (gr. 7-10). tchr. ed., spiral bd. 8.95 (978-1-56077-628-4(5)) Ctr. for Learning, The.

—Grammar Mastery 1: For Better Writing — Workbook Level 1. 2nd ed. 2000. (English Ser.). 158p. (YA). (gr. 7-9). stu. ed., per., wbk. ed. 7.95 (978-1-56077-629-1(3)) Ctr. for Learning, The.

—Grammar Mastery 2: For Better Writing — Workbook Level 2. 2000. (English Ser.). 123p. (YA). (gr. 8-10). stu. ed., per., wbk. ed. 7.95 (978-1-56077-630-7(7)) Ctr. for Learning, The.

—Grammar Power Student Workbook: The Essential Elements. 1999. (English Ser.). 170p. (YA). (gr. 6-8). pap., stu. ed., wbk. ed. 10.95 (978-1-56077-593-5(9)) Ctr. for Learning, The.

Center for Performance Assessment. Write to Know: Nonfiction Writing Prompts for Algebra. 2005. 128p. pap. 9.95 (978-1-933196-07-7(6)) Advanced Learning Pr.

Chaitkin, Carol. Let's Review: English. 3rd ed. 2005. (Let's Review Ser.). (Illus.). 336p. pap. 13.99 (978-0-7641-2378-8(5)) Barron's Educational Series, Inc.

Champlin, DeeAnn. Eddie E & the Eggs. Champlin, DeeAnn, illus. Date not set. (Little Lyrics Short Vowel Collection: Vol. 2). (Illus.). (J). (gr. k-2). pap. 12.00 (978-1-893429-26-0(1)) Little Lyrics Pubns.

—Five Funny A's. Champlin, DeeAnn, illus. 1998. (Little Lyrics Short Vowel Collection: Vol. 1). (Illus.). (J). (gr. k-2). pap. 12.00 (978-1-893429-25-3(3)) Little Lyrics Pubns.

—Incredible I. 1998. (Little Lyrics Short Vowel Collection: Vol. 3). (Illus.). (J). (gr. k-2). pap. 12.00 (978-1-893429-27-7(X)) Little Lyrics Pubns.

—The Land of U. 1998. (Little Lyrics Short Vowel Collection: Vol. 5). (Illus.). (J). (gr. k-2). pap. 12.00 (978-1-893429-29-1(6)) Little Lyrics Pubns.

—Let's Do the Vowel Sounds. 1998. (Little Lyrics Short Vowel Collection: Vol. 6). (Illus.). 11p. (J). (gr. k-2). pap. 12.00 (978-1-893429-30-7(X)) Little Lyrics Pubns.

—Oliver O & the Olives. Champlin, DeeAnn, illus. 1998. (Little Lyrics Short Vowel Collection: Vol. 4). (Illus.). (J). (gr. k-2). pap. 12.00 (978-1-893429-28-4(8)) Little Lyrics Pubns.

Chapman, Rhonda. Building Grammar. 2001. (Homework Booklets Ser.). 80p. (J). (gr. 5-6). pap. 2.99 (978-0-7424-0151-8(0) , IF0372); (YA). (gr. 7-8). pap. 2.99 (978-0-7424-0152-5(9) , IF0373) School Specialty Publishing.

Choy, Penelope. Basic Grammar. 2002. pap. 9.95 (978-0-8384-7415-0(2)) Thomson Heinle.

Christopher Lee Publications Staff. Webster's English Grammar Made Easy. 2002. (Webster's... Made Easy Flippers Ser.). (Illus.). (J). pap. 7.95 (978-1-59125-137-8(0)) Penton Overseas, Inc.

—Webster's English Grammar Made Easy Flippers. 2002. (Webster's... Made Easy Flippers Ser.). (Illus.). (J). pap. 7.95 (978-1-59125-166-8(4)) Penton Overseas, Inc.

—Webster's Language Terms Made Easy. 2002. (Webster's... Made Easy Flippers Ser.). (Illus.). (J). pap. 7.95 (978-1-59125-140-8(0)); 50p. pap. 7.95 (978-1-59125-167-5(2)) Penton Overseas, Inc.

Cimochowski, Anna. PassWord Decoder for Prefix, Root Word & Suffix Meanings. 2003. 72p. (gr. 3-5). wbk. ed. (978-1-56762-183-9(X)) Modern Learning Pr.

—PassWord Decoder for Tricky Letter Teams. 2003. 48p. (gr. 2-4). wbk. ed. (978-1-56762-182-2(1)) Modern Learning Pr.

Cleary, Brian P. Dearly, Nearly, Insincerely: What Is an Adverb? Gable, Brian, illus. 2005. 32p. (J). (ps-ps). pap. 5.95 (978-1-57505-919-8(3)) Lerner Publishing Group.

—Hairy, Scary, Ordinary: What Is an Adjective? Prosmitsky, Jenya, illus. 2005. (Words Are Categorical Ser.). 32p. (gr. 2-5). 14.95 (978-1-57505-401-8(9)) Lerner Publishing Group.

—Hairy, Scary, Ordinary: What Is an Adjective? 2000. (gr. 3-6). lib. bdg. 14.10 (978-0-613-43829-2(9)) Tandem Library Bks.

—A Mink, a Fink, a Skating Rink: What Is a Noun? Prosmitsky, Jenya, illus. (Words Are Categorical Ser.). 32p. (gr. 2-5). 2005. 14.95 (978-1-57505-402-5(7)); 2003. (J). pap. 5.95 (978-1-57505-417-9(5)) Lerner Publishing Group.

—Neatly, Sweetly, Quite Completely: More about Adverbs. Gable, Brian, illus. 2008. (Words Are CATegorical trade; Ser.). (J). lib. bdg. 15.95 (***978-0-8225-7848-2(4)**, Millbrook Pr.) Lerner Publishing Group.

—Quirky, Jerky, Extra-Perky: More about Adjectives. Gable, Brian, illus. 2007. (Words Are CATegorical Ser.). 32p. (J). (gr. 2-6). 15.95 (978-0-8225-6709-7(1) , Millbrook Pr.) Lerner Publishing Group.

—Slide & Slurp, Scratch & Burp: More about Verbs. Gable, Brian, illus. 2007. (Words Are CATegorical trade; Ser.). 32p. (J). (gr. 2-6). 15.95 (978-0-8225-6207-8(3) , Millbrook Pr.) Lerner Publishing Group.

—To Root, to Toot, to Parachute: What is a Verb? Prosmitsky, Jenya, illus. 2003. (Words Are Categorical Ser.). 32p. (J). (gr. 2-4). pap. 5.95 (978-1-57505-418-6(3)) Lerner Publishing Group.

—To Root, to Toot, to Parachute: What Is a Verb? Prosmitsky, Jenya, illus. (Words Are Categorical Ser.). (gr. 2-5). 2005. 32p. 14.95 (978-1-57505-403-2(5)); 1999. (J). 5.95 (978-0-8225-2110-5(5) , Lerner Pubns.) Lerner Publishing Group.

—Under, over, by the Clover: What Is A Preposition? 2002. (gr. 3-6). lib. bdg. 14.10 (978-0-613-68140-7(1)) Tandem Library Bks.

Cleary, Brian P. & Gable, Brian, illus. A Lime, a Mime, a Pool of Slime: More about Nouns. 2006. (Words Are Categorical Ser.). 32p. (J). (gr. 2-5). 15.95 (978-1-57505-937-2(1) , Millbrook Pr.) Lerner Publishing Group.

Correct Writing. (J). 16.00 (978-1-931555-01-2(X)) Our Lady of Victory Schl.

Critical Thinking Publishing Staff & Hockett, M. A. Punctuation Puzzler Bk. 1: Commas & More. 2003. (J). pap. 9.99 (978-0-89455-815-3(3)) Critical Thinking Bks. & Software.

—Punctuation Puzzler Bk. 1: Commas & More Level A. 2003. Orig. Title: Language Logic Twisters: Punctuation Puzzlers. (J). pap. 9.99 (978-0-89455-839-9(0)) Critical Thinking Bks. & Software.

Cutting, Robert. Languageworks 7: English Skills Resource. 2000. ix, 101p. (J). (978-0-13-026283-7(8)) Prentice Hall PTR.

Dahl, Michael. If You Were a Noun. Gray, Sara, illus. 2006. (Word Fun Ser.). 24p. (J). (gr. 2-4). 23.95 (978-1-4048-1355-7(1)) Picture Window Bks.

—If You Were a Verb. Gray, Sara, illus. 2006. (Word Fun Ser.). 24p. (J). (gr. 2-4). 23.95 (978-1-4048-1354-0(3)) Picture Window Bks.

—If You Were an Adjective. Gray, Sara, illus. 2006. (Word Fun Ser.). 24p. (J). (gr. 2-4). 23.95 (978-1-4048-1356-4(X)) Picture Window Bks.

—If You Were an Adverb. Gray, Sara, illus. 2006. (Word Fun Ser.). 24p. (J). (gr. 2-4). 23.95 (978-1-4048-1357-1(8)) Picture Window Bks.

Daily Grams Workbook Grade 5. 2003. 180p. pap. 12.95 (978-0-936981-38-3(5)) Isha Enterprises, Inc.

Daily Grams Workbook Grade 7. 2003. 180p. pap. 12.95 (978-0-936981-37-6(7)) Isha Enterprises, Inc.

Dora the Explorer Nouns-First Object Words. 2007. (J). pap. 2.95 (***978-1-59545-159-0(5)**) Learning Horizons, Inc.

Dorothea Lange: Fifth Grade Guided Comprehension Level O. (On Our Way to English Ser.). (gr. 5 up). 34.50 (978-0-7578-6607-4(7)) Rigby Education.

Doudna, Kelly. Adjectives. l.t. ed. 2001. (Sentences Ser.). (Illus.). 24p. (J). (ps-3). lib. bdg. 19.93 (978-1-57765-617-3(2) , SandCastle) ABDO Publishing Co.

—Adverbs. l.t. ed. 2001. (Sentences Ser.). (Illus.). 24p. (J). (ps-3). lib. bdg. 19.93 (978-1-57765-616-6(4) , SandCastle) ABDO Publishing Co.

—Ida & Ike. 2005. (First Sounds Ser.). (Illus.). 23p. (J). pap. (978-1-59679-165-7(9)); 19.93 (978-1-59679-164-0(0)) ABDO Publishing Co.

—Nouns. l.t. ed. 2001. (Sentences Ser.). (Illus.). 24p. (J). (ps-3). lib. bdg. 19.93 (978-1-57765-614-2(8) , SandCastle) ABDO Publishing Co.

—Pronouns. l.t. ed. 2001. (Sentences Ser.). (Illus.). 24p. (J). (ps-3). lib. bdg. 19.93 (978-1-57765-619-7(9) , SandCastle) ABDO Publishing Co.

—Proper Nouns. l.t. ed. 2001. (Sentences Ser.). (Illus.). 24p. (J). (ps-3). lib. bdg. 19.93 (978-1-57765-618-0(0) , SandCastle) ABDO Publishing Co.

—Sentences, Set. l.t. ed. Incl. Adjectives. lib. bdg. 19.93 (978-1-57765-617-3(2)); Adverbs. lib. bdg. 19.93 (978-1-57765-616-6(4)); Nouns. lib. bdg. 19.93 (978-1-57765-614-2(8)); Pronouns. lib. bdg. 19.93 (978-1-57765-619-7(9)); Proper Nouns. lib. bdg. 19.93 (978-1-57765-618-0(0)); Verbs. lib. bdg. 19.93 (978-1-57765-615-9(6)); 24p. (J). (ps-3). (Illus.). 2001. Set lib. bdg. 119.58 (978-1-57765-513-8(3) , SandCastle) ABDO Publishing Co.

—Verbs. l.t. ed. 2001. (Sentences Ser.). (Illus.). 24p. (J). (ps-3). lib. bdg. 19.93 (978-1-57765-615-9(6) , SandCastle) ABDO Publishing Co.

E F G

Douglas, Vincent & School Specialty Publishing Staff. The Complete Book of Grammar & Punctuation. 2005. (Complete Book Ser.). (Illus.). 352p. (J). pap. 14.95 (978-0-7696-4332-8(9) , American Education Publishing) School Specialty Publishing.

Dreamers & Doers: Fifth Grade Guided Comprehension Level S. (On Our Way to English Ser.). (gr. 5 up). 34.50 (978-0-7578-6627-2(1)) Rigby Education.

Early Fluency Skills Guide. (Sunshine Skills Guides). 25.95 (978-0-7802-9811-8(X)) Wright Group, The.

Egan, Lorraine Hopping. Noun Hounds & Other Great Grammar Games: 20 Fun & Easy Reproducible Games That Help Every Kid Grasp the Essential Rules of Grammar. 2001. (Illus.). 96p. (gr. 3-6). pap. 12.95 (978-0-439-05174-3(6)) Scholastic, Inc.

Elbaum. Grammar in Context: Sampling Letter. 3rd ed. 2000. (978-0-8384-2393-6(0)) Thomson Heinle.

Elliott, Rebecca. Painless Grammar. Hamilton, Laurie, illus. 2nd ed. 2006. (Painless Ser.). 224p. pap., stu. ed. 8.99 (978-0-7641-3436-4(1)) Barron's Educational Series, Inc.

English: Grade 5. 2000. (Master Skills Ser.). (Illus.). 128p. (J). (gr. k-6). pap., wbk. ed. 6.95 (978-1-56189-025-5(1) , 12015, American Education Publishing) School Specialty Publishing.

English Grammar Skills, Chapter 1, Activities. 2005. (Illus.). 64p. (YA). pap. 7.00 (978-1-59476-126-3(4)) Paradigm Accelerated Curriculum.

English Grammar Skills, Chapter 1, Text. 2005. (Illus.). 54p. (YA). pap. 7.00 (978-1-59476-121-8(3)) Paradigm Accelerated Curriculum.

English Grammar Skills, Chapter 2, Activities. 2005. (Illus.). 54p. (YA). pap. 5.00 (978-1-59476-127-0(2)) Paradigm Accelerated Curriculum.

English Grammar Skills, Chapter 2, Text. 2005. (Illus.). 46p. (YA). pap. 7.00 (978-1-59476-122-5(1)) Paradigm Accelerated Curriculum.

English Grammar Skills, Chapter 3, Activities. 2005. (Illus.). 50p. (YA). pap. 5.00 (978-1-59476-128-7(0)) Paradigm Accelerated Curriculum.

English Grammar Skills, Chapter 3, Text. 2005. (Illus.). 44p. (YA). pap. 7.00 (978-1-59476-123-2(X)) Paradigm Accelerated Curriculum.

English Grammar Skills, Chapter 4, Activities. 2005. (Illus.). 46p. (YA). pap. 5.00 (978-1-59476-129-4(9)) Paradigm Accelerated Curriculum.

English Grammar Skills, Chapter 4, Text. 2005. (Illus.). 40p. (YA). pap. 7.00 (978-1-59476-124-9(8)) Paradigm Accelerated Curriculum.

English Grammar Skills, Chapter 5, Activities. 2005. (Illus.). 48p. (YA). pap. 5.00 (978-1-59476-130-0(2)) Paradigm Accelerated Curriculum.

English Grammar Skills, Chapter 5, Text. 2005. (Illus.). 46p. (YA). pap. 7.00 (978-1-59476-125-6(6)) Paradigm Accelerated Curriculum.

English Grammar Skills, Full Course Kit. 2005. (Illus.). 736p. (YA). 75.00 (978-1-59476-092-1(6)) Paradigm Accelerated Curriculum.

English I: Language Skills, Chapter 2 Text. 2005. (Illus.). 54p. (YA). pap. 7.00 (978-1-59476-133-1(7)) Paradigm Accelerated Curriculum.

English I: Language Skills, Chapter 3 Text. 2005. (Illus.). 54p. (YA). pap. 7.00 (978-1-59476-134-8(5)) Paradigm Accelerated Curriculum.

English I: Language Skills, Chapter 4 Activities. 2005. (Illus.). 72p. (YA). pap. 5.00 (978-1-59476-140-9(X)) Paradigm Accelerated Curriculum.

English I: Language Skills, Chapter 4 Text. 2005. (Illus.). 62p. (YA). pap. 7.00 (978-1-59476-135-5(3)) Paradigm Accelerated Curriculum.

English I: Language Skills, Chapter 5 Activites. 2005. (Illus.). 66p. (YA). pap. 5.00 (978-1-59476-141-6(8)) Paradigm Accelerated Curriculum.

English I: Language Skills, Chapter 5 Text. 2005. (Illus.). 76p. (YA). pap. 7.00 (978-1-59476-136-2(1)) Paradigm Accelerated Curriculum.

Espanol Activo: Septimo Grado. (SPA & ENG.). (YA). (gr. 7). 14.25 (978-84-499-4721-6(9) , CPR82) Prous, J. R. S.A. ESP. *Dist:* Continental Bk. Co., Inc.

Exercises in English: Grammar for Life; Level C. 2004. (gr. 3 up). tchr. ed. (978-0-8294-2016-6(9)); stu. ed. (978-0-8294-1741-8(9)) Loyola Pr.

Exercises in English: Grammar for Life; Level E. 2004. (Illus.). (gr. 5 up). stu. ed. (978-0-8294-1745-6(1)) Loyola Pr.

Exercises in English: Grammar for Life; Level F. 2004. (gr. 6 up). tchr. ed. (978-0-8294-2019-7(3)); stu. ed. (978-0-8294-1748-7(6)) Loyola Pr.

Exercises in English: Grammar for Life; Level G. 2004. (gr. 7 up). stu. ed. (978-0-8294-1750-0(8)) Loyola Pr.

Exercises in English: Grammar for Life; Level H. 2004. (gr. 8 up). tchr. ed. (978-0-8294-2021-0(5)); stu. ed. (978-0-8294-1752-4(4)) Loyola Pr.

Fenick, Ruth & Dion, Elaine. Using Standards Grammar Gr 7-8. 2003. (100+ Seriestm Ser.). 128p. (YA). (gr. 7-8). pap. 12.99 (978-0-7424-1807-3(3) , IFG99056) School Specialty Publishing.

Fisk, Sally. A Christian Child's Guide to Grammar: Grade 2. Fisk, Sally, illus. 2000. (Illus.). 28p. (J). (gr. 2-3). pap. 6.95 (978-1-930338-04-3(X) , G1002) Praise Pubns.

—A Christian Child's Guide to Grammar: Grade 4, 3 vols., Vol. 3. Fisk, Sally, illus. 2000. (Illus.). 28p. (J). (gr. 4-6). pap. 6.95 (978-1-930338-06-7(6) , G1004) Praise Pubns.

—A Christian Child's Guide to Grammar Vol. 2: Grade 3. Fisk, Sally, illus. 2000. (Illus.). 28p. (J). (gr. 3-5). pap. 6.95 (978-1-930338-05-0(8) , G1003) Praise Pubns.

Food - Set 2: Adjective-Noun. 2004. (J). spiral bd. 23.40 (978-0-9770248-2-7(2)) Sidedoor Publishing LLC.

Fry. Picture Nouns. 2004. (Reading Ser.). (Illus.). 48p. 7.99 (978-1-57690-763-4(5)) Teacher Created Materials, Inc.

Fun-to-Learn: Beginning Consonants. (ps-1). 2.99 (978-0-7424-0175-4(8) , IF0408) School Specialty Publishing.

Gerngross, Gunter & Puchta, Herbert. Join in, Bk. 1. 2000. (Join In Ser.). (Illus.). 32p. pap., act. bk. ed. 6.00 (978-0-521-77521-2(3)) Cambridge Univ. Pr.

Gifford, Myrna. Name Those Vowels: A Read-and-Sing Book. Cooper, Frances, illus. 2003. 12p. (J). 9.95 (978-0-9720763-4-0(4)) Action Factor, Inc.

—Oh, Do You Know? A Read-and-Sing Book. Cooper, France, illus. 2003. 12p. (J). 9.95 (978-0-9720763-5-7(2)) Action Factor, Inc.

Gill, Kim & DeNinno, Joanne P. Say & Do Grammar Gameboards Fun Sheets. DeShong, Molly et al, eds. 2002. (Illus.). (J). (ps-5). spiral bd. 29.95 (978-1-58650-222-5(0)) Super Duper Pubns.

Gill, Kim A. & DeNinno, Joanne P. Fun Deck & Do. DeShong, Molly & Webber, Thomas, eds. 2001. (Illus.). 218p. (J). (gr. k-6). spiral bd. 33.95 (978-1-58650-169-3(0) , BK-287) Super Duper Pubns.

Gillham, Bill, et al. Essential Skills, 4 bks. (Illus.). 128p. (YA). pap. 15.99 (978-0-340-71583-3(9) , Hodder & Stoughton) Hodder General Publishing Division GBR. *Dist:* Trafalgar Square Publishing.

Goldenberg, Phyllis, et al. Grammar for Writing, Complete Course. Incl. Grammar for Writing, Complete Course : Student Test Booklet. 48p. stu. ed. (978-0-8215-0352-2(9)); Grammar for Writing, Complete Course, Grade 12. 400p. tchr. ed. 18.99 (978-0-8215-0322-5(7)); (YA). (gr. 12 up). 1999. (Grammar for Writing Ser.). 384p. 1999. pap., stu. ed. (978-0-8215-0312-6(X)) Sadlier, William H. Inc.

—Grammar for Writing, Complete Course: Student Test Booklet. 1999. (Grammar for Writing Ser.). 48p. (YA). (gr. 12 up). stu. ed. (978-0-8215-0352-2(9)) Sadlier, William H. Inc.

—Grammar for Writing, Fifth Course. Incl. Grammar for Writing, Fifth Course : Student Test Booklet. 48p. stu. ed. (978-0-8215-0350-8(2)); Grammar for Writing, Fifth Course, Grades 10-11. 400p. tchr. ed. 18.99 (978-0-8215-0320-1(0)); (YA). (gr. 10 up). (Grammar for Writing Ser.). 352p. 1999. pap., stu. ed. (978-0-8215-0310-2(3)) Sadlier, William H. Inc.

—Grammar for Writing, Fourth Course: Student Test Booklet. 1999. (Grammar for Writing Ser.). 48p. (YA). (gr. 9 up). stu. ed. (978-0-8215-0349-2(9)) Sadlier, William H. Inc.

—Grammar for Writing, Sixth Course. Incl. Grammar for Writing, Sixth Course : Student Test Booklet. 48p. stu. ed. (978-0-8215-0351-5(0)); Grammar for Writing, Sixth Course, Grades 11-12. 400p. tchr. ed. 18.99 (978-0-8215-0321-8(9)); (YA). (gr. 11 up). (Grammar for Writing Ser.). 352p. 1999. pap., stu. ed. (978-0-8215-0311-9(1)) Sadlier, William H. Inc.

—Grammar for Writing, Sixth Course: Student Test Booklet. 1999. (Grammar for Writing Ser.). 48p. (YA). (gr. 11 up). stu. ed. (978-0-8215-0351-5(0)) Sadlier, William H. Inc.

Graham, Leland. Grammar Grade 4. 2003. (Skill Builders Ser.). 80p. (gr. 4 up). 2.95 (978-1-932210-11-8(3)) Rainbow Bridge Publishing.

—Grammar Grade 5. 2003. (Skill Builders Ser.). 80p. (gr. 5 up). 2.95 (978-1-932210-12-5(1)) Rainbow Bridge Publishing.

—Grammar Grade 6. 2003. (Skill Builders Ser.). 80p. (gr. 6 up). 2.95 (978-1-932210-13-2(X)) Rainbow Bridge Publishing.

Grammar Ad Libs. 2003. (J). pap. 9.95 (978-1-56911-106-2(5)) Learning Resources, Inc.

Grammar & Literature Games: Making Learning Fun through Friendly Classroom Competition. 2003. 48p. (gr. 5-8). 8.99 (978-0-7682-0656-2(1) , GA13089) School Specialty Publishing.

Grammar & Punctuation. 2002. (J). 112p. (gr. 1). per. 19.99 incl. cd-rom (978-1-55799-845-3(0) , EMC 2711); 112p. (gr. 2). per. 19.99 incl. cd-rom (978-1-55799-846-0(9) , EMC 2712); (gr. 3). per. 19.99 incl. cd-rom (978-1-55799-847-7(7) , EMC 2713); (gr. 4). per. 19.99 incl. cd-rom (978-1-55799-848-4(5) , EMC 2714); (gr. 5). per. 19.99 incl. cd-rom (978-1-55799-849-1(3) , EMC 2715); (gr. 6). per. 19.99 incl. cd-rom (978-1-55799-850-7(7) , EMC 2716) Evan-Moor Educational Pubs.

Grammar & Usage: English in Context. 2000. (Illus.). 112p. per., wbk. ed. 8.95 (978-1-56254-352-5(0) , SP 3520) Saddleback Educational Publishing.

Grammar Basics Plus: Level A. 2003. 128p. (C). pap. 13.99 (978-0-7424-1856-1(1) , LL90014) School Specialty Publishing.

Grammar in Action: Class Pack; 10 of Each Title. 2004. (Grammar Pocket Handbook Ser.). (978-0-8294-1050-1(3)); (978-0-8294-1052-5(X)) Loyola Pr.

Grammar in Action: Parts of Speech. 2004. (Grammar Practice Book Ser.). tchr. ed. (978-0-8294-0952-9(1)) Loyola Pr.

Grammar in Action: Punctuation, Capitalization, & Sentence Structure. 2004. (Grammar Practice Book Ser.). tchr. ed. (978-0-8294-0954-3(8)) Loyola Pr.

Grammar in Action: Student Pack; One of Each Title. 2004. (Grammar Practice Book Ser.). (978-0-8294-1051-8(1)) Loyola Pr.

Grammar Practice. 2004. 144p. (J). (gr. 5-6). 14.99 (978-0-7439-3622-4(1)); (Illus.). (gr. 1-2). 14.99 (978-0-7439-3620-0(5)); (Illus.). (gr. 3-4). 14.99 (978-0-7439-3621-7(3)) Teacher Created Materials, Inc.

Grammar Practice Book. 2004. (gr. 1 up). suppl. ed. 1.95 (978-0-328-01175-9(4)); (gr. 1 up). wbk. ed. 5.25 (978-0-328-00664-9(5)); (gr. 2 up). 5.25 (978-0-328-00665-6(3)); (gr. 2 up). suppl. ed. 1.95 (978-0-328-01176-6(2)); (gr. 3 up). 5.25 (978-0-328-00666-3(1)); (gr. 3 up). 1.95 (978-0-328-01177-3(0) , Scott Foresman); (gr. 4 up). 5.25 (978-0-328-00667-0(X)); (gr. 4 up). 1.95 (978-0-328-01178-0(9)); (gr. 5 up). 5.25 (978-0-328-00668-7(8)); (gr. 5 up). 1.95 (978-0-328-01179-7(7) , Scott Foresman); (gr. 6 up). 5.25 (978-0-328-00669-4(6)); (gr. 6 up). 1.95 (978-0-328-01180-3(0)) Addison-Wesley Educational Pubs., Inc.

Grammar Readers Classroom Library Set. 2004. (J). pap. 249.95 (978-1-56911-185-7(5)) Learning Resources, Inc.

Grammar Readers Foundation Set. 2004. (J). pap. 44.95 (978-1-56911-184-0(7)) Learning Resources, Inc.

Grammar Rules! 2003. 128p. (J). per. 11.99 (978-0-88724-976-1(0) , CD-4338); per. 11.99 (978-0-88724-977-8(9) , CD-4339) Carson-Dellosa Publishing Co., Inc.

Grammer Rules! 2003. 128p. (J). per. 11.99 (978-0-88724-975-4(2)) Carson-Dellosa Publishing Co., Inc.

Gravois, Michael. Fill-in Flip Books for Grammar, Vocabulary, & More: Grades 3-5. 2005. (Illus.). 80p. (gr. 3-5). pap. 12.99 (978-0-439-67682-3(7) , Teaching Resources) Scholastic, Inc.

Greenberg, Dan. Comic-Strip Grammar: 40 Reproducible Cartoons with Engaging Practice Exercises That Make Learning Grammar Fun. 2000. (Illus.). 64p. pap. 10.95 (978-0-439-08681-3(7)) Scholastic, Inc.

Growing with Grammar Grade 3 Student Manual Grade 3. 2005. (J). stu. ed., spiral bd. 17.99 (978-0-9772923-0-1(4)) Davis, Tamela.

Growing with Grammar Grade 3 Student Workbook Grade 3. 2005. (J). spiral bd., wbk. ed. 13.99 (978-0-9772923-1-8(2)) Davis, Tamela.

Growing with Grammar Grade 4 Student Manual. 2006. (J). spiral bd. 17.99 (978-0-9772923-2-5(0)) Davis, Tamela.

Growing with Grammar Grade 4 Student Workbook. 2006. (J). spiral bd. 13.99 (978-0-9772923-3-2(9)) Davis, Tamela.

Hall, Prentice. Ph Literature, Gold Level. 5th ed. 1999. (YA). (gr. 9). stu. ed. 54.97 (978-0-13-434056-2(6)) Prentice Hall PTR.

Halverson, Jim. Parts of Speech Made Fun: A-Maze-Ing Practice Pages with Mini-Lessons & Grammar Tips. 2004. 64p. (gr. 5 up). pap. 11.99 (978-0-439-51892-5(X)) Scholastic, Inc.

—Ready-to-Go Reproducibles: Grammar. 2001. pap. 4.99 (978-0-439-05186-6(X)) Scholastic, Inc.

Harcourt School Publishers Staff. Collections: Reading & Language Skills: Standardized Test Preparation. 2003. (Trophies Ser.). (Illus.). (gr. 1 up). 7.50 (978-0-15-321227-7(6)) Harcourt Schl. Pubs.

—Harcourt Language Arts. 2nd ed. 2002. (Harcourt Language Ser.). (Illus.). (gr. k-6). pap., pupil's gde. ed. 21.00 (978-0-15-317998-3(8)); (gr. 2 up). pap., pupil's gde. ed. 47.60 (978-0-15-319094-0(9)); (gr. 4 up). pap., pupil's gde. ed. 58.70 (978-0-15-317834-4(5)); (gr. 5 up). pap., pupil's gde. ed. 63.80 (978-0-15-317836-8(1)) Harcourt Schl. Pubs.

—Harcourt Language Arts: Consumable Edition. 2nd ed. 2002. (Harcourt Language Ser.). (Illus.). (gr. 1 up). pap., pupil's gde. ed. 28.00 (978-0-15-317831-3(0)) Harcourt Schl. Pubs.

—Harcourt Language Arts: Practice Workbook. 2nd ed. 2002. (Harcourt Language Ser.). (Illus.). (gr. 2 up). pap., wbk. ed. 10.70 (978-0-15-317984-6(8)); (gr. 3 up). pap., wbk. ed. 10.70 (978-0-15-317985-3(6)); (gr. 4 up). pap., wbk. ed. 10.70 (978-0-15-317986-0(4)); (gr. 5 up). pap., wbk. ed. 10.70 (978-0-15-317987-7(2)) Harcourt Schl. Pubs.

—Harcourt Language Arts, Grade 1: Language Skills & Writing Assessment. 2nd ed. 2002. (Harcourt Language Ser.). (gr. 1 up). pap., tchr. ed. 57.50 (978-0-15-319123-7(6)) Harcourt Schl. Pubs.

—No, It's Not a Mouse! 3rd ed. 2002. (Trophies English Language Learners Ser.). (Illus.). pap. 5.10 (978-0-15-327877-8(3)) Harcourt Schl. Pubs.

—Nothing Will Stop Me! 3rd ed. 2002. (Trophies English Language Learners Ser.). (Illus.). pap. 5.10 (978-0-15-327885-3(4)) Harcourt Schl. Pubs.

—Success for Elements in Literature. 2nd ed. 2002. (gr. 1). pap. 26.60 (978-0-15-336543-0(9)) Harcourt Schl. Pubs.

—Test Best: Elements of Grammar - Reading. 2002. (J). (gr. 1). pap. (978-0-7398-7344-1(X)); (gr. 2). pap. (978-0-7398-7347-2(4)) Steck-Vaughn.

—Treasury of Literature: Grammar Practice. 95th ed. 1998. (gr. 6). pap. 9.40 (978-0-15-303588-3(9)); (gr. 7). pap. 10.50 (978-0-15-303589-0(7)) Harcourt Schl. Pubs.

—Walk the Moon. 3rd ed. 2002. (Trophies English Language Learners Ser.). (Illus.). pap. 5.10 (978-0-15-327824-2(2)) Harcourt Schl. Pubs.

Harper, Charise Mericle. The Little Book of Not So. 2005. (Illus.). 32p. (J). (ps-k). 9.95 (978-0-618-47319-9(X)) Houghton Mifflin Co. Trade & Reference Div.

Harte, May. ABCs in My House. 2004. (Look-And-Learn Books). (Illus.). (J). lib. bdg. 7.95 (978-1-4042-2824-5(1) , PowerKids Pr.) Rosen Publishing Group, Inc., The.

Hazan, Maurice. ESL Book 1 Michael's Friends. Hazan, Maurice, illus. 2002. 126p. spiral bd. 20.00 (978-1-932770-96-4(8) , EB1-SM) Symtalk, Inc.

—ESL Book 2 Symtalk ESL. Hazan, Maurice, illus. 2002. (Illus.). 133p. spiral bd. 22.00 (978-1-932770-25-4(9) , EB2-SM) Symtalk, Inc.

Headway: Level E from Sea to Sea. (J). (gr. 2-3). (978-0-89688-457-1(0) , 88-457) Open Court Publishing Co.

Heath Grammar & Composition: Grade 12. (YA). (gr. 12). pap. (978-0-669-15971-4(9)) Houghton Mifflin Co. (Schl. Div.).

Heinrichs, Ann. Adjectives. 2004. (Fun with Grammar Ser.). 32p. (J). (gr. 1-5). 27.07 (978-1-59296-067-5(7)) Child's World, Inc.

—Adverbs. 2004. (Fun with Grammar Ser.). 32p. (J). (gr. 1-5). 27.07 (978-1-59296-069-9(3)) Child's World, Inc.

—Conjunctions. 2004. (Fun with Grammar Ser.). 32p. (J). (gr. 1-5). 27.07 (978-1-59296-071-2(5)) Child's World, Inc.

—Interjections. 2004. (Fun with Grammar Ser.). 32p. (J). (gr. 1-5). 27.07 (978-1-59296-072-9(3)) Child's World, Inc.

—Nouns. 2004. (Fun with Grammar Ser.). 32p. (J). (gr. 1-5). 27.07 (978-1-59296-065-1(0)) Child's World, Inc.

—Prepositions. 2004. (Fun with Grammar Ser.). 32p. (J). (gr. 1-5). 27.07 (978-1-59296-070-5(7)) Child's World, Inc.

—Pronouns. 2004. (Fun with Grammar Ser.). 32p. (J). (gr. 1-5). 27.07 (978-1-59296-066-8(9)) Child's World, Inc.

—Verbs. 2004. (Magic of Language Ser.). 32p. (J). (gr. 1-5). 27.07 (978-1-59296-068-2(5)) Child's World, Inc.

Heller, Ruth. Behind the Mask: A Book about Prepositions. Heller, Ruth, illus. 1998. (World of Language Ser.). (Illus.). 48p. (J). (gr. k up). pap. 7.99 (978-0-698-11698-6(4) , Putnam Juvenile) Penguin Group (USA) Inc.

—Behind the Mask: A Book about Prepositions. 1998. (Illus.). (J). (ps-17). lib. bdg. 15.30 (978-0-613-10368-8(8)) Tandem Library Bks.

—Fantastic! Wow! & Unreal! A Book about Interjections & Conjunctions. 2000. 13.79 (978-0-606-20358-6(3)); (J). (978-0-606-20234-3(X)) Tandem Library Bks.

—Kites Sail High. 1998. (World of Language Ser.). (Illus.). 48p. (J). (gr. k-3). pap. 7.99 (978-0-698-11389-3(6) , Putnam Juvenile) Penguin Group (USA) Inc.

—Many Luscious Lollipops: A Book about Adjectives. 1998. (World of Language Ser.). (Illus.). 48p. (J). (gr. k-3). pap. 7.99 (978-0-698-11641-2(0) , Putnam Juvenile) Penguin Group (USA) Inc.

—Merry-Go-Round: A Book about Nouns. 1998. (World of Language Ser.). (Illus.). 48p. (J). (gr. k-3). pap. 7.99 (978-0-698-11642-9(9) , Putnam Juvenile) Penguin Group (USA) Inc.

—Mine, All Mine: A Book about Pronouns. Heller, Ruth, illus. 1999. (Ruth Heller's World of Nature Ser.). (Illus.). 48p. (J). (ps-3). pap. 6.99 (978-0-698-11797-6(2) , Putnam Juvenile) Penguin Group (USA) Inc.

—Mine, All Mine: A Book about Pronouns. 1999. (gr. k-3). lib. bdg. 15.50 (978-0-613-22007-1(2)) Tandem Library Bks.

—Up, up & Away: A Book about Adverbs. Heller, Ruth, illus. 1998. (World of Language Ser.). (Illus.). 48p. (J). (gr. k-3). pap. 7.99 (978-0-698-11663-4(1) , Putnam Juvenile) Penguin Group (USA) Inc.

Herzog, Joyce. Expedition with Vowels: Student Activity Book. Sinclair, Angie & Sinclair, Dan, eds. 2005. (J). spiral bd. 15.00 (***978-1-887225-44-1(7)**) JoyceHerzog.com, Inc.

—Expedition with Vowels Reader: Part of the Little Beginner's Book Series. 2005. (J). spiral bd. 15.00 (***978-1-887225-34-2(X)**) JoyceHerzog.com, Inc.

Hex, Kathleen. Using Standards Grammar Gr 3. 2003. (100+ Seriestm Ser.). 128p. (J). (gr. 3 up). pap. 12.99 (978-0-7424-1803-5(0) , IFG99052) School Specialty Publishing.

High-Interest Reading Comprehension Skills & Strategies Level 5. 2002. (Illus.). 144p. per. 16.95 (978-1-56254-032-6(7) , SP 0327) Saddleback Educational Publishing.

High-Interest Reading Comprehension Skills & Strategies Level 6. 2002. (Illus.). 144p. per. 16.95 (978-1-56254-033-3(5) , SP 0335) Saddleback Educational Publishing.

High Point. (High Point Ser.). (gr. 6-12). 57.61 (978-0-7362-0969-4(7)); 7.52 (978-0-7362-0967-0(0)); 7.52 (978-0-7362-0935-9(2)); tchr. ed. 33.37 (978-0-7362-0981-6(6)); tchr. ed. 33.37 (978-0-7362-0949-6(2)); suppl. ed. 57.61 (978-0-7362-0937-3(9)); tchr.'s assessmt. gde. ed. 27.50 (978-0-7362-0950-2(6)); instr.'s hndbk. ed. 27.50 (978-0-7362-0982-3(4)); 2002. tchr. ed. 91.16 (978-0-7362-1224-3(8)); 2002. tchr. ed. 33.37 (978-0-7362-1261-8(2)); 2002. stu. ed. 37.74 (978-0-7362-

1223-6(X)); 2002. instr.'s hndbk. ed. 19.96 (978-0-7362-1227-4(2)); 2000. 57.61 (978-0-7362-0905-2(0)); 2000. 7.52 (978-0-7362-0903-8(4)); 2000. tchr. ed. 33.37 (978-0-7362-0917-5(4)); 2000. tchr.'s assessmt. gde. ed. 27.50 (978-0-7362-0918-2(2)); 2000. tchr. ed. 14.19 (978-0-7362-0904-5(2)); tchr. ed. 14.19 (978-0-7362-0936-6(0)); tchr. ed. 14.19 (978-0-7362-0968-7(9)); Level C. stu. ed. 43.80 (978-0-7362-0965-6(4)); Level A. 2000. stu. ed. 43.80 (978-0-7362-0901-4(8)); Level B. stu. ed. 43.80 (978-0-7362-0933-5(6)) Hampton-Brown Bks.

Hockett, M. A. Punctuation Puzzler: Commas & More Level C1. 2003. (YA). pap. 9.99 (978-0-89455-816-0(1)) Critical Thinking Bks. & Software.

—Punctuation Puzzler: Run-Ons Level C1. 2005. (YA). pap. 9.99 (978-0-89455-819-1(6)) Critical Thinking Bks. & Software.

Holt, Rinehart and Winston Staff. Allez Viens! Level 1: Grammar & Vocabulary Workbook. 1998. pap., tchr. ed. 21.86 (978-0-03-052642-8(6)) Holt, Rinehart & Winston.

—Daily Language Activities Transparencies: Elements of Language. 2000. trans. 145.53 (978-0-03-056014-9(4)); trans. 145.53 (978-0-03-056018-7(7)); trans. 145.53 (978-0-03-056019-4(5)); trans. 145.53 (978-0-03-056022-4(5)); trans. 145.53 (978-0-03-056017-0(9)) Holt, Rinehart & Winston.

—Daily Language Acttivities Transparencies: Elements of Language. 2000. trans. 145.53 (978-0-03-056013-2(6)) Holt, Rinehart & Winston.

—Elements of Language: Combining Sentences. (Elements of Language Ser.). 2003. pap. 10.93 (978-0-03-056306-5(2)); 2000. pap. 10.93 (978-0-03-056307-2(0)); 2000. pap. 10.93 (978-0-03-056308-9(9)); 2000. pap. 10.93 (978-0-03-056311-9(9)); 2000. pap. 10.93 (978-0-03-056309-6(7)) Holt, Rinehart & Winston.

—Elements of Language: Combining Sentences - Grade 11. 2000. pap. 10.93 (978-0-03-056312-6(7)) Holt, Rinehart & Winston.

—Elements of Language: Combining Sentences - Grade 12. 2000. pap. 10.93 (978-0-03-056313-3(5)) Holt, Rinehart & Winston.

—Elements of Language: Developing Language Skills Answer Key. 4th ed. Date not set. (YA). (gr. 10). pap. 12.80 (978-0-03-070072-9(8)); (gr. 11). pap. 12.80 (978-0-03-070073-6(6)); (gr. 12). pap. 12.80 (978-0-03-070074-3(4)); (gr. 9). pap. 12.80 (978-0-03-070071-2(X)) Holt, Rinehart & Winston.

—Elements of Language: Grammar & Language Links. 1999. 29.20 (978-0-03-052359-5(1)); 29.20 (978-0-03-052364-9(8)); 29.20 (978-0-03-052358-8(3)); 29.20 (978-0-03-052362-5(1)); 29.20 (978-0-03-052363-2(X)) Holt, Rinehart & Winston.

—Elements of Language: Grammar, Usage & Mechanics: Language Skills Answer Key - Grade 10. 2000. pap. 23.13 (978-0-03-056363-8(1)) Holt, Rinehart & Winston.

—Elements of Language: Grammar, Usage & Mechanics: Language Skills Answer Key - Grade 12. 2000. pap. 23.13 (978-0-03-056366-9(6)) Holt, Rinehart & Winston.

—Elements of Language: Grammar, Usage & Mechanics: Language Skills Answer Key - Grade 7. 2000. pap. 23.13 (978-0-03-056359-1(3)) Holt, Rinehart & Winston.

—Elements of Language: Grammar, Usage & Mechanics: Language Skills Answer Key - Grade 8. 2000. pap. 23.13 (978-0-03-056361-4(5)) Holt, Rinehart & Winston.

—Elements of Language: Grammar, Usage & Mechanics: Language Skills Answer Key - Grade 9. 2000. pap. 23.13 (978-0-03-056362-1(3)) Holt, Rinehart & Winston.

—Elements of Language: Grammar, Usage & Mechanics: Language Skills Answer Key Grade 11. 2000. pap. 23.13 (978-0-03-056364-5(X)) Holt, Rinehart & Winston.

—Elements of Language: How-to Handbook for High School. 2000. pap. 28.40 (978-0-03-056324-9(0)) Holt, Rinehart & Winston.

—Elements of Language: How-to Handbook for Middle School. 2000. pap. 28.40 (978-0-03-056323-2(2)) Holt, Rinehart & Winston.

—Elements of Language: Sentences & Paragraphs - Grade 6. 2003. (Elements of Language Ser.). 11.33 (978-0-03-056314-0(3)) Holt, Rinehart & Winston.

—Elements of Language: Sentences & Paragraphs - Grade 7. 2000. pap. 11.33 (978-0-03-056316-4(X)) Holt, Rinehart & Winston.

—Elements of Language: Sentences & Paragraphs - Grade 8. 2000. pap. 11.33 (978-0-03-056317-1(8)) Holt, Rinehart & Winston.

—Elements of Language: Sentences & Paragraphs - Grade 9. 2000. pap. 11.33 (978-0-03-056318-8(6)) Holt, Rinehart & Winston.

—Elements of Language: Sentences, Paragraphs & Compositions - Grade 10. 2001. pap. 11.33 (978-0-03-056319-5(4)) Holt, Rinehart & Winston.

—Elements of Language: Sentences, Paragraphs & Compositions - Grade 11. 2001. pap. 11.33 (978-0-03-056321-8(6)) Holt, Rinehart & Winston.

—Elements of Language: Sentences, Paragraphs & Compositions - Grade 12. 2001. pap. 11.33 (978-0-03-056322-5(4)) Holt, Rinehart & Winston.

—Elements of Language: Standard Format Chapter Tests: Illinois Edition. 2001. (gr. 10). pap. 4.00 (978-0-03-066979-8(0)); (gr. 11). pap. 4.00 (978-0-03-066981-1(2)); (gr. 12). pap. 4.00 (978-0-03-066982-8(0)); (gr. 6). pap. 4.00 (978-0-03-066974-3(X)); (gr. 7). pap. 4.00 (978-0-03-066976-7(6)); (gr. 8). pap. 4.00 (978-0-03-066977-4(4)); (gr. 9). pap. 4.00 (978-0-03-066978-1(2)) Holt, Rinehart & Winston.

—Elements of Language: Standard Format Chapter Tests: Kansas Edition. 2001. (gr. 6). pap. 13.46 (978-0-03-066983-5(9)) Holt, Rinehart & Winston.

—Elements of Language: Support & Practice - Grade 11. 2000. pap. 37.80 (978-0-03-056401-7(8)) Holt, Rinehart & Winston.

—Elements of Language -2001: Preparation for LEAP: Middle School - Louisiana Edition. 2001. pap. 13.86 (978-0-03-064582-2(4)) Holt, Rinehart & Winston.

—Elements of Language 2000: Practicing for TAAS - Grade 6. 2000. pap. 13.86 (978-0-03-064732-1(0)) Holt, Rinehart & Winston.

—Elements of Language 2000: Practicing for TAAS - Grade 8. 2000. pap. 13.86 (978-0-03-064734-5(7)) Holt, Rinehart & Winston.

—Elements of Language 2001: Preparation for LEAP: High School - Louisiana Edition. 2001. pap. 13.86 (978-0-03-064583-9(2)) Holt, Rinehart & Winston.

—Elements of Language, Grade 10: One-Step Lesson Planner & Standard Chapter Tests: Indiana Edition. 2001. pap. 13.46 (978-0-03-067011-4(X)) Holt, Rinehart & Winston.

—Elements of Language, Grade 10: Standard Format Chapter Tests: Kansas Edition. 2001. pap. 13.46 (978-0-03-066988-0(X)) Holt, Rinehart & Winston.

—Elements of Language, Grade 10: Standard Format Chapter Tests: Missouri Edition. 2001. pap. 13.46 (978-0-03-066997-2(9)) Holt, Rinehart & Winston.

—Elements of Language, Grade 11: Standard Format Chapter Tests: Kansas Edition. 2001. pap. 13.46 (978-0-03-066989-7(8)) Holt, Rinehart & Winston.

—Elements of Language, Grade 11: Standard Format Chapter Tests: Missouri Edition. 2001. pap. 13.46 (978-0-03-066998-9(7)) Holt, Rinehart & Winston.

—Elements of Language, Grade 12: Standard Format Chapter Tests: Kansas Edition. 2001. pap. 13.46 (978-0-03-066991-0(X)) Holt, Rinehart & Winston.

—Elements of Language, Grade 12: With Correlations: Indiana Edition. annot. ed. 2001. pap., tchr. ed. 132.93 (978-0-03-067161-6(2)) Holt, Rinehart & Winston.

—Elements of Language, Grade 6: Standard Format Chapter Tests: Missouri Edition. 2001. pap. 13.46 (978-0-03-066992-7(8)) Holt, Rinehart & Winston.

—Elements of Language, Grade 7: Communications - Louisiana Edition. 2002. pap., wbk. ed. 113.40 (978-0-03-068326-8(2)) Holt, Rinehart & Winston.

—Elements of Language, Grade 7: Standard Format Chapter Tests: Kansas Edition. 2001. pap. 13.46 (978-0-03-066984-2(7)) Holt, Rinehart & Winston.

—Elements of Language, Grade 7: Standard Format Chapter Tests: Missouri Edition. 2001. pap. 13.46 (978-0-03-066993-4(6)) Holt, Rinehart & Winston.

—Elements of Language, Grade 8: One-Step Lesson Planner & Standard Chapter Tests: Indiana Edition. 2001. pap. 13.46 (978-0-03-067008-4(X)) Holt, Rinehart & Winston.

—Elements of Language, Grade 8: Standard Format Chapter Tests: Kansas Edition. 2001. pap. 13.46 (978-0-03-066986-6(3)) Holt, Rinehart & Winston.

—Elements of Language, Grade 8: Standard Format Chapter Tests: Missouri Edition. 2001. pap. 13.46 (978-0-03-066994-1(4)) Holt, Rinehart & Winston.

—Elements of Language, Grade 9: One-Step Lesson Planner & Standard Chapter Tests: Indiana Edition. 2001. pap. 13.46 (978-0-03-067009-1(8)) Holt, Rinehart & Winston.

—Elements of Language, Grade 9: Standard Format Chapter Tests: Kansas Edition. 2001. pap. 13.46 (978-0-03-066987-3(1)) Holt, Rinehart & Winston.

—Elements of Languge, Grade 7: One-Step Lesson Planner & Standard Chapter Tests: Indiana Edition. 2001. pap. 13.46 (978-0-03-067007-7(1)) Holt, Rinehart & Winston.

—Elements of Literature: Daily Oral Grammar: Texas Edition. 1999. (gr. 10). 145.53 (978-0-03-053763-9(0)) Holt, Rinehart & Winston.

—Elements of Literature, Grade 7: Daily Oral Grammar: Georgia Edition. 3rd ed. 2003. pap. 148.26 (978-0-03-068613-9(X)) Holt, Rinehart & Winston.

—Elements of Literature, Grade 8: Daily Oral Grammar: Georgia Edition. 3rd ed. 2003. pap. 148.26 (978-0-03-068614-6(8)) Holt, Rinehart & Winston.

—Workshop: Course 4. 95th ed. 1998. pap. 19.60 (978-0-03-097177-8(2)) Holt, Rinehart & Winston.

—Workshop: Course 5. 95th ed. 1999. pap. 19.60 (978-0-03-097178-5(0)) Holt, Rinehart & Winston.

How Did They Do That? Fifth Grade Guided Comprehension Level Q. (On Our Way to English Ser.). (gr. 5 up). 34.50 (978-0-7578-6615-9(8)) Rigby Education.

Howell, Brandy. Sustantivos. 2007. (Dora The Explorer Ser.). (SPA & ENG.). 32p. (J). pap. 2.95 (*978-1-59545-075-3(0)) Learning Horizons, Inc.

Howell, Jennifer. Tracking down the Parts of Speech Game. 2005. (YA). 49.95 (978-1-58804-387-0(8)) PCI Educational Publishing.

How's the Weather? Fifth Grade Guided Comprehension Level T. (On Our Way to English Ser.). (gr. 5 up). 34.50 (978-0-7578-6630-2(1)) Rigby Education.

Hubbard, L. Ron. Grammar & Communication for Children. 496p. (J). (gr. 3-7). 62.50 (978-0-88404-746-9(6)) Bridge Pubns., Inc.

Huber, Marcia. Literature Circles: Using Student Interaction to Improve Reading Comprehension, 2271. Samoiloff, Sheri, ed. Yamada, Jane, illus. 2001. 80p. pap. 9.99 (978-1-57471-790-7(1)) Creative Teaching Pr., Inc.

Hughes, Linda. Dominie Vocabulary Builders. Peh, Sherlyne, illus. 1999. (J). (978-0-7685-0362-3(0)) Dominie Pr., Inc.

I & You & Don't Forget Who: What Is a Pronoun? 2006. (Illus.). 32p. (J). pap. 5.95 (978-0-8225-6469-0(6) , First Avenue Editions) Lerner Publishing Group.

Improving Student Reading Comprehension - Grades 1-2. 2004. (J). pap. 14.95 (978-1-56911-166-6(9)) Learning Resources, Inc.

Improving Student Reading Comprehension - Grades 3-4. 2004. (J). pap. 14.95 (978-1-56911-167-3(7)) Learning Resources, Inc.

Improving Student Reading Comprehension - Grades 5-6. 2004. (J). pap. 14.95 (978-1-56911-168-0(5)) Learning Resources, Inc.

Improving Student Writing: Grammar. 2004. (J). per. 12.95 (978-1-56911-527-5(3)) Learning Resources, Inc.

Jackson, Abby. Donde? 2005. Tr. of Where?. (SPA., Illus.). 16p. (J). (gr. k-1). lib. bdg. 15.93 (978-0-7368-4133-7(4)) Capstone Pr., Inc.

Jones, Beau, et al. Insights Reading As Thinking: Comprehension Strategies: Responding to Literature - Purple Level Student Book. 1998. (Illus.). (YA). (gr. 7). pap., stu. ed. 7.00 (978-1-57091-064-7(2) , R710) Charlesbridge Publishing, Inc.

—Insights Reading As Thinking: Comprehension Strategies: Responding to Literature - Silver Level Student Book. 1998. (Illus.). (YA). (gr. 8). pap., stu. ed. 7.00 (978-1-57091-066-1(9) , R810) Charlesbridge Publishing, Inc.

Jones, Vernie O. & Jensen, Frode M. A Journey Through Grammar Land, Parts 1 And 2. 2007. (Illus.). 184p. per. 29.00 (*978-1-886061-41-5(6)) Wordsmiths.

—A Journey Through Grammar Land, Parts 1 & 2 Tests & Answers. 2007. 40p. 1.00 (*978-1-886061-42-2(4)) Wordsmiths.

Jordan, Sara. Thematic Songs for Learning Language. Howard, Joan, ed. Filipov, Alex, illus. 2000. 48p. pap. 14.95 incl. audio (978-1-894262-33-0(6) , JMP120K) Jordan Music Productions, Inc.

A Journey Through Grammar Land, 5 vols., Vol. 1. 2nd ed. 2000. (Journey Through Grammar Land Ser.: Vol. 1). 120p. (YA). pap. 15.00 (978-1-886061-15-6(7)) Wordsmiths.

Journey Through Grammar Land 3. 2004. (gr. 5-7). pap. 30.00 (978-1-886061-32-3(7)) Wordsmiths.

Kohl, David. Upper Grammar Reading Comprehension Book I. 2000. (Logos School Literature Ser.). (YA). (gr. 4 up). 119p. spiral bd. 25.00 (978-1-930443-21-1(8) , C115); 103p. spiral bd. 25.00 (978-1-930443-22-8(6) , C116) Logos Schl.

Konrad, Dee C. Grammar Handbook. 2004. 146p. pap. (978-0-673-58662-9(6)) Good Year Bks.

Kooistra, Alison, et al. The Power Drill Grammar Book. 2000. (Illus.). 74p. spiral bd. (978-1-895451-35-1(3)) Full Blast Productions.

Krensky, Stephen. 50 Great Reproducible Writing Workouts: Awesome Activity Sheets to Build Skills in Grammar Usage. 1999. 64p. pap. 9.95 (978-0-590-98408-9(X)) Scholastic, Inc.

Kumon Publishing, creator. My Book of Simple Sentences: Learning about Nouns & Verbs. 2005. (Illus.). 80p. (J). (ps-3). per. 6.95 (978-1-933241-05-0(5)) Kumon Publishing North America, Inc.

—My Book of Writing Words: Learning about Consonants & Vowels. 2005. (Illus.). 80p. (J). (gr. k-2). per. 6.95 (978-1-933241-04-3(7)) Kumon Publishing North America, Inc.

Kumon Publishing Staff, ed. ABCs Write & Wipe Lowercase Letters. 2007. 32p. 9.95 (*978-1-933241-44-9(6)) Kumon Publishing North America, Inc.

—My Book of Sentences. 2007. 80p. pap. 6.95 (*978-1-933241-38-8(1)) Kumon Publishing North America, Inc.

Lakeshore Learning Materials, contrib. by. The Big Surprise: A Homophone Story, Set of 6 Student Books. 2007. (J). pap. 18.95 (*978-1-59746-028-6(1)) Lakeshore Learning Materials.

—The Big Surprise: A Homophone Story Big Book. 2007. (J). pap. 19.95 (*978-1-59746-024-8(9)) Lakeshore Learning Materials.

—The Game: A Multiple Meaning Story, Set of 6 Student Books. 2007. (J). pap. 18.95 (*978-1-59746-029-3(X)) Lakeshore Learning Materials.

—The Game: A Multiple Meaning Story Big Book. 2007. (J). pap. 19.95 (*978-1-59746-025-5(7)) Lakeshore Learning Materials.

—The Great Race: A Synonym Story Big Book. 2007. (J). pap. 19.95 (*978-1-59746-022-4(2)) Lakeshore Learning Materials.

—Partner Reading Book Set. 2007. (J). pap. 39.95 (*978-1-59746-021-7(4)) Lakeshore Learning Materials.

—Reading Comprehension Mystery Readers, Set of 18 Books. 2007. (J). 49.95 (*978-1-59746-017-0(6)) Lakeshore Learning Materials.

Language Network. 2001. (gr. 10 up). tchr. ed. (978-0-395-96747-8(3) , 2-22042); (gr. 10 up). tchr. ed. (978-0-618-05269-1(0) , 2-22376); (gr. 10 up). tchr. ed. (978-0-618-05333-9(6) , 2-22426); (gr. 10 up). stu. ed. (978-0-395-96740-9(6) , 2-22035); (gr. 10 up). stu. ed., wbk. ed. (978-0-618-05262-2(3) , 2-22369); (gr. 10 up). pap. incl. cd-rom (978-0-618-21274-3(4) , 2-19251); (gr. 10 up). tchr. ed. incl. cd-rom (978-0-618-05380-3(8) , 2-22445); (gr. 10 up). cd-rom (978-0-618-24588-8(X) , 2-22616); (gr. 11 up). tchr. ed. (978-0-618-05270-7(4) , 2-22377); (gr. 11 up). tchr. ed. (978-0-618-05334-6(4) , 2-22427); (gr. 11 up). tchr. ed. (978-0-395-96748-5(1) , 2-22043); (gr. 11 up). stu. ed. (978-0-395-96741-6(4) , 2-22036); (gr. 11 up). stu. ed., wbk. ed. (978-0-618-05263-9(1) , 2-22370); (gr. 11 up). pap. incl. cd-rom (978-0-618-21276-7(0) , 2-19253); (gr. 11 up). tchr. ed. incl. cd-rom (978-0-618-05379-7(4) , 2-22444); (gr. 11 up). cd-rom (978-0-618-24589-5(8) , 2-22617); (gr. 12 up). tchr. ed. (978-0-395-96749-2(X) , 2-22044); (gr. 12 up). tchr. ed. (978-0-618-05271-4(2) , 2-22378); (gr. 12 up). tchr. ed. (978-0-618-05335-3(2) , 2-22428); (gr. 12 up). stu. ed. (978-0-395-96742-3(2) , 2-22037); (gr. 12 up). stu. ed., wbk. ed. (978-0-618-05264-6(X) , 2-22371); (gr. 12 up). pap. incl. cd-rom (978-0-618-21278-1(7) , 2-19255); (gr. 12 up). tchr. ed. incl. cd-rom (978-0-618-05378-0(6) , 2-22443); (gr. 6 up). tchr. ed. (978-0-618-05268-4(2) , 2-22375); (gr. 6 up). tchr. ed. (978-0-618-05332-2(8) , 2-22425); (gr. 6 up). tchr. ed. (978-0-395-96746-1(5) , 2-22041); (gr. 6 up). tchr. ed. (978-0-395-96743-0(0) , 2-22038); (gr. 6 up). tchr. ed. (978-0-618-11894-6(2) , 2-80960); (gr. 6 up). stu. ed. (978-0-395-96739-3(2) , 2-22034); (gr. 6 up). stu. ed. (978-0-395-96736-2(8) , 2-22031); (gr. 6 up). stu. ed., wbk. ed. (978-0-618-05261-5(5) , 2-22368); (gr. 6 up). pap. incl. cd-rom (978-0-618-18242-8(X) , 2-22027); (gr. 6 up). pap. incl. cd-rom (978-0-618-21272-9(8) , 2-19249); (gr. 6 up). tchr. ed. incl. cd-rom (978-0-618-05381-0(6) , 2-22446); (gr. 6 up). tchr. ed. incl. cd-rom (978-0-618-16654-1(8) , 2-80954); (gr. 6 up). cd-rom (978-0-618-24587-1(1) , 2-22615); (gr. 6 up). cd-rom (978-0-618-24584-0(7) , 2-22612); (gr. 7 up). tchr. ed. (978-0-618-11895-3(0) , 2-80961); (gr. 7 up). tchr. ed. (978-0-395-96744-7(9) , 2-22039); (gr. 7 up). stu. ed. (978-0-395-96737-9(6) , 2-22032); (gr. 7 up). pap. incl. cd-rom (978-0-618-18251-0(9) , 2-22028); (gr. 7 up). tchr. ed. incl. cd-rom (978-0-618-16655-8(6) , 2-80955); (gr. 7 up). cd-rom (978-0-618-24585-7(5) , 2-22613); (gr. 8 up). tchr. ed. (978-0-395-96745-4(7) , 2-22040); (gr. 8 up). tchr. ed. (978-0-618-16814-9(1) , 2-80962); (gr. 8 up). stu. ed. (978-0-395-96738-6(4) , 2-22033); (gr. 8 up). pap. incl. cd-rom (978-0-618-18252-7(7) , 2-22029); (gr. 8 up). tchr. ed. incl. cd-rom (978-0-618-16656-5(4) , 2-80956); (gr. 8 up). cd-rom (978-0-618-24586-4(3) , 2-22614) McDougal Littell Inc.

Language Network: Grammar Coach CD-ROM with User's Guide. 2001. (gr. 6 up). cd-rom (978-0-618-05375-9(1) , 2-22440) McDougal Littell Inc.

Language Network: Grammar Coach Lab Pack. 2001. (gr. 6 up). cd-rom (978-0-618-09565-0(9) , 2-22558) McDougal Littell Inc.

Language Network: Grammar Coach Site License. 2001. (gr. 6 up). (978-0-618-09564-3(0) , 2-22557); (978-0-618-09566-7(7) , 2-22559) McDougal Littell Inc.

Language Network: Grammar Coach User's Guide. 2001. (gr. 6 up). cd-rom (978-0-618-05374-2(3) , 2-22439) McDougal Littell Inc.

Larousse Mexico Staff. Ingles para Todos Gramatica. (SPA & ENG.). 256p. (J). pap. 9.95 (978-970-607-305-1(1) , LA3051) Larousse, Ediciones, S. A. de C. V. MEX. *Dist:* Continental Bk. Co., Inc.

Larson, Randy. Bunches of Grammar Fun - Binder 3. 2004. (YA). ring bd. 79.95 (978-1-58804-320-7(7)) PCI Educational Publishing.

—Bunches of Grammar Fun 3. 2004. (YA). ring bd. 79.95 (978-1-58804-399-3(1)) PCI Educational Publishing.

LD COACH. TEH Learns to Read: Pronouns & Possessive Adjectives, Volume Three. 2004. (Illus.). 40p. (J). 34.95 (978-0-9745938-3-8(4)) LD Coach, LLC.

Le Patner, Michelle, et al. Nonfiction Writing Prompts for Upper Elementary Science. Whited, Amy M., ed. 2005. (Illus.). 128p. pap. 9.95 (978-1-933196-05-3(X)) Advanced Learning Pr.

—Nonfiction Writing Prompts for Upper Elementary Social Studies. Whited, Amy M., ed. 2005. (Illus.). 128p. pap. 9.95 (978-1-933196-06-0(8)) Advanced Learning Pr.

—Write to Know: Nonfiction Writing Prompts for Kindergarten Math, Science, & Social Studies. Whited, Amy M., ed. 2005. 128p. pap. 9.95 (978-1-933196-00-8(9)) Advanced Learning Pr.

—Write to Know: Nonfiction Writing Prompts for Lower Elementary Science. Whited, Amy M., ed. 2005. 128p. pap. 9.95 (978-1-933196-02-2(5)) Advanced Learning Pr.

—Write to Know: Nonfiction Writing Prompts for Lower Elementary Social Studies. Whited, Amy M., ed. 2005. 128p. pap. 9.95 (978-1-933196-03-9(3)) Advanced Learning Pr.

Learning Company Books Staff, ed. Reader Rabbit: Writing Mechanics. 2003. (Illus.). 32p. (J). pap., wbk. ed. 3.99 (978-0-7630-7642-9(2)) Learning Co. Bks.

Leist, Susan. Grammatical Literacy. 2001. 160p. (YA). pap. 20.95 (978-0-595-13826-5(8)) iUniverse, Inc.

Lewis, Starin. Comprehension E-Book. 2005. 80p. (J). per. 10.99 (978-1-59441-561-6(7) , CD-104014-E) Carson-Dellosa Publishing Co., Inc.

Lindsay, Elizabeth, ed. Learning Library-Reading, Spelling & Grammar. 2003. 128p. 19.95 (978-1-56234-532-7(X) , Mailbox Bks., The) Education Ctr., Inc.

Literature: Timeless Voices, Timeless Themes. 2001. Bronze Level. (SPA.). (gr. 7). pap., tchr.'s training gde. ed. 5.47 (978-0-13-052391-4(7)); Bronze Level (SPA.). (YA). (gr. 7). pap. 29.97 (978-0-13-052388-4(7)); Copper Level. (J). (gr. 6). suppl. ed. 10.97 (978-0-13-050903-1(5)); Copper Level (J). (gr. 6). pap. 12.47 (978-0-13-050910-9(8)); Copper Level (J). (gr. 6). trans. 134.97 (978-0-13-050819-5(5)); Gold Level (YA). (gr. 9). pap., stu. ed. 12.97 (978-0-13-050921-5(3)); Silver Level. (SPA.). (gr. 8). pap., tchr.'s training gde. ed. 5.47 (978-0-13-052392-1(5)); Silver Level (SPA.). (YA). (gr. 8). pap. 29.97 (978-0-13-052389-1(5)) Prentice Hall PTR.

Locker-Halmy, Barbara. Key Paragraphs, Vol. 2263. Hamaguchi, Carla, ed. 2002. pap. 12.00 (978-1-57471-908-6(4)) Creative Teaching Pr., Inc.

Loewen, Nancy. If You Were a Conjunction. Gray, Sara, illus. 2006. (Word Fun Ser.). (J). 25.26 (978-1-4048-2385-3(9)) Picture Window Bks.

—If You Were a Interjection. Gray, Sara, illus. 2006. (Word Fun Ser.). (J). 25.26 (978-1-4048-2636-6(X)) Picture Window Bks.

—If You Were a Preposition. Gray, Sara, illus. 2006. (Word Fun Ser.). (J). 25.26 (978-1-4048-2386-0(7)) Picture Window Bks.

—If You Were a Pronoun. Gray, Sara, illus. 2006. (Word Fun Ser.). (J). 25.26 (978-1-4048-2637-3(8)) Picture Window Bks.

Lubben, Amy & Williams, Rozanne Lanczak. Build-a-Skill Instant Books Word Families-Long Vowels. Shiotsu, Vicky & Faulkner, Stacey, eds. Campbell, Jenny & Tom, Darcy, illus. 2007. (J). 4.99 (***978-1-59198-409-2(2)***) Creative Teaching Pr., Inc.

—Build-a-Skill Instant Books Word Families-Short Vowels. Shiotsu, Vicky & Faulkner, Stacey, eds. Campbell, Jenny & Tom, Darcy, illus. 2007. (J). 4.99 (***978-1-59198-408-5(4)***) Creative Teaching Pr., Inc.

Lucas, Jerry. Grammar Graphics & Picture Perfect Punctuation: A Fun & Easy Way to Learn Through Pictures! 2000. (Ready - Set - Remember Ser.). (Illus.). 120p. (J). pap. 23.95 (978-1-930853-04-1(1) , 967-005) Lucas Educational Systems.

Mack, Nancy. Teaching Grammar with Playful Poems: Grades 3-5. 2005. (Illus.). 80p. (gr. 3-5). pap. 14.99 (978-0-439-57411-2(0) , Teaching Strategies) Scholastic, Inc.

Manser, Martin. Getting to Grips with Grammar. 2003. (First Guides). (Illus.). 32p. (J). (gr. 1-4). 14.95 (978-1-57768-557-9(1) , Waterbird Bks.) School Specialty Publishing.

Mara, Wil. Quite Enough Hot Dogs. Whitehead, Pete, illus. 2007. (Rookie Reader': Silent Letters Ser.). 32p. (J). pap. 4.95 (***978-0-531-17782-2(3)*** , Children's Pr.) Scholastic Library Publishing.

Masonis, Tracy. Story Starters: Adventure Stories. 2000. (Gifted & Talented Ser.). (Illus.). 64p. (J). (gr. 1-3). pap. 5.95 (978-0-7373-0546-3(0)) Lowell Hse. Juvenile.

Mazzeo, J. L. Aimee¿s A Book (BL) el libro A de Aimée, 1. 2007. (My Letter Library Ser.: 1). (SPA., Illus.). (J). lib. bdg. 22.60 (***978-1-59646-419-3(4)***) Dingles & Co.

—Aimee¿s A Book (BL) el libro A de Aimée (PB), 1. 2007. (My Letter Library Ser.: 1). (SPA., Illus.). (J). pap. 9.95 (***978-1-59646-420-9(8)***) Dingles & Co.

—Cassie's C Book (BL) el libro C de Cassie: S, 3 vols. 2007. (My Letter Library Ser.: 3). (SPA & ENG., Illus.). (J). lib. bdg. 22.60 (***978-1-59646-431-5(3)***) Dingles & Co.

—Cassie's C Book (BL) el libro C de Cassie (PB), 3 vols. 2007. (My Letter Library Ser.: 3). (SPA & ENG., Illus.). (J). pap. 9.95 (***978-1-59646-432-2(1)***) Dingles & Co.

—Uri's U Book, 21 vols. 2007. (My Letter Library Ser.: 21). (Illus.). (J). lib. bdg. 22.60 (***978-1-59646-536-7(0)***) Dingles & Co.

—Uri's U Book (PB), 21 vols. 2007. (My Letter Library Ser.: 21). (Illus.). (J). pap. 9.95 (***978-1-59646-537-4(9)***) Dingles & Co.

—Yola's Y Book, 25 vols. 2007. (My Letter Library Ser.: 25). (Illus.). (J). lib. bdg. 22.60 (***978-1-59646-560-2(3)***) Dingles & Co.

—Yola's Y Book (PB), 25 vols. 2007. (My Letter Library Ser.: 25). (Illus.). (J). pap. 9.95 (***978-1-59646-561-9(1)***) Dingles & Co.

—Zach's Z Book (BL) el libro Z de Zach, 26 vols. 2007. (My Letter Library Ser.: 26). (SPA & ENG., Illus.). (J). lib. bdg. 22.60 (***978-1-59646-569-5(7)***) Dingles & Co.

—Zach's Z Book (BL) el libro Z de Zach (PB), 26 vols. 2007. (My Letter Library Ser.: 26). (SPA & ENG., Illus.). (J). pap. 9.95 (***978-1-59646-570-1(0)***) Dingles & Co.

McCarty, Diane Bischoff. Copywork for Children: For Grades 1-3. 2004. (Illus.). 63p. (J). (978-0-9712124-1-1(4)) Angel Heart Children's Pr.

McClarnon M.S., Marciann. Painless Junior: Grammar. Hohn, Tracy, illus. 2007. (Painless Junior Ser.). 208p. pap. 8.99 (978-0-7641-3561-3(9)) Barron's Educational Series, Inc.

McGraw-Hill Staff. Glencoe Language Arts: Grammar & Language, Grade 12. 1999. pap., wbk. ed. 20.64 (978-0-02-818312-1(6) , 9780028183121) Glencoe/McGraw-Hill.

—Glencoe Language Arts, Grade 10, Grammar & Composition Handbook. 2001. 593p. 39.96 (978-0-07-825117-7(6) , 9780078251177) Glencoe/McGraw-Hill.

—Glencoe Language Arts, Grade 11, Grammar & Composition Handbook. 2001. 594p. 39.96 (978-0-07-825118-4(4) , 9780078251184) Glencoe/McGraw-Hill.

—Glencoe Language Arts, Grade 12, Grammar & Composition Handbook. 2001. 594p. 39.96 (978-0-07-825119-1(2) , 9780078251191) Glencoe/McGraw-Hill.

—Glencoe Language Arts, Grade 6, Grammar & Composition Handbook. 2001. 39.96 (978-0-07-825113-9(3) , 9780078251139) Glencoe/McGraw-Hill.

—Glencoe Language Arts, Grade 7, Grammar & Composition Handbook. 2001. (C). 39.96 (978-0-07-825114-6(1) , 9780078251146) Glencoe/McGraw-Hill.

—Glencoe Language Arts, Grade 8, Grammar & Composition Handbook. 2001. (C). 39.96 (978-0-07-825115-3(X) , 9780078251153) Glencoe/McGraw-Hill.

—Glencoe Language Arts, Grade 9, Grammar & Composition Handbook. 2001. 39.96 (978-0-07-825116-0(8) , 9780078251160) Glencoe/McGraw-Hill.

—Glencoe Language Arts, Grammar & Language. 1999. (C). Grade 6. pap., wbk. ed. 20.64 (978-0-07-820539-2(5) , 9780078205392); Grade 7. pap., wbk. ed. 20.64 (978-0-07-820540-8(9) , 9780078205408) Glencoe/McGraw-Hill.

—Glencoe Language Arts Grammar & Language Book. 1999. Grade 8. pap., wbk. ed. 20.64 (978-0-07-820541-5(7) , 9780078205415); Grade 9. (C). pap., wbk. ed. 20.64 (978-0-02-818294-0(4) , 9780028182940) Glencoe/McGraw-Hill.

—Glencoe Language Arts Grammar & Language Book Grade 11. 1999. pap., wbk. ed. 20.64 (978-0-02-818303-9(7) , 9780028183039) Glencoe/McGraw-Hill.

—Glencoe Language Arts Grammar Practice Grade 6. 2000. pap., wbk. ed. 18.00 (978-0-07-823941-0(9) , 9780078239410) Glencoe/McGraw-Hill.

—Glencoe Language Arts, Middle School, Grammar & Composition Handbook. 1999. 41.32 (978-0-02-817298-9(1) , 9780028172989) Glencoe/McGraw-Hill.

—Glencoe Literature, British Literature, Grammar Practice, Grade 12. 2000. pap., wbk. ed. 18.00 (978-0-07-823947-2(8) , 9780078239472) Glencoe/McGraw-Hill.

—Glencoe Literature Grade 10, Grammar Practice. 2000. pap., wbk. ed. 18.00 (978-0-07-823945-8(1) , 9780078239458) Glencoe/McGraw-Hill.

—Glencoe Literature Grade 11, American Literature, Grammar Practice. 2000. (C). pap., wbk. ed. 18.00 (978-0-07-823946-5(X) , 9780078239465) Glencoe/McGraw-Hill.

—Glencoe Literature Grade 9 Grammar Practice. 2000. pap., wbk. ed. 18.00 (978-0-07-823944-1(3) , 9780078239441) Glencoe/McGraw-Hill.

—Glencoe Literature, Grammar Practice, Grade 8. 2000. (C). pap., wbk. ed. 18.00 (978-0-07-823943-4(5) , 9780078239434) Glencoe/McGraw-Hill.

—Glencoe Literature Grammar Practice Grade 7. 2000. pap., wbk. ed. 18.00 (978-0-07-823942-7(7) , 9780078239427) Glencoe/McGraw-Hill.

—Glencoe Literature Interactive Reading Grade 7. 2001. pap., wbk. ed. 18.00 (978-0-07-825175-7(3) , 9780078251757) Glencoe/McGraw-Hill.

—Writer's Choice: Grammer & Composition, Grade 6. 2001. stu. ed. 73.32 incl. cd-rom (978-0-07-827065-9(0) , 9780078270659) Glencoe/McGraw-Hill.

—Writer's Choice Grade 6: Grammar & Composition, Grade 6. 2004. stu. ed. 74.60 (978-0-07-829814-1(8) , 9780078298141) Glencoe/McGraw-Hill.

—Writer's Choice Grade 8: Grammar & Composition, Grade 8. 2004. stu. ed. 74.60 (978-0-07-829816-5(4) , 9780078298165) Glencoe/McGraw-Hill.

—Writer's Choice Grade 9: Grammar & Composition. 2004. stu. ed. 78.00 (978-0-07-829817-2(2) , 9780078298172) Glencoe/McGraw-Hill.

—Writer's Choice Grammar. 2000. Grade 6. pap., wbk. ed. 17.32 (978-0-07-823352-4(6) , 9780078233524); Grade. 7. pap., wbk. ed. 17.32 (978-0-07-823353-1(4) , 9780078233531) Glencoe/McGraw-Hill.

—Writer's Choice Grammar Grade 10. 2000. pap., wbk. ed. 17.32 (978-0-07-823356-2(9) , 9780078233562) Glencoe/McGraw-Hill.

—Writer's Choice, Grammar Grade 8. 2000. (C). pap., wbk. ed. 17.32 (978-0-07-823354-8(2) , 9780078233548) Glencoe/McGraw-Hill.

—Writer's Choice Grammar Practice. 2000. Grade 9. pap., wbk. ed. 17.32 (978-0-07-823355-5(0) , 9780078233555); Grade 12. pap., wbk. ed. 17.32 (978-0-07-823358-6(5) , 9780078233586) Glencoe/McGraw-Hill.

—Writer's Choice Grammar Practice Grade 11. 2000. (C). pap., wbk. ed. 17.32 (978-0-07-823357-9(7) , 9780078233579) Glencoe/McGraw-Hill.

—Writer's Choice Interactive Student Edition Grade 10 Florida Edition 2001. 2001. (C). stu. ed. 65.32 incl. cd-rom (978-0-07-827062-8(6) , 9780078270628) Glencoe/McGraw-Hill.

McKerns, Dorothy & Motchkavitz, Leslie. The Kid's Guide to Good Grammar. 1998. (Illus.). 96p. (J). (gr. 4-7). pap. 8.95 (978-1-56565-697-0(0) , 06970W) Lowell Hse. Juvenile.

Mcree Christen, Nancy. Phonics: Level 1 - Beginning & Ending Consonant Sounds. 1999. (Homework Booklets Ser.). 80p. (C). pap. 2.99 (978-0-88012-970-1(0) , IF0261) School Specialty Publishing.

—Phonics: Level 2 - Long & Short Vowel Sounds. 1999. (Homework Booklets Ser.). 80p. (C). pap. 2.99 (978-0-88012-971-8(9) , IF0262) School Specialty Publishing.

—Phonics: Level 3 - Digraphs, Combinations, Blends, & Consonant Review. 1999. (Homework Booklets Ser.). 80p. (C). pap. 2.99 (978-0-88012-972-5(7) , IF0263) School Specialty Publishing.

Menken, John. Hands-on English with Linking Blocks Program Handbook. 2006. 31p. spiral bd. 17.00 (***978-0-9797375-1-0(6)***) E3 Concepts LLC.

—Hands-on English with Linking Blocks Student Workbook. 2006. 139p. spiral bd. 39.00 (***978-0-9797375-2-7(4)***) E3 Concepts LLC.

Modern Staff. Paco's Pockets: Consonants p, s. (J). (gr. k-1). 38.95 (978-0-8136-1328-4(0)) Modern Curriculum Pr.

Molter, Carey. Silent Letters. 2004. (J). (ps-3). lib. bdg. 119.58 (978-1-59197-442-0(9) , SandCastle) ABDO Publishing Co.

Monaghan, Elizabeth. Grammar Skills 2. 1999. (Cambridge Secondary Grammar Ser.). 96p. pap. 12.00 (978-0-521-59757-9(9)) Cambridge Univ. Pr.

—Grammar Skills 3. 2000. (Cambridge Secondary Grammar Ser.). 96p. pap. 10.00 (978-0-521-59758-6(7)) Cambridge Univ. Pr.

Moore, Jo Ellen. Blends & Digraphs Word Machines. Evans, Marilyn, ed. Larsen, Jo, illus. 2000. (Word Machines Ser.). 28p. (J). (gr. 1-3). pap., tchr. ed. 12.95 (978-1-55799-759-3(4) , EMC 782) Evan-Moor Educational Pubs.

Moreau, Maryellen Rooney & Welch, Brian Scott. Talk to Write, Write to Learn: A Teachers' Manual for Differentiated Instruction & Tiered Intervention. 2007. pap. 60.00 (***978-0-9761393-9-3(1)***) Mindwing Concepts, Inc.

Mulvey, Dan. Grammar the Easy Way. 2002. (Easy Way Ser.). 300p. pap. 14.95 (978-0-7641-1989-7(3)) Barron's Educational Series, Inc.

O'Conner, Patricia T. Woe Is I Jr: The Junior Grammarphobe's Guide to Better English in Plain English. Stiglich, Tom, illus. 2007. 176p. (YA). (gr. 4 up). 16.99 (978-0-399-24331-8(3) , Putnam Juvenile) Penguin Group (USA) Inc.

Orient, Jane. Professor Klugimkopf's Old Fashioned English Grammar. 2002. 24.95 (978-0-942487-11-4(7)); per. 14.95 (978-0-942487-10-7(9)) Oregon Institute of Science & Medicine.

Our Journey: Fourth Grade Guided Comprehension Level P. (On Our Way to English Ser.). (gr. 4 up). 34.50 (978-0-7578-7174-0(7)) Rigby Education.

Parts of Speech (Gr. 1-3) 2003. (J). (978-1-58232-048-9(9)) Bryan Hse. Pubs., Inc.

Parts of Speech (Gr. 3+) 2003. (J). (978-1-58232-054-0(3)) Bryan Hse. Pubs., Inc.

Pearce, Q L. Using Standards Grammar Gr 1. 2003. (100+ Seriestm Ser.). 128p. (J). (gr. 1 up). pap. 12.99 (978-0-7424-1801-1(4) , IFG99050) School Specialty Publishing.

—Using Standards Grammar Gr 2. 2003. (100+ Seriestm Ser.). 128p. (J). (gr. 2 up). pap. 12.99 (978-0-7424-1802-8(2) , IFG99051) School Specialty Publishing.

Petelinsek, Kathleen & Primm, E. Russell. Actions/Acciones. 2006. (Talking Hands Ser.). (ENG & SPA., Illus.). 24p. (J). 21.36 (978-1-59296-679-0(9)) Child's World, Inc.

Peterson. Mastering Grammar Skills: Entertaining Instruction & Cool Activities for High School Students Who Want to Get Wise. 2002. (Get Wise! Ser.). (Illus.). 207p. pap. 12.95 (978-0-7689-1077-3(3)) Peterson's.

Phillips, Wanda C. Easy Grammar Grade 3 Student Test Booklet. 2006. pap. 4.95 (***978-0-936981-49-9(0)***) Isha Enterprises, Inc.

—Easy Grammar Grade 3 Student Workbook. 2006. pap. 13.95 (***978-0-936981-48-2(2)***) Isha Enterprises, Inc.

—Easy Grammar Grade 4 Student Test Booklet. 2006. pap. 4.95 (***978-0-936981-50-5(4)***) Isha Enterprises, Inc.

—Easy Grammar Grade 5 Student Test Booklet. 2006. pap. 4.95 (***978-0-936981-51-2(2)***) Isha Enterprises, Inc.

—Easy Grammar Grade 5 Student Workbook. 2006. pap. 13.95 (***978-0-936981-45-1(8)***) Isha Enterprises, Inc.

—Easy Grammar Grade 6 Student Test Booklet. 2006. pap. 4.95 (***978-0-936981-52-9(0)***) Isha Enterprises, Inc.

—Easy Grammar Grade 6 Student Workbook. 2006. pap. 13.95 (***978-0-936981-46-8(6)***) Isha Enterprises, Inc.

—Easy Grammar Plus Student Test Booklet. 2006. pap. 4.95 (***978-0-936981-53-6(9)***) Isha Enterprises, Inc.

—Easy Grammar Plus Student Workbook. 2006. 347p. (gr. 6 up). pap., wbk. ed. 13.95 (978-0-936981-14-7(8)) Isha Enterprises, Inc.

—Easy Grammar Plus teacher Edition. 2006. 663p. (gr. 6 up). pap. 32.95 (978-0-936981-13-0(X)) Isha Enterprises, Inc.

Phonics: Level 4 - Controlled Vowels, Vowel Digraphs, & Long & Short Vowel Review. (Homework Booklets Ser.). 80p. 2.99 (978-0-88012-973-2(5) , IF0264) School Specialty Publishing.

Phonics Ad Libs: Vowels & Consonants. 2003. (J). pap. 9.95 (978-1-56911-104-8(9)) Learning Resources, Inc.

Pike, Katy. Apples & Ants. Jurevicius, Luke, illus. 2006. (Funny Photo Alphabet Ser.). (J). pap. (978-0-8225-6267-2(7) , Lerner Pubns.) Lerner Publishing Group.

—Big Bad Bears. Jurevicius, Luke, illus. 2006. (Funny Photo Alphabet Ser.). 11p. (J). pap. (978-0-8225-6268-9(5) , Lerner Pubns.) Lerner Publishing Group.

—Candles on a Cake. Jurevicius, Luke, illus. 2006. (Funny Photo Alphabet Ser.). 11p. (J). pap. (978-0-8225-6269-6(3) , Lerner Pubns.) Lerner Publishing Group.

—Dancing Dog. Jurevicius, Luke, illus. 2006. (Funny Photo Alphabet Ser.). 11p. (J). pap. (978-0-8225-6270-2(7) , Lerner Pubns.) Lerner Publishing Group.

—Eggs & Elephants. Jurevicius, Luke, illus. 2006. (Funny Photo Alphabet Ser.). 11p. (J). pap. (978-0-8225-6271-9(5) , Lerner Pubns.) Lerner Publishing Group.

—Funny Fish. Jurevicius, Luke, illus. 2006. (Funny Photo Alphabet Ser.). 11p. (J). pap. (978-0-8225-6272-6(3) , Lerner Pubns.) Lerner Publishing Group.

—Giggly Goat. Jurevicius, Luke, illus. 2006. (Funny Photo Alphabet Ser.). 11p. (J). pap. (978-0-8225-6273-3(1) , Lerner Pubns.) Lerner Publishing Group.

—Happy Horse. Jurevicius, Luke, illus. 2006. (Funny Photo Alphabet Ser.). 11p. (J). pap. (978-0-8225-6274-0(X) , Lerner Pubns.) Lerner Publishing Group.

—Icky Insects. Jurevicius, Luke, illus. 2006. (Funny Photo Alphabet Ser.). 11p. (J). pap. (978-0-8225-6275-7(8) , Lerner Pubns.) Lerner Publishing Group.

—Jolly Jellybeans. Jurevicius, Luke, illus. 2006. (Funny Photo Alphabet Ser.). 11p. (J). pap. (978-0-8225-6276-4(6) , Lerner Pubns.) Lerner Publishing Group.

—Lots of Lizards. Jurevicius, Luke, illus. 2006. (Funny Photo Alphabet Ser.). 11p. (J). pap. (978-0-8225-6278-8(2) , Lerner Pubns.) Lerner Publishing Group.

—Mini Mouse. Jurevicius, Luke, illus. 2006. (Funny Photo Alphabet Ser.). 11p. (J). pap. (978-0-8225-6279-5(0) , Lerner Pubns.) Lerner Publishing Group.

—Nine Nuts. Jurevicius, Luke, illus. 2006. (Funny Photo Alphabet Ser.). 11p. (J). pap. (978-0-8225-6280-1(4) , Lerner Pubns.) Lerner Publishing Group.

—Orange Octopus. Jurevicius, Luke, illus. 2006. (Funny Photo Alphabet Ser.). 11p. (J). pap. (978-0-8225-6281-8(2) , Lerner Pubns.) Lerner Publishing Group.

—Penguin Pond. Jurevicius, Luke, illus. 2006. (Funny Photo Alphabet Ser.). 11p. (J). pap. (978-0-8225-6282-5(0) , Lerner Pubns.) Lerner Publishing Group.

—The Queen's Question. Jurevicius, Luke, illus. 2006. (Funny Photo Alphabet Ser.). 11p. (J). pap. (978-0-8225-6283-2(9) , Lerner Pubns.) Lerner Publishing Group.

—Rabbit on a Raft. Jurevicius, Luke, illus. 2006. (Funny Photo Alphabet Ser.). 11p. (J). pap. (978-0-8225-6284-9(7) , Lerner Pubns.) Lerner Publishing Group.

—Silly Seagulls. Jurevicius, Luke, illus. 2006. (Funny Photo Alphabet Ser.). 11p. (J). pap. (978-0-8225-6285-6(5) , Lerner Pubns.) Lerner Publishing Group.

—Talking Tigers. Jurevicius, Luke, illus. 2006. (Funny Photo Alphabet Ser.). 11p. (J). pap. (978-0-8225-6286-3(3) , Lerner Pubns.) Lerner Publishing Group.

—Under Umbrellas. Jurevicius, Luke, illus. 2006. (Funny Photo Alphabet Ser.). 11p. (J). pap. (978-0-8225-6287-0(1) , Lerner Pubns.) Lerner Publishing Group.

—Vegetables in a Van. Jurevicius, Luke, illus. 2006. (Funny Photo Alphabet Ser.). 11p. (J). pap. (978-0-8225-6288-7(X) , Lerner Pubns.) Lerner Publishing Group.

—Wet Whales. Jurevicius, Luke, illus. 2006. (Funny Photo Alphabet Ser.). 11p. (J). pap. (978-0-8225-6289-4(8) , Lerner Pubns.) Lerner Publishing Group.

—X As in Fox. Jurevicius, Luke, illus. 2006. (Funny Photo Alphabet Ser.). 11p. (J). pap. (978-0-8225-6290-0(1) , Lerner Pubns.) Lerner Publishing Group.

—Yellow Yo-Yo. Jurevicius, Luke, illus. 2006. (Funny Photo Alphabet Ser.). (J). pap. (978-0-8225-6291-7(X) , Lerner Pubns.) Lerner Publishing Group.

—Zebras in a Zoo. Jurevicius, Luke, illus. 2006. (Funny Photo Alphabet Ser.). pap. (978-0-8225-6292-4(8) , Lerner Pubns.) Lerner Publishing Group.

Pike, Katy & Jurevicius, Luke. Kicking Kangaroo: Pictures by Luke Jurevicius. 2006. (Funny Photo Alphabet Ser.). (Illus.). 11p. (J). pap. (978-0-8225-6277-1(4) , Lerner Pubns.) Lerner Publishing Group.

Plurals & Possessives (Gr. 2-3) 2003. (J). (978-1-58232-122-6(1)) Bryan Hse. Pubs., Inc.

Polston, Deborah. Eagle Child Series 4-6. 2007. (YA). per. 12.99 (***978-1-59886-381-9(9)***) Tate Publishing & Enterprises, L.L.C.

PowerPhonics Skill Set II: Includes Animals II, Community Helpers, Where I Live, 18 bks. 2001. (Illus.). (J). (gr. 1). lib. bdg. 324.00 (978-0-8239-7208-1(9) , PowerKids Pr.) Rosen Publishing Group, Inc., The.

PowerPhonics Skill Set III: Includes Going Places, Self II, Seasons/Weather, 18 bks. 2001. (Illus.). (J). (gr. 1). lib. bdg. 324.00 (978-0-8239-7212-8(7) , PowerKids Pr.) Rosen Publishing Group, Inc., The.

PowerPhonics Skill Sets I, II, III, 54 bks. 2001. (Illus.). (J). (gr. 1). lib. bdg. 972.00 (978-0-8239-7215-9(1) , PowerKids Pr.) Rosen Publishing Group, Inc., The.

Prefixes, Suffixes, & Root Words (Gr. 2-3) 2003. (J). (978-1-58232-123-3(X)) Bryan Hse. Pubs., Inc.

Prefixes, Suffixes, & Root Words (Gr. 4-5) 2004. (J). (978-1-58232-137-0(X)) Bryan Hse. Pubs., Inc.

Prentice-Hall Staff. PH Grammar & Composition. 3rd ed. (J). (978-0-13-708926-0(0)); (978-0-13-708934-5(1)); (978-0-13-708942-0(2)); (978-0-13-708868-3(X)) Prentice Hall (Schl. Div.).

Prepositional Phrases, 8 vols., Set. 2004. (Beastieville Ser.). 103.95 (978-0-516-25149-3(X) , Children's Pr.) Scholastic Library Publishing.

Pulse- Fun with Grammar. 2006. cd-rom 4.99 (***978-1-60245-037-0(4)***) GDL Multimedia, LLC.

Punctuate & Capitalize. 2003. (Practice Makes Perfect Ser.). (Illus.). 48p. (J). (gr. 3). pap. 4.99 (978-0-7439-3777-1(5)); (gr. 4). pap. 4.99 (978-0-7439-3778-8(3)) Teacher Created Materials, Inc.

Quiz Show: Fifth Grade Guided Comprehension Level N. (On Our Way to English Ser.). (gr. 5 up). 34.50 (978-0-7578-6598-5(4)) Rigby Education.

Rainbow Bridge Publishing Staff. Grammar First Grade: Mastering Basic Skills. 2002. (Mastering Basic Skills Ser.). (Illus.). 48p. (gr. 1 up). 5.95 (978-1-887923-66-8(7)) Rainbow Bridge Publishing.

—Grammar Second Grade: Mastering Basic Skills. 2002. (Mastering Basic Skills Ser.). (Illus.). 48p. (gr. 2 up). 5.95 (978-1-887923-67-5(5)) Rainbow Bridge Publishing.

—Grammar Third Grade: Mastering Basic Skills. 2002. (Mastering Basic Skills Ser.). (Illus.). 48p. (gr. 3 up). 5.95 (978-1-887923-68-2(3)) Rainbow Bridge Publishing.

Rau, Dana Meachen. Blow Out. 2006. (Bookworms Ser.). (Illus.). 32p. (J). lib. bdg. 22.79 (978-0-7614-2288-4(9) , Benchmark Bks.) Cavendish, Marshall Corp.

—Bookworms: Verbs in Action, 6 bks., Set. Incl. Dig In. (ps-3). lib. bdg. (978-0-7614-1937-2(3)); Fall Down. (ps-3). lib. bdg. (978-0-7614-1936-5(5)); Grow Up. (ps-3). lib. bdg. (978-0-7614-1932-7(2)); On the Run. (gr. 1-2). lib. bdg. (978-0-7614-1934-1(9)); Spin Around. (ps-3). lib. bdg. (978-0-7614-1933-4(0)); Spring Out. (ps-3). lib. bdg. (978-0-7614-1935-8(7)); (Illus.). 32p. (J). 2005. (978-0-7614-1931-0(4) , Benchmark Bks.) Cavendish, Marshall Corp.

—Carry On. 2006. (Bookworms Ser.). (Illus.). 32p. (J). lib. bdg. 22.79 (978-0-7614-2289-1(7) , Benchmark Bks.) Cavendish, Marshall Corp.

—Dig In. 2005. (Bookworms Ser.). (Illus.). 32p. (J). (ps-3). lib. bdg. (978-0-7614-1937-2(3) , Benchmark Bks.) Cavendish, Marshall Corp.

—Fall Down. 2005. (Bookworms Ser.). (Illus.). 32p. (J). (ps-3). lib. bdg. (978-0-7614-1936-5(5) , Benchmark Bks.) Cavendish, Marshall Corp.

—Family Photo. Gordon, Mike, illus. 2006. (Rookie Reader Skill Set Ser.). 32p. (J). (gr. k-2). 19.50 (978-0-531-12469-7(X) , Children's Pr.) Scholastic Library Publishing.

—Grow Up. 2005. (Bookworms Ser.). (Illus.). 32p. (J). (ps-3). lib. bdg. (978-0-7614-1932-7(2) , Benchmark Bks.) Cavendish, Marshall Corp.

—Make a Face. 2006. (Bookworms Ser.). (Illus.). 32p. (J). lib. bdg. 22.79 (978-0-7614-2290-7(0) , Benchmark Bks.) Cavendish, Marshall Corp.

—Move Along. 2006. (Bookworms Ser.). (Illus.). 32p. lib. bdg. 22.79 (978-0-7614-2291-4(9) , Benchmark Bks.) Cavendish, Marshall Corp.

—On the Run. 2005. (Bookworms Ser.). (Illus.). 32p. (J). (gr. 1-2). lib. bdg. (978-0-7614-1934-1(9) , Benchmark Bks.) Cavendish, Marshall Corp.

—Play Ball. 2006. (Bookworms Ser.). (Illus.). 32p. (J). lib. bdg. 22.79 (978-0-7614-2292-1(7) , Benchmark Bks.) Cavendish, Marshall Corp.

—Spin Around. 2005. (Bookworms Ser.). (Illus.). 32p. (J). (ps-3). lib. bdg. (978-0-7614-1933-4(0) , Benchmark Bks.) Cavendish, Marshall Corp.

—Spring Out. 2005. (Bookworms Ser.). (Illus.). 32p. (J). (ps-3). lib. bdg. (978-0-7614-1935-8(7) , Benchmark Bks.) Cavendish, Marshall Corp.

—Turn Into. 2006. (Bookworms Ser.). (Illus.). 32p. (J). lib. bdg. 22.79 (978-0-7614-2293-8(5) , Benchmark Bks.) Cavendish, Marshall Corp.

Rau, Dana Meachen. Verbs in Action Group 2, 6 bks., Set. Incl. Blow Out. (J). lib. bdg. 22.79 (978-0-7614-2288-4(9)); Carry On. (J). lib. bdg. 22.79 (978-0-7614-2289-1(7)); Make a Face. (J). lib. bdg. 22.79 (978-0-7614-2290-7(0)); Move Along. lib. bdg. 22.79 (978-0-7614-2291-4(9)); Play Ball. (J). lib. bdg. 22.79 (978-0-7614-2292-1(7)); Turn Into. (J). lib. bdg. 22.79 (978-0-7614-2293-8(5)); (Illus.). 32p. 2006. 2007. Set lib. bdg. 136.71 (***978-0-7614-2287-7(0)*** , Benchmark Bks.) Cavendish, Marshall Corp.

Read All about It! Fifth Grade Guided Comprehension Level S. (On Our Way to English Ser.). (gr. 5 up). 34.50 (978-0-7578-6623-4(9)) Rigby Education.

Reader's Clubhouse Staff. Coach Bo Will Show You. 2007. (Reader's Clubhouse Ser.). 24p. (J). (gr. k-2). pap. 3.99 (978-0-7641-3723-5(9)) Barron's Educational Series, Inc.

Reading & Language, Set. 2002. (gr. 6-12). 9.42 (978-0-7362-1228-1(0)); tchr. ed. 22.76 (978-0-7362-1229-8(9)) Hampton-Brown Bks.

Reading Rods Readers: Advanced Vowel Mastery Set. 2004. (J). per. 44.95 (978-1-56911-532-9(X)) Learning Resources, Inc.

Reading Rods Readers: Advanced Vowel Mastery Set Classpack. 2004. (J). per. 249.95 (978-1-56911-574-9(5)) Learning Resources, Inc.

Reading Rods Readers: Long Vowel Mastery Set. 2004. (J). per. 32.95 (978-1-56911-531-2(1)) Learning Resources, Inc.

Reading Rods Readers: Long Vowel Mastery Set Classpack. 2004. (J). per. 184.95 (978-1-56911-549-7(4)) Learning Resources, Inc.

Reading Rods Readers: Short Vowel Mastery Set. 2004. (J). per. 32.95 (978-1-56911-530-5(3)) Learning Resources, Inc.

Ready Reader Staff. The Lucky Duck: Short Vowels, 6 bks., set, Level B. 2003. (J). (ps-3). 24.50 (978-0-8136-2013-8(9)) Modern Curriculum Pr.

Realtime Associates and Mazer Corporation Staff & LeapFrog Staff, compiled by. Distinguish Connotative & Denotative Meanings. 2002. (J). (gr. 4). 66.75 (978-1-58605-443-4(0) , LeapFrog Schl. Hse.) LeapFrog Enterprises, Inc.

—Distinguish Connotative from Denotative Meanings. 2002. (J). (gr. 5). 66.75 (978-1-58605-506-6(2) , LeapFrog Schl. Hse.) LeapFrog Enterprises, Inc.

—Draw Conclusions. 2002. (J). (gr. 2). 66.75 (978-1-58605-297-3(7)); (J). (gr. 3). 66.75 (978-1-58605-359-8(0)); (gr. 4). 66.75 (978-1-58605-415-1(5)); (J). (gr. 5). 66.75 (978-1-58605-474-8(0)) LeapFrog Enterprises, Inc. (LeapFrog Schl. Hse.).

—Identify Nouns & Verbs. 2002. (J). (gr. 2). 66.75 (978-1-58605-310-9(8)); (gr. 3). 66.75 (978-1-58605-378-9(7)) LeapFrog Enterprises, Inc. (LeapFrog Schl. Hse.).

—Recognize Common Word Families. 2002. (J). (gr. 2). 66.75 (978-1-58605-329-1(9) , LeapFrog Schl. Hse.) LeapFrog Enterprises, Inc.

—Recognize Compound Words. 2002. (J). (gr. 2). 66.75 (978-1-58605-325-3(6)); (gr. 3). 66.75 (978-1-58605-385-7(X)); (gr. 4). 66.75 (978-1-58605-444-1(9)) LeapFrog Enterprises, Inc. (LeapFrog Schl. Hse.).

—Recognize Contractions. 2002. (J). (gr. 3). 66.75 (978-1-58605-386-4(8)); (gr. 4). 66.75 (978-1-58605-445-8(7)) LeapFrog Enterprises, Inc. (LeapFrog Schl. Hse.).

—Recognize Contradictions. 2002. (J). (gr. 2). 66.75 (978-1-58605-326-0(4) , LeapFrog Schl. Hse.) LeapFrog Enterprises, Inc.

—Recognize Regular & Irregular Plurals. 2002. (J). (gr. 2). 66.75 (978-1-58605-327-7(2)); (gr. 3). 66.75 (978-1-58605-387-1(6)); (gr. 4). 66.75 (978-1-58605-446-5(5)) LeapFrog Enterprises, Inc. (LeapFrog Schl. Hse.).

—Recognize Short Vowels. 2002. (J). (gr. 2). 66.75 (978-1-58605-322-2(1) , LeapFrog Schl. Hse.) LeapFrog Enterprises, Inc.

—Use a Dictionary & a Thesaurus. 2002. (J). (gr. 4). 66.75 (978-1-58605-435-9(X) , LeapFrog Schl. Hse.) LeapFrog Enterprises, Inc.

—Use a Dictionary & Glossary. 2002. (J). (gr. 2). 66.75 (978-1-58605-305-5(1) , LeapFrog Schl. Hse.) LeapFrog Enterprises, Inc.

—Use a Dictionary, Thesaurus, & Glossary. 2002. (J). (gr. 5). 66.75 (978-1-58605-497-7(X) , LeapFrog Schl. Hse.) LeapFrog Enterprises, Inc.

—Use Roots & Affixes. 2002. (J). (gr. 2). 66.75 (978-1-58605-312-3(4)); (gr. 3). 66.75 (978-1-58605-381-9(7)); (gr. 4). 66.75 (978-1-58605-439-7(2)) LeapFrog Enterprises, Inc. (LeapFrog Schl. Hse.).

—Use Structural Analysis: Root Words & Affixes. 2002. (J). (gr. 5). 66.75 (978-1-58605-509-7(7) , LeapFrog Schl. Hse.) LeapFrog Enterprises, Inc.

—Use Structural Analysis Root Words & Affixes. 2002. (J). (gr. 4). 66.75 (978-1-58605-449-6(X) , LeapFrog Schl. Hse.) LeapFrog Enterprises, Inc.

Reilly, Geoff. Skills in Grammar & Style, Bk. 2. 2004. (Illus.). (J). pap., stu. ed. 19.95 (978-0-7487-7794-5(6)) Nelson Thornes Ltd. GBR. *Dist:* Trans-Atlantic Pubns., Inc.

Rondeau, Amanda. Compound Words. 2004. (J). (ps-3). lib. bdg. 239.16 (978-1-59197-429-1(1) , SandCastle) ABDO Publishing Co.

—Months. l.t. ed. 2001. (Capital Letters Ser.). (Illus.). 24p. (J). (ps-3). lib. bdg. 19.93 (978-1-57765-612-8(1) , SandCastle) ABDO Publishing Co.

Rooney Moreau, Maryellen & Welch, Brian Scott. Talk to Write, Write to Learn Kit. 2006. pap. (***978-0-9769527-5-6(0)***) Mindwing Concepts, Inc.

Rosenberg, Mandie. Mastering Grammar Skills. 2002. lib. bdg. 22.20 (978-0-613-52139-0(0)) Tandem Library Bks.

Roy, Jennifer Rozines. You Can Write Using Good Grammar. 2004. (You Can Write Ser.). (Illus.). 64p. (J). lib. bdg. 22.60 (978-0-7660-2084-9(3)) Enslow Pubs., Inc.

Rules of the Game. 2004. Bk. 1. (gr. 5-6). pap., stu. ed. 9.15 (978-0-8388-2237-1(1)); Bk. 2. (gr. 7-8). pap., stu. ed. 9.15 (978-0-8388-2239-5(8)); Bk. 3 (gr. 9-10). pap., stu. ed. 9.15 (978-0-8388-2241-8(X)) Educators Publishing Service, Inc.

Ruthven, Rosemary. Write to Know: Nonfiction Writing Prompts for Lower Elementary Math. Whited, Amy M., ed. 2005. 128p. pap. 9.95 (978-1-933196-01-5(7)) Advanced Learning Pr.

—Write to Know: Nonfiction Writing Prompts for Upper Elementary Math. Whited, Amy M., ed. 2005. 128p. pap. 9.95 (978-1-933196-04-6(1)) Advanced Learning Pr.

Salisbury, Cynthia. Building Grammar. 2001. (Homework Booklets Ser.). 80p. (J). (gr. 1-2). pap. 2.99 (978-0-7424-0149-5(9) , IF0370); (gr. 3-4). pap. 2.99 (978-0-7424-0150-1(2) , IF0371) School Specialty Publishing.

Salzmann, Mary Elizabeth. Apostrophe. l.t. ed. 2001. (Punctuation Ser.). (Illus.). 24p. (J). (ps-3). lib. bdg. 19.93 (978-1-57765-625-8(3) , SandCastle) ABDO Publishing Co.

—Comma. l.t. ed. 2001. (Punctuation Ser.). (Illus.). 24p. (J). (ps-3). lib. bdg. 19.93 (978-1-57765-620-3(2) , SandCastle) ABDO Publishing Co.

—Exclamation Point. l.t. ed. 2001. (Punctuation Ser.). (Illus.). 24p. (J). (ps-3). lib. bdg. 19.93 (978-1-57765-621-0(0) , SandCastle) ABDO Publishing Co.

Sarris, Eno & Aihara, Masaaki, eds. Long Vowels Write & Wipe. 2008. (J). 9.95 (***978-1-933241-48-7(9)***) Kumon Publishing North America, Inc.

Sarris, Eno & Masaaki, Aihara, eds. Short Vowels Write & Wipe. 2008. (J). 9.95 (***978-1-933241-47-0(0)***) Kumon Publishing North America, Inc.

Saslow, Joan M. & Collins, Tim. Living & Working In English, 4 vols. 2004. (Illus.). xii, 148p. (C). pap. 21.67 (978-0-13-192802-2(3)) Pearson ESL.

—Workplace Plus 1 with Grammar Booster, 4 vols. 2004. (Illus.). (C). pap. 21.67 (978-0-13-192799-5(X)) Pearson ESL.

—Workplace Plus 2 with Grammar Booster, 4 vols. 2004. (Illus.). xiii, 148p. (C). pap. 21.67 (978-0-13-192800-8(7)) Pearson ESL.

—Workplace Plus 3 with Grammar Booster, 4 vols. 2004. (Illus.). 162p. (C). pap. 21.67 (978-0-13-192801-5(5)) Pearson ESL.

Schatz, Mary S. Grammar Rules. 2002. 250p. (YA). pap. 14.95 (978-1-930820-02-9(X) , GP-102) Garlic Pr.

Scheunemann, Pam. Days. l.t. ed. 2001. (Capital Letters Ser.). (Illus.). 24p. (J). (ps-3). lib. bdg. 19.93 (978-1-57765-611-1(3) , SandCastle) ABDO Publishing Co.

—Places. l.t. ed. 2001. (Capital Letters Ser.). (Illus.). 24p. (J). (ps-3). lib. bdg. 19.93 (978-1-57765-609-8(1) , SandCastle) ABDO Publishing Co.

—States. l.t. ed. 2001. (Capital Letters Ser.). (Illus.). 24p. (J). (ps-3). lib. bdg. 19.93 (978-1-57765-613-5(X) , SandCastle) ABDO Publishing Co.

Schneider, Melissa. G. U. M. Drops 1-2. 2005. 128p. 12.95 (978-1-933407-00-5(X)) In the Think of Things.

—G. U. M. Drops 3. 2005. 12.95 (978-1-933407-01-2(8)) In the Think of Things.

—G. U. M. Drops 4. 2005. 12.95 (978-1-933407-02-9(6)) In the Think of Things.

School Specialty Publishing. Adjectives & Adverbs. 2003. (Modified Basic Skills Ser.). 48p. (J). (gr. k-4). pap. 6.99 (978-0-7424-1924-7(X) , LL90001) School Specialty Publishing.

—Beginning Consonants. 2001. (Flip-Flashtm Ser.). 160p. (J). (gr. k up). pap. 7.99 (978-1-56451-383-0(1) , ID2422) School Specialty Publishing.

—Blends & Digraphs. 2001. (Flip-Flashtm Ser.). 160p. (J). (gr. k up). pap. 7.99 (978-1-56451-384-7(X) , ID2423) School Specialty Publishing.

—Compounds & Contractions. 2001. (Flip-Flashtm Ser.). 160p. (J). (gr. k up). pap. 7.99 (978-1-56451-385-4(8) , ID2424) School Specialty Publishing.

—Flip-Flash Phonics: Homonyms. 2002. (Flip-Flashtm Phonics Ser.). 160p. (J). (gr. 1 up). pap. 7.99 (978-1-56451-392-2(0) , ID2427) School Specialty Publishing.

—Long Vowels. 2001. (Flip-Flashtm Ser.). 160p. (J). (gr. k up). pap. 7.99 (978-1-56451-382-3(3) , ID2421) School Specialty Publishing.

—Nouns & Verbs. 2003. (Modified Basic Skills Ser.). 48p. (J). (gr. k-4). pap. 6.99 (978-0-7424-1927-8(4) , LL90004) School Specialty Publishing.

—Regular Verbs. 2003. (Modified Basic Skills Ser.). 48p. (J). (gr. k-4). pap. 6.99 (978-0-7424-1929-2(0) , LL90006) School Specialty Publishing.

—Sentences & Punctuation. 2003. (Modified Basic Skills Ser.). 48p. (J). (gr. k-4). pap. 6.99 (978-0-7424-1934-6(7) , LL90007) School Specialty Publishing.

—Words & Pictures. 2002. (Flip-Flashtm Phonics Ser.). 160p. (J). (gr. k up). pap. 7.99 (978-1-56451-391-5(2) , ID2426) School Specialty Publishing.

School Zone Staff. Nouns, Verbs & More. 2005. (Illus.). 56p. (J). 2.79 (978-1-58947-420-8(1)) School Zone Publishing Co.

Scrambled Sentences (Gr. 1-2) 2003. (J). (978-1-58232-126-4(4)) Bryan Hse. Pubs., Inc.

Self I - PowerPhonics Skill, 6 bks., Set I. Incl. Be Safe on the Bus : Learning the B Sound. Smith, Kathy. lib. bdg. 18.50 (978-0-8239-5900-6(7)); Day with My Dad : Learning the D Sound. Baron, Larry. lib. bdg. 18.00 (978-0-8239-5902-0(3)); Family Fun : Learning the F Sound. Moskal, Greg. lib. bdg. 18.00 (978-0-8239-5901-3(5)); Meet My Mom : Learning the M Sound. Moore, M. lib. bdg. 18.00 (978-0-8239-5913-6(9)); On the Job : Learning the Short O Sound. Metz, Lynn. lib. bdg. 18.50 (978-0-8239-5905-1(8)); You Need Your Nose : Learning the N Sound. Sarkisian, Kevin. lib. bdg. 18.50 (978-0-8239-5910-5(4)); 24p. (J). (gr. 1). 2002. (Illus.). 2001. Set lib. bdg. 108.50 (978-0-8239-7202-9(X) , PowerKids Pr.) Rosen Publishing Group, Inc., The.

Self II - PowerPhonics Skill, 6 bks., Set III. Incl. All Sorts of Sports : Learning the OR Sound. Hogenkamp, Susan. lib. bdg. 18.50 (978-0-8239-5949-5(X)); Friends : Learning the FR Sound. Santos, Dina. lib. bdg. 18.50 (978-0-8239-5944-0(9)); I Can Draw : Learning the DR Sound. Santos, Dina. lib. bdg. 18.50 (978-0-8239-5946-4(5)); Let's Bring Mom Breakfast : Learning the BR Sound. McConnell, Sharon. lib. bdg. 18.50 (978-0-8239-5936-5(8)); My Birthday : Learning the IR Sound. Hogenkamp, Susan. lib. bdg. 18.50 (978-0-8239-5948-8(1)); My New Glasses : Learning the GL Sound. Santos, Dina. lib. bdg. 18.50 (978-0-8239-5945-7(7)); 24p. (J). (gr. 1). 2002. (Illus.). 2001. Set lib. bdg. 108.00 (978-0-8239-7210-4(0) , PowerKids Pr.) Rosen Publishing Group, Inc., The.

Shehan, L. English Can Be Easy. 2001. (Illus.). (J). pap. 3.73 (978-0-03-002540-2(0)) Holt, Rinehart & Winston.

Short & R-Controlled Vowel Sounds. (Modified Basic Skills Ser.). 48p. (gr. k-4). 5.99 (978-0-7424-0272-0(X) , LL80026) School Specialty Publishing.

Short Vowel Sounds & R-Controlled Vowels. 2004. (Basic Skills Ser.). 48p. (J). pap. 6.99 (978-0-88724-143-7(3) , CD-4707) Carson-Dellosa Publishing Co., Inc.

Shostak, Jerome. Vocabulary Workshop: Level Blue. 1999. (Vocabulary Workshop Ser.). (YA). (gr. 5 up). 6.90 (978-0-8215-0405-5(3)) Sadlier, William H. Inc.

Soars, John & Soars, Liz. New Headway English Course. 2002. (Illus.). 144p. 18.95 (978-0-19-436670-0(7)); 159p. 18.95 (978-0-19-436671-7(5)) Oxford Univ. Pr., Inc.

—New Headway English Course: With Key. 2002. (Illus.). 96p. (J). 10.50 (978-0-19-436672-4(3)) Oxford Univ. Pr., Inc.

Solloway, Jeff. Grammar Smart: A Guide to Perfect Usage. 2001. 18.65 (978-0-606-22342-3(8)) Tandem Library Bks.

Spence, Bill & Bremner, Sue. Language Works Book 4: Grammar in Context. 2007. (Language Works: Grammar in Context Ser.). pap. 10.50 (***978-0-521-69257-1(1)***) Cambridge Univ. Pr.

—Language Works Book 5: Grammar in Context. 2007. (Language Works: Grammar in Context Ser.). pap. 10.50 (***978-0-521-69258-8(X)***) Cambridge Univ. Pr.

—Language Works Book 6: Grammar in Context. 2007. (Language Works: Grammar in Context Ser.). pap. 10.50 (***978-0-521-69259-5(8)***) Cambridge Univ. Pr.

SpongeBob Grammar Wipe Off. 2007. (J). 4.99 (***978-1-59545-105-7(6)***) Learning Horizons, Inc.

Sprick, Marilyn, et al. Student Workbook 3 (Plain Text) Unit 19 through Vowel Review Unit. 2003. (Read Well Level K Ser.). (J). (978-1-59318-168-0(X)) Sopris West Educational Services.

—Student Workbook 3 (Slant Text) Unit 19 through Vowel Review Unit. 2003. (Read Well Level K Ser.). (Illus.). 104p. (J). (978-1-59318-171-0(X)) Sopris West Educational Services.

Steck-Vaughn Staff. Access Writing. 2004. pap., tchr. ed. 5.95 (978-0-7398-8933-6(8)) Steck-Vaughn.

—At-Home Workbooks: Vowels. 2004. (Illus.). pap., wbk. ed. (978-0-7398-8535-2(9)) Steck-Vaughn.

—English ASAP Level 1. 1998. pap., tchr. ed. 17.60 (978-0-8172-7954-7(7)) Steck-Vaughn.

—Head for Home: Consonant Blends. 2004. (Illus.). pap. 5.99 (978-0-7398-8536-9(7)) Steck-Vaughn.

—Language Skills Set. 2002. (Illus.). (J). (gr. 2). (978-0-7398-6821-8(7)); (gr. 3). (978-0-7398-6822-5(5)); (gr. 4). (978-0-7398-6823-2(3)) Steck-Vaughn.

—Middle School Capitalization & Punctuation. 1999. (Illus.). (J). pap. (978-0-7398-1304-1(8)) Steck-Vaughn.

—Notetaking & Outlining. 1999. pap. (978-0-7398-2926-4(2)) Steck-Vaughn.

—Reading Comprehension. 2002. (Illus.). Bk. C. pap. (978-0-7398-5822-6(X)); Bk. D. pap. (978-0-7398-5823-3(8)); Bk. A. (J). pap. (978-0-7398-5820-2(3)); Bk. B. pap. (978-0-7398-5821-9(1)) Steck-Vaughn.

—Steck-Vaughn Spelling Book: Level 5. 2001. (J). pap., stu. ed. 19.90 (978-0-7398-5057-2(1)) Steck-Vaughn.

—Steck-Vaughn Spelling Book: Level 6. 2001. (J). pap., stu. ed. 19.90 (978-0-7398-5058-9(X)) Steck-Vaughn.

Steele, Anne L. Using Standards Grammar Gr 4. 2003. (100+ Seriestm Ser.). 128p. (J). (gr. 4 up). pap. 12.99 (978-0-7424-1804-2(9) , IFG99053) School Specialty Publishing.

—Using Standards Grammar Gr 5. 2003. (100+ Seriestm Ser.). 128p. (J). (gr. 5 up). pap. 12.99 (978-0-7424-1805-9(7) , IFG99054) School Specialty Publishing.

Suarez, Elizabeth. Comprehension E-Book. 2005. 80p. (J). per. 10.99 (978-1-59441-562-3(5) , CD-104015-EB) Carson-Dellosa Publishing Co., Inc.

—Fluency, Vocabulary, & Comprehension E-Book. 2005. 80p. (J). per. 10.99 (978-1-59441-564-7(1) , CD-104017-EB) Carson-Dellosa Publishing Co., Inc.

Sullivan, Vicki Gallo. Grammar. 1998. (Kelley Wingate Grammar Ser.). v, 129p. (gr. 1-2). pap. 11.99 (978-0-88724-497-1(1) , CD-3741); (gr. 3-4). pap. 11.99 (978-0-88724-498-8(X) , CD-3742); (gr. 5-6). pap. 11.99 (978-0-88724-499-5(8) , CD-3743); (gr. 7-8). pap. 11.99 (978-0-88724-500-8(5) , CD-3744); (gr. 9-10). pap. 11.99 (978-0-88724-501-5(3) , CD-3745) Carson-Dellosa Publishing Co., Inc.

Sunley, Laura. Fun with Grammar: 75 Quick Activities & Games That Help Kids Learn about Nouns, Verbs, Adjectives, Adverbs & More. 2002. 64p. pap. 10.95 (978-0-439-28234-5(9)) Scholastic, Inc.

Tabor, Nancy. See What You Say. 2000. Tr. of Ve Lo Que Dices. (ENG & SPA., Illus.). (J). (978-1-57091-375-4(7)) Charlesbridge Publishing, Inc.

—See What You Say. 2000. Tr. of Ve Lo Que Dices. (SPA.). (gr. k-3). lib. bdg. 15.25 (978-0-613-28312-0(0)) Tandem Library Bks.

Terban, Marvin. Verbs! Verbs! Verbs! The Trickiest Action-Packed Words in English. Hobbs, Pamela, illus. 2002. 160p. (J). pap. 7.95 (978-0-439-40164-7(X) , Scholastic Reference) Scholastic, Inc.

—Verbs! Verbs! Verbs! The Trickiest Action-Packed Words in English. 2002. (gr. 3-6). lib. bdg. 15.25 (978-0-613-53119-1(1)) Tandem Library Bks.

Terban, Marvin. Your Foot's on My Feet! And Other Tricky Nouns. Maestro, Giulio, illus. 2008. 64p. (J). (gr. 2-5). pap. 6.95 (***978-0-618-19166-6(6)*** , Clarion Bks.) Houghton Mifflin Co. Trade & Reference Div.

Thomson, Ruth. Go Further with Grammar. 2002. (Adventures in Literacy Ser.). (Illus.). 32p. (J). lib. bdg. 24.25 (978-1-931983-07-5(0)) Chrysalis Education.

—Grammar Is Great! 2002. (Adventures in Literacy Ser.). (Illus.). 32p. (J). lib. bdg. 24.25 (978-1-931983-06-8(2)) Chrysalis Education.

Timeless Voices, Timeless Themes. (YA). 2000. (gr. 11). trans. 160.97 (978-0-13-435111-7(8)); 2000. (gr. 12). 24.47 (978-0-13-436134-5(2)); 2000. (gr. 12). trans. 160.97 (978-0-13-435112-4(6)); Gold Level. 2000. (gr. 9). trans. 160.97 (978-0-13-435106-3(1)); Gold Level 2000. (gr. 9). pap. 8.47 (978-0-13-436008-9(7)); Platinum Level 2000. (gr. 10). pap. 8.47 (978-0-13-436009-6(5)); Platinum Level 1999. (gr. 10). stu. ed. 54.97 (978-0-13-434057-9(4)); Silver Level. 2001. (gr. 8). trans. 161.47 (978-0-13-436021-8(4)) Prentice Hall PTR.

Timeless Voices, Timeless Themes: Bronze, Lesson Planner. 2001. (YA). (gr. 7). pap. 9.97 (978-0-13-050904-8(3)) Prentice Hall PTR.

Timeless Voices, Timeless Themes: Bronze, Literary Analysis Activity Book. 2001. (YA). (gr. 7). pap. 6.97 (978-0-13-052367-9(4)) Prentice Hall PTR.

Timeless Voices, Timeless Themes: Bronze, Standardized Test Preparation Answers & Explanations. 2001. (YA). (gr. 7). 129.97 (978-0-13-050810-2(1)) Prentice Hall PTR.

Timeless Voices, Timeless Themes: Bronze, Standardized Test Preparation Blackline Masters. 2001. (YA). (gr. 7). pap. 19.97 (978-0-13-043576-7(7)) Prentice Hall PTR.

Timeless Voices, Timeless Themes: Bronze, Standardized Test Preparation Workbook. 2001. (YA). (gr. 7). pap., wbk. ed. 6.97 (978-0-13-050609-2(5)) Prentice Hall PTR.

Timeless Voices, Timeless Themes: Bronze, Vocabulary & Spelling Practice Book. 2001. (YA). (gr. 7). pap. 6.97 (978-0-13-052345-7(3)) Prentice Hall PTR.

Timeless Voices, Timeless Themes: Copper, Reading Selection Summaries Practice Book. 2001. (J). (gr. 6). pap. 6.97 (978-0-13-044102-7(3)) Prentice Hall PTR.

Timeless Voices, Timeless Themes: Copper, Vocabulary & Spelling Practice Book. 2001. (J). (gr. 6). pap. 6.97 (978-0-13-052344-0(5)) Prentice Hall PTR.

Timeless Voices, Timeless Themes: Gold. 2001. (YA). (gr. 9). stu. ed. 52.97 (978-0-13-050287-2(1)) Prentice Hall PTR.

Timeless Voices, Timeless Themes: Gold, Assessment Success Planning Guide. 2001. (YA). (gr. 9). pap. 4.97 (978-0-13-051082-2(3)) Prentice Hall PTR.

Timeless Voices, Timeless Themes: Gold, Lesson Planner. 2001. (YA). (gr. 9). pap. 9.97 (978-0-13-050906-2(X)) Prentice Hall PTR.

Timeless Voices, Timeless Themes: Gold, Standardized Test Preparation. 2000. (YA). (gr. 9). pap., wbk. ed. 6.97 (978-0-13-050612-2(5)) Prentice Hall PTR.

Timeless Voices, Timeless Themes: Grammar Practice Book. Bronze Level 2001. (YA). (gr. 7). pap. 7.47 (978-0-13-434640-3(8)); Copper Level 2001. (J). (gr. 6). pap. 7.47 (978-0-13-434639-7(4)); Gold Level 2000. (YA). (gr. 9). 7.47 (978-0-13-434642-7(4)); Silver Level 2001. (YA) (gr. 8). pap. 7.47 (978-0-13-434641-0(6)) Prentice Hall PTR.

Timeless Voices, Timeless Themes: Platinum. 2001. (YA). (gr. 10). stu. ed. 52.97 (978-0-13-050288-9(X)) Prentice Hall PTR.

Timeless Voices, Timeless Themes: Platinum, Standardized Test Preparation Blackline Masters. 2001. (YA). (gr. 10). pap. 6.97 (978-0-13-437470-3(3)) Prentice Hall PTR.

Timeless Voices, Timeless Themes: Selection Support, Skills Development Practice Book, Silver Level 2001. (YA). (gr. 8). pap. 8.47 (978-0-13-436583-1(6)) Prentice Hall PTR.

Timeless Voices, Timeless Themes: Silver, Lesson Planner. 2001. (YA). (gr. 8). pap. 9.97 (978-0-13-050905-5(1)) Prentice Hall PTR.

Timeless Voices, Timeless Themes: Silver, Standardized Test Preparation Blackline Masters. 2001. (YA). (gr. 8). pap. 19.40 (978-0-13-043577-4(5)) Prentice Hall PTR.

Timeless Voices, Timeless Themes: Silver, Standardized Test Preparation Workbook. 2001. (YA). (gr. 8). pap., wbk. ed. 6.97 (978-0-13-050611-5(7)) Prentice Hall PTR.

Timeless Voices, Timeless Themes: Silver, Vocabulary & Spelling Practice Book. 2001. (YA). (gr. 8). pap. 6.97 (978-0-13-052346-4(1)) Prentice Hall PTR.

Timeless Voices, Timeless Themes: The American Experience, Fine Art. 2000. (YA). (gr. 11). trans. 31.97 (978-0-13-051237-6(0)) Prentice Hall PTR.

Timeless Voices, Timeless Themes: The American Experience, Grammar Practice Book. 2001. (YA). (gr. 11). pap. 7.47 (978-0-13-434644-1(0)) Prentice Hall PTR.

Timeless Voices, Timeless Themes: The American Experience, Literary Focus & Reading. 2000. (YA). (gr. 11). trans. 109.97 (978-0-13-051282-6(6)) Prentice Hall PTR.

Timeless Voices, Timeless Themes: The American Experience, Reading Selection Summaries Practice Book. 2000. (YA). (gr. 11). pap. 6.97 (978-0-13-044107-2(4)) Prentice Hall PTR.

Timeless Voices, Timeless Themes: The American Experience, Standardized Test Preparation Notes. 2000. trans. 109.97 (978-0-13-052188-0(4)) Prentice Hall PTR.

Timeless Voices, Timeless Themes: The British Tradition, Fine Art. 2000. (YA). (gr. 12). trans. 31.97 (978-0-13-051238-3(9)) Prentice Hall PTR.

Timeless Voices, Timeless Themes: The British Tradition, Literary Focus & Reading. 2000. (YA). (gr. 12). trans. 109.97 (978-0-13-051283-3(4)) Prentice Hall PTR.

Timeless Voices, Timeless Themes: The British Tradition, Standardized Test Prep. Answers & Explanations. 2000. (YA). (gr. 12). trans. 129.97 (978-0-13-050826-3(8)) Prentice Hall PTR.

Timeless Voices, Timeless Themes: The British Tradition, Standardized Test Preparation Notes. 2000. (YA). (gr. 12). trans. 109.97 (978-0-13-052189-7(2)) Prentice Hall PTR.

Timeless Voices, Timeless Themes: World Literature, Literary Analysis Activity Book. 2000. (YA). (gr. 10). pap. 6.97 (978-0-13-052967-1(2)) Prentice Hall PTR.

Turrell, Linda. The Comma Book Student Activities Book: Mastering Language Arts Series. Matthews, Douglas L., ed. 2003. (Illus.). stu. ed., wbk. ed. (978-1-931680-73-8(6) , Expert Systems for Teachers) Teaching Point, Inc.

—The Noun Book Student Activities Book: Mastering Language Arts Series. Matthews, Douglas L., ed. 2003. (Mastering Language Arts Ser.). (Illus.). stu. ed., per., wbk. ed. (978-1-931680-59-2(0) , Expert Systems for Teachers) Teaching Point, Inc.

—The Sentence Book Student Activities Book: Mastering Language Arts Series. Matthews, Douglas L., ed. 2003. (Illus.). stu. ed., wbk. ed. (978-1-931680-79-0(5) , Expert Systems for Teachers) Teaching Point, Inc.

—The Verb Book Student Activities Book: Mastering Language Arts Series. Matthews, Douglas L., ed. 2003. (Illus.). stu. ed., wbk. ed. (978-1-931680-61-5(2) , Expert Systems for Teachers) Teaching Point, Inc.

Tyler, Jenny. Usborne First Learning Opposites. 2001. (gr. k-3). lib. bdg. 12.95 (978-0-613-90433-9(8)) Tandem Library Bks.

Using Capitalization (Gr. 3+) 2003. (J). (978-1-58232-051-9(9)) Bryan Hse. Pubs., Inc.

Vale, David. Picture Grammar for Children 1: Topic-Based Grammar Practice. 64p. pap., stu. ed. (978-0-435-29734-3(1)) Heinemann.

—Picture Grammar for Children 1: Topic-Based Grammar Practice, Answer Key. 34p. pap. (978-0-435-29735-0(X)) Heinemann.

—Picture Grammar for Children 2: Topic-Based Grammar Practice. 64p. pap., stu. ed. (978-0-435-29736-7(8)) Heinemann.

—Picture Grammar for Children 2: Topic-Based Grammar Practice, Answer Key. 34p. pap. (978-0-435-29737-4(6)) Heinemann.

Vandyck, William & Burt, Angela. Grammar Repair Kit. 2005. (Illus.). (YA). pap. 9.99 (978-0-340-89336-4(2) , Hodder & Stoughton) Hodder General Publishing Division GBR. *Dist:* Trafalgar Square Publishing.

Vastola, Pam. Rain: Learning the AI Sound. 2001. (PowerPhonics Ser.). (Illus.). 23p. (J). pap. 26.40 (978-0-8239-8288-2(2) , PowerKids Pr.) Rosen Publishing Group, Inc., The.

Venolia, Jan. Kids Write Right! 2000. (978-0-606-20316-6(8)) Tandem Library Bks.

—Kids Write Right! What You Need to Be a Writing Powerhouse. 2000. (J). (ps-7). (Illus.). 156p. lib. bdg. 17.60 (978-0-613-87430-4(7)); (978-0-606-20278-7(1)) Tandem Library Bks.

—Kids Write Right! What You Need to Be a Writing Powerhouse. McMahon, Bob, illus. 2004. 156p. (YA). (gr. 6-8). 8.95 (978-1-58246-028-4(0) , Tricycle Pr.) Ten Speed Pr.

Verb Endings, 10 vols., Set. 2004. (Beastieville Ser.). (J). 135.10 (978-0-516-25147-9(3) , Children's Pr.) Scholastic Library Publishing.

Vowel Sounds, 10 vols., Set. 2004. (Beastieville Ser.). 129.50 (978-0-516-25141-7(4) , Children's Pr.) Scholastic Library Publishing.

Voyages in English: Writing & Grammar. 2004. (gr. 1 up). tchr. ed. (978-0-8294-0980-2(7)); (gr. 1 up). tchr. ed., wbk. ed. (978-0-8294-1383-0(9)); (gr. 1 up). stu. ed. (978-0-8294-0981-9(5)); (gr. 1 up). stu. ed., wbk. ed. (978-0-8294-1382-3(0)); (gr. 2 up). tchr. ed. (978-0-8294-0982-6(3)); (gr. 2 up). tchr. ed., wbk. ed. (978-0-8294-1385-4(5)); (gr. 2 up). stu. ed. (978-0-8294-0983-3(1)); (gr. 2 up). stu. ed., wbk. ed. (978-0-8294-1384-7(7)); (gr. 3 up). (978-0-8294-1303-8(0)); (gr. 3 up). tchr. ed. (978-0-8294-0985-7(8)); (gr. 3 up). tchr. ed., wbk. ed. (978-0-8294-1319-9(7)); (gr. 3 up). stu. ed. (978-0-8294-0986-4(6)); (gr. 3 up). stu. ed., wbk. ed. (978-0-8294-1318-2(9)); (gr. 4 up). tchr. ed., wbk. ed. (978-0-8294-1321-2(9)); (gr. 4 up). stu. ed. (978-0-8294-0988-8(2)) Loyola Pr.

Ward-Beech, Linda. Great Grammar Skill Builders. 2001. (Joyful Learning Ser.). 48p. (gr. 2-3). pap., tchr. ed. 8.95 (978-0-439-40805-9(9)); (gr. 4-5). pap., tchr. ed. 8.95 (978-0-439-40806-6(7)); (gr. 6-8). pap., tchr. ed. 8.95 (978-0-439-40807-3(5)) Scholastic, Inc. (Teaching Resources).

The Weather Box: Fifth Grade Guided Comprehension Level Q. (On Our Way to English Ser.). (gr. 5 up). 34.50 (978-0-7578-6613-5(1)) Rigby Education.

Wernham, Sara. Jolly Readers Level 2 Inky & Friends Level 2: 6 Titles in a Pack, 6 vols. 2003. (Jolly Phonics Ser.). (Illus.). 12p. 9.95 (978-1-903619-86-5(6) , JL866) Jolly Learning, Ltd. GBR. *Dist:* American International Distribution Corp.

Whited, Amy. Write to Know: Nonfiction Writing Prompts for Secondary PE. 2006. (Write to Know Ser.). 128p. pap. 9.95 (978-1-933196-21-3(1)) Advanced Learning Pr.

Whited, Amy M., ed. Nonfiction Writing Prompts for Geometry. 2005. (Illus.). 128p. pap. 9.95 (978-1-933196-08-4(4)) Advanced Learning Pr.

—Nonfiction Writing Prompts for Secondary Art. 2005. 128p. pap. 9.95 (978-1-933196-09-1(2)) Advanced Learning Pr.

—Nonfiction Writing Prompts for Secondary Music. 2005. (Illus.). 128p. pap. 9.95 (978-1-933196-10-7(6)) Advanced Learning Pr.

Whiteford, Rhona. Complete English, 3 bks. in 1. (Illus.). 96p. (YA). pap. 15.99 (978-0-340-71582-6(0) , Hodder & Stoughton) Hodder General Publishing Division GBR. *Dist:* Trafalgar Square Publishing.

—Grammar & Punctuation. 2003. (Hodder Home Learning Ser.). (Illus.). 32p. (J). pap. 6.99 (978-0-340-79185-1(3) , Hodder & Stoughton) Hodder General Publishing Division GBR. *Dist:* Trafalgar Square Publishing.

WHS Staff, contrib. by. Vocabulary Workshop, Level Green, Test Booklets Cycle One. 2005. (Illus.). 44p. (YA). (gr. 3 up). 39.00 (978-0-8215-0430-7(4)) Sadlier, William H. Inc.

—Vocabulary Workshop, Level Green, Test Booklets Cycle Two. 2005. (Illus.). 44p. (YA). (gr. 3 up). 39.00 (978-0-8215-0440-6(1)) Sadlier, William H. Inc.

Wilson, Nancy. Our Mother Tongue: A Guide to English Grammar. 2003. 184p. (J). per. 20.00 (978-1-59128-011-8(7)) Canon Pr.

Wilson, Nancy. Our Mother Tongue: Answer Key. 2004. 60p. (J). per. 5.00 (***978-1-59128-016-3(8)***) Canon Pr.

Windsor, Lucinda. Grammar in Story Vol. 2: The Transparencies, 2 vols. 2004. 410p. pap. 38.50 (978-1-888842-17-3(2)) Absey & Co.

Wise, Jessie. First Language Lessons for the Well-Trained Mind. Park, Sarah, illus. 2002. 422p. (J). (gr. 1-2). pap. 18.95 (978-0-9714129-2-7(8) , FLL-PB) Peace Hill Pr.

Wise, Sue. How Do I Say That? Como Se Dice? Coirault, Christine, illus. 2006. (ENG & SPA.). 32p. (J). pap. 8.95 (978-0-8368-6583-7(9)); lib. bdg. 23.33 (978-0-8368-6259-1(7)) Stevens, Gareth Inc.

Wright, Marsha. Sentences & Vowel Pairs - Digraphs, 8 vols. 2003. 48p. (J). per. 7.99 (978-1-56472-195-2(7)) Edupress, Inc.

—Sentences for Consonant Blends - Digraphs, 8 vols. 2003. 48p. (J). per. 7.99 (978-1-56472-193-8(0)) Edupress, Inc.

—Sentences for R-Controlled Vowels - Diphthongs, 8 vols. 2003. 48p. (J). per. 7.99 (978-1-56472-197-6(3)) Edupress, Inc.

—Sentences for Short - Long Vowels, 8 vols. 2003. (Illus.). 48p. (J). per. 7.99 (978-1-56472-191-4(4)) Edupress, Inc.

—Stories for Consonant Blends - Digraphs, 8 vols. 2003. 48p. (J). per. (978-1-56472-194-5(9)) Edupress, Inc.

—Stories for R-Controlled Vowels - Diphthongs, 8 vols. 2003. 48p. (J). per. 7.99 (978-1-56472-198-3(1)) Edupress, Inc.

—Stories for Short - Long Vowels, 8 vols. 2003. 48p. (J). per. 7.99 (978-1-56472-192-1(2)) Edupress, Inc.

—Stories for Vowel Pairs - Digraphs, 8 vols. 2003. 48p. (J). per. 7.99 (978-1-56472-196-9(5)) Edupress, Inc.

Writer's Solution Bronze Level: Grammar Practice Book Answer Key. (YA). (gr. 7). 1.97 (978-0-13-434759-2(5)) Prentice Hall PTR.

Writer's Solution Diamond Level: Grammar Practice Book Answer Key. (YA). (gr. 12). 1.97 (978-0-13-434766-0(8)) Prentice Hall PTR.

Writer's Solution Gold Level: Grammar Practice Book Answer Key. (YA). (gr. 9). 1.97 (978-0-13-434761-5(7)) Prentice Hall PTR.

Writer's Solution Platinum Level: Grammar Practice Book Answer Key. (YA). (gr. 10). 1.97 (978-0-13-434763-9(3)) Prentice Hall PTR.

Writer's Solution Ruby Level: Grammar Practice Book Answer Key. (YA). (gr. 11). 1.97 (978-0-13-434764-6(1)) Prentice Hall PTR.

Writer's Solution Silver Level: Grammar Practice Book Answer Key. (YA). (gr. 8). 1.97 (978-0-13-434760-8(9)) Prentice Hall PTR.

Writing Sentences (Gr. 2-3) 2003. (J). (978-1-58232-127-1(2)) Bryan Hse. Pubs., Inc.

Writing Works with NC Wordcrafter & Joey: Grade 3+ 2004. 28.00 (***978-0-9790796-0-3(8)***) PJR Assocs., Ltd.

Writing Works with NC Wordcrafter & Joey: Grade 4+ 2004. 28.00 (***978-0-9790796-1-0(6)***) PJR Assocs., Ltd.

Writing Works with NC Wordcrafter & Joey: Grade 5+ 2004. 28.00 (***978-0-9790796-2-7(4)***) PJR Assocs., Ltd.

Yates, Irene. How to Be a Wizard at Grammer. Ford, Kate, illus. 48p. (J). (gr. 3-6). pap. (978-1-876367-29-9(6)) Wizard Bks.

Zile, Susan Van. Awesome Hands-On Activities for Teaching Grammar: Easy, Learning-Rich Activities That Tap into Students' Multiple Intelligences - And Bring Excitement & Fun to Your Grammar Lessons. 2003. (Illus.). 80p. (gr. 4). pap. 12.99 (978-0-439-43460-7(2) , Teaching Resources) Scholastic, Inc.

Zocchi, Judith Mazzeo. Uri's "U" Book. Revutsky, Helen Ross, illus. 2007. (J). (***978-1-59646-538-1(7)***) Dingles & Co.

—Yola's "Y" Book. Revutsky, Helen Ross, illus. 2007. (J). (***978-1-59646-562-6(X)***) Dingles & Co.

Zocchi, Judith Mazzeo, et al. Aimee's a Book: El Libro a de Aimee. Revutsky, Helen Ross, illus. 2005. (J). (***978-1-59646-421-6(6)***) Dingles & Co.

—Zach's "Z" Book: El Libro "Z" de Zach. Revutsky, Helen Ross, illus. 2005. (SPA & ENG.). (J). (***978-1-59646-571-8(9)***) Dingles & Co.

Zocchi, Judy. Cassie's "C" Book: El Libro "C" de Cassie. 2005. (SPA & ENG., Illus.). (J). (***978-1-59646-433-9(X)***) Dingles & Co.

4th Grammer Booster. 2005. 64p. (J). per. 1.49 (978-1-59441-352-0(5) , C04028) Carson-Dellosa Publishing Co., Inc.

ENGLISH LANGUAGE—HISTORY

Atkinson, Mary. What Do You Mean? Communication Isn't Easy. 2007. (Shockwave: People & Communities Ser.). (Illus.). 36p. (J). (gr. 4-6). lib. bdg. 25.00 (***978-0-531-17571-2(5)*** , Children's Pr.) Scholastic Library Publishing.

ENGLISH LANGUAGE—HOMONYMS

Alda, Arlene. Did You Say Pears? 2006. (Illus.). 32p. (J). (ps-3). 16.95 (978-0-88776-739-5(7)) Tundra Bks., Inc./Livres Toundra, Inc. CAN. *Dist:* Random Hse., Inc.

Cleary, Brian P. How Much Can a Bare Bear Bear? What Are Homonyms & Homophones? Gable, Brian, illus. (Words Are CATegorical Ser.). 32p. (J). 2007. (gr. 2-6). pap. 6.95 (***978-0-8225-6710-3(5)*** , First Avenue Editions); 2005. (ps-ps). 15.95 (978-1-57505-824-5(3)) Lerner Publishing Group.

Doudna, Kelly. A Bat Hangs from the Bat. l.t. ed. 2002. (Homonyms Ser.). (Illus.). 24p. (J). (ps-3). lib. bdg. 19.93 (978-1-57765-785-9(3) , SandCastle) ABDO Publishing Co.

—Do Not Squash the Squash. l.t. ed. 2002. (Homonyms Ser.). (Illus.). 24p. (J). (ps-3). lib. bdg. 19.93 (978-1-57765-791-0(8) , SandCastle) ABDO Publishing Co.

—An Ear Is Not an Ear. l.t. ed. 2002. (Homonyms Ser.). (Illus.). 24p. (J). (ps-3). lib. bdg. 19.93 (978-1-57765-788-0(8) , SandCastle) ABDO Publishing Co.

—A Fly Can Fly. l.t. ed. 2002. (Homonyms Ser.). (Illus.). 24p. (J). (ps-3). lib. bdg. 19.93 (978-1-57765-786-6(1) , SandCastle) ABDO Publishing Co.

—Homonyms, Set. l.t. ed. Incl. Bat Hangs from the Bat. lib. bdg. 19.93 (978-1-57765-785-9(3)); Do Not Squash the Squash. lib. bdg. 19.93 (978-1-57765-791-0(8)); Ear Is Not an Ear. lib. bdg. 19.93 (978-1-57765-788-0(8)); Fly Can Fly. lib. bdg. 19.93 (978-1-57765-786-6(1)); Line up on the Line. lib. bdg. 19.93 (978-1-57765-787-3(X)); Palm in My Palm. lib. bdg. 19.93 (978-1-57765-790-3(X)); Rose Rose from the Garden. lib. bdg. 19.93 (978-1-57765-789-7(6)); Top Is on Top. lib. bdg. 19.93 (978-1-57765-792-7(6)); 24p. (J). (ps-3). (Illus.). 2002. Set lib. bdg. 159.44 (978-1-57765-524-4(9) , SandCastle) ABDO Publishing Co.

—Line up on the Line. l.t. ed. 2002. (Homonyms Ser.). (Illus.). 24p. (J). (ps-3). lib. bdg. 19.93 (978-1-57765-787-3(X) , SandCastle) ABDO Publishing Co.

—A Palm in My Palm. l.t. ed. 2002. (Homonyms Ser.). (Illus.). 24p. (J). (ps-3). lib. bdg. 19.93 (978-1-57765-790-3(X) , SandCastle) ABDO Publishing Co.

—The Rose Rose from the Garden. l.t. ed. 2002. (Homonyms Ser.). (Illus.). 24p. (J). (ps-3). lib. bdg. 19.93 (978-1-57765-789-7(6) , SandCastle) ABDO Publishing Co.

—The Top Is on Top. l.t. ed. 2002. (Homonyms Ser.). (Illus.). 24p. (J). (ps-3). lib. bdg. 19.93 (978-1-57765-792-7(6) , SandCastle) ABDO Publishing Co.

Fun with Homonyms - Crossword Puzzles & Word Searches. 2004. pap. 7.99 (978-1-4206-3143-2(8)) Teacher Created Materials, Inc.

Ghigna, Charles. See the Yak Yak. 1999. (Step into Reading Ser.). (978-0-606-16888-5(5)) Tandem Library Bks.

Gwynne, Fred. A Chocolate Moose for Dinner. Gwynne, Fred, illus. 2005. (Stories to Go! Ser.). (Illus.). 48p. (J). pap. 4.99 (978-0-689-87827-5(3) , Aladdin) Simon & Schuster Children's Publishing.

—The King Who Rained. Gwynne, Fred, illus. 2006. (Stories to Go! Ser.). (Illus.). 40p. (J). 4.99 (978-1-4169-1858-5(2) , Aladdin) Simon & Schuster Children's Publishing.

Homophones, Set II. Incl. Bella Blew Blue Bubbles. Rondeau, Amanda. lib. bdg. 19.93 (978-1-57765-784-2(5)); Knight Waits at Night. Salzmann, Mary Elizabeth. lib. bdg. 19.93 (978-1-57765-651-7(2)); My Deer Is a Dear. Salzmann, Mary Elizabeth. lib. bdg. 19.93 (978-1-57765-652-4(0)); Prince Left His Prints. Rondeau, Amanda. lib. bdg. 19.93 (978-1-57765-781-1(0)); Sue Threw the Goop Through the Hoop. Rondeau, Amanda. lib. bdg. 19.93 (978-1-57765-783-5(7)); We Have a Wee Whale. Rondeau, Amanda. lib. bdg. 19.93 (978-1-57765-779-8(9)); 24p. (J). (ps-3). (Illus.). 2002. Set lib. bdg. 119.58 (978-1-57765-522-0(2)); Set lib. bdg. 119.58 (978-1-57765-527-5(3)) ABDO Publishing Co. (SandCastle).

Loewen, Nancy. If You Were a Homonym or a Homophone. Gray, Sara, illus. 2006. 24p. (J). (978-1-4048-3161-2(4)) Picture Window Bks.

Molter, Carey. Bass Cannot Play Bass. l.t. ed. 2002. (Homographs Ser.). (Illus.). 24p. (J). (ps-3). lib. bdg. 19.93 (978-1-57765-793-4(4) , SandCastle) ABDO Publishing Co.

—Fruit Trees Produce Produce. l.t. ed. 2002. (Homographs Ser.). (Illus.). 24p. (J). (ps-3). lib. bdg. 19.93 (978-1-57765-794-1(2) , SandCastle) ABDO Publishing Co.

—Homographs, Set. l.t. ed. Incl. Bass Cannot Play Bass. lib. bdg. 19.93 (978-1-57765-793-4(4)); Fruit Trees Produce Produce. lib. bdg. 19.93 (978-1-57765-794-1(2)); Live Lions Live on Land. lib. bdg. 19.93 (978-1-57765-795-8(0)); Pete Presents the Presents. lib. bdg. 19.93 (978-1-57765-796-5(9)); 24p. (J). (ps-3). (Illus.). 2002. Set lib. bdg. 79.72 (978-1-57765-523-7(0) , SandCastle) ABDO Publishing Co.

—Live Lions Live on Land. l.t. ed. 2002. (Homographs Ser.). (Illus.). 24p. (J). (ps-3). lib. bdg. 19.93 (978-1-57765-795-8(0) , SandCastle) ABDO Publishing Co.

—Pete Presents the Presents. l.t. ed. 2002. (Homographs Ser.). (Illus.). 24p. (J). (ps-3). lib. bdg. 19.93 (978-1-57765-796-5(9) , SandCastle) ABDO Publishing Co.

Presson, Leslie. What in the World Is a Homophone? Bosson, Jo-Ellen, illus. 192p. (J). 11.95 (978-0-7641-2698-7(9)) Barron's Educational Series, Inc.

Rayevsky, Kim. Antonyms, Synonyms, Homonyms. Rayevsky, Robert, illus. 2006. 32p. (J). (ps-3). 16.95 (978-0-8234-1889-3(8)) Holiday Hse., Inc.

Rondeau, Amanda. Bella Blew Blue Bubbles. l.t. ed. 2002. (Homophones Ser.). (Illus.). 24p. (J). (ps-3). lib. bdg. 19.93 (978-1-57765-784-2(5) , SandCastle) ABDO Publishing Co.

—Can You Hear Me from Here? l.t. ed. 2002. (Homophones Ser.). (Illus.). 24p. (J). (ps-3). lib. bdg. 19.93 (978-1-57765-780-4(2) , SandCastle) ABDO Publishing Co.

—Do We By, Buy, or Bye Tickets? l.t. ed. 2002. (Homophones Ser.). (Illus.). 24p. (J). (ps-3). lib. bdg. 19.93 (978-1-57765-782-8(9) , SandCastle) ABDO Publishing Co.

—The Prince Left His Prints. l.t. ed. 2002. (Homophones Ser.). (Illus.). 24p. (J). (ps-3). lib. bdg. 19.93 (978-1-57765-781-1(0) , SandCastle) ABDO Publishing Co.

—Sue Threw the Goop Through the Hoop. l.t. ed. 2002. (Homophones Ser.). (Illus.). 24p. (J). (ps-3). lib. bdg. 19.93 (978-1-57765-783-5(7) , SandCastle) ABDO Publishing Co.

—We Have a Wee Whale. l.t. ed. 2002. (Homophones Ser.). (Illus.). 24p. (J). (ps-3). lib. bdg. 19.93 (978-1-57765-779-8(9) , SandCastle) ABDO Publishing Co.

Salzmann, Mary Elizabeth. The Knight Waits at Night. l.t. ed. 2002. (Homophones Ser.). (Illus.). 24p. (J). (ps-3). lib. bdg. 19.93 (978-1-57765-651-7(2) , SandCastle) ABDO Publishing Co.

—My Deer Is a Dear. l.t. ed. 2002. (Homophones Ser.). (Illus.). 24p. (J). (ps-3). lib. bdg. 19.93 (978-1-57765-652-4(0) , SandCastle) ABDO Publishing Co.

—They're There in Their Boat. l.t. ed. 2002. (Homophones Ser.). (Illus.). 24p. (J). (ps-3). lib. bdg. 19.93 (978-1-57765-650-0(4) , SandCastle) ABDO Publishing Co.

—Where Do I Wear Water Wings? l.t. ed. 2002. (Homophones Ser.). (Illus.). 24p. (J). (gr. 1-2). lib. bdg. 19.93 (978-1-57765-799-6(3) , SandCastle) ABDO Publishing Co.

—Who's on Whose Spot? l.t. ed. 2002. (Homophones Ser.). (Illus.). 24p. (J). (ps-3). lib. bdg. 19.93 (978-1-57765-798-9(5) , SandCastle) ABDO Publishing Co.

—You're on Your Phone. l.t. ed. 2002. (Homophones Ser.). (Illus.). 24p. (J). (ps-3). lib. bdg. 19.93 (978-1-57765-797-2(7) , SandCastle) ABDO Publishing Co.

Scheunemann, Pam. Flour Does Not Flower. l.t. ed. 2002. (Homophones Ser.). (Illus.). 24p. (J). (ps-3). lib. bdg. 19.93 (978-1-57765-742-2(X) , SandCastle) ABDO Publishing Co.

—Fred Read the Red Book. l.t. ed. 2002. (Homophones Ser.). (Illus.). 24p. (J). (ps-3). lib. bdg. 19.93 (978-1-57765-745-3(4) , SandCastle) ABDO Publishing Co.

—Harry Is Not Hairy. l.t. ed. 2002. (Homophones Ser.). (Illus.). 24p. (J). (ps-3). lib. bdg. 19.93 (978-1-57765-743-9(8) , SandCastle) ABDO Publishing Co.

—Homophones, Set I. l.t. ed. Incl. Flour Does Not Flower. lib. bdg. 19.93 (978-1-57765-742-2(X)); Fred Read the Red Book. lib. bdg. 19.93 (978-1-57765-745-3(4)); Harry Is Not Hairy. lib. bdg. 19.93 (978-1-57765-743-9(8)); Moose Is in the Mousse. lib. bdg. 19.93 (978-1-57765-746-0(2)); Sam Has a Sundae on Sunday. lib. bdg. 19.93 (978-1-57765-744-6(6)); Two Kids Got to Go Too. lib. bdg. 19.93 (978-1-57765-747-7(0)); 24p. (J). (ps-3). (Illus.). 2002. Set lib. bdg. 119.58 (978-1-57765-518-3(4) , SandCastle) ABDO Publishing Co.

—The Moose Is in the Mousse. l.t. ed. 2002. (Homophones Ser.). (Illus.). 24p. (J). (ps-3). lib. bdg. 19.93 (978-1-57765-746-0(2) , SandCastle) ABDO Publishing Co.

—Sam Has a Sundae on Sunday. l.t. ed. 2002. (Homophones Ser.). (Illus.). 24p. (J). (ps-3). lib. bdg. 19.93 (978-1-57765-744-6(6) , SandCastle) ABDO Publishing Co.

—Two Kids Got to Go Too. l.t. ed. 2002. (Homophones Ser.). (Illus.). 24p. (J). (ps-3). lib. bdg. 19.93 (978-1-57765-747-7(0) , SandCastle) ABDO Publishing Co.

Sickels, Chris. The Look Book. 2007. (Illus.). 80p. 17.99 (***978-1-58180-940-4(9)*** , HOW Bks.) F & W Pubns., Inc.

Synonyms, Antonyms, & Homonyms (Gr. 4-5) 2004. (J). (978-1-58232-138-7(8)) Bryan Hse. Pubs., Inc.

Zeitzoff, Helen. Hooray for HHH!¿ Workbook & CD-ROM. Ward, Wendy & Webber, Thomas, eds. 2006. (J). per. 21.95 (***978-1-58650-630-8(7)***) Super Duper Pubns.

ENGLISH LANGUAGE—IDIOMS

Brennan-Nelson, Denise. My Grandma Likes to Say. Donovan, Jane Monroe, illus. rev. ed. 2007. 32p. (J). (ps-3). 16.95 (978-1-58536-284-4(0)) Sleeping Bear Pr.

—My Momma Likes to Say. Donovan, Jane Monroe, illus. 2003. 32p. (J). 15.95 (978-1-58536-106-9(2)) Sleeping Bear Pr.

—My Teacher Likes to Say. Monroe Donovan, Jane, illus. rev. ed. 2004. 32p. (J). 15.95 (978-1-58536-212-7(3)) Sleeping Bear Pr.

Edwards, Wallace. Monkey Business. 2005. (Illus.). 32p. (YA). (978-1-55337-462-6(2)) Kids Can Pr., Ltd.

Fun with Idioms - Crossword Puzzles & Word Searches. 2004. pap. 7.99 (978-1-4206-3144-9(6)) Teacher Created Materials, Inc.

Hambleton, Laura & Turhan, Sedat. Monkey Business: Fun with Idioms. Tullet, Herve, illus. 2007. (Milet Wordwise Ser.). 28p. (J). pap. 6.95 (***978-1-84059-499-7(3)***) Milet Publishing.

Landner, Cobi. Why Is an Orange Called an Orange? Smith, Lisa, illus. 2003. 14.95 (978-1-55278-328-3(6)) McArthur & Co. CAN. *Dist:* National Bk. Network.

Snodgrass, Catherine S. Super Silly Sayings That Are over Your Head: A Children's Illustrated Book of Idioms. 2004. (Illus.). 29p. (J). (gr. 1-4). bds. 16.95 (978-0-9666529-4-9(0)) Starfish Specialty Pr., LLC.

Tabor, Nancy. See What You Say. 2000. Tr. of Ve Lo Que Dices. (ENG & SPA., Illus.). (J). (978-1-57091-375-4(7)) Charlesbridge Publishing, Inc.

—See What You Say. 2000. Tr. of Ve Lo Que Dices. (SPA.). (gr. k-3). lib. bdg. 15.25 (978-0-613-28312-0(0)) Tandem Library Bks.

Terban, Marvin. In a Pickle: And Other Funny Idioms. Maestro, Giulio, illus. 2007. 64p. (J). (gr. k-3). pap. 6.95 (***978-0-618-83001-5(4)***, Clarion Bks.) Houghton Mifflin Co. Trade & Reference Div.

—Mad as a Wet Hen! And Other Funny Idioms. Maestro, Giulio, illus. 2007. 64p. (J). (gr. k-3). pap. 6.95 (***978-0-618-83003-9(0)***, Clarion Bks.) Houghton Mifflin Co. Trade & Reference Div.

—Scholastic Dictionary of Idioms. 1998. (gr. 3-6). lib. bdg. 17.60 (978-0-613-88717-5(4)) Tandem Library Bks.

—The Scholastic Dictionary of Idioms. 1998. (Illus.). 256p. (J). (gr. 3-7). reprint ed. 8.95 (978-0-590-38157-4(1)) Scholastic, Inc.

—Scholastic Dictionary of Idioms. rev. ed. 2006. 304p. (J). pap. 9.99 (978-0-439-77083-5(1), Scholastic Reference) Scholastic, Inc.

ENGLISH LANGUAGE—ORTHOGRAPHY

see English Language—Spelling

ENGLISH LANGUAGE—PHRASES AND TERMS

see English Language—Terms and Phrases

ENGLISH LANGUAGE—PUNCTUATION

see Punctuation

ENGLISH LANGUAGE—READERS

see Readers

also subdivision readers for languages other than English, e.g. French Language—Readers

ENGLISH LANGUAGE—RHETORIC

see Rhetoric

ENGLISH LANGUAGE—RHYME

Body, Wendy. Blinki's Shopping List. 2006. (Illus.). 24p. (J). lib. bdg. 15.95 (978-1-59566-224-8(3)) QEB Publishing Inc.

Bryant-Mole, Karen. Rhyming Words. Mukhida, Zul, illus. 2000. (Mortimer's Fun with Words Ser.). 24p. (J). (ps up). lib. bdg. 22.00 (978-0-8368-2751-4(1)) Stevens, Gareth Inc.

Bulloch, Ivan & James, Diane. Learn with Me 123. Pangbourne, Daniel, illus. Pangbourne, Daniel, photos by. 2007. (J). pap. (***978-1-58728-622-3(X)***, Two Can Publishing) T&N Children's Publishing.

Chang, Maria, ed. Flip Open Flash Cards Rhyming Words. 2005. lthr. 9.99 (978-0-439-73298-7(0)) Scholastic, Inc.

Charlip, Remy. Arm in Arm: A Collection of Connections, Endless Tales, Reiterations, & Other Echolalia. Charlip, Remy, illus. 2004. (Illus.). 48p. (gr. 2). 16.95 (978-1-883672-50-8(3), Tricycle Pr.) Ten Speed Pr.

Doudna, Kelly. Art from the Mart. (First Rhymes Ser.). (Illus.). (J). (ps-3). 2006. 24p. lib. bdg. 19.93 (978-1-59679-449-8(6), SandCastle); 2005. 23p. pap. (978-1-59679-450-4(X)) ABDO Publishing Co.

—Billy Goat Can Float. (First Rhymes Ser.). (Illus.). (J). (ps-3). 2006. 24p. lib. bdg. 19.93 (978-1-59679-453-5(4), SandCastle); 2005. 23p. pap. (978-1-59679-454-2(2)) ABDO Publishing Co.

—Bret & His Pet. (First Rhymes Ser.). (Illus.). (J). (ps-3). 2006. 24p. lib. bdg. 19.93 (978-1-59679-489-4(5), SandCastle); 2005. 23p. pap. (978-1-59679-490-0(9)) ABDO Publishing Co.

—The Bride & the Slide. (First Rhymes Ser.). (Illus.). (J). (ps-3). 2006. 24p. lib. bdg. 19.93 (978-1-59679-455-9(0), SandCastle); 2005. 23p. pap. (978-1-59679-456-6(9)) ABDO Publishing Co.

—The Crook Can Cook! (First Rhymes Ser.). (Illus.). (J). (ps-3). 2006. 24p. lib. bdg. 19.93 (978-1-59679-467-2(4), SandCastle); 2005. 23p. pap. (978-1-59679-468-9(2)) ABDO Publishing Co.

—Dip the Chip! 2005. (First Rhymes Ser.). (Illus.). 23p. (J). pap. (978-1-59679-470-2(4)) ABDO Publishing Co.

—Dip the Chip. 2006. (First Rhymes Ser.). (Illus.). 24p. (J). (ps-3). lib. bdg. 19.93 (978-1-59679-469-6(0), SandCastle) ABDO Publishing Co.

—The Flock on the Dock. (First Rhymes Ser.). (Illus.). (J). (ps-3). 2006. 24p. lib. bdg. 19.93 (978-1-59679-481-8(X), SandCastle); 2005. 23p. pap. (978-1-59679-482-5(8)) ABDO Publishing Co.

—Grant's Aunts from France. 2005. (See It, Say It, Hear It, Read It! Ser.). (Illus.). 23p. (J). pap. (978-1-59197-898-5(X)); lib. bdg. 19.93 (978-1-59197-792-6(4)) ABDO Publishing Co.

—Gwen the Hen. (First Rhymes Ser.). (Illus.). (J). (ps-3). 2006. 24p. lib. bdg. 19.93 (978-1-59679-487-0(9), SandCastle); 2005. 23p. pap. (978-1-59679-488-7(7)) ABDO Publishing Co.

—The Jelly Bean Machine. 2005. (See It, Say It, Hear It, Read It! Ser.). (Illus.). 23p. (J). pap. (978-1-59197-901-2(3)); lib. bdg. 19.93 (978-1-59197-795-7(9), SandCastle) ABDO Publishing Co.

—Jump from the Stump. (First Rhymes Ser.). (Illus.). (J). (ps-3). 2006. 24p. lib. bdg. 19.93 (978-1-59679-485-6(2), SandCastle); 2005. 23p. pap. (978-1-59679-486-3(0)) ABDO Publishing Co.

—Knead with Speed, Chef Mead! 2005. (See It, Say It, Hear It, Read It! Ser.). (Illus.). 23p. (J). pap. (978-1-59197-905-0(6)); lib. bdg. 19.93 (978-1-59197-799-5(1)) ABDO Publishing Co.

—The Mermaid Parade. 2005. (See It, Say It, Hear It, Read It! Ser.). (Illus.). 23p. (J). pap. (978-1-59197-910-4(2)); lib. bdg. 19.93 (978-1-59197-804-6(1)) ABDO Publishing Co.

—Moe's Toes Froze. 2005. (See It, Say It, Hear It, Read It! Ser.). (Illus.). 23p. (J). pap. (978-1-59197-911-1(0)); lib. bdg. 19.93 (978-1-59197-805-3(X)) ABDO Publishing Co.

—The Pin in the Bin. (First Rhymes Ser.). (Illus.). (J). (ps-3). 2006. 24p. lib. bdg. 19.93 (978-1-59679-539-6(5), SandCastle); 2005. 23p. pap. (978-1-59679-540-2(9)) ABDO Publishing Co.

—The Sheep Is Asleep. (First Rhymes Ser.). (Illus.). (J). (ps-3). 2006. 24p. lib. bdg. 19.93 (978-1-59679-521-1(2), SandCastle); 2005. 23p. pap. (978-1-59679-522-8(0)) ABDO Publishing Co.

—Squeak from My Cheek. 2005. (See It, Say It, Hear It, Read It! Ser.). (Illus.). 23p. (J). pap. (978-1-59197-923-4(4)); lib. bdg. 19.93 (978-1-59197-817-6(3)) ABDO Publishing Co.

—The Tweet Fleet. (First Rhymes Ser.). (Illus.). (J). (ps-3). 2006. 24p. lib. bdg. 19.93 (978-1-59679-523-5(9), SandCastle); 2005. 23p. pap. (978-1-59679-524-2(7)) ABDO Publishing Co.

Fisher, Jeff & Gaga. Pass the Celery, Ellery! 2000. (Illus.). 48p. (J). (gr. 2-7). 14.95 (978-1-58479-031-0(8)) Stewart, Tabori & Chang.

Gemmen, Heather & McNeil, Mary. God & You, Level 2. Ulrich, George, tr. Ulrich, George, illus. abr. ed. 2004. (Rocket ReaderT2 Ser.). 40p. (J). (gr. 2 up). pap., pap. 8.99 (978-0-7814-4014-1(9), 0781440149) Cook, David C. Publishing Co.

—Little Things, Pre-Level 1. Stormer, Karen, illus. 2003. (Rocket Readers Ser.). 40p. (J). (ps-1). pap. 8.99 (978-0-7814-3981-7(0), 0781439817) Cook, David C. Publishing Co.

—Time's Up, Pre-Level 1. Williams, Jenny, tr. Williams, Jenny, illus. 2004. (Rr2 Ser.). 40p. (J). (ps-1). pap., pap. 8.99 (978-0-7814-4009-7(2), 0781440092) Cook, David C. Publishing Co.

—Walk This Way, Pre-Level 1. Ochoa, Ana, tr. Ochoa, Ana, illus. 2003. (Rocket Readers Ser.). 40p. (J). (ps-1). pap. 8.99 (978-0-7814-3983-1(3), 0781439833) Cook, David C. Publishing Co.

Hanson, Anders. Adell & the Secret Well. (First Rhymes Ser.). (Illus.). (J). (ps-3). 2006. 24p. lib. bdg. 19.93 (978-1-59679-447-4(X), SandCastle); 2005. 23p. pap. (978-1-59679-448-1(8)) ABDO Publishing Co.

—A Career for Mr. Lear. 2005. (See It, Say It, Hear It, Read It! Ser.). (Illus.). 23p. (J). pap. (978-1-59197-885-5(8)); lib. bdg. 19.93 (978-1-59197-779-7(7)) ABDO Publishing Co.

—Chuck Has a Big Truck. (First Rhymes Ser.). 23p. (J). (ps-3). 2006. 19.93 (978-1-59679-463-4(1), SandCastle); 2005. pap. (978-1-59679-464-1(X)) ABDO Publishing Co.

—Claire's Bear Scare. 2005. (Rhyme Time Ser.). (Illus.). 23p. (J). (ps-3). lib. bdg. 19.93 (978-1-59197-780-3(0)) ABDO Publishing Co.

—The Cow with a Plow. (First Rhymes Ser.). (Illus.). (J). (ps-3). 2006. 24p. lib. bdg. 19.93 (978-1-59679-465-8(8), SandCastle); 2005. 23p. pap. (978-1-59679-466-5(6)) ABDO Publishing Co.

—The Deer on Mount Ranier. 2005. (Rhyme Time Ser.). (Illus.). 23p. (J). (ps-3). lib. bdg. 19.93 (978-1-59197-784-1(3)) ABDO Publishing Co.

—Don't Hop with Pop! (First Rhymes Ser.). (Illus.). (J). (ps-3). 2006. 24p. lib. bdg. 19.93 (978-1-59679-471-9(2), SandCastle); 2005. 23p. pap. (978-1-59679-472-6(0)) ABDO Publishing Co.

—Dunk-Tank Frank. (First Rhymes Ser.). (Illus.). (J). (ps-3). 2006. 24p. lib. bdg. 19.93 (978-1-59679-475-7(5), SandCastle); 2005. 23p. pap. (978-1-59679-476-4(3)) ABDO Publishing Co.

—Elaine's Rain Cane. 2005. (See It, Say It, Hear It, Read It! Ser.). (Illus.). 23p. (J). pap. (978-1-59197-894-7(7)); lib. bdg. 19.93 (978-1-59197-788-9(6)) ABDO Publishing Co.

—Eli & the High Pie. 2005. (See It, Say It, Hear It, Read It! Ser.). (Illus.). 23p. (J). pap. (978-1-59197-895-4(5)); lib. bdg. 19.93 (978-1-59197-789-6(4)) ABDO Publishing Co.

—Hun Plays One-on—One. 2005. (Rhyme Time Ser.). (Illus.). 23p. (J). (ps-3). lib. bdg. 19.93 (978-1-59197-794-0(0), SandCastle) ABDO Publishing Co.

—The Hun Plays One-On-One. 2005. (See It, Say It, Hear It, Read It! Ser.). (Illus.). 23p. (J). pap. (978-1-59197-900-5(5)) ABDO Publishing Co.

—Jill & the Giant Spill. (First Rhymes Ser.). (Illus.). (J). (ps-3). 2006. 24p. lib. bdg. 19.93 (978-1-59679-491-7(7), SandCastle); 2005. 23p. pap. (978-1-59679-492-4(5)) ABDO Publishing Co.

—Joe Grows Tomatoes. 2005. (See It, Say It, Hear It, Learn It! Ser.). (Illus.). 23p. (J). pap. (978-1-59197-902-9(1)); lib. bdg. 19.93 (978-1-59197-796-4(7), SandCastle) ABDO Publishing Co.

—Kay's Maze Phase. 2005. (See It, Say It, Hear It, Read It! Ser.). (Illus.). 23p. (J). pap. (978-1-59197-904-3(8)); lib. bdg. 19.93 (978-1-59197-798-8(3)) ABDO Publishing Co.

—Let's Sled Instead. 2005. (See It, Say It, Hear It, Read It! Ser.). (Illus.). 23p. (J). pap. (978-1-59197-908-1(0)); lib. bdg. 19.93 (978-1-59197-802-2(5)) ABDO Publishing Co.

—May by the Bay. (First Rhymes Ser.). (Illus.). (J). (ps-3). 2006. 24p. lib. bdg. 19.93 (978-1-59679-495-5(X), SandCastle); 2005. 23p. pap. (978-1-59679-496-2(8)) ABDO Publishing Co.

—Nate Is Great. 2005. (See It, Say It, Hear It, Read It! Ser.). (Illus.). 23p. (J). pap. (978-1-59197-913-5(7)); lib. bdg. 19.93 (978-1-59197-807-7(6)) ABDO Publishing Co.

—Neil & His Meal Mobile. 2005. (See It, Say It, Hear It, Read It! Ser.). (Illus.). 23p. (J). pap. (978-1-59197-914-2(5)); lib. bdg. 19.93 (978-1-59197-808-4(4)) ABDO Publishing Co.

—The Owl Swings a Dowel. 2005. (See It, Say It, Hear It, Read It! Ser.). (Illus.). 23p. (J). pap. (978-1-59197-915-9(3)); lib. bdg. 19.93 (978-1-59197-809-1(2)) ABDO Publishing Co.

—The Pest with a Vest. (First Rhymes Ser.). (Illus.). (J). (ps-3). 2006. 24p. lib. bdg. 19.93 (978-1-59679-503-7(4), SandCastle); 2005. 23p. pap. (978-1-59679-504-4(2)) ABDO Publishing Co.

—The Pig with a Wig. 2005. (First Rhymes Ser.). (Illus.). 23p. (J). (978-1-59679-508-2(5)) ABDO Publishing Co.

—The Pig with the Wig. 2006. (First Rhymes Ser.). (Illus.). 24p. (J). (gr. k-1). lib. bdg. 19.93 (978-1-59679-507-5(7), SandCastle) ABDO Publishing Co.

—The Pink Mink. (First Rhymes Ser.). (Illus.). (J). (ps-3). 2006. 24p. lib. bdg. 19.93 (978-1-59679-509-9(3), SandCastle); 2005. 23p. pap. (978-1-59679-510-5(7)) ABDO Publishing Co.

—Rob the Blob. 2006. (First Rhymes Ser.). (Illus.). 23p. (J). pap. (978-1-59679-478-8(X)); 19.93 (978-1-59679-477-1(1), SandCastle) ABDO Publishing Co.

—Simone on the Throne. (First Rhymes Ser.). (Illus.). (J). (ps-3). 2006. 24p. lib. bdg. 19.93 (978-1-59679-505-1(0), SandCastle); 2005. 23p. pap. (978-1-59679-506-8(9)) ABDO Publishing Co.

—The Waste Is Traced. 2005. (See It, Say It, Hear It, Read It! Ser.). (Illus.). 23p. (J). pap. (978-1-59197-926-5(9)); lib. bdg. 19.93 (978-1-59197-820-6(3)) ABDO Publishing Co.

Hanson, Anders, et al. First Rhymes. 2006. (J). (ps-3). 956.64 (978-1-59679-446-7(1), SandCastle) ABDO Publishing Co.

Kido, Yukiko. Flip-a-Word. 2006. (Illus.). 32p. (J). pap. 5.95 (978-1-59354-178-1(3)) Blue Apple Bks.

—Flip-a-Word: Stop Pop. 2007. (Illus.). 32p. 12.95 (***978-1-59354-620-5(3)***) Handprint Bks.

—Pig Wig. 2006. (Illus.). 32p. (J). 12.95 (978-1-59354-175-0(9)) Blue Apple Bks.

—Snow Bow: Flip-a-Word. 2007. (Flip-A-Word Ser.). (Illus.). 32p. (ps-2). pap. 5.95 (***978-1-59354-623-6(8)***) Blue Apple Bks.

—Snow Bow: Flip-a-Word. 2007. (Illus.). 32p. 12.95 (***978-1-59354-622-9(X)***) Handprint Bks.

—Stop Pop. 2007. (Illus.). 32p. (ps-2). pap. 5.95 (***978-1-59354-621-2(1)***) Blue Apple Bks.

Kompelien, Tracy. A Calico in the Window. 2005. (See It, Say It, Hear It, Read It! Ser.). (Illus.). 23p. (J). pap. (978-1-59197-884-8(X)); lib. bdg. 19.93 (978-1-59197-778-0(9)) ABDO Publishing Co.

—Dwight & the Magic Kite. 2005. (Rhyme Time Ser.). (Illus.). 23p. (J). (ps-3). lib. bdg. 19.93 (978-1-59197-787-2(8), SandCastle) ABDO Publishing Co.

—The Mole with a Goal. 2005. (See It, Say It, Hear It, Read It! Ser.). (Illus.). 23p. (J). pap. (978-1-59197-912-8(9)); lib. bdg. 19.93 (978-1-59197-806-0(8)) ABDO Publishing Co.

—Scott the Astronaut. 2005. (See It, Say It, Hear It, Read It! Ser.). (Illus.). 23p. (J). pap. (978-1-59197-921-0(8)); lib. bdg. 19.93 (978-1-59197-815-2(7)) ABDO Publishing Co.

—The Thumb & His Chum. 2005. (Rhyme Time Ser.). (Illus.). 23p. (J). (ps-3). lib. bdg. 19.93 (978-1-59197-819-0(X)) ABDO Publishing Co.

—The Yaks Relax. 2005. (See It, Say It, Hear It, Read It! Ser.). (Illus.). 23p. (J). pap. (978-1-59197-927-2(7)); lib. bdg. 19.93 (978-1-59197-821-3(1)) ABDO Publishing Co.

LeapFrog Staff, compiled by. Rhyme & Sing with Mother Goose. 2002. (YA). (ps up). spiral bd. 9.99 (978-1-58605-795-4(2)) LeapFrog Enterprises, Inc.

Realtime Associates and Mazer Corporation Staff & LeapFrog Staff, compiled by. Identify Rhyming Words. 2002. (J). (gr. 2). 66.75 (978-1-58605-317-8(5), LeapFrog Schl. Hse.) LeapFrog Enterprises, Inc.

A Rookie Reader Skill Set: Rhyme, 4 bks. Incl. Germs. Oetting, Judy. Herr, Tad, illus. 19.50 (978-0-516-24980-3(0)); Old Mo. Hsu, Stacey W. Ritter, Adam, illus. 19.50 (978-0-516-24981-0(9)); One Smart Fish. Manivong, Laura. Beaky, Suzanne, illus. 19.50 (978-0-516-24982-7(7)); Rainy-Day Music. Hyde, Judith Jensen. Abbott, Jason, illus. 19.50 (978-0-516-24983-4(5)); 32p. (J). (gr. k-2). 2006. 78.00 (978-0-516-25411-1(1), Children's Pr.) Scholastic Library Publishing.

Ryan, Pam Muñoz. Our California. Lopez, Rafael, illus. 2008. (J). lib. bdg. (***978-1-58089-116-5(0)***) Charlesbridge Publishing, Inc.

Salzmann, Mary Elizabeth. Bee & Flea Go to the Sea. 2005. (See It, Say It, Hear It, Read It! Ser.). (Illus.). 23p. (J). pap. (978-1-59197-882-4(3)); lib. bdg. 19.93 (978-1-59197-776-6(2)) ABDO Publishing Co.

—Cash for Trash. (First Rhymes Ser.). (Illus.). (J). (ps-3). 2006. 24p. lib. bdg. 19.93 (978-1-59679-457-3(7), SandCastle); 2005. 23p. pap. (978-1-59679-458-0(5)) ABDO Publishing Co.

—The Chap & the Cap. (First Rhymes Ser.). (Illus.). (J). (ps-3). 2006. 24p. lib. bdg. 19.93 (978-1-59679-459-7(3), SandCastle); 2005. 23p. pap. (978-1-59679-460-3(7)) ABDO Publishing Co.

—Don't Sneeze on Skis. 2005. (Rhyme Time Ser.). (Illus.). 23p. (J). (ps-3). lib. bdg. 19.93 (978-1-59197-785-8(1), SandCastle) ABDO Publishing Co.

—The Fan in the Can. (First Rhymes Ser.). (Illus.). (J). (ps-3). 2006. 24p. lib. bdg. 19.93 (978-1-59679-479-5(8), SandCastle); 2005. 23p. pap. (978-1-59679-480-1(1)) ABDO Publishing Co.

—Fay Loves Ballet. 2005. (Rhyme Time Ser.). (Illus.). 23p. (J). (ps-3). lib. bdg. 19.93 (978-1-59197-790-2(8)) ABDO Publishing Co.

—Kangaroo & the Crew. 2005. (See It, Say It, Hear It, Read It! Ser.). (Illus.). 23p. (J). pap. (978-1-59197-903-6(X)); lib. bdg. 19.93 (978-1-59197-797-1(5)) ABDO Publishing Co.

—Kyle Wears a Smile. 2005. (See It, Say It, Hear It, Read It! Ser.). (Illus.). 23p. (J). pap. (978-1-59197-906-7(4)); lib. bdg. 19.93 (978-1-59197-800-8(9)) ABDO Publishing Co.

—Lady Bauer in the Tower. 2005. (See It, Say It, Hear It, Read It! Ser.). (Illus.). 23p. (J). pap. (978-1-59197-907-4(2)); lib. bdg. 19.93 (978-1-59197-801-5(7)) ABDO Publishing Co.

—Nate, Let's Skate. (First Rhymes Ser.). (Illus.). (J). (ps-3). 2006. 24p. lib. bdg. 19.93 (978-1-59679-497-9(6), SandCastle); 2005. 23p. pap. (978-1-59679-498-6(4)) ABDO Publishing Co.

—The Paw That Can Draw. (First Rhymes Ser.). (Illus.). (J). (ps-3). 2006. 24p. lib. bdg. 19.93 (978-1-59679-501-3(8), SandCastle); 2005. 23p. (978-1-59679-502-0(6)) ABDO Publishing Co.

—Pete the Parakeet. 2005. (Illus.). 23p. (J). pap. (978-1-59197-917-3(X)); lib. bdg. 19.93 (978-1-59197-811-4(4)) ABDO Publishing Co.

—The Race for the Vase. 2005. (See It, Say It, Hear It, Read It! Ser.). (Illus.). 23p. (J). pap. (978-1-59197-919-7(6)); lib. bdg. 19.93 (978-1-59197-813-8(0)) ABDO Publishing Co.

—The Ram & the Clam. 2005. (First Rhymes Ser.). (Illus.). 23p. (J). pap. (978-1-59679-518-1(2)) ABDO Publishing Co.

—The RAM & the Clam. 2006. (First Rhymes Ser.). (Illus.). 24p. (J). (ps-3). lib. bdg. 19.93 (978-1-59679-517-4(4), SandCastle) ABDO Publishing Co.

—Scat the Fat Cat. (First Rhymes Ser.). (Illus.). (J). (ps-3). 2006. 24p. lib. bdg. 19.93 (978-1-59679-519-8(0), SandCastle); 2005. 23p. pap. (978-1-59679-520-4(4)) ABDO Publishing Co.

—A Snack for Jack. (First Rhymes Ser.). (Illus.). (J). (ps-3). 2006. 24p. lib. bdg. 19.93 (978-1-59679-527-3(1), SandCastle); 2005. 23p. pap. (978-1-59679-528-0(X)) ABDO Publishing Co.

—The Snail Tale. 2005. (See It, Say It, Hear It, Read It! Ser.). (Illus.). 23p. (J). pap. (978-1-59197-922-7(6)); lib. bdg. 19.93 (978-1-59197-816-9(5)) ABDO Publishing Co.

—The Snake by the Lake. (First Rhymes Ser.). (Illus.). (J). (ps-3). 2006. 24p. lib. bdg. 19.93 (978-1-59679-529-7(8), SandCastle); 2005. 23p. pap. (978-1-59679-530-3(1)) ABDO Publishing Co.

—A Stag in the Bag. (First Rhymes Ser.). (Illus.). (J). (ps-3). 2006. 24p. lib. bdg. 19.93 (978-1-59679-531-0(X), SandCastle); 2005. 23p. pap. (978-1-59679-532-7(8)) ABDO Publishing Co.

—Thad & His Dad. (First Rhymes Ser.). (Illus.). (J). (ps-3). 2006. 24p. lib. bdg. 19.93 (978-1-59679-537-2(9), SandCastle); 2005. 23p. pap. (978-1-59679-538-9(7)) ABDO Publishing Co.

—The Train to Spain. (First Rhymes Ser.). (Illus.). (J). (ps-3). 2006. 24p. lib. bdg. 19.93 (978-1-59679-541-9(7), SandCastle); 2005. 23p. pap. (978-1-59679-542-6(5)) ABDO Publishing Co.

Scheunemann, Pam. The Band in the Sand. 2005. (First Rhymes Ser.). (Illus.). 23p. (J). pap. (978-1-59679-452-8(6)) ABDO Publishing Co.

—Band in the Sand. 2006. (First Rhymes Ser.). (Illus.). 24p. (J). (ps-3). lib. bdg. 19.93 (978-1-59679-451-1(8), SandCastle) ABDO Publishing Co.

—The Chick on the Thick Brick. (First Rhymes Ser.). (Illus.). (J). (ps-3). 2006. 24p. lib. bdg. 19.93 (978-1-59679-461-0(5), SandCastle); 2005. 23p. pap. (978-1-59679-462-7(3)) ABDO Publishing Co.

—The Crane Loves Grain. 2005. (Rhyme Time Ser.). (Illus.). 23p. (J). (ps-3). lib. bdg. 19.93 (978-1-59197-781-0(9)) ABDO Publishing Co.

—Drew & the Crew. (First Rhymes Ser.). (Illus.). (J). (ps-3). 2006. 24p. lib. bdg. 19.93 (978-1-59679-473-3(9), SandCastle); 2005. 23p. pap. (978-1-59679-474-0(7)) ABDO Publishing Co.

—Four Soar & Roar. 2005. (See It, Say It, Hear It, Read It! Ser.). (Illus.). 23p. (J). pap. (978-1-59197-897-8(1)); lib. bdg. 19.93 (978-1-59197-791-9(6), SandCastle) ABDO Publishing Co.

—The Frog in the Clog. (First Rhymes Ser.). (Illus.). (J). (gr. k-1). 2006. 24p. lib. bdg. 19.93 (978-1-59679-483-2(6), SandCastle); 2005. 23p. pap. (978-1-59679-484-9(4)) ABDO Publishing Co.

—The King on a Spring. (First Rhymes Ser.). (Illus.). (J). (gr. k-1). 2006. 24p. lib. bdg. 19.93 (978-1-59679-493-1(3), SandCastle); 2005. 23p. pap. (978-1-59679-494-8(1)) ABDO Publishing Co.

—Lou Flew Too! 2005. (See It, Say It, Hear It, Read It! Ser.). (Illus.). 23p. (J). pap. (978-1-59197-909-8(9)); lib. bdg. 19.93 (978-1-59197-803-9(3)) ABDO Publishing Co.

—The One-Cent Tent. (First Rhymes Ser.). (Illus.). (J). (ps-3). 2006. 24p. lib. bdg. 19.93 (978-1-59679-499-3(2), SandCastle); 2005. 23p. pap. (978-1-59679-500-6(X)) ABDO Publishing Co.

—Peas & Cheese. 2005. (Illus.). 23p. (J). pap. (978-1-59197-916-6(1)); lib. bdg. 19.93 (978-1-59197-810-7(6)) ABDO Publishing Co.

—The Pot with a Dot. (First Rhymes Ser.). (Illus.). (ps-3). 2006. 24p. (J). lib. bdg. 19.93 (978-1-59679-511-2(5), SandCastle); 2005. 23p. pap. (978-1-59679-512-9(3)) ABDO Publishing Co.

—The Pug with a Mug. (First Rhymes Ser.). (Illus.). (J). (ps-3). 2006. 24p. lib. bdg. 19.93 (978-1-59679-513-6(1), SandCastle); 2005. 23p. pap. (978-1-59679-514-3(X)) ABDO Publishing Co.

—The Raccoon & the Balloon. (First Rhymes Ser.). (Illus.). (J). (ps-3). 2006. 24p. lib. bdg. 19.93 (978-1-59679-515-0(8), SandCastle); 2005. 23p. pap. (978-1-59679-516-7(6)) ABDO Publishing Co.

—The Rare Fair. 2005. (See It, Say It, Hear It, Read It! Ser.). (Illus.). 23p. (J). pap. (978-1-59197-918-0(8)); lib. bdg. 19.93 (978-1-59197-814-5(9)) ABDO Publishing Co.

E F G

—The Skunk & His Junk. (First Rhymes Ser.). (Illus.). (J). (ps-3). 2006. 24p. lib. bdg. 19.93 (978-1-59679-525-9(5) , SandCastle); 2005. 23p. pap. (978-1-59679-526-6(3)) ABDO Publishing Co.

—The Sub Club. (First Rhymes Ser.). (Illus.). (J). (ps-3). 2006. 24p. lib. bdg. 19.93 (978-1-59679-533-4(6) , SandCastle); 2005. 23p. pap. (978-1-59679-534-1(4)) ABDO Publishing Co.

—Ted's Red Sled. (First Rhymes Ser.). (Illus.). (J). (ps-3). 2006. 24p. lib. bdg. 19.93 (978-1-59679-535-8(2) , SandCastle); 2005. 23p. pap. (978-1-59679-536-5(0)) ABDO Publishing Co.

—Tennis in Venice. 2005. (See It, Say It, Hear It, Read It! Ser.). (Illus.). 23p. (J). pap. (978-1-59197-924-1(2)); lib. bdg. 19.93 (978-1-59197-818-3(1)) ABDO Publishing Co.

Sprick, Marilyn, et al. Rhyming Fun: Read Well Level K Unit 6 Storybook. Jerde, Susan, illus. 2003. (Read Well Level K Ser.). 20p. (J). (978-1-57035-678-0(5)) Sopris West Educational Services.

Webb, Steve. Tanka Tanka Skunk! 2004. (Illus.). 32p. (J). 15.95 (978-0-439-57844-8(2) , Orchard Bks.) Scholastic, Inc.

Westberg, Jan. The Athlete with Big Feet. 2005. (See It, Say It, Hear It, Read It! Ser.). (Illus.). 23p. (J). pap. (978-1-59197-880-0(7)); lib. bdg. 19.93 (978-1-59197-774-2(6)) ABDO Publishing Co.

—The Bale of Mail. 2005. (See It, Say It, Hear It, Read It! Ser.). (Illus.). 23p. (J). pap. (978-1-59197-881-7(5)); lib. bdg. 19.93 (978-1-59197-775-9(4)) ABDO Publishing Co.

—Bo Loves to Row. 2005. (See It, Say It, Hear It, Read It! Ser.). (Illus.). 23p. (J). pap. (978-1-59197-883-1(1)); lib. bdg. 19.93 (978-1-59197-777-3(0)) ABDO Publishing Co.

—Curious Miss Muss. 2005. (Rhyme Time Ser.). (Illus.). 23p. (J). (ps-3). lib. bdg. 19.93 (978-1-59197-782-7(7)) ABDO Publishing Co.

—The Cute Boot. 2005. (Rhyme Time Ser.). (Illus.). 23p. (J). (ps-3). lib. bdg. 19.93 (978-1-59197-783-4(5)) ABDO Publishing Co.

—Door to the Shore. 2005. (Rhyme Time Ser.). (Illus.). 23p. (J). (ps-3). lib. bdg. 19.93 (978-1-59197-786-5(X) , SandCastle) ABDO Publishing Co.

—Guy the Shy Fly. 2005. (See It, Say It, Hear It, Read It! Ser.). (Illus.). 23p. (J). pap. (978-1-59197-899-2(8)); lib. bdg. 19.93 (978-1-59197-793-3(2) , SandCastle) ABDO Publishing Co.

—The Polite Knight. 2005. (See It, Say It, Hear It, Read It! Ser.). (Illus.). 23p. (J). pap. (978-1-59197-920-3(X)); lib. bdg. 19.93 (978-1-59197-812-1(2)) ABDO Publishing Co.

ENGLISH LANGUAGE—RHYME—DICTIONARIES

Learning to Rhyme. 2003. (Kermit the Frog & Friends Ser.). (Illus.). 16p. (J). (ps-k). pap., act. bk. ed. 4.99 (978-1-57768-716-0(7)) School Specialty Publishing.

Terban, Marvin. Time to Rhyme: A Rhyming Dictionary. Demarest, Chris L., illus. 2003. 96p. (J). (gr. 2-4). pap. 10.95 (978-1-56397-630-8(7)) Boyds Mills Pr.

ENGLISH LANGUAGE—SPELLING

Accelerated Grammar & Spelling. 2004. cd-rom 2995.00 (978-1-59455-196-3(0)) Renaissance Learning, Inc.

Accelerated Grammar & Spelling High School Edition. 2004. cd-rom 2995.00 (978-1-59455-197-0(9)) Renaissance Learning, Inc.

Arnold, Ellen. Brilliant Brain Selects Spelling Strategies. Farber, Deborah, illus. 2001. (MI Strategies for Kids Ser.). 32p. (J). (gr. 1-5). pap. 7.00 (978-1-56976-113-7(2) , 1142, Zephyr Pr.) Chicago Review Pr., Inc.

Barker, Ray & Moorcroft, Christine. Spelling First 1. 2002. 48p. stu. ed. (978-0-7487-6814-1(9)) Nelson Thornes Ltd.

—Spelling First 2. 2002. 48p. pap., stu. ed. (978-0-7487-6815-8(7)) Nelson Thornes Ltd.

—Spelling First 3. 2003. pap., stu. ed. (978-0-7487-6816-5(5)) Nelson Thornes Ltd.

BJU Staff. Spelling Worktext Grd 2. 2004. pap. 12.50 (978-1-57924-322-7(3)) Jones, Bob Univ. Pr.

—Spelling Worktext Grd 3. 2004. pap. 12.50 (978-1-57924-340-1(1)) Jones, Bob Univ. Pr.

—Spelling Worktext Grd 4. 2004. pap. 12.50 (978-1-57924-373-9(8)) Jones, Bob Univ. Pr.

—Spelling Worktext Grd 6. 2004. pap. 12.50 (978-1-57924-410-1(6)) Jones, Bob Univ. Pr.

Blanchard, Cherie. Word Roots Level A2: Learning the Building Blocks of Better Spelling & Vocabulary. 2005. (J). pap. 16.99 (978-0-89455-865-8(X)) Critical Thinking Bks. & Software.

—Word Roots Level B Bk. 2: Learning the Building Blocks of Better Spelling & Vocabulary. 2005. (YA). pap. 18.99 (978-0-89455-866-5(8)) Critical Thinking Bks. & Software.

Bluedorn, Harvey. Handy English Encoder Decoder: All the Spelling & Phonics Rules You Could Ever Want to Know. 2nd ed. 2004. 104p. per. 9.00 (978-0-9743616-2-8(3)) Trivium Pursuit.

Bottino, Marlane. My Language Book for Spelling, Writing & Vocabulary: Level D. Bottino, Marlane, illus. 2000. (My Language Books for Spelling, Writing & Vocabulary Ser.: Vol. 4). (Illus.). (J). (gr. k-6). pap. 6.50 (978-1-893615-05-2(7)) Creative Enterprises.

—My Language Book for Spelling, Writing & Vocabulary: Level E. Bottino, Marlane, illus. 2000. (My Language Books for Spelling, Writing & Vocabulary Ser.: Vol. 5). (Illus.). (J). (gr. k-6). pap. 6.50 (978-1-893615-06-9(5)) Creative Enterprises.

—My Language Book for Spelling, Writing & Vocabulary: Level F. Bottino, Marlane, illus. 2000. (My Language Books for Spelling, Writing & Vocabulary Ser.: Vol. 6). (Illus.). (J). (gr. k-6). pap. 6.50 (978-1-893615-07-6(3)) Creative Enterprises.

Buckton, Chris & Corbett, Pie. Searchlights for Spelling Year 2. 2002. (Searchlights for Spelling Ser.). (Illus.). (J). 48p. pap. 73.70 (978-0-521-89183-7(3)); 50p. pap., stu. ed. 9.00 (978-0-521-89168-4(X)) Cambridge Univ. Pr.

—Searchlights for Spelling Year 2: For Interactive Whole-Class Teaching. 2003. (Searchlights for Spelling Ser.). (Illus.). cd-rom 83.00 (978-0-521-75579-5(4)) Cambridge Univ. Pr.

—Searchlights for Spelling Year 3: For Interactive Whole-Class Teaching. 2003. (Searchlights for Spelling Ser.). cd-rom 83.00 (978-0-521-75580-1(8)) Cambridge Univ. Pr.

—Searchlights for Spelling Year 4. 2002. (Searchlights for Spelling Ser.). (Illus.). 48p. pap., stu. ed. 9.00 (978-0-521-89170-7(1)) Cambridge Univ. Pr.

—Searchlights for Spelling Year 5. 2002. (Searchlights for Spelling Ser.). (Illus.). 48p. pap., stu. ed. 9.00 (978-0-521-89171-4(X)) Cambridge Univ. Pr.

Building Spelling Skills. 2002. (J). (gr. 2). per. 16.99 (978-1-55799-840-8(X) , EMC 2706); (J). (gr. 3). per. 16.99 (978-1-55799-841-5(8) , EMC 2707); (J). (gr. 4). per. 16.99 (978-1-55799-842-2(6) , EMC 2708); (J). (gr. 5). per. 16.99 (978-1-55799-843-9(4) , EMC 2709); (J). (gr. 6). per. 16.99 (978-1-55799-844-6(2) , EMC 2710); (gr. 1). per. 16.99 (978-1-55799-839-2(6) , EMC 2705) Evan-Moor Educational Pubs.

Burgess, Chris. English Skills: Spelling Module. 1999. (J). (gr. 4-8). pap. 35.00 (978-0-7217-0605-4(3)) Schofield & Sims Ltd. GBR. *Dist:* State Mutual Bk. & Periodical Service, Ltd.

Burt, A. Spelling. (Illus.). 32p. (J). (gr. 4-6). pap. (978-0-340-72651-8(2) , Hodder & Stoughton) Hodder General Publishing Division.

Campbell, Rod. I Can Spell! With Consonants B C D F G H. 2000. (Illus.). 24p. (J). (ps-k). pap. (978-1-85292-172-9(2) , Campbell Bks.) Pan Macmillan.

—I Can Spell! With Consonants R S T V W Z. 2000. (Illus.). 24p. (J). (ps-k). pap. (978-1-85292-174-3(9) , Campbell Bks.) Pan Macmillan.

—I Can Spell! With Vowels A E I O U. 2000. (Illus.). 24p. (J). (ps-k). pap. (978-1-85292-171-2(4) , Campbell Bks.) Pan Macmillan.

Carroll, Joyce Armstrong, et al. Literature: Timeless Voices, Timeless Themes. 2001. Bronze Level. (YA). (gr. 7). pap., stu. ed., wbk. ed. 7.47 (978-0-13-043487-6(6)); Copper Level. (J). (gr. 6). pap., stu. ed., wbk. ed. 7.47 (978-0-13-043486-9(8)); Diamond Level. (YA). (gr. 12). pap., stu. ed., wbk. ed. 7.47 (978-0-13-043492-0(2)); Gold Level. (YA). (gr. 9). pap., stu. ed., wbk. ed. 7.47 (978-0-13-043489-0(2)); Platinum Level. (YA). (gr. 10). pap., stu. ed., wbk. ed. 7.47 (978-0-13-043490-6(6)); Ruby Level. (YA). (gr. 11). pap., stu. ed., wbk. ed. 7.47 (978-0-13-043491-3(4)); Silver Level. (YA). (gr. 8). pap., stu. ed., wbk. ed. 7.47 (978-0-13-043488-3(4)) Prentice Hall PTR.

Cernak, Kim. Build-a-Skill Instant Books R-Controled Vowels & Vowel Digraphs. shiotsu, Vicky & Faulkner, Stacey, eds. Campbell, Jenny & Tom, Darcy, illus. 2007. (J). 4.99 (***978-1-59198-413-9(0)***) Creative Teaching Pr., Inc.

Concerned Communications Staff. Reason for Spelling B. 2004. pap., stu. ed. 12.99 (978-0-936785-27-1(6)) Concerned Communications.

—Reason for Spelling C. 2004. pap., stu. ed. 12.99 (978-0-936785-29-5(2)) Concerned Communications.

—Reason for Spelling D. 2004. stu. ed. 12.99 (978-0-936785-31-8(4)) Concerned Communications.

Cunningham, Patricia. Making Places. 2005. (Four-Blocks Ser.). (J). per. 24.99 (978-1-59441-199-1(9) , CD-104108) Carson-Dellosa Publishing Co., Inc.

Dalmatian Press Staff. Spelling 1. 2002. (Tools Ser.). (Illus.). 32p. (J). (gr. 1 up). pap. 2.29 (978-1-57759-194-8(1)) Dalmatian Pr.

DK Publishing Staff. Count & Spell. 2006. 10p. (J). 3.99 (978-0-7566-2710-2(9)) Dorling Kindersley Publishing, Inc.

Edutech Systems Staff. Searchlights for Spelling Year 4: For Interactive Whole-Class Teaching. Buckton, Chris & Corbett, Pie, eds. 2003. (Searchlights for Spelling Ser.). cd-rom 83.00 (978-0-521-75581-8(6)) Cambridge Univ. Pr.

—Searchlights for Spelling Year 5: For Interactive Whole-Class Teaching. Buckton, Chris & Corbett, Pie, eds. 2003. (Searchlights for Spelling Ser.). cd-rom 83.00 (978-0-521-75582-5(4)) Cambridge Univ. Pr.

Everyday Spelling. 2000. (gr. 8 up). stu. ed. 15.00 (978-0-673-60142-1(0)); stu. ed. 26.10 (978-0-673-60154-4(4)) Addison-Wesley Educational Pubs., Inc.

Falletta, Bernadette. We Love to Read Stories Coloring Book & Word Search Puzzles. 2005. 23p. (J). 10.95 (978-1-4116-6291-9(1)) Lulu.com.

Faulkner, Keith. Spelling Machine. Teel, Gina, illus. 2006. 16p. (J). pap. 7.99 (978-0-439-82090-5(1) , Cartwheel Bks.) Scholastic, Inc.

Forster, Anne & Martin, Paul. Early Spellings. 1999. (Illus.). 29p. (J). (gr. 1-3). Bk. 1. pap. 19.95 (978-0-7217-0667-2(3)); Bk. 2. pap. 19.95 (978-0-7217-0668-9(1)); Bk. 3. pap. 19.95 (978-0-7217-0669-6(X)) Schofield & Sims Ltd. GBR. *Dist:* State Mutual Bk. & Periodical Service, Ltd.

—Key Spellings. 1999. (Illus.). 31p. (J). (gr. 2-6). Bk. 2. pap. 22.00 (978-0-7217-0752-5(1)); Bk. 3. pap. 22.00 (978-0-7217-0753-2(X)); Bk. 4. pap. 22.00 (978-0-7217-0754-9(8)) Schofield & Sims Ltd. GBR. *Dist:* State Mutual Bk. & Periodical Service, Ltd.

Gale, John E. Speedyread: A Phonics-Based Reading & Spelling Program. 2005. 353p. ring bd. 275.00 (978-0-9777683-0-1(9)) Mirror Pond Publishing.

Gateman, Ryan, creator. Spelling the Number Words: From a Child's View. 2004. (Illus.). 24p. (J). 8.95 (978-1-932226-23-2(0)) Wizard Academy Pr.

Gerber, Carole & School Specialty Publishing Staff. Spelling & Writing. 1999. (Master Skills Ser.). (Illus.). 128p. (J). (gr. k-6). pap., wbk. ed. 6.95 (978-1-56189-031-6(6) , 13011, American Education Publishing) School Specialty Publishing.

Gifford, Myrna. Spelling Families: A Read-and-Sing Book. Cooper, Frances, illus. 2003. 12p. (J). 9.95 (978-0-9720763-6-4(0)) Action Factor, Inc.

Gobo Books Staff. My Magnetic Spelling Book. 2006. 20p. 9.95 (978-1-932915-18-1(4)) National Bk. Network.

Hall, Nancy. Spellwell B Gr 3 Student. 2004. (J). pap. 6.65 (978-0-8388-2193-0(6)) Educators Publishing Service, Inc.

Harcourt School Publishers Staff. Collections: Spelling Practice. (Illus.). 2000. (gr. 4). pap. 6.80 (978-0-15-313347-3(3)); 2000. (gr. 5). pap. 6.80 (978-0-15-313348-0(1)); 2000. (gr. 6). pap. 7.10 (978-0-15-313349-7(X)); 1999. (J). (gr. 1). pap. 6.60 (978-0-15-314994-8(9)); 1999. (gr. 2). pap. 6.70 (978-0-15-313345-9(7)); 1999. (gr. 3). pap. 6.70 (978-0-15-313346-6(5)) Harcourt Schl. Pubs.

—Integrated Spelling. 99th ed. 1999. (Signatures Ser.). (Illus.). (gr. 3). pap. 10.50 (978-0-15-310825-9(8)); (gr. 1). pap. 10.50 (978-0-15-310824-2(X)) Harcourt Schl. Pubs.

—Integrated Spelling, Grade 1. 99th ed. 1999. (Signatures Ser.). pap., tchr. ed. 38.00 (978-0-15-310826-6(6)) Harcourt Schl. Pubs.

—Integrated Spelling, Grade 3. 99th ed. 1999. (Signatures Ser.). pap., tchr. ed. 42.10 (978-0-15-310827-3(4)) Harcourt Schl. Pubs.

—Practice Book On-Level Grade 1, Vol. 2. 3rd ed. 2002. (Trophies Reading Program Ser.). (gr. 1 up). pap., tchr. ed. 16.20 (978-0-15-323508-5(X)) Harcourt Schl. Pubs.

—Spelling Practice Book. 3rd ed. (Trophies Reading Program Ser.). (Illus.). 2003. (gr. 1 up). 6.80 (978-0-15-323498-9(9)); 2002. (gr. 2 up). pap. 8.00 (978-0-15-323499-6(7)); 2002. (gr. 3 up). pap. 8.00 (978-0-15-323500-9(4)); 2002. (gr. 4 up). pap. 8.00 (978-0-15-323501-6(2)); 2002. (gr. 5 up). pap. 8.00 (978-0-15-323502-3(0)); 2002. (gr. 6 up). pap. 8.00 (978-0-15-323503-0(9)) Harcourt Schl. Pubs.

—Spelling Practice Book, Grade 1. 3rd ed. 2002. (Trophies Reading Program Ser.). (gr. 1 up). pap., tchr. ed. 14.10 (978-0-15-323550-4(0)) Harcourt Schl. Pubs.

—Spelling Practice Book, Grade 2. 3rd ed. 2002. (Trophies Reading Program Ser.). (gr. 2 up). pap., tchr. ed. 14.90 (978-0-15-323551-1(9)) Harcourt Schl. Pubs.

—Spelling Practice Book, Grade 3. 3rd ed. 2002. (Trophies Reading Program Ser.). (gr. 3 up). pap., tchr. ed. 14.90 (978-0-15-323552-8(7)) Harcourt Schl. Pubs.

—Spelling Practice Book, Grade 4. 3rd ed. 2002. (Trophies Reading Program Ser.). (gr. 4 up). pap., tchr. ed. 14.90 (978-0-15-323553-5(5)) Harcourt Schl. Pubs.

—Spelling Practice Book, Grade 5. 3rd ed. 2002. (Trophies Reading Program Ser.). (gr. 5 up). pap., tchr. ed. 14.90 (978-0-15-323554-2(3)) Harcourt Schl. Pubs.

—Spelling Practice Book, Grade 6. 3rd ed. 2002. (Trophies Reading Program Ser.). (gr. 6 up). pap., tchr. ed. 14.90 (978-0-15-323555-9(1)) Harcourt Schl. Pubs.

—Vamos de Fiesta: Spelling Practice. (SPA., Illus.). 2001. pap. 9.50 (978-0-15-316155-1(8)); 2001. (gr. 5). pap. 9.50 (978-0-15-316165-0(5)); 1999. (gr. 1). pap. 9.50 (978-0-15-315929-9(4)); 1999. pap. 9.50 (978-0-15-316139-1(6)); 1999. pap. 9.50 (978-0-15-316146-9(9)) Harcourt Schl. Pubs.

Holt, Rinehart and Winston Staff. Holt Literature & Language Arts, Grade 7: Spelling Lessons - California Edition. 3rd ed. 2001. pap. 10.00 (978-0-03-066127-3(7)) Holt, Rinehart & Winston.

—Holt Literature & Language Arts, Grade 8: Spelling Lessons - California Edition. 3rd ed. 2001. pap. 10.00 (978-0-03-066128-0(5)) Holt, Rinehart & Winston.

Hoover, Sharon. Spelling. 2000. (Step Ahead Workbooks Ser.). (Illus.). 32p. (J). (gr. 1-2). pap., wbk. ed. 2.99 (978-0-307-23570-1(X) , 03570, Golden Bks.) Random Hse. Children's Bks.

Hop, L. L. C. Hooked on First Grade: Spelling. 2006. 64p. 3.79 (978-1-931020-77-0(9)) HOP, LLC.

How to Spell, Bk. 1. 2004. pap. 7.15 (978-0-8388-1848-0(X)) Educators Publishing Service, Inc.

How to Spell Grd 7-12, Bk. 4. 2004. pap. 9.20 (978-0-8388-1854-1(4)) Educators Publishing Service, Inc.

Hyperion Staff. Finger Spelling Pack. 2007. 16p. (J). (ps-3). 12.99 (978-1-4231-0249-6(5)) Hyperion Pr.

Johnson, Kristin & Bayrd, Polly. Megawords 1: Multisyllabic Words for Reading, Spelling, & Vocabulary. 2004. 91p. (gr. 4 up). pap. 6.80 (978-0-8388-1825-1(0)) Educators Publishing Service, Inc.

Josephina, M., et al. Word Power Through Spelling, 7 vols. , Set. 1999. (Illus.). (J). (gr. 3-9). 75.00 (978-0-911845-89-1(5)) Neumann Pr., The.

Kellaher, Karen. Spelling Secrets! 2003. (Illus.). 80p. pap., tchr. ed. 12.95 (978-0-439-37073-8(6) , Teaching Resources) Scholastic, Inc.

Kemmerer, Susan. Apples: Daily Spelling Drills for Secondary Students. 2nd ed. 2005. 172p. (YA). per. 14.95 (978-0-9758543-0-3(5)) Schoolhouse Publishing.

Kimble, Paige, et al. How to Spell Like a Champ. 2006. (Illus.). 192p. (J). 10.95 (978-0-7611-4369-7(6)) Workman Publishing Co., Inc.

Kottmeyer, William A. Basic Goals in Spelling: Grade 5. 8th ed. (J). 148.20 (978-0-07-036155-3(X)) Macmillan/McGraw-Hill Schl. Div.

Learning Horizons, creator. Berrylicious Spelling. 2005. 10p. (J). (ps-3). bds. 5.99 (978-1-59545-017-3(3)) Learning Horizons, Inc.

Lindsay, Elizabeth, ed. Learning Library-Reading, Spelling & Grammar. 2003. 128p. 19.95 (978-1-56234-532-7(X) , Mailbox Bks., The) Education Ctr., Inc.

Literature: Timeless Voices, Timeless Themes. 2001. (YA). (gr. 10). pap. 7.47 (978-0-13-053412-5(9)) Prentice Hall PTR.

Ludwig, Benjamin. Sound Spelling: An Individualized Spelling Program from WriteGuide. com. 2000. 182p. (YA). (gr. 5-9). per. 20.00 (978-1-886061-25-5(4)) Wordsmiths.

McGraw-Hill Staff. Glencoe Language Arts, Spelling Power. 2nd ed. 2001. Grade. 6. pap., wbk. ed. 18.00 (978-0-07-826238-8(0) , 9780078262388); Grade 7. (C). pap., wbk. ed. 18.00 (978-0-07-826240-1(2) , 9780078262401); Grade 8. (C). pap., wbk. ed. 18.00 (978-0-07-826242-5(9) , 9780078262425); Grade 10. pap., wbk. ed. 18.00 (978-0-07-826246-3(1) , 9780078262463); Grade 11. pap., wbk. ed. 18.00 (978-0-07-826248-7(8) , 9780078262487) Glencoe/McGraw-Hill.

—Glencoe Language Arts Spelling Power, Grade 12. 2nd ed. 2001. pap., wbk. ed. 18.00 (978-0-07-826250-0(X) , 9780078262500) Glencoe/McGraw-Hill.

—Glencoe Language Arts Spelling Power Grade 9. 2nd ed. 2001. (C). pap., wbk. ed. 18.00 (978-0-07-826244-9(5) , 9780078262449) Glencoe/McGraw-Hill.

—Spelling: Grades 4-6. 1999. (J). (gr. 4-6). pap. 19.95 (978-1-57768-301-8(3)) School Specialty Publishing.

Modern Curriculum Press Staff. MCP Spelling Workout. 3rd ed. (J). Bk. C. (gr. 3). stu. ed. 11.95 net. (978-0-8136-2817-2(2)); Bk. D. (gr. 4). stu. ed. 11.95 net. (978-0-8136-2818-9(0)); Bk. E. (gr. 5). stu. ed. 11.95 net. (978-0-8136-2819-6(9)) Modern Curriculum Pr.

—McP Spelling Workout Student B, Bk. B. 3rd ed. (J). (gr. 2). 11.95 net. (978-0-8136-2816-5(4)) Modern Curriculum Pr.

Moore, Jo Ellen. Blends & Digraphs Word Machines. Evans, Marilyn, ed. Larsen, Jo, illus. 2000. (Word Machines Ser.). 28p. (J). (gr. 1-3). pap., tchr. ed. 12.95 (978-1-55799-759-3(4) , EMC 782) Evan-Moor Educational Pubs.

Nilsen, Anna. I Can Spell Words with Four Letters. 1998. (I Can Spell Ser.). (Illus.). 26p. (J). (ps-k). tchr. ed. 9.95 (978-0-7534-5125-0(5) , Kingfisher) Houghton Mifflin Co. Trade & Reference Div.

Orient, Jane. Professor Klugimkopf's Spelling Method. 2002. 19.95 (978-0-942487-09-1(5)); per. 12.95 (978-0-942487-08-4(7)) Oregon Institute of Science & Medicine.

Ortografia: Grades 1-2, Class Set B. 2001. (SPA., Illus.). (J). (gr. 1-2). stu. ed., wbk. ed. 159.00 (978-1-56014-295-9(2)) Santillana USA Publishing Co., Inc.

Ortografia: Grades 2-3, Class Set C. 2001. (SPA., Illus.). (J). (gr. 2-3). tchr. ed., stu. ed. 159.00 (978-1-56014-296-6(0)) Santillana USA Publishing Co., Inc.

Ortografia: Grades 3-4, Class Set D. 2001. (SPA., Illus.). (J). (gr. 3-4). tchr. ed., stu. ed. 159.00 (978-1-56014-984-2(1)) Santillana USA Publishing Co., Inc.

Oz, Emily. Spelling Bee. 2006. (Trollz Ser.). 80p. (J). pap. 3.99 (978-0-439-82955-7(0)) Scholastic, Inc.

Parker, Victoria. Test Your Spelling. 1999. (Test Yourself Ser.). (Illus.). 32p. (J). (gr. 5-9). lib. bdg. 13.95 (978-0-88110-754-8(9)) EDC Publishing.

Patullo, Pat & Patullo, Dulcie. Spelling Patterns. (Cambridge Primary Spelling Ser.). (Illus.). 72p. Bk. 1. 1998. pap. 8.00 (978-0-521-64981-0(1)); Bk. 2. 1998. pap. 8.00 (978-0-521-64982-7(X)); Bk. 3. 1999. pap. 8.00 (978-0-521-64983-4(8)); Bk. 4. 1999. pap. 8.00 (978-0-521-64984-1(6)); Bk. 5. 1999. pap. 8.00 (978-0-521-64985-8(4)); Bk. 6. 1999. pap. 8.00 (978-0-521-64986-5(2)) Cambridge Univ. Pr.

Pescosolid. Seck Vaughn Spelling Permabound: Level 6. 1999. (J). 17.68 (978-0-7398-2811-3(8)) Steck-Vaughn.

—Seck Vaughn Spelling Permabound: Level 7. 1999. (J). 17.68 (978-0-7398-2812-0(6)) Steck-Vaughn.

—Seck Vaughn Spelling Permabound: Level 8. 1999. (J). 17.68 (978-0-7398-2813-7(4)) Steck-Vaughn.

Piccirilli, Richard & Zuk, Todd A. Making Spelling Words Stick: 50 Fun, Teacher-Tested Ideas for All Learners. 2004. 80p. pap. 12.99 (978-0-439-57626-0(1) , Teaching Resources) Scholastic, Inc.

Prefixes & Suffixes: Systematic Sequential Phonics & Spelling. 2002. (Four-Blocks Ser.). 192p. pap. 24.99 (978-0-88724-695-1(8) , CD-2413) Carson-Dellosa Publishing Co., Inc.

Priddy, Roger. Simple Spelling. rev. ed. 2005. (Wipe Clean Ser.). 20p. (J). spiral bd. 9.95 (978-0-312-49454-4(8) , Priddy Bks.) St. Martin's Pr.

Rasinski, Timothy. Daily Word Ladders: 100 Reproducible Word Study Lessons That Help Kids Boost Reading, Vocabulary, Spelling & Phonics Skills-Independently! 2005. (Daily Word Ladders Ser.). (Illus.). 112p. (gr. 4-6). pap. 15.99 (978-0-439-77345-4(8) , Teaching Resources) Scholastic, Inc.

Read & Spell with Zoo-phonics. 2004. (J). cd-rom 29.95 (978-1-886441-46-0(4)) Zoo-phonics, Inc.

Read & Spell with Zoo=Phonics Guide for CD-ROM. 2004. (J). 14.95 (978-1-886441-45-3(6)) Zoo-phonics, Inc.

Reading Rods Spelling: Instruction & Activity Book. 2002. (J). pap. 12.95 (978-1-56911-097-3(2)) Learning Resources, Inc.

Reading Rods Spelling Double-Sided Activity Cards. 2002. (J). 12.95 (978-1-56911-099-7(9)) Learning Resources, Inc.

Salzmann, Mary Elizabeth. Vowel Blends, Set. l.t. ed. Incl. Ai : See It Say It Hear It. lib. bdg. 19.93 (978-1-57765-453-7(6)); Ea : See It Say It Hear It. lib. bdg. 19.93 (978-1-57765-454-4(4)); Ee : See It Say It Hear It. lib. bdg. 19.93 (978-1-57765-455-1(2)); Oa : See It Say It Hear It. lib. bdg. 19.93 (978-1-57765-456-8(0)); Oo : See It Say It Hear It. lib. bdg. 19.93 (978-1-57765-457-5(9)); Ou : See It Say It Hear It. lib. bdg. 19.93 (978-1-57765-458-2(7)); 24p. (J). (ps-3). 2001. (Illus.). 2001. Set lib. bdg. 119.58 (978-1-57765-299-1(1) , SandCastle) ABDO Publishing Co.

Say It, Rhyme It, Spell It Game 2. 2005. (J). 49.95 (978-1-58804-404-4(1)) PCI Educational Publishing.

Scarborough. Target Spelling 1020. 2004. pap., tchr. ed. 15.10 incl. cd-rom (978-0-7398-9198-8(7)); (Illus.). pap. 16.00 incl. cd-rom (978-0-7398-9192-6(8)) Steck-Vaughn.

—Target Spelling 1260. 2004. pap. 16.00 incl. cd-rom (978-0-7398-9193-3(6)); pap., tchr. ed. 15.10 incl. cd-rom (978-0-7398-9199-5(5)) Steck-Vaughn.

—Target Spelling 180. 2004. pap., tchr. ed. 15.10 incl. cd-rom (978-0-7398-9194-0(4)); (Illus.). pap. 16.00 incl. cd-rom (978-0-7398-9188-9(X)) Steck-Vaughn.

—Target Spelling 360. 2004. pap. 16.00 incl. cd-rom (978-0-7398-9189-6(8)); pap., tchr. ed. 15.10 incl. cd-rom (978-0-7398-9195-7(2)) Steck-Vaughn.

—Target Spelling 540. 2004. pap., tchr. ed. 15.10 incl. cd-rom (978-0-7398-9196-4(0)); (Illus.). pap. 16.00 incl. cd-rom (978-0-7398-9190-2(1)) Steck-Vaughn.

—Target Spelling 780. 2004. pap. 16.00 incl. cd-rom (978-0-7398-9191-9(X)); pap., tchr. ed. 15.10 incl. cd-rom (978-0-7398-9197-1(9)) Steck-Vaughn.

School Specialty Publishing. I Can Spell & Rhyme. 2006. (Brighter Child I Can... Ser.). 128p. (J). pap. 3.95 (978-0-7696-4898-9(3) , Brighter Child) School Specialty Publishing.

—100 Lifelong Words: Recognizing & Using High-Frequency Words. 2006. 112p. (J). (gr. 3-6). pap. 12.99 (978-0-7682-3373-5(9) , Schaffer, Frank) Schaffer, Frank Pubns.

School Zone Interactive Staff, et al. Spelling 1-2. 2006. 64p. (J). (gr. 1-3). pap. 15.99 incl. cd-rom (***978-1-58947-827-5(4)**) School Zone Publishing Co.

School Zone Publishing Company Staff. Spelling 2. (Illus.). (J). 19.99 incl. audio compact disk (978-0-88743-939-1(X)) School Zone Publishing Co.

School Zone Staff, ed. Kindergarten Spelling Bee. 2006. 6p. (J). 5.99 (***978-1-58947-847-3(9)**) School Zone Publishing Co.

Shifflett, Christa. Hands on Reading & Spelling: Grades 3-6. 2002. 16.95 (978-0-9740367-0-0(6)) Shifflett, Christa.

SIPPS Beginning Package of Little Books. 2004. (978-1-57621-458-9(3)) Developmental Studies Ctr.

SIPPS Beginning Reproducible Book. 2004. (978-1-57621-459-6(1)) Developmental Studies Ctr.

Skill Sharpeners, Spell & Write, Grade 1. 2005. (J). pap. 9.99 (978-1-59673-045-8(5) , emc 4537) Evan-Moor Educational Pubs.

Skill Sharpeners, Spell & Write, Grade 2. 2005. (J). pap. 9.99 (978-1-59673-046-5(3) , emc 4538) Evan-Moor Educational Pubs.

Skill Sharpeners, Spell & Write, Grade 3. 2005. (J). pap. 9.99 (978-1-59673-047-2(1) , emc 4539) Evan-Moor Educational Pubs.

Skill Sharpeners, Spell & Write, Grade 4. 2005. (J). pap. 9.99 (978-1-59673-048-9(X) , emc 4540) Evan-Moor Educational Pubs.

Skill Sharpeners, Spell & Write, Grade 5. 2005. (J). pap. 9.99 (978-1-59673-049-6(8) , emc 4542) Evan-Moor Educational Pubs.

Skill Sharpeners, Spell & Write, Grade 6. 2005. (J). pap. 9.99 (978-1-59673-050-2(1) , emc 4542) Evan-Moor Educational Pubs.

Skill Sharpeners, Spell & Write, Grade PreK. 2005. (J). pap. 9.99 (978-1-59673-043-4(9) , emc 4535) Evan-Moor Educational Pubs.

Smith, Marilyn K. & Forbes, Victoria Q. Spelling Skills Practice & Apply: Grade 5. 2000. (Illus.). 128p. (J). (gr. 5). pap. 10.95 (978-1-58037-135-3(3)) Twain, Mark Media, Inc. Pubs.

—Spelling Skills Practice & Apply: Grade 6. 2000. (Illus.). 128p. (J). (gr. 6). pap. 10.95 (978-1-58037-136-0(1)) Twain, Mark Media, Inc. Pubs.

Snap! Spelling. 2002. cd-rom 4.99 (978-1-59150-164-0(4)) TOPICS Entertainment.

Spelling: English in Context. 2000. (Illus.). 112p. per., wbk. ed. 8.95 (978-1-56254-354-9(7) , SP 3547) Saddleback Educational Publishing.

Spelling Ad Libs. 2004. (J). pap. 10.95 (978-1-56911-159-8(6)) Learning Resources, Inc.

Spelling & Writing. 2000. (gr. 1 up). 52.95 (978-0-673-28977-3(X)); (gr. 2 up). 52.95 (978-0-673-61803-0(X)); (gr. 3 up). 52.95 (978-0-673-28979-7(6)); (gr. 4 up). 52.95 (978-0-673-28980-3(X)); (gr. 5 up). 52.95 (978-0-673-28981-0(8)); (gr. 6 up). 52.95 (978-0-673-28982-7(6)); (gr. 7 up). 52.95 (978-0-673-28983-4(4)); (gr. 8 up). 52.95 (978-0-673-28984-1(2)) Addison-Wesley Educational Pubs., Inc.

Spelling & Writing. 2002. (Home Workbooks Ser.). 64p. pap. 2.49 (978-0-88724-732-3(6) , CD-4534) Carson-Dellosa Publishing Co., Inc.

Spelling & Writing: Grade 3. 2000. (Master Skills Ser.). (Illus.). 128p. (J). (gr. k-6). pap., wbk. ed. 6.95 (978-1-56189-033-0(2) , 13013, American Education Publishing) School Specialty Publishing.

Spelling & Writing: Grade 4. 2000. (Master Skills Ser.). (Illus.). 128p. (J). (gr. k-6). mass mkt., wbk. ed. 6.95 (978-1-56189-034-7(0) , 13014, American Education Publishing) School Specialty Publishing.

Spelling Power Book a Student. 2004. pap. 11.95 (978-0-7609-0880-8(X)) Curriculum Assocs., Inc.

Spelling Power Book B Student. 2004. pap. 11.95 (978-0-7609-0883-9(4)) Curriculum Assocs., Inc.

Spelling Power Book C Student. 2004. pap. 11.95 (978-0-7609-0886-0(9)) Curriculum Assocs., Inc.

Spelling Power Book D Student. 2004. pap. 11.95 (978-0-7609-0889-1(3)) Curriculum Assocs., Inc.

Spelling Power Book E Student. 2004. pap. 11.95 (978-0-7609-0892-1(3)) Curriculum Assocs., Inc.

Spelling Power Book F Student. 2004. pap. 11.95 (978-0-7609-0895-2(8)) Curriculum Assocs., Inc.

Spelling Power Book G Student. 2004. pap. 11.95 (978-0-7609-0898-3(2)) Curriculum Assocs., Inc.

Spelling Power Book H Student. 2004. pap. 11.95 (978-0-7609-0901-0(6)) Curriculum Assocs., Inc.

Spelling Power Book H Teacher. 2004. pap. 26.95 (978-0-7609-0902-7(4)) Curriculum Assocs., Inc.

Spelling Skills 2-3. 2004. (Basic Skills Ser.). 48p. (J). pap. 6.99 (978-0-88724-150-5(6) , CD-4711) Carson-Dellosa Publishing Co., Inc.

Spelling Skills 3-4. 2004. (Basic Skills Ser.). 48p. (J). pap. 6.99 (978-0-88724-151-2(4) , CD-4712) Carson-Dellosa Publishing Co., Inc.

Spelling Skills 4-5. 2004. (Basic Skills Ser.). 48p. (J). pap. 6.99 (978-0-88724-152-9(2) , CD-4713) Carson-Dellosa Publishing Co., Inc.

Spelling Skills 5-6. 2004. (Basic Skills Ser.). 48p. (J). pap. 6.99 (978-0-88724-163-5(8) , CD-4714) Carson-Dellosa Publishing Co., Inc.

Spelling Steps 1. 2nd ed. 2001. 96p. ring bd. 27.95 (978-1-56254-144-6(7) , SP 1447) Saddleback Educational Publishing.

Spelling Steps 2. 2nd ed. 2001. 140p. ring bd. 28.95 (978-1-56254-145-3(5) , SP 1455) Saddleback Educational Publishing.

Spelling Steps 3. 2nd ed. 2001. 176p. ring bd. 29.95 (978-1-56254-146-0(3) , SP 1463) Saddleback Educational Publishing.

Spelling Steps 4. 2001. 160p. ring bd. 30.95 (978-1-56254-142-2(0) , SP 1420) Saddleback Educational Publishing.

Splat! Spelling Software. 2000. (gr. 6 up). 20.76 (978-0-673-28928-5(1)) Addison-Wesley Educational Pubs., Inc.

Steck-Vaughn Staff. Language Art & Spelling, 8, Pack. 2004. pap. 68.00 (978-0-7398-9933-5(3)) Harcourt Schl. Pubs.

—Language Arts & Spelling. 2004. pap. 8.50 (978-0-7398-9848-2(5)); pap. 68.00 (978-0-7398-9929-8(5)); pap., tchr. ed. 10.00 (978-0-7398-9904-5(X)) Harcourt Schl. Pubs.

Sterling Publishing Company Staff. Learning to Write with Benjamin the Bear: Wipe & Clean Book. 1998. (Balloon Ser.). (Illus.). 14p. (J). (ps-1). pap. 5.95 (978-0-8069-3824-0(2)) Sterling Publishing Co., Inc.

Stevenson, Nancy. Basic Blue Level. Gallager, Ann & Stevenson, William, eds. Semple, Janice, illus. 1998. (Language Skills Program Ser.). 90p. (J). (gr. 1-7). A. 2nd ed. pap., wbk. ed. 4.75 (978-0-941112-48-2(9)); C. pap., wbk. ed. 4.75 (978-0-941112-50-5(0)) Stevenson Learning Skills, Inc.

—Basic Blue Level Spelling Manual. Gallager, Ann & Stevenson, William, eds. Semple, Janice, illus. 1998. (Language Skills Program Ser.). 289p. (J). (gr. 2-6). pap. 18.95 (978-0-941112-51-2(9)) Stevenson Learning Skills, Inc.

Stoneman, Sonya. First Aid in Spelling. (Illus.). (J). pap. (978-1-876367-53-4(9)) Wizard Bks.

Terban, Marvin. Scholastic Dictionary of Spelling. 1998. 224p. (J). (gr. 4-7). pap. 16.95 (978-0-590-30697-3(9)) Scholastic, Inc.

—Scholastic Dictionary of Spelling. 2000. (gr. 3-6). lib. bdg. 17.60 (978-0-613-28633-6(2)) Tandem Library Bks.

Timeless Voices, Timeless Themes: Bronze, Vocabulary & Spelling Practice Book. 2001. (YA). (gr. 7). pap. 6.97 (978-0-13-052345-7(3)) Prentice Hall PTR.

Timeless Voices, Timeless Themes: Copper, Vocabulary & Spelling Practice Book. 2001. (J). (gr. 6). pap. 6.97 (978-0-13-052344-0(5)) Prentice Hall PTR.

Timeless Voices, Timeless Themes: Gold, Vocabulary & Spelling Practice Book. 2000. (YA). (gr. 9). pap. 6.97 (978-0-13-437572-4(6)) Prentice Hall PTR.

Timeless Voices, Timeless Themes: Platinum, Vocabulary & Spelling Practice Book. 2000. (YA). (gr. 10). pap. 6.97 (978-0-13-437576-2(9)) Prentice Hall PTR.

Timeless Voices, Timeless Themes: Silver, Vocabulary & Spelling Practice Book. 2001. (YA). (gr. 8). pap. 6.97 (978-0-13-052346-4(1)) Prentice Hall PTR.

Traditional Catholic Speller. (J). (gr. 1). wbk. ed. 12.00 (978-1-931555-33-3(8)); (J). (gr. 2). wbk. ed. 12.00 (978-1-931555-34-0(6)); (J). (gr. 3). wbk. ed. 12.00 (978-1-931555-35-7(4)); (J). (gr. 4) wbk. ed. 12.00 (978-1-931555-36-4(2)); (J). (gr. 5). wbk. ed. 12.00 (978-1-931555-37-1(0)); (J). (gr. 6). wbk. ed. 12.00 (978-1-931555-38-8(9)); (YA). (gr. 7). wbk. ed. 12.00 (978-1-931555-39-5(7)); (YA). (gr. 8). wbk. ed. 12.00 (978-1-931555-40-1(0)) Our Lady of Victory Schl.

Tulip, Jenny. On the Farm. 2000. (Illus.). 16p. (ps-k). pap. 5.00 (978-0-7548-0133-7(0)) Anness Publishing, Inc.

Valentino, Catherine. Blue Ribbon Spelling & Vocabulary, Level 1. (J). pap. 7.95 (978-0-86651-196-4(2)) Seymour, Dale Pubns.

Vandyck, William & Burt, Angela. Spelling Repair Kits. 2005. (Illus.). 96p. (YA). pap. 9.99 (978-0-340-89335-7(4) , Hodder & Stoughton) Hodder General Publishing Division GBR. *Dist:* Trafalgar Square Publishing.

Webster, Noah. The Elementary Spelling Book: Being an Improvement on the American Spelling Book. 3rd rev. ed. 1998. (Illus.). 176p. (J). (gr. 2-9). reprint ed. spiral bd. 11.00 (978-0-9668921-1-6(9)) Weisman Pubns.

Whiteford, Rhona. Complete English, 3 bks. in 1. (Illus.). 96p. (YA). pap. 15.99 (978-0-340-71582-6(0) , Hodder & Stoughton) Hodder General Publishing Division GBR. *Dist:* Trafalgar Square Publishing.

—Spelling. 2003. (Hodder Home Learning Ser.). (Illus.). 32p. (J). pap. 6.99 (978-0-340-79184-4(5) , Hodder & Stoughton) Hodder General Publishing Division GBR. *Dist:* Trafalgar Square Publishing.

Wickings, Ruth. Letter Box. 2007. (Illus.). 14p. 19.95 (***978-1-84560-036-5(3)**) Mercury Bks. Ltd. GBR. *Dist:* International Publishers Marketing.

Windridge, C. How to Better Your Words: Exercises. 1999. 24p. (J). (gr. 2-4). 39.00 (978-0-7217-0503-3(0)) Schofield & Sims Ltd. GBR. *Dist:* State Mutual Bk. & Periodical Service, Ltd.

Wolf, Kathy, ed. Learning Library Phonics, Reading & Spelling. 2002. 128p. 19.95 (978-1-56234-483-2(8) , Mailbox Bks., The) Education Ctr., Inc.

Yates, Irene. How to Be a Wizard at Spelling. 48p. (J). (gr. 2-6). pap. (978-1-875739-65-3(3)) Wizard Bks.

Zoo-phonics Quick Tests for the Classroom. 2004. cd-rom (978-1-886441-41-5(3)) Zoo-phonics, Inc.

100 Lifelong Words: Helping Students Become Better Spellers. 112p. (gr. 3-6). 14.99 (978-0-7682-0107-9(1) , GA13011) School Specialty Publishing.

ENGLISH LANGUAGE—STUDY AND TEACHING

Ada, Alma Flor. How Happy I Would Be! Escriva, Vivi, illus. (Stories for the Telling Ser.). 16p. (J). (gr. k-3). pap. 6.95 (978-1-58105-228-2(6)) Santillana USA Publishing Co., Inc.

Adams, Colleen. On My Sled: Learning the SL Sound. (PowerPhonics Ser.). (Illus.). (J). 2002. 24p. (gr. 1). lib. bdg. 18.50 (978-0-8239-5952-5(X)); 2001. 23p. pap. (978-0-8239-8297-4(1)) Rosen Publishing Group, Inc., The. (PowerKids Pr.).

Albright, Thomas B. Universal English: Second Language for All. unabr. l.t. ed. 2003. (Languages: Universal English for All). (ENM.). 128p. pap. 7.00 (978-1-888264-17-3(9)) Twenty-First Century Co., The.

Baron, Larry. A Day with My Dad: Learning the D Sound. 2002. (PowerPhonics Ser.). (Illus.). 24p. (J). (gr. 1). lib. bdg. 18.00 (978-0-8239-5902-0(3) , PowerKids Pr.) Rosen Publishing Group, Inc., The.

Battistoni, Ilse. I Fight Fires: Learning the Long I Sound. (PowerPhonics Ser.). (Illus.). (J). 2002. 24p. (gr. 1). lib. bdg. 18.50 (978-0-8239-5928-0(7)); 2001. 23p. pap. 26.40 (978-0-8239-8273-8(4)) Rosen Publishing Group, Inc., The. (PowerKids Pr.).

—What a Whale! Learning the WH Sound. (PowerPhonics Ser.). (Illus.). (J). 2002. 24p. (gr. 1). lib. bdg. 18.50 (978-0-8239-5929-7(5)); 2001. 23p. pap. 26.40 (978-0-8239-8274-5(2)) Rosen Publishing Group, Inc., The. (PowerKids Pr.).

Beech, Linda Ward. Great Grammar Skill Builders. 2000. (Ready-to-Go Reproducibles Ser.). (Illus.). 48p. (YA). (gr. 6-8). pap. 8.95 (978-0-439-10544-6(7)); (J). pap. 8.95 (978-0-439-10543-9(9)) Scholastic, Inc.

Braidich, Shelby & Roza, Greg. Meet Me on the Farm: Learning the Long E Sound. (PowerPhonics Ser.). (Illus.). (J). 2002. 24p. (gr. 1). lib. bdg. 18.50 (978-0-8239-5920-4(1)); 2001. 23p. pap. 26.40 (978-0-8239-8265-3(3)) Rosen Publishing Group, Inc., The. (PowerKids Pr.).

Bryant-Mole, Karen. Beginning Letters. Mukhida, Zul, illus. 2000. (Mortimer's Fun with Words Ser.). 24p. (J). (ps up). lib. bdg. 22.00 (978-0-8368-2746-0(5)) Stevens, Gareth Inc.

—Ending Letters. Mukhida, Zul, photos by. 2000. (Mortimer's Fun with Words Ser.). (Illus.). 24p. (J). (ps up). lib. bdg. 22.00 (978-0-8368-2747-7(3)) Stevens, Gareth Inc.

—Letters Make Words. Mukhida, Zul, photos by. 2000. (Mortimer's Fun with Words Ser.). (Illus.). 24p. (J). (ps up). lib. bdg. 22.00 (978-0-8368-2748-4(1)) Stevens, Gareth Inc.

Burnard, Damon. I Spy in the Ocean. Cairns, Julia, illus. 2001. 24p. (J). (ps-5). bds. 6.95 (978-0-8118-2988-5(X)) Chronicle Bks. LLC.

Campell, Dawn & Halderman, Karen. Word Walls Activities. Apodaca-LaBounty, Blanca, illus. 1999. 208p. (J). (gr. k-3). pap., tchr. ed. 16.99 (978-1-57690-481-7(4) , TCM2481) Teacher Created Materials, Inc.

Carroll, Joyce Armstrong, et al. Writing & Grammar, Grade 9: Communication in Action, Diamond Level. 2001. (YA). (gr. 12). trans. 20.97 (978-0-13-043965-9(7)) Prentice-Hall.

Carson, Janet. Visiting the Vet: Learning the V Sound. (PowerPhonics Ser.). (Illus.). (J). 2002. 24p. (gr. 1). lib. bdg. 18.50 (978-0-8239-5934-1(1)); 2001. 23p. pap. 26.40 (978-0-8239-8279-0(3)) Rosen Publishing Group, Inc., The. (PowerKids Pr.).

Chapman, Joan. Pet Pals: Learning the P Sound. 2002. (PowerPhonics Ser.). (Illus.). 24p. (J). (gr. 1). lib. bdg. 18.50 (978-0-8239-5915-0(5) , PowerKids Pr.) Rosen Publishing Group, Inc., The.

—Pet Pals: Learning the Short U Sound. 2001. (PowerPhonics Ser.). (Illus.). 23p. (J). lib. bdg. 26.40 (978-0-8239-8260-8(2) , PowerKids Pr.) Rosen Publishing Group, Inc., The.

Dahl, Michael. Alphabet Soup: A Book of Riddles about Letters. Reibeling, Brandon, illus. 2004. (Read-It! Joke Books). 24p. (C). (gr. k-3). 18.60 (978-1-4048-0228-5(2)) Picture Window Bks.

Dalmatian Press Staff. Phonics Review. 2002. (Tools Ser.). (Illus.). 32p. (J). (gr. 2-3). pap. 2.29 (978-1-57759-196-2(8)) Dalmatian Pr.

Daniel, Pauline, illus. Alphabet Songs. 2001. (ENG.). 30p. (J). suppl. ed. 15.00 (978-0-9702826-9-9(9)) Breaking The Sounds' Barrier, Reading By Ear.

Dufresne, Michele. Teacher Notes: Early Emergent Set 2. 1999. (J). pap. (978-1-58453-042-8(1)) Pioneer Valley Educational Pr., Inc.

Edutech Systems Staff. Searchlights for Spelling Year 4: For Interactive Whole-Class Teaching. Buckton, Chris & Corbett, Pie, eds. 2003. (Searchlights for Spelling Ser.). cd-rom 83.00 (978-0-521-75581-8(6)) Cambridge Univ. Pr.

—Searchlights for Spelling Year 5: For Interactive Whole-Class Teaching. Buckton, Chris & Corbett, Pie, eds. 2003. (Searchlights for Spelling Ser.). cd-rom 83.00 (978-0-521-75582-5(4)) Cambridge Univ. Pr.

Elliott, Rebecca. Painless Grammar. Hamilton, Laurie, illus. 2nd ed. 2006. (Painless Ser.). 224p. pap., stu. ed. 8.99 (978-0-7641-3436-4(1)) Barron's Educational Series, Inc.

Far from the Madding Crowd: Teaching Unit. 2003. 92p. (YA). ring bd. (978-1-58049-471-7(4) , TU4714) Prestwick Hse., Inc.

Fenner, Matthew. On My Block: Learning the BL Sound. (PowerPhonics Ser.). (Illus.). (J). 2002. 24p. (gr. 1). lib. bdg. 18.50 (978-0-8239-5924-2(4)); 2001. 23p. pap. 26.40 (978-0-8239-8269-1(6)) Rosen Publishing Group, Inc., The. (PowerKids Pr.).

Figorito, Christine. Go Far in the Car: Learning the AR Sound. (PowerPhonics Ser.). (Illus.). (J). 2002. 24p. (gr. 1). lib. bdg. 18.50 (978-0-8239-5938-9(4)); 2001. 23p. pap. 26.40 (978-0-8239-8283-7(1)) Rosen Publishing Group, Inc., The. (PowerKids Pr.).

Finn, Perdita. Teaching Memoir Writing: 20 Easy Mini-lessons & Thought-Provoking Activities That Inspire Kids. 1999. (Illus.). 48p. pap. 10.95 (978-0-439-04390-8(5)) Scholastic, Inc.

Gerngross, Gunter & Puchta, Herbert. Playway to English 2 Picture Cards. 1999. (Playway to English Ser.). 2p. 36.00 (978-0-521-65681-8(8)) Cambridge Univ. Pr.

—Playway to English 2 Story Cards. 1999. (Playway to English Ser.). 2p. 64.00 (978-0-521-65680-1(X)) Cambridge Univ. Pr.

Giglio, Julie. Third Grade Enrichment. 2001. (Enrichment Wkbks.). (Illus.). 32p. (J). (gr. 3). pap. 2.49 (978-0-88743-458-7(4) , 02153) School Zone Publishing Co.

Gill, Kim & DeNinno, Joanne P. Fun Deck & Say Fun Sheets. DeShong, Molly & Webber, Thomas, eds. 2001. (Illus.). spiral bd. 33.96 (978-1-58650-189-1(5)) Super Duper Pubns.

Hall, M. C. First Grade Enrichment. 2001. (Enrichment Wkbks.). 32p. (J). (gr. 1). pap., wbk. ed. 2.49 (978-0-88743-456-3(8) , 02151) School Zone Publishing Co.

—Second Grade Enrichment. 2001. (Enrichment Wkbks.). (Illus.). 32p. (J). (gr. 2). pap., wbk. ed. 2.49 (978-0-88743-457-0(6) , 02152) School Zone Publishing Co.

Harcourt School Publishers Staff. Collections: Language Handbook. 1999. (Illus.). (gr. 1). pap. 8.60 (978-0-15-313355-8(4)) Harcourt Schl. Pubs.

—Intervention Solution: Teacher Resource Guide: California Edition. 2nd ed. 2002. (Horizons Ser.). (gr. 1). pap., tchr. ed. 22.70 (978-0-15-338209-3(0)) Harcourt Schl. Pubs.

—Intervention Solutions: Teacher Resource Guide: California Edition. 2nd ed. 2002. (Horizons Ser.). (gr. 2). pap., tchr. ed. 22.70 (978-0-15-338210-9(4)); (gr. 3). pap., tchr. ed. 22.70 (978-0-15-338211-6(2)); (gr. 4). pap., tchr. ed. 22.70 (978-0-15-338212-3(0)); (gr. 5). pap., tchr. ed. 22.70 (978-0-15-338213-0(9)); (gr. 6). pap., tchr. ed. 22.70 (978-0-15-338214-7(7)) Harcourt Schl. Pubs.

—Teacher's Edition Package: Texas Edition. 3rd ed. 2003. (gr. 1). tchr. ed. 237.70 (978-0-15-320185-1(1)); (gr. 2). 252.30 (978-0-15-320186-8(X)); (gr. 3). 252.30 (978-0-15-320187-5(8)); (gr. 4). 277.90 (978-0-15-320188-2(6)) Harcourt Schl. Pubs.

Harris, Julie, narrated by. The Fairies. unabr. ed. 2001. (World of Words Ser.). (J). (gr. k-3). pap. 22.00 incl. audio (978-0-8045-6708-4(5) , 6500-H/10) Spoken Arts, Inc.

—The Little Match Girl. unabr. ed. 2001. (World of Words Ser.). (J). (gr. k-3). pap. 22.00 incl. audio (978-0-8045-6702-2(6) , 6500-B/10) Spoken Arts, Inc.

Hawes, Alison. Come Top in English 4: Ages 6-7. 2004. (Illus.). 32p. pap. 5.99 (978-0-7548-1146-6(8) , Lorenz Bks.) Anness Publishing GBR. *Dist:* National Bk. Network.

—Coming Top... English: Ages 3-4. 2004. (Illus.). 32p. pap. 5.99 (978-0-7548-1141-1(7)) Anness Publishing GBR. *Dist:* National Bk. Network.

—Coming TOP English: Ages 5-6. 2004. (Illus.). 32p. pap. 5.99 (978-0-7548-1145-9(X)) Anness Publishing GBR. *Dist:* National Bk. Network.

Hereford, Jane. Passing the Georgia High School Graduation Test in English Language Arts. 1999. (Illus.). 216p. (J). pap. 12.00 (978-0-89892-192-2(9)) Contemporary Publishing Co. of Raleigh, Inc.

Hoffman, Joan. Readiness Basics: Grades K-1. 2001. (Super-Deluxe Wkbks.). (Illus.). 128p. (J). (gr. k-1). pap., wbk. ed. 7.99 (978-1-58947-005-7(2) , 02456) School Zone Publishing Co.

Holt, Rinehart and Winston Staff. Call to Freedom: Beginning-1914: Main Idea Activities. 3rd ed. 2001. pap. 25.80 (978-0-03-065791-7(1)) Holt, Rinehart & Winston.

—Holt Literature & Language Arts, Grade 8: Universal Access Word & Language Skills Answer Key: California Edition. 3rd ed. 2001. pap. 24.33 (978-0-03-066059-7(9)) Holt, Rinehart & Winston.

—In English Study Guide with Ansky Economics. 3rd ed. 2002. (J). pap. 19.20 (978-0-03-069996-2(7)) Holt, Rinehart & Winston of Canada, Ltd. CAN. *Dist:* Harcourt Canada, Ltd.

—Language Arts: Preparation for Proficiency Test - Ohio Edition. 3rd ed. 2003. (J). pap. 12.20 (978-0-03-068553-8(2)) Holt, Rinehart & Winston.

—Middle School Practice for Middle School English Subject Area. 3rd ed. 2003. (YA). (gr. 6-8). pap. 12.16 (978-0-03-070908-1(3)) Holt, Rinehart & Winston.

Janeczko, Paul B. How to Write Poetry, Grades 4 to 9. 2001. 15.75 (978-0-606-21239-7(6)) Tandem Library Bks.

Jarnow, Jill. Writing to Instruct. 2006. (Write Now Ser.). (J). 17.25 (978-1-4042-2834-4(9) , PowerKids Pr.) Rosen Publishing Group, Inc., The.

La Raja, Taryn & Pruger, Elizabeth. Smart Start! A Preparatory Guide. 1999. (Smart Start Ser.). (Illus.). 64p. (YA). (gr. 8). pap. 5.95 (978-1-893110-05-2(2)) Silver Moon Pr.

Lang. Arts: Student Testing Kit. 2004. (gr. 1-8). stu. ed. 5.00 (978-0-86717-287-4(8) , LD001, Lifepac) Alpha Omega Pubns., Inc.

E F G

Laraja, Taryn & Kaplan, Farida. Smart Start! Grade 3. 2000. (Illus.). 68p. (J). pap. 5.95 (978-1-893110-14-4(1)) Silver Moon Pr.

Learning Company Books Staff, ed. Reader Rabbit: Phonics. 2003. (Illus.). 32p. (J). pap., wbk. ed. 3.99 (978-0-7630-7579-8(5)); pap., wbk. ed. 3.99 (978-0-7630-7580-4(9)); pap., wbk. ed. 3.99 (978-0-7630-7576-7(0)) Learning Co. Bks.

Leigh, Autumn. Giant Giraffes: Learning the Soft G Sound. (PowerPhonics Ser.). (Illus.). (J). 2002. 24p. (gr. 1). lib. bdg. 18.50 (978-0-8239-5919-8(8)); 2001. 23p. pap. 26.40 (978-0-8239-8264-6(5)) Rosen Publishing Group, Inc., The. (PowerKids Pr.).

—It Grows in Spring: Learning the GR Sound. 2002. (PowerPhonics Ser.). (Illus.). (J). 23p. lib. bdg. (978-0-8239-8286-8(6)); 24p. (gr. 1). lib. bdg. 18.50 (978-0-8239-5941-9(4)) Rosen Publishing Group, Inc., The. (PowerKids Pr.).

McGraw-Hill Staff. Mummy Mystery: Language Arts. 1999. (J). (gr. 5). 19.95 (978-1-57768-335-3(8)) School Specialty Publishing.

—Network Nightmare: Language Arts. 1999. (J). (gr. 4-5). 19.95 (978-1-57768-334-6(X)) School Specialty Publishing.

—Phonics: Grades 2-3. 1999. (J). (gr. 2-3). pap. 19.95 (978-1-57768-037-6(5)) School Specialty Publishing.

McMahon, Helen. Workbook for English Language Learners: Twelve Month Student Curriculum. McMahon, Terry, illus. 2000. vi, 173p. (J). pap., wbk. ed. 39.95 (978-0-9704195-0-7(3)) Torus Pr.

McMorrow, Annalisa. A Diller, a Dollar. 1999. (Illus.). 80p. (J). pap. 9.95 (978-1-57612-109-2(7)) Monday Morning Bks., Inc.

—Sticks & Stones. 1999. (Illus.). 80p. (J). pap. 9.95 (978-1-57612-107-8(0)) Monday Morning Bks., Inc.

—Wheels on the Bus. 1999. (Illus.). 80p. (J). pap. 9.95 (978-1-57612-108-5(9)) Monday Morning Bks., Inc.

Metz, Lynn. Every Egg: Learning the Short E Sound. (PowerPhonics Ser.). (Illus.). (J). 2002. 24p. (gr. 1). lib. bdg. 18.50 (978-0-8239-5909-9(0)); 2001. 23p. pap. 26.40 (978-0-8239-8254-7(8)) Rosen Publishing Group, Inc., The. (PowerKids Pr.).

Molinsky, Steven J. & Bliss, Bill. Side by Side. 3rd ed. (J). (gr. 1-9). 2001. 208p. pap., wbk. ed., act. bk. ed. 10.50 (978-0-13-040647-7(3)); Bk. 1A. 2000. (Illus.). 64p. pap., stu. ed., wbk. ed. 19.93 (978-0-13-029298-8(2)) Longman Publishing Group.

Moore, Jo Ellen. Daily Language Review. 1998. (Daily Language Review Ser.). (Illus.). 112p. (J). (gr. 2). pap., tchr. ed. 14.95 (978-1-55799-656-5(3) , EMC 580); (gr. 5). pap., tchr. ed. 14.95 (978-1-55799-659-6(8) , EMC 583) Evan-Moor Educational Pubs.

Moore, M. Meet My Mom: Learning the M Sound. 2002. (PowerPhonics Ser.). (Illus.). 24p. (J). (gr. 1). lib. bdg. 18.00 (978-0-8239-5913-6(9) , PowerKids Pr.) Rosen Publishing Group, Inc., The.

Moore, Sharon. Meet My Mom: Learning the M Sound. 2002. (PowerPhonics Ser.). (Illus.). 23p. (J). lib. bdg. (978-0-8239-8258-5(0) , PowerKids Pr.) Rosen Publishing Group, Inc., The.

—Tiger Talk: Learning the T Sound. 2002. (PowerPhonics Ser.). (Illus.). 24p. (J). (gr. 1). lib. bdg. 18.50 (978-0-8239-5914-3(7) , PowerKids Pr.) Rosen Publishing Group, Inc., The.

Moskal, Greg. I Like Winter: Learning the ER Sound. (PowerPhonics Ser.). (Illus.). (J). 2002. 24p. (gr. 1). lib. bdg. 18.50 (978-0-8239-5939-6(2)); 2001. 23p. pap. 26.40 (978-0-8239-8284-4(X)) Rosen Publishing Group, Inc., The. (PowerKids Pr.).

My First 100 Words in French/English. 2003. (First Words & Pictures Book Ser.).Tr. of My First 100 Words. (FRE.). 32p. (J). 11.95 (978-0-7525-7768-5(9)) Parragon, Inc.

NCPTA Staff. Home Learning 5-7 English. (Illus.). 24p. pap. 6.99 (978-0-340-71679-3(7) , Coronet) Hodder General Publishing Division GBR. *Dist:* Trafalgar Square Publishing.

New Tools for English Language Development: Student Kit. 2001. (J). act. bk. ed. (978-1-58105-942-7(6)); (Illus.). (gr. 1). stu. ed., act. bk. ed. (978-1-58105-943-4(4)); (Illus.). (gr. 2). stu. ed., act. bk. ed. (978-1-58105-944-1(2)); (Illus.). (gr. 3). stu. ed., act. bk. ed. (978-1-58105-945-8(0)); (Illus.). (gr. 5). stu. ed., act. bk. ed. (978-1-58105-947-2(7)); (Illus.). (gr. 6). stu. ed., act. bk. ed. (978-1-58105-948-9(5)) Santillana USA Publishing Co., Inc.

Norris, Jill. Daily Language Review. (Daily Language Review Ser.). 112p. (J). 2000. (gr. 6). pap., tchr. ed. 14.95 (978-1-55799-792-0(6) , EMC 576); 1998. (Illus.). (gr. 1). pap., tchr. ed. 14.95 (978-1-55799-655-8(5) , EMC 579) Evan-Moor Educational Pubs.

Nuevo Siglo de Espanol: Student Kit, 15 bks., Set. 2001. (SPA & ENG., Illus.). (J). (gr. 4). stu. ed., wbk. ed. (978-1-58105-877-2(2)) Santillana USA Publishing Co., Inc.

O'Connor, John. Language to Analyse, Review & Comment Student's Book. 2001. (Literacy in Context Ser.). 80p. pap., stu. ed. 12.00 (978-0-521-80554-4(6)) Cambridge Univ. Pr.

O'Donnell, Kerri. So Many Seeds: Learning the S Sound. (PowerPhonics Ser.). (Illus.). (J). 2002. 24p. (gr. 1). lib. bdg. 18.50 (978-0-8239-5908-2(2)); 2001. 23p. pap. 26.40 (978-0-8239-8253-0(X)) Rosen Publishing Group, Inc., The. (PowerKids Pr.).

Pruger, Elizabeth & Zernone, Michelle. Smart Start! A Preparatory Guide. 1999. (Smart Start Ser.). (Illus.). 64p. (YA). (gr. 4). pap. 5.95 (978-1-893110-06-9(0)) Silver Moon Pr.

Pruger, Liz & Zernone, Michelle. Listen, Take Note!, Level A. 2000. (Illus.). 48p. (J). pap. 5.95 (978-1-893110-18-2(4)) Silver Moon Pr.

—Smart Start! Grade 7. 2000. (Illus.). 60p. (YA). (gr. 7). pap. 5.95 (978-1-893110-21-2(4)) Silver Moon Pr.

Richter, Abigail. By the Ocean: Learning the Long O Sound. (PowerPhonics Ser.). (Illus.). (J). 2002. 24p. (gr. 1). lib. bdg. 18.50 (978-0-8239-5922-8(8)); 2001. 23p. pap. 26.40 (978-0-8239-8267-7(X)) Rosen Publishing Group, Inc., The. (PowerKids Pr.).

Rosenberg, Mary. Learning Sight Words Is Easy! 50 Fun & Easy Reproducible Activities That Help Every Child Master the Top 100 High-Frequency Words. 2000. (Illus.). 96p. pap. 10.95 (978-0-439-14113-0(3)) Scholastic, Inc.

Ross, Michael & West, Keith. Delivering the Framework for Teaching English. 2001. (Level Best Ser.: No. 1). (Illus.). 128p. (YA). (gr. 6-9). pap. 19.95 (978-0-7487-6058-9(X)) Nelson Thornes Ltd. GBR. *Dist:* Trans-Atlantic Pubns., Inc.

Roy, Jennifer Rozines & Haney, Johannah. You Can Write an Essay. 2004. (You Can Write Ser.). (Illus.). 64p. (J). lib. bdg. 22.60 (978-0-7660-2091-7(6)) Enslow Pubs., Inc.

Roza, Greg. Lots of Leaves: Learning the L Sound. (PowerPhonics Ser.). (Illus.). (J). 2002. 24p. (gr. 1). lib. bdg. 18.50 (978-0-8239-5899-3(X)); 2001. 23p. lib. bdg. 26.40 (978-0-8239-8244-8(0)) Rosen Publishing Group, Inc., The. (PowerKids Pr.).

—On Flat Land: Learning the FL Sound. (PowerPhonics Ser.). (Illus.). (J). 2002. 24p. (gr. 1). lib. bdg. 18.50 (978-0-8239-5925-9(2)); 2001. 23p. pap. 26.40 (978-0-8239-8270-7(X)) Rosen Publishing Group, Inc., The. (PowerKids Pr.).

Santillana Intensive English: Grade 1 - Homework Activity Book Set, 15 bks. 2001. (J). (gr. 1). pap. 147.95 (978-1-58105-853-6(5)) Santillana COL. *Dist:* Santillana USA Publishing Co., Inc.

Santillana Intensive English: Grade 2 - Homework Activity Book Set, 15 bks. 2001. (J). (gr. 2). pap., act. bk. ed. 147.95 (978-1-58105-854-3(3)) Santillana USA Publishing Co., Inc.

Santillana Intensive English: Grade 3 - Homework Activity Book Set, 15 bks., Set. 2001. (J). (gr. 3). pap. 147.95 (978-1-58105-855-0(1)) Santillana USA Publishing Co., Inc.

Santillana Intensive English: Grade 4 - Homework Activity Book Set, 15 bks. 2001. (J). (gr. 4). pap. 147.95 (978-1-58105-856-7(X)) Santillana USA Publishing Co., Inc.

Santillana Intensive English: Grade 5 - Homework Activity Book Set, 15 bks. 2001. (J). (gr. 5). pap. 147.95 (978-1-58105-857-4(8)) Santillana USA Publishing Co., Inc.

Santillana Intensive English: Grade 6 - Homework Activity Book Set, 15 bks. 2001. (J). (gr. 6). pap. 147.95 (978-1-58105-858-1(6)) Santillana USA Publishing Co., Inc.

Santillana Intensive English: Grade K - Homework Activity Book Set, 15 bks. 2001. (J). pap. 147.95 (978-1-58105-852-9(7)) Santillana USA Publishing Co., Inc.

Santillana Intensive English Opening Doors: Achievement Test Correlated Activities, Grade 1, 15 bks., Set. 2001. (J). (gr. 1). wbk. ed. (978-1-58105-937-3(X)) Santillana USA Publishing Co., Inc.

Santillana Intensive English Opening Doors: Achievement Test Correlated Activities, Grade 2, 15 bks., Set. 2001. (J). (gr. 2). wbk. ed. (978-1-58105-938-0(8)) Santillana USA Publishing Co., Inc.

Santillana Intensive English Opening Doors: Achievement Test Correlated Activities, Grade 3, 30 bks., Set. 2001. (J). (gr. 3). wbk. ed. (978-1-58105-939-7(6)) Santillana USA Publishing Co., Inc.

Santillana Intensive English Opening Doors: Achievement Test Correlated Activities, Grade K, 16 bks., Set. 2001. (J). wbk. ed., tchr.'s training gde. ed. (978-1-58105-936-6(1)) Santillana USA Publishing Co., Inc.

Santos, Dina. Friends: Learning the FR Sound. (PowerPhonics Ser.). (Illus.). (J). 2002. 24p. (gr. 1). lib. bdg. 18.50 (978-0-8239-5944-0(9)); 2001. 23p. pap. 26.40 (978-0-8239-8289-9(0)) Rosen Publishing Group, Inc., The. (PowerKids Pr.).

Sarkisian, Kevin. I Have a Horse: Learning the H Sound. (PowerPhonics Ser.). (Illus.). (J). 2002. 24p. (gr. 1). lib. bdg. 18.50 (978-0-8239-5906-8(6)); 2001. 23p. lib. bdg. 26.40 (978-0-8239-8251-6(3)) Rosen Publishing Group, Inc., The. (PowerKids Pr.).

Saslow, Joan M. & Collins, Tim. Workplace Plus 1 with Grammar Booster, 4 vols. 2004. (Illus.). (C). pap. 21.67 (978-0-13-192799-5(X)) Pearson ESL.

School Zone Publishing Company Staff. First Grade Scholar. rev. ed. 2001. (Super-Deluxe Wkbks.). (Illus.). 128p. (J). (gr. k-1). pap. 7.99 (978-1-58947-009-5(5) , 02460) School Zone Publishing Co.

—Grades 3-4 Big Get Ready! 2002. (Big Get Ready Ser.). (Illus.). 320p. (J). (gr. 3-4). pap. 9.99 (978-1-58947-017-0(6) , 06320) School Zone Publishing Co.

School Zone Staff, ed. Third Grade Scholar. 2005. (Illus.). 128p. (J). (gr. k-3). pap. 7.99 (978-1-58947-015-6(X) , 02466) School Zone Publishing Co.

Schwartz, Sara Jo & Irvin, Barbara Bando. Second Grade Scholar: Grade 2. Speir, Nancy, illus. rev. ed. 2002. (Super-Deluxe Wkbks.). 128p. (J). (gr. k-2). pap. 7.99 (978-1-58947-012-5(5) , 02463) School Zone Publishing Co.

Scott, James. The Odyssey: Student Response Journal. 2002. 32p. (YA). (gr. 8-12). 19.95 (978-1-58049-945-3(7)) Prestwick Hse., Inc.

Sheffield, Sarah. A Train on the Track: Learning the TR Sound. 2002. (PowerPhonics Ser.). (Illus.). 24p. (J). (gr. 1). lib. bdg. 18.50 (978-0-8239-5937-2(6) , PowerKids Pr.) Rosen Publishing Group, Inc., The.

—When Leaves Turn: Learning the UR Sound. 2002. (PowerPhonics Ser.). (Illus.). (J). 23p. lib. bdg. (978-0-8239-8285-1(8)); 24p. (gr. 1). lib. bdg. 18.50 (978-0-8239-5940-2(6)) Rosen Publishing Group, Inc., The. (PowerKids Pr.).

Soars, Liz. American Headway. 2003. (American Headway Ser.). (Illus.). Bk. 3. 158p. stu. ed. 9.25 (978-0-19-437938-0(8)); Bk. B. 109p. stu. ed. 9.25 (978-0-19-437939-7(6)) Oxford Univ. Pr., Inc.

Steck-Vaughn Staff. Classroom Library: Levels H-J. 2003. pap., stu. ed. (978-0-7398-7960-3(X)) Steck-Vaughn.

—Classroom Library: Levels J-M. 2003. pap., stu. ed. (978-0-7398-7963-4(4)) Steck-Vaughn.

—Map Comm Arts A: 10 Pack with Key Soaring Scores. 2002. pap. (978-0-7398-5636-9(7)) Steck-Vaughn.

—Map Comm Arts B: 10 Pack with Key Soaring Scores. 2002. pap. (978-0-7398-5637-6(5)) Steck-Vaughn.

—Map Comm Arts D: 10 Pack with Key Soaring Scores. 2002. pap. (978-0-7398-5639-0(1)) Steck-Vaughn.

—Map Comm Arts E: 10 Pack with Key Soaring Scores. 2002. pap. (978-0-7398-5640-6(5)) Steck-Vaughn.

—Map Comm Arts E: Answer Key Soaring Scores. 2002. pap. (978-0-7398-5629-1(4)) Steck-Vaughn.

—Map Comm Arts F: 10 Pack with Key Soaring Scores. 2002. pap. (978-0-7398-5641-3(3)) Steck-Vaughn.

—Map Comm Arts F: Answer Key Soaring Scores. 2002. pap. (978-0-7398-5631-4(6)) Steck-Vaughn.

—Map Comm Arts H: 10 Pack with Key Scoring Scores. 2002. pap. (978-0-7398-5643-7(X)) Steck-Vaughn.

—Map Comm Arts H: Answer Key Soaring Scores. 2002. pap. (978-0-7398-5635-2(9)) Steck-Vaughn.

—Map Comm Arts H: Soaring Scores. 2002. pap. (978-0-7398-5634-5(0)) Steck-Vaughn.

—Map Commerical Arts A: Answer Key: Soaring Scores. 2002. pap. (978-0-7398-5621-5(9)) Steck-Vaughn.

—Map Commerical Arts A: Soaring Scores. 2002. pap. (978-0-7398-5620-8(0)) Steck-Vaughn.

—Map Commerical Arts B: Answer Key: Soaring Scores. 2002. pap. (978-0-7398-5623-9(5)) Steck-Vaughn.

—Map Commerical Arts B: Soaring Scores. 2002. pap. (978-0-7398-5622-2(7)) Steck-Vaughn.

—Map Commerical Arts D: Answer Key: Soaring Scores. 2002. pap. (978-0-7398-5627-7(8)) Steck-Vaughn.

—Map Commerical Arts D: Soaring Scores. 2002. pap. (978-0-7398-5626-0(X)) Steck-Vaughn.

—Map Commerical Arts E: Soaring Scores. 2002. pap. (978-0-7398-5628-4(6)) Steck-Vaughn.

—March New Product Package. 2003. (J). pap. (978-0-7398-7971-9(5)) Steck-Vaughn.

Tears of a Tiger: Teaching Unit. 2003. 88p. (YA). ring bd. (978-1-58049-429-8(3) , TU4293) Prestwick Hse., Inc.

Third Grade Workbook. 2002. (English Made Easy Ser.). 200p. (J). pap. 12.95 (978-0-7894-8585-4(0)) Dorling Kindersley Publishing, Inc.

Thomas, Maryann. I Jog Around: Learning the J Sound. (PowerPhonics Ser.). (Illus.). (J). 2002. 24p. (gr. 1). lib. bdg. 18.50 (978-0-8239-5932-7(5)); 2001. 23p. pap. 26.40 (978-0-8239-8277-6(7)) Rosen Publishing Group, Inc., The. (PowerKids Pr.).

—Summer at the Beach: Learning the EA Sound. 2002. (PowerPhonics Ser.). (Illus.). 24p. (J). (gr. 1). lib. bdg. 18.50 (978-0-8239-5950-1(3) , PowerKids Pr.) Rosen Publishing Group, Inc., The.

Vastola, Pam. Huge Animals: Learning the Long U Sound. (PowerPhonics Ser.). (Illus.). (J). 2002. 24p. (gr. 1). lib. bdg. 18.50 (978-0-8239-5931-0(7)); 2001. 23p. pap. 26.40 (978-0-8239-8276-9(9)) Rosen Publishing Group, Inc., The. (PowerKids Pr.).

—Rain: Learning the AI Sound. 2002. (PowerPhonics Ser.). (Illus.). 24p. (J). (gr. 1). lib. bdg. 18.50 (978-0-8239-5943-3(0) , PowerKids Pr.) Rosen Publishing Group, Inc., The.

Venolia, Jan. Kids Write Right! What You Need to Be a Writing Powerhouse. McMahon, Bob, illus. 2004. 156p. (YA). (gr. 6-8). 8.95 (978-1-58246-028-4(0) , Tricycle Pr.) Ten Speed Pr.

Williams, Laurie. Daily Language Review. 1998. (Daily Language Review Ser.). (Illus.). 112p. (J). (gr. 3). pap., tchr. ed. 14.95 (978-1-55799-657-2(1) , EMC 581); (gr. 4). pap., tchr. ed. 14.95 (978-1-55799-658-9(X) , EMC 582) Evan-Moor Educational Pubs.

Winter, Douglas O. Literacy Trails & Explorer 4.0. (J). 2001. spiral bd. 15000.00 incl. cd-rom (978-1-893586-02-4(2)); 1998. spiral bd. 12025.00 incl. cd-rom (978-1-893586-10-9(3)) OpenBook Learning, Inc.

Wood, Ira. Sharks: Learning the SH Sound. (PowerPhonics Ser.). (Illus.). (J). 2002. 24p. (gr. 1). lib. bdg. 18.50 (978-0-8239-5921-1(X)); 2001. 23p. pap. 26.40 (978-0-8239-8266-0(1)) Rosen Publishing Group, Inc., The. (PowerKids Pr.).

World Book, Inc. Staff. The Wonderful World of English. Date not set. (Illus.). 35p. (J). (gr. 1-5). (978-0-7166-5301-1(X) , 6164) World Bk., Inc.

ENGLISH LANGUAGE—SYNONYMS AND ANTONYMS

Ackroyd, Dorothea. What Do You Know? 1999. bds. 3.95 (978-1-58185-207-3(X)) Quadrillion Media LLC.

Agee, Jon. Who Ordered the Jumbo Shrimp? 2002. (gr. 3-6). lib. bdg. 17.60 (978-0-613-53880-0(3)) Tandem Library Bks.

American Heritage Dictionary Editors, ed. The American Heritage Essential Student Thesaurus. 2nd ed. 2003. 96p. (gr. 7). pap. 6.95 (978-0-618-28017-9(0)) Houghton Mifflin Co. Trade & Reference Div.

American Heritage Essential Student Thesaurus. 2003. (gr. 3-6). lib. bdg. 15.25 (978-0-613-66861-3(8)) Tandem Library Bks.

Antonyms. 2007. (J). 119.58 (***978-1-59928-713-3(7)*** , SandCastle) ABDO Publishing Co.

Beal, George. Kingfisher First Thesaurus. Chatterton, Martin, illus. rev. ed. 2004. (Kingfisher First Reference Ser.). 144p. (J). (gr. k-3). pap. 9.95 (978-0-7534-5808-2(X) , Kingfisher) Houghton Mifflin Co. Trade & Reference Div.

Beall, Pamela Conn & Nipp, Susan Hagen. Wee Sing & Learn Opposites. Moran, Michael, illus. 2007. (Wee Sing & Learn Ser.). 20p. (J). (ps-2). 9.99 (978-0-8431-2186-5(6) , Price Stern Sloan) Penguin Group (USA) Inc.

Bentley, Joyce. Soft. 2006. (Things Around Us Ser.). (J). (978-1-59389-278-4(0)) Chrysalis Education.

—Wet. 2006. (Things Around Us Ser.). (J). (978-1-59389-279-1(9)) Chrysalis Education.

Berenstain, Stan & Berenstain, Jan. The Berenstain Bears Big Bear Small Bear. 1998. (Berenstain Bears Ser.). (J). 10.79 (978-0-606-13953-3(2)) Tandem Library Bks.

Bollard, John. Scholastic Student Thesaurus. rev. ed. 2007. 208p. (J). pap. 16.99 (***978-0-439-02588-1(5)***) Scholastic, Inc.

Bollard, John K. Scholastic Children's Thesaurus. Reed, Mike, illus. (Scholastic Reference Ser.). (J). 1998. 256p. (gr. 4-8). pap. 15.95 (978-0-590-96785-3(1)); 2006. 240p. pap. 16.99 (978-0-439-79831-0(0)) Scholastic, Inc. (Scholastic Reference).

Brimner, Larry Dane. Quiet Wyatt. Fletcher, Rusty, illus. 2007. (Rookie Reader': Opposites Ser.). 32p. (J). pap. 4.95 (***978-0-531-17777-8(7)***); 19.50 (978-0-531-17543-9(X)) Scholastic Library Publishing. (Children's Pr.).

Brimner, Larry Dane. Slower Than a Slug. Zemke, Deborah, illus. 2007. (Rookie Reader Skill Set Ser.). 32p. (J). (gr. k-2). pap. 4.95 (***978-0-531-17776-1(9)***); 19.50 (978-0-531-17542-2(1)) Scholastic Library Publishing. (Children's Pr.).

Brown, Janet Allison. My First Book of Opposites. Endersby, Frank, illus. 2004. (Early Learning Ser.). 18p. (J). bds. 5.99 (978-1-85854-530-1(7)) Brimax Books Ltd. GBR. *Dist:* Byeway Bks.

Bullard, Lisa. Animal Opposites. 2005. (Illus.). (J). (gr. k-1). lib. bdg. 135.60 (978-0-7368-4409-3(0)) Capstone Pr., Inc.

Burg, Ann. Pirate Pickle & the White Balloon. Janovitz, Marilyn, illus. 2007. (Rookie Reader': Opposites Ser.). 32p. (J). pap. 4.95 (***978-0-531-17778-5(5)*** , Children's Pr.) Scholastic Library Publishing.

Burg, Ann E. Pirate Pickle & the White Balloon. Janovitz, Marilyn, illus. 2007. (Rookie Reader Skill Set Ser.). 32p. (J). (gr. k-2). 19.50 (***978-0-531-17544-6(8)*** , Children's Pr.) Scholastic Library Publishing.

Callella, Kim & Williams, Rozanne Lanczak. Build-a-SKill Instant Books Synonyms & Antonyms. Faulkner, Stacey, ed. Campbell, Jenny, illus. 2007. (J). 4.99 (***978-1-59198-419-1(X)***) Creative Teaching Pr., Inc.

Carle, Eric. Opposites. 2007. 16p. (J). 5.99 (978-0-448-44565-6(4) , Grosset & Dunlap) Penguin Group (USA) Inc.

Cleary, Brian P. Pitch & Throw, Grasp & Know: What Is a Synonym? Gable, Brian, illus. 2005. (Words Are CATegorical trade; Ser.). 32p. (J). (gr. 2-5). 15.95 (978-1-57505-796-5(4)) Lerner Publishing Group.

—Stop & Go, Yes & No: What Is an Antonym? Gable, Brian, illus. 2006. (Words Are CATegorical trade; Ser.). (J). 15.95 (978-1-57505-860-3(X) , Millbrook Pr.) Lerner Publishing Group.

Collin, Peter Hodgson, ed. Basic English Thesaurus: For Elementary & Pre-Intermediate Students. 2002. 280p. (J). pap. (978-1-901659-98-6(4) , T&AD Poyser) A & C Black.

Colores, Formas y Opuestos. 2007. (Sesame Street Ser.). (SPA & ENG., Illus.). 50p. (J). 2.95 (***978-1-59545-059-3(9)***) Learning Horizons, Inc.

Cox, Steve, illus. Barron's First Thesaurus. 2005. 128p. (J). pap. 12.95 (978-0-7641-3159-2(1)) Barron's Educational Series, Inc.

Crawford, Andy. Fun with Opposites. Crawford, Andy, photos by. (Illus.). (J). pap. 9.99 (978-0-590-24640-8(2)) Scholastic, Inc.

Dahl, Michael. If You Were a Synonym. Gray, Sara, illus. 2006. 24p. (J). (978-1-4048-2387-7(5)) Picture Window Bks.

Davis, Lee. The Lifesize Animal Opposites Book. (Illus.). 32p. (J). pap. 16.95 (978-0-590-24372-8(1)) Scholastic, Inc.

DeGrie, Eve. Opposites. Rose, Drew, illus. 2004. (Baby Looney Toons Ser.). 12p. (J). bds. 6.95 (978-0-8249-6559-4(0)) Ideals Pubns.

DK Publishing Staff. Opposites. 2005. 12p. (J). bds. 4.99 (978-0-7566-0990-0(9)) Dorling Kindersley Publishing, Inc.

Dobkin, Bonnie. Go-With Words. Payne, Tom, illus. rev. ed. 2000. (Rookie Reader Skill Set Ser.). (J). (gr. k-2). pap. 4.95 (978-0-516-27048-7(6)); (gr. 1-2). 19.50 (978-0-516-22031-4(4)) Scholastic Library Publishing. (Children's Pr.).

Dorling Kindersley Publishing Staff. DK Dictionary Thesaurus: Over 100,000 Definitions & Synonyms. 1999. (Illus.). (978-0-606-20632-7(9)) Tandem Library Bks.

—My First Opposites. 2nd ed. 2006. (Illus.). 36p. (J). (ps-3). bds. 5.99 (978-0-7566-0503-2(2)) Dorling Kindersley Publishing, Inc.

Doudna, Kelly. Big & Small. l.t. ed. 2000. (Opposites Ser.). (Illus.). 24p. (J). (ps-3). lib. bdg. 19.93 (978-1-57765-144-4(8) , SandCastle) ABDO Publishing Co.

—Light & Dark. l.t. ed. 2000. (Opposites Ser.). (Illus.). 24p. (J). (ps-3). lib. bdg. 19.93 (978-1-57765-145-1(6) , SandCastle) ABDO Publishing Co.

—Long & Short. l.t. ed. 2000. (Opposites Ser.). (Illus.). 24p. (J). (ps-3). lib. bdg. 19.93 (978-1-57765-146-8(4) , SandCastle) ABDO Publishing Co.

—Near & Far. l.t. ed. 2000. (Opposites Ser.). (Illus.). 24p. (J). (ps-3). lib. bdg. 19.93 (978-1-57765-147-5(2) , SandCastle) ABDO Publishing Co.

—New & Old. l.t. ed. 2000. (Opposites Ser.). (Illus.). 24p. (J). (ps-3). lib. bdg. 19.93 (978-1-57765-148-2(0) , SandCastle) ABDO Publishing Co.

—Opposites, Set. l.t. ed. Incl. Big & Small. lib. bdg. 19.93 (978-1-57765-144-4(8)); Light & Dark. lib. bdg. 19.93 (978-1-57765-145-1(6)); Long & Short. lib. bdg. 19.93 (978-1-57765-146-8(4)); Near & Far. lib. bdg. 19.93 (978-1-57765-147-5(2)); New & Old. lib. bdg. 19.93 (978-1-57765-148-2(0)); Wet & Dry. lib. bdg. 19.93 (978-1-57765-149-9(9)); (J). (ps-3). 2000. (Illus.). 24p. 2000. Set lib. bdg. 119.58 (978-1-57765-282-3(7) , SandCastle) ABDO Publishing Co.

—Wet & Dry. l.t. ed. 2000. (Opposites Ser.). (Illus.). 24p. (J). (ps-3). lib. bdg. 19.93 (978-1-57765-149-9(9) , SandCastle) ABDO Publishing Co.

Douglas, Vincent & School Specialty Publishing Staff. The AEP Children's Thesaurus. 2002. (Wordsmyth Reference Ser.). (Illus.). 320p. (J). (gr. 3 up). 19.95 (978-1-57768-296-7(3)) School Specialty Publishing.

Eck, Kristin. Opposites in My House. 2004. (Look-And-Learn Books). (Illus.). (J). lib. bdg. 7.95 (978-1-4042-2700-2(8) , PowerKids Pr.) Rosen Publishing Group, Inc., The.

Falk, Laine. Let's Talk about Opposites, Morning to Night. 2007. (Let's Find Out Early Learning Bks.). (Illus.). 24p. (J). (ps-k). 18.00 (978-0-531-14872-3(6) , Children's Pr.) Scholastic Library Publishing.

Feldman, Thea. My Magnetic Opposites: Big & Little: Best Friends. 2007. 8p. bds. 9.95 (*978-1-932915-39-6(7)*) Sandvik Innovations, LLC.

The Five Senses/Opposites & Position Words, 4 bks., Set. Incl. Let's Explore the Five Senses with City Dog & Country Dog. Falk, Laine. 18.00 (978-0-531-14873-0(4)); Let's Find Rain Forest Animals : Up, down, Around. Behrens, Janice. 18.00 (*978-0-531-14874-7(2));* Let's Play a Five Senses Guessing Game. Miller, Amanda. 18.00 (978-0-531-14871-6(8)); Let's Talk about Opposites, Morning to Night. Falk, Laine. 18.00 (978-0-531-14872-3(6)); (Illus.). 24p. (J). (ps-k). (Let's Find Out Early Learning Bks.). 2007. 72.00 (*978-0-531-17574-3(X)* , Children's Pr.) Scholastic Library Publishing.

Freymann, Saxton, illus. Food for Thought: The Complete Book of Concepts for Growing Minds. 2005. 61p. (J). lib. bdg. (978-1-4155-7707-3(2) , Levine, Arthur A. Bks.) Scholastic, Inc.

Fun with Antonyms - Crossword Puzzles & Word Searches. 2004. pap. 7.99 (978-1-4206-3146-3(2)) Teacher Created Materials, Inc.

Fun with Synonyms - Crossword Puzzles & Word Searches. 2004. pap. 7.99 (978-1-4206-3145-6(4)) Teacher Created Materials, Inc.

Furgang, Kathy. Building Bridges. 2004. (Navigators Ser.). (J). pap. 38.00 (978-1-4108-0404-4(6)) Benchmark Education Co.

Gerver, Jane E. Little Sister, Big Mess! Dieterichs, Shelley, illus. 2007. (Rookie Reader': Opposites Ser.). 32p. (J). pap. 4.95 (*978-0-531-17779-2(3));* 19.50 (*978-0-531-17545-3(6))* Scholastic Library Publishing. (Children's Pr.).

Gordon, Bob & Holmen, Lene. Lift & Learn Opposites. Snaith, Andy, photos by. 2006. (Illus.). 24p. (ps-ps). per., bds. 5.95 (978-1-84610-031-4(3)) Make Believe Ideas GBR. *Dist:* Ingram Pub. Services.

Gordon, Sharon. Dirty Clean (Sucio Limpio) 2006. (Bookworms Ser.). (SPA & ENG., Illus.). 24p. (J). lib. bdg. 22.79 (978-0-7614-2446-8(6)) Cavendish, Marshall Corp.

—Duro Blando. 2006. (Bookworms Ser.). (SPA & ENG., Illus.). 24p. (J). lib. bdg. 22.79 (978-0-7614-2368-3(0)) Cavendish, Marshall Corp.

—Fast Slow (Rapido Lento) 2006. (Bookworms Ser.). (ENG & SPA., Illus.). 24p. (J). lib. bdg. 22.79 (978-0-7614-2447-5(4)) Cavendish, Marshall Corp.

—Hard Soft (Duro Blando) 2006. (Bookworms Ser.). (ENG & SPA., Illus.). 24p. (J). lib. bdg. 22.79 (978-0-7614-2448-2(2)) Cavendish, Marshall Corp.

—Mojado Seco. 2006. (Bookworms Ser.). (SPA & ENG., Illus.). 24p. (J). lib. bdg. 22.79 (978-0-7614-2370-6(2)) Cavendish, Marshall Corp.

—Rapido Lento. 2006. (Bookworms Ser.). (SPA & ENG., Illus.). 24p. (J). lib. bdg. 22.79 (978-0-7614-2367-6(2)) Cavendish, Marshall Corp.

—Wet Dry (Mojado Seco) 2006. (Bookworms Ser.). (ENG & SPA., Illus.). 24p. (J). lib. bdg. 22.79 (978-0-7614-2450-5(4)) Cavendish, Marshall Corp.

Gould, Vera Dobson & Hughes, Patricia J. The Dominie Thesaurus for Young Writers. 2003. 393p. (J). 18.95 (978-0-7685-2298-3(6)) Dominie Pr., Inc.

Group/McGraw-Hill, Wright. Opposites: Collection 4. (Storyteller Interactive Writing Cards Ser.). (gr. k-3). (978-0-322-09326-3(0)) Wright Group, The.

Gunzi, Christiane. My Very First Look at Opposites. 2007. (My Very First Look at Ser.). 22p. (J). (ps). bds. 6.95 (978-1-58728-591-2(6) , Two Can Publishing) T&N Children's Publishing.

—Opposites. (My Very First Look at Ser.). (SPA., Illus.). 24p. (ps-k). 2004. (J). pap. 5.95 (978-1-58728-683-4(1)); 2003. 9.95 (978-1-58728-669-8(6)) T&N Children's Publishing. (Two Can Publishing).

Hall, Kirsten. Oops! All about Opposites. Luedecke, Bev, illus. 2003. (Beastieville Ser.). 32p. (J). 19.50 (978-0-516-22895-2(1) , Children's Pr.) Scholastic Library Publishing.

Heinrichs, Ann. Synonyms & Antonyms. 2005. (Magic of Language Ser.). (Illus.). 32p. (J). (gr. 1-5). 27.07 (978-1-59296-430-7(3)) Child's World, Inc.

Hellweg, Paul. The American Heritage Children's Thesaurus. American Heritage Dictionary Editors, ed. 2006. 288p. (J). (gr. 4-6). 17.95 (978-0-618-70166-7(4)) Houghton Mifflin Co.

Hierlmaier Nelson, Christine M. Green Yellow Go! Nat Knows Bananas. Hierlmaier, Joy, illus. 2004. 26p. (J). spiral bd. 14.95 (978-0-9759362-0-7(4)) Expressive Ink.

Hills, Tad. What's up Duck? Hills, Tad, illus. 2008. (Illus.). 22p. (J). bds. (*978-0-375-84738-7(3)* , Schwartz & Wade Bks.) Random Hse. Children's Bks.

Hine, Eileen, illus. Desert Opposites. 2005. 12p. (J). bds. 5.95 (978-0-87358-890-4(8) , Rising Moon Bks. for Young Readers) Northland Publishing.

Holland, Gini. Alive & Not Alive: Vivo y No Vivo. 2007. (SPA & ENG.). (J). pap. (*978-0-8368-8308-4(X)* , Weekly Reader Early Learning Library) Stevens, Gareth Inc.

—Alive & Not Alive/Vivo y No Vivo. 2007. (I Know Opposites/Conceptos Contrarios Ser.). (SPA & ENG.). 24p. (J). (gr. k-2). lib. bdg. 17.27 (*978-0-8368-8303-9(9)* , Weekly Reader Early Learning Library) Stevens, Gareth Inc.

—Hot & Cold: Caliente y Frío. 2007. (SPA & ENG.). (J). pap. (*978-0-8368-8309-1(8)* , Weekly Reader Early Learning Library) Stevens, Gareth Inc.

—Hot & Cold/Caliente y Frio. 2007. (I Know Opposites/ Conceptos Contrarios Ser.). (SPA & ENG.). 24p. (J). (gr. k-2). lib. bdg. 17.27 (*978-0-8368-8304-6(7)* , Weekly Reader Early Learning Library) Stevens, Gareth Inc.

Hunt, Laura. Disney's Winnie the Pooh's Opposites: Opposites Learn & Grow Board Book. 1999. (Disney's Winnie the Pooh Ser.). (Illus.). 20p. (J). (ps-3). bds. 4.99 (978-0-7364-0034-3(6) , RH/Disney) Random Hse. Children's Bks.

Innovative Kids Staff. Big & Little. Filipowich, Bob, illus. 2000. (Soft Shapes Ser.). 8p. (J). (ps-ps). 8.99 (978-1-58476-021-4(4)) Innovative Kids.

Jackaman, Philippa. Fun to Learn Opposites: Kaleidoscope Book. Daniel, Carol, illus. 16p. (J). (978-1-84322-125-8(X)) Bookmart Ltd.

Jim Henson Staff. Bear Loves Opposites! 2000. (Illus.). 20p. (J). (gr. k-3). pap. 4.99 (978-0-671-77447-9(6) , Simon & Schuster Children's Publishing) Simon & Schuster Children's Publishing.

Kannas, C. Larousse Dictionnaire Mini Debutants. 2000. Tr. of Larousse Mini Beginners Dictionary. (FRE., Illus.). 512p. (J). 29.95 (978-2-03-532168-8(9)) Librairie Larousse FRA. *Dist:* Continental Bk. Co., Inc., Distribooks, Inc.

Kingfisher Editors, ed. Kingfisher Illustrated Pocket Thesaurus. 2007. 160p. (J). (gr. 5-9). pap. 10.95 (978-0-7534-6117-4(X) , Kingfisher) Houghton Mifflin Co. Trade & Reference Div.

Kirk, Bev. Which Way? 2005. (Illus.). (J). lib. bdg. (*978-0-9768706-2-3(2))* Learning Props.

Kompelien, Tracy. The Castle Is Cold, Ancient & Old! 2007. (Synonyms Ser.). (Illus.). 24p. (J). (gr. 2-5). lib. bdg. 19.93 (*978-1-59928-728-7(5)* , SandCastle) ABDO Publishing Co.

—Ella Is Right, Smart & Bright! 2007. (Synonyms Ser.). (Illus.). 24p. (J). (gr. 2-5). lib. bdg. 19.93 (*978-1-59928-729-4(3)* , SandCastle) ABDO Publishing Co.

—The Pickle Is Dilly, Cool & Chilly! 2007. (Illus.). 24p. (J). 19.93 (*978-1-59928-730-0(7))* ABDO Publishing Co.

—Why Are You Sad & Blue? 2007. (Synonyms Ser.). (Illus.). 24p. (J). (gr. 2-5). lib. bdg. 19.93 (*978-1-59928-731-7(5)* , SandCastle) ABDO Publishing Co.

—Why Is Today Cloudy & Gray? 2007. (Sandcastle 3 Ser.). (Illus.). 23p. (J). (gr. k-3). lib. bdg. 19.93 (*978-1-59928-732-4(3)* , SandCastle) ABDO Publishing Co.

—Yell & Scream for Your Team! 2007. (Illus.). 24p. (J). 19.93 (*978-1-59928-733-1(1))* ABDO Publishing Co.

Krulik, Nancy E., et al. Opposites Everywhere. 2004. (Illus.). 20p. (J). pap. 12.95 (978-0-7624-2152-7(5) , Running Pr. Kids) Running Pr. Bk. Pubs.

Land of Opposites. (Illus.). 12p. (J). bds. (978-2-7643-0125-8(1)) Phidal Publishing, Inc./Editions Phidal, Inc.

Larousse Mexico Staff. Larousse Sinonimos y Antonimos (Larousse Synonyms & Antonyms) 1999. (SPA.). (J). pap. (978-970-607-127-9(X)) Larousse.

LD COACH. TEH Learns to Read: Opposites, Volume Four. 2004. (Illus.). 40p. (J). 34.95 (978-0-9745938-4-5(2)) LD Coach, LLC.

Lluch, Alex A. I Like to Learn: Alphabet, Numbers, Colors, & Opposites. 2008. 19.95 (*978-1-887169-95-0(4))* Wedding Solutions Publishing, Inc.

Loewen, Nancy. If You Were an Antonym. Gray, Sara, illus. 2006. 24p. (J). (*978-1-4048-2384-6(0))* Picture Window Bks.

Mara, Wil. The Frog in the Pond. Mendenhall, Cheryl, illus. 2007. (Rookie Reader Skill Set Ser.). 32p. (J). (gr. k-2). pap. 4.95 (*978-0-531-17775-4(0));* 19.50 (*978-0-531-17541-5(3))* Scholastic Library Publishing. (Children's Pr.).

Marshall, George W. The Kingfisher Children's Illustrated Dictionary & Thesaurus. 2003. (Illus.). 320p. (J). (gr. 2-5). tchr. ed. 12.95 (978-0-7534-5653-8(2) , Kingfisher) Houghton Mifflin Co. Trade & Reference Div.

McLaughlin, Patrick & MacLeod, Iseaball. In Other Words Exercises. 1999. (Illus.). 40p. (J). (gr. 3-7). 45.00 (978-0-7217-0722-8(X)) Schofield & Sims Ltd. GBR. *Dist:* State Mutual Bk. & Periodical Service, Ltd.

McMahon, Kara. Opposites. 2004. (Elmo's World Ser.). (Illus.). 22p. (J). (gr. k-ps). bds. 6.99 (978-0-375-82716-7(1) , Random Hse. Bks. for Young Readers) Random Hse. Children's Bks.

Meister, Cari. Catch That Cat! Brooks, David J., illus. 2000. (Rookie Reader Espanol Ser.). 24p. (J). (gr. k-2). pap. 4.95 (978-0-516-26541-4(5) , Children's Pr.) Scholastic Library Publishing.

—Catch That Cat! 2000. lib. bdg. 12.95 (978-0-613-51443-9(2)) Tandem Library Bks.

—Detenlo a Ese Gato! Brooks, David J., illus. 2000. (Rookie Espanol Ser.). (SPA.). 24p. (J). (gr. k-2). 19.50 (978-0-516-21689-8(9) , CP1137, Children's Pr.) Scholastic Library Publishing.

Milne, Barbara L. W. Opposites Are Fun. Munoz, Olga M., illus. l.t. ed. 2005. 40p. (J). 19.95 (978-0-9708796-0-8(1) , TLConcepts, Inc.) Tender Learning Concepts.

Mitter, Matt. Same & Different. 2000. (Talking Pages Deluxe Ser.). (Illus.). (J). (ps-3). 12.95 (978-1-58224-132-6(5)) Futech Interactive Products, Inc.

Murphy. The Greatest Gymnast of All: Opposites Big Book. 2002. (Illus.). pap. (978-0-7398-6780-8(6)) Steck-Vaughn.

—Opposites. 1998. (J). 4.99 (978-0-87628-980-8(4)) Ctr. for Applied Research in Education, The.

Murphy, Chuck. Chuck Murphy's Black Cat, White Cat: A Pop-Up Book of Opposites. 2000. (Illus.). 12p. (J). (gr. k-3). per. (978-0-689-83507-0(8) , Simon & Schuster Children's Publishing) Simon & Schuster Children's Publishing.

Murphy, Stuart J. The Greatest Gymnast of All. Jabar, Cynthia, illus. 1998. (MathStart Ser.). 40p. (J). (ps up). 15.95 (978-0-06-027608-9(8)); 15.89 (978-0-06-027609-6(6)) HarperCollins Pubs.

Novick, Mary. Opposites. Harlin, Sybel, illus. 2002. (Double Delight Ser.). 24p. (J). (ps). 9.95 (978-1-57145-781-3(X) , Silver Dolphin Bks.) Advantage Pubs. Group.

Opposites, 11 vols., Set. 2004. (Beastieville Ser.). 142.80 (978-0-516-25138-7(4) , Children's Pr.) Scholastic Library Publishing.

Opposites. 2004. (Early Days Ser.). (Illus.). 18p. (J). bds. (978-1-84229-974-6(3)) Top That! Publishing PLC.

Opposites. 2003. 16p. (J). 3.79 (978-1-58792-053-0(0)) Trend Enterprises, Inc.

Opposites & Visual Skills. 2003. (Right Start for Early Learners Ser.). (Illus.). 48p. (J). (ps-1). pap. 7.99 (978-0-7439-3229-5(3)) Teacher Created Materials, Inc.

Paré, Roger. Les Contraires. ed. 2004. (J). (ps-2). spiral bd. (978-0-616-01847-7(9)) Canadian National Institute for the Blind/Institut National Canadien pour les Aveugles.

—Opposites. Paré, Roger, illus. 2001. (Smart Start Ser.). (Illus.). 24p. (J). (ps up). lib. bdg. 22.00 (978-0-8368-2846-7(1)) Stevens, Gareth Inc.

Parker, Ant. Opposites. 1999. (Touch & Feel Ser.). (Illus.). 12p. (J). (ps). pap. 4.95 (978-0-7373-0294-3(1) , 02941W, Roxbury Park) Lowell Hse.

Pelham, David. Applebee's Opposites: A Cat & Mouse. 2005. (Illus.). 16p. (J). (ps-3). 12.95 (978-0-7624-2552-5(0) , Running Pr. Kids) Running Pr. Bk. Pubs.

Pesiri, Evelyn. The Thesaurus for Kids. Bild, Linda, illus. 1998. 144p. (J). (gr. 3-7). pap. 8.95 (978-1-56565-694-9(6) , 06946W); (gr. 4-7). 12.95 (978-1-56565-693-2(8) , 06938W) Lowell Hse. Juvenile.

Pfister, Marcus. Rainbow Fish Opposites Mini Board Book. Pfister, Marcus, illus. 2005. (Illus.). 24p. (J). bds. 4.99 (978-0-7358-1982-5(3)) North-South Bks., Inc.

Phillips, Sarah & Wallace, Bruce. Flip Flaps Opposites. 2005. (Flip Flaps (Make Believe Ideas) Ser.). (Illus.). 12p. (ps-k). per., bds. 5.95 (978-1-905051-95-3(6)) Make Believe Ideas GBR. *Dist:* Ingram Pub. Services.

Pitch & Throw, Grasp & Know: What Is a Synonym? 2007. 32p. (J). (gr. 2-6). pap. 5.95 (*978-0-8225-6877-3(2)* , First Avenue Editions) Lerner Publishing Group.

Pittau, Francesco & Gervais, Bernadette. Elephant Elephant: A Book of Opposites. 2001. (Illus.). 80p. (J). (ps-k). 17.95 (978-0-8109-3699-7(2)) Abrams, Harry N. , Inc.

Potter, Tony & Kolanovic, Dubravka. Opposites with Albert & Amy: The Fun Way! Kolanovic, Dubravka, illus. 2005. (Illus.). 10p. (J). (gr. 2-5). bds. 5.95 (978-1-59125-568-0(6)) Penton Overseas, Inc.

Preller, James. NBA Book of Opposites. 2000. (978-0-606-18585-1(2)) Tandem Library Bks.

Rayevsky, Kim. Antonyms, Synonyms, Homonyms. Rayevsky, Robert, illus. 2006. 32p. (J). (ps-3). 16.95 (978-0-8234-1889-3(8)) Holiday Hse., Inc.

Realtime Associates and Mazer Corporation Staff & LeapFrog Staff, compiled by. Clarify Word Meanings. 2002. (J). (gr. 5). 66.75 (978-1-58605-507-3(0) , LeapFrog Schl. Hse.) LeapFrog Enterprises, Inc.

—Identify Synonyms & Antonyms. 2002. (J). (gr. 2). 66.75 (978-1-58605-308-6(6)); (gr. 3). 66.75 (978-1-58605-377-2(9)); (gr. 4). 66.75 (978-1-58605-436-6(8)); (gr. 5). 66.75 (978-1-58605-499-1(6)) LeapFrog Enterprises, Inc. (LeapFrog Schl. Hse.).

A Rookie Reader Skill Set: Opposites, 5 bks. Incl. Frog in the Pond. Mara, Wil. Mendenhall, Cheryl, illus. 19.50 (*978-0-531-17541-5(3));* Little Sister, Big Mess! Gerver, Jane E. Dieterichs, Shelley, illus. 19.50 (*978-0-531-17545-3(6));* Pirate Pickle & the White Balloon. Burg, Ann E. Janovitz, Marilyn, illus. 19.50 (*978-0-531-17544-6(8));* Quiet Wyatt. Brimner, Larry Dane. Fletcher, Rusty, illus. 19.50 (978-0-531-17543-9(X)); Slower Than a Slug. Brimner, Larry Dane. Zemke, Deborah, illus. 19.50 (978-0-531-17542-2(1)); 32p. (J). (gr. k-2). 2007. 2007. 97.50 (*978-0-531-17735-8(1)* , Children's Pr.) Scholastic Library Publishing.

Salzmann, Mary Elizabeth. Can a Giraffe Cry or Laugh? 2007. (Illus.). 24p. (J). 19.93 (*978-1-59928-714-0(5))* ABDO Publishing Co.

—Can You Go Fast or Slow? 2007. (Illus.). 24p. (J). 19.93 (*978-1-59928-715-7(3))* ABDO Publishing Co.

—Did I Hear a Hello from above or Below? 2007. (Illus.). 24p. (J). 19.93 (*978-1-59928-716-4(1))* ABDO Publishing Co.

—Does It Fly Away in the Night or Day? 2007. (Illus.). 24p. (J). 19.93 (*978-1-59928-717-1(X))* ABDO Publishing Co.

—Is It a Day for Work or Play? 2007. (Illus.). 24p. (J). 19.93 (*978-1-59928-718-8(8))* ABDO Publishing Co.

—Is the Treat Sour or Sweet? 2007. (Illus.). 24p. (J). 19.93 (*978-1-59928-719-5(6))* ABDO Publishing Co.

Scholastic Dictionary of Synonyms, Antonyms, & Homonyms. 2001. (gr. 5-8). lib. bdg. 12.95 (978-0-613-35745-6(0)) Tandem Library Bks.

School Specialty Publishing. Flip-Flash Phonics: Opposites. 2002. (Flip-Flashtm Phonics Ser.). 160p. (J). (gr. 1 up). pap. 7.99 (978-1-56451-394-6(7) , ID2429) School Specialty Publishing.

—Flip-Flash Phonics: Synonyms. 2002. (Flip-Flashtm Phonics Ser.). 160p. (J). (gr. 1 up). pap. 7.99 (978-1-56451-393-9(9) , ID2428) School Specialty Publishing.

—Opposites. 2004. (On-File Ser.). 4p. (J). (gr. k-k). ring bd. 4.99 (978-0-7424-2878-2(8) , Instructional Fair) Schaffer, Frank Pubns.

Seeger, Laura Vaccaro. Black? White! Day? Night! A Book of Opposites. 2006. (Illus.). 24p. (J). (ps-2). 16.95 (978-1-59643-185-0(7)) Roaring Brook Pr.

Sesame's: A Giant Coloring Book that Teaches about Opposites. 2006. (J). 6.99 (978-1-59949-497-5(3)) Food Marketing Consultants, Inc.

Shapes & Opposites: Fun to Learn. 1999. (Illus.). 32p. (ps-2). 1.99 (978-1-58279-010-7(8) , 96) Trident Pr. International.

Simon & Schuster. Simon & Schuster Thesaurus for Children: Non Returnable. 2005. 912p. (J). 16.95 (978-0-689-04989-7(7)) Simon & Schuster Children's Publishing.

—Simon & Schuster Thesaurus for Children: The Ultimate Student Thesaurus. 2005. 272p. (J). 9.95 (978-0-689-86657-9(7)) Simon & Schuster Children's Publishing.

Simon and Schuster Staff. Simon & Schuster Thesaurus for Children: The Ultimate Student Thesaurus. Latimer, Jonathan P. & Nolting, Karen Stray, eds. 2001. 296p. (J). (gr. 4-11). 16.95 (978-0-689-84322-8(4)) Simon & Schuster Children's Publishing.

SpongeBob Opposites. 2007. (J). 2.95 (*978-1-59545-103-3(X))* Learning Horizons, Inc.

Swinburne, Stephen R. What's Opposite? 2000. (J). (978-0-606-20105-6(X)); lib. bdg. 17.60 (978-0-613-46115-3(0)) Tandem Library Bks.

Synonyms. 2007. (J). 119.58 (*978-1-59928-727-0(7)* , SandCastle) ABDO Publishing Co.

Synonyms & Antonyms. (Modified Basic Skills Ser.). 48p. (gr. k-4). 5.99 (978-0-7424-1937-7(1) , LL90010) School Specialty Publishing.

Synonyms, Antonyms, & Homonyms (Gr. 2-3) 2003. (J). (978-1-58232-124-0(8)) Bryan Hse. Pubs., Inc.

Synonyms, Antonyms, & Homonyms (Gr. 4-5) 2004. (J). (978-1-58232-138-7(8)) Bryan Hse. Pubs., Inc.

Tetro, Marc. Opposites. 2006. (Illus.). 6.99 (978-1-55278-503-4(3)) McArthur & Co. CAN. *Dist:* National Bk. Network.

Thomson, Ruth. A First Thesaurus. 2002. (Adventures in Literacy Ser.). (Illus.). 64p. (J). lib. bdg. 28.50 (978-1-931983-08-2(9)) Chrysalis Education.

Traditional Catholic Speller. (J). (gr. 1). wbk. ed. 12.00 (978-1-931555-33-3(8)); (J). (gr. 2). wbk. ed. 12.00 (978-1-931555-34-0(6)); (J). (gr. 3). wbk. ed. 12.00 (978-1-931555-35-7(4)); (J). (gr. 4). wbk. ed. 12.00 (978-1-931555-36-4(2)); (J). (gr. 5). wbk. ed. 12.00 (978-1-931555-37-1(0)); (J). (gr. 6). wbk. ed. 12.00 (978-1-931555-38-8(9)); (YA). (gr. 7). wbk. ed. 12.00 (978-1-931555-39-5(7)); (YA). (gr. 8). wbk. ed. 12.00 (978-1-931555-40-1(0)) Our Lady of Victory Schl.

Tullet, Herve. Yellow & Round. 2002. (Illus.). 24p. (J). 7.99 (978-1-84059-344-0(X)) Milet Publishing.

Turrell, Linda. Synonyms, Antonyms, & Homonyms Student Activities Book: Mastering Language Arts Series. Matthews, Douglas L., ed. 2003. (Illus.). stu. ed., wbk. ed. (978-1-931680-81-3(7) , Expert Systems for Teachers) Teaching Point, Inc.

Vischer, Phil. Archibald's Opposites: A Veggiecational Book about Opposites! (Veggiecational Ser.). (Illus.). (J). (ps-3). 1999. 12p. 8.99 (978-0-8499-5987-5(X)); 1998. 32p. 8.99 (978-0-8499-1533-8(3)) Nelson, Thomas Inc.

Watt, Melanie. Opposites. 2005. (Learning with Animals Board Bks.). (Illus.). 24p. (J). (gr. k up). (978-1-55337-832-7(6)) Kids Can Pr., Ltd.

Webster's Dictionary & Thesaurus for Students with Full-Color World Atlas. 2006. (Illus.). 880p. pap. 9.98 (978-1-59695-017-7(X)) Federal Street Pr.

Webster's New World Staff. Websters New World College Dictionary: Webster's New World Roget's A-Z Thesaurus, 2 vols. 4th ed. 1999. (Illus.). (J). 39.95 (978-0-02-863559-0(0)) Wiley, John & Sons, Inc.

Webster's Thesaurus for Students. 2003. (gr. 3-6). lib. bdg. 10.10 (978-0-613-68551-1(2)) Tandem Library Bks.

Wen, Dref. Fy Llyfr Geiriau Croes Cyntaf. 2005. Tr. of My First Opposites. (WEL., Illus.). 32p. bds. (978-1-85596-671-0(9)) Dref Wen.

Wilbur, Richard. Opposites, More Opposites & a Few Differences. 2000. (978-0-606-18186-0(5)) Tandem Library Bks.

Wittels, Harriet & Greisman, Joan. A First Thesaurus. Block, Alex, illus. 2001. 128p. (J). (gr. 3-7). pap. 8.99 (978-0-307-15835-2(7) , Golden Bks.) Random Hse. Children's Bks.

Yates, Gene. The Dragon Opposites Book. 2005. (Illus.). 14p. (J). (*978-1-58865-283-6(1))* Kidsbooks, Inc.

Yee, T. Island Opposites. 2002. pap. 3.99 (978-0-89610-465-5(6)) Island Heritage Publishing.

Yoon, Jung-Huyn. Popposites: A Lift, Pull, & Pop Book of Opposites. (Illus.). 14p. (J). pap. 16.99 (978-0-590-24937-9(1)) Scholastic, Inc.

Yoon, Salina, illus. Foil Fun Opposites. 2000. (Foil Fun Board Bks.). 10p. (J). (ps). bds. 4.95 (978-1-58117-063-4(7) , Intervisual/Piggy Toes) Dalmatian Pr.

ENGLISH LANGUAGE—TERMS AND PHRASES

Cleary, Brian P. I & You & Don't Forget Who: What Is a Pronoun? Gable, Brian, illus. 2004. (Words Are Categorical Ser.). 32p. (J). (gr. 2-5). 15.95 (978-1-57505-596-1(1)) Lerner Publishing Group.

Heinrichs, Ann. Similes & Metaphors. 2005. (Magic of Language Ser.). (Illus.). 32p. (J). (gr. 1-5). 27.07 (978-1-59296-434-5(6)) Child's World, Inc.

E
F
G

Juster, Norton. As Silly as Knees, as Busy as Bees: An Astounding Assortment of Similes. Small, David, illus. 1998. 80p. (J). (gr. 3 up). pap. 4.95 (978-0-688-16360-0(2)) HarperCollins Pubs.

Leedy, Loreen & Street, Pat. There's a Frog in My Throat: 440 Animal Sayings a Little Bird Told Me. Leedy, Loreen, illus. 2003. (Ala Notable Book Ser.). (Illus.). 48p. (J). (gr. k-3). reprint ed. pap. 6.95 (978-0-8234-1819-0(7)) Holiday Hse., Inc.

—There's a Frog in My Throat: 440 Animal Sayings from the Horse's Mouth. 2002. (Illus.). 56p. (J). 18.95 (978-1-890817-24-4(4)) Winslow Pr.

Realtime Associates and Mazer Corporation Staff & LeapFrog Staff, compiled by. Derive Word & Phrase Meaning. 2002. (J). (gr. 4). 66.75 (978-1-58605-419-9(8) , LeapFrog Schl. Hse.) LeapFrog Enterprises, Inc.

Tabor, Nancy Maria Grande. Ve Lo Que Dices. 2000. Tr. of See What You Say. (978-0-606-18031-3(1)) Tandem Library Bks.

Terban, Marvin. In a Pickle: And Other Funny Idioms. Maestro, Giulio, illus. 2007. 64p. (J). (gr. k-3). pap. 6.95 (***978-0-618-83001-5(4)** , Clarion Bks.) Houghton Mifflin Co. Trade & Reference Div.

—Mad as a Wet Hen! And Other Funny Idioms. Maestro, Giulio, illus. 2007. 64p. (J). (gr. k-3). pap. 6.95 (***978-0-618-83003-9(0)** , Clarion Bks.) Houghton Mifflin Co. Trade & Reference Div.

Your Baby Can Learn! Patterns, Vol. 1. 2007. (J). 7.95 (***978-1-931026-15-4(7))** Infant Learning Co., The.

Your Baby Can Learn! Prepositions, Vol. 1. 2007. (J). 7.95 (***978-1-931026-16-1(5))** Infant Learning Co., The.

ENGLISH LANGUAGE—TEXTBOOKS FOR FOREIGN SPEAKERS

Arengo, Sue. Beauty & the Beast. Pound, Clare, illus. 2001. 18p. (J). act. bk. ed. 2.95 (978-0-19-422060-6(5)) Oxford Univ. Pr., Inc.

—Cinderella Activity Book. Kimber, Kevin, illus. 2001. 18p. (J). 2.95 (978-0-19-422067-5(2)) Oxford Univ. Pr., Inc.

—Classic Tales: Classic Tales Activity Books : The Shoemaker & the Elves. 2002. (Illus.). (J). 2.95 (978-0-19-422081-1(8)) Oxford Univ. Pr., Inc.

—Goldilocks & the Three Bears. 2001. (Illus.). (J). act. bk. ed. 2.95 (978-0-19-422064-4(8)) Oxford Univ. Pr., Inc.

Baker, Ann. Tree or Three? 2nd ed. 2006. (Illus.). 136p. pap., stu. ed. 31.00 incl. audio compact disk (978-0-521-68527-6(3)) Cambridge Univ. Pr.

—Tree or Three? An Elementary Pronunciation Course. 2nd rev. ed. 2006. (Illus.). 136p. pap. 18.00 (978-0-521-68526-9(5)) Cambridge Univ. Pr.

BBC Staff. English Pronunciation: Learning the Sounds of American English. unabr. ed. 128p. (YA). pap. 49.50 incl. audio (978-0-88432-674-8(8) , S32560) Norton, Jeffrey Pubs., Inc.

Big Books for ESL/ELD: Grade 1 Collection. (J). (gr. k-2). 270.93 (978-0-7362-2989-0(2)) Hampton-Brown Bks.

Big Books for ESL/ELD: Grade 2 Collection. (J). (gr. k-2). 270.93 (978-0-7362-2990-6(6)) Hampton-Brown Bks.

Big Books for ESL/ELD: Kindergarten Collection. (J). (gr. k-2). 317.99 (978-0-7362-2988-3(4)) Hampton-Brown Bks.

Bluedorn, Harvey. Handy English Encoder Decoder: All the Spelling & Phonics Rules You Could Ever Want to Know. 2nd ed. 2004. 104p. per. 9.00 (978-0-9743616-2-8(3)) Trivium Pursuit.

Bouchard, Margaret. Comprehension Strategies for English Language Learners: 30 Research-Based Reading Strategies That Help Students Read, Understand, & Really Learn Content from Their Textbooks & Other Nonfiction Materials. 2005. 128p. pap. 17.99 (978-0-439-55428-2(4) , Teaching Strategies) Scholastic, Inc.

Brennan, Frank. Three Tomorrows: Level 1 Beginner/Elementary. 2007. (Cambridge English Readers Ser.). (Illus.). 32p. pap. 6.00 (***978-0-521-69377-6(2))** Cambridge Univ. Pr.

—Three Tomorrows Book/Audio CD Pack: Level 1 Beginner/Elementary. 2007. (Cambridge English Readers Ser.). (Illus.). 32p. pap. 11.00 incl. audio compact disk (***978-0-521-69378-3(0))** Cambridge Univ. Pr.

Clayborn, Cynthia Cavazos. No Te Vayas ~ Please Dont Go. 2004. (Illus.). 16p. (J). 16.95 (978-1-932373-12-7(8)) Cedar Hill Publishing.

Cook, Betty Segal. Linking the ESL Student to the Mainstream. (Teaching English Through Total Physical Response Ser.). 58p. (YA). (gr. 3-12). pap. 14.50 (978-0-938395-39-3(4) , BSC5394) Segal, Berty Inc.

Cooper-Pete, Beverly. Tootie Fruity Bear's Sing-a-Long Tunes. 4th l.t. ed. 2001. Tr. of Para que cantes junto con el oso Tootie Fruity. (ENG & POL.). 32p. pap. (978-0-9714093-0-9(7)) Trey-Ish & Co.

Cummins & Chamot, Anna Uhl. Scott Foresman ESL Little Book - Kindergarten. 2nd ed. 2000. (J). Bk. 4. 24p. pap. 8.80 (978-0-13-027517-2(4)); Bk. 5. (Illus.). 24p. pap. 8.80 (978-0-13-027518-9(2)); Bk. 6. pap. 8.80 (978-0-13-027519-6(0)); Bk. 8. (Illus.). 24p. pap. 8.80 (978-0-13-027521-9(2)) Longman Publishing Group.

Cummins, et al. Scott Foresman ESL Grade 1. 2nd ed. 2000. (J). stu. ed. 24.93 (978-0-13-027486-1(0)) Longman Publishing Group.

Cummins, Jim P., et al. Scott Foresman ESL Grade 7. 2nd ed. 2000. (C). (gr. 7). pap., stu. ed. 30.00 (978-0-13-027499-1(2)) Longman Publishing Group.

Eichten, Philip. Two Words Together: A Picture Book of Line Drawings For Two-Word Phrases. Thornton, Andrew, illus. 2000. 32p. (J). (ps). spiral bd. 7.95 (978-0-9639415-3-4(4)) Pi Communication Materials, Inc.

English At Your Command! Beginning Level: Add-on Components. (J). (gr. k). 7.99 (978-0-7362-2910-4(8)) Hampton-Brown Bks.

English At Your Command! Beginning Level: Classroom Set. (J). (gr. k). 273.54 (978-0-7362-2986-9(8)) Hampton-Brown Bks.

English At Your Command! Primary Level: Add-on Components. (J). (gr. 1). 8.23 (978-0-7362-2913-5(2)) Hampton-Brown Bks.

English At Your Command! Primary Level: Classroom Set. (J). (gr. 1). 219.03 (978-0-7362-2987-6(6)) Hampton-Brown Bks.

English for All Book 2 Student's Book: Elt. 1999. (Illus.). 208p. pap., stu. ed. (978-1-929310-17-3(X)) ALL Publishing Hse.

English for All Book 3 Student's Book: Elt. 2000. (Illus.). 160p. pap., stu. ed. (978-1-929310-20-3(X)) ALL Publishing Hse.

English for All Book 4 Student's Book: Elt. 2000. (Illus.). 160p. pap., stu. ed. (978-1-929310-23-4(4)) ALL Publishing Hse.

English, "Living Language Courses" For French Speakers. (YA). pap. 29.95 incl. audio (978-0-88432-930-5(5) , SEN605) Norton, Jeffrey Pubs., Inc.

English, "Living Language Courses" For German Speakers. (YA). pap. 29.95 incl. audio (978-0-88432-931-2(3) , AFE610) Norton, Jeffrey Pubs., Inc.

English, "Living Language Courses" For Italian Speakers. (YA). pap. 29.95 incl. audio (978-0-88432-932-9(1) , SEN615) Norton, Jeffrey Pubs., Inc.

Fancy, Robin Lyn & Welch, Vala J. My Filipino Word Book. Ronny, Lynn, illus. 2007. 28p. 14.95 (***978-1-57306-276-3(6))** Bess Pr., Inc.

Gerngross, Gunter & Puchta, Herbert. Join in. 2000. (Join In Ser.). (Illus.). Bk. 1. 96p. pap., stu. ed. 13.00 (978-0-521-77524-3(8)); Bk. 1. 32p. pap., act. bk. ed. 6.00 (978-0-521-77521-2(3)); Bk. 2. 96p. pap., stu. ed. 13.00 (978-0-521-77523-6(X)); Bk. 2. 32p. pap., act. bk. ed. 6.00 (978-0-521-77520-5(5)); Bk. 3. 96p. pap., stu. ed. 13.00 (978-0-521-77522-9(1)); Bk. 3. 32p. pap., act. bk. ed. 6.00 (978-0-521-77519-9(1)) Cambridge Univ. Pr.

—Join In: French Edition. 2000. (Join In Ser.). (FRE., Illus.). 88p. pap., stu. ed. 12.00 (978-0-521-78591-4(X)) Cambridge Univ. Pr.

—Join in Starter. 2000. (Join In Ser.). 48p. pap., stu. ed. 10.00 (978-0-521-77525-0(6)); (POL., Illus.). pap., stu. ed. 7.00 (978-0-521-78597-6(9)) Cambridge Univ. Pr.

—Join Us for English 1 Flashcards Polish Edition. 2006. 28.00 (978-0-521-69433-9(7)) Cambridge Univ. Pr.

—Join Us for English 1 Portfolio Polish Edition. 2006. pap. 4.00 (***978-0-521-68905-2(8))** Cambridge Univ. Pr.

Gerngross, Gunter & Puchta, Herbert. Join Us for English 1 Pupil's Book Polish Edition. 2006. pap., stu. ed. 15.50 (978-0-521-68903-8(1)) Cambridge Univ. Pr.

Goodey, Diana & Goodey, Noel. Messages 1, 3 vols. 2005. (Messages Ser.). (Illus.). 144p. pap., stu. ed. 22.00 (978-0-521-54707-9(5)) Cambridge Univ. Pr.

Goodey, Diana, et al. Messages 3, 3 vols. 2005. (Messages Ser.). (Illus.). 146p. pap., stu. ed. 21.00 (978-0-521-61433-7(3)) Cambridge Univ. Pr.

Grant, David & McLarty, Robert. Business Basics. 2002. (Illus.). 16.50 (978-0-19-457340-5(0)) Oxford Univ. Pr., Inc.

Handle with Care. 64p. (YA). (gr. 9-12). pap. 9.95 (978-0-8224-7151-6(5) , 7151) Globe Fearon Educational Publishing.

Harcourt School Publishers Staff. Collections: For Transition & ESL Students. 1999. (Illus.). pap. 47.10 (978-0-15-312790-8(2)) Harcourt Schl. Pubs.

—Collections: Transition/ESL Students. 2000. (Illus.). (gr. 2). pap. 47.10 (978-0-15-318670-7(4)); (gr. 3). pap. 47.10 (978-0-15-318671-4(2)); (gr. 4). pap. 50.20 (978-0-15-318672-1(0)); (gr. 5). pap. 50.20 (978-0-15-318673-8(9)); (gr. 6). pap. 50.20 (978-0-15-318675-2(5)) Harcourt Schl. Pubs.

—Esl Support Book Horizons. 3rd ed. 2003. (gr. 1). pap. 9.50 (978-0-15-338321-2(6)); (gr. 2). pap. 9.50 (978-0-15-338322-9(4)); (gr. 3). pap. 12.70 (978-0-15-338323-6(2)) Harcourt Schl. Pubs.

—Harcourt Language: ESL/Transition Manual. 2nd ed. 2002. (Harcourt Language Ser.). (Illus.). (gr. 5 up). pap. 53.60 (978-0-15-319134-3(1)) Harcourt Schl. Pubs.

—Harcourt Language Arts. 2nd ed. 2002. (Harcourt Language Ser.). (Illus.). (gr. 3 up). pap., pupil's gde. ed. 58.70 (978-0-15-317833-7(7)) Harcourt Schl. Pubs.

—Harcourt Language Arts: ESL/Transition Manual. 2nd ed. 2002. (Harcourt Language Ser.). (Illus.). (gr. 2 up). pap. 53.60 (978-0-15-319130-5(9)); (gr. 3 up). pap. 53.60 (978-0-15-319132-9(5)); (gr. 4 up). pap. 53.60 (978-0-15-319133-6(3)) Harcourt Schl. Pubs.

—Let's Have a Picnic. 3rd ed. 2002. (Trophies English Language Learners Ser.). (Illus.). (J). pap. 3.20 (978-0-15-327577-7(4)) Harcourt Schl. Pubs.

Hardy, Thomas & Bassett, Jennifer. Tales from Longpuddle. Walker, Brian, illus. 2004. (Oxford Bookworms Ser.). 56p. 6.50 (978-0-19-422993-7(9)) Oxford Univ. Pr., Inc.

Hayes, Rosemary. The Big Shrink Play. 2005. (Cambridge Storybooks Ser.). 32p. pap. 7.00 (978-0-521-67476-8(X)) Cambridge Univ. Pr.

Heath, Roberta Mae & Simms, Candace Michelle. Let's Make Conbersation. 2003. 197p. pap. 19.95 (978-1-59286-815-5(0)) PublishAmerica, Inc.

Herrera, Mario. Backpack, Level 5. 2004. (C). pap. 18.67 (978-0-13-182710-3(3)) Pearson ESL.

Herrera, Mario & Zanatta, Theresa. New Parade Level 1: First Grade. 2nd ed. 1999. 109p. (C). pap., stu. ed. 18.67 (978-0-201-60427-6(2)) Pearson ESL.

Herrick, Mark P., illus. Rock U. S. A. & the American Way CONNECT-IT: Fun Projects & Activity Pages. 2004. 128p. per. 29.95 (978-0-9749412-1-9(2)) EDCO Publishing, Inc.

Hicks, Diana & Littlejohn, Andrew. American English Primary Colors 3. 2004. (Primary Colours Ser.). pap. 8.00 (978-0-521-60799-5(X)); pap. 12.00 (978-0-521-60803-9(1)) Cambridge Univ. Pr.

—American English Primary Colors 4. 2004. (Primary Colours Ser.). pap. 8.00 (978-0-521-60794-0(9)); pap., stu. ed. 12.00 (978-0-521-60798-8(1)) Cambridge Univ. Pr.

Hicks, Diana & Littlejohn, Andrew. Primary Colours Level 2. 2007. (Primary Colours Ser.). pap., stu. ed. 14.00 (***978-0-521-69815-3(4))** Cambridge Univ. Pr.

Hojel, Barbara & Guy, Ginger F. Where's Andy? 1999. Bk. 2. (Illus.). 16p. (C). pap. 7.66 (978-0-201-35144-6(7)) Longman Publishing Group.

Hoskins, Barbara. The Costume Contest - Carnival Luck, Level 3. 2000. (Let's Go Readers Ser.). (Illus.). 30p. (J). 7.25 (978-0-19-436466-9(6)) Oxford Univ. Pr., Inc.

—The Homestay Friends - Kid Power, Level 6. 2000. (Let's Go Readers Ser.). (Illus.). 32p. (J). 7.25 (978-0-19-436496-6(8)) Oxford Univ. Pr., Inc.

—Kate's Grandma - Rusty's Cookies, Level 1. 2000. (Let's Go Readers Ser.). (Illus.). 32p. (J). 7.25 (978-0-19-436446-1(1)) Oxford Univ. Pr., Inc.

—The Treasure Hunt - The Pet Sitter, Level 5. 2000. (Let's Go Readers Ser.). (Illus.). 32p. (J). 7.25 (978-0-19-436486-7(0)) Oxford Univ. Pr., Inc.

Howard, Lori. Read All about It. 2000. (Illus.). 16.95 (978-0-19-435224-6(2)) Oxford Univ. Pr., Inc.

Interlink Resources International. New Bridges - Book 3: Connecting People Through Language & Culture. 2007. (Illus.). 138p. spiral bd. 14.00 net. (***978-0-9796411-4-5(4))** Interlink Resources International.

Irving, N. Improve Your English. 2004. 96p. (J). lib. bdg. 22.95 (978-1-58086-611-8(5) , Usborne) EDC Publishing.

Johnson-Stefanidou, Catherine. Primary Colours 1 Companion. 2002. (Primary Colours Ser.). (Illus.). 64p. pap. (978-0-521-52163-5(7)) Cambridge Univ. Pr.

Kampa, Kathleen & Vilina, Charles. Magic Time, Bk. 1. 2001. (Illus.). 81p. (J). 14.95 (978-0-19-436180-4(2)) Oxford Univ. Pr., Inc.

Kehe, David & Kehe, Peggy Dustin. Conversation Strategies. 2nd ed. 2004. 150p. pap. 16.50 (978-0-86647-189-3(8)) Pro Lingua Assocs., Inc.

Kellas, Lydia. Our CSEC English: Volume 0, Part 0. 2008. pap. (***978-0-521-69176-5(1))** Cambridge Univ. Pr.

—Our English 1 Student Book: Volume 0, Part 0: Integrated Course for the Caribbean. 2007. (Illus.). 260p. pap., stu. ed. 16.95 (***978-0-521-69168-0(0))** Cambridge Univ. Pr.

—Our English 3 Student Book: Volume 0, Part 0: Integrated Course for the Caribbean. 2007. pap., stu. ed. (***978-0-521-69177-2(X))** Cambridge Univ. Pr.

Konda, Cynthia. Okasan & Me: Japanese American Educational Program. 2003. (JPN., Illus.). 26p. (J). (ps up). spiral bd. 19.99 (978-0-9743613-0-7(5)) Okasan & Me.

Kozyrev, Joann. Text with Audio Cassette: Volume of ... Kozyrev-Talk It up!: Listening, Speaking, & Pronunciation, 1. 2nd ed. 2001. 172p. (YA). pap., stu. ed. 41.16 (978-0-618-14399-3(8) , 330525) Houghton Mifflin College Div.

—Text with Audio CD: Talk It Up!: Listening, Speaking, & Pronunciation, 1. 2nd ed. 2001. 172p. (YA). pap., stu. ed. 41.16 (978-0-618-14400-6(5) , 330526) Houghton Mifflin College Div.

Lee, Linda. Explorations, 2 vols. 2000. (Illus.). 80p. wbk. ed. 9.95 (978-0-19-435038-9(X)) Oxford Univ. Pr., Inc.

Lesley, Tay. Connect Placement & Evaluation Package CD-ROM. 2007. (Connect Ser.). cd-rom 100.00 (***978-0-521-69003-4(X))** Cambridge Univ. Pr.

Littlejohn, Andrew & Hicks, Diana. Cambridge English for Polish Schools, Bk. 4. 1999. (Cambridge English for Schools Ser.). (ENG & POL., Illus.). 160p. pap., stu. ed. 9.00 (978-0-521-58882-9(0)) Cambridge Univ. Pr.

—Primary Colours 3. 2003. (Primary Colours Ser.). (Illus.). 64p. pap., act. bk. ed. 9.00 (978-0-521-66728-9(3)); Bk. 3. pap., tchr. ed., stu. ed. 14.00 (978-0-521-66732-6(1)) Cambridge Univ. Pr.

Littlejohn, Andrew, et al. Cambridge English for Polish Schools, Bk. 3. 1998. (Cambridge English for Schools Ser.). (Illus.). 160p. pap., stu. ed. 9.00 (978-0-521-58883-6(9)) Cambridge Univ. Pr.

Maggart, Kaye Wiley. Shining Star, Introductory Level. 2004. (Illus.). xiv, 289p. 64.67 (978-0-13-111285-8(6)) Pearson ESL.

Marsh, Carole. Way to Go Amigo!English for Kids! 2007. 32p. pap. 5.95 (***978-0-635-06369-4(7))** Gallopade International.

McCarthy, Michael, et al. Touchstone, Bk. 2. 2005. (Touchstone Ser.). 104p. pap., stu. ed., wbk. ed. 12.00 (978-0-521-66604-6(X)) Cambridge Univ. Pr.

McFarlane, Mike. Open House: Step Up! 1999. (Illus.). 48p. wbk. ed. 8.25 (978-0-19-435848-4(8)) Oxford Univ. Pr., Inc.

McFarlane, Mike & Whitney, Norman. Open House: Come In! 1999. (Illus.). 48p. wbk. ed. 8.25 (978-0-19-435844-6(5)) Oxford Univ. Pr., Inc.

McKeegan, David, et al. Get Together. 2003. (Illus.). 109p. Bk. 1. stu. ed. 13.25 (978-0-19-437484-2(X)); Bk. 2. stu. ed. 13.25 (978-0-19-437485-9(8)); Bk. 3. stu. ed. 13.25 (978-0-19-437486-6(6)); Bk. 4. stu. ed. 13.25 (978-0-19-437487-3(4)) Oxford Univ. Pr., Inc.

Ministry of Education Zambia Staff. Step in to English/Pathway to English. 2002. 144p. (gr. 2). pap., act. bk. ed. 0.85 (978-0-521-53151-1(9)) Cambridge Univ. Pr.

Mixon, Myrtis. Stories from American History. 2001. 96p. (J). tchr. ed. (978-0-8442-0444-4(7)) McGraw-Hill/Contemporary.

Monckeberg, Paulina. Artilugia English 2008. 2007. (Pascualina Family of Products Ser.). 114p. (J). spiral bd. 14.99 (***978-956-8222-62-8(6))** Pascualina Producciones S.A.

Montgomery, Karen & Ollerhead, Sue. English for Zambia Basic Education Grade 6 Pupil's Book. 2006. pap. 4.00 (978-0-521-69870-2(7)) Cambridge Univ. Pr.

Nakata, Ritsuko, et al. Let's Go: Level 1. 2nd ed. 2000. (Let's Go Second Edition Ser.). (Illus.). 80p. stu. ed. 13.75 (978-0-19-436443-0(7)) Oxford Univ. Pr., Inc.

—Let's Go: Level 2. 2nd ed. 2000. (Let's Go Second Edition Ser.). (Illus.). 80p. pap., wbk. ed. 8.25 (978-0-19-436454-6(2)) Oxford Univ. Pr., Inc.

O'Connor, John. Literacy in Context for GCSE. Ward, Joan, ed. 2002. (Literacy in Context Ser.). (Illus.). 182p. pap., stu. ed. 18.00 (978-0-521-52715-6(5)) Cambridge Univ. Pr.

Petelinsek, Kathleen & Primm, E. Russell. Greetings & Phrases: Saludos y Frases. 2006. (Talking Hands Ser.). (ENG & SPA., Illus.). 24p. (J). 21.36 (978-1-59296-682-0(9)) Child's World, Inc.

Redston, Chris & Cunningham, Gillie. Face2face Elementary Student's Book with CD-ROM/Audio CD & Workbook Pack Italian Edition. 2006. pap. 25.00 incl. cd-rom (978-0-521-68409-5(9)) Cambridge Univ. Pr.

—Face2face Pre-Intermediate Student's Book with CD-ROM/Audio CD & Workbook Pack Italian Edition. 2006. pap. 25.00 incl. cd-rom (978-0-521-68411-8(0)) Cambridge Univ. Pr.

Rempel, Cherie J., ed. New Bridges - Book 1: Connecting People Through Language & Culture. 2008. (Illus.). 138p. spiral bd. 14.00 net. (***978-0-9796411-0-7(1))** Interlink Resources International.

—New Bridges - Book 2: Connecting People Through Language & Culture. 2007. (Illus.). 138p. spiral bd. 14.00 net. (***978-0-9796411-2-1(8))** Interlink Resources International.

—New Bridges - Book 4: Connecting People Through Language & Culture. 2007. (Illus.). 138p. spiral bd. 14.00 net. (***978-0-9796411-6-9(0))** Interlink Resources International.

—New Bridges - Book 5: Connecting People Through Language & Culture. 2008. (Illus.). 138p. spiral bd. 14.00 net. (***978-0-9796411-8-3(7))** Interlink Resources International.

Rivers, Susan & Toyama, Setsuko. English Time. (Illus.). (J). 2003. (978-0-19-436435-5(6)); Bk. 1. 2001. 80p. (978-0-19-436306-8(6)); Bk. 2. 2001. 80p. (978-0-19-436403-4(8)); Bk. 3. 2002. 80p. (978-0-19-436411-9(9)); Bk. 4. 2002. 80p. (978-0-19-436419-5(4)); Bk. 5. 2003. 96p. (978-0-19-436427-0(5)) Oxford Univ. Pr., Inc.

The Rosetta Stone Language Library: English Level 1 (British) 2005. (J). (gr. 1 up). cd-rom 209.00 (978-1-58022-042-2(8)) Fairfield Language Technologies.

The Rosetta Stone Language Library: English Level 2 (British) 2005. (J). (gr. 1 up). cd-rom 239.00 (978-1-58022-044-6(4)) Fairfield Language Technologies.

Scraper, Katherine. Horsing Around. 2004. 64p. pap. (978-0-673-61735-4(1)) Good Year Bks.

Second Language Support Package. 2000. (gr. 2 up). suppl. ed. 46.65 (978-0-673-61814-6(5)); (gr. 3 up). suppl. ed. 46.65 (978-0-673-61815-3(3)); (gr. 4 up). suppl. ed. 43.60 (978-0-673-61816-0(1)); (gr. 5 up). suppl. ed. 46.65 (978-0-673-61817-7(X)); (gr. 6 up). suppl. ed. 46.65 (978-0-673-61818-4(8)); (gr. 7 up). suppl. ed. 46.65 (978-0-673-61819-1(6)); (gr. 8 up). suppl. ed. 46.65 (978-0-673-61820-7(X)); (Illus.). (gr. 1 up). suppl. ed. 46.65 (978-0-673-30105-5(2)) Addison-Wesley Educational Pubs., Inc.

Soars, John & Soars, Liz. American Headway, Bk. 2. 2001. (American Headway Ser.). (Illus.). 88p. wbk. ed. 9.75 (978-0-19-435380-9(X)) Oxford Univ. Pr., Inc.

Stamper Bauer, Judith & Ross Keyes, Joan. Sweet Surprise. 2005. (Oxford Picture Dictionary for Kids Ser.). (Illus.). 16p. 4.50 (978-0-19-430933-2(9)) Oxford Univ. Pr., Inc.

Steck-Vaughn Staff. CRCT: Answer Key - Reading & Language Arts - Level A. 2002. (Soaring Scores Ser.). pap. (978-0-7398-5546-1(8)) Steck-Vaughn.

—CRCT: Answer Key - Reading & Language Arts - Level B. 2002. (Soaring Scores Ser.). pap. (978-0-7398-5548-5(4)) Steck-Vaughn.

—CRCT: Reading & Language Arts - Level A. 2002. (Soaring Scores Ser.). pap. (978-0-7398-5545-4(X)) Steck-Vaughn.

—CRCT: Reading & Language Arts - Level B. 2002. (Soaring Scores Ser.). pap. (978-0-7398-5547-8(6)) Steck-Vaughn.

—English ASAP: Level 1. 2000. (J). pap., tchr. ed. (978-0-7398-2965-3(3)) Steck-Vaughn.

—Esl/ell. 2003. (J). (gr. k-1). pap. (978-0-7398-7096-9(3)); (gr. 2-3). pap. 15.99 (978-0-7398-7097-6(1)); (gr. 4-6). pap. 15.99 (978-0-7398-7098-3(X)) Steck-Vaughn.

Sykes, Helen. The Text Book 5 Standard: Resources for English. 2005. pap., stu. ed. 12.95 (978-0-521-61543-3(7)) Cambridge Univ. Pr.

Tell Me More Kids Ingles. 2001. (J). (gr. 2-4). mass mkt. 49.95 incl. cd-rom (978-1-893197-78-7(6) , 5K-1-2); (gr. 4-7). mass mkt. 49.95 incl. cd-rom (978-1-893197-79-4(4) , 5K-1-3); (ps-2). mass mkt. 49.95 incl. cd-rom (978-1-893197-77-0(8) , 5K-1-1) Auralog, Inc.

Through the Looking Glass. (Read-Along Ser.). (YA). pap., stu. ed. 34.95 incl. audio (978-0-88432-971-8(2) , S23946) Norton, Jeffrey Pubs., Inc.

Toyama, Setsuko. English Time. 2003. (Illus.). 48p. (J). (978-0-19-436441-6(0)) Oxford Univ. Pr., Inc.

—English Time Storybook 1: Annie & the Map. 2001. (Illus.). 48p. (J). (978-0-19-436312-9(0)) Oxford Univ. Pr., Inc.

—English Time Storybook 2: Coco & Digger. 2001. (Illus.). 44p. (J). (978-0-19-436409-6(7)) Oxford Univ. Pr., Inc.

—English Time Storybook 3: A Day at Storyland. 2002. (Illus.). (J). (978-0-19-436417-1(8)) Oxford Univ. Pr., Inc.

—English Time Storybook 4: A Medal for Ranger Day. 2002. (Illus.). 48p. (J). (978-0-19-436425-6(9)) Oxford Univ. Pr., Inc.

Toyama, Setsuko & Rivers, Susan. English Time Storybook 5: Digger & the Thief. 2003. (Illus.). 48p. (J). (978-0-19-436433-1(X)) Oxford Univ. Pr., Inc.

Traynor, Tracy. English with Abby & Zak. 2007. (Abby & Zak Ser.). (Illus.). 48p. (J). pap. 16.95 (978-1-84059-491-1(8)) Milet Publishing.

Ur, Penny & Hancock, Mark. New Ways to Go, Bk. 3. 2002. (SPA.). 80p. pap., wbk. ed. 12.00 (978-84-8323-285-9(5)); (CAT.). 112p. pap., stu. ed. 19.00 (978-84-8323-284-2(7)); (SPA.). 112p. pap., stu. ed. 19.00 (978-84-8323-283-5(9)) Cambridge Univ. Pr.

Ur, Penny, et al. New Ways to Go, Bk. 1. 2002. (SPA.). 80p. pap., wbk. ed. 12.00 (978-84-8323-261-3(8)); 96p. pap., stu. ed. 19.00 (978-84-8323-258-3(8)) Cambridge Univ. Pr.

Viney, Peter. The Collector. 1998. (Illus.). 24p. (J). 4.95 (978-0-19-421954-9(2)) Oxford Univ. Pr., Inc.

Whitney, Norman & McKeegan, David. Open House. (Illus.). 2000. 80p. stu. ed. 12.25 (978-0-19-435846-0(1)); 1999. 78p. 12.25 (978-0-19-435850-7(X)) Oxford Univ. Pr., Inc.

Whitney, Norman & Ward, Ann. Open House: Open Up! 2000. (Illus.). 46p. wbk. ed. 8.25 (978-0-19-435856-9(9)) Oxford Univ. Pr., Inc.

Zelman, Nancy Ellen. Conversation Inspirations. 2005. 114p. pap. 18.00 (978-0-86647-195-4(2)) Pro Lingua Assocs., Inc.

ENGLISH LANGUAGE—TEXTBOOKS FOR FOREIGN SPEAKERS—SPANISH

Beaton, Clare, illus. English-Spanish Bilingual First Books, 6 bks. (J). lib. bdg. 86.70 (978-1-56674-944-2(1)) Forest Hse. Publishing Co., Inc.

Ferrandiz, Elena, illus. My First 1,000 Words/Mis Primeras 1,000 Palabras. 2004. (ENG & SPA.). 76p. (J). (978-1-58394-100-3(2) , Frog Ltd.) North Atlantic Bks.

Finnie, Sue & Bourdais, Daniele. Julia Aprende Ingles. Tempest, Annabel, illus. 2003. (Language Learners Ser.). (SPA & ENG.). 32p. (J). (gr. 2-5). 9.95 (978-0-7641-7632-6(3)) Barron's Educational Series, Inc.

Inglés Basico para niños: Edad 7-12, Basic English for Children: ¡Aprenda las 250 Palabras Mas Importantes en Inglés!, Learn the 250 Most Important Words in English! 2005. 30.00 (978-0-9769266-2-7(8)) Weapons of Mass Instruction.

Mahmout, Ulfet & Thompson, Alan. My Life Story. 2004. (CZE, SPA, SER, URD & SOM., Illus.). 34p. (J). (978-1-85269-885-0(3)) Mantra Publishing, Ltd.

Morton, Lone. Space Postman/el Cartero Espacial: English-Spanish Edition. Ursell, Martin, illus. 2005. (I Can Read Spanish Ser.). (SPA & ENG.). 28p. (J). (ps). 7.99 (978-0-7641-5875-9(9)) Barron's Educational Series, Inc.

Ninos Aprenden Ingles Corp. Children Learning English. 2004. (Illus.). 119p. (J). pap. 19.95 ***(978-1-934665-03-9(7))*** Ninos Aprenden Ingles Corp.

Pirz, Therese S. Kids Stuff Ingles: English Phrases for Spanish Speakers. 2002. Tr. of Frases Faciles en Ingles Para Personas Que Hablan Espanol. (SPA.). (J). pap. 18.95 net. (978-0-9716605-0-2(6)) Chou-Chou Pr.

Practice Pal Bilingual Addition/Subtraction Practice Book. 2004. (Illus.). 16p. (J). (gr. k-2). spiral bd. (978-1-930355-50-7(5)) Greenbrier/Scentex.

Timeless Voices, Timeless Themes: Gold, Spanish Support Practice Book. 2000. (YA). (gr. 10). pap. 15.97 (978-0-13-050922-2(1)) Prentice Hall PTR.

Timeless Voices, Timeless Themes: Platinum, Spanish Support Practice Book. 2000. (YA). (gr. 10). pap. 15.97 (978-0-13-050924-6(8)) Prentice Hall PTR.

Timeless Voices, Timeless Themes: The American Experience, Spanish Support Planning Guide. 2000. (YA). (gr. 11). pap. 4.97 (978-0-13-050918-5(3)) Prentice Hall PTR.

Timeless Voices, Timeless Themes: The British Tradition, Spanish Support Planning Guide. 2000. (YA). (gr. 12). pap. 4.97 (978-0-13-050919-2(1)) Prentice Hall PTR.

Timeless Voices, Timeless Themes: The British Tradition, Spanish Support Practice Book. 2000. (YA). (gr. 12). pap. 15.97 (978-0-13-050926-0(4)) Prentice Hall PTR.

Villafane-Leon, Ines. A Story for All Seasons: Un Cuento Para Cada Estacion: Immigration of One. 2004. (ENG & SPA.). xiii, 367p. (YA). pap. 22.95 (978-1-882897-78-0(1)) Lost Coast Pr.

ENGLISH LANGUAGE—VERSIFICATION

see Versification

ENGLISH LITERATURE

see also Authors, English; English Drama; English Poetry; English Wit and Humor; Parodies; Short Stories

AfterSchool Kidzlit. 2000. spiral bd. 1813.00 (978-1-57621-398-8(6)) Developmental Studies Ctr.

Brown, Robin. Practice Papers: English. 2nd ed. (Illus.). 32p. (YA). pap. 6.99 (978-0-340-72687-7(3) , Hodder & Stoughton) Hodder General Publishing Division GBR. *Dist:* Trafalgar Square Publishing.

Center for Learning Network Staff. British Literature 2: Romantics to the Present. rev. ed. 2000. (English Ser.). 281p. (YA). (gr. 10-12). spiral bd. 39.95 (978-1-56077-623-9(4)) Ctr. for Learning, The.

Cromwell Productions Limited, prod. The Arthurian Tradition-on CD-ROM. (YA). cd-rom 149.95 (978-0-7365-0621-2(7)) Films Media Group.

Harcourt School Publishers Staff. Hidden Treasures Anthology. 99th ed. 1998. (Signatures Ser.). (Illus.). (gr. 6). 75.10 (978-0-15-310112-0(1)) Harcourt Schl. Pubs.

—Hold on Tight Bk. 5: Standard Anthology. 95th ed. 1999. (Treasury of Literature Ser.). (Illus.). 44.20 (978-0-15-301251-8(X)) Harcourt Schl. Pubs.

—Jump Right In Bk. 2: Standard Anthology. 95th ed. 1998. (Treasury of Literature Ser.). (Illus.). 37.30 (978-0-15-301248-8(X)) Harcourt Schl. Pubs.

—Out of This World: Standard Anthology. 95th ed. 1998. (Treasury of Literature Ser.). (Illus.). (gr. 5). 77.30 (978-0-15-301235-8(8)) Harcourt Schl. Pubs.

—Treasury of Literature: Practice Book, Bks. 1-3. 95th ed. 1998. (Treasury of Literature Ser.). (Illus.). (gr. 1). pap. 12.30 (978-0-15-301288-4(9)) Harcourt Schl. Pubs.

—Treasury of Literature Bk. 1: Practice Book. 95th ed. 1998. (Treasury of Literature Ser.). (Illus.). (gr. 3). pap. 10.00 (978-0-15-301293-8(5)); (gr. 2). pap., tchr. ed. 25.70 (978-0-15-302061-2(X)); (gr. 3). pap., tchr. ed. 25.70 (978-0-15-302063-6(6)) Harcourt Schl. Pubs.

—Treasury of Literature Bk. 2: Practice Book. 95th ed. 1998. (Treasury of Literature Ser.). (Illus.). pap. 10.00 (978-0-15-301292-1(7)); pap. 10.00 (978-0-15-301294-5(3)) Harcourt Schl. Pubs.

—Treasury of Literature Bk. 4: Practice Book. 95th ed. 1998. (Treasury of Literature Ser.). (Illus.). pap. 8.30 (978-0-15-301289-1(7)) Harcourt Schl. Pubs.

—Treasury of Literature Bk. 5: Practice Book. 95th ed. 1998. (Treasury of Literature Ser.). (Illus.). pap. 8.30 (978-0-15-301290-7(0)) Harcourt Schl. Pubs.

Holt, Rinehart and Winston Staff. TAKS Practice Tests, Grade 3: Elemental Literature & Language. 2002. pap. 14.73 (978-0-03-069188-1(5)) Holt, Rinehart & Winston.

—TAkS Practice Tests, Grade 6: Elemental Literature & Language. 2002. pap. 14.73 (978-0-03-069192-8(3)) Holt, Rinehart & Winston.

Lord, Roberta. Reflections: French Version. 2003. 200p. 9.95 net. (978-1-931934-25-1(8)) Back Yard Pub.

Montgomery, Karen & Lloyd, Glynis. English Matters Grade 6 Anthology. 2002. (English Matters Ser.). pap. (978-0-521-00379-7(2)) Cambridge Univ. Pr.

—English Matters Grade 6 Learner's Book. 2002. (English Matters Ser.). pap. (978-0-521-00378-0(4)) Cambridge Univ. Pr.

Moulton, Carroll. Authors in Depth: The British Tradition. 2001. (Prentice Hall Literature Library). v, 246p. (J). 8.97 (978-0-13-050405-0(X)) Prentice Hall PTR.

O'Connor, John. Literacy in Context for AQA A. 2003. (Literacy in Context Ser.). (Illus.). 208p. pap. 19.35 (978-0-521-53528-1(X)) Cambridge Univ. Pr.

Prentice-Hall Staff, contrib. by. Authors in Depth. 2000. (Prentice Hall Literature Library). (Illus.). iv, 212p. (J). 8.97 (978-0-13-050401-2(7)) Prentice Hall PTR.

Probst. Elements of Literature: Course 6. 97th ed. 1998. (J). (gr. 1). 82.60 (978-0-03-096834-1(8)) Holt, Rinehart & Winston.

Strickland, Dorothy. Listen Children: An Introduction to Black Literature for All Young People. 1999. (J). (978-0-606-15818-3(9)) Tandem Library Bks.

ENGLISH LITERATURE—COLLECTIONS

Center for Learning Network Staff. British Literature 1: Beginnings to Age of Reason. 2000. (English Ser.). 168p. (YA). (gr. 10-12). tchr. ed., spiral bd. 39.95 (978-1-56077-622-2(6)) Ctr. for Learning, The.

Great Illustrated Classics. 2005. (J). (gr. 3-8). 427.00 (978-1-59679-233-3(7) , ABDO & Daughters) ABDO Publishing Co.

Harcourt School Publishers Staff. Trophies: Distant Voyages. 3rd ed. 2003. (Illus.). (gr. 5). 65.40 (978-0-15-339788-2(8)) Harcourt Schl. Pubs.

—Trophies Level 1-4: Time Together. 3rd ed. 2003. (Illus.). 31.40 (978-0-15-339779-0(9)) Harcourt Schl. Pubs.

—Trophies Level 1-5: Gather Around. 3rd ed. 2003. (Illus.). pap. 32.90 (978-0-15-339781-3(0)) Harcourt Schl. Pubs.

—Trophies Level 2-1: Just for You. 3rd ed. 2003. (Illus.). (gr. 2). 44.70 (978-0-15-339782-0(9)) Harcourt Schl. Pubs.

Hunt, Peter. Children's Literature: An Anthology, 1801-1902. 2000. (Anthologies Ser.). (Illus.). 480p. 117.95 (978-0-631-21048-1(2)); pap. 54.95 (978-0-631-21049-8(0)) Blackwell Publishing Ltd. GBR. *Dist:* Blackwell Publishing, Inc.

McGraw-Hill Staff. World Literature. 2nd ed. 2003. 832p. (gr. 6-12). stu. ed. 61.32 (978-0-07-860353-2(6) , 9780078603532); pap., stu. ed. 53.32 (978-0-07-860352-5(8) , 9780078603525) Glencoe/McGraw-Hill.

The Students of Animo Inglewood Charter High School. Rhythm of the Chain: Young Writers Explore Team work. 2006. 182p. pap. 12.00 (978-0-9768467-0-3(5)) 826 Valencia.

ENGLISH LITERATURE—CRITICISM

see English Literature—History and Criticism

ENGLISH LITERATURE—HISTORY AND CRITICISM

Beers. Elements of Literature: Premier Online Edition. 5th ed. 2004. (gr. 9). 82.20 (978-0-03-073847-0(4)) Holt, Rinehart & Winston.

Bloom, Harold. London. 2005. (Bloom's Literary Places Ser.). (Illus.). 150p. (gr. 9-13). 40.00 (978-0-7910-7841-9(8) , Chelsea Hse.) Facts On File, Inc.

Bloom, Harold, ed. Emily Bronte's Wuthering Heights, Vol. 1. 1999. (Bloom's Reviews Comprehensive Research & Study Guides). 80p. (YA). (gr. 8-11). pap. 4.95 (978-0-7910-4170-3(0) , Chelsea Hse.) Facts On File, Inc.

—Frankenstein. 2006. (Bloom's Modern Critical Interpretations Ser.). (Illus.). 264p. (YA). (gr. 9 up). 45.00 (978-0-7910-9303-0(4)) Facts On File, Inc.

—Jane Eyre - Charlotte Bronte. 2006. (Bloom's Modern Critical Interpretations Ser.). 248p. (YA). (gr. 9 up). 45.00 (978-0-7910-9304-7(2) , Chelsea Hse.) Facts On File, Inc.

—London. 2005. (Bloom's Literary Places Ser.). (Illus.). 150p. (gr. 9-13). pap. 40.00 (978-0-7910-8360-4(8) , Chelsea Hse.) Facts On File, Inc.

—1984 - George Orwell. 2nd rev. ed. 2006. (Bloom's Modern Critical Interpretations Ser.). 216p. (YA). (gr. 9 up). 45.00 (978-0-7910-9300-9(X) , Chelsea Hse.) Facts On File, Inc.

Bloom, Harold, intro. Lord of the Flies. 2004. (Bloom's Guides Ser.). (Illus.). 80p. (J). (gr. 9-13). 30.00 (978-0-7910-7878-5(7) , Chelsea Hse.) Facts On File, Inc.

Bridges to Literature: Power Words: A Bridge to Reading. 2002. (gr. 6-12). Vol. 2. (978-0-618-36410-7(2) , 2-04684); Vol. 3. (978-0-618-36411-4(0) , 2-04685) McDougal Littell Inc.

British Literature, 6 vols., Set. 2004. (Illus.). (YA). (gr. 9). tchr. ed., stu. ed. 38.95 (978-0-7403-0203-9(5) , ES9515, Lifepac) Alpha Omega Pubns., Inc.

British Literature. (gr. 12 up). 2004. stu. ed. (978-0-618-17075-3(8) , 2-71108); 2004. cd-rom (978-0-618-30391-5(X) , 2-04296); 2001. tchr. ed. incl. cd-rom (978-0-395-97280-9(9) , 2-80751) McDougal Littell Inc.

Critical Companion Set. 2005. (Literary A to Z Ser.). 320p. (gr. 9). 299.50 (978-0-8160-6529-5(2)) Facts On File, Inc.

Dougall, Alastair. James Bond: The Secret World of 007. Worrall, Dave, ed. Stewart, Roger, illus. 2000. 144p. (J). 19.99 (978-0-7894-6691-4(0)) Dorling Kindersley Publishing, Inc.

Greenhill, Wendy, contrib. by. Romeo & Juliet. 2000. (Shakespeare Library). (Illus.). 32p. (J). lib. bdg. 21.36 (978-1-57572-285-6(2)) Heinemann Library.

Heims, Neil. J. R. R. Tolkien. 2004. (Great Writers Ser.). (Illus.). 128p. (YA). (gr. 9-13). 31.95 (978-0-7910-7847-1(7) , Chelsea Hse.) Facts On File, Inc.

Joyce, James. James Joyce's A Portrait of the Artist As a Young Man. Bloom, Harold, ed. 1999. (Bloom's Notes Ser.). (Illus.). 90p. (YA). (gr. 8-12). 30.00 (978-0-7910-4570-1(6) , Chelsea Hse.) Facts On File, Inc.

Kirk, E. J. Step into Narnia: A Journey Through the Lion, the Witch & the Wardrobe. 2005. (Narnia Ser.). (Illus.). 64p. (J). lib. bdg. 20.89 (978-0-06-074234-8(8)) HarperCollins Pubs.

Linking Literature: Using Oral History to Connect Books to the World. 2004. per. (978-1-932948-07-3(4)) Student Pr. Initiative.

Loos, Pamela. Reading Sounder. 2005. (Engaged Reader Ser.). (Illus.). 74p. (J). (ps-8). lib. bdg. 25.00 (978-0-7910-8833-3(2) , Chelsea Hse.) Facts On File, Inc.

Mitchell, Hayley R. Readings on "Wuthering Heights" 1998. (Literary Companion to American Literature Ser.). (Illus.). 156p. (YA). (gr. 9 up). pap. 22.45 (978-1-56510-832-5(9) , Greenhaven Pr., Inc.) Thomson Gale.

Nardo, Don. Frankenstein. 2003. (Understanding Great Literature Ser.). (Illus.). 128p. (J). 29.95 (978-1-59018-147-8(6) , Lucent Bks.) Thomson Gale.

—Understanding the Lord of the Rings. 2003. (Understanding Great Literature Ser.). (Illus.). 96p. (J). (gr. 8-11). lib. bdg. 29.95 (978-1-59018-234-5(0) , Lucent Bks.) Thomson Gale.

School Zone Publishing Company Staff. Story Problems: Grades 1 & 2. (Illus.). (J). 19.99 incl. audio compact disk (978-0-88743-936-0(5)) School Zone Publishing Co.

Scott, James. The Strange Case of Dr. Jekyll & Mr. Hyde: A Student Response Journal. 2002. 32p. (YA). (gr. 7-12). pap., wbk. ed. 19.95 (978-1-58049-971-2(6) , RJ47) Prestwick Hse., Inc.

Shakespeare, William. Hamlet. Mueller, Jenny, ed. 2002. (Simply Shakespeare Ser.). (Illus.). 346p. pap. 8.99 (978-0-7641-2084-8(0)) Barron's Educational Series, Inc.

—The Tempest. Ermitage, Kathleen, ed. 2002. (Simply Shakespeare Ser.). (Illus.). 288p. pap. 8.99 (978-0-7641-2087-9(5)) Barron's Educational Series, Inc.

Shakespeare, William & Roth, Robert R., eds. Macbeth. 2002. (Simply Shakespeare Ser.). (Illus.). 288p. pap. 8.99 (978-0-7641-2086-2(7)) Barron's Educational Series, Inc.

Stevens, David. The Gothic Tradition. 2000. (Cambridge Contexts in Literature Ser.). (Illus.). 128p. (gr. 9-12). pap. 16.00 (978-0-521-77732-2(1)) Cambridge Univ. Pr.

Stobaugh, James. British Literature Student. 2005. (Broadman & Holman Literature Ser.). 288p. stu. ed. 24.99 (978-0-8054-5894-7(8)) B&H Publishing Grp.

Streissguth, Thomas. Legends of Dracula. 1998. (Biography Ser.). (Illus.). 112p. (gr. 6-12). lib. bdg. 27.93 (978-0-8225-4942-0(5)) Lerner Publishing Group.

Streissguth, Thomas & Streissguth, Tom. Legends of Dracula. 2003. (Biography Ser.). (Illus.). 112p. (YA). (gr. 6 up). pap. 7.95 (978-0-8225-9682-0(2) , Carolrhoda Bks.) Lerner Publishing Group.

Tibbets, Stacy Glenn. Reading Roll of Thunder, Hear My Cry. 2005. (Engaged Reader Ser.). (Illus.). 88p. (gr. 4-8). 25.00 (978-0-7910-8832-6(4) , Chelsea Hse.) Facts On File, Inc.

Watts, Cedric. Macbeth. Shakespeare, William, ed. 2001. 118p. audio compact disk (978-1-903342-15-2(5)) Wordsworth Educational.

ENGLISH PARODIES

see Parodies

ENGLISH POETRY

Agard, John. Baby Poems. Bent, Jenny, illus. 2005. 24p. (J). 14.95 (978-1-84507-084-7(4)) Lincoln, Frances Ltd. GBR. *Dist:* Perseus Distribution.

Andreae, Giles. Commotion in the Ocean. Wojtowycz, David, illus. 1998. 32p. (J). (ps-2). 14.95 (978-1-888444-39-1(8)) Little Tiger Pr.

Bloom, Valerie. Hot Like Fire. 2002. (Illus.). 96p. (J). pap. 8.99 (978-0-7475-5647-3(4)) Bloomsbury Publishing Plc GBR. *Dist:* Independent Pubs. Group.

Brownjohn, Sandy. In & Out of the Shadows. 2000. (Illus.). 64p. (J). (978-0-19-276246-7(X)) Oxford Univ. Pr., Inc.

Bruce, Lisa. Row Your Boat. Corfield, Robin Bell, illus. 2001. 32p. (J). (ps-k). 16.99 (978-0-7112-1557-3(X)) Lincoln, Frances Ltd. GBR. *Dist:* Antique Collectors' Club.

Bruce, Lisa & Corfield, Robin Bell. Row Your Boat. (Illus.). 20p. pap. (978-0-7112-1750-8(5)); 2004. 24p. (J). pap. 7.95 (978-1-84507-230-8(8)) Lincoln, Frances Ltd. GBR. *Dist:* Transition Vendor, Perseus Distribution.

Causely, Charles. Bring in the Holly. Kopper, Lisa, illus. 2000. 32p. (J). (gr. k-5). pap. 10.99 (978-0-7112-1571-9(5)) Lincoln, Frances Ltd. GBR. *Dist:* Antique Collectors' Club.

Crossley-Holland, Kevin, tr. from ANG. Beowulf. Keeping, Charles, illus. 1999. 48p. (YA). 12.95 (978-0-19-272369-7(3)) Oxford Univ. Pr., Inc.

de la Mare, Walter. Rhymes & Verses: Collected Poems for Young People. Blaisdell, Elinore, illus. 2002. 370p. (J). 18.95 (978-0-8050-7192-4(X) , Holt, Henry & Co. Bks. For Young Readers) Holt, Henry & Co.

DiTerlizzi, Tony. The Spider & the Fly. 2002. (Illus.). 40p. (J). 17.99 (978-0-689-85289-3(4)) Simon & Schuster Children's Publishing.

Dowswell, Paul. Victorians. (Illus.). 32p. pap. 9.99 (978-0-7502-2613-4(7) , Hodder & Stoughton) Hodder General Publishing Division GBR. *Dist:* Trafalgar Square Publishing.

Dunbar, Polly, illus. Here's a Little Poem: A Very First Book of Poetry. 2007. 112p. (J). (ps-k). 21.99 (978-0-7636-3141-3(8)) Candlewick Pr.

Fairer, David. English Poetry of the Eighteenth Century, 1700-1789. 2003. (Longman Literature in English Ser.). 320p. (C). pap. 47.80 (978-0-582-22777-4(1)) Longman Publishing.

Fyleman, Rose. Mary Middling & Other Silly Folk: Nursery Rhymes & Nonsense Poems. Bandlow, Katja, illus. 2004. 32p. (J). (gr. k-3). tchr. ed. 16.00 (978-0-618-38141-8(4) , Clarion Bks.) Houghton Mifflin Co. Trade & Reference Div.

Hegley, John. My Dog Is a Carrot. Hegley, John, illus. 2003. (Illus.). 64p. (J). (gr. 1). 12.99 (978-0-7636-1932-9(9)) Candlewick Pr.

Hooper, Mary. The Remarkable Life & Times of Eliza Rose. McGough, Roger, ed. 2006. 336p. (YA). 16.95 (978-1-58234-854-4(5)) Bloomsbury Publishing.

Kalaidjian, Walter B. Understanding Poetry, & Understanding Literature Cd. 2004. (YA). pap. 61.56 incl. cd-rom (978-0-618-46485-2(9) , 387591) Houghton Mifflin College Div.

Keats, John. A Song about Myself. Prosek, James, illus. 2005. (J). 16.95 (978-0-689-86829-0(4) , Simon & Schuster Children's Publishing) Simon & Schuster Children's Publishing.

Kipling, Rudyard. If: A Father's Advice to His Son. Smith, Charles R., illus. Smith, Charles R., photos by. 2007. (J). ***(978-1-4287-3329-9(9))*** Simon & Schuster Children's Publishing.

Kipling, Rudyard. Rudyard Kipling. Gillooly, Eileen, ed. Sharpe, Jim, illus. 2000. (Poetry for Young People Ser.). 48p. (gr. 4-7). 14.95 (978-0-8069-4484-5(6)) Sterling Publishing Co., Inc.

Lear, Edward. Book of Nonsense. 2nd fac. rev. ed. 2002. (Classics Ser.). (Illus.). 240p. (YA). (gr. 13). 99.95 (978-0-415-28599-5(2)); 15.95 (978-0-415-28600-8(X)) Routledge.

—The Quangle Wangle's Hat. Voce, Louise, illus. 2005. 40p. (J). (ps-2). 15.99 (978-0-7636-1289-4(8)) Candlewick Pr.

Martin, Peggy-Lou. Songs, Seas, & Green Peas: Poems for Anywhere. 2000. (Poetry Parade Ser.). (Illus.). 32p. (J). 21.36 (978-1-57572-400-3(6)) Heinemann Library.

Milne, A. A. Now We Are Six Deluxe Edition. 2008. 128p. (J). (ps). 19.99 ***(978-0-525-47929-1(5)*** , Dutton Juvenile) Penguin Group (USA) Inc.

Mitton, Tony. Plum. GrandPré, Mary, illus. 2003. (J). (978-0-439-36410-2(8)); 64p. pap. 17.95 (978-0-439-36409-6(4)) Scholastic, Inc. (Levine, Arthur A. Bks.).

Moses, Brian. I'm Telling on You! Poems about Brothers & Sisters. Maddison, Lucy, illus. 2003. 60p. (J). pap. (978-0-330-36867-4(2) , Pan) Pan Macmillan.

Nister, Ernest. Moving Pictures. (Illus.). (J). (978-0-399-22390-7(8) , Philomel) Penguin Group (USA) Inc.

Peters, Andrew & Peters, Polly. Poems with Attitude: Uncensored. (YA). mass mkt. (978-0-7502-4117-5(9) , Hodder Wayland) Hodder Children's Division.

Rogasky, Barbara. Winter Poems, Vol. 1. Hyman, Trina Schart & Cooper, Martha, illus. 1999. 40p. (J). (gr. 2-6). pap. 5.99 (978-0-590-42873-6(X)) Scholastic, Inc.

Shakespeare, William & Burto, William. The Sonnets. 1999. 210p. (gr. 7-12). lib. bdg. 12.95 (978-0-613-17523-4(9)) Tandem Library Bks.

Strand, Mark & Boland, Eavan. The Making of a Poem: A Norton Anthology of Poetic Forms. 2001. 448p. (YA). 27.50 (978-0-393-04916-9(7)) Norton, W. W. & Co., Inc.

Taylor, Jane & O'Neal, Debbie Trafton. Twinkle, Twinkle, Little Star. Huang, Benrei, illus. 2003. (Sing-It! Ser.). 32p. 8.99 (978-0-8066-4350-2(1) , Augsburg Bks.) Augsburg Fortress, Pubs.

Temperley, Howard. In the Days of Dinosaurs: A Rhyming Romp Through Dino History. Kline, Michael P., illus. 2004. (J). pap. 9.95 (978-1-885593-81-8(3) , Williamson Bks.) Ideals Pubns.

Tolkien, J. R. R. Bilbo's Last Song. Baynes, Pauline, illus. 2002. 32p. (J). 12.95 (978-0-375-82373-2(5) , Knopf Bks. for Young Readers) Random Hse. Children's Bks.

Willard, Nancy. Step Lightly: Poems for the Journey. 1998. (Illus.). 112p. (J). (gr. 5-9). pap. 12.00 (978-0-15-202052-1(7) , Harcourt Paperbacks) Harcourt Children's Bks.

ENGLISH POETRY—COLLECTIONS

Andreae, Giles. Cock-a-Doodle-Doo! Barnyard Hullabaloo. Wojtowycz, David, illus. 2002. 32p. (J). tchr. ed. 16.95 (978-1-58925-020-8(6) , tiger tales) ME Media LLC.

—Commotion in the Ocean. Wojtowycz, David, illus. 32p. (J). 2002. pap. 7.95 (978-1-58925-366-7(3)); 2001. tchr. ed. 16.95 (978-1-58925-000-0(1)) ME Media LLC. (tiger tales).

—Commotion in the Ocean. 2002. (gr. k-3). lib. bdg. 15.25 (978-0-613-55208-0(3)) Tandem Library Bks.

E F G

—Rumble in the Jungle. Wojtowycz, David, illus. 2002. 36p. (J). pap. 7.95 (978-1-58925-367-4(1) , tiger tales) ME Media LLC.

—Rumble in the Jungle. 2002. (ps-2). lib. bdg. 15.25 (978-0-613-46096-5(0)) Tandem Library Bks.

Andreae, Giles & Wojtowycz, David. Cock-a-Doodle-Doo! Barnyard Hullabaloo. Andreae, Giles & Wojtowycz, David, illus. 2000. (Illus.). 32p. (J). (ps-3). pap. 14.95 (978-1-888444-75-9(4)) Little Tiger Pr.

Goodings, Christina, compiled by. Baby Rhymes & Bedtime Blessings. 1999. (Illus.). 48p. (J). 19.99 (978-0-7459-4166-0(4) , Lion) Lion Hudson plc GBR. *Dist:* Trafalgar Square Publishing.

Harrison, Michael. The Oxford Treasury of Classic Poems. 2nd rev. ed. 2004. (Illus.). 160p. (YA). 19.95 (978-0-19-276289-4(3)) Oxford Univ. Pr., Inc.

Martin, Peggy-Lou. Wishes, Wings, & Other Things: Poems for Anytime. 2000. (Poetry Parade Ser.). (Illus.). 32p. (J). 21.36 (978-1-57572-399-0(9)) Heinemann Library.

McGough, Roger. The Kingfisher Book of Funny Poems. Holden, Caroline, illus. 2002. 256p. (J). (gr. 3-5). tchr. ed. 18.95 (978-0-7534-5480-0(7) , Kingfisher) Houghton Mifflin Co. Trade & Reference Div.

Pearson, Susan, ed. The Drowsy Hours: Poems for Bedtime. Malone, Peter, illus. 2002. 40p. (J). (ps up). 16.95 (978-0-688-16603-8(2)) HarperCollins Pubs.

Peters, Andrew Fusek. Out of Order. 1999. (Illus.). 96p. pap. 19.95 (978-0-237-52316-9(7) , Evans Brothers, Limited) Evans Publishing Group GBR. *Dist:* Independent Pubs. Group.

Philip, Neil. Hot Potato: Mealtime Rhymes. Henley, Claire, tr. Henley, Claire, illus. 2004. 32p. (J). (ps-k). tchr. ed. 16.00 (978-0-618-31554-3(3) , Clarion Bks.) Houghton Mifflin Co. Trade & Reference Div.

Rivers, Ruth, illus. This Amazing World: Poems & Prayers about Everything under the Sun. 2002. 48p. (J). (gr. 1-7). 16.00 (978-1-56148-363-1(X)) Good Bks.

Ross, Harriet, ed. Great English Story Poems: Collections. 160p. (YA). (gr. 5-12). pap. 8.95 (978-0-87460-364-4(1)) Lion Bks.

Snell, Gordon. Thursday Club. Flintoft, Anthony, illus. 96p. (J). pap. 8.99 (978-1-85881-831-3(1)) Orion Bks. Ltd. GBR. *Dist:* Trafalgar Square Publishing.

Stuart-Clark, Christopher. One Hundred Years of Poetry for Children. 2000. (Illus.). (J). (978-0-606-20831-4(3)) Tandem Library Bks.

Tripp, Wallace. Rose's Are Red, Violet's Are Blue: And Other Silly Poems. Tripp, Wallace, illus. 1999. (Illus.). 32p. (YA). (gr. 2-5). 15.95 (978-0-316-85440-5(9)) Little Brown & Co.

Waters, Fiona. If the Sea Was in the Sky. 2002. (Illus.). 96p. 22.99 (978-0-237-52126-4(1) , Evans Brothers, Limited) Evans Publishing Group GBR. *Dist:* Independent Pubs. Group.

Williamson, Melanie, illus. Drift upon a Dream: Poems for Sleepy Babies. 2004. 32p. (J). 16.95 (978-1-57091-577-2(6)) Charlesbridge Publishing, Inc.

ENGLISH POETRY—HISTORY AND CRITICISM

Fandel, Jennifer. Keats, Shakespeare, & Other Wordsmiths: Understanding Poetry. 2005. (Illus.). 48p. (gr. 5-9). 21.95 (978-1-58341-343-2(X) , Creative Education) Creative Co., The.

Granfield, Linda. In Flanders Fields. Wilson, Janet, illus. 2000. 32p. (gr. 4-7). 8.95 (978-0-7737-5925-1(5)) Stoddart Kids CAN. *Dist:* Fitzhenry & Whiteside, Ltd.

Moses, Brian. Favourite Classic Poets. (Illus.). 32p. pap. (978-0-7502-4292-9(2) , Hodder Wayland) Hodder Children's Division.

Sellars, Roy & Allen, Graham, eds. Salt Companion to Harold Bloom. 2007. (ENG.). 536p. per. (***978-1-876857-20-2(X)**) Salt Publishing.

ENGLISH SHORT STORIES

see Short Stories

ENGLISH WIT AND HUMOR

Anderson, Scoular. My First Joke Book. 1998. (Young Corgis Ser.). (Illus.). 90p. pap. 7.99 (978-0-552-54278-4(4)) Transworld Publishers Ltd. GBR. *Dist:* Independent Pubs. Group.

Byrne, John. The Alien Joke Book. 2000. (Illus.). 108p. (J). pap. 6.95 (978-0-552-54562-4(7)) Transworld Publishers Ltd. GBR. *Dist:* Trafalgar Square Publishing.

ENLISTMENT

see United States—Army—Recruiting, Enlistment, etc.

ENSEMBLES (MATHEMATICS)

see Set Theory

ENSIGNS

see Flags

ENTERTAINERS

see also Actors and Actresses; Clowns; Dancers

Anderson, Marilyn D. Chris Farley. 2000. (They Died Too Young Ser.). (Illus.). 48p. (J). (gr. 4-7). 21.95 (978-0-7910-5860-2(3) , Chelsea Hse.) Facts On File, Inc.

Blair, Eric. Annie Oakley, Sharp Shooter: A Retelling of the Classic Traditional Tale. Chambers-Goldbert, Micah, illus. 2005. (Read-It! Readers Ser.). 32p. (C). (gr. k-3). 18.60 (978-1-4048-0970-3(8)) Picture Window Bks.

Cole, Melanie. Sinbad. 1998. (Real-Life Reader Biographies Ser.). (Illus.). 32p. (J). (gr. 3-8). lib. bdg. 24.95 (978-1-883845-73-5(4)) Mitchell Lane Pubs., Inc.

Covington, Karen. The Performing Artists: Actors, Directors, Dancers, Entertainers, Musicians. 2002. (Remarkable Women). (Illus.). 80p. (YA). (gr. 6-9). lib. bdg. 32.85 (978-0-8172-5727-9(6)) Raintree.

Donovan, Sandra. Will Rogers: Cowboy, Comedian, & Commentator. 2006. (Signature Lives Ser.). (Illus.). 112p. (J). (gr. 4-8). lib. bdg. 31.93 (978-0-7565-2463-0(6)) Compass Point Bks.

Feinstein, Stephen. Read about Annie Oakley. 2006. (I Like Biographies! Ser.). (Illus.). 24p. (J). lib. bdg. 21.26 (978-0-7660-2583-7(7) , Enslow Elementary) Enslow Pubs., Inc.

Gale Research Staff. Performing Artists: From Alvin Ailey to Julia Roberts, Vol. 4. 1999. (Illus.). 285p. 67.00 (978-0-7876-5687-4(9) , GML00502-175302, UXL) Thomson Gale.

Gilbert, Sara. Annie Oakley. 2005. (Illus.). 48p. (gr. 5-9). 21.95 (978-1-58341-334-0(0) , Creative Education) Creative Co., The.

Goodman, Michael E. Buffalo Bill. 2005. (Illus.). 48p. (gr. 5-9). 21.95 (978-1-58341-336-4(7) , Creative Education) Creative Co., The.

Graves, Karen Marie. Michael Jackson. 2000. (People in the News Ser.). (Illus.). 112p. (J). (gr. 6-9). (978-1-56006-707-8(1) , Lucent Bks.) Thomson Gale.

Haugen, Brenda. Annie Oakley: American Sharpshooter. (Illus.). 112p. (J). 2007. pap. (***978-0-7565-1974-2(8));** 2006. lib. bdg. (***978-0-7565-1869-1(5)**) Compass Point Bks.

Johns, Michael-Anne. Cool in School. 1999. (gr. 3-6). lib. bdg. 11.80 (978-0-613-24678-1(0)) Tandem Library Bks.

—Stars in School: Celebrity Yearbook. 2002. (Illus.). 48p. (J). (978-0-439-44381-4(4)) Scholastic, Inc.

Korb, Rena B. Pulling down the Walls: The Struggle of African American Performers. 2005. (Illus.). 24p. (J). (***978-0-328-13625-4(5)** , Scott Foresman) Addison-Wesley Educational Pubs., Inc.

Krohn, Katherine E. Rosie O'Donnell. 1998. (Biography Ser.). (Illus.). 112p. (YA). (gr. 6-12). lib. bdg. 27.93 (978-0-8225-4939-0(5) , Lerner Pubns.) Lerner Publishing Group.

Kunstler, James Howard. Annie Oakley. Warter, Fred, illus. 2005. (Rabbit Ears-A Classic Tale Ser.). 40p. (J). (gr. k-5). 25.65 (978-1-59197-759-9(2)) Spotlight.

Landau, Elaine. Annie Oakley: Wild West Sharpshooter. 2004. (Best of the West Biographies Ser.). (Illus.). 48p. (J). lib. bdg. 23.93 (978-0-7660-2205-8(6)) Enslow Pubs., Inc.

Macy, Sue. Bulls - Eye: A Photobiography of Annie Oakley. 2001. (Illus.). 64p. (J). (gr. 3-7). 17.95 (978-0-7922-7008-9(8) , National Geographic Children's Bks.) National Geographic Society.

—Bull's Eye: A Photobiography of Annie Oakley. 2006. 64p. (gr. 5). pap. 7.95 (978-0-7922-5933-6(5) , National Geographic Children's Bks.) National Geographic Society.

Saks, Diane. So You Want to Be a Rock n' Roll Bride. 2001. 336p. (YA). pap. 17.95 (978-0-595-18276-3(3)) iUniverse, Inc.

Schoell, William. "I Can Do Anything" The Sammy Davis, Jr. Story. 2004. (Avisson Young Adult Ser.). (Illus.). 116p. (J). pap. 19.95 (978-1-888105-61-2(5)) Avisson Pr., Inc.

Stone, Tanya Lee. Rosie O' Donnell: America's Favorite Grown-Up Kid. 2000. (Gateway Biography Ser.). (Illus.). 48p. (gr. 2-4). lib. bdg. 23.90 (978-0-7613-1724-1(4) , Millbrook Pr.) Lerner Publishing Group.

Wadsworth, Ginger. Annie Oakley. 2006. (History Maker Bios Ser.). (Illus.). 48p. (J). (gr. 3-7). 26.60 (978-0-8225-2940-8(8) , Lerner Pubns.) Lerner Publishing Group.

The Wiggles Sticker Activity Books. 2004. (J). act. bk. ed. (978-0-7666-1084-2(5) , 69585) Modern Publishing.

Williams, Brian. Sport & Entertainment: Biggest & Best. 2003. (Biggest & Best Ser.). (Illus.). 40p. (J). pap. 7.95 (978-1-84236-063-7(9)) Miles Kelly Publishing, Ltd. GBR. *Dist:* Independent Pubs. Group.

Woo, Dianne J. How to Reach Your Favorite Superstar, Vol. 2. 2001. (Illus.). 96p. (J). (gr. 3-7). pap. 4.95 (978-0-7373-0577-7(0)) Lowell Hse. Juvenile.

Woog, Adam. Frank Sinatra. 2000. (Importance of Ser.). (Illus.). 112p. (YA). (gr. 7-10). 32.45 (978-1-56006-749-8(7) , Lucent Bks.) Thomson Gale.

—Lucille Ball. 2002. (Importance of Ser.). (Illus.). 120p. (YA). (gr. 7-10). 27.45 (978-1-56006-746-7(2) , Lucent Bks.) Thomson Gale.

Zannos, Susan. Paula Abdul. 1998. (Real-Life Reader Biographies Ser.). (Illus.). 32p. (J). (gr. 4-7). lib. bdg. 15.95 (978-1-883845-74-2(2)) Mitchell Lane Pubs., Inc.

ENTERTAINING

see also Amusements; Etiquette; Games; Parties

American Girl Editorial Staff, ed. Snooze-A-Palooza! More Than 100 Slumber Party Ideas. Yoshizumi, Carol, illus. 2005. (American Girl Library). 80p. (J). pap. 9.95 (978-1-58485-978-9(4)) American Girl Publishing, Inc.

Bell, Alison. Let's Party! Chung, Kun-Sung, illus. 2005. 64p. (J). pap. 14.95 (978-1-894222-99-0(7)) Lobster Pr. CAN. *Dist:* Univ. of Toronto Pr.

Bruder, Mikyla. The Star Wars Party Book: Recipes & Ideas for Galactic Occasions. Frankeny, Frankie, illus. Frankeny, Frankie, photos by. 2002. (Star Wars Ser.). 60p. (J). (gr. 3-5). 17.95 (978-0-8118-3491-9(3)) Chronicle Bks. LLC.

Bull, Jane. Parties. 2005. (Sticker activity Bks.). 16p. (J). pap. 6.99 (978-0-7566-1223-8(3)) Dorling Kindersley Publishing, Inc.

Bull, Jane & Dorling Kindersley Publishing Staff. The Party Book. 2005. (Illus.). 48p. (J). 12.99 (978-0-7566-1028-9(1)) Dorling Kindersley Publishing, Inc.

Claycomb, Patty. Celebrations: Ages 3-5. 2002. (Early Learner Photo Fun Activities Ser.). 8p. 6.95 (978-1-56472-384-0(4)) Edupress, Inc.

Dalgleish, Sharon. Party Food. 2006. (Illus.). 32p. (J). (978-1-58340-746-2(4)) Smart Apple Media.

Dann, Penny. The Secret Fairy Party Book: Or How to Have Your Own Secret Fairy Party. Dann, Penny, illus. 1999. (Secret Fairy Ser.). (Illus.). 16p. (J). (ps-3). pap. 14.95 (978-0-531-30183-8(4) , Orchard Bks.) Scholastic, Inc.

Dorling Kindersley Publishing Staff. Party Time. 2005. (J). bds. 6.99 (978-0-7566-1110-1(5)) Dorling Kindersley Publishing, Inc.

Erwin, Vicki B. Scooby-Doo! Groovy Guide to Party Fun. 2002. (Illus.). 32p. (J). (978-0-439-37462-0(6)) Scholastic, Inc.

Evans, Lynn. Peas & Honey: A Young Persons Guide to Gracious Dining. 1999. (Illus.). (J). (gr. k-5). 10.00 (978-0-9669658-6-5(8)) Poole & Smith Publishing.

Galloway, L. A. This Is NOT Your Parents' Prom: A Handbook to Proms, Parties & Promises, 2 vols. Medick, Mike G., illus. 2002. 152p. (YA). (gr. 8-13). per. 14.99 (978-0-9718915-0-0(8)) Have Vision Pubns.

Hospitality & Tourism Careers (AVA) 2001. (YA). pap. 6.00 (978-1-57078-018-9(8) , CEV00018); pap. 8.00 (978-1-57078-019-6(6) , CEV00019) C E V Multimedia, Ltd.

Medved, Denise Sullivan. The Tiny Kitchen: Cooking & Entertaining. Healy, Todd, illus. Wellens, Jeri Pinson, photos by. 2002. 152p. 16.95 (978-0-9716028-0-9(8)) Tiny Kitchen Publishing.

Mission City Press Inc. Staff, ed. Elsie's Christmas Party: How to Plan, Prepare & Host an Old-Fashioned Christmas Party. 2000. (Elsie Dinsmore). (Illus.). 112p. (YA). (gr. 5-9). 9.99 (978-1-928749-52-3(6)) Zonderkidz.

Moreton, Daniel & Berger, Samantha. It's a Party. 1999. (Learning Center Emergent Readers Ser.). (J). pap. 2.50 (978-0-439-04587-2(8)) Scholastic, Inc.

Smith, Thomasina. I Can Have a Party: Party Activity Projects for Children. 2000. (Show Me How Ser.). (Illus.). 48p. (ps-2). pap. 7.95 (978-0-7548-0224-2(8)) Anness Publishing GBR. *Dist:* National Bk. Network.

Souter, Gillian. Perfect Parties. Watson, Clare, illus. Martin, Andre, photos by. 2001. (Handy Crafts Ser.). 48p. (J). (gr. 2 up). lib. bdg. 24.67 (978-0-8368-2822-1(4)) Stevens, Gareth Inc.

Stacy, Lori Moore. It's My Party: How to Throw a Great Bash for Any Occasion. 2000. (All about You Ser.). 144p. (J). (gr. 4-7). pap. 4.50 (978-0-439-16137-4(1)) Scholastic, Inc.

Swain, Gwenyth. Celebrating. 2003. (Small World Ser.). (Illus.). 24p. (J). (ps-2). pap. 6.95 (978-1-57505-372-1(1)) Lerner Publishing Group.

—Celebrating. 1999. (gr. k-3). lib. bdg. 15.25 (978-0-613-42480-6(8)) Tandem Library Bks.

Warner, Penny. Kids' Pick-a-Party Book: 50 Fun Party Themes for Kids, Ages 2 to 16. 1998. (Illus.). 150p. (J). 9.00 (978-0-88166-293-1(3)) Meadowbrook Pr.

Zakarin, Debra Mostow. Ultimate Sleepover Party Book. 2000. (Illus.). 160p. (YA). (gr. 3 up). pap. 5.95 (978-1-902618-99-9(8)) Element Children's Bks.

ENTERTAINING—FICTION

Aguila, Priscilla. An Unexpected Visitor. 2006. 48p. pap. 17.96 (978-1-4116-5734-2(9)) Lulu.com.

Bailey, Helen. Topaz in the Limelight. 2007. (Illus.). 144p. pap. 7.95 (***978-0-340-89348-7(6)**) Hodder Children's Division GBR. *Dist:* Independent Pubs. Group.

—Topaz Steals the Show. 2007. (Illus.). 128p. pap. 7.95 (***978-0-340-89346-3(X)**) Hodder Children's Division GBR. *Dist:* Independent Pubs. Group.

—Topaz Takes a Chance. 2007. (Illus.). 128p. pap. 7.95 (***978-0-340-89347-0(8)**) Hodder Children's Division GBR. *Dist:* Independent Pubs. Group.

Baker, Barbara. One Saturday Evening. Duke, Kate, illus. 2007. 48p. (J). (gr. 1-4). 13.99 (978-0-525-47103-5(0) , Dutton Juvenile) Penguin Group (USA) Inc.

Bourgeois, Paulette & Clark, Brenda, creators. Hurry up, Franklin. 2000. (Franklin Ser.). (Illus.). 180p. (J). (ps-3). (978-1-55074-682-2(0)) Kids Can Pr., Ltd.

Bruna, Dick. Auntie Alice's Party: A Miffy Storybook. 2000. (Miffy Ser.). (Illus.). 28p. (J). (ps-k). 4.95 (978-1-56836-304-2(4)) Kodansha America, Inc.

Burkett, Larry. Different Kind of Party. 2000. (Great Smoky Mountain Storybook Ser.). (Illus.). 32p. (J). (ps-3). 7.99 (978-0-8024-0983-6(0)) Moody Pubs.

The Costume Party. 2001. (YA). (gr. 6-12). pap. incl. audio (978-0-8224-3288-3(9)) Globe Fearon Educational Publishing.

Depisco, Dorothea. Beetle Bugs Party: A Counting Book. Parry, Jo, illus. 2005. 10p. (J). (ps-ps). 10.95 (978-1-58117-415-1(2) , Intervisual/Piggy Toes) Dalmatian Pr.

Disney Staff. Pooh's Hero Party, No. 12. 1999. (Winnie the Pooh First Readers Ser.: No. 12). (Illus.). 37p. (J). (gr. k-3). pap. 3.99 (978-0-7868-4270-4(9)) Disney Pr.

Drew, Rosa. The Block Party, Vol. 4410. Kupperstein, Joel, ed. O'Malley, Kathleen, illus. 1998. (Learn to Read Social Studies). 16p. (J). (ps-2). pap. 2.75 (978-1-57471-333-6(7) , 4410) Creative Teaching Pr., Inc.

Falwell, Cathryn. Fiesta Para 10. 2004. (SPA., Illus.). 14p. (J). (gr. k-ps). bds. 4.95 (978-0-618-44215-7(4) , Clarion Bks.) Houghton Mifflin Co. Trade & Reference Div.

French, Vivian. Princess Sophia & the Prince's Party. Gibb, Sarah, illus. 2007. (J). (***978-0-06-112450-1(8));** (Tiara Club Ser.: No. 11). 80p. pap. 3.99 (***978-0-06-112449-5(4)** , Harper Trophy) HarperCollins Pubs.

Gillham, Bill. My Dog's Party ELT Edition. Snow, Alan, illus. 2001. (Cambridge Storybooks Ser.). 8p. pap. 3.00 (978-0-521-00654-5(6)) Cambridge Univ. Pr.

Hall, Kirsten. Our Tea Party. Maccarone, Grace, ed. deRosa, Dee, illus. 2003. 32p. (J). pap. 3.99 (978-0-439-59428-8(6)) Scholastic, Inc.

Hill, Eric. Spot Goes to a Party. Hill, Eric, illus. 2004. (Illus.). 24p. (J). pap. 6.99 (978-0-14-240082-1(3) , Puffin) Penguin Group (USA) Inc.

Inui, Sekihiko. Comic Party, 3 vols., Vol. 1. 2004. (Illus.). 192p. pap. 9.99 (978-1-59182-854-9(6) , Tokyopop Adult) TOKYOPOP, Inc.

—Comic PartyTM, 3 vols., Vol. 2. Kiefl, Mike, tr. from JPN. rev. ed. 2004. (Illus.). 192p. pap. 9.99 (978-1-59182-855-6(4) , Tokyopop Adult) TOKYOPOP, Inc.

Inui, Sekihiko, creator. Comic Party, 3 vols., Vol. 3. rev. ed. 2004. (Illus.). 192p. pap. 9.99 (978-1-59182-856-3(2) , Tokyopop Adult) TOKYOPOP, Inc.

Inui, Sekihiko, illus. & creator. Comic Party, Vol. 4. Inui, Sekihiko, creator. rev. ed. 2004. 192p. pap. 9.99 (978-1-59532-584-6(0) , Tokyopop Adult) TOKYOPOP, Inc.

Lovelace, Maud Hart. Carney's House Party: A Deep Valley Book. Neville, Vera, illus. 2000. 288p. (YA). (gr. 3 up). 16.89 (978-0-06-028874-7(4)) HarperCollins Pubs.

Lutz, Nancie Anne. Patsy Ann Back Again. Lutz, Nancie Anne, illus. 2005. (Illus.). 25p. (J). pap. 14.50 (978-0-9760064-0-4(5)) Dollworks.

Maar, Paul & Schulte, T. Gloria the Cow. 2006. (Illus.). 32p. (J). 16.95 (978-0-7358-2096-8(1)) North-South Bks., Inc.

Malot, Hector & Crewe-Jones, Florence. Nobody's Boy: Companion Story to Nobody's Girl. Gooch, Thelma & Gruelle, Johnny, illus. 2006. 237p. (J). pap. (978-1-894666-75-6(5)) Inheritance Pubns.

Martin, Ann M. Karen's Show & Share. 1999. (Baby-Sitters Little Sister Ser.: No. 109). 112p. (J). (gr. 3-7). pap. 3.99 (978-0-590-50061-6(9)) Scholastic, Inc.

Older, Effin. Birthday Party. 1998. (You're Invited to Mary-Kate & Ashley's Ser.). (Illus.). 48p. (J). (gr. 2-4). pap. 12.95 (978-0-590-22593-9(6)) Scholastic, Inc.

Park, Barbara. Junie B. Jones Is a Party Animal. unabr. ed. 2004. (Junie B. Jones Ser.: No. 10). 71p. (J). (gr. k-3). pap. 17.00 incl. audio (978-0-8072-0531-0(1) , Listening Library) Random Hse. Audio Publishing Group.

Pinkwater, Daniel M. Rainy Morning. Pinkwater, Jill, illus. 1999. (Pinkwater Ser.: Vol. 1). 32p. (J). (gr. k-3). 16.00 (978-0-689-81143-2(8) , Atheneum) Simon & Schuster Children's Publishing.

Santillo, LuAnn. The Tune. Santillo, LuAnn, ed. 2003. (Half-Pint Kids Readers Ser.). (Illus.). 7p. (J). (ps-1). pap. (978-1-59256-102-5(0)) Half-Pint Kids, Inc.

Seuss, Dr. Hooper Humperdink... ? Not Him! Stevenson, James & Nash, Scott, illus. (Bright & Early Bks.). 48p. (J). (gr. k-1). 2006. 8.99 (978-0-679-88129-2(8)); 1999. lib. bdg. 12.99 (978-0-679-98129-9(2)) Random Hse. Children's Bks. (Random Hse. Bks. for Young Readers).

Thaler, Mike. The Talent Show from the Black Lagoon. D. Lee, Jared, illus. 2004. (Black Lagoon Ser.). 64p. (J). pap. 3.99 (978-0-439-43894-0(2) , Scholastic Paperbacks) Scholastic, Inc.

Trease, Christine K. The Enchanted Tea Party. Trease, Christine K., illus. 1999. (J). (ps-7). 11p. cd-rom 14.95 (978-1-929450-09-1(5)); (Illus.). 23p. 7.97 (978-1-929450-08-4(7)) Lexico.

Wells, Carolyn & E. C. CASWELL. Two Little Women on a Holiday. l.t. ed. 2006. 178p. pap. 14.99 (978-1-4264-2807-4(3)) BiblioBazaar.

ENTERTAINMENTS

see Amusements

ENTOMOLOGY

see Insects

ENTOMOLOGY, ECONOMIC

see Insects, Injurious and Beneficial

ENTOZOA

see Parasites

ENTRANCE REQUIREMENTS FOR COLLEGE AND UNIVERSITIES

see Universities and Colleges—Entrance Requirements

ENVIRONMENT

see Adaptation (Biology); Ecology; Human Beings—Effect of Environment on; Human Geography; Nature—Effect of Human Beings on

ENVIRONMENT AND PESTICIDES

see Pesticides—Environmental Aspects

ENVIRONMENTAL EFFECTS ON HUMAN BEINGS

see Human Beings—Effect of Environment on

ENVIRONMENTAL PROTECTION

see also Conservation of Natural Resources

Ada, Alma Flor & Campoy, F. Isabel. Vuelo del Quetzal. (Gateway to the Sun Ser.). (SPA.). 48p. (J). (gr. k-6). pap. 13.95 (978-1-58105-811-6(X)) Santillana USA Publishing Co., Inc.

African-American Environmentalists. Date not set. (My Ancestors—My Heroes Ser.: Vol. 32). (J). (gr. 3-4). (978-1-893091-31-3(7)) Parker Publishing Co.

Ansary, Mir Tamim. Earth Day. (Holiday Histories Ser.). (Illus.). 32p. (J). 2006. (***978-1-4034-8884-8(3));** 2001. lib. bdg. 21.36 (978-1-58810-220-1(3)) Heinemann Library.

—Earth Day. 2001. 13.75 (978-0-606-22384-3(3)) Tandem Library Bks.

Appelt, Kathi. Miss Lady Bird's Wildflowers: How a First Lady Changed America. Hein, Joy Fisher, illus. 2005. 40p. (J). 16.99 (978-0-06-001107-9(6)); lib. bdg. 17.89 (978-0-06-001108-6(4)) HarperCollins Pubs.

Baird, Nicola. A Green World? 1998. (Viewpoints Ser.). (Illus.). 32p. (J). (gr. 5-8). 23.00 (978-0-531-14451-0(8) , Watts, Franklin) Scholastic Library Publishing.

—A Green World? 2005. (Illus.). 32p. (J). (gr. 5-9). lib. bdg. 27.10 (978-1-932889-57-4(4)) Sea-To-Sea Pubns.

Bang, Molly. Nobody Particular: One Woman's Fight to Save the Bays; the Diane Wilson Story. 2005. (Illus.). 48p. (J). (gr. 4-7). pap. 10.00 (978-1-931498-94-4(6)) Chelsea Green Publishing.

Barraclough, Sue. Reusing Things. 2007. (***978-1-59771-109-8(8)**) Sea-To-Sea Pubns.

Bellamy, David & Dow, Jill. Our Changing World: The Rockpool. 2004. (Our Changing World Ser.). (Illus.). 32p. (J). pap. 7.95 (978-1-84507-220-9(0)) Lincoln, Frances Ltd. GBR. *Dist:* Perseus Distribution.

Binns, Tristan Boyer. The EPA: Environmental Protection Agency. (Government Agencies Ser.). 48p. (J). (gr. 3-5). 2003. (Illus.). lib. bdg. 27.07 (978-1-58810-497-7(4)); 2002. pap. 7.95 (978-1-58810-981-1(X) , 91596) Heinemann Library.

Bortolotti, Dan. Panda Rescue: Changing the Future for Endangered Wildlife. 2003. (Firefly Animal Rescue Ser.). (Illus.). 64p. (J). (gr. 5). pap. 9.95 (978-1-55297-557-2(6)); lib. bdg. 19.95 (978-1-55297-598-5(3)) Firefly Bks., Ltd.

—Panda Rescue: Changing the Future for Endangered Wildlife. 2003. (gr. 5-8). lib. bdg. 18.75 (978-0-613-78595-2(9)) Tandem Library Bks.

—Tiger Rescue: Changing the Future for Endangered Wildlife. 2003. (Firefly Animal Rescue Ser.). (Illus.). 64p. (J). (gr. 5). pap. 9.95 (978-1-55297-558-9(4)); lib. bdg. 19.95 (978-1-55297-599-2(1)) Firefly Bks., Ltd.

—Tiger Rescue: Changing the Future for Endangered Wildlife. 2003. (gr. 5-8). lib. bdg. 18.75 (978-0-613-78596-9(7)) Tandem Library Bks.

Bowden, Rob. Transportation & the Environment. 2004. (21st Century Debates Ser.). (Illus.). 64p. (J). 28.56 (978-0-7398-5505-8(0)) Raintree.

Brown, Paul. Global Pollution. 2003. (Face the Facts Ser.). (Illus.). 56p. (J). lib. bdg. 28.56 (978-0-7398-6433-3(5)) Raintree.

Bryan, Nichol. Environmental Disasters, 6 bks. Incl. Alamos : Wildfires. lib. bdg. 30.00 (978-0-8368-5507-4(8)); Bhopal : Chemical Plant Accident. lib. bdg. 30.00 (978-0-8368-5503-6(5)); Chernobyl : Nuclear Disaster. lib. bdg. 30.00 (978-0-8368-5504-3(3)); Danube : Cyanide Spill. lib. bdg. 30.00 (978-0-8368-5505-0(1)); Exxon Valdez : Oil Spill. lib. bdg. 30.00 (978-0-8368-5506-7(X)); Love Canal : Pollution Crisis. lib. bdg. 30.00 (978-0-8368-5508-1(6)); 48p. (YA). (gr. 5 up). (Illus.). 2003. Set lib. bdg. 180.00 (978-0-8368-5502-9(7) , World Almanac Library) Stevens, Gareth Inc.

—Love Canal: Pollution Crisis. 2003. (Environmental Disasters Ser.). (Illus.). 48p. (gr. 5 up). (YA). lib. bdg. 30.00 (978-0-8368-5508-1(6)); (J). pap. 11.95 (978-0-8368-5515-9(9)) Stevens, Gareth Inc. (World Almanac Library).

Buffett, Howard G. Cuidando Nuestro Mundo. Buffett, Devon G., ed. 2001. Tr. of Taking Care of Our World. (SPA., Illus.). 48p. (J). (gr. 2-5). (978-0-9707385-2-3(8)) BioImages.

—Taking Care of Our World. 2002. (Illus.). 46p. (J). reprint ed. (978-0-9707385-5-4(2)) BioImages.

Buffett, Howard G. & Buffett, Devon G. Taking Care of Our World. 2001. (Illus.). 48p. (J). (gr. 2-5). (978-0-9707385-1-6(X)) BioImages.

Bull, Jane. Make It! 2008. 128p. (J). (gr. 2-6). 16.99 (***978-0-7566-3837-5(2)***) Dorling Kindersley Publishing, Inc.

Burstein, Chaya M. The Kids' Catalog of Animals & the Earth. 2005. (Illus.). 200p. (J). pap. 16.95 (978-0-8276-0785-9(7)) Jewish Pubn. Society.

Burton, John, ed. The Atlas of Endangered Species. 2nd ed. 1998. (Illus.). 276p. (YA). 135.00 (978-0-02-865034-0(4) , GML00502-166800, Macmillan Reference USA) Thomson Gale.

Burton, Margie, et al. Are We Hurting the Earth. Adams, Alison, ed. 1999. (Early Connections Ser.). 16p. (J). (gr. k-2). pap. 4.50 (978-1-58344-053-7(4)) Benchmark Education Co.

—Reduce, Reuse, & Recycle. Adams, Alison, ed. 1999. (Early Connections Ser.). 16p. (J). (gr. k-2). pap. 4.50 (978-1-58344-079-7(8)) Benchmark Education Co.

Byles, Monica. Los Polos. (Coleccion Tierra Viva).Tr. of Polar Lands. (SPA.). 32p. (YA). (gr. 5-8). (978-84-348-3372-2(7)) SM Ediciones.

Byrnes, Patricia. Environmental Pioneers. 1998. (Profiles Ser.). (Illus.). 160p. (gr. 5 up). lib. bdg. 19.95 (978-1-881508-45-8(5)) Oliver Pr., Inc.

Cefrey, Holly. What If the Hole in the Ozone Layer Grows Larger? 2002. (High Interest Bks.). (Illus.). 48p. (YA). (gr. 7-12). pap. 6.95 (978-0-516-23476-2(5) , Children's Pr.) Scholastic Library Publishing.

—What If the Hole in the Ozone Layer Grows Larger? 2002. (gr. 7-12). lib. bdg. 15.25 (978-0-613-58816-4(9)) Tandem Library Bks.

Challen, Paul C. Environmental Disaster Alert! 2004. (Disaster Alert! Ser.). (Illus.). 32p. (J). (978-0-7787-1581-8(7)); pap. (978-0-7787-1613-6(9)) Crabtree Publishing Co.

Chandler, Gary & Graham, Kevin. Making a Better World, 4 bks. Incl. Guardians of Wildlife. (YA). lib. bdg. 25.90 (978-0-8050-4626-7(7) , Twenty-First Century Bks.); Kids Who Make a Difference. lib. bdg. 25.90 (978-0-8050-4625-0(9) , Millbrook Pr.); Natural Foods & Products. lib. bdg. 25.90 (978-0-8050-4623-6(2) , Millbrook Pr.); Recycling. lib. bdg. 25.90 (978-0-8050-4622-9(4) , Twenty-First Century Bks.); 64p. (gr. 5 up). 1997. (Illus.). Set lib. bdg. 103.60 (978-0-7613-3066-0(6) , Twenty-First Century Bks.) Lerner Publishing Group.

Christy, Judith. Green - Our Heritage, Our Home. Mazgaj, Sharon Frank, illus. 2002. (YA). (gr. 4 up). 15.00 (978-0-9717616-0-5(4)) Green Local Schl. District.

Connolly, Sean. Safeguarding the Environment. 2005. (Campaigns for Change Ser.). (Illus.). 48p. (J). (gr. 6-9). lib. bdg. 29.95 (978-1-58340-519-2(4)) Smart Apple Media.

Cooper, Jason. Earth Day. 2002. (Rourke Discovery Library). (Illus.). 24p. (J). lib. bdg. 20.64 (978-1-58952-218-3(4)) Rourke Publishing, LLC.

Dalgleish, Sharon. Cleaning the Air. 2002. (Our World - Our Future Ser.). (Illus.). 32p. (gr. 4-8). 28.00 (978-0-7910-7019-2(0) , Chelsea Hse.) Facts On File, Inc.

—Managing the Land. 2003. (Our World - Our Future Ser.). (Illus.). 32p. (gr. 4-8). 27.00 (978-0-7910-7020-8(4) , Chelsea Hse.) Facts On File, Inc.

David C. Cook. Families, the Environment, Sports & Competition. 2003. (Domain 456 Ser.). 128p. (J). (gr. 4-6). pap., pap. 15.99 (978-0-7814-5514-5(6) , 0781455146) Cook, David C. Publishing Co.

Donald, Rhonda Lucas. The Ozone Layer. 2002. (978-0-606-22876-3(4)) Tandem Library Bks.

Engineering Animation Inc., Staff. Environmental Science ESP. 2nd ed. 2001. (C). (gr. 6-12). cd-rom 20.63 (978-0-07-239912-7(0) , 9780072399127) Glencoe/McGraw-Hill.

Environment. (YA). (gr. 6-12). 19.47 (978-0-673-21549-9(0)) Addison-Wesley Educational Pubs., Inc.

Environmental - Saving Our Earth, 6 bks., Set. (J). (gr. k-6). lib. bdg. 111.70 (978-1-56674-933-6(6)) Forest Hse. Publishing Co., Inc.

Featherstone, Jane. Energy. 1999. (Ecology Alert Ser.). 32p. (YA). (gr. 3-7). 25.69 (978-0-8172-5374-5(2)) Raintree.

Fourment, Tiffany. My Water Comes from the Mountains. Emerling, Dorothy, illus. 2004. 32p. 19.95 (978-1-57098-387-0(9)) Rinehart, Roberts Pubs.

Franklin Watts, Inc. Staff & Myers, Chris. The Dictionary of the Environment & Its Biomes. 2001. (Reference Ser.). (Illus.). 128p. (J). (gr. 2-6). 35.00 (978-0-531-11983-9(1) , Watts, Franklin) Scholastic Library Publishing.

Freeman, Marcia. Wetlands. Whitfield, Jennifer, ed. 1998. (Early Science Ser.). 16p. (J). (ps-2). pap., stu. ed. 3.33 (978-1-56784-382-8(4)); (Illus.). pap. 16.95 (978-1-56784-381-1(6)) Sundance/Newbridge Educational Publishing.

Galko, Francine. Earth Friends, 4 bks. 2004. (J). (gr. k-2). lib. bdg. 96.86 (978-1-4034-4899-6(X)) Heinemann Library.

—Earth Friends at Home. 2004. (Heinemann First Library). (Illus.). 32p. (J). pap. 7.25 (978-1-4034-4900-9(7)) Heinemann Library.

—Earth Friends at Play. 2004. (Heinemann First Library). (Illus.). 32p. (J). pap. 6.95 (978-1-4034-4901-6(5)) Heinemann Library.

—Earth Friends at School. 2004. (Heinemann First Library). (Illus.). 32p. (J). pap. 6.95 (978-1-4034-4902-3(3)); lib. bdg. 22.79 (978-1-4034-4897-2(3)) Heinemann Library.

—Earth Friends at the Grocery Store. 2004. (Heinemann First Library). (Illus.). 32p. (J). pap. (978-1-4034-4903-0(1)) Heinemann Library.

—Ecology at Home. 2004. (Heinemann First Library). (Illus.). 32p. (J). lib. bdg. 22.79 (978-1-4034-4895-8(7)) Heinemann Library.

—Ecology at the Grocery Store. 2004. (Heinemann First Library). (Illus.). 32p. (J). lib. bdg. 22.79 (978-1-4034-4898-9(1)) Heinemann Library.

—Ecology on the Playground. 2004. (Heinemann First Library). (Illus.). 32p. (J). lib. bdg. 22.79 (978-1-4034-4896-5(5)) Heinemann Library.

Garrett, Leslie. Earth Smart. 2006. (Dk Readers Ser.). (Illus.). 32p. (J). 14.99 (978-0-7566-1913-8(0)); pap. 3.99 (978-0-7566-1912-1(2)) Dorling Kindersley Publishing, Inc.

Gifford, Clive. Sustainable Development. 2003. (Face the Facts Ser.). (Illus.). 56p. (J). lib. bdg. 28.56 (978-0-7398-6851-5(9)) Raintree.

Globe-Fearon Staff. Working Together Against Destruction of the Environment. 64p. (YA). (gr. 6-12). pap. 15.95 (978-0-8359-1130-6(6)) Globe Fearon Educational Publishing.

Green Alert Set 1, 7 vols., Set. 2004. (Illus.). (J). 171.36 (978-0-7398-7017-4(3)) Raintree.

Green, Jen. The Polluted Planet. 2004. (J). lib. bdg. (978-1-59389-140-4(7)) Chrysalis Education.

—Why Should I Protect Nature? Gordon, Mike, illus. 2005. (Why Should I? Bks.). 32p. (J). pap. 5.95 (978-0-7641-3154-7(0)) Barron's Educational Series, Inc.

Green, Jen & Inskipp, Carol. Improving Our Environment, 4 Vols. 98.68 (978-0-8368-4427-6(0)) Stevens, Gareth Inc.

The Green World. 2006. (Illus.). (gr. 6-12). 195.65 (978-0-7910-9098-5(1)) Facts On File, Inc.

Gresham, Joel. Our Bearable World: Featuring the Imagination Bears. 2005. 19.95 (***978-0-9708446-8-2(9)***) Gresham, Joel.

Hare, Tony. Capa de Ozono. 6th ed. Tr. of Ozone Layer. (SPA., Illus.). 32p. (J). 10.95 (978-84-348-3260-2(7)) SM Ediciones ESP. *Dist:* AIMS International Bks., Inc.

Harmon, Daniel E. The Environmental Protection Agency. 2002. (Your Government Ser.). (Illus.). 64p. (J). 25.00 (978-0-7910-6792-5(0) , Chelsea Hse.) Facts On File, Inc.

Haynes, Diane. Flight or Fight. 2006. (Wildlife Rescue Ser.). 284p. (J). (gr. 7-11). pap. 6.95 (978-1-55285-658-1(5) , Walrus Bks.) Whitecap Bks., Ltd. CAN. *Dist:* Firefly Bks., Ltd.

Hillstrom, Laurie Collier & Hillstrom, Kevin, eds. Biography Today: Profiles of People of Interest to Young Readers. 2000. (World Leaders Ser.: Vol. 3). (Illus.). 200p. (YA). (gr. 5 up). lib. bdg. 39.00 (978-0-7808-0418-0(X)) Omnigraphics, Inc.

Holt, Rinehart and Winston Staff. Environmental Science: Assessments. 4th ed. 2004. (SPA.). pap. 16.33 (978-0-03-068344-2(0)) Holt, Rinehart & Winston.

—Environmental Science 2004. 4th ed. 2004. (SPA.). pap., stu. ed. 11.13 (978-0-03-068343-5(2)) Holt, Rinehart & Winston.

—Holt Science & Technology Chapter 21: Life Science: Environmental Problems & Solutions. 5th ed. 2004. (Illus.). pap. 12.86 (978-0-03-030236-7(6)) Holt, Rinehart & Winston.

Jeffers, Susan. Brother Eagle, Sister Sky. Jeffers, Susan, illus. 2002. (Illus.). 32p. (J). (gr. k up). pap. 7.99 (978-0-14-230132-6(9) , Puffin) Penguin Group (USA) Inc.

—Brother Eagle, Sister Sky. 2002. (gr. 3-6). lib. bdg. 16.45 (978-0-613-45249-6(6)) Tandem Library Bks.

Jerome, Kate Boehm. Protecting the Planet. 2003. (Life Science Ser.). (Illus.). 32p. (J). pap. (978-0-7922-8864-0(5)) National Geographic Society.

Kruger, Leanne Flett. Taking Care of Mother Earth. Hamelin, Marie-Micheline, illus. 2006. 20p. (J). pap. 10.95 (978-1-894778-30-5(8)) Theytus Bks., Ltd. CAN. *Dist:* Orca Bk. Pubs. USA.

Landau, Elaine. Earth Day: Keeping Our Planet Clean. 2002. (Finding Out about Holidays Ser.). (Illus.). 48p. (J). (gr. 1-4). lib. bdg. 23.93 (978-0-7660-1778-8(8)) Enslow Pubs., Inc.

Leedy, Loreen. The Great Trash Bash. Leedy, Loreen, illus. 2005. (Illus.). 32p. (J). (gr. k-3). pap. 6.95 (978-0-8234-1634-9(8)) Holiday Hse., Inc.

Llewellyn, Claire. Let's Recycle. 2005. (Illus.). 32p. (YA). (gr. 1 up). lib. bdg. 27.10 (978-1-932333-22-0(3)) Chrysalis Education.

—Protect Natural Habitats. 2005. (Illus.). 32p. (YA). (gr. 1 up). lib. bdg. 27.10 (978-1-932333-20-6(7)) Chrysalis Education.

Loeschnig, L. V. Experimentos Sencillos Sobre el Espacio y el Vuelo. (Juego de la Ciencia Ser.). (SPA.). 128p. (gr. 5-8). 5.20 (978-84-95456-56-4(7) , 87803) Ediciones Oniro S.A. ESP. *Dist:* Bilingual Pubns. Co., The, Lectorum Pubns., Inc., Libros Sin Fronteras.

Lopatka, Michael, creator. A. P. Environmental Science. 2002. (YA). lib. bdg., stu. ed., wbk. ed. 15.95 (978-0-9703694-6-8(8)) Awesome Guides, Inc.

Mallory, Kenneth. A Home by the Sea: Protecting Coastal Wildlife. 2003. (Illus.). 64p. (YA). (gr. 4-8). reprint ed. 20.00 (978-0-7567-6562-0(5)) DIANE Publishing Co.

Mandell, M. Experimentos Sencillos Sobre el Tiempo. (Juego de la Ciencia Ser.). (SPA.). 118p. (gr. 5-8). 5.20 (978-84-95456-78-6(8) , 87805) Ediciones Oniro S.A. ESP. *Dist:* Bilingual Pubns. Co., The, Lectorum Pubns., Inc., Libros Sin Fronteras.

Manos, John. It's Earth Day! 2006. (Early Explorers Ser.). (J). 36.00 (***978-1-4108-6124-5(4)***) Benchmark Education Co.

Margaret, Amy. Earth Day. 2002. (Library of Holidays). (Illus.). 24p. (J). lib. bdg. 18.75 (978-0-8239-5787-3(X) , PowerKids Pr.) Rosen Publishing Group, Inc., The.

Marx, David F. Earth Day. 2001. (Rookie Read-About Holidays Ser.). (Illus.). 32p. (J). (gr. 1-2). pap. 5.95 (978-0-516-27174-3(1) , Children's Pr.) Scholastic Library Publishing.

—Earth Day: Holidays. 2001. (Rookie Read-About Holidays Ser.). (Illus.). 32p. (J). (gr. 1-2). 19.50 (978-0-516-22231-8(7) , Children's Pr.) Scholastic Library Publishing.

Maze, Stephanie. I Want to Be an Environmentalist. 2000. (I Want to Be Ser.). (Illus.). 48p. (YA). (gr. 4-9). lib. bdg. 27.12 (978-0-7398-3071-0(6)) Raintree.

—I Want to Be an Environmentalist. 2000. 15.80 (978-0-606-20327-2(3)); (gr. 3-6). lib. bdg. 17.65 (978-0-613-30505-1(1)) Tandem Library Bks.

Mazur, Ivan & Mazur, Elena. Neptune's Kingdom. Freedman, Stella, ed. Piatikop, Alexander, illus. 1998. (Ecology for Children Ser.: Vol. 1). 48p. (J). (gr. 2-6). 11.95 (978-1-892316-03-5(X)) Rama Pr., Inc.

McCauley, John. Harley Teaches. McCauley, John, illus. 1998. (Illus.). 34p. (J). (gr. k-6). 12.95 (978-0-9664005-7-1(7)) American Health Pr.

Mir Tamim Ansary. Earth Day. 2nd ed. 2006. (Holiday Histories Ser.). (Illus.). 32p. (J). pap. (***978-1-4034-8897-8(5)***) Heinemann Library.

Murdico, Suzanne J. Volunteering to Help the Environment. 2000. (High Interest Bks.). (Illus.). 48p. (YA). (gr. 7-12). 23.00 (978-0-516-23373-4(4)); pap. 6.95 (978-0-516-23573-8(7)) Scholastic Library Publishing. (Children's Pr.).

—Volunteering to Help the Environment. 2000. (gr. 3-6). lib. bdg. 15.25 (978-0-613-89020-5(5)) Tandem Library Bks.

Nelson, Robin. Earth Day. 2003. (First Step Nonfiction Ser.). (Illus.). 24p. (J). (gr. k-2). lib. bdg. 18.60 (978-0-8225-1283-7(1)) Lerner Publishing Group.

Nobleman, Marc Tyler. Earth Day. 2004. (Let's See Ser.). 24p. (J). (gr. 1 up). lib. bdg. 19.93 (978-0-7565-0645-2(X)) Compass Point Bks.

Nolan, Andrea J. Understanding Garbage & Our Environment. Sarquis, Mickey, ed. 1999. 305p. (J). pap. 23.95 (978-1-883822-35-4(1)) Terrific Science Pr.

On the Verge of Extinction: Crisis in the Environment, 5 vols., Set. Incl. Frogs in Danger. Whiting, Jim. lib. bdg. 25.70 (***978-1-58415-585-0(X));*** Polar Bears on the Hudson Bay. Leathers, Dan. lib. bdg. 25.70 (***978-1-58415-586-7(8));*** Snows of Kilimanjaro. Leathers, Dan. lib. bdg. 25.70 (***978-1-58415-584-3(1));*** Threat of the Monarch Butterfly. Thatcher, Rebecca. lib. bdg. 25.70 (***978-1-58415-587-4(6));*** Threat to Ancient Egyptian Treasures. Whiting, Jim. lib. bdg. 25.70 (***978-1-58415-588-1(4));*** (Illus.). 32p. (J). (gr. 1-4). 2007. Set lib. bdg. 128.50 (***978-1-58415-589-8(2)***) Mitchell Lane Pubs., Inc.

Ostopowich, Melanie. Greenpeace. 2002. (International Organizations Ser.). (Illus.). 32p. (J). lib. bdg. 16.95 (978-1-59036-020-0(6)) Weigl Pubs., Inc.

Our Future. 2003. (Our World Ser.). (Illus.). (gr. 4-8). lib. bdg. 113.70 (978-0-7910-7059-8(X) , Chelsea Hse.) Facts On File, Inc.

Parry, Ann. Greenpeace. 2005. (Humanitarian Organizations Ser.). (Illus.). 32p. (J). (gr. 5-8). lib. bdg. 22.95 (978-0-7910-8815-9(4) , Chelsea Hse.) Facts On File, Inc.

Petersen, Christine. Land Preservation. 2004. (True Book Ser.). (Illus.). 48p. (J). 25.00 (978-0-516-22806-8(4) , Children's Pr.) Scholastic Library Publishing.

Peterson, Virginia, et al, eds. The Environment: Protecting Our Home. 3rd rev. ed. 1998. (Information Plus Compact Ser.). (Illus.). 88p. (YA). (gr. 6-9). pap. 22.00 (978-1-57302-080-0(X)) Thomson Gale.

Pinderhughes, John, photos by. Hurt No Living Thing. 1999. (Illus.). 18p. (J). (ps-k). mass mkt. 4.99 (978-0-7681-0104-1(2) , McClanahan Bk.) Learning Horizons, Inc.

Pratt-Serafini, Kristin Joy. A Swim Through the Sea. Pratt-Serafini, Kristin Joy, illus. 2006. (Illus.). 26p. (J). bds. 7.95 (978-1-58469-080-1(1)) Dawn Pubns.

Pringle, Laurence P. The Environmental Movement. 2000. (Illus.). 144p. (J). (gr. 5 up). 16.95 (978-0-688-15626-8(6)) HarperCollins Pubs.

—Taking Care of the Earth Vol. 1: Kids in Action. Moore, Bobbie, illus. 2003. 64p. (J). (gr. 2-4). pap. 9.95 (978-1-56397-634-6(X)) Boyds Mills Pr.

Protecting Habitats. (YA). 148.02 (978-0-8368-4990-5(6)) Stevens, Gareth Inc.

Rettungsaktion Planet Erde. (GER., Illus.). 96p. (978-3-411-08011-3(6)) Bibliographisches Institut & F. A. Brockhaus AG DEU. *Dist:* i.b.d., Ltd.

Riley, Karen. Don't Trash My Planet. 2004. (Illus.). 20p. (J). (gr. k-5). pap. 10.00 (978-0-9708135-4-1(6) , "5,000") S.C.R.A.P. Gallery.

Roop, Connie, et al. Let's Celebrate Earth Day. 2001. (Let's Celebrate Ser.). (Illus.). 32p. (gr. k-3). lib. bdg. 22.90 (978-0-7613-1812-5(7) , Millbrook Pr.) Lerner Publishing Group.

Roop, Peter & Roop, Connie. Let's Celebrate Earth Day. Connelly, Gwen, illus. 2001. 32p. pap. 6.95 (978-0-7613-1690-9(6) , Millbrook Pr.) Lerner Publishing Group.

Sanders, Nancy I. Earth Day. 2003. (True Book Ser.). (Illus.). 48p. (J). 25.00 (978-0-516-22762-7(9) , Children's Pr.) Scholastic Library Publishing.

—Earth Day, April 22. 2003. (gr. 3-6). lib. bdg. 15.25 (978-0-613-89013-7(2)) Tandem Library Bks.

Saving Our Planet. (J). (gr. 1). (978-1-56189-401-7(X) , 22011); (gr. 2). (978-1-56189-402-4(8) , 22012); (gr. 3). (978-1-56189-403-1(6) , 22013); (gr. 4). (978-1-56189-404-8(4) , 22014); (gr. 5). (978-1-56189-405-5(2) , 22015); (gr. 6). (978-1-56189-406-2(0) , 22016) School Specialty Publishing. (American Education Publishing).

Sheather, Allan. One Less Fish. Toft, Kim Michelle, illus. 1998. 32p. (J). (ps-3). 15.95 (978-0-88106-322-6(3)); pap. 6.95 (978-0-88106-323-3(1)) Charlesbridge Publishing, Inc.

Sheehan, Sean. Greenpeace. 2004. (World Watch Ser.). (Illus.). 48p. (YA). (gr. 6-8). lib. bdg. 18.99 (978-0-7398-6612-2(5)) Raintree.

Sonneborn, Liz. The Environmental Movement: Protecting Our Natural Resources. 2007. (Reform Movements in American History Ser.). 128p. (J). (gr. 6-12). 30.00 (***978-0-7910-9537-9(1)***, Chelsea Hse.) Facts On File, Inc.

Spilsbury, Richard & Spilsbury, Louise. The Earth's Resources. 2006. (Science in Focus Ser.). 48p. (J). 27.00 (978-0-7910-8863-0(4) , Chelsea Hse.) Facts On File, Inc.

Stein, Paul. Biomes of the Future. 2001. (Library of Future Weather & Climate). (Illus.). 64p. (YA). (gr. 4-6). lib. bdg. 26.50 (978-0-8239-3410-2(1)) Rosen Publishing Group, Inc., The.

Suzuki, David, narrated by. Connections: Finding Out about the Environment. 2002. (Illus.). 64p. (J). (ps-3). mass mkt. (978-0-7736-7356-4(3)) Stoddart Kids.

Taylor, Barbara. How to Save the Planet. Anderson, Scoular, illus. 2001. (How to Ser.). 96p. (J). (gr. 5-7). 16.00 (978-0-531-14640-8(5)); pap. 4.95 (978-0-531-14821-1(1)) Scholastic Library Publishing. (Watts, Franklin).

—How to Save the Planet. 2001. (gr. 5-8). lib. bdg. 12.95 (978-0-613-54552-5(4)) Tandem Library Bks.

Tesar, Jenny. Global Warming. 1999. (Illus.). 114p. (YA). (gr. 7-12). lib. bdg. 23.95 (978-0-7351-0214-9(7)) Replica Bks.

Thompson, Gare. Take Care of Our Earth. 1998. (Illus.). 32p. (ps-3). pap. 4.95 (978-0-8172-7982-0(2)) Steck-Vaughn.

Trueit, Trudi Strain. Earth Day. 2006. (Rookie Read-About Holidays Ser.). (Illus.). 31p. (978-0-531-12455-0(X)) Children's Pr., Ltd.

United Nations Environment Programme Staff & Peace Child International Staff, contrib. by. UNEP/Peace Child International. 1999. (Illus.). 96p. pap. 19.99 (978-0-237-52119-6(9) , Evans Brothers, Limited) Evans Publishing Group GBR. *Dist:* Independent Pubs. Group.

Vanase, Jessica, ed. Farms As Factories: Issues in Animal Welfare, Environmental Protection & Public Health. 2000. 32p. (YA). 3.00 (978-0-941246-11-8(6)) National Assn. for Humane & Environmental Education.

Wall, Suzy. The Earth Day Garden. 2005. 22.00 (***978-1-4108-4189-6(8)***) Benchmark Education Co.

Watson, Susan. Living Sustainably. 2003. 32p. (J). lib. bdg. 24.25 (978-1-58340-404-1(X)) Smart Apple Media.

Watts, Claire. Earth Alert. 2000. (gr. 3-6). lib. bdg. 11.80 (978-0-613-46068-2(5)) Tandem Library Bks.

Watts, Claire & Nicholson, Robert. Earth Alert. 2000. (Info Adventure Ser.). (Illus.). 32p. (J). (gr. 3-6). pap. 3.95 (978-1-58728-106-8(6) , Two Can Publishing) T&N Children's Publishing.

West, Krista. Critical Perspectives on Environmental Protection. 2006. (Scientific American Critical Anthologies on Environment & Climate Ser.). (Illus.). 224p. (YA). (gr. 9-12). lib. bdg. 31.95 (978-1-4042-0691-5(4)) Rosen Publishing Group, Inc., The.

Williams, Brenda. Your Environment. 1998. (Geography Starts Here Ser.). (Illus.). 32p. (J). (gr. 1-4). lib. bdg. 25.69 (978-0-8172-5117-8(0)) Raintree.

Wines, Jacquie. You Can Save the Planet: 101 Ways You can Make a Difference. 2008. 112p. (J). pap. 4.99 (***978-0-545-05332-7(3)***, Scholastic Reference) Scholastic, Inc.

Wolf, Ann M. & Spitz, Anna H. What's Hazardous in Our Home? 1998. (Environmental Ser.). (Illus.). 93p. (Orig.). (J). (gr. 6-8). pap. 9.50 (978-1-892816-01-6(6) , SER-201) Sonora Environmental Research Institute, Inc.

Wood, Jenny. Los Desiertos. (Coleccion Tierra Viva).Tr. of Deserts. (SPA.). 32p. (YA). (gr. 5-8). (978-84-348-3266-4(6)) SM Ediciones.

Woods, Mae. Protecting the Rain Forest. 1999. (Rain Forest Ser.). (Illus.). 24p. (J). (gr. k-6). lib. bdg. 21.35 (978-1-57765-022-5(0) , Checkerboard Library) ABDO Publishing Co.

Woodward, John & Skancke, Jennifer. Conserving the Environment. 2006. (Current Controversies Ser.). (Illus.). 244p. (YA). (gr. 7 up). pap. 24.95 (978-0-7377-2477-6(3)); lib. bdg. 36.20 (978-0-7377-2476-9(5)) Thomson Gale. (Greenhaven Pr., Inc.).

ENVIRONMENTAL PROTECTION—FICTION

Amis, Yana. The Adventurers of Crystal Lake. 1998. (978-0-921252-85-6(4)) LEGAS.

Anholt, Laurence. Eco-Wolf & the Three Pigs. 2004. (Illus.). 64p. (C). (gr. 3-5). 13.26 (978-0-7565-0630-8(1)) Compass Point Bks.

Baby Lauren & Theodore, Paperback. 2007. (J). pap. 9.95 (***978-0-9779643-0-7(2)***) Healing Tree Arts.

Banks, John. Doorway to Darkness. Liew, Sonny, illus. 2007. (J). 80p. (***978-1-59889-351-9(3)***); 75p. pap. (***978-1-59889-446-2(3)***) Stone Arch Bks.

Baskwill, Jane. Touch the Earth. Fiore, Peter M., illus. 1999. 32p. (J). (gr. 1-5). pap. 4.95 (978-1-57255-428-3(2)) Mondo Publishing.

Beadle, David M. The Day the Trash Came Out to Play. Faust, Laurie A., illus. 2004. 32p. (J). 16.95 (978-0-9727855-0-1(7)) Ezra's Earth Publishing.

Bjork, Linda. Salmon Cavern. 2006. 92p. pap. 10.95 (978-1-59800-546-2(4)) Outskirts Press, Inc.

Brimner, Larry Dane. Trash Trouble. Tripp, Christine, illus. 2003. (Rookie Choices Ser.). 32p. (J). 20.50 (978-0-516-22547-0(2) , Children's Pr.) Scholastic Library Publishing.

Burningham, John. Whadayamean. 1999. (Illus.). (J). lib. bdg. (978-0-375-90177-5(9)) Crown Publishing Group.

—Whadayamean. 1999. (Illus.). (J). 19.00 (978-0-375-80177-8(4)) Knopf, Alfred A. Inc.

Carlson, Melody. Project, Take Charge. 2007. (Faithgirlz!#8482; / Girls of 622 Harbor View Ser.). 144p. (J). pap. 6.99 (978-0-310-71189-6(4)) Zonderkidz.

Child, Lauren. What Planet Are You from, Clarice Bean? Child, Lauren, illus. 2002. (Illus.). 32p. (J). (gr. 1-5). 16.99 (978-0-7636-1696-0(6)) Candlewick Pr.

Cole, Sheila. The Canyon. 2002. 160p. (J). (gr. 3-7). 15.89 (978-0-06-029496-0(5)) HarperCollins Pubs.

Cooper, Susan. Green Boy. (Illus.). 208p. (J). 2003. pap. 5.99 (978-0-689-84760-8(2) , Aladdin); 2002. (gr. 4-6). 16.00 (978-0-689-84751-6(3) , McElderry, Margaret K.) Simon & Schuster Children's Publishing.

Delaney, Mark. The Kingfisher's Tale. 2000. (Misfits, Inc. Ser.: No. 4). 216p. (J). (gr. 7-11). pap. 5.95 (978-1-56145-226-2(2)) Peachtree Pubs., Ltd.

—The Kingfisher's Tale. 2000. (Misfits, Inc. Ser.). (J). (978-0-606-19862-2(8)) Tandem Library Bks.

—Kingfisher's Tale. 2000. (gr. 7-12). lib. bdg. 14.10 (978-0-613-85287-6(7)) Tandem Library Bks.

Doolittle, Bev & Maclay, Elise. The Earth Is My Mother. Doolittle, Bev, illus. 2000. (Illus.). 176p. (J). (gr. 4-7). tchr. ed. 17.95 (978-0-86713-044-7(X) , 85163) Greenwich Workshop Pr.

Ellis, A. G. A Trellis for Mr. Ellis: Or How I Saved the World from Global Warming. Ellis, A. G. & Deaton, T. K., illus. l.t. ed. 2002. 32p. (J). per. 8.95 (978-0-9717451-1-7(0) , Louisa May Allcat Children's Bks.) Allcat Pr.

Garrett, Ann. Keeper of the Swamp. 1999. (gr. 3-6). lib. bdg. 17.60 (978-0-613-50211-5(6)) Tandem Library Bks.

—Keeper of the Swamp. Chandler, Karen, illus. 40p. (J). 2001. (ps-3). pap. 8.95 (978-1-890515-27-0(2)); 1998. (SPA.). (gr. 1-4). 16.95 (978-1-890515-12-6(4)) Turtle Bks.

Golding, Julia. The Gorgon's Gaze. 2007. (Companions Quartet Ser.). 320p. (YA). (gr. 5 up). 16.99 (***978-0-7614-5377-2(6)***) Cavendish, Marshall Corp.

—Secret of the Sirens. Wyatt, David, illus. 2007. 384p. (YA). (gr. 5 up). 16.99 (***978-0-7614-5371-0(7)***) Cavendish, Marshall Corp.

Golio, Janet & Golio, Mike. Present from the Past. 2nd ed. 2007. 120p. (YA). pap. 14.99 (***978-1-59092-145-6(3)*** , Blue Works) Windstorm Creative.

Golio, Janet, et al. A Present from the Past: Multimedia Edition. 2000. (Illus.). III, 157p. (J). (gr. 4-7). cd-rom 14.95 (978-0-9704202-0-6(X)) GAGA.

Hallinan, P. K. Por Amor a Nuestra Tierra. Marcuse, Aida E., tr. 2000. (SPA., Illus.). (J). (gr. k-3). pap. 6.95 (978-1-880507-58-2(7) , LC4712) Lectorum Pubns., Inc.

Hallinan, P. K., illus. For the Love of Our Earth. 2001. 24p. (J). (ps-3). 7.95 (978-0-8249-5384-3(3)); pap. 5.95 (978-0-8249-5385-0(1)) Ideals Pubns. (Ideals).

Halsey, Megan. Three Pandas Planting. 1999. mass mkt. 3.99 (978-0-689-83304-5(0) , Aladdin) Simon & Schuster Children's Publishing.

Hamilton, Elizabeth L. Secret of Cachuma Lake. 2001. (Travel Adventure Ser.: Bk. 1). (Illus.). 144p. (YA). per. 9.95 (978-0-9713749-7-3(X)) Quiet Impact, Inc.

Hautman, Pete & Logue, Mary. Skullduggery. 2007. (Bloodwater Mysteries Ser.). 176p. (J). (gr. 5-9). 16.99 (978-0-399-24378-3(X) , Putnam Juvenile) Penguin Group (USA) Inc.

Hiaasen, Carl. Flush. 272p. (J). (gr. 5). 2007. pap. 8.99 (***978-0-375-84185-9(7)***); 2005. lib. bdg. 18.99 (978-0-375-92182-7(6)); 2005. 16.95 (978-0-375-82182-0(1)) Random Hse. Children's Bks. (Knopf Bks. for Young Readers).

—Flush. l.t. ed. 2005. 335p. (YA). 23.95 (978-0-7862-7908-1(7)) Thorndike Pr.

—Hoot. 304p. (gr. 5 up). 2002. (Illus.). (J). 15.95 (978-0-375-82181-3(3)); 2002. (Illus.). (J). lib. bdg. 17.99 (978-0-375-92181-0(8)); 2004. (YA). reprint ed. pap. 8.95 (978-0-375-82916-1(4)) Random Hse. Children's Bks. (Knopf Bks. for Young Readers).

—Hoot. 2003. 25.95 (978-0-7862-5014-1(3)) Thorndike Pr.

Hoobler, Dorothy & Hoobler, Thomas. The 1980s: Earthsong. Hoffman, Robin, illus. 2002. (Century Kids Ser.). 160p. (gr. 5-8). lib. bdg. 22.90 (978-0-7613-1608-4(6) , Twenty-First Century Bks.) Lerner Publishing Group.

Joslin, Mary. The Tale of the Heaven Tree. So, Meilo, illus. 1999. 32p. (J). (ps-3). 16.00 (978-0-8028-5190-1(8) , Eerdmans Bks For Young Readers) Eerdmans, William B. Publishing Co.

Koss, Amy Goldman. Kailey. Howe, Philip, illus. 2003. (American Girl of Today Ser.). 152p. (J). pap. 6.95 (978-1-58485-591-0(6)) American Girl Publishing, Inc.

—Kailey. 2003. (gr. 3-6). lib. bdg. 15.25 (978-0-613-86379-7(8)) Tandem Library Bks.

LeBox, Annette. Miracle at Willowcreek. 1998. (Illus.). 288p. pap. 6.95 (978-1-896764-04-7(5)) Second Story Pr. CAN. *Dist:* Orca Bk. Pubs. USA.

Lee, Julia Elizabeth. Seahorses Down Under. Weiser, Robert, ed. (Defenders of Wildlife Ser.). (Illus.). 50+p. (J). (gr. k-3). lib. bdg. 9.95 (978-0-9666857-0-1(9)) Dawn of Day Childrens Publishing Co., Inc.

Livingston, Timothy J. & Livingston, Mary A. Working with Nature Set, 2 bks. Livingston, Timothy J., illus. 2006th ed. 2006. (Illus.). (J). 32.95 (***978-0-9635757-3-9(2)***) Red Tail Publishing.

Lowery, Paul. Do You Know Where Sea Turtles Go? 2007. (J). 15.99 (***978-0-9792379-0-4(4)***) PBL Stories LLC.

Lyons, Dana. The Tree. Danioth, David, illus. l.t. ed. 2002. 32p. 16.95 (978-0-9701907-1-0(9)) Illumination Arts Publishing Co., Inc.

Mark of the Stone. 2000. 45p. (J). (gr. 3-6). per. 9.99 (978-0-9707770-0-3(0)) Blue Horse Mukwa Publishing.

Markowitz-Meredith, Susan. Environmentally Friendly World. checkpt. ed. 2003. (Early Connections Ser.). (J). pap. 35.00 (978-1-4108-1561-3(7)) Benchmark Education Co.

Markowitz, Susan Meredith. The el gran bosque verde & Great Green Forest. 2005. spiral bd. 66.00 (***978-1-4108-5653-1(4)***) Benchmark Education Co.

McCluskey, J. E. The Adventures of Peter the Pleasant Platypus & Friends: First Adventure, Tidy Time. 2004. 48p. pap. 19.95 (978-1-4137-2546-9(5)) PublishAmerica, Inc.

McDonald, Megan. Judy Moody Saves the World! Reynolds, Peter H., illus. (Judy Moody Ser.: No. 3). 160p. (J). (gr. 1-5). 2004. pap. 5.99 (978-0-7636-2087-5(4)); 2002. 15.99 (978-0-7636-1446-1(7)) Candlewick Pr.

Medlicott, Mary. Open Secret. 2004. 156p. pap. 12.95 (978-1-84323-289-6(8)) Beekman Bks., Inc.

Montgomery, R. A. Forecast from Stonehenge. 2007. (Choose Your Own Adventure Ser.: No. 19). (Illus.). 144p. (J). mass mkt. 6.99 (***978-1-933390-19-2(0)***) Chooseco LLC.

Remnant-Ashton, Rod. The Roseland Mysteries. 2005. 128p. (J). pap. 15.00 (978-1-4116-5166-1(9)) Lulu.com.

Schimmel, Schim. Children of the Earth Remember. 2002. (Illus.). 22p. (J). (ps up). bds. 6.95 (978-1-55971-834-9(X) , NorthWord Bks. for Young Readers) T&N Children's Publishing.

Sherrell, Deborah. Baby Lauren & Theodore,hardcover. 2007. (J). bds. 17.95 (***978-0-9779643-5-2(3)***) Healing Tree Arts.

Sullivan, Jenny. Nowhere Again. 2004. 228p. pap. 13.95 (978-1-84323-297-1(9)) Beekman Bks., Inc.

Terry & the Ecological Disaster. pap. (978-1-56002-792-8(4)) Univ. Editions.

Thomas, Rob. Green Thumb. unabr. ed. 2000. (YA). pap. 59.00 incl. audio (978-0-7887-3641-4(8) , 41007) Recorded Bks., LLC.

—Green Thumb. 2000. (978-0-606-20048-6(7)) Tandem Library Bks.

Tomkins, D. Michael. The World Below. 2006. (YA). lib. bdg. 39.95 (978-0-9774451-2-7(7)) DSA Publishing & Design, Inc.

Wilson, Barbara. A Clear Spring. 2002. (Girls First! Ser.: Vol. 1). 112p. 12.50 (978-1-55861-277-8(7)) Feminist Pr. at The City Univ. of New York.

Yolen, Jane. Where Have the Unicorns Gone. Sanderson, Ruth, illus. 2003. 32p. (J). 6.99 (978-0-689-86359-2(4) , Aladdin) Simon & Schuster Children's Publishing.

—Where Have the Unicorns Gone. 2003. (gr. k-3). lib. bdg. 15.30 (978-0-613-90038-6(3)) Tandem Library Bks.

EOLITHIC PERIOD

see Stone Age

EPILEPSY

Bjorklund, Ruth. Epilepsy. 2006. (Health Alert Ser.). (Illus.). 64p. (J). lib. bdg. 31.36 (978-0-7614-2206-8(4) , Benchmark Bks.) Cavendish, Marshall Corp.

Carson, Mary Kay. Epilepsy. 1998. (Diseases & People Ser.). (Illus.). 112p. (YA). (gr. 6-12). lib. bdg. 26.60 (978-0-7660-1049-9(X)) Enslow Pubs., Inc.

Chillemi, Stacey. My Mommy Has Epilepsy. 2004. 31p. 12.96 (978-1-4116-1957-9(9)) Lulu.com.

Dudley, Mark Edward. Epilepsy. rev. ed. 2001. (Health Watch Ser.). (Illus.). 48p. (YA). (gr. 4-10). lib. bdg. 23.93 (978-0-7660-1661-3(7)) Enslow Pubs., Inc.

Emanuele, Patricia. Everything You Need to Know about Epilepsy. 2005. (Need to Know Library). (Illus.). 64p. (YA). (gr. 7-12). 25.25 (978-0-8239-3161-3(7) , NTEPIL) Rosen Publishing Group, Inc., The.

Gay, Kathlyn. Epilepsy: The Ultimate Teen Guide. 2007. 112p. pap. 12.95 (***978-0-8108-5835-0(5)***) Scarecrow Pr., Inc.

Gay, Kathlyn & McGarrahan, Sean. Epilepsy: The Ultimate Teen Guide. 2002. (It Happened to Me Ser.). (Illus.). 112p. 37.50 (978-0-8108-4339-4(0)) Scarecrow Pr., Inc.

Goodfellow, Greg. Epilepsy. 2000. (Diseases & Disorders Ser.). (Illus.). 120p. (YA). (gr. 6-9). 32.45 (978-1-56006-701-6(2) , GML12001-178053, Lucent Bks.) Thomson Gale.

Gordon, Melanie Apel. Let's Talk about Epilepsy. 2000. (Let's Talk Library). (Illus.). 24p. (J). (gr. 3). lib. bdg. 18.75 (978-0-8239-5414-8(5) , PowerKids Pr.) Rosen Publishing Group, Inc., The.

Gosselin, Kim. Taking Seizure Disorders to School: A Story about Epilepsy. Freedman, Moss, illus. 2nd ed. 2001. (Special Kids in School Ser.: Vol. 3). 32p. (J). pap. 11.95 (978-1-891383-16-8(7)) JayJo Bks., LLC.

Gray, Shirley W. Living with Epilepsy. 2002. (Living Well: Chronic Conditions Ser.). (Illus.). 32p. (J). (gr. 2-6). 27.07 (978-1-56766-103-3(3)) Child's World, Inc.

Haugen, Hayley Mitchell. Epilepsy. 2004. (Understanding Diseases & Disorders Ser.). (Illus.). (J). (gr. 4-7). 26.20 (978-0-7377-2168-3(5) , Greenhaven Pr., Inc.) Thomson Gale.

Llewellyn, Claire. Epilepsy. 2001. (Illus.). 32p. (J). lib. bdg. 24.25 (978-1-929298-96-9(X)) Chrysalis Education.

O'Neill, Linda. Imagine Having Epilepsy. 2000. (Imagine Ser.). (Illus.). 32p. (J). (gr. 1-4). lib. bdg. 26.60 (978-1-57103-381-9(5)) Rourke Publishing, LLC.

Peacock, Judith. Epilepsy. 1999. (Perspectives on Disease & Illness Ser.). (Illus.). 64p. (J). (gr. 4-6). lib. bdg. 23.93 (978-0-7368-0278-9(9) , LifeMatters Bks.) Capstone Pr., Inc.

Routh, Kristina. Epilepsy. 2003. (Just the Facts Ser.). (Illus.). 56p. (J). lib. bdg. (978-1-4034-4601-5(6)) Heinemann Library.

Vander Hook, Sue. Epilepsy. 2000. (Understanding Illness Ser.). (Illus.). 32p. (J). lib. bdg. 16.95 (978-1-58340-025-8(7)) Smart Apple Media.

Westcott, Patsy. Living with Epilepsy. 1999. 32 p. (J). lib. bdg. 27.12 (978-0-8172-5570-1(2)) Raintree.

EPILEPSY—FICTION

Benjamin, E. M. Takedown. 1999. 205p. (J). (gr. 7-12). pap. 9.95 (978-1-889199-04-7(4)) Banks Channel Bks.

Charlton-Trujillo, E. E. Prizefighter en Mi Casa. (J). (gr. 5-7). 2007. 192p. 5.99 (***978-0-440-42117-7(9)*** , Yearling); 2006. 224p. 15.95 (978-0-385-73325-0(9) , Delacorte Bks. for Young Readers); 2006. 224p. lib. bdg. 17.99 (978-0-385-90344-8(8) , Delacorte Bks. for Young Readers) Random Hse. Children's Bks.

Jinks, Catherine. Pagan's Scribe. 2006. (Pagan Chronicles Ser.: Bk. 4). 368p. (YA). (gr. 7). pap. 6.99 (978-0-7636-2973-1(1)) Candlewick Pr.

Lears, Laurie. Becky the Brave: A Story about Epilepsy. Piazza, Gail, illus. 2002. 32p. (J). (gr. 1-4). 15.95 (978-0-8075-0601-1(X)) Whitman, Albert & Co.

Philbrick, Rodman. The Last Book in the Universe. 2005. 240p. mass mkt. 2.99 (978-0-439-77133-7(1)) Scholastic, Inc.

—The Last Book in the Universe. 2001. (gr. 5-8). lib. bdg. 13.00 (978-0-613-45598-5(3)) Tandem Library Bks.

Trembath, Don. Lefty Carmichael Has a Fit. 2004. 176p. (J). (gr. 7-12). pap. 6.95 (978-1-55143-166-6(1)) Orca Bk. Pubs. USA.

—Lefty Carmichael Has a Fit. 2000. (Illus.). (J). (978-0-606-18328-4(0)) Tandem Library Bks.

Woodworth, Adam. Monsters under My Bed. 2006. (J). per. 12.00 (***978-0-9769132-7-6(5)***) Capri Publishing.

EPISTEMOLOGY

see Knowledge, Theory of

EPIZOA

see Parasites

EQUALITY

see also Democracy; Social Classes; Socialism

Benchmark Education Staff, compiled by. Fairness & Equality. 2006. spiral bd. 125.00 (***978-1-4108-7068-1(5)***) Benchmark Education Co.

Hermann, Spring. The Struggle for Equality: Women & Minorities in America. 2006. (American Saga Ser.). (Illus.). 128p. (J). lib. bdg. 31.93 (978-0-7660-2573-8(X)) Enslow Pubs., Inc.

January, Brendan. Globalize It! The Stories of the IMF, the World Bank, the WTO - And Those Who Protest. 2003. (Single Titles Ser.). (Illus.). 144p. (gr. 7 up). 26.90 (978-0-7613-2417-1(8) , Twenty-First Century Bks.) Lerner Publishing Group.

Kallen, Stuart A. Are America's Wealthy Too Powerful? 2006. (Illus.). 128p. (gr. 10-12). 21.20 (978-0-7377-3430-0(2)); pap. 29.95 (978-0-7377-3429-4(9)) Thomson Gale. (Greenhaven Pr., Inc.).

—Does Equality Exist in America? 2006. (Illus.). 128p. (gr. 10-12). 21.20 (978-0-7377-3434-8(5)); pap. 29.95 (978-0-7377-3433-1(7)) Thomson Gale. (Greenhaven Pr., Inc.).

McGowan, Keith. Sexual Harassment. 1998. (Overview Ser.). (Illus.). 112p. (YA). (gr. 6-9). lib. bdg. 29.95 (978-1-56006-507-4(9) , LML00902-177867, Lucent Bks.) Thomson Gale.

Perfection Learning Staff, contrib. by. And Justice for All. 2000. (Literature & Thought Ser.). (Illus.). 144p. (J). (978-0-7807-9665-2(9)); pap. (978-0-7891-5228-2(2)) Perfection Learning Corp.

Rossi, Anna Maria. The Struggle for Equality: 1955-1975. 2004. (Illus.). 40p. (J). (978-0-7922-4559-9(8)) National Geographic Society.

EQUESTRIANISM

see Horsemanship

ERICSSON, JOHN, 1803-1889

Wooldridge, Connie N. Thank You Very Much, Captain Ericsson! Glass, Andrew, photos by. 2004. (Illus.). 32p. (J). (gr. k-3). tchr. ed. 16.95 (978-0-8234-1626-4(7)) Holiday Hse., Inc.

ERIKSSON, LEIF, D. CA. 1020

Kimmel, Elizabeth Cody. Before Columbus: The Leif Eriksson Expedition. 2004. 112p. (J). (gr. 3-5). pap. 5.99 (978-0-375-82307-7(7) , Random Hse. Bks. for Young Readers) Random Hse. Children's Bks.

—Before Columbus: The Leif Eriksson Expedition: A True Adventure. 2003. (Landmark Books Ser.). (Illus.). 112p. (J). (gr. 4). lib. bdg. 16.99 (978-0-375-91347-1(5) , Random Hse. Bks. for Young Readers) Random Hse. Children's Bks.

Klingel, Cynthia Fitterer & Noyed, Robert B. Leif Eriksson: Norwegian Explorer. 2002. (Spirit of America: Our People Ser.). (Illus.). 32p. (J). (gr. 2-6). 27.07 (978-1-56766-163-7(7)) Child's World, Inc.

Knudsen, Shannon. Leif Eriksson. Oldroyd, Mark, illus. 2005. (On My Own Biography Ser.). 48p. (J). (gr. 3-7). pap. 5.95 (978-1-57505-828-3(6)) Lerner Publishing Group.

ERIE, LAKE

Ylvisaker, Anne. Lake Erie. 2003. (Fact Finders Ser.). (Illus.). 32p. (J). lib. bdg. 22.60 (978-0-7368-2208-4(9) , Bridgestone Bks.) Capstone Pr., Inc.

ERIE, LAKE—FICTION

Arthur M. Winfield (Staff. The Rover Boys on the Great Lakes or the. 2006. pap. 57.99 (***978-1-4219-9669-1(3)***) IndyPublish.com.

Winfield, Arthur M. The Rover Boys on the Great Lakes. 2004. reprint ed. pap. 22.95 (978-1-4191-8119-1(X)) Kessinger Publishing, LLC.

Winfield, Arthur M. The Rover Boys on the Great Lakes. 2004. reprint ed. pap. 1.99 (978-1-4192-8119-8(4)) Kessinger Publishing, LLC.

ERIE CANAL (N.Y.)

Coleman, Wim & Perrin, Pat. The Amazing Erie Canal & How a Big Ditch Opened up the West. 2006. (Wild History of the American West Ser.). (Illus.). 128p. (J). lib. bdg. 33.27 (978-1-59845-017-0(4) , MyReportLinks.com Bks.) Enslow Pubs., Inc.

The Erie Canal. 2004. 24.95 incl. audio (978-0-7882-0562-0(5)); pap. 14.95 incl. audio (978-1-56008-197-5(X)) Weston Woods Studios, Inc.

Harness, Cheryl. The Amazing Impossible Erie Canal. Harness, Cheryl, illus. 1999. (Illus.). 32p. (J). (ps-3). pap. 7.99 (978-0-689-82584-2(6) , 076714005990, Aladdin) Simon & Schuster Children's Publishing.

—The Amazing Impossible Erie Canal. 1999. (J). 13.79 (978-0-606-16315-6(8)) Tandem Library Bks.

—Amazing Impossible Erie Canal. 1999. (gr. 3-6). lib. bdg. 15.30 (978-0-613-18230-0(8)) Tandem Library Bks.

Levy, Janey. A Journey along the Erie Canal: Dividing Multidigit Numbers by a One-Digit Number Without Remainders. 2004. (PowerMath Ser.). (Illus.). 32p. (J). pap. (978-0-8239-8904-1(6)); lib. bdg. 22.50 (978-0-8239-8991-1(7)) Rosen Publishing Group, Inc., The.

Lourie, Peter. Erie Canal: Canoeing America's Great Waterway. Lourie, Peter, photos by. 2003. (Illus.). 48p. (J). (gr. 2-5). 17.95 (978-1-56397-669-8(2)) Boyds Mills Pr.

—Erie Canal: Canoeing America's Great Waterway. 2003. (Illus.). 48p. (YA). (gr. 4-6). pap. 10.95 (978-1-56397-764-0(8)) Boyds Mills Pr.

Murray, Julie. Erie Canal. 2005. (All Aboard America Ser.). (Illus.). 24p. (J). (gr. k-4). lib. bdg. 21.35 (978-1-59197-504-5(2)) ABDO Publishing Co.

National Geographic Society Staff. Erie Canal. 2008. (Illus.). 128p. (gr. 5-9). 18.95 (978-1-4263-0022-6(0)); 28.90 (978-1-4263-0023-3(9)) National Geographic Society. (National Geographic Children's Bks.).

Santella, Andrew. The Erie Canal. 2004. 48p. (J). (gr. 4 up). lib. bdg. 22.60 (978-0-7565-0679-7(4)) Compass Point Bks.

Stein, R. Conrad. The Erie Canal. 2004. (Cornerstones of Freedom Ser.). (J). 26.00 (978-0-516-24243-9(1) , Children's Pr.) Scholastic Library Publishing.

ERIE CANAL (N.Y.)—FICTION

Kimmel, Eric A. The Erie Canal Pirates. Glass, Andrew, illus. 2002. 32p. (J). (gr. k-3). tchr. ed. 16.95 (978-0-8234-1657-8(7)) Holiday Hse., Inc.

Murphy, Jim. Desperate Journey. 2006. (Illus.). 288p. (J). pap. 16.99 (978-0-439-07806-1(7) , Scholastic Pr.) Scholastic, Inc.

Myers, Anna. Hoggee. 2004. 160p. (J). 16.95 (978-0-8027-8926-6(9)) Walker & Co.

Rizzo, Kay D. Old Friends & New. 2003. 96p. (J). (978-0-8163-1975-6(8)) Pacific Pr. Publishing Assn.

Thomas, Peggy. Joshua & the Giant Frog. 2005. (Illus.). 32p. (J). 15.95 (978-1-58980-267-4(5)) Pelican Publishing Co., Inc.

EROSION

Bailey, Jacqui. Cracking Up: A Story about Erosion. Lilly, Matthew, illus. 2006. 32p. (J). (gr. 3-6). 23.93 (978-1-4048-1594-0(5)) Picture Window Bks.

Benchmark Education Staff. Weathering & Erosion. 2005. 2.00 (***978-1-4108-4648-8(2)***) Benchmark Education Co.

Brannon, Barbara. Discover Erosion. 2005. 39.00 (***978-1-4108-5133-8(8)***) Benchmark Education Co.

Colson, Mary. Crumbling Earth Erosion & Landslides. 2005. (Turbulent Planet Ser.). pap. (978-1-4109-1751-5(7)); lib. bdg. (978-1-4109-1741-6(X)) Steck-Vaughn.

Ganeri, Anita. Crumbling Earth. 2004. (Turbulent Planet Ser.). (Illus.). 48p. (J). 28.56 (978-1-4109-0586-4(1)) Raintree.

—The Crumbling Earth. 2004. (Turbulent Planet Ser.). (Illus.). pap. 8.50 (978-1-4109-1024-0(5)) Raintree.

—The Crumbling Earth 6-Pack. 2004. (Turbulent Planet Ser.). (Illus.). pap. 45.90 (978-1-4109-1029-5(6)) Raintree.

Gifford, Clive. Weathering & Erosion. 2005. (Looking at Landscapes Ser.). (Illus.). 47p. (J). (gr. 6-9). lib. bdg. 29.95 (978-1-58340-731-8(6)) Smart Apple Media.

Holt, Rinehart and Winston Staff. Holt Science & Technology Chapter 12: Earth Science: Agents of Erosion. 5th ed. 2004. (Illus.). pap. 12.86 (978-0-03-030318-0(4)) Holt, Rinehart & Winston.

Koontz, Robin Michal. Erosion: Changing the Earth's Surface. Harrad, Matthew, illus. 2007. (Amazing Science Ser.). (J). 23.93 (978-1-4048-2195-8(3)) Picture Window Bks.

Mattern, Joanne. Weathering & Erosion & the Rock Cycle. 2006. lib. bdg. (978-1-4042-3198-6(6) , PowerKids Pr.) Rosen Publishing Group, Inc., The.

Olien, Becky. Erosion. (Exploring the Earth Ser.). 24p. (J). pap. 6.95 (978-0-7368-3365-3(X)) Capstone Pr., Inc.

Olien, Rebecca. Erosion. 2001. (Bridgestone Science Library). (Illus.). 24p. (J). (gr. 2-3). lib. bdg. 18.60 (978-0-7368-0950-4(3) , Bridgestone Bks.) Capstone Pr., Inc.

Reader dsm-3 erosion Ea. 2004. (J). (978-1-59242-523-5(2)) Delta Education, LLC.

Redlin, Janice L. Land Abuse & Soil Erosion. 2004. (Understanding Global Issues Ser.). (J). lib. bdg. (978-1-59036-237-2(3)) Weigl Pubs., Inc.

Riley, Joelle. Erosion. 2007. (Early Bird Earth Science Ser.). (J). 25.26 (978-0-8225-5949-8(8) , Lerner Pubns.) Lerner Publishing Group.

Sheehan, Thomas F. Wind & Water at Work: A Book about Change. 2008. (J). ***978-1-60044-538-5(1))** Rourke Publishing, LLC.

Spilsbury, Louise & Spilsbury, Richard. The Disappearing Mountain & Other Earth Mysteries: Erosion & Weathering. 2005. (Illus.). 32p. (J). lib. bdg. (978-1-4109-1924-3(2)); (gr. 6-9). 7.85 (978-1-4109-1955-7(2)) Steck-Vaughn.

Stille, Darlene R. Erosion: How Land Forms, How It Changes. 2004. (Exploring Science Ser.). (Illus.). 48p. 25.27 (978-0-7565-0854-8(1)) Compass Point Bks.

Stradling, Jan. Erosion & Weathering: Level K, 6 vols., Vol. 2. (First Explorers Ser.). 24p. (gr. 1-2). 34.95 (978-0-7699-1457-2(8)) Shortland Pubns. (U. S. A.) Inc.

Trumbauer, Lisa. Weathering & Erosion. 2005. 39.00 (***978-1-4108-4600-6(8))** Benchmark Education Co.

Winner, Cherie. Erosion. 1999. (Earth Watch Ser.). (Illus.). 56p. (gr. 4-6). lib. bdg. 21.27 (978-1-57505-223-6(7)) Lerner Publishing Group.

ERUPTIONS

see Volcanoes

ESCAPES

Dowswell, Paul. True Escape Stories. Tyler, Jenny, ed. 2004. (True Adventure Stories Ser.). (Illus.). 144p. (J). pap. 4.95 (978-0-7945-0087-0(0) , Usborne) EDC Publishing.

Kaplan, William & Tanaka, Shelley. One More Border: The True Story of One Family's Escape from War-Torn Europe. Taylor, Stephen, illus. 2004. 61p. (J). (gr. 3-6). pap. 9.95 (978-0-88899-638-1(1)) Groundwood Bks. CAN. *Dist:* Perseus Distribution.

Scandiffio, Laura. Escapes! MacEachern, Stephen, illus. 2003. (True Stories from the Edge Ser.). 176p. (J). (gr. 4-7). 18.95 (978-1-55037-823-8(6)); pap. 7.95 (978-1-55037-822-1(8)) Annick Pr., Ltd. CAN. *Dist:* Firefly Bks., Ltd.

—Escapes! 2003. (gr. 3-6). lib. bdg. 16.40 (978-0-613-78416-0(2)) Tandem Library Bks.

Schanzer, Rosalyn. John Smith Escapes Again! Schanzer, Rosalyn, illus. 2006. (Illus.). 64p. (J). (gr. 4-9). 16.95 (978-0-7922-5930-5(0)); lib. bdg. 25.90 (978-0-7922-5931-2(9)) National Geographic Society. (National Geographic Children's Bks.).

Simms, Patsy Ford. Harriet's Freedom Train. 2000. (J). stu. ed. 12.50 (978-0-7692-9377-6(8)); tchr. ed. 24.95 (978-0-7692-9376-9(X)) Alfred Publishing Co., Inc. (Warner Bros. Pubns.).

Townsend, John. Breakouts & Blunders. 48p. (J). 2006. pap. 8.90 (978-1-4109-1433-0(X)); 2005. lib. bdg. 31.43 (978-1-4109-1427-9(5)) Raintree.

Weil, Ann. Great Escapes. 2006. (Atomic Ser.). (Illus.). 32p. (J). (gr. 4-6). lib. bdg. 28.21 (978-1-4109-2497-1(1)) Raintree.

—Great Escapes. 2006. (Illus.). 32p. (J). pap. (978-1-4109-2502-2(1)) Steck-Vaughn.

ESCAPES—FICTION

Applegate, Katherine. The Escape. 1998. (Animorphs Ser.: No. 15). (J). (gr. 3-7). (978-0-606-12876-6(X)) Tandem Library Bks.

Borden, Louise & Daly, Niki. The Greatest Skating Race: A World War II Story from the Netherlands. 2004. (Illus.). 48p. (J). 18.95 (978-0-689-84502-4(2) , McElderry, Margaret K.) Simon & Schuster Children's Publishing.

Castle, Caroline. Funny! 2005. (Illus.). 32p. (J). pap. 11.95 (978-0-09-943302-6(8) , Red Fox) Random Hse. Children's Bks. GBR. *Dist:* Trafalgar Square Publishing.

Dunckel, Mona. Escape. 1999. 101p. (J). (gr. 1-2). pap. 6.49 (978-1-57924-068-4(2) , 113100) Jones, Bob Univ. Pr.

Egielski, Richard. Gingerbread Boy. 2000. (gr. k-3). lib. bdg. 14.15 (978-0-613-29964-0(7)) Tandem Library Bks.

Eustache, Harold. Shuswap Journey. 2004. 176p. pap. 15.95 (978-1-894778-15-2(4)) Theytus Bks., Ltd. CAN. *Dist:* Orca Bk. Pubs. USA.

Garland, Michael. Last Night at the Zoo. Garland, Michael, illus. 2003. (Illus.). 32p. (J). (gr. k-2). pap. 8.95 (978-1-59078-167-8(8)) Boyds Mills Pr.

—Last Night at the Zoo. 2001. (Illus.). 32p. (J). (gr. k-2). 15.95 (978-1-56397-759-6(1)) Boyds Mills Pr.

—Last Night at the Zoo. 2003. (gr. k-3). lib. bdg. 17.60 (978-0-613-79885-3(6)) Tandem Library Bks.

Grifalconi, Ann. The Village That Vanished. Nelson, Kadir A., illus. 2004. 40p. (J). reprint ed. pap. 6.99 (978-0-14-240190-3(0) , Puffin) Penguin Group (USA) Inc.

Hobrecker, Ginny. Magic Memories of Mutts & More. 2006. 49p. per. 8.95 (***978-1-59824-371-0(3))** E-BookTime LLC.

Holman, Felice. Slake's Limbo. unabr. ed. 2004. 117p. (J). (gr. 7 up). pap. 29.00 incl. audio (978-0-8072-8744-6(X) , YA254SP, Listening Library) Random Hse. Audio Publishing Group.

Jackson, Dave & Jackson, Neta. Hostage on the Nighthawk: William Penn. McLaughlin, Catherine R., illus. 2000. (Trailblazer Bks.: Vol. 32). 144p. (J). (gr. 3-7). pap. 6.99 (978-0-7642-2265-8(1)) Bethany Hse. Pubs.

Langlois, Annie. L' Evasion d'Alfred le Dindon. Beaulieu, Jimméy, illus. 2004. (Roman Jeunesse Ser.). (FRE.). 96p. (J). (gr. 4-7). pap. (978-2-89021-687-7(X)) Diffusion du livre Mirabel.

McDonnell, Vincent. The Knock Airport Mystery. 2006. (Illus.). 203p. (J). pap. 9.95 (978-1-903464-87-8(0)) Collins Pr., The IRL. *Dist:* Dufour Editions, Inc.

Napoli, Donna Jo. Stones in Water. 1999. 224p. (J). (gr. 5-9). reprint ed. pap. 5.99 (978-0-14-130600-1(9) , Puffin) Penguin Group (USA) Inc.

—Stones in Water. 1999. (978-0-606-17262-2(9)) Tandem Library Bks.

Nerette-Louis, Liliane. Zenga. 2001. (CRP.). (J). (gr. 3-5). 8.50 (978-1-58432-043-2(5)); (Illus.). 16p. pap. 8.50 (978-1-58432-087-6(7)) Educa Vision.

Norton, Mary. Borrowers Avenged. 2003. (gr. 3-6). lib. bdg. 14.10 (978-0-613-66945-0(2)) Tandem Library Bks.

Nostlinger, Christine. Por Favor, Vuelve a Casa (Please, Come Back Home) (SPA.). 176p. (YA). (gr. 7-9). 9.95 (978-958-04-2379-9(2) , 10266266) Norma S.A. COL. *Dist:* Distribuidora Norma, Inc.

Peel, John. Traitor. 2000. (Twenty Ninety-Nine Ser.: Bk. 3). (Illus.). 160p. (J). (gr. 3-7). pap. 4.99 (978-0-439-06032-5(X) , Scholastic Paperbacks) Scholastic, Inc.

Reid, John. Escape! 2005. 128p. (J). pap. 10.95 (978-1-55266-147-5(4)) Fernwood Publishing Co., Ltd. CAN. *Dist:* Independent Pubs. Group.

Reynolds, Aaron. Breaking Out of the Bungle Bird: Based on Proverbs 13:10. Whitehead, Peter, illus. 2005. (Insect-Inside Ser.). 40p. (J). 9.99 (978-0-310-70956-5(3)) Zonderkidz.

Robison, Dan, Jr. Kimo's Escape: The Story of a Hawaiian Boy Who Learns to Believe in Himself. 2005. 100p. (J). per. 19.95 (978-0-922993-28-4(9)) Marquette Bks., LLC.

Rue, Nancy N. The Escape. 1998. (Christian Heritage Ser.). 192p. (J). (gr. 3-7). pap. 5.99 (978-1-56179-639-7(5)) Bethany Hse. Pubs.

Shaw, Janet Beeler. Kaya's Escape. 2002. (gr. 3-6). lib. bdg. 14.10 (978-0-613-46223-5(8)) Tandem Library Bks.

—Kaya's Escape! A Survival Story, Bk. 2. Farnsworth, Bill & McAliley, Susan, illus. 2002. (American Girls Collection: Bk. 2). 88p. (gr. 2-7). (J). 12.95 (978-1-58485-426-5(X)); 6.95 (978-1-58485-425-8(1)) American Girl Publishing, Inc.

Simmons, Ted. Sandstorm. 2006. (Illus.). 140p. (YA). pap. 13.95 (***978-0-9776958-4-3(0))** CyPress Pubns.

Smith, Roland. Jack's Run. 256p. (gr. 5-17). 2007. pap. 5.99 (***978-1-4231-0407-0(2));** 2005. 15.99 (978-0-7868-5592-6(4)) Hyperion Pr.

Spaht-Gill, Janie. Gator's Out, Said the Trout. Reese, Bob, illus. (J). (gr. k-2). 5.95 (978-0-89868-305-9(X)) ARO Publishing Co.

ESKIMOS

Ansary, Mir Tamim. Arctic Peoples. (Native Americans Ser.). (Illus.). 32p. (J). 2002. (gr. 1-4). pap. 7.50 (978-1-58810-450-2(8) , 91169); 1999. (gr. 2-4). lib. bdg. 21.36 (978-1-57572-920-6(2)) Heinemann Library.

Bial, Raymond. The Inuit. 2001. (Lifeways Ser.). (Illus.). 128p. (J). (gr. 5-9). lib. bdg. 34.21 (978-0-7614-1212-0(3) , Benchmark Bks.) Cavendish, Marshall Corp.

Cordoba, Yasmine A. Igloo. Dawson, Kimberly L., illus. 2000. (Native American Homes Ser.). 32p. (J). (gr. 3-6). lib. bdg. 28.50 (978-1-55916-277-7(5)) Rourke Publishing, LLC.

Corriveau, Danielle. The Inuit of Canada. 2005. (First Peoples Ser.). (Illus.). 48p. (J). (gr. 4-8). lib. bdg. 23.95 (978-0-8225-4850-8(X)) Lerner Publishing Group.

Gray-Kanatiiosh, Barbara A. Inuit. Kanietakeron, David, illus. 2002. (Native Americans Ser.). 32p. (J). (gr. k-6). lib. bdg. 22.78 (978-1-57765-599-2(0) , Checkerboard Library) ABDO Publishing Co.

Harper, Kenn. Give Me My Fathers Body: The Life of Minik the New York Eskimo. 2001. (gr. 7-12). lib. bdg. 23.40 (978-0-613-45765-1(X)) Tandem Library Bks.

Haslam, Andrew. Arctic Peoples: The Hands-on Approach to History. 2001. (gr. 3-6). lib. bdg. 16.40 (978-0-613-43299-3(1)) Tandem Library Bks.

Kalman, Bobbie. Life in the Far North. 2003. (gr. 3-6). lib. bdg. 17.60 (978-0-613-85053-7(X)) Tandem Library Bks.

Kalman, Bobbie & Sjonger, Rebecca. Life in the Far North. 2003. (Native Nations of North America Ser.). (Illus.). 32p. (J). (gr. 5). (978-0-7787-0377-8(0)); pap. (978-0-7787-0469-0(6)) Crabtree Publishing Co.

Koestler-Grack, Rachel A. The Inuit: Ivory Carvers of the Far North. 2003. (America's First Peoples Ser.). (Illus.). 32p. (J). (gr. 2-3). lib. bdg. 23.93 (978-0-7368-2171-1(6) , Bridgestone Bks.) Capstone Pr., Inc.

Lassieur, Allison. The Inuit. 2000. (Native Peoples Ser.). (Illus.). 24p. (J). (gr. 2-3). lib. bdg. 18.60 (978-0-7368-0498-1(6) , Bridgestone Bks.) Capstone Pr., Inc.

Lectorum Publications Staff. Lo Que Cuentan los Inuit. 2000. Tr. of Tales of the Inuit. (SPA.). (gr. 3-6). lib. bdg. 16.40 (978-0-613-82034-9(7)) Tandem Library Bks.

Rau, Dana Meachen. Igloo. 2006. (Bookworms Ser.). (Illus.). 24p. (J). lib. bdg. 22.79 (978-0-7614-2273-0(0) , Benchmark Bks.) Cavendish, Marshall Corp.

Santella, Andrew. The Inuit. 2001. (True Bks.). (Illus.). 48p. (J). (gr. 3-5). pap. 6.95 (978-0-516-27319-8(1) , Children's Pr.) Scholastic Library Publishing.

—Inuit. 2001. (gr. 3-6). lib. bdg. 15.25 (978-0-613-53513-7(8)) Tandem Library Bks.

Schwatka, Frederick. The Children of the Cold. (J). reprint ed. 34.50 (978-0-404-11683-5(3)) AMS Pr., Inc.

Steltzer, Ulli. Building an Igloo. Steltzer, Ulli, photos by. (Illus.). 32p. (J). (ps-2). pap. (978-0-88899-118-8(5)) Groundwood Bks.

—Building an Igloo. rev. ed. 1999. (Illus.). 32p. (J). (gr. k-3). pap. 7.95 (978-0-8050-6313-4(7) , Holt, Henry & Co. Bks. For Young Readers) Holt, Henry & Co.

Strudwick, Leslie. Inuit. 2003. (Indigenous Peoples Ser.). (J). pap. 7.95 (978-1-59036-157-3(1)); (Illus.). 32p. lib. bdg. 18.20 (978-1-59036-122-1(9)) Weigl Pubs., Inc.

Titus, David. Native Alaskan String Figures. 2007. (Illus.). 32p. (J). 5.99 (***978-0-9744562-7-0(6))** WRDSMTH Productions.

Wolfson, Evelyn. Inuit Mythology. Bock, William Sauts, illus. 2001. (Mythology Ser.). 128p. (J). (gr. 6-12). lib. bdg. 26.60 (978-0-7660-1559-3(9)) Enslow Pubs., Inc.

ESKIMOS—FICTION

Amundson, Susan. Free to Be Me: The Eskimo Way. Geiken, Brenda, illus. 2003. 56p. lib. bdg. 16.95 (978-1-883477-65-3(4)) Lone Oak Pr., Ltd.

Andrews, Jan. Very Last First Time. Wallace, Ian, illus. 2003. 32p. (J). 18.95 (978-0-88899-043-3(X)) Groundwood Bks. CAN. *Dist:* Perseus Distribution.

Ballantyne, R. M. The Walrus Hunters. 2004. reprint ed. pap. 26.95 (978-1-4191-8706-3(6)); pap. 1.99 (978-1-4192-8706-0(0)) Kessinger Publishing, LLC.

Bania, Michael. Kumak's Fish: A Tall Tale from the Far North. 2005. (Illus.). 32p. 15.95 (978-0-88240-583-4(7)); pap. 8.95 (978-0-88240-584-1(5)) Graphic Arts Ctr. Publishing Co.

Berlin, James, Sr. Cup'igtat Laanguarrutenka. Berlin, James & Nevak, Caroline, illus. l.t. ed. 1999. Tr. of My Yup'ik Eskimo Toys. (ESK.). 12p. (J). (gr. k-3). pap. 17.00 (978-1-58084-112-2(0)) Lower Kuskokwim Schl. District.

—My Yupik Eskimo Toys. Berlin, James & Nevak, Caroline, illus. l.t. ed. 1999. 12p. (J). (gr. k-3). pap. 17.00 (978-1-58084-074-3(4)) Lower Kuskokwim Schl. District.

—Yugtaat Naanguat. Berlin, James & Nevak, Caroline, illus. l.t. ed. 1999. Tr. of My Yup'ik Eskimo Toys. (ESK.). 12p. (J). (gr. k-3). pap. 17.00 (978-1-58084-075-0(2)) Lower Kuskokwim Schl. District.

Brown, Kerry Hannula. Tupaq the Dreamer. Sapport, Linda, illus. 2001. 32p. (J). (ps-3). 15.95 (978-0-7614-5076-4(9) , Cavendish Children's Bks.) Cavendish, Marshall Corp.

Dewey, Jennifer Owings. Minik's Story. 2003. (Illus.). 160p. (YA). 15.95 (978-0-7614-5134-1(X)) Cavendish, Marshall Corp.

Edwardson, Debby Dahl. Whale Snow. Patterson, Annie, illus. 2004. 32p. (J). (ENG.). pap. 7.95 (978-1-57091-496-6(6)); pap. (978-1-57091-394-5(3)); 15.95 (978-1-57091-393-8(5)) Charlesbridge Publishing, Inc.

George, Jean Craighead. Arctic Son. 1999. (J). (978-0-606-17381-0(1)) Tandem Library Bks.

—Julie of the Wolves. Schoenherr, John, illus. 2003. (Julie of the Wolves Ser.). 208p. (YA). (gr. 7 up). pap. 5.99 (978-0-06-054095-1(8) , Harper Trophy) HarperCollins Pubs.

—Julie of the Wolves. l.t. ed. 2004. (Beeler Mystery Ser.). 32.95 (978-1-58118-121-0(3)) LRS.

—Julie of the Wolves. l.t. ed. 2005. 180p. (YA). pap. 10.95 (978-0-7862-7955-5(9)) Thorndike Pr.

—Julie's Wolf Pack. Minor, Wendell, illus. 1999. (Julie of the Wolves Ser.). 208p. (J). (gr. 5 up). pap. 5.99 (978-0-06-440721-2(7) , Harper Trophy) HarperCollins Pubs.

—Nutik & Amaroq Play Ball. 2000. 32p. (J). (gr. k-3). pap. 5.95 (978-0-06-443523-9(7)) HarperCollins Pubs.

—Nutik, the Wolf Pup. Rand, Ted, illus. 2001. 40p. (J). (gr. k-3). 15.99 (978-0-06-028164-9(2)); lib. bdg. 17.89 (978-0-06-028165-6(0)) HarperCollins Pubs.

—Nutik, the Wolf Pup. 2000. 32p. (J). (gr. k-3). pap. 5.95 (978-0-06-443522-2(9)) HarperCollins Pubs.

—Snow Bear. 2003. (gr. k-3). lib. bdg. 14.15 (978-0-613-75033-2(0)) Tandem Library Bks.

Gerber, Carole. Arctic Dreams. Husted, Marty, illus. 1999. (J). (ps-2). 15.95 (978-1-58089-021-2(0)) Charlesbridge Publishing, Inc.

He Who Listens: Individual Title Six-Packs. (Literatura 2000 Ser.). (gr. 2-3). 33.00 (978-0-7635-0171-6(9)) Rigby Education.

Heinz, Brian J. Kayuktuk: An Arctic Quest. Van Zyle, Jon, illus. 2004. (J). pap. 6.95 (978-0-936335-09-4(2)) Ballyhoo BookWorks, Inc.

Ilutsik, Paul, et al. Kuvyastek. Smart, B. George, illus. l.t. ed. 1999. Tr. of Two Fishermen. (ESK.). 20p. (J). (gr. 3-5). pap. 6.00 (978-1-58084-172-6(4)) Lower Kuskokwim Schl. District.

Joshua, Mary. Cayunqegtua. Athanas, Reyne, illus. 1998. Tr. of I Like To. (ESK.). 8p. (J). (gr. k-3). pap. 6.00 (978-1-58084-026-2(4)) Lower Kuskokwim Schl. District.

Kittredge, Frances. Neeluk: An Eskimo Boy in the Days of the Whaling Ships. Rock, Howard, illus. 2005. 88p. (J). (gr. 3-7). 18.95 (978-0-88240-545-2(4)) Graphic Arts Ctr. Publishing Co.

—Neeluk: An Eskimo Boy in the Days of the Whaling Ships. Rock, Howard B., illus. 2005. 88p. (J). (gr. 3-7). pap. 11.95 (978-0-88240-546-9(2)) Graphic Arts Ctr. Publishing Co.

—Neeluk: An Eskimo Boy in the Days of the Whaling Ships. 2001. (gr. 3-6). lib. bdg. 21.05 (978-0-613-55638-5(0)) Tandem Library Bks.

Lehman-Wilzig, Tami. Keeping the Promise: A Torah's Journey. Orback, Craig, illus. 2004. (J). 16.95 (978-0-929371-79-5(8)) Kar-Ben Publishing.

Lerangis, Peter. Smiler's Bones. 2007. 176p. (J). pap. 4.99 (978-0-439-34488-3(3) , Scholastic Paperbacks) Scholastic, Inc.

Lincoln, Kelly J. Let's Go Storyknifing. Nevak, Caroline, illus. l.t. ed. 1999. 12p. (J). (gr. k-3). pap. 17.00 (978-1-58084-066-8(3)) Lower Kuskokwim Schl. District.

—Yaaruiyarciqukug. Nevak, Caroline, illus. l.t. ed. 1999. Tr. of Let's Go Story Knifing. (ESK.). 12p. (J). (gr. k-3). pap. 17.00 (978-1-58084-108-5(2)) Lower Kuskokwim Schl. District.

—Yaaruiyarluk. Nevak, Caroline, illus. l.t. ed. 1999. Tr. of Let's Go Story Knifing. (ESK.). 12p. (J). (gr. k-3). pap. 17.00 (978-1-58084-067-5(1)) Lower Kuskokwim Schl. District.

Lincoln, Rosalie. Arnat Castun Pillerkat Assigeskuneng. Lincoln, Rosalie & Nevak, Caroline, illus. l.t. ed. 1999. Tr. of What Girls Should Do When Eskimo Dancing. (ESK.). 16p. (J). (gr. k-3). pap. 21.00 (978-1-58084-111-5(2)) Lower Kuskokwim Schl. District.

—Nasaurluum Yurallra. Lincoln, Rosalie & Nevak, Caroline, illus. l.t. ed. 1999. Tr. of What Girls Should Do When Eskimo Dancing. (ESK.). 16p. (J). (gr. k-3). pap. 21.00 (978-1-58084-065-1(5)) Lower Kuskokwim Schl. District.

—What Girls Should Do When Eskimo Dancing. Lincoln, Rosalie & Nevak, Caroline, illus. l.t. ed. 1999. 16p. (J). (gr. k-3). pap. 20.00 (978-1-58084-064-4(7)) Lower Kuskokwim Schl. District.

MacDiarmid, Jim. Neqem Ayuqucia Nallunritellruan-qaa... Nega! Collidge, Joseph, tr. l.t. ed. 1999. Tr. of Meet... a Fish!. (ESK., Illus.). 20p. (J). (gr. 3-5). pap. 7.00 (978-1-58084-176-4(7)) Lower Kuskokwim Schl. District.

Magdanz, James. Go Home, River. Widom, Dianne, illus. 2002. 32p. (ps up). 8.95 (978-0-88240-568-1(3)) Graphic Arts Ctr. Publishing Co.

Marceau-Chenkie, Brittany. Naya, the Inuit Cinderella. Brookes, Shelley, illus. l.t. ed. 1999. 24p. (J). (ps-3). pap. (978-1-894303-05-7(9)) Raven Rock Publishing.

Nicolai, Margaret. Kitaq Goes Ice Fishing. Rubin, David, illus. 32p. (gr. k up). 2002. pap. 8.95 (978-0-88240-569-8(1)); 1998. 15.95 (978-0-88240-504-9(7)) Graphic Arts Ctr. Publishing Co.

Olick, Hilda. Kaviam Iqvaryallra. Olick, Hilda & Nevak, Caroline, illus. l.t. ed. 1999. (ESK.). 8p. (J). (gr. k-3). pap. 14.50 (978-1-58084-057-6(4)) Lower Kuskokwim Schl. District.

Orenstein, Denise Gosliner. Unseen Companion. 2003. 368p. (J). 15.99 (978-0-06-052056-4(6)); lib. bdg. 16.89 (978-0-06-052057-1(4)) HarperCollins Pubs.

Paulsen, Gary. Dogsong. 1999. (YA). 9.95 (978-1-56137-342-0(7)) Novel Units, Inc.

—Dogsong. 192p. 2007. (J). pap. 6.99 (978-1-4169-3962-7(8) , Aladdin); 2007. (YA). mass mkt. 6.99 (978-1-4169-3919-1(9) , Simon Pulse); 2000. (YA). (gr. 7 up). 17.99 (978-0-689-83960-3(X) , Atheneum/Richard Jackson Bks.) Simon & Schuster Children's Publishing.

—Dogsong. 1999. (J). 11.64 (978-0-606-16328-6(X)) Tandem Library Bks.

—Dogsong. l.t. ed. 2000. (Illus.). 184p. (J). (gr. 8-12). 21.95 (978-0-7862-2845-4(8)) Thorndike Pr.

Perkins, Lucy Fitch. Eskimo Twins. 2006. 62.99 (***978-1-4280-3721-2(7));** pap. 55.99 (***978-1-4280-3694-9(6))** IndyPublish.com.

—The Eskimo Twins. 2004. reprint ed. pap. 15.95 (978-1-4191-6126-1(1)); pap. 1.99 (978-1-4192-6126-8(6)) Kessinger Publishing, LLC.

Perkins, Lucy Fitch. The Eskimo Twins (Yesterday's Classics) 2006. (J). per. 9.95 (***978-1-59915-059-8(X))** Yesterday's Classics.

Peterson, Sara Budinger. Alice Meets Inupiat Eskimos. 2000. (Illus.). 68p. 11.95 (978-0-9665282-1-3(2)) Saranjon Publishing.

Price, Susan. Can Yr Ysbrydion. 2005. (WEL.). 172p. pap. (978-1-85596-217-0(9)) Dref Wen.

Prins, Piet. Stefan Derksen's Polar Adventure. 2004. (Illus.). 237p. (J). pap. (978-1-894666-67-1(4)) Inheritance Pubns.

Repp, Gloria. Charlie. 2002. (Illus.). 147p. (J). (gr. 4-7). 7.49 (978-1-57924-817-8(9)) Jones, Bob Univ. Pr.

Rogers, Jean. Goodbye, My Island. Munoz, Rie, illus. 2005. 96p. (gr. 2 up). pap. 9.95 (978-0-88240-538-4(1)) Graphic Arts Ctr. Publishing Co.

—Goodbye, My Island. 2001. (gr. 3-6). lib. bdg. 18.75 (978-0-613-77288-4(1)) Tandem Library Bks.

Scott, Ann Herbert. On Mother's Lap. Coalson, Glo, illus. 2002. (J). 14.74 (978-0-7587-3318-4(6)) Book Wholesalers, Inc.

—On Mother's Lap. Coalson, Glo, illus. 2000. 14p. (J). (gr. k-ps). bds. 5.95 (978-0-618-05159-5(7) , Clarion Bks.) Houghton Mifflin Co. Trade & Reference Div.

Shaw-MacKinnon, Margaret & Gal, Laszlo. Tiktala. (Illus.). 30p. 13.95 (978-0-7737-2920-9(8)) Stoddart Kids CAN. *Dist:* Fitzhenry & Whiteside, Ltd.

Shield, Sophie. Can'giiq. Smart, S. George & Horesh, David, illus. l.t. ed. 1999. Tr. of Blackfish. (ESK.). 12p. (J). (gr. 3-5). pap. 6.00 (978-1-58084-175-7(9)) Lower Kuskokwim Schl. District.

Sis, Peter. A Small, Tall Tale from the Far Far North. (Illus.). (J). pap. 7.95 (978-0-88899-431-8(1)) Groundwood Bks. CAN. *Dist:* Transition Vendor.

E
F
G

—Small Tall Tale from the Far Far North. 2001. (gr. k-3). lib. bdg. 15.25 (978-0-613-82503-0(9)) Tandem Library Bks.

—A Small Tall Tale from the Far Far North. Sis, Peter, illus. 2001. (Illus.). 40p. (J). (gr. 1-4). 17.00 (978-0-374-37075-6(3) , Farrar, Straus & Giroux (BYR)); pap. 6.95 (978-0-374-46725-8(0) , Sunburst) Farrar, Straus & Giroux.

Stafford, Liliana. Snow Bear. Davis, Lambert, illus. 32p. (J). pap. (978-0-88899-441-7(9)) Groundwood Bks.

—Snow Bear. Davis, Lambert, illus. 2001. 32p. (J). (gr. 1-3). 15.95 (978-0-439-26977-3(6)) Scholastic, Inc.

Taylor, Theodore. Ice Drift. (Illus.). 240p. (J). 2006. pap. 5.95 (978-0-15-205550-9(9) , Harcourt Paperbacks); 2005. 16.00 (978-0-15-205081-8(7)) Harcourt Children's Bks.

ESKIMOS—FOLKLORE

Dabcovich, Lydia. The Polar Bear Son: An Inuit Tale. Dabcovich, Lydia, illus. 1999. (FRE., Illus.). 40p. (J). (gr. k-3). pap. 6.95 (978-0-395-97567-1(0) , Clarion Bks.) Houghton Mifflin Co. Trade & Reference Div.

Fox, Esther. Kegginaquq. Fox, Esther & Shantz, Joy, illus. 1998. Tr. of Mask. (ESK.). 8p. (J). (gr. k-3). pap. 6.00 (978-1-58084-025-5(6)) Lower Kuskokwim Schl. District.

Jones, Ayaprun L. Kui. Brunk, Cara, illus. l.t. ed. 1999. Tr. of I Am. (ESK.). 20p. (J). (gr. k-3). pap. 25.00 (978-1-58084-113-9(9)) Lower Kuskokwim Schl. District.

—Wiinga (I Am) Brunk, Cara, illus. l.t. ed. 1999. (ESK.). 20p. (J). (gr. k-3). pap. 25.00 (978-1-58084-071-2(X)) Lower Kuskokwim Schl. District.

Olick, Hilda. Kavviar Paunerssuyallrim. Olick, Hilda & Nevak, Caroline, illus. l.t. ed. 1999. (ESK.). 8p. (J). (gr. k-3). pap. 14.50 (978-1-58084-114-6(7)) Lower Kuskokwim Schl. District.

—Kayuqtuq Aullaqsrugiaman. Olick, Hilda & Nevak, Caroline, illus. l.t. ed. 1999. (ESK.). 8p. (J). (gr. k-3). pap. 14.50 (978-1-58084-119-1(8)) Lower Kuskokwim Schl. District.

Renner, Michelle. The Girl Who Swam with the Fish: An Athabascan Legend. Cox, Christine, illus. 1999. 32p. (gr. 2-4). 8.95 (978-0-88240-523-0(3)) Graphic Arts Ctr. Publishing Co.

—The Girl Who Swam with the Fish: An Athabascan Legend. 1999. (Illus.). (J). (978-0-606-17948-5(8)) Tandem Library Bks.

White, Timothy, illus. A Kayak Full of Ghosts: Eskimo Folk Tales. 2004. (International Folk Tales Ser.). 208p. 13.95 (978-1-56656-525-7(1)) Interlink Publishing Group, Inc.

ESP

see Extrasensory Perception

ESQUIMAUX

see Eskimos

ESSEX (WHALESHIP)

Cook, Peter. You Wouldn't Want to Sail on 19th Century Whaling Ship. Antram, David, illus. 2004. (You Wouldn't Want to Ser.). 32p. (J). (gr. 2-5). pap. 9.95 (978-0-531-16399-3(7) , Watts, Franklin) Scholastic Library Publishing.

ESTHER, QUEEN OF PERSIA

Chronicles of Faith - Esther. 2007. 224p. (J). pap. 4.97 ***(978-1-59789-924-6(0))*** Barbour Publishing, Inc.

DeBoer, Rondi & Tangvald, Christine. Brave Queen Esther. Conger, Holli, illus. 2007. (J). 5.99 ***(978-0-7847-1947-3(0))*** Standard Publishing.

Freed, Shirley & Moon, Louise. Esther Becomes Queen. Morelan, Bill, ed. Butler, Steven, illus. 2002. 24p. (J). (gr. 2 up). pap. 3.99 (978-1-58938-048-6(7)) Concerned Communications.

Gemmen, Heather & McNeil, Mary. Spare Me, Level 3. Mahan, Ben, tr. Mahan, Ben, illus. 1999. (Rocket Readers Ser.). 24p. (J). (gr. 3 up). pap., pap. 8.99 (978-0-7814-3985-5(X) , 078143985X) Cook, David C. Publishing Co.

Nystrom, Carolyn. Courage, Esther! Dahl, Sharon, illus. 1998. (Follow the Leader Stories Ser.). 32p. (J). (ps-3). 7.99 (978-0-8024-2206-4(3)) Moody Pubs.

Pulley, Kelly, illus. Esther & the King. 2007. (I Can Read!). 32p. (J). pap. 3.99 ***(978-0-310-71460-6(5))*** Zonderkidz.

Slater, Teddy. Esther Saves Her People. 2007. 32p. (J). pap. 3.99 (978-0-439-86395-7(3)) Scholastic, Inc.

Taylor, Damon. Beauty & the Booster: The Story of Esther. 2002. (Child Sockology Ser.). (Illus.). 32p. (J). 10.99 (978-0-8254-3858-5(6)) Kregel Pubns.

ESTHER, QUEEN OF PERSIA—FICTION

Moscowitz, Moshe & Resnick, Yael. The Queen of Persia. Sokoloff, David, illus. 2004. 107p. ***(978-1-930925-09-0(3)*** , Shazak Productions) Torah Excel.

Pakulak, Eric. At the Side of Esther: A Multiple-Ending Bible Adventure. Bulanadi, Danny, illus. 2000. 96p. (J). pap. 6.95 (978-0-8198-0769-4(9)) Pauline Bks. & Media.

Tenney, Tommy. Hadassah: The Girl Who Became Queen Esther. 2005. (Illus.). 168p. (J). 9.99 (978-0-7642-2738-7(6)) Bethany Hse. Pubs.

ESTONIA

Hiisjarv, Piret & Hiiepuu, Ene. Estonia. Bultje, Jan Willem, photos by. 2006. (Looking at Europe Ser.). 48p. (YA). (gr. 5-8). 22.95 (978-1-881508-32-8(3)) Oliver Pr., Inc.

Libal, Autumn. Estonia. 2006. (European Union Ser.). (Illus.). 88p. (J). (gr. 5 up). lib. bdg. (978-1-4222-0044-5(2) , 1247996) Mason Crest Pubs.

Spilling, Michael. Estonia. 1999. (Cultures of the World Ser.). (Illus.). 128p. (J). (gr. 5-12). lib. bdg. 37.07 (978-0-7614-0951-9(3) , Benchmark Bks.) Cavendish, Marshall Corp.

ESTONIA—FICTION

Uncle Markie. Piglettė & Bobo Have Visitors. 2003. (YA). ring bd. 9.95 (978-1-933129-12-9(3)) Studio 403.

—Piglettė & Bobo in Estonia. 2003. (YA). ring bd. 9.95 (978-1-933129-13-6(1)) Studio 403.

ETERNAL LIFE

see Future Life

ETHICAL EDUCATION

see Religious Education

ETHICS

see also Good and Evil; Values

Altman, Linda Jacobs. Bioethics: Who Lives, Who Dies, & Who Decides? 2006. (Issues in Focus Today). (Illus.). 104p. (YA). (gr. 6-9). lib. bdg. 31.93 (978-0-7660-2546-2(2)) Enslow Pubs., Inc.

Artson, Bradley Shavit & Gevirtz, Gila. Making a Difference: Putting Jewish Spirituality into Action, One Mitzvah at a Time. 2001. (Illus.). 144p. (J). (gr. 7-9). pap. 8.95 (978-0-87441-712-8(0)) Behrman Hse., Inc.

Bender, Marie. Fairness Counts. 2003. (Character Counts Ser.). (Illus.). 32p. (J). (gr. k-6). lib. bdg. 22.78 (978-1-57765-870-2(1)) ABDO Publishing Co.

Bergstrom, Amy, et al. The Seventh Generation: Native Students Speak about Finding the Good Path. 2003. 300p. (YA). (gr. 7-12). pap. 25.00 (978-1-880785-25-6(0)) ERIC Clearinghouse on Rural Education & Small Schls.

Blumenthal, Scott. A Kid's Mensch Handbook: Step by Step to a Lifetime of Jewish Values. 2004. (J). (978-0-87441-700-5(7)) Behrman Hse., Inc.

Boatman, Marva. A Children's Book of Morals. 2003. 16p. pap. 7.00 (978-0-8059-5767-9(7)) Dorrance Publishing Co., Inc.

Bottoms, James "Bud". Kid Ethics: From a to Z. 2006. (J). per. 12.95 (978-0-9772078-5-5(4)) Journey Pubns., LLC.

Boyd, Kenneth. A Right to Life - & Death? (Illus.). 64p. (J). (978-0-237-51877-6(5) , Evans Brothers, Limited) Evans Publishing Group.

Burch, Regina G. I Can Accept Others. Jarrett, Michael, photos by. 2004. (J). lib. bdg. 19.33 (978-0-8368-4244-9(8)) Stevens, Gareth Inc.

—I Can Be Responsible. Burris, Priscilla, illus. 2004. (J). lib. bdg. 19.33 (978-0-8368-4245-6(6)) Stevens, Gareth Inc.

—I Can Share with Others. Jarrett, Michael, photos by. 2004. (J). lib. bdg. 19.33 (978-0-8368-4246-3(4)) Stevens, Gareth Inc.

Christopher, Matt. Run for It. 2002. (#1 Sports Series for Kids). 128p. (J). (gr. 2-4). pap. 4.50 (978-0-316-34914-7(3)) Little, Brown Bks. for Young Readers.

—Run for It. 2002. (gr. 3-6). lib. bdg. 12.40 (978-0-613-50638-0(3)) Tandem Library Bks.

Dowswell, Paul. Genetics: The Impact on Our Lives. 2001. (Twenty-First Century Debates Ser.). (Illus.). 64p. (YA). (gr. 6-8). lib. bdg. 27.12 (978-0-7398-3174-8(7)) Raintree.

Elster, Jean Alicia. I Have a Dream, Too! Tadgell, Nicole, illus. 2002. (Joe Joe in the City Ser.: No. 2). 32p. (gr. 1-5). 12.00 (978-0-8170-1397-4(0)) Judson Pr.

Estrin, Leibel. Rabbi Riddle. Sears, Dovid, illus. 2000. (J). (978-1-58330-206-4(9)) Feldheim Pubs.

Ethics & Values, 8 vols., Set. 1998. (Illus.). (J). lib. bdg. 275.00 (978-0-7172-9274-5(6) , Grolier) Scholastic Library Publishing.

Fireside, Bryna J. & Ferguson, John E. The Right to Die. 2007. (Point/Counterpoint Ser.). 112p. (J). (gr. 9). 32.95 ***(978-0-7910-9287-3(9)*** , Chelsea Hse.) Facts On File, Inc.

Grishaver, Joel Lurie. You Be the Judge: A Collection of Ethical Cases. 1999. (Family Bet Din Ser.). (Illus.). 128p. (J). (gr. 7-11). pap. 9.95 (978-1-891662-00-3(7)) Torah Aura Productions.

Halman, Jacqueline. The Karma Queen's Little Book of Big Tips on Living a Lucky Life. 2003. 144p. (YA). 10.95 (978-1-931722-27-8(7) , Sixth Avenue Bks.) Grand Central Publishing.

Humphrey, Sandra McLeod. It's up to You... What Do You Do? Strassburg, Brian, illus. 1999. (Young Readers Ser.). 114p. (gr. 1 up). pap. 14.00 (978-1-57392-263-0(3) , Pyr Bks.) Prometheus Bks., Pubs.

Humphrey, Sandra McLeod & Barker, Dan. More-If You Had to Choose, What Would You Do? Strassburg, Brian, illus. 2004. 110p. pap. 13.00 (978-1-59102-077-6(8) , Pyr Bks.) Prometheus Bks., Pubs.

Hyde, Margaret O. & Setaro, John F. Medicine's Brave New World: Bioengineering & the New Genetics. 2001. (Single Titles Ser.). (Illus.). 144p. (gr. 7 up). lib. bdg. 29.90 (978-0-7613-1706-7(6) , Twenty-First Century Bks.) Lerner Publishing Group.

Jamiolkowski, Raymond M. A Baby Doesn't Make the Man: Alternative Sources of Power & Manhood for Young Men. rev. ed. 2005. (Teen Pregnancy Prevention Library). (Illus.). 64p. (YA). (gr. 7-12). lib. bdg. 23.95 (978-0-8239-3470-6(5)) Rosen Publishing Group, Inc., The.

Kehrwald, Leif. Morality 6 Booklets: Meeting Jesus' Challenge in Everyday Life. 1998. (Illus.). (YA). (gr. 9-13). pap., stu. ed. 7.45 (978-0-89837-165-9(1)) Pflaum Publishing Group.

Levy, Debbie. Medical Ethics. 2001. (Overview Ser.). (Illus.). 128p. (YA). (gr. 6-9). lib. bdg. 29.95 (978-1-56006-547-0(8) , LML00902-177904, Lucent Bks.) Thomson Gale.

Lishinski, Ann King. Let Your Light Shine. Morello, Charles, ed. Lishinski, Jamie, illus. 2003. (J). pap. 9.95 (978-0-9709575-0-4(5)) Singing River Pubns.

Loewen, Nancy. Do I Have To? Kids Talk about Responsibility. Wesley, Omarr, illus. 2004. (Kids Talk Ser.). 32p. (C). (gr. 2-5). 23.93 (978-1-4048-0030-4(1)) Picture Window Bks.

—How Could You? Kids Talk about Trust. Wesley, Omarr, illus. 2004. (Kids Talk Ser.). 32p. (C). (gr. 2-5). 23.93 (978-1-4048-0031-1(X)) Picture Window Bks.

—No Fair! Kids Talk about Fairness. Wesley, Omarr, illus. 2004. (Kids Talk Ser.). 32p. (C). (gr. 2-5). 23.93 (978-1-4048-0033-5(6)) Picture Window Bks.

—Treat Me Right! Kids Talk about Respect. Wesley, Omarr, illus. 2004. (Kids Talk Ser.). 32p. (C). (gr. 2-5). 23.93 (978-1-4048-0034-2(4)) Picture Window Bks.

—We Live Here Too! Kids Talk about Good Citizenship. Wesley, Omarr, illus. 2004. (Kids Talk Ser.). 32p. (C). (gr. 2-5). pap. 23.93 (978-1-4048-0035-9(2)) Picture Window Bks.

MacGregor, Cynthia. Think for Yourself: A Kid's Guide to Solving Life's Dilemmas & Other Sticky Problems. Farias, Susan Norberg, illus. 2004. 96p. (J). (gr. 4-7). pap. 7.95 (978-1-894222-73-0(3)) Lobster Pr. CAN. *Dist:* Univ. of Toronto Pr.

Marcovitz, Hal. Teens, Religion, & Values. 2004. (Gallup Youth Survey, Major Issues & Trends Ser.). (Illus.). 112,128p. (J). (gr. 7-9). lib. bdg. 22.95 (978-1-59084-726-8(1)) Mason Crest Pubs.

Mayer, Cassie. Being Fair. 2007. (J). pap. ***(978-1-4034-9491-7(6))*** Heinemann Library.

—Being Responsible. 2007. (J). ***(978-1-4034-9489-4(4));*** pap. ***(978-1-4034-9497-9(5))*** Heinemann Library.

Mayled, Jon & Ahluwalia, Libby. Philosophy & Ethics for OCR GCSE Religious Studies. 2003. (Illus.). 208p. pap. (978-0-7487-7157-8(3)) Nelson Thornes Ltd.

McFarlane, Evelyn & Saywell, James. If... Questions for Teens. 2001. (Illus.). 144p. 10.95 (978-0-375-50555-3(5) , Villard Bks.) Random House Publishing Group.

Newell, Karmel H. Come Follow Me: A Child's Guide to Faith, Hope, & Charity. Smith, Mary Ann Free, illus. 2003. (J). 16.95 (978-1-57008-809-4(8)) Scribbulations LLC.

Parker, David. I Accept You As You Are! Fiammenghi, Gioia, illus. 2004. (J). ***(978-0-439-62811-2(3))*** Scholastic, Inc.

—I Can Cooperate! Dubin, Jill, illus. 2004. (J). ***(978-0-439-62812-9(1))*** Scholastic, Inc.

Pinderhughes, John, photos by. The Golden Rule. 1999. (Large-Size Photo Board Bks.). (Illus.). 20p. (J). (ps-k). mass mkt. 4.99 (978-0-7681-0105-8(0) , McClanahan Bk.) Learning Horizons, Inc.

Raatma, Lucia. Forgiveness. 2002. (Character Education Ser.). (Illus.). 24p. (J). (gr. 1-2). lib. bdg. 18.60 (978-0-7368-1132-3(X) , Bridgestone Bks.) Capstone Pr., Inc.

Responsibility. (Everyday Character Education Ser.). 24p. (J). 6.95 (978-0-7368-5151-0(8)); 6.95 (978-0-7368-9156-1(0)) Capstone Pr., Inc.

Rue, Nancy N. The Blurry Rules Book: It's a God Thing. 2001. (Ywof Library). 96p. (J). pap. 7.99 (978-0-310-70152-1(X)) Zondervan.

Salzmann, Mary Elizabeth. I Am Fair. 2003. (Building Character Ser.). (Illus.). 24p. (J). (ps-3). lib. bdg. 19.93 (978-1-57765-826-9(4)) ABDO Publishing Co.

—Responsibility Counts. 2003. (Character Counts Ser.). 32p. (J). (gr. k-6). lib. bdg. 22.78 (978-1-57765-874-0(4)) ABDO Publishing Co.

Sawyer, Kem Knapp. Freedom Calls: Journey of a Slave Girl. 2001. v, 181p. (J). (gr. 3-6). lib. bdg. 17.95 (978-1-57249-206-6(6) , White Mane Kids) White Mane Publishing Co., Inc.

Schuette, Sarah L. I Am Generous. 2004. (Character Values Ser.). (Illus.). 24p. (J). lib. bdg. 15.93 (978-0-7368-2570-2(3) , Pebble Bks.) Capstone Pr., Inc.

Seder, Isaac. Justice & Fairness. (J). 2003. pap. 7.50 (978-1-4109-0330-3(3)); 2002. (Illus.). 32p. lib. bdg. 24.26 (978-0-7398-5805-9(X)) Raintree.

Shafer, Jean. Our Core Democratic Values: Civic Virtue in Action. 1999. (Illus.). 32p. (J). (gr. 3-7). pap., wbk. ed. 14.95 (978-0-938682-54-7(7)) River Road Pubns., Inc.

Small, Mary. Caring Is. Ouren, Todd, illus. 2004. (J). (978-1-4048-0273-5(8)) Picture Window Bks.

Snedden, Robert. Medical Ethics: Changing Attitudes, 1900-2000. 1999. (Twentieth Century Issues Ser.). (Illus.). 64p. (J). (gr. 4-6). lib. bdg. 28.54 (978-0-8172-5893-1(0)) Raintree.

Taylor, Kenneth N. Right Choices. Shoemaker, Kathryn E., illus. 1999. 64p. (J). 12.99 (978-0-8423-5299-4(6)) Tyndale Hse. Pubs.

Teen Issues, 26 bks., Set. (Illus.). (YA). (gr. 6-12). lib. bdg. 344.10 (978-0-89490-887-3(1)) Enslow Pubs., Inc.

Teitelbaum, Michael. Sportsmanship. 2003. (Illus.). 32p. (J). pap. 7.50 (978-1-4109-0327-3(3)); lib. bdg. 24.28 (978-0-7398-7008-2(4)) Raintree.

—Sportsmanship. 2003. (gr. 3-6). lib. bdg. 15.90 (978-0-613-78296-8(8)) Tandem Library Bks.

Torr, James D. Medical Ethics. 2000. (Current Controversies Ser.). (Illus.). 176p. (YA). (gr. 7-12). pap. 21.20 (978-0-7377-0144-9(7) , Greenhaven Pr., Inc.) Thomson Gale.

Turner, Dale. Free to Be. Summer, Angel, ed. Smart, Ross, illus. 2003. 112p. (J). (gr. k-5). 16.95 (978-1-892696-28-1(2)) High Tide Pr.

Williams, Bernard. The A-Z of PSE. 1999. (Illus.). 144p. (J). (gr. 6-11). pap. 24.00 (978-0-7487-3892-2(4)) Nelson Thornes Ltd. GBR. *Dist:* Trans-Atlantic Pubns., Inc.

ETHICS, CHRISTIAN

see Christian Ethics

ETHICS, SEXUAL

see Sexual Ethics

ETHIOPIA

Berg, Elizabeth. Ethiopia. (Countries of the World Ser.). (Illus.). (J). 2000. 96p. (gr. 6 up). lib. bdg. 30.00 (978-0-8368-2324-0(9)); 1999. 32p. (gr. 3 up). lib. bdg. 24.67 (978-0-8368-2032-4(0)) Stevens, Gareth Inc.

Britton, Tamara L. Ethiopia. 2002. (Countries Ser.). (Illus.). 40p. (J). (gr. k-6). lib. bdg. 22.78 (978-1-57765-757-6(8) , Checkerboard Library) ABDO Publishing Co.

Campbell, Andrew. Ethiopia. 2007. (978-1-59920-016-3(3)) Smart Apple Media.

Chelsea House Publishing Staff. Ethiopia. 2002. (Exploration of Africa). (Illus.). 112p. (J). (gr. 7-12). 35.00 (978-0-7910-5745-2(3) , Chelsea Hse.) Facts On File, Inc.

Corona, Laurel. Ethiopia. 2000. (Modern Nations of the World Ser.). (Illus.). 128p. (J). (gr. 7-10). 29.95 (978-1-56006-823-5(X) , Lucent Bks.) Thomson Gale.

Corrigan, Jim. Ethiopia. 2004. (Africa Ser.). (Illus.). 79p. (J). lib. bdg. (978-1-59084-818-0(7)) Mason Crest Pubs.

Delzio, Suzanne. Ethiopia. 2004. (Many Cultures, One World Ser.). (Illus.). 32p. (J). (gr. 2-3). lib. bdg. 23.93 (978-0-7368-2449-1(9) , Bridgestone Bks.) Capstone Pr., Inc.

Dubois, Muriel L. Ethiopia. 2001. (Countries of the World Ser.). (Illus.). 126p. (J). (gr. 2-3). 18.60 (978-0-7368-0813-2(2) , Bridgestone Bks.) Capstone Pr., Inc.

Englar, Mary. Ethiopia: A Question & Answer Book. 2006. (Fact Finders Ser.). (Illus.). 32p. (J). (978-0-7368-4354-6(X) , Fact Finders) Capstone Pr., Inc.

Gillespie, Carol Ann. Ethiopia. (Modern World Nations Ser.). (Illus.). (gr. 6-12). 2003. 200p. pap. 30.00 (978-0-7910-7106-9(5)); 2002. 150p. 30.00 (978-0-7910-6780-2(7)) Facts On File, Inc. (Chelsea Hse.).

Glaser, Elizabeth & Biel, Timothy Levi. The Ethiopian Famine. 2002. (World Disasters Ser.). (Illus.). 64p. (YA). (gr. 4-12). lib. bdg. 26.20 (978-1-56006-014-7(X) , Lucent Bks.) Thomson Gale.

Grunsell, Angela. Ethiopia. 1998. (Worldfocus Ser.). (Illus.). 32p. (J). pap. (978-1-57572-032-6(9)) Heinemann Library.

Heinemann Staff. Ethiopia. (World Focus Ser.). (Illus.). 31p. (J). (gr. 3-7). pap. 3.99 (978-0-431-07262-3(0)) Oxfam Publishing GBR. *Dist:* Stylus Publishing, LLC.

Heinrichs, Ann. Ethiopia. 2005. (Enchantment of the World, Second Ser.). (Illus.). 144p. (J). (gr. 5-9). 36.00 (978-0-516-23680-3(6) , Children's Pr.) Scholastic Library Publishing.

Lassieur, Allison. Ethiopia. 2003. (Countries & Cultures Ser.). (Illus.). 64p. (J). lib. bdg. 25.26 (978-0-7368-2175-9(9) , Bridgestone Bks.) Capstone Pr., Inc.

Macknish, Neil & Berg, Elizabeth. Welcome to Ethiopia. 2001. (Welcome to My Country Ser.). (Illus.). 48p. (J). (gr. 2 up). lib. bdg. 26.00 (978-0-8368-2524-4(1)) Stevens, Gareth Inc.

Morris, Noelle. Ethiopia. 2003. (World Tour Ser.). (Illus.). 48p. (J). lib. bdg. 25.70 (978-0-7398-6810-2(1)) Raintree.

NgCheong-Lum, Roseline. Eritrea. 2001. (Cultures of the World Ser.). (Illus.). 128p. (J). (gr. 5-12). lib. bdg. 37.07 (978-0-7614-1192-5(5) , Benchmark Bks.) Cavendish, Marshall Corp.

ETHIOPIA—FICTION

Dunckel, Mona. Escape. 1999. 101p. (J). (gr. 1-2). pap. 6.49 (978-1-57924-068-4(2) , 113100) Jones, Bob Univ. Pr.

Guillain, Adam. Bella Balistica & the African Safari. 2007. (Bella Balistica Ser.). (Illus.). 234p. (J). (gr. 5-8). pap. 9.95 (978-1-84059-482-9(9)) Milet Publishing.

Kessler, Cristina. The Best Beekeeper of Lalibela: A Tale from Africa. Jenkins, Leonard, illus. 2006. 32p. (J). 16.95 (978-0-8234-1858-9(8)) Holiday Hse., Inc.

Kurtz, Jane. Faraway Home. Lewis, Earl, illus. 2000. 32p. (J). (gr. 1-5). 17.00 (978-0-15-200036-3(4) , Gulliver Bks.) Harcourt Children's Bks.

—The Storyteller's Beads. Van Doren, Liz, ed. Bryant, Michael, illus. 1998. 160p. (YA). (gr. 3-7). 16.00 (978-0-15-201074-4(2) , Gulliver Bks.) Harcourt Children's Bks.

Mohamed, Sultan, tr. & illus. The Story of Coffee. Mohamed, Sultan, illus. 2003. (ENG & AMH.). 24p. (J). (gr. 4-5). 15.99 (978-0-9605670-9-6(7)) Ananse Pr.

Morgan, Anna. Daughters of the Ark. 2005. (Illus.). 230p. (J). (gr. 5-9). pap. 7.95 (978-1-896764-92-4(4)) Second Story Pr. CAN. *Dist:* Orca Bk. Pubs. USA, Univ. of Toronto Pr.

Zephaniah, Benjamin. Refugee Boy. 2004. 296p. (J). (gr. 5-12). reprint ed. pap. 7.95 (978-1-58234-908-4(8) , Bloomsbury Children) Bloomsbury Publishing.

ETHNIC GROUPS

see Ethnic Relations; Minorities; Racially Mixed People

ETHNIC RELATIONS

Ancona, George. Mis Amigos: My Friends. 2004. (Somos Latino (We Are Latinos) Ser.). 20.00 (978-0-516-23690-2(3) , Watts, Franklin) Scholastic Library Publishing.

Cooper, Michael L. Indian School: Teaching the White Man's Way. 1999. (Illus.). 112p. (J). (gr. 5-9). tchr. ed. 18.00 (978-0-395-92084-8(1) , Clarion Bks.) Houghton Mifflin Co. Trade & Reference Div.

Finkelstein, Norman H. Forged in Freedom: Shaping the Jewish-American Experience. 2002. (Illus.). 192p. (gr. 6-12). 19.95 (978-0-8276-0748-4(2)) Jewish Pubn. Society.

Gottfried, Ted. Northern Ireland: Peace in Our Time? 2002. (Headliners Ser.). (Illus.). 64p. (gr. 5-8). lib. bdg. 25.90 (978-0-7613-2252-8(3) , Millbrook Pr.) Lerner Publishing Group.

Hanes, Richard Clay, et al. Prejudice in the Modern World. 2007. (J). ***(978-1-4144-0205-5(8)); (978-1-4144-0206-2(6))*** Thomson Gale.

Holman, Sandy Lynne. We All Have a Heritage. Kowetiawi, Lela, illus. l.t. ed. 2002. (People Ser.: Pt. II). 35p. (J). (gr. k-6). 18.95 (978-0-9644655-2-7(3)) Culture C.O.-O.P., The.

Jaskol, Julie & Lewis, Brian. City of Angels: In & Around Los Angeles. Kleven, Elisa, illus. 1999. 48p. (J). (ps-3). 16.99 (978-0-525-46214-9(7) , Dutton Juvenile) Penguin Group (USA) Inc.

King, Dr. Dorothy. What Is Ethnophobia? 2005. 64p. pap. 22.13 (978-1-4116-4348-2(8)) Lulu.com.

Malaspina, Ann. The Ethnic & Group Identity Movements: Earning Recognition. 2007. (Reform Movements in American History Ser.). 160p. (J). (gr. 6-12). 30.00 (***978-0-7910-9571-3(1)** , Chelsea Hse.) Facts On File, Inc.

Nickles, Greg. Japanese. 2001. (gr. 3-6). lib. bdg. 17.60 (978-0-613-43459-1(5)) Tandem Library Bks.

Russo, Marisabina. Always Remember Me: How One Family Survived World War II. Russo, Marisabina, illus. 2005. (Illus.). 48p. (J). (gr. 1-5). 17.99 (978-0-689-86920-4(7) , Atheneum) Simon & Schuster Children's Publishing.

Stotsky, Sandra. Ethnic Answer Books, 11 bks., Ueda, Reed, ed. 1999. (Illus.). 120-136p. (YA). (gr. 5 up). pap. 109.45 (978-0-7910-4804-7(7) , Chelsea Hse.) Facts On File, Inc.

Thomson Gale Staff. Prejudice in the Modern World: Almanac, 2 vols. Hanes, Richard C. et al, eds. rev. ed. 2007. (Prejudice Throughout History Reference Library). 462p. (YA). 120.00 (978-1-4144-0204-8(X) , UXL) Thomson Gale.

—Prejudice in the Modern World: Biographies. Hanes, Richard C. & Rudd, Kelly, eds. rev. ed. 2007. (Prejudice Throughout History Reference Library). 920p. (YA). 67.00 (978-1-4144-0207-9(4) , UXL) Thomson Gale.

—Prejudice in the Modern World: Cumulative Index. Hermsen, Sarah, ed. rev. ed. 2007. (Prejudice Throughout History Reference Library). 34p. (YA). 5.00 (978-1-4144-0209-3(0) , UXL) Thomson Gale.

—Prejudice in the Modern World: Primary Sources. Hanes, Sharon M., ed. rev. ed. 2007. (Prejudice Throughout History Reference Library). 214p. (YA). 67.00 (978-1-4144-0208-6(2) , UXL) Thomson Gale.

ETHNOGRAPHY

see Ethnology

ETHNOLOGY

see also Anthropology; Anthropometry; Archaeology; Civilization; Costume; Ethnic Relations; Folklore; Human Geography; Human Skin Color; Language and Languages; Manners and Customs; Prehistoric Peoples; Primitive Societies; Race; Race Relations; Totems and Totemism

All about Us Interactive Packages: Here I Am. (Pebble Soup Explorations Ser.). (ps up). 52.00 (978-0-7578-5227-5(0)) Rigby Education.

All about Us Interactive Packages: Making Friends. (Pebble Soup Explorations Ser.). (ps up). 52.00 (978-0-7578-5228-2(9)) Rigby Education.

Ancona, George. The People: Viva Mexico. 2001. (Viva Mexico! Ser.). (Illus.). 48p. (J). (gr. 3 up). lib. bdg. 27.07 (978-0-7614-1329-5(4) , Benchmark Bks.) Cavendish, Marshall Corp.

Ansary, Mir Tamim. People of California. 2003. (Heinemann State Studies). (Illus.). 48p. (J). (gr. 3-5). lib. bdg. (978-1-4034-0342-1(2)) Heinemann Library.

Ashanti to Zulu. 2004. (J). pap. 14.95 incl. audio (978-0-7882-0674-0(5)) Weston Woods Studios, Inc.

Banting, Erinn. Afghanistan - The People. 2003. (Lands, Peoples & Cultures Ser.). (Illus.). 32p. (J). (gr. 2-9). (978-0-7787-9336-6(2)); pap. (978-0-7787-9704-3(X)) Crabtree Publishing Co.

Breaud, Odile, et al. Cultures of the World. 1998. (Creative Discoveries Ser.: Vol. 8). Orig. Title: Living Around the World. (Illus.). 75p. (J). (gr. 2-8). lib. bdg. 23.95 (978-0-88682-957-5(7) , Creative Education) Creative Co., The.

Castner, James L. Native Peoples: Deep in the Amazon. 2001. (Deep in the Amazon Ser.). (Illus.). 32p. (J). (gr. 5 up). lib. bdg. 28.50 (978-0-7614-1128-4(3) , Benchmark Bks.) Cavendish, Marshall Corp.

Chelsea House Publishing Staff. People & Customs of the World, 4 bks. 1998. (Illus.). (J). (gr. 5-12). 79.80 (978-0-7910-5137-5(4) , Chelsea Hse.) Facts On File, Inc.

Clarke, Ann. People Are So Different! Smith, Duncan, illus. 2006. (J). 14.95 (***978-0-9787235-0-7(3))** Precious Little Bks.

Claybourne, Anna & Doherty, Gillian. Peoples of the World. rev. ed. 2005. 96p. (J). pap. 14.95 (978-0-7945-1025-1(6) , Usborne) EDC Publishing.

Conrad, David C. Empires of Medieval West Africa: Ghana, Mali, & Songhay. 2005. (Great Empires of the Past Ser.). (Illus.). 128p. (J). (gr. 6-12). 35.00 (978-0-8160-5562-3(9)) Facts On File, Inc.

Cultures of the World - Group 16, 6 vols. Incl. Belarus. Levy, Patricia. lib. bdg. 37.07 (978-0-7614-0811-6(8)); Guatemala. Sheehan, Sean. lib. bdg. 37.07 (978-0-7614-0812-3(6)); Liberia. Levy, Patricia. lib. bdg. 37.07 (978-0-7614-0810-9(X)); New Zealand. Smelt, Roselynn. lib. bdg. 37.07 (978-0-7614-0808-6(8)); Papua New Guinea. Gascoigne, Ingrid. lib. bdg. 37.07 (978-0-7614-0813-0(4)); Tanzania. Heale, Jay. lib. bdg. 37.07 (978-0-7614-0809-3(6)); 128p. (gr. 5-12). 1998. (Illus.). 1998. 222.43 (978-0-7614-0807-9(X) , Benchmark Bks.) Cavendish, Marshall Corp.

Cultures of the World - Group 17, 6 vols. Incl. Bangladesh. Whyte, Mariam. (gr. 5-12). 1999. lib. bdg. 37.07 (978-0-7614-0869-7(X)); Czech Republic. Sioras, Efstathia. (gr. 5-12). 1999. lib. bdg. 37.07 (978-0-7614-0870-3(3)); Democratic Republic of the Congo. Heale, Jay. (gr. 5-12). 1999. lib. bdg. 37.07 (978-0-7614-0874-1(6)); Kuwait. O'Shea, Maria. (gr. 5-12). 1999. lib. bdg. 37.07 (978-0-7614-0871-0(1)); Senegal. Berg, Elizabeth. (gr. 5-12). 1999. lib. bdg. 37.07 (978-0-7614-0872-7(X)); Uruguay. Jermyn, Leslie. (J). (gr. k-17). 1998. lib. bdg. 37.07 (978-0-7614-0873-4(8)); 128p. (Illus.). 222.43 (978-0-7614-0868-0(1) , Benchmark Bks.) Cavendish, Marshall Corp.

Cultures of the World - Group 20, 6 vols. Incl. Bahamas. Barlas, Robert. lib. bdg. 37.07 (978-0-7614-0992-0(0)); Fiji. NgCheong-Lum, Roseline. lib. bdg. 37.07 (978-0-7614-0996-0(3)); Guyana. Jermyn, Leslie. lib. bdg. 37.07 (978-0-7614-0994-6(7)); Malta. Sheehan, Sean. lib. bdg. 37.07 (978-0-7614-0993-9(9)); Moldova. Sheehan, Patricia. lib. bdg. 37.07 (978-0-7614-0997-7(1)); Niger. Seffal, Rabah. lib. bdg. 37.07 (978-0-7614-0995-3(5)); 128p. (gr. 5-12). 2000. (Illus.). 222.43 (978-0-7614-0991-5(2) , Benchmark Bks.) Cavendish, Marshall Corp.

Cultures of the World - Group 21, 6 vols. Incl. Bahrain. Cooper, Robert. 2000. lib. bdg. 37.07 (978-0-7614-1161-1(5)); Cameroon. Sheehan, Sean. (J). 2001. lib. bdg. 37.07 (978-0-7614-1158-1(5)); Croatia. Cooper, Robert. (J). 2000. lib. bdg. 37.07 (978-0-7614-1156-7(9)); Grenada. Cheng, Pang Guek. 2000. lib. bdg. 37.07 (978-0-7614-1160-4(7)); Maldives. NgCheong-Lum, Roseline. 2000. lib. bdg. 37.07 (978-0-7614-1157-4(7)); Scotland. Levy, Patricia. (J). 2000. lib. bdg. 37.07 (978-0-7614-1159-8(3)); 128p. (gr. 5-12). (Illus.). 2000. 222.43 (978-0-7614-1155-0(0) , Benchmark Bks.) Cavendish, Marshall Corp.

Douglas, Vincent & School Specialty Publishing Staff. People of the World. 2006. (Just the Facts Ser.). (Illus.). 64p. (J). (gr. 5-8). pap. 9.95 (978-0-7696-4257-4(8)) School Specialty Publishing.

Fleischman, Paul, ed. Cannibal in the Mirror. Whalen, John, photos by. 2000. (Single Titles Ser.: up). (Illus.). 64p. (gr. 7 up). lib. bdg. 24.90 (978-0-7613-0968-0(3) , Twenty-First Century Bks.) Lerner Publishing Group.

Fox, Mem. Whoever You Are: Quienquiera Que Seas. Ada, Alma Flor & Campoy, F. Isabel, trs. Staub, Leslie, illus. 2007. (ENG & SPA.). 28p. (J). bds. 6.95 (978-0-15-205891-3(5) , Voyager Bks./Libros Viajeros) Harcourt Children's Bks.

Fox, Mem & Staub, Leslie. Quienquiera Que Seas. Ada, Alma Flor & Campoy, F. Isabel, trs. Staub, Leslie, illus. 2002. (ENG & SPA., Illus.). 32p. (J). pap. 7.00 (978-0-15-216460-7(X) , HB31513, Voyager Bks./Libros Viajeros) Harcourt Children's Bks.

Freeman, Dena & Alexander, Bryan. How People Live. 2003. (Illus.). 304p. (J). 29.99 (978-0-7894-9867-0(7)) Dorling Kindersley Publishing, Inc.

Gall, Susan B. & Gall, Timothy L. Junior Worldmark Encyclopedia of World Cultures, 9 vols. 1998. (Illus.). 2090p. (J). (gr. 4-7). lib. bdg. 470.00 (978-0-7876-1756-1(3) , GML00502-111157, UXL) Thomson Gale.

Gayle-Evans, Guda. An Annotated Bibliography of Multi-Cultural Literature for Children Three to Ten Years. 2004. (Mellen Studies in Children's Literature: Vol. 6). (Illus.). 204p. 109.95 (978-0-7734-6474-2(3)) Mellen, Edwin Pr., The.

Gustafson, Angela. Imagine a House: A Journey to Fascinating Houses Around the World. 2003. (What a World We Live in Ser.). (Illus.). 32p. (J). (gr. k-6). lib. bdg. 16.95 (978-0-9726849-0-3(5)) Out of the Box.

Harris, Nicholas, ed. People of the World. 2002. (Blackbirch Visual Encyclopedia Ser.). (Illus.). 64p. (J). 37.44 (978-1-56711-518-5(7) , Blackbirch Pr., Inc.) Thomson Gale.

Hathersmith, June. From Akebu to Zapotec: A Book of Bibleless Peoples. Roder, Alice, illus. 2002. 31p. (J). pap. (978-0-938978-28-2(4)) Wycliffe Bible Translators.

Hollander, Malika. Brazil - The People. 2003. (Lands, Peoples & Cultures Ser.). (Illus.). 32p. (J). (gr. 2-9). (978-0-7787-9339-7(7)); pap. (978-0-7787-9707-4(4)) Crabtree Publishing Co.

Horn, Geoffrey M. Margaret Mead. 2004. (Trailblazers of the Modern World Ser.). (Illus.). 48p. (J). (gr. 5 up). pap. 11.95 (978-0-8368-5259-2(1)); lib. bdg. 30.00 (978-0-8368-5099-4(8)) Stevens, Gareth Inc. (World Almanac Library).

Jenson-Elliott, Cynthia L. East Africa. 2002. (Indigenous Peoples of Africa Ser.). (Illus.). 112p. (YA). (gr. 4-12). 29.95 (978-1-56006-969-0(4) , Lucent Bks.) Thomson Gale.

—Southern Africa. 2002. (Indigenous Peoples of Africa Ser.). (Illus.). 112p. (J). 29.95 (978-1-59018-084-6(4) , Lucent Bks.) Thomson Gale.

Knotts, Bob. People of Florida. 2002. (State Studies). (Illus.). 48p. (J). pap. 8.50 (978-1-4034-0565-4(4)); (gr. 3-5). lib. bdg. (978-1-4034-0349-0(X)) Heinemann Library.

Kroll, Virginia L. With Love, to Earth's Endangered People. 1998. (gr. 5-8). lib. bdg. 17.60 (978-0-613-70737-4(0)) Tandem Library Bks.

—With Love, to Earth's Endangered Peoples. Collier-Morales, Roberta, illus. 1998. 48p. (YA). (gr. 4-7). pap. 8.95 (978-1-883220-82-2(3)); 17.95 (978-1-883220-83-9(1)) Dawn Pubns.

Lehman, Jeffrey, ed. Gale Encyclopedia of Multicultural America, 2 vols. 1999. (Illus.). xiv, 820p. (J). (978-0-7876-3991-4(5)) Thomson Gale.

—Gale Encyclopedia of Multicultural America Set: Primary Documents, 2 vols. 1999. (Illus.). xiv, 820p. (YA). (gr. 9 up). 225.00 (978-0-7876-3990-7(7) , GML00502-113793, Gale Research International, Ltd.) Thomson Gale.

MacQuitty, Miranda & Dorling Kindersley Publishing Staff. Desert. 2000. (Eyewitness Bks.). (Illus.). 64p. (J). (gr. 4-7). lib. bdg. 19.99 (978-0-7894-6600-6(7)) Dorling Kindersley Publishing, Inc.

Mason, Antony. People Around the World. 2002. (Illus.). 256p. (J). (gr. 5-9). tchr. ed. 25.00 (978-0-7534-5497-8(1) , Kingfisher) Houghton Mifflin Co. Trade & Reference Div.

Millett, Sandra. The Hmong of Southeast Asia. 2002. (First Peoples Ser.). (Illus.). 48p. (J). (gr. 4-8). lib. bdg. 23.93 (978-0-8225-4852-2(6)) Lerner Publishing Group.

Nathan, Emma. La Gente. 2002. (Abre los Ojos y Aprende Serie).Tr. of Eyeopeners: People. (SPA.). 24p. (J). (-3). 24.94 (978-1-4103-0019-5(6) , Blackbirch Pr., Inc.) Thomson Gale.

—People. 2002. (Eyeopeners Ser.). (Illus.). 24p. (J). 22.45 (978-1-56711-652-6(3) , Blackbirch Pr., Inc.) Thomson Gale.

Nile, Richard. Threatened Cultures. 1999. pap. 152.82 (978-0-8172-9645-2(X)) Raintree.

People of the World. (J). (gr. 6). (978-0-8374-1460-7(1) , 208) Weekly Reader Corp.

Peoples of North America, 10 vols. 2003. (Illus.). (J). 359.00 (978-0-7172-5777-5(0) , Grolier) Scholastic Library Publishing.

Peoples of the World: Customs & Cultures, 10 vols. 1998. (Illus.). (J). lib. bdg. 305.00 (978-0-7172-9236-3(3) , Grolier) Scholastic Library Publishing.

Philbrick, Nathaniel. Sea of Glory: America's Voyage of Discovery, the U. S. Exploring Expedition, 1838-1842. 2004. (Illus.). 452p. per. 22.65 (978-0-606-33469-3(6)) Tandem Library Bks.

Santella, Andrew. People of Illinois. 2002. (State Studies). (Illus.). 48p. (J). (gr. 3-5). pap. 8.50 (978-1-4034-0571-5(9) , 91876); lib. bdg. 27.07 (978-1-4034-0010-9(5)) Heinemann Library.

Schonberg, Marcia. People of Michigan. 2003. (Heinemann State Studies). (Illus.). 48p. (J). pap. 8.50 (978-1-4034-2680-2(5)); 27.07 (978-1-4034-0661-3(8)) Heinemann Library.

Steward, Mark. People of New York. 2003. (Heinemann State Studies). (Illus.). 48p. (J). (gr. 3-5). lib. bdg. (978-1-4034-0355-1(4)) Heinemann Library.

Stewart, Mark. People of New York. 2003. (Heinemann State Studies). (Illus.). 48p. (J). pap. 8.50 (978-1-4034-0577-7(8)) Heinemann Library.

—People of New York. 2003. (gr. 3-6). lib. bdg. 17.05 (978-0-613-60979-1(4)) Tandem Library Bks.

Stone, Lynn M. America's People. 2002. (Illus.). 24p. (J). lib. bdg. 25.64 (978-1-58952-309-8(1)) Rourke Publishing, LLC.

Ueda, Reed & Stotsky, Sandra, eds. Anglo-American Answer Book. 1999. (Ethnic Answer Book Ser.). (Illus.). 136p. (YA). (gr. 5 up). pap. 9.95 (978-0-7910-4893-1(4)); lib. bdg. 17.95 (978-0-7910-4892-4(6)) Facts On File, Inc. (Chelsea Hse.).

We Come From..., 10 bks., Set. Incl. Brazil. Lichtenberger, Andre. 2000. lib. bdg. 25.69 (978-0-8172-5514-5(1)); China. Waterlow, Julia. 2000. lib. bdg. 25.69 (978-0-8172-5219-9(3)); France. Fisher, Teresa. 1999. lib. bdg. 25.69 (978-0-8172-5212-0(6)); Germany. Hurst, Mike. 1999. lib. bdg. 25.69 (978-0-8172-5218-2(5)); India. Cumming, David. 1999. lib. bdg. 25.69 (978-0-8172-5213-7(4)); Jamaica. Brownlie, Alison. 1999. lib. bdg. 25.69 (978-0-8172-5511-4(7)); Japan. Fisher, Teresa. 1999. lib. bdg. 25.69 (978-0-8172-5217-5(7)); Kenya. Kairi, Wambui. 2000. lib. bdg. 25.69 (978-0-8172-5512-1(5)); Nigeria. Brownlie, Alison. 2000. lib. bdg. 25.69 (978-0-8172-5513-8(3)); South Africa. Brownlie, Alison. 2000. lib. bdg. 25.69 (978-0-8172-5221-2(5)); 32p. (J). (gr. 1-4). (Illus.). 1998. Set lib. bdg. 256.90 (978-0-7398-1005-7(7)) Raintree.

Zurlo, Tony. Native Peoples of West Africa. 2001. (Indigenous Peoples of Africa Ser.). (Illus.). 112p. (J). (gr. 4-12). 29.95 (978-1-56006-832-7(9) , LML00902-178164, Lucent Bks.) Thomson Gale.

ETIQUETTE

see also Courtesy; Dance; Dating (Social Customs); Entertaining; Letter Writing; Manners and Customs

also names of countries with the subdivision Social life and customs

Aikins, Anne Marie. Misconduct: Without Bending the Rules. Murray, Steven, illus. 2005. (Deal with It Ser.). 32p. (J). (gr. 4-8). 12.95 (978-1-55028-871-1(7)) Lorimer, James & Co., Ltd., Pubs. CAN. *Dist:* Casemate Pubs. & Bk. Distributors, LLC.

Amos, Janine. After You! Spenceley, Annabel, illus. 2001. (Courteous Kids Ser.). 32p. (J). (ps up). lib. bdg. 23.33 (978-0-8368-2802-3(X)) Stevens, Gareth Inc.

—Courteous Kids, 18 bks. Spenceley, Annabel, illus. Incl. Admitting Mistakes. 2002. lib. bdg. 23.33 (978-0-8368-3168-9(3)); After You! 2001. lib. bdg. 23.33 (978-0-8368-2802-3(X)); Being Helpful. 2002. lib. bdg. 23.33 (978-0-8368-3169-6(1)); Being Kind. 2002. lib. bdg. 23.33 (978-0-8368-3170-2(5)); Don't Do That! 2002. lib. bdg. 23.33 (978-0-8368-3605-9(7)); Don't Say That! 2002. lib. bdg. 23.33 (978-0-8368-3606-6(5)); Go Away! 2002. lib. bdg. 23.33 (978-0-8368-3607-3(3)); Hello! 2001. lib. bdg. 23.33 (978-0-8368-2803-0(8)); I'm Sorry! 2001. lib. bdg. 23.33 (978-0-8368-2804-7(6)); It Won't Work! 2002. lib. bdg. 23.33 (978-0-8368-3608-0(1)); It's Mine! 2002. lib. bdg. 23.33 (978-0-8368-3609-7(X)); Making Friends. 2002. lib. bdg. 23.33 (978-0-8368-3171-9(3)); Move Over! 2002. lib. bdg. 23.33 (978-0-8368-3610-3(3)); No, Thank You! 2001. lib. bdg. 23.33 (978-0-8368-2805-4(4)); Please! 2001. lib. bdg. 23.33 (978-0-8368-2806-1(2)); Sharing. 2002. lib. bdg. 23.33 (978-0-8368-3172-6(1)); Taking Turns. 2002. lib. bdg. 23.33 (978-0-8368-3173-3(X)); Thank You! 2001. lib. bdg. 23.33 (978-0-8368-2807-8(0)); 32p. (J). (ps up). (Illus.). Set lib. bdg. 419.94 (978-0-8368-3644-8(8)) Stevens, Gareth Inc.

—Courteous Kids: Don't Do That!; Don't Say That!; Go Away!; It Won't Work!; It's Mine!; Move Over!, 6 bks. Spenceley, Annabel, illus. 2002. (J). (ps up). lib. bdg. 127.60 (978-0-8368-3604-2(9)) Stevens, Gareth Inc.

—Don't Do That! Spenceley, Annabel, illus. 2002. (Courteous Kids Ser.). 32p. (J). (ps up). lib. bdg. 23.33 (978-0-8368-3605-9(7)) Stevens, Gareth Inc.

—Don't Say That! Spenceley, Annabel, illus. 2002. (Courteous Kids Ser.). 32p. (J). (ps up). lib. bdg. 23.33 (978-0-8368-3606-6(5)) Stevens, Gareth Inc.

—Hello! Spenceley, Annabel, illus. 2001. (Courteous Kids Ser.). 32p. (J). (ps up). lib. bdg. 23.33 (978-0-8368-2803-0(8)) Stevens, Gareth Inc.

—I'm Sorry! Spenceley, Annabel, illus. 2001. (Courteous Kids Ser.). 32p. (J). (ps up). lib. bdg. 23.33 (978-0-8368-2804-7(6)) Stevens, Gareth Inc.

—It's Mine! Spenceley, Annabel, illus. 2002. (Courteous Kids Ser.). 32p. (J). (ps up). lib. bdg. 23.33 (978-0-8368-3609-7(X)) Stevens, Gareth Inc.

—Move Over! Spenceley, Annabel, illus. 2002. (Courteous Kids Ser.). 32p. (J). (ps up). lib. bdg. 23.33 (978-0-8368-3610-3(3)) Stevens, Gareth Inc.

—No, Thank You! Spenceley, Annabel, illus. 2001. (Courteous Kids Ser.). 32p. (J). (ps up). lib. bdg. 23.33 (978-0-8368-2805-4(4)) Stevens, Gareth Inc.

—Please! Spenceley, Annabel, illus. 2001. (Courteous Kids Ser.). 32p. (J). (ps up). lib. bdg. 23.33 (978-0-8368-2806-1(2)) Stevens, Gareth Inc.

—Taking Turns. Spenceley, Annabel, illus. 2002. (Courteous Kids Ser.). 32p. (J). (ps up). lib. bdg. 23.33 (978-0-8368-3173-3(X)) Stevens, Gareth Inc.

—Thank You! Spenceley, Annabel, illus. 2001. (Courteous Kids Ser.). 32p. (J). (ps up). lib. bdg. 23.33 (978-0-8368-2807-8(0)) Stevens, Gareth Inc.

Anastasio, Dina. Pass the Peas, Please: A Book of Manners. 1999. (Roxbury Park Bks.). (Illus.). 32p. (J). (ps-2). pap. 7.95 (978-0-7373-0193-9(7) , 01937W) McGraw-Hill/Contemporary.

—Pass the Peas, Please: A Book of Manners. 1999. (978-0-606-18269-0(1)) Tandem Library Bks.

Backer, Barbara F. Introducing Concepts at Circle Time. Hodges, Susan, ed. Burris, Priscilla, illus. 2001. (Circle Time Book Ser.). 96p. (J). (ps-k). pap. 10.99 (978-1-57029-239-2(6) , WPH04901, Totline Pubns.) Schaffer, Frank Pubns.

Barnes, Emilie. A Little Book of Manners: Etiquette for Young Ladies. Buchanan, Anne C., ed. Sparks, Michal, illus. 1998. 32p. (ps-3). 14.99 (978-1-56507-678-5(8)) Harvest Hse. Pubs.

Beker, Jeanne. The Big Night Out. Dion, Nathalie, illus. 2005. 80p. (J). (gr. 4). pap. 15.95 (978-0-88776-719-7(2)) Tundra Bks., Inc./Livres Toundra, Inc. CAN. *Dist:* Random Hse., Inc.

Berry, Joy Wilt. Being in Public: A Good Manners Book About. Bartholomew & Pace, Don, illus. rev. ed. 2000. (Living Skills Ser.: Vol. 8). 48p. (J). (gr. 1-7). pap. 4.95 (978-1-58634-123-7(5)) Goldstar Publishing, Inc.

—Rude People: Get over It! Bartholomew, illus. rev. ed. 2000. (Winning Skills Ser.: Vol. 4). 48p. (YA). (gr. 4-7). pap. 2.95 (978-1-58634-163-3(4)) Goldstar Publishing, Inc.

Bloch, Lyudmila & Civitano, Tom. The Golden Rules of Etiquette at the Plaza. Carroll, Rosemary, illus. 2004. 48p. (J). lib. bdg. 16.95 (978-0-9755390-0-2(0)) Fifth Ave Pr.

Buehner, Caralyn. It's a Spoon Not a Shovel. Buehner, Mark, illus. 1998. 40p. (J). (ps-3). pap. 6.99 (978-0-14-056427-3(6) , Puffin) Penguin Group (USA) Inc.

Burgess, Gelett. Goops - 1900: And How to Be Them. 2006. 100p. pap. 10.45 (978-1-59462-233-5(7) , 266, Book Jungle) Standard Pubns., Inc.

Candell, Arianna. Mind Your Manners: At Parties. Curto, Rosa M., illus. 2005. (Mind Your Manners Ser.). (ENG & SPA.). 36p. (J). pap. 6.95 (978-0-7641-3167-7(2)) Barron's Educational Series, Inc.

—Mind Your Manners: At the Park. Curto, Rosa M., illus. 2005. (Mind Your Manners Ser.). 36p. (J). pap. 6.95 (978-0-7641-3168-4(0)) Barron's Educational Series, Inc.

—Mind Your Manners: In School. Curto, Rosa M., illus. 2005. (Mind Your Manners Ser.). 36p. (J). pap. 6.95 (978-0-7641-3166-0(4)) Barron's Educational Series, Inc.

Chronicle Books LLC Staff. Fiona the Flower Girl. 2008. 40p. (J). 15.99 (978-0-8118-5903-5(7)) Chronicle Bks. LLC.

Cook, Bev. In God's House: A Guidebook for Children on Using Good Manners at Church. McIntosh, Chuck, illus. 1998. iv, 32p. (J). (gr. k-5). pap. 5.95 (978-0-9667718-0-0(X)) Bright Eyes, Inc.

Crots, Marcia. Manners. 1998. (Illus.). 24p. (gr. k-3). 6.95 (978-1-57197-086-2(X)) Pentland Pr., Inc.

David C. Cook. Manners. 2003. (My Jesus Pocket Bks.). (Illus.). 32p. (J). (gr. 5-3). pap., pap. 8.90 (978-1-55513-128-9(X) , 155513128X) Cook, David C. Publishing Co.

DeGezelle, Terri. Manners at a Friend's Home. 2004. (First Facts Ser.). (Illus.). 24p. (J). (gr. k-2). lib. bdg. 21.26 (978-0-7368-2643-3(2) , First Facts) Capstone Pr., Inc.

—Manners at a Restaurant. 2004. (First Facts Ser.). (Illus.). 24p. (J). (gr. k-2). lib. bdg. 21.26 (978-0-7368-2644-0(0) , First Facts) Capstone Pr., Inc.

—Manners at the Library. 2004. (First Facts Ser.). (Illus.). 24p. (J). (gr. k-2). lib. bdg. 21.26 (978-0-7368-2645-7(9) , First Facts) Capstone Pr., Inc.

—Manners in the Classroom. 2004. (First Facts Ser.). (Illus.). 24p. (J). (gr. k-2). lib. bdg. 21.26 (978-0-7368-2646-4(7) , First Facts) Capstone Pr., Inc.

—Manners on the Playground. 2004. (First Facts Ser.). (Illus.). 24p. (J). (gr. k-2). lib. bdg. 21.26 (978-0-7368-2647-1(5) , First Facts) Capstone Pr., Inc.

—Manners on the Telephone. 2004. (First Facts Ser.). (Illus.). 24p. (J). (gr. k-2). lib. bdg. 21.26 (978-0-7368-2648-8(3) , First Facts) Capstone Pr., Inc.

Dorling Kindersley Publishing Staff. Dinner Time! 2006. (Illus.). 12p. (J). 6.99 (978-0-7566-2583-2(1)) Dorling Kindersley Publishing, Inc.

—Please, Sorry, Thank You. 2006. 12p. (J). 6.99 (978-0-7566-2287-9(5)) Dorling Kindersley Publishing, Inc.

Doudna, Kelly. Excuse Me. l.t. ed. 2001. (Good Manners Ser.). (Illus.). 24p. (J). (ps-3). lib. bdg. 19.93 (978-1-57765-574-9(5) ; SandCastle) ABDO Publishing Co.

—Good Manners, Set. l.t. ed. Incl. Excuse Me. lib. bdg. 19.93 (978-1-57765-574-9(5)); Hello. lib. bdg. 19.93 (978-1-57765-575-6(3)); I Am Sorry. lib. bdg. 19.93 (978-1-57765-573-2(7)); May I? lib. bdg. 19.93 (978-1-

E F G

57765-572-5(9)); Please. lib. bdg. 19.93 (978-1-57765-570-1(2)); Thank You. lib. bdg. 19.93 (978-1-57765-571-8(0)); 24p. (J). (ps-3). 2001. (Illus.). 2001. Set lib. bdg. 119.58 (978-1-57765-507-7(9) , SandCastle) ABDO Publishing Co.

—Hello. l.t. ed. 2001. (Good Manners Ser.). (Illus.). 24p. (J). (ps-3). lib. bdg. 19.93 (978-1-57765-575-6(3) , SandCastle) ABDO Publishing Co.

—I Am Sorry. l.t. ed. 2001. (Good Manners Ser.). (Illus.). 24p. (J). (ps-3). lib. bdg. 19.93 (978-1-57765-573-2(7) , SandCastle) ABDO Publishing Co.

—May I? l.t. ed. 2001. (Good Manners Ser.). (Illus.). 24p. (J). (ps-3). lib. bdg. 19.93 (978-1-57765-572-5(9) , SandCastle) ABDO Publishing Co.

—Please. l.t. ed. 2001. (Good Manners Ser.). (Illus.). 24p. (J). (ps-3). lib. bdg. 19.93 (978-1-57765-570-1(2) , SandCastle) ABDO Publishing Co.

—Thank You. l.t. ed. 2001. (Good Manners Ser.). (Illus.). 24p. (J). (ps-3). lib. bdg. 19.93 (978-1-57765-571-8(0) , SandCastle) ABDO Publishing Co.

Dougherty, Karla. The Rules to Be Cool: Etiquette & Netiquette. 2001. (Teen Issues Ser.). (Illus.). 64p. (J). (gr. 6-12). lib. bdg. 22.60 (978-0-7660-1607-1(2)) Enslow Pubs., Inc.

Elerding, Louise. You've Got Social Manners! Party Pointers from A to Z for Kids of All Ages. 2005. (to Z Guides). (Illus.). 64p. (J). 15.95 (978-0-9729237-4-3(8)) Grandy Pubns.

Excuse Me, Please!, 4 bks.; set. 2002. (J). bds. 7.98 (978-0-7525-8878-0(8)) Parragon, Inc.

Fehlmann, Sonja. Helping Mom & Dad, Vol. 4419. Kupperstein, Joel, ed. Jarrett, Michael, photos by. 1998. (Learn to Read Social Studies). (Illus.). 16p. (J). (ps-2). pap. 2.75 (978-1-57471-342-8(6) , 4419) Creative Teaching Pr., Inc.

Finn, Carrie. Kids Talk about Respect. Muehlenhardt, Amy Bailey, illus. 2006. (Kids Talk Junior Ser.). (J). 23.93 (978-1-4048-2318-1(2)) Picture Window Bks.

—Kids Talk about Sharing. Muehlenhardt, Amy Bailey, illus. 2006. (Kids Talk Junior Ser.). (J). 23.93 (978-1-4048-2319-8(0)) Picture Window Bks.

—Manners at the Table. Lensch, Chris, illus. 2006. 24p. (J). (*978-1-4048-3155-1(X)) Picture Window Bks.

—Manners in Public. Lensch, Chris, illus. 2006. (Way to Be! Ser.). 24p. (J). (ps-2). lib. bdg. 23.93 (*978-1-4048-3153-7(3)) Picture Window Bks.

—Manners in the Library. 2007. (Way to Be! Ser.). (Illus.). 24p. (*978-1-4048-3557-3(1) , 1265722) Picture Window Bks.

—Manners in the Library. Lensch, Chris, illus. 2006. (Way to Be! Ser.). 24p. (*978-1-4048-3152-0(5) , 1265722) Picture Window Bks.

—Manners on the Playground. Lensch, Chris, illus. 2006. (Way to Be! Ser.). 24p. (J). (ps-2). lib. bdg. 23.93 (*978-1-4048-3154-4(1)) Picture Window Bks.

—Manners on the Telephone. Lensch, Chris, illus. 2006. 24p. (J). (*978-1-4048-3156-8(8)) Picture Window Bks.

Fundamental Table Etiquette. 1999. (YA). (gr. 7 up). cd-rom 99.00 (978-1-57078-587-0(2) , CEV90587) C E V Multimedia, Ltd.

Galloway, L. A. This Is NOT Your Parents' Prom: A Handbook to Proms, Parties & Promises, 2 vols. Medick, Mike G., illus. 2002. 152p. (YA). (gr. 8-13). per. 14.99 (978-0-9718915-0-0(8)) Have Vision Pubns.

Gibbs, Lynne. Don't Slurp Your Soup! A First Guide to Letter Writing, E-Mail Etiquette, & Other Everyday Manners. Eastwood, John, illus. 2003. (First Guides). 32p. (J). (gr. 1-4). 14.95 (978-1-57768-556-2(3) , Waterbird Bks.) School Specialty Publishing.

Gillis, Jennifer Blizin. You & Me ABC. 2003. (You & Me Ser.). (Illus.). 24p. (J). lib. bdg. 18.50 (978-1-4034-2510-2(8)) Heinemann Library.

Gold, Shannon & Gold, Erica. Flower Petals Falling Down: How to Be a Flower Girl. Masar, Corey N., illus. 2000. 43p. (J). (ps-7). pap. 14.95 (978-0-9671047-0-6(X)) Peacock Publishing.

Goode, Diane. Mind Your Manners! 2005. (Illus.). 32p. (J). (ps-3). 16.00 (978-0-374-34975-2(4)) Farrar, Straus & Giroux.

Gray, Carolyn. All about M. E. Manners & Etiquette for TWEENS & TEENS. 2007. 28p. (J). pap. 12.95 (*978-1-60131-010-1(2)) Big Tent Bks.

Grisinger Reilly, Teresa Kathryn. Etiquette Lessons: Volume Two. 2007. 132p. (gr. 4-7). per. 13.95 (*978-0-595-44020-7(7)) iUniverse, Inc.

Hallinan, P. K. Let's Be Patient. 2005. (Illus.). 28p. (J). bds. 7.95 (978-0-8249-6586-0(8)) Ideals Pubns.

—Let's Be Thankful. 2005. (Illus.). 28p. (J). bds. 7.95 (978-0-8249-6585-3(X)) Ideals Pubns.

Hill, Sandi. A Great Attitude, Vol. 4418. Kupperstein, Joel, ed. Ember, Kathi, illus. 1998. (Learn to Read Social Studies). 16p. (J). (ps-2). pap. 2.99 (978-1-57471-341-1(8) , 4418) Creative Teaching Pr., Inc.

Hillings, Phyllis & Hillings, Pamela. A Web of Good Manners - Grown-up Manners for Young People. Mumper-Drumm, Heidrun, illus. (J). 19.95 (978-0-9725364-1-7(8)) Perrin & Kabel Publishing.

Holyoke, Nancy. A Smart Girl's Guide to Manners: The Secrets to Grace, Confidence, & Being Your Best. Watkins, Michelle, ed. Mingus, Cathi, illus. 2005. (American Girl Library). 120p. (J). (gr. 3). pap. 9.95 (978-1-58485-983-3(0) , American Girl) American Girl Publishing, Inc.

Jarrell, Pamela R. Giving Gifts. Linke, Don, Jr., illus. l.t. ed. 1999. (CB Ser.). 7p. (J). (ps-1). pap. 10.95 (978-1-57332-156-3(7)) HighReach Learning, Inc.

—Good Manners. Metzger, Jeanne, illus. l.t. ed. 1999. (CB Ser.). 8p. (J). (ps-1). pap. 10.95 (978-1-57332-151-8(6)) HighReach Learning, Inc.

Johnson, Dorthea. Children's Tea & Etiquette. 2006. 36p. (J). 19.95 (978-0-9663478-9-0(7)) Benjamin Pr.

Jones, Myoushi. Etiquette Vol. 3: On the Places We Go. Reams, Damaris, illus. 2000. 35p. (J). (gr. 2-6). pap. 6.95 (978-0-9703537-6-4(6)) Myoushi Enterprises.

—Minding My Manners, Vol. 1. Reams, Damaris, illus. 2000. 35p. (J). (gr. 2-6). pap. 6.95 (978-0-9703537-2-6(3)) Myoushi Enterprises.

Jordan, Denise. You & Me ABC. 2003. (Heinemann Read & Learn Ser.). (Illus.). 24p. (J). pap. 5.25 (978-1-4034-2512-6(4)) Heinemann Library.

Joslin, Sesyle. What Do You Say, Dear? Sendak, Maurice, illus. (J). (gr. k-2). 14.45 incl. audio (978-0-8045-6525-7(2) , SAC 6525) Spoken Arts, Inc.

Keller, Irene. Thingamajig Book of Manners. Keller, Dick, illus. 2005. 30p. (J). bds. 7.95 (978-0-8249-6590-7(6)) Ideals Pubns.

—Thingumajig Book of Manners. Kelley, Dick, illus. 1999. 32p. (J). (ps-3). 6.95 (978-1-57102-148-9(5)) Warehousing & Fulfillment Specialists, LLC (WFS, LLC).

Kelley, Michelle. Rules, Rules, Rules! 2007. (ENG & SPA.). (J). (978-1-59515-957-1(6)) Rourke Publishing, LLC.

Krauss, Ronnie. Captain Kangaroo & Manners. 2000. (J). pap. 8.99 (978-0-06-107156-0(0) , Harper Entertainment) HarperCollins Pubs.

Leaf, Munro. Manners Can Be Fun. 2004. (Illus.). 48p. (J). (gr. k). 14.95 (978-0-7893-1061-3(9)) Universe Publishing.

Leigh, Susan K. God, I Need to Talk to You About Bad Manners. 2005. (J). 5.99 (978-0-7586-0813-0(6)) Concordia Publishing Hse.

MacGregor, Cynthia. What Do You Know about Manners? A Funny Quiz for Kids. 2000. (Illus.). viii, 149p. (J). (978-0-88166-354-9(9)) Meadowbrook Pr.

—What Do You Know about Manners? A Funny Quiz for Kids. Oertel, Lev & Fuller, Jim, illus. 2000. 200p. (J). (gr. 1-7). pap. 6.99 (978-0-689-83292-5(3)) Meadowbrook Pr.

—What Do You Know about Manners? a Funny Manners Quiz. 2000. (gr. 3-6). lib. bdg. 15.30 (978-0-613-22602-8(X)) Tandem Library Bks.

Manners Matter. 1999. (Health & Human Development Resource Library). (J). (gr. 4-6). 69.95 (978-1-55942-124-9(X) , 9223V9) Marsh Media.

Marciano, John Bemelmans. Madeline Says Merci: The Always Be Polite Book. Marciano, John Bemelmans, illus. 2001. (Madeline Ser.). (Illus.). 48p. (J). (ps-3). 12.99 (978-0-670-03505-2(X) , Viking Juvenile) Penguin Group (USA) Inc.

Maurer, Tracy. A to Z of Ps & Qs. 2002. (A to Z Ser.). (Illus.). 48p. (J). lib. bdg. 20.95 (978-1-58952-062-2(9)) Rourke Publishing, LLC.

McGrath, Bob. Oops! Excuse Me, Please! And Other Mannerly Tales. 1998. (Barron's Educational Ser.). (Illus.). 32p. (J). (ps-3). 6.99 (978-0-7641-5083-8(9)) Barron's Educational Series, Inc.

Meiners, Cheri J. Respect & Take Care of Things. Johnson, Meredith, illus. 2004. (Learning to Get Along Ser.). 40p. (J). (ps-3). pap. 10.95 (978-1-57542-160-5(7)) Free Spirit Publishing, Inc.

Mission City Press Inc. Staff & Cone, Cindy. Simply Etiquette. 2003. (Elsie Dinsmore). 112p. (J). (gr. 5-9). 14.99 (978-1-928749-53-0(4)) Mission City Pr., Inc.

Morgan, Richard. Oops, Sorry! A First Book of Manners. 2002. (Illus.). 24p. (J). pap. 3.95 (978-0-7641-2287-3(8)) Barron's Educational Series, Inc.

Moses, Brian. Que Me Importa: Aprender a Respetar. Gordon, Mike, illus. 2000. (SPA.). 32p. (J). (ps-k). 7.95 (978-950-24-0807-1(1)) Lectorum Pubns., Inc.

—Yo lo Hago: Aprender a Ser Responsable. Gordon, Mike, illus. 2000. (SPA.). 32p. (J). (ps-k). 7.95 (978-950-24-0805-7(5)) Lectorum Pubns., Inc.

My Good Manners Book. 1998. (Illus.). 8p. (J). (ps). 35.00 (978-1-888074-78-9(7)) Pockets of Learning.

Packer, Alex J. The How Rude! Handbook of Family Manners for Teens: Avoiding Strife in Family Life. 2004. (How Rude! Handbooks Ser.). (Illus.). 128p. (YA). (gr. 8 up). pap. 9.95 (978-1-57542-163-6(1)) Free Spirit Publishing, Inc.

—The How Rude! Handbook of Friendship & Dating Manners for Teens: Surviving the Social Scene. 2004. (How Rude! Handbooks Ser.). (Illus.). 128p. (YA). (gr. 8 up). pap. 9.95 (978-1-57542-165-0(8)) Free Spirit Publishing, Inc.

—The How Rude! Handbook of School Manners for Teens: Civility in the Hallowed Halls. 2004. (How Rude! Handbooks Ser.). (Illus.). 128p. (J). (gr. 8 up). pap. 9.95 (978-1-57542-164-3(X)) Free Spirit Publishing, Inc.

Polisar, Barry Louis. Don't Do That! A Child's Guide to Bad Manners, Ridiculous Rules, & Inadequate Etiquette. Clark, David, illus. 2003. (Rainbow Morning Music Picture Bks.). 32p. (J). (gr. 2-6). reprint ed. 14.95 (978-0-938663-20-1(8)) Rainbow Morning Music Alternatives.

Popov, Linda Kavelin. The Virtues Project Educator's Guide: Simple Ways to Create a Culture of Character. 2000. (Illus.). 208p. (J). (gr. k-12). pap. 24.95 (978-1-880396-84-1(X)) Jalmar Pr.

Post, Peggy & Senning, Cindy Post. Emily's Everyday Manners. Bjorkman, Steve, illus. 2006. 32p. (J). lib. bdg. 17.89 (978-0-06-076177-6(6)) HarperCollins Pubs.

—Emily's Everyday Manners for Children. Bjorkman, Steve, illus. 2006. 32p. (J). 16.99 (978-0-06-076174-5(1)) HarperCollins Pubs.

—Emily's Magic Words. Landry, Leo, illus. 2007. 32p. (J). (ps-1). 15.99 (978-0-06-111680-3(7)) HarperCollins Pubs.

—The Guide to Good Manners for Kids. Bjorkman, Steve, illus. 2006. 144p. (J). (gr. 4-8). reprint ed. 16.00 (978-1-4223-5621-0(3)) DIANE Publishing Co.

—Teen Manners: From Malls to Meals to Messaging & Beyond. Watts, Sharon, illus. 2007. 134p. (J). (gr. 3-7). 15.99 (978-0-06-088198-6(4)); lib. bdg. 16.89 (978-0-06-088199-3(2)) HarperCollins Pubs.

Precious Moments, illus. Precious Moments' Book of Manners for Boys. 2006. 48p. 15.99 (978-0-7369-1526-7(5)) Harvest Hse. Pubs.

—Precious Moments' Book of Manners for Girls. 2006. 48p. 15.99 (978-0-7369-1525-0(7)) Harvest Hse. Pubs.

Raatma, Lucia. Politeness. 2002. (Character Education Ser.). (Illus.). 24p. (J). (gr. 1-2). lib. bdg. 18.60 (978-0-7368-1134-7(6) , Bridgestone Bks.) Capstone Pr., Inc.

Radabaugh, Melinda Beth. Dormir en otra parte. (La Primera Vez (First Time) Ser.). 24p. pap. 5.25 (978-1-4034-0477-0(1)) Heinemann Library.

Richey, Lisa. Manners to Go. 2003. (J). 22.95 (978-0-9743210-0-4(1)) Eat Your Peas Publishing.

Rigby Education Staff. Let's Eat. (Sails Literacy Ser.). (Illus.). 16p. (gr. 1-2). 27.00 (978-0-7635-9885-3(2) , 698852C99) Rigby Education.

Roca, Nuria. Mind Your Manners: On Vacation. Curto, Rosa M., illus. 2005. (Mind Your Manners Ser.). 36p. (J). pap. 6.95 (978-0-7641-3169-1(9)) Barron's Educational Series, Inc.

Rondina, Catherine. Rudeness: If You Please. Workman, Dan, illus. 2005. (Deal with It Ser.). 32p. (J). (gr. 4-8). 12.95 (978-1-55028-870-4(9)) Lorimer, James & Co., Ltd., Pubs. CAN. *Dist:* Casemate Pubs. & Bk. Distributors, LLC.

Rosenthal, Amy Krouse. Cookies: Bite-Size Life Lessons. Dyer, Jane, illus. 2006. 40p. (J). 12.99 (978-0-06-058081-0(X)) HarperCollins Pubs.

Rosson, Denise & Turnblacer, Margaret. Tadpole Dreams Etiquette & Good Manners Program Handbook. 2005. 25p. (J). 12.95 (978-0-9769320-1-7(6) , ss0002) Smith, S. Pubns.

Rupprecht, Karen. Miss Prudence Pennypack's a Month of Manners. Graham, Laurel Elderkin, illus. 2000. 40p. (J). (ps-4). pap. (978-1-893116-13-9(1)) Baltimore Sun, The.

—Miss Prudence Pennypack's Perfectly Proper. Graham, Laurel Elderkin, illus. 1999. 68p. (J). (ps-4). 16.95 (978-1-893116-09-2(3)) Baltimore Sun, The.

Santorum, Karen. Everyday Graces: A Child's Book of Good Manners. Torode, Sam, illus. 2003. (Foundations Ser.). 407p. (J). 25.00 (978-1-932236-09-5(0)) ISI Bks.

Schoberle, Cecile. Thank You, Angelica: The Rugrats Book of Manners. Resto, Ed, illus. 1999. (Rugrats Ser.). 32p. (J). (ps-2). per. 3.50 (978-0-671-02865-7(0) , Simon & Schuster Children's Publishing) Simon & Schuster Children's Publishing.

Schuette, Sarah L. I Am Polite. 2004. (Character Values Ser.). (Illus.). 24p. (J). lib. bdg. 15.93 (978-0-7368-2572-6(X) , Pebble Bks.) Capstone Pr., Inc.

Senning, Cindy Post & Post, Emily. Emily Post's the Guide to Good Manners for Kids. Bjorkman, Steve, illus. 2004. 144p. (J). 16.99 (978-0-06-057196-2(9)) HarperCollins Pubs.

Senning, Cindy Post & Post, Peggy. Emily's Sharing & Caring Book. Landry, Leo, illus. 2008. 32p. (J). 16.99 (*978-0-06-111697-1(1)) HarperCollins Pubs.

Shaw, Tucker. What's That Smell? 2003. (gr. 3-6). lib. bdg. 16.45 (978-0-613-61666-9(9)) Tandem Library Bks.

Smith, Mavis. Mind Your Manners, Ben Bunny: A Life-the-Flap Book about Table Manners. Smith, Mavis, illus. 1998. (Lift-the-Flap Book Ser.). (Illus.). 24p. (J). (ps-1). pap. 8.95 (978-0-590-06844-4(X)) Scholastic, Inc.

Sparks, Michal. A Boy's First Book of Manners. Sparks, Michal, illus. 2001. (Illus.). 10p. 5.99 (978-0-7369-0762-0(9)) Harvest Hse. Pubs.

—My Very First Book of Manners. 2000. (Illus.). 10p. (J). (ps). 5.99 (978-0-7369-0244-1(9)) Harvest Hse. Pubs.

Steinhorst, Steff. Move Over! Teenage Manners Coming Through. 2001. (Illus.). viii, 49p. (J). (978-0-89390-535-4(6)) Resource Pubns., Inc.

Stuart, Carole. The Thank You Book. Robins, Arthur, illus. 2001. 32p. (J). (ps-3). 16.00 (978-1-56858-170-5(X)) Running Pr. Bk. Pubs.

—Thank You Book. 2003. (gr. k-3). lib. bdg. 17.60 (978-0-613-68944-1(5)) Tandem Library Bks.

Stuart, Carole & Robins, Arthur. The Thank You Book. Robins, Arthur, illus. 2003. (Illus.). 32p. (J). (ps-3). pap. 8.95 (978-1-56858-237-5(4)) Running Pr. Bk. Pubs.

Tadpole Dreams Etiquette & Good Manners Curriculum. 2005. (YA). ring bd. 249.95 (978-0-9769320-0-0(8) , ss0001) Smith, S. Pubns.

Teen Etiquette: Lessons in Gracious Living. 2004. (YA). tchr. ed., spiral bd. (978-0-9758940-0-2(5)) Whitaker, Thurston Information Services, LLC.

Teen Etiquette: Lessons in Gracious Living Student Workbook. 2004. (YA). (978-0-9758940-1-9(3)) Whitaker, Thurston Information Services, LLC.

Thompson, Robin. Be the Best You Can Be: A Guide to Etiquette & Self-Improvement for Children. 1999. (Illus.). 106p. (YA). (gr. 3-12). pap. 15.95 (978-0-9675318-0-9(2)) Robin Thompson Charm Schl.

Underwood, Deborah. Where Are Your Manners? 2006. (Illus.). 32p. (J). (978-1-4109-2594-7(3)); pap. (978-1-4109-2623-4(0)) Steck-Vaughn.

Verdick, Elizabeth. Words Are Not for Hurting. Heinlen, Marieka, illus. 2004. (Best Behavior Ser.). 40p. (J). (ps-2). pap. 11.95 (978-1-57542-156-8(9)) Free Spirit Publishing, Inc.

Waters, Jennifer. Be a Good Sport! 2002. (Spyglass Books). (Illus.). 24p. (J). (gr. 1 up). lib. bdg. 18.60 (978-0-7565-0375-8(2)) Compass Point Bks.

Weatherill, Steve. Baby Goz - When I Grow Up. 1999. (Illus.). 16p. (J). (ps-k). pap. (978-0-7112-0884-1(0)) Lincoln, Frances Ltd. GBR. *Dist:* Transition Vendor.

Whitaker, Ginger. Teen Etiquette. 2004. (YA). stu. ed., spiral bd., wbk. ed. (978-0-9758940-3-3(X)) Whitaker, Thurston Information Services, LLC.

Willems, Mo. Time to Say Please ! Willems, Mo, illus. 2005. (Illus.). 40p. (ps-1). 15.99 (978-0-7868-5293-2(3)) Hyperion Bks. for Children.

ETIQUETTE—FICTION

Allen, Kathryn Madeline. This Little Piggy's Book of Manners. Wolff, Nancy, illus. rev. ed. 2003. 32p. (J). 15.95 (978-0-8050-6769-9(8) , Holt, Henry & Co. Bks. For Young Readers) Holt, Henry & Co.

Bartell, Lindy. It's Neat to Eat at the Table. 2006. 16p. (J). bds. 6.95 (978-1-57921-843-0(1)) WinePress Publishing.

Bauer, Marion Dane. Thank You! Sweet, Melissa, illus. 2008. (J). (978-0-689-85788-1(8) , Simon & Schuster Children's Publishing) Simon & Schuster Children's Publishing.

Benenfeld, Rikki. I Go Visiting. 2007. (Illus.). 32p. (J). 10.95 (978-1-929628-33-9(1)) Hachai Publishing.

Berenstain, Stan & Berenstain, Jan. The Berenstain Bears Catch the Bus. Berenstain, Stan & Berenstain, Jan, illus. 2002. (Berenstain Bears Ser.). (Illus.). (J). (gr. k-3). 11.91 (978-0-7587-0977-6(3)) Book Wholesalers, Inc.

—The Berenstain Bears Catch the Bus. 1999. (Berenstain Bears Ser.). (Illus.). 32p. (J). (ps-3). lib. bdg. 11.99 (978-0-679-99227-1(8)); pap. 3.99 (978-0-679-89227-4(3)) Random Hse. Children's Bks. (Random Hse. Bks. for Young Readers).

—The Berenstain Bears Catch the Bus. 1999. (Berenstain Bears Ser.). (J). (ps). (Illus.). 32p. lib. bdg. 11.80 (978-0-613-16056-8(8)); 10.79 (978-0-606-16944-8(X)) Tandem Library Bks.

Bloom, Suzanne. Piggy Monday: A Tale about Manners. Bloom, Suzanne, illus. 2001. (Illus.). 32p. (J). (gr. k-4). 16.95 (978-0-8075-6529-2(6)) Whitman, Albert & Co.

Bourgeois, Paulette & Clark, Brenda. Franklin Says Sorry. (Franklin TV StoryBks.). (Illus.). 32p. (J). (gr. k-3). 2004. (978-1-55074-712-6(6)); 1999. (978-1-55074-714-0(2)) Kids Can Pr., Ltd.

Brimner, Larry Dane. School Rules. Tripp, Christine, illus. 2002. (Rookie Choices Ser.). 32p. (J). (gr. 1-2). pap. 5.95 (978-0-516-27389-1(2) , Children's Pr.) Scholastic Library Publishing.

—School Rules. 2002. (gr. k-3). lib. bdg. 14.10 (978-0-613-50237-5(X)) Tandem Library Bks.

Brouwer, Sigmund. Strunk Soup. 2003. (Watch Out for Joel Ser.). (Illus.). 32p. (J). pap. 3.99 (978-0-7642-2585-7(5)) Bethany Hse. Pubs.

Brown, Marc. D. W. 's Guide to Perfect Manners. 2006. (D. W. Ser.). (Illus.). 32p. (J). (ps-3). 15.99 (978-0-316-12106-4(1)) Little Brown & Co.

Cazet, Denys. Elvis the Rooster & the Magic Words. 2004. (Illus.). 48p. (J). lib. bdg. 13.85 (*978-1-4242-0562-2(X)) Fitzgerald Bks.

—Elvis the Rooster & the Magic Words. Cazet, Denys, illus. (I Can Read Bks.). 48p. (J). 2005. pap. 3.99 (978-0-06-000511-5(4) , Harper Trophy); 2004. (Illus.). 15.99 (978-0-06-000509-2(2)) HarperCollins Pubs.

—Elvis the Rooster & the Magic Words. unabr. ed. 2006. (Readalongs for Beginning Readers Ser.). (J). 29.95 incl. audio (978-1-59519-694-1(3)); 28.95 incl. audio compact disk (978-1-59519-695-8(1)); pap. 16.95 incl. audio (978-1-59519-690-3(0)); pap. 18.95 incl. audio compact disk (978-1-59519-691-0(9)); Set. pap. 29.95 incl. audio (978-1-59519-692-7(7)); Set. pap. 31.95 incl. audio compact disk (978-1-59519-693-4(5)) Live Oak Media.

Cole, Babette. Lady Lupin's Book of Etiquette. 2002. (Illus.). 32p. (J). (gr. 1-5). 14.95 (978-1-56145-257-6(2)) Peachtree Pubs., Ltd.

—El Libro de Etiqueta de Lady Lupina. 2003. (Babette Cole Ser.). (SPA.). (J). 18.95 (978-84-233-3337-0(X)) Ediciones Destino ESP. *Dist:* Planeta Publishing Corp.

Cooney, Doug. I Know Who Likes You. Bernardin, James, illus. 2005. 224p. (J). pap. 4.99 (978-1-4169-0261-4(9) , Aladdin) Simon & Schuster Children's Publishing.

Cosgrove, Stephen. Squabbles. 2003. (gr. k-3). lib. bdg. 13.00 (978-0-613-64600-0(2)) Tandem Library Bks.

Crawford, Joanne Sneed. Respectfully Yours Buford: Program on Respect. Norcross, Harry, illus. 1999. 31p. (J). (ps-2). pap. 6.95 (978-1-57543-076-8(2)) MAR*CO Products, Inc.

Cuneo, Diane. Mary Louise Loses Her Manners. Davis, Jack E., illus. 2000. (J). (978-0-606-20019-6(3)) Tandem Library Bks.

Cuyler, Margery. Please Play Safe! Penguin's Guide to Playground Safety. Hillenbrand, Will, illus. 2006. 32p. (J). pap. 15.99 (978-0-439-52832-0(1) , Scholastic Pr.) Scholastic, Inc.

Cuyler, Margery. Please Say Please! Penguin's Guide to Manners. Hillenbrand, Will, illus. 2005. (J). (*978-0-439-67874-2(9)) Scholastic, Inc.

—Please Say Please! Penguin's Guide to Manners. Hillenbrand, Will, tr. Hillenbrand, Will, illus. 2004. 32p. (J). pap. 15.95 (978-0-590-29224-5(2)) Scholastic, Inc.

de Brunhoff, Laurent. Babar's World Tour. 2005. (Illus.). 48p. (J). (978-0-8109-5982-8(8)) Abrams, Harry N. , Inc.

Dutton, Sandra. Dear Miss Perfect: A Beast's Guide to Proper Behavior. 2007. (Illus.). 48p. (J). (gr. k-3). 16.00 (978-0-618-67717-7(8)) Houghton Mifflin Co.

Edwards, Pamela Duncan & Nascimbeni, Barbara. Rude Mule. 2002. (Illus.). 32p. (J). (ps-3). 15.95 (978-0-8050-7007-1(9) , Holt, Henry & Co. Bks. For Young Readers) Holt, Henry & Co.

Faulkner, Keith. Please & Thank You. James, Rhian Nest, illus. 1998. 4p. (J). bds. 7.99 (978-1-58048-037-6(3)) Sandvik Publishing.

Fienberg, Anna. Horrendo's Curse. Gamble, Kim, illus. 2002. 160p. (J). (gr. 2-6). 18.95 (978-1-55037-773-6(6)); pap. 6.95 (978-1-55037-772-9(8)) Annick Pr., Ltd. CAN. *Dist:* Firefly Bks., Ltd.

Fontes, Justine. Henry's Turn. Hefferan, Rob, illus. 2004. (J). (978-1-59336-004-7(5)); pap. (978-1-59336-005-4(3)) Mondo Publishing.

EFG

—Rude Ralph. Jordan, Charles, tr. Jordan, Charles, illus. 2004. (Rookie Reader Ser.). 31p. (J). 19.50 (978-0-516-24567-6(8) , Children's Pr.) Scholastic Library Publishing.

George, Michele Naylor. The Rainbow of Respect & Responsibility. 1999. (J). (978-0-9672049-0-1(9)) Grace & Mercy Publishing.

Gillis, Jennifer B. What Do You Say? 2006. (Reader's Clubhouse Set B Ser.). (Illus.). 24p. (J). pap. 3.99 (978-0-7641-3298-8(9)) Barron's Educational Series, Inc.

Give, Save, Spend. 2006. 16p. (J). pap. 1.99 (978-0-7847-1691-5(9) , 02993) Standard Publishing.

Goldberg, Malky. What Else Do I Say? A Lift the Flap Book. Argoff, Patti, illus. 2007. (J). (ps-k). bds. 9.95 ***(978-1-929628-34-6(X))*** Hachai Publishing.

Gurney, Stella & Sparklington, Madame. Princess: A Glittering Guide for Young Ladies. Allsop, Sophie et al, illus. 2006. (Genuine & Moste Authentic Gdes Ser.). 32p. (J). (gr. 1-4). 17.99 (978-0-7636-3430-8(1)) Candlewick Pr.

Hallinan, P. K. Let's Be Polite. 2004. (Illus.). 26p. (J). bds. 7.95 (978-0-8249-6562-4(0)) Ideals Pubns.

Holm, Jennifer L. An Adventure. 2002. (Boston Jane Ser.). 288p. (J). (gr. k-17). pap. 6.99 (978-0-06-440849-3(3)) HarperCollins Pubs.

—Wilderness Days. (Boston Jane Ser.). 256p. (J). (gr. 5 up). 2004. pap. 5.99 (978-0-06-440881-3(7) , Harper Trophy); 2002. 16.99 (978-0-06-029043-6(9)); 2002. lib. bdg. 18.89 (978-0-06-029044-3(7)) HarperCollins Pubs.

Katz, Alan. Don't Say That Word! Catrow, David, illus. 2007. 40p. (J). (ps-3). 16.99 (978-0-689-86971-6(1) , McElderry, Margaret K.) Simon & Schuster Children's Publishing.

Katz, Karen. Excuse Me: A Little Book of Manners. Katz, Karen, illus. 2002. (Lift-the-Flap Bks.). (Illus.). 14p. (J). (ps-1). 5.99 (978-0-448-42585-6(8) , Grosset & Dunlap) Penguin Group (USA) Inc.

—No Biting. Katz, Karen, illus. 2002. (Illus.). 14p. (J). (ps-1). 5.99 (978-0-448-42584-9(X) , Grosset & Dunlap) Penguin Group (USA) Inc.

Keep Trying, Travis! 2006. 16p. (J). pap. 1.99 (978-0-7847-1705-9(2) , 04166) Standard Publishing.

Kimmelman, Leslie. Everybody Bonjours! McMenemy, Sarah, illus. 2008. (J). 16.99 ***(978-0-375-84443-0(0));*** lib. bdg. 19.99 ***(978-0-375-94443-7(5))*** Knopf, Alfred A. Inc.

Kopelke, Lisa. Excuse Me! Kopelke, Lisa, illus. 2003. (Illus.). 32p. (J). (gr. k-3). 16.95 (978-0-689-85111-7(1)) Simon & Schuster Children's Publishing.

—Tissue, Please! Kopelke, Lisa, illus. 2004. (Illus.). 32p. (J). 15.95 (978-0-689-86248-9(2)) Simon & Schuster Children's Publishing.

Livermore, Edward. Phebe the Blackberry Girl. 2004. reprint ed. pap. 15.95 (978-1-4191-4126-3(0)); pap. 1.99 (978-1-4192-4126-0(5)) Kessinger Publishing, LLC.

Lukas, Catherine. Say Please. 2007. 24p. (J). 21.35 ***(978-1-59961-160-0(0))*** Spotlight.

MacDonald, Betty Bard, ed. Mrs. Piggle-Wiggle's Bad Table-Manners Cure. Whatley, Bruce, illus. 2000. (Mrs. Piggle-Wiggle Adventure Ser.). (J). 12.95 (978-0-06-027632-4(0)); 12.89 (978-0-06-027633-1(9)) HarperCollins Pubs.

McConduit, Denise Walter. D. J. & the Debutante Ball. Henriquez, Emile F., illus. 2004. 32p. (J). pap. 15.95 (978-1-58980-173-8(3)) Pelican Publishing Co., Inc.

Morris, Jennifer E. May I Please Have a Cookie? Morris, Jennifer E., illus. 2005. (Scholastic Reader Ser.). (Illus.). 32p. (J). (ps-3). pap. 3.99 (978-0-439-73819-4(9) , Cartwheel Bks.) Scholastic, Inc.

Mouse Works Staff. The Lady & the Tramp: We're All Different. 1999. (Illus.). (J). 2.99 (978-0-7364-0044-2(3)) Mouse Works.

Ms. Hilda's Adventure into the World of Manners. 2001. 24p. (YA). pap., tchr.'s planning gde. ed. 9.99 (978-0-9712300-5-7(6)) Schryver Enterprises, LLC.

Oops! Excuse Me Please! And Other Mannerly Tales. 1998. 47.60 (978-0-7641-7199-4(2)) Barron's Educational Series, Inc.

A Perfectly Proper Christmas Video & Book Gift Set. 2001. (J). pap. 22.00 incl. VHS (978-0-9714334-1-0(0)) Visual Bk. Co., LLC, The.

Raintree Steck-Vaughn Staff. Los Modales de Manolo. 1999. (Coleccion en Parejas). (SPA.). (J). pap., stu. ed. 21.50 (978-0-7398-0836-8(2)) Steck-Vaughn.

Rovetch, Lissa & Whitman, Emily. Sir Henry, the Polite Knight. Barnard, Bryn, illus. 2006. (J). ***(978-1-58987-204-2(5))*** Kindermusik International.

Ruth, Annie. No! Not on the Pews. Ruth, Annie, illus. l.t. ed. 1999. (Illus.). 20p. (J). (gr. k-3). 2.50 (978-0-9656306-1-0(7)) Ruth, A. Creations.

Schoberle, Cecile. Thank You, Angelica! 1999. (gr. k-3). lib. bdg. 11.25 (978-0-613-16006-3(1)) Tandem Library Bks.

Schoberle, Cecile. Thank You, Angelica. 2007. 24p. (J). 21.35 ***(978-1-59961-359-8(X))*** Spotlight.

Sierra, Judy. Mind Your Manners, B. B. Wolf. Seibold, J. Otto, illus. 2007. 40p. (J). (ps-3). 16.99 (978-0-375-83532-2(6)); lib. bdg. 19.99 (978-0-375-93532-9(0)) Random Hse. Children's Bks. (Knopf Bks. for Young Readers).

Spaht-Gill, Janie. Pigouts. Reese, Bob, illus. 1998. 24p. (J). (ps-3). 5.95 (978-0-89868-317-2(3)) ARO Publishing Co.

Stephens, Helen. Ahoyty-Toyty. 2004. (Illus.). 32p. (J). (ps-3). 14.95 (978-0-385-75039-4(0) , Fickling, David Bks.) Random Hse. Children's Bks.

Tayleur, Karen. Manners! David Mortimore Baxter. Garvey, Brann, illus. 2007. 77p. (J). pap. ***(978-1-59889-207-9(X))*** Stone Arch Bks.

Tryon, Leslie. Patsy Says. Tryon, Leslie, illus. 2001. (Illus.). 40p. (J). (gr. k-3). 16.00 (978-0-689-82297-1(9) , Atheneum) Simon & Schuster Children's Publishing.

Turpin, Nick. Sorry Sam, Level P. NASCIMBENI, Barbara, illus. 2006. (Lightning Readers Ser.). 32p. (J). pap. 3.95 (978-0-7696-4186-7(5) , Gingham Dog Pr.) School Specialty Publishing.

Wax, Wendy. What Do You Say? Please & Thank You. Dillard, Sarah, illus. 2005. (J). (978-1-58987-108-3(1)) Kindermusik International.

Williams, Suzanne. My Dog Never Says Please. 2000. (978-0-606-18435-9(X)) Tandem Library Bks.

Yolen, Jane. How Do Dinosaurs Eat Their Food? Teague, Mark, illus. 2005. 40p. (J). (ps-k). pap. 15.99 (978-0-439-24102-1(2) , Blue Sky Pr., The) Scholastic, Inc.

Ziefert, Harriet. What's Polite? Brown, Rick & Brown, Richard, illus. 2004. 20p. pap. 6.95 (978-1-4027-1790-1(3)) Sterling Publishing Co., Inc.

ETIQUETTE—POETRY

Burgess, Gelett. Goops: And How to Be Them. 2001. 96p. (J). (ps-3). pap. 12.95 (978-0-89716-851-9(8)) Peanut Butter Publishing.

—Goops & How to Be Them: A Manual of Manners for Polite Infants. 2004. (Illus.). 108p. per. 17.95 (978-1-55709-392-9(X)) Applewood Bks.

Greenberg, David. Don't Forget Your Etiquette! The Essential Guide to Misbehavior. Westcott, Nadine Bernard, illus. 2006. 40p. (J). 16.00 (978-0-374-34990-5(8) , Farrar, Straus & Giroux (BYR)) Farrar, Straus & Giroux.

ETRURIANS

see Etruscans

ETRUSCANS

Nardo, Don. The Etruscans. 2004. (Illus.). 112p. (YA). (gr. 7-12). lib. bdg. 29.95 (978-1-59018-564-3(1) , Lucent Bks.) Thomson Gale.

EUPHRATES RIVER

Mountjoy, Shane. The Tigris & Euphrates Rivers. 2004. (Rivers in World History Ser.). (Illus.). 120p. (J). (gr. 9-13). 30.00 (978-0-7910-8246-1(6) , Chelsea Hse.) Facts On File, Inc.

Whitcraft, Melissa. The Tigris & Euphrates River. 2000. (Watts Library Ser.). (Illus.). 64p. (J). (gr. 5-7). pap. 8.95 (978-0-531-16432-7(2) , Watts, Franklin) Scholastic Library Publishing.

—The Tigris & Euphrates Rivers. 1999. (Watts Library). (Illus.). 64p. (J). (gr. 5-7). 25.50 (978-0-531-11741-5(3) , Watts, Franklin) Scholastic Library Publishing.

—Tigris & Euphrates Rivers. 1999. (gr. 3-6). lib. bdg. 17.60 (978-0-613-37561-0(0)) Tandem Library Bks.

EUROPE

Aloian, Molly & Kalman, Bobbie. Explore Europe. 2007. (Explore the Continents Ser.). (Illus.). 32p. (J). (gr. 1-7). ***(978-0-7787-3074-3(3));*** pap. ***(978-0-7787-3088-0(3))*** Crabtree Publishing Co.

Bingham, Jane. Europe. 2007. (Illus.). 32p. ***(978-1-4034-8245-7(4))*** Heinemann Library.

—Exploring Europe. 2007. (Illus.). 32p. pap. ***(978-1-4034-8253-2(5))*** Heinemann Library.

Carlson, Laurie M. Days of Knights & Damsels: An Activity Guide. 2003. (Kid's Guide Ser.). (Illus.). 184p. (J). (gr. k-7). pap. 14.95 (978-1-55652-291-8(6)) Chicago Review Pr., Inc.

CultureGrams 2005 World Edition - Europe. 2004. (YA). per. 39.99 (978-1-931694-90-2(7)) ProQuest CSA.

Donaldson, Madeline. Europe. 2005. (Pull Ahead Bks.). (Illus.). 32p. (J). (gr. k-3). lib. bdg. 22.60 (978-0-8225-4719-8(8)) Lerner Publishing Group.

Eastwood, Kay. Medieval Society. 2003. (Medieval World Ser.). (Illus.). 32p. (J). (gr. 5). (978-0-7787-1345-6(8)) Crabtree Publishing Co.

Encyclopaedia Britannica Publishers, Inc. Staff. Views of Europe. 2004. (Britannica Learning Library). (Illus.). (J). 14.95 (978-1-59339-009-9(2)) Encyclopaedia Britannica, Inc.

Foster, Leila Merrell. Europe. (Illus.). 32p. (J). 2006. ***(978-1-4034-8543-4(7));*** 2001. lib. bdg. 21.36 (978-1-57572-213-9(5)) Heinemann Library.

Foster, Leila Merrell & Fox, Mary Virginia. Europe. 2002. (Continents Ser.). (Illus.). 32p. (J). (gr. k-2). pap. 6.95 (978-1-58810-949-1(6) , 91439) Heinemann Library.

Fowler, Allan. Europe. (Rookie Read-About Geography Ser.). (Illus.). 32p. (J). (gr. 1-2). 2002. pap. 5.95 (978-0-516-25981-9(4)); 2001. 20.50 (978-0-516-22236-3(8)) Scholastic Library Publishing. (Children's Pr.).

—Europe. 2002. (Illus.). 31p. (J). (ps-ps). lib. bdg. 14.10 (978-0-613-54205-0(3)) Tandem Library Bks.

Graf, Mike. Europe. 2002. (Continents Ser.). (Illus.). 79p. (J). (gr. 1-2). 18.60 (978-0-7368-1418-8(3) , Bridgestone Bks.) Capstone Pr., Inc.

Hovanec, Erin M. An Online Visit to Europe. (Internet Field Trips Ser.). 24p. (J). 2002. lib. bdg. 18.75 (978-0-8239-6419-2(1)); 2001. (Illus.). (gr. 3). lib. bdg. 18.75 (978-0-8239-5657-9(1)) Rosen Publishing Group, Inc., The. (PowerKids Pr.).

Klingel, Cynthia Fitterer. Europe. 2003. (Continents Ser.). (Illus.). 32p. (J). (gr. 2-6). 27.07 (978-1-59296-060-6(X)) Child's World, Inc.

Knowlton, MaryLee. Albania. 2004. (Cultures of the World Ser.). (Illus.). 144p. (J). 37.07 (978-0-7614-1852-8(0)) Cavendish, Marshall Corp.

McGraw-Hill Staff. Exploring Our World, Eastern Hemisphere, Interactive Tutor Self Assessment CD-ROM. 2007. (C). cd-rom 93.32 ***(978-0-07-879098-0(0)*** , 9780078790980) Glencoe/McGraw-Hill.

—Exploring Our World, Eastern Hemisphere, Reading Essentials & Note-Taking Guide Workbook. 2007. (C). pap. 18.00 ***(978-0-07-878166-7(3)*** , 9780078781667) Glencoe/McGraw-Hill.

—Exploring Our World, Eastern Hemisphere, Standardized Test Practice Workbook. 2007. (C). pap. 10.00 ***(978-0-07-877743-1(7)*** , 9780078777431) Glencoe/McGraw-Hill.

—Exploring Our World, Eastern Hemisphere, Student Edition. 2nd ed. 2007. 69.32 ***(978-0-07-874578-2(0)*** , 9780078745782) Glencoe/McGraw-Hill.

—Exploring Our World, Western Hemisphere with Europe & Russia, Interactive Tutor Self-Assesment CD-ROM. 2007. (C). cd-rom 93.32 ***(978-0-07-879088-1(3)*** , 9780078790881) Glencoe/McGraw-Hill.

—Exploring Our World, Western Hemisphere with Europe & Russia, Reading Essentials & Note-Taking Guide Workbook. 2007. (C). pap. 18.00 ***(978-0-07-878170-4(1)*** , 9780078781704) Glencoe/McGraw-Hill.

—Exploring Our World, Western Hemisphere with Europe & Russia, Spanish Reading Essentials & Note-Taking Guide Workbook. 2007. (C). pap. 18.00 ***(978-0-07-878172-8(8)*** , 9780078781728) Glencoe/McGraw-Hill.

—Exploring Our World, Western Hemisphere with Europe & Russia, Standardized Test Practice Workbook. 2007. (C). pap. 10.00 ***(978-0-07-877728-8(3)*** , 9780078777288) Glencoe/McGraw-Hill.

—Exploring Our World, Western Hemisphere with Europe & Russia, Student Edition. 2nd ed. 2007. 69.32 ***(978-0-07-874580-5(2)*** , 9780078745805) Glencoe/McGraw-Hill.

Morris, Neil. Europe. 2007. ***(978-1-4034-9896-0(2));*** pap. ***(978-1-4034-9905-9(5))*** Heinemann Library.

Nollen, Tim. Czech Republic. 1999. (Festivals of the World Ser.). (Illus.). 32p. (J). (gr. 3 up). lib. bdg. 24.67 (978-0-8368-2031-7(2)) Stevens, Gareth Inc.

Otfinoski, Steven. The Baltic Republics. 2004. (Nations in Transition Ser.). (Illus.). 192p. (J). (gr. 6-12). 40.00 (978-0-8160-5117-5(8)) Facts On File, Inc.

Pelusey, Michael & Pelusey, Jane. Europe. 2004. (Continents Ser.). (Illus.). 32p. (J). (gr. 2-4). 23.00 (978-0-7910-8279-9(2) , Chelsea Hse.) Facts On File, Inc.

Petersen, David. Europe. 1998. (True Bks.). (Illus.). 48p. (J). (gr. 3-5). pap. 6.95 (978-0-516-26375-5(7) , Children's Pr.) Scholastic Library Publishing.

Petra Press Staff. European Union. 2003. (International Organizations Ser.). (Illus.). 48p. (J). (gr. 5 up). lib. bdg. 30.00 (978-0-8368-5518-0(3) , World Almanac Library) Stevens, Gareth Inc.

Press, Petra, tr. European Union. 2003. (International Organizations Ser.). (Illus.). 48p. (J). (gr. 5 up). pap. 14.60 (978-0-8368-5527-2(2) , World Almanac Library) Stevens, Gareth Inc.

Pundyk, Grace. Welcome to the Czech Republic. 2005. (Welcome to My Country Ser.). (Illus.). 48p. (J). lib. bdg. 26.00 (978-0-8368-3127-6(6)) Stevens, Gareth Inc.

Reynolds, Jan. Far North: Vanishing Cultures. 2007. 32p. (J). ***(978-1-60060-127-9(8)); (978-1-60060-142-2(1))*** Lee & Low Bks., Inc.

Sammis, Fran. Europe & the Middle East. 1998. (Mapping Our World Ser.). (Illus.). 64p. (J). (gr. 4-8). lib. bdg. 27.07 (978-0-7614-0370-8(1) , Benchmark Bks.) Cavendish, Marshall Corp.

Sayre, April Pulley. Europe. 1998. (Seven Continents Ser.: 8). (Illus.). 64p. (gr. 5-8). lib. bdg. 25.90 (978-0-7613-3008-0(9) , Millbrook Pr.) Lerner Publishing Group.

—Hello Europe! 2003. (Illus.). 32p. (J). (gr. 2-5). pap. 7.95 (978-0-7613-1990-0(5) , Millbrook Pr.) Lerner Publishing Group.

Striveildi, Cheryl. Europe. 2003. (Continents Ser.). (Illus.). 32p. (J). (gr. k-4). lib. bdg. 22.78 (978-1-57765-962-4(7)) ABDO Publishing Co.

Watson, Galadriel Findlay. Europe. 2005. (Illus.). 32p. pap. 7.95 (978-1-59036-327-0(2)); (J). (gr. 4-6). lib. bdg. 26.00 (978-1-59036-320-1(5)) Weigl Pubs., Inc.

Weintraub, Aileen. Discovering Europe's Land, People, & Wildlife: A MyReportLinks. com Book. 2004. (Continents of the World Ser.). (Illus.). 48p. (J). lib. bdg. 25.26 (978-0-7660-5203-1(6) , MyReportLinks.com Bks.) Enslow Pubs., Inc.

EUROPE, CENTRAL

Bultje, Jan Willem. The Czech Republic. 2006. (Looking at Europe Ser.). (Illus.). 48p. (J). (gr. 4-7). 22.95 (978-1-881508-29-8(3)) Oliver Pr., Inc.

Kollar, Daniel. Slovakia. 2006. (Looking at Europe Ser.). (Illus.). 48p. (J). (gr. 4-7). 22.95 (978-1-881508-49-6(8)) Oliver Pr., Inc.

Roux, Lindy. Czech Republic. 2004. (Countries of the World Ser.). (Illus.). 96p. (J). (gr. 6 up). lib. bdg. 30.00 (978-0-8368-3109-2(8)) Stevens, Gareth Inc.

Van Cleaf, Kristin. Czech Republic. 2007. (Countries Set VI Ser.). (Illus.). 40p. (J). (gr. k-6). lib. bdg. 24.21 ***(978-1-59928-782-9(X)*** , Checkerboard Library) ABDO Publishing Co.

Veceric, Danica. Slovenia. 2006. (Looking at Europe Ser.). (Illus.). 48p. (J). (gr. 4-7). 22.95 (978-1-881508-74-8(9)) Oliver Pr., Inc.

EUROPE—CIVILIZATION—HISTORY

Albania-Belgium, Vol. 1. 2002. (J). (978-0-7614-7379-4(3)) Cavendish, Marshall Corp.

Benchmark Education Staff, compiled by. Historical Communities. 2006. spiral bd. 109.00 ***(978-1-4108-7097-1(9))*** Benchmark Education Co.

Bosnia-Herzegovina—Czech Republic, Vol. 2. 2002. (YA). (978-0-7614-7380-0(7)) Cavendish, Marshall Corp.

Denmark-France, Vol. 3. 2002. (J). (978-0-7614-7381-7(5)) Cavendish, Marshall Corp.

Eastwood, Kay. Medieval Society. 2003. (Medieval World Ser.). (Illus.). 32p. (J). (gr. 5). pap. (978-0-7787-1377-7(6)) Crabtree Publishing Co.

Flint, David. Europe. 2005. (Illus.). 64p. (J). pap. (978-0-8368-5920-1(0)); lib. bdg. 32.67 (978-0-8368-5913-3(8)) Stevens, Gareth Inc. (World Almanac Library).

Germany-Hungary, Vol. 4. 2002. (J). (978-0-7614-7382-4(3)) Cavendish, Marshall Corp.

Grant, Neil, et al. The Atlas of the Renaissance World. Ravaglia, Paola, illus. 2001. (Atlas Ser.). 64p. (J). (gr. 5 up). 19.95 (978-0-87226-692-6(3) , Bedrick, Peter Bks.) School Specialty Publishing.

Hay, Jeff. Renaissance. 2001. (gr. 7-12). lib. bdg. 39.05 (978-0-613-73785-2(7)) Tandem Library Bks.

Haywood, John. Medieval Europe. 2007. (J). ***(978-1-4109-2909-9(4));*** pap. ***(978-1-4109-2915-0(9))*** Steck-Vaughn.

Huff, Toby E. An Age of Science & Revolutions, 1600-1800. (Illus.). 2006. 173p. (J). 32.95 (978-0-19-522269-2(5)); 2005. 176p. (YA). (gr. 7 up). 32.95 (978-0-19-517724-4(X)) Oxford Univ. Pr., Inc.

Iceland-Liechtenstein, Vol. 5. 2002. (J). (978-0-7614-7383-1(1)) Cavendish, Marshall Corp.

Index, Vol. 11. 2002. (J). (978-0-7614-7389-3(0)) Cavendish, Marshall Corp.

Kenney, Karen Latchana. Harsh or Heroic? The Middle Ages. 2007. (Shockwave: History & Politics Ser.). 36p. (J). pap. 6.95 ***(978-0-531-18794-4(2)*** , Children's Pr.) Scholastic Library Publishing.

Langley, Andrew & Dorling Kindersley Publishing Staff. Medieval Life. 2004. (Eyewitness Books). (Illus.). 72p. (J). lib. bdg. 19.99 (978-0-7566-0704-3(3)) Dorling Kindersley Publishing, Inc.

Lassieur, Allison. The Ancient Romans. (People of the Ancient World Ser.). (J). 2005. (Illus.). 112p. (gr. 6-8). pap. 9.95 (978-0-531-16742-7(9)); 2004. 30.50 (978-0-531-12338-6(3)) Scholastic Library Publishing. (Watts, Franklin).

Lithuania-Netherlands, Vol. 6. 2002. (J). (978-0-7614-7384-8(X)) Cavendish, Marshall Corp.

Norway-Romania, Vol. 7. 2002. (J). (978-0-7614-7385-5(8)) Cavendish, Marshall Corp.

Peoples of Europe, 11 vols., Set. Incl. Vol. 1. Albania-Belgium. (J). (978-0-7614-7379-4(3)); Vol. 2. Bosnia-Herzegovina—Czech Republic. (YA). (978-0-7614-7380-0(7)); Vol. 3. Denmark-France. (J). (978-0-7614-7381-7(5)); Vol. 4. Germany-Hungary. (J). (978-0-7614-7382-4(3)); Vol. 5. Iceland-Liechtenstein. (J). (978-0-7614-7383-1(1)); Vol. 6. Lithuania-Netherlands. (J). (978-0-7614-7384-8(X)); Vol. 7. Norway-Romania. (J). (978-0-7614-7385-5(8)); Vol. 8. Russia-Slovakia. (J). (978-0-7614-7386-2(6)); Vol. 9. Slovenia-Switzerland. (J). (978-0-7614-7387-9(4)); Vol. 10. Ukraine-Yugoslavia. (J). (978-0-7614-7388-6(2)); Vol. 11. Index. (J). (978-0-7614-7389-3(0)). (Illus.). 704p. 2002. 471.36 (978-0-7614-7378-7(5) , Cavendish, Marshall Reference Bks.) Cavendish, Marshall Corp.

Quigley, Mary. The Renaissance. 2003. (Understanding People in the Past Ser.). (Illus.). 64p. (J). (gr. 4-6). pap. 28.50 (978-1-4034-0388-9(0)); pap. 8.95 (978-1-4034-0608-8(1)) Heinemann Library.

Russia-Slovakia, Vol. 8. 2002. (J). (978-0-7614-7386-2(6)) Cavendish, Marshall Corp.

Slovenia-Switzerland, Vol. 9. 2002. (J). (978-0-7614-7387-9(4)) Cavendish, Marshall Corp.

Steele, Philip. Medieval World. 2000. (978-0-606-20790-4(2)) Tandem Library Bks.

Thomas, Keltie. Sweden — The People. 2003. (Lands, Peoples & Cultures Ser.). (Illus.). 32p. (J). (gr. 4-5). (978-0-7787-9328-1(1)); pap. (978-0-7787-9696-1(5)) Crabtree Publishing Co.

Ukraine-Yugoslavia, Vol. 10. 2002. (J). (978-0-7614-7388-6(2)) Cavendish, Marshall Corp.

Weintraub, Aileen. Discovering Europe's Land, People, & Wildlife: A MyReportLinks. com Book. 2004. (Continents of the World Ser.). (Illus.). 48p. (J). lib. bdg. 25.26 (978-0-7660-5203-1(6) , MyReportLinks.com Bks.) Enslow Pubs., Inc.

EUROPE—DESCRIPTION AND TRAVEL

Albania-Belgium, Vol. 1. 2002. (J). (978-0-7614-7379-4(3)) Cavendish, Marshall Corp.

Allison, Amy. Germany. 2001. (Dropping in on Ser.). (Illus.). 32p. (J). lib. bdg. 28.50 (978-1-55916-284-5(8)) Rourke Publishing, LLC.

Barish, David & Deen, Neila. Bakpak Travelers Guide Europe 2002 - the Essential Guide for Travelers on a Budget. 2nd ed. 2002. 96p. (YA). 6.95 (978-0-9669752-5-3(1)) Bakpak Travelers Guide.

Bateman, Helen & Denshire, Jayne. Europe. 2006. (Illus.). 32p. (J). (978-1-58340-803-2(7)) Smart Apple Media.

Bosnia-Herzegovina—Czech Republic, Vol. 2. 2002. (YA). (978-0-7614-7380-0(7)) Cavendish, Marshall Corp.

Bramwell, Martyn. Europe. 2000. (World in Maps Ser.). (Illus.). 48p. (YA). (gr. 5-12). lib. bdg. 23.93 (978-0-8225-2913-2(0) , Lerner Pubns.) Lerner Publishing Group.

Chanek, Sherilin. Europe & Russia. 2003. (National Geographic Reading Expeditions Ser.). (Illus.). 64p. (978-0-7922-4374-8(9)); (J). (978-0-7922-4375-5(7)) National Geographic Society.

Denmark-France, Vol. 3. 2002. (J). (978-0-7614-7381-7(5)) Cavendish, Marshall Corp.

Germany-Hungary, Vol. 4. 2002. (J). (978-0-7614-7382-4(3)) Cavendish, Marshall Corp.

Graf, Mike. Europe. 2002. (Continents Ser.). (Illus.). 79p. (J). (gr. 1-2). 18.60 (978-0-7368-1418-8(3) , Bridgestone Bks.) Capstone Pr., Inc.

Haughwout, Pixie & Folsom, Ralph. Canal Cruising in the South of France: The Romantic Canal Du Midi. 5th ed. 2004. 162p. stu. ed., spiral bd. 39.95 (978-0-9676620-9-1(5)) Kalmia Publishing.

Iceland-Liechtenstein, Vol. 5. 2002. (J). (978-0-7614-7383-1(1)) Cavendish, Marshall Corp.

Index, Vol. 11. 2002. (J). (978-0-7614-7389-3(0)) Cavendish, Marshall Corp.

Jackson, Ellen, ed. My Tour of Europe: By Teddy Roosevelt, Age 10. Brighton, Catherine, illus. 2003. 40p. 14.95 (978-0-7613-1998-6(0) , Millbrook Pr.) Lerner Publishing Group.

Kat, Kika & Chickena, Hib. Off the Map. Maul, Paul F., ed. 2002. (Illus.). 120p. pap. 3.00 (978-0-9709101-3-4(4)) CrimethInc. Workers' Collective.

Lithuania-Netherlands, Vol. 6. 2002. (J). (978-0-7614-7384-8(X)) Cavendish, Marshall Corp.

Moore, Jo Ellen. Europe. Evans, Marilyn, ed. Davis, Cindy & Winters, Keli, illus. 1999. (Geography Units Ser.). 80p. (J). (gr. 3-6). pap., tchr. ed. 12.95 (978-1-55799-714-2(4) , EMC 767) Evan-Moor Educational Pubs.

Norway-Romania, Vol. 7. 2002. (J). (978-0-7614-7385-5(8)) Cavendish, Marshall Corp.

Peoples of Europe, 11 vols., Set. Incl. Vol. 1. Albania-Belgium. (J). (978-0-7614-7379-4(3)); Vol. 2. Bosnia-Herzegovina—Czech Republic. (YA). (978-0-7614-7380-0(7)); Vol. 3. Denmark-France. (J). (978-0-7614-7381-7(5)); Vol. 4. Germany-Hungary. (J). (978-0-7614-7382-4(3)); Vol. 5. Iceland-Liechtenstein. (J). (978-0-7614-7383-1(1)); Vol. 6. Lithuania-Netherlands. (J). (978-0-7614-7384-8(X)); Vol. 7. Norway-Romania. (J). (978-0-7614-7385-5(8)); Vol. 8. Russia-Slovakia. (J). (978-0-7614-7386-2(6)); Vol. 9. Slovenia-Switzerland. (J). (978-0-7614-7387-9(4)); Vol. 10. Ukraine-Yugoslavia. (J). (978-0-7614-7388-6(2)); Vol. 11. Index. (J). (978-0-7614-7389-3(0)); (Illus.). 704p. 2002. 471.36 (978-0-7614-7378-7(5) , Cavendish, Marshall Reference Bks.) Cavendish, Marshall Corp.

Roosevelt, Theodore. The Boyhood Diary of Theodore Roosevelt, 1869-1870: Early Travels of the 26th U. S. President. Saterern, Shelley Swanson, ed. 2000. (Blue Earth Books). (Illus.). 32p. (J). (gr. 3-4). lib. bdg. 22.60 (978-0-7368-0601-5(6) , Bridgestone Bks.) Capstone Pr., Inc.

—My Tour of Europe: By Teddy Roosevelt. Jackson, Ellen B., ed. Brighton, Catherine, illus. 2003. 40p. lib. bdg. 23.90 (978-0-7613-2516-1(6) , Millbrook Pr.) Lerner Publishing Group.

Ross, N. J. Mick & Megan Visit the French Riviera. 2000. (J). (gr. k-4). incl. audio (978-1-930303-07-2(6)) Angelic Enterprises.

Russia-Slovakia, Vol. 8. 2002. (J). (978-0-7614-7386-2(6)) Cavendish, Marshall Corp.

Slovenia-Switzerland, Vol. 9. 2002. (J). (978-0-7614-7387-9(4)) Cavendish, Marshall Corp.

Thomas, Keltie. Sweden — The Land. 2003. (Lands, Peoples & Cultures Ser.). (Illus.). 32p. (J). (gr. 4-5). (978-0-7787-9327-4(3)); pap. (978-0-7787-9695-4(7)) Crabtree Publishing Co.

Ukraine-Yugoslavia, Vol. 10. 2002. (J). (978-0-7614-7388-6(2)) Cavendish, Marshall Corp.

Vierow, Wendy. Europe. 2004. (Atlas of the Seven Continents Ser.). (Illus.). 24p. (J). lib. bdg. 21.25 (978-0-8239-6691-2(7) , PowerKids Pr.) Rosen Publishing Group, Inc., The.

Walker, Ida. Belgium. 2006. (European Union Ser.). (Illus.). 88p. (J). (gr. 5 up). lib. bdg. (978-1-4222-0040-7(X) , 1247982) Mason Crest Pubs.

EUROPE, EASTERN

Cooper, Robert. Croatia. 2000. (Cultures of the World Ser.). (Illus.). 128p. (J). (gr. 5-12). lib. bdg. 37.07 (978-0-7614-1156-7(9) , Benchmark Bks.) Cavendish, Marshall Corp.

Grabowski, John F. The Baltics. 2001. (Former Soviet Republics Ser.). (Illus.). 128p. (J). (gr. 6-9). 29.95 (978-1-56006-734-4(9) , Lucent Bks.) Thomson Gale.

Grandjean, Samuel. Genovieva: O Povestire Adevarata Din Romania. Beattie, Genovieva Sfatcu & Beattie, Stephen, trs. from FRE. Nussbaumer, Danielle, illus. 1998. Tr. of Genovieva Histoire Vecue en Roumanie. (RUM.). 112p. (J). (gr. 3-6). pap. 10.00 (978-1-893179-12-7(5)) Eastern Europe Aid Assn.

Horrell, Sarah. Eastern Europe. 1998. (Origins Ser.). (Illus.). 32p. (YA). (gr. 5-8). 21.00 (978-0-531-14449-7(6) , Watts, Franklin) Scholastic Library Publishing.

Kirby, D. G. & Hinkkanen, Merja-Liisa. Baltic & North Seas. 2000. (Seas in History Ser.). (Illus.). 368p. 105.00 (978-0-415-13282-4(7)) Routledge.

Levy, Patricia. Belarus. 1998. (Cultures of the World Ser.). (Illus.). 128p. (gr. 5-12). lib. bdg. 37.07 (978-0-7614-0811-6(8) , Benchmark Bks.) Cavendish, Marshall Corp.

Rihosek, Jacob. Czech Republic. 2004. (Changing Face Of... Ser.). (Illus.). (J). 28.56 (978-0-7398-6828-7(4)) Harcourt Schl. Pubs.

Sheehan, Sean. Romania. 2005. (Cultures of the World Ser.). (Illus.). 144p. (J). 37.07 (978-0-7614-1848-1(2) , Benchmark Bks.) Cavendish, Marshall Corp.

EUROPE—FICTION

Alexander, Lloyd. The Illyrian Adventure. 2000. (Vesper Holly Ser.). (Illus.). 144p. (J). (gr. 5-9). pap. 5.99 (978-0-14-130313-0(1) , Puffin) Penguin Group (USA) Inc.

—The Illyrian Adventure. 1999. (Vesper Holly Ser.). (YA). (gr. 7 up). 12.64 (978-0-606-16832-8(X)) Tandem Library Bks.

Bennett, Veronica. Angelmonster. 2007. (Illus.). 240p. (YA). (gr. 9). pap. 7.99 (***978-0-7636-3407-0(7)***) Candlewick Pr.

Brooks, Kevin. Being. 2007. 336p. (J). (gr. 7 up). pap. 16.99 (978-0-439-89973-4(7) , Chicken Hse., The) Scholastic, Inc.

Burnett, Eric. Gymnastics Jenny Stands on Her Own. 2003. 108p. pap. 9.95 (978-0-595-27919-7(8)) iUniverse, Inc.

Burnham, Niki. Royally Jacked. 2004. (gr. 7-12). lib. bdg. 14.15 (978-0-613-73454-7(8)) Tandem Library Bks.

Burnham, Niki & Saidens, Amy. Royally Jacked. 2003. (Romantic Comedies Ser.). 208p. (YA). pap. 6.99 (978-0-689-86668-5(2) , Simon Pulse) Simon & Schuster Children's Publishing.

Cohen, Barbara. Here Come the Purim Players! Mekibel, Shoshana, illus. 1998. (gr. k-3). 13.95 (978-0-8074-0645-8(7) , 101251) URJ Pr.

Connelly, Peggy. My Quirky, Oddball, Eccentric, Unpredictable Grandma. 2006. (ENG.). 112p. per. 16.95 (***978-1-4241-4486-0(8)***) PublishAmerica, Inc.

Coolidge, Susan. What Katy Did Next EasyRead Comfort Edit. 2006. pap. (***978-1-4250-0872-7(0)***) Assistedreadingbooks.com Inc.

—What Katy Did Next EasyRead Edition. 2006. pap. (***978-1-4250-0281-7(1)***) Assistedreadingbooks.com Inc.

—What Katy Did Next EasyRead Large Editio. 2006. pap. (***978-1-4250-1337-0(6)***) Assistedreadingbooks.com Inc.

Court, Georgia. Traitor of Bled. 2005. 108p. pap. 16.95 (978-1-4137-9595-0(1)) PublishAmerica, Inc.

Cutchin, Marcia, illus. Feathers: A Jewish Tale from Eastern Europe. 2005. 32p. (gr. 2-5). 16.95 (978-0-87483-755-1(3) , 1249133) August Hse. Pubs., Inc.

D'Elia, Amy & Clerman, Lisa. Dreams Come True: A story about the blessing of Adoption. 2007. (***978-0-9777744-1-8(4)***) Finneran, Lisa.

Dickinson, Peter. Tears of the Salamander. 2005. 208p. (gr. 5). reprint ed. pap. 7.95 (978-0-440-23823-2(4) , Lamb, Wendy) Random Hse. Children's Bks.

Englehart, Steve & Englehart, Terry. The DNAgers. 2001. 128p. (YA). (gr. 4-7). pap. 9.95 (978-0-595-16697-8(0)) iUniverse, Inc.

Erenberger, Timothy D. Abacar the Wizard Book One: A Tale of Magic, War, Elves, Goblins, Orcs, Monsters, Fantasy, & Adventure. 2001. 210p. pap. 14.95 (978-0-595-21261-3(1) , Writer's Showcase Pr.) iUniverse, Inc.

Finch, Mary. La Gallinita Roja Y la Espiga Trigo. 2001. (SPA.). (ps-2). lib. bdg. 14.15 (978-0-613-53814-5(5)) Tandem Library Bks.

Fleischman, Sid. The Entertainer & the Dybbuk. 2007. 192p. (J). (gr. 4-9). 16.99 (***978-0-06-134445-9(1)***); lib. bdg. 17.89 (***978-0-06-134446-6(X)***) HarperCollins Pubs. (Greenwillow Bks.).

Freymann-Weyr, Garret. The Kings Are Already Here. 2003. 160p. (YA). (gr. 7). tchr. ed. 15.00 (978-0-618-26363-9(2)) Houghton Mifflin Co. Trade & Reference Div.

Hawthorne, Rachel. A Year in Europe: Three Novels. 2007. 544p. (YA). (gr. 7-11). pap. 7.99 (***978-0-375-84073-9(7)***); lib. bdg. 11.99 (***978-0-375-94073-6(1)***) Random Hse. Children's Bks. (Laurel Leaf).

Hicks, Clifford B. Alvin Fernald Foreign Trader. Schluenderfritz, Theodore, illus. 2007. (J). pap. 11.95 (***978-1-883937-74-4(4)***) Bethlehem Bks.

Keller, Bill. Beowulf. McLean, J., illus. 2007. (Kingfisher Epics Ser.). 176p. (J). (gr. 5-9). pap. 7.95 (***978-0-7534-6134-1(X)***, Kingfisher) Houghton Mifflin Co. Trade & Reference Div.

Kindt, Matt. Super Spy. 2007. 304p. (YA). pap. 19.95 (***978-1-891830-96-9(1)***) Top Shelf Productions.

Konigsburg, E. L. The Second Mrs. Gioconda. 2005. 160p. (YA). pap. 7.99 (978-1-4169-0342-0(9) , Simon Pulse) Simon & Schuster Children's Publishing.

Marsh, Carole. Snow Bank. 2002. (Carole Marsh Bks.). (Illus.). 32p. (J). (gr. 1-6). pap. 7.95 (978-0-635-01359-0(2) , 13592); (gr. 3-9). lib. bdg. 21.95 (978-0-635-01360-6(6) , 13606, Marsh, Carole Bks.) Gallopade International.

McNamara, Joan. Borya & the Burps: An Eastern European Adoption Story. Majewski, Dawn, illus. 2005. 30p. (J). (ps-ps). 18.00 (978-0-944934-31-9(5)) Perspectives Pr., Inc.

Mooney, Bel. Voices of Silence. 1998. (978-0-606-13887-1(0)) Tandem Library Bks.

Nislick, June Levitt. Zayda Was a Cowboy. 2005. 128p. (J). pap. 9.95 (978-0-8276-0817-7(9)) Jewish Pubn. Society.

Peart, Hendry. Red Falcons of Tremoine. Brevannes, Maurice, illus. 2007. 239p. (J). pap. 12.95 (***978-1-932350-15-9(2)***) Bethlehem Bks.

Rennie, C. Goal Behind the Curtain. Date not set. 176p. (YA). mass mkt. 4.99 (978-1-871676-47-1(9) , Christian Focus) Christian Focus Pubns, GBR. *Dist:* Riverside, Spring Arbor Distributors, Inc.

Rennie, Gordon. Glimmer Rats. 2002. 64p. pap. 14.95 (978-1-56971-698-4(6)) Dark Horse Comics.

Runholt, Susan. The Mystery of the Third Lucretia. 2008. (J). (gr. 6). 16.99 (***978-0-670-06252-2(9)***, Viking Juvenile) Penguin Group (USA) Inc.

Spyri, Johanna. Erick & Sally. 2006. 41.99 (***978-1-4280-0242-5(1)***); pap. 34.99 (***978-1-4280-0239-5(1)***) Indy-Publish.com.

Standish, Burt L. Frank Merriwell in Europe. Rudman, Jack, ed. (Frank Merriwell Ser.). (YA). (gr. 9 up). 29.95 (978-0-8373-9308-7(6)); pap. 9.95 (978-0-8373-9008-6(7) , FM-008) Merriwell, Frank Inc.

Stein, Tammar. High Dive. 2008. 240p. (YA). (gr. 7). lib. bdg. 18.99 (***978-0-375-93024-9(8)***, Knopf Bks. for Young Readers) Random Hse. Children's Bks.

Stevermer, Caroline & Wrede, Patricia C. The Grand Tour: Being a Revelation of Matters of High Confidentiality & Greatest Importance, Including Extracts from the Intimate Diary of a Noblewoman & the Sworn Testimony of a Lady of Quality. 2006. (Illus.). 480p. (J). pap. 6.95 (978-0-15-205556-1(8) , Magic Carpet Bks.) Harcourt Children's Bks.

Taylor, G. P. Wormwood. 2005. (Illus.). 272p. (YA). (gr. 7). pap. 7.99 (978-0-14-240469-0(1) , Puffin) Penguin Group (USA) Inc.

Touring Europe on a Magic Carpet. 2004. (J). ring bd. 4.50 (978-0-9762740-9-4(4)) Smart Smiles Co., The.

Van Dyne, Edith. Aunt Jane's Nieces at Work. 2007. 154p. pap. 11.99 (***978-1-4264-6763-9(X)***) BiblioBazaar.

Verlaque, Amanda. Lurgan Champagne & Other Tales. Fearon, Kate, ed. 2001. 112p. (J). pap. 9.99 (978-0-7043-4971-1(X)) Women's Pr., Ltd., The GBR. *Dist:* Independent Pubs. Group.

Ward, John. Le Secret de l'Alchimiste. Guitard, Agnes & Pineau, Severine, trs. from ENG. 2004. (FRE., Illus.). 336p. (J). pap. (978-2-89021-672-3(1)) Diffusion du livre Mirabel.

Wrede, Patricia C. & Stevermer, Caroline. The Mislaid Magician or Ten Years After: Being the Private Correspondence Between Two Prominent Families Regarding a Scandal Touching the Highest Levels of Government & the Security of the Realm. 2006. (Illus.). 336p. (J). (gr. 8 up). 17.00 (978-0-15-205548-6(7)) Harcourt Trade Pubs.

EUROPE—HISTORY

Albania-Belgium, Vol. 1. 2002. (J). (978-0-7614-7379-4(3)) Cavendish, Marshall Corp.

Aloian, Molly & Kalman, Bobbie. Explora Europa. 2007. (SPA.). 32p. (gr. 6-10). pap. (***978-0-7787-8299-5(9)***) Crabtree Publishing Co.

Altman, Linda Jacobs. Trade & Commerce. 2007. (Colonial Life Ser.). (Illus.). 96p. (gr. 6 up). 37.95 (***978-0-7656-8111-9(0)***) Sharpe, M.E. Inc.

Anderson, Dale. Churches & Religion in the Middle Ages. 2005. (World Almanac Library of the Middle Ages). (J). pap. (978-0-8368-5901-0(4)); (Illus.). 48p. (YA). lib. bdg. 30.00 (978-0-8368-5892-1(1)) Stevens, Gareth Inc. (World Almanac Library).

Bosnia-Herzegovina—Czech Republic, Vol. 2. 2002. (YA). (978-0-7614-7380-0(7)) Cavendish, Marshall Corp.

Brocklehurst, Ruth. Victorians - Internet Linked. 2005. (History of Britain Ser.). 48p. (J). pap. 8.95 (978-0-7945-0873-9(1) , Usborne) EDC Publishing.

Broida, Marian. Projects about Nineteenth-Century European Immigrants. 2005. (Hands-On History Ser.). (Illus.). 47p. (J). (978-0-7614-1980-8(2) , Benchmark Bks.) Cavendish, Marshall Corp.

Calvert, Patricia. The Ancient Celts. 2005. (People of the Ancient World Ser.). (Illus.). (gr. 6-8). 112p. (J). pap. 9.95 (978-0-531-16845-5(X)); 30.50 (978-0-531-12359-1(6)) Scholastic Library Publishing. (Watts, Franklin).

Chibi, Andrew A. The European Reformation: A Student's Guide to the Key Ideas & the Events They Shaped. 2002. (Illus.). 144p. (YA). pap. 23.50 (978-1-84025-130-2(1)) Studymates Ltd. GBR. *Dist:* Trans-Atlantic Pubns., Inc.

Coletti, Sharon. Everything You Need to Teach Europe. 2005. (YA). ring bd. 149.95 (978-1-933558-02-8(4)) InspirEd Educators.

The Crusades from Medieval European & Muslim Perspectives. (YA). (gr. 6-9). spiral bd., tchr.'s planning gde. ed. 12.00 (978-0-382-44469-2(8)) Cobblestone Publishing Co.

Davey, Frances. A Brief Political & Geographic History of Europe: Where Are Prussia, Gaul, & the Holy Roman Empire? 2007. (Places in Time Ser.). (Illus.). 112p. (YA). (gr. 5-10). lib. bdg. 37.10 (***978-1-58415-625-3(2)***) Mitchell Lane Pubs., Inc.

Day, Nancy. Your Travel Guide to Renaissance Europe. 2005. (Passport to History Ser.). (Illus.). 96p. (gr. 5-8). lib. bdg. 26.50 (978-0-8225-3080-0(5)) Lerner Publishing Group.

DBQ Practice: European History. 2003. spiral bd. 19.95 (978-1-56004-146-7(3)) Social Studies Schl. Service.

Denmark-France, Vol. 3. 2002. (J). (978-0-7614-7381-7(5)) Cavendish, Marshall Corp.

Downing, David. Toward Genocide. 2005. (World Almanac Library of the Holocaust). (Illus.). 48p. pap. (978-0-8368-5952-2(9)); (YA). (gr. 10-12). lib. bdg. 30.00 (978-0-8368-5945-4(6)) Stevens, Gareth Inc. (World Almanac Library).

Europe: Regions of the World. 2003. spiral bd. 16.95 (978-1-56004-157-3(9)) Social Studies Schl. Service.

Fischell, Emma. Northern Europe. 2002. (Cultures & Costumes Ser.). (Illus.). 64p. (J). (gr. 7 up). lib. bdg. (978-1-59084-439-7(4)) Mason Crest Pubs.

Germany-Hungary, Vol. 4. 2002. (J). (978-0-7614-7382-4(3)) Cavendish, Marshall Corp.

Goldberg, Enid A. & Itzkowitz, Norman. Grigory Rasputin: Holy Man or Mad Monk? 2007. (Wicked History Ser.). (Illus.). 128p. (YA). (gr. 8-12). lib. bdg. 30.00 (***978-0-531-12594-6(7)***, Watts, Franklin) Scholastic Library Publishing.

Groves, Marsha. Manners & Customs in the Middle Ages. 2005. (Medieval World Ser.). (Illus.). 32p. (J). (gr. 4-9). (978-0-7787-1357-9(1)) Crabtree Publishing Co.

Haberle, Susan E. Jewish Immigrants, 1880-1924. 2002. (Blue Earth Books). (Illus.). 32p. (J). (gr. 4). lib. bdg. 22.60 (978-0-7368-1207-8(5) , Bridgestone Bks.) Capstone Pr., Inc.

Hamme. Thorgal Child of the Stars. Rosinski, Grzegorz, illus. 2007. 96p. pap. 14.99 (***978-1-905460-23-6(6)***) CineBook GBR. *Dist:* Biblio Distribution.

Hirsch, E. D., ed. Europe in the Middle Ages, Level 4. 2003. stu. ed. 49.95 (978-0-7690-2847-7(0)) Pearson Learning.

Hunt, Norman Bancroft. Living in Medieval Europe. 2007. (Living in the Ancient World Ser.). 96p. (gr. 6-12). 35.00 (978-0-8160-6341-3(9)) Facts On File, Inc.

Iceland-Liechtenstein, Vol. 5. 2002. (J). (978-0-7614-7383-1(1)) Cavendish, Marshall Corp.

Index, Vol. 11. 2002. (J). (978-0-7614-7389-3(0)) Cavendish, Marshall Corp.

Jane Shuter. The Renaissance. 2nd ed. 2007. (Illus.). 32p. (J). pap. (***978-1-4034-8821-3(5)***) Heinemann Library.

Johnson, Robert. European History 1870-1918: The Rise of Nationalism. 2003. (Studymates Ser.). (Illus.). 16p. (C). pap. 27.50 (978-1-84285-031-2(8)) Studymates Ltd. GBR. *Dist:* Trans-Atlantic Pubns., Inc.

Jovinelly, Joann. The Crafts & Culture of a Medieval Guild. 2006. (Illus.). 48p. (J). lib. bdg. (978-1-4042-0757-8(0)) Rosen Publishing Group, Inc., The.

Jovinelly, Joann & Netelkos, Jason. The Crafts & Culture of a Medieval Castle. 2006. (Illus.). 47p. (J). (978-1-4042-0760-8(0)) Rosen Publishing Group, Inc., The.

—The Crafts & Culture of a Medieval Cathedral. 2006. (Illus.). 28p. (J). lib. bdg. (978-1-4042-0758-5(9)) Rosen Publishing Group, Inc., The.

—The Crafts & Culture of a Medieval Manor. 2006. (Illus.). 48p. (J). lib. bdg. (978-1-4042-0756-1(2)) Rosen Publishing Group, Inc., The.

—The Crafts & Culture of a Medieval Monastery. 2006. (Crafts & Culture of the Middle Ages Ser.). (Illus.). 48p. (J). (gr. 4-8). lib. bdg. 29.25 (978-1-4042-0759-2(7)) Rosen Publishing Group, Inc., The.

Knox, Barbara J. Castle Dracula: Romania's Vampire Home. 2005. (Castles, Palaces, & Tombs Ser.). (Illus.). 32p. (J). lib. bdg. 25.27 (978-1-59716-000-1(8)) Bearport Publishing Co., Inc.

Lilly, Melinda. Peasant. 2002. (People of the Middle Ages Ser.). (Illus.). 32p. (J). lib. bdg. 26.60 (978-1-58952-229-9(X)) Rourke Publishing, LLC.

Lithuania-Netherlands, Vol. 6. 2002. (J). (978-0-7614-7384-8(X)) Cavendish, Marshall Corp.

MacDonald, Fiona. Charlemagne. 2000. (World in the Time of... Ser.). (Illus.). 48p. (J). (gr. 4-7). 22.95 (978-0-7910-6030-8(6) , Chelsea Hse.) Facts On File, Inc.

—How to Be a Medieval Knight. Bergin, Mark, illus. 2005. (How to Be Ser.). 32p. (J). (gr. 3-7). 21.90 (978-0-7922-3634-4(3) , National Geographic Children's Bks.) National Geographic Society.

MacDonald, Fiona & Bergin, Mark. How to Be a Medieval Knight. 2005. (How to Be Ser.). (Illus.). 32p. (J). (gr. 3-7). 14.95 (978-0-7922-3619-1(X) , National Geographic Children's Bks.) National Geographic Society.

Mason, Antony. New Europe. 2005. (Issues of the World Ser.). (Illus.). 48p. (J). (gr. 6-9). lib. bdg. 29.95 (978-1-59604-073-1(4)) Stargazer Bks.

McGraw-Hill Staff. The American Journey: Building a Nation, Spanish Student Edition. 2000. (SPA.). 91.52 (978-0-02-821869-4(8) , 9780028218694) Glencoe/McGraw-Hill.

McIntosh, Jane R. Handbook to Life in Prehistoric Europe. 2006. (Handbook to Life Ser.). (Illus.). 400p. (YA). (gr. 9 up). 70.00 (978-0-8160-5779-5(6)) Facts On File, Inc.

McNab, Chris. Eastern Europe. 2002. (Cultures & Costumes Ser.). (Illus.). 64p. (J). (gr. 7 up). lib. bdg. (978-1-59084-441-0(6)) Mason Crest Pubs.

Medieval Europe: PowerPoint Presentations in World History. 2005. cd-rom 49.95 net. (978-1-56004-231-0(1)) Social Studies Schl. Service.

Medieval Europe DBA. 2002. spiral bd 16.95 (978-1-56004-138-2(2)) Social Studies Schl. Service.

Middle Ages Europe: Mr Donn & Maxie's World History Series. 2006. spiral bd. 29.95 net. (978-1-56004-243-3(5)) Social Studies Schl. Service.

Nardo, Don. The Age of Colonialism. 2006. (World History Ser.). (Illus.). 112p. (J). (gr. 7-10). 32.45 (978-1-59018-833-0(0) , Lucent Bks.) Thomson Gale.

Norway-Romania, Vol. 7. 2002. (J). (978-0-7614-7385-5(8)) Cavendish, Marshall Corp.

Peoples of Europe, 11 vols., Set. Incl. Vol. 1. Albania-Belgium. (J). (978-0-7614-7379-4(3)); Vol. 2. Bosnia-Herzegovina—Czech Republic. (YA). (978-0-7614-7380-0(7)); Vol. 3. Denmark-France. (J). (978-0-7614-7381-7(5)); Vol. 4. Germany-Hungary. (J). (978-0-7614-7382-4(3)); Vol. 5. Iceland-Liechtenstein. (J). (978-0-7614-7383-1(1)); Vol. 6. Lithuania-Netherlands. (J). (978-0-7614-7384-8(X)); Vol. 7. Norway-Romania. (J). (978-0-7614-7385-5(8)); Vol. 8. Russia-Slovakia. (J). (978-0-7614-7386-2(6)); Vol. 9. Slovenia-Switzerland. (J). (978-0-7614-7387-9(4)); Vol. 10. Ukraine-Yugoslavia. (J). (978-0-7614-7388-6(2)); Vol. 11. Index. (J). (978-0-7614-7389-3(0)); (Illus.). 704p. 2002. 471.36 (978-0-7614-7378-7(5) , Cavendish, Marshall Reference Bks.) Cavendish, Marshall Corp.

Russia-Slovakia, Vol. 8. 2002. (J). (978-0-7614-7386-2(6)) Cavendish, Marshall Corp.

Saari, Peggy & Saari, Aaron Maurice. Renaissance & Reformation: Biographies, 2 vols. 2002. (Illus.). (J). 400p. 120.00 (978-0-7876-5470-2(1) , GML00502-173752); xxxiv, 386p. (978-0-7876-5472-6(8)); xxxiv, 386p. (978-0-7876-5471-9(X)) Thomson Gale. (UXL).

Sayre, April Pulley. Hello Europe! 2003. (Exploring Our Continents Ser.: 4). (Illus.). 32p. lib. bdg. 21.90 (978-0-7613-2151-4(9) , Millbrook Pr.) Lerner Publishing Group.

Schley, Michael. The Heart of Prague. 2004. (Illus.). 96p. 45.00 (978-0-9759645-0-7(X)) Schley, Michael.

Shukin, Barbara. Renaissance History Portfolio: A History of Europe & the Americas from the 14th -18th Centuries. 2004. (J). spiral bd. 24.95 (978-0-9762918-2-4(7)) Homeschool Journey.

Shuter, Jane. The Renaissance. 2007. (Illus.). 32p. (J). (***978-1-4034-8814-5(2)***) Heinemann Library.

Slovenia-Switzerland, Vol. 9. 2002. (J). (978-0-7614-7387-9(4)) Cavendish, Marshall Corp.

Stanley, George Edward. The European Settlement of North America (1492-1754) 2005. (Illus.). 48p. (J). pap. (978-0-8368-5833-4(6)); lib. bdg. 30.00 (978-0-8368-5824-2(7)) Stevens, Gareth Inc. (World Almanac Library).

Synge, M. B. The Awakening of Europe (Yesterday's Classics) Synge, E. M., illus. l.t. ed. 2006. 268p. (J). per. 11.95 (978-1-59915-015-4(8)) Yesterday's Classics.

Ukraine-Yugoslavia, Vol. 10. 2002. (J). (978-0-7614-7388-6(2)) Cavendish, Marshall Corp.

Walker, Ida. Belgium. 2006. (European Union Ser.). (Illus.). 88p. (J). (gr. 5 up). lib. bdg. (978-1-4222-0040-7(X) , 1247982) Mason Crest Pubs.

Wells, Donald. The Silk Road. 2004. (Great Journeys Ser.). (Illus.). 32p. (J). lib. bdg. 26.00 (978-1-59036-207-5(1)) Weigl Pubs., Inc.

Zocchi, Judy. In Sweden. Brodie, Neale, illus. 2005. (Global Adventures II Ser.). 32p. (J). pap. 9.95 (978-1-59646-176-5(4)) Dingles & Co.

—In Sweden/en Suecia. Brodie, Neale, illus. 2005. (Global Adventures I Ser.).Tr. of En Japon. (ENG & SPA.). 32p. (J). pap. 9.95 (978-1-59646-178-9(0)) Dingles & Co.

—In Switzerland. Brodie, Neale, illus. 2005. (Global Adventures I Ser.). 32p. (J). pap. 9.95 (978-1-59646-156-7(X)); lib. bdg. 20.65 (978-1-59646-006-5(7)) Dingles & Co.

—In Switzerland/en Suiza. Brodie, Neale, illus. 2005. (Global Adventures I Ser.).Tr. of En Suiza. (ENG & SPA.). 32p. (J). pap. 9.95 (978-1-59646-158-1(6)); lib. bdg. 20.65 (978-1-59646-007-2(5)) Dingles & Co.

EUROPE—HISTORY—FICTION

Comrie, Margaret S. The Heroes of Castle Bretten. 2003. (Illus.). 229p. (J). (978-1-894666-65-7(8)) Inheritance Pubns.

Cutler, Jane. The Cello of Mr. O. Couch, Greg, illus. 2004. (Picture Puffin Ser.). 32p. (J). (gr. k up). pap. 6.99 (978-0-14-240174-3(9), Puffin) Penguin Group (USA) Inc.

Harcourt School Publishers Staff. Quiet Heroes Advanced Level. 3rd ed. 2002. (Trophies Reading Program Ser.). (Illus.). pap. 5.10 (978-0-15-323466-8(0)) Harcourt Schl. Pubs.

Heuston, Kimberley Burton. Book of Jude. 2008. (J). (***978-1-932425-26-0(8)***, Front Street) Boyds Mills Pr.

Lake, A. J. The Book of the Sword: The Darkest Age II. 2007. 240p. (J). 16.95 (***978-1-59990-039-1(4)***, Bloomsbury Children) Bloomsbury Publishing.

Petrie, Glen. Lucy & the Pirates. Harrison, Matilda, illus. 32p. (J). (gr. k-5). 2001. pap. (978-1-896580-38-8(6)); 2000. (978-1-896580-02-9(5)) Tradewind Bks.

Priestley, Chris. Death & the Arrow. l.t. ed. 2005. (J). pap. (978-0-7540-7899-9(X), CLP 467) BBC Audio.

—Death & the Arrow. 2005. 176p. (YA). (gr. 7). pap. 5.50 (978-0-440-23811-9(0), Laurel Leaf) Random Hse. Children's Bks.

Riordan, James. Escape from War. 2005. (My Side of the Story Ser.). 192p. (J). (gr. 4-6). pap. 7.95 (978-0-7534-5794-8(6), Kingfisher) Houghton Mifflin Co. Trade & Reference Div.

Ross, Stewart. The Terror Trail. 2007. 48p. (J). 14.99 (978-0-7566-2570-2(X)); pap. 3.99 (978-0-7566-2569-6(6)) Dorling Kindersley Publishing, Inc.

Schraff, Anne. Gingerbread Heart. 1999. 114p. (J). pap. (978-0-7891-4926-8(5)); (gr. 5-12). lib. bdg. 13.95 (978-0-7807-8005-7(1)) Perfection Learning Corp.

Scott, Elaine. The Spanish Web: An Encounter with Picasso. 2004. (Art Encounters Ser.). (J). 15.95 (978-0-8230-0410-2(4)); pap. 6.99 (978-0-8230-0413-3(9)) Watson-Guptill Pubns., Inc.

Steiner, Connie Colker. Shoes for Amelie. Rodier, Denis, illus. 2005. 48p. (J). (gr. 3-7). 6.95 (978-1-894222-37-2(7)) Lobster Pr. CAN. *Dist:* Univ. of Toronto Pr.

Van Ryk, Laverne. A Garland of Emeralds. 2006. (Illus.). 305p. (***978-1-4122-0156-8(X)***) Trafford Publishing.

Welsh, T. K. Resurrection Men. 2007. 214p. (J). (gr. 9 up). 16.99 (978-0-525-47699-3(7), Dutton Juvenile) Penguin Group (USA) Inc.

Wilson, John. Lost in Spain. (Illus.). 174p. 2000. (YA). (gr. 8-12). (978-1-55041-550-6(6)); 1999. (gr. 7-10). (978-1-55041-523-0(9)) Fitzhenry & Whiteside, Ltd.

—Lost in Spain. 2001. (gr. 7-12). lib. bdg. 18.75 (978-0-613-43694-6(6)) Tandem Library Bks.

Winter, Kathryn. Katarina. 1999. (J). (978-0-606-17441-1(9)) Tandem Library Bks.

Wisniewski, David, illus. & retold by. Golem. Wisniewski, David, retold by. 2007. 32p. (J). (gr. 1-5). 6.95 (***978-0-618-89424-6(1)***, Clarion Bks.) Houghton Mifflin Co. Trade & Reference Div.

Wrede, Patricia C. & Stevermer, Caroline. The Grand Tour: Being a Revelation of Matters of High Confidentiality & Greatest Importance, Including Extracts from the Intimate Diary of a Noblewoman & the Sworn Testimony of a Lady of Quality. 2004. (Illus.). 480p. (YA). 17.00 (978-0-15-204616-3(X)) Harcourt Children's Bks.

EUROPE—HISTORY—476-1492

see also Holy Roman Empire; Hundred Years' War, 1339-1453

Barron's Educational Editorial Staff. Life in the Middle Ages. 1998. (Megascope Ser.). (Illus.). 64p. (J). (gr. 3-7) 6.95 (978-0-7641-5094-4(4)) Barron's Educational Series, Inc.

Claybourne, Anna. The Renaissance. 2007. (J). (***978-1-4109-2910-5(8)***); pap. (***978-1-4109-2916-7(7)***) Steck-Vaughn.

Grant, Neil, et al. The Atlas of the Renaissance World. Ravaglia, Paola, illus. 2001. (Atlas Ser.). 64p. (J). (gr. 5 up). 19.95 (978-0-87226-692-6(3), Bedrick, Peter Bks.) School Specialty Publishing.

Hanawalt, Barbara. The European World, 400-1450. (Illus.). 2006. 189p. 32.95 (978-0-19-522267-8(9)); 2005. 192p. (YA). 32.95 (978-0-19-517844-9(0)) Oxford Univ. Pr., Inc.

Kenney, Karen Latchana. Harsh or Heroic? The Middle Ages. 2007. (Shockwave: History & Politics Ser.). 36p. (J). pap. 6.95 (***978-0-531-18794-4(2)***); (Illus.). (gr. 4-6). lib. bdg. 25.00 (***978-0-531-17754-9(8)***) Scholastic Library Publishing. (Children's Pr.).

Langley, Andrew. Renaissance: An Eyewitness Book. Scott, Carey, ed. Crawford, Andy, photos by. 2004. (Illus.). 60p. (J). (gr. 4-8). reprint ed. 16.00 (978-0-7567-8157-6(4)) DIANE Publishing Co.

Macdonald, Fiona. Monarchs in the Middle Ages. 2005. (World Almanac Library of the Middle Ages). (Illus.). 48p. pap. (978-0-8368-5905-8(7), World Almanac Library) Stevens, Gareth Inc.

MacDonald, Fiona. Monarchs in the Middle Ages. 2005. (World Almanac' Library of the Middle Ages). (Illus.). 48p. (YA). (gr. 10-12). lib. bdg. 30.00 (978-0-8368-5896-9(4), World Almanac Library) Stevens, Gareth Inc.

Marshall, Chris. Warfare in the Medieval World. 1999. (History of Warfare Ser.). (Illus.). 80p. (YA). (gr. 7-12). lib. bdg. 29.97 (978-0-8172-5443-8(9)) Raintree.

Student Study Guide to the European World, 400-1450. 2005. (Medieval & Early Modern World Ser.). 48p. (YA). 9.95 (978-0-19-522336-1(5)) Oxford Univ. Pr., Inc.

Willard, Barbara. Son of Charlemagne. Weiss, Emil, illus. 1998. (Living History Library). 208p. (J). (gr. 5 up). reprint ed. pap. 12.95 (978-1-883937-30-0(2), 30-2) Bethlehem Bks.

EUROPE—HISTORY—1492-1789

Claybourne, Anna. The Renaissance. 2007. (J). (***978-1-4109-2910-5(8)***); pap. (***978-1-4109-2916-7(7)***) Steck-Vaughn.

Grant, Neil, et al. The Atlas of the Renaissance World. Ravaglia, Paola, illus. 2001. (Atlas Ser.). 64p. (J). (gr. 5 up). 19.95 (978-0-87226-692-6(3), Bedrick, Peter Bks.) School Specialty Publishing.

Hinds, Kathryn. The Countryside. (Illus.). (J). 2004. 72p. 29.93 (978-0-7614-1656-2(0)); 2000. 80p. (gr. 5 up). lib. bdg. 29.93 (978-0-7614-1006-5(6)) Cavendish, Marshall Corp. (Benchmark Bks.).

Prum, Deborah M. Rats, Bulls & Flying Machines: A History of the Renaissance & Reformation. Holdren, John, ed. 1999. (Core Chronicles Ser.: Vol. 1). (Illus.). (YA). (gr. 5-10). 106p. 21.95 (978-1-890517-19-9(4)); pap. 11.95 (978-1-890517-18-2(6)) Core Knowledge Foundation.

Shapiro, Stephen. The Siege: Under Attack in Renaissance Europe. Mantha, John, illus. 2007. 56p. (J). (gr. 5-12). pap. 12.95 (***978-1-55451-107-5(0)***); lib. bdg. 21.95 (***978-1-55451-108-2(9)***) Annick Pr., Ltd. CAN. *Dist:* Firefly Bks., Ltd.

Wagner, John A. Historical Dictionary of the Elizabethan World. (Illus.). 432p. (gr. 9). pap. 24.95 (978-0-8160-4657-7(3), Checkmark Bks.) Facts On File, Inc.

EUROPE—HISTORY—18TH CENTURY

Laver, John, et al. European History, 1815-1914. 2001. (Illus.). 480p. (J). pap. 29.99 (978-0-340-72127-8(8), Hodder & Stoughton) Hodder General Publishing Division GBR. *Dist:* Trafalgar Square Publishing.

EUROPE—HISTORY—1789-1900

Bacchin, Giorgio, illus. Industrial Revolution, 1800-1850: A Social History. 2002. (Road to Globalization Ser.). 32p. (YA). 22.95 (978-0-7910-7092-5(1)) Facts On File, Inc.

Baycroft, Timothy. Nationalism in Europe 1789-1945. 1998. (Cambridge Perspectives in History Core Texts Ser.). (Illus.). 104p. pap. 15.00 (978-0-521-59871-2(0)) Cambridge Univ. Pr.

Maybury, Richard J. World War I: The Rest of the Story & How It Affects You Today, 1870 To 1935. Williams, Jane A., ed. rev. ed. 2003. ("Uncle Eric" Bk.). 253p. (YA). pap. 17.95 (978-0-942617-42-9(8)) Bluestocking Pr.

EUROPE—HISTORY—20TH CENTURY

Gunderson, Cory. Great Depression. 2005. (American Moments Ser.). (Illus.). 48p. (J). (gr. 4-8). lib. bdg. 25.65 (978-1-59197-286-0(8), ABDO & Daughters) ABDO Publishing Co.

Smith, William Herbert Cecil. Twentieth Century Europe. 2004. (Twentieth Century History Ser.). (Illus.). 127p. (978-0-298-76285-9(4), Weidenfeld & Nicolson) Orion Publishing Group, Ltd.

Taylor, David. The Wars in Former Yugoslavia. 2002. (Troubled World Ser.). (Illus.). 64p. (J). (gr. 6 up). lib. bdg. 28.54 (978-0-7398-6343-5(6)) Raintree.

EUROPE—HISTORY—1914-1945

see also World War, 1939-1945

Gutierrez, Peter. The Story Behind Erich Maria Remarque's All Quiet on the Western Front. 2006. (History in Literature Ser.). 56p. (J). (978-1-4034-8210-5(1)) Heinemann Library.

Heinemann Library Staff. The Great Depression. 2003. (Illus.). 56p. (J). pap. 8.95 (978-1-4034-4576-6(1)) Heinemann Library.

Klam, Julie. Europe in Flames. 2002. (Illus.). 48p. (J). lib. bdg. 28.50 (978-1-58340-187-3(3)) Smart Apple Media.

EUROPE—HISTORY—1945-

European Commission Staff, contrib. by. May Day: Young Literature from the Ten New Member States of the European Union. 2005. (ENG & MUL., Illus.). 152p. (***978-92-894-9358-1(5)***) Office for Official Pubns. of the European Communities.

Post-Cold War Europe. 2003. (Eye on History Ser.). 32p. (gr. 5-12). 5.99 (978-1-56822-944-7(5), IF2677) School Specialty Publishing.

EUROPE—KINGS AND RULERS

Gunther, John. Sterling Point Books: Alexander the Great. 2007. (Sterling Point Bks.). (Illus.). 176p. (J). 12.95 (978-1-4027-4519-5(2)); pap. 6.95 (978-1-4027-4139-5(1)) Sterling Publishing Co., Inc.

EUROPE—POLITICS AND GOVERNMENT

Haugen, Brenda. Winston Churchill: British Soldier, Writer, Statesman. 2006. (Signature Lives Ser.). (Illus.). 112p. (J). (gr. 5-7). 30.60 (978-0-7565-1582-9(3)) Compass Point Bks.

Kelly, Martin & Kelly, Melissa. Government. 2007. (Colonial Life Ser.). (Illus.). 96p. (gr. 6 up). 37.95 (***978-0-7656-8112-6(9)***) Sharpe, M.E. Inc.

Lee, Stephen J. Gladstone & Disraeli. 2005. (Questions & Analysis in History Ser.). (Illus.). 208p. 20.95 (978-0-415-32357-4(6)) Routledge.

Macdonald, Fiona. Monarchs in the Middle Ages. 2005. (World Almanac Library of the Middle Ages). (Illus.). 48p. pap. (978-0-8368-5905-8(7), World Almanac Library) Stevens, Gareth Inc.

MacDonald, Fiona. Monarchs in the Middle Ages. 2005. (World Almanac' Library of the Middle Ages). (Illus.). 48p. (YA). (gr. 10-12). lib. bdg. 30.00 (978-0-8368-5896-9(4), World Almanac Library) Stevens, Gareth Inc.

Whiting, Jim. The Life & Times of Pericles. 2005. (Biography from Ancient Civilizations Ser.). (Illus.). 48p. (J). (ps-7). lib. bdg. 29.95 (978-1-58415-339-9(3)) Mitchell Lane Pubs., Inc.

EUROPEAN COMMON MARKET

see European Economic Community

EUROPEAN ECONOMIC COMMUNITY

Docalavich, Heather. Sweden. 2006. (European Union Ser.). (Illus.). 88p. (J). (gr. 5 up). lib. bdg. (978-1-4222-0063-6(9)) Mason Crest Pubs.

Etingoff, Kim. Greece. 2006. (European Union Ser.). (Illus.). 88p. (J). (gr. 5 up). lib. bdg. (978-1-4222-0049-0(3)) Mason Crest Pubs.

—Portugal. 2006. (European Union Ser.). (Illus.). 88p. (J). (gr. 5 up). lib. bdg. (978-1-4222-0059-9(0)) Mason Crest Pubs.

Powell, Jillian. The European Union. 2001. (World Organizations Ser.). (Illus.). 32p. (J). (gr. 6-8). 24.00 (978-0-531-14620-0(0), Watts, Franklin) Scholastic Library Publishing.

Sadik, Ademola O. Italy. 2006. (European Union Ser.). (Illus.). 88p. (J). (gr. 5 up). lib. bdg. (978-1-4222-0052-0(3)) Mason Crest Pubs.

Sanna, Jeanine. France. 2006. (European Union Ser.). (Illus.). 88p. (J). (gr. 5 up). lib. bdg. (978-1-4222-0047-6(7), 1247999) Mason Crest Pubs.

Simons, Rae. Luxembourg. 2006. (European Union Ser.). (Illus.). 88p. (J). (gr. 5 up). lib. bdg. (978-1-4222-0055-1(8)) Mason Crest Pubs.

Stafford, James. The European Union: Facts & Figures. 2007. (European Union Ser.). (Illus.). 88p. (YA). (gr. 5 up). lib. bdg. (978-1-4222-0045-2(0)) Mason Crest Pubs.

—Malta. 2006. (European Union Ser.). (Illus.). 88p. (J). (gr. 5 up). lib. bdg. (978-1-4222-0056-8(6)) Mason Crest Pubs.

EUROPEAN WAR, 1939-1945

see World War, 1939-1945

EUTHANASIA

see also Assisted Suicide

Altman, Linda Jacobs. Death: An Introduction to Medical-Ethical Dilemmas. 2000. (Illus.). 112p. (J). (gr. 6-12). lib. bdg. 26.60 (978-0-7660-1246-2(8)) Enslow Pubs., Inc.

Cavan, Seamus & Dolan, Sean. Euthanasia: Debate Over the Right to Die. 2000. (Focus on Science & Society Ser.). (Illus.). 64p. (YA). (gr. 4-6). lib. bdg. 26.50 (978-0-8239-3215-3(X), FSEUTH) Rosen Publishing Group, Inc., The.

Engdahl, Sylvia Louise. Euthanasia. 2006. 192p. (J). (gr. 10-12). 36.20 (978-0-7377-3251-1(2)); pap. 24.95 (978-0-7377-3252-8(0)) Thomson Gale. (Greenhaven Pr., Inc.).

Fireside, Bryna J. & Ferguson, John E. The Right to Die. 2007. (Point/Counterpoint Ser.). 112p. (J). (gr. 9). 32.95 (***978-0-7910-9287-3(9)***, Chelsea Hse.) Facts On File, Inc.

Jackson, Linda. Euthanasia. 2005. (Face the Facts Ser.). (Illus.). 56p. (J). (gr. 4-6). lib. bdg. 28.56 (978-1-4109-1068-4(7)) Harcourt Schl. Pubs.

Rebman, Renee C. Euthanasia & the Right to Die: A Pro/Con Issue. 2002. (Hot Pro/Con Issues Ser.). (Illus.). 64p. (YA). (gr. 6-12). lib. bdg. 27.93 (978-0-7660-1816-7(4)) Enslow Pubs., Inc.

Torr, James D. Euthanasia. 2000. (Opposing Viewpoints Ser.). (Illus.). 208p. (YA). (gr. 10-12). pap. (978-0-7377-0126-5(9)); (gr. 9-12). lib. bdg. 32.45 (978-0-7377-0127-2(7)) Thomson Gale. (Greenhaven Pr., Inc.).

Walker, Richard. The Right to Die? 2005. (Illus.). 32p. (J). (gr. 5-9). lib. bdg. 27.10 (978-1-932889-56-7(6)) Sea To-Sea Pubns.

Williams, Mary E. Terminal Illness. 2001. (Opposing Viewpoints Ser.). (Illus.). 208p. (YA). (gr. 10-12). 32.45 (978-0-7377-0526-3(4), Greenhaven Pr., Inc.) Thomson Gale.

Williams, Mary E., ed. Terminal Illness. 2001. (Opposing Viewpoints Ser.). (Illus.). 208p. (YA). (gr. 10-12). pap. 21.20 (978-0-7377-0525-6(6), Greenhaven Pr., Inc.) Thomson Gale.

Woolf, Alex. Euthanasia. 2004. (World Issues Ser.). (J). lib. bdg. (978-1-59389-156-5(3)) Chrysalis Education.

Young, Mitchell. Euthanasia. 2007. (Issues on Trial Ser.). 240p. (gr. 10-12). 36.20 (***978-0-7377-2789-0(6)***, Greenhaven Pr., Inc.) Thomson Gale.

Yount, Lisa. Euthanasia. 2nd rev. ed. 2000. (Overview Ser.). (Illus.). 112p. (YA). (gr. 6-9). lib. bdg. 29.95 (978-1-56006-697-2(0), LML00902-178049, Lucent Bks.) Thomson Gale.

EVALUATION OF LITERATURE

see Books and Reading; Criticism; Literature—History and Criticism

EVANGELICALISM

Donahue, Laurie. God's Plan My Response. Rittenhouse, Ralph, ed. 2003. (Illus.). 100p. pap. 9.99 (978-0-9718306-0-8(6)) LifeSong Pubs.

Donahue, Laurie & Rittenhouse, Ralph. God... Should I Be Baptized? 2003. (Illus.). 96p. pap. 10.99 (978-0-9718306-1-5(4)) LifeSong Pubs.

Filleul, Liz. Tumbler. Field, Susan Anna, illus. 2004. 32p. (gr. 2-5). 16.99 (978-0-8066-4268-0(8), Augsburg Bks.) Augsburg Fortress, Pubs.

Kids in Evangelism. 2000. pap. 10.00 (978-1-59185-165-3(3)) CharismaLife Pubs.

School of Evangelism for Kids. 2002. (ENG, SWA & GER.). 187p. ring bd. 74.95 (978-0-9767647-1-7(7)) Kids in Ministry International.

Six Steps to Successful Film Evangelism. 2000. (Illus.). 13p. (YA). pap. 1.75 (978-1-888568-57-8(7)) Doughten, Russ Films, Inc.

EVANGELISTS

Davis, Rebecca. George Mueller: A Father to the Fatherless. 2004. (Illus.). 135p. (J). pap. 7.49 (978-1-59166-255-6(9)) Jones, Bob Univ. Pr.

Shaw, S. B. The Great Revival in Wales. 2002. per. 10.99 (978-1-931393-01-0(X)) Christian Life Bks.

Sheafer, Silvia Anne. Aimee Semple McPherson. 2004. (Spiritual Leaders & Thinkers Ser.). (Illus.). 120p. (gr. 9-13). 30.00 (978-0-7910-7867-9(1), Chelsea Hse.) Facts On File, Inc.

Wellman, Sam. Billy Graham: The Great Evangelist. 1999. (Heroes of the Faith Ser.). (Illus.). 208p. (YA). (gr. 4-7). 14.95 (978-0-7910-5031-6(9), Chelsea Hse.) Facts On File, Inc.

Wooten, Sara McIntosh. Billy Graham: World-Famous Evangelist. 2001. (People to Know Ser.). (Illus.). 112p. (YA). (gr. 6-12). lib. bdg. 26.60 (978-0-7660-1533-3(5)) Enslow Pubs., Inc.

EVANGELISTS—FICTION

Paulsen, Gary. The Tent. 2006. (Illus.). 96p. (J). pap. 5.95 (978-0-15-205833-3(8), Harcourt Paperbacks) Harcourt Children's Bks.

EVEREST, MOUNT (CHINA AND NEPAL)

Coburn, Broughton. My Triumph on Everest: A Photobiography of Sir Edmund Hillary. 2000. (Illus.). 64p. (J). (gr. 3-7). 17.95 (978-0-7922-7114-7(9), National Geographic Children's Bks.) National Geographic Society.

—Triumph on Everest: A Photobiography of Sir Edmund Hillary. 2003. (Illus.). 64p. (J). (gr. 5). 7.95 (978-0-7922-7932-7(8), National Geographic Children's Bks.) National Geographic Society.

De Capua, Sarah. Mount Everest. 2002. (Rookie Read-About Geography Ser.). (Illus.). 32p. (J). (gr. 1-2). pap. 5.95 (978-0-516-27391-4(4)); 20.50 (978-0-516-22015-4(2)) Scholastic Library Publishing. (Children's Pr.).

Dorling Kindersley Publishing Staff. Everest. Stephens, Rebecca, ed. 2001. (Eyewitness Bks.: Vol. 116). (Illus.). 64p. (J). (gr. 4-7). lib. bdg. 19.99 (978-0-7894-7396-7(8)) Dorling Kindersley Publishing, Inc.

Dowswell, Paul. True Everest Adventures. Woodcock, John, illus. 2004. (True Adventure Stories Ser.). 144p. (J). pap. 4.95 (978-0-7945-0373-4(X), Usborne) EDC Publishing.

Everest, 6 Packs. 32p. (gr. 5 up). 44.00 (978-0-7578-0990-3(1)) Rigby Education.

Expedition Everest Yetiology Journal. 2006. (J). (ps-17). pap. 15.95 (978-1-4231-0232-8(0), Disney Editions) Disney Pr.

Gammelgaard, Lene. Climbing High: A Woman's Account of Surviving the Everest Tragedy. 2000. (Illus.). (J). (978-0-606-18683-4(2)) Tandem Library Bks.

Glassman, Jackie. La conquista del Monte Everest. ed. 2004. (SPA.). 32p. (J). pap. 6.00 (978-1-4108-2343-4(1), A23431) Benchmark Education Co.

Hirschmann, Kris. The Highest Mountain. 2002. (Extreme Places Ser.). (Illus.). 48p. (J). (gr. 3-5). 26.20 (978-0-7377-1373-2(9), Kidhaven) Thomson Gale.

Jenkins, Steve. The Top of the World: Climbing Mount Everest. Jenkins, Steve, illus. 2002. (Illus.). 32p. (J). (gr. k-3). pap. 6.95 (978-0-618-19676-0(5)) Houghton Mifflin Co. Trade & Reference Div.

—The Top of the World: Climbing Mount Everest. 1999. (Illus.). 32p. (J). (gr. k-3). tchr. ed. 16.00 (978-0-395-94218-5(7)) Houghton Mifflin Co. Trade & Reference Div.

—Top of the World: Climbing Mount Everest. 1999. (gr. 3-6). lib. bdg. 15.25 (978-0-613-60732-2(5)) Tandem Library Bks.

Jones, Brenn. Learning about Teamwork from the Lives of Sir Edmund Hillary & Tenzig Norgay. 2002. (Character Building Book Ser.). (Illus.). 24p. (J). (gr. 3). lib. bdg. 18.75 (978-0-8239-5778-1(0), PowerKids Pr.) Rosen Publishing Group, Inc., The.

Kalz, Jill. Mount Everest. 2004. (Natural Wonders of the World Ser.). (Illus.). 32p. (J). lib. bdg. (978-1-58341-325-8(1), Creative Education) Creative Co., The.

Kerr, James. Hillary & Norgay's Mount Everest Adventure. 2007. (J). (***978-1-4034-9755-0(9)***) Heinemann Library.

Lappi, Megan. Mount Everest. 2004. (J). lib. bdg. (978-1-59036-450-5(3)); lib. bdg. (978-1-59036-271-6(3)) Weigl Pubs., Inc.

O'Shei, Tim. Left for Dead! Lincoln Hall's Story of Survival. 2008. (J). (***978-1-4296-0090-3(X)***) Capstone Pr., Inc.

Pastan, Amy & Dorling Kindersley Publishing Staff. First Ladies. 2001. (Eyewitness Bks.: Vol. 117). (Illus.). 64p. (J). (gr. 4-7). lib. bdg. 19.99 (978-0-7894-7398-1(4)) Dorling Kindersley Publishing, Inc.

Pfetzer, Mark. Within Reach: My Everest Story. 2000. (gr. 3-6). lib. bdg. 16.45 (978-0-613-15316-4(2)) Tandem Library Bks.

Pfetzer, Mark & Galvin, Jack. Within Reach: My Everest Story. 2000. 208p. (J). (gr. 7-12). pap. 7.99 (978-0-14-130497-7(9), Puffin) Penguin Group (USA) Inc.

—Within Reach: My Everest Story. 2000. (978-0-606-16770-3(6)) Tandem Library Bks.

Platt, Richard, contrib. by. Everest. 2000. (Dorling Kindersley Discoveries Ser.). (Illus.). 48p. (J). 14.95 (978-0-7894-6110-0(2)) Dorling Kindersley Publishing, Inc.

Salkeld, Audrey. Climbing Everest: Tales of Triumph & Tragedy on the World's Highest Mountain. 2003. (Illus.). 128p. (J). (gr. 5). 21.00 (978-0-7922-5105-7(9), National Geographic Children's Bks.) National Geographic Society.

E F G

—Mystery on Everest: A Photobiography of George Mallory. 2000. (Illus.). 64p. (J). (gr. 5-8). 17.95 (978-0-7922-7222-9(6) , National Geographic Children's Bks.) National Geographic Society.

Sandler, Michael. Mountains: Surviving on Mt. Everest. 2005. (X-treme Places Ser.). (Illus.). 32p. (J). (gr. 3-7). lib. bdg. 25.27 (978-1-59716-086-5(5)) Bearport Publishing Co., Inc.

Seddon, Tony. Big Book of Climbing Mount Everest. 2000. (Cambridge Reading Routes Ser.). (Illus.). 24p. pap. 12.40 (978-0-521-77888-6(3)) Cambridge Univ. Pr.

Shea, Therese. Climbing Mount Everest: Understanding Commutative, Associative, & Distributive Properties. 2005. (PowerMath Ser.). (Illus.). 32p. (J). 22.50 (978-1-4042-2939-6(6)); (978-1-4042-5143-4(X)); pap. (978-1-4042-5142-7(1)) Rosen Publishing Group, Inc., The. (PowerKids Pr.).

Skreslet, Laurie. To the Top of Everest. 2003. (gr. 3-6). lib. bdg. 17.60 (978-0-613-84973-9(6)) Tandem Library Bks.

Skreslet, Laurie & MacLeod, Elizabeth. To the Top of Everest. (Illus.). 56p. (J). (gr. 4-6). 2003. (978-1-55074-814-7(9)); 2001. (978-1-55074-721-8(5)) Kids Can Pr., Ltd.

Stephens, Rebecca. Everest. Parsons, Jayne, ed. 2001. (Eyewitness Bks.: Vol. 116). (Illus.). 64p. (J). (gr. 4-7). 15.99 (978-0-7894-7395-0(X)) Dorling Kindersley Publishing, Inc.

Weintraub, Aileen. Mount Everest: The Highest Mountain. 2001. (Great Record Breakers in Nature Ser.). (Illus.). 24p. (J). lib. bdg. 18.75 (978-0-8239-5636-4(9) , PowerKids Pr.) Rosen Publishing Group, Inc., The.

Werther, Scott P. Jon Krakauer's Adventure on Mt. Everest. 2002. (Survivors Ser.). (Illus.). 48p. (YA). (gr. 7-12). 24.00 (978-0-516-23902-6(3)); pap. 6.95 (978-0-516-23488-5(9)) Scholastic Library Publishing. (Children's Pr.).

EVERGLADES (FLA.)

Adams, Colleen. The Everglades: Analyzing Graphs, Tables, & Charts. 2005. (PowerMath Ser.). (J). 22.50 (978-1-4042-2933-4(7)); pap. (978-1-4042-5127-4(8)) Rosen Publishing Group, Inc., The. (PowerKids Pr.).

Benjamin, Lisa. People of the Wetlands. 2005. (Voices Reading Ser.). (Illus.). 32p. (J). (978-0-7367-2947-5(X)) Zaner-Bloser, Inc.

Blaustein, Daniel. The Everglades & the Gulf Coast. 2000. (Ecosystems of North America Ser.). (Illus.). 64p. (YA). (gr. 6 up). lib. bdg. 28.50 (978-0-7614-0896-3(7) , Benchmark Bks.) Cavendish, Marshall Corp.

Doherty, Kieran. Marjory Stoneman Douglas: Guardian of the 'Glades. 2002. (Techies Ser.). (Illus.). 160p. (gr. 7 up). lib. bdg. 24.90 (978-0-7613-2371-6(6) , Twenty-First Century Bks.) Lerner Publishing Group.

Furstinger, Nancy. The Everglades. (Natural Wonders of the U. S. A. Ser.). (J). 2004. pap. 7.95 (978-1-59036-160-3(1)); 2003. (Illus.). 32p. lib. bdg. 18.20 (978-1-59036-039-2(7)) Weigl Pubs., Inc.

George, Jean Craighead. Autumn Moon. 2003. (J). (gr. 3-7). 20.75 (978-0-8446-7241-0(6)) Smith, Peter Pub., Inc.

Kinser, Kathy. The Everglades. ed. 2003. (Early Connections Ser.). (J). pap. 35.00 (978-1-4108-1543-9(9)) Benchmark Education Co.

Leotti-Bachem, Janice. The Everglades. 2005. (Rookie Read-About Geography Ser.). (Illus.). 32p. (J). (gr. 1-2). 20.50 (978-0-516-22750-4(5) , Children's Pr.) Scholastic Library Publishing.

—Everglades. 2005. (Rookie Read-about Geography Ser.). (Illus.). 31p. (J). (gr. 1-2). pap. 5.95 (978-0-516-25929-1(6) , Children's Pr.) Scholastic Library Publishing.

Marx, Trish. Everglades Forever. Karp, Cindy, illus. Karp, Cindy, photos by. 2004. 40p. (J). 17.95 (978-1-58430-164-6(3)) Lee & Low Bks., Inc.

Quigley, Mary. Wetlands Explorer. 2004. (Habitat Explorer Ser.). lib. bdg. 25.70 (978-1-4109-0514-7(4)) Raintree.

Repko, Marya. The Story of Everglades City: A History for Younger Readers. 2004. (Illus.). 48p. (YA). per. 5.00 (978-0-9716006-1-4(9)) Repko, Marya.

Tyler, Ann Spann. Torry Island Boy of the Everglades. 2000. (Illus.). 119p. (J). (978-0-9679351-0-2(5)); pap. (978-0-9679351-1-9(3)) Tyler Reproductions.

EVERGLADES (FLA.)—FICTION

Coman, Carolyn. Sneaking Suspicions. Shepperson, Rob, illus. 2007. 204p. (J). (gr. 3-7). 16.95 (***978-1-59078-491-4(X)*** , Front Street) Boyds Mills Pr.

Dexter, Anthony. The Adventures of Manny the Manatee. 2004. 45p. pap. 19.95 (978-1-4137-2751-7(4)) PublishAmerica, Inc.

Douglas, Marjory Stoneman. Alligator Crossing. Nicholson, Trudy, illus. 2003. 192p. (J). (gr. 3-8). pap. 6.95 (978-1-57131-644-8(2)) Milkweed Editions.

—Alligator Crossing. 2003. (gr. 3-6). lib. bdg. 15.25 (978-0-613-79196-0(7)) Tandem Library Bks.

Everglades Environmental Storybook: Coastal Creatures. l.t. ed. 1999. (Voices of the Earth Ser.: Vol. I). (Illus.). 48p. (J). (gr. k-4). pap. 6.95 (978-0-9666720-1-5(1)) Earthwing Pubns.

Hanson, Ed. The Swamp. 2003. (Barclay Family Adventure Ser.: Bk. 10). 64p. (J). (gr. k-6). per. 3.95 (978-1-56254-558-1(2)) Saddleback Educational Publishing.

Harcourt School Publishers Staff. The Everglades Forever, On Level. 3rd ed. 2002. (Trophies Reading Program Ser.). (Illus.). pap. 5.10 (978-0-15-323273-2(0)) Harcourt Schl. Pubs.

Raffa, Edwina & Rigsby, Annelle. Escape to the Everglades. 2006. pap., tchr. ed., act. bk. ed. 6.00 (978-1-56164-362-2(9)); (Illus.). 100p. (J). 12.95 (978-1-56164-351-6(3)) Pineapple Pr., Inc.

Rust, Ann O'Connell. Torry Island. Rust, Allen F., ed. 2002. (Nonie of the Everglades Ser.: Vol. II). 94p. (J). (gr. 4-7). pap. 7.95 (978-1-883203-06-1(6)) Amaro Bks.

Shaler, Robert. The Boy Scouts on Picket Duty. 2006. pap. 33.99 (***978-1-4219-7290-9(5)***) IndyPublish.com.

Wildes, Shirley Ann. The Life of Old Big Daddy, the Bullfrog. 2006. 52p. per. 9.95 (978-1-59453-929-9(4) , Airleaf Publishing) Airleaf Publishing & Bookselling.

EVERGLADES NATIONAL PARK (FLA.)

Fazio, Wende. Everglades National Park. (True Bks.). (Illus.). 48p. (J). (gr. 3-5). 1999. pap. 6.95 (978-0-516-26433-2(8)); 1998. 25.00 (978-0-516-20667-7(2)) Scholastic Library Publishing. (Children's Pr.).

Graf, Mike. Everglades National Park. 2003. (National Parks Ser.). (Illus.). 24p. (J). lib. bdg. 19.93 (978-0-7368-2219-0(4) , Bridgestone Bks.) Capstone Pr., Inc.

Harcourt School Publishers Staff. Exploring the Everglades Below Level. 3rd ed. 2002. (Trophies Reading Program Ser.). (Illus.). pap. 5.10 (978-0-15-323321-0(4)) Harcourt Schl. Pubs.

Higgins, Nadia. Welcome to Everglades National Park. 2006. (Visitor Guides Ser.). (Illus.). 32p. (J). (gr. 1-5). 27.07 (978-1-59296-702-5(7)) Child's World, Inc.

Leotti-Bachem, Janice. The Everglades. 2005. (Rookie Read-About Geography Ser.). (Illus.). 32p. (J). (gr. 1-2). 20.50 (978-0-516-22750-4(5) , Children's Pr.) Scholastic Library Publishing.

Lourie, Peter. Everglades: Buffalo Tiger & the River of Grass. 2003. (River Ser.). (Illus.). 48p. (YA). (gr. 4-6). pap. 11.95 (978-1-56397-702-2(8)) Boyds Mills Pr.

Stewart, Melissa. Life in a Wetland. 2003. (Ecosystems in Action Ser.). (Illus.). 72p. (J). (gr. 6-12). lib. bdg. 26.60 (978-0-8225-4687-0(6)) Lerner Publishing Group.

Wade, Linda R. Everglades National Park. 2005. (National Parks Ser.). (Illus.). 32p. (J). (gr. 3-8). lib. bdg. 24.21 (978-1-59197-424-6(0)) ABDO Publishing Co.

EVERWORLD (IMAGINARY PLACE)—FICTION

Applegate, Katherine. Brave the Betrayal. 2000. (EverWorld Ser.: No. 8). (Illus.). (J). (gr. 4-7). 11.64 (978-0-606-18541-7(0)) Tandem Library Bks.

—Discover the Destroyer. (EverWorld Ser.: No. 5). 2000. (gr. 7-12). lib. bdg. 13.00 (978-0-613-21502-2(8)); 1999. (Illus.). (J). (gr. 4-7). 11.64 (978-0-606-18539-4(9)) Tandem Library Bks.

—Enter the Enchanted. 1999. (EverWorld Ser.: No. 3). (J). (gr. 4-7). 11.64 (978-0-606-17279-0(3)) Tandem Library Bks.

—Fear the Fantastic. 2000. (EverWorld Ser.: No. 6). (Illus.). 192p. (J). (gr. 4-7). pap. 4.99 (978-0-590-87764-0(X)) Scholastic, Inc.

—Fear the Fantastic. 2000. (EverWorld Ser.: No. 6). (Illus.). (J). (gr. 4-7). 11.64 (978-0-606-18540-0(2)) Tandem Library Bks.

—Gateway to the Gods. 7th ed. 2000. (EverWorld Ser.: No. 7). (Illus.). 192p. (J). (gr. 4-7). pap. 4.99 (978-0-590-87766-4(6)) Scholastic, Inc.

—Gateway to the Gods. 2000. (EverWorld Ser.: No. 7). (Illus.). (J). (gr. 4-7). (978-0-606-18872-2(X)) Tandem Library Bks.

—Inside the Illusion. 2000. (EverWorld Ser.: No. 9). (J). (gr. 4-7). 11.64 (978-0-606-19558-4(0)) Tandem Library Bks.

—Land of Loss. 1999. (EverWorld Ser.: No. 2). 192p. (J). (gr. 4-7). pap. 4.99 (978-0-590-87751-0(8)) Scholastic, Inc.

—Land of Loss. 1999. (EverWorld Ser.: No. 2). (J). (gr. 4-7). (978-0-606-16927-1(X)) Tandem Library Bks.

—Realm of the Reaper. 1999. (EverWorld Ser.: No. 4). (J). (gr. 4-7). (978-0-606-17541-8(5)) Tandem Library Bks.

—Search for Senna. 1999. (EverWorld Ser.: No. 1). (J). (gr. 4-7). (978-0-606-16926-4(1)) Tandem Library Bks.

—Understand the Unknown. 2000. (EverWorld Ser.: No. 10). 208p. (J). (gr. 4-7). pap. 4.99 (978-0-590-87986-6(3)) Scholastic, Inc.

—Understand the Unknown. 2000. (EverWorld Ser.: No. 10). (J). (gr. 4-7). (978-0-606-19557-7(2)); (978-0-606-19917-9(9)) Tandem Library Bks.

EVOLUTION

see also Adaptation (Biology); Anatomy, Comparative; Biology; Creation; Embryology; Human Beings—Effect of Environment on; Human Beings—Origin; Human Skin Color; Natural Selection; Religion and Science; Social Change

Ackroyd, Peter. In the Beginning. 2003. (Voyages Through Time Ser.). (Illus.). 144p. (J). 19.99 (978-0-7894-9836-6(7)) Dorling Kindersley Publishing, Inc.

Adamson, Heather. Charles Darwin & the Theory of Evolution. Purcell, Gordon & Milgrom, Al, illus. 2008. (J). (***978-1-4296-0145-0(0)***) Capstone Pr., Inc.

Anderson, Dale. How Do We Know the Nature of Humankind. 2005. (Great Scientific Questions & the Scientists Who Answered Them Ser.). (Illus.). 112p. (J). (gr. 7-12). lib. bdg. 26.50 (978-1-4042-0077-7(0)) Rosen Publishing Group, Inc., The.

Bailey, Jacqui. The Stick & Stone Age, 4 vols. Lilly, Matthew, illus. 2001. (Cartoon History of the Earth Ser.). 32p. (J). (gr. 4-6). (978-1-55337-083-3(X)); Vol. 4. (978-1-55337-074-1(0)) Kids Can Pr., Ltd.

Barron's Educational Editorial Staff. Searching for Human Origins. 1998. (Megascope Ser.). (Illus.). 64p. (J). (gr. 3-7). 6.95 (978-0-7641-5092-0(8)) Barron's Educational Series, Inc.

Biological Evolution: An Anthology of Current Thought. 2005. (Contemporary Discourse in the Field of Biology Ser.). (Illus.). 187p. (J). (ps-7). lib. bdg. 30.60 (978-1-4042-0403-4(2)) Rosen Publishing Group, Inc., The.

Bradley, James V. How Species Change. 2006. (Nature Walk Ser.). (Illus.). 80p. (J). 28.00 (978-0-7910-9118-0(X) , Chelsea Hse.) Facts On File, Inc.

Crewe, Sabrina & Uschan, Michael V. The Scopes "Monkey" Trial. 2005. (Events That Shaped America Ser.). (Illus.). 32p. (J). lib. bdg. 24.67 (978-0-8368-3415-4(1)) Stevens, Gareth Inc.

Diagram Group, contrib. by. First Life. 2004. (Life on Earth Ser.). (Illus.). 112p. (J). (gr. 4-9). 35.00 (978-0-8160-5046-8(5)) Facts On File, Inc.

—On the Land. 2004. (Life on Earth Ser.). (Illus.). 112p. (J). (gr. 4-9). 35.00 (978-0-8160-5047-5(3)) Facts On File, Inc.

DK Publishing. Prehistoric Life. 2008. (DK Eyewitness Bks.). 48p. (J). (gr. 2-8). pap. 9.99 (***978-0-7566-3784-2(8)***) Dorling Kindersley Publishing, Inc.

Ecology & Evolution Complete Materials Package W/Teacher's Guide. 2001. (Illus.). (YA). ring bd. (978-1-887725-40-8(7)) Lab-Aids, Inc.

Ecology & Evolution Complete Materials Package W/Teacher's Guide & Student Books. 2001. (Illus.). (YA). ring bd. (978-1-887725-57-6(1)) Lab-Aids, Inc.

Fitzgerald, Stephanie. The Scopes Trial: The Battle over Teaching Evolution. 2006. 96p. (978-0-7565-2018-2(5)) Compass Point Bks.

Fleisher, Paul. Evolution. 2006. (Great Ideas of Science Ser.). (Illus.). 80p. (J). (gr. 3-7). 27.93 (978-0-8225-2134-1(2) , Twenty-First Century Bks.) Lerner Publishing Group.

Gallant, Roy A. The Origins of Life. 2000. (Story of Science Ser.). (Illus.). 80p. (J). (gr. 5 up). lib. bdg. 29.93 (978-0-7614-1151-2(8) , Benchmark Bks.) Cavendish, Marshall Corp.

Gamlin, Linda. Evolution. 2000. (Eyewitness Bks.). (Illus.). 64p. (J). (gr. 4-7). 15.99 (978-0-7894-5579-6(X)) Dorling Kindersley Publishing, Inc.

Gamlin, Linda & Dorling Kindersley Publishing Staff. Evolution. 2000. (Eyewitness Bks.). (Illus.). 64p. (J). (gr. 4-7). lib. bdg. 19.99 (978-0-7894-6719-5(4)) Dorling Kindersley Publishing, Inc.

Gardner, Robert. Genetics & Evolution Science Fair Projects: Using Skeletons, Cereal, Earthworms, & More. 2005. (Biology! Best Science Projects Ser.). (Illus.). 128p. (J). (gr. 6-13). lib. bdg. 26.60 (978-0-7660-1175-5(5)) Enslow Pubs., Inc.

—Human Evolution. 1999. (Venture Bks.). (Illus.). 144p. (YA). (gr. 8-12). 21.00 (978-0-531-11528-2(3) , Watts, Franklin) Scholastic Library Publishing.

Gareth Stevens Publishing Staff, contrib. by. Evolution. 2002. (Discovery Channel School Science Ser.). (Illus.). 32p. (J). (gr. 5 up). lib. bdg. 24.67 (978-0-8368-3211-2(6)) Stevens, Gareth Inc.

Graves, Renee. The Scopes Trial. 2007. (Cornerstones of Freedomtrade;, Second Ser.). 48p. (J). pap. 5.95 (***978-0-531-18769-2(1)*** , Children's Pr.) Scholastic Library Publishing.

Green, Jen. Evolution. 2004. (Routes of Science Ser.). (Illus.). 40p. (J). pap. 11.20 (978-1-4103-0302-8(0)); (gr. 4-7). 24.95 (978-1-4103-0303-5(9)) Thomson Gale. (Blackbirch Pr., Inc.).

Hurtak, J. J. Beyond Darwinism. 1999. 37p. (YA). 5.00 (978-1-892139-06-1(5)) Academy for Future Science.

Hynes, Margaret. The Best Book of Early People. White, Mike, illus. 2003. (Best Book of... Ser.). 32p. (J). (gr. k-3). tchr. ed. 12.95 (978-0-7534-5577-7(3) , Kingfisher) Houghton Mifflin Co. Trade & Reference Div.

Jackson, Ellen B. The Tree of Life: The Wonders of Evolution. Winter, Judeanne, illus. 2004. 41p. pap. 12.00 (978-1-59102-240-4(1) , Pyr Bks.) Prometheus Bks., Pubs.

Jackson, Jerry. How Can an Animal Turn into a Man? 1998. (Illus.). 24p. (J). (gr. 4-8). pap. 7.00 (978-0-8059-4174-6(6)) Dorrance Publishing Co., Inc.

Jenkins, Steve. Life on Earth: The Story of Evolution. 2002. (Illus.). 40p. (J). (gr. 3-5). tchr. ed. 16.00 (978-0-618-16476-9(6)) Houghton Mifflin Co. Trade & Reference Div.

Johnson, Anne Janette. The Scopes "Monkey Trial" 2006. (Defining Moments Ser.). (Illus.). 246p. (YA). (gr. 9 up). lib. bdg. 49.00 (978-0-7808-0955-0(6)) Omnigraphics, Inc.

Johnson, Kevin W. What's with the Mutant in the Microscope? 1999. (Illus.). 144p. (J). (gr. 7-12). pap. 7.99 (978-0-7642-2187-3(6)) Bethany Hse. Pubs.

Lyons, Eric & Butt, Kyle. Truth Be Told: Exposing the Myth of Evolution. 2006. (Illus.). 179p. (978-0-932859-84-6(4)) Apologetics Pr., Inc.

McCutcheon, Marc. The Beast in You! Activities & Questions to Explore Evolution. Kline, Michael P., illus. 1999. (Kaleidoscope Kids Bks.). 96p. (YA). (gr. 2-8). pap. 10.95 (978-1-885593-36-8(8) , Williamson Bks.) Ideals Pubns.

McNulty, Faith. How Whales Walked into the Sea. Lewin, Ted, illus. 1999. (J). pap. (978-0-590-89831-7(0)) Scholastic, Inc.

Myers, Jack. How Dogs Came from Wolves: And Other Explorations of Science in Action. Rice, John, illus. 2004. 64p. (YA). (gr. 4-6). 17.95 (978-1-56397-411-3(8)) Boyds Mills Pr.

Naff, Clay Farris. Evolution. 2005. (Exploring Science & Medical Discoveries Ser.). (Illus.). 222p. (YA). (gr. 7 up). lib. bdg. 34.95 (978-0-7377-2823-1(X) , Greenhaven Pr., Inc.) Thomson Gale.

O'Donnell, Kerri. Birds: Modern-Day Dinosaurs. 2002. (Reading Room Collection). (Illus.). 24p. (J). pap. 4.40 (978-0-8239-8170-0(3)); lib. bdg. 18.75 (978-0-8239-3733-2(X)) Rosen Publishing Group, Inc., The.

Patkau, Karen. Creatures Yesterday & Today. 2008. (Illus.). 32p. 18.95 (***978-0-88776-833-0(4)***) Tundra Bks., Inc./ Livres Toundra, Inc. CAN. *Dist:* Random Hse. of Canada, Ltd.

Peters, Lisa Westberg. Our Family Tree: An Evolution Story. Stringer, Lauren, illus. 2003. 48p. (J). 17.00 (978-0-15-201772-9(0)) Harcourt Children's Bks.

PH Inc. Staff. PH Science Evolution. 2nd ed. (J). pap., act. bk. ed. (978-0-13-225541-7(3)) Prentice Hall (Schl. Div.).

Pye, Claire. The Wild World of the Future. 2003. (Illus.). 96p. (J). (gr. 5-9). 24.95 (978-1-55297-727-9(7)); pap. 14.95 (978-1-55297-725-5(0)) Firefly Bks., Ltd.

Silverstein, Alvin, et al. Evolution. 1998. (Science Concepts Ser.: 8). (Illus.). 64p. (gr. 5-8). lib. bdg. 26.90 (978-0-7613-3003-5(8) , Twenty-First Century Bks.) Lerner Publishing Group.

—Symbiosis. 1998. (Science Concepts Ser.). (Illus.). 64p. (gr. 5-8). lib. bdg. 26.90 (978-0-7613-3001-1(1) , Twenty-First Century Bks.) Lerner Publishing Group.

Snedden, Robert. The Diversity of Life: From Single Cells to Multicellular Organizations. 2003. (Cells & Life Ser.). (Illus.). 48p. (YA). (gr. 6-8). pap. 8.50 (978-1-58810-935-4(6)) Heinemann Library.

Sproule, Anna. Charles Darwin: Visionary Behind the Theory of Evolution. 2002. (Scientists Who Have Changed the World Ser.). (Illus.). 64p. (J). 26.20 (978-1-56711-655-7(8) , Blackbirch Pr., Inc.) Thomson Gale.

Stein, Sara. The Evolution Book. Stein, Sara, illus. 1999. (Illus.). 400p. (YA). (gr. 7-12). pap. 12.95 (978-0-89480-927-9(X) , 927) Workman Publishing Co., Inc.

Stewart, Robin. Darwin's Tortoise: The Amazing Story of Harriet, the World's Oldest Living Creature. Crichton, Anna, illus. 2006. 160p. (J). pap. (978-1-86395-373-3(6) , Black Inc. Agenda) Schwartz Publishing Pty, Ltd.

Suzuki, David. From Naked Ape to Superspecies. abr. ed. 2005. (gr. 9-12). (978-0-660-17795-3(1)) Canadian Broadcasting Corp./Societe Radio-Canada.

Thompson, Bruce. Evolution. 2003. (Fact or Fiction Ser.). (Illus.). (YA). 160p. pap. 23.70 (978-0-7377-1592-7(8)); 192p. lib. bdg. 32.45 (978-0-7377-1591-0(X)) Thomson Gale. (Greenhaven Pr., Inc.).

Tubbs, Joseph. Did Evolution Really Happen? 2001. vi, 56p. (YA). pap. 12.00 (978-0-9711285-0-7(2)) Tubbs, Joseph G.

Uschan, Michael V. The Scopes "Monkey" Trial. 2004. (Landmark Events in American History Ser.). (Illus.). 48p. (J). pap. 11.95 (978-0-8368-5424-4(1)); lib. bdg. 30.00 (978-0-8368-5396-4(2)) Stevens, Gareth Inc. (World Almanac Library).

Whiting, Jim. The Scopes Monkey Trial. 2006. (Monumental Milestones Ser.). 48p. (J). (gr. 6-9). lib. bdg. 29.95 (978-1-58415-468-6(3)) Mitchell Lane Pubs., Inc.

Williams, Brian. Earth Time. 2002. (Illus.). 32p. (J). lib. bdg. 24.25 (978-1-58340-210-8(1)) Smart Apple Media.

EWING, PATRICK ALOYSIUS, 1962-

Armstrong, Robb. Got Game? Smith, Bruce, illus. 1998. (Patrick's Pals Ser.: No. 3). 96p. (J). (gr. 2-7). mass mkt. 3.99 (978-0-06-107069-3(6) , Harper Entertainment) HarperCollins Pubs.

EXCAVATION

Eick, Jean. Diggers. 1998. (Machines at Work Ser.). (Illus.). 24p. (J). (ps-3). 21.36 (978-1-56766-529-1(2)) Child's World, Inc.

Knopf, Susan. Welcome to Merriweather Farm. Walstead, Curt, illus. 2005. 10p. (J). pap. 11.95 (978-0-7624-2342-2(0) , Running Pr. Kids) Running Pr. Bk. Pubs.

Litchfield, Jo & Brooks, Felicity. Diggers. 2004. (Chunky Board Bks.). (Illus.). 10p. (J). 4.95 (978-0-7945-0350-5(0) , Usborne) EDC Publishing.

Running Press Staff & Newberger, Devra. Busy Days in Deerfield Valley. Wakelin, Bob, illus. 2005. 10p. (J). pap. 11.95 (978-0-7624-2343-9(9) , Running Pr.) Running Pr. Bk. Pubs.

Tractors & Diggers. 2003. (Illus.). 32p. 12.98 (978-1-4054-2005-1(7)) Parragon, Inc.

Whitehouse, Patricia. Dig & Dump. (Illus.). 24p. 2007. (J). (978-1-60044-207-0(2)); 2005. pap. 27.00 (***978-1-59515-564-1(3)***) Rourke Publishing, LLC.

—What Can Dig? 2003. (Heinemann Read & Learn Ser.). (Illus.). 24p. (J). pap. 5.25 (978-1-4034-4376-2(9)) Heinemann Library.

EXCAVATION—FICTION

Dorling Kindersley Publishing Staff. Digger. 2004. (Machines at Work Ser.). (Illus.). 32p. (J). 8.99 (978-0-7566-0216-1(5)) Dorling Kindersley Publishing, Inc.

EXCAVATIONS (ARCHAEOLOGY)

see also Mounds and Mound Builders

Alexander, Suzanna M., et al. Prehistoric People of Moccasin Bend, Chattanooga, Tennessee: An Educational Coloring Book. 2006. (J). (***978-0-9779189-3-5(9)***) Waldenhouse Pub., Inc.

Aronovsky, Ilona. The Indus Valley. 2004. (Excavating the Past Ser.). (J). pap. 8.50 (978-1-4034-5460-7(4)); lib. bdg. 27.07 (978-1-4034-4840-8(X)) Heinemann Library.

Behr, Alexandra. Lost in Time. 2005. (Real Deal Ser.). (Illus.). 32p. (J). 18.50 (978-0-7910-8771-8(9) , Chelsea Hse.) Facts On File, Inc.

Burnham, Brad. Qumran Caves: Hiding Place for the Dea Sea Scrolls. 2003. (Famous Caves of the World Ser.). (Illus.). 24p. (J). lib. bdg. 18.75 (978-0-8239-6259-4(8) , PowerKids Pr.) Rosen Publishing Group, Inc., The.

Cressey, Pamela J. & Anderson, Margaret Jean. Alexandria, Virginia. 2006. (Digging for the Past Ser.). (Illus.). 48p. (YA). 22.95 (978-0-19-517334-5(1)) Oxford Univ. Pr., Inc.

Deem, James M. Bodies from the Ash: Life & Death in Ancient Pompeii. 2005. (Illus.). 64p. (J). (gr. 4-6). 17.00 (978-0-618-47308-3(4)) Houghton Mifflin Co. Trade & Reference Div.

Goodman, Susan E. Digging into Southwest Archaeology. 2000. (Ultimate Field Trip Ser.: Vol. 2). (YA). 13.79 (978-0-606-19252-1(2)) Tandem Library Bks.

Hatt, Christine. The Viking World. 2004. (Excavating the Past Ser.). (J). pap. 8.50 (978-1-4034-5461-4(2)); lib. bdg. 27.07 (978-1-4034-4841-5(8)) Heinemann Library.

Holliday, Diane Young & Malone, Bobbie. Digging & Discovery: Wisconsin Archaeology. 2nd ed. 2006. (New Badger History Ser.). (Illus.). 120p. pap. 15.95 (978-0-87020-376-3(2)) Wisconsin Historical Society.

Inserra, Rose. Archaeologists. 2004. (J). lib. bdg. 27.10 (978-1-58340-544-4(5)) Smart Apple Media.

Kaplan, Sarah Pitt. Pompeii: City of Ashes. 2005. (Illus.). 48p. (J). (ps-7). 24.00 (978-0-516-25122-6(8)); (YA). (gr. 7-12). pap. 6.95 (978-0-516-25091-5(4)) Scholastic Library Publishing. (Children's Pr.).

Kops, Deborah. Palenque. 2008. (J). lib. bdg. (*978-0-8225-7504-7(3)) Twenty First Century Bks.

Lewin, Ted. The Search for the Lost City: The Discovery of Machu Picchu. Lewin, Ted, illus. 2003. (Illus.). 48p. (J). (gr. 3-6). 17.99 (978-0-399-23302-9(4) , Philomel) Penguin Group (USA) Inc.

Lindeen, Mary. Ashes to Ashes: Uncovering Pompeii. 2007. (Shockwave: People & Communities Ser.). (Illus.). 36p. (J). (gr. 4-6). lib. bdg. 25.00 (*978-0-531-17745-7(9) , Children's Pr.) Scholastic Library Publishing.

MacDonald, Fiona. Mysterious Mummies. 2003. (History Hunters Ser.). (Illus.). 32p. (J). (gr. 3 up). lib. bdg. 24.67 (978-0-8368-3742-1(8)) Stevens, Gareth Inc.

Morris, Neil. Lost Cities. 2007. (J). (*978-1-59920-108-5(9)) Smart Apple Media.

Orna-Ornstein, John. Archaeology: Discovering the Past. 2002. (Illus.). 48p. (YA). 21.95 (978-0-19-521909-8(0)) Oxford Univ. Pr., Inc.

Patent, Dorothy Hinshaw. Secrets of the Ice Man. 1999. (Frozen in Time Ser.). (Illus.). 72p. (J). (gr. 5-9). lib. bdg. 28.50 (978-0-7614-0782-9(0) , Benchmark Bks.) Cavendish, Marshall Corp.

Pauketat, Timothy R. & Bernard, Nancy Stone. Cahokia Mounds. 2004. (Digging for the Past Ser.). (Illus.). 48p. (YA). 22.95 (978-0-19-515810-6(5)) Oxford Univ. Pr., Inc.

Rinaldo, Denise. Cities of the Dead. 2007. (24/7 - Science Behind the Scenes Ser.). 64p. (J). (gr. 8-12). 26.00 (978-0-531-12079-8(1) , Watts, Franklin) Scholastic Library Publishing.

Rinaldo, Denise. Cities of the Dead: Finding Lost Civilizations. 2008. (24/7: Science Behind the Scenes: Mystery Files Ser.). 64p. (J). pap. 7.95 (*978-0-531-18739-5(X) , Watts, Franklin) Scholastic Library Publishing.

Rosebrough, Amy & Malone, Bobbie. Water Panthers, Bears, & Thunderbirds: Exploring the Effigy Mounds of Wisconsin. 2003. (New Badger History Ser.). (Illus.). 32p. (J). pap. 9.95 (978-0-87020-357-2(6)) Wisconsin Historical Society.

Schlitz, Laura Amy. The Hero Schliemann: The Dreamer Who Dug up Troy. Byrd, Robert, illus. 2006. 80p. (J). (gr. 4-8). 17.99 (978-0-7636-2283-1(4)) Candlewick Pr.

Shone, Rob. Ancient Treasures. Spender, Nick, illus. 2007. (Graphic Discoveries Ser.). (J). 48p. (gr. 3-7). lib. bdg. (*978-1-4042-1089-9(X)); (*978-1-4042-9594-0(1)); pap. (*978-1-4042-9593-3(3)) Rosen Publishing Group, Inc., The.

Shuter, Jane. Ancient China. 2004. (Excavating the Past Ser.). (Illus.). 48p. (J). (gr. 4-6). lib. bdg. 31.43 (978-1-4034-5995-4(9)) Heinemann Library.

—Life in a Roman Fort. 2004. (Picture the Past Ser.). (Illus.). 32p. (J). 24.22 (978-1-4034-5829-2(4)); pap. (978-1-4034-5837-7(5)) Heinemann Library.

Smith, K. C. Shipwrecks of the Explorers. 2000. (Watts Library). (Illus.). 64p. (J). (gr. 5-7). 25.50 (978-0-531-20378-1(6) , Watts, Franklin) Scholastic Library Publishing.

—Shipwrecks of the Explorers. 2000. (gr. 3-6). lib. bdg. 17.60 (978-0-613-36667-0(0)) Tandem Library Bks.

Sonneborn, Liz. Pompeii. 2008. (J). lib. bdg. (*978-0-8225-7505-4(1)) Twenty First Century Bks.

Spilsbury, Louise & Spilsbury, Richard. Scientists at Work: History Detectives: Archaeologists Hardback. 2007. (Illus.). 32p. (J). (*978-0-431-14924-0(0)) Heinemann Library.

—Scientists at Work: History Detectives: Archaeologists Paperback. 2007. (Illus.). 32p. (J). (*978-0-431-14931-8(3)) Heinemann Library.

Woods, Michael & Woods, Mary B. The Tomb of King Tutankhamun. 2008. (J). lib. bdg. (*978-0-8225-7506-1(X)) Twenty First Century Bks.

EXCAVATIONS (ARCHAEOLOGY)—FICTION

Dahl, Michael. Worm Tunnel. 1999. (Illus.). (J). (978-0-606-21798-9(3)) Tandem Library Bks.

Herr, Melody. Summer of Discovery. 2006. 111p. (J). pap. 10.95 (978-0-8032-2437-7(0)); 112p. pap. 10.95 (978-0-8032-7362-7(2) , A Bison Original) Univ. of Nebraska Pr.

Jones, Allan Frewin. The Wreckers. 2003. 163p. (J). mass mkt. (978-0-330-36810-0(9) , Pan) Pan Macmillan.

Moss, Marissa. The All-New Amelia. Moss, Marissa, illus. 2007. (Amelia's Notebooks). (Illus.). 40p. (J). (gr. 2-5). 9.99 (978-1-4169-0908-8(7) , Simon & Schuster/Paula Wiseman Bks.) Simon & Schuster Children's Publishing.

—The All-New Amelia. 1999. (Amelia's Notebooks). (J). (gr. 3-5). 12.75 (978-0-606-19866-0(0)) Tandem Library Bks.

Priestley, Chris. Redwulf's Curse: A Tom Marlowe Adventure. 2005. (Illus.). 176p. (YA). (gr. 6-10). 16.99 (978-0-385-60695-0(8) , Doubleday) Transworld Publishers Ltd. GBR. *Dist:* Trafalgar Square Publishing.

Rees, Celia. Trap in Time. 2002. (Celia Rees Supernatural Trilogy: Bk. 2). 229p. (J). (gr. 3-6). pap. 7.99 (978-0-340-81801-5(8) , Hodder & Stoughton) Hodder General Publishing Division GBR. *Dist:* Trafalgar Square Publishing.

Travis, Alva. Secret of the Hidden Chamber. 2006. pap. 12.95 (978-1-4241-2071-0(3)) PublishAmerica, Inc.

EXECUTIONS

see Capital Punishment

EXECUTIVE POWER

Quiri, Patricia Ryon. The Presidency. 1998. (True Bks.). (Illus.). 48p. (J). (gr. 3-5). 25.00 (978-0-516-20674-5(5) , Children's Pr.) Scholastic Library Publishing.

EXECUTIVES

Aller, Susan Bivin. Madam C. J. Walker. 2007. (History Maker Biographies Ser.). (J). 26.60 (978-0-8225-6582-6(X) , Lerner Pubns.) Lerner Publishing Group.

Krohn, Katherine E. Madam C.J. Walker & New Cosmetics. Dominguez, Richard, illus. 2007. (Graphic Library). 32p. (*978-0-7368-9647-4(3)) Capstone Pr., Inc.

Stille, Darlene R. Madam C.J. Walker: Entrepreneur & Millionaire. 2006. (Signature Lives Ser.). (Illus.). 112p. (J). (*978-0-7565-1883-7(0) , 1265883) Compass Point Bks.

Vitale, Ann E. Manager. 2002. (Careers with Character Ser.). (Illus.). 96p. (J). (gr. 7 up). (978-1-59084-317-8(7)) Mason Crest Pubs.

Woog, Adam. Pierre M. Omidyar: Creator of Ebay. 2007. (Innovators Ser.). (Illus.). 64p. (J). (gr. 4-8). 24.95 (*978-0-7377-3864-3(2) , Kidhaven) Thomson Gale.

EXERCISE

see also Gymnastics; Physical Education and Training; Physical Fitness

also names of special kinds of exercises, e.g. Rowing, etc.

Aliotti, Johnny. Johnny's Simple Dumbbell Workout. 2004. spiral bd. 14.95 (978-0-9740600-1-9(1)); (Illus.). 102p. per. 13.95 (978-0-9740600-0-2(3)) ProTips(TM) Media.

American Girl Editorial Staff. Real Fitness: Games to Get Girls Going! Yoshizumi, Carol, illus. 2006. 96p. (J). pap. 9.95 (978-1-59369-147-9(5) , American Girl) American Girl Publishing, Inc.

Bassett, Carol. Walk Like a Bear, Stand Like a Tree, Run Like the Wind. 2004. 40p. (978-0-9740485-0-5(X)) Nubod Concept, Inc.

Benchmark Education Staff, compiled by. Nutrition & Exercise. 2006. spiral bd. 85.00 (*978-1-4108-7036-0(7)) Benchmark Education Co.

Brown, Marc. Arthur & the Seventh-Inning Stretcher. Brown, Marc, illus. 2nd ed. 2001. (Arthur Good Sports Ser.: Bk. 2). (Illus.). 64p. (J). (gr. 2-4). 13.95 (978-0-316-11861-3(3)) Little, Brown Bks. for Young Readers.

Bundey, Nikki. In the Gym. Gray, Virginia, illus. 1999. (First Sports Science Ser.). 32p. (J). (gr. 2-4). lib. bdg. 21.27 (978-1-57505-358-5(6) , Carolrhoda Bks.) Lerner Publishing Group.

Burstein, John. Exercising. 2006. (Illus.). 32p. (J). lib. bdg. (*978-0-8368-7741-0(1)) Stevens, Gareth Inc.

Carle, Eric. From Head to Toe. 1999. (Illus.). 32p. (J). (gr. k-3). pap. 6.99 (978-0-06-443596-3(2) , Harper Trophy) HarperCollins Pubs.

—From Head to Toe. Carle, Eric, illus. 1999. (Illus.). 26p. (J). (ps-k). bds. 7.99 (978-0-694-01301-2(3) , Harper Festival) HarperCollins Pubs.

—From Head to Toe. 1999. lib. bdg. 15.30 (978-0-613-22852-7(9)) Tandem Library Bks.

—From Head to Toe (Spanish Edition) De la cabeza a los Pies. Carle, Eric, illus. 2007. (SPA.). 32p. (J). pap. 6.99 (978-0-06-051313-9(6) , Rayo) HarperCollins Pubs.

Coleman, Lori & Savage, Jeff. Beginning Strength Training. Clarke, Jimmy, illus. 1998. (Beginning Sports Ser.). 80p. (gr. 3-5). lib. bdg. 22.60 (978-0-8225-3511-9(4)) Lerner Publishing Group.

CosmoGIRL! Editors. Total Body Workout: Fun Moves to Look & Feel Your Best. 2008. (CosmoGirl! Ser.). (Illus.). 128p. (J). pap. 9.95 (*978-1-58816-663-0(5)) Hearst Bks.

Dalgleish, Sharon. Exercise & Rest. 2006. (Illus.). 32p. (J). (978-1-58340-755-4(3)) Smart Apple Media.

de Brunhoff, Laurent. Babar's Yoga for Elephants. (Illus.). 48p. (J). (ps-3). 2006. 9.95 (978-0-8109-3076-6(5)); 2002. 16.95 (978-0-8109-1021-8(7)) Abrams, Harry N., Inc.

De La Hoya, Oscar. Super Oscar. Montejo, Andrea, tr. Kopelke, Lisa, illus. 2006. (ENG & SPA.). 32p. (J). (ps-3). 15.95 (978-1-4169-0611-7(8)) Simon & Schuster Children's Publishing.

Evans, Lynette. Move Your Bones. 2007. (Shockwave: the Human Experience Ser.). 36p. (J). (gr. 3-5). pap. 6.95 (*978-0-531-18795-1(0)); (Illus.). (gr. 4-6). lib. bdg. 25.00 (*978-0-531-17761-7(0)) Scholastic Library Publishing. (Children's Pr.).

Feeney, Kathy. Get Moving: Tips on Exercise. 2001. (Your Health Ser.). (Illus.). 24p. (J). (gr. 1-2). lib. bdg. 18.60 (978-0-7368-0973-3(2) , Bridgestone Bks.) Capstone Pr., Inc.

Fuerst, Jeffrey B. The Kids' Baseball Workout: How to Get in Shape & Improve Your Game. Green, Anne Canevari, illus. 2002. 80p. (gr. 4 up). lib. bdg. 24.90 (978-0-7613-2307-5(4) , Millbrook Pr.) Lerner Publishing Group.

Gaff, Jackie. Why Must I... Exercise? Fairclough, Chris, photos by. 2005. (Illus.). 32p. (J). (gr. 2-5). lib. bdg. (978-1-84234-348-7(3) , Cherrytree Books) Evans Publishing Group.

Gedatus, Gus. Exercise for Weight Management. 2000. (Nutrition & Fitness Ser.). (Illus.). 64p. (J). (gr. 4-6). lib. bdg. 23.93 (978-0-7368-0706-7(3) , LifeMatters Bks.) Capstone Pr., Inc.

Get Moving. (Your Health Ser.). 24p. (J). 6.95 (978-0-7368-4449-9(X)) Capstone Pr., Inc.

Goodger, Beverley. Exercise. 2005. (It's Your Health Ser.). (Illus.). 45p. (J). (gr. 6-9). lib. bdg. 29.95 (978-1-58340-593-2(3)) Smart Apple Media.

Goodrow, Carol. Happy Feet, Healthy Food: Your Child's First Journal of Exercise & Healthy Eating. Goodrow, Carol, illus. 2004. (Illus.). 112p. 14.00 (978-1-891369-46-9(6)) Breakaway Bks.

Gordon, Sharon. Exercise. 2003. (Rookie Read-About Health Ser.). (Illus.). 32p. (J). (gr. k-2). pap. 5.95 (978-0-516-26950-4(X) , Children's Pr.) Scholastic Library Publishing.

—Exercise. 2002. (gr. k-3). lib. bdg. 14.10 (978-0-613-59471-4(1)) Tandem Library Bks.

Gray, Shirley W. Exercising for Good Health. 2003. (Living Well). (Illus.). 32p. (J). (gr. 2-6). 27.07 (978-1-59296-081-1(2)) Child's World, Inc.

Green, Emily K. Keeping Fit. 2006. (Blastoff! Readers Ser.). (Illus.). 24p. (J). lib. bdg. 16.95 (978-1-60014-006-8(8)) Bellwether Media.

Green, Tamara. Exercise Is Fun! 1998. (Good Health Guides). (Illus.). 32p. (J). (gr. 4 up). lib. bdg. 22.60 (978-0-8368-2180-2(7)) Stevens, Gareth Inc.

Hallinan, P. K. Let's Be Fit! 2007. (Illus.). 32p. (J). (ps-2). 8.99 (*978-0-8249-5528-1(5) , Candy Cane Pr.) Ideals Pubns.

Hughes, Mary. Body Building. 2000. (Composite Guides Ser.). (Illus.). 64p. (J). (gr. 8-12). 12.95 (978-0-7910-5861-9(1) , Chelsea Hse.) Facts On File, Inc.

Johnson, Marlys. Understanding Exercise Addiction. 2005. (Teen Eating Disorder Prevention Book Ser.). (Illus.). 192p. (YA). (gr. 7-12). lib. bdg. 25.25 (978-0-8239-2990-0(6) , E2EXAD) Rosen Publishing Group, Inc., The.

Kalman, Bobbie. Active Kids. 2003. (gr. 3-6). lib. bdg. 17.60 (978-0-613-59126-3(7)) Tandem Library Bks.

Keeping Fit New Food Guide Pyramid. 2006. (Illus.). 24p. (J). (gr. k-2). 18.50 (*978-0-531-17853-9(6)) Scholastic Library Publishing.

Lark, Liz. Yoga for Kids. Park, Clare, photos by. 2005. (Illus.). 127p. (J). reprint ed. pap. 20.00 (978-0-7567-9410-1(2)) DIANE Publishing Co.

Lee, Ilchi. Meridian Exercise for Self-Healing Bk. 1: Classified by Common Symptoms, 2 vols. 2003. (Dahnhak, the Way to Perfect Health Ser.: Vol. 1). (Illus.). 152p. pap. 17.95 (978-0-9720282-7-1(7)) Healing Society, Inc.

—Meridian Exercise for Self-Healing Book 2: Classified by Common Symptoms, 2 vols., Vol. 2. 2003. (Dahnhak, the Way to Perfect Health Ser.: 2). (Illus.). 196p. pap. 17.95 (978-0-9720282-8-8(5)) Healing Society, Inc.

Let's Get Moving, 4 bks., Set 1. 2004. Tr. of Diviertete en Movimiento. (Illus.). (J). 74.24 (978-1-4109-0870-4(4)); pap. 19.80 (978-1-4109-0875-9(5)) Raintree.

Libal, Autumn. The Importance of Physical Activity & Exercise: The Fitness Factor. 2005. (Obesity Ser.). (Illus.). 104p. (J). (ps-7). lib. bdg. 23.95 (978-1-59084-945-3(0)) Mason Crest Pubs.

Llewellyn, Claire. Estoy Sano? Aprender Sobre Alimentacion y Actividad Fisica. Gordon, Mike, illus. (SPA.). (J). (gr. k-2). pap. (978-950-24-0945-0(0)) Albatros ARG. *Dist:* Lectorum Pubns., Inc.

Llewelyn, Clair. Exercise. 2006. (QEB Looking After Me Ser.). (Illus.). 24p. (J). lib. bdg. 19.95 (978-1-59566-192-0(1)) QEB Publishing Inc.

—Get Active! 2006. (QEB Looking After Me Ser.). (Illus.). 24p. (J). lib. bdg. 16.95 (978-1-59566-193-7(X)) QEB Publishing Inc.

Lynch, Emma. Safari. 2004. (Raintree Sprouts Ser.). (Illus.). 24p. (J). pap. 5.50 (978-1-4109-0872-8(0)); lib. bdg. 18.56 (978-1-4109-0867-4(4)) Raintree.

Mason, Paul. Training for the Top: Nutrition & Exercise. 2005. (Illus.). 32p. (J). (978-1-4109-1964-9(1)); lib. bdg. (978-1-4109-1933-5(1)) Steck-Vaughn.

Minden, Cecilia. Exercise by the Numbers. 2008. (J). lib. bdg. 25.26 (*978-1-60279-010-0(8)) Cherry Lake Publishing.

Nagler, Michelle H. Get Fit! Eat Right! Be Active! Girls Guide to Health & Fitness. 2001. (WNBA Ser.). (Illus.). 64p. (gr. 3-9). pap. 5.99 (978-0-439-24113-7(8)) Scholastic, Inc.

Nelson, Robin. Exercising. 2006. (Pull Ahead Bks.). (Illus.). 32p. (J). 22.60 (978-0-8225-3489-1(4) , Lerner Pubns.) Lerner Publishing Group.

Rockwell, Lizzy. The Busy Body Book. Rockwell, Lizzy, illus. 2004. (Illus.). 40p. (J). (gr. k-4). lib. bdg. 17.99 (978-0-375-92203-9(2) , Crown Books For Young Readers) Random Hse. Children's Bks.

—The Busy Body Book: A Kid's Guide to Fitness. Rockwell, Lizzy, illus. 2004. (Illus.). 40p. (J). (gr. k-4). 15.95 (978-0-375-82203-2(8) , Crown Books For Young Readers) Random Hse. Children's Bks.

Royston, Angela. Get Some Exercise! 2003. (Illus.). 32p. (J). pap. 6.95 (978-1-4034-4449-3(8)); lib. bdg. 22.79 (978-1-4034-4440-0(4)) Heinemann Library.

—A Healthy Body. 1999. (Illus.). 32p. (J). (gr. k-2). lib. bdg. 21.36 (978-1-57572-983-1(0)) Heinemann Library.

—Why Do We Need to Be Active? 2005. (Heinemann Read & Learn Ser.). (Illus.). 24p. (J). (978-1-4034-7609-8(8)); pap. (978-1-4034-7614-2(4)) Heinemann Library.

Sadgrove, Judy. Exercise. 1999. (Health & Fitness Ser.). (Illus.). 48p. (J). (gr. 4-6). lib. bdg. 27.12 (978-0-7398-1347-8(1)) Raintree.

Safari 6-Pack. 2004. (Illus.). (J). pap. 29.70 (978-1-4109-0877-3(1)) Raintree.

Salzmann, Mary Elizabeth. Being Active. 2004. (Healthy Habits Ser.). (Illus.). 23p. (J). (ps-3). lib. bdg. 19.93 (978-1-59197-550-2(6)) ABDO Publishing Co.

Savage, Jeff. Fundamentals Strength Training. Clarke, Jimmy, photos by. 1998. (Fundamental Sports Ser.). (Illus.). 80p. (gr. 5-9). lib. bdg. 22.60 (978-0-8225-3461-7(4)) Lerner Publishing Group.

Schuh, Mari C. Being Active. 2006. (Illus.). 24p. (J). 19.93 (978-0-7368-5368-2(5) , Pebble Bks.) Capstone Pr., Inc.

Sheen, Barbara. Keeping Fit. 2007. (J). pap. (*978-1-4034-9702-4(8)); (Illus.). 32p. (gr. 4-7). lib. bdg. (*978-1-4034-9695-9(1)) Heinemann Library.

Smithyman, Kathryn & Kalman, Bobbie. Active Kids: Fun Ways to Be Active. 2003. (Kid Power Ser.). (Illus.). 32p. (J). (gr. 3). (978-0-7787-1253-4(2)); pap. (978-0-7787-1275-6(3)) Crabtree Publishing Co.

Spilsbury, Louise. Why Should I Get off the Couch? And Other Questions about Health & Exercise. 2003. (Body Matters Ser.). (Illus.). 32p. (J). lib. bdg. 16.95 (978-1-4034-4681-7(4)) Heinemann Library.

Steck-Vaughn Staff. Sports/Exercise: Rabbit Turtle. 1998. (Illus.). (J). pap. (978-0-8172-8647-7(0)) Steck-Vaughn.

Stewart, Georgiana. Good Morning Exercises for Kids, 2001. (J). pap. 11.95 incl. audio (978-0-937124-22-2(2) , KIM 9098C) Kimbo Educational.

Strauss, Greg. Eleven Minute Workout: Total Fitness in 11 Minutes a Day. 2003. (Illus.). 124p. per. 11.00 (978-0-9744568-0-5(2) , EMW:0974456802) Motion Fitness LLC.

Vedral, Joyce L. Toning for Teens: The 20-Minute Workout That Makes You Look Good & Feel Great! 2002. (Illus.). 192p. pap. 15.95 (978-0-446-67815-5(5)) Grand Central Publishing.

Vogel, Elizabeth. Let's Exercise. 2001. (PowerKids Readers Ser.). (Illus.). 24p. (J). (gr. 1). lib. bdg. 16.00 (978-0-8239-5687-6(3) , PKEXER, PowerKids Pr.) Rosen Publishing Group, Inc., The.

Winchester, Bob. Excercise & Eating Right Are Okay, I Guess, 8 vols., Vol. 2. 2002. (Illus.). (J). per. (978-1-932062-09-0(2)) Hability Solution Services, Inc.

Windsor, Jo. Exercise Time, 6 Packs. Taylor, Clive, illus. (Sails Literacy Ser.). 16p. (gr. 2-3). 27.00 (978-0-7578-0706-0(2)) Rigby Education.

Winkler, Peter. Keeping Fit. 2003. (Human Body Ser.). (Illus.). 32p. (J). pap. (978-0-7922-8863-3(7)) National Geographic Society.

EXHIBITIONS

Anonymous. The World's Fair or Children's Prize Gif. 2006. 77.99 (*978-1-4280-1986-7(3)) IndyPublish.com.

Jackson, Robert. Meet Me in St. Louis: A Trip to the 1904 World's Fair. 2004. (Illus.). 144p. (J). (gr. 3 up). 17.99 (978-0-06-009267-2(X)) HarperCollins Pubs.

Radtke, Becky. At the State Fair Coloring Book. 2004. (Dover Coloring Bks.). (Illus.). 32p. (J). pap. 2.95 (978-0-486-43339-4(0)) Dover Pubns., Inc.

Settembrini, Luigi, ed. The Ideal City. 2003. (Illus.). 516p. (YA). (gr. 13 up). pap. 42.95 (978-88-8158-437-6(9)) Charta ITA. *Dist:* D.A.P./Distributed Art Pubs.

Then, Raya. Pan-American Exposition: Sights & Sounds. 2001. (Illus.). 36p. 19.95 (978-0-9671480-7-6(3)) Canisius College Pr.

EXILES

see Refugees

EXORCISM

see Witchcraft

EXPEDITIONS, ANTARCTIC AND ARCTIC

see Antarctica; Arctic Regions

EXPEDITIONS, SCIENTIFIC

see Scientific Expeditions

EXPERIMENTS, SCIENTIFIC

see Science—Experiments

EXPLORATION, SUBMARINE

see Underwater Exploration

EXPLORATION AND DISCOVERY

see Discoveries in Geography

EXPLORATION, UNDERWATER

see Underwater Exploration

EXPLORERS

see also America—Discovery and Exploration; Discoveries in Geography; Travelers; Voyages and Travels

also names of countries with the subdivision Description and Travel and Exploring Expeditions, e.g. United States—Description and Travel; United States—Exploring Expeditions, etc.; and names of individual explorers

Aaseng, Nathan. You Are the Explorer. 2000. (Great Decisions Ser.). (Illus.). 160p. (gr. 5 up). lib. bdg. 19.95 (978-1-881508-55-7(2)) Oliver Pr., Inc.

Abnett, Dan. Christopher Columbus & the Voyage of 1492. Q2A, illus. 2007. (Jr. Graphic Biographies Ser.). 24p. (J). (978-1-4042-2333-2(9)); pap. (978-1-4042-2143-7(3)); (gr. 2-6). lib. bdg. 21.25 (978-1-4042-3390-4(3)) Rosen Publishing Group, Inc., The. (PowerKids Pr.).

Abramson, Jordan. Masterpieces. 2004. (Start Exploring Ser.). (Illus.). 16p. (J). pap. 19.95 (978-0-7624-1850-3(8) , Running Pr. Kids) Running Pr. Bk. Pubs.

Adler, David A. A Picture Book of Lewis & Clark. Himler, Ronald, illus. 2003. 32p. (J). (gr. k-3). tchr. ed. 16.95 (978-0-8234-1735-3(2)) Holiday Hse., Inc.

Aller, Susan Bivin. Christopher Columbus. 2003. (History Maker Bios Ser.). (Illus.). 48p. (J). (gr. 3-5). lib. bdg. 26.60 (978-0-8225-0398-9(0)) Lerner Publishing Group.

Alphin, Elaine Marie. Around the World in 1500. 2001. (Around the World Ser.: Vol. 1). (Illus.). 96p. (J). lib. bdg. 29.93 (978-0-7614-1082-9(1) , Benchmark Bks.) Cavendish, Marshall Corp.

Alter, Judy. Christopher Columbus: Explorer. 2002. (Spirit of America: Our People Ser.). (Illus.). 32p. (J). (gr. 2-6). 27.07 (978-1-56766-161-3(0)) Child's World, Inc.

Anema, Durlynn. Louise Arner Boyd: Arctic Explorer. 2004. (Women Adventurers Ser.). (Illus.). 112p. (gr. 5 up). 21.95 (978-1-883846-42-8(0)) Reynolds, Morgan Inc.

Angelis, Gina De. Hernando Cortes & the Conquest of Mexico. 2007. (Illus.). 63p. (J). 25.00 (*978-1-4223-6717-9(7)) DIANE Publishing Co.

Ansary, Mir Tamim. Columbus Day. 2006. (Illus.). 32p. (J). (*978-1-4034-8883-1(5)) Heinemann Library.

Anthony, Laurence. John Cabot. 2001. (Great Explorers Ser.). (Illus.). 48p. (J). (gr. 5 up). lib. bdg. 30.00 (978-0-8368-5012-3(2) , World Almanac Library) Stevens, Gareth Inc.

Ariganello, Lisa. Henry the Navigator: Prince of Portuguese Exploration. 2006. (In the Footsteps of Explorers Ser.). (Illus.). 32p. (J). (gr. 3-9). (978-0-7787-2433-9(6)); pap. (978-0-7787-2469-8(7)) Crabtree Publishing Co.

Aronson, Marc, et al. The World Made New: Why the Age of Exploration Happened & How It Changed the World. 2007. (National Geographic Timelines Ser.). (Illus.). 64p. (J). (gr. 4-6). 17.95 (978-0-7922-6454-5(1) , National Geographic Children's Bks.) National Geographic Society.

Arruda, Suzanne Middendorf. From Kansas to Cannibals: The Story of Osa Johnson. 2001. (Illus.). 96p. (J). (gr. 6-12). pap. 19.95 (978-1-888105-50-6(X)) Avisson Pr., Inc.

Atkins, Jeannine. How High Can We Climb? The Story of Women Explorers. Petricic, Dusan, illus. 2005. 224p. (J). 17.00 (978-0-374-33503-8(6) , Farrar, Straus & Giroux (BYR)) Farrar, Straus & Giroux.

Bailey, Katharine. Vasco da Gama: Quest for the Spice Trade. 2007. (Illus.). 32p. (J). (gr. 3-9). ***978-0-7787-2421-6(2));** pap. (***978-0-7787-2457-5(3))** Crabtree Publishing Co.

Bailey, Katie. Ferdinand Magellan: Circumnavigating the World. 2005. (In the Footsteps of Explorers Ser.). (Illus.). 32p. (J). (gr. 3-9). (978-0-7787-2416-2(6)); pap. (978-0-7787-2452-0(2)) Crabtree Publishing Co.

—Radisson & Groseilliers: Fur Traders of the North. 2006. (In the Footsteps of Explorers Ser.). (Illus.). 32p. (J). (gr. 3-14). pap. (978-0-7787-2458-2(1) , 1253444); (978-0-7787-2422-3(0) , 1253444) Crabtree Publishing Co.

Bandon, Alex & O'Brien, Patrick. The Travels of Marco Polo. 1999. (Explorers & Exploration Ser.). (Illus.). 48p. (J). (gr. 4-7). lib. bdg. 22.83 (978-0-7398-1485-7(0)) Raintree.

Bastable, Tony. Ferdinand Magellan. 2003. (Great Explorers Ser.). (Illus.). 48p. (J). (gr. 5 up). pap. 14.60 (978-0-8368-5176-2(5) , World Almanac Library) Stevens, Gareth Inc.

Beales, R. A. James Cook: The Pacific Coast & Beyond. 2005. (In the Footsteps of Explorers Ser.). (Illus.). 32p. (J). (gr. 3-9). (978-0-7787-2415-5(8)); pap. (978-0-7787-2451-3(4)) Crabtree Publishing Co.

Bedesky, Baron. Peary & Henson: The Race to the North Pole. 2006. (In the Footsteps of Explorers Ser.). (Illus.). 32p. (J). (gr. 3-9). (978-0-7787-2426-1(3)) Crabtree Publishing Co.

—Sir Walter Raleigh: Founding the Virginia Colony. 2006. (In the Footsteps of Explorers Ser.). (Illus.). 32p. (J). (gr. 3-9). (978-0-7787-2424-7(7) , 1253445) Crabtree Publishing Co.

Benchmark Education Staff. England Explores the Americas. 2005. 2.00 (***978-1-4108-4659-4(8))** Benchmark Education Co.

—France Explores the Americas. 2005. 2.00 (***978-1-4108-4652-5(0))** Benchmark Education Co.

—Spain Explores the Americas. 2005. 2.00 (***978-1-4108-4645-7(8))** Benchmark Education Co.

Benchmark Education Staff, compiled by. Early Explorers. 2006. spiral bd. 330.00 (***978-1-4108-7009-4(X));** 2006. spiral bd. 119.00 (***978-1-4108-7124-4(X));** 2005. (J). spiral bd. 265.00 (***978-1-4108-5770-5(0))** Benchmark Education Co.

—Social Studies Theme: Early Explorers. 2005. spiral bd. 115.00 (***978-1-4108-5324-0(1))** Benchmark Education Co.

Benge, Janet & Benge, Geoff. Christopher Columbus: Across the Ocean Sea. 2005. 190p. (J). (978-1-932096-23-1(X)) Emerald Bks.

—Daniel Boone: Frontiersman. 2004. pap. 8.99 (978-1-932096-09-5(4)) Emerald Bks.

—John Smith: A Foothold in the New World. 2006. (Illus.). 192p. (J). pap. (978-1-932096-36-1(1)) Emerald Bks.

Benge, Janet Hazel & Benge, Geoffrey Francis. Meriwether Lewis: Off the Edge of the Map. 2001. 232p. pap. 8.99 (978-1-883002-80-0(X)) Emerald Bks.

Bergen. Earth's Explorers: Sieur de La Salle. 2000. (SPA., Illus.). pap. (978-0-7398-3340-7(5)) Steck-Vaughn.

Bergen, Lara Rice. Francisco Pizarro. 1999. (Illus.). 48p. (J). 136.98 (978-0-7398-1489-5(3)) Raintree.

—The Travels of Francisco Pizarro. 2000. (Explorers & Exploration Ser.). (Illus.). 48p. (J). (gr. 4-7). lib. bdg. 22.83 (978-0-7398-1487-1(7)) Raintree.

—The Travels of Lewis & Clark. 2000. (Explorers & Exploration Ser.). (Illus.). 48p. (J). (gr. 4-7). lib. bdg. 22.83 (978-0-7398-1486-4(9)) Raintree.

—The Travels of Sieur de la Salle. 1999. (Explorers & Exploration Ser.). (Illus.). 48p. (J). (gr. 4-7). lib. bdg. 22.83 (978-0-7398-1495-6(8)) Raintree.

Bingham, Jane. Captain Cook's Pacific Explorations. 2007. (J). (***978-1-4034-9756-7(7))** Heinemann Library.

Blashfield, Jean F. Cartier: Jacques Cartier in Search of the Northwest Passage. 2001. (Exploring the World Ser.). (Illus.). 48p. (J). (gr. 4 up). lib. bdg. 22.60 (978-0-7565-0122-8(9)) Compass Point Bks.

Blue, Rose. Exploring the Arctic. 2004. (Illus.). (J). pap. 9.50 (978-1-4109-0675-5(2)) Raintree.

—Exploring the Western Mountains. 2004. (Illus.). (J). pap. 9.50 (978-1-4109-0676-2(0)) Raintree.

Blue, Rose & Naden, Corinne J. Exploring Central America, Mexico, & the Caribbean. 2003. (Illus.). 64p. pap. 9.50 (978-1-4109-0334-1(6)); lib. bdg. 28.56 (978-0-7398-4952-1(2)) Raintree.

—Exploring Northeastern America. 2003. (Illus.). 64p. (J). lib. bdg. 28.56 (978-0-7398-4948-4(4)) Raintree.

—Exploring South America. 2003. (Illus.). 64p. (J). pap. 9.50 (978-1-4109-0335-8(4)) Raintree.

—Exploring the Arctic. 2004. (J). lib. bdg. 32.79 (978-1-4109-0673-1(6)) Raintree.

—Exploring the Mississippi River Valley. 2003. (Illus.). 64p. (J). lib. bdg. 28.56 (978-0-7398-4949-1(2)) Raintree.

—Exploring the Pacific Northwest. 2003. (Illus.). 64p. (J). lib. bdg. 28.56 (978-0-7398-4950-7(6)) Raintree.

—Exploring the Southeastern United States. 2003. (Illus.). 64p. (J). lib. bdg. 28.56 (978-0-7398-4951-4(4)) Raintree.

—Exploring the Southwestern United States. 2003. (Illus.). 64p. (J). pap. 9.50 (978-1-4109-0336-5(2)) Raintree.

—Exploring the St. Lawrence River Region. 2003. (Illus.). 64p. (J). pap. 9.50 (978-1-4109-0337-2(0)) Raintree.

—Exploring the Western Mountains. 2004. (J). lib. bdg. 32.79 (978-1-4109-0674-8(4)) Raintree.

—St. Lawrence Explorers. 2003. (Illus.). 64p. (J). lib. bdg. 28.56 (978-0-7398-4955-2(7)) Raintree.

Boraas, Tracey. Daniel Boone: Frontier Scout. 2002. (Let Freedom Ring Ser.). (Illus.). 48p. (J). (gr. 3-4). lib. bdg. 22.60 (978-0-7368-1347-1(0) , Bridgestone Bks.) Capstone Pr., Inc.

Brannon, Barbara. Discover English Explorers. 2005. 39.00 (***978-1-4108-5155-0(9))** Benchmark Education Co.

—Discover French Explorers. 2005. 39.00 (***978-1-4108-5154-3(0))** Benchmark Education Co.

—Discover Spanish Explorers. 2005. 39.00 (***978-1-4108-5153-6(2))** Benchmark Education Co.

Bredeson, Carmen. After the Last Dog Died: The True-Life, Hair-Raising Adventure of Douglas Mawson's 1912 Antarctic Expedition. 2003. (Illus.). 64p. (J). (gr. 5). 18.95 (978-0-7922-6140-7(2) , National Geographic Children's Bks.) National Geographic Society.

Broderick, Enid. Capt. James Cook. 2003. (Great Explorers Ser.). (Illus.). 48p. (J). (gr. 5 up). pap. 14.60 (978-0-8368-5174-8(9) , World Almanac Library) Stevens, Gareth Inc.

—Captain James Cook. 2001. (Great Explorers Ser.). (Illus.). 48p. (J). (gr. 5 up). lib. bdg. 30.00 (978-0-8368-5014-7(9) , World Almanac Library) Stevens, Gareth Inc.

—Roald Amundsen. (Great Explorers Ser.). (Illus.). 48p. (J). (gr. 5 up). 2002. pap. 14.60 (978-0-8368-5171-7(4)); 2001. lib. bdg. 30.00 (978-0-8368-5011-6(4)) Stevens, Gareth Inc. (World Almanac Library).

Brown, Janet Hubbard. Hernando de Soto: And His Expeditions Across the Americas. Goetzmann, William H., ed. 2005. (Explorers of New Lands Ser.). (Illus.). 138p. (J). (gr. 4-8). lib. bdg. 30.00 (978-0-7910-8610-0(0) , Chelsea Hse.) Facts On File, Inc.

Brown, John Mason. Sterling Point Books: Daniel Boone: the Opening of the Wilderness. 2007. (Sterling Point Bks.). 176p. (J). pap. 6.95 (***978-1-4027-5119-6(2))** Sterling Publishing Co., Inc.

Burgan, Michael. Marco Polo: Marco Polo & the Silk Road to China. 2002. (Exploring the World Ser.). (Illus.). 48p. (J). (gr. 4 up). lib. bdg. 22.60 (978-0-7565-0180-8(6)) Compass Point Bks.

Burger, James P. The Mountain Men of the West. 2002. (Library of the Westward Expansion). (Illus.). 24p. (J). (gr. 3). lib. bdg. 19.95 (978-0-8239-5853-5(1) , PowerKids Pr.) Rosen Publishing Group, Inc., The.

Burleigh, Robert. Black Whiteness: Admiral Byrd Alone in the Antarctic. Krudop, Walter Lyon, illus. 1998. 40p. (J). (gr. 2-7). 17.95 (978-0-689-81299-6(X) , Atheneum) Simon & Schuster Children's Publishing.

Calvert, Patricia. Hernando Cortes: Fortune Favored the Bold. 2002. (Great Explorations Ser.). (Illus.). 80p. (J). 29.93 (978-0-7614-1482-7(7) , Benchmark Bks.) Cavendish, Marshall Corp.

—Sir Ernest Shackleton: By Endurance We Conquer. 2002. (Great Explorations Ser.). (Illus.). 80p. (J). 29.93 (978-0-7614-1485-8(1) , Benchmark Bks.) Cavendish, Marshall Corp.

—Vasco Da Gama: So Strong a Spirit. 2003. (Great Explorations Ser.). (Illus.). 96p. (J). 29.93 (978-0-7614-1611-1(0) , Benchmark Bks.) Cavendish, Marshall Corp.

—Zebulon Pike: Lost in the Rockies. 2003. (Great Explorations Ser.). (J). (978-0-7614-1740-8(0)); 29.93 (978-0-7614-1612-8(9)) Cavendish, Marshall Corp. (Benchmark Bks.).

Capstone Press. Christopher Columbus: Famous Explorer. 2007. (Graphic Library). (Illus.). 32p. (J). (***978-0-7368-6853-2(4)** , 1264941) Capstone Pr., Inc.

Champion, Neil. John Cabot. (Groundbreakers Ser.). (Illus.). 48p. (J). (gr. 5-7). 2002. pap. 8.50 (978-1-58810-370-3(6) , 91095); 2001. lib. bdg. 25.64 (978-1-58810-046-7(4)) Heinemann Library.

Chipman, Donald & Joseph, Harriett Denise. Explorers & Settlers of Spanish Texas: Men & Women of Spanish Texas. 2001. (Illus.). 272p. (J). (gr. 7-12). pap. 19.95 (978-0-292-71231-7(6)) Univ. of Texas Pr.

Chrisp, Peter. Christopher Columbus. 2006. (DK Discoveries Ser.). 48p. (J). pap. 6.99 (978-0-7566-1965-7(3)) Dorling Kindersley Publishing, Inc.

—Christopher Columbus: Admiral of the Ocean Sea. Parsons, Jayne, ed. Dennis, Peter, illus. 2001. (DK Discoveries Ser.). 48p. (J). 14.95 (978-0-7894-7936-5(2)) Dorling Kindersley Publishing, Inc.

Christopher Columbus, 6 vols. (gr. k-2). 28.95 (978-0-7368-9369-5(5)) Red Brick Learning.

Clements, Gillian. The Picture History of Great Explorers. 2005. (Illus.). 96p. (J). (gr. 3-17). 19.95 (978-1-84507-075-5(5)) Lincoln, Frances Ltd. GBR. *Dist:* Perseus Distribution.

Clifton, Chuck & Clifton, Joyce. A Daily Walk with Lewis & Clark - 1804. 2003. 308p. (J). spiral bd. 14.95 (978-0-9669760-3-8(7)) Maple Canyon Co.

—A Daily Walk with Lewis & Clark - 1805. 2003. 390p. (J). spiral bd. 14.95 (978-0-9669760-4-5(5)) Maple Canyon Co.

—A Daily Walk with Lewis & Clark - 1806. 2003. 292p. (J). spiral bd. 14.95 (978-0-9669760-5-2(3)) Maple Canyon Co.

Collier, James Lincoln. Christopher Columbus: To the New World. 2006. (Great Explorations Ser.). (Illus.). 80p. (J). lib. bdg. 32.79 (978-0-7614-2221-1(8) , Benchmark Bks.) Cavendish, Marshall Corp.

Como Funcionan Algunas Cosas, 6 vols., Vol. 3. (Explorers. Exploradores Nonfiction Sets Ser.). (SPA.). (gr. 3-6). (978-0-7699-0656-0(7)) Shortland Pubns. (U. S. A.) Inc.

La Conquista de Las Alturas, 6 vols., Vol. 3. (Explorers. Exploradores Nonfiction Sets Ser.). (SPA.). (gr. 3-6). (978-0-7699-0655-3(9)) Shortland Pubns. (U. S. A.) Inc.

Cox, Caroline & Albala, Ken. Opening up North America, 1497-1800. 2005. (Discovery & Exploration (John S. Bowman & Maurice Isserman Are General Editors of the Set.) Ser.). (Illus.). 208p. (J). (gr. 6-12). 40.00 (978-0-8160-5261-5(1)) Facts On File, Inc.

Craats, Rennay. Exploration of North America. 2005. (Great Journeys Ser.). (Illus.). 32p. (J). pap. 7.95 (978-1-59036-258-7(6)) Weigl Pubs., Inc.

Crisfield. Earth's Explorers: Juan Ponce de Leon. 2000. (SPA., Illus.). pap. (978-0-7398-3336-0(7)) Steck-Vaughn.

Crisfield, Deborah. The Travels of Francisco de Coronado. 1999. (Explorers & Exploration Ser.). (Illus.). 48p. (J). (gr. 4-7). lib. bdg. 22.83 (978-0-7398-1493-2(1)) Raintree.

—The Travels of Hernan Cortes. 2000. (Explorers & Exploration Ser.). (Illus.). 48p. (J). (gr. 4-7). lib. bdg. 22.83 (978-0-7398-1488-8(5)) Raintree.

Crompton, Samuel Willard. Ferdinand Magellan: And the Quest to Circle the Globe. Goetzmann, William H., ed. 2005. (Explorers of New Lands Ser.). (Illus.). 144p. (J). (ps-8). lib. bdg. 30.00 (978-0-7910-8608-7(9) , Chelsea Hse.) Facts On File, Inc.

—Francis Drake & the Oceans of the World. 2005. (Explorers of New Worlds Ser.). (Illus.). 160p. (J). (gr. 4-8). 30.00 (978-0-7910-8615-5(1) , Chelsea Hse.) Facts On File, Inc.

Curlee, Lynn. Into the Ice: The Story of Arctic Exploration. 1998. (Illus.). 40p. (J). (gr. 4-6). tchr. ed. 16.00 (978-0-395-83013-0(3)) Houghton Mifflin Co. Trade & Reference Div.

Currie, Stephen. Travels to Distant Lands: 1000-1400. 2004. (Reading Expeditions Ser.). (Illus.). 32p. (J). (978-0-7922-4542-1(3)) National Geographic Society.

Davenport, John. Juan Ponce de Leon: And His Lands of Discovery. Goetzmann, William H., ed. 2005. (Explorers of New Lands Ser.). (Illus.). 142p. (J). (ps-8). lib. bdg. 30.00 (978-0-7910-8607-0(0) , Chelsea Hse.) Facts On File, Inc.

De Angelis, Gina. Hernan Cortes & the Conquest of Mexico. 1999. (Explorers of the New World Ser.). (Illus.). 64p. (YA). (gr. 4 up). 31.00 (978-0-7910-5516-8(7) , Chelsea Hse.) Facts On File, Inc.

DeLucenayLeon, George. Explorers of the Americas Before Columbus. 1999. (Illus.). 64p. (J). (gr. 5-7). 17.00 (978-0-7881-6846-8(0)) DIANE Publishing Co.

Devillier, Christy. Christopher Columbus. 2001. (First Biographies Ser.). (Illus.). 32p. (J). (gr. k-4). lib. bdg. 22.78 (978-1-57765-594-7(X) , Buddy Bks.) ABDO Publishing Co.

Ditchfield, Christin. The Lewis & Clark Expedition. 2006. 48p. (gr. 3-5). (YA). pap. 6.95 (978-0-516-25222-3(4)); (Illus.). (J). 25.00 (978-0-516-22835-8(8)) Scholastic Library Publishing. (Children's Pr.).

Doak, Robin S. Cabot: John Cabot & the Journey to North America. 2003. (Exploring the World Ser.). (Illus.). 48p. (J). (gr. 4 up). lib. bdg. 22.60 (978-0-7565-0420-5(1)) Compass Point Bks.

—Christopher Columbus: Explorer of the New World. 2004. (Signature Lives Ser.). (Illus.). 112p. (J). 30.60 (978-0-7565-0811-1(8) , 1240120) Compass Point Bks.

—Coronado: Francisco Vazques de Coronado Explores the Southwest. 2001. (Exploring the World Ser.). (Illus.). 48p. (J). (gr. 4 up). lib. bdg. 22.60 (978-0-7565-0123-5(7)) Compass Point Bks.

—Hudson: Henry Hudson Searches for a Passage to Asia. 2003. (Exploring the World Ser.). (Illus.). 48p. (J). (gr. 4 up). lib. bdg. 22.60 (978-0-7565-0422-9(8)) Compass Point Bks.

—Smith: John Smith & the Settlement of Jamestown. 2003. (Exploring the World Ser.). (Illus.). 48p. (J). (gr. 4 up). lib. bdg. 22.60 (978-0-7565-0423-6(6)) Compass Point Bks.

—Zebulon Pike: Explorer & Soldier. 2005. (Signature Lives Ser.). (Illus.). 112p. (J). (gr. 5-7). (978-0-7565-0998-9(X)) Compass Point Bks.

Dodson Wade, Mary. Christopher Columbus: Famous Explorer. 2007. (Graphic Library). (Illus.). 32p. (J). (***978-0-7368-7905-7(6)** , 1264941) Capstone Pr., Inc.

Doherty, Kieran. Explorers, Missionaries & Trappers: Trailblazers of the West. 2000. (Shaping America Ser.). (Illus.). 176p. (gr. 7 up). lib. bdg. 22.95 (978-1-881508-52-6(8)) Oliver Pr., Inc.

Donaldson-Forbes, Jeff. Famous Explorers - Set 3, 6 bks. Incl. Amerigo Vespucci. lib. bdg. 18.75 (978-0-8239-5833-7(7)); Francisco Pizarro. lib. bdg. 18.75 (978-0-8239-5831-3(0)); Hernan Cortes. lib. bdg. 18.75 (978-0-8239-5832-0(9)); Jacques Cartier. lib. bdg. 18.75 (978-0-8239-5834-4(5)); Jacques Marquette & Louis Jolliet. lib. bdg. 18.75 (978-0-8239-5835-1(3)); La Salle. lib. bdg. 18.75 (978-0-8239-5830-6(2)); 24p. (J). (gr. 3). 2002. (Illus.). Set lib. bdg. 112.50 (978-0-8239-7181-7(3) , PowerKids Pr.) Rosen Publishing Group, Inc., The.

—Hernan Cortes. 2002. (Famous Explorers Ser.). (Illus.). 24p. (J). (gr. 3). lib. bdg. 18.75 (978-0-8239-5832-0(9) , PowerKids Pr.) Rosen Publishing Group, Inc., The.

—Jacques Cartier. 2002. (Famous Explorers Ser.). (Illus.). 24p. (J). (gr. 3). lib. bdg. 18.75 (978-0-8239-5834-4(5) , PowerKids Pr.) Rosen Publishing Group, Inc., The.

Dorling Kindersley Publishing Staff. Explorer. (Eye Wonder Ser.). (Illus.). (J). 2006. 48p. 9.99 (978-0-7566-1978-7(5)); 2006. 48p. lib. bdg. 17.99 (978-0-7566-1979-4(3)); 2005. 72p. 15.99 (978-0-7566-1071-5(0)) Dorling Kindersley Publishing, Inc.

Eagen, Rachel. Ponce de Léon: Exploring Florida & Puerto Rico. 2005. (In the Footsteps of Explorers Ser.). (Illus.). 32p. (J). (gr. 3-9). (978-0-7787-2412-4(3)); pap. (978-0-7787-2448-3(4)) Crabtree Publishing Co.

Edwards, Judith. Henry Hudson & His Voyages of Exploration in World History. 2002. (In World History Ser.). (Illus.). 128p. (YA). (gr. 5-12). lib. bdg. 26.60 (978-0-7660-1885-3(7)) Enslow Pubs., Inc.

Englar, Mary. Sieur de la Salle. 2004. (Fact Finders Ser.). (Illus.). 32p. (J). lib. bdg. 22.60 (978-0-7368-2666-2(1)) Capstone Pr., Inc.

Espinosa, Rod. Lewis & Clark. 2007. (Bio-Graphics Ser.). (Illus.). 32p. (J). (gr. 3-6). lib. bdg. 27.07 (***978-1-60270-069-7(9)** , Graphic Planet) Magic Wagon.

Everett, Felicity & Reid, Struan. Explorers. rev. ed. 2007. (Famous Lives Ser.). 48p. (J). pap. 8.99 (***978-0-7945-1533-1(9)** , Usborne) EDC Publishing.

Exploradores. 2003. (Megabites Ser.). (SPA., Illus.). (J). pap. 8.95 (978-0-9715256-8-9(4)) Planeta Publishing Corp.

Explorers & Exploration, 6 vols. 2000. (Illus.). (J). 136.98 (978-0-7398-2849-6(5)); Set. (978-0-7398-4173-0(4)) Raintree.

Explorers & Exploration, Set 1. 1999. (Illus.). (J). pap. (978-0-7398-2205-0(5)) Steck-Vaughn.

Explorers & Exploration Collection. 2001. (Illus.). (J). pap. (978-0-7398-4554-7(3)) Steck-Vaughn.

Explorers of New Worlds. 2005. pap. 500.00 (978-0-7910-9154-8(6) , Chelsea Hse.) Facts On File, Inc.

Explorers Set 2. 2007. (J). 273.36 (***978-1-59679-739-0(8)** , Checkerboard Library) ABDO Publishing Co.

Extraordinary Women Explorers. 2005. (Women's Hall of Fame Ser.). (Illus.). 118p. (YA). (gr. 4-7). pap. 7.95 (978-1-896764-98-6(3)) Second Story Pr. CAN. *Dist:* Orca Bk. Pubs. USA, Univ. of Toronto Pr.

Faber, Harold. John Charles Fremont: Pathfinder to the West. 2002. (Great Explorations Ser.). (Illus.). 79p. (J). 29.93 (978-0-7614-1481-0(9) , Benchmark Bks.) Cavendish, Marshall Corp.

Faber, Harold, et al. La Salle: Down the Mississippi. 2002. (Great Explorations Ser.). (Illus.). 80p. (J). (gr. 4 up). lib. bdg. 29.93 (978-0-7614-1239-7(5) , Benchmark Bks.) Cavendish, Marshall Corp.

Fact Finders Biographies: Great Explorers. (Fact Finders Ser.). (Illus.). (J). (gr. 3-4). lib. bdg. 226.00 (978-0-7368-2759-1(5)) Capstone Pr., Inc.

Feeney, Kathy. Marco Polo: Explorer of China. 2004. (Explorers! Ser.). (Illus.). 48p. (J). lib. bdg. 23.93 (978-0-7660-2145-7(9)) Enslow Pubs., Inc.

Fine, Jil. Shackleton Expedition. 2002. (gr. 7-12). lib. bdg. 15.25 (978-0-613-58800-3(2)) Tandem Library Bks.

Fish, Bruce & Fish, Becky Durost. The Congo. 2001. (Exploration of Africa Ser.). (Illus.). 112p. (J). 35.00 (978-0-7910-6198-5(1) , Chelsea Hse.) Facts On File, Inc.

Fisher, Ann Richmond. Explorers of the New World Time Line. Mitchell, Judy & Lindeen, Mary, eds. Smith, Bron, illus. 2007. 112p. (J). pap. 12.95 (***978-1-57310-523-1(6))** Teaching & Learning Co.

Freedman, Frances. David Livingstone. (Great Explorers Ser.). (Illus.). 48p. (J). (gr. 5 up). 2002. pap. 14.60 (978-0-8368-5175-5(7)); 2001. lib. bdg. 30.00 (978-0-8368-5015-4(7)) Stevens, Gareth Inc. (World Almanac Library).

Freedman, Russell. Who Was First? Discovering the Americas. 2007. (Illus.). 96p. (J). (gr. 4-7). 19.00 (***978-0-618-66391-0(6)** , Clarion Bks.) Houghton Mifflin Co. Trade & Reference Div.

Gallagher, Jim. Ferdinand Magellan & the First Voyage Around the World. 1999. (Explorers of the New World Ser.). (Illus.). 63p. (YA). (gr. 4 up). 31.00 (978-0-7910-5508-3(6) , Chelsea Hse.) Facts On File, Inc.

—Hernando de Soto & the Exploration of Florida. 1999. (Explorers of the New World Ser.). (Illus.). 63p. (J). (gr. 4 up). 31.00 (978-0-7910-5512-0(4) , Chelsea Hse.) Facts On File, Inc.

—Vasco da Gama & the Portuguese Explorers. 1999. (Explorers of the New World Ser.). (Illus.). 63p. (J). (gr. 4 up). 31.00 (978-0-7910-5514-4(0) , Chelsea Hse.) Facts On File, Inc.

Ganeri, Anita. The Story of Columbus, Vol. 2. Ling, Mary, ed. 2001. (Readers Ser.). (Illus.). 32p. (J). (gr. 5-3). pap. 3.99 (978-0-7894-7878-8(1)) Dorling Kindersley Publishing, Inc.

Ganeri, Anita & Dorling Kindersley Publishing Staff. The Story of Columbus. 2001. (Readers Ser.). (Illus.). 32p. (J). (gr. 1-3). 14.99 (978-0-7894-7877-1(3)) Dorling Kindersley Publishing, Inc.

Gefen, Keren. Marco Polo. (Great Explorers Ser.). (Illus.). 48p. (J). (gr. 5 up). 2002. pap. 14.60 (978-0-8368-5177-9(3)); 2001. lib. bdg. 30.00 (978-0-8368-5017-8(3)) Stevens, Gareth Inc. (World Almanac Library).

Gibson-Hardie, Stephanie Kim. The 10 Boldest Explorers. 2008. (Tentrade; Ser.). 48p. (J). pap. 14.99 (***978-1-55448-456-0(1)** , Watts, Franklin) Scholastic Library Publishing.

Gifford, Clive. Ten Explorers Who Changed the World. 2007. 64p. (J). (gr. 5). 14.95 (978-0-7534-6103-7(X) , Kingfisher) Houghton Mifflin Co. Trade & Reference Div.

Glaser, Jason. Leif Eriksson. 2004. (Fact Finders Ser.). (Illus.). 32p. (J). lib. bdg. 22.60 (978-0-7368-2664-8(5)) Capstone Pr., Inc.

—Lewis & Clark. 2004. (Fact Finders Ser.). (Illus.). 32p. (J). lib. bdg. 22.60 (978-0-7368-2665-5(3)) Capstone Pr., Inc.

Gleason, Carrie. Henry Hudson: Seeking the Northwest Passage. 2005. (In the Footsteps of Explorers Ser.). (Illus.). 32p. (J). (ps-9). (978-0-7787-2408-7(5)); pap. (978-0-7787-2444-5(1)) Crabtree Publishing Co.

Glover, David. Flying & Floating. 2002. (Young Discoverers Ser.). (Illus.). 32p. (J). (gr. k-3). pap. 7.95 (978-0-7534-5511-1(0) , Kingfisher) Houghton Mifflin Co. Trade & Reference Div.

Goetzmann, William H. & Crouch, Tom D., eds. The Explorers of Distant Frontiers Series, 7 bks. 1999. (World Explorers Ser.). (Illus.). 112-128p. (gr. 5). (978-0-7910-3532-0(8) , Chelsea Hse.) Facts On File, Inc.

Goodman, Joan Elizabeth. A Long & Uncertain Journey: The 27,000 Mile Voyage of Vasco Da Gama. McNeely, Tom, illus. 2001. (Great Explorers Ser.). 48p. (ps-12). 22.95 (978-0-9650493-7-5(X)) Mikaya Pr.

Gough, Barry M., ed. Geographers & Explorers. 2001. (Scribner Science Reference Ser.: Vol. 4). (Illus.). 225p. (J). 115.00 (978-0-684-80662-4(2) , GML00502-173594, Charles Scribner's Sons) Thomson Gale.

Graf, Mike & McFarren, Kathleen. History Pockets: Explorers of North America. McClain, Lynn, illus. 2003. (History Pockets Ser.). 96p. (J). (gr. 4-6). suppl. ed. 12.99 (978-1-55799-905-4(8) , EMC 3708) Evan-Moor Educational Pubs.

Grant, Kevin Patrick. Exploration in the Age of Empire, 1750-1953, 10 vols. 2004. (Discovery & Exploration Ser.). (Illus.). 176p. (J). (gr. 6-12). 40.00 (978-0-8160-5260-8(3)) Facts On File, Inc.

Great Explorations - Group 3, 6 Bks, Set. 2004. (J). 179.57 (978-0-7614-1606-7(4)) Cavendish, Marshall Corp.

Great Explorations Group 4, 6 bks., Set. Incl. Christopher Columbus : To the New World. Collier, James Lincoln. (J). 2006. lib. bdg. 32.79 (978-0-7614-2221-1(8)); David Livingstone : Deep in the Heart of Africa. Otfinoski, Steven. (YA). (gr. 5-9). 2006. lib. bdg. 32.79 (978-0-7614-2226-6(9)); Edmund Hillary : First to the Top. Elish, Dan. (YA). (gr. 5-9). 2007. lib. bdg. 32.79 (***978-0-7614-2224-2(2)***); Henry Hudson : In Search of the Northwest Passage. Otfinoski, Steven. (J). 2007. lib. bdg. 32.79 (***978-0-7614-2225-9(0)***); Kit Carson : He Led the Way. Calvert, Patricia. (J). 2006. lib. bdg. 32.79 (978-0-7614-2223-5(4)); Richard Francis Burton : Explorer, Scholar, Spy. Young, Serenity. (YA). (gr. 5-9). 2007. lib. bdg. 32.79 (***978-0-7614-2222-8(6)***); (Illus.). 80p. 2007. Set lib. bdg. 196.71 (***978-0-7614-2219-8(6)*** , Benchmark Bks.) Cavendish, Marshall Corp.

Great Explorers, 8 bks. Incl. Captain James Cook. Broderick, Enid. lib. bdg. 30.00 (978-0-8368-5014-7(9)); Christopher Columbus. Green, Tamara. lib. bdg. 30.00 (978-0-8368-5013-0(0)); David Livingstone. Freedman, Frances. lib. bdg. 30.00 (978-0-8368-5015-4(7)); Ferdinand Magellan. Anthony, Laurence. lib. bdg. 30.00 (978-0-8368-5016-1(5)); John Cabot. Anthony, Laurence. lib. bdg. 30.00 (978-0-8368-5012-3(2)); Juan Ponce de Leon. Green, Tamara. lib. bdg. 30.00 (978-0-8368-5018-5(1)); Marco Polo. Gefen, Keren. lib. bdg. 30.00 (978-0-8368-5017-8(3)); Roald Amundsen. Broderick, Enid. lib. bdg. 30.00 (978-0-8368-5011-6(4)); 48p. (J). (gr. 5 up). 2001. (Illus.). 2002. Set lib. bdg. 240.00 (978-0-8368-5557-9(4) , World Almanac Library) Stevens, Gareth Inc.

Great Explorers: Captain James Cook; Christopher Columbus; Ferdinand Magellan; John Cabot, 4 bks. 2002. (Illus.). (J). (gr. 5 up). pap. (978-0-8368-5179-3(X)); lib. bdg. 117.06 (978-0-8368-5019-2(X)) Stevens, Gareth Inc. (World Almanac Library).

Great Explorers: Roald Amundsen; David Livingstone; Marco Polo; Juan Ponce de Leon, 4 bks. 2002. (Illus.). (J). (gr. 5 up). pap. (978-0-8368-5170-0(6) , World Almanac Library) Stevens, Gareth Inc.

Green, Jen. You Wouldn't Want to Be a Polar Explorer! An Expedition You'd Rather Not Go On. Antram, David, illus. 2001. (You Wouldn't Want to Ser.). 32p. (J). (gr. 2-5). 28.50 (978-0-531-14601-9(4)); pap. 9.95 (978-0-531-16207-1(9)) Scholastic Library Publishing. (Watts, Franklin).

Green, Tamara. Juan Ponce de Leon. (Great Explorers Ser.). (Illus.). 48p. (J). (gr. 5 up). 2002. pap. 14.60 (978-0-8368-5178-6(1)); 2001. lib. bdg. 30.00 (978-0-8368-5018-5(1)) Stevens, Gareth Inc. (World Almanac Library).

Greenwood, Rosie. I Wonder Why Columbus Crossed the Ocean: And Other Questions about Explorers. 2005. (I Wonder Why Ser.). (Illus.). 32p. (J). (gr. k-3). 11.95 (978-0-7534-5860-0(8) , Kingfisher) Houghton Mifflin Co. Trade & Reference Div.

Group/McGraw-Hill, Wright. First Explorers: Student Book Set - 1 Each of 12 Titles. (First Explorers. Primeros Exploradores Nonfiction Sets Ser.). (gr. 1-2). 59.95 (978-0-7699-1363-6(6)) Shortland Pubns. (U. S. A.) Inc.

—Twentieth-Century Explorers, 6 vols. (Book2WebTM Ser.). (gr. 4-8). 36.50 (978-0-322-04468-5(5)) Wright Group, The.

Gunderson, Jessica Sarah. The Lewis & Clark Expedition. 2007. (Graphic Library). (Illus.). 32p. (J). 25.26 (978-0-7368-6493-0(8)) Capstone Pr., Inc.

Habitat Explorer Series, 9 vols., Set. 2004. (Illus.). pap. 60.75 (978-1-4109-1394-4(5)) Raintree.

Hacker, Carlotta. Explorers. 1998. (Women in Profile Ser.). (Illus.). 48p. (J). (gr. 4). pap. (978-0-7787-0026-5(7)); lib. bdg. (978-0-7787-0004-3(6)) Crabtree Publishing Co.

Hammond Inc. Staff. Hammond Explorer Atlas. 2005. (Atlas Ser.). (Illus.). 32p. pap. 10.95 (978-0-8437-0919-3(7) , 709197) Langenscheidt Pubs Inc.

Harcourt School Publishers Staff. The First Voyage Around the World. 3rd ed. 2002. (Horizons Ser.). (Illus.). (J). pap. 7.30 (978-0-15-333559-4(9)) Harcourt Schl. Pubs.

Harmon, Daniel E. Jacques Cartier & the Exploration of Canada. 2001. (gr. 3-6). lib. bdg. 17.60 (978-0-613-32700-8(4)) Tandem Library Bks.

Harris, Laurie Lanzen, ed. Biography for Beginners: World Explorers. 2003. (Illus.). xxi, 598p. (J). (gr. 3-6). 55.00 (978-1-931360-20-3(0)) Favorable Impressions.

Haskins, Jim. Against All Opposition: Black Explorers in America. 2003. (gr. 5-8). lib. bdg. 17.60 (978-0-613-91054-5(0)) Tandem Library Bks.

—Against All Opposition: Black Explorers in America. 2003. 96p. (J). pap. 8.95 (978-0-8027-7672-3(8)) Walker & Co.

Heckscher, Melissa & Shulman, Mark. The Explorer's Gazette: Amazing Stories of 30 Real-Life Journeys. 2004. (Illus.). (J). pap. (978-0-439-67653-3(3)) Scholastic, Inc.

Hendrickson, Sue. Hunt for the Past: My Life as an Explorer. 2001. (J). 10.79 (978-0-606-21243-4(4)) Tandem Library Bks.

Higgins, Nadia. Columbus & the Age of Explorers. 2007. (Illus.). 48p. (J). (978-1-60044-119-6(X)) Rourke Publishing, LLC.

High-Interest Nonfiction: Explorers 3-5. 2003. 128p. (J). per. 10.99 (978-0-88724-951-8(5) , CD-4321) Carson-Dellosa Publishing Co., Inc.

Hirschfelder, Arlene B. Photo Odyssey: Solomon Carvalho's Remarkable Western Adventure 1853-54. 2000. (Illus.). 128p. (J). (gr. 5-9). tchr. ed. 18.00 (978-0-395-89123-0(X) , Clarion Bks.) Houghton Mifflin Co. Trade & Reference Div.

Hitchcock, Susan Tyler. Sylvia A. Earle: Deep Sea Explorer. 2004. (Women Explorers Ser.). (Illus.). 120p. 30.00 (978-0-7910-7712-2(8) , Chelsea Hse.) Facts On File, Inc.

Hoena, B. A. Matthew Henson: Arctic Adventurer. Miller, Phil & Barnett, Charles, III, illus. 2005. (Graphic Library). 32p. (J). (gr. 3-7). lib. bdg. 25.26 (978-0-7368-4634-9(4)) Capstone Pr., Inc.

Holub, Joan. Who Was Marco Polo? O'Brien, John & Harrison, Nancy, illus. 2007. (Who Was... ? Ser.). 112p. (J). (gr. 2-6). pap. 4.99 (978-0-448-44540-3(9) , Grosset & Dunlap) Penguin Group (USA) Inc.

Hoogenboom, Lynn. Amerigo Vespucci: A Primary Source Biography. 2006. (Illus.). 24p. (J). lib. bdg. (978-1-4042-3037-8(8) , PowerKids Pr.) Rosen Publishing Group, Inc., The.

—Christopher Columbus: A Primary Source Biography. 2006. (Illus.). 24p. (J). lib. bdg. (978-1-4042-3036-1(X) , PowerKids Pr.) Rosen Publishing Group, Inc., The.

—Ferdinand Magellan: A Primary Source Biography. 2006. (J). lib. bdg. (978-1-4042-3039-2(4) , PowerKids Pr.) Rosen Publishing Group, Inc., The.

—Francisco Pizarro: A Primary Source Biography. 2006. (J). lib. bdg. (978-1-4042-3038-5(6) , PowerKids Pr.) Rosen Publishing Group, Inc., The.

—Juan Ponce de Leon: A Primary Source Biography. 2006. (Illus.). 24p. (J). lib. bdg. (978-1-4042-3040-8(8) , PowerKids Pr.) Rosen Publishing Group, Inc., The.

—Sir Francis Drake: A Primary Source Portrait. 2006. (J). lib. bdg. (978-1-4042-3035-4(1) , PowerKids Pr.) Rosen Publishing Group, Inc., The.

Hooper, Meredith. Antarctic Adventure: Exploring the frozen Continent. Martin, Linda, ed. 2000. (Eyewitness Bks.). (Illus.). 48p. (J). (gr. 2-4). pap. 3.99 (978-0-7894-6684-6(8)) Dorling Kindersley Publishing, Inc.

Hurwicz, Claude. Famous Explorers - Set 2, 6 bks. Incl. Ferdinand Magellan. lib. bdg. 18.75 (978-0-8239-5562-6(1)); Francisco Vasquez de Coronado. lib. bdg. 18.75 (978-0-8239-5564-0(8)); Henry Hudson. lib. bdg. 18.75 (978-0-8239-5561-9(3)); Henry the Navigator. lib. bdg. 18.75 (978-0-8239-5560-2(5)); Juan Ponce de Leon. lib. bdg. 18.75 (978-0-8239-5563-3(X)); Samuel de Champlain. lib. bdg. 18.75 (978-0-8239-5559-6(1)); 24p. (J). (gr. 3). (Illus.). 2001. Set lib. bdg. 112.50 (978-0-8239-7064-3(7) , PowerKids Pr.) Rosen Publishing Group, Inc., The.

—Francisco Vasquez de Coronado. 2001. (Famous Explorers Ser.). (Illus.). 24p. (J). (gr. 3). lib. bdg. 18.75 (978-0-8239-5564-0(8) , PowerKids Pr.) Rosen Publishing Group, Inc., The.

—Henry Hudson. 2001. (Famous Explorers Ser.). (Illus.). 24p. (J). (gr. 3). lib. bdg. 18.75 (978-0-8239-5561-9(3) , PowerKids Pr.) Rosen Publishing Group, Inc., The.

—Juan Ponce de Leon. 2001. (Famous Explorers Ser.). (Illus.). 24p. (J). (gr. 3). lib. bdg. 18.75 (978-0-8239-5563-3(X) , PowerKids Pr.) Rosen Publishing Group, Inc., The.

Isserman, Maurice. Across America: The Lewis & Clark Expedition. 2004. (Discovery & Exploration Ser.). (Illus.). 192p. (J). (gr. 6-12). 40.00 (978-0-8160-5256-1(5)) Facts On File, Inc.

—Exploring North America, 1800-1900. 2005. (Discovery & Exploration Ser.). (Illus.). 208p. (J). (gr. 6-12). 40.00 (978-0-8160-5263-9(8)) Facts On File, Inc.

Jackson, Garnet N. Famous Explorers. Brown, Dan, illus. 2000. (Hello Reader! Ser.). (J). lib. bdg. (978-0-439-20629-7(4)) Scholastic, Inc.

January, Brendan. Explorers of North America. 2000. (gr. 3-6). lib. bdg. 15.25 (978-0-613-51644-0(3)) Tandem Library Bks.

—New York Public Library Amazing Explorers: A Book of Answers for Kids. 2001. (gr. 5-8). lib. bdg. 22.20 (978-0-613-85110-7(2)) Tandem Library Bks.

Johnson, Dolores. Onward: A Photobiography of African-American Polar Explorer Matthew Henson. 2005. (National Geographic Photographer Ser.). (Illus.). 64p. (J). (gr. k-3). 17.95 (978-0-7922-7914-3(X)); 27.90 (978-0-7922-7915-0(8)) National Geographic Society. (National Geographic Children's Bks.).

Johnson, Rebecca L. Ernest Shackleton: Gripped by the Antarctic. 2003. (Trailblazers Biographies Ser.). (Illus.). 112p. (J). (gr. 5-9). 30.60 (978-0-87614-920-1(4)) Lerner Publishing Group.

Johnston, Charles H. Famous Discoverers & Explorers of Amer. 2006. pap. 38.95 (***978-1-4254-9677-7(6)***) Kessinger Publishing, LLC.

Johnstone, Michael. Explorers. 2001. (History News Ser.). (Illus.). 32p. (J). (gr. 3 up). lib. bdg. 24.67 (978-0-8368-2875-7(5)) Stevens, Gareth Inc.

—Explorers News. 2000. (History News Ser.). (Illus.). 32p. (J). (gr. 4-9). pap. 6.99 (978-0-7636-0985-6(4)) Candlewick Pr.

—Explorers News. 2000. (News Ser.). (J). (978-0-606-19314-6(6)) Tandem Library Bks.

Joly, Dominique & Garel, Beatrice. The Adventures of the Great Explorers. 1999. (Megascope Ser.). (Illus.). 61p. (J). (gr. 5-9). 6.95 (978-0-7641-5182-8(7)) Barron's Educational Series, Inc.

Jones, Charlotte Foltz. Westward Ho! Eleven Explorers of the American West. 2005. (Illus.). 240p. (J). (gr. 4-6). tchr. ed. 22.95 (978-0-8234-1586-1(4)) Holiday Hse., Inc.

Kachurek, Sandra J. Francisco Pizarro: Explorer of South America. 2004. (Explorers! Ser.). (Illus.). 48p. (J). lib. bdg. 23.93 (978-0-7660-2178-5(5)) Enslow Pubs., Inc.

Karner, Julie. Roald Amundsen: The Conquest of the South Pole. 2006. (In the Footsteps of Explorers Ser.). (Illus.). 32p. (J). (gr. 3-9). pap. (978-0-7787-2468-1(9)) Crabtree Publishing Co.

Kelly Allen, Nancy. Daniel Boone: Trailblazer. Waites, Joan C., illus. 2005. 32p. (J). (gr. 2-4). 15.95 (978-1-58980-212-4(8)) Pelican Publishing Co., Inc.

Kimmel, Elizabeth Cody. Before Columbus: The Leif Eriksson Expedition: A True Adventure. 2003. (Landmark Books Ser.). (Illus.). 112p. (J). (gr. 4). lib. bdg. 16.99 (978-0-375-91347-1(5) , Random Hse. Bks. for Young Readers) Random Hse. Children's Bks.

—Ice Story: Shackleton's Lost Expedition. 1999. (Illus.). 128p. (J). (gr. 4-6). tchr. ed. 19.00 (978-0-395-91524-0(4) , Clarion Bks.) Houghton Mifflin Co. Trade & Reference Div.

—The Look-It-Up Book of Explorers. Barnard, Bryn, illus. 2004. 128p. (J). (gr. 3-5). pap. 10.99 (978-0-375-82478-4(2) , Random Hse. Bks. for Young Readers) Random Hse. Children's Bks.

—The Look-It-up Book of Explorers. Barnard, Bryn, illus. 2004. 128p. (J). (gr. 3-5). 17.99 (978-0-375-92478-1(7) , Random Hse. Bks. for Young Readers) Random Hse. Children's Bks.

Kirkpatrick, Katherine. The Snow Baby: The Arctic Childhood of Robert E. Peary's Daring Daughter. 2006. (Illus.). 48p. (J). 16.95 (978-0-8234-1973-9(8)) Holiday Hse., Inc.

Kline, Trish. Captain John Smith. 2001. (Discover the Life of an Explorer Ser.). (Illus.). 24p. (J). (gr. 1-4). lib. bdg. 20.64 (978-1-58952-065-3(3)) Rourke Publishing, LLC.

—Christopher Columbus. 2001. (Discover the Life of an Explorer Ser.). (Illus.). 24p. (J). (gr. 1-4). lib. bdg. 20.64 (978-1-58952-066-0(1)) Rourke Publishing, LLC.

—Descubre la Vida de un Explorador. 2002. (SPA.). 115.62 (978-1-58952-425-5(X)) Rourke Publishing, LLC.

—Francisco Coronado. 2002. (ENG & SPA.). (J). lib. bdg. 19.27 (978-1-58952-428-6(4)) Rourke Publishing, LLC.

—Francisco Pizarro: Descubre la Vida de un Explorador. 2002. (J). lib. bdg. 19.27 (978-1-58952-431-6(4)) Rourke Publishing, LLC.

—Francisco Vazquez de Coronado. 2003. (Rourke Discovery Library). (Illus.). 24p. (gr. 2-5). 14.95 (978-1-58952-294-7(X)) Rourke Publishing, LLC.

—Henry Hudson. (Discover the Life of an Explorer Ser.). 2003. (Illus.). 24p. (gr. 2-5). 14.95 (978-1-58952-296-1(6)); 2002. (SPA.). 19.27 (978-1-58952-430-9(6)) Rourke Publishing, LLC.

—Hernan Cortes. (Rourke Discovery Library). 2003. (Illus.). 24p. (gr. 2-5). 14.95 (978-1-58952-293-0(1)); 2002. 19.27 (978-1-58952-427-9(6)) Rourke Publishing, LLC.

—James Cook. (Rourke Discovery Library). 2003. (Illus.). 24p. (gr. 2-5). 14.95 (978-1-58952-292-3(3)); 2002. lib. bdg. 19.27 (978-1-58952-426-2(8)) Rourke Publishing, LLC.

—Lewis & Clark. 2002. (Discover the Life of an Explorer Ser.). (Illus.). 24p. (gr. 2-5). 14.95 (978-1-58952-067-7(X)) Rourke Publishing, LLC.

—Ponce de Leon. 2001. (Discover the Life of an Explorer Ser.). (Illus.). 24p. (J). (gr. 1-4). lib. bdg. 20.64 (978-1-58952-068-4(8)) Rourke Publishing, LLC.

—Robert la Salle. 2002. (Discover the Life of an Explorer Ser.). (Illus.). 24p. (gr. 2-5). 14.95 (978-1-58952-069-1(6)) Rourke Publishing, LLC.

—Samuel de Champlain. 2001. (Illus.). 24p. (J). (gr. 1-4). lib. bdg. 20.64 (978-1-58952-070-7(X)) Rourke Publishing, LLC.

Klingel, Cynthia Fitterer & Noyed, Robert B. Lewis & Clark: Explorers. 2002. (Spirit of America: Our People Ser.). (Illus.). 32p. (J). (gr. 2-6). 27.07 (978-1-56766-164-4(5)) Child's World, Inc.

Knudsen, Anders. Antoine de la Mothe Cadillac: French Settlements at Detroit & Louisiana. 2006. (In the Footsteps of Explorers Ser.). (Illus.). 32p. (J). (gr. 3-9). (978-0-7787-2429-2(8)); pap. (978-0-7787-2465-0(4)) Crabtree Publishing Co.

Knudsen, Anders. Sir John Franklin: The Search for the Northwest Passage. 2007. (Illus.). 32p. (J). (gr. 3-9). (***978-0-7787-2420-9(4)***); pap. (***978-0-7787-2456-8(5)***) Crabtree Publishing Co.

Knudsen, Shannon. Leif Eriksson. Oldroyd, Mark, illus. 2005. (On My Own Biography Ser.). 48p. (J). (gr. 3-7). pap. 5.95 (978-1-57505-828-3(6)); (ps-7). 25.26 (978-1-57505-649-4(6) , Carolrhoda Bks.) Lerner Publishing Group.

Koestler-Grack, Rachel A. Hernando Cortes: And the Fall of the Aztecs. Goetzmann, William H., ed. 2005. (Explorers of New Lands Ser.). (Illus.). 158p. (J). (ps-8). lib. bdg. 30.00 (978-0-7910-8609-4(7) , Chelsea Hse.) Facts On File, Inc.

—Vasco Da Gama: And the Sea Route to India. Goetzmann, William H., ed. 2005. (Explorers of New Lands Ser.). (Illus.). 146p. (J). (ps-8). lib. bdg. 30.00 (978-0-7910-8611-7(9) , Chelsea Hse.) Facts On File, Inc.

Kozar, Richard. Lewis & Clark: Explorers of the Louisiana Purchase. 2000. (Explorers of the New World Ser.). (Illus.). 64p. (J). (gr. 4 up). 25.00 (978-0-7910-5513-7(2) , Chelsea Hse.) Facts On File, Inc.

Kramer, S. A. Who Was Ferdinand Magellan? Wolf, Elizabeth & Harrison, Nancy, illus. 2004. (Who Was...? Ser.). 112p. (J). (gr. 3-7). pap. 4.99 (978-0-448-43105-5(X) , Grosset & Dunlap) Penguin Group (USA) Inc.

Kramer, Sydelle. Who Was Daniel Boone? Ulrich, George, illus. 2006. (Who Was... ? Ser.). 112p. (J). (gr. 2-5). pap. 4.99 (978-0-448-43902-0(6) , Grosset & Dunlap) Penguin Group (USA) Inc.

Kudlinski, Kathleen. Christopher Columbus: Young Explorer. 2005. 199p. (J). lib. bdg. 18.46 (***978-1-4242-1727-4(X)***) Fitzgerald Bks.

Lackey, Jennifer D. B. Jacques Cartier: Exploring the St. Lawrence River. 2006. (In the Footsteps of Explorers Ser.). (Illus.). 32p. (J). (gr. 3-9). pap. (978-0-7787-2466-7(2)); lib. bdg. (978-0-7787-2430-8(1)) Crabtree Publishing Co.

Landau, Elaine. Ferdinand Magellan. 2006. (History Maker Bios Ser.). (Illus.). 48p. (J). (gr. 3-7). 26.60 (978-0-8225-2942-2(4) , Lerner Pubns.) Lerner Publishing Group.

Larkin, Tanya. Christopher Columbus. 2001. (Famous Explorers Ser.). (Illus.). 24p. (J). (gr. 3). lib. bdg. 18.75 (978-0-8239-5554-1(0) , PowerKids Pr.) Rosen Publishing Group, Inc., The.

—Famous Explorers - Set 1, 6 bks. Incl. Christopher Columbus. lib. bdg. 18.75 (978-0-8239-5554-1(0)); Hernando de Soto. lib. bdg. 18.75 (978-0-8239-5557-2(5)); John Cabot. lib. bdg. 18.75 (978-0-8239-5553-4(2)); Sir Francis Drake. lib. bdg. 18.75 (978-0-8239-5556-5(7)); Sir Walter Raleigh. lib. bdg. 18.75 (978-0-8239-5558-9(3)); Vasco da Gama. lib. bdg. 18.75 (978-0-8239-5555-8(9)); 24p. (J). (gr. 3). 2001. (Illus.). Set lib. bdg. 112.50 (978-0-8239-7063-6(9) , PowerKids Pr.) Rosen Publishing Group, Inc., The.

—Sir Francis Drake. 2001. (Famous Explorers Ser.). (Illus.). 24p. (J). (gr. 3). lib. bdg. 18.75 (978-0-8239-5556-5(7) , PowerKids Pr.) Rosen Publishing Group, Inc., The.

—Sir Walter Raleigh. 2001. (Famous Explorers Ser.). (Illus.). 24p. (J). (gr. 3). lib. bdg. 18.75 (978-0-8239-5558-9(3) , PowerKids Pr.) Rosen Publishing Group, Inc., The.

—Vasco da Gama. 2001. (Famous Explorers Ser.). (Illus.). 24p. (J). (gr. 3). lib. bdg. 18.75 (978-0-8239-5555-8(9) , PowerKids Pr.) Rosen Publishing Group, Inc., The.

Leavitt, Amie. Christopher Columbus. 2007. (What's So Great About... ? Ser.). 32p. (J). lib. bdg. 25.70 (***978-1-58415-578-2(7)***) Mitchell Lane Pubs., Inc.

Levene, Rebecca. Captain Cook. 2005. (Illus.). 64p. (J). 8.95 (978-0-7945-1051-0(5) , Usborne) EDC Publishing.

The Library of Explorers & Exploration: Sets 1 & 2, 12 bks. 2002. (Illus.). (YA). (gr. 5-8). lib. bdg. 273.00 (978-0-8239-4073-8(X) , Rosen Central) Rosen Publishing Group, Inc., The.

Lilly, Melinda. The Journey of Columbus. 2002. (Rourke Discovery Library). (Illus.). 24p. (J). lib. bdg. 20.64 (978-1-58952-358-6(X)) Rourke Publishing, LLC.

Loker, Aleck. Fearless Captain: The Adventures of John Smith. 2006. (Founders of the Republic Ser.). 176p. (J). lib. bdg. 26.95 (978-1-931798-83-9(4)) Reynolds, Morgan Inc.

Lorenz Books Staff & Adams, Simon. Exploration & Discovery: Charts Extraordinary Journeys into the Unknown, 4 vols. 2000. (Exploring History Ser.). (Illus.). 64p. (gr. 3-7). 12.95 (978-0-7548-0443-7(7)) Anness Publishing GBR. *Dist:* National Bk. Network.

Malam, John. Thor Heyerdahl. 1999. (Tell Me about Ser.). (Illus.). 24p. (gr. 2-5). lib. bdg. 19.93 (978-1-57505-364-6(0)) Lerner Publishing Group.

Manning, Ruth. Francisco Pizarro. (Groundbreakers Ser.). (Illus.). 48p. (J). (gr. 5-7). 2002. pap. 8.50 (978-1-58810-341-3(2) , 91092); 2000. lib. bdg. 25.64 (978-1-57572-369-3(7)) Heinemann Library.

—Francisco Pizarro. 2001. (gr. 5-8). lib. bdg. 17.05 (978-0-613-87922-4(8)) Tandem Library Bks.

—Henry Hudson. (Groundbreakers Ser.). 48p. (J). (gr. 5-7). 2002. pap. 8.50 (978-1-58810-342-0(0) , 91093); 2000. (Illus.). lib. bdg. 25.64 (978-1-57572-370-9(0)) Heinemann Library.

—Henry Hudson. 2001. (gr. 5-8). lib. bdg. 17.05 (978-0-613-86815-0(3)) Tandem Library Bks.

—Hernando de Soto. 2000. (Groundbreakers Ser.). (Illus.). 48p. (J). (gr. 5-7). lib. bdg. 25.64 (978-1-57572-388-4(3)) Heinemann Library.

—Juan Ponce de Leon. 2000. (Groundbreakers Ser.). (Illus.). 48p. (J). (gr. 5-7). lib. bdg. 25.64 (978-1-57572-376-1(X)) Heinemann Library.

Manson, Ainslie. Alexander MacKenzie: From Canada by Land. 2003. (Illus.). (J). pap. (978-0-88899-483-7(4)) Douglas & McIntyre, Ltd.

Marcovitz, Hal. Coronado to Escalate: Francisco Coronado & the Exploration of the American Southwest. 1999. (Explorers of the New World Ser.). (Illus.). 64p. (J). (gr. 4 up). 31.00 (978-0-7910-5515-1(9) , Chelsea Hse.) Facts On File, Inc.

—John C. Fremont: Pathfinder of the West. 2001. (Explorers of New Worlds Ser.). (Illus.). (J). 63p. pap. 25.00 (978-0-7910-6431-3(X)); 64p. 25.00 (978-0-7910-6430-6(1)) Facts On File, Inc. (Chelsea Hse.).

Marsh, Carole. Francisco de Coronado. 2002. (One Thousand Readers Ser.). (Illus.). 12p. (J). (gr. k-4). 2.95 (978-0-635-01567-9(6) , 15676) Gallopade International.

—Jacques Cartier. 2002. (One Thousand Readers Ser.). (Illus.). 12p. (J). (gr. k-4). 2.95 (978-0-635-01540-2(4) , 15404) Gallopade International.

—Jean Nicolet. 2002. (One Thousand Readers Ser.). (Illus.). 12p. (J). (gr. k-4). 2.95 (978-0-635-01551-8(X), 1551X) Gallopade International.

—Lewis & Clark Go on a Hike. 2003. 32p. (J). (gr. 3-8). pap. 5.95 (978-0-635-02122-9(6)) Gallopade International.

—Louis Jolliet. 2002. (One Thousand Readers Ser.). (Illus.). 12p. (J). (gr. k-4). 2.95 (978-0-635-01494-8(7), 14947) Gallopade International.

—Medard Groseilliers. 2002. (One Thousand Readers Ser.). (Illus.). 12p. (J). (gr. k-4). 2.95 (978-0-635-01539-6(0), 15390) Gallopade International.

—Nicolas Perrot. 2002. (One Thousand Readers Ser.). (Illus.). 12p. (J). (gr. k-4). 2.95 (978-0-635-01528-0(5), 15285) Gallopade International.

—Robert de La Salle. 2002. (One Thousand Readers Ser.). (Illus.). 12p. (J). (gr. k-4). 2.95 (978-0-635-01522-8(6), 15226) Gallopade International.

Marzollo, Jean. En 1492. 2002. (SPA., Illus.). 32p. (J). (ps-3). pap. 4.99 (978-0-590-49442-7(2), SO5713, Scholastic en Espanol) Scholastic, Inc.

Mass, Wendy. John Cabot: Early Explorer. 2004. (Explorers! Ser.). (Illus.). 48p. (J). lib. bdg. 23.93 (978-0-7660-2144-0(0)) Enslow Pubs., Inc.

Mattern. Earth's Explorers: John & Sebastian Cabot. 2000. (SPA., Illus.). pap. (978-0-7398-3337-7(5)) Steck-Vaughn.

Mattern, Joanne. Leif Eriksson: Viking Explorer. 2004. (Explorers! Ser.). (Illus.). 48p. (J). lib. bdg. 23.93 (978-0-7660-2146-4(7)) Enslow Pubs., Inc.

—The Travels of Ferdinand Magellan. 2000. (Explorers & Exploration Ser.). (Illus.). 48p. (J). (gr. 4-7). lib. bdg. 22.83 (978-0-7398-1484-0(2)) Raintree.

—The Travels of John & Sebastian Cabot. 1999. (Explorers & Exploration Ser.). (Illus.). 48p. (J). (gr. 4-7). lib. bdg. 22.83 (978-0-7398-1492-5(3)) Raintree.

—The Travels of Samuel de Champlain. 1999. (Explorers & Exploration Ser.). (Illus.). 48p. (J). (gr. 4-7). lib. bdg. 22.83 (978-0-7398-1494-9(X)) Raintree.

—The Travels of Vasco da Gama. 1999. (Explorers & Exploration Ser.). (Illus.). 48p. (J). (gr. 4-7). lib. bdg. 22.83 (978-0-7398-1490-1(7)) Raintree.

Matthews, Rupert & Dorling Kindersley Publishing Staff. Explorer. 2005. (Eyewitness Books). (Illus.). 72p. (J). (ps-7). lib. bdg. 19.99 (978-0-7566-1072-2(9)) Dorling Kindersley Publishing, Inc.

Maynard, Charles W. Jedediah Smith: Mountain Man of the American West. 2003. (Famous Explorers of the American West Ser.). (Illus.). 24p. (J). lib. bdg. 18.75 (978-0-8239-6287-7(3), PowerKids Pr.) Rosen Publishing Group, Inc., The.

—John Wesley Powell: Soldier, Scientist, & Explorer. 2003. (Famous Explorers of the American West Ser.). (Illus.). 24p. (J). lib. bdg. 18.75 (978-0-8239-6290-7(3), PowerKids Pr.) Rosen Publishing Group, Inc., The.

McCarthy, Shaun. Sir Walter Raleigh. 2002. (Groundbreakers Ser.). (Illus.). 48p. (J). (gr. 5-7). lib. bdg. 27.07 (978-1-58810-599-8(7)) Heinemann Library.

—Sir Walter Raleigh. 2002. (gr. 5-8). lib. bdg. 16.40 (978-0-613-45831-3(1)) Tandem Library Bks.

McCarthy, Shaun & Cook, James. James Cook. 2002. (Groundbreakers Ser.). (Illus.). 48p. (J). (gr. 5-7). lib. bdg. 27.07 (978-1-58810-595-0(4)) Heinemann Library.

McCormick, Lisa Wade. Christopher Columbus. 2005. (Scholastic News Nonfiction Readers Ser.). (Illus.). 24p. (J). (gr. 1-2). 19.00 (978-0-516-24938-4(X), Children's Pr.) Scholastic Library Publishing.

—Lewis & Clark. 2006. 32p. (gr. 1-2). (YA). pap. 4.95 (978-0-516-21443-6(8)); (Illus.). (J). 20.50 (978-0-516-25039-7(6)) Scholastic Library Publishing. (Children's Pr.).

McCurdy, Michael. Trapped by the Ice! Shackleton's Amazing Antarctic Adventure. McCurdy, Michael, illus. 2002. (Illus.). 40p. (J). pap. 8.95 (978-0-8027-7633-4(7)) Walker & Co.

—Trapped by the Ice: Shackleton's Amazing Antarctic Adventure. 2002. (gr. 3-6). lib. bdg. 17.60 (978-0-613-75493-4(X)) Tandem Library Bks.

McFarren, Kathleen. Marco Polo. 2004. (Fact Finders Ser.). (Illus.). 32p. (J). 16.95 (978-0-7368-2490-3(1)) Capstone Pr., Inc.

—Vasco Da Gama. 2004. (Fact Finders Ser.). (Illus.). 32p. (J). 16.95 (978-0-7368-2491-0(X)) Capstone Pr., Inc.

McNeese, Tim. Christopher Columbus & the Discovery of the Americas. Goetzmann, William H., ed. 2005. (Explorers of New Lands Ser.). (Illus.). 166p. (J). (gr. 4-8). lib. bdg. 30.00 (978-0-7910-8613-1(5), Chelsea Hse.) Facts On File, Inc.

—Marco Polo: And the Realm of Kublai Khan. Goetzmann, William H., ed. 2005. (Explorers of New Lands Ser.). (Illus.). 158p. (J). (gr. 4-8). lib. bdg. 30.00 (978-0-7910-8612-4(7), Chelsea Hse.) Facts On File, Inc.

McPherson, Stephanie Sammartino. Sir Walter Raleigh. 2006. (History Maker Bios Ser.). (Illus.). 48p. (J). (gr. 3-7). 26.60 (978-0-8225-2945-3(9), Lerner Pubns.) Lerner Publishing Group.

Menard, Valerie. Alvar Nunez Cabeza de Vaca. 2002. (Latinos in American History). (Illus.). 56p. (gr. 4-8). lib. bdg. 29.95 (978-1-58415-153-1(6)) Mitchell Lane Pubs., Inc.

Mir Tamim Ansary. Columbus Day. 2nd ed. 2006. (Illus.). 32p. (J). pap. (***978-1-4034-8896-1(7)***) Heinemann Library.

Mitchell, Mark. Raising la Belle. Mitchell, Mark, illus. (Professor Wigglestix & the Weather Ser.). (Illus.). 112p. 10.95 (978-1-57168-703-6(3)) Eakin Pr.

Molzahn, Arlene Bourgeois. Ferdinand Magellan: First Explorer Around the World. 2003. (Illus.). 48p. (J). (gr. 1-4). lib. bdg. 23.93 (978-0-7660-2068-9(1)) Enslow Pubs., Inc.

—Henry Hudson: Explorer of the Hudson River. 2003. (Explorers! Ser.). (Illus.). 48p. (J). lib. bdg. 23.93 (978-0-7660-2070-2(3)) Enslow Pubs., Inc.

—Lewis & Clark: American Explorers. 2003. (Explorers! Ser.). (Illus.). 48p. (J). (gr. 1-4). lib. bdg. 23.93 (978-0-7660-2067-2(3)) Enslow Pubs., Inc.

—Ponce de Leon: Explorer of Florida. 2003. (Explorers! Ser.). (Illus.). 48p. (J). lib. bdg. 23.93 (978-0-7660-2071-9(1)) Enslow Pubs., Inc.

—Vasco Nunez de Balboa: Explorer to the Pacific Ocean. 2004. (Explorers! Ser.). (Illus.). 48p. (J). lib. bdg. 23.93 (978-0-7660-2142-6(4)) Enslow Pubs., Inc.

Morganelli, Adrianna. Christopher Columbus: Sailing to a New World. 2005. (In the Footsteps of Explorers Ser.). (Illus.). 32p. (J). (ps-9). (978-0-7787-2409-4(3)); pap. (978-0-7787-2445-2(X)) Crabtree Publishing Co.

—Samuel de Champlain: From New France to Cape Cod. 2005. (In the Footsteps of Explorers Ser.). (Illus.). 32p. (J). (gr. 3-9). (978-0-7787-2414-8(X)); pap. (978-0-7787-2450-6(6)) Crabtree Publishing Co.

Mountjoy, Shane. Francisco Coronado & the Seven Cities of Gold. Goetzmann, William H., ed. 2005. (Explorers of New Lands Ser.). (Illus.). 142p. (J). (gr. 4-8). lib. bdg. 30.00 (978-0-7910-8631-5(3), Chelsea Hse.) Facts On File, Inc.

—Francisco Pizarro & the Conquest of the Inca. Goetzmann, William H., ed. 2005. (Explorers of New Lands Ser.). (Illus.). 150p. (J). (gr. 4-8). 30.00 (978-0-7910-8614-8(3), Chelsea Hse.) Facts On File, Inc.

Un Mundo Oculto, 6 vols., Vol. 3. (Explorers. Exploradores Nonfiction Sets Ser.). (SPA.). (gr. 3-6). (978-0-7699-0652-2(4)) Shortland Pubns. (U. S. A.) Inc.

Nardo, Don. Sieur de la Salle. 2001. (Exploration Ser.). (Illus.). 64p. (J). (gr. 5-7). 25.50 (978-0-531-11973-0(4), Watts, Franklin) Scholastic Library Publishing.

National Geographic Society Staff. Cultural & Geographical Exploration: Chronicles from National Geographic, 8 bks. 1998. (gr. 5-12). 19.95 (978-0-7910-5096-5(3), Chelsea Hse.) Facts On File, Inc.

Nelson, Sharlene P. & Nelson, Ted W. Jedediah Smith. 2004. (Watts Library). (Illus.). 64p. (J). 25.50 (978-0-531-12287-7(5), Watts, Franklin) Scholastic Library Publishing.

Nemerson, Roy. Daniel Boone. 2005. (Heroes of America Ser.). (Illus.). 240p. (J). (gr. 3-8). lib. bdg. 21.35 (978-1-59679-256-2(6)) ABDO Publishing Co.

New York Public Library Staff & January, Brendan. The New York Public Library Amazing Explorers: A Book of Answers for Kids. 2001. (New York Public Library Books for Kids: Vol. 11). (Illus.). 176p. (gr. 3-7). pap. 13.95 (978-0-471-39291-0(X), Wiley) Wiley, John & Sons, Inc.

Nichols, Catherine. Polar Adventures: A Chapter Book. 2003. (True Tales Ser.). (Illus.). 48p. (J). 22.50 (978-0-516-22920-1(6), Children's Pr.) Scholastic Library Publishing.

Nobleman, Marc Tyler. Juan Ponce de Leon. 2004. (Fact Finders Ser.). (Illus.). 32p. (J). lib. bdg. 22.60 (978-0-7368-2667-9(X)) Capstone Pr., Inc.

Otfinoski, Steven. David Livingstone: Deep in the Heart of Africa. 2006. (Great Explorations Ser.). (Illus.). 80p. (YA). (gr. 5-9). lib. bdg. 32.79 (978-0-7614-2226-6(9), Benchmark Bks.) Cavendish, Marshall Corp.

—Francisco Coronado: In Search of the Seven Cities of Gold. 2002. (Great Explorations Ser.). (Illus.). 76p. (J). 29.93 (978-0-7614-1484-1(3), Benchmark Bks.) Cavendish, Marshall Corp.

—Henry Hudson: In Search of the Northwest Passage. 2007. (Great Explorations Ser.). (Illus.). 80p. (J). lib. bdg. 32.79 (***978-0-7614-2225-9(0)***, Benchmark Bks.) Cavendish, Marshall Corp.

—Juan Ponce de Leon: Discoverer of Florida. 2003. (Great Explorations Ser.). (J). (978-0-7614-1741-5(9)); 29.93 (978-0-7614-1610-4(2)) Cavendish, Marshall Corp. (Benchmark Bks.).

—Vasco Nunez de Balboa: Explorer of the Pacific. 2004. (Great Explorations Ser.). (Illus.). 79p. (J). 29.93 (978-0-7614-1609-8(9), Benchmark Bks.) Cavendish, Marshall Corp.

Owens, Ann-Maureen & Yealland, Jane. The Kids Book of Canadian Exploration. Mantha, John, illus. 2004. (Kids Books Of ... Ser.). 56p. (J). (gr. 3-7). (978-1-55337-353-7(7)) Kids Can Pr., Ltd.

Parker, Lewis K. Spanish Colonies in the Americas. 2003. (Reading Power Ser.). (Illus.). 24p. (J). lib. bdg. 17.25 (978-0-8239-6471-0(X), PowerKids Pr.) Rosen Publishing Group, Inc., The.

Penner, Lucille Recht. Ice Wreck. LaFleur, David, illus. 2004. (Stepping Stones Ser.). 48p. (J). (gr. k-3). pap. 3.99 (978-0-307-26408-4(4), Random Hse. Bks. for Young Readers) Random Hse. Children's Bks.

Petrie, Kristin. Christopher Columbus. 2004. (Explorers Set I Ser.). (Illus.). 32p. (J). (gr. k-6). lib. bdg. 22.78 (978-1-59197-595-3(6)) ABDO Publishing Co.

—Daniel Boone. 2004. (Explorers Set I Ser.). (J). (gr. k-6). lib. bdg. 22.78 (978-1-59197-592-2(1)) ABDO Publishing Co.

—Explorers Set I. 2004. (Illus.). (J). (gr. k-6). lib. bdg. 273.36 (978-1-59197-591-5(3), Checkerboard Library) ABDO Publishing Co.

—Ferdinand Magellan. 2007. (Illus.). 32p. (J). 22.78 (978-1-59679-744-4(4)) ABDO Publishing Co.

—Francisco Vasquez de Coronado. 2004. (Explorers Set I Ser.). (J). (gr. k-6). lib. bdg. 22.78 (978-1-59197-597-7(2)) ABDO Publishing Co.

—Henry Hudson. 2007. (Illus.). 32p. (J). 22.78 (978-1-59679-741-3(X)) ABDO Publishing Co.

—Hernan Cortes. 2004. (Explorers Set I Ser.). (Illus.). 32p. (J). (gr. k-6). lib. bdg. 22.78 (978-1-59197-598-4(0)) ABDO Publishing Co.

—Hernando de Soto. 2004. (Explorers Set I Ser.). (J). (gr. k-6). lib. bdg. 22.78 (978-1-59197-600-4(6)) ABDO Publishing Co.

—Jacques Cartier. 2004. (Explorers Set I Ser.). (Illus.). 32p. (J). (gr. k-6). lib. bdg. 22.78 (978-1-59197-594-6(8)) ABDO Publishing Co.

—James Cook. 2004. (Explorers Set I Ser.). (Illus.). 32p. (J). (gr. k-6). lib. bdg. 22.78 (978-1-59197-596-0(4)) ABDO Publishing Co.

—John C. Fremont. 2004. (Explorers Ser.). (Illus.). 32p. (J). (gr. k-6). lib. bdg. 22.78 (978-1-59197-602-8(2), Checkerboard Library) ABDO Publishing Co.

—John Cabot. 2004. (Explorers Set I Ser.). (J). (gr. k-6). lib. bdg. 22.78 (978-1-59197-593-9(X)) ABDO Publishing Co.

—John Smith. 2007. (Illus.). 32p. (J). 22.78 (978-1-59679-751-2(7)) ABDO Publishing Co.

—Juan Ponce de Leon. 2007. (Illus.). 32p. (J). 22.78 (978-1-59679-742-0(8)) ABDO Publishing Co.

—Lewis & Clark. 2007. (Illus.). 32p. (J). 22.78 (978-1-59679-743-7(6)) ABDO Publishing Co.

—Marco Polo. 2007. (Rabbit Ears Ser.). (Illus.). 32p. (J). (gr. k-5). 22.78 (978-1-59679-747-5(9)) ABDO Publishing Co.

—Marquette & Jolliet. 2007. (Illus.). 32p. (J). 22.78 (978-1-59679-745-1(2)) ABDO Publishing Co.

—Robert Peary. 2007. (Rabbit Ears Ser.). (Illus.). 32p. (J). (gr. k-5). 22.78 (978-1-59679-746-8(0)) ABDO Publishing Co.

—La Salle. 2007. (Illus.). 32p. (J). 22.78 (978-1-59679-750-5(9)) ABDO Publishing Co.

—Sir Francis Drake. 2004. (Explorers Ser.). (Illus.). 32p. (J). (gr. k-6). lib. bdg. 22.78 (978-1-59197-601-1(4), Checkerboard Library) ABDO Publishing Co.

—Sir Walter Raleigh. 2007. (Illus.). 32p. (J). 22.78 (978-1-59679-748-2(7)) ABDO Publishing Co.

—Vasco Da Gama. 2004. (Explorers Ser.). (Illus.). 32p. (J). (gr. k-6). lib. bdg. 22.78 (978-1-59197-603-5(0), Checkerboard Library) ABDO Publishing Co.

—Vasco Nuñez de Balboa. 2007. (Illus.). 32p. (J). 22.78 (978-1-59679-740-6(1)) ABDO Publishing Co.

Play Bac Edu-Team, ed. Explorers: From Egypt to Mars. 2007. (Illus.). 10p. (J). 6.95 (***978-1-60214-007-3(3)***) Play Bac Publishing, USA.

Polking, Kirk. Oceanographers & Explorers of the Sea. 1999. (Collective Biographies Ser.). (Illus.). 128p. (YA). (gr. 6-12). lib. bdg. 20.95 (978-0-7660-1113-7(5)) Enslow Pubs., Inc.

Powell, John Wesley. The Diary of John Wesley Powell: Exploring the Grand Canyon. Roop, Connie & Roop, Peter, eds. 2000. (In My Own Words Ser.). (Illus.). 96p. (J). (gr. 5 up). lib. bdg. 24.21 (978-0-7614-1013-3(9), Benchmark Bks.) Cavendish, Marshall Corp.

Price Hossell, Karen. Francisco Coronado. (Groundbreakers Ser.). (Illus.). 48p. (J). 2003. (gr. 5-7). lib. bdg. 27.07 (978-1-4034-0242-4(6)); 2002. pap. 8.50 (978-1-4034-0478-7(X)) Heinemann Library.

—John C. Fremont. (Groundbreakers Ser.). (Illus.). 48p. (J). 2003. (gr. 5-7). lib. bdg. 27.07 (978-1-4034-0244-8(2)); 2002. pap. 8.50 (978-1-4034-0480-0(1)) Heinemann Library.

Que Pasa Alla Afuera?, 6 vols., Vol. 2. (Explorers. Exploradores Nonfiction Sets Ser.). (SPA.). 32p. (gr. 3-6). 44.95 (978-0-7699-0644-7(3)) Shortland Pubns. (U. S. A.) Inc.

Ransom, Candice. Daniel Boone. 2006. (History Maker Bios Ser.). (Illus.). 48p. (J). (gr. 3-7). 26.60 (978-0-8225-2941-5(6), Lerner Pubns.) Lerner Publishing Group.

Ransom, Candice F. Lewis & Clark. (History Maker Bios Ser.). (J). 2003. (Illus.). 48p. (gr. 2-4). 26.60 (978-0-8225-0394-1(8), Lerner Pubns.); 2002. pap. 6.95 (978-0-8225-1562-3(8)) Lerner Publishing Group.

Raum, Elizabeth. Explorers. 2007. (J). (***978-1-4109-2963-1(9)***); pap. (***978-1-4109-2984-6(1)***) Steck-Vaughn.

—Lewis & Clark's Continental Journey. 2007. (J). (***978-1-4034-9757-4(5)***) Heinemann Library.

Ray, Deborah Kogan. Down the Colorado: The Story of John Wesley Powell, the One-Armed Explorer. 2007. (Illus.). 48p. (J). (gr. 3 up). 17.00 (978-0-374-31838-3(7)) Farrar, Straus & Giroux.

Reid, Struan. Christopher Columbus. 2002. (Groundbreakers Ser.). 48p. (J). (gr. 5-7). (Illus.). lib. bdg. 27.07 (978-1-58810-593-6(8)); pap. 8.50 (978-1-58810-986-6(0), 91601) Heinemann Library.

—Ferdinand Magellan. (Groundbreakers Ser.). (Illus.). 48p. (J). (gr. 5-7). 2002. pap. 8.50 (978-1-58810-369-7(2), 91091); 2001. lib. bdg. 25.64 (978-1-58810-045-0(6)) Heinemann Library.

—Marco Polo. (Groundbreakers Ser.). 48p. (J). (gr. 5-7). 2002. pap. 8.50 (978-1-58810-371-0(4), 91097); 2001. (Illus.). lib. bdg. 25.64 (978-1-58810-047-4(2)) Heinemann Library.

Reid, Struan & Champion, Neil. Explorers, 8 bks. (Illus.). (J). Set. (gr. 4-6). lib. bdg. 204.22 (978-1-58810-182-2(7)); Set 2. 2001. (gr. 5-7). lib. bdg. 102.56 (978-1-58810-010-8(3)) Heinemann Library.

Rice, Earle. Alexandra David-Neel: Explorer at the Roof of the World. 2004. (Women in Explorers Ser.). 30.00 (978-0-7910-7715-3(2), Chelsea Hse.) Facts On File, Inc.

Rink, Paul. Admiral Richard Byrd: Alone in the Antarctic. 2006. (Sterling Point Bks.). (Illus.). 192p. (J). 12.95 (978-1-4027-3189-1(2)) Sterling Publishing Co., Inc.

Roberts, Russell. Pedro Menendez de Aviles. 2002. (Latinos in American History). (Illus.). 56p. (gr. 4-8). lib. bdg. 29.95 (978-1-58415-150-0(1)) Mitchell Lane Pubs., Inc.

Rodger, Ellen. Lewis & Clark: Opening the American West. 2005. (In the Footsteps of Explorers Ser.). (Illus.). 32p. (J). (ps-9). pap. (978-0-7787-2446-9(8)) Crabtree Publishing Co.

Roop, Connie, et al. Escape from the Ice: Shackleton & the Endurance. 2001. (Hello Reader! Ser.). (Illus.). 48p. (J). (gr. 2-4). pap. 3.99 (978-0-439-20640-2(5), Cartwheel Bks.) Scholastic, Inc.

Ross, Michael Elsohn. Exploring the Earth with John Wesley Powell. Smith, Wendy, illus. 2006. 48p. (J). (gr. 4-10). reprint ed. 19.00 (978-1-4223-5581-7(0)) DIANE Publishing Co.

—Exploring the Earth with John Wesley Powell. Smith, Wendy, illus. 2005. (Naturalist's Apprentice Biographies Ser.). 48p. (gr. 3-6). lib. bdg. 19.93 (978-1-57505-254-0(7)) Lerner Publishing Group.

Ryan, P. Explorers & Mapmakers. 2000. 48p. (J). pap. 13.99 (978-0-237-52231-5(4), Evans Brothers, Limited) Evans Publishing Group GBR. *Dist:* Independent Pubs. Group.

Saffer, Barbara. Henry Hudson: Ill-Fated Explorer of North America's Coast. 2001. (Explorers of New Worlds Ser.). (Illus.). (J). 63p. pap. 25.00 (978-0-7910-6437-5(9)); 64p. 25.00 (978-0-7910-6436-8(0)) Facts On File, Inc. (Chelsea Hse.).

—Henry Hudson: Ill-Fated Explorer of North America's Coast. 2002. (gr. 3-6). lib. bdg. 17.60 (978-0-613-65422-7(6)) Tandem Library Bks.

—Polar Exploration Adventures. 2000. (Dangerous Adventures Ser.). (Illus.). 48p. (J). (gr. 3-4). lib. bdg. 21.26 (978-0-7368-0572-8(9), Capstone High-Interest Bks.) Capstone Pr., Inc.

Salem Press Staff, ed. Explorers, 2 vols., Vol. 2. 1998. (Magill's Choice Ser.). (Illus.). 590p. (gr. 9 up). lib. bdg. 104.00 (978-0-89356-970-9(4), L7, Magill's Choice) Salem Pr., Inc.

Sanders, Walter. England Explores the Americas. 2005. 42.00 (***978-1-4108-4611-2(3)***) Benchmark Education Co.

—France Explores the Americas. 2005. 39.00 (***978-1-4108-4604-4(0)***) Benchmark Education Co.

—Spain Explores the Americas. 2005. 39.00 (***978-1-4108-4597-9(4)***) Benchmark Education Co.

Sanderson, Jeanette. Read-aloud Plays. 2002. (Read Aloud Plays Ser.). (Illus.). 64p. (gr. 4-8). pap. 11.95 (978-0-439-25181-5(8)) Scholastic, Inc.

Sandler, Michael. Explorers of the Americas. 2005. (Navigators Ser.). (J). pap. 42.00 (***978-1-4108-5107-9(9)***) Benchmark Education Co.

Santella, Andrew. Daniel Boone & the Cumberland Gap. (Cornerstones of Freedomtrade;, Second Ser.). 48p. (J). 2007. 5.95 (***978-0-531-18687-9(3)***); 2002. (Illus.). (gr. 4-6). 26.00 (978-0-516-22526-5(X)) Scholastic Library Publishing. (Children's Pr.).

—Henry Hudson. 2001. (gr. 3-6). lib. bdg. 17.60 (978-0-613-51651-8(6)) Tandem Library Bks.

—Sieur de La Salle. 2002. (Groundbreakers Ser.). (Illus.). 48p. (J). (gr. 5-7). lib. bdg. 27.07 (978-1-58810-598-1(9)) Heinemann Library.

Sapp, Richard. Lewis & Clark on Their Journey to the Pacific. 2006. (In the Footsteps of American Heroes Ser.). (Illus.). 64p. (J). pap. (978-0-8368-6434-2(4)); lib. bdg. 32.67 (978-0-8368-6429-8(8)) Stevens, Gareth Inc. (World Almanac Library).

Schaefer, Lola M. Christopher Columbus. Saunders-Smith, Gail, ed. 2002. (First Biographies Ser.). (Illus.). 24p. (J). (gr. k-1). lib. bdg. 15.93 (978-0-7368-1173-6(7), Pebble Bks.) Capstone Pr., Inc.

—Christopher Columbus. 2005. (First Biographies Ser.). 24p. (YA). (gr. k-3). pap. (978-0-7368-9368-8(7), Pebble Bks.) Capstone Pr., Inc.

Schanzer, Rosalyn. How Ben Franklin Stole the Lightning. Schanzer, Rosalyn, illus. 2003. (Illus.). 40p. (J). lib. bdg. 17.89 (978-0-688-16994-7(5)); (gr. 1-6). 16.99 (978-0-688-16993-0(7)) HarperCollins Pubs.

—John Smith Escapes Again! Schanzer, Rosalyn, illus. 2006. (Illus.). 64p. (J). (gr. 4-9). 16.95 (978-0-7922-5930-5(0)); lib. bdg. 25.90 (978-0-7922-5931-2(9)) National Geographic Society. (National Geographic Children's Bks.).

Senker, Cath. Magellan's Voyage Around the World. 2007. (J). (***978-1-4034-9754-3(0)***) Heinemann Library.

—Marco Polo's Travels on Asia's Silk Road. 2007. (J). (***978-1-4034-9751-2(6)***) Heinemann Library.

Seres Extranos, 6 vols. (Explorers. Exploradores Nonfiction Sets Ser.). (SPA.). 32p. (gr. 3-6). 44.95 (978-0-7699-0628-7(1)) Shortland Pubns. (U. S. A.) Inc.

Shafer, Susan. Ponce de Leon & the Fountain of Youth. 2005. 40.00 (***978-1-4108-4231-2(2)***) Benchmark Education Co.

Shields, Charles J. John Cabot & the Rediscovery of North America. 2001. (Explorers of New Worlds Ser.). (Illus.). (J). (gr. 4-8). 63p. pap. 25.00 (978-0-7910-6439-9(5)); 64p. 25.00 (978-0-7910-6438-2(7)) Facts On File, Inc. (Chelsea Hse.).

—John Cabot & the Rediscovery of North America. 2002. (gr. 3-6). lib. bdg. 17.60 (978-0-613-65430-2(7)) Tandem Library Bks.

Slavicek, Louise Chipley. Juan Ponce de Leon. 2003. (Great Hispanic Heritage Ser.). (Illus.). 112p. (gr. 6-12). 30.00 (978-0-7910-7255-4(X)); pap. 30.00 (978-0-7910-7518-0(4)) Facts On File, Inc. (Chelsea Hse.).

Smalley, Roger. The Adventures of Marco Polo. Carter, Greg, illus. 2005. (Graphic Library). 32p. (J). 22.60 (978-0-7368-3830-6(9)) Capstone Pr., Inc.

Smith, James K. David Thompson. 2001. (Canadians Ser.). (Illus.). 64p. (978-1-55041-493-6(3)) Fitzhenry & Whiteside, Ltd.

Smith, K. C. Shipwrecks of the Explorers. 2000. (Illus.). (978-0-606-20915-1(8)) Tandem Library Bks.

Smith, M. Ice Man: The Remarkable Adventures of Antarctic Explorer Tom Crean. 2004. (Illus.). 128p. (J). pap. 13.95 (978-1-903464-44-1(7)) Collins Pr., The IRL. *Dist:* Dufour Editions, Inc.

Smith, Michael. Boss: The Remarkable Adventures of Ernest Shackleton, Heroic Antarctic Explorer. Brady, Annie, illus. 2005. (SPA.). 128p. pap. 12.95 (978-1-903464-57-1(9)) Collins Pr., The IRL. *Dist:* Dufour Editions, Inc.

E F G

Snowden, Maxine. Polar Explorers for Kids: Historic Expeditions to the Arctic & Antarctic with 21 Activities. 2003. (For Kids Ser.). 160p. (J). pap. 16.95 (978-1-55652-500-1(1)) Chicago Review Pr., Inc.

Somervill, Barbara A. Francisco Pizarro: Conqueror of the Incas. 2004. (Signature Lives Ser.). (Illus.). 112p. (J). 30.60 (978-0-7565-0815-9(0) , 1240121) Compass Point Bks.

Sonneborn, Liz. Samuel de Champlain. 2002. (Watts Library). (Illus.). 64p. (J). (gr. 5-7). pap. 8.95 (978-0-531-16580-5(9) , Watts, Franklin) Scholastic Library Publishing.

Southwater Staff. Encyclopedia of Civilizations, Explorers & Conquerers. 2000. (Illus.). 256p. (J). 29.95 (978-1-84215-157-0(6)) Anness Publishing, Inc.

Souza, Dorothy M. John C. Fremont. 2004. (Watts Library). (Illus.). 64p. (J). (gr. 5-7). pap. 8.95 (978-0-531-16652-9(X)); 25.50 (978-0-531-12288-4(3)) Scholastic Library Publishing. (Watts, Franklin).

—John Wesley Powell. 2004. (Watts Library). (Illus.). 64p. (J). (gr. 5-7). pap. 8.95 (978-0-531-16653-6(8)); 25.50 (978-0-531-12289-1(1)) Scholastic Library Publishing. (Watts, Franklin).

Spangenburg, Ray & Moser, Diane Kit. Robert Ballard: Tbd. 2008. (Makers of Modern Science Ser.). 160p. (gr. 6-12). 29.95 (****978-0-8160-6173-0(4)*** , Chelsea Hse.) Facts On File, Inc.

St. George, Judith. So You Want to Be an Explorer? Small, David, illus. 2005. 56p. (J). (gr. 3-6). 16.99 (978-0-399-23868-0(9) , Philomel) Penguin Group (USA) Inc.

Steck-Vaughn Staff. Explorers & Exploration, Set 2. 2001. (Illus.). (J). pap. (978-0-7398-4124-2(6)) Steck-Vaughn.

Stefoff, Rebecca. Exploration. 2004. (J). 27.07 (978-0-7614-1640-1(4) , Benchmark Bks.) Cavendish, Marshall Corp.

—Exploring the New World. 2000. (North American Historical Atlases Ser.). (Illus.). 48p. (J). (gr. 4-8). lib. bdg. 27.07 (978-0-7614-1056-0(2) , Benchmark Bks.) Cavendish, Marshall Corp.

Strathloch, Robert. Marco Polo. 2002. (Historical Biographies Ser.). (Illus.). 32p. (J). (gr. 2-4). lib. bdg. 22.79 (978-1-58810-567-7(9)) Heinemann Library.

—Marco Polo. 2002. (gr. 3-6). lib. bdg. 15.25 (978-0-613-45790-3(0)) Tandem Library Bks.

Streissguth, Thomas. Lewis & Clark: Explorers of the Northwest. 1998. (Historical American Biographies Ser.). (Illus.). 128p. (YA). (gr. 6-12). lib. bdg. 26.60 (978-0-7660-1016-1(3)) Enslow Pubs., Inc.

Streissguth, Thomas, tr. Francisco Pizarro. 2004. (Fact Finders Ser.). (Illus.). 32p. (J). 16.95 (978-0-7368-2488-0(X)) Capstone Pr., Inc.

Suen, Anastasia. Trappers & Mountain Men. 2007. (Events in American History Ser.). (Illus.). 48p. (J). (gr. 4-6). lib. bdg. 29.93 (978-1-60044-134-9(3)) Rourke Publishing, LLC.

Sundel, Al. Christopher Columbus & the Age of Exploration in World History. 2002. (In World History Ser.). (Illus.). 128p. (YA). (gr. 5-12). lib. bdg. 26.60 (978-0-7660-1820-4(2)) Enslow Pubs., Inc.

Sundling, Charles W. Explorers of the Frontier. 2000. (Frontier Land Ser.). (Illus.). 32p. (J). (gr. 3-8). lib. bdg. 24.21 (978-1-57765-044-7(1) , ABDO & Daughters) ABDO Publishing Co.

Sussman, Ellen. Early Explorers. Carrozza, John & Rogers, Kathy, eds. Adams, Elizabeth, illus. 2000. (Famous Faces Ser.). 8p. (J). pap. 6.95 (978-1-56472-278-2(3)) Edupress, Inc.

Sutcliffe, Jane. Juan Ponce de Leon. 2006. (History Maker Bios Ser.). (Illus.). 48p. (J). (gr. 3-7). 26.60 (978-0-8225-2944-6(0) , Lerner Pubns.) Lerner Publishing Group.

Taylor-Butler, Christine. Explorers of North America. (True Booktrade;: American History Ser.). 48p. (J). 2008. pap. 6.95 (****978-0-531-14782-5(7));*** 2007. (Illus.). (gr. 3-5). lib. bdg. 26.00 (****978-0-531-12632-5(3))*** Scholastic Library Publishing. (Children's Pr.).

Todd, Margaret. Explorers. 2004. (Illus.). (J). (gr. 4-7). 48.00 (978-1-57336-399-0(5) , I5003) Interaction Pubs., Inc.

Vail, Martha. Exploring the Pacific. Bowman, John S. & Isserman, Maurice, eds. 2005. (Discovery & Exploration Ser.). (Illus.). 176p. (J). (gr. 6-12). 40.00 (978-0-8160-5258-5(1)) Facts On File, Inc.

Vergés, Gloria & Vergés, Oiol. La Edad Moderna: Viaje a Traves de la Historia. Rius, María, illus. 2002. (SPA.). 29p. (J). (gr. 2-6). reprint ed. pap. 15.00 (978-0-7567-6061-8(5)) DIANE Publishing Co.

Wade, Mary Dodson. Christopher Columbus. 2003. (Rookie Biographies Ser.). (Illus.). 32p. (J). (gr. 1-2). 20.50 (978-0-516-22851-8(X) , Children's Pr.) Scholastic Library Publishing.

Wagner, Heather Lehr. Mary Kingsley: Explorer of the Congo. 2004. (Women Explorers Ser.). 120p. 30.00 (978-0-7910-7714-6(4) , Chelsea Hse.) Facts On File, Inc.

Waldman, Stuart. The Last River: John Wesley Powell & the Colorado River Exploring Expedition. Manchess, Gregory, illus. 2005. (Great Explorers Ser.). 48p. (J). (gr. 4-12). 19.95 (978-1-931414-09-8(2)) Mikaya Pr.

—Magellan's World. Manchess, Gregory, illus. 2007. (Great Explorers Ser.). 48p. (J). (gr. 4-8). 22.95 (****978-1-931414-19-7(X))*** Mikaya Pr.

Waldman, Stuart. We Asked for Nothing: The Remarkable Journey of Cabeza de Vaca. McNeely, Tom, illus. 2003. (Great Explorers Ser.). 48p. (J). (gr. 4-8). 19.95 (978-1-931414-07-4(6)) Mikaya Pr.

Warrick, Karen Clemens. The Perilous Search for the Fabled Northwest Passage in American History. 2004. (In American History Ser.). (Illus.). 128p. (J). lib. bdg. 26.60 (978-0-7660-2148-8(3)) Enslow Pubs., Inc.

—The Race for the North Pole & Robert Peary in World History. 2003. (In World History Ser.). (Illus.). 128p. (J). (gr. 5-12). lib. bdg. 26.60 (978-0-7660-1933-1(0)) Enslow Pubs., Inc.

Weatherford, Carole Boston. I, Matthew Henson. Velasquez, Eric, illus. 2007. 32p. (J). 16.95 (****978-0-8027-9688-2(5))*** Walker & Co.

Weidt, Maryann N. Matthew Henson. (History Maker Bios Ser.). (Illus.). 48p. (J). 2003. (gr. 2-4). 26.60 (978-0-8225-0397-2(2)); 2002. pap. 6.95 (978-0-8225-1565-4(2)) Lerner Publishing Group. (Lerner Pubns.).

Weinberger, Kimberly. Let's Read about Christopher Columbus. Van Wright, Cornelius & Hu, Ying-Hwa, illus. 2001. (Scholastic First Biographies Ser.). (J). (978-0-439-29546-8(7)) Scholastic, Inc.

Wellman, Sam. David Livingstone: Missionary & Explorer. 1999. (Heroes of the Faith Ser.). (Illus.). 208p. (YA). (gr. 4-7). 14.95 (978-0-7910-5038-5(6) , Chelsea Hse.) Facts On File, Inc.

West, David & Gaff, Jackie. Christopher Columbus: The Life of a Master Navigator & Explorer. 2005. (Illus.). 48p. (J). (gr. 4-6). lib. bdg. 26.50 (978-1-4042-0243-6(9)) Rosen Publishing Group, Inc., The.

Whiting, Jim. Francisco Vasquez de Coronado. 2002. (Latinos in American History). (Illus.). 56p. (gr. 4-8). lib. bdg. 29.95 (978-1-58415-146-3(3)) Mitchell Lane Pubs., Inc.

—Juan Ponce de Leon. 2002. (Latinos in American History). (Illus.). 56p. (gr. 4-8). lib. bdg. 29.95 (978-1-58415-149-4(8)) Mitchell Lane Pubs., Inc.

—The Life & Times of Hernando Cortes. 2006. (Profiles in American History Ser.). (Illus.). 48p. (J). (gr. 4-8). lib. bdg. 29.95 (978-1-58415-449-5(7)) Mitchell Lane Pubs., Inc.

Wilkinson, Paul & Wilkinson, Philip. Explorers. 2002. (Best Ever Ser.). (Illus.). 64p. (J). (gr. 5-9). tchr. ed. 16.95 (978-0-7534-5452-7(1) , Kingfisher) Houghton Mifflin Co. Trade & Reference Div.

Wilkinson, Philip. Civilizations, Exploration & Conquest: The Illustrated History Encyclopedia. 2001. (gr. 3-6). lib. bdg. 30.35 (978-0-613-82097-4(5)) Tandem Library Bks.

Wilkinson, Philip. Explorers. 2007. (Illus.). 63p. (J). reprint ed. 17.00 (****978-1-4223-6727-8(4))*** DIANE Publishing Co.

Williams, Jean Kinney. Cook: Captain James Cook Charts the Pacific Ocean. 2003. (Exploring the World Ser.). (Illus.). 48p. (J). (gr. 4 up). lib. bdg. 22.60 (978-0-7565-0421-2(X)) Compass Point Bks.

Wilson, Wayne. Gaspar de Portola. 2002. (Latinos in American History). (Illus.). 56p. (gr. 4-8). lib. bdg. 29.95 (978-1-58415-148-7(X)) Mitchell Lane Pubs., Inc.

Witteman, Barbara. John Charles Fremont: Western Pathfinder. 2002. (Let Freedom Ring Ser.). (Illus.). 48p. (J). (gr. 3-4). lib. bdg. 22.60 (978-0-7368-1348-8(9) , Bridgestone Bks.) Capstone Pr., Inc.

—Zebulon Pike: Soldier & Explorer. 2002. (Let Freedom Ring Ser.). (Illus.). 48p. (J). (gr. 3-4). lib. bdg. 22.60 (978-0-7368-1351-8(9) , Bridgestone Bks.) Capstone Pr., Inc.

Wittmann, Kelly. The European Rediscovery of America. 2002. (Exploration & Discovery Ser.). (Illus.). 64p. (J). (gr. 5 up). lib. bdg. (978-1-59084-052-8(6)) Mason Crest Pubs.

—Explorers of the American West. 2002. (Exploration & Discovery Ser.). (Illus.). 64p. (YA). (gr. 5 up). lib. bdg. (978-1-59084-049-8(6)) Mason Crest Pubs.

Women Explorers. (J). pap. 4.95 (978-0-88388-203-0(5)) Bellerophon Bks.

Workman Publishing Company Staff & Aronson, Steven M. Explorers. 1999. (Fandex Family Field Guides Ser.). (Illus.). 96p. (J). (gr. 4-7). 9.95 (978-0-7611-1444-4(0) , 11444) Workman Publishing Co., Inc.

Worsley, Frank Arthur. Shackleton's Boat Journey: The Narrative from the Captain of the 'Endurance' 1998. (Illus.). 224p. (gr. 3). pap. 13.95 (978-0-393-31864-7(8) , Norton Paperbacks) Norton, W. W. & Co., Inc.

Worth, Richard. Ponce de Leon & the Age of Spanish Exploration in World History. 2003. (In World History Ser.). (Illus.). 112p. (J). (gr. 5-12). lib. bdg. 26.60 (978-0-7660-1940-9(3)) Enslow Pubs., Inc.

Young, Ian. Amazing Journeys: Following in History's Footsteps. 2003. (High Five Reading Ser.). (Illus.). (J). 64p. lib. bdg. 22.60 (978-0-7368-2790-4(0)); 48p. pap. 23.93 (978-0-7368-2831-4(1)) Capstone Pr., Inc.

Young, Serenity. Richard Francis Burton: Explorer, Scholar, Spy. 2007. (Great Explorations Ser.). (Illus.). 80p. (YA). (gr. 5-9). lib. bdg. 32.79 (****978-0-7614-2222-8(6)*** , Benchmark Bks.) Cavendish, Marshall Corp.

Zannos, Susan. The Life & Times of Marco Polo. 2004. (Biography from Ancient Civilizations Ser.). (Illus.). 48p. (J). (gr. 4-8). lib. bdg. 29.95 (978-1-58415-264-4(8)) Mitchell Lane Pubs., Inc.

Zelenyi, Alexander. Marquette & Jolliet: Quest for the Mississippi. 2006. (In the Footsteps of Explorers Ser.). (Illus.). 32p. (J). (gr. 3-9). (978-0-7787-2431-5(X)); pap. (978-0-7787-2467-4(0)) Crabtree Publishing Co.

Zelenyj, Alexander. Marco Polo: Overland to China. 2005. (In the Footsteps of Explorers Ser.). (Illus.). 32p. (J). (gr. 3-9). (978-0-7787-2417-9(4)); pap. (978-0-7787-2453-7(0)) Crabtree Publishing Co.

Zronik, John Paul. Daniel Boone: Woodsman of Kentucky. 2006. (In the Footsteps of Explorers Ser.). (Illus.). 32p. (J). (gr. 3-9). pap. (978-0-7787-2464-3(6) , 1253442); (978-0-7787-2428-5(X) , 1253442) Crabtree Publishing Co.

—Francisco Pizarro: Journeys Through Peru & South America. 2005. (In the Footsteps of Explorers Ser.). (Illus.). 32p. (J). (ps-9). (978-0-7787-2411-7(5)); pap. (978-0-7787-2447-6(6)) Crabtree Publishing Co.

—Hernando Cortés: Spanish Invader of Mexico. 2006. (In the Footsteps of Explorers Ser.). (Illus.). 32p. (J). (gr. 3-9). (978-0-7787-2434-6(4)) Crabtree Publishing Co.

—Sieur de La Salle: New World Adventurer. 2005. (In the Footsteps of Explorers Ser.). (Illus.). 32p. (J). (gr. 3-9). (978-0-7787-2413-1(1)); pap. (978-0-7787-2449-0(2)) Crabtree Publishing Co.

EXPLORERS—FICTION

Aikins, Dave, illus. At the Carnival. 2005. (J). (****978-1-4156-0769-5(9)*** , Simon Spotlight/Nickelodeon) Simon & Schuster Children's Publishing.

Aikins, Dave, illus. Dance to the Rescue. 2005. (Dora the Explorer Ser.). 24p. (J). pap. 3.99 (978-1-4169-0216-4(3) , Simon Spotlight/Nickelodeon) Simon & Schuster Children's Publishing.

Beinstein, Phoebe. Dora's Color Adventure! Hall, Susan T., illus. 2002. (Dora the Explorer Ser.). 20p. (J). bds. 6.99 (978-0-689-84663-2(0) , Simon Spotlight/Nickelodeon) Simon & Schuster Children's Publishing.

Clancy, Tom. Gameprey. 2000. (gr. 7-12). lib. bdg. 13.00 (978-0-613-81160-6(7)) Tandem Library Bks.

Dixon, George. The Adventures of Yin & Yang. 2002. (Illus.). 193p. (YA). mass mkt. 9.95 (978-0-9721833-2-1(9)) Sleepy D Publishing.

Duble, Kathleen Benner. Quest. 2008. 256p. (J). 15.99 (****978-1-4169-3386-1(7)*** , McElderry, Margaret K.) Simon & Schuster Children's Publishing.

The Explorer: Individual Title Six-Packs. (ps-2). 27.00 (978-0-7635-9448-0(2)) Rigby Education.

Explorer Guide: Leader's Handbook. 2004. (Caravan Ser.). 272p. pap. 12.99 (978-0-8341-2120-1(4)) Beacon Hill Pr. of Kansas City.

Explorer Scout. 2004. (Caravan Ser.). 128p. pap., stu. ed. 9.50 (978-0-8341-2122-5(0)) Beacon Hill Pr. of Kansas City.

Explorer Sentry. 2004. (Caravan Ser.). 128p. pap., stu. ed. 9.50 (978-0-8341-2121-8(2)) Beacon Hill Pr. of Kansas City.

Frederick, Heather Vogel. The Education of Patience Goodspeed. 2004. (Illus.). 320p. (J). 16.95 (978-0-689-86411-7(6)) Simon & Schuster Children's Publishing.

French, Jackie. Rover. 2007. (Illus.). 304p. (J). (gr. 5-8). 16.99 (978-0-06-085078-4(7)); lib. bdg. 17.89 (978-0-06-085079-1(5)) HarperCollins Pubs.

Garfield, Henry. The Lost Voyage of John Cabot. 2004. (Illus.). 320p. (YA). 16.95 (978-0-689-85173-5(1) , Atheneum/Richard Jackson Bks.) Simon & Schuster Children's Publishing.

—The Lost Voyage of John Cabot. l.t. ed. 2004. 326p. 20.95 (978-0-7862-7085-9(3)) Thorndike Pr.

Golden Books Staff. All Around the World! 2007. (Book & CD Ser.). (Illus.). 32p. (J). (ps-2). 9.99 (978-0-375-84026-5(5) , Golden Bks.) Random Hse. Children's Bks.

—Backyard Explorers! 2007. (Color Plus Gatefold Sticker Ser.). (Illus.). 16p. (J). (ps-2). pap. 3.99 (978-0-375-84122-4(9) , Golden Bks.) Random Hse. Children's Bks.

Greene, Janice. Gulliver's Travels. abr. ed. 2001. (gr. 7-12). lib. bdg. 15.25 (978-0-613-36384-6(1)) Tandem Library Bks.

Greenwood, Mark. The Legend of Lasseter's Reef. 2003. (Illus.). 32p. 22.50 (978-1-876268-99-2(9)) Univ. of Western Australia Pr. AUS. *Dist:* International Specialized Bk. Services.

Harcourt School Publishers Staff. Wait for Me, Captain! On Level. 3rd ed. 2002. (Trophies Reading Program Ser.). (Illus.). pap. 5.10 (978-0-15-323099-8(1)) Harcourt Schl. Pubs.

Histories presents Christopher Cowlumbus. 2006. (J). bds. 14.99 (978-0-9763233-3-4(8)) Little Germ That Could-...Creations, Inc., The.

Horse, Harry, illus. The Last Polar Bears. 2007. 76p. (J). (gr. 1-5). 12.95 (****978-1-56145-379-5(X)*** , Peachtree Junior) Peachtree Pubs., Ltd.

Inches, Alison. Just Like Dora! Aikins, Dave, illus. 2005. (Ready-To-Read Ser.: Vol. 8). 24p. (J). pap. 3.99 (978-0-689-87675-2(0) , Simon Spotlight/Nickelodeon) Simon & Schuster Children's Publishing.

—Just Like Dora! Aikins, Dave, illus. 2005. 32p. (J). (ps-ps). lib. bdg. 11.19 (978-0-606-33920-9(5)) Tandem Library Bks.

Johnson, Vargie. Eric the Red the Fearless: What Made Them Famous? 2006. (J). per. 15.00 (978-1-931195-94-2(3)) KiwE Publishing, Ltd.

Karwoski, Gail Langer. Seaman: The Dog Who Explored the West with Lewis & Clark. 1999. (978-0-606-17742-9(6)) Tandem Library Bks.

—SeaMan: The Dog Who Explored the West with Lewis & Clark. Watling, James, illus. 2003. 192p. (J). 14.95 (978-1-56145-276-7(9) , Q20194); (gr. 3-7). pap. 8.95 (978-1-56145-190-6(8) , Q20194) Peachtree Pubs., Ltd.

—Surviving Jamestown: The Adventures of Young Sam Collier. Casale, Paul, illus. 2001. 192p. (J). (gr. 3-7). 14.95 (978-1-56145-239-2(4)); pap. 8.95 (978-1-56145-245-3(9)) Peachtree Pubs., Ltd.

—Surviving Jamestown: The Adventures of Young Sam Collier. 2001. (gr. 3-6). lib. bdg. 17.60 (978-0-613-51595-5(1)) Tandem Library Bks.

Kramer, Candice. Matthew Henson en el Polo Norte & Matthew Henson at the North Pole. 2005. spiral bd. 76.00 (****978-1-4108-5790-3(5))*** Benchmark Education Co.

Lasky, Kathryn. The Journal of Augustus Pelletier: The Lewis & Clark Expedition, 1804. 2000. (My Name Is America Ser.). (Illus.). 192p. (J). (gr. 4-8). pap. 10.95 (978-0-590-68489-7(2)) Scholastic, Inc.

Lawlor, Laurie. Dead Reckoning: A Pirate Voyage with Captain Drake. 2007. 336p. (J). pap. 5.99 (978-0-689-86578-7(3) , Aladdin) Simon & Schuster Children's Publishing.

Lawlor, Laurie & Barkat, Jonathan. Dead Reckoning: A Pirate Voyage with Captain Drake. 2005. (Illus.). 272p. (J). 15.95 (978-0-689-86577-0(5) , Simon & Schuster Children's Publishing) Simon & Schuster Children's Publishing.

Lendroth, Susan. Why Explore? Moreiro, Enrique S., illus. 2005. 32p. (J). (ps-ps). 15.95 (978-1-58246-150-2(3) , Tricycle Pr.) Ten Speed Pr.

Luna, Rachel Nickerson. The Haunting of Captain Snow. 2005. (Eel Grass Girls Mystery Ser.: No. 2). (Illus.). 332p. pap. 11.95 (978-1-886551-08-4(1)) Howard, Emma Bks.

Mayhew, James. Miranda the Explorer: A Magical-Round-the-World Adventure. 2003. (Illus.). (J). pap. 9.99 (978-1-84255-280-3(5)); 32p. 20.00 (978-1-84255-000-7(4)) Dolphin Paperbacks GBR. *Dist:* Trafalgar Square Publishing.

McAndrews, Anita. Blessed Be the Light of Day. Kabak, Carrie, illus. 2001. 48p. (J). (gr. 2-5). 14.95 (978-1-930093-02-7(0)) Brookfield Reader, Inc., The.

Peake, Mervyn. Letters from a Lost Uncle. 2004. (Illus.). 19.95 (978-0-413-74590-3(2)) Methuen Publishing Ltd. GBR. *Dist:* Consortium Bk. Sales & Distribution.

Place, Francois. The Last Giants. 2001. (Illus.). 74p. (J). pap. 11.00 (978-1-86205-289-5(1) , Pavilion Bks., Ltd.) Anova Bks. GBR. *Dist:* Trafalgar Square Publishing.

—A Voyage of Discovery Vol. 1: From the Land of the Amazons to the Indigo Isles. 2001. (Illus.). 144p. (YA). (gr. 3 up). 22.99 (978-1-86205-213-0(1) , Pavilion Bks., Ltd.) Anova Bks. GBR. *Dist:* Trafalgar Square Publishing.

Ricci, Christine. Dora's Costume Party! Saunders, Zina, illus. 2005. 24p. (J). lib. bdg. 9.00 (****978-1-4242-0978-1(1))*** Fitzgerald Bks.

Ricci, Christine. Dora's Costume Party. 2006. (J). (ps-2). 21.35 (978-1-59961-071-9(X)) Spotlight.

Roberts, Laura Peyton. New Beginnings. 1999. (Clearwater Crossing Ser.: No. 7). (J). (978-0-606-16380-4(8)) Tandem Library Bks.

Rocca, Al. Explorer Courage: The First Voyage of Christopher Columbus. l.t. ed. 2006. (Illus.). 72p. (J). per. 4.95 (****978-0-9643378-1-7(9))*** Renown Publishing Co.

Sargent, Dave & Sargent, Pat. Chalky No. 12: (Chalky Grullo) I'm Forgetful, 25, 12. Lenoir, Jane, illus. 2001. (Saddle Up Ser.: 12). 36p. (J). pap. 6.95 (978-1-56763-604-8(7)); lib. bdg. 22.60 (978-1-56763-603-1(9)) Ozark Publishing.

Smith, Roland. The Captain's Dog: My Journey with the Lewis & Clark Tribe. 2000. (Great Episodes Ser.). (Illus.). 304p. (YA). (gr. 4-7). pap. 6.00 (978-0-15-202696-7(7) , Harcourt Paperbacks) Harcourt Children's Bks.

—The Captain's Dog: My Journey with the Lewis & Clark Tribe. 2000. (J). 12.65 (978-0-606-19000-8(7)); (gr. 3-6). lib. bdg. 14.15 (978-0-613-29900-8(0)) Tandem Library Bks.

Stanley, John. Little Lulu Explorers, Vol. 15. 2007. 240p. pap. 9.95 (****978-1-59307-684-9(3))*** Dark Horse Comics.

Stilton, Geronimo. All Because of a Cup of Coffee. 2004. (Geronimo Stilton Ser.: No. 10). (Illus.). 112p. (J). (gr. 2-5). lib. bdg. 13.94 (978-0-606-33273-6(1)) Tandem Library Bks.

Stilton, Geronimo & Wolf, Matt. All Because of a Cup of Coffee. 2004. (Geronimo Stilton Ser.: No. 10). (Illus.). 112p. (J). lib. bdg. 10.00 (****978-1-4242-0279-9(5))*** Fitzgerald Bks.

Valdes, Leslie. At the Carnival. Roper, Robert, illus. 2005. 24p. (J). lib. bdg. 9.00 (****978-1-4242-0982-8(X))*** Fitzgerald Bks.

Verne, Jules. Jules Verne/Journey to the Center of the Earth. 2005. (Illus.). 48p. (gr. 5-8). 25.50 (978-0-7910-9105-0(8)) Facts On File, Inc.

Winston, Annie. Admiral Wright's Heroical Storicals: Daniel Boone & the Battle of Boonesborough. 3rd ed. 2007. (Illus.). 288p. (J). 12.99 (****978-0-9779535-4-7(8)*** , Sonship Pr.) 21st Century Pr.

EXPLORING EXPEDITIONS

see names of countries with the subdivision Exploring Expeditions (e.g. United States—Exploring Expeditions; etc.) and names of Expeditions, e.g. Lewis and Clark Expedition; etc.

Bergin, Mark. You Wouldn't Want to Travel with Captain Cook. Antram, David, illus. 2006. 32p. (J). (gr. 2-5). pap. 9.95 (978-0-531-12446-8(0) , Watts, Franklin) Scholastic Library Publishing.

Explorers & Exploration, 6 vols. 2000. (Illus.). (J). 136.98 (978-0-7398-2849-6(5)); Set. (978-0-7398-4173-0(4)) Raintree.

EXPLOSIVES

Cobb, Vicki. Fireworks. 2006. (Where's the Science Here? Ser.). (Illus.). 48p. (J). (gr. 3-5). 23.93 (978-0-7613-2771-4(1) , Millbrook Pr.) Lerner Publishing Group.

Trueit, Trudi Strain. Gunpowder. 2006. 80p. (YA). (gr. 5-8). pap. 9.95 (978-0-531-16744-1(5) , Watts, Franklin) Scholastic Library Publishing.

Wright, John D. Fire & Explosives. 2007. (Forensic Evidence Ser.). (Illus.). 96p. (gr. 6 up). 39.95 (****978-0-7656-8117-1(X))*** Sharpe, M.E. Inc.

EXTINCT ANIMALS

see also names of extinct animals, e.g. Mastodon, etc.

Batten, Mary. Extinct! Creatures of the Past. Doyle, Beverly, illus. 2004. (J). pap. (978-0-375-82554-5(1)); lib. bdg. (978-0-375-92554-2(6)) Random Hse. Children's Bks. (Random Hse. Bks. for Young Readers).

—Extinct! Creatures of the Past. 2000. (J). 10.79 (978-0-606-18926-2(2)) Tandem Library Bks.

Bertolucci, Cristiano, et al. Past & Present. Cucchiariani, Fer, illus. 2003. (Contrasts Ser.). 32p. (J). (gr. 1-4). 14.95 (978-1-57768-525-8(3) , Waterbird Bks.) School Specialty Publishing.

E
F
G

Charman, Andrew. Dodo Is Dead & other questions about extinct & endangered Animals. 2007. (I Wonder Why Ser.). (Illus.). 32p. (J). pap. 6.95 (****978-0-7534-6095-5(5)*** , Kingfisher) Houghton Mifflin Co. Trade & Reference Div.

Draw 50 Dinosaurs & Other Prehistoric Animals. 2002. (Draw 50 Ser.). (Illus.). (J). 17.60 (978-0-7587-4163-9(4)) Book Wholesalers, Inc.

Ehrlich, Fred. You Can't See a Dodo at the Zoo. Haley, Amanda, illus. 2007. 36p. pap. 6.95 (****978-1-59354-624-3(6)***) Handprint Bks.

Fisher, Enid Broderick. True-Life Monsters of the Prehistoric Seas. Grant, Richard, illus. 1999. (World of Dinosaurs Ser.). 32p. (J). (gr. 4 up). lib. bdg. 21.26 (978-0-8368-2293-9(5)) Stevens, Gareth Inc.

—True-Life Monsters of the Prehistoric Skies. Grant, Richard, illus. 1999. (World of Dinosaurs Ser.). 32p. (J). (gr. 4 up). lib. bdg. 21.26 (978-0-8368-2294-6(3)) Stevens, Gareth Inc.

Green, Tamara. The Dodo: Extinct Species. Gibbons, Tony, illus. 2007. 24p. (J). reprint ed. 15.00 (****978-1-4223-6677-6(4)***) DIANE Publishing Co.

Grolier Educational Staff, contrib. by. Atlas of Extinction, 10 vols., Vol. 10. 2002. (Illus.). (J). (978-0-7172-5574-0(3) , Grolier) Scholastic Library Publishing.

—Extinct Birds, 10 vols., Vol. 5. 2002. (Illus.). (J). (978-0-7172-5569-6(7) , Grolier) Scholastic Library Publishing.

—Extinct Invertebrates & Plants, 10 vols., Vol. 8. 2002. (Illus.). (J). (978-0-7172-5572-6(7) , Grolier) Scholastic Library Publishing.

—Extinct Mammals, 10 vols., Vol. 4. 2002. (Illus.). (J). (978-0-7172-5568-9(9) , Grolier) Scholastic Library Publishing.

—Extinct Reptiles & Amphibians, 10 vols., Vol. 7. 2002. (Illus.). (J). (978-0-7172-5571-9(9) , Grolier) Scholastic Library Publishing.

—Extinct Species, 10 vols., Set. Incl. Vol. 1. Why Extinction Occurs. (978-0-7172-5565-8(4)); Vol. 2. Prehistoric Animal Life. (978-0-7172-5566-5(2)); Vol. 3. Fossil Hunting. (978-0-7172-5567-2(0)); Vol. 4. Extinct Mammals. (978-0-7172-5568-9(9)); Vol. 5. Extinct Birds. (978-0-7172-5569-6(7)); Vol. 6. Extinct Underwater Life. (978-0-7172-5570-2(0)); Vol. 7. Extinct Reptiles & Amphibians. (978-0-7172-5571-9(9)); Vol. 8. Extinct Invertebrates & Plants. (978-0-7172-5572-6(7)); Vol. 9. Hominids. (978-0-7172-5573-3(5)); Vol. 10. Atlas of Extinction. (978-0-7172-5574-0(3)); (J). (Illus.). 2002. (978-0-7172-5564-1(6) , Grolier) Scholastic Library Publishing.

—Extinct Underwater Life, 10 vols., Vol. 6. 2002. (Illus.). (J). (978-0-7172-5570-2(0) , Grolier) Scholastic Library Publishing.

—Fossil Hunting, 10 vols., Vol. 3. 2002. (Illus.). (J). (978-0-7172-5567-2(0) , Grolier) Scholastic Library Publishing.

—Hominids, 10 vols., Vol. 9. 2002. (Illus.). (J). (978-0-7172-5573-3(5) , Grolier) Scholastic Library Publishing.

—Prehistoric Animal Life, 10 vols., Vol. 2. 2002. (Illus.). (J). (978-0-7172-5566-5(2) , Grolier) Scholastic Library Publishing.

—Why Extinction Occurs, 10 vols., Vol. 1. 2002. (Illus.). (J). (978-0-7172-5565-8(4) , Grolier) Scholastic Library Publishing.

Gunzi, Christiane. The Best Book of Endangered & Extinct Animals. 2004. (Best Book of... Ser.). (Illus.). 32p. (J). (gr. k-3). 12.95 (978-0-7534-5757-3(1) , Kingfisher) Houghton Mifflin Co. Trade & Reference Div.

Henderson, Doug. Asteroid Impact. 2000. (Illus.). 40p. (J). (gr. 1-5). 16.99 (978-0-8037-2500-3(0) , Dial) Penguin Group (USA) Inc.

Kimble, Evan & Kimble, Lael. Ice Age Creatures Dot-to-Dot. 2004. (Illus.). 80p. pap. 5.95 (978-1-4027-0994-4(3)) Sterling Publishing Co., Inc.

Lessem, Don. Dinosaurs to Dodos: An Encyclopedia of Extinct Animals. Sovak, Jan, illus. 1999. (Jurassic Park Ser.). 112p. (J). (gr. 3-7). pap. 16.95 (978-0-590-31684-2(2) , Scholastic Reference) Scholastic, Inc.

Lindeen, Carol. Giant Kangaroo: Procoptodon Goliah. 2008. (J). (****978-1-4296-0114-6(0)***) Capstone Pr., Inc.

—Tasmanian Tiger: Thylacine Cynocephalus. 2008. (J). (****978-1-4296-0118-4(3)***) Capstone Pr., Inc.

McDaniel, Melissa. Mysterious Nature: A Chapter Book. (True Tales Ser.). (Illus.). 48p. (J). 2006. (gr. 2-4). pap. 4.95 (978-0-516-25453-1(7)); 2005. (ps-ps). 22.50 (978-0-516-25183-7(X)) Scholastic Library Publishing. (Children's Pr.).

Ring, Susan. Animals of Long Ago. Nelson, Will, illus. 2002. 16p. (J). (978-0-439-35123-2(5)) Scholastic, Inc.

Sabuda, Robert & Reinhart, Matthew. Encyclopedia Prehistorica: Sharks & Other Sea Monsters. Sabuda, Robert & Reinhart, Matthew, illus. 2006. (Illus.). 12p. (J). (gr. k). 27.99 (978-0-7636-2229-9(X)) Candlewick Pr.

Scholastic, Inc. Staff. Endangered Animals. 2007. (Scholastic First Discovery Ser.). 24p. (J). (ps-k). pap. 5.99 (****978-0-545-00143-4(9)*** , Scholastic Reference) Scholastic, Inc.

EXTINCT CITIES

see Cities and Towns, Ruined, Extinct, Etc.

EXTINCT PLANTS

see Plants, Fossil

EXTINCTION (BIOLOGY)

Andryszewski, Tricia. Mass Extinction: Examining the Current Crisis. 2008. (J). lib. bdg. (****978-0-8225-7523-8(X)***) Twenty First Century Bks.

Appelt, Kathi. Bats Around the Clock. Sweet, Melissa, illus. 2000. 32p. (J). (gr. k-5). 16.99 (978-0-688-16469-0(2)) HarperCollins Pubs.

Batten, Mary. Extinct! Creatures of the Past. Doyle, Beverly, illus. 2004. (J). pap. (978-0-375-82554-5(1)); lib. bdg. (978-0-375-92554-2(6)) Random Hse. Children's Bks. (Random Hse. Bks. for Young Readers).

—Extinct! Creatures of the Past. 2000. (J). 10.79 (978-0-606-18926-2(2)) Tandem Library Bks.

Beck, Katie. The Moas. Thatch, Nancy R., ed. 1999. (Books for Students by Students). (Illus.). 29p. (J). (gr. 4-7). lib. bdg. 15.95 (978-0-933849-73-0(7)) Landmark Editions, Inc.

Berger, Melvin & Berger, Gilda. Why Did the Dinosaurs Disappear? The Great Dinosaur Mystery. Harrison, Susan J., illus. 1999. (Discovery Readers Ser.). 48p. (YA). (gr. 4-7). lib. bdg. 17.55 (978-0-7910-5074-3(2) , Chelsea Hse.) Facts On File, Inc.

Branley, Franklyn M. What Happened to the Dinosaurs? 2001. 24.75 (978-0-06-000343-2(X)) HarperCollins Pubs.

—What Happened to the Dinosaurs? Simont, Marc, illus. 2000. (Let's-Read-and-Find-Out Science Ser.). 32p. (J). (gr. k-4). 15.89 (978-0-690-04749-3(5)) HarperCollins Pubs.

Erickson, Jon. Lost Creatures of the Earth: Mass Extinction in the History of Life. 2001. (Living Earth Ser.). (Illus.). 272p. (YA). (gr. 6-12). 55.00 (978-0-8160-4337-8(X)) Facts On File, Inc.

Grolier Educational Staff, contrib. by. Atlas of Extinction, 10 vols., Vol. 10. 2002. (Illus.). (J). (978-0-7172-5574-0(3) , Grolier) Scholastic Library Publishing.

—Extinct Birds, 10 vols., Vol. 5. 2002. (Illus.). (J). (978-0-7172-5569-6(7) , Grolier) Scholastic Library Publishing.

—Extinct Invertebrates & Plants, 10 vols., Vol. 8. 2002. (Illus.). (J). (978-0-7172-5572-6(7) , Grolier) Scholastic Library Publishing.

—Extinct Mammals, 10 vols., Vol. 4. 2002. (Illus.). (J). (978-0-7172-5568-9(9) , Grolier) Scholastic Library Publishing.

—Extinct Reptiles & Amphibians, 10 vols., Vol. 7. 2002. (Illus.). (J). (978-0-7172-5571-9(9) , Grolier) Scholastic Library Publishing.

—Extinct Species, 10 vols., Set. Incl. Vol. 1. Why Extinction Occurs. (978-0-7172-5565-8(4)); Vol. 2. Prehistoric Animal Life. (978-0-7172-5566-5(2)); Vol. 3. Fossil Hunting. (978-0-7172-5567-2(0)); Vol. 4. Extinct Mammals. (978-0-7172-5568-9(9)); Vol. 5. Extinct Birds. (978-0-7172-5569-6(7)); Vol. 6. Extinct Underwater Life. (978-0-7172-5570-2(0)); Vol. 7. Extinct Reptiles & Amphibians. (978-0-7172-5571-9(9)); Vol. 8. Extinct Invertebrates & Plants. (978-0-7172-5572-6(7)); Vol. 9. Hominids. (978-0-7172-5573-3(5)); Vol. 10. Atlas of Extinction. (978-0-7172-5574-0(3)); (J). (Illus.). 2002. (978-0-7172-5564-1(6) , Grolier) Scholastic Library Publishing.

—Extinct Underwater Life, 10 vols., Vol. 6. 2002. (Illus.). (J). (978-0-7172-5570-2(0) , Grolier) Scholastic Library Publishing.

—Fossil Hunting, 10 vols., Vol. 3. 2002. (Illus.). (J). (978-0-7172-5567-2(0) , Grolier) Scholastic Library Publishing.

—Hominids, 10 vols., Vol. 9. 2002. (Illus.). (J). (978-0-7172-5573-3(5) , Grolier) Scholastic Library Publishing.

—Prehistoric Animal Life, 10 vols., Vol. 2. 2002. (Illus.). (J). (978-0-7172-5566-5(2) , Grolier) Scholastic Library Publishing.

—Why Extinction Occurs, 10 vols., Vol. 1. 2002. (Illus.). (J). (978-0-7172-5565-8(4) , Grolier) Scholastic Library Publishing.

Henderson, Doug. Asteroid Impact. 2000. (Illus.). 40p. (J). (gr. 1-5). 16.99 (978-0-8037-2500-3(0) , Dial) Penguin Group (USA) Inc.

Henry, Chad. Dogbreath Victorious. 1999. 192p. (J). (gr. 7 up). tchr. ed. 16.95 (978-0-8234-1458-1(2)) Holiday Hse., Inc.

Kinsner, Kathy. ¿Condenadas a desaparecer? Especies en peligro de extincion & Doomed to Disappear? Endangered Species. 2005. spiral bd. 84.00 (****978-1-4108-5698-2(4)***) Benchmark Education Co.

Lessem, Don. Dinosaurs to Dodos: An Encyclopedia of Extinct Animals. Sovak, Jan, illus. 1999. (Jurassic Park Ser.). 112p. (J). (gr. 3-7). pap. 16.95 (978-0-590-31684-2(2) , Scholastic Reference) Scholastic, Inc.

Matthews, Rupert. End of the Dinosaurs. 2002. (Dinosaurs Undercover Ser.). (Illus.). 40p. (J). 29.94 (978-1-56711-603-8(5) , Blackbirch Pr., Inc.) Thomson Gale.

Nardo, Don. The Extinction of the Dinosaur. 2004. (KidHaven Science Library). (Illus.). (J). (gr. 4-7). 26.20 (978-0-7377-2637-4(7) , Greenhaven Pr., Inc.) Thomson Gale.

—The Extinction of the Dinosaurs. 2001. (Mystery Library). (Illus.). 112p. (YA). (gr. 4-12). 27.45 (978-1-56006-890-7(6) , Lucent Bks.) Thomson Gale.

Oxlade, Chris. The Mystery of the Death of the Dinosaurs. 2002. (Can Science Solve? Ser.). 32p. (J). (gr. 4-7). (Illus.). lib. bdg. 22.79 (978-1-58810-664-3(0)); pap. 7.50 (978-1-58810-931-6(3) , 91567) Heinemann Library.

Vergoth, Karin & Lampton, Christopher. Endangered Species. rev. ed. 1999. (Impact Bks.). (Illus.). 112p. (YA). (gr. 8-12). 26.00 (978-0-531-11480-3(5) , Watts, Franklin) Scholastic Library Publishing.

EXTRACURRICULAR ACTIVITIES

see Student Activities

EXTRASENSORY PERCEPTION

Claybourne, Anna. ESP? 1999. (Paranormal Guides Ser.). (Illus.). 48p. (J). lib. bdg. 13.95 (978-1-58086-199-1(7)) EDC Publishing.

Gorman, Jacqueline Laks. ESP. 2002. (X Science Ser.). (Illus.). 24p. (YA). (gr. 2 up). lib. bdg. 22.00 (978-0-8368-3198-6(5)) Stevens, Gareth Inc.

Harvey, Gill. Percepcion Extrasensorial. 1999. Tr. of Extrasensory Perception. (978-0-606-18131-0(8)) Tandem Library Bks.

Herbst, Judith. ESP. (Unexplained Ser.). (Illus.). 48p. (J). 2005. (gr. 5-12). lib. bdg. 26.60 (978-0-8225-1628-6(4)); 2004. pap. 7.95 (978-0-8225-2405-2(8)) Lerner Publishing Group.

Innes, Brian. Powers of the Mind. 1999. (Unsolved Mysteries Ser.). 48p. (YA). (gr. 4-7). lib. bdg. 25.69 (978-0-8172-5488-9(9)) Raintree.

Johnson, Julie Tallard. Teen Psychic: Exploring Your Intuitive Spiritual Powers. 2003. (Illus.). 256p. 14.95 (978-0-89281-094-9(7)) Inner Traditions International, Ltd.

Martin, Michael. Esp: Extrasensory Perception. 2006. (Unexplained Ser.). (Illus.). 32p. (J). (gr. 3-9). 23.93 (978-0-7368-5451-1(7) , Edge Bks.) Capstone Pr., Inc.

Needham, Kate, ed. ESP: The Evidence & the Arguments. 1999. (Paranormal Guides Ser.). (Illus.). 48p. (YA). (gr. 5 up). pap. 5.95 (978-0-7460-3060-8(6)) EDC Publishing.

Netzley, Patricia D. The Mystery Library - ESP. 2000. (Mystery Library). (Illus.). 96p. (YA). (gr. 4-12). 29.95 (978-1-56006-770-2(5) , Lucent Bks.) Thomson Gale.

Oxlade, Chris. The Mystery of ESP. 2002. (Can Science Solve? Ser.). 32p. (Illus.). (J). (gr. 4-7). lib. bdg. 22.79 (978-1-58810-665-0(9)); pap. 7.50 (978-1-58810-928-6(3) , 91563) Heinemann Library.

Parks, Peggy J. Esp. 2007. (YA). lib. bdg. (****978-1-60152-025-8(5)***) ReferencePoint Pr., Inc.

Rudy, Lisa Jo. Mind Readers: The Science of ESP. 2007. (24/7 - Science Behind the Scenes Ser.). 64p. (J). (gr. 8-12). 26.00 (978-0-531-12075-0(9) , Watts, Franklin) Scholastic Library Publishing.

EXTRASENSORY PERCEPTION—FICTION

Augarde, Steve. Celandine. 2008. 496p. (J). (gr. 5). 6.99 (****978-0-440-42216-7(7)*** , Yearling) Random Hse. Children's Bks.

Barnes, Jennifer Lynn. Golden. 2006. 256p. (YA). (gr. 7). pap. 7.95 (978-0-385-73311-3(9)); lib. bdg. 9.99 (978-0-385-90330-1(8)) Random Hse. Children's Bks. (Delacorte Bks. for Young Readers).

Barnes, Jennifer Lynn. Platinum. 2007. 224p. (YA). (gr. 7). 10.99 (****978-0-385-90409-4(6));*** pap. 7.99 (****978-0-385-73395-3(X)***) Random Hse. Children's Bks. (Delacorte Bks. for Young Readers).

Berry, Liz. China Garden. 1999. (gr. 5-8). lib. bdg. 15.30 (978-0-613-22975-3(4)) Tandem Library Bks.

—The China Garden. 1999. (Illus.). 288p. (J). pap. 7.99 (978-0-380-73228-9(9)) HarperCollins Pubs.

Bo, Ben. Skullcrack. 2003. 168p. (J). pap. 6.95 (978-0-8225-3311-5(1)); (gr. 9-12). 14.95 (978-0-8225-3308-5(1)) Lerner Publishing Group.

—Skullcrack. 2000. (gr. 5-8). lib. bdg. 15.25 (978-0-613-58938-3(6)) Tandem Library Bks.

Clayton, John. Alexander Fox & the Amazing Mind Reader. Egan, Emily, illus. 1998. (Young Readers Ser.). 78p. (ps-3). pap. 16.00 (978-1-57392-221-0(8)) Prometheus Bks., Pubs.

Clement-Davies, David. Fell. 2007. 542p. (YA). (gr. 7-17). 19.95 (****978-0-8109-1185-7(X)***) Abrams, Harry N. , Inc.

Clement-Davies, David. The Sight. 2002. (gr. 7-12). lib. bdg. 16.45 (978-0-613-68285-5(8)) Tandem Library Bks.

Cowley, Joy. Hunter. 2004. 176p. (YA). (gr. 5). 17.99 (978-0-399-24227-4(9) , Philomel) Penguin Group (USA) Inc.

Davies, Nicola. Tangled Webs. 2000. 120p. (YA). pap. 12.95 (978-1-85902-847-6(0)) Beekman Bks., Inc.

Devaney, Patrick. The Psychic Edge. 2000. 137p. (YA). (gr. 5-9). per. (978-1-84210-020-2(3)) Mentor Bks.

Dokey, Cameron. Lost & Found. 1999. (Enchanted Hearts Ser.: No. 3). 208p. (YA). (gr. 7-12). pap. 4.50 (978-0-380-80083-4(7)) HarperCollins Pubs.

—Lost & Found. 1999. (Enchanted Hearts Ser.). (Illus.). (YA). (978-0-606-17965-2(8)) Tandem Library Bks.

Gavin, Jamila. The Blood Stone. 2005. (Illus.). 352p. (YA). (gr. 6-8). 18.00 (978-0-374-30846-9(2)) Farrar, Straus & Giroux.

Geras, Adele. Family Files. Ross, Tony, illus. 1998. (Fabulous Fantoras Ser.: Vol. 1). 144p. (J). (gr. 3-7). 14.00 (978-0-380-97547-1(5)) HarperCollins Pubs.

Grunwell, Jeanne Marie. Mind Games. 2006. 144p. (YA). (gr. 5-9). pap. 5.95 (978-0-618-68947-7(8)) Houghton Mifflin Co.

—Mind Games. 2003. (Illus.). 144p. (YA). (gr. 5-9). tchr. ed. 15.00 (978-0-618-17672-4(1)) Houghton Mifflin Co. Trade & Reference Div.

Hamilton, Virginia. Dustland. 1998. (Justice Cycle Ser.: Bk. 2). 214p. (YA). (gr. 6-12). pap. 4.50 (978-0-590-36217-7(8)) Scholastic, Inc.

—Dustland. 1998. (Justice Cycle Ser.). (978-0-606-12927-5(8)) Tandem Library Bks.

—The Gathering. 1998. (Justice Cycle Ser.: Bk. 3). 214p. (J). (gr. 6-12). mass mkt. 4.50 (978-0-590-36216-0(X)) Scholastic, Inc.

—The Gathering. 1998. (Justice Cycle Ser.). (978-0-606-13414-9(X)) Tandem Library Bks.

Kibbe, Pat. The Hocus-Pocus Dilemma. Capozzi, Dan, illus. 2001. 140p. (YA). (gr. 4-7). pap. 9.95 (978-0-595-16569-8(9) , Backinprint.com) iUniverse, Inc.

Lester, Julius. The Old African. Pinkney, Jerry, illus. 2005. 80p. (J). (gr. 3). 19.99 (978-0-8037-2564-5(7) , Dial) Penguin Group (USA) Inc.

Levithan, David. Sixth Sense. 2000. (Illus.). (YA). pap. 59.88 (978-0-439-21195-6(6)) Scholastic, Inc.

Lubar, David. Hidden Talents. 2007. 240p. (J). 2.99 (978-0-7653-5766-3(6) , Starscape) Doherty, Tom Assocs., LLC.

—Hidden Talents Sequel. 2008. 320p. (J). 5.99 (978-0-7653-4856-2(X) , Tor Bks.) Doherty, Tom Assocs., LLC.

McNish, Cliff. Breathe: A Ghost Story. 2006. 264p. (J). 15.95 (978-0-8225-6443-0(2) , Carolrhoda Bks.) Lerner Publishing Group.

Radford, Michelle. Almost Fabulous. 2008. 256p. (J). pap. 8.99 (****978-0-06-125235-8(2)*** , HarperTeen) HarperCollins Pubs.

Richards, Justin. The Invisible Detective: Double Life. 2005. 160p. (J). (gr. 4). 10.99 (978-0-399-24313-4(5) , Putnam Juvenile) Penguin Group (USA) Inc.

Roberts, Katherine. Song Quest. 2002. lib. bdg. 13.00 (978-0-613-54676-8(8)); (Illus.). 271p. (J). lib. bdg. 13.04 (978-0-606-24222-6(8)) Tandem Library Bks.

Satten, Sandra C. In the Thirteenth Year. Spark, illus. 1999. 72p. (YA). (ps up). pap. 7.95 (978-1-881283-24-9(0)) Alef Design Group.

Sedgwick, Marcus. The Foreshadowing. 2008. 304p. (J). (gr. 9). mass mkt. 6.50 (****978-0-553-48785-5(X)*** , Laurel Leaf) Random Hse. Children's Bks.

Stolarz, Laurie Faria. The Blue Is for Nightmares Collection. 2006. 1224p. pap., pap. 29.95 (978-0-7387-0988-8(3) , Flux) Llewellyn Pubns.

—Silver Is for Secrets. 2005. (Blue Is for Nightmares Ser.: Vol. 3). 288p. pap. 8.95 (978-0-7387-0631-3(0)) Llewellyn Pubns.

EXTRATERRESTRIAL BEINGS

Brookes, Philip. Invaders from Outer Space: Real Life Stories of UFOs. 1999. (Eyewitness Readers Ser.). (J). 10.75 (978-0-606-16985-1(7)) Tandem Library Bks.

—Invaders from Outer Space: Real-Life Stories of UFOs. 1999. (Eyewitness Readers). (Illus.). 48p. (J). (ps-4). pap. 3.99 (978-0-7894-3998-7(0) , 0-7894-4762-2) Dorling Kindersley Publishing, Inc.

Brooks, Philip & Dorling Kindersley Publishing Staff. Invaders from Outer Space: Real-Life Stories of UFOs. 1999. (Eyewitness Readers). (Illus.). 48p. (J). (ps-3). 14.99 (978-0-7894-3999-4(9)) Dorling Kindersley Publishing, Inc.

Campbell, Peter A. Alien Encounters. 2000. (Women at War Ser.). (Illus.). 48p. (gr. 4-8). lib. bdg. 23.90 (978-0-7613-1402-8(4) , Millbrook Pr.) Lerner Publishing Group.

Gifford, Clive. How to Meet Aliens. Anderson, Scoular, illus. 2001. (How to Ser.). 96p. (J). (gr. 5-7). 16.00 (978-0-531-14642-2(1)); pap. 4.95 (978-0-531-14820-4(3)) Scholastic Library Publishing. (Watts, Franklin).

—How to Meet Aliens. 2001. (gr. 5-8). lib. bdg. 12.95 (978-0-613-54551-8(6)) Tandem Library Bks.

Herbst, Judith. Aliens. (Unexplained Ser.). (Illus.). 48p. (J). 2005. (gr. 5-12). lib. bdg. 26.60 (978-0-8225-0960-8(1)); 2004. pap. 7.95 (978-0-8225-2402-1(3) , Lerner Pubns.) Lerner Publishing Group.

Innes. Unsolved Mysteries Series, 14 bks., Set. 2000. (Unsolved Mysteries Ser.). (Illus.). 359.66 (978-0-7398-4285-0(4)) Steck-Vaughn.

Innes, Brian. Alien Visitors & Abductions. 1999. (Unsolved Mysteries Ser.). (Illus.). 48p. (YA). (gr. 3-7). lib. bdg. 25.69 (978-0-8172-5478-0(1)) Raintree.

—Alien Visitors & Abductions. 1998. (Unsolved Mysteries Ser.). (Illus.). 48p. (J). (gr. 3-7). pap. 8.05 (978-0-8172-4275-6(9)) Steck-Vaughn.

Jefferis, David. Alien Lifesearch: Quest for Extraterrestrial Organisms. 1999. (Megatech Ser.). (Illus.). 32p. (J). (gr. 4-5). pap. (978-0-7787-0059-3(3)); lib. bdg. (978-0-7787-0049-4(6)) Crabtree Publishing Co.

Kallen, Stuart A. Alien Abductions. 2008. (J). lib. bdg. (****978-1-60152-023-4(9)***) ReferencePoint Pr., Inc.

Krull, Kathleen. What Really Happened in Roswell? Just the Facts (Plus the Rumors) about UFOs & Aliens. Santoro, Christopher, illus. 2003. 64p. (J). (gr. 3 up). lib. bdg. 16.89 (978-0-688-17249-7(0)) HarperCollins Pubs.

Netzley, Patricia D. Alien Abductions. 2000. (Mystery Library). (Illus.). 96p. (YA). (gr. 4-12). 27.45 (978-1-56006-767-2(5) , Lucent Bks.) Thomson Gale.

Parker. Space Aliens. 2003. (Space Busters Ser.). (Illus.). 32p. (J). pap. 7.95 (978-1-4109-0072-2(X)) Raintree.

Parker, Steve. Space Aliens. 2002. (Young Library - Space Busters Ser.). 32p. (J). lib. bdg. 25.69 (978-0-7398-4849-4(6)) Raintree.

Perry, Janet & Gentle, Victor. Aliens. 1999. (Imagination Library). (Illus.). 24p. (J). (gr. 2 up). lib. bdg. 22.00 (978-0-8368-2435-3(0)) Stevens, Gareth Inc.

Roleff, Tamara L., ed. Alien Abductions. 2003. (Illus.). 160p. (J). pap. 23.70 (978-0-7377-1590-3(1) , Greenhaven Pr., Inc.) Thomson Gale.

Silverstein, Janna. Close Encounters with Aliens. 2005. (Unsolved Mysteries Ser.). (Illus.). 48p. (YA). (gr. 5-8). lib. bdg. 25.25 (978-0-8239-3562-8(0)) Rosen Publishing Group, Inc., The.

EXTRATERRESTRIAL BEINGS—FICTION

Alexander, Alec. My Fantastic Dream of the Marshmallow Martians. 2000. (Marshmallow Martian Ser.: Vol. 1). (Illus.). 32p. (J). (ps-5). 5.95 (978-0-9670091-0-0(3)) Smart Alec Toys Publishing.

—My Magical Christmas Dream of the Marshmallow Martians. 2000. (Marshmallow Martian Ser.: Vol. 2). (Illus.). 32p. (J). (ps-5). 5.95 (978-0-9670091-1-7(1)) Smart Alec Toys Publishing.

The Alien, 6 vols., Pack. (gr. 1-2). 25.00 (978-0-7635-9192-2(0)) Rigby Education.

Alien at the Zoo, 6 vols. (Sunshinetm Ser.). 16p. (gr. k up). 29.50 (978-0-7802-5429-9(5)) Wright Group, The.

Alien in Space. Date not set. (Illus.). (J). bds. 1.98 (978-0-7525-9838-3(4)) Parragon, Inc.

The Alien Next Door. 2005. (J). audio, cd-rom 24.95 (978-0-9771381-8-0(6)) Williams, Geoffrey T.

Aliens & Space. Date not set. (Illus.). 64p. (J). 2.98 (978-1-4054-0446-4(9)) Parragon, Inc.

Aliens on the Lawn, 6 vols., Pack. (gr. 1-2). 25.00 (978-0-7635-9126-7(2)) Rigby Education.

Anderson, Dwayne. Partially Human. 2006. (YA). per. 12.00 (****978-0-9788612-0-9(5)***) Capri Publishing.

Applegate, Katherine. Animorphs Boxed Set: The Change; The Unknown; The Escape; The Warning, No. 4. 2001. (Animorphs Ser.). (J). (gr. 3-7). 19.96 (978-0-590-28434-9(7) , Scholastic Paperbacks) Scholastic, Inc.

—Animorphs Boxed Set: The Threat; The Solution; The Pretender; The Suspicion, 4 vols., No. 6. 2001. (Animorphs Ser.: Nos. 21-24). (J). (gr. 3-7). 19.96 (978-0-590-28543-8(2)) Scholastic, Inc.

—Animorphs Boxed Set: The Weakness; the Arrival; the Hidden; the Other, No. 10. 2000. (Animorphs Ser.: Nos. 37-40). (Illus.). (J). (gr. 3-7). 19.96 (978-0-439-10688-7(5) , Scholastic Paperbacks) Scholastic, Inc.

—Animorphs Series Boxed Set. 1998. (Animorphs Ser.). (J). (gr. 3-7). pap. 143.64 (978-0-590-51066-0(5)) Scholastic, Inc.

—The Arrival. l.t. ed. 2001. (Animorphs Ser.: No. 38). 148p. (J). (gr. 4 up). lib. bdg. 23.33 (978-0-8368-2771-2(6)) Stevens, Gareth Inc.

—The Arrival. 2000. (Animorphs Ser.: No. 38). (gr. 3-6). lib. bdg. 13.00 (978-0-613-21111-6(1)); (Illus.). (J). 11.64 (978-0-606-18509-7(7)) Tandem Library Bks.

—The Attack. 1999. (Animorphs Ser.: No. 26). (gr. 3-6). lib. bdg. 13.00 (978-0-613-11262-8(8)); (J). (978-0-606-15834-3(0)) Tandem Library Bks.

—Back to Before. 2000. (Animorphs Ser.: No. 4). (Illus.). 192p. (J). (gr. 3-7). pap. 5.99 (978-0-439-17307-0(8) , Scholastic Paperbacks) Scholastic, Inc.

—The Conspiracy. l.t. ed. 2001. (Animorphs Ser.: No. 31). 138p. (J). (gr. 4 up). lib. bdg. 23.33 (978-0-8368-2754-5(6)) Stevens, Gareth Inc.

—The Conspiracy. 1999. (Animorphs Ser.: No. 31). (Illus.). (J). (gr. 3-7). 11.64 (978-0-606-16928-8(8)) Tandem Library Bks.

—The Decision. 1998. (Animorphs Ser.: No. 18). (J). (gr. 3-7). 11.64 (978-0-606-13138-4(8)) Tandem Library Bks.

—The Departure. 1998. (Animorphs Ser.: No. 19). 176p. (J). (gr. 3-7). pap. 4.99 (978-0-590-49451-9(1) , Scholastic Paperbacks) Scholastic, Inc.

—The Departure. 1998. (Animorphs Ser.: No. 19). (J). (gr. 3-7). 11.64 (978-0-606-13139-1(6)) Tandem Library Bks.

—The Discovery. 1998. (Animorphs Ser.: No. 20). 153p. (J). (gr. 3-7). pap. 4.99 (978-0-590-49637-7(9) , Scholastic Paperbacks) Scholastic, Inc.

—The Discovery. 1998. (Animorphs Ser.: No. 20). (J). (gr. 3-7). (978-0-606-13140-7(X)) Tandem Library Bks.

—The Experiment. 1999. (Animorphs Ser.: No. 28). 160p. (J). (gr. 3-7). pap. 4.99 (978-0-590-76261-8(3)) Scholastic, Inc.

—The Experiment. 1999. (Animorphs Ser.: No. 28). (gr. 3-6). lib. bdg. 13.00 (978-0-613-16892-2(5)); (J). (978-0-606-16608-9(4)) Tandem Library Bks.

—The Exposed. 1999. (Animorphs Ser.: No. 27). (J). (gr. 3-7). (978-0-606-16589-1(4)) Tandem Library Bks.

—The Extreme. 1999. (Animorphs Ser.: No. 25). 146p. (J). (gr. 3-7). pap. 4.99 (978-0-590-76258-8(3)) Scholastic, Inc.

—The Familiar. l.t. ed. 2001. (Animorphs Ser.: No. 41). 143p. (J). (gr. 4 up). lib. bdg. 23.33 (978-0-8368-2774-3(0)) Stevens, Gareth Inc.

—The Familiar. 2000. (Animorphs Ser.: No. 41). (Illus.). (J). (gr. 3-7). 11.64 (978-0-606-18512-7(7)) Tandem Library Bks.

—The First Journey. 1999. (Animorphs Ser.: No. 1). (J). (gr. 3-7). (978-0-606-16606-5(8)) Tandem Library Bks.

—The Hidden. l.t. ed. 2001. (Animorphs Ser.: No. 39). 121p. (J). (gr. 4 up). lib. bdg. 23.33 (978-0-8368-2772-9(4)) Stevens, Gareth Inc.

—The Hork-Bajir Chronicles. 1998. (Animorphs Ser.). (Illus.). 206p. (J). (gr. 3-7). pap. 13.95 (978-0-439-04291-8(7)) Scholastic, Inc.

—The Hork-Bajir Chronicles. 1999. (Animorphs Ser.). (J). (gr. 3-7). (978-0-606-17284-4(X)) Tandem Library Bks.

—The Illusion. l.t. ed. 2000. (Animorphs Ser.: No. 33). 156p. (J). (gr. 4 up). lib. bdg. 23.33 (978-0-8368-2755-2(4)) Stevens, Gareth Inc.

—The Illusion. 1999. (Animorphs Ser.: No. 33). (J). (gr. 3-7). 11.64 (978-0-606-17287-5(4)) Tandem Library Bks.

—In the Time of Dinosaurs. 1998. (Animorphs Ser.: No. 2). 229p. (J). (gr. 3-7). pap. 4.99 (978-0-590-95615-4(9) , Scholastic Paperbacks) Scholastic, Inc.

—In the Time of Dinosaurs. 1998. (Animorphs Ser.: No. 2). (J). (gr. 3-7). (978-0-606-13142-1(6)) Tandem Library Bks.

—L' Invasion. 1999. (Animorphs Ser.: No. 1). Tr. of Invasion. (FRE & SPA.). 128p. (J). (gr. 3-7). pap. 4.99 (978-0-439-05602-1(0)) Scholastic, Inc.

—La Invasion. 1999. (Animorphs Ser.: No. 1). Tr. of Invasion. (J). (gr. 3-7). (978-0-606-16607-2(6)) Tandem Library Bks.

—The Journey. l.t. ed. 2001. (Animorphs Ser.: No. 42). 139p. (J). (gr. 4 up). lib. bdg. 23.33 (978-0-8368-2775-0(9)) Stevens, Gareth Inc.

—The Journey. 2000. (Animorphs Ser.: No. 42). (Illus.). (J). (gr. 3-7). 11.64 (978-0-606-18860-9(6)) Tandem Library Bks.

—El Mensaje. 1999. (Animorphs Ser.: No. 4). (SPA., Illus.). 164p. (J). (gr. 3-7). pap. 4.99 (978-0-439-08783-4(X) , SO5398) Scholastic, Inc.

—El Mensaje. 1999. No. 4. (J). (978-0-606-17290-5(4)) Tandem Library Bks.

—The Message. 2000. (Animorphs Ser.: No. 4). (Illus.). (J). (gr. 3-7). 11.64 (978-0-606-18510-3(0)) Tandem Library Bks.

—The Mutation. l.t. ed. 2000. (Animorphs Ser.: No. 36). 142p. (J). (gr. 4 up). lib. bdg. 23.33 (978-0-8368-2756-9(2)) Stevens, Gareth Inc.

—The Mutation. 1999. (Animorphs Ser.: No. 36). (Illus.). (J). (gr. 3-7). (978-0-606-18507-3(0)) Tandem Library Bks.

—The Next Passage. 2000. (Animorphs Ser.: No. 2). (Illus.). 128p. (J). (gr. 3-7). pap. 4.99 (978-0-439-14263-2(6)) Scholastic, Inc.

—The Next Passage. 2000. (Animorphs Ser.: No. 2). (Illus.). (J). (gr. 3-7). (978-0-606-18506-6(2)) Tandem Library Bks.

—The Other. 2000. (Animorphs Ser.: No. 40). (Illus.). 144p. (J). (gr. 3-7). pap. 4.99 (978-0-439-10679-5(6)) Scholastic, Inc.

—The Other. l.t. ed. 2001. (Animorphs Ser.: No. 40). 130p. (J). (gr. 4 up). lib. bdg. 23.33 (978-0-8368-2773-6(2)) Stevens, Gareth Inc.

—The Other. 2000. (Animorphs Ser.: No. 40). (Illus.). (J). (gr. 3-7). (978-0-606-18511-0(9)) Tandem Library Bks.

—The Prophecy. l.t. ed. 2000. (Animorphs Ser.: No. 34). 141p. (J). (gr. 4 up). lib. bdg. 23.33 (978-0-8368-2757-6(0)) Stevens, Gareth Inc.

—The Prophecy. 1999. (Animorphs Ser.: No. 34). (J). (gr. 3-7). (978-0-606-17283-7(1)) Tandem Library Bks.

—The Proposal. l.t. ed. 2000. (Animorphs Ser.: No. 35). 147p. (J). (gr. 4 up). lib. bdg. 23.33 (978-0-8368-2758-3(9)) Stevens, Gareth Inc.

—The Proposal. 1999. (Animorphs Ser.: No. 35). (gr. 3-6). lib. bdg. 13.00 (978-0-613-21114-7(6)); (J). (978-0-606-17289-9(0)) Tandem Library Bks.

—The Revelation. 2000. (Animorphs Ser.: No. 45). (Illus.). 144p. (J). (gr. 3-7). pap. 4.99 (978-0-439-11519-3(1)) Scholastic, Inc.

—The Separation. 1999. (Animorphs Ser.: No. 32). 176p. (J). (gr. 3-7). pap. 4.99 (978-0-439-07032-4(5)) Scholastic, Inc.

—The Separation. l.t. ed. 2000. (Animorphs Ser.: No. 32). 158p. (J). (gr. 4 up). lib. bdg. 23.33 (978-0-8368-2759-0(7)) Stevens, Gareth Inc.

—The Separation. 1999. (Animorphs Ser.: No. 32). (gr. 3-6). lib. bdg. 13.00 (978-0-613-16895-3(X)); (J). (978-0-606-17060-4(X)) Tandem Library Bks.

—The Sickness. 1999. (Animorphs Ser.: No. 29). 176p. (J). (gr. 3-7). pap. 4.99 (978-0-590-76262-5(1)) Scholastic, Inc.

—The Sickness. 1999. (Animorphs Ser.: No. 29). (J). (978-0-606-16618-8(1)); (gr. 3-6). lib. bdg. 13.00 (978-0-613-16896-0(8)) Tandem Library Bks.

—The Solution. 1998. (Animorphs Ser.: No. 22). 152p. (J). (gr. 3-7). pap. 4.99 (978-0-590-76255-7(9)) Scholastic, Inc.

—The Suspicion. 1998. (Animorphs Ser.: No. 24). 176p. (J). (gr. 3-7). pap. 4.99 (978-0-590-76257-1(5)) Scholastic, Inc.

—The Test. 2000. (Animorphs Ser.: No. 43). (Illus.). (J). (gr. 3-7). (978-0-606-18861-6(4)) Tandem Library Bks.

—The Threat. 1998. (Animorphs Ser.: No. 21). (J). (gr. 3-7). (978-0-606-13141-4(8)) Tandem Library Bks.

—The Underground. 1998. (Animorphs Ser.: No. 17). (J). (gr. 3-7). (978-0-606-13137-7(X)) Tandem Library Bks.

—El Visitante. 1999. (Animorphs Ser.: No. 2). (SPA., Illus.). 192p. (J). (gr. 3-7). pap. 4.99 (978-0-439-07163-5(1) , SO5396) Scholastic, Inc.

—El Visitante. 1999. (Animorphs Ser.: No. 2). (J). (gr. 3-7). (978-0-606-16929-5(6)) Tandem Library Bks.

—The Warning. 1998. (Animorphs Ser.: No. 16). (J). (gr. 3-7). (978-0-606-13136-0(1)) Tandem Library Bks.

—The Weakness. l.t. ed. 2001. (Animorphs Ser.: No. 37). (Illus.). 129p. (J). (gr. 4 up). lib. bdg. 23.33 (978-0-8368-2770-5(8)) Stevens, Gareth Inc.

—The Weakness. 2000. (Animorphs Ser.: No. 37). (gr. 3-6). lib. bdg. 13.00 (978-0-613-21115-4(4)); (Illus.). (J). (978-0-606-18508-0(9)) Tandem Library Bks.

Appleton, Victor. Tom Swift & the Visitor from Planet X. 2006. pap. (***978-1-4065-0913-7(2)***) Dodo Pr.

Ashley, Elana. Splunkunio Splunkey Detective & Peacemaker: Case One: The Missing Friendship Bracelet. 2003. (ENG & SPA., Illus.). 32p. (J). 17.95 (978-0-9744812-0-3(3)) Dream Image Pr., LLC.

—Splunkunio Splunkey Detective & Peacemaker Detective y Pacificador: Case One: The Missing Friendship Bracelet Caso Primero: El Brazalete de la Amistad Desaparecido. Nikolov, Stefan V., tr. Ashley, Elana, photos by. 2005. (SPA & ENG., Illus.). 32p. (J). (gr. k-3). 17.95 (978-0-9744812-1-0(1)) Dream Image Pr., LLC.

Balawajder, Thomas, et al. The Ultimate Homework Survival Guide: A Reality Horror Production. Wise, Noreen, ed. 2nd ed. 2003. (Illus.). 64p. (J). per. 6.95 (978-1-58584-559-0(0)) Huckleberry Pr.

Ball, Justin & Croker, Evan. Space Dogs. 2006. 272p. (J). (gr. 3-7). 15.95 (978-0-375-83256-7(4)); lib. bdg. 17.99 (978-0-375-93256-4(9)) Random Hse. Children's Bks. (Knopf Bks. for Young Readers).

Barker, M. A. R. Prince of Skulls. 2002. (Illus.). 204p. (YA). per. 19.95 (978-0-9725880-3-0(0) , 1) Zottola Publishing, Inc.

Beechen, Adam. What I Did on My Hypergalactic Interstellar Summer Vacation. Hipp, Dan, illus. 2006. 129p. (J). 12.95 (978-0-9742803-6-3(4)) Komikwerks, LLC.

Bellavia, Timothy D. We Are All the Same Inside. Bellavia, William D., ed. Bellavia, Timothy D., illus. Becket, Logan, photos by. 2nd l.t. ed. 2000. (Illus.). 28p. (J). (ps-3). reprint ed. per. 10.95 (978-0-615-11395-1(8)) T.I.M.M.-E. Co., Inc.

Benton, Jim. Howard Hubbins Half Hour Hero. 2008. (J). pap. (***978-0-06-059774-0(7)***) HarperCollins Pubs.

Biro, Val. Gumdrop & the Martians. (Illus.). 32p. (J). (978-0-340-71485-0(9) , Hodder & Stoughton) Hodder General Publishing Division.

Blacker, Terence. The Angel Factory. (Illus.). 224p. 2003. (J). (gr. k-17). pap. 5.99 (978-0-689-86413-1(2) , Aladdin); 2002. (YA). (gr. 6-9). 16.95 (978-0-689-85171-1(5)) Simon & Schuster Children's Publishing.

Blackman, Malorie. Whizziwig Returns. unabr. l.t. ed. 2003. (Read-Along Ser.). 160p. (J). 24.95 incl. audio (978-0-7540-6235-9(1) , RA035, Galaxy Children's Large Print) BBC Audiobooks America.

Blundell, Judy. Star Wars: The Last of the Jedi #9. 2008. 160p. pap. 5.99 (***978-0-439-68142-1(1)***) Scholastic, Inc.

Breathed, Berkeley. Mars Needs Moms! Breathed, Berkeley, illus. 2007. 48p. (J). (ps). 16.99 (978-0-399-24736-1(X) , Philomel) Penguin Group (USA) Inc.

Brennan, Herbie. Zartog's Remote. Layton, Neal, illus. 2003. (Middle Grade Fiction Ser.). 96p. (J). (gr. 3-6). 14.95 (978-1-57505-507-7(4) , Carolrhoda Bks.) Lerner Publishing Group.

Brezina, Thomas. El Ataque del Caballero de Piedra (The Attack of the Stone Knight) Jos, A. Santiago Tagle, tr. Kruger, Dietmar, illus. 2001. (Corazon de Dragon Ser.: No. 3). (SPA.). 126p. 11.95 (978-84-348-7826-6(7)) SM Ediciones ESP. *Dist:* AIMS International Bks., Inc.

Broderick, Damien. Time Zones. 2000. (gr. 7-12). lib. bdg. 12.10 (978-0-613-29108-8(5)) Tandem Library Bks.

Brooks, Walter R. Freddy & the Baseball Team from Mars. Wiese, Kurt, illus. 1999. 256p. (J). (gr. 3-7). 23.95 (978-0-87951-942-1(8)) Overlook Pr., The.

—Freddy & the Baseball Team from Mars. 2000. (J). pap. 67.95 incl. audio (978-0-7887-4461-7(5) , 41150) Recorded Bks., LLC.

—Freddy & the Men from Mars. Wiese, Kurt, illus. 2002. 246p. (J). 23.95 (978-1-58567-269-1(6)) Overlook Pr., The.

Buchanan, Paul. Uncle from Another Planet. 1999. (Heebie Jeebies Ser.: Vol. 4). 144p. (YA). pap. 5.99 (978-0-8054-1650-3(1)) B&H Publishing Grp.

Budhos, Marina. Ask Me No Questions. 2007. 176p. (YA). pap. 8.99 (***978-1-4169-4920-6(8)*** , Simon Pulse) Simon & Schuster Children's Publishing.

Bunting, Eve. Wanna Buy an Alien? Bush, Timothy, illus. 2000. 96p. (J). (gr. 4-6). tchr. ed. 14.00 (978-0-395-69719-1(0) , Clarion Bks.) Houghton Mifflin Co. Trade & Reference Div.

Caldwell, Denise. Our Alien Friends. 2004. 35p. pap. 17.95 (978-1-4137-1066-3(2)) PublishAmerica, Inc.

Calvert, Patricia. Picking up the Pieces. 1999. (978-0-606-15922-7(3)) Tandem Library Bks.

Cannon, Janell. Trupp: A Fuzzhead Tale. 1998. (Illus.). 48p. (J). pap. 7.00 (978-0-15-201695-1(3) , Harcourt Paperbacks) Harcourt Children's Bks.

—Trupp: A Fuzzhead Tale. 1998. (J). (978-0-606-13876-5(5)) Tandem Library Bks.

Cazet, Denys. Minnie & Moo: Minnie & Moo Save the Earth. Cazet, Denys, illus. 2001. (Live Oak Readalong Ser.). (Illus.). (J). pap. 18.95 incl. audio compact disk (978-1-59112-396-5(8)) Live Oak Media.

—Minnie & Moo & the Potato from Planet X. Cazet, Denys, illus. (I Can Read Bks.). (Illus.). 48p. (J). (gr. k-3). 2003. pap. 3.99 (978-0-06-444312-8(4)); 2002. lib. bdg. 16.89 (978-0-06-623751-0(3)) HarperCollins Pubs.

—Minnie & Moo & the Potato from Planet X. Cazet, Denys, illus. 2005. (Readalongs for Beginning Readers Ser.). (Illus.). (J). pap. 16.95 incl. audio (978-1-59112-257-9(0)) Live Oak Media.

—Minnie & Moo & the Potato from Planet X. 2003. (gr. k-3). lib. bdg. 11.80 (978-0-613-65813-3(2)) Tandem Library Bks.

—Minnie & Moo Save the Earth. Cazet, Denys, illus. 2001. (Illus.). 25.95 incl. audio (978-0-87499-771-2(2)); 28.95 incl. audio compact disk (978-1-59112-597-6(9)); pap. 29.95 incl. audio (978-0-87499-772-9(0)); pap. 31.95 incl. audio compact disk (978-1-59112-596-9(0)) Live Oak Media.

Cazet, Denys, reader. Minnie & Moo & the Potato from Planet X. (Readalongs for Beginning Readers Ser.). (Illus.). (J). (ps-3). 2005. pap. 18.95 incl. audio compact disk (978-1-59112-879-3(X)); 2004. 25.95 incl. audio (978-1-59112-258-6(9)); 2004. 28.95 incl. audio compact disk (978-1-59112-880-9(3)); 2004. pap. 29.95 incl. audio (978-1-59112-259-3(7)); 2004. pap. 31.95 incl. audio compact disk (978-1-59112-881-6(1)) Live Oak Media.

Cazet, Denys & Dorling Kindersley Publishing Staff. Minnie & Moo Save the Earth, Vol. 3. 1999. (Minnie & Moo Ser.: Vol. 3). (Illus.). 48p. (J). (gr. 1-3). 12.99 (978-0-7894-2594-2(7)); pap. 3.99 (978-0-7894-3929-1(8)) Dorling Kindersley Publishing, Inc.

Chartrand, Kenneth. A Martian's Dream of Christmas. 2006. 48p. pap. 12.95 (978-1-4241-4123-4(0)) PublishAmerica, Inc.

Chase, Jeffrey Scott. Andy the Alien. 2006. (J). pap. 16.00 (978-0-8059-7081-4(9)) Dorrance Publishing Co., Inc.

Childress, Jamie. Galactic Treasure Hunt: Lost City of Atlantis. Braun, Chris, illus. 2006. 120p. (J). pap. 4.99 (978-1-931882-62-0(2)) Adventures Unlimited Pr.

—Galactic Treasure Hunt: Lost City of the Moon. Braun, Chris, illus. 2005. 115p. (J). (ps-7). pap. 4.99 (978-1-931882-45-3(2)) Adventures Unlimited Pr.

Chiodo, Stephen & Strain, Jim. Chiodo Bros.' Alien Xmas. Chiodo, Charles, illus. 2006. 40p. (J). 17.95 (978-0-9729388-4-6(2)) Baby Tattoo Bks.

Clarke, Carol Page. The Cuddly Mogs. 2006. (Illus.). 72p. pap. (***978-1-84401-620-4(X)***) Athena Pr.

Clevenger, Lee. IncrediBoy: Be Careful What You Wish. 2004. 267p. (J). pap. 12.95 (978-0-9764052-0-7(2)) Thomas Max Publishing.

Cole, Stephen & Gardner, Lousie. Alien Olympics. 1998. (Alien Pop-Ups Ser.). (Illus.). 10p. (J). 4.95 (978-1-899607-65-5(X)) Sterling Publishing Co., Inc.

Collins, Terry. Digest Novelization. 2002. (E. T. the Extra-Terrestrial Ser.). (Illus.). 144p. (J). pap. 4.99 (978-0-689-84367-9(4) , Simon Spotlight) Simon & Schuster Children's Publishing.

Conly, Jane Leslie. The Rudest Alien on Earth. rev. ed. 2002. 272p. (J). (gr. 5-8). 16.95 (978-0-8050-6069-0(3) , Holt, Henry & Co. Bks. For Young Readers) Holt, Henry & Co.

Connely, Chris L. & Vaughan, Mark. An Alien from Earth. 2003. 175p. per. 9.95 (978-0-9745544-0-2(5)) Lewis Lynn Bks.

Corey, Shana. First Graders from Mars. Teague, Mark, illus. 2003. (First Graders from Mars Ser.: No. 4). 32p. (J). pap. 4.99 (978-0-439-45219-9(8) , Scholastic Pr.) Scholastic, Inc.

Corey, Shana & Teague, Mark. Tera, Star Student. 2003. (First Graders from Mars Ser.: No. 4). (Illus.). 32p. (J). pap. 15.95 (978-0-439-26634-5(3) , Scholastic Pr.) Scholastic, Inc.

Coville, Bruce. Aliens Ate My Homework. Coville, Katherine, illus. 2007. (Alien Adventures Ser.). 192p. (J). pap. 5.99 (978-1-4169-3883-5(4) , Aladdin) Simon & Schuster Children's Publishing.

—Aliens Stole My Body. 1998. (Bruce Coville's Alien Adventures Ser.). (J). (gr. 3-7). 11.64 (978-0-606-13115-5(9)) Tandem Library Bks.

—The Attack of the Two-Inch Teacher. unabr. ed. 2000. (I Was a Sixth Grade Alien Ser.). 165p. (J). (gr. 3-5). pap. 28.00 incl. audio (978-0-8072-8354-7(1) , YA170SP, Listening Library) Random Hse. Audio Publishing Group.

—The Attack of the Two-Inch Teacher. 1999. (I Was a Sixth Grade Alien Ser.). (Illus.). (J). 10.64 (978-0-606-18374-1(4)) Tandem Library Bks.

—Bruce Coville's UFOs. 2000. (Illus.). (J). 11.64 (978-0-606-18679-7(4)) Tandem Library Bks.

—Don't Fry My Veeblax! Sansekers, Tony, illus. 2000. (I Was a Sixth Grade Alien Ser.: Vol. 6). (J). 10.64 (978-0-606-19849-3(0)) Tandem Library Bks.

—I Left My Sneakers in Dimension X. Coville, Katherine, illus. 2007. (Alien Adventures Ser.). 192p. (J). pap. 5.99 (978-1-4169-3882-8(6) , Aladdin) Simon & Schuster Children's Publishing.

—I Lost My Grandfather's Brain. unabr. ed. 2004. (I Was a Sixth Grade Alien Ser.). 160p. (J). (gr. 3-6). pap. 29.00 incl. audio (978-0-8072-8385-1(1) , YA180SP, Listening Library) Random Hse. Audio Publishing Group.

—I Lost My Grandfather's Brain. 1999. (I Was a Sixth Grade Alien Ser.). (Illus.). (J). 10.64 (978-0-606-18306-2(X)) Tandem Library Bks.

—I Was a Sixth Grade Alien. (I Was a Sixth Grade Alien Ser.). 170p. (J). (gr. 4-6). pap. 3.99 (978-0-8072-8202-1(2)); 2004. (gr. 3-6). pap. 29.00 incl. audio (978-0-8072-8201-4(4) , S YA 138 SP) Random Hse. Audio Publishing Group. (Listening Library).

—I Was a Sixth Grade Alien. 1999. (I Was a Sixth Grade Alien Ser.). (J). 11.64 (978-0-606-17089-5(8)) Tandem Library Bks.

—The Monsters of Morley Manor. 2002. (J). lib. bdg. 24.00 incl. audio (978-0-9717540-3-4(9) , 02003L) Full Cast Audio.

—The Monsters of Morley Manor: A Madcap Adventure. 240p. (YA). (gr. 3-6). 2003. pap. 5.95 (978-0-15-204705-4(0) , Magic Carpet Bks.); 2001. 16.00 (978-0-15-216382-2(4)) Harcourt Children's Bks.

—My Teacher Flunked the Planet. Pierard, John, illus. 2005. 162p. (J). (gr. 3-7). lib. bdg. 12.04 (978-0-606-33892-9(6)) Tandem Library Bks.

—My Teacher Fried My Brains. Pierard, John, illus. 2005. 138p. (J). (gr. 3-7). lib. bdg. 12.04 (978-0-606-33890-5(X)) Tandem Library Bks.

—My Teacher Is an Alien. unabr. ed. 2004. (My Teacher Is an Alien Ser.). 123p. (J). (gr. 3-6). pap. 29.00 incl. audio (978-0-8072-8029-4(1) , S YA 971 SP, Listening Library) Random Hse. Audio Publishing Group.

—My Teacher Is an Alien. Wimmer, Mike, illus. 2005. (My teacher Bks.). 128p. (J). (ps-7). pap. 5.99 (978-1-4169-0334-5(8) , Aladdin) Simon & Schuster Children's Publishing.

—My Teacher Is an Alien. Wimmer, Mike, illus. 2005. 124p. (J). (ps-7). lib. bdg. 12.04 (978-0-606-33889-9(6)) Tandem Library Bks.

—Peanut Butter Lover Boy. 2000. (I Was a Sixth Grade Alien Ser.). (Illus.). (J). (978-0-606-18307-9(8)) Tandem Library Bks.

—The Revolt of the Miniature Mutants. No. 10. 2000. (I Was a Sixth Grade Alien Ser.). (Illus.). (J). (978-0-606-20716-4(3)) Tandem Library Bks.

—The Search for Snout. Coville, Katherine, illus. 2007. (Rod Allbright & the Galactic Patrol Ser.). 224p. (J). pap. 5.99 (***978-1-4169-4980-0(1)*** , Aladdin) Simon & Schuster Children's Publishing.

—There's an Alien in My Classroom! l.t. ed. 2000. (Illus.). 184p. (J). pap. 16.95 (978-0-7540-6108-3(6) , Galaxy Children's Large Print) BBC Audiobooks America.

—There's an Alien in My Classroom! (Illus.). 201p. (J). pap. 8.95 (978-0-340-73634-0(8) , Hodder & Stoughton) Hodder General Publishing Division GBR. *Dist:* Trafalgar Square Publishing.

—There's an Alien in My Underwear. 2001. (Illus.). 150p. (J). (gr. 3-6). lib. bdg. 11.04 (978-0-606-22824-4(1)) Tandem Library Bks.

—Zombies of the Science Fair. 2000. (I Was a Sixth Grade Alien Ser.). (Illus.). (J). (978-0-606-18308-6(6)) Tandem Library Bks.

Crilley, Mark. Akiko & the Intergalactic Zoo. Crilley, Mark, illus. 2003. (Illus.). 160p. (gr. 3 up). pap. 5.50 (978-0-440-41891-7(7) , Yearling) Random Hse. Children's Bks.

—Akiko & the Intergalactic Zoo. 2003. (gr. k-3). lib. bdg. 13.00 (978-0-613-82973-1(5)) Tandem Library Bks.

Crisp, Dan, illus. Five Little Men in a Flying Saucer. 2005. (Classic Books with Holes). 16p. (J). bds. 5.99 (978-1-904550-58-7(4)) Child's Play-International.

Cross, Susan & Sullivan, Mary Beth. Journey from Nimmsvib. Picard, Lynne, illus. 2002. ii, 70p. (YA). (gr. 3-11). pap. 22.00 (978-0-9723691-0-7(4)) Caleidoscope Creations.

Cullimore, Stan. Alien Swap. Schon, Nick, illus. 2005. 24p. (J). lib. bdg. 22.65 (***978-1-59646-744-6(4)***) Dingles & Co.

E
F
G

Dark Horse Comics Staff & Schultz, Mark. Apocalypse - The Destroying Angels. 1999. (Aliens Ser.). (Illus.). 96p. (gr. 11 up). pap. 10.95 (978-1-56971-399-0(5)) Dark Horse Comics.

Deacon, Alexis. Beegu. Deacon, Alexis, illus. 2003. (Illus.). 40p. (J). 16.00 (978-0-374-30667-0(2) , Farrar, Straus & Giroux (BYR)) Farrar, Straus & Giroux.

—Beegu. 2004. (Illus.). 32p. (J). pap. (978-0-09-941744-6(8) , Red Fox) Random Hse. Children's Bks.

DeAndrea, William L. & DeAndrea, Matthew. The Pizza That Time Forgot. 1999. (J). (gr. 3-7). pap. 3.99 (978-0-380-79155-2(2)) HarperCollins Pubs.

Desrosiers, Sylvie. Ma Mère Est un Extraterrestre. Franson, Leanne, illus. 2002. (Premier Roman Ser.). (FRE.). 64p. (J). (gr. 1-4). pap. (978-2-89021-561-0(X)) Diffusion du livre Mirabel.

Diggs, Dylan. Palladium: Second Contact. 2006. (J). mass mkt. 3.80 (978-1-886366-13-8(6) , 5,000) Sights Productions.

Disney Press Staff. Lilo & Stitch. 2nd rev. ed. 2006. (Illus.). 48p. (gr. 1-4). pap. 3.99 (978-1-4231-0141-3(3)) Disney Pr.

DK Publishing Staff. Little Lost Alien. 2007. 12p. (J). (ps-1). 12.99 (978-0-7566-2931-1(4)) Dorling Kindersley Publishing, Inc.

Duey, Kathleen. Beware the Alien Invasion! 2000. (Alone in the Dark Ser.). (Illus.). 32p. (J). pap. 3.95 (978-1-891100-15-4(7)) Smart Kids Publishing.

Duffey, Betsy. Alien for Rent. 2000. (978-0-606-17889-1(9)) Tandem Library Bks.

Eason, Alethea. Hungry. 2007. 208p. (J). (gr. 5 up). 15.99 (***978-0-06-082554-6(5)***); lib. bdg. 16.89 (***978-0-06-082555-3(3)***) HarperCollins Pubs. (Eos).

Ed's Terrestrials. 2006. (J). per. 19.99 net. (978-0-9789168-1-7(6)) Blue Dream Studios.

Edwards, Pat. Monster from Mercury. 1999. (gr. 3-6). lib. bdg. 10.95 (978-0-613-19402-0(0)) Tandem Library Bks.

Elish, Dan. Attack of the Frozen Woodchucks. 2008. 256p. (J). 17.89 (***978-0-06-113871-3(1)*** , Geringer, Laura Book) HarperCollins Pubs.

—Attack of the Frozen Woodchucks. Call, Greg, illus. 2008. 256p. (J). 16.99 (***978-0-06-113870-6(3)*** , Geringer, Laura Book) HarperCollins Pubs.

Elliott, David. Hazel Nutt, Alien Hunter. Kelley, True, illus. 2005. 32p. (J). tchr. ed. 16.95 (978-0-8234-1843-5(X)) Holiday Hse., Inc.

Faller, Regis. Polo: The Runaway Book. Faller, Regis, illus. rev. ed. 2007. (Illus.). 80p. (J). (gr. k-3). 16.95 (978-1-59643-189-8(X)) Roaring Brook Pr.

Fallon, Joe. Quailman Battles the Giant Space Slug. Truong, Vinh et al, illus. 1999. (Golden Book Ser.). (J). pap. (978-0-307-13141-6(6) , Golden Bks.) Random Hse. Children's Bks.

Farber, Erica. The Alien from Outer Space. Mayer, Mercer, illus. 2006. (Critter Kids Adventure Ser.). 32p. (J). (gr. 2-3). pap. 4.95 (978-0-7696-4763-0(4) , Gingham Dog Pr.) School Specialty Publishing.

Farrell, Robert E., Jr. Alien Log. 2004. 250p. per. 12.95 (978-1-59196-523-7(3)) Instantpublisher.com.

Freedman, Claire. Aliens Love Underpants. Cort, Ben, illus. 2007. 32p. (J). (ps-2). 14.99 (***978-0-7641-6087-5(7)***) Barron's Educational Series, Inc.

French, Vivian. I Wish I Were an Alien. Williams, Lisa, illus. 2005. (Lightning Readers Ser.). 32p. (J). (ps-ps). pap., pap. 3.95 (978-0-7696-4020-4(6) , Gingham Dog Pr.) School Specialty Publishing.

—Ojala fuera un Extraterrestre. Williams, Lisa, illus. 2005. (Lightning Readers Ser.). (SPA.). 32p. (J). (gr. k-1). pap. 3.95 (978-0-7696-4060-0(5) , Gingham Dog Pr.) School Specialty Publishing.

Friesner, Esther M. Men in Black II: The Official Novelization. 2002. (gr. 7-12). lib. bdg. 15.30 (978-0-613-56978-1(4)) Tandem Library Bks.

Gaarder, Jostein. Hello? Is Anybody There? Gardner, Sally, illus. l.t. ed. 2002. 152p. (J). 16.95 (978-0-7540-7814-2(0) , Galaxy Children's Large Print) BBC Audiobooks America.

Gauthier, Gail. My Life among the Aliens. 1998. (J). (978-0-606-12997-8(9)) Tandem Library Bks.

Gershon, Gina & Gershon, Dann. Camp Creepy Time: The Adventures of Einstein P. Fleet. 2007. 224p. (J). (gr. 5 up). 16.99 (978-0-399-24737-8(6) , Putnam Juvenile) Penguin Group (USA) Inc.

Gilden, Mel. Britney Spears Is a Three-Headed Alien: The Inside Story. 2001. (gr. 7-12). lib. bdg. 18.80 (978-0-613-82444-6(X)) Tandem Library Bks.

Gilmore, Kate. The Exchange Student. 2006. 222p. (J). (gr. 7). pap. 6.95 (978-0-618-68948-4(6)) Houghton Mifflin Co.

—The Exchange Student. 1999. 224p. (J). (gr. 5-9). tchr. ed. 15.00 (978-0-395-57511-6(7)) Houghton Mifflin Co. Trade & Reference Div.

Golden Books Staff. Space Signals - Muppets from Space: Paint Box Book. 1999. (Muppets Ser.). (Illus.). 32p. (ps-3). pap. (978-0-307-09243-4(7)) Golden Bks. Publishing (Canada), Inc.

Greenburg, Dan. Attack of the Evil Elvises. Pamintuan, Macky, illus. 2007. (Weird Planet Ser.: No. 4). 96p. (J). (gr. 2-4). lib. bdg. 11.99 (978-0-375-93347-9(6)); 3.99 (978-0-375-83347-2(1)) Random Hse. Children's Bks. (Random Hse. Bks. for Young Readers).

—Chilling with the Great Ones. Pamintuan, Macky, illus. 2006. 96p. (J). (gr. 2-5). lib. bdg. 11.99 (978-0-375-93346-2(8)); (Weird Planet Ser.: No. 3). (gr. 1-4). pap. 3.99 (978-0-375-83346-5(3)) Random Hse. Children's Bks. (Random Hse. Bks. for Young Readers).

—Just Add Water...and Scream! Davis, Jack E., illus. 2003. (Zack Files Ser.: No. 29). 64p. (gr. 1-4). mass mkt. 4.99 (978-0-448-42887-1(3) , Grosset & Dunlap) Penguin Group (USA) Inc.

—Just Add Water...and Scream! 2002. (gr. 3-6). lib. bdg. 13.00 (978-0-613-61637-9(5)) Tandem Library Bks.

—Weird Planet: Lights, Camera... Liftoff! Pamintuan, Macky, illus. 2007. (Weird Planet Ser.: No. 5). 96p. (J). (gr. 2-5). pap. 3.99 (***978-0-375-84336-5(1)*** , Random Hse. Bks. for Young Readers) Random Hse. Children's Bks.

—Weird Planet No. 5: Lights, Camera... Liftoff! Pamintuan, Macky, illus. 2007. (Stepping Stone Bks.). 96p. (J). (gr. 2-5). lib. bdg. 11.99 (***978-0-375-94336-2(6)*** , Random Hse. Bks. for Young Readers) Random Hse. Children's Bks.

Greenwood, Kerry. Alien Invasions. 2000. (gr. 7-12). lib. bdg. 12.10 (978-0-613-28728-9(2)) Tandem Library Bks.

Greeson, Ewell. Aegis. 2003. 436p. (YA). per. 19.95 (978-1-59453-024-1(6) , 1701) Airleaf Publishing & Bookselling.

Gregar, Steve. Al the Alien. 2004. 23p. pap. 14.98 (978-1-4116-1149-8(7)) Lulu.com.

Griffiths, Andy. Zombie Butts from Uranus! 2004. 288p. (Orig.). (J). 4.99 (978-0-439-42470-7(4)) Scholastic, Inc.

Gutman, Dan. Funny Boy Meets the Airsick Alien from Andromeda. Dykes, John, illus. 3rd rev. ed. 1999. (L.A.F. Ser.: No. 3). 128p. (gr. 2-6). pap. 3.99 (978-0-7868-1330-8(X)) Hyperion Pr.

—Funny Boy Meets the Airsick Alien from Andromeda. 1999. (gr. 3-6). lib. bdg. 11.80 (978-0-613-21571-8(0)) Tandem Library Bks.

—Funny Boy Takes on the Chit-Chatting Cheese from Chattanooga. 2001. (L.A.F. Bks.). (Illus.). 128p. (gr. 2-6). pap. 4.99 (978-0-7868-1445-9(4)) Disney Pr.

—Funny Boy Takes on the Chit-Chatting Cheese from Chattanooga. 2000. (gr. 3-6). lib. bdg. 13.00 (978-0-613-31228-8(7)) Tandem Library Bks.

Haarsma, P. J. The Softwire: Virus on Orbis 1. 2008. (Illus.). 288p. (J). (gr. 5). 6.99 (***978-0-7636-3638-8(X)***) Candlewick Pr.

Haber, Karen. Crossing Infinity. 2006. 239p. pap. 9.95 (978-1-59687-411-4(2)) ibooks, Inc.

Hannan, Peter. Attack of the 50-Foot Alien Creep-Oids! Hannan, Peter, illus. 2007. (Super Goofballs Ser.: Bk. 4). 144p. (J). (gr. 2-6). pap. 4.99 (***978-0-06-085217-7(8)*** , Harper Trophy) HarperCollins Pubs.

Hansen, Lynne. Reckless Revolution. 2007. (YA). (***978-1-4114-9672-9(8)***) Spark Publishing Group.

—Shades of Blue & Gray. 2007. (YA). pap. (***978-1-4114-9674-3(4)***) Spark Publishing Group.

—A Time for Witches. 2007. (YA). (***978-1-4114-9671-2(X)***) Spark Publishing Group.

Hayes, Malcolm. The Dreamcatchers. 2006. 282p. pap. (***978-1-4120-8320-1(6)***) Trafford Publishing.

Herman, Gail. Be Good, Gertie! 2002. (E. T. the Extra-Terrestrial Ser.). (Illus.). 24p. (J). pap. 3.50 (978-0-689-84364-8(X) , Simon Spotlight) Simon & Schuster Children's Publishing.

—Be Good, Gertie! 2002. (gr. k-3). lib. bdg. 11.25 (978-0-613-82939-7(5)) Tandem Library Bks.

—A Friend for E. T. 2002. (E. T. the Extra-Terrestrial Ser.). (Illus.). 24p. (J). (ps-3). pap. 3.50 (978-0-689-84363-1(1) , Simon Spotlight) Simon & Schuster Children's Publishing.

—Scooby-Doo & Aliens Too! del Sur, Duendes, illus. 2000. (Scooby-Doo Movie Storybooks). 32p. (J). (ps-3). 3.50 (978-0-439-17701-6(4)) Scholastic, Inc.

—Scooby-Doo & Aliens Too! 2000. (gr. k-3). lib. bdg. 11.25 (978-0-613-33034-3(X)) Tandem Library Bks.

—Scooby Doo! & the Football Fright. 2002. (gr. k-3). lib. bdg. 11.80 (978-0-613-58152-3(0)) Tandem Library Bks.

Hoena, B. A. & Harpster, Steve. Invaders from the Great Goo Galaxy. 2007. (Graphic Sparks Ser.). (Illus.). (J). 19.93 (978-1-59889-052-5(2)) Stone Arch Bks.

Homzie, H. B. & Phillips, Matthew. The Baby-Sitters Wore Diapers, No. 3. 2003. (Alien Clones from Outer Space Ser.). 80p. (J). pap. 3.99 (978-0-689-82344-2(4) , Aladdin) Simon & Schuster Children's Publishing.

Homzie, Hillary. Two Heads Are Better Than One. 2002. (gr. k-3). lib. bdg. 11.80 (978-0-613-57587-4(3)) Tandem Library Bks.

Homzie, Hillary & Phillips, Matthew. Two Heads Are Better Than One, Vol. 1. 2002. (Alien Clones from Outer Space Ser.). 80p. (J). pap. 3.99 (978-0-689-82342-8(8) , Aladdin) Simon & Schuster Children's Publishing.

Hood, Robert. Gadgets & Gizmos. 2000. (gr. 7-12). lib. bdg. 12.10 (978-0-613-28848-4(3)) Tandem Library Bks.

Howe, James. Invasion of the Mind Swappers from Asteroid 6! 2004. (Tales from the House of Bunnicula Ser.). 112p. (J). (gr. 3-6). pap. 17.00 incl. audio (978-1-4000-8633-7(7) , Listening Library) Random Hse. Audio Publishing Group.

—Invasion of the Mind Swappers from Asteroid 6! Helquist, Brett, illus. (Tales from the House of Bunnicula Ser.). (J). 2003. 112p. pap. 3.99 (978-0-689-83950-4(2) , Aladdin); 2002. 96p. (gr. 2-4). 9.95 (978-0-689-83949-8(9) , Atheneum) Simon & Schuster Children's Publishing.

—Invasion of the Mind Swappers from Asteroid 6! 2003. (Tales from the House of Bunnicula Ser.). (gr. 3-6). lib. bdg. 11.80 (978-0-613-66414-1(0)) Tandem Library Bks.

—It Came from Beneath the Bed! Helquist, Brett, illus. 2002. (Tales from the House of Bunnicula Ser.). 96p. (J). (gr. 2-4). 9.95 (978-0-689-83947-4(2) , Atheneum) Simon & Schuster Children's Publishing.

Huggins-Cooper, Lynn. Alien Invaders/Invasores Extraterrestres. de la Vega, Eida, tr. Leick, Bonnie, illus. 2005. Tr. of Invasores Extraterrestres. (SPA & ENG.). 32p. (J). (gr. 1-3). 16.95 (978-0-9724973-9-8(0) , 626999) Raven Tree Pr.

—Alien Invaders/Invasores Extraterrestres. Leick, Bonnie, illus. 2005. Tr. of Invasores Extraterrestres. (SPA & ENG.). 32p. (J). pap. 4.99 (978-0-9741992-7-6(3) , 626999) Raven Tree Pr.

Iacobucci, Vincent. The Little Book All about Fluguls. ed. 2006. (Illus.). (J). (***978-0-9779390-0-8(6)***) Flugul Pubng.

Ikumi, Mia. Tokyo Mew Mew (en Español) 2006. (SPA., Illus.). 176p. reprint ed. Vol. 2. pap. 10.95 (978-1-59497-170-9(6)); Vol. 3. pap. 10.95 (978-1-59497-171-6(4)) Public Square Bks.

Jaffe, Elizabeth. Alien Alert, Vol. 2. Steck, Jim, illus. 2005. 32p. (J). (ps-7). lib. bdg. 12.04 (978-0-606-33922-3(1)) Tandem Library Bks.

Janos, Robert, illus. Jasmin & the Wugling. 2000. (It's up to You Ser.). 101p. (J). (gr. 2-7). per. 8.95 (978-0-9726099-2-0(X)) BurnsBooks.

Jeapes, Ben. The Ark. 2000. 352p. (YA). (gr. 8-12). pap. 4.99 (978-0-439-21917-4(5)) Scholastic, Inc.

—Xenocide Mission. 2004. (gr. 7-12). lib. bdg. 14.75 (978-0-613-72334-3(1)) Tandem Library Bks.

Jeffers, Oliver. The Way Back Home. Jeffers, Oliver, illus. 2008. 32p. (J). (ps). 16.99 (***978-0-399-25074-3(3)*** , Philomel) Penguin Group (USA) Inc.

Johnson, David. Trapped in Space. Liew, Sonny, illus. 2007. (J). 80p. (***978-1-59889-354-0(8)***); 74p. pap. (***978-1-59889-449-3(8)***) Stone Arch Bks.

Johnson, Pete. Eyes of the Alien. l.t. ed. 2005. (Illus.). 200p. (J). pap. (978-0-7540-6127-4(2) , CLP 321) BBC Audio.

—Eyes of the Alien. unabr. l.t. ed. 2003. (Read-Along Ser.). 184p. (J). 24.95 incl. audio (978-0-7540-6239-4(2) , RAO40, Galaxy Children's Large Print) BBC Audiobooks America.

Johnston, Tony. Alien & Possum: Friends No Matter What. 2002. (gr. 3-6). lib. bdg. 11.80 (978-0-613-57565-2(2)) Tandem Library Bks.

—Alien & Possum: Hanging Out. DiTerlizzi, Tony, illus. (Ready-to-Reads Ser.). 48p. (J). 2003. pap. 3.99 (978-0-689-85771-3(3) , Aladdin); 2002. (gr. 1-3). 15.00 (978-0-689-83836-1(0)) Simon & Schuster Children's Publishing.

—Alien & Possum: Hanging Out. 2003. (gr. k-3). lib. bdg. 11.80 (978-0-613-66391-5(8)) Tandem Library Bks.

—Alien & Possum No. 1: Friends No Matter What. DiTerlizzi, Tony, illus. 2002. (Ready-to-Read Ser.). 48p. (J). pap. 3.99 (978-0-689-85326-5(2) , Aladdin) Simon & Schuster Children's Publishing.

Joosse, Barbara M. Alien Brain Fryout. Truesdell, Sue, illus. 2000. (Wild Willie Mystery Ser.). 108p. (J). (gr. 4-6). tchr. ed. 15.00 (978-0-395-68964-6(3) , Clarion Bks.) Houghton Mifflin Co. Trade & Reference Div.

Karas, G. Brian. Bebe 2. 2001. (J). (978-0-06-029273-7(3)); lib. bdg. (978-0-06-029274-4(1)) HarperCollins Pubs.

—Bebe's Bad Dream. 2000. (Illus.). 32p. (J). (gr. k up). 15.89 (978-0-688-16183-5(9)) HarperCollins Pubs.

Katz, Z. L. Aliens Are Everywhere. 2002. (gr. 3-6). lib. bdg. 11.80 (978-0-613-50402-7(X)) Tandem Library Bks.

Kennedy, Mike & Robinson, Roger. Alien vs. Predator: Thrill of the Hunt. 2004. (Illus.). 96p. pap. 6.95 (978-1-59307-257-5(0)) Dark Horse Comics.

Kennedy Tosten, S. Troy's Amazing Universe: A for Aliens. 2005. 124p. pap. 12.95 (978-1-59113-672-9(5)) Booklocker.com, Inc.

Kerr, P. B. One Small Step. 2008. 304p. (J). 16.99 (978-1-4169-4213-9(0)) Simon & Schuster Children's Publishing.

Kido, Yukiko. Who's at the Movies? 2006. (I'm Going to Read Ser.). (Illus.). 32p. (J). pap. 3.95 (978-1-4027-3340-6(2)) Sterling Publishing Co., Inc.

Klause, Annette Curtis. Alien Secrets. 1999. 240p. (YA). (gr. 5-12). mass mkt. 5.99 (978-0-440-22851-6(4) , Laurel Leaf) Random Hse. Children's Bks.

—Alien Secrets. 1999. (gr. 5-8). lib. bdg. 13.55 (978-0-613-72273-5(6)) Tandem Library Bks.

Kline, Trish. Earth Academy 7, Purple Book One: Journey to Earth. 2003. (J). per. 7.50 (978-0-9717234-7-4(8)) Ghost Hunter Productions.

—Earth Academy 7, Red Book One: The Aliens Are Coming! 2003. (J). per. 7.50 (978-0-9717234-4-3(3)) Ghost Hunter Productions.

Koge-Donbo. Di Gi Charat Theater - Dejiko's Summer Vacation. Yamashita, Saki, ed. Hina., illus. 2003. (Di Gi Charat Theater Ser.). 176p. pap. 9.99 (978-1-932480-07-8(2) , Broccoli Bks.) Broccoli International USA, Inc.

Korman, Gordon. Invasion of the Nose Pickers. Vaccaro, Victor, illus. 2000. (L.A.F. Bks.). 138p. (J). (gr. 2-6). lib. bdg. 14.49 (978-0-7868-2590-5(1)) Hyperion Paperbacks for Children.

—Planet of the Nose Pickers, Vol. 2. Vaccaro, Victor, illus. 2000. (Planet of the Nose Pickers Ser.: Vol. 2). 140p. 14.49 (978-0-7868-2571-4(5)) Hyperion Bks. for Children.

—Planet of the Nose Pickers. 2000. (gr. 3-6). lib. bdg. 11.80 (978-0-613-26612-3(9)) Tandem Library Bks.

—The Ultimate Nose Picker Collection. Vaccaro, Victor, illus. 2006. 592p. (gr. 2-6). pap. 9.99 (978-0-7868-3740-3(3)) Hyperion Pr.

Krull, Kathleen. How to Trick or Treat in Outer Space. Brewer, Paul, illus. 2004. 32p. (J). (gr. k-3). tchr. ed. 16.95 (978-0-8234-1844-2(8)) Holiday Hse., Inc.

Kulling, Monica. Go, Stitch, Go! Shimabukuro, Denise & Disney Storybook Artists Staff, illus. 2002. (Step into Reading Ser.). 32p. (J). (ps-1). pap. 3.99 (978-0-7364-1350-3(2) , RH/Disney) Random Hse. Children's Bks.

Labatt, Mary. Aliens in Woodford. Hill-Jackson, Troy, illus. 2000. (Sam Ser.). 120p. (J). (gr. 4-6). (978-1-55074-607-5(3)); (978-1-55074-611-2(1)) Kids Can Pr., Ltd.

Lantz, Francess L. Stepbaby from Planet Weird. 2001. (Illus.). (J). 3.99 (978-0-375-81259-0(8) , Random Hse. Bks. for Young Readers) Random Hse. Children's Bks.

Locke, Terry. Spencer Hurley & the Aliens: Book One: the Abduction. 2007. (Spencer Hurley & the Aliens Ser.: 1). (Illus.). 224p. (YA). 12.95 (978-0-9786940-0-5(7) , SHAB1V1E1CB) Dream Workshop Publishing Co., LLC, The.

Lofficier, Randy & Lofficier, Jean-Marc. Robonocchio. Pijuan Aragon, Miren, tr. Martiniere, Stephan, illus. 2004. (SPA.). 128p. (YA). per. 14.95 (978-1-932983-25-8(2) , Black Coat Pr.) HollywoodComics.com, LLC.

—Robonocchio. Martiniere, Stephan, illus. 2004. (FRE.). 128p. (YA). per. 14.95 (978-1-932983-04-3(X) , Black Coat Pr.) HollywoodComics.com, LLC.

Lorimer, Janet. Flashback. 2001. (PageTurner Science Fiction Ser.). 80p. (YA). per. 3.95 (978-1-56254-132-3(3) , SP 1323) Saddleback Educational Publishing.

—Flashback. 2001. (gr. 7-12). lib. bdg. 11.80 (978-0-613-34211-7(9)) Tandem Library Bks.

Luzzatto, Caroline. Interplanetary Avenger. 2005. (Illus.). 128p. (J). (gr. 3-7). 16.95 (978-0-8234-1933-3(9)) Holiday Hse., Inc.

Lytle, Casey. Alien in the Mirror Bk. 1: Homeworld. 2000. (Homeworld Ser.: Vol. 1). 218p. (YA). (gr. 4-9). mass mkt. 5.99 (978-0-9678933-0-3(5)) Mcnarn Group, The.

Ma, Jyoti. Sparkling Together: Starbright & His Earthling Friends. Devi, Chandra, illus. 2004. 96p. pap. 19.95 (978-0-932040-54-1(3)) Integral Yoga Pubns.

Mackel, Kathy. Alien in a Bottle. 2004. 208p. (J). 16.99 (978-0-06-029281-2(4)); lib. bdg. 16.89 (978-0-06-029282-9(2)) HarperCollins Pubs.

—Can of Worms. 2000. (Illus.). (J). 10.64 (978-0-606-17962-1(3)); 1999. (gr. 3-6). lib. bdg. 11.80 (978-0-613-23590-7(8)) Tandem Library Bks.

—Eggs in One Basket. (J). 2002. 208p. pap. 6.99 (978-0-380-81399-5(8)); 2000. (Illus.). 195p. (gr. 5-7). 15.95 (978-0-380-97847-2(4)) HarperCollins Pubs.

—From the Horse's Mouth. 2002. 224p. (J). (gr. 3-7). 15.95 (978-0-06-029414-4(0)) HarperCollins Pubs.

Maguire, Gregory. Five Alien Elves. Clayton, Elaine, illus. 2000. (J). 12.64 (978-0-606-19970-4(5)) Tandem Library Bks.

Manchester, Deborah M. & Davis, Madeline. Bula's Surprise Visit, 53 vols., Vol. 1. Manchester, Deborah M., ed. Johnson, Brook L., illus. 1999. 32p. (J). 4.95 (978-0-9673099-0-3(5)) Zula Ltd.

Mangels, Andy & Martin, Michael A. Pursuit. 2003. (Roswell Ser.). (Illus.). 272p. (YA). pap. 5.99 (978-0-689-85522-1(2) , Simon Pulse) Simon & Schuster Children's Publishing.

Marr, Andrew. Born in the Darkest Time of Year: Stories for the Season of the Christ Child. 2004. 180p. (J). pap. 13.95 (978-0-595-32633-4(1)) iUniverse, Inc.

Marsh, Carole. Dear Alien: The Little Green Man Mystery. 2007. (Postcard Mysteries Ser.). 128p. (J). (gr. 2-9). 14.95 (***978-0-635-06397-7(2)***); pap. 5.99 (***978-0-635-06341-0(7)***) Gallopade International. (Marsh, Carole Family CD-Rom).

Mason, Jane. Flinstones in Viva Rock Vegas: Flinstones Movie Storybook. 2000. (Illus.). 32p. (J). (ps-3). pap. 5.99 (978-0-439-17304-9(3)) Scholastic, Inc.

McBride, R. J. Temple of the Rainbow. 2004. 151p. pap. 19.95 (978-1-4137-1934-5(1)) PublishAmerica, Inc.

McCann, Jesse Leon. Scooby-Doo & the Alien Invaders. 2000. (Golden Book Ser.). (Illus.). 32p. (J). (ps-3). pap. 3.99 (978-0-307-10474-8(5) , 10474, Golden Bks.) Random Hse. Children's Bks.

McCann, Jesse Leon, adapted by. Scooby-Doo & the Alien Invaders. 2000. (Scooby-Doo Movie Storybooks). (Illus.). 32p. (J). (ps-3). 3.50 (978-0-439-17700-9(6)) Scholastic, Inc.

McElroy, Laurie. Alien Invasion. 2007. (Teenick Ser.: No. 5). 112p. (J). pap. 4.99 (978-0-439-89044-1(6)) Scholastic, Inc.

McGrath, Raymond, illus. My Alien: Individual Title Six-Packs. (Sails Literacy Ser.). 16p. (gr. k up). 27.00 (978-0-7635-4394-5(2)) Rigby Education.

McPhail, David M. Tinker & Tom & the Star Baby. 2000. (Illus.). 32p. (J). (ps-3). pap. 5.95 (978-0-316-56389-5(7)) Little Brown & Co.

—Tinker & Tom & the Star Baby. McPhail, David M., illus. 1998. (Illus.). 32p. (J). (ps-3). 14.95 (978-0-316-56349-9(8)) Little Brown & Co.

Meganck, Glenn. Big Deal. 1998. 67p. (Illus.). (gr. 4-7). pap. 4.99 (978-1-892339-01-0(3)); 11.99 (978-1-892339-00-3(5)) Beachfront Publishing.

—No Big Deal. Ward, Jon, illus. 2000. 76p. (gr. 3-5). pap. 4.99 (978-1-892339-05-8(6)) Beachfront Publishing.

Metz, Melinda. Stowaway. 2000. (gr. 5-8). lib. bdg. 14.15 (978-0-613-17535-7(2)) Tandem Library Bks.

Metzger, Joanna. The Space Program. Elizalde, Marcelo, illus. 2006. 142p. (J). (978-1-59336-695-7(7)) Mondo Publishing.

Miller, Lee. Ete: (Extraterrestrial Elements) 2006. 80p. pap. 14.95 (978-1-4241-3498-4(6)) PublishAmerica, Inc.

Mitchell, Richard, illus. The Man from Mars. 1999. (J). (978-0-7608-3201-1(3)) Sundance/Newbridge Educational Publishing.

—The Monster from Mercury. 1999. (J). (978-0-7608-3200-4(5)) Sundance/Newbridge Educational Publishing.

Montgomery, R. A. Prisoner of the Ant People. 2005. (Illus.). 115p. (J). pap. (***978-0-7608-9698-3(4)***) Sundance/Newbridge Educational Publishing.

Myers, Bill. The Encounter. 2002. (Forbidden Doors Ser.: Vol. 6). 160p. (J). mass mkt. 4.99 (978-0-8423-5738-8(6)) Tyndale Hse. Pubs.

—My Life As a Prickly Porcupine from the Planet Pluto. 2004. (Incredible Worlds of Wally McDoogle Ser.). 128p. (J). pap. 6.99 (978-0-8499-5994-3(2)) Nelson, Thomas Inc.

E F G

Nastasic, Susan. The Galaxy Diner. Bryant, Laura J., tr. Bryant, Laura J., illus. 2001. (Cover-To-Cover Novel Ser.). 72p. (J). (gr. 2-5). lib. bdg. 13.95 (978-0-7807-9716-1(7)) Perfection Learning Corp.

Nguyen, Tao. Mighty Mite: A New Beginning. Nguyen, Tao, illus. 2006. (J). 14.95 (978-0-9776282-1-6(3)) Amazing Factory, The.

Nix, Garth. One Beastly Beast: Two Aliens, Three Inventors, Four Fantastic Tales. Biggs, Brian, illus. 2007. 176p. (J). (gr. 2-6). 15.99 (***978-0-06-084319-9(5)***); lib. bdg. 16.89 (***978-0-06-084320-5(9)***) HarperCollins Pubs. (Eos).

Noriss, Andrew. Aquila. 1999. (J). pap. 29.95 incl. audio (978-0-7540-6213-4(9)) BBC Audiobooks America.

Oberne, Sharon. Kelsey. 2006. 88p. (YA). pap. 13.95 (978-1-58909-340-9(2)) Bookstand Publishing.

Ostrow, Kim. E. T. & Me. Obrero, Rudy, illus. 2002. (E. T. the Extra-Terrestrial Ser.). 64p. (J). pap. 3.99 (978-0-689-84366-2(6) , Simon Spotlight) Simon & Schuster Children's Publishing.

—The Extra Terrestrial Movie Storybook Proprietary. 2002. 32p. 17.80 (978-0-689-85650-1(4) , Simon Spotlight/ Nickelodeon) Simon & Schuster Children's Publishing.

Parsons, Garry. Krong! Parsons, Garry, illus. 2006. (Illus.). 36p. (J). 15.95 (978-1-58925-061-1(3) , tiger tales) ME Media LLC.

Passen, Lisa. Attack of the 50-Foot Teacher. 2003. (gr. k-3). lib. bdg. 15.25 (978-0-613-75618-1(5)) Tandem Library Bks.

Pausacker, Jenny. Freedom Fighters: Mindfire, Starfight, Endgame. 2005. (Triple Play Ser.). (Illus.). 48p. (gr. 4-8). 41.85 (978-0-7910-9073-2(6)) Facts On File, Inc.

Pearson. Alien Draw. 214p. (J). pap. (978-0-340-68077-3(6) , Hodder & Stoughton) Hodder General Publishing Division.

Penguin Books Staff. The Flintstones in Viva Rock Vegas, Level 2. 2001. (Illus.). 32p. (C). pap. 9.00 (978-0-582-45190-2(6)) Longman Publishing Group.

Philips, Gretchen, et al. The Quizm Message: Trash Landing. 1999. (Illus.). 36p. (J). (gr. k-2). 11.99 (978-0-9671611-0-5(X)); pap. 7.99 (978-0-9671611-1-2(8)) KRW International, Inc.

Photo Novel. 2007. (Transformers Ser.). 96p. (J). (gr. 2-5). pap. 7.99 (***978-0-06-088805-3(9)*** , Harper Entertainment) HarperCollins Pubs.

Pienkowski, Jan, illus. Small Talk. 2000. (Monsterpops Ser.). 12p. (J). (ps-3). 5.95 (978-1-58117-025-2(4) , Intervisual/Piggy Toes) Dalmatian Pr.

Pilkey, Dav. Captain Underpants & the Invasion of the Incredibly Naughty Cafeteria Ladies from Outer Space: And the Subsequent Assault of the Equally Evil Lunchroom Zombie Nerds. ed. 2005. (Captain Underpants Ser.: No. 3). (Illus.). 144p. (J). lib. bdg. 15.00 (978-1-59054-681-9(4)) Fitzgerald Bks.

Pinkwater, Daniel M. Mush's Jazz Adventure. 2002. (gr. 3-6). lib. bdg. 11.80 (978-0-613-57577-5(6)) Tandem Library Bks.

Pinkwater, Daniel M. & Pinkwater, Jill. Mush's Jazz Adventure. 2002. (Ready-for-Chapters Ser.). (Illus.). 48p. (J). pap. 6.99 (978-0-689-84572-7(3) , Aladdin) Simon & Schuster Children's Publishing.

Pocket Books Staff. Intruder. 2000. (gr. 7-12). lib. bdg. 14.15 (978-0-613-73179-9(4)) Tandem Library Bks.

Powell, Jillian. Big Brother at School. Savage, Paul, illus. 2007. (J). 40p. (***978-1-59889-244-4(4)***); 33p. (gr. 5-8). lib. bdg. 19.93 (978-1-59889-091-4(3)) Stone Arch Bks.

Power Ranger Wild Force: Red Lion Roar. 2007. 24p. pap. 3.50 (***978-1-4037-3567-6(0)***) Dalmatian Pr.

Priddy, Roger. Funny Faces Alien Al. 2007. 24p. (J). bds. 14.95 (***978-0-312-49893-1(4)*** , Priddy Bks.) St. Martin's Pr.

Pringle, Eric. Big George. 2001. (gr. 3-6). lib. bdg. 18.75 (978-0-613-62506-7(4)) Tandem Library Bks.

—Big George: A Novel. Paine, Colin, illus. 2001. 160p. (J). (gr. 3-7). 18.95 (978-1-55037-713-2(2)); pap. 9.95 (978-1-55037-712-5(4)) Annick Pr., Ltd. CAN. *Dist:* Firefly Bks., Ltd.

Reisman, Michael. Simon Bloom, the Gravity Keeper. 2008. 256p. (J). (gr. 4-12). 15.99 (978-0-525-47922-2(8) , Dutton Juvenile) Penguin Group (USA) Inc.

Rex, Michael. Pals, Level 1. Rex, Michael, illus. 2003. (Word-by-Word First Reader Ser.). (Illus.). 32p. (J). pap. 3.99 (978-0-439-49310-9(2) , Cartwheel Bks.) Scholastic, Inc.

Richards, Douglas E. Captured! 2007. 160p. (J). pap. 7.95 (***978-1-933255-33-0(1)***) DNA Pr.

Richards, Kitty. Meet the Sparkplugs. Simard, Remy, illus. 2006. (Phonics Comics Ser.). 24p. (J). (gr. 1-17). pap. 3.99 (978-1-58476-419-9(8) , IKIDS) Innovative Kids.

Richter, Dana. E. T. Phone Home. 2002. (Illus.). (J). 16.95 (978-0-7853-5530-4(8)) Publications International, Ltd.

Rigby Education Staff. Aliens. (Sails Literacy Ser.). (Illus.). 16p. (gr. 1-2). 27.00 (978-0-7635-9912-6(3) , 699123C99) Rigby Education.

Rodríguez, Antonio Orlando. Earthlings, How Weird They Are! / !Qué extraños son los Terrícolas¡. 2006. 52p. pap. (978-958-30-1737-7(X)) Panamericana Editorial.

Rovetch, L. Bob. Hot Dog & Bob & the Dangerously Dizzy Attack of the Alien Hypno Hamsters. Whamond, Dave, illus. 2007. 96p. (J). pap. 4.95 (978-0-8118-5602-7(X)) Chronicle Bks. LLC.

—Hot Dog & Bob & the Exceptionally Eggy Attack of the Game Gators. Whamond, Dave, illus. 2007. 96p. (J). pap. 4.95 (978-0-8118-5604-1(6)) Chronicle Bks. LLC.

Rovetch, Lissa. Hot Dog & Bob Adventure. Whamond, Dave, illus. 2007. 96p. (J). 15.50 (978-0-8118-5601-0(1)) Chronicle Bks. LLC.

—Hot Dog & Bob & the Exceptionally Eggy Attack of the Game Gators. Whamond, Dave, illus. 2007. 96p. (J). 15.50 (978-0-8118-5603-4(8)) Chronicle Bks. LLC.

Ryan, Kevin. Nightscape. 2003. (Roswell Ser.). (Illus.). 208p. (YA). pap. 5.99 (978-0-689-85521-4(4) , Simon Pulse) Simon & Schuster Children's Publishing.

—Nightscape. 2003. (gr. 7-12). lib. bdg. 14.15 (978-0-613-66528-5(7)) Tandem Library Bks.

Sachar, Louis. A Flying Birthday Cake? Wummer, Amy, illus. 1999. (Marvin Redpost Ser.: Bk. 6). (J). (gr. k-3). 96p. lib. bdg. 11.99 (978-0-679-99000-0(3)); 80p. pap. 3.99 (978-0-679-89000-3(9)) Random Hse. Children's Bks. (Random Hse. Bks. for Young Readers).

—A Flying Birthday Cake? 1999. (Marvin Redpost Ser.: Bk. 6). (978-0-606-17524-1(5)) Tandem Library Bks.

—A Flying Birthday Cake. Wummer, Amy, illus. 1999. (Marvin Redpost Ser.: Bk. 6). 76p. (J). (ps-ps). lib. bdg. 11.80 (978-0-613-19523-2(X)) Tandem Library Bks.

San Souci, Daniel. Space Station Mars. 2005. (Illus.). 40p. (J). (gr. 1-4). 15.95 (978-1-58246-142-7(2) , Tricycle Pr.) Ten Speed Pr.

Sander, Heather. Robbie Packford - Alien Monster. 2004. (Robbie Packford Ser.). (Illus.). 96p. (J). (gr. 3-7). pap. 6.95 (978-1-55143-259-5(5)) Orca Bk. Pubs. USA.

Sasaki, Chris & Wells, H. G. The War of the Worlds. Akib, Jamel, illus. 2007. (Classic Starts Ser.). 151p. (J). (***978-1-4287-4208-6(5)***) Sterling Publishing Co., Inc.

Satten, Sandra C. In the Thirteenth Year. Spark, illus. 1999. 72p. (YA). (ps up). pap. 7.95 (978-1-881283-24-9(0)) Alef Design Group.

Sava, Scott C. Eds Terrestrials. 2005. (Illus.). 80p. 19.99 (978-1-933428-64-2(3)) Alias Enterprises LLC.

Schaefer, Carole Lexa. Beep! Beep! It's Beeper. Lacome, Julie, illus. 2001. (Brand New Readers Ser.). 32p. (J). (ps-2). pap. 5.99 (978-0-7636-1204-7(9)) Candlewick Pr.

—Beeper's Friends. Lacome, Julie, illus. 2002. (Brand New Readers Ser.). 8p. (J). (ps-2). pap. 5.99 (978-0-7636-1244-3(8)) Candlewick Pr.

Schanback, Mindy. Princess from Another Planet. 2005. 254p. (J). (gr. 5-9). 16.95 (978-0-8234-1847-3(2)) Holiday Hse., Inc.

Schneider, John Lee. Extinction: Dragons of Earth: A Novel. 2005. 173p. (YA). pap. (978-1-890109-79-0(7) , Cross Time) Crossquarter Publishing Group.

Scholastic, Inc. Staff & West, Tracey. Cyborg, Come Home! MacKenzie, Kevin, illus. 2004. (Teen Titans Ser.). 64p. (J). 3.99 (978-0-439-63620-9(5) , Scholastic Paperbacks) Scholastic, Inc.

—Teen Titans, Bk. 2. MacKenzie, Kevin, illus. 2004. (Teen Titans Ser.). 64p. (J). pap. 3.99 (978-0-439-63618-6(3) , Scholastic Paperbacks) Scholastic, Inc.

Scrimger, Richard. The Nose from Jupiter. 1998. (Illus.). 156p. (J). (ps-6). per. 16.40 (978-0-613-10237-7(1)) Tandem Library Bks.

—The Nose from Jupiter. 1998. 160p. (J). (gr. 3-7). pap. 7.95 (978-0-88776-428-8(2)) Tundra Bks., Inc./Livres Toundra, Inc. CAN. *Dist:* Random Hse., Inc.

Service, Pamela F. My Cousin, the Alien. 2008. (J). lib. bdg. (***978-0-8225-7627-3(9)*** , Carolrhoda Bks.) Lerner Publishing Group.

Shusterman, Neal. The Dark Side of Nowhere. 2002. 192p. (J). (gr. 5 up). 5.99 (978-0-7653-4243-0(X) , Starscape) Doherty, Tom Assocs., LLC.

Simons, Jamie & Scollon, E. W. Double Trouble. Evans, Michael, illus. 1999. (Goners Ser.: No. 9). 160p. (J). (gr. 3-7). pap. 3.99 (978-0-380-80725-3(4)) HarperCollins Pubs.

Singleton, Linda Joy. Oh No! UFO! Karre, Andrew, ed. 2004. (Strange Encounters Ser.). 192p. (gr. 8-12). pap. 4.99 (978-0-7387-0579-8(9)) Llewellyn Pubns.

Sleator, William. The Night the Heads Came. 1998. (J). (978-0-606-13663-1(0)) Tandem Library Bks.

Smillie, Bryan. A Time for Evron. Rooth, Mike, illus. 2004. 190p. 11.95 (978-0-9689516-0-6(0)) Shabrya Publishing CAN. *Dist:* Hushion Hse. Publishing, Ltd.

Smith, Dean Wesley & Rusch, Kristine Kathryn. Little Green Men. 2002. (Roswell Ser.: Vol. 3). 208p. (YA). pap. 6.99 (978-0-7434-1836-2(0) , Simon Pulse) Simon & Schuster Children's Publishing.

Smith, Stu. Goldilocks & the Three Martians. Garland, Michael, tr. Garland, Michael, illus. 2004. 32p. (J). (ps). 15.99 (978-0-525-46972-8(9) , Dutton Juvenile) Penguin Group (USA) Inc.

St. Aubin, Bruno. Daddy's an Alien. St. Aubin, Bruno, illus. 2005. (Read-It! Readers Ser.). (Illus.). 32p. (J). (gr. k-3). 18.60 (978-1-4048-1067-9(6)) Picture Window Bks.

Stewart, Paul & Riddell, Chris. Blobheads Go Boing! l.t. ed. 2005. (J). pap. (978-1-4056-6002-0(3)) BBC Audio.

Strasser, Todd. Help! I'm Trapped in an Alien's Body. 1998. (Help! I'm Trapped Ser.). (Illus.). 160p. (J). (gr. 4-7). pap. 4.50 (978-0-590-76271-7(0) , Scholastic Paperbacks) Scholastic, Inc.

Strauss, Elizabeth. Message on a Rocket. 2000. (gr. k-3). lib. bdg. 11.80 (978-0-613-29696-0(6)) Tandem Library Bks.

Suter, Joanne. War of the Worlds. 2003. (gr. 7-12). lib. bdg. 15.25 (978-0-613-65749-5(7)) Tandem Library Bks.

Thames, S. R. Crystal Star: Legend of the Mecha Fighters. 2002. 148p. pap. 11.95 (978-0-595-26119-2(1) , Writers Club Pr.) iUniverse, Inc.

Thomas, Nigel. Tom Travis: The Lost People of Orion. 2006. 193p. pap. 19.95 (978-1-4241-0382-9(7)) PublishAmerica, Inc.

Thorpe, Kiki. Lilo & Stitch: The Junior Novelization. 2002. (ps-2). lib. bdg. 13.00 (978-0-613-50630-4(8)) Tandem Library Bks.

Tiller, Steve. Rudolf the Red Nose Rocket. Cremeans, Robert, illus. 2002. 28p. (J). (gr. k-3). 15.95 (978-0-9704597-9-4(3)) MichaelsMind LLC.

Tomizawa, Hitoshi. Alien Nine: Emulators. Pannone, Frank, ed. Jackson, Laura & Kobayashi, Yoko, trs. from JPN. Tomizawa, Hitoshi, illus. 2004. (Illus.). 248p. pap. 9.99 (978-1-58664-924-1(8) , CMX 65004G, CPM Manga) Central Park Media Corp.

—Alien Nine 1, Vol. 1. Pannone, Frank, ed. Jackson, Laura & Kobayashi, Yoko, trs. from JPN. Tomizawa, Hitoshi, illus. 2003. (Illus.). 224p. (gr. 11 up). pap. 15.95 (978-1-58664-891-6(8) , CMX 64201G, CPM Manga) Central Park Media Corp.

—Alien Nine 2, Vol. 2. Pannone, Frank, ed. Jackson, Laura & Kobayashi, Yoko, trs. from JPN. Tomizawa, Hitoshi, illus. 2003. (Illus.). 224p. (gr. 11 up). pap. 15.95 (978-1-58664-892-3(6) , CMX 64202G, CPM Manga) Central Park Media Corp.

—Alien Nine 3, Vol. 3. Pannone, Frank, ed. Jackson, Laura & Kobayashi, Yoko, trs. from JPN. Tomizawa, Hitoshi, illus. 2003. (Illus.). 224p. pap. 15.95 (978-1-58664-893-0(4) , CMX 64203G, CPM Manga) Central Park Media Corp.

Ward, Jon, illus. No Big Deal. 2000. 76p. (J). (978-1-892339-08-9(0)) Beachfront Publishing.

Warner, James. An Alien Adventure - The Magic Sled. Holder, Harry, illus. 1999. 107p. (YA). (gr. 5-8). pap. 14.95 (978-1-890549-08-4(8)) Alpha Publishing Group.

Watson, Jude. Death on Naboo. 2006. (Star Wars Ser.: No. 4). 135p. (J). lib. bdg. 13.00 (***978-1-4242-0777-0(0)***) Fitzgerald Bks.

—Underworld. 2005. (Star Wars Ser.: No. 3). 137p. (J). lib. bdg. 20.00 (***978-1-4242-0776-3(2)***) Fitzgerald Bks.

Waugh, Sylvia. Space Race. 2001. 256p. (gr. 5 up). 5.50 (978-0-440-41714-9(7) , Yearling) Random Hse. Children's Bks.

—Space Race. 2001. (gr. 5-8). lib. bdg. 13.00 (978-0-613-88327-6(6)) Tandem Library Bks.

—Space Race. l.t. ed. 2001. 300p. (J). 20.95 (978-0-7862-3606-0(X)) Thorndike Pr.

—Who Goes Home? 2005. 224p. (gr. 4-7). 5.99 (978-0-440-41839-9(9) , Yearling) Random Hse. Children's Bks.

Wells, H. G. & Card, Orson Scott. War of the Worlds: With an Introduction by Orson Scott Card. 2004. (Scholastic Classics Ser.). 304p. (J). pap. 3.99 (978-0-439-51849-9(0) , Scholastic Paperbacks) Scholastic, Inc.

Weston, Martha. Space Guys: A Holiday House Reader. Weston, Martha, illus. 2000. (Holiday House Reader Ser.). (Illus.). 32p. (J). (gr. k-3). tchr. ed. 14.95 (978-0-8234-1487-1(6)) Holiday Hse., Inc.

Wilson, Sarah. George Hogglesberry, Grade School Alien. Cameron, Chad, illus. 2004. 38p. (J). 14.95 (978-1-58246-063-5(9) , Tricycle Pr.) Ten Speed Pr.

Yaccarino, Dan. First Day on a Strange New Planet. 2000. (Blast Off Boy & Blorp Ser.: Vol. 1). (Illus.). 40p. (gr. k-3). 15.49 (978-0-7868-2499-1(9)) Hyperion Bks. for Children.

—First Day on a Strange New Planet. 2002. (gr. k-3). lib. bdg. 13.00 (978-0-613-74971-8(5)) Tandem Library Bks.

—New Pet. 2003. (ps-2). lib. bdg. 13.00 (978-0-613-74973-2(1)) Tandem Library Bks.

Yackety-Yak, the Alien's Back. 2005. (Illus.). (J). lib. bdg. 27.10 (978-1-59389-141-1(5)) Chrysalis Education.

Yorinks, Arthur. Company's Coming. 2000. (Illus.). 32p. (gr. k-4). 16.49 (978-0-7868-2433-5(6)) Hyperion Bks. for Children.

—Company's Coming. Small, David, illus. 2000. 32p. (gr. k-4). 15.99 (978-0-7868-0500-6(5)) Hyperion Bks. for Children.

—Company's Going. (J). pap. 14.99 (978-0-06-205125-7(3)) HarperCollins Pubs.

—Company's Going. Small, David, illus. 2001. 40p. (gr. k-4). 15.99 (978-0-7868-0415-3(7)); 16.49 (978-0-7868-2363-5(1)) Hyperion Bks. for Children.

—Tomatoes from Mars. Drucker, Mort, illus. 1999. (Michael di Capua Bks.). 32p. (J). (ps-3). 14.95 (978-0-06-205070-0(2)) HarperCollins Pubs.

Yorinks, Arthur, et al. Company's Going. Date not set. (J). lib. bdg. 15.89 (978-0-06-205126-4(1)) HarperCollins Pubs.

Zucker, Jonny. Alien Attack. Smith, Pete, illus. 2007. 35p. (J). pap. (***978-1-59889-425-7(0)***); 40p. (YA). (gr. 5-9). lib. bdg. 21.26 (***978-1-59889-329-8(7)***) Stone Arch Bks.

Zucker, Jonny. Basketball War. Savage, Paul, illus. 2006. 40p. (J). (gr. 2-3). lib. bdg. (978-1-59889-009-9(3)) Stone Arch Bks.

EXTRATERRESTRIAL LIFE

see Extraterrestrial Beings; Life on Other Planets

EXTREME SPORTS

Abraham, Philip. Extreme Sports Stars. 2007. (Sports Stars Ser.). (Illus.). 48p. (J). pap. (978-0-531-18702-9(0)) Children's Pr., Ltd.

—Extreme Sports Stars. 2006. (Sports Stars Ser.). (Illus.). 48p. (J). (978-0-531-12585-4(8) , Children's Pr.) Scholastic Library Publishing.

Bass, Scott. Extreme Sports: Your Guide to Longboarding, Shortboarding, Tubing, Aerials, Hanging Ten, & More. 2003. (Illus.). 64p. (J). (gr. 4-7). pap. 8.95 (978-0-7922-5108-8(3) , National Geographic Children's Bks.) National Geographic Society.

Behind the Moves: Extreme Bicycle Stunt Riding Moves; Extreme In-Line Skating Moves; Extreme Skateboarding Moves; Extreme Snowboarding Moves, 4 bks. 2000. (Illus.). (J). (gr. 3-4). lib. bdg. 85.04 (978-0-7368-0874-3(4) , Capstone High-Interest Bks.) Capstone Pr., Inc.

Bloomquist, Christopher. BMX in the X Games. 2003. (Kids Guide to the X Games Ser.). (Illus.). 24p. (J). lib. bdg. 19.95 (978-0-8239-6298-3(9) , PowerKids Pr.) Rosen Publishing Group, Inc., The.

Christopher, Matt. Wild Ride. Koelsch, Michael, illus. 2005. 55p. (J). (ps-ps). lib. bdg. 12.19 (978-0-606-33464-8(5)) Tandem Library Bks.

Christopher, Matt & Christopher, Matthew F. Matt Christopher Extreme Sports, 8 vols., Set. #1 Sports Writer for Kids Staff, illus. 2004. (J). (gr. 3-7). pap., pap. 6.50 (978-0-316-01143-3(6)) Little Brown & Co.

Clemson, Wendy. Using Math to Conquer Extreme Sports. 2004. (Mathworks!). (Illus.). 31p. (J). lib. bdg. 24.67 (978-0-8368-4210-4(3)) Stevens, Gareth Inc.

Crossingham, John. Extreme BMX. 2003. (Extreme Sports - No Limits Ser.). (Illus.). 32p. (J). (gr. 3). (978-0-7787-1666-2(X)); pap. (978-0-7787-1712-6(7)) Crabtree Publishing Co.

—Extreme in-Line Skating. 2003. (gr. 3-6). lib. bdg. 15.25 (978-0-613-82413-2(X)) Tandem Library Bks.

—Extreme Skateboarding. 2003. (Extreme Sports - No Limits Ser.). (Illus.). 32p. (J). (gr. 3). pap. (978-0-7787-1714-0(3)) Crabtree Publishing Co.

—Extreme Skateboarding. 2003. (gr. 3-6). lib. bdg. 15.25 (978-0-613-87231-7(2)) Tandem Library Bks.

—Extreme Sports - No Limits, 4 bks. Incl. Extreme BMX. pap. (978-0-7787-1712-6(7)); Extreme in-Line Skating. Kalman, Bobbie. pap. (978-0-7787-1713-3(5)); Extreme Skateboarding. pap. (978-0-7787-1714-0(3)); Extreme Surfing. Kalman, Bobbie. pap. (978-0-7787-1715-7(1)); 32p. (J). (gr. 3). 2003. (Illus.). 2003. Set pap. (978-0-7787-1711-9(9)); Set lib. bdg. (978-0-7787-1665-5(1)) Crabtree Publishing Co.

Crossingham, John & Kalman, Bobbie. Extreme in-Line Skating. 2003. (Extreme Sports - No Limits Ser.). (Illus.). 32p. (J). (gr. 3). (978-0-7787-1667-9(8)); pap. (978-0-7787-1713-3(5)) Crabtree Publishing Co.

—Extreme Skateboarding. 2003. (Extreme Sports - No Limits Ser.). (Illus.). 32p. (J). (gr. 3). (978-0-7787-1668-6(6)) Crabtree Publishing Co.

—Extreme Surfing. 2003. (Extreme Sports - No Limits Ser.). (Illus.). 32p. (J). (gr. 3). (978-0-7787-1669-3(4)); pap. (978-0-7787-1715-7(1)) Crabtree Publishing Co.

Crossingham, John & Kalman, Bobbie. La planche a roulette Extrême. rev. ed. 2007. (FRE., Illus.). 32p. (J). (gr. 3-4). pap. (***978-2-89579-123-2(6)***) Editions Banjo.

Dangerous Adventures, 8 bks. Incl. Airplane Adventures. Bledsoe, Karen & Bledsoe, Glen. 2001. lib. bdg. 21.26 (978-0-7368-0903-0(1)); Ballooning Adventures. Bledsoe, Glen & Bledsoe, Karen. 2000. lib. bdg. 21.26 (978-0-7368-0574-2(5)); Bicycling Adventures. Bledsoe, Karen & Bledsoe, Glen. 2001. lib. bdg. 21.26 (978-0-7368-0904-7(X)); Caving Adventures. Todd, Anne M. 2001. lib. bdg. 21.26 (978-0-7368-0905-4(8)); Deep Diving Adventures. Vander Hook, Sue. 2000. lib. bdg. 21.26 (978-0-7368-0573-5(7)); Mountaineering Adventures. Doeden, Matt. 2000. lib. bdg. 21.26 (978-0-7368-0575-9(3)); Polar Exploration Adventures. Saffer, Barbara. 2000. lib. bdg. 21.26 (978-0-7368-0572-8(9)); Sailing Adventures. Todd, Anne M. 2001. lib. bdg. 21.26 (978-0-7368-0906-1(6)); 48p. (J). (gr. 3-4). (Illus.). Set lib. bdg. 170.08 (978-0-7368-1001-2(3) , Capstone High-Interest Bks.) Capstone Pr., Inc.

Deady, Kathleen W. Extreme Mountain Biking Moves. 2003. (Behind the Moves Ser.). (Illus.). 32p. (J). (gr. 3-4). lib. bdg. 21.26 (978-0-7368-1513-0(9) , Capstone High-Interest Bks.) Capstone Pr., Inc.

—Extreme Rock Climbing Moves. 2003. (Behind the Moves Ser.). (Illus.). 32p. (J). (gr. 3-4). lib. bdg. 21.26 (978-0-7368-1514-7(7) , Capstone High-Interest Bks.) Capstone Pr., Inc.

Doeden, Matt. BMX Freestyle. 2004. (To the Extreme Ser.). (Illus.). 149p. (J). 19.93 (978-0-7368-2728-7(5)) Capstone Pr., Inc.

—Motocross Freestyle. 2004. (To the Extreme Ser.). (Illus.). 32p. (J). lib. bdg. 19.93 (978-0-7368-2729-4(3)) Capstone Pr., Inc.

—Skateboarding. 2004. (To the Extreme Ser.). (Illus.). 32p. (J). lib. bdg. 19.93 (978-0-7368-2730-0(7)) Capstone Pr., Inc.

—Snowboarding. 2004. (To the Extreme Ser.). (Illus.) 149p. (J). 19.93 (978-0-7368-2731-7(5)) Capstone Pr., Inc.

Evans, Lynette. Camp Extreme. 2007. (Shockwave: the Human Experience Ser.). (Illus.). 36p. (J). (gr. 4-6). lib. bdg. 25.00 (***978-0-531-17758-7(0)*** , Children's Pr.) Scholastic Library Publishing.

—Extreme Sports. 2007. (Shockwave: the Human Experience Ser.). (Illus.). 36p. (J). (gr. 4-6). lib. bdg. 25.00 (***978-0-531-17759-4(9)*** , Children's Pr.) Scholastic Library Publishing.

Extreme Sports Classroom Library. (gr. 4 up). lib. bdg. 24.95 (978-0-7368-7066-5(0)) Red Brick Learning.

Extreme Sports Coloring Book. 2004. (J). mass mkt. 5.99 (978-0-9763757-0-8(2)) Cypress Knees Publishing.

Extreme Sports Complete Unit. (gr. 4 up). 142.95 (978-0-7368-7067-2(9)) Red Brick Learning.

Firestone, Mary. Extreme Downhill BMX Racing Moves. 2003. (Behind the Moves Ser.). (Illus.). 32p. (J). lib. bdg. 22.60 (978-0-7368-2152-0(X) , Capstone High/Low Bks.) Capstone Pr., Inc.

—Extreme Downhill Skiing Moves. 2003. (Behind the Moves Ser.). (Illus.). 32p. (J). lib. bdg. 22.60 (978-0-7368-2153-7(8)) Capstone Pr., Inc.

—Extreme Snowboard Halfpipe Moves. 2003. (Behind the Moves Ser.). (Illus.). 32p. (J). lib. bdg. 22.60 (978-0-7368-2154-4(6) , Capstone High/Low Bks.) Capstone Pr., Inc.

—Extreme Waterskiing Moves. 2003. (Behind the Moves Ser.). (Illus.). 32p. (J). lib. bdg. 22.60 (978-0-7368-2155-1(4)) Capstone Pr., Inc.

Gikow, Louise. Extreme Sports: A Chapter Book. 2004. (True Tales Ser.). (J). 22.50 (978-0-516-23730-5(6) , Children's Pr.) Scholastic Library Publishing.

Glidewell, Steve. Inline Skating. 2004. (Extreme Sports Ser.). (Illus.). 32p. (J). (gr. 3-6). lib. bdg. 22.60 (978-0-8225-1244-8(0)) Lerner Publishing Group.

Harris, David. Daredevils & Show-offs. 2005. (X-Zone Ser.). (Illus.). 30p. (gr. 4-8). 23.00 (978-0-7910-8973-6(8)) Facts On File, Inc.

Hayhurst, Chris. Wakeboarding! Throw a Tantrum. 2000. (Illus.). 64p. (YA). per. 9.95 (978-1-56254-307-5(5) , SP 3075) Saddleback Educational Publishing.

Herran, Joe & Thomas, Ron. Motocross. 2003. (Action Sports Ser.). (Illus.). 32p. (J). (gr. 4-8). 28.00 (978-0-7910-7536-4(2) , Chelsea Hse.) Facts On File, Inc.

Herzog, Brad. E Is for Extreme: An Extreme Sports Alphabet. Rose, Melanie, illus. rev. ed. 2007. 40p. (J). 17.95 (***978-1-58536-310-0(3)***) Sleeping Bear Pr.

High Interest Books: X-Treme Outdoors. 2004. (Illus.). 100.00 (978-0-516-29634-0(5)) Scholastic Library Publishing.

Hintz, Martin & Hintz, Kate. Drag Racing, 4 bks. Incl. Monster Truck Drag Racing. lib. bdg. 21.26 (978-1-56065-390-5(6)); Motorcycle Drag Racing. lib. bdg. 21.26 (978-1-56065-387-5(6)); Pro Stock Drag Racing. lib. bdg. 21.26 (978-1-56065-388-2(4)); Top Fuel Drag Racing. lib. bdg. 21.26 (978-1-56065-389-9(2)); 48p. (J). (gr. 3-4). 1996. (Illus.). Set lib. bdg. 85.04 (978-1-56065-643-2(3) , Capstone High-Interest Bks.) Capstone Pr., Inc.

Horton, Ron. Awesome Athletes. 2003. (History Makers Ser.). (Illus.). 112p. (J). 29.95 (978-1-59018-307-6(X) , Lucent Bks.) Thomson Gale.

—Extreme Athletes. 2004. (History Makers Ser.). (Illus.). 112p. (J). (gr. 7-10). 29.95 (978-1-59018-519-3(6) , Lucent Bks.) Thomson Gale.

Job, Chris. BMX. 2004. (Extreme Sports Ser.). (Illus.). 32p. (J). (gr. 3-6). lib. bdg. 22.60 (978-0-8225-1243-1(2)) Lerner Publishing Group.

Kalman, Bobbie. Extreme BMX. 2003. (gr. 3-6). lib. bdg. 15.25 (978-0-613-82412-5(1)) Tandem Library Bks.

—Extreme Wakeboarding. 2006. (Extreme Sports No Limits! Ser.). (Illus.). 32p. (J). (gr. 3-9). pap. (978-0-7787-1726-3(7)); (978-0-7787-1680-8(5)) Crabtree Publishing Co.

Kalman, Bobbie & Crossingham, John. Extreme Climbing. 2004. (Extreme Sports No Limits! Ser.). (Illus.). 32p. (J). (978-0-7787-1671-6(6)); pap. (978-0-7787-1717-1(8)) Crabtree Publishing Co.

—Extreme Motocross. 2003. (Extreme Sports No Limits! Ser.). (Illus.). 32p. (J). (978-0-7787-1670-9(8)); pap. (978-0-7787-1716-4(X)) Crabtree Publishing Co.

—Extreme Skydiving. 2006. (Extreme Sports No Limits! Ser.). (Illus.). 32p. (J). (gr. 3-9). pap. (978-0-7787-1730-0(5)); (978-0-7787-1684-6(8)) Crabtree Publishing Co.

—Extreme Sports. 2004. (Extreme Sports - No Limits Ser.). (Illus.). 32p. (J). (978-0-7787-1673-0(2)); pap. (978-0-7787-1719-5(4)) Crabtree Publishing Co.

Kalman, Bobbie & MacAulay, Kelley. Extreme Snowboarding. 2003. (Extreme Sports - No Limits Ser.). (Illus.). 32p. (J). (978-0-7787-1672-3(4)); pap. (978-0-7787-1718-8(6)) Crabtree Publishing Co.

Lorimer, Janet. Extreme Sports Reproducibles. 2001. (Illus.). 64p. (YA). tchr. ed., per. 16.95 (978-1-56254-299-3(0) , SP 2990) Saddleback Educational Publishing.

MacAulay, Kelley & Kalman, Bobbie. Extreme Mountain Biking. 2006. (Extreme Sports No Limits! Ser.). (Illus.). 32p. (J). (gr. 3-9). pap. (978-0-7787-1724-9(0)); (978-0-7787-1678-5(3)) Crabtree Publishing Co.

—Extreme Skiing. 2006. (Extreme Sports No Limits! Ser.). (Illus.). 32p. (J). (gr. 3-9). pap. (978-0-7787-1728-7(3) , 1253447); (978-0-7787-1682-2(1) , 1253447) Crabtree Publishing Co.

Mahaney, Ian F. Taig Khris: In-Line Skate Champion. 2005. (Extreme Sports Biographies Ser.). (Illus.). 24p. (J). 19.95 (978-1-4042-2746-0(6) , PowerKids Pr.) Rosen Publishing Group, Inc., The.

Maurer, Tracy. Surfing. 2003. (Radsports Guides Ser.). (Illus.). 48p. (gr. 4-8). 20.95 (978-1-58952-280-0(X)) Rourke Publishing, LLC.

—Wakeboarding. 2003. (Radsports Guides Ser.). (Illus.). 48p. (gr. 4-8). 20.95 (978-1-58952-281-7(8)) Rourke Publishing, LLC.

Maxwell, E. J. Xtreme Sports: Cutting Edge. 2003. (Xtreme Sports Ser.). (Illus.). 96p. (J). (gr. 3-6). pap. 4.99 (978-0-439-46854-1(X) , Scholastic Paperbacks) Scholastic, Inc.

—Xtreme Sports: Cutting Edge. 2003. (gr. 3-6). lib. bdg. 13.00 (978-0-613-71994-0(8)) Tandem Library Bks.

McNab, Chris. Extreme Sports. 2003. (Sports Injuries Ser.). (Illus.). 64p. (J). lib. bdg. (978-1-59084-630-8(3)) Mason Crest Pubs.

Murdico, Suzanne J. Skateboarding in the X-Games. 2005. (World of Skateboarding Ser.). (Illus.). 48p. (YA). (gr. 5-8). lib. bdg. 26.50 (978-0-8239-3645-8(7)) Rosen Publishing Group, Inc., The.

—Street Luge & Dirtboarding. 2005. (World of Skateboarding Ser.). (Illus.). 48p. (YA). (gr. 5-8). lib. bdg. 26.50 (978-0-8239-3647-2(3)) Rosen Publishing Group, Inc., The.

Murray, Julie. Tony Hawk. 2004. (Awesome Athletes Ser.). (Illus.). 32p. (J). (gr. k-6). lib. bdg. 22.78 (978-1-59197-489-5(5)) ABDO Publishing Co.

On the Edge. 2006. (Illus.). (gr. 4-8). 406.80 (978-0-7910-9096-1(5)) Facts On File, Inc.

Osborne, Ian. Mountain Biking. 2004. (Extreme Sports Ser.). (Illus.). 32p. (J). (gr. 3-6). lib. bdg. 22.60 (978-0-8225-1245-5(9)) Lerner Publishing Group.

—Mountain Biking. 2004. (gr. 3-6). lib. bdg. 15.25 (978-0-613-81323-5(5)) Tandem Library Bks.

O'Shei, Tim. The World's Most Dangerous Stunts. 2006. (Edge Books, the World's Top Tens). (Illus.). 32p. (J). (978-0-7368-5457-3(6)) Capstone Pr., Inc.

Parr, Danny. Extreme In-Line Skating Moves. 2001. (Behind the Moves Ser.). (Illus.). 32p. (J). (gr. 3-4). lib. bdg. 21.26 (978-0-7368-0782-1(9) , Capstone High-Interest Bks.) Capstone Pr., Inc.

Ramsden, Julie & Ramsden, Michael. Made for Speed. 2005. (X-Zone Ser.). (Illus.). 30p. (gr. 4-8). 23.00 (978-0-7910-8995-8(9)) Facts On File, Inc.

—To the Max. 2005. (X-Zone Ser.). (Illus.). 30p. (gr. 4-8). 23.00 (978-0-7910-8982-8(7)) Facts On File, Inc.

A Robbie Reader¿Extreme Sports. 2007. (J). lib. bdg. (***978-1-58415-599-7(X)***) Mitchell Lane Pubs., Inc.

Rosenberg, Aaron. Taig Khris:In-Line Skating. 2005. (Illus.). 64p. (J). (gr. 5-8). lib. bdg. 26.50 (978-1-4042-0069-2(X)) Rosen Publishing Group, Inc., The.

Schaefer, A. R. Extreme Freestyle Motocross Moves. 2003. (Behind the Moves Ser.). (Illus.). 32p. (J). (gr. 3-4). lib. bdg. 21.26 (978-0-7368-1512-3(0) , Capstone High-Interest Bks.) Capstone Pr., Inc.

Seelig, Tina L. Games for Your Brain: Extreme. 2007. (Illus.). 61p. (J). 9.95 (978-0-8118-5708-6(5)) Chronicle Bks. LLC.

Shafran, Michael. Skate! Your Guide to Blading, Aggressive, Vert, Street, Roller Hockey, Speed Skating, Dance, Fitness Training, & More. 2003. (Illus.). 64p. (J). (gr. 4-7). pap. 8.95 (978-0-7922-5107-1(5) , National Geographic Children's Bks.) National Geographic Society.

Spurdens, Dave, photos by. Extreme Sports. 2004. (Twenty4Sevens Ser.). (Illus.). 48p. (J). pap. (978-0-439-68106-3(5)) Scholastic, Inc.

Top That Publishing Staff. Extreme Sports. 2006. (Illus.). 48p. (978-1-84510-101-5(4)) Top That! Publishing PLC.

Voeller, Edward A. Extreme Surfing. 2000. (Extreme Sports Ser.). (Illus.). 48p. (J). (gr. 3-4). lib. bdg. 21.26 (978-0-7368-0485-1(4) , Capstone High-Interest Bks.) Capstone Pr., Inc.

Weigl Publishers Staff & Craats, Rennay. For the Love of Skateboarding. Nault, Jennifer & Turner, Kara, eds. 2003. (For the Love of Sports Ser.). (Illus.). 24p. (J). pap. 6.95 (978-1-59036-070-5(2)) Weigl Pubs., Inc.

Weil, Ann. Aggressive In-Line Skating. 2004. (Edge Books, X-Sports). (Illus.). 32p. (J). lib. bdg. 22.60 (978-0-7368-2708-9(0)) Capstone Pr., Inc.

—BMX Racing. 2004. (Edge Books, X-Sports). (Illus.). 32p. (J). lib. bdg. 22.60 (978-0-7368-2709-6(9)) Capstone Pr., Inc.

X-Sports. 2005. (Illus.). (J). (gr. 3-4). lib. bdg. 226.00 (978-0-7368-3824-5(4)) Capstone Pr., Inc.

X-Treme Sports. 2003. (J). (gr. k-6). lib. bdg. 136.68 (978-1-57765-925-9(2) , Checkerboard Library) ABDO Publishing Co.

EXTREME SPORTS—FICTION

Dixon, Franklin W. Extreme Danger. 2005. 165p. (J). lib. bdg. 16.92 (***978-1-4242-0383-3(X)***) Fitzgerald Bks.

—Extreme Danger. 2005. (Illus.). 165p. (J). (***978-1-4156-0379-6(0)*** , Aladdin) Simon & Schuster Children's Publishing.

Hobbs, Will. Go Big or Go Home. 2008. 192p. (J). 15.99 (***978-0-06-074141-9(4)***); lib. bdg. 16.89 (***978-0-06-074142-6(2)***) HarperCollins Pubs.

Withers, Pam. BMX Tunnel Run. 2007. (Take It to the Xtreme Ser.). 231p. (YA). (gr. 7-10). pap. 6.95 (***978-1-55285-904-9(5)*** , Walrus Bks.) Whitecap Bks., Ltd. CAN. *Dist:* Firefly Bks., Ltd.

—Dirt Bike Daredevils. 2006. (Take it to the Xtreme Ser.). 247p. (YA). (gr. 7-10). pap. 6.95 (978-1-55285-804-2(9) , Walrus Bks.) Whitecap Bks., Ltd. CAN. *Dist:* Firefly Bks., Ltd.

Withers, Pam. Wake's Edge. 2007. (Take It to the Xtreme Ser.). 196p. (YA). (gr. 7-10). pap. 6.95 (***978-1-55285-856-1(1)*** , Walrus Bks.) Whitecap Bks., Ltd. CAN. *Dist:* Firefly Bks., Ltd.

EXTREMISM (POLITICAL SCIENCE)

see Right and Left (Political Science)

EYE

see also Vision

Aguirre Cox, Maria Victoria & Aguirre Cox, Ernest. The Patch. 2005. (Illus.). 50p. (J). (***978-0-9767994-0-5(5)***) Aguirre Cox, Vicki & Ernest.

All Kinds of Eyes, 6 vols., Pack. (Discovery World Ser.). 16p. (gr. 1-2). 28.00 (978-0-7635-8456-6(8)) Rigby Education.

Arledge, Judith. With My Glasses on My Face! Walsh, Donna, illus. 2002. 50p. (J). per. 12.00 (978-0-9720735-0-9(7)) Arledge, Judith.

Ballard, Carol. Eyes. 2003. (Body Focus Ser.). (Illus.). 48p. (J). lib. bdg. 27.07 (978-1-4034-0750-4(9)); pap. (978-1-4034-3298-8(8)) Heinemann Library.

Baumbusch, Brigitte. Eyes in Art. 2005. (Illus.). 32p. (J). lib. bdg. 22.00 (978-0-8368-4445-0(9)) Stevens, Gareth Inc.

Button, M. A. The Eye Book: A Coloring Book. 2000. (Illus.). 26p. (J). pap. 9.95 (978-0-7414-0424-4(9)) Infinity Publishing.

Cobb, Vicki. Open Your Eyes: Discover Your Sense of Sight. Lewis, Cynthia C., illus. 2002. 32p. (gr. 2-4). lib. bdg. 22.90 (978-0-7613-1705-0(8) , Millbrook Pr.) Lerner Publishing Group.

Curry, Don L. Take Care of Your Eyes. 2005. (Rookie Read-about Health Ser.). (Illus.). (J). (gr. k-2). 31p. pap. 5.95 (978-0-516-27914-5(9)); 32p. 20.50 (978-0-516-25874-4(5)) Scholastic Library Publishing. (Children's Pr.).

DeGezelle, Terri. Taking Care of My Eyes. 2006. (Pebble Plus Ser.). (Illus.). 24p. (J). (978-0-7368-4260-0(8)) Capstone Pr., Inc.

Douglas, Lloyd G. My Eyes. 2004. (Wel-My Body Ser.). (J). 18.00 (978-0-516-24060-2(9)); 24p. pap. 4.95 (978-0-516-22127-4(2)) Scholastic Library Publishing. (Children's Pr.).

Eye. 2001. (Human Anatomy Ser.). (J). (gr. k-12). vinyl bd. 4.95 (978-1-58845-081-4(3)) School Specialty Publishing.

Eyes. (Amazing Animals Ser.). 32p. (J). (gr. 1). pap. (978-1-882210-76-3(X)) Action Publishing, Inc.

Eyes: Level C, 6 vols. (Wonder Worldtm Ser.). 16p. 24.95 (978-0-7802-1992-2(9)) Wright Group, The.

Eyes & Ears Sets: 1 Each of 3 Big Books. (Sunshinetm Science Ser.). (gr. 1-2). 111.50 (978-0-7802-1445-3(5)) Wright Group, The.

Eyes & Ears Sets: 1 Each of 3 Student Books. (Sunshinetm Science Ser.). (gr. 1-2). 20.95 (978-0-7802-1747-8(0)) Wright Group, The.

Fernandez, A. & Fernandez, Q. Hooray for My Eyes. (Hooray for My Senses Ser.). (Illus.). (J). 19.27 (978-1-58952-374-6(1)) Rourke Publishing, LLC.

Gordon, Sharon. Pinkeye. 2003. (Rookie Read-About Health Ser.). (Illus.). (J). (gr. k-2). 31p. pap. 5.95 (978-0-516-27396-9(5)); 32p. 20.50 (978-0-516-22583-8(9)) Scholastic Library Publishing. (Children's Pr.).

—Pinkeye. 2003. (Illus.). 31p. (J). (ps-3). lib. bdg. 14.10 (978-0-613-67921-3(0)) Tandem Library Bks.

Grambo, Rebecca L. Eyes. 2002. (Amazing Animals Ser.). (Illus.). 32p. (gr. 2-5). 18.95 (978-1-58952-145-2(5)) Rourke Publishing, LLC.

Gray, Susan Heinrichs. The Eyes. 2005. (Human Body Ser.). (Illus.). 32p. (J). (gr. 2-6). 27.07 (978-1-59296-426-0(5)) Child's World, Inc.

Hall, Peg. Whose Eyes Are These? A Look at Animal Eyes - Big, Round, & Narrow. Landmark, Ken, illus. 2004. (Whose Is It? Ser.). 24p. (C). (gr. k-2). 22.60 (978-1-4048-0005-2(0)) Picture Window Bks.

Harris, David & Van Til, Meaghan. Eye See. 2005. (X-Zone Ser.). (Illus.). 30p. (gr. 4-8). 23.00 (978-0-7910-8975-0(4)) Facts On File, Inc.

Hidalgo, Maria. Sight. 2003. 24p. (J). lib. bdg. 21.35 (978-1-58340-303-7(5)) Smart Apple Media.

Klingel, Cynthia Fitterer & Noyed, Robert B. Eyes. Andersen, Gregg, photos by. 2002. (Weekly Reader Early Learning Library). (Illus.). 24p. (J). (ps up). pap. 5.95 (978-0-8368-3152-8(7)); lib. bdg. 19.33 (978-0-8368-3063-7(6)) Stevens, Gareth Inc. (Weekly Reader Early Learning Library).

—Eyes/Ojos. Acosta, Tatiana & Gutiérrez, Guillermo, trs. Andersen, Gregg, photos by. 2002. (Weekly Reader Early Learning Library). (ENG & SPA., Illus.). 24p. (J). (ps up). pap. (978-0-8368-3321-8(X)); lib. bdg. 19.33 (978-0-8368-3072-9(5)) Stevens, Gareth Inc. (Weekly Reader Early Learning Library).

Labella, Susan. Owls & Other Animals with Amazing Eyes. 2005. (Scholastic News Nonfiction Readers Ser.). (Illus.). 24p. (J). (gr. 1-2). 19.00 (978-0-516-24927-8(4) , Children's Pr.) Scholastic Library Publishing.

Llewellyn, Claire. Seeing. 2004. (Body in Action Ser.). (J). pap. (978-1-58340-438-6(4)) Smart Apple Media.

Miles, Elizabeth. Eyes. (Animal Parts Ser.). (Illus.). 32p. (J). 2003. pap. 6.95 (978-1-4034-0424-4(0)); 2002. lib. bdg. 21.36 (978-1-4034-0015-4(6)) Heinemann Library.

—Eyes. 2003. (gr. k-3). lib. bdg. 14.75 (978-0-613-45749-1(8)) Tandem Library Bks.

Miller, Sara Swan. All Kinds of Eyes. 2007. (All Kinds Of Ser.). (Illus.). 48p. (J). (ps-3). lib. bdg. 28.50 (978-0-7614-2519-9(5)) Cavendish, Marshall Corp.

Mitchell, Melanie S. Eyes. 2003. (First Step Nonfiction Ser.). (J). pap. 3.95 (978-0-8225-3911-7(X) , Lerner Pubns.) Lerner Publishing Group.

Moses, B., et al. Winking, Blinking, Wiggling & Waggling. 2000. (Eyewitness Readers). (Illus.). 32p. (J). (gr. 1-3). 12.95 (978-0-7894-5414-0(9)) Dorling Kindersley Publishing, Inc.

Moses, Brian, et al. Winking, Blinking, Wiggling & Waggling, Vol. 2. 2000. (Eyewitness Readers). (Illus.). 32p. (J). (gr. 1-3). pap. 3.99 (978-0-7894-5413-3(0)) Dorling Kindersley Publishing, Inc.

Nelson, Robin. Seeing & Hearing Well. 2006. (Pull Ahead Bks.). (J). 22.60 (978-0-8225-3488-4(6) , Lerner Pubns.) Lerner Publishing Group.

Nunn, Daniel. Eyes. 2006. (Illus.). 24p. (J). pap. (978-1-4034-8479-6(1)); lib. bdg. 20.71 (978-1-4034-8474-1(0)) Heinemann Library.

Olson, Karen W. Eyes, Ears, Nose & Mouth. George, Leonard, Jr., illus. 2006. 20p. (J). pap. 10.95 (978-1-894778-34-3(0)) Theytus Bks., Ltd. CAN. *Dist:* Orca Bk. Pubs. USA.

Our Eyes. (Sunshinetm Science Ser.). 24p. (gr. 1-2). 37.50 (978-0-7802-1420-0(X)) Wright Group, The.

Our Eyes: 6 Each of 1 Student Book, 6 vols. (Sunshinetm Science Ser.). 24p. (gr. 1-2). 41.95 (978-0-7802-1419-4(6)) Wright Group, The.

Perkins, Wendy. Animal Eyes. 2007. (Pebble Plus Ser.). (Illus.). 24p. (J). 19.93 (978-0-7368-6349-0(4)) Capstone Pr., Inc.

Phillips, Carey R. & Johannen, Kevin C. Physiology of the Eye. Doggett, W. Kirk, illus. 2nd ed. 2005. (C). cd-rom 95.00 (978-0-9759464-1-1(2) , Interactive Eye, L.L.C.) Interactive Knowledge, Inc.

Phillips, Carey R., et al. Physiology of the Eye. 2000. (Illus.). (YA). cd-rom (978-0-9759464-0-4(4)) Interactive Knowledge, Inc.

Pringle, Laurence P. Sight. 2000. (Explore Your Senses Ser.). (Illus.). 32p. (J). (gr. 4-8). lib. bdg. 25.64 (978-0-7614-0734-8(0) , Benchmark Bks.) Cavendish, Marshall Corp.

Pryor, Kimberley Jane. Seeing. 2003. (Senses Ser.). (Illus.). 32p. (gr. 2-4). 23.00 (978-0-7910-7555-5(9) , Chelsea Hse.) Facts On File, Inc.

Rau, Dana Meachen. Look Around! A Book about Your Sense of Sight. Peterson, Rick, illus. 2005. (Amazing Body Ser.). 24p. (C). (gr. k-3). 22.60 (978-1-4048-1019-8(6)) Picture Window Bks.

Rice, Judith Anne. Those Ooey Gooey Winky Blinky but... Invisible Pinkeye Germs. de la Vega, Eida, tr. Stricklin, Julie A., illus. 2004. (Children's Health Ser.: Vol. 4). Tr. of Esos Pringosos Viscosos Pestaneantes Parpadeantes Pero... Invisibles Germenes Que Causan Conjuntivitis. (ENG & SPA.). 32p. (J). (ps-3). pap. 13.95 (978-1-884834-89-9(2) , 181801) Redleaf Pr.

Royston, Angela. Healthy Eyes & Ears. 2003. (Illus.). 32p. (J). pap. 6.95 (978-1-4034-4455-4(2)); lib. bdg. (978-1-4034-4446-2(3)) Heinemann Library.

—Pink Eye. 2001. (It's Catching Ser.). (Illus.). 32p. (J). (gr. k-2). lib. bdg. 21.36 (978-1-58810-230-0(0)) Heinemann Library.

School Specialty Publishing. The Eye. 2004. (On-File Ser.). 4p. (J). (gr. 4-6). ring bd. 4.99 (978-0-7424-2904-8(0) , Instructional Fair) Schaffer, Frank Pubns.

Seeing Eye to Eye. 2002. (Illus.). (J). pap. (978-0-7398-5142-5(X)) Steck-Vaughn.

Sideri, Simona. Eyes. Noble, Sheilagh, tr. Noble, Sheilagh, illus. 2004. (J). lib. bdg. (978-1-58340-495-9(3)) Smart Apple Media.

—Let's Look at Eyes. Noble, Sheilagh, illus. 2003. (Let's Look at Ser.). 24p. (J). (978-1-84089-146-1(7) , Zero to Ten, Limited) Evans Publishing Group.

Silverstein, Alvin, et al. Seeing. 2001. (Senses & Sensors Ser.). (Illus.). 64p. (gr. 5-8). lib. bdg. 25.90 (978-0-7613-1663-3(9) , Millbrook Pr.) Lerner Publishing Group.

Simon, Seymour. Eyes & Ears. (Illus.). (J). 2005. 32p. pap. 6.99 (978-0-06-073302-5(0) , Harper Trophy); 2003. 15.99 (978-0-688-15303-8(8)) HarperCollins Pubs.

Sirret, Dawn. Winking, Blinking, Wiggling, & Waggling. 2000. (Eyewitness Readers Ser.). (978-0-606-18121-1(0)); lib. bdg. 11.80 (978-0-613-27596-5(9)) Tandem Library Bks.

Spilsbury, Louise. Why Should I Turn down the Volume? And Other Questions about Healthy Ears & Eyes. 2003. (Body Matters Ser.). (Illus.). 32p. (J). lib. bdg. 16.95 (978-1-4034-4683-1(0)) Heinemann Library.

Stanley, Debbie. Coping with Vision Disorders. 2005. (Coping Ser.). (Illus.). 192p. (YA). (gr. 7-12). lib. bdg. 26.50 (978-0-8239-3198-9(6)) Rosen Publishing Group, Inc., The.

—Everything You Need to Know about Vision Disorders. 2005. (Need to Know Library). (Illus.). 64p. (YA). (gr. 7-12). 25.25 (978-0-8239-3225-2(7)) Rosen Publishing Group, Inc., The.

Stone, Lynn M. How Do Animals Use Their Eyes? 2008. (J). (***978-1-60044-504-0(7)***) Rourke Publishing, LLC.

Take Care of Your Eyes! With Annie Funelli & the Funsters. 2002. (Lessons for a Healthy Childhood Ser.). (J). (gr. k-3). instr.'s gde. ed. 69.95 (978-1-55942-189-8(4) , 9235V9) Marsh Media.

Tildes, Phyllis Limbacher. Eye Guess: A Foldout Guessing Game. 2005. (Illus.). 36p. (J). (ps-ps). per. 9.95 (978-1-57091-650-2(0)) Charlesbridge Publishing, Inc.

Viegas, Jennifer. The Eye: Learning How We See. 2002. (3-D Library of the Human Body). (Illus.). 48p. (YA). (gr. 5-8). lib. bdg. 26.50 (978-0-8239-3530-7(2) , Rosen Central) Rosen Publishing Group, Inc., The.

Vv. La Vista. (Coleccion Mundo Maravilloso). (SPA., Illus.). 48p. (J). (gr. 2-4). (978-84-348-4318-9(8) , SM0099) SM Ediciones ESP. *Dist:* Lectorum Pubns., Inc.

Windsor, Jo. Eyes: Emergent Level Satellite Individual Title Six-Packs. (Sails Literacy Ser.). (gr. k-1). 27.00 (978-0-7578-7926-5(8)) Rigby Education.

EYEGLASSES

see also Lenses

Flanagan, Alice K. Choosing Eyeglasses with Mrs. Koutris. Rau, Dana, ed. 1998. (Our Neighborhood Ser.). (Illus.). 32p. (J). (gr. 1-2). pap. 6.95 (978-0-516-26294-9(7) , Children's Pr.) Scholastic Library Publishing.

Santos, Dina. My New Glasses: Learning the GL Sound. 2002. (PowerPhonics Ser.). (Illus.). (J). 23p. pap. (978-0-8239-8290-5(4)); 24p. (gr. 1). lib. bdg. 18.50 (978-0-8239-5945-7(7)) Rosen Publishing Group, Inc., The. (PowerKids Pr.).

EYEGLASSES—FICTION

Boonstra, Jean Elizabeth. A New Life down Under. 2004. 95p. (J). (978-0-8163-2017-2(9)) Pacific Pr. Publishing Assn.

Calvert, Pam. Princess Peepers. Mourning, Tuesday, illus. 2008. (J). (***978-0-7614-5437-3(3)***) Cavendish, Marshall Corp.

Cohen, Bernard. Paul Needs Specs. Kelly, Geoff, illus. 2004. 32p. (J). 15.95 (978-1-929132-61-4(1)) Kane/Miller Bk. Pubs., Inc.

Cohen, Peter. Boris's Glasses. Sandin, Joan, tr. Landstrom, Olof, illus. 2003. 28p. (J). (gr. k-3). 15.00 (978-91-29-65942-9(6)) R & S Bks. SWE. *Dist:* Macmillan.

Coulton, Mia. Carla's New Glasses. Totire, Valerie, illus. 2005. (J). pap. 4.95 (978-1-57874-092-5(4)) Kaeden Corp.

Cowley, Joy. Agapanthus Hum & the Eyeglasses. Plecas, Jennifer, illus. 1999. 1p. (J). (gr. k-3). 14.99 (978-0-399-23211-4(7) , Philomel) Penguin Group (USA) Inc.

Day, Shirley. Luna & the Big Blur: A Story for Children Who Wear Glasses. 2000. (Illus.). 32p. (J). (ps-3). pap. 8.95 (978-1-55798-777-8(7)) American Psychological Assn.

Dooley, Virginia. I Need Glasses: My Visit to the Optometrist. Roth, Stephanie, illus. 2002. 32p. (J). (ps-2). pap. 6.00 (978-1-59034-040-0(X)) Mondo Publishing.

Driscoll, Laura. Super Specs. Gott, Barry, illus. 2005. 32p. (J). lib. bdg. 20.00 (***978-1-4242-1074-9(7)***) Fitzgerald Bks.

—Super Specs. Adams, Lynn, illus. 2005. (Math Matters Ser.). 32p. (J). pap. 4.95 (978-1-57565-145-3(9)) Kane Pr., The.

Guiffre, William. Gramma's Glasses. Pippin, Barbara, illus. 1998. (J). pap. 6.95 (978-1-56763-347-4(1)); lib. bdg. 19.95 (978-1-56763-346-7(3)) Ozark Publishing.

Headley, Justina Chen. The Patch. Vane, Mitch, illus. (J). 2007. pap. 7.95 (***978-1-58089-170-7(5)***); 2006. 32p. 15.95 (978-1-58089-049-6(0)) Charlesbridge Publishing, Inc.

E F G

Heling, Kathryn & Hembrook, Deborah. I Wish I Had Glasses Like Rosa/Quisiera tener lentes como Rosa. de la Vega, Eida, tr. Adamson, Bonnie, illus. Tr. of Quisiera tener lentes como Rosa. (SPA.). (J). 2006. 4.99 (978-0-9770906-5-5(5)); 2005. 32p. 16.95 (978-0-9724973-7-4(4) , 626999) Raven Tree Pr.

Hodgson, Mona Gansberg. Goofy Glasses. 2000. (ps-2). lib. bdg. 13.00 (978-0-613-72834-8(3)) Tandem Library Bks.

Hodgson, Mona Gansberg & Sharp, Chris. Goofy Glasses. 2000. (Desert Critter Friends Ser.: Vol. 10). (Illus.). 48p. (J). (ps-2). 4.99 (978-0-570-07011-5(2)) Concordia Publishing Hse.

Jones, Christianne C. Robin's New Glasses. Lee, Ji Sun, illus. 2006. (Read-It! Readers Ser.). 32p. (J). (ps-3). 18.60 (978-1-4048-1587-2(2)) Picture Window Bks.

London, Sara. Good Luck Glasses. (Hello Reader! Ser.). 2001. (Illus.). (J). 10.79 (978-0-606-21216-8(7)); 2000. lib. bdg. 11.80 (978-0-613-35519-3(9)) Tandem Library Bks.

—The Good Luck Glasses. Rogers, Jacqueline, illus. 2001. (Hello Reader! Ser.). 32p. (J). (gr. 1-3). pap. 3.99 (978-0-590-97212-3(X)) Scholastic, Inc.

Manson, Sheri. Bumpy & Boo Visit the Eye Doctor: Guess Who Needs Glasses? 2006. 32p. 15.95 (978-0-9744307-3-7(0)) Merry Lane Pr.

McKinlay, Penny. Bumposaurus. Teckentrup, Britta, illus. 2006. 32p. (J). pap. 7.95 (978-1-84507-516-3(1)) Lincoln, Frances Ltd. GBR. *Dist:* Perseus Distribution.

Nanette. Oinky the Yellow Pig. 2004. (Life on Granny's Farm Ser.). (J). 12.95 (978-0-9741269-4-4(2)) St. Bernard Publishing, LLC.

Park, Barbara. Junie B. , First Grader (at Last!) Brunkus, Denise, illus. (Junie B. Jones Ser.: No. 18). 96p. (J). 2002. (gr. k-3). pap. 3.99 (978-0-375-81516-4(3)); 2001. (gr. k-3). 11.95 (978-0-375-80293-5(2)); 2001. (gr. 1-4). lib. bdg. 13.99 (978-0-375-90293-2(7)) Random Hse. Children's Bks. (Random Hse. Bks. for Young Readers).

—Junie B. , First Grader (at Last!) 2001. (Junie B. Jones Ser.: No. 18). (J). (gr. k-3). lib. bdg. 11.80 (978-0-613-57510-2(5)) Tandem Library Bks.

Payne, Yadira V. Brown Eyes: Ojos Marrones. Payne, Yadira V., ed. Payne, Emerald M., illus. 2004. (MUL.). (J). pap. 12.50 (978-0-9747350-1-6(9)) Payne, Yadira V. Publishing.

Sadler, Marilyn. Honey Bunny's Honey Bear. Bollen, Roger, illus. 2008. (Step into Reading Ser.). (J). (978-0-375-84326-6(4)); lib. bdg. 11.99 (978-0-375-94326-3(9)) Random Hse. Children's Bks.

Santa Gets New Glasses. 2005. (J). 5.95 (978-0-9769321-2-3(1)) Steingart, Nathan Publishing.

Smith, Lane. Glasses: Who Needs 'Em? Smith, Lane, illus. 2006. (Illus.). 29p. (J). (gr. k-4). reprint ed. 17.00 (978-1-4223-5451-3(2)) DIANE Publishing Co.

Stair, Karen Smith. Glasses, Glasses Oh What Do I See. 2004. (Illus.). 32p. 14.95 (978-0-9755407-1-8(8)) Bk. Pubs. Network.

Sweeney, Jacqueline. Just Call Me J. P. Hart, G. K. & Empey, Mark, illus. 2000. (We Can Read! Ser.). 32p. (J). (gr. 1-2). lib. bdg. 21.36 (978-0-7614-0922-9(X) , Benchmark Bks.) Cavendish, Marshall Corp.

Thomas, Charlie. I Need Glasses. Goldfinger, Jennifer P., illus. (J). (gr. k-2). 2006. 32p. pap. 4.95 (978-0-516-25024-3(8)); 2005. 31p. 19.50 (978-0-516-24863-9(4)) Scholastic Library Publishing. (Children's Pr.).

Thomas, Valerie. Winnie Flies Again. 2000. (978-0-606-19823-3(7)) Tandem Library Bks.

Willson, Sarah. Hocus Focus. Wummer, Amy, illus. 2004. 32p. (J). lib. bdg. 20.00 (***978-1-4242-1093-0(3)***) Fitzgerald Bks.

Wilson, Sarah. Hocus Focus. Wummer, Amy, tr. Wummer, Amy, illus. 2004. (Science Solves It! Ser.). (J). pap. 4.99 (978-1-57565-136-1(X)) Kane Pr., The.

F

FABLES

see also Animals—Fiction; Folklore; Parables

Aesop. Aesop's Fables. Salter, Safaya, illus. 2000. 128p. (J). pap. 8.99 (978-1-86205-215-4(8) , Pavilion Bks., Ltd.) Anova Bks. GBR. *Dist:* Trafalgar Square Publishing.

—Aesop's Fables. Salter, Safaya, illus. 2003. (Chrysalis Children's Classics Ser.). 111p. (YA). pap. (978-1-84365-035-5(5)) Chrysalis Children's Bks.

—Aesop's Fables. Jones, V. S. Vernon, tr. from GEC. Rackham, Arthur, illus. 2003. (Barnes & Noble Classics Ser.). 304p. pap. 5.95 (978-1-59308-062-4(X)) Barnes & Noble, Inc.

—Aesop's Fables. Zwerger, Lisbeth, illus. ed. 2006. 32p. (J). pap. 6.95 (978-0-7358-2069-2(4)); (YA). 16.95 (978-0-7358-2068-5(6)) North-South Bks., Inc.

—Aesop's Fables. Winter, Nilo, illus. l.t. ed. Date not set. (J). (gr. 1-12). lib. bdg. 22.95 (978-0-88411-991-3(2)) Amereon LTD.

—Aesop's Fables. Hague, Michael, illus. rev. ed. 1999. 32p. (J). (ps-3). pap. 7.95 (978-0-8050-6315-8(3) , Holt, Henry & Co. Bks. For Young Readers) Holt, Henry & Co.

—Aesop's Fox. Sogabe, Aki, illus. 1999. 32p. (J). (gr. k-3). 16.00 (978-0-15-201671-5(6)) Harcourt Children's Bks.

—Belling the Cat: A Retelling of Aesop's Fable. Silverman, Diane, illus. 2004. (Read-It! Readers Ser.). 24p. (C). (gr. k-3). 18.60 (978-1-4048-0321-3(1)) Picture Window Bks.

—The Boy Who Cried Wolf: A Retelling of Aesop's Fable. Silverman, Diane, illus. 2004. (Read-It! Readers Ser.). 24p. (C). (gr. k-3). 18.60 (978-1-4048-0319-0(X)) Picture Window Bks.

—The Boy Who Cried Wolf: Sincerity. Goodell, Jon, illus. 2005. (J). (***978-1-4127-3760-9(5)***) Publications International, Ltd.

—The Country Mouse & the City Mouse: A Retelling of Aesop's Fable. Silverman, Diane, illus. 2004. (Read-It! Readers Ser.). 24p. (C). (gr. k-3). 18.60 (978-1-4048-0318-3(1)) Picture Window Bks.

—The Crow & the Pitcher: A Retelling of Aesop's Fable. Silverman, Diane, illus. 2004. (Read-It! Readers Ser.). 24p. (C). (gr. k-3). 18.60 (978-1-4048-0322-0(X)) Picture Window Bks.

—The Dog & the Wolf: A Retelling of Aesop's Fable. Silverman, Diane, illus. 2004. (Read-It! Readers Ser.). 24p. (C). (gr. k-3). 18.60 (978-1-4048-0323-7(8)) Picture Window Bks.

—The Donkey in the Lion's Skin: A Retelling of Aesop's Fable. Silverman, Diane, illus. 2004. (Read-It! Readers Ser.). 24p. (C). (gr. k-3). 18.60 (978-1-4048-0320-6(3)) Picture Window Bks.

—Fabulas de Esopo.Tr. of Aesop's Fables. (SPA., Illus.). 28p. (J). 18.50 (978-84-233-1922-0(9)) Ediciones Destino ESP. *Dist:* AIMS International Bks., Inc., Lectorum Pubns., Inc., Planeta Publishing Corp.

—The Miller & the Donkey: A Tale about Thinking for Yourself. Branch, Beverly, illus. 2006. (J). (978-1-59939-087-1(6) , Reader's Digest Young Families, Inc.) Reader's Digest Children's Publishing, Inc.

—The Town Mouse & the Country Mouse. Watts, Bernadette, illus. 1998. 32p. (J). (ps-3). 16.50 (978-1-55858-988-9(0)) North-South Bks., Inc.

—Unwitting Wisdom. Ward, Helen, illus. 2004. 64p. (J). 18.95 (978-0-8118-4450-5(1)) Chronicle Bks. LLC.

—The Wolf in Sheep's Clothing: A Tale about Appearances. 2006. (J). (978-1-59939-086-4(8) , Reader's Digest Young Families, Inc.) Reader's Digest Children's Publishing, Inc.

Aesop, as told by. Aesop's Fables: Digital Classics. 2002. cd-rom 5.00 (978-1-931457-09-5(3)) Stargate Electronic Library, Inc.

Aesop & Lawrence, Jacob. Aesop's Fables. 2003. (Illus.). 56p. 22.50 (978-0-295-97641-9(1)) Univ. of Washington Pr.

Aesop & Pinkney, Jerry. Aesop's Fables. 2000. (Illus.). 87p. (J). pap. (978-1-58717-003-4(5) , SeaStar Bks.) Chronicle Bks. LLC.

Aesop & Pirotta, Saviour. Aesop's Fables. Johnson, Richard, illus. 2005. 80p. (J). (gr. 3-5). 12.95 (978-0-7534-5919-5(1) , Kingfisher) Houghton Mifflin Co. Trade & Reference Div.

Aesop's Fables. Date not set. 88p. (J). 7.98 (978-0-7525-9844-4(9)) Parragon, Inc.

Alex, Ben. Fables of Spiritual Wisdom: From Around the World. Imhoff, Ruth, illus. 1998. 70p. 16.95 (978-87-7247-532-5(3)) Scandinavia Publishing Hse. DNK. *Dist:* National Bk. Network.

Andersen, Hans Christian & White, Mus. For Sure! for Sure! Czernecki, Stefan, illus. 2004. 32p. 16.95 (978-0-87483-742-1(1)) August Hse. Pubs., Inc.

Avalon, Dawn. Bubbels. Een Vochtig Draakje. 2006. 60p. pap. 8.23 (978-1-4116-1193-1(4)) Lulu.com.

—Bubbles. A Wet Dragon. 2006. 59p. pap. 8.21 (978-1-4116-1177-1(2)) Lulu.com.

Backstein, Karen. The Blind Men & the Elephant. Mitra, Annie, illus. 2004. 48p. (J). lib. bdg. 15.00 (978-1-59054-401-3(3)) Fitzgerald Bks.

Barber, Antonia & So, Meilo. The Monkey & the Panda. 1999. (Illus.). 32p. (J). (ps-4). pap. 7.99 (978-0-7112-1085-1(3)) Lincoln, Frances Ltd. GBR. *Dist:* Transition Vendor.

Bauld, Jane S. Parables for Children. 1998. (J). (ps-2). 8.95 (978-1-880384-16-9(7)) Coldwater Pr.

Bellamy, Marian Meredith. Goldic & Androcles—A Fable for the 21st Century. Bellamy, Marian Meredith, illus. 2005. (Illus.). 91p. (YA). per. 20.00 (978-0-9765341-0-5(X)) Meredith Group Ltd., The.

Boyce, Christopher. Little Ha-Ha. 2000. viii, 40p. (J). (gr. 2-7). pap. 5.95 (978-0-9703704-7-1(4)) Kissing Deer Pr., LLC.

Boyd, Roland. The Fisherman & His Wife. Wright, Carol, ed. Zarvatski, Derek, illus. rev. ed. 20p. (J). (gr. 1-2). pap. 6.95 (978-0-9701573-0-0(4)) Chameleon Designs.

Brett, Jan. Town Mouse, Country Mouse. Brett, Jan, illus. 2002. (Illus.). (J). 23.64 (978-0-7587-3852-3(8)) Book Wholesalers, Inc.

—Town Mouse, Country Mouse. Brett, Jan, illus. 2003. (Illus.). 32p. (J). (ps-3). pap. 6.99 (978-0-698-11986-4(X) , Putnam Juvenile) Penguin Group (USA) Inc.

—Town Mouse, Country Mouse. 2003. (ps-2). lib. bdg. 15.30 (978-0-613-59140-9(2)) Tandem Library Bks.

Brown, Stephanie Gwyn. Professor Aesop's the Crow & the Pitcher. 2004. (Illus.). 30p. (J). tchr. ed. 15.95 (978-1-58246-087-1(6) , Tricycle Pr.) Ten Speed Pr.

Il Brutto Anatroccolo. 1999. Tr. of Ugly Duckling. (ITA., Illus.). 24p. (J). (ps-5). pap. 7.95 (978-88-8148-256-6(8)) European Language Institute ITA. *Dist:* Distribooks, Inc., Midwest European Pubns.

Bryan, Ashley & Bryan, Ashley. Ashley Bryan's African Tales, Uh-Huh. Bryan, Ashley & Bryan, Ashley, illus. 1998. (Illus.). 208p. (J). (gr. 3-7). 22.95 (978-0-689-82076-2(3) , Atheneum) Simon & Schuster Children's Publishing.

Cappucceto Rosso. 1999. Tr. of Little Red Riding Hood. (ITA., Illus.). 24p. (J). (ps-5). pap. 7.95 (978-88-8148-254-2(1)) European Language Institute ITA. *Dist:* Distribooks, Inc., Midwest European Pubns.

Chatellard, Isabelle, illus. City Mouse & Country Mouse: A Classic Fairy Tale. 1999. (Little Pebbles Ser.). 32p. (J). (ps-1). 6.95 (978-0-7892-0513-1(0) , Abbeville Kids) Abbeville Pr., Inc.

Cleveland, Rob. The Bear, the Bat & the Dove: Three Stories from Aesop. 2006. (Illus.). 32p. (J). pap. 3.95 (978-0-87483-810-7(X)) August Hse. Pubs., Inc.

Clynes, Kate. Little Red Hen & Wheat. 2004. (Illus.). (J). (978-1-84444-058-0(3)) Mantra Publishing, Ltd.

Comtesse De Segur, Sophie. Les Petites Filles Modeles. Cote, Anne, illus. 1998. (Collection Comtesse de Segur: Vol. 2). Tr. of Perfect Little Girls. (FRE.). (J). (gr. 1-7). audio, audio compact disk 12.95 (978-2-921997-18-8(5)) Coffragants CAN. *Dist:* Penton Overseas, Inc.

Cote, Anne, illus. Les Malheurs de Sophie. 1998. Tr. of Sophie's Misfortune. (FRE.). (J). (gr. 1-7). audio, audio compact disk 12.95 (978-2-921997-47-8(9)) Coffragants CAN. *Dist:* Penton Overseas, Inc.

Cox, Judy. Weird Stories from the Lonesome Cafe. 2001. (Illus.). 80p. pap. 3.99 (978-0-439-21942-6(6)) Scholastic, Inc.

Czernecki, Stefan. Huevos Rancheros. Czernecki, Stefan, illus. 2006. (Illus.). 32p. (J). (ps-3). pap. 7.95 (978-1-896580-04-3(1)) Tradewind Bks. CAN. *Dist:* Orca Bk. Pubs. USA.

Daily, Don, illus. The Classic Treasury of Aesop's Fables. 1999. 56p. (J). (ps-3). 9.98 (978-0-7624-0413-1(2) , Courage Bks.) Running Pr. Bk. Pubs.

de La Fontaine, Jean. Fables. Marsh, Edward, tr. from FRE. 2001. (Everyman's Library Children's Classics Ser.). (Illus.). 176p. 14.95 (978-0-375-41334-6(0) , Everyman's Library) Knopf Publishing Group.

De La Fontaine, Jeannine. Fables, Tome II. 2001. Tr. of Fables, Vol. II. (FRE.). (J). (gr. 1-7). pap. 18.95 incl. audio compact disk (978-2-89558-020-1(0)) Coffragants CAN. *Dist:* Penton Overseas, Inc.

Dominie Press Staff. Aesop's Fables. (J). pap., tchr.'s training gde. ed. 15.50 (978-0-7685-0177-3(6)) Dominie Pr., Inc.

Donnelly, Anthony James. When the Trees Held Their Breath. Whitler, Larry, illus. deluxe ed. 2000. 44p. (YA). pap. 12.95 (978-0-9702052-3-0(6)) Antix Pr., Inc.

Enderle, Dotti. Aesop's Opposites: Interactive Aesop Fables. Mitchell, Judy, ed. Shalansky, Len, illus. 2004. 64p. (J). pap. 9.95 (978-1-57310-424-1(8)) Teaching & Learning Co.

Esopo. Faules de Isop. 2002. Tr. of Aesop. (CAT & SPA.). 28p. (J). 14.95 (978-84-233-1920-6(2)) Ediciones Destino ESP. *Dist:* AIMS International Bks., Inc.

Fables of Bah Ya Bah. 2002. 40p. (J). pap., tchr. ed. 10.00 (978-1-932008-11-1(X)) Fine Media Group.

Fabulas. (Coleccion Estrella).Tr. of Fables. (SPA., Illus.). 64p. (J). 14.95 (978-950-11-0006-8(5) , SGM006) Sigmar ARG. *Dist:* Continental Bk. Co., Inc.

Fabulas de la Fontaine. (SPA., Illus.). (YA). 11.95 (978-84-201-0304-4(7) , AF1100) Auriga, Ediciones S.A. ESP. *Dist:* Continental Bk. Co., Inc.

Feathery Fables: Individual Title Six-Packs. (Action Packs Ser.). 128p. (gr. 3-5). 44.00 (978-0-7635-3312-0(2)) Rigby Education.

Fish, Becky Durost & Fish, Bruce. Fables & Their Morals Vol. 2: The Fighting Roosters & the Eagle to the Lion in Love. 1999. (Illus.). 64p. (J). 19.24 (978-0-7910-5212-9(5) , Chelsea Hse.) Facts On File, Inc.

Fish, Bruce & Fish, Becky Durost. Fables & Their Morals Vol. 1: Androcles & the Lion to The Field of Treasure. 1999. (Illus.). 64p. (J). 19.23 (978-0-7910-5211-2(7) , Chelsea Hse.) Facts On File, Inc.

Fisher, Robert & Kelly, Beth. El Buho Que No Podia Ulular. 2nd ed. 2004. Tr. of Owl Who Didn't Give a Hoot. (SPA., Illus.). 99p. (J). (978-84-7720-685-9(6) , OB10849) Obelisco, Ediciones S.A.

Floyd, Lucy. Rabbit & Turtle Go to School. Denise, Christopher, illus. 2003. (Green Light Readers Level 1 Ser.). 24p. (J). 11.95 (978-0-15-204811-2(1)); pap. 3.95 (978-0-15-204851-8(0)) Harcourt Children's Bks. (Green Light Readers).

Rabbit & Turtle Go to School. 2000. (Green Light Readers Ser.). (J). (978-0-606-20034-9(7)); lib. bdg. 11.80 (978-0-613-63339-0(3)) Tandem Library Bks.

Fox, Mem. Feathers & Fools. Wilton, Nicholas, illus. 2000. 36p. (J). (gr. k-3). pap. 7.00 (978-0-15-202365-2(8) , Harcourt Paperbacks) Harcourt Children's Bks.

—Feathers & Fools. 2000. (Illus.). (J). (978-0-606-18740-4(5)) Tandem Library Bks.

Franco, Betsy. Why the Frog Has Big Eyes. Kim, Joung Un, illus. 2003. (Green Light Readers Level 2 Ser.). 24p. (J). 11.95 (978-0-15-204874-7(X)); pap. 3.95 (978-0-15-204834-1(0)) Harcourt Children's Bks. (Green Light Readers).

—Why the Frog Has Big Eyes. 2000. (Green Light Readers Ser.). (978-0-606-20337-1(0)); (J). (978-0-606-20175-9(0)); lib. bdg. 11.80 (978-0-613-64618-5(5)) Tandem Library Bks.

Griffin, Sandi Z. Yea Us Series (Tails with a Moral), 3 bks., Set. Griffin, Sandi Z., illus. Incl. Becca Bumbum Bunny. 14.00 (978-1-883838-03-4(7)); Curly Pig. 14.00 (978-1-883838-02-7(9)); Lumpa Lou Elephant. 14.00 (978-1-883838-01-0(0)); (Illus.). 28p. (J). (ps-2). 1993. (978-1-883838-00-3(2)) Griffin, Sandi Zambarano.

Gross, Ila Lane. Trickster Tales Around the World. 2001. (Global Understanding - Cultural Literacy Ser.). (Illus.). 72p. (J). (gr. 3-5). pap. 4.45 (978-0-9713649-0-5(7)) L.E.A.P. (Learning through an Expanded Arts Program, Inc).

Hague, Michael. Aesop's Fables. 1999. (gr. k-3). lib. bdg. 15.25 (978-0-613-75404-0(2)) Tandem Library Bks.

—Fabulas de Esopo. 2000. (SPA.). 32p. (J). (gr. k-3). 14.99 (978-84-241-3346-7(3) , EV1921) Everest de Ediciones y Distribucion, S.L. ESP. *Dist:* Lectorum Pubns., Inc.

Haley, Helen. Magical Friends. 2002. 32p. (J). pap. 8.00 (978-0-8059-5753-2(7)) Dorrance Publishing Co., Inc.

Harris, John. Pop-Up Aesop. Brown, Calef, illus. 2005. (Getty Trust Publications: J. Paul Getty Museum Ser.). 10p. (ps-7). 19.95 (978-0-89236-814-3(4)) Getty Pubns.

Hayashi, Leslie Ann. Fables from the Sea. Bishop, Kathleen Wong, illus. 2000. (Kolowalu Bks.). 40p. (ps-5). 14.95 (978-0-8248-2224-8(2) , Kolowalu Bk.) Univ. of Hawaii Pr.

Hennessy, B. G. The Boy Who Cried Wolf. Kulikov, Boris, illus. 2006. 40p. (J). (ps-2). 15.95 (978-0-689-87433-8(2)) Simon & Schuster Children's Publishing.

Herman, Gail. The Lion & the Mouse. McCue, Lisa, illus. 1998. 28p. lib. bdg. 10.79 (978-0-606-15973-9(8)) Tandem Library Bks.

Herman, Gail & Aesop. The Lion & the Mouse. McCue, Lisa, illus. 1998. (Step into Reading Ser.). 32p. (J). (ps-k). lib. bdg. 11.99 (978-0-679-98674-4(X)); pap. 3.99 (978-0-679-88674-7(5)) Random Hse. Children's Bks. (Random Hse. Bks. for Young Readers).

Hernandez, Norberto, tr. The Goose with the Golden Eggs: A Fable by Aesop. Leonard, Card, illus. 2000. Tr. of Ganso con los Huevos de Oro: Una Fabula de Esopo. (ENG & SPA.). (J). (gr. 1-4). pap. 12.95 incl. audio (978-0-9678821-0-9(9)) Libie Alone Pubns.

Heurtelou, Maude. Aesop's Fables. Heurtelou, Maude et al, trs. Gautier, G. et al, illus. 1999. (CRP & SPA.). 52p. (J). (gr. 3-5). pap. 16.00 incl. audio (978-1-881839-93-4(1)) Educa Vision.

Hopkins, Lee Bennett. Mother Goose & Her Children: Theme 1. Fehlau, Dagmar et al, illus. l.t. ed. 1999. (Sadlier Phonics Reading Program). 16p. (YA). (ps-1). 29.85 (978-0-8215-0462-8(2)) Sadlier, William H. Inc.

—Mother Goose Around the World: Theme 4. Fehlau, Dagmar et al, illus. l.t. ed. 1999. (Sadlier Phonics Reading Program). 20p. (YA). (ps-1). 29.85 (978-0-8215-0492-5(4)) Sadlier, William H. Inc.

Jacobs, Joseph, ed. The Fables of Aesop. 2002. (Dover Juvenile Classics Ser.). (Illus.). 208p. (J). (gr. 4-7). pap. 3.00 (978-0-486-41859-9(6)) Dover Pubns., Inc.

Jaekel, Susan, illus. The Tortoise & the Hare: A Tale about Determination. 2006. (J). 6.99 (978-1-59939-015-4(9)) Reader's Digest Young Families, Inc.

Jaekel, Susan M., illus. Tug of War: A Tale about Being Resourceful. 2006. (J). (***978-1-59939-091-8(4)*** , Reader's Digest Young Families, Inc.) Reader's Digest Children's Publishing, Inc.

Johnson, Richard. Little Red Hen & the Grains of Wheat: Big Book English Only. 2004. (Illus.). (J). (978-1-84444-298-0(5)) Mantra Publishing, Ltd.

Kahn, Sheryl & Walsh-Balducci, Rita. Disney's Family Storybook Collection: 75 Fables for Living, Loving, & Learning. 1998. (Disneys Ser.). (Illus.). 304p. (J). (ps-17). 19.95 (978-0-7868-3200-2(2)) Disney Pr.

Keyser, Samuel Jay. The Pond God & Other Stories. 2003. (gr. 7-12). lib. bdg. 18.75 (978-0-613-67077-7(9)) Tandem Library Bks.

Keyser, Samuel Jay & Boyds Mills Press Staff. The Pond God & Other Stories. 2004. (Illus.). 96p. (YA). 14.95 (978-1-886910-96-6(0) , Lemniscaat) Boyds Mills Pr.

Kilaka, John. True Friends: A Tale from Tanzania. 2006. (Illus.). 32p. (J). 16.95 (978-0-88899-698-5(5)) Groundwood Bks. CAN. *Dist:* Perseus Distribution.

L. A. Goal Members, contrib. by. Disabled Fables: Aesop's Fables Retold & Illustrated by Artists with Developmental Disabilities. 2005. (Illus.). 52p. (J). (gr. 1 up). 19.95 (978-1-932065-97-8(0)) Star Bright Bks., Inc.

La Fontaine, Jean De. Fables. Cote, Anne, illus. (J). (gr. 1-7). Tome 1. 1998. (FRE.). audio, audio compact disk 12.95 (978-2-921997-44-7(4)); Tome II. 2000. pap. 12.95 incl. audio (978-2-89517-061-7(4)) Coffragants CAN. *Dist:* Penton Overseas, Inc.

—Fables. 2000. (FRE.). (J). 5.95 (978-2-89393-448-8(X)) Phidal Publishing, Inc./Editions Phidal, Inc. CAN. *Dist:* AIMS International Bks., Inc.

Lang, Andrew. The Hut in the Forest: A Tale about Being Kind to Animals. Johnson, Meredith, illus. 2006. (J). (978-1-59939-083-3(3) , Reader's Digest Young Families, Inc.) Reader's Digest Children's Publishing, Inc.

Larsen, Ron A. The Little Owl Who Couldn't Say Who: A Freethought Fable. Turpen, John A., illus. 2002. 34p. (J). 15.00 (978-0-9704968-0-5(X)) Freethought Publishing Group.

Lasky, Kathryn. The Hatchling. 2005. (Guardians of Ga'Hoole Ser.: Bk. 7). 240p. (J). (gr. 4-7). pap. 4.99 (978-0-439-73950-4(0) , Scholastic Paperbacks) Scholastic, Inc.

Leyendas, Fabulas y Cuentos. 2003. (SPA., Illus.). 112p. (YA). (gr. 3 up). 9.95 (978-968-6966-14-5(5)) EDITER'S Publishing Hse. MEX. *Dist:* EDITER'S Publishing Hse.

The Little Red Hen. 2004. (J). (978-1-58453-270-5(X)) Pioneer Valley Educational Pr., Inc.

Little Red Hen & the Grains of Wheat. 2004. (J). (ALB & ENG.). (978-1-84444-594-3(1)); (ARA & ENG.). (978-1-84444-595-0(X)); (BEN & ENG.). (978-1-84444-596-7(8)); (CHI & ENG.). (978-1-84444-597-4(6)); (CHI & ENG.). (978-1-84444-598-1(4)); (CRO & ENG.). (978-1-84444-599-8(2)); (ENG & PER.). (978-1-84444-600-1(X)); (ENG & FRE.). (978-1-84444-601-8(8)); (ENG & GRE.). (978-1-84444-602-5(6)); (ENG & GUJ.). (978-1-84444-603-2(4)); (ENG & HIN.). (978-1-84444-604-9(2)); (ENG & ITA.). (978-1-84444-605-6(0)); (ENG & JPN.). (978-1-84444-606-3(9)); (ENG & KOR.). (978-1-84444-607-0(7)); (ENG & KUR.). (978-1-84444-608-7(5)); (ENG & PAN.). (978-1-84444-609-4(3)); (ENG & POL.). (978-1-84444-610-0(7)); (ENG & POR.). (978-1-84444-612-4(3)); (ENG & RUS.). (978-1-84444-613-1(1)); (ENG & SOM.). (978-1-84444-614-8(X)); (ENG & SPA.). (978-1-84444-615-5(8)); (ENG & TAG.). (978-1-84444-616-

2(6)); (ENG & TAM.). (978-1-84444-617-9(4)); (ENG & TUR.). (978-1-84444-618-6(2)); (ENG & URD.). (978-1-84444-619-3(0)); (ENG & VIE.). (978-1-84444-620-9(4)) Mantra Publishing, Ltd.

Little Red HenGrains. 2004. (J). cd-rom (978-1-84444-462-5(7)) Mantra Publishing, Ltd.

Lobel, A. Fables, Vol. 1. 2002. (FRE.). (J). 18.95 incl. audio compact disk (978-2-89558-027-0(8)) Editions Alexandre Stanke CAN. *Dist:* Penton Overseas, Inc.

Lobel, Arnold. Fabulas.Tr. of Fables. (SPA.). 48p. (J). (gr. 2-3). 21.99 (978-84-8470-138-5(7) , COR32443) Corimbo, Editorial S.L. ESP. *Dist:* Lectorum Pubns., Inc.

Lynch, Tom & Aesop. Fables from Aesop. 2000. (Illus.). 32p. (J). (ps-3). 15.99 (978-0-670-88948-8(2) , Viking Juvenile) Penguin Group (USA) Inc.

MacLaren, Dorothy H. Esopus Hodie, Aesop Today, Vol. 1. (ENG & LAT.). 64p. (YA). (gr. 9-12). 9.75 (978-0-939507-06-1(4) , B20) American Classical League, The.

Masson, J. Moussaieff. The Cat Who Came in from the Cold: A Fable. 2004. 107p. (978-0-345-47867-2(3) , Ballantine Bks.) Random House Publishing Group.

McAllister, Angela. Barkus, Sly & the Golden Egg. Lambert, Sally Anne, illus. 2002. 32p. (J). 15.95 (978-1-58234-764-6(6) , Bloomsbury Children) Bloomsbury Publishing.

McClintock, Barbara. Animal Fables from Aesop. 2000. (Illus.). 48p. (J). (gr. 1 up). reprint ed. pap. 10.95 (978-1-56792-144-1(2)) Godine, David R. Pub.

—Animal Fables from Aesop. 2000. (gr. k-3). lib. bdg. 19.90 (978-0-613-78971-4(7)) Tandem Library Bks.

McNamee, Gregory. The North Wind & the Sun: And Other Fables of Aesop. 2004. 107p. pap. 19.95 (978-3-85630-636-6(6) , 255-082) Daimon Verlag CHE. *Dist:* Bookworld Trade, Inc.

Mooney, Margaret. Sour Grapes. 2001. (gr. k-3). lib. bdg. 11.65 (978-0-613-33434-1(5)) Tandem Library Bks.

Morgan, Richard, illus. The Fox & the Stork. 2005. (Reading Corner Ser.). 24p. (J). (gr. k-3). lib. bdg. 22.80 (978-1-59771-011-4(3)) Sea-To-Sea Pubns.

Morpurgo, Michael & Aesop. The McElderry Book of Aesop's Fables. Clark, Emma Chichester, illus. 2005. 96p. (J). 21.99 (978-1-4169-0290-4(2) , McElderry, Margaret K.) Simon & Schuster Children's Publishing.

Morrow, Lesley Mandel & Vacca, Richard T. Getting Ready to Read with Mother Goose, Teacher's Resource Guide. 2001. (Sadlier Phonics Reading Program). (Illus.). 160p. (YA). (ps-k). tchr. ed. 69.00 (978-0-8215-6951-1(1)) Sadlier, William H. Inc.

Nazoa, Aquiles. Fabula de la Avispa Ahogada. 2002. (SPA., Illus.). 36p. (J). 6.50 (978-980-257-099-7(0) , EK4926) Ekare, Ediciones VEN. *Dist:* Lectorum Pubns., Inc.

Nottingham, Theodore J. The Color of the Wind: Fables for a New Age. Moore, Susan, illus. 1999. 107p. (gr. 4-7). pap. 12.95 (978-0-9664960-0-0(0)) Nottingham Publishing.

Oh, Cirro. Greek & Roman Mythology. Chun, C. S., illus. 2005. 192p. (J). Vol. 1. pap. 12.95 (978-981-05-2240-7(1)); Vol. 2. pap. 12.95 (978-981-05-2241-4(X)) Youngjin.com Publishing Co., Ltd. KOR. *Dist:* Transition Vendor.

Olivelle, Patrick. Pancatantra: The Book of India's Folk Wisdom. Olivelle, Patrick, tr. from SAN. 2002. (Oxford World's Classics Ser.). (Illus.). 256p. (Orig.). 12.95 (978-0-19-283988-6(8)) Oxford Univ. Pr., Inc.

Orgel, Doris. The Bremen Town Musicians: And Other Animal Tales from Grimm. Kitchen, Bert, illus. rev. ed. 2004. 48p. (J). 18.95 (978-1-59643-010-5(9)) Roaring Brook Pr.

Osborne, M. D. The Rescue of Mr. Goldsmith. l.t. ed. 2005. (Illus.). 40p. (J). 12.95 (978-0-9762852-1-2(5)) Wooden Shoe Pr.

Ovani, Germano, tr. from SPA. & illus. The Illustrated Book of Aesop's Fables. Ovani, Germano, illus. Bucan, Simona et al, illus. 2006. 128p. (J). (gr. 2-4). 18.99 (978-0-7641-5930-5(5)) Barron's Educational Series, Inc.

Ownby, Karen. Once upon a Time Tales, Vol. 2. 2000. (Illus.). 53p. (J). (gr. k-7). pap. 23.95 (978-1-930002-24-1(6)) I & L Publishing.

—Once upon a Times Tales, Vol. 1. 2000. (Illus.). 43p. (J). (gr. k-6). pap. 23.95 (978-1-930002-15-9(7)) I & L Publishing.

Parable Venture Partners Staff. Ethan's Parables: Ethan & the Good Samantha. 2005. 16p. cd-rom 14.95 (978-0-9728501-1-7(2)) Parable Venture Partners, LLC.

Pinkney, Jerry. Aesop's Fables. 2000. (Illus.). 87p. (J). (gr. 4-7). 19.95 (978-1-58717-000-3(0) , SeaStar Bks.) Chronicle Bks. LLC.

Price, Nick, illus. Aesop's Fables. 2004. (Young Reading Series Two Ser.). 64p. (J). (gr. 2 up). pap. 5.95 (978-0-7945-0409-0(4) , Usborne) EDC Publishing.

Le Rat de Ville et le Rat des Champs: Opposites, Means of Transport, Utensils, Prepositions. 1999. (FRE & ENG., Illus.). 24p. (J). (ps-5). pap., stu. ed. 7.95 (978-88-8148-242-9(8)) European Language Institute ITA. *Dist:* Distribooks, Inc., Midwest European Pubns.

El Raton de Ciudad y el Raton de Campo: Opposites, Means of Transport, Utensils, Prepositions. 1999. (SPA & ENG., Illus.). (J). (ps-5). pap. 7.95 (978-88-8148-252-8(5)) European Language Institute ITA. *Dist:* Distribooks, Inc., Midwest European Pubns.

Repchuk, Caroline & Aesop. The Race. Jay, Alison, illus. 2002. 32p. (J). (gr. k-1). 15.95 (978-0-8118-3500-8(6)) Chronicle Bks. LLC.

Rojas, Emilio. Mitos, Leyendas, Cuentos, Fabulas, Apologos y Parabolas. 2003. (SPA., Illus.). 224p. (YA). (gr. 5 up). Vol. I. 15.95 (978-968-6966-03-9(X)); Vol. II. 15.95 (978-968-6966-11-4(0)); Vol. III. 15.95 (978-968-6966-17-6(X)) EDITER'S Publishing Hse. MEX. *Dist:* EDITER'S Publishing Hse.

Rosenthal, Paul. Yo, Aesop! Get a Load of These Fables. Rosenthal, Marc, illus. 2005. 51p. reprint ed. pap. 16.00 (978-0-7567-8761-5(0)) DIANE Publishing Co.

Scieszka, Jon. Squids Will Be Squids: Fresh Morals, Beastly Fables. 2002. (Illus.). (J). 24.55 (978-0-7587-5392-2(6)) Book Wholesalers, Inc.

—Squids Will Be Squids: Fresh Morals, Beastly Fables. Smith, Lane, illus. 1998. 48p. (J). (gr. 3-3). 17.99 (978-0-670-88135-2(X) , Viking Juvenile) Penguin Group (USA) Inc.

—Squids Will Be Squids: Fresh Morals, Beastly Fables. 2003. (gr. k-3). lib. bdg. 16.45 (978-0-613-67305-1(0)) Tandem Library Bks.

Scieszka, Jon & Smith, Lane. Squids Will Be Squids: Fresh Morals, Beastly Fables. 2003. (Illus.). 48p. (J). pap. 7.99 (978-0-14-250040-8(2) , Puffin) Penguin Group (USA) Inc.

Selections from the Flower Fables by Louisa Mae Alcott. 2003. (J). cd-rom (978-0-9724995-5-2(5)) Alcazar AudioWorks.

Shapiro, Norman R. & LA Fontaine, Jean De. Once Again, la Fontaine: Sixty New Translations from the "Fables" Schorr, David, illus. 2001. (Wesleyan Poetry Ser.). (ENG & FRE.). 248p. pap. 19.95 (978-0-8195-6458-0(3)) Wesleyan Univ. Pr.

Sherman, Pat. The Sun's Daughter. Christie, R. Gregory, illus. 2005. 32p. (J). (gr. k-3). 16.00 (978-0-618-32430-9(5) , Clarion Bks.) Houghton Mifflin Co. Trade & Reference Div.

Stevens, Janet. The Tortoise & the Hare. Stevens, Janet, illus. 2002. (Illus.). (J). 15.49 (978-0-7587-3847-9(1)) Book Wholesalers, Inc.

Thistle, Louise. Dramatizando la Gallinita Roja: Un Cuento para Contar y Actuar. Packer, Emily, illus. l.t. ed. 2003. Tr. of Dramatizing the Little Red Hen. (SPA.). 32p. (J). (gr. k-2). pap. 10.00 (978-0-9644186-4-6(9)) Literature Dramatization Pr.

—Dramatizing the Little Red Hen. Landes, William-Alan, ed. Packer, Emily, illus. l.t. ed. 2003. 32p. (J). (gr. k-2). pap. 10.00 (978-0-9644186-5-3(7)) Literature Dramatization Pr.

Thornhill, Jan, illus. The Rumor: A Jataka Tale from India. 2005. 32p. pap. 6.95 (978-1-897066-27-0(9)) Maple Tree Pr. CAN. *Dist:* Perseus Distribution.

I Tre Porcellini. 1999. Tr. of Three Little Pigs. (ITA., Illus.). 24p. (J). (ps-5). pap. 7.95 (978-88-8148-255-9(X)) European Language Institute ITA. *Dist:* Distribooks, Inc., Midwest European Pubns.

Treanor, Francis. How the Eagle Got His Beak. 2002. 110p. (J). pap. 9.95 (978-0-595-22451-7(2) , Writers Club Pr.) iUniverse, Inc.

Ungerer, Tomi. Moon Man. 1998. (Illus.). 40p. (J). (ps-1). pap. 6.95 (978-1-57098-207-1(4)) Rinehart, Roberts Pubs.

Verne, Jules. Vingt Mille Lieues sous les Mers. Langlois, Suzane, illus. 1998. (FRE.). (J). audio, audio compact disk 12.95 (978-2-921997-22-5(3)) Coffragants CAN. *Dist:* Penton Overseas, Inc.

Walbesser,, Henry. Imagination. 2003. 96p. pap. 8.95 (978-0-595-27851-0(5)) iUniverse, Inc.

Ward, Helen. Hare & Tortoise. 2005. (Illus.). 32p. (J). (ENG & ARA.). pap. 12.95 (978-1-84444-780-0(4)); (ENG & BEN., pap. 12.95 (978-1-84444-781-7(2)); (ENG & CHI., pap. 12.95 (978-1-84444-783-1(9)); (ENG, PER & FAR., pap. 12.95 (978-1-84444-786-2(3)); (ENG & FRE., pap. 12.95 (978-1-84444-787-9(1)); (ENG & GUJ., pap. 12.95 (978-1-84444-789-3(8)); (ENG & HIN., pap. 12.95 (978-1-84444-790-9(1)); (ENG & PAN., pap. 12.95 (978-1-84444-793-0(6)); (ENG & POL., pap. 12.95 (978-1-84444-794-7(4)); (POR & ENG., pap. 12.95 (978-1-84444-795-4(2)); (ENG, RUM & ROM., pap. 12.95 (978-1-84444-796-1(0)); (RUS & ENG., pap. 12.95 (978-1-84444-797-8(9)); (ENG & SOM., pap. 12.95 (978-1-84444-799-2(5)); (ENG & SPA., pap. 12.95 (978-1-84444-800-5(2)); (ENG & TAG., pap. 12.95 (978-1-84444-801-2(0)); (ENG & TUR., pap. 12.95 (978-1-84444-803-6(7)); (ENG & URD., pap. 12.95 (978-1-84444-805-0(3)); (ENG & VIE., pap. 12.95 (978-1-84444-806-7(1)) Mantra Lingua GBR. *Dist:* Mantra Publishing, Ltd.

Ward, Helen & Aesop. Hare & Tortoise. 2005. (Illus.). 32p. (J). (ENG & GRE.). pap. 12.95 (978-1-84444-788-6(X)); (JPN & ENG., pap. 12.95 (978-1-84444-791-6(X)); (ENG & SWA., pap. 12.95 (978-1-84444-798-5(7)) Mantra Lingua GBR. *Dist:* Mantra Publishing, Ltd.

Weale, David. Three Tall Trees. McNevin, Dale, illus. 2004. 24p. pap. 6.95 (978-1-894838-13-9(0)) Acorn Pr., The CAN. *Dist:* Goose Lane Editions.

White, Mark. The Ant & the Grasshopper: A Retelling of Aesop's Fable. Rojo, Sara, illus. 2004. (Read-It! Readers Ser.). 24p. (C). (gr. k-3). 18.60 (978-1-4048-0217-9(7)) Picture Window Bks.

—The Fox & the Grapes: A Retelling of Aesop's Fable. Rojo, Sara, illus. 2004. (Read-It! Readers Ser.). 24p. (C). (gr. k-3). 18.60 (978-1-4048-0218-6(5)) Picture Window Bks.

—The Goose That Laid the Golden Egg: A Retelling of Aesop's Fable. Rojo, Sara, illus. 2004. (Read-It! Readers Ser.). 24p. (C). (gr. k-3). 18.60 (978-1-4048-0219-3(3)) Picture Window Bks.

—The Lion & the Mouse: A Retelling of Aesop's Fable. Rojo, Sara, illus. 2004. (Read-It! Readers Ser.). 24p. (C). (gr. k-3). 18.60 (978-1-4048-0216-2(9)) Picture Window Bks.

—The Tortoise & the Hare: A Retelling of Aesop's Fable. Rojo, Sara, illus. 2004. (Read-It! Readers Ser.). 24p. (C). (gr. k-3). 18.60 (978-1-4048-0215-5(0)) Picture Window Bks.

—The Wolf in Sheep's Clothing: A Retelling of Aesop's Fable. Rojo, Sara, illus. 2004. (Read-It! Readers Ser.). 24p. (C). (gr. k-3). 18.60 (978-1-4048-0220-9(7)) Picture Window Bks.

Wooldridge, Jack. The Hidden Children. Wooldridge, Jack, illus. 1999. (Potawatomi Fable Bk.: No. 11). (Illus.). 32p. (J). (gr. 1-6). pap. 7.00 (978-1-887963-14-5(6)) Pota Pr.

—Misho Tells a Story: A Potawatomi Fable. Wooldridge, Jack, illus. 1998. (Potawatomi Fables Ser.: Vol. 10). (Illus.). 32p. (J). (gr. 1-5). pap. 7.00 (978-1-887963-13-8(8)) Pota Pr.

Wormell, Christopher. Mice, Morals & Monkey Business: Lively Lessons from Aesop's Fables. Wormell, Christopher, illus. 2007. (Illus.). 20p. (J). pap. 6.95 (978-0-7624-2932-5(1) , Running Pr. Kids) Running Pr. Bk. Pubs.

—Mice, Morals & Monkey Business: Lively Lessons from Aesop's Fables. 2005. (Illus.). 64p. (J). 18.95 (978-0-7624-2404-7(4) , Running Pr. Kids); 18.95 (978-0-7624-2611-9(X)) Running Pr. Bk. Pubs.

Yolen, Jane. A Sip of Aesop. Barbour, Karen, illus. 2000. 32p. (J). (gr. 4-5). pap. 5.99 (978-0-590-47896-0(6)) Scholastic, Inc.

Young, Ed. Seven Blind Mice. Young, Ed, illus. 2002. (Illus.). 14.04 (978-1-4046-0752-1(8)) Book Wholesalers, Inc.

Young, Ed & Adams, Tracey. The Lost Horse: A Chinese Folktale. 2004. (Illus.). 32p. (J). pap. 6.00 (978-0-15-205023-8(X) , Voyager Bks./Libros Viajeros) Harcourt Children's Bks.

Young, Russell. Dragonsong: A Fable for the New Millennium. Cheng, Civi, illus. 2000. 32p. (J). (gr. 1-7). 16.95 (978-1-885008-12-1(0)) Shen's Bks.

FABRIC PICTURES

see Collage

FABRICS

see Textile Industry

FACE PAINTING

Caudron, Chris & Childs, Caro. Face Painting. (Activity Bks). (J). 2007. 48p. spiral bd. 12.99 (***978-0-7945-1783-0(8)*** , Usborne); 2004. (Illus.). 32p. pap. 7.95 (978-0-7945-0236-2(9) , Usborne); 2004. (Illus.). 32p. lthr. 15.95 (978-1-58086-460-2(0)) EDC Publishing.

Caun, Chris. Usborne Book of Face Painting. 2003. (gr. 3-6). lib. bdg. 16.40 (978-0-613-90011-9(1)) Tandem Library Bks.

Cool Cats Face Painting. 2004. (Fun Kits Ser.). (Illus.). 48p. (J). (978-1-84229-731-5(7)) Top That! Publishing PLC.

Emberley, Ed. Ed Emberley's Drawing Book of Faces. Emberley, Ed, illus. 2006. (Illus.). 30p. (J). (gr. 2-17). pap. 6.99 (978-0-316-78970-7(4)) Little Brown & Co.

Face Painting. 2004. (Whizz Kits Ser.). (Illus.). 48p. (J). (978-1-84229-944-9(1)) Top That! Publishing PLC.

Funtastic Face Painting. 2004. (How 2 Kits Ser.). (Illus.). 48p. (J). (978-1-84229-933-3(6)) Top That! Publishing PLC.

Henson, Paige. Painting with Face Paints. 1999. (How to Paint & Draw Ser.). (Illus.). 32p. (J). (gr. 3-6). lib. bdg. 26.60 (978-1-57103-314-7(9)) Rourke Publishing, LLC.

Mason, Jane B. & Hines Stephens, Sarah. Gymboree Face Painting: Imaginative Designs Plus Fun-Filled Activities! rev. ed. 2007. (Illus.). 36p. (J). (ps-2). bds. 16.95 (***978-1-55263-962-7(2)***) Key Porter Bks. CAN. *Dist:* Perseus Distribution.

Scary Faces. 2002. 64p. (YA). 7.98 (978-0-7525-8691-5(2)) Parragon, Inc.

Wild Things Face Painting. 2004. (Fun Kits Ser.). (Illus.). 48p. (J). (978-1-84229-858-9(5)) Top That! Publishing PLC.

FACETIAE

see Anecdotes; Wit and Humor

FACTORIES

Anderson, Catherine. Fire Truck Factory. 2004. (Field Trip! Ser.). (Illus.). 24p. (J). pap. (978-1-4034-6168-1(6)); lib. bdg. 18.50 (978-1-4034-6162-9(7)) Heinemann Library.

Bial, Raymond. The Mills: Building America. 2001. (Building America Ser.). (Illus.). 56p. (J). (gr. 4-7). lib. bdg. 27.07 (978-0-7614-1333-2(2) , Benchmark Bks.) Cavendish, Marshall Corp.

DeAngelis, Gina. Triangle Shirtwaist Company Fire of 1911. 2000. (Great Disasters, Reforms & Ramifications Ser.). (Illus.). 112p. (J). (gr. 5 up). 30.00 (978-0-7910-5267-9(2) , Chelsea Hse.) Facts On File, Inc.

Houle, Michelle M. Triangle Shirtwaist Factory Fire: Flames of Labor Reform. 2002. (American Disasters Ser.). (Illus.). 48p. (J). (gr. 4-10). lib. bdg. 23.93 (978-0-7660-1785-6(0)) Enslow Pubs., Inc.

Lieurance, Suzanne. The Triangle Shirtwaist Fire & Sweatshop Reform in American History. 2003. (In American History Ser.). (Illus.). 128p. (J). (gr. 5-12). lib. bdg. 26.60 (978-0-7660-1839-6(3)) Enslow Pubs., Inc.

Richardson, Adele D. Historic Mills. 2001. (Let's Investigate Ser.). (J). lib. bdg. 19.95 (978-1-58341-007-3(4) , Creative Education) Creative Co., The.

FACULTY (EDUCATION)

see Educators; Teachers

FAIENCE

see Pottery

FAIR EMPLOYMENT PRACTICE

see Discrimination in Employment

FAIRIES

see also Fairy Tales

Adams, Georgie. Historias de Hadas Contadas Por Hadas. Gardner, Sally, tr. 2004. (SPA., Illus.). 42p. (J). 18.99 (978-84-8488-072-1(9)) Serres, Ediciones, S. L. ESP. *Dist:* Lectorum Pubns., Inc.

Allen, Judy & Hook, Richard. Fantasy Encyclopedia. Howe, John et al, illus. 2005. 144p. (J). (gr. 5-9). 19.95 (978-0-7534-5847-1(0) , Kingfisher) Houghton Mifflin Co. Trade & Reference Div.

Arengo, Sue. The Shoemaker & the Elves. 2001. (Illus.). 24p. 5.50 (978-0-19-422073-6(7)) Oxford Univ. Pr., Inc.

Barker, Cicely Mary. Enchanted Garden Sticker Book. 2004. (Flower Fairies Ser.). (Illus.). 24p. pap. 4.99 (978-0-7232-5232-0(7) , Warne) Penguin Group (USA) Inc.

—Flower Fairies Dress-Up for the Ball Boo. 2005. (Illus.). 8p. pap. 7.99 (978-0-7232-5376-1(5) , Warne) Penguin Group (USA) Inc.

—How to Host a Flower Fairy Tea Party. 2004. (Flower Fairies Ser.). (Illus.). 48p. (J). (ps). 7.99 (978-0-7232-5360-0(9) , Warne) Penguin Group (USA) Inc.

Barker, Cicely Mary & Potter, Beatrix. A Deluxe Book of Flower Fairies. gif. ed. 2003. (Illus.). 272p. (J). (ps). 16.99 (978-0-7232-4939-9(3) , Warne) Penguin Group (USA) Inc.

Batt, Tanya Robyn. A Child's Book of Faeries. Newey, Gail, illus. 2002. 64p. (J). (gr. 3). pap. 19.99 (978-1-84148-954-4(9)) Barefoot Bks., Inc.

Berger, Thomas & Berger, Petra. The Gnome Craft Book. 2001. (Illus.). 80p. pap. 15.95 (978-0-86315-300-6(3)) Floris Bks. GBR. *Dist:* Gryphon Hse., Inc., Steiner-Books, Inc.

Bulloch, Ivan. A Fairy. James, Diane, illus. rev. ed. 2004. (I Wish I Were Ser.). 24p. (ps-2). 12.95 (978-1-58728-036-8(1) , Two Can Publishing) T&N Children's Publishing.

—I Wish I Were a Fairy. 1999. (ps-2). lib. bdg. 15.25 (978-0-613-43331-0(9)) Tandem Library Bks.

Burns, Jan. Fairies. 2007. (Mysterious Encounters Ser.). 48p. (J). (gr. 4-8). 26.20 (***978-0-7377-3635-9(6)*** , Kidhaven) Thomson Gale.

Busquets, Jordi. Leo y Veo, los Gnomos.Tr. of I Read & See, the Elves. (SPA.). 24p. (J). 3.48 (978-84-305-9407-8(8)) Susaeta Ediciones, S.A. ESP. *Dist:* AIMS International Bks., Inc.

Carroll, Yvonne. The Very Little Leprechaun Tale. 2000. (Illus.). 8p. (J). (ps-3). 9.95 (978-1-56554-781-0(0)) Pelican Publishing Co., Inc.

Clemmer, Charlotte. Murfy: The Littlest Elf. Clemmer, Charlotte, illus. l.t. ed. 2000. (Illus.). 95p. (J). (gr. 1-6). pap. 15.00 (978-0-9677716-0-1(9)) Chandler-Day.

Clibbon, Meg. Imagine You're a Fairy! Clibbon, Lucy, illus. 2002. (Imagine This! Ser.). 32p. (J). (ps-4). 19.95 (978-1-55037-743-9(4)); pap. 7.95 (978-1-55037-742-2(6)) Annick Pr., Ltd. CAN. *Dist:* Firefly Bks., Ltd.

—Imagine You're a Fairy! 2002. (gr. k-3). lib. bdg. 16.40 (978-0-613-56442-7(1)) Tandem Library Bks.

Clibbon, Meg & Clibbon, Lucy, trs. The Fairyspotters Guide. Clibbon, Meg & Clibbon, Lucy, illus. 2007. (Illus.). 24p. (J). 5.95 (***978-1-84089-297-0(8)*** , Zero to Ten, Limited) Evans Publishing Group GBR. *Dist:* Independent Pubs. Group.

Crane, Walter. Flower Fairies in Full Color. 2002. (Illus.). 48p. (J). (gr. 4-7). pap. 8.95 (978-0-486-41858-2(8)) Dover Pubns., Inc.

D'Aulaire, Ingri & D'Aulaire, Edgar Parin. D'aulaires' Book of Trolls. 2006. (New York Review Children's Collection Ser.). (Illus.). 72p. (J). (ps-3). 19.95 (978-1-59017-217-9(5) , NYR Children's Collection) New York Review of Bks., Inc., The.

de Paola, Tomie. Jamie O'Rourke & the Pooka. Frith, Margaret, ed. de Paola, Tomie, illus. 2000. (Illus.). 32p. (J). (ps-3). 16.99 (978-0-399-23467-5(5) , Putnam Juvenile) Penguin Group (USA) Inc.

Disney. Disney Fairies: Learn to Draw the Fairies of Pixie Hollow. 2006. (Disney Magic Artist Learn to Draw Bks.). 32p. (J). pap. 5.95 (978-1-56010-958-7(0)) Foster, Walter Publishing, Inc.

Doherty, Gillian. 1001 Cosas Que Buscar en el Mundo de las Hadas. 2007. 32p. (J). 9.99 (***978-0-7460-8346-8(7)*** , Usborne) EDC Publishing.

Dorling Kindersley Publishing Staff, ed. Fairy. 2005. (Make-Believe Ser.). (Illus.). 12p. (J). bds. 6.99 (978-0-7566-1016-6(8)) Dorling Kindersley Publishing, Inc.

Dover Staff. Fairies Fun Books, 10 vols. 1998. (J). pap. 10.00 (978-0-486-40252-9(5)) Dover Pubns., Inc.

Doyle, Richard. Fairyland Stained Glass Coloring Book. 2003. (Illus.). 16p. (J). (gr. 3). pap. 5.95 (978-0-486-43049-2(9)) Dover Pubns., Inc.

Gardner, Sally. The Fairytale Catalog: All You Need to Make a Fairy Tale. 2001. (Illus.). 40p. (J). 15.95 (978-0-8118-3320-2(8)) Chronicle Bks. LLC.

Gilpin, Rebecca. Christmas fairy things to make & Do. Fearn, Katrina, illus. 2004. 34p. (J). pap. 6.95 (978-0-7945-0835-7(9) , Usborne) EDC Publishing.

A Gnome's Home: A Princess Book Collection by Princess Ena. 2000. (J). per. (978-0-9705133-8-0(0)) World of Wonders, Inc.

Hague, Michael. Book of Fairies. 2000. (J). lib. bdg. 19.89 (978-0-06-029211-9(3)) HarperCollins Pubs.

Hamilton, John. Elves & Fairies. 2005. (Fantasy & Folklore Ser.). (Illus.). 32p. (J). (gr. 4-8). lib. bdg. 24.21 (978-1-59197-712-4(6)) ABDO Publishing Co.

—Goblins & Trolls. 2005. (Fantasy & Folklore Ser.). (Illus.). 32p. (J). (gr. 4-8). lib. bdg. 24.21 (978-1-59197-713-1(4)) ABDO Publishing Co.

Hamilton, Sue L. Ghosts & Goblins. 2007. (ENG., Illus.). 32p. (J). lib. bdg. 24.21 (***978-1-59928-767-6(6)*** , ABDO & Daughters) ABDO Publishing Co.

Hawkins, Al. The Story of Jingle the Magic Elf: How Jingle Bells Came to Be. Edwards, Ken, illus. 2001. 30p. (J). pap. 10.00 (978-0-9640056-3-1(8)) Arrowhead Publishing.

Hodges, Margaret & Root, Kimberly B. The Wee Christmas Cabin. 2001. (Illus.). (J). (978-0-8234-1528-1(7)) Holiday Hse., Inc.

Hoffman, Nancy. Fairies. 2003. (Illus.). 112p. (J). 29.95 (978-1-56006-973-7(2) , Lucent Bks.) Thomson Gale.

Kane, Barry & Kane, Tracy. Fairy Houses ... Everywhere! 2006. (Fairy Houses Ser.). 56p. (J). 14.95 (978-0-9708104-4-1(X)) Light-Beams Publishing.

Kerven, Rosalind. The Fairy-Spotter's Handbook. Anderson, Wayne, illus. 2004. 48p. (J). 14.95 (978-1-84507-152-3(2)) Lincoln, Frances Ltd. GBR. *Dist:* Perseus Distribution.

Krensky, Stephen. Watchers in the Woods. 2007. (Monster Chronicles Ser.). 48p. (J). (gr. 4-8). lib. bdg. 26.60 (*978-0-8225-6763-9(6) , Lerner Pubns.) Lerner Publishing Group.

Larkspur, Penelope. The Secret Life of Fairies. Watts, Leslie Elizabeth, illus. 1999. 32p. (J). (gr. 4-6). (978-1-55074-547-4(6)) Kids Can Pr., Ltd.

Larkspur, Penelope & Watts, Leslie Elizabeth. The Secret Life of Fairies. 1999. (Illus.). 32p. (J). (gr. 4-6). (978-1-55074-555-9(7)) Kids Can Pr., Ltd.

Litalien, Theresa L. The Secret of the Tooth Fairy. Buckley, Diane, illus. 1998. 26p. (J). (ps-6). pap. 3.99 (978-0-9664625-1-7(3)) Twinkle Toes, Inc.

Lowell, Susan. The Bootmaker & the Elves. Curry, Tom, illus. 1999. 32p. (J). (ps-3). pap. 6.95 (978-0-531-07138-0(3) , Orchard Bks.) Scholastic, Inc.

Luppens, Michel. What Do the Fairies Do with All Those Teeth. Béha, Philippe, illus. 2003. 24p. (J). (gr. k-3). pap. 4.95 (978-1-55209-002-2(7)) Firefly Bks., Ltd.

Mortensen, Lori. Leprechauns. 2007. (Mysterious Encounters Ser.). (Illus.). 48p. (J). (gr. 4-8). 26.20 (*978-0-7377-3663-2(1) , Kidhaven) Thomson Gale.

My Dolly Dressing Book of Fairies. 2002. 16p. (J). pap. 2.98 (978-0-7525-8043-2(4)) Parragon, Inc.

Noble, Marty. Garden Fairies Activity Book. 1998. (Illus.). 64p. (J). (ps-3). pap. 1.50 (978-0-486-40495-0(1)) Dover Pubns., Inc.

Paxton, Tom. The Story of the Tooth Fairy. Sauber, Robert G., illus. 2000. 32p. (YA). (ps-3). pap. 5.95 (978-0-688-17523-8(6) , Harper Trophy) HarperCollins Pubs.

Penelope Jane Fairy Stickers. 2000. (J). (978-0-06-029069-6(2)) HarperCollins Pubs.

Pratt, L. Christmas Fairy Cooking Pb. 2006. 32p. (J). pap. 8.99 (978-0-7945-1118-0(X) , Usborne) EDC Publishing.

Repchuk, Caroline. Fairy Colors. 2007. (J). bds. 5.99 (978-0-439-88704-5(6) , Cartwheel Bks.) Scholastic, Inc.

—Fairy Numbers. 2007. (J). bds. 5.99 (978-0-439-88705-2(4) , Cartwheel Bks.) Scholastic, Inc.

Ross, Kathy. Fairies. Bosch, Nicole in den, illus. 2008. (Girl Crafts Ser.). (J). lib. bdg. 25.26 (*978-0-8225-7509-2(4) , Millbrook Pr.) Lerner Publishing Group.

Ryland Peters and Small, Inc, creator. Now I Am a Fairy. 2007. (Illus.). 48p. (*978-1-84597-498-5(0)) Ryland Peters & Small.

Schoberle, Cecile. Sweetheart Fairies. Couri, Kathy, illus. 2003. 16p. (J). pap. 4.99 (978-0-689-85023-3(9) , Little Simon) Simon & Schuster Children's Publishing.

Silver Dolphin en Español Editors. Serie Aprendizaje: Drawing with Fairies. 2006. (SPA., Illus.). 22p. (J). bds. 16.95 (978-970-718-331-5(4)) Advantage Pubs. Group.

Streit, Jakob. Liputto: Stories of Gnomes & Trolls. Mitchell, David, ed. Mitchell, Susanne, illus. 2000. 58p. 20.00 (978-1-888365-26-9(9)) Assn. of Waldorf Schls. of North America Pubns. (AWSNA).

Timmerman, Charles & Timmerman, Calla. Everything Kids' Fairies Puzzle & Activity Book: Enter the make-believe world of these magical Creatures. 2007. 144p. pap. 7.95 (*978-1-59869-394-2(8)) Adams Media Corp.

Vornholt, John. The Troll King. 2002. 224p. (J). (gr. 7-9). pap. 4.99 (978-0-7434-2412-7(3) , Aladdin) Simon & Schuster Children's Publishing.

Watt, Fiona. Fairies. Cartwright, Stephen & Bird, Glen, illus. 2004. 10p. (J). (ps-ps). per. 15.95 (978-0-7945-0811-1(1) , Usborne) EDC Publishing.

—Fairy Things to Stitch & Sew. Fearn, Katrina, illus. 2006. 32p. (J). pap. 6.99 (978-0-7945-1235-4(6) , Usborne) EDC Publishing.

Watt, Fiona & Gilpin, Rebecca. Big Bk of Fairy Things to Make & Do. 2006. 96p. (J). pap. 14.99 (978-0-7945-1437-2(5) , Usborne) EDC Publishing.

Yolen, Jane & Christiana, David. The Book of Fairy Holidays. 1998. (J). (978-0-590-60356-0(6) , Blue Sky Pr., The) Scholastic, Inc.

Zschock, Martha. Flower Fairies Scratch & Sketch: An Art Activity Book for Magical Artists & Believers of All Ages. Zschock, Martha, illus. 2007. (Activity Book Ser.). (Illus.). 64p. (J). 12.99 (*978-1-59359-870-9(X)) Peter Pauper Pr. Inc.

FAIRIES—FICTION

Abbott, Tony. Kringle. Call, Greg, illus. 2005. 304p. (J). (gr. 4-7). pap. 14.99 (978-0-439-74942-8(5) , Scholastic Pr.) Scholastic, Inc.

Albee, Sarah. A Visit from the Tooth Fairy. Craig, Karen, illus. 2003. (Blue's Clues Ser.). 24p. (J). pap. 3.50 (978-0-689-86271-7(7) , Simon Spotlight/Nickelodeon) Simon & Schuster Children's Publishing.

Alexander, Jason. Dad, Are You the Tooth Fairy? Spears, Ron, illus. 2005. 32p. (J). pap. 16.95 (978-0-439-66745-6(3)) Scholastic, Inc.

Alice in Wonderland. 2006. 64p. (J). 8.99 (978-0-7945-1239-2(9) , Usborne) EDC Publishing.

Alton, Steve. The Firehills. 2005. 192p. (J). (gr. 7-13). 15.95 (978-1-57505-798-9(0) , Carolrhoda Bks.) Lerner Publishing Group.

Andersen, Hans Christian. Hans Christian Andersen's Fairy Tales. 2006. (Illus.). 200p. (J). 12.99 (978-0-517-22718-3(5) , Gramercy) Random Hse. Value Publishing.

Augarde, Steve. Celandine. 496p. (J). (gr. 5). 2008. 6.99 (*978-0-440-42216-7(7) , Yearling); 2006. 16.95 (978-0-385-75048-6(X) , Fickling, David Bks.); 2006. lib. bdg. 18.99 (978-0-385-75049-3(8) , Fickling, David Bks.) Random Hse. Children's Bks.

Augarde, Steve. The Various. 2005. 448p. (J). (gr. 5). reprint ed. 6.99 (978-0-440-42029-3(6) , Yearling) Random Hse. Children's Bks.

Auxier, Bryan. Where Have All the Fairies Gone? Ramey, Cindy, illus. l.t. ed. 2005. 24p. (J). pap. 7.95 (978-0-9719144-3-8(5)) Where? Pr., Inc.

Baker, E. D. No Place for Magic: The Fourth Tale of the Frog Princess. 2006. (Tales of the Frog Princess Ser.). 250p. (YA). 15.95 (978-1-58234-654-0(2)) Bloomsbury Publishing.

—Once upon a Curse: More Tales of the Frog Princess. 2004. (Illus.). 225p. (J). 15.95 (978-1-58234-892-6(8) , Bloomsbury Children) Bloomsbury Publishing.

Banks, Lynne Reid. The Fairy Rebel. 2004. (Illus.). 128p. (gr. 4-7). 5.50 (978-0-440-41925-9(5) , Yearling) Random Hse. Children's Bks.

—The Fairy Rebel. Geldart, William, illus. 2003. 128p. (gr. 4-7). reprint ed. 15.95 (978-0-385-73076-1(4) , Delacorte Bks. for Young Readers) Random Hse. Children's Bks.

Banks, Steven. Lemonade with a Twist. 2004. (gr. k-3). lib. bdg. 11.80 (978-0-613-73465-3(3)) Tandem Library Bks.

Banks, Steven & Thomas, Jack. Lemonade with a Twist. Miller, Victoria, illus. 2004. (Ready-to-Read Ser.: Vol. 2). 32p. (J). pap. 3.99 (978-0-689-86321-9(7) , Simon Spotlight/Nickelodeon) Simon & Schuster Children's Publishing.

Barber, Shirley. The Enchanted Woods. 2002. (Illus.). 96p. (J). reprint ed. (978-1-86503-781-3(8)) Summit Pr.

—Spellbound: and the Fairy Book: Packed with 3-D Pictures. Barber, Shirley, illus. 2005. (Illus.). 64p. (J). incl. audio compact disk (978-1-74124-486-1(2)) Five Mile Pr. Pty Ltd. The.

Barker, Cicely. Rose's Special Secret. 2006. (Flower Fairies Ser.: Bk. 3). 80p. (J). (gr. 2). 3.99 (978-0-7232-5827-8(9) , Warne) Penguin Group (USA) Inc.

Barker, Cicely Mary. Almond Blossom's Mystery No. 6. 2007. (Flower Fairies Ser.). 80p. (J). pap. 3.99 (978-0-7232-5848-3(1) , Warne) Penguin Group (USA) Inc.

—Buttercup Goes to the Ball: Book, Bag & Necklace. 2005. (Flower Fairies Ser.). 24p. (J). (ps). pap. 5.99 (978-0-7232-5375-4(7) , Warne) Penguin Group (USA) Inc.

—Candytuft's Enchanting Treats. 2007. 80p. (J). pap. 3.99 (978-0-7232-5904-6(6) , Warne) Penguin Group (USA) Inc.

—Fairy Whispers. 2007. (Flower Fairies Friends Ser.). (Illus.). 32p. (J). pap. 12.99 (978-0-7232-5737-0(X) , Warne) Penguin Group (USA) Inc.

—Fairyopolis: A Flower Fairies Journal. 2005. (Illus.). 32p. (J). 19.99 (978-0-7232-5724-0(8) , Warne) Penguin Group (USA) Inc.

—Flower Fairies Book & Fairy Doll. 2006. (Illus.). 32p. 12.99 (978-0-7232-5709-7(4) , Warne) Penguin Group (USA) Inc.

—Flower Fairies Masks & Wings Book. 2006. 24p. (J). pap. 5.99 (978-0-7232-5731-8(0) , Warne) Penguin Group (USA) Inc.

—Flower Fairies of the Autumn: With the Nuts & Berries They Bring. Barker, Cicely Mary, illus. 2002. (Illus.). 64p. (J). 6.99 (978-0-7232-4828-6(1) , Warne) Penguin Group (USA) Inc.

—Flower Fairies of the Garden. 2002. (Illus.). 56p. (J). 6.99 (978-0-7232-4831-6(1) , Warne) Penguin Group (USA) Inc.

—Flower Fairies of the Spring. Barker, Cicely Mary, illus. 2002. (Illus.). 64p. (J). 6.99 (978-0-7232-4826-2(5) , Warne) Penguin Group (USA) Inc.

—Flower Fairies of the Summer. 2002. (Illus.). 56p. (J). 6.99 (978-0-7232-4827-9(3) , Warne) Penguin Group (USA) Inc.

—Flower Fairies of the Trees. Barker, Cicely Mary, illus. 2002. (Illus.). 56p. (J). 6.99 (978-0-7232-4833-0(8) , Warne) Penguin Group (USA) Inc.

—Flower Fairies of the Wayside. Barker, Cicely Mary, illus. 2002. (Illus.). 56p. (J). 6.99 (978-0-7232-4830-9(3) , Warne) Penguin Group (USA) Inc.

—Flower Fairies of the Winter. Barker, Cicely Mary, illus. 2002. (Illus.). 56p. (J). 6.99 (978-0-7232-4829-3(X) , Warne) Penguin Group (USA) Inc.

—Flower Fairies Sparkly Sticker Book. 2005. (Flower Fairies Ser.). (Illus.). 16p. (J). (ps). 5.99 (978-0-7232-5377-8(3) , Warne) Penguin Group (USA) Inc.

—Flower Fairy Springtime Dance. 2006. (Flower Fairies Ser.). (Illus.). 24p. (J). 4.99 (978-0-7232-5726-4(4) , Warne) Penguin Group (USA) Inc.

—How to Find Flower Fairies. 2007. (Flower Fairies Ser.). 24p. (J). (gr. 2). 19.99 (*978-0-7232-5890-2(2)); 19.99 (*978-0-7232-5962-6(3)) Penguin Group (USA) Inc. (Warne).

—Jasmine's Starry Night. 2008. (Flower Fairies Ser.). 168p. (gr. 2). 3.99 (*978-0-7232-5922-0(4) , Warne) Penguin Group (USA) Inc.

—Lavender's Midsummer Mix-up. 2006. 80p. (J). (gr. 2). 3.99 (978-0-7232-5773-8(6) , Warne) Penguin Group (USA) Inc.

—Lily's Seaside Adventure: A Flower Fairies Friends Chapter Book. 2008. (Flower Fairies Ser.). 80p. (J). (gr. 2). pap. 3.99 (*978-0-7232-6286-2(1) , Warne) Penguin Group (USA) Inc.

—Magical Moonlight Feast. 2007. (Flower Fairies Ser.). (Illus.). 24p. (J). pap. 14.99 (978-0-7232-5784-4(1) , Warne) Penguin Group (USA) Inc.

—Merry Fairy Holidays: Three Enchanted Christmas Stories. 2007. 244p. (J). (gr. 2). 8.99 (*978-0-7232-5972-5(0) , Warne) Penguin Group (USA) Inc.

—My Garden of Flower Fairies. 2004. (Flower Fairies Ser.). (Illus.). 48p. (J). (gr. k-3). 12.99 (978-0-7232-4926-9(1) , Warne) Penguin Group (USA) Inc.

—Poppy's Perfect Home: A Flower Fairies Friends Chapter Book. 2007. 80p. (J). (gr. 2). 3.99 (*978-0-7232-5951-0(8) , Warne) Penguin Group (USA) Inc.

—Strawberry's New Friend. 2007. 80p. (J). 3.99 (978-0-7232-5905-3(4) , Warne) Penguin Group (USA) Inc.

—Sweet Pea's Precious Promise: A Flower Fairies Friends Chapter Book. 2007. (Flower Fairies Ser.). 80p. (J). (gr. 2). 3.99 (*978-0-7232-5921-3(6) , Warne) Penguin Group (USA) Inc.

—Tansy's New Petals: A Flower Fairies Friends Chapter Book. 2008. (Flower Fairies Ser.). 80p. (J). (gr. 2). pap. 3.99 (*978-0-7232-6285-5(3) , Warne) Penguin Group (USA) Inc.

Barker, Cicely Mary. Wild Cherry Makes a Wish: Flower Fairies Chapter Book #4. 2006. (Flower Fairies Ser.). 80p. (J). 3.99 (978-0-7232-5826-1(0) , Warne) Penguin Group (USA) Inc.

Barker, Cicely Mary & Le Quesne, Pippa. Buttercup & the Fairy Gold. 2007. (Flower Fairies Ser.: Bk. 5). 80p. (J). 3.99 (978-0-7232-5840-7(6) , Warne) Penguin Group (USA) Inc.

Barker, Cicely Mary & Swain-Smith, Justine. Return to Fairyopolis. 2008. 24p. (J). (gr. k). 19.99 (*978-0-7232-5996-1(8) , Warne) Penguin Group (USA) Inc.

Barrera, F. M. Tales of the Blue Wizard: The Children of Jamomere. Barrera, F. M., illus. 2005. (Illus.). 180p. (YA). (gr. 4-9). per. 12.95 (978-0-9670848-1-7(4)) Talisman Pr.

Bateman, Teresa. Fiona's Luck. Murphy, Kelly, illus. 2007. 32p. (J). (ps-3). 15.95 (978-1-57091-651-9(9)) Charlesbridge Publishing, Inc.

Batt Tanya Robyn. Faeries Gift. Ceccoli Nicoletta, illus. 2006. 0032p. pap. 6.99 (978-1-905236-73-2(5)) Barefoot Bks., Inc.

Baum, L. Frank. The Enchanted Island of Yew. l.t. ed. 2005. 228p. pap. (978-1-84637-102-8(3)) Echo Library.

Baxter, Nicola & Jones, Deborah. Rainbow Fairies. (Illus.). 16p. (J). (978-1-84322-052-7(0) , Armadillo Bks.) Advance Bks. Co.

Bell, Nick. Mary the Tooth Fairy. Bell, Nick, illus. 2007. 32p. (J). (ps-2). 15.95 (*978-1-60108-015-8(8)) Red Cygnet Pr.

Bell-Rehwoldt, Sheri. You Think It's Easy Being the Tooth Fairy? Slonim, David, illus. 2007. 32p. (J). (ps-3). 15.95 (978-0-8118-5460-3(4)) Chronicle Bks. LLC.

Bennett, Holly. The Bonemender. 2005. (Illus.). 208p. (YA). (gr. 7-12). pap. 7.95 (978-1-55143-336-3(2)) Orca Bk. Pubs. USA.

Bentley, Dawn. Lucky Leprechaun. Berg, Michelle, illus. 2003. 10p. (J). (ps-1). bds. 5.99 (978-0-8431-4587-8(0) , Price Stern Sloan) Penguin Group (USA) Inc.

Benz, Derek & Lewis, J. S. The Fall of the Templar. 2008. (Grey Griffins Ser.). 304p. (J). 12.99 (*978-0-439-83776-7(6) , Orchard Bks.) Scholastic, Inc.

—The Revenge of the Shadow King. 2006. (J). 384p. (gr. 4-7). pap. 10.99 (978-0-439-79574-6(5) , Orchard Bks.); 39.95 (978-0-439-87592-9(7) , Scholastic) Scholastic, Inc.

—Revenge of the Shadow King Audio (library Edition) 2006. (Grey Griffins Ser.). (J). 84.95 (978-0-439-87913-2(2)) Scholastic, Inc.

Berenstain, Jan & Berenstain, Michael. The Berenstain Bears' Big Bedtime Book. 2008. (Berenstain Bears Ser.). 48p. (J). 12.99 (*978-0-06-057434-5(8)); lib. bdg. 13.89 (*978-0-06-057435-2(6)) HarperCollins Pubs.

Bergen, Lara. Flower Fashions: Book & Flower Press. Disney Storybook Artists Staff, illus. 2007. 24p. (gr. 1-5). pap. 14.99 (*978-1-4231-0181-9(2)) Disney Pr.

Bergen, Lara. A Masterpiece for Bess. Clarke, Judith H., illus. 2006. (Stepping Stone Bks.). 128p. (J). (gr. 1-5). 5.99 (978-0-7364-2418-9(0) , RH/Disney) Random Hse. Children's Bks.

Bergsma, Jody Lynn. Faerie. 2002. (Illus.). 40p. (J). 15.95 (978-0-9717117-0-9(4)) Gallery Press Publishing, Inc.

Bergstrom, William. The Magic Telescope. 2006. 9.95 (978-0-9787648-0-7(3)) Bergstrom Bks.

Beylon, Cathy. Fairyland Activity Book. 2003. (Dover Little Activity Bks.). (Illus.). 64p. (J). pap., act. bk. ed. 1.50 (978-0-486-42996-0(2)) Dover Pubns., Inc.

Bib, Betty. Betty Bib's Fairy Handbook: A Field Guide to Fairies & their Habitats. 2005. (Illus.). 72p. (978-1-84483-194-4(9)) Duncan Baird Pubs.

Billingsley, Franny. The Folk Keeper. unabr. ed. 2004. 176p. (J). (gr. 5-9). pap. 36.00 incl. audio (978-0-8072-0662-1(8) , Listening Library) Random Hse. Audio Publishing Group.

—The Folk Keeper. Gore, Leonid, illus. 2001. 176p. (J). pap. 4.99 (978-0-689-84461-4(1) , Aladdin) Simon & Schuster Children's Publishing.

—The Folk Keeper. 2001. 11.64 (978-0-606-22111-5(5)) Tandem Library Bks.

—The Folk Keeper. l.t. ed. 2000. 224p. (YA). (gr. 5-9). 20.95 (978-0-7862-2461-6(4)) Thorndike Pr.

Billingsley, Franny & Gore, Leonid. The Folk Keeper. 1999. (Illus.). 176p. (YA). (gr. 5-9). 16.95 (978-0-689-82876-8(4) , Atheneum) Simon & Schuster Children's Publishing.

Bingham, Jane. Billy Goat's Gruff Cd Pack. rev. ed. 2007. (Young Reading CD Packs Ser.). 48p. (J). 9.99 (*978-0-7945-1867-7(2) , Usborne) EDC Publishing.

Birch, Beverley. Midsummer Nights Dream. 2007. (Illus.). 80p. 13.95 (*978-0-7502-4963-8(3) , Hodder Wayland) Hodder Children's Division GBR. *Dist:* Independent Pubs. Group.

Bishop, Debbie. The Fairies of Bladderwhack Pond. Park, Andy, illus. 2007. (Fairies of Bladderwhack Pond Ser.: Vol. 1). 152p. 19.99 (978-1-932431-01-8(2) , Angel Gate) Left Field Ink.

Black, Holly. Ironside: A Modern Faery's Tale. 2007. 336p. (YA). (gr. 4-7). 16.99 (978-0-689-86820-7(0) , McElderry, Margaret K.) Simon & Schuster Children's Publishing.

—Tithe: A Modern Faerie Tale. (YA). 2002. 320p. (gr. 7 up). 17.99 (978-0-689-84924-4(9)); 2004. 336p. reprint ed. pap. 6.99 (978-0-689-86704-0(2) , Simon Pulse) Simon & Schuster Children's Publishing.

—Tithe: A Modern Faerie Tale. 2004. (gr. 7-12). lib. bdg. 15.30 (978-0-613-73456-1(4)); 331p. (YA). per. 13.64 (978-0-606-30074-2(0)) Tandem Library Bks.

Black, Holly & DiTerlizzi, Tony. The Chronicles of Spiderwick: A Grand Tour of the Enchanted World, Navigated by Thimbletack. 2007. (Spiderwick Chronicles). 32p. (J). 21.99 (*978-1-4169-5038-7(9)) Simon & Schuster Children's Publishing.

—Deluxe Collector's Trunk: The Field Guide, the Seeing Stone, Lucinda's Secret, the Ironwood Tree, the Wrath of Mulgarath, Untitled, Set. DiTerlizzi, Tony, illus. 2007. (Spiderwick Chronicles). 672p. (J). 65.00 (*978-1-4169-5015-8(X)) Simon & Schuster Children's Publishing.

—Spiderwick Chronicles Set: The Field Guide, the Seeing Stone, Lucinda's Secret, the Ironwood Tree, the Wrath of Mulgarath. DiTerlizzi, Tony, illus. movie tie-in ed. 2008. (Spiderwick Chronicles). 672p. (J). 49.99 (*978-1-4169-5016-5(8)) Simon & Schuster Children's Publishing.

Blackford, Ami. Quest for the Elfin Elixir: A Duncan Family Adventure. Blackford, Ami, illus. 2007. 80p. (J). (gr. 3-7). 16.95 (*978-1-60108-021-9(2)) Red Cygnet Pr.

Blair, Eric. Los Duendes Zapateros: Version del Cuento de los Hermanos Grimm. Dickson, Bill, illus. 2006. (Read-It! Readers en Espanol Ser.).Tr. of Shoemaker & His Elves: A Retelling of the Grimm's Fairy Tale. (SPA.). 32p. (J). (ps-3). 19.95 (978-1-4048-1638-1(0)) Picture Window Bks.

Blaylock, Kathy. Adventures of Buddy Fairy & Friends. 2007. 48p. 12.95 (*978-1-4137-9195-2(6)) PublishAmerica, Inc.

Bliss, Bob, illus. The Hardest Lessons: The Lost Babies Series #3. 2007. 118p. (J). per. 5.99 (*978-0-9792499-2-1(9)) Howell, M Kay.

—The Ruby Hind: The Lost Babies Series #1. 2007. 116p. (J). per. 5.99 (*978-0-9792499-0-7(2)) Howell, M Kay.

—Too Many Parents: The Lost Babies Series #2. 2007. 109p. (J). per. 5.99 (*978-0-9792499-1-4(0)) Howell, M Kay.

Block, Francesca Lia. I Was a Teenage Fairy. 192p. (gr. 7 up). 1998. (J). 14.89 (978-0-06-027748-2(3)); 1998. (YA). 14.95 (978-0-06-027747-5(5) , Cotler, Joanna Books); 2000. (J). reprint ed. pap. 7.99 (978-0-06-440862-2(0) , Cotler, Joanna Books) HarperCollins Pubs.

—I Was a Teenage Fairy. 2000. (gr. 7-12). lib. bdg. 16.45 (978-0-613-28529-2(8)); (Illus.). (J). 14.64 (978-0-606-18903-3(3)) Tandem Library Bks.

Blyton, Enid. Mister Meddle's Muddles. (Illus.). 111p. (J). pap. 6.95 (978-0-7475-3860-8(3)) Bloomsbury Publishing Plc GBR. *Dist:* Trafalgar Square Publishing.

Bolliger, Max. The Happy Troll. Ignatowicz, Nina, tr. from GER. Sis, Peter, illus. 2005. 32p. (J). reprint ed. 16.95 (978-0-8050-6982-2(8) , Holt, Henry & Co. Bks. For Young Readers) Holt, Henry & Co.

Bottner, Barbara. Pish & Posh. Bottner, Barbara, illus. 2005. (I Can Read Bks.). 48p. (J). pap. 3.99 (978-0-06-051418-1(3) , Harper Trophy) HarperCollins Pubs.

Bottner, Barbara. Pish & Posh Wish for Fairy Wings. Bottner, Barbara, illus. 2007. (I Can Read Bks.). 48p. (J). pap. 3.99 (*978-0-06-051421-1(3) , Harper Trophy) HarperCollins Pubs.

Bottner, Barbara & Kruglik, Gerald. Pish & Posh. Bottner, Barbara, illus. 2004. (I Can Read Bks.). (Illus.). 48p. (J). (gr. k-3). pap. 15.99 (978-0-06-051416-7(7)) HarperCollins Pubs.

—Pish & Posh Wish for Fairy Wings. Bottner, Barbara, illus. 2006. (I Can Read Bks.). (Illus.). 48p. (J). 15.99 (978-0-06-051419-8(1) , HarperCollins); lib. bdg. 16.89 (978-0-06-051420-4(5)) HarperCollins Pubs.

Bottner/Kruglik. Pish & Posh. Bottner, Barbara, illus. 2004. 48p. (J). lib. bdg. 13.85 (*978-1-4242-0513-4(1)) Fitzgerald Bks.

Bouchard, David. Fairy. Griffiths, Dean, illus. 2001. 32p. (J). (ps-2). 16.95 (978-1-55143-212-0(9)) Orca Bk. Pubs. USA.

Bourgeois, Paulette. Franklin & the Tooth Fairy. Clark, Brenda, illus. 2002. (Franklin Ser.). 12.40 (978-1-4046-0311-0(5)) Book Wholesalers, Inc.

Bow, James. Fathom Five: A Rosemary & Time Book. 2007. 232p. (YA). pap. 12.99 (*978-1-55002-692-4(5) , Boardwalk Bks.) Dundurn Group, The CAN. *Dist:* Univ. of Toronto Pr.

Bow, Patricia. The Bone Flute. 2004. 144p. (J). (gr. 5-12). pap. 6.95 (978-1-55143-301-1(X)) Orca Bk. Pubs. USA.

Boyd, William T. The Pumpkin Fairy. Roberts, Mary Jo, illus. 2003. 32p. (J). (gr. k-1). 14.95 (978-0-9718161-0-7(7)) Wyatt Pr.

Bradman, Tony. Flora the Fairy. 2005. (Green Bananas Ser.). (Illus.). 48p. (J). (ps). pap. (978-0-7787-1038-7(6)) Crabtree Publishing Co.

Brennan, Herbie. Faerie Lord. 2007. (Faerie Wars Chronicles Ser.). 432p. (YA). (gr. 7 up). 18.95 (*978-1-59990-120-6(X) , Bloomsbury Children) Bloomsbury Publishing.

—Faerie Wars. 2003. (Illus.). 370p. (J). 17.95 (978-1-58234-810-0(3) , Bloomsbury Children) Bloomsbury Publishing.

—Faerie Wars. 2007. 384p. mass mkt. 6.99 (978-0-7653-5674-1(0) , Tor Bks.) Doherty, Tom Assocs., LLC.

—The Purple Emperor. 2006. (Faerie Wars Chronicles Ser.). 432p. (J). pap. 8.95 (978-1-58234-746-2(8) , Bloomsbury Children) Bloomsbury Publishing.

—The Purple Emperor: Faerie Wars II. 2004. 400p. (J). 17.95 (978-1-58234-880-3(4) , Bloomsbury Children) Bloomsbury Publishing.

—Ruler of the Realm. 2006. (Faerie Wars Chronicles Ser.: Bk. 3). (Illus.). 432p. (YA). 18.95 (978-1-58234-881-0(2)) Bloomsbury Publishing.

Brett, Jan. The Trouble with Trolls. Brett, Jan, illus. 1999. (Illus.). 32p. (J). (ps-3). pap. 6.99 (978-0-698-11791-4(3) , Putnam Juvenile) Penguin Group (USA) Inc.

—The Trouble with Trolls. 1999. (978-0-606-17433-6(8)) Tandem Library Bks.

Brian, Janeen. Party Time! Join Mia in the Mystery & Magic of the Fairy Shop! Norling, Beth, illus. 2006. (Nibbles Ser.). 72p. (J). (gr. 1-4). pap. 3.95 (978-0-7624-2627-0(6) , Running Pr. Kids) Running Pr. Bk. Pubs.

Bridwell, Norman. Tiny Family. 1999. (Hello Reader! Ser.). (978-0-606-16632-4(7)) Tandem Library Bks.

Bridwell, Norman & Lewison, Wendy Cheyette. Clifford's Loose Tooth. Kurtz, Sandrina & Kurtz, John, illus. 2002. (Clifford Big Red Readers Ser.). 32p. (J). (ps-1). pap. 3.99 (978-0-439-33245-3(1)) Scholastic, Inc.

Brooks, Stephen J. Alexander Asenby's Great Adventure. Rajesh, illus. 2006. 32p. (J). 16.96 (978-0-9769017-2-3(2)) Purple Sky Publishing.

—The Fairy Ball. Seah, Denise, illus. 2006. 32p. (J). 16.95 (978-0-9769017-4-7(9)) Purple Sky Publishing.

Bull, Emma. War for the Oaks. 2001. (gr. 7-12). lib. bdg. 23.40 (978-0-613-60631-8(0)) Tandem Library Bks.

Bunting, Eve. That's What Leprechauns Do. McCully, Emily Arnold, illus. 2006. 32p. (J). (gr. k-3). 16.00 (978-0-618-35410-8(7) , Clarion Bks.) Houghton Mifflin Co. Trade & Reference Div.

Burke, David. Cinderella (English to Italian - Level 1) Learn ITALIAN Through Fairy Tales. 2007. (Learn Italian Through Fairy Tales Ser.). (ENG & ITA., Illus.). (J). per. 14.95 incl. audio compact disk (*978-1-891888-77-9(3)) Slangman Publishing.

—Cinderella (English to Spanish - Level 1) Learn SPANISH Through Fairy Tales. 2007. (Learn Spanish Through Fairy Tales Ser.). (ENG & SPA., Illus.). (J). per. 14.95 incl. audio compact disk (*978-1-891888-74-8(9)) Slangman Publishing.

—Goldilocks (English to Spanish - Level 2) Learn SPANISH Through Fairy Tales. 2007. (Learn Spanish Through Fairy Tales Ser.). (ENG & SPA., Illus.). (J). per. 14.95 incl. audio compact disk (*978-1-891888-80-9(3)) Slangman Publishing.

Burke, David, adapted by. Goldilocks (English to French - Level 2) Learn FRENCH Through Fairy Tales. 2007. (Learn French Through Fairy Tales Ser.). (ENG & FRE., Illus.). (J). per. 14.95 incl. audio compact disk (*978-1-891888-81-6(1)) Slangman Publishing.

Burnett, Frances Hodgson. The Racketty-Packetty House. Halperin, Wendy Anderson, illus. 100th anniv. ed. 2006. 96p. (J). 17.95 (978-0-689-86974-7(6)) Simon & Schuster Children's Publishing.

—RackettyPacketty House. l.t. ed. 2006. 52p. pap. (978-1-84637-262-9(3)) Echo Library.

Burton, Martin Nelson. Fooling the Tooth Fairy. Hansen, Clint, illus. 2005. (J). pap. (*978-0-9666490-3-1(6)) London Town Pr.

Campbell, Ellie. The Visiting Elf. 2006. (ENG., Illus.). 32p. per. 25.49 (*978-1-4259-7562-3(3)) AuthorHouse.

Capone, Deb. Tooth Fairy Tales. 2005. (J). 14.95 (*978-0-9728666-7-5(1)) As Simple As That Publishing.

Carlow, Emma. Flora the Fairy. Carlow, Emma, illus. 2005. (Green Bananas Ser.). (Illus.). 48p. (J). (978-0-7787-1022-6(X)) Crabtree Publishing Co.

Carmody, Isobelle. A Fox Called Sorrow. (Little Fur Ser.). (Illus.). (J). (gr. 1-7). 2008. 272p. 5.99 (978-0-375-83857-6(0)); 2007. 256p. 14.99 (978-0-375-83856-9(2) , Random Hse. Bks. for Young Readers); 2007. 256p. lib. bdg. 16.99 (978-0-375-93856-6(7) , Random Hse. Bks. for Young Readers) Random Hse. Children's Bks.

—The Legend Begins. 2006. (Illus.). 208p. (J). (gr. 1-7). 12.95 (978-0-375-83854-5(6)); (gr. 3-7). lib. bdg. 14.99 (978-0-375-93854-2(0)) Random Hse. Children's Bks. (Random Hse. Bks. for Young Readers).

—Little Fur: The Legend Begins. 2006. (Illus.). 272p. (J). (978-0-375-83855-2(4)) Random Hse., Inc.

—Magic Night. Lee, Declan, illus. 2007. (Picture Book Ser.). 40p. (J). (ps-1). 16.99 (*978-0-375-83918-4(6)); lib. bdg. 19.99 (*978-0-375-93918-1(0)) Random Hse. Children's Bks. (Random Hse. Bks. for Young Readers).

—A Mystery of Wolves: Little Fur #3. 2008. (J). pap. (*978-0-375-83859-0(7)); (Little Fur: 3). 12.99 (*978-0-375-83858-3(9)); (Little Fur: 3). lib. bdg. 15.99 (*978-0-375-93858-0(3)) Random Hse., Inc.

Carroll, Yvonne. Great Irish Legends for Children. Lawrie, Robin, illus. 2005. 64p. (J). (ps-ps). 16.95 (978-1-58980-345-9(0)) Pelican Publishing Co., Inc.

Carville, Declan. The Fairy Glen. (Illus.). 36p. pap. 7.95 (978-0-9538222-3-2(0)) Discovery Pubns. GBR. *Dist:* Irish Bks. & Media, Inc.

Cash, Rosanne. Penelope Jane: A Fairy's Tale. Karas, G. Brian, illus. 2006. 32p. (J). pap. 6.99 (978-0-06-084230-7(X) , Harper Trophy) HarperCollins Pubs.

Chan, Ching. Mystery of the Black Sun: Songs of the Unicorn. 2006. (Anime Sticker Stories Ser.). 16p. (J). (ps-1). 4.99 (978-0-448-44340-9(6) , Grosset & Dunlap) Penguin Group (USA) Inc.

Chan, Gillian. The Turning. 2005. (Illus.). 200p. (YA). (gr. 7 up). (978-1-55337-576-0(9)); (978-1-55337-575-3(0)) Kids Can Pr., Ltd.

Chipponeri, Kelli. The Timmy Touch. Moore, Harry, illus. 2005. (Ready-to-Read Ser. Level 1). 24p. (J). lib. bdg. 15.00 (978-1-59054-966-7(X)) Fitzgerald Bks.

Christensen, Margaret Kate. The Hollyhock Fairies. 2004. 48p. per. (978-1-932077-85-8(5)) Athena Pr.

Clark, CoraMarie. Emily's Magical Journey with Toothena the Tooth Fairy. Lawton, Val, illus. 2007. 32p. (J). (*978-0-9783779-0-8(7)) Strategix Ltd.

Coleman, David R. Old Troop, Rainbow Fairies, & the Forget-Me-Now Potion. 2007. (J). pap. 8.99 (*978-1-60247-054-5(5)) Tate Publishing & Enterprises, L.L.C.

Colfer, Eoin. The Arctic Incident. l.t. ed. 2003. (Artemis Fowl Ser.: Bk. 2). 296p. (J). (gr. 3-6). 16.95 (978-0-7540-7839-5(6) , Galaxy Children's Large Print) BBC Audiobooks America.

—The Arctic Incident. (Artemis Fowl Ser.: Bk. 2). 288p. (ps-17). 2003. (J). pap. 7.99 (978-0-7868-1708-5(9)); 2002. 16.95 (978-0-7868-0855-7(1)) Hyperion Bks. for Children.

—The Arctic Incident. l.t. ed. 2003. (Artemis Fowl Ser.: Bk. 2). 313p. (J). (gr. 3-6). 25.95 (978-0-7862-4825-4(4)) Thorndike Pr.

—Artemis Fowl. (Artemis Fowl Ser.: Bk. 1). (FRE.). pap. 34.95 (978-2-07-054681-7(0)) Gallimard, Editions FRA. *Dist:* Distribooks, Inc.

—Artemis Fowl. 2003. (Artemis Fowl Ser.: Bk. 1). (Illus.). 416p. (ps-17). pap. 5.99 (978-0-7868-1787-0(9)) Hyperion Bks. for Children.

—Artemis Fowl. 2002. (Artemis Fowl Ser.: Bk. 1). 304p. (J). (ps-17). pap. 7.99 (978-0-7868-1707-8(0)) Hyperion Paperbacks for Children.

—Artemis Fowl. 2001. (Artemis Fowl Ser.: Bk. 1). 288p. (gr. 8-17). 16.95 (978-0-7868-0801-4(2)) Miramax Bks.

—Artemis Fowl. abr. ed. 2001. (Artemis Fowl Ser.: Bk. 1). (Illus.). 2p. (J). (gr. 3-6). cd-rom (978-0-14-180286-2(3) , Penguin AudioBooks) Penguin Group (USA) Inc.

—Artemis Fowl. (Artemis Fowl Ser.: Bk. 1). 2003. (gr. 7-12). lib. bdg. 14.15 (978-0-613-75035-6(7)); 2002. (gr. 5-8). lib. bdg. 16.15 (978-0-613-60637-0(X)) Tandem Library Bks.

—Artemis Fowl. l.t. ed. 2001. (Artemis Fowl Ser.: Bk. 1). 312p. (J). (gr. 3-6). 28.95 (978-1-58724-092-8(0) , Wheeler Publishing, Inc.) Thomson Gale.

—Artemis Fowl: The Graphic Novel. Rigano, Giovanni & Lamanna, Paolo, illus. 2007. (Artemis Fowl Ser.). 112p. (gr. 5 up). 18.99 (*978-0-7868-4881-2(2)) Miramax Bks.

—Artemis Fowl: The Graphic Novel. Lamanna, Paolo, illus. 2007. (Artemis Fowl Ser.). 112p. (gr. 5 up). pap. 9.99 (*978-0-7868-4882-9(0)) Miramax Bks.

—Artemis Fowl Encuentro en el Artico: Encuentro en el Artico. 2005. (SPA., Illus.). 320p. (J). pap. 13.95 (978-0-307-34310-9(3) , Montena) Random House Mondadori ESP. *Dist:* Random Hse., Inc.

—The Artemis Fowl Files. 2004. (Artemis Fowl Ser.). (Illus.). 208p. (J). (gr. 7-17). 12.95 (978-0-7868-5639-8(4)) Hyperion Bks. for Children.

—El Cubo B. 2005. (Artemis Fowl Ser.: No. 3). (SPA., Illus.). 352p. (J). pap. 13.95 (978-0-307-34311-6(1) , Montena) Random House Mondadori ESP. *Dist:* Random Hse., Inc.

—The Eternity Code. (Artemis Fowl Ser.: Bk. 3). 2005. 446p. (YA). (gr. 5-17). mass mkt. 5.99 (978-0-7868-5628-2(9)); 2003. 320p. (ps-17). 16.95 (978-0-7868-1914-0(6)) Hyperion Bks. for Children.

—The Lost Colony. 2006. (Artemis Fowl Ser.: Bk. 5). 400p. (J). (gr. 5-17). 16.95 (978-0-7868-4956-7(8)) Miramax Bks.

Colfer, Eoin. The Opal Deception. 2005. (Artemis Fowl Ser.: Bk. 4). 352p. (gr. 5-17). 16.95 (978-0-7868-5289-5(5)) Hyperion Bks. for Children.

—The Opal Deception. (Artemis Fowl Ser.). 2007. 528p. (gr. 5 up). pap. 5.99 (*978-1-4231-0399-8(8)); 2005. (J). pap. 7.99 (978-0-7868-3640-6(7)); 2006. 352p. (J). (gr. 5-17). reprint ed. pap. 7.99 (978-0-7868-5290-1(9)) Miramax Bks.

—The Opal Deception. l.t. ed. 2005. (Artemis Fowl Ser.: Bk. 4). 421p. (J). 23.95 (978-0-7862-7754-4(8) , Large Print Pr.) Thorndike Pr.

Corbett, Terry. Nicholas & the Elves. Corbett, Mary Lark, illus. 1999. 20p. (Orig.). (J). pap. 5.99 (978-1-929731-03-9(5)) Rowfant Pr.

Corby, Linda. The girl who believed in Fairies. 2005. 36p. (J). pap. 7.25 (978-1-4116-5135-7(9)) Lulu.com.

Cosgrove, Stephen. Gnome from Nome. James, Robin, illus. 2003. (Serendipity Bks.). 32p. (J). (gr. k-3). pap. 4.99 (978-0-8431-0585-8(2) , Price Stern Sloan) Penguin Group (USA) Inc.

—Gnome from Nome. 2003. (gr. k-3). lib. bdg. 13.00 (978-0-613-70763-3(X)) Tandem Library Bks.

Coville, Bruce. The Weeping Werewolf. Coville, Katherine, illus. (Moongobble & Me Ser.). 80p. (J). (gr. 1-4). 2006. pap. 3.99 (978-0-689-85759-1(4) , Aladdin); 2004. 15.99 (978-0-689-85756-0(X)) Simon & Schuster Children's Publishing.

Cowen-Fletcher, Jane. Nell's Elf. Cowen-Fletcher, Jane, illus. 2006. (Illus.). 32p. (J). (ps-2). 14.99 (978-0-7636-2391-3(1)) Candlewick Pr.

Cowley, Joy. The Wishing of Biddy Malone. Denise, Christopher, illus. 2006. 40p. (J). reprint ed. pap. 6.99 (978-0-14-240589-5(2) , Puffin) Penguin Group (USA) Inc.

Cox, Karen. Gwyneira, the Crystal Fairy. 2005. 35p. 14.84 (978-1-4116-4777-0(7)) Lulu.com.

Crew, Gary. The End of the Line. Rogers, Gregory, illus. 2008. 80p. (J). pap. (*978-1-59889-915-3(5)); (YA). (gr. 5-9). lib. bdg. 16.95 (*978-1-59889-859-0(0)) Stone Arch Bks.

Cross, Frances. Mystery of the Green Elephant. 2007. (Blobber Trilogy Ser.). 96p. pap. 7.95 (*978-1-84167-559-6(8)) Ransom Publishing Ltd. GBR. *Dist:* International Publishers Marketing.

Curry, Don, ed. Gingerbread Man. 2006. (My Turn! Your Turn! Ser.). 24p. (J). pap. 3.99 (978-0-696-22853-7(X)) Meredith Bks.

Curtis, Christopher Paul. Mr. Chickee's Messy Mission. 2008. 240p. (J). (gr. 4-7). 6.50 (*978-0-440-22922-3(7) , Yearling) Random Hse. Children's Bks.

Dakin, Margaret. Secrets of the Flower Fairies. 2004. (Fairy Dust Tales: Bk. 1). (Illus.). 77p. (J). (gr. 1-6). pap. 16.95 (978-1-930002-60-9(2)) I & L Publishing.

Dale, Penny. Princess, Princess. Dale, Penny, illus. (Illus.). 32p. (J). (ps-1). 2007. pap. 4.99 (*978-0-7636-3565-7(0)); 2003. 14.99 (978-0-7636-2212-1(5)) Candlewick Pr.

Dale, Penny & Platt, Richard. Pirate Diary. Ridell, Chris, illus. 2003. 128p. (J). (gr. 4). pap. 6.99 (978-0-7636-2169-8(2)) Candlewick Pr.

Dalmatian Press Staff. Disney Seven Dwarfs. 2006. 16p. (J). pap. 3.99 (978-1-4037-2338-3(9)) Dalmatian Pr.

Dann, Penny. The Secret Fairy Boutique. Dann, Penny, illus. 2000. (Secret Fairy Ser.). (Illus.). 16p. (J). (ps-3). pap. 14.95 (978-0-531-30308-5(X) , Orchard Bks.) Scholastic, Inc.

Datlow, Ellen & Windling, Terri, eds. The Faery Reel: Tales from the Twilight Realm. 2006. (Illus.). 544p. (YA). (gr. 7). pap. 9.99 (978-0-14-240406-5(3) , Puffin) Penguin Group (USA) Inc.

d'Aulaire, Edgar & d'Aulaire, Ingri. The Terrible Troll-Bird. 2007. (Illus.). 48p. (J). (ps-3). 15.95 (*978-1-59017-252-0(3) , NYR Children's Collection) New York Review of Bks., Inc., The.

Davidson, Susanna. Fairyland. Ligi, Raffaella, illus. 2007. (See Inside Board Bks). 16p. (J). bds. 12.99 (978-0-7945-1570-6(3) , Usborne) EDC Publishing.

Davis, Elena. Where Do the Balloons Go? Jurinich, Anna, illus. 2004. 32p. (ps-3). 16.95 (978-0-9714372-3-4(8)) National Bk. Network.

Day, Nancy Raines. Fairy Childs Busy Week. 2006. (978-0-06-052751-8(X)); lib. bdg. (978-0-06-052752-5(8)) HarperCollins Canada, Ltd.

de Brun, Kieran Christopher. The Talking Llama: la Llama Que Habla. de Brun, Brendan Joseph, illus. 2005. (J). pap. 16.00 (978-0-8059-6910-8(1)) Dorrance Publishing Co., Inc.

De Lint, Charles. The Blue Girl. (YA). (gr. 7). 2004. 368p. 17.99 (978-0-670-05924-9(2) , Viking Juvenile); 2006. 384p. reprint ed. pap. 7.99 (978-0-14-240545-1(0) , Puffin) Penguin Group (USA) Inc.

De Mari, Silvana. The Last Dragon. Whiteside, Shaun, tr. from ITA. 2006. (Illus.). 368p. (gr. 5 up). 16.95 (978-0-7868-3636-9(9)) Miramax Bks.

DeGoede, Jeannette. Tulip Fairy's Holiday. 2006. (J). 5.00 (978-0-9778374-0-3(8)) grafixCORP.

Demeritt, Mary Anne. The Twilight Ride of the Pink Fairy. Daniel, Ellen, illus. 2006. (J). 17.95 (*978-1-58597-410-8(2)) Leathers Publishing.

Demers, Dominique. Old Thomas & the Little Fairy. ed. 2004. (Illus.). (J). (ps up). spiral bd. (978-0-616-07229-5(5)) Canadian National Institute for the Blind/Institut National Canadien pour les Aveugles.

Dergachov, Oleg. The Yellow Elves. Andryczyk, Mark, tr. from UKR. 2004. (Illus.). 14p. (J). pap. (*978-0-9735003-0-1(1)) StudioNib Publishing.

DiCerto, Joseph. The Wall People. 2006. 19.95 (978-1-58752-112-6(1)) Timberwolf Pr., Inc.

Disney Press Staff. In the Realm of the Never Fairies: The Secret World of Pixie Hollow. 2006. 144p. (gr. 2-17). 18.99 (978-0-7868-4765-5(4)) Disney Pr.

—Make Your Own Fairies: Storybook with Shrinkydinks Charms. Disney Storybook Artists Staff, illus. 2006. 12p. (gr. 1-17). 18.99 (978-1-4231-0059-1(X)) Disney Pr.

DiTerlizzi, Tony & Black, Holly. Arthur Spiderwick's Field Guide to the Fantastical World Around You. DiTerlizzi, Tony, illus. 2005. (Spiderwick Chronicles). (Illus.). 142p. (J). 24.95 (978-0-689-85941-0(4)) Simon & Schuster Children's Publishing.

—The Field Guide. DiTerlizzi, Tony, illus. (Spiderwick Chronicles: Bk. 1). 128p. (J). 2003. (Illus.). 10.99 (978-0-689-85936-6(8) , 53409542); 2008. 10.99 (*978-1-4169-5017-2(6)) Simon & Schuster Children's Publishing.

—The Field Guide. l.t. ed. 2006. (Spiderwick Chronicles: Bk. 1). 120p. (J). 23.95 (978-0-7862-8284-5(3)) Thorndike Pr.

—The Ironwood Tree. movie tie-in ed. 2008. (Spiderwick Chronicles: Bk. 4). 128p. (J). 10.99 (*978-1-4169-5020-2(6)) Simon & Schuster Children's Publishing.

—The Ironwood Tree. l.t. ed. 2006. (Spiderwick Chronicles: Bk. 4). 90p. (YA). (gr. 2 up). 23.95 (978-0-7862-8583-9(4)) Thorndike Pr.

—The Seeing Stone. DiTerlizzi, Tony, illus. movie tie-in ed. (Spiderwick Chronicles: Bk. 2). 128p. (J). 2008. 10.99 (*978-1-4169-5018-9(4)); Bk. 2. 2003. (Illus.). 10.99 (978-0-689-85937-3(6) , 53409541) Simon & Schuster Children's Publishing.

—The Seeing Stone. l.t. ed. 2006. (Spiderwick Chronicles: No. 2). (YA). 23.95 (978-0-7862-8581-5(8)) Thorndike Pr.

—The Wrath of Mulgarath. DiTerlizzi, Tony, illus. movie tie-in ed. 2008. (Spiderwick Chronicles: Bk. 5). 160p. (J). (gr. 2 up). 10.99 (*978-1-4169-5021-9(4)) Simon & Schuster Children's Publishing.

—The Wrath of Mulgarath. l.t. ed. 2006. (Spiderwick Chronicles: Bk. 5). 183p. (YA). 23.95 (978-0-7862-8579-2(6)) Thorndike Pr.

DK Publishing. Playful Little Fairy: Plush Board Book. 2008. 10p. (J). bds. 8.99 (*978-0-7566-3444-5(X)) Dorling Kindersley Publishing, Inc.

Dolan, Penny. Mary & the Fairy. Allwright, Deborah, illus. 2004. (Read-It! Readers Ser.). 32p. (C). (gr. k-3). 18.60 (978-1-4048-0066-3(2)) Picture Window Bks.

Donnell, Frances. Goblins Will Be Seen: When it's time for Halloween. Hebert, Catherine, ed. Merchant, Donna, illus. 2005. 38p. (J). per. 16.95 incl. audio compact disk (978-0-9770893-0-7(4)) 2 Donn Bks.

Down, Reg. The Magic Knot: And other Tangles. 2007. (Illus.). 100p. (J). pap. 14.95 (*978-0-9794452-0-0(5)) Lightly Pr.

Dozier, Kim. The Confused Tooth Fairy. Dozier, Ashlyn & Dozier, Makenna Joy, illus. 2005. (ENG.). 28p. (J). 10.00 (978-0-9745839-3-8(6) , Fun to Read Bks. with Royally Good Morals) MKADesigns.

Drescher, Daniela. In the Land of Fairies. 2004. (Illus.). 24p. (J). 16.99 (978-0-86315-450-8(6)) Floris Bks. GBR. *Dist:* SteinerBooks, Inc.

Driscoll, Laura. Beck & the Great Berry Battle. Clarke, Judith, illus. 2006. (Stepping Stone Bks.). 128p. (J). (gr. 2-4). 5.99 (978-0-7364-2373-1(7) , RH/Disney) Random Hse. Children's Bks.

—Vidia & the Fairy Crown. Clarke, Judith, illus. 2006. (Stepping Stone Bks.). 128p. (J). (gr. 2-4). 5.99 (978-0-7364-2372-4(9) , RH/Disney) Random Hse. Children's Bks.

Duffy, Carol Ann. The Tear Thief. Ceccoli, Nicoletta, illus. 2007. 32p. (J). (ps-5). 16.99 (*978-1-84686-045-4(8)) Barefoot Bks., Inc.

Dunkle, Clare B. Close Kin. Simonsen, Reka, ed. 2nd rev. ed. 2004. (Hollow Kingdom Trilogy Ser.: Bk. II). (Illus.). 224p. (YA). 16.95 (978-0-8050-7497-0(X) , Holt, Henry & Co. Bks. For Young Readers) Holt, Henry & Co.

Durant, Alan. Dear Tooth Fairy. Cabban, Vanessa, illus. 32p. (J). (ps-2). 2004. 14.99 (978-0-7636-2175-9(7)); 2006. 6.99 (978-0-7636-2991-5(X)) Candlewick Pr.

Eberhard, Phyllis Lunde Brees. Little Miss Neat-As-A-Pin. Jacoby, Nickolina Dye, illus. 2007. (J). (*978-0-9722741-7-3(0)) Publishing Factory, The.

Eberhart, Nancy. Anabeele's Wish. 2007. (J). pap. 9.99 (*978-1-59879-370-3(5)) Lifevest Publishing, Inc.

—Anabelle's Wish. 2007. (J). per. 13.99 (*978-1-59879-371-0(3)) Lifevest Publishing, Inc.

Edgson, Alison, et al, illus. The Elves & the Shoemaker. 2007. 24p. pap. 5.99 (*978-1-84643-076-3(3)) Child's Play International Ltd. GBR. *Dist:* Child's Play-International.

Edwards. Dear Tooth Fairy. 2000. mass mkt. 5.95 (978-0-06-443877-3(5)) HarperCollins Pubs.

Eliot, Ethel Cook. The Little House in the Fairy Wood. 2006. 40.99 (*978-1-4280-0247-0(2)); pap. 34.99 (*978-1-4280-0243-2(X)) IndyPublish.com.

—The Little House in the Fairy Wood. 2004. reprint ed. pap. 1.99 (978-1-4192-7023-9(0)) Kessinger Publishing, LLC.

Ellerton, Sarah. Inverloch, Vol. 1. 2006. (Illus.). 160p. pap. 14.99 (978-1-933164-13-7(1)) Seven Seas Entertainment, LLC.

Ellsworth, Nick. Twinkle the Tooth Fairy. White, Michelle, illus. Date not set. 32p. (J). 5.98 (978-0-7525-7628-2(3)) Parragon, Inc.

Elves & the Shoemaker. Date not set. (J). 4.99 (978-0-7214-5407-8(0)) Nickel Pr.

Engelbrecht, Carla. Professor Dalrymple's Patented Fairy Catching System. 2007. 48p. pap. 6.95 (978-0-7624-2918-9(6) , Running Pr. Minature Editions) Running Pr. Bk. Pubs.

England, Brooke. Guardian Fairies. 2006. 17p. 12.00 (978-1-4116-7923-8(7)) Lulu.com.

Eubank, Patti Reeder, illus. The Princess & the Snarls. 2006. 32p. (J). (ps). 16.95 (978-0-8249-5536-6(6) , Ideals Children's Bks.) Ideals Pubns.

Fairies are Fun. 2002. (Little Friends Ser.). 32p. (J). 2.98 (978-1-84273-423-0(7) , Exclusive Editions) Parragon, Inc.

Fairy Fern. 2002. (Dolly Board Book Ser.). bds. 4.98 (978-0-7525-8279-5(8)) Parragon, Inc.

Fairy Tale- Cinderella. 2005. (J). bds. (978-1-4194-0039-1(8)) Paradise Pr., Inc.

Fairy tales - Cinderella. 2005. (J). bds. (978-1-4194-0100-8(9)) Paradise Pr., Inc.

Fairy talse s/s - CInderella. 2005. (J). bds. (978-1-4194-0066-7(5)) Paradise Pr., Inc.

The Fairy Who Lost His Wings. 2004. (J). 10.00 (*978-0-9760076-0-9(6)) Juniper Berry Pr.

Farmer, Nancy. The Land of the Silver Apples. Sardinha, Rick, illus. 2007. 512p. (J). (gr. 5-9). 18.99 (*978-1-4169-0735-0(1) , Atheneum/Richard Jackson Bks.) Simon & Schuster Children's Publishing.

Farmer, Nancy. The Sea of Trolls. 2006. 480p. (J). (gr. 5-9). reprint ed. pap. 9.99 (978-0-689-86746-0(8) , Simon Pulse) Simon & Schuster Children's Publishing.

Farrow, Edward Georg. The Mysterious Shin Shira. 2006. 40.99 (*978-1-4280-1467-1(5)); pap. 34.99 (*978-1-4280-1471-8(3)) IndyPublish.com.

The Fearful Fairy. ed. 2007. (Illus.). 40p. (J). 16.95 (*978-0-9793823-0-7(0)) StonesThrow Publishing LLC.

Fields, Frever. Frumpy McDoogle: And the Legend of the Ruby Toad. 2003. 40p. 16.95 (978-0-9632675-1-1(5)) Kimberlite Publishing Co.

Finsterbusch, Monika. Princess Lillifee's Secret. 2006. 28p. (J). (ps-3). 12.95 (978-0-8109-5724-4(8) , Abrams Bks. for Young Readers) Abrams, Harry N. , Inc.

Fisher, Catherine. Lammas Field. 2003. 240p. pap. (978-0-340-73699-9(2) , Hodder Children's Books) Hodder Children's Division.

Fitzgerald, Gyleen Xavier. The Dream: A Magical Journey in Colourful Stitches. 2006. (Illus.). 96p. (J). 29.95 (978-0-9768215-1-9(6)) FPI Publishing.

Forrester, Emma. Uncle Arthur's Art Studio. Nunn, Paul E., illus. 2008. (Spiderwick Chronicles). 48p. (J). 10.99 (*978-1-4169-4955-8(0) , Simon Scribbles) Simon & Schuster Children's Publishing.

Fox, Mem. Fairy, Fairy Quite Contrary. Swearingen, Greg, illus. 2005. (J). (978-0-15-202260-0(0)) Holt, Rinehart & Winston.

Francis, Marnie, et al. Green Isles of the Ocean. Evans, Fran et al, illus. 2005. 32p. pap. 12.95 (978-1-84323-421-0(1)) Beekman Bks., Inc.

Freeman, Faith L. Beyond the Magic Waterfall. 2006. 79p. pap. 26.38 (978-1-4116-8202-3(5)) Lulu.com.

Freeman, R. Gregory. A Carpenter¿s Tale: The Mystery of Kidron Valley. 2006. (Illus.). 44p. (J). per. 10.95 (978-1-60002-118-3(2) , 3901, Airleaf Publishing) Airleaf Publishing & Bookselling.

French, Vivian. Princess Emily & the Substitute Fairy. Gibb, Sarah, illus. 2007. (Tiara Club Ser.: No. 6). 80p. (J). pap. 3.99 (***978-0-06-112436-5(2)*** , Harper Trophy) HarperCollins Pubs.

Gabriel Jr., Carl L. Jester's Quest: Book One. 2007. (ENG.). 52p. per. 12.95 (***978-1-4241-7364-8(7))*** PublishAmerica, Inc.

Gainsley, Margaret. The Faerie of Kalla. 2007. (J). per. 9.99 (***978-1-59886-764-0(4))*** Tate Publishing & Enterprises, L.L.C.

Gardner, Sally. I, Coriander. 2007. 288p. (J). (gr. 5 up). pap. 6.99 (978-0-14-240763-9(1) , Puffin) Penguin Group (USA) Inc.

Gaudissart, Martine. Kanyon & the Rainbow Stone. Gaudissart, Martine, illus. 2000. (Illus.). 64p. (J). (gr. k-3). 17.95 (978-0-9677547-0-3(4)) Angie Blue Bks., LLC.

Gay, Marie-Louise. Estela, Hada del Bosque. 2002. (SPA.). 36p. (J). pap. (978-980-257-272-4(1)) Ekare, Ediciones.

—Stella, Fairy of the Forest. 2006. (Stella Ser.). (Illus.). 32p. (J). 7.95 (978-0-88899-710-4(8)) Groundwood Bks. CAN. *Dist:* Perseus Distribution.

Gelsey, James. Gruesome Goblin. del Sur, Duendes, illus. 2004. (Scooby-Doo Mysteries Ser.: No. 29). 64p. (J). pap. 3.99 (978-0-439-42076-1(8) , Scholastic Paperbacks) Scholastic, Inc.

Giles, Chauncey. The Magic Spectacles: A Fairy Story. 2004. reprint ed. pap. 22.95 (978-0-7661-8731-3(4)) Kessinger Publishing, LLC.

Gili, Phillida. Cinderella: A Pop-up Book. Gili, Phillida, illus. 2007. (Illus.). 12p. (J). 25.00 (***978-1-4223-9031-3(4))*** DIANE Publishing Co.

Gliori, Debi. Pure Dead Frozen. 2007. (J). (gr. 5). 320p. 15.99 (***978-0-375-83317-5(X));*** 304p. lib. bdg. 18.99 (***978-0-375-93317-2(4))*** Random Hse. Children's Bks. (Knopf Bks. for Young Readers).

Goldberg, Dennis. Double Bubble Trouble. 2007. (J). 14.95 (***978-1-933769-19-6(X))*** Level 4 Press, Inc.

Golden Bks Staff. Enchanted. Akyaka, Sarl, illus. 2007. 48p. (J). (ps-2). pap. 6.99 (***978-0-7364-2482-0(2)*** , Bolder Bks.) Random Hse. Children's Bks.

Golden Books Staff. Barbie Fairytopia: Mermaidia Board Book. 2007. 24p. (J). (gr. k-k). bds. 4.99 (978-0-375-83851-4(1) , Golden Bks.) Random Hse. Children's Bks.

—Fairy Dance. 2007. (Deluxe Coloring Book Ser.). (Illus.). 96p. (J). (ps-2). 3.99 (978-0-375-83973-3(9) , Golden Bks.) Random Hse. Children's Bks.

Golden Books Staff & Man-Kong, Mary. Mermaidia: A Storybook. 2006. (Barbie's Fairytopia Ser.). (Illus.). 16p. (J). (gr. k-k). pap., pap. 3.99 (978-0-375-87492-5(5) , Golden Bks.) Random Hse. Children's Bks.

Goldstone, Bruce & Poortvliet, Rien. A Gnome's Christmas. 2004. (Illus.). 48p. 14.95 (978-0-8109-5017-7(0)) Abrams, Harry N. , Inc.

Gomez, Rebecca. Graduation Day at Elf School. 2005. 40.00 (***978-1-4108-4208-4(8))*** Benchmark Education Co.

Graham, Bob. Jethro Byrd, Fairy Child. Graham, Bob, illus. (Illus.). 32p. (J). (ps-2). 2002. 15.99 (978-0-7636-1772-1(5)); 2005. reprint ed. pap. 6.99 (978-0-7636-2697-6(X)) Candlewick Pr.

—Jethro Byrd, Fairy Child. Graham, Bob, illus. 2002. (Illus.). 32p. (J). (978-0-7445-8863-7(4)) Walker & Co.

Grambling, Lois G. This Whole Tooth Fairy Thing's Nothing but a Big Rip-off! Payne, Thomas, illus. 2002. 32p. (J). (gr. k-3). 15.95 (978-0-7614-5104-4(8) , Cavendish Children's Bks.) Cavendish, Marshall Corp.

Grimm, Jacob W. Cinderella/Cenicienta. 2004. (Illus.). (J). (978-1-933530-13-0(8)) Bingo Bks., Inc.

—Cinderella/Cenicienta Take Home Version. 2004. (Illus.). (J). cd-rom (978-1-933530-39-0(1)) Bingo Bks., Inc.

Grimm, Wilhelm K., et al. Elves & Shoemaker. 2004. 48p. (J). (gr. 2 up). pap. 5.95 (978-0-7945-0758-9(1) , Usborne) EDC Publishing.

Gunzi, Christina. Pretty in Pink: My Day. 2007. (Illus.). 10p. (J). bds. 6.95 (***978-1-59223-755-5(X)*** , Silver Dolphin Bks.) Advantage Pubs. Group.

—Pretty in Pink: My Things. 2007. (Illus.). 10p. (J). bds. 6.95 (***978-1-59223-756-2(8)*** , Silver Dolphin Bks.) Advantage Pubs. Group.

Hague, Kathleen. Good Night, Fairies. Hague, Michael, illus. 2002. 40p. (J). (ps-2). 16.99 (978-1-58717-134-5(1) , SeaStar Bks.) Chronicle Bks. LLC.

—Good Night Fairies. Hague, Michael, illus. 2006. 40p. (J). pap. 6.95 (978-0-8118-5762-8(X)) Chronicle Bks. LLC.

Hague, Michael. The Book of Fairies. Hague, Michael, illus. 2006. 128p. (J). pap. 9.99 (978-0-06-089187-9(4) , Harper Trophy) HarperCollins Pubs.

Hahn, Mary Downing. Witch Catcher. 2006. 240p. (J). (gr. 4-6). 16.00 (978-0-618-50457-2(5) , Clarion Bks.) Houghton Mifflin Co. Trade & Reference Div.

Halfmann, Janet. Ogre Hunter No. 2: With Stencils. Karl, Linda, illus. 2004. (Shrek 2 Ser.). 32p. (J). act. bk. ed. 3.99 (978-0-439-57633-8(4)) Scholastic, Inc.

Hall, Kirsten. Revamp Your Room. 2005. (Illus.). 48p. pap. (***978-0-439-80296-3(2))*** Scholastic, Inc.

Hall, Kirsten. The Tooth Fairy. 2004. (My First Reader Ser.). (Illus.). 31p. (J). (gr. k-1). pap. 3.95 (978-0-516-24640-6(2) , Children's Pr.) Scholastic Library Publishing.

Hamilton, C. After Ever Happily. 2006. 80p. pap. 14.95 (978-1-4241-3190-7(1)) PublishAmerica, Inc.

Hamilton, Tisha, adapted by. Five Times the Trouble. 2006. (Trollz Ser.). (Illus.). 32p. (J). (***978-1-4156-8962-2(8))*** Scholastic, Inc.

Hanken, Sandra. Sky Castle. Bergsma, Jody Lynn, illus. 1998. 32p. (ps-3). 15.95 (978-0-935699-14-2(7)) Illumination Arts Publishing Co., Inc.

Hanson-Roberts, Mary, illus. Cinderella: A Tale of Kindness. 2006. (J). 6.99 (978-1-59939-001-7(9) , Reader's Digest Young Families, Inc.) Reader's Digest Children's Publishing, Inc.

Hargreaves, Roger. Little Miss Naughty & the Good Fairy. 2007. 32p. (J). pap. 3.99 (978-0-8431-2122-3(X) , Price Stern Sloan) Penguin Group (USA) Inc.

Hayes, Drew & Davidsen, Keith. Poison Elves Ventures 1: Hyena. 2006. (Illus.). 128p. pap. 14.95 (978-1-57989-084-1(9)) Diamond Bk. Distributors.

Hays, Helen Ashe. The Adventures of Prince Lazybones: And Other Stories. 2007. 152p. pap. 11.99 (***978-1-4264-8474-2(7));*** 168p. pap. 14.99 (***978-1-4264-8532-9(8))*** BiblioBazaar.

Hearn, Julie. The Minister's Daughter. 2006. 272p. (YA). pap. 7.99 (978-0-689-87691-2(2) , Simon Pulse) Simon & Schuster Children's Publishing.

Hearn, Julie & Frost, Michael. The Minister's Daughter. 2005. 272p. (YA). (gr. 7 up). 17.99 (978-0-689-87690-5(4) , Atheneum) Simon & Schuster Children's Publishing.

Hearson, Ruth. Cinnamon's Fairy Sleepover. Hearson, Ruth, illus. 2006. (Illus.). 14p. (J). 5.99 (978-1-4169-1401-3(3) , Little Simon) Simon & Schuster Children's Publishing.

—Daisy's Fairy Flowers. Hearson, Ruth, illus. abr. ed. 2006. (Flips & Flaps Book Ser.). (Illus.). 14p. (J). 5.99 (978-1-4169-1221-7(5) , Little Simon) Simon & Schuster Children's Publishing.

Helgerson, Joseph. Horns & Wrinkles. Ceccoli, Nicoletta, illus. 2006. 368p. (J). (gr. 4-6). 16.00 (978-0-618-61679-4(9)) Houghton Mifflin Co.

Heller, Sarah & Reader's Digest Staff. Disney Tinker Bell Music Player & Storybook. 2008. (RD Innovative Book & Player Format Ser.). 36p. (J). 24.99 (***978-0-7944-1300-2(5))*** Reader's Digest Assn., Inc., The.

Helliwell, Sheila. Hoonraki Moon: The Murphy Stories. 2006. (J). pap. 9.00 (978-0-8059-7027-2(4)) Dorrance Publishing Co., Inc.

Henkel, Donald G. Painted Treasures or the Original 288 Tree Gnomes. Henkel, D. B., VIII, illus. 2006. (J). mass mkt. 20.50 (978-0-9673504-1-7(7)) Quillpen.

Herman, Gail. Dulcie's Taste of Magic. Clarke, Judith et al, illus. 2008. 128p. (J). (gr. 1-5). 5.99 (***978-0-7364-2454-7(7))*** Random Hse., Inc.

—Fira & the Full Moon. Clarke, Judith, illus. 2006. (Stepping Stone Bks.). 128p. (J). (gr. 1-5). 5.99 (978-0-7364-2417-2(2) , RH/Disney) Random Hse. Children's Bks.

Herman, Gail. Silvermist & the Ladybug Curse. 2008. (Stepping Stone Book(TM) Ser.). 128p. (J). (gr. 1-5). 5.99 (***978-0-7364-2508-7(X)*** , RH/Disney) Random Hse. Children's Bks.

Hinman, Bobbie. The Knot Fairy. 2007. 32p. 15.95 (***978-0-9786791-0-1(5))*** Hinman, Bobbie E. Inc.

Hirt, Kelly K. Lucy & the Leprechaun Seekers. Laurie, Kane A., illus. 2001. (J). (gr. k-4). pap. 14.95 (978-0-9708027-0-5(6) , 14009) Passion Works, LLC.

Hoel, Charlotte. The Magical Mischief Maker. 2004. (J). spiral bd. (978-0-9754004-0-1(1)) Magical Mischief Maker.

Holabird, Katharine. The Rose Fairy Princess. Craig, Helen, illus. 2006. (Angelina Ballerina Ser.). 24p. (J). (ps-1). 3.99 (978-0-448-44465-9(8) , Grosset & Dunlap) Penguin Group (USA) Inc.

Hundal, Nancy. Twilight Fairies. Kilby, Don, illus. 2002. 32p. (J). (gr. k-3). (978-1-55041-645-9(6)) Fitzhenry & Whiteside, Ltd.

—Twilight Fairies. Kilby, Don, illus. 2006. 32p. pap. 7.95 (978-1-55041-961-0(7)) Fitzhenry & Whiteside, Ltd. CAN. *Dist:* F & W Pubns., Inc.

Hurston, Nancy. The Enchanted Pixie Gardens: Hide & Seek. 2007. 32p. per. 13.99 (***978-1-59886-807-4(1))*** Tate Publishing & Enterprises, L.L.C.

Hutchison, Gary. The Ambassador & the Touchperson. 2nd ed. 2005. (Little People of the Ozark Mountains Ser.: 3). pap. 10.99 (***978-1-885631-95-4(2))*** Hutchison, G.F. Pr.

—Man of the Clan. 2nd ed. 2005. (Little People of the Ozark Mountains Ser.: 3). pap. 10.99 (***978-1-885631-97-8(9))*** Hutchison, G.F. Pr.

—Ring of the Farjumpers. 2nd ed. 2005. (Little People of the Ozark Mountains Ser.: 1). pap. 10.99 (***978-1-885631-94-7(4))*** Hutchison, G.F. Pr.

—Twiggs & Cinnamon. 2nd ed. 2005. (Little People of the Ozark Mountains Ser.). pap. 10.95 (***978-1-885631-96-1(0))*** Hutchison, G.F. Pr.

Hyman, Trina Schart, illus. Herschel & the Hanukkah Goblins. (Caldecott Honor Book Ser.). 32p. (gr. k-3). 6.95 (978-0-8234-1131-3(1)) Holiday Hse., Inc.

Ingelow, Jean. Mopsa the Fairy. 2004. reprint ed. pap. 19.95 (978-1-4191-3510-1(4)); pap. 1.99 (978-1-4192-3510-8(9)) Kessinger Publishing, LLC.

Ivanov, Aleksey & Ivanov, Olga, illus. The Tall Book of Fairies. 2007. 80p. (J). (ps-2). 6.99 (***978-0-06-085051-7(5)*** , Harper Festival) HarperCollins Pubs.

Jackson, Shirley. Sleeping Beauty & Other Fairy Sticker Stories. Prole, Helen, illus. 2004. 80p. (J). pap. 8.99 (978-1-4052-1408-7(2)) Egmont Bks., Ltd. GBR. *Dist:* Independent Pubs. Group.

Jacobsen, Annie. Ivar, the Short, but Brave Viking. Hanson, Susan Jo, illus. 2007. (J). lib. bdg. 16.95 (***978-0-9778276-1-9(5))*** Pickled Herring Pr.

Jeffers, Susan. The Nutcracker. Jeffers, Susan, illus. 2007. 40p. (J). (ps-3). lib. bdg. 17.89 (***978-0-06-074387-1(5));*** (Illus.). 16.99 (***978-0-06-074386-4(7))*** HarperCollins Pubs.

A Job for Little Elf. 2006. (J). (***978-1-932570-72-4(1))*** Literacy Footprints Inc.

Johnson, Lisa. All Hallows' Eve: The Story of the Halloween Fairy. Johnson, Tucker, illus. l.t. ed. 2005. 32p. (J). 12.95 (978-0-9773096-0-3(6)) Positive Spin Pr.

Johnson, Lisa Sferlazza. All Hallows Eve: The Story of the Halloween Fairy. Johnson, Tucker, illus. 2006. 32p. (J). 15.95 (978-0-9773096-1-0(4)) Positive Spin Pr.

Johnson, Lisa Sferlazza. Winter's Eve: Love & Lights. Johnson, Tucker, illus. 2007. 32p. (J). (ps-k). 15.95 (***978-0-9773096-3-4(0))*** Positive Spin Pr.

Johnson, Margaret. Seven Magical Tooth Fairies. 2005. (ENG.). 88p. per. 9.95 (***978-0-595-37420-5(4))*** iUniverse, Inc.

Johnson, Paul Brett, tr. & illus. Little Bunny Foo Foo: Told & Sung by the Good Fairy. Johnson, Paul Brett, illus. 2004. 32p. (J). pap. 15.95 (978-0-439-37301-2(8)) Scholastic, Inc.

Jones, Christianne C. Rapunzel. Muehlenhardt, Amy Bailey, illus. 2006. (Read-It! Readers en Espanol Ser.).Tr. of Rapunzel. (SPA.). 32p. (J). (ps-3). 19.95 (978-1-4048-1636-7(4)) Picture Window Bks.

Jones, Frewin. The Faerie Path. 2008. (Faerie Path Ser.: Bk. 1). 336p. (J). pap. 8.99 (***978-0-06-087104-8(0)*** , Eos) HarperCollins Pubs.

—The Lost Queen. 2007. (Faerie Path Ser.: Bk. 2). 352p. (J). lib. bdg. 17.89 (***978-0-06-087106-2(7));*** 335p. (YA). (gr. 7 up). 16.99 (***978-0-06-087105-5(9))*** HarperCollins Pubs. (Eos).

—The Sorcerer King. 2008. (Faerie Path Ser.: Bk. 3). 336p. (J). 16.99 (***978-0-06-087108-6(3));*** lib. bdg. 17.89 (***978-0-06-087109-3(1))*** HarperCollins Pubs. (Eos).

Jones, Heulwen. O'Grady's Well. 2005. (Illus.). 96p. pap. (***978-1-84401-578-8(5))*** Athena Pr.

Jones, Margaret. Nat. 2004. (Illus.). 111p. pap. 13.95 (978-1-84323-327-5(4)) Beekman Bks., Inc.

Jones, Miranda. Little Genie: A Puff of Pink. Calver, David, tr. Calver, David, illus. 2004. 128p. (gr. 1-3). lib. bdg. 10.99 (978-0-385-90188-8(7) , Delacorte Bks. for Young Readers) Random Hse. Children's Bks.

—Little Genie No. 4: Castle Magic. Calver, David, illus. 2004. 144p. (gr. 1-3). 8.95 (978-0-385-73165-2(5) , Delacorte Bks. for Young Readers) Random Hse. Children's Bks.

Joy, Flora. The Pride Piper. Harroll, Pat, illus. 1999. 48p. (J). 7.00 (978-1-884624-10-0(3)) Storytelling World Pr.

Joyce, Robert Dwyer. The Leaping Leprechaun. Rutherford, Peter, illus. 2001. 10p. pap. 8.95 (978-1-56554-915-9(5)) Pelican Publishing Co., Inc.

Kane, Tracy. Fairy Boat. Kane, Tracy, illus. 2nd ed. 2002. (Fairy Houses Ser.). (Illus.). 40p. (J). act. bk. ed. 15.95 net. (978-0-9708104-7-2(4)) Light-Beams Publishing.

—Fairy Flight. Kane, Tracy, illus. l.t. ed. 2003. (Fairy Houses Ser.). (Illus.). 40p. (J). (gr. k-3). 15.95 (978-0-9708104-2-7(3)) Light-Beams Publishing.

Katz, Alan & Slack, Michael. The Flim-Flam Fairies. 2008. (Illus.). 32p. (J). 14.95 (***978-0-7624-2996-7(8)*** , Running Pr. Kids) Running Pr. Bk. Pubs.

Kavanagh, Herminie Templeton. Darby O'Gill. rev. ed. 2006. 224p. 5.99 (978-0-7653-5462-4(4) , Tor Bks.) Doherty, Tom Assocs., LLC.

Keegan, Shannon. Legend of the Sea Fairies. 2006. (J). per. 14.99 (978-0-9773433-0-0(8)) Bixie Gate Publishing.

Keen, Donna. Flossy, a Tooth Fairy Tale: Including Red Velvet Bag for Tooth. Keen, Donna, illus. 2nd ed. 1998. (Illus.). 32p. (YA). (ps up). reprint ed. spiral bd. (978-1-56021-273-7(X) , 171) W.J. Fantasy, Inc.

Keenan, Sheila. Looking for Leprechauns. Meisel, Paul, illus. 2005. (J). (***978-0-439-68057-8(3))*** Scholastic, Inc.

Kendall, Cassie. Laurel & the Lost Treasure. Spector, Joel, illus. 2nd ed. 1998. (Stardust Classics). 117p. (J). (gr. 2-6). pap. 5.95 (978-1-889514-10-9(1)) Dolls Corp.

—Laurel the Woodfairy. Spector, Joel, illus. 2nd ed. 1998. (Stardust Classics). 114p. (J). (gr. 2-6). 12.95 (978-1-889514-05-5(5)); pap. 5.95 (978-1-889514-06-2(3)) Dolls Corp.

Kimmel, Eric A. Herschel & the Hanukkah Goblins. Hyman, Trina Schart, illus. (Caldecott Honor Book Ser.). 32p. (gr. k-3). pap., tchr. ed. 17.95 (978-0-8234-0769-9(1)) Holiday Hse., Inc.

Kingsley, Charles. The Water Babies: A Fairy Tale for a Land-Baby. Goble, Warwick, illus. 2006. 160p. pap. 14.95 (978-0-486-45000-1(7)) Dover Pubns., Inc.

Kline, Suzy. Horrible Harry Bugs the Three Bears. Remkiewicz, Frank, illus. 2008. (J). (gr. 2). 13.99 (***978-0-670-06293-5(6)*** , Viking Juvenile) Penguin Group (USA) Inc.

Knoos, Sara Marie. A Fairy's Tail. Van Eps, Ann, illus. 2002. 29p. (J). (ps-6). pap. 14.99 (978-0-9721276-0-8(7)) Mermaid Utopia, Inc.

Kochalka, James. Squirrelly Gray. 2007. (Picture Book Ser.). (Illus.). 40p. (J). (gr. k-2). 12.99 (***978-0-375-83975-7(5));*** lib. bdg. 15.99 (***978-0-375-93975-4(X))*** Random Hse. Children's Bks. (Random Hse. Bks. for Young Readers).

Koski, Mary B. Stowaway Fairy Goes to Japan. 2002. (J). 8.99 (978-0-89610-203-3(3)) Island Heritage Publishing.

Krensky, Stephen. How Santa Lost His Job. Schindler, S. D., illus. 2005. 29p. (J). (gr. k-4). reprint ed. 15.00 (978-0-7567-9405-7(6)) DIANE Publishing Co.

—Too Many Leprechauns: Or How That Pot o' Gold Got to the End of the Rainbow. Andreasen, Dan, illus. 2007. 32p. (J). 12.99 (978-0-689-85112-4(X) , Simon & Schuster Children's Publishing) Simon & Schuster Children's Publishing.

—The Youngest Fairy Godmother Ever. Bluthenthal, Diana Cain, illus. 2003. 32p. (J). 6.99 (978-0-689-86143-7(5) , Aladdin) Simon & Schuster Children's Publishing.

—Youngest Fairy Godmother Ever. 2003. (gr. k-3). lib. bdg. 14.15 (978-0-613-66446-2(9)) Tandem Library Bks.

Krishnaswami, Uma. The Big Party. 2006. (Early Explorers Ser.). (J). 36.00 (***978-1-4108-6133-7(3))*** Benchmark Education Co.

La Fevers, R. L. The True Blade of Power. 2006. (Lowthar's Blade Ser.: Bk. 3). 160p. (J). (gr. 2). pap. 5.99 (978-0-14-240559-8(0) , Puffin) Penguin Group (USA) Inc.

Lamb, Charles & Lamb, Mary. Tales from Shakespeare: "A Midsummer Night's Dream" Strang, Kay, ed. Andrews, Gary, illus. rev. ed. 2005. 40p. pap. 4.95 (978-0-9542905-3-5(4)) Capercaillie Bks., Ltd GBR. *Dist:* Wilson & Assocs.

Lampman, Annette. Nicole's Wish. 2006. 23.00 (***978-0-8059-9146-8(8))*** Dorrance Publishing Co., Inc.

Lander, C. F. Willow & the Ice Fairies. 2004. 88p. pap. 14.95 (978-1-4137-1638-2(5)) PublishAmerica, Inc.

Landolf, Diane Wright. Barbie: Fairytopia. 2006. (Step into Reading Ser.). (Illus.). 32p. (J). (ps-2). pap. 3.99 (978-0-375-83696-1(9)); lib. bdg. 11.99 (978-0-375-93696-8(3)) Random Hse. Children's Bks. (Random Hse. Bks. for Young Readers).

Lang, Andrew. The Green Fairy Book. l.t. ed. 2005. 636p. pap. (978-1-84637-147-9(3)) Echo Library.

—The Lilac Fairy Book. l.t. ed. 2005. 508p. pap. (978-1-84637-149-3(X)) Echo Library.

—The Pink Fairy Book. 2005. 31.95 (978-1-4218-0004-2(7) , 1st World Library - Literary Society) 1st World Publishing, Inc.

Langrish, Katherine. Troll Fell. (J). 2005. 368p. (gr. 7 up). pap. 6.99 (978-0-06-058306-4(1)); 2004. (Illus.). 272p. (gr. 5 up). 16.99 (978-0-06-058304-0(5)) HarperCollins Pubs.

Langrish, Katherine. Troll Mill. 2008. 384p. (J). 7.99 (***978-0-06-058309-5(6)*** , Eos) HarperCollins Pubs.

Larsen, Kirsten, et al. Lily's Pesky Plant. Clarke, Judith, illus. 2006. (Stepping Stone Bks.). 128p. (J). (gr. 2-4). 5.99 (978-0-7364-2374-8(5) , RH/Disney) Random Hse. Children's Bks.

Laura & the Leprechauns. 2007. (J). 19.95 (***978-0-9795933-0-7(1))*** Chrysalis Pr.

Laurain, L. G. The Brain Fairy. 2005. (Illus.). 16p. 12.95 (978-1-59453-725-7(9) , Airleaf Publishing) Airleaf Publishing & Bookselling.

Laymance, Cherilyn. A Faerie's Tale. 2005. 214p. pap. 19.95 (978-1-4137-9018-4(6)) PublishAmerica, Inc.

Leaf, Munro. Noodle. Bemelmans, Ludwig, illus. 2006. 56p. (J). 15.99 (978-0-590-04310-6(2)); pap. 15.99 (978-0-590-04309-0(9)) Scholastic, Inc. (Levine, Arthur A. Bks.).

LeMieux, Anne Connelly. A Safe Place. 1998. (Fairy Lair Ser.: 2). 160p. (J). (gr. 3-7). mass mkt. 4.50 (978-0-689-81726-7(6) , Simon Pulse) Simon & Schuster Children's Publishing.

Lester, Anna. Fairies. Gower, Teri, illus. 2006. 48p. (J). 8.99 (978-0-7945-1326-9(3) , Usborne) EDC Publishing.

Lester, Anna. Fairytale Castles. Cascio, Lo & Cristina, Maria, illus. 2007. (Young Reading Series 1 Gift Bks). 48p. (J). 8.99 (***978-0-7945-1679-6(3)*** , Usborne) EDC Publishing.

Levine, Gail Carson. Fairy Dust & the Quest for the Egg. 2008. 208p. (J). (gr. 1-5). pap. 9.99 (***978-1-4231-0819-1(1))*** Disney Pr.

—Fairy Dust & the Quest for the Egg. Christiana, David, illus. 2005. 208p. (gr. 1-5). 16.99 (978-0-7868-3491-4(9)) Disney Pr.

—Fairy Haven & the Quest for the Wand. Christiana, David, illus. rev. ed. 2007. 208p. (gr. 1-5). 17.99 (***978-1-4231-0100-0(6))*** Disney Pr.

Levine, Gail Carson. The Fairy's Return & Other Princess Tales. 2006. (Princess Tales Ser.). 400p. (J). 14.99 (978-0-06-113061-8(3)) HarperCollins Pubs.

Levine, Terri. Abigail & the Purple Fairy. Harr, Lynn, illus. 2007. 34p. (J). (ps-3). per. 14.99 (***978-1-60002-314-9(2)*** , Airleaf Publishing) Airleaf Publishing & Bookselling.

Lewis, Regina N. The Smallest Schoolhouse. Moore, P. M., illus. 2007. 56p. (J). pap. 12.95 (***978-0-9776958-3-6(2))*** CyPress Pubns.

Lin, Grace. Red Thread: An Adoption Fairy Tale. Lin, Grace, illus. 2007. (Illus.). 32p. (J). (ps-3). 16.95 (***978-0-8075-6922-1(4))*** Whitman, Albert & Co.

Lindner, Simone. Aelin the Water Fairy. Unzner, Christa, illus. 2008. 32p. (J). (ps). 9.99 (***978-0-698-40070-2(4)*** , Minedition) Penguin Group (USA) Inc.

—Gobulus the Earth Fairy. Unzner, Christa, illus. 2008. 32p. (J). (ps). 9.99 (***978-0-698-40072-6(0)*** , Minedition) Penguin Group (USA) Inc.

—Runia the Fire Fairy. Unzner, Christa, illus. 2008. 32p. (J). (ps). 9.99 (***978-0-698-40071-9(2)*** , Minedition) Penguin Group (USA) Inc.

—Tara the Air Fairy. Unzner, Christa, illus. 2008. 32p. (J). (ps). 9.99 (***978-0-698-40069-6(0)*** , Minedition) Penguin Group (USA) Inc.

Lisle, Janet Taylor. Afternoon of the Elves. 1999. (J). 11.64 (978-0-606-16789-5(7)) Tandem Library Bks.

Little Elf Set 1. 2006. (J). (***978-1-932570-70-0(5))*** Literacy Footprints Inc.

Lodico, Cheryl Madeleine. The Ice Princess Trilogy. 2007. pap. 20.00 (***978-0-8059-8967-0(6))*** Dorrance Publishing Co., Inc.

Luberto, Bradley. Clide & Druce: A Repulsive Tale of Trolls & Tax Money. 2006. (ENG.). 48p. per. 12.95 (***978-1-4241-5012-0(4))*** PublishAmerica, Inc.

Lyons, Mary E. Knockabeg: A Famine Tale. 2001. (Illus.). 128p. (J). (gr. 4-6). tchr. ed. 15.00 (978-0-618-09283-3(8)) Houghton Mifflin Co. Trade & Reference Div.

Lyons, Sarah. Fairy stories about sally & Mignonette. 2007. pap. 9.99 (*978-1-60034-860-0(2)) Xulon Pr., Inc.

MacDonald, George. Far above Rubies. 2006. pap. (*978-1-4250-0932-8(8)) Assistedreadingbooks.com Inc.

—The Light Princess & Other Fairy Stori. 2006. 94.99 (*978-1-4280-4431-9(0)); pap. 88.99 (*978-1-4280-4437-1(X)) IndyPublish.com.

—The Light Princess (Clear Print) 2006. pap. (*978-1-4068-2160-4(8)) Echo Library.

—The Princess & Curdie. l.t. ed. 2005. 320p. pap. (978-1-84637-020-5(5)) Echo Library.

—The Princess & the Goblin. 2003. (Illus.). 160p. (J). 19.95 (978-1-81514-970-2(1)) Antique Collectors' Club.

—The Princess & the Goblin. Hughes, Arthur, illus. 2003. 136p. pap. 12.99 (978-1-57646-633-9(7)) Quiet Vision Publishing.

MacInnis, Katherine Grace. Kelsar. 2006. 140p. 19.95 (978-1-58939-877-1(7)) Virtualbookworm.com Publishing, Inc.

Maguire, Gregory. Leaping Beauty: And Other Animal Fairy Tales. Demarest, Chris L., illus. 2004. 208p. (J). lib. bdg. 16.89 (978-0-06-056418-6(0)) HarperCollins Pubs.

Maguire, Gregory. What-the-Dickens: The Story of a Rogue Tooth Fairy. 2007. (Illus.). 304p. (J). (gr. 5-8). 15.99 (*978-0-7636-2961-8(8)) Candlewick Pr.

Maiden, Cecil. The Molliwumps. Price, Christine, illus. 2004. 160p. 12.95 (978-0-9714612-9-1(5)) Green Mansion Pr. LLC.

Mallen, Lisa. Elton the Elf. Pavanel, Jane, ed. Roge, illus. 2000. 24p. (J). pap. 8.95 (978-1-894222-13-6(X)) Lobster Pr. CAN. *Dist:* Univ. of Toronto Pr.

—Elton the Elf. Roge, illus. 2nd adapted ed. 2001. 24p. (J). (ps-k). 12.95 (978-1-894222-33-4(4)) Lobster Pr. CAN. *Dist:* Univ. of Toronto Pr.

Man-Kong, Mary. Barbie Fairytopia: The Magic of the Rainbow: A Storybook. 2007. (Pictureback(R) Ser.). (Illus.). 16p. (J). (ps-2). 3.99 (978-0-375-83985-6(2) , Golden Bks.) Random Hse. Children's Bks.

—Fairytopia. 2006. (Board Books). (Illus.). 22p. (J). (gr. k-ps). bds. 4.99 (978-0-375-83538-4(5) , Golden Bks.) Random Hse. Children's Bks.

Man-Kong, Mary. The Magic of the Rainbow. 2008. 24p. (J). (gr. k-k). bds. 4.99 (*978-0-375-84796-7(0) , Golden Bks.) Random Hse., Inc.

Mark, Jan. Eyes Wide Open. 2003. (ENG., Illus.). 105p. (*978-0-7136-7648-8(5)) A & C Black.

Markowitz-Meredith, Susan. Frances & the Fairy Dressmaker. ed. 2003. (Early Connections Ser.). (J). pap. 35.00 (978-1-4108-1557-6(9)) Benchmark Education Co.

Marks, Melanie. The Tooth Fairy Rules. Kalis, Jennifer, illus. 2006. 14p. (J). (gr. k-17). 12.99 (978-1-58476-488-5(0) , IKIDS) Innovative Kids.

Marr, Melissa. Wicked Lovely. 2007. 336p. (gr. 7 up). (J). lib. bdg. 17.89 (*978-0-06-121466-0(3)); (YA). 16.99 (*978-0-06-121465-3(5)) HarperCollins Pubs. (HarperTeen).

Marshall, Ken. The Adventures of Maya & Grampa. 2005. 64p. pap. 9.95 (978-0-7414-2472-3(X)) Infinity Publishing.

McDonald, Ann-Eve. The Bad Day. 2004. (J). (978-0-9770158-1-8(5)) BeachWalk Bks. Inc.

McGraw, Eloise. The Moorchild. 2007. 256p. (J). pap. 2.99 (*978-1-4169-4819-3(8) , Aladdin) Simon & Schuster Children's Publishing.

McGraw, Eloise Jarvis. The Moorchild. 2002. (Illus.). (J). 13.40 (978-0-7587-4123-3(5)) Book Wholesalers, Inc.

—The Moorchild. 256p. (J). 2006. pap. 5.99 (978-1-4169-2768-6(9)); 1998. (gr. 4-7). pap. 5.99 (978-0-689-82033-5(X)) Simon & Schuster Children's Publishing. (Aladdin).

—The Moorchild. 1998. (J). (978-0-606-13621-1(5)) Tandem Library Bks.

—The Moorchild. l.t. ed. 2002. 291p. (YA). 24.95 (978-0-7862-4787-5(8)) Thorndike Pr.

McKain, Kelly. Fairy for a Day. 2008. (Fairy House Ser.: No. 2). 96p. (J). pap. 6.99 (*978-0-545-04238-3(0)) Scholastic, Inc.

—Fairy Friends. 2008. (Fairy House Ser.). 112p. (J). pap. 6.99 (*978-0-545-04237-6(2)) Scholastic, Inc.

McLean, Wendy & Book Company Staff. Follow an Elf. Worthington, Leonie, illus. 2003. (Sparkle Bks.). 10p. (J). bds. 8.95 (978-1-74047-314-9(0)) Book Co. Publishing Pty, Ltd., The AUS. *Dist:* Penton Overseas, Inc.

Meacham, Margaret. A Fairy's Guide to Understanding Humans. 2007. 160p. (YA). (gr. 5 up). 16.95 (*978-0-8234-2078-0(7)) Holiday Hse., Inc.

Meacham, Margaret. A Mid-Semester Night's Dream. 2004. 160p. (J). (gr. 4-6). tchr. ed. 16.95 (978-0-8234-1815-2(4)) Holiday Hse., Inc.

Meadows, Daisy. Abigail the Breeze Fairy. 2006. (Weather Fairies Ser.: No. 2). (Illus.). 80p. (J). pap. 4.99 (978-0-439-81386-0(7) , Scholastic Paperbacks) Scholastic, Inc.

—Amber the Orange Fairy. Ripper, Georgie, illus. 2nd ed. 2005. (Rainbow Magic Ser.: No. 2). 80p. (J). 4.99 (978-0-439-74465-2(2)) Scholastic, Inc.

—Amy the Amethyst Fairy. 2007. (Jewel Fairies Ser.). 80p. (Orig.). (J). pap. 4.99 (*978-0-439-93532-6(6) , Scholastic Paperbacks) Scholastic, Inc.

—Chloe the Topaz Fairy. 2007. (Jewel Fairies Ser.: No. 4). 80p. (Orig.). (J). 4.99 (*978-0-439-93531-9(8)) Scholastic, Inc.

—Emily the Emerald Fairy. 2007. (Jewel Fairies Ser.: No. 3). 80p. (Orig.). (J). 4.99 (*978-0-439-93530-2(X)) Scholastic, Inc.

—Evie the Mist Fairy. 2006. (Weather Fairies Ser.: No. 5). 80p. (Orig.). (J). pap. 4.99 (978-0-439-81390-7(5) , Scholastic Paperbacks) Scholastic, Inc.

—Fern the Green Fairy. Ripper, Georgie, illus. 2005. (Rainbow Magic Ser.: No. 4). 80p. (Orig.). (J). (ps-ps). pap. 4.99 (978-0-439-74467-6(9) , Scholastic Paperbacks) Scholastic, Inc.

—Goldie the Sunshine Fairy. 2006. (Weather Fairies Ser.: No. 4). (Illus.). 80p. (Orig.). (J). pap. 4.99 (978-0-439-81389-1(1) , Scholastic Paperbacks) Scholastic, Inc.

—Goldie the Sunshine Fairy. 2007. (Weather Fairies Ser.: No. 4). 80p. (J). pap. 2.99 (*978-0-545-01039-9(X)) Scholastic, Inc.

—Hayley the Rain Fairy. 2007. (Weather Fairies Ser.: No. 7). 80p. (Orig.). (J). pap. 4.99 (978-0-439-81392-1(1) , Scholastic Paperbacks) Scholastic, Inc.

—Heather the Violet Fairy. 2005. 71p. (J). (978-0-439-69192-5(3)) Scholastic, Inc.

—Holly the Christmas Fairy. 2007. (Rainbow Magic Ser.). 176p. (Orig.). (J). pap. 6.99 (*978-0-439-92880-9(X) , Scholastic Paperbacks) Scholastic, Inc.

—India the Moonstone Fairy. 2007. (Jewel Fairies Ser.: No. 1). 80p. (Orig.). (J). 4.99 (*978-0-439-93528-9(8)) Scholastic, Inc.

—Joy the Summer Vacation Fairy. 2007. (Rainbow Magic Ser.). 192p. (J). pap. 6.99 (*978-0-439-93442-8(7) , Scholastic Paperbacks) Scholastic, Inc.

—Lucy the Diamond Fairy. 2008. (Scholastic First Discovery Ser.: No. 7). 80p. (Orig.). (J). pap. 4.99 (*978-0-439-93534-0(2) , Scholastic Paperbacks) Scholastic, Inc.

—Pet Fairies #1 Katie the Kitten Fairy. 2008. (Pet Fairies Ser.). 80p. (J). pap. 4.99 (*978-0-545-02816-5(7) , Scholastic Paperbacks) Scholastic, Inc.

—Pet Fairies #2 Bella the Bunny Fairy. 2008. (Pet Fairies Ser.). 80p. (J). pap. 4.99 (*978-0-545-04185-0(6) , Scholastic Paperbacks) Scholastic, Inc.

—Pet Fairies #3 Georgia the Guinea Pig Fairy. 2008. (Pet Fairies Ser.). 80p. (J). pap. 4.99 (*978-0-545-04186-7(4) , Scholastic Paperbacks) Scholastic, Inc.

—Pet Fairies #4 Lauren the Puppy Fairy. 2008. (Pet Fairies Ser.). 80p. (J). pap. 4.99 (*978-0-545-04187-4(2) , Scholastic Paperbacks) Scholastic, Inc.

—Rainbow Magic: Heather the Violet Fairy. Ripper, Georgie, illus. 2006. 80p. (J). pap. 4.99 (978-0-439-74686-1(8) , Scholastic Paperbacks) Scholastic, Inc.

—Rainbow Magic: Inky the Indigo Fairy. Ripper, Georgie, illus. 2006. (Rainbow Magic Ser.: No. 6). 80p. (J). pap. 4.99 (978-0-439-74685-4(X) , Scholastic Paperbacks) Scholastic, Inc.

—Ruby the Red Fairy, Vol. 1. Ripper, Georgie, illus. 2005. (Rainbow Magic Ser.). 80p. (Orig.). (J). (ps-ps). pap. 4.99 (978-0-439-73861-3(X)) Scholastic, Inc.

—Scarlett the Garnet Fairy. 2007. (Jewel Fairies Ser.: No. 2). 80p. (Orig.). (J). 4.99 (*978-0-439-93529-6(6)) Scholastic, Inc.

—Sky the Blue Fairy. Ripper, Georgie, illus. 2005. (Rainbow Magic Ser.: No. 5). 80p. (Orig.). (J). (gr. 1-4). pap. 4.99 (978-0-439-74684-7(1) , Scholastic Paperbacks) Scholastic, Inc.

—Sophie the Sapphire Fairy. 2007. (Jewel Fairies Ser.). 80p. (Orig.). (J). pap. 4.99 (*978-0-439-93533-3(4) , Scholastic Paperbacks) Scholastic, Inc.

—Storm the Lightning Fairy. 2007. (Weather Fairies Ser.). 80p. (Orig.). (J). pap. 4.99 (978-0-439-81391-4(3) , Scholastic Paperbacks) Scholastic, Inc.

—Sunny the Yellow Fairy. Ripper, Georgie, illus. 2005. (Rainbow Magic Ser.: No. 3). 70p. (J). 4.99 (978-0-439-74466-9(0)) Scholastic, Inc.

—Weather Fairies: Crystal the Snow Fairy. Ripper, Georgie, illus. 2006. 80p. (J). pap. 4.99 (978-0-439-81387-7(5) , Scholastic Paperbacks) Scholastic, Inc.

Melling, O. R. The Hunter's Moon. 2005. (Chronicles of Faerie Ser.: No. 1). (Illus.). 296p. (J). (gr. 5-10). 16.95 (978-0-8109-5857-9(0)) Abrams, Harry N. , Inc.

—Hunter's Moon. 2006. (Chronicles of Faerie Ser.: No. 1). 304p. (J). (gr. 5-10). pap. 7.95 (978-0-8109-9214-6(0)) Abrams, Harry N. , Inc.

—The Summer King. (Chronicles of Faerie Ser.). 2007. 368p. (J). (gr. 2-8). pap. 7.95 (*978-0-8109-9321-1(X) , Amulet Bks.); 2006. (Illus.). 380p. (YA). (gr. 5-10). 16.95 (978-0-8109-5969-9(0)) Abrams, Harry N. , Inc.

Mendo, Miguel Angel, tr. Blancanieves. Barrett, Angela, illus. 2007. (SPA.). (J). (gr. 2-5). 24.95 (*978-84-96629-17-2(1)) S.A. Kokinos ESP. *Dist:* Lectorum Pubns., Inc.

Milord, Susan. Willa the Wonderful. (Illus.). 32p. (J). (gr. k-3). 2005. 5.95 (978-0-618-58543-4(5)); 2003. tchr. ed. 15.00 (978-0-618-27522-9(3)) Houghton Mifflin Co. Trade & Reference Div.

Mitchell, Joni. Chelsea Morning. Froud, Brian, illus. 2004. 32p. (J). (978-0-689-03593-7(4) , Milk & Cookies) ibooks, Inc.

Mitchell, N. J. W. Saraly & the Dragons. 2003. 124p. pap. 10.95 (978-0-595-30264-2(5)) iUniverse, Inc.

Mitchell, Stephen, et al. Iron Hans. Mitchell, Stephen, tr. Tavares, Matt, illus. 2007. 40p. (J). (gr. 1-5). 16.99 (978-0-7636-2160-5(9)) Candlewick Pr.

Morris, Gerald. The Princess, the Crone, & the Dung-Cart Knight. (Squire's Tales Ser.). 320p. (YA). (gr. 5-9). 2006. pap. 6.95 (978-0-618-73748-2(0)); 2004. tchr. ed. 16.00 (978-0-618-37823-4(5)) Houghton Mifflin Co. Trade & Reference Div.

Morris, Kimberly. Beck Beyond the Sea. Clarke, Judith, illus. 2007. 128p. (J). (gr. 1-5). 5.99 (*978-0-7364-2456-1(3) , RH/Disney) Random Hse. Children's Bks.

Mueller, Martina. Pico the Gnome. 2001. (Illus.). 28p. (J). (gr. k-2). 16.95 (978-0-86315-278-8(3)) Floris Bks. GBR. *Dist:* Gryphon Hse., Inc., SteinerBooks, Inc.

Muneefa. My Tales for Children. 2006. 90p. (J). pap. 13.95 (978-1-58909-339-3(9)) Bookstand Publishing.

Munsch, Robert. Andrew's Loose Tooth. 2002. (ps-2). lib. bdg. 11.80 (978-0-613-72077-9(6)) Tandem Library Bks.

Myers, Tim. Good Babies: A Tale of Trolls, Humans, a Witch & a Switch. Murphy, Kelly, illus. 2005. 32p. (J). (ps-3). 15.99 (978-0-7636-2227-5(3)) Candlewick Pr.

Namy, Verna. Ancient Secrets in the Garden. Martin, Mary, illus. 2001. 32p. (J). 18.95 (978-0-944851-18-0(5)) Earth Star Pubns.

Nelson, Brett Alan. The Magical Forest. Ueda, Kumiko, illus. 2003. 42p. (J). (978-0-9655078-7-5(4)) Windsong Publishing Co.

Nesbit, E. Five Children & IT. 207p. 20.95 (978-0-8488-2523-2(3)) Amereon LTD.

—Five Children & IT. 2002. (Dover Evergreen Classics Ser.). (Illus.). 160p. (J). (gr. 4-7). pap. 2.50 (978-0-486-42366-1(2)) Dover Pubns., Inc.

—Five Children & IT. Zelinsky, Paul O., illus. 1999. (Books of Wonder). 256p. (gr. 4-7). 22.95 (978-0-688-13545-4(5)) HarperCollins Pubs.

—Five Children & IT. Nesbit, E. & Millar, H. R., illus. 2004. 240p. (gr. 12). pap. 10.00 (978-0-14-303915-0(6) , Penguin Classics) Penguin Group (USA) Inc.

—Five Children & IT. 2002. 192p. pap. 14.95 (978-1-59224-938-1(8)); lib. bdg. 24.95 (978-1-59224-942-8(6)) Wildside Pr.

Nesbit, E. Five Children & It. 2006. pap. (*978-1-4068-3501-4(3)); 2005. 296p. pap. (978-1-84637-200-1(3)) Echo Library.

Nguy, Hoa X. The Bamboo Girl. 2007. 84p. (J). pap. 20.00 (*978-0-8059-7562-8(4)) Dorrance Publishing Co., Inc.

Norris, Christine. Talisman of Zandria, 1. Nagy, Robert, illus. 2005. 187p. (YA). pap. 14.95 (978-1-885093-44-8(6) , LBF/Hadrosaur) Hadrosaur Pr.

O'Connor, Edwin. Benjy: A Ferocious Fairy Tale. O'Neill, Catharine, illus. 2006. 96p. (J). reprint ed. pap. 12.00 (978-1-4223-5421-6(0)) DIANE Publishing Co.

O'Connor, Jane. Dear Tooth Fairy, Vol 2. Allen, Joy, illus. 2002. (All Aboard Reading Ser.). 48p. (J). 3.99 (978-0-448-42849-9(0) , Grosset & Dunlap) Penguin Group (USA) Inc.

—Dear Tooth Fairy. 2002. (gr. k-3). lib. bdg. 11.80 (978-0-613-64036-7(5)) Tandem Library Bks.

Oddino, Licia. Finn & the Fairies. Toni, Alessandra, illus. 2006. 32p. (J). 16.50 (978-1-933327-18-1(9)); 15.95 (978-1-933327-17-4(0)) Purple Bear Bks., Inc.

O'Dea, Kendra. The Stolen Sleigh. McGovern, Sarah, illus. 2006. (J). pap. (978-0-922993-53-6(X)) Marquette Bks., LLC.

Once upon a Time Spanish Version-the Elves & the Shoemaker. 2005. (J). (978-1-57022-559-8(1)) ECS Learning Systems, Inc.

Ondrias, Rachel. Cindy Lou Ella: A Country Fairy Tale. Scarborough, Casey, illus. 2007. (YA). 18.95 (*978-1-933660-28-8(7) , Tadpole Pr. 4 Kids) Smooth Sailing Pr.

Ostrow, Kim. Up All Night. Saunders, Zina, illus. 2004. (Ready-to-Read Ser.: Vol. 1). 32p. (J). pap. 3.99 (978-0-689-86320-2(9) , Simon Spotlight/Nickelodeon) Simon & Schuster Children's Publishing.

—Up All Night. 2004. (gr. k-3). lib. bdg. 11.80 (978-0-613-73459-2(9)) Tandem Library Bks.

Outside Your Back Door. 2004. (J). bds. 12.00 net. (978-0-9747081-0-2(0)) Cohen, Deanna Moreau.

Page, Nick, et al. Seashore. 2006. (Ready to Read Sticker Ser.). (Illus.). 12p. (J). (ps-3). pap., pap., wbk. ed. 3.95 (978-1-84610-127-4(1)) Make Believe Ideas GBR. *Dist:* Ingram Pub. Services.

Page, Nick & Claire. Read with Me - Sticker Activity Books: Elves & the Shoemaker. 2006. (Read with Me (Make Believe Ideas) Ser.). (Illus.). 12p. (J). (gr. k-2). pap. 4.95 (978-1-84610-177-9(8)) Make Believe Ideas GBR. *Dist:* Ingram Pub. Services.

Page, Nick And Claire. Giant Sticker Activity Story Book. 2006. (Giant Sticker Bks.). (Illus.). 144p. (J). (ps-k). pap. 12.95 (978-1-84610-303-2(7)) Make Believe Ideas GBR. *Dist:* Ingram Pub. Services.

Palatini, Margie & Davis, Jack E. Sweet Tooth. 2004. (Illus.). 40p. (J). 16.95 (978-0-689-85159-9(6)) Simon & Schuster Children's Publishing.

Papademetriou, Lisa. Rani in the Mermaid Lagoon. Clarke, Judith, illus. 2006. (Stepping Stone Bks.). 128p. (J). (gr. 2-4). 5.99 (978-0-7364-2375-5(3) , RH/Disney) Random Hse. Children's Bks.

Papademitriou, Lisa. Prilla's Prize. Disney Storybook Artists Staff, illus. 2006. 28p. (gr. 1-4). 12.99 (978-1-4231-0111-6(1)) Disney Pr.

Park, Barbara. Junie B., First Grader: Toothless Wonder. Brunkus, Denise, illus. 2003. (Junie B. Jones Ser.: No. 20). 96p. (J). (gr. k-3). pap. 3.99 (978-0-375-82223-0(2) , Random Hse. for Young Readers) Random Hse. Children's Bks.

—Junie B., First Grader: Toothless Wonder. 2002. (Junie B. Jones Ser.: No. 20). (Illus.). 96p. (J). (gr. k-3). lib. bdg. 13.99 (978-0-375-90295-6(3) , Random Hse. Bks. for Young Readers) Random Hse. Children's Bks.

—Junie B., First Grader: Toothless Wonder. Brunkus, Denise, illus. 2002. (Junie B. Jones Ser.: No. 20). 96p. (J). (gr. 1-4). 11.95 (978-0-375-80295-9(9) , Random Hse. Bks. for Young Readers) Random Hse. Children's Bks.

—Junie B., First Grader: Toothless Wonder. 2003. (Junie B. Jones Ser.: No. 20). (J). (gr. k-3). lib. bdg. 11.80 (978-0-613-71014-5(2)) Tandem Library Bks.

Pearce, Philippa. The Squirrel Wife. Anderson, Wayne, illus. 2007. 32p. (J). (gr. k-3). 16.99 (*978-0-7636-3551-0(0)) Candlewick Pr.

Penney, Shannon. Mariposa. 2008. (Barbie Fairytopia Ser.). 80p. (J). pap. 3.99 (*978-0-545-03590-3(2) , Scholastic Paperbacks) Scholastic, Inc.

Perez, Baltazar Gomez. Cuentos de Ogros para Ninos. 2000. (Stories for Children Ser.).Tr. of Ogre Stories for Kids. (SPA., Illus.). 125p. (J). (gr. 4-7). 7.98 (978-970-643-207-0(8)) Selector, S.A. de C.V. MEX. *Dist:* Libros Sin Fronteras.

—Cuentos de Ogros para Ninos. 2000. Tr. of Ogre Stories for Kids. (SPA.). (gr. 3-6). lib. bdg. 16.45 (978-0-613-87847-0(7)) Tandem Library Bks.

Perrault, Charles. The Fairies. 2005. 12p. pap. (978-958-30-1779-7(5)) Panamericana Editorial.

Petalwink Learns to Fly. 2006. (J). 15.95 (978-0-9789426-0-1(4)) Three Trees, Inc.

Peters, Stephanie True. A Princess Primer: A Fairy Godmother's Guide to Being a Princess. Oberdieck, Bernhard & Gordeev, Denis, illus. 2006. 32p. (J). (ps). 19.99 (978-0-525-47765-5(9) , Dutton Juvenile) Penguin Group (USA) Inc.

Peterson, Janice & Peterson, Macy. The Sleep Fairy. Newlun, Shawn, illus. 2003. 32p. (J). (ps-5). 16.95 (978-0-9714405-0-0(6)) Behavenkids Pr.

Petty, J. T. Clemency Pogue: Fairy Killer. Davis, Will, illus. 2005. (Clemency Pogue Ser.). 128p. (J). 9.95 (978-0-689-87236-5(4) , Simon & Schuster Children's Publishing) Simon & Schuster Children's Publishing.

—The Hobgoblin Proxy. Davis, Will, illus. 2006. (Clemency Pogue Ser.). 160p. (J). (gr. 3-7). 9.95 (978-1-4169-0768-8(8) , Simon & Schuster Children's Publishing) Simon & Schuster Children's Publishing.

—The Scrivener Bees. Friend, David Michael, illus. 2007. (Clemency Pogue Ser.). 176p. (J). (gr. 3-7). 11.99 (978-1-4169-0769-5(6) , Simon & Schuster Children's Publishing) Simon & Schuster Children's Publishing.

Picard, Anne M. Peace & Pancakes. 2006. 48p. bds. 25.00 (978-1-59298-149-6(6)) Beaver's Pond Pr., Inc.

Picouly, Daniel. Thumbelina of Toulaba. Bedrick, Claudia Zoe, tr. Tallac, Olivier, illus. 2007. 32p. (J). (ps-3). 16.95 (*978-1-59270-069-1(1)) Enchanted Lion Bks., LLC.

Pike, Christopher, pseud. The Shaktra. 2006. (Alosha Trilogy: No. 2). 336p. (YA). 6.99 (978-0-7653-4961-3(2) , Tor Bks.) Doherty, Tom Assocs., LLC.

—The Yanti. 2006. (Alosha Trilogy: No. 3). 400p. (YA). (gr. 8 up). 18.95 (978-0-7653-1100-9(3) , Tor Bks.) Doherty, Tom Assocs., LLC.

Pikey, Mikey. The Diamond Tree, Episode III: the Beginning of the Rainbow. 2006. 153p. pap. 16.76 (*978-1-84728-099-2(4)) Lulu.com.

Piscetta, Colleen McCauley. Dandelion Delilah: The Tale of the Dandelion Fairies. Wolf, Gwynn, illus. 2002. (J). 24.95 (978-1-888683-87-5(2)) Wooster Bk. Co., The.

Polette, Keith. Paco & the Giant Chile Plant/Paco y las Planta de Chile Gigante. de la Vega, Eida, tr. Dulemba, Elizabeth, illus. 2008. (SPA.). (J). lib. bdg. 16.95 (978-0-9770906-2-4(0)) Raven Tree Pr.

Pollack, Pam. Winx Club: Fairy Insider. 2005. (Winx Club Ser.). 65p. (J). pap. 5.99 (978-0-439-68512-2(5)) Scholastic, Inc.

Potter, Beatrix & Barker, Cicely Mary. Flower Fairies Best Friends. 2005. 24p. (J). pap. 9.99 (978-0-7232-5395-2(1) , Warne) Penguin Group (USA) Inc.

Powell, Stacy A. The Legend of Auggie the Awkard Elf. 2001. (Illus.). 120p. (J). (ps-8). pap. 12.50 (978-0-9713551-0-1(X)) Candle Fly Pr.

Powers, Lindsay. Christmas Elf. 2006. (Illus.). 32p. pap. 6.95 (978-0-7624-2884-7(8) , Running Pr.) Running Pr. Bk. Pubs.

Prasadam, Smriti & Finn, Rebecca. My Fairy Glade: Through Play Books. 2008. (Illus.). 12p. (J). bds. 6.95 (*978-0-7475-8809-2(0)) Bloomsbury Publishing Plc GBR. *Dist:* Independent Pubs. Group.

Pratchett, Terry. A Hat Full of Sky. 2004. (Discworld Ser.). 288p. (J). (gr. 7 up). 16.99 (978-0-06-058660-7(5)) HarperCollins Pubs.

—The Wee Free Men. Player, Stephen, illus. 2007. 256p. (J). 24.99 (*978-0-06-134080-2(4)) HarperCollins Pubs.

—The Wee Free Men. (gr. 7 up). 2003. 272p. (J). 16.99 (978-0-06-001236-6(6)); 2004. 400p. (YA). reprint ed. pap. 6.99 (978-0-06-001238-0(2) , Harper Trophy) HarperCollins Pubs.

—Wintersmith. (J). 2007. 464p. pap. 7.99 (*978-0-06-089033-9(9)); 2006. 336p. (gr. 6-8). 16.99 (978-0-06-089031-5(2)); 2006. 336p. (gr. 6-8). lib. bdg. 17.89 (978-0-06-089032-2(0)) HarperCollins Pubs. (HarperTeen).

Rainbow Magic Staff & Meadows, Daisy. Ruby the Red Fairy. 2007. (Rainbow Magic Ser.). 80p. (J). pap. 2.99 (*978-0-545-01037-5(3)) Scholastic, Inc.

The Rainbow's End. 2003. 14.95 (978-1-929489-75-6(7)) Platinum Medallion Children's Bks.

Ralph, Grampa. How Santa Knows. 2007. 56p. pap. 12.95 (*978-1-4241-2284-4(8)) PublishAmerica, Inc.

Random House Disney Staff. Actual Fairy Size. 2007. 32p. (J). (gr. 1-5). 7.99 (*978-0-7364-2495-0(4) , RH/Disney) Random Hse. Children's Bks.

—Cinderella III: A Twist in Time. 2006. (Pictureback(R) Ser.). (Illus.). 24p. (J). (gr. k-3). pap. 3.99 (978-0-7364-2429-5(6) , RH/Disney) Random Hse. Children's Bks.

—Walt Disney's Peter Pan. Dempster, Al, illus. 2007. (Little Golden Book Ser.). 24p. (J). (gr. k-k). 2.99 (978-0-7364-0238-5(1) , Golden/Disney) Random Hse. Children's Bks.

Ray, Belinda. Fairy: Blinda Ray. 2004. 136p. (J). (978-0-439-56013-9(6)) Scholastic, Inc.

Reader's Digest Editors. Barbie Fairytopia (board book) the Magic of the Rainbow. 2007. 10p. (J). bds. 9.99 (978-0-7944-1214-2(9)) Reader's Digest Assn., Inc., The.

—Barbie Fairytopia (panorama sticker book) the Magic of the Rainbow. 2007. 16p. (J). bds. 7.99 (978-0-7944-1215-9(7)) Reader's Digest Assn., Inc., The.

Reader's Digest Staff. Disney Fairies Tinker Bell & Friends Storybook & Kaleidoscope Viewer. 2007. (RD Innovative Book & Player Format Ser.). 40p. (J). bds. 24.99 (*978-0-7944-1350-7(1)) Reader's Digest Assn., Inc., The.

Redbank, Tennant. Fairy Lantern. Disney Storybook Artists Staff, illus. rev. ed. 2007. 24p. (gr. 1). pap. 17.99 (***978-1-4231-0818-4(3))*** Disney Pr.

Reif, Charles Braddock. Toxamok, a Troll at Summer Camp. Ashcraft, Wanda, illus. 1999. 75p. (J). (gr. 4-6). (978-0-9666156-1-6(1)) Keepsake Chronicles.

The Return of the Brownies. 2004. (Illus.). 260p. (J). bds. 22.50 (978-0-9749382-0-2(3)) Celestine Pr.

RH Disney. The Fairy Berry Bake-off. 2008. (Step into Reading Ser.). 48p. (J). (gr. k-3). pap. 3.99 (***978-0-7364-2525-4(X));*** lib. bdg. 11.99 (***978-0-7364-8061-1(7))*** Random Hse. Children's Bks. (RH/Disney).

—The Great Fairy Race. 2008. (Step into Reading Ser.). 48p. (J). (gr. k-3). lib. bdg. 11.99 (***978-0-7364-8060-4(9)*** , RH/Disney) Random Hse. Children's Bks.

Richards, Kitty. Prilla & the Butterfly Lie. Shimabukuro, Denise, illus. 2007. (Stepping Stone Bks.). 128p. (J). (gr. 1-5). 5.99 (978-0-7364-2419-6(9) , RH/Disney) Random Hse. Children's Bks.

—Prilla & the Butterfly Lie. Shimabukuro, Denise, illus. 2007. (Disney Fairies Ser.). 113p. (J). (***978-1-4287-2536-2(9))*** Random Hse., Inc.

Riley, Christine. Saving the Tooth Fairy. Warren, Mnetha, illus. 2005. (J). per. 16.00 (978-0-9754298-4-6(1) , Ithaca Pr.) Authors & Artists Publishers of New York, Inc.

Risso, Eduardo. Los misterios de la Luna Roja Vol. 1: Mysteries of the Red Moon. 2006. (SPA.). 48p. pap. 16.95 (978-1-59497-162-4(5)) Public Square Bks.

—Mysteries of the Red Moon, Vol. 3. 2006. (SPA.). 48p. pap. 16.95 (978-1-59497-163-1(3)) Public Square Bks.

Ritchie, Madonna, ed. & illus. The English Roses. Ritchie, Madonna, illus. Fulvimari, Jeffrey, illus. 2003. 48p. (J). 19.95 (978-0-670-03678-3(1)) Callaway Editions, Inc.

—The English Roses. Ritchie, Madonna, illus. ed. 2006. 48p. (J). (ps-6). 9.95 (978-0-670-06180-8(8)) Callaway Editions, Inc.

Roberts, Esyllt Nest & Owen, Carys Eurwen. Elidir A'r Tylwyth Teg. 2005. (WEL., Illus.). 35p. (978-0-86381-530-0(8)) Gwasg Carreg Gwalch.

Robinson, Hilary & Sharratt, Nick. Mixed up Fairy Tales. 2005. (Illus.). (J). (ps-ps). 17.99 (978-0-340-87557-5(7)) Hodder Headline Ltd. GBR. *Dist:* Trafalgar Square Publishing.

Rodda, Emily. The Charm Bracelet. Vitale, Raoul, illus. 2003. (Fairy Realm Ser.: No. 1). 128p. (J). (gr. 2-5). 8.99 (978-0-06-009583-3(0)); lib. bdg. 15.89 (978-0-06-009584-0(9)) HarperCollins Pubs.

—The Charm Bracelet. Vitale, Raoul, illus. 2007. (Fairy Realm Ser.). 128p. (J). (gr. 3-6). 25.65 (978-1-59961-323-9(9)) Spotlight.

—The Flower Fairies. Vitale, Raoul, illus. 2003. (Fairy Realm Ser.: No. 2). 128p. (J). 8.99 (978-0-06-009586-4(5)); lib. bdg. 15.89 (978-0-06-009587-1(3)) HarperCollins Pubs.

—The Flower Fairies. Vitale, Raoul, illus. 2007. (Fairy Realm Ser.). 128p. (J). (gr. 3-6). 25.65 (978-1-59961-324-6(7)) Spotlight.

—The Last Fairy-Apple Tree. Vitale, Raoul, illus. 2003. (Fairy Realm Ser.: No. 4). 128p. (J). 8.99 (978-0-06-009592-5(X)); lib. bdg. 15.89 (978-0-06-009593-2(8)) HarperCollins Pubs.

—The Last Fairy-Apple Tree. Vitale, Raoul, illus. 2007. (Fairy Realm Ser.). 128p. (J). (gr. 3-6). 25.65 (978-1-59961-326-0(3)) Spotlight.

—The Magic Key. Vitale, Raoul, illus. 2004. (Fairy Realm Ser.: No. 5). 128p. (J). lib. bdg. 15.89 (978-0-06-009596-3(2)); Book 5. 8.99 (978-0-06-009595-6(4)) HarperCollins Pubs.

—The Magic Key. Vitale, Raoul, illus. 2007. (Fairy Realm Ser.). 128p. (J). (gr. 3-6). 25.65 (978-1-59961-327-7(1)) Spotlight.

—The Peskie Spell. Vitale, Raoul, illus. 2006. (Fairy Realm Ser.). 128p. (J). 8.99 (978-0-06-077764-7(8)); lib. bdg. 14.89 (978-0-06-077766-1(4)) HarperCollins Pubs.

—The Peskie Spell. Vitale, Raoul, illus. 2007. (Fairy Realm Ser.). 128p. (J). (gr. 3-6). 25.65 (978-1-59961-331-4(X)) Spotlight.

—The Rainbow Wand. Vitale, Raoul, illus. 2006. (Fairy Realm Ser.: No. 10). 128p. (J). lib. bdg. 14.89 (978-0-06-077769-2(9)); 8.99 (978-0-06-077768-5(0)) HarperCollins Pubs.

—The Rainbow Wand. Vitale, Raoul, illus. 2007. (Fairy Realm Ser.). 128p. (J). (gr. 3-6). 25.65 (978-1-59961-332-1(8)) Spotlight.

—The Star Cloak. Vitale, Raoul, illus. 2005. (Fairy Realm Ser.: No. 7). 128p. (J). lib. bdg. 14.89 (978-0-06-077759-3(1)); 8.99 (978-0-06-077758-6(3)) HarperCollins Pubs.

—The Star Cloak. Vitale, Raoul, illus. 2007. (Fairy Realm Ser.). 128p. (J). (gr. 3-6). 25.65 (978-1-59961-329-1(8)) Spotlight.

—The Third Wish. Vitale, Raoul, illus. 2007. (Fairy Realm Ser.). 128p. (J). (gr. 3-6). 25.65 (978-1-59961-325-3(5)) Spotlight.

—The Unicorn. Vitale, Raoul, illus. 2004. (Fairy Realm Ser.: No. 6). 112p. (J). 8.99 (978-0-06-009598-7(9)); lib. bdg. 14.89 (978-0-06-009599-4(7)) HarperCollins Pubs.

—The Unicorn. Vitale, Raoul, illus. 2007. (Fairy Realm Ser.). 112p. (J). (gr. 3-6). 25.65 (978-1-59961-328-4(X)) Spotlight.

—The Water Sprites. Vitale, Raoul, illus. 2007. (Fairy Realm Ser.). 128p. (J). (gr. 3-6). 25.65 (978-1-59961-330-7(1)) Spotlight.

Rodriguez, AJ. Theodore Da Baer Ii: A New Beginning. 2006. 207p. pap. 19.95 (978-1-4241-1125-1(0)) PublishAmerica, Inc.

Rogers, Gregory. Midsummer Knight. Rogers, Gregory, illus. 2007. (Illus.). 32p. (J). (gr. 1-4). 16.95 (***978-1-59643-183-6(0))*** Roaring Brook Pr.

Rogers, Joe. The War of the Elves (Book Two of the Changeling) 2006. 221p. pap. (978-1-84685-164-3(5) , Exposure Publishing) Meadow Bks.

Root, Phyllis. Lucia & the Light. GrandPré, Mary, illus. 2006. 40p. (J). (gr. k-3). 16.99 (978-0-7636-2296-1(6)) Candlewick Pr.

Rowe, Melissa J. When the Tooth Fairy Comes... 2007. (J). per. 10.99 (***978-1-59879-369-7(1))*** Lifevest Publishing, Inc.

Ryan, Brittney. Holly Claus: The Christmas Princess. Long, Laurel & Bedrick, Jeffrey K., illus. 2007. 48p. (J). lib. bdg. 19.89 (***978-0-06-144023-6(X));*** 18.99 (***978-0-06-144022-9(1))*** HarperCollins Pubs. (Julie Andrews Collection).

Ryan, Margaret. Magic Mess! Murfin, Teresa, illus. 2005. (Airy Fairy Bks.). 80p. (J). pap. 3.95 (978-0-7641-3188-2(5)) Barron's Educational Series, Inc.

—Magic Muddle! Murfin, Teresa, illus. 2005. (Airy Fairy Bks.). 80p. (J). pap. 3.95 (978-0-7641-3187-5(7)) Barron's Educational Series, Inc.

Salas, Macarena, ed. La Bella Durmiente: Sleeping Beauty. 2007. (Bilingual Tales Ser.). (ENG & SPA.). 24p. (J). pap. 3.99 (978-0-439-87199-0(9) , Scholastic en Espanol) Scholastic, Inc.

Samuel, Catherine. Timmy's Eggs-Ray Vision. Saunders, Zina, illus. 2005. 16p. (J). lib. bdg. 12.00 (***978-1-4242-0968-2(4))*** Fitzgerald Bks.

Samuel, Catherine & Hartman, Butch. Timmy's Eggs-Ray Vision. Saunders, Zina, illus. 2005. (J). (***978-1-4155-8053-0(7)*** , Simon Spotlight/Nickelodeon) Simon & Schuster Children's Publishing.

Sawyer, Ruth. The Primrose Ring. 2006. 77.99 (***978-1-4280-4665-8(8));*** pap. 70.99 (***978-1-4280-4664-1(X))*** IndyPublish.com.

Sawyer, Ruth. The Wee Christmas Cabin of Carn-Na-Ween. Grafe, Max, illus. 2005. 40p. (J). (gr. 3 up). 14.99 (978-0-7636-2553-5(1)) Candlewick Pr.

Scalora, Suza. The Fairies. Scalora, Suza, illus. 1999. (Illus.). 48p. (gr. 5 up). 19.99 (978-0-06-028234-9(7) , Cotler, Joanna Books) HarperCollins Pubs.

Schoberle, Cecile. Sweetheart Fairy Wings. Couri, Kathy, illus. 2006. 16p. (J). 12.95 (978-1-4169-1162-3(6) , Little Simon) Simon & Schuster Children's Publishing.

Schoop, Bernice F. The Legend of Moon-Goblin Town. 2003. pap. 8.95 (978-0-533-14342-9(X)) Vantage Pr., Inc.

Scott, Kathleen. We are All Special... Babies are Very Special! l.t. ed. 2002. (Illus.). 40p. (J). 5.00 (978-0-9749177-4-0(5)) A New Day...A New Way!.

Seibold, J. Otto. The Fuchsia Is Now. 2006. (Illus.). 40p. (J). (ps-k). pap. 16.99 (978-0-439-63559-2(4) , Orchard Bks.) Scholastic, Inc.

Selections from the Flower Fables by Louisa Mae Alcott. 2003. (J). cd-rom (978-0-9724995-5-2(5)) Alcazar AudioWorks.

Shannon, David. Alice the Fairy. 2004. (Illus.). 40p. (J). pap. 15.95 (978-0-439-49025-2(1) , Blue Sky Pr., The) Scholastic, Inc.

Shaw, Irene. Cosy Cottage. 2006. (Illus.). 48p. pap. (***978-1-84401-792-8(3))*** Athena Pr.

Sheryl the pearl productions, Sheryl Clayton. Teeny the Magic Genie. 2007. (Illus.). 170p. (J). per. 12.95 (***978-0-9795862-0-0(8))*** Sheryl Da Pearl Productions.

Shetterly, Will. Nevernever. 2004. 226p. (YA). (gr. 9-12). lib. bdg. 13.60 (978-0-606-33013-8(5)) Tandem Library Bks.

Shortridge, Retha. Gnome in the House. 2005. 78p. pap. 14.95 (978-1-4137-5188-8(1)) PublishAmerica, Inc.

Shu, Sammy. There's a Season for All. Cone, Carl, illus. 2006. 54p. (J). per. 16.95 (978-0-9778211-0-5(2) , Raynestorm Bks.) Silver Rose Publishing.

Shulman, Mark. Magic Fairy Forest. Wilburn, Kathy, illus. 2005. (Storytime Stickers Ser.). 16p. (J). pap. 4.95 (978-1-4027-1806-9(3)) Sterling Publishing Co., Inc.

Sidell, Yvonne. The Fairy Twins: Land of New Friends. 2006. (ENG.). 48p. per. 23.99 (***978-1-4259-4840-5(5))*** AuthorHouse.

Silver Dolphin en Español Staff. Imanes Magicos: Fairies Forever: Magnets on the Move: Fairies Forever, Spanish-Language Edition. 2006. (Illus.). 8p. (J). bds. 12.95 (978-970-718-370-4(5) , Silver Dolphin en Español) Advanced Marketing, S. de R. L. de C. V. MEX. *Dist:* Perseus Distribution.

Simmons, Jane. El Vuelo de las Hadas. 2002. Tr. of Where the Fairies Fly. (SPA.). 102p. (J). 17.95 (978-84-488-1193-8(3) , BS31494) Beascoa, Ediciones S.A. ESP. *Dist:* Lectorum Pubns., Inc.

Sisk, Glenda. The Snow Fairy. Sparks, Sandra Ann, illus. 2000. (J). lib. bdg. 14.95 (978-0-9705727-2-1(7)) Coastal Publishing Carolina, Inc.

Skead, Robert. Elves Can't Dunk. 2000. 96p. (YA). (gr. 3-10). pap. 5.95 (978-1-929478-14-9(3)) Cross Training Publishing.

—Elves Can't Kick. 2005. 84p. per. 7.99 (978-1-929478-66-8(6)) Cross Training Publishing.

Slater, Teddy. The Luckiest St Patrick's Day Ever. 2008. 32p. pap. 5.99 (***978-0-545-03943-7(6)*** , Cartwheel Bks.) Scholastic, Inc.

Smith, James. I'm so over Fairies. Smith, Alice, illus. 2007. 32p. (J). (ps-k). pap. 5.99 (978-1-84255-542-2(1)) Orion Children's Bks. GBR. *Dist:* Independent Pubs. Group.

Smith, James & Smith, Alice. I'm So over Fairies. 2007. (Illus.). 32p. (J). (ps-k). 8.99 (978-1-84255-500-2(6)) Orion Children's Bks. GBR. *Dist:* Independent Pubs. Group.

Smith, Jane Denitz. Fairy Dust. (J). Date not set. (gr. 3-7). mass mkt. 4.99 (978-0-06-440961-2(9)); 2002. (Illus.). 160p. 15.89 (978-0-06-029280-5(6)) HarperCollins Pubs.

Space Fairy. 2005. (J). (978-1-932570-34-2(9)) Literacy Footprints Inc.

Spitzer, Linda & Myers, Sarah. Tales of the Paper Bag Fairies/Color Version. 2005. 54p. (J). pap. 14.95 (978-1-4116-4095-5(0)) Lulu.com.

Springer, Nancy. I Am Morgan le Fay: A Tale from Camelot. 2002. (Firebird Ser.). 240p. (YA). pap. 6.99 (978-0-698-11974-1(6) , Puffin) Penguin Group (USA) Inc.

—I Am Morgan le Fay: A Tale from Camelot. 2002. (gr. 7-12). lib. bdg. 14.15 (978-0-613-55214-1(8)) Tandem Library Bks.

—Rowan Hood: Outlaw Girl of Sherwood Forest. 2002. (Tales of Rowan Hood Ser.: No. 1). (gr. 5-8). lib. bdg. 14.15 (978-0-613-53860-2(9)) Tandem Library Bks.

—Rowan Hood Returns: The Final Chapter. 2006. (Tales of Rowan Hood Ser.: No. 5). 176p. (J). (gr. 3). pap. 5.99 (978-0-14-240685-4(6) , Puffin) Penguin Group (USA) Inc.

Stanek, Robert. The Kingdoms & the Elves of the Reaches IV (Special Illustrated Edition) 2009. (Keeper Martin's Tales Ser.: Bk. 4). (Illus.). 256p. (YA). pap. 18.95 (978-1-57545-508-2(0) , Reagent Pr. Signature Editions) Reagent Pr.

Stanton, Andy. You're a Bad Man, Mr. Gum! Dezern, Chad, illus. 2008. 144p. (J). 9.99 (***978-0-06-115240-5(4));*** lib. bdg. 14.89 (***978-0-06-115243-6(9))*** HarperCollins Pubs.

Star the Tooth Fairy from Treasure Cloud Shares Secrets with You! 2006. (J). per. 9.99 (***978-0-9792992-0-9(9))*** Twinkle Bks.

Star the Tooth Fairy Is Checking on You! 2004. (J). per. 9.99 (***978-0-9792992-2-3(5))*** Twinkle Bks.

Star the Tooth Fairy Wants to Know if You Need Braces? 2006. (J). per. 9.99 (***978-0-9792992-1-6(7))*** Twinkle Bks.

Starcke, Rod M. Seven Fairy Tales. 2006. pap. 9.95 (978-0-533-15288-9(7)) Vantage Pr., Inc.

Stegman-Bourgeois, Karen M. Trollerella. Long, Ethan, illus. 2006. 32p. (J). 14.95 (978-0-8234-1918-0(5)) Holiday Hse., Inc.

Stein-Aubert, Danielle. The Blossoms' Ball. Peyre, Virginie, illus. 2004. 34p. (J). 12.95 (978-1-58246-096-3(5) , Tricycle Pr.) Ten Speed Pr.

Sterling Publishing Co., Inc. & Fernleigh Books Staff. Fairies: A Magic 3-Dimensional World of Fairies. 2007. (Step Inside Ser.). (Illus.). 12p. (J). (ps-1). 9.95 (***978-1-4027-4898-1(1))*** Sterling Publishing Co., Inc.

Stine, R. L. Have You Met My Ghoulfriend? 2004. (Mostly Ghostly Ser.). 144p. (J). (gr. 2-5). 6.95 (978-0-385-74664-9(4)); lib. bdg. 8.99 (978-0-385-90914-3(4)) Random Hse. Children's Bks. (Delacorte Bks. for Young Readers).

Stohner, Anu. Santa's Littlest Helper Travels the World. Wilson, Henrike, illus. 2007. 32p. (J). (ps-3). 15.95 (***978-1-59990-187-9(0)*** , Bloomsbury Children) Bloomsbury Publishing.

Story of the Christmas Elves. 2001. 26p. (J). 12.95 (978-0-9712332-0-1(9)) G. D. Stewart Publishing.

Strauss, Linda Leopold. A Fairy Called Hilary. Truesdell, Sue, illus. 1999. 96p. (J). (gr. 4-6). tchr. ed. 15.95 (978-0-8234-1418-5(3)) Holiday Hse., Inc.

—A Fairy Called Hilary. Truesdell, Sue, illus. 2001. 128p. (J). (gr. 2-5). pap. 3.99 (978-0-439-17519-7(4)) Scholastic, Inc.

Streit, Jakob. Puck trhe Gnome. Mitchell, David S., ed. Kuettel, Nina, tr. 2004. Orig. Title: Puck der Zwerg. (J). per. 14.00 (978-1-888365-54-2(4)) Assn. of Waldorf Schls. of North America Pubns. (AWSNA).

Stringer. Fairies of Spencer Meadow: Fairy Tales. 2004. (Illus.). 60p. (978-1-4120-1667-4(3)) Trafford Publishing.

Sullivan, Ellen. How Santa Got His Elves. Eldredge, Ernie, illus. 1998. (J). (978-1-58173-148-4(5)) Sweetwater Pr.

Sweet, J. H. Dragonfly & the Web of Dreams. Chang, Tara Larsen, illus. 2007. (Fairy Chronicles Ser.). 128p. (J). (gr. 2-4). pap. 6.99 (***978-1-4022-0873-7(1)*** , Sourcebooks Jabberwocky) Sourcebooks, Inc.

—The Fairy Chronicles: Thistle & the Shell of Laughter. 2007. (Illus.). 128p. (J). pap. 6.99 (***978-1-4022-0874-4(X)*** , Sourcebooks Jabberwocky) Sourcebooks, Inc.

—Marigold & the Feather of Hope, the Journey Begins. Chang, Tara Larsen, illus. 2007. (Fairy Chronicles Ser.). 128p. (J). (gr. 2-4). pap. 6.99 (***978-1-4022-0872-0(3)*** , Sourcebooks Jabberwocky) Sourcebooks, Inc.

Sweet, J.H. & Sierra, Holly. Periwinkle & the Cave of Courage: The Fairy Chronicles. 2007. (Fairy Chronicles Ser.). (Illus.). 128p. (J). (gr. 2 up). pap. 6.99 (***978-1-4022-1026-6(4)*** , Sourcebooks Jabberwocky) Sourcebooks, Inc.

—Spiderwort & the Princess of Haiku: The Fairy Chronicles. 2007. (Fairy Chronicles Ser.). (Illus.). 128p. (J). (gr. 2 up). pap. 6.99 (***978-1-4022-1025-9(6)*** , Sourcebooks Jabberwocky) Sourcebooks, Inc.

Taylor, Laini. Blackbringer. 2007. (Faeries of Dreamdark Ser.). 368p. (J). (gr. 5 up). 17.99 (978-0-399-24630-2(4) , Putnam Juvenile) Penguin Group (USA) Inc.

Thompson, Kate. The New Policeman. 2007. 448p. (gr. 7-10). (J). lib. bdg. 17.89 (978-0-06-117428-5(9)); (YA). 16.99 (978-0-06-117427-8(0) , Greenwillow Bks.) HarperCollins Pubs.

Thomson, Emma. Felicity Wishes Friendship & Fairyschool. 2002. 20p. (J). 14.99 (978-0-670-03593-9(9) , Viking Juvenile) Penguin Group (USA) Inc.

—Felicity Wishes Little Book of Friendship. 2002. 20p. (J). 5.99 (978-0-670-03590-8(4) , Viking Juvenile) Penguin Group (USA) Inc.

Thorpe, Kiki. Tink, North of Never Land. Disney Storybook Artists Staff, illus. 2007. 128p. (J). (gr. 1-5). 5.99 (***978-0-7364-2455-4(5)*** , RH/Disney) Random Hse. Children's Bks.

Thorpe, Kiki. The Trouble with Tink. Clarke, Judith, illus. 2006. (Stepping Stone Bks.). 128p. (J). (gr. 2-4). 5.99 (978-0-7364-2371-7(0) , RH/Disney) Random Hse. Children's Bks.

Throckmorton, Patricia. The Adventures of Ish & Parr: Land of Happiness. 2007. (J). per. 10.99 (***978-1-59886-910-1(8))*** Tate Publishing & Enterprises, L.L.C.

Tich, Jan & Jantti, Mariana. The Sea Fairy's Hat. 2006. (Magical Stories Ser.). (Illus.). 28p. (J). 16.95 (978-9974-7896-8-5(0)) Hardenville SA URY. *Dist:* Independent Pubs. Group.

Top That Publishing Staff, ed. Goldilocks & Three Bears. 2006. (Illus.). 10p. bds. (978-1-905359-93-6(4)) Top That! Publishing PLC.

Trent, Tiffany. In the Serpent's Coils. 2007. (Hallowmere Ser.). 312p. (YA). (gr. 7-11). 8.95 (***978-0-7869-4229-9(0)*** , Mirrorstone) Wizards of the Coast.

Trondheim, Lewis. Happy Halloween, Li'l Santa. Robin, Thierry, illus. 2003. 48p. 14.95 (978-1-56163-361-6(5)) NBM Publishing Co.

Turin, Adela. La Herencia del Hada. Bosnia, Nella, illus. (SPA.). 40p. (J). (gr. 3-5). (978-84-264-3556-9(4)) Editorial Lumen ESP. *Dist:* Lectorum Pubns., Inc.

Tutt, Ann Chamberlain. Red Wings & Fairy Things. 2006. 78p. pap. 14.95 (978-1-4241-2219-6(8)) PublishAmerica, Inc.

Ullman, Barb Bentler. The Fairies of Nutfolk Wood. 256p. (J). 2008. pap. 5.99 (***978-0-06-134563-0(6)*** , Harper Trophy); 2006. 15.99 (978-0-06-073614-9(3) , Tegen, Katherine Bks); 2006. lib. bdg. 16.89 (978-0-06-073615-6(1) , Tegen, Katherine Bks) HarperCollins Pubs.

Uncle Henry. How the Tooth Fairy, of All People, Saved the Day, Uncle Henry, illus. 100th ed. 2004. (Illus.). 64p. pap. 5.99 (978-1-932568-00-4(X) , UHB001) Uncle Henry Bks.

Uribe, Veronica. El Libro de Oro de las Fabulas. Bravo, Constanza, illus. 2004. (SPA.). 126p. (J). (ps-3). 9.99 (978-980-257-209-0(8)) Ekare, Ediciones VEN. *Dist:* Lectorum Pubns., Inc., Iaconi, Mariuccia Bk. Imports.

Vance, L. K. Jennadi. 2006. 73p. pap. 14.95 (978-1-4241-1574-7(4)) PublishAmerica, Inc.

Vornholt, John. The Troll Queen. l.t. ed. 2004. (Troll King Ser.). 241p. 20.95 (978-0-7862-6517-6(5)) Thorndike Pr.

Wagner, Jerri. The Adventures of "Jako", the Florida Troll. 1999. 53p. (J). pap. 9.95 (978-0-7414-0111-3(8)) Infinity Publishing.

Wahl, Jan. Elf Night. Weevers, Peter, illus. 2005. (Picture Bks.). 32p. (gr. k-2). 15.25 (978-1-57505-512-1(0)) Lerner Publishing Group.

Walther, William. A Collection of Fairy Tales: Volume One. 2007. (YA). per. 12.95 (***978-0-9795087-0-7(3))*** Ctr. Stage Puppets.

Ward, Helen. Little Moon Dog. Anderson, Wayne, illus. 2007. 32p. (J). (ps-3). 16.99 (978-0-525-47727-3(6) , Dutton Juvenile) Penguin Group (USA) Inc.

Ward, Helen. Moon Dog. 2005. (Illus.). 40p. (J). (***978-1-84011-864-3(4))*** Templar Publishing, Dorking.

Washington, Linda & Pyykkonen, Carrie. Secrets of the Wee Free Men & Discworld: The Myths & Legends of Terry Pratchett's Multiverse. 2008. (Illus.). 192p. (J). pap. 9.95 (***978-0-312-37243-9(4)*** , St. Martin's Griffin) St. Martin's Pr.

Watt, Fiona. (Fairies Luxury Touchy-Feely) - Spanish. 2006. 12p. (J). bds. 15.99 (978-0-7460-7405-3(0) , Usborne) EDC Publishing.

Wax, Wendy. For Love or Money. Piluso, Piero, illus. 2006. 32p. (J). lib. bdg. 9.00 (***978-1-4242-0955-2(2))*** Fitzgerald Bks.

Wax, Wendy. Too Many Turners. Moore, Harry, Jr., illus. 2004. (Ready-to-Read Ser.). 32p. (J). pap. 3.99 (978-0-689-86859-7(6) , Simon Spotlight/Nickelodeon) Simon & Schuster Children's Publishing.

Weather Fairies Staff & Meadows, Daisy. Pearl the Cloud Fairy. 2006. (Weather Fairies Ser.: No. 3). (Illus.). 80p. (J). pap. 4.99 (978-0-439-81388-4(3) , Scholastic Paperbacks) Scholastic, Inc.

Webb, Carla. The Magic in Believing: The Tooth Fairies. Lee, Kim, illus. (Magic in Believing Ser.). 36p. (J). (gr. k-5). (978-0-9705726-0-8(3)) Ageless Treasures.

Weber, Jen Funk. Thimbletack's Activity Book. 2008. (Spiderwick Chronicles). 64p. (J). pap. 4.99 (***978-1-4169-4954-1(2)*** , Simon Scribbles) Simon & Schuster Children's Publishing.

Webster, Christy. Barbie Mariposa. 2008. (Step into Reading Ser.). (Illus.). 32p. (J). (ps-1). lib. bdg. 11.99 (***978-0-375-95198-5(9));*** pap. 3.99 (***978-0-375-85198-8(4))*** Random Hse. Children's Bks. (Random Hse. Bks. for Young Readers).

Weinberg, Jennifer. Surprise for a Princess. Emslie, Peter & Marrucchi, Elisa, illus. 2003. (Disney Princess Ser.). 32p. (J). (ps-1). pap. 3.99 (978-0-7364-2132-4(7) , RH/Disney) Random Hse. Children's Bks.

—Surprise for a Princess. 2003. (Disney Princess Ser.). (ps-2). lib. bdg. 11.80 (978-0-613-73686-2(9)) Tandem Library Bks.

Weiser, Joey. The Ride Home. 2007. (Illus.). 168p. pap. 8.95 (***978-0-9770304-4-6(X))*** AdHouse Bks.

West, Tracey. The Greedy Gremlin. 2006. (Pixie Tricks Ser.: No. 2). (Illus.). 128p. (J). (gr. 1-4). 3.99 (978-0-439-17219-6(5) , Scholastic Paperbacks) Scholastic, Inc.

—The Halloween Goblin. 2000. (gr. 3-6). lib. bdg. 11.80 (978-0-613-25435-9(X)) Tandem Library Bks.

—The Movie Storybook. 2008. (Spiderwick Chronicles). 32p. (J). (gr. k-4). 8.99 (***978-1-4169-4947-3(X)*** , Simon Spotlight) Simon & Schuster Children's Publishing.

—The Pet Store Sprite. 2000. (gr. 3-6). lib. bdg. 11.80 (978-0-613-26575-1(0)) Tandem Library Bks.

—Sporty Sprite. 2001. (gr. 3-6). lib. bdg. 11.80 (978-0-613-33086-2(2)) Tandem Library Bks.

Where the Leprechauns Hide. 2007. pap. 12.99 (***978-0-9792258-9-5(2))*** Bezalel Bks.

Wickings, Ruth. Fairies. 2007. (Enchanted World Ser.). (Illus.). 10p. (J). (ps-3). 9.95 (***978-1-84560-030-3(4))*** Mercury Bks. Ltd. GBR. *Dist:* International Publishers Marketing.

E
F
G

Wilcox, Leah. Waking Beauty. Monks, Lydia, illus. 2008. 32p. (J). (ps). 16.99 (*978-0-399-24615-9(0) , Putnam Juvenile) Penguin Group (USA) Inc.

Wood, Maggie. The Princess Mage. 2006. 296p. (YA). pap. 9.95 (978-1-894549-52-3(X)) Sumach Pr. CAN. *Dist:* Orca Bk. Pubs. USA.

Wooding, Chris. Poison. 288p. (J). 2006. pap. 7.99 (978-0-439-75571-9(9) , Scholastic Paperbacks); 2005. (gr. 7 up). pap. 16.99 (978-0-439-75570-2(0) , Orchard Bks.) Scholastic, Inc.

Woods, Tonita. Mystical Forest of Wise. 2001. 120p. pap. 10.95 (978-0-595-19147-5(9) , Writers Club Pr.) iUniverse, Inc.

Wright, Jonathan B. Who's Behind the Fairy Doors? Wright, Jonathan B., illus. 2007. (Illus.). 64p. (*978-0-9793585-0-0(7)) Urban Fairies Operations, LLC.

Yoon, Salina. The Secret Life of Fairies. 2007. (Salina Yoon Bks.). 10p. (J). (ps-1). pap. 8.99 (978-0-8431-2488-0(1) , Price Stern Sloan) Penguin Group (USA) Inc.

Zobel-Nolan, Allia. The Secret Fairy Garden. Ember, Kathi, illus. 2005. 12p. (J). bds. 12.99 (978-0-7944-0513-7(4)) Reader's Digest Assn., Inc., The.

FAIRIES—POETRY

Barker, Cecily M. Flower Fairies Box Set. 2007. pap. 16.99 (*978-0-7232-5976-3(3)) Penguin Group (USA) Inc.

Barker, Cicely Mary. Alphabet. 2002. (Illus.). 64p. (J). 6.99 (978-0-7232-4832-3(X) , Warne) Penguin Group (USA) Inc.

—The Complete Book of the Flower Fairies. 2002. (Illus.). 192p. (J). (ps-3). 25.00 (978-0-7232-4839-2(7) , Warne) Penguin Group (USA) Inc.

Joyce, Hale. Faerys, Dragons & Unicorns. Hale, Joyce & Kirk, Joan, illus. 2002. (J). 12.95 (978-0-9715926-3-6(2)) Passage Publishing.

Lach, William, ed. Fairyland: In Art & Poetry. Doyle, Richard, illus. 2001. 40p. (J). (978-0-87099-995-6(8)) Metropolitan Museum of Art, The.

—Fairyland in Art & Poetry. Doyle, Richard, illus. rev. ed. 2002. 40p. (J). 16.95 (978-0-8050-7006-4(0) , Holt, Henry & Co. Bks. For Young Readers) Holt, Henry & Co.

FAIRS

see also Exhibitions; Markets

Color All About: A Giant Coloring Book about the County Fair: the County Fair. 2004. (SPA & ENG., Illus.). 36p. (J). (978-1-59949-004-5(8)) Food Marketing Consultants, Inc.

Color All About: The County Fair: A Giant Coloring Book about Having Fun When the Fair Comes to Town. 2004. (Illus.). (J). (978-0-9763307-6-9(8)) Food Marketing Consultants, Inc.

Foley, Cate. Let's Go to a Fair. (Weekend Fun Ser.). (Illus.). 24p. (J). (ps-2). 2001. 17.00 (978-0-516-23190-7(1)); 2001. pap. 4.95 (978-0-516-29580-0(2)); 2000. lib. bdg. (978-0-516-23293-5(2)) Scholastic Library Publishing. (Children's Pr.).

—Let's Go to a Fair. 2001. (gr. k-3). lib. bdg. 12.95 (978-0-613-58986-4(6)) Tandem Library Bks.

Harcourt School Publishers Staff. County Fair. 3rd ed. 2002. (Trophies English Language Learners Ser.). (Illus.). pap. 5.10 (978-0-15-327777-1(7)) Harcourt Schl. Pubs.

—Ohio State Fair. 3rd ed. 2002. (Horizons Ser.). (Illus.). (J). pap. 5.50 (978-0-15-333415-3(0)) Harcourt Schl. Pubs.

Jackson, Robert. Meet Me in St. Louis: A Trip to the 1904 World's Fair. 2004. (Illus.). 144p. (J). (gr. 3 up). 17.99 (978-0-06-009267-2(X)) HarperCollins Pubs.

Libal, Joyce. Getting Ready for the Fair: Crafts, Projects, & Prize-Winning Animals. 2006. (Youth in Rural North America Ser.). (J). (978-1-4222-0019-3(1)) Mason Crest Pubs.

Tu, Alice. A Fair Is Fun. 2003. (Compass Point Phonics Readers Ser.). (Illus.). 16p. (J). (gr. 1 up). 13.26 (978-0-7565-0501-1(1)) Compass Point Bks.

FAIRS—FICTION

Anastasio, Dina. Matematicas divertidas en la feria & Math Fun at the Fair. 2005. spiral bd. 66.00 (*978-1-4108-5639-5(9)) Benchmark Education Co.

Anderson, Jane. Inspector Insector. 2005. 22.00 (*978-1-4108-4196-4(0)) Benchmark Education Co.

Axelrod, Amy. Pigs at Odds: Fun with Math & Games. McGinley-Nally, Sharon, illus. 2000. 40p. (J). (gr. 2-4). 15.95 (978-0-689-81566-9(2)) Simon & Schuster Children's Publishing.

—Pigs at Odds: Fun with Math & Games. 2003. (gr. k-3). lib. bdg. 15.30 (978-0-613-67156-9(2)) Tandem Library Bks.

Axelrod, Amy & McGinley-Nally, Sharon. Pigs at Odds. 2003. (Illus.). 40p. (J). pap. 6.99 (978-0-689-86144-4(3) , Aladdin) Simon & Schuster Children's Publishing.

Banscherus, Jurgen & Baron, Daniel C. The Puzzle of the Power Drain. Butschkow, Ralf, illus. 2008. (J). pap. (*978-1-59889-912-2(0)); lib. bdg. (*978-1-59889-876-7(0)) Stone Arch Bks.

Barker, Cicely Mary. Flower Fairies Best Friends. Barker, Cicely Mary, illus. 2005. 24p. (J). 9.99 (978-0-7232-5714-1(0) , Warne) Penguin Group (USA) Inc.

Barkley, Brad & Hepler, Heather. Scrambled Eggs at Midnight. 2007. 288p. (J). (gr. 7 up). pap. 7.99 (978-0-14-240867-4(0) , Puffin); 2006. 272p. (YA). (gr. 6). 16.99 (978-0-525-47760-0(8) , Dutton Juvenile) Penguin Group (USA) Inc.

Bodel, Garrett. A Day at the Fair. 2002. (Doll's Life Story Ser.: Vol. 4). (Illus.). 32p. (J). pap. 7.90 (978-0-9720072-1-4(0)) Doll's Life.

Brown, Marc. Arthur's Lost Puppy. 2001. (Arthur Ser.). (J). (ps-1). spiral bd. 14.99 (978-1-58605-223-2(3)) Leap-Frog Enterprises, Inc.

Bunting, Eve. Market Day. 1999. (J). (978-0-606-14263-2(0)) Tandem Library Bks.

—The Pumpkin Fair. Christelow, Eileen, illus. 2001. 40p. (J). (gr. k-3). pap. 5.95 (978-0-618-13051-1(9) , Clarion Bks.) Houghton Mifflin Co. Trade & Reference Div.

Burns, Laura. A Fine State of Affairs, No. 3. 2006. (Darcy's Wild Life Ser.: Bk. 3). 176p. (J). (gr. 4-7). pap. 4.99 (978-0-448-44260-0(4) , Grosset & Dunlap) Penguin Group (USA) Inc.

Clarissa - Evaluation Guide: Evaluation Guide. 2006. (J). (978-1-55942-402-8(8)) Marsh Media.

Colato Lainez, Rene. Playing Loteria Mexicana: El Juego de la Loteria Mexicana. Arena, Jillayne, illus. 2005. (ENG & SPA.). 32p. (gr. 1-3). 15.95 (978-0-87358-881-2(9) , Rising Moon Bks. for Young Readers) Northland Publishing.

Cole, Joanna & Calmenson, Stephanie. Gator Halloween. Munsinger, Lynn, illus. 1999. (Gator Girls Ser.: Vol. 3). 64p. (J). (gr. 1-4). 14.89 (978-0-688-14785-3(2)) HarperCollins Pubs.

Crews, Donald. Night at the Fair. Crews, Donald, illus. 1998. (Illus.). (J). (ps-3). 32p. 16.99 (978-0-688-11483-1(0)); 24p. 14.89 (978-0-688-11484-8(9)) HarperCollins Pubs.

Dad at the Fair: Individual Title Six-Packs. (Sails Literacy Ser.). (gr. 1-2). 36.00 (978-0-7578-6719-4(7)) Rigby Education.

Danziger, Paula. It's a Fair Day, Amber Brown. Ross, Tony, illus. 2003. 28.95 incl. audio compact disk (978-1-59112-565-5(0)); pap. 31.95 incl. audio compact disk (978-1-59112-564-8(2)) Live Oak Media.

—It's a Fair Day, Amber Brown. Ross, Tony, illus. 48p. (J). (gr. k-2). 2003. pap. 3.99 (978-0-698-11982-6(7) , Puffin); 2002. 12.99 (978-0-399-23606-8(6) , Putnam Juvenile) Penguin Group (USA) Inc.

—It's a Fair Day, Amber Brown. 2003. (gr. k-3). lib. bdg. 11.80 (978-0-613-61635-5(9)) Tandem Library Bks.

—Orange You Glad It's Halloween, Amber Brown? Ross, Tony, illus. 2005. 48p. (J). (gr. 2-5). 13.99 (978-0-399-23471-2(3) , Putnam Juvenile) Penguin Group (USA) Inc.

Derrick, Patricia. Farley the Ferret of Farkleberry Farm. 2007. 32p. 18.95 (978-1-933818-12-2(3)) Animalations.

deRubertis, Barbara. Bouncy Mouse. Cockrille, Eva V., illus. 1998. (Let's Read Together Ser.). 32p. (J). (ps-3). pap. 4.95 (978-1-57565-043-2(6)) Kane Pr., The.

Edwards, Frank B. Crowded Ride in the Countryside. 1999. (ps-2). lib. bdg. 12.95 (978-0-613-80351-9(5)) Tandem Library Bks.

Egan, Kate. Fun at the Fair. Edwards, Ken, illus. 2004. (My Little Pony Ser.). 24p. (J). (ps-1). pap. 3.99 (978-0-06-055400-2(2) , Harper Festival) HarperCollins Pubs.

Ellsberry, Sharon. The Spaniel Family Goes to the State Fair. Espinosa, Chris, illus. 2004. 24p. (J). 9.00 (978-0-9724637-2-0(0)) Sky Rocket Pr.

Enderle, Dotti. The Cotton Candy Catastrophe at the Texas State Fair. Galey, Chuck, illus. 2004. 32p. (J). pap. 15.95 (978-1-58980-189-9(X)) Pelican Publishing Co., Inc.

Evans, Gwen & Collins, Darluniau Mike. Delyth a'r Ffair Haf. 2005. (WEL., Illus.). 12p. (978-1-85644-758-4(8)) Univ. of Wales, Aberystwyth, Centre for Educational Studies.

Finley, Martha. Elsie at the Worlds Fair. 2006. 78.99 (*978-1-4280-3168-5(5)) IndyPublish.com.

Gelsey, James. Scooby-Doo!TM & the Fairground Phantom. del Sur, Duendes, illus. 2000. (Scooby-Doo Mysteries Ser.: No. 11). 64p. (J). (ps-3). 3.99 (978-0-439-10664-1(8)) Scholastic, Inc.

Greene, Stephanie. Pig Pickin' Mathieu, Joseph, illus. 2006. (Marshall Cavendish Chapter Book Ser.). 64p. (J). 14.99 (978-0-7614-5324-6(5)) Cavendish, Marshall Corp.

Hall, Patricia. Day at the Fair. 2000. (gr. k-3). lib. bdg. 11.80 (978-0-613-31111-3(6)) Tandem Library Bks.

Harcourt School Publishers Staff. Little Pig at the State Fair Advanced Level. 3rd ed. 2002. (Trophies Reading Program Ser.). (Illus.). pap. 5.10 (978-0-15-323038-7(X)) Harcourt Schl. Pubs.

—Science Fair! 3rd ed. 2002. (Trophies English Language Learners Ser.). (Illus.). pap. 5.10 (978-0-15-327751-1(3)) Harcourt Schl. Pubs.

Hats for the Carnival: Individual Title Six-Pack Pouch - Level I. (Lighthouse Ser.). 16p. (gr. 1 up). 26.00 (978-0-7578-0851-7(4)) Rigby Education.

Healy, Nick. The Big Pig. Rooney, Ronnie, illus. 2006. 32p. (J). (*978-1-4048-3385-2(4)) Picture Window Bks.

Hensley, Sarah M. Cailloo Goes to the Fair. Coray, Stacy A., illus. l.t. ed. 2005. (Hrl Board Book Ser.). (J). (gr. k up). pap. 10.95 (978-1-57332-328-4(4)) HighReach Learning, Inc.

Hill, David. Ghosts & Ghoulies. 2005. (Thrillogy Ser.). (Illus.). 48p. (gr. 4-8). 17.50 (978-0-7910-8888-3(X)) Facts On File, Inc.

Hoffman, Elizabeth. Miss Renee's Mice Go to an Exhibition. Peterson, Dawn, illus. 2003. (Miss Rene's Mice Ser.: No. 2). 32p. (gr. k-2). 15.95 (978-0-89272-581-6(8)) Down East Bks.

Holabird, Katharine. Angelina at the Fair. Craig, Helen, illus. 2007. 32p. (J). 12.99 (978-0-670-06234-8(0) , Viking Juvenile) Penguin Group (USA) Inc.

—Angelina at the Fair. 2006. (Illus.). 32p. (J). pap. 5.99 (978-0-14-240591-8(4) , Puffin) Penguin Group (USA) Inc.

Hollar, Cheryl Faye. Billy the Bunny Goes to the State Fair. 2005. (J). pap. 7.97 (978-0-9763826-0-7(1)) Hollar, Cheryl Public Relations.

Holley, Marietta. Samantha at the St. Louis Exposition. 2007. 188p. pap. 11.99 (*978-1-4264-6038-8(4)) BiblioBazaar.

—Samantha at the World's Fair. 2007. 428p. pap. 16.99 (*978-1-4264-5101-0(6)) BiblioBazaar.

Hood, Susan. Pup & Hound Lost & Found. Hendry, Linda, illus. 2006. 32p. (J). lib. bdg. 15.38 (*978-1-4242-0250-8(7)) Fitzgerald Bks.

Hughes, Shirley. Alfie Wins a Prize. 2007. (Illus.). 32p. (J). pap. 8.95 (*978-0-09-945638-4(9) , Red Fox) Random Hse. Children's Bks. GBR. *Dist:* Independent Pubs. Group.

—Alfie Wins a Prize. 2006. (Illus.). 32p. (J). 19.95 (*978-0-370-32824-9(8)) Transworld Publishers Ltd. GBR. *Dist:* Independent Pubs. Group.

Inches, Alison. Hooray for Polka Dots! Chernichaw, Ian, illus. ed. 2005. 22p. (J). lib. bdg. 15.00 (978-1-59054-972-8(4)) Fitzgerald Bks.

—Hooray for Polka Dots! Chernichaw, Ian, illus. 2005. (Blue's Clues Ser.: Vol. 10). 24p. (J). pap. 3.99 (978-0-689-87210-5(0) , Simon Spotlight/Nickelodeon) Simon & Schuster Children's Publishing.

Jeanne Marie at the Fair. 2004. (Illus.). 34p. (J). mass mkt. (978-0-9740599-4-5(3)) Omnibus Publishing.

Katschke, Judy. Case of the Weird Science Mystery. 2002. (gr. 3-6). lib. bdg. 12.40 (978-0-613-50431-7(3)) Tandem Library Bks.

Kent, Renee Holmes. Cassie, You're a Winner! 2004. (Adventures in Misty Falls Ser.: Vol. 1). (Illus.). 100p. (gr. 4-7). pap. 2.99 (978-1-56309-735-5(4) , N007116) New Hope Pubs.

Lawson, Robert. The Great Wheel. 2004. (Illus.). 192p. (J). pap. 6.95 (978-0-8027-7705-8(8)) Walker & Co.

Lloyd, Gita. Meet Me at the Fair. 2001. (gr. k-3). lib. bdg. 11.80 (978-0-613-85714-7(3)) Tandem Library Bks.

Loughead, Deb. Pet Fair. Birke, Lisa, illus. 2000. vi, 48p. (J). pap. 5.95 (978-0-9686899-3-6(0)) Hodgepog Bks. CAN. *Dist:* Coteau Bks.

Lunn, Janet. Come to the Fair. 2001. (gr. k-3). lib. bdg. 16.40 (978-0-613-77327-0(6)) Tandem Library Bks.

—Come to the Fair. Pelletier, Gilles, illus. 2001. 24p. (J). (gr. 1-4). pap. 7.95 (978-0-88776-576-6(9)) Tundra Bks., Inc./Livres Toundra, Inc. CAN. *Dist:* Random Hse., Inc.

Marsh, Carole. Dear Granny: The Spooky State Fair Fiasco. 2007. (Postcard Mysteries Ser.). 128p. (J). (gr. 2-9). 14.95 (*978-0-635-06399-1(9)); pap. 5.99 (*978-0-635-06343-4(3)) Gallopade International. (Marsh, Carole Family CD-Rom).

Mayer, Mercer. Country Fair. (Little Critter Ser.). (Illus.). 24p. (J). (ps-2). 2003. 10.95 (978-1-57768-633-0(0)); 2002. pap. 3.95 (978-1-57768-827-3(9)) School Specialty Publishing.

—Country Fair. 2001. (gr. k-3). lib. bdg. 11.80 (978-0-613-67607-6(6)) Tandem Library Bks.

McCann, Jesse Leon. Scooby-Doo & the Creepy Carnival. 1998. (Scooby-Doo 3-D Storybooks: No. 1). (Illus.). 16p. (J). (ps-3). pap. 5.99 (978-0-590-38654-8(9)) Scholastic, Inc.

McCullough, Sharon Pierce. Bunbun at the Fair. 2002. (Bunbun Ser.). (Illus.). 24p. (J). (gr. k-2). 14.99 (978-1-84148-900-1(X)) Barefoot Bks., Inc.

McOmber, Rachel B., ed. McOmber Phonics Storybooks: At the Fair. rev. ed. (Illus.). (J). (978-0-944991-60-2(2)) Swift Learning Resources.

Moore, Nancy Delano. Kiernan's Jam. Peck, Bill, illus. 2006. (J). 10.00 (978-0-9785775-0-6(7)) Moore, Hullihen.

Morgan, Melissa J. Fair to Remember, Vol. 13. 2007. (Camp Confidential Ser.). 160p. (J). pap. 4.99 (978-0-448-44451-2(8) , Grosset & Dunlap) Penguin Group (USA) Inc.

Papp, Robert, illus. The Sword of the Silver Knight, Vol. 103. 2005. (Boxcar Children Mysteries Ser.: 103). 112p. (J). (ps-7). 14.95 (978-0-8075-0877-0(2)) Whitman, Albert & Co.

Peck, Richard. Fair Weather. 2001. (Illus.). 160p. (J). (gr. 4-8). 16.99 (978-0-8037-2516-4(7) , Dial) Penguin Group (USA) Inc.

Proysen, Alf. Mrs. Pepperpot at the Bazaar. Offen, Hilda, illus. 2007. 32p. pap. 4.99 (*978-0-09-945158-7(1)) Transworld Publishers Ltd. GBR. *Dist:* Independent Pubs. Group.

Pugliano-Martin, Carol. BarbieTM: A Day at the Fair. S. I. International Staff, illus. 2003. (Step into Reading Ser.). 32p. (J). (ps-1). pap. 3.99 (978-0-375-82368-8(9) , Random Hse. Bks. for Young Readers) Random Hse. Children's Bks.

Rau, Dana Meachen. At a Fair. 2007. (Fun Time Ser.). 24p. (J). lib. bdg. 22.79 (*978-0-7614-2606-6(X) , Benchmark Bks.) Cavendish, Marshall Corp.

Rice, Judy. Counting Fair. 2007. 20p. (J). per. 10.95 (*978-1-59594-173-2(8) , Wingspan Pr.) WingSpan Publishing.

Roth, Julie Jersild. Knitting Nell. 2006. (Illus.). 32p. (J). (gr. k-3). 16.00 (978-0-618-54033-4(4)) Houghton Mifflin Co.

Ruurs, Margriet. Emma at the Fair. Spurll, Barbara, illus. 2005. 24p. (J). (gr. k-2). (978-1-55005-126-1(1)) Fitzhenry & Whiteside, Ltd.

Sargent, Dave & Sargent, Pat. Fancy Fannie: Show Off!, 56 vols., 28. Huff, Jeane, illus. 2001. (Animal Pride Ser.: Vol. 28). 36p. (J). pap. 19.95 (978-1-56763-373-3(0)) Ozark Publishing.

Sculthorp, Jeffrey A. The Wickleville Fair. Wingate, Lynae & Kober, John R., eds. Walter, Lorin, illus. 2000. (Wickleville Woods Ser.). 28p. (J). (ps-2). pap. 4.99 (978-1-889319-71-1(6) , Wickleville Woods) Trend Enterprises, Inc.

Shaw, Deirdre & Prince, Jonathan. Fair Play. 2005. (American Dreams Ser.). 168p. (YA). (978-1-4155-7940-4(7) , Simon Spotlight) Simon & Schuster Children's Publishing.

Spinelli, Jerry. Blue Ribbon Blues. Nelson, Donna, illus. 1998. (Stepping Stone Books 2: Vol. 2). 80p. (gr. 2-5). lib. bdg. 11.99 (978-0-679-98753-6(3) , Random Hse. Bks. for Young Readers) Random Hse. Children's Bks.

—Blue Ribbon Blues: A Tooter Tale. Nelson, Donna, illus. 1998. (Tooter Tale Ser.: Vol. 2). 80p. (J). (gr. 1-4). pap. 3.99 (978-0-679-88753-9(9) , Random Hse. Bks. for Young Readers) Random Hse. Children's Bks.

Stamper, Judith Bauer & Blevins, Wiley. Monster Town Fair. Evans, Nate, illus. 1998. (Hello Reader! Ser.). 160p. (J). (gr. 1-2). pap. 3.99 (978-0-590-76268-7(0)) Scholastic, Inc.

Stoeke, Janet Morgan. Minerva Louise at the Fair. Stoeke, Janet Morgan, illus. 2002. (Minerva Louise Ser.). (Illus.). 14.21 (978-1-4046-1705-6(1)) Book Wholesalers, Inc.

Thaler, Mike. Science Fair from the Black Lagoon. Lee, Jared D., illus. 2004. 64p. (J). lib. bdg. 15.00 (*978-1-4242-2259-9(1)) Fitzgerald Bks.

Train, Mary. Time for the Fair. Hayes, Karel, illus. 2005. (ps). 15.95 (978-0-89272-694-3(6)) Down East Bks.

Tudor, Tasha. Corgiville Fair. Tudor, Tasha, illus. 1998. (Illus.). 48p. (J). (ps-17). 17.99 (978-0-316-85312-5(7)) Little Brown & Co.

—The County Fair. 1998. (Illus.). 56p. (J). 6.95 (978-0-446-91249-5(2)) Grand Central Publishing.

Umansky, Kaye. Sophie in Charge. Currey, Anna, illus. 2005. 30p. (J). 3.95 (978-1-56148-480-5(6)); 9.95 (978-1-56148-478-2(4)) Good Bks.

Unknown. Strawberry Shortcake's Country Fair Fun. 2008. (Strawberry Shortcake Ser.). 32p. (J). (ps-1). pap. 5.99 (*978-0-448-44861-9(0) , Grosset & Dunlap) Penguin Group (USA) Inc.

Warner, Gertrude Chandler, creator. The Sword of the Silver Knight, Vol. 103. 2005. (Boxcar Children Mysteries Ser.: 103). (Illus.). 128p. (J). pap. 4.50 (978-0-8075-0876-3(4)) Whitman, Albert & Co.

Weaver, Tess. Frederick Finch, Loudmouth. 2008. (J). (*978-0-618-45239-2(7) , Clarion Bks.) Houghton Mifflin Co. Trade & Reference Div.

Wells, Rosemary. Wingwalker. Selznick, Brian, illus. 2002. 80p. (gr. 2-5). 15.99 (978-0-7868-0397-2(5)); 16.49 (978-0-7868-2347-5(X)) Hyperion Bks. for Children.

Wilder, Laura Ingalls. County Fair. Wheeler, Jody, illus. 1998. (My First Little House Bks.). 32p. (J). (ps-3). pap. 6.99 (978-0-06-443493-5(1) , Harper Trophy) HarperCollins Pubs.

Wilsdon, Christina. A Wild Ride in Texas. Jaekel, Susan, illus. 2006. 26p. (J). 7.99 (978-1-59939-011-6(6) , Reader's Digest Young Families, Inc.) Reader's Digest Children's Publishing, Inc.

Wood, Brian. The Cramp Twins. 2001. (J). pap. 9.95 (978-0-385-32714-5(5) , Random Hse. Bks. for Young Readers) Random Hse. Children's Bks.

FAIRY PLAYS

Coville, Bruce. William Shakespeare's A Midsummer Night's Dream. Nolan, Dennis, illus. 2003. 48p. (J). (gr. 2). pap. 7.99 (978-0-14-250168-9(9) , Puffin) Penguin Group (USA) Inc.

Grimm, Jacob W. & Grimm, Wilhelm K. We Both Read-the Frog Prince. Ulrich, George, illus. 1998. (We Both Read Ser.). 44p. (J). (gr. 1-2). 7.99 (978-1-891327-02-5(X)) Treasure Bay, Inc.

McKay, Sindy. We Both Read-Jack & the Beanstalk. 1998. (We Both Read Ser.). (Illus.). 44p. (J). (gr. 1-2). 7.99 (978-1-891327-00-1(3)) Treasure Bay, Inc.

FAIRY TALES

see also Folklore

A&J Studios Staff. Dora's Three Little Fairy Tales. 2005. (Dora the Explorer Ser.). (Illus.). 36p. (J). bds. 8.99 (978-1-4169-0640-7(1) , Simon Spotlight/Nickelodeon) Simon & Schuster Children's Publishing.

Aaron, Hugh. Suzy, Fair Suzy. Sproch, Lynnette, illus. l.t. ed. 1998. 32p. (J). (gr. k-4). pap. 8.95 (978-1-882521-07-4(2)) Stones Point Pr.

Abello, Ruiz. El Flautista de Hamelin. 3rd ed. 2002. (Troquelados Clasicos Ser.). (ENG & SPA., Illus.). 16p. pap. 2.95 (978-84-7864-281-6(1)) Combel Editorial, S.A. ESP. *Dist:* Independent Pubs. Group.

Aber, Linda Williams. Princess & the Pauper Jr. Novelization. 2004. (Barbie Ser.). (Illus.). 80p. (J). (ps-3). mass mkt. 3.99 (978-0-439-63600-1(0)) Scholastic, Inc.

Abeya, Elisabet. Hansel & Gretel/Hansel y Gretel. Losantos, Cristina, illus. 2005. (ENG & SPA.). 32p. (J). (ps-ps). pap. 6.95 (978-0-8118-4794-0(2)) Chronicle Bks. LLC.

Abrahams, Roger D. African American Folktales: Stories from Black Traditions in the New World. 1999. (gr. 3-6). lib. bdg. 25.75 (978-0-613-71849-3(6)) Tandem Library Bks.

Ada, Alma Flor. Yours Truly, Goldilocks. 2001. (gr. k-3). lib. bdg. 15.30 (978-0-613-90802-3(3)); (Illus.). (J). (978-0-606-21541-1(7)) Tandem Library Bks.

Adams, Eve. Christmas Eve. 2000. (Illus.). 10p. (J). pap. (978-0-9538369-0-1(8)) E. V. Bks.

Adams, Georgie. The Real Fairy Story Book. Gardner, Sally, illus. 96p. (J). 19.99 (978-1-85881-624-1(6)) Orion Children's Bks. GBR. *Dist:* Trafalgar Square Publishing.

—Real Fairy Story Book: Stories the Fairies Tell Themselves. Gardner, Sally, illus. 2001. (J). (gr. 2-5). pap. 11.99 (978-1-85881-681-4(5)) Dolphin Paperbacks GBR. *Dist:* Trafalgar Square Publishing.

Adams, H. J. Of Dragons, Kings, Sages & Little Folk. 1999. 120p. (J). 22.50 (978-0-923687-52-6(1)) Celo Valley Bks.

—Twice Six Tales All Told. 2003. 86p. 22.50 (978-0-923687-63-2(7)) Celo Valley Bks.

Adeney, Anne, retold by. The Pied Piper of Hamelin. 2007. (First Fairy Tales Ser.). (Illus.). 30p. (J). (*978-1-59771-072-5(5)) Sea-To-Sea Pubns.

Aesop & Miles, Betty. The Tortoise & the Hare. Meisel, Paul, illus. 1998. (Starting to Read Ser.). (J). (978-0-606-13858-1(7)) Tandem Library Bks.

Aesop & Perrault, Charles. Animal Fables, 4 bks., Set. Roederer, Charlotte et al, illus. 2007. (Classic Fairy Tales Ser.). 112p. (J). (ps-3). 19.95 (***978-0-7892-0951-1(9)***) Abbeville Pr., Inc.

Ahlberg, Allan. Previously. Ingman, Bruce, illus. 2007. 32p. (J). (ps-3). 16.99 (***978-0-7636-3542-8(1)***) Candlewick Pr.

Alcott, Louisa May. Flower Fables. Shealy, Daniel, ed. Preiss, Leah P., illus. 1998. 112p. (J). 22.00 (978-0-9660933-0-8(5)) OKey-Doke Productions, Inc.

Alexander, Lloyd. Taran Wanderer. rev. ed. 1999. (Chronicles of Prydain Ser.: Bk. 4). 256p. (J). (gr. 3-7). 19.95 (978-0-8050-6134-5(7) , Holt, Henry & Co. Bks. For Young Readers) Holt, Henry & Co.

Ali Baba & the Forty Thieves. 2004. (J). (ARA & ENG.). (978-1-84444-527-1(5)); (BEN & ENG.). (978-1-84444-528-8(3)); (CHI & ENG.). (978-1-84444-529-5(1)); (CHI & ENG.). (978-1-84444-530-1(5)); (ENG & GUJ.). (978-1-84444-646-9(8)); (ENG & ITA.). (978-1-84444-535-6(6)); (ENG & PAN.). (978-1-84444-537-0(2)); (ENG & POL.). (978-1-84444-538-7(0)); (ENG & RUS.). (978-1-84444-540-0(2)); (ENG & SOM.). (978-1-84444-541-7(0)); (ENG & SPA.). (978-1-84444-542-4(9)); (ENG & TAM.). (978-1-84444-544-8(5)); (ENG & TUR.). (978-1-84444-545-5(3)); (ENG & URD.). (978-1-84444-546-2(1)); (ENG & VIE.). (978-1-84444-547-9(X)) Mantra Publishing, Ltd.

Ali BabaForty Thieves. 2004. (J). cd-rom (978-1-84444-452-6(X)) Mantra Publishing, Ltd.

Allen, Constance. Elmo's Mother Goose. Swanson, Maggie, illus. 2000. (Big Bird's Favorite Bird Bks.). 12p. (J). (gr. k-ps). bds. 4.99 (978-0-375-80541-7(9) , Random Hse. Bks. for Young Readers) Random Hse. Children's Bks.

Allen, Debbie. Brothers of the Knight. 2001. 13.79 (978-0-606-22528-1(5)) Tandem Library Bks.

Almendros, Herminio. Habia una Vez. 2000. (SPA., Illus.). 200p. (J). (gr. 2-4). pap. 13.00 (978-968-439-521-3(3) , PA5131) Publicaciones Cultural, S.A. de C.V. MEX. *Dist:* Ediciones Universal, Lectorum Pubns., Inc.

Alonso, Fernando. The Little Red Hen (La Gallina Paulina) Gimeno, J. M., illus. 16p. (J). (gr. k-3). pap. 6.95 (978-0-88272-468-3(1)) Santillana USA Publishing Co., Inc.

Alvarez, Julia. The Secret Footprints. 2002. (ps-2). lib. bdg. 15.30 (978-0-613-87802-9(7)) Tandem Library Bks.

Amery, H. & Cartwright, S. Cinderella. 2004. (First Stories Ser.). 16p. (J). pap. 4.99 (978-0-7945-0605-6(4)) EDC Publishing.

—Little Red Riding Hood. 2004. (First Stories Ser.). 16p. (J). lib. bdg. 12.95 (978-1-58086-620-0(4) , Usborne); pap. 4.99 (978-0-7945-0607-0(0)) EDC Publishing.

—Sleeping Beauty. 2004. (First Stories Ser.). 16p. (J). pap. 4.95 (978-0-7945-0604-9(6)) EDC Publishing.

—The Story of Rumpelstiltskin. 2004. (First Stories Ser.). 16p. (J). lib. bdg. 12.95 (978-1-58086-621-7(2) , Usborne) EDC Publishing.

Amery, H. & Cartwright, Stephen. Sleeping Beauty. 16p. (J). lib. bdg. 12.95 (978-1-58086-622-4(0) , Usborne) EDC Publishing.

Amery, Heather. Princess Stories. 2005. (First Stories Ser.). 64p. (J). 12.95 (978-0-7945-0898-2(7) , Usborne) EDC Publishing.

—Traditional Fairy Tales. 2005. (First Stories Ser.). 96p. (J). 13.95 (978-0-7945-0865-4(0) , Usborne) EDC Publishing.

Amery, Heather & Howell, Laura. Cinderella Sticker Bk. 2006. 16p. (J). pap. 6.99 (978-0-7945-1311-5(5) , Usborne) EDC Publishing.

—Sleeping Beauty Sticker Bk. 2006. 16p. (J). pap. 6.99 (978-0-7945-1313-9(1) , Usborne) EDC Publishing.

—Three Little Pigs Sticker Bk. 2006. 16p. (J). pap. 6.99 (978-0-7945-1386-3(7) , Usborne) EDC Publishing.

Amoss, Berthe. The Cajun Gingerbread Boy. 1999. (J). 13.95 (978-0-922589-66-1(6)) More Than a Card, Inc.

Andersen, Christian. Stories from Hans Andersen. 2006. 94.99 (***978-1-4280-1510-4(8)***); pap. 88.99 (***978-1-4280-1501-2(9)***) IndyPublish.com.

Andersen, Hans Christian. Andersen Fairy Tales. Klanten, Robert, cd. 2004. (Illus.). 208p. 39.00 (978-3-89955-059-7(5)) Die Gestalten Verlag DEU. *Dist:* Prestel Publishing.

—Andersen's Fairy Tales. 2006. pap. (***978-1-4250-0519-1(5)***); pap. (***978-1-4250-1059-1(8)***); pap. (***978-1-4250-1549-7(2)***) Assistedreadingbooks.com Inc.

—The Emperor & the Nightingale. Van Nutt, Robert, illus. 2007. (J). 25.65 (978-1-59961-307-9(7)) ABDO Publishing Co.

—The Emperor's New Clothes. Durual, Christophe, illus. 2001. (Little Pebbles Ser.). 32p. (J). (ps-3). 6.95 (978-0-7892-0691-6(9)) Abbeville Pr., Inc.

—The Emperor's New Clothes. Archipowa, Anastassija, illus. 1998. 32p. (J). (ps-4). 15.95 (978-1-56397-699-5(4)) Boyds Mills Pr.

—The Emperor's New Clothes. Lanning, Rosemary, tr. from GER. Tharlet, Eve, illus. 2002. 32p. (J). (ps-2). pap. 6.95 (978-0-7358-1701-2(4)) North-South Bks., Inc.

—The Emperor's New Clothes. 2005. 12p. pap. (978-958-30-1782-7(5)) Panamericana Editorial.

—The Emperor's New Clothes. 2000. (YA). (978-0-606-19757-1(5)) Tandem Library Bks.

—The Emperor's New Clothes. Van Nutt, Robert, illus. 2005. (J). (gr. k-5). 25.65 (978-1-59197-746-9(0)) Spotlight.

—The Emperor's New Clothes. Hall, Francois, illus. 2006. (First Fairy Tales Ser.). 30p. (J). (978-1-59771-071-8(7) , 1262700) Sea-To-Sea Pubns.

—The Emperor's New Clothes: An All-Star Illustrated Retelling of the Classic Fairy Tale. 2004. (Illus.). 85p. (J). (gr. k-4). reprint ed. (978-0-7567-7720-3(8)) DIANE Publishing Co.

—The Emperor's New Clothes: Honesty. Neidigh, Sherry, illus. 2005. (J). pap. (978-1-4127-3759-3(1)) Publications International, Ltd.

—For Sure! for Sure! White, Mus, tr. from DAN. Czernecki, Stefan, illus. 2006. 29p. (J). (gr. k-4). reprint ed. 17.00 (978-1-4223-5208-3(0)) DIANE Publishing Co.

—Hans Christian Andersen: Illustrated Fairy Tales, Vol. 2. 2001. (Illus.). 416p. 29.95 (978-87-7247-271-3(5)) Scandinavia Publishing Hse. DNK. *Dist:* National Bk. Network.

—Hans Christian Andersen: The Complete Stories, 2 vols. 2005. (Illus.). 980p. 60.00 (978-0-7123-0682-9(X)) British Library, The GBR. *Dist:* Chicago Distribution Ctr.

—Hans Christian Andersen Illustrated Fairytales. 2005. (Illus.). 144p. (ps-7). 12.95 (978-87-7247-264-5(2)) Scandinavia Publishing Hse. DNK. *Dist:* National Bk. Network.

—Hans Christian Andersen Illustrated Fairytales Vol. 1: The Snow Queen; The Little Match Girl; The Little Mermaid; She Was Good for Nothing. 2004. (Illus.). 144p. 12.95 (978-87-7247-256-0(1)) Scandinavia Publishing Hse. DNK. *Dist:* National Bk. Network.

—Hans Christian Andersen Illustrated Fairytales Vol. II: It's Absolutely True; The Pigkeeper; Little Claus & Big Claus; The Racers; The Buckwheat. 2005. (Illus.). 144p. 12.95 (978-87-7247-258-4(8)) Scandinavia Publishing Hse. DNK. *Dist:* National Bk. Network.

—Hans Christian Andersen Illustrated Fairytales Vol. IV: The Snowdrop; There Is a Difference; The Emperor's New Clothes; Thumbelina; What the Old Man Does. 2005. 144p. 12.95 (978-87-7247-265-2(0)) Scandinavia Publishing Hse. DNK. *Dist:* National Bk. Network.

—Hans Christian Andersen Illustrated Fairytales Vol. V: The Brave Tin Soldier; Clod Hans; A Gift for Hans; The Ugly Duckling. 2005. 144p. 12.95 (978-87-7247-270-6(7)) Scandinavia Publishing Hse. DNK. *Dist:* National Bk. Network.

—Hans Christian Andersen Illustrated Fairytales Vol. VI: The Wild Swans; The Traveling Companion; The Jewish Maiden; The Toad. 2005. 144p. 12.95 (978-87-7247-278-2(2)) Scandinavia Publishing Hse. DNK. *Dist:* National Bk. Network.

—Hans Christian Andersen's Fairy Tales. Zwerger, Lisbeth, illus. 2006. 104p. (J). (ps-12). 19.99 (978-0-698-40035-1(6) , Minedition) Penguin Group (USA) Inc.

—Hans Christian Andersen's the Snow Queen. Hofer, Ernst & Hofer, Nelly, illus. 2000. 48p. (J). (gr. 3-7). 17.95 (978-0-88776-497-4(5)) Tundra Bks., Inc./Livres Toundra, Inc. CAN. *Dist:* Random Hse., Inc.

—IceMaiden & Other Tales. 2006. pap. (***978-1-4068-0421-8(5)***) Echo Library.

—The Little Match Girl. Bell, Anthea, tr. from DAN. Pacovska, Kveta, illus. 2005. 40p. (J). (ps-3). 18.99 (978-0-698-40027-6(5) , Minedition) Penguin Group (USA) Inc.

—The Little Match Girl. 2002. (Illus.). (J). (ps-3). lib. bdg. 15.30 (978-0-613-83546-6(8)) Tandem Library Bks.

—The Little Match Seller. 2005. 12p. pap. (978-958-30-1509-0(1)) Panamericana Editorial.

—The Little Mermaid. Bell, Anthea, tr. from DAN. Zwerger, Lisbeth, illus. 2004. 48p. (J). (ps). 16.99 (978-0-698-40001-6(1) , Minedition) Penguin Group (USA) Inc.

—The Little Mermaid. 2000. (Illus.). (J). (978-0-606-18420-5(1)) Tandem Library Bks.

—The Little Mermaid. Michel, Petra, tr. Wulfing, Sulamith, illus. 2004. 32p. (ps-3). 18.95 (978-1-885394-17-0(9)) Amber Lotus Publishing.

—The Little Mermaid & Other Fairy Tales. unabr. ed. 2003. (Dover Evergreen Classics Ser.). (Illus.). 112p. (J). (gr. 4-7). pap. 2.00 (978-0-486-42365-4(4)) Dover Pubns., Inc.

—The Nightingale. Ibatoulline, Bagram, illus. 2006. 48p. (J). (gr. 1-5). pap. 6.99 (978-0-7636-2406-4(3)) Candlewick Pr.

—The Nightingale. Pinkney, Jerry, illus. 2002. Tr. of Nattergalen. 40p. (J). 16.99 (978-0-8037-2464-8(0) , Dial) Penguin Group (USA) Inc.

—El Patito Feo. (SPA., Illus.). 48p. (J). (gr. 3-5). (978-84-241-5525-4(4) , EV0572) Everest de Ediciones y Distribucion, S.L. ESP. *Dist:* Lectorum Pubns., Inc.

—El Patito Feo: Farm Animals, The Farm, Seasons, The Weather. 1999. (Mi Primeros Cuentos Ser.). (SPA & ENG., Illus.). (J). (ps-3). pap. 7.95 (978-88-8148-251-1(7)) European Language Institute ITA. *Dist:* Distribooks, Inc., Midwest European Pubns.

—Pictures of Sweden. 2006. pap. (***978-1-4065-0860-4(8)***) Dodo Pr.

—Poucette. Dyer, Berenice, ed. Stone, Petula, illus. (French Language Editions Ser.: No. 600-6). (FRE.). 52p. (J). (gr. 1). 3.50 (978-0-7214-1274-0(2) , Dutton Juvenile) Penguin Group (USA) Inc.

—The Princess & the Pea. (Fairy Tale Fun Ser.).Tr. of Prindsessen Paa Aerten. (J). 3.95 (978-0-7214-5433-7(X) , Dutton Juvenile) Penguin Group (USA) Inc.

—The Princess & the Pea. Oberdieck, Bernhard, illus. 2007. (Classic Fairy Tale Collection). 24p. (J). (ps-2). 14.95 (978-1-4027-3065-8(9)) Sterling Publishing Co., Inc.

—The Princess & the Pea: A Fairy Tale. Semelet, Camille, illus. 1999. (Little Pebbles Ser.). 32p. (J). (ps-1). 6.95 (978-0-7892-0515-5(7) , Abbeville Kids) Abbeville Pr., Inc.

—Pulgarcita. 1998. (SPA., Illus.). 32p. (J). 4.95 (978-84-392-8301-0(6)) Everest Publishing.

—The Snow Queen. 2002. (Illus.). 96p. 13.95 (978-0-375-41512-8(2) , Everyman's Library) Knopf Publishing Group.

—The Snow Queen. Tatarnikov, Pavel, illus. 2006. 48p. (J). 16.50 (978-1-933327-23-5(5)); 15.95 (978-1-933327-22-8(7)) Purple Bear Bks., Inc.

—Snow Queen. 2006. (Illus.). 48p. (J). (ps-3). 16.95 (978-1-84732-001-8(5)) Carlton Bks., Ltd. GBR. *Dist:* Ingram Pub. Services.

—The Snow Queen. ed. 2007. (ENG., Illus.). 34p. (***978-1-890568-12-2(0)*** , A-BA-BA-HA-LA-MA-HA Pubs.) Anderson House Foundation.

—The Snow Queen. Bogdanovic, Toma, illus. adapted ed. 32p. (J). (ps-5). 16.95 (978-0-87592-048-1(9)) Scroll Pr., Inc.

—The Steadfast Tin Soldier. Lemoine, Georges, illus. 2000. Tr. of Standhaftige Tinsoldat. 32p. (YA). lib. bdg. 13.95 (978-1-56846-132-8(1) , Creative Education) Creative Co., The.

—The Steadfast Tin Soldier. de Conno, Gianni, illus. 2006. Tr. of Standhaftige Tinsoldat. 44p. (J). 16.50 (978-1-933327-25-9(1)); 15.95 (978-1-933327-24-2(3)) Purple Bear Bks., Inc.

—The Steadfast Tin Soldier. Jorgensen, David, illus. 2006. Tr. of Standhaftige Tinsoldat. (J). (gr. 2-6). 25.65 (978-1-59679-346-0(5)) Spotlight.

—Stories for Girls: Lovingly Adapted for Twenty-First Century Children. l.t. ed. 2001. (Illus.). 148p. (J). pap. 11.95 (978-1-58742-009-2(0)) Inkling Bks.

—The Swineherd. (Illus.). 28p. pap. 15.95 (978-0-86315-129-3(9) , 1297) Floris Bks. GBR. *Dist:* SteinerBooks, Inc.

—Tales & Stories. 2nd rev. ed. 2002. (Classics Ser.). (Illus.). 416p. (YA). (gr. 13). 17.95 (978-0-415-28598-8(4)); 105.00 (978-0-415-28597-1(6)) Routledge.

—Tales from Hans Christian Andersen, Level 2. 2001. (Illus.), 48p. (C). pap. 9.00 (978-0-582-42112-7(8)) Pearson ESL.

—Tales of Hans Christian Andersen. Lewis, Naomi, tr. from DAN. Stewart, Joel, illus. 2004. 208p. (J). (gr. 3-7). 22.99 (978-0-7636-2515-3(9)) Candlewick Pr.

—Thumbelina. Pinkney, Brian, illus. 2003. 40p. (J). 17.89 (978-0-688-17477-4(9)) HarperCollins Pubs.

—Thumbelina. Sneed, Brad, tr. Sneed, Brad, illus. 2004. 40p. (J). (ps). 16.99 (978-0-8037-2812-7(3) , Dial) Penguin Group (USA) Inc.

—Thumbelina. Johnson, David, illus. 2005. (J). (gr. k-5). 25.65 (978-1-59197-756-8(8)) Spotlight.

—Thumbeline. Zwerger, Lisbeth, illus. 2000. Tr. of Tommelise. 32p. (J). (gr. k-3). pap. 6.95 (978-0-7358-1210-9(1)) North-South Bks., Inc.

—Thumbeline. Bell, Anthea, tr. Zwerger, Lisbeth, illus. 2000. Tr. of Tommelise. (J). (ps-ps). lib. bdg. 15.25 (978-0-613-27246-9(3)) Tandem Library Bks.

—The Tinderbox. Ibatoulline, Bagram, illus. 2007. 48p. (J). (gr. 1-5). 17.99 (978-0-7636-2078-3(5)) Candlewick Pr.

—The Ugly Duckling. Furukawa, Masumi et al, illus. 2006. 24p. pap. 5.99 (978-1-84643-022-0(4)) Child's Play-International.

—The Ugly Duckling. Andersen, Hans Christian, illus. (Fairy Tale Fun Ser.). (J). 3.95 (978-0-7214-5432-0(1) , Dutton Juvenile) Penguin Group (USA) Inc.

—The Ugly Duckling. Angeldorff, W., tr. from DAN. Angaramo, Roberta, illus. 2006. 32p. (J). 15.95 (978-1-933327-09-9(X)) Purple Bear Bks., Inc.

—The Ugly Duckling. Andersen, Hans Christian, illus. 1999. (Golden Book Ser.). (Illus.). 20p. (J). (ps-3). bds. 3.99 (978-0-307-16076-8(9) , Golden Bks.) Random Hse. Children's Bks.

—The Ugly Duckling. Andersen, Hans Christian & Bogdanovic, Toma, illus. 32p. (J). (ps-3). 16.95 (978-0-87592-055-9(1)) Scroll Pr., Inc.

—The Ugly Duckling. Andersen, Hans Christian & Van Nutt, Robert, illus. 2006. (J). (gr. 2-6). 25.65 (978-1-59679-348-4(1)) Spotlight.

—The Ugly Duckling. Andersen, Hans Christian & Hanff, Margitta, illus. 1998. (Froggy's Country Storybook Ser.: Vol. 3). 16p. (J). (gr. k-3). pap. 12.98 incl. audio (978-1-890818-28-9(3)) Virginia Records, Inc.

—The Ugly Duckling. Johnson, Steve & Francher, Lou, illus. 2008. 40p. (J). (ps-3). 16.99 (***978-0-7636-2159-9(5)***) Candlewick Pr.

—The Ugly Duckling. Bell, Anthea, tr. from DAN. Andersen, Hans Christian & Ingpen, Robert R., illus. anniv. ed. 2005. 36p. (J). (ps). 16.99 (978-0-698-40010-8(0) , Minedition) Penguin Group (USA) Inc.

—The Ugly Duckling Signed Edition. Tatar, Maria, ed. Galeron, Henri, illus. 2007. 32p. (J). (gr. k). 250.00 (***978-0-670-01104-9(5)*** , Viking Juvenile) Penguin Group (USA) Inc.

—We Both Read-Thumbelina (Picture Book Edition) Greban, Quentin, illus. 2007. (We Both Read Ser.). 32p. (J). 14.95 (***978-1-60115-007-3(5)***) Treasure Bay, Inc.

—The Wild Swans. Lewis, Naomi, tr. from DAN. Gilbert, Yvonne, illus. 2005. 48p. (J). 17.99 (978-1-84148-164-7(5)) Barefoot Bks., Inc.

Andersen, Hans Christian. The Wild Swans: A Tale of Persistence. Lohmann, Renate, illus. 2006. (J). (***978-1-59939-093-2(0)*** , Reader's Digest Young Families, Inc.) Reader's Digest Children's Publishing, Inc.

Andersen, Hans Christian, ed. Andersen's Fairy Tales. 1998. (Children's Classics). (ENG., Illus.). 400p. (J). (gr. 4-7). pap. (978-1-85326-100-8(9) , 1009WW) Wordsworth Editions, Ltd.

Andersen, Hans Christian, illus. Thumbelina. 2000. Tr. of Tommelise. (J). (978-0-606-21769-9(X)) Tandem Library Bks.

Andersen, Hans Christian, tr. Andersen's Fairy Tales. 2004. 220p. pap. 12.95 (978-1-59540-305-6(1) , 1st World Library - Literary Society) 1st World Publishing, Inc.

—Andersen's Fairy Tales. (Twelve-Point Ser.). 2001. 165p. lib. bdg. 24.00 (978-1-58287-146-2(9)); 2004. 266p. 25.00 (978-1-58287-629-0(0)) North Bks.

—Andersen's Fairy Tales. 2004. (ENG.). 172p. 28.95 (***978-0-8095-9507-5(9)***) Wildside Pr.

—Andersen's Fairy Tales. l.t. ed. 2002. cd-rom 11.50 (978-0-9721271-0-3(0)) Woolf, Virginia M. Foundation.

Andersen, Hans Christian & Capdevila, Bas. Ugly Duckling (El Patito Feo) A Bilingual Book. Capdevila, Francesc, illus. 2004. (ENG & SPA.). 32p. (J). 14.95 (978-0-8118-4454-3(4)) Chronicle Bks. LLC.

Andersen, Hans Christian & Davidson, Susanna. The Emperor's New Clothes. 2005. 48p. (J). (gr. 2 up). 8.99 (978-0-7945-1057-2(4) , Usborne) EDC Publishing.

—Ugly Duckling. 2006. 48p. (J). 8.99 (978-0-7945-1274-3(7) , Usborne) EDC Publishing.

Andersen, Hans Christian & Lynch, P. J. The Steadfast Tin Soldier. Lewis, Naomi, tr. from DAN. 2005. Tr. of Standhaftige Tinsoldat. (Illus.). 32p. (J). pap. 7.99 (978-1-84270-443-1(5)) Andersen GBR. *Dist:* Independent Pubs. Group.

Andersen, Hans Christian & Pinkney, Brian, illus. Thumbelina. 2003. Tr. of Tommelise. 40p. (J). 16.99 (978-0-688-17476-7(0)) HarperCollins Pubs.

Angstrom, Gwen. Ruthie's Extraordinarily Ordinary Summer: A Tale of Happy Valley. 2005. 59p. pap. 12.95 (978-1-4137-6323-2(5)) PublishAmerica, Inc.

Anholt, Laurence. Foolish Jack & the Bean Stack. 2004. (Illus.). 64p. (J). (gr. 3 up). 13.26 (978-0-7565-0629-2(8)) Compass Point Bks.

—Rumply Crumply Stinky Pin. 2004. (Illus.). 64p. (J). (gr. 3 up). 13.26 (978-0-7565-0633-9(6)) Compass Point Bks.

—Shampoozel. 2004. (Illus.). 64p. (J). (gr. 3 up). 13.26 (978-0-7565-0634-6(4)) Compass Point Bks.

—Snow White & the Seven Aliens. 2004. (Illus.). 64p. (J). (gr. 3 up). 13.26 (978-0-7565-0635-3(2)) Compass Point Bks.

Anholt, Laurence & Robins, Arthur. Silly Jack & the Bean Stack. 1999. (J). pap. (978-0-88166-348-8(4)) Meadowbrook Pr.

Anjelae, Samara. My Fairy Godmother. Ferguson, Martha-Elizabeth, illus. 2002. (Wonder Window Ser.). 32p. (J). 16.95 (978-0-9634910-8-4(3) , BelleTress Bks.) Red Wheel/Weiser.

Anonymous. The Arabian Nights. Goodenow, Earle, illus. deluxe ed. 2002. (Illustrated Junior Library Ser.). 352p. (J). (gr. 4-7). reprint ed. 17.99 (978-0-448-06006-4(X) , Grosset & Dunlap) Penguin Group (USA) Inc.

La Aranita de Belen. 2002. (Troquelados Clasicos Ser.). (ENG & SPA., Illus.). 16p. pap. 2.95 (978-84-7864-598-5(5)) Combel Editorial, S.A. ESP. *Dist:* Independent Pubs. Group.

Archipowa, Anastassija, illus. Favorite Grimm's Tales. 2000. (GER.). 198p. (J). (ps-3). 24.95 (978-0-86315-318-1(6)) Floris Bks. GBR. *Dist:* SteinerBooks, Inc.

Arengo, Sue. The Three Billy-Goats: Beginner Level 1. 1998. (Illus.). (J). 5.50 (978-0-19-422003-3(6)) Oxford Univ. Pr., Inc.

Argueta, Jorge. El Zipitio. Calderon, Gloria, illus. 2003. (SPA.). 32p. (J). 16.95 (978-0-88899-539-1(3)) Groundwood Bks. CAN. *Dist:* Perseus Distribution.

Arndt, Rhonda. Mac's Adventure. 2006. 48p. pap. 12.95 (978-1-4241-1321-7(0)) PublishAmerica, Inc.

Arnold, Tedd. More Parts. 2003. (Illus.). 32p. (J). pap. 5.99 (978-0-14-250149-8(2) , Puffin) Penguin Group (USA) Inc.

—More Parts. Arnold, Tedd, illus. 2001. (Illus.). 32p. (J). (ps-3). 16.99 (978-0-8037-1417-5(3) , Dial) Penguin Group (USA) Inc.

Arraras, Maria Celeste. El Baston Magico (The Magic Cane) 2008. (I Love My Mommy Ser.). 32p. (J). pap. 5.99 (***978-0-545-00532-6(9)*** , Scholastic en Espanol) Scholastic, Inc.

Arraras, María Celeste. The Magic Cane. Raimondi, Pablo, illus. 2007. 32p. (J). (ps-3). pap. 16.99 (***978-0-439-57419-8(6)*** , Orchard Bks.) Scholastic, Inc.

Artell, Mike. Petite Rouge: A Cajun Red Riding Hood. 2001. lib. bdg. 15.30 (978-0-613-67470-6(7)) Tandem Library Bks.

Artful Doodlers Limited Staff, illus. It's Absolutely True. 2006. (Famous Fables Ser.). (J). 6.99 (978-1-59939-029-1(9)) Reader's Digest Young Families, Inc.

Asbjornsen, Peter Christen. The Three Billy Goats Gruff. Jorgensen, David, illus. 2005. (J). (gr. k-5). 25.65 (978-1-59197-754-4(1)) Spotlight.

—The Three Billy Goats Gruff. Carpenter, Stephen, illus. 1998. (Growing Tree Ser.). 24p. (J). (ps up). 9.99 (978-0-694-01033-2(2)) HarperCollins Pubs.

Asbjornsen, Peter Christen, et al. East O' the Sun & West O' the Moon & Other Norwegian Fairy Tales. 2001. (Dover Juvenile Classics Ser.). (Illus.). 128p. (J). (gr. 4-7). pap. 2.00 (978-0-486-41724-0(7)) Dover Pubns., Inc.

Ashley, Catherine C. N. Butterfly Girl. 2006. (J). per. 9.95 (978-0-9672699-3-1(8) , Papillon Children's Bks.) Ashcafe Publishing.

Aspengren, Michael A., illus. Tales of Silliness: Retold Timeless Classics. 1999. (Cover-to-Cover Timeless Classics Ser.). 63p. (J). pap. (978-0-7891-2328-2(2)); (gr. 1-4). lib. bdg. 13.95 (978-0-7807-7749-1(2)) Perfection Learning Corp.

Attard, Enebor. Ali Baba & the Forty Thieves. Holland, Richard, illus. 2005. (GRE & ENG.). 32p. (J). pap. 12.95 (978-1-84444-526-4(7)) Mantra Lingua GBR. *Dist:* Mantra Publishing, Ltd.

Auch, Mary Jane & Auch, Herm. The Princess & the Pizza. 2002. (Illus.). 32p. (J). (gr. k-3). 6.95 (978-0-8234-1798-8(0)) Holiday Hse., Inc.

Audio. Little Red Riding Hood. 2000. (Classic Stories Ser.). (Illus.). 48p. (J). (ps-2). audio, audio compact disk (978-2-921997-83-6(5)) Coffragants.

Auerbach, Annie. Cindy Big Hair: A Twisted (and Teased & Braided) Cinderella Story. Maxey, David, illus. 2005. 16p. (J). 12.95 (978-1-58117-387-1(3) , Intervisual/Piggy Toes) Dalmatian Pr.

Aylesworth, Jim. Full Belly Bowl. Halperin, Wendy Anderson, illus. 1999. 40p. (J). (ps-3). 17.99 (978-0-689-81033-6(4) , Atheneum) Simon & Schuster Children's Publishing.

Babbitt, Natalie. Elsie Times Eight. Babbitt, Natalie, illus. 2005. (Illus.). 26p. (J). (gr. k-4). reprint ed. 16.00 (978-0-7567-9640-2(7)) DIANE Publishing Co.

—Kneeknock Rise. 2003. (J). (gr. 3-7). 20.75 (978-0-8446-7236-6(X)) Smith, Peter Pub., Inc.

—Ouch! Marcellino, Fred, illus. pap. 18.95 incl. audio compact disk (978-1-59112-350-7(X)); pap. incl. audio compact disk (978-1-59112-558-7(8)); 2002. 28.95 incl. audio compact disk (978-1-59112-351-4(8)) Live Oak Media.

—Ouch! Marcellino, Fred, illus. unabr. ed. 2000. (J). (gr. 1-4). 25.95 incl. audio (978-0-87499-679-1(1)) Live Oak Media.

Babcock, Bruce. Christmas with the Little People. Babcock, Bruce, illus. unabr. ed. 1998. (Illus.). 46p. (J). (ps-6). pap. 7.95 (978-1-892161-04-8(4)) Babcock Publishing Co.

Baca, Ana. Benito's Bizcochitos. Castilla, Julia Mercedes, tr. Accardo, Anthony, illus. 1999. Tr. of Bizcochitos de Benito. (ENG & SPA.). 32p. (J). (ps-3). 14.95 (978-1-55885-264-8(6) , Piñata Books) Arte Publico Pr.

Baker, E. D. Dragon's Breath. 2003. 250p. (J). 15.95 (978-1-58234-858-2(8) , Bloomsbury Children) Bloomsbury Publishing.

—Dragon's Breath: Read-Along/Homework Pack. unabr. ed. 2005. (YA). (gr. 5-8). 92.70 incl. audio (978-1-4193-3563-1(4) , 42041) Recorded Bks., LLC.

—The Frog Princess. 2002. 200p. (J). (gr. 3-9). 15.95 (978-1-58234-799-8(9) , Bloomsbury Children) Bloomsbury Publishing.

Baker, E. D. The Salamander Spell. 2007. (Tales of the Frog Princess Ser.). 250p. (J). (gr. 3-7). 16.95 (***978-1-59990-018-6(1)** , Bloomsbury Children) Bloomsbury Publishing.

Balaguae, Lin & Long, Robert. La Dama y el Leaon. 2000. (Cuentos y Leyendas Bilingues Ser.).Tr. of Princess & the Lion. (ENG & SPA.). (J). 22.48 (978-0-658-01013-2(1)) National Textbook Co.

Balaguae, Lin & Long, Robert, contrib. by. Alai Babaa y los 40 Ladrones: Ali Baba & the 40 Thieves. 2000. (Cuentos y Leyendas Bilingues Ser.). (ENG & SPA.). (J). 21.20 (978-0-658-01023-1(9) , National Textbook Co.) McGraw-Hill/Contemporary.

—Hansel y Gretel: Hansel & Gretel. 2000. (Cuentos y Leyendas Bilingues Ser.). (ENG & SPA.). (J). 21.20 (978-0-658-01037-8(9) , National Textbook Co.) McGraw-Hill/Contemporary.

Balague, Lin & Long, Robert. Ali Baba y los 40 Ladrones (Ali Baba & the 40 Thieves) 2000. (Cuentos y Leyendas Bilingues Ser.). (SPA & ENG., Illus.). (J). 17.68 (978-0-658-01024-8(7)) McGraw-Hill/Contemporary.

—Hansel y Gretel (Hansel & Gretel) 2000. (Cuentos y Leyendas Bilingues Ser.). (SPA & ENG., Illus.). (J). 19.88 (978-0-658-01038-5(7)) McGraw-Hill/Contemporary.

Ballesteros, Adriana Esther. Los Cuentos de Villa Disparate. 2002. (J). (978-956-240-349-8(1)) Arrayan Editores S.A.

Ballesteros, Xose. El Flautista de Hamelin. Ribeyron, Samuel, illus. 2002. (Libros para Soñar Ser.). (SPA.). 40p. (J). (978-84-8464-010-3(8)) Kalandraka Editora, S.L.

Bang, Molly Garrett. Dawn. 2002. (gr. k-3). lib. bdg. 14.10 (978-0-613-62742-9(3)) Tandem Library Bks.

Banks, Lynne Reid. The Farthest-Away Mountain. 2004. (gr. 3-6). lib. bdg. 13.00 (978-0-613-86689-7(4)) Tandem Library Bks.

Bannerman, Helen. Little Black Sambo (Illustrated Edition) 2006. (Illus.). pap. (***978-1-4065-0769-0(5)**) Dodo Pr.

Bar-El, Dan. Such a Prince. Manders, John, illus. 2007. 32p. (J). (ps-3). 16.00 (978-0-618-71468-1(5) , Clarion Bks.) Houghton Mifflin Co. Trade & Reference Div.

Barber, Antonia. The Cape of Rushes. 2005. (Cambridge Storybooks Ser.). 32p. pap. 7.00 (978-0-521-67486-7(7)) Cambridge Univ. Pr.

—Tales from Grimm. Chamberlain, Margaret, illus. 1999. 112p. (J). (ps-4). pap. 13.99 (978-0-7112-1341-8(0)) Lincoln, Frances Ltd. GBR. *Dist:* Transition Vendor.

Barber, Antonia & Chamberlain, Margaret. Tales from Grimm. 1998. (Illus.). 112p. (J). pap. 12.95 (978-1-84507-237-5(5)) Lincoln, Frances Ltd. GBR. *Dist:* Perseus Distribution.

Barcita, Pamela. The Dancing Bears. 2007. (J). (ps up). 19.95 (***978-1-933982-00-7(4)** , TDB) Bumble Bee Publishing.

Baring-Gould, S. The Crock of Gold: Twelve Fairy Tales, O. 2006. pap. 27.95 (***978-1-4254-9842-9(6)**) Kessinger Publishing, LLC.

Barker, Cicely Mary. Blackthorn's Changing Seasons. 2005. (Flower Fairies Friends Ser.). (Illus.). 24p. (J). (ps). 4.99 (978-0-7232-5378-5(1) , Warne) Penguin Group (USA) Inc.

Barker, Cicely Mary. Willow's Underwater World. 2008. (Flower Fairies Ser.). 80p. 3.99 (***978-0-7232-5952-7(6)** , Warne) Penguin Group (USA) Inc.

Barkow, Henriette. Ali Baba & the Forty Thieves. Brazell, Derek, illus. 2004. (ENG, POR & SWE.). (J). (978-1-84444-539-4(9)) Mantra Publishing, Ltd.

—Three Billy Goats Gruff. Johnson, Richard, illus. 2004. (ENG & ITA.). 24p. (J). (978-1-85269-786-0(5)) Mantra Publishing, Ltd.

Barkow, Henriette & Finlay, Lizzie, illus. Buri & the Marrow: Buri Dhe Kungulli. 2004. (ALB & ENG.). 24p. (J). pap. (978-1-85269-578-1(1)) Mantra Publishing, Ltd.

Barkow, Henriette & Johnson, Richard, illus. Don't Cry, Sly! Mos Qaj Dhelperush! 2004. (TAM, CZE, VIE, SPA & GUJ.). 24p. (J). pap. (978-1-85269-648-1(6)) Mantra Publishing, Ltd.

Barkow, Henriette & Reed, Nathan, illus. The Buskers of Bremen: Kengetaret Endacak Te Bremenit. 2004. (TAM, CZE, VIE, SPA & GUJ.). 24p. (J). pap. (978-1-85269-764-8(4)) Mantra Publishing, Ltd.

Barrett, Dean. The Boat Girl & the Magic Fish. 2nd ed. 2002. 32p. 6.95 (978-0-9661899-5-7(7)) Village East Bks.

Barrie, J. M. Peter Pan. 2002. (Spot the Classics Ser.). (Illus.). 178p. (J). (gr. k-5). 4.99 (978-1-57759-548-9(3)) Dalmatian Pr.

Bas, Merce Escardo & Capdevila, Francesc. Ugly Duckling. 2004. Tr. of Patito Feo. (Illus.). 32p. (J). pap. 6.95 (978-0-8118-4455-0(2)) Chronicle Bks. LLC.

Bassa, Josep, illus. La cigarra y la Hormiga. 2005. (Caballo alado clasicos-Al Trote Ser.). (SPA.). 24p. (J). 6.95 (978-84-7864-869-6(0)) Combel Editorial, S.A. ESP. *Dist:* Independent Pubs. Group.

Bateman, Teresa. The Princesses Have a Ball. Cravath, Lynne W., illus. 2002. 32p. (J). (gr. 2-5). 16.95 (978-0-8075-6626-8(8)) Whitman, Albert & Co.

—The Princesses Have a Ball. Cravath, Lynne, illus. 2005. (Albert Whitman Prairie Bks.). 32p. (J). (gr. 2-5). reprint ed. pap. 6.95 (978-0-8075-6628-2(4)) Whitman, Albert & Co.

—Traveling Tom & the Leprechaun. Potter, Mélisande, illus. 2007. 32p. (J). (ps-3). 16.95 (978-0-8234-1976-0(2)) Holiday Hse., Inc.

Batory, Edward. Genevieve in Ashram. 2001. 276p. (J). pap. 15.95 (978-0-595-19209-0(2) , Authors Choice Pr.) iUniverse, Inc.

Batt, Tanya Robyn. The Fabrics of Fairy Tale: Stories Spun from Far & Wide. Griffin, Rachel, illus. 2000. 80p. (J). (gr. 1-7). 19.99 (978-1-84148-061-9(4)) Barefoot Bks., Inc.

Batt Tanya Robyn. Faeries Gift. Ceccoli Nicoletta, illus. 2006. 0032p. pap. 6.99 (978-1-905236-73-2(5)) Barefoot Bks., Inc.

Batt, Tanya Robyn. The Princess & the White Bear King. Ceccoli, Nicoletta, illus. 2004. 40p. (J). 16.99 (978-1-84148-339-9(7)) Barefoot Bks., Inc.

Baum, L. Frank. The Discontented Gopher. Conahan, Carolyn, illus. 2006. vii, 31p. (J). (978-0-9749195-9-1(4) , South Dakota State Historical Society Pr.) South Dakota State Historical Society.

—El Maravilloso Mago de Oz. 2004. (SPA.). 192p. pap. (978-84-7720-736-8(4)) Obelisco, Ediciones S.A.

Baum, L. Frank. Queen Zixi of Ix; or, Story of the Magic. 2006. pap. (***978-1-4250-0681-5(7)**) Assistedreading-books.com Inc.

Beauty & the Beast. (Look & Find Ser.). 24p. (J). (978-0-7853-4151-2(X) , 3031707) Publications International, Ltd.

Beauty & the Beast: Individual Title Six-Packs. 32p. (gr. 2 up). 37.00 (978-0-7635-9404-6(0)) Rigby Education.

Beer, Barbara Vagnozzi. Jack & the Beanstalk. (Illus.). 24p. pap. (978-1-904550-20-4(7)); 2004. (J). 7.99 (978-0-85953-676-9(9)) Child's Play-International.

Béha, Philippe, illus. Fairy Tale Feasts: A Literary Cookbook for Young Readers & Eaters. 2006. 200p. (J). 24.95 (978-1-56656-643-8(6)) Interlink Publishing Group, Inc.

La Bella Durmiente. 2001. (First Class Ser.).Tr. of Sleeping Beauty. (SPA.). 20p. (J). (ps-3). pap. (978-968-5308-31-1(4) , Silver Dolphin en Español) Advanced Marketing, S. de R. L. de C. V.

La Bella Durmiente. 4th ed. 2002. (Troquelados Clasicos Ser.).Tr. of Sleeping Beauty. (SPA & ENG., Illus.). 16p. pap. 2.95 (978-84-7864-219-9(6)) Combel Editorial, S.A. ESP. *Dist:* Independent Pubs. Group.

La Bella Durmiente. 2000. Tr. of Sleeping Beauty. (SPA., Illus.). (J). 12.95 incl. audio (978-84-207-6728-4(X)) Grupo Anaya, S.A. ESP. *Dist:* Distribooks, Inc.

La Belle au Bois Dormant. (FRE.). 48p. pap. 12.95 incl. audio compact disk (978-2-89558-067-6(7)) Coffragants CAN. *Dist:* Penton Overseas, Inc.

Benthe. Do Not Enter. 2003. (Illus.). 106p. pap. 12.95 (978-0-9721640-7-8(3)) Whispering Wind Publishing Inc.

Bentley, Dawn. Floaties! Fairy Magic. Brown, Amy, illus. 2004. (Floaties Ser.). 12p. (J). bds. 5.98 (978-1-4027-2153-3(6)) Sterling Publishing Co., Inc.

Bergen, Lara. Disney's the Little Mermaid. 2006. 96p. (ps-2). 12.99 (978-0-7868-4942-0(8)) Disney Pr.

—Under the Sea. 2006. (Disney's the Little Mermaid Ser.). 24p. (ps-2). 18.99 (978-1-4231-0057-7(3)) Disney Pr.

—Walt Disney's Snow White & the Seven Dwarfs. 2005. (Disney Princess Ser.). (Illus.). 96p. (ps-2). 12.99 (978-0-7868-3827-1(2)) Disney Pr.

Bib, Betty. Betty Bib's Fairy Handbook: A Field Guide to Fairies & their Habitats. 2005. (Illus.). 72p. (978-1-84483-194-4(9)) Duncan Baird Pubs.

Bilan, J. Jack & the Beanstalk. 2007. 6p. 16.95 (***978-1-58117-595-0(7)** , Intervisual/Piggy Toes) Dalmatian Pr.

Birdseye, Tom. Look Out Jack! Giant Is Back! Hillenbrand, Will, illus. 2005. 32p. (J). (gr. k-3). 6.95 (978-0-8234-1776-6(X)) Holiday Hse., Inc.

Birkbeck, Paul H., illus. The Emperor & the Nightingale. 2001. (Children's Classic Ser.). 25p. (J). (gr. 3-6). 19.95 (978-0-7475-3559-1(0)) Bloomsbury Publishing Plc GBR. *Dist:* Trafalgar Square Publishing.

Birmingham, Christian, tr. & illus. Sleeping Beauty. Birmingham, Christian, illus. 2004. 64p. (J). pap. 18.95 (978-0-439-58180-6(X) , Orchard Bks.) Scholastic, Inc.

Blackaby, Susan. The Emperor's New Clothes: A Retelling of the Hans Christian Andersen Fairy Tale. DeLage, Charlene, illus. 2004. (Read-It! Readers Ser.). 32p. (C). (gr. k-3). 18.60 (978-1-4048-0224-7(X)) Picture Window Bks.

—The Little Mermaid: A Retelling of the Hans Christian Andersen Fairy Tale. DeLage, Charlene, illus. 2004. (Read-It! Readers Ser.). 32p. (C). (gr. k-3). 18.60 (978-1-4048-0221-6(5)) Picture Window Bks.

—El Patito Feo: Version del Cuento de Hans Christian Andersen. Delage, Charlene, illus. 2006. (Read-It! Readers en Espanol Ser.).Tr. of Ugly Duckling: A Retelling of the Hans Christian Andersen Fairy Tale. (SPA.). 32p. (J). (ps-3). 19.95 (978-1-4048-1644-2(5)) Picture Window Bks.

—La Princesa del Guisante: Version del Cuento de los Hermanos Grimm. Delage, Charlene, illus. 2006. (Read-It! Readers en Espanol Ser.).Tr. of Princess & the Pea: A Retelling of the Grimm's Fairy Tale. (SPA.). 32p. (J). (ps-3). 19.95 (978-1-4048-1634-3(8)) Picture Window Bks.

—The Princess & the Pea: A Retelling of the Hans Christian Andersen Fairy Tale. DeLage, Charlene, illus. 2004. (Read-It! Readers Ser.). 32p. (C). (gr. k-3). 18.60 (978-1-4048-0223-0(1)) Picture Window Bks.

—La Sirenita: Version del Cuento de los Hermanos Grimm. Delage, Charlene, illus. 2006. (Read-It! Readers en Espanol Ser.).Tr. of Little Mermaid: A Retelling of the Grimm's Fairy Tale. (SPA.). 32p. (J). (ps-3). 19.95 (978-1-4048-1633-6(X)) Picture Window Bks.

—El Soldadito de Plomo: Version del Cuento de Hans Christian Andersen. Delage, Charlene, illus. 2006. (Read-It! Readers en Espanol Ser.).Tr. of Steadfast Tin Soldier: A Retelling of the Hans Christian Andersen Fairy Tale. (SPA.). 32p. (J). (ps-3). 19.95 (978-1-4048-1641-1(0)) Picture Window Bks.

—The Steadfast Tin Soldier: A Retelling of the Hans Christian Andersen Fairy Tale. DeLage, Charlene, illus. 2004. (Read-It! Readers Ser.). 32p. (C). (gr. k-3). 18.60 (978-1-4048-0226-1(6)) Picture Window Bks.

—Thumbelina: A Retelling of the Hans Christian Andersen Fairy Tale. DeLage, Charlene, illus. 2004. (Read-It! Readers Ser.). 32p. (C). (gr. k-3). 18.60 (978-1-4048-0225-4(8)) Picture Window Bks.

—El Traje Nuevo del Emperador: Version del Cuento de los Hermanos Grimm. Delage, Charlene, illus. 2006. (Read-It! Readers en Espanol Ser.).Tr. of Emperor's New Clothes: A Retelling of the Grimm's Fairy Tale. (SPA.). 32p. (J). (ps-3). 19.95 (978-1-4048-1629-9(1)) Picture Window Bks.

—The Ugly Duckling: A Retelling of the Hans Christian Andersen Fairy Tale. DeLage, Charlene, illus. 2004. (Read-It! Readers Ser.). 32p. (C). (gr. k-3). 18.60 (978-1-4048-0222-3(3)) Picture Window Bks.

Blackstone, Stella. Storytime: First Tales for Sharing. Wilson, Anne, illus. 2005. 96p. (J). (ps-3). 19.99 (978-1-84148-345-0(1)) Barefoot Bks., Inc.

Blair, Eric. La Bella Durmiente: Version del Cuento de los Hermanos Grimm. Ouren, Todd, illus. 2006. (Read-It! Readers en Espanol Ser.).Tr. of Sleeping Beauty: A Retelling of the Grimm's Fairy Tale. (SPA.). 32p. (J). (ps-3). 19.95 (978-1-4048-1639-8(9)) Picture Window Bks.

—Blanca Nieves: Version del Cuento de los Hermanos Grimm. Wolf, Claudia, illus. 2006. (Read-It! Readers en Espanol Ser.).Tr. of Snow White: A Retelling of the Grimm's Fairy Tale. (SPA.). 32p. (J). (ps-3). 19.95 (978-1-4048-1640-4(2)) Picture Window Bks.

—The Bremen Town Musicians. 2004. (Illus.). (J). pap. 13.95 (978-1-4048-0536-1(2)) Picture Window Bks.

—Los Duendes Zapateros: Version del Cuento de los Hermanos Grimm. Dickson, Bill, illus. 2006. (Read-It! Readers en Espanol Ser.).Tr. of Shoemaker & His Elves: A Retelling of the Grimm's Fairy Tale. (SPA.). 32p. (J). (ps-3). 19.95 (978-1-4048-1638-1(0)) Picture Window Bks.

—El Lobo y los Siete Cabritos: Version del Cuento de los Hermanos Grimm. Petrusek, Brett, illus. 2006. (Read-It! Readers en Espanol Ser.).Tr. of Wolf & the Seven Little Kids: A Retelling of the Grimm's Fairy Tale. (SPA.). 32p. (J). (ps-3). 19.95 (978-1-4048-1645-9(3)) Picture Window Bks.

—Los Musicos de Bremen: Version del Cuento de los Hermanos Grimm. Dickson, Bill, illus. 2006. (Read-It! Readers en Espanol Ser.).Tr. of Bremen Town Musicians: A Retelling of the Grimm's Fairy Tale. (SPA.). 32p. (J). (ps-3). 19.95 (978-1-4048-1628-2(3)) Picture Window Bks.

—El Ninito de Jengibre. Peterson, Ben, illus. 2006. (Read-It! Readers en Espanol Ser.).Tr. of Gingerbread Man. (SPA.). 32p. (J). (ps-3). 19.95 (978-1-4048-1647-3(X)) Picture Window Bks.

—El Principe Encantado: Version del Cuento de los Hermanos Grimm. Ouren, Todd, illus. 2006. (Read-It! Readers en Espanol Ser.).Tr. of Frog Prince: A Retelling of the Grimm's Fairy Tale. (SPA.). 32p. (J). (ps-3). 19.95 (978-1-4048-1631-2(3)) Picture Window Bks.

—Puss in Boots: A Retelling of the Grimms' Fairy Tale. Ouren, Todd, illus. 2004. (Read-It! Readers Ser.). 32p. (J). (gr. k-3). 18.60 (978-1-4048-0591-0(5)) Picture Window Bks.

—The Shoemaker & His Elves. 2004. (Read-It! Readers Ser.). (Illus.). 32p. (J). (978-1-4048-0540-8(0)) Picture Window Bks.

—Sleeping Beauty: A Retelling of the Grimms' Fairy Tale. Ouren, Todd, illus. 2004. (Read-It! Readers Ser.). 32p. (C). (gr. k-3). 18.60 (978-1-4048-0592-7(3)) Picture Window Bks.

—Tom Thumb: A Retelling of the Classic Fairy Tale. Ouren, Todd, illus. 2004. (Read-It! Readers Ser.). 32p. (J). (gr. k-3). 18.60 (978-1-4048-0593-4(1)) Picture Window Bks.

—The Wolf & the Seven Little Kids: A Retelling of the Grimms' Fairy Tale. Petrusek, Brett, illus. 2004. (Read-It! Readers Ser.). 32p. (J). (gr. k-3). 18.60 (978-1-4048-0594-1(X)) Picture Window Bks.

Blanca Nieves - (Estrella de Mar) 2003. (SPA., Illus.). 16p. 2.95 (978-968-855-185-1(6)) Suromex, Ediciones, S.A. MEX. *Dist:* Giron Bks.

Blancanieves y los Siete Enanitos. 4th ed. 2002. (Troquelados Clasicos Ser.). (SPA & ENG., Illus.). 16p. pap. 2.95 (978-84-7864-217-5(X)) Combel Editorial, S.A. ESP. *Dist:* Independent Pubs. Group.

Blaylock, Kathy. Adventures of Buddy Fairy & Friends. 2007. 48p. 12.95 (***978-1-4137-9195-2(6)**) PublishAmerica, Inc.

Block, Francesca Lia. Beautiful Boys: Two Weetzie Bat Books. 2004. (Weetzie Bat Ser.). (Illus.). 304p. (J). pap. 7.99 (978-0-06-059435-0(7) , Cotler, Joanna Books) HarperCollins Pubs.

—Goat Girls: Two Weetzie Bat Books. 2004. (Weetzie Bat Ser.). 240p. (J). pap. 7.99 (978-0-06-059434-3(9) , Cotler, Joanna Books) HarperCollins Pubs.

—The Rose & the Beast: Fairy Tales Retold. 2001. (gr. 7-12). lib. bdg. 15.25 (978-0-613-44249-7(0)) Tandem Library Bks.

Bluege, Wilor. The Golden Bough: A Fairytale Ballet for Children. 2000. (Illus.). 28p. (J). (ps-12). pap. 25.00 (978-1-883477-39-4(5)) Lone Oak Pr., Ltd.

Boada, Francesc. Cinderella. Surges, James, tr. Fransoy, Monse, illus. 2001. (SPA & ENG.). 32p. (J). (ps-3). pap. 6.95 (978-0-8118-3090-4(X)) Chronicle Bks. LLC.

—Princess & the Pea; La Princesa y Pea: A Bilingual Book. Estrada, Pau, illus. 2004. 32p. (J). pap. 6.95 (978-0-8118-4452-9(8)) Chronicle Bks. LLC.

Boada, Francesc & Andersen, Hans Christian. The Princess & the Pea (La Princesa y el Guisante) A Bilingual Book. Estrada, Pau, illus. 2004. (ENG & SPA.). 32p. (J). 14.95 (978-0-8118-4451-2(X)) Chronicle Bks. LLC.

Boada, Francesc & Perrault, Charles. Puss in Boots: A Bilingual Book. Merino, Jose Luis, tr. from CAT. Merino, Jose Luis, illus. 2004. Tr. of El Gato con Botas. (ENG & SPA.). 32p. (J). pap. 6.95 (978-0-8118-3924-2(9)) Chronicle Bks. LLC.

Boada, Francesc, et al. Puss in Boots: A Bilingual Book. 2004. Tr. of El Gato con Botas. (ENG & SPA., Illus.). 32p. (J). (gr. k-3). 14.95 (978-0-8118-3923-5(0)) Chronicle Bks. LLC.

Boada I Moret, Francesc. Caperucita Roja. (Coleccion Fabulas y Cuentos Populares). (SPA.). 24p. (J). (gr. 2-4). (978-84-246-1921-3(8) , GL0132) La Galera, S.A. Editorial ESP. *Dist:* Lectorum Pubns., Inc.

Bockus, William, Jr. A Faerie Tale. 2001. (Illus.). 144p. (Orig.). (J). (gr. 1-6). pap. 12.00 (978-0-9647151-3-4(9)) Print Place.

Boelts, Maribeth. Dogerella. Wu, Donald, illus. 2008. (J). (***978-0-375-83393-9(5)**); lib. bdg. (***978-0-375-93393-6(X)**) Random Hse., Inc.

Bofill, Francesc. Juan y los Frijoles Magicos. Alejandro, Alis, tr. from SPA. Ballester, Arnal, illus. 1998. Tr. of Jack & the Beanstalk. (SPA.). 32p. (J). (ps-3). 14.95 (978-0-8118-2062-2(9)) Chronicle Bks. LLC.

Bofill, Francesc & Ballester, Arnal. Jack & the Beanstalk. Alejandro, Alis, tr. Ballester, Arnal, illus. 1998. Tr. of Juan y los Frijoles Magicos. (ENG & SPA., Illus.). 32p. (J). (ps-3). pap. 6.95 (978-0-8118-1843-8(8)) Chronicle Bks. LLC.

Bolton, Michael. The Secret of the Lost Kingdom. 2006. 44p. (J). 12.95 (978-1-59764-218-7(5)) New Line Bks.

Bonder, Dianna, illus. Three Royal Tales: The Frog Prince; The Emperor's New Clothes; The Princess & the Pea. 2004. (Once-upon-a-Time Ser.). 32p. (J). (gr. k-3). (978-1-55074-939-7(0)) Kids Can Pr., Ltd.

Le Bonhomme de Pain d'Epice. 2000. Tr. of Gingerbread Man. (FRE., Illus.). 32p. (J). pap. 13.95 (978-2-09-202101-9(X)) Nathan, Fernand FRA. *Dist:* Distribooks, Inc.

Book Company Staff. Lift-A-Flap Guess Who. 2005. (J). bds. 10.95 (978-1-74047-620-1(4)) Book Co. Publishing Pty, Ltd., The AUS. *Dist:* Penton Overseas, Inc.

Bordoy, Irene, illus. Las Fresas. 2005. (Caballo alado clasicos-Al Trote Ser.). (SPA.). 24p. (J). 6.95 (978-84-7864-870-2(4)) Combel Editorial, S.A. ESP. *Dist:* Independent Pubs. Group.

—El Patito Feo. 2004. (Caballo Alado Clasico Ser.). (SPA.). 24p. (J). 6.95 (978-84-7864-764-4(3)) Combel Editorial, S.A. ESP. *Dist:* Independent Pubs. Group.

Borsten, Joan & Vidov, Oleg, eds. Mikhail Baryshnikov's Stories from My Childhood: Beloved Fairy Tales from the Snow Queen to Ivan & His Magicpony to Cinderella. 2005. (Illus.). 128p. (J). (gr. 4-8). reprint ed. 25.00 (978-0-7567-8941-1(9)) DIANE Publishing Co.

Bosom, Monica. Peter Pan: Fairy Tale Theater. Rius, Roser, illus. 2005. 29p. (J). (gr. k-4). reprint ed. 9.00 (978-0-7567-8817-9(X)) DIANE Publishing Co.

Bosom, Monica, ed. The Ugly Duckling. Peris, Carme, illus. 1999. 32p. (J). (ps-3). 8.95 (978-0-7641-5149-1(5)) Barron's Educational Series, Inc.

Bouchard, David. The Great Race - The Legend of the Chinese Zodiac. ed. 2004. (J). (gr. k-3). spiral bd. (978-0-616-01430-1(9)) Canadian National Institute for the Blind/Institut National Canadien pour les Aveugles.

Boucle d'Or et les Trois Ours. 2000. Tr. of Goldilocks. (FRE., Illus.). 32p. (J). pap. (978-2-09-202102-6(8)) Editions Rouge et Or.

Boucle d'Or et les Trois Ours. 2000. (Musicontes Ser.).Tr. of Goldilocks. (FRE.). (J). 24.95 incl. audio (978-2-09-230441-9(0)) Nathan, Fernand FRA. *Dist:* Distribooks, Inc.

Bradman, Tony. Has Anyone Seen Jack. rev. ed. 2007. (Illus.). 24p. (J). 7.95 (***978-1-84507-706-8(7)**) Lincoln, Frances Ltd. GBR. *Dist:* Perseus Distribution.

—Look Out, He's Behind You! Chamberlain, Margaret, illus. 2007. 28p. (J). 7.95 (***978-1-84507-734-1(2)**) Lincoln, Frances Ltd. GBR. *Dist:* Perseus Distribution.

Branch, Beverly, illus. Thumbelina: A Tale about Being Nice. 2006. (J). 6.99 (978-1-59939-024-6(8)) Reader's Digest Young Families, Inc.

Bredin, Henrietta & McEwen, Priscilla. The Prince & the Goosegirl: A Story with Activities Based on the Opera by Humperdinck. 2006. (Illus.). 30p. (J). (gr. k-4). reprint ed. pap. 17.00 (978-1-4223-5538-1(1)) DIANE Publishing Co.

Brimax, S. Fairy Tales. 1998. (Illus.). 96p. (J). 80.00 (978-81-86982-75-4(2)) Business Pubns. Inc. IND. *Dist:* State Mutual Bk. & Periodical Service, Ltd.

Brothers Grimm Staff. Grimm's Fairy Tales. 2002. (Illus.). (J). (gr. k-3). lib. bdg. 31.55 (978-0-613-86552-4(9)) Tandem Library Bks.

—Grimms Fairy Tales Clear Print. 2006. pap. ***(*978-1-4068-2141-3(1))*** Echo Library.

—Hansel & Gretel. Price, Margaret Evans, illus. 2005. 16p. (J). (ps-3). 9.95 (978-1-59583-012-8(X) , Green Tiger Pr.) Laughing Elephant.

—Hansel y Gretel. Martinez, Miriam, tr. Browne, Anthony, illus. 2004. (SPA.). (J). 9.95 (978-968-16-7062-7(0)) Fondo de Cultura Economica MEX. *Dist:* Lectorum Pubns., Inc.

Brothers Grimm Staff. Household Tales by Brothers Grimm, V1. 2006. 67.99 ***(*978-1-4280-1855-6(7))*** IndyPublish.com.

Brothers Grimm Staff & Daynes, Katie. Hansel & Gretel. 2005. 48p. (J). (gr. 2 up). 8.95 (978-0-7945-1053-4(1) , Usborne) EDC Publishing.

Brown, Arlene E. The Legend of Fairy Tale Trail, Vol. 1. Wheeler, Dianne, ed. Boden, A., illus. 2000. 22p. (J). (gr. 2-3). pap. 7.95 (978-0-9700135-0-7(7) , 1001A) Fairy Tale Trail Pubns.

Brown, Beth, compiled by. Fairy Tales of Birds & Beasts. 1999. (Illus.). 128p. (J). (gr. 3-7). lib. bdg. 15.95 (978-0-87460-375-0(7)) Lion Bks.

Brown, Calef. Polkabats & Octopus Slacks: 14 Stories. 2005. 32p. (J). (gr. k-3). 5.95 (978-0-618-11129-9(8)) Houghton Mifflin Co. Trade & Reference Div.

Brown, Marc. Arthur Tricks the Tooth Fairy. 1998. (Arthur Ser.). (Illus.). 24p. (J). (gr. k-3). lib. bdg. 11.99 (978-0-679-98464-1(X) , Random Hse. Bks. for Young Readers) Random Hse. Children's Bks.

Browne, Francis. Granny's Wonderful Chair. 1999. (Illus.). 128p. (gr. 4-7). 19.95 (978-1-85149-706-5(4)) Antique Collectors' Club.

Brundage, Frances, illus. Cinderella: A Fairy Story. 2004. reprint ed. pap. 15.95 (978-1-4179-8713-9(8)) Kessinger Publishing, LLC.

Bryant, Megan E. Berry Fairy Tales: Cinderella. Neely, Scott, illus. 2005. (Strawberry Shortcake Ser.). 32p. (J). (ps-3). pap. 6.99 (978-0-448-43979-2(4) , Grosset & Dunlap) Penguin Group (USA) Inc.

—The Little Mermaid. Huxtable, John, illus. 2006. (Berry Fairy Tales Ser.). 32p. (J). pap. 3.99 (978-0-448-44346-1(5) , Grosset & Dunlap) Penguin Group (USA) Inc.

—The Little Mermaid: Berry Fairy Tales. Huxtable, John & Huxtable, Tonja, illus. 2006. (Strawberry Shortcake Ser.). 32p. (J). 6.99 (978-0-448-44523-6(9) , Grosset & Dunlap) Penguin Group (USA) Inc.

—Rapunzel: Berry Fairy Tales. Huxtable, John & Huxtable, Tonja, illus. 2007. (Strawberry Shortcake Ser.). 32p. (J). (ps-2). 6.99 (978-0-448-44556-4(5) , Grosset & Dunlap) Penguin Group (USA) Inc.

—Snow White: Berry Fairy Tales. Huxtable, John & Huxtable, Tonja, illus. 2007. (Strawberry Shortcake Ser.). 32p. (J). 6.99 (978-0-448-44458-1(5) , Grosset & Dunlap) Penguin Group (USA) Inc.

Buckler, Carol. Feathered Tales from the Barnyard. l.t. ed. 2004. (J). per. 5.95 (978-1-932496-20-8(3)) Penman Publishing, Inc.

Buckley, Michael. The Fairy Tale Detectives. Ferguson, Peter, illus. 2005. (Sisters Grimm Ser.: Bk. 1). 288p. (J). (gr. 3-7). 14.95 (978-0-8109-5925-5(9) , Abrams Bks. for Young Readers) Abrams, Harry N. , Inc.

—The Unusual Suspects. Ferguson, Peter, illus. 2005. (Sisters Grimm Ser.: Bk. 2). 192p. (J). (gr. 3-7). 14.95 (978-0-8109-5926-2(7) , Abrams Bks. for Young Readers) Abrams, Harry N. , Inc.

Buffett, Jimmy & Buffett, Savannah Jane. The Jolly Mon. Davis, Lambert, illus. 2006. 32p. (J). 17.95 (978-0-15-205786-2(2)) Harcourt Children's Bks.

Burke, David. Beauty & the Beast (English to French - Level 3) Learn FRENCH Through Fairy Tales. 2007. (Learn French Through Fairy Tales Ser.). (ENG & FRE., Illus.). (J). per. 14.95 incl. audio compact disk ***(*978-1-891888-87-8(0))*** Slangman Publishing.

—Beauty & the Beast (English to German - Level 3) Learn GERMAN Through Fairy Tales. 2007. (Learn German Through Fairy Tales Ser.). (ENG & GER., Illus.). (J). per. 14.95 incl. audio compact disk ***(*978-1-891888-88-5(9))*** Slangman Publishing.

—Beauty & the Beast (English to Italian - Level 3) Learn ITALIAN Through Fairy Tales. 2007. (Learn Italian Through Fairy Tales Ser.). (ENG & ITA., Illus.). (J). per. 14.95 incl. audio compact disk ***(*978-1-891888-89-2(7))*** Slangman Publishing.

—Beauty & the Beast (English to Spanish - Level 3) Learn SPANISH Through Fairy Tales. 2007. (Learn Spanish Through Fairy Tales Ser.). (ENG & SPA., Illus.). (J). per. 14.95 incl. audio compact disk ***(*978-1-891888-86-1(2))*** Slangman Publishing.

—Cinderella (English to German - Level 1) Learn GERMAN Through Fairy Tales. 2007. (Learn German Through Fairy Tales Ser.). (ENG & GER., Illus.). (J). per. 14.95 incl. audio compact disk ***(*978-1-891888-76-2(5))*** Slangman Publishing.

—Cinderella (English to Italian - Level 1) Learn ITALIAN Through Fairy Tales. 2007. (Learn Italian Through Fairy Tales Ser.). (ENG & ITA., Illus.). (J). per. 14.95 incl. audio compact disk ***(*978-1-891888-77-9(3))*** Slangman Publishing.

—Cinderella (English to Spanish - Level 1) Learn SPANISH Through Fairy Tales. 2007. (Learn Spanish Through Fairy Tales Ser.). (ENG & SPA., Illus.). (J). per. 14.95 incl. audio compact disk ***(*978-1-891888-74-8(9))*** Slangman Publishing.

—Goldilocks (English to German - Level 2) Learn GERMAN Through Fairy Tales. 2007. (Learn German Through Fairy Tales Ser.). (ENG & GER., Illus.). (J). per. 14.95 incl. audio compact disk ***(*978-1-891888-83-0(8))*** Slangman Publishing.

—Goldilocks (English to Italian - Level 2) Learn ITALIAN Through Fairy Tales. 2007. (Learn Italian Through Fairy Tales Ser.). (ENG & ITA., Illus.). (J). per. 14.95 incl. audio compact disk ***(*978-1-891888-82-3(X))*** Slangman Publishing.

Burke, David, adapted by. Beauty & the Beast (English to Chinese - Level 3) Learn MANDARIN CHINESE Through Fairy Tales. 2007. (Learn Chinese Through Fairy Tales Ser.). (ENG & CHI., Illus.). (J). per. 14.95 incl. audio compact disk ***(*978-1-891888-91-5(9))*** Slangman Publishing.

—Cinderella (English to Chinese - Level 1) Learn MANDARIN CHINESE Through Fairy Tales. 2007. (Learn Chinese Through Fairy Tales Ser.). (ENG & CHI., Illus.). (J). per. 14.95 incl. cd-rom ***(*978-1-891888-79-3(X))*** Slangman Publishing.

—Cinderella (English to French - Level 1) Learn FRENCH Through Fairy Tales. 2007. (Learn French Through Fairy Tales Ser.). (ENG & FRE., Illus.). (J). per. 14.95 incl. audio compact disk ***(*978-1-891888-75-5(7))*** Slangman Publishing.

—GOLDILOCKS (English to Chinese - Level 2) Learn MANDARIN CHINESE Through Fairy Tales. 2007. (Learn Chinese Through Fairy Tales Ser.). (ENG & CHI., Illus.). (J). per. 14.95 incl. audio compact disk ***(*978-1-891888-85-4(4))*** Slangman Publishing.

—Goldilocks (English to French - Level 2) Learn FRENCH Through Fairy Tales. 2007. (Learn French Through Fairy Tales Ser.). (ENG & FRE., Illus.). (J). per. 14.95 incl. audio compact disk ***(*978-1-891888-81-6(1))*** Slangman Publishing.

Burnett, Frances Hodgson. The Land of the Blue Flower. 2002. (J). cd-rom (978-0-9724995-7-6(1)) Alcazar AudioWorks.

Burton, Richard F. The Arabian Nights. 1999. (gr. 7-12). lib. bdg. 15.25 (978-0-613-21126-0(X)) Tandem Library Bks.

Butts, Christina. Horse & the Dog A Grand Fairy Tale A. 2006. pap. 15.38 ***(*978-1-4116-1235-8(3))*** Lulu.com.

Buzzati, Dino & Lobb, Frances. The Bears' Famous Invasion of Sicily. 2003. (New York Review Children's Collection). (Illus.). 152p. (J). 18.95 (978-1-59017-076-2(8) , NYR Children's Collection) New York Review of Bks., Inc., The.

Buzzati, Dino & Snicket, Lemony. The Bears' Famous Invasion of Sicily. Buzzati, Dino, illus. 2005. (Illus.). 192p. (J). pap. 5.99 (978-0-06-072608-9(3)) HarperCollins Pubs.

Cabal, Graciela Beatriz. Azul. (SPA.). 32p. pap. 8.95 (978-950-07-2052-6(3)) Editorial Sudamericana S.A. ARG. *Dist:* Distribooks, Inc.

Caldwell, J. Lynn. The Tooth Fairy's Guide to Lost Teeth: A Fortune for Every Day a Tooth Is Lost. Jepson, Beth, illus. 2005. (J). per. 11.95 (978-0-9774463-0-8(1)) Caldwell, Judy.

Cane, Rochelle. Barbie Glitter Fun. 2006. (Style Bks.). 12p. (J). bds. 12.99 (978-0-7944-0943-2(1)) Reader's Digest Assn., Inc., The.

Capek, Jindra, illus. The Firebird: A Traditional Russian Folk-Tale. 1999. 32p. (J). pap. 19.99 (978-0-86315-302-0(X)) Floris Bks. GBR. *Dist:* SteinerBooks, Inc.

Caperucita Roja. 3rd ed. 2002. (Troquelados Clasicos Ser.). (SPA & ENG., Illus.). 16p. pap. 2.95 (978-84-7864-183-3(1)) Combel Editorial, S.A. ESP. *Dist:* Independent Pubs. Group.

Caperucita Roja: Clothing, Food, Nature, the Human Body. 1999. (SPA & ENG., Illus.). (J). (ps-5). pap. 7.95 (978-88-8148-249-8(5)) European Language Institute ITA. *Dist:* Distribooks, Inc., Midwest European Pubns.

Cardenoso, Concha, adapted by. Cuentame un Cuento, No. 3. (SPA.). 96p. (J). (gr. k-3). (978-84-480-1144-4(9) , TM3382) Timun Mas, Editorial S.A. ESP. *Dist:* Lectorum Pubns., Inc.

Carroll, Lewis, pseud. Alice au Pays des Merveilles. (FRE.). (J). (gr. 3-8). 7.95 (978-0-8288-6095-6(5) , M5497) French & European Pubns., Inc.

—Alice's Adventures in Wonderland. Steadman, Ralph, illus. 2006. 128p. pap. 19.95 (978-1-55407-203-3(4)) Firefly Bks., Ltd.

—Alice's Adventures in Wonderland & Through the Looking-Glass: And What Alice Found There. 2002. (Modern Library Classics). (Illus.). 304p. pap. 8.95 (978-0-375-76138-6(1) , Modern Library) Random House Publishing Group.

—Alicia en el Pais de las Maravillas. 2000. (Coleccion "Clasicos Juveniles" Ser.). (SPA.). 156p. pap. 10.95 (978-0-595-13544-8(7)) iUniverse, Inc.

Carroll, Yvonne. Great Irish Legends for Children. Lawrie, Robin, illus. 2005. 64p. (J). (ps-ps). 16.95 (978-1-58980-345-9(0)) Pelican Publishing Co., Inc.

—The Leprechaun Library, 5. 1999. (Illus.). 116p. (J). 16.95 (978-0-7171-3251-5(X)) Gill & MacMillan, Ltd. IRL. *Dist:* Irish Bks. & Media, Inc.

Cartwright, Stephen, illus. Fairytale Jigsaw Book. 2004. (Jigsaw Books Ser.). 20p. (J). 14.95 (978-0-7945-0771-8(9) , Usborne) EDC Publishing.

Cason, Sue. Dragon Trouble. Grimwood, Tracie, illus. 1999. (Supa Doopers Ser.). 64p. (J). (978-0-7608-3289-9(7)) Sundance/Newbridge Educational Publishing.

—Dragon Trouble. 1999. (gr. 3-6). lib. bdg. 12.60 (978-0-613-30364-4(4)) Tandem Library Bks.

Cassidy, Anne. Snow White. 2006. (First Fairy Tales Ser.). (Illus.). 32p. (J). (978-1-59771-074-9(1)) Sea-To-Sea Pubns.

La Castanera. 2nd ed. 2002. (Troquelados Clasicos Ser.). (ENG & SPA., Illus.). 16p. pap. 2.95 (978-84-7864-376-9(1)) Combel Editorial, S.A. ESP. *Dist:* Independent Pubs. Group.

Catanese, P. W. The Thief & the Beanstalk. 2005. 288p. (J). (gr. 4-7). pap. 4.99 (978-0-689-87173-3(2) , Aladdin) Simon & Schuster Children's Publishing.

Cattie, Ray. Ard Righ: The Sword on the Stone. 2005. (Illus.). 280p. 19.95 (978-0-9748765-2-8(6)) DNA Pr.

Cavalieri, Felicia. La Petite Fille Aux Allumettes. 2000. (Best-Sellers Ser.).Tr. of Little Match Girl. (FRE., Illus.). 40p. (J). (ps-2). audio, audio compact disk 9.95 (978-2-921997-31-7(2)) Coffragants CAN. *Dist:* Penton Overseas, Inc.

Ceccoli, Nicoletta, illus. Barefoot Book of Fairy Tales. 2005. 160p. (J). 19.99 (978-1-84148-798-4(8)) Barefoot Bks., Inc.

—Little Red Riding Hood. 2004. 32p. (J). 16.99 (978-1-84148-621-5(3)) Barefoot Bks., Inc.

Cendrars, Blaise. Petits Contes Negres pour les Enfants. (FRE.). (J). pap. 19.95 (978-2-07-051787-9(X)) Gallimard, Editions FRA. *Dist:* Distribooks, Inc.

Cendrillon.Tr. of Cinderella. (FRE.). 48p. pap. 12.95 incl. audio compact disk (978-2-89558-065-2(0)) Coffragants CAN. *Dist:* Penton Overseas, Inc.

Cenicienta. 2001. (First Class Ser.). (SPA.). 20p. (J). (ps-3). pap. (978-968-5308-29-8(2) , Silver Dolphin en Español) Advanced Marketing, S. de R. L. de C. V.

Cenicienta. 4th ed. 2002. (Troquelados Clasicos Ser.). (SPA & ENG., Illus.). 16p. pap. 2.95 (978-84-7864-216-8(1)) Combel Editorial, S.A. ESP. *Dist:* Independent Pubs. Group.

Cethial and Bossche Publishing Staff. Fairy Tale Garden Castle Games: Cinderella & Dracula. 1999. (Illus.). (J). (ps-3). (978-1-55274-036-1(6)) Cethial & Bossche Co.

Chalvin, Marc, illus. The Sly Fox & the Little Red Hen: Based on a Traditional Folk Tale. 1999. (First Favourite Tales Ser.). 32p. (J). 4.95 (978-0-7214-9741-9(1) , Dutton Juvenile) Penguin Group (USA) Inc.

Charko, Kasia, illus. Three Tuneful Tales. 2004. (Once-upon-a-Time Ser.). 32p. (J). (gr. k-3). (978-1-55074-941-0(2)) Kids Can Pr., Ltd.

Charles, Veronika Martenova. Stretch, Swallow & Stare. Charles, Veronika Martenova, illus. l.t. ed. 1999. (Illus.). 31p. (J). (ps-3). 16.95 (978-0-7737-3098-4(2)) Stoddart Kids CAN. *Dist:* Fitzhenry & Whiteside, Ltd.

Chester, Laura. Hiding Glory. Lippincott, Gary, illus. 2007. 160p. (J). 18.95 ***(*978-1-59543-616-0(2))*** Willow Creek Pr., Inc.

Child, Lauren. The Princess & the Pea. Borland, Polly, photos by. 2006. (Illus.). 40p. (gr. k-17). 16.99 (978-0-7868-3886-8(8)) Hyperion Pr.

Chinchinian, Harry. The Princess & the Beggar II: Continuing Adventures. Chinchinian, Harry, illus. 2005. (Illus.). 176p. (J). lib. bdg. 18.95 (978-1-892476-11-1(8)) Plum Tree Pr.

Christianánders, Hans & Falloon, Jane. Thumbelina. Clark, Emma Chichester, illus. 2006. 38p. (J). (gr. k-4). reprint ed. 16.00 (978-1-4223-5373-8(7)) DIANE Publishing Co.

Chronicle Books LLC Staff. Snow White (Bilingual) 2008. (SPA & ENG.). (J). 14.95 (978-0-8118-6030-7(2)); pap. 6.95 (978-0-8118-6031-4(0)) Chronicle Bks. LLC.

Cinderella. 1999. (Little Golden Bks.). (J). pap. 4.99 (978-0-307-98064-9(2) , 98064, Golden Bks.) Random Hse. Children's Bks.

Cinderella. 2002. (Classic Tales Ser.). (Illus.). 32p. (J). incl. audio compact disk (978-1-59069-101-4(6) , T1103); (978-1-59069-034-5(6) , T1003) Studio Mouse LLC.

Cinderella. unabr. ed. (Read-Along Ser.). (J). 7.99 incl. audio (978-1-55723-007-2(2)) Walt Disney Records.

Cinderella: 6 Small Books. (gr. k-2). 23.00 (978-0-7635-8514-3(9)) Rigby Education.

Cinderella: Individual Title Six-Packs. 32p. (gr. 2 up). 37.00 (978-0-7635-9400-8(8)) Rigby Education.

Cinderella: Treasures from the Library of Congress. 2004. (Shape Bks.). (Illus.). 20p. (J). reprint ed. 3.95 (978-1-55709-166-6(8)) Applewood Bks.

Cinderfella's Big Night: Individual Title Six-Packs. (Action Packs Ser.). 104p. (gr. 3-5). 44.00 (978-0-7635-2984-0(2)) Rigby Education.

Clark, Margaret & Malone, Peter. The Classic Treasury of Princess Fairy Tales. 2005. (Illus.). 56p. 9.98 (978-0-7624-1890-9(7) , Courage Bks.) Running Pr. Bk. Pubs.

Claybourne, Anna. Don't Kiss the Frog. Waters, Fiona, ed. Burfoot, Ella et al, illus. 2007. 80p. (J). 14.95 ***(*978-0-7534-5953-9(1)*** , Kingfisher) Houghton Mifflin Co. Trade & Reference Div.

Climo, Shirley. Irish Cinderlad. 2000. 12.79 (978-0-606-17881-5(3)); lib. bdg. 14.15 (978-0-613-28540-7(9)) Tandem Library Bks.

—The Persian Cinderella. Florczak, Robert, illus. 32p. (J). (gr. k-4). 2001. pap. 6.99 (978-0-06-443853-7(8) , Harper Trophy); 1999. 16.99 (978-0-06-026763-6(1)) HarperCollins Pubs.

—Persian Cinderella. 2002. (978-0-606-22280-8(4)); 2001. lib. bdg. 14.10 (978-0-613-44245-9(8)) Tandem Library Bks.

—Pride of Princesses: Princess Tales from Around the World. 1999. (978-0-606-16696-6(3)) Tandem Library Bks.

Clynes, Kate & Anstey, David. Ali Baba & the Forty Thieves. 2005. (Illus.). 32p. (J). (ALB & ENG.). pap. 12.95 (978-1-84444-400-7(7)); (ARA & ENG., pap. 12.95 (978-1-84444-401-4(5)); (BEN & ENG., pap. 12.95 (978-1-84444-402-1(3)); (BUL & ENG., pap. 12.95 (978-1-84444-403-8(1)); (CHI & ENG., pap. 12.95 (978-1-84444-404-5(X)); (CHI & ENG., pap. 12.95 (978-1-84444-405-2(8)); (CRO, SER & ENG., pap. 12.95 (978-1-84444-406-9(6)); (ENG, PER & FAR., pap. 12.95 (978-1-84444-407-6(4)); (ENG & FRE., pap. 12.95 (978-1-84444-408-3(2)); (ENG & GER., pap. 12.95 (978-1-84444-409-0(0)); (ENG & GUJ., pap. 12.95 (978-1-84444-410-6(4)); (ENG & HIN., pap. 12.95 (978-1-84444-411-3(2)); (ENG & ITA., pap. 12.95 (978-1-84444-412-0(0)); (ENG & KUR., pap. 12.95 (978-1-84444-413-7(9)); (ENG & PAN., pap. 12.95 (978-1-84444-414-4(7)); (ENG & POL., pap. 12.95 (978-1-84444-415-1(5)); (ENG & POR., pap. 12.95 (978-1-84444-416-8(3)); (ENG & RUS., pap. 12.95 (978-1-84444-417-5(1)); (ENG & SHO., pap. 12.95 (978-1-84444-418-2(X)); (ENG & SOM., pap. 12.95 (978-1-84444-419-9(8)); (ENG & SPA., pap. 12.95 (978-1-84444-420-5(1)); (ENG & TAM., pap. 12.95 (978-1-84444-421-2(X)); (ENG & TUR., pap. 12.95 (978-1-84444-422-9(8)); (ENG & URD., pap. 12.95 (978-1-84444-424-3(4)); (ENG & VIE., pap. 12.95 (978-1-84444-425-0(2)); (ENG, RUM & ROM., pap. 12.95 (978-1-84444-427-4(9)) Mantra Lingua GBR. *Dist:* Mantra Publishing, Ltd.

Coburn, Jewell R. Angkat: The Cambodian Cinderella. Flotte, Edmund, illus. 1998. 32p. (gr. 1-3). 16.95 (978-1-885008-09-1(0)) Shen's Bks.

Cohen, Della, adapted by. Cinderella: A Read-Aloud Storybook. 1999. (Disney's Read-Aloud Storybooks Ser.). (Illus.). 72p. (J). (ps-2). 8.99 (978-0-7364-0124-1(5) , RH/Disney) Random Hse. Children's Bks.

Cohen, Sheldon, illus. La Chasse-Galerie. 2004. (FRE.). 24p. (J). (gr. 3-7). 15.95 (978-0-88776-635-0(8)) Tundra Bks., Inc./Livres Toundra, Inc. CAN. *Dist:* Random Hse., Inc.

Cole, Babette. Princess Smartypants. Cole, Babette, illus. 2005. 32p. (J). (ps-3). 15.99 (978-0-399-24398-1(4) , Putnam Juvenile) Penguin Group (USA) Inc.

Cole, Brock. The Giant's Toe. Cole, Brock, illus. 2001. (Sunburst Ser.). (Illus.). 32p. (J). (ps-3). pap. 6.95 (978-0-374-42557-9(4) , Sunburst) Farrar, Straus & Giroux.

Collins, Sheila Hebert. Jacques et la Canne a Sucre: A Cajun Jack & the Beanstalk. Lyne, Alison Davis, illus. 2004. (FRE.). 32p. (J). pap. 15.95 (978-1-58980-191-2(1)) Pelican Publishing Co., Inc.

Collins, Sheila Hebert, et al. 'T Pousette et 't Poulette: A Cajun Hansel & Gretel. Hebert, Barbara H., ed. Soper, Patrick, illus. 2001. 32p. (J). (gr. 1-3). 15.95 (978-1-56554-764-3(0)) Pelican Publishing Co., Inc.

Collinson, Roger. Grisel & the Tooth Fairy: And Other Stories. Ross, Tony, illus. 1998. 80p. (J). pap. (978-0-86264-689-9(8)) Andersen GBR. *Dist:* Random Hse. of Canada, Ltd.

Collodi, C. The Adventures of Pinocchio. 2006. pap. ***(*978-1-4250-1282-3(5))*** Assistedreadingbooks.com Inc.

—The Adventures of Pinocchio. Della Chiesa, Carol, tr. 2007. (ENG.). 160p. per. ***(*978-1-4065-1463-6(2))*** Dodo Pr.

—Pinocchio: the Tale of a Puppet. Carsey, Alice, illus. 2007. (ENG.). 196p. per. ***(*978-1-4065-1462-9(4))*** Dodo Pr.

Collodi, Carlo. Avventure Di Pinocchio. pap. 19.95 (978-88-451-2911-7(X)) Fabbri - RCS Libri ITA. *Dist:* Distribooks, Inc.

—Pinocchio. Fanelli, Sara & Rose, Emma, trs. from ITA. Fanelli, Sara, illus. 2003. 192p. (J). (gr. 2). 18.99 (978-0-7636-2261-9(3)) Candlewick Pr.

—Pinocchio. 2000. (ITA.). (J). pap. 15.95 (978-88-452-4182-6(3)) Fabbri - RCS Libri ITA. *Dist:* Distribooks, Inc.

—Pinocchio. Murray, M. A., tr. from ITA. 2002. (Penguin Classics Ser.). (Illus.). 192p. (gr. 12). pap. 10.00 (978-0-14-243706-3(9) , Penguin Classics) Penguin Group (USA) Inc.

—Pinocchio. Grimly, Gris, illus. 2002. 224p. (J). 5.99 (978-0-7653-4458-8(0) , Starscape) Doherty, Tom Assocs., LLC.

—Pinocchio. Ajhar, Brian, illus. 2005. (Rabbit Ears Ser.). 40p. (J). (gr. k-5). 25.65 (978-1-59679-228-9(0)) Spotlight.

—Pinocchio. Grimly, Gris & Grimly, Gus, illus. rev. ed. 2002. 224p. (J). 15.95 (978-0-7653-0591-6(7) , Tor Bks.) Doherty, Tom Assocs., LLC.

—Pinochio. 1998. (Fairy Tales Ser.). (978-2-215-06193-9(6)) Editions Fleurus.

Collodi, Carlo & Edens, Cooper. Pinocchio. 2001. (Classic Illustrated Treasury Ser.). (Illus.). 176p. (J). 19.95 (978-0-8118-2283-1(4)) Chronicle Bks. LLC.

Colshorn, Carl & Colshorn, Theodore. The Porridge Pot. Carls, Claudia, illus. 2007. 32p. (J). (ps). 16.99 ***(*978-0-698-40073-3(9)*** , Minedition) Penguin Group (USA) Inc.

Combel Editorial Staff. Ali Baba y los cuarenta Ladrones. 2004. (Troquelados clasicos Ser.). (SPA., Illus.). 16p. pap. 2.95 (978-84-7864-736-1(8)) Combel Editorial, S.A. ESP. *Dist:* Independent Pubs. Group.

—Amahal y los tres Reyes. 2004. (Troquelados clasicos Ser.). (SPA., Illus.). 16p. pap. 2.95 (978-84-7864-735-4(X)) Combel Editorial, S.A. ESP. *Dist:* Independent Pubs. Group.

—La Bella Durmiente. 2004. (Caballo alado clasicos-Al Trote Ser.). (SPA., Illus.). 24p. 6.95 (978-84-7864-775-0(9)) Combel Editorial, S.A. ESP. *Dist:* Independent Pubs. Group.

—Blancanieves. 2004. (Caballo alado clasicos-Al Trote Ser.). (SPA., Illus.). 24p. 6.95 (978-84-7864-778-1(3)) Combel Editorial, S.A. ESP. *Dist:* Independent Pubs. Group.

—Cenicienta. 2004. (Caballo alado clasicos-Al Trote Ser.). (SPA., Illus.). 24p. 6.95 (978-84-7864-777-4(5)) Combel Editorial, S.A. ESP. *Dist:* Independent Pubs. Group.

—Como la Sal. 2004. (Caballo alado clasicos-Al Galope Ser.). (SPA., Illus.). 24p. 6.95 (978-84-7864-786-6(4)) Combel Editorial, S.A. ESP. *Dist:* Independent Pubs. Group.

—El Cuento de la Lechera. 2003. (Troquelados Clasicos Ser.). (SPA & ENG., Illus.). 16p. pap. 2.95 (978-84-7864-676-0(0)) Combel Editorial, S.A. ESP. *Dist:* Independent Pubs. Group.

—Pedrito y el Rey Gloton. 2004. (Troquelados Clasicos Ser.). (SPA., Illus.). 16p. pap. 2.95 (978-84-7864-738-5(4)) Combel Editorial, S.A. ESP. *Dist:* Independent Pubs. Group.

—El Ruisenor. 2004. (Troquelados clasicos Ser.). (SPA., Illus.). 16p. pap. 2.95 (978-84-7864-737-8(6)) Combel Editorial, S.A. ESP. *Dist:* Independent Pubs. Group.

—La Vendedora de Fosforos. 2003. (Troquelados Clasicos Ser.). (ENG & SPA., Illus.). 16p. pap. 2.95 (978-84-7864-675-3(2)) Combel Editorial, S.A. ESP. *Dist:* Independent Pubs. Group.

—La Vieja del Bosque. 2004. (Caballo alado clasicos-Al Trote Ser.). (SPA., Illus.). 24p. 6.95 (978-84-7864-776-7(7)) Combel Editorial, S.A. ESP. *Dist:* Independent Pubs. Group.

—El Zapatero y los Duendes. 2004. (Caballo alado clasicos-Al Galope Ser.). (SPA., Illus.). 24p. 6.95 (978-84-7864-785-9(6)) Combel Editorial, S.A. ESP. *Dist:* Independent Pubs. Group.

—Los Zapatos Bailarines. 2003. (Troquelados Clasicos Ser.). (SPA & ENG., Illus.). 16p. pap. 2.95 (978-84-7864-678-4(7)) Combel Editorial, S.A. ESP. *Dist:* Independent Pubs. Group.

Como te Portas. (SPA.). pap. 9.95 (978-84-272-8327-5(X)) Molino, Editorial ESP. *Dist:* Distribooks, Inc.

Comotto, Agustin. La Selva Azul. 2005. (SPA.). (J). (gr. k-1). 8.99 (978-980-257-298-4(5)) Ekare, Ediciones VEN. *Dist:* Iaconi, Mariuccia Bk. Imports.

Conejito Azul: Es un Valiente Socorrista.Tr. of Little Blue Bunny: Fairy Tale Story of Bunny Rabbit to the Rescue. (SPA.). (J). 2.98 (978-970-22-0018-5(0)) Larousse, Ediciones, S. A. de C. V. MEX. *Dist:* Continental Bk. Co., Inc.

Coombs, Kate. The Runaway Princess. 2006. 288p. (J). 17.00 (978-0-374-35546-3(0)) Farrar, Straus & Giroux.

Cooper, Janet E. Three Proud Princesses. 2006. (Illus.). 64p. (J). pap. 19.95 (978-0-913720-86-8(0)) Beil, Frederic C. Pub., Inc.

Cooper, Susan. The Magician's Boy. Riglietti, Serena, illus. 2006. 112p. (J). (gr. 3-7). pap. 6.99 (978-1-4169-1555-3(9), Aladdin) Simon & Schuster Children's Publishing.

Copper, Melinda. Snow White. 2005. (Illus.). 44p. (J). (ps). 16.99 (978-0-525-47474-6(9), Dutton Juvenile) Penguin Group (USA) Inc.

Corazza, Joe, illus. The Frog Prince: A Story about Keeping Your Word. 2006. (J). 6.99 (978-1-59939-008-6(6), Reader's Digest Young Families, Inc.) Reader's Digest Children's Publishing, Inc.

Corey, Shana, ed. The Random House Book of Fairy Tales. Goode, Diane, illus. 2000. (Random House Book of... Ser.). 224p. (J). (gr. k-3). 19.95 (978-0-394-85693-3(7), Random Hse. Bks. for Young Readers) Random Hse. Children's Bks.

Corke, Estelle, et al, illus. The Gingerbread Man. 2007. 24p. pap. 5.99 (*978-1-84643-078-7(X)*) Child's Play International Ltd. GBR. *Dist:* Child's Play-International.

Corke, Estelle, illus. Goldilocks & the Three Bears. 2005. 24p. pap. (978-1-904550-19-8(3)) Child's Play-International.

Corkran, Alice. Bairn's Annual of Old Fashioned Fairy Tales. 2003. (gr. k-3). lib. bdg. 26.90 (978-0-613-74872-8(7)) Tandem Library Bks.

Cornelison, Sue F., illus. Tales of Beauty. 1999. (Cover-to-Cover Timeless Classics Ser.). 63p. (J). pap. (978-0-7891-2326-8(6)); (gr. 1-4). lib. bdg. 13.95 (978-0-7807-7747-7(6)) Perfection Learning Corp.

Corser-Gay, Joan. The Tales of Mannikin & Bubbikin. 2000. (J). pap. 9.95 (978-0-7414-0491-6(5)) Infinity Publishing.

Corvino, Lucy, illus. Arabian Nights: Retold from the Original. 2008. (Classic Starts Ser.). 160p. (J). 5.95 (*978-1-4027-4573-7(7)*) Sterling Publishing Co., Inc.

Couch, Greg, illus. Aladdin & the Magic Lamp. 2005. (Rabbit Ears Ser.). 40p. (J). (gr. k-5). 25.65 (978-1-59679-221-0(3)) Spotlight.

Courage Books Staff. Mother Goose: The Children's Classic Edition. 2002. (Courage Children's Ser.). (Illus.). 56p. (J). 9.98 (978-0-7624-0015-7(3), Courage Bks.) Running Pr. Bk. Pubs.

Courtauld, Sarah & Dickins, Rosie. Illustrated Fairy Tales. 2007. (Illustrated Stories Ser.). 352p. (J). 19.99 (*978-0-7945-1717-5(X)*, Usborne) EDC Publishing.

Coventry, Anna. The Princess Who Lost Her Hair. 1998. (Illus.). 28p. pap. 13.95 (978-1-899874-06-4(2)) Goblinshead GBR. *Dist:* Dufour Editions, Inc.

Coville, Bruce. The Dragon of Doom. Coville, Katherine, illus. (Moongobble & Me Ser.). 80p. (J). 2005. pap. 3.99 (978-0-689-85757-7(8), Aladdin); 2003. (gr. 1-5). 14.95 (978-0-689-85754-6(3)) Simon & Schuster Children's Publishing.

—The Dragonslayers. unabr. ed. 2004. (Words Take Wingtm Ser.). 119p. (J). (gr. 3-6). pap. 29.00 incl. audio (978-0-8072-7988-5(9), S YA 958 SP, Listening Library) Random Hse. Audio Publishing Group.

—The Mischief Monster. Coville, Katherine, illus. 2007. (Moongobble & Me Ser.). 80p. (J). 15.99 (978-1-4169-0807-4(2), Simon & Schuster Children's Publishing) Simon & Schuster Children's Publishing.

—The Weeping Werewolf. Coville, Katherine, illus. (Moongobble & Me Ser.). (J). (gr. 1-4). 2006. 80p. pap. 3.99 (978-0-689-85759-1(4)); 2005. 71p. pap. 3.99 (978-0-689-85758-4(6)) Simon & Schuster Children's Publishing. (Aladdin).

Craft, Kinuko. Cinderella. 2000. (Illus.). 32p. (J). (ps-3). 16.95 (978-1-58717-004-1(3), SeaStar Bks.) Chronicle Bks. LLC.

Craft, Kinuko Y., illus. Cinderella. 2000. 32p. (J). (ps-4). 16.50 (978-1-58717-005-8(1), SeaStar Bks.) Chronicle Bks. LLC.

Craft, Mahlon & Craft, Mahlon F. Le Sleeping Beauty. Craft, K. Y., illus. 2002. 32p. (J). (gr. k-3). 16.50 (978-1-58717-121-5(X), SeaStar Bks.) Chronicle Bks. LLC.

Craft, Mahlon F. & Craft, K. Y., illus. Sleeping Beauty. 2002. 32p. (J). (gr. k-3). 15.95 (978-1-58717-120-8(1), SeaStar Bks.) Chronicle Bks. LLC.

Craik, Dinah Maria Mulock. The Adventures of a Brownie. 2006. (ENG.). pap. (*978-1-4250-1648-7(0)*) Assistedreadingbooks.com Inc.

—Little Lame Prince EasyRead Comfort Edit. 2006. pap. (*978-1-4250-2001-9(1)*) Assistedreadingbooks.com Inc.

—Little Lame Prince EasyRead Edition. 2006. pap. (*978-1-4250-1718-7(5)*) Assistedreadingbooks.com Inc.

—Little Lame Prince EasyRead Large Editio. 2006. pap. (*978-1-4250-2260-0(X)*) Assistedreadingbooks.com Inc.

—Little Lame Prince the. 2006. pap. (*978-1-4250-2683-7(4)*) Assistedreadingbooks.com Inc.

Crane, Walter. Beauty & the Beast, & Other Tales. [47] p. :p. (978-0-87099-303-9(8)) Bow Historical Bks.

Cresswell, Helen & Player, Stephen. Rumpelstiltskin. 2004. (Stories to Collect & Treasure Ser.). (Illus.). (gr. k-3). pap. (978-0-340-87787-6(1), Hodder Children's Books) Hodder Children's Division.

Croall, Marie P. & Hilinski, Clint. Ali Baba Fooling the Forty Thieves: An Arabian Tale: Story. 2008. (Graphic Myths & Legends Ser.). (J). lib. bdg. 26.60 (*978-0-8225-7525-2(6)*, Graphic Universe) Lerner Publishing Group.

Cross, Ruth Belov. Hansel y Cretel. Pels, Winslow Pinney, illus. 2003. (SPA.). pap. (978-0-439-19894-3(1), SO30113) Scholastic GBR. *Dist:* Lectorum Pubns., Inc.

Crossley-Holland, Kevin. Enchantment: Fairy Tales, Ghost Stories & Tales of Wonder. Clark, Emma Chichester, illus. 2003. 128p. (YA). reprint ed. 22.00 (978-0-7567-6961-1(2)) DIANE Publishing Co.

Crowson, Andrew. Flip Flap Fairytale. 2003. (Illus.). 12p. bds. (978-1-85602-444-0(X)) Chrysalis Children's Bks.

Crump, Fred, Jr. Three Little Brown Piggies. 2006. 32p. pap. 9.95 (978-1-932715-83-5(5)) UMI (Urban Ministries, Inc.).

Cuentos de Andersen. (Coleccion Estrella).Tr. of Tales of Andersen. (SPA., Illus.). 64p. (J). 14.95 (978-950-11-0011-2(1), SGM011) Sigmar ARG. *Dist:* Continental Bk. Co., Inc.

cummings, e e & Firmage, George James. Fairy Tales. So, Meilo, illus. 2004. 48p. (J). 17.95 (978-0-87140-658-3(6)) Liveright Publishing Corp.

Cummings, Pat. The Blue Lake. 2001. (Illus.). 64p. (J). (gr. 1-5). 14.95 (978-0-06-021535-4(6)); lib. bdg. 14.89 (978-0-06-021536-1(4)) HarperCollins Pubs.

Curry, Don, ed. The Little Red Hen. 2006. (My Turn! Your Turn! Ser.). (ENG.). 24p. (J). pap. 3.99 (978-0-696-22887-2(4)) Meredith Bks.

—The Three Little Pigs. 2006. (My Turn! Your Turn! Ser.). (ENG.). 24p. (J). pap. 3.99 (978-0-696-22855-1(6)) Meredith Bks.

Curry, Jane Louise. Beneath the Hill. 2001. 228p. (YA). (gr. 7-11). pap. 14.95 (978-0-595-15522-4(7)) iUniverse, Inc.

Curtis, S. R. Los Muertos No Hablan: El Zorro. 1999. Tr. of Dead Don't Talk. (SPA.). (978-0-606-17702-3(7)) Tandem Library Bks.

Curto, Rosa Maria, illus. Pequeno Abeto. 2005. (Caballo alado clasicos-Al Trote Ser.). (SPA.). 24p. (J). 6.95 (978-84-7864-867-2(4)) Combel Editorial, S.A. ESP. *Dist:* Independent Pubs. Group.

—La Ratita Presumida. 2004. (Caballo Alado Clasico Ser.). (SPA.). 24p. (J). 6.95 (978-84-7864-763-7(5)) Combel Editorial, S.A. ESP. *Dist:* Independent Pubs. Group.

Dahl, Michael. The Princess & the Tower. Zhurkina, Svetlana A., illus. 2005. (Read-It! Readers Ser.). 32p. (J). (ps). lib. bdg. 18.60 (978-1-4048-1184-3(2)) Picture Window Bks.

Dahl, Roald. James & the Giant Peach. 2007. 96p. (J). 5.99 (978-0-14-240791-2(7), Puffin) Penguin Group (USA) Inc.

—James und der Riesenpfirsich.Tr. of James & the Giant Peach. (GER.). (J). pap. 12.50 (978-3-499-20433-3(9)) Rowohlt Taschenbuch Verlag GmbH DEU. *Dist:* Distribooks, Inc.

Dale, Penny. Princess, Princess. Dale, Penny, illus. 2003. (Illus.). 32p. (J). (ps-1). 14.99 (978-0-7636-2212-1(5)) Candlewick Pr.

Dale, Penny & Platt, Richard. Pirate Diary. Ridell, Chris, illus. 2003. 128p. (J). (gr. 4). pap. 6.99 (978-0-7636-2169-8(2)) Candlewick Pr.

Dalmatian Press Staff. Favorite Fairy Tales & Fables: Keepsake Treasury. rev. ed. 2004. (Keepsake Treasuries Ser.). (Illus.). 224p. (J). 10.99 (978-1-4037-0770-3(7)) Dalmatian Pr.

Daly, Jude. Fair, Brown & Trembling: An Irish Cinderella Story. 2005. (Illus.). 32p. (J). reprint ed. pap. 6.95 (978-0-374-42257-8(5), Sunburst) Farrar, Straus & Giroux.

Daly, Niki. Pretty Salma: A Little Red Riding Hood Story from Africa. Daly, Niki, illus. 2007. (Illus.). 32p. (J). (gr. k-3). 16.00 (978-0-618-72345-4(5), Clarion Bks.) Houghton Mifflin Co. Trade & Reference Div.

Danson, Lesley, et al, illus. Snow White. 2006. 24p. pap. 5.99 (978-1-84643-023-7(2)) Child's Play-International.

Datlow, Ellen. The Green Man: Tales from the Mythic Forest. Windling, Terri & Vess, Charles, illus. 2002. 400p. (J). 18.99 (978-0-670-03526-7(2), Viking Juvenile) Penguin Group (USA) Inc.

—A Wolf at the Door: And Other Retold Fairy Tales. Windling, Terri, ed. Ellwell, Tristan, illus. 2000. 192p. (J). (gr. 4-6). 16.00 (978-0-689-82138-7(7)) Simon & Schuster Children's Publishing.

—A Wolf at the Door: And Other Retold Fairy Tales. 2001. (gr. 3-6). lib. bdg. 13.00 (978-0-613-73230-7(8)); (978-0-606-22138-2(7)) Tandem Library Bks.

d'Aulaire, Edgar & d'Aulaire, Ingri. The Terrible Troll-Bird. 2007. (Illus.). 48p. (J). (ps-3). 15.95 (*978-1-59017-252-0(3)*, NYR Children's Collection) New York Review of Bks., Inc., The.

D'Aulaire, Ingri & Edgar. D'Aulaires' Book of Norse Myths. 2005. (New York Review Children's Collection). (Illus.). 160p. (J). pap. 24.95 (978-1-59017-125-7(X), NYR Children's Collection) New York Review of Bks., Inc., The.

D'Aulnoy, Marie-Catherine. Beauty & the Beast. Delessert, Etienne, illus. 2000. 48p. (gr. 5-12). 17.95 (978-1-56846-129-8(1), Creative Editions) Creative Co., The.

Davenport, Victoria & Davenport, Nigel. Once Upon Another Time - Another Place. 2001. 216p. pap. 14.95 (978-0-595-18338-8(7), Writers Club Pr.) iUniverse, Inc.

David, Stuart. Nalda Said. 2003. (gr. 7-12). lib. bdg. 24.55 (978-0-613-61144-2(6)) Tandem Library Bks.

Davidson, Susanna. Emperor's New Clothes. 2006. 24p. (J). 9.99 (978-0-7945-1350-4(6), Usborne) EDC Publishing.

Davidson, Susannah, retold by. Cinderella. 2005. (Young Reading Gift Books Ser.). 48p. (J). (gr. 2 up). 8.99 (978-0-7945-0920-0(7), Usborne) EDC Publishing.

Davis, Aubrey. Jody Salleratus. Daniel, Alan & Daniel, Lea, illus. unabr. ed. 2001. 32p. (J). (gr. k-3). (978-1-55337-069-7(4)) Kids Can Pr., Ltd.

Daykin, Louise, illus. Goldilocks & the Three Bears. 2004. 32p. (J). (ENG & ALB.). (978-1-84444-035-1(4)); (ENG & ARA.). (978-1-84444-036-8(2)); (ENG & BEN.). (978-1-84444-037-5(0)); (ENG & CHI.). (978-1-84444-038-2(9)); (ENG & PER.). (978-1-84444-039-9(7)); (ENG & FRE.). (978-1-84444-040-5(0)); (ENG & GER.). (978-1-84444-041-2(9)); (ENG & GUJ.). (978-1-84444-042-9(7)); (ENG & PAN.). (978-1-84444-043-6(5)); (POR & ENG.). (978-1-84444-044-3(3)); (ENG & SOM.). (978-1-84444-045-0(1)); (ENG & SPA.). (978-1-84444-046-7(X)); (ENG & TUR.). (978-1-84444-047-4(8)); (ENG & URD.). (978-1-84444-048-1(6)); (CZE & ENG.). (978-1-84444-049-8(4)); (ENG & ITA.). (978-1-84444-050-4(8)); (ENG & POL.). (978-1-84444-051-1(6)); (RUS & ENG.). (978-1-84444-052-8(4)); (SBC, ENG & SER.). (978-1-84444-053-5(2)); (TAM & ENG.). (978-1-84444-054-2(0)); (ENG & HIN.). (978-1-84444-059-7(1)) Mantra Publishing, Ltd.

Daykin, Louise, tr. & illus. Goldilocks & the Three Bears. Daykin, Louise, illus. 2004. (J). (ENG & VIE.). 32p. (978-1-84444-055-9(9)); 31p. (978-1-84444-057-3(5)) Mantra Publishing, Ltd.

De Beaumont, Leprince, et al. Beauty & the Beast & Other Fairy Tales. 2001. (Dover Juvenile Classics Ser.). (Illus.). 96p. (J). (gr. 4-7). pap. 2.00 (978-0-486-41716-5(6)) Dover Pubns., Inc.

De Graaf, Anne. Best of the Classics: Retold for Today's Children. 2003. (Illus.). 370p. 18.95 (978-87-7247-182-2(4)) Scandinavia Publishing Hse. DNK. *Dist:* National Bk. Network.

De La Paz, Myrna J. Abadeha: The Philippine Cinderella. Tang, You-shan, illus. 2004. 32p. (J). (gr. 2-4). 16.95 (978-1-885008-17-6(1)) Shen's Bks.

De Lafayette, Madame. The Princess de Montpensier. 2004. reprint ed. pap. 1.99 (978-1-4192-7870-9(3)) Kessinger Publishing, LLC.

De Matos, Isabel Freire. El Pececito Magico. Torres, Walter, illus. 2004. (SPA.). 22p. (J). pap. 6.95 (978-1-57581-578-7(8)) Santillana USA Publishing Co., Inc.

de Paola, Tomie. Adelita: A Mexican Cinderella Story. (SPA., Illus.). (J). (gr. k-3). 2004. 40p. pap. 6.99 (978-0-14-240187-3(0), Puffin); 2002. 32p. 16.99 (978-0-399-23866-6(2), Putnam Juvenile) Penguin Group (USA) Inc.

—Tomie's Three Bears & Other Tales. 2004. (Illus.). 36p. (J). (ps-1). bds. 6.99 (978-0-399-24327-1(5), Putnam Juvenile) Penguin Group (USA) Inc.

de Saint-Exupery, Antoine. The Little Prince. l.t. ed. 2005. 100p. (J). 22.95 (978-0-7862-7538-0(3)) Thorndike Pr.

De Valera, Sinead. The Magic Gifts: Classic Irish Fairytales. (Illus.). 224p. 16.95 (978-0-86327-822-8(1)) Wolfhound Pr. IRL. *Dist:* Irish Bks. & Media, Inc.

Dean, Judith, retold by. Aladdin & the Enchanted Lamp, Level 1. 2000. (Bookworms Ser.). (Illus.). 64p. 6.50 (978-0-19-422937-1(8)) Oxford Univ. Pr., Inc.

Dean Wafstet, Cindi. Wings of Light. 2005. 31p. 15.00 (978-1-4116-5567-6(2)) Lulu.com.

DeFelice, Cynthia C. One Potato, Two Potato. U'Ren, Andrea, illus. 2006. 32p. (J). (ps-3). 16.00 (978-0-374-35640-8(8)) Farrar, Straus & Giroux.

DeLisa, Patricia, illus. Little Red Riding Hood: A Book for the Thoughtful Parent. 2006. 32p. (J). 14.95 (978-0-88010-571-2(2), Bell Pond Bks.) SteinerBooks, Inc.

Demi. The Emperor's New Clothes: A Tale Set in China. Demi, illus. 2000. (Illus.). 42p. (J). (ps-k). 19.95 (978-0-689-83068-6(8), McElderry, Margaret K.) Simon & Schuster Children's Publishing.

dePaola, Tomie. Tomie dePaola's Front Porch Stories & North Country Whoppers. dePaola, Tomie, illus. 2007. 64p. (J). (ps). 17.99 (*978-0-399-24754-5(8)*, Putnam Juvenile) Penguin Group (USA) Inc.

Desclot, Miquel. Sleeping Beauty. Abbrederis, Christoph, illus. 2003. Tr. of Bella Durmiente. (ENG & SPA.). 32p. (J). pap. 6.95 (978-0-8118-3913-6(3)) Chronicle Bks. LLC.

Desclot, Miquel & DC Comics Staff. The Sleeping Beauty. Abbrederis, Christoph, illus. 2003. Tr. of La Bella Durmiente. (ENG & SPA.). 32p. (J). 14.95 (978-0-8118-3912-9(5)) Chronicle Bks. LLC.

DeSpain, Pleasant. Tales of Tricksters. 2001. (gr. k-3). lib. bdg. 11.80 (978-0-613-88805-9(7)) Tandem Library Bks.

Diaz-Pimienta, Alexis. Cuentos Clasicos en Verso.Tr. of Classic Stories in Verse. (SPA.). (J). (gr. 2-4). pap. 7.98 (978-970-643-142-4(X)) Selector, S.A. de C.V. MEX. *Dist:* Lectorum Pubns., Inc.

DiCamillo, Kate. The Tale of Despereaux. Ering, Timothy Basil, illus. 272p. (J). (gr. 2-7). 2003. 17.99 (978-0-7636-1722-6(9)); 2005. 0.99 (978-0-7636-2928-1(6)) Candlewick Pr.

—The Tale of Despereaux. 2004. (J). (gr. 3-4). stu. ed. 11.95 (978-1-58130-524-1(9)) Novel Units, Inc.

—The Tale of Despereaux. Ering, Timothy B., illus. l.t. ed. 2004. 255p. 23.95 (978-0-7862-6578-7(7), Large Print Pr.) Thorndike Pr.

—The Tale of Despereaux: Being the Story of a Mouse, a Princess, Some Soup & a Spool of Thread. Ering, Timothy Basil, illus. 2006. 272p. (J). (gr. 2-7). reprint ed. pap. 7.99 (978-0-7636-2529-0(9)) Candlewick Pr.

Dickens, Charles. The Cricket on the Hearth. 2004. reprint ed. pap. 15.95 (978-1-4191-5807-0(4)); pap. 1.99 (978-1-4192-5807-7(9)) Kessinger Publishing, LLC.

—The Cricket on the Hearth. l.t. ed. 2005. 128p. pap. 17.95 (978-1-59688-048-1(1), 1-59688-048-1) Large Print Bk. Co., The.

Dickens, Charles & De Graaf, Anne. The Best of Charles Dickens' Classics. Montero, Jose Perez, illus. 2003. 240p. 16.95 (978-87-7247-184-6(0)) Scandinavia Publishing Hse. DNK. *Dist:* National Bk. Network.

Dickson, Bill, illus. The Bremen Town Muscians: A Retelling of the Grimms' Fairy Tale. 2004. (Read-It! Readers Ser.). 32p. (C). (gr. k-3). 18.60 (978-1-4048-0310-7(6)) Picture Window Bks.

—The Shoemaker & His Elves: A Retelling of the Grimms' Fairy Tale. 2004. (Read-It! Readers Ser.). 32p. (J). (gr. k-3). 18.60 (978-1-4048-0314-5(9)) Picture Window Bks.

Diego, Rapi. El Sapo Hechizado. (SPA.). (J). pap. (978-968-7791-20-3(9)) SM Ediciones ESP. *Dist:* Lectorum Pubns., Inc.

Disney Staff. Aladdin. (FRE.). 96p. (J). (gr. k-5). pap. 9.95 (978-0-7859-8852-6(1)) French & European Pubns., Inc.

—Beauty & the Beast. ed. 2004. (J). (ps-2). spiral bd. (978-0-616-01631-2(X)) Canadian National Institute for the Blind/Institut National Canadien pour les Aveugles.

—Disney's the Little Mermaid & Sebastian. (FRE.). 96p. (J). (gr. k-5). pap. 9.95 (978-0-7859-8846-5(7)) French & European Pubns., Inc.

—The Princess Collection Friendship Box: Cinderella; The Little Mermaid; Sleeping Beauty; Snow White & the Seven Dwarfs. 2001. (Illus.). 48p. (J). (ps-3). bds. 9.99 (978-0-7364-1138-7(0), RH/Disney) Random Hse. Children's Bks.

—The Sleeping Beauty. (FRE.). 96p. (J). (gr. k-5). pap. 9.95 (978-0-7859-8854-0(8)) French & European Pubns., Inc.

—Snow White & the Seven Dwarfs. ed. 2004. (J). (ps-2). spiral bd. (978-0-616-01632-9(8)); spiral bd. (978-0-616-01633-6(6)) Canadian National Institute for the Blind/Institut National Canadien pour les Aveugles.

—Snow White & the Seven Dwarfs. (FRE.). 96p. (J). (gr. k-5). pap. 9.95 (978-0-7859-8853-3(X)) French & European Pubns., Inc.

Disney Storybook Artists Staff, contrib. by. Princess Treasury. 2005. (Illus.). 318p. (*978-1-4127-3276-5(X)*) Publications International, Ltd.

Disney Storybook Artists Staff, illus. Sleeping Beauty: A Read-Aloud Storybook. 2003. 72p. (J). (ps-3). 8.99 (978-0-7364-2098-3(3), RH/Disney) Random Hse. Children's Bks.

Disney's Beauty & the Beast. 2007. 48p. (ps-2). 12.99 incl. audio compact disk (978-1-4231-0269-4(X)) Disney Pr.

Disney's Beauty & the Beast in Touch-a-Vision Dimensional Technology. (J). (978-1-878444-02-8(6)) Minardi Photography.

DiTerlizzi, Tony. The Wrath of Mulgarath. 2004. (Spiderwick Chronicles: Bk. 5). (Illus.). 160p. (gr. 1-5). 10.99 (978-0-689-85940-3(6)) Simon & Schuster Children's Publishing.

DiTerlizzi, Tony & Black, Holly. Notebook for Fantastical Observations. DiTerlizzi, Tony, illus. 2005. (Spiderwick Chronicles). (Illus.). 240p. (J). 9.95 (978-1-4169-0345-1(3)) Simon & Schuster Children's Publishing.

DK Publishing. Goldilocks & the Three Bears: Read-along Paperbacks. 2007. 16p. (J). (ps-5). pap. 4.99 (*978-0-7566-3456-8(3)*) Dorling Kindersley Publishing, Inc.

DK Publishing Staff. Fairy Tale Sticker Storybook. 2007. 10p. (J). (ps-2). pap. 4.99 (*978-0-7566-3089-8(4)*) Dorling Kindersley Publishing, Inc.

Dockray, Tracy Arah, illus. Grimm's Grimmest. 2005. 144p. 22.95 (978-0-8118-5046-9(3)) Chronicle Bks. LLC.

Doherty, Berlie. Cuentos Magicos. Ray, Jane, illus. 2003. (FRE & SPA.). 224p. 29.95 (978-84-89396-98-2(1)) Blume ESP. *Dist:* Independent Pubs. Group.

—Cuentos Magicos. 2003. (SPA.). 126p. (978-84-348-6710-9(9), NR30568) SM Ediciones ESP. *Dist:* Lectorum Pubns., Inc.

—The Famous Adventures of Jack. unabr. ed. 2001. (Read-Along Ser.). 128p. (J). 24.95 incl. audio (978-0-7540-6237-0(6), RAO38, Chivers Children's Audio Bks.) BBC Audiobooks America.

Dokey, Cameron. Sunlight & Shadow. 2004. (Once upon a Time Ser.). 192p. (YA). pap. 5.99 (978-0-689-86999-0(1), Simon Pulse) Simon & Schuster Children's Publishing.

Dole, Nathan Haskell, tr. The Russian Fairy Book. 2000. 128p. (J). (gr. 4-7). pap. 5.95 (978-0-486-41019-7(6)) Dover Pubns., Inc.

Doman, Regina. Black as Night: A Fairy Tale Retold. 2004. (Illus.). 440p. (YA). pap. 11.95 (978-1-883937-88-1(4)) Bethlehem Bks.

Donnelly, Jennifer & Gammell, Stephen. Humble Pie. 2002. (Illus.). 32p. (J). (gr. k-2). 16.95 (978-0-689-84435-5(2) , Atheneum/Richard Jackson Bks.) Simon & Schuster Children's Publishing.

Donnet, Beatriz & Murray, G. Cuentos Clasicos de Hadas.Tr. of Classical Fairy Tales. (SPA.). (J). 9.98 (978-968-403-949-0(2)) Selector, S.A. de C.V. MEX. *Dist:* AIMS International Bks., Inc.

Donoghue, Emma. Kissing the Witch: Old Tales in New Skins. 1999. 240p. (J). (gr. 7-10). pap. 11.99 (978-0-06-440772-4(1) , Harper Trophy) HarperCollins Pubs.

—Kissing the Witch: Old Tales in New Skins. 1999. (J). (978-0-606-17465-7(6)); (gr. 7-12). lib. bdg. 19.95 (978-0-613-18260-7(X)) Tandem Library Bks.

Douglas, Vincent. The Little Mermaid. 2001. (Disney Parent & Child Read Together Ser.). (Illus.). 40p. (ps-k). 4.99 (978-1-57768-734-4(5)) School Specialty Publishing.

Douglas, Vincent & School Specialty Publishing Staff. Fairy Tales. 2002. (Rhythm & Rhyme Ser.). (Illus.). 53p. (J). (ps up). bds. 19.95 (978-1-58845-497-3(5)) School Specialty Publishing.

—The Ugly Duckling. 2004. (Handle Book with CD Ser.). (Illus.). 24p. (J). 3.99 (978-1-58845-730-1(3)) School Specialty Publishing.

Dover Staff. Listen & Color: Hans Christian Andersen Fairy Tales. O'Brien, Joan, illus. 2004. 48p. (J). pap. 6.95 (978-0-486-43773-6(6)) Dover Pubns., Inc.

Doyle, Malachy. Una and the Sea Cloak. Jay, Alison, illus. 2004. 32p. (J). 15.95 (978-1-84507-010-6(0)) Lincoln, Frances Ltd. GBR. *Dist:* Perseus Distribution.

—Tales from Old Ireland. 2006. (Illus.). 96p. (J). 16.99 (978-1-905236-32-9(8)) Barefoot Bks., Inc.

Doyle, Malachy & Walker, Sholto. Long Gray Norris. 2006. (Yellow Bananas Ser.). (Illus.). 46p. (J). (978-0-7787-0956-5(6)) Crabtree Publishing Co.

Doyle, Richard. Jack the Giant Killer. Doyle, Richard, illus. 2004. (Illus.). 96p. (J). reprint ed. 19.00 (978-0-7567-7478-3(0)) DIANE Publishing Co.

—Jack the Giant Killer. 2000. (Everyman's Library Children's Classics Ser.). (Illus.). 96p. (gr. 4-7). 14.00 (978-0-375-41070-3(8) , Everyman's Library) Knopf Publishing Group.

Drummer Hoff. 2004. (J). pap. 18.95 incl. audio compact disk (978-1-55592-405-8(0)) Weston Woods Studios, Inc.

Dudley, Maywill. The Story of Little Red Riding Hood. 2005. reprint ed. pap. 15.95 (978-1-4191-5430-0(3)) Kessinger Publishing, LLC.

Los Duendes Zapateros. 2nd ed. 2002. (Troquelados Clasicos Ser.).Tr. of Shoemaker & the Elves. (SPA & ENG., Illus.). 16p. pap. 2.95 (978-84-7864-374-5(5)) Combel Editorial, S.A. ESP. *Dist:* Independent Pubs. Group.

Dunbar, Joyce. The Glass Garden. French, Fiona, illus. 2001. 32p. (J). (gr. k-4). pap. 8.99 (978-0-7112-1445-3(X)) Lincoln, Frances Ltd. GBR. *Dist:* Transition Vendor.

—Kingfisher Read-Aloud Storybook. 2000. (J). (978-0-606-19436-5(3)) Tandem Library Bks.

Dunbar, Joyce & French, Fiona. The Glass Garden. 1999. (Illus.). 32p. (J). (gr. k-4). (978-0-7112-1350-0(X)) Lincoln, Frances Ltd.

—Glass Garden. 2004. (Illus.). 32p. (J). pap. 7.95 (978-1-84507-193-6(X)) Lincoln, Frances Ltd. GBR. *Dist:* Perseus Distribution.

Duncan, Lois. The Magic of Spider Woman. 2000. (J). (978-0-606-19576-8(9)) Tandem Library Bks.

Dunrea, Olivier. Hanne's Quest. 2006. (Illus.). 96p. (J). (gr. 3). 16.99 (978-0-399-24216-8(3) , Philomel) Penguin Group (USA) Inc.

Dwyer, Mindy. Aurora: A Tale of the Northern Lights. Dwyer, Mindy, illus. 2005. (Illus.). 32p. (ps up). pap. 8.95 (978-0-88240-549-0(7)) Graphic Arts Ctr. Publishing Co.

—Aurora: A Tale of the Northern Lights. 2001. (gr. k-3). lib. bdg. 17.60 (978-0-613-77291-4(1)) Tandem Library Bks.

Edens, Cooper, compiled by. Princess Stories: A Classic Illustrated Edition. 2004. (Illus.). 136p. (J). (gr. 1-5). 19.95 (978-0-8118-4032-3(8)) Chronicle Bks. LLC.

Edgson, Alison, et al, illus. The Elves & the Shoemaker. 2007. 24p. pap. 5.99 (***978-1-84643-076-3(3)***) Child's Play International Ltd. GBR. *Dist:* Child's Play-International.

Edgson, Alison, et al, illus. The Emperor's New Clothes. 24p. pap. 5.99 (978-1-84643-020-6(8)) Child's Play-International.

Edgson, Alison, et al. Cinderella. 2006. (Flip up Fairy Tales Ser.). (Illus.). 24p. (J). 9.99 (978-1-904550-46-4(0)) Child's Play-International.

—Hansel & Gretel. 2006. (Illus.). 24p. pap. 5.99 (978-1-904550-73-0(8)); pap. 9.99 (978-1-904550-45-7(2)) Child's Play-International.

—The Little Red Hen. 2006. (Illus.). 24p. pap. 9.99 (978-1-904550-47-1(9)) Child's Play-International.

Eggleton, Jill. What's Your Opinion? Individual Title. 6 packs. Taylor, Clive, illus. (Sails Literacy Ser.). 20p. (gr. 4 up). 27.00 (978-0-7578-0792-3(5)) Rigby Education.

Ehrlich, Amy. The Snow Queen. Jeffers, Susan, illus. 2006. 32p. (J). (ps). 16.99 (978-0-525-47694-8(6) , Dutton Juvenile) Penguin Group (USA) Inc.

Eilenberg, Max. Beauty & the Beast. Barrett, Angela, illus. 2006. 64p. (J). (gr. 1-5). 17.99 (978-0-7636-3160-4(4)) Candlewick Pr.

Eisner, Will. The Princess & the Frog. Eisner, Will, illus. 2003. (Illus.). 32p. 7.95 (978-1-56163-346-3(1)); 15.95 (978-1-56163-244-2(9)) NBM Publishing Co.

Eliot, Ethel Cook. The Little House in the Fairy Wood. 2004. reprint ed. pap. 15.95 (978-1-4191-7023-2(6)) Kessinger Publishing, LLC.

Ellwand, David, des. Cinderlily: A Floral Fairy Tale. 2003. (Illus.). 32p. (J). 16.99 (978-0-7636-2328-9(8)) Candlewick Pr.

Emperors. 2001. (Little Pebbles Ser.). (J). pap. (978-0-7892-6588-3(5)) Abbeville Pr., Inc.

En el Mundo de los Cuentos. (Coleccion Estrella). (SPA., Illus.). 64p. (J). 14.95 (978-950-11-0000-6(6) , SGM000) Sigmar ARG. *Dist:* Continental Bk. Co., Inc.

Ensor, Barbara. Cinderella (As If You Didn't Already Know the Story) Ensor, Barbara, illus. 2006. (Illus.). 128p. (J). (gr. 2-7). 12.95 (978-0-375-83620-6(9) , Schwartz & Wade Bks.) Random Hse. Children's Bks.

Ensor, Barbara. Thumbelina: Tiny Little Runaway Bride. 2008. (J). (***978-0-375-83960-3(7)); (*978-0-375-93960-0(1)***) Random Hse. Children's Bks. (Schwartz & Wade Bks.).

Equipo Staff. Blanca Nieves.Tr. of Snow White. (SPA.). 24p. (J). 9.98 (978-84-305-9089-6(7)) Susaeta Ediciones, S.A. ESP. *Dist:* AIMS International Bks., Inc., Giron Bks.

Ernst, Lisa Campbell. Little Red Riding Hood: A Newfangled Prairie Tale. Ernst, Lisa Campbell, illus. (Stories to Go! Ser.). (Illus.). 40p. (J). 2005. 4.99 (978-0-689-87831-2(1)); 1998. (gr. 4-6). reprint ed. pap. 7.99 (978-0-689-82191-2(3)) Simon & Schuster Children's Publishing. (Aladdin).

Escobar, Melba. Los Siete Mejores Cuentos Rabes. Neira, Muyi, illus. 2004. (SPA.). (J). (gr. 3-5). (978-958-04-7212-4(2)) Norma S.A.

Escott, Jamison. The Clockmaker of Mullen. Escott, Esther, illus. 2004. 24p. (J). pap. 8.95 (978-1-57733-127-8(3) , Papillon Publishing) Blue Dolphin Publishing, Inc.

Espluga, Maria, illus. Ricitos de Oro. 2005. (Caballo alado clasico series-Al Paso Ser.). (SPA.). 24p. (J). 6.95 (978-84-7864-854-2(2)) Combel Editorial, S.A. ESP. *Dist:* Independent Pubs. Group.

Eubank, Patti Reeder, illus. The Princess & the Snarls. 2006. 32p. (J). (ps). 16.95 (978-0-8249-5536-6(6) , Ideals Children's Bks.) Ideals Pubns.

Evans, Latonya, adapted by. Jack & the Beanstalk. l.t. ed. 2005. (Fairy Tales of Special Children Ser.: Book 1). (Illus.). 25p. (J). (978-0-9767258-0-0(0)) Diversity Ink Publishing.

Ewing, Juliana Horatia. Old-Fashioned Fairy Tales. 2006. 77.99 (***978-1-4280-4762-4(X));*** pap. 70.99 (***978-1-4280-4770-9(0)***) IndyPublish.com.

Fabulas Doradas.Tr. of Golden Fables. (SPA.). (J). 22.48 (978-84-8426-215-2(4)) Susaeta Ediciones, S.A. ESP. *Dist:* AIMS International Bks., Inc.

Fairy Tale- Aladdin. 2005. (J). bds. (978-1-4194-0037-7(1)) Paradise Pr., Inc.

Fairy Tale- Beauty & the Beast. 2005. (J). bds. (978-1-4194-0038-4(X)) Paradise Pr., Inc.

Fairy Tale- Cinderella. 2005. (J). bds. (978-1-4194-0039-1(8)) Paradise Pr., Inc.

Fairy Tale Literacy Center with Puppet Theater. 2001. (Illus.). (J). (ps-2). 219.00 (978-0-9673268-5-6(0)) Learning Fasten-Ations, Inc.

Fairy Tales. (J). 2.29 (978-1-59445-060-0(9)) Dogs in Hats Children's Publishing Co.

Fairy Tales. 2003. (J). per. (978-1-57657-912-1(3)); per. (978-1-57657-913-8(1)) Paradise Pr., Inc.

Fairy Tales. (Little Lift-A-Flaps Ser.). (J). bds. (978-1-4127-3441-7(X) , 3910601) Publications International, Ltd.

Fairy Tales - Beauty & the Beast. 2005. (J). bds. (978-1-4194-0099-5(1)) Paradise Pr., Inc.

Fairy tales - Cinderella. 2005. (J). bds. (978-1-4194-0100-8(9)) Paradise Pr., Inc.

Fairy Tales - Pinocchio. 2005. (J). bds. (978-1-4194-0101-5(7)) Paradise Pr., Inc.

Fairy Tales - Snow White. 2005. (J). bds. (978-1-4194-0102-2(5)) Paradise Pr., Inc.

Fairy Tales: Cinderella, Rumplestiltskin & the Frog Prince. 2002. (J). cd-rom (978-0-9724995-9-0(8)) Alcazar AudioWorks.

Fairy Tales- Jack & the Beanstalk. 2005. (J). bds. (978-1-4194-0040-7(1)) Paradise Pr., Inc.

Fairy Tales- Pinocchio. 2005. (J). bds. (978-1-4194-0041-4(X)) Paradise Pr., Inc.

Fairy Tales- Sleeping Beauty. 2005. (J). bds. (978-1-4194-0042 1(8)) Paradise Pr., Inc.

Fairy Tales- Snow White. 2005. (J). bds. (978-1-4194-0043-8(6)) Paradise Pr., Inc.

Fairy Tales- Three little Pigs. 2005. (J). bds. (978-1-4194-0044-5(4)) Paradise Pr., Inc.

Fairy Tales, Fables, & Folktales (Gr. PreK-5) 2003. (J). (978-1-58232-020-5(9)) Bryan Hse. Pubs., Inc.

Fairy Tales (Gr. 2-3) 2003. (J). (978-1-58232-071-7(3)) Bryan Hse. Pubs., Inc.

Fairy Tales s/s - Pinocchio. 2005. (J). bds. (978-1-4194-0067-4(3)) Paradise Pr., Inc.

Fairy tales s/s - SNow White. 2005. (J). bds. (978-1-4194-0068-1(1)) Paradise Pr., Inc.

Fairy Tales s/s Beauty & the Beast. 2005. (J). bds. (978-1-4194-0065-0(7)) Paradise Pr., Inc.

Fairy talse s/s - CInderella. 2005. (J). bds. (978-1-4194-0066-7(5)) Paradise Pr., Inc.

Farhat-Holzman, Laina, tr. The Slave Who Lied but Once a Year & Other Persian Tales. 2001. (YA). per. 15.00 (978-1-58684-119-5(X)) Global Academic Publishing.

Farley, Carol J. Mr. Pak Buys a Store. 1999. (Illus.). (J). (978-0-606-21860-3(2)) Tandem Library Bks.

Farrell, Liam. The True Story of the Three Little Pigs & the Big Bad Wolf. 2002. (Illus.). 64p. (YA). (gr. 1 up). pap. 8.95 (978-1-901737-35-6(7)) Anvil Bks., Ltd. IRL. *Dist:* Dufour Editions, Inc.

Farrer, Vashti. Princess Euphorbia. Bodsworth, Nan, illus. 1999. (Supa Doopers Ser.). 64p. (J). (978-0-7608-1923-4(8)) Sundance/Newbridge Educational Publishing.

Favorite Fairy Tales Series, 6 bks. (Illus.). (J). (gr. 2-4). lib. bdg. 71.70 (978-1-56674-924-4(7)) Forest Hse. Publishing Co., Inc.

Fernandez Paz, Agustín & Martínez, Maribel G. La Ciudad de Los Deseos. Uhía, Manolo & Martínez, Maribel G., trs. Uhía, Manolo, illus. 2002. (Joven Coleccion Ser.). (SPA.). 48p. (978-84-89804-04-3(4)) Loguez Ediciones ESP. *Dist:* Lectorum Pubns., Inc.

Ferris, Jean. Once upon a Marigold. 2002. 272p. (YA). (gr. 5 up). 17.00 (978-0-15-216791-2(9)); 2004. 288p. (J). reprint ed. pap. 5.95 (978-0-15-205084-9(1) , Harcourt Paperbacks) Harcourt Children's Bks.

—Once upon a Marigold. 2004. (gr. 5-8). lib. bdg. 14.10 (978-0-613-71637-6(X)) Tandem Library Bks.

Fielding, William H., Jr. Three Tales for You. Fielding, William H., Jr., illus. 2001. (J). spiral bd. (978-0-945069-13-3(8)) Freedom Pr. Assocs.

Finch, Mary. Gallinita Roja y la Espiga de Trigo. 1999. Tr. of Little Red Hen & the Ear of Wheat. (SPA., Illus.). (J). 12.79 (978-0-606-20669-3(8)) Tandem Library Bks.

—Los tres chivitos Gruff (The Three Billy Goats Gruff) Arenson, Roberta, illus. 2003. (SPA.). 32p. (J). pap. 6.99 (978-1-84148-145-6(9)) Barefoot Bks., Inc.

Findlay, Lisa. Puss in Boots. Bowers, Tim, illus. 2008. (J). pap. (***978-0-375-84671-7(9));*** 48p. lib. bdg. 11.99 (***978-0-375-94671-4(3)***) Random Hse., Inc.

First Fairy Tales Staff. Tres Chivos Testarudos. (Primeros Cuentos Ser.). (SPA., Illus.). 28p. (J). (gr. k-3). pap. 7.95 (978-1-56014-457-1(2)) Santillana USA Publishing Co., Inc.

Fischman, Sheila, tr. from FRE. The Flying Canoe. Oberman, Sheldon & Cohen, Sheldon, illus. 2004. 24p. (J). (gr. 3-7). 15.95 (978-0-88776-636-7(6)) Tundra Bks., Inc./Livres Toundra, Inc. CAN. *Dist:* Random Hse., Inc.

Fish, Bruce & Fish, Becky Durost. Fables & Their Morals Vol. 1: Androcles & the Lion to The Field of Treasure. 1999. (Illus.). 64p. (J). 19.23 (978-0-7910-5211-2(7) , Chelsea Hse.) Facts On File, Inc.

Flanagan, John. The Burning Bridge. 2006. (Ranger's Apprentice Ser.: Bk. 2). 256p. (YA). (gr. 5). 16.99 (978-0-399-24455-1(7) , Philomel) Penguin Group (USA) Inc.

Floca, Brian, illus. The Hinky Pink. 2008. 48p. (J). (***978-0-689-87588-5(6)***) Simon & Schuster Children's Publishing.

Foglio, Phil & Foglio, Kaja. Agatha Heterodyne & the Clockwork Princess. 2006. (Girl Genius Ser.: Vol. 5). (Illus.). 112p. (YA). pap. 19.95 (978-1-890856-39-7(8)) Studio Foglio, LLC.

Ford, Ford Madox. The Queen Who Flew. reprint ed. (J). lib. bdg. 98.00 (978-0-7426-3057-4(9)); 2001. pap. 28.00 (978-0-7426-8057-9(6)) Classic Bks.

Foreman, Michael, illus. & retold by. Classic Fairy Tales. Foreman, Michael, retold by. 2005. 176p. (J). (ps-k). 12.95 (978-1-4027-2865-5(4)) Sterling Publishing Co., Inc.

Fowler, Sharon H. Fairies of Spencer's Meadow: Fairy Tales. Gooch, ed. Fowler, Sharon H. & Hargis, illus. 1999. 75p. (J). (gr. k-7). 19.95 (978-0-9651588-3-1(7)) Stringer, Alicia.

Frank, Jeffrey & Frank, Diana, trs. from DAN. The Stories of Hans Christian Andersen: A New Translation from the Danish. Frolich, Lorenz & Pederson, Vilhelm, illus. 2003. 304p. tchr. ed. 30.00 (978-0-618-22456-2(4)) Houghton Mifflin Co. Trade & Reference Div.

Fransoy, Monse, illus. Cinderella. 2001. (SPA & ENG.). 32p. (J). (ps-3). 12.95 (978-0-8118-3084-3(5)) Chronicle Bks. LLC.

French, Fiona. Little Inchkin. (Illus.). 32p. (J). 2004. pap. 19.95 (978-1-84507-009-0(7)); 2000. pap. 7.99 (978-0-7112-0917-6(0)) Lincoln, Frances Ltd. GBR. *Dist:* Transition Vendor.

French, Vivian. The Kingfisher Mini Treasury of Fairy Tales. Malone, Peter, illus. 2004. (Kingfisher Mini Treasury Ser.). 96p. (J). (ps-k). 9.95 (978-0-7534-5703-0(2) , Kingfisher) Houghton Mifflin Co. Trade & Reference Div.

French, Vivian & McDonald, Ronald L. Once upon a Time. Prater, John, illus. 1999. (Read & Share Ser.). 32p. (J). (ps). pap. 3.99 (978-0-7636-0858-3(0)) Candlewick Pr.

Friederich, Peggy. Storytime Vol. II: Many Years AGo. Friederich, Peggy, illus. 2002. (Illus.). 88p. (J). pap. (978-1-57579-240-8(0)) Pine Hill Pr., Inc.

Friedlander, Gerald. Jewish Fairy Tales. 2001. (Dover Juvenile Classics Ser.). 96p. (J). (gr. 4-7). pap. 2.00 (978-0-486-41982-4(7)) Dover Pubns., Inc.

Fukazawa, Kuniro, illus. Little Red Riding Hood. 2004. (Heian's Origami Fairy Tales Ser.: Vol. 3). 16p. (gr. k-3). pap. 7.95 (978-0-89346-912-2(2)) Heian International Publishing, Inc.

Gag, Wanda. More Tales from Grimm. 2006. (Fesler-Lampert Minnesota Heritage Ser.). (Illus.). 272p. 51.00 (978-0-8166-4937-2(5)); pap. 16.95 (978-0-8166-4938-9(3)) Univ. of Minnesota Pr.

—Tales from Grimm. 2006. (Fesler-Lampert Minnesota Heritage Ser.). (Illus.). 256p. 51.00 (978-0-8166-4935-8(9)) Univ. of Minnesota Pr.

Gag, Wanda. Tales from Grimm. 2006. (Fesler-Lampert Minnesota Heritage Ser.). (Illus.). 256p. pap. 16.95 (978-0-8166-4936-5(7)) Univ. of Minnesota Pr.

Galdone, Paul. Henny Penny. Galdone, Paul, illus. 2002. (Illus.). (J). 14.72 (978-0-7587-2712-1(7)) Book Wholesalers, Inc.

—Rumpelstiltskin. Galdone, Paul, illus. 2002. (Illus.). (J). 14.74 (978-0-7587-3543-0(X)) Book Wholesalers, Inc.

Garbancito. 3rd ed. 2002. (Troquelados Clasicos Ser.). (ENG & SPA., Illus.). 16p. pap. 2.95 (978-84-7864-186-4(6)) Combel Editorial, S.A. ESP. *Dist:* Independent Pubs. Group.

Garcia, Jose Enrique. Un Pueblo Llamado Pan y Otros Cuentos Infantiles. 2003. (SPA.). 10.36 net. (978-0-9710710-1-8(2) , SLT30784) Spanish Language Texts, Inc.

Gardner, Sally. El Catalogo para Hadas. 2002. (Illus.). (J). (SPA.). 32p. 17.95 (978-84-8488-022-6(2)); (CAT., 40p. 17.95 (978-84-8488-023-3(0)) Serres, Ediciones, S. L. ESP. *Dist:* Lectorum Pubns., Inc.

Gatty, Alfred. The Fairy Godmothers & Other Tales. 2004. reprint ed. pap. 15.95 (978-1-4191-6178-0(4)); pap. 1.99 (978-1-4192-6178-7(9)) Kessinger Publishing, LLC.

Gay, Marie-Louise. Rumplestinskin. (Buenas Noches Coleccion). (SPA.). (J). (gr. k-3). pap. 7.95 (978-958-04-5091-7(9)) Norma S.A. COL. *Dist:* Distribuidora Norma, Inc., Lectorum Pubns., Inc.

Geist, Ken, ed. Carebears: 4 Easy-to-Read Stories. 2005. (Scholastic Reader Collection Level 2 Ser.). 144p. (J). (ps-ps). pap. 6.99 (978-0-439-76310-3(X) , Cartwheel Bks.) Scholastic, Inc.

Gell, Jay & McMahan, Virginia. Where the Mushgnomes Live. 2nd ed. 2003. (J). per. 11.15 (978-1-4116-0221-2(8)) Lulu.com.

German Craftsmen Staff, illus. King Winter: Treasures from the Library of Congress. 2001. (Shape Bks.). 20p. (J). (gr. 4-7). reprint ed. pap. 3.95 (978-1-55709-168-0(4)) Applewood Bks.

Gerstein, Mordecai. Carolinda Clatter! unabr. ed. 2007. (Illus.). (J). (ps-2). 28.95 incl. audio compact disk (***978-1-59519-958-4(6)***) Live Oak Media.

Gerstein, Mordicai. Carolinda Clatter! 2005. (Illus.). 40p. (J). 16.95 (978-1-59643-063-1(X)) Roaring Brook Pr.

Gerver, Jane E. Penny. Papp, Lisa, illus. 2006. (Breyer Stablemates Ser.). 48p. (J). pap. 4.99 (978-0-439-72235-3(7) , Cartwheel Bks.) Scholastic, Inc.

Gerver, Jane E., et al. Barbie As Rapunzel: A Storybook. 2002. (Pictureback(R) Ser.). (Illus.). 24p. (J). (gr. k-k). pap. 3.99 (978-0-307-10425-0(7) , Golden Bks.) Random Hse. Children's Bks.

Gieselmann, Reinhard. Oscar Wilde, Fairy Tales. 2007. (Illus.). 96p. 39.00 (978-3-936681-13-0(9)) Edition Axel Menges GmbH DEU. *Dist:* National Bk. Network.

El Gigante Egoista. 2002. (Troquelados Clasicos Ser.). (ENG & SPA., Illus.). 16p. pap. 2.95 (978-84-7864-597-8(7)) Combel Editorial, S.A. ESP. *Dist:* Independent Pubs. Group, Libros Sin Fronteras.

Gilbertsen, Neal W. Little Red Snapperhood: A Fishy Fairy Tale. Zerbetz, Evon, illus. 2005. 32p. 15.95 (978-1-55868-683-0(5)); pap. 8.95 (978-1-55868-684-7(3)) Graphic Arts Ctr. Publishing Co.

Gili, Phillida. Cinderella: A Pop Up Book. 2006. (Illus.). 14p. (J). 17.95 (978-1-58234-712-7(3) , Bloomsbury Children) Bloomsbury Publishing.

Gill, Vince. The Emperor's New Clothes: A Country Storybook. Newsom, Carol, illus. 2006. 30p. (J). (gr. 4-8). reprint ed. 17.00 (978-1-4223-5729-3(5)) DIANE Publishing Co.

Ginsburg, Mirra. Two Greedy Bears: Adapted from a Hungarian Folktale. 1998. (J). (978-0-606-13881-9(1)) Tandem Library Bks.

Gitomer, Helaine D. & Weinstock, Harriett. The Magic Cow: A Gift. Gitomer, Helaine D. & Weinstock, Harriett, illus. 2000. (Illus.). (J). (978-0-9676205-0-3(3)) Orbin Publishing, Ltd.

Glassman, Peter. King Stork. 1998. (Books of Wonder). (Illus.). 48p. (gr. k-3). reprint ed. 16.00 (978-0-688-15813-2(7)) HarperCollins Pubs.

Gleeson, Brian. Anansi. Guarnaccia, Steven, illus. 2006. (J). (gr. 2-6). 25.65 (978-1-59679-342-2(2)) Spotlight.

—Koi & the Kola Nuts. Ruffins, Reynold, illus. 2007. (J). 25.65 (978-1-59961-310-9(7)) ABDO Publishing Co.

Gmeyner, Elizabeth. The Key of the Kingdom: A Book of Stories & Poems for Children. Russell, Joyce, illus. 2004. 100p. (J). pap. 15.00 (978-0-88010-549-1(6) , Bell Pond Bks.) SteinerBooks, Inc.

Goble, Paul. The Girl Who Loved Wild Horses. Goble, Paul, illus. 2001. (Illus.). 28.95 incl. audio compact disk (978-1-59112-752-9(1)); pap. 39.95 incl. audio compact disk (978-1-59112-534-1(0)) Live Oak Media.

God's Little Angel Twins, Maryknoll Coloring & Activity Book, Grades Pre-K & K: Rhyming Tales of Mary & Knoll from Maryknoll Land. 2005. (J). 2.00 (978-0-941395-12-0(X)) Maryknoll Missioners.

Goethe, Johann Wolfgang von. The Green Snake & the Beautiful Lily: A Fairy Tale. Allen, Joan deRis, ed. Linde, Hermann, illus. 2006. 48p. (J). 25.00 (978-0-88010-570-5(4)) SteinerBooks, Inc.

Golden Books Staff. Barbie as the Princess & the Pauper. Falkenstern, Lisa, illus. 2004. (Barbie Ser.). 32p. (J). (ps-2). 8.99 (978-0-375-82972-7(5) , Golden Bks.) Random Hse. Children's Bks.

—The House that Jack Built. Miller, J. P., illus. 2008. (Little Golden Book Ser.). 24p. (J). 2.99 (978-0-375-83530-8(X) , Golden Bks.) Random Hse. Children's Bks.

—The Story of Cinderella. 2007. (Color Plus Chunky Crayons Ser.). (Illus.). 48p. (J). (ps-2). 3.99 (978-0-375-83972-6(0) , Golden Bks.) Random Hse. Children's Bks.

—The Three Bears. Hefferan, Rob, illus. 2003. (Little Golden Book Ser.). 24p. (J). (gr. k-k). 2.99 (978-0-375-82576-7(2) , Golden Bks.) Random Hse. Children's Bks.

Goldenburg, Dorothea & Killian, Bette. Treasury of Fairy Tales. LoFaro, Jerry et al, illus. 2004. 320p. (J). 15.98 (978-0-7853-7771-9(9) , 3049205) Publications International, Ltd.

Goldilocks & the Three Bears. 2004. (My First Fairy Tales Ser.). (Illus.). 24p. (J). pap. 3.99 (978-1-85854-686-5(9)) Brimax Books Ltd. GBR. *Dist:* Byeway Bks.

Goldilocks & the Three Bears. 2002. (Puppy Tales Ser.). (Illus.). 24p. (J). (gr. k-3). 1.49 (978-1-57759-219-8(0)); pap. 2.99 (978-1-57759-479-6(7)) Dalmatian Pr.

Goldilocks & the Three Bears. (Ladybird Bks.). (ARA., Illus.). 52p. (J). 12.95 incl. audio (978-0-86685-254-8(9) , LDL109C) International Bk. Ctr., Inc.

E F G

E F G

GoldilocksThree Bears. 2004. (J). E-Book incl. cd-rom (978-1-84444-460-1(0)) Mantra Publishing, Ltd.

Goldsberry, U'i. The Shark Man of Hana. Chang, Roy, illus. 2004. (HAW.). 32p. (J). 14.95 (978-1-933067-01-8(2)) Beachhouse Publishing, LLC.

Gonzalez, Lucia. Romance de Don Gato. 1999. Tr. of Senor Cat's Romance. (978-0-606-17272-1(6)) Tandem Library Bks.

Goodman, Judith. A Fairy's Tale about Honesty. 2005. (J). 15.00 (978-0-9663144-3-4(3)) Women & Addiction Counseling & Educational Services.

Gould, Robert. Father & Son Read-Aloud Stories. Gurin, Lara, illus. 2006. 56p. (J). 12.95 (978-1-929945-67-2(1)) Big Guy Bks., Inc.

Gramercy Staff. Classic Fairy Tales: Enchanting Stories from Around the World. 2006. (Illus.). 192p. (J). 11.99 (978-0-517-22726-8(6) , Gramercy) Random Hse. Value Publishing.

Gray, Margaret. The Lovesick Salesman. Cecil, Randy, illus. rev. ed. 2004. 192p. (J). 16.95 (978-0-8050-7558-8(5) , Holt, Henry & Co. Bks. For Young Readers) Holt, Henry & Co.

Great Children's Stories. 2002. (Illus.). 160p. (J). (gr. k-7). 9.99 (978-1-57759-423-9(1)) Dalmatian Pr.

Greaves, Margaret. Tattercoats. Chamberlain, Margaret, illus. 32p. (J). (ps-2). pap. 9.99 (978-0-7112-0649-6(X)) Lincoln, Frances Ltd. GBR. *Dist:* Transition Vendor.

Green, Yuko. Cinderella, the Little Mermaid & Other Fairy Tale Paper Dolls. 2000. 32p. (J). (gr. k-5). pap. 4.95 (978-0-486-41044-9(7)) Dover Pubns., Inc.

Greenway, Betty, ed. Twice-Told Childrens Tales Vol. 35: The Influence of Childhood Reading on Writers for Adults. 2005. (Children's Literature & Culture Ser.: Vol. 35). 280p. 100.00 (978-0-415-97205-5(1)) Routledge.

Gresko, Marcia S. Monster Stew, Vol. 4474. Kupperstein, Joel, ed. Dunne, Kathleen, illus. 1998. (Learn to Read Math Ser.). 16p. (J). pap. 2.75 (978-1-57471-381-7(7) , 4474) Creative Teaching Pr., Inc.

Gribben, Valerie. Fairytale. 2003. (gr. 7-12). lib. bdg. 18.75 (978-0-613-79795-5(7)) Tandem Library Bks.

Griffis, William Elliot. Dutch Fairy Tales for Young Folks. 2004. reprint ed. pap. 1.99 (978-1-4192-1705-0(4)) Kessinger Publishing, LLC.

Grimm. Beauty & the Beast. (Illus.). 32p. (J). (ps). 7.95 (978-1-904668-64-0(X)) Mercury Bks. Ltd. GBR. *Dist:* International Publishers Marketing.

—Little Red Riding Hood. Mantovani, Maria & Barsotti, Renzo, illus. 32p. (J). (ps). 7.95 (978-1-904668-57-2(7)) Mercury Bks. Ltd. GBR. *Dist:* International Publishers Marketing.

—The Musicians of Bremen. Puttapipat, Niroot, illus. 2005. 32p. (J). (gr. k-3). 15.99 (978-0-7636-2758-4(5)) Candlewick Pr.

—Repunzel. 2005. 24p. incl. cd-rom (978-84-494-2900-2(5)) Oceano Grupo Editoria, S.A.

—Die Schoensten Kinder und Hausmaerchen. (GER.). cd-rom (978-3-15-120018-5(4)) Reclam, Philip jun., Verlag GmbH DEU. *Dist:* International Bk. Import Service, Inc.

—Sleeping Beauty. Mantovani, Maria & Barsotti, Renzo, illus. 32p. (J). (ps). 7.95 (978-1-904668-60-2(7)) Mercury Bks. Ltd. GBR. *Dist:* International Publishers Marketing.

—The Ugly Duckling. Mantovani, Maria & Barsotti, Renzo, illus. 32p. (J). (ps). 7.95 (978-1-904668-62-6(3)) Mercury Bks. Ltd. GBR. *Dist:* International Publishers Marketing.

Grimm, Jacob W. Grimm's Fairy Stories. 2006. pap. 26.99 (****978-1-4280-4819-5(7)***) IndyPublish.com.

—Household Stories. 2006. 99.00 (****978-1-4280-5072-3(8));*** pap. 90.99 (****978-1-4280-5106-5(6)***) IndyPublish.com.

Grimm, Jacob W. & Grimm, Wilhelm K. The Bremen Town Musicians: A Tale about Working Together. Catalano, Dominic, illus. 2006. (Famous Fables Ser.). (J). (978-1-59939-039-0(6) , Reader's Digest Young Families, Inc.) Reader's Digest Children's Publishing, Inc.

—Cinderella & Other Tales. 2005. (Charming Classics). (Illus.). 224p. (J). 6.99 (978-0-06-059602-6(3) , Harper Festival) HarperCollins Pubs.

—The Classic Treasury of Grimm's Fairy Tales. Daily, Don, illus. 2001. 56p. (J). 9.98 (978-0-7624-1115-3(5) , Courage Bks.) Running Pr. Bk. Pubs.

—The Elves & the Shoemaker. Stevens, Molly, tr. from FRE. Thibault, Dominique, illus. 2001. (Little Pebbles Ser.). 32p. 6.95 (978-0-7892-0731-9(1)) Abbeville Pr., Inc.

—The Elves & the Shoemaker. Chelushkin, Kirill, illus. 2007. (Classic Fairy Tale Collection). 24p. (J). (gr. 1-4). 14.95 (978-1-4027-3067-2(5)) Sterling Publishing Co., Inc.

—Fairy Tales: Hans Christian Andersen, 14 bks., Set. Incl. Three Feathers. Schmid, Eleanor, illus. (ps-3). lib. bdg. 13.95 (978-0-87191-941-0(9) , 1178-8); Three Languages. Chermayeff, Ivan, illus. (gr. 5 up). lib. bdg. 13.95 (978-0-87191-940-3(0) , 1178-9); 32p. (YA). 1984. 195.30 o.p. (978-0-87191-933-5(8) , Creative Education) Creative Co., The.

—Family Favorites, 4 bks., Set. Thibault, Dominique & Durual, Christophe, illus. 2007. (Classic Fairy Tales Ser.). 112p. (J). (ps-3). 19.95 (****978-0-7892-0952-8(7)***) Abbeville Pr., Inc.

—Favorite Fairy Tales. 2001. (gr. 3-6). lib. bdg. 9.50 (978-0-613-88890-5(1)) Tandem Library Bks.

—Favorite Fairy Tales of the Brothers Grimm. unabr. ed. 2001. (Dover Juvenile Classics Ser.). 96p. (J). (gr. 4-7). pap. 2.50 (978-0-486-41979-4(7)) Dover Pubns., Inc.

—The Fisherman & His Wife. Bryan, Diana, illus. 2005. (J). (gr. k-5). 25.65 (978-1-59197-747-6(9)) Spotlight.

—The Fisherman & His Wife: A Tale about Being Happy & Satisfied. Ebert, Len, illus. 2006. (J). (****978-1-59939-097-0(3)*** , Reader's Digest Young Families, Inc.) Reader's Digest Children's Publishing, Inc.

—The Fisherman & the Turtle. AvileI[81]s Junco, Martha, illus. 2008. (J). (****978-0-7614-5387-1(3)***) Cavendish, Marshall Corp.

—The Frog Prince. Gilbert, Anne Yvonne, illus. 2007. 32p. (J). 18.95 (978-1-58726-279-1(7) , Mitten Pr.) Ann Arbor Media Group, LLC.

—Grandpa Mouse & Little Mouse: A Tale about Respect for Elders. Lonaytis, Olga, illus. 2006. (J). (978-1-59939-088-8(4) , Reader's Digest Young Families, Inc.) Reader's Digest Children's Publishing, Inc.

—Grimm's Fairy Tales. 2007. 276p. pap. 5.95 (****978-1-58726-489-4(7)***) Ann Arbor Media Group, LLC.

—Grimm's Fairy Tales. 2007. (Thrift Edition Ser.). (Illus.). 208p. pap. 3.95 (****978-0-486-45656-0(0)***) Dover Pubns., Inc.

—Grimm's Fairy Tales. 2001. (Twelve-Point Ser.). 270p. lib. bdg. 25.00 (978-1-58287-143-1(4)) North Bks.

—Grimm's Fairy Tales. 1998. (Children's Classics). (ENG., Illus.). 272p. (J). (gr. 4-7). pap. (978-1-85326-101-5(7) , 1017WW) Wordsworth Editions, Ltd.

—Hansel & Gretel. Felix, Monique, illus. 2001. 32p. (gr. 5 up). 17.95 (978-1-56846-137-3(2) , Creative Editions) Creative Co., The.

—Hansel & Gretel. Duntze, Dorothee, illus. 2006. 24p. (J). (gr. k-4). reprint ed. 17.00 (978-1-4223-5008-9(8)) DIANE Publishing Co.

—Household Stories from the Collection of the Brothers Grimm. (J). 23.95 (978-0-88411-663-9(8)) Amereon LTD.

—Rapunzel. Bell, Anthea, tr. from GER. Duntze, Dorothie, illus. 2005. 24p. (J). (ps-17). 16.95 (978-0-7358-2013-5(9)) North-South Bks., Inc.

—Sleeping Beauty. Stevens, Molly, tr. from FRE. Novi, Nathalie, illus. 2001. (Little Pebbles Ser.). 32p. 6.95 (978-0-7892-0734-0(6)) Abbeville Pr., Inc.

—Snow White. Santore, Charles, illus. 2004. 48p. (J). (gr. k-3). 19.95 (978-0-375-83001-3(4) , Random Hse. Bks. for Young Readers) Random Hse. Children's Bks.

—The Wolf & the Seven Little Kids. Routiaux, Claudine, illus. 2001. (Little Pebbles Ser.).Tr. of Wolf und die Sieben Jungen Geisslein. 32p. 6.95 (978-0-7892-0735-7(4)) Abbeville Pr., Inc.

Grimm, Jacob W. & Wilhelm. Rapunzel. 2005. (Illus.). 32p. (J). (ps up). 17.50 (978-0-7358-2014-2(7)) North-South Bks., Inc.

Grimm, Jacob W., et al. The Bremen Town Musicians. Bell, Anthea, tr. from GER. 2007. (Illus.). 32p. (J). (ps-3). 16.99 (978-0-698-40042-9(9) , Minedition) Penguin Group (USA) Inc.

—The Complete Fairy Tales of the Brothers Grimm. 3rd ed. 2003. (Bantam Classics Ser.). (Illus.). 800p. reprint ed. 20.00 (978-0-553-38216-7(0) , Bantam) Bantam Bks.

—The Fisherman & His Wife. 2001. (Illus.). 32p. (gr. 6). 17.95 (978-1-56846-140-3(2)) Creative Co., The.

—Little Red Riding Hood/Capercuita Roja: A Bilingual Book. Surges, James, tr. from CAT. Estrada, Pau, illus. 1999. (ENG & SPA.). 32p. (J). (ps-3). pap. 6.95 (978-0-8118-2562-7(0)) Chronicle Bks. LLC.

—The Queen Bee. James, Elisabeth, tr. from GER. Ghiuselev, Iassen, illus. 2003. 32p. 16.95 (978-0-9688768-4-8(6)) Simply Read Bks. CAN. *Dist:* Perseus Distribution.

—Tales from the Brothers Grimm. 2007. (Classic Illustrated Edition Ser.). (Illus.). 148p. (J). 19.95 (978-0-8118-5459-7(0)) Chronicle Bks. LLC.

Grimm, Jakob & Grimm, Wilhelm K. Grimm's Fairy Tales. l.t. ed. 2004. (Large Print Ser.). 477p. 26.00 (978-1-58287-627-6(4)) North Bks.

Grimm, Wilhelm K. & Grimm, Jacob W. Hansel & Gretel. Wolf, Claudia, tr. Wolf, Claudia, illus. 2003. (J). pap. (978-1-4048-0542-2(7)) Picture Window Bks.

—The McElderry Book of Grimms' Fairy Tales. Chichester-Clark, Emma, illus. 2006. 128p. (J). 19.95 (978-1-4169-1798-4(5) , McElderry, Margaret K.) Simon & Schuster Children's Publishing.

—Snow White & the Seven Dwarfs. Deru, Myriam, illus. 2001. (Little Pebbles Ser.). 32p. (ps-3). 6.95 (978-0-7892-0693-0(5)) Abbeville Pr., Inc.

—We Both Read-Hansel & Gretel. Barnes, Tim, illus. 1999. (We Both Read Ser.). 44p. (J). (gr. 1-2). 7.99 (978-1-891327-13-1(5)); pap. 3.99 (978-1-891327-17-9(8)) Treasure Bay, Inc.

Grimm, Wilhelm K., et al. Elves & Shoemaker. 2004. 48p. (J). (gr. 2 up). pap. 5.95 (978-0-7945-0758-9(1) , Usborne) EDC Publishing.

—Grimm's Fairy Tales. 2005. (Great Illustrated Classics Ser.). (Illus.). 237p. (J). (gr. 3-8). 21.35 (978-1-59679-241-8(8) , ABDO & Daughters) ABDO Publishing Co.

—The Rabbit's Bride. Meade, Holly, illus. 2001. 32p. (J). (ps-3). 15.95 (978-0-7614-5081-8(5) , Cavendish Children's Bks.) Cavendish, Marshall Corp.

Grindley, Sally. Who Is It? Lots of Fairytale Fun. Beardshaw, Rosalind, illus. 2000. 32p. (J). (ps-1). 16.95 (978-1-56145-224-8(6)) Peachtree Pubs., Ltd.

Grodin, Elissa. The Happy Prince. Stutzman, Laura, illus. rev. ed. 2006. 48p. (J). 17.95 (978-1-58536-264-6(6)) Sleeping Bear Pr.

Gross, Ruth B. Hansel y Gretel. 2001. Tr. of Hansel & Gretel. (978-0-606-22654-7(0)) Tandem Library Bks.

Gross, Ruth Belov. The Emperor's New Clothes. Kent, Jack, illus. 2000. 32p. (J). (ps-3). pap. 4.99 (978-0-590-43267-2(2)) Scholastic, Inc.

Grosset and Dunlap Staff. Cinderella. Brooks, Nan, illus. 2000. (Glow Sticker Stories Ser.). 16p. (J). (ps-3). mass mkt. 4.99 (978-0-448-42174-2(7) , Grosset & Dunlap) Penguin Group (USA) Inc.

Gruber, Michael. The Witch's Boy. (gr. 6-9). 2006. 400p. (J). pap. 7.99 (978-0-06-076167-7(9)); 2005. 384p. (YA). 16.99 (978-0-06-076164-6(4)) HarperCollins Pubs. (HarperTeen).

—The Witch's Boy. l.t. ed. 2006. 448p. (YA). 22.95 (978-0-7862-8580-8(X)) Thorndike Pr.

Gruelle, Johnny. My Very Own Fairy Stories. 2000. (Illus.). 48p. (J). (gr. k-5). reprint ed. 14.99 (978-1-57860-076-2(6)) Emmis Bks.

Guell, Fernando. Snow White & the Seven Dwarfs. 2001. (gr. k-3). lib. bdg. 10.95 (978-0-613-73676-3(1)) Tandem Library Bks.

La Habichuela Magica. 2002. (Troquelados Clasicos Ser.). (ENG & SPA., Illus.). 16p. pap. 2.95 (978-84-7864-599-2(3)) Combel Editorial, S.A. ESP. *Dist:* Independent Pubs. Group.

Haddix, Margaret Peterson. Just Ella. 2001. (gr. 5-8). lib. bdg. 14.15 (978-0-613-90928-0(3)); (J). 12.64 (978-0-606-21275-5(2)) Tandem Library Bks.

Hague, Michael. The Book of Fairies. Hague, Michael, illus. 2000. (Illus.). 128p. (J). (ps up). 21.99 (978-0-688-10881-6(4)) HarperCollins Pubs.

—The Nutcracker. ed. 2005. (Illus.). 56p. (J). (ps-7). 7.95 (978-0-8118-5027-8(7)) Chronicle Bks. LLC.

Hague, Michael, illus. Michael Hague's Favourite Hans Christian Andersen Fairy Tales. rev. ed. 2003. 168p. (J). (gr. 1 up). 18.95 (978-0-8050-7239-6(X) , Holt, Henry & Co. Bks. For Young Readers) Holt, Henry & Co.

—The Nutcracker. 2003. 48p. (J). 17.50 (978-1-58717-255-7(0)); 16.95 (978-1-58717-254-0(2)) Chronicle Bks. LLC. (SeaStar Bks.).

Hahner, Aaron. The Magic of Midnight. 2004. per. 8.95 (978-1-932560-58-9(0)) Media Creations, Inc.

Hale, Bruce. Snoring Beauty. 2006. (J). 16.00 (978-0-15-216314-3(X) , Harcourt Children's Bks) Harcourt Children's Bks.

Hale, Shannon. Enna Burning. (J). 2006. 336p. pap. 8.95 (978-1-58234-906-0(1)); 2004. (Illus.). 300p. 17.95 (978-1-58234-889-6(8)) Bloomsbury Publishing. (Bloomsbury Children).

—The Goose Girl. 2003. (Illus.). 300p. (J). (gr. 5 up). 18.95 (978-1-58234-843-8(X)); 2005. 400p. (YA). (gr. 7-17). reprint ed. pap. 8.95 (978-1-58234-990-9(8)) Bloomsbury Publishing. (Bloomsbury Children).

—River Secrets. 2006. (Illus.). 304p. (J). 17.95 (978-1-58234-901-5(0)) Bloomsbury Publishing.

Hall, Amanda. Giant Tales from Around the World. Waters, Fiona, illus. 2004. 96p. (J). 17.95 (978-1-84458-143-6(8)) Chrysalis Children's Bks. GBR. *Dist:* Transition Vendor.

Halverson, Lydia, illus. We Both Read-Jack & the Beanstalk. 2nd ed. 1999. (We Both Read Ser.). 44p. (J). (gr. 1-2). pap. 3.99 (978-1-891327-15-5(1)) Treasure Bay, Inc.

Han, Carolyn. Koa's Seed. Peterson, Kathleen, illus. 2004. 32p. (J). 14.95 (978-1-933067-02-5(0)) Beachhouse Publishing, LLC.

Hansel & Gretel. 2003. (SPA.). (978-84-246-2535-1(8) , GL7967) La Galera, S.A. Editorial ESP. *Dist:* Lectorum Pubns., Inc.

Hansel & Gretel. (Ladybird Bks.). (ARA., Illus.). 14.95 incl. audio (978-0-86685-637-9(4) , LDL102C) Librairie du Liban Pubns. FRA. *Dist:* International Bk. Ctr., Inc.

Hansel & Gretel. 2005. (J). pap. 18.95 incl. audio compact disk (978-0-439-80423-3(X)); pap. 14.95 incl. audio (978-0-439-80422-6(1)) Weston Woods Studios, Inc.

Hansel e Gretel. pap. 7.95 (978-88-8148-547-5(8)) European Language Institute ITA. *Dist:* Distribooks, Inc.

Hansel et Gretel.Tr. of Hansel & Gretel. pap. 7.95 (978-88-8148-544-4(3)) European Language Institute ITA. *Dist:* Distribooks, Inc.

Hansel und Gretel. pap. 7.95 (978-88-8148-545-1(1)) European Language Institute ITA. *Dist:* Distribooks, Inc.

Hanson, Mary Elizabeth. How to Save Your Tail: If You Are a Rat Nabbed by Cats Who Really Like Stories about Magic Spoons, Wolves with Snout-Warts, Big Hairy Chimney Trolls—And Cookies Too. Hendrix, John, illus. 2007. 112p. (J). (gr. 1-5). 15.99 (978-0-375-83755-5(8) , Schwartz & Wade Bks.) Random Hse. Children's Bks.

—How to Save Your Tail: If You Are a Rat Nabbed by Cats Who Really Like Stories about Magic Spoons, Wolves with Snout-Warts, Big Hairy Chimney Trolls—and Cookies Too. 2007. (Illus.). 112p. (J). (gr. 1-5). lib. bdg. 18.99 (978-0-375-93755-2(2) , Schwartz & Wade Bks.) Random Hse. Children's Bks.

Hanson-Roberts, Mary, illus. Cinderella: A Tale of Kindness. 2006. (J). 6.99 (978-1-59939-001-7(9) , Reader's Digest Young Families, Inc.) Reader's Digest Children's Publishing, Inc.

Harcourt School Publishers Staff. Tales of Mr. Map Advanced Level. 3rd ed. 2002. (Trophies Reading Program Ser.). (Illus.). pap. 5.10 (978-0-15-323026-4(6)) Harcourt Schl. Pubs.

Hargreaves, Martin, illus. Rumpelstiltskin. 2008. (J). (****978-1-4027-3066-5(7)***) Sterling Publishing Co., Inc.

Harmel, Kristin. When You Wish. 2008. 288p. (J). (gr. 7). lib. bdg. 18.99 (****978-0-385-90474-2(6)*** , Delacorte Bks. for Young Readers) Random Hse. Children's Bks.

Harold's Fairy Tale. 2004. (J). pap. 14.95 incl. audio (978-0-7882-0686-3(9)) Weston Woods Studios, Inc.

Harper, Wilhelmina. The Gunniwolf. Upton, Barbara, illus. 2003. 32p. (J). (ps). 15.99 (978-0-525-46785-4(8) , Dutton Juvenile) Penguin Group (USA) Inc.

HarperCollins Children's Books. Fairy Tales. 2007. (Word Play Ser.). 208p. (J). pap. 5.95 (****978-0-00-724336-5(7)***) HarperCollins Pubs. Ltd. GBR. *Dist:* Independent Pubs. Group.

Harris, Jim. Jack & the Giant: A Story Full of Beans. Harris, Jim, illus. 2000. (Illus.). 32p. (gr. k-3). 15.95 (978-0-87358-680-1(8) , Rising Moon Bks. for Young Readers) Northland Publishing.

Harris, L. Little Girl in Paris. 2004. (Madame Juliette & the Inchanded Crate Ser.: Vol. 1). (Illus.). 330p. (J). pap. 19.95 (978-0-9749950-2-1(9)) Granny's Pub Co.

Harrison, David L. The Book of Giant Stories. Fix, Philippe, illus. 2003. 40p. (J). (gr. k-2). 17.95 (978-1-56397-976-7(4)); pap. 10.95 (978-1-56397-797-8(4)) Boyds Mills Pr.

—Book of Giant Stories. 2001. (gr. 3-6). lib. bdg. 19.90 (978-0-613-56248-5(8)) Tandem Library Bks.

Harrison, Mette. Mira, Mirror. 2006. 320p. (YA). (gr. 7). pap. 6.99 (978-0-14-240643-4(0) , Puffin) Penguin Group (USA) Inc.

Hart, Melissa. Tale of Despereaux Literature Unit. 2005. 48p. pap. 7.99 (978-1-4206-3164-7(0)) Teacher Created Resources, Inc.

Hartland, Edwin Sidney, ed. English Fairy & Folk Tales. 2000. 320p. pap. 8.95 (978-0-486-41135-4(4)) Dover Pubns., Inc.

Harvey, Amanda, illus. Up the Chimney. 1998. 32p. (J). (ps-3). tchr. ed. 15.95 (978-0-8234-1354-6(3)) Holiday Hse., Inc.

Harvey-Fitzhenry, Alyxandra. Waking: A Fairy Tale. 2006. 176p. (gr. 7-12). pap. 8.95 (978-1-55143-489-6(X)) Orca Bk. Pubs. USA.

Hassett, John & Hassett, Ann. The Three Silly Girls Grubb. Hassett, John & Hassett, Ann, illus. 2002. (Illus.). 32p. (J). (gr. k-3). tchr. ed. 15.00 (978-0-618-14183-8(9) , Walter Lorraine) Houghton Mifflin Co. Trade & Reference Div.

—Three Silly Girls Grubb. 2006. (Illus.). 32p. (J). (gr. k-3). reprint ed. pap. 6.95 (978-0-618-69334-4(3)) Houghton Mifflin Co.

Hauff, Wilhelm & Pak, Boris. Little Mook & Dwarf Longnose. 2004. (Illus.). 124p. 19.95 (978-1-56792-222-6(8)) Godine, David R. Pub.

Haviland, C. S. Faith & Fairies. 2004. 258p. (YA). pap. 14.95 (978-0-9759355-0-7(X)) LegendMaker Scriptoria.

Hawthorn, P. Little Book of Fairy Stories. 2004. (Mini Storybooks Ser.). (Illus.). 96p. (J). 7.95 (978-0-7945-0297-3(0) , Usborne) EDC Publishing.

Hawthorne, Grace. Healthy Air: Book C of Healthy Me, 3 books. Blyth, Eileen, illus. 2004. 48p. (J). pap. 73.75 (978-0-944235-49-2(2)) American Cancer Society, Inc.

—Healthy Bodies: Book A of Healthy Me, 3 books. Blyth, Eileen, illus. 2004. 48p. (J). pap. 73.75 (978-0-944235-47-8(6)) American Cancer Society, Inc.

—Healthy Food: Book B of Healthy Me, 3 bks. Blyth, Eileen, illus. 2004. 48p. (J). pap. 73.75 (978-0-944235-48-5(4)) American Cancer Society, Inc.

—Healthy Me: A Read-along Coloring & Activity Book. Blyth, Eileen, illus. 2004. 144p. pap., act. bk. ed. 6.95 (978-0-944235-46-1(8) , 9780944235461) McGraw-Hill Cos., The.

Hayes, Joe. Little Gold Star: A Cinderella Cuento. 2002. (gr. k-3). lib. bdg. 16.40 (978-0-613-77773-5(5)) Tandem Library Bks.

Hays, J. W. Adventures of Prince Lazybones & Other. 2006. 78.99 (****978-1-4280-3786-1(1));*** pap. 71.99 (****978-1-4280-3813-4(2)***) IndyPublish.com.

Hearn, Lafcadio, et al. The Boy Who Drew Cats & Other Japanese Fairy Tales. Green, Yuko, illus. 1998. (Dover Children's Thrift Classics Ser.). 64p. (J). (gr. 3-6). pap. 2.00 (978-0-486-40348-9(3)) Dover Pubns., Inc.

Helbrough, Emma. First Picture Fairytales. Litchfield, Jo, illus. 2007. 16p. (J). bds. 11.99 (978-0-7945-1460-0(X) , Usborne) EDC Publishing.

Helbrough, Emma, retold by. Nutcracker. 2005. (Young Reading Gift Books Ser.). 48p. (J). (gr. 2 up). 8.99 (978-0-7945-0921-7(5) , Usborne) EDC Publishing.

Helmer, Marilyn. Three Prince Charming Tales: Cinderella, Snow White, Rapunzel. Charko, Kasia, illus. 2004. (Once-upon-a-Time Ser.). 32p. (J). (gr. k-3). (978-1-55074-761-4(4)) Kids Can Pr., Ltd.

—Three Tales of Enchantment: Sleeping Beauty, The Little Mermaid, Beauty & the Beast. Charko, Kasia, illus. 2004. (Once-upon-a-Time Ser.: No. 4). 32p. (J). (gr. k-3). (978-1-55074-843-7(2)) Kids Can Pr., Ltd.

—Three Tales of Trickery. Pajouhesh, Noushin, illus. 2004. (Once-upon-a-Time Ser.). 32p. (J). (gr. k-3). (978-1-55074-937-3(4)) Kids Can Pr., Ltd.

—Three Teeny Tiny Tales. Tomova, Veselina, illus. unabr. ed. 2004. (Once-upon-a-Time Ser.). 32p. (J). (gr. k-3). (978-1-55074-841-3(6)) Kids Can Pr., Ltd.

Henkel, Julie Anne. Jungle Seek in the Rainforest: An Enchanted Fairy Tale. 2004. (Illus.). 66p. (J). per. (978-1-932077-09-4(X)) Athena Pr.

Herman, Gail. Tooth Fairy Travels. 1999. (Fairy School Ser.). (J). (978-0-606-19293-4(X)) Tandem Library Bks.

Heurtelou, Maude. Sandra: Cinderalla in Haiti. 2004. (CRP., Illus.). 24p. (J). 8.50 (978-1-58432-176-7(8)) Educa Vision.

Heyer, Carol. The Sleeping Beauty in the Wood. 2001. (J). (gr. 4-7). 14.95 (978-0-8249-5401-7(7)) Ideals Pubns.

Hibbs, Joan Arlin. Cinderella's Daughter. 2004. 93p. pap. 14.95 (978-1-4137-2935-1(5)) PublishAmerica, Inc.

HighReach Learning. Fabulous Fairy Tales. 2001. (Learning Fun for Little Ones Ser.). (Illus.). 64p. (ps-1). pap. 8.99 (978-0-88724-586-2(2) , CD-6413) Carson-Dellosa Publishing Co., Inc.

Hilario. Yuck!! A Toad. 2006. (Stories for Smaller Kids Ser.). (Illus.). 16p. (J). bds. 5.95 (978-9974-7925-4-8(1)) Hardenville SA URY. *Dist:* Independent Pubs. Group.

Hill, William. Dragon Pawns: Jules & the Runt Dragon. 2005. 358p. (J). 24.95 (978-1-890611-37-8(9)) Atlas-Books Distribution.

Hillert, Margaret. Cinderella at the Ball. 2002. (Illus.). (YA). 15.00 (978-1-4046-2003-2(6)) Book Wholesalers, Inc.

—Cinderella at the Ball. LaSalle, Janet, illus. rev. exp. ed. 2007. (Beginning to Read Ser.). 32p. (J). lib. bdg. (978-1-59953-046-8(5)) Norwood Hse. Pr.

—The Cookie House: Hansel & Gretel Retold. Craft, Kinuko, illus. rev. exp. ed. 2007. (Beginning to Read Ser.). 28p. (J). lib. bdg. (978-1-59953-051-2(1)) Norwood Hse. Pr.

—Four Good Friends: The Bremen Town Musicians Retold. Stasiak, Krystyna, illus. rev. exp. ed. 2007. (Beginning to Read Ser.). 32p. (J). lib. bdg. (978-1-59953-047-5(3)) Norwood Hse. Pr.

—Magic Nutcracker. (Illus.). (J). 4.95 (978-0-87895-667-8(0)) Modern Curriculum Pr.

Hillert, Margaret & Andersen. The Funny Baby: The Ugly Duckling Retold. Depper, Hertha, illus. rev. exp. ed. 2007. (Beginning to Read Ser.). 32p. (J). lib. bdg. (978-1-59953-048-2(1)) Norwood Hse. Pr.

Historias Doradas.Tr. of Golden Stories for Children. (SPA.). (J). 22.98 (978-84-8426-214-5(6)) Susaeta Ediciones, S.A. ESP. *Dist:* AIMS International Bks., Inc.

Hoberman, Mary Ann. You Read to Me, I'll Read to You: Very Short Fairy Tales to Read Together. Emberley, Michael, illus. 2004. 32p. (J). (ps-3). 16.99 (978-0-316-14611-1(0)) Little Brown & Co.

Hofer, Nelly & Hofer, Ernst, illus. Clever Katarina: A Tale in Six Parts. 2006. 40p. (J). (gr. 3-5). 17.95 (978-0-88776-764-7(8)) Tundra Bks., Inc./Livres Toundra, Inc. CAN. *Dist:* Random Hse., Inc.

Hoffman, Mary. Clever Katya: A Fairy Tale from Old Russia. Cameron, Marie, illus. 32p. (J). (gr. k-5). 2005. pap. 6.99 (978-1-905236-05-3(0)); 1998. 15.95 (978-1-901223-64-4(7)) Barefoot Bks., Inc.

—A First Book of Fairy Tales. Downing, Julie, illus. 2006. 80p. (J). pap. 9.99 (978-0-7566-2107-0(0)) Dorling Kindersley Publishing, Inc.

Hoffmann, E. T. A. The Nutcracker. Manheim, Ralph, tr. from GER. Sendak, Maurice, illus. 2004. 102p. (YA). (gr. 4-8). reprint ed. 40.00 (978-0-7567-8041-8(1)) DIANE Publishing Co.

—The Nutcracker. Zwerger, Lisbeth, illus. 2004. 32p. (J). 16.50 (978-0-7358-1733-3(2)) North-South Bks., Inc.

—The Nutcracker. Daily, Don, illus. gif. ed. 2003. (Heirloom Editions Ser.). 56p. (J). 16.95 (978-0-7624-1668-4(8) , Running Pr.) Running Pr. Bk. Pubs.

—The Story of the Nutcracker. 2000. (YA). 19.95 (978-0-8488-2936-0(0)) Amereon LTD.

Holder, Nancy. Spirited. 2004. (Once upon a Time Ser.). 272p. (YA). pap. 13.95 (978-0-689-87063-7(9) , Simon Pulse) Simon & Schuster Children's Publishing.

Holmes, Sarah. Letters from Rapunzel. 2007. 192p. (J). (gr. 5-8). 15.99 (978-0-06-078073-9(8)); lib. bdg. 16.89 (978-0-06-078074-6(6)) HarperCollins Pubs.

Hong, Michele. Cho Noi: Little Straw Maiden. 2000. (Illus.). 16p. (J). pap. 7.00 (978-0-8059-4846-2(5)) Dorrance Publishing Co., Inc.

Honold, Alexander & Scherpe, Klaus R. Das Fremde: Reiseerfahrungen, Schreibformen und Kulturelles Wissen. 2000. (Zeitschrift fur Germanistik Ser.: Bd. 2). (GER.). 341p. (J). 45.95 (978-3-906765-28-0(8)) Lang, Peter CHE. *Dist:* Lang, Peter Publishing, Inc.

Hood, Karen Jean Matsko. Adventures of My Dentist & the Tooth Fairy Activity & Coloring Book Second Edition. 2nd ed. 2005. (Educational Activity & Coloring Book Ser.).Tr. of Japanese. (J). spiral bd. 15.95 (978-1-59649-233-2(3)) Whispering Pine Pr., Inc.

—Jesus Loves the Little Children Activity & Coloring Book. 2005. (Educational Activity & Coloring Book Ser.). (ENG & SPA.). (J). spiral bd. 15.95 (978-1-59649-607-1(X)); cd-rom 7.95 (978-1-59434-087-1(0)) Whispering Pine Pr., Inc.

Hood, Karen Jean Matsko, told to. Adventures of My Dentist & the Tooth Fairy Activity & Coloring Book Second Edition. 2nd ed. 2005. (Educational Activity & Coloring Book Ser.).Tr. of Japanese. (J). cd-rom 13.95 (978-1-59649-234-9(1)) Whispering Pine Pr., Inc.

Hopkins, Jackie & Asbjornsen, Peter Christen. The Three Armadillies Tuff. Brooks, S. G., illus. 2002. (J). 15.95 (978-1-56145-258-3(0) , Q34266) Peachtree Pubs., Ltd.

Hopkins, Lee Bennett. Mother Goose & Her Animal Friends: Theme 2. Fehlau, Dagmar et al, illus. l.t. ed. 1999. (Sadlier Phonics Reading Program). 16p. (YA). (ps-2). 29.85 (978-0-8215-0472-7(X)) Sadlier, William H. Inc.

Housman, Laurence. Field of Clover. 2006. pap. 33.99 (***978-1-4280-4897-3(9))** IndyPublish.com.

Howard, Arthur. Serious Trouble. (Illus.). 32p. (J). 2007. pap. 6.00 (978-0-15-205853-1(2) , Voyager Bks./Libros Viajeros); 2003. 16.00 (978-0-15-202664-6(9)) Harcourt Children's Bks.

Howe, John, illus. & retold by. Jack & the Beanstalk. Howe, John, retold by. 1998. 32p. (J). (gr. 1-5). pap. 5.95 (978-0-316-37562-7(4)) Little Brown & Co.

Howell, Gill. Snow King. Cann, Helen, illus. 2005. 24p. (J). lib. bdg. 22.65 (***978-1-59646-742-2(8))** Dingles & Co.

Howland, Naomi. Latkes, Latkes, Good to Eat: A Chanukah Story. 2004. (Illus.). 32p. (J). (ps-3). pap. 5.95 (978-0-618-49295-4(X) , Clarion Bks.) Houghton Mifflin Co. Trade & Reference Div.

—Latkes, Latkes, Good to Eat: A Chanukah Story. Howland, Naomi, illus. 1999. (Illus.). 32p. (J). (gr. k-3). tchr. ed. 16.00 (978-0-395-89903-8(6) , Clarion Bks.) Houghton Mifflin Co. Trade & Reference Div.

—The Matzah Man: A Passover Story. 2002. (Illus.). 32p. (J). (gr. k-3). 16.00 (978-0-618-11750-5(4) , Clarion Bks.) Houghton Mifflin Co. Trade & Reference Div.

Hoyos, Hector. Los Siete Mejores Cuentos Chinos. Cuellar, Olga, illus. 2004. (SPA.). (J). (gr. 3-5). (978-958-04-7210-0(6)) Norma S.A.

—Los Siete Mejores Cuentos Indios. Cuellar, Olga, illus. 2004. (SPA.). 55p. (J). (gr. 3-5). (978-958-04-7213-1(0)) Norma S.A.

Hughes, Shirley. Ella's Big Chance. Hughes, Shirley, illus. 2004. (Illus.). 48p. (J). 16.95 (978-0-689-87399-7(9) , Simon & Schuster Children's Publishing) Simon & Schuster Children's Publishing.

Hurt-Newton, Tania, illus. The Magic Porridge Pot: Based on a Traditional Folk Tale. 1999. (First Favourite Tales Ser.). 32p. (J). 4.95 (978-0-7214-9742-6(X) , Dutton Juvenile) Penguin Group (USA) Inc.

Hyman. Sleeping Beauty. 2000. (J). (978-0-606-19844-8(X)) Tandem Library Bks.

Hyman, Tina Schart. Snow White. 2000. (J). (978-0-606-19845-5(8)) Tandem Library Bks.

Ibbotson, Eva. The Secret of Platform 13. 2002. (Illus.). 13.19 (978-1-4046-1491-8(5)) Book Wholesalers, Inc.

—The Secret of Platform 13. Porter, Sue, illus. 1999. 240p. (gr. 3-7). pap. 6.99 (978-0-14-130286-7(0) , Puffin) Penguin Group (USA) Inc.

—The Secret of Platform 13. Porter, Sue, illus. 1999. 231p. (J). (ps-7). per. 14.15 (978-0-613-23032-2(9)) Tandem Library Bks.

—The Secret of Platform 13. 1999. (978-0-606-17261-5(0)) Tandem Library Bks.

—The Secret of Platform 13. Porter, Sue, illus. l.t. ed. 2001. 250p. (J). (gr. 4-7). 22.95 (978-0-7862-3074-7(6)) Thorndike Pr.

Ikeda, Hiroaki, illus. Snow White. 2004. (Heian's Origami Fairy Tales Ser.: Vol. 4). 16p. (gr. k-3). pap. 7.95 (978-0-89346-911-5(4)) Heian International Publishing, Inc.

Imperato, Teresa. This Little Piggy. Haskamp, Steve, illus. 2005. 22p. (J). 9.95 (978-1-58117-281-2(8) , Intervisual/Piggy Toes) Dalmatian Pr.

Impey, Martin, illus. Rapunzel. 2007. (First Fairy Tales Ser.). 31p. (J). (***978-1-59771-076-3(8))** Sea-To-Sea Pubns.

Ingelow, Jean. Mopsa the Fairy. 2006. pap. 19.95 (***978-1-4304-4177-9(1))** Kessinger Publishing, LLC.

Inu Yasha: A Feudal Fairy Tale. 2002. Vol. 9. (YA). 23.19 (978-0-7587-9968-5(3)); (Inu Yasha Ser.: Vol. 1). (Illus.). 23.19 (978-1-4046-2212-8(8)); Vol. 10. (Illus.). (J). 23.19 (978-0-7587-9942-5(X)); (Inu Yasha Ser.: Vol. 11). (Illus.). (YA). 23.19 (978-1-4046-2211-1(X)); (Inu Yasha Ser.: Vol. 12). (Illus.). 23.19 (978-1-4046-1626-4(8)); (Inu Yasha Ser.: Vol. 2). (Illus.). 23.19 (978-1-4046-2213-5(6)); (Inu Yasha Ser.: Vol. 3). (Illus.). 23.19 (978-1-4046-2214-2(4)); (Inu Yasha Ser.: Vol. 4). (Illus.). 23.19 (978-1-4046-2215-9(2)); (Inu Yasha Ser.: Vol. 5). (Illus.). (YA). 23.19 (978-1-4046-2208-1(X)); (Inu Yasha Ser.: Vol. 6). (Illus.). (YA). 23.19 (978-1-4046-0206-9(2)); (Inu Yasha Ser.: Vol. 7). (Illus.). 23.19 (978-1-4046-2209-8(8)); (Inu Yasha Ser.: Vol. 8). (Illus.). 23.19 (978-1-4046-2210-4(1)) Book Wholesalers, Inc.

Irving, Washington. Rip Van Winkle & the Legend of Sleepy Hollow, Level 1. abr. ed. 2000. (SPA., Illus.). 32p. (C). pap. 9.00 (978-0-582-42051-9(2)) Longman Publishing Group.

Isadora, Rachel. The Fisherman & His Wife. Isadora, Rachel, illus. 2008. 32p. (J). (ps). 16.99 (***978-0-399-24771-2(8)** , Putnam Juvenile) Penguin Group (USA) Inc.

Isadora, Rachel & Andersen, Han. The Princess & the Pea. Isadora, Rachel, illus. 2007. (Illus.). 32p. (J). (ps-2). 16.99 (978-0-399-24611-1(8) , Putnam Juvenile) Penguin Group (USA) Inc.

Ivanova, Olga V. The Tall Book of Nursery Tales. Ivanov, Aleksey, illus. 2006. 80p. (J). 6.99 (978-0-06-054372-3(8) , Harper Festival) HarperCollins Pubs.

Jack & the Bean Stalk. 2005. (J). (978-1-58453-307-8(2)) Pioneer Valley Educational Pr., Inc.

Jack & the Beanstalk. 2002. (Puppy Tales Ser.). (Illus.). 24p. (J). (gr. k-3). 1.49 (978-1-57759-256-3(5)) Dalmatian Pr.

Jack & the Beanstalk. 2005. (J). bds. 3.99 (978-1-933200-10-1(3)) Family Bks. at Home.

Jackson, Ellen. Cinder Edna. O'Malley, Kevin, illus. 1998. (J). (ps-ps). lib. bdg. 14.15 (978-0-613-10499-9(4)) Tandem Library Bks.

Jackson, Ellen B. Cinder Edna. O'Malley, Kevin, illus. 1998. 32p. (J). (ps-3). pap. 6.99 (978-0-688-16295-5(9) , Harper Trophy) HarperCollins Pubs.

Jacob, Max. The Story of King Kabul the First & Gawain the Kitchen-Boy & Vulcan's Crown. Black, Moishe & Green, Maria, trs. Blachon, Roger, illus. 2000. 78p. (YA). (gr. 8-10). reprint ed. 20.00 (978-0-7881-6926-7(2)) DIANE Publishing Co.

Jacobs, Joseph. Irish Fairy Tales. Batten, John D., illus. 2001. (Children's Classics). (ENG.). 240p. (J). (gr. 3-6). pap. (978-1-84022-434-4(7)) Wordsworth Editions, Ltd.

Jacobs, Joseph, ed. English Fairy Tales. 2005. (Twelve-Point Ser.). lib. bdg. 24.00 (978-1-58287-370-1(4)); lib. bdg. 25.00 (978-1-58287-862-1(5)) North Bks.

Jaffrey, Saeed. The Monkey King. 1998. (Karadi Tales Ser.). (Illus.). 24p. (YA). (gr. 1 up). 9.99 incl. audio (978-81-86838-12-9(0)) APG Sales and Fulfillment.

—The Musical Donkey. 1998. (Karadi Tales Ser.). (Illus.). 24p. (YA). (gr. 1 up). 9.99 incl. audio (978-81-86838-37-2(6)) APG Sales and Fulfillment.

Jago, illus. Ali Baba & the Forty Thieves. 2004. (ENG, TAG, KUR & ITA.). 31p. (J). (978-1-84444-543-1(7)) Mantra Publishing, Ltd.

James, Grace. Japanese Fairy Tales. Goble, Warwick, illus. 1998. 280p. (J). reprint ed. pap. 15.00 (978-0-7881-5397-6(8)) DIANE Publishing Co.

—The Moon Maiden & Other Japanese Fairy Tales. Goble, Warwick, illus. 2005. 192p. (J). (gr. 3). pap. 9.95 (978-0-486-44392-8(2)) Dover Pubns., Inc.

James, Ian. The Gingerbread Boy Uptown. 2006. spiral bd. 42.00 (***978-1-4108-7169-5(X))** Benchmark Education Co.

Janik, Dan. Sourdough Scott's Bedtime Fairy Tales from Alaska. 2005. (J). per. 12.95 net. (978-1-59433-031-5(X)) Publication Consultants.

The Jar: A Tale from the East. 2002. (ARA.). (J). 9.99 incl. audio (978-1-932008-00-5(4)); 2002. pap., tchr. ed. 10.00 (978-0-9716826-4-1(X)); 2000. (J). 9.99 incl. audio (978-0-9716826-6-5(6)) Fine Media Group.

Jeffers, Susan, illus. Thumbelina. 2005. 32p. (J). (ps). 16.99 (978-0-525-47508-8(7) , Dutton Juvenile) Penguin Group (USA) Inc.

Jeffrey, Linda, tr. & illus. The Gingerbread Man. Jeffrey, Linda, illus. 2003. 24p. (J). 9.99 (978-0-85953-464-2(2)) Child's Play-International.

Jennings, Linda. Mary Had a Little Lamb. Hurt-Newton, Tania, illus. 2000. (Mini Finger Puppet Bks.). 16p. (J). (ps-k). 6.95 (978-1-86233-122-8(7)) Sterling Publishing Co., Inc.

Jennings, Linda & Hurt-Newton, Tania. Mary Had a Little Lamb. 1999. (Finger Puppet Bks.). (Illus.). 16p. (J). 10.95 (978-1-86233-069-6(7)) Sterling Publishing Co., Inc.

Johnson, A. E. (Trans). Perraults Fairy Tales. 2004. (ENG.). 144p. pap. (***978-1-84022-482-5(7))** Wordsworth Editions, Ltd.

Johnson, David, illus. The Bremen Town Musicians. 2005. (Rabbit Ears Ser.). 40p. (J). (gr. k-5). 25.65 (978-1-59679-222-7(1)) Spotlight.

Johnson, Jane. Very Pretty Story. 2005. (Illus.). 78p. pap. 25.00 (978-1-85124-065-4(9)) Bodleian Library GBR. *Dist:* Chicago Distribution Ctr.

Johnson, Ollie. Rapunzel: Fairy Tale Classics. Kurtz, John, illus. 2007. 24p. (ps-2). pap. 3.50 (978-0-7868-5653-4(X) , Jump at the Sun) Hyperion Bks. for Children.

Johnson, Richard. Little Red Hen & the Grains. 2005. (ENG & KOR., Illus.). 32p. (J). pap. 12.95 (978-1-84444-210-2(1)) Mantra Lingua GBR. *Dist:* Mantra Publishing, Ltd.

—Little Red Hen & the Grains of Wheat. 2005. (Illus.). 32p. (J). (ENG & ALB.). pap. 12.95 (978-1-84444-198-3(9)); (ENG & ARA., pap. 12.95 (978-1-84444-199-0(7)); (ENG & BEN., pap. 12.95 (978-1-84444-200-3(4)); (ENG & CHI., pap. 12.95 (978-1-84444-201-0(2)); (ENG & CHI., pap. 12.95 (978-1-84444-202-7(0)); (CRO, ENG & SER., pap. 12.95 (978-1-84444-203-4(9)); (FAR, ENG & PER., pap. 12.95 (978-1-84444-204-1(7)); (ENG & FRE., pap. 12.95 (978-1-84444-205-8(5)); (ENG & GER., pap. 12.95 (978-1-84444-206-5(3)); (ENG & GUJ., pap. 12.95 (978-1-84444-207-2(1)); (ENG & HIN., pap. 12.95 (978-1-84444-208-9(X)); (ENG & ITA., pap. 12.95 (978-1-84444-209-6(8)); (ENG & PAN., pap. 12.95 (978-1-84444-211-9(X)); (POR & ENG., pap. 12.95 (978-1-84444-212-6(8)); (ENG & SOM., pap. 12.95 (978-1-84444-213-3(6)); (ENG & SPA., pap. 12.95 (978-1-84444-214-0(4)); (TAM & ENG., pap. 12.95 (978-1-84444-215-7(2)); (ENG & TUR., pap. 12.95 (978-1-84444-216-4(0)); (ENG & URD., pap. 12.95 (978-1-84444-217-1(9)); (ENG & VIE., pap. 12.95 (978-1-84444-218-8(7)); (YOR & ENG., pap. 12.95 (978-1-84444-219-5(5)); (ENG, BUL & GRE., pap. 12.95 (978-1-84444-393-2(0)); (ENG, POL & JPN., pap. 12.95 (978-1-84444-394-9(9)); (ENG, TAG & SWA., pap. 12.95 (978-1-84444-395-6(7)); (ENG, TWI & GRE., pap. 12.95 (978-1-84444-396-3(5)); (ENG, RUM, IRI & ROM., pap. 12.95 (978-1-84444-397-0(3)); (RUS, ENG & JPN., pap. 12.95 (978-1-84444-398-7(1)); (ENG & SWA., pap. 12.95 (978-1-84444-399-4(X)); (ENG & GRE., pap. 12.95 (978-1-84444-445-8(7)); (JPN & ENG., pap. 12.95 (978-1-84444-446-5(5)); (KUR & ENG., pap. 12.95 (978-1-84444-447-2(3)); (SHO & ENG., pap. 12.95 (978-1-84444-448-9(1)) Mantra Lingua GBR. *Dist:* Mantra Publishing, Ltd.

Johnson, Richard, illus. Don't Cry, Sly! 2004. (TAM, CZE, SPA, VIE & GUJ.). 24p. (J). pap. (978-1-85269-672-6(9)) Mantra Publishing, Ltd.

—Three Little Pigs. 24p. pap. (978-1-904550-21-1(5)) Child's Play-International.

Johnson, Richard, tr. & illus. Jack & the Beanstalk. Johnson, Richard, illus. 2004. 31p. (J). (978-1-84444-108-2(3)) Mantra Publishing, Ltd.

Johnston, Tony. Bigfoot Cinderrrrrella. 2000. (J). (978-0-606-20222-0(6)) Tandem Library Bks.

Joma, Bofill, illus. Rapunzel. 2006. (CAT & ENG.). 32p. (J). 14.95 (978-0-8118-5059-9(5)) Chronicle Bks. LLC.

Joma, Bofill & Bofill, Francesc. Rapunzel. 2006. (CAT & ENG., Illus.). 32p. (J). pap. 6.95 (978-0-8118-5060-5(9)) Chronicle Bks. LLC.

Jones, Carol. The Gingerbread Man. 2002. (J). 15.00 (978-0-618-18823-9(1)); (Illus.). 32p. 16.00 (978-0-618-18822-2(3)) Houghton Mifflin Co. Trade & Reference Div. (Walter Lorraine).

Jones, Christianne C. Beauty & the Beast: A Retelling of the Classic Fairy Tale. Muehlenhardt, Amy Bailey, illus. 2005. (Read-It! Readers Ser.). 32p. (J). (gr. k-3). 18.60 (978-1-4048-0981-9(3)) Picture Window Bks.

—Rapunzel: A Retelling of the Classic Fairy Tale. Muehlenhardt, Amy Bailey, illus. 2005. (Read-It! Readers Ser.). 32p. (J). (gr. k-3). 18.60 (978-1-4048-0982-6(1)) Picture Window Bks.

Jones, Diana Wynne. Howl's Moving Castle. 2001. (gr. 5-8). lib. bdg. 15.30 (978-0-613-37151-3(8)) Tandem Library Bks.

Jones, Terry & Foreman, Michael, trs. Fairy Tales & Fantastic Stories. Jones, Terry & Foreman, Michael, illus. 10th anniv. ed. 2003. (Illus.). 256p. (YA). (978-1-84365-055-3(X)) Chrysalis Children's Bks.

Jungman, Ann & Ayto, Russell. Cinderella & the Hot Air Balloon. 1999. (Illus.). 24p. (J). (ps-2). pap. (978-0-7112-1051-6(9)) Lincoln, Frances Ltd. GBR. *Dist:* Transition Vendor.

Kain, Karen. The Nutcracker. Kupesic, Rajka, illus. 2005. 32p. (J). (ps-7). 18.95 (978-0-88776-696-1(X)) Tundra Bks., Inc./Livres Toundra, Inc. CAN. *Dist:* Random Hse., Inc.

Kale, Ann Stephanian. Marco & Princess Gina. Kale, Ann Stephanian, illus. 2003. (Illus.). 24p. (J). (gr. k-3). pap. 10.00 (978-0-9704131-5-4(7)) Abril BookStore & Publishing.

Kane, Tracy. Fairy Houses. Kane, Tracy, illus. 3rd ed. 2001. (Fairy Houses Ser.). (Illus.). 40p. (J). (ps-3). per., act. bk. ed. 15.95 (978-0-9708104-5-8(8)) Light-Beams Publishing.

Karlin, Barbara. Cinderella. 2001. 13.79 (978-0-606-22509-0(9)); lib. bdg. 15.30 (978-0-613-67073-9(6)) Tandem Library Bks.

—Cinderella. Marshall, James, illus. unabr. ed. 2006. (J). (ps-4). pap. 14.95 incl. audio (978-0-439-84889-3(X) , WPRA671); 24.95 incl. audio (978-0-439-84887-9(3) , WHRA671); 29.95 incl. audio compact disk (978-0-439-84888-6(1) , WHCD671); pap. 18.95 incl. audio compact disk (978-0-439-84890-9(3) , WPCD671) Weston Woods Studios, Inc.

—James Marshall's Cinderella. Marshall, James, illus. 2001. 32p. (J). pap. 6.99 (978-0-14-230048-0(9) , Puffin) Penguin Group (USA) Inc.

Kassirer, Sue. Thumbelina. 2003. (Illus.). 16p. (J). (gr. k-k). 2.99 (978-0-307-10452-6(4) , Golden Bks.) Random Hse. Children's Bks.

Kaur, Bibi Inderjit. Historias para Ganar el Mundo. Medina, Eduardo, ed. Soto, Carolina, tr. 2000. (SPA., Illus.). 214p. (J). 15.00 (978-1-930531-00-0(1)) Nam Pubs.

Kaye, M. M. The Ordinary Princess. Kaye, M. M., illus. 2002. (Illus.). 128p. (J). (gr. 4-7). reprint ed. pap. 5.99 (978-0-14-230085-5(3) , Puffin) Penguin Group (USA) Inc.

—The Ordinary Princess. 2002. (gr. 7-12). lib. bdg. 14.15 (978-0-613-83544-2(1)) Tandem Library Bks.

Keen, Donna. Flossy, a Tooth Fairy Tale: Including Red Velvet Bag for Tooth. Keen, Donna, illus. 2nd ed. 1998. (Illus.). 32p. (YA). (ps up). reprint ed. spiral bd. (978-1-56021-273-7(X) , 171) W.J. Fantasy, Inc.

Keens-Douglas, Richardo. Tales from the Isle of Spice. Bourbonnière, Sylvie, illus. 2004. 48p. (J). (gr. 2-6). pap. 6.95 (978-1-55037-866-5(X)); lib. bdg. 19.95 (978-1-55037-867-2(8)) Annick Pr., Ltd. CAN. *Dist:* Firefly Bks., Ltd.

Keith, Adrienne. Fairies from A to Z: A Fairy Box Book. Malinow, Wendy Wallin, illus. 2004. 48p. (J). (ps up). 14.95 (978-1-883672-10-2(4) , Tricycle Pr.) Ten Speed Pr.

Kellogg, Steven. Sally Ann Thunder Ann Whirlwind Crockett: A Tall Tale. 1999. (978-0-606-17396-4(X)) Tandem Library Bks.

—Three Sillies. 2004. (Illus.). 40p. (J). (ps-3). reprint ed. pap. 6.99 (978-0-7636-1056-2(9)) Candlewick Pr.

Kendall, Gladys E. Why Pansies Have Faces. Klatt, Eileen, illus. l.t. ed. 1998. 15p. (J). (ps-5). pap. 10.95 (978-0-9659942-8-6(7) , 8-7) Erda Publishing Co.

Kennedy, Richard. Porcelain Man. Date not set. 32p. (J). (ps-3). 15.89 (978-0-06-027216-6(3)); 14.99 (978-0-06-027215-9(5)) HarperCollins Pubs.

Kerven, Rosalind. The Enchanted Forest: A Scottish Fairy Tale. Marks, Alan, illus. 1999. 32p. (J). (978-0-7112-1352-4(6)) Lincoln, Frances Ltd.

—The Enchanted Forest: A Scottish Fairy Tale. 2001. (Illus.). 32p. (J). (gr. k-4). pap. 8.99 (978-0-7112-1527-6(8)) Lincoln, Frances Ltd. GBR. *Dist:* Transition Vendor.

Kessler, Brad. The Firebird. Van Nutt, Robert, illus. 2005. (Rabbit Ears Ser.). 40p. (J). (gr. k-5). 25.65 (978-1-59679-224-1(8)) Spotlight.

Ketchedjian, Armen G. & Ketch. Golden Apples. 2007. 12.95 (978-0-9778274-0-4(2)) Parental Interventional Tools, Inc.

Ketteman, Helen. Waynetta & the Cornstalk: A Texas Fairy Tale. Greenseid, Diane, illus. 2007. 32p. (J). 16.95 (978-0-8075-8687-7(0)) Whitman, Albert & Co.

Kilgras, Heidi. Cinderella's Countdown to the Ball. Harchy, Atelier Philippe, illus. 2002. 32p. (J). (ps-1). pap. 3.99 (978-0-7364-1225-4(5) , RH/Disney) Random Hse. Children's Bks.

—Cinderella's Countdown to the Ball. 2002. (gr. k-3). lib bdg. 11.80 (978-0-613-73603-9(6)) Tandem Library Bks.

Killion, Kathleen. The Glass Heart. Lang, Gary, illus. 2005. 19.95 (978-0-9723067-2-0(2)) Imagine That Enterprises.

Kimmel, Eric A. Anansi & the Magic Stick. Stevens, Janet, illus. (J). 2005. pap. 16.95 incl. audio (978-1-59112-481-8(6)); 2005. pap. 18.95 incl. audio compact disk (978-1-59112-506-8(5)); 2003. 25.95 incl. audio (978-1-59112-482-5(4)); 2003. 28.95 incl. audio compact disk (978-1-59112-507-5(3)); 2003. pap. 37.95 incl. audio (978-1-59112-483-2(2)); 2003. pap. 39.95 incl. audio compact disk (978-1-59112-519-8(7)) Live Oak Media.

—The Castle of Cats: A Story from Ukraine. Krenina, Katya, illus. 2004. 32p. (J). (gr. k-3). tchr. ed. 16.95 (978-0-8234-1565-6(1)) Holiday Hse., Inc.

—The Gingerbread Man. 2004. (Illus.). (J). pap. 18.95 incl. audio compact disk (978-1-59112-785-7(8)) Live Oak Media.

Kimmel, Eric A. & Asbjornsen, Peter Christen. The Three Cabritos. Gilpin, Stephen, illus. 2007. (J). 32p. 16.99 (978-0-7614-5343-7(1)); (***978-1-4287-3709-9(X)** , Cavendish Children's Bks.) Cavendish, Marshall Corp.

Kincaid, Lucy & Kincaid, Eric, illus. Felices Cuentos. 2004. Tr. of Happy Tales. (SPA.). (J). 12.99 (978-84-241-9316-4(4)) Everest de Ediciones y Distribucion, S.L. ESP. *Dist:* Lectorum Pubns., Inc.

Kindl, Patrice. Goose Chase. 2002. 224p. (YA). pap. 5.99 (978-0-14-230208-8(2) , Puffin) Penguin Group (USA) Inc.

—Goose Chase. 2002. (gr. 5-8). lib. bdg. 14.15 (978-0-613-60805-3(4)) Tandem Library Bks.

King-Smith, Dick. Huge Red Riding Hood. Eastwood, John, illus. abr. ed. 32p. (J). pap. 7.95 (978-0-14-130034-4(5)) Penguin Bks., Ltd. GBR. *Dist:* Trafalgar Square Publishing.

—Robin Hood & His Miserable Men & Other Topsy-Turvy Stories. abr. ed. (Illus.). 32p. (J). pap. 7.95 (978-0-14-130035-1(3)) Penguin Bks., Ltd. GBR. *Dist:* Trafalgar Square Publishing.
—Thinderella & Other Topsy-Turvy Stories. abr. ed. (Illus.). 32p. (J). pap. 7.95 (978-0-14-130036-8(1)) Penguin Bks., Ltd. GBR. *Dist:* Trafalgar Square Publishing.
Kingfisher Editors, ed. The Kingfisher Book of Classic Boy Stories. 2005. (J). (gr. 3-5). pap. 9.95 (978-0 7534-5843-3(8) , Kingfisher) Houghton Mifflin Co. Trade & Reference Div.
—The Kingfisher Book of Classic Girl Stories. 2005. (J). (gr. 3-5). pap. 9.95 (978-0-7534-5844-0(6) , Kingfisher) Houghton Mifflin Co. Trade & Reference Div.
Kingsley, Charles. The Water Babies. 2001. (Children's Classics). (ENG.). 224p. (J). (gr. 3-6). pap. (978-1-85326-148-0(3)) Wordsworth Editions, Ltd.
Kirk, Daniel. Humpty Dumpty. Kirk, Daniel, illus. 2002. (Illus.). 32p. (J). pap. 5.99 (978-0-698-11945-1(2) , Putnam Juvenile) Penguin Group (USA) Inc.
—Humpty Dumpty. 2002. (gr. k-3). lib. bdg. 14.15 (978-0-613-45280-9(1)) Tandem Library Bks.
Kirkwood, Ian. Rob & the Black Mill. 2004. (Illus.). 32p. pap. 9.95 (978-0-9545206-7-0(X)) Capercaillie Bks., Ltd GBR. *Dist:* Wilson & Assocs.
Kliros, Thea, illus. Three Billy Goats Gruff. 2003. 20p. (J). (ps-1). 5.99 (978-0-06-008237-6(2)) HarperCollins Pubs.
—Three Little Pigs. 2003. 20p. (J). (ps-1). 5.99 (978-0-06-008236-9(4)) HarperCollins Pubs.
Knight, Hilary. Hilary Knight's Cinderella. 2001. (Illus.). 40p. (J). (ps-1). 14.95 (978-0-375-81422-8(1) , Random Hse. Bks. for Young Readers) Random Hse. Children's Bks.
Konnikov, Svetlana. Grapette, the Runaway Who Rolled Away. Smishliaev, Anatoli, illus. 2007. (Grapette's Adventures Ser.). 32p. (J). 15.95 (***978-0-9791758-0-0(1)***) Aurora Pubs., Inc.
Korba, Joanna. Sleepless Beauty. 2006. spiral bd. 42.00 (***978-1-4108-7171-8(1)***) Benchmark Education Co.
Kovalski, Maryann. Pizza for Breakfast. ed. 2004. (J). (gr. k-3). spiral bd. (978-0-616-01692-3(1)) Canadian National Institute for the Blind/Institut National Canadien pour les Aveugles.
Kubinyi, Laszlo, illus. Red Riding Hood. 2006. (J). (gr. 2-6). 25.65 (978-1-59197-752-0(5)) Spotlight.
Kubler, Annie. The Wheels on the Bus. Kubler, Annie, illus. (ENG, PER & IRA., Illus.). 16p. (J). 2005. bds. (978-1-84444-532-5(1)); 2005. bds. (978-1-84444-533-2(X)); 2004. bds. (978-1-84444-534-9(8)) Mantra Publishing, Ltd.
Kunhardt, Dorothy, ed. Pinocchio. (FRE.). 96p. (J). (gr. k-5). pap. 9.95 (978-0-7859-8845-8(9)) French & European Pubns., Inc.
Kurita, Miwa & Matsutani, Miyoko. Chinese Fables Remembered. Mitsukuri, Saoko, illus. 2006. (Asian Folktales Retold Ser.). 32p. 16.95 (978-0-89346-945-0(9)) Consortium Bk. Sales & Distribution.
Kurtz, John. Beauty & the Beast - Fairy Tale Classics. Kurtz, John, illus. 2007. (Jump at the Sun Ser.). (Illus.). 24p. (ps-2). pap. 3.50 (978-0-7868-5652-7(1) , Jump at the Sun) Hyperion Bks. for Children.
Kurtz, John. Jack & the Beanstalk. Kurtz, John, illus. 2004. (Illus.). 24p. (J). lib. bdg. 8.00 (***978-1-4242-0636-0(7)***) Fitzgerald Bks.
Kurtz, John, illus. Cinderella. 2004. (Jump at the Sun Fairy-Tale Classics Ser.). 24p. (ps-2). pap. 3.50 (978-0-7868-0955-4(8)) Hyperion Bks. for Children.
—Goldilocks & the Three Bears. 2004. (Jump at the Sun Fairy-Tale Classics Ser.). 24p. (ps-2). pap. 3.50 (978-0-7868-0952-3(3)) Hyperion Bks. for Children.
—Jack & the Beanstalk. 2004. (Jump at the Sun Fairy-Tale Classics Ser.). 24p. (ps-2). pap. 3.50 (978-0-7868-0954-7(X)) Hyperion Bks. for Children.
Kushner, Ellen. The Golden Dreydl. Winn-Lederer, Ilene, illus. 2007. 128p. (J). (gr. 3-6). 15.95 (978-1-58089-135-6(7)) Charlesbridge Publishing, Inc.
Ladybird Books Staff. Cinderella. (First Fairy Tales Ser.: No. S852-1). (Illus.). (J). (ps-2). pap. 3.95 (978-0-7214-5058-2(X) , Dutton Juvenile) Penguin Group (USA) Inc.
—The Elves & the Shoemaker: First Favourite Tales. Hurt-Newton, Tania, illus. 1999. (First Favourite Tales Ser.). 32p. (J). 4.95 (978-0-7214-9737-2(3) , Dutton Juvenile) Penguin Group (USA) Inc.
—Red Riding Hood. (First Fairy Tales Ser.: No. S852-10). (Illus.). 25p. (J). (ps-2). pap. 3.95 (978-0-7214-5103-9(9) , Dutton Juvenile) Penguin Group (USA) Inc.
Lafayette, Madame de. The Princess de Montpensier. 2004. reprint ed. pap. 15.95 (978-1-4191-7870-2(9)) Kessinger Publishing, LLC.
Lagonegro, Melissa & Random House Disney Staff. A Dream for a Princess. Saichann, Alberto, illus. 2005. 32p. (J). (ps-2). pap. 3.99 (978-0-7364-2340-3(0) , RH/Disney) Random Hse. Children's Bks.
Lahens, Yanick. La Petite Corruption. 1999. (FRE.). 123p. pap. (978-1-58437-006-2(8)) Editions Memoire.
Lakeshore Learning Materials Staff, contrib. by. The Gingerbread Boy Packet. 2000. (J). pap. 19.95 (978-1-929255-32-0(2)) Lakeshore Learning Materials.
—Jack & the Beanstalk Packet. 2000. (J). pap. 19.95 (978-1-929255-29-0(2)) Lakeshore Learning Materials.
—Rumpelstiltskin Packet. 2000. (J). pap. 19.95 (978-1-929255-27-6(6)) Lakeshore Learning Materials.
Lamb, Charles. Othello. Chieux, Benoit, illus. 1999. (J). 14.95 (978-962-7609-11-7(0)) Reader's Digest Children's Publishing, Inc.
Lamm, C. Drew. The Prog Frince: A Mixed-Up Tale. McClintock, Barbara, illus. 1999. 32p. (J). (gr. k-4). pap. 16.95 (978-0-531-30135-7(4) , Orchard Bks.) Scholastic, Inc.
Lang, Andrew. The Blue Fairy Book. l.t. ed. 2005. 720p. pap. (978-1-84637-144-8(9)) Echo Library.
—The Blue Fairy Book. 1998. (Twelve-Point Ser.). 390p. reprint ed. lib. bdg. 25.00 (978-1-58287-018-2(7)) North Bks.
—The Crimson Fairy Book. 2005. 364p. pap. 15.95 (978-1-4218-0106-3(X) , 1st World Library - Literary Society) 1st World Publishing, Inc.
—The Green Fairy Book. l.t. ed. 2005. 636p. pap. (978-1-84637-147-9(3)) Echo Library.
—The Green Fairy Book. 2004. reprint ed. pap. 28.95 (978-1-4191-6492-7(9)); pap. 1.99 (978-1-4192-6492-4(3)) Kessinger Publishing, LLC.
—The Grey Fairy Book. 2006. 264p. pap. 13.99 (***978-1-4264-4988-8(7)***); 294p. pap. 17.99 (***978-1-4264-5289-5(6)***) BiblioBazaar.
—The Lilac Fairy Book. 2005. 384p. pap. 15.95 (978-1-4218-0105-6(1) , 1st World Library - Literary Society) 1st World Publishing, Inc.
—The Lilac Fairy Book. 2004. reprint ed. pap. 27.95 (978-1-4191-7006-5(6)); pap. 1.99 (978-1-4192-7006-2(0)) Kessinger Publishing, LLC.
—The Pink Fairy Book. 2005. 388p. pap. 15.95 (978-1-4218-0104-9(3) , 1st World Library - Literary Society) 1st World Publishing, Inc.
—The Pink Fairy Book. 2004. reprint ed. pap. 27.95 (978-1-4191-7753-8(2)); pap. 1.99 (978-1-4192-7753-5(7)) Kessinger Publishing, LLC.
—Prince Prigio. 2004. reprint ed. pap. 19.95 (978-1-4179-0522-5(0)) Kessinger Publishing, LLC.
—Prince Ricardo of Pantouflia: Being the. 2006. (Illus.). pap. 24.95 (***978-1-4286-0645-6(9)***) Kessinger Publishing, LLC.
—The Queen & the Mouse: A Story about Friendship. Lohmann, Renate, illus. 2006. (J). (978-1-59939-081-9(7) , Reader's Digest Young Families, Inc.) Reader's Digest Children's Publishing, Inc.
—The Rainbow Fairy Book. 2007. (Illus.). 224p. (J). pap. 12.95 (***978-0-486-45455-9(X)***) Dover Pubns., Inc.
—The Violet Fairy Book. 2005. 404p. pap. 16.95 (978-1-4218-0107-0(8) , 1st World Library - Literary Society) 1st World Publishing, Inc.
Lang, Andrew. Violet Fairy Book. 2006. pap. 14.95 (***978-1-59605-994-8(X)*** , Cosimo Classics) Cosimo, Inc.
Lang, Andrew, ed. Brown Fairy Book. 2004. (Twelve-Point Ser.). lib. bdg. 25.00 (978-1-58287-282-7(1)) North Bks.
—The Chronicles of Pantouflia. (J). 20.95 (978-0-89190-088-7(8)) Amereon LTD.
—Green Fairy Book. 2004. (Twelve-Point Ser.). lib. bdg. 25.00 (978-1-58287-283-4(X)) North Bks.
—Grey Fairy Book. 2006. (Twelve-Point Ser.). lib. bdg. 25.00 (***978-1-58287-393-0(3)***); lib. bdg. 26.00 (***978-1-58287-884-3(6)***) North Bks.
—The Lilac Fairy Book. (J). 26.95 (978-0-89190-084-9(5)) Amereon LTD.
—Lilac Fairy Book. 2004. (Twelve-Point Ser.). lib. bdg. 25.00 (978-1-58287-284-1(8)); lib. bdg. 26.00 (978-1-58287-778-5(5)) North Bks.
—The Orange Fairy Book. (J). 26.95 (978-0-89190-083-2(7)) Amereon LTD.
—Pink Fairy Book. 2004. (Twelve-Point Ser.). lib. bdg. 25.00 (978-1-58287-287-2(2)); lib. bdg. 26.00 (978-1-58287-781-5(5)) North Bks.
—The Red Fairy Book. 2002. (ENG.). 352p. 26.99 (***978-1-4043-2856-3(4)***) IndyPublish.com.
—The Red Fairy Book. 1998. (Twelve-Point Ser.). 365p. reprint ed. lib. bdg. 25.00 (978-1-58287-063-2(2)) North Bks.
—Yellow Fairy Book. (Twelve-Point Ser.). 2003. lib. bdg. 25.00 (978-1-58287-206-3(6)); 2004. 529p. 26.00 (978-1-58287-690-0(8)) North Bks.
Lang, Andrew & Ford, H. J. The Tale of the Cid: And Other Stories of Knights & Chivalry. Ford, H. J., illus. 2007. (Illus.). 208p. pap. 9.95 (***978-0-486-45470-2(3)***) Dover Pubns., Inc.
Lanza, Barbara. Little Mermaid. 2003. (gr. k-3). lib. bdg. 11.80 (978-0-613-71999-5(9)) Tandem Library Bks.
—Time to Fly: A Fairy Lane Book. Lanza, Barbara, illus. 2005. (Illus.). 32p. 19.95 (978-0-9724853-7-1(6)) Keene Publishing.
Larkin, Rochelle. Beauty & the Beast & Other Stories. 2005. (Great Illustrated Classics Ser.). (Illus.). 238p. (J). (gr. 3-8). 21.35 (978-1-59679-236-4(1) , ABDO & Daughters) ABDO Publishing Co.
—Cinderella & Other Stories. 2005. (Great Illustrated Classics Ser.). (Illus.). 236p. (J). (gr. 3-8). 21.35 (978-1-59679-239-5(6) , ABDO & Daughters) ABDO Publishing Co.
—The Little Mermaid & Other Stories. 2005. (Great Illustrated Classics Ser.). (Illus.). 238p. (J). (gr. 3-8). 21.35 (978-1-59679-245-6(0) , ABDO & Daughters) ABDO Publishing Co.
—Sleeping Beauty & Other Stories. 2005. (Great Illustrated Classics Ser.). (Illus.). 236p. (J). (gr. 3-8). 21.35 (978-1-59679-251-7(5) , ABDO & Daughters) ABDO Publishing Co.
—Snow White & Other Stories. 2005. (Great Illustrated Classics Ser.). (Illus.). 238p. (J). (gr. 3-8). 21.35 (978-1-59679-252-4(3) , ABDO & Daughters) ABDO Publishing Co.
Larkin, Rochelle, ed. Beauty & the Beast & Other Stories. (Illus.). 339p. (J). (978-0-86611-674-9(5)) Waldman Publishing Corp.
—The Little Mermaid & Other Stories. (Illus.). 239p. (J). 9.95 (978-0-86611-676-3(1)) Waldman Publishing Corp.
LaRochelle, David. The End. Egielski, Richard, illus. (J). (ps-3). 2007. 40p. pap. 16.99 (978-0-439-64011-4(3)); 2006. 16.99 (978-0-439-64012-1(1)) Scholastic, Inc. (Levine, Arthur A. Bks.).
Latin American Tales & Myths, 6 bks., Set. 1998. (Illus.). (J). (gr. 2-5). lib. bdg. 159.60 (978-1-57103-261-4(4)) Rourke Publishing, LLC.
Lavarello, Jose Maria, illus. Cuentame un Cuento, No. 2. (SPA.). 366p. (J). (gr. k-3). (978-84-480-1124-6(4) , TM2346) Timun Mas, Editorial S.A. ESP. *Dist:* Lectorum Pubns., Inc.
Law, Karina. The Truth about Hansel & Gretel. Counsell, Elke, illus. 2004. (Read-It! Readers Ser.). 32p. (C). (gr. k-3). 18.60 (978-1-4048-0559-0(1)) Picture Window Bks.
Laymance, Cherilyn. A Faerie's Tale. 2005. 214p. pap. 19.95 (978-1-4137-9018-4(6)) PublishAmerica, Inc.
LeapFrog Staff, compiled by. Classic Fairy Tales. 2001. (J). spiral bd. 14.99 (978-1-58605-048-1(6)) LeapFrog Enterprises, Inc.
—Favorite Fairy Tales. 2002. (J). (gr. 3-7). 14.95 (978-1-58605-918-7(1) , LeapFrog Schl. Hse.) LeapFrog Enterprises, Inc.
Learning Through Literature. 2004. pap. 32.75 incl. audio (978-1-55592-528-4(6)) Weston Woods Studios, Inc.
Learning Through Literature: Amazing Grace. 2004. pap. 32.75 incl. audio (978-1-55592-527-7(8)) Weston Woods Studios, Inc.
Learning Through Literature: Mufaro's Beautiful Daughters. 2004. pap. 32.75 incl. audio (978-1-55592-525-3(1)) Weston Woods Studios, Inc.
Learning Through Literature: Paperboy. 2004. pap. 32.75 incl. audio (978-1-55592-524-6(3)) Weston Woods Studios, Inc.
Leavy, Una. The O'Brien Book of Irish Fairy Tales & Legends. Field, Susan Anna, illus. 2002. 96p. (J). (gr. 3-6). 19.95 (978-0-86278-482-9(4)) O'Brien Pr., Ltd., The IRL. *Dist:* Independent Pubs. Group.
Leber, Nancy. The Elves & the Shoemaker. Hovell, John, illus. 2002. 16p. (J). (978-0-439-35083-9(2)) Scholastic, Inc.
Lee, Alvin Benedict. Arena of Sorcery. 2002. 204p. (YA). pap. 13.95 (978-0-595-25678-5(3) , Writers Club Pr.) iUniverse, Inc.
Lefèvre, A. M. Hugan Fach Goch. 2005. (WEL., Illus.). 10p. (978-0-86381-645-1(2)) Gwasg Carreg Gwalch.
—Pws Esgid Uchel. 2005. (WEL., Illus.). 10p. (978-0-86381-647-5(9)) Gwasg Carreg Gwalch.
Lendler, Ian. An Undone Fairy Tale. Martin, Whitney, illus. 2005. 32p. (J). (gr. 1-3). 15.95 (978-0-689-86677-7(1) , Simon & Schuster Children's Publishing) Simon & Schuster Children's Publishing.
Lenihan, Edmund. Gruesome Irish Tales for Children. 1998. 96p. (J). (gr. 4-7). pap. 7.95 (978-1-85635-197-3(1)) Mercier Pr., Ltd., The IRL. *Dist:* Irish Bks. & Media, Inc.
Leonard, Barry, ed. Alice in Wonderland. 2003. (Illus.). 12p. (J). (gr. k-4). reprint ed. 17.00 (978-0-7567-6864-5(0)) DIANE Publishing Co.
—The Little Tin Soldier. 2003. (Illus.). 12p. (J). (gr. k-4). reprint ed. 17.00 (978-0-7567-6867-6(5)) DIANE Publishing Co.
—Sleeping Beauty. 2003. (Illus.). 12p. (J). (gr. k-4). reprint ed. 17.00 (978-0-7567-6865-2(9)) DIANE Publishing Co.
—The Three Little Pigs. 2003. (Illus.). 12p. (J). (gr. k-4). reprint ed. 17.00 (978-0-7567-6860-7(8)) DIANE Publishing Co.
—The Ugly Duckling. 2003. (Illus.). 12p. (J). (gr. k-4). reprint ed. 17.00 (978-0-7567-6858-4(6)) DIANE Publishing Co.
Leprince de Beaumont, Marie. La Bella y la Bestia. (SPA.). 72p. (J). (gr. 3). 7.95 (978-84-372-1851-9(9)) Santillana USA Publishing Co., Inc.
Lesser, Rika. Hansel & Gretel. Zelinsky, Paul O., illus. 1999. 40p. (J). (ps-3). 17.99 (978-0-525-46152-4(3) , Dutton Juvenile) Penguin Group (USA) Inc.
Levine, Gail Carson. Fairest. 2006. 336p. (J). (gr. 3-9). 16.99 (978-0-06-073408-4(6)); lib. bdg. 17.89 (978-0-06-073409-1(4)) HarperCollins Pubs.
—Fairest. l.t. rev. ed. 2007. 356p. (YA). 23.95 (***978-0-7862-9270-7(9)***) Thorndike Pr.
—The Fairy's Mistake. Elliott, Mark, illus. 1999. (Princess Tales Ser.). 96p. (J). (gr. 2-7). 10.99 (978-0-06-028060-4(3)) HarperCollins Pubs.
—The Fairy's Return. Elliott, Mark, illus. 2002. (Princess Tales Ser.). 112p. (J). (gr. 2-6). 9.99 (978-0-06-623800-5(5)) HarperCollins Pubs.
—For Biddle's Sake. Elliott, Mark, illus. 2002. (Princess Tales Ser.). 112p. (J). (gr. 2-6). 9.99 (978-0-06-000094-3(5)) HarperCollins Pubs.
—The Princess Tales. Elliott, Mark, illus. (Princess Tales Ser.). (J). No. 2. 2004. 256p. pap. 6.99 (978-0-06-056043-0(6) , Harper Trophy); Vol. 1. 2002. 240p. (gr. 2-6). pap. 6.99 (978-0-06-051841-7(3)) HarperCollins Pubs.
—The Princess Tales. (gr. 3-6). 2004. lib. bdg. 15.30 (978-0-613-83563-3(8)); 2002. lib. bdg. 15.30 (978-0-613-85148-0(X)) Tandem Library Bks.
Lewis, Elizabeth. At the Back of the North Wind. 2006. 94.99 (***978-1-4280-4029-8(3)***); pap. 88.99 (***978-1-4280-4031-1(5)***) IndyPublish.com.
Lewis, Hara. Cinderella. 2004. (gr. k-3). lib. bdg. 11.80 (978-0-613-71998-8(0)) Tandem Library Bks.
Lewis, Hara, et al. Cinderella. 2004. (Scholastic Readers Ser.). (Illus.). 32p. (J). pap. 3.99 (978-0-439-47153-4(2)) Scholastic, Inc.
Lewis, Jan & Amery, Heather. Jan Lewis' Fairy Tales. Lewis, Jan, illus. 2000. (Illus.). 90p. (J). (ps-1). 12.95 (978-1-57145-404-1(7) , Silver Dolphin Bks.) Advantage Pubs. Group.
Lewis, Naomi. Elf Hill: And Other Tales from Hans Andersen. Chichester-Clark, Emma, illus. 1999. 72p. (J). (gr. k-4). 20.95 (978-0-7112-1426-2(3)) Lincoln, Frances Ltd. GBR. *Dist:* Star Bright Bks., Inc.
—Elf Hill: Tales from Hans Christian Andersen. Chichester-Clark, Emma, illus. 1999. 72p. (J). (gr. k-4). 20.95 (978-1-887734-70-7(8)) Star Bright Bks., Inc.
—Tales from Hans Christian Andersen. Clark, Emma Chicester, illus. 2005. 72p. (J). pap. 9.95 (978-1-84507-432-6(7)) Lincoln, Frances Ltd. GBR. *Dist:* Perseus Distribution.
Lewis, Naomi, et al. Elf Hill: Tales from Hans Christian Andersen. (Illus.). 68p. pap. (978-0-7112-1830-7(7)) Lincoln, Frances Ltd. GBR. *Dist:* Transition Vendor.
Lewis, Stephen, illus. Rumpelstiltskin: A German Tale. 2000. (Scholastic At-Home Phonics Reading Program Ser.: Vol. 56). 24p. (J). (978-0-590-68858-1(8)) Scholastic, Inc.
Liammoir, Micheal Mac. Faery Nights (Oicheanta Si) 2nd ed. (IRI & ENG., Illus.). 127p. pap. 7.95 (978-0-86278-681-6(9)) O'Brien Pr., Ltd., The IRL. *Dist:* Irish Bks. & Media, Inc.
Light, Steve. Puss in Boots. 2002. (Illus.). 32p. (J). (ps-1). 14.95 (978-0-8109-4368-1(9)) Abrams, Harry N. , Inc.
—The Shoemaker Extraordinaire. 2003. (Illus.). 32p. (J). (ps-3). 14.95 (978-0-8109-4236-3(4)) Abrams, Harry N. , Inc.
Lilly, Melinda. Aletin y el Dia Que el Cielo Se Vino Abajo. Fernandez, Queta, tr. Reasoner, Charles, illus. (Cuentos y Mitos de America Latina (Latin American Tales & Myths) Ser.).Tr. of Aletin & the Falling Sky. (SPA.). 32p. 2002. mass mkt. 6.95 (978-1-58952-076-9(9) , RK31438); 2001. (J). (gr. 2-5). lib. bdg. 26.60 (978-1-58952-189-6(7) , RK4883) Rourke Publishing, LLC.
—Aletin y el Dia Que el Cielo Se Vino Abajo. 2002. Tr. of Aletin & the Falling Sky. (SPA.). (gr. 3-6). lib. bdg. 15.25 (978-0-613-79402-2(8)) Tandem Library Bks.
—La Cancion del Sol. Fernandez, Queta, tr. Reasoner, Charles, illus. 2002. (Cuentos y Mitos de America Latina (Latin American Tales & Myths) Ser.).Tr. of Song of the Sun. (SPA.). 32p. mass mkt. 6.95 (978-1-58952-079-0(3) , RK31441) Rourke Publishing, LLC.
—La Cancion del Sol. 2002. Tr. of Song of the Sun. (SPA.). (gr. 3-6). lib. bdg. 15.25 (978-0-613-79403-9(6)) Tandem Library Bks.
—La Gente de la Luna. Fernandez, Queta, tr. Reasoner, Charles, illus. (Cuentos y Mitos de America Latina (Latin American Tales & Myths) Ser.).Tr. of Moon People. (SPA.). 32p. 2002. mass mkt. 6.95 (978-1-58952-080-6(7) , RK31442); 2001. (J). (gr. 2-5). lib. bdg. 26.60 (978-1-58952-193-3(5) , RK2054) Rourke Publishing, LLC.
—La Gente de la Luna. 2002. Tr. of Moon People. (SPA.). (gr. 3-6). lib. bdg. 15.25 (978-0-613-79404-6(4)) Tandem Library Bks.
—Huatya Curi y los Cinco Condores. Fernandez, Queta, tr. Reasoner, Charles, illus. (Cuentos y Mitos de America Latina (Latin American Tales & Myths) Ser.).Tr. of Huatya Curi & the Five Condors. (SPA.). 32p. 2002. mass mkt. 6.95 (978-1-58952-077-6(7) , RK31439); 2001. (J). (gr. 2-5). lib. bdg. 26.60 (978-1-58952-190-2(0) , RK5265) Rourke Publishing, LLC.
—Mira y la Piedra. Fernandez, Queta, tr. Reasoner, Charles, illus. (Cuentos y Mitos de America Latina (Latin American Tales & Myths) Ser.).Tr. of Mira & the Stone Tortoise. (SPA.). 32p. 2002. mass mkt. 6.95 (978-1-58952-078-3(5) , RK31440); 2001. (J). (gr. 2-5). lib. bdg. 26.60 (978-1-58952-191-9(9) , RK7238) Rourke Publishing, LLC.
Lindskoog, Kathryn & Hunsicker, Ranelda Mack, eds. Faerie Gold: Treasures from the Lands of Enchantment. 2005. (Classics for Young Readers Ser.). 304p. (J). per. 11.99 (978-0-87552-738-3(8)) P & R Publishing.
The Lion of Ain Jaloot: Fun Pack. 2000. (J). 29.99 incl. audio, VHS (978-0-9716826-5-8(8)) Fine Media Group.
Lionni, Leo. Tico & the Golden Wings. 2000. (J). (978-0-606-19774-8(5)) Tandem Library Bks.
Lionni, Leo. Tico & the Golden Wings. 2007. 32p. (J). (ps-3). 16.99 (***978-0-394-81749-1(4)*** , Knopf Bks. for Young Readers) Random Hse. Children's Bks.
Lisle, Janet Taylor. Afternoon of the Elves. 2000. 66p. (J). pap. 6.25 (978-0-87129-959-8(3) , A86) Dramatic Publishing Co.
—The Afternoon of the Elves. 1999. 126p. (J). (gr. 2-5). pap. 6.99 (978-0-698-11806-5(5) , Putnam Juvenile) Penguin Group (USA) Inc.
Litos, Michael. Cinderella: Inside the Rise of Mid-Major College Basketball. 2007. 272p. (YA). (gr. 8 up). 22.95 (***978-1-4022-0867-6(7)***) Sourcebooks, Inc.
Little Golden Books Staff. Cinderella. 1999. (J). (ps-2). bds. 2.99 (978-0-307-01035-3(X) , Golden Bks.) Random Hse. Children's Bks.
—The Little Mermaid: The Whole Story. 2000. (Illus.). 24p. (J). (ps-2). bds. 2.99 (978-0-307-00106-1(7) , Golden Bks.) Random Hse. Children's Bks.
The Little Mermaid. 2002. (Classic Tales Mini Bks.). (Illus.). 32p. (J). (978-1-59069-038-3(9) , T1007); incl. audio compact disk (978-1-59069-105-2(9) , T1107) Studio Mouse LLC.
Little Reader Digital Storybook: Cinderella. 2005. (J). cd-rom 8.99 (978-0-9767657-7-6(2)) Mullings Media.
Little Red Riding Hood. 2005. (J). bds. 3.99 (978-1-933200-15-6(4)) Family Bks. at Home.
Little Red Riding Hood. Date not set. (J). 4.99 (978-0-7214-5405-4(4)) Nickel Pr.
Little Red Riding Hood. 2004. (J). (978-1-58453-272-9(6)) Pioneer Valley Educational Pr., Inc.
Little Red Riding Hood. 2005. (J). per. 8.95 (978-1-59566-147-0(6)) QEB Publishing Inc.
Little Red Riding Hood. 2003. reprint ed. pap. 9.95 (978-1-891419-27-0(7)) State Historical Society of North Dakota.
Little Red Riding Hood. 2002. (Classic Tales Ser.). (Illus.). 32p. (J). incl. audio compact disk (978-1-59069-100-7(8) , T1102); (978-1-59069-033-8(8) , T1002) Studio Mouse LLC.

Little Red Riding Pooh: A Fairy Tale Friend a Board Book & Plush Figure. 2004. (Pooh's Fairy Tale Theater Ser.). 12p. (J). 6.99 (978-0-7364-2239-0(0) , RH/Disney) Random Hse. Children's Bks.

Littlest, Pet Shop. Rapunzel. 2008. (Littlest Pet Shop Ser.). 32p. (J). pap. 3.99 (*978-0-545-00795-5(X) , Scholastic) Scholastic, Inc.

Lively, Penelope & Gliori, Debi. Goldilocks & the Three Bears. 2004. (Stories to Collect & Treasure Ser.). (Illus.). 32p. pap. (978-0-340-87785-2(5) , Hodder Children's Books) Hodder Children's Division.

Lodge, Jo. Ali Baba & the Forty Thieves. 2004. (COR, ENG & SWA., Illus.). 10p. (J). (978-1-84444-531-8(3)) Mantra Publishing, Ltd.

Lohmann, Renate, illus. The Lucky Boots. 2006. (Famous Fables Ser.). (J). 6.99 (978-1-59939-027-7(2)) Reader's Digest Young Families, Inc.

London, Jonathan. What Newt Could Do for Turtle. 1998. (J). (978-0-606-13902-1(8)) Tandem Library Bks.

Losantos, Christina, illus. Beauty & the Beast/La Bella y la Bestia: A Bilingual Book! 2007. (ENG & SPA.). 32p. (J). (ps-3). pap. 6.95 (978-0-8118-5970-7(3)) Chronicle Bks. LLC.

Losantos, Cristina, illus. Beauty & the Beast/La Bella y la Bestia: A Bilingual Book! 2007. (ENG & SPA.). 32p. (J). (ps-3). 14.95 (978-0-8118-5969-1(X)) Chronicle Bks. LLC.

Louie, Ai-Ling. Cenicienta. 2001. Tr. of Cinderella. (SPA., Illus.). (J). 13.75 (978-0-606-20606-8(X)) Tandem Library Bks.

Love, D. Anne. The Secret Prince. 2005. 240p. (J). 16.95 (978-0-689-84426-3(3) , McElderry, Margaret K.) Simon & Schuster Children's Publishing.

Lovejoy, Robert. The Golden Dog Book of Fairy Tales & Animals Stories. 2004. 140p. pap. 9.99 (978-0-919614-66-6(3)) Golden Dog Pr. CAN. *Dist:* Univ. of Toronto Pr.

Lowell, Susan. Cindy Ellen: A Wild Western Cinderella. Manning, Jane, illus. 2000. (Joanna Cotler Bks.). 40p. (J). (ps-3). 16.99 (978-0-06-027446-7(8)) ; lib. bdg. 17.89 (978-0-06-027447-4(6)) HarperCollins Pubs. (Cotler, Joanna Books).

Lunge-Larsen, Lise. The Hidden Folk: Stories of Fairies, Dwarves, Selkies, & Other Secret Beings. Krommes, Beth, illus. 2004. 80p. (J). (gr. k-3). tchr. ed. 18.00 (978-0-618-17495-9(8)) Houghton Mifflin Co. Trade & Reference Div.

Lyons, Mary E. Roy Makes a Car. Widener, Terry, illus. 2005. 32p. (J). 16.95 (978-0-689-84640-3(1) , Atheneum) Simon & Schuster Children's Publishing.

Mabie, Wright Hamilt. Young Folks Treasury, Volume 3. 2006. 84.99 (*978-1-4280-4742-6(5)); pap. 77.99 (*978-1-4280-4741-9(7)) IndyPublish.com.

Mabie, Wright Hamilto. Fairy Tales Every Child Should Know. 2006. 79.99 (*978-1-4280-3192-0(8)) IndyPublish.com.

—Young Folks Treasury Volume 2. 2006. 85.99 (*978-1-4280-3829-5(9)); pap. 78.99 (*978-1-4280-3833-2(7)) IndyPublish.com.

MacDonald, George. The Golden Key. 2006. pap. (*978-1-4250-0937-3(9)) Assistedreadingbooks.com Inc.

—Golden Key EasyRead Comfort Edition. 2006. pap. (*978-1-4250-1057-7(1)) Assistedreadingbooks.com Inc.

—Golden Key EasyRead Edition. 2006. pap. (*978-1-4250-0517-7(9)) Assistedreadingbooks.com Inc.

—Golden Key EasyRead Large Edition. 2006. pap. (*978-1-4250-1544-2(1)) Assistedreadingbooks.com Inc.

—Gutta Percha Willie a Duplex. Hughes, Arthur, illus. unabr. ed. 1998. (George MacDonald Original Works Ser.: Series III). 384p. reprint ed. lib. bdg. 24.00 (978-1-881084-62-4(0)) Johannesen Printing & Publishing.

—Light Princess Large Print. 2006. pap. (*978-1-84702-350-6(9)) Echo Library.

—La Llave de Oro. 2004. (SPA.). 64p. (978-84-7720-881-5(6)) Obelisco, Ediciones S.A.

—The Princess & Curdie. l.t. ed. 2005. 320p. pap. (978-1-84637-020-5(5)) Echo Library.

—The Princess & Curdie. 2004. reprint ed. pap. 1.99 (978-1-4192-7867-9(3)) Kessinger Publishing, LLC.

—The Princess & Curdie. 1998. (Twelve-Point Ser.). 177p. reprint ed. lib. bdg. 24.00 (978-1-58287-059-5(4)) North Bks.

—The Princess & the Goblin. 2005. 108p. per. 5.99 (978-1-4209-2557-9(1)) Digireads.com.

—The Princess & the Goblin. 2004. reprint ed. pap. 1.99 (978-1-4192-7868-6(1)) Kessinger Publishing, LLC.

—The Princess & the Goblin. 1998. (Twelve-Point Ser.). 154p. reprint ed. lib. bdg. 24.00 (978-1-58287-060-1(8)) North Bks.

—The Wise Woman. 1998. (George MacDonald Original Works Ser.: Series III). (Illus.). 384p. reprint ed. 22.00 (978-1-881084-17-4(5)) Johannesen Printing & Publishing.

MacDonald, George & Walton, Nick. The Princess & the Goblin. 1998. (Illus.). 160p. 19.95 (978-1-85149-701-0(3)) Antique Collectors' Club.

MacDonald, Margaret Read. The Old Woman Who Lived in a Vinegar Bottle. 2003. (Illus.). 32p. pap. 6.95 (978-0-87483-723-0(5)) August Hse. Pubs., Inc.

Macdonell, Anne & Williams, Morris Meredith. Biancabella & Other Italian Fairy Tales. 2001. (Dover Children's Thrift Classics Ser.). (Illus.). 64p. (J). (gr. 3-6). pap. 1.50 (978-0-486-41661-8(5)) Dover Pubns., Inc.

Macedo, Blanca, illus. Cuentos Clasicos Infantiles. 2005. (SPA.). 159p. pap. 8.90 (978-968-7748-16-0(8)) LD Bks., Inc.

MacHale, D. J. East of the Sun, West of the Moon. Flesher, Vivienne, illus. 2007. (J). 25.65 (978-1-59961-306-2(9)) ABDO Publishing Co.

Mackenzie, Robert, illus. Jack & the Beanstalk. 2008. (Classic Fairy Tale Collection). 32p. (J). 14.95 (*978-1-4027-3064-1(0)) Sterling Publishing Co., Inc.

Mackinnon, Mairi. Runaway Pancake. Provantini, Silvia, illus. 2006. 48p. (J). 8.99 (978-0-7945-1276-7(3) , Usborne) EDC Publishing.

MacManus, Seumas. Donegal Fairy Stories. Greenleaf, Joseph A., ed. Verbeck, Frank & Quigley, John, illus. rev. ed. 2003. 160p. (YA). pap. (978-0-9544530-0-8(X)) Swordpoint Intercontinental, Ltd.

—Favorite Irish Folk Tales. 1999. (gr. 3-6). lib. bdg. 14.10 (978-0-613-90223-6(8)) Tandem Library Bks.

Madina, Alex & Berry, Mary. Tales from Times Past: Sinister Stories from the 19th Century. 1998. (Cambridge School Anthologies Ser.). (Illus.). 128p. pap. 15.00 (978-0-521-58566-8(X)) Cambridge Univ. Pr.

Madonna. The Adventures of Abdi, the (Las Aventuras de Abdi) Dugina, Olga & Dugin, Andrej, illus. 2004. 40p. (J). (ps-6). 19.95 (978-0-670-05889-1(0)) Callaway Editions, Inc.

The Magical Horses Vol. 2000: A Fairy Tale for the Young & the Young at Heart. l.t. ed. 2005. (Illus.). 127p. (J). per. (978-0-9738625-0-8(5)) Blue Cat Publishing.

Maguire, Gregory. Leaping Beauty: And Other Animal Fairy Tales. Demarest, Chris L., illus. (J). 2004. 208p. 15.99 (978-0-06-056417-9(2)); 2006. 224p. reprint ed. pap. 5.99 (978-0-06-056419-3(9) , Harper Trophy) HarperCollins Pubs.

Malak, Annabel, illus. Cinderella. (Classic Stories Ser.). 48p. (J). (ps-2). incl. audio (978-2-921997-75-1(4)) Coffragants.

Malcolm, Jahnna N. The Emerald Princess Finds a Fairy. 1998. (Jewel Kingdom Ser.: No. 8). (Illus.). 66p. (J). (gr. 3-5). pap. 3.99 (978-0-590-11738-8(6) , Scholastic Paperbacks) Scholastic, Inc.

Malone, Peter, illus. The Classic Treasurey of Princess Fairy Tales. 2007. 54p. (J). 7.98 (*978-0-7624-3162-5(8) , Courage Bks.) Running Pr. Bk. Pubs.

Man-Kong, Mary. BarbieTM as the Princess & the Pauper. 2004. (Illus.). 24p. (J). (ps-2). pap. 3.99 (978-0-375-82990-1(3) , Golden Bks.) Random Hse. Children's Bks.

Mann, Pamela. The Frog Princess? (Illus.). (J). 2002. (TUR & ENG.). 24p. 15.95 (978-1-85269-324-4(X)); 2000. (BEN & ENG., 24p. 19.95 (978-1-85269-317-6(7)); 2000. (GUJ & ENG., 25p. 19.95 (978-1-85269-322-0(3)); 2000. (PAN & ENG., 24p. 17.95 (978-1-85269-323-7(1)); 2000. (SOM & ENG., 24p. 15.95 (978-1-85269-319-0(3)); 2000. (URD & ENG., 24p. 17.95 (978-1-85269-321-3(5)) Mantra Publishing, Ltd. GBR. *Dist:* AIMS International Bks., Inc.

Manners, Richard. Girl Child Saturday: A Children's Fantasy. 2000. 152p. (J). (gr. 1-7). pap. 9.95 (978-0-595-12673-6(1)) iUniverse, Inc.

Mantovani, Maria. Fairy Tales. 2006. (Illus.). 224p. 18.95 (*978-1-84560-034-1(7)) Mercury Bks. Ltd. GBR. *Dist:* International Publishers Marketing.

Mantovani, Maria & Barsotti, Renzo, illus. Classic Fairy Tales - Town Mouse & Country Mouse. 32p. 7.95 (978-1-904668-53-4(4)) Mercury Bks. Ltd. GBR. *Dist:* International Publishers Marketing.

Marcantonio, Patricia Santos, et al. Red Ridin' in the Hood: And Other Cuentos. Alarcao, Renato, illus. 2005. 192p. (J). 16.00 (978-0-374-36241-6(6) , Farrar, Straus & Giroux (BYR)) Farrar, Straus & Giroux.

Marshall, James. Goldilocks & the Three Bears. Marshall, James, illus. 2002. (Illus.). (J). 14.04 (978-0-7587-2613-1(9)) Book Wholesalers, Inc.

—Goldilocks & the Three Bears. 1998. (J). 13.79 (978-0-606-12946-6(4)) Tandem Library Bks.

Marshall, Rita. The Illustrated Treasury of Fairy Tales. 2003. (Illus.). 356p. 29.95 (978-1-56846-144-1(5)) Creative Co., The.

Marsoli, Lisa Ann. Ask Fickle Fairy. 2007. 16p. (J). (gr. 2-4). 9.99 (978-0-7641-6010-3(9)) Barron's Educational Series, Inc.

Martin, Lynn & Hogg, Glenda. Funky Fairy Tales. (J). (gr. 5-6). pap. (978-1-875739-81-3(5)) Wizard Bks.

Martin, Rafe. The Girl & the Sea. Lefleur, Dave, illus. 2002. (J). 16.00 (978-0-15-201322-6(9)) Harcourt Trade Pubs.

—The Twelve Months. Krykorka, Vladyana Langer, illus. 2001. 28p. (ps-3). 15.95 (978-0-7737-3249-0(7)) Stoddart Kids CAN. *Dist:* Fitzhenry & Whiteside, Ltd.

Martinez, Rocio. Matias Pierde Su Lapiz. 2005. Tr. of Matthew Loses His Pencil. (SPA.). (J). (gr. k up). 8.95 (978-980-257-299-1(3)) Ekare, Ediciones VEN. *Dist:* Iaconi, Mariuccia Bk. Imports.

Masini, Beatrice. A Brave Little Princess. Handley, Diana, tr. Monaco, Octavia, illus. 2000. 32p. (J). (gr. k-2). lib. bdg. 16.99 (978-1-84148-267-5(6)) Barefoot Bks., Inc.

Mason, Eva. Berry Fairy Tales: Sleeping Beauty. Huxtable, John, illus. 2006. (Strawberry Shortcake Ser.). 32p. (J). (ps-3). 6.99 (978-0-448-44274-7(4) , Grosset & Dunlap) Penguin Group (USA) Inc.

Masson, Sophie. Malkin. 2000. (StarMaker Bks.). 153p. (J). pap. 5.50 (978-0-88489-669-2(2)) St. Mary's Pr.

—Malkin. 2001. (gr. 7-12). lib. bdg. 13.55 (978-0-613-83395-0(3)) Tandem Library Bks.

Mata, Marta & Ballester, Arnal. Goldilocks & the Three Bears. Alejandro, Alis, tr. from SPA. Ballester, Arnal, illus. 1998. Orig. Title: Ricitos de Oro y los Tres Osos. (ENG & SPA., Illus.). 32p. (J). (ps-3). pap. 6.95 (978-0-8118-1835-3(7)) Chronicle Bks. LLC.

Matthews, John. Classic Celtic Fairy Tales. Daniels, Ian, illus. 1999. 208p. (gr. 4-7). pap. 14.95 (978-0-7137-2783-8(7)) Blandford Pr. GBR. *Dist:* Sterling Publishing Co., Inc.

Matthews, John & Matthews, Caitlin. The Wizard King: And Other Spellbinding Tales. Press, Jenny, illus. 2000. 80p. (J). (ps-3). 18.95 (978-1-901223-84-2(1)) Barefoot Bks., Inc.

Maugham, W. Somerset. A Siamese Fairy Tale. 2006. (Illus.). 19.95 (978-974-8304-26-7(4)) White Orchid THA. *Dist:* Antique Collectors' Club, Weatherhill, Inc.

Maxwell, Marc C. B. The Wallace Dream: The Adventures of the Baby Seekers. 2006. 148p. pap. 12.95 (978-1-59113-933-1(3)) Booklocker.com, Inc.

Mayer, Marianna. The Adventures of Tom Thumb. Craft, Kinuko Y., illus. 2005. 28p. (J). (gr. k-4). reprint ed. 16.00 (978-0-7567-9642-6(3)) DIANE Publishing Co.

—Beauty & the Beast. Mayer, Mercer, illus. 2002. 48p. (J). pap. 5.95 (978-1-58717-148-2(1) , SeaStar Bks.) Chronicle Bks. LLC.

—Beauty & the Beast. 2002. (ps-2). lib. bdg. 14.10 (978-0-613-56213-3(5)) Tandem Library Bks.

—Iron John. 1999. (Illus.). 40p. (J). (gr. k-3). 15.89 (978-0-688-11555-5(1)) HarperCollins Pubs.

—Twelve Dancing Princesses. Craft, Kinuko Y., illus. 1998. (Mulberry Bks.). 40p. (J). (ps-3). pap. 6.99 (978-0-688-14392-3(X) , Harper Trophy) HarperCollins Pubs.

McAllister, Angela. The Tortoise & the Hare: An Aesop's Fable. Heale, Jonathan, illus. 2004. 32p. (J). pap. 7.95 (978-1-84507-142-4(5)) Lincoln, Frances Ltd. GBR. *Dist:* Perseus Distribution.

McAlpine, Helen & McAlpine, William. Tales from Japan. Kiddell-Monroe, Joan & Fowler, Rosamund, illus. 2002. (Oxford Myths & Legends Ser.). 160p. (YA). 11.95 (978-0-19-275175-1(1)) Oxford Univ. Pr., Inc.

McBratney, Sam & Chichester-Clark, Emma. Little Red Riding Hood. 2004. (Stories to Collect & Treasure Ser.). (Illus.). 32p. (J). (gr. k-3). pap. (978-0-340-87786-9(3) , Hodder Children's Books) Hodder Children's Division.

McCafferty, Catherine. Rapunzel. Spong, Clive, illus. 2002. (Brighter Child Keepsake Stories Ser.). 32p. (J). (ps-3). pap. 3.99 (978-1-57768-379-7(X) , Brighter Child) School Specialty Publishing.

McCaffrey, Anne. Dragonsong. 2005. (Harper Hall Trilogy: Vol. 1). 208p. (J). pap. 2.99 (978-1-4169-0534-9(0) , Aladdin) Simon & Schuster Children's Publishing.

McCann, Jesse Leon, adapted by. Shrek 2: The Movie Novel. 2004. (Illus.). 110p. (J). (978-0-439-74048-7(7)) Scholastic, Inc.

McCann, Michelle Roehm & Monson-Burton, Marianne. Finding Fairies: Secrets for Attracting Little People from Around the World. Hohn, David, illus. 2004. 48p. (J). (gr. 4-7). 17.95 (978-1-57178-165-9(X) , 1235428) Council Oak Bks.

McCaughrean, Geraldine. Beauty & the Beast. Blythe, Gary, illus. 2003. (Picture Bks.). 32p. (J). (ps-3). 15.95 (978-1-57505-491-9(4) , Carolrhoda Bks.) Lerner Publishing Group.

McClintock, Barbara. Cinderella. 2005. (Illus.). 32p. (J). (gr. k-4). pap. 15.99 (978-0-439-56145-7(0) , Scholastic Pr.) Scholastic, Inc.

McClintock, Barbara, illus. Goldilocks & the Three Bears. 2003. 32p. (J). (ps-2). pap. 15.95 (978-0-439-39545-8(3) , Scholastic Pr.) Scholastic, Inc.

McCue, Lisa, illus. My First Mother Goose. 1999. 20p. (J). (ps-3). bds. 12.99 (978-1-57584-254-7(8) , Reader's Digest Children's Bks.) Reader's Digest Children's Publishing, Inc.

McDermott, Gerald. Tim O'Toole & the Wee Folk: An Irish Tale. McDermott, Gerald, illus. 2002. (Illus.). (J). 13.19 (978-0-7587-3812-7(9)) Book Wholesalers, Inc.

—Tim O'Toole & the Wee Folk: An Irish Tale. McDermott, Gerald, illus. 2004. (Illus.). 32p. (J). (ps-ps). lib. bdg. 13.19 (978-0-606-30057-5(0)) Tandem Library Bks.

McGraw-Hill Staff. Jack & the Beanstalk. 2001. (gr. k-3). lib. bdg. 11.80 (978-0-613-87940-8(6)) Tandem Library Bks.

—Little Red Hen. 2001. (gr. k-3). lib. bdg. 11.80 (978-0-613-86841-9(2)) Tandem Library Bks.

—Rapunzel. 2001. (gr. k-3). lib. bdg. 11.80 (978-0-613-87941-5(4)) Tandem Library Bks.

McKenzie, Nancy. Guinevere's Gift. 2008. 336p. (J). (gr. 5-9). 15.99 (*978-0-375-84345-7(0) , Knopf Bks. for Young Readers) Random Hse. Children's Bks.

McKinley, Robin. Beauty: A Retelling of the Story of Beauty & the Beast. 2005. 336p. (YA). (gr. 7 up). pap. 6.99 (978-0-06-075310-8(2)) HarperCollins Pubs.

—Door in the Hedge. 2003. (gr. 7-12). lib. bdg. 15.30 (978-0-613-73478-3(5)) Tandem Library Bks.

—The Spindle's End. 2002. (Firebird Ser.). 432p. (YA). pap. 6.99 (978-0-698-11950-5(9) , Puffin) Penguin Group (USA) Inc.

—Spindle's End. (gr. 7-12). 2002. lib. bdg. 15.30 (978-0-613-73477-6(7)); 2001. lib. bdg. 14.75 (978-0-613-35237-6(8)) Tandem Library Bks.

McMahan, Virginia. The Mushgnome Fairy & the Silver Bell. 2003. (J). pap. 13.81 (978-1-4116-0162-8(9)) Lulu.com.

McNaughton, Janet. Brave Jack & the Unicorn. Tooke, Susan, illus. 2005. 32p. (J). (gr. k-3). 15.95 (978-0-88776-677-0(3)) Tundra Bks., Inc./Livres Toundra, Inc. CAN. *Dist:* Random Hse., Inc.

McTaggart, William R. Butternut Moon. Hibbard, Eugene J., illus. 2000. 112p. (J). (gr. 2-7). 13.95 (978-0-9669285-4-9(7)) Gramma Bks. Publishing Co.

Meidell, Sherry. The Devil with the Three Golden Hairs: The Classic Brothers Grimm Folktale. 2006. (Illus.). 32p. (J). 16.95 (978-1-933317-50-2(7)) Silverleaf Pr.

Meik, Mitchell. Molly the Milkmaid. Muggli, Glorianne, illus. 2003. (J). pap. 7.95 (978-1-57665-089-9(8)) Muggli Graphics.

Melling, David. The Kiss That Missed. 2007. 32p. (J). (gr. k-2). pap. 7.99 (978-0-7641-3624-5(0)) Barron's Educational Series, Inc.

Melmed, Laura Krauss. Moishe's Miracle: A Hanukkah Story. Slonim, David, illus. 2005. 32p. (J). (ps-3). pap. 6.95 (978-0-8118-5234-0(2)) Chronicle Bks. LLC.

—Rainbabies. 2004. (gr. k-3). lib. bdg. 15.30 (978-0-613-89754-9(4)) Tandem Library Bks.

Menchu, Rigoberta & Liano, Dante. El Vaso de Miel. Tebalan, Helman, illus. 2003. (SPA.). 96p. (J). (gr. 5-8). pap. 13.95 (978-970-29-0985-9(6)) Santillana USA Publishing Co., Inc.

Mercer, Gary. Justin Flowers & the Orb of Time. 2003. 147p. pap. 16.95 (978-1-59286-530-7(5)) PublishAmerica, Inc.

Metaxas, Eric. The Fool & the Flying Ship. Drescher, Henrik, illus. 2007. (J). 25.65 (978-1-59961-308-6(5)) ABDO Publishing Co.

—Jack & the Beanstalk. Sorel, Edward, illus. 2006. (J). (gr. 2-6). 25.65 (978-1-59679-345-3(7)) Spotlight.

—Puss in Boots. Le-Tan, Pierre, illus. 2007. (J). 25.65 (978-1-59961-311-6(5)) ABDO Publishing Co.

Michka, el Osito. 2002. 16p. pap. 2.95 (978-84-7864-485-8(7)) Casals Editorial ESP. *Dist:* Libros Sin Fronteras.

Michka, el Osito. 2nd ed. 2002. (Troquelados Clasicos Ser.). (SPA & ENG., Illus.). 16p. pap. 2.95 (978-84-7864-489-6(X)) Combel Editorial, S.A. ESP. *Dist:* Independent Pubs. Group.

Miguel, Calero, illus. Caperucita Roja. 2006. (SPA.). 16p. pap. 3.50 (978-84-95994-30-1(5)) Mestas, Jorge A. Ediciones Escolares La Escuela Nueva y Alinorma, S.L. ESP. *Dist:* Fondo de Cultura Economica USA.

Miles, Linda, et al. Amanda Salamander & the Secret of Happily Ever After. 2005. (J). cd-rom 7.99 (978-0-9778623-4-4(8)) Miles and Associates.

Millard, Anne. A First Book of Fairy Tales. Downing, Julie, illus. 2001. 80p. (J). 14.99 (978-0-7894-7906-8(0)) Dorling Kindersley Publishing, Inc.

Miller, Edward. 3 Tales Retold & Illustrated: The Three Little Pigs, Goldilocks & the Three Bears, Three Billy Goats Gruff. Miller, Edward, illus. 2007. (Illus.). 48p. (J). (ps-2). 17.95 (978-0-8050-7916-6(5)) Holt, Henry & Co.

Mills, J. Elizabeth. Beauty & the Beast. 2003. (gr. k-3). lib. bdg. 11.80 (978-0-613-63534-9(5)) Tandem Library Bks.

Minh Quoc. Tam & Cam/Tam Cam: The Ancient Vietnamese Cinderella Story. Smith, William, tr. from VIE. Mai Long, illus. 2006. (ENG & VIE.). 32p. (J). (gr. 1-4). 16.95 (978-0-9701654-4-2(7)) East West Discovery Pr.

Mini Cuentos: Atletas se Entrenan, Zorro y la Ciguena.Tr. of Mini Fairy Tales: Fox & the Swan. (SPA.). (J). (gr. k-4). 4.98 (978-970-607-621-2(2)) Larousse, Ediciones, S. A. de C. V. MEX. *Dist:* Continental Bk. Co., Inc.

Mini Cuentos: Hazanas de Baltazar, Pipo, el Perro Fiel.Tr. of Mini Faiy Tales: Pipo, the Loyal Dog. (SPA.). (J). (gr. k-4). 4.98 (978-970-607-622-9(0)) Larousse, Ediciones, S. A. de C. V. MEX. *Dist:* Continental Bk. Co., Inc.

Mini Cuentos: Relampago, Caballo Salvaje, Pelirrojo y Tania.Tr. of Mini Faiy Tales: Lightning the Wild Horse. (SPA.). (J). (gr. k-4). 4.98 (978-970-607-620-5(4)) Larousse, Ediciones, S. A. de C. V. MEX. *Dist:* Continental Bk. Co., Inc.

Mini Cuentos: Rey de los Sapos, Sapatillas Rojas.Tr. of Mini Fairy Tales: King & His Shoes. (SPA.). (J). (gr. k-4). 4.98 (978-970-607-619-9(0)) Larousse, Ediciones, S. A. de C. V. MEX. *Dist:* Continental Bk. Co., Inc.

Mitchell, Marianne. Joe Cinders. Langdo, Bryan, illus. rev. ed. 2002. 48p. (J). (ps-3). 17.95 (978-0-8050-6529-9(6) , Holt, Henry & Co. Bks. For Young Readers) Holt, Henry & Co.

Mitchell, N. J. W. The Search. 2003. 110p. pap. 9.95 (978-0-595-27251-8(7)) iUniverse, Inc.

Mitchell, Stephen, et al. Iron Hans. Mitchell, Stephen, tr. Tavares, Matt, illus. 2007. 40p. (J). (gr. 1-5). 16.99 (978-0-7636-2160-5(9)) Candlewick Pr.

Moerbeck, Kees, illus. & des. Cinderella. Moerbeck, Kees, des. 2006. 9.99 (978-1-84643-019-0(4)) Child's Play-International.

El Mono Azul. (Fantasmas de Fear Street Coleccion). (SPA.). (YA). (gr. 5-8). pap. 7.95 (978-950-04-2022-8(8) , EM10965) Emecé Editores S.A. ARG. *Dist:* Lectorum Pubns., Inc., Planeta Publishing Corp.

Montana, Marta, illus. Los Siete Cabritillos y el Lobo. 2004. (Caballo Alado Clasico Ser.). (SPA.). 24p. (J). 6.95 (978-84-7864-766-8(X)) Combel Editorial, S.A. ESP. *Dist:* Independent Pubs. Group.

Moon, Fabio. Ursula. Pinto, Joan De Sola & Pinto, Guilherme, trs. 2004. (Illus.). 72p. pap. 9.95 (978-1-932051-22-3(8)) A i T/Planet Lar.

Moore, Billy. Cracker's Mule. 2002. 256p. 12.95 (978-1-58838-105-7(6)) NewSouth, Inc.

—Cracker's Mule. 2002. (gr. 7-12). lib. bdg. 22.20 (978-0-613-79796-2(5)) Tandem Library Bks.

Moore, Raina. A Charming Princess Collection Book & Charm. 2005. (Charming Classics). 256p. (J). pap. 6.99 (978-0-06-059604-0(X) , Harper Festival) HarperCollins Pubs.

Mora, Pat. Dona Flor. Colon, Raul, illus. 2005. (SPA.). 40p. (J). (ps-3). pap. 7.99 (978-0-440-41768-2(6) , Dragonfly Bks.) Random Hse. Children's Bks.

—Dona Flor: Un Cuento de una Mujer Gigante con un Gran Corazo. Mlawer, Teresa, tr. Colon, Raul, illus. 2005. (SPA.). 40p. (J). (ps-3). lib. bdg. 17.99 (978-0-679-98002-5(4) , Knopf Bks. for Young Readers) Random Hse. Children's Bks.

Morecambe, Gary. The Tall Tales of Dracula's Daggers: Count Krinkelfiend's Quest. l.t. ed. 2005. (J). pap. (978-0-7540-7931-6(7) , CLP 483) BBC Audio.

Morgenstern, Susie. Princesses Are People, Too: Two Modern Fairy Tales. 2004. (gr. 3-6). lib. bdg. 13.00 (978-0-613-89800-3(1)) Tandem Library Bks.

Moroney, Tracey. Goldilocks & the Three Bears. 1999. (Lamaze Ser.). (Illus.). 16p. (J). (ps-k). 7.99 (978-1-56799-899-3(2) , Friedman-Fairfax) Friedman, Michael Publishing Group, Inc.

—Little Red Riding Hood. 1999. (Lamaze Ser.). (Illus.). 16p. (J). (ps-k). 7.99 (978-1-56799-898-6(4) , Friedman-Fairfax) Friedman, Michael Publishing Group, Inc.

Morris, Jackie. The Seal Children. 2004. (Illus.). 32p. (J). 16.95 (978-1-84507-040-3(2)) Lincoln, Frances Ltd. GBR. *Dist:* Perseus Distribution.

Moseley, James. The Ninth Jewel of the Mughal Crown: The Birbal Tales Vol. 1: From the Oral Traditions of India, 3 vols. Moseley, James, illus. l.t. ed. 2001. (Birbal Tales). (Illus.). 160p. (J). (gr. 3-6). 24.95 (978-0-9704447-1-4(0) , 1011092) Summerwind Marketing, Inc.

Moses, Will. Hansel & Gretel. Moses, Will, illus. 2006. (Illus.). 40p. (J). (ps). 16.99 (978-0-399-24234-2(1) , Philomel) Penguin Group (USA) Inc.

Moss, Miriam. The Horse Girl. Cockcroft, Jason, illus. 2004. 32p. (J). (978-0-7112-1876-5(5)) Lincoln, Frances Ltd. GBR. *Dist:* Transition Vendor.

—The Horse Girl. Cockroft, Jason, illus. 2004. 32p. (J). pap. 7.95 (978-1-84507-149-3(2)) Lincoln, Frances Ltd. GBR. *Dist:* Perseus Distribution.

Mounter, Paddy, illus. Ali Baba & the Forty Thieves. 2004. (Young Reading Series One Ser.). 48p. (J). (gr. 2 up). pap. 5.95 (978-0-7945-0667-4(4) , Usborne) EDC Publishing.

Mouse Works Staff. Alice in Wonderland. 2002. (Classic Storybook Ser.). (J). 7.99 (978-1-57082-976-5(4)) Mouse Works.

—Disney's Easy to Read Stories: A Collection of 6 Favorite Tales. 1999. (Illus.). 192p. (gr. k-2). 9.99 (978-0-7868-3244-6(4)) Disney Pr.

—Snow White & the Seven Dwarfs - Cinderella, 2. 75th anniv. ed. 1998. 9.99 (978-0-7364-0087-9(7)) Mouse Works.

—Snow White Classic. rev. ed. 7.99 (978-1-57082-977-2(2)) Mouse Works.

Mueller, Martina, illus. Sleeping Beauty: A Grimm's Fairy Tale. 2001. 28p. (J). 16.95 (978-0-86315-342-6(9)) Floris Bks. GBR. *Dist:* Gryphon Hse., Inc., SteinerBooks, Inc.

Mufari's Beautiful Daughters. 2004. pap. 14.95 incl. audio (978-1-55592-052-4(7)) Weston Woods Studios, Inc.

Mufaro's Beautiful Daughters. 2004. pap. 32.75 incl. audio (978-1-55592-280-1(5)) Weston Woods Studios, Inc.

Muldrow, Diane. Jacky & the Giant. Andriani, Vincent, illus. 1999. (Scholastic At-Home Phonics Reading Program Ser.: Vol. 42). 24p. (J). (978-0-590-68810-9(3)) Scholastic, Inc.

Murdock, Hy. Hansel & Gretel. (First Fairy Tales Ser.: No. S852-8). (Illus.). 25p. (J). (ps-2). pap. 3.95 (978-0-7214-5101-5(2) , Dutton Juvenile) Penguin Group (USA) Inc.

Murphy, Breena. The Fairy Seekers - the Sand Fairy. Waid, Sara Joyce & Waid, Antoinette M., illus. l.t. ed. 2006. 284p. (J). 24.95 (978-0-9788010-1-4(6)) Edes Publishing Co.

—The Fairy Seekers - the Sand Fairy, 1. Waid, Sara J. & Waid, Antoinette M., illus. l.t. ed. 2006. 284p. (J). per. 14.95 (978-0-9788010-0-7(8)) Edes Publishing Co.

Murphy, Shirley Rousseau. Wind Child. Dillon, Leo & Dillon, Diane, illus. 1999. 40p. (J). (gr. k-4). 15.95 (978-0-06-024903-8(X)); 15.89 (978-0-06-024904-5(8)) HarperCollins Pubs.

My Dentist & the Tooth Fairy Christian Adventures in Learning Book. 2005. (J). cd-rom 13.95 (978-1-59649-319-3(4)) Whispering Pine Pr., Inc.

My Dentist & the Tooth Fairy Hood Christian Educational Curriculum. 2005. (J). 34.95 (978-1-59649-452-7(2)) Whispering Pine Pr., Inc.

My Dentist & the Tooth Fairy Hood Christian Educational Curriculum Book. 2005. (J). cd-rom 13.95 (978-1-59649-320-9(8)) Whispering Pine Pr., Inc.

My Dentist & the Tooth Fairy Story Book. 2005. (J). 15.95 (978-1-59649-432-9(8)) Whispering Pine Pr., Inc.

Myers, Walter Dean. The Dragon Takes a Wife. French, Fiona, illus. rev. ed. 2000. 32p. (ps-3). pap. 5.99 (978-0-590-46694-3(1)) Scholastic, Inc.

—The Dragon Takes a Wife. 2000. (Illus.). (J). (978-0-606-18871-5(1)) Tandem Library Bks.

N a Staff. Fairy Tales. 2005. (Bright Lights Ser.). (Illus.). 224p. 18.95 (978-1-904668-99-2(2)) Mercury Bks. Ltd. GBR. *Dist:* International Publishers Marketing.

Naidu, Vayu. A Curly Tale. 1998. (Under the Banyan Ser.). (Illus.). 22p. (YA). (gr. 2 up). 11.99 incl. audio (978-81-86838-33-4(3)) APG Sales and Fulfillment.

—Eyes on the Peacock's Tail. 1998. (Under the Banyan Ser.). (Illus.). 22p. (YA). (gr. 2 up). 11.99 incl. audio (978-81-86838-27-3(9)) APG Sales and Fulfillment.

—Hiss, Don't Bite. 1998. (Under the Banyan Ser.). (Illus.). 22p. (YA). (gr. 2 up). 11.99 incl. audio (978-81-86838-31-0(7)) APG Sales and Fulfillment.

—Magic Vessels. 1998. (Under the Banyan Ser.). (Illus.). 22p. (YA). (gr. 2 up). 11.99 incl. audio (978-81-86838-29-7(5)) APG Sales and Fulfillment.

Naomi, Aunt. Jewish Fairy Tales & Legends. 2006. pap. 28.95 (***978-1-4254-9788-0(8)***) Kessinger Publishing, LLC.

Napoli, Donna Jo. Beast. 272p. (YA). 2004. pap. 6.99 (978-0-689-87005-7(1)); 2002. (gr. 7 up). pap. 8.99 (978-0-689-83590-2(6)) Simon & Schuster Children's Publishing. (Simon Pulse).

—Beast. 2002. (gr. 7-12). lib. bdg. 16.45 (978-0-613-73277-2(4)) Tandem Library Bks.

—Crazy Jack. 2000. (YA). pap., stu. ed. 51.95 incl. audio (978-0-7887-4159-3(4) , 41099) Recorded Bks., LLC.

—Crazy Jack. l.t. ed. 2000. 183p. (YA). (gr. 8-12). 20.95 (978-0-7862-3047-1(9)) Thorndike Pr.

—Spinners. 2001. (gr. 7-12). lib. bdg. 14.15 (978-0-613-36016-6(8)) Tandem Library Bks.

—Ugly. Judge, Lita, illus. 2006. 192p. (gr. 2-5). 14.99 (978-0-7868-3753-3(5)) Hyperion Pr.

—Zel. 2005. 240p. (J). (gr. 5-9). 21.00 (978-0-8446-7278-6(5) , 3593) Smith, Peter Pub., Inc.

Naruse, Kaori. Pretear Vol. 2: The New Legend of Snow White. 2004. (Illus.). 198p. (YA). pap. (978-1-4139-0145-0(X)) ADV Manga.

Naruse, Kaori & Satou, Junichi. Pretear Vol. 1: The New Legend of Snow White. 2004. (Illus.). 188p. (YA). pap. (978-1-4139-0144-3(1)) ADV Manga.

Nash, Margaret. The Princess & the Frog. Remphry, Martin, illus. 2004. (Read-It! Readers Ser.). 32p. (C). (gr. k-3). 18.60 (978-1-4048-0562-0(1)) Picture Window Bks.

Nesbit, E. Irish Fairy Tales. Rackham, Arthur, illus. 1998. (Children's Classics). 224p. (J). (gr. 4-7). pap. 3.95 (978-1-85326-157-2(2) , 1572WW) Wordsworth Editions, Ltd. GBR. *Dist:* Combined Publishing.

—Jack & the Beanstalk. Tavares, Matt, illus. 2006. 48p. (J). (ps-1). 16.99 (978-0-7636-2124-7(2)) Candlewick Pr.

—Lionel & the Book of Beasts. Hague, Michael, illus. 2006. 48p. (J). (gr. 2-4). lib. bdg. 17.89 (978-0-06-084272-7(5)); 16.99 (978-0-688-14006-9(8)) HarperCollins Pubs.

—Melisande. 1999. (J). (978-0-606-16399-6(9)) Tandem Library Bks.

—Story of the Amulet. 2006. pap. (***978-1-4068-3506-9(4)***) Echo Library.

Nesbit, E. The Story of the Amulet. l.t. ed. 2005. 396p. pap. (978-1-84637-206-3(2)) Echo Library.

Nightingale, Sandy. Dear Fairies: A Book of Letters. Nightingale, Sandy, illus. 1999. (Illus.). 18p. (J). (ps-3). 14.95 (978-0-689-83121-8(8) , Little Simon) Simon & Schuster Children's Publishing.

Nishimoto, Keiske. Japanese Fairy Tales, Vol. 1. Imoto, Yoko, illus. 2004. (Japanese Fairy Tale Ser.: Vol. 1). 32p. (gr. k-4). reprint ed. 14.95 (978-0-89346-845-3(2)) Heian International Publishing, Inc.

Nobisso, Josephine. The Weight of a Mass: A Tale of Faith. Szegedi, Katalin, illus. 2005. 32p. (J). (ps-ps). 17.95 (978-0-8146-2930-7(X)) Liturgical Pr.

Noble, Marty. Cinderella Sticker Paper Doll. 1998. 4p. (J). (gr. k-5). pap. 1.50 (978-0-486-40321-2(1)) Dover Pubns., Inc.

—Nutcracker Tattoos. 1998. 2p. (J). (ps-5). pap. 1.00 (978-0-486-40537-7(0)) Dover Pubns., Inc.

—Thumbelina Sticker Storybook. 1998. (Illus.). (J). pap. 1.00 (978-0-486-40082-2(4)) Dover Pubns., Inc.

Noël, Christopher. Rumpelstiltskin. Sís, Peter, illus. 2005. (Rabbit Ears Ser.). 40p. (J). (gr. k-5). 25.65 (978-1-59679-229-6(9)) Spotlight.

Not Again Red Riding Hood. 2004. (J). E-Book incl. cd-rom (978-1-84444-464-9(3)) Mantra Publishing, Ltd.

Novi, Nathalie. La Belle au Bois Dormant. 2001. Tr. of Sleeping Beauty. (FRE., Illus.). 32p. (J). 13.95 (978-2-09-202110-1(9)) Nathan, Fernand FRA. *Dist:* Distribooks, Inc.

Ogburn, Jacqueline K. The Lady & the Lion. 2003. (Illus.). 32p. (J). (gr. k). 16.99 (978-0-8037-2651-2(1) , Dial) Penguin Group (USA) Inc.

—The Magic Nesting Doll. Long, Laurel, illus. (J). (gr. k-3). 2003. 32p. pap. 6.99 (978-0-14-250065-1(8) , Puffin); 2000. 1p. 16.99 (978-0-8037-2414-3(4) , Dial) Penguin Group (USA) Inc.

—Magic Nesting Doll. 2003. (gr. k-3). lib. bdg. 15.30 (978-0-613-67460-7(X)) Tandem Library Bks.

Okoye-Johnson, Ogo. Oma the Faithful Daughter. Johnson, Desing, illus. 1999. 32p. (J). (gr. k-8). 15.00 (978-0-9670024-9-1(4)) Noon Productions.

Old-Time Fairy Tales. 2002. (Illus.). 96p. (J). (gr. k-7). 9.99 (978-1-57759-422-2(3)) Dalmatian Pr.

O'Leary-Coggins, Annette C. Nanny Reilly. 2007. 116p. per. 10.95 (***978-0-595-44994-1(8)***) iUniverse, Inc.

Olson, Mary W. & Tillotson, Katherine. Nice Try, Tooth Fairy. 2000. Orig. Title: Dear Tooth Fairy. (Illus.). 32p. (J). (ps-3). 15.00 (978-0-689-82422-7(X)) Simon & Schuster Children's Publishing.

O'Malley, Kevin. Once upon a Cool Motorcycle Dude. O'Malley, Kevin et al, illus. 2005. 32p. (J). 16.95 (978-0-8027-8947-1(1)) Walker & Co.

Once upon a Time Spanish Version-Jack & the Beanstalk. 2005. (J). (978-1-57022-560-4(5)) ECS Learning Systems, Inc.

Once upon a Time Spanish Version-Little Red Riding Hood. 2005. (J). (978-1-57022-562-8(1)) ECS Learning Systems, Inc.

Once upon a Time Spanish Version-the Gingerbread Man. 2005. (J). (978-1-57022-556-7(7)) ECS Learning Systems, Inc.

O'Neal, Shaquille. Shaq & the Beanstalk: And Other Very Tall Tales. Evans, Shane W., illus. 1999. 80p. (J). (gr. 1-4). pap. 15.95 (978-0-590-91823-7(0) , Cartwheel Bks.) Scholastic, Inc.

The Ooshes A Wish Comes True. 2005. (J). (978-1-932233-05-6(9)) Aurora Libris Corp.

The Ooshes the Night Before Christmas. 2004. (J). mass mkt. (978-1-932233-03-2(2)) Aurora Libris Corp.

Orihuela, Luz. Los Tres Cerditos. Rius, Maria, illus. 2004. (Caballo Alado Clasico Ser.). (SPA.). 24p. (J). 6.95 (978-84-7864-765-1(1)) Combel Editorial, S.A. ESP. *Dist:* Independent Pubs. Group.

Osborne, Mary Pope. Kate & the Beanstalk. Potter, Giselle, illus. 2000. 40p. (J). (ps-3). 17.95 (978-0-689-82550-7(1) , Atheneum/Anne Schwartz Bks.) Simon & Schuster Children's Publishing.

Osborne, Mary Pope & Osborne, Will. Sleeping Bobby. Potter, Giselle, illus. 2005. 40p. (J). (gr. k-3). 16.95 (978-0-689-87668-4(8) , Atheneum) Simon & Schuster Children's Publishing.

Osborne, Mary Pope & Potter, Giselle. The Brave Little Seamstress. (Illus.). 40p. (J). (ps-3). 2002. 16.00 (978-0-689-84486-7(7) , Atheneum/Anne Schwartz Bks.); 2006. reprint ed. pap. 6.99 (978-1-4169-1620-8(2) , Aladdin) Simon & Schuster Children's Publishing.

Osmond, Alan. If the Shoe Fits. Aarrestad, Thomas, illus. 1998. (Twice Upon a Time Ser.). 32p. (J). (ps-2). 11.95 (978-1-57102-133-5(7)) Warehousing & Fulfillment Specialists, LLC (WFS, LLC).

Ottolenghi, Carol. Jack & the Beanstalk/Juan y los Frijoles Magicos. Porfirio, Guy, illus. 2005. (Keepsake Stories Ser.). (SPA.). 32p. (J). (ps-ps). pap. 3.99 (978-0-7696-3816-4(3) , Brighter Child) School Specialty Publishing.

—John Henry. 2004. (Keepsake Stories Ser.). (Illus.). 32p. (J). pap. 3.99 (978-0-7696-3284-1(X) , American Education Publishing) School Specialty Publishing.

—Johnny Appleseed. 2004. (Keepsake Stories Ser.). (Illus.). 32p. (J). pap. 3.99 (978-0-7696-3281-0(5) , American Education Publishing) School Specialty Publishing.

—Johnny Appleseed. 2004. lib. bdg. 11.80 (978-0-613-88035-0(8)) Tandem Library Bks.

—Paul Bunyan. 2004. (Keepsake Stories Ser.). (Illus.). 32p. (J). pap. 3.99 (978-0-7696-3283-4(1) , American Education Publishing) School Specialty Publishing.

—Paul Bunyan. 2004. lib. bdg. 11.80 (978-0-613-90012-6(X)) Tandem Library Bks.

—Rip Van Winkle. 2004. (Keepsake Stories Ser.). (Illus.). 32p. (J). pap. 3.99 (978-0-7696-3282-7(3) , American Education Publishing) School Specialty Publishing.

Ouren, Todd, illus. The Fisherman & His Wife: A Retelling of the Grimms' Fairy Tale. 2004. (Read-It! Readers Ser.). 32p. (C). (gr. k-3). 18.60 (978-1-4048-0317-6(3)) Picture Window Bks.

—The Frog Prince: A Retelling of the Grimms' Fairy Tale. 2004. (Read-It! Readers Ser.). 32p. (C). (gr. k-3). 18.60 (978-1-4048-0313-8(0)) Picture Window Bks.

Ouriou, Susan. Little Book of Fables. Bravo, Constanza, illus. 2004. 128p. (J). 8.95 (978-0-88899-573-5(3)) Groundwood Bks. CAN. *Dist:* Perseus Distribution.

Ozaki, Yei Theodora. Japanese Fairy Tales. 2005. 28.95 (978-1-4218-0697-6(5)); 2004. 280p. pap. 13.95 (978-1-59540-147-2(4)) 1st World Publishing, Inc. (1st World Library - Literary Society).

—Japanese Fairy Tales. 2004. reprint ed. pap. 22.95 (978-1-4191-2730-4(6)); pap. 1.99 (978-1-4192-2730-1(0)) Kessinger Publishing, LLC.

—Japanese Fairy Tales. 2007. (Illus.). 288p. pap. 16.95 (***978-4-8053-0881-3(8)***) Periplus Editions (HK), Ltd. HKG. *Dist:* Tuttle Publishing.

Ozaki, Yei Theodora, ed. Japanese Fairy Tales. (Twelve-Point Ser.). 2003. lib. bdg. 25.00 (978-1-58287-266-7(X)); 2004. 335p. 26.00 (978-1-58287-750-1(5)) North Bks.

Pacovska, Kveta. The Little Flower King. Pacovska, Kveta, illus. 2007. 40p. (J). 17.99 (978-0-698-40054-2(2) , Minedition) Penguin Group (USA) Inc.

Padron, Mary E. Anna Victoria: With Doll. Pendergast, Patrice, illus. gif. collector's l.t. ed. 2002. 32p. (J). per. 25.95 (978-0-9648284-2-1(1)) Pink Hse. Pr.

Page, Nick & Page, Claire. The Little Mermaid. 2007. (Ready to Read: Level 1 (Make Believe Ideas) Ser.). (Illus.). 31p. (J). (gr. k-2). 3.99 (***978-1-84610-442-8(4)***) Make Believe Ideas GBR. *Dist:* Ingram Pub. Services.

—Read with Me Three Billy Goats Gruff: Sticker Activity Book. Saunders, Katie, illus. 2006. (Read with Me (Make Believe Ideas) Ser.). 12p. (J). (gr. k-2). pap. 4.95 (978-1-84610-181-6(6)) Make Believe Ideas GBR. *Dist:* Ingram Pub. Services.

—Sleeping Beauty: Ready to Read Level 1. 2007. (Ready to Read: Level 1 (Make Believe Ideas) Ser.). (Illus.). 31p. (J). (gr. k-2). 3.99 (***978-1-84610-441-1(6)***) Make Believe Ideas GBR. *Dist:* Ingram Pub. Services.

Page, Nick & Page, Claire. Three Billy Goats Gruff. 2006. (Read with Me (Make Believe Ideas) Ser.). (Illus.). 32p. (J). (gr. k-2). 3.95 (978-1-84610-165-6(4)) Make Believe Ideas GBR. *Dist:* Ingram Pub. Services.

Page, Nick, et al. Seashore. 2006. (Ready to Read Sticker Ser.). (Illus.). 12p. (J). (ps-3). pap., pap., wbk. ed. 3.95 (978-1-84610-127-4(1)) Make Believe Ideas GBR. *Dist:* Ingram Pub. Services.

Page, Nick & Claire. Elves & the Shoemaker. 2006. (Read with Me (Make Believe Ideas) Ser.). (Illus.). 32p. (J). (gr. k-2). 3.95 (978-1-84610-161-8(1)) Make Believe Ideas GBR. *Dist:* Ingram Pub. Services.

—Jack & the Beanstalk. 2006. (Read with Me (Make Believe Ideas) Ser.). (Illus.). 32p. (J). (gr. k-2). 3.95 (978-1-84610-164-9(6)) Make Believe Ideas GBR. *Dist:* Ingram Pub. Services.

—The King of Spring. 2006. (Read with Me (Make Believe Ideas) Ser.). (Illus.). 31p. (J). (gr. k-2). 3.95 (978-1-84610-169-4(7)) Make Believe Ideas GBR. *Dist:* Ingram Pub. Services.

—Read with Me Rumpelstiltskin: Sticker Activity Book. 2006. (Read with Me (Make Believe Ideas) Ser.). (Illus.). 12p. (J). (gr. k-2). pap. 4.95 (978-1-84610-182-3(4)) Make Believe Ideas GBR. *Dist:* Ingram Pub. Services.

Palacios, Maria Eugenia Blanco. El Kan Kanay. Tane Arte y Diseno, illus. rev. ed. 2001. (Castillo de la Lectura, Serie Blanca). (SPA.). 96p. (J). pap. 6.95 (978-970-20-0171-3(4)) Castillo, Ediciones, S. A. de C. V. MEX. *Dist:* Macmillan.

Parker, Robert Andrew, illus. The People with Five Fingers: A Native Californian Creation Tale. 2000. (Accelerated Reader Bks.). 32p. (J). (ps-k). 15.95 (978-0-7614-5058-0(0) , Cavendish Children's Bks.) Cavendish, Marshall Corp.

Parrish, Frank. Pancho & the Power. 2000. (Illus.). 48p. (J). (ps-3). pap. 11.95 (978-0-9678566-2-9(0)) Barbed Wire Publishing.

Paterson, Judy. Peerifool. Collins, Sally J., illus. 1998. 32p. (J). (gr. k-4). pap. (978-1-871512-59-5(X)) Glowworm Bks., Ltd.

—Tamlane. Collins, Sally J., illus. 1999. 32p. (J). (gr. k-4). pap. (978-1-871512-62-5(X)) Glowworm Bks., Ltd.

Paterson, Katherine. Igual Al Rey. Vagin, Vladimir, illus. (Buenas Noches Coleccion). (SPA.). (J). (gr. 3-5). pap. 7.16 (978-958-04-4167-0(7)) Norma S.A. COL. *Dist:* Lectorum Pubns., Inc.

—The King's Equal. Woodbridge, Curtis, illus. 1999. (Trophy Chapter Bks.). 64p. (J). (gr. 2-5). pap. 4.25 (978-0-06-442090-7(6) , Harper Trophy) HarperCollins Pubs.

—The King's Equal. 1999. (gr. 3-6). lib. bdg. 12.10 (978-0-7857-8016-8(5)) Tandem Library Bks.

—The Tale of the Mandarin Ducks. Dillon, Leo & Dillon, Diane, illus. 2004. 32p. (J). (gr. k-4). reprint ed. 15.00 (978-0-7567-7698-5(8)) DIANE Publishing Co.

El Patito Feo. 3rd ed. 2002. (Troquelados Clasicos Ser.).Tr. of Ugly Duckling. (ENG & SPA., Illus.). 16p. pap. 2.95 (978-84-7864-184-0(X)) Combel Editorial, S.A. ESP. *Dist:* Independent Pubs. Group.

Patrick & the Leprechaun: Individual Title Six-Packs. 16p. (gr. 2 up). 35.00 (978-0-7635-9378-0(8)) Rigby Education.

Pattou, Edith. East. (YA). 2005. 516p. pap. 8.95 (978-0-15-205221-8(6) , Magic Carpet Bks.); 2003. 512p. (gr. 6 up). 18.00 (978-0-15-204563-0(5)) Harcourt Children's Bks.

—East. 2005. 507p. (YA). (gr. 7-12). per. 14.60 (978-0-606-33423-5(8)) Tandem Library Bks.

Paul, Ann Whitford. Manana, Iguana. Long, Ethan, illus. 2005. 32p. (J). 6.95 (978-0-8234-1980-7(0)) Holiday Hse., Inc.

Payton, David. Cinderella. Proto, Todd, illus. 1998. 32p. (J). (gr. k-4). pap. 9.95 (978-1-58066-012-9(6) , Covered Bridge Pr.) Douglas Charles, Ltd.

PC Treasures, prod. Cinderella. 2007. (J). (***978-1-60072-032-1(3)***) PC Treasures, Inc.

—The Gingerbread Man. 2007. (J). (***978-1-60072-015-4(3)***) PC Treasures, Inc.

—Hansel & Gretel. 2007. (J). (***978-1-60072-030-7(7)***) PC Treasures, Inc.

—The Little Mermaid. 2007. (J). (***978-1-60072-020-8(X)***) PC Treasures, Inc.

—The Ugly Duckling. 2007. (J). (***978-1-60072-018-5(8)***) PC Treasures, Inc.

Pearce, Philippa. The Squirrel Wife. Anderson, Wayne, illus. 2007. 32p. (J). (gr. k-3). 16.99 (***978-0-7636-3551-0(0)***) Candlewick Pr.

Penguin Young Readers Sample Little Red Riding Hood. 2000. (Illus.). (YA). (978-0-582-46864-1(7)) Pearson Education.

Percy, Graham, illus. Caperucita Roja. l.t. ed. 2001. Tr. of Little Red Riding Hood. (SPA.). 28p. (J). (ps-3). 8.99 incl. audio (978-84-86154-06-6(5)) Peralt Montagut ESP. *Dist:* imaJen, Inc.

—Cinderella. l.t. ed. 2001. (SPA.). 28p. (ps-3). incl. audio compact disk (978-84-8214-091-9(4) , 1622) Peralt Montagut.

—Cinderella. l.t. ed. 2001. 28p. (J). (ps-2). 8.99 incl. audio (978-84-87650-25-3(2)) Peralt Montagut ESP. *Dist:* imaJen, Inc.

—The City Mouse & the Country Mouse. l.t. ed. 2001. (SPA.). 28p. (ps-3). incl. audio compact disk (978-84-8214-092-6(2) , 1622) Peralt Montagut.

—The City Mouse & the Country Mouse. l.t. ed. 2001. 28p. (J). (ps-3). 8.99 incl. audio (978-84-86154-62-2(6)) Peralt Montagut ESP. *Dist:* imaJen, Inc.

—The Gingerbread Man. l.t. ed. 2001. (SPA.). 28p. (ps-3). incl. audio compact disk (978-84-8214-094-0(9) , 1622) Peralt Montagut.

—The Gingerbread Man. l.t. ed. 2001. 28p. (J). (ps-3). 8.99 incl. audio (978-84-86154-40-0(5)) Peralt Montagut ESP. *Dist:* imaJen, Inc.

—Goldilocks & the Three Bears. l.t. ed. 2001. (SPA.). 28p. (ps-3). incl. audio compact disk (978-84-8214-087-2(6) , 1622) Peralt Montagut.

—Goldilocks & the Three Bears. l.t. ed. 2001. 28p. (J). (ps-3). 8.99 incl. audio (978-84-86154-91-2(X)) Peralt Montagut ESP. *Dist:* imaJen, Inc.

—Henny-Penny. l.t. ed. 2001. (SPA.). 28p. (ps-3). incl. audio compact disk (978-84-8214-084-1(1) , 1622) Peralt Montagut.

—Henny-Penny. l.t. ed. 2001. 28p. (J). (ps-3). 8.99 incl. audio (978-84-86154-39-4(1)) Peralt Montagut ESP. *Dist:* imaJen, Inc.

—Little Red Riding Hood. l.t. ed. 2001. (SPA.). 28p. (ps-3). incl. audio compact disk (978-84-8214-086-5(8) , 1622) Peralt Montagut.

—Little Red Riding Hood. l.t. ed. 2001. 28p. (J). (ps-3). 8.49 incl. audio (978-84-86154-90-5(1)) Peralt Montagut ESP. *Dist:* imaJen, Inc.

—The Nutcracker. l.t. ed. 2001. (SPA.). 28p. (ps-3). incl. audio (978-84-86154-60-8(X) , 1622) Peralt Montagut.

—The Nutcracker. l.t. ed. 2001. 28p. (J). (ps-3). 8.99 incl. audio compact disk (978-84-8214-089-6(2)) Peralt Montagut ESP. *Dist:* imaJen, Inc.

—Puss in Boots. l.t. ed. 2001. 28p. (J). (ps-3). 8.99 incl. audio compact disk (978-84-8214-090-2(6)); 8.99 incl. audio (978-84-87650-24-6(4)) Peralt Montagut ESP. *Dist:* imaJen, Inc.

—The Steadfast Tin Soldier. l.t. ed. 2001. (SPA.). 28p. (ps-3). incl. audio compact disk (978-84-8214-095-7(7) , 1622) Peralt Montagut.

—The Steadfast Tin Soldier. l.t. ed. 2001. 28p. (J). (ps-3). 8.99 incl. audio (978-84-86154-59-2(6)) Peralt Montagut ESP. *Dist:* imaJen, Inc.

—The Three Billy Goats Gruff. l.t. ed. 2001. (SPA.). 28p. (ps-3). incl. audio compact disk (978-84-8214-088-9(4) , 1622) Peralt Montagut.

—The Three Billy Goats Gruff. l.t. ed. 2001. 28p. (J). (ps-3). 8.99 incl. audio (978-84-86154-89-9(8)) Peralt Montagut ESP. *Dist:* imaJen, Inc.

—The Ugly Duckling. l.t. ed. 2001. (SPA.). 28p. (ps-3). incl. audio compact disk (978-84-8214-093-3(0) , 1622) Peralt Montagut.

—The Ugly Duckling. l.t. ed. 2001. 28p. (J). (ps-3). 8.99 incl. audio (978-84-87650-23-9(6)) Peralt Montagut ESP. *Dist:* imaJen, Inc.

Perez-Vidal, Angel. Cuentos Infantiles Para Que Adultos Lean. 2001. (Coleccion Caniqui Ser.). (SPA.). 175p. 16.00 (978-0-89729-961-9(2) , x961-2) Ediciones Universal.

Peris, Carme. La Caperucita Roja. 1998. (Fairy Tale Theater Ser.).Tr. of Little Red Riding Hood. (SPA., Illus.). 32p. (J). (gr. k-3). pap. 8.95 (978-0-7641-5146-0(0)) Barron's Educational Series, Inc.

—Goldilocks & the Three Bears. 1998. (Fairy Tale Theater Ser.). (Illus.). 32p. (J). (gr. k-3). pap. 8.95 (978-0-7641-5116-3(9)) Barron's Educational Series, Inc.

—Little Red Riding Hood. 1998. (Fairy Tale Theater Ser.). (Illus.). 32p. (J). (gr. k-3). pap. 8.95 (978-0-7641-5114-9(2)) Barron's Educational Series, Inc.

—Ricitos de Oro y Los Tres Osos. 1998. (Fairy Tale Theater Ser.).Tr. of Goldilocks & the Three Bears. (SPA., Illus.). 32p. (J). (gr. k-3). pap. 8.95 (978-0-7641-5148-4(7)) Barron's Educational Series, Inc.

Peris, Carme, illus. Puss 'n Boots. 1999. 32p. (J). (ps-3). 8.95 (978-0-7641-5156-9(8)) Barron's Educational Series, Inc.

Peris, Carmie, illus. Snow White & the Seven Dwarfs. 1999. 32p. (J). (gr. k-3). 8.95 (978-0-7641-5151-4(7)) Barron's Educational Series, Inc.

Perrault. Bella Durmiente (Caracola) 2003. (SPA.). 3.48 (978-968-855-183-7(X)) Suromex, Ediciones, S.A. MEX. *Dist:* Giron Bks.

Perrault, Charles. Cendrillon. Baudrand, Edith, illus. 2000. (FRE.). 32p. (J). 13.95 (978-2-09-202114-9(1)) Nathan, Fernand FRA. *Dist:* Distribooks, Inc.

—Cenicienta. 2002. (SPA.). (gr. k-3). lib. bdg. 15.25 (978-0-613-73572-8(2)) Tandem Library Bks.

—La Cenicienta.Tr. of Cinderella. (SPA.). (J). 12.95 (978-84-7183-326-6(3) , EV6475) El Hogar y La Moda, S.A. ESP. *Dist:* AIMS International Bks., Inc., Lectorum Pubns., Inc.

—Cinderella. Innocenti, Roberto, illus. 2000. (Mouse Bks.). 32p. (gr. 6). 17.95 (978-1-56846-130-4(5) , Creative Editions) Creative Co., The.

—Cinderella. Bell, Anthea, tr. from GER. Koopmans, Loek, illus. 2002. 32p. (J). (gr. k-3). pap. 6.95 (978-0-7358-1486-8(4)) North-South Bks., Inc.

—Cinderella. 2002. (gr. k-3). lib. bdg. 15.25 (978-0-613-73574-2(9)) Tandem Library Bks.

—Cinderella: A Fairy Tale. Baudrand, Edith, illus. 1999. (Little Pebbles Ser.). 32p. (ps-1). 6.95 (978-0-7892-0512-4(2)) Abbeville Pr., Inc.

—The Fairies. 2005. 12p. pap. (978-958-30-1779-7(5)) Panamericana Editorial.

—Las Hadas. Trias, Margarida, tr. Dumas, Philippe, illus. 2002. (SPA.). 52p. (978-84-8470-058-6(5)) Corimbo, Editorial S.L.

—Little Red Riding Hood. Moon, Sarah, illus. 2000. 32p. (YA). (gr. 5 up). lib. bdg. 13.95 (978-1-56846-131-1(3) , Creative Education) Creative Co., The.

—Perrault's Complete Fairy Tales. 2000. (978-0-606-18444-1(9)) Tandem Library Bks.

—Puss in Boots. Arthur, Malcolm, tr. Marcellino, Fred, illus. 1998. (J). (ps-17). lib. bdg. 17.60 (978-0-613-10524-8(9)) Tandem Library Bks.

—Tales of Mother Goose. 2006. pap. ***(978-1-84702-444-2(0))*** Echo Library.

—The Tales of Mother Goose (As First Coll. 2006. pap. 87.99 ***(978-1-4280-0315-6(0))*** IndyPublish.com.

Perrault, Charles. Tom Thumb. Roederer, Charlotte, illus. 2001. (Little Pebbles Ser.). 32p. (J). (ps-3). 6.95 (978-0-7892-0694-7(3)) Abbeville Pr., Inc.

Perrault, Charles & Grimm, Jacob W. Princess Tales, 4 bks., Set. Deru, Myriam et al, illus. 2007. (Classic Fairy Tales Ser.). 112p. (J). (ps-3). 19.95 ***(978-0-7892-0950-4(0))*** Abbeville Pr., Inc.

Perrault, Charles & Moon, Sarah. Little Red Riding Hood. 2002. (Illus.). 40p. (gr. 9 up). 17.95 (978-1-56846-143-4(7) , Creative Editions) Creative Co., The.

Perrotti, P. J. Jason & the Enchanted Forest. 2004. 48p. pap. 12.95 (978-1-4137-4593-1(8)) PublishAmerica, Inc.

Peters, Amy. The Everything Fairy Tales Book: A Magical Collection of All-Time Favorites to Delight the Whole Family. 2001. (Illus.). 304p. 14.95 (978-1-58062-546-3(0)) Adams Media Corp.

Le Petit Chaperon Rouge: Clothing, Food, Nature, The Human Body. 1999. (FRE & ENG., Illus.). 24p. (J). (ps-5). pap., stu. ed. 7.95 (978-88-8148-239-9(8)) European Language Institute ITA. *Dist:* Distribooks, Inc., Midwest European Pubns.

La Petite Fille Aux Allumettes.Tr. of Little Match Girl. (FRE.). 48p. pap. 12.95 incl. audio compact disk (978-2-89558-068-3(5)) Coffragants CAN. *Dist:* Penton Overseas, Inc.

Petty, J. T. Clemency Pogue: Fairy Killer. Davis, Will, illus. 2005. (Clemency Pogue Ser.). 128p. (J). 9.95 (978-0-689-87236-5(4) , Simon & Schuster Children's Publishing) Simon & Schuster Children's Publishing.

—The Hobgoblin Proxy. Davis, Will, illus. 2006. (Clemency Pogue Ser.). 160p. (J). (gr. 3-7). 9.95 (978-1-4169-0768-8(8) , Simon & Schuster Children's Publishing) Simon & Schuster Children's Publishing.

—The Scrivener Bees. Friend, David Michael, illus. 2007. (Clemency Pogue Ser.). 176p. (J). (gr. 3-7). 11.99 (978-1-4169-0769-5(6) , Simon & Schuster Children's Publishing) Simon & Schuster Children's Publishing.

Phelps, Karen. Grass Is Always Greener, the & Let Sleeping Dogs Lie: Two Original Fairy Tales. 2006. spiral bd. 23.00 ***(978-1-4108-7155-8(X))*** Benchmark Education Co.

Philip, Neil. American Fairy Tales: From Rip Van Winkle to the Rootabaga Stories. 1998. (J). (978-0-606-13122-3(1)) Tandem Library Bks.

—Las aventuras de Ulises. Julia Brugues, Berta, tr. Malone, Peter, illus. 2004. (SPA.). 72p. 19.95 (978-84-95939-70-8(3)) Blume ESP. *Dist:* Independent Pubs. Group.

—The Pirate Princess: And Other Fairy Tales. Weber, Mark, illus. 2005. 96p. (J). (ps-3). pap. 19.99 (978-0-590-10855-3(7) , Levine, Arthur A. Bks.) Scholastic, Inc.

Philip, Neil, ed. American Fairy Tales: From Rip Van Winkle to the Rootabaga Stories. McCuroy, Michael, illus. 2004. 160p. (J). (gr. k-4). reprint ed. pap. 13.00 (978-0-7567-8068-5(3)) DIANE Publishing Co.

Philpot, Graham, illus. Hansel & Gretel. 2007. (First Fairy Tales Ser.). 31p. (J). ***(978-1-59771-075-6(X))*** Sea-To-Sea Pubns.

Pichon, Liz, illus. Goldilocks & the Three Bears: Based on a Traditional Folk Tale. 1999. (First Favourite Tales Ser.). 32p. (J). (gr. k-3). 4.95 (978-0-7214-9733-4(0) , Dutton Juvenile) Penguin Group (USA) Inc.

—The Little Red Hen: Based on a Traditional Folk Tale. 1999. (First Favourite Tales Ser.). 32p. (J). 4.95 (978-0-7214-9739-6(X) , Dutton Juvenile) Penguin Group (USA) Inc.

Picture-Book People, 6 Packs. (Story Steps Ser.). (gr. k-2). 32.00 (978-0-7635-9819-8(4)) Rigby Education.

Pienkowski, Jan. The Fairy Tales. Walser, David, tr. from FRE. Pienkowski, Jan, illus. 2006. (Illus.). 188p. (J). (gr. 1-5). 19.99 (978-0-670-06189-1(1) , Viking Juvenile) Penguin Group (USA) Inc.

Pierre et le Loup. 2000. (Musicontes Ser.).Tr. of Peter & the Wolf. (FRE.). (J). 24.95 incl. audio (978-2-09-230475-4(5)) Nathan, Fernand FRA. *Dist:* Distribooks, Inc.

Pikey, Mikey. The Diamond Tree, Episode I: Coronation Day. 2006. 96p. pap. 14.00 (978-1-4116-7798-2(6)) Lulu.com.

Pileggi-Gabbamonte, Anne J. Cinderella in Rhyme. 1999. 32p. (J). (gr. k-6). pap. 10.00 (978-0-8059-4686-4(1)) Dorrance Publishing Co., Inc.

Pilzer, Karl. The Treasure of the Tear. Capps, Barbara, illus. Date not set. 40p. (J). pap. (978-0-936015-51-4(9)) Pocahontas Pr., Inc.

Pinkney, Brian & Andersen, Hans Christian. Thumbelina. Pinkney, Brian, illus. 2005. (Illus.). 37p. (J). (gr. k-4). reprint ed. 17.00 (978-0-7567-8834-6(X)) DIANE Publishing Co.

Pinkney, Jerry. Little Red Riding Hood. 2007. 40p. (J). (ps-3). 16.99 ***(978-0-316-01355-0(2))*** Little Brown & Co.

Pinkney, Jerry, et al. The Ugly Duckling (Spanish Version) El Patito Feo. Pinkney, Jerry, illus. 2007. (SPA.). 40p. (J). pap. 6.99 ***(978-0-06-111727-5(7)*** , Rayo) HarperCollins Pubs.

Pinocchio: The Human Body, Sea Life, The Bedroom. 1999. (FRE & ENG., Illus.). 24p. (J). (ps-5). pap., stu. ed. 7.95 (978-88-8148-243-6(6)) European Language Institute ITA. *Dist:* Distribooks, Inc., Midwest European Pubns.

Pinocho. 4th ed. 2002. (Troquelados Clasicos Ser.). (SPA & ENG., Illus.). 16p. pap. 2.95 (978-84-7864-218-2(8)) Combel Editorial, S.A. ESP. *Dist:* Independent Pubs. Group.

Pirotta, Saviour & Marks, Alan. The Enchanted Gazelle. 2007. (J). ***(978-1-59771-081-7(4))*** Sea-To-Sea Pubns.

—The Giant Oak Tree. 2007. (J). ***(978-1-59771-080-0(6))*** Sea-To-Sea Pubns.

—The Glass Palace. 2007. (J). ***(978-1-59771-078-7(4))*** Sea-To-Sea Pubns.

—The Golden Slipper. 2007. (J). ***(978-1-59771-077-0(6))*** Sea-To-Sea Pubns.

—Guess My Name. 2007. (J). ***(978-1-59771-082-4(2))*** Sea-To-Sea Pubns.

—The Lonely Princess. 2007. (J). ***(978-1-59771-079-4(2))*** Sea-To-Sea Pubns.

Pitman, Hinsdale Nor. A Chinese Wonder Book. 2006. 41.99 ***(978-1-4280-4098-4(6));*** pap. 34.99 ***(978-1-4280-4114-1(1))*** IndyPublish.com.

Plourde, Becky. Rose of Many Colors. 2005. 268p. pap. 21.95 (978-1-4137-6775-9(3)) PublishAmerica, Inc.

Plume, Ilse, illus. & retold by. The Bremen Town Musicians. Plume, Ilse, retold by. 1998. (ps-2). lib. bdg. 15.30 (978-0-8335-2036-4(9)) Tandem Library Bks.

Poer, Nancy Jewel. Mia's Apple Tree. Poer, Nancy Jewel, illus. 2004. (Illus.). 34p. (J). 21.95 (978-0-9740413-1-5(9)) White Feather Publishing.

Pohrte, Kathysue, et al. In the Land of Liviaann. Pohrte, Kathysue, ed. Pohrte, Olivia & Pohrte, Juliann, illus. l.t. ed. 2003. 36p. (J). pap. 17.95 (978-0-9722296-0-9(4) , 872493); 12.95 (978-0-9722296-1-6(2) , 872493) Pohrte, Dorey Publishing, Inc.

Polacco, Patricia. Luba & the Wren. 1999. (Illus.). 32p. (J). (ps-3). 16.99 (978-0-399-23168-1(4) , Philomel) Penguin Group (USA) Inc.

Polette, Keith. Isabel & the Hungry Coyote/Isabel y el Coyote Hambriento. de la Vega, Eida, tr. Szegedy, Esther, illus. 2006. Tr. of Isabel y el coyote Hambriento. (SPA.). (J). 4.99 (978-0-9770906-4-8(7)) Raven Tree Pr.

Ponsot, Marie. The Golden Book of Fairy Tales. Segur, Adrienne, illus. 1999. (Golden Book Ser.). 160p. (J). (ps-2). 19.99 (978-0-307-17025-5(X) , Golden Bks.) Random Hse. Children's Bks.

Poole, Amy Lowry & Andersen, Hans Christian. The Pea Blossom. 2005. (Illus.). 32p. (J). (ps-3). 16.95 (978-0-8234-1864-0(2)) Holiday Hse., Inc.

Poole, Josephine & Hess, Paul. Jack & the Beanstalk. 2004. (Stories to Collect & Treasure Ser.). (Illus.). 32p. (J). (gr. k-3). pap. (978-0-340-87784-5(7) , Hodder Children's Books) Hodder Children's Division.

Poortvliet, Rien. Gnome Clock Book. 1998. (Illus.). 24p. (J). 8.95 (978-1-57909-019-7(2)) Kabouter Products.

Porte, Barbara Ann. Hearsay: Tales from the Middle Kingdom. Covey, Rosemary, illus. 1998. 144p. (YA). (gr. 5 up). 15.00 (978-0-688-15381-6(X)) HarperCollins Pubs.

Posener, Alan. Marchenland. 2002. (GER.). (YA). pap. 6.95 (978-0-8219-1852-4(4) , 45316) EMC/Paradigm Publishing.

—Olli Aus Ossiland. 2002. (GER.). (YA). pap. 6.95 (978-0-8219-1463-2(4) , 45315) EMC/Paradigm Publishing.

Potpara, Lili, tr. Slovenian Folk Tales: The Shepherd; The Three Peas; The Golden Bird; The Riverman; Three Vixens; Harry the Hedgehog. Gosnik-Godec, Anèka, illus. 2002. 82p. (J). 29.00 (978-86-11-16248-5(X)) Mladinska Knjiga Zalozba, d.d. SVN. *Dist:* Bks. of Slovenia.

Potter, Beatrix. Selected Tales from Beatrix Potter. 2007. (Illus.). 128p. (J). 7.99 (978-0-7232-5859-9(7) , Warne) Penguin Group (USA) Inc.

Pouzadoux, Claude. Cuentos y Leyendas de la Mitologia Griega. 2003. (Fables & Legends Ser.). (SPA., Illus.). 160p. (J). 9.95 (978-84-239-9056-6(7)) Espasa Calpe, S.A. ESP. *Dist:* Libros Sin Fronteras, Planeta Publishing Corp.

Poveda, Mabel, illus. La Lechera. 2005. (Caballo alado clasico series-Al Paso Ser.). (SPA.). 24p. (J). 6.95 (978-84-7864-852-8(6)) Combel Editorial, S.A. ESP. *Dist:* Independent Pubs. Group.

Price, Kathy. The Bourbon Street Musicians. Glass, Andrew, illus. 2002. 40p. (J). (gr. k-3). 16.00 (978-0-618-04076-6(5) , Clarion Bks.) Houghton Mifflin Co. Trade & Reference Div.

Priceman, Marjorie. Little Red Riding Hood. Priceman, Marjorie, illus. 2001. (Classic Collectible Pop-Up Ser.). (Illus.). 14p. (J). 19.95 (978-0-689-83116-4(1) , Little Simon) Simon & Schuster Children's Publishing.

Prince, Sarah. Mr Wolf Tries Again. 1999. (gr. k-3). lib. bdg. 11.80 (978-0-613-19404-4(7)) Tandem Library Bks.

Principals New Cloth. 1998. (J). pap. 3.95 (978-0-439-04435-6(9)) Scholastic, Inc.

El Principe Feliz. 2nd ed. 2003. (Troquelados Clasicos Ser.). (SPA., Illus.). 16p. pap. 2.95 (978-84-7864-492-6(X)) Combel Editorial, S.A. ESP. *Dist:* Independent Pubs. Group.

El Prmncipe Feliz. 2002. 16p. pap. 2.95 (978-84-7864-488-9(1)) Casals Editorial ESP. *Dist:* Libros Sin Fronteras.

Prokofiev, Sergei. Peter & the Wolf. Johnson, Joe, tr. from FRE. Prado, Miguelanxo, illus. 1998. 32p. (ps-3). 15.95 (978-1-56163-200-8(7)) NBM Publishing Co.

—Peter & the Wolf. (Live Oak Readalong Ser.). pap. 18.95 incl. audio compact disk (978-1-59519-339-1(1)) Live Oak Media.

Prokofiev, Sergei & Gozzi, Carlo. The Love for Three Oranges. Gaudasinska, Elzbieta, illus. 2006. (Musical Stories Ser.: Vol. 1). 40p. (J). 16.95 (978-0-9646010-3-1(6)) Pumpkin Hse., Ltd.

Prole, Helen, illus. Cuentos con Calcomanios: Blanca Nieves y los Siete Enanitos. 2001. (First Class Ser.). (SPA.). 20p. (J). (ps-3). pap. (978-968-5308-30-4(6) , Silver Dolphin en Español) Advanced Marketing, S. de R. L. de C. V.

Proulx-Willis, Dana. Cinderella vs. the Stepfamily: A Fairy Tale Courtroom Event. 2007. 28p. pap. 6.00 ***(978-0-88734-696-5(0))*** Players Pr., Inc.

Publications International, creator. Disney Princess. 2004. (Disney Princess Ser.). (Illus.). (J). (ps). per. 12.98 (978-0-7853-9019-0(7) , 7195600) Publications International, Ltd.

Pullman, Philip. Puss in Boots: The Adventures of That Most Enterprising Feline. Beck, Ian, illus. 2001. 32p. (J). (gr. k-3). 16.95 (978-0-375-81354-2(3) , Knopf Bks. for Young Readers) Random Hse. Children's Bks.

Pullman, Philip & Parker, Kim. Aladdin & the Enchanted Lamp. Williams, Sophy, illus. 2005. 64p. (J). pap. 16.95 (978-0-439-69255-7(5) , Levine, Arthur A. Bks.) Scholastic, Inc.

Puss in Boots. 2002. (Classic Tales Mini Bks.). (Illus.). 32p. (J). (978-1-59069-035-2(4) , T1004); incl. audio compact disk (978-1-59069-102-1(4) , T1104) Studio Mouse LLC.

Pyle, Howard. Pepper & Salt & the Wonder Clock, Set. 2006. (Foundations Ser.). 385p. (J). 45.00 (978-1-933859-14-9(8)) ISI Bks.

—Twilight Land. 2006. 192p. pap. 11.99 (978-1-4264-0425-2(5)) BiblioBazaar.

—Twilight Land. 2006. (ENG.). pap. ***(978-1-4068-3431-4(9))*** Echo Library.

—Twilight Land. 2004. reprint ed. pap. 22.95 (978-1-4191-9142-8(X)) Kessinger Publishing, LLC.

Rackham, Arthur. A Fairy Book 1923. 2004. reprint ed. pap. 20.95 (978-1-4179-7656-0(X)) Kessinger Publishing, LLC.

Rackham, Arthur, illus. Cuentos de Andersen. 2003. (SPA.). 240p. 24.95 (978-84-261-0273-7(5) , JV30115) Juventud, Editorial ESP. *Dist:* Distribooks, Inc., Lectorum Pubns., Inc.

Rainbabies. 2004. 29.95 incl. cd-rom (978-1-55592-112-5(4)) Weston Woods Studios, Inc.

Randall, Ronne. Sleeping Beauty. (First Fairy Tales Ser.: No. S852-7). (Illus.). 25p. (J). (ps-2). pap. 3.95 (978-0-7214-5100-8(4) , Dutton Juvenile) Penguin Group (USA) Inc.

Random House Disney Staff. Ariel's Secret. Harchy, Atelier Philippe, illus. 2005. (Princess Secrets Ser.). 32p. (J). (ps-2). 4.99 (978-0-7364-2324-3(9) , RH/Disney) Random Hse. Children's Bks.

—Cinderella. Random House Disney Staff, tr. (FRE.). 96p. (J). (gr. k-5). pap. 9.95 (978-0-7859-8855-7(6)) French & European Pubns., Inc.

—Cinderella. 2005. (Illus.). 16p. (J). (ps). pap. 6.99 (978-0-7364-2355-7(9) , RH/Disney) Random Hse. Children's Bks.

—Cinderella. Dias, Ron & Lorencz, Bill, illus. 2005. (Little Golden Storybook Ser.). 24p. (J). (gr. k-k). lib. bdg. 2.99 (978-0-7364-2362-5(1) , Golden/Disney) Random Hse. Children's Bks.

—Cinderella. 2003. (Read-Aloud Board Bks.). (Illus.). 24p. (J). (gr. k-k). bds. 4.99 (978-0-7364-2204-8(8) , RH/Disney) Random Hse. Children's Bks.

—Cinderella. Random House Disney Staff, tr. 2002. (Illus.). (J). lib. bdg. 14.99 (978-0-7364-8020-8(X) , RH/Disney) Random Hse. Children's Bks.

—Cinderella. Dias, Ron, illus. 2002. 24p. (J). (gr. k-3). pap. 3.99 (978-0-7364-1296-4(4) , RH/Disney) Random Hse. Children's Bks.

—Cinderella. 2002. (gr. k-3). lib. bdg. 10.95 (978-0-613-73670-1(2)) Tandem Library Bks.

—The Little Mermaid. 2006. (Illus.). 12p. (J). (ps-1). pap. 6.99 (978-0-7364-2414-1(8) , RH/Disney) Random Hse. Children's Bks.

—Princess Story Collection. 2007. (Step into Reading Ser.). (Illus.). 160p. (J). (ps-1). pap. 7.99 ***(978-0-7364-2486-8(5)*** , RH/Disney) Random Hse. Children's Bks.

Random House Disney Staff. Snow White & the Seven Dwarfs. 2006. (Illus.). 24p. (J). (gr. k-k). bds. 4.99 (978-0-7364-2426-4(1) , RH/Disney) Random Hse. Children's Bks.

Random House Disney Staff & Liberts, Jennifer. Sleeping Beauty. 2002. (Shaped Coloring Book Ser.). (Illus.). 48p. (J). (ps-1). pap. 2.99 (978-0-7364-1286-5(7) , Golden/Disney) Random Hse. Children's Bks.

Random House Disney Staff & Posner-Sanchez, Andrea. Lovely Cinderella. 2004. (Illus.). 16p. (J). (gr. k-ps). bds. 3.99 (978-0-7364-2212-3(9) , RH/Disney) Random Hse. Children's Bks.

Random House Disney Staff & Teitelbaum, Michael. Sleeping Beauty. DiCicco, Sue, illus. 2003. (Disney Princess Ser.). 24p. (J). (gr. k-3). pap. 3.99 (978-0-7364-1318-3(9) , RH/Disney) Random Hse. Children's Bks.

Ransom, Candice. Little Red Riding Hood: Caperucita Roja. 2005. (Dual Language Keepsake Stories Ser.). (ENG & SPA., Illus.). 32p. (J). (gr. k-3). pap. 3.99 (978-0-7696-3817-1(1) , Brighter Child) School Specialty Publishing.

Ransom, Candice F. Goldilocks & the Three Bears. Bryant, Laura J., illus. 2002. (Brighter Child Keepsake Stories Ser.). 32p. (J). (ps-3). pap. 3.99 (978-1-57768-178-6(9) , Brighter Child) School Specialty Publishing.

—Little Red Riding Hood. Lyon, Tammie Speer, illus. 2002. (Brighter Child Keepsake Stories Ser.). 32p. (J). (ps-3). pap. 3.99 (978-1-57768-198-4(3) , Brighter Child) School Specialty Publishing.

Ransome, Arthur. The Firebird & Other Russian Fairy Tales. 2004. (Illus.). 128p. (J). pap. 5.95 (978-0-486-43893-1(7)) Dover Pubns., Inc.

—Little Daughter of the Snow. Guild, Shena, ed. Bower, Tom, illus. 2005. 32p. (J). 15.95 (978-1-84507-297-1(9)) Lincoln, Frances Ltd. GBR. *Dist:* Perseus Distribution.

Raote, Komilla. The Princess with the Longest Hair. Bist, Vandana, illus. 26p. (J). (978-81-85586-78-6(0)) Katha.

Rapunzel. 2002. (Classic Tales Mini Bks.). (Illus.). 32p. (J). (978-1-59069-032-1(X) , T1001); incl. audio compact disk (978-1-59069-099-4(0) , T1101) Studio Mouse LLC.

La Ratita Presumida. 3rd ed. 2002. (Troquelados Clasicos Ser.). (SPA & ENG., Illus.). 16p. pap. 2.95 (978-84-7864-185-7(8)) Combel Editorial, S.A. ESP. *Dist:* Independent Pubs. Group.

La Ratita Presumida. (Coleccion Fabulas y Cuentos Populares). (SPA.). (J). (gr. 2-4). (978-84-246-1603-8(0) , GL1026) La Galera, S.A. Editorial ESP. *Dist:* Lectorum Pubns., Inc.

El Ratoncito Perez. 2nd ed. 2002. (Troquelados Clasicos Ser.). (SPA & ENG., Illus.). 16p. pap. 2.95 (978-84-7864-490-2(3)) Combel Editorial, S.A. ESP. *Dist:* Independent Pubs. Group, Libros Sin Fronteras.

Ray, Jane, illus. Fairy Tales. 2000. 224p. (J). (gr. 3-7). 19.99 (978-0-7636-0997-9(8)) Candlewick Pr.

Read-It! Readers Fairy Tales, 24 bks. Incl. Brave LittleTailor : A Retelling of the Grimms' Fairy Tale. Shaw, David, illus. (C). 18.60 (978-1-4048-0315-2(7)); Bremen Town Muscians : A Retelling of the Grimms' Fairy Tale. Dickson, Dill, illus. (C). 18.60 (978-1-4048-0310-7(6)); Cinderella. Wade, Barrie. Monks, Julie, illus. (C). 18.60 (978-1-4048-0052-6(2)); Emperor's New Clothes : A Retelling of the Hans Christian Andersen Fairy Tale. Blackaby, Susan. DeLage, Charlene, illus. (C). 18.60 (978-1-4048-0224-7(X)); Fisherman & His Wife : A Retelling of the Grimms' Fairy Tale. Ouren, Todd, illus. (C). 18.60 (978-1-4048-0317-6(3)); Frog Prince : A Retelling of the Grimms' Fairy Tale. Ouren, Todd, illus. (C). 18.60 (978-1-4048-0313-8(0)); Goldilocks & the Three Bears. Wade, Barrie. Stephenson, Kristina, illus. (C). 18.60 (978-1-4048-0057-1(3)); Hansel & Gretel : A Retelling of the Grimms' Fairy Tale. Wolf, Claudia, illus. (C). 18.60 (978-1-4048-0316-9(5)); Jack & the Beanstalk. Moore, Maggie. Cox, Steve, illus. (C). 18.60 (978-1-4048-0059-5(X)); Little Mermaid : A Retelling of the Hans Christian Andersen Fairy Tale. Blackaby, Susan. DeLage, Charlene, illus. (C). 18.60 (978-1-4048-0221-6(5)); Little Red Riding Hood. Moore, Maggie. Knight, Paula, illus. (C). 18.60 (978-1-4048-0064-9(6)); Princess & the Pea : A Retelling of the Hans Christian Andersen Fairy Tale. Blackaby, Susan. DeLage, Charlene, illus. (C). 18.60 (978-1-4048-0223-0(1)); Puss in Boots : A Retelling of the Grimms' Fairy Tale. Blair, Eric. Ouren, Todd, illus. (J). 18.60 (978-1-4048-0591-0(5)); Rumpelstiltskin : A Retelling of the Grimms' Fairy Tale. Shaw, David, illus. (C). 18.60 (978-1-4048-0311-4(4)); Shoemaker & His Elves : A Retelling of the Grimms' Fairy Tale. Dickson, Bill, illus. (J). 18.60 (978-1-4048-0314-5(9)); Sleeping Beauty : A Retelling of the Grimms' Fairy Tale. Blair, Eric. Ouren, Todd, illus. (C). 18.60 (978-1-4048-0592-7(3)); Snow White : A Retelling of the Grimms' Fairy Tale. Wolf, Claudia, illus. (C). 18.60 (978-1-4048-0312-1(2)); Steadfast Tin Soldier : A Retelling of the Hans Christian Andersen Fairy Tale. Blackaby, Susan.

E
F
G

DeLage, Charlene, illus. (C). 18.60 (978-1-4048-0226-1(6)); Three Billy Goats Gruff. Wade, Barrie. (C). 18.60 (978-1-4048-0070-0(0)); Three Little Pigs. Moore, Maggie. Hefferan, Rob, illus. (C). 18.60 (978-1-4048-0071-7(9)); Thumbelina : A Retelling of the Hans Christian Andersen Fairy Tale. Blackaby, Susan. DeLage, Charlene, illus. (C). 18.60 (978-1-4048-0225-4(8)); Tom Thumb : A Retelling of the Classic Fairy Tale. Blair, Eric. Ouren, Todd, illus. (J). 18.60 (978-1-4048-0593-4(1)); Ugly Duckling : A Retelling of the Hans Christian Andersen Fairy Tale. Blackaby, Susan. DeLage, Charlene, illus. (C). 18.60 (978-1-4048-0222-3(3)); Wolf & the Seven Little Kids : A Retelling of the Grimms' Fairy Tale. Blair, Eric. Petrusek, Brett, illus. (J). 18.60 (978-1-4048-0594-1(X)); 32p. (gr. k-3). 2004. 2003. Set lib. bdg. 446.40 (978-1-4048-0639-9(3)) Picture Window Bks.

Reader's Digest Staff & Katschke, Judy. Barbie Pretty Hairstyle Revised. 2006. (Style Bks.). 12p. (J). bds. 12.99 (978-0-7944-1009-4(X)) Reader's Digest Assn., Inc., The.

Reasoner, Charles. Humpty Dumpty... after the Fall. Reasoner, Charles, illus. 2005. (Illus.). 12p. (J). (ps-ps). bds. 7.99 (978-0-8431-1347-1(2) , Price Stern Sloan) Penguin Group (USA) Inc.

Redbank, Tennant. Barbie in the Twelve Dancing Princesses. 2006. (Step into Reading Ser.). (Illus.). 32p. (J). (ps-2). lib. bdg. 11.99 (978-0-375-93780-4(3) , Random Hse. Bks. for Young Readers) Random Hse. Children's Bks.

Redbank, Tennant & Golden Books Staff. Barbie in the Twelve Dancing Princesses. 2006. (Step into Reading Ser.: No. 2). (Illus.). 32p. (J). (ps-2). pap. 3.99 (978-0-375-83780-7(9) , Random Hse. Bks. for Young Readers) Random Hse. Children's Bks.

Reece, Bernadette. Nervy the Ghost. 2004. 21p. pap. 14.95 (978-1-4137-2021-1(8)) PublishAmerica, Inc.

Reed, Nathan, illus. The Buskers of Bremen. 2004. 24p. (J). (TAM, CZE, VIE, SPA & GUJ.). (978-1-85269-800-3(4)); (TAM, CZE, VIE, SPA & GUJ.). pap. (978-1-85269-765-5(2)); (TAM, CZE, VIE, SPA & GUJ.). pap. (978-1-85269-766-2(0)); (TAM, CZE, VIE, SPA & GUJ.). pap. (978-1-85269-767-9(9)); (TAM, CZE, VIE, SPA & GUJ.). pap. (978-1-85269-768-6(7)); (TAM, CZE, VIE, SPA & GUJ.). pap. (978-1-85269-770-9(9)); (TAM, CZE, VIE, SPA & GUJ.). pap. (978-1-85269-771-6(7)); (TAM, CZE, VIE, SPA & GUJ.). pap. (978-1-85269-772-3(5)); (TAM, CZE, VIE, SPA & GUJ.). pap. (978-1-85269-773-0(3)); (TAM, CZE, VIE, SPA & GUJ.). pap. (978-1-85269-225-4(1)); (TAM, CZE, VIE, SPA & GUJ.). pap. (978-1-85269-775-4(X)); (TAM, CZE, VIE, SPA & GUJ.). pap. (978-1-85269-776-1(8)); (TAM, CZE, VIE, SPA & GUJ.). pap. (978-1-85269-777-8(6)); (TAM, CZE, VIE, SPA & GUJ.). pap. (978-1-85269-778-5(4)); (CZE, TAM, VIE, SPA & GUJ.). pap. (978-1-85269-779-2(2)); (TAM, CZE, VIE, SPA & GUJ.). pap. (978-1-85269-780-8(6)); (TAM, CZE, VIE, SPA & GUJ.). pap. (978-1-85269-781-5(4)); (TAM, CZE, SPA, VIE & GUJ.). pap. (978-1-85269-782-2(2)); (TAM, CZE, VIE, SPA & GUJ.). pap. (978-1-85269-774-7(1)) Mantra Publishing, Ltd.

Rees, Gwyneth. Fairy Dust. 2005. (Read-along Ser.). (Illus.). (J). audio (978-0-7540-6286-8(4)) BBC Audio.

Reese, Kevin M., adapted by. Santa's Elves & the Shoemaker: Musical Version. 2000. pap. (978-1-932240-42-9(X)) KMR Scripts.

Regenold, Theresa. Not Your Average Princess: A Real-Life Fairy Tale. 2005. 117p. pap. 16.95 (978-1-4137-9308-6(8)) PublishAmerica, Inc.

Reichenstetter, Friederun. Andersens Fairy Tales. Leffler, Silke, illus. 2007. 0096p. 19.95 (***978-0-7358-2141-5(0)***) North-South Bks., Inc.

La Reina De Las Abejas. 2002. 16p. pap. 2.95 (978-84-7864-487-2(3)) Casals Editorial ESP. *Dist:* Libros Sin Fronteras.

La Reina de las Abejas. 2nd ed. 2002. (Troquelados Clasicos Ser.). (SPA & ENG., Illus.). 16p. pap. 2.95 (978-84-7864-491-9(1)) Combel Editorial, S.A. ESP. *Dist:* Independent Pubs. Group.

Reinhart, Matthew. Cinderella: A Pop-up Fairy Tale. Reinhart, Matthew, illus. 2005. (Illus.). 12p. (J). 25.99 (978-1-4169-0501-1(4) , Little Simon) Simon & Schuster Children's Publishing.

Reynolds, Patrick M. Texas Lore, Vols. 1-4. 2000. (gr. 7-12). lib. bdg. 24.55 (978-0-613-77643-1(7)) Tandem Library Bks.

Rhys, Ernest. Fairy Gold: A Book of Classic English Fairy Tales. Cole, Herbert, illus. 1999. (Library of Folklore). 236p. (gr. 4-7). 14.95 (978-0-7818-0700-5(X)) Hippocrene Bks., Inc.

Ricci, Christine. Dora's Fairy-Tale Adventure. Hall, Susan', illus. ed. 2005. (Dora the Explorer Ser.: No. 9). 22p. (J). lib. bdg. 15.00 (978-1-59054-795-3(0)) Fitzgerald Bks.

Ricitos de Oro. 2nd ed. 2002. (Troquelados Clasicos Ser.). (ENG & SPA., Illus.). 16p. pap. 2.95 (978-84-7864-324-0(9)) Combel Editorial, S.A. ESP. *Dist:* Independent Pubs. Group.

Ricitos de Oro. (SPA.). (J). 12.00 (978-958-02-1237-9(6)) Editorial Voluntad S.A. COL. *Dist:* Distribuidora Norma, Inc.

Ricitos de Oro y los Tres Osos. 2001. (SPA.). (978-968-6347-34-0(8)) Larousse, Ediciones, S. A. de C. V.

Rieger, Anja, illus. The Gingerbread Man: Based on a Traditional Folk Tale. 1999. (First Favourite Tales Ser.). 32p. (J). 4.95 (978-0-7214-9731-0(4) , Dutton Juvenile) Penguin Group (USA) Inc.

Rigby Education Staff. Cinderella: Jumbled Tumble. (gr. k-2). 26.00 (978-0-7635-2420-3(4)) Rigby Education.

Riggio, Anita, retold by. Beware the Brindlebeast. 2003. (Illus.). 32p. (J). (ps-1). pap. 8.95 (978-1-56397-684-1(6)) Boyds Mills Pr.

Riordan, James, ed. Stories from the Sea. Hall, Amanda, illus. 2002. 79p. (J). (gr. 4-6). 20.00 (978-0-7567-5638-3(3)) DIANE Publishing Co.

Rissik, Maureen. The Tooth Fairy Box: A Magical Gift to Unlock & Treasure. 1999. (Illus.). 24p. (J). (ps-3). pap. 9.95 (978-0-7624-0538-1(4) , Running Pr. Kids) Running Pr. Bk. Pubs.

Rius, Maria, illus. La Castanera. 2005. (Caballo alado clasicos-Al Trote Ser.). (SPA.). 24p. (J). 6.95 (978-84-7864-868-9(2)) Combel Editorial, S.A. ESP. *Dist:* Independent Pubs. Group.

Rius, R. Los Tres Cerditos. 1998. (Fairy Tale Theater Ser.).Tr. of Three Little Pigs. (SPA., Illus.). 32p. (J). (gr. k-3). pap. 8.95 (978-0-7641-5147-7(9)) Barron's Educational Series, Inc.

Rius, Roser. Hansel & Gretel. 1998. (Fairy Tale Theater Ser.). (Illus.). 32p. (J). (gr. k-3). pap. 8.95 (978-0-7641-5113-2(4)) Barron's Educational Series, Inc.

—Hansel y Gretel. 1998. (Fairy Tale Theater Ser.). (SPA., Illus.). 32p. (J). (gr. k-3). 8.95 (978-0-7641-5145-3(2)) Barron's Educational Series, Inc.

—The Three Little Pigs. 1998. (Fairy Tale Theater Ser.). (Illus.). 32p. (J). (gr. k-3). pap. 8.95 (978-0-7641-5115-6(0)) Barron's Educational Series, Inc.

Robbins, John. The Tooth Fairy Is Broke. Owings, Rae, illus. 2002. 48p. (J). (gr. 2-4). 14.99 (978-0-88092-569-3(8) , 5698) Royal Fireworks Publishing Co.

Roberts, Lynn. Cinderella: An Art Deco Love Story. Roberts, David, illus. 2001. 32p. (J). (ps-3). 16.95 (978-0-8109-4168-7(6)) Abrams, Harry N. , Inc.

—Little Red: A Fizzingly Good Yarn. Roberts, David, illus. 2005. 32p. (J). (ps-3). 16.95 (978-0-8109-5783-1(3) , Abrams Bks. for Young Readers) Abrams, Harry N. , Inc.

—Rapunzel: A Groovy Fairy Tale. Roberts, David, illus. 2003. 32p. (J). (ps-3). 16.95 (978-0-8109-4242-4(9)) Abrams, Harry N. , Inc.

Robinson, Hilary & Sharratt, Nick. Mixed up Fairy Tales. 2005. (Illus.). (J). (ps-ps). 17.99 (978-0-340-87557-5(7)) Headway GBR. *Dist:* Trafalgar Square Publishing.

—Mixed up Fairy Tales. 2007. (Illus.). 30p. pap. 11.95 (***978-0-340-87558-2(5)***) Hodder Children's Division GBR. *Dist:* Independent Pubs. Group.

Rodda, Emily. Enter the Realm: Three Fairy Realm Adventures. Vitale, Raoul, illus. 2007. (Fairy Realm Ser.). 352p. (J). 9.99 (***978-0-06-120845-4(0)***) HarperCollins Pubs.

Rogers, Beth. Barbie As Rapunzel. 2006. 16p. (J). 7.99 (978-0-7944-0945-6(8)) Reader's Digest Assn., Inc., The.

Roldan, Gustavo. Cuentos del Zorro. (Cuentamerica Ser.). (SPA.). 64p. (J). (gr. 4-6). (978-950-07-1557-7(0) , SA30061) Editorial Sudamericana S.A. ARG. *Dist:* Lectorum Pubns., Inc.

Ross, Kathy. Crafts from Your Favorite Fairy Tales. Enright, Vicky, illus. 2001. 51p. 20.00 (978-0-7881-9963-9(3)) DIANE Publishing Co.

—Crafts from Your Favorite Fairy Tales. 1998. 3. (Illus.). 48p. (J). (gr. k-4). pap. 8.95 (978-0-7613-0342-8(1) , Millbrook Pr.) Lerner Publishing Group.

Ross, M. Little Red Riding Hood. Rieger, Anja, illus. 1999. (First Favourite Tales Ser.). 32p. (J). (gr. k-3). pap. 4.95 (978-0-7214-9734-1(9) , Dutton Juvenile) Penguin Group (USA) Inc.

Roszel, Karen, illus. The Diamond Button. l.t. ed. 2005. 32p. (J). bds. 14.95 (978-0-9709630-7-9(6)) Coal Hole Productions.

Rothman, Cynthia. Tell Me a Story. Tormey, Carlotta, illus. 2002. 16p. (J). (978-0-439-35088-4(3)) Scholastic, Inc.

Rovira, Francesc, illus. Caperucita Roja. 2005. (Caballo alado clasico series-Al Paso Ser.). (SPA.). 24p. (J). 6.95 (978-84-7864-851-1(8)) Combel Editorial, S.A. ESP. *Dist:* Independent Pubs. Group.

Rox, Steven. The Adventures of Grassie Green in the Colored Worlds: The Flower Country & the Green World, 3 vols. 500th ed. 2006. Orig. Title: The Flower Country & the Green World. (Illus.). 437p. (YA). cd-rom 14.95 (978-0-9773406-0-6(0)) SR Publishing Co.

Royde-Smith, N. G. Una and the Red Cross Knight & Other T. 2006. (Illus.). pap. 28.95 (***978-1-4254-8407-1(7)***) Kessinger Publishing, LLC.

El Ruisenor: he Nightingale. 2004. (Troquelados Clasicos Ser.). (SPA.). 16p. (J). pap. 2.95 (978-84-7864-733-0(3)) Combel Editorial, S.A. ESP. *Dist:* Independent Pubs. Group.

Ruiz. La Bella y la Bestia. 2nd ed. 2002. (Troquelados Clasicos Ser.). (SPA & ENG., Illus.). 16p. pap. 2.95 (978-84-7864-327-1(3)) Combel Editorial, S.A. ESP. *Dist:* Independent Pubs. Group.

Ruiz Abello, Margarita. El Gato con Botas. 3rd ed. 2002. (Troquelados Clasicos Ser.).Tr. of Puss in Boots. (SPA & ENG., Illus.). 16p. pap. 2.95 (978-84-7864-280-9(3)) Combel Editorial, S.A. ESP. *Dist:* Independent Pubs. Group.

—La Princesa y el Guisante. 2003. (Troquelados Clasicos Ser.). (SPA & ENG., Illus.). 16p. pap. 2.95 (978-84-7864-677-7(9)) Combel Editorial, S.A. ESP. *Dist:* Independent Pubs. Group.

Ruiz, Margarita, illus. Aladino. 2nd ed. 2002. (Troquelados Clasicos Ser.).Tr. of Aladdin. (SPA & ENG.). 16p. pap. 2.95 (978-84-7864-325-7(7)) Combel Editorial, S.A. ESP. *Dist:* Independent Pubs. Group.

—Historia de un Conejito. 2005. (Troquelados clasicos Ser.). (SPA.). 16p. (J). pap. 2.95 (978-84-7864-898-6(4)) Combel Editorial, S.A. ESP. *Dist:* Independent Pubs. Group.

—El Pez de Oro. 2005. (Troquelados clasicos Ser.). (SPA.). 16p. (J). pap. 2.95 (978-84-7864-897-9(6)) Combel Editorial, S.A. ESP. *Dist:* Independent Pubs. Group.

—El rey Midas. 2005. (Troquelados clasicos Ser.). (SPA.). 16p. (J). pap. 2.95 (978-84-7864-895-5(X)) Combel Editorial, S.A. ESP. *Dist:* Independent Pubs. Group.

—El sastrecillo Valiente. 2005. (Troquelados clasicos Ser.). (SPA.). 16p. (J). pap. 2.95 (978-84-7864-896-2(8)) Combel Editorial, S.A. ESP. *Dist:* Independent Pubs. Group.

Rumpelstiltskin. (Ladybird Bks.). (ARA., Illus.). 52p. (J). 4.95 (978-0-86685-222-7(0)) International Bk. Ctr., Inc.

Russell, Janice. Goldilocks. Russell, Janice, illus. 2003. (Illus.). 32p. (YA). (ps up). 8.95 (978-1-56397-430-4(4)) Boyds Mills Pr.

Russell, P. Craig. Fairy Tales of Oscar Wilde: The Birthday of the Infanta. 2003. (Illus.). 32p. (gr. 3-6). (Fairy Tales of Oscar Wilde Ser.: Vol. 3). 15.95 (978-1-56163-213-8(9)); 45.00 (978-1-56163-214-5(7)) NBM Publishing Co.

Russell, P. Craig, illus. The Young King & Remarkable Rocket, Vol. 2. aut. num. ltd. ed. 2003. (Fairy Tales of Oscar Wilde Ser.: Vol. 2). 45.00 (978-1-56163-099-8(3)) NBM Publishing Co.

Russler, Sydney. Ella of Frell. 2002. (AFR.). 253p. (YA). pap. 14.95 (978-0-595-22965-9(4) , Writers Club Pr.) iUniverse, Inc.

Ryan, Brittney. The Legend of Holly Claus. Long, Laurel, illus. 2004. 544p. (J). (gr. 4 up). 16.99 (978-0-06-058511-2(0)); lib. bdg. 17.89 (978-0-06-058514-3(5)) HarperCollins Pubs. (Julie Andrews Collection).

—Legend of Holly Claus. Long, Laurel, illus. 2006. 544p. (J). pap. 7.99 (978-0-06-058515-0(3) , Julie Andrews Collection) HarperCollins Pubs.

Ryan, Margaret. Magic Mess! Murfin, Teresa, illus. 2005. (Airy Fairy Bks.). 80p. (J). pap. 3.95 (978-0-7641-3188-2(5)) Barron's Educational Series, Inc.

—Magic Mischief! Murfin, Teresa, illus. 2005. (Airy Fairy Bks.: Vol. 1). 80p. (J). pap. 3.95 (978-0-7641-3186-8(9)) Barron's Educational Series, Inc.

—Magic Mix-up! Murfin, Teresa, illus. 2005. (Airy Fairy Bks.: Vol. 4). 80p. (J). pap. 3.95 (978-0-7641-3189-9(3)) Barron's Educational Series, Inc.

—Magic Muddle! Murfin, Teresa, illus. 2005. (Airy Fairy Bks.). 80p. (J). pap. 3.95 (978-0-7641-3187-5(7)) Barron's Educational Series, Inc.

Rymer, Alta M. Up from Uzam. Rymer, Alta M., illus. (Tharma Lo Fairyland Ser.: Story 1). (Illus.). 28p. (Orig.). (J). (gr. 2-4). pap. 20.00 (978-0-9600792-8-5(9)) Rymer Bks.

Saint-Exupéry, Antoine de. Friends of The Little Prince. 2003. (Illus.). (J). bds. (978-0-15-204729-0(8)) Harcourt Trade Pubs.

Saint-Exupery, Antoine De. Inkosana Encane. 2006. 90p. pap. 11.95 (***978-1-919855-65-3(3)***) STE Pubs. ZAF. *Dist:* Independent Pubs. Group.

Saint-Exupéry, Antoine de. The Little Prince. Howard, Richard, tr. from FRE. Saint-Exupéry, Antoine de, illus. 2000. (Illus.). 96p. (gr. 4-7). pap. 10.00 (978-0-15-601219-5(7) , Harvest Bks.) Harcourt Trade Pubs.

—The Little Prince. Howard, Richard, tr. from FRE. 2000. (Illus.). 96p. (YA). (gr. 4-7). 19.00 (978-0-15-202398-0(4)) Harcourt Trade Pubs.

—The Little Prince. 2000. (gr. 3-6). lib. bdg. 22.25 (978-0-613-71610-9(8)); (gr. 5-8). lib. bdg. 17.65 (978-0-8085-6337-2(8)) Tandem Library Bks.

—Le Petit Prince. 2001. Tr. of Little Prince. (FRE.). (J). audio 22.50 (978-0-8442-1383-5(7)) Glencoe/McGraw-Hill.

—Regulus. Haury, Augusto, tr. 2001. (LAT., Illus.). 96p. pap. 10.00 (978-0-15-601404-5(1) , Harvest Bks.) Harcourt Trade Pubs.

Salan, Felipe Lopez, illus. Jack & the Beanstalk. 2006. 32p. (J). 15.95 (978-1-933327-11-2(1)) Purple Bear Bks., Inc.

The Salt Mountain. 2004. (Illus.). 32p. 3.99 (978-1-894998-06-2(5)) Lake, Jack Productions, Inc. CAN. *Dist:* Hushion Hse. Publishing, Ltd.

San Jose, Christine. Sleeping Beauty. Catalano, Dominic, illus. 2003. 32p. (YA). (gr. 2-4). 14.95 (978-1-56397-636-0(6)) Boyds Mills Pr.

San José, Christine, et al. The Six Swans. Cole, Jes, illus. 2006. (J). 16.95 (978-1-59078-056-5(6)) Boyds Mills Pr.

San Souci, Robert D. Brave Margaret: An Irish Adventure. Comport, Sally Wern, illus. 1999. 40p. (J). (gr. k-5). 17.95 (978-0-689-81072-5(5)) Simon & Schuster Children's Publishing.

—Brave Margaret: An Irish Adventure. 2002. (gr. 3-6). lib. bdg. 15.30 (978-0-613-45016-4(7)) Tandem Library Bks.

—Cendrillon: A Caribbean Cinderella. Pinkney, Brian, illus. 2002. 40p. (J). (gr. k-5). 7.99 (978-0-689-84888-9(9) , Aladdin) Simon & Schuster Children's Publishing.

—Cendrillon: A Caribbean Cinderella. 2002. (gr. 3-6). lib. bdg. 15.30 (978-0-613-45021-8(3)) Tandem Library Bks.

—Cinderella Skeleton. Catrow, David, illus. 2000. 32p. (J). (ps-2). 16.00 (978-0-15-202003-3(9) , Silver Whistle) Harcourt Trade Pubs.

—Cinderella Skeleton. Catrow, David, illus. 2004. 32p. (J). reprint ed. pap. 6.00 (978-0-15-205069-6(8) , Voyager Bks./Libros Viajeros) Harcourt Children's Bks.

—A Weave of Words. Colon, Raul, illus. 1998. 32p. (J). (gr. k-4). 17.99 (978-0-531-33053-1(2)); pap. 16.95 (978-0-531-30053-4(6)) Scholastic, Inc. (Orchard Bks.).

San Souci, Robert D. & Comport, Sally. Brave Margaret: An Irish Adventure. 2002. (Illus.). 40p. (J). pap. 7.99 (978-0-689-84850-6(1) , Aladdin) Simon & Schuster Children's Publishing.

Sandburg, Carl. Rootabaga Stories. Petersham, Maud & Petersham, Miska, illus. 2004. 240p. (J). (gr. 4-7). reprint ed. per. 15.95 (978-1-55709-490-2(X)) Applewood Bks.

—Rootabaga Stories. Petersham, Maud & Petersham, Miska, illus. 2002. 256p. 24.95 (978-0-87483-697-4(2)); pap. 14.95 (978-0-87483-698-1(0)) August Hse. Pubs., Inc.

—Rootabaga Stories. Petersham, Maud & Petersham, Miska, illus. 2003. 192p. (YA). pap. 5.95 (978-0-15-204714-6(X) , Odyssey Classics) Harcourt Children's Bks.

Sanderson, Ruth. Cinderella: Grades 1-3. 2002. 32p. pap., tchr. ed. 15.95 (978-0-316-07248-9(6)) Little, Brown Bks. for Young Readers.

—Papa Gatto: An Italian Fairy. 1999. (978-0-606-17849-5(X)) Tandem Library Bks.

—The Snow Princess. 2005. (J). (ps-3). pap. 1.45 (978-0-316-10582-8(1)) Little Brown & Co.

Santillo, LuAnn. Jack. Santillo, LuAnn, ed. 2003. (Half-Pint Kids Readers Ser.). (Illus.). 7p. (J). (ps-1). pap. (978-1-59256-062-2(8)) Half-Pint Kids, Inc.

Sarin, Amita. Akbar & Birbal. 2005. (Illus.). 160p. (J). pap. 8.00 (978-0-14-333494-1(8) , Penguin Global) Penguin Group (USA) Inc.

Satrapi, Marjane. Monsters Are Afraid of the Moon. 2006. (Illus.). 32p. (J). 15.95 (978-1-58234-744-8(1) , Bloomsbury Children) Bloomsbury Publishing.

Saunders, Catherine. The Essential Guide. 2005. (Illus.). 48p. (J). (ps-7). 12.99 (978-0-7566-1333-4(7)) Dorling Kindersley Publishing, Inc.

Saunders, Catherine & Dorling Kindersley Publishing Staff. Barbie Princess Tales. 2005. (Ultimate sticker Bks.). (Illus.). 16p. (J). (ps-7). pap. 6.99 (978-0-7566-1332-7(9)) Dorling Kindersley Publishing, Inc.

Saunders, George. The Very Persistent Gappers of Frip. Smith, Lane, illus. 2006. 84p. (J). 20.00 (978-1-932416-37-4(4)) McSweeney's Publishing.

Sauvant, Henriette. Rapunzel & Other Magic Fairy Tales. Bell, Anthea, tr. from MUL. 2007. (Illus.). 160p. (J). (gr. k-2). pap. 15.95 (***978-1-4052-2702-5(8)***) Egmont Bks., Ltd. GBR. *Dist:* Independent Pubs. Group.

Scalora, Suza. The Fairies. 1999. 48p. (J). pap. 9.95 (978-0-06-440752-6(7)) HarperCollins Pubs.

Scarry, Richard. Richard Scarry's Animal Nursery Tales. 2006. (Illus.). 72p. (J). (ps-3). 14.95 (978-0-375-83791-3(4) , Golden Bks.) Random Hse. Children's Bks.

Schleh, Joy. Jack & the Beanstalk: How a Small Fellow Solved a Big Problem. Lorenz, Albert, illus. 2002. 40p. (J). (ps-4). 16.95 (978-0-8109-1160-4(4)) Abrams, Harry N. , Inc.

Schmidt, Gary D. Straw into Gold. 2001. (Illus.). 176p. (J). (gr. 4-6). tchr. ed. 15.00 (978-0-618-05601-9(7) , Clarion Bks.) Houghton Mifflin Co. Trade & Reference Div.

Schmidt, Karen Lee. The Gingerbread Man. 2007. (Illus.). 31p. (J). (ps-3). pap. 18.95 incl. audio compact disk (***978-0-545-01781-7(5)***) Scholastic, Inc.

Schneider, Evanne. Pass the SAT the Humorous Way: Lampooning Fairy Tales. Yaras, Adam, illus. 2000. 315p. (YA). (gr. 8-11). pap. 18.95 (978-0-9700747-2-0(7)) Westcreek Industries/Westcreek Publishing.

Scholastic, Inc. Staff. Thumbelina/Pulgarcita. Andrada, Javier, illus. 2007. (Bilingual Tales Ser.). (ENG & SPA.). 24p. (J). pap. 3.99 (***978-0-439-87196-9(4)***) Scholastic, Inc.

Scholastic, Inc. Staff, et al. The Little Mermaid. Lanza, Barbara, illus. 2003. (Scholastic Reader Ser.). 32p. (J). pap. 3.99 (978-0-439-47154-1(0) , Cartwheel Bks.) Scholastic, Inc.

School Specialty Publishing, retold by. Princess Tales. 2004. (Handle Book with CD Ser.). 96p. (J). 14.95 (978-1-58845-736-3(2)) School Specialty Publishing.

Schulman, Janet. The Nutcracker. Graef, Renee, illus. 2005. 40p. (J). pap. 6.99 (978-0-06-443790-5(6) , Harper Trophy) HarperCollins Pubs.

Schulman, Janet & Hoffmann, E. T. A. The Nutcracker. Graef, Renee, illus. 1999. 40p. (J). (gr. k-3). 19.99 (978-0-06-027814-4(5)) HarperCollins Pubs.

Schumacher, Stef. The Gingerbread Man. Catusanu, Mircea, illus. 2002. 16p. (J). (978-0-439-35087-7(5)) Scholastic, Inc.

Scieszka, Jon. The Frog Prince, Continued. 2003. (Live Oak Readalong Ser.). (Illus.). (J). 25.95 incl. audio (978-1-59112-229-6(5)); 28.95 incl. audio compact disk (978-1-59112-515-0(4)); pap. 18.95 incl. audio compact disk (978-1-59112-490-0(5)); pap. 16.95 incl. audio (978-1-59112-228-9(7)) Live Oak Media.

—The Frog Prince, Continued. Johnson, Steve, illus. 2003. pap. 39.95 incl. audio compact disk (978-1-59112-522-8(7)) Live Oak Media.

—The Frog Prince, Continued, 4 bks. 2003. (Live Oak Readalong Ser.). (J). pap. 37.95 incl. audio (978-1-59112-230-2(9)) Live Oak Media.

Scieszka, Jon. The Stinky Cheese Man & Other Fairly Stupid Tales. 2002. (Illus.). (J). 13.19 (978-0-7587-0147-3(0)) Book Wholesalers, Inc.

—The Stinky Cheese Man & Other Fairly Stupid Tales. Smith, Lane, illus. 2004. 48p. (J). (gr. k-4). reprint ed. 22.00 (978-0-7567-7699-2(6)) DIANE Publishing Co.

—The Stinky Cheese Man & Other Fairly Stupid Tales. Smith, Lane, illus. 2007. 56p. (J). (ps). pap. 9.99 (***978-0-670-06300-0(2)*** , Viking Juvenile) Penguin Group (USA) Inc.

Sedgwick, Marcus & Andersen, Hans Christian. Emperor's New Clothes. Jay, Alison, illus. 2004. 32p. (J). 16.95 (978-0-8118-4569-4(9)) Chronicle Bks. LLC.

Segal, Lore. The Juniper Tree: And Other Tales from Grimm. Segal, Lore & Jarrell, Randall, trs. from GER. Sendak, Maurice, illus. 2003. 368p. (J). 28.00 (978-0-374-33971-5(6) , Farrar, Straus & Giroux (BYR)) Farrar, Straus & Giroux.

Seibert, Patricia. The Three Little Pigs. Elena, Horacio, illus. 2002. (Brighter Child Keepsake Stories Ser.). 32p. (J). (ps-3). pap. 3.99 (978-1-57768-367-4(6) , Brighter Child) School Specialty Publishing.

Seleccion de Oro: Libro Azul.Tr. of Golden Selection of Tales - Blue Book. (SPA.). (J). 13.48 (978-84-8426-241-1(3)) Susaeta Ediciones, S.A. ESP. *Dist:* AIMS International Bks., Inc.

Seleccion de Oro: Libro Morado.Tr. of Golden Selection: Purple Book. (SPA.). (J). 13.48 (978-84-8426-240-4(5)) Susaeta Ediciones, S.A. ESP. *Dist:* AIMS International Bks., Inc.

Seleccion de Oro: Libro Rojo.Tr. of Golden Selection: Red Book. (SPA.). (J). 13.48 (978-84-8426-243-5(X)) Susaeta Ediciones, S.A. ESP. *Dist:* AIMS International Bks., Inc.

Seleccion de Oro: Libro Verde.Tr. of Golden Selection - Green Book. (SPA.). (J). 13.48 (978-84-8426-242-8(1)) Susaeta Ediciones, S.A. ESP. *Dist:* AIMS International Bks., Inc.

Selected Classic Fairy Tales Series, 2 bks. (Illus.). (J). (gr. k-6). lib. bdg. 27.90 (978-1-56674-945-9(X)) Forest Hse. Publishing Co., Inc.

Sengupta, Poile. Vikram & Vetal. 2005. 144p. (J). pap. 8.00 (978-0-14-333498-9(0) , Penguin Global) Penguin Group (USA) Inc.

Serra, Sebastia, illus. Garbancito. 2005. (Caballo alado clasico series-Al Paso Ser.). (SPA.). 24p. (J). (ps-k). 6.95 (978-84-7864-853-5(4)) Combel Editorial, S.A. ESP. *Dist:* Independent Pubs. Group.

Seuss, Dr. The King's Stilts. Seuss, Dr., illus. 2002. (Illus.). (J). 22.40 (978-0-7587-2934-7(0)) Book Wholesalers, Inc.

Shah, Idries. Neem the Half-boy. Revels, Robert & Mori, Midori, illus. 1998. 32p. (J). (gr. 4-7). 17.00 (978-1-883536-10-7(3) , NEHB1, Hoopoe Bks.) ISHK.

Shah, Naseeruddin. The Blue Jackal - The Foolish Lion. 1998. (Karadi Tales Ser.). (Illus.). 24p. (YA). (gr. 1 up). 15.99 incl. audio (978-81-86838-00-6(7)) APG Sales and Fulfillment.

—The Crows & the Serpent - The Monkey & the Crocodile. 1998. (Karadi Tales Ser.). 24p. (YA). (gr. 1-4). 15.99 incl. audio (978-81-86838-04-4(X)) APG Sales and Fulfillment.

—The Monkey & the Crocodile. 1998. (Karadi Tales Ser.). (Illus.). 24p. (YA). (gr. 1 up). 9.99 incl. audio (978-81-86838-35-8(X)) APG Sales and Fulfillment.

Shannon, Margaret. The Red Wolf. 2006. (Illus.). 32p. (J). (gr. k-3). 6.95 (978-0-618-73744-4(8)) Houghton Mifflin Co. Trade & Reference Div.

Shannon, Monica. California Fairy Tales. Millard, C. E., illus. 2004. reprint ed. pap. 30.95 (978-1-4179-4211-4(8)) Kessinger Publishing, LLC.

Shapiro, Brigette. The Tale of the Tooth Fairy. 2004. 21p. pap. 14.95 (978-1-4137-3479-9(0)) PublishAmerica, Inc.

Sharkey, Niamh, illus. Tales of Wisdom & Wonder. 2005. 64p. (J). (978-1-84148-231-6(5)) Barefoot Bks., Inc.

Shaw, David, illus. The Brave LittleTailor: A Retelling of the Grimms' Fairy Tale. 2004. (Read-It! Readers Ser.). 32p. (C). (gr. k-3). 18.60 (978-1-4048-0315-2(7)) Picture Window Bks.

—Rumpelstiltskin: A Retelling of the Grimms' Fairy Tale. 2004. (Read-It! Readers Ser.). 32p. (C). (gr. k-3). 18.60 (978-1-4048-0311-4(4)) Picture Window Bks.

Shepard, Aaron. La Hija del Rey de los Mares. Spirin, Gennady, illus. (SPA.). 32p. (J). (gr. 3-5). (978-84-264-3725-9(7) , LM5051) Editorial Lumen ESP. *Dist:* Lectorum Pubns., Inc.

—One-Eye! Two-Eyes! Three-Eyes! A Very Grimm Fairy Tale. Clement, Gary, illus. 2006. 32p. (J). 16.95 (978-0-689-86740-8(9) , Atheneum) Simon & Schuster Children's Publishing.

Shepard, Aaron & Gore, Leonid. The Princess Mouse: A Tale of Finland. 2003. (Illus.). 32p. (J). (gr. k-3). 16.95 (978-0-689-82912-3(4) , Atheneum) Simon & Schuster Children's Publishing.

Shinozaki, Mitsuo, illus. Hansel & Gretel. 2004. (Origami Fairy Tale Ser.: Vol. 2). 16p. (gr. k-12). pap. 7.95 (978-0-89346-913-9(0)) Heian International Publishing, Inc.

Shrestha, Sophie & Shrestha, Romio, illus. In Search of the Thunder Dragon. 2007. 32p. (J). 16.95 (978-1-60109-100-0(1)) Mandala Publishing.

Shulman, Lisa. The Matzo Ball Boy. Litzinger, Rosanne, illus. 32p. (J). 2007. pap. 5.99 (978-0-14-240769-1(0) , Puffin); 2005. 15.99 (978-0-525-47169-1(3) , Dutton Juvenile) Penguin Group (USA) Inc.

Sierra i Fabra, Jordi. Cuentos Imposibles. 2002. (J). (978-956-240-369-6(6)) Arrayan Editores S.A.

Sierra, Judy. Can You Guess My Name? Traditional Tales Around the World. Vitale, Stefano, illus. 2002. 128p. (J). (gr. k-3). tchr. ed. 20.00 (978-0-618-13328-4(3) , Clarion Bks.) Houghton Mifflin Co. Trade & Reference Div.

Los Siete Cabritillos y el Lobo. 3rd ed. 2002. (Troquelados Clasicos Ser.). (SPA & ENG., Illus.). 16p. pap. 2.95 (978-84-7864-279-3(X)) Combel Editorial, S.A. ESP. *Dist:* Independent Pubs. Group, Libros Sin Fronteras.

Siks, Geraldine B. Ali Baba & the Forty Thieves. (Illus.). (YA). (gr. 6-12). 6.00 (978-0-87602-103-3(8)) Anchorage Pr.

Silver Dolphin en Español Editors. Disney Princesa Cine en Casa. 2003. (Cine en casa Disney Ser.). (SPA.). 46p. (J). 24.95 (978-970-718-111-3(7) , Silver Dolphin en Español) Advanced Marketing, S. de R. L. de C. V. MEX. *Dist:* Perseus Distribution.

—Llegs la hora del baile: Time for the Ball, Spanish-Language Edition. 2005. (SPA., Illus.). 22p. (J). 18.95 (978-970-718-287-5(3) , Silver Dolphin en Español) Advanced Marketing, S. de R. L. de C. V. MEX. *Dist:* Perseus Distribution.

—Tesoros para llevar Disney: Disney Princess CarryAlong Treasury, Spanish-Language Edition. 2004. (SPA., Illus.). 24p. (J). bds. 14.95 (978-970-718-239-4(3) , Silver Dolphin en Español) Advanced Marketing, S. de R. L. de C. V. MEX. *Dist:* Perseus Distribution.

Silverman, Erica. Raisel's Riddle. Gaber, Susan, illus. 1999. 40p. (J). (ps-3). 16.00 (978-0-374-36168-6(1) , Farrar, Straus & Giroux (BYR)) Farrar, Straus & Giroux.

—Raisel's Riddle. 2003. lib. bdg. 14.10 (978-0-613-59711-1(7)) Tandem Library Bks.

Simon, Francesca. Horrid Henry Tricks the Tooth Fairy. l.t. ed. 2003. (Illus.). 88p. (J). 16.95 (978-0-7540-7851-7(5) , Galaxy Children's Large Print) BBC Audiobooks America.

Sis, Peter. The Three Golden Keys. Sis, Peter, illus. 2001. (Illus.). 64p. (J). 23.00 (978-0-374-37525-6(9) , Farrar, Straus & Giroux (BYR)) Farrar, Straus & Giroux.

Sleeping Beauty. (Read-Along Ser.). (J). 7.99 incl. audio (978-1-55723-010-2(2)) Walt Disney Records.

Smallfield, Jane. The Bedtime Treasury of Real Fairy Tales. Smallfield, Graeme, illus. 2005. 96p. 17.95 (978-0-689-03923-2(9) , Milk & Cookies) ibooks, Inc.

Smith, Emily. Joe v. the Fairies. 2005. (Illus.). 80p. (J). (gr. 2-4). pap. 7.50 (978-0-552-55174-8(0) , Corgi) Transworld Publishers Ltd. GBR. *Dist:* Trafalgar Square Publishing.

Smith, George Harmon. The Voice of Turtle Ann. 2001. 127p. (YA). pap. 10.95 (978-0-595-20757-2(X) , Writers Club Pr.) iUniverse, Inc.

Smith, Jane. Fairytale Mix-up. Raynor, Jackie, illus. 2005. 12p. (J). (ps-ps). per. 10.95 (978-1-58117-419-9(5) , Intervisual/Piggy Toes) Dalmatian Pr.

Smith, Robert Kimmel. Jelly Belly. 155p. (J). (gr. 3-5). pap. 4.50 (978-0-8072-1406-0(X) , Listening Library) Random Hse. Audio Publishing Group.

Snow White. 2001. (Little Pebbles Ser.). (J). pap. (978-0-7892-6523-4(0)) Abbeville Pr., Inc.

Snow White. (Read-Along Ser.). (J). 7.99 incl. audio (978-1-55723-387-5(X)) Walt Disney Records.

Snow White & Rose Red. (Ladybird Bks.). (ARA., Illus.). 52p. (J). 4.95 (978-0-86685-225-8(5) , LDL181) International Bk. Ctr., Inc.

Snyder, Laurel. Up & down the Scratchy Mountains, or, the Search for a Suitable Princess. Dorman, Brandon, illus. 2008. (J). (***978-0-375-84719-6(7)**); lib. bdg. (***978-0-375-94719-3(1)**) Random Hse., Inc.

So, Meilo. Emperor & the Nightingale. 2000. (gr. k-3). lib. bdg. 18.80 (978-0-613-73530-8(7)) Tandem Library Bks.

Soecknick, Avril, tr. from MUL. UNICEF Book of Fairy Tales. Scheffler, Axel et al, illus. 1998. 48p. (J). 14.95 (978-0-7892-0437-0(1) , Abbeville Kids) Abbeville Pr., Inc.

El Soldadito de Plomo. 2nd ed. 2002. (Troquelados Clasicos Ser.).Tr. of Staunch Tin Soldier. (ENG & SPA., Illus.). 16p. pap. 2.95 (978-84-7864-375-2(3)) Combel Editorial, S.A. ESP. *Dist:* Independent Pubs. Group.

Soling, Cevin. Boris the Dog. Kille, Steve, illus. 2008. 16.95 (978-0-9767771-6-8(9)) Spectacle Films, Inc.

Souci, Robert D. San. Well at the End of the World. Walsh, Rebecca, illus. 2004. 48p. (J). 16.95 (978-1-58717-212-0(7) , SeaStar Bks.) Chronicle Bks. LLC.

Souhami, Jessica. Rama & the Demon King, Bengali/English-Language Edition: An Ancient Tale from India. 2005. (Illus.). 36p. (J). pap. 7.95 (978-1-84507-417-3(3)) Lincoln, Frances Ltd. GBR. *Dist:* Perseus Distribution.

—Rama & the Demon King, Gujarati/English-Language Edition: An Ancient Tale from India. 2005. (Illus.). 36p. (J). pap. 7.95 (978-1-84507-416-6(5)) Lincoln, Frances Ltd. GBR. *Dist:* Perseus Distribution.

—Rama & the Demon King, Punjabi/English-Language Edition: An Ancient Tale from India. 2005. (Illus.). 36p. (J). pap. 7.95 (978-1-84507-384-8(3)) Lincoln, Frances Ltd. GBR. *Dist:* Perseus Distribution.

Souhami, Jessica, illus. Rama & the Demon King, Urdu/English-Language Edition: An Ancient Tale from India. 2005. 36p. (J). pap. 7.95 (978-1-84507-415-9(7)) Lincoln, Frances Ltd. GBR. *Dist:* Perseus Distribution.

Soundprints. Fairy Tales. 2005. (Studio Mouse Ser.). (Illus.). 256p. (J). (ps-2). 14.95 (978-1-59069-229-5(2)) Studio Mouse LLC.

Southwater Books Staff. Fabulous Fairytales. 2000. (Superstickers Ser.). (Illus.). 64p. (ps-2). pap. 7.95 (978-1-84215-131-0(2)) Anness Publishing, Inc.

Sowers, Sherry. Tallulah & the Three Cowgirls. 2004. 23p. pap. 10.00 (978-1-4116-0771-2(6)) Lulu.com.

Sperling, Vatsala. Ram the Demon Slayer. 2005. (Illus.). 32p. (J). 15.95 (978-1-59143-057-5(7) , Bear Cub Bks.) Bear & Co.

Spiegelman, Art. Folklore & Fairy Tale Funnies. Mouly, Francoise, ed. Spiegelman, Art, illus. 2000. (Little Lit Ser.: Vol. 1). (Illus.). 64p. (J). (ps up). 19.95 (978-0-06-028624-8(5) , Cotler, Joanna Books) HarperCollins Pubs.

—Little Lit Three-Book Collection: Strange Stories for Strange Kids; Folklore & Fairytale Funnies; It Was a Dark & Silly Night. 2001. (Illus.). 176p. (J). (978-0-06-059826-6(3)) HarperCollins Pubs.

Spirin, Gennady. The Tale of the Firebird. Popova, Tatiana, tr. Spirin, Gennady, illus. 2002. (Illus.). 32p. (J). (ps-3). 16.99 (978-0-399-23584-9(1) , Philomel) Penguin Group (USA) Inc.

Squires, Janet. The Gingerbread Cowboy. Berry, Holly, illus. 2006. 32p. (J). (ps-2). 16.99 (978-0-06-077863-7(6) , Geringer, Laura Book); lib. bdg. 17.89 (978-0-06-077864-4(4)) HarperCollins Pubs.

Stadther, Michael. A Treasure's Trove: A Fairy Tale about Real Treasure for Parents & Children of All Ages. Stadther, Michael, illus. 2005. (Treasure's Trove Ser.). (Illus.). 102p. (J). pap. 19.95 (978-0-9760618-0-9(5)) Treasure Trove, Inc.

Stanley, Diane. Rumpelstiltskin's Daughter. 2002. (gr. k-3). lib. bdg. 15.25 (978-0-613-46097-2(9)) Tandem Library Bks.

Starbright Foundation Staff. Once upon a Fairy Tale: Four Favorite Stories Retold by the Stars. 2001. (Illus.). 80p. (J). 30.00 (978-0-670-03500-7(9) , Viking Juvenile) Penguin Group (USA) Inc.

Starcke, Rod M. Seven Fairy Tales. 2006. pap. 9.95 (978-0-533-15288-9(7)) Vantage Pr., Inc.

Steadman, Barbara. Hansel & Gretel Sticker Activity Book. 1999. (Dover Little Activity Bks.). (Illus.). (J). pap. 1.00 (978-0-486-40750-0(0)) Dover Pubns., Inc.

Stegman-Bourgeois, Karen M. Trollerella. Long, Ethan, illus. 2006. 32p. (J). 14.95 (978-0-8234-1918-0(5)) Holiday Hse., Inc.

Steig, Jeanne. A Handful of Beans: Six Fairy Tales Retold. 2001. (J). pap. (978-0-06-443746-2(9) , Harper Trophy) HarperCollins Pubs.

—A Handful of Beans: Six Fairy Tales Retold by Jeanne Steig with Illustrations by Wiliam Steig. Steig, William, illus. 1998. 144p. (J). 21.99 (978-0-06-205162-2(8)) HarperCollins Pubs.

Steig, William, illus. A Handful of Beans: Six Fairy Tales Retold. 1998. 144p. (J). (ps-3). 17.89 (978-0-06-205163-9(6)) HarperCollins Pubs.

Stein, Meg. Elves & the Shoemaker. 2000. (gr. k-3). lib. bdg. 11.80 (978-0-613-29609-0(5)) Tandem Library Bks.

—Ugly Duckling. 2001. (gr. k-3). lib. bdg. 11.65 (978-0-613-33447-1(7)) Tandem Library Bks.

Steiner, Rudolf. Cinderella at the Ball. (Illus.). (J). lib. bdg. 6.00 (978-0-87895-625-8(5)) Modern Curriculum Pr.

Steptoe, John. Mufaro's Beautiful Daughters. Steptoe, John, illus. 2001. Tr. of Las Bellas Hijas De Mufaro. (Illus.). 28.95 incl. audio compact disk (978-1-59112-542-6(1)); pap. 35.95 incl. audio compact disk (978-1-59112-541-9(3)); pap. 33.95 incl. audio (978-1-59112-132-9(9)) Live Oak Media.

Steptoe, John L. Las Bellas Hijas de Mufaro. Steptoe, John L., illus. 1998. Tr. of ghters. (Illus.). pap. 43.95 incl. audio compact disk (978-1-59519-139-7(9)); (SPA., (J). pap. 18.95 incl. audio compact disk (978-1-59519-138-0(0)) Live Oak Media.

Stevens, Molly, tr. from FRE. The Gingerbread Man: A Classic Fairy Tale. Thibault, Dominique, illus. 2001. (Little Pebbles Ser.). 32p. 6.95 (978-0-7892-0733-3(8)) Abbeville Pr., Inc.

Stevenson, James. The Oldest Elf. 1998. (Illus.). 32p. (J). (ps-3). pap. 4.95 (978-0-688-16154-5(5)) HarperCollins Pubs.

Stevenson, Peter, illus. Hansel & Gretel. 1999. (Finger Puppet Theater Bks.). 16p. (J). (ps-1). pap. 14.95 (978-0-439-04005-1(1) , Cartwheel Bks.) Scholastic, Inc.

Stewart, Chantal. Fairy Godmother's Diary. 2001. (gr. k-3). lib. bdg. 11.80 (978-0-613-33364-1(0)) Tandem Library Bks.

Stewart, Pat. Invisible Fairy Tales Magic Picture Book. 2003. (Dover Little Activity Bks.). (Illus.). 16p. (J). (ps-2). pap. 1.50 (978-0-486-43022-5(7)) Dover Pubns., Inc.

Stockham, Jess, et al, illus. The Frog Prince. 2007. 24p. pap. 5.99 (***978-1-84643-077-0(1)**) Child's Play International Ltd. GBR. *Dist:* Child's Play-International.

—Puss in Boots. 2007. 24p. pap. 5.99 (***978-1-84643-075-6(5)**) Child's Play International Ltd. GBR. *Dist:* Child's Play-International.

Stockham, Jess, et al, illus. Stone Soup. 2006. 24p. pap. 5.00 (978-1-84643-021-3(6)) Child's Play-International.

Stockham, Jessica. Little Red Riding Hood. 2004. (Flip up Fairy Tales Ser.). (Illus.). 24p. (J). 7.99 (978-0-85953-675-2(0)) Child's Play-International.

Stockham, Jessica, illus. Little Red Riding Hood. 2005. 24p. pap. (978-1-904550-22-8(3)) Child's Play-International.

Stockton, Frank Richard. The Bee-Man of Orn. Lynch, P. J., illus. 2004. 48p. (J). (gr. 1-5). 17.99 incl. DVD (978-0-7636-2239-8(7)) Candlewick Pr.

—The Bee Man of Orn. 1999. (Notable American Authors Ser.). reprint ed. lib. bdg. 125.00 (978-0-7812-8927-6(0)) Reprint Services Co.

—The Bee Man of Orn & Other Fanciful Tales. 2004. reprint ed. pap. 20.95 (978-1-4191-5383-9(8)); pap. 1.99 (978-1-4192-5383-6(2)) Kessinger Publishing, LLC.

Stone, David Lee. The Ratastrophe Catastrophe. Lea, Bob, illus. 2004. (Illmoor Chronicles Ser.: Bk. 1). 288p. (gr. 5-9). 16.99 (978-0-7868-5128-7(7)) Hyperion Bks. for Children.

STORYBOOK. Disney's Princess Treasury. 2001. (Illus.). 576p. (J). (ps 17). 19.99 (978-0-7868-3348-1(3)) Disney Pr.

Stowell, Louie. Beauty & the Beast. Tavares, Victor, illus. 2007. 64p. (J). 8.99 (978-0-7945-1456-3(1) , Usborne) EDC Publishing.

Sullivan, Joe E. Giant Tales. 1999. (Illus.). 109p. (J). mass mkt. (978-0-7541-0873-3(2)) Minerva Pr. GBR. *Dist:* Unity Distribution.

Sultzer, Randy T. The Wicca: And Other Tales. 2002. 150p. (J). pap. 11.95 (978-0-595-22490-6(3) , Writers Club Pr.) iUniverse, Inc.

Sutherland, Dianne, illus. Rashiecoat: A Story in Scots for Young Readers. 16p. pap. 6.95 (978-1-899827-19-0(6)) Scottish Children's Pr. GBR. *Dist:* Wilson & Assocs.

Swan. Five Famous Fairy Tales, Level 2. 2001. (Illus.). 48p. (C). pap. 9.00 (978-0-582-42125-7(X)) Pearson ESL.

—Rumpelstiltskin. Date not set. (Illus.). 31p. pap. 25.95 (978-0-582-02567-7(2)) Addison-Wesley Longman, Ltd. GBR. *Dist:* Trans-Atlantic Pubns., Inc.

—Sleeping Beauty. Date not set. (Illus.). 32p. pap. 25.95 (978-0-582-02568-4(0)) Addison-Wesley Longman, Ltd. GBR. *Dist:* Trans-Atlantic Pubns., Inc.

Swedeen, Staci. Phoebe & the Flame-Bellied Toad: An Original Fairy Tale. 2006. spiral bd. 42.00 (***978-1-4108-7153-4(3)**) Benchmark Education Co.

—The Toad Bridegroom: A Fairy Tale from Korea. 2006. spiral bd. 42.00 (***978-1-4108-7152-7(5)**) Benchmark Education Co.

—Tombi-Ende & the Frog: A Fairy Tale from South Africa. 2006. spiral bd. 42.00 (***978-1-4108-7151-0(7)**) Benchmark Education Co.

Swope, Sam. Jack & the Seven Deadly Giants. Cneut, Carll, illus. 2004. 112p. (J). 16.00 (978-0-374-33670-7(9) , Frances Foster Bks.) Farrar, Straus & Giroux.

T/K. Read to Me Treasury, Vol. 2. 2001. (Illus.). 400p. (ps-2). 19.99 (978-0-7868-3301-6(7)) Disney Pr.

Taback, Simms. Kibitzers & Fools: Tales My Zayda Told Me. 2008. 48p. (J). (ps). pap. 6.99 (***978-0-14-241065-3(9)** , Puffin) Penguin Group (USA) Inc.

Tabori, Lena & Fried, Natasha Tabori. A Little Box of Books: Fairy Tales, Nursery Rhymes, Songs, 3 vols. (Illus.). 48p. 16.95 (978-0-941807-64-7(9) , Welcome Bks.) Welcome Enterprises, Inc.

Tagg, Christine. Cinderlily: A Floral Fairy Tale. Ellwand, David, ed. Ellwand, David, photos by. 2006. (Illus.). 26p. (J). (gr. k-4). reprint ed. 17.00 (978-1-4223-5558-9(6)) DIANE Publishing Co.

Talbott, Hudson, et al. Into the Woods. Talbott, Hudson, ed. 2006. (Illus.). 91p. (J). (gr. 4-8). pap. 20.00 (978-1-4223-5331-8(1)) DIANE Publishing Co.

Tarcov, Edith. Frog Prince. 1999. (Illus.). (J). (gr. k-3). lib. bdg. 11.80 (978-0-7857-1145-2(7)) Tandem Library Bks.

Tatar, Maria. The Annotated Classic Fairy Tales. Tatar, Maria, ed. annot. ed. 2002. (Illus.). 448p. 35.00 (978-0-393-05163-6(3)) Norton, W. W. & Co., Inc.

Tchaikovsky, Peter Illich. Swan Lake. Martens, Marianne, tr. from GER. Zwerger, Lisbeth, illus. 2002. 32p. (J). (gr. 2-4). 15.95 (978-0-7358-1702-9(2)) North-South Bks., Inc.

Tchana, Katrin. The Serpent Slayer: And Other Stories of Strong Women. Hyman, Trina Schart, illus. 2000. 128p. (J). (ps-17). 22.99 (978-0-316-38701-9(0)) Little Brown & Co.

Teis, Kyra, adapted by. The Magic Flute. 2006. 32p. (J). 17.95 (978-1-59572-058-0(8)) Star Bright Bks., Inc.

Tesch, Lisa. The Little Princess. 2005. 54p. (J). per. 12.95 (978-1-933290-01-0(3)) Tate Publishing & Enterprises, L.L.C.

Thomas, Becky, et al. Little Red-Cap. Zwerger, Lisbeth, illus. 2006. 32p. (J). (gr. k). 16.99 (978-0-698-40053-5(4) , Minedition) Penguin Group (USA) Inc.

Thomas, W. Jenkyn. The Welsh Fairy Book. 2001. (Illus.). 256p. (J). pap. 7.95 (978-0-486-41711-0(5)) Dover Pubns., Inc.

—The Welsh Fairy Book. 2001. (Illus.). 310p. (C). reprint ed. pap. 16.95 (978-0-7083-1257-5(8)) Univ. of Wales Pr. GBR. *Dist:* Chicago Distribution Ctr.

Three Billy Goats Gruff. 2002. (Puppy Tales Ser.). (Illus.). 24p. (J). (gr. k-3). 1.49 (978-1-57759-255-6(7)) Dalmatian Pr.

Three Billy Goat's Gruff. 2004. (J). E-Book incl. cd-rom (978-1-84444-467-0(8)) Mantra Publishing, Ltd.

The Three Little Pigs. 2004. (J). (978-1-58453-271-2(8)) Pioneer Valley Educational Pr., Inc.

Three Little Pigs. 2004. (My First Fairy Tales Ser.). (Illus.). 24p. (J). pap. 3.99 (978-1-85854-687-2(7)) Brimax Books Ltd. GBR. *Dist:* Byeway Bks.

Three Minute Stories: Best-Loved Tales. (Illus.). 160p. (J). 9.98 (978-0-7853-6877-9(9) , 7167900) Publications International, Ltd.

Thumbelina. 2002. (Classic Tales Mini Bks.). (Illus.). 32p. (J). (978-1-59069-036-9(2) , T1005); incl. audio compact disk (978-1-59069-103-8(2) , T1105) Studio Mouse LLC.

Thurber, James. Many Moons. Simont, Marc, illus. 2002. (J). 14.79 (978-0-7587-0084-1(9)) Book Wholesalers, Inc.

—Many Moons. Simont, Marc, illus. 1998. 48p. (J). (ps-3). pap. 7.00 (978-0-15-201895-5(6) , Harcourt Paperbacks) Harcourt Children's Bks.

Toksvig, Sandi, reader. The Fwog Pwince: The Twuth! l.t. ed. 2003. (Read-Along Ser.). (Illus.). (J). pap. 24.95 incl. audio (978-0-7540-6209-7(0) , Galaxy Children's Large Print) BBC Audiobooks America.

Tolstoy, Alexei. Enormous Turnip. 2003. (gr. k-3). lib. bdg. 11.80 (978-0-613-64495-2(6)) Tandem Library Bks.

—The Gigantic Turnip. 2000. (J). 13.79 (978-0-606-19699-4(4)) Tandem Library Bks.

Tolstoy, Leo. Classic Tales & Fables for Children. Blaisdell, Bob, ed. Weiner, Leo & Dole, Nathan, trs. from RUS. 2004. (Literary Classics). (Illus.). 126p. pap. 14.00 (978-1-57392-939-4(5) , Pyr Bks.) Prometheus Bks., Pubs.

—Classic Tales & Fables for Children. 2001. (gr. 7-12). lib. bdg. 19.95 (978-0-613-83698-2(7)) Tandem Library Bks.

Tomlinson, Heather. The Swan Maiden. 2007. 304p. (YA). (gr. 7 up). 17.95 (***978-0-8050-8275-3(1)**) Holt, Henry & Co.

Townley, Roderick. Great Good Thing. 2002. (gr. 5-8). lib. bdg. 13.00 (978-0-613-91045-3(1)) Tandem Library Bks.

Traditional Fairy Tales. Jack & the Beanstalk. Stevenson, Peter, illus. 2001. (Finger Puppet Theater Bks.). 16p. (J). bds. 14.95 (978-0-439-28890-3(8) , Cartwheel Bks.) Scholastic, Inc.

El Traje del Emperador. 2002. (Troquelados Clasicos Ser.). (ENG & SPA., Illus.). 16p. pap. 2.95 (978-84-7864-600-5(0)) Combel Editorial, S.A. ESP. *Dist:* Independent Pubs. Group, Libros Sin Fronteras.

Treahy, Iona & Ladybird Books Staff. Jack & the Beanstalk: Based on a Traditional Folk Tale. Rivers, Ruth, illus. 1999. (First Favourite Tales Ser.). 32p. (J). 4.95 (978-0-7214-9740-2(3) , Dutton Juvenile) Penguin Group (USA) Inc.

A Treasury for Six Year Olds. 2002. 96p. (J). 7.98 (978-0-7525-8712-7(9)) Parragon, Inc.

A Treasury for Three Year Olds. 2002. 96p. (J). 7.98 (978-0-7525-8709-7(9)) Parragon, Inc.

Los Tres Cerditos: The Family, the House, Verbs. 1999. (SPA., Illus.). (J). (ps-5). pap. 7.95 (978-88-8148-250-4(9)) European Language Institute ITA. *Dist:* Distribooks, Inc., Midwest European Pubns.

Tresselt, Alvin R. The Mitten. Sternhagen, Frances, illus. 2001. (J). (gr. k-3). pap. 16.90 incl. audio Spoken Arts, Inc.

Trewellard, J. M. Butterfingers. Beck, Ian, illus. 2007. 208p. (J). (gr. 3-7). 15.99 (***978-0-385-75123-0(0)***); lib. bdg. 18.99 (***978-0-385-75124-7(9)***) Random Hse. Children's Bks. (Fickling, David Bks.).

Les Trois Petits Cochons: The Family, The House, Verbs. 1999. (FRE., Illus.). 24p. (J). (ps-5). pap., stu. ed. 7.95 (978-88-8148-240-5(1)) European Language Institute ITA. *Dist:* Distribooks, Inc., Midwest European Pubns.

Tseng, Grace. White Tiger, Blue Serpent. Tseng, Jean & Tseng, Mou-Sien, illus. 1999. 32p. (J). (ps-3). 16.00 (978-0-688-12515-8(8)) HarperCollins Pubs.

Tucker Slingsby Ltd., Staff. My Big Book of Fairy Tales in Rhyme! Lewis, Jan, illus. 2004. 224p. (J). (978-1-902272-31-3(5)) Tucker Slingsby, Ltd.

Tyrrell, Melissa. Beauty & the Beast. McMullen, Nigel, illus. 2005. (Fairytale Friends Ser.). 12p. (J). bds. 5.95 (978-1-58117-153-2(6), Intervisual/Piggy Toes) Dalmatian Pr.

—The Gingerbread Man. McMullen, Nigel, illus. 2005. (Fairytale Friends Ser.: Vol. 8). 12p. (J). (ps-k). bds. 5.95 (978-1-58117-154-9(4), Intervisual/Piggy Toes) Dalmatian Pr.

—Goldilocks & the Three Bears. 1998. (Fairytale Friends Ser.). (Illus.). 12p. (J). (gr. 2 up). bds. 5.95 (978-1-58117-014-6(9), Intervisual/Piggy Toes) Dalmatian Pr.

—Hansel & Gretel. McMullen, Nigel, illus. 2005. (Fairytale Friends Ser.). 12p. (J). bds. 5.95 (978-1-58117-152-5(8), Intervisual/Piggy Toes) Dalmatian Pr.

—Jack & the Beanstalk. 1998. (Fairytale Friends Ser.). (Illus.). 12p. (J). (gr. 2 up). bds. 5.95 (978-1-58117-015-3(7), Intervisual/Piggy Toes) Dalmatian Pr.

—Little Red Riding Hood. 1998. (Fairytale Friends Ser.: Vol. 3). (Illus.). 12p. (J). (ps up). bds. 5.95 (978-1-58117-016-0(5), Intervisual/Piggy Toes) Dalmatian Pr.

—Pinocchio. McMullen, Nigel, illus. 2005. (Fairytale Friends Ser.: Vol. 7). 12p. (J). (ps-k). bds. 5.95 (978-1-58117-151-8(X), Intervisual/Piggy Toes) Dalmatian Pr.

—The Three Little Pigs. 1998. (Fairytale Friends Ser.: Vol. 4). (Illus.). 12p. (J). (ps up). bds. 5.95 (978-1-58117-017-7(3), Intervisual/Piggy Toes) Dalmatian Pr.

The Ugly Duckling. 2005. (J). (978-1-58453-302-3(1)) Pioneer Valley Educational Pr., Inc.

The Ugly Duckling. 2004. 24.95 incl. audio (978-1-55592-074-6(8)) Weston Woods Studios, Inc.

Umansky, Kaye. Cinderella: Photocopiable Plays. 2nd unabr. ed. 2003. (Curtain up! Ser.: Vol. 5). (Illus.). 48p. (J). (gr. 1-4). pap. 15.95 (978-0-7136-4341-1(2)) A & C Black GBR. *Dist:* Empire Publishing Service, Lubrecht & Cramer, Ltd., Players Pr., Inc.

Ungerer, Tomi. Zeralda's Ogre. 1999. (Illus.). 32p. (J). (gr. 1-5). reprint ed. pap. 6.95 (978-1-57098-267-5(8)) Rinehart, Roberts Pubs.

Uribe, Veronica. Little Book of Fairy Tales. Ouriou, Susan, tr. from SPA. Murkasek & Arevalo, Gisela, illus. 2004. 132p. (J). 8.95 (978-0-88899-583-4(0)) Groundwood Bks. CAN. *Dist:* Perseus Distribution.

Vaes, Alain. The Princess & the Pea. Vaes, Alain, illus. 2001. (Illus.). 32p. (J). (gr. 1-3). 15.95 (978-0-316-89633-7(0)) Little, Brown Bks. for Young Readers.

Vagin, Vladimir. The Nutcracker Ballet. 2002. (Illus.). 32p. (J). pap. 5.99 (978-0-439-08185-6(8)) Scholastic, Inc.

—Nutcracker Ballet. 2002. (ps-2). lib. bdg. 14.15 (978-0-613-85386-6(5)) Tandem Library Bks.

Vagnozzi, Barbara, illus. Sleeping Beauty. 2007. (First Fairy Tales Ser.). 31p. (J). (***978-1-59771-073-2(3)***) Sea-To-Sea Pubns.

Valentine, Johnny. The Duke Who Outlawed Jelly Beans: And Other Stories. Schmidt, Lynette, illus. 2nd ed. 2004. 32p. pap. 10.95 (978-1-55583-847-8(2)) Alyson Pubns.

Valldejuly, Frances Bragan. Keka en el Museo de Arte de Ponce. Rabenau, Francesca von, illus. 2004. (SPA.). 60p. 21.95 (978-1-56328-269-0(0)) Editorial Plaza Mayor, Inc.

Valriu, Caterina. Thumbelina: A Bilingual Book. Max, illus. 2004. Tr. of Pulgarcita. (ENG & SPA.). 32p. (J). (gr. k-3). pap. 6.95 (978-0-8118-3928-0(1)) Chronicle Bks. LLC.

—Thumbelina/Pulgarcita: A Bilingual Book. Max, illus. 2004. Tr. of Pulgarcita. (ENG & SPA.). 32p. (J). (gr. k-3). 13.95 (978-0-8118-3927-3(3)) Chronicle Bks. LLC.

Van Gool, A, illus. Cuentos y Leyendas. 2001. (SPA.). 312p. (J). per. 14.95 (978-1-58087-058-0(9)) Stampley, C.D. Enterprises, Inc.

Vande Velde, Vivian. The Rumpelstiltskin Problem. 2000. (Illus.). 128p. (YA). (gr. 7-6). tchr. ed. 15.00 (978-0-618-05523-4(1)) Houghton Mifflin Co. Trade & Reference Div.

—The Rumpelstiltskin Problem. 2002. 128p. (J). pap. 4.50 (978-0-439-30529-7(2)) Scholastic, Inc.

Vera, Luisa, illus. Ali Baba & the Forty Thieves. 2004. (ENG & KUR.). (J). (978-1-84444-536-3(4)) Mantra Publishing, Ltd.

Very, Lydia L. Goody Two Shoes: Treasures from the Library of Congress. 2001. (Shape Bks.). (Illus.). 20p. (J). (ps-3). reprint ed. 3.95 (978-1-55709-169-7(2)) Applewood Bks.

—Little Red Riding Hood: Treasures from the Library of Congress. 2004. (Shape Bks.). (Illus.). 20p. (J). reprint ed. 3.95 (978-1-55709-167-3(6)) Applewood Bks.

Vilagut, Xavier. Los Siete Cabritillos y el Lobo. 2002. (SPA.). 48p. 6.95 (978-84-241-8015-7(1), EV30611) Everest de Ediciones y Distribucion, S.L. ESP. *Dist:* Lectorum Pubns., Inc.

Le Vilain Petit Canard.Tr. of Ugly Duckling. (FRE.). 48p. (J). pap. 12.95 incl. audio compact disk (978-2-89558-063-8(4)) Coffragants CAN. *Dist:* Penton Overseas, Inc.

Le Vilain Petit Canard: Farm Animals, The Farm, Seasons, The Weather. 1999. (FRE & ENG., Illus.). 24p. (J). (ps-5). pap., stu. ed. 7.95 (978-88-8148-241-2(X)) European Language Institute ITA. *Dist:* Distribooks, Inc., Midwest European Pubns.

Von Drogas, Johann. Beauty & the Beast, the Full Story. 2000. 33p. (YA). (gr. 5-12). pap. 6.50 (978-0-9620016-5-9(1)) Great Lakes Publishing Co.

—Cinderella, Little Red Riding Hood, Jack & the Beanstalk: What Really Happened? 2000. 49p. (YA). (gr. 5-12). pap. 6.50 (978-0-9620016-4-2(3)) Great Lakes Publishing Co.

—Those Famous Fairy Tales, What Really Happened? 2000. (Illus.). 180p. (YA). (gr. 7-12). pap. 5.90 (978-0-9620016-6-6(X)) Great Lakes Publishing Co.

von Olfers, Sibylle. Mother Earth & Her Children: A Quilted Fairy Tale. Zipes, Jack, tr. from GER. Schoen-Smith, Sieglinde, illus. 2007. 32p. (J). (ps-2). 17.95 (***978-1-933308-18-0(4)***) Breckling Pr.

Vornholt, John. The Troll Queen. 2003. (Illus.). 208p. (J). pap. 4.99 (978-0-689-85833-8(7), Aladdin) Simon & Schuster Children's Publishing.

Wade, Barrie. Cinderella. Monks, Julie, illus. 2004. (Read-It! Readers Ser.). 32p. (C). (gr. k-3). 18.60 (978-1-4048-0052-6(2)) Picture Window Bks.

Wahl, Jan. Cabbage Moon. Johnson-Petrov, Arden, illus. 1998. 32p. (J). (ps-1). 15.95 (978-1-56397-584-4(X)) Boyds Mills Pr.

Walker, Richard. Jack & Beanstalk. Sharkey, Niamh, illus. 2006. 0040p. 9.99 (978-1-905236-69-5(7)) Barefoot Bks., Inc.

—Jack & the Beanstalk. 2002. (Illus.). 40p. (J). pap. 6.99 (978-1-84148-158-6(0)) Barefoot Bks., Inc.

—Jack & the Beanstalk. Sharkey, Niamh, illus. 1999. 40p. (J). (ps-3). 15.95 (978-1-902283-13-5(9)) Barefoot Bks., Inc.

—Juan Y Los Frijoles Magicos. 1999. (SPA.). (ps-2). lib. bdg. 15.30 (978-0-613-53825-1(0)) Tandem Library Bks.

Wallner, S. J. Hans & the Golden Stirrup. (Illus.). 48p. (J). (gr. 2-3). lib. bdg. 10.95 (978-0-87783-016-0(9)); pap. 3.94 (978-0-87783-093-1(2)) Oddo Publishing, Inc.

Walt Disney Company Staff & Disney Staff. Classic Disney Adventures CD Storybook: Lion King, Aladdin, Little Mermaid & Toy Story. Hinkler Books Staff, ed. rev. ed. 2004. (Disney CD Storybooks Ser.). (Illus.). 128p. (J). (gr. 4-12). 14.95 incl. cd-rom (978-1-86515-304-9(4)) Hinkler Bks. Pty, Ltd. AUS. *Dist:* Penton Overseas, Inc.

Walt Disney's Beauty & the Beast. 2002. spiral bd. (978-0-9720651-3-9(X)) Story Reader, Inc.

Walt Disney's Snow White & the Seven Dwarfs. 2002. (J). spiral bd. (978-0-9720651-6-0(4)) Story Reader, Inc.

Walt Disney's The Lion King. 2002. (J). spiral bd. (978-0-9720651-4-6(8)) Story Reader, Inc.

Washington, LaVonne & LaShawn. Proverbial Tales for Kids Volume 1. 2005. 30p. 10.91 (978-1-4116-2427-6(0)) Lulu.com.

Waters, Fiona. Fairy Tales from Far & Wide. Berkshire, Lisa, illus. 1999. 48p. (J). (ps-2). 15.95 (978-1-902283-14-2(7)) Barefoot Bks., Inc.

Waters, Fiona, retold by. Faithful Sister. (Illus.). 94p. (J). pap. 10.99 (978-0-7475-4704-4(1)) Bloomsbury Publishing Plc GBR. *Dist:* Trafalgar Square Publishing.

—Sisters with Glass Hearts. 2000. (Illus.). 93p. (J). pap. 10.99 (978-0-7475-4709-9(2)) Bloomsbury Publishing Plc GBR. *Dist:* Independent Pubs. Group.

—Widow & Her Daughters. 2000. (Illus.). 95p. (J). pap. 9.99 (978-0-7475-4719-8(X)) Bloomsbury Publishing Plc GBR. *Dist:* Independent Pubs. Group.

Watson, Laura, illus. Three Barnyard Tales. unabr. ed. 2004. (Once-upon-a-Time Ser.). 32p. (J). (gr. k-3). (978-1-55074-796-6(7)) Kids Can Pr., Ltd.

Watson, Patrick. Wittgenstein & the Goshawk: A Fable. 2005. (Illus.). 14.95 (978-1-55278-449-5(5)) McArthur & Co. CAN. *Dist:* National Bk. Network.

Watson, T. E. Glen Robbie: A Scottish Fairy Tale. Ferchaud, Steve, illus. ed. 2006. (J). lib. bdg. 22.95 (978-1-58478-013-7(4), Highland Children's Pr.) Heather & Highlands Publishing.

Watts, Bernadette. Ugly Duckling. Watts, Bernadette, illus. 2008. 0032p. pap. 6.95 (***978-0-7358-2146-0(1)***) North-South Bks., Inc.

Wax, Wendy A. Musica en Casa: Libro de Cuentos. de Alba, Arlette, tr. 2005. (SPA., Illus.). 32p. (J). (ps-7). 24.95 (978-970-718-289-9(X), Silver Dolphin en Español) Advanced Marketing, S. de R. L. de C. V. MEX. *Dist:* Perseus Distribution.

Webb, Mack Henry, Jr. Webb's Wondrous Tales Book 1. Webb, Celia, illus. 2006. 184p. (YA). per. 14.95 (978-0-9779576-1-3(6)) Pilinut Pr., Inc.

Weber, Lou, ed. El Tesoro de Los Cuentos de Hadas. Lo-Faro, Jerry, illus. 2004. (SPA & ESP.). 384p. (J). 15.98 (978-1-4127-0165-5(1), 3995001) Publications International, Ltd.

Weinberg, Jennifer Liberts. The Disney Princess: A Read-Aloud Storybook. 2002. (Illus.). 72p. (J). (ps-3). 8.99 (978-0-7364-1261-2(1), RH/Disney) Random Hse. Children's Bks.

Wells, Rosemary. The Fisherman & His Wife. Hubbard, Eleanor, illus. 1998. 32p. (J). (ps-3). 16.99 (978-0-8037-1850-0(0), Dial) Penguin Group (USA) Inc.

Wenzel, Karen M. The Fan Tom Spider: A Flower Forest Wedding. Stadlberger, Kristy G., illus. 1999. 39p. (J). (gr. k-4). pap. (978-0-9656714-7-7(X)) WNZ Pubns.

Wheeler, Jeff. The Wishing Lantern. Gallegos, Randy, illus. 1999. 14p. lib. bdg. 18.95 (978-1-58649-000-3(1)) Amberlin Group, The.

Wiesner, David, illus. & retold by. The Loathsome Dragon. Wiesner, David, retold by. 2005. 32p. (J). (gr. k-3). 16.00 (978-0-618-54359-5(7), Clarion Bks.) Houghton Mifflin Co. Trade & Reference Div.

Wiggin, Kate Douglas, ed. Tales of Wonder Every Child Should Know. 2007. (ENG.). 344p. 98.99 (***978-1-4280-7383-8(3)***); per. 92.99 (***978-1-4280-7381-4(7)***) IndyPublish.com.

Wilcox, Leah. Falling for Rapunzel. Monks, Lydia, illus. 2005. 32p. (J). (gr. k-3). pap. 5.99 (978-0-14-240399-0(7), Puffin) Penguin Group (USA) Inc.

Wilde, Oscar. El Gigante Egoista. Zwerger, Lisbeth, illus. 2nd ed. (SPA.). 48p. (J). (978-84-392-8674-5(0)) Gaviota Ediciones ESP. *Dist:* Lectorum Pubns., Inc.

—El Gigante Egoista. Gallagher, S. Saelig, illus. 2nd ed. 2000. (SPA.). 32p. (J). (gr. 3-5). 14.99 (978-84-241-3360-3(9)) Everest de Ediciones y Distribucion, S.L. ESP. *Dist:* Lectorum Pubns., Inc.

—The Happy Prince & Other Fairy Tales. unabr. ed. 2001. (Dover Juvenile Classics Ser.). 160p. (J). (gr. 4-7). pap. 2.50 (978-0-486-41723-3(9)) Dover Pubns., Inc.

—El Principe Feliz y Otros Cuentos. 2003. (SPA., Illus.). 180p. (978-84-392-8015-6(7), EV0874) Gaviota Ediciones ESP. *Dist:* Lectorum Pubns., Inc.

—The Selfish Giant: A Tale about Being Unselfish. Ebert, Len, illus. 2006. (J). (978-1-59939-085-7(X), Reader's Digest Young Families, Inc.) Reader's Digest Children's Publishing, Inc.

—The Star Child. Capek, Jindra, illus. 1999. 32p. pap. 19.99 (978-0-86315-303-7(8)) Floris Bks. GBR. *Dist:* Steiner-Books, Inc.

Wilhelm, Hans. Los Musicos de Bremen. 2001. (978-0-606-22655-4(9)) Tandem Library Bks.

Wilhelm, Hans, retold by. Los Musicos de Bremen. (SPA.). (J). pap. 4.80 net. (978-0-439-17707-8(3), SO30111) Scholastic, Inc.

Willard, Nancy. Cinderella's Dress. Dyer, Jane, illus. 2003. 32p. (J). pap. 16.95 (978-0-590-56927-9(9), Blue Sky Pr., The) Scholastic, Inc.

—The Flying Bed. Thompson, John, illus. 2007. 48p. (J). (ps-3). pap. 16.99 (978-0-590-25610-0(6), Blue Sky Pr., The) Scholastic, Inc.

Williams, Brenda. The Real Princess. 2006. (J). (978-1-905236-88-6(3)) Barefoot Bks., Inc.

Williams, Marcia, illus. & retold by. Chaucer's Canterbury Tales. Williams, Marcia, retold by. 2007. 48p. (J). (gr. 3-7). 16.99 (978-0-7636-3197-0(3)) Candlewick Pr.

Williams, Sophy, illus. Aladdin & the Enchanted Lamp. 2007. 70p. (J). (978-0-439-69257-1(1), Levine, Arthur A. Bks.) Scholastic, Inc.

Willson, Sarah. Visit from the Tooth Fairy. 2004. (ps-2). lib. bdg. 11.25 (978-0-613-73458-5(0)) Tandem Library Bks.

Wilson Hills, Atheen. Little Crane: A Fairy Tale for All Ages. 2008. (J). pap. 10.00 (***978-0-9792371-5-7(7)***, Moo Pr.) Keene Publishing.

Wilson, Jacqueline. Beauty & the Beast. 2003. (Curtain up! Ser.: Vol. 1). (Illus.). 48p. (J). (gr. 1-4). pap. 15.95 (978-0-7136-4390-9(0)) A & C Black GBR. *Dist:* Lubrecht & Cramer, Ltd., Players Pr., Inc.

Windling, Terri & Datlow, Ellen, eds. Swan Sister: Fairy Tales Retold. 2005. 176p. (J). pap. 4.99 (978-0-689-87837-4(0), Aladdin) Simon & Schuster Children's Publishing.

Windling, Terri & Vojnar, Kamil. Swan Sister Fairy Tales Retold. Datlow, Ellen, ed. 2003. (Illus.). 176p. (J). (gr. 3-6). 16.95 (978-0-689-84613-7(4)) Simon & Schuster Children's Publishing.

Winterson, Jeanette. The King of Capri. Ray, Jane, illus. 2003. 32p. (J). 16.95 (978-1-58234-830-8(8), Bloomsbury Children) Bloomsbury Publishing.

Wiseman, Lisa, ed. Disney's Nursery Rhymes & Fairy Tales. 2005. (Illus.). 320p. (J). (ps-3). 15.99 (978-0-7868-3463-1(3)) Disney Pr.

Wisnewski, Andrea, illus. & retold by. Little Red Riding Hood. Wisnewski, Andrea, retold by. 2007. 32p. (J). (ps-3). 18.95 (978-1-56792-303-2(8)) Godine, David R. Pub.

Wisniewski, David & Wisniewski, David. Wave of the Sea-Wolf. Wisniewski, David, illus. 1999. (Illus.). (J). (gr. k-4). lib. bdg. 14.10 (978-0-613-19489-1(6)) Tandem Library Bks.

Wolf, Claudia, illus. Hansel & Gretel: A Retelling of the Grimms' Fairy Tale. 2004. (Read-It! Readers Ser.). 32p. (C). (gr. k-3). 18.60 (978-1-4048-0316-9(5)) Picture Window Bks.

—Snow White: A Retelling of the Grimms' Fairy Tale. 2004. (Read-It! Readers Ser.). 32p. (C). (gr. k-3). 18.60 (978-1-4048-0312-1(2)) Picture Window Bks.

Wolkstein, Diane. The Glass Mountain. Bauer, Louisa, illus. 1999. 32p. (gr. k-3). (J). 15.89 (978-0-688-14848-5(4)); (YA). 16.00 (978-0-688-14847-8(6)) HarperCollins Pubs.

Wood, Audrey. The Christmas Adventure of Space Elf Sam. Wood, Bruce Robert, illus. 1998. 40p. (J). (ps-4). pap. 15.95 (978-0-590-03143-1(0), Blue Sky Pr., The) Scholastic, Inc.

—Heckedy Peg. Wood, Audrey, illus. 2002. (Illus.). (J). 14.04 (978-0-7587-2710-7(0)) Book Wholesalers, Inc.

—Heckedy Peg. Wood, Don, illus. 2001. 36p. (J). (ps-5). pap. 6.95 (978-0-9629298-6-1(7), MHC-6-7) Minnesota Humanities Commission.

World of Fairy Tales. unabr. ed. 2004. (Chrysalis Children's Classics Ser.). (Illus.). (YA). pap. (978-1-84365-064-5(9)) Chrysalis Children's Bks.

Woyiwada, Allison. The Little Fir Tree: A Musical for Primary Children Based on a Story by Hans Christian Andersen. 2003. (Musicals for Young Audiences Ser.). 16p. (J). (gr. k-6). pap. 5.00 (978-0-88734-428-2(3)) Players Pr., Inc.

Yaroslavskaya, Lyudmila. The Great Lakes Legends & Fairy Tales. 2006. (ENG & RUS., Illus.). (J). per. (***978-0-9791248-0-8(8)***) Yaroslavskaya, Lyudmila.

Yep, Laurence. Auntie Tiger. Lee, Insu, illus. 2008. (J). (***978-0-06-029551-6(1)***); lib. bdg. (***978-0-06-029552-3(X)***) HarperCollins Pubs.

Yep, Laurence. The Dragon Prince: A Chinese Beauty & the Beast Tale. Mak, Kam, illus. 1999. 32p. (J). (gr. k-3). reprint ed. pap. 6.99 (978-0-06-443518-5(0), Harper Trophy) HarperCollins Pubs.

—The Dragon Prince: A Chinese Beauty & the Beast Tale. 1999. (J). 13.79 (978-0-606-15845-9(6)) Tandem Library Bks.

Yep, Laurence & Yep, Laurence. The Dragon Prince: A Chinese Beauty & the Beast Tale. Mak, Kam, illus. 1999. (J). (ps-ps). lib. bdg. 15.25 (978-0-613-11493-6(0)) Tandem Library Bks.

Yolen, Jane. Baba Yaga. Date not set. 32p. (J). (ps-1). pap. 5.99 (978-0-06-443599-4(7)) HarperCollins Pubs.

—Briar Rose. 2002. (gr. 7-12). lib. bdg. 15.30 (978-0-613-46051-4(0)) Tandem Library Bks.

—Firebird. 1999. 32p. (J). (ps-1). pap. 5.95 (978-0-06-443600-7(4)) HarperCollins Pubs.

—The Firebird. Vagin, Vladimir, illus. 2002. 32p. (J). (ps-1). lib. bdg. 17.89 (978-0-06-028539-5(7)); 15.95 (978-0-06-028538-8(9)) HarperCollins Pubs.

—The Flying Witch. Vagin, Vladimir, illus. 2003. 40p. (J). (ps-1). 15.99 (978-0-06-028536-4(2)) HarperCollins Pubs.

Yolen, Jane & Stemple, Adam. Troll Bridge. 2006. 240p. (J). 16.95 (978-0-7653-1426-0(6), Starscape) Doherty, Tom Assocs., LLC.

Yolen, Jane & Stemple, Adam. Troll Bridge: A Rock 'n' Roll Fairy Tale. 2007. 240p. (J). 5.99 (***978-0-7653-5284-2(2)***, Starscape) Doherty, Tom Assocs., LLC.

Yorinks, Arthur. The Witch's Child. Smith, Joseph A., illus. 2007. 34p. (J). (gr. k-4). 16.95 (***978-0-8109-9349-5(X)***, Abrams Bks. for Young Readers) Abrams, Harry N., Inc.

Young, Ed. Lon Po Po: A Red Riding Hood Story from China. Young, Ed, illus. 2002. (Illus.). (J). 14.04 (978-0-7587-0055-1(5)) Book Wholesalers, Inc.

—Pinocchio. Young, Ed, illus. 2002. (Illus.). (J). 25.43 (978-0-7587-3421-1(2)) Book Wholesalers, Inc.

Young, Laurie. Princess Polly & the Pea. 2007. 14p. pap. 12.95 (***978-1-58117-558-5(2)***) Dalmatian Pr.

Youngquist, Cathrene Valente. The Three Billygoats Gruff & Mean Calypso Joe. Sorra, Kristin, illus. 2002. 32p. (J). (ps-3). 16.00 (978-0-689-82824-9(1), Atheneum) Simon & Schuster Children's Publishing.

Zavrel, Stepan. Vodnik. Zavrel, Stepan, illus. (Illus.). 32p. (J). (ps-3). 14.95 (978-0-87592-058-0(6)) Scroll Pr., Inc.

Zelinsky, Paul O. Rapunzel. Zelinsky, Paul O., illus. 2002. (Illus.). 14.89 (978-1-4046-1755-1(8)) Book Wholesalers, Inc.

—Rapunzel. 2002. (Illus.). (J). (ps-ps). lib. bdg. 16.45 (978-0-613-60832-9(1)) Tandem Library Bks.

—Rumpelstiltskin. Zelinsky, Paul O., illus. 2002. (Illus.). (J). 14.89 (978-0-7587-0140-4(3)) Book Wholesalers, Inc.

Zelinsky, Paul O., reader. Rapunzel. unabr. ed. 1998. (J). (ps-4). 24.95 incl. audio (978-0-7882-0684-9(2), HRA379) Weston Woods Studios, Inc.

Zelinsky, Paul O., et al. Rapunzel. 2002. (Illus.). 48p. (J). pap. 7.99 (978-0-14-230193-7(0), Puffin) Penguin Group (USA) Inc.

Zemach, Margot. The Three Little Pigs: An Old Story. Zemach, Margot, illus. 2002. (Illus.). (J). 14.43 (978-0-7587-3806-6(4)) Book Wholesalers, Inc.

Zeman, Ludmila, illus. & retold by. The Last Quest of Gilgamesh. Zeman, Ludmila, retold by. 1998. (J). (ps-7). lib. bdg. 17.60 (978-0-613-09459-7(X)) Tandem Library Bks.

Zern, Linda L. The Pocket Fairies of Middleburg. Day, Linda S., illus. 2004. (J). per. 9.95 (978-0-9753098-0-3(3)) Linwood Hse. Publishing.

Ziefert, Harriet. Little Red Riding Hood. Bolam, Emily, illus. 2000. (Viking Easy-to-Read Ser.). 32p. (J). (ps-2). pap. 3.99 (978-0-14-056529-4(9), Puffin) Penguin Group (USA) Inc.

Ziegler, Argentina Palacios, tr. Aventura magica de Dora (Dora's Fairy-Tale Adventure) Hall, Susan', illus. 2006. (Dora la Exploradora Ser.). (SPA.). 24p. (J). pap. 3.99 (978-1-4169-1184-5(7), Libros Para Ninos) Simon & Schuster Children's Publishing.

Zimelman, Nathan. Little Red Baseball Stockings & Other Stories. 2005. 80p. pap. 11.95 (978-1-889658-22-3(7)) New Canaan Publishing Co. LLC.

Zourelias, Diana. Fairy Tale Search-a-Word. 2006. 64p. (J). pap. 1.50 (978-0-486-45206-7(9)) Dover Pubns., Inc.

3-Minute Stories: Fairy Tales. 2002. (Illus.). 160p. (J). (978-0-7853-6300-2(9), 7158600) Publications International, Ltd.

365 Historias Lectura a Partir de 3 Anos.Tr. of Three Hundred Sixty-Five Fairy Tales. (SPA.). (J). 14.98 (978-970-22-0042-0(3)) Larousse, Ediciones, S. A. de C. V. MEX. *Dist:* Continental Bk. Co., Inc., Giron Bks.

FAITH

Anderson, Joel. Big Topics for Little Kids: Tell Me about Faith. Smith, Kristi Carter, illus. 2005. 32p. (J). 9.99 (978-1-4003-0615-2(9)) Nelson, Thomas Inc.

Arrington, French L. Exploring the Declaration of Faith. 2003. 112p. spiral bd. 7.99 (978-0-87148-396-6(3)) Pathway Pr.

Baker, Harold S. Just a Man in Preacher's Clothing: One Man's Journey to Share His Faith. 2001. 143p. per. 9.95 (978-0-9714196-0-5(4)) Washburn Design & Consulting, Inc.

Balfour, R. C., III. Fishing for the Abundant Life 2 Journey to Faith. 2004. (gr. 9 up). 26.00 (978-1-889574-21-9(X)) Sentry Pr., Inc.

Barry, John F. One Faith, One Lord: A Study of Basic Catholic Belief. 4th ed. 2001. (J). per. (978-0-8215-2207-3(8), Sadlier) Sadlier, William H. Inc.

Becker, Mary Lee, contrib. by. Living Our Faith Church: A Community of Faith. 2002. (Living Our Faith Ser.). (Illus.). 112p. pap., stu. ed. 8.95 (978-0-15-900500-2(0)) Harcourt Religion Pubs.

Becoming a Girl of Faith: According to God's Word. l.t. ed. 2004. 90p. (YA). 12.95 (978-0-9764304-2-1(8)) Girls of Faith.

Bible Visuals International, compiled by. Faith Volume 02: Old Testament. 2006. (Illus.). pap. (978-1-932381-67-2(8) , 2002) Bible Visuals International, Inc.

Bogard, Michael. The Bold & the Dutiful: The Book of James. 2000. (Generation Why Ser.: No. 5, Pt. 3). 37p. (YA). (gr. 9-12). pap. 12.95 (978-0-87303-389-3(2)) Faith & Life Pr.

Bruinsma, Sheryl. Meet My Imaginary Elephant: And More Stories for Kids. 2001. (FaithBuilders for Kids Ser.: Vol. 3). 96p. (J). (ps-3). reprint ed. pap. 4.99 (978-0-8010-6347-3(7) , Object Lessons) Baker Bks.

Buller, Laura & Dorling Kindersley Publishing Staff. A Faith Like Mine: A Celebration of the World's Religions—Seen Through the Eyes of Children. 2005. (Illus.). 80p. (J). (ps-7). 19.99 (978-0-7566-1177-4(6)) Dorling Kindersley Publishing, Inc.

Callaghan, William. What's Right? What's Wrong? Participant Book. Sawyer, Kieran, ed. 2004. (Developing Faith Ser.). 80p. (gr. 9-12). 6.95 (978-0-87793-608-4(0)) Ave Maria Pr.

Carotta, Michael. Celebrating Our Faith: Reconciliation/Eucharist, Level II. 2001. (Celebrating Our Faith). 208p. pap. 19.95 (978-0-15-901141-6(8)) Harcourt Religion Pubs.

—Reconciliation/Eucharist: Level 2. 2002. (Celebrating Our Faith). (Illus.). 144p. pap. 12.95 (978-0-15-901135-5(3)) Harcourt Religion Pubs.

Courtney, Claudia. Saved by Faith: Noah & the Ark. 1998. (ps-2). lib. bdg. 10.65 (978-0-613-72652-8(9)) Tandem Library Bks.

Days of Faith: Student Planner & Assignment Book, Intermediate Grades 2006-2007. 2006. (Illus.). 108p. (J). 4.95 (978-1-933178-33-2(7)) Pflaum Publishing Group.

Dotterweich, Kass P. 25 Stories for Sharing Faith with Teens: Making Connections. Cannizzo, Karen A., ed. 2004. (Youth Ministry Resource Library). 96p. pap. 19.95 (978-0-937997-58-1(7) , 702) Pflaum Publishing Group.

Elkins, Stephen. First Steps in Faith. Colton, Ellie, illus. 2006. 32p. (J). 9.99 (978-0-8054-2662-5(0)) B&H Publishing Grp.

A Few Who Dared to Trust God: With Imprimatur. 2000. (Illus.). 234p. (J). pap. 17.62 (978-1-58516-295-6(7)) American Bible Society.

Fischer, Carl. Days of Faith Assignment Book & Student Planner. Homberg, Ansgar, illus. 2003. 108p. (J). spiral bd. 4.99 (978-0-89837-232-8(1) , 9804) Pflaum Publishing Group.

Gaskins, Pearl Fuyo. I Believe In. . . Christian, Jewish, & Muslim Young People Speak about Their Faiths. 2004. (Illus.). 160p. (J). 18.95 (978-0-8126-2713-8(X)) Cricket Bks.

Gellman, Marc. And God Cried, Too: A Kid's Book of Healing & Hope. Bliss, Harry, illus. 2002. 128p. (J). (gr. 2 up). pap. 5.99 (978-0-06-009886-5(4)); 17.89 (978-0-06-009887-2(2)) HarperCollins Pubs.

Gemmen, Heather & McNeil, Mary. Fun & Games, Pre-Level 1. Frazier, Victoria Ponikvar, illus. 2004. (Rocket ReaderT2 Ser.). 40p. (J). (ps-1). pap., pap. 8.99 (978-0-7814-4008-0(4) , 0781440084) Cook, David C. Publishing Co.

—What Will You Do?, Level 4. Burris, Priscilla, tr. Burris, Priscilla, illus. 1999. (Rocket Readers Ser.). 32p. (J). (gr. 4 up). pap., pap. 4.99 (978-0-7814-3979-4(5) , 0781439795) Cook, David C. Publishing Co.

Gleason, Kenneth. Now the Good News: Participant Book. Sawyer, Kieran, ed. 2003. (Developing Faith Ser.). 80p. (gr. 9-12). 6.95 (978-0-87793-610-7(2)) Ave Maria Pr.

God Always Cares. 2006. 16p. (J). pap. 1.99 (978-0-7847-1452-2(5) , 22131) Standard Publishing.

Groome, Thomas H., et al. Acercandote a Dios (Coming to God) 1998. (Acercandote a la Fe Ser.). (SPA & ENG., Illus.). 288p. (J). (gr. 1). pap. (978-0-8215-4461-7(6)) Sadlier, William H. Inc.

—Acercandote a Dios (Coming to God), Grade 1, Guia. 1998. (Acercandote a la Fe Ser.). (SPA & ENG., Illus.). 286p. (J). (gr. 1-2). pap. 20.55 net. (978-0-8215-4471-6(3)) Sadlier, William H. Inc.

—Acercandote a la Iglesias (Coming to the Church) 1998. (Acercandote a la Fe Ser.). (SPA & ENG., Illus.). 288p. (J). (gr. 3). pap. 12.36 net. (978-0-8215-4463-1(2)) Sadlier, William H. Inc.

—Acercandote a la Iglesias (Coming to the Church), Guia. 1998. (Acercandote a la Fe Ser.). (SPA & ENG., Illus.). 286p. (J). (gr. 3). pap. 20.55 net. (978-0-8215-4473-0(X)) Sadlier, William H. Inc.

—Acercandote a la Palabra de Dios (Coming to God's Word), Guia. 1998. (Acercandote a la Fe Ser.). (SPA & ENG., Illus.). 286p. (YA). (gr. 6). pap. 20.55 net. (978-0-8215-4476-1(4)) Sadlier, William H. Inc.

—Acercandote a la Vida de Dios (Coming to God's Life) 1999. (Acercandote a la Fe Ser.). (SPA & ENG., Illus.). 304p. (J). (gr. 5). pap. 12.00 net. (978-0-8215-4465-5(9)) Sadlier, William H. Inc.

—Acercandote a la Vida de Dios (Coming to God's Life), Grade 5, Guia. 1999. (Acercandote a la Fe Ser.). (SPA & ENG., Illus.). 286p. (J). (gr. 5-6). pap. 20.55 net. (978-0-8215-4475-4(6)) Sadlier, William H. Inc.

—Acercandote al Amor de Dios (Coming to God's Love), Guia. 1998. (Acercandote a la Fe Ser.). (SPA & ENG., Illus.). 286p. (J). (gr. 4-5). pap. 19.95 net. (978-0-8215-4474-7(8)) Sadlier, William H. Inc.

Hendrick, Kathy. One Faith, Onr Lord, Review & Resource Book. 4th ed. 2001. (J). (978-0-8215-2209-7(4) , Sadlier) Sadlier, William H. Inc.

Hendricks, Kathy & Hutchinson, Gloris. One Faith, One Lord, Catechist's Guide. 4th ed. 2001. (J). per. (978-0-8215-2208-0(6) , Sadlier) Sadlier, William H. Inc.

Johnson, Kevin W. Stick Tight: Glue Yourself to Godly Friends. 2001. (Early Teen Discipleship Ser.). 128p. (J). pap. 7.99 (978-0-7642-2434-8(4)) Bethany Hse. Pubs.

Johnson, Nevlynn L., Sr. Faith, Courage & Wisdom: A Journey to Manhood. 3rd rev. l.t. ed. 2003. Orig. Title: Finding My Way: a Journey to Manhood. 240p. per. 14.95 (978-0-9741413-0-5(5)) In The Lead Publishing.

Labosh, Kathy. The Child with Autism Learns the Faith: The Sunday School Guide. 2007. per. 14.00 (978-0-9744341-4-8(0)) Labosh Publishing.

Larkin, Jean K. Days of Faith: Student Planner & Assignment Book, Primary Grades 2006-2007. 2006. (Illus.). 108p. (J). spiral bd. 4.95 (978-1-933178-31-8(0)) Pflaum Publishing Group.

Lauren, Emily. Trustworthiness. (Illus.). (J). 2003. pap. 7.50 (978-1-4109-0333-4(8)); 2002. 32p. lib. bdg. 24.26 (978-0-7398-5782-3(7)) Raintree.

—Trustworthiness. 2003. (gr. k-3). lib. bdg. 15.90 (978-0-613-78300-2(X)) Tandem Library Bks.

Leeper, Angela. Depend on Me. 2004. (You & Me Ser.). (Illus.). 24p. (J). pap. (978-1-4034-6079-0(5)); lib. bdg. 20.64 (978-1-4034-6071-4(X)) Heinemann Library.

Let's Practice Faith: Bible Story Flipbook. 2004. (Firelight Ser.). (gr. 3-4). 4.99 (978-0-8066-6512-2(2)) Augsburg Fortress, Pubs.

Let's Practice Faith: Bible Story Magazine. 2004. (Firelight Ser.). (gr. 5-6). 4.99 (978-0-8066-6514-6(9)) Augsburg Fortress, Pubs.

Let's Practice Faith: Bible Storybook. 2004. (Firelight Ser.). (gr. 1-2). 4.99 (978-0-8066-6510-8(6)) Augsburg Fortress, Pubs.

Let's Practice Faith, Ages 2-3: Bible Story Album. 2004. (Firelight Ser.). (ps-k). 4.99 (978-0-8066-6508-5(4)) Augsburg Fortress, Pubs.

MacArthur, John. A Faith to Grow On. 2004. 192p. (J). 16.99 (978-1-4003-0442-4(3)) Nelson, Thomas Inc.

—My Faith & Prayer Journal. 2004. 64p. (J). pap. 4.99 (978-1-4003-0441-7(5)) Nelson, Thomas Inc.

Media, the Journey of Faith: The Holy Spirit, the Potter & the Clay. 2000. (Connect Ser.: Vol. 9). (YA). 20.00 (978-0-687-72641-7(7)) Abingdon Pr.

Miller, Robbie R. Faith That Works: Serving God's Vision. 1999. (Generation Why Ser.: Vol. 4.7). 41p. (YA). (gr. 9-12). pap. 12.95 (978-0-87303-287-2(X)) Faith & Life Pr.

Morrow, Lesley Mandel, et al, contrib. by. Discovering God's Love: A Faith Development Program for Five Year Olds. rev. ed. 1999. (Discovering God Ser.). (Illus.). 128p. (J). (gr. k-1). pap. 11.58 net. (978-0-8215-2470-1(4)) Sadlier, William H. Inc.

Naseem, Hina. Our Faith & Worship Workbook Vol. 2: Companion to the textbook of Islamic Aqa'id & Arkan. Abiva, Huseyn, ed. 1998. 100p. (J). (gr. 1-3). pap. 6.00 (978-1-56316-065-3(X)) IQRA International Educational Foundation.

Palmer, Alison. Walking the Path of Faith: More Fun Character-Building Activities for LDS Children - a Companion Volume to Planting Seeds of Faith. 2004. (J). per. 9.99 (978-0-88290-764-2(6) , Horizon Pubs.) Cedar Fort, Inc./CFI Distribution.

Reed, Judy. Faith in Action: Discovering Real-Life Heroes. 2004. (Faith Rules Ser.). 96p. (J). (gr. 5-11). pap. 4.99 (978-0-7424-2828-7(1) , In Celebration) Schaffer, Frank Pubns.

Riley, Jim. Spiritual Grit: Pass It on to Kids, 2004. (Illus.). 125p. per. 8.95 (978-1-57166-315-3(0)) Quixote Pr.

Ross & Guymon-King. Primary Partners: Faith in God: We Love Activity Days. 2004. cd-rom 12.95 (978-1-59156-344-0(5)) Covenant Communications, Inc.

Schulz, Charles M. Seguridad es un Pulgar y una Manta. (SPA.). (J). 7.00 (978-84-7655-664-1(0) , PI3929) Plaza Joven, S.A. ESP. *Dist:* Lectorum Pubns., Inc.

Sexuality. 2003. (Faith 4 Life Ser.). 48p. 14.99 (978-0-7644-2479-3(3) , Flagship Church Resources) Group Publishing, Inc.

Sexuality. 2000. (SPA.). (J). pap. 7.95 (978-3-8290-2107-4(0)) Konemann.

Stolpe, Norman D. Discover Your Faith: And Learn How to Live It. 2001. (Discover Series for Junior High Ser.). 32p. (gr. 7-10). stu. ed. 4.75 (978-1-56212-525-7(7) , 120700, Faith Alive Christian Resources) CRC Pubns.

Stradford, Eric & Stradford, Stephanie Walker. The Enterprize: From Slaveship to Spaceship. 2001. 212p. per. 19.95 (978-0-9715153-0-7(1)) Youth Achievers USA.

Strobel, Lee & Vogel, Jane. The Case for Faith. 2002. (Evangelism Ser.). (Illus.). 112p. (YA). pap., stu. ed. 8.99 (978-0-310-24188-1(X) , 230034) Zondervan.

Sublett, Kit. After Camp: Beginning the Christian Adventure. 2003. (YA). pap. 3.95 (978-0-9758577-0-0(3)) Whitecaps Media.

Tada, Joni Eareckson & Wolgemuth, Bobbie. Hymns for a Kid's Heart, 2 vols., Vol. 2. Martinez, Sergio, illus. 2005. 96p. 21.99 incl. audio compact disk (978-1-58134-582-7(8) , Crossway Bibles) Crossway Bks.

Trujillo, Michelle L. Teens Talkin' Faith: A Christian Perspective. 2001. 400p. (YA). pap. 12.95 (978-1-55874-941-2(1)) Health Communications, Inc.

Trust. 2000. (Lion Cub Upside-Down Bks.). (J). (ps-3). pap. 5.95 (978-0-87162-824-4(4)) Warner Pr. Pubs.

Vander Griend, Donna & Von Hulzen, Gary. Share Your Faith: And Keep Your Friends. 1999. (Evangelism Ser.). 100p. (gr. 8-12). 27.95 (978-1-56212-415-1(3) , 131305, Faith Alive Christian Resources) CRC Pubns.

Vida Publishers Staff, ed. Promesas de Dios para Ninos. 2000. (Bible Promises Ser.). (SPA.). 160p. (J). pap. 3.99 (978-0-8297-2370-0(6)) Vida Pubs.

VonSeggen, Liz. Mission Possible: Adventures in Faith. 1998. (Illus.). 131p. pap. 30.00 (978-1-58302-050-0(0) , BTU-11) One Way St., Inc.

Walker, Joyce MacKichan. Faithful Questions Student Book. 2nd ed. 2004. (YA). spiral bd. 14.99 (978-0-9752605-7-9(X)) LOGOS System Assocs.

Ward, Elaine M. Answering Children's Faith Questions: Through Parables, Poetry & Prayer. 1999. 100p. (J). (gr. 1-6). pap. 10.95 (978-1-57438-031-6(1) , 5302) Educational Ministries, Inc.

Warner Press Staff. Faith. 2000. (Lion Cub Upside-Down Books Ser.). (Illus.). (J). (ps-3). pap. 5.95 (978-0-87162-828-2(7)) Warner Pr. Pubs.

What Is Faith? 2006. (J). 16p. pap. 1.99 (978-0-7847-1688-5(9) , 02990); (Illus.). 24p. bds. 6.99 (978-0-7847-1396-9(0) , 04056) Standard Publishing.

Why Sharing Faith Matters. 1998. (Core Belief Bible Study Ser.). (YA). (gr. 10-12). pap. 11.99 (978-0-7644-0897-7(6)) Group Publishing, Inc.

Zizek, Slavoj. On Belief. 2001. (Thinking in Action Ser.). (Illus.). 176p. 19.95 (978-0-415-25532-5(5)) Routledge.

FAITH-CURE

see Spiritual Healing

FALCONRY—FICTION

Lasky, Kathryn. Robin Hood: The Boy Who Became a Legend. 1999. (J). (978-0-590-25933-0(4) , Blue Sky Pr., The) Scholastic, Inc.

FALCONS

Bailey, Jill. Falcons. 2002. (Secret World Of... Ser.). (Illus.). 48p. (J). lib. bdg. 27.12 (978-0-7398-4985-9(9)) Raintree.

Collard, Sneed B., III. Birds of Prey: A Look at Daytime Raptors. 1999. (Watts Library). (Illus.). 64p. (J). (gr. 5-7). 25.50 (978-0-531-20363-7(8) , Watts, Franklin) Scholastic Library Publishing.

Deborah Kops. Los Halcones. 2004. (Illus.). (J). lib. bdg. 22.45 (978-1-4103-0281-6(4) , Blackbirch Pr., Inc.) Thomson Gale.

The Falcon: Individual Chapter Book Title Six-Packs. Vol. 25. 32p. (gr. 3-4). 44.00 (978-0-7635-4471-3(X)) Rigby Education.

Harcourt School Publishers Staff. Return of the Peregrine Falcon Advanced Level. 3rd ed. 2002. (Trophies Reading Program Ser.). (Illus.). pap. 5.10 (978-0-15-323121-6(1)) Harcourt Schl. Pubs.

Lynch, Wayne. Falcons. Neidigh, Sherry, illus. 2005. (Our Wild World Ser.). 48p. (J). pap. 7.95 (978-1-55971-912-4(5) , NorthWord Bks. for Young Readers) T&N Children's Publishing.

—Falcons. Neidigh, Sherry, illus. 2005. 47p. (J). (gr. 2-5). lib. bdg. 15.15 (978-0-606-33697-0(4)) Tandem Library Bks.

Lynch, Wayne, contrib. by. Falcons. 2005. (Our Wild World Ser.). (Illus.). 48p. 10.95 (978-1-55971-911-7(7) , NorthWord Bks. for Young Readers) T&N Children's Publishing.

Povey, Karen D. Falcons. 2005. (Nature's Predators Ser.). (Illus.). 48p. (J). (ps-8). lib. bdg. 26.20 (978-0-7377-2347-2(5) , Greenhaven Pr., Inc.) Thomson Gale.

Priebe, Mac. FalconQuest CD-ROM + the Peregrine Falcon Book. 2003. (J). 29.95 (978-0-9669551-5-6(3)) Mindfull Publishing.

—The Peregrine Falcon: Endangered No More. Priebe, Jennifer, illus. 1999. (Wildlife Winners). 30p. (J). (gr. 2-5). 15.95 (978-0-9669551-9-4(6)) Mindfull Publishing.

Unwin, Mike. Peregrine Falcon. 2004. (Animals under Threat Ser.). (Illus.). 48p. (J). lib. bdg. (978-1-4034-4862-0(0)) Heinemann Library.

—The Peregrine Falcon. 2004. (Animals under Threat Ser.). (Illus.). 48p. (J). pap. 8.50 (978-1-4034-5436-2(1)) Heinemann Library.

Warhol, Tom. Hawks. 2005. (Animalways Ser.). (Illus.). 112p. (J). (gr. 4-7). lib. bdg. (978-0-7614-1744-6(3) , Benchmark Bks.) Cavendish, Marshall Corp.

Wechsler, Doug. Peregrine Falcons. 2001. (Really Wild Life of Birds of Prey Ser.). (Illus.). 24p. (J). lib. bdg. 18.75 (978-0-8239-5598-5(2) , PowerKids Pr.) Rosen Publishing Group, Inc., The.

FALCONS—FICTION

Atwater-Rhodes, Amelia. Falcondance. 2005. 192p. (YA). (gr. 7-12). lib. bdg. 16.99 (978-0-385-90334-9(0) , Delacorte Bks. for Young Readers) Random Hse. Children's Bks.

—Falcondance Vol. III: The Kiesha'ra. 2007. 208p. (YA). (gr. 7). pap. 7.99 (978-0-440-23885-0(4) , Delacorte Bks. for Young Readers) Random Hse. Children's Bks.

—Falcondance Vol. 3: The Kiesha'ra. 2005. 192p. (YA). (gr. 7-12). 14.95 (978-0-385-73194-2(9) , Delacorte Bks. for Young Readers) Random Hse. Children's Bks.

—Snakecharm. 2006. 176p. (YA). (gr. 7-11). mass mkt. 5.99 (978-0-440-23804-1(8) , Laurel Leaf) Random Hse. Children's Bks.

Dans, Peter E. Perry's Baltimore Adventure: A Bird's-Eye View of Charm City. Harrell, Kim, illus. 2007. (J). 14.95 (***978-1-933822-08-2(2)***) Camino Bks., Inc.

Dixon, Sean. The Feathered Cloak. rev. ed. 2007. (Trilogy of the Tree Ser.: Pt. 1). 200p. (J). (gr. 7 up). 12.95 (***978-1-55263-936-8(3)***) Key Porter Bks. CAN. *Dist:* Perseus Distribution.

Douglas, Babette. Falcon Eddie. 2004. (J). 9.99 (978-1-890343-21-7(8)) Kiss A Me Productions, Inc.

Dunphy, Madeleine. The Peregrine's Journey: A Story of Migration. Kest, Kristin, illus. 2008. 32p. (J). 16.95 (***978-0-9777539-3-2(X)***); pap. 9.95 (***978-0-9777539-2-5(1)***) Web of Life Children's Bks.

George, Jean Craighead. Frightful's Daughter. San Souci, Daniel, illus. 2002. 32p. (J). (ps-3). 16.99 (978-0-525-46907-0(9) , Dutton Juvenile) Penguin Group (USA) Inc.

—Frightful's Daughter Meets the Baron Weasel. San Souci, Daniel, illus. 2007. 48p. (J). (ps). 16.99 (***978-0-525-47202-5(9)*** , Dutton Juvenile) Penguin Group (USA) Inc.

—Frightful's Mountain. 1999. (Illus.). 272p. (J). (gr. 4-7). 15.99 (978-0-525-46166-1(3) , Dutton Juvenile) Penguin Group (USA) Inc.

—On the Far Side of the Mountain. 1999. (Illus.). 144p. (J). (gr. 4-7). 16.99 (978-0-525-46348-1(8) , Dutton Juvenile) Penguin Group (USA) Inc.

La Fontaine, Jean De. The Falcon & the Little Dog. 2004. reprint ed. pap. 15.95 (978-1-4191-6181-0(4)) Kessinger Publishing, LLC.

Linklater, Eric. The Wind on the Moon. Bentley, Nicolas, illus. 2004. (New York Review Children's Collection). 376p. (J). 18.95 (978-1-59017-100-4(4) , NYR Children's Collection) New York Review of Bks., Inc., The.

Roy, Ron. The Falcon's Feathers. Gurney, John Steven, illus. 1998. (A to Z Mysteries Ser.: No. 6). 96p. (gr. k-3). lib. bdg. 11.99 (978-0-679-99055-0(0)); (J). pap. 3.99 (978-0-679-89055-3(6)) Random Hse. Children's Bks. (Random Hse. Bks. for Young Readers).

Schraff, Anne. The Phantom Falcon. Taylor, Marjorie, illus. rev. ed. 1999. (Take Ten Ser.). 51p. (YA). (gr. 4-12). pap. 3.95 (978-1-58659-031-4(6)) Artesian Pr.

FALL

see Autumn

FALLACIES

see Logic

FALLING STARS

see Meteors

FALSEHOOD

see Truthfulness and Falsehood

FAMILY

see also Divorce; Domestic Relations; Marriage; Parent and Child; Single-Parent Families; Stepfamilies

also names of members of the family, e.g., Fathers; Mothers; etc.

Adams, Pamela L. Once upon a Family: A Son's Journey of Love, Loss, & Hope. Henderson, Ken, illus. l.t. ed. 2003. 116p. per. (978-1-891029-35-6(5)) Henderson Publishing.

Adamson, Heather. Families in Many Cultures. 2008. (J). (***978-1-4296-0019-4(5)*** , Pebble Bks.) Capstone Pr., Inc.

Ages 4-5 Take Home Fall 2002. 2002. pap. 14.99 (978-1-59185-017-5(7)) CharismaLife Pubs.

Alcott, Louisa May. Under the Lilacs. l.t. ed. 2005. 444p. pap. (978-1-84637-059-5(0)) Echo Library.

Alpern, Michele. The Effects of Job Loss on the Family. 2002. (Focus on Family Matters Ser.). (Illus.). 64p. (YA). (gr. 10 up). 25.00 (978-0-7910-6690-4(8) , Chelsea Hse.) Facts On File, Inc.

Apel, Melanie Ann. Home Life in Ancient Greece. 2004. (Primary Sources of Ancient Civilizations Ser.). (Illus.). 24p. (J). lib. bdg. (978-0-8239-8940-9(2)); lib. bdg. 19.95 (978-0-8239-6772-8(7)) Rosen Publishing Group, Inc., The. (PowerKids Pr.).

Armitage, Ronda. Violence in Society. 2004. (21st Century Debates Ser.). lib. bdg. 28.56 (978-0-7398-6469-2(6)) Raintree.

Auld, Mary. Meet the Family, 6 bks. Incl. My Aunt & Uncle. lib. bdg. 20.67 (978-0-8368-3923-4(4)); My Brother. lib. bdg. 20.67 (978-0-8368-3924-1(2)); My Dad. lib. bdg. 20.67 (978-0-8368-3925-8(0)); My Grandparents. lib. bdg. 20.67 (978-0-8368-3926-5(9)); My Mom. lib. bdg. 20.67 (978-0-8368-3927-2(7)); My Sister. lib. bdg. 20.67 (978-0-8368-3928-9(5)); 24p. (J). (gr. 1 up). (Illus.). 2004. Set lib. bdg. 124.02 (978-0-8368-3922-7(6)) Stevens, Gareth Inc.

—Mi Hermana. 2004. (Conoce la Familia Ser.). (SPA., Illus.). 24p. (J). (gr. 1 up). lib. bdg. 20.67 (978-0-8368-3930-2(1)) Stevens, Gareth Inc.

—Mi Hermano. 2004. (Conoce la Familia Ser.). (SPA., Illus.). 24p. (J). (gr. 1 up). lib. bdg. 20.67 (978-0-8368-3931-9(5)) Stevens, Gareth Inc.

—Mi Mama. 2004. (Conoce la Familia Ser.). (SPA., Illus.). 24p. (J). (gr. 1 up). lib. bdg. 20.67 (978-0-8368-3932-6(3)) Stevens, Gareth Inc.

—Mi Papa. 2004. (Conoce la Familia Ser.). (SPA., Illus.). 24p. (J). (gr. 1 up). lib. bdg. 20.67 (978-0-8368-3933-3(1)) Stevens, Gareth Inc.

—Mis Abuelos. 2004. (Conoce la Familia Ser.). (SPA., Illus.). 24p. (J). (gr. 1 up). lib. bdg. 20.67 (978-0-8368-3934-0(X)) Stevens, Gareth Inc.

—Mis Tios. 2004. (Conoce la Familia Ser.). (SPA., Illus.). 24p. (J). (gr. 1 up). lib. bdg. 20.67 (978-0-8368-3935-7(8)) Stevens, Gareth Inc.

—My Aunt & Uncle. 2004. (Meet the Family Ser.). (Illus.). 24p. (J). (gr. 1 up). lib. bdg. 20.67 (978-0-8368-3923-4(4)) Stevens, Gareth Inc.

—My Dad. 2004. (Meet the Family Ser.). (Illus.). 24p. (J). (gr. 1 up). lib. bdg. 20.67 (978-0-8368-3925-8(0)) Stevens, Gareth Inc.

—My Grandparents. 2004. (Meet the Family Ser.). (Illus.). 24p. (J). (gr. 1 up). lib. bdg. 20.67 (978-0-8368-3926-5(9)) Stevens, Gareth Inc.

—My Mom. 2004. (Meet the Family Ser.). (Illus.). 24p. (J). (gr. 1 up). lib. bdg. 20.67 (978-0-8368-3927-2(7)) Stevens, Gareth Inc.

—My Sister. 2004. (Meet the Family Ser.). (Illus.). 24p. (J). (gr. 1 up). lib. bdg. 20.67 (978-0-8368-3928-9(5)) Stevens, Gareth Inc.

Backes, Michel & Brun-Cosme, Nadine. Hoy lo Hace Papa! Ros, Rafael, tr. Backes, Michael, illus. 2003. (SPA.). 164p. (978-84-8470-116-3(6)) Corimbo, Editorial S.L.

E
F
G

Baggette, Susan K. Jonathan Goes to the Airport. Moriarty, William J., photos by. 1998. (Jonathan Adventures Ser.). (Illus.). 16p. (J). (ps-k). bds. 5.95 (978-0-9660172-6-7(9)) Brookfield Reader, Inc., The.

Bailey, Debbie. Families. Huszar, Susan, photos by. 1999. (Talk-about-Books). (Illus.). 104p. (J). (gr. k-ps). lib. bdg. 19.95 (978-1-55037-594-7(6)) Annick Pr., Ltd. CAN. *Dist:* Firefly Bks., Ltd.

—My Family. Huszar, Susan, photos by. 1998. (Talk-about-Books: Vol. 11). (Illus.). 14p. (J). (gr. k-ps). bds. 5.95 (978-1-55037-510-7(5)) Annick Pr., Ltd. CAN. *Dist:* Firefly Bks., Ltd.

Banks, Pat & Davidson, Carolyn. Where Grandma Lives, Love Is Forever. 1998. (Illus.). 34p. (J). (gr. 3-6). 7.50 (978-1-56469-033-3(4)) Harmony Hse. Pubs.

Barbara, Diane & Beccaria, Dominique. Grandmother & Me: A Special Book for You & Your Grandmother to Fill in Together & Share with Each Other. 2004. (Illus.). 52p. (J). 16.95 (978-0-8109-4936-2(9)) Abrams, Harry N., Inc.

Beaton, Clare, illus. Family: La Familia. l.t. ed. 1998. (English-Spanish Bilingual First Bks.). (ENG & SPA.). 24p. (J). (ps up). lib. bdg. 14.45 (978-1-56674-250-4(1)) Forest Hse. Publishing Co., Inc.

Belinsky, Ruth. We Are a Family. Hill, Linda W., ed. Harris, Rhonda, illus. l.t. ed. 2001. 30p. (J). (gr. k-5). pap. 9.95 (978-1-892614-37-7(5)) Briarwood Pubns.

Benchmark Education Staff, compiled by. Families & Friends. 2006. spiral bd. 249.00 (***978-1-4108-7069-8(3)***) Benchmark Education Co.

Beren, Norris L. When Disaster Strikes Home! 101+ Ways to Protect Your Family from Unthinkable Emergencies. 2003. (Illus.). 240p. per. 17.95 (978-0-9729065-0-0(9)) EPEI Pr.

Bishop, Keeley & Tripp, Penny. Family Break Up. 2003. (Just the Facts Ser.). (Illus.). 56p. (YA). lib. bdg. 25.64 (978-1-4034-0819-8(X)) Heinemann Library.

Bolchazy, Marie Carducci. Quis Me Amat?/Who Loves Me? 2003. (I Am Reading Latin Ser.). (ENG & LAT., Illus.). 64p. (J). (gr. k-3). 12.00 (978-0-86516-541-0(6)) Bolchazy-Carducci Pubs.

Bratton, Heidi. Celebrate Family. 2000. (Illus.). 32p. (J). (ps-2). 8.99 (978-0-570-07094-8(5)) Concordia Publishing Hse.

Brieske, Joel. Being Different Is Being Normal. 2005. 32p. (J). pap. 12.95 (978-1-4116-3378-0(4)) Lulu.com.

Broqueville, Paulette-Renee. Unraveling Your Past Relationships. 2003. 288p. per. 20.00 (978-0-9719413-2-8(7)) Broqueville Publishing, Inc.

Burton, Margie, et al. Families. Adams, Alison, ed. 1999. (Early Connections Ser.). 16p. (gr. k-2). pap. 4.50 (978-1-58344-060-5(7)) Benchmark Education Co.

Casselman, Grace. A Hole in the Hedge. 2004. 215p. (J). (gr. 6 up). pap. 8.95 (978-0-929141-99-2(7)) Napoleon Publishing/Rendezvous Pr. CAN. *Dist:* AtlasBooks Distribution.

Catala, Ellen. Who Keeps Us Safe? 2006. (Illus.). 18p. (J). (978-0-7368-5984-4(5)) Capstone Pr., Inc.

—Who Keeps Us Safe? 2006. (Illus.). 8,16p. (J). 6.50 (978-0-7368-1720-2(4)) Red Brick Learning.

—Who Keeps Us Safe. 2006. (ENG & SPA., Illus.). 18p. (J). (978-0-7368-6020-8(7)) Yellow Umbrella Pr.

Catching People in the Love Net. 2005. (YA). 9.75 (978-1-58942-261-2(9)) R.H. Boyd Publishing Corp.

Charlip, Remy & Moore, Lilian. Hooray for Me! Williams, Vera B., illus. 2004. 40p. (YA). (ps up). 14.95 (978-1-883672-43-0(0), Tricycle Pr.) Ten Speed Pr.

Ching, Carrie. Tons of Things to Do for Hawaii's Kids: Activities, Adventures & Excursions for Keiki Eager to Explore Oahu. Bowen, Lance, illus. 2004. 160p. (J). pap. 14.95 (978-0-9729905-2-3(6)) Beachhouse Publishing, LLC.

Clark, Jan. Family Survival. 2004. (Illus.). 32p. (J). lib. bdg. 25.64 (978-1-4109-0569-7(1)) Raintree.

Clarkson, Clay. Our 24 Family Ways: Family Devotional Guide. Jarboe, Marvin, illus. 2004. 112p. (J). pap. 14.95 (978-1-888692-07-5(3)) Whole Heart Ministries.

Clinch, Lori. Are We There Yet? From Diapers to Puberty. 2004. (Illus.). 308p. (YA). per. 15.95 (978-0-9721613-9-8(2)) Old Hundred & One Pr. Publishing Co., The.

D'Andrea, Joseph C. Picture Me with Grandma. Rasmussen, Wendy, illus. 1998. 10p. (J). (ps up). bds. 4.99 (978-1-57151-545-2(3)) Playhouse Publishing.

Daronco, Mickey & Ohanesian, Diane. Home with Mom & Dad. 2003. (BuildUp Ser.). (J). pap. 22.00 (978-1-4108-0753-3(3)) Benchmark Education Co.

David C. Cook. Families, the Environment, Sports & Competition. 2003. (Domain 456 Ser.). 128p. (J). (gr. 4-6). pap., pap. 15.99 (978-0-7814-5514-5(6), 0781455146) Cook, David C. Publishing Co.

—My Loving Family. 2003. (My Jesus Pocket Bks.). (Illus.). 32p. (J). (ps-3). pap., pap. 8.90 (978-1-55513-858-5(6), 1555138586) Cook, David C. Publishing Co.

Davis, James (Jim) W. Out-takes of 55 Years of Camping. 2004. (Illus.). 168p. (YA). per. 5.95 (978-0-9760960-0-9(5)) Davis, James (Jim).

De Muchas Maneras (Many Ways) Como las Familias Practican Sus Creencias y Religiones (How Families Practice Their Beliefs & Religions) 2006. (Spanish Picture Bks.). (SPA.). 32p. (J). lib. bdg. 15.95 (978-0-8225-6506-2(4), Ediciones Lerner) Lerner Publishing Group.

Dennis, Jep & Dennis, Bill. It Really Was a Lovely Village: Auburn, Alabama. 2002. (Illus.). 244p. (YA). (gr. 11 up). pap. 16.95 (978-0-9632180-9-4(3)) Chinaberry Hse.

Dk Millennium Family Encyclopedia W/Ew Children's. (J). 149.95 (978-0-7894-2934-6(9)) Dorling Kindersley Publishing, Inc.

Donahue, Jill L. Family Follies: A Book of Family Jokes. Trover, Zachary, illus. 2006. (Read-It! Joke Books—Supercharged!). (J). 19.93 (978-1-4048-2362-4(X)) Picture Window Bks.

Dotlich, Rebecca Kai. A Family Like Yours. Lyon, Tammie Speer, illus. 2003. 32p. (YA). (gr. k-2). 14.95 (978-1-56397-916-3(0)) Boyds Mills Pr.

Douglas, Ann. Family Tree Detective. 1999. (gr. 3-6). lib. bdg. 18.75 (978-0-613-25125-9(3)) Tandem Library Bks.

Drake, Jane & Love, Ann. My Baby Brother & Me. Ritchie, Scot, illus. 2000. (Memory Scrapbks. for Kids). 32p. (J). (gr. k-3). (978-1-55074-639-6(1)) Kids Can Pr., Ltd.

—My Baby Sister & Me. Ritchie, Scot, illus. 2000. (Memory Scrapbks. for Kids). 32p. (J). (gr. k-3). (978-1-55074-641-9(3)) Kids Can Pr., Ltd.

Dunwell, Anna. Guide to the 400 Best Children's & Adults Books about Grandparents. 1999. 50p. (J). (gr. k-12). spiral bd. 29.95 (978-1-891657-33-7(X), S3079) Lift Every Voice.

Dwight, Laura. Brothers & Sisters. 2005. (Illus.). 40p. (J). 15.95 (978-1-887734-80-6(5)) Star Bright Bks., Inc.

Easterling, Lisa. Families. 2007. (J). (***978-1-4034-9402-3(9)***); pap. (***978-1-4034-9411-5(8)***) Heinemann Library.

Elton, Richard & Elton, Candice. My Family Album. 2004. (Illus.). 28p. pap. 19.95 (978-1-58685-586-4(7)) Gibbs Smith, Publisher.

Epstein, Brad, ed. Cornell University 101: My First Text-Board-Book. l.t. ed. 2004. (101—My First Text-Board Books). (Illus.). 20p. (J). bds. 9.95 (978-1-932530-00-1(2)) Michaelson Entertainment.

—Penn State University 101: My First Text-Board-Book. l.t. ed. 2004. (101—My First Text-Board Books). (Illus.). 20p. (J). bds. 9.95 (978-1-932530-04-9(5)) Michaelson Entertainment.

—Stanford University 101: My First Text-Board-Book. l.t. ed. 2003. (101—My First Text-Board Books). (Illus.). 20p. (J). bds. 9.95 (978-1-932530-05-6(3), 101 Bk.) Michaelson Entertainment.

—University of Michigan 101: My First Text-Board-Book. l.t. ed. 2003. (101—My First Text-Board Books). (Illus.). 20p. (J). bds. 9.95 (978-1-932530-02-5(9)) Michaelson Entertainment.

—University of Nebraska 101: My First Text-Board-Book. l.t. ed. 2003. (101—My First Text-Board Books). (Illus.). 20p. (J). bds. 9.95 (978-1-932530-03-2(7)) Michaelson Entertainment.

Especially for Dads: Introducing Dads with Young Children to Literacy, Language & Learning Through Great Children's Literature. 2004. (J). (978-0-9753985-4-8(7)) Mother Goose Programs.

Espeland, Pamela & Verdick, Elizabeth. People Who Care about You: The Support Assets. 2004. (Adding Assets Series for Kids: Bk. 1). (Illus.). 80p. (J). (gr. 3-7). pap. 9.95 (978-1-57542-162-9(3)) Free Spirit Publishing, Inc.

Families & Careers Activity Center with Puppet Theater. 2001. (Illus.). (J). (ps-2). 219.00 (978-0-9673268-3-2(4)) Learning Fasten-Ations, Inc.

Families & Careers Activity Center with Velcro Penguin Board. 2001. (Illus.). (J). (ps-2). pap. 199.00 (978-0-9673268-4-9(2)) Learning Fasten-Ations, Inc.

Family. (YA). tchr. ed. 41.95 (978-0-382-40668-3(0)) Cobblestone Publishing Co.

Family, Vol. II. 2nd fac. ed. 723p. (YA). reprint ed. pap. 99.00 (978-0-7404-0383-5(4)) Higginson Bk. Co.

Family Matters, 6 bks. Incl. You & a Death in Your Family. Wilson, Antoine. (YA). lib. bdg. 23.95 (978-0-8239-3355-6(5)); You & an Illness in Your Family. Wainwright, Tabitha. (YA). lib. bdg. 23.95 (978-0-8239-3352-5(0)); You & the Rules in Your Family. MacAdam, Lea. (YA). lib. bdg. 23.95 (978-0-8239-3350-1(4)); You & Violence in Your Family. Giacobello, John. (J). lib. bdg. 23.95 (978-0-8239-3353-2(9)); You & Your Parents' Divorce. Krohn, Katherine E. (YA). lib. bdg. 23.95 (978-0-8239-3354-9(7)); You, Your Friends & Your Family. Bishop, Vincent. (J). lib. bdg. 23.95 (978-0-8239-3351-8(2)); (gr. 5-8). (Illus.). 48p. 2005. Set lib. bdg. 143.70 (978-0-8239-9313-0(2)) Rosen Publishing Group, Inc., The.

Famous Families, 8 Bks., Set. 2005. (YA). 202.00 (978-1-4042-0376-1(1)) Rosen Publishing Group, Inc., The.

Fannoun, Kathy. Our Loving Grandparents. Date not set. 20p. (J). 4.50 (978-1-884187-30-8(7)) AMICA Publishing Hse.

Fletcher, Ralph J. Relatively Speaking: Poems about Family. Krudop, Walter L., illus. 1999. 48p. (J). (ps-3). 15.99 (978-0-531-33141-5(5)); (gr. 2-4). pap. 14.95 (978-0-531-30141-8(9)) Scholastic, Inc. (Orchard Bks.).

Fox-Lee, Kyme & Fox-Lee, Susan. What Are Parents? Daddys Edition. Jennings, Randy, illus. 2007. 32p. 15.95 (978-0-9753699-1-3(1)) StoryTyme Publishing.

Fox-Lee, Susan & Fox-Lee, Kyme. "What Are Parents?" Jennings, Randy, illus. 2005. 32p. 15.95 (978-0-9753699-0-6(3)) StoryTyme Publishing.

Frasier, Debra. El Dia en Que Tu Naciste. Ada, Alma Flor & Campoy, F. Isabel, trs. 1998. (SPA., Illus.). 32p. (J). (gr. k-2). pap. 7.00 (978-0-15-201709-5(7), HB7090, Red Wagon Bks.) Harcourt Children's Bks.

Friedler, Anna Dunwell. My Very Own Multicultural Family. 2001. (Illus.). 16p. (J). (gr. k-12). spiral bd. 24.95 (978-1-891657-34-4(8), S3090) Lift Every Voice.

Garon, Risa J. A Kid's Guide to Coming toTerms with Separation & Divorce. 2000. (Illus.). 23p. (YA). pap. 10.00 (978-0-9729415-1-8(7)) National Family Resiliency Ctr., Inc.

Goldenstern, Joyce. American Women Against Violence. 1998. (Collective Biographies Ser.). (Illus.). 128p. (YA). (gr. 6-12). lib. bdg. 26.60 (978-0-7660-1025-3(2)) Enslow Pubs., Inc.

Gonzales Bertrand, Diane. Family, Familia. Castilla, Julia Mercedes, tr. Howard, Pauline Rodriguez, illus. 1999. (SPA & ENG.). 32p. (J). (ps-3). 14.95 (978-1-55885-269-3(7), Piñata Books) Arte Publico Pr.

The Good, the Bad, & Everything Else: Individual Title Six-Packs. (Action Packs Ser.). 104p. (gr. 3-5). 44.00 (978-0-7635-2994-9(X)) Rigby Education.

Gordon, Sol. All Families Are Different. Cohen, Vivien, illus. 2004. 53p. (gr. 2 up). pap. 12.00 (978-1-57392-765-9(1)) Prometheus Bks., Pubs.

—All Families Are Different. 2000. (gr. k-3). lib. bdg. 19.35 (978-0-613-88483-9(3)) Tandem Library Bks.

Grace, Roz. Trina's Family Reunion. Melvin, James, illus. 1998. 32p. (J). (ps-6). 14.95 (978-0-9659181-1-4(4)) BMF Pr.

Greene, Judybeth, illus. Mommy, Open up the Secrets of the World. 2005. (J). pap. 9.95 (978-1-932672-76-3(1)) Outskirts Press, Inc.

Halpern. Theme Pack: Family. 2002. (Pair-It Bks.). (Illus.). (J). pap. (978-0-7398-6369-5(X)) Steck-Vaughn.

Hammersmith, Craig & Stewart, Joan. What Is a Family? 2002. (Spyglass Books). (Illus.). 24p. (J). (gr. 1 up). lib. bdg. 18.60 (978-0-7565-0367-3(1)) Compass Point Bks.

Haywood, John. Families at Home: Home Family & Everyday Life Through the Ages. 2003. (How We Lived Ser.). (Illus.). 64p. (gr. 3-7). pap. 7.99 (978-1-84215-812-8(0), Southwater) Anness Publishing GBR. *Dist:* National Bk. Network.

Herrera, Juan Felipe. Calling the Doves: El Canto de las Palomas. 2001. (J). 14.75 (978-0-606-21098-0(9)) Tandem Library Bks.

Heyman, Carly. My Extra Special Brother: How to Love, Understand, & Celebrate Your Sibling with Special Needs. Conley, Stephanie, illus. l.t. ed. 2003. 112p. pap. 12.95 (978-0-9727865-0-8(3), 1003894) Fragile X Assn. of Georgia.

Hoffman, Don. Good Morning, Good Night Billy & Abigail. Dakins, Todd, illus. 2004. (Billy & Abigail Ser.). 20p. (J). (ps-k). bds. 5.99 (978-1-4037-0542-6(9)) Dalmatian Pr.

Hood, Karen Jean Matsko. Holiday Help for Foster Children: A Basic Guide to Help Foster Children During the Holidays. 2002. 19.95 (978-1-59210-462-8(2)); cd-rom 13.95 (978-1-59210-483-3(5)) Whispering Pine Pr., Inc.

Hutchison, G. F. How to Handle Your Parents: A Guide for Teens. 2003. 160p. (YA). per. 13.99 (978-1-885631-78-7(2), Family Of Man Pr., The) Hutchison, G.F. Pr.

I Love My Family: Big Book: Level C. Group 1. (Sunshinetm Ser.). 8p. 20.95 (978-0-7802-5723-8(5)) Wright Group, The.

I Need a Rest! Individual Title, 6 Packs. (ps-2). 23.00 (978-0-7635-8818-2(0)) Rigby Education.

Janice M.Yuwiler. Family Violence. 2004. (Lucent Overview Ser.). (Illus.). 112p. (J). 29.95 (978-1-59018-189-8(1)) Thomson Gale.

Johnson, Jennifer Hunt & Hansen, Holly T. Family Folklore, 715 vols. 2003. (Illus.). 27p. 9.95 (978-0-9729610-8-0(9), CMB7) Tapis & Assocs., Inc.

Johnson, Julie. Our Stepfamily. 2007. (J). (***978-1-59604-154-7(4)***) Stargazer Bks.

Johnson, Nevlynn L., Sr. Faith, Courage & Wisdom: A Journey to Manhood. 3rd rev. l.t. ed. 2003. Orig. Title: Finding My Way: a Journey to Manhood. 240p. per. 14.95 (978-0-9741413-0-5(5)) In The Lead Publishing.

Kalar, Bonnie. Jack. Spreen, Kathe, illus. Date not set. 12p. (J). (ps-2). pap. (978-1-891619-13-7(6)) Corona Pr.

Kaplan, Leslie C. Home Life in Ancient Egypt. 2004. (Primary Sources of Ancient Civilizations Ser.). (Illus.). 24p. (J). lib. bdg. (978-0-8239-8935-5(6)); lib. bdg. 19.95 (978-0-8239-6784-1(0)) Rosen Publishing Group, Inc., The. (PowerKids Pr.).

Kent, Susan. Let's Talk about Living with a Grandparent. 2000. (Let's Talk Library). (Illus.). 24p. (J). (gr. 3). lib. bdg. 18.75 (978-0-8239-5421-6(8), PowerKids Pr.) Rosen Publishing Group, Inc., The.

Kinkade, Sheila. My Family. Little, Elaine, illus. 2006. 32p. (J). pap. 6.95 (978-1-57091-691-5(8)) Charlesbridge Publishing, Inc.

Kuklin, Susan. Families. 2006. (Illus.). 36p. (J). (978-1-4156-6281-6(9)) Hyperion Bks. for Children.

—Families. Kuklin, Susan, illus. 2006. (Illus.). 40p. (ps-3). 15.99 (978-0-7868-0822-9(5)) Hyperion Pr.

—How My Family Lives in America. Kuklin, Susan, illus. 1998. (Illus.). 40p. (J). (ps-2). 6.99 (978-0-689-82221-6(9), Aladdin) Simon & Schuster Children's Publishing.

Lanese, Janet. Grandfathers Are Like Gold: Every Family's Treasure. 2000. (Illus.). 128p. pap. 10.00 (978-0-684-86217-0(4), Fireside) Simon & Schuster.

Law, Felicia. Family: A First Poem Book about Family. Knight, Paula, illus. (Patchwork First Poem Bks.). 24p. (ps). 8.95 (978-1-904668-83-1(6)) Mercury Bks. Ltd. GBR. *Dist:* International Publishers Marketing.

Lawrence, Kenneth. Korah's Travels: The Saga of an Israelite Family. l.t. ed. 2007. (Illus.). 256p. (Orig.). (YA). per. 19.95 (978-0-910653-14-5(3), 8404143, Red River Pr.) Red River Pr.

Ligon, Susan. There's a Brand-New Baby at Our House & ... I'm the Big Sister! 2007. 48p. (J). pap. 9.99 (978-1-4003-0966-5(2)) Nelson, Thomas Inc.

—There's a Brand-New Baby at Our House and... I'm the Big Brother! 2007. 48p. (J). pap. 9.99 (978-1-4003-0967-2(0)) Nelson, Thomas Inc.

Lound, Karen. Girl Power in the Family. 1999. (Girl Power Ser.). (Illus.). 80p. (YA). (gr. 6-9). lib. bdg. (978-0-8225-2692-6(1), Lerner Pubns.) Lerner Publishing Group.

Lynch, Emma. Brazil. 2005. (We're from Ser.). (Illus.). 32p. (J). (ps-ps). pap. 7.60 (978-1-4034-5811-7(1)) Heinemann.

—China (We're From) 2005. (Heinemann First Libary Ser.). (Illus.). 32p. (J). lib. bdg. (978-1-4034-5803-2(0)) Heinemann Library.

—We're from Brazil. 2005. (We're from Ser.). (Illus.). 32p. (J). (978-1-4034-5802-5(2)) Heinemann Library.

—We're from Indonesia. 2005. (We're from Ser.). (Illus.). 32p. (J). pap. (978-1-4034-5813-1(8)); lib. bdg. (978-1-4034-5804-9(9)) Heinemann.

—We're from Italy. 2005. (Heinemann First Library). (Illus.). 32p. (J). (978-1-4034-5805-6(7)); pap. (978-1-4034-5814-8(6)) Heinemann.

—We're from Kenya. 2005. (We're from Ser.). (Illus.). 32p. (J). pap. (978-1-4034-5815-5(4)); lib. bdg. (978-1-4034-5806-3(5)) Heinemann Library.

—We're from Pakistan. 2005. (We're from Ser.). (J). lib. bdg. 24.21 (978-1-4034-5807-0(3)) Heinemann.

—We're from Pakistan. 2005. 32p. (J). pap. 7.60 (978-1-4034-5816-2(2)) Heinemann Library.

Lynn, Vicki, concept. Hilda Is Here. 2003. per. 14.95 (978-0-9715737-1-0(9)) Aradiance Publishing.

MacDonald, Fiona. Home, Family & Everyday Life. 2001. (Through the Ages Ser.). (Illus.). 64p. (gr. 3-7). 12.95 (978-0-7548-0816-9(5)) Anness Publishing GBR. *Dist:* National Bk. Network.

MacGregor, Kim. Yummy Yummy Nummy Nummy, Should I Put This in My Tummy? 2004. 24p. pap. (978-0-9731301-2-6(1)) Beautiful Beginnings Youth, Inc.

Malam, John. Ancient Egyptian Homes. 2003. (People in the Past Ser.). (Illus.). 48p. (J). (gr. 4-6). lib. bdg. 27.07 (978-1-4034-0310-0(4)) Heinemann Library.

—Homes. 2002. (People in the Past Ser.). (Illus.). 48p. (J). pap. (978-1-4034-0514-2(X)) Heinemann Library.

Marcovitz, Hal. Teens & Family Issues. 2004. (Gallup Youth Survey, Major Issues & Trends Ser.). (Illus.). 112,128p. (J). (gr. 7-9). lib. bdg. 22.95 (978-1-59084-725-1(3)) Mason Crest Pubs.

Maurer, Tracy. A to Z of Friends & Family. 2002. (A to Z Ser.). (Illus.). 48p. (gr. k-2). 20.95 (978-1-58952-060-8(2)) Rourke Publishing, LLC.

McDonald, Stacy. Raising Maidens of Virtue: A Study of Feminine Loveliness for Mothers & Daughters. 2004. (Illus.). 226p. (YA). 18.00 (978-0-9743390-1-6(6)) Books on the Path.

McGraw-Hill Staff & Sasse, Connie R. Families Today, 2 vols. 4th ed. 2003. 728p. (C). (gr. 9-12). stu. ed. 61.32 (978-0-07-829840-0(7), 9780078298400) Glencoe/McGraw-Hill.

Mi Familia: Individual Title Six-Packs. (Coleccion Pm Ser.: Vol. 1). Tr. of My family. (SPA.). 16p. (gr. k-1). 26.00 (978-0-7578-0663-6(5)) Rigby Education.

Michels, Dia L. Look What I See! Where Can I Be?, 3 vols. 2001. (Look What I See! Where Can I Be? Ser.). (Illus.). (J). 39.95 (978-1-930775-37-4(7)) Platypus Media, L.L.C.

Millennium Male: Separating the Men from the Boys. 2003. 88p. pap. 7.50 (978-0-9712585-6-3(2)) JuDe Publishing.

Minden, Cecilia. Family Dinnertime by the Numbers. 2008. (J). lib. bdg. 25.26 (***978-1-60279-013-1(2)***) Cherry Lake Publishing.

Moore-Malinos, Jennifer. When My Parents Forgot How to Be Friends. Fabrega, Marta, illus. 2005. (Let's Talk about It! Ser.). 32p. (J). (ps-3). pap. 6.95 (978-0-7641-3172-1(9)) Barron's Educational Series, Inc.

Morris, Alison. I Love My Family. 2004. (Look at Me... I Love Ser.). (Illus.). 10p. (J). bds. 4.99 (978-1-85854-342-0(8)) Brimax Books Ltd. GBR. *Dist:* Byeway Bks.

Morris, Ann. Families. 2000. (Illus.). 32p. (J). (ps-3). 15.99 (978-0-688-17198-8(2)) HarperCollins Pubs.

My Family. (All about Me Ser.). 24p. (J). 6.95 (978-1-4048-0160-8(X)) Picture Window Bks.

My Family Tree 6 Packs. Individual Title. (Story Steps Ser.). (gr. k-2). 29.00 (978-0-7635-9599-9(3)) Rigby Education.

Nadelson, Carol C. & Reinburg, Claire E., eds. Sibling Rivalry: Relational Disorders Between Brothers & Sisters. 1999. (Encyclopedia of Psychological Disorders Ser.). (Illus.). 88p. (YA). (gr. 4-7). 35.00 (978-0-7910-4952-5(3), Chelsea Hse.) Facts On File, Inc.

Nana's Sweet Potato Pie, 6 vols. (Multicultural Programs Ser.). 16p. (gr. 1-3). 24.95 (978-0-7802-9211-6(1)) Wright Group, The.

Nelson, Robin. Home. 2003. (First Step Nonfiction Ser.). (Illus.). 24p. (J). (gr. k-2). lib. bdg. 18.60 (978-0-8225-4642-9(6)) Lerner Publishing Group.

—Where Is My Country? (First Step Nonfiction Ser.). (gr. k-2). 2005. (Illus.). 24p. lib. bdg. 17.27 (978-0-8225-0192-3(9)); 2001. (J). pap. 3.95 (978-0-8225-1981-2(X), Lerner Pubns.) Lerner Publishing Group.

Norac, Carl & Dubois, Claude K. Las Palabras Dulces. 2003. (SPA.). 32p. (978-84-95150-18-9(2)) Corimbo, Editorial S.L.

Nuestros Padres 6 Packs. Individual Title. (Coleccion Pm Ser.).Tr. of Our parents. (SPA.). 16p. (gr. 1 up). 26.00 (978-0-7578-3028-0(5)) Rigby Education.

Palmore, Julie. Big Brothers & Big Sisters Are VIP's (Very Important Persons) A Color Me Book. Engle, Jenny, illus. III, 56p. (J). (ps-1). spiral bd. 9.95 (978-0-9722653-0-0(9)) Palmore, Julie.

Parker, Victoria. Greece. 2005. (Illus.). 32p. (J). (ps-7). lib. bdg. 24.21 (978-1-4034-5784-4(0)) Heinemann.

—India. 2005. (We're from Ser.). (Illus.). 32p. (J). (gr. k-2). lib. bdg. 25.36 (978-1-4034-5785-1(9)) Heinemann.

—Mexico. 2005. (We're from Ser.). (Illus.). 32p. (J). (gr. 3-7). lib. bdg. 24.21 (978-1-4034-5787-5(5)) Heinemann.

—We're from Australia. 2005. (We're from Ser.). (Illus.). 32p. (J). pap. (978-1-4034-5789-9(1)) Heinemann.

—We're from Greece. 2005. (Illus.). 32p. (J). pap. 7.25 (978-1-4034-5791-2(3)) Heinemann.

—We're from India. 2005. (We're from Ser.). (Illus.). 32p. (J). pap. (978-1-4034-5792-9(1)) Heinemann.

—We're from Japan. 2005. (Illus.). 32p. (J). (978-1-4034-5786-8(7)); pap. (978-1-4034-5793-6(X)) Heinemann.

—We're from Mexico. 2005. (We're from Ser.). (Illus.). 32p. (J). pap. 7.25 (978-1-4034-5794-3(8)) Heinemann.

Parker, Victoria & Parker, Vic. Australia. 2005. (We're from Ser.). (Illus.). 32p. (J). (ps-ps). lib. bdg. 25.36 (978-1-4034-5782-0(4)) Heinemann.

E
F
G

Parr, Todd. We Belong Together: A Book About Adoption & Families. 2007. (Illus.). 32p. (J). (ps-1). 15.99 (***978-0-316-01668-1(3)***) Little, Brown Bks. for Young Readers.

Passey, Marion. My Tiny Book of Family. 2004. (Illus.). (J). 5.95 (978-1-59038-242-4(0)) Deseret Bk. Co.

Peavler, Amy & Peavler, Jan. The King the Queen & the Princess. Peavler, Amy & Peavler, Jan, illus. 2006. (Illus.). 40p. (J). per. (978-0-9787672-2-8(5)) Lotus Petal Publishing.

Playing with My Family: Second Grade Newcomer Books. (On Our Way to English Ser.). (gr. 2 up). 29.50 (978-0-7578-7209-9(3)) Rigby Education.

Powell, Jillian. Family Matters. 1999. (Life Files Ser.). (Illus.). 64p. (J). pap. 15.99 (978-0-237-51887-5(2)); 24.99 (978-0-237-51886-8(4)) Evans Publishing Group GBR. (Evans Brothers, Limited). *Dist:* Independent Pubs. Group.

Powell, Jillian. Me & My Family. 2007. (J). (***978-1-59771-088-6(1)***) Sea-To-Sea Pubns.

Presma, Frances & Edelson, Paula. Straight Talk about Today's Families. 1999. (Straight Talk Ser.). 160p. (YA). (gr. 6-12). 27.45 (978-0-8160-3905-0(4)) Facts On File, Inc.

Pugliano-Martin, Carol. Our Families. 2003. (Early Connections Ser.). (J). pap. 33.00 (978-1-4108-1066-3(6)) Benchmark Education Co.

Quateman, Bill & Quateman, India. Daddy Daughter Dinner Dance: A Father's Steps to a Blended Family That Really Works. Quateman, India, illus. 2003. (Illus.). 96p. 17.95 (978-0-9729866-0-1(X)) Angel Mind.

Reeves, Rhonda. Families Are Special. 2000. (Missions & Me Ser.). (Illus.). 16p. (J). (ps). 7.99 (978-1-56309-312-8(X)) Woman's Missionary Union.

Richards, Linda. Family Violence. 2006. (Social Issues Firsthand Ser.). 224p. (gr. 10-12). 29.95 (978-0-7377-2887-3(6) , Greenhaven Pr., Inc.) Thomson Gale.

Richardson, Adele. Manners at Home. 2006. (First Facts Ser.). (J). (978-0-7368-4293-8(4)) Capstone Pr., Inc.

Rickard, Cathy. That's Mine! A Lesson in Sharing. 2004. (Illus.). 16p. (YA). 16.95 (978-1-932373-55-4(1) , Cedar Hill Pr.) Cedar Hill Publishing.

Roca, Nuria. La Familia (del Pequeno al Mayor) Your Family from Youngest to Oldest, Spanish Edition. Curto, Rosa Maria, illus. 2000. (SPA.). 36p. (J). (ps-1). pap. 6.95 (978-0-7641-1688-9(6)) Barron's Educational Series, Inc.

Roche, Hannah. My Grandma Is Great. 1998. (Illus.). (J). (ps-3). pap. (978-1-84089-014-3(2) , 868237Q, Zero to Ten, Limited) Evans Publishing Group.

Rosa-Mendoza, Gladys. My Family & I. Cifuentes, Carolina, ed. Snider, Jackie, illus. 2004. (English-Spanish Foundations Ser.: Vol. 4). Tr. of Mi Familia y Yo. (ENG & SPA.). 20p. (J). (ps-4). bds. 6.95 (978-0-9679748-4-2(4)) Me+Mi Publishing.

Ross, Allison J. Coping When a Parent Is Mentally Ill. 2005. (Coping Ser.). (Illus.). 192p. (YA). (gr. 7-12). lib. bdg. 26.50 (978-0-8239-3359-4(8)) Rosen Publishing Group, Inc., The.

Rubin, Howie. Dads. Hastings, Doug, illus. 2001. 32p. (J). (ps-9). 20.00 (978-0-9703971-1-9(9)) Howie Haus Bks.

Ruth, Angie. My Aunt: Early My Adventure. 2007. 44p. (J). 8.99 (978-1-59092-477-8(0) , Orchard Academy Pr.) Windstorm Creative.

—My Cousin: Early My Adventure. 2007. 44p. (J). 8.99 (978-1-59092-479-2(7) , Orchard Academy Pr.) Windstorm Creative.

—My Uncle: Early My Adventure. 2007. 44p. (J). 8.99 (978-1-59092-487-7(8) , Orchard Academy Pr.) Windstorm Creative.

Saunders-Smith, Gail. Families. 1998. (J). pap. 13.25 (978-0-516-21240-1(0) , Children's Pr.) Scholastic Library Publishing.

Schaefer, Lola M. Aunts. 2008. (***978-1-4296-1220-3(7)*** , Pebble Bks.) Capstone Pr., Inc.

—Aunts. Saunders-Smith, Gail, ed. 1999. (Families Ser.). (Illus.). 24p. (J). (gr. k-1). lib. bdg. 15.93 (978-0-7368-0252-9(5) , Pebble Bks.) Capstone Pr., Inc.

—Cousins. 2008. (J). (***978-1-4296-1222-7(3)***) Capstone Pr., Inc.

—Grandmothers. Saunders-Smith, Gail, ed. 1999. (Families Ser.). (Illus.). 24p. (J). (gr. k-1). lib. bdg. 15.93 (978-0-7368-0258-1(4) , Pebble Bks.) Capstone Pr., Inc.

—Sisters. Saunders-Smith, Gail, ed. 1999. (Families Ser.). (Illus.). 24p. (J). (gr. k-1). lib. bdg. 15.93 (978-0-7368-0260-4(6) , Pebble Bks.) Capstone Pr., Inc.

Schaefer, Lola M. Uncles. 2008. (J). (***978-1-4296-1229-6(0)*** , Pebble Bks.) Capstone Pr., Inc.

Sharp, N. L. Today I'm Going Fishing with My Dad. Demarest, Chris L., illus. 2003. 32p. (J). (gr. k-2). pap. 12.50 (978-1-56397-613-1(7)) Boyds Mills Pr.

Skutch, Robert. Who's in a Family? Nienhaus, Laura, illus. 2004. 32p. (J). (ps-3). 7.95 (978-1-883672-66-9(X) , Tricycle Pr.) Ten Speed Pr.

Slamp, Kathy. Little House in the Arctic: An Adventure Story. l.t. ed. 2004. Orig. Title: Our Little House in the Arctic. (Illus.). 228p. pap. 17.95 (978-0-9713345-3-3(6)) Vessel Ministries.

Smith, Carrie. Our Family Stories. ed. 2004. (Shared Connections Ser.). (J). pap. 27.00 (978-1-4108-1640-5(0)); pap., instr.'s gde. ed. 27.00 (978-1-4108-1616-0(8)) Benchmark Education Co.

Snyder, Gail. Marriage & Family Issues. 2006. (Gallup Major Trends & Events Ser.). (Illus.). 112p. (J). (gr. 7 up). lib. bdg. (978-1-59084-966-8(3) , 1260831) Mason Crest Pubs.

Steck-Vaughn Staff. A Family Is Special. 2000. (Illus.). (J). bds. (978-0-7398-4449-6(0)) Steck-Vaughn.

—A Part of Our Family. 2000. (Illus.). (J). bds. (978-0-7398-4448-9(2)) Steck-Vaughn.

Swain, Cynthia. Families Have Rules. 2006. (Early Explorers Ser.). (J). 30.00 (***978-1-4108-6028-6(0)***) Benchmark Education Co.

Sweeney, Joan. Me & My Family Tree. Cable, Annette, illus. 2000. (Me Ser.). 32p. (J). (gr. k-3). 6.99 (978-0-517-88597-0(2) , Dragonfly Bks.) Random Hse. Children's Bks.

—Me & My Family Tree. 2000. (978-0-606-18091-7(5)); lib. bdg. 15.30 (978-0-613-26171-5(2)) Tandem Library Bks.

Tax, Meredith. Familias. Wiener, Leonora & Festinger, Nancy, trs. from SPA. Hafner, Marylin, illus. 2004. Tr. of Families. (SPA.). 32p. (gr. 1-6). pap. 7.95 (978-1-55861-183-2(5) , FEM1835) Feminist Pr. at The City Univ. of New York.

—Familias. 1998. Tr. of Families. (SPA.). (gr. 3-6). lib. bdg. 16.40 (978-0-613-84288-4(X)) Tandem Library Bks.

—Families. Hafner, Marylin, illus. 2004. 32p. (gr. 1-6). reprint ed. pap. 8.95 (978-1-55861-157-3(6) , FEM1576) Feminist Pr. at The City Univ. of New York.

They Were Strong & Good. 2004. 24.95 incl. audio (978-1-56008-248-4(8)) Weston Woods Studios, Inc.

Thomas, Pat. My Family's Changing: A First Look at Family Break-Up. Harker, Lesley, illus. 1999. (First Look at Bks.). 32p. (J). (ps-2). pap. 6.95 (978-0-7641-0995-9(2)) Barron's Educational Series, Inc.

Tierney, Tom. American Family of the 1980s Paper Dolls. 2003. (Paper Dolls Ser.). (Illus.). 32p. (J). (gr. 3). pap. 5.95 (978-0-486-43052-2(9)) Dover Pubns., Inc.

Townsend, John. Dreary Dwellings & Frightful Families. 2006. (Illus.). 48p. (J). (978-1-4109-1873-4(4)) Steck-Vaughn.

Treadwell, Perry. Grandfather Stories: The Family Farm of the 1930's & 40's. 2000. (Illus.). 112p. pap. 10.95 (978-0-595-00087-6(8) , Writer's Showcase Pr.) iUniverse, Inc.

Trumbauer, Lisa. Families. 2000. (Yellow Umbrella Books). (Illus.). 16p. (J). (gr. 1). lib. bdg. 14.60 (978-0-7368-0734-0(9) , Pebble Bks.) Capstone Pr., Inc.

Tyler, John C. Friendships: Lovers, Huggers & Others. 2000. (Illus.). 126p. (YA). (gr. 7 up). 9.95 (978-0-9674350-0-8(5)) Tyler, John C.

Vaugelade, Anais. Una Sopa de Piedra. 2005. Tr. of Stone Soup. (SPA.). (J). 9.95 (978-84-8470-137-8(9)) Corimbo, Editorial S.L. ESP. *Dist:* Iaconi, Mariuccia Bk. Imports.

Vogel, Elizabeth. Dealing with Being the Middle Child in Your Family. 2000. (Conflict Resolution Library). (Illus.). 24p. (J). (gr. 3). lib. bdg. 18.75 (978-0-8239-5408-7(0) , PowerKids Pr.) Rosen Publishing Group, Inc., The.

—Dealing with Being the Oldest Child in Your Family. 2000. (Conflict Resolution Library). (Illus.). 24p. (J). (gr. 3). lib. bdg. 18.75 (978-0-8239-5409-4(9) , PowerKids Pr.) Rosen Publishing Group, Inc., The.

—Dealing with Being the Youngest Child in Your Family. 2000. (Conflict Resolution Library). (Illus.). 24p. (J). (gr. 3). lib. bdg. 18.75 (978-0-8239-5407-0(2) , PowerKids Pr.) Rosen Publishing Group, Inc., The.

von Konigslow, Andrea Wayne. Me Querrias Tu? von Konigslow, Andrea Wayne, illus. 2003. (Hablemos Ser.). (SPA., Illus.). 32p. (J). (gr. k). pap. 5.95 (978-1-55037-449-0(4)) Annick Pr., Ltd. CAN. *Dist:* Firefly Bks., Ltd.

Weitzman, Elizabeth. Let's Talk about Living with a Single Parent. 1999. (Let's Talk Library). (Illus.). 24p. (J). (gr. 3). lib. bdg. 18.75 (978-0-8239-2314-4(2) , PowerKids Pr.) Rosen Publishing Group, Inc., The.

Weston, Carol. Girltalk: All the Stuff Your Sister Never Told You. 4th ed. 2004. 448p. pap. 14.95 (978-0-06-058575-4(7)) HarperCollins Pubs.

What Did I Get?, 6 vols. 8p. (gr. k-1). 21.50 (978-0-322-02077-1(8)) Wright Group, The.

Williams, Brian. Ancient Roman Homes. (People in the Past Ser.). (Illus.). 48p. (J). 2003. (gr. 4-6). lib. bdg. 25.64 (978-1-58810-631-5(4)); 2002. pap. 8.50 (978-1-4034-0519-7(0)) Heinemann Library.

Yacoubou, Jeanne. What's My Heritage? Coloring-Story Book. Stebakova, Elena, illus. 2006. 24p. (J). (978-0-9788737-2-1(6)) Alaafia Kids Co.

Yates, Vicki. Life at Home. 2007. (J). (***978-1-4034-9833-5(4)***); pap. (***978-1-4034-9841-0(5)***) Heinemann Library.

FAMILY—FICTION

Abbott, Jacob. Stories Told to Rollo's Cousin Lucy. 2005. pap. 22.95 (978-1-4179-5651-7(8)) Kessinger Publishing, LLC.

Abolade, Caroline, told to. I'm Going to Be a Big Brother. 2003. 14p. 9.44 (978-1-4116-0123-9(8)) Lulu.com.

Acampora, Paul. Defining Dulcie. 2008. 176p. (YA). (gr. 7). pap. 6.99 (***978-0-14-241183-4(3)*** , Puffin) Penguin Group (USA) Inc.

Ad Break, 6, Pack. (Bookweb Ser.). 32p. (gr. 4 up). 34.00 (978-0-7635-3722-7(5)) Rigby Education.

Ada, Alma Flor. Actividades para el Hogar. 2001. (SPA.). (J). (gr. k-3). pap. 7.65 (978-1-58105-356-2(8)) Santillana USA Publishing Co., Inc.

Adams, L. Dawn. Happy Memories: A Continuing Family Saga for Young Adults. 2003. (gr. 7-12). lib. bdg. 38.45 (978-0-613-85675-1(9)) Tandem Library Bks.

Adams-Treska, Lucille. The Twig Tops: Thunder in the Woods. 2002. 32p. pap. 8.00 (978-0-8059-5650-4(6)) Dorrance Publishing Co., Inc.

Adapted from the King James Bible Staff. Love Is ... Halperin, Wendy Anderson, illus. 2003. 32p. (J). pap. 6.99 (978-0-689-86675-3(5) , Aladdin) Simon & Schuster Children's Publishing.

Adkins, Jan. A Storm Without Rain: A Novel in Time. 2004. 179p. 14.95 (978-0-937822-80-7(9)) WoodenBoat Pubns.

Agnew, Kate, ed. Family Like Mine. Parsons, Gary, illus. 2003. 128p. (J). pap. 6.99 (978-1-4052-0519-1(9)) Egmont Bks., Ltd. GBR. *Dist:* Independent Pubs. Group.

Ahlberg, Allan. Master Track's Train. Amstutz, Andre, illus. 24p. (J). pap. 6.95 (978-0-14-037881-8(2)) Penguin Bks., Ltd. GBR. *Dist:* Trafalgar Square Publishing.

—My Brother's Ghost. l.t. ed. 2005. (Illus.). 64p. (J). pap. (978-0-7540-6181-6(7) , CLP 372) BBC Audio.

Alcott, Louisa May. Jo's Boys. l.t. ed. 2005. 424p. pap. (978-1-84637-067-0(1)) Echo Library.

Alcott, Louisa May. Rose in Bloom. 2002. (ENG.). 252p. pap. 20.99 (***978-1-4043-2865-5(3)***) IndyPublish.com.

—Rose in Bloom. l.t. ed. 2005. 456p. 29.95 (978-0-7862-7294-5(5) , Large Print Pr.) Thorndike Pr.

Alexander, Martha. When the New Baby Comes, I'm Moving Out. Alexander, Martha, illus. 2006. (Illus.). 32p. (J). 9.95 (978-1-57091-678-6(0)) Charlesbridge Publishing, Inc.

Alexander, Michael. Until Wishes Are Fulfilled. 2007. (ENG.). 160p. per. (***978-1-84426-408-7(4)***) Upfront Publishing Ltd.

Alger Jr. Horatio Staff. Andy Grants Pluck. rev. ed. 2006. 312p. 29.95 (978-1-4218-1762-0(4)); pap. 14.95 (978-1-4218-1862-7(0)) 1st World Publishing, Inc. (1st World Library - Literary Society).

Alma, Ann. Skateway to Freedom. 2008. 136p. (YA). pap. 11.99 (***978-1-55002-719-8(0)*** , Sandcastle Bks.) Dundurn Group, The CAN. *Dist:* Univ. of Toronto Pr.

Alonso, Fernando. La Historia de un Hombrecillo de Papel. (Leer Es Vivir Serie Teatro). (SPA.). 96p. (J). (gr. 3-5). 6.36 (978-84-241-7711-9(8)) Everest de Ediciones y Distribucion, S.L. ESP. *Dist:* Lectorum Pubns., Inc.

Alphin, Elaine Marie. Counterfeit Son. 2000. (Illus.). 192p. (YA). (gr. 9 up). 17.00 (978-0-15-202645-5(2)) Harcourt Children's Bks.

Altan. Here Comes Timpa. Altan, illus. 2007. (Illus.). 48p. (J). pap. 14.95 (***978-1-933372-28-0(1)***) Europa Editions, Inc.

Alvarez, Julia. Antes de Ser Libre. Valenzuela, Liliana, tr. 2004. (SPA.). 192p. (YA). (gr. 7). mass mkt. 5.99 (978-0-375-81545-4(7) , Laurel Leaf) Random Hse. Children's Bks.

—Cuando Tia Lola Vino (de Visita) a Quedarse. Valenzuela, Liliana, tr. 2004. Tr. of How Tia Lola Came to (Visit) Stay. (SPA.). 144p. (gr. 3-7). pap. 5.50 (978-0-375-81552-2(X) , Yearling) Random Hse. Children's Bks.

—Cuando Tia Lola Vino (de Visita) a Quedarse. 2004. Tr. of How Tia Lola Came to (Visit) Stay. (SPA.). (gr. 3-6). lib. bdg. 13.55 (978-0-613-83279-3(5)) Tandem Library Bks.

—Cuando Tía Lola Vino (De Visita) a Quedarse. Valenzuela, Liliana, tr. 2004. (SPA.). 144p. (J). (gr. 3-7). lib. bdg. 17.99 (978-0-375-91552-9(4) , Yearling) Random Hse. Children's Bks.

—How Tia Lola Came to Stay. 2002. (Illus.). 160p. (gr. 3-7). 5.99 (978-0-440-41870-2(4) , Yearling) Random Hse. Children's Bks.

—How Tia Lola Came to (Visit) Stay. Cascardi, Andrea, ed. 2001. (Illus.). 160p. (J). (gr. 3-5). 15.95 (978-0-375-80215-7(0)); lib. bdg. 17.99 (978-0-375-90215-4(5)) Random Hse. Children's Bks. (Knopf Bks. for Young Readers).

—How Tia Lola Came to (Visit) Stay. 2002. (gr. 3-6). lib. bdg. 13.00 (978-0-613-57907-0(0)) Tandem Library Bks.

Alyson Publications Staff & Valentine, Johnny. The Daddy Machine. 2nd ed. 2004. (Illus.). 16.95 (978-1-55583-887-4(1)) Alyson Pubns.

Amerel. The Summer Holidays: A Story for Childre. 2006. pap. (***978-1-4065-0808-6(X)***) Dodo Pr.

Anders, Bill. Becoming Noah. 2004. 114p. (J). pap. 7.95 (978-0-9762059-0-6(4)) Leaping Antelope Productions.

Andersen, C. B. The Book of Mormon Sleuth. 2000. v, 279p. (J). pap. 9.95 (978-1-57345-664-7(0)) Deseret Bk. Co.

Anderson, Doug. Hadley & the Bean. 2004. (Illus.). (J). 16.95 (978-1-59404-038-2(9)) Peanut Butter Publishing.

Anderson, S.N. Desperate for a Family. 2005. 57p. pap. 8.98 (978-1-4116-6162-2(1)) Lulu.com.

Andrews, Jan. The Auction. Reczuch, Karen, illus. 2007. 32p. (J). pap. 6.95 (***978-0-88899-842-2(2)***) Groundwood Bks. CAN. *Dist:* Perseus Distribution.

Andrews, V. C. Rain. 2000. (gr. 7-12). lib. bdg. 16.45 (978-0-613-28031-0(8)) Tandem Library Bks.

Anna, Jennifer. Yen Shei & the American Bonsai. 2007. (Illus.). 88p. (YA). pap. 14.99 (***978-1-59092-153-1(4)*** , Blue Works) Windstorm Creative.

Answer the Phone, Fiona! Individual Title Six-Pack Pouch - Level H. (Lighthouse Ser.). 16p. (gr. 1 up). 26.00 (978-0-7578-0844-9(1)) Rigby Education.

Applegate, Cathy. Red Sand, Blue Sky. 2002. (Girls First! Ser.). 144p. (gr. 4-7). pap. 13.50 (978-1-55861-278-5(5)) Feminist Pr. at The City Univ. of New York.

Armstrong, Jeannette. Dancing with the Cranes. 2005. (Illus.). 24p. (J). pap. 11.95 (978-1-894778-17-6(0)) Theytus Bks., Ltd. CAN. *Dist:* Orca Bk. Pubs. USA.

As Told by Milo: My Very Own Family. 2005. (J). 14.95 (978-0-9772000-0-9(0)) Andrus, Ashley.

Asare, Meshack. Noma's Sand. 2002. pap. (978-9988-550-56-1(1)) Sub-Saharan Pubs. & Traders.

Asch, Frank. Star Jumper: Journal of a Cardboard Genius. 2006. (Illus.). 128p. 5.95 (978-1-55337-887-7(3)) Kids Can Pr., Ltd. CAN. *Dist:* Wybel Marketing Group.

Ashkenas, Bruce. Auntie's Ghost. 2007. 108p. 34.50 (***978-1-4303-1929-0(1)***) Lulu.com.

Aska, Warabe. Tapicero Tap Tap. 2006. (Illus.). 24p. (J). (gr. 1-3). 16.95 (978-0-88776-760-9(5)) Tundra Bks., Inc./Livres Toundra, Inc. CAN. *Dist:* Random Hse., Inc.

Aumann, Jane & Ladage, Cindy. The Christmas Tractor. Freitag, Charles, illus. 2003. 30p. (J). (gr. k-4). pap. 8.95 (978-0-9703319-2-2(4)) Roots & Wings.

Auth, Tony. My Curious Uncle Dudley. Yourgrau, Barry, illus. 2004. 224p. (J). (gr. 4-7). 15.99 (978-0-7636-1935-0(3)) Candlewick Pr.

Autumn, Kyla. Time Era: Back in Salem's Hunt. 2005. 78p. pap. 14.95 (978-1-4137-7605-8(1)) PublishAmerica, Inc.

Avi Staff. Crispin: At the Edge of the World. 2nd rev. ed. 2006. 240p. (gr. 5-9). 16.99 (978-0-7868-5152-2(X)) Hyperion Pr.

Azore, Barbara. Wanda & the Wild Hair. Graham, Georgia, illus. 2005. 32p. (J). (ps-1). 15.95 (978-0-88776-717-3(6)) Tundra Bks., Inc./Livres Toundra, Inc. CAN. *Dist:* Random Hse., Inc.

Bailey, Debbie. My Family. Huszar, Susan, photos by. 1998. (Talk-about-Books: Vol. 11). (Illus.). 14p. (J). (gr. k-ps). bds. 5.95 (978-1-55037-510-7(5)) Annick Pr., Ltd. CAN. *Dist:* Firefly Bks., Ltd.

Bain, Tracie. Peanuts & Life. 2004. 84p. (YA). pap. 8.95 (978-0-595-33239-7(0)) iUniverse, Inc.

Baker, Ryan. How I Would Paint the World? 2006. (ENG.). 48p. per. 15.95 (***978-1-59800-969-9(9)***) Outskirts Press, Inc.

Banks, Kate. Dillon Dillon. 160p. (J). 2002. (gr. 3-6). 16.00 (978-0-374-31786-7(0) , Farrar, Straus & Giroux (BYR)); 2005. reprint ed. pap. 5.95 (978-0-374-41715-4(6) , Sunburst) Farrar, Straus & Giroux.

Banting, Celia. I only said I couldn't Cope. 2006. 240p. (YA). per. 14.99 (***978-0-9786648-2-4(5)***) Wighita Pr.

Baptiste, Tracey. Angel's Grace. 2005. 176p. (J). 15.95 (978-0-689-86773-6(5) , Simon & Schuster/Paula Wiseman Bks.) Simon & Schuster Children's Publishing.

Baran, Robin. Flight of the Robbins. 2006. pap. 7.95 (978-0-533-15430-2(8)) Vantage Pr., Inc.

Baraou, Anne & Sardon, Vincent. The Skeleton Family: The Neighbors from Elsewhere. 2005. (Illus.). 64p. (978-1-59687-825-9(8) , ipicturebooks) ibooks, Inc.

Barclay Family Adventures Series 2 Resource Guide. 2004. 48p. (YA). per. 9.95 (978-1-56254-813-1(1) , SP8131) Saddleback Educational Publishing.

Barensfeld, Debrae. Fox: Lost & Found. 2006. 12.95 (978-0-9776617-0-1(9)) CreoXimius Publishing Company.

The Barnabys' New House, 6 Packs. (Literatura 2000 Ser.). (gr. 1-2). 28.00 (978-0-7635-0458-8(0)) Rigby Education.

Battle, Cleaton D. A Saturday Surprise. Cooper, Emmanuel B., illus. 2006. 68p. (J). pap. 11.95 (978-1-59663-504-3(5) , Castle Keep Pr.) Rock, James A. & Co. Pubs.

Bauer, Joan. Rules of the Road. 2005. 208p. (YA). (gr. 7). pap. 7.99 (978-0-14-240425-6(X) , Puffin) Penguin Group (USA) Inc.

—Rules of the Road. 2000. 201p. (YA). (gr. 7-12). lib. bdg. 13.64 (978-0-606-20370-8(2)) Tandem Library Bks.

Bauer, Marion Dane. Land of the Buffalo Bones: The Diary of Mary Elizabeth Rodgers, an English Girl in Minnesota. 2003. (Dear America Ser.). (Illus.). 224p. (J). pap. 12.95 (978-0-439-22027-9(0)) Scholastic, Inc.

Baum, L. Frank & Van Dyne, Edith. Aunt Jane's Nieces. 2003. 25.00 (978-1-930764-08-8(1)) International Wizard of Oz Club, The.

Baylor, Byrd. The Table Where Rich People Sit. 1998. (978-0-606-13832-1(3)) Tandem Library Bks.

Belgue, Nancy. Summer on the Run. 2005. 144p. (J). (gr. 3-7). pap. 7.95 (978-1-55143-372-1(9)) Orca Bk. Pubs. USA.

Beliveau, Beverly Hicks. Noelle's Wish. 2003. (Illus.). 27p. pap. 7.95 (978-0-533-14205-7(9)) Vantage Pr., Inc.

Bell, Michele Ashman. Dragon's Jaw: A Heart-Pounding Adventure. 2005. 241p. (J). (978-1-59156-880-3(3)) Covenant Communications.

Belle Prater's Boy. 1999. (Pathways to Critical Thinking Ser.). 32p. (YA). pap., stu. ed., tchr.'s training gde. ed. 19.95 (978-1-58303-081-3(6)) Pathways Publishing.

Bellingham, Brenda. Storm Child. 2003. (gr. 5-8). lib. bdg. 15.25 (978-0-613-77352-2(7)) Tandem Library Bks.

Belshe, Judy. The Fry Family Goes to Hollywood. 2007. (Illus.). 50p. (J). spiral bd. 10.00 (***978-0-9655530-4-9(3)***) Belshe, Judy.

Belton, Sandra. Store-Bought Baby. 2006. 256p. (J). 15.99 (978-0-06-085086-9(8)); lib. bdg. 16.89 (978-0-06-085087-6(6)) HarperCollins Pubs.

Benedict, Helen. Opposite of Love. 2007. 256p. (J). (gr. 6 up). 16.99 (***978-0-670-06135-8(2)*** , Viking Juvenile) Penguin Group (USA) Inc.

Bennett, Dean. The Late Loon. 2006. (Illus.). 32p. 15.95 (978-0-89272-730-8(6)) Down East Bks.

Bercun, Brenda. I'm Going to be a Big Brother. Gross, Sue, illus. 2007. 33p. (J). 15.95 (978-0-9767198-7-8(8)) Nurturing Your Children Pr.

Berenstain, Stan & Berenstain, Jan. The Berenstain Bears, 7 vols., Date not set. (Early Childhood First Bks.). (Illus.). (J). (ps-2). lib. bdg. 97.65 (978-1-56674-942-8(5)) Forest Hse. Publishing Co., Inc.

Birdseye, Tom. A Tough Nut to Crack. 2006. 128p. (J). (gr. 3-7). 16.95 (978-0-8234-1967-8(3)) Holiday Hse., Inc.

Bjornson, Nancy. Llamas, Ponies & Pyrite. 2007. (J). (***978-1-930596-82-5(0)***) Amherst Pr.

—Mustangs, Fires & Snakes. 2007. (J). (***978-1-930596-84-9(7)***) Amherst Pr.

—Sleds, Skins & Snow. 2007. (J). (***978-1-930596-83-2(9)***) Amherst Pr.

Black, Judith. Adult Children of ... Parents. (J). 12.00 (978-0-9701073-2-9(3)) Black, Judith Storyteller.

Black, Robert A. Lunar Pioneers. 2008. 280p. (YA). pap. 14.99 (978-1-59092-397-9(9) , Blue Works) Windstorm Creative.

Blackington, Debbie. Mama's Wish/Daughter's Wish. Sommer, Xiaolan, tr. from CHI. 2004. (Illus.). 48p. (J). 17.95 (978-0-9760011-0-2(1)) Pebbleton Pr.

Blackstone, Stella. Bear's Busy Family. Harter, Debbie, illus. 2000. 24p. (J). (ps). reprint ed. bds. 6.99 (978-1-84148-391-7(5)) Barefoot Bks., Inc.

E F G

—Bear's Busy Family. 2000. (ps-2). lib. bdg. 14.15 (978-0-613-33672-7(0)) Tandem Library Bks.

—La Familia activa de Oso (Bear's Busy Family) Sarfatti, Esther, tr. Harter, Debbie, illus. 2003. (Bear Ser.). (SPA.). 24p. (J). 5.99 (978-1-84148-777-9(5)) Barefoot Bks., Inc.

Blake, Bronwyn. Find Me a River. 2002. 272p. (YA). pap. (978-0-7344-0261-5(9) , Lothian Bks.) Hachette Livre Australia.

Blake, Emily. Playing with Fire. 2008. (Little Secrets Ser.: No. 1). 224p. (J). pap. 4.99 (***978-0-545-02824-0(8)*** , Scholastic Paperbacks) Scholastic, Inc.

Blake, Emily. Playing with Fire -library. 2006. (Little Secrets Ser.). (J). 39.95 (978-0-439-89846-1(3)) Scholastic, Inc.

Blossom, J. I Should Have Been a Long Distance Truck. 2006. 71p. pap. 14.95 (978-1-4241-3720-6(9)) PublishAmerica, Inc.

Blume, Judy. Double Fudge. (Fudge Ser.). (SPA.). 250p. (J). (gr. 5-8). pap. 9.95 (978-1-59437-814-0(2)) Santillana USA Publishing Co., Inc.

Blumenthal, Deborah. Aunt Claire's Yellow Beehive Hair. GrandPré, Mary, illus. 2007. 32p. (J). 15.95 (***978-1-58980-491-3(0)***) Pelican Publishing Co., Inc.

Blyton, Enid. Four in a Family. (Illus.). 87p. (J). pap. 5.95 (978-0-09-935680-6(5)) Random Hse. GBR. *Dist:* Trafalgar Square Publishing.

Boie, Kirsten. Todo Cambio con Jakob. Raul, illus. 2003. (SPA.). 166p. (J). (gr. 3-5). pap. 8.95 (978-84-204-4764-3(1)) Santillana USA Publishing Co., Inc.

Bond, Juliet C. Sam's Sister. Majewski, Dawn, illus. 2004. (J). 18.00 (978-0-944934-30-2(7)) Perspectives Pr., Inc.

Bond, Rebecca. Just Like a Baby. Bond, Rebecca, illus. 1999. (Illus.). 32p. (J). (ps-3). 15.95 (978-0-316-10416-6(7)) Little Brown & Co.

Bonners, Susan. Edwina Victorious. Bonners, Susan, illus. (Illus.). 144p. (J). 2007. pap. 5.95 (978-0-374-41960-8(4) , Sunburst); 2000. (gr. 2-5). 16.00 (978-0-374-31968-7(5) , Farrar, Straus & Giroux (BYR)) Farrar, Straus & Giroux.

—Vanishing Point. 2005. (Illus.). 304p. (J). 18.00 (978-0-374-38081-6(3) , Farrar, Straus & Giroux (BYR)) Farrar, Straus & Giroux.

Booth, David. The Dust Bowl. Reczuch, Karen, illus. 2002. 32p. (J). (gr. k-3). (978-1-55074-746-1(0)) Kids Can Pr., Ltd.

Bordons, Paloma. La Tierra de las Papas. 5th ed. 2005. (SPA., Illus.). 144p. (J). (gr. 6-8). 7.95 (978-84-348-5053-8(2)) SM Ediciones ESP. *Dist:* Lectorum Pubns., Inc., Iaconi, Mariuccia Bk. Imports.

Boring Old Bed: Individual Title Six-Pack Pouch - Level J. (Lighthouse Ser.). 16p. (gr. 2 up). 28.00 (978-0-7578-0868-5(9)) Rigby Education.

Bosak, Susan V. Something to Remember Me By: A Story about Love & Legacies. McGaw, Laurie, illus. 2003. 32p. (gr. 1-6). (978-1-896232-01-0(9) , TCP Pr.) Communication Project, The.

Bostrom's, Kathleen. Josie's Gift. Ordaz, Frank, illus. 2005. 40p. (J). (ps-3). 16.99 (978-0-8054-3020-2(2)) B&H Publishing Grp.

Bougie, Victoria. Welcome Little One. Stanley, Ron, illus. 2002. 32p. per. 9.95 (978-0-9725022-0-7(3)) Alvin Bks., Inc.

Bowman, Andy. Indian Slim. Travis, Stephanie, illus. 29p. (J). (gr. 1-6). pap. 6.95 (978-1-931650-06-9(3)); lib. bdg. 14.95 (978-1-931650-07-6(1)) Coastal Publishing Carolina, Inc.

Boyce, Frank Cottrell. Framed. 2006. 320p. pap. 15.95 (***978-0-330-43425-6(X)***) Macmillan Publishers Ltd. GBR. *Dist:* Trans-Atlantic Pubns., Inc.

Boyd, David. Closer to Hamlet. 2003. 120p. (YA). pap. 4.95 (978-0-921156-93-2(6)) Rubicon Publishing, Inc. CAN. *Dist:* International Publishers Marketing.

—Closer to Hamlet. 2003. (gr. 7-12). lib. bdg. 12.95 (978-0-613-77672-1(0)) Tandem Library Bks.

Bradley, Kimberly Brubaker. The President's Daughter. 2004. (Illus.). 176p. (gr. 3-7). 15.95 (978-0-385-73147-8(7) , Delacorte Bks. for Young Readers) Random Hse. Children's Bks.

Bradman, Tony. Has Anyone Seen Jack. rev. ed. 2007. (Illus.). 24p. (J). 7.95 (***978-1-84507-706-8(7)***) Lincoln, Frances Ltd. GBR. *Dist:* Perseus Distribution.

Bradman, Tony, compiled by. My Dad's a Punk: 12 Stories about Boys & Their Fathers. 2006. 240p. (J). (gr. 5-9). pap. 7.95 (978-0-7534-5870-9(5) , Kingfisher) Houghton Mifflin Co. Trade & Reference Div.

Brannen, Sarah S. Uncle Bobby's Wedding. Brennen, Sarah S., illus. 2008. 32p. (J). (ps). 15.99 (***978-0-399-24712-5(2)*** , Putnam Juvenile) Penguin Group (USA) Inc.

The Breadwinner. braille ed. 2000. (gr. 2). spiral bd. (978-0-616-08845-6(0)) Canadian National Institute for the Blind/Institut National Canadien pour les Aveugles.

Bridgers, Sue E. Notes for Another Life. 1998. 258p. (YA). lib. bdg. 29.95 (978-0-7351-0044-2(6)) Replica Bks.

Briggs, Jay. Giants Child. 2006. pap. (***978-1-905665-07-5(5)***) Pollinger In Print.

Brignole, Giancarla, tr. El Pueblo de los Silencios. Bersanetti, Sandra, illus. (Fabulas De Familia Ser.). (SPA.). 32p. (978-970-20-0271-0(0)) Castillo, Ediciones, S. A. de C. V.

Brin, Susannah. Pack. 2002. (gr. 3-6). lib. bdg. 11.80 (978-0-613-57859-2(7)) Tandem Library Bks.

Brisson, Pat. The Star Blanket. Magnus, Erica, illus. 2003. 32p. (YA). (gr. k-2). 15.95 (978-1-56397-889-0(X)) Boyds Mills Pr.

Broach, Elise. Cousin John Is Coming! Lilly, Nate, illus. 2006. 32p. (J). (ps). 16.99 (978-0-8037-3013-7(6) , Dial) Penguin Group (USA) Inc.

Broder, Lynn. The Long Winding Road. 2006. (ENG.). 37p. per. 15.95 (***978-1-59526-366-7(7)***) Media Creations, Inc.

Brokaw, Nancy Steele. Leaving Emma. 1999. 144p. (J). (gr. 4-6). tchr. ed. 15.00 (978-0-395-90699-6(7) , Clarion Bks.) Houghton Mifflin Co. Trade & Reference Div.

Bronzan, William M., Sr. A Time to Dream. 2006. 41p. (J). pap. 8.95 (978-0-7414-3158-5(0)) Infinity Publishing.

Brown, Gladys M. Home Away from Home. 2005. 36p. pap. 6.95 (978-1-4116-3026-0(2)) Lulu.com.

Brown, Marc. D. W. the Big Boss. 2005. (Arthur's 8 x 8 Bks.). (Illus.). 23p. (J). (ps-7). lib. bdg. 11.19 (978-0-606-34230-8(3)) Tandem Library Bks.

Brown, Margaret Wise. Mon Petit Monde (French edition of My World) 2004. 40p. 29.95 (978-0-320-06689-4(4)) French & European Pubns., Inc.

Brown, Stacia Bradley. A Family of His Own. DeKnight, Cathy, illus. 2004. (J). 14.95 (978-1-58597-283-8(5)) Leathers Publishing.

Bruna, Dick. Auntie Alice's Party: A Miffy Storybook. 2000. (Miffy Ser.). (Illus.). 28p. (J). (ps-k). 4.95 (978-1-56836-304-2(4)) Kodansha America, Inc.

Brundige, Patricia. Traveling with Aunt Patty: Aunt Patty Visits London. Wright, Cindy, ed. Hanlon, Leslie, illus. Date not set. (J). (gr. 1-4). 12.95 (978-0-9659668-0-1(1)) Aunt Patty's Travels-London.

Brunson, Jodi. A Year Without Dad. Cramer, illus. 2003. (J). per. 10.00 (978-0-9740683-1-2(4)) Authors & Artists Publishers of New York, Inc.

Buehner, Caralyn. Would I Ever Lie to You? Davis, Jack E., illus. 2007. 32p. (J). (ps up). 16.99 (978-0-8037-2793-9(3) , Dial) Penguin Group (USA) Inc.

Buggs, Michael A. Tabard. Buggs, Michael A., illus. (Illus.). 64p. (Orig.). (J). (gr. 2-6). pap. 15.00 (978-0-9657723-0-3(6)) Mogul Comics.

Bullard, Lisa. My Family: Love & Care, Give & Share. Wesley, Omarr, illus. 2004. (All about Me Ser.). 24p. (C). (gr. k-1). 21.26 (978-1-4048-0044-1(1)) Picture Window Bks.

—Trick-or-Treat on Milton Street. Oeltjenbruns, Joni, illus. 2004. (Carolrhoda Picture Books Ser.). 32p. (J). (ps-3). pap. 6.95 (978-1-57505-793-4(X)) Lerner Publishing Group.

Bundschuh, Rick & Hamilton, Bethany. Storm. 2007. (Soul Surfer#8482; Ser.). 144p. (J). pap. 6.99 (978-0-310-71224-4(6)) Zonderkidz.

Bunt, Barbara & Karram, Mona. LuLu's Friend Teag. Chouan, Joe, illus. 2002. 16p. (J). (ps-1). 18.95 (978-0-9724929-1-1(7)) LuLu Bks Ltd.

Bunting, Eve. I Have an Olive Tree. unabr. ed. 2000. (YA). pap. 31.95 incl. audio (978-0-7887-3644-5(2) , 41010X4) Recorded Bks., LLC.

—My Backpack. Cocca-Leffler, Maryann, illus. 2004. 32p. (J). (gr. k-2). 16.95 (978-1-56397-433-5(9)) Boyds Mills Pr.

—A Picnic in October. Carpenter, Nancy, illus. 2004. 32p. (J). reprint ed. pap. 7.00 (978-0-15-205065-8(5) , Voyager Bks./Libros Viajeros) Harcourt Children's Bks.

Burch, Robert. Queenie Peavey. l.t. ed. 2003. (LRS Large Print Cornerstone Ser.). 166p. (J). lib. bdg. 29.95 (978-1-58118-115-9(9)) LRS.

Burchett, Loni. Bear & Katie in A Riverboat Ride, 4 vols., Vol. 4. 2006. (Illus.). 104p. (J). per. 12.95 (978-0-9742815-3-7(0)) Black Lab Publishing LLC.

Burgess, Lynn. Family Reunion. Duckworth, John, illus. 1998. 16p. (J). (ps-k). pap. 5.95 (978-0-9655442-7-6(3)) Business Word, The.

Burgess, Melvin. Doing It. rev. ed. 2004. 336p. (YA). 15.95 (978-0-8050-7565-6(8) , Holt, Henry & Co. Bks. For Young Readers) Holt, Henry & Co.

Burke, Kevin, illus. A Wing & a Prayer. 2005. 32p. (J). (ps-ps). 14.99 (978-1-4003-0114-0(9)) Nelson, Thomas Inc.

Burshek, Edward & Burshek, Tonja. Explorers of the Word: Episode 1: the Creation. Peterson, Melanie, illus. 2007. (ENG.). 76p. per. 14.95 (***978-1-4241-6691-6(8)***) PublishAmerica, Inc.

Burton, Rick. Running on Empty. 2005. 72p. pap. 14.95 (978-1-4137-6600-4(5)) PublishAmerica, Inc.

Butcher, Kristin. Hemingway Tradition. 2002. (gr. 7-12). lib. bdg. 16.40 (978-0-613-62955-3(8)) Tandem Library Bks.

—The Hemingway Tradition. 2002. (Orca Soundings Ser.). 96p. (J). (gr. 7-12). pap. 7.95 (978-1-55143-242-7(0)) Orca Bk. Pubs. USA.

Butler, Dori Hillestad. Do You Know the Monkey Man? 2005. 224p. (J). 14.95 (978-1-56145-340-5(4)) Peachtree Pubs., Ltd.

—Trading Places with Tank Talbott. 2003. 136p. (J). (gr. 3-6). pap. 6.95 (978-0-8075-8060-8(0)) Whitman, Albert & Co.

Buzzy. One Sunny Day. Martin, John, ed. Simpkins, Iravis, illus. 2003. 52p. (J). (ps-2). pap. 7.99 (978-0-9719054-1-2(X)) Buzzy's Bks.

Byars, Betsy. The Not-Just-Anybody Family. 149p. (J). (gr. 4-6). pap. 4.50 (978-0-8072-1429-9(9) , Listening Library) Random Hse. Audio Publishing Group.

Cahill, Byron. Space Pox. 2005. 40.00 (***978-1-4108-4220-6(7)***) Benchmark Education Co.

Caletti, Deb. The Nature of Jade. 2007. 288p. (YA). (***978-1-4287-2344-3(7)*** , Simon & Schuster Children's Publishing) Simon & Schuster Children's Publishing.

Call of the Selkie: Individual Title Six-Packs. (Action Packs Ser.). 104p. (gr. 3-5). 44.00 (978-0-7635-2991-8(5)) Rigby Education.

Canady, Pat. Boots the World's Best Kid-Sitter: Springtime Adventures. Bartley, Michael, illus. 2000. 6p. (J). (ps-4). pap. 10.00 (978-1-929889-02-0(X)) Canady SW Publishing.

Cann, Kate. Hard Cash. 2003. (Illus.). 336p. (YA). mass mkt. 5.99 (978-0-689-85905-2(8) , Simon Pulse) Simon & Schuster Children's Publishing.

—Hard Cash. 2003. (gr. 7-12). lib. bdg. 14.15 (978-0-613-73411-0(4)) Tandem Library Bks.

Cano, Robin B. Lucita Regresa a Oaxaca (Lucita Comes Home to Oaxaca) Ricardez, Rafael E., tr. Smith, Kerry, illus. 1998. (ENG & SPA.). 32p. (J). (gr. 3-6). 16.95 (978-1-56492-111-6(5)) Laredo Publishing Co., Inc.

Capdevila, Roser & Vendrell, Maria Martinez. Los Conflictos de Ana. 2003. Tr. of Ana's Problems. (SPA.). 24p. (J). 7.95 (978-84-233-1627-4(0)) Ediciones Destino ESP. *Dist:* Planeta Publishing Corp.

Carey, Elizabeth Doyle. Keeping Cool. 3rd ed. 2006. (Callahan Cousins Ser.). (Illus.). 226p. (J). (gr. 3-7). 10.99 (978-0-316-73693-0(7)) Little Brown & Co.

Carlson, Nancy. My Family Is Forever. 2006. 32p. (J). pap. 5.99 (978-0-14-240561-1(2) , Puffin) Penguin Group (USA) Inc.

—My Family Is Forever. Carlson, Nancy, illus. 2004. (Illus.). 32p. (J). 15.99 (978-0-670-03650-9(1) , Viking Juvenile) Penguin Group (USA) Inc.

Carr, Diane & Earley, Kira. River Dragon. 2003. (Illus.). 44p. (J). 16.95 incl. audio compact disk (978-1-59094-024-2(5) , 1590940245) Jawbone Publishing Corp.

Carr, Lawrence. Under the Peach Tree. 2006. pap. 8.00 (978-0-8059-7019-7(3)) Dorrance Publishing Co., Inc.

Cart, Michael. Necessary Noise: Stories about Our Families as They Really Are. Noruzi, Charlotte, illus. 256p. (J). 2003. (gr. 12 up). 15.99 (978-0-06-027499-3(9)); 2006. reprint ed. pap. 8.99 (978-0-06-051437-2(X) , HarperTeen) HarperCollins Pubs.

Carter, Alden R. Crescent Moon. 1999. 160p. (YA). (gr. 7 up). tchr. ed. 16.95 (978-0-8234-1521-2(X)) Holiday Hse., Inc.

—Crescent Moon. 1999. (J). 15.95 (978-0-590-29882-7(8)) Scholastic, Inc.

—Up Country. 2004. 256p. (J). (gr. 5). pap. 6.99 (978-0-14-240243-6(5) , Puffin) Penguin Group (USA) Inc.

Carter, Kristin. What Matters Most: A Children's Book of Families. 2005. 47p. pap. 19.95 (978-1-4137-3631-1(9)) PublishAmerica, Inc.

Casselman, Grace. A Walk in the Park. 2005. (Illus.). 152p. (YA). (ps-7). pap. 7.95 (978-1-894917-19-3(7)) Napoleon Publishing/Rendezvous Pr. CAN. *Dist:* AtlasBooks Distribution.

Cassidy, Cathy. Dizzy. 2005. 272p. (J). (gr. 3-6). pap. 6.99 (978-0-14-240474-4(8) , Puffin) Penguin Group (USA) Inc.

Castleberry, Stephen B., Sr. & Castleberry, Susie. Where There's Smoke. 2004. (Farm Mystery Ser.). (J). per. 8.50 (978-1-891907-14-2(X)) Castleberry Farms Pr.

Castlemon, Harry. The Sportsman's Club among the Trappers. 2005. pap. 28.95 (978-1-4179-5498-8(1)) Kessinger Publishing, LLC.

Castlemon, Harry. Sportsmans Club in the Saddle. 2006. pap. 30.95 (***978-1-4286-5231-6(0)***) Kessinger Publishing, LLC.

Catching Air! Individual Chapter Book Title Six-Pack. Vol. 29. 32p. (gr. 5 up). 44.00 (978-0-7578-0974-3(X)) Rigby Education.

Catran, Wendy. Katie Raven's Fire. 2003. 205p. (Orig.). pap. (978-0-7344-0497-8(2) , Lothian Bks.) Hachette Livre Australia.

Caudill, Rebecca. Up & down the River. Merwin, Decie, illus. 2005. 143p. (J). (ps-17). pap. 11.95 (978-1-883937-81-2(7)) Bethlehem Bks.

Caught in the Storm: Individual Title Six-Packs. (gr. k-1). 23.00 (978-0-7635-9046-8(0)) Rigby Education.

Cesena, Denise. Caring - Companion Book. Perez, Maureen T., illus. l.t. ed. 2003. 12p. (J). 2.00 (978-0-9740418-7-2(4)) Night LIght Pubns., LLC.

Cesena, Denise & Perez, Maureen T. Caring. Perez, Maureen T., illus. l.t. ed. 2003. (Illus.). 28p. (J). 10.00 (978-0-9740418-6-5(6)) Night LIght Pubns., LLC.

Chapman, Brenda. Running Scared. 2004. 122p. (YA). pap. 7.95 (978-1-894917-14-8(6)) Napoleon Publishing/Rendezvous Pr. CAN. *Dist:* AtlasBooks Distribution.

Charles, Norma M. All the Way to Mexico. 2003. (gr. 5-8). lib. bdg. 15.25 (978-0-613-78580-8(0)) Tandem Library Bks.

—Sophie Sea to Sea: Star Girl's Cross-Canada Adventures! 2005. 152p. (YA). (gr. 3-8). pap., tchr. ed. (978-0-88878-404-9(X) , Sandcastle Bks.) Dundurn Group, The.

Charlton-Trujillo, E. E. Prizefighter en Mi Casa. 2006. 224p. (J). (gr. 5-7). 15.95 (978-0-385-73325-0(9)); lib. bdg. 17.99 (978-0-385-90344-8(8)) Random Hse. Children's Bks. (Delacorte Bks. for Young Readers).

Cheng, Andrea. Anna the Bookbinder. Rand, Ted, illus. 2003. 32p. (J). (gr. k-4). 16.95 (978-0-8027-8831-3(9)) Walker & Co.

Cherrington, Janelle. Drawing the Line. Goldberg, Barry, illus. 2000. (Wild Thornberrys Ready-to-Read Ser. : Vol. 2). 32p. (J). (gr. 4-6). pap. 3.99 (978-0-689-83231-4(1) , Simon Spotlight/Nickelodeon) Simon & Schuster Children's Publishing.

—Drawing the Line. 2000. (gr. k-3). lib. bdg. 11.80 (978-0-613-24899-0(6)) Tandem Library Bks.

Chess, Victoria. The Costume Party. Chess, Victoria, illus. 2005. (Illus.). 32p. (J). (ps-ps). 15.95 (978-1-929132-87-4(5)) Kane/Miller Bk. Pubs., Inc.

Chester. 2007. (Illus.). 32p. (J). (ps-3). 16.99 (***978-0-698-40062-7(3)*** , Minedition) Penguin Group (USA) Inc.

Chesterfield, Sadie. A Family for Lewis. Disney Storybook Artists Staff, illus. 2007. (I Can Read Bks.). 32p. (J). pap. 3.99 (978-0-06-112470-9(2) , Harper Trophy) HarperCollins Pubs.

Child, Lauren. Clarice Bean, Guess Who's Babysitting? Child, Lauren, illus. 2001. (Illus.). 32p. (J). (gr. 1-5). 16.99 (978-0-7636-1373-0(8)) Candlewick Pr.

Child, Lauren, et al. Carys Blodyn, Dyma Fi. 2005. (WEL., Illus.). 30p. (978-1-85596-670-3(0)) Dref Wen.

—Fi'n Hollol, Carys Blodyn. 2005. (WEL., Illus.). 192p. pap. (978-1-85596-675-8(1)) Dref Wen.

Choldenko, Gennifer. Al Capone Does My Shirts. l.t. ed. 2005. 299p. (YA). 22.95 (978-0-7862-8043-8(3)) Thorndike Pr.

—Notes from a Liar & Her Dog. 2003. 224p. (J). (gr. 5-7). pap. 6.99 (978-0-14-250068-2(2) , Puffin) Penguin Group (USA) Inc.

—Notes from a Liar & Her Dog. 2004. 224p. (J). (gr. 4-7). pap. 38.00 incl. audio (978-0-8072-2097-9(3) , Listening Library) Random Hse. Audio Publishing Group.

Christie, Amanda. Camp Camden. 2001. (gr. 3-6). lib. bdg. 13.00 (978-0-613-85126-8(9)) Tandem Library Bks.

Christmas. 2004. (J). mass mkt. 8.99 (978-0-9741215-4-3(1)) Stories of My Life, The.

Chronicle Books LLC Staff. Just Like a Baby. 2009. (J). 14.95 (978-0-8118-5026-1(9)) Chronicle Bks. LLC.

Chumbley, Peggy Lucinda. Mommy & Daddy Take Me to Church. 1999. (Illus.). 32p. (J). pap. 9.95 (978-0-9672309-0-0(X)) PLC Publishing.

Citra, Becky. Never to Be Told: Becky Citra. 2006. 224p. (J). pap. 7.95 (978-1-55143-567-1(5)) Orca Bk. Pubs. USA.

Clark, Abbie. Way down Yonder in the Paw Paw Patch. 2006. (J). per. 16.95 (***978-1-59858-129-4(5)***) Dog Ear Publishing, LLC.

Clark, Eleanor. Katie Sue: Heading West. 2007. (Eleanor Jo Ser.). (J). pap. 14.99 (978-0-9788726-0-1(6)) HonorNet.

Clay, Ian. Coyote Lake. 2007. 104p. per. 9.95 (***978-0-595-44590-5(X)***) iUniverse, Inc.

Cleaver, Vera & Cleaver, Bill. Donde Florecen los Lirios. (SPA.). 168p. (YA). (gr. 5-8). (978-84-204-3648-7(8) , AF0285) Alfaguara, Ediciones, S.A.- Grupo Santillana ESP. *Dist:* Lectorum Pubns., Inc.

Clements, Andrew. Lunch Money. Selznick, Brian, illus. 2005. 224p. (J). 16.99 (978-0-689-86683-8(6)) Simon & Schuster Children's Publishing.

—Lunch Money. Selznick, Brian, illus. l.t. ed. 2005. 231p. (J). (gr. 3-7). 21.95 (978-0-7862-8036-0(0) , Large Print Pr.) Thorndike Pr.

—Slippers Loves to Run. Bynum, Janie, illus. 2006. 32p. (J). (ps-1). 12.99 (978-0-525-47648-1(2) , Dutton Juvenile) Penguin Group (USA) Inc.

Clements, Bruce. What Erika Wants. 2005. 224p. (YA). (gr. 7-17). 16.00 (978-0-374-32304-2(6) , Farrar, Straus & Giroux (BYR)) Farrar, Straus & Giroux.

Coatsworth, Elizabeth. Away Goes Sally. 2004. (Illus.). 118p. (J). pap. 10.95 (978-1-883937-83-6(3)) Bethlehem Bks.

Cogan, Karen. Mi Hermanito Ben. Romo, Alberto, tr. Treatner, Meryl, illus. 1999. (Books for Young Learners).Tr. of My Little Brother Ben. (SPA.). 12p. (J). (gr. k-2). pap. 5.00 (978-1-57274-343-4(3) , A2878) Owen, Richard C. Pubs., Inc.

Cohen, Miriam. Say Hi, Backpack Baby! Cohen, Miriam, illus. l.t. ed. 2001. (Backpack Baby Stories Ser.). (Illus.). 12p. (J). (ps). bds. 5.95 (978-1-887734-82-0(1)) Star Bright Bks., Inc.

—Wah! Wah! A Backpack Baby Story. l.t. ed. 2001. (Backpack Baby Stories Ser.). (Illus.). 12p. (J). (ps). bds. 5.95 (978-1-887734-81-3(3)) Star Bright Bks., Inc.

Cole, Babette. Los Problemas con Mi Tio.Tr. of Trouble with Uncle. (SPA.). 28p. (J). 12.95 (978-84-233-2126-1(6)) Ediciones Destino ESP. *Dist:* Planeta Publishing Corp.

Coll, Ivar Da. Carlos. Coll, Ivar Da, illus. 2003. (SPA., Illus.). 52p. (J). (gr. k-3). pap. 9.95 (978-958-8061-64-1(4)) Santillana USA Publishing Co., Inc.

Collier, James Lincoln. The Rich & Famous. 2001. (Lost Treasures Ser.: No. 6). (Illus.). 240p. (gr. 3-7). pap. 1.99 (978-0-7868-1519-7(1) , Volo) Hyperion Bks. for Children.

Coman, Carolyn. Bee & Jacky. 2006. 104p. pap. 9.95 (978-1-932425-37-6(3) , Lemniscaat) Boyds Mills Pr.

Coman, Carolyn. Sneaking Suspicions. Shepperson, Rob, illus. 2007. 204p. (J). (gr. 3-7). 16.95 (***978-1-59078-491-4(X)*** , Front Street) Boyds Mills Pr.

Condi-Babich, Kris. 4Cam. us. 2004. 71p. pap. 14.95 (978-1-4137-2241-3(5)) PublishAmerica, Inc.

Connelly, Neil. St. Michael's Scales. 2004. 320p. (J). reprint ed. pap. 6.99 (978-0-439-49171-6(1) , Scholastic Paperbacks) Scholastic, Inc.

Contreras-Rosado, Rosalina. Adventures of Two Little Sisters in El Salvador: Tatiana & Irene Visit for the First Time Their Mother's Homeland. 2002. 46p. 15.40 (978-0-9726541-0-4(0)) Adventures In Books.

Conway, David. The Most Important Gift of All. Littlewood, Karin, illus. 2006. 32p. (J). 15.95 (978-0-7696-4618-3(2) , Gingham Dog Pr.) School Specialty Publishing.

Cooley, Beth. Ostrich Eye. 2005. 192p. (YA). (gr. 7-12). reprint ed. pap. 5.99 (978-0-440-23828-7(5) , Laurel Leaf) Random Hse. Children's Bks.

Coolidge, Susan. Clover. Mcdermot, Jessie, illus. 2007. (ENG.). 168p. per. (***978-1-4065-1524-4(8)***) Dodo Pr.

—What Katy Did. 2006. 62.99 (***978-1-4280-3108-1(1)***) IndyPublish.com.

Coombs, Corinne. My Brother Sam Is Dead. Chaney, Howard, illus. 1999. (Literature Units Ser.). 48p. (J). pap., tchr. ed. 7.99 (978-1-57690-507-4(1) , TCA2507) Teacher Created Materials, Inc.

Cooney, Barbara. Miss Rumphius. Cooney, Barbara, illus. 2002. (Illus.). (J). 14.04 (978-0-7587-3148-7(5)) Book Wholesalers, Inc.

—Miss Rumphius. Cooney, Barbara, illus. 2004. (Illus.). 28p. (J). (gr. k-2). reprint ed. pap. 6.00 (978-0-7567-7107-2(2)) DIANE Publishing Co.

Cooney, Caroline B. Family Reunion. 2004. 208p. (J). (gr. 5). lib. bdg. 11.99 (978-0-385-90167-3(4) , Delacorte Bks. for Young Readers) Random Hse. Children's Bks.

—A Friend at Midnight. 2006. 192p. (YA). (gr. 7). 15.95 (978-0-385-73326-7(7)); lib. bdg. 17.99 (978-0-385-90345-5(6)) Random Hse. Children's Bks. (Delacorte Bks. for Young Readers).

Copeland, Mark. The Bundle at Blackthorpe Heath. 2006. (Illus.). 208p. (J). (gr. 5). 15.00 (978-0-618-56302-9(4)) Houghton Mifflin Co.

Corazon. (Coleccion Estrella). (SPA., Illus.). 64p. (J). 14.95 (978-950-11-0005-1(7) , SGM005) Sigmar ARG. *Dist:* Continental Bk. Co., Inc.

Cory, Kim Delmar. Home to Mackinac: The Tale of Young Jack Murphy's Discovery of Loyalty, Family & Forgiveness. Evans, Laura, illus. 2007. 175p. (J). pap. 9.95 (978-0-911872-87-3(6)) Mackinac State Historic Parks.

—Lilly's Way. Austin, Jane G., ed. 1998. 187p. (YA). (gr. 4-6). 9.99 (978-0-88092-363-7(6) , 3636) Royal Fireworks Publishing Co.

Costella, Deborah. Cooking with Granddad. Morisson, Connie, ed. 2002. 42p. pap. 14.95 (978-0-9718155-5-1(0) , 14) Inkwell Productions, LLC.

Couloumbis, Audrey. Getting near to Baby. 2002. (Illus.). (J). 13.19 (978-0-7587-6515-4(0)) Book Wholesalers, Inc.

—Getting near to Baby. 224p. (J). (gr. 5-9). 2001. pap. 5.99 (978-0-698-11892-8(8)); 1999. 17.99 (978-0-399-23389-0(X)) Penguin Group (USA) Inc. (Putnam Juvenile).

—Getting near to Baby. 2001. (gr. 5-8). lib. bdg. 14.15 (978-0-613-44208-4(3)) Tandem Library Bks.

—Getting near to Baby. l.t. ed. 2000. (Juvenile Ser.). (Illus.). 215p. (J). (gr. 4-7). 22.95 (978-0-7862-2705-1(2)) Thorndike Pr.

—Summer's End. 2005. 192p. (YA). (gr. 4). 16.99 (978-0-399-23555-9(8) , Putnam Juvenile) Penguin Group (USA) Inc.

Courcy, Jon. Scourges: Seeds of Dissent. 2005. Tr. of Scourges. (YA). per. 19.95 (978-0-9741864-4-3(9)) NT Publishing, L.L.C.

CourseCrafters Staff, des. Interactive Storybooks - the Family Home. 2003. (J). spiral bd. 14.95 (978-1-58605-965-1(3)) LeapFrog Enterprises, Inc.

Covert, Joshua. Josiah & the Lost Mill. Shelton, Diane et al, illus. 2002. 54p. 4.50 (978-0-9719108-0-5(4)) Rumsey Family Ministries.

Cox, Tory. A Silent Cry in the Night. 2005. 148p. pap. 19.95 (978-1-4137-8255-4(8)) PublishAmerica, Inc.

Craddock, Sonia. Runaway Gran. 2006. (Streetlights Ser.). 168p. (J). (gr. 2-5). 7.95 (***978-1-55028-953-4(5)***) Lorimer, James & Co., Ltd., Pubs. CAN. *Dist:* Casemate Pubs. & Bk. Distributors, LLC.

Craft, Jerry. Mama's Boyz: Home Schoolin' Because Learning Shouldn't Stop at 3 O'clock!, 2. 2007. (Illus.). 112p. (YA). per. 9.95 (***978-0-9796132-0-3(5)***) Mama's Boyz, Inc.

Crisis Maximus! Individual Title Six-Packs. (Bookweb Ser.). 32p. (gr. 6 up). 34.00 (978-0-7578-0902-6(2)) Rigby Education.

Crouse, Rodney Ivan. Night Song of the Little Smokies. Bowden, Gary, illus. 2000. 375p. (J). pap. 27.00 (978-0-9677000-3-8(5)) Foxsong Enterprises, LLC.

—Wind Song of the Little Smokies. Bowden, Gary, illus. 1999. iv, 283p. (J). 27.00 (978-0-9677000-0-7(0)) Foxsong Enterprises, LLC.

Crowe, Carole. Groover's Heart. 2003. (Illus.). 144p. (J). (gr. 4-6). 15.95 (978-1-56397-953-8(5)) Boyds Mills Pr.

Crutcher, Chris. Chinese Handcuffs. 2004. 304p. (J). pap. 7.99 (978-0-06-059839-6(5) , HarperTeen) HarperCollins Pubs.

Culver, Steven. The Magic Christmas Reindeer Bell: A Ho. 2006. pap. 11.00 (***978-1-4259-7114-4(8)***) AuthorHouse.

Cummings, Priscilla. What Mr. Mattero Did. 2007. 224p. (J). (gr. 3). pap. 6.99 (978-0-14-240856-8(5) , Puffin) Penguin Group (USA) Inc.

Cuno, Sabine. Abre, cierra y Aprende: Open, Close, & Learn, Spanish-Lanaguage Edition. 2007. (Illus.). 12p. (J). 14.95 (***978-970-718-489-3(2)*** , Silver Dolphin en Español) Advanced Marketing, S. de R. L. de C. V. MEX. *Dist:* Perseus Distribution.

Curley, Marianne. El Circulo de Fuego. Puig, Fernando Gari, tr. 2001. (SPA.). 256p. (978-84-7888-710-1(5) , 1952) Emece Editores.

Curtis, Sandra R. Gabriel's Ark. Spark, illus. 1998. 64p. (J). (gr. 3 6). pap. 7.95 (978-1-881283-23-2(2)) Alef Design Group.

Daddy Saved the Day: Six-Pack. (Greetings Ser.: Vol. 3). 24p. (gr. 2-3). 31.00 (978-0-7635-9417-6(2)) Rigby Education.

Dadey, Debbie. Whistler's Hollow. 2002. 130p. (J). 14.95 (978-1-58234-789-9(1) , Bloomsbury Children) Bloomsbury Publishing.

Dagenais, Linda Lee. Through Jacob's Eyes. Mori, Andy, illus. 2004. 77p. pap. 14.95 (978-1-4137-2523-0(6)) PublishAmerica, Inc.

Danziger, Paula. Ambar Quiere Buenas Notas. Ross, Tony, tr. Ross, Tony, illus. 8th ed. (SPA.). 128p. (J). (gr. 4-5). 9.95 (978-84-204-6589-0(5) , AF31904) Alfaguara, Ediciones, S.A.- Grupo Santillana ESP. *Dist:* Lectorum Pubns., Inc.

—United Tates of America. Danziger, Paula, illus. 2002. (Illus.). 144p. (J). (gr. 3-7). pap. 17.95 (978-0-590-69221-2(6) , Scholastic Pr.) Scholastic, Inc.

—United Tates of America: The Story & the Scrapbook. 2002. (gr. 3-6). lib. bdg. 14.15 (978-0-613-67042-5(6)) Tandem Library Bks.

David, Luke. Oh, Brother! UK Edition. Peters, James, illus. 1999. (Rugrats Ser.). 24p. (J). (ps-3). per. 3.50 (978-0-671-02871-8(5) , Simon & Schuster Children's Publishing) Simon & Schuster Children's Publishing.

Davis, Catherine. Abby & Alex Feel Their Hearts' Little. 2006. 57p. pap. 12.95 (***978-1-4241-4586-7(4)***) PublishAmerica, Inc.

Davis, L. J. A Simple Brown Leaf. 2006. (Illus.). 32p. 17.95 (978-0-9762007-8-9(3)) Abovo Publishing.

Davis, Lee. Beware the Last Cousins. 2003. (J). per. (978-0-9741294-1-9(0) , MSP) Main St Publishing, Inc.

de Brunhoff, Jean & de Brunhoff, Laurent. Babar en Famille. 1999. (Babar Ser.).Tr. of Babar & His Children. (FRE., Illus.). (J). (ps-3). 15.95 (978-2-01-002516-7(4)) Distribooks, Inc.

de Brunhoff, Laurent. Babar in Famiglia. pap. 12.95 (978-88-04-46271-2(X)) Mondadori ITA. *Dist:* Distribooks, Inc.

De Lint, Charles. The Dreaming Place. 2002. (gr. 7-12). lib. bdg. 14.15 (978-0-613-56338-3(7)) Tandem Library Bks.

de Paola, Tomie. Tomie's Family. 2000. (Illus.). (J). (978-0-698-11718-1(2) , Puffin) Penguin Group (USA) Inc.

Deborah Sue. All Things Remembered. 2004. 56p. (YA). pap. 8.95 (978-0-595-31286-3(1)) iUniverse, Inc.

Debrecht, Katharine. Help! Mom! There Are Liberals under My Bed! A Small Lesson in Conservatism. Hummel, Jim, illus. 2005. 60p. 15.95 (978-0-9767269-0-6(4) , Kids Ahead Bks.) World Ahead Media.

Dee, Barbara. Just Another Day in My Insanely Real Life. 2006. (Illus.). 256p. (J). 15.95 (978-1-4169-0861-6(7) , McElderry, Margaret K.) Simon & Schuster Children's Publishing.

Deedy, Carmen Agra. The Secret of Old Zeb. White, Michael P., illus. 2002. 36p. (J). (gr. 1-5). pap. 8.95 (978-1-56145-280-4(7)) Peachtree Pubs., Ltd.

DeFatta Barattini, Kathryn. I Live in Shreveport-Bossier! by Louise E. Ana, Ladybug. 2006. 36p. (J). pap. 15.00 (978-1-4116-5197-5(9)) Lulu.com.

DeFelice, Cynthia C. The Real, True Dulcie Campbell. Alley, R. W., illus. 2002. 32p. (J). (gr. k-3). 16.00 (978-0-374-36220-1(3) , Farrar, Straus & Giroux (BYR)) Farrar, Straus & Giroux.

Defosse, Rosana Curiel. Santiago in the the World of I Want To. Barradas, Leticia, illus. (SPA.). 38p. (J). (gr. 3-5). pap. 7.95 (978-970-29-0136-5(7)) Santillana USA Publishing Co., Inc.

Del Moral, Susana, tr. Sr. Cuadrado. 2005. (Mis figuras Geometricas Ser.). (SPA., Illus.). 6p. (J). (ps-7). 9.95 (978-970-718-294-3(6) , Silver Dolphin en Español) Advanced Marketing, S. de R. L. de C. V. MEX. *Dist:* Perseus Distribution.

Delano, Poli. Policarpo Y el Tio Pablo. 2005. (SPA.). 49p. pap. 7.95 (978-0-307-27363-5(6)) Editorial Sudamericana S.A. ARG. *Dist:* Random Hse., Inc.

Delton, Judy. Angel Bites the Bullet. Weber, Jill, illus. 2003. 144p. (J). (gr. 3-5). pap. 4.95 (978-0-618-36920-1(1)) Houghton Mifflin Co. Trade & Reference Div.

Denton, Kady MacDonald. Watch Out, William. 2006. (I Am Reading Ser.). (Illus.). 48p. (J). (gr. k-3). pap. 3.95 (978-0-7534-5960-7(4) , Kingfisher) Houghton Mifflin Co. Trade & Reference Div.

Dessen, Sarah. Keeping the Moon. 1999. (Illus.). 288p. (J). (gr. 7-12). 16.99 (978-0-670-88549-7(5) , Viking Juvenile) Penguin Group (USA) Inc.

Dessen, Sarah. Lock & Key. 2008. 432p. (YA). (gr. 7). 18.99 (***978-0-670-01088-2(X)*** , Viking Juvenile) Penguin Group (USA) Inc.

Dhami, Narinder. Bindi Babes. 2004. 192p. (J). (gr. 3-7). 14.95 (978-0-385-73177-5(9) , Delacorte Bks. for Young Readers) Random Hse. Children's Bks.

DiCamillo, Kate. Because of Winn-Dixie. pap. 17.95 (978-3-423-70771-8(2)) Deutscher Taschenbuch Verlag GmbH & Co KG DEU. *Dist:* Distribooks, Inc.

Dickinson, Peter. The Ropemaker. 2003. 384p. (YA). (gr. 7). pap. 7.95 (978-0-385-73063-1(2) , Delacorte Bks. for Young Readers) Random Hse. Children's Bks.

DiLorenzo, Michael A. Adventures with Jonny: Let's Go Fishing! Julich, Jenniffer, illus. 2006. 68p. (J). 17.95 (978-0-9777210-0-9(0)) Running Moose Publications.

DK Publishing. Vote for Mom. 2008. 18p. (J). (ps-k). 14.99 (***978-0-7566-3809-2(7)***) Dorling Kindersley Publishing, Inc.

Dodge, Mary Mapes. Po No Kah an Indian Tale of Long Ago. 2004. reprint ed. pap. 15.95 (978-1-4191-4185-0(6)) Kessinger Publishing, LLC.

Dodge, Wayne. The Bongo Boys: An Almost True Story. 2004. 172p. 25.95 (978-1-932852-63-9(8)) Wasteland Pr.

Dorie & Me. 2003. (YA). per. (978-1-59431-071-3(8) , Ebks. On The Net) ebooksonthe.net.

Douglas, Ann. Freddy & Flossy Flutterby. Douglas, Ann, illus. 2002. (Illus.). 40p. (J). 16.95 (978-0-9723184-0-2(2)) Betta Place, Inc.

Douglas, Erin. Get That Pest! Yee, Wong Herbert, illus. 2003. (Green Light Readers Level 2 Ser.). 24p. (J). 11.95 (978-0-15-204873-0(1)); pap. 3.95 (978-0-15-204833-4(2)) Harcourt Children's Bks. (Green Light Readers).

Dowd, Siobhan. The London Eye Mystery. 2008. 336p. (J). (***978-0-375-84976-3(9)*** ; lib. bdg. (***978-0-375-94976-0(3)***) Random Hse. Children's Bks. (Fickling, David Bks.).

Doyle, Brian. Uncle Ronald. 2004. 138p. (J). pap. 6.95 (978-0-88899-621-3(7)) Groundwood Bks. CAN. *Dist:* Perseus Distribution.

Draper, Sharon M. The Battle of Jericho. 2003. (Illus.). 304p. (YA). 17.95 (978-0-689-84232-0(5) , Atheneum) Simon & Schuster Children's Publishing.

Draper, Sharon M. & Bascoul, Eric. The Battle of Jericho. 2004. 352p. (YA). mass mkt. 6.99 (978-0-689-84233-7(3) , Simon Pulse) Simon & Schuster Children's Publishing.

Dream Boat: Individual Title Six-Packs. (Action Packs Ser.). 120p. (gr. 3-5). 44.00 (978-0-7635-8429-0(0)) Rigby Education.

Dreams of Glory: A Penny Parrish Story. 2001. (Penny Parrish Story). 190p. (YA). pap. 12.95 (978-1-930009-27-1(5)) Image Cascade Publishing.

Dreibrodt, Stacie Champlin. Where the Lilies Bloom. 2000. (YA). 9.95 (978-1-58130-634-7(2)); 11.95 (978-1-58130-635-4(0)) Novel Units, Inc.

Driscoll, Laura. Name That Ed. 2002. (gr. k-3). lib. bdg. 11.80 (978-0-613-45297-7(6)) Tandem Library Bks.

Dube, Jasmine. Gratelle au Bois Mordant. ed. 2004. (FRE., Illus.). (J). (ps-3). spiral bd. (978-0-616-01848-4(7)) Canadian National Institute for the Blind/Institut National Canadien pour les Aveugles.

Dube, Jasmine & Paré, Roger. Elvis Presente Sa Famille. 2000. (Elvis Ser.). (Illus.). 24p. (YA). (ps up). pap. (978-2-89021-419-4(2)) Diffusion du livre Mirabel.

Duble, Kathleen Benner. Bravo Zulu, Samantha! 2007. 144p. (J). (gr. 4-7). 14.95 (***978-1-56145-401-3(X)*** , Peachtree Junior) Peachtree Pubs., Ltd.

Dubosarsky, Ursula. The Red Shoe. 2007. 192p. (J). (gr. 7 up). 16.95 (978-1-59643-265-9(9)) Roaring Brook Pr.

Dubowski, Cathy East & West, Cathy. Substitute Sister. 2000. (Full House Sisters Ser.: No. 9). (Illus.). 160p. (J). (gr. 4-6). pap. 3.99 (978-0-671-04089-5(8) , Simon Spotlight) Simon & Schuster Children's Publishing.

Duey, Kathleen & Bale, Karen A. Blizzard: Colorado, 1886. 1998. (Survival! Ser.: No. 3). (J). (gr. 4-7). (978-0-606-13827-7(7)) Tandem Library Bks.

DuJardin, Rosamond. Double Date: A Pam & Penny Story. 2002. 191p. (YA). pap. 12.95 (978-1-930009-49-3(6) , 800-691-7779) Image Cascade Publishing.

—Double Feature: A Pam & Penny Story. 2002. 182p. (YA). pap. 12.95 (978-1-930009-50-9(X) , 800-691-7779) Image Cascade Publishing.

—Showboat Summer: A Pam & Penny Story. 2002. 192p. (YA). pap. 12.95 (978-1-930009-51-6(8)) Image Cascade Publishing.

Dumas, Bianca. Tia Luisa, the Magical Cook: A Tale in English & Spanish. Dumas, Bianca, illus. 2000. (SPA & ENG., Illus.). 32p. (J). (gr. k-4). per. 7.95 (978-0-9669645-4-7(3) , AlterLingo Bks.) O'Hollow Publishing.

Dumont, Virginie & Soria, Bernard. Enredos de Familia. Boucher, Michel, illus. 2004. (Arbol de la Vida Ser.). (SPA.). 64p. (J). 13.99 (978-84-8488-098-1(2)) Serres, Ediciones, S. L. ESP. *Dist:* Lectorum Pubns., Inc.

Dunn-Dern, Lisa. Dr. Duncan Dog on Duty! 2007. (J). per. 16.99 (***978-1-933156-20-0(1)*** , Visikid Bks.) GSVQ Publishing.

Duras, Marguerite. La Pluie d'Ete. (FRE.). pap. 14.95 (978-2-07-038705-2(4)) Gallimard, Editions FRA. *Dist:* Distribooks, Inc.

Dygard, Thomas J. River Danger. 1998. 160p. (J). (gr. 7 up). 16.99 (978-0-688-14852-2(2)) HarperCollins Pubs.

Dyson, Tony. The Crystal Wand. 2005. 242p. pap. 14.01 (978-1-4116-5596-6(6)) Lulu.com.

Eager, Edward. The Time Garden. 1999. (gr. 5-8). lib. bdg. 14.15 (978-0-613-70941-5(1)) Tandem Library Bks.

Earls, Nick. 48 Shades of Brown. 1999. 300p. (YA). pap. (978-0-14-028769-1(8)) Penguin Group (USA) Inc.

East, Jacqueline. Ed the Pup Ed's New Baby Sister. 1999. (Ed the Pup Ser.). (ps-3). (978-1-894155-67-0(X)) Cethial & Bossche Co.

—Ed the Pup I Won't Eat That. 1999. (Ed the Pup Ser.). (ps-3). (978-1-894155-76-2(9)) Cethial & Bossche Co.

Eastman, P. D. ¿Eres Mi Mama? Eastman, P. D., illus. 2001. (Bright & Early Board Bks.). (SPA., Illus.). 24p. (J). (gr. k-ps). bds. 4.99 (978-0-375-81505-8(8) , Random Hse. Bks. for Young Readers) Random Hse. Children's Bks.

Educational Adventures, creator. Blazin' Hot: Picture Book (Spanish) 9x9. 2006. (SPA., Illus.). (J). (***978-0-9770455-4-9(4)***) Educational Adventures.

Edwards, Hazel. Fake ID. 2004. (Illus.). 144p. pap. (978-0-7344-0442-8(5) , Lothian Bks.) Hachette Livre Australia.

Edwards, Pamela Duncan. Rosie's Roses. Cole, Henry, illus. 2003. 32p. (J). (ps-1). 16.99 (978-0-06-028997-3(X)) HarperCollins Pubs.

Edwards, Pat. A Visit to Cousin Boris. Selway, Martina, illus. 1999. 24p. (J). (978-0-7608-3196-0(3)) Sundance/Newbridge Educational Publishing.

Eggleton, Jill. Passport to Earth: Individual Title Six-Packs. Hawley, Kelvin, illus. (Sails Literacy Ser.). 20p. (gr. 4 up). 27.00 (978-0-7578-0791-6(7)) Rigby Education.

Ellis, Sarah. Odd Man Out. 2008. 168p. (J). pap. 8.95 (***978-0-88899-703-6(5)***); 2006. 16p. (gr. 4-7). 16.95 (978-0-88899-702-9(7)) Groundwood Bks. CAN. *Dist:* Perseus Distribution.

Ellis, Sarah. Out of the Blue. 2001. 120p. (J). (gr. 5-9). pap. 5.95 (978-0-88899-236-9(X)) Groundwood Bks. CAN. *Dist:* Perseus Distribution.

Emmons, Katherine M. Keep Moving Forward. Husband, Ron, illus. 2007. (Meet the Robinsons Ser.). 24p. (J). pap. 3.99 (978-0-06-112469-3(9)) HarperCollins Pubs.

Emmy's Question. 2007. (J). 16.99 (***978-0-9790395-2-2(5)***) Morningtide Pr.

Erb, Sharlyne. A hug from Daddy. 2005. 83p. pap. 22.71 (978-1-4116-5970-4(8)) Lulu.com.

Erlbruch, Wolf. The Miracle of the Bears. Reynolds, Michael, tr. from GER. 2006. (Illus.). 32p. pap. 14.95 (978-1-933372-21-1(4)) Europa Editions, Inc.

Everett Hale, Edward. Last of the Peterkins with Others of the. 2006. pap. (***978-1-4068-1087-5(8)***) Echo Library.

Eversole, Barbara. My Name Is Zorro. 2005. 25p. 11.07 (978-1-4116-4438-0(7)) Lulu.com.

Everstine, Andrew D. Seth: A Visitor's Pass. 2003. 286p. (YA). pap. 16.95 (978-0-595-26368-4(2) , Writers Club Pr.) iUniverse, Inc.

Exclaim Entertainment Staff. I Love My Family. 2007. (BOZ#8482; Ser.). 14p. (J). 4.99 (***978-0-310-71404-0(4)***) Zonderkidz.

Face to Face: Individual Title Six-Packs. (Bookweb Ser.). 32p. (gr. 4 up). 34.00 (978-0-7635-3731-9(4)) Rigby Education.

Faerber, Jay. Family Secrets, Vol. 2. 120p. pap. 12.95 (978-1-58240-348-9(1)) Image Comics.

Faerber, Jay, et al. Extended Family, No. 2. 2004. 80p. pap. 7.95 (978-1-58240-370-0(8)) Image Comics.

Fajardo, Renee & Ruby, Carl. Ole Posole & Other Tummy Tales. Fajardo, Renee, ed. 2005. (Illus.). 110p. (YA). (gr. 4-8). pap. 14.00 (978-0-9724472-3-2(7)) Just Enjoyable Memorable Story Bks.

Falletta, Bernadette & Gasparro, Marie. Reflections of the Dog That Learned English. 2005. 16p. (J). 14.95 (978-1-4116-6524-8(4)) Lulu.com.

Falwell, Cathryn. We Have a Baby. Falwell, Cathryn, illus. 2002. (Illus.). (J). 13.79 (978-0-7587-3939-1(7)) Book Wholesalers, Inc.

—We Have a Baby. Falwell, Cathryn, illus. 1999. (Illus.). 32p. (J). (gr. k-ps). 6.95 (978-0-395-73970-9(5) , Clarion Bks.) Houghton Mifflin Co. Trade & Reference Div.

Family Stories: Individual Packs Pack A. (SPA.). (gr. k-2). 15.40 (978-0-7362-0492-7(X)) Hampton-Brown Bks.

Family Stories: Individual Packs Pack B. (SPA.). (gr. k-2). 15.40 (978-0-7362-0494-1(6)) Hampton-Brown Bks.

Family Stories: Jumbo Packs. (SPA.). (gr. k-2). 157.08 (978-0-7362-0052-3(5)) Hampton-Brown Bks.

Family Ties Set. (Illus.). (J). (gr. 1-3). 74.75 (978-1-881889-82-3(3)) Silver Moon Pr.

Family Tree. (Poster Projects Ser.). (gr. 3-6). 9.99 (978-0-7424-0698-8(9) , IF22455) School Specialty Publishing.

Fann, Lisa. Uprooted. 2002. (YA). 128p. 18.50 (978-0-9719167-3-9(X)); per. 10.00 (978-0-9719167-0-8(5)) Open Bk. Publishing.

Farrell, John. Dear Child. Manning, Maurie, illus. 2008. (J). (***978-1-59078-495-2(2)***) Boyds Mills Pr.

Favorite, Deborah. The Tush People. Arinsberg, Norman, illus. (J). 11.95 (978-0-9722514-0-2(5)) Tush People, The.

Feil, Denise J. Praze B. a Growing, Loving Day: Forgiveness & Responsibility. Feil, Denise J., illus. 2004. (J). per. 5.50 (978-0-9741588-0-8(1)) Feil.

Feldman, Eve B. Seymour, the Formerly Fearful. 2000. 164p. (J). (gr. 4-7). pap. 11.95 (978-0-595-00391-4(5) , Backinprint.com) iUniverse, Inc.

Fennell, Haywood. Coota & the Magic Quilt. 2004. (J). (978-0-9720404-0-2(4)) Tri-Ad veterans League, Inc.

Fernandez, Nacho. La nueva era del sueno vol. 2: Los desiertos del Norte: The New Age of Dreams vol. 2: the Deserts of the North. 2007. (SPA.). 48p. 22.95 (***978-1-59497-398-7(9)***) Public Square Bks.

Ferrer, Caridad. It's Not about the Accent. 2007. 288p. (YA). (gr. 7 up). pap. 9.95 (***978-1-4165-2491-5(6)*** , MTV) Simon & Schuster.

Ferris, Jean. Of Sound Mind. 224p. (YA). 2001. (gr. 8 up). 16.00 (978-0-374-35580-7(0) , Farrar, Straus & Giroux (BYR)); 2004. reprint ed. pap. 6.95 (978-0-374-45584-2(8) , Sunburst) Farrar, Straus & Giroux.

—Of Sound Mind. l.t. ed. 2004. 225p. 21.95 (978-0-7862-7036-1(5) , Large Print Pr.) Thorndike Pr.

Field, Matthew S. Father Like A Tree. Hedderich, Tom, illus. 2005. (J). pap. 19.95 (978-0-9761528-0-4(0)) Matting Leah Publishing Co.

Fienberg. Power to Burn. 167p. (J). pap. (978-0-340-70930-6(8) , Hodder & Stoughton) Hodder General Publishing Division.

Findon, Joanne. When Night Eats the Moon. 2004. 175p. (YA). (gr. 7-12). per. 16.60 (978-0-613-93942-3(5)) Tandem Library Bks.

Fine, Anne & Trimmer, Tony. Countdown. 2006. (Yellow Bananas Ser.). (Illus.). 48p. (J). pap. (978-0-7787-1004-2(1)) Crabtree Publishing Co.

Finley, Martha. Elsies Girlhood. 2006. 27.99 (***978-1-4280-2220-1(1)***) IndyPublish.com.

—Elsie's Girlhood: A Sequel to Elsie Dinsmore & Elsie's Holidays at Roselands. l.t. ed. 2006. 296p. pap. 17.99 (***978-1-4264-3884-4(2)***) BiblioBazaar.

—Elsies Kith & Kin. 2006. 79.99 (***978-1-4280-2573-8(1)***) IndyPublish.com.

—Elsie's New Relations, Bk. 9. 2001. (J). pap. 5.99 (978-1-931343-00-8(1)) Hibbard Pubns., Inc.

—Elsie's Stolen Heart, Vol. 4. 2006. (Life of Faith': Elsie Dinsmore Ser.). 224p. (J). pap. 7.99 (978-1-928749-83-7(6)) Zonderkidz.

—Mildred at Home, Vol. 5. (Mildred Classics Ser.: Vol. 5). 288p. pap. 6.95 (978-1-58182-231-1(6)) Cumberland Hse. Publishing.

—Mildred Keith, Vol. 1. (Mildred Classics Ser.: Vol. 1). 288p. pap. 6.95 (978-1-58182-227-4(8)) Cumberland Hse. Publishing.

—Mildred's Boys & Girls, Vol. 6. (Mildred Classics Ser.: Vol. 6). 288p. pap. 6.95 (978-1-58182-232-8(4)) Cumberland Hse. Publishing.

—Mildred's New Daughter, 7 Vols., Vol. 7. (Mildred Classics: Vol. 7). 288p. pap. 6.95 (978-1-58182-233-5(2)) Cumberland Hse. Publishing.

Fitzgerald, Dawn. Getting in the Game. rev. ed. 2005. 144p. (J). 15.95 (978-1-59643-044-0(3)) Roaring Brook Pr.

Fitzhugh, Louise. Sport. 2002. 240p. (gr. 5). 6.50 (978-0-440-41818-4(6) , Yearling) Random Hse. Children's Bks.

—Sport. 2002. (gr. 5-8). lib. bdg. 14.15 (978-0-613-83532-9(8)) Tandem Library Bks.

Fitzpatrick, Marie-Louise. Silly Mommy, Silly Daddy. Fitzpatrick, Marie-Louise, illus. 2006. (Illus.). 32p. 15.95 (978-1-84507-547-7(1)) Lincoln, Frances Ltd. GBR. *Dist:* Perseus Distribution.

Fleming, Charles & Schirripa, Steven R. Nicky Deuce: Welcome to the Family. 2005. 176p. (J). (gr. 3-7). 15.95 (978-0-385-73257-4(0) , Delacorte Bks. for Young Readers) Random Hse. Children's Bks.

Fletcher, Ralph J. Uncle Daddy. rev. ed. 2001. (Illus.). 144p. (J). (gr. 4-6). 16.95 (978-0-8050-6663-0(2) , Holt, Henry & Co. Bks. For Young Readers) Holt, Henry & Co.

Flood, Pansie Hart. Secret Holes. Marshall, Felicia, illus. 2004. 128p. (J). (gr. 3-6). 15.95 (978-0-87614-923-2(9) , Carolrhoda Bks.) Lerner Publishing Group.

Forney, Melissa. Oonawassee Summer: Something is Lurking Beneath the Surface... Scott, Gregg, illus. 2000. 126p. (J). (gr. 4-8). pap. 14.95 (978-1-928961-04-8(5)) Barker Creek Publishing, Inc.

Forrester, Izola. Kit of Greenacre Farm. 2006. 33.99 ***(978-1-4280-3401-3(3))*** IndyPublish.com.

Forrester, Izola L. Kit of Greenacre Farm. 2007. 158p. pap. 11.99 ***(978-1-4264-8431-5(3));*** 174p. pap. 14.99 ***(978-1-4264-8489-6(5))*** BiblioBazaar.

Fox, Paula. La Habitacion de Mauricio. 2003. (SPA., Illus.). 96p. (J). (gr. 3-5). (978-84-279-3457-3(2) , NG4695) Noguer y Caralt Editores, S. A. ESP. *Dist:* Lectorum Pubns., Inc.

Fraggalosch, Audrey. Grizzly Bear Family. 2003. (gr. k-3). lib. bdg. 15.25 (978-0-613-71037-4(1)) Tandem Library Bks.

Frank, E. R. Wrecked. 2005. (Illus.). 256p. (YA). (gr. 7 up). 16.99 (978-0-689-87383-6(2) , Atheneum) Simon & Schuster Children's Publishing.

Frank, E. R. & Dorling Kindersley Publishing Staff. Life Is Funny. 2000. (Richard Jackson Bks.). (Illus.). 272p. (J). (gr. 7-12). 19.99 (978-0-7894-2634-5(X)) Dorling Kindersley Publishing, Inc.

Freeman, Marilyn. Pasquale's Journey. 2003. 49p. pap. 8.95 (978-0-595-30311-3(0)) iUniverse, Inc.

French, Jennifer. Fidgets. 2007. 132p. pap. 9.95 ***(978-1-59663-531-9(2)*** , Castle Keep Pr.) Rock, James A. & Co. Pubs.

Friedlander, Eleanor. Mrs. Digger's Roots. Traverso, Laura, illus. 1999. 44p. (J). (ps-3). 17.95 (978-0-9672124-0-1(5)) Jadeda Pr.

Friesen, Gayle. Men of Stone. 2000. (gr. 7-12). lib. bdg. 15.25 (978-0-613-44529-0(5)) Tandem Library Bks.

—Men of stone. 2000. (Gayle Friessen Ser.). (Illus.). 216p. (YA). (gr. 13 up). (978-1-55074-781-2(9)) Kids Can Pr., Ltd.

Fritz, T. J. Katey's Dream List. 1999. 90p. (gr. 4-7). 7.95 (978-1-56315-084-5(0)) SterlingHouse Pubs., Inc.

Froissart, Benedicte. Uncle Henry's Dinner Guests. ed. 2004. (Illus.). (J). (gr. k-3). spiral bd. (978-0-616-01644-2(1)) Canadian National Institute for the Blind/Institut National Canadien pour les Aveugles.

Fromm, Pete. How All This Started: A Novel. 2001. (gr. 7-12). lib. bdg. 23.45 (978-0-613-45189-5(9)) Tandem Library Bks.

Frost, Helen. The Braid. 2006. (Illus.). 112p. (YA). (gr. 7 up). 16.00 (978-0-374-30962-6(0) , Frances Foster Bks.) Farrar, Straus & Giroux.

Fuchs, Menucha. A Coat for Two & Other Stories. Miri, illus. 2000. (Children's Learning Ser.: Vol. 9). 48p. (J). (gr. k-5). pap. 4.95 (978-1-880582-58-9(9)) Judaica Pr., Inc., The.

—Pesach with the Cohen Family. Greenberg, Chana, illus. 2000. (Children's Learning Ser.: Vol. 7). 48p. (J). (gr. k-5). pap. 4.95 (978-1-880582-55-8(4)) Judaica Pr., Inc., The.

—Safety First: Having Fun & Staying Safe. Miri, illus. 2000. (Children's Learning Ser.: Vol. 8). 48p. (J). (gr. k-5). pap. 4.95 (978-1-880582-54-1(6)) Judaica Pr., Inc., The.

Fujita, Maki, illus. & creator. Platinum Garden. Fujita, Maki, creator. 2006. (YA). pap. 9.99 (978-1-59816-361-2(2) , Tokyopop Kids) TOKYOPOP, Inc.

Fuller, Jill. John's Book. Toop, Bill, illus. 2004. 88p. (J). 20.00 (978-0-7188-2870-7(4)) Lutherworth Pr., The GBR. *Dist:* Parkwest Pubns., Inc.

Fun with Our Family. 2004. (Dick & Jane Ser.). (Illus.). 144p. (J). (ps-2). 7.99 (978-0-448-43568-8(3) , Grosset & Dunlap) Penguin Group (USA) Inc.

Furcron, Bertha Phillips. No Half, No Step, Just a Whole. Hendrick, Betty Acey, illus. 2003. Orig. Title: Yes. 32p. (J). (gr. 1-3). lib. bdg. 15.95 (978-1-884242-55-7(3)); pap. 7.95 (978-1-884242-57-1(X)) Multicultural Pubns.

Fusco, Kimberly Newton. Tending to Grace. 2005. 192p. (YA). (gr. 7 up). pap. 5.99 (978-0-553-49423-5(6) , Laurel Leaf) Random Hse. Children's Bks.

Fussell, Bonnie. More Than a Stove. Sadler, Dale, illus. l.t. ed. 2004. 32p. (J). pap. 7.99 (978-0-615-12702-6(9)) Blackberry Pubs.

Gaberman, Judith. Superbowl Upset. 2000. 164p. (J). (gr. 4-7). pap. 11.95 (978-0-595-16096-9(4) , Backinprint.com) iUniverse, Inc.

Gaines, Isabel. Pooh's Family Tree, Vol. 20. 2000. (Winnie the Pooh Ser.). (Illus.). 34p. (J). (gr. k-3). pap. 3.99 (978-0-7868-4367-1(5)) Disney Pr.

Gallagher, Diana G. A Dog's Life. 2001. (Full House Sisters Ser.: No. 13). (Illus.). 176p. (J). (gr. 4-6). pap. 3.99 (978-0-671-04093-2(6) , Simon Spotlight) Simon & Schuster Children's Publishing.

Gallagher, Mary. Mulhern Twins. 2007. (Illus.). 126p. pap. 10.95 ***(978-1-905172-17-7(6))*** Collins Pr., The IRL. *Dist:* Dufour Editions, Inc.

Galvin, Kim. RJ's Farm. 2000. 208p. (J). (gr. 4-7). pap. 12.95 (978-0-595-13989-7(2) , Writers Club Pr.) iUniverse, Inc.

Gantos, Jack. What Would Joey Do? A Dazzling Conclusion to the Joey Pigza Trilogy! 2004. 240p. (J). (gr. 5-9). pap. 36.00 incl. audio (978-1-4000-9020-4(2) , Listening Library) Random Hse. Audio Publishing Group.

García, Cristina. I Wanna Be Your Shoebox. 2008. 208p. (J). ***(978-1-4169-3928-3(8)*** , Simon & Schuster Children's Publishing) Simon & Schuster Children's Publishing.

Garcia, Molly. G. G. The Diary fo a Space Case. 2007. 77p. pap. 9.95 ***(978-0-7414-3838-6(0))*** Infinity Publishing.

Garcia, Richard. Los Espiritus de Mi Tia Otilia. ed. 2004. (ENG & SPA., Illus.). (J). (gr. k-3). spiral bd. (978-0-616-14606-4(X)) Canadian National Institute for the Blind/Institut National Canadien pour les Aveugles.

Garis, Howard Roger. Uncle Wiggily's Happy Days. Date not set. 226p. (J). 21.95 (978-0-8488-2650-5(7)) Amereon LTD.

Garland, Michael. Mystery Mansion: A Look Again Book. Garland, Michael, illus. 2001. (Illus.). 32p. (J). 15.99 (978-0-525-46675-8(4) , Dutton Juvenile) Penguin Group (USA) Inc.

Garon, Risa J. Snowman. 2000. (Illus.). 5p. (J). pap. 5.00 (978-0-9729415-0-1(9)) National Family Resiliency Ctr., Inc.

Garza, Xavier. Lucha Libre: The Man in the Silver Mask. Garza, Xavier, illus. 2007. (SPA.). 40p. (J). pap. 8.95 ***(978-1-933693-10-1(X))*** Cinco Puntos Pr.

Gauthier, Gilles. La Petite Lili Est un Genie. Deromer, Pierre-André, illus. 2004. (Premier Roman Ser.). (FRE.). 64p. (J). (gr. 1-4). pap. (978-2-89021-686-0(1)) Diffusion du livre Mirabel.

Gay, Marie-Louise & Homel, David. Travels with My Family. 2006. (Illus.). 80p. (J). 15.95 (978-0-88899-688-6(8)) Groundwood Bks. CAN. *Dist:* Perseus Distribution.

Gaydos, Nora. Innovative Kids Readers: the Long Ride. Sharp, Chris, illus. 2007. 24p. (J). (gr. k-2). pap. 6.99 (978-1-58476-544-8(5)) Innovative Kids.

Genechten, Guido van. The Cuddle Book. Genechten, Guido van, illus. 2004. (Illus.). 32p. (J). (ps-k). 14.99 (978-0-06-075306-1(4)) HarperCollins Pubs.

Geras, Adele. Family Files. 1999. (Fabulous Fantoras Ser.: Vol. 1). (Illus.). 80p. (J). (gr. 4-7). mass mkt. 3.99 (978-0-380-79359-4(8)) HarperCollins Pubs.

Gerber, Carole. Artic Dreams. Husted, Marty, illus. 2006. 32p. (J). pap. 7.95 (978-1-58089-074-8(1)) Charlesbridge Publishing, Inc.

Gerlach-Babb nee Maines, Mary & Gerlach, Susan. Best Christmas Gift. 2007. (ENG.). 52p. per. 12.95 ***(978-1-4241-6389-2(7))*** PublishAmerica, Inc.

Gertein, Sherry & Fleet, Mara Van. My Great Aunt Phibian. 2007. 10p. (J). bds. 6.99 (978-0-7944-1281-4(5)) Reader's Digest Assn., Inc., The.

Gibbons, Faye. Emma Jo's Song. Meidell, Sherry, illus. 2003. 32p. (J). (gr. k-2). 15.95 (978-1-56397-935-4(7)) Boyds Mills Pr.

Giff, Patricia Reilly. Pictures of Hollis Woods. 176p. (gr. 3-8). 2004. (J). pap. 6.50 (978-0-440-41578-7(0) , Yearling); 2002. lib. bdg. 17.99 (978-0-385-90070-6(8) , Lamb, Wendy) Random Hse. Children's Bks.

—Pictures of Hollis Woods. Giff, Patricia Reilly, illus. 2002. (Illus.). 176p. (gr. 3-8). 15.95 (978-0-385-32655-1(6) , Lamb, Wendy) Random Hse. Children's Bks.

—Pictures of Hollis Woods. l.t. ed. 2003. 158p. (J). 23.95 (978-0-7862-5094-3(1)) Thorndike Pr.

—Water Street. (gr. 4-7). 2008. 144p. 6.50 ***(978-0-440-41921-1(2)*** , Yearling); 2006. 176p. (J). 15.95 (978-0-385-73068-6(3) , Lamb, Wendy); 2006. 176p. (J). lib. bdg. 17.99 (978-0-385-90097-3(X) , Lamb, Wendy) Random Hse. Children's Bks.

—Water Street. l.t. rev. ed. 2007. 193p. (YA). 23.95 ***(978-0-7862-9277-6(6))*** Thorndike Pr.

Gikow, Louise. A Day with Daddy. Mazali, Gustavo, illus. 2004. (My First Reader Pb Ser.). 32p. (J). (gr. k-1). pap. 3.95 (978-0-516-25501-9(0) , Children's Pr.) Scholastic Library Publishing.

Gilkey, Gail. Would You Still Love Me? Greene, Mary Lamb, illus. 2001. 32p. (J). (ps-2). pap. 6.95 (978-0-9662983-2-1(2)) Windy Hill Pr.

Gilstrap, John. At All Costs. 1999. (gr. 7-12). lib. bdg. 15.90 (978-0-613-24254-7(8)) Tandem Library Bks.

Gingras, Charlotte. Emily's Piano. Ouriou, Susan, tr. from FRE. Jorisch, Stephane, illus. 2005. 64p. (J). (gr. 4-7). 18.95 (978-1-55037-913-6(5)); pap. 7.95 (978-1-55037-912-9(7)) Annick Pr., Ltd. CAN. *Dist:* Firefly Bks., Ltd.

Gire, Ken. Treasure in an Oatmeal Box: The Story of a Special Boy & the People Who Loved. 2000. (gr. 3-6). lib. bdg. 13.00 (978-0-613-74893-3(X)) Tandem Library Bks.

Gittus, Mark, ed. Sunshine Acres Children's Home: Miracle in the Desert. Dingman, Rolland, illus. 2001. 136p. per. 5.00 (978-0-9711814-0-3(3)) Dingman, Vera.

Glassman, Miriam. Box Top Dreams. 1999. (J). 10.64 (978-0-606-15910-4(X)) Tandem Library Bks.

Glick, Shifra. Shikufitsky, Vol. 2. Glick, Shifra, illus. (Illus.). 100p. (J). 19.99 (978-1-58330-640-6(4)) Feldheim Pubs.

Glory Be! A Penny Parrish Story. 2001. (Penny Parrish Story). 207p. pap. 12.95 (978-1-930009-28-8(3)) Image Cascade Publishing.

Glover, Sandra. Spiked! 2006. 176p. (J). pap. (978-1-84270-520-9(2)) Andersen.

Godby, Ron. The King of Imperial Hill. 2006. 76p. pap. 14.95 (978-1-4241-1061-2(0)) PublishAmerica, Inc.

Godden, Rumer. Miss Happiness & Miss Flower. 2002. (Illus.). 128p. (J). (gr. 3-7). 14.89 (978-0-06-029193-8(1)) HarperCollins Pubs.

Godolphin, Mary. The Swiss Family Robinson Told in Words. 2006. 24.99 ***(978-1-4280-4168-4(0));*** pap. 18.99 ***(978-1-4280-4195-0(8))*** IndyPublish.com.

Golden Books Staff. Little Golden Book Favorites by Richard Scarry. 2008. (Little Golden Book Ser.). (Illus.). 72p. (J). 5.99 ***(978-0-375-84580-2(1)*** , Golden Bks.) Random Hse., Inc.

Golden, Marcellus. The Fabulous Crabulous Family in Pee-Wee Learns about Moving. Golden, Marcellus, illus. 2004. (Illus.). 51p. (J). (gr. 2-5). pap. 12.95 (978-1-4137-2341-0(1)) PublishAmerica, Inc.

Golding, Theresa Martin. The Truth about Twelve. 2004. (Illus.). 176p. (J). (gr. 4-6). pap. 16.95 (978-1-59078-291-0(7)) Boyds Mills Pr.

Gomes, Linda Nunes. Special Words: A Story about Multicultural Families & Their Pets. Levine, Lenora D., illus. 2007. (YA). per. 12.99 ***(978-1-934400-02-9(5))*** Rock Village Publishing.

Gonzalez, Gabriela & Triana, Gaby. Backstage Pass. 2004. (Illus.). 224p. (J). (gr. 7 up). lib. bdg. 16.89 (978-0-06-056018-8(5)) HarperCollins Pubs.

Goudge, Elizabeth. Linnets & Valerians. 2001. 256p. (J). pap. 6.99 (978-0-14-230026-8(8) , Puffin) Penguin Group (USA) Inc.

Graef, Renee, illus. Little House Farm Days. 1998. (Little House Chapter Bks.: No. 7). (J). (gr. 3-6). (978-0-606-13576-4(6)) Tandem Library Bks.

Grannie Annie, Vol. 1. 2006. (Illus.). 81p. (J). pap. 14.95 (978-0-9677685-9-5(4)) McIntyre, Connie.

Grannie Annie: Selections from the 2007 Grannie Annie Family Story Celebration, 2. 2007. (Illus.). 86p. (J). pap. 14.95 ***(978-0-9793296-1-6(2)*** , Thumbprint Pr.) McIntyre, Connie.

Granowsky, Alvin. My Family. 2001. (978-0-606-22434-5(3)) Tandem Library Bks.

Grant, Cynthia D. White Horse. 2000. (978-0-606-17945-4(3)) Tandem Library Bks.

Grantner, Anne M. & Haggart, Gary. Without a Home. Hannon, Kenneth, photos by. 2003. (Illus.). 35p. (YA). (gr. 5 up). pap. 12.95 (978-0-9740929-0-4(8)) Shelter of Flint, Inc.

Graves, Anna Louise. How Can You Lose Something as Big as a Farm? 2007. 102p. pap. 10.95 ***(978-0-7414-4029-7(6))*** Infinity Publishing.

Gravley, Debbie Bybee. Golden Lace & the Magical Mossy Woods. 2005. 25.00 (978-0-9771793-0-5(3)) Gravley, Debbie Bybee.

Gray, Nigel. Full House. Graham, Bob, illus. 2002. 20p. pap. (978-0-85091-879-3(0) , Lothian Bks.) Hachette Livre Australia.

Greenburg, J. C. In the Deep. Gerardi, Jan, illus. 2004. (Andrew Lost Ser.: Bk. 8). 96p. (J). (gr. 2-5). pap. 3.99 (978-0-375-82526-2(6) , Random Hse. Bks. for Young Readers) Random Hse. Children's Bks.

—In the Deep, No. 8. Reed, Mike, illus. 2004. (Andrew Lost Ser.: Bk. 8). 96p. (J). (gr. 2-5). lib. bdg. 11.99 (978-0-375-92526-9(0) , Random Hse. Bks. for Young Readers) Random Hse. Children's Bks.

—In the Desert. Gerardi, Jan, illus. 2008. (Andrew Lost: 17). 96p. (J). ***(978-0-375-84667-0(0))*** Random Hse., Inc.

—In the Kitchen. Palen, Debbie, illus. 2002. (Andrew Lost Ser.: Bk. 3). 96p. (J). (gr. 2-5). pap. 3.99 (978-0-375-81279-8(2) , Random Hse. Bks. for Young Readers) Random Hse. Children's Bks.

—In Uncle Al. Gerardi, Jan, illus. 2007. (Andrew Lost Ser.: Bk. 16). 96p. (J). (gr. 2-4). 3.99 ***(978-0-375-83565-0(2));*** lib. bdg. 11.99 ***(978-0-375-93565-7(7))*** Random Hse. Children's Bks. (Random Hse. Bks. for Young Readers).

Greenburg, J. C. Under Water. Reed, Mike, illus. 2003. (Andrew Lost Ser.: Bk. 5). 96p. (J). (gr. 2-5). mass mkt. 3.99 (978-0-375-82523-1(1) , Random Hse. Bks. for Young Readers) Random Hse. Children's Bks.

Greene, Brenda. Dog Gone: Boomer's Story. Cheryl H. Hahn, illus. 2005. 127p. (YA). per. 8.99 (978-0-9770279-0-3(2)) Three Willows Pr.

Greene, Janice. The House on the Hill, Set 2. 2002. 32p. (YA). 2.95 (978-1-56254-419-5(5) , SP 4195) Saddleback Educational Publishing.

Greenhalgh, Miranda. Rapid Duck. 2007. (Illus.). 38p. (J). per. 14.99 ***(978-1-59879-348-2(9)*** , Lifevest) Lifevest Publishing, Inc.

Greenwald, Sheila. Rosy Cole's Worst Ever, Best yet Tour of New York City. Greenwald, Sheila, illus. 2003. (Rosie Cole Ser.). (Illus.). 128p. (J). 16.00 (978-0-374-36349-9(8) , Farrar, Straus & Giroux (BYR)) Farrar, Straus & Giroux.

Gregory, Jeannette. Honor Your Father & Mother. 2004. (J). 6.99 (978-0-9754779-5-3(1)) Chosen Word Publishing.

Gremila, Elaine Demetri. Seasons of the Heart. l.t. ed. 2003. (Illus.). 140p. per. 11.95 (978-1-932338-16-4(0)) Lifevest Publishing, Inc.

Griffin, Adele. Son of Liberty. 2003. (LRS Large Print Cornerstone Ser.). (J). lib. bdg. 29.95 (978-1-58118-096-1(9) , 25333) LRS.

Griffis, Molly Levite. Simon Says. 2004. vi, 263p. (J). 22.95 (978-1-57168-836-1(6)); pap. (978-1-57168-847-7(1)) Eakin Pr. (Eakin Pr.).

Grimes, Cookie. A New Year's Family. 2007. 36p. (J). 11.99 ***(978-1-60247-154-2(1))*** Tate Publishing & Enterprises, L.L.C.

Grimm, Jacob W. & Grimm, Wilhelm K. The Fisherman & His Wife: A Tale about Being Happy & Satisfied. Ebert, Len, illus. 2006. (J). ***(978-1-59939-097-0(3)*** , Reader's Digest Young Families, Inc.) Reader's Digest Children's Publishing, Inc.

Grove, Ella. A Surprise for Tommy. 2005. (Illus.). 24p. (ps-5). 2.70 (978-0-7399-2341-2(2) , 2780) Rod & Staff Pubs., Inc.

Grover, Lorie Ann. Hold Me Tight. 2005. 352p. (J). 16.95 (978-0-689-85248-0(7) , McElderry, Margaret K.) Simon & Schuster Children's Publishing.

Guest, Jacqueline. Wild Ride. 2005. (SideStreets Ser.). 168p. (YA). (gr. 7-12). ***(978-1-55028-881-0(4));*** 7.95 (978-1-55028-880-3(6)) Lorimer, James & Co., Ltd., Pubs. CAN. *Dist:* Casemate Pubs. & Bk. Distributors, LLC.

Guibert, Emmanuel & Sfar, Joann. The Professor's Daughter. 2007. 80p. (YA). pap. 16.95 (978-1-59643-130-0(X) , First Second Bks.) Roaring Brook Pr.

Gunn, Robin Jones. A Promise Is Forever. rev. ed. 1999. (Christy Miller Ser.: Bk. 12). 160p. (J). (gr. 7-12). pap. (978-1-56179-733-2(2)) Focus on the Family Publishing.

—Seventeen Wishes. rev. ed. 1999. (Christy Miller Ser.: Bk. 9). 160p. (J). (gr. 7-12). pap. (978-1-56179-730-1(8)) Focus on the Family Publishing.

—Sweet Dreams. rev. ed. 1999. (Christy Miller Ser.: Bk. 11). 160p. (J). (gr. 7-12). pap. (978-1-56179-732-5(4)) Focus on the Family Publishing.

—A Time to Cherish. rev. ed. 1999. (Christy Miller Ser.: Bk. 10). 176p. (J). (gr. 7-12). pap. (978-1-56179-731-8(6)) Focus on the Family Publishing.

Gurnick, Isabella Grace & Beals, Stephen Naayvek. Girls Have Eyelashes. 2004. 39p. pap. 11.63 (978-1-4116-1696-7(0)) Lulu.com.

Gutierrez, Debbi Miller. Cactus Factory. 2007. (J). 6.00 ***(978-0-9740173-4-1(5))*** Prints By Mail.

Gutman, Anne & Hallensleben, Georg. Lisa in New York. 2002. (Illus.). 32p. (J). (gr. k-3). 9.95 (978-0-375-81119-7(2) , Knopf Bks. for Young Readers) Random Hse. Children's Bks.

Gwaltney, Doris. Homefront. 2006. 320p. (J). 17.99 (978-0-689-86842-9(1)) Simon & Schuster Children's Publishing.

Haas, Jessie. Keeping Barney. 1998. 160p. (J). (gr. 3 up). pap. 4.50 (978-0-688-15859-0(5)) HarperCollins Pubs.

Haddix, Margaret Peterson. Double Identity. 2007. 192p. (J). (gr. 5-9). pap. 5.99 (978-0-689-87379-9(4) , Aladdin) Simon & Schuster Children's Publishing.

—Takeoffs & Landings. 2003. (Illus.). 208p. (J). pap. 4.99 (978-0-689-85543-6(5) , Aladdin) Simon & Schuster Children's Publishing.

Hahn, Mary Downing. Following My Own Footsteps. 1998. (Camelot Bks.). 192p. (J). (gr. 3-7). reprint ed. pap. 4.95 (978-0-380-72990-6(3)) HarperCollins Pubs.

Hallagin, Janet. The Way of Courage. 2006. 30.99 ***(978-1-4257-1249-5(5));*** pap. 20.99 ***(978-1-4257-1248-8(7))*** Xlibris Corp.

Halvorsen Schreck, Karen. Lucy's Family Tree. Gassler, Stephen, illus. 2006. 40p. (J). 7.95 ***(978-0-88448-292-5(8))*** Tilbury Hse. Pubs.

Hamilton, Virginia. M. C. Higgins, the Great. l.t. ed. 2005. 372p. (J). 22.95 (978-0-7862-7541-0(3)) Thorndike Pr.

—Primos. 2002. Tr. of Cousins. (SPA., Illus.). 126p. (YA). (gr. 5-8). pap. 12.95 (978-968-19-0787-7(6)) Aguilar Editorial MEX. *Dist:* Santillana USA Publishing Co., Inc.

—Primos. 2003. Tr. of Cousins. (SPA., Illus.). 126p. (J). (gr. 5-8). pap. 9.95 (978-84-204-4747-6(1) , LEC7471) Santillana USA Publishing Co., Inc.

—Second Cousins. 2000. (Illus.). 176p. (J). (gr. 4-8). pap. 4.99 (978-0-590-47369-9(7) , Scholastic Reference) Scholastic, Inc.

—Second Cousins. 2000. (978-0-606-18602-5(6)) Tandem Library Bks.

—Zeely. 1998. (C). pap. 3.95 (978-0-87628-345-5(8)) Simon & Schuster.

Hamley, Dennis. Without Warning: Ellen's Story, 1914-1918. 2007. (Illus.). 336p. (YA). (gr. 7). 17.99 ***(978-0-7636-3338-7(0))*** Candlewick Pr.

Hampton, Randall. A Christmas Kiss. l.t. ed. 2005. (Illus.). 48p. (J). per. 16.95 (978-1-59879-048-1(X)) Lifevest Publishing, Inc.

Hands, Cynthia. Odd Couples. 2001. 70p. (J). (ps-3). pap. 2.99 (978-0-307-33771-9(5) , Golden Bks.) Random Hse. Children's Bks.

Hansen, Francis & Hansen, Caroline. Finally a Friend. 2003. (Illus.). 117p. (J). per. (978-0-9722501-1-5(5)) Backwoods Publishing Co.

Harcourt School Publishers Staff. Beethoven Is Upstairs Level D: Library Edition. 2001. (Collections Ser.). (Illus.). (J). (gr. 5). 5.90 (978-0-15-314403-5(3)) Harcourt Schl. Pubs.

—The Best Thanksgiving On Level. 3rd ed. 2002. (Trophies Reading Program Ser.). (Illus.). pap. 5.10 (978-0-15-323176-6(9)) Harcourt Schl. Pubs.

—Ella & Her Mean Cousins Below Level. 3rd ed. 2002. (Trophies Reading Program Ser.). (Illus.). pap. 5.10 (978-0-15-323149-0(1)) Harcourt Schl. Pubs.

—Faces to the Sun On Level. 3rd ed. 2002. (Trophies Reading Program Ser.). (Illus.). pap. 5.10 (978-0-15-323259-6(5)) Harcourt Schl. Pubs.

—A Family Farm: A Reader. 1999. (Collections Ser.). (Illus.). (J). pap. 2.10 (978-0-15-313446-3(1)) Harcourt Schl. Pubs.

—Family Pictures. 3rd ed. 2002. (Trophies English Language Learners Ser.). (Illus.). pap. 5.10 (978-0-15-327636-1(3)) Harcourt Schl. Pubs.

—Family Ties: Practice Book. 3rd ed. 2001. (Trophies Reading Program Ser.). (Illus.). (J). pap. 1.80 (978-0-15-325085-9(2)) Harcourt Schl. Pubs.

—Family Ties: Practice Book: Florida Edition. 3rd ed. 2002. (Trophies Reading Program Ser.). (Illus.). (J). pap. 2.00 (978-0-15-326600-3(7)) Harcourt Schl. Pubs.

—Finding a Home at Last Advanced Level. 3rd ed. 2002. (Trophies Reading Program Ser.). (Illus.). pap. 5.10 (978-0-15-323484-2(9)) Harcourt Schl. Pubs.

—A Good Combination On Level. 3rd ed. 2002. (Trophies Reading Program Ser.). (Illus.). pap. 5.10 (978-0-15-323253-4(6)) Harcourt Schl. Pubs.

—Home Sweet Home. 3rd ed. 2002. (Trophies English Language Learners Ser.). (Illus.). pap. 5.10 (978-0-15-327709-2(2)) Harcourt Schl. Pubs.

—I Can Help. 3rd ed. 2002. (Trophies English Language Learners Ser.). (Illus.). (J). pap. 3.20 (978-0-15-327565-4(0)) Harcourt Schl. Pubs.

—Meet My Family. 3rd ed. 2002. (Trophies English Language Learners Ser.). (Illus.). (J). pap. 4.10 (978-0-15-327583-8(9)) Harcourt Schl. Pubs.

—Olga's Bakery On Level. 3rd ed. 2002. (Trophies Reading Program Ser.). (Illus.). pap. 5.10 (978-0-15-323275-6(7)) Harcourt Schl. Pubs.

—Short for Estrallita Advanced Level. 3rd ed. 2002. (Trophies Reading Program Ser.). (Illus.). pap. 5.10 (978-0-15-323394-4(X)) Harcourt Schl. Pubs.

E F G

—Snowshoe Thompson: Library Edition. 1999. (Collections Ser.). (Illus.). (J). 5.30 (978-0-15-314329-8(0)) Harcourt Schl. Pubs.

—Stacy's Surprise: Take-Home Book. 1999. (Collections Ser.). (Illus.). (J). pap. 1.90 (978-0-15-317298-4(3)) Harcourt Schl. Pubs.

—Student of the Week On Level. 3rd ed. 2002. (Trophies Reading Program Ser.). (Illus.). pap. 5.10 (978-0-15-323181-0(5)) Harcourt Schl. Pubs.

—The Subway Series On Level. 3rd ed. 2002. (Trophies Reading Program Ser.). (Illus.). pap. 5.10 (978-0-15-323174-2(2)) Harcourt Schl. Pubs.

—The Subway Series - 5 Pack - Grade 3, On Level. 3rd ed. 2002. (Trophies Reading Program Ser.). pap. 25.60 (978-0-15-327030-7(6)) Harcourt Schl. Pubs.

—Taming the Land Below Level. 3rd ed. 2002. (Trophies Reading Program Ser.). (Illus.). pap. 5.10 (978-0-15-323326-5(5)) Harcourt Schl. Pubs.

—Things Will Get Better On Level. 3rd ed. 2002. (Trophies Reading Program Ser.). (Illus.). pap. 5.10 (978-0-15-323262-6(5)) Harcourt Schl. Pubs.

—Thunder Lake Advanced Level. 3rd ed. 2002. (Trophies Reading Program Ser.). (Illus.). pap. 5.10 (978-0-15-323469-9(5)) Harcourt Schl. Pubs.

—Travels with Dad On Level. 3rd ed. 2002. (Trophies Reading Program Ser.). (Illus.). pap. 5.10 (978-0-15-323098-1(3)) Harcourt Schl. Pubs.

—Under One Roof. 3rd ed. 2002. (Trophies English Language Learners Ser.). (Illus.). pap. 5.10 (978-0-15-327760-3(2)) Harcourt Schl. Pubs.

—The Unwelcome Uncle: Take Home Book. 1999. (Signatures Ser.). (Illus.). (J). pap. 1.90 (978-0-15-313972-7(2)) Harcourt Schl. Pubs.

—Wagon Wheels. 3rd ed. 2002. (Trophies English Language Learners Ser.). (Illus.). pap. 5.10 (978-0-15-327776-4(9)) Harcourt Schl. Pubs.

—Walking to Nebraska On Level. 3rd ed. 2002. (Trophies Reading Program Ser.). (Illus.). pap. 5.10 (978-0-15-323277-0(3)) Harcourt Schl. Pubs.

—What a Great Team! 3rd ed. 2002. (Trophies English Language Learners Ser.). (Illus.). (J). pap. 4.10 (978-0-15-327580-7(4)) Harcourt Schl. Pubs.

—Where I Come From. 3rd ed. 2002. (Trophies English Language Learners Ser.). (Illus.). pap. 5.10 (978-0-15-327875-4(7)) Harcourt Schl. Pubs.

—Working Hard: On Level. 3rd ed. 2002. (Trophies Reading Program Ser.). (Illus.). (J). pap. 4.10 (978-0-15-322987-9(X)) Harcourt Schl. Pubs.

Harmel, Kristin. When You Wish. 2008. 288p. (J). (gr. 7). lib. bdg. 18.99 (***978-0-385-90474-2(6)*** , Delacorte Bks. for Young Readers) Random Hse. Children's Bks.

Harmon, Lyn. Clyde's Clam Farm. 2001. (Illus.). 132p. (gr. 4-7). pap. 9.95 (978-0-595-16339-7(4) , Backinprint-.com) iUniverse, Inc.

Harmon, Michael. Skate. 2008. 256p. (J). (gr. 9). mass mkt. 6.50 (***978-0-553-49510-2(0)*** , Laurel Leaf) Random Hse. Children's Bks.

Harness, Cheryl. Just for You to Know. 2006. 320p. (J). 16.99 (978-0-06-078313-6(3)); lib. bdg. 17.89 (978-0-06-078314-3(1)) HarperCollins Pubs.

Harper, Jo. Delfino's Journey. 2000. viii, 184p. (J). (gr. 8-12). 15.95 (978-0-89672-437-2(9)) Texas Tech Univ. Pr.

—Delfino's Journey, Grades 8-12. 2000. (Illus.). viii, 184p. (J). tchr. ed. 5.95 (978-0-89672-442-6(5)) Texas Tech Univ. Pr.

Harper, Jo & Harper, Josephine. Buscando A Papa: Un Cuento Sobre la Epoca de la Gran Depresion. Peluffo, Ana, tr. Mazellan, Ron, illus. 2005. (SPA.). 32p. (J). (ps-17). 16.95 (978-1-890515-32-4(9)) Turtle Bks.

—Como los Perros de la Pradera. Gutiérrez, Guillermo, tr. Spearing, Craig, illus. 2000. (SPA.). 48p. (J). (ps-3). pap. 8.95 (978-1-890515-24-9(8)) Turtle Bks.

Harris, Bradley K. My Brother & I. Harris, Phyllis, illus. 2005. 26p. (J). 18.95 (978-0-9710278-6-2(2)) All About Kids Publishing.

Harrison, Emma, et al. Slipping Away. 2005. 163p. (YA). (978-1-4155-8181-0(9) , Simon Spotlight) Simon & Schuster Children's Publishing.

Hart, Joy F. A New Family for Semoj. 2004. (Illus.). 242p. 9.65 (978-0-7399-2320-7(X) , 2403) Rod & Staff Pubs., Inc.

Hartfield, Claire. Me & Uncle Romie: A Story Inspired by the Life & Art of Romare Beardon. Lagarrigue, Jerome, illus. 2002. 40p. (J). 16.99 (978-0-8037-2520-1(5) , Dial) Penguin Group (USA) Inc.

Hautman, Pete. Mr. Was. 1998. 256p. (YA). (gr. 7-12). mass mkt. 5.99 (978-0-689-81914-8(5) , Simon Pulse) Simon & Schuster Children's Publishing.

Haven, Eloise Amy. Families Are Forever: Book 1 of the Rissy Series. 2004. 90p. pap. 14.95 (978-1-4137-4770-6(1)) PublishAmerica, Inc.

Hawes, Alison. A Quiet Morning for Mom: Individual Title Six-Pack Pouch - Level H. Shearing, Leonie, illus. (Lighthouse Ser.). 16p. (gr. 1 up). 26.00 (978-0-7578-0845-6(X)) Rigby Education.

Hawthorne, Nathaniel & Larkin, Rochelle. The House of the Seven Gables. Marcos, Pablo, illus. 2005. (Great Illustrated Classics Ser.). 240p. (J). (gr. 3-8). 21.35 (978-1-59679-242-5(6) , ABDO & Daughters) ABDO Publishing Co.

Hayes, Rosemary. Bright Horizon. 2004. (J). pap. 11.95 (978-0-340-85471-6(5) , Hodder & Stoughton) Hodder General Publishing Division GBR. *Dist:* Trafalgar Square Publishing.

Hayward, Linda. Monster Bug. Palmisciano, Diane, illus. 2004. 32p. (J). lib. bdg. 20.00 (***978-1-4242-1097-8(6)***) Fitzgerald Bks.

Healy, Nick. The Big Pig. Rooney, Ronnie, illus. 2006. 32p. (J). (***978-1-4048-3385-2(4)***) Picture Window Bks.

Hébert, Marie-Francine & Germain, Philippe. Une Tempete dans un Verre d'Eau. 2001. (FRE., Illus.). 64p. (J). pap. (978-2-89021-477-4(X)) Diffusion du livre Mirabel.

Heller, Andrew. A Mouthful of Teeth. 2002. (Illus.). 16p. (J). 7.99 (978-0-9722038-4-5(2)) Mr Do It All, Inc.

Hellings, Collete. Un Bebe Caido del Cielo. Jacobs, Nadine, illus. 2003. (SPA.). 32p. (J). (gr. k-1). 16.95 (978-84-95150-10-3(7) , COR4033) Corimbo, Editorial S.L. ESP. *Dist:* Distribooks, Inc., Lectorum Pubns., Inc.

Henderson, Kathy. And the Good Brown Earth. Henderson, Kathy, illus. 2004. (Illus.). 40p. (J). (ps up). 15.99 (978-0-7636-2301-2(6)) Candlewick Pr.

Herman, Charlotte. The Memory Cupboard: A Thanksgiving Story. Stahl, Ben F., illus. 2003. 32p. (J). (gr. 1-4). 16.95 (978-0-8075-5055-7(8)) Whitman, Albert & Co.

Herrera, Juan Felipe. Cinnamon Girl: Letters Found Inside a Cereal Box. 2005. 176p. (J). 15.99 (978-0-06-057984-5(6) , Cotler, Joanna Books) HarperCollins Pubs.

Herrick, Steven. Love, Ghosts, & Facial Hair. 2004. (Illus.). 128p. (YA). pap. 6.99 (978-0-689-86710-1(7) , Simon Pulse) Simon & Schuster Children's Publishing.

—Love, Ghosts, & Facial Hair. 2004. (gr. 7-12). lib. bdg. 15.30 (978-0-613-73420-2(3)) Tandem Library Bks.

Hest, Amy. Guess Who, Baby Duck! Barton, Jill, illus. 2004. 32p. (J). (gr. k-k). 15.99 (978-0-7636-1981-7(7)) Candlewick Pr.

Heynen, Jim. Being Youngest. 2000. 272p. (J). (gr. 3-7). pap. 4.95 (978-0-380-73204-3(1) , Harper Trophy) HarperCollins Pubs.

—Being Youngest. 2000. (978-0-606-17829-7(5)) Tandem Library Bks.

Hickey, Jack. A Storyteller's Book of Tales. 2002. 114p. (J). pap. 9.95 (978-0-595-22333-6(8) , Writer's Showcase Pr.) iUniverse, Inc.

Higginson, Hadley. Keeker & the Not-So-Sleepy Hollow. Perrett, Lisa, illus. 2008. (J). (***978-0-8118-6073-4(6));*** 56p. pap. 3.99 (***978-0-8118-6074-1(4)***) Chronicle Bks. LLC.

Hilbrecht, Kirk. My Daddy Is an Airman. 2005. 32p. pap. 6.95 (978-1-889658-38-4(3)) New Canaan Publishing Co. LLC.

Hill, Grace Livingston. Cloudy Jewel. (J). reprint ed. lib. bdg. 24.95 (978-0-89190-037-5(3) , Rivercity Pr.) Amereon LTD.

Himelblau, Linda. The Trouble Begins. 2005. 208p. (J). (gr. 3-7). 14.95 (978-0-385-73273-4(2) , Delacorte Bks. for Young Readers) Random Hse. Children's Bks.

Hinds, Ruth McNaughton. Puppy & I. 2006. (J). per. 7.95 (978-0-9764232-2-5(7)) River City Pr.

Hip Hip Hooray, It's Monsoon Day! 2007. (ENG & SPA.). (YA). pap. 15.95 (***978-1-886679-36-8(3)***) Arizona Sonora Desert Museum Pr.

Hite, Sid. Those Darn Dithers. 1998. (J). (978-0-606-13846-8(3)) Tandem Library Bks.

Hoban, Russell. The Little Brute Family. Hoban, Lillian, illus. 2002. 32p. (J). pap. 5.95 (978-0-374-44483-9(8) , Sunburst) Farrar, Straus & Giroux.

—The Little Brute Family. 2002. (gr. k-3). lib. bdg. 14.10 (978-0-613-71008-4(8)) Tandem Library Bks.

Hobbs, William. Jackie's Wild Seattle. 208p. (J). (gr. 5 up). 2004. pap. 5.99 (978-0-380-73311-8(0) , Harper Trophy); 2003. 16.99 (978-0-688-17474-3(4)); 2003. lib. bdg. 16.89 (978-0-06-051631-4(3)) HarperCollins Pubs.

Hodge, Deborah. Emma's Story. Zhang, Song Nan, illus. 2003. 24p. (J). (gr. k-3). 17.95 (978-0-88776-632-9(3)) Tundra Bks., Inc./Livres Toundra, Inc. CAN. *Dist:* Random Hse., Inc.

Hodgson, Guinn. Family in a Blender. 2005. 48p. pap. 12.95 (978-1-4137-8765-8(7)) PublishAmerica, Inc.

Hoffman, Alice. Indigo. 2003. (gr. 5-8). lib. bdg. 13.00 (978-0-613-67496-6(0)) Tandem Library Bks.

Hoffman, Nina Kiriki. A Stir of Bones. 2005. 224p. (J). (gr. 7). pap. 6.99 (978-0-14-240361-7(X) , Puffin) Penguin Group (USA) Inc.

Hoffman, Sanford. Too Much Tooting. 2006. (I'm Going to Read Ser.). (Illus.). 32p. (J). pap. 3.95 (978-1-4027-3680-3(0)) Sterling Publishing Co., Inc.

Hogan, Mary. Tigger's Family. 2000. (Winnie the Pooh Ser.) (Illus.). 10p. (J). (ps-k). bds. 4.99 (978-0-7364-1062-5(7)) Mouse Works.

Hohenthal, K. D. Herman Goes Home: A Duffy Family Adventure. 2003. (Illus.). 46p. (J). per. 15.95 (978-0-9716907-3-8(1) , Ridgewood Publishing) Ridgewood Group, The.

Holman, John. Luminous Mysteries. 2000. (gr. 7-12). lib. bdg. 21.10 (978-0-613-21942-6(2)) Tandem Library Bks.

Holsather, Kent /Wilson. Sara's Moon. 2007. (Illus.). 176p. (YA). per. 12.95 (***978-0-9729101-3-2(1)***) Lonejack Mountain Pr.

Homel, David. Travels with My Family. Gay, Marie-Louise, illus. 2007. 120p. (J). pap. 7.95 (***978-0-88899-833-0(3)***) Groundwood Bks. CAN. *Dist:* Perseus Distribution.

Hoobler, Dorothy & Hoobler, Thomas. The 1970's: Arguments. Hoffman, Robin, illus. 2002. (Century Kids Ser.). 160p. (gr. 5-8). lib. bdg. 22.90 (978-0-7613-1607-7(8) , Twenty-First Century Bks.) Lerner Publishing Group.

—The 1990s: Families. Hoffman, Robin, illus. 2002. (Century Kids Ser.). 160p. (gr. 5-8). lib. bdg. 22.90 (978-0-7613-1609-1(4) , Twenty-First Century Bks.) Lerner Publishing Group.

Hope, Laura Lee. Six Little Bunkers at Cousin Tom's. rev. ed. 2006. 192p. 26.95 (978-1-4218-1795-8(0)); pap. 11.95 (978-1-4218-1895-5(7)) 1st World Publishing, Inc. (1st World Library - Literary Society).

Hopkins, Cathy. Discount Diva. 2007. (Zodiac Girls Ser.). 184p. (J). (gr. 4-7). pap. 5.95 (***978-0-7534-6131-0(5)*** , Kingfisher) Houghton Mifflin Co. Trade & Reference Div.

Hopkins, Ellen. Crank. 2004. 544p. (YA). (gr. 9 up). pap. 8.99 (978-0-689-86519-0(8) , Simon Pulse) Simon & Schuster Children's Publishing.

Hopkinson, Deborah. Cabin in the Snow. Faricy, Patrick, illus. ed. 2005. 74p. (J). lib. bdg. 15.00 (978-1-59054-896-7(5)) Fitzgerald Bks.

Horn, Peter. Cuando Sea Grande... Kadmon, Cristina, illus. 2001. (SPA.). 32p. (J). (gr. k-3). pap. 6.95 (978-0-7358-1435-6(X) , NS30340) North-South Bks., Inc.

—When I Grow Up... Cuando Sea Grande. Almohar, Ariel, tr. from GER. Kadmon, Cristina, illus. 2001. 32p. (J). (ps-3). pap. 6.95 (978-0-7358-1418-9(X)) North-South Bks., Inc.

Horvath, Polly. The Vacation. pap. 12.95 (978-0-88899-693-0(4)) Groundwood Bks. CAN. *Dist:* Transition Vendor.

Howard, Elizabeth Fitzgerald. What's in Aunt Mary's Room? Lucas, Cedric, illus. 2002. 32p. (J). (gr. k-3). pap. 5.95 (978-0-618-24621-2(5) , Clarion Bks.) Houghton Mifflin Co. Trade & Reference Div.

—What's in Aunt Mary's Room? 2002. (gr. k-3). lib. bdg. 14.10 (978-0-613-72911-6(0)) Tandem Library Bks.

Howard, Joanne. Not So Long Ago. 2005. 48p. pap. 12.95 (978-1-4137-6324-9(3)) PublishAmerica, Inc.

Howe, James. Pinky & Rex & the Perfect Pumpkin. 2000. (Pinky & Rex Ser.). (J). (gr. 1-4). pap., stu. ed. 23.24 incl. audio (978-0-7887-4459-4(3) , 41149) Recorded Bks., LLC.

—Watcher. (gr. 7-12). 2001. lib. bdg. 13.00 (978-0-613-18288-1(X)); 1999. lib. bdg. 16.45 (978-0-613-73278-9(2)) Tandem Library Bks.

Huber, Penelope. Three's a Crowd. 1999. 118p. pap. 13.00 (978-1-877135-26-2(7)) Longacre Pr. NZL. *Dist:* Pacific Island Bks.

Hughes, Shirley. Alfie's World. 2007. (Illus.). 48p. (J). 19.95 (***978-0-370-32894-2(9)***) Transworld Publishers Ltd. GBR. *Dist:* Independent Pubs. Group.

—Helpers. 2007. (Illus.). 32p. (J). pap. 8.95 (***978-0-09-992650-4(4)*** , Red Fox) Random Hse. Children's Bks. GBR. *Dist:* Independent Pubs. Group.

Humes, Kristin Joy. My Dad Wears Polka-Dotted Socks! Barr, Loel, illus. 2005. 32p. (ps-7). 15.95 (978-0-9744307-2-0(2)) Merry Lane Pr.

Hussey, Charmian. The Valley of Secrets. Crump, Christopher, illus. 400p. 2006. (J). pap. 9.99 (978-1-4169-0015-3(2) , Simon Pulse); 2005. (YA). 17.95 (978-0-689-87862-6(1)) Simon & Schuster Children's Publishing.

Hutchins, Pat. There's Only One of Me! Hutchins, Pat, illus. 2003. (Illus.). 24p. (J). 16.99 (978-0-06-029819-7(7)) HarperCollins Pubs.

—There's Only One of Me! Hutchins, Pat, illus. 2006. (J). (ps-2). 25.95 incl. audio (978-1-59519-490-9(8)); (Illus.). 28.95 incl. audio compact disk (978-1-59519-494-7(0)) Live Oak Media.

I Like Me. 2004. (J). per. (978-1-57657-395-2(8)) Paradise Pr., Inc.

I Like Me. 2004. 8p. (gr. k-2). 20.95 (978-0-322-00630-0(9)) Wright Group, The.

Idleman, Juli. Finding America: A Novel. 2005. 211p. pap. 19.95 (978-1-4137-8234-9(5)) PublishAmerica, Inc.

Iguerabide, Juan Cruz. La Pena de Jonas. 2002. (SPA., Illus.). 56p. 6.95 (978-84-241-7933-5(1) , EV30302) Everest de Ediciones y Distribucion, S.L. ESP. *Dist:* Lectorum Pubns., Inc.

Ilogienboh, Caroline. Nowhere to Hide. 2004. 220p. (YA). pap. 14.95 (978-0-9712781-4-1(8) , 0-9712781) Sun Rose Pubs.

In My Father's House. 2004. (Literature Connections Ser.). (gr. 6-12). (978-0-395-88933-6(2) , 2-70865) McDougal Littell Inc.

In the Month of Kislev. unabr. ed. 2004. (J). (ps-3). pap. 14.95 incl. audio (978-0-7882-0685-6(0) , PRA357) Weston Woods Studios, Inc.

Inchy Goes the Extra Mile, 3 bks. 2004. (Illus.). (J). 9.95 (978-0-9725286-1-0(X)) Sheppard Publishing.

Inns, Dennis & Kanaan, Salah. Fattish & Fattoush: The Revelation. 2005. 143p. pap. 19.95 (978-1-4137-4397-5(8)) PublishAmerica, Inc.

Inserra, Rose. Wedding Day Disaster. Hill, Trish, illus. 1999. (Supa Doopers Ser.). 64p. (J). (978-0-7608-3288-2(9)) Sundance/Newbridge Educational Publishing.

Inteli, Nancy. Tutter Family Reunion. 2001. (gr. k-3). lib. bdg. 14.15 (978-0-613-51327-2(4)) Tandem Library Bks.

Isadora, Rachel. What a Family! A Fresh Look at Family Trees. 2006. (Illus.). (J). (***978-1-4156-5634-1(7)*** , Putnam Juvenile) Penguin Group (USA) Inc.

Ivey, Tracie. Queen of Beans. 2004. 78p. pap. 14.95 (978-1-4137-1873-7(6)) PublishAmerica, Inc.

Jaffe, Nina. In the Month of Kislev. August, Louise, illus. unabr. ed. 2004. (J). (ps-3). 24.95 incl. audio (978-0-7882-0660-3(5) , HRA357) Weston Woods Studios, Inc.

James, Betsy. Long Night Dance. 2005. (Seeker Chronicles Ser.). (Illus.). 224p. (J). pap. 5.99 (978-0-689-85071-4(9) , Simon Pulse) Simon & Schuster Children's Publishing.

James, Henry. Washington Square, Level 4. abr. ed. 2000. (Bookworms Ser.). (Illus.). 96p. 6.50 (978-0-19-423052-0(X)) Oxford Univ. Pr., Inc.

—Washington Square, Level 2. abr. ed. 1999. (Illus.). 48p. (C). pap. 9.00 (978-0-582-40162-4(3)) Pearson ESL.

—Washington Square. 2001. (Washington Square Press Enriched Classic Ser.). (Illus.). (J). (978-0-606-21510-7(7)) Tandem Library Bks.

James, Sara & Ruckdeschel, Liz. What If ... All the Boys Wanted You. 2006. 288p. (YA). (gr. 7). pap. 8.95 (978-0-385-73297-0(X) , Delacorte Bks. for Young Readers) Random Hse. Children's Bks.

James, Simon. Jake & His Cousin Sidney. 2002. (gr. 3-6). lib. bdg. 13.00 (978-0-613-53737-7(8)) Tandem Library Bks.

—Little One Step. James, Simon, illus. 2003. (Illus.). 32p. (J). (ps-3). 15.99 (978-0-7636-2070-7(X)) Candlewick Pr.

James, Will. Uncle Bill. Carey, Jennifer, ed. (Tumbleweed Ser.). (Illus.). 185p. (gr. 4 up). reprint ed. 26.00 (978-0-87842-379-8(6) , 695) Mountain Pr. Publishing Co., Inc.

Jantti, Mariana. Pope y su oveja Ba. 2005. (Grandes lugares para la Aventura Ser.). (SPA., Illus.). 28p. (J). 14.95 (978-84-933955-9-9(5)) Hardenville SA URY. *Dist:* Independent Pubs. Group.

Jarrell, Pamela R. Caillou's Family & Friends. Meier, Kerry L., illus. l.t. ed. 2005. (Hrl Board Book Ser.). (J). (gr. k up). pap. 10.95 (978-1-57332-327-7(6)) HighReach Learning, Inc.

Jaysree. Drama. 2004. 134p. (YA). pap. 11.95 (978-0-595-29662-0(9)) iUniverse, Inc.

Jeanne-Marie in Gay Paris. 2003. (Illus.). 32p. (J). mass mkt. 9.99 (978-0-9740599-1-4(9) , 2) Omnibus Publishing.

Jeeva Raghunath & Nayar, Deeya. Malli: Malli. Nancy Raj, illus. 2005. (HIN & ENG.). 16p. (J). (***978-81-8146-089-9(8)***) Tulika Pubs.

Jenisch, Betty. Rennie. 2007. 9.00 (***978-0-8059-8947-2(1)***) Dorrance Publishing Co., Inc.

Jennings, Sharon. The Bye-Bye Pie. Ohi, Ruth, illus. 1999. 31p. (J). (gr. k-3). (978-1-55041-405-9(4)) Fitzhenry & Whiteside, Ltd.

—Into My Mother's Arms. Ohi, Ruth, illus. 2000. 32p. (J). (ps-k). (978-1-55041-533-9(6)) Fitzhenry & Whiteside, Ltd.

—Into My Mother's Arms: With Sticker & Card. Ohi, Ruth, illus. 2001. 32p. (J). (ps-k). (978-1-55041-669-5(3)) Fitzhenry & Whiteside, Ltd.

Jimmy Gimmy & the Raid on Burkey Run. 2005. (Illus.). 192p. (J). pap. 12.95 (978-0-9767646-0-1(1)) Team EEK!.

Johnson, Angela. The Wedding. Soman, David, illus. 1999. 32p. (J). (ps-2). 17.99 (978-0-531-33139-2(3)); pap. 16.95 (978-0-531-30139-5(7)) Scholastic, Inc. (Orchard Bks.).

Johnson, Donna. The Story of the Little Red Leaf. Johnson, Emily, illus. l.t. ed. 2006. 22p. (J). 25.00 (***978-0-9778774-0-9(X)***) Choicepoint Editions.

Johnson, Lindsay Lee. Worlds Apart. 2005. 176p. (J). (gr. 5). 16.95 (978-1-932425-28-4(4) , Lemniscaat) Boyds Mills Pr.

Johnson, Maureen. 13 Little Blue Envelopes. (Illus.). (J). 2005. 336p. (gr. 7 up). 16.99 (978-0-06-054141-5(5)); 2005. 336p. (gr. 7 up). lib. bdg. 17.89 (978-0-06-054142-2(3)); 2006. 352p. reprint ed. pap. 8.99 (978-0-06-054143-9(1) , HarperTeen) HarperCollins Pubs.

Johnston. Hero of Lesser Causes. 2003. (gr. 7-12). lib. bdg. 18.75 (978-0-613-77314-0(4)) Tandem Library Bks.

Johnston, Annie Fell. Two Little Knights of Kentucky (Illustra. 2006. pap. (***978-1-4065-1133-8(1)***) Dodo Pr.

Johnston, Julie. In Spite of Killer Bees. 2002. (gr. 5-8). lib. bdg. 17.60 (978-0-613-77264-8(4)) Tandem Library Bks.

—In Spite of Killer Bees. 2002. 264p. (J). (gr. 6 up). pap. 9.95 (978-0-88776-601-5(3)) Tundra Bks., Inc./Livres Toundra, Inc. CAN. *Dist:* Random Hse., Inc.

Johnston, Tony & Johnston, Tony. Uncle Rain Cloud. VandenBroeck, Fabricio, illus. 2003. (J). (ps-3). lib. bdg. 15.25 (978-0-613-90105-5(3)) Tandem Library Bks.

Johnston, Tony & Vanden Broeck, Fabrizio. Uncle Rain Cloud. 2003. pap. 6.95 (978-0-88106-372-1(X)) Charlesbridge Publishing, Inc.

Jones, Diana Wynne. Aunt Maria. 2003. 288p. (J). (gr. 5 up). 16.99 (978-0-06-623742-8(4)) HarperCollins Pubs.

Jones, Jennifer B. Dear Mrs. Ryan, You're Ruining My Life. 2004. 144p. (J). pap. 5.95 (978-0-8027-7653-2(1)) Walker & Co.

Jones, Lara. I Love Hugs. Jones, Lara, illus. 2002. (Illus.). 16p. (J). bds. 6.95 (978-0-439-36767-7(0) , Cartwheel Bks.) Scholastic, Inc.

Jones, Molly. Something in the Air. Welch, Sheila Kelly, illus. 2005. (J). (978-1-893516-03-8(2)) Our Child Pr.

Jongman, Mariken & Boeke, Wanda. Rits. 2008. (J). (***978-1-59078-545-4(2)*** , Front Street) Boyds Mills Pr.

Jopling, Heather. The Not-So-Only Child. 2006. (J). (978-0-9780739-4-7(0)) Nickname Pr.

Jordan, Annie Laurie. Bogwaddle Pond. La Grange, Myrtle, illus. 2004. 25p. pap. 14.95 (978-1-4137-2013-6(7)) PublishAmerica, Inc.

Joyal, Lisa. Swahili for Beginners: A Young Adult Novel. 2007. (Illus.). 176p. pap. 9.95 (***978-1-894549-69-1(4)***) Sumach Pr. CAN. *Dist:* Univ. of Toronto Pr.

Joyce, William. Rolie Polie Olie Christmas Sticker Book! 2002. (Illus.). 10p. (YA). (ps up). pap. 6.99 (978-0-7868-4532-3(5)) Disney Pr.

Julian, Alison. Brave as a Bunny Can Be. Julian, Alison, illus. 2001. (Illus.). 40p. (J). (gr. 2 up). 15.95 (978-0-931674-46-4(8)) Waldman Hse. Pr., Inc.

Julik, Edie. Sailing Through the Storm: To the Ocean of Peace. Julik, Edie, illus. 1998. (Illus.). 42p. (J). (gr. k-2). 16.95 (978-1-880090-70-1(8)) Galde Pr., Inc.

Kahler, Janet C. 1918 Covered Wagon Adventure. 2006. (Illus.). 94p. (J). per. 10.95 (978-1-57258-444-0(0) , 945-6305) TEACH Services, Inc.

Kalish, Ginny. Rachel Rude Rowdy. 2001. (Illus.). 128p. (J). pap. 15.95 (978-1-56976-127-4(2) , 1148, Zephyr Pr.) Chicago Review Pr., Inc.

Kass, Pnina Moed. Real Time. 2006. 192p. (YA). (gr. 7). reprint ed. pap. 7.99 (978-0-618-69174-6(X)) Houghton Mifflin Co.

Katschke, Judy. If I Were President. 1999. (gr. 3-6). lib. bdg. 11.80 (978-0-613-21748-4(9)) Tandem Library Bks.

Katz, Jennifer A. The Era of Courting. 2006. 119p. pap. 16.95 (978-1-4241-3321-5(1)) PublishAmerica, Inc.

Katz, Karen. Baby's Box of Family Fun. Katz, Karen, illus. 2006. 56p. (J). bds. 19.95 (978-1-4169-2795-2(6) , Little Simon) Simon & Schuster Children's Publishing.

—Grandpa & Me. Katz, Karen, illus. 2004. (Illus.). 14p. (J). 6.99 (978-0-689-86644-9(5) , Little Simon) Simon & Schuster Children's Publishing.

—What Does Baby Say? Katz, Karen, illus. 2004. (Robin Hill School Ser.). (Illus.). 16p. (J). 5.99 (978-0-689-86645-6(3) , Little Simon) Simon & Schuster Children's Publishing.

Katzakian, Norma. Naomi - A First Generation American. Chidester, Ardis & Folchi, Robert A., eds. Heggie, Dolores, illus. l.t. ed. 2000. (J). (gr. 4-7). pap. 12.95 (978-0-9662228-1-4(4)) Dab Publishing Co.

Kay, Alan N. On the Trail of John Brown's Body. 2001. (Young Heroes of History Ser.: Vol. 2). (Illus.). 175p. (J). (gr. 4-7). pap. 5.95 (978-1-57249-239-4(2) , 1572492406, Burd Street Pr.) White Mane Publishing Co., Inc.

Keane, Bil. The Family Circus by Request. Keane, Bil, illus. 2001. (Guideposts Ser.). (Illus.). 120p. 12.95 (978-0-8249-4603-6(0)) Ideals Pubns.

Keats, Ezra Jack. Louie's Search. Keats, Ezra Jack, illus. 2002. (Illus.). (J). 13.19 (978-0-7587-5737-1(9)) Book Wholesalers, Inc.

—Louie's Search. 2001. (978-0-606-20775-1(9)); lib. bdg. 15.30 (978-0-613-31436-7(0)) Tandem Library Bks.

Keenan, Carolyn. Annie Belle. 2005. 94p. pap. 14.95 (978-1-4137-8263-9(9)) PublishAmerica, Inc.

Kehoe, Lindy, illus. Home on a Giggle. 2004. (J). (978-0-9752801-0-2(4)) Beres, Nancy.

Keith, Harold. Chico & Dan. Arbuckle, Scott, illus. 1998. 120p. (gr. 4-7). 16.95 (978-1-57168-216-1(3)) Eakin Pr.

Kelgard, Todd. Outside In. 2001. 173p. (YA). (gr. 7-10). pap. 9.99 (978-0-88092-567-9(1) , 567-1) Royal Fireworks Publishing Co.

Keller, Holly. What a Hat! Keller, Holly, illus. 2003. (Illus.). 24p. (J). 15.99 (978-0-06-051479-2(5)) HarperCollins Pubs.

Kelly, Theresa. Aloha Cove Set, 7 vols. (Aloha Cove Ser.). (YA). 39.99 (978-0-7586-0005-9(4)) Concordia Publishing Hse.

Kendall, Jack. The Magic Apple Tree. Bostrom, Sally, illus. l.t. ed. 2006. (ENG.). 48p. (J). per. 9.95 (978-0-9787740-4-2(3)) Peppertree Pr., The.

Kerr, Judith. Mog Collection, 6 vols. Kerr, Judith, illus. 2007. 1p. (J). (gr. k-2). pap., pap., pap. 35.00 (***978-0-00-725944-1(1)***) HarperCollins Pubs. Ltd. GBR. *Dist:* Independent Pubs. Group.

Kerr, M. E. I Stay near You: One Story in Three. 2006. (Illus.). 216p. (YA). pap. 6.95 (978-0-15-205589-9(4) , Harcourt Paperbacks) Harcourt Children's Bks.

Keyes, Pamela. Legend of Zamiel Zimbalist: Book Two of the Connedim Series. 2005. 280p. (YA). pap. 14.99 (978-1-59092-062-6(7) , Blue Works) Windstorm Creative.

Kimmel, Elizabeth Cody. In the Stone Circle. 1998. 225p. (J). (gr. 5-9). pap. 15.95 (978-0-590-21308-0(3)) Scholastic, Inc.

King, Diane. Sr. Desconocido y el Perrito Perdido. Jones, Jerrold, illus. 2007. Tr. of Mr. Stranger & the Lost Puppy. (ENG & SPA.). 32p. (J). 8.95 (***978-0-9798036-0-4(8)***) DK Novels & Playwrights.

King, Donna. Slam Dunk. 2007. 160p. (J). (gr. 4-7). pap. 5.95 (***978-0-7534-6155-6(2)*** , Kingfisher) Houghton Mifflin Co. Trade & Reference Div.

Kinsey-Warnock, Natalie. As Long As There Are Mountains. 2001. (gr. 5-8). lib. bdg. 13.00 (978-0-613-35902-3(X)) Tandem Library Bks.

Kir-On, Calanitte. The Adventures of the Gimmel Gang II: The Secret in the Basement. 2002. (Illus.). 110p. (J). pap. 8.95 (978-1-931681-36-0(8)) Israel Bk. Shop.

Kirkman, Robert. Eight Is Enough. (Invincible Ser.: Vol. 2). 128p. (YA). pap. 12.95 (978-1-58240-347-2(3)) Image Comics.

Kitze, Carrie A. I Don't Have Your Eyes. 2003. (Illus.). 32p. (J). lib. bdg. 16.95 (978-0-9726244-2-8(2)) EMK Pr.

Kleinberg, Naomi. Baby Says. 2007. (Illus.). 12p. (J). (gr. k-ps). bds. 4.99 (***978-0-375-84201-6(2)*** , Random Hse. Bks. for Young Readers) Random Hse. Children's Bks.

Kleyla, Mary Pat. Identity Unknown. 2003. (gr. 7-12). lib. bdg. 22.20 (978-0-613-83502-2(6)) Tandem Library Bks.

—Identity Unknown. 2003. 154p. (YA). 22.95 (978-0-595-65812-1(1)); pap. 12.95 (978-0-595-28473-3(6)) iUniverse, Inc.

Klingel, Cynthia Fitterer & Noyed, Robert B. Uncle Russ & the Letter U. 2003. (Alphaphonics Ser.). (Illus.). 24p. (J). (ps-2). 21.36 (978-1-59296-111-5(8)) Child's World, Inc.

Kloepfer, Marguerite. Hope's Beat: The Story of a Teenager, Her Stepmother, & a Rock Star. 2003. (YA). 12.95 (978-1-932173-19-2(6)) Stephens Pr. LLC.

Knott, Joan. Merry Christmas, Marushka! Frohliche Weihnachten, Marie! Knott, Marie, ed. 2006. (J). 7.95 (978-0-9779895-1-5(8)) Knott, Joan.

Knudsen, Michelle. Mother's Day Ribbons. Wallace, John, illus. 2005. 12p. (J). bds. 6.99 (978-0-689-86381-3(0) , Little Simon) Simon & Schuster Children's Publishing.

Koertge, Ronald. Margaux with an X. 2004. 176p. (YA). (gr. 9 up). 15.99 (978-0-7636-2401-9(2)) Candlewick Pr.

Kohlhepp, Michael. Within the Hearthstone: Book 1: the Trea. 2006. 127p. pap. 17.95 (978-1-4241-3744-2(6)) PublishAmerica, Inc.

Konigsburg, E. L. The Outcasts of 19 Schuyler Place. 304p. 2004. 16.95 (978-0-689-86636-4(4) , Atheneum); 2005. (J). reprint ed. pap. 5.99 (978-0-689-86637-1(2) , Aladdin) Simon & Schuster Children's Publishing.

—The Outcasts of 19 Schuyler Place. l.t. ed. 2004. (Thorndike Press Large Print the Literary Bridge Ser.). 346p. (J). 22.95 (978-0-7862-6483-4(7)) Thorndike Pr.

Koski, Mary B. Impatient Pamela Wants a Bigger Family. Brown, Dan, illus. 2002. (Impatient Pamela Ser.). 32p. (J). (ps-3). 14.95 (978-1-930650-04-6(3)) Trellis Publishing, Inc.

Kranowitz, Carol Stock. The Goodenoughs Get in Sync: A Story for Kids about the Tough Day When Filibuster Grabbed Darwin's Rabbit's Foot... Wylie, T. J., illus. 2004. 86p. (J). 14.95 (978-1-931615-17-4(9) , 978-1-931615-17-4) Sensory Resources.

Kraus, Robert. Leo the Late Bloomer. Aruego, Jose, illus. 1999. (Share a Story Ser.). (J). (ps up). 9.95 incl. reel tape (978-0-694-70098-1(3) , Harper Festival) HarperCollins Pubs.

Kregel Publications Staff. The Long Ride. 2004. 32p. 13.99 (978-0-8254-3577-5(3)) Kregel Pubns.

Krogh, Kevin. The Willow Switch. 2004. 252p. (YA). per. 22.00 (978-1-58982-210-8(2) , Bedside Bks.) American Bk. Publishing Group.

Krueger, Kathryn L. Road to Grandma's House. 2005. 128p. pap. 13.95 (978-1-59800-366-6(6)) Outskirts Press, Inc.

Krulik, Nancy E. Home Is Where the Heart Is. 2000. (Moffatts on the Road Ser.: No. 1). (Illus.). 112p. (J). (gr. 3-7). pap. 4.99 (978-0-439-13686-0(5)) Scholastic, Inc.

—Home Is Where the Heart Is. 2000. (gr. 3-6). lib. bdg. 13.00 (978-0-613-25542-4(9)) Tandem Library Bks.

—Tommy's Last Stand. 1999. (gr. 3-6). lib. bdg. 11.80 (978-0-613-16014-8(2)) Tandem Library Bks.

Krushner, Tony. Brundibar. 2002. 64p. (J). (978-0-7868-0905-9(1) , Di Capua, Michael) Scholastic, Inc.

Kuehnel, Judy Lyons. The Autumn of Aunt Charlotte. 2006. (ENG.). 132p. per. 9.95 (***978-1-59800-688-9(6)***) Outskirts Press, Inc.

Kurtis-Kleinman, Eileen. When Aunt Lena Did the Rhumba. 1999. (978-0-606-16664-5(5)) Tandem Library Bks.

Kurtz, Jane. River Friendly, River Wild. Brennan, Neil, illus. 2007. 40p. (J). 7.99 (978-1-4169-3487-5(1) , Aladdin) Simon & Schuster Children's Publishing.

Kuskin, Karla. I Am Me. Wolcott, Dyanna, illus. 2000. 32p. (J). (ps-3). 15.99 (978-0-689-81473-0(9)) Simon & Schuster Children's Publishing.

Laguna, Sofie. Surviving Aunt Marsha. 2005. 208p. (J). pap. 15.95 (978-0-439-64485-3(2)) Scholastic, Inc.

Lambert, Janet. A Bright Tomorrow. 2001. (Jordon Ser.: Vol. 9). (YA). pap. 12.95 (978-1-930009-40-0(2)) Image Cascade Publishing.

—Candy Kane. 2001. (Candy Kane Ser.: Vol. 1). (YA). pap. 12.95 (978-1-930009-45-5(3)) Image Cascade Publishing.

—Introducing Parri. 2001. (Parri MacDonald Series by Janet Lambert: Vol. 1). (YA). pap. 12.95 (978-1-930009-41-7(0)) Image Cascade Publishing.

—The Odd Ones: A Campbell Story. 2002. (J). per. 9.95 (978-1-930009-61-5(5)) Image Cascade Publishing.

—The Precious Days: A Campbell Story. 2002. (J). per. 9.95 (978-1-930009-56-1(9) , 800-691-7779) Image Cascade Publishing.

—That's My Girl. 2001. (Parri MacDonald Series by Janet Lambert: Vol. 2). (YA). pap. 12.95 (978-1-930009-42-4(9)) Image Cascade Publishing.

Lamote, Lisa Edman. Booklet Goes to the Doctor. 2006. (J). 15.99 (978-1-933673-02-8(8) , BookMann Pr.) Mann Publishing Group.

—A Day Out for Opus. 2006. (J). 15.99 (978-1-933673-03-5(6) , BookMann Pr.) Mann Publishing Group.

—Don't Judge a Book by Its Cover. 2006. (J). 15.99 (978-1-933673-01-1(X) , BookMann Pr.) Mann Publishing Group.

Lane, Queen, illus. & creator. It's Christmas Time (Babytown Storybook) Lane, Queen, creator. 2005. (BABYTOWN Ser.: Bk. 4). 36p. (J). spiral bd. 15.00 (978-0-9772738-1-2(4)) Quebla.

Langan, Paul. The Bully, No. 5. 2007. (Bluford Ser.: No. 5). 208p. (J). pap. 3.99 (***978-0-439-86546-3(8)*** , Scholastic Paperbacks) Scholastic, Inc.

—The Bully. Langan, Paul, ed. 2002. (Bluford Ser.: 5). 190p. (YA). mass mkt. 4.95 (978-0-944210-00-0(7)) Townsend Pr.

Langrish, Katherine. Troll Fell. (J). 2005. 368p. (gr. 7 up). pap. 6.99 (978-0-06-058306-4(1)); 2004. (Illus.). 272p. (gr. 5 up). 16.99 (978-0-06-058304-0(5)); 2004. (Illus.). 272p. (gr. 5 up). lib. bdg. 16.89 (978-0-06-058305-7(3)) HarperCollins Pubs.

Lankester-Brisley, Joyce. Milly-Molly-Mandy Storybook. 2001. (Milly-Molly-Mandy Ser.). (Illus.). 224p. (J). (gr. k-3). tchr. ed. 13.95 (978-0-7534-5332-2(0) , Kingfisher) Houghton Mifflin Co. Trade & Reference Div.

Laurain, L. G. The Brain Fairy. 2005. (Illus.). 16p. 12.95 (978-1-59453-725-7(9) , Airleaf Publishing) Airleaf Publishing & Bookselling.

Lazewnik, Libby. On the Road & Other Stories. 2000. 248p. (gr. 3-9). 15.95 (978-1-56871-162-1(X)) Targum Pr., Inc.

Lazewnik, Libby, et al. Baker's Dozen: Three-in-One: On Our Own; Ghosthunters; And the Winners. 1999. (Illus.). 139p. (J). (gr. 3-9). 16.99 (978-1-56871-190-4(5)) Targum Pr., Inc.

Le Feuvre, Amy. Harebell's Friend. 2004. (Golden Inheritance Ser.: Vol. 8). (Illus.). 140p. (J). pap. (978-0-921100-84-3(1)) Inheritance Pubns.

Leblanc, Louise. Leo & Julio. Cummins, Sarah, tr. Brochard, Phillippe, illus. 1999. (First Novels Ser.). 64p. (gr. 1-5). 4.95 (978-0-88780-478-6(0)) Formac Publishing Co., Ltd. CAN. *Dist:* Casemate Pubs. & Bk. Distributors, LLC.

Lectura en Familia: Jumbo Pack. (SPA.). (ps-2). 392.63 (978-0-7362-1489-6(5)) Hampton-Brown Bks.

Lee, Marie G. Night of the Chupacabras. 1999. 128p. (gr. 3-7). pap. 3.99 (978-0-380-79773-8(9)) HarperCollins Pubs.

Lehmkuhl, Pat, illus. Starlight, Star Bright: (the Starlight Books, 3), 6 vols. 2003. (Starlight Bks.: Bk. 3). 192p. (J). (gr. 3-7). per. 9.00 (978-0-9714161-2-3(5)) Raven Publishing Inc. of Montana.

L'Engle, Madeleine. The Other Dog. Davenier, Christine, illus. 2003. 37p. (J). (gr. 2-5). reprint ed. 16.00 (978-0-7567-6970-3(1)) DIANE Publishing Co.

Lenhard, Elizabeth. One Agent Too Many. 2nd ed. 2003. (Spy Kids 2 Ser.: Bk. 1). 144p. (J). (gr. 3-7). pap. 4.99 (978-0-7868-1715-3(1) , Volo) Hyperion Bks. for Children.

Leon, Georgina Lazaro. My Dad Is the Best. Alvarez, David, illus. 2004. (Yellow Ser.). (SPA.). 31p. (J). (gr. k-3). pap. 5.95 (978-1-57581-442-1(0)) Santillana USA Publishing Co., Inc.

Leota Crawford, Macy. Just Because Drago. 2006. (ENG.). 36p. per. 16.95 (***978-1-4259-5426-0(X)***) AuthorHouse.

Lethcoe, Jason. Wishful Thinking. 2007. (Benjamin Bartholomew Piff Ser.: No. 2). 224p. (J). (gr. 3-7). 9.99 (978-0-448-44497-0(6) , Grosset & Dunlap) Penguin Group (USA) Inc.

Let's Go Downtown: Individual Title Six-Packs. (ps-2). 27.00 (978-0-7635-9458-9(X)) Rigby Education.

Leung, Helen. Toni. 2006. 251p. pap. 21.95 (978-1-4137-8990-4(0)) PublishAmerica, Inc.

Levine, Gail Carson. Dave at Night. 2001. 304p. (J). (gr. 3-7). reprint ed. pap. 6.99 (978-0-06-440747-2(0) , Harper Trophy) HarperCollins Pubs.

—Dave at Night. unabr. ed. 2004. 278p. (J). (gr. 4-7). pap. 38.00 incl. audio (978-0-8072-8379-0(7) , YA174SP, Listening Library) Random Hse. Audio Publishing Group.

—Dave at Night. 1999. (YA). pap., stu. ed. 69.95 incl. audio (978-0-7887-3794-7(5) , 41038) Recorded Bks., LLC.

Levine, Phyllis. At the Skylight with Matlida. 2007. 156p. pap. 12.95 (***978-1-60047-089-9(0)***) Wasteland Pr.

Levine, Phyllis. Matilda. 2002. 114p. (YA). pap. 10.95 (978-1-891429-31-6(0) , 31-0) Armadillo Publishing Corp.

Levinson, Robin K. Miriam's Journey: Discovering a New World. 2006. (Illus.). 64p. (J). per. 12.00 (978-0-9773673-0-6(4)) Gali Girls, Inc.

Levitin, Sonia. Strange Relations. 2007. 304p. (gr. 7). (J). 15.99 (978-0-375-83751-7(5)); (YA). lib. bdg. 18.99 (978-0-375-93751-4(X)) Random Hse. Children's Bks. (Knopf Bks. for Young Readers).

Lewis, Orane. Miss Henn & Family. Vest, Dianne, illus. l.t. ed. 2006. 25p. (J). per. 10.99 (978-1-59879-141-9(9)) Lifevest Publishing, Inc.

Lightle, Lugenia L. Ruguma: New to America. 2005. 135p. pap. 19.95 (978-1-4137-6723-0(0)) PublishAmerica, Inc.

Linda, Brooks. Meet Toado & Friends. l.t. ed. 2006. (Illus.). 34p. (J). per. 12.99 (***978-1-59879-314-7(4)***) Lifevest Publishing, Inc.

Lindenbaum, Pija. Mini Mia & Her Darling Uncle. Dysseg-aard, Elisabeth Kallick, tr. from SWE. 2007. (Illus.). 40p. (J). (ps-3). 16.00 (***978-91-29-66734-9(8)***) R & S Bks. SWE. *Dist:* Macmillan.

Lindgren, Astrid. Happy Times in Noisy Village. Wikland, Ilon, illus. 2003. Orig. Title: Bullerby Boken. 128p. (J). pap. 10.95 (978-1-883937-66-9(3)) Bethlehem Bks.

Lindsay, Jeanne Warren. Do I Have a Daddy? A Story about a Single-Parent Child. rev. ed. 2003. (Illus.). 48p. (J). (ps). 14.95 (978-1-885356-62-8(5)) Morning Glory Pr., Inc.

—Yo Tengo Papa? Un Cuento Sobre Un Nino de Madre Soltera. Palacios, Argentina, tr. from SPA. Boeller, Cheryl, illus. 1999. Tr. of Do I Have a Daddy?: A Story about a Single-Parent Child. 48p. (J). (ps-3). 12.95 (978-0-930934-83-5(0)) Morning Glory Pr., Inc.

Linn, Margot. The Big Red Blanket. Jacobson, David, illus. 2005. (I'm Going to Read Ser.). 28p. (J). 11.95 (978-1-4027-2069-7(6)) Sterling Publishing Co., Inc.

Lipscomb, Wilma. The Growing Cane's. 2003. (J). per. 9.95 (978-1-932301-27-4(5) , 1135) Airleaf Publishing & Bookselling.

Lisle, Janet Taylor. The Art of Keeping Cool. 2002. 256p. (J). (gr. 5-9). pap. 5.99 (978-0-689-83788-3(7) , Aladdin) Simon & Schuster Children's Publishing.

—The Art of Keeping Cool. Goldstrom, Robert, illus. 2000. 216p. (J). (gr. 5-7). 17.00 (978-0-689-83787-6(9) , Atheneum/Richard Jackson Bks.) Simon & Schuster Children's Publishing.

Literature Connections English: Go Tell It on the Mountain. 2004. (gr. 6-12). (978-0-395-86994-9(3) , 2-70830) McDougal Littell Inc.

Literature Connections English: Trouble River. 2004. (gr. 6-12). (978-0-395-77526-4(4) , 2-80095) McDougal Littell Inc.

The Littles to the Rescue. 2002. (Littles Ser.). (J). 12.17 (978-0-7587-8429-2(5)) Book Wholesalers, Inc.

Lobel, Anita. Potatoes, Potatoes. 2004. 40p. (J). 15.99 (978-0-06-023927-5(1)); lib. bdg. 16.89 (978-0-06-023928-2(X)) HarperCollins Pubs.

—Potatoes, Potatoes. Lobel, Anita, illus. 2004. (Illus.). 40p. (J). reprint ed. 15.99 (978-0-06-051817-2(0)) HarperCollins Pubs.

Look, Lenore. Uncle Peter's Amazing Chinese Wedding. Heo, Yumi, illus. 2006. 40p. (J). (ps-3). 16.95 (978-0-689-84458-4(1) , Atheneum/Anne Schwartz Bks.) Simon & Schuster Children's Publishing.

Looper, Grace W. Molasses Making Time. l.t. ed. 2004. 152p. (YA). pap. 8.95 (978-0-9747685-5-7(3)) Bella Rosa Bks.

Lopez, Lorraine. Call Me Henri. 2006. 242p. 17.95 (978-1-931896-27-6(5)) Curbstone Pr.

Lorimer, Janet. The Mystery Quilt: Set 1. 2002. 32p. (YA). 2.95 (978-1-56254-410-2(1) , SP 4101) Saddleback Educational Publishing.

—Tug-of-War: Set 2. 2002. 32p. (YA). 2.95 (978-1-56254-423-2(3) , SP 4233) Saddleback Educational Publishing.

Lottridge, Celia B. Wings to Fly. 2007. 144p. (J). pap. 8.95 (***978-0-88899-844-6(9)***) Groundwood Bks. CAN. *Dist:* Perseus Distribution.

Lottridge, Celia Barker. Ticket to Curlew. 2007. 144p. (J). pap. 7.95 (***978-0-88899-843-9(0)***) Groundwood Bks. CAN. *Dist:* Perseus Distribution.

Love, D. Anne. Picture Perfect. 2007. 291p. (YA). (***978-1-4287-3275-9(6)*** , McElderry, Margaret K.) Simon & Schuster Children's Publishing.

Lowrey, Becky. Chirps. 2004. 45p. pap. 19.95 (978-1-4137-2984-9(3)) PublishAmerica, Inc.

Lutz, Norma Jean. Grace & the Bully: Drought on the Frontier. 2006. 144p. (J). pap. 4.97 (978-1-59789-102-8(9)) Barbour Publishing, Inc.

Lynch, Marcia. United in Freedom. Cornelison, Sue F., illus. 2000. (Cover-to-Cover Bks.). 92p. (J). pap. (978-0-7891-5102-5(2)); (gr. 2-5). lib. bdg. 13.95 (978-0-7807-9068-1(5)) Perfection Learning Corp.

MacBride, Roger Lea. Missouri Bound. 1999. (Little House Chapter Bks.: No. 1). (J). (gr. 3-6). (978-0-606-18717-6(0)) Tandem Library Bks.

MacCracken, Joan. Trisba & Sula: A Miskitu Folktale from Nicaragua (Una Leyenda de los Miskitos de Nicaragua) Macdonald, Isabel et al, trs. Silva, Augusto Alves da, illus. 2005. (ENG & SPA.). 16.95 (978-0-9646018-2-6(6)) Tiffin Pr. of Maine.

MacCullough, Carolyn. Drawing the Ocean. 2006. 176p. (YA). (gr. 7 up). 16.95 (978-1-59643-092-1(3)) Roaring Brook Pr.

MacDonald, Amy. No More Nice. 1998. (Illus.). 144p. (J). (gr. 3-7). pap. 4.95 (978-0-380-73055-1(3) , Harper Trophy) HarperCollins Pubs.

The MacGregors & MacDougalls: Individual Title Six-Packs. (Bookweb Ser.). 32p. (gr. 5 up). 34.00 (978-0-7635-3783-8(7)) Rigby Education.

MacHado, Ana Maria. Todo al Mismo Tiempo Ahora. 2003. (SPA.). (YA). 8.95 (978-958-04-6030-5(2) , NR30567) Norma S.A. COL. *Dist:* Distribuidora Norma, Inc., Lectorum Pubns., Inc.

MacIntyre, R. P. & MacIntyre, Wendy. Apart. 2007. 192p. (J). (gr. 8 up). 16.95 (***978-0-88899-750-0(7)***) Groundwood Bks. CAN. *Dist:* Perseus Distribution.

Mackler, Carolyn. Love & Other Four-Letter Words. 2002. (gr. 7-12). lib. bdg. 13.55 (978-0-613-72272-8(8)) Tandem Library Bks.

MacLean, Christine. Even Firefighters Hug Their Moms. Reed, Mike, illus. 2004. 32p. (J). (gr. k-3). pap. 5.99 (978-0-14-240191-0(9) , Puffin) Penguin Group (USA) Inc.

Madrzak, Carole. In the Shadows of Bington Manor. 2006. (ENG.). 132p. per. 19.95 (***978-1-4241-5168-4(6)***) PublishAmerica, Inc.

Madrzak, Carole. Secrets Inside Bington Manor. 2005. 108p. pap. 16.95 (978-1-4241-0720-9(2)) PublishAmerica, Inc.

Man-Kong, Mary. Fairytopia: A Storybook. 2005. (Illus.). 16p. (J). (ps-2). pap. 3.99 (978-0-375-83318-2(8) , Golden Bks.) Random Hse. Children's Bks.

Mandeville, Terry M. Just Waiting for My Family. l.t. ed. 2005. (Illus.). 52p. (J). 14.95 (978-0-9762475-0-0(X)) Mandeville, Terry M.

Manning, Maurie J. The Aunts Go Marching. Manning, Maurie J., illus. 2003. (Illus.). 32p. (J). (ps up). 15.95 (978-1-59078-026-8(4)) Boyds Mills Pr.

Mansur, Motesem. The Terry Tornado Story: The Wake-up Call. 2004. 25p. pap. 14.95 (978-1-4137-2133-1(8)) PublishAmerica, Inc.

Manzur, Vivian Mansour. Familias Familiares. Gedovius, Juan, illus. 2000. (SPA.). 40p. (J). (gr. k-17). pap. 7.50 (978-968-16-6005-5(6) , FC2875) Fondo de Cultura Economica MEX. *Dist:* Lectorum Pubns., Inc.

Marchetta, Melina. Looking for Alibrandi. 1999. 256p. (YA). (gr. 7-12). pap. 16.95 (978-0-531-30142-5(7)); lib. bdg. 17.99 (978-0-531-33142-2(3)) Scholastic, Inc. (Orchard Bks.).

Margaret, Linda. Footprints in the Pies: (and Other Excit. 2005. 64p. pap. 12.95 (978-1-4137-7151-0(3)) PublishAmerica, Inc.

Margolis, Leslie. Price of Admission. 2007. 224p. (YA). pap. 8.99 (978-1-4169-2455-5(8) , Simon Pulse) Simon & Schuster Children's Publishing.

Martin, Ann M. Belle Teal. 2005. 240p. (J). (ps-7). pap. 2.99 (978-0-439-77126-9(9)) Scholastic, Inc.

Martin, Nora. A Perfect Snow. 2004. 144p. (J). pap. 6.95 (978-1-58234-925-1(8) , Bloomsbury Children) Bloomsbury Publishing.

Martinez, Migdalia Fonseca & Martinez-Radio, Jorge Baez. Maina. 2004. (Yellow Ser.). (SPA., Illus.). 32p. (J). (gr. k-3). pap. 5.95 (978-1-57581-441-4(2)) Santillana USA Publishing Co., Inc.

Martino, Alfred C. Pinned. 2005. 320p. (YA). 17.00 (978-0-15-205355-0(7)) Harcourt Children's Bks.

Maslen, John R. & Maslen, Bobby Lynn. Word Families. 2006. (Bob Books Set 3 Ser.). (Illus.). 16p. (J). pap. 16.99 (978-0-439-84509-0(2) , Scholastic Paperbacks) Scholastic, Inc.

Mason, Jane B. & Stephens, Sarah Hines. Bella Baxter Inn Trouble. Shelley, John, illus. 2005. (Bella Baxter Ser.). 80p. (J). pap. 3.99 (978-0-689-86280-9(6) , Aladdin) Simon & Schuster Children's Publishing.

Mason, Simon. Quigleys: Not for Sale. Stephens, Helen, illus. 2004. 176p. (J). (gr. k-7). 14.95 (978-0-385-75043-1(9)); lib. bdg. 16.99 (978-0-385-75047-9(1)) Random Hse. Children's Bks. (Fickling, David Bks.).

Mass, Wendy. Rapunzel: The One with All the Hair. 2006. (Twice upon a Time Ser.: No. 1). 208p. (J). pap. 5.99 (978-0-439-79656-9(3) , Scholastic Paperbacks) Scholastic, Inc.

Massi, Jeri. Some Through the Fire, 2 vols. 2003. (Great Stories That Teach Eternal Truths Ser.). 496p. pap. 12.99 (978-0-8024-1513-4(X)) Moody Pubs.

Masurel, Claire. Emily & Her Daddy. Calitri, Susan, illus. 2003. (Lift-the-Flap Ser.). 16p. (J). (gr. k-1). pap. 6.99 (978-0-14-250080-4(1) , Puffin) Penguin Group (USA) Inc.

Mathews, Eleanor. The Linden Tree. 2007. 224p. (J). pap. 6.95 (***978-1-57131-674-5(4)**); (gr. 3-6). 16.95 (***978-1-57131-673-8(6)***) Milkweed Editions.

Maxwell, Marc C. B. The Wallace Dream: The Adventures of the Baby Seekers. 2006. 148p. pap. 12.95 (978-1-59113-933-1(3)) Booklocker.com, Inc.

Mayer, Mercer. Little Critter's the Picnic. l.t. ed. 1999. (Early Childhood First Bks.: No. 1). (Illus.). 20p. (J). (gr. k-1). lib. bdg. 13.95 (978-1-56674-219-1(6)) Forest Hse. Publishing Co., Inc.

—Little Critter's the Trip. 1999. (Early Childhood First Bks.: No. 2). (Illus.). 20p. (J). (gr. k-1). lib. bdg. 13.95 (978-1-56674-254-2(4)) Forest Hse. Publishing Co., Inc.

Mayhew, James. Boy. 2004. (Illus.). 32p. (J). (gr. k). pap. 15.95 (978-0-439-65106-6(9) , Chicken Hse., The) Scholastic, Inc.

Maynard, Joyce. The Cloud Chamber. 2005. 288p. (YA). (gr. 6-9). 16.95 (978-0-689-87152-8(X) , Atheneum) Simon & Schuster Children's Publishing.

Mayoral, Juana Aurora. Cuerpos de Cobre, Corazones de Jade. (SPA.). 176p. (YA). (gr. 5-8). (978-84-321-2688-8(8) , RP6168) Rialp, Ediciones, S.A. ESP. *Dist:* Lectorum Pubns., Inc.

Mazer, Anne. Have Wheels, Will Travel. 2001. (Amazing Days of Abby Hayes Ser.: No. 4). 144p. (gr. 4-7). mass mkt. 4.99 (978-0-439-17878-5(9)) Scholastic, Inc.

Mazer, Norma Fox. What I Believe. 2005. 176p. (YA). (gr. 5-9). 16.00 (978-0-15-201462-9(4) , Harcourt Children's Bks) Harcourt Children's Bks.

—When She Was Good. 2000. 240p. (J). (gr. 7-12). pap. 16.95 (978-0-590-13506-1(6)); (Illus.). pap. 5.99 (978-0-590-31990-4(6) , Scholastic Paperbacks) Scholastic, Inc.

—When She Was Good. 2000. (978-0-606-18615-5(8)) Tandem Library Bks.

McBratney, Sam. Guess How Much I Love. Jeram, Anita & McBratney, Sam, illus. 10th anniv. ltd. ed. 2004. 32p. (J). 35.00 (978-0-7636-2729-4(1)) Candlewick Pr.

Mccabe, Jr. Planting the Wilderness or, the Pioneer Boys: a Story of Frontier Life. 2007. pap. 27.95 (***978-1-4304-8187-4(0)***) Kessinger Publishing, LLC.

McCann, Jesse Leon, adapted by. Shrek 2: The Movie Novel. 2004. (Illus.). 110p. (J). (978-0-439-74048-7(7)) Scholastic, Inc.

McCann, Thomas P. "Tom". The Tree Nobody Wanted: A Christmas Story. 2007. 14.95 (***978-0-9797407-0-1(3)***) Exeter Pr.

McCaughrean, Geraldine. The Kite Rider. 2003. (Illus.). 320p. (J). (gr. 7 up). pap. 6.99 (978-0-06-441091-5(9)) HarperCollins Pubs.

—The Kite Rider. 2002. (gr. 7-12). lib. bdg. 15.30 (978-0-613-68440-8(0)) Tandem Library Bks.

—My Grandmother's Clock. Lambert, Stephen, illus. 2002. 32p. (J). (gr. k-3). 15.00 (978-0-618-21695-6(2) , Clarion Bks.) Houghton Mifflin Co. Trade & Reference Div.

McClain, Lee. My Loco Life. 2006. (YA). mass mkt. 5.99 (978-0-8439-5661-0(5) , SMOOCH) Dorchester Publishing Co., Inc.

McClintock, Barbara. Adèle & Simon in America. 2008. (J). (***978-0-374-39924-5(7)***) Farrar, Straus & Giroux.

McClintock, Norah. Snitch. 2005. (Orca Soundings Ser.). 112p. (J). (gr. 7-12). pap. 7.95 (978-1-55143-484-1(9)) Orca Bk. Pubs. USA.

Mcclung, L. Nellie. Sowing Seeds in Danny. 2006. 52.99 (***978-1-4219-8132-1(7)***); pap. 45.99 (***978-1-4219-8124-6(6)***) IndyPublish.com.

McCourt, Lisa. The Most Thankful Thing. Moore, Cyd, illus. 2004. 32p. (J). (gr. k). pap. 15.95 (978-0-439-65083-0(6) , Cartwheel Bks.) Scholastic, Inc.

McElligott, Walter Lee. A Blessed Bethlehem Birth: As told by Abraham & Anna Mousenstern. Collier, Kevin Scott, illus. 2006. 28p. (J). E-Book 5.00 incl. cd-rom (***978-1-933090-21-4(9)***) Guardian Angel Publishing, Inc.

McEwan, Ian. The Daydreamer. 2003. (gr. 3-6). lib. bdg. 14.15 (978-0-613-58678-8(6)) Tandem Library Bks.

McGrath, Liz & Quick, Barbara. Even More/Todavía Mas. de la Vega, Eida, tr. McGrath, Liz, illus. 2004. Tr. of Todavía Mas. (SPA & ENG., Illus.). 34p. (J). (gr. k-3). 16.95 (978-0-9720192-8-6(6) , 626999) Raven Tree Pr.

McKee, David. The Hill & the Rock. 1999. (Illus.). 32p. (J). pap. 9.99 (978-0-86264-784-1(3)) Andersen GBR. *Dist:* Trafalgar Square Publishing.

McKissack, Patricia C. Loved Best. Marshall, Felicia, illus. 2005. (Ready-for-Chapters Ser.). 64p. (J). pap. 3.99 (978-0-689-86151-2(6) , Aladdin) Simon & Schuster Children's Publishing.

—Messy Bessey's Family Reunion. 2000. (gr. k-3). lib. bdg. 12.95 (978-0-613-54613-3(X)) Tandem Library Bks.

McMenemy, Sarah. Jack's New Boat. McMenemy, Sarah, illus. 2005. (Illus.). 32p. (J). (ps-k). 15.99 (978-0-7636-2477-4(2)) Candlewick Pr.

McMillan, Ernest. Psalms of Passion. 2006. 48p. pap. 8.95 (978-1-59800-224-9(4)) Outskirts Press, Inc.

McMurchy-Barber, Gina. Reading the Bones. 2008. 152p. (YA). pap. 9.99 (***978-1-55002-732-7(8)*** , Sandcastle Bks.) Dundurn Group, The CAN. *Dist:* Univ. of Toronto Pr.

McMurtrey, Martin. Loose to the Wilds. 2nd ed. 162p. (YA). reprint ed. pap. 6.00 (978-0-9623961-0-6(9)) McMurtrey, Martin A.

McNatt, Martha. Grandmother's Face in the Mirror. 2003. (YA). per. 14.00 (978-0-9741294-0-2(2)) Main St Publishing, Inc.

Mead. Junebug in Trouble. 2003. (gr. 3-6). lib. bdg. 13.00 (978-0-613-89785-3(4)) Tandem Library Bks.

Mead, Alice. Dawn & Dusk. 2007. (Illus.). 151p. (J). (***978-1-4287-3319-0(1)***) Farrar, Straus & Giroux.

Meade, T. L. Polly (a New-Fashioned Girl) 2006. 43.99 (***978-1-4280-4099-1(4)***); pap. 37.99 (***978-1-4280-4078-6(1)***) IndyPublish.com.

Mechelke, Violet. The Woodshed. Miller, Arlene, illus. 2002. 165p. (YA). (gr. 4-9). pap. 12.00 (978-0-9719623-0-9(8)) Whispering Hope Publishing.

Meddaugh, Susan. Martha Habla. 1999. (SPA., Illus.). (J). (gr. k-2). pap. 6.95 (978-1-880507-55-1(2) , LC2799) Lectorum Pubns., Inc.

Meehl, Brian. Out of Patience. 2008. 304p. 6.50 (***978-0-440-42090-3(3)*** , Yearling) Dell Bks. for Young Readers CAN. *Dist:* Random Hse., Inc.

—Out of Patience. 2006. 304p. (gr. 4-7). (J). 15.95 (978-0-385-73299-4(6)); lib. bdg. 17.99 (978-0-385-90320-2(0)) Random Hse. Children's Bks. (Delacorte Bks. for Young Readers).

—Out of Patience. l.t. ed. 2006. (J). 22.95 (978-0-7862-8968-4(6)) Thorndike Pr.

Mendes, Valerie. Look at Me, Grandma! Fletcher, Claire, illus. 2001. 32p. (J). (ps-1). pap. 15.95 (978-0-439-29654-0(4) , Chicken Hse., The) Scholastic, Inc.

Menning, Lori. One Was Not Enough. Christy, Jana, illus. 2000. 16p. (J). pap. 5.95 (978-1-891846-18-2(3)) Business Word, The.

Merwin, Decie, illus. Happy Little Family. 2004. 107p. (J). pap. 10.95 (978-1-883937-72-0(8)) Bethlehem Bks.

Messinger, Robert M. & Messinger, Laura M. Why Me? Why Did I Have to Get Diabetes? l.t. ed. 2004. (Illus.). 64p. 12.95 (978-1-893237-02-5(8)) Little Mai Pr.

Meyers, Susan. Everywhere Babies. Frazee, Marla, illus. 2004. 30p. (J). bds. 6.95 (978-0-15-205315-4(8) , Red Wagon Bks.) Harcourt Children's Bks.

Milgrim, David. Thank You, Thanksgiving. 2006. (Illus.). 32p. (J). (ps-k). 5.95 (978-0-618-75243-0(9) , Clarion Bks.) Houghton Mifflin Co. Trade & Reference Div.

Miller-Burke, Jude. Snowball, Come Home! 2005. (Illus.). 32p. (J). bds. 16.95 (978-1-59298-093-2(7)) Beaver's Pond Pr., Inc.

Millman, M. C. Always Something Else: The whimsical adventures of Elisheva Raskin. 2005. (Illus.). 160p. (J). 14.95 (978-1-932443-23-3(1) , ASEH) Judaica Pr., Inc., The.

—Always Something Else 2. 2006. (Illus.). 160p. (J). 14.95 (978-1-932443-43-1(6) , ASE2H) Judaica Pr., Inc., The.

Millman, Selena. Anyone Can Make A Difference. 2006. 109p. (YA). per. (***978-0-9793058-6-3(1)***) Millman, Selena.

Mills, Claudia. Gus & Grandpa & Show-and-Tell. 2002. (gr. k-3). lib. bdg. 12.95 (978-0-613-71863-9(1)) Tandem Library Bks.

Mills, David. Lima's Red Hot Chilli. Brazell, Derek, illus. 2004. (ENG & SPA.). 24p. (J). (978-1-85269-942-0(6)) Mantra Publishing, Ltd.

Mills, Linda Sue. Meet Toado & Friends. Mills, Lori, illus. l.t. ed. 2006. 34p. (J). 23.99 (***978-1-59879-246-1(6)***) Lifevest Publishing, Inc.

Milner, Claudette. Children of Plaines Estates. 2003. 165p. pap. 16.95 (978-1-4137-0424-2(7)) PublishAmerica, Inc.

Minne. I Love... Fortier, Nathalie, illus. 2005. 128p. (J). pap. 11.95 (978-1-929132-75-1(1)) Kane/Miller Bk. Pubs., Inc.

Minshull, Evelyn. Eaglet's World. Gabriel, Andrea, illus. 2002. 32p. (J). (ps-3). pap. 6.95 (978-0-8075-1760-4(7)) Whitman, Albert & Co.

Minter, J. The Insiders. 2004. 200p. (gr. 9 up). pap. 8.95 (978-1-58234-895-7(2) , Bloomsbury Children) Bloomsbury Publishing.

Miranda, Hialeah. One Fun Summer's Day. 2004. 48p. pap. 12.95 (978-1-4137-1858-4(2)) PublishAmerica, Inc.

Mitchel, Pratima. Petar's Song. Binch, Caroline, illus. 2004. 32p. (J). 15.95 (978-1-84507-266-7(9)) Lincoln, Frances Ltd. GBR. *Dist:* Perseus Distribution.

Mitchell, Chris. The Realm Legends. 2006. pap. 40.99 (***978-1-4208-9129-4(4)***) AuthorHouse.

Mitchell, Pratima. Petar's Song. Binch, Caroline, illus. 2004. 32p. (J). pap. 7.95 (978-1-84507-352-7(5)) Lincoln, Frances Ltd. GBR. *Dist:* Perseus Distribution.

Mitzo Thompson, Kim. My Family. 2006. (Dual Language Readers Ser.). 32p. (J). pap., pap. 4.99 incl. audio compact disk (978-0-7696-4613-8(1)) School Specialty Publishing.

—My Grandma Likes to Cook / A mi abuela le gusta Cocinar. 2006. (Dual Language Readers Ser.). 32p. (J). pap. 4.99 (978-0-7696-4624-4(7)) School Specialty Publishing.

Molinet, Michael & Molinet, Kelly. Before You Were Born. Molinet, Michael, illus. 2003. (Illus.). 22p. (J). 12.99 (978-0-9705996-7-4(6)) Green Key Bks.

Monk, Isabell. Family. Porter, Janice Lee, illus. 32p. (J). (ps-ps). 2005. pap. 6.95 (978-1-57505-917-4(7)); 2003. 15.95 (978-1-57505-485-8(X) , Carolrhoda Bks.) Lerner Publishing Group.

—Hope. Porter, Janice Lee, illus. 1998. (Picture Bks.). 32p. (J). (ps-3). 15.95 (978-1-57505-230-4(X)) Lerner Publishing Group.

Montgomery Buvens, Norma O'Rene. A Salute for Trixey. Smith, Normareen Buvens, illus. 2001. 40p. 16.95 (978-1-57168-943-6(5)) Eakin Pr.

Montgomery Gibson, Jane. Daddy's Valentine. Montgomery Gibson, Jane, illus. 2005. (J). bds. 8.99 (978-1-4183-0046-3(2)) Christ Inspired, Inc.

Montgomery, L. M. Dreams, Schemes & Mysteries, Bk. 4. 2004. (Story Girl#8482; Ser.). (Illus.). 112p. (J). pap. 4.99 (978-0-310-70601-4(7)) Zonderkidz.

—The King Cousins. 2004. (Story Girl Ser.). (Illus.). 112p. (J). pap. 4.99 (978-0-310-70598-7(3)) Zonderkidz.

Moodie, Craig. The Sea Singer. 2005. (Illus.). 176p. (J). (gr. 6-9). 16.95 (978-1-59643-050-1(8)) Roaring Brook Pr.

Moonshower, Candie. The Legend of Zoey. 2006. 224p. (J). (gr. 4-7). 15.95 (978-0-385-73280-2(5)); lib. bdg. 17.99 (978-0-385-90298-4(0)) Random Hse. Children's Bks. (Delacorte Bks. for Young Readers).

Moore, Ishbel L. Daughter. 216p. (YA). (gr. 13 up). 1999. (978-1-55074-535-1(2)); 2002. (Illus.). (978-1-55074-537-5(9)) Kids Can Pr., Ltd.

Moore, Karen. Daddy Loves Me. Stanley, Mandy, illus. gif. ed. 2005. 20p. (J). (ps-ps). per. 6.99 (978-1-57791-183-8(0)) Brighter Minds Children's Publishing.

Moore, Martha A. Matchit. 2003. lib. bdg. 11.85 (978-0-613-63216-4(8)) Tandem Library Bks.

Moore, Peter G. Caught in the Act. 2005. 274p. (J). (gr. 7). 16.99 (978-0-670-05990-4(0) , Viking Juvenile) Penguin Group (USA) Inc.

Moore, Shahari. It's Good Sunday. Waddington, Nicole, illus. 2003. (J). (978-0-9743394-0-5(7)) More Pr.

Mora, Eddy G. Toby & Dad at Work. Martin, April, illus. deluxe ed. 2000. (Toby & Tig Ser.). (J). (gr. 3-8). 13.99 (978-0-9671753-1-7(3)) Mora Art Studio.

Morgan, Allen, et al. Cours Vite, Mathieu! 2000. (Drtles d'Histoires Ser.). (FRE., Illus.). 24p. (YA). (ps up). pap. (978-2-89021-417-0(6)) Diffusion du livre Mirabel.

Morpurgo, Michael. Snakes & Ladders. Wilson, Anne, illus. 2006. 48p. (J). pap. (978-0-7787-0998-5(1)) Crabtree Publishing Co.

Morris, Ann. Grandma Lai Goon Remembers: A Chinese-American Family Story. 2002. (Illus.). 32p. (J). (gr. 5 up). pap. 7.95 (978-0-7613-1730-2(9) , Millbrook Pr.) Lerner Publishing Group.

—Grandma Lois Remembers: An African-American Family Story. 2002. (Illus.). 32p. (J). (gr. 5 up). pap. 7.95 (978-0-7613-1729-6(5) , Millbrook Pr.) Lerner Publishing Group.

—Grandma Maxine Remembers: A Native American Family Story. 2002. (Illus.). 32p. (J). (gr. 5 up). pap. 7.95 (978-0-7613-1728-9(7) , Millbrook Pr.) Lerner Publishing Group.

—Grandma Susan Remembers: A British-American Family Story. 2002. (Illus.). 32p. (J). (gr. 5 up). pap. 7.95 (978-0-7613-1732-6(5) , Millbrook Pr.) Lerner Publishing Group.

Morris, Gilbert. Dixie & Sandy. 1998. (Dixie Morris Animal Adventure Ser.: No. 4). 128p. (Orig.). (J). (gr. 4-7). pap. 5.99 (978-0-8024-3366-4(9)) Moody Pubs.

Morrison, P. R. Wind Tamer. 2007. 336p. (YA). pap. 7.95 (***978-1-59990-147-3(1)*** , Bloomsbury Children) Bloomsbury Publishing.

Moses, Shelia P. The Return of Buddy Bush. 2008. 176p. (YA). pap. 5.99 (***978-1-4169-3925-2(3)*** , Simon Pulse); 2005. (Illus.). 160p. (J). 15.95 (978-0-689-87431-4(6) , McElderry, Margaret K.) Simon & Schuster Children's Publishing.

Moss, Marissa. Amelia's Longest, Biggest, Most-Fights-Ever Family Reunion. Moss, Marissa, illus. 2006. (Amelia's Notebooks). (Illus.). 80p. (J). 9.95 (978-0-689-87447-5(2) , Simon & Schuster Children's Publishing) Simon & Schuster Children's Publishing.

Moss, Miriam. One Day It Was Wet: American English Edition. 2000. (Cambridge Reading Ser.). (Illus.). 12p. pap. 5.00 (978-0-521-79529-6(X)) Cambridge Univ. Pr.

Mostacchi, Massimo. El Rey Perezoso. Brignole, Giancarla, tr. Miceli, Monica, illus. rev. ed. 2006. (Fabulas De Familia Ser.). (SPA.). 32p. (J). pap. 6.95 (978-970-20-0274-1(5)) Castillo, Ediciones, S. A. de C. V. MEX. *Dist:* Macmillan.

Moulton, Mark Kimball. The Night at Humpback Bridge. Winget, Susan, illus. 2001. 48p. (J). (gr. k-3). 22.00 (978-0-7412-0823-1(7)) Lang Graphics, Ltd.

Mubiru, Bertha, ed. Kabaka,Kulabako & Kakookolo. 2004. (Illus.). 30p. pap. 9.95 (978-9970-02-437-7(X)) Fountain Pubs. Ltd. UGA. *Dist:* Michigan State Univ. Pr.

Mubiru, Betha. Muzinge the Bird. 2004. (Illus.). 16p. pap. 9.95 (978-9970-02-447-6(7)) Fountain Pubs. Ltd. UGA. *Dist:* Michigan State Univ. Pr.

Muhammad, King Nazir. Black 8. 28. 2004. 68p. pap. 14.95 (978-1-4137-3348-8(4)) PublishAmerica, Inc.

Muldrow, Diane. On the Back Burner with Other. 2003. (gr. 3-6). lib. bdg. 13.00 (978-0-613-72488-3(7)) Tandem Library Bks.

Muluka, B. Kandu & the Lake. 2004. (Illus.). 40p. 13.95 (978-9966-25-165-7(0)) Heinemann Kenya, Limited (East African Educational Publishers Ltd E.A.E.P.) KEN. *Dist:* Michigan State Univ. Pr.

Mundy, Dawn. The Gift: A Woodsong Story. Tigue, Terry & Turner, Diane, illus. 2003. (J). lib. bdg. (978-1-932139-16-7(8)) DEMDACO.

Munsch, Robert. Alligator Baby. 2002. (gr. k-3). lib. bdg. 11.80 (978-0-613-58282-7(9)) Tandem Library Bks.

Murail, Marie-Aude. Un Domingo Con Los Dinosaurios. (la Orilla Del Viento Ser.). (SPA., Illus.). 48p. (J). reprint ed. 6.99 (978-968-16-5798-7(5) , 108) Fondo de Cultura Economica USA.

Murciano, Carlos. El Mar Sigue Esperando. 2003. (SPA.). 112p. (978-84-279-3139-8(5) , NG3602) Noguer y Caralt Editores, S. A. ESP. *Dist:* Lectorum Pubns., Inc.

—El Mar Sigue Esperando. 2001. (SPA.). (gr. 7-12). lib. bdg. 17.05 (978-0-613-80646-6(8)) Tandem Library Bks.

Murphy, Barbara Beasley. Ace Flies Like an Eagle. 2003. (Can't Stop Ace Ser.: No. 3). 180p. (J). pap. 16.95 (978-0-86534-409-9(4)) Sunstone Pr.

Murphy, Elspeth Campbell. The Mystery of the Golden Reindeer. 2000. (Three Cousins Detective Club Ser.: No. 30). (Illus.). 64p. (J). (gr. 2-5). pap. 3.99 (978-0-7642-2138-5(8)) Bethany Hse. Pubs.

Murphy, Rita. Looking for Lucy Buick. 176p. (YA). (gr. 7). 2007. mass mkt. 6.50 (***978-0-440-22924-7(3)*** , Laurel Leaf); 2005. 15.95 (978-0-385-72939-0(1) , Delacorte Bks. for Young Readers); 2005. lib. bdg. 17.99 (978-0-385-90176-5(3) , Delacorte Bks. for Young Readers) Random Hse. Children's Bks.

Murray, Martine. The Slightly True Story of Cedar B. Hartley: (Who Planned to Live an Unusual Life) 2002. (Illus.). 204p. (J). (978-1-86508-623-1(1)) Allen & Unwin.

—Slightly True Story of Cedar B. Hartley: (Who Planned to Live an Unusual Life) 2004. (Illus.). 240p. (J). reprint ed. pap. 4.99 (978-0-439-48623-1(8) , Levine, Arthur A. Bks.) Scholastic, Inc.

My Time on Nantucket Coloring Book. 2005. (J). 3.95 (978-0-9755078-1-0(8)) Sweet Punkin Pr.

Myers, Walter Dean. The Glory Field. 1999. 420p. (J). 15.60 (978-0-03-054616-7(8)) Holt, Rinehart & Winston.

—Shooter. (J). 2004. (Illus.). 240p. lib. bdg. 16.89 (978-0-06-029520-2(1) , HarperTeen); 2005. 256p. reprint ed. pap. 7.99 (978-0-06-447290-6(6) , Amistad) HarperCollins Pubs.

Na, An. Wait for Me. 2006. 240p. (YA). (gr. 4). 15.99 (978-0-399-24275-5(9) , Putnam Juvenile) Penguin Group (USA) Inc.

Natti, Susanna, illus. Lionel in the Summer. 2002. (Lionel Ser.). (J). 11.49 (978-0-7587-4120-2(0)) Book Wholesalers, Inc.

—Lionel in the Winter. 2002. (Lionel Ser.). (J). 11.49 (978-0-7587-1393-3(2)) Book Wholesalers, Inc.

Naylor, Phyllis Reynolds. I Can't Take You Anywhere! Kaminsky, Jef, illus. 2001. 32p. (J). (ps-3). 6.99 (978-0-689-84116-3(7) , Aladdin) Simon & Schuster Children's Publishing.

—Lovingly Alice. 2006. 166p. (J). (***978-1-4156-5199-5(X)*** , Aladdin) Simon & Schuster Children's Publishing.

Naylor, Phyllis Reynolds. The World of Alice Set: The Agony of Alice; Alice in Rapture, Sort of; Reluctantly Alice; All but Alice, 4 vols. 2003. (Alice Ser.). 672p. (J). (gr. 3-6). pap. 19.95 (978-0-689-03028-4(2) , Aladdin) Simon & Schuster Children's Publishing.

Nelson, Theresa. 25 Cents Miracle. 2000. (gr. 3-6). lib. bdg. 24.55 (978-0-613-88322-1(5)) Tandem Library Bks.

Nesbit, E. The Railway Children. 2002. (gr. 3-6). lib. bdg. 23.40 (978-0-613-86551-7(0)) Tandem Library Bks.

—Railway Children. Brock, C. E., illus. (YA). 14.95 (978-0-8118-4933-3(3)) Chronicle Bks. LLC.

Ness, Berthetta. Originals: Short Stories for Children. 2007. (YA). pap. (***978-1-57579-351-1(2)***) Pine Hill Pr., Inc.

Neuschafer-Carlon, Mercedes. Antonio en el Pais del Silencio. (SPA.). 96p. (J). (gr. 3-5). 6.36 (978-84-241-7896-3(3)) Everest de Ediciones y Distribucion, S.L. ESP. *Dist:* Lectorum Pubns., Inc.

Newton, Robert. Khaki Kid. Schaffner, Laurie, ed. 2002. 136p. pap. 13.95 (978-0-7022-3296-1(3)) Univ. of Queensland Pr. AUS. *Dist:* International Specialized Bk. Services.

Nixon, Joan Lowery. The Haunting. Horowitz, Beverly, ed. 2000. 192p. (YA). (gr. 7-12). mass mkt. 5.99 (978-0-440-22008-4(4) , Laurel Leaf) Random Hse. Children's Bks.

—The Haunting. 2000. (YA). 11.64 (978-0-606-19191-3(7)) Tandem Library Bks.

Nixon-Roulet, Mary F. Kalitan Our Little Alaskan Cousin. 2004. reprint ed. pap. 15.95 (978-1-4191-2838-7(8)); pap. 1.99 (978-1-4192-2838-4(2)) Kessinger Publishing, LLC.

No Extras: Individual Title, 6 packs. (Literatura 2000 Ser.). (gr. 1-2). 28.00 (978-0-7635-0103-7(4)) Rigby Education.

No Way Home: Individual Title Six-Packs. (Bookweb Ser.). 32p. (gr. 6 up). 34.00 (978-0-7578-0896-8(4)) Rigby Education.

Nolan, Han. Dancing on the Edge. 1999. 256p. (gr. 3-6). pap. 6.99 (978-0-14-130203-4(8) , Puffin) Penguin Group (USA) Inc.

—Dancing on the Edge. 1999. (J). 12.64 (978-0-606-16836-6(2)); (gr. 7-12). lib. bdg. 14.15 (978-0-613-15338-6(3)) Tandem Library Bks.

Noonan, Rosalind. Sarah: Don't Say You Love Me. 1998. (gr. 7-12). lib. bdg. 12.40 (978-0-613-73055-6(0)) Tandem Library Bks.

Norac, Carl. La Isla de los Mimos. 2003. Tr. of I Love to Cuddle. (SPA., Illus.). 32p. (J). (978-84-95150-66 0(2) , COR3070) Corimbo, Editorial S.L. ESP. *Dist:* Lectorum Pubns., Inc.

—Las Palabras Dulces. 2003. (SPA., Illus.). 32p. (J). (978-84-95150-05-9(0) , COR1690) Corimbo, Editorial S.L. ESP. *Dist:* Lectorum Pubns., Inc.

Norton, Mary. Borrowers Aloft: Plus the Short Tale, Poor Stainless. 2003. (gr. 3-6). lib. bdg. 14.10 (978-0-613-66944-3(4)) Tandem Library Bks.

—The Borrowers Aloft: Plus the Short Tale Poor Stainless. Krush, Beth & Krush, Joe, illus. 50th anniv. ed. 2003. (Borrowers Ser.). 224p. (J). (gr. 3-7). pap. 5.95 (978-0-15-204734-4(4) , Odyssey Classics) Harcourt Children's Bks.

Nugent, Cynthia. Francesca & the Magic Bike Teacher Guide. 2005. 4p. (J). pap. (978-1-55192-825-8(6)) Raincoast Bk. Distribution CAN. *Dist:* Transition Vendor.

Nyikos, Stacy. Dragon Wishes. 2008. (J). 16.95 (***978-1-933831-11-4(1)***) Blooming Tree Pr.

Oates, Joyce Carol. Freaky Green Eyes. 2003. tchr. ed. (978-0-06-056885-6(2)); 2005. 368p. (YA). reprint ed. pap. 7.99 (978-0-06-447348-4(1) , HarperTeen) HarperCollins Pubs.

—Where Is Little Reynard? Graham, Mark, illus. 2003. 32p. (J). 16.89 (978-0-06-029583-7(X)) HarperCollins Pubs.

O'Callaghan, Elena. What's Going On? Fanlo, Africa, illus. 2008. 32p. (J). 15.95 (***978-1-933605-65-4(0)***) Kane/Miller Bk. Pubs., Inc.

O'Connor, Barbara. Moonpie & Ivy. 160p. (J). 2001. (gr. 5 up). 16.00 (978-0-374-35059-8(0) , Farrar, Straus & Giroux (BYR)); 2004. (Illus.). reprint ed. pap. 7.95 (978-0-374-45320-6(9) , Sunburst) Farrar, Straus & Giroux.

—Moonpie & Ivy. l.t. ed. 2004. 140p. 20.95 (978-0-7862-7037-8(3) , Large Print Pr.) Thorndike Pr.

O'Connor, Ilett. A Born Leader - Our Francine. Kahn, Alisha, illus. Wells, Wadell, photos by. 2002. 32p. pap. 10.00 (978-0-9717003-1-4(1)) O'Connor, Ilett K.

O'Connor, Jane & Schindler, S. D. The Snow Globe Family. 2006. (Illus.). 40p. (J). (ps-3). 16.99 (978-0-399-24242-7(2)) Penguin Group (USA) Inc.

Ohi, Ruth. And You Can Come Too. Ohi, Ruth, illus. 2005. (Illus.). 32p. (J). (ps-1). pap. 5.95 (978-1-55037-904-4(6)); lib. bdg. 19.95 (978-1-55037-905-1(4)) Annick Pr., Ltd. CAN. *Dist:* Firefly Bks., Ltd.

Okoro, Jeremiah A. Telepathic Revelations & Confessions of My Family Goldfish. Okoro, Jeremiah A., illus. 2005. (Illus.). 69p. 18.95 (978-1-57197-440-2(7) , Ivy House Publishing Group) Pentland Pr., Inc.

Oldfield, Jenny. Running Wilde. Nayler, Sarah, tr. Nayler, Sarah, illus. 2003. pap. (978-0-340-87320-5(5) , Hodder Children's Books) Hodder Children's Division.

Oliver, Lin. The Mighty Mogul. Lindberg, Jeffrey, illus. 1999. (Great Railway Adventures Ser.: Vol. 2;1). 32p. (J). (gr. k-4). 14.95 (978-1-890647-56-8(X)); pap. 14.99 incl. audio (978-1-890647-57-5(8)) RC2 Corp.

Opperman, Jennifer N. Silent Cry: Katy's Story. 2004. 124p. (YA). pap. 12.95 (978-1-58736-264-4(3) , Starbound Bks.) Wheatmark.

Optic, Oliver. Through by Daylight: The Young Engineer. unabr. ed. 1998. (Lakeshore Ser.: Vol. 1). 312p. reprint ed. 15.00 (978-1-889128-50-4(3)) Mantle Ministries.

Orme, Helen. New Man. 2008. (Siti's Sisters Ser.). 36p. pap. 7.95 (*978-1-84167-686-9(1)) Ransom Publishing Ltd. GBR. *Dist:* International Publishers Marketing.

Osmond, Alan. If the Shoe Fits. Aarrestad, Thomas, illus. 1998. (Twice Upon a Time Ser.). 32p. (J). (ps-2). 11.95 (978-1-57102-133-5(7)) Warehousing & Fulfillment Specialists, LLC (WFS, LLC).

Ostow, Micol. Emily Goldberg Learns to Salsa. 2007. 288p. (J). (gr. 7). pap. 7.99 (*978-1-59514-144-6(8) , Razorbill) Penguin Group (USA) Inc.

Ostrow, Kim. Ask Me Anything! Piluso, Piero, illus. 2004. (Fairly OddParents Ser.). 12p. (J). bds. 12.95 (978-0-689-86719-4(0) , Simon Spotlight/Nickelodeon) Simon & Schuster Children's Publishing.

Oswald, Michael. Dear Jenny. 2000. 61p. (J). pap. 11.95 (978-0-7414-0455-8(9)) Infinity Publishing.

Ot, Elli. Docto y los Jazmines. Brignole, Giancarla, tr. rev. ed. 2007. (Fabulas De Familia Ser.). (SPA.). 32p. (J). pap. 6.95 (978-970-20-0267-3(2)) Castillo, Ediciones, S. A. de C. V. MEX. *Dist:* Macmillan.

Otte, Wanda. Hidden Secrets of the Knob. 2007. (ENG.). 228p. (J). per. 17.99 (*978-1-4141-0810-0(9)) Pleasant Word.

Ouriou, Katie. Luv Ya Like a Sister: A Story of Friendship. 1999. (gr. 5-8). lib. bdg. 16.40 (978-0-613-77268-6(7)) Tandem Library Bks.

Pacheco, Miguel Angel. La Familia de Mic. Escriva, Ana Lopez, illus. 2003. (SPA.). (J). (978-970-690-761-5(0)) Planeta Mexicana Editorial S. A. de C. V.

Palatini, Margie. Moosekitos: A Moose Family Reunion. Cole, Henry, illus. 2004. 40p. (ps-3). 15.99 (978-0-7868-1955-3(3)) Hyperion Bks. for Children.

Palmer, Robin. Cindy Ella. 2008. 304p. (YA). (gr. 7). 7.99 (*978-0-14-240392-1(X) , Puffin) Penguin Group (USA) Inc.

Paratore, Coleen Murtagh. The Wedding Planner's Daughter. 2005. (Wedding Planner's Daughter Ser.). 208p. (J). 15.95 (978-0-689-87340-9(9)) Simon & Schuster Children's Publishing.

Parish, Peggy. Amelia Bedelia's Family Album. Sweat, Lynn, illus. 2003. (I Can Read Bks.). 48p. (J). (gr. k-3). pap. 3.99 (978-0-06-051116-6(8) , Harper Trophy) HarperCollins Pubs.

—Amelia Bedelia's Family Album. 2003. (gr. k-3). lib. bdg. 11.80 (978-0-613-62129-8(8)) Tandem Library Bks.

Park, Linda Sue. The Kite Fighters. 2000. (Illus.). 144p. (J). (gr. 5-9). tchr. ed. 15.00 (978-0-395-94041-9(9) , Clarion Bks.) Houghton Mifflin Co. Trade & Reference Div.

Parkinson, Curtis. Emily's Eighteen Aunts. ed. 2004. (Illus.). (J). (gr. k-3). spiral bd. (978-0-616-11134-5(7)); spiral bd. (978-0-616-11135-2(5)) Canadian National Institute for the Blind/Institut National Canadien pour les Aveugles.

—Emily's Eighteen Aunts. von Königslow, Andrea Wayne, illus. 2002. 30p. (J). 15.95 (978-0-7737-3336-7(1)) Stoddart Kids CAN. *Dist:* Fitzhenry & Whiteside, Ltd.

Parkinson, Siobhan. Four Kids, Three Cats, Two Cows, One Witch. 2002. (gr. 7-12). lib. bdg. 16.40 (978-0-613-86137-3(X)) Tandem Library Bks.

—Four Kids, Three Cats, Two Cows, One Witch (Maybe) 2002. 192p. (J). (gr. 5-9). pap. 7.95 (978-0-86278-515-4(4)) O'Brien Pr., Ltd., The IRL. *Dist:* Independent Pubs. Group, Irish American Bk. Co.

Parr, Todd. The Family Book. Parr, Todd, illus. 2003. (Illus.). 32p. (J). (ps-1). 15.99 (978-0-316-73896-5(4)) Little Brown & Co.

Partridge, Elizabeth. Oranges on Golden Mountain. Sogabe, Aki, illus. 2003. 36p. (J). pap. 6.99 (978-0-14-250033-0(X) , Puffin) Penguin Group (USA) Inc.

—Oranges on Golden Mountain. 2003. (gr. k-3). lib. bdg. 15.30 (978-0-613-61651-5(0)) Tandem Library Bks.

Pasch, J. A. Arthur P. Snittles: The Magic Barrel. 2006. 116p. (YA). per. 10.95 (978-1-59886-199-0(9)) Tate Publishing & Enterprises, L.L.C.

Paterson, Katherine. Park's Quest. 2000. (J). (gr. 5-8). pap., stu. ed. 42.24 incl. audio (978-0-7887-4345-0(7) , 41139) Recorded Bks., LLC.

Patrick, Patsy S. Willie Wonders Why. Heiser, Aline L., illus. l.t. ed. 2003. 32p. (J). (ps-6). 14.95 (978-0-9726832-0-3(8)) Lu, Melissa Productions.

Patton, Lee. Toe Jam & Boo Boo's. 2004. 33p. pap. 17.95 (978-1-4137-1508-8(7)) PublishAmerica, Inc.

Paul, Dominique. The Possibility of Fireflies. 2007. 224p. (YA). pap. 8.99 (*978-1-4169-1311-5(4) , Simon Pulse) Simon & Schuster Children's Publishing.

Paulsen, Gary. The Schernoff Discoveries. 1998. 112p. (gr. 5-9). 4.99 (978-0-440-41463-6(6) , Yearling) Random Hse. Children's Bks.

—The Schernoff Discoveries. 1998. (978-0-606-13761-4(0)) Tandem Library Bks.

Pearsall, Shelley. All of the Above: A Novel. 2008. 128p. (J). (gr. 3-7). pap. 5.99 (*978-0-316-11526-1(6)) Little, Brown Bks. for Young Readers.

Pearson, Debora. Sophie's Wheels. Hilb, Nora, illus. 2006. 24p. (J). (ps-1). pap. 6.95 (978-1-55451-037-5(6)); lib. bdg. 18.95 (978-1-55451-038-2(4)) Annick Pr., Ltd. CAN. *Dist:* Firefly Bks., Ltd.

Peck, Robert Newton. Extra Innings. 2001. 192p. (J). (gr. 7 up). 16.99 (978-0-06-028867-9(1)) HarperCollins Pubs.

Peel, John. Book of War. 2005. (Diadem: Worlds of Magic Ser.: Book 7). 264p. pap. 4.99 (978-0-7387-0611-5(6)) Llewellyn Pubns.

Pelow, Lawrence. Little Larry of Lewiston Meets Bobby the Backyard Bully. 2006. 2p. 6.71 (978-1-4116-9172-8(5)) Lulu.com.

Pendziwol, Jean E. Marja's Skis. Marton, Jirina, illus. 2007. 32p. (J). (ps-3). 17.95 (*978-0-88899-674-9(8)) Groundwood Bks. CAN. *Dist:* Perseus Distribution.

Penrose, Margaret. Dorothy Dale. rev. ed. 2006. 196p. 26.95 (978-1-4218-1801-6(9)); pap. 11.95 (978-1-4218-1901-3(5)) 1st World Publishing, Inc. (1st World Library - Literary Society).

Perez, Angela J. Zack Attack! Hazard, Andrea, illus. 2007. 36p. (J). 17.95 (*978-0-9778328-9-7(9)) His Work Christian Publishing.

Perez, Jonathan. Sasp. 2005. (Illus.). 239p. (YA). per. 13.95 (978-0-9708922-6-3(8) , 0970892268) Stansbury Publishing.

Perkins, Mitali. First Daughter: Extreme American Makeover. 2007. 192p. (YA). (gr. 7-9). 16.99 (978-0-525-47800-3(0) , Dutton Juvenile) Penguin Group (USA) Inc.

Perl, Erica S. Ninety-Three in My Family. Lester, Mike, illus. 2006. 32p. (J). (ps-3). 15.95 (978-0-8109-5760-2(4)) Abrams, Harry N. , Inc.

Perry, Michael. Daniel's Ride. Ballard, Lee, illus. 2001. 32p. (J). (gr. 2-5). 16.00 (978-0-9701771-9-3(4)) Free Will Pr.

Peters, Andrew Fusek & Peters, Polly. Roar Bull, Roar! Weckmann, Anke, illus. 2007. 155p. (J). pap. 8.95 (978-1-84507-520-0(X)) Lincoln, Frances Ltd. GBR. *Dist:* Perseus Distribution.

Peters, Julie Anne. Between Mom & Jo. 2006. 240p. (J). (gr. 7-17). 16.99 (978-0-316-73906-1(5)) Little Brown & Co.

—Define Normal. 2003. (Illus.). 208p. (J). (gr. 7-17). pap. 7.99 (978-0-316-73489-9(6)) Little, Brown Bks. for Young Readers.

—Luna. 2006. 254p. (J). (gr. 9-17). reprint ed. pap. 7.99 (978-0-316-01127-3(4) , Tingley, Megan Bks.) Little, Brown Bks. for Young Readers.

Piccirillo, Renee. Big Mister Little Mister Baby Sister. Gumm, Susan Kathleen, illus. 2006. (J). per. 12.50 (978-0-9771482-0-2(3) , Ithaca Pr.) Authors & Artists Publishers of New York, Inc.

Pighin, Marcel. Tickles the Bear Goes on a Cruise, 1 bk. Mitchell, Hazel, illus. 2006. 48p. (J). per. 10.49 (*978-0-9776679-7-0(9)) MP2ME Enterprise.

Pilney, Dovie. Charlie, the Cocky Rooster. 2007. (ENG., Illus.). 28p. (J). per. 15.95 (*978-1-4327-0220-5(3)) Outskirts Press, Inc.

Pittar, Gill. Milly, Molly & Different Dads. 2004. 28p. (978-1-86972-019-3(9)) Milly Molly Bks.

—Milly, Molly & Different Dads (book W/dolls) 2006. 28p. pap. (978-1-86972-099-5(7)) Milly Molly Bks.

Piumini, Roberto. Matias y el Abuelo. 2nd ed. 2003. (SPA., Illus.). 133p. pap. (978-84-236-3261-9(X) , ED6273) La Galera, S.A. Editorial ESP. *Dist:* Lectorum Pubns., Inc.

Plourde, Becky. Rose of Many Colors. 2005. 268p. pap. 21.95 (978-1-4137-6775-9(3)) PublishAmerica, Inc.

Polacco, Patricia. The Graves Family. Gauch, Patricia Lee, ed. 2006. 48p. (J). (gr. 1). reprint ed. pap. 6.99 (978-0-14-240635-9(X) , Puffin) Penguin Group (USA) Inc.

Pollet, Alison. Nobody Was Here: Seventh Grade in the Life of Me, Penelope. (Nobody Was Here Ser.). 2004. 224p. (J). pap. 15.95 (978-0-439-58394-7(2)); 2005. 240p. reprint ed. 5.99 (978-0-439-58395-4(0)) Scholastic, Inc. (Orchard Bks.).

Porter, Eleanor H. Classic Starts: Pollyanna. Akib, Jamel, illus. 2007. (Classic Starts Ser.). 160p. (J). 4.95 (978-1-4027-3692-6(4)) Sterling Publishing Co., Inc.

Porter, H. Eleanor. Pollyanna. 2006. 52.99 (*978-1-4219-7974-8(8)); pap. 46.99 (*978-1-4219-7968-7(3)) IndyPublish.com.

—Pollyanna Grows up. 2006. pap. 58.99 (*978-1-4280-1137-3(4)) IndyPublish.com.

Porter, Marylyn Kight. Speedy the Snail & His New Family. 2006. 10.00 (978-0-8059-9134-5(4)) Dorrance Publishing Co., Inc.

Porter, Tracey. Billy Creekmore. 2007. 320p. (J). (gr. 4-7). 16.99 (*978-0-06-077570-4(X)); lib. bdg. 17.89 (*978-0-06-077571-1(8)) HarperCollins Pubs. (Cotler, Joanna Books).

Portis, Nathanial. Things in Between. 2005. 268p. (YA). per. 14.75 (978-0-9760372-0-0(3)) Quick Quest Pubns. LLC.

Potter, Ellen. Olivia Kidney Stops for No One. 2007. 272p. (J). (gr. 3-7). pap. 6.99 (978-0-14-240772-1(0) , Puffin) Penguin Group (USA) Inc.

Potter, G. L. Keeping Secerts. 2003. 141p. (YA). per. (978-1-931524-04-9(1)) Moondance Publishing.

Practically Perfect: A Penny Parrish Story. 2001. (Penny Parrish Story). 192p. (YA). pap. 12.95 (978-1-930009-30-1(5)) Image Cascade Publishing.

Precourt, Barbara. Waiting for Mr. Right. 2004. 207p. (YA). per. 14.95 (978-1-932338-42-3(X)) Lifevest Publishing, Inc.

Prigger, Mary Skillings. Aunt Minnie & the Twister. Lewin, Betsy, illus. 2002. 40p. (J). (gr. k-3). 15.00 (978-0-618-11136-7(0) , Clarion Bks.) Houghton Mifflin Co. Trade & Reference Div.

Pullman, Philip. Count Karlstein. Bryan, Diana, illus. 2000. 256p. (YA). (gr. 5-8). 5.99 (978-0-375-80348-2(3) , Yearling) Random Hse. Children's Bks.

—Count Karlstein. 1998. 256p. (J). (gr. 5-8). 17.00 (978-0-679-89255-7(9) , Knopf Bks. for Young Readers) Random Hse. Children's Bks.

—Count Karlstein. 2000. 12.64 (978-0-606-17845-7(7)); (gr. 7-12). lib. bdg. 14.15 (978-0-613-28451-6(8)) Tandem Library Bks.

—Les Royaumes du Nord. (FRE.). pap. 19.95 (978-2-07-054188-1(6)) Gallimard, Editions FRA. *Dist:* Distribooks, Inc.

—La Tour des Anges. (FRE.). pap. 19.95 (978-2-07-054189-8(4)) Gallimard, Editions FRA. *Dist:* Distribooks, Inc.

Purtill, C. Leigh. Love, Meg. 2007. 304p. (YA). 16.99 (978-1-59514-116-3(2) , Razorbill) Penguin Group (USA) Inc.

Puzzle Track Staff, ed. Our Family Vacation. 2007. (Puzzle Track Ser.). 20p. (J). bds. 18.95 (*978-0-7696-5609-0(9)) School Specialty Publishing.

Qualey, Marsha. Thin Ice. 1999. (978-0-606-17348-3(X)) Tandem Library Bks.

A Queen's Command: The Story of Our Lady of Lourdes & Bernadette. 2003. (Illus.). 138p. 18.00 (978-1-930873-85-8(9)) Neumann Pr., The.

Ragawa, Mirimo. Baby & Me, Vol. 2. Ragawa, Mirimo, illus. 2006. (Baby & Me Ser.). 208p. (YA). pap. 8.99 (978-1-4215-0573-2(8)) Viz Media.

Raintree Steck-Vaughn Staff. Pasteles de Manzana en Familia. 1999. (SPA.). (J). pap., stu. ed. 31.05 (978-0-7398-0759-0(5)) Steck-Vaughn.

—A Picnic in October. 2000. 32p. (J). (gr. k-5). 16.98 (978-0-7398-1367-6(6)) Raintree.

Randall, Barbara. I'm Baby Caleb & I Can Do What I Want. Herning, Kathy, ed. 2006. (Mimi's Kids Ser.: vol. 5). (Illus.). 32p. (J). pap. 12.95 (978-0-9712383-9-8(1)) Culture Connection, The.

Ranoia, Sharon Curry. The uninvited Houseguest. 2006. pap. 7.95 (978-0-533-15470-8(7)) Vantage Pr., Inc.

Ransburg, Ashley, illus. Evie Finds Her Family Tree. 2006. (J). 14.95 (978-0-87195-187-8(8)) Indiana Historical Society.

Ransom, Candice F. The Promise Quilt. Beier, Ellen, illus. 2002. 32p. (J). (gr. k-3). pap. 7.95 (978-0-8027-7648-8(5)) Walker & Co.

Ratto, Linda Lee. Where Dreams Come True. 2004. (J). per. (978-0-9748508-0-1(2)) Power Pr.

Rawlings, John S. Sometimes Boxes Make the Best Forts. Espina, Vito, illus. 2006. (J). pap. 15.00 (*978-0-8059-7181-1(5)) Dorrance Publishing Co., Inc.

Razzell, Mary. Snow Apples. 2006. 216p. (J). pap. 6.95 (978-0-88899-728-9(0)) Groundwood Bks. CAN. *Dist:* Perseus Distribution.

Red & Green Choices by Green Irene: Niki's Next Grade. 2003. (J). per. 14.50 (978-0-9742280-1-3(X)) Green Irene.

Reddekopp, Sharon. A New Baby for Paige. Pamplin, Terry, illus. 2000. 16p. (J). (ps-3). pap. (978-1-894303-07-1(5)) Raven Rock Publishing.

Reeder, Carolyn. Foster's War. 2000. (J). 11.15 (978-0-606-19697-0(8)) Tandem Library Bks.

Rees, Douglas. Uncle Pirate. Auth, Tony, illus. 2008. 112p. (J). (*978-1-4169-4762-2(0) , McElderry, Margaret K.) Simon & Schuster Children's Publishing.

Reetz, Kurt. The Shorteners: Family Day. 2000. mass mkt. 4.50 (978-1-931179-21-8(2)); mass mkt. 8.95 incl. audio compact disk (978-1-931179-32-4(8)) Long Hill Productions, Inc.

Regan, Dian Curtis. I Know God Is Near. Mitchell, Susan, illus. 2006. 14p. (J). 7.99 (978-1-4169-1497-6(8) , Little Simon Inspirations) Simon & Schuster Children's Publishing.

Reid, William. North of Nowhere. 2002. 196p. pap. (978-1-55313-077-2(4)) Adventure Bk. Pubs.

Reiken, Frederick. Lost Legends of New Jersey. 2001. (gr. 7-12). lib. bdg. 22.25 (978-0-613-36486-7(4)) Tandem Library Bks.

Reiser, Lynn W. Cherry Pies & Lullabies. Reiser, Lynn W., illus. 1998. (Illus.). 40p. (J). (ps-3). 18.99 (978-0-688-13391-7(6)) HarperCollins Pubs.

The Reluctant Heart: A Penny Parrish Story. 2001. (Penny Parrish Story). 192p. (YA). pap. 12.95 (978-1-930009-31-8(3)) Image Cascade Publishing.

Rennie Pattison, Caroline. The Law of Three: A Sarah Martin Mystery. 2007. 200p. (YA). pap. 10.99 (*978-1-55002-733-4(6) , Boardwalk Bks.) Dundurn Group, The CAN. *Dist:* Univ. of Toronto Pr.

Reyes, Yolanda. A Bed for Three. Coll, Ivar Da, illus. 2004. (SPA.). 36p. (J). (gr. k-3). 14.95 (978-958-704-055-5(4)) Santillana USA Publishing Co., Inc.

Reynolds, Marilyn. No More Sad Goodbyes. 2007. (Hamilton High Ser.). 192p. (YA). 18.95 (*978-1-932538-72-4(0)); pap. 9.95 (*978-1-932538-71-7(2)) Morning Glory Pr., Inc.

Rhema, Dan. One Tiny Twig. 1. Leonard, Michael, illus. 2003. 32p. (J). per. 19.95 (978-0-9729835-0-1(3)) Mesquite Tress Pr., LLC.

Rice, David. Crazy Loco. Clayton, Christian, illus. 2003. 144p. (YA). (gr. 6-11). pap. 5.99 (978-0-14-250056-9(9) , Puffin) Penguin Group (USA) Inc.

Richards. Magic Sky Board Book. 2007. (Illus.). 22p. (J). (ps-k). 7.99 (*978-1-4052-2441-3(X)) Egmont Bks., Ltd. GBR. *Dist:* Independent Pubs. Group.

Richards, Kitty. Have Yourself a Thornberry Little Christmas. 2000. (gr. k-3). lib. bdg. 14.15 (978-0-613-31296-7(1)) Tandem Library Bks.

Richardson, Dorothea M. Moose Girl. 2001. (gr. 7-12). lib. bdg. 26.85 (978-0-613-85254-8(0)) Tandem Library Bks.

Richardson, Tom. Dominic Is Strong. 2005. (Illus.). 26p. (J). lib. bdg. 16.95 (978-1-932338-99-7(3)) Lifevest Publishing, Inc.

Richter, Conrad. The Light in the Forest. (YA). (gr. 7 up). 21.95 (978-0-89190-333-8(X)) Amereon LTD.

Rifkin, L. & Hartman, Kurt. The Nine Lives of Romeo Crumb: Life Three. 2006. (Illus.). 276p. 16.95 (978-0-9743221-2-4(1)) Stratford Road Pr., Ltd.

Rigby Education Staff. The Very Noisy Family. (Illus.). 16p. (J). bds. 30.00 (978-0-7635-6430-8(3) , 764303C99) Rigby Education.

Rinaldi, Ann. The Last Silk Dress. 1999. (gr. 7-12). lib. bdg. 14.15 (978-0-613-72274-2(4)) Tandem Library Bks.

Ringler, Matt. One Little, Two Little, Three Little Apples. Kennedy, Anne, illus. 2005. (J). pap. (*978-0-439-77500-7(0)) Scholastic, Inc.

Ritchey, Melissa. The Kabeezles. 2006. (Illus.). 16p. (J). lib. bdg. 18.95 (978-0-9761128-5-3(X)) Hafabanana Pr.

Rivera, Jeff. Forever My Lady: A Novel. 2004. per. 12.95 (978-0-9762838-0-5(8)) JoAnne/Horatio Bks.

—Forever My Lady: Young Adult. 2005. (YA). per. 12.95 (978-0-9762838-1-2(6)) JoAnne/Horatio Bks.

Robbins, Terrie C. Bushtail Is Our Cousin. Mezza, J. Di, illus. 2002. 32p. (J). (gr. 3-6). pap. 7.99 (978-0-9711577-0-5(7)) Possibilities Unlimited.

Roberts, Dannel. Me & Uncle Mike & the 3-Toed Bear. Tapia, Lonnie C., illus. l.t. ed. 1999. (Me & Uncle Mike Children's Book Ser.: Bk. 1). 36p. (J). (gr. k-5). per. 14.95 (978-1-893459-00-7(4)) Lions & Tigers & Bears Publishing, Inc.

—Me & Uncle Mike & the Purple Gorilla, 5 bks, Bk. 5. l.t. ed. 2003. (Me & Uncle Mike Children's Book Ser.: Bk. 5). (Illus.). 32p. (J). per. 14.95 (978-1-893459-04-5(7)) Lions & Tigers & Bears Publishing, Inc.

Roberts, Willo Davis. Buddy Is a Stupid Name for a Girl. Cipolla, Karen, illus. 2002. 224p. (J). pap. 5.99 (978-0-689-85164-3(2) , Aladdin) Simon & Schuster Children's Publishing.

—Buddy Is a Stupid Name for a Girl. 2001. (Illus.). 224p. (J). (gr. 3-7). 16.00 (978-0-689-81670-3(7) , Atheneum) Simon & Schuster Children's Publishing.

—Undercurrents. 2003. (Illus.). 240p. (J). pap. 4.99 (978-0-689-85994-6(5) , Aladdin) Simon & Schuster Children's Publishing.

—Undercurrents. Downey, Mark, illus. 2002. 240p. (J). (gr. 5-8). 16.95 (978-0-689-81671-0(5) , Atheneum) Simon & Schuster Children's Publishing.

—Undercurrents. 2002. (gr. 3-6). lib. bdg. 13.00 (978-0-613-66553-7(8)) Tandem Library Bks.

Robertson, Barbara. Rosemary in Paris: Back to 1889. 2001. (Hourglass Adventures Ser.: Bk. 2). (Illus.). 121p. (J). (gr. 4-7). pap. 4.95 (978-1-890817-56-5(2)) Winslow Pr.

—Rosemary Meets Rosemarie Bk. 1: Berlin in 1870. 2001. (Hourglass Adventures Ser.: Bk. 1). (Illus.). 128p. (J). (gr. 4-6). pap. 5.95 (978-1-890817-55-8(4)) Winslow Pr.

Robinson, Gwen. The Renshaw Diversion. 2007. 204p. per. (*978-0-7552-0275-1(9)) Authors OnLine, Ltd.

Robinson, Linda. Dear Grandchild: When You Come for a Visit. Larkins, Mona, illus. 2005. (J). 15.99 (978-0-9740841-4-5(X)) K&B Products.

Rodowsky, Colby. Not My Dog. Yezerski, Thomas F., illus. 1999. 80p. (J). (gr. 2-5). 15.00 (978-0-374-35531-9(2) , Farrar, Straus & Giroux (BYR)) Farrar, Straus & Giroux.

Rodowsky, Colby F. That Fernhill Summer. 2006. 176p. (J). 16.00 (978-0-374-37442-6(2)) Farrar, Straus & Giroux.

Romero, Sensi. La familia de Nieve. 2004. (Cuentos con miga Ser.). 47p. (J). pap. 11.00 (978-84-95895-22-6(6)) Editorial Brief ESP. *Dist:* Independent Pubs. Group.

Root, Phyllis. Aunt Nancy & Old Man Trouble. ed. 2000. (J). (gr. 2). spiral bd. (978-0-616-01775-3(8)) Canadian National Institute for the Blind/Institut National Canadien pour les Aveugles.

Ross, Odette. Families. 2007. (Wordless Board Bks.). (Illus.). 12p. (J). (ps). bds. 5.95 (*978-1-894965-92-7(2)) Simply Read Bks. CAN. *Dist:* Perseus Distribution.

Roth, Rhonda. The Most Important Thing. Grajczyk, Shane, illus. 2007. 32p. (J). 16.95 (*978-0-9770141-0-1(X) , Crossing Guard Bks.) Longs Peak Publishing, Inc.

Rottman, S. L. Rough Waters. 1998. (Illus.). 144p. (YA). (gr. 7-11). 14.95 (978-1-56145-172-2(X) , Q17398) Peachtree Pubs., Ltd.

—Shadow of a Doubt. 224p. (YA). 2005. pap. 7.95 (978-1-56145-354-2(4)); 2003. (gr. 6-10). 14.95 (978-1-56145-291-0(2)) Peachtree Pubs., Ltd.

Rouss, Sylvia A. Tali's Jerusalem Scrapbook. Oppenheimer, Nancy, illus. 2003. 32p. (gr. 1-4). 14.95 (978-1-930143-68-5(0)); pap. 9.95 (978-1-930143-69-2(9)) Pitspopany Pr.

—Tali's Jerusalem Scrapbook. 2003. (gr. k-3). lib. bdg. 18.75 (978-0-613-81198-9(4)) Tandem Library Bks.

Roy, Arundhati. Le Dieu des Petits Riens. pap. 19.95 (978-2-07-041172-6(9)) Gallimard, Editions FRA. *Dist:* Distribooks, Inc.

Rubcic, Michael. Native Soul. 2004. 216p. (Orig.). (J). pap. 14.95 (978-0-9746848-0-2(5)) Native Sun Pr.

Rubin, Cathy. Eleanor, Ellatony, Ellencake, & Me. Fowler, Christopher, illus. 2003. (Eleanor Ser.). 32p. (J). (gr. k-3). 14.95 (978-1-57768-412-1(5) , Gingham Dog Pr.) School Specialty Publishing.

Rudner, Rebecca. My Grandma Lives at the Airport. 2002. (Illus.). 32p. (J). (gr. k-3). (978-0-9708217-0-6(0)) Red Hill Pr.

Rue, Nancy N. The Chase. 1999. (Christian Heritage Ser.). 192p. (J). (gr. 3-7). pap. (978-1-56179-735-6(9)) Focus on the Family Publishing.

—The Trick. 1999. (Christian Heritage Ser.). (Illus.). 208p. (J). (gr. 3-7). pap. (978-1-56179-734-9(0)) Focus on the Family Publishing.

Rugrats Back to School Riser. 1998. (978-0-689-00701-9(9) , Simon & Schuster Children's Publishing) Simon & Schuster Children's Publishing.

Rushton, Rosie. How Could You Do This to Me, Mum? 2005. 224p. (J). pap. 5.99 (978-0-7868-5187-4(2)) Hyperion Bks. for Children.

—Last Seen Wearing Trainers. 2003. 224p. (J). pap. 9.95 (978-1-84270-216-1(5)) Andersen GBR. *Dist:* Trafalgar Square Publishing.

Ruttledge, Nancy. If I Were My Mommy & Daddy. 2003. (J). per. 11.95 (978-1-932205-51-0(9)) Word Association Pubs.

Ryan, Darlene. Rules for Life. 2004. 176p. (J). (gr. 7-12). pap. 7.95 (978-1-55143-350-9(8) , 1234553) Orca Bk. Pubs. USA.

Ryan, Darlene & Manchester, Peter. Kisses, Kisses, Kisses. 2004. (Illus.). 24p. (J). (***978-1-55131-092-3(9)***) Univ. of New Brunswick, Dept. of Graphic Services.

Ryan, Pam Muñoz. Esperanza Renace. 2002. (SPA.). (gr. 3-6). lib. bdg. 13.00 (978-0-613-82250-3(1)) Tandem Library Bks.

—Esperanza Rising. 2001. (gr. 5-8). lib. bdg. 13.00 (978-0-613-53807-7(2)) Tandem Library Bks.

—Mice & Beans. Cepeda, Joe, illus. 2005. (Bookshelf Ser.). 32p. (J). pap. 5.99 (978-0-439-70136-5(8) , Scholastic Paperbacks) Scholastic, Inc.

Ryherd, Tim. My Hurricane Book. 2006. (J). 12.95 (978-0-9749974-1-4(2)) Ryherd, Tim Publishing.

Rylant, Cynthia. Annie & Snowball & the Tea Cup Club. Stevenson, Sucie, illus. 2008. (Annie & Snowball Ser.). 32p. (J). 15.99 (***978-1-4169-0940-8(0)*** , Simon & Schuster Children's Publishing) Simon & Schuster Children's Publishing.

—Henry & Mudge & the Funny Lunch. Bracken, Carolyn, illus. 2005. (Henry & Mudge Ser.). 40p. (J). pap. 3.99 (978-0-689-83444-8(6) , Aladdin) Simon & Schuster Children's Publishing.

—Henry & Mudge & the Tall Tree House. Bracken, Carolyn, illus. 2003. (Henry & Mudge Ser.). 40p. (J). pap. 3.99 (978-0-689-83445-5(4) , Aladdin) Simon & Schuster Children's Publishing.

—Henry & Mudge & the Tall Tree House. 2003. (Henry & Mudge Ser.). (gr. k-3). lib. bdg. 11.80 (978-0-613-90605-0(5)) Tandem Library Bks.

—Henry & Mudge in the Family Trees. Stevenson, Sucie, illus. 2002. (Henry & Mudge Ser.). (J). 11.91 (978-0-7587-1273-8(1)) Book Wholesalers, Inc.

—Henry & Mudge in the Family Trees. Stevenson, Sucie, illus. 1998. (Henry & Mudge Ser.). 40p. (J). (gr. k-3). pap. 3.99 (978-0-689-82317-6(7) , Aladdin) Simon & Schuster Children's Publishing.

—In Aunt Lucy's Kitchen. Halperin, Wendy Anderson, illus. 2000. (Cobble Street Cousins Ser.: No. 1). 64p. (J). (gr. 2-5). pap. 3.99 (978-0-689-81708-3(8) , Aladdin) Simon & Schuster Children's Publishing.

—In Aunt Lucy's Kitchen & a Little Shopping. Halperin, Wendy Anderson, illus. 2004. (Cobble Street Cousins Ser.: Nos. 1-2). 144p. (J). pap. 3.99 (978-0-689-87103-0(1) , Aladdin) Simon & Schuster Children's Publishing.

—Some Good News. Halperin, Wendy Anderson, illus. 2001. (Cobble Street Cousins Ser.: No. 4). 64p. (J). (gr. 4-7). pap. 3.99 (978-0-689-81712-0(6) , Aladdin) Simon & Schuster Children's Publishing.

—Some Good News. 2001. (Cobble Street Cousins Ser.: No. 3). (gr. 3-6). lib. bdg. 11.80 (978-0-613-35677-0(2)) Tandem Library Bks.

—Special Gifts. Halperin, Wendy Anderson, illus. 2000. (Cobble Street Cousins Ser.: No. 4). 64p. (J). pap. 3.99 (978-0-689-81715-1(0) , Aladdin) Simon & Schuster Children's Publishing.

—Special Gifts. Halperin, Wendy Anderson, illus. 2000. (Cobble Street Cousins Ser.: No. 4). (J). (978-0-606-20026-4(6)) Tandem Library Bks.

—Summer Party. Halperin, Wendy Anderson, illus. 2001. (Cobble Street Cousins Ser.: No. 5). 64p. (J). (gr. 2-8). 15.00 (978-0-689-83241-3(9)) Simon & Schuster Children's Publishing.

—Summer Party. 2002. (Cobble Street Cousins Ser.: No. 5). (gr. 3-6). lib. bdg. 11.80 (978-0-613-46174-0(6)) Tandem Library Bks.

Rylant, Cynthia & Halperin, Wendy Anderson. Summer Party. 2002. (Cobble Street Cousins Ser.: No. 5). (Illus.). 64p. (J). (gr. 2-5). pap. 3.99 (978-0-689-83417-2(9) , Aladdin) Simon & Schuster Children's Publishing.

Samuel, Lynette M. Mommy's Hat. Capps, Leigh, illus. 2005. (J). per. (978-0-9727703-3-0(X)) P.R.A. Publishing.

Sandburg, Carl. The Huckabuck Family: And How They Raised Popcorn in Nebraska & Quit & Came Back. Small, David, illus. 40p. (J). (ps-3). 1999. 16.00 (978-0-374-33511-3(7)); 2004. reprint ed. pap. 6.95 (978-0-374-43449-6(2)) Farrar, Straus & Giroux. (Farrar, Straus & Giroux (BYR)).

Sanders, Scott Russell. Warm as Wool. Cogancherry, Helen, illus. 2007. (J). lib. bdg. 18.00 (***978-1-59098-421-5(8)***) Wooster Bk. Co., The.

Sandoval, Lynda. Who's Your Daddy? 2004. 320p. (YA). pap. 6.99 (978-0-689-86440-7(X) , Simon Pulse) Simon & Schuster Children's Publishing.

Saneshige, Norio, illus. Wu-lung & I-lung. l.t. deluxe ed. 2004. 36p. (J). 26.95 (978-0-9759251-1-9(3)) Forest Hill Publishing, LLC.

—Wu-lung & I-lung: Color Edition. 2004. 36p. (J). pap. 16.00 (978-0-9759251-0-2(5)) Forest Hill Publishing, LLC.

Santillo, LuAnn. Chip. Santillo, LuAnn, ed. 2003. (Half-Pint Kids Readers Ser.). (Illus.). 7p. (J). (ps-1). pap. (978-1-59256-075-2(X)) Half-Pint Kids, Inc.

—Digging for Clams. Santillo, LuAnn, ed. 2003. (Half-Pint Kids Readers Ser.). (Illus.). 7p. (J). (ps-1). pap. (978-1-59256-092-9(X)) Half-Pint Kids, Inc.

—The Wish. Santillo, LuAnn, ed. 2003. (Half-Pint Kids Readers Ser.). (Illus.). 7p. (J). (ps-1). pap. (978-1-59256-048-6(2)) Half-Pint Kids, Inc.

Sasloff, Jackie. Mommy Got Bigger: And So Did Our Family. Doriand, Stephen, Jr., illus. 2001. 24p. (J). (ps-5). 12.95 (978-0-9712942-0-2(8)) Terrapin Pubns.

Savage, Deborah. Kotuku. 2002. 304p. (YA). (gr. 7 up). 16.00 (978-0-618-04756-7(5)) Houghton Mifflin Co. Trade & Reference Div.

Sawyers, William. The Nest That Could Fly. 2005. 43p. (J). pap. 16.69 (978-1-4116-5446-4(3)) Lulu.com.

Schaefer, Lola M. Loose Tooth. Wickstrom, Sylvie Kantorovitz, illus. 2005. (My First I Can Read Bks.). 32p. (J). (ps-ps). pap. 3.99 (978-0-06-052778-5(1)) HarperCollins Pubs.

Schaller, Bob. Arlington Family Adventures, 4 vols. 2000. (J). (gr. 4-7). 19.95 (978-0-8010-8493-5(8)) Baker Bks.

Scheunemann, Pam. Bear Claws. Chawla, Neena, illus. 2006. (Fact & Fiction Ser.). 24p. (J). pap. (978-1-59679-926-4(9)); (gr. 1-3). 21.35 (978-1-59679-925-7(0) , Sand-Castle) ABDO Publishing Co.

Schietinger-Cachina, Daryl A. Hey New Baby in There. Schietinger-Cachina, Daryl A., illus. 1999. (Illus.). 8p. (J). (ps-5). pap. 5.00 (978-1-928641-02-5(4)) Daryl Ann Pubns.

Schneider, Antonie. Leo's Dream. Cole, Alison, tr. from GER. Bansch, Helga, illus. 2006. 32p. 22.95 (978-0-7475-8184-0(3) , Bloomsbury Children) Bloomsbury Publishing Plc GBR. *Dist:* Independent Pubs. Group.

Scholastic, Inc. Staff. Fluffy Bunny. Harper, Piers, illus. 2004. 32p. (J). 15.95 (978-0-439-57825-7(6) , Cartwheel Bks.) Scholastic, Inc.

Schraff, Ann. Until We Meet Again. 2007. (Bluford Ser.: No. 7). 160p. (J). pap. 3.99 (***978-0-439-90488-9(9)*** , Scholastic Paperbacks) Scholastic, Inc.

Schraff, Anne. Someone to Love Me. Langan, Paul, ed. 2002. (Bluford Ser.: 4). 162p. (YA). mass mkt. 4.95 (978-0-944210-06-2(6)) Townsend Pr.

—Sounds of Terror: Set 3. 2002. 32p. (YA). 2.95 (978-1-56254-433-1(0) , SP 4330) Saddleback Educational Publishing.

—Until We Meet Again. Langan, Paul, ed. 2002. (Bluford Ser.: 7). 144p. (YA). mass mkt. 4.95 (978-0-944210-07-9(4)) Townsend Pr.

Schultz, Jan Neubert. Horse Sense: The Story of Will Sasse, His Horse Star & the Outlaw Jesse James. (Adventures in Time Ser.). (J). 2005. (Illus.). 180p. (gr. 4-8). 15.95 (978-1-57505-998-3(3)); 2001. lib. bdg. 6.95 (978-1-57505-999-0(1) , Carolrhoda Bks.) Lerner Publishing Group.

Schwartz, Amy. What James Likes Best. Schwartz, Amy, illus. 2003. (Illus.). 32p. (J). 16.95 (978-0-689-84059-3(4) , Atheneum/Richard Jackson Bks.) Simon & Schuster Children's Publishing.

Schwartz, Ellen. Yossi's Goal. 2006. (Illus.). 144p. (J). pap. 5.95 (978-1-55143-492-6(X)) Orca Bk. Pubs. USA.

Schwartz, Noa. Old Timers: The One That Got Away. Vipond, Erica, illus. 1998. (J). pap. 5.95 (978-0-9683303-1-9(2)) Tumbleweed Pr.

Scott, Kathy. Beacon Hill. 2005. 85p. pap. 14.95 (978-1-4137-8423-7(2)) PublishAmerica, Inc.

The Secret Hideaway: Individual Title, 6 packs. 16p. (gr. 2 up). 35.00 (978-0-7635-9376-6(1)) Rigby Education.

Selvadurai, Shyam. Swimming in the Monsoon Sea. 2007. 280p. (J). (gr. 8). pap. 9.95 (***978-0-88776-834-7(2)***) Tundra Bks., Inc./Livres Toundra, Inc. CAN. *Dist:* Random Hse., Inc.

Shape Family. (J). (978-1-58209-079-5(3)) Books Are Fun, Ltd.

Shaw, Janet Beeler. Kaya Shows the Way Bk. 5: A Sister Story. Farnsworth, Bill & McAliley, Susan, illus. 2002. (American Girls Collection: Bk. 5). 88p. (gr. 2-7). (J). 12.95 (978-1-58485-432-6(4)); 6.95 (978-1-58485-431-9(6)) American Girl Publishing, Inc.

Shaw, Susan. Black-Eyed Suzie. 2004. (J). pap. 9.95 (978-1-59078-257-6(7)) Boyds Mills Pr.

Sheath, Irene. Lippy Lime Juice. 2004. 144p. (J). per. (978-1-904502-48-7(2)) MediaWorld/BestBooks.

Shemin, Craig. Families Are Forever. McCoy, John, illus. l.t. ed. 2004. 34p. 9.95 (978-0-9728666-1-3(2) , 1) As Simple As That Publishing.

Shepherd, Donna J. OUCH! Sunburn. Collier, Kevin Scott, illus. 2007. 27p. (J). E-Book 9.95 incl. cd-rom (***978-1-933090-60-3(X)***) Guardian Angel Publishing, Inc.

Shepherd, JaiLeen. Lea's Song: The Life of a Special Little Horse. 2006. (J). per. 13.95 (978-1-889743-54-7(2)) Robbie Dean Pr.

Sheppard, Hazel A. Inch Worm Goes a Mile. 2002. (Illus.). 20p. 8.95 (978-0-9725286-0-3(1)) Sheppard Publishing.

Sherrard, Valerie. Three Million Acres of Flame. 2007. 180p. (YA). pap. 10.99 (***978-1-55002-727-3(1)*** , Boardwalk Bks.) Dundurn Group, The CAN. *Dist:* Univ. of Toronto Pr.

Shifflett, Stephen. Josie Unlimited. 2007. 136p. (YA). per. 11.95 (***978-0-595-43013-0(9)***) iUniverse, Inc.

Shimko, Bonnie. Kat's Promise. 2006. 288p. (J). 17.00 (978-0-15-205473-1(1)) Harcourt Children's Bks.

Shook, Karl. The Family Thing. 2004. 166p. (YA). pap. 12.95 (978-0-595-31121-7(0)) iUniverse, Inc.

The Shooting Star, 6 vols., Pack. 16p. (gr. 2 up). 35.00 (978-0-7635-9386-5(9)) Rigby Education.

Shuster, Bud. Double Buckeyes: A Story of the Way America Used to Be. (Illus.). vi, 149p. (J). (gr. 4-7). 2000. pap. 7.95 (978-1-57249-177-9(9) , White Mane Kids); 1999. 19.95 (978-1-57249-176-2(0) , White Mane Bks.) White Mane Publishing Co., Inc.

Siburt, Ruth. The Trouble with Alex. 1998. 93p. (J). (gr. k-9). pap. 9.99 (978-0-88092-366-8(0) , 3660) Royal Fireworks Publishing Co.

Siegel, Elizabeth. Taj. Toye, Derek, illus. 2007. 48p. (J). lib. bdg. 23.08 (***978-1-4242-1632-1(X)***) Fitzgerald Bks.

Silberberg, Alan. Pond Scum. 2007. 288p. (gr. 3-7). pap. 5.99 (978-0-7868-5635-0(1)) Hyperion Pr.

Silver Dolphin en Español Editors. Seqorita Cmrculo: Miss Circle, Spanish-Language Edition. 2005. (Mis figuras Geometricas Ser.). (SPA., Illus.). 6p. (J). 9.95 (978-970-718-293-6(8) , Silver Dolphin en Español) Advanced Marketing, S. de R. L. de C. V. MEX. *Dist:* Perseus Distribution.

Simmons, Michael. Vandal. 2007. 176p. (YA). pap. 6.99 (***978-0-312-37147-0(0)***) Square Fish.

Simon. Like to Win! 2000. (J). (gr. k-6). 11.79 (978-0-606-19158-6(5)) Tandem Library Bks.

Simon, Norma. All Families Are Special. Flavin, Teresa, illus. 2003. 32p. (J). (gr. k-3). 16.95 (978-0-8075-2175-5(2)) Whitman, Albert & Co.

Simont, Marc. The Stray Dog. Simont, Marc, illus. (Illus.). 32p. (J). (ps-3). 2003. pap. 6.99 (978-0-06-443669-4(1)); 2001. 15.99 (978-0-06-028933-1(3)) HarperCollins Pubs.

Simpson, Lesley B. The Hug. Simpson, Lesley B., illus. 2003. (Annikins Ser.: Vol. 4). (Illus.). 24p. (J). (ps-2). pap. 1.25 (978-0-920303-23-8(4)) Annick Pr., Ltd. CAN. *Dist:* Firefly Bks., Ltd.

Sims, Janet. Mark's Big Surprise. 2007. (J). pap. 8.00 (***978-0-8059-7355-6(9)***) Dorrance Publishing Co., Inc.

Sinclair, Upton. Jungle. 2001. (gr. 7-12). lib. bdg. 14.10 (978-0-613-46082-8(0)) Tandem Library Bks.

Singer, Marilyn. Didi & Daddy on the Promenade. Gay, Marie-Louise, illus. 2001. 32p. (J). (gr. k-3). tchr. ed. 14.00 (978-0-618-04640-9(2) , Clarion Bks.) Houghton Mifflin Co. Trade & Reference Div.

Sinke, Janet. I Wanna Go to Grandma's House. 2003. (Illus.). 50p. (J). (978-0-9742732-0-4(1)) My Grandma & Me Pubs.

Skarmeta, Antonio. La Composicion. Ruano, Alfonso, illus. 2000. (SPA.). 36p. (J). (gr. 3-5). 11.95 (978-980-257-215-1(2)) Ekare, Ediciones VEN. *Dist:* Lectorum Pubns., Inc.

Slade, Arthur. Megiddo's Shadow. 2008. 304p. (YA). (gr. 7). mass mkt. 6.50 (***978-0-553-49507-2(0)*** , Laurel Leaf) Random Hse. Children's Bks.

Slater, Nicola, illus. We're Bored. 2005. 12p. (J). 12.95 (978-1-58117-384-0(9) , Intervisual/Piggy Toes) Dalmatian Pr.

Smith, Alexander McCall. Harriet Bean & the League of Cheats. Rankin, Laura, illus. 2007. 80p. (J). pap. 4.95 (978-1-59990-054-4(8) , Bloomsbury Children) Bloomsbury Publishing.

Smith, Bruce L. When My Dad Was Little. l.t. ed. 2006. (Illus.). 32p. (J). lib. bdg. (***978-1-934190-09-8(8)***) Ocean Front Bk. Publishing, Inc.

Smith-Leckie, Nina. The Fall & Rise of Abuse-a-Saurus Rex. Gordon, Danny, illus. 2003. 28p. (YA). (gr. 5 up). pap. 6.95 (978-0-9725382-0-6(8)) Prairie Arts, Inc.

Smith, Linda. The Minstrel's Daughter. 2004. (Juvenile Novel Ser.: Vol. 1). (Illus.). 282p. (J). (gr. 5-9). pap. 8.95 (978-1-55050-309-8(X)) Coteau Bks. CAN. *Dist:* Fitzhenry & Whiteside, Ltd.

Smith, Montez Roller. A Summer to Grow On: House upon a Hill Series - Book 1. 2005. 220p. per. 14.95 (978-1-933148-95-3(0)) Tate Publishing & Enterprises, L.L.C.

Smothers, Ethel Footman. Auntee Edna. Clay, Wil, illus. 2004. 32p. (J). pap. 8.00 (978-0-8028-5246-5(7)); 16.00 (978-0-8028-5154-3(1)) Eerdmans, William B. Publishing Co.

—Auntee Edna. 2002. (gr. k-3). lib. bdg. 16.45 (978-0-613-75338-8(0)) Tandem Library Bks.

Snead, Kathi. My Mom Has a Job. Christine, Grove, illus. 2004. (J). (978-0-9747385-1-2(4)) City of Manassas Department of Social Services.

Snedeker, Caroline Dale. Lysis Goes to the Play. Clark, Elizabeth Palmer, illus. 2003. 62p. (J). per. 8.95 (978-0-9667067-4-1(9)) American Home-School Publishing, LLC.

Snicket, Lemony, pseud. The End. Helquist, Brett, illus. 2006. (Series of Unfortunate Events Ser.: Bk. 13). (J). 368p. lib. bdg. 15.89 (978-0-06-029644-5(5)); 384p. (gr. 5 up). 12.99 (978-0-06-441016-8(1)) HarperCollins Pubs.

—The Grim Grotto. Helquist, Brett, illus. 2004. (Series of Unfortunate Events Ser.: Bk. 11). 352p. (YA). (gr. 3-6). 12.99 (978-0-06-441014-4(5) , HarperCollins) HarperCollins Pubs.

Snyder, Zilpha Keatley. The Bronze Pen. 2008. 208p. (J). 16.99 (***978-1-4169-4201-6(7)***) Simon & Schuster Children's Publishing.

Snyder, Zilpha Keatley. Spyhole Secrets. 2005. 192p. (J). (gr. 3-7). pap. 5.99 (978-0-440-41708-8(2) , Yearling) Random Hse. Children's Bks.

—Spyhole Secrets. 2002. (gr. 3-6). lib. bdg. 13.00 (978-0-613-88326-9(8)) Tandem Library Bks.

Sommer, A. M. Tucker's Christmas. 2006. pap. 7.95 (978-0-533-15278-0(X)) Vantage Pr., Inc.

Sommer, Carl. No Longer a Dilly Dally Read-Along, 2003. (Another Sommer-Time Story Ser.). (Illus.). 48p. (J). lib. bdg. 23.95 incl. audio compact disk (978-1-57537-701-8(2)); lib. bdg. 23.95 incl. audio (978-1-57537-751-3(9)) Advance Publishing, Inc.

—You Move You Lose Read-along, 2003. (Another Sommer-Time Story Ser.). (Illus.). 48p. (J). lib. bdg. 23.95 incl. audio compact disk (978-1-57537-705-6(5)); lib. bdg. 23.95 incl. audio (978-1-57537-755-1(1)) Advance Publishing, Inc.

Son, John. Finding My Hat. 2005. (First Person Fiction Ser.). 192p. (J). reprint ed. pap. 6.99 (978-0-439-43539-0(0) , Scholastic Paperbacks) Scholastic, Inc.

Sonney, Dale N. Dog, Duck & Dade: May the Country in Them, Tease the Youth in You. 2001. 276p. (YA). pap. 15.95 (978-0-595-19233-5(5)) iUniverse, Inc.

Soto, Gary & Widener, Terry. If the Shoe Fits. 2002. (Illus.). 32p. (J). (gr. 4-8). 15.99 (978-0-399-23420-0(9) , Putnam Juvenile) Penguin Group (USA) Inc.

Souhami, Jessica. The Little, Little House. 2005. (Illus.). 32p. (J). 15.95 (978-1-84507-108-0(5)) Lincoln, Frances Ltd. GBR. *Dist:* Perseus Distribution.

Spalding, Andrea. The Keeper & the Crows. 1999. (Young Reader Ser.). (Illus.). 128p. (J). (gr. 3-6). pap. 5.95 (978-1-55143-141-3(6)) Orca Bk. Pubs. USA.

Speregen, Devra Newberger. Hero for a Day. 1999. (gr. 3-6). lib. bdg. 11.80 (978-0-613-23257-9(7)) Tandem Library Bks.

Spiegler, Louise. The Amethyst Road. 2005. 336p. (YA). (gr. 7-12). 16.00 (978-0-618-48572-7(4) , Clarion Bks.) Houghton Mifflin Co. Trade & Reference Div.

Spoon, Cynthia. The Ice Angel. 2006. (Illus.). 32p. (J). per. 8.50 (***978-1-60002-280-7(4)*** , 4233, Airleaf Publishing) Airleaf Publishing & Bookselling.

Spruill, Ed. Jordan Wants a Brother. l.t. ed. 2005. (Illus.). 26p. (J). lib. bdg. 15.95 (978-0-9772578-0-5(0)) Tree Branch Publishing.

Spyropolous, Angelo. RV. 2005. pap. 12.99 (978-1-894869-98-0(2) , PO 00128) Zumaya Pubns. LLC.

St. John, Patricia. Nothing Else Matters. 2003. 176p. 6.49 (978-0-85421-972-8(2)) Scripture Union GBR. *Dist:* Gabriel Resources.

—The Tanglewoods' Secret. Rees, Gary, illus. 2001. 224p. (J). pap. 6.99 (978-0-8024-6576-4(5)) Moody Pubs.

Star Spangled Summer. 2001. (Penny Parrish Story Ser.). 281p. (YA). (gr. 5 up). pap. 12.95 (978-1-930009-26-4(7)) Image Cascade Publishing.

Starr, Claire. They Called Me Beautiful: A Dog's Search for Love & the Family That Rescued Him. Starr, Claire, illus. 2002. (Illus.). 128p. (J). (ps-4). pap. 10.95 (978-0-9706377-1-0(3)) Lucky Pr., LLC.

Staunton, Ted. Two False Moves. Lafontaine, Roger, illus. 2004. (Monkey Mountain Bks.). 64p. (J). (gr. 2-5). pap. 4.95 (978-0-88995-205-8(1)) Red Deer Pr. CAN. *Dist:* Fitzhenry & Whiteside, Ltd.

Stein, Aidel, et al. Baker's Dozen Three-in-One: Ima Come Home; Hey, Walter!; Through Thick & Thin, 3 vols. 2000. (Illus.). 143p. 16.99 (978-1-56871-285-7(5)) Targum Pr., Inc.

—Baker's Dozen Three-in-One: Stars in Their Eyes; The Inside Story; Trapped, 3 vols. 2000. (Illus.). 169p. (gr. 3-9). 16.99 (978-1-56871-163-8(8)) Targum Pr., Inc.

Steptoe, Javaka. The Jones Family Express. 2003. (Illus.). 40p. (J). (ps-4). 17.95 (978-1-58430-047-2(7)) Lee & Low Bks., Inc.

Steptoe, John. Mufaro's Beautiful Daughters. Steptoe, John, illus. 2001. Tr. of Las Bellas Hijas De Mufaro. (Illus.). 28.95 incl. audio compact disk (978-1-59112-542-6(1)); pap. 33.95 incl. audio (978-1-59112-132-9(9)); pap. 35.95 incl. audio compact disk (978-1-59112-541-9(3)); (J). pap. 18.95 incl. audio compact disk (978-1-59112-318-7(6)); (J). 25.95 incl. audio (978-0-87499-656-2(2)); (J). pap. 33.95 incl. audio (978-0-87499-657-9(0)) Live Oak Media.

Steptoe, John L. Mufaro's Beautiful Daughters. 2001. (Live Oak Readalong Ser.). (Illus.). (J). (ps-4). pap. 16.95 incl. audio (978-0-87499-655-5(4)) Live Oak Media.

Stern, Ricki. Beryl E. Bean. 2nd ed. 2002. (Beryl E Bean Ser.). (Illus.). 64p. (J). 14.89 (978-0-06-028772-6(1)) HarperCollins Pubs.

Stevenson, Robert Louis. The Moon. Pearson, Tracey Campbell, illus. 2006. 40p. (J). (gr. k-4). 16.00 (978-0-374-35046-8(9) , Farrar, Straus & Giroux (BYR)) Farrar, Straus & Giroux.

Stewart, Sarah. The Gardener. Small, David, illus. 2002. (J). 15.49 (978-0-7587-2567-7(1)) Book Wholesalers, Inc.

—The Gardener. Small, David, illus. 2000. (J). pap. 19.97 incl. audio (978-0-7366-9203-8(7)) Books on Tape, Inc.

—The Gardener. Small, David, illus. 1999. (J). (gr. k-3). pap. 16.95 incl. audio (978-0-87499-431-5(4)); pap., tchr. ed. 37.95 incl. audio (978-0-87499-432-2(2)) Live Oak Media.

—The Gardener. 2000. 13.75 (978-0-606-17840-2(6)) Tandem Library Bks.

Stiegemeyer, Julie. Cheep! Cheep! Baicker-McKee, Carol, illus. 2006. 24p. (J). 9.95 (978-1-58234-682-3(8)) Bloomsbury Publishing.

Stilton, Geronimo. Merry Christmas, Geronimo! Wolf, Matt, illus. 2004. (Geronimo Stilton Ser.: No. 12). 113p. (J). lib. bdg. 10.00 (***978-1-4242-0281-2(7)***) Fitzgerald Bks.

Stine, R. L. Terror Trips. 2007. (Goosebumps Graphix Ser.). 144p. (J). pap. 16.99 (978-0-439-85777-2(5)); (Illus.). pap. 8.99 (978-0-439-85780-2(5)) Scholastic, Inc. (Graphix).

Stinson, Kathy. Red Is Best. Lewis, Robin Baird, illus. 25th ed. 2006. 32p. (J). (ps-1). lib. bdg. 19.95 (978-1-55451-052-8(X)); pap. 5.95 (978-1-55451-051-1(1)) Annick Pr., Ltd. CAN. *Dist:* Firefly Bks., Ltd.

—Those Green Things. Betteridge, Deirdre, illus. 2003. 32p. (J). (ps-1). pap. 4.95 (978-1-55037-376-9(5)) Annick Pr., Ltd. CAN. *Dist:* Firefly Bks., Ltd.

Stockton, Frank Richard. What Might Have Been Expected. 2006. 41.99 (***978-1-4280-4102-8(8)***); pap. 35.99 (***978-1-4280-4103-5(6)***) IndyPublish.com.

Stokes, Anthony, ed. Voices on Violence: The Lives of Children in Their Own Words. l.t. ed. 2002. (Illus.). 80p. 10.00 (978-0-9724803-0-7(7)) Orange Boy Bks.

Stolz, Mary. Ready or Not. 2000. 256p. (YA). pap. 15.95 (978-0-595-15119-6(1) , Backinprint.com) iUniverse, Inc.

Stout, Steve. The Day It Rained Leaves: A Starved Rock Park Adventure. Funk, Charles, illus. 2002. (Orig.). (J). (gr. k-5). pap. 9.95 (978-0-9609296-3-4(0)) Utica Hse. Publishing Co.

Strasser, Todd. For Money & Love. 2007. (Mob Princess Ser.). 208p. (YA). (gr. 9 up). pap. 8.99 (*978-1-4169-3533-9(9) , Simon Pulse) Simon & Schuster Children's Publishing.

—Stolen Kisses, Secrets, & Lies. Trisolini, Matteo, photos by. 2007. (Mob Princess Ser.). 224p. (YA). (gr. 9 up). pap. 8.99 (*978-1-4169-3541-4(X) , Simon Pulse) Simon & Schuster Children's Publishing.

Strauss, Linda Leopold. Really, Truly, Everything's Fine. 2004. 160p. (YA). 15.95 (978-0-7614-5163-1(3)) Cavendish, Marshall Corp.

Students of Galileo Academy of Science and Technology. Home Wasn't Built in a Day: Constructing the Stories of Our Families. 2006. 279p. (J). (gr. 7 up). pap. 16.00 (978-0-9770844-7-0(7)) 826 Valencia.

Sullivan, Sarah. Dear Baby: Letters from Your Big Brother. Meisel, Paul, illus. 2005. 40p. (J). (gr. k-2). 14.99 (978-0-7636-2126-1(9)) Candlewick Pr.

Sundberg, Angela M., et al. The Pottamus Family & the Unhappy Pottamus. Sundberg, Angela M. et al, illus. 2007. (J). pap. 16.00 (*978-0-8059-7478-2(4)) Dorrance Publishing Co., Inc.

Sweet, J. H. Marigold & the Feather of Hope, the Journey Begins. Chang, Tara Larsen, illus. 2007. (Fairy Chronicles Ser.). 128p. (J). (gr. 2-4). pap. 6.99 (*978-1-4022-0872-0(3) , Sourcebooks Jabberwocky) Sourcebooks, Inc.

Swigut, Bernadetta. First Star: Vigilja- First Star. 2006. (J). 16.99 (978-0-9790026-0-1(5)) Steinschneider, Bernadetta.

Swoish, Tammy. Hot Scots, Castles, & Kilts. 2008. (YA). (gr. 7). 208p. pap. 7.99 (*978-0-385-73447-9(6)); 224p. lib. bdg. 10.99 (*978-0-385-90450-6(9)) Random Hse. Children's Bks. (Delacorte Bks. for Young Readers).

Sykes, Shelley & Szymanski, Lois. The Soldier in the Cellar. 2004. (Gettysburg Ghost Gang Ser.: Vol. 5). 96p. (J). pap. 5.95 (978-1-57249-299-8(6) , White Mane Kids) White Mane Publishing Co., Inc.

Szekeres, Cyndy. I Can Count 100 Bunnies: And So Can You! 1999. (Illus.). 48p. (J). (ps-2). pap. 12.95 (978-0-590-38361-5(2)) Scholastic, Inc.

Talbert, Marc. Double or Nothing. 2001. 136p. (gr. 4-7). pap. 9.95 (978-0-595-15009-0(8) , Backinprint.com) iUniverse, Inc.

Tanabe, Yellow. Kekkaishi, Vol. 6. 2006. (Kekkaishi Ser.). (Illus.). 208p. (YA). pap. 9.99 (978-1-4215-0487-2(1)) Viz Media.

Tankoos, Sandra. A Growing Family: Ettie & the Evil Eye. 2000. (gr. 7-12). lib. bdg. 31.55 (978-0-613-73943-6(4)) Tandem Library Bks.

Tarpley, Natasha. Joe-Joe's First Flight. Lewis, Earl, illus. 2003. 40p. (J). (gr. k-3). 15.95 (978-0-375-81053-4(6) , Knopf Bks. for Young Readers) Random Hse. Children's Bks.

Tate, Eleanora E. A Blessing in Disguise. 2004. 192p. (J). pap. 6.95 (978-0-940975-66-8(1) , Sankofa Bks.) Just Us Bks., Inc.

Tate, Nikki. No Cafes in Narnia. 2000. (gr. 3-6). lib. bdg. 12.95 (978-0-613-78495-5(2)) Tandem Library Bks.

—No Cafes in Narnia: A Mystery on Tarragon Island. 2001. 174p. (J). (gr. 3-7). pap. 7.95 (978-1-55039-107-7(0)) Sono Nis Pr. CAN. Dist: Orca Bk. Pubs. USA.

Taylor, Bonnie Highsmith. Kodi's Mare. Marks, Dea, illus. 2000. (Cover-to-Cover Novel Ser.). 82p. (J). pap. (978-0-7891-2929-1(9)); (gr. 2-5). lib. bdg. 13.95 (978-0-7807-8962-3(8)) Perfection Learning Corp.

Taylor, Jeannie St. John. Out at Home: A Novel. 2004. 144p. (J). pap. 6.99 (978-0-8254-3724-3(5)) Kregel Pubns.

Taylor, Joanne. Making Room. Rankin, Peter, illus. 2004. 24p. (J). (gr. 1-4). 15.95 (978-0-88776-651-0(X)) Tundra Bks., Inc./Livres Toundra, Inc. CAN. Dist: Random Hse., Inc.

—There You Are. 2004. 208p. (J). (gr. 3-7). pap. 8.95 (978-0-88776-658-9(7)) Tundra Bks., Inc./Livres Toundra, Inc. CAN. Dist: Random Hse., Inc.

Taylor, Kim. Cissy Funk. 2001. 224p. (J). (gr. 5 up). 15.89 (978-0-06-029042-9(0)) HarperCollins Pubs.

Taylor, Mildred D. Lloro por la Tierra. 2000. (gr. 5-8). lib. bdg. 19.90 (978-0-613-70978-1(0)) Tandem Library Bks.

Teaster, Gerald Fred. Spirit up the People: Four Days to the Cowpens. 2006. (Illus.). 236p. per. 12.95 (978-0-9744556-2-4(8)) Junior History Pr.

Teixido, Emilio. Federico, Federico, Federico. 1999. 15.60 (978-0-606-17655-2(1)) Tandem Library Bks.

The Terrible Twos: 6 Small Books. (gr. k-3). 24.00 (978-0-7635-6244-1(0)) Rigby Education.

Testa, Maria. Almost Forever. 2003. (Illus.). 80p. (J). (gr. 4-8). 14.99 (978-0-7636-1996-1(5)) Candlewick Pr.

Thiel, Annie. Chloe's New Baby Brother. 2006. (Playdate Kids Ser.). (Illus.). 32p. 14.95 (978-1-933721-01-9(4)) Playdate Kids Publishing.

—Cosmos' Mom & Dad Are Moving Apart. 2006. (Playdate Kids Ser.). (Illus.). 32p. 14.95 (978-1-933721-04-0(9)) Playdate Kids Publishing.

—Dakota's Mom Goes to the Hospital. 2006. (Playdate Kids Ser.). (Illus.). 14.95 (978-1-933721-03-3(0)) Playdate Kids Publishing.

Thomas, Alisa. Anne of Green Gables. 2001. 72p. (J). stu. ed., ring bd. 12.99 (978-1-58609-179-8(4)) Progeny Pr.

Thomas, Carroll. Matty's War. Howard, Larry, illus. 1999. 164p. (J). (gr. 4-7). pap. 9.95 (978-1-57525-206-3(6)) Smith and Kraus Publishers, Incorporated.

—Matty's War. 1999. (J). (978-1-57525-205-6(8)) Smith and Kraus Publishers, Incorporated.

—Matty's War. 1999. (gr. 3-6). lib. bdg. 18.75 (978-0-613-62686-6(9)) Tandem Library Bks.

—Ring Out Wild Bells: A Matty Trescott Novel. 2001. (Illus.). viii, 169p. (J). 9.95 (978-1-57525-291-9(0)) Smith and Kraus Publishers, Incorporated.

Thomassie, Tynia. Cajun Through & Through. Glass, Andrew, illus. 2000. 32p. (J). (ps-3). 14.95 (978-0-316-84189-4(7)) Little Brown & Co.

Thompson, Lisa. Digging for Buried Treasure. Cantell, Brenda, illus. 2005. (Treasure Trackers Ser.). 80p. (gr. 5-9). 19.00 (978-0-7910-8872-2(3) , Chelsea Hse.) Facts On File, Inc.

Thorpe, Kiki. Snowbound. 2000. (gr. k-3). lib. bdg. 11.80 (978-0-613-31727-6(0)) Tandem Library Bks.

Thorup, Bryce. Doctor Matthews' Family Christmas. Muller, Ruth, illus. 2005. (J). 18.95 (978-0-9765964-1-7(5)) Round Tower Pr.

Tich, Jan. Pope Meets Pin. 2006. (Adventures in Unusual Places Ser.). (Illus.). 28p. (J). 12.95 (978-9974-7925-7-9(6)) Hardenville SA URY. Dist: Independent Pubs. Group.

Tiddle, Deanna Hessedal. Hold on, Jessica, Don't Let Go. 2001. (gr. 3-6). lib. bdg. 28.00 (978-0-613-74714-1(3)) Tandem Library Bks.

Tiernan, Cate. A Feather of Stone, No. 3. 2005. (Balefire Ser.). 240p. (YA). (gr. 7-12). mass mkt. 5.99 (978-1-59514-047-0(6) , Razorbill) Penguin Group (USA) Inc.

Tinkler, David. Headmaster Went Splat. 2005. (Illus.). 104p. (J). pap. 8.99 (*978-1-84270-457-8(5)) Transworld Publishers Ltd. GBR. Dist: Independent Pubs. Group.

To the Other Side: Individual Chapter Book Title Six-Packs. Vol. 30. 32p. (gr. 5 up). 44.00 (978-0-7578-0981-1(2)) Rigby Education.

Tomblin, Marian Strong. The Mystery at Hotel Ormond. 2004. (Illus.). 142p. (J). per. 9.95 (978-0-9766620-0-6(0)) Avery Goode-Reid Pubs.

—Where's Capone's Cash? 2005. (Illus.). 232p. (J). per. 9.95 (978-0-9766620-1-3(9)) Avery Goode-Reid Pubs.

Tomey, Ingrid. Grandfather's Day. McKay, Robert A., illus. 2003. 64p. (YA). (gr. 4-6). pap. 9.95 (978-1-56397-947-7(0)) Boyds Mills Pr.

Torrey, Michele. Bottles of Eight & Pieces of Rum. 1998. 138p. (J). (ps-7). pap. 9.99 (978-0-88092-321-7(0) , 3210) Royal Fireworks Publishing Co.

—Voyage of Midnight. 2006. 240p. (gr. 5). (J). 17.99 (978-0-375-92382-1(9)); (YA). 15.95 (978-0-375-82382-4(4)) Random Hse. Children's Bks. (Knopf Bks. for Young Readers).

Toten, Teresa. Game. 2001. (gr. 7-12). lib. bdg. 16.40 (978-0-613-60557-1(8)) Tandem Library Bks.

Town, Florida Ann. With a Silent Companion. 1999. (gr. 7-12). lib. bdg. 16.40 (978-0-613-89150-9(3)) Tandem Library Bks.

Townley, Roderick. The Red Thread: A Novel in Three Incarnations. 2007. 304p. (YA). 17.99 (*978-1-4169-2930-7(4) , Atheneum) Simon & Schuster Children's Publishing.

Townson, Hazel. Your Dad, My Mom. 2000. (Illus.). 96p. (J). (gr. 3 up). 16.99 (978-0-86264-961-6(7)) Andersen GBR. Dist: Independent Pubs. Group.

Treis, Connie. Bartrob. 2003. 44p. per. 12.95 (978-1-932344-52-3(7)) Thornton Publishing.

Tricking Tracy: 6 Small Books. (gr. k-3). 24.00 (978-0-7635-6245-8(9)) Rigby Education.

Trotter, Deborah W. A Summer's Trade. Manavi, Lorraine Begay, tr. Toddy, Irving, illus. 2008. (ENG & NAV.). 32p. (gr. 2-5). 17.95 (*978-1-893354-71-5(7)) Salina Bookshelf.

Troughton, Ruth. The Invisible Ones. 2003. 88p. pap. 9.95 (978-0-595-29592-0(4)) iUniverse, Inc.

Uff, Caroline, reader. Hola, Lulu! 2003. (Lovable Lulu Ser.). (SPA., Illus.). (J). pap. (978-970-690-564-2(2)) Planeta Mexicana Editorial S. A. de C. V.

Uhlig, Richard Allen. Last Dance at the Frosty Queen. 2007. 368p. (YA). (gr. 9). lib. bdg. 18.99 (*978-0-375-93967-9(9)); 15.99 (*978-0-375-83967-2(4)) Random Hse. Children's Bks. (Knopf Bks. for Young Readers).

Uncle Markie. Pigletté & Bobo Go Home. 2002. 22p. (YA). ring bd. 9.95 (978-1-933129-02-0(6)) Studio 403.

Underdahl, S. T. The Other Sister. 2007. 264p. (J). (gr. 7 up). pap. 8.95 (978-0-7387-0933-8(6) , Flux) Llewellyn Pubns.

Ungerer, Tomi. The Mellops Go Spelunking. Ungerer, Tomi, illus. 1998. (Illus.). 32p. (J). (gr. k-4). pap. 5.95 (978-1-57098-228-6(7)) Rinehart, Roberts Pubs.

—Ningun Beso Para Mama. 1998. (Spanish Ser.). (SPA.). 40p. (ps-3). 11.00 (978-84-264-3590-3(4)) Lectorum Pubns., Inc.

Unknown. Ruby's Sandcastle. 2008. (Max & Ruby Ser.). 10p. (J). (ps-k). bds. 7.99 (*978-0-448-44864-0(5) , Grosset & Dunlap) Penguin Group (USA) Inc.

Ure, Jean. Family Fan Club. l.t. ed. 2005. (J). pap. (978-0-7540-7934-7(1) , CLP 484) BBC Audio.

—Family Fan Club. 2004. (Diary Ser.). (Illus.). 160p. (J). pap. 8.99 (*978-0-00-717237-5(0)) HarperCollins Pubs. Ltd. GBR. Dist: Independent Pubs. Group.

Ure, Jean. Passion Flower. l.t. ed. 2005. 268p. (J). pap. (978-0-7540-7910-1(4) , CLP 472) BBC Audio.

—Passion Flower. 2003. (Diary Ser.). (Illus.). 202p. (J). pap. 9.99 (978-0-00-715619-1(7)) HarperCollins Pubs. Ltd. GBR. Dist: Independent Pubs. Group.

Vafides, Debbi. Here Comes B. B. 2002. pap. 7.00 (978-0-8059-5612-2(3)) Dorrance Publishing Co., Inc.

Valentine, Johnny. The Daddy Machine. Schmidt, Lynette, illus. 2nd ed. 2004. 32p. (Orig.). pap. 10.95 (978-1-55583-846-1(4)) Alyson Pubns.

—The Duke Who Outlawed Jelly Beans: And Other Stories. Schmidt, Lynette, illus. 2nd ed. 2004. 32p. pap. 10.95 (978-1-55583-847-8(2)) Alyson Pubns.

—One Dad, Two Dads, Brown Dad, Blue Dads. Sarecky, Melody, illus. 2004. 32p. (J). pap. 10.95 (978-1-55583-848-5(0)) Alyson Pubns.

Vallejo-Nagera, Alejandra. Cuanto me Quieren! Guerrero, Andrés, illus. 2003. (SPA.). 23p. (J). (gr. k-1). 8.95 (978-84-204-4951-7(2)) Santillana USA Publishing Co., Inc.

—Los Bigotes de Chocolate. 2003. (SPA., Illus.). 27p. (J). (gr. k-1). 8.95 (978-968-19-1020-4(6)) Santillana USA Publishing Co., Inc.

Van Dyne, Edith. Aunt Jane's Nieces. l.t. ed. 2006. 170p. pap. 11.99 (*978-1-4264-3951-3(2)); 186p. pap. 14.99 (*978-1-4264-4009-0(X)) BiblioBazaar.

—Aunt Jane's Nieces at Millville. l.t. ed. 2006. 158p. pap. 11.99 (*978-1-4264-4058-8(8)); 172p. pap. 14.99 (*978-1-4264-4117-2(7)) BiblioBazaar.

—Aunt Jane's Nieces in Society. 2006. 144p. pap. 10.99 (*978-1-4264-4161-5(4)); 156p. pap. 14.99 (*978-1-4264-4202-5(5)) BiblioBazaar.

—Aunt Jane's Nieces Out West. 2006. 180p. pap. 14.99 (*978-1-4264-4188-2(6)); 164p. pap. 11.99 (*978-1-4264-4145-5(2)) BiblioBazaar.

Van Leeuwen, Jean. Amanda Pig & the Awful, Scary Monster. Schweninger, Ann, illus. 2004. (Easy-to-Read, Puffin Ser.). 48p. (J). (gr. k-2). pap. 3.99 (978-0-14-240203-0(6) , Puffin) Penguin Group (USA) Inc.

Van Steenwyk, Elizabeth. Three Dog Winter. 1999. (978-0-606-16440-5(5)) Tandem Library Bks.

Vander Zee, Ruth & Sneider, Marian. Eli Remembers. Farnsworth, Bill, illus. 2007. 32p. (J). (gr. 3-7). 18.00 (*978-0-8028-5309-7(9) , Eerdmans Bks For Young Readers) Eerdmans, William B. Publishing Co.

Varela, Barry. Palmer's Gate. 2006. 112p. (J). 16.95 (978-1-59643-073-0(7)) Roaring Brook Pr.

Vasiliu, Mircea. A Day at the Beach. 2007. (Illus.). 36p. (J). 7.95 (*978-1-59091-068-9(0)) Eastern National.

Venable, Leslie Allgood. The Not So Wicked Stepmother. Harrison, Julie M., illus. 1999. 24p. (J). (gr. 1-7). per. 9.95 (978-0-9666817-0-3(3)) Venable, L.A. Publishing Co.

Veneziano, Chuckie. My Time on Nantucket. 2005. (Illus.). 56p. (J). lib. bdg. 17.95 (978-0-9755078-0-3(X)) Sweet Punkin Pr.

The Very Noisy Family: Lap Book. (Pebble Soup Explorations Ser.). 16p. (ps up). 21.00 (978-0-7578-2109-7(X)) Rigby Education.

The Very Noisy Family: Small Book. (Pebble Soup Explorations Ser.). 16p. (ps up). 5.00 (978-0-7578-2110-3(3)) Rigby Education.

Vescio & LohnRiver, Jenna. Rainbow Journey Screen Play (with Pictures) 2005. 65p. pap. 20.00 (978-1-4116-3288-2(5)) Lulu.com.

Victoria & the Baby Tree. 2005. pap. 14.95 (*978-1-59526-525-8(2)) Media Creations, Inc.

Vijayaraghavan, Vineeta. Motherland. 2001. (gr. 7-12). lib. bdg. 21.10 (978-0-613-61041-4(5)) Tandem Library Bks.

Viky Toma Unas Vacaciones Divetidas. 2003. (SPA.). 62p. (J). (ps-1). (978-968-5308-80-9(2) , Silver Dolphin en Español) Advanced Marketing, S. de R. L. de C. V.

Vision, David & Vision, Mutiya Sahar. Missing You. Alcantara, Ignacio, illus. 2005. 40p. (J). mass mkt. 17.00 (978-0-9659538-6-3(6)) Soul Vision Works Publishing.

Vogelaar, Alie. Not So High, Margreet!, 5 bks. VanBrugge, J., tr. Kramer, K. J., illus. 2001. 128p. (YA). lib. bdg. 10.95 (978-0-9670728-2-1(4)) Early Foundations Pubs.

Voigt, Cynthia. Los Tillerman Encuentran Hogar. 2001. (SPA.). (gr. 3-6). lib. bdg. 18.20 (978-0-613-80661-9(1)) Tandem Library Bks.

Vrettos, Adrienne Maria. Skin. 2006. (Illus.). 240p. (J). (gr. 7 up). 16.95 (978-1-4169-0655-1(X) , McElderry, Margaret K.) Simon & Schuster Children's Publishing.

W. I. T. C. H. collector's ed. 2004. 144p. (J). pap. 12.99 (978-0-7868-0973-8(6)) Disney Pr.

Waite, Judy. A Trick of the Mind. 2005. (Illus.). 272p. (YA). (gr. 7). 16.95 (978-0-689-87014-9(0) , Atheneum) Simon & Schuster Children's Publishing.

—Trick of the Mind. 2006. 288p. (YA). pap. 6.99 (978-0-689-87015-6(9) , Simon Pulse) Simon & Schuster Children's Publishing.

Waldorf, Heather. Fighting the Current. Lee, Karen, ed. 2004. 224p. 19.95 (978-1-894222-93-8(8)) Lobster Pr. CAN. Dist: Univ. of Toronto Pr.

Walker, Susan Eileen. Secret of the Dance. 2006. 232p. pap. 15.00 (978-0-9766805-4-3(8)) Keene Publishing.

Wallace, Karen. The Secret of the Crocodiles. 2007. (Lady Violet's Casebook Ser.). 208p. (J). (gr. 4-7). pap. 9.95 (*978-0-689-87483-3(9)) Simon & Schuster, Ltd. GBR. Dist: Independent Pubs. Group.

—The Unrivalled Spangles. 2006. 224p. (YA). 16.95 (978-1-4169-1503-4(6)) Simon & Schuster Children's Publishing.

—Wendy. 320p. (J). 2003. (978-0-689-83747-0(X) , Simon & Schuster Children's Publishing); 2005. reprint ed. pap. 6.99 (978-1-4169-0314-7(3) , Simon Pulse) Simon & Schuster Children's Publishing.

Wallace, Karen & Frost, Michael. Wendy. 2003. 320p. (J). 16.95 (978-0-689-86769-9(7)) Simon & Schuster Children's Publishing.

Wallace, Michael. You, Mommy & Me. 2006. 22p. spiral bd. 8.50 (978-1-4116-9761-4(8)) Lulu.com.

Wallace, Rich. Takedown, No. 8. 2007. (Winning Season Ser.: No. 8). 128p. (YA). (gr. 2). pap. 4.99 (*978-0-14-240919-0(7) , Puffin) Penguin Group (USA) Inc.

Walsh, Alice. Uncle Farley's False Teeth. ed. 2004. (Illus.). (J). (gr. k-3). spiral bd. (978-0-616-01807-1(X)) Canadian National Institute for the Blind/Institut National Canadien pour les Aveugles.

—Uncle Farley's False Teeth. Martchenko, Michael, illus. 1998. 32p. (J). (ps-2). lib. bdg. 15.95 (978-1-55037-543-5(1)) Firefly Bks., Ltd.

Walsh, Laurence & Walsh, Suella. In the Middle of the Night. 2006. (J). pap. (*978-0-88092-473-3(X)) Royal Fireworks Publishing Co.

Walsh, Sheila. Gigi, God's Little Princess. Johnson, Meredith, illus. 2005. 32p. (J). 12.99 (978-1-4003-0529-2(2)) Nelson, Thomas Inc.

Wang, Adria. My World: My Family. Nicholls, Paul, illus. 2005. (My World Bks.). 10p. (J). 4.95 (978-1-58117-252-2(4) , Intervisual/Piggy Toes) Dalmatian Pr.

Ware-Holmes, Barbara. Letters to Julia. 1999. (J). (978-0-606-17466-4(4)) Tandem Library Bks.

Wargin, Kathy-Jo. Mitt & Minn at the Wisconsin Cheese Jamboree. Busch Holman, Karen, illus. 2007. 144p. (J). 14.95 (*978-1-58726-305-7(X) , Mitten Pr.) Ann Arbor Media Group, LLC.

Warner, Sally. It's Only Temporary. 2008. 160p. (J). (gr. 4). 15.99 (*978-0-670-06111-2(5) , Viking Juvenile) Penguin Group (USA) Inc.

Watson, Sally. Highland Rebel. 2002. (J). pap. 12.95 (978-1-930009-63-9(1) , 800-691-7779) Image Cascade Publishing.

Wax, Wendy. A Fairly Odd Recess: A Funny Fill-ins Book. Style Guide Staff, illus. 2005. (Fairly OddParents Ser.). 48p. (J). pap. 3.99 (978-1-4169-0646-9(0) , Simon Spotlight) Simon & Schuster Children's Publishing.

—Top-Secret Handbook. Artful Doodlers Limited Staff, illus. 2005. (Totally Spies! Ser.). 48p. (J). pap. 3.99 (978-0-689-87729-2(3) , Simon Spotlight) Simon & Schuster Children's Publishing.

Weaver, K. C. For the Sake of the Children. 2007. 75p. 14.95 (*978-1-4241-0647-9(8)) PublishAmerica, Inc.

Weaver, Will. Claws. 240p. (J). 2003. lib. bdg. 16.89 (978-0-06-009474-4(5)); 2004. reprint ed. pap. 6.99 (978-0-06-009475-1(3) , HarperTeen) HarperCollins Pubs.

—Claws. 2004. lib. bdg. 15.30 (978-0-613-71445-7(8)) Tandem Library Bks.

Webb, Terry. Manning the Light. 2003. 148p. (J). pap. 12.99 (978-1-57921-669-6(2)) Pleasant Word.

Weber, Jill. Angel Bites the Bullet. 2003. (gr. 3-6). lib. bdg. 12.95 (978-0-613-88088-6(9)) Tandem Library Bks.

Weimer, Heidi R. I Love You More Than... Sharp, Chris, illus. 2006. 16p. (J). (ps). bds. 12.99 (978-0-8249-6679-9(1) , Candy Cane Pr.) Ideals Pubns.

Weller, Duncan. Night Wall. 2005. (Illus.). 32p. (J). 16.95 (978-1-894965-13-2(2)) Simply Read Bks. CAN. Dist: Perseus Distribution.

Welles, Lee. Gaia Girls Way of Water. 2007. (Gaia Girls Ser.). 336p. (J). pap. 12.95 (*978-1-933609-03-4(6)) Daisyworld Pr.

Wells, Carolyn. Marjorie's Maytime. 2007. 152p. pap. 11.99 (*978-1-4264-8435-3(6)) BiblioBazaar.

—Patty at Home. 2007. (ENG.). 204p. per. 12.95 (*978-1-4218-3321-7(2)) 1st World Publishing, Inc.

Wells, Rosemary. Leale a Su Conejito. 2000. (SPA.). (gr. k-3). lib. bdg. 10.65 (978-0-613-25929-3(7)) Tandem Library Bks.

—Max & Ruby's Midas: Another Greek Myth. 2003. (Max & Ruby Ser.). (Illus.). 32p. (J). (gr. k-2). pap. 5.99 (978-0-14-250066-8(6) , Puffin) Penguin Group (USA) Inc.

—The Small World of Binky Braverman. Egielski, Richard, illus. 2003. 40p. (J). (ps-3). 15.99 (978-0-670-03636-3(6) , Viking Juvenile) Penguin Group (USA) Inc.

Werlin, Nancy. The Killer's Cousin. 2000. 240p. (YA). (gr. 9-12). mass mkt. 5.99 (978-0-440-22751-9(8) , Laurel Leaf) Random Hse. Children's Bks.

—The Killer's Cousin. 2000. (978-0-606-17820-4(1)) Tandem Library Bks.

—The Killer's Cousin. l.t. ed. 1999. 277p. (YA). (gr. 9-12). 21.95 (978-0-7862-2188-2(7)) Thorndike Pr.

Wesley, Valerie Wilson. How to Fish for Trouble. Roos, Maryn, illus. 2004. 89p. (J). lib. bdg. 15.00 (*978-1-4242-0643-8(X)) Fitzgerald Bks.

West, Colin. Uncle Pat & Auntie Pat. 2006. (Read-It! Chapter Books). (J). 21.26 (978-1-4048-2734-9(X)) Picture Window Bks.

West, Keith. Young Runaways: A Teenage Adventure. Andrews, Gary, illus. 2001. (Star Plays Ser.). 48p. (gr. 4-6). pap. 8.99 (978-0-237-52191-2(1) , Evans Brothers, Limited) Evans Publishing Group GBR. Dist: Independent Pubs. Group.

Westfall, Tom. Piney the Porcupine Finally Finds a Family. 2005. 40p. per. 10.95 (978-1-59453-798-1(4) , 2949) Airleaf Publishing & Bookselling.

Whale Watch, 6 Packs. (Bookweb Ser.). 32p. (gr. 6 up). 34.00 (978-0-7578-0895-1(6)) Rigby Education.

What Kind of a Name Is That? 2006. (J). per. 6.49 net. (978-0-9759665-3-2(7)) Pilate, Victoria.

Wheeler, Jordan & Jackson, Dennis. Christmas at Wapos Bay. 2006. 176p. (J). pap. (*978-1-55050-324-1(3)) Coteau Bks.

Whelan, Gloria. Farewell to the Island. 1998. 208p. (J). (gr. 4 up). 16.95 (978-0-06-027751-2(3)) HarperCollins Pubs.

Whint, Ana Lee. Espalemit. 2003. (ENG.). 112p. pap. 9.95 (*978-0-595-26259-5(7) , Writers Club Pr.) iUniverse, Inc.

White, Ruth. Belle Prater's Boy. unabr. ed. 2004. 196p. (J). (gr. 5-9). pap. 38.00 incl. audio (978-0-8072-8682-1(6) , YA234SP, Listening Library) Random Hse. Audio Publishing Group.

—Belle Prater's Boy. 1998. (YA). 12.15 (978-0-606-12610-6(4)) Tandem Library Bks.

—Belle Prater's Boy. l.t. ed. 2000. (Illus.). 221p. (YA). (gr. 4-7). 21.95 (978-0-7862-2885-0(7)) Thorndike Pr.

—Buttermilk Hill. 2006. 176p. (J). reprint ed. pap. 6.95 (978-0-374-41003-2(8)) Macmillan.

 For book reviews, descriptive annotations, tables of contents, cover images, author biographies & additional information, updated daily, subscribe to www.booksinprint.com

White, Steve. Family Vacations & Other Hazards of Growing Up. 2001. (Illus.). 206p. per. 14.95 (978-0-9679092-8-8(7)) Chloe Pr.

Whitehouse, Elizabeth. The Bag Babies & the Secret of Civilization: A Jensen Family Story. 2004. (Illus.). 96p. (J). pap. 5.95 (978-1-933031-54-5(9)) Whitehouse Publishing.

Who Will Look Out for Danny? Individual Title Six-Packs. (Action Packs Ser.). 120p. (gr. 3-5). 44.00 (978-0-7635-8420-7(7)) Rigby Education.

Whos's in My Family? (Peek A Boo Pockets Ser.). 12p. (J). bds. (978-2-7643-0107-4(3)) Phidal Publishing, Inc./ Editions Phidal, Inc.

Wibking, Ben & Dittus, Janet. The Happy Ending: A Family for Quin Quin. Wibking, Tim, illus. 1999. 32p. (J). (gr. k-3). 16.95 (978-0-9651747-1-8(9)) Foxhaven Pr.

Wiesner, David, adapted by. Gonna Roll the Bones. 2004. 32p. 16.95 (978-1-59687-176-2(8) , Milk & Cookies) ibooks, Inc.

Wiggin, Kate Douglas. New Chronicles of Rebecca. 2006. 128p. pap. (978-1-84637-648-1(3)) Echo Library.

—Rebecca of Sunnybrook Farm. (J). 23.95 (978-0-8488-0854-9(1)) Amereon LTD.

—Rebecca of Sunnybrook Farm. McClintock, Barbara, illus. anniv. ed. 2006. 290p. (J). (gr. 4-8). reprint ed. 22.00 (978-1-4223-5332-5(X)) DIANE Publishing Co.

—Rebecca of Sunnybrook Farm. 2003. (Dover Evergreen Classics Ser.). 208p. (J). (gr. 4-7). pap. 3.00 (978-0-486-42845-1(1)) Dover Pubns., Inc.

—Rebecca of Sunnybrook Farm. McClintock, Barbara, illus. 2003. 304p. (J). (gr. 5 up). tchr. ed. 20.00 (978-0-618-34694-3(5)) Houghton Mifflin Co. Trade & Reference Div.

—Rebecca of Sunnybrook Farm. 2004. reprint ed. pap. 19.95 (978-1-4179-9996-5(9)); pap. 1.99 (978-1-4179-9946-0(2)) Kessinger Publishing, LLC.

—Rebecca of Sunnybrook Farm. 2003. (Aladdin Classics Ser.). 368p. (J). pap. 4.99 (978-0-689-86001-0(3) , Aladdin) Simon & Schuster Children's Publishing.

—Rebecca of Sunnybrook Farm. Akib, Jamel, illus. 2007. (Classic Starts Ser.). 160p. (J). 4.95 (978-1-4027-3693-3(2)) Sterling Publishing Co., Inc.

Wilburn, Garlyn Webb. Désirée's Quest for Freedom. 2004. 143p. pap. 19.95 (978-1-4137-2825-5(1)) PublishAmerica, Inc.

Wilder, Laura Ingalls. The Long Winter. 2003. (gr. 3-6). lib. bdg. 14.15 (978-0-613-71424-2(5)) Tandem Library Bks.

—My Little House Book & Diary Set. 1999. (Illus.). (J). (gr. 3-7). 14.95 (978-0-694-01253-4(X)) HarperCollins Pubs.

Wilkins, Celia. Across the Rolling River. Andreasen, Dan, illus. 2001. (Little House Ser.). 272p. (J). 16.95 (978-0-06-027004-9(7)); 16.89 (978-0-06-027005-6(5)); (gr. 5 up). pap. 6.99 (978-0-06-440734-2(9) , Harper Trophy) HarperCollins Pubs.

—Across the Rolling River. Andreasen, Dan, illus. 2001. (gr. 3-6). lib. bdg. 14.15 (978-0-613-51524-5(2)) Tandem Library Bks.

Willcox, James. Pixie Howard: Her Adventures in Faith. 2004. 116p. pap. 16.95 (978-1-4137-2499-8(X)) PublishAmerica, Inc.

Willey, Margaret. Thanksgiving with Me. Bloom, Lloyd, illus. 1998. 32p. (J). (ps-3). 15.95 (978-0-06-027113-8(2) , Geringer, Laura Book) HarperCollins Pubs.

Williams, Barbara. Michi y Su Nueva Familia. 1998. (SPA.). 136p. (gr. 6-8). (978-84-239-7127-5(9)) Espasa Calpe, S.A.

Williams, Carol Lynch. Mother to Embarrass Me. 2003. (gr. 3-6). lib. bdg. 13.00 (978-0-613-83531-2(X)) Tandem Library Bks.

Williams, Jennifer. Stringbean's Trip to the Shining Sea. Williams, Vera B., illus. 1999. 48p. (J). (ps-3). pap. 6.99 (978-0-688-16701-2(2) , Harper Trophy) HarperCollins Pubs.

Williams, Kethette. The Ghosts on the Hill. 2007. (ENG.). 56p. per. 12.95 (*978-1-4241-6767-8(1)*) PublishAmerica, Inc.

Williams, Vera B. Stringbean's Trip to the Shining Sea. 1999. (978-0-606-16744-4(7)); lib. bdg. 14.10 (978-0-613-18280-5(4)) Tandem Library Bks.

Willis, Judith (Tran & Farre, Lluis. Grey Boy. 2007. 44p. (J). pap. 12.95 (*978-1-905341-08-5(3)*) WingedChariot Pr. GBR. *Dist:* Independent Pubs. Group.

Willner-Pardo, Gina. My Mom & Other Mysteries of the Universe. 2004. 176p. (YA). (gr. 4-6). tchr. ed. 15.00 (978-0-618-43020-8(2) , Clarion Bks.) Houghton Mifflin Co. Trade & Reference Div.

Winn, Christine M. & Walsh, David. Clover's Secret. Winn, Christine M., illus. 2004. (Illus.). 28p. (J). (gr. k-4). reprint ed. 15.00 (978-0-7567-7653-4(8)) DIANE Publishing Co.

Wiseman, Eva. No One Must Know. 2004. 200p. (J). (gr. 5). pap. 8.95 (978-0-88776-680-0(3)) Tundra Bks., Inc./ Livres Toundra, Inc. CAN. *Dist:* Random Hse., Inc.

Wixom, Jason Kay & Wixom, Tedi Tuttle. Cock-a-Doodle-Doo, I Love You. Lancaster, Derek, illus. 2nd ed. 2003. (Ralph Rooster Ser.: Vol. 1). 16p. (J). (ps-2). 6.95 (978-1-885227-05-8(1)) TNT Bks.

Wolf, Joan M. Someone Named Eva. 2007. 208p. (J). (gr. 5-9). 16.00 (978-0-618-53579-8(9) , Clarion Bks.) Houghton Mifflin Co. Trade & Reference Div.

Wolfer, Dianne. Border Line. 1998. 190p. (J). pap. 11.95 (978-1-86368-208-4(2)) Fremantle Pr. AUS. *Dist:* International Specialized Bk. Services.

Wollman, Jessica. Bunches of Fun. MacNeil, Chris, illus. 2006. 149p. (J). (*978-1-4156-5003-5(9)* , Aladdin) Simon & Schuster Children's Publishing.

Woodson, Jacqueline. The House You Pass on the Way. 2003. 112p. (YA). reprint ed. pap. 5.99 (978-0-14-250191-7(3) , Puffin); (gr. 5). 16.99 (978-0-399-23969-4(3) , Putnam Juvenile) Penguin Group (USA) Inc.

—The House You Pass on the Way. 1999. (J). (978-0-606-16085-8(X)) Tandem Library Bks.

—The House You Pass on the Way. l.t. ed. 2004. 109p. (J). 22.95 (978-0-7862-6428-5(4)) Thorndike Pr.

—Miracle's Boys. 2000. 1p. (YA). (gr. 5 up). 15.99 (978-0-399-23113-1(7) , Putnam Juvenile) Penguin Group (USA) Inc.

Woolson, Constance Fenimore (A. K. A. Anne March). The Old Stone House. 2006. 140p. pap. (978-1-84637-478-4(2)) Echo Library.

The World of Dick & Jane & Friends. 2004. (Dick & Jane Ser.). (Illus.). 192p. (J). (ps-2). 10.99 (978-0-448-43646-3(9) , Grosset & Dunlap) Penguin Group (USA) Inc.

Wright, Barbara R. Harry Berry. 1999. (gr. 7-12). lib. bdg. 31.55 (978-0-613-73938-2(8)) Tandem Library Bks.

Wright, Betty Ren. Crandall's Castle. 2005. 184p. (YA). (gr. 4-6). tchr. ed. 16.95 (978-0-8234-1726-1(3)) Holiday Hse., Inc.

Wyeth, Sharon Dennis. A Piece of Heaven. 2002. (gr. 5-8). lib. bdg. 13.00 (978-0-613-64761-8(0)) Tandem Library Bks.

Wynne-Jones, Tim. Rex Zero & the End of the World. 2007. 186p. (J). (*978-1-4287-3318-3(3)*) Farrar, Straus & Giroux.

Wyss, Johann David. Classic Starts: the Swiss Family Robinson. Akib, Jamel, illus. 2007. (Classic Starts Ser.). 160p. (J). 4.95 (978-1-4027-3694-0(0)) Sterling Publishing Co., Inc.

—The Swiss Family Robinson. 2006. (Charming Classics). 208p. (J). pap. 6.99 (978-0-06-087587-9(9) , Harper Festival) HarperCollins Pubs.

Wyss, Johann David. The Swiss Family Robinson: Or Adventures in a Desert Island. l.t. ed. 2006. 354p. pap. 18.99 (*978-1-4264-5633-6(6)*) BiblioBazaar.

Yacoubou, Jeanne. I Am a Rainbow Child Coloring-Story Book. Stebakova, Elena, illus. 2005. 16p. (J). (978-0-9788737-4-5(2)) Alaafia Kids Co.

Yates, Elizabeth. American Haven. 2002. (Illus.). 112p. (J). (gr. 4-7). 7.49 (978-1-57924-896-3(9)) Jones, Bob Univ. Pr.

Yates, Irene. Ollie. 1998. (Cambridge Reading Ser.). (Illus.). 32p. (gr. 2-6). pap. 9.00 (978-0-521-63944-6(1)) Cambridge Univ. Pr.

Ye, Ting-Xing. Share the Sky. Langlois, Suzane, illus. 1999. 32p. (J). (ps-2). lib. bdg. 17.95 (978-1-55037-579-4(2)) Annick Pr., Ltd. CAN. *Dist:* Firefly Bks., Ltd.

—Share the Sky. 1999. (gr. k-3). lib. bdg. 15.25 (978-0-613-26907-0(1)) Tandem Library Bks.

Yep, Laurence. The Amah. 2001. (gr. 7-12). lib. bdg. 14.15 (978-0-613-35896-5(1)) Tandem Library Bks.

Ylvisaker, Anne. Little Klein. 2007. (Illus.). 192p. (J). (gr. 3-7). 15.99 (*978-0-7636-3359-2(3)*) Candlewick Pr.

Yuki, Kaori. Godchild, Vol. 4. 2007. (GodChild Ser.). 200p. (YA). pap. 8.99 (978-1-4215-0478-0(2)) Viz Media.

Yukish, Joe. The Fishing Contest. Palmer, Kate Salley, illus. 2002. 24p. (J). (gr. k-2). pap. 5.25 (978-1-57874-031-4(2)) Kaeden Corp.

Zagwyn, Deborah Turney. The Sea House. Zagwyn, Deborah Turney, illus. 2004. (Illus.). 32p. (J). (gr. k-3). 15.95 (978-1-58246-030-7(2) , Tricycle Pr.) Ten Speed Pr.

Zaikine, Zak. A Mother's Love. Zaikine, Zak & O'Keefe, Karin, eds. deluxe ed. 2005. Vol. 2. (Illus.). 42p. (J). 24.95 (978-0-934290-01-2(6)) Moon Valley Productions.

Zalben, Jane Breskin. Brenda Berman, Wedding Expert. Chess, Victoria, illus. 2007. (J). (*978-0-618-31321-1(4)* , Clarion Bks.) Houghton Mifflin Co. Trade & Reference Div.

Zemser, Amy Bronwen. Beyond the Mango Tree. 1998. (Illus.). 156p. (YA). (gr. 5 up). 14.95 (978-0-688-16005-0(0)) HarperCollins Pubs.

Ziarko, Greg. The Waylaid: Asheth. ed. 2007. 280p. (YA). (*978-0-9792694-0-0(7)*) gaZko Entertainment.

Ziefert, Harriet. Baby Talk. Sami, illus. 2005. 24p. (ps). bds. 8.95 (978-1-59354-105-7(8)) Blue Apple Bks.

—Ready, Alice? Level 2. Haley, Amanda, illus. 2005. (I'm Going to Read Ser.). 32p. (J). 11.95 (978-1-4027-2718-4(6)) Sterling Publishing Co., Inc.

Ziefert, Harriet & Zemke, Deborah. Families Have Together. 2005. (Illus.). 40p. (J). 15.95 (978-1-59354-071-5(X)) Blue Apple Bks.

Zinnen, Linda. The Dragons of Spratt, Ohio. 2004. 240p. (J). 15.99 (978-0-06-000021-9(X)); lib. bdg. 17.89 (978-0-06-000022-6(8)) HarperCollins Pubs.

Zoehfeld, Kathleen Weidner. Billy. 2001. (Rolie Polie Olie Ser.). (Illus.). 12p. (J). (gr. k-2). bds. 3.99 (978-0-7364-1023-6(6)) Mouse Works.

Zolotow, Charlotte. This Quiet Lady. Lobel, Anita, illus. 2000. 24p. (J). (ps-3). pap. 6.99 (978-0-688-17527-6(9) , Harper Trophy) HarperCollins Pubs.

—This Quiet Lady. 2000. (ps-2). lib. bdg. 14.10 (978-0-613-27232-2(3)) Tandem Library Bks.

Zubizarreta, Patxi. Paloma, Llegaste Por el Aire. Balzola, Asun, illus. 2003. (SPA.). 74p. (978-84-246-5913-4(9) , GL3212) La Galera, S.A. Editorial ESP. *Dist:* Lectorum Pubns., Inc.

Zucker, Jonny. Fasting & Dates: A Ramadan & Eid-ul-Fitr Story. Cohen, Jan Barger, illus. 2004. (Festival Time! Ser.). 24p. (J). pap. 6.95 (978-0-7641-2671-0(7)) Barron's Educational Series, Inc.

—Lighting a Lamp: A Diwali Story. Cohen, Jan Barger, illus. 2004. (Festival Time! Ser.). 24p. (J). pap. 6.95 (978-0-7641-2670-3(9)) Barron's Educational Series, Inc.

FAMILY LIFE

Ambrose-Van Lee, Doreen. Raised in the Sun: Shades of Black. 2001. (978-0-7951-0034-5(5)) Watermark Pr.

Apel, Melanie Ann. Let's Talk about Living with Your Single Dad. 2001. (Let's Talk Library). (Illus.). 24p. (J). (gr. 3). lib. bdg. 18.75 (978-0-8239-5619-7(9) , PowerKids Pr.) Rosen Publishing Group, Inc., The.

Bernstein, Robin. Terrible, Terrible! A Folktale Retold. Kawasaki, Shauna Mooney, illus. 1998. 32p. (J). (ps-5). 15.95 (978-1-58013-016-5(X)) Kar-Ben Publishing.

Bigmama's. 1998. (J). pap. 3.95 (978-0-439-04436-3(7)) Scholastic, Inc.

Bishop, Jennie. Jesus Must Be Really Special. Wummer, Amy, illus. 2006. (Heritage Builders Ser.). 32p. (J). 14.99 (978-0-7847-1379-2(0) , 04029) Standard Publishing.

Blue, Rose & Naden, Corine J. Staying Out of Trouble in A Troubled Family. 1998. (Single Titles Ser.: up). 112p. (gr. 7-12). lib. bdg. 24.90 (978-0-7613-0365-7(0) , Millbrook Pr.) Lerner Publishing Group.

Brown, Roman & Brown, Ramsey. 101 Ways Kids Can Spoil Their Parents . . . Gift Book: And Increase Their Allowance. Davis, Rich, illus. 1998. 128p. (J). (gr. k-10). 5.99 (978-1-881830-92-4(6)) Garborg's, Inc.

Building a Culture of Life Leader's Manual. 2nd ed. 2004. (YA). per. 19.95 (978-0-9764572-0-6(2)) Together, Inc.

Building a Culture of Life Study Guide. 2004. (YA). per. 17.95 (978-0-9764572-1-3(0)) Together, Inc.

Cadier, Florence & Daly, Melissa. My Parents Are Getting Divorced: How to Keep It Together When Your Mom & Dad Are Splitting Up, 4 vols. Gandini, Claire, illus. 2004. (Sunscreen Ser.). 112p. (J). (gr. 6-11). pap. 9.95 (978-0-8109-9163-7(2) , Amulet Bks.) Abrams, Harry N., Inc.

Cann, Kate. Breaking Up. 2002. 150p. pap. 9.95 (978-0-7043-4976-6(0)) Women's Pr., Ltd., The GBR. *Dist:* Trafalgar Square Publishing.

Christakis, Dimitri A. & Zimmerman, Frederick J. The Elephant in the Living Room: Make Television Work for Your Kids. 2006. (Illus.). 256p. 24.95 (978-1-59486-276-2(1)) Rodale Pr., Inc.

Civardi, Anne. New Baby. 2001. (gr. k-3). lib. bdg. 12.95 (978-0-613-67651-9(3)) Tandem Library Bks.

Clarkson, Clay. Our 24 Family Ways: Kids Color-In Book. Jarboe, Marvin, illus. 2004. 64p. (J). pap. 4.95 (978-1-888692-10-5(3)) Whole Heart Ministries.

Concepcion, Jorge L., creator. A Tale of Innovation & Persistence. 2004. (Illus.). 125p. (YA). per. 12.95 (978-0-9761779-0-6(0)) Concepcion, Jorge.

Crews, Donald. Bigmama's. 2001. (J). (gr. k-3). pap. 16.90 incl. audio (978-0-8045-6840-1(5) , 6840) Spoken Arts, Inc.

Dorling Kindersley Publishing Staff, ed. Good Morning, Baby! 2004. (SPA & ENG., Illus.). 18p. (J). bds. 4.99 (978-0-7566-0437-0(0)) Dorling Kindersley Publishing, Inc.

Drake, Jane & Love, Ann. My Family & Me: A Memory Scrapbook for Kids. Ritchie, Scot, illus. 2002. (Memory Scrapbks. for Kids). 32p. (J). (gr. k-3). (978-1-55337-002-4(3)) Kids Can Pr., Ltd.

Fajardo, Renee & Ruby, Carl. Pinch a Lotta Enchiladas & Other Tummy Tales. Fajardo, Renee & Ruby, Carl, eds. 2002. (Illus.). 104p. (YA). (gr. 4-8). pap. 14.00 (978-0-9724472-0-1(2)) Just Enjoyable Memorable Story Bks.

Family Celebrations. 2005. 80p. (J). per. 6.99 (978-1-59441-205-9(7) , CD-204018) Carson-Dellosa Publishing Co., Inc.

Faye, Joanne & Whaley, Stacey Lynn. Conversations with Kids Ages 3 to 6. l.t. ed. 2004. (Illus.). 24p. (J). 9.95 (978-0-9747375-0-8(X)) Joanne Faye Pr.

Focus on Family Matters. 2005. pap. 275.00 (978-0-7910-9163-0(5)); 2003. (Illus.). 249.00 (978-0-7910-7205-9(3)); Set. (Illus.). 64p. (YA). (gr. 5 up). 118.50 (978-0-7910-6689-8(4)) Facts On File, Inc. (Chelsea Hse.).

Garza, Carmen Lomas. In My Family. 2000. Tr. of En Mi Familia. (SPA.). (gr. 3-6). lib. bdg. 16.40 (978-0-613-28536-0(0)) Tandem Library Bks.

Gesme, Carole & Pearson, Douglas. Time Together Learning about Family Values. (Time-Together Ser.). (J). (gr. k-6). wbk. ed. 9.95 (978-1-888384-02-4(6)) Time-Together Pr.

Giacobello, John. You & Violence in Your Family. 2005. (Family Matters Ser.). (Illus.). 48p. (J). (gr. 5-8). lib. bdg. 23.95 (978-0-8239-3353-2(9)) Rosen Publishing Group, Inc., The.

Gilbreth, Frank B., Jr. Cheaper by the Dozen. 2000. (YA). (gr. 7 up). (978-0-606-19692-5(7)) Tandem Library Bks.

Gilbreth, Frank B., Jr. & Carey, Ernestine Gilbreth. Cheaper by the Dozen. 188p. (YA). (gr. 7 up). reprint ed. lib. bdg. 24.95 (978-0-88411-289-1(6)) Amereon LTD.

—Cheaper by the Dozen. 2002. (Perennial Classics Ser.). 224p. (gr. 7 up). pap. 11.95 (978-0-06-008460-8(X)) HarperCollins Pubs.

—Cheaper by the Dozen. 180p. (YA). (gr. 7 up). pap. 5.50 (978-0-8072-8308-0(8)); 2004. (J). (gr. 4-7). pap. 38.00 incl. audio (978-0-8072-8307-3(X) , YA157SP) Random Hse. Audio Publishing Group. (Listening Library).

Hirschman, Jessica Elin & Cole, Jennifer Elin. I'm in the Bathroom! Bright, Bonnie, illus. 2002. 24p. (J). per. 6.95 (978-0-9701155-2-2(0) , 0970115520) Cookie Bear Pr., Inc.

Honan, Linda & Kosmer, Ellen. Spend the Day in Ancient Greece: Projects & Activities that Bring the Past to Life. 1998. (Spend the Day Ser.: Vol. 1). (Illus.). 128p. (gr. 3-7). pap. 12.95 (978-0-471-15454-9(7) , Wiley) Wiley, John & Sons, Inc.

Hoobler, Dorothy & Hoobler, Thomas. The American Family Albums, 10 vols., Set. 1998. (American Family Albums Ser.). (Illus.). 1280p. (YA). pap. 149.95 (978-0-19-512416-3(2)) Oxford Univ. Pr., Inc.

Hood, Karen Jean Matsko. Getting to Know Each Other in the Hood Family: A Keepsake Guide for Our Family to Enjoy. 2003. (J). 15.95 (978-1-59210-839-8(3)); 2002. 15.95 (978-1-59210-715-5(X)) Whispering Pine Pr., Inc.

Jackson, J. S. Keeping Family First: A Kid's Guide. Alley, R. W., illus. 2004. (J). per. 7.95 (978-0-87029-390-0(7)) Abbey Pr.

Jennings, Patti. Rise & Shine. 2002. (Illus.). 6p. (J). 6.95 (978-0-8069-8473-5(2)) Sterling Publishing Co., Inc.

Jennings, Sharon. Into My Mother's Arms. Ohi, Ruth, illus. 2003. 32p. (J). (ps-1). pap. (978-1-55041-800-2(9)) Fitzhenry & Whiteside, Ltd.

Johnson, et al. Love Through the Generations: The Inspirational Journey of an African-American Family for Children of All Ages. Minter, Amani, illus. Minter, Kendall, photos by. 2001. 104p. pap. 8.95 (978-0-9655064-8-9(7)) Amber Bks.

Johnson, Charlotte Russell. The Flip Side: A Journey to Hell & Back. 2004. 256p. (YA). per. 15.95 (978-0-9741893-2-1(4)) Reaching Beyond, Inc.

Johnson, Leona. Strengthening Family & Self. rev. ed. 2002. (Illus.). 749p. (J). 53.00 (978-1-56637-780-5(3)) Goodheart-Willcox Pub.

Kenney, Cindy & Peterson, Doug. VeggieTales Family Devotional. 2005. (Illus.). 224p. (gr. 4-7). 14.99 (978-1-59145-261-4(9)) Nelson, Thomas Inc.

Look Who's Popping Up: At Home. 2003. (J). (ps-k). 4.98 (978-0-7525-8901-5(6)) Parragon, Inc.

Lynch, Amy. Real Families: Figuring Out Your Family & Where You Fit In. 2007. 88p. (J). pap. 9.95 (*978-1-59369-167-7(X)* , Pleasant Co.) American Girl Publishing, Inc.

Mackenzie, Carine. Our New Baby. 16p. (J). pap. 3.99 (978-1-85792-547-0(5) , Christian Focus) Christian Focus Pubns. GBR. *Dist:* Riverside.

McMahon, Patricia. One Belfast Boy. O'Connor, Alan, photos by. 1999. (Illus.). 64p. (J). (gr. 4-6). tchr. ed. 16.00 (978-0-395-68620-1(2)) Houghton Mifflin Co. Trade & Reference Div.

McMahon, Patricia & McCarthy, Conor Clarke. Just Add One Chinese Sister. Jerome, Karen A., illus. 2005. 32p. (J). (ps-ps). 16.95 (978-1-56397-989-7(6)) Boyds Mills Pr.

Meredith-Markowitz, Susan. A Family Celebration. 2003. (Early Connections Ser.). (J). pap. 33.00 (978-1-4108-1078-6(X)) Benchmark Education Co.

Michels, Dia L. Look What I See! Where Can I Be?, 5. 2005. (Look What I See! Where Can I Be? Ser.). (Illus.). 32p. 69.95 (978-1-930775-22-0(9)) Platypus Media, L.L.C.

Millard, Anne. My Busy Day. 2001. (Early Learners Ser.). (Illus.). 12p. (J). (ps-3). bds. 9.95 (978-0-7894-7407-0(7)) Dorling Kindersley Publishing, Inc.

Momma, Please Forgive Me! 2001. 195p. (YA). per. 13.95 (978-0-9713221-0-3(4)) TM Pubns.

Moskal, Greg. Family Fun: Learning the F Sound. (PowerPhonics Ser.). (Illus.). (J). 2002. 24p. (gr. 1). lib. bdg. 18.00 (978-0-8239-5901-3(5)); 2001. 23p. lib. bdg. 26.40 (978-0-8239-8246-2(7)) Rosen Publishing Group, Inc., The. (PowerKids Pr.).

Muhammad, Maryum. My Dad Moved Yesterday. 2000. (J). (gr. k-2). 10.95 (978-0-533-13230-0(4)) Vantage Pr., Inc.

The Need to Know Library: Dealing with Family Problems & More, 8 bks. Incl. Everything You Need to Know about a Drug-Abusing Parent. Shuker-Haines, Frances. Rosen, Ruth C., ed. (YA). (gr. 7-12). 1997. lib. bdg. 25.25 (978-0-8239-2613-8(3) , NTDRPA); Everything You Need to Know about Breaking the Cycle of Domestic Violence. Kinstlinger-Bruhn, Charlotte. (J). (gr. 4-6). 1997. lib. bdg. 25.25 (978-0-8239-2434-9(3) , NTDOVI); Everything You Need to Know about Codependency. Septien, Al & Nathan. (YA). (gr. 7-12). 1997. lib. bdg. 25.25 (978-0-8239-2563-6(3) , NTCODE); Everything You Need to Know about Date Rape. Shuker-Haines, Frances. (YA). (gr. 7-12). 1998. lib. bdg. 25.25 (978-0-8239-2882-8(9) , NTDARA); Everything You Need to Know about Sexual Abstinence. Moe, Barbara. (YA). (gr. 7-12). 1998. lib. bdg. 25.25 (978-0-8239-2747-0(4) , NTSABS); Everything You Need to Know about Sexual Abuse. Stark, Evan. (YA). (gr. 7-12). 1998. lib. bdg. 25.25 (978-0-8239-2871-2(3) , NTSEAB); Everything You Need to Know If Your Family Is on Welfare. Erlbach, Arlene. (YA). (gr. 7-12). 1998. lib. bdg. 25.25 (978-0-8239-2433-2(5) , NTFAWE); Everything You Need to Know When a Parent Dies. Bratman, Fred. (YA). (gr. 7-12). 1998. lib. bdg. 25.25 (978-0-8239-2870-5(5) , NTPADI); 64p. (Illus.). 2005. Set lib. bdg. 176.75 (978-0-8239-9440-3(6)) Rosen Publishing Group, Inc., The.

Nelson, Robin. Where Is My Home? (First Step Nonfiction Ser.). (gr. k-2). 2005. (Illus.). 24p. lib. bdg. 17.27 (978-0-8225-0189-3(9)); 2001. (J). pap. 3.95 (978-0-8225-1978-2(X) , Lerner Pubns.) Lerner Publishing Group.

—Where Is My Town? (First Step Nonfiction Ser.). (gr. k-2). 2005. (Illus.). 24p. lib. bdg. 17.27 (978-0-8225-0190-9(2)); 2001. (J). pap. 3.95 (978-0-8225-1979-9(8) , Lerner Pubns.) Lerner Publishing Group.

Nicodemus, Laura Konger. Grandma's Onion Patch, 4 vols. Nicodemus, Laura Konger, illus. 2002. (Illus.). 16p. (J). (gr. 1-4). 3.99 (978-0-9722216-3-4(8)) Grandma's Stories, Inc.

—Grandma's Scary Mean Gander, 4 vols., Set. Nicodemus, Laura Konger, illus. 2002. (Illus.). 16p. (J). (gr. 1-4). 3.99 (978-0-9722216-0-3(3)) Grandma's Stories, Inc.

Patrick, Jean L. S. Cows, Cats, & Kids: A Veterinarian's Family at Work. Upitis, Alvis, illus. 2003. 48p. (YA). (gr. 4-6). 17.95 (978-1-56397-111-2(9)) Boyds Mills Pr.

Power Twins Handbook Volume One. 2006. (J). spiral bd. (*978-0-9742355-1-6(2)*) Brda, Tracy.

Quattlebaum, Mary. Family Reunion. Shine, Andrea, illus. 2004. 32p. 16.00 (978-0-8028-5237-3(8)) Eerdmans, William B. Publishing Co.

Rice, David L. Because Brian Hugged His Mother. 2004. (Sharing Nature with Children Book Ser.). (Illus.). 32p. (YA). (ps-3). 16.95 (978-1-883220-90-7(4)) ; pap. 7.95 (978-1-883220-89-1(0)) Dawn Pubns.

Roca, Nuria. La Familia. 2001. (SPA.). (gr. k-3). lib. bdg. 15.25 (978-0-613-82938-0(7)) Tandem Library Bks.

Rondeau, Amanda. Do Something in Your Family. 2004. (Do Something about It! Ser.). (Illus.). 23p. (J). (ps-3). lib. bdg. 19.93 (978-1-59197-574-8(3)) ABDO Publishing Co.

Schwartz, Stuart B. & Conley, Craig. Finding an Apartment. 1998. (Career Books). (Illus.). 32p. (J). (gr. 3-4). lib. bdg. 21.26 (978-0-7368-0046-4(8) , LifeMatters Bks.) Capstone Pr., Inc.

Shumway, Lindsey. I Chose You. 2005. (Illus.). 31p. (J). 15.99 (978-1-55517-861-1(8)) Cedar Fort, Inc./CFI Distribution.

Sonnenberg, Roger, et al. 501 Practical Ways to Love Your Grandparents. 2000. (Illus.). 208p. (J). (ps-3). pap. 10.99 (978-0-570-05237-1(8) , 12-4043) Concordia Publishing Hse.

Steck-Vaughn Staff. Homes & Families, Level A. 2001. (Steck-Vaughn Social Studies). (J). tchr. ed., ring bd. 107.94 (978-0-7398-2959-2(9)) Steck-Vaughn.

Tubbs, Janet. Sibling Rivalry. 2000. (Spud Packs Ser.). (Illus.). 16p. (J). (ps-4). pap. 19.95 (978-1-881185-23-9(0)) Arcadia Pr.

Tym, Kate. Coping with Families. 2004. (Illus.). 48p. (J). 28.56 (978-1-4109-0574-1(8)) Harcourt Schl. Pubs.

Weaver, Mary Wenger. Mommy Stayed in Bed This Morning: Helping Children Understand Depression. Chambers, Mary, illus. 2002. 40p. (J). (ps-3). pap. 12.99 (978-0-8361-9150-9(1)) Herald Pr.

Weimer, Heidi. You're My Little Love Bug. Sharp, Chris, illus. 2005. 16p. (J). bds. 12.99 (978-0-8249-6589-1(2)) Ideals Pubns.

Weitzman, Elizabeth. Living in a Blended Family. 2004. (Lets Talk Library). (Illus.). 24p. (J). lib. bdg. 18.75 (978-0-8239-6929-6(0) , PowerKids Pr.) Rosen Publishing Group, Inc., The.

Wenzel, Doris, et al. Ten Little Sisters. Hill, Lana, illus. 1999. 32p. (J). (gr. 3-6). pap. 14.95 (978-1-878044-38-9(9) , Wild Rose) Mayhaven Publishing.

Willard, Nancy. Cracked Corn & Snow Ice Cream: A Family Almanac. Dyer, Jane, illus. 2005. 56p. (YA). (gr. 4-8). 18.00 (978-0-7567-8835-3(8)) DIANE Publishing Co.

Williams, Dave. Windgalore Farm. 2005. (Illus.). 182p. pap. 21.95 (978-0-937921-56-2(4)) Acorn Publishing.

Williams, Thelma. Our Family Table: Recipes & Food Memories from African-American Life Models. 2004. (Illus.). 94p. (YA). reprint ed. 15.00 (978-0-7567-8093-7(4)) DIANE Publishing Co.

Winchester, Kent. My Two Homes Magic Words Handbook for Kids. 1998. (Illus.). 28p. (J). (gr. 2-6). spiral bd. 5.95 (978-0-9650296-1-2(1)) LadyBug Pr.

FAMILY LIFE—FICTION

Abelove, Joan. Saying It Out Loud. 2001. (YA). 136p. (gr. 8-12). lib. bdg. 14.15 (978-0-613-44252-7(0)); (978-0-606-21410-0(0)) Tandem Library Bks.

Aboff, Marcie. Giant Jelly Bean Jar. Billin-Frye, Paige, illus. 2004. (Easy-to-Read, Puffin Ser.). 32p. (J). pap. 3.99 (978-0-14-240049-4(1) , Puffin) Penguin Group (USA) Inc.

Abraham, Michelle Shapiro. Good Morning, Boker Tov. Alko, Selina, illus. 2004. pap. 6.95 (978-0-8074-0783-7(6) , 101974) URJ Pr.

—Good Night, Lilah Tov. Alko, Selina, illus. 2004. pap. 6.95 (978-0-8074-0784-4(4) , 101975) URJ Pr.

Abraham, Susan Gonzales. Cecilia's Year. 2004. (Latino Fiction for Young Adults Ser.). (Illus.). 160p. (J). (gr. 5 up). 16.95 (978-0-938317-87-6(3)) Cinco Puntos Pr.

Abraham, Susan Gonzales & Abraham, Denise Gonzales. Cecilia's Year. 2007. (Latino Fiction for Young Adults Ser.). 210p. (J). pap. 11.95 (978-1-933693-02-6(9)) Cinco Puntos Pr.

—Surprising Cecilia. 2005. (Latino Fiction for Young Adults Ser.). 216p. (YA). 16.95 (978-0-938317-96-8(2)) Cinco Puntos Pr.

Acampora, Paul. Defining Dulcie. 2006. 176p. (J). (gr. 7). 16.99 (978-0-8037-3046-5(2) , Dial) Penguin Group (USA) Inc.

Adams, Chanelle. Myra. 2006. 22p. 12.16 (978-1-4116-9426-2(0)) Lulu.com.

Adams, Jewel. Elise's Heart. 2nd unabr. ed. 2001. 146p. pap. 9.95 (978-1-930980-21-1(3) , 80213) Granite Publishing & Distribution.

Adams, L. Happy Memories: A Continuing Family Saga for Young Adults. 2003. 516p. pap. 26.95 (978-0-595-29210-3(0)) iUniverse, Inc.

Adams, Lenora. Baby Girl. 2007. 240p. (YA). pap. 6.99 (978-1-4169-2512-5(0) , Simon Pulse) Simon & Schuster Children's Publishing.

Adler, C. S. The No Place Cat. 2002. 160p. (YA). (gr. 5-9). 15.00 (978-0-618-09644-2(2) , Clarion Bks.) Houghton Mifflin Co. Trade & Reference Div.

Adler, David A. Andy & Tamika. Hillenbrand, Will, illus. (Andy Russell Ser.). 144p. 2005. (J). pap. 4.95 (978-0-15-205446-5(4)); 1999. (YA). (gr. 2-5). 14.00 (978-0-15-201735-4(6)) Harcourt Children's Bks. (Gulliver Bks.).

—Don't Talk to Me about the War. 2008. (YA). (gr. 5). 15.99 (***978-0-670-06307-9(X)*** , Viking Adult) Penguin Group (USA) Inc.

—It's a Baby, Andy Russell. Franson, Leanne, illus. (Andy Russell Ser.). 128p. (J). 2006. pap. 4.95 (978-0-15-205610-0(6) , Harcourt Paperbacks); 2005. 14.00 (978-0-15-216742-4(0) , Gulliver Bks.) Harcourt Children's Bks.

—Mama Played Baseball. O'Leary, Chris, illus. 2003. 32p. (J). 16.00 (978-0-15-202196-2(5) , Gulliver Bks.) Harcourt Children's Bks.

—The Many Troubles of Andy Russell. Hillenbrand, Will, illus. 2005. (Andy Russell Ser.). 144p. (J). pap. 5.95 (978-0-15-205440-3(5) , Gulliver Bks.) Harcourt Children's Bks.

Adoff, Arnold. Black Is Brown Is Tan. McCully, Emily Arnold, illus. 40p. (J). (ps-3). 2004. reprint ed. pap. 6.99 (978-0-06-443644-1(6)); 2002. 16.99 (978-0-06-028776-4(4)) HarperCollins Pubs.

Adshead, Paul S. Incredible Reversing Peppermints. 1999. (Child's Play Library). (Illus.). 120p. (J). (gr. k-7). 5.99 (978-0-85953-629-5(7)) Child's Play-International.

Ahlberg, Allan. The Cat Who Got Carried Away. McEwen, Katharine, illus. 2003. 96p. (J). (gr. 1-4). 15.99 (978-0-7636-2073-8(4)) Candlewick Pr.

Aksomitis, Linda. Snowmobile Challenge. Cummins, Sandy, ed. 2004. (YA). pap. (978-1-920741-10-5(0)) Writers Exchange E-Publishing Australia.

Al-Chokhachy, Elissa. How Can I Help, Papa? A Child's Journey Through Loss & Healing. Graf, Ulrike, illus. 2002. 32p. (J). (ps-7). 15.95 (978-0-9712481-0-6(9)) Works of Hope Publishing.

Albee, Sarah. Off to Bed. Ebert, Len, illus. 2006. (Step-By-Step Readers Ser.). (J). pap. (978-1-59939-060-4(4) , Reader's Digest Young Families, Inc.) Reader's Digest Children's Publishing, Inc.

Alberto, Daisy. No Rules for Rex! Smath, Jerry, illus. 2005. 32p. (J). lib. bdg. 20.00 (***978-1-4242-1112-8(3)***) Fitzgerald Bks.

—No Rules for Rex! Smath, Jerry, illus. 2005. (Social Studies Connects). 32p. (J). pap. 4.99 (978-1-57565-146-0(7)) Kane Pr., The.

Alberto, Daisy & Wyss, Johann. Swiss Family Robinson. 2006. (Illus.). 112p. (J). (gr. 1-4). lib. bdg. 11.99 (978-0-375-97525-7(X) , Random Hse. Bks. for Young Readers) Random Hse. Children's Bks.

—Swiss Family Robinson. Hunt, Robert, illus. 2006. 112p. (J). (gr. 1-4). pap. 3.99 (978-0-375-87525-0(5) , Random Hse. Bks. for Young Readers) Random Hse. Children's Bks.

Alcott, Louisa May. Eight Cousins. 2000. 252p. (J). pap. 9.95 (978-0-594-06118-2(0)) 1873 Pr.

—Eight Cousins. 2005. 29.95 (978-1-4218-0976-2(1)); 300p. pap. 14.95 (978-1-59540-676-7(X)) 1st World Publishing, Inc. (1st World Library - Literary Society).

—Eight Cousins. 2005. 120p. per. 4.95 (978-1-4209-2569-2(5)) Digireads.com.

—Eight Cousins. 2007. (Dover Evergreen Classics Ser.). 224p. pap. 4.95 (***978-0-486-45559-4(9)***) Dover Pubns., Inc.

—Eight Cousins. 2003. (ENG.). pap. 13.99 (***978-1-4043-6290-1(8)***) IndyPublish.com.

—Eight Cousins. 2004. reprint ed. pap. 1.99 (978-1-4192-1740-1(2)) Kessinger Publishing, LLC.

—The Inheritance. 1998. (Classics Ser.). 208p. pap. 14.00 (978-0-14-043666-2(9) , Penguin Classics) Penguin Group (USA) Inc.

—Jack & Jill. Date not set. 352p. (YA). 25.95 (978-0-8488-2671-0(X)) Amereon LTD.

—Jo's Boys. 2000. 252p. (J). pap. 9.95 (978-0-594-05147-3(9)) 1873 Pr.

—Jo's Boys. (Dover Juvenile Classics Ser.). (J). 2002. 288p. (gr. 4-7). pap. 3.00 (978-0-486-42226-8(7)); 1999. (Illus.). 80p. pap. 1.00 (978-0-486-40789-0(6)) Dover Pubns., Inc.

—Jo's Boys. l.t. ed. 2005. 424p. pap. (978-1-84637-067-0(1)) Echo Library.

—Little Men: Life at Plumfield with Jo's Boys. 2001. (Dover Juvenile Classics Ser.). 304p. (J). (gr. 4-7). pap. 3.00 (978-0-486-41808-7(1)) Dover Pubns., Inc.

—Little Men: Life at Plumfield with Jo's Boys. 2004. 352p. (gr. 12). pap. 4.95 (978-0-451-52935-0(9) , Signet Classics) Penguin Group (USA) Inc.

—Little Women. 2002. (Great Illustrated Classics Ser.). (Illus.). 240p. (J). (gr. 3-8). 21.35 (978-1-57765-693-7(8) , ABDO & Daughters) ABDO Publishing Co.

—Little Women. Dryhurst, Dinah, illus. 2000. 288p. (J). pap. 8.99 (978-1-86205-220-8(4) , Pavilion Bks., Ltd.) Anova Bks. GBR. *Dist:* Trafalgar Square Publishing.

—Little Women. Alton, Anne Hiebert, ed. 2001. (Broadview Literary Texts Ser.). (Illus.). 619p. (J). pap. (978-1-55111-191-9(8)) Broadview Pr.

—Little Women. 2001. (Young Reader's Classics Ser.). 94p. (J). pap. 9.95 (978-1-55013-783-5(2) , Key Porter kids) Key Porter Bks. CAN. *Dist:* Firefly Bks., Ltd.

—Little Women. Lauter, Richard, illus. 192p. (J). 9.95 (978-1-56156-371-5(4)) Kidsbooks, Inc.

—Little Women. Smith, Jessie Willcox, illus. 2002. (Illustrated Library for Children). 400p. (J). 12.99 (978-0-517-22116-7(0) , Gramercy) Random Hse. Value Publishing.

—Little Women. 1998. (Children's Classics Ser.). (Illus.). 400p. (J). 6.99 (978-0-517-18954-2(2)) Random Hse. Value Publishing.

—Little Women. 2000. 576p. (J). (gr. 4-7). pap. 4.99 (978-0-439-10136-3(0)) Scholastic, Inc.

—Little Women. 2001. (Signature Classics Ser.). (Illus.). 544p. (J). 12.95 (978-1-58279-069-5(8) , 64) Trident Pr. International.

—Little Women. Dryhurst, Dinah & Rust, Graham, illus. 2001. (Storytime Classics Ser.). 32p. (J). (ps-3). pap. 5.99 (978-0-14-131202-6(5) , Puffin) Penguin Group (USA) Inc.

—Little Women. Corvino, Lucy, illus. 2005. (Classic Starts Ser.). 160p. 4.95 (978-1-4027-1236-4(7)) Sterling Publishing Co., Inc.

—Little Women. unabr. ed. 2000. (Dover Juvenile Classics Ser.). (Illus.). 608p. (J). (gr. 4-7). pap. 4.00 (978-0-486-41023-4(4)) Dover Pubns., Inc.

—Little Women. 1998. 559p. (J). reprint ed. lib. bdg. 25.00 (978-1-58287-046-5(2)) North Bks.

—Little Women, Bk. 1. 2003. (gr. 3-6). lib. bdg. 15.30 (978-0-613-70764-0(8)) Tandem Library Bks.

—Little Women. deluxe ed. 2000. (Signature Classics Ser.). (Illus.). 544p. (J). (978-1-58279-075-6(2)) Trident Pr. International.

—Little Women: Book & Charm. (Charming Classics). (Illus.). (J). 2003. 384p. 6.99 (978-0-06-051180-7(X)); 2000. 5.95 (978-0-694-01527-6(X)) HarperCollins Pubs. (Harper Festival).

—Little Women: With a Discussion of Family. Lauter, Richard, illus. 2003. (Values in Action Illustrated Classics Ser.). 191p. (J). (978-1-59203-032-3(7)) Learning Challenge, Inc.

—Little Women Bk. 2: Good Wives: Book with Charm. 2004. (Charming Classics). 416p. (J). pap. 6.99 (978-0-06-055991-5(8) , Harper Festival) HarperCollins Pubs.

—Little Women & Good Wives. 1998. (Children's Classics). (ENG.). 224p. (J). (gr. 4-7). pap. (978-1-85326-116-9(5) , 1165WW) Wordsworth Editions, Ltd.

—The Little Women Pop-Up Dollhouse. Krystanovich, Vesna, illus. 2000. 8p. (J). 21.95 (978-1-55263-290-1(3)) Key Porter Bks. CAN. *Dist:* Firefly Bks., Ltd.

—A Modern Cinderella. l.t. ed. 2005. 224p. pap. (978-1-84637-050-2(7)) Echo Library.

—Modern Cinderella or the Little Old Shoe. 2006. pap. 44.99 (***978-1-4219-8892-4(5)***) IndyPublish.com.

—A Modern Mephistopheles. Date not set. (J). lib. bdg. 16.95 (978-0-8488-0412-1(0)) Amereon LTD.

—Mujercitas. (SPA., Illus.). 192p. (YA). 11.95 (978-84-7281-101-0(8) , AF1101) Auriga, Ediciones S.A. ESP. *Dist:* Continental Bk. Co., Inc.

—Mujercitas. 2002. (Classics for Young Readers Ser.). (SPA.). (YA). 14.95 (978-84-392-0901-0(0) , EV30608) Lectorum Pubns., Inc.

—Mujercitas. (YA). 7.95 (978-84-95311-16-0(X)) Mestas, Jorge A. Ediciones Escolares La Escuela Nueva y Alinorma, S.L. ESP. *Dist:* Continental Bk. Co., Inc.

—Mujercitas. 1998. (SPA., Illus.). 304p. (J). (978-84-01-46257-3(6)) Plaza & Janes Editories, S.A.

—Mujercitas. (Coleccion Estrella). (SPA., Illus.). 64p. (J). 14.95 (978-950-11-0010-5(3) , SGM010) Sigmar ARG. *Dist:* Continental Bk. Co., Inc.

—Mujercitas. 2000. (Coleccion "Clasicos Juveniles" Ser.). (SPA., Illus.). 292p. (gr. 4-7). pap. 12.95 (978-1-58348-784-6(0)) iUniverse, Inc.

—An Old-Fashioned Thanksgiving. Bernardin, James, illus. 2005. 32p. (J). (ps-3). 15.99 (978-0-06-000450-7(9)); lib. bdg. 16.89 (978-0-06-000451-4(7)) HarperCollins Pubs.

—The Works of Louisa May Alcott. (J). (gr. 5-6). 40.95 (978-0-88411-173-3(3)) Amereon LTD.

Alcott, Louisa May & Dorling Kindersley Publishing Staff. Little Women. Gerver, Jane E., ed. Molan, Chris, illus. 1999. (Eyewitness Classics Ser.). 64p. (J). (gr. 2 up). 14.99 (978-0-7894-4767-8(3)) Dorling Kindersley Publishing, Inc.

Alcott, Louisa May, et al. Mujercitas. Prunier, James, tr. 2002. (SPA., Illus.). 268p. (J). 29.95 (978-84-348-5324-9(8)) SM Ediciones ESP. *Dist:* AIMS International Bks., Inc.

Alda, Arlene. Morning Glory Monday. Kovalski, Maryann, illus. 2003. 32p. (J). (gr. k-3). 17.95 (978-0-88776-620-6(X)) Tundra Bks., Inc./Livres Toundra, Inc. CAN. *Dist:* Random Hse., Inc.

Alexander, Marge. Adventures at the Grandparents' House. 2001. 96p. 9.99 (978-1-58169-064-4(9) , Evergreen Pr.) Genesis Communications, Inc.

Alexander, Sue. One More Time, Mama. Soman, David, illus. 1999. (Accelerated Reader Bks.). 32p. (J). (ps-k). 15.95 (978-0-7614-5051-1(3) , Cavendish Children's Bks.) Cavendish, Marshall Corp.

Alford, Carrie. My Christmas Story. 2003. (J). per. 14.25 (978-1-932301-18-2(6) , 1045) Airleaf Publishing & Bookselling.

All in the Family, 6 vols., Pack. (Rigby Infoquest Ser.). (gr. 6 up). 37.00 (978-0-7578-7992-0(6)) Rigby Education.

Allen, Jonathan. I'm Not Cute. 2006. (Illus.), 32p. (ps-k). 14.99 (978-0-7868-3720-5(9)) Hyperion Pr.

Allison, Jennifer. Gilda Joyce: Psychic Investigator. 2005. 208p. (YA). 12.99 (978-0-525-47375-6(0) , Dutton Juvenile); 2006. 336p. (J). (gr. 5). reprint ed. pap. 6.99 (978-0-14-240698-4(8) , Puffin) Penguin Group (USA) Inc.

Alma, Ann. Summer of Adventures. 2003. (Summer Ser.). 160p. (J). pap. 5.95 (978-1-55039-122-0(4)) Sono Nis Pr. CAN. *Dist:* Orca Bk. Pubs. USA.

Almond, David. En el Lugar de las Alas. (Barco de Vapor). (SPA.). 218p. (YA). (gr. 5-8). (978-84-348-6421-4(5)) SM Ediciones.

—Skellig. 2001. (Illus.). 208p. (gr. 5). mass mkt. 6.50 (978-0-440-22908-7(1) , Laurel Leaf) Random Hse. Children's Bks.

—Skellig. Wojtyla, Karen, ed. 2000. (Illus.). 192p. (gr. 5-7). 6.50 (978-0-440-41602-9(7) , Yearling) Random Hse. Children's Bks.

—Skellig. 1999. 192p. (gr. 5 up). 16.95 (978-0-385-32653-7(X) , Delacorte Bks. for Young Readers) Random Hse. Children's Bks.

—Skellig. 2001. (gr. 5-8). lib. bdg. 14.15 (978-0-613-84565-6(X)); 2000. (J). (978-0-606-19192-0(5)); 2000. (gr. 5-8). lib. bdg. 13.00 (978-0-613-28330-4(9)) Tandem Library Bks.

Alvarez, Julia. Antes de Ser Libre. 2004. (SPA.). (gr. 7-12). lib. bdg. 14.15 (978-0-613-71931-5(X)) Tandem Library Bks.

Amado, Elisa. Cousins. Garay, Luis, tr. Garay, Luis, illus. 2004. 32p. (J). 16.95 (978-0-88899-459-2(1)) Groundwood Bks. CAN. *Dist:* Perseus Distribution.

—Primas. Iribarren, Elena & Iribarren, Leopoldo, trs. from ENG. Garay, Luis, illus. 2004. (SPA & ENG.). 32p. (J). 16.95 (978-0-88899-548-3(2)) Groundwood Bks. CAN. *Dist:* Perseus Distribution.

Amend, Bill. His Code Name Was the Fox: A FoxTrot Collection. 2002. (gr. 7-12). lib. bdg. 17.60 (978-0-613-67552-9(5)) Tandem Library Bks.

Amico, Tom & Proimos, James. The Day the Dog Dressed Like Dad. 2004. (Illus.). 32p. (J). 16.95 (978-1-58234-877-3(4) , Bloomsbury Children) Bloomsbury Publishing.

Andersen, C. B. The Forgotten Treasure. 2004. 215p. (J). pap. (978-1-59038-314-8(1)) Deseret Bk. Co.

Anderson, Janet. The Last Treasure. 2004. 272p. (J). (gr. 5). pap. 6.99 (978-0-14-240217-7(6) , Puffin) Penguin Group (USA) Inc.

Anderson, Jodi Lynn. Peaches. 2006. 320p. (J). reprint ed. pap. 8.99 (978-0-06-073307-0(1) , Harper Trophy) HarperCollins Pubs.

Anderson, Launi K. Jillian's Discovery. 1999. (Choose the Right Ser.: Bk. 3). 60p. (J). pap. (978-1-57008-673-1(7)) Scribbulations LLC.

Anderson, Laurie Halse. Fever 1793. unabr. ed. 2004. 256p. (J). (gr. 5-9). pap. 38.00 incl. audio (978-0-8072-8719-4(9) , LYA 246 SP, Listening Library) Random Hse. Audio Publishing Group.

—Fever 1793. 2002. (gr. 5-8). lib. bdg. 14.15 (978-0-613-45039-3(6)) Tandem Library Bks.

—Prom. 2006. 224p. (YA). (gr. 7). reprint ed. pap. 8.99 (978-0-14-240570-3(1) , Puffin) Penguin Group (USA) Inc.

—Prom. l.t. ed. 2005. 288p. (YA). (gr. 7-12). per. 21.95 (978-0-7862-7813-8(7) , Large Print Pr.) Thorndike Pr.

Anderson, Peggy Perry. Joe on the Go. 2007. (Illus.). 32p. (J). (gr. 3-5). 16.00 (978-0-618-77331-2(2)) Houghton Mifflin Co.

Andreae, Giles. Heaven Is Having You. Cabban, Vanessa, illus. 2007. 24p. (J). (ps-k). bds. 7.95 (***978-1-58925-820-4(7)*** , tiger tales) ME Media LLC.

Angle, Kimberly Greene. Hummingbird. 2008. 256p. (J). 16.95 (***978-0-374-33376-8(9)***) Farrar, Straus & Giroux.

Antieau, Kim. Mercy, Unbound. 2006. (Illus.). 176p. (YA). pap. 6.99 (978-1-4169-0893-7(5) , Simon Pulse) Simon & Schuster Children's Publishing.

Appelt, Kathi. Oh My Baby, Little One. Dyer, Jane, illus. 2002. (J). 23.40 (978-0-7587-3298-9(8)) Book Wholesalers, Inc.

—Oh My Baby, Little One. Dyer, Jane, illus. 32p. (J). (ps-k). 2000. 16.00 (978-0-15-200041-7(0)); 2005. reprint ed. pap. 6.00 (978-0-15-205242-3(9) , Voyager Bks./Libros Viajeros) Harcourt Children's Bks.

—Someone's Come to Our House. Carpenter, Nancy, illus. 1999. 24p. (J). (ps-3). 16.00 (978-0-8028-5144-4(4) , Eerdmans Bks For Young Readers) Eerdmans, William B. Publishing Co.

April Morning. 1999. (YA). 9.95 (978-1-56137-119-8(X)) Novel Units, Inc.

Arcellana, Francisco. The Mats. Alegre, Hermes, illus. 1999. 24p. (J). (ps-3). 13.95 (978-0-916291-86-0(3)) Kane/Miller Bk. Pubs., Inc.

Ardagh, Philip. Rise of the House Mcnally. 2006. (Unlikely Exploits Trilogy Ser.). 160p. (J). pap. 5.99 (978-0-439-73018-1(X) , Scholastic Paperbacks) Scholastic, Inc.

Armstrong, William H. Sounder. 2001. (Perennial Classics Ser.). 96p. (gr. 4-7). pap. 7.00 (978-0-06-093548-1(0)) HarperCollins Pubs.

—Sounder. Barkley, James, illus. l.t. ed. 1999. (LRS Large Print Cornerstone Ser.). 230p. (YA). (gr. 6-12). lib. bdg. 27.95 (978-1-58118-054-1(3) , 22768) LRS.

—Sounder. 2001. (gr. 3-6). lib. bdg. 15.30 (978-0-613-85745-1(3)) Tandem Library Bks.

—Sounder. l.t. ed. 2005. 111p. (YA). pap. 10.95 (978-0-7862-7915-9(X)) Thorndike Pr.

Aronson, Sarah. Head Case. 2007. 192p. (YA). (gr. 9 up). 16.95 (***978-1-59643-214-7(4)***) Roaring Brook Pr.

Arraras, Maria Celeste. El Baston Magico (The Magic Cane) 2008. (I Love My Mommy Ser.). 32p. (J). pap. 5.99 (***978-0-545-00532-6(9)*** , Scholastic en Espanol) Scholastic, Inc.

Arraras, María Celeste. The Magic Cane. Raimondi, Pablo, illus. 2007. 32p. (J). (ps-3). pap. 16.99 (***978-0-439-57419-8(6)*** , Orchard Bks.) Scholastic, Inc.

Arrington, Frances. Prairie Whispers. 2005. 192p. (J). (gr. 5). pap. 6.99 (978-0-14-240306-8(7) , Puffin) Penguin Group (USA) Inc.

Arrington, Gladys. Dallas: On Book One: Jo/Jo KIDS. Arrington, Chiquila, illus. 2006. 49p. pap. 12.95 (978-1-4241-1162-6(5)) PublishAmerica, Inc.

Asher Penny. Mommy & Daddy Are Going on a Trip. 2006. 32p. 12.95 (978-0-9755902-1-8(9)) Change Is Strange, Inc.

Ashman, Linda. To the Beach! Westcott, Nadine Bernard, illus. 2005. 32p. (J). 16.00 (978-0-15-216490-4(1)) Harcourt Children's Bks.

Atkins, Catherine. When Jeff Comes Home. 2001. (Illus.). 240p. (YA). pap. 6.99 (978-0-698-11915-4(0) , Putnam Juvenile) Penguin Group (USA) Inc.

—When Jeff Comes Home. 2001. (gr. 7-12). lib. bdg. 15.30 (978-0-613-44430-9(2)) Tandem Library Bks.

Atkins, Jeannine. Anne Hutchinson's Way. Dooling, Michael, illus. 2007. 32p. (J). (gr. 3 up). 17.00 (978-0-374-30365-5(7)) Farrar, Straus & Giroux.

Atkinson, Beth. From Alice to Zen & Everyone in Between: A Novel. 2008. (Exceptional Reading & Language Arts Titles for Intermediate Grades Ser.). (J). 15.95 (***978-0-8225-7271-8(0)*** , Carolrhoda Bks.) Lerner Publishing Group.

Atkinson, Chryssa. Lindsey. 2001. (American Girl Today Ser.). (Illus.). 128p. (J). pap. 6.95 (978-1-58485-450-0(2)) American Girl Publishing, Inc.

—Lindsey. 2003. (gr. 3-6). lib. bdg. 15.25 (978-0-613-85868-7(9)) Tandem Library Bks.

Atwell, Debby. Pearl. 2001. (Illus.). 32p. (J). (gr. k-3). tchr. ed. 16.00 (978-0-395-88416-4(0) , Walter Lorraine) Houghton Mifflin Co. Trade & Reference Div.

Auch, M. J. One-Handed Catch. 2006. 256p. (J). 16.95 (978-0-8050-7900-5(9) , Holt, Henry & Co. Bks. For Young Readers) Holt, Henry & Co.

Aumann, Jane & Ladage, Cindy. Tucker's Surprise. Craig, Christy, illus. 2000. 16p. (J). (ps-7). pap. 8.00 (978-0-9703319-0-8(8)) Roots & Wings.

Aunt Lucy's Rolls. 2005. (J). per. (978-0-9772209-0-8(7)) Spann Productions.

Auseon, Andrew. Funny Little Monkey. 2005. 304p. (YA). (gr. 9-12). 17.00 (978-0-15-205334-5(4)) Harcourt Children's Bks.

Austen, Jane. Pride & Prejudice. Miralles, Joseph, illus. 2005. (Great Illustrated Classics Ser.). 236p. (J). (gr. 3-8). 21.35 (978-1-59679-249-4(3) , ABDO & Daughters) ABDO Publishing Co.

Autumn Moon, 6 Pcks. (Bookweb Ser.). 32p. (gr. 6 up). 34.00 (978-0-7578-0894-4(8)) Rigby Education.

Avi. The Traitors' Gate. Raude, Karina, illus. 2007. 368p. (J). (gr. 6-9). 17.99 (978-0-689-85335-7(1) , Atheneum/Richard Jackson Bks.) Simon & Schuster Children's Publishing.

Ayres, Katherine. Macaroni Boy. 2004. 192p. (J). (gr. 3-7). pap. 5.99 (978-0-440-41884-9(4) , Yearling) Random Hse. Children's Bks.

Baggette, Susan K. Jonathan Goes to the Grocery Store. Moriarty, William J., photos by. 1998. (Jonathan Adventures Ser.). (Illus.). 16p. (J). (ps-k). bds. 5.95 (978-0-9660172-2-9(6)) Brookfield Reader, Inc., The.

Baicker, Karen. I Can Do It Too! Wilson-Max, Ken, illus. 2003. 24p. (J). 13.95 (978-1-929766-83-3(1)) Handprint Bks.

Bailey, Barbara. When I Get Older I'll Understand. 2000. 192p. (gr. 7-12). 7.95 (978-1-56315-211-5(8)) Sterling-House Pubs., Inc.

—When I Get Older I'll Understand. 2000. (gr. 7-12). lib. bdg. 16.40 (978-0-613-83337-0(6)) Tandem Library Bks.

Bajaj, Varsha. How Many Kisses Do You Want Tonight? Bates, Ivan, illus. 2007. 26p. (J). bds. 6.99 (*978-0-316-06735-5(0)) Little, Brown Bks. for Young Readers.

Baker, Barbara. One Saturday Evening: By Barbara Baker: Pictures by Kate Duke. Duke, Kate, illus. 2007. (J). (*978-0-525-47850-8(7) , Dutton Juvenile) Penguin Group (USA) Inc.

Ballard, Robin. When We Get Home. 1999. lib. bdg. (978-0-688-16169-9(3)) HarperCollins Pubs.

Balzola, Asun. Babi es Barbara. (SPA.). 72p. 8.95 (978-84-392-8113-9(7)) Baker & Taylor Bks.

—Munia y Sra. Piltronera (Munia & Mrs. Piltronera) (SPA.). 36p. (J). 16.95 (978-84-233-1290-0(9)) Ediciones Destino ESP. *Dist:* AIMS International Bks., Inc.

Banim, Lisa. Case at Camp Get-Me-Outie! Junior Novel. 2nd novel rev. ed. 2004. (Lizzie McGuire Original Mystery Ser.: No. 2). (Illus.). 128p. (gr. 3-7). pap. 4.99 (978-0-7868-4621-4(6) , Disney Editions) Disney Pr.

Banks, Kate. Friends of the Heart: Amici Del Cuore. 2005. 144p. (J). 16.00 (978-0-374-32455-1(7)) Farrar, Straus & Giroux.

—Mama's Coming Home. Bogacki, Tomek, illus. 2003. 32p. (J). (ps-1). 16.00 (978-0-374-34747-5(6) , Farrar, Straus & Giroux (BYR)) Farrar, Straus & Giroux.

Banks, Lynne Reid. The Key to the Indian. 1999. (gr. 3-6). lib. bdg. 13.00 (978-0-613-23006-3(X)) Tandem Library Bks.

Banting, Celia. I only said I was telling the Truth. 2006. 240p. (YA). per. 14.99 (*978-0-9786648-4-8(1)) Wighita Pr.

—I Only Said Yes So That They'd Like Me. 2006. 224p. (YA). per. 14.99 (*978-0-9786648-1-7(7)) Wighita Pr.

Barkley, Brad & Hepler, Heather. Scrambled Eggs at Midnight. 2006. 272p. (YA). (gr. 6). 16.99 (978-0-525-47760-0(8) , Dutton Juvenile) Penguin Group (USA) Inc.

Barrett, Mary Brigid. Day Care Days. Murphy, Patti B., illus. 1999. 32p. (J). (ps-1). 12.95 (978-0-316-08456-7(5)) Little Brown & Co.

Bartek, Mary. Funerals & Fly Fishing. rev. ed. 2004. (Illus.). 160p. (J). 16.95 (978-0-8050-7409-3(0) , Holt, Henry & Co. Bks. For Young Readers) Holt, Henry & Co.

Barth, Jeff. The Homesteaders. Barth, Marge, ed. 2002. (Illus.). 304p. pap. (978-1-891484-04-9(4)) Barth Family Ministries.

Baskin, Nora Raleigh. Basketball (or Something Like It) 176p. (J). 2007. (gr. 4-7). pap. 5.99 (978-0-06-059612-5(0) , Harper Trophy); 2005. 15.99 (978-0-06-059610-1(4)); 2005. lib. bdg. 16.89 (978-0-06-059611-8(2)) HarperCollins Pubs.

Bateman, Teresa. Red, White, Blue & Uncle Who? The Story Behind Some of America's Patriotic Symbols. O'Brien, John, illus. 2001. 64p. (J). (gr. 4-6). tchr. ed. 16.95 (978-0-8234-1285-3(7)) Holiday Hse., Inc.

Bateson, Catherine. Being Bee. 2007. 136p. (J). (gr. 3-7). 16.95 (*978-0-8234-2104-6(X)) Holiday Hse., Inc.

Bauer, Joan. Backwater. 2005. 185p. (YA). (gr. 7-12). pap. 7.99 (978-0-14-240434-8(9) , Puffin) Penguin Group (USA) Inc.

—Backwater. 2000. (978-0-606-20077-6(0)) Tandem Library Bks.

—Best Foot Forward. (YA). 2005. 183p. (gr. 5). 16.99 (978-0-399-23474-3(8) , Putnam Juvenile); 2006. 192p. (gr. 7). reprint ed. pap. 7.99 (978-0-14-240690-8(2) , Puffin) Penguin Group (USA) Inc.

—Rules of the Road. 1998. 208p. (J). (gr. 7-12). 16.99 (978-0-399-23140-7(4) , Putnam Juvenile) Penguin Group (USA) Inc.

—Rules of the Road. 2000. (YA). (978-0-606-20252-7(8)) Tandem Library Bks.

Bauer, Marion Dane. Killing Miss Kitty & Other Sins. 2007. 176p. (YA). (gr. 7). 16.00 (*978-0-618-69000-8(X) , Clarion Bks.) Houghton Mifflin Co. Trade & Reference Div.

Baxter, Linda. River of Ice. 2001. (J). 104p. 11.90 (978-0-7891-5392-0(0)); 103p. (gr. 2-5). lib. bdg. 13.95 (978-0-7807-9805-2(8)) Perfection Learning Corp.

Beard, Darleen Bailey. Operation Clean Sweep. 2004. (Illus.). 160p. (J). 16.00 (978-0-374-38034-2(1) , Farrar, Straus & Giroux (BYR)) Farrar, Straus & Giroux.

Beaudoin, Sean. Going Nowhere Faster. 2007. 240p. (J). (gr. 8 up). 16.99 (*978-0-316-01415-1(X)) Little, Brown Bks. for Young Readers.

Beechen, Adam. Wild Thornberrys Survival Guide. 2000. (gr. 3-6). lib. bdg. 10.65 (978-0-613-27582-8(9)) Tandem Library Bks.

Beiler, Edna. Mattie Mae. Graber, Esther Rose, illus. 2nd ed. 2000. 112p. (J). (ps-4). pap. 6.99 (978-0-8361-9141-7(2)) Herald Pr.

Bell, Julia. Massive. 2005. (Illus.). 272p. (YA). (gr. 7 up). pap. 6.99 (978-1-4169-0207-2(4) , Simon Pulse) Simon & Schuster Children's Publishing.

Bell, Krista. Get a Life. 2002. (Takeaways Ser.). (Illus.). 164p. (YA). pap. (978-0-7344-0187-8(6) , Lothian Bks.) Hachette Livre Australia.

Bencastro, Mario. A Promise to Keep. Giersbach-Rascon, Susan, tr. from SPA. 2005. 134p. (J). (gr. 3-7). pap. 9.95 (978-1-55885-457-4(6) , Piñata Books) Arte Publico Pr.

Bender, Carrie. Hemlock Hill Hideaway. 2000. (Whispering Brook Ser.: Bk. 4). (Illus.). 168p. (J). (gr. 4-8). pap. 8.99 (978-0-8361-9128-8(5)) Herald Pr.

—Hemlock Hill Hideaway: Whispering Brook Series #4. 2007. (Illus.). 168p. pap. 8.99 (*978-1-60126-022-2(9)) Masthof Pr.

—Summerville Days. 2001. (Whispering Brook Ser.). (Illus.). 183p. (J). 25.95 (978-0-7862-3081-5(9) , Five Star) Thomson Gale.

—Summerville Days: Whispering Brook Series #2. 2007. (Illus.). 224p. pap. 8.99 (*978-1-60126-023-9(7)) Masthof Pr.

Bender, Carrie. Timber Lane Cove. 2003. (Whispering Brook Ser.: Bk. 6). 144p. (YA). pap. 8.99 (978-0-8361-9202-5(8)) Herald Pr.

Bender, Esther. Elisabeth & the Windmill. 2003. (Lemon Tree Ser.). 112p. (J). (gr. 3-7). pap. 6.99 (978-0-8361-9204-9(4)) Herald Pr.

—Virginia & the Tiny One. Keenan, Joy Dunn, illus. 1998. (Lemon Tree Ser.: Vol. 2). 104p. (J). (gr. 3-7). pap. 6.99 (978-0-8361-9090-8(4)) Herald Pr.

Benjamin, A. H. It Could Have Been Worse. Warnes, Tim, illus. (J). (ps-k). 2000. 28p. 6.95 (978-1-58431-015-0(4)); 1999. 32p. pap. 5.95 (978-1-58431-006-8(5)) Little Tiger Pr.

Benjamin, Ruth. The Lost Treasure of Chelton. 2004. viii, 170p. (J). 13.95 (978-1-932443-02-8(9)) Judaica Pr., Inc., The.

Benjamin, Ruth. The Mysterious Lighthouse of Chelton. 2006. (ENG.). 160p. (J). 14.95 (*978-1-932443-57-8(6)) Judaica Pr., Inc., The.

Bennett, Jill. Grandad's Tree: Poems about Families. Cairns, Julia, illus. 2003. 32p. (J). 16.99 (978-1-84148-541-6(1)) Barefoot Bks., Inc.

Benson, Linda. Finding Chance. Lane, Nancy, illus. 2006. 112p. (J). (978-1-59336-696-4(5)) Mondo Publishing.

Berenstain, Stan & Berenstain, Jan. The Berenstain Bears & Baby Makes Five. 2000. (Berenstain Bears First Time Bks.). (Illus.). 32p. (J). (gr. k-1). pap. 3.25 (978-0-679-88960-1(4) , Random Hse. Bks. for Young Readers) Random Hse. Children's Bks.

—The Berenstain Bears & Baby Makes Five. 2000. (Berenstain Bears First Time Bks.). (J). (ps-2). lib. bdg. 10.95 (978-0-613-24332-2(3)); (Illus.). 10.05 (978-0-606-18485-4(6)) Tandem Library Bks.

—The Berenstain Bears & the Big Spelling Bee, No. 6. Berenstain, Jan, illus. 2007. (Berenstain Bears Ser.). (Illus.). 32p. (J). 3.99 (*978-0-06-057386-7(4) , Harper Festival) HarperCollins Pubs.

—The Berenstain Bears & the Trouble with Chores. 2005. (Berenstain Bears Ser.). (Illus.). 32p. (J). (ps-2). 8.99 (978-0-06-057398-0(8)); pap. 3.99 (978-0-06-057382-9(1)) HarperCollins Pubs. (Harper Festival).

—The Berenstain Bears & Too Much Car Trip. 2006. (Berenstain Bears Ser.). (Illus.). 32p. (J). (ps-2). 8.99 (978-0-06-057400-0(3)); pap. 3.99 (978-0-06-057384-3(8)) HarperCollins Pubs. (Harper Festival).

—The Berenstain Bears Hug & Make Up. 2006. (Berenstain Bears Ser.). (Illus.). 32p. (J). pap. 3.99 (978-0-06-057385-0(6) , Harper Festival) HarperCollins Pubs.

—The Berenstain Bears Hug & Make Up, No. 5. Berenstain, Stan & Berenstain, Jan, illus. 2006. (Berenstain Bears Ser.). (Illus.). 32p. (J). 8.99 (978-0-06-057401-7(1) , Harper Festival) HarperCollins Pubs.

—The Berenstain Bears' Report Card Trouble. ed. 2004. (Berenstain Bears First Time Bks.). (J). (gr. k-3). spiral bd. (978-0-616-11095-9(2)); spiral bd. (978-0-616-11096-6(0)) Canadian National Institute for the Blind/Institut National Canadien pour les Aveugles.

—The Berenstain Bears' Report Card Trouble. 2002. (Berenstain Bears First Time Bks.). (Illus.). 32p. (J). (gr. k-3). pap. 3.99 (978-0-375-81127-2(3) , Random Hse. Bks. for Young Readers) Random Hse. Children's Bks.

—The Berenstain Bears' Report Card Trouble. 2002. (Berenstain Bears First Time Bks.). (J). (gr. k-3). lib. bdg. 3.80 (978-0-613-70585-1(8)) Tandem Library Bks.

Beserra, Donna. Twirly Shirley & the Brother Like No Other. 2004. (J). pap. 12.00 (978-0-9729484-2-5(2)) Seventh Street Pr.

The Big Balloon Festival: Individual Title Six-Packs. 16p. (gr. 2 up). 35.00 (978-0-7635-9381-0(8)) Rigby Education.

The Big Mix-up: Individual Title Six-Packs. (ps-2). 27.00 (978-0-7635-9438-1(5)) Rigby Education.

Bildner, Phil. Turkey Bowl. Payne, C. F., illus. 2006. (J). 16.99 (978-0-689-87896-1(6) , Simon & Schuster Children's Publishing) Simon & Schuster Children's Publishing.

Birdsall, Jeanne. The Penderwicks. 2005. 272p. (J). (gr. 3-7). lib. bdg. 17.99 (978-0-375-93143-7(0) , Knopf Bks. for Young Readers) Random Hse. Children's Bks.

—The Penderwicks: A Summer Tale of Four Sisters, Two Rabbits, & a Very Interesting Boy. 2005. 272p. (J). (gr. 3-7). 15.95 (978-0-375-83143-0(6) , Knopf Bks. for Young Readers) Random Hse. Children's Bks.

Birdsall, Olivia. Notes on a Near-Life Experience. 2007. 272p. (YA). (gr. 7). 15.99 (978-0-385-73370-0(4)); lib. bdg. 18.99 (978-0-385-90385-1(5)) Random Hse. Children's Bks. (Delacorte Bks. for Young Readers).

Birney, Betty G. The Princess & the Peabodys. 2007. 256p. (J). lib. bdg. 16.89 (*978-0-06-084721-0(2)); (gr. 5 up). 15.99 (*978-0-06-084720-3(4)) HarperCollins Pubs.

—The Seven Wonders of Sassafras Springs. Phelan, Matt, illus. 2005. 224p. (J). (ps-7). 16.95 (978-0-689-87136-8(8) , Atheneum) Simon & Schuster Children's Publishing.

—The Seven Wonders of Sassafras Springs. Phelan, Matt, illus. 2007. 224p. (J). pap. 5.99 (978-1-4169-3489-9(8) , Aladdin) Simon & Schuster Children's Publishing.

—The Seven Wonders of Sassafras Springs. l.t. ed. 2006. 206p. (J). 22.95 (978-0-7862-8287-6(8)) Thorndike Pr.

Bittner, Wolfgang. Despierta, Osogris! 1999. (gr. k-3). (SPA.). lib. bdg. 15.25 (978-0-613-73509-4(9)); 13.75 (978-0-606-17635-4(7)) Tandem Library Bks.

Bjorkquist, Elena Diaz. Water from the Moon. 2002. 202p. (YA). pap. 13.95 (978-0-595-23561-2(1) , Writers Club Pr.) iUniverse, Inc.

Black, Sonia W. Mommy's Bed. Kindert, Jennifer, illus. 2004. 32p. (J). lib. bdg. 15.00 (*978-1-4242-0223-2(X)) Fitzgerald Bks.

Blackaby, Susan. Moving Day. Haugen, Ryan, illus. 2005. (Read-It! Readers Ser.). 32p. (J). (gr. k-3). 18.60 (978-1-4048-1006-8(4)) Picture Window Bks.

—Mudanza. Haugen, Ryan, illus. 2006. (Read-It! Readers en Espanol Ser.).Tr. of Moving Day. (SPA.). 32p. (J). (ps-3). 19.95 (978-1-4048-1686-2(0)) Picture Window Bks.

Blackaby, Susan. Todd's Fire Drill. Greathouse, Justin, illus. 2007. (J). lib. bdg. (*978-1-4048-2332-7(8)) Picture Window Bks.

Blacker, Terence. The Angel Factory. (Illus.). 224p. 2003. (J). (gr. k-17). pap. 5.99 (978-0-689-86413-1(2) , Aladdin); 2002. (YA). (gr. 6-9). 16.95 (978-0-689-85171-1(5)) Simon & Schuster Children's Publishing.

—Parent Swap. 2006. 240p. (J). 16.00 (978-0-374-35752-8(8) , Farrar, Straus & Giroux (BYR)) Farrar, Straus & Giroux.

Blackmon, D. J. una. Ghetto Waterfront Christmas. 2005. (Illus.). per. 8.99 (978-0-9719943-6-2(6)) Creative Enigma Enterprises.

Blades, Ann. Too Small. Blades, Ann, illus. 2000. (Illus.). 32p. (J). (ps-3). 15.95 (978-0-88899-400-4(1)) Groundwood Bks. CAN. *Dist:* Perseus Distribution.

Blair, Eric. El Pescador y su Mujer: Version del Cuento de los Hermanos Grimm. Ouren, Todd, illus. 2006. (Read-It! Readers en Espanol Ser.).Tr. of Fisherman & His Wife: A Retelling of the Grimm's Fairy Tale. (SPA.). 32p. (J). (ps-3). 19.95 (978-1-4048-1630-5(5)) Picture Window Bks.

Blake, Claire, et al. The Paper Chain. Parksinson, Kathy, illus. 1999. 32p. (J). (gr. k-6). pap. 8.95 (978-0-929173-28-3(7)) Health Pr. NA, Inc.

Blanchard, E. Amy. Sweet Little Maid. 2006. 95.99 (*978-1-4280-5035-8(3)); pap. 88.99 (*978-1-4280-5022-8(1)) IndyPublish.com.

Blasi, Kathleen McAlpin. A Name of Honor. Bowman, Leslie W., illus. 2006. (J). (978-1-59336-692-6(2)) Mondo Publishing.

Blue, Martha. Little Prankster Girl: At'Eed Adilahi Yazhi. Ruffenach, Jessie, ed. Thomas, Peter, tr. Smith, Keith, illus. 2003. (NAV & ENG.). 32p. 17.95 (978-1-893354-36-4(9)) Salina Bookshelf.

Bluedorn, Johannah. My Mommy, My Teacher. Bluedorn, Johannah, illus. 2002. (Illus.). 53p. (J). per. 12.00 (978-0-9743616-5-9(8)) Trivium Pursuit.

Blume, Judy. Best of Judy Blume Set: Are You There God? It's Me, Margaret; Blubber; Iggie's House; Starring Sally J. Freedman as Herself, 4 vols. 2004. (gr. 3-7). pap. 23.47 (978-0-440-42022-4(9) , Yearling) Random Hse. Children's Bks.

—BFF: Two novels by Judy Blume—Just As Long As We're Together/Here's to You, Rachel Robinson (Best Friends Forever), 2 vols. 2007. (Illus.). 512p. (J). (gr. 4-7). lib. bdg. 22.99 (978-0-385-90416-2(9) , Delacorte Bks. for Young Readers) Random Hse. Children's Bks.

—BFF 2: Two Novels by Judy Blume—Just As Long As We're Together/Here's to You, Rachel Robinson (Best Friends Forever) 2007. (Illus.). 512p. (J). (gr. 4-7). 18.99 (978-0-385-73407-3(7) , Delacorte Bks. for Young Readers) Random Hse. Children's Bks.

—Cool Zone with the Pain & the Great One. Stevenson, James, illus. 2008. (J). 12.99 (*978-0-385-73306-9(2)); 16.99 (*978-0-385-90325-7(1)) Dell Publishing. (Delacorte Pr.).

—Double Fudge. (Fudge Ser.). 2007. 224p. (J). (gr. 2). 5.99 (*978-0-14-240878-0(6) , Puffin); 2004. 192p. (gr. 12). mass mkt. 5.99 (978-0-425-19647-2(X) , Berkley); 2002. 224p. (gr. 3-7). 15.99 (978-0-525-46926-1(5) , Dutton Juvenile) Penguin Group (USA) Inc.

—Double Fudge. 2004. (Fudge Ser.). 160p. (J). (gr. 3-7). pap. 36.00 incl. audio (978-0-8072-2036-8(1) , Listening Library) Random Hse. Audio Publishing Group.

—Estas Ahi Dios? Soy Yo, Margaret. rev. ed. 2001. Tr. of Are You There God? It's Me, Margaret. (SPA.). 176p. (J). (gr. 4-6). 17.00 (978-0-689-84688-5(6) , Atheneum/Richard Jackson Bks.) Simon & Schuster Children's Publishing.

—Fudge-a-Mania. (Fudge Ser.). 2007. 160p. (J). (gr. 2). pap. 5.99 (978-0-14-240877-3(8) , Puffin); 2004. 176p. (gr. 12). mass mkt. 5.99 (978-0-425-19382-2(9) , Berkley) Penguin Group (USA) Inc.

—Fudge-a-Mania. (Fudge Ser.). (gr. 3-6). 2004. lib. bdg. 14.15 (978-0-613-87580-6(X)); 2003. lib. bdg. 14.15 (978-0-613-63936-1(7)) Tandem Library Bks.

—It's Not the End of the World. 2002. (Illus.). (J). 13.94 (978-0-7587-9132-0(1)) Book Wholesalers, Inc.

—It's Not the End of the World. 174p. (YA). (gr. 5 up). pap. 4.50 (978-0-8072-1365-0(9) , Listening Library) Random Hse. Audio Publishing Group.

—It's Not the End of the World. 2002. 176p. (J). 17.99 (978-0-689-84293-1(7) , Atheneum/Richard Jackson Bks.) Simon & Schuster Children's Publishing.

—Superfudge. 2002. (Fudge Ser.). (Illus.). (J). 13.40 (978-0-7587-6668-7(8)) Book Wholesalers, Inc.

—Superfudge. l.t. ed. 2000. (Fudge Ser.). 216p. (YA). (gr. 5-10). lib. bdg. 28.95 (978-1-58118-061-9(6) , 23475) LRS.

—Superfudge. 1999. (Fudge Ser.). (J). 9.95 (978-1-56137-175-4(0)) Novel Units, Inc.

—Superfudge. (Fudge Ser.). 2004. 192p. (gr. 12). mass mkt. 5.99 (978-0-425-19381-5(0) , Berkley); 2002. (Illus.). 176p. (J). 15.99 (978-0-525-46930-8(3) , Dutton Juvenile) Penguin Group (USA) Inc.

—Superfudge. (Fudge Ser.). 166p. (J). (gr. 2-4). pap. 4.99 (978-0-8072-1457-2(4) , Listening Library) Random Hse. Audio Publishing Group.

—Superfudge. (Fudge Ser.). (SPA.). 159p. (J). (gr. 5-8). pap. 9.95 (978-1-56014-665-0(6)) Santillana USA Publishing Co., Inc.

Blumenthal, Deborah. The Pink House at the Seashore. Chayka, Doug, illus. 2005. 32p. (J). (gr. 3-5). 16.00 (978-0-618-37886-9(3) , Clarion Bks.) Houghton Mifflin Co. Trade & Reference Div.

Blyton, Enid. Family Christmas. (Illus.). 151p. (J). pap. 6.95 (978-0-09-987830-8(5)) Random Hse. GBR. *Dist:* Trafalgar Square Publishing.

—Four Cousins. (Illus.). 93p. (J). pap. 5.95 (978-0-09-926640-2(7)) Random Hse. GBR. *Dist:* Trafalgar Square Publishing.

Bockol, Leslie. Peek-a-Boo! Larranaga, Ana & Parsons, Jackie, illus. 2006. (IBaby Ser.). 10p. (J). (ps-ps). bds. 10.99 (978-1-58476-416-8(3) , IKIDS) Innovative Kids.

Bodett, Tom. Norman Tuttle on the Last Frontier. 208p. (YA). (gr. 7). 2006. mass mkt. 5.99 (978-0-553-49493-8(7) , Laurel Leaf); 2004. 15.95 (978-0-679-89031-7(9) , Knopf Bks. for Young Readers) Random Hse. Children's Bks.

—Norman Tuttle on the Last Frontier: A Novel in Stories. 2004. 208p. (J). (gr. 7). lib. bdg. 17.99 (978-0-679-99031-4(3) , Knopf Bks. for Young Readers) Random Hse. Children's Bks.

Boling, Katharine. January 1905. 2006. 192p. (YA). pap. 5.95 (978-0-15-205121-1(X) , Harcourt Paperbacks) Harcourt Children's Bks.

Boonstra, Jean Elizabeth. Secret in the Family A: Sarah 1842-1844. 2002. 95p. (J). (978-0-8163-1887-2(5)) Pacific Pr. Publishing Assn.

Borden, Louise. Just in Time for Christmas. 2000. (Illus.). (J). pap. 5.99 (978-0-590-45356-1(4)) Scholastic, Inc.

—Just in Time for Christmas. 2000. (J). 12.79 (978-0-606-19573-7(4)) Tandem Library Bks.

Borntrager, Mary Christner. Andy. l.t. ed. 2002. 161p. 25.95 (978-0-7862-4029-6(6)) Thomson Gale.

—Ellie. l.t. ed. 2001. (Christian Fiction Ser.). 208p. 23.95 (978-0-7862-3383-0(4)) Thorndike Pr.

—Mandy Bk. 9: Ellie's People. l.t. ed. 2002. (Christian Fiction Ser.). 25.95 (978-0-7862-4539-0(5)) Thorndike Pr.

—Rebecca. l.t. ed. 2001. (Thorndike Christian Fiction Ser.). 245p. 24.95 (978-0-7862-3252-9(8)) Thorndike Pr.

—Sarah. l.t. ed. 2002. (Christian Fiction Ser.). 177p. 25.95 (978-0-7862-4526-0(3)) Thorndike Pr.

Bostrom, Kathleen Long. Waiting for Christmas: A Story about the Advent Calendar. Natchev, Alexi, illus. 2006. (Traditions of Faith Ser.). 40p. (J). 15.99 (978-0-310-71015-8(4)) Zonderkidz.

Bourgeois, Paulette. The Franklin Annual, Vol. 2. Clark, Brenda, illus. 2004. (Franklin Annual Ser.). 96p. (J). (gr. k-3). (978-1-55337-531-9(9)) Kids Can Pr., Ltd.

—El Principe y el Mendigo. Jorisch, Stephane, illus. 2004. (SPA.). (J). 14.99 (978-84-241-8644-9(3)) Everest de Ediciones y Distribucion, S.L. ESP. *Dist:* Lectorum Pubns., Inc.

Bousman, Cindy. Pete & P. J. Sing, Dance & Read with Me, Read-Along with Small Book & Cassette. 2000. 12p. (J). (ps-3). pap. 9.95 incl. audio (978-1-931127-37-0(9) , 986-004) Kindermusik International.

Bowen, Anne. Christmas Is Coming. Bogacki, Tomasz, illus. 2007. (Carolrhoda Picture Bks.). 32p. (J). (ps-4). 16.95 (*978-1-57505-934-1(7) , Carolrhoda Bks.) Lerner Publishing Group.

Bowler, Tim. Storm Catchers. 2003. (Illus.). 208p. (YA). 16.95 (978-0-689-84573-4(1) , McElderry, Margaret K.) Simon & Schuster Children's Publishing.

Boyce, Frank Cottrell, ed. Framed. 2006. 320p. (J). 16.99 (978-0-06-073402-2(7)); lib. bdg. 17.89 (978-0-06-073403-9(5)) HarperCollins Pubs.

Boyce, Julia G. Not Very Messy, Unless... Durney, Ryan, illus. 1998. 8p. (J). (gr. k-2). pap. 3.75 (978-1-880612-79-8(8) , Seedling Pubns.) Continental Pr., Inc.

Bradby, Marie. Some Friend. 2007. 240p. (J). pap. 5.99 (978-1-4169-3452-3(9) , Aladdin) Simon & Schuster Children's Publishing.

E F G

Bradfield, Carl. Hawaii Calls Wendell & Myrtle: The Wendells Family Make It to the Big Island. (Illus.). 196p. (Orig.). (YA). (gr. 8-12). pap. (978-0-9632319-5-6(2)) ASDA Publishing, Inc.

Bradley-McBeth, Anna E. & Bradley-McBeth, Nilaja A. I Eat at Mommy's. Bradley-McBeth, Anna E., illus. 1999. (Illus.). v, 41p. (J). 14.99 (978-0-9670636-4-5(7)) Big Brain Publishing, LLC.

Bradman, Tony. A Goodnight Kind of Feeling. Scruton, Clive, illus. 1998. 32p. (J). (ps-k). tchr. ed. 15.95 (978-0-8234-1351-5(9)) Holiday Hse., Inc.

Bradman, Tony & Chatterton, Martin. The Mummy Family Finds Fame. 2006. (Illus.). 46p. (J). (978-0-7787-1076-9(9)) Crabtree Publishing Co.

Braids for Naya, 6, Pack. (ps-2). 27.00 (978-0-7635-9439-8(3)) Rigby Education.

Brandeis, Batsheva. Faiga Finds the Way. Levitas, Alexander, illus. 2005. (Fun to Read Book Ser.). 120p. (J). pap. 8.95 (978-1-929628-28-5(5)) Hachai Publishing.

Bredsdorff, Bodil. The Crow-Girl: The Children of Crow Cove. Ingwersen, Faith, tr. 2006. 160p. (J). reprint ed. pap. 5.95 (978-0-374-40003-3(2) , Farrar, Straus & Giroux (BYR)) Farrar, Straus & Giroux.

Brennan, Herbie. Faerie Wars. 2007. 384p. mass mkt. 6.99 (978-0-7653-5674-1(0) , Tor Bks.) Doherty, Tom Assocs., LLC.

—Faerie Wars. l.t. ed. 2004. 448p. 22.95 (978-0-7862-6831-3(X) , Large Print Pr.) Thorndike Pr.

Brennan-Nelson, Denise. Someday Is Not a Day of the Week. O'Malley, Kevin, illus. 2005. 32p. (J). 15.95 (978-1-58536-243-1(3)) Sleeping Bear Pr.

Bridwell, Norman. Clifford's Family. Bridwell, Norman, illus. 2002. (Clifford, the Big Red Dog Ser.). (Illus.). (J). 11.45 (978-0-7587-6708-0(0)) Book Wholesalers, Inc.

Brimner, Larry Dane. Elliot Fry's Good-Bye. Fernandes, Eugenie, illus. 2003. 32p. (J). (gr. k-2). 8.95 (978-1-56397-715-2(X)) Boyds Mills Pr.

Brisac, Genevieve. Olga. 2000. (la Orilla Del Viento Ser.). (SPA., Illus.). 47p. (J). (ps-ps). pap. 6.99 (978-968-16-5436-8(6) , 104) Fondo de Cultura Economica USA.

Brochu, Lisa. Dad Still Smiles. Butterfield, Ned, illus. 2003. (Books for Young Learners). 12p. (J). pap. 5.00 net. (978-1-57274-601-5(7) , 2731) Owen, Richard C. Pubs., Inc.

Brokaw, Nancy Steele. Leaving Emma. 1999. 144p. (J). (gr. 4-6). tchr. ed. 15.00 (978-0-395-90699-6(7) , Clarion Bks.) Houghton Mifflin Co. Trade & Reference Div.

Brooke, Lauren. Out of the Darkness. 2002. (Heartland Ser.: No. 7). 160p. (gr. 3-7). mass mkt. 4.99 (978-0-439-31714-6(2)) Scholastic, Inc.

—Out of the Darkness. 2002. (gr. 3-6). lib. bdg. 12.40 (978-0-613-62913-3(2)) Tandem Library Bks.

Brooks, Regina. Never Finished, Never Done! Borgella, Marjorie, illus. 2004. 32p. (J). lib. bdg. 15.00 (*978-1-4242-0229-4(9)) Fitzgerald Bks.

Brooks, Ron. Oscar y la Gata de Medianoche. 2nd ed. 2002. (Rosa y Manzana Ser.). (SPA.). 32p. (J). (978-84-89804-05-0(2)) Loguez Ediciones ESP. *Dist:* Lectorum Pubns., Inc.

Brouwer, Sigmund. Hitmen Triumph. 2007. (Orca Sports Ser.). 176p. (YA). (gr. 5 up). pap. (*978-1-55143-873-3(9)) Orca Bk. Pubs.

Brown, Elizabeth Ferguson. Coal Country Christmas. Stevenson, Harvey, illus. 2003. 32p. (J). (gr. k-2). 15.95 (978-1-59078-020-6(5)) Boyds Mills Pr.

Brown, Jeff. Flat Stanley. Nash, Scott, illus. 2006. (Flat Stanley Ser.). 40p. (J). 16.99 (978-0-06-112904-9(6)) HarperCollins Pubs.

Brown, Marc. Arthur Loses His Patience, 18 vols. 2001. (Arthur's Family Values: Vol. 11). (Illus.). 28p. 3.79 (978-1-57973-117-5(1)) Advance Pubs. LLC.

—Arthur the Brave, 18 vols., Vol. 10. 2001. (Arthur's Family Values: Vol. 10). (Illus.). 28p. (J). 3.79 (978-1-57973-116-8(3)) Advance Pubs. LLC.

—Arthur's Family Treasury: Three Arthur Adventures in One Volume. Brown, Marc, illus. 2000. (Illus.). 112p. (J). (ps-3). 18.95 (978-0-316-12147-7(9)) Little Brown & Co.

—Arthur's Science Project, 18 vols., Vol. 9. 2001. (Arthur's Family Values: Vol. 9). (Illus.). 28p. (J). 3.79 (978-1-57973-115-1(5)) Advance Pubs. LLC.

—Buried Treasure, 18 vols., Vol. 8. 2001. (Illus.). 28p. (J). 3.79 (978-1-57973-114-4(7)) Advance Pubs. LLC.

—D. W., Go to Your Room! Brown, Marc, illus. 2001. (D. W. Ser.). (Illus.). 24p. (J). (ps-1). pap. 5.99 (978-0-316-10670-2(4)) Little, Brown Bks. for Young Readers.

—D. W., Go to Your Room! (D. W. Ser.). 2001. (Illus.). (J). 12.75 (978-0-606-21133-8(0)); 1999. lib. bdg. 14.10 (978-0-613-58320-6(5)) Tandem Library Bks.

—D. W. Saves the Day. 2001. (D. W. Ser.). (Illus.). 28p. (J). 3.79 (978-1-57973-121-2(X)) Advance Pubs. LLC.

—D. W.'s Lost Blankie. Brown, Marc, illus. 2002. (D. W. Ser.). (Illus.). (J). 13.15 (978-0-7587-2330-7(X)) Book Wholesalers, Inc.

—D. W.'s Lost Blankie. Brown, Marc, illus. 1998. (D. W. Ser.). (Illus.). 32p. (J). (ps-1). 13.95 (978-0-316-10914-7(2)) Little, Brown Bks. for Young Readers.

—Family Stories You Can Relate To. 2001. (gr. 3-6). lib. bdg. 11.80 (978-0-613-56364-2(6)) Tandem Library Bks.

—Manners Matter. Brown, Marc, ed. 2001. (Arthur's Family Values: Vol. 1). (Illus.). 28p. (J). 3.49 (978-1-57973-108-3(2)) Advance Pubs. LLC.

—Queen for a Day, 18 vols., Vol. 3. 2001. (Arthur's Family Values: Vol. 3). (Illus.). 28p. (J). 3.79 (978-1-57973-109-0(0)) Advance Pubs. LLC.

—Say Cheese, 18 vols., Vol. 17. 2001. (Arthur's Family Values: Vol. 17). (Illus.). 28p. (J). 3.79 (978-1-57973-123-6(6)) Advance Pubs. LLC.

—The Truth Pops Out, 18 vols., Vol. 5. 2001. (Arthur's Family Values: Vol. 5). (Illus.). 28p. (J). 3.79 (978-1-57973-111-3(2)) Advance Pubs. LLC.

—Try It, You'll Like It!, 18 vols., Vol. 4. 2001. (Arthur's Family Values: Vol. 4). (Illus.). 28p. (J). 3.79 (978-1-57973-110-6(4)) Advance Pubs. LLC.

—Vacaciones de Arturo. 1999. Tr. of Arthur's Family Vacation. (978-0-606-17376-6(5)); (SPA.). lib. bdg. 15.25 (978-0-613-18151-8(4)) Tandem Library Bks.

—What a Mess!, 18 vols., Vol. 12. 2001. (Arthur's Family Values: Vol. 12). (Illus.). 28p. (J). 3.79 (978-1-57973-118-2(X)) Advance Pubs. LLC.

Brown, Margaret Wise. My World: A Companion to Goodnight Moon. Hurd, Clement, illus. (J). (ps up). 2004. 40p. pap. 5.99 (978-0-694-01660-0(8) , Harper Trophy); 2003. 36p. bds. 7.99 (978-0-694-00862-9(1) , Harper Festival); 2001. 32p. 15.95 (978-0-06-024798-0(3) , Harper Festival) HarperCollins Pubs.

—Where Have You Been? Dillon, Leo & Dillon, Diane, illus. 2004. 32p. (J). (ps-1). 16.99 (978-0-06-028378-0(5)) HarperCollins Pubs.

—Where Have You Been? rev. ed. Date not set. 32p. (J). (ps-1). pap. 6.99 (978-0-06-443569-7(5)) HarperCollins Pubs.

Brown, Ruth. The Big Sneeze. Date not set. (Illus.). 32p. (J). pap. (978-0-05-004391-2(9)) Addison-Wesley Longman, Inc.

Bruchac, Joseph. Hidden Roots. 2006. 160p. (J). pap. 5.99 (978-0-439-35359-5(9) , Scholastic Paperbacks) Scholastic, Inc.

Brunner, Celeste Walker. Louisiana Lessie. 2001. (Illus.). 40p. (J). pap. 11.00 (978-1-57921-333-6(2)) WinePress Publishing.

Bryant, Ann. She's No Angel. 2005. (Step-Chain Ser.). 190p. (J). pap. 4.95 (978-1-894222-75-4(X)) Lobster Pr. CAN. *Dist:* Univ. of Toronto Pr.

—Too Good to Be True. 2005. (Step-Chain Ser.). 190p. (J). pap. 4.95 (978-1-894222-76-1(8)) Lobster Pr. CAN. *Dist:* Univ. of Toronto Pr.

Buchanan, Paul. House Divided. 2001. (gr. 3-6). lib. bdg. 14.15 (978-0-613-72848-5(3)) Tandem Library Bks.

Buchanan, Paul & Randall, Rod. A House Divided, Vol. 20. 2001. (Misadventures of Willie Plummett Ser.: Vol. 20). (Illus.). 128p. (J). (gr. 3-7). 5.99 (978-0-570-07131-0(3)) Concordia Publishing Hse.

Budhos, Marina. Ask Me No Questions. 176p. (YA). 2007. pap. 8.99 (*978-1-4169-4920-6(8) , Simon Pulse); 2006. (Illus.). (gr. 5-9). 16.95 (978-1-4169-0351-2(8) , Atheneum) Simon & Schuster Children's Publishing.

Bullard, Lisa. My Day: Morning, Noon & Night. Wesley, Omarr, illus. 2004. (All about Me Ser.). 24p. (C). (gr. k-1). 21.26 (978-1-4048-0045-8(X)) Picture Window Bks.

Bunting, Eve. I Don't Want to Go to Camp. 2003. (ps-2). lib. bdg. 17.60 (978-0-613-58326-8(4)) Tandem Library Bks.

Bunting, Eve. You Were Loved Before You Were Born. Barbour, Karen, illus. 2008. 32p. pap. 16.99 (*978-0-439-04061-7(2)); pap. (*978-0-439-04062-4(0)) Scholastic, Inc. (Blue Sky Pr., The).

Burch, Christian. The Manny Files. 2006. (Illus.). 304p. (J). (gr. 4-7). 15.95 (978-1-4169-0039-9(X) , Atheneum) Simon & Schuster Children's Publishing.

Burch, Robert. Queenie Peavy. abr. ed. 1999. (J). (gr. 4-7). pap. 15.95 incl. audio (978-0-670-58427-7(4)) Live Oak Media.

Burgess, Melvin. Doing It. 2006. 336p. (YA). reprint ed. pap. 6.95 (978-0-8050-8079-7(1) , Holt, Henry & Co. Bks. For Young Readers) Holt, Henry & Co.

Burnett, Frances Hodgson. The Secret Garden: A Young Reader's Edition of the Classic Story. 1999. (978-0-606-17320-9(X)) Tandem Library Bks.

Butcher, Kristin. The Gramma War. 2001. (Illus.). 176p. (J). (gr. 4-7). pap. 6.95 (978-1-55143-183-3(1)) Orca Bk. Pubs. USA.

—Gramma War. 2001. (gr. 3-6). lib. bdg. 15.25 (978-0-613-45662-3(9)) Tandem Library Bks.

—Zee's Way. 2004. (Orca Soundings Ser.). 112p. (J). (gr. 7-12). pap. 7.95 (978-1-55143-279-3(X)) Orca Bk. Pubs. USA.

Butterworth, Nick. My Grandpa Is Amazing. Butterworth, Nick, illus. 2003. (My Relative Ser.). (Illus.). 32p. (J). (ps-3). 5.99 (978-0-7636-2057-8(2)) Candlewick Pr.

Byalick, Marcia. Quit It. 2004. 176p. (J). (gr. 3-7). pap. 5.99 (978-0-440-41865-8(8) , Yearling) Random Hse. Children's Bks.

Byars, Betsy. Keeper of the Doves. (J). 2002. 96p. (gr. 3-7). 14.99 (978-0-670-03576-2(9) , Viking Juvenile); 2004. (Illus.). 128p. reprint ed. pap. 5.99 (978-0-14-240063-0(7) , Puffin) Penguin Group (USA) Inc.

—The Summer of the Swans. Coconis, Ted, illus. 2002. (J). 13.19 (978-0-7587-0217-3(5)) Book Wholesalers, Inc.

—The Summer of the Swans. CoConis, Ted, illus. l.t. ed. 2000. (LRS Large Print Cornerstone Ser.). 176p. (YA). (gr. 5-12). lib. bdg. 27.95 (978-1-58118-060-2(8) , 23474) LRS.

—The Summer of the Swans. 2004. (Puffin Modern Classics Ser.). 144p. (gr. 3). pap. 5.99 (978-0-14-240114-9(5) , Puffin) Penguin Group (USA) Inc.

Byrd, Sandra. Red Velvet. 2005. (Friends for a Season Ser.). 256p. (J). (gr. 8-12). pap. 10.99 (978-0-7642-0022-9(4)) Bethany Hse. Pubs.

Cabot, Meg. Ready or No. 2008. 256p. (J). pap. 7.99 (*978-0-06-147996-0(9) , HarperTeen) HarperCollins Pubs.

Cabot, Meg. Ready or Not. 2nd ed. 2005. 256p. (YA). (gr. 7 up). 16.99 (978-0-06-072450-4(1)) HarperCollins Pubs.

—Ready or Not. l.t. ed. 2006. 322p. (YA). 23.95 (978-0-7862-8282-1(7)) Thorndike Pr.

Caho, Cheryl. Jumbo's Tiny Tale - Volume 1: Family Fun. 2007. (Illus.). 84p. per. 15.97 (*978-0-9779960-7-0(7)) Thornton Publishing.

Caldwell, V. M. The Ocean Within. Magnus, Erica, illus. 1999. (Milkweed Prize for Children's Literature Ser.). 236p. (J). (gr. 3-8). pap. 6.95 (978-1-57131-624-0(8)) Milkweed Editions.

—The Ocean Within. 1999. (J). (gr. 3-9). (978-0-606-19035-0(X)) Tandem Library Bks.

Caletti, Deb. The Fortunes of Indigo Skye. 2008. 304p. (YA). 15.99 (*978-1-4169-1007-7(7) , Simon & Schuster Children's Publishing) Simon & Schuster Children's Publishing.

Caletti, Deb. Queen of Everything. 2002. (gr. 7-12). lib. bdg. 15.30 (978-0-613-57580-5(6)) Tandem Library Bks.

Callahan, Thera S. All Wrapped Up. 2004. (Rookie Reader Espanol Ser.). (Illus.). 31p. (J). (gr. k-2). pap. 4.95 (978-0-516-21949-3(9) , Children's Pr.) Scholastic Library Publishing.

Calvert, Patricia. Glennis, Before & After. 1999. 144p. (J). (gr. 3-7). pap. 3.99 (978-0-380-73132-9(0)) HarperCollins Pubs.

—Glennis, Before & After. 1999. (J). (978-0-606-15932-6(0)) Tandem Library Bks.

Cameron, Ann. Gloria's Way. 2001. 11.64 (978-0-606-22055-2(0)) Tandem Library Bks.

—Julian, Dream Doctor. 2002. (J). 12.32 (978-0-7587-6155-2(4)) Book Wholesalers, Inc.

—More Stories Huey Tells. Toft, Lis, illus. 1999. 128p. (J). (gr. k-4). pap. 4.99 (978-0-679-88363-0(0) , Random Hse. Bks. for Young Readers) Random Hse. Children's Bks.

—More Stories Huey Tells. 1998. (J). pap. 4.99 (978-0-679-88576-4(5) , Knopf Bks. for Young Readers) Random Hse. Children's Bks.

—More Stories Huey Tells. 1999. (J). (978-0-606-16567-9(3)) Tandem Library Bks.

—More Stories Huey Tells. Toft, Lis, illus. 1999. 117p. (J). (ps-ps). per. 13.00 (978-0-613-10978-9(3)) Tandem Library Bks.

—The Secret Life of Amanda K. Woods. 1999. (Illus.). 208p. (J). (gr. 5-9). pap. 6.99 (978-0-14-130642-1(4) , Puffin) Penguin Group (USA) Inc.

—Secret Life of Amanda K Woods. 1999. (gr. 3-6). lib. bdg. 14.15 (978-0-613-23031-5(0)) Tandem Library Bks.

—The Stories Julian Tells. 1999. (J). 9.95 (978-1-56137-671-1(X)) Novel Units, Inc.

Campbell, Terry. Harlem & Momma: A Short Children Story. 2005. 42p. (J). pap. 10.00 (978-0-9761560-0-0(8)) Sweet T. C. Campbell.

Canales, Viola. The Tequila Worm. 208p. (YA). (gr. 7-11). 2007. pap. 7.99 (978-0-375-84089-0(3)); 2005. 15.95 (978-0-385-74674-8(1)); 2005. 17.99 (978-0-385-90905-1(5)) Random Hse. Children's Bks. (Lamb, Wendy).

Canals, Sonia. Castanets. 1999. (Music Time Ser.). (Illus.). 8p. (J). (ps). 6.95 (978-1-899607-75-4(7)) Sterling Publishing Co., Inc.

Canfield, Jack L., et al. Chicken Soup for Little Souls Reader: The Best Night Out with Dad. Dodson, Bert, illus. 2005. 48p. (J). pap. 3.95 (978-0-7573-0281-7(5)) Health Communications, Inc.

Capone, Deb. Families Are Forever. 2004. (J). 16.95 (*978-0-9728666-6-8(3)) As Simple As That Publishing.

Card, Orson Scott, ed. Future on Ice. rev. ed. 1998. 432p. (YA). (gr. 7 up). 24.95 (978-0-312-86694-5(1) , Tor Bks.) Doherty, Tom Assocs., LLC.

Carey, Janet Lee. The Double Life of Zoe Flynn. 2004. (Illus.). 240p. (J). 16.95 (978-0-689-85604-4(0) , Atheneum) Simon & Schuster Children's Publishing.

Carlson, Nancy, tr. & illus. Louanne Pig in the Perfect Family. Carlson, Nancy, illus. 2nd rev. ed. 2004. (Nancy Carlson's Neighborhood Ser.). 32p. (J). (gr. k-2). 15.95 (978-1-57505-611-1(9)); pap. (978-1-57505-616-6(X)) Lerner Publishing Group.

Carlson, Ron. The Speed of Light. 2003. (Illus.). 288p. (J). 15.99 (978-0-380-97837-3(7) , HarperTeen) HarperCollins Pubs.

Carlton, Susan. Lobsterland. 2007. 224p. (YA). (gr. 9 up). 16.95 (*978-0-8050-8096-4(1)) Holt, Henry & Co.

Carson, Diana Pastora. All the Muchos in the World: A Special Story about Love. Pruitt, Ginny, illus. 2006. 32p. (J). pap. 8.95 (978-0-8198-0779-3(6)) Pauline Bks. & Media.

Carter, Anne. My Home Bay. Daniel, Alan, illus. 2004. 32p. (J). (gr. k-2). 17.95 (978-0-88995-284-3(1)) Red Deer Pr. CAN. *Dist:* Fitzhenry & Whiteside, Ltd.

Cartoon Network Staff, contrib. by. Attack of the 50 Foot Sister: Dexter's Laboratory. 2000. (Illus.). 16p. (J). (ps-3). pap. 4.99 (978-0-307-29952-9(X) , Golden Bks.) Random Hse. Children's Bks.

Casanova, Mary. Klipfish Code. 2007. 240p. (J). (gr. 5-7). 16.00 (*978-0-618-88393-6(2)) Houghton Mifflin Co. Trade & Reference Div.

Cassidy, Cathy. Indigo Blue. 2006. 240p. (J). (gr. 5). pap. 5.99 (978-0-14-240703-5(8) , Puffin) Penguin Group (USA) Inc.

—Scarlett. 2006. 272p. (YA). 16.99 (978-0-670-06068-9(2) , Viking Juvenile) Penguin Group (USA) Inc.

Center for Learning Network Staff. Belle Prater's Boy/ My Louisiana Sky: Curriculum Unit — Novel Series. 2001. (Novel Ser.). 77p. (YA). tchr. ed., spiral bd. 19.95 (978-1-56077-662-8(5)) Ctr. for Learning, The.

Chaikin, Miriam. Finders Weepers. Egielski, Richard, illus. 2001. 136p. (YA). pap. 11.95 (978-0-595-19878-8(3) , Backinprint.com) iUniverse, Inc.

—I Should Worry, I Should Care. 2000. (Illus.). 116p. (gr. 4-7). pap. 9.95 (978-0-595-09011-2(7) , Backinprint.com) iUniverse, Inc.

Chalifour, Francis. After. 2005. 144p. (J). (gr. 7). pap. 7.95 (978-0-88776-705-0(2)) Tundra Bks., Inc./Livres Toundra, Inc. CAN. *Dist:* Random Hse., Inc.

Chall, Marsha Wilson. Happy Birthday, America! Porfirio, Guy, illus. 2000. 32p. (J). (ps-3). 17.99 (978-0-688-13051-0(8)) HarperCollins Pubs.

—Sugarbush Spring. 2000. (Illus.). 24p. (J). (gr. 1 up). 16.89 (978-0-688-14908-6(1)) HarperCollins Pubs.

—Sugarbush Spring. Daly, Jim, illus. 2000. 24p. (J). (gr. 1 up). 16.99 (978-0-688-14907-9(3)) HarperCollins Pubs.

Chapman, Jean. Favourite Live Thing. (Illus.). 62p. pap. 10.95 (978-0-7022-2888-9(5)) Univ. of Queensland Pr. AUS. *Dist:* International Specialized Bk. Services.

Chapra, Mimi. Sparky's Bark/El Ladrido de Sparky. Escriva, Vivi, illus. 2006. (ENG & SPA.). 32p. (J). 16.99 (978-0-06-053172-0(X)) HarperCollins Pubs.

Charles, Norma M. All the Way to Mexico. 2003. (Illus.). 168p. (J). pap. 6.95 (978-1-55192-598-1(2)) Raincoast Bk. Distribution CAN. *Dist:* Perseus Distribution.

Charlton-Trujillo, E. E. Feels Like Home. 2007. 224p. (YA). (gr. 7 up). 15.99 (978-0-385-73332-8(1)); lib. bdg. 18.99 (978-0-385-90349-3(9)) Random Hse. Children's Bks. (Delacorte Bks. for Young Readers).

Charlton-Trujillo, E. E. Prizefighter en Mi Casa. 2007. 192p. (J). (gr. 5-7). 5.99 (*978-0-440-42117-7(9) , Yearling) Random Hse. Children's Bks.

Cheaney, J. B. My Friend the Enemy. 2007. 272p. (J). (gr. 5-9). 6.50 (*978-0-440-42102-3(0) , Yearling) Random Hse. Children's Bks.

Cheng, Andrea. Eclipse. 2006. 320p. (J). 16.95 (978-1-932425-21-5(7) , Front Street) Boyds Mills Pr.

—Shanghai Messenger. Young, Ed, illus. 2005. 40p. (J). (ps-7). 17.95 (978-1-58430-238-4(0)) Lee & Low Bks., Inc.

Chessa, Francesca. The Mysterious Package. Chessa, Francesca, illus. 2007. (Illus.). 32p. (J). (ps-2). 16.95 (*978-1-59990-028-5(9)) Bloomsbury Publishing.

Child, Lauren. Ana Tarambana Me Llaman. 2000. (Illus.). (J). (CAT.). 32p. (gr. 3-5). 17.95 (978-84-95040-37-4(9)); (SPA., 48p. (ps-3). 17.95 (978-84-95040-36-7(0)) Serres, Ediciones, S. L. ESP. *Dist:* Lectorum Pubns., Inc.

—Clarice Bean, Guess Who's Babysitting? Child, Lauren, illus. 2001. (Illus.). 32p. (J). (gr. 1-5). 16.99 (978-0-7636-1373-0(8)) Candlewick Pr.

—Clarice Bean Spells Trouble. Child, Lauren, illus. 2006. (Clarice Bean Ser.). 192p. (J). (gr. 3-6). pap. 5.99 (978-0-7636-2903-8(0)) Candlewick Pr.

—Para Tio el Mio, Dice Ana Tarambana. 2001. (CAT., Illus.). 28p. (J). (gr. 2-4). 17.95 (978-84-95040-85-5(9)) Serres, Ediciones, S. L. ESP. *Dist:* Lectorum Pubns., Inc.

—Para Tio el Mio, Dice Ana Tarambana. Rubio, Esther, tr. Child, Lauren, illus. 2001. (SPA., Illus.). 146p. (J). (ps-3). 17.95 (978-84-95040-84-8(0)) Serres, Ediciones, S. L. ESP. *Dist:* Lectorum Pubns., Inc.

—Utterly Me, Clarice Bean. Child, Lauren, illus. 2003. (Illus.). 192p. (J). (gr. 3-7). 15.99 (978-0-7636-2186-5(2)) Candlewick Pr.

—Utterly Me, Clarice Bean. 2002. (Illus.). 160p. (J). 5.99 (978-1-84121-918-9(5) , Orchard Bks.) Scholastic, Inc.

—What Planet Are You from, Clarice Bean? Child, Lauren, illus. 2002. (Illus.). 32p. (J). (gr. 1-5). 16.99 (978-0-7636-1696-0(6)) Candlewick Pr.

Choldenko, Gennifer. Al Capone Does My Shirts. 2006. 240p. (J). (gr. 5). reprint ed. pap. 6.99 (978-0-14-240370-9(9) , Puffin) Penguin Group (USA) Inc.

—If a Tree Falls at Lunch Period. 2007. (Illus.). 224p. (J). (gr. 5 up). 17.00 (*978-0-15-205753-4(6)) Harcourt Trade Pubs.

Choldenko, Gennifer. Notes from a Liar & Her Dog. 2001. (Illus.). 1p. (J). (gr. 5-9). 16.99 (978-0-399-23591-7(4) , Putnam Juvenile) Penguin Group (USA) Inc.

—Notes from a Liar & Her Dog. 2001. lib. bdg. 14.15 (978-0-613-67468-3(5)) Tandem Library Bks.

Choyce, Lesley. Shoulder the Sky. 2004. 220p. pap. 8.99 (978-1-55002-415-9(9)) Dundurn Group, The CAN. *Dist:* Univ. of Toronto Pr.

—Shoulder the Sky. 2002. (gr. 7-12). lib. bdg. 17.60 (978-0-613-90074-4(X)) Tandem Library Bks.

Christopher, Matt. Soccer Halfback. 2007. 144p. (J). lib. bdg. (*978-1-59953-110-6(0)) Norwood Hse. Pr.

Christopher, Matt. Stealing Home. 2004. 144p. (J). (gr. 4-7). pap. 4.99 (978-0-316-60742-1(8)) Hachette Bk. Group.

Chronicle Books LLC Staff. Football Heroes. 2008. (J). 14.95 (978-0-8118-5661-4(5)) Chronicle Bks. LLC.

Clairday, Robynn. Confessions of a Boyfriend Stealer. 2005. 240p. (YA). (gr. 7-12). pap. 7.95 (978-0-385-73242-0(2) , Delacorte Bks. for Young Readers) Random Hse. Children's Bks.

Clark, Catherine. The Alison Rules. 2004. 272p. (J). lib. bdg. 16.89 (978-0-06-055981-6(0) , HarperTeen) HarperCollins Pubs.

—Frozen Rodeo. 2003. 304p. (J). (gr. 8 up). 15.99 (978-0-06-009070-8(7)) HarperCollins Pubs.

—Frozen Rodeo. 2004. lib. bdg. 15.30 (978-0-613-71502-7(0)) Tandem Library Bks.

—I Do, Don't I? 2002. (Gilmore Girls Ser.: No. 3). (Illus.). 176p. mass mkt. 6.50 (978-0-06-009757-8(4) , Harper Entertainment) HarperCollins Pubs.

Clarke, Judith. Night Train. 2007. (J). pap. 9.95 (*978-1-932425-92-5(6) , Front Street) Boyds Mills Pr.

—One Whole & Perfect Day. 2007. 250p. (YA). (gr. 7 up). 16.95 (*978-1-932425-95-6(0) , Front Street) Boyds Mills Pr.

Class Cnct Family Rel. (Illus.). (J). pap. (978-0-698-11710-5(7) , Putnam Juvenile) Penguin Group (USA) Inc.

Cleary, Beverly. Beezus & Ramona. Dockray, Tracy, illus. 2006. 183p. (J). lib. bdg. 20.00 (*978-1-4242-0409-0(7)) Fitzgerald Bks.

—Beezus & Ramona. (Ramona Quimby Ser.). 142p. (J). (gr. 3-5). pap. 4.99 (978-0-8072-1441-1(8) , Listening Library) Random Hse. Audio Publishing Group.

—Ramona & Her Family. (J). Dell Publishing.

—Ramona & Her Father. 2002. (Illus.). (J). 13.83 (978-0-7587-5636-7(4)) Book Wholesalers, Inc.

—Ramona & Her Father. (Ramona Quimby Ser.). 186p. (J). (gr. 3-5). pap. 4.99 (978-0-8072-1439-8(6) , Listening Library) Random Hse. Audio Publishing Group.

—Ramona & Her Mother. (Ramona Quimby Ser.). 208p. (J). (gr. 3-5). pap. 4.99 (978-0-8072-1435-0(3) , Listening Library) Random Hse. Audio Publishing Group.

—The Ramona Collection, 4 vols., Vol. 1. Dockray, Tracy, illus. 1999. (Ramona Quimby Ser.). (J). (gr. 3-7). pap. 23.96 (978-0-380-81468-8(4)) HarperCollins Pubs.

—Ramona Forever. 2001. (Ramona Ser.). (J). (gr. 3-5). pap., wbk. ed. (978-1-58130-690-3(3)); pap., wbk. ed. (978-1-58130-691-0(1)) Novel Units, Inc.

—Ramona Forever. (Ramona Quimby Ser.). 182p. (J). (gr. 3-5). pap. 4.99 (978-0-8072-1437-4(X) , Listening Library) Random Hse. Audio Publishing Group.

—Ramona Quimby, Age 8. 2002. (Illus.). (J). 13.83 (978-0-7587-5637-4(2)) Book Wholesalers, Inc.

—Ramona Quimby, Age 8. (Ramona Ser.). (J). (gr. 3-5). Dell Publishing.

—Ramona Quimby, Age 8. (Ramona Ser.). (J). (gr. 3-5). 1999. 9.95 (978-1-56137-448-9(2)); 1998. 44p. 11.95 (978-1-56137-708-4(2) , NU7082SP) Novel Units, Inc.

—Ramona Quimby, Age 8. (Ramona Quimby Ser.). 190p. (J). (gr. 3-5). pap. 4.99 (978-0-8072-1436-7(1) , Listening Library) Random Hse. Audio Publishing Group.

—Ramona the Brave. 2000. (Ramona Ser.). (J). (gr. 3-5). 9.95 (978-1-56137-444-1(X)) Novel Units, Inc.

—Ramona the Brave. (Ramona Quimby Ser.). 190p. (J). (gr. 3-5). pap. 4.99 (978-0-8072-1440-4(X) , Listening Library) Random Hse. Audio Publishing Group.

—Ramona the Pest. (Ramona Ser.). (J). (gr. 3-5). Dell Publishing.

—Ramona the Pest. (Ramona Quimby Ser.). 192p. (J). (gr. 3-5). pap. 4.99 (978-0-8072-1438-1(8) , Listening Library) Random Hse. Audio Publishing Group.

—Ramona's World. Tiegreen, Alan & Dockray, Tracy, illus. 2001. (Ramona Quimby Ser.). 240p. (J). (gr. 3-5). 16.99 (978-0-688-16816-2(7)) HarperCollins Pubs.

—Ramona's World. Tiegreen, Alan, illus. 1999. (Ramona Quimby Ser.). 208p. (gr. 3-5). pap. 5.99 (978-0-380-73272-2(6)) HarperCollins Pubs.

Cleary, Jon. The Sundowners. (J). 25.95 (978-0-88411-467-3(8)) Amereon LTD.

Clinton, Cathryn. The Eyes of Van Gogh. 2007. (Illus.). 224p. (YA). (gr. 9 up). 16.99 (***978-0-7636-2245-9(1)***) Candlewick Pr.

—Simeon's Fire. 2007. 128p. (J). (gr. 3-7). pap. 5.99 (978-0-7636-3294-6(5)) Candlewick Pr.

—Stone in My Hand. 2004. (Illus.). 208p. (YA). (gr. 6 up). reprint ed. pap. 5.99 (978-0-7636-2561-0(2)) Candlewick Pr.

Cocks, Nancy & Marton, Jirina. Fergie Counts His Blessings. 2003. (Illus.). 16p. pap. (978-2-89507-302-4(3)) Novalis Publishing.

Cohen, Miriam. My Big Brother. Himler, Ronald, illus. 2005. 40p. (J). 15.95 (978-1-59572-007-8(3)) Star Bright Bks., Inc.

Cohn, Rachel. The Steps. 14p. (J). 2003. (Illus.). (gr. 3-7). 15.95 (978-0-689-84549-9(9)); 2004. reprint ed. pap. 4.99 (978-0-689-87414-7(6) , Aladdin) Simon & Schuster Children's Publishing.

—Two Steps Forward. 2007. 240p. (J). (gr. 4-8). pap. 8.99 (***978-0-689-86615-9(1)***) Kaplan Bks.

—Two Steps Forward. 2006. (Illus.). 240p. (J). 15.95 (978-0-689-86614-2(3)) Simon & Schuster Children's Publishing.

Cohn, Rachel. You Know Where to Find Me. 2008. 208p. (YA). 15.99 (***978-0-689-87859-6(1)*** , Simon & Schuster Children's Publishing) Simon & Schuster Children's Publishing.

Coleman, Evelyn. Freedom Train. Riley, David, illus. 2008. 160p. (J). 15.99 (***978-0-689-84716-5(5)*** , McElderry, Margaret K.) Simon & Schuster Children's Publishing.

Colfer, Eoin. Benny & Omar. 2007. 288p. (gr. 5-17). 18.95 (***978-1-4231-0281-6(9));*** pap. 7.95 (***978-1-4231-0282-3(7)***) Miramax Bks.

—Benny & Omar. 2003. 240p. (YA). (gr. 5 up). pap. 7.95 (978-0-86278-567-3(7)) O'Brien Pr., Ltd., The IRL. *Dist:* Independent Pubs. Group.

—The Wish List. 2004. 256p. (J). reprint ed. pap. 6.99 (978-0-439-44336-4(9)) Scholastic, Inc.

Collicott, Sharleen. Mildred & Sam & Their Babies. Collicott, Sharleen, illus. (I Can Read Bks.). 48p. (J). 2007. pap. 3.99 (***978-0-06-058113-8(1)*** , Harper Trophy); 2005. (Illus.). 15.99 (978-0-06-058111-4(5) , Geringer, Laura Book); 2005. (Illus.). lib. bdg. 16.89 (978-0-06-058112-1(3) , Geringer, Laura Book) HarperCollins Pubs.

Collier, James Lincoln. My Brother Sam Is Dead. 1999. (YA). 9.95 (978-1-56137-380-2(X)) Novel Units, Inc.

—My Brother Sam Is Dead. 2000. (Pathways to Critical Thinking Ser.). 32p. (J). pap., stu. ed., tchr.'s training gde. ed. 19.95 (978-1-58303-086-8(7)) Pathways Publishing.

Collier, James Lincoln & Collier, Christopher. My Brother Sam Is Dead. 1999. 11.95 (978-1-56137-823-4(2)) Novel Units, Inc.

Collins, Pat L. Just Imagine. 2001. (Illus.). 224p. (J). (gr. 5-9). tchr. ed. 15.00 (978-0-618-05603-3(3)) Houghton Mifflin Co. Trade & Reference Div.

Collins, Yvonne & Rideout, Sandy. The Black Sheep. 2007. 352p. (gr. 5 up). 15.99 (***978-1-4231-0156-7(1)***) Hyperion Pr.

Coman, Carolyn. Many Stones. 2002. 160p. (YA). pap. 5.99 (978-0-14-230148-7(5) , Puffin) Penguin Group (USA) Inc.

—Many Stones. 2002. 157p. (YA). (gr. 7-9). lib. bdg. 14.15 (978-0-613-45291-5(7)) Tandem Library Bks.

—Many Stones. l.t. ed. 2001. 24.95 (978-0-7862-3399-1(0)) Thorndike Pr.

—What Jamie Saw. 2002. (Illus.). (J). 12.81 (978-0-7587-0330-9(9)) Book Wholesalers, Inc.

—What Jamie Saw. unabr. ed. 2004. 128p. (J). (gr. 7 up). pap. 29.00 incl. audio (978-0-8072-8788-0(1) , YA268SP, Listening Library) Random Hse. Audio Publishing Group.

Comino, Sandra. Morning Glory. Amado, Elisa, tr. Max, illus. 2006. 64p. (J). 14.95 (978-0-88899-642-8(X)) Groundwood Bks. CAN. *Dist:* Perseus Distribution.

Compestine, Ying Chang. Revolution Is Not a Dinner Party. 2007. 256p. (YA). (gr. 5 up). 16.95 (***978-0-8050-8207-4(7)*** , Holt, Henry & Co. Bks. For Young Readers) Holt, Henry & Co.

Compestine, Ying Chang. The Story of Noodles. Xuan, Yong-Sheng, illus. 2002. 32p. (J). (gr. k-3). tchr. ed. 16.95 (978-0-8234-1600-4(3)) Holiday Hse., Inc.

Condra, Estelle. See the Ocean. Crockett-Blassingame, Linda, illus. 2002. 32p. (gr. k-3). 9.95 (978-1-59093-067-0(3)) Warehousing & Fulfillment Specialists, LLC (WFS, LLC).

Connor, Leslie. Waiting for Normal. 2008. 304p. (J). 16.99 (***978-0-06-089088-9(6));*** lib. bdg. 17.89 (***978-0-06-089089-6(4)***) HarperCollins Pubs.

Cooley, Beth. Shelter. 2006. 224p. (YA). (gr. 7). 15.95 (978-0-385-73330-4(5)); lib. bdg. 17.99 (978-0-385-90347-9(2)) Random Hse. Children's Bks. (Delacorte Bks. for Young Readers).

Coolidge, Susan. Clover. 2005. (Illus.). 133p. pap. (***978-1-59569-026-5(3)***) Mondial.

—What Katy Did. 2007. (ENG.). 148p. per. (***978-1-4065-1527-5(2)***) Dodo Pr.

—What Katy Did. 2006. 160p. (J). pap. 6.95 (978-0-486-44760-5(X)) Dover Pubns., Inc.

—What Katy Did. 2005. (ENG.). pap. 71.99 (***978-1-4219-1393-3(3)***) IndyPublish.com.

Cooney, Barbara. Lost Treasures Bk. 1: The Kellyhorns. 2001. 256p. (J). 13.49 (978-0-7868-2596-7(0)) Hyperion Pr.

Cooney, Caroline B. Diamonds in the Shadow. 2007. (YA). (gr. 7). 240p. lib. bdg. 18.99 (***978-0-385-90278-6(6));*** 228p. 15.99 (***978-0-385-73261-1(9)***) Random Hse. Children's Bks. (Delacorte Bks. for Young Readers).

—Family Reunion. 2004. 208p. (J). (gr. 5). lib. bdg. 11.99 (978-0-385-90167-3(4) , Delacorte Bks. for Young Readers) Random Hse. Children's Bks.

—A Friend at Midnight. 2006. 192p. (YA). 15.95 (978-1-4000-7208-8(5) , WaterBrook Pr.) WaterBrook Pr.

—Tune in Anytime. 2001. (J). (978-0-606-21495-7(X)) Tandem Library Bks.

Cooper, Ilene. Sam I Am. 256p. (J). 2006. pap. 5.99 (978-0-439-43968-8(X)); 2004. (gr. 4-7). pap. 15.95 (978-0-439-43967-1(1) , Scholastic Pr.) Scholastic, Inc.

Cooper, Melrose. Gettin' Through Thursday. 2000. (Illus.). 32p. (J). (ps-5). 6.95 (978-1-58430-014-4(0)) Lee & Low Bks., Inc.

—Gettin' Through Thursday. Bennett, Nneka, illus. 1999. 32p. (J). (ps-5). 15.95 (978-1-880000-67-0(9)) Lee & Low Bks., Inc.

—Gettin' Through Thursday. Bennett, Nneka, illus. 2000. (J). 13.75 (978-0-606-19831-8(8)) Tandem Library Bks.

Corbet, Robert. Fifteen Love. 2005. 192p. (YA). pap. 6.95 (978-0-8027-7714-0(7)) Walker & Co.

Cornman, Sabrina. Lepi's Golden America. Pierce, Kim, illus. 2003. 108p. 20.00 (978-0-9719167-6-0(4)); per. 12.00 (978-0-9719167-5-3(6)) Open Bk. Publishing.

Corpi, Lucha. Where Fireflies Dance (Ahi, Donde Bailan las Luciernagas) Reisberg, Mira, illus. 2002. 32p. (J). (gr. 1 up). pap. 7.95 (978-0-89239-177-6(4)) Children's Bk. Pr.

Corrigan, Eireann. Splintering. 2005. 184p. (YA). (gr. 8-12). lib. bdg. 15.04 (978-0-606-33304-7(5)) Tandem Library Bks.

Corso, Erika. The Day You Came. 2006. (ENG., Illus.). 28p. per. 12.95 (978-1-59800-242-3(2)) Outskirts Press, Inc.

Cosby, Bill. Shipwreck Saturday. Honeywood, Varnette P., illus. 1998. (Little Bill Books for Beginning Readers Ser.: No. 5). 40p. (J). (gr. k-3). pap. 3.99 (978-0-590-95620-8(5)) Scholastic, Inc.

Cosgrove, Stephen. The Bigg Family: Getting along with Others. Arroyo, Fian, illus. 2004. (J). (978-1-58804-354-2(1)) PCI Educational Publishing.

—Flynn "Flea" Flicker: Sticking to the Truth. Arroyo, Fian, illus. 2004. (J). (978-1-58804-353-5(3)) PCI Educational Publishing.

—Katy Didd Bigg: Standing up for Yourself. Arroyo, Fian, illus. 2004. (J). (978-1-58804-378-8(9)) PCI Educational Publishing.

Cotten, Cynthia. Abbie in Stitches. Peck, Beth, illus. 2006. 32p. (J). 16.00 (978-0-374-30004-3(6) , Farrar, Straus & Giroux (BYR)) Farrar, Straus & Giroux.

Cottrell Boyce, Frank. Framed. 2008. 320p. (J). pap. 6.99 (***978-0-06-073404-6(3)*** , Harper Trophy) HarperCollins Pubs.

Couloumbis, Audrey. Love Me Tender. 2008. (J). (***978-0-375-83839-2(2));*** lib. bdg. (***978-0-375-93839-9(7)***) Random Hse., Inc.

Couloumbis, Audrey. Summer's End. 2007. 192p. (YA). (gr. 7 up). pap. 5.99 (978-0-14-240783-7(6) , Puffin) Penguin Group (USA) Inc.

Cousain, Hattie M. When I Was Little. (J). 8.95 (978-0-9640459-0-3(7)) Cole's, C. Consultant & Pubns.

Cousins, Lucy. Maisy Takes a Bath. Cousins, Lucy, illus. 2000. (Maisy Bks.). (Illus.). 24p. (J). (gr. k-k). pap. 3.99 (978-0-7636-1084-5(4)) Candlewick Pr.

—Za-Za's Baby Brother. Cousins, Lucy, illus. 2002. (Illus.). (J). 15.74 (978-0-7587-4072-4(7)) Book Wholesalers, Inc.

Coville, Bruce. The Skull of Truth. 1999. (gr. 3-6). lib. bdg. 13.00 (978-0-613-17061-1(X)) Tandem Library Bks.

—The Skull of Truth: A Magic Shop Book. Lippincott, Gary A., illus. 2007. (Magic Shop Book Ser.). 208p. (J). pap. 5.95 (978-0-15-206084-8(7) , Magic Carpet Bks.) Harcourt Children's Bks.

Coward, Fiona. Swing High, Swing Low: A Day of Opposites. Manna, Giovanni, illus. 2005. 32p. (J). 16.99 (978-1-84148-170-8(X)) Barefoot Bks., Inc.

Crabtree, Dianne. On the Road to Royalty. 2005. 222p. (YA). pap. 14.95 (978-1-932898-32-3(8) , 98328) Spring Creek Bk. Co.

Crawford, Ann Fears. Vangie: The Ghost of the Pines. 2002. 142p. (J). 17.95 (978-1-57168-710-4(6) , Eakin Pr.) Eakin Pr.

Cree, Ronald. Desert Blood 10pm/9c. 2006. (Illus.). 320p. (YA). pap. 7.99 (978-1-4169-1156-2(1) , Simon Pulse) Simon & Schuster Children's Publishing.

Creech, Sharon. Bloomability. unabr. ed. 2004. 273p. (J). (gr. 4-7). pap. 38.00 incl. audio (978-0-8072-8754-5(7) , YA257SP, Listening Library) Random Hse. Audio Publishing Group.

—Bloomability. 1999. 12.64 (978-0-606-17460-2(5)); (gr. 3-6). lib. bdg. 14.15 (978-0-613-22826-8(X)) Tandem Library Bks.

—Chasing Redbird. l.t. ed. 2005. 259p. (J). (gr. 3-7). per. 22.95 (978-0-7862-7779-7(3) , Large Print Pr.) Thorndike Pr.

—Fishing in the Air. Raschka, Chris, illus. 2003. (J). 25.95 incl. audio (978-1-59112-225-8(2)); pap. 37.95 incl. audio (978-1-59112-226-5(0)); pap. 39.95 incl. audio compact disk (978-1-59112-521-1(9)) Live Oak Media.

—Fishing in the Air. Rashka, Chris, illus. 2000. 29p. (J). (ps-3). 28.95 (978-1-59112-513-6(8)) Live Oak Media.

—Replay. 240p. (J). (gr. 3-7). 2007. pap. 5.99 (978-0-06-054021-0(4) , Harper Trophy); 2005. 15.99 (978-0-06-054019-7(2) , Cotler, Joanna Books); 2005. lib. bdg. 16.89 (978-0-06-054020-3(6) , Cotler, Joanna Books) HarperCollins Pubs.

—Walk Two Moons. 2002. (Illus.). (J). 15.00 (978-0-7587-0223-4(X)) Book Wholesalers, Inc.

—Walk Two Moons. 2004. 304p. (J). (gr. 7 up). pap. 6.99 (978-0-06-056013-3(4) , Harper Trophy) HarperCollins Pubs.

—Walk Two Moons. 1999. (J). 9.95 (978-1-56137-770-1(8)); 11.95 (978-1-56137-771-8(6)) Novel Units, Inc.

—Walk Two Moons. 1998. (Assessment Packs Ser.). 15p. (J). pap., tchr.'s training gde. ed. 15.95 (978-1-58303-067-7(0)) Pathways Publishing.

—Walk Two Moons. 280p. (J). (gr. 4-6). pap. 4.95 (978-0-8072-1509-8(0) , Listening Library) Random Hse. Audio Publishing Group.

—Walk Two Moons. 2004. (gr. 7-12). lib. bdg. 14.75 (978-0-613-81971-8(3)) Tandem Library Bks.

—Walk Two Moons. l.t. ed. 287p. 2003. pap. 10.95 (978-0-7862-6185-7(4)); 2000. (Illus.). (J). 21.95 (978-0-7862-2773-0(7)) Thorndike Pr.

—The Wanderer. Diaz, David, illus. 320p. 2002. (gr. 3-7). pap. 6.99 (978-0-06-441032-8(3)); 2000. (J). (ps-3). 16.99 (978-0-06-027730-7(0) , Cotler, Joanna Books); 2000. (J). (ps-3). lib. bdg. 17.89 (978-0-06-027731-4(9) , Cotler, Joanna Books) HarperCollins Pubs.

—The Wanderer. 2002. (gr. 3-6). lib. bdg. 14.15 (978-0-613-49702-2(3)) Tandem Library Bks.

—The Wanderer. l.t. ed. 2003. 263p. pap. 10.95 (978-0-7862-6186-4(2)) Thorndike Pr.

—The Wanderer. Diaz, David, illus. l.t. ed. 2002. 263p. (J). 24.95 (978-0-7862-4125-5(X)) Thorndike Pr.

Crew, Linda. Nekomah Creek. Robinson, Charles, illus. 2001. 192p. (gr. 4-7). pap. 12.00 (978-0-375-89506-7(X) , Yearling) Random Hse. Children's Bks.

Crews, Dana-Susan. Our Daddy's Cancer: How We Helped Him Fight. 2007. (J). per. 10.99 (***978-1-60247-409-3(5)***) Tate Publishing & Enterprises, L.L.C.

Crockett-Blassingame, Linda, illus. See the Ocean. 2006. 32p. (J). 14.95 (978-0-9778143-0-5(0)) Inclusive Books LLC.

Crook, Connie Brummel. Hungry Year. 2001. (gr. 5-8). lib. bdg. 16.10 (978-0-613-46140-5(1)) Tandem Library Bks.

Crowley, Suzanne Carlisle. The Very Ordered Existence of Merilee Marvelous. 2007. (J). (gr. 5 up). 256p. 16.99 (***978-0-06-123197-1(5));*** 384p. lib. bdg. 17.89 (***978-0-06-123198-8(3)***) HarperCollins Pubs. (Greenwillow Bks.).

Cruise, Robin. Little Mama Forgets. Dressen-McQueen, Stacey, illus. 2006. 40p. (J). 16.00 (978-0-374-34613-3(5) , Farrar, Straus & Giroux (BYR)) Farrar, Straus & Giroux.

—Top-Secret Journal of Fiona Claire Jardin. 2000. (978-0-606-18192-1(X)) Tandem Library Bks.

Crum, Shutta. Spitting Image. 2003. 224p. (J). tchr. ed. 15.00 (978-0-618-23477-6(2) , Clarion Bks.) Houghton Mifflin Co. Trade & Reference Div.

Cruz, Maria Colleen. Border Crossing. 128p. (YA). pap. 9.95 (978-1-55885-405-5(3) , Piñata Books) Arte Publico Pr.

—Border Crossing. 2003. (gr. 7-12). lib. bdg. 18.75 (978-0-613-90255-7(6)) Tandem Library Bks.

Cry, the Beloved Country. 1999. (YA). 11.95 (978-1-56137-355-0(9)) Novel Units, Inc.

Cullen, Lynn. The Three Lives of Harris Harper. 1998. 160p. (J). pap. 3.99 (978-0-380-72901-2(6) , Harper Trophy) HarperCollins Pubs.

Currey, Anna. Truffle Goes to Town. Currey, Anna, illus. 2003. (Illus.). 32p. (YA). (978-1-85602-429-7(6)) Chrysalis Children's Bks.

Curtis, Christopher Paul. The Watsons Go to Birmingham - 1963. 2002. (Illus.). (J). 14.47 (978-0-7587-0328-6(7)) Book Wholesalers, Inc.

—The Watsons Go to Birmingham - 1963. 1998. 15p. pap., stu. ed., tchr.'s training gde. ed. 15.95 (978-1-58303-068-4(9)) Pathways Publishing.

—The Watsons Go to Birmingham - 1963. 210p. (YA). (gr. 5 up). pap. 5.50 (978-0-8072-8336-3(3)); 2004. (J). (gr. 4 up). pap. 38.00 incl. audio (978-0-8072-8335-6(5) , YA166SP) Random Hse. Audio Publishing Group. (Listening Library).

—The Watsons Go to Birmingham - 1963. 2000. 224p. (YA). (gr. 5-7). pap. 6.50 (978-0-440-22800-4(X) , Laurel Leaf) Random Hse. Children's Bks.

—The Watsons Go to Birmingham - 1963. 2000. (gr. 5-8). lib. bdg. 14.15 (978-0-613-85111-4(0)) Tandem Library Bks.

—The Watsons Go to Birmingham - 1963. l.t. ed. 2004. 254p. pap. 10.95 (978-0-7862-6406-3(3)) Thorndike Pr.

Curtis, Marci. Big Sister, Little Sister. Curtis, Marci, illus. 2002. (Illus.). 32p. (J). pap. 6.99 (978-0-14-230078-7(0) , Puffin) Penguin Group (USA) Inc.

—Big Sister, Little Sister. 2002. (ps-2). lib. bdg. 15.30 (978-0-613-43609-0(1)) Tandem Library Bks.

Cushman, Karen. The Loud Silence of Francine Green. 2006. 240p. (J). (gr. 5-9). 16.00 (978-0-618-50455-8(9) , Clarion Bks.) Houghton Mifflin Co. Trade & Reference Div.

Cusick, Richie Tankersley. The Unseen 1 It Begins. 2005. 304p. (YA). (gr. 7). pap. 6.99 (978-0-14-240463-8(2) , Puffin) Penguin Group (USA) Inc.

Czernecki, Stefan & Peterson, Jeanne Whitehouse. Don't Forget Winona. Root, Kimberly B., illus. 2004. 32p. (J). (ps-3). 15.99 (978-0-06-027197-8(3)) HarperCollins Pubs.

D C Thomson Staff, ed. The Broons 2004. 2003. (Illus.). 96p. (J). 9.95 (978-0-85116-835-7(3)) Thomson, D.C. & Co., Ltd. GBR. *Dist:* APG Sales and Fulfillment.

—The Broons & Oor Wullie 2004: More Classics from the Fifties. 2003. (Illus.). 144p. (J). 12.95 (978-0-85116-836-4(1)) Thomson, D.C. & Co., Ltd. GBR. *Dist:* APG Sales and Fulfillment.

da Costa, Deborah. Hanukkah Moon. Mosz, Gosia, illus. 2007. (Hanukkah Ser.). (J). (gr. 1-5). pap. 7.95 (***978-1-58013-245-9(6)***) Kar-Ben Publishing.

Danziger, Paula. Amber Brown Is Green with Envy. Ross, Tony, illus. 2003. (Amber Brown Ser.: No. 9). 160p. (J). (gr. 2-5). 15.99 (978-0-399-23181-0(1) , Putnam Juvenile) Penguin Group (USA) Inc.

—Amber Brown Is Green with Envy. Ross, Tony, illus. 2004. (Amber Brown Ser.: No. 9). 160p. (J). (gr. 3-6). pap. 4.99 (978-0-439-07171-0(2) , Scholastic Paperbacks) Scholastic, Inc.

—Can You Sue Your Parents for Malpractice? 1998. 160p. (J). (gr. 4-7). pap. 4.99 (978-0-698-11688-7(7) , Putnam Juvenile) Penguin Group (USA) Inc.

—Can You Sue Your Parents for Malpractice? (gr. 5-6). 144p. (J). pap. 3.99 (978-0-8072-1375-9(6)); 152p. (YA). pap. 3.99 (978-0-8072-1540-1(6)) Random Hse. Audio Publishing Group. (Listening Library).

—It's an Aardvark-Eat-Turtle World. 2007. 144p. (J). (gr. 5). pap. 5.99 (978-0-14-240679-3(1) , Puffin) Penguin Group (USA) Inc.

—Make Like a Tree & Leave. 1998. (Matthew Martin Ser.: No. 2). 128p. (J). (gr. 4-7). pap. 5.99 (978-0-698-11686-3(0) , Putnam Juvenile) Penguin Group (USA) Inc.

—Make Like a Tree & Leave. 1998. (Matthew Martin Ser.: No. 2). (J). (978-0-606-13593-1(6)) Tandem Library Bks.

—P. S. Longer Letter Later: A Novel in Letters. 1999. (978-0-606-17062-8(6)) Tandem Library Bks.

—The Pistachio Prescription. 2006. (J). 160p. (gr. 5). pap. 5.99 (978-0-14-240682-3(1)); 154p. (***978-1-4156-7490-1(6)***) Penguin Group (USA) Inc. (Puffin).

—The Pistachio Prescription. 1999. 154p. (J). (gr. k-9). per. 14.45 (978-0-88103-335-9(9)) Tandem Library Bks.

—Snail Mail No More. 2000. (gr. 3-6). lib. bdg. 13.00 (978-0-613-35753-1(1)) Tandem Library Bks.

—United Tates of America. 2002. (J). (gr. 4-7). lib. bdg. 20.00 incl. audio (978-0-9717540-5-8(5) , 02002) Full Cast Audio.

Danziger, Paula & Martin, Ann M. P. S. Longer Letter Later: A Novel in Letters. unabr. ed. 1999. 240p. (J). (gr. 3-7). pap. 36.00 incl. audio (978-0-8072-8085-0(2) , YA998SP, Listening Library) Random Hse. Audio Publishing Group.

—Snail Mail No More. unabr. ed. 2004. 307p. (J). (gr. 3-7). pap. 36.00 incl. audio (978-0-8072-8413-1(0) , Listening Library) Random Hse. Audio Publishing Group.

—Snail Mail No More. 2001. (Illus.). 320p. (J). (gr. 3-7). pap. 5.99 (978-0-439-06336-4(1) , Scholastic Paperbacks) Scholastic, Inc.

Danziger, Paula, et al. United Tates of America. 2003. (Illus.). 144p. (J). mass mkt. 5.99 (978-0-590-69222-9(4) , Scholastic Paperbacks) Scholastic, Inc.

Darrow, Sharon. Painters of Lexieville. 2003. (Illus.). 192p. (YA). (gr. 9). 16.99 (978-0-7636-1437-9(8)) Candlewick Pr.

Daval, Josie. The Wright Twist. 2006. (Illus.). 151p. (J). (978-1-933197-19-7(6)) Orange Frazer Pr.

Davidson, Mary Janice & Alongi, Anthony. Jennifer Scales & the Ancient Furnace. 2007. 224p. (gr. 12). mass mkt. 6.99 (978-0-441-01474-3(7) , Ace Bks.) Penguin Group (USA) Inc.

—Jennifer Scales & the Messenger of Light. (gr. 12). 2007. 288p. mass mkt. 6.99 (***978-0-441-01510-8(7)*** , Ace Bks.); 2006. 336p. (YA). pap. 9.99 (978-0-425-21011-6(1) , Berkley Trade) Penguin Group (USA) Inc.

Davoll, Barbara. Christopher & His Family. Hockerman, Dennis, illus. 2003. (Christopher Churchmouse Ser.). 128p. (J). 14.99 (978-0-8423-5735-7(1)) Tyndale Hse. Pubs.

Day, Alexandra. Carl's Sleepy Afternoon. 2005. (Carl Ser.). (Illus.). 40p. (J). (ps-1). 12.95 (978-0-374-31088-2(2) , Farrar, Straus & Giroux (BYR)) Farrar, Straus & Giroux.

De Lint, Charles. The Dreaming Place. 2002. (Firebird Ser.). 160p. (YA). pap. 5.99 (978-0-14-230218-7(X) , Puffin) Penguin Group (USA) Inc.

de Paola, Tomie. Big Anthony: His Story. de Paola, Tomie, illus. 2002. (Illus.). (J). 23.64 (978-0-7587-2090-0(4)) Book Wholesalers, Inc.

—Big Anthony: His Story. 2001. (Illus.). 32p. (J). (ps-3). pap. 5.99 (978-0-698-11893-5(6) , Putnam Juvenile) Penguin Group (USA) Inc.

—Big Anthony: His Story. 2001. (gr. k-3). lib. bdg. 14.15 (978-0-613-36050-0(8)) Tandem Library Bks.

—Guess Who's Coming to Santa's for Dinner? 2004. (Illus.). 48p. (J). (ps-3). 16.99 (978-0-399-24271-7(6) , Putnam Juvenile) Penguin Group (USA) Inc.

—Now One Foot, Now the Other. 2006. 48p. (J). pap. 7.99 (978-0-14-240104-0(8) , Puffin) Penguin Group (USA) Inc.

—Things Will Never Be the Same. 2004. (Illus.). 80p. (J). (gr. 2 up). reprint ed. pap. 5.99 (978-0-14-240155-2(2) , Puffin) Penguin Group (USA) Inc.

De Young, C. Coco. A Letter to Mrs. Roosevelt. 2000. 112p. (J). (gr. 3-7). pap. 5.50 (978-0-440-41529-9(2) , Yearling) Random Hse. Children's Bks.

de Young, C. Coco. Letter to Mrs. Roosevelt. 2000. 105p. (J). (ps-7). lib. bdg. 12.40 (978-0-613-28551-3(4)) Tandem Library Bks.

DeClements, Barthe. Liar, Liar. 1998. (Accelerated Reader Bks.). 144p. (J). (gr. 3-7). lib. bdg. 14.95 (978-0-7614-5021-4(1) , Cavendish Children's Bks.) Cavendish, Marshall Corp.

Dee, Barbara. Just Another Day in My Insanely Real Life. 2007. 256p. (J). pap. 5.99 (*978-1-4169-4739-4(6)) Kaplan Bks.

DeFelice, Cynthia. The Missing Manatee. 2008. 192p. (J). pap. 6.95 (*978-0-374-40020-0(2) , Farrar, Straus & Giroux (BYR)) Farrar, Straus & Giroux.

DeFelice, Cynthia C. The Missing Manatee. l.t. ed. 2005. 183p. (J). 20.95 (978-0-7862-8178-7(2)) Thorndike Pr.

Del Canizo, Jose Antonio. Las Cosas del Abuelo. (SPA.). 96p. (J). (gr. 3-5). (978-84-279-3345-3(2) , NG4456) Noguer y Caralt Editores, S. A. ESP. *Dist:* Lectorum Pubns., Inc.

Dellasega, Cheryl. Nugrl90 (Sadie) LaPierre, Karina, illus. 2007. (Bloggrls Ser.). (YA). (gr. 7 up). 200p. 15.99 (*978-0-7614-5375-8(X)); 190p. per. 6.99 (*978-0-7614-5396-3(2)) Cavendish, Marshall Corp.

Delton, Judy. Angel Bites the Bullet. 2000. (Illus.). 144p. (J). (gr. 4-6). tchr. ed. 15.00 (978-0-618-04085-8(4)) Houghton Mifflin Co. Trade & Reference Div.

—Angel in Charge. 1999. (Illus.). 160p. (J). (gr. 4-6). pap. 5.95 (978-0-395-96061-5(4)) Houghton Mifflin Co. Trade & Reference Div.

—Angel in Charge. 1999. (gr. 3-6). lib. bdg. 12.95 (978-0-613-18232-4(4)); (Illus.). (J). 11.60 (978-0-606-18206-5(3)) Tandem Library Bks.

Delval, Marie-Helene. Los Tres Hermanos Osos. Courtin, Thierry, illus. 2002. (Palabras Menudas Ser.).Tr. of Three Brother Bears. (SPA.). 14p. (ps). 4.95 (978-84-7864-513-8(6)) Combel Editorial, S.A. ESP. *Dist:* Independent Pubs. Group.

Dennis-Wyeth, Sharon. Something Beautiful. 2002. 32p. (J). (gr. 2-4). pap. 6.99 (978-0-440-41210-6(2) , Dragonfly Bks.) Random Hse. Children's Bks.

DePaola, Tomie. Guess Who's Coming to Santa's for Dinner? DePaola, Tomie, illus. 2006. 40p. (J). (ps). pap. 6.99 (978-0-14-240699-1(6) , Puffin) Penguin Group (USA) Inc.

D'Erasmo, Stacey. Tea: A Novel. 2001. (Washington Square Press Enriched Classic Ser.). (Illus.). (J). (978-0-606-20936-6(0)) Tandem Library Bks.

Deriso, Christine Hurley. The Right-Under Club. 2007. 208p. (J). (gr. 4-7). lib. bdg. 18.99 (*978-0-385-90351-6(0) , Delacorte Bks. for Young Readers) Random Hse. Children's Bks.

Desnick, Chaim. The Little Room. Zwebner, Janet, illus. 2005. 32p. (J). (ps-1). 14.95 (978-1-930143-81-4(8)); pap. 9.95 (978-1-930143-86-9(9)) Pitspopany Pr. (Devora Publishing).

Desrosiers, Sylvie & Franson, Leanne. Je Suis Thomas. 2003. (Premier Roman Ser.). (FRE., Illus.). 64p. (J). (gr. 1-4). pap. (978-2-89021-617-4(9)) Diffusion du livre Mirabel.

Deuker, Carl. Gym Candy. 2007. 320p. (J). (gr. 7 up). 16.00 (*978-0-618-77713-6(X)) Houghton Mifflin Co. Trade & Reference Div.

Dewey, Jennifer Owings. Navajo Summer. 2000. (gr. 3-6). lib. bdg. 18.75 (978-0-8085-8012-6(4)) Tandem Library Bks.

Diakite, Penda. I Lost My Tooth in Africa. Diakite, Baba Wague, illus. 2006. 32p. (J). (ps-3). pap. 16.99 (978-0-439-66226-0(5) , Scholastic Pr.) Scholastic, Inc.

Dickinson, Mary & Charlotte. Alex's Bed. Date not set. 32p. (J). pap. (978-0-05-004389-9(7)) Addison-Wesley Longman, Inc.

A Different Kind of Family. 2006. (J). (*978-0-9793568-0-3(6)) Merlin, Debbi.

DiMarco, Carol. Alchemy. DiMarco, Carol, illus. 2nd rev. ed. 2002. (Illus.). 24p. (J). pap. 11.95 (978-1-886383-65-4(0) , Little Blue Works) Windstorm Creative.

Dines, Carol. Talk to Me: Stories & a Novella. 1999. (978-0-606-16451-1(0)) Tandem Library Bks.

Dion. Fishing with Balloons. 2004. (Illus.). 68p. (J). (978-1-881929-34-5(5)) Oxton Hse., Pubs.

DiPucchio, Kelly S. Bed Hogs. Fine, Howard, illus. 2004. 32p. (ps-k). 15.99 (978-0-7868-1884-6(0)) Hyperion Bks. for Children.

DiSalvo-Ryan, DyAnne. Spaghetti Park. DiSalvo-Ryan, DyAnne, illus. 2002. (Illus.). 32p. (J). (gr. k-3). tchr. ed. 16.95 (978-0-8234-1682-0(8)) Holiday Hse., Inc.

Dobkin, Bonnie. Dream Spinner. 2006. 288p. pap. 8.95 (978-0-7387-0919-2(0) , Flux) Llewellyn Pubns.

E F G

Donald, Margaret. Tipsy: The Hurricane Hero. 2007. 26p. (J). 14.95 (*978-81-8386-050-5(8)) India Research Pr. IND. *Dist:* Independent Pubs. Group.

Dorris, Michael. Morning Girl. rev. ed. 1999. 80p. (gr. 4-17). pap. 4.99 (978-0-7868-1358-2(X)) Hyperion Pr.

Dostis, Isaac & Haddad Ikonomopoulos, Marcia. Ten Gold Medals: Glory or Freedom. 2005. (Illus.). ii, 72p. (J). (978-0-8197-0770-3(8)) Bloch Publishing Co.

Dotlich, Rebecca Kai. Mama Loves. Brown, Kathryn, illus. 2004. 32p. (J). (ps-2). 14.99 (978-0-06-029407-6(8)); lib. bdg. 15.89 (978-0-06-029408-3(6)) HarperCollins Pubs.

Doucet, Sharon Arms. Fiddle Fever. 176p. (J). (gr. 5-9). 2007. pap. 6.95 (978-0-618-77682-5(6)); 2000. (Illus.). tchr. ed. 15.00 (978-0-618-04324-8(1)) Houghton Mifflin Co. Trade & Reference Div. (Clarion Bks.).

—Fiddle Fever. l.t. ed. 2001. 174p. (J). 20.95 (978-0-7862-3548-3(9)) Thomson Gale.

Dowd, Siobhan. A Swift Pure Cry. 2007. 320p. (YA). (gr. 7). 16.99 (978-0-385-75108-7(7)); lib. bdg. 19.99 (978-0-385-75109-4(5)) Random Hse. Children's Bks. (Fickling, David Bks.).

Dowell, Frances O'Roark. Chicken Boy. Krause, George, photos by. 2007. 208p. (J). (gr. 5 up). pap. 5.99 (978-1-4169-3482-0(0) , Aladdin) Simon & Schuster Children's Publishing.

—Chicken Boy. 2005. (Illus.). 208p. (J). 15.95 (978-0-689-85816-1(7) , Atheneum) Simon & Schuster Children's Publishing.

—Chicken Boy. l.t. ed. 2006. 169p. (YA). 22.95 (978-0-7862-8280-7(0)) Thorndike Pr.

Dower, Laura. From the Files of Madison Finn: Sink or Swim. 2003. (gr. 3-6). lib. bdg. 13.00 (978-0-613-88965-0(7)) Tandem Library Bks.

—Sink or Swim. rev. ed. 2003. (From the Files of Madison Finn Ser.: No. 13). 176p. (J). (gr. 3-7). pap. 4.99 (978-0-7868-1735-1(6) , Volo) Hyperion Bks. for Children.

Doyle, Brian. Boy O'Boy. 2005. (YA). pap. (978-0-88899-590-2(3) , Libros Tigrillo); 162p. pap. 6.95 (978-0-88899-654-1(3)) Groundwood Bks. CAN. *Dist:* Transition Vendor, Perseus Distribution.

Doyle, Malachy & Jones, Jac. Lake of the Shadows. 2002. (Illus.). 32p. pap. 12.95 (978-1-84323-076-2(3)) Beekman Bks., Inc.

Doyle, Roddy. The Meanwhile Adventures. Ajhar, Brian, illus. 176p. (J). 2006. pap. 5.99 (978-0-439-66211-6(7)); 2004. (gr. 4-7). pap. 16.95 (978-0-439-66210-9(9)) Scholastic, Inc. (Levine, Arthur A. Bks.).

Dragonwagon, Crescent. The Sun Begun. Shaffer, Terea, illus. 1999. (J). 16.00 (978-0-689-81159-3(4) , Atheneum) Simon & Schuster Children's Publishing.

Draper, Sharon. Fire from the Rock. 2007. 240p. (YA). (gr. 7). 16.99 (*978-0-525-47720-4(9) , Dutton Juvenile) Penguin Group (USA) Inc.

Dreyer, Ellen. The Glow Stone. 2006. 186p. (J). 15.95 (978-1-56145-370-2(6) , Peachtree Junior) Peachtree Pubs., Ltd.

Duble, Kathleen Benner & Vojnar, Kamil. The Sacrifice. 2005. 224p. (J). (gr. 4-8). 16.99 (978-0-689-87650-9(5) , McElderry, Margaret K.) Simon & Schuster Children's Publishing.

Duey, Kathleen. Silence & Lily: 1773. 2007. 176p. (J). (gr. 5). pap. 5.99 (*978-0-14-240909-1(X) , Puffin) Penguin Group (USA) Inc.

Duey, Kathleen. The Silver Thread. Rayyan, Omar, illus. 2001. (Unicorn's Secret Ser.: No. 2). 80p. (J). pap. 3.99 (978-0-689-84270-2(8) , Aladdin) Simon & Schuster Children's Publishing.

Duffy, Daniel M., illus. Meet the Boxcar Children. 1998. (Adventures of Benny & Watch: Vol. No. 1). 48p. (J). (ps-2). pap. 3.95 (978-0-8075-5034-2(5)) Whitman, Albert & Co.

Dunbar, James. When I Was Young. Remphry, Martin, illus. 1999. (Picture Bks.). 32p. (J). (ps-3). lib. bdg. 15.95 (978-1-57505-359-2(4) , Carolrhoda Bks.) Lerner Publishing Group.

Durbin, William. Song of Sampo Lake. 2004. 224p. (J). (gr. 5). reprint ed. pap. 5.50 (978-0-440-22899-8(9) , Yearling) Random Hse. Children's Bks.

—Song of Sampo Lake. 2004. (gr. 5-8). lib. bdg. 13.55 (978-0-613-85112-1(9)) Tandem Library Bks.

Durin-Valois, Marc. Chamelle. l.t. ed. 2003. (French Ser.). (Illus.). 236p. 30.99 (978-2-84011-524-3(7)) Ulverscroft Large Print Bks. GBR. *Dist:* Ulverscroft Large Print Bks., Ltd.

Durrant, Sabine. Bon Voyage, Connie Pickles. 2008. 240p. (J). 16.99 (*978-0-06-085482-9(0)); lib. bdg. 17.89 (*978-0-06-085483-6(9)) HarperCollins Pubs. (HarperTeen).

Dyahnne. Sweetie's Place: A Moving Adventure. 2004. 26p. (J). per. 7.99 (978-1-4116-0760-6(0)) Lulu.com.

Eason, Cassandra & Sterling Publishing Company Staff. Benjamin Helps Mommy & Daddy. 1998. (Balloon Ser.). (Illus.). 16p. (J). (ps-k). 4.95 (978-0-8069-9516-8(5)) Sterling Publishing Co., Inc.

Easton, Kelly. The Life History of a Star. 2002. 208p. (YA). pap. 6.99 (978-0-689-85270-1(3) , Simon Pulse) Simon & Schuster Children's Publishing.

—The Life History of a Star. 2002. (gr. 7-12). lib. bdg. 15.30 (978-0-613-60641-7(8)) Tandem Library Bks.

—The Life History of a Star. l.t. ed. 2002. 200p. 22.95 (978-0-7862-4786-8(X)) Thorndike Pr.

—Walking on Air. 2004. (Illus.). 240p. (YA). 16.95 (978-0-689-84875-9(7) , McElderry, Margaret K.) Simon & Schuster Children's Publishing.

Eberhard, Phyllis Lunde Brees. Little Miss Neat-As-A-Pin. Jacoby, Nickolina Dye, illus. 2007. (J). (*978-0-9722741-7-3(0)) Publishing Factory, The.

Edwards, Nancy. Mom for Mayor. Chesworth, Michael, illus. 2006. 96p. (J). 16.95 (978-0-8126-2743-5(1)) Cricket Bks.

Edwards, Pamela. Oliver Has Something to Say! Pilon, Louis, illus. 2007. 24p. (J). (ps-1). (978-1-897073-52-0(6)) Lobster Pr.

Ehrlich, Amy. When I Was Your Age Vol. 2: Original Stories about Growing Up. 2001. (gr. 5-8). lib. bdg. 16.45 (978-0-613-74735-6(6)); (Illus.). (J). (978-0-606-20988-5(3)) Tandem Library Bks.

Ehrlich, Amy, ed. When I Was Your Age: Original Stories about Growing Up. 2002. 192p. (J). (gr. 4-9). pap. 7.99 (978-0-7636-1734-9(2)) Candlewick Pr.

Eisch, Beverly. In the Woods. Eisch, Lisa & Grabner, Mike, illus. 2002. 12p. (J). pap. 5.00 (978-0-9724517-0-3(6)) Eisch, Beverly.

Elizabeti's Doll. 2004. 24.95 incl. audio (978-1-55592-053-1(5)); (J). pap. 14.95 incl. audio (978-1-55592-716-5(5)) Weston Woods Studios, Inc.

Ellison, Laura. Hard Rock, Hard Times: Coming of Age in Butte Montana, 1911-1917. 2005. 195p. (YA). per. (978-0-9722217-7-1(8)) Horse Creek Pubns.

Elvgren, Jennifer Riesmeyer. Josias, Hold the Book. Tadgell, Nicole, illus. 2006. 32p. (J). 15.95 (978-1-59078-318-4(2)) Boyds Mills Pr.

Emerson, Charlotte. Amy's True Prize. 1999. (Little Women Journals Ser.). (J). (978-0-606-16348-4(4)) Tandem Library Bks.

—Beth's Snow Dancer. 1999. (Little Women Journals Ser.). (J). (978-0-606-16347-7(6)) Tandem Library Bks.

—Meg's Dearest Wish. 1999. (Little Women Journals). (J). (978-0-606-16350-7(6)) Tandem Library Bks.

Emerson, Charlotte & Alcott, Louisa May. Amy's True Prize. Wasden, Kevin, illus. 1999. (Little Women Journals). 128p. (J). (gr. 3-7). mass mkt. 3.99 (978-0-380-79706-6(2)) HarperCollins Pubs.

—Beth's Snow Dancer. Wasden, Kevin, illus. 1999. (Little Women Journals). 128p. (J). (gr. 3-7). pap. 3.99 (978-0-380-79704-2(6)) HarperCollins Pubs.

—Jo's Troubled Heart. Wasden, Kevin, illus. 1999. (Little Women Journals). 128p. (J). (gr. 3-7). pap. 3.99 (978-0-380-79669-4(4)) HarperCollins Pubs.

—Meg's Dearest Wish. Wasden, Kevin, illus. 1999. (Little Women Journals). 128p. (J). (gr. 3-7). pap. 3.99 (978-0-380-79705-9(4)) HarperCollins Pubs.

Emmett, Jonathan. Ruby in Her Own Time. 2007. 32p. (J). pap. 5.99 (978-0-439-86278-3(7)) Scholastic, Inc.

Enderle, Dotti. Hidden. Gentry, T. Kyle, illus. 2007. 120p. (YA). (gr. 5-9). pap. 8.95 (*978-1-58980-481-4(3)) Pelican Publishing Co., Inc.

English, Karen. Just Right Stew. Rich, Anna, illus. 32p. (J). (gr. k-2). pap. 8.95 (978-1-59078-168-5(6)) Boyds Mills Pr.

—Just Right Stew. 2003. (Illus.). 32p. (J). (gr. k-4). 15.95 (978-1-56397-487-8(8)) Boyds Mills Pr.

—Neeny Coming, Neeny Going. 1998. (978-0-606-13656-3(8)) Tandem Library Bks.

English, Travis. Knights of Paris. 2004. (J). per. 11.95 (978-0-9759903-1-5(4)) Blue Tiger Publishing.

Enright, Elizabeth. The Four-Story Mistake. Enright, Elizabeth, illus. rev. ed. 2002. (Melendy Quartet Ser.: Bk. 2). (Illus.). 208p. (J). (gr. 3-7). 16.95 (978-0-8050-7061-3(3) , Holt, Henry & Co. Bks. For Young Readers) Holt, Henry & Co.

—The Saturdays. 2008. (Melendy Quartet Ser.). (Illus.). 208p. (J). pap. 6.99 (*978-0-312-37598-0(0)) Square Fish.

—Spiderweb for Two: A Melendy Maze. Enright, Elizabeth, illus. rev. ed. 2002. (Melendy Quartet Ser.: Bk. 4). (Illus.). 224p. (J). (gr. 3-7). 16.95 (978-0-8050-7063-7(X) , Holt, Henry & Co. Bks. For Young Readers) Holt, Henry & Co.

—Spiderweb for Two: A Melendy Maze. 2008. (Melendy Quartet Ser.). (Illus.). 240p. (J). pap. 6.99 (*978-0-312-37601-7(4)) Square Fish.

Entara Ltd. Staff, photos by. The Lost Shamrock. 2007. (Jakers! Ser.). 24p. (J). pap. 3.99 (978-1-4169-4067-8(7) , Simon Spotlight) Simon & Schuster Children's Publishing.

Epstein, Estelle Pottern. I Heard My Father's Voice. 2007. 124p. pap. 11.95 (*978-0-7414-4053-2(9)) Infinity Publishing.

Eriksson, Eva. A Crash Course for Molly. Dyssegaard, Elisabeth Kallick, tr. from SWE. 2005. (Illus.). 32p. (J). 16.00 (978-91-29-66156-9(0)) R & S Bks. SWE. *Dist:* Macmillan.

Erskine, Kathryn. Quaking. 2007. 272p. (YA). (gr. 6 up). 16.99 (*978-0-399-24774-3(2) , Philomel) Penguin Group (USA) Inc.

Eschbacher, Roger. Road Trip! Wickstrom, Thor, illus. 2006. 32p. (J). (ps). 16.99 (978-0-8037-2927-8(8) , Dial) Penguin Group (USA) Inc.

Esckilsen, Erik E. Outside Groove. 2006. 272p. (J). (gr. 5). 16.00 (978-0-618-66854-0(3)) Houghton Mifflin Co.

Estes, Eleanor. The Middle Moffat. 2001. (978-0-606-20799-7(6)); (gr. 3-6). lib. bdg. 14.15 (978-0-613-35462-2(1)) Tandem Library Bks.

—The Moffat Museum. 2001. (Odyssey Classics). (Illus.). 256p. (gr. 3 up). pap. 6.00 (978-0-15-202553-3(7) , Odyssey Classics) Harcourt Children's Bks.

—The Moffat Museum. 2001. (J). (978-0-606-20805-5(4)); (gr. 3-6). lib. bdg. 14.15 (978-0-613-35463-9(X)) Tandem Library Bks.

—The Moffats. Tusa, Tricia & Slobodkin, Louis, illus. 2001. (Young Classics). 224p. (YA). (gr. 3 up). 17.00 (978-0-15-202535-9(9) , Odyssey Classics) Harcourt Children's Bks.

—The Moffats. Slobodkin, Louis, illus. 2001. (Odyssey Classics). 224p. (YA). (gr. 3 up). pap. 6.00 (978-0-15-202541-0(3) , Odyssey Classics) Harcourt Children's Bks.

—The Moffats. 2001. (J). (978-0-606-20806-2(2)); (gr. 3-6). lib. bdg. 14.15 (978-0-613-35538-4(5)) Tandem Library Bks.

—Pinky Pye. Ardizzone, Edward, illus. 2000. 272p. (YA). (gr. 3-7). pap. 6.00 (978-0-15-202565-6(0) , Odyssey Classics); (gr. 4-7). 17.00 (978-0-15-202559-5(6)) Harcourt Children's Bks.

—Pinky Pye. 2000. (J). (978-0-606-20042-4(8)); (J). (978-0-606-20170-4(X)); (gr. 3-6). lib. bdg. 14.15 (978-0-613-30671-3(6)) Tandem Library Bks.

—Rufus M. 2001. (gr. 3-6). lib. bdg. 14.15 (978-0-613-35468-4(0)) Tandem Library Bks.

—Rufus M. Slobodkin, Louis, illus. 2001. (Odyssey Classics). 256p. (YA). (gr. 3 up). pap. 6.00 (978-0-15-202577-9(4) , Odyssey Classics) Harcourt Children's Bks.

—Rufus M. 2001. (Illus.). (J). (978-0-606-20893-2(3)) Tandem Library Bks.

Estevis, Anne. Down Garrapata Road. 128p. pap. 12.95 (978-1-55885-397-3(9)) Arte Publico Pr.

Evans, Alwyn. Old MacDonald's Farm: A Three-Dimensional Playset with Sound! Bell, Owen, illus. 2001. (J). (ps-k). act. bk. ed. 16.95 (978-1-58117-145-7(5) , Intervisual/Piggy Toes) Dalmatian Pr.

Evans, Douglas. The Elevator Family. 2001. (J). 11.30 (978-0-606-21173-4(X)) Tandem Library Bks.

Eversole, Barbara. Adventures of Zorro. 2005. 42p. 14.49 (978-1-4116-5523-2(0)) Lulu.com.

Ewing, Juliana Horatia. Six to Sixteen. 2007. (ENG.). 192p. 13.99 (*978-1-4280-7181-0(4)); per. 19.99 (*978-1-4280-7175-9(X)) IndyPublish.com.

Faine, Edward Allan. Little Ned Stories. Waites, Joan C., illus. 1999. 128p. (J). (gr. k-3). pap. 9.99 (978-0-9654651-5-1(2)) IM Pr.

Fajardo, Renee & Ruby, Carl. Chili Today, Hot Tamale & Other Tummy Tales. Fajardo, Renee & Ruby, Carl, eds. 2004. (Illus.). 110p. (YA). (gr. 4-8). pap. 14.00 (978-0-9724472-2-5(9)) Just Enjoyable Memorable Story Bks.

Fallon, Joan & Feltenstein, Arlene. Will the New Baby Be Bigger Than Me? Escriva, Viví, illus. 1998. (J). (ps-3). 9.95 (978-1-56492-252-6(9)) Laredo Publishing Co., Inc.

Falwell, Cathryn. Feast for 10. Falwell, Cathryn, illus. 2002. (Illus.). (J). 14.74 (978-0-7587-2485-4(3)) Book Wholesalers, Inc.

—Feast for 10. Falwell, Cathryn, illus. 2003. (Illus.). 28p. (J). (gr. k-ps). bds. 4.95 (978-0-618-38226-2(7) , Clarion Bks.) Houghton Mifflin Co. Trade & Reference Div.

Family under the Bridge. 1999. (J). 9.95 (978-1-56137-368-0(0)) Novel Units, Inc.

Farnes, Catherine. Snowblind. 2004. 108p. (J). (978-1-59166-329-4(6)) Jones, Bob Univ. Pr.

Fearnley, Jan. Are We There Yet? Fearnley, Jan, illus. 2008. (Illus.). 32p. (J). pap. 7.95 (*978-0-00-720785-5(9)) HarperCollins Pubs. Ltd. GBR. *Dist:* Independent Pubs. Group.

Feiffer, Jules. The House Across the Street. Feiffer, Jules, illus. 2003. (Illus.). 28p. (J). (gr. 1-4). reprint ed. 16.00 (978-0-7567-6845-4(4)) DIANE Publishing Co.

—The House Across the Street. 2002. (Illus.). 32p. (J). (ps-17). (978-0-7868-0910-3(8)) Hyperion Bks. for Children.

—I Lost My Bear. Feiffer, Jules, illus. 2002. (Illus.). (J). 14.43 (978-0-7587-4249-0(5)) Book Wholesalers, Inc.

—I Lost My Bear. Feiffer, Jules, illus. 2000. (Illus.). 40p. (J). (ps-2). pap. 6.99 (978-0-688-17722-5(0) , Harper Trophy) HarperCollins Pubs.

—I Lost My Bear. 1998. (Illus.). 40p. (J). (ps-2). 15.89 (978-0-688-15148-5(5)) HarperCollins Pubs.

—I Lost My Bear. 2000. (YA). pap. 34.25 incl. audio (978-0-7887-4095-4(4) , 41091) Recorded Bks., LLC.

—I Lost My Bear. 2000. (gr. k-3). lib. bdg. 14.15 (978-0-613-29984-8(1)) Tandem Library Bks.

Feiffer, Jules. A Room with a Zoo. Feiffer, Jules, illus. 2007. (Illus.). 182p. (J). (gr. 2-7). per. 7.99 (*978-0-7868-3703-8(9)) Hyperion Bks. for Children.

Feigenbaum, Lawrence. Bennett & His Bubbe's Beau. 2002. 32p. pap. 9.00 (978-0-8059-5840-9(1)) Dorrance Publishing Co., Inc.

Felin, M. Sindy. Touching Snow. 2007. 240p. (YA). (gr. 7 up). 16.99 (978-1-4169-1795-3(0) , Atheneum) Simon & Schuster Children's Publishing.

Fenner, Carol. Yolonda's Genius. unabr. ed. 2004. 211p. (J). (gr. 4-6). pap. 38.00 incl. audio (978-0-8072-0462-7(5) , Listening Library) Random Hse. Audio Publishing Group.

Fernandes, Eugenie. A Difficult Day. 2002. (Illus.). 32p. (J). (gr. k-3). (978-0-921103-80-6(8)) Kids Can Pr., Ltd.

Ferraro, Tina. How to Hook a Hottie. 2008. 208p. (J). pap. (*978-0-385-73438-7(7) , Delacorte Pr.) Dell Publishing.

—How to Hook a Hottie. 2008. 208p. (YA). (gr. 7). lib. bdg. 11.99 (*978-0-385-90444-5(4) , Delacorte Bks. for Young Readers) Random Hse. Children's Bks.

—Top Ten Uses for an Unworn Prom Dress. 2007. 240p. (YA). (gr. 7). pap. 7.99 (978-0-385-73368-7(2)); lib. bdg. 12.99 (978-0-385-90383-7(9)) Random Hse. Children's Bks. (Delacorte Bks. for Young Readers).

Ferraro, Tina. Top Ten Uses for an Unworn Prom Dress: A Novel. 2006. 222p. (YA). (*978-1-4287-2694-9(2) , Delacorte Pr.) Dell Publishing.

Ferris, Jean. Love among the Walnuts. (YA). 2008. (Illus.). 240p. pap. 6.95 (*978-0-15-206227-9(0) , Harcourt Paperbacks); 1998. 224p. (gr. 5-9). 16.00 (978-0-15-201590-9(6)) Harcourt Children's Bks.

—Love among the Walnuts. 2001. (gr. 7-12). lib. bdg. 14.15 (978-0-613-33709-0(3)); (Illus.). (J). (978-0-606-20776-8(7)) Tandem Library Bks.

—Love among the Walnuts: Or, How I Saved My Entire Family from Being Poisoned. November, S., ed. 2001. 224p. (J). (gr. 5-9). pap. 6.99 (978-0-14-131099-2(5) , Puffin) Penguin Group (USA) Inc.

—Once upon a Marigold. 2002. 272p. (YA). (gr. 5 up). 17.00 (978-0-15-216791-2(9)); 2004. 288p. (J). reprint ed. pap. 5.95 (978-0-15-205084-9(1) , Harcourt Paperbacks) Harcourt Children's Bks.
—Once upon a Marigold. 2004. (gr. 5-8). lib. bdg. 14.10 (978-0-613-71637-6(X)) Tandem Library Bks.
Few, Cyndi. My Family Loves Me: For My Grandson, Talon. 2005. 27p. pap. 14.95 (978-1-4137-3189-7(9)) PublishAmerica, Inc.
Fidler, Mark. Pond Puckster. 2nd ed. 2003. 148p. (J). (gr. 4-8). reprint ed. pap. 11.95 (978-0-9721839-0-1(6)) BLR Bks.
—Signed Ball. 2002. 146p. (J). pap. 11.95 (978-0-595-21780-9(X) , Writers Club Pr.) iUniverse, Inc.
Figiel, Lisa. Another Bird in Our Nest. 2007. (J). per. 6.99 (*978-1-60247-356-0(0)) Tate Publishing & Enterprises, L.L.C.
Fine, Anne. Crummy Mummy & Me. Douglass, Claire, illus. l.t. ed. 2002. 176p. (J). 16.95 (978-0-7540-7813-5(2) , Galaxy Children's Large Print) BBC Audiobooks America.
Fine, Anne. The Road of Bones. 2008. 224p. (YA). 16.95 (*978-0-374-36316-1(1)) Farrar, Straus & Giroux.
Finley, Martha. Elsie at Nantucket A Sequel to Elsies Ne. 2006. 34.99 (*978-1-4280-2289-8(9)) IndyPublish.com.
—Elsie's Endless Wait. 224p. 2006. (Life of Faith Ser.). (J). pap. 7.99 (978-1-928749-80-6(1)); Bk. 1. 1999. (Elsie Dinsmore: Bk. 1). (Illus.). (YA). (gr. 5-9). 12.99 (978-1-928749-01-1(1)) Zonderkidz.
—Elsie's Great Hope, Vol. 8. 2006. (Life of Faith': Elsie Dinsmore Ser.). 224p. (J). pap. 7.99 (978-1-928749-87-5(9)) Zonderkidz.
—Elsie's Stolen Heart, Bk. 4. 1999. (Elsie Dinsmore: Bk. 4). (Illus.). 224p. (YA). (gr. 5-9). 12.99 (978-1-928749-04-2(6)) Zonderkidz.
—Elsie's Tender Mercies, Vol. 7. 2006. (Life of Faith': Elsie Dinsmore Ser.). 224p. (J). pap. 7.99 (978-1-928749-86-8(0)) Zonderkidz.
—Mildred's Married Life, Vol. 4. (Mildred Classics Ser.: Vol. 4). 288p. pap. 6.95 (978-1-58182-230-4(8)) Cumberland Hse. Publishing.
—Violet's Defiant Daughter, Bk. 7. 2006. (Life of Faith Ser.). 224p. (J). 12.99 (978-1-928749-23-3(2)) Zonderkidz.
Finley, Martha & Hamilton, Kersten. Life of Faith Collection. 2006. (Life of Faith' Ser.). 992p. (J). pap. 14.99 (978-1-928749-85-1(2)) Mission City Pr., Inc.
Finn, Felicity. Jeremy & the Aunties. 1998. (Illus.). 199p. (YA). (gr. 4-8). pap. 5.95 (978-0-929005-40-9(6)) Second Story Pr. CAN. *Dist:* Orca Bk. Pubs. USA.
Finnegan, Evelyn M. My Little Friend Goes to a Baseball Game. Houghton, Diane R., illus. 2006. 32p. (J). (ps-3). reprint ed. pap. 7.00 (978-1-4223-5403-2(2)) DIANE Publishing Co.
Finney, Patricia. I, Jack. Bailey, Peter, illus. 192p. (J). 2005. pap. 5.99 (978-0-06-052209-4(7) , Harper Trophy); 2004. 15.99 (978-0-06-052207-0(0)); 2004. lib. bdg. 16.89 (978-0-06-052208-7(9)) HarperCollins Pubs.
Fitch, Michele. When Lizzi & Kathryn Get Together. 2007. 18p. 10.00 (*978-0-615-14996-7(0)) Fitch, Michele Marko.
Fitch, Sheree. One More Step. 2002. (Orca Soundings Ser.). 96p. (J). (gr. 7-12). pap. 7.95 (978-1-55143-248-9(X)) Orca Bk. Pubs. USA.
—One More Step. 2002. (gr. 7-12). lib. bdg. 16.40 (978-0-613-62978-2(7)) Tandem Library Bks.
Fitzgerald, Dawn. Soccer Chick Rules. 2006. 160p. (J). 16.95 (978-1-59643-137-9(7)) Roaring Brook Pr.
FitzGerald, Dawn. Soccer Chick Rules. 2007. 160p. (J). pap. 6.99 (*978-0-312-37662-8(6)) Square Fish.
Flake, Sharon G. Bang! 2005. 320p. (gr. 7-17). 16.99 (978-0-7868-1844-0(1) , Jump at the Sun) Hyperion Bks. for Children.
Flam, Chanie. Good Night. (Goldie Gold Board Book Ser.: Vol. 6). (Illus.). (J). (ps-1). bds. 4.95 (978-1-58330-030-5(9)) Feldheim Pubs.
Fleischman, Paul. A Fate Totally Worse Than Death. 2004. (Illus.). 128p. (YA). (gr. 9 up). reprint ed. pap. 5.99 (978-0-7636-2189-6(7)) Candlewick Pr.
Fleischman, Sid. McBroom Tells a Lie. Wummer, Amy, illus. 1999. (Adventures of McBroom Ser.). 64p. (J). (gr. 2-6). pap. 4.99 (978-0-8431-7497-7(8) , Price Stern Sloan) Penguin Group (USA) Inc.
—McBroom Tells a Lie. 1999. (J). (978-0-606-19073-2(2)); (gr. 3-6). lib. bdg. 13.00 (978-0-613-14983-9(1)) Tandem Library Bks.
—McBroom Tells the Truth. Wummer, Amy, illus. 1998. (Adventures of McBroom Ser.). 62p. (J). (gr. 2-5). pap. 4.99 (978-0-8431-7947-7(3) , Price Stern Sloan) Penguin Group (USA) Inc.
Fletcher, Ralph J. Fig Pudding. unabr. ed. 2000. (YA). (gr. 5 up). pap. 39.75 incl. audio (978-0-7887-3181-5(5) , 40916X4) Recorded Bks., LLC.
Flood, Pansie Hart. Secret Holes. Marshall, Felicia, illus. 2004. 128p. (J). (gr. 3-6). 15.95 (978-0-87614-923-2(9) , Carolrhoda Bks.) Lerner Publishing Group.
—Sometimey Friend. Marshall, Felicia, illus. 2005. 128p. (J). (gr. 4-6). 15.95 (978-1-57505-866-5(9)) Lerner Publishing Group.
—Sylvia & Miz Lula Maye. Marshall, Felicia, illus. 2003. (Middle Grade Fiction Ser.). 120p. (J). (gr. 3-6). 15.95 (978-0-87614-204-2(8) , Carolrhoda Bks.) Lerner Publishing Group.
Flores, Carlos Nicolas. Our House on Hueco. 2006. 248p. (YA). pap. 17.95 (978-0-89672-573-7(1)) Texas Tech Univ. Pr.
Floyd, Lucy. A Place for Nicholas. McPhail, David M., illus. 2005. (Green Light Readers Level 2 Ser.). 24p. (J). 12.95 (978-0-15-205150-1(3)); pap. 3.95 (978-0-15-205149-5(X)) Harcourt Children's Bks. (Green Light Readers).
Flynn, Pat. Alex Jackson: Grommet. 2001. 136p. (Orig.). (YA). pap. 14.95 (978-0-7022-3223-7(8)) Univ. of Queensland Pr. AUS. *Dist:* International Specialized Bk. Services.
Fogelin, Adrian. My Brother's Hero. (Peachtree Junior Publication Ser.). 224p. (J). 2002. (gr. 3-7). 14.95 (978-1-56145-274-3(2)); 2005. reprint ed. pap. 6.95 (978-1-56145-352-8(8)) Peachtree Pubs., Ltd.
Foland, Constance M. Flying High, Pogo! 2002. (gr. 3-6). lib. bdg. 14.10 (978-0-613-89603-0(3)) Tandem Library Bks.
Forbing, Shirley E. Sylvester: A Squirrel for Suzie. Zapp, Marilyn, illus. 2001. (YA). pap. 21.95 incl. audio compact disk Wild Animal XPress.
Ford, Christine. Scout. 2007. 224p. (J). (gr. 4-7). pap. 5.50 (*978-0-440-42041-5(5) , Yearling) Random Hse. Children's Bks.
Foreman, Michael. Mia's Story: A Sketchbook of Hopes & Dreams. Foreman, Michael, illus. 2006. (Illus.). 32p. (J). (gr. k-3). 15.99 (978-0-7636-3063-8(2)) Candlewick Pr.
Foreman, Wilmoth & Boyds Mills Press Staff. Summer of the Skunks. 2004. 152p. (J). 15.95 (978-1-886910-80-5(4) , Lemniscaat) Boyds Mills Pr.
Forrestal, Elaine. Graffiti on the Fence. 1999. 144p. (J). pap. (978-0-14-130519-6(3) , Puffin) Penguin Group (USA) Inc.
Forrester, Izola. Kit of Greenacre Farm. 2006. pap. 26.99 (*978-1-4280-3376-4(9)) IndyPublish.com.
Forsberg, Crystal. Michael's Brothers. Hayes, John, illus. 1998. 16p. (J). (ps-k). pap. 5.95 (978-0-9655442-3-8(0)) Business Word, The.
Fox, Mem. Noam Mechapes Zichronot. Dash Greenspan, Shari, tr. from ENG. Vivas, Julie, illus. 2005. Orig. Title: Wilfrid Gordon McDonald Partridge. (HEB.). 32p. 14.00 (978-965-7108-43-7(8)) Urim Pubns. ISR. *Dist:* Biblio Distribution.
Fox, Paula. Ivan. 2002. (SPA.). (YA). pap. 8.50 (978-84-279-3245-6(6) , NG31202) Molino, Editorial ESP. *Dist:* Lectorum Pubns., Inc.
Frame, Jeron Ashford. Yesterday I Had the Blues. Christie, Gregory R., illus. 2004. 30p. (J). (gr. k-3). 14.95 (978-1-58246-084-0(1) , Tricycle Pr.) Ten Speed Pr.
Frank, E. R. Wrecked. 2007. 256p. (YA). (gr. 7 up). pap. 8.99 (978-0-689-87384-3(0) , Simon Pulse) Simon & Schuster Children's Publishing.
Frank, Hillary. I Can't Tell You. 2004. 208p. (YA). (gr. 7). 16.00 (978-0-618-41202-0(6)); pap. 7.99 (978-0-618-49491-0(X) , Graphia) Houghton Mifflin Co. Trade & Reference Div.
Franklin, Emily. The Other Half of Me. 2007. 256p. (YA). (gr. 9). 15.99 (*978-0-385-73445-5(X)); lib. bdg. 18.99 (*978-0-385-90449-0(5)) Random Hse. Children's Bks. (Delacorte Bks. for Young Readers).
Franklin, Kristine L. Dove Song. 2006. 192p. (J). (gr. 5-9). pap. 5.99 (978-0-7636-3219-9(8)) Candlewick Pr.
Frasier, Debra. El Dia en Que Tu Naciste. 1998. 13.80 (978-0-606-13363-0(1)) Tandem Library Bks.
Frazier, Sundee Tucker. Brendan Buckley's Universe & Everything in It. 2007. 208p. (J). (gr. 4-7). 14.99 (*978-0-385-73439-4(5)); lib. bdg. 17.99 (*978-0-385-90445-2(2)) Random Hse. Children's Bks. (Delacorte Bks. for Young Readers).
Freeman, Martha. The Polyester Grandpa. 1998. 160p. (J). (gr. 4-7). tchr. ed. 15.95 (978-0-8234-1398-0(5)) Holiday Hse., Inc.
—The Trouble with Twins. Smith, Cat Bowman, illus. 2007. 112p. (J). (gr. 2-6). 16.95 (978-0-8234-2025-4(6)) Holiday Hse., Inc.
French, Jackie. My Dog the Dinosaur. King, Stephen Michael, illus. 2007. (J). 112p. (*978-1-59889-344-1(0)); 107p. pap. (*978-1-59889-437-0(4)) Stone Arch Bks.
—My Uncle the Werewolf. King, Stephen Michael, illus. 2007. (J). 112p. (*978-1-59889-346-5(7)); 107p. pap. (*978-1-59889-439-4(0)) Stone Arch Bks.
French, Renee. The Soap Lady. unabr. ed. 2001. (Illus.). 112p. 19.95 (978-1-891830-24-2(4)) Top Shelf Productions.
Freymann-Weyr, Garret. My Heartbeat. 2002. 160p. (YA). (gr. 7-12). 15.00 (978-0-618-14181-4(2)) Houghton Mifflin Co. Trade & Reference Div.
Friedman, Laurie. Mallory Se Muda (Mallory on the Move) Anaya, Josefina, tr. Schmitz, Tamara, illus. 2007. (Mallory en español (Mallory in Spanish) Ser.). (SPA.). (J). (gr. 2-6). pap. 5.95 (*978-0-8225-7493-4(4) , Ediciones Lerner) Lerner Publishing Group.
Friedman, Laurie. Mallory vs. Max. Schmitz, Tamara, illus. 2006. (J). pap. 5.95 (978-1-57505-863-4(4) , First Avenue Editions) Lerner Publishing Group.
Friedman, Laurie B. Back to School, Mallory. Schmitz, Tamara, illus. (J). 2005. 175p. (ps-7). pap. 5.95 (978-1-57505-865-8(0)); 2004. 160p. (gr. 2-5). 15.95 (978-1-57505-658-6(5)) Lerner Publishing Group.
—Mallory on Board. Pollak, Barbara, illus. 2007. 160p. (J). (gr. 2-6). 15.95 (978-0-8225-6194-1(8) , Carolrhoda Bks.) Lerner Publishing Group.
—Mallory vs. Max. Schmitz, Tamara, illus. 2005. 160p. (J). (ps-k). 15.95 (978-1-57505-795-8(6)) Lerner Publishing Group.
Friend, Natasha. Bounce. 2007. 192p. (YA). (gr. 6-8). pap. 16.99 (*978-0-439-85350-7(5) , Scholastic Pr.) Scholastic, Inc.
Friend, Natasha. Lush. 192p. (J). 2007. (gr. 7 up). pap. 6.99 (*978-0-439-85347-7(8)); 2006. pap. 16.99 (978-0-439-85346-0(X)) Scholastic, Inc. (Scholastic Paperbacks).
From the Hillside: Individual Chapter Book Title Six-Packs. Vol. 30. 32p. (gr. 5 up). 44.00 (978-0-7578-0980-4(4)) Rigby Education.
Frost, Helen. Diamond Willow. 2008. 128p. (J). 16.00 (*978-0-374-31776-8(3)) Farrar, Straus & Giroux.
—Keesha's House. l.t. ed. 2005. 173p. (YA). (gr. 7-12). per. 20.95 (978-0-7862-7697-4(5) , Large Print Pr.) Thorndike Pr.
—Spinning Through the Universe. 2004. (Illus.). 112p. (J). 16.00 (978-0-374-37159-3(8) , Farrar, Straus & Giroux (BYR)) Farrar, Straus & Giroux.
Fuqua, Jonathon Scott. The Reappearance of Sam Webber. 2001. (978-0-606-21397-4(X)) Tandem Library Bks.
Gail, Cornelia. Juvey. 2007. 153p. (YA). per. 14.95 net. (*978-0-9674454-4-1(2)) Girls In Da Game Publishing.
Gallup, Tracy. Shell Crazy. Gallup, Tracy, illus. 2007. (Crazy Little Ser.). (Illus.). 40p. (J). 9.95 (*978-1-934133-14-9(0)) Mackinac Island Pr., Inc.
Gantos, Jack. What Would Joey Do? 2002. (Joey Pigza Ser.). 240p. (J). (gr. 5-9). 16.00 (978-0-374-39986-3(7) , Farrar, Straus & Giroux (BYR)) Farrar, Straus & Giroux.
—What Would Joey Do? 2004. 240p. (J). (gr. 5 up). reprint ed. pap. 5.99 (978-0-06-054403-4(1) , Harper Trophy) HarperCollins Pubs.
—What Would Joey Do? l.t. ed. 2003. (Juvenile Ser.). 264p. (J). 22.95 (978-0-7862-5468-2(8)) Thorndike Pr.
Garber, Linda. Don't Leave the Lawn! Garber, Linda, illus. l.t. ed. 1999. (Illus.). (J). (gr. 1-4). spiral bd. 9.95 (978-1-892218-04-9(6)) Murlin Pubns.
Garden, Nancy. Endgame. 2006. (Illus.). 304p. (YA). 17.00 (978-0-15-205416-8(2)) Harcourt Children's Bks.
—Molly's Family. Wooding, Sharon, illus. 2004. 32p. (J). 16.00 (978-0-374-35002-4(7) , Farrar, Straus & Giroux (BYR)) Farrar, Straus & Giroux.
Garfinkle, Debra. Storky: How I Lost My Nickname & Won the Girl. 192p. (YA). 2007. (gr. 7 up). pap. 5.99 (978-0-14-240782-0(8) , Puffin); 2005. (gr. 6). 16.99 (978-0-399-24284-7(8) , Putnam Juvenile) Penguin Group (USA) Inc.
Garis, Howard Roger. Uncle Wiggily's Fortune. Date not set. 192p. (J). 20.95 (978-0-8488-2280-4(3)) Amereon LTD.
Gates, Susan. Beyond the Billboard. 2007. (Illus.). 224p. (YA). (gr. 6-8). 16.00 (978-0-15-205983-5(0)) Harcourt Children's Bks.
Gavalda, Anna. 95 Libras de Esperanza. 2004. Tr. of 95 Pounds of Hope. (SPA.). (YA). 13.99 (978-1-930332-64-5(5)) Lectorum Pubns., Inc.
Gerber, Linda. Now & Zen. Pilkington, Roger, ed. 2006. (S. A. S. S. (Students Across the Seven Seas) Ser.). 224p. (YA). (gr. 7). pap. 6.99 (978-0-14-240657-1(0) , Puffin) Penguin Group (USA) Inc.
Gibala-Broxholm, Scott. Scary Fright, Are You All Right? Gibala-Broxholm, Scott, illus. 2002. (Illus.). 48p. (J). 14.99 (978-0-8037-2588-1(4) , Dial) Penguin Group (USA) Inc.
Gibbons, Faye. Mountain Wedding. Rand, Ted, illus. 2004. 32p. (YA). pap. 8.95 (978-1-59078-324-5(7)) Boyds Mills Pr.
Gifford, Griselda. Second Sight. 2003. (Illus.). 96p. (YA). pap. 9.99 (978-1-84270-217-8(3)) Andersen GBR. *Dist:* Independent Pubs. Group.
Gifford, Peggy. Moxy Maxwell Does Not Love Stuart Little. Fisher, Valorie, photos by. 2007. (Illus.). 104p. (J). (gr. 2-6). 12.99 (978-0-375-83915-3(1)); lib. bdg. 15.99 (978-0-375-93915-0(6)) Random Hse. Children's Bks. (Schwartz & Wade Bks.).
Gifford, Peggy. Moxy Maxwell Does Not Love Stuart Little. Fisher, Valorie, photos by. 2008. (Illus.). 112p. (J). (gr. 2-6). 5.50 (*978-0-440-42230-3(2) , Yearling) Random Hse. Children's Bks.
Gifford, Peggy Elizabeth. Moxy Maxwell Does Not Love Writing Thank-You Notes. Fisher, Valorie, illus. Fisher, Valorie, photos by. 2008. (J). (*978-0-375-84270-2(5)); (*978-0-375-94552-6(0)) Random Hse. Children's Bks. (Schwartz & Wade Bks.).
Giles, Gail. Playing in Traffic. 2006. (Illus.). 176p. (YA). reprint ed. pap. 6.99 (978-1-4169-0926-2(5) , Simon Pulse) Simon & Schuster Children's Publishing.
—Right Behind You. 2007. 304p. (YA). (gr. 10 up). 15.99 (*978-0-316-16636-2(7)) Little, Brown Bks. for Young Readers.
—What Happened to Cass Mcbride. 2007. 240p. (J). (gr. 7-17). pap. 7.99 (*978-0-316-16639-3(1)) Little, Brown Bks. for Young Readers.
Giles, Gail. What Happened to Cass McBride? 2006. 212p. (YA). pap. 16.99 (*978-0-316-01703-9(5)); 224p. (J). (gr. 7-17). 16.99 (978-0-316-16638-6(3)) Little Brown & Co.
Gilkey, Gail. Miriam's Holiday. Kittell, Kathy, illus. 1998. 32p. (J). (gr. k-5). pap. 5.95 (978-0-9662983-1-4(4)) Windy Hill Pr.
Gilleland, Rebecca. The Swiss Family Robinson Study Guide. 2003. stu. ed., ring bd. 14.99 (978-1-58609-194-1(8)) Progeny Pr.
Gillmor, Don. The Fabulous Song. Gay, Marie-Louise, illus. 2003. 32p. (J). pap. 7.95 (978-1-929132-48-5(4)) Kane/Miller Bk. Pubs., Inc.
—The Fabulous Song. Gay, Marie-Louise, illus. 2006. 36p. 16.95 (978-2-923163-17-8(6)) La Montagne Secrete CAN. *Dist:* National Bk. Network.
Gilmore, Rachna. Mina's Spring of Colors. 2000. 150p. (J). (gr. 4-7). (978-1-55041-549-0(2)); (978-1-55041-534-6(4)) Fitzhenry & Whiteside, Ltd.
—Mina's Spring of Colors. 2000. (gr. 3-6). lib. bdg. 17.60 (978-0-613-43201-6(0)) Tandem Library Bks.
—A Screaming Kind of Day. Sauve, Gordon, illus. 2001. 38p. (J). (gr. k-2). lib. bdg. 16.40 (978-0-613-78441-2(3)) Tandem Library Bks.
Gipson, Fred. Savage Sam. Date not set. pap. 371.40 (978-0-671-75819-6(5) , Atria) Simon & Schuster.
Glasgow, Geraldine. Troublesome Comforts (a Story for Childr. 2006. pap. 87.99 (*978-1-4280-2964-4(8)) IndyPublish.com.
Glass, Linzi Alex. The Year the Gypsies Came. 2006. 272p. (YA). 16.95 (978-0-8050-7999-9(8)) Holt, Henry & Co.
Gleeson, Libby. Cuddle Time. Vivas, Julie, illus. 2004. 32p. (J). (gr. k-k). 16.99 (978-0-7636-2320-3(2)) Candlewick Pr.
Glencoe McGraw-Hill Staff & McGraw-Hill - Jamestown Education Staff. Topics from the Restless, Bk. 1. unabr. ed. 1999. (Wordsworth Classics Ser.). (gr. 10 up). pap. 24.64 (978-0-89061-116-6(5) , 9780890611166) Jamestown.
Gliori, Debi. Pure Dead Frozen. 2007. (J). (gr. 5). 320p. 15.99 (*978-0-375-83317-5(X)); 304p. lib. bdg. 18.99 (*978-0-375-93317-2(4)) Random Hse. Children's Bks. (Knopf Bks. for Young Readers).
—Pure Dead Magic. 2002. (Illus.). 208p. (gr. 5). mass mkt. 6.50 (978-0-440-41849-8(6) , Yearling) Random Hse. Children's Bks.
—Pure Dead Wicked. 2003. 240p. (gr. 5 up). 6.50 (978-0-440-41936-5(0) , Yearling) Random Hse. Children's Bks.
Godolphin, Mary. The Swiss Family Robinson Told in Words. 2004. reprint ed. pap. 15.95 (978-1-4191-8466-7(6)) Kessinger Publishing, LLC.
—The Swiss Family Robinson Told in Words of One Syllable. 2004. reprint ed. pap. 1.99 (978-1-4192-8466-3(5)) Kessinger Publishing, LLC.
Gohman, Amy. I Have Just the Gift for You. 2005. (Illus.). 47p. per. 9.99 (978-1-932338-87-4(X)) Lifevest Publishing, Inc.
Going, K. L. The Garden of Eve. 2007. (Illus.). 240p. (J). (gr. 3-7). 17.00 (*978-0-15-205986-6(5)) Harcourt Children's Bks.
Going, K. L. Saint Iggy. 2006. (Illus.). 272p. (YA). 17.00 (978-0-15-205795-4(1)) Harcourt Children's Bks.
Golden Books Staff. Eloise Wilkin Stories. Wilkin, Eloise, illus. 2005. (Little Golden Book Treasury Ser.). 224p. (J). (ps-3). 10.95 (978-0-375-82928-4(8) , Golden Bks.) Random Hse. Children's Bks.
—My Family & Me. Butcher, Samuel J., illus. 2004. 64p. (J). (ps-2). pap. 2.99 (978-0-375-82790-7(0) , Golden Bks.) Random Hse. Children's Bks.
Goldin, Barbara Diamond. The Best Hanukkah Ever. Katz, Avi, illus. 2007. 32p. (J). (gr. k-3). 16.99 (*978-0-7614-5355-0(5)) Cavendish, Marshall Corp.
Gonder, Glen W. Micmacs. Gonder, Sharon J., ed. Grove, Gladys, illus. 1999. (Adventures of Willy Whacker Ser.). 125p. (YA). (gr. 6-8). lib. bdg. 8.95 (978-1-58389-003-5(3)) Osage Bend Publishing Co.
Gonzales Bertrand, Diane. Family, Familia. Castilla, Julia Mercedes, tr. Howard, Pauline Rodriguez, illus. 1999. (SPA & ENG.). 32p. (J). (ps-3). 14.95 (978-1-55885-269-3(7) , Piñata Books) Arte Publico Pr.
Gonzales Bertrand, Diane & Castilla, Julie Mercedes. El Dilema de Trino. (SPA.). 144p. pap. 9.95 (978-1-55885-458-1(4) , Piñata Books) Arte Publico Pr.
Gonzalez, Gabriela & Triana, Gaby. Backstage Pass. 2004. (Illus.). 224p. (J). (gr. 7 up). 15.99 (978-0-06-056017-1(7)) HarperCollins Pubs.
Goobie, Beth. The Lottery. 2004. 272p. (J). (gr. 7-12). pap. 7.95 (978-1-55143-280-9(3)) Orca Bk. Pubs. USA.
Goode, Diane. Thanksgiving Is Here! Goode, Diane, illus. 2003. (Illus.). 32p. (J). (ps-3). 17.99 (978-0-06-051588-1(0)); lib. bdg. 16.89 (978-0-06-051589-8(9)) HarperCollins Pubs.
Goodhart, Pippa. House that Jack Built. Parker, Andy, illus. 2004. 24p. (J). lib. bdg. 22.65 (*978-1-59646-700-2(2)) Dingles & Co.
Grab, Daphne. Alive & Well in Prague, NY. 2008. 256p. (J). 16.99 (*978-0-06-125670-7(6)); lib. bdg. 17.89 (*978-0-06-125671-4(4)) HarperCollins Pubs. (Geringer, Laura Book).
Grabenstein, Chris. The Crossroads. 2008. 368p. (J). (gr. 4-7). 16.99 (*978-0-375-84697-7(2) , Random Hse. Bks. for Young Readers) Random Hse. Children's Bks.
Graef, Renee, illus. Hard Times on the Prairie. 1998. (Little House Chapter Bks.: No. 8). (J). (gr. 3-6). 11.05 (978-0-606-13458-3(1)) Tandem Library Bks.
—Laura & Nellie. 1998. (Little House Chapter Bks.: No. 5). (J). (gr. 3-6). (978-0-606-12979-4(0)) Tandem Library Bks.
—Laura's Ma. 1999. (Little House Ser.: No. 11). 80p. (J). (gr. 3-6). 14.89 (978-0-06-027897-7(8)) HarperCollins Pubs.
Graff, Lisa. Bernetta Wallflower: A Novel. 2008. 256p. (J). 16.99 (*978-0-06-087592-3(5)); lib. bdg. 17.89 (*978-0-06-087593-0(3)) HarperCollins Pubs. (Geringer, Laura Book).
Graff, Lisa. The Thing about Georgie. 2007. 224p. (J). (gr. 3-6). 15.99 (978-0-06-087589-3(5)); lib. bdg. 16.89 (978-0-06-087590-9(9)) HarperCollins Pubs. (Geringer, Laura Book).
Graham, Bob. Queenie, One of the Family. Graham, Bob, illus. 2001. (Illus.). 32p. (J). (gr. k-3). pap. 6.99 (978-0-7636-1400-3(9)) Candlewick Pr.
—Queenie, One of the Family. 2001. (gr. k-3). lib. bdg. 14.15 (978-0-613-74724-0(0)) Tandem Library Bks.
Grandma Moves In: Six-Pack. (Greetings Ser.: Vol. 2). (gr. 2-3). 31.00 (978-0-7635-9429-9(6)) Rigby Education.
Grandma's Pictures: Individual Title Six-Packs. (gr. k-1). 23.00 (978-0-7635-8842-7(3)) Rigby Education.
Grantham, Jared. Ashley & the Mooncorn People. 2002. 64p. (J). 16.00 (978-1-58597-134-3(0)) Leathers Publishing.
Gratz, Alan M. Something Rotten: A Horatio Wilkes Mystery. 2007. 208p. (J). (gr. 6). 16.99 (*978-0-8037-3216-2(3) , Dial) Penguin Group (USA) Inc.
Graves, Sue. A Busy Week. Sharp, Melanie, illus. 2005. (Reading Corner Ser.). 24p. (J). (gr. k-3). lib. bdg. 22.80 (978-1-59771-005-3(9)) Sea-To-Sea Pubns.
Gray, Nigel. A Country Far Away. Dupasquier, Philippe, illus. 1999. 32p. (J). (ps-3). pap. 11.95 (978-0-86264-860-2(2)) Andersen GBR. *Dist:* Trafalgar Square Publishing.

E F G

Green, Jessica. Diary of a Would-Be Princess: The Journal of Jillian James, 5B. 2007. (Illus.). 236p. (J). (gr. 4-7). 15.95 (978-1-58089-166-0(7)) Charlesbridge Publishing, Inc.

Green, Jose. Castro's Diary. 2004. 174p. pap. 19.95 (978-1-4137-4556-6(3)) PublishAmerica, Inc.

Green, Julia. Hunter's Heart. 2007. 264p. (YA). (gr. 7-12). 16.95 (*978-0-7613-9493-8(1) , Carolrhoda Bks.) Lerner Publishing Group.

Green, Sylvia. The Best Christmas Ever. 2001. 128p. (J). pap. 3.99 (978-0-439-34013-7(6)) Scholastic, Inc.

Greenberg, Polly. Oh Lord, I Wish I Was a Buzzard. Aliki, illus. 2002. 32p. (J). (gr. k-3). 15.95 (978-1-58717-122-2(8) , SeaStar Bks.) Chronicle Bks. LLC.

Greenburg, Dan. The Day That Went from Bad to Verse. Davis, Jack E., illus. 2000. (Zack Files Ser.: No. 20). 64p. (J). (gr. 2-5). pap. 4.99 (978-0-448-42042-4(2) , Grosset & Dunlap) Penguin Group (USA) Inc.

—The Day That Went from Bad to Verse. 2000. (gr. 3-6). lib. bdg. 13.00 (978-0-613-24777-1(9)) Tandem Library Bks.

Greene, Constance C. Beat the Turtle Drum. 128p. (J). (gr. 4-6). pap. 3.99 (978-0-8072-1411-4(6) , Listening Library) Random Hse. Audio Publishing Group.

Greene, Renea Russ. Thunder in the Coffee Pot. Greene, Laura Hampton, illus. 2002. 36p. (J). pap. 8.95 (978-0-9723719-0-2(7)) FUN 4 5 Pubns.

Greene, Stephanie. Christmas at Stony Creek. Sheban, Chris, illus. 2007. 96p. (J). (gr. 2-7). 14.99 (*978-0-06-121486-8(8)); lib. bdg. 15.89 (*978-0-06-121487-5(6)) HarperCollins Pubs. (Greenwillow Bks.).

—Falling into Place. 128p. (J). (gr. 4-6). 2006. pap. 5.95 (978-0-618-68928-6(1)); 2002. (Illus.). tchr. ed. 15.00 (978-0-618-17744-8(2)) Houghton Mifflin Co. Trade & Reference Div. (Clarion Bks.).

—Owen Foote, Money Man. Weston, Martha, illus. 96p. (J). 2003. (gr. k-3). pap. 4.95 (978-0-618-37837-1(5)); 2000. (gr. 5-9). tchr. ed. 15.00 (978-0-618-02369-1(0)) Houghton Mifflin Co. Trade & Reference Div. (Clarion Bks.).

—Queen Sophie Hartley. 2005. 144p. (J). (gr. 3-5). 15.00 (978-0-618-49461-3(8) , Clarion Bks.) Houghton Mifflin Co. Trade & Reference Div.

—Sophie Hartley, on Strike. 2006. 160p. (J). (gr. 3-5). 15.00 (978-0-618-71960-0(1) , Clarion Bks.) Houghton Mifflin Co. Trade & Reference Div.

Greenwood, Barbara. Secret Garden. 2001. (Young Reader's Classics Ser.). (Illus.). 94p. (J). 16.95 (978-1-55013-548-0(1) , Key Porter kids) Key Porter Bks. CAN. Dist: Firefly Bks., Ltd.

Gregerson, Judy. Bad Girls Club. 2007. 288p. (YA). (gr. 8 up). 16.95 (978-1-933831-01-5(4)) Blooming Tree Pr.

Griessman, Annette. The Fire. Gore, Leonid, illus. 2005. 32p. (J). (ps-3). 16.99 (978-0-399-24019-5(5) , Putnam Juvenile) Penguin Group (USA) Inc.

Griffin, Adele. The Other Shepards. 1999. (978-0-606-17144-1(4)) Tandem Library Bks.

—The Other Shepards. l.t. ed. 2000. (Illus.). 209p. (J). (gr. 4-7). 20.95 (978-0-7862-2914-7(4)) Thorndike Pr.

—Rainy Season. 1998. (978-0-606-13726-3(2)) Tandem Library Bks.

—Sons of Liberty. 1998. 230p. (gr. 5-17). pap. 4.95 (978-0-7868-1300-1(8)) Disney Pr.

Griffin, Peni R. The Music Thief. rev. ed. 2002. 160p. (YA). (gr. 5-8). 16.95 (978-0-8050-7055-2(9) , Holt, Henry & Co. Bks. For Young Readers) Holt, Henry & Co.

—The Music Thief. l.t. ed. 2003. 190p. (J). 21.95 (978-0-7862-5606-8(0)) Thorndike Pr.

Griffiths, Corinne Escobar. Corky Eckelsbriar. 2004. (J). pap. 6.95 (978-0-9760271-0-2(0)) Cappella Publishing, A.

Grimes, Nikki. My Man Blue. Lagarrigue, Jerome, illus. 2002. 32p. (J). (ps-3). pap. 6.99 (978-0-14-230197-5(3) , Puffin) Penguin Group (USA) Inc.

—My Man Blue. 2002. (gr. 3-6). lib. bdg. 15.30 (978-0-613-60823-7(2)) Tandem Library Bks.

Grindley, Sally. Spilled Water. 2004. 224p. (J). 15.95 (978-1-58234-937-4(1) , Bloomsbury Children) Bloomsbury Publishing.

Grisham, John. La Casa Dipinta. pap. 21.95 (978-88-04-50528-0(1)) Mondadori ITA. Dist: Distribooks, Inc.

Grossman, Linda Sky. A Tale Worth Telling. Bockus, Petra, illus. 2002. (I'm a Great Little Kid Ser.). 24p. pap. 4.95 (978-1-896764-60-3(6)); (gr. 3 up). 11.95 (978-1-896764-62-7(2)) Second Story Pr. CAN. Dist: Orca Bk. Pubs. USA.

Grote, JoAnn A. Queen Anne's War. 1999. (American Adventure Ser.: No. 5). 144p. (J). (gr. 3-7). lib. bdg. 15.95 (978-0-7910-5045-3(9) , Chelsea Hse.) Facts On File, Inc.

Grove, Vicki. Reaching Dustin. 2000. (Illus.). 208p. (J). (gr. 4-9). pap. 6.99 (978-0-698-11839-3(1) , Putnam Juvenile) Penguin Group (USA) Inc.

—Reaching Dustin. 2000. (978-0-606-18844-9(4)); (gr. 5-8). lib. bdg. 14.15 (978-0-613-28619-0(7)) Tandem Library Bks.

Groves. Best Duster Bk. 5. Date not set. (Illus.). 16p. (J). pap. 129.15 (978-0-582-18766-5(4)) Addison-Wesley Longman, Ltd. GBR. Dist: Trans-Atlantic Pubns., Inc.

—Sticky Trousers. Date not set. (Illus.). 32p. (J). pap. 129.15 (978-0-582-18304-9(9)) Addison-Wesley Longman, Ltd. GBR. Dist: Trans-Atlantic Pubns., Inc.

Gugler, Laurel Dee. Facing the Day. Betteridge, Deirdre, illus. 1999. 24p. (J). (gr. k-ps). lib. bdg. 15.95 (978-1-55037-577-0(6)) Annick Pr., Ltd. CAN. Dist: Firefly Bks., Ltd.

Gunn, Robin Jones. Only You, Sierra. 1998. (Sierra Jensen Ser.: Bk. 1). 176p. (J). (gr. 7-11). pap. 6.99 (978-1-56179-370-9(1)) Bethany Hse. Pubs.

—Time Will Tell. 1998. (Sierra Jensen Ser.: Bk. 8). 160p. (YA). (gr. 7-11). pap. (978-1-56179-568-0(2)) Focus on the Family Publishing.

Gunning, Monica. Under the Breadfruit Tree: Island Poems. 2004. (Illus.). 48p. (J). (gr. 2-4). pap. 9.95 (978-1-59078-258-3(5)) Boyds Mills Pr.

Gutman, Dan. The Edison Mystery: Back in Time. 2002. (Illus.). 201p. lib. bdg. 13.00 (978-0-613-62098-7(4)) Tandem Library Bks.

Haas, Jessie. Unbroken. 2001. 208p. (J). (gr. 5 up). pap. 6.99 (978-0-380-73313-2(7) , Harper Trophy) HarperCollins Pubs.

Hadcroft, Will. Anne Droyd & Century Lodge. 2004. 282p. (J). pap. (978-1-84310-282-3(X)) Kingsley, Jessica Ltd.

Hafer, Todd. Stealing Home. 2004. (Spirit of the Game, Sports Fiction Ser.). 144p. (J). pap. 4.99 (978-0-310-70671-7(8)) Zonderkidz.

Hahn, Mary Downing. Anna All Year Round. deGroat, Diane, illus. 2001. 144p. (J). (gr. 4-7). pap. 4.95 (978-0-380-73317-0(X) , Harper Trophy) HarperCollins Pubs.

—Anna All Year Round. 2001. (Illus.). (J). (978-0-606-21037-9(7)) Tandem Library Bks.

—Anna All Year Round. deGroat, Diane, illus. 1999. 144p. (J). (gr. 4-6). tchr. ed. 15.00 (978-0-395-86975-8(7) , Clarion Bks.) Houghton Mifflin Co. Trade & Reference Div.

Hale, Lucretia. The Peterkin Papers. Brett, Harold M., illus. 2005. reprint ed. pap. 24.95 (978-1-4179-3265-8(1)) Kessinger Publishing, LLC.

Hale, Lucretia P. The Peterkin Papers. 2002. (ENG.). 23.99 (*978-1-4043-2416-9(X)); pap. 18.99 (*978-1-4043-2417-6(8)) IndyPublish.com.

—The Peterkin Papers. 2004. reprint ed. pap. 20.95 (978-1-4191-7709-5(5)); pap. 1.99 (978-1-4192-7709-2(X)) Kessinger Publishing, LLC.

—The Peterkin Papers. 2006. (New York Review Children's Collection). (Illus.). 320p. (J). (gr. 4). 18.95 (978-1-59017-212-4(4) , NYR Children's Collection) New York Review of Bks., Inc., The.

Hale, Marian. The Truth about Sparrows. rev. ed. 2004. (Illus.). 272p. (J). 16.95 (978-0-8050-7584-7(4) , Holt, Henry & Co. Bks. For Young Readers) Holt, Henry & Co.

—The Truth about Sparrows. 2007. 288p. (J). pap. 6.99 (*978-0-312-37133-3(0)) Square Fish.

Hale, P. Lucretia. The Last of the Peterkins, with Others O. 2006. 77.99 (*978-1-4280-4816-4(2)); pap. 71.99 (*978-1-4280-4814-0(6)) IndyPublish.com.

Hall, Barbara. Dixie Storms. 2006. (Illus.). 224p. (J). pap. 6.95 (978-0-15-205756-5(0) , Harcourt Paperbacks) Harcourt Children's Bks.

—The Noah Confessions. 2007. 224p. (YA). (gr. 7). lib. bdg. 18.99 (978-0-385-90346-2(4)); 15.99 (978-0-385-73328-1(3)) Random Hse. Children's Bks. (Delacorte Bks. for Young Readers).

Hall, Kirsten. Oops! All about Opposites. 2004. (Beastieville Ser.). (J). (gr. k-1). pap. 3.95 (978-0-516-24657-4(7) , Children's Pr.) Scholastic Library Publishing.

Hallinan, P. K. Thanksgiving at Our House. 2006. (Illus.). 32p. (J). (gr. k). 8.95 (978-0-8249-5534-2(X) , 1262730, Ideals Children's Bks.) Ideals Pubns.

Halperin, Wendy Anderson. Once upon a Company. 1998. (Illus.). 40p. (J). (gr. k-4). 17.99 (978-0-531-33089-0(3)); pap. 16.95 (978-0-531-30089-3(7)) Scholastic, Inc. (Orchard Bks.).

Halperin, Wendy Anderson, tr. & illus. The Peterkins' Thanksgiving. Halperin, Wendy Anderson, illus. 2005. 32p. (J). (gr. 2-4). 17.95 (978-0-689-84142-2(6) , Atheneum) Simon & Schuster Children's Publishing.

Hamilton, Richard & McCord, Patricia. Pictures in the Dark. 2004. (Illus.). 225p. (J). (gr. 5 up). 16.95 (978-1-58234-848-3(0) , Bloomsbury Children) Bloomsbury Publishing.

Hamilton, Virginia. M. C. Higgins, the Great. 1998. (J). pap. 4.50 (978-0-87628-568-8(X)) Ctr. for Applied Research in Education, The.

—M. C. Higgins, the Great. (J). pap., stu. ed. (978-0-13-620246-2(2)); 3rd ed. pap. 23.70 (978-0-13-620220-2(9)); 3rd ed. pap. 3.95 (978-0-13-800137-7(5)) Prentice Hall (Schl. Div.).

—M. C. Higgins, the Great. 2006. (Illus.). 288p. (J). pap. 5.99 (978-1-4169-1407-5(2) , Aladdin) Simon & Schuster Children's Publishing.

—M. C. Higgins, the Great. Palencar, John J., illus. 25th anniv. ed. 1999. 240p. (J). (gr. 7). 19.99 (978-0-689-83074-7(2)) Simon & Schuster Children's Publishing.

Hannigan, Katherine. Ida B: ... And Her Plans to Maximize Fun, Avoid Disaster, & (Possibly) Save the World. 256p. 2004. (J). (gr. 4 up). 16.99 (978-0-06-073024-6(2)); 2004. (J). (gr. 4 up). lib. bdg. 16.89 (978-0-06-073025-3(0)); 2007. reprint ed. pap. 5.99 (978-0-06-073026-0(9) , Harper Trophy) HarperCollins Pubs.

Harcourt School Publishers Staff. Family Day. 3rd ed. 2002. (Trophies English Language Learners Ser.). (Illus.). pap. 5.10 (978-0-15-327698-9(3)) Harcourt Schl. Pubs.

—Family Life Advanced Level. 3rd ed. 2002. (Trophies Reading Program Ser.). (Illus.). pap. 5.10 (978-0-15-323028-8(2)) Harcourt Schl. Pubs.

—Girasoles On Level. 3rd ed. 2002. (Trofeos Ser.).Tr. of Sunflowers. (SPA., Illus.). pap. 6.80 (978-0-15-324169-7(1)) Harcourt Schl. Pubs.

—Mommy Needs a New Baby: Take-Home Book. 1999. (Collections Ser.). (Illus.). (J). pap. 1.90 (978-0-15-317303-5(3)) Harcourt Schl. Pubs.

Hargreaves, Roger & Hargreaves, Roger. Mr. Tickle. Hargreaves, Roger, illus. 1998. (Mr. Men & Little Miss Ser.). (Illus.). 32p. (J). (gr. k up). pap. 3.99 (978-0-8431-7422-9(6) , Price Stern Sloan) Penguin Group (USA) Inc.

Harker, Lesley. Charlie's Dragon. (Illus.). 32p. (J). 13.95 (978-0-241-13069-8(7) , Hamilton, Hamish) Penguin Bks., Ltd. GBR. Dist: Trafalgar Square Publishing.

Harlow, Joan Hiatt. Blown Away! 2007. 272p. (J). (gr. 4-7). 15.99 (978-1-4169-0781-7(5) , McElderry, Margaret K.) Simon & Schuster Children's Publishing.

—Thunder from the Sea. 2004. (Illus.). 256p. (J). 16.99 (978-0-689-86403-2(5) , McElderry, Margaret K.) Simon & Schuster Children's Publishing.

Harmon, Michael B. Skate. 2006. 256p. (YA). (gr. 9). 15.95 (978-0-375-87516-8(6)); 17.99 (978-0-375-97516-5(0)) Random Hse. Children's Bks. (Knopf Bks. for Young Readers).

Harness, Cheryl. Just for You to Know. 2008. (J). pap. (*978-0-06-078315-0(X)) HarperCollins Pubs.

Harper, Charise Mericle. Flashcards of My Life. (J). 2007. 224p. (gr. 3-7). pap. 6.99 (978-0-316-16676-8(6)); 2006. (Illus.). 240p. (gr. 4-7). 15.99 (978-0-316-75621-1(0)) Little Brown & Co.

Harper, Suzanne. The Secret Life of Sparrow Delaney. 2007. 368p. (gr. 7 up). (J). lib. bdg. 17.89 (978-0-06-113159-2(8)); (YA). 16.99 (978-0-06-113158-5(X)) HarperCollins Pubs.

Harris, Robie H. Hi New Baby. Emberley, Michael, illus. 2003. 32p. (J). (gr. k-2). pap. 6.99 (978-0-7636-1826-1(8)) Candlewick Pr.

Harris, Ruth Elwin. Gwen's Story. 2002. (gr. 7-12). lib. bdg. 14.15 (978-0-613-74775-2(5)) Tandem Library Bks.

—Gwen's Story: Sisters of the Quantock Hills. 2002. (Quantock's Quartet Ser.). (Illus.). 288p. (YA). (gr. 7 up). pap. 5.99 (978-0-7636-1705-9(9)) Candlewick Pr.

—Julia's Story. 2002. (gr. 7-12). lib. bdg. 14.15 (978-0-613-74777-6(1)) Tandem Library Bks.

—Sarah's Story. 2002. (Quantock's Quartet Ser.). (Illus.). 288p. (YA). (gr. 7 up). pap. 5.99 (978-0-7636-1707-3(5)) Candlewick Pr.

—Sarah's Story. 2002. (gr. 7-12). lib. bdg. 14.15 (978-0-613-74779-0(8)) Tandem Library Bks.

Harrison, Jean & Cristnogol, Cymorth. Shompa o India. 2005. (978-0-904379-43-3(4)) Christian Aid.

Harrison, Pam & Worthington, Denise. Snuggle Up. Gorman, Kate S., illus. 1998. 8p. (J). (gr. k-2). pap. 3.75 (978-1-880612-75-0(5) , Seedling Pubns.) Continental Pr., Inc.

Harrison, Troon. A Bushel of Light. 2001. 244p. (gr. 7-9). pap. 7.95 (978-0-7737-6140-7(3)) Stoddart Kids CAN. Dist: Fitzhenry & Whiteside, Ltd.

Hartinger, Brent. The Last Chance Texaco. 2005. 240p. (J). reprint ed. pap. 7.99 (978-0-06-050914-9(7) , Harper-Teen) HarperCollins Pubs.

—Split Screen: Attack of the Soul-Sucking Brain Zombies/ Bride of the Soul-Sucking Brain Zombies. 2007. 304p. (J). (gr. 9 up). 16.99 (978-0-06-082408-2(5)); lib. bdg. 17.89 (978-0-06-082409-9(3)) HarperCollins Pubs. (HarperTeen).

Hartman, Bob. Granny Mae's Christmas Play. Cravath, Lynne W., illus. 2004. 40p. (gr. k-5). 16.99 (978-0-8066-4063-1(4) , Augsburg Bks.) Augsburg Fortress, Pubs.

Hartnett, Sonya. Stripes of the Sidestep Wolf. 2005. 208p. (J). (gr. 7 up). 16.99 (978-0-7636-2644-0(9)) Candlewick Pr.

—Surrender. 2006. 256p. (YA). (gr. 9). 16.99 (978-0-7636-2768-3(2)) Candlewick Pr.

—Thursday's Child. 272p. (YA). (gr. 9). 2003. (Illus.). pap. 7.99 (978-0-7636-2203-9(6)); 2002. 15.99 (978-0-7636-1620-5(6)) Candlewick Pr.

—Thursday's Child. 2000. 240p. pap. (978-0-14-029732-4(4)) Penguin Group (USA) Inc.

—Thursday's Child. 2002. (gr. 7-12). lib. bdg. 16.45 (978-0-613-69466-7(X)) Tandem Library Bks.

Harvey, Sarah N. Bull's Eye. 2007. (Orca Soundings Ser.). 112p. (YA). (gr. 7 up). (*978-1-55143-679-1(5)); lib. bdg. (*978-1-55143-681-4(7)) Orca Bk. Pubs.

Haskins, James. The March on Washington. 2004. (Illus.). 192p. (J). (gr. 5 up). pap. 10.95 (978-0-940975-93-4(9) , Sankofa Bks.) Just Us Bks., Inc.

Hassler, Kurt. Hannah & the Homunculus. Darnell, K. L., illus. 2001. 32p. (J). 15.95 (978-1-58536-043-7(0)) Sleeping Bear Pr.

Hatton, Caroline K. Vero & Philippe. McDaniels, Preston, illus. 2001. 144p. (J). (gr. 3-7). 14.95 (978-0-8126-2940-8(X)) Cricket Bks.

Haufsk, Violet. The Gathering Spot: A Story for Children about Death. 2001. 24p. (J). 14.99 (978-0-933675-96-4(8)) Scratch & Scribble Pr., Inc.

Hausman, Gerald & Hinds, Uton. The Jacob Ladder. 2001. (Illus.). 128p. (J). (gr. 5-8). pap. 15.95 (978-0-531-30331-3(4) , Orchard Bks.) Scholastic, Inc.

Hautzig, Deborah. Little Witch Learns to Read. Wickstrom, Sylvie K., illus. 2003. (Step into Reading Ser.). 48p. (J). (gr. 1-3). pap. 3.99 (978-0-375-82179-0(1) , Random Hse. Bks. for Young Readers) Random Hse. Children's Bks.

—Little Witch Learns to Read. 2003. (gr. k-3). lib. bdg. 11.80 (978-0-613-89789-1(7)) Tandem Library Bks.

Hautzig, Esther. A Picture of Grandmother. Peck, Beth, illus. 2002. 80p. (J). (gr. 2-5). 15.00 (978-0-374-35920-1(2) , Farrar, Straus & Giroux (BYR)) Farrar, Straus & Giroux.

Hayes, Joe. Little Gold Star (Estrellita de Oro) A Cinderella Cuento. 2002. (SPA & ENG.). 32p. (J). pap. 7.95 (978-0-938317-68-5(7)) Cinco Puntos Pr.

—Little Gold Star (Estrellita de Oro) A Cinderella Cuento. Perez, Gloria Osuna & Perez, Lucia Angela, illus. 2000. (SPA & ENG.). 32p. (ps-3). 15.95 (978-0-938317-49-4(0) , CPP7490) Cinco Puntos Pr.

—A Spoon for Every Bite/Una Cuchara para Cada Bocado. Leer, Rebecca, illus. 2005. (SPA & ENG.). 32p. (gr. 1-4). reprint ed. pap. 8.95 (978-0-938317-93-7(8)) Cinco Puntos Pr.

Haywood, Carolyn. Here's a Penny. 2005. (Illus.). 160p. (J). 16.00 (978-0-15-205227-0(5) , Harcourt Young Classics); pap. 5.95 (978-0-15-205225-6(9) , Odyssey Classics) Harcourt Children's Bks.

Hazell, Mark. Miners of the Rainbow Stone (the Forest Children Series) 2006. 308p. pap. (*978-1-84401-625-9(0)) Athena Pr.

Headley, Justina Chen. Girl Overboard. 2008. 352p. (J). (gr. 7-17). 16.99 (*978-0-316-01130-3(4)) Little Brown & Co.

Heàrtling, Peter. Algo Pasa en la Liberia. Blanco, Rosa Pilar, tr. 2001. (SPA., Illus.). 160p. (J). 15.95 (978-84-204-4425-3(1)) Alfaguara, Ediciones, S.A.- Grupo Santillana ESP. Dist: Santillana USA Publishing Co., Inc.

Hébert, Marie-Francine & Perkes, Carolyn. Daddy, Can I Have the Moon? Pratt, Mylene, illus. 2001. 32p. (J). (ps up). pap. (978-1-894363-79-2(5)) Dominique & Friends.

Hedlund, Daniel Levine. The Trouble with Tomatoes. 2003. 108p. 19.95 (978-0-595-74776-4(0)); pap. 9.95 (978-0-595-28313-2(6)) iUniverse, Inc.

Heibel, Dorothy. Message for a Spy. 2004. (Illus.). 94p. (J). pap. (978-1-932663-07-5(X)) History Compass, LLC.

Heide, Florence Parry & Pierce, Roxanne H. Tio Armando. Grifalconi, Ann, illus. 1998. 32p. (YA). (gr. 5 up). 15.00 (978-0-688-12107-5(1)) HarperCollins Pubs.

Heitzmann, Kristen. Chestnut Ridge Acres. 2001. 220p. (J). 25.95 (978-0-7862-3415-8(6) , Five Star) Thomson Gale.

Helmso, Candy Grant. Freedom Quilt. Friar, Joanne, illus. 2003. (Books for Young Learners). 16p. (J). pap. 5.00 net. (978-1-57274-529-2(0) , 2744) Owen, Richard C. Pubs., Inc.

Hemphill, Helen. Runaround. 2007. 117p. (YA). (gr. 8 up). 16.95 (978-1-932425-83-3(7) , Front Street) Boyds Mills Pr.

Henderson, Aileen Kilgore. Hard Times for Jake Smith. 2004. (Historical Fiction for Young Readers Ser.). 232p. pap. 6.95 (978-1-57131-649-3(3)) Milkweed Editions.

Hendry, Diana. Que Ocupado Estoy! Chapman, Jane, illus. 2002. Tr. of Very Busy Day. (SPA.). 124p. (J). 14.95 (978-84-488-1154-9(2)) Lectorum Pubns., Inc.

Heneghan, James. Payback. 2007. 144p. (YA). (gr. 7 up). 17.95 (*978-0-88899-701-2(9)) Groundwood Bks. CAN. Dist: Perseus Distribution.

Henkes, Kevin. The Birthday Room. Henkes, Kevin, illus. 1999. (Illus.). 160p. (J). (gr. 3 up). 19.99 (978-0-688-16733-2(0)) HarperCollins Pubs.

—The Birthday Room. unabr. ed. 2004. 160p. (J). (gr. 3-7). pap. 29.00 incl. audio (978-0-8072-0444-3(7) , Listening Library) Random Hse. Audio Publishing Group.

—The Birthday Room. 2001. (gr. 5-8). lib. bdg. 14.15 (978-0-613-44190-2(7)); (Illus.). (J). 12.64 (978-0-606-21070-6(9)) Tandem Library Bks.

—Chester's Way. 2005. (Illus.). (J). pap. 16.95 incl. audio (978-1-59112-967-7(2)); pap. 18.95 incl. audio compact disk (978-1-59112-971-4(0)) Live Oak Media.

—Olive's Ocean. 2005. (HarperClassics Ser.). 224p. (J). (gr. k-9). reprint ed. pap. 6.99 (978-0-06-053545-2(8) , Harper Trophy) HarperCollins Pubs.

—The Zebra Wall. 2005. 147p. (J). (gr. 3-7). per. 13.04 (978-0-606-33331-3(2)) Tandem Library Bks.

Hennessy, B. G. Once upon a Time Map Book. Joyce, Peter, illus. 2004. 16p. (J). (gr. 1-5). 11.99 (978-0-7636-2521-4(3)) Candlewick Pr.

Hennessy, Claire. Afterwards. 2005. 188p. (YA). pap. (*978-1-84223-207-1(X)) Poolbeg Pr.

Hermes, Patricia. Emma Dilemma & the New Nanny. 2006. (Illus.). 112p. (J). 15.95 (978-0-7614-5286-7(9)) Cavendish, Marshall Corp.

—Emma Dilemma & the Two Nannies. 2007. (J). 112p. (gr. 2-4). 15.99 (*978-0-7614-5353-6(9)); 117p. (*978-1-4287-3961-1(0)) Cavendish, Marshall Corp.

—Everything Stinks. MacDonald, Patricia, ed. 1999. (Cousins' Club Ser.). 176p. (J). 14.00 (978-0-671-89653-9(9) , Simon & Schuster Children's Publishing) Simon & Schuster Children's Publishing.

—Fly Away Home. 2005. (Illus.). 160p. pap. 7.95 (978-1-55704-308-5(6)) Newmarket Pr.

—A Perfect Place Bk. 2: Joshua's Oregon Trail Diary. 2002. (My America Ser.: Bk. 2). 112p. (J). (gr. 2-5). pap. 10.95 (978-0-439-19999-5(9) , Scholastic Pr.) Scholastic, Inc.

—A Perfect Place Bk. 2: Joshua's Oregon Trail Diary. 2002. (gr. 3-6). lib. bdg. 13.00 (978-0-613-57261-3(0)) Tandem Library Bks.

Hernandez, David. Suckerpunch. 2008. 224p. (J). 16.99 (*978-0-06-117330-1(4)); lib. bdg. 17.89 (*978-0-06-117331-8(2)) HarperCollins Pubs. (HarperTeen).

Herrick, Steven. A Place Like This. 1998. 137p. (J). pap. 16.95 (978-0-7022-2984-8(9)) Univ. of Queensland Pr. AUS. Dist: International Specialized Bk. Services.

—The Wolf. 2007. 214p. (YA). (gr. 7 up). 17.95 (978-1-932425-75-8(6) , Front Street) Boyds Mills Pr.

Hershberger, Noah. Salamonie Farm. Koehler, Chris, illus. 1998. 240p. pap. 12.95 (978-1-879863-53-8(7)) Goosefoot Acres Pr.

Hesse, Karen. Just Juice. Parker, Robert Andrew, illus. 1999. 144p. (J). (gr. 3-5). pap. 4.99 (978-0-590-03383-1(2) , Scholastic Paperbacks) Scholastic, Inc.

—Just Juice. 1999. (gr. 3-6). lib. bdg. 13.00 (978-0-613-23005-6(1)) Tandem Library Bks.

Hesser, Terry Spencer. Kissing Doorknobs. 1999. (J). (978-0-606-17347-6(1)) Tandem Library Bks.

Hest, Amy. The Great Green Notebook of Katie Roberts: Who Just Turned 12 on Monday. Lamut, Sonja, illus. 1998. 112p. (J). (gr. 3-7). 16.99 (978-0-7636-0464-6(X)) Candlewick Pr.

Heuston, Kimberley B. Dante's Daughter. 2004. 304p. (YA). 16.95 (978-1-886910-97-3(9) , Lemniscaat) Boyds Mills Pr.

Heuston, Kimberley Burton. Book of Jude. 2008. (J). (*978-1-932425-26-0(8) , Front Street) Boyds Mills Pr.

Hickey, Caroline. Cassie Was Here. 2007. 192p. (J). (gr. 4-7). 16.95 (*978-1-59643-205-5(5)) Roaring Brook Pr.

Hicks, Barbara Jean. Jitterbug Jam: A Monster Tale. Deacon, Alexis, illus. 2005. 40p. (J). 16.00 (978-0-374-33685-1(7) , Farrar, Straus & Giroux) Farrar, Straus & Giroux.

Hicks, Betty. Get Real. 2006. 192p. (J). 16.95 (978-1-59643-089-1(3)) Roaring Brook Pr.

Hidier, Tanuja Desai. Born Confused. 2003. 512p. mass mkt. 7.99 (978-0-439-51011-0(2) , PUSH) Scholastic, Inc.

Highway, Tomson. Dragonfly Kites: Kiweeginapiseek. ed. 2004. (Illus.). (J). (gr. k-3). spiral bd. (978-0-616-14619-4(1)) Canadian National Institute for the Blind/ Institut National Canadien pour les Aveugles.

Hilbtecht, Kirk. My Mommy Is a Guardsman. 2005. 30p. pap. 6.95 (978-1-889658-33-9(2)) New Canaan Publishing Co. LLC.

Hill, Becky. The Duck That Stayed Behind. 2007. (J). per. 8.99 (***978-1-60247-417-8(6)***) Tate Publishing & Enterprises, L.L.C.

Hill, Eric. Spot Loves His Mommy. Hill, Eric, illus. 2006. 12p. (J). (ps-k). bds. 5.99 (978-0-399-24511-4(1) , Putnam Juvenile) Penguin Group (USA) Inc.

Hill, Janet Muirhead. Danny's Dragon: A Story of Wartime Loss. Lehmkuhl, Pat & Ore, Peter, illus. 2006. 192p. (J). per. 10.00 (978-0-9772525-0-3(7)) Raven Publishing Inc. of Montana.

—Miranda & Starlight: (the Starlight Books, 1), 6 vols. Lehmkuhl, Pat, illus. 2nd rev. ed. 2003. (Starlight Bks.: 1). 168p. (J). (gr. 3-7). per. 9.00 (978-0-9714161-4-7(1)) Raven Publishing Inc. of Montana.

Hill, Kirkpatrick. Do Not Pass Go. 2007. 240p. (J). 15.99 (978-1-4169-1400-6(5) , McElderry, Margaret K.) Simon & Schuster Children's Publishing.

Hill, Stuart. Blade of Fire. 2007. (Icemark Chronicles Ser.: Bk. 2). 584p. (J). (gr. 7 up). pap. 18.99 (978-0-439-84122-1(4) , Chicken Hse., The) Scholastic, Inc.

Hinton, S. E. The Outsiders. 2002. (YA). 14.04 (978-0-7587-7753-9(1)) Book Wholesalers, Inc.

—The Outsiders. l.t. ed. 2002. (LRS Large Print Cornerstone Ser.). (J). lib. bdg. 32.95 (978-1-58118-089-3(6) , 24874) LRS.

—The Outsiders. 2006. (Penguin Classics Ser.). 160p. (J). (gr. 12). pap. 13.00 (978-0-14-303985-3(7) , Penguin Classics); 208p. (YA). pap. 10.00 (978-0-14-240733-2(X) , Puffin) Penguin Group (USA) Inc.

—The Outsiders. 156p. (YA). (gr. 7 up). pap. 5.99 (978-0-8072-1430-5(2) , Listening Library) Random Hse. Audio Publishing Group.

—The Outsiders. 1999. (J). pap. 19.00 (978-0-88103-039-6(2)) Tandem Library Bks.

—The Outsiders. l.t. ed. 2005. 264p. pap. 10.95 (978-0-7862-7362-1(3) , Large Print Pr.) Thorndike Pr.

Hobbs, Valerie. Carolina Crow Girl. 2000. (Illus.). 144p. (J). (gr. 5-9). pap. 5.99 (978-0-14-130976-7(8) , Puffin) Penguin Group (USA) Inc.

—Carolina Crow Girl. 2000. (J). (ps-7). 137p. per. 14.15 (978-0-613-29902-2(7)); 12.64 (978-0-606-19066-4(X)) Tandem Library Bks.

Hobbs, Will. Changes in Latitudes. 2004. 176p. (YA). pap. 9.95 (978-0-689-87069-9(8) , Simon Pulse) Simon & Schuster Children's Publishing.

—Leaving Protection. 2004. 192p. (J). (gr. 5 up). 15.99 (978-0-688-17475-0(2)) HarperCollins Pubs.

Hobbs, William. Leaving Protection. 2004. 192p. (J). (gr. 5 up). lib. bdg. 16.89 (978-0-06-051632-1(1)) HarperCollins Pubs.

Hodge, Merle. For the Life of Laetitia. 2003. 21.25 (978-0-8446-7246-5(7)) Smith, Peter Pub., Inc.

Hodges, Lynn & Buchanan, Sue. I Love You This Much. Bendall-Brunello, John, illus. 2006. (Song of God's Love Ser.). 16p. (J). 6.99 (978-0-310-70961-9(X)) Zonderkidz.

Hodges, Lynn, et al. I Love You This Much. Bendall-Brunello, John, illus. 2001. (Song of God's Love Ser.). 36p. (J). 14.99 incl. audio compact disk (978-0-310-23268-1(6)) Zonderkidz.

Hofer, Ernst & Hofer, Nelly, illus. The Wild Swans. 2003. 40p. (J). (gr. 3-5). 17.95 (978-0-88776-615-2(3)) Tundra Bks., Inc./Livres Toundra, Inc. CAN. *Dist:* Random Hse., Inc.

Hoffman, Mary. Boundless Grace. Binch, Caroline, illus. 2002. (J). 25.45 (978-0-7587-2139-6(0)) Book Wholesalers, Inc.

—Boundless Grace. Binch, Caroline, illus. 2000. 32p. (J). (ps-3). pap. 6.99 (978-0-14-055667-4(2) , Puffin) Penguin Group (USA) Inc.

—Boundless Grace. Binch, Caroline, illus. 2000. (J). (ps-ps). 26p. 12.79 (978-0-606-20350-0(8)); lib. bdg. 14.15 (978-0-613-33678-9(X)) Tandem Library Bks.

—Boundless Grace. 2000. (J). (978-0-606-20224-4(2)) Tandem Library Bks.

Hogan, Mary. Perfect Girl. 2008. 208p. (J). 7.99 (***978-0-06-084110-2(9)*** , HarperTeen) HarperCollins Pubs.

Hogan, Mary. The Serious Kiss. 2005. 256p. (J). pap. 7.99 (978-0-06-072208-1(8) , Harper Trophy); (YA). (gr. 7 up). 16.99 (978-0-06-072206-7(1)) HarperCollins Pubs.

Holder, Nancy. The Rose Bride: A Retelling of the White Bride & the Black Bride. 2007. (Once upon a Time Ser.). 256p. (YA). pap. 5.99 (***978-1-4169-3535-3(5)*** , Simon Pulse) Simon & Schuster Children's Publishing.

Holeman, Linda. Mercy's Birds. 1998. (gr. 5-8). lib. bdg. 15.25 (978-0-613-77269-3(5)) Tandem Library Bks.

—Mercy's Birds. 1998. 208p. (J). (gr. 6-9). pap. 6.95 (978-0-88776-463-9(0)) Tundra Bks., Inc./Livres Toundra, Inc. CAN. *Dist:* Random Hse., Inc.

—Raspberry House Blues. 2000. 238p. (J). (gr. 4-7). per. 15.25 (978-0-613-53300-3(3)) Tandem Library Bks.

—Raspberry House Blues. 2000. 248p. (J). (gr. 6-9). pap. 6.95 (978-0-88776-493-6(2)) Tundra Bks., Inc./Livres Toundra, Inc. CAN. *Dist:* Random Hse., Inc.

Holland, Maryjo. Susannah & Henry: Making the Best of T. 2005. 73p. pap. 14.95 (978-1-4137-6485-7(1)) PublishAmerica, Inc.

Holm, Jennifer L. Penny from Heaven. (Illus.). (J). 2007. 272p. (gr. 5-7). 6.99 (978-0-375-83689-3(6) , Yearling); 2006. 288p. (gr. 3-7). 15.95 (978-0-375-83687-9(X) , Random Hse. Bks. for Young Readers); 2006. 288p. (gr. 3-7). lib. bdg. 17.99 (978-0-375-93687-6(4) , Random Hse. Bks. for Young Readers) Random Hse. Children's Bks.

Holman, T. A. Stop It, Tyrone! (Illus.). 42p. (J). (gr. k-4). pap. 7.50 (978-0-9660617-1-0(3)) PLEO.

Holmes, Elizabeth. Pretty Is. 2007. 224p. (J). (gr. 4-6). 16.99 (978-0-525-47813-3(2) , Dutton Juvenile) Penguin Group (USA) Inc.

Holt, Kimberly Willis. Dancing in Cadillac Light. 2002. 176p. (J). (gr. 5 up). pap. 5.99 (978-0-698-11970-3(3) , Putnam Juvenile) Penguin Group (USA) Inc.

—Dancing in Cadillac Light. 2004. 176p. (J). (gr. 4-7). pap. 36.00 incl. audio (978-0-8072-2095-5(7) , Listening Library) Random Hse. Audio Publishing Group.

—Dancing in Cadillac Light. 2002. (gr. 5-8). lib. bdg. 14.15 (978-0-613-66873-6(1)) Tandem Library Bks.

—Keeper of the Night. 2005. 309p. (YA). (gr. 7-12). lib. bdg. 13.55 (978-0-606-33249-1(9)) Tandem Library Bks.

—Mister & Me. 2000. (gr. 3-6). lib. bdg. 13.00 (978-0-613-33713-7(1)) Tandem Library Bks.

—Part of Me: Stories of a Louisiana Family. 2006. 224p. (J). 16.95 (978-0-8050-6360-8(9) , Holt, Henry & Co. Bks. For Young Readers) Holt, Henry & Co.

—Piper Reed, Navy Brat. Davenier, Christine, illus. 2007. 160p. (J). (gr. 3-6). 14.95 (***978-0-8050-8197-8(6)*** , Holt, Henry & Co. Bks. For Young Readers) Holt, Henry & Co.

—Piper Reed, Navy Brat. Davenier, Christine, illus. 2008. 176p. (J). pap. 6.99 (***978-0-312-38020-5(8)***) Square Fish.

—Waiting for Gregory. Swiatkowska, Gabriela, illus. 2006. (J). (***978-1-4156-7424-6(8)***) Holt, Henry & Co.

—Waiting for Gregory. Swiatkowska, Gabi, illus. rev. ed. 2006. 32p. (J). 16.95 (978-0-8050-7388-1(4) , Holt, Henry & Co. Bks. For Young Readers) Holt, Henry & Co.

Holt, Rinehart and Winston Staff. And Now Miguel. 3rd ed. 2003. (Illus.). 16.80 (978-0-03-035916-3(3)) Holt, Rinehart & Winston.

—M. C. Higgins the Great: With Connections. 1998. (J). pap., stu. ed. 13.20 (978-0-03-054353-1(3)) Holt, Rinehart & Winston.

—Wish You Well. 3rd ed. 2002. pap., stu. ed. 13.20 (978-0-03-068009-0(3)) Holt, Rinehart & Winston.

—Wish You Well: With Connections. 3rd ed. 2002. 14.64 (978-0-03-068008-3(5)) Holt, Rinehart & Winston.

Holub, Joan. Company's Coming. Andriani, Renee W., illus. 2002. 16p. (J). pap. 6.99 (978-0-14-230062-6(4) , Puffin) Penguin Group (USA) Inc.

Holub, Joan & Kurisu, Jane. Backwards Day. 2000. (Hello Reader! Ser.). (J). pap. (978-0-439-12964-0(8)) Scholastic, Inc.

Honeycutt, Natalie. Twilight in Grace Falls. 1999. 192p. (J). (gr. 3-7). pap. 4.50 (978-0-380-73128-2(2)) HarperCollins Pubs.

—Twilight in Grace Falls. 1999. (978-0-606-15928-9(2)) Tandem Library Bks.

Honeywood, Varnette P., illus. The Treasure Hunt. 2002. (Little Bill Ser.). (J). 11.91 (978-0-7587-1766-5(0)) Book Wholesalers, Inc.

Hoobler, Dorothy & Hoobler, Thomas. The Second Decade: Voyages. Hoffman, Robin, illus. 2000. (Century Kids Ser.). 160p. (gr. 5-8). lib. bdg. 22.90 (978-0-7613-1601-5(9) , Twenty-First Century Bks.) Lerner Publishing Group.

—The 1970's: Arguments. Hoffman, Robin, illus. 2002. (Century Kids Ser.). 160p. (gr. 5-8). lib. bdg. 22.90 (978-0-7613-1607-7(8) , Twenty-First Century Bks.) Lerner Publishing Group.

Hood, Ann. How I Saved My Father's Life (and Ruined Everything Else) 2008. 224p. (J). pap. 16.99 (***978-0-439-92819-9(2)*** , Scholastic Pr.) Scholastic, Inc.

Hooks, William H. Where's Lulu? Alley, R. W., illus. 1998. (Bank Street Reader Collection). 48p. (J). (ps-2). lib. bdg. 22.60 (978-0-8368-1768-3(0)) Stevens, Gareth Inc.

Hooray for Midsommar! 6 Small Books. (Greetings Ser.: Vol. 1). 24p. (gr. 2-3). 31.00 (978-0-7635-9410-7(5)) Rigby Education.

Hooray for Midsommar! Big Book. (Greetings Ser.: Vol. 1). 24p. (gr. 2-3). 31.00 (978-0-7635-5694-5(7)) Rigby Education.

Hopkins, Ellen. Burned. 544p. (YA). 2007. pap. 9.99 (***978-1-4169-0355-0(0)*** , Simon Pulse); 2006. (Illus.). 17.99 (978-1-4169-0354-3(2) , McElderry, Margaret K.) Simon & Schuster Children's Publishing.

Hopkins, Ellen. Glass. 2007. 688p. (YA). (gr. 9 up). 16.99 (978-1-4169-4090-6(1) , McElderry, Margaret K.) Simon & Schuster Children's Publishing.

Hopkinson, Deborah. Prairie Skies: Pioneer Summer. 2002. (gr. 3-6). lib. bdg. 11.80 (978-0-613-45093-5(0)) Tandem Library Bks.

Horne, Constance. Papa's Surprise. Hansen, Mia, illus. 2005. 60p. (J). 5.95 (978-0-9730831-1-8(5)) Hodgepog Bks. CAN. *Dist:* Coteau Bks., Fitzhenry & Whiteside, Ltd.

Horning, Katherine. World of Shadows. 2005. 128p. pap. 17.95 (978-1-4137-6500-7(9)) PublishAmerica, Inc.

Horvath, Polly. Everything on a Waffle. 2008. 176p. (J). pap. 6.99 (***978-0-312-38004-5(6)***) Square Fish.

—The Happy Yellow Car. 2004. (Illus.). 128p. (J). pap. 5.95 (978-0-374-42879-2(4) , Sunburst) Farrar, Straus & Giroux.

—The Trolls. 1999. 144p. (J). (gr. 3-7). 16.00 (978-0-374-37787-8(1) , Farrar, Straus & Giroux (BYR)) Farrar, Straus & Giroux.

—Trolls. 2001. (gr. 3-6). lib. bdg. 12.95 (978-0-613-82505-4(5)) Tandem Library Bks.

—The Trolls. 2001. (Sunburst Bks.). (Illus.). 144p. (J). (gr. 3-7). reprint ed. pap. 5.95 (978-0-374-47991-6(7) , Sunburst) Farrar, Straus & Giroux.

—The Vacation. 2005. 208p. (J). 16.00 (978-0-374-38070-0(8) , Farrar, Straus & Giroux (BYR)) Farrar, Straus & Giroux.

Howard, Elizabeth Fitzgerald. Flower Girl Butterflies. Kromer, Christiane, illus. 2004. 32p. (J). 16.89 (978-0-688-17810-9(3)); 15.99 (978-0-688-17809-3(X)) HarperCollins Pubs.

Howard, Ellen. The Log Cabin Wedding. Himler, Ronald, illus. 2006. 64p. (J). 15.95 (978-0-8234-1989-0(4)) Holiday Hse., Inc.

Howe, James. La Mirona. 1999. Tr. of Watcher. (J). (978-0-606-20217-6(X)) Tandem Library Bks.

—Totally Joe. 2005. (Illus.). 208p. (J). (gr. 5-9). 16.99 (978-0-689-83957-3(X) , Atheneum) Simon & Schuster Children's Publishing.

—Totally Joe. 2007. 208p. (J). (gr. 4-8). pap. 5.99 (***978-0-689-83958-0(8)***) Kaplan Bks.

Howe, James. The Watcher. 1999. 192p. (YA). (gr. 7-12). pap. 8.99 (978-0-689-82662-7(1) , 076714008007, Simon Pulse) Simon & Schuster Children's Publishing.

—The Watcher. 1999. (978-0-606-16319-4(0)) Tandem Library Bks.

Howe, James & Howe, James. There's a Dragon in My Sleeping Bag. Rose, David S., illus. 1998. 40p. (J). (ps-2). 6.99 (978-0-689-81922-3(6) , Aladdin) Simon & Schuster Children's Publishing.

Hubbell, Patricia. Bouncing Time. Sweet, Melissa, illus. 2000. 32p. (YA). (ps up). 15.95 (978-0-688-17376-0(4)) HarperCollins Pubs.

Hughes, Dean. As Wide As the River. 2005. 156p. (J). pap. (978-1-59038-450-3(4)) Deseret Bk. Co.

—Facing the Enemy. 2005. (Illus.). 153p. (J). pap. (978-1-59038-449-7(0)) Deseret Bk. Co.

—Under the Same Stars. 2005. viii, 152p. (J). pap. (978-1-59038-448-0(2)) Deseret Bk. Co.

Hughes, Mark Peter. I Am the Wallpaper. 2007. 256p. (YA). (gr. 7-11). pap. 7.99 (978-0-440-42046-0(6)); 2005. 240p. (J). (gr. 5). 15.95 (978-0-385-73241-3(4)); 2005. 240p. (J). (gr. 5). lib. bdg. 17.99 (978-0-385-90265-6(4)) Random Hse. Children's Bks. (Delacorte Bks. for Young Readers).

Hughes, Pat. The Breaker Boys. 2004. (Illus.). 256p. (J). 18.00 (978-0-374-30956-5(6) , Farrar, Straus & Giroux (BYR)) Farrar, Straus & Giroux.

The Hundred Penny Box. 1999. (J). 9.95 (978-1-56137-386-4(9)) Novel Units, Inc.

Hunt, Irene. Up a Road Slowly. 2003. (gr. 3-6). lib. bdg. 13.00 (978-0-613-58744-0(8)) Tandem Library Bks.

Hurst, Carol Otis. You Come to Yokum. Life, Kay, illus. 2005. 144p. (YA). (gr. 4-6). 15.00 (978-0-618-55122-4(0) , Walter Lorraine) Houghton Mifflin Co. Trade & Reference Div.

Hurwitz, Johanna. Ethan at Home. Floca, Brian, illus. 2003. (Brand New Readers Ser.). 32p. (J). (ps-2). pap. 5.99 (978-0-7636-1092-0(5)) Candlewick Pr.

—Summer with Elisa. Maione, Heather Harms & Tilley, Debbie, illus. 2000. 96p. (J). (ps-2). 16.99 (978-0-688-17095-0(1)) HarperCollins Pubs.

—Superduper Teddy. 2001. (Illus.). (J). (978-0-606-22039-2(9)) Tandem Library Bks.

—The Unsigned Valentine: And Other Events in the Life of Emma Meade. Azarian, Mary, illus. 2006. 176p. (J). 15.99 (978-0-06-056053-9(3)); lib. bdg. 16.89 (978-0-06-056054-6(1)) HarperCollins Pubs.

Hyppolite, Joanne. Seth & Samona. Bootman, Colin, illus. 2001. 128p. (gr. 3-7). pap. 12.00 (978-0-375-89508-1(6) , Yearling) Random Hse. Children's Bks.

—Seth & Samona. 2001. lib. bdg. 21.10 (978-0-613-82989-2(1)) Tandem Library Bks.

I Know Why the Caged Bird Sings. 1998. 44p. (YA). 11.95 (978-1-56137-634-6(5) , NU6345SP) Novel Units, Inc.

I Love You Like Crazy Cakes. 2004. (J). 24.95 incl. audio (978-1-55592-095-1(0)); 29.95 incl. cd-rom (978-1-55592-135-4(3)) Weston Woods Studios, Inc.

Ihimaera, Witi. The Whale Rider. 2003. Orig. Title: Te Kaieke Tohora. (YA). (gr. 3-6). 152p. 17.00 (978-0-15-205017-7(5)); 168p. pap. 8.00 (978-0-15-205016-0(7) , Harcourt Paperbacks) Harcourt Children's Bks.

—Whale Rider. 2003. (gr. 5-8). lib. bdg. 16.45 (978-0-613-70660-5(9)) Tandem Library Bks.

I'll Run Away: Individual Title Six-Packs. (ps-2). 23.00 (978-0-7635-8793-2(1)) Rigby Education.

Inches, Alison. I Love You Coupons for Dad. 2004. (Illus.). 24p. (J). (ps-4). pap. 3.99 (978-0-8431-0661-9(1) , Price Stern Sloan) Penguin Group (USA) Inc.

Ingle, Sheila C. Courageous Kate: A Daughter of the American Revolution. 2006. (J). (***978-1-891885-52-5(9)***) Hub City Writers Project.

Ingold, Jeanette. Airfield. 2001. (J). 12.64 (978-0-606-21017-1(2)) Tandem Library Bks.

—Mountain Solo. 320p. (YA). 2005. (gr. 7-17). pap. 6.95 (978-0-15-205358-1(1) , Harcourt Paperbacks); 2003. 17.00 (978-0-15-202670-7(3)) Harcourt Children's Bks.

—The Window. 2003. 208p. (YA). pap. 6.95 (978-0-15-204926-3(6)) Harcourt Trade Pubs.

Ioannides, Mara W. Cohen. A Shout in the Sunshine. 2007. 120p. (J). pap. 12.95 (***978-0-8276-0838-2(1)***) Jewish Pubn. Society.

Irgens, Barbara E. Finding the Way. 2001. 187p. (YA). pap. 14.95 (978-1-930580-06-0(1) , Luminary Media Group) Pine Orchard, Inc.

—Finding the Way. 2001. (gr. 7-12). lib. bdg. 24.55 (978-0-613-80418-9(X)) Tandem Library Bks.

It's Time for Dinner. 2002. 12p. (J). bds. 7.95 (978-1-84250-495-6(9) , Bright Sparks) Parragon, Inc.

Iwamura. Une Nouvelle Maison de Famille. 2000. (FRE.). (J). pap. 14.95 (978-2-211-01700-8(2)) Archimede Editions FRA. *Dist:* Distribooks, Inc.

Jablonski, Carla. Thicker Than Water. 2007. 272p. (YA). (gr. 9-12). pap. 8.99 (978-1-59514-123-1(5) , Razorbill) Penguin Group (USA) Inc.

Jackson, Chris. Edmund for Short: A Tale from China Plate Farm. 2000. (Illus.). 24p. (J). pap. 6.99 (978-0-00-648165-2(5)) HarperCollins Pubs.

Jackson, Jill L. Fine Feathers Don't Make a Peacock. Kirby, Bertha, illus. 2000. (Lessons for Lucile Ser.). 79p. (J). 24.95 (978-0-9700692-0-7(0)) Noble Endeaver.

—How Dan Patch Got His Name. Kirby, Bertha, illus. deluxe ed. 2001. (Lessons for Lucile Ser.). 104p. (YA). (gr. 2-7). 24.95 (978-0-9700692-2-1(7)) Noble Endeaver.

Jackson, Kamichi. You're Too Much, Reggie Brown. Goldberg, Jeff A., illus. l.t. ed. 2000. 110p. (J). (gr. 2-5). pap. 5.95 (978-0-615-11287-9(0)) Pen Poised Pr.

Janke, Katelan. Survival in the Storm: The Dust Bowl Diary of Grace Edwards. 2002. (Dear America Ser.). (Illus.). 192p. (J). (gr. 4-9). pap. 10.95 (978-0-439-21599-2(4)) Scholastic, Inc.

Janover, Caroline D. The Worst Speller in Jr. High. 2001. 208p. (YA). (gr. 4-7). pap. 13.95 (978-0-595-15328-2(3) , Backinprint.com) iUniverse, Inc.

Jefferies, Cindy. Solo Star #7. 2008. (Fame School Ser.). 128p. (J). (gr. 1-3). pap. 5.99 (***978-0-14-241103-2(5)*** , Puffin) Penguin Group (USA) Inc.

Jenkins, A. M. Breaking Boxes. 2000. (978-0-606-17834-1(1)) Tandem Library Bks.

Jenkins, Emily & Bogacki, Tomek. Five Creatures. 2005. (Illus.). 32p. (J). (ps-ps). reprint ed. pap. 5.95 (978-0-374-42328-5(8) , Sunburst) Farrar, Straus & Giroux.

Jenkins, Jerry B. & Fabry, Chris. Double Fault. 2005. (Tyndale Kids Ser.). 272p. (J). pap. 5.99 (978-1-4143-0146-4(4)) Tyndale Hse. Pubs.

—Phantom Writer. 2005. (Red Rock Mysteries Ser.). 256p. (J). pap. 5.99 (978-1-4143-0145-7(6)) Tyndale Hse. Pubs.

Jensen, Patricia. My House. 2004. (My First Reader Ser.). 29p. (J). (gr. k-1). pap. 3.95 (978-0-516-24636-9(4) , Children's Pr.) Scholastic Library Publishing.

Jimenez, Francisco. Senderos Fronterizos. 2002. (SPA.). (gr. 7-12). lib. bdg. 15.25 (978-0-613-60784-1(8)) Tandem Library Bks.

Jocelyn, Marthe. Would You? 2008. (YA). (***978-0-375-83703-6(5));*** lib. bdg. (***978-0-375-93703-3(X)***) Dell Publishing. (Delacorte Pr.).

Johnson, Allen. My Brothers Story. 2006. 192p. pap. 7.95 (978-0-944353-17-2(7)) Rivendell Bk. Factory.

Johnson, Angela. Daddy Calls Me Man. Mitchell, Rhonda, illus. 2000. (Richard Jackson Bks.). 32p. (J). (ps-k). pap. 6.95 (978-0-531-07175-5(8) , Orchard Bks.) Scholastic, Inc.

—Daddy Calls Me Man. 2000. (J). 13.75 (978-0-606-19856-1(3)); lib. bdg. 15.25 (978-0-613-44555-9(4)) Tandem Library Bks.

—Songs of Faith. 1998. (Illus.). 112p. (J). (gr. 3-7). 16.99 (978-0-531-33023-4(0)); pap. 15.95 (978-0-531-30023-7(4)) Scholastic, Inc. (Orchard Bks.).

—Songs of Faith. 1999. (978-0-606-17374-2(9)) Tandem Library Bks.

—Toning the Sweep. 2002. (J). 13.19 (978-0-7587-0401-6(1)) Book Wholesalers, Inc.

—Toning the Sweep. 2003. 112p. (J). (gr. 7 up). pap. 5.99 (978-0-590-48142-7(8) , Scholastic Paperbacks) Scholastic, Inc.

—The Wedding. Soman, David, illus. 1999. 32p. (J). (ps-2). 17.99 (978-0-531-33139-2(3)); pap. 16.95 (978-0-531-30139-5(7)) Scholastic, Inc. (Orchard Bks.).

Johnson, Gillian. Gracie's Baby Chub Chop. 2004. 32p. (J). (ps-k). 14.95 (978-0-88776-693-0(5)) Tundra Bks., Inc./Livres Toundra, Inc. CAN. *Dist:* Random Hse., Inc.

Johnson, Kathleen Jeffrie. Dumb Love. 2005. 176p. (YA). (gr. 7-17). 16.95 (978-1-59643-062-4(1)) Roaring Brook Pr.

Johnson, Kathleen Jeffrie. A Fast & Brutal Wing. 2007. 208p. (YA). pap. 6.99 (***978-0-312-37148-7(9)***) Square Fish.

Johnson, Maureen. The Bermudez Triangle. 384p. (YA). (gr. 9-12). 2007. 7.99 (978-1-59514-155-2(3)); 2005. reprint ed. pap. 7.99 (978-1-59514-033-3(6)) Penguin Group (USA) Inc. (Razorbill).

Johnston, Annie Fell. The Story of Dago (Illustrated Edition) 2006. (Illus.). pap. (***978-1-4065-1127-7(7)***) Dodo Pr.

Johnston, Fellows An. The Story of the Red Cross As Told to Th. 2006. pap. 33.99 (***978-1-4280-4120-2(6)***) Indy-Publish.com.

Johnston, Norma. Feather in the Wind. 2001. (Illus.). 172p. (J). (gr. 5-9). 14.95 (978-0-7614-5063-4(7) , Cavendish Children's Bks.) Cavendish, Marshall Corp.

Johnston, Tony. Any Small Goodness: A Novel of the Barrio. Colon, Raul, illus. 2001. 128p. (J). (gr. 4 up). 16.95 (978-0-439-18936-1(5) , Blue Sky Pr., The) Scholastic, Inc.

—That Summer. Moser, Barry, illus. 2007. 32p. (J). (gr. 1-4). pap. 6.00 (978-0-15-205856-2(7) , Voyager Bks./Libros Viajeros) Harcourt Children's Bks.

Jolin, Paula. In the Name of God. 2007. 208p. (YA). (gr. 9 up). 16.95 (978-1-59643-211-6(X)) Roaring Brook Pr.

Jones, Elizabeth Orton. Twig. Jones, Elizabeth Orton, illus. anniv. ed. 2002. (Illus.). 152p. (J). (gr. 1-6). 18.95 (978-1-930900-05-9(8)) Purple Hse. Pr.

Jones, Jasmine, adapted by. Family Affair. rev. ed. 2005. (That's So Raven Ser.). (Illus.). 144p. (J). (gr. 3-7). pap. 4.99 (978-0-7868-4660-3(7)) Disney Pr.

Jones, Kimberly K. Sand Dollar Summer. 2006. 224p. (J). 15.95 (978-1-4169-0362-8(3) , McElderry, Margaret K.) Simon & Schuster Children's Publishing.

Jones, Molly. The Choosing Tree. 2006. 126p. pap. 17.95 (***978-1-4241-5076-2(0)***) PublishAmerica, Inc.

Jones, Patrick. Chasing Tail Lights. 2007. 304p. (YA). (gr. 9 up). 16.95 (***978-0-8027-9628-8(1)***) Walker & Co.

—Cheated. 2008. 208p. (YA). 16.95 ***(978-0-8027-9699-8(0))*** Walker & Co.

Jones, Traci L. Standing Against the Wind. 2006. 192p. (J). 16.00 (978-0-374-37174-6(1)) Farrar, Straus & Giroux.

Jonsberg, Barry. The Crimes & Punishments of Miss Payne. 2006. 288p. (YA). (gr. 7). pap. 8.95 (978-0-375-84022-7(2) , Knopf Bks. for Young Readers) Random Hse. Children's Bks.

Joosse, Barbara M. Nugget & Darling. 2001. (Illus.). (J). (978-0-606-21360-8(0)) Tandem Library Bks.

—Snow Day! Plecas, Jennifer, illus. 1999. 32p. (J). (gr. k-3). pap. 5.95 (978-0-395-96890-1(9) , Clarion Bks.) Houghton Mifflin Co. Trade & Reference Div.

Jordan, Apple. Big Enough for a Bed. Barrett, John E., photos by. 2002. (Illus.). 12p. (J). (gr. k-ps). bds. 4.99 (978-0-375-82270-4(4) , Random Hse. Bks. for Young Readers) Random Hse. Children's Bks.

Jordan, Rosa. The Goatnappers. 2007. 224p. (J). (gr. 5-7). 14.95 ***(978-1-56145-400-6(1)*** , Peachtree Junior) Peachtree Pubs., Ltd.

Jordan, Rosa. Lost Goat Lane. 2004. 192p. (J). 14.95 (978-1-56145-325-2(0)) Peachtree Pubs., Ltd.

Joseph, Lynn. El Color de Mis Palabras. 2004. (SPA., Illus.). (YA). pap. 5.99 (978-1-930332-75-1(0)) Lectorum Pubns., Inc.

—The Color of My Words. 2002. 144p. (J). (gr. 5 up). pap. 5.99 (978-0-06-447204-3(3) , Harper Trophy) HarperCollins Pubs.

—Color of My Words. 2002. (gr. 3-6). lib. bdg. 12.95 (978-0-613-44515-3(5)) Tandem Library Bks.

Joslin, Sesyle. What Do You Do, Dear? Sendak, Maurice, illus. 2001. (J). (gr. k-2). pap. 17.90 incl. audio (978-0-8045-6526-4(0) , 6526) Spoken Arts, Inc.

Jossel, Joylynn M. When the Clock Strikes Eight. l.t. ed. 2002. (Illus.). 18p. (J). (ps-6). 8.95 (978-0-9706726-2-9(4)) End Of The Rainbow Projects.

Jougla, Fréderic. Tricked on Halloween: Rina & Jax's Stories. Jougla, Karina, illus. l.t. ed. 2004. 36p. (J). bds. 14.99 (978-0-9754287-0-2(5)) Imagery Pr.

Joy Luck Club. 1999. (YA). 11.95 (978-1-56137-895-1(X)) Novel Units, Inc.

Juby, Susan. Alice, I Think. 2003. (Illus.). 304p. (J). lib. bdg. 16.89 (978-0-06-051544-7(9) , HarperTeen) HarperCollins Pubs.

—Alice MacLeod, Realist at Last. 2006. 320p. (J). pap. 8.99 (978-0-06-051552-2(X) , HarperTeen) HarperCollins Pubs.

—Another Kind of Cowboy. 2007. 352p. (J). lib. bdg. 17.89 ***(978-0-06-076518-7(6));*** (YA). lib. bdg. ***(978-0-06-076521-7(6));*** 352p. (YA). (gr. 9 up). 16.99 ***(978-0-06-076517-0(8))*** HarperCollins Pubs. (HarperTeen).

Juby, Susan. Miss Smithers. 2004. (Illus.). 336p. (J). 15.99 (978-0-06-051546-1(5)); lib. bdg. 16.89 (978-0-06-051547-8(3)) HarperCollins Pubs. (HarperTeen).

Jukes, Mavis. Cinderella 2000. 2001. (Illus.). (J). (978-0-606-20605-1(1)) Tandem Library Bks.

—Planning the Impossible. 2000. (J). (978-0-606-20022-6(3)) Tandem Library Bks.

Justus, Barbara & Starbird, Caroline. The Day Papa Came Home. Newman, Timothy, ed. Bennett, Brent, illus. 2004. 20p. (YA). (978-0-9755996-0-0(7)) Heifer Project International.

Kalar, Bonnie. Clair at Home. Spreen, Kathe, illus. Date not set. 12p. (J). (ps-2). pap. (978-1-891619-44-1(6)) Corona Pr.

—A Good Day. Spreen, Kathe, illus. Date not set. 12p. (J). (ps-2). pap. (978-1-891619-41-0(1)) Corona Pr.

Kantor, Melissa. If I Have a Wicked Stepmother, Where's My Prince? 2005. 288p. (gr. 7-17). 15.99 (978-0-7868-0960-8(4)) Hyperion Pr.

Karbo, Karen. Minerva Clark Gives up the Ghost. 2007. 244p. (J). (gr. 5 up). 16.95 ***(978-1-58234-679-3(8)*** , Bloomsbury Children) Bloomsbury Publishing.

Karim, Roberta. Faraway Grandpa. Rand, Ted, illus. rev. ed. 2004. 40p. (J). 16.95 (978-0-8050-6785-9(X) , Holt, Henry & Co. Bks. For Young Readers) Holt, Henry & Co.

—Kindle Me a Riddle: A Pioneer Story. Andersen, Bethanne, illus. 1999. 32p. (J). (gr. k-3). 16.89 (978-0-688-16204-7(5)) HarperCollins Pubs.

Katz, Karen. Best-Ever Big Brother. 2006. (Illus.). 14p. (J). (ps-k). bds. 5.99 (978-0-448-43914-3(X) , Grosset & Dunlap) Penguin Group (USA) Inc.

—Best-Ever Big Sister. 2006. (Illus.). 14p. (J). (ps-k). bds. 5.99 (978-0-448-43915-0(8) , Grosset & Dunlap) Penguin Group (USA) Inc.

—Over the Moon: An Adoption Tale. 2001. (J). (978-0-606-21373-8(2)) Tandem Library Bks.

Kay, Alan N. Crossroads at Gettysburg. 2005. (Young Heroes of History: 6). (Illus.). 166p. (J). (gr. 3-7). pap. 7.95 (978-1-57249-359-9(3) , White Mane Kids) White Mane Publishing Co., Inc.

Kaye, Bernard. A Coconut for Christmas. 2006. 52p. per. 9.95 (978-1-59886-146-4(8)) Tate Publishing & Enterprises, L.L.C.

Kaye, Marilyn. Penelope. movie tie-in ed. 2007. 240p. (YA). pap. 6.99 ***(978-0-312-37559-1(X)*** , St. Martin's Griffin) St. Martin's Pr.

Keehn, Sally M. Magpie Gabbard & the Quest for the Buried Moon. 2007. 208p. (YA). (gr. 5-8). 16.99 (978-0-399-24340-0(2) , Philomel) Penguin Group (USA) Inc.

Keep, Linda Lowery. Truth & Salsa. 2006. 176p. (J). 14.95 (978-1-56145-366-5(8) , Peachtree Junior) Peachtree Pubs., Ltd.

Kehret, Peg. Cages. 2001. (J). 11.64 (978-0-606-21097-3(0)); (gr. 3-6). lib. bdg. 13.00 (978-0-613-36051-7(6)) Tandem Library Bks.

Kellogg, Steven. Much Bigger Than Martin. Kellogg, Steven, illus. 2005. (Illus.). 25p. (J). (gr. k-4). reprint ed. 17.00 (978-0-7567-9639-6(3)) DIANE Publishing Co.

Kelly, Katy. Busy Like You Can't Believe. Rex, Adam, illus. 2006. (Lucy Rose Ser.). 176p. (J). (gr. 3-7). 12.95 (978-0-385-73319-9(4) , Delacorte Bks. for Young Readers) Random Hse. Children's Bks.

—Lucy Rose: Big on Plans. Rex, Adam, illus. 2005. 176p. (gr. 3-7). (J). 12.95 (978-0-385-73204-8(X)); lib. bdg. 14.99 (978-0-385-90235-9(2)) Random Hse. Children's Bks. (Delacorte Bks. for Young Readers).

—Lucy Rose: Here's the Thing about Me. Rex, Adam, illus. (J). (gr. 3-7). 2004. 144p. 12.95 (978-0-385-73203-1(1) , Delacorte Bks. for Young Readers); 2004. 144p. lib. bdg. 14.99 (978-0-385-90234-2(4) , Delacorte Bks. for Young Readers); 2006. 160p. reprint ed. 5.99 (978-0-440-42026-2(1) , Yearling) Random Hse. Children's Bks.

—Lucy Rose: Working Myself to Pieces & Bits. Ferguson, Peter, illus. 2007. (J). (gr. 3-7). 208p. 12.99 ***(978-0-385-73408-0(5));*** 128p. lib. bdg. 15.99 ***(978-0-385-90425-4(8))*** Random Hse. Children's Bks. (Delacorte Bks. for Young Readers).

—Lucy Rose: Big on Plans. Rex, Adam, illus. 2007. 192p. (gr. 3-5). 5.50 (978-0-440-42027-9(X) , Yearling) Random Hse. Children's Bks.

—Lucy Rose: Busy Like You Can't Believe. Rex, Adam, illus. 2006. 176p. (J). (gr. 3-7). lib. bdg. 14.99 (978-0-385-90338-7(3) , Delacorte Bks. for Young Readers) Random Hse. Children's Bks.

Kemp, Gene. The Hairy Hands. unabr. ed. 2000. (Read-Along Ser.). 168p. (J). pap. 24.95 incl. audio (978-0-7540-6223-3(6) , RA024, Chivers Children's Audio Bks.) BBC Audiobooks America.

Kenneally, Christy. Second Son. 2007. 464p. (Orig.). pap. 8.99 ***(978-0-340-89620-4(5)*** , Hodder & Stoughton) Hodder General Publishing Division GBR. *Dist:* Independent Pubs. Group.

Kennedy, Pamela. Moving Day for Sam. Petrov, Anton, illus. 2007. 32p. (J). (gr. k-3). 8.99 ***(978-0-8249-5558-8(7)*** , GPKids) Ideals Pubns.

Kennemore, Tim. Circle of Doom. 2003. 208p. (J). 16.00 (978-0-374-31284-8(2) , Farrar, Straus & Giroux (BYR)) Farrar, Straus & Giroux.

Kennemore, Tim & Archbold, Tim. Circle of Doom. 2006. (Illus.). 208p. (J). pap. 6.95 (978-0-374-41198-5(0)) Macmillan.

Kent, Renee Holmes. Girl Talk, Vol. 7. 2004. (Adventures in Misty Falls Ser.: Vol. 7). (Illus.). 100p. (J). (gr. 4-7). pap. 4.99 (978-1-56309-455-2(X) , N017103) New Hope Pubs.

Kephart, Beth. Undercover. 2007. 288p. (gr. 7 up). (J). 16.99 ***(978-0-06-123893-2(7));*** (YA). lib. bdg. 17.89 ***(978-0-06-123894-9(5))*** HarperCollins Pubs. (HarperTeen).

Kerley, Barbara. Greetings from Planet Earth. 2007. (Illus.). 256p. (J). (gr. 4-7). pap. 16.99 (978-0-439-80203-1(2) , Scholastic Pr.) Scholastic, Inc.

Kerr, Judith. When Hitler Stole Pink Rabbit.Tr. of Cuando Hitler Robo el Conejo Rosa. (SPA.). 172p. (J). 11.95 (978-84-204-3201-4(6)) Santillana USA Publishing Co., Inc.

Kerr, M. E. Dinky Hocker Shoots Smack! 2007. 224p. (J). pap. 6.99 (978-0-06-113989-5(0) , HarperTeen) HarperCollins Pubs.

—Your Eyes in Stars. 2006. 240p. (J). lib. bdg. 16.89 (978-0-06-075683-3(7)); (YA). 15.99 (978-0-06-075682-6(9)) HarperCollins Pubs.

Kerr, Rita. The Good Old Days. 1999. (Illus.). 120p. 13.95 (978-1-57168-362-5(3)) Eakin Pr.

Kim, Kelly. My Busy, Busy Day. 2000. 12p. (J). 5.99 (978-0-310-23206-3(6)) Zonderkidz.

Kimmel, Elizabeth Cody. Lily B. on the Brink of Cool. 2003. 256p. (J). (gr. 3-7). 15.99 (978-0-06-000586-3(6)) HarperCollins Pubs.

King, Ron S. The Quantum July. 2007. 256p. (YA). (gr. 5). 15.99 ***(978-0-385-73418-9(2));*** lib. bdg. 18.99 ***(978-0-385-90432-2(0))*** Random Hse. Children's Bks. (Delacorte Bks. for Young Readers).

King-Smith, Dick. Sophie's Snail. 1999. (Sophie Bks.). (978-0-606-16402-3(2)) Tandem Library Bks.

—The Stray. unabr. ed. 2002. (J). pap. 24.95 incl. audio (978-0-7540-6201-1(5)) BBC Audiobooks America.

King, Sue. Wake Up. 2004. (Magic Picture Book Ser.). (Illus.). 10p. (J). bds. 5.95 (978-0-8118-4402-4(1)) Chronicle Bks. LLC.

King, Susan. Amy & the Birthday Story; Amy & the Labor Day Lamentations. King, Susan, illus. 2002. (Illus.). 79p. (J). (ps-5). 7.00 (978-0-9714446-6-9(8)) King RIT - ACKS Pubs.

Kingsolver, Barbara. The Bean Trees. 1999. (YA). 9.95 (978-1-56137-890-6(9)) Novel Units, Inc.

Kinkade, Thomas. Katherine's Story. 2004. (Girls of Lighthouse Lane Ser.). 176p. (J). (gr. 5 up). 13.89 (978-0-06-054342-6(6)) HarperCollins Pubs.

Kinkade, Thomas & Tamar, Erika. Rose's Story. 2004. (Girls of Lighthouse Lane Ser.: No. 2). (Illus.). 192p. (J). (gr. 5 up). 12.99 (978-0-06-054344-0(2)) HarperCollins Pubs.

Kinsey-Warnock, Natalie. From Dawn till Dusk. Azarian, Mary, illus. 2006. 40p. (J). (gr. k-3). reprint ed. pap. 6.95 (978-0-618-73750-5(2)) Houghton Mifflin Co. Trade & Reference Div.

Kirby. Ida Lou's Story. 2000. (American Quilts Ser.: Vol. 4). (J). 11.64 (978-0-606-20082-0(7)) Tandem Library Bks.

Kirby, Susan E. Ellen's Story. 2000. (gr. 3-6). lib. bdg. 13.00 (978-0-613-31156-4(6)) Tandem Library Bks.

Kirwan, Wednesday. Nobody Notices Minerva. 2007. (Illus.). 32p. (J). (ps up). 14.95 ***(978-1-4027-4728-1(4))*** Sterling Publishing Co., Inc.

Kisseloff, Jeff & Wells, Rosemary. Ruby's Tea for Two. 2003. (Max & Ruby Ser.). 12p. (J). bds. 5.99 (978-0-670-03652-3(8) , Puffin) Penguin Group (USA) Inc.

Klassen, Kirsten L. Katelyn's Affection. 2004. 280p. pap. 11.99 (978-0-8361-9281-0(8)) Herald Pr.

Klingel, Cynthia Fitterer & Noyed, Robert B. Carmen & the Letter C. 2003. (Alphaphonics Ser.). (Illus.). 24p. (J). (ps-2). 21.36 (978-1-59296-093-4(6)) Child's World, Inc.

Klise, Kate. Deliver Us from Normal. 2005. 240p. (YA). (gr. 5-9). 16.95 (978-0-439-52322-6(2)) Scholastic, Inc.

—Deliver Us from Normal: Read-Along/Homework Pack. unabr. ed. 2005. (YA). (gr. 5-8). 65.70 incl. audio (978-1-4193-3619-5(3) , 42050) Recorded Bks., LLC.

—Far from Normal. 2006. 240p. (J). pap. 16.99 (978-0-439-79447-3(1) , Scholastic Pr.) Scholastic, Inc.

Knipe, Floyd P. Forest & the Family Reunion. Jackson, James K., illus. 2000. (Forest the Huggable Dog Ser.: Vol. 5). 23p. (J). (ps-3). pap. 4.95 (978-1-930130-08-1(2)) Nature's Nest Bks.

—Forest & the Family Reunion Coloring Book. Jackson, James K., illus. 2000. (Forest the Huggable Dog Ser.: Vol. 5). 23p. (J). (ps-3). pap. 2.00 (978-1-930130-09-8(0)) Nature's Nest Bks.

Knox, Elizabeth. Dreamhunter. 2006. (Dreamhunter Duet Ser.: Bk. 1). (Illus.). 384p. (YA). (gr. 7 up). 19.00 (978-0-374-31853-6(0)) Farrar, Straus & Giroux.

—Dreamquake. 2007. (Dreamhunter Duet Ser.: Bk. 2). (Illus.). 464p. (YA). (gr. 7 up). 19.00 (978-0-374-31854-3(9)) Farrar, Straus & Giroux.

Knox, Elizabeth. Dreamquake: Book Two of the Dreamhunter Duet. 2007. (Illus.). 449p. (J). ***(978-1-4287-3321-3(3))*** Farrar, Straus & Giroux.

Koda-Callan, Elizabeth, illus. The Squiggly Wigglys. 2003. 24p. (J). (gr. k-3). 14.95 (978-0-7611-2821-2(2) , 12821) Workman Publishing Co., Inc.

Koertge, Ronald. Margaux with an X. 2006. 176p. (YA). (gr. 9). reprint ed. pap. 6.99 (978-0-7636-2679-2(1)) Candlewick Pr.

Kogler, Jennifer Anne. Ruby Tuesday. 2005. 320p. (J). (gr. 7 up). 15.99 (978-0-06-073956-0(8)) HarperCollins Pubs.

Komaiko, Leah. Annie Bananie. Cornell, Laura, illus. 32p. (J). (ps-3). 2003. pap. 6.99 (978-0-06-051912-4(6)); 2001. 15.89 (978-0-06-023261-0(7)) HarperCollins Pubs. (Geringer, Laura Book).

—Annie Bananie. 2003. (gr. k-3). lib. bdg. 14.15 (978-0-613-63577-6(9)) Tandem Library Bks.

Konigsburg, E. L. George. 2007. (Illus.). 168p. (J). (gr. 3-7). per. 5.99 ***(978-1-4169-4957-2(7)*** , Aladdin) Simon & Schuster Children's Publishing.

Koss, Amy Goldman. How I Saved Hanukkah. 2000. (J). 11.64 (978-0-606-20239-8(0)) Tandem Library Bks.

Koss, Amy Goldman. Side Effects. 2006. 144p. (YA). 16.95 ***(978-1-59643-294-9(2));*** 143p. (J). ***(978-1-4287-0203-5(2))*** Roaring Brook Pr.

Krahn, Fernando. La Familia Numerozzi. 2001. (SPA.). 13.75 (978-0-606-20756-0(2)) Tandem Library Bks.

Krauss, Ruth. The Backward Day. Simont, Marc, illus. 2007. 40p. (J). (ps-2). 14.95 ***(978-1-59017-237-7(X)*** , NYR Children's Collection) New York Review of Bks., Inc., The.

Kray, Reg. A Way of Life: Over Thirty Years of Blood, Sweat & Tears. 2002. (Illus.). 224p. pap. 13.99 (978-0-330-48511-1(3) , Pan) Pan Macmillan GBR. *Dist:* Trafalgar Square Publishing.

Krishnaswami, Uma. Chachaji's Cup. Sitaraman, Soumya, illus. 2003. 32p. (J). (gr. 1 up). 16.95 (978-0-89239-178-3(2)) Children's Bk. Pr.

—Naming Maya. 2004. (Illus.). 192p. (J). 16.00 (978-0-374-35485-5(5) , Farrar, Straus & Giroux (BYR)) Farrar, Straus & Giroux.

Krossing, Karen. Take the Stairs. 2005. 183p. (YA). pap. 7.95 (978-1-896764-76-4(2)) Second Story Pr. CAN. *Dist:* Orca Bk. Pubs. USA, Univ. of Toronto Pr.

Kuhn, Betsy. Not Exactly Nashville. 1999. (978-0-606-16708-6(0)) Tandem Library Bks.

Kuijer, Guus. The Book of Everything. Nieuwenhuizen, John, tr. from DUT. 2006. 112p. (J). (gr. 4-7). pap. 16.99 (978-0-439-74918-3(2) , Levine, Arthur A. Bks.) Scholastic, Inc.

Kuijer, Guus & Nieuwenhuizen, John. The Book of Everything. 2006. ix, 101p. (J). 16.99 (978-0-439-74919-0(0) , Levine, Arthur A. Bks.) Scholastic, Inc.

Kurtz, Carmen. Veva. (SPA.). 128p. (J). (gr. 3-5). (978-84-279-3120-6(4)) Noguer y Caralt Editores, S. A. ESP. *Dist:* Lectorum Pubns., Inc.

—Veva. 2001. (SPA.). (gr. 3-6). lib. bdg. 17.05 (978-0-613-79908-9(9)) Tandem Library Bks.

Kwasney, Michelle D. Baby Blue. rev. ed. 2004. (Illus.). 208p. (YA). 16.95 (978-0-8050-7050-7(8) , Holt, Henry & Co. Bks. For Young Readers) Holt, Henry & Co.

Kyi, Tanya Lloyd. Truth. 2003. (YA). (gr. 7 up). pap. 7.95 (978-1-55143-235-9(8)) Orca Bk. Pubs. USA.

—Truth. 2003. (gr. 7-12). lib. bdg. 16.40 (978-0-613-70627-8(7)) Tandem Library Bks.

Lachtman, Ofelia Dumas. Pepita Finds Out/lo que Pepita Descubre. Villarroel, Carolina, tr. DeLange, Alex Pardo, illus. (ENG & SPA.). 32p. (J). 15.95 (978-1-55885-375-1(8) , Piñata Books) Arte Publico Pr.

—The Trouble with Tessa. 122p. (J). (ps-7). pap. 9.95 (978-1-55885-448-2(7) , Piñata Books) Arte Publico Pr.

LaFaye, A. Nissa's Place. 2001. (J). (978-0-606-21355-4(4)) Tandem Library Bks.

—Strawberry Hill. 2000. (J). (978-0-606-19953-7(5)) Tandem Library Bks.

LaFevers, R. L. Theodosia & the Serpents of Chaos. Tanaka, Yoko, illus. 2007. 368p. (J). (gr. 5-7). 16.00 ***(978-0-618-75638-4(8))*** Houghton Mifflin Co. Trade & Reference Div.

Lamba, Marie. What I Meant... 2007. 320p. (gr. 5-11). (J). 16.99 (978-0-375-84091-3(5)); (YA). lib. bdg. 19.99 (978-0-375-94091-0(X)) Random Hse. Children's Bks. (Random Hse. Bks. for Young Readers).

Lambert, Janet. Love Taps Gently. 2001. (Jordon Ser.: Vol. 5). (YA). pap. 12.95 (978-1-930009-36-3(4)) Image Cascade Publishing.

—My Davy. 2001. (Parri MacDonald Series by Janet Lambert: Vol. 4). (YA). pap. 12.95 (978-1-930009-44-8(5)) Image Cascade Publishing.

Laminack, Lester. Saturdays & Teacakes. Soentpiet, Chris K., illus. 2004. 32p. (J). (gr. 1-2). 16.95 (978-1-56145-303-0(X)) Peachtree Pubs., Ltd.

Lamstein, Sarah. Hunger Moon. 2004. (Illus.). 112p. (YA). 15.95 (978-1-932425-05-5(5) , Lemniscaat) Boyds Mills Pr.

Landolf, Diane Wright. What a Good Big Brother! Johnson, Steve & Fancher, Lou, illus. 2008. (J). (978-0-375-84258-0(6)); lib. bdg. (978-0-375-94258-7(0)) Random Hse. Children's Bks.

Landry, Leo. Space Boy. 2007. 32p. (J). (gr. k-3). 16.00 ***(978-0-618-60568-2(1))*** Houghton Mifflin Co.

Lane, Dakota. Orpheus Obsession. 2005. (Illus.). 288p. (J). 16.99 (978-0-06-074173-0(2) , Tegen, Katherine Bks); lib. bdg. 17.89 (978-0-06-074174-7(0) , HarperTeen) HarperCollins Pubs.

Lane, Rose Wilder. Young Pioneers. Andreasen, Dan, illus. 1998. (Little House Ser.). 192p. (J). (gr. 3 up). pap. 6.99 (978-0-06-440698-7(9) , Harper Trophy) HarperCollins Pubs.

Langston, Laura. A Taste of Perfection. 2002. (Illus.). 190p. (J). (gr. 5 up). pap. 6.95 (978-0-7737-6274-9(4)) Stoddart Kids CAN. *Dist:* Fitzhenry & Whiteside, Ltd.

Langton, Jane. The Mysterious Circus. 2005. (Hall Family Chronicles). 224p. (J). lib. bdg. 16.89 (978-0-06-009487-4(7)) HarperCollins Pubs.

Lankester-Brisley, Joyce. Milly-Molly-Mandy Stories. 2002. (Kingfisher Modern Classics Ser.). (Illus.). 240p. (J). (gr. k-3). tchr. ed. 15.95 (978-0-7534-5559-3(5) , Kingfisher) Houghton Mifflin Co. Trade & Reference Div.

Lanthier, Jennifer. The Mystery of the Martello Tower. 2008. 272p. (J). 16.99 ***(978-0-06-125712-4(5));*** lib. bdg. 17.89 ***(978-0-06-125713-1(3))*** HarperCollins Pubs. (Geringer, Laura Book).

Laskas, Gretchen Moran. The Miner's Daughter. 2007. 256p. (YA). 15.99 (978-1-4169-1262-0(2)) Simon & Schuster Children's Publishing.

Lasky, Kathryn. Dreams in the Golden Country: The Diary of Zipporah Feldman, a Jewish Immigrant Girl, New York City, 1903. 1998. (Dear America Ser.). (Illus.). 192p. (J). (gr. 4-9). pap. 10.95 (978-0-590-02973-5(8)) Scholastic, Inc.

—The Last Girls of Pompeii. 2007. 160p. (J). (gr. 5 up). 15.99 (978-0-670-06196-9(4) , Viking Juvenile) Penguin Group (USA) Inc.

The Last Wild Run. 2006. (J). per. 14.95 (978-1-933791-05-7(5)) Finial Publishing.

Lat. Kampung Boy. Lat, illus. rev. ed. 2006. (Illus.). 144p. (J). (gr. 6-8). pap. 16.95 (978-1-59643-121-8(0) , First Second Bks.) Roaring Brook Pr.

Lathan, Tamala. Black Butterflies. 2000. 250p. (J). 7.99 (978-0-9700599-0-1(6)) Sybrell Publishing.

Latimer, Miriam. Shrinking Sam. 2007. (Illus.). 32p. (J). (gr. 1-3). 16.99 ***(978-1-84686-038-6(5))*** Barefoot Bks., Inc.

Lawrence, Caroline. The Enemies of Jupiter. 2005. (Roman Mysteries Ser.). (Illus.). 192p. (J). 16.95 (978-1-59643-048-8(6)) Roaring Brook Pr.

Lawrence, Iain. B for Buster. 2004. (Illus.). 336p. (YA). (gr. 7). 15.95 (978-0-385-73086-0(1) , Delacorte Bks. for Young Readers) Random Hse. Children's Bks.

—Gemini Summer. 2006. 272p. (J). (gr. 3-7). 15.95 (978-0-385-73089-1(6)); lib. bdg. 17.99 (978-0-385-90111-6(9)) Random Hse. Children's Bks. (Delacorte Bks. for Young Readers).

Lawton, Wendy. Flip Flop. 2004. (Real Tv - Real Transformations Series (Take 2) Ser.). 208p. (J). pap. 10.99 (978-0-8024-5414-0(3)) Moody Pubs.

Lee, Marie G. Necessary Roughness. 1998. 240p. (J). (gr. 7 up). pap. 6.50 (978-0-06-447169-5(1) , Harper Trophy) HarperCollins Pubs.

—Necessary Roughness. 1998. (J). (978-0-606-13000-4(4)) Tandem Library Bks.

Lehri, R. M. Cut & Make Festival Masks from India: 6 Full-Color Designs. 2001. (Illus.). 16p. (J). (gr. 3). pap. 5.95 (978-0-486-41667-0(4)) Dover Pubns., Inc.

Leininger, Tracy M. Alone, yet Not Alone: The Story of Barbara & Regina Leininger. Ingram, Charles, illus. 2001. 203p. (J). 16.00 (978-1-929241-36-1(4)) Vision Forum, Inc., The.

—Nothing Can Separate Us: The Story of Nan Harper. Pulley, Kelly & Reed, Lisa, illus. 2000. 63p. (J). 16.00 (978-1-929241-21-7(6)) Vision Forum, Inc., The.

Leman, Kevin. My Firstborn, There's No One Like You. Leman, Kevin, II, illus. 2004. 32p. (J). 12.99 (978-0-8007-1829-9(1)) Revell.

—My Youngest, There's No One Like You. Leman, Kevin, II, illus. 2005. 32p. (J). 12.99 (978-0-8007-1831-2(3)) Revell.

Leman, Kevin & Leman, Kevin, II. My Only Child, There's No One Like You. 2005. (Illus.). 32p. (J). (ps). 12.99 (978-0-8007-1864-0(X)) Revell.

Lendroth, Susan. Ocean Wide, Ocean Deep. Allen, Raul, illus. 2007. (J). ***(978-1-58246-232-5(1)*** , Tricycle Pr.) Ten Speed Pr.

L'Engle, Madeleine. Meet the Austins. 2002. (Austin Family Ser.: No. 1). (Illus.). (J). 13.94 (978-0-7587-8955-6(6)) Book Wholesalers, Inc.

Lenski, Lois. Papa Small. Lenski, Lois, illus. 2004. (Little Treasures from Lois Lenski Ser.). (Illus.). 56p. (J). (ps-1). 11.95 (978-0-375-82749-5(8) , Random Hse. Bks. for Young Readers) Random Hse. Children's Bks.

Lerner, Harriet & Goldhor, Susan. Franny B. Kranny, There's a Bird in Your Hair! Oxenbury, Helen, illus. 2001. 40p. (J). (ps-3). 15.89 (978-0-06-029503-5(1)) HarperCollins Pubs.

Les Becquets, Diane. Love, Cajun Style. 2007. (Illus.). 304p. (YA). pap. 7.95 (978-1-59990-030-8(0) , Bloomsbury Children) Bloomsbury Publishing.

Leshe, Leta. Precious Memories—May They Linger: A Leshe Family Reminiscence. Leshe, Leta, ed. 2000. viii,39p. pap. 5.00 (978-1-890770-01-3(9) , Swann Pubns.) Swann, Francine Pubns.

Leske, Staci. Butterfly That Loved the Firefly. 2006. 21.95 (***978-1-4259-7645-3(X)**); pap. 11.95 (***978-1-4259-7644-6(1)***) AuthorHouse.

Let's Get Ready! (Illus.). (J). pap. 2.79 (978-0-88743-713-7(3)) School Zone Publishing Co.

Levchuk, Lisa. Everything Beautiful in the World. 2008. (YA). (***978-0-374-32238-0(4)***) Farrar, Straus & Giroux.

Levine, Abby. This Is the Turkey. Billin-Frye, Paige, illus. 2000. 32p. (J). (ps-1). pap. 6.95 (978-0-8075-7889-6(4)) Whitman, Albert & Co.

Levine, Phyllis. Matilda's Way. 2007. 188p. pap. 12.95 (***978-1-60047-073-8(4)***) Wasteland Pr.

Levinson, Marilyn. No Boys Allowed. 2005. 144p. (J). pap. 4.99 (978-0-439-71965-0(8) , Scholastic Paperbacks) Scholastic, Inc.

Levithan, David. 101 Ways to Get Away with Anything! 2002. (Malcolm in the Middle Ser.). (Illus.). 96p. (J). (gr. 3-7). pap. 4.50 (978-0-439-35132-4(9)) Scholastic, Inc.

Levitin, Sonia. Dream Freedom. 2000. 192p. (YA). (gr. 4-7). 17.00 (978-0-15-202404-8(2) , Silver Whistle) Harcourt Trade Pubs.

—Junkmans Girl. Porfirio, Guy, illus. rev. ed. 2007. (Tales of Young Americans Ser.). 40p. 17.95 (***978-1-58536-315-5(4)***) Sleeping Bear Pr.

Levitin, Sonia. Singing Mountain. 2000. (978-0-606-17938-6(0)) Tandem Library Bks.

Levy, Barry. How the Rules Were Made. 2005. 31p. (J). 7.99 (978-1-4116-3482-4(9)) Lulu.com.

Lewin, Terry. God Remembered Us. Gumm, Susan Kathleen, illus. 2006. 36p. (J). per. 19.00 (***978-0-9771482-1-9(1)*** , Ithaca Pr.) Authors & Artists Publishers of New York, Inc.

Lewis, Maggie. Morgy Coast to Coast. Chesworth, Michael, illus. 2005. 144p. (J). (gr. 3-5). 15.00 (978-0-618-44896-8(9)) Houghton Mifflin Co. Trade & Reference Div.

—Morgy Makes His Move. Chesworth, Michael, illus. 80p. (J). 2002. (gr. 1-4). pap. 4.95 (978-0-618-19680-7(3)); 1999. (gr. 4-6). tchr. ed. 15.00 (978-0-395-92284-2(4)) Houghton Mifflin Co. Trade & Reference Div.

—Morgy Makes His Move. 1999. (gr. 3-6). lib. bdg. 12.95 (978-0-613-60698-1(1)) Tandem Library Bks.

Lin, Grace. Dim Sum for Everyone! Lin, Grace, illus. 2003. (Illus.). 32p. (J). (gr. k-3). pap. 6.99 (978-0-440-41770-5(8) , Dragonfly Bks.) Random Hse. Children's Bks.

—The Year of the Dog. (Illus.). (J). (gr. 3-7). 2007. 162p. pap. 5.99 (978-0-316-06002-8(X)); 2005. 144p. 14.99 (978-0-316-06000-4(3)) Little Brown & Co.

Lin, Grace. The Year of the Rat. rev. ed. 2008. 208p. (J). (gr. 3-7). 14.99 (***978-0-316-11426-4(X)***) Little, Brown Bks. for Young Readers.

Lindsey, Kathleen D. Sweet Potato Pie. Riley-Webb, Charlotte, illus. 2003. (J). 16.95 (978-1-58430-061-8(2)) Lee & Low Bks., Inc.

Lion, Melissa. Upstream. 160p. (YA). (gr. 7). 2006. pap. 8.95 (978-0-375-83954-2(2)); 2005. 15.95 (978-0-385-74643-4(1)) Random Hse. Children's Bks. (Lamb, Wendy).

Lish, Ted. Ese No Es Mi Trabajo. Jordan, Charles, illus. 2002. (J). lib. bdg. 15.95 (978-0-7940-0011-0(8)) Munchweiler Pr.

—It's Not My Job! Jordan, Charles, illus. 2002. 24p. (J). 14.95 (978-0-7940-0004-2(5)); lib. bdg. 15.95 (978-0-7940-0005-9(3)) Munchweiler Pr.

Lisle, Janet Taylor. The Art of Keeping Cool. 2002. (gr. 5-8). lib. bdg. 13.00 (978-0-613-54109-1(X)) Tandem Library Bks.

Littke, Lael. Searching for Selene. 2003. 203p. (J). pap. 13.95 (978-1-59038-179-3(3)) Deseret Bk. Co.

Littman, Sarah. Confessions of a Closet Catholic. McClelland, Charles E. & Scher, Steven P., eds. 2005. 176p. (J). (gr. 5-8). 15.99 (978-0-525-47365-7(3) , Dutton Juvenile) Penguin Group (USA) Inc.

—Confessions of a Closet Catholic. 2006. 208p. (J). (gr. 5). reprint ed. pap. 5.99 (978-0-14-240597-0(3) , Puffin) Penguin Group (USA) Inc.

Lloyd-Jones, Sally. The Ultimate Guide to Grandmas & Grandpas. Emberley, Michael, illus. 2008. 32p. (J). 16.99 (***978-0-06-075687-1(X)***); lib. bdg. 17.89 (***978-0-06-075688-8(8)***) HarperCollins Pubs.

Lobel, Steven. Remains of Elliot Brown. 2004. 135p. pap. 19.95 (978-1-4137-4999-1(2)) PublishAmerica, Inc.

Lollino, Jessica. Little Lily Mays & the Daddy Dilemma. Kendrick-TaZiyah, Brandi, illus. 2006. (Little Lily Mays Ser.: vol. 1). 32p. (J). per. 20.00 (978-0-9712383-1-2(6)) Culture Connection, The.

Lombard, Jenny. Drita, My Homegirl. (J). (gr. 4-6). 2008. 144p. pap. 5.99 (***978-0-14-240905-3(7)*** , Puffin); 2006. 176p. 15.99 (978-0-399-24380-6(1) , Putnam Juvenile) Penguin Group (USA) Inc.

The Long Walk Home: Individual Title Six-Packs. (Action Packs Ser.). 120p. (gr. 3-5). 44.00 (978-0-7635-8430-6(4)) Rigby Education.

Look, Lenore. Ruby Lu, Brave & True. 2004. (Illus.). 104p. (J). lib. bdg. 15.00 (***978-1-4242-0914-9(5)***) Fitzgerald Bks.

—Ruby Lu, Brave & True. Wilsdorf, Anne, illus. 2006. (Ready-for-Chapters Ser.). 112p. (J). pap. 3.99 (978-1-4169-1389-4(0) , Aladdin) Simon & Schuster Children's Publishing.

Look, Lenore & Wilsdorf, Anne. Ruby Lu, Brave & True. 2004. (Illus.). 176p. (J). (gr. 1-2). 15.95 (978-0-689-84907-7(9) , Atheneum/Anne Schwartz Bks.) Simon & Schuster Children's Publishing.

Lopez, Diana. Confetti Girl. 2007. 144p. (J). pap. 5.99 (***978-0-316-02956-8(4)***) Little, Brown Bks. for Young Readers.

Lopez, Jack. In the Break. 2006. (Illus.). 208p. (J). (gr. 7-17). 16.99 (978-0-316-00874-7(5)) Little Brown & Co.

Lough, Loree. Fire by Night: The Great Fire Devastates Boston. 1999. (American Adventure Ser.: No. 4). 144p. (J). (gr. 3-7). lib. bdg. 15.95 (978-0-7910-5044-6(0) , Chelsea Hse.) Facts On File, Inc.

Love & Roast Chicken: A Trickster Tale from the Andes Mountains. 2005. (Libros Ilustrados (Picture Bks.)). (SPA., Illus.). 40p. (J). (ps-ps). 16.95 (978-0-8225-3190-6(9) , Ediciones Lerner) Lerner Publishing Group.

Love, D. Anne. Picture Perfect. 2007. (YA). 304p. (gr. 7 up). 16.99 (978-0-689-87390-4(5)); 291p. (***978-1-4287-3275-9(6)***) Simon & Schuster Children's Publishing. (McElderry, Margaret K.).

—Semiprecious. 2006. 304p. (J). (gr. 5-9). 16.95 (978-0-689-85638-9(5) , McElderry, Margaret K.) Simon & Schuster Children's Publishing.

—A Year Without Rain. 2000. (Illus.). 128p. (J). (gr. 4-6). tchr. ed. 15.95 (978-0-8234-1488-8(4)) Holiday Hse., Inc.

Lowry, Lois. Anastasia de Nuevo. 2003. (Juvenil Ser.: Vol. 77). Tr. of Anastasia Again. (SPA., Illus.). 112p. (J). (gr. 5-7). 9.95 (978-84-239-9047-4(8)) Espasa Calpe, S.A. ESP. *Dist:* Lectorum Pubns., Inc., Planeta Publishing Corp.

—Anastasia Esta al Mando. 2003. Tr. of Anastasia on Her Own. (SPA.). 168p. (J). 9.95 (978-84-239-7095-7(7)) Espasa Calpe, S.A. ESP. *Dist:* Lectorum Pubns., Inc., Planeta Publishing Corp.

—Anastasia Krupnik. 7th ed. 2003. (SPA., Illus.). 140p. (J). (gr. 4-7). 9.95 (978-84-239-7061-2(2)) Espasa Calpe, S.A. ESP. *Dist:* Lectorum Pubns., Inc.

—Anastasia Krupnik. 2001. (J). 16.60 (978-0-606-22686-8(9)); (SPA.). (gr. 3-6). lib. bdg. 18.75 (978-0-613-86338-4(0)) Tandem Library Bks.

Lowry, Lois. The Willoughbys. 2008. (J). (***978-0-618-97974-5(3)***) Houghton Mifflin Co.

Lucia, Ruth. The Sad Little Cloud. 2004. (Illus.). 25p. (J). pap. 9.95 (978-1-932373-14-1(4)) Cedar Hill Publishing.

Luddy, Karon. Spelldown: The Big-Time Dreams of a Small-Town Word Whiz. 2007. 224p. (YA). 15.99 (978-1-4169-1610-9(5)) Simon & Schuster Children's Publishing.

Luisi, Nancy. Unwanted Changes. 2005. 131p. pap. 19.95 (978-1-4137-8250-9(7)) PublishAmerica, Inc.

Luke, Deanna. Marky & the Cat. Chambers, Lynne, illus. 2000. (Marky Ser.: Vol. No. 2). 40p. (J). (gr. 2-7). 8.95 (978-1-928777-06-9(6) , BOW Bks.) Blessing Our World, Inc.

Lupton, Hugh. The Gingerbread Man. Mayo, Diana, illus. 2003. 24p. (J). (gr. k-3). 14.99 (978-1-84148-056-5(8)) Barefoot Bks., Inc.

Lynch, Chris. The Gravedigger's Cottage. 2004. 208p. (J). (gr. 7 up). 15.99 (978-0-06-623940-8(0)) HarperCollins Pubs.

—Inexcusable. 176p. (YA). 2007. (gr. 9 up). pap. 6.99 (978-1-4169-3972-6(5) , Simon Pulse); 2005. (Illus.). (gr. 7 up). 16.95 (978-0-689-84789-9(0) , Atheneum) Simon & Schuster Children's Publishing.

—Inexcusable. l.t. ed. 2006. 180p. (YA). 22.95 (978-0-7862-8812-0(4)) Thorndike Pr.

—Me, Dead Dad, & Alcatraz. 3rd ed. 2005. 240p. (J). 15.99 (978-0-06-059709-2(7)) HarperCollins Pubs.

MacBride, Roger Lea. The Adventures of Rose & Swiney. Ettlinger, Doris, illus. 2000. (Little House Chapter Bks.: No. 4). 80p. (J). (gr. 2-5). 14.89 (978-0-06-028553-1(2)) HarperCollins Pubs.

—The Adventures of Rose & Swiney. Ettlinger, Doris, illus. 2000. (Little House Chapter Bks.). (J). (978-0-606-19996-4(9)) Tandem Library Bks.

Maccarone, Grace. It's Graduation Day! 2005. 32p. (J). pap. 2.99 (978-0-439-69384-4(5)) Scholastic, Inc.

MacCullough, Carolyn. Stealing Henry. rev. ed. 2005. 208p. (YA). 16.95 (978-1-59643-045-7(1)) Roaring Brook Pr.

MacDonald, Marianne. Secondhand Star. Christelow, Eileen, illus. 1998. (Lots of O'Leary's Ser.). (978-0-606-13769-0(6)) Tandem Library Bks.

MacDonald, Steven. Just Clowning Around: Two Stories. McPhail, David M., illus. 2003. (Green Light Readers Level 1 Ser.). 24p. (J). 11.95 (978-0-15-204816-7(2)); pap. 3.95 (978-0-15-204856-3(1)) Harcourt Children's Bks. (Green Light Readers).

MacHado, Ana Maria. Bisa Bea, Bisa Bel. (SPA.). (J). (gr. 4-5). 6.00 (978-968-16-5463-4(3) , FC6391) Fondo de Cultura Economica MEX. *Dist:* Lectorum Pubns., Inc.

Mackall, Dandi. Larger-Than-Life Lara. 2006. 195p. (J). (gr. 5). 16.99 (978-0-525-47726-6(8) , Dutton Juvenile) Penguin Group (USA) Inc.

Mackall, Dandi Daley. Grace Notes. 2006. (Faithgirlz Ser.). (Illus.). 128p. (J). pap. 6.99 (978-0-310-71093-6(6)) Zonderkidz.

Mackey, Weezie Kerr. Throwing a Like Girl. 2007. 272p. (J). (gr. 7 up). 16.99 (***978-0-7614-5342-0(3)***) Cavendish, Marshall Corp.

Mackler, Carolyn. The Earth, My Butt, & Other Big Round Things. 2005. 256p. (YA). (gr. 9 up). reprint ed. pap. 8.99 (978-0-7636-2091-2(2)) Candlewick Pr.

—Love & Other Four-Letter Words. 2002. (Laurel-Leaf Books). 256p. (YA). (gr. 7). pap. 5.99 (978-0-440-22831-8(X) , Laurel Leaf) Random Hse. Children's Bks.

MacLachlan, Patricia. Caleb's Story. 2002. (SPA., Illus.). 112p. 8.99 (978-84-279-3252-4(9) , NG31208) Noguer y Caralt Editores, S. A. ESP. *Dist:* Lectorum Pubns., Inc.

—Caleb's Story. 2002. (SPA.). (gr. 3-6). lib. bdg. 17.05 (978-0-613-64342-9(9)) Tandem Library Bks.

—Edward's Eyes. 2007. 128p. (J). (gr. 3-7). 15.99 (***978-1-4169-2743-3(3)*** , Atheneum) Simon & Schuster Children's Publishing.

—Grandfather's Dance. (Sarah, Plain & Tall Ser.). 96p. (J). 2008. pap. 5.99 (***978-0-06-134003-1(0)***); 2006. lib. bdg. 15.89 (978-0-06-027561-7(8)) HarperCollins Pubs. (Cotler, Joanna Books).

—More Perfect Than the Moon. 2005. (Sarah, Plain & Tall Ser.). 96p. (J). pap. 4.99 (978-0-06-075179-1(7) , Harper Trophy) HarperCollins Pubs.

—What You Know First. Moser, Barry, illus. 1998. (Trophy Picture Bk.). 32p. (J). (ps-3). pap. 6.99 (978-0-06-443492-8(3) , Harper Trophy) HarperCollins Pubs.

Maclean, Christine. Mary Margaret & the Perfect Pet Plan. Vicky, Lowe, illus. 2007. 192p. (J). (gr. 3). pap. 5.99 (978-0-14-240767-7(4) , Puffin) Penguin Group (USA) Inc.

MacLeod, Doug. I'm Being Stalked by a Moonshadow. 2007. 212p. (YA). (gr. 8 up). 16.95 (***978-1-59078-501-0(0)*** , Front Street) Boyds Mills Pr.

Madden, Kerry. Gentle's Holler. 2007. 272p. (YA). (gr. 4 up). 6.99 (978-0-14-240751-6(8) , Puffin) Penguin Group (USA) Inc.

—Louisiana's Song. 2007. 256p. (YA). (gr. 5 up). 16.99 (978-0-670-06153-2(0) , Viking Juvenile) Penguin Group (USA) Inc.

Maine, Margarita. Un Gran Resfrio. 2002. (SPA.). 32p. (J). pap. 8.95 (978-1-4000-0033-3(5)) Random Hse., Inc.

Maisner, Heather. Our New Baby. Stephenson, Kristina, illus. 2005. (First Time Stories Ser.). 24p. (J). (gr. k-ps). pap. 3.95 (978-0-7534-5738-2(5) , Kingfisher) Houghton Mifflin Co. Trade & Reference Div.

Maizel, Karen, illus. Jake Helps Out. 2007. (I Can Read!). 32p. (J). pap. 3.99 (***978-0-310-71457-6(5)***) Zonderkidz.

Malokas, Ann. The Tag-a-long Trio: Zak, Lizze & Ben Too! Nicholas, Corasue, illus. 2007. (J). 15.95 (***978-0-9708415-8-2(2)***) Guilty Mom Pr.

Maloney, Peter & Zekauskas, Felicia. His Mother's Nose. Maloney, Peter & Zekauskas, Felicia, illus. 2001. (Illus.). 40p. (J). (ps-3). 15.99 (978-0-8037-2545-4(0) , Dial) Penguin Group (USA) Inc.

Mammay, Judith. Knowing Joseph. 2008. (Illus.). 256p. (YA). (gr. 2-7). 16.95 (***978-1-933831-05-3(7)***) Blooming Tree Pr.

Marchetta, Melina. Saving Francesca. 2006. 256p. (YA). (gr. 7). reprint ed. pap. 8.95 (978-0-375-82983-3(0) , Knopf Bks. for Young Readers) Random Hse. Children's Bks.

Marcum, Lance. The Cottonmouth Club. 2005. 336p. (J). 18.00 (978-0-374-31562-7(0) , Farrar, Straus & Giroux (BYR)) Farrar, Straus & Giroux.

Marillier, Juliet. Cybele's Secret. 2008. 432p. (YA). (gr. 7). lib. bdg. 20.99 (***978-0-375-93365-3(4)*** , Knopf Bks. for Young Readers) Random Hse. Children's Bks.

Marino, Peter. Dough Boy. 2007. 176p. (YA). (gr. 7 up). pap. 6.95 (***978-0-8234-2096-4(5)***) Holiday Hse., Inc.

Marsden, Carolyn. Silk Umbrellas. 2007. (Illus.). 144p. (J). (gr. 3-7). 5.99 (***978-0-7636-3376-9(3)***) Candlewick Pr.

—Silk Umbrellas. Swiatkowska, Gabi, illus. 2004. 144p. (J). (gr. 3-7). 15.99 (978-0-7636-2257-2(5)) Candlewick Pr.

Marshall, Janet. A Honey of a Day. 2000. (Illus.). 24p. (J). (ps up). 15.95 (978-0-688-16917-6(1)) HarperCollins Pubs.

Marshall, Robert T. & Arbuckle, Wendall S. Ice Cream. 5th ed. 2000. 364p. reprint ed. 87.00 (978-0-8342-1917-5(4) , Aspen Pubs.) Wolters Kluwer Law & Business.

Martin, Ann M. Belle Teale. 2004. 224p. (J). pap. 5.99 (978-0-439-09824-3(6) , Scholastic Paperbacks) Scholastic, Inc.

—A Corner of the Universe. 208p. (J). 2004. pap. 5.99 (978-0-439-38881-8(3) , Scholastic Paperbacks); 2002. (gr. 5-8). pap. 15.95 (978-0-439-38880-1(5) , Scholastic Pr.) Scholastic, Inc.

—A Corner of the Universe. 2003. (gr. 7-12). lib. bdg. 14.15 (978-0-613-72078-6(4)) Tandem Library Bks.

—Dawn on the Coast. (Baby-Sitters Club Ser.: No. 23). 10p. (J). (gr. 3-7). pap. 3.95 (978-0-590-42007-5(0)) Scholastic, Inc.

—Here Today. (J). 2005. 336p. (gr. 5-9). pap. 5.99 (978-0-439-57945-2(7) , Scholastic Paperbacks); 2004. 320p. (gr. 4-7). pap. 16.95 (978-0-439-57944-5(9) , Scholastic Pr.) Scholastic, Inc.

—Karen's Promise. 1998. (Baby-Sitters Little Sister Ser.: No. 95). (J). (gr. 3-7). (978-0-606-13171-1(X)) Tandem Library Bks.

—Karen's Snow Princess. 1998. (Baby-Sitters Little Sister Ser.: No. 94). (J). (gr. 3-7). (978-0-606-13170-4(1)) Tandem Library Bks.

—Sunny: Diary Three. 1999. (California Diaries: Bk. 12). 160p. (YA). (gr. 6-8). pap. 4.50 (978-0-590-02390-0(X)) Scholastic, Inc.

Martin, Cathy. Uff Da! Clark, Richard, tr. Clark, Richard, illus. 2004. 32p. (J). 14.95 (978-1-58246-117-5(1) , Tricycle Pr.) Ten Speed Pr.

Martin, David. Five Little Piggies. Meddaugh, Susan, illus. 2002. (J). 14.79 (978-0-7587-2513-4(2)) Book Wholesalers, Inc.

—Five Little Piggies. Meddaugh, Susan, illus. 2000. 40p. (J). (ps-1). pap. 6.99 (978-0-7636-1081-4(X)) Candlewick Pr.

—Five Little Piggies. 2000. (J). 13.79 (978-0-606-19315-3(4)); lib. bdg. 15.30 (978-0-613-28488-2(7)) Tandem Library Bks.

—I, Piggy & Dad. 2000. (Brand New Readers Ser.). (Illus.). (J). (978-0-7636-1328-0(2)) Candlewick Pr.

Martin, Hugo. Pablo's Christmas. Chapman, Lee, illus. 2006. 24p. (J). 14.95 (978-1-4027-2560-9(4)) Sterling Publishing Co., Inc.

Martínez, Arturo O. Pedrito's World. 2007. (Illus.). 160p. (J). 16.95 (***978-0-89672-600-0(2)***) Texas Tech Univ. Pr.

Martinez, Raul. Rooly & Flora's Reunion: A Story of Cuba. Prieto, Antonio, illus. 2006. 32p. (J). (***978-1-59249-657-0(1)***); pap. (***978-1-59249-658-7(X)***) Soundprints.

Martinez, Victor. El Loro en el Horno. 2001. (SPA.). (gr. 7-12). lib. bdg. 19.90 (978-0-613-80733-3(2)) Tandem Library Bks.

—Parrot in the Oven: Mi Vida. Scott, Steve, illus. rev. ed. 1998. 240p. (J). (gr. 7 up). pap. 5.99 (978-0-06-447186-2(1) , Harper Trophy) HarperCollins Pubs.

—Parrot in the Oven: Mi Vida. 1998. (978-0-606-13695-2(9)) Tandem Library Bks.

Martino, Carmela. Rosa, Sola. 2005. 256p. (J). (gr. 4-7). 15.99 (978-0-7636-2395-1(4)) Candlewick Pr.

Marusak, Elaine. Truly Tales & Girl Fish Stories. 2006. 93p. pap. 14.95 (978-1-4241-3244-7(4)) PublishAmerica, Inc.

Masilela, Johnny. We Shall Not Weep. 2003. 132p. pap. 17.00 (978-0-7957-0147-4(0)) Kwela Bks. ZAF. *Dist:* Independent Pubs. Group.

Mason, Simon. The Quigleys. Stephens, Helen, illus. 160p. (gr. k-7). 2003. 4.99 (978-0-440-41898-6(4) , Yearling); 2002. (J). 14.95 (978-0-385-75006-6(4) , Fickling, David Bks.) Random Hse. Children's Bks.

—The Quigleys: Not for Sale. Stephens, Helen, illus. 2006. 176p. (J). (gr. k-7). 5.50 (978-0-440-42084-2(9) , Yearling) Random Hse. Children's Bks.

—The Quigleys in a Spin. Stephens, Helen, illus. 2006. 192p. (J). (gr. k-7). 14.95 (978-0-385-75098-1(6)); lib. bdg. 16.99 (978-0-385-75099-8(4)) Random Hse. Children's Bks. (Fickling, David Bks.).

Mass, Wendy. A Mango-Shaped Space. 2005. 240p. (J). (gr. 5-8). pap. 6.99 (978-0-316-05825-4(4)) Little Brown & Co.

Masters, Susan Rowan. The Secret Life of Hubie Hartzel. 2000. 112p. (J). (gr. 4-7). pap. 9.95 (978-0-595-08893-5(7)) iUniverse, Inc.

Masurel, Claire. Two Homes. MacDonald Denton, Kady, illus. 2003. 40p. (J). (ps-1). pap. 6.99 (978-0-7636-1984-8(1)) Candlewick Pr.

Masurel, Claire & Bond, Barbara Higgins. Sticker Stories Penguins. Calitri, Susan & Bond, Barbara Higgins, illus. 2003. (Giant Lift-the-Flap Ser.). 16p. (J). pap. 4.99 (978-0-448-42527-6(0) , Grosset & Dunlap) Penguin Group (USA) Inc.

Matas, Carol. Rebecca. 2000. (Illus.). 160p. (J). pap. (978-0-439-98718-9(0)) Scholastic, Inc.

—Sparks Fly Upward. 2002. 192p. (YA). (gr. 5-9). 15.00 (978-0-618-15964-2(9) , Clarion Bks.) Houghton Mifflin Co. Trade & Reference Div.

Mateos, Pilar. El Cuento Interrumpido. (SPA.). 128p. (YA). (gr. 5-8). (978-84-279-3149-7(2) , NG0388) Noguer y Caralt Editores, S. A. ESP. *Dist:* Lectorum Pubns., Inc.

Mathis, Sharon Bell. The Hundred-Penny Box. Dillon, Leo & Dillon, Diane, illus. 2006. 48p. (J). (gr. 1). pap. 7.99 (978-0-14-240702-8(X) , Puffin) Penguin Group (USA) Inc.

Mattingley, Christobel. Asmir No Quiere Pistolas. (SPA.). 129p. (J). (gr. 5-8). pap. 9.95 (978-84-204-4891-6(5)) Santillana USA Publishing Co., Inc.

Matute, Ana M. El Polizon del Ulises. (SPA.). 96p. (J). (978-84-264-3401-2(0) , LM4015) Editorial Lumen ESP. *Dist:* Lectorum Pubns., Inc.

Mayer, Mercer. Bye-Bye, Mom & Dad. Mayer, Mercer, illus. 2004. (Little Critter Ser.). (Illus.). 24p. (J). (ps-2). pap. 3.99 (978-0-06-053945-0(3) , Harper Festival) HarperCollins Pubs.

—No Dancing in the Bathtub. 1998. (Pictureback Ser.). (J). pap. 3.25 (978-0-679-88708-9(3) , Random Hse. Bks. for Young Readers) Random Hse. Children's Bks.

—There's Something in My Attic. Mayer, Mercer, illus. 2002. (Illus.). (J). 13.19 (978-0-7587-3785-4(8)) Book Wholesalers, Inc.

Mazer, Anne. Everything New under the Sun. 2003. (Amazing Days of Abby Hayes Ser.: No. 10). (Illus.). 112p. (J). 4.99 (978-0-439-35369-4(6)) Scholastic, Inc.

—Everything New under the Sun. 2003. (Amazing Days of Abby Hayes Ser.: No. 10). (gr. 3-6). lib. bdg. 12.40 (978-0-613-66626-8(7)) Tandem Library Bks.

—The More, the Merrier. 2002. (gr. 3-6). lib. bdg. 12.40 (978-0-613-50473-7(9)) Tandem Library Bks.

—Two Heads Are Better Than One. 2002. (Amazing Days of Abby Hayes Ser.: No. 7). (gr. 3-6). lib. bdg. 12.40 (978-0-613-50519-2(0)) Tandem Library Bks.

Mazer, Anne & Gesue, Monica. Two Heads Are Better Than One. 2002. (Amazing Days of Abby Hayes Ser.: No. 7). (Illus.). 144p. (J). (gr. 4-7). mass mkt. 4.99 (978-0-439-35366-3(1)) Scholastic, Inc.

Mazer, Norma Fox. Babyface. 2007. (Illus.). 176p. (YA). pap. 6.95 (978-0-15-206277-4(7) , Harcourt Paperbacks) Harcourt Children's Bks.

—Girlhearts. 2002. (gr. 7-12). lib. bdg. 15.30 (978-0-613-58571-2(2)) Tandem Library Bks.

—The Missing Girl. 2008. 288p. (J). 16.99 (***978-0-06-623776-3(9)***); lib. bdg. 17.89 (***978-0-06-623777-0(7)***) HarperCollins Pubs. (HarperTeen).

—Ten Ways to Make My Sister Disappear. 2007. (J). (***978-0-439-83984-6(X)***); 160p. (gr. 4-7). pap. 16.99 (***978-0-439-83983-9(1)***) Scholastic, Inc. (Levine, Arthur A. Bks.).

—What I Believe. 2007. (Illus.). 176p. (J). pap. 6.95 (978-0-15-206283-5(1) , Harcourt Paperbacks) Harcourt Children's Bks.

—When She Was Good. 2003. 228p. (YA). (gr. 7-12). per. 14.15 (978-0-613-23050-6(7)) Tandem Library Bks.

McCann, Daryl & Forbes, Debbie. Wish You Weren't Here. 2000. 144p. (YA). pap. 14.95 (978-0-7022-3103-2(7)) Univ. of Queensland Pr. AUS. *Dist:* International Specialized Bk. Services.

McCarthy, Maureen. Rose by Any Other Name. 2008. 336p. (YA). 16.95 (***978-1-59643-372-4(8)***) Roaring Brook Pr.

E F G

McClain, Lee. My Abnormal Life. 2005. (YA). mass mkt. 5.99 (978-0-8439-5466-1(3)) Dorchester Publishing Co., Inc.

McClements, George. Night of the Veggie Monster. 2008. (Illus.). 32p. (J). 15.85 (*978-1-59990-234-0(6)) Bloomsbury Publishing.

—Night of the Veggie Monster. McClements, George, illus. 2008. (Illus.). 32p. (J). 14.95 (*978-1-59990-061-2(0)) Bloomsbury Publishing.

McCloskey, Robert. Time of Wonder. McCloskey, Robert, illus. 2002. (Illus.). (J). 14.04 (978-0-7587-0079-7(2)) Book Wholesalers, Inc.

McCormick, Patricia. Cut. unabr. ed. 2004. 168p. (J). (gr. 7 up). pap. 36.00 incl. audio (978-0-8072-0868-7(X), LYA 320 SP, Listening Library) Random Hse. Audio Publishing Group.

—Cut. 2002. (Illus.). 160p. (J). (gr. 7 up). pap. 6.99 (978-0-439-32459-5(9), PUSH) Scholastic, Inc.

—Cut. 2002. 13.64 (978-0-606-22261-7(8)); (gr. 7-12). lib. bdg. 15.30 (978-0-613-49394-9(X)) Tandem Library Bks.

—My Brother's Keeper. 2005. 192p. (gr. 5-17). 15.99 (978-0-7868-5173-7(2)) Hyperion Bks. for Children.

—My Brother's Keeper. 2006. 192p. (gr. 5-17). reprint ed. pap. 5.99 (978-0-7868-5174-4(0)) Hyperion Pr.

McCormick, Wendy. Papa, Me Echaras de Menos? Eachus, Jennifer, illus. 2000. (SPA.). 32p. (J). (ps-1). (978-84-241-7899-4(8), EV2384) Everest de Ediciones y Distribucion, S.L. ESP. *Dist:* Lectorum Pubns., Inc.

McCourt, Lisa. Te Quiero, Carita Sucia. 2006. (SPA., Illus.). 30p. (J). (gr. 1-2). 10.40 (978-84-95620-66-8(9), BRO33536) Brosquil Edicions, S.L. ESP. *Dist:* Lectorum Pubns., Inc.

McCusker, Paul. Danger Lies Ahead. 2006. (Adventures in Odyssey Ser.: No. 2). 336p. (J). pap. 13.99 (978-1-58997-329-9(1)) Focus on the Family Publishing.

McDaniel, Lurlene. Garden of Angels. 2005. 288p. (YA). (gr. 7). pap. 5.50 (978-0-553-49432-7(5), Laurel Leaf) Random Hse. Children's Bks.

—Letting Go of Lisa. (YA). (gr. 7). 2007. 176p. mass mkt. 6.50 (*978-0-440-23868-3(4), Laurel Leaf); 2006. 192p. 10.95 (978-0-385-73159-1(0), Delacorte Bks. for Young Readers); 2006. 192p. lib. bdg. 12.99 (978-0-385-90196-3(8), Delacorte Bks. for Young Readers) Random Hse. Children's Bks.

—One Last Wish: Three Novels: Mother, Help Me Live; Let Him Live; Sixteen & Dying. 1998. (One Last Wish Ser.). (gr. 7-12). lib. bdg. 15.30 (978-0-613-88880-6(4)) Tandem Library Bks.

—The Time Capsule. 2005. 224p. (YA). (gr. 7). mass mkt. 5.99 (978-0-553-49431-0(7), Laurel Leaf) Random Hse. Children's Bks.

McDonald, Joyce. Comfort Creek. 1998. 10.64 (978-0-606-13289-3(9)) Tandem Library Bks.

—Swallowing Stones. 1999. 272p. (YA). (gr. 7-12). mass mkt. 6.99 (978-0-440-22672-7(4), Laurel Leaf) Random Hse. Children's Bks.

—Swallowing Stones. 1999. 245p. lib. bdg. 13.55 (978-0-606-16721-5(8)); (gr. 7-12). lib. bdg. 13.55 (978-0-613-19465-5(9)) Tandem Library Bks.

McDonald, Megan. Julie Tells Her Story, Bk. 2. McAliley, Susan, illus. 2007. 104p. (YA). (gr. 3 up). 12.95 (*978-1-59369-289-6(7)) American Girl Publishing, Inc.

—Julie Tells Her Story, Bk. 2. McAliley, Susan & Hunt, Robert, illus. 2007. 104p. (YA). (gr. 3 up). pap. 6.95 (*978-1-59369-288-9(9)) American Girl Publishing, Inc.

McElmurry, Jill. I'm Not a Baby! 2005. (J). 15.95 (978-0-689-87008-8(6), Atheneum) Simon & Schuster Children's Publishing.

—I'm Not a Baby. McElmurry, Jill, illus. 2006. (Illus.). 40p. (J). (ps-3). 16.95 (978-0-375-83614-5(4), Schwartz & Wade Bks.) Random Hse. Children's Bks.

McEwan, Ian. The Daydreamer. Browne, Anthony, illus. 2002. 208p. (J). (gr. 3 up). pap. 8.99 (978-0-06-053015-0(4), Harper Trophy) HarperCollins Pubs.

—The Daydreamer. 2000. 160p. (gr. 4-7). pap. 10.95 (978-0-385-49805-0(5), Anchor) Knopf Publishing Group.

Mcfarlane, Seth, creator. Family Guy, 3 vols., Vol. 1. 2004. (Cine-Manga Ser.). (Illus.). 192p. pap. 7.99 (978-1-59532-166-4(7), Tokyopop Adult) TOKYOPOP, Inc.

McGill, Alice. Mile's Song. 2002. (Illus.). 224p. (YA). (gr. 6-8). pap. 4.99 (978-0-439-28070-9(2), Scholastic Pr.) Scholastic, Inc.

McGowan, Anthony. Hellbent. 2006. 272p. (YA). pap. 8.99 (978-1-4169-0814-2(5), Simon & Schuster Children's Publishing) Simon & Schuster Children's Publishing.

McGuigan, Mary Ann. Morning in a Different Place. 2008. (J). (*978-1-59078-551-5(7), Front Street) Boyds Mills Pr.

McKay, Hilary. Caddy Ever After. 224p. (J). 2007. pap. 5.99 (*978-1-4169-0931-6(1), Aladdin); 2006. (gr. 5-9). 15.95 (978-1-4169-0930-9(3), McElderry, Margaret K.) Simon & Schuster Children's Publishing.

—Forever Rose. 2008. 304p. (J). 16.99 (*978-1-4169-5486-6(4), McElderry, Margaret K.) Simon & Schuster Children's Publishing.

—Indigo's Star. 272p. (J). (gr. 3-7). 2004. (Illus.). 16.95 (978-0-689-86563-3(5), McElderry, Margaret K.); 2006. reprint ed. pap. 5.99 (978-1-4169-1403-7(X), Aladdin) Simon & Schuster Children's Publishing.

—Permanent Rose. (J). (gr. 3-7). 2005. 240p. 16.99 (978-1-4169-0372-7(0), McElderry, Margaret K.); 2006. 256p. reprint ed. pap. 5.99 (978-1-4169-2804-1(9), Aladdin) Simon & Schuster Children's Publishing.

—El Perro Viernes. (Barco de Vapor). (SPA.). (YA). (gr. 5-8). pap. (978-84-348-6214-2(X)) SM Ediciones.

—Saffy's Angel. 2004. 160p. (J). (gr. 4-7). pap. 36.00 incl. audio (978-0-8072-2098-6(1), Listening Library) Random Hse. Audio Publishing Group.

—Saffy's Angel. 160p. (J). (gr. 3-7). 2003. (Illus.). pap. 4.99 (978-0-689-84934-3(6), Aladdin); 2002. 16.99 (978-0-689-84933-6(8), McElderry, Margaret K.) Simon & Schuster Children's Publishing.

—Saffy's Angel. l.t. ed. 2003. (Juvenile Ser.). 227p. (J). 21.95 (978-0-7862-5500-9(5)) Thorndike Pr.

McKee, David. El Cochinito de Carlota. 2000. (Los Especials de A la Orilla Del Viento Ser.). (SPA., Illus.). 24p. (J). (ps-ps). per. 13.99 (978-968-16-6021-5(8), FC5896) Fondo de Cultura Economica USA.

McKissack, Pat. Stitchin' & Pullin' A Gee's Bend Quilt. Cabrera, Cozbi S., illus. 2007. (J). (*978-0-375-83163-8(0)); lib. bdg. (*978-0-375-93163-5(5)) Random Hse., Inc.

McKissack, Patricia C. Color Me Dark: The Diary of Nellie Lee Love, the Great Migration North, Chicago, Illinois, 1919. 2000. (Dear America Ser.). (J). 9.95 (978-0-439-26653-6(X)) Scholastic, Inc.

—Color Me Dark: The Diary of Nellie Lee Love, the Great Migration North, Chicago, Illinois, 1919. 2000. (Dear America Ser.). (Illus.). 224p. (J). (gr. 4-9). pap. 10.95 (978-0-590-51159-9(9)) Scholastic, Inc.

McKissack, Patricia C. & McKissack, Fredrick L. Messy Bessey's Family Reunion. Regan, Dana, illus. 2000. (Rookie Reader Skill Set Ser.). 32p. (J). (gr. k-2). pap. 4.95 (978-0-516-26552-0(0), Children's Pr.) Scholastic Library Publishing.

McKissack, Patricia C., et al. Messy Bessey's Closet, Level C. rev. ed. 2001. (Rookie Readers Ser.). (Illus.). 32p. (J). (gr. 1-2). 19.50 (978-0-516-21659-1(7), Children's Pr.) Scholastic Library Publishing.

—Messy Bessey's Family Reunion. 2000. (Rookie Readers Ser.). (Illus.). 32p. (J). (gr. 1-2). 19.50 (978-0-516-20830-5(6), Children's Pr.) Scholastic Library Publishing.

McKnight, Penny. Nix. 2006. (Illus.). 84p. (J). (978-1-59166-610-3(4)) Jones, Bob Univ. Pr.

McLaren, Clemence. Aphrodite's Blessings: Love Stories from the Greek Myth. 2002. 208p. (YA). (gr. 8 up). 16.00 (978-0-689-84377-8(1), Atheneum) Simon & Schuster Children's Publishing.

—Dance for the Aina. 2003. 160p. 9.95 (978-1-57306-151-3(4)) Bess Pr., Inc.

McMullan, Kate. Sir Lancelot, Where Are You? 2007. (Dragon Slayers' Academy Ser.: No. 6). 112p. (J). (gr. 1-6). 24.21 (*978-1-59961-379-6(4)) Spotlight.

McMullan, Margaret. How I Found the Strong. 2004. 144p. (J). (gr. 5-9). tchr. ed. 15.00 (978-0-618-35008-7(X)) Houghton Mifflin Co. Trade & Reference Div.

—How I Found the Strong. 2006. 144p. (YA). (gr. 7). reprint ed. mass mkt. 5.50 (978-0-553-49492-1(9), Laurel Leaf) Random Hse. Children's Bks.

McNamee, Graham. Hate You. 2000. (Illus.). (J). 12.15 (978-0-606-18803-6(7)) Tandem Library Bks.

McNeill, J. D. The Last Codfish. rev. ed. 2005. 192p. (YA). (gr. 9-17). 16.95 (978-0-8050-7489-5(9), Holt, Henry & Co. Bks. For Young Readers) Holt, Henry & Co.

McNish, Cliff. Angel. 2008. (Exceptional Reading & Language Arts Titles for Upper Grades Ser.). (J). 16.95 (*978-0-8225-8900-6(1), Carolrhoda Bks.) Lerner Publishing Group.

Mead, Alice. Dawn & Dusk. 2007. (Illus.). 160p. (J). (gr. 5-9). 16.00 (978-0-374-31708-9(9)) Farrar, Straus & Giroux.

Mead, Alice & Weber James, Alice. Isabella's Above-Ground Pool. Cocca-Leffler, Maryann, illus. 2006. 112p. (J). 16.00 (978-0-374-33617-2(2), Farrar, Straus & Giroux (BYR)) Farrar, Straus & Giroux.

Meckley, Stephanie R., et al. Just Like Mom. 1998. (Illus.). 24p. (J). (gr. k-2). pap. 3.00 (978-1-892464-03-3(9)) Meckley Publishing Co.

Meldrum, Christina. Madapple. 2008. 416p. (J). (gr. 9). 16.99 (*978-0-375-85176-6(3)); lib. bdg. 19.99 (*978-0-375-95176-3(8)) Random Hse. Children's Bks. (Knopf Bks. for Young Readers).

Meltzer, Milton. Tough Times. 2007. 176p. (J). (gr. 7 up). 16.00 (*978-0-618-87445-3(3), Clarion Bks.) Houghton Mifflin Co. Trade & Reference Div.

Merkel, Ruth. Hannah's Girls: Ann. 2006. 112p. (J). pap. 9.99 (*978-0-8280-1951-4(7)) Review & Herald Publishing Assn.

—Hannah's Girls: Grace, 6. 2006. (Illus.). 128p. (J). pap. 9.99 (*978-0-8280-1953-8(3)) Review & Herald Publishing Assn.

—Hannah's Girls: Marilla, 6 bks. 2006. (Illus.). 144p. (J). pap. 9.99 (*978-0-8280-1952-1(5)) Review & Herald Publishing Assn.

—Hannah's Girls: Ruthie. 2007. 144p. (J). pap. 9.99 (*978-0-8280-1954-5(1)) Review & Herald Publishing Assn.

Merrell, Mar'ce. Trading Riley. 2001. (Middle Readers Ser.). (Illus.). 96p. (J). (gr. 3-7). pap. 6.95 (978-1-896184-88-3(X)) Roussan Pubs., Inc./Roussan Editeur, Inc. CAN. *Dist:* Orca Bk. Pubs. USA.

Merrifield, Margaret. Come Sit by Me. Collins, Heather, illus. 2nd ed. 1998. 32p. (J). (ps-3). reprint ed. pap. 5.50 (978-0-7737-5958-9(1)) Stoddart Kids CAN. *Dist:* Fitzhenry & Whiteside, Ltd.

Merritt, Susan E. The Stone Orchard. 1999. 168p. (J). (gr. 3-7). pap. (978-1-55125-030-4(6)) Vanwell Publishing, Ltd.

Messinger, Carla & Katz, Susan. When the Shadbush Blooms. Fadden, David Kanietakeron, illus. 2007. 32p. (J). (ps-2). 15.95 (978-1-58246-192-2(9), Tricycle Pr.) Ten Speed Pr.

Metzler, Chris & Kim, Sunyoung. Me & 10 Babies. (Illus.). 36p. (978-0-9688338-4-1(5)) Cadence Publishing.

Meyer, Adam. The Last Domino. 2005. 272p. (YA). (gr. 6). 16.99 (978-0-399-24332-5(1), Putnam Juvenile) Penguin Group (USA) Inc.

Michels, Dia L. Look What I See! Where Can I Be? at Home. Bowles, Michael J N., photos by. 2002. 32p. 16.95 (978-1-930775-06-0(7)) Platypus Media, L.L.C.

—Look What I See! Where Can I Be? with My Animal Friends. Bowles, Michael J. N. & Bowles, Michael J. N., photos by. 2007. (Illus.). (J). pap. 9.95 (978-1-930775-08-4(3)) Platypus Media, L.L.C.

—Look What I See! Where Can I Be? with My Animal Friends. Bowles, Michael J. N., photos by l.t. ed. 2002. (Look What I See! Where Can I Be? Ser.: Vol. 3). (Illus.). 32p. 16.95 (978-1-930775-07-7(5)) Platypus Media, L.L.C.

—Zack in the Middle. Bell, Fred, illus. 2001. 48p. 16.95 (978-1-930775-01-5(6)) Platypus Media, L.L.C.

Milgrim, David. My Dog, Buddy. 2008. (J). pap. (*978-0-545-03593-4(7)) Scholastic, Inc.

Miller, Paula. One-Eyed Jack. Forrest, Chris, illus. 144p. (J). 2007. per. 8.95 (978-0-9769417-0-5(8)); 2006. 13.95 (978-0-9718348-8-0(1)) Blooming Tree Pr.

Mills, Charles. Wings over Oshkosh. 2005. (Honors Club Story Ser.: Vol. 5). 127p. (J). (978-0-8163-2089-9(6)) Pacific Pr. Publishing Assn.

Mills, Claudia. The Totally Made-Up Civil War Diary of Amanda MacLeish. 2008. 208p. (J). 16.00 (*978-0-374-37696-3(4)) Farrar, Straus & Giroux.

Minarik, Else Holmelund. Lost in Little Bear's Room. Wenzel, David T., illus. 2004. (Festival Reader Ser.). 32p. (J). (ps-2). pap. 3.99 (978-0-694-01706-5(X), Harper Festival) HarperCollins Pubs.

Minter, J. The Sweetest Thing: An Inside Girl Novel. 2007. (Insiders Novel Ser.). 224p. (J). (gr. 7 up). pap. 8.95 (*978-1-59990-087-2(4), Bloomsbury Children) Bloomsbury Publishing.

Mitchell, Rhonda. The Talking Cloth. 2001. (Illus.). 32p. (J). (ps-2). pap. 6.95 (978-0-531-07182-3(0), Orchard Bks.) Scholastic, Inc.

Mitchell, Todd. The Traitor King. 2007. 368p. (J). (gr. 4-7). pap. 16.99 (978-0-439-82788-1(4), Scholastic Pr.) Scholastic, Inc.

Mogdics, Teresa. Jimmy Johnson. 2001. 117p. (YA). pap. 16.95 (978-1-58851-574-2(5)) PublishAmerica, Inc.

Mohr, Nicholasa. Going Home. 1999. 192p. (J). (gr. 3-7). reprint ed. pap. 5.99 (978-0-14-130644-5(0), Puffin) Penguin Group (USA) Inc.

—Going Home. 1999. (gr. 3-6). lib. bdg. 14.15 (978-0-8335-2939-8(0)) Tandem Library Bks.

Molloy, Michael. The House on Falling Star Hill. 2004. (Illus.). 384p. (J). pap. 16.95 (978-0-439-57740-3(3), Chicken Hse., The) Scholastic, Inc.

Molzahn, Arlene Bourgeois. The Goat Who Wouldn't Come Home. Dillard, Kristine, illus. 1998. 12p. (J). (gr. k-2). pap. 3.75 (978-1-880612-82-8(8), Seedling Pubns.) Continental Pr., Inc.

Montes, Marisa. A Crazy Mixed-Up Spanglish Day. Cepeda, Joe, illus. 2003. (Get Ready for Gabi Ser.). 128p. (J). pap. 12.95 (978-0-439-51710-2(9), Scholastic Paperbacks) Scholastic, Inc.

Montgomery, L. M. Akin to Anne: Tales of Other Orphans. (YA). 22.95 (978-0-8488-2656-7(6)) Amereon LTD.

—Anne of Green Gables. 2005. (My First Classics Ser.). 112p. (J). (gr. k-3). pap. 4.99 (978-0-06-079147-6(0), Harper Festival) HarperCollins Pubs.

—Anne of Ingleside. 2000. (Avonlea Ser.: No. 10). (YA). (gr. 5-8). 23.95 (978-0-8488-0890-7(8)) Amereon LTD.

—Anne of Ingleside, Vol. 6. 1999. 384p. (J). pap. 3.99 (978-0-14-036801-7(9), Putnam Juvenile) Penguin Group (USA) Inc.

—The Complete Anne of Green Gables: Anne of Green Gables; Anne of the Island; Anne of Avonlea; Anne of Windy Poplars; Anne's House of Dreams; Anne of Ingleside; Rainbow Valley; Rilla of Ingleside, 8 vols. gif. ed. 1998. (J). (gr. 4-7). mass mkt. 40.43 (978-0-553-60941-7(6), Starfire) Random Hse. Children's Bks.

—Rainbow Valley. 2004. 184p. (YA). pap. 8.95 (978-1-57646-890-6(9)) Quiet Vision Publishing.

—The Story Girl. Date not set. 22.95 (978-0-8488-2372-6(9)) Amereon LTD.

—The Story Girl. 2000. (Sara Stanley of Avonlea Ser.: Vol. vol 1). 178p. 24.95 (978-1-57646-322-2(2)); (Sara Stanley of Avonlea Ser.: Vol. vol 1). 220p. pap. 12.99 (978-1-57646-321-5(4)); (Sara Stanley of Avonlea: Vol. 1). 370p. pap. 21.99 (978-1-57646-323-9(0)) Quiet Vision Publishing.

Mooney, Bel. Voices of Silence. 1998. (978-0-606-13887-1(0)) Tandem Library Bks.

Moore, Stephanie Perry. Golden Spirit. 2006. (Carmen Browne Ser.). 144p. (YA). pap. 5.99 (978-0-8024-8169-6(8)) Moody Pubs.

Mora, Pat. A Birthday Basket for Tia. Lang, Cecily, illus. unabr. ed. 2001. (J). (gr. k-3). pap. 15.95 incl. audio (978-0-8045-6841-8(3), 6841) Spoken Arts, Inc.

—Let's Eat! A Comer! Suarez, Maribel, illus. 2008. (My Family: Mi Familia Ser.). (SPA & ENG.). 24p. (J). 12.99 (*978-0-06-085038-8(8)); lib. bdg. 14.89 (*978-0-06-085039-5(6)) HarperCollins Pubs. (Rayo).

Mora, Pat. Maria Paints the Hills. Hesch, Maria, illus. 2002. 32p. 19.95 (978-0-89013-401-6(4)); 1p. pap. 9.95 (978-0-89013-410-8(3)) Museum of New Mexico Pr.

Morales, Maximino. Juan & the Three Wise Men (Juan y los Tres Reyes Mogos) 2002. (ENG & SPA., Illus.). 28p. (J). (gr. k-3). pap. 6.95 (978-0-9740308-1-4(3)) Maximum Publishing Co.

Moranville, Sharelle Byars. Over the River. rev. ed. 2002. 240p. (J). (gr. 4-9). 16.95 (978-0-8050-7049-1(4), Holt, Henry & Co. Bks. For Young Readers) Holt, Henry & Co.

—Over the River. 2004. 240p. (gr. 5). 5.99 (978-0-440-41977-8(8), Yearling) Random Hse. Children's Bks.

—The Purple Ribbon. Alter, Anna, illus. rev. ed. 2003. 80p. (J). (gr. 1-4). 17.95 (978-0-8050-6659-3(4), Holt, Henry & Co. Bks. For Young Readers) Holt, Henry & Co.

Morey, Walt. Year of the Black Pony. 2006. (Living History Library). 172p. (J). pap. 11.95 (*978-1-932350-08-1(X)) Bethlehem Bks.

Morganstern, Mimi. The House at Hemlock Farms. Morganstern, Mimi, illus. 2000. (Illus.). vi, 54p. (J). (gr. 3-6). pap. 6.95 (978-0-9700522-3-0(5)) Morganstern, Mimi.

—The House at Hemlock Farms-"Read-Along with Mimi" A Cool Chapterbook-Package. Morganstern, Mimi, illus. 2000. (Illus.). vi, 54p. (J). (gr. 3-6). per. 9.99 incl. audio (978-0-9700522-4-7(3)) Morganstern, Mimi.

Moriarty, Jaclyn. The Spell Book of Listen Taylor. 2007. (YA). (*978-0-439-84679-0(X)); 496p. (J). (gr. 9 up). 16.99 (*978-0-439-84678-3(1)) Scholastic, Inc. (Levine, Arthur A. Bks.).

Morris, Taylor. Class Favorite. 2007. 304p. (J). (gr. 4-8). pap. 5.99 (*978-1-4169-3598-8(3), Aladdin) Simon & Schuster Children's Publishing.

Morrison, Toni & Morrison, Slade. La Gran Caja. Potter, Giselle, illus. 2001. (SPA.). 56p. (YA). (gr. 3 up). 15.16 (978-84-406-9535-2(7)) Ediciones B ESP. *Dist:* Lectorum Pubns., Inc.

Morton, Lone & Risk, Mary. Get Dressed, Roberto. 1998. (Language Learning Story Bks.).Tr. of Vistete, Roberto. (ENG & SPA., Illus.). 28p. (J). (ps-3). 7.99 (978-0-7641-5129-3(0), BA290) Barron's Educational Series, Inc.

Moses, Shelia P. The Baptism. 2007. 144p. (YA). (gr. 7 up). 15.99 (978-1-4169-0671-1(1), McElderry, Margaret K.) Simon & Schuster Children's Publishing.

—The Legend of Buddy Bush. unabr. ed. 2005. (J). (gr. 3-7). 55.70 incl. audio (978-1-4193-3575-4(8), 42043) Recorded Bks., LLC.

—The Legend of Buddy Bush. (Illus.). 224p. 2005. (YA). pap. 5.99 (978-1-4169-0716-9(5), Simon Pulse); 2003. (J). 15.95 (978-0-689-85839-0(6), McElderry, Margaret K.) Simon & Schuster Children's Publishing.

—The Legend of Buddy Bush. l.t. ed. 2005. 179p. 22.95 (978-0-7862-7311-9(9)) Thorndike Pr.

Moss, Marissa. Amelia Writes Again. Moss, Marissa, illus. 2006. (Amelia's Notebooks). (Illus.). 32p. (J). 9.95 (978-1-4169-0904-0(4), Simon & Schuster/Paula Wiseman Bks.) Simon & Schuster Children's Publishing.

—Amelia Writes Again. 1999. (Amelia's Notebooks). (Illus.). 48p. (gr. 3-5). lib. bdg. 12.75 (978-0-606-17252-3(1)) Tandem Library Bks.

—Amelia's 5th-Grade Notebook. Moss, Marissa, illus. 2006. (Amelia's Notebooks). (J). 5.99 (978-1-4169-1292-7(4)) Simon & Schuster, Inc.

—Rose's Journal: The Story of a Girl in the Great Depression. 2003. (Young American Voices Ser.). (Illus.). 56p. (J). pap. 7.00 (978-0-15-204605-7(4), Silver Whistle) Harcourt Trade Pubs.

—Rose's Journal: The Story of a Girl in the Great Depression. Moss, Marissa, illus. 2001. (Young American Voices Ser.). (Illus.). 56p. (YA). (gr. 3-7). 15.00 (978-0-15-202423-9(9), Silver Whistle) Harcourt Trade Pubs.

Mowll, Joshua. Operation Typhoon Shore. Mowll, Joshua et al, illus. 2006. (Guild of Specialists Ser.). 288p. (YA). (gr. 5 up). 15.99 (978-0-7636-3122-2(1)) Candlewick Pr.

Mueller, Miranda, illus. Mishka: An Adoption Tale. 2007. 32p. (J). 16.95 (978-1-933084-01-5(4)) DRT Pr.

Mullen, Paul Michael. The Day I Hit a Home Run at Great American Ball Park. 2007. (J). (*978-1-933197-29-6(3)) Orange Frazer Pr.

Mullin, Penn. Along the Santa Fe Trail. 1999. (gr. 7-12). lib. bdg. 11.60 (978-0-613-23075-9(2)) Tandem Library Bks.

—Gold Rush Fever. 1999. (gr. 7-12). lib. bdg. 11.60 (978-0-613-28855-2(6)) Tandem Library Bks.

—Off to Oregon. 1999. (gr. 7-12). lib. bdg. 11.60 (978-0-613-28988-7(9)) Tandem Library Bks.

Munsch, Robert. On Partage Tout. ed. 2004. (FRE., Illus.). (J). (gr. k-3). spiral bd. (978-0-616-01838-5(X)) Canadian National Institute for the Blind/Institut National Canadien pour les Aveugles.

—Tengo Que Ir! Martchenko, Michael, illus. 2001. (Hablemos Ser.). (SPA.). 24p. (J). (gr. k-2). pap. 5.95 (978-1-55037-682-1(9), AP30494) Annick Pr., Ltd. CAN. *Dist:* Firefly Bks., Ltd.

—Up, Up, Down! Martchenko, Michael, illus. 2002. 32p. (J). pap. 4.99 (978-0-439-31796-2(7)) Scholastic, Inc.

—Up, up, Down. ed. 2004. (Illus.). (J). (gr. k-3). spiral bd. (978-0-616-11126-0(6)); spiral bd. (978-0-616-11127-7(4)) Canadian National Institute for the Blind/Institut National Canadien pour les Aveugles.

Murphy, Barbara. Life! How I Love You! Baca, Elena, illus. 2004. (Museo Kids Ser.). 1p. 16.95 (978-0-89013-468-9(5)) Museum of New Mexico Pr.

Murphy, Jill. Mr. Large in Charge. Murphy, Jill, illus. 2007. (Illus.). 40p. (J). (ps-2). 16.99 (978-0-7636-3504-6(9)); pap. 6.99 (978-0-7636-2739-3(9)) Candlewick Pr.

Murphy, Jim. Desperate Journey. 2006. (Illus.). 288p. (J). pap. 16.99 (978-0-439-07806-1(7), Scholastic Pr.) Scholastic, Inc.

Murray, Brendan. Tev. Rubin, Barry & Veremis, Thanos, eds. 2002. 152p. (YA). pap. 13.95 (978-1-86368-334-0(8)) Fremantle Pr. AUS. *Dist:* International Specialized Bk. Services.

Murray, Carol. Hurry Up! Garbot, Dave, illus. 2003. (Rookie Reader Skill Set Ser.). (J). (gr. k-2). pap. 4.95 (978-0-516-27831-5(2), Children's Pr.) Scholastic Library Publishing.

—Hurry Up! 2003. (gr. k-3). lib. bdg. 12.95 (978-0-613-67634-2(3)) Tandem Library Bks.

Murray, Jaye. Bottled Up. 2004. 220p. (J). (gr. 2-13). lib. bdg. 13.04 (978-0-606-32733-6(9)) Tandem Library Bks.

Murray, Martine. Henrietta: There's No One Better. 2006. (Illus.). (J). 88p. 9.99 (978-0-439-80749-4(2)); 96p. pap. 9.99 (978-0-439-80747-0(6)) Scholastic, Inc. (Levine, Arthur A. Bks.).

My Great Grandma Clara. 2006. (J). pap. 12.95 (978-0-9677047-8-4(2)) Marble House Editions.

My little Brother, 6 vols., Pack. (gr. 1-2). 22.00 (978-0-7635-9164-9(5)) Rigby Education.

My Two Families: Individual Title Six-Packs. (gr. 3 up). 35.00 (978-0-7635-9661-3(2)) Rigby Education.

Myers, Anna. Captain's Command. 2001. 11.15 (978-0-606-22411-6(4)) Tandem Library Bks.

Myers, Anna. Wart. 2007. 224p. (J). (gr. 5-9). 16.95 (****978-0-8027-8977-8(3))*** Walker & Co.

Myers, Walter Dean. The Dream Bearer. 2003. 192p. (J). (gr. 5 up). 15.99 (978-0-06-029521-9(X) , Amistad) HarperCollins Pubs.

—The Dream Bearer. l.t. ed. 2003. 207p. (J). 25.95 (978-0-7862-5923-6(X)) Thorndike Pr.

—Game. 2008. 240p. (J). 16.99 (****978-0-06-058294-4(4));*** lib. bdg. 17.89 (****978-0-06-058295-1(2))*** HarperCollins Pubs. (HarperTeen).

—It Ain't All for Nothin' 2003. (Amistad Ser.). 240p. (gr. 7 up). pap. 6.99 (978-0-06-447311-8(2) , Harper Trophy) HarperCollins Pubs.

—It Ain't All for Nothin' 2003. (gr. 7-12). lib. bdg. 14.15 (978-0-613-67203-0(8)) Tandem Library Bks.

—Shooter. 2004. 224p. (J). 15.99 (978-0-06-029519-6(8) , HarperTeen) HarperCollins Pubs.

Myracle, Lauren. Eleven. 208p. (J). (gr. 3-7). 2004. 16.99 (978-0-525-47165-3(0) , Dutton Juvenile); 2005. reprint ed. pap. 6.99 (978-0-14-240346-4(6) , Puffin) Penguin Group (USA) Inc.

—The Fashion Disaster That Changed My Life. 2008. 160p. (J). (gr. 5). 6.99 (978-0-14-240717-2(8) , Puffin); 2005. 144p. (YA). (gr. 4-6). 15.99 (978-0-525-47222-3(3) , Dutton Juvenile) Penguin Group (USA) Inc.

—Thirteen. 2008. 224p. (J). (gr. 5). 15.99 (****978-0-525-47896-6(5)*** , Dutton Juvenile) Penguin Group (USA) Inc.

Myracle, Lauren. Twelve. (YA). (gr. 5-8). 2008. 224p. 6.99 (****978-0-14-241091-2(8)*** , Puffin); 2007. 208p. 15.99 (978-0-525-47784-6(5) , Dutton Juvenile) Penguin Group (USA) Inc.

Na, An. A Step from Heaven. 2003. 160p. (YA). (gr. 7-11). pap. 7.99 (978-0-14-250027-9(5) , Puffin) Penguin Group (USA) Inc.

—A Step from Heaven. l.t. ed. 2002. 193p. (J). 22.95 (978-0-7862-4126-2(8)) Thomson Gale.

Namioka, Lensey. Half & Half. 2004. 144p. (gr. 3-7). pap. 5.50 (978-0-440-41890-0(9) , Yearling) Random Hse. Children's Bks.

—Mismatch. 224p. (gr. 5-9). 2007. (YA). mass mkt. 6.50 (978-0-440-23879-9(X) , Laurel Leaf); 2006. (J). 15.95 (978-0-385-73183-6(3) , Delacorte Bks. for Young Readers) Random Hse. Children's Bks.

Napoli, Donna Jo. Crazy Jack. 2001. 12.15 (978-0-606-20617-4(5)) Tandem Library Bks.

—Daughter of Venice. 2003. 288p. (YA). (gr. 7). pap. 6.50 (978-0-440-22928-5(6) , Laurel Leaf) Random Hse. Children's Bks.

—Daughter of Venice. 2003. (gr. 7-12). lib. bdg. 13.55 (978-0-613-72327-5(9)) Tandem Library Bks.

Napoli, Donna Jo & Tchen, Richard. Spinners. November, S., ed. 2001. 208p. (YA). pap. 6.99 (978-0-14-131110-4(X) , Puffin) Penguin Group (USA) Inc.

Nash, Mary. Lost Treasures Bk. 2: Mrs. Coverlet's Magician. 2001. 128p. (J). 13.49 (978-0-7868-2597-4(9)) Hyperion Pr.

Natti, Susanna, illus. Lionel at Large. 2002. (J). 11.49 (978-0-7587-1389-6(4)) Book Wholesalers, Inc.

Naylor, Phyllis Reynolds. Alice in April. 2002. (Alice Ser.). 176p. (J). pap. 5.99 (978-0-689-81686-4(3) , Aladdin) Simon & Schuster Children's Publishing.

—Alice in April. 2002. (Alice Ser.). (gr. 3-6). lib. bdg. 13.00 (978-0-613-88873-8(1)) Tandem Library Bks.

—Alice In-Between. Vaccaro, Nick, photos by. 2004. (Alice Ser.). (Illus.). 160p. (J). pap. 4.99 (978-0-689-81685-7(5) , Aladdin) Simon & Schuster Children's Publishing.

—Alice in the Know. (Alice Ser.). (YA). 2007. 320p. pap. 5.99 (****978-0-689-87093-4(0)*** , Simon Pulse); 2006. 288p. (gr. 7 up). 15.95 (978-0-689-87092-7(2)) Simon & Schuster Children's Publishing.

—Alice on Her Way. 2006. (Alice Ser.). 352p. (YA). mass mkt. 5.99 (978-0-689-87091-0(4) , Simon Pulse) Simon & Schuster Children's Publishing.

—Dangerously Alice. 2007. (Alice Ser.). 304p. (YA). (gr. 9 up). 15.99 (978-0-689-87094-1(9) , Atheneum) Simon & Schuster Children's Publishing.

—I Can't Take You Anywhere! 2001. (J). 12.79 (978-0-606-20714-0(7)); lib. bdg. 14.15 (978-0-613-34773-0(0)) Tandem Library Bks.

—Lovingly Alice. (Alice Ser.). 176p. (J). 2006. pap. 5.99 (978-0-689-84400-3(X) , Aladdin); 2004. (Illus.). 15.95 (978-0-689-84399-0(2) , Atheneum) Simon & Schuster Children's Publishing.

—Outrageously Alice. 1998. (Alice Ser.). 144p. (J). (gr. 5-9). pap. 5.99 (978-0-689-80596-7(9) , Aladdin) Simon & Schuster Children's Publishing.

—Patiently Alice. (Alice Ser.). 256p. (YA). 2004. mass mkt. 5.99 (978-0-689-87073-6(6) , Simon Pulse); 2003. (Illus.). 15.95 (978-0-689-82636-8(2) , Atheneum) Simon & Schuster Children's Publishing.

—Peril in the Bessledorf Parachute Factory. Bernardin, James, illus. 2000. 160p. (J). (gr. 3-7). 16.95 (978-0-689-82539-2(0) , Atheneum) Simon & Schuster Children's Publishing.

—Saving Shiloh. 144p. (J). 1999. (Shiloh Ser.: No. 3). (gr. 4-7). reprint ed. pap. 5.99 (978-0-689-81461-7(5)); 2nd ed. 2006. (Illus.). (gr. 3-7). pap. 5.99 (978-1-4169-1422-8(6)) Simon & Schuster Children's Publishing. (Aladdin).

—Saving Shiloh. 1999. (978-0-606-14310-3(6)); (Shiloh Ser.: No. 3). (J). (gr. 3-6). lib. bdg. 13.55 (978-0-613-12073-9(6)) Tandem Library Bks.

—Saving Shiloh. l.t. ed. 2002. 193p. (J). 22.95 (978-0-7862-3713-5(9)) Thorndike Pr.

—Shiloh. (SPA.). 146p. (YA). (gr. 5-8). (978-968-16-5805-2(1) , FC0086) Fondo de Cultura Economica MEX. *Dist:* Lectorum Pubns., Inc.

—Shiloh. l.t. ed. 2000. (Shiloh Ser.: No. 1). 155p. (J). (gr. 4-7). lib. bdg. 27.95 (978-1-58118-058-9(6) , 23472) LRS.

—Shiloh. 144p. (J). (Shiloh Ser.: No. 1). (gr. 4-7). pap. 4.99 (978-0-8072-8330-1(4)); No. 1. 2004. (gr. 3-7). pap. 29.00 incl. audio (978-0-8072-8329-5(0) , YA164SP) Random Hse. Audio Publishing Group. (Listening Library).

—Shiloh. Moser, Barry, illus. 2000. (Shiloh Ser.: No. 1). 144p. (J). (gr. 3-7). pap. 5.99 (978-0-689-83582-7(5) , Aladdin) Simon & Schuster Children's Publishing.

—Shiloh. movie tie-in ed. 2000. (Shiloh Ser.: No. 6). (Illus.). 144p. (J). (gr. 4-7). pap. 5.99 (978-0-689-83583-4(3) , Aladdin) Simon & Schuster Children's Publishing.

—Shiloh. 2000. (gr. 3-6). lib. bdg. 14.15 (978-0-613-73274-1(X)); (J). (978-0-606-19724-3(9)); (gr. 3-6). lib. bdg. 14.15 (978-0-613-30125-1(0)) Tandem Library Bks.

—Shiloh Season. unabr. ed. 2004. (Shiloh Ser.: No. 2). 120p. (J). (gr. 3-7). pap. 29.00 incl. audio (978-0-8072-8707-1(5) , YA242SP, Listening Library) Random Hse. Audio Publishing Group.

—Shiloh Season. Moser, Barry, illus. (Shiloh Ser.: No. 2). 128p. (J). 1999. (gr. 3-7). pap. 5.99 (978-0-689-82931-4(0)); 1998. (gr. 4-7). pap. 5.99 (978-0-689-80646-9(9)) Simon & Schuster Children's Publishing. (Aladdin).

—Shiloh Season. 1999. (gr. 3-6). lib. bdg. 13.55 (978-0-613-90607-4(1)); 1998. (Shiloh Ser.: No. 2). (J). (gr. 4-7). (978-0-606-13085-1(3)) Tandem Library Bks.

—Shiloh Trilogy. (J). 2000. 432p. (gr. 3-7). pap. 16.99 (978-0-689-01525-0(9) , Aladdin); 1998. (Shiloh Ser.: Nos. 1-3). (gr. 4-7). 35.00 (978-0-689-82327-5(4) , Atheneum) Simon & Schuster Children's Publishing.

—Starting with Alice. (Alice Ser.). 192p. (J). 2004. (Illus.). pap. 4.99 (978-0-689-84396-9(8) , Aladdin); 2002. 15.95 (978-0-689-84395-2(X) , Atheneum) Simon & Schuster Children's Publishing.

—Starting with Alice. 2004. (gr. 3-6). lib. bdg. 13.00 (978-0-613-87056-6(5)) Tandem Library Bks.

—Walker's Crossing. unabr. ed. 2004. 232p. (J). (gr. 5-9). pap. 36.00 incl. audio (978-0-8072-8410-0(6) , Listening Library) Random Hse. Audio Publishing Group.

—Walker's Crossing. 2001. (J). (978-0-606-21506-0(9)); (gr. 7-12). lib. bdg. 13.00 (978-0-613-35030-3(8)) Tandem Library Bks.

Naylor, Phyllis Reynolds & Vaccaro, Nick. Alice on Her Way. 2005. (Alice Ser.). 336p. (YA). 16.99 (978-0-689-87090-3(6) , Atheneum) Simon & Schuster Children's Publishing.

Neale, Cynthia. Hope in New York City: The Continuing Story of the Irish Dresser. 2007. (ENG.). 176p. (J). pap. 7.95 (****978-1-57249-387-2(9)*** , White Mane Kids) White Mane Publishing Co., Inc.

Nelson, Annabelle. Ricardo's Pain: A Story for Young People & Their Parents about Staying Strong, Finding Courage & Overcoming Adversity. Palomares, Franz, illus. 2003. (SPA.). (978-0-9656732-8-0(6)) WHEEL Council, Inc., The.

Nelson, R. A. Breathe My Name. 2007. 288p. (J). (gr. 7). 16.99 (****978-1-59514-094-4(8)*** , Razorbill) Penguin Group (USA) Inc.

Nelson, Theresa. Empress of Elsewhere. 2000. (Illus.). (J). 12.64 (978-0-606-18836-4(3)) Tandem Library Bks.

Nervelle, Rosemarie. The Witch of Beaver Creek Mine. 2007. 160p. (gr. 5-9). 14.95 (****978-0-89272-741-4(1))*** Down East Bks.

Nesbit, E. Five Children & IT. 2002. (Children's Classics). (ENG., Illus.). 192p. (J). pap. (978-1-85326-124-4(6)) Wordsworth Editions, Ltd.

—The Railway Children. Dryhurst, Dinah, illus. 2000. 224p. (J). pap. 8.99 (978-1-86205-235-2(2) , Pavilion Bks., Ltd.) Anova Bks. GBR. *Dist:* Trafalgar Square Publishing.

—The Railway Children. Dryhurst, Dinah, tr. Dryhurst, Dinah, illus. 2004. 184p. 18.95 (978-1-56792-261-5(9)) Godine, David R. Pub.

—The Railway Children. 1998. (Children's Classics). (ENG., Illus.). 208p. (J). (gr. 4-7). pap. (978-1-85326-107-7(6) , 1076WW) Wordsworth Editions, Ltd.

—Railway Children. 2000. (Dover Juvenile Classics Ser.). (Illus.). 208p. (J). (gr. 4-7). pap. 2.50 (978-0-486-41022-7(6)) Dover Pubns., Inc.

—Railway Children. 2006. pap. (****978-1-4068-3505-2(6))*** Echo Library.

—Railway Children. (J). (978-0-340-71497-3(2) , Hodder & Stoughton) Hodder General Publishing Division.

—Railway Children. 2004. (ENG.). 580p. (****978-0-9548401-2-9(7))*** Shoes & Ships & Sealing Wax Ltd.

—The Railway Children. Brock, C. E., illus. 100th ed. 2005. 240p. (J). (ps-7). 14.95 (978-1-58717-279-3(8)); pap. 9.95 (978-1-58717-280-9(1)) Chronicle Bks. LLC. (SeaStar Bks.).

—The Railway Children. unabr. ed. 2004. (Chrysalis Children's Classics Ser.). (Illus.). 190p. (YA). pap. (978-1-84365-050-8(9)) Chrysalis Children's Bks.

—The Railway Children. 2004. reprint ed. pap. 22.95 (978-1-4191-7972-3(1)); pap. 1.99 (978-1-4192-7972-0(6)) Kessinger Publishing, LLC.

—The Railway Children. l.t. ed. 2006. (Large Print Ser.). lib. bdg. 26.00 (****978-1-58287-890-4(0))*** North Bks.

—The Railway Children, Level 3. 2nd ed. 2000. (Bookworms Ser.). (Illus.). 74p. 6.50 (978-0-19-423013-1(9)) Oxford Univ. Pr., Inc.

—The Railway Children, Level 2. 2000. (Illus.). 48p. (C). pap. 9.00 (978-0-582-41790-8(2)) Pearson ESL.

—Story of the Treasure Seekers. 2006. pap. (****978-1-4068-3507-6(2))*** Echo Library.

Nesbit, E. The Story of the Treasure Seekers: Being the Adventures of the Bastable Children in Search of A Fortune. l.t. ed. 2005. 288p. pap. (978-1-84637-207-0(0)) Echo Library.

Newbery, Linda. Set in Stone. 2006. 368p. (YA). (gr. 9). lib. bdg. 18.99 (978-0-385-75103-2(6)) Knopf, Alfred A. Inc.

—Set in Stone. 2006. 368p. (YA). (gr. 9). 16.95 (978-0-385-75102-5(8) , Fickling, David Bks.) Random Hse. Children's Bks.

Newton, Samantha. Being Nine Isn't So Bad. 2006. 52p. pap. 12.95 (978-1-4241-1902-8(2)) PublishAmerica, Inc.

Nickerson, Sara. How to Disappear Completely & Never Be Found. Comport, Sally Wern, illus. 288p. (J). (gr. 5 up). 2003. pap. 5.99 (978-0-06-441027-4(7)); 2002. 16.99 (978-0-06-029771-8(9)); 2002. lib. bdg. 17.89 (978-0-06-029772-5(7)) HarperCollins Pubs.

—How to Disappear Completely & Never Be Found. 2003. (gr. 7-12). lib. bdg. 14.15 (978-0-613-62207-3(3)) Tandem Library Bks.

Nielsen-Fernlund, Susin. Mormor Moves In. Laliberte, Louise-Andree, illus. 2004. 32p. (J). (ps-2). 16.95 (978-1-55143-291-5(9)) Orca Bk. Pubs. USA.

Nielson, Ane O. The Lone Star G Brand on My Behind. 2004. (Illus.). 96p. (J). per. 9.95 (978-1-930580-56-5(8) , Luminary Media Group) Pine Orchard, Inc.

Nilsson, Per. Seventeen. Chace, Tara, tr. 2007. 264p. (YA). (gr. 7 up). 17.95 (****978-1-932425-89-5(6))*** Boyds Mills Pr.

Nixon, Joan Lowery. John's Story, 1775. 2004. (J). (978-0-87935-228-8(0)) Colonial Williamsburg Foundation.

—Land of Promise. l.t. ed. 2001. (Ellis Island Stories Ser.). 169p. (J). (gr. 4 up). lib. bdg. 23.33 (978-0-8368-2812-2(7)) Stevens, Gareth Inc.

Nixon-Weaver, Elizabeth. Rooster. 2001. (Illus.). 320p. (J). (gr. 7 up). 16.95 (978-1-58837-001-3(1)) Winslow Pr.

Noble, Sheilagh. Uh Oh! 2003. (Toddler Ser.). (Illus.). 24p. (J). (ps up). (978-1-84089-182-9(3) , Zero to Ten, Limited) Evans Publishing Group.

Noble, Trinka Hakes. The Orange Shoes. Ettlinger, Doris, illus. rev. ed. 2007. (General Ser.). 40p. (J). (gr. 1-7). 16.95 (****978-1-58536-277-6(8))*** Sleeping Bear Pr.

Nolan, Han. Dancing on the Edge. 2007. (Illus.). 264p. (YA). pap. 6.95 (978-0-15-205884-5(2) , Harcourt Paperbacks) Harcourt Children's Bks.

—A Face in Every Window. 2001. (J). 12.64 (978-0-606-21184-0(5)) Tandem Library Bks.

—A Summer of Kings. 2006. (Illus.). 352p. (YA). 17.00 (978-0-15-205108-2(2)) Harcourt Children's Bks.

—A Summer of Kings. 2006. 334p. (J). (978-1-4156-7340-9(3)) Harcourt Trade Pubs.

Nolen, Jerdine. In My Momma's Kitchen. 2001. (Illus.). (J). 12.75 (978-0-606-21246-5(9)) Tandem Library Bks.

Nolen, Jerdine. Pitching in for Eubie. Lewis, E. B., illus. 2007. 32p. (J). lib. bdg. 17.89 (****978-0-06-056960-0(3));*** 16.99 (****978-0-688-14917-8(0))*** HarperCollins Pubs. (Amistad).

Noonan, Brandon. Plenty Porter. 2006. 240p. (YA). (gr. 7-17). 16.95 (978-0-8109-5996-5(8)) Abrams, Harry N. , Inc.

Novara, Joe. Road Wrangler: Cowboys on Wheels. Lawson, Robert & Spatrisano, Kimberly, illus. 2007. (J). pap. 7.95 (****978-1-58980-507-1(0))*** Pelican Publishing Co., Inc.

Nye, Naomi. Habibi. 1999. (gr. 7-12). lib. bdg. 14.15 (978-0-613-18312-3(6)) Tandem Library Bks.

Nye, Naomi Shihab. Habibi. unabr. ed. 2000. (YA). pap. 49.24 incl. audio (978-0-7887-3642-1(6) , 41008X4) Recorded Bks., LLC.

—Habibi. 1999. 272p. (YA). (gr. 5 up). pap. 5.99 (978-0-689-82523-1(4) , Simon Pulse) Simon & Schuster Children's Publishing.

—Habibi. 1999. (J). 12.64 (978-0-606-16320-0(4)) Tandem Library Bks.

O'Connell, Tyne. Dueling Princes: The Calypso Chronicles, Book 3. 2006. 272p. (YA). pap. 7.95 (978-1-58234-900-8(2) , Bloomsbury Children) Bloomsbury Publishing.

O'Connor, Barbara. How to Steal a Dog. 2007. 176p. (J). (gr. 3-7). 16.00 (978-0-374-33497-0(8)) Farrar, Straus & Giroux.

—Taking Care of Moses. 2004. 144p. (J). 16.00 (978-0-374-38038-0(4) , Frances Foster Bks.) Farrar, Straus & Giroux.

O'connor, George. Uncle Bigfoot. 2008. (Illus.). 32p. (J). 15.95 (****978-1-59643-271-0(3))*** Roaring Brook Pr.

O'Connor, Jane. Fancy Nancy. Glasser, Robin Preiss, illus. 2005. (Fancy Nancy Ser.). 32p. (J). 16.99 (978-0-06-054209-2(8)); lib. bdg. 17.89 (978-0-06-054210-8(1)) HarperCollins Pubs.

O'Dell, Scott. Zia. 2002. (J). 13.94 (978-0-7587-5209-3(1)) Book Wholesalers, Inc.

Offerman, Lynn. Where Is It? Hers. Chambers, Sally, illus. 1998. (Nuk Bks.). 8p. (J). 6.95 (978-0-7641-7233-5(6)) Barron's Educational Series, Inc.

Offill, Jenny. 17 Things I'm Not Allowed to Do Anymore. Carpenter, Nancy, illus. 2006. 32p. (J). (ps-3). 15.99 (978-0-375-83596-4(2) , Schwartz & Wade Bks.) Random Hse. Children's Bks.

Ogilvie, Elizabeth. The Pigeon Pair. (J). reprint ed. lib. bdg. 19.95 (978-0-88411-336-2(1)) Amereon LTD.

Oh, Jina, reader. A Step from Heaven. 2004. 160p. (J). (gr. 6 up). pap. 36.00 incl. audio (978-0-8072-2287-4(9) , Listening Library) Random Hse. Audio Publishing Group.

Oheal, Katherine. Family Series Clutter Family. 2008. (J). (978-0-310-70985-5(7)) Zonderkidz.

O'Keefe, Susan. My Life & Death by Alexandra Canarsie. 2006. 224p. pap. 7.95 (978-1-56145-387-0(0) , Peachtree Junior) Peachtree Pubs., Ltd.

Oliver, Lin. Attack of the Growling Eyeballs. 2008. (Who Shrunk Daniel Funk? Ser.). 112p. (J). 14.99 (****978-1-4169-0951-4(6)*** , Simon & Schuster Children's Publishing) Simon & Schuster Children's Publishing.

Once upon a Time. Date not set. (978-0-517-80128-4(0)) Random Hse. Value Publishing.

Oppenheim, Joanne. Could It Be? Schindler, S. D., illus. 1998. (Bank Street Reader Collection). 48p. (J). (gr. 1-3). lib. bdg. 22.60 (978-0-8368-1770-6(2)) Stevens, Gareth Inc.

Oriev, Uri. Lidia, Reina de Palestina. (SPA.). 158p. (YA). (gr. 5-8). (978-84-279-3237-1(5) , NG8035) Noguer y Caralt Editores, S. A. ESP. *Dist:* Lectorum Pubns., Inc.

Orlando, Linda M. Island Boy. 2004. (YA). pap. 14.95 (978-1-59088-776-9(X)) Wings ePress, Inc.

Ormerod, Jan. Sunshine. 2005. (Illus.). 32p. pap. 14.95 (978-1-84507-390-9(8)) Lincoln, Frances Ltd. GBR. *Dist:* Transition Vendor.

—Who's Whose. 1998. (Illus.). 40p. (J). (gr. k-3). 16.00 (978-0-688-14678-8(3)) HarperCollins Pubs.

—Who's Whose? 1998. (Illus.). 32p. (J). (gr. k-3). 15.89 (978-0-688-14679-5(1)) HarperCollins Pubs.

Ortega, Cristina. The Key to Grandpa's House. Ortega, Luis Armando, illus. 2007. 24p. (J). (gr. 1 up). 14.95 (****978-0-8263-4205-8(1))*** Univ. of New Mexico Pr.

Osborne, Mary Pope. Happy Birthday, America. Catalanotto, Peter, illus. 2008. 32p. (J). pap. 6.99 (****978-0-312-38050-2(X))*** Square Fish.

—Happy Birthday, America. Catalanotto, Peter, illus. 2005. 32p. (J). (gr. k-4). lib. bdg. 13.15 (978-0-606-33702-1(4)) Tandem Library Bks.

Osborne, Rick. The Legend of the Christmas Stocking: An Inspirational Story of a Wish Come True. Griffin, Jim, illus. (J). 2006. 28p. 6.99 (978-0-310-71157-5(6)); 2004. 32p. 15.99 (978-0-310-70898-8(2)) Zonderkidz.

Oughton, Jerrie. The War in Georgia. 1999. (978-0-606-16444-3(8)) Tandem Library Bks.

Padian, Maria. Brett McCarthy: Work In Progress. 2008. (J). 288p. (****978-0-375-84675-5(1)); (*978-0-375-94675-2(6))*** Knopf, Alfred A. Inc.

Pagratis, Maggie. My Sister the Bee. 2004. 29p. (J). per. 11.38 (978-1-4116-1098-9(9)) Lulu.com.

Palatini, Margie. The Wonder Worm Wars. 1999. (978-0-606-16660-7(2)) Tandem Library Bks.

Palmer, Angela Elsberry. Promise Wishes. 2005. (J). 19.95 (978-1-58597-311-8(4)) Leathers Publishing.

Palmer, Kate S. A Gracious Plenty. Palmer, Kate S., illus. 1998. (Illus.). 32p. (J). (gr. 1-4). reprint ed. pap. 7.95 (978-0-9667114-0-0(8)) Warbranch Pr., Inc.

Panagopoulos, Janie Lynn. A Place Called Home: Michigan's Mill Creek Story. van Frankenhuyzen, Gijsbert, illus. 2001. 48p. (J). 18.95 (978-1-58536-054-3(6)) Sleeping Bear Pr.

Paradine, Mike. King of Toys. 2006. 83p. pap. 14.95 (978-1-4241-2694-1(0)) PublishAmerica, Inc.

Paratore, Coleen. Mack McGinn's Big Win. 2007. 192p. (J). (gr. 4-7). 15.99 (****978-1-4169-1613-0(X)*** , Simon & Schuster Children's Publishing) Simon & Schuster Children's Publishing.

Park, Linda Sue. Project Mulberry. 2005. 240p. (J). (gr. 5-9). 16.00 (978-0-618-47786-9(1) , Clarion Bks.) Houghton Mifflin Co. Trade & Reference Div.

—Project Mulberry. 2007. 240p. (J). (gr. 4-7). pap. 6.50 (978-0-440-42163-4(2) , Yearling) Random Hse. Children's Bks.

—When My Name Was Keoko. 2002. 208p. (YA). (gr. 5-9). 16.00 (978-0-618-13335-2(6) , Clarion Bks.) Houghton Mifflin Co. Trade & Reference Div.

—When My Name Was Keoko. 2004. (Illus.). 208p. (J). (gr. 5). pap. 6.50 (978-0-440-41944-0(1) , Yearling) Random Hse. Children's Bks.

Parker, Toni Trent. Sienna's Scrapbook: Our African American Heritage Trip. Genovese, Janell, illus. 2005. 64p. (J). 15.95 (978-0-8118-4300-3(9)) Chronicle Bks. LLC.

Parkinson, Siobhan. Something Invisible. 2006. 160p. (J). 16.95 (978-1-59643-123-2(7)) Roaring Brook Pr.

Partridge, Elizabeth. Annie & Bo & the Big Surprise. Weston, Martha, illus. 2002. (Easy-to-Read Ser.). 48p. (J). pap. 3.99 (978-0-14-230071-8(3) , Puffin) Penguin Group (USA) Inc.

Pascal, Francine. Atrapada. Orig. Title: Married Woman. (SPA.). 208p. (J). 10.50 (978-84-272-3165-8(2)) Molino, Editorial ESP. *Dist:* AIMS International Bks., Inc.

Paterson, Katherine. Preacher's Boy. 2001. 192p. (J). (gr. 5 up). pap. 5.99 (978-0-06-447233-3(7) , Harper Trophy) HarperCollins Pubs.

—Preacher's Boy. 1999. (Illus.). 176p. (J). (gr. 5-9). tchr. ed. 15.00 (978-0-395-83897-6(5) , Clarion Bks.) Houghton Mifflin Co. Trade & Reference Div.

—Preacher's Boy. 2001. (J). (978-0-606-20861-1(5)); (gr. 5-8). lib. bdg. 12.95 (978-0-613-34906-2(7)) Tandem Library Bks.

—The Same Stuff As Stars. 2004. 288p. (J). reprint ed. pap. 6.99 (978-0-06-055712-6(5) , Harper Trophy) HarperCollins Pubs.

Patrick, Denise Lewis. Ma Dear's Old Green House. Sadler, Sonia Lynn, illus. 2004. (J). (gr. k-3). 16.95 (978-0-940975-55-2(6) , Sankofa Bks.) Just Us Bks., Inc.

Patterson, Nancy Ruth. The Winner's Walk. Yezerski, Thomas, illus. 2006. 128p. (J). 16.00 (978-0-374-38445-6(2)) Farrar, Straus & Giroux.

Paul, Dominique. The Possibility of Fireflies. 2006. 224p. (J). 15.95 (978-1-4169-1310-8(6)) Simon & Schuster Children's Publishing.

Pavlicin, Karen. Perch, Mrs. Sackets, & Crow's Nest. 2007. (J). 160p. 16.95 ***(*978-1-934617-00-7(8));*** pap. ***(*978-1-934617-01-4(6))*** Elva Resa Publishing, LLC. (Alma Little).

Pearce, Emily Smith. Isabel & the Miracle Baby. 2007. 144p. (YA). (gr. 3 up). 15.95 ***(*978-1-932425-44-4(6)***, Front Street) Boyds Mills Pr.

Pearce, Jonathan. Little Honesty: Trials & Triumphs of a Prince of Balona. 2001. (gr. 7-12). lib. bdg. 34.30 (978-0-613-74561-1(2)) Tandem Library Bks.

Pearsall, Shelley. All of the Above: A Novel. Steptoe, Javaka, illus. 2006. 256p. (J). (gr. 3-7). 15.99 (978-0-316-11524-7(X)) Little Brown & Co.

—Crooked River. (J). (gr. 5-9). 2007. 272p. pap. 6.50 (978-0-440-42101-6(2) , Yearling); 2005. 256p. 15.95 (978-0-375-82389-3(1) , Knopf Bks. for Young Readers); 2005. 256p. lib. bdg. 17.99 (978-0-375-92389-0(6) , Knopf Bks. for Young Readers) Random Hse. Children's Bks.

Pearson, Kit. Awake & Dreaming. 1999. (J). (978-0-606-21048-5(2)) Tandem Library Bks.

Pearson, Mary E. A Room on Lorelei Street. rev. ed. 2005. 272p. (YA). 16.95 (978-0-8050-7667-7(0)) Holt, Henry & Co.

Peck, Richard. Fair Weather. (Illus.). 160p. 2003. (YA). pap. 5.99 (978-0-14-250034-7(8) , Puffin); 2001. (J). (gr. 4-8). 16.99 (978-0-8037-2516-4(7) , Dial) Penguin Group (USA) Inc.

—Fair Weather. 2003. (gr. 3-6). lib. bdg. 14.15 (978-0-613-57895-0(3)) Tandem Library Bks.

—Fair Weather. 2004. 146p. (J). (gr. 5-9). pap. 36.00 incl. audio (978-0-8072-2038-2(8) , Listening Library) Random Hse. Audio Publishing Group.

—Fair Weather. l.t. ed. 2002. 161p. (YA). 24.95 (978-0-7862-3922-1(0)) Thomson Gale.

—The River Between Us. 176p. (J). 2003. (gr. 7). 16.99 (978-0-8037-2735-9(6) , Dial); 2005. (gr. 5-7). reprint ed. pap. 6.99 (978-0-14-240310-5(5) , Puffin) Penguin Group (USA) Inc.

—The River Between Us. 2005. 164p. (J). (ps-7). lib. bdg. 12.64 (978-0-606-33120-3(4)) Tandem Library Bks.

Peck, Robert Newton. Extra Innings. 2001. 192p. (J). (gr. 7 up). 16.99 (978-0-06-028867-9(1)) HarperCollins Pubs.

—Extra Innings. 2003. (gr. 5-8). lib. bdg. 14.15 (978-0-613-61762-8(2)) Tandem Library Bks.

Penn, Audrey. A Pocket Full of Kisses. Gibson, Barbara Leonard, illus. 2004. (New Child & Family Press Titles Ser.). 32p. (ps-1). 16.95 (978-0-87868-894-4(3) , 8943, Child & Family Pr.) Child Welfare League of America, Inc.

—A Pocket Full of Kisses. Gibson, Barbara, illus. 2006. 32p. 16.95 (978-1-933718-02-6(1)) Tanglewood Pr.

Pennypacker, Sara. Clementine. Frazee, Marla, illus. 2006. 144p. (gr. 1-5). 14.99 (978-0-7868-3882-0(5)) Hyperion Pr.

Penson, Mary. Martha Mary Overstreet, M. D. 2007. (Chaparral Book for Young Readers Ser.). 142p. (J). pap. 11.95 ***(*978-0-87565-345-7(6))*** Texas Christian Univ. Pr.

Perera, Hilda. La Jaula del Unicornio. (SPA.). 102p. (YA). (gr. 8 up). 8.95 (978-84-279-3205-0(7) , NG4205) Noguer y Caralt Editores, S. A. ESP. *Dist:* Lectorum Pubns., Inc.

Perez, Amada Irma. Mi Propio Cuartito. ed. 2004. (SPA & ENG., Illus.). (J). (gr. k-3). spiral bd. (978-0-616-14609-5(4)) Canadian National Institute for the Blind/Institut National Canadien pour les Aveugles.

—My Diary from Here to There / Mi Diario de Aqui Hasta Alla. Gonzalez, Maya Christina, illus. 2002. Tr. of Mi Diario de Aqui Hasta Alla. (ENG & SPA.). 32p. (J). (gr. 2-5). 16.95 (978-0-89239-175-2(8)) Children's Bk. Pr.

—My Very Own Room (Mi Propio Cuartito) Gonzalez, Maya Christina, illus. 2000. (ENG & SPA.). 32p. (J). (gr. 1 up). 16.95 (978-0-89239-164-6(2)) Children's Bk. Pr.

Perez, L. King. Remember As You Pass Me By. 2007. 224p. (J). (gr. 4-8). 16.95 ***(*978-1-57131-677-6(9))*** Milkweed Editions.

—Remember as You Pass Me By. 2007. 184p. (J). (gr. 2-7). per. 6.95 ***(*978-1-57131-678-3(7))*** Milkweed Editions.

Perez-Mercado, Mary Margaret. Zas! Torrey, Richard L., illus. 2000. (Rookie Espanol Ser.). (SPA.). 24p. (J). (gr. k-2). 19.50 (978-0-516-21692-8(9) , Children's Pr.) Scholastic Library Publishing.

Perez, Norah A. Breaker. 2002. (Pitt Golden Triangle Bks.). 216p. pap. 9.95 (978-0-8229-5778-2(7) , Golden Triangle Bks.) Univ. of Pittsburgh Pr.

Perkins, Larry B. Jake the Cow Hand. 2004. 27p. pap. 9.97 (978-1-4116-1344-7(9)) Lulu.com.

Perkins, Lynne Rae. All Alone in the Universe. 2001. (Illus.). 224p. (J). (gr. 5 up). reprint ed. 5.99 (978-0-380-73302-6(1) , Harper Trophy) HarperCollins Pubs.

Perkins, Lynne Rae. Pictures from Our Vacation. Perkins, Lynne Rae, illus. 2007. (Illus.). (J). (gr. 2-5). 40p. 16.99 ***(*978-0-06-085097-5(3));*** 32p. lib. bdg. 17.89 ***(*978-0-06-085098-2(1))*** HarperCollins Pubs. (Greenwillow Bks.).

Perkins, Mitali. First Daughter: Extreme American Makeover. 2008. 288p. (YA). (gr. 7). pap. 7.99 ***(*978-0-14-241154-4(X)***, Puffin) Penguin Group (USA) Inc.

—Monsoon Summer. 2006. 272p. (YA). (gr. 7). mass mkt. 6.50 (978-0-440-23840-9(4) , Laurel Leaf) Random Hse. Children's Bks.

—Rickshaw Girl. Hogan, Jamie, illus. 2007. 91p. (J). (gr. 2-5). 13.95 (978-1-58089-308-4(2)) Charlesbridge Publishing, Inc.

Perrin, Randy, et al. Time Like a River. 2004. 144p. (gr. 5 up). 14.95 (978-1-57143-061-8(X)) RDR Bks.

Perry, Naresha S. Zora's Valentine. 2005. (J). per. 13.00 ***(*978-0-9767189-0-1(1))*** Better Day Publishing Co.

Peterson, Jeanne Whitehouse. Don't Forget Winona. Root, Kimberly B., illus. 2004. 32p. (J). (ps-3). lib. bdg. 15.89 (978-0-06-027198-5(1)) HarperCollins Pubs.

Peterson, John. The Littles Go on a Hike. Rogers, Jaqueline, illus. 2002. (Littles First Readers Ser.: No. 9). 32p. (J). pap. 3.99 (978-0-439-31718-4(5) , Scholastic Paperbacks) Scholastic, Inc.

Petty, Kate. Moving Day. 2007. (J). ***(*978-1-59604-157-8(9))*** Stargazer Bks.

Pevsner, Stella. Would My Fortune Cookie Lie? 1999. (978-0-606-14369-1(6)) Tandem Library Bks.

Pevsner, Stella & Tang, Fay. Sing for Your Father, Su Phan. 1999. (978-0-606-16709-3(9)) Tandem Library Bks.

Pfeffer, Susan Beth. Amy's Story. 2001. (Portraits of Little Women Ser.). (Illus.). (J). (978-0-606-21030-0(X)) Tandem Library Bks.

—Ghostly Tales: Four Stories. 2002. (Portraits of Little Women Ser.). (gr. 3-6). lib. bdg. 12.40 (978-0-613-85700-0(3)) Tandem Library Bks.

—Jo's Story. 2001. (Portraits of Little Women Ser.). (Illus.). (J). (978-0-606-21270-0(1)) Tandem Library Bks.

—Life As We Knew It. 2006. (Illus.). 352p. (J). 17.00 (978-0-15-205826-5(5)) Harcourt Children's Bks.

Philbrick, Rodman. The Young Man & the Sea. 2005. 192p. (J). reprint ed. pap. 5.99 (978-0-439-36830-8(8) , Scholastic Paperbacks) Scholastic, Inc.

Phillips, Jan. Just for Today. Shapiro, Alison Bonds, illus. 2005. 32p. (J). (ps-5). 15.95 (978-1-932073-07-2(8)) Kramer, H.J. Inc.

Phillips, Suzanne. Chloe Doe. 2007. 192p. (YA). (gr. 10 up). 16.99 ***(*978-0-316-01413-7(3))*** Little, Brown Bks. for Young Readers.

Pierotti, Jr. Toward the Setting Sun. 2007. 268p. per. 17.95 ***(*978-0-595-45469-3(0))*** iUniverse, Inc.

Pinkney, Andrea Davis. Raven in a Dove House. 1999. (978-0-606-17789-4(2)) Tandem Library Bks.

Pintozzi, Nick. Bentley & the Great Fire. Pintozzi, Nick et al, illus. l.t. ed. 2004. 120p. per. 17.95 (978-0-9749465-1-1(6)) BentDaiSha, LLC.

Piven, Hanoch. My Dog Is As Smelly As Dirty Socks: And Other Funny Family Portraits. 2007. (Illus.). 40p. (J). (ps-3). 15.99 (978-0-375-84052-4(4)); lib. bdg. 18.99 (978-0-375-94052-1(9)) Random Hse. Children's Bks. (Schwartz & Wade Bks.).

Plummer, Louise. Finding Daddy. 2007. 176p. (YA). (gr. 7). 15.99 (978-0-385-73092-1(6) , Delacorte Bks. for Young Readers) Random Hse. Children's Bks.

Polacco, Ernest L. When Lightning Comes in a Jar. Polacco, Patricia, illus. 2007. 40p. (J). (gr. k). pap. 6.99 (978-0-14-240350-1(4) , Puffin) Penguin Group (USA) Inc.

Polacco, Patricia. The Butterfly. Polacco, Patricia, illus. 2002. (Illus.). (J). 23.64 (978-0-7587-2166-2(8)) Book Wholesalers, Inc.

—The Butterfly. unabr. ed. 2001. (J). (gr. 1-6). 27.95 incl. audio (978-0-8045-6875-3(8) , 6875) Spoken Arts, Inc.

—Chicken Sunday. 1998. (Illus.). 32p. (J). (gr. k-3). reprint ed. pap. 7.99 (978-0-698-11615-3(1) , Putnam Juvenile) Penguin Group (USA) Inc.

—The Graves Family Vacation. Polacco, Patricia, illus. 2008. 48p. (J). (gr. k). pap. 6.99 ***(*978-0-14-241175-9(2)***, Puffin) Penguin Group (USA) Inc.

Polacco, Patricia. When Lightning Comes in a Jar: Come to a Family Reunion. Polacco, Patricia, illus. 2002. (Illus.). 40p. (J). 16.99 (978-0-399-23164-3(1) , Philomel) Penguin Group (USA) Inc.

Polak, Monique. Home Invasion. 2005. (Orca Soundings Ser.). 112p. (J). (gr. 7-12). pap. 7.95 (978-1-55143-482-7(2)) Orca Bk. Pubs. USA.

Pollack, Pam. Bad Luck Charm. 2001. (gr. 3-6). lib. bdg. 13.00 (978-0-613-32298-0(3)) Tandem Library Bks.

Pomes Leiz, Juliet. Mama Sale Esta Noche. 2003. (SPA.). 36p. (978-84-8310-869-7(0) , 6012) Tusquets Editores.

—Sabado Que Vamos a Hacer Hoy? 2003. (SPA.). 36p. (978-84-8310-873-4(9) , 6012) Tusquets Editores.

Porter, Eleanor H. Pollyanna. 2000. (Historias de Siempre Ser.). (SPA., Illus.). 198p. (YA). (gr. 4-7). 15.95 (978-84-204-5730-7(2)) Alfaguara, Ediciones, S.A.- Grupo Santillana ESP. *Dist:* Santillana USA Publishing Co., Inc.

—Pollyanna. (J). 21.95 (978-0-8488-1445-8(2)) Amereon LTD.

—Pollyanna. 2002. 256p. (J). pap. 7.99 (978-1-84222-615-5(0)) Carlton Bks., Ltd. GBR. *Dist:* Independent Pubs. Group.

—Pollyanna. Date not set. (J). 14.99 (978-0-06-028226-4(6)); 32p. pap. 4.99 (978-0-06-443536-9(9)) HarperCollins Pubs.

—Pollyanna. l.t. ed. 2000. (Large Print Heritage Ser.). 310p. (J). (gr. 7-12). lib. bdg. 29.95 (978-1-58118-069-5(1) , 23663) LRS.

—Pollyanna. 2002. (gr. 3-6). lib. bdg. 11.80 (978-0-613-63223-2(0)) Tandem Library Bks.

—Pollyanna Grows Up. Date not set. 216p. (J). 21.95 (978-0-8488-1447-2(9)) Amereon LTD.

Poryes, Michael, et al. Family Affair. 2005. (Illus.). 128p. (J). ***(*978-1-4155-6887-3(1))*** Disney Pr.

Poupeney, Mollie. Her Father's Daughter. 2002. (gr. 7-12). lib. bdg. 13.55 (978-0-613-49493-9(8)) Tandem Library Bks.

Powell, Jillian. Henry & the Hand-Me-Downs. Worsley, Belinda, illus. 2005. 32p. (J). lib. bdg. 9.00 ***(*978-1-4242-0886-9(6))*** Fitzgerald Bks.

—Henry & the Hand-Me-Downs, Level 1. Worsley, Belinda, illus. 2005. (Lightning Readers Ser.). 32p. (J). (ps-k). pap., pap. 3.95 (978-0-7696-4209-3(8) , Gingham Dog Pr.) School Specialty Publishing.

—Henry y las Cosas Usadas, Level 1. Worsley, Belinda, illus. 2005. (Lightning Readers Ser.). 32p. (J). (ps-3). pap., pap. 3.95 (978-0-7696-4229-1(2) , Gingham Dog Pr.) School Specialty Publishing.

Pray, Ralph. Jingu: The Hidden Princess. Li, Xiaojun, illus. 2002. 80p. (YA). 14.95 (978-1-885008-21-3(X) , 188500821x) Shen's Bks.

Prigger, Mary Skillings. Aunt Minnie McGranahan. Lewin, Betsy, illus. 1999. 40p. (J). (gr. k-3). tchr. ed. 15.00 (978-0-395-82270-8(X) , Clarion Bks.) Houghton Mifflin Co. Trade & Reference Div.

The Prince & the Pauper. 2000. (Illus.). 80p. (YA). per. 6.95 (978-1-56254-287-0(7) , SP2877) Saddleback Educational Publishing.

Prince, Sarah. If I Were Invisible. 2001. (gr. k-3). lib. bdg. 11.80 (978-0-613-33379-5(9)) Tandem Library Bks.

Prosek, James. The Day My Mother Left. Prosek, James, illus. 2007. (Illus.). 304p. (J). 15.99 (978-1-4169-0770-1(X)) Simon & Schuster Children's Publishing.

Puccini, Giacomo. Madame Butterfly. Fucíkova, Renata, illus. 2005. 40p. (J). 15.95 (978-1-933327-04-4(9)) Purple Bear Bks., Inc.

—Madame Butterfly. Fuc#0237;kov#0225;, Ren#0225;ta, illus. 2005. 40p. (J). 16.85 (978-1-933327-08-2(1)) Purple Bear Bks., Inc.

Puerto, Carlos. No Mires Ahora. 1999. Tr. of Don't Look Now. (978-0-606-17722-1(1)) Tandem Library Bks.

Pullman, Philip. The Broken Bridge. 2002. 20.50 (978-0-8446-7229-8(7)) Smith, Peter Pub., Inc.

—The Firework-Maker's Daughter. Gallagher, Susan Saelig, illus. 2001. 112p. (J). (gr. 3-7). pap. 4.99 (978-0-439-22420-8(9)) Scholastic, Inc.

Purmell, Ann. Maple Syrup Spring. Weber, Jill, illus. 2007. (J). (978-0-8234-1891-6(X)) Holiday Hse., Inc.

Qamar, Amjed. Beneath My Mother's Feet. 2008. 208p. (J). ***(*978-1-4169-4728-8(0))*** Simon & Schuster Children's Publishing.

Qualey, Marsha. Just Like That. 240p. (YA). (gr. 7). 2007. pap. 6.99 (978-0-14-240830-8(1) , Puffin); 2005. 16.99 (978-0-8037-2840-0(9) , Dial) Penguin Group (USA) Inc.

—Too Big a Storm. 2004. 256p. (J). (gr. 9). 16.99 (978-0-8037-2839-4(5) , Dial) Penguin Group (USA) Inc.

Quarles, Heather. A Door Near Here. 2000. 11.64 (978-0-606-17796-2(5)) Tandem Library Bks.

—A Door near Here. 2000. (Illus.). 240p. (YA). (gr. 7 up). pap. 5.50 (978-0-440-22761-8(5) , Laurel Leaf) Random Hse. Children's Bks.

R. Friend -Panic in the PigPen. 2007. (J). per. ***(*978-0-9743627-7-9(8))*** Sunflower Seeds Pr.

Ramona Quimby, Age 8. 2005. (J). (978-1-59564-976-8(X)) Steps To Literacy, LLC.

Rand, T. & Rand, G. Sailing Home. 2006. (Illus.). 40p. (J). reprint ed. pap. 6.95 (978-0-7358-2079-1(1)) North-South Bks., Inc.

Randall, Barbara. Alexandra's Special Day. Herning, Kathy, ed. 2006. (Mimi's Kids Ser.: vol. 3). (Illus.). 32p. (J). pap. 12.95 (978-0-9712383-7-4(5)) Culture Connection, The.

—Baby Nadia Learns To Talk. Herning, Kathy, ed. 2006. (Mimi's Kids Ser.: vol. 1). (Illus.). 32p. (J). pap. 12.95 (978-0-9712383-5-0(9)) Culture Connection, The.

Random House Staff. Keep in Touch: Letters, Notes, & More from the Sisterhood of the Traveling Pants. 2005. 144p. (J). (gr. 7). lib. bdg. 9.99 (978-0-385-90943-3(8) , Delacorte Bks. for Young Readers) Random Hse. Children's Bks.

Random House Staff, ed. Mary's Story. 1999. (gr. 5-8). lib. bdg. 13.00 (978-0-613-21976-1(7)) Tandem Library Bks.

Ranulfo. Joker. 2006. 208p. (J). 15.99 (978-0-06-054158-3(X)); lib. bdg. 16.89 (978-0-06-054159-0(8)) HarperCollins Pubs. (Cotler, Joanna Books).

Raphael, Taffy E. Missing May. 2002. (Book Club Novel Guide Ser.). 48p. 17.95 (978-1-931376-08-2(5)) Small Planet Communications, Inc.

Rapp, Adam. Under the Wolf, under the Dog. 2004. 320p. (YA). (gr. 9 up). 16.99 (978-0-7636-1818-6(7)) Candlewick Pr.

Raudenbush, Amy. Lucy More Needs Less. 2006. 48p. (J). pap. 13.99 (978-1-4116-6120-2(6)) Lulu.com.

Ravel, Edeet. The Thrilling Life of Pauline de Lammermoor. 2007. 168p. pap. 9.95 ***(*978-1-55192-988-0(0))*** Raincoast Bk. Distribution CAN. *Dist:* Perseus Distribution.

Ray, Delia. Singing Hands. 2006. (Illus.). 224p. (J). (gr. 5-9). 16.00 (978-0-618-65762-9(2) , Clarion Bks.) Houghton Mifflin Co. Trade & Reference Div.

Rayburn, Tricia. The Melting of Maggie Bean. 2007. 256p. (J). (gr. 4-8). pap. 5.99 (978-1-4169-3348-9(4) , Aladdin) Simon & Schuster Children's Publishing.

Reeder, Carolyn. Foster's War. 2000. 272p. (J). (gr. 4-7). pap. 4.99 (978-0-590-09856-4(X)) Scholastic, Inc.

—Foster's War. 2000. (gr. 5-8). lib. bdg. 12.40 (978-0-613-29960-2(4)) Tandem Library Bks.

—Moonshiner's Son. 2003. (gr. 3-6). lib. bdg. 13.00 (978-0-613-61803-8(3)) Tandem Library Bks.

Reinhardt, Dana. A Brief Chapter in My Impossible Life. (gr. 7). 2007. 256p. (YA). pap. 8.99 ***(*978-0-375-84691-5(3));*** 2006. 240p. (J). 15.95 (978-0-385-74698-4(9)); 2006. 240p. (J). lib. bdg. 17.99 (978-0-385-90940-2(3)) Random Hse. Children's Bks. (Lamb, Wendy).

Reiser, Lynn W. Tortillas & Lullabies. Corazones, Valientes, illus. 1998. Tr. of Tortillas y Cancioncitas. (SPA & ENG.). 48p. (J). (ps-3). 16.99 (978-0-688-14628-3(7) , Rayo) HarperCollins Pubs.

Reisfeld, Randi, ed. Romeo: Chapter Book. 2006. (Teenick Ser.). (Illus.). 96p. (J). pap. 4.99 (978-0-439-79667-5(9)) Scholastic, Inc.

Reiss, Johanna. The Upstairs Room. 2002. (Illus.). (J). 14.47 (978-0-7587-0326-2(0)) Book Wholesalers, Inc.

—The Upstairs Room. 1999. (J). 9.95 (978-1-56137-657-5(4)) Novel Units, Inc.

Reiss, Kathryn. Blackthorn Winter: A Murder Mystery. 2007. (Illus.). 348p. (YA). pap. 6.95 ***(*978-0-15-206109-8(6)***, Harcourt Paperbacks) Harcourt Children's Bks.

Reiss, Kathryn. Riddle of the Prairie Bride. 2001. (American Girl Collection). (Illus.). (J). (978-0-606-21400-1(3)) Tandem Library Bks.

Reiss, Mike. Merry Un-Christmas. Catrow, David, illus. 2006. 32p. (J). 15.99 (978-0-06-059126-7(9)) HarperCollins Pubs.

Rempel, Leah. Hey, Hmong Girl, Whassup? The Journal of Choua Vang. 2004. (Illus.). v, 138p. (YA). pap. ***(*978-0-9723721-5-2(6))*** Hamline Univ. Pr.

Rennison, Louise. Dancing in My Nuddy-Pants: Even Further Confessions of Georgia Nicolson. (Confessions of Georgia Nicolson Ser.). 2003. 224p. (J). 15.99 (978-0-06-009746-2(9)); 2004. 240p. (YA). reprint ed. pap. 7.99 (978-0-06-009748-6(5)) HarperCollins Pubs. (HarperTeen).

—On the Bright Side, I'm Now the Girlfriend of a Sex God: Further Confessions Of. 2002. (gr. 7-12). lib. bdg. 15.30 (978-0-613-49344-4(3)) Tandem Library Bks.

—On the Bright Side, I'm Now the Girlfriend of a Sex God: Further Confessions of Georgia Nicolson. (Confessions of Georgia Nicolson Ser.). 2003. 256p. (J). pap. 6.99 (978-0-06-052185-1(6)); 2002. 272p. (YA). pap. 7.99 (978-0-06-447226-5(4)); 2001. 256p. (J). (gr. 7 up). 17.99 (978-0-06-028813-6(2)) HarperCollins Pubs.

Rettig, Liz. My Desperate Love Diary. 2007. 314p. (YA). (gr. 9 up). 16.95 (978-0-8234-2033-9(7)) Holiday Hse., Inc.

Reynolds, Cynthia Furlong. Across the Reach. 2007. 144p. (J). 16.95 ***(*978-1-58726-518-1(4)***, Mitten Pr.) Ann Arbor Media Group, LLC.

Reynolds, Marilynn. Goodbye to Griffith Street. Benoit, Renne, illus. 2004. 32p. (J). (ps-2). 16.95 (978-1-55143-285-4(4)) Orca Bk. Pubs. USA.

Reynolds, Peter H. My Very Big Little World: A SugarLoaf Book. 2006. (Illus.). 40p. (J). (ps-2). 15.95 (978-0-689-87621-9(1) , Atheneum) Simon & Schuster Children's Publishing.

Reynolds, Sheila. Daddy's Penny. 2004. 48p. pap. 12.95 (978-1-4137-4085-1(5)) PublishAmerica, Inc.

Rhyason, Sharon. Utopia, Where Are You? 2003. 164p. (YA). pap. 11.95 (978-0-595-26401-8(8) , Writers Club Pr.) iUniverse, Inc.

Rice, David L. Because Brian Hugged His Mother. 2004. (Sharing Nature with Children Book Ser.). (Illus.). 32p. (YA). (ps-3). 16.95 (978-1-883220-90-7(4)); pap. 7.95 (978-1-883220-89-1(0)) Dawn Pubns.

Richards, Kitty. Thornberry Thanksgiving. 2001. (gr. k-3). lib. bdg. 14.15 (978-0-613-43963-3(5)) Tandem Library Bks.

Richter, Conrad. The Light in the Forest. 2005. (Illus.). 176p. ***(*978-1-85715-515-0(7))*** Knopf, Alfred A. Inc.

Rinaldi, Ann. The Coffin Quilt: The Feud Between the Hatfields & the McCoys. 2nd ed. 2002. (J). 4.80 (978-0-03-073522-6(X)) Holt, Rinehart & Winston.

—The Coffin Quilt: The Feud Between the Hatfields & the McCoys. 2001. (J). 12.65 (978-0-606-20507-8(1)) Tandem Library Bks.

—Come Juneteenth. 2007. (Great Episodes Ser.). (Illus.). 256p. (YA). 17.00 (978-0-15-205947-7(4)) Harcourt Children's Bks.

—Millicent's Gift. 2002. (Illus.). 224p. (J). (ps-3). 15.95 (978-0-06-029636-0(4)) HarperCollins Pubs.

—Or Give Me Death: A Novel of Patrick Henry's Family. (Great Episodes Ser.). 240p. (YA). 2004. pap. 6.95 (978-0-15-205076-4(0)); 2003. 17.00 (978-0-15-216687-8(4)) Harcourt Children's Bks. (Gulliver Bks.).

Risk, Mary & Morton, Lone. What's for Supper? Que Hay Para Cenar? 1998. (Language Learning Story Bks.). (ENG & SPA., Illus.). 28p. (J). (ps up). 8.99 (978-0-7641-5127-9(4) , BA274) Barron's Educational Series, Inc.

Risk, Mary, et al. Hurry up Molly/English-French: Depechtoi, Molly. Scriven, Gill, illus. 2000. (I Can Read Bks.). (ENG & FRE.). 28p. (J). (ps-2). 8.99 (978-0-7641-5287-0(4)) Barron's Educational Series, Inc. Inc.

Ritter, John H. Choosing up Sides. 2001. (J). 12.64 (978-0-606-20603-7(5)) Tandem Library Bks.

—Over the Wall. 2002. 320p. (J). pap. 6.99 (978-0-698-11931-4(2) , Putnam Juvenile) Penguin Group (USA) Inc.

Rivers, Karen. Surviving Sam. 2002. (Illus.). 176p. (YA). (gr. 9 up). pap. 6.95 (978-1-55192-506-6(0)) Raincoast Bk. Distribution CAN. *Dist:* Perseus Distribution.

Roberts, Judson. Viking Warrior. (Strongbow Saga Ser.: Bk. 1). 368p. 2007. (J). pap. 7.99 ***(*978-0-06-079999-1(4)***, HarperTeen); 2006. (Illus.). (YA). 16.99 (978-0-06-079996-0(X)); Bk. 1. 2006. (Illus.). (YA). lib. bdg. 17.89 (978-0-06-079997-7(8)) HarperCollins Pubs.

Roberts, Ken. Past Tense. 2002. (Illus.). 112p. (J). (gr. 3-5). pap. 6.95 (978-0-88899-214-7(9)) Groundwood Bks. CAN. *Dist:* Perseus Distribution.

Roberts, Laura Peyton. Queen B. 368p. (gr. 7-11). 2007. (YA). mass mkt. 6.50 ***(*978-0-440-23872-0(2)***, Laurel Leaf); 2006. (J). lib. bdg. 17.99 (978-0-385-90201-4(8) , Delacorte Bks. for Young Readers); 2006. (YA). 15.95 (978-0-385-73163-8(9) , Delacorte Bks. for Young Readers) Random Hse. Children's Bks.

—The Queen of Second Place. 336p. (YA). (gr. 7). 2006. pap. 5.99 (978-0-440-23871-3(4) , Laurel Leaf); 2005. 15.95 (978-0-385-73162-1(0) , Delacorte Bks. for Young Readers) Random Hse. Children's Bks.

—Reality Check. 1998. (Clearwater Crossing Ser.: No. 2). (YA). (gr. 5-8). (978-0-606-13283-1(X)) Tandem Library Bks.

Roberts, Willo Davis. Blood on His Hands. 192p. (J). 2005. mass mkt. 5.99 (978-0-689-85082-0(4) , Simon Pulse); 2004. (Illus.). 16.95 (978-0-689-85074-5(3) , Atheneum/ Richard Jackson Bks.) Simon & Schuster Children's Publishing.

Robichaud, Janeen. They Killed Me. 2002. 108p. (YA). pap. 9.95 (978-0-595-26143-7(4) , Writers Club Pr.) iUniverse, Inc.

Robinet, Harriette Gillem. Walking to the Bus-Rider Blues. Colon, Raul, illus. 2002. 160p. (J). pap. 4.99 (978-0-689-83886-6(7) , Aladdin) Simon & Schuster Children's Publishing.

Robinson, Barbara. My Brother Louis Measures Worms: And Other Louis Stories. 2005. 240p. (J). (ps-7). pap. 5.99 (978-0-06-076672-6(7) , Harper Trophy) HarperCollins Pubs.

Robinson, Sharon. Safe at Home. 160p. (J). 2007. (gr. 4-7). pap. 4.99 (***978-0-439-67198-9(1)*** , Scholastic Paperbacks); 2006. pap. 16.99 (978-0-439-67197-2(3) , Scholastic) Scholastic, Inc.

—Slam Dunk! 2007. 160p. (J). (gr. 4-7). pap. 16.99 (***978-0-439-67199-6(X)*** , Scholastic Pr.) Scholastic, Inc.

Robinson, Susan. Edward's Magic Paintbox. Leach, Helen May Keedwell, illus. 2002. 32p. (J). (978-0-7344-0193-9(0) , Lothian Bks.) Hachette Livre Australia.

Rocklin, Joanne. The Very Best Hanukkah Gift. 2001. (978-0-606-22400-0(9)) Tandem Library Bks.

—Very Best Hanukkah Gift. 2001. (gr. 3-6). lib. bdg. 12.40 (978-0-613-85709-3(7)) Tandem Library Bks.

Rodman, Mary Ann. Jimmy's Stars. 2008. 272p. (J). 16.95 (***978-0-374-33703-2(9)***) Farrar, Straus & Giroux.

Rodowsky, Colby. Not Quite a Stranger. 2003. 192p. (J). (gr. 5 up). 16.00 (978-0-374-35548-7(7) , Farrar, Straus & Giroux (BYR)) Farrar, Straus & Giroux.

Rogers, Joe. The Changeling. 2005. 183p. pap. 19.95 (978-1-4137-8032-1(6)) PublishAmerica, Inc.

Rogers, Karen M. Mingo y Yo. Alvarado, Ana María, tr. Bullet, Getty, illus. 2000. (Think-Kids Book Collection).Tr. of Max & Me. (SPA.). 16p. (J). (gr. 1-4). pap. 2.95 (978-1-58237-050-7(8)) Creative Thinkers, Inc.

Rogers, Kenny. Christmas in Canaan. 2002. (gr. 7-12). lib. bdg. 15.30 (978-0-613-68413-2(3)) Tandem Library Bks.

Rogers, Kenny & Davenport, Donald. Christmas in Canaan. 2002. 336p. (J). (gr. 6-9). 15.99 (978-0-06-000746-1(X)) HarperCollins Pubs.

Rogue Robot: Individual Title Six-Packs. (Bookweb Ser.). 32p. (gr. 4 up). 34.00 (978-0-7635-3735-7(7)) Rigby Education.

Romanelli, Serena. Little Bobo. 1999. (gr. k-3). lib. bdg. 15.25 (978-0-613-73589-6(7)); (J). (978-0-606-16194-7(5)) Tandem Library Bks.

Romano, Ray. Raymie, Dickie, & the Bean: Why I Love & Hate My Brothers. Locke, Gary, illus. 2007. 30p. (J). 18.00 (***978-1-4223-6806-0(8)***) DIANE Publishing Co.

Room for One More, 6 Packs. (ps-2). 27.00 (978-0-7635-9472-5(5)) Rigby Education.

Roop, Peter. Eye for an Eye: A Story of the Revolutionary War. 2000. (gr. 5-8). lib. bdg. 15.70 (978-0-613-36805-6(3)) Tandem Library Bks.

Roop, Peter & Roop, Connie. An Eye for an Eye: A Story of the American Revolution. 2001. (Jamestown Classics Ser.). (Illus.). 168p. (J). (gr. 5-8). 15.32 (978-0-8092-0587-5(4) , 9780809205875) Jamestown.

—An Eye for an Eye: A Story of the Revolutionary War. 2004. (Jamestown's American Portraits Ser.). (Illus.). 176p. (J). (gr. 5-7). pap. 4.95 (978-0-7696-3422-7(2) , Waterbird Bks.) School Specialty Publishing.

Roop, Peter and Connie. An Eye for an Eye. 2004. 168p. (J). lib. bdg. 16.92 (***978-1-4242-0772-5(X)***) Fitzgerald Bks.

Rosa-Casanova, Sylvia. Mama Provi & the Pot of Rice. ed. 2004. (Illus.). (J). (gr. k-3). spiral bd. (978-0-616-07257-8(0)) Canadian National Institute for the Blind/ Institut National Canadien pour les Aveugles.

—Mama Provi & the Pot of Rice. 2001. (Illus.). (J). (978-0-606-20782-9(1)) Tandem Library Bks.

Rosado, Maria. Wild Thornberrys Trivia Book. 2000. (gr. 3-6). lib. bdg. 10.65 (978-0-613-27583-5(7)) Tandem Library Bks.

Rosen, Michael J. A Drive in the Country. Burckhardt, Marc, illus. 2007. 32p. (J). (gr. k-5). 16.99 (***978-0-7636-2140-7(4)***) Candlewick Pr.

Rosenberg, Liz. The Silence in the Mountains. Soentpiet, Chris K., illus. 32p. (J). (gr. k-4). 1999. 16.99 (978-0-531-33084-5(2)); 1998. pap. 15.95 (978-0-531-30084-8(6)) Scholastic, Inc. (Orchard Bks.).

Rosenberry, Vera. Vera Runs Away. Rosenberry, Vera, illus. rev. ed. 2000. (Illus.). 32p. (J). (ps-2). 16.00 (978-0-8050-6267-0(X) , Holt, Henry & Co. Bks. For Young Readers) Holt, Henry & Co.

Rosoff, Meg. How I Live Now. 2006. 224p. (YA). (gr. 7). reprint ed. pap. 7.99 (978-0-553-37605-0(5) , Lamb, Wendy) Random Hse. Children's Bks.

—How I Live Now. 2006. 250p. (YA). 23.95 (978-0-7862-8878-6(7)) Thorndike Pr.

Ross, Tony. Happy Rag. 2002. (Illus.). 28p. (Orig.). pap. 8.99 (978-1-84270-053-2(7)) Andersen GBR. *Dist:* Trafalgar Square Publishing.

Rosseau, Paul. Lucifer, Mon Grand-Père, Tome 1. Guénette, Geneviève, illus. 2004. (Mon Roman Ser.). (FRE.). 160p. (J). (gr. 2). pap. (978-2-89021-650-1(0)) Diffusion du livre Mirabel.

Rothstein, Nancy. My Daddy Snores. 2007. 32p. (J). pap. 5.99 (***978-0-545-02834-9(5)***) Scholastic, Inc.

Rottman, S. L. Slalom. 2004. 256p. (YA). (gr. 7). 16.99 (978-0-670-05913-3(7) , Viking Juvenile) Penguin Group (USA) Inc.

Rowlands, Avril. Animals to the Rescue & Other Stories. 2002. (Illus.). 128p. (J). pap. 7.99 (978-0-7459-4764-8(6) , Lion) Lion Hudson plc GBR. *Dist:* Independent Pubs. Group.

Roy, Jennifer Rozines. Yellow Star. 2006. 256p. (YA). (gr. 5-9). 16.95 (978-0-7614-5277-5(X)) Cavendish, Marshall Corp.

Roy, Ron. The Empty Envelope. Gurney, John Steven, illus. 1998. (A to Z Mysteries Ser.: No. 5). 96p. (gr. 1-4). lib. bdg. 11.99 (978-0-679-99054-3(2) , Random Hse. Bks. for Young Readers) Random Hse. Children's Bks.

Rubel, Nicole. It's Hot & Cold in Miami. 2006. (Illus.). 208p. (J). 17.00 (978-0-374-33611-0(3)) Farrar, Straus & Giroux.

Ruby, Lois. Shanghai Shadows. 2006. 256p. (J). (gr. 7 up). 16.95 (978-0-8234-1960-9(6)) Holiday Hse., Inc.

Rue, Nancy. Sophie Tracks a Thief, Vol. 8. 2005. (Faithgirlz Ser.). (Illus.). 144p. (J). pap. 6.99 (978-0-310-71023-3(5)) Zonderkidz.

Rue, Nancy N. The Pursuit. 2000. (Christian Heritage Ser.). 192p. (J). (gr. 3-7). pap. 5.99 (978-1-56179-856-8(8)) Bethany Hse. Pubs.

—Pursuit. 2000. (gr. 3-6). lib. bdg. 14.15 (978-0-613-86405-3(0)) Tandem Library Bks.

—Sophie & the Scoundrels, Bk. 3. Chen, Grace, illus. 2005. (Faithgirlz Ser.). 128p. (J). pap. 6.99 (978-0-310-70758-5(7)) Zonderkidz.

—The Trap. 1998. (Christian Heritage Ser.). 208p. (J). (gr. 3-7). pap. (978-1-56179-567-3(4)) Focus on the Family Publishing.

Ruelle, Karen Gray. Spookier Than a Ghost. Ruelle, Karen Gray, illus. 2001. (Illus.). 32p. (J). (gr. k-3). tchr. ed. 14.95 (978-0-8234-1667-7(4)) Holiday Hse., Inc.

—Spookier Than a Ghost. (Holiday House Readers Ser.). (Illus.). 32p. (J). (gr. k-3). pap. 4.95 (978-0-8234-1801-5(4)) Holiday Hse., Inc.

Rushford, Patricia H. Secrets of Ghost Island. 2007. (J). (***978-88-02-46255-4(0)***) Moody Pubs.

Russell, Barbara Timberlake. Maggie's Amerikay. Burke, Jim, illus. 2006. 40p. (J). 17.00 (978-0-374-34722-2(0) , Farrar, Straus & Giroux (BYR)) Farrar, Straus & Giroux.

Ryan, Pam Muñoz. Paint the Wind. 2007. 336p. (J). (gr. 4-7). pap. 16.99 (***978-0-439-87362-8(2)*** , Scholastic Pr.) Scholastic, Inc.

Rylant, Cynthia. A Blue-Eyed Daisy. 112p. (J). (gr. 4-7). 2001. pap. 4.99 (978-0-689-84495-9(6) , Aladdin); 2000. 15.00 (978-0-689-84217-7(1) , Atheneum/Richard Jackson Bks.) Simon & Schuster Children's Publishing.

—A Blue-Eyed Daisy. 2001. (J). 11.64 (978-0-606-21074-4(1)); (gr. 3-6). lib. bdg. 13.00 (978-0-613-65738-9(1)) Tandem Library Bks.

—The Blue Hill Meadows. 2001. (gr. 3-6). lib. bdg. 14.15 (978-0-613-35490-5(7)); (Illus.). (J). 12.80 (978-0-606-21075-1(X)) Tandem Library Bks.

—Bunny Bungalow. Hayashi, Nancy, illus. 2002. 32p. (J). (ps-k). pap. 6.00 (978-0-15-216316-7(6) , Voyager Bks./ Libros Viajeros) Harcourt Children's Bks.

—Bunny Bungalow. Hayashi, Nancy, illus. 2002. (J). (ps-3). lib. bdg. 14.15 (978-0-613-53798-8(X)) Tandem Library Bks.

—Family Time with Henry & Mudge. Stevenson, Sucie, illus. 2002. pap. 61.95 incl. audio (978-0-87499-997-6(9)); pap. 68.95 incl. audio compact disk (978-1-59112-854-0(4)) Live Oak Media.

—Old Town in the Green Groves: Laura Ingalls Wilder's Lost Little House Years. 2007. (Little House Ser.). 192p. (J). pap. 6.99 (978-0-06-088546-5(7) , Harper Trophy) HarperCollins Pubs.

—Old Town in the Green Groves: Laura Ingalls Wilder's Lost Little House Years. LaMarche, Jim, illus. (Little House Ser.). 176p. (J). 2004. pap. 5.99 (978-0-06-440990-2(2) , Harper Trophy); 2002. 15.99 (978-0-06-029561-5(9)) HarperCollins Pubs.

—The Relatives Came. Gammell, Stephen, illus. unabr. ed. 1999. (J). (gr. k-3). pap. 16.95 incl. audio (978-0-87499-532-9(9)) BBC Audiobooks America.

—The Relatives Came. Gammell, Stephen, illus. 2000. (J). pap. 19.97 incl. audio (978-0-7366-9212-0(6)) Books on Tape, Inc.

—The Relatives Came. Gammell, Stephen, illus. 1999. 28.95 incl. audio compact disk (978-1-59112-546-4(4)); pap. 39.95 incl. audio compact disk (978-1-59112-545-7(6)); (J). pap. 18.95 incl. audio compact disk (978-1-59112-324-8(0)); (J). pap., tchr. ed. 37.95 incl. audio (978-0-87499-534-3(5)); (J). 25.95 incl. audio (978-0-87499-533-6(7)) Live Oak Media.

—The Relatives Came. Gammell, Stephen, illus. 32p. (J). 2002. mass mkt. 1.00 (978-0-689-85586-3(9) , Aladdin); 2001. 17.99 (978-0-689-84508-6(1) , Atheneum/Richard Jackson Bks.) Simon & Schuster Children's Publishing.

—Some Good News, Bk. 4. 2001. (Cobble Street Cousins Ser.: No. 3). (Illus.). (J). (978-0-606-21115-4(2)) Tandem Library Bks.

Sachar, Louis. Kidnapped at Birth? Hughes, Neal, illus. 2004. (Marvin Redpost Ser.: Vol. 1). 80p. (J). (gr. k-3). 11.99 (978-0-679-91946-9(5) , Random Hse. Bks. for Young Readers) Random Hse. Children's Bks.

Sachs, Marilyn. First Impressions. 2006. 128p. (YA). 16.95 (978-1-59643-117-1(2)) Roaring Brook Pr.

Saenz, Benjamin Alire. He Forgot to Say Good-Bye. 2008. 272p. (YA). (***978-1-4169-4963-3(1)*** , Simon & Schuster Children's Publishing) Simon & Schuster Children's Publishing.

Saldana, Rene, Jr. The Jumping Tree. 2002. (Illus.). 192p. (YA). (gr. 5). pap. 5.99 (978-0-440-22881-3(6) , Laurel Leaf) Random Hse. Children's Bks.

Salmansohn, Karen. Girl Wonders. 2007. 128p. (J). 6.95 (***978-1-58246-162-5(7)*** , Tricycle Pr.) Ten Speed Pr.

Salmansohn, Karen. Wherever I Go, There I Am. 2004. (Alexandra Rambles on! Ser.). (Illus.). 70p. (YA). (gr. 4-7). 12.95 (978-1-58246-079-6(5) , Tricycle Pr.) Ten Speed Pr.

Samuels, Gertrude. Yours, Brett. 2000. 180p. (YA). (gr. 4-7). pap. 13.95 (978-0-595-00806-3(2)) iUniverse, Inc.

Sandoval, Victor. Roll over, Big Toben. 128p. (YA). pap. 9.95 (978-1-55885-401-7(0) , Piñata Books) Arte Publico Pr.

Sanroman, Susana. Senora Reganona: A Mexican Bedtime Story. ed. 2004. (SPA., Illus.). (J). (gr. k-3). spiral bd. (978-0-616-07280-6(5)) Canadian National Institute for the Blind/Institut National Canadien pour les Aveugles.

Santana, Patricia. Motorcycle Ride on the Sea of Tranquility. 2002. 270p. (YA). 19.95 (978-0-8263-2435-1(5)) Univ. of New Mexico Pr.

Santiago, Esmeralda. A Doll for Navidades. Sanchez, Enrique O., illus. 2005. 32p. (J). (ps-3). pap. 16.99 (978-0-439-55398-8(9) , Scholastic Pr.) Scholastic, Inc.

Santillo, LuAnn. Family Fun, 6 vols. Santillo, LuAnn, ed. 2003. (Half-Pint Kids Readers Ser.). (Illus.). 42p. (J). (ps-1). pap. 6.99 (978-1-59256-098-1(9)) Half-Pint Kids, Inc.

Santos, Rosario. Play Date. Fiammenghi, Gioia, illus. 2001. (Math Matters Ser.). 32p. (J). (ps-1). pap. 4.95 (978-1-57565-105-7(X)) Kane Pr., The.

—Play Date. 2001. (gr. k-3). lib. bdg. 12.95 (978-0-613-39351-5(1)); (Illus.). (J). (978-0-606-20857-4(7)) Tandem Library Bks.

Santucci, Barbara. Anna's Corn. Bloom, Lloyd, illus. 2004. 32p. (J). (gr. 1 up). 16.00 (978-0-8028-5119-2(3)) Eerdmans, William B. Publishing Co.

Sargent, Dave & Sargent, Pat. Amy Armadillo: Mind Your Mama, 15 vols. Huff, Jeane, illus. 2003. (Animal Pride Ser.: 15). 42p. (J). pap. 6.95 (978-1-56763-788-5(4)); lib. bdg. 19.95 (978-1-56763-787-8(6)) Ozark Publishing.

—Bandit: I Help Others, 38 bks., 14. Huff, Jeane, illus. 2nd rev. ed. 2003. (Animal Pride Ser.: No. 14). 42p. (J). pap. 6.95 (978-1-56763-786-1(8)) Ozark Publishing.

Sargent, Pat L. The Cheetah, 6 vols, Vol. 6. Lenoir, Jane, illus. l.t. ed. 2004. (Barney the Bear Killer Ser.: No. 6). 146p. (YA). pap. 9.95 (978-1-56763-974-2(7)); lib. bdg. 25.25 (978-1-56763-973-5(9)) Ozark Publishing.

Satrapi, Marjane. Persépolis (En Español), Vol. 4. Agut, Albert, tr. from FRE. 2005. (SPA., Illus.). 160p. pap. 22.95 (978-1-59497-096-2(3)) Public Square Bks.

Saunders, Joanne D. Secret at the Winthrop House. 2007. 192p. per. 12.99 (***978-1-59886-622-3(2)***) Tate Publishing & Enterprises, L.L.C.

Schaefer, Lola M. Frankie Stein. Atteberry, Kevan, illus. 2007. 32p. (J). (ps-2). 16.99 (***978-0-7614-5358-1(X)***) Cavendish, Marshall Corp.

Schanback, Mindy. Princess from Another Planet. 2005. 254p. (J). (gr. 5-9). 16.95 (978-0-8234-1847-3(2)) Holiday Hse., Inc.

Schein, Herman, et al. Story for a Black Night. 2004. 112p. (YA). (gr. 7). pap. 6.99 (978-0-618-49483-5(9) , Graphia) Houghton Mifflin Co. Trade & Reference Div.

Schirripa, Steven R. & Fleming, Charles. Nicky Deuce: Home for the Holidays. 2006. 208p. (J). (gr. 4-7). 15.95 (978-0-385-73258-1(9)); lib. bdg. 17.99 (978-0-385-90276-2(X)) Random Hse. Children's Bks. (Delacorte Bks. for Young Readers).

Schlein, Miriam. The Story about Me. Stephenson, Kristina, illus. 2004. 32p. (J). (ps-1). 15.95 (978-0-8075-7631-1(X)) Whitman, Albert & Co.

Schmidt, C. A. Useful Fools. 2007. 272p. (YA). (gr. 8 up). 18.99 (***978-0-525-47814-0(0)*** , Dutton Juvenile) Penguin Group (USA) Inc.

Schmidt, Gary D. The Wednesday Wars. 2007. 272p. (J). (gr. 5-9). 16.00 (978-0-618-72483-3(4) , Clarion Bks.) Houghton Mifflin Co. Trade & Reference Div.

Schnur, Steven. The Koufax Dilemma. Treatner, Meryl, illus. 2001. 196p. (YA). pap. 14.95 (978-0-595-19998-3(4) , Backinprint.com) iUniverse, Inc.

—Koufax Dilemma. 2001. (gr. 3-6). lib. bdg. 24.55 (978-0-613-85103-9(X)) Tandem Library Bks.

Scholastic, Inc. Staff & Black, Sonia. Mommy's Bed. 2004. (Just for You! Ser.). (Illus.). 32p. pap. 3.99 (978-0-439-56857-9(9) , Teaching Resources) Scholastic, Inc.

Schotter, Roni. The House of Joyful Living. Widener, Terry, illus. 2008. (J). (***978-0-374-33429-1(3)***) Farrar, Straus & Giroux.

Schotter, Roni. When the Wizzy Foot Goes Walking. Wohnoutka, Mike, illus. 2007. (J). (***978-5-525-47791-9(2)***); 32p. 16.99 (978-0-525-47791-4(8)) Penguin Group (USA) Inc. (Dutton Juvenile).

Schraff, Anne. The Greatest Heroes. 2000. 143p. (J). pap. (978-0-7891-5133-9(2)); (gr. 5-12). lib. bdg. 13.95 (978-0-7807-9271-5(8)) Perfection Learning Corp.

—Lost & Found. Langan, Paul, ed. 2002. (Bluford Ser.: 1). 133p. (J). mass mkt. 4.95 (978-0-944210-02-4(3)) Townsend Pr.

—Memories Are Forever. 1999. 135p. (J). pap. (978-0-7891-4924-4(9)); (gr. 5-12). lib. bdg. 13.95 (978-0-7807-8008-6(6)) Perfection Learning Corp.

Schreiber, Anne. Word Play. Ong, Cristina, illus. 2000. (Scholastic At-Home Phonics Reading Program Ser.: Vol. 60). 24p. (J). (978-0-590-68864-2(2)) Scholastic, Inc.

Schulte, Mary. Who Do I Look Like? Roos, Maryn, illus. 2006. (Rookie Reader Skill Set Ser.). 32p. (J). (gr. k-2). 19.50 (978-0-516-24978-0(9) , Children's Pr.) Scholastic Library Publishing.

Schulte, Mary & Roos, Maryn. Who Do I Look Like? 2006. (Illus.). 32p. (YA). pap. 4.95 (978-0-516-24758-8(1) , Children's Pr.) Scholastic Library Publishing.

Schultz, Betty K. Mom of Mystery. Diehl, Diana, ed. Kott, Betty A., illus. num. ed. 2002. 158p. (Orig.). (J). (gr. 6-8). lib. bdg. 18.95 (978-0-929568-02-7(8)) Raspberry Pr., Ltd.

Schumacher, Julie. The Chain Letter. 2005. 208p. (J). (gr. 5-9). lib. bdg. 17.99 (978-0-385-90205-2(0) , Delacorte Bks. for Young Readers) Random Hse. Children's Bks.

—Grass Angel. 2004. 208p. (gr. 5-9). lib. bdg. 17.99 (978-0-385-90163-5(1) , Delacorte Bks. for Young Readers) Random Hse. Children's Bks.

—Grass Angel. 2005. 196p. (J). (gr. k-9). per. 12.55 (978-0-606-33725-0(3)) Tandem Library Bks.

Schuster, Judith. The Eddie Brewster Adventures, Bk. 1. 2006. 142p. pap. 19.95 (***978-1-4241-4418-1(3)***) PublishAmerica, Inc.

Schwartz, Virginia Frances. Messenger. 2002. 290p. (J). (gr. 7 up). tchr. ed. 17.95 (978-0-8234-1716-2(6)) Holiday Hse., Inc.

Scillian, Devin. Pappy's Handkerchief. Ellison, Chris, illus. rev. ed. 2007. (Tales of Young Americans Ser.). 40p. (J). (gr. 3-7). 17.95 (***978-1-58536-316-2(2)***) Sleeping Bear Pr.

Scott, Adam. Joe Moves In. Levy, David B., illus. 2002. (Blue's Clues Ser.). 24p. (J). (ps-1). pap. 3.50 (978-0-689-84943-5(5) , 12, Simon Spotlight/Nickelodeon) Simon & Schuster Children's Publishing.

Seckar, Alvena Vajdak. Misko. Merwin, Decie, illus. 1999. 159p. (J). 19.00 (978-0-86516-465-9(7)) Bolchazy-Carducci Pubs.

—Trapped in the Old Mine. Gotlieb, Jules, illus. 1999. 224p. (J). 19.00 (978-0-86516-466-6(5)) Bolchazy-Carducci Pubs.

Seiler, E. Building Paper Bridges. 2005. 207p. pap. 19.95 (978-1-4137-5459-9(7)) PublishAmerica, Inc.

Sesame Workshop Staff & SoftPlay (Firm) Staff, contrib. by. Happy Families in Elmo's World. 2002. (Elmo's World Ser.). (Illus.). (J). (978-1-931312-47-9(8)) SoftPlay, Inc.

Seuling, Barbara. Robert Finds a Way. Brewer, Paul, illus. 2005. (Robert Bks.). 150p. (J). 15.95 (978-0-8126-2734-3(2)) Cricket Bks.

Shanahan, Lisa. The Sweet, Terrible, Glorious Year I Truly, Completely Lost It. 2007. 304p. (YA). (gr. 7-10). 15.99 (***978-0-385-73516-2(2)***); lib. bdg. 18.99 (***978-0-385-90505-3(X)***) Random Hse. Children's Bks. (Delacorte Bks. for Young Readers).

Shawver, Margaret. What's Wrong with Grandma? A Family's Experience with Alzheimer's. Bagby, Jeffrey K., illus. 2004. 62p. pap. 16.00 (978-1-59102-174-2(X)) Prometheus Bks., Pubs.

Shelby, Anne. Homeplace. Halperin, Wendy Anderson, illus. 2000. 32p. (J). (ps-2). pap. 6.95 (978-0-531-07178-6(2) , Orchard Bks.) Scholastic, Inc.

Sheldon, Dyan. Confessions of a Teenage Drama Queen. 2005. 272p. (YA). (gr. 7 up). pap. 7.99 (978-0-7636-2827-7(1)); 2004. (J). 107.82 (978-0-7636-2538-2(8)); 2004. (Illus.). 308p. (YA). (gr. 7 up). pap. 5.99 (978-0-7636-2416-3(0)) Candlewick Pr.

—Confessions of a Teenage Drama Queen. 2002. (gr. 7-12). lib. bdg. 15.30 (978-0-613-74762-2(3)) Tandem Library Bks.

Shemin, Craig. Families Are Forever. McCoy, John, illus. l.t. ed. 2003. 34p. 9.95 (978-0-9728666-0-6(4) , 1) As Simple As That Publishing.

Sheppard, Caroline H. Shadow Moves: A Story for Families & Children Experiencing a Difficult or Traumatic Move. Manikoff, John, illus. 2003. (J). pap. 10.00 (978-1-931310-26-0(2)) National Institute for Trauma & Loss in Children, The/TLC.

Sheth, Kashmira. Koyal Dark, Mango Sweet. 224p. (gr. 7-17). 2006. 15.99 (978-0-7868-3857-8(4)); 2007. pap. 7.99 (***978-0-7868-3858-5(2)***) Hyperion Pr.

Shields, Carol Diggory. Lucky Pennies & Hot Chocolate. Nakata, Hiroe, illus. 2002. 32p. (J). pap. 5.99 (978-0-14-230190-6(6) , Puffin) Penguin Group (USA) Inc.

Shimko, Bonnie. Kat's Promise. 2006. 288p. (J). 17.00 (978-0-15-205473-1(1)) Harcourt Children's Bks.

Shipley, Jocelyn. Getting a Life: A Young Adult Novel. 2003. 224p. (J). pap. 7.95 (978-1-894549-18-9(X)) Sumach Pr. CAN. *Dist:* Orca Bk. Pubs. USA.

Shreve, Susan Richards. Blister. 2003. (Illus.). 176p. (J). (gr. 3-7). pap. 4.99 (978-0-439-19314-6(1) , Scholastic Paperbacks) Scholastic, Inc.

Shulman, Mark. Mom & Dad Are Palindromes: A Dilemma for Words... & Backwards. McCauley, Adam, illus. 2006. 36p. (J). 15.95 (978-0-8118-4328-7(9)) Chronicle Bks. LLC.

Shusterman, Neal. Dread Locks, No. 1. 2006. (Dark Fusion Ser.). 176p. (YA). (gr. 7). pap. 6.99 (978-0-14-240599-4(X) , Puffin) Penguin Group (USA) Inc.

—Dread Locks: Dark Fusion # 1. 2005. 176p. (J). (gr. 6-12). 15.99 (978-0-525-47554-5(0) , Dutton Juvenile) Penguin Group (USA) Inc.

Shyer, Marlene Fanta. Fleabiscuit Sings! 2005. 160p. (J). 15.95 (978-0-7614-5213-3(3)) Cavendish, Marshall Corp.

Sidney, Margaret. Five Little Peppers & How They Grew. (J). 23.95 (978-0-8488-0629-3(8)) Amereon LTD.

—Five Little Peppers & How They Grew. 2006. (Dover Value Editions Ser.). (Illus.). 224p. (J). pap. 5.95 (978-0-486-45267-8(0)) Dover Pubns., Inc.

—Five Little Peppers Grown Up. 2006. 236p. pap. 12.99 (978-1-4264-2517-2(1)) BiblioBazaar.

—Five Little Peppers Grown up. l.t. ed. 2006. 250p. pap. 16.99 (978-1-4264-2540-0(6)) BiblioBazaar.

Siegrist, Bonnie. Little Farm down the Lane -Book IV. 2007. pap. 10.99 (***978-1-60034-912-6(9)***) Xulon Pr., Inc.

Silver Dolphin en Español Editors, creator. Mis Figuras Geometricas. 2005. (Mis figuras Geometricas Ser.). (SPA., Illus.). 6p. (J). (ps-k). 9.95 (978-970-718-296-7(2) , Silver Dolphin en Español) Advanced Marketing, S. de R. L. de C. V. MEX. *Dist:* Perseus Distribution.

Simmons, H. J. The Little House on the Corner. 2004. 63p. pap. 12.95 (978-1-4137-2934-4(7)) PublishAmerica, Inc.

Simmons, Michael. Pool Boy. 2005. 192p. (YA). (gr. 7). reprint ed. pap. 7.95 (978-0-385-73196-6(5) , Delacorte Bks. for Young Readers) Random Hse. Children's Bks.

—Vandal. 2006. 176p. (YA). 16.95 (978-1-59643-070-9(2)) Roaring Brook Pr.

E F G

Simon, Charnan. Pumpkin Fever. Bryan-Hunt, Jan, illus. 2007. (Rookie Reader Ser.). 30p. (J). pap. (***978-0-531-12488-6(6))*** Children's Pr., Ltd.

—Pumpkin Forever. Bryan-Hunt, Jan, illus. 2006. (Rookie Reader Skill Set Ser.). 32p. (J). (gr. k-2). 19.50 (978-0-531-12086-6(4) , Children's Pr.) Scholastic Library Publishing.

—Tressa the Musical Princess. Allen, Joy, illus. 2005. 25p. (J). (978-1-58987-112-0(X)) Kindermusik International.

—What Makes You Happy? Bryan-Hunt, Jan, illus. 2006. (Magic Door to Learning Ser.). 24p. (J). 21.36 (978-1-59296-623-3(3)) Child's World, Inc.

Skolmoski, Stephanie. A Paper Hug. Bennion, Anneliese, illus. 2006. (J). 6.95 (978-0-9786425-0-1(3)) Design-Ability.

Skolsky, Mindy Warshaw. You're the Best Hannah! 2000. (978-0-606-18733-6(2)) Tandem Library Bks.

Skurzynski, Gloria. Cliff-Hanger. 2001. (National Parks Mystery Ser.). (Illus.). (J). 12.60 (978-0-606-21111-6(X)) Tandem Library Bks.

—Deadly Waters. 2001. (gr. 3-6). lib. bdg. 14.10 (978-0-613-81327-3(8)); (Illus.). (J). 12.60 (978-0-606-21142-0(X)) Tandem Library Bks.

Sloan, Glenna. A Year on the Dot. 2000. 91p. (J). (gr. k-8). pap. 9.99 (978-0-88092-545-7(0) , 5450) Royal Fireworks Publishing Co.

Smalls-Hector, Irene. Because You're Lucky. Hays, Michael, illus. 2004. 48p. (J). (ps-ps). lib. bdg. 13.19 (978-0-606-30471-9(1)) Tandem Library Bks.

Smith, Anne Warren. Turkey Monster Thanksgiving. 2003. 112p. (J). (gr. 2-5). 14.95 (978-0-8075-8125-4(9)) Whitman, Albert & Co.

Smith, D. James. The Boys of San Joaquin. 240p. (J). (gr. 3-7). 2006. pap. 5.99 (978-1-4169-1619-2(9) , Aladdin); 2005. (Illus.). 16.99 (978-0-689-87606-6(8) , Atheneum) Simon & Schuster Children's Publishing.

—Probably the World's Best Story about a Dog & the Girl Who Loved Me. 2006. 240p. (J). (gr. 4-7). 15.95 (978-1-4169-0542-4(1)) Simon & Schuster Children's Publishing.

Smith, Debra West. Hattie Marshall & the Prowling Panther. 2005. 144p. (J). 6.95 (978-1-56554-940-1(6)) Pelican Publishing Co., Inc.

—Yankees on the Doorstep: The Story of Sarah Morgan. 2001. (Illus.). 176p. (J). (gr. 3-7). pap. 10.95 (978-1-56554-872-5(8)) Pelican Publishing Co., Inc.

Smith, Doris Buchanan. Return to Bitter Creek. 2002. (J). (gr. 3-7). 19.75 (978-0-8446-7212-0(2)) Smith, Peter Pub., Inc.

Smith, Greg Andrew. The Pledge of Three Bk. 1: The Z. O. Chronicles. 2005. 240p. (J). pap. 8.95 (978-0-9760576-5-9(4) , 0976057654) Lucky Pr., LLC.

Smith, Greg Leitich. Ninjas, Piranhas, & Galileo. 2005. 192p. (J). (gr. 5-8). pap. 6.99 (978-0-316-01181-5(9)) Little Brown & Co.

Smith, Jennifer E. The Comeback Season. 2008. 256p. (YA). 15.99 (***978-1-4169-3847-7(8)*** , Simon & Schuster Children's Publishing) Simon & Schuster Children's Publishing.

Smith, Lane. The Happy Hocky Family Moves to the Country! 2003. (Illus.). 64p. (J). 16.99 (978-0-670-03594-6(7) , Viking Juvenile) Penguin Group (USA) Inc.

—The Happy Hocky Family Moves to the Country. Smith, Lane, illus. 2005. 64p. (J). pap. 6.99 (978-0-14-240297-9(4) , Puffin) Penguin Group (USA) Inc.

Smith, Patrick. Land Remembered. 2001. (gr. 5-8). lib. bdg. 16.40 (978-0-613-55622-4(4)) Tandem Library Bks.

Smith, Patrick D. A Land Remembered, 2 vols. 2001. (Illus.). Vol. 1. 240p. (J). (gr. 5-12). pap., stu. ed. 7.95 (978-1-56164-223-6(1)); Vol. 1. 240p. (gr. 5-12). stu. ed. 14.95 (978-1-56164-230-4(4)); Vol. 2. 200p. (J). pap., stu. ed. 7.95 (978-1-56164-224-3(X)); Vol. 2. 200p. (J). (gr. 5-12). stu. ed. 14.95 (978-1-56164-231-1(2)) Pineapple Pr., Inc.

Smith, S. C. Mabell. Ethel Morton at Rose House. 2006. 77.99 (***978-1-4280-4780-8(8));*** pap. 70.99 (***978-1-4280-4784-6(0))*** IndyPublish.com.

Smith, Sherri L. Hot, Sour, Salty, Sweet. 2008. 176p. (J). (***978-0-385-73417-2(4));*** lib. bdg. (***978-0-385-90431-5(2))*** Dell Publishing. (Delacorte Pr.).

Smith, Stephen D. & Caldwell, Lise. Rivals on the Waves. 2006. 128p. (J). pap. 5.99 (978-0-7847-1470-6(3) , 42141) Standard Publishing.

Smothers, Ethel Footman. Down in the Piney Woods. 2004. 128p. (J). pap. 7.00 (978-0-8028-5248-9(3)) Eerdmans, William B. Publishing Co.

—Down in the Piney Woods. 2003. (gr. 3-6). lib. bdg. 15.30 (978-0-613-75341-8(0)) Tandem Library Bks.

Smucker, Barbara. Nubes Negras. (SPA.). (YA). (gr. 5-8). pap. (978-84-279-3148-0(4) , NG3493) Noguer y Caralt Editores, S. A. ESP. *Dist:* Lectorum Pubns., Inc.

Snadowsky, Daria. Anatomy of a Boyfriend. 2007. 272p. (YA). (gr. 9). 16.99 (978-0-385-73320-5(8)); 16.99 (978-0-385-90339-4(1)) Random Hse. Children's Bks. (Delacorte Bks. for Young Readers).

Snedeker, Caroline. Downright Dencey. Barney, Maginel Wright, illus. 2003. (Young Adult Library). 274p. (YA). pap. 11.95 (978-1-883937-79-9(5)) Bethlehem Bks.

Snelling, Lauraine. Class Act. 2000. (High Hurdles Ser.: No. 10). 176p. (J). (gr. 6-9). pap. 5.99 (978-0-7642-2038-8(1)) Bethany Hse. Pubs.

Snyder, Zilpha Keatley. The Headless Cupid. 2002. (Illus.). (J). 13.38 (978-0-7587-0269-2(8)) Book Wholesalers, Inc.

—The Magic Nation Thing. (gr. 3-7). 2007. 192p. 6.50 (***978-0-440-41931-0(X)*** , Yearling); 2005. 176p. (J). 15.95 (978-0-385-73085-3(3) , Delacorte Bks. for Young Readers) Random Hse. Children's Bks.

Snyder, Zilpha Keatley. The Unseen. l.t. ed. 2005. 276p. 22.95 (978-0-7862-7265-5(1) , Large Print Pr.) Thorndike Pr.

Sommer, Carl. No Longer a Dilly Dally, 1 bk. 2003. (Another Sommer-Time Story Ser.). (Illus.). 48p. (J). 16.95 incl. audio (978-1-57537-550-2(8)); (gr. 1-4). 16.95 incl. audio compact disk (978-1-57537-501-4(X)) Advance Publishing, Inc.

Sommer, Carl. The Richest Poor Kid. Martinez, Jorge, illus. 2007. (J). (***978-1-57537-025-5(5));*** lib. bdg. (***978-1-57537-074-3(3))*** Advance Publishing, Inc.

Son, John. Finding My Hat. 2003. (First Person Fiction Ser.). 192p. (J). (gr. 6-10). pap. 16.95 (978-0-439-43538-3(2) , Orchard Bks.) Scholastic, Inc.

Sonenklar, Carol. My Own Worst Enemy. 1999. 152p. (J). (gr. 7 up). tchr. ed. 15.95 (978-0-8234-1456-7(6)) Holiday Hse., Inc.

Sonnenblick, Jordan. Dodger & Me. 2008. 176p. (J). 16.95 (***978-0-312-37793-9(2))*** Feiwel & Friends.

Sonnenblick, Jordan. Notes from the Midnight Driver. 2007. 288p. (J). pap. 6.99 (***978-0-439-75781-2(9)*** , Scholastic Paperbacks); 2006. 272p. (YA). pap. 16.99 (978-0-439-75779-9(7) , Scholastic Pr.) Scholastic, Inc.

Sorensen, Virginia. Miracles on Maple Hill. Davis, Lambert, illus. 2002. (J). 13.19 (978-0-7587-0203-6(5)) Book Wholesalers, Inc.

—Miracles on Maple Hill. 2003. (Illus.). 256p. (YA). pap. 5.95 (978-0-15-204718-4(2) , Odyssey Classics) Harcourt Children's Bks.

—Miracles on Maple Hill. Krush, Joe & Krush, Beth, illus. 2003. 256p. (J). 17.00 (978-0-15-204719-1(0) , Harcourt Young Classics) Harcourt Children's Bks.

—Miracles on Maple Hill. 2003. (gr. 5-8). lib. bdg. 6.95 (978-0-613-70527-1(0)) Tandem Library Bks.

Sorrells, Walter. Silent Room. 2006. 240p. (YA). (gr. 7). 16.99 (978-0-525-47697-9(0) , Dutton Juvenile) Penguin Group (USA) Inc.

Spalding, Andrea. Heart of the Hill. 2005. (Dinah Galloway Mystery Ser.: Bk. 3Three). 192p. (J). (gr. 3-7). pap. 7.95 (978-1-55143-486-5(5)) Orca Bk. Pubs. USA.

—Me & Mr. Mah. Wilson, Janet, illus. 32p. (J). (ps-2). 2001. 7.95 (978-1-55143-177-2(7)); 2000. 14.95 (978-1-55143-168-0(8)) Orca Bk. Pubs. USA.

Sparks, Matthew. All I Need. 2005. 48p. pap. 12.95 (978-1-4137-4004-2(9)) PublishAmerica, Inc.

Speregen, Devra Newberger. Brother's Keeper: Hero for a Day. 1999. 10.64 (978-0-606-17621-7(7)) Tandem Library Bks.

Spinelli, Eileen. The Perfect Thanksgiving. Adinolfi, JoAnn, illus. 2007. 32p. (J). pap. 6.99 (***978-0-312-37505-8(0))*** Square Fish.

—Someday. Winstead, Rosie, illus. 2007. 32p. (J). (ps). 16.99 (978-0-8037-2941-4(3) , Dial) Penguin Group (USA) Inc.

—Summerhouse Time. Lew-Vriethoff, Joanne, illus. 2007. 224p. (J). (gr. 3-7). 12.99 (978-0-375-84061-6(3)); lib. bdg. 15.99 (978-0-375-94061-3(8)) Random Hse. Children's Bks. (Knopf Bks. for Young Readers).

—Thanksgiving at the Tappletons' Lloyd, Megan, illus. 32p. (J). (ps-3). 2003. 16.99 (978-0-06-008670-1(X)); 2004. pap. 6.99 (978-0-06-008672-5(6) , Harper Trophy) HarperCollins Pubs.

—When Mama Comes Home Tonight. Dyer, Jane, illus. (J). (gr. k-3). 1999. 30p. bds. 14.00 (978-0-689-82714-3(8) , Simon & Schuster Children's Publishing); 2002. 32p. reprint ed. 6.99 (978-0-689-84897-1(8) , Aladdin) Simon & Schuster Children's Publishing.

—When Mama Comes Home Tonight. 2002. (gr. k-3). lib. bdg. 15.30 (978-0-613-62881-5(0)) Tandem Library Bks.

—When You Are Happy. Valerio, Geraldo, illus. 2006. 40p. (J). (ps-1). 16.95 (978-0-689-86251-9(2)) Simon & Schuster Children's Publishing.

—Where I Live. 2007. (Illus.). 112p. (J). (gr. 2-4). 16.99 (978-0-8037-3122-6(1) , Dial) Penguin Group (USA) Inc.

Spinelli, Eileen & Lisker, Emily, illus. Summerhouse Time. 2001. (J). 16.00 (978-0-689-82418-0(1) , Simon & Schuster Children's Publishing) Simon & Schuster Children's Publishing.

Spinelli, Jerry. Blue Ribbon Blues. Nelson, Donna, illus. 1998. (Stepping Stone Books 2: Vol. 2). 80p. (gr. 2-5). lib. bdg. 11.99 (978-0-679-98753-6(3) , Random Hse. Bks. for Young Readers) Random Hse. Children's Bks.

—Blue Ribbon Blues: A Tooter Tale. Nelson, Donna, illus. 1998. (Tooter Tale Ser.: Vol. 2). 80p. (J). (gr. 1-4). pap. 3.99 (978-0-679-88753-9(9) , Random Hse. Bks. for Young Readers) Random Hse. Children's Bks.

—Eggs. 2007. 224p. (J). (gr. 3-7). 15.99 (***978-0-316-16646-1(4))*** Little, Brown Bks. for Young Readers.

Spinelli, Jerry. Loser. 224p. 2003. pap. 5.99 (978-0-06-054074-6(5)); 2002. (J). (gr. 4-7). 15.99 (978-0-06-000193-3(3) , Cotler, Joanna Books); 2002. (Illus.). (J). (gr. 4-6). lib. bdg. 16.89 (978-0-06-000483-5(5) , Cotler, Joanna Books) HarperCollins Pubs.

—Loser. 2002. (gr. 3-6). lib. bdg. 14.15 (978-0-613-66899-6(5)) Tandem Library Bks.

Spizman, Robyn Freedman & Johnston, Mark. Secret Agent. 240p. (J). 2006. (gr. 4-7). pap. 5.99 (978-1-4169-1862-2(0) , Aladdin); 2005. 16.95 (978-0-689-87044-6(2) , Atheneum) Simon & Schuster Children's Publishing.

Spyri, Johanna. Heidi. reprint ed. lib. bdg. 48.00 (978-0-7426-1047-7(0)); 2001. (Illus.). pap. 28.00 (978-0-7426-6047-2(8)) Classic Bks.

—Heidi. l.t. ed. 2004. (Large Print Ser.). 433p. 26.00 (978-1-58287-666-5(5)) North Bks.

—Heidi. l.t. ed. 2002. (Perennial Bestsellers Ser.). 394p. 29.95 (978-0-7862-4886-5(6)) Thorndike Pr.

Spyri, Johanna. Uncle Titus & His Visit to the Country. 2006. 77.99 (***978-1-4280-3143-2(X))*** IndyPublish.com.

St. Anthony, Jane. Grace above All. 2007. 176p. (J). (gr. 5-8). 16.00 (978-0-374-39940-5(9) , Farrar, Straus & Giroux (BYR)) Farrar, Straus & Giroux.

St-Aubin, Bruno, illus. Daddy's a Dinosaur. 2005. (Read-It! Readers Ser.). 32p. (J). (gr. k-3). 18.60 (978-1-4048-1028-0(5)) Picture Window Bks.

St. George, Judith. The Ghost, the White House, & Me. 2007. 128p. (J). (gr. 3-7). 16.95 (978-0-8234-2045-2(0)) Holiday Hse., Inc.

St. John, Patricia. I Needed a Neighbour. 2003. 128p. 6.49 (978-0-86201-454-4(9)) Scripture Union GBR. *Dist:* Gabriel Resources.

—The Secret at Pheasant Cottage. 2002. (Illus.). 144p. (YA). pap. 5.99 (978-0-8024-6579-5(X)) Moody Pubs.

Stahler, David, Jr. Doppelganger. 2006. 272p. (J). 16.99 (978-0-06-087232-8(2)); lib. bdg. 17.89 (978-0-06-087233-5(0)) HarperCollins Pubs.

Staples, Suzanne Fisher. Jameel & the House of Djinn. 2008. 224p. (YA). 16.95 (***978-0-374-39936-8(0))*** Farrar, Straus & Giroux.

Starks, R. The Fish Gut Experiment. Jellett, Tom, illus. 2008. (J). lib. bdg. (***978-1-59889-862-0(0));*** 80p. pap. (***978-1-59889-918-4(X))*** Stone Arch Bks.

Staunton, Ted. Stinky. Gardos, Susan, illus. 2004. (Northern Lights Young Novels Ser.). 64p. (J). (gr. 2-5). pap. 4.95 (978-0-88995-263-8(9)) Red Deer Pr. CAN. *Dist:* Fitzhenry & Whiteside, Ltd.

—Stinky. 2003. (gr. 3-6). lib. bdg. 12.95 (978-0-613-84450-5(5)) Tandem Library Bks.

Steinhofel, Andreas. The Center of the World. 2007. 480p. (YA). (gr. 9). pap. 7.99 (978-0-440-22932-2(4) , Laurel Leaf) Random Hse. Children's Bks.

Step from Heaven. 2002. (gr. 7-12). lib. bdg. 16.45 (978-0-613-60366-9(4)) Tandem Library Bks.

Stewart, Sarah. The Gardener. Small, David, illus. 2007. 40p. (J). pap. 6.95 (***978-0-312-36749-7(X))*** Square Fish.

Stiegemeyer, Julie. Merry Christmas, Cheeps! Baicker-McKee, Carol, illus. 2007. 24p. (J). (ps). 9.95 (978-1-59990-064-3(5)) Bloomsbury Publishing.

Stites, Clara. Rosalba of Santa Juanita: A California Story. 2002. (Illus.). 80p. (J). pap. 8.95 (978-1-56474-394-7(2)) Fithian Pr.

Stockham, Leslie C. What's the Matter with the Baby? 1999. Tr. of Que le Pasa Al Bebito?. (Illus.). 18p. (J). (ps). 19.98 (978-1-893447-00-4(6)) Bilingual Language Materials.

Stone, Phoebe. Deep down Popular. 2008. (J). 288p. pap. 16.99 (***978-0-439-80245-1(8)); (978-0-439-80244-4(X))*** Scholastic, Inc. (Levine, Arthur A. Bks.).

Stork, Francisco X. Behind the Eyes. 2006. 256p. (YA). (gr. 9). 16.99 (978-0-525-47735-8(7) , Dutton Adult) Penguin Group (USA) Inc.

Strasser, Todd. Boot Camp. 2007. 256p. (YA). (gr. 8 up). 15.99 (978-1-4169-0848-7(X)) Simon & Schuster Children's Publishing.

—Count Your Blessings. 2007. (Mob Princess Ser.). 240p. (YA). (gr. 9 up). pap. 8.99 (***978-1-4169-3542-1(8)*** , Simon Pulse) Simon & Schuster Children's Publishing.

Strasser, Todd. Dance Magic. 1999. (Illus.). (J). (978-0-606-18372-7(8)) Tandem Library Bks.

Stuchner, Joan Betty. Honey Cake. Nugent, Cynthia, illus. 2008. (J). (***978-0-375-85189-6(5));*** pap. (***978-0-375-85190-2(9));*** lib. bdg. (***978-0-375-95189-3(X))*** Random Hse., Inc.

Studio, Marcel S. Arthur's Promise, 18. Studio, Marcel S., ed. 2001. (Arthur's Family Values: Vol. 1). (Illus.). 28p. (J). (ps). 3.49 (978-1-57973-107-6(4)) Advance Pubs. LLC.

Stuve-Bodeen, Stephanie. Elizabeti's School. Hale, Christy, illus. 2002. 32p. (J). (gr. k-3). 16.95 (978-1-58430-043-4(4)) Lee & Low Bks., Inc.

Stuve-Bodeen, Stephanie. La escuela de Elizabeti. Christy, Hale, illus. 2007. (SPA.). (J). pap. 7.95 (***978-1-60060-235-1(5))*** Lee & Low Bks., Inc.

Sula, Sondra. The Expanders: Quest for the Flubulator. 2000. mass mkt. 8.95 (978-1-931179-11-9(5)) Long Hill Productions, Inc.

—The Expanders: Quest for the Flubulator. Johnson, Terri L., illus. 2000. 32p. (J). (gr. 1-3). pap. (978-0-9701450-2-4(0)) Long Hill Productions, Inc.

Sullivan, Jaqueline Levering. Annie's War. 2007. 190p. (J). (gr. 3-7). 15.00 (***978-0-8028-5325-7(0)*** , Eerdmans Bks For Young Readers) Eerdmans, William B. Publishing Co.

Sullivan, Therese M. & Bitner, Pamela. A Gift from Valentine. 2007. 24p. (J). per. 12.95 (***978-1-58939-981-5(1))*** Virtualbookworm.com Publishing, Inc.

Surprise Cake: Individual Title Six-Packs. (Literatura 2000 Ser.). (gr. k-1). 28.00 (978-0-7635-0065-8(8)) Rigby Education.

Sweeney, Joyce. Takedown. 2004. 208p. (J). 15.95 (978-0-7614-5175-4(7)) Cavendish, Marshall Corp.

Swicord, Robin. Little Women: The Children's Picture Book. 2004. (Illus.). 96p. (gr. 2 up). 15.95 (978-1-55704-216-3(0)) Newmarket Pr.

Swindells, Robert. Abomination! 2000. (Yearling Book Ser.). 208p. (J). pap. 9.99 (978-0-440-86362-5(7)) Transworld Publishers Ltd. GBR. *Dist:* Trafalgar Square Publishing.

Swiss Family Robinson Study Guide. 2002. (Illus.). 48p. (YA). per. 17.95 (978-1-56254-532-1(9) , SP5329) Saddleback Educational Publishing.

Sykes, Julie. Despierta, Tigrito. 2002. (Little Tiger Board Book Ser.). (SPA., Illus.). 76p. 8.95 (978-84-488-0929-4(7) , BS7937) Beascoa, Ediciones S.A. ESP. *Dist:* Lectorum Pubns., Inc.

Sylvera, Jana. Men Are from Mars, Women Are from Venus. 2005. 62p. pap. 12.95 (978-1-4137-7440-5(7)) PublishAmerica, Inc.

Tabor, Nancy. Las Botellas Se Rompen. 1999. Tr. of Bottles Break. (SPA., Illus.). 32p. (J). (gr. k-3). pap. 6.95 (978-0-88106-320-2(7)) Charlesbridge Publishing, Inc.

Tafuri, Nancy. Mama's Little Bears. 2004. (J). bds. 7.99 (978-0-439-57357-3(2)) Scholastic, Inc.

Tait, Chris & Wyss, Johann David. The Swiss Family Robinson. Akib, Jamel, illus. 2007. 151p. (J). (***978-1-4287-4213-0(1))*** Sterling Publishing Co., Inc.

Takabayashi, Mari. I Live in Brooklyn. 2004. (Illus.). 32p. (J). (gr. k-3). tchr. ed. 16.00 (978-0-618-30899-6(7)) Houghton Mifflin Co. Trade & Reference Div.

Takacs, Dalma. Meet Me at the Globe: A Novel for Young People. 2002. 204p. (YA). pap. 13.95 (978-0-595-21155-5(0) , Writer's Showcase Pr.) iUniverse, Inc.

Tangvald, Christine Harder. Hip, Hug, Hooray! Griego, Tony, illus. 2002. 32p. (J). (ps-k). 9.99 (978-0-7642-2540-6(5)) Bethany Hse. Pubs.

Tarshis, Lauren. Emma Jean Lazarus Fell Out of a Tree. 2007. (Illus.). 144p. (J). (gr. 4 up). 16.99 (978-0-8037-3164-6(7) , Dial) Penguin Group (USA) Inc.

Tate, Nikki. Grandparents' Day. Laverdière, Benoit, illus. 2004. 32p. (J). (gr. k-3). pap. 7.95 (978-1-55037-842-9(2)); lib. bdg. 18.95 (978-1-55037-843-6(0)) Annick Pr., Ltd. CAN. *Dist:* Firefly Bks., Ltd.

Taulbert, Clifton L. Little Cliff & the Porch People. Kane, Cindy, ed. Lewis, Earl, illus. 1999. 32p. (J). (ps-3). 16.99 (978-0-8037-2174-6(9) , Dial) Penguin Group (USA) Inc.

Taylor, Bonnie Highsmith. Gypsy in the Cellar. Marks, Dea, illus. 1999. (Cover-to-Cover Bks.). 99p. (J). (gr. 4-6). pap. 5.60 (978-0-7891-5112-4(X)) Perfection Learning Corp.

Taylor, Kim. Cissy Funk. 2001. 224p. (J). (gr. 5 up). 15.95 (978-0-06-029041-2(2)) HarperCollins Pubs.

Taylor, Mildred D. The Gold Cadillac. Hays, Michael & Ginsberg, Max, illus. 1998. 48p. (YA). (gr. 2-6). pap. 4.99 (978-0-14-038963-0(6) , Puffin) Penguin Group (USA) Inc.

—The Gold Cadillac. 1998. 11.79 (978-0-606-13433-0(6)) Tandem Library Bks.

—The Land. Ginsburg, Max, illus. 2001. 392p. (J). (gr. 7 up). 17.99 (978-0-8037-1950-7(7) , Dial) Penguin Group (USA) Inc.

—Roll of Thunder, Hear My Cry. l.t. ed. 2000. (LRS Large Print Cornerstone Ser.). 348p. (YA). (gr. 5-12). lib. bdg. 32.95 (978-1-58118-057-2(8) , 23471) LRS.

—Roll of Thunder, Hear My Cry. 1998. (J). (gr. 5). pap. 3.95 (978-0-439-04476-9(6)) Scholastic, Inc.

Taylor, Sydney. All-of-a-Kind Family. John, Helen, illus. 2002. 13.94 (978-0-7587-9169-6(0)) Book Wholesalers, Inc.

—All-of-a-Kind Family. 2000. (All-of-a-Kind Family Ser.). (Illus.). 189p. (J). (gr. 4-7). reprint ed. pap. 13.95 (978-0-929093-08-6(9) , Taylor Productions) GRM Assocs.

—All-of-a-Kind Family. John, Helen, illus. 2005. 192p. (J). (gr. 3-7). lib. bdg. 17.99 (978-0-385-90316-5(2) , Delacorte Bks. for Young Readers) Random Hse. Children's Bks.

—All-of-a-Kind Family Downtown. Krush, Beth & Krush, Joe, illus. 2001. (All-of-a-Kind Family Ser.). 187p. (J). (gr. 5 up). reprint ed. pap. 13.95 (978-0-929093-07-9(0) , Taylor Productions) GRM Assocs.

—All-of-a-Kind Family Uptown. Stevens, Mary, illus. 2001. (All-of-a-Kind Family Ser.). 160p. (J). (gr. 5 up). pap. 13.95 (978-0-929093-09-3(7) , Taylor Productions) GRM Assocs.

—Ella of All-of-a-Kind Family. 2000. (All-of-a-Kind Family Ser.). 144p. (J). (gr. 4-7). reprint ed. pap. 12.95 (978-0-929093-05-5(4) , Taylor Productions) GRM Assocs.

—More All-of-a-Kind Family. Stevens, Mary, illus. 2001. (All-of-a-Kind Family Ser.). 160p. (J). (gr. 5 up). pap. 13.95 (978-0-929093-10-9(0)); reprint ed. 16.95 (978-0-929093-02-4(X)) GRM Assocs. (Taylor Productions).

Taylor, Sydney & John, Helen. All-of-a-Kind Family. 2005. (Illus.). 192p. (J). (gr. 3-7). 15.95 (978-0-385-73295-6(3) , Delacorte Bks. for Young Readers) Random Hse. Children's Bks.

Taylor, Theodore. Maldonado Miracle. 2003. (gr. 5-8). lib. bdg. 6.95 (978-0-613-70532-5(7)) Tandem Library Bks.

—The Maldonado Miracle. 2003. 176p. (YA). (gr. 3-6). pap. 6.95 (978-0-15-205036-8(1) , Harcourt Paperbacks) Harcourt Children's Bks.

A Teeny Tiny Taste: Individual Title Six-Packs. (ps-2). 27.00 (978-0-7635-9478-7(4)) Rigby Education.

That Was Then, This Is Now. 1999. (YA). 9.95 (978-1-56137-522-6(5)) Novel Units, Inc.

Thermes, Jennifer. Sam Bennett's New Shoes. 2006. (Illus.). (J). 15.95 (978-1-57505-822-1(7) , Carolrhoda Bks.) Lerner Publishing Group.

Things Fall Apart. (YA). 1999. 9.95 (978-1-56137-812-8(7)); 1998. 40p. 11.95 (978-1-56137-813-5(5) , NU8135SP) Novel Units, Inc.

Thompson, Richard. Foo. Fernandes, Eugenie, illus. 2000. (Annikins Ser.). 24p. (J). (ps-k). pap. 1.25 (978-1-55037-641-8(1)) Annick Pr., Ltd. CAN. *Dist:* Firefly Bks., Ltd.

Thompson, Vivian L. Camp-in-the-Yard. 2002. 32p. pap. 8.95 (978-0-7414-1062-7(1)) Infinity Publishing.

Tildes, Phyllis L. Billy's Big-Boy Bed. Tildes, Phyllis L., illus. 2003. 32p. pap. 6.95 (978-1-57091-606-9(3)) Charlesbridge Publishing, Inc.

Tillman, Nancy. On the Night You Were Born, 1. l.t. ed. 2005. (Illus.). 32p. (J). 17.95 (978-0-9765761-0-5(4)) Darling Pr. LLC.

Timberlake, Amy. That Girl Lucy Moon. 2006. 304p. (gr. 4-7). 15.99 (978-0-7868-5298-7(4)) Hyperion Pr.

Tobesman, Rachmiel. The Magic Glasses: Stories & Other Activities for Children of Separation & Divorce. 1998. (Illus.). 38p. (J). (ps-12). spiral bd. 12.95 (978-0-9677266-0-1(3)) Project Shalom.

Tolan, Stephanie S. Ordinary Miracles. 2002. (gr. 5-8). lib. bdg. 14.10 (978-0-613-89267-4(4)) Tandem Library Bks.

—Surviving the Applewhites. 2002. 224p. (J). (gr. 5 up). 16.99 (978-0-06-623602-5(9)) HarperCollins Pubs.

 For book reviews, descriptive annotations, tables of contents, cover images, author biographies & additional information, updated daily, subscribe to **www.booksinprint.com**

—Welcome to the Ark. 2000. (gr. 5-8). lib. bdg. 15.30 (978-0-613-10539-2(7)) Tandem Library Bks.

Tomlinson, Sylvia. Maddie. Cartmell, Ginny, illus. 2002. 124p. (J). (gr. 3-7). 12.95 (978-0-9720293-0-8(3)) Redbud Publishing Co.

Tondreau Levert, Louise & Perkes, Carolyn. Parents Do the Weirdest Things! Girard, Roge, illus. 2001. (Little Wolf Bks.: Level 2). 32p. (J). (gr. 1 up). pap. (978-1-894363-75-4(2)) Dominique & Friends.

Tony's Dad, 6 Packs. (Sails Literacy Ser.). (gr. 1-2). 36.00 (978-0-7578-4015-9(9)) Rigby Education.

Too Hot! Individual Title Six-Pack Pouch - Level C. (Lighthouse Ser.). 12p. (gr. k-1). 24.00 (978-0-7578-0824-1(7)) Rigby Education.

Too Many Tamales. 2004. (J). (ps-3). 24.95 incl. audio (978-1-55592-098-2(5)); 29.95 incl. cd-rom (978-1-55592-137-8(X)) Weston Woods Studios, Inc.

Torres, Leyla. The Kite Festival. Torres, Leyla, illus. 2004. (Illus.). 32p. (J). 16.00 (978-0-374-38054-0(6) , Farrar, Straus & Giroux (BYR)) Farrar, Straus & Giroux.

Toten, Teresa. The Game. 2004. (Illus.). 160p. (YA). (gr. 9 up). pap. 7.95 (978-0-88995-232-4(9)) Red Deer Pr. CAN. *Dist:* Fitzhenry & Whiteside, Ltd.

—Game. 2001. (gr. 7-12). lib. bdg. 16.40 (978-0-613-60557-1(8)) Tandem Library Bks.

Townley, Roderick. The Red Thread: A Novel in Three Incarnations. 2007. 304p. (YA). (gr. 7 up). 17.99 (978-1-4169-0894-4(3) , Atheneum/Richard Jackson Bks.) Simon & Schuster Children's Publishing.

Townley, Roderick. The Red Thread: A Novel in Three Incarnations. 2007. 304p. (YA). 17.99 (***978-1-4169-2930-7(4)*** , Atheneum) Simon & Schuster Children's Publishing.

Travers, P. L. Mary Poppins from A to Z. Shepard, Mary, illus. 2006. 64p. (J). 14.00 (978-0-15-205834-0(6)) Harcourt Children's Bks.

Travers, Pamela L. Mary Poppins. 202p. (J). (gr. 3-5). pap. 6.00 (978-0-8072-1536-4(8) , Listening Library) Random Hse. Audio Publishing Group.

Treasure in the Attic. Date not set. (Illus.). 12p. (J). (gr. k-2). pap. 3.75 (978-1-58323-024-4(6) , Seedling Pubns.) Continental Pr., Inc.

Tremblay, Alain Ulysse. L' Héritage de Julien. Malépart, Céline, illus. 2004. (Roman Jeunesse Ser.). (FRE.). 96p. (J). (gr. 4-7). pap. (978-2-89021-682-2(9)) Diffusion du livre Mirabel.

Trewin, Trudie. I Lost My Kisses. 2008. 32p. (J). pap. 14.99 (***978-0-545-05557-4(1)*** , Orchard Bks.) Scholastic, Inc.

Tristan, Sarah. Cheat Codes. 2003. 234p. (YA). pap. 15.95 (978-0-595-29670-5(X)) iUniverse, Inc.

Trottier, Maxine. Prairie Willow. Fernandez, Laura & Jacobson, Rick, illus. 2000. 22p. (J). (gr. k-5). 7.95 (978-0-7737-6100-1(4)) Stoddart Kids CAN. *Dist:* Fitzhenry & Whiteside, Ltd.

—Prairie Willow. 2000. (J). (978-0-606-19956-8(X)) Tandem Library Bks.

Trudel, Sylvain. L' Ange de Monsieur Chose. 1999. (Premier Roman Ser.). (Illus.). 64p. (J). (gr. 2-5). pap. (978-2-89021-347-0(1)) Diffusion du livre Mirabel.

Trueman, Terry. Cruise Control. 2005. 160p. (J). pap. 7.99 (978-0-06-447377-4(5) , HarperTeen) HarperCollins Pubs.

Trumbore, Cindy. The Genie in the Book. Alley, R. W., illus. 2004. 120p. (J). (gr. 3-6). 15.95 (978-1-59354-042-5(6)) Handprint Bks.

Truss, Jan. Red. (J). pap. 6.95 (978-0-88899-135-5(5)) Groundwood Bks. CAN. *Dist:* Transition Vendor.

Tuey. Doug E Do. Martin, Susan, illus. 2006. 76p. pap. 14.95 (978-1-4241-0295-2(2)) PublishAmerica, Inc.

Turner, Ethel. Seven Little Australians. 2006. (ENG.). 25.99 (***978-1-4280-4145-5(1)***) IndyPublish.com.

Tym, Kate. We Love the Seaside. 2007. (J). lib. bdg. 16.95 (***978-1-59566-369-6(X)***) QEB Publishing Inc.

Tyner, Christopher. I'll Do It Tommarra Laura. 2004. 37p. (J). pap. 17.95 (978-1-4137-2753-1(0)) PublishAmerica, Inc.

Uff, Caroline. Hello, Lulu. 2004. (Illus.). 14p. (J). bds. 5.95 (978-0-8027-8928-0(5)) Walker & Co.

Uncle Tease: Individual Title Six Packs. (Action Packs Ser.). 120p. (gr. 3-5). 44.00 (978-0-7635-8388-0(X)) Rigby Education.

Uncle Teds Big Jump: Individual Title Six-Packs. (Sails Literacy Ser.). (gr. 1-2). 36.00 (978-0-7578-4011-1(6)) Rigby Education.

Uncle Walt's Christmas Box. 2001. 36p. (J). (gr. k-3). 10.99 (978-0-8254-7243-5(1)) Kregel Pubns.

Ungerer, Tomi. The Mellops Go Spelunking. Ungerer, Tomi, illus. 1998. (Illus.). 32p. (J). (gr. k-4). pap. 5.95 (978-1-57098-228-6(7)) Rinehart, Roberts Pubs.

Urban, Linda. A Crooked Kind of Perfect. 2007. (Illus.). 224p. (J). (gr. 3-7). 16.00 (***978-0-15-206007-7(3)***) Harcourt Children's Bks.

Ure, Jean. Pumpkin. 2002. (Diary Ser.). (Illus.). 176p. (J). pap. 9.99 (978-0-00-714392-4(3)) HarperCollins Pubs. Ltd. GBR. *Dist:* Independent Pubs. Group.

Vail, Rachel. If You Only Knew: Zoe. 1998. (Friendship Ring Ser.: No. 1). 240p. (J). (gr. 4-8). pap. 14.95 (978-0-590-03370-1(0)); pap. 4.99 (978-0-590-37451-4(6)) Scholastic, Inc.

—Not That I Care: Morgan. 1998. (Friendship Ring Ser.: No. 3). (J). (gr. 4-8). 59.88 (978-0-590-95214-9(5)); 240p. pap. 4.99 (978-0-590-37453-8(2)); 240p. pap. 14.95 (978-0-590-03476-0(6)) Scholastic, Inc.

Valgardson, W. D. Garbage Creek: And Other Stories. 1998. (Illus.). 136p. (J). (gr. 3-7). 5.95 (978-0-88899-339-7(0)) Groundwood Bks. CAN. *Dist:* Perseus Distribution.

Vallejo-Nagera, Alejandra. Mira Como He Crecido. Guerrero, Andrés, illus. (SPA.). 31p. (J). (gr. k-1). 8.95 (978-1-58986-547-1(2)) Santillana USA Publishing Co., Inc.

van de Ruit, John. Spud. 2007. 352p. (YA). (gr. 7 up). 16.99 (***978-1-59514-170-5(7)*** , Razorbill) Penguin Group (USA) Inc.

Van Draanen, Wendelin. Flipped. 224p. (gr. 5-9). 2003. (J). pap. 8.95 (978-0-375-82544-6(4)); 2001. (J). 14.95 (978-0-375-81174-6(5)); 2001. lib. bdg. 16.99 (978-0-375-91174-3(X)) Random Hse. Children's Bks. (Knopf Bks. for Young Readers).

—Flipped. 2003. (YA). 24.95 (978-0-7862-4798-1(3)) Thorndike Pr.

Van Dyne, Edith. Aunt Jane's Nieces. 2006. 96.99 (***978-1-4219-7428-6(2)***); pap. 89.99 (***978-1-4219-7440-8(1)***) IndyPublish.com.

—Aunt Jane's Nieces & Uncle John. 2006. 95.99 (***978-1-4219-7416-3(9)***); pap. 88.99 (***978-1-4219-7434-7(7)***) IndyPublish.com.

—Aunt Jane's Nieces at Millville. 2006. 95.99 (***978-1-4219-7454-5(1)***); pap. 89.99 (***978-1-4219-7453-8(3)***) IndyPublish.com.

—Aunt Jane's Nieces at Work. 2006. 78.99 (***978-1-4142-5888-1(7)***); pap. 71.99 (***978-1-4142-5882-9(8)***) IndyPublish.com.

—Aunt Jane's Nieces in Society. 2006. 41.99 (***978-1-4280-0211-1(1)***); pap. 35.99 (***978-1-4280-0196-1(4)***) IndyPublish.com.

—Aunt Jane's Nieces on Vacation. 2006. 95.99 (***978-1-4219-7507-8(6)***) IndyPublish.com.

—Aunt Jane's Nieces Out West. 2006. 42.99 (***978-1-4280-0248-7(0)***); pap. 35.99 (***978-1-4280-0254-8(5)***) IndyPublish.com.

van Kampen, Vlasta. It Couldn't Be Worse. van Kampen, Vlasta, illus. 2003. (Folk Tales Ser.). (Illus.). 32p. (J). (ps-1). pap. 6.95 (978-1-55037-782-8(5)) Annick Pr., Ltd. CAN. *Dist:* Firefly Bks., Ltd.

Van Leeuwen, Jean. Amanda Pig & the Really Hot Day. Schweninger, Ann, illus. 2007. 48p. (J). pap. 3.99 (978-0-14-240775-2(5) , Puffin) Penguin Group (USA) Inc.

Van Leeuwen, Jean & Van Leeuwen, Jean. Amanda Pig & the Really Hot Day. Schweninger, Ann, illus. 2005. (Easy-to-Read, Dial Ser.). 48p. (J). (ps-ps). 14.99 (978-0-8037-2887-5(5) , Dial) Penguin Group (USA) Inc.

Van Steenwyk, Elizabeth. Maggie in the Morning. 2002. (gr. 3-6). lib. bdg. 14.15 (978-0-613-88116-6(8)) Tandem Library Bks.

Vaughn, Margaret Britton, et al. The Birthday Dolly. 2000. (Illus.). 47p. (J). pap. (978-1-882845-09-5(9)) Bell Buckle Pr.

Vega, Denise. Fact of Life #31. 2008. 304p. (J). (gr. 7). 16.99 (***978-0-375-84819-3(3)***); lib. bdg. 19.99 (***978-0-375-94819-0(8)***) Random Hse. Children's Bks. (Knopf Bks. for Young Readers).

Velasquez, Gloria. Tyrone's Betrayal. 144p. (J). pap. 9.95 (978-1-55885-465-9(7) , Piñata Books) Arte Publico Pr.

Venkatraman, Padma. Climbing the Stairs. 2008. 256p. (YA). (gr. 7). 15.99 (***978-0-399-24746-0(7)*** , Putnam Juvenile) Penguin Group (USA) Inc.

Verne, Jules. Los Hijos del Capitan Grant (Captain Grant's Children) (SPA., Illus.). 192p. (YA). 11.95 (978-84-7281-077-8(1) , AF1077) Auriga, Ediciones S.A. ESP. *Dist:* Continental Bk. Co., Inc.

Vidal, Clara. Like a Thorn. Maudet, Y., tr. 2008. 128p. (J). (gr. 9). 14.99 (***978-0-385-73564-3(2)*** , Delacorte Bks. for Young Readers) Random Hse. Children's Bks.

View from Saturday. 1999. (J). 9.95 (978-1-56137-935-4(2)) Novel Units, Inc.

Vinette, Arnold D. Reid's Adventures - 1st Year Breaking in Your New Parents. Vinette, Dorothy V., ed. 2004. (J). 576p. 35.99 (978-1-4149-0002-5(3)); 592p. pap. 24.50 (978-1-4149-0004-9(X)) Time Capsule eBooks, Inc. (Time Capsule Bks.).

Viorst, Judith. Nobody Here but Me. Davenier, Christine, illus. 2008. (J). (***978-0-374-35540-1(1)***) Farrar, Straus & Giroux.

Vision, David & Vision, Mutiya Sahar, illus. Daddy Loves His Baby Girl. 2005. 32p. (J). 16.00 (978-0-9659538-7-0(4)) Soul Vision Works Publishing.

Voigt, Cynthia. Dicey's Song. l.t. ed. 2002. (Tillerman Cycle Ser.: Bk. 2). 370p. (YA). lib. bdg. 35.95 (978-1-58118-106-7(X) , 25790) LRS.

Dicey's Song. (Tillerman Cycle Ser.: Bk. 2). 368p. 2003. (Illus.). (J). pap. 5.99 (978-0-689-86362-2(4) , Aladdin); 2002. (YA). (gr. 7 up). mass mkt. 6.99 (978-0-689-85131-5(6) , Simon Pulse) Simon & Schuster Children's Publishing.

—Dicey's Song. (Tillerman Cycle Ser.: Bk. 2). 2003. (gr. 5-8). lib. bdg. 14.15 (978-0-613-73434-9(3)); 2002. (gr. 7-12). lib. bdg. 14.15 (978-0-613-45028-7(0)) Tandem Library Bks.

—Dicey's Song. l.t. ed. 2004. (Tillerman Cycle Ser.: Bk. 2). 355p. (J). 22.95 (978-0-7862-6288-5(5)); pap. 10.95 (978-0-7862-6352-3(0)) Thorndike Pr.

—Homecoming. l.t. ed. 2002. (Tillerman Cycle Ser.: Bk. 1). (J). lib. bdg. 35.95 (978-1-58118-090-9(X)) LRS.

—Homecoming. (Tillerman Cycle Ser.: Bk. 1). 416p. 2003. (Illus.). (J). pap. 6.99 (978-0-689-86361-5(6) , Aladdin); 2002. (YA). (gr. 7 up). mass mkt. 6.99 (978-0-689-85132-2(4) , Simon Pulse) Simon & Schuster Children's Publishing.

—Homecoming. 2002. (Tillerman Cycle Ser.: Bk. 1). (gr. 7-12). lib. bdg. 14.15 (978-0-613-45063-8(9)) Tandem Library Bks.

—The Runner. 2005. (Tillerman Cycle Ser.: Bk. 4). 320p. (YA). mass mkt. 6.99 (978-1-4169-0341-3(0) , Simon Pulse) Simon & Schuster Children's Publishing.

—Seventeen Against the Dealer. 2002. (Tillerman Cycle Ser.: Bk. 7). (Illus.). 352p. (YA). (gr. 7 up). mass mkt. 6.99 (978-0-689-85133-9(2) , Simon Pulse) Simon & Schuster Children's Publishing.

—Seventeen Against the Dealer. 2002. (Tillerman Cycle Ser.: Bk. 7). (gr. 7-12). lib. bdg. 14.15 (978-0-613-45099-7(X)) Tandem Library Bks.

—Los Tillerman Encuentran Hogar. (SPA.). 190p. (YA). (gr. 5-8). (978-84-279-3219-7(7) , NG1573) Noguer y Caralt Editores, S. A. ESP. *Dist:* Lectorum Pubns., Inc.

Voland, Wanda. Ivan Icicle's Wedding. 2007. (J). per. 10.99 (***978-1-60247-064-4(2)***) Tate Publishing & Enterprises, L.L.C.

Volponi, Paul. Rooftop. (gr. 7). 2007. 224p. (J). pap. 6.99 (978-0-14-240844-5(1) , Puffin); 2006. 208p. (YA). 15.99 (978-0-670-06069-6(0) , Viking Adult) Penguin Group (USA) Inc.

Voorhees, Coert. Los Torres. 2008. 320p. 16.99 (***978-1-4231-0304-2(1)***) Hyperion Pr.

Vrettos, Adrienne Maria. Skin. 2007. 272p. (YA). pap. 6.99 (***978-1-4169-0656-8(8)*** , Simon Pulse) Simon & Schuster Children's Publishing.

Waber, Bernard. Funny, Funny Lyle. Waber, Bernard, illus. 2002. (Lyle the Crocodile Ser.). (Illus.). (J). 14.74 (978-0-7587-2559-2(0)) Book Wholesalers, Inc.

Waddell, Martin. Bee Frog. Firth, Barbara, illus. 2007. 32p. (J). (ps-2). 14.99 (978-0-7636-3310-3(0)) Candlewick Pr.

Wait, Lea. Wintering Well. 2006. (Illus.). 192p. (J). pap. 5.99 (978-0-689-85647-1(4) , Aladdin) Simon & Schuster Children's Publishing.

Walker, Jan. An Inmate's Daughter. Leonhard, Herb, illus. 2006. 171p. (J). per. 9.00 (978-0-9714161-9-2(2)) Raven Publishing Inc. of Montana.

Wallace, Bill. The Dog Who Thought He Was Santa. 2007. 224p. (J). (gr. 3-7). 16.95 (***978-0-8234-2114-5(7)***) Holiday Hse., Inc.

—Eye of the Great Bear. 1999. 176p. (J). (gr. 3-6). pap. 9.95 (978-0-671-02502-1(3) , Aladdin) Simon & Schuster Children's Publishing.

—Eye of the Great Bear. 1999. (J). 11.64 (978-0-606-19050-3(3)); (gr. 3-6). lib. bdg. 13.00 (978-0-613-21509-1(5)) Tandem Library Bks.

—No Dogs Allowed! 2004. 214p. (J). (gr. 4-6). tchr. ed. 16.95 (978-0-8234-1818-3(9)) Holiday Hse., Inc.

Wallace, Carol. The Santa Secret. Bjorkman, Steve, illus. 2007. 40p. (J). (gr. k-3). 15.95 (***978-0-8234-2022-3(1)***); pap. 4.95 (***978-0-8234-2126-8(0)***) Holiday Hse., Inc.

Wallace, Karen. Colour Young Puffin Developing Reader's Freaky Families. (Illus.). 64p. (J). 7.95 (978-0-14-038499-4(5)) Penguin Bks., Ltd. GBR. *Dist:* Trafalgar Square Publishing.

Wallace, Karen. Queen Carrion's Big Bear Hug. Flook, Helen, illus. 2007. (J). lib. bdg. (***978-1-4048-3709-6(4)***) Picture Window Bks.

Wallace, Karen & Barrie, J. M. Wendy. 2005. 307p. (J). (***978-1-4156-1690-1(6)*** , Simon Pulse) Simon & Schuster Children's Publishing.

Wallace, Rich. Losing Is Not an Option. 2003. 144p. (YA). (gr. 5-9). 15.95 (978-0-375-81351-1(9) , Knopf Bks. for Young Readers) Random Hse. Children's Bks.

—Second String Center. 2007. (Winning Season Ser.). 128p. (J). (gr. 4). 14.99 (***978-0-670-06150-1(6)*** , Viking Juvenile) Penguin Group (USA) Inc.

Wallace, Rich. Takedown: Winning Season 8. 2006. (Winning Season Ser.). 128p. (J). (gr. 3). 14.99 (978-0-670-06096-2(8) , Viking Juvenile) Penguin Group (USA) Inc.

Walmsley, Tom. Kid Stuff: A Novel. 2003. 288p. pap. 17.95 (978-1-55152-153-4(9)) Arsenal Pulp Pr. CAN. *Dist:* Consortium Bk. Sales & Distribution.

Walsh, Sheila. Gigi, No. 4. 2007. (Gigi, God's Little Princess Ser.). (Illus.). 32p. (J). 12.99 (978-1-4003-0804-0(6)) Nelson, Thomas Inc.

Walter, Mildred Pitts. Justin & the Best Biscuits in the World. Stock, Catherine, illus. 2002. (J). 13.40 (978-0-7587-0371-2(6)) Book Wholesalers, Inc.

—Justin & the Best Biscuits in the World. 1999. (Illus.). 128p. (J). (gr. 3-5). pap. 4.99 (978-0-679-89448-3(9)) Knopf, Alfred A. Inc.

Walters, Jennie. House of Secrets. 2007. (Swallowcliffe Hall Ser.: Bk. 1). 224p. (J). pap. 9.99 (***978-0-689-87526-7(6)*** , Pocket Bks.) Simon & Schuster, Ltd. GBR. *Dist:* Independent Pubs. Group.

Walton, Rick. Bunny Christmas: A Family Celebration. Miglio, Paige, illus. 2004. 32p. (J). 15.99 (978-0-06-008415-8(4)); lib. bdg. 16.89 (978-0-06-008416-5(2)) HarperCollins Pubs.

—Bunny Day: Telling Time from Breakfast to Bedtime. Miglio, Paige, illus. 2002. 32p. (J). (gr. 2 up). 16.99 (978-0-06-029183-9(4)) HarperCollins Pubs.

Wargin, Kathy-Jo. The Legend of Thanksgiving. Papp, Robert, illus. 2008. (J). (978-0-310-71179-7(7)) Zonderkidz.

—The Voyageur's Paddle. Geister, David, illus. rev. ed. 2007. 40p. (J). (ps-5). 17.95 (978-1-58536-007-9(4)) Sleeping Bear Pr.

Warner, Gertrude Chandler. The Boxcar Children. Date not set. (Boxcar Children Ser.: No. 1). (J). (gr. 2-5). lib. bdg. 18.95 (978-0-8488-1712-1(5)) Amereon LTD.

—The Boxcar Children. Deal, L Kate, illus. 2004. (Boxcar Children Ser.: No. 1). 128p. (gr. 2-7). reprint ed. mass mkt. 4.50 (978-0-8075-0852-7(7)) Whitman, Albert & Co.

—Meet the Boxcar Children. Duffy, Daniel Mark, illus. 1998. (J). (ps-ps). lib. bdg. 11.80 (978-0-613-08335-5(0)) Tandem Library Bks.

—The Mystery of the Midnight Dog. 2001. (Boxcar Children Ser.). (Illus.). (J). (978-0-606-21080-5(6)) Tandem Library Bks.

—The Mystery of the Screech Owl. 2001. (Boxcar Children Special Ser.). (Illus.). (J). (978-0-606-21085-0(7)) Tandem Library Bks.

Warner, Gertrude Chandler, creator. Meet the Boxcar Children. 1998. (Adventures of Benny & Watch: No. 1). (J). (gr. 1-3). (978-0-606-13215-2(5)) Tandem Library Bks.

Warner, Sally. Sister Split. 2001. (gr. 3-6). lib. bdg. 14.10 (978-0-613-85509-9(4)) Tandem Library Bks.

Watson, Kim. Just Like Dad. 2001. (Little Bill Books for Beginning Readers Ser.). (Illus.). (J). 12.79 (978-0-606-21276-2(0)) Tandem Library Bks.

Weatherly, Lee. Breakfast at Sadie's. 208p. (gr. 7). 2008. (YA). mass mkt. 6.99 (***978-0-440-24069-3(7)*** , Laurel Leaf); 2006. (J). 15.95 (978-0-385-75094-3(3) , Fickling, David Bks.); 2006. (J). lib. bdg. 17.99 (978-0-385-75095-0(1) , Fickling, David Bks.) Random Hse. Children's Bks.

Weatherly, Lee. Child X. 2003. 224p. (gr. 4-9). 5.99 (978-0-440-41904-4(2) , Yearling) Random Hse. Children's Bks.

Weathers, Anah D. Secrets of the Cave. Weathers, Luther, illus. Weathers, Luther, photos by. unabr. ed. 2000. (Treasures from the Past Ser.). x, 104p. (J). (gr. 4-8). pap. 7.98 (978-0-9702584-0-3(2)) Creative Services.

Weaver, Elizabeth Nixon. Rooster. 2005. 208p. (J). reprint ed. pap. 5.95 (978-0-7614-5218-8(4)) Cavendish, Marshall Corp.

Weber, Lenora Mattingly. Beany Has a Secret Life. 1999. (Beany Malone Ser.). 296p. (J). pap. 12.95 (978-0-9639607-7-1(6)) Image Cascade Publishing.

—A Bright Star Falls. 1999. (Beany Malone Ser.). 278p. (J). reprint ed. pap. 12.95 (978-1-930009-01-1(1)) Image Cascade Publishing.

—Come Back, Wherever You Are. 1999. (Beany Malone Ser.). 259p. (J). pap. 12.95 (978-1-930009-06-6(2)) Image Cascade Publishing.

Weber, Lori. Split. 2005. (SideStreets Ser.). 152p. (YA). (gr. 7-12). (***978-1-55028-879-7(2)***); 7.95 (978-1-55028-878-0(4)) Lorimer, James & Co., Ltd., Pubs. CAN. *Dist:* Casemate Pubs. & Bk. Distributors, LLC.

Weber, Lou, ed. Fairly Oddparents: Interactive Play-a-Sound. 2005. 24p. (J). 15.98 (978-1-4127-3241-3(7) , 7236100) Publications International, Ltd.

Weedn, Flavia M. Flavia & the Dream Maker. 1999. (Illus.). 48p. (J). (ps-3). 14.95 (978-0-7683-2102-9(6)) CEDCO Publishing.

Wegman, Marcia. Lula Belle. 2007. (ENG.). 32p. per. 16.95 (***978-1-4327-0146-8(0)***) Outskirts Press, Inc.

Weigel, Jeff, illus. Atomic Ace & the Robot Rampage. 2006. 32p. (J). 15.95 (978-0-8075-0484-0(X)); pap. 6.95 (978-0-8075-0485-7(8)) Whitman, Albert & Co.

Weiner, Kimberly. Not My Reality. 2004. pap. 12.50 (978-0-9753262-0-6(1)) YNR Media L.L.C.

Weinheimer, Beckie. Converting Kate. 2007. 288p. (YA). (gr. 7 up). 16.99 (978-0-670-06152-5(2) , Viking Juvenile) Penguin Group (USA) Inc.

Weiss, Ellen. Nose Knows. 2002. (gr. k-3). lib. bdg. 13.00 (978-0-613-53756-8(4)) Tandem Library Bks.

Weiss, Ellen & Lucas, Margeaux. The Nose Knows. 2002. (Science Solves It! Ser.). (Illus.). 32p. (J). 4.99 (978-1-57565-120-0(3)) Kane Pr., The.

Welch, Leah. Pretty on the Inside. 2007. (J). per. 10.00 (***978-1-59872-779-1(6)***) Instantpublisher.com.

Wells, Rosemary. Hide-and-Seek. 2008. (Max & Ruby Ser.). 12p. (J). (ps-k). bds. 7.99 (***978-0-448-44784-1(3)*** , Grosset & Dunlap) Penguin Group (USA) Inc.

—Julieta, Estate Quieta! (SPA.). 43p. (J). 5.50 (978-84-372-1523-5(4)) Santillana USA Publishing Co., Inc.

—Lassie. Jeffers, Susan, illus. 2000. (SPA.). 48p. (J). (gr. 3-5). 12.95 (978-84-241-3362-7(5) , EV8276) Everest de Ediciones y Distribucion, S.L. ESP. *Dist:* Lectorum Pubns., Inc.

—Max & Ruby's Busy Week. Wells, Rosemary, illus. 2002. (Sticker Stories Ser.). (Illus.). 16p. (J). (ps-1). pap. 4.99 (978-0-448-42853-6(9) , Grosset & Dunlap) Penguin Group (USA) Inc.

—Max & Ruby's Show-and-Tell. 2006. (All Aboard Bks.). 24p. (J). (ps-ps). pap. 3.99 (978-0-448-43952-5(2) , Grosset & Dunlap) Penguin Group (USA) Inc.

—Max's ABC. 2006. (Illus.). 32p. (J). (ps). 15.99 (978-0-670-06074-0(7) , Viking Juvenile) Penguin Group (USA) Inc.

—Max's Easter Surprise. 2008. (Max & Ruby Ser.). 24p. (J). (ps-k). pap. 3.99 (***978-0-448-44783-4(5)*** , Grosset & Dunlap) Penguin Group (USA) Inc.

—McDuff & the Baby. Jeffers, Susan, illus. 2020. 24p. (J). pap. 4.99 (978-0-7868-1191-5(9)) Hyperion Paperbacks for Children.

—Noisy Nora. 2000. (gr. k-3). lib. bdg. 15.30 (978-0-8085-3632-1(X)) Tandem Library Bks.

Weninger, Brigitte. Dany, Mira lo Que Has Hecho! 1999. (gr. k-3). (SPA.). lib. bdg. 15.25 (978-0-613-81373-0(1)); 13.75 (978-0-606-17631-6(4)) Tandem Library Bks.

We're Having a Baby. 2004. (J). 14.00 (978-0-9755902-0-1(0)) Change Is Strange, Inc.

Werlin, Nancy. Are You Alone on Purpose? 2007. 208p. (YA). (gr. 7). pap. 7.99 (978-0-14-240777-6(1) , Puffin) Penguin Group (USA) Inc.

—Killer's Cousin. 2000. (gr. 7-12). lib. bdg. 13.00 (978-0-613-23909-7(1)) Tandem Library Bks.

—Locked Inside. 2001. 272p. (YA). (gr. 7). mass mkt. 5.99 (978-0-440-22829-5(8) , Laurel Leaf) Random Hse. Children's Bks.

Wesley, Mary. Haphazard House. Date not set. (Sky Bks.). 200p. pap. 54.75 (978-0-582-08108-6(4)) Addison-Wesley Longman, Ltd. GBR. *Dist:* Trans-Atlantic Pubns., Inc.

West, Tracey. Connor's Guide to Bubble Town. 2002. (Cubix Ser.). 24p. (J). (ps). pap. 4.99 (978-0-439-38056-0(1)) Scholastic, Inc.

Weston, Carol. The Diary of Melanie Martin. 2001. (Illus.). 144p. (J). (ps-7). per. 13.00 (978-0-613-33751-9(4)) Tandem Library Bks.

—The Diary of Melanie Martin: Or How I Survived Matt the Brat, Michelangelo & the Leaning Tower of Pizza. Roth, Marci Doane, illus. 2001. 160p. (gr. 3-7). 5.50 (978-0-440-41667-8(1) , Yearling) Random Hse. Children's Bks.

E F G

—Melanie in Manhattan. 288p. (J). (gr. 3-7). 2006. 5.99 (978-0-440-42040-8(7) , Yearling); 2005. (Illus.). 15.95 (978-0-375-83028-0(6) , Knopf Bks. for Young Readers) Random Hse. Children's Bks.

Weston, Martha. Act I, Act II, Act Normal. rev. ed. 2003. (Roman Mysteries Ser.). 160p. (J). (gr. 5-9). 22.90 (978-0-7613-2859-9(9)) Roaring Brook Pr.

—Owen Foote, Money Man. 2003. (gr. k-3). lib. bdg. 12.95 (978-0-613-73020-4(8)) Tandem Library Bks.

Weston, Tamson. Hey, Pancakes! Gammell, Stephen, illus. 2003. 32p. (J). 17.00 (978-0-15-216502-4(9)) Harcourt Trade Pubs.

Wetter, Bruce. The Boy with the Lampshade on His Head. 2004. (Illus.). 304p. (J). 16.95 (978-0-689-85032-5(8) , Atheneum) Simon & Schuster Children's Publishing.

Weyr, Garret. My Heartbeat. 2003. 176p. (YA). pap. 7.99 (978-0-14-240066-1(1) , Puffin) Penguin Group (USA) Inc.

—My Heartbeat. 2003. (gr. 7-12). lib. bdg. 16.45 (978-0-613-81700-4(1)) Tandem Library Bks.

Whelan, Gloria. Chu Ju's House. 2005. 240p. (J). reprint ed. pap. 5.99 (978-0-06-050726-8(8) , Harper Trophy) HarperCollins Pubs.

—Farewell to the Island. 208p. (gr. 4 up). 1999. (Illus.). (YA). pap. 5.99 (978-0-06-440821-9(3) , Harper Trophy); 1998. (J). 16.95 (978-0-06-027751-2(3)) HarperCollins Pubs.

—Farewell to the Island. 1999. (J). (978-0-606-17462-6(1)) Tandem Library Bks.

—Farewell to the Island. 2004. 200p. (J). (ps-7). pap. 7.95 (978-1-882376-92-6(7)) Thunder Bay Pr.

—Fruitlands: Louisa May Alcott Made Perfect. 2002. 128p. (J). (gr. 4-7). 15.99 (978-0-06-623815-9(3)) HarperCollins Pubs.

Whelan, Gloria. Summer of the War. 2006. (J). 176p. 15.99 (978-0-06-008072-3(8)); 176p. lib. bdg. 16.89 (978-0-06-008073-0(6)); 163p. ***(978-1-4287-0030-7(7))*** HarperCollins Pubs.

When I Go. 2003. (Illus.). (J). bds. 7.98 (978-0-7525-8657-1(2)) Parragon, Inc.

White, Ruth. The Search for Belle Prater. 2005. (Illus.). 176p. (J). (gr. 8-12). 16.00 (978-0-374-30853-7(5) , Farrar, Straus & Giroux (BYR)) Farrar, Straus & Giroux.

—The Search for Belle Prater. 2007. 176p. (J). (gr. 4-7). 6.50 (978-0-440-42164-1(0) , Yearling) Random Hse. Children's Bks.

—The Search for Belle Prater. l.t. ed. 2006. 205p. (J). 23.95 (978-0-7862-8278-4(9)) Thorndike Pr.

—Tadpole. 2004. 208p. (gr. 5). 5.99 (978-0-440-41979-2(4) , Yearling) Random Hse. Children's Bks.

Whitehouse, Elizabeth. Ogham in Orkney: A Jensen Family Story. 2004. (J). pap. 5.95 (978-1-933031-36-1(0)) Whitehouse Publishing.

Whitmore, Arvella. The Bread Winner. 2004. 144p. (J). (gr. 4-6). pap. 5.95 (978-0-618-49479-8(0)) Houghton Mifflin Co. Trade & Reference Div.

Whitney, Kim Ablon. See You down the Road: A Novel. 2004. 192p. (gr. 7). (J). lib. bdg. 17.99 (978-0-375-92467-5(1)); (YA). 15.95 (978-0-375-82467-8(7)) Random Hse. Children's Bks. (Knopf Bks. for Young Readers).

Whittenberg, Allison. Sweet Thang. 160p. (J). (gr. 3-7). 2007. pap. 5.99 (978-0-440-42086-6(5) , Yearling); 2006. 15.95 (978-0-385-73292-5(9) , Delacorte Bks. for Young Readers); 2006. lib. bdg. 17.99 (978-0-385-90313-4(8) , Delacorte Bks. for Young Readers) Random Hse. Children's Bks.

Wienski, Vera. Erkuleese & Tobias. 2002. (J). per. 7.99 (978-1-930200-98-2(6)) Martell Publishing Co.

Wiess, Laura. Leftovers. 2008. 256p. pap. 12.00 ***(978-1-4165-4662-7(6)*** , MTV) Simon & Schuster.

Wiggin, Kate Douglas. New Chronicles of Rebecca. 2004. reprint ed. pap. 28.95 (978-1-4179-2096-9(3)); pap. 15.95 (978-1-4179-9994-1(2)); pap. 1.99 (978-1-4179-9944-6(6)) Kessinger Publishing, LLC.

Wiggin, Kate Douglas. The Romance of a Christmas Card. 2006. pap. 33.99 ***(978-1-4280-0238-8(3))*** IndyPublish.com.

Wiggins, Leah Holder. My Neighbor Is Gone. Wiggins, Margaret W., illus. 2006. 28p. (J). per. 17.99 ***(978-0-9768579-5-2(2))*** eVision, LLC.

Wigington, Patti. Summer's Ashes. 2007. 208p. (YA). pap. 15.00 ***(978-0-9766805-9-8(9))*** Keene Publishing.

Wikler, Linda. Alfonse, Where Are You? 1998. (J). (978-0-606-13113-1(2)) Tandem Library Bks.

Wilcox, Edee. Saved Times Three. 2007. (YA). pap. 14.95 ***(978-1-59705-813-1(0))*** Wings ePress, Inc.

Wilcox, Mary. Caught on Tape. 2007. (Hollywood Sisters Ser.). 208p. (J). (gr. 5). 7.99 ***(978-0-385-73356-4(9));*** lib. bdg. 10.99 ***(978-0-385-90371-4(5))*** Random Hse. Children's Bks. (Delacorte Bks. for Young Readers).

Wilder, Laura Ingalls. By the Shores of Silver Lake. 2007. (Little House Ser.). 384p. (J). pap. 6.99 (978-0-06-088541-0(6) , Harper Trophy) HarperCollins Pubs.

—The Deer in the Wood. Graef, Renee, illus. 1999. (My First Little House Bks.). 32p. (J). (ps-3). pap. 6.99 (978-0-06-443498-0(2) , Harper Trophy) HarperCollins Pubs.

—The Deer in the Wood. 1999. (My First Little House Bks.). (J). 12.79 (978-0-606-15841-1(3)) Tandem Library Bks.

—Farmer Boy. Williams, Garth, illus. 2004. (Little House Ser.). 384p. (J). pap. 8.99 (978-0-06-058182-4(4) , Harper Trophy) HarperCollins Pubs.

—Farmer Boy. Williams, Garth, illus. l.t. ed. 2000. (Little House Ser.). 400p. (J). (gr. 3-6). lib. bdg. 33.95 (978-1-58118-079-4(9) , 24071) LRS.

—A Farmer Boy Christmas. Wheeler, Jody, illus. 1999. (My First Little House Bks.). (J). (ps-1). 12.95 (978-0-06-025940-2(X)); lib. bdg. 12.89 (978-0-06-025941-9(8)) HarperCollins Pubs.

—Laura's Ma. 1999. (Little House Chapter Bks.: No. 11). (J). (gr. 3-6). (978-0-606-15839-8(1)) Tandem Library Bks.

—Laura's Pa. 1999. (Little House Chapter Bks.: No. 12). (J). (gr. 3-6). (978-0-606-15840-4(5)) Tandem Library Bks.

—A Little House Christmas Treasury: Festive Holiday Stories. Williams, Garth, illus. 2005. (Little House Ser.). 144p. (J). 12.99 (978-0-06-076918-5(1)) HarperCollins Pubs.

—The Little House Collection, Set. Williams, Garth, illus. 2004. (Little House Ser.). (J). pap. 44.99 (978-0-06-075428-0(1) , Harper Trophy) HarperCollins Pubs.

—Little House "History Comes to Life" Event Kit. 2000. (J). (978-0-06-028839-6(6)) HarperCollins Pubs.

—Little House in the Big Woods. 2007. (Little House Ser.). 224p. (J). pap. 6.99 (978-0-06-088537-3(8) , Harper Trophy) HarperCollins Pubs.

—Little House in the Big Woods. Williams, Garth, illus. (Little House Ser.). 256p. (J). 2004. pap. 8.99 (978-0-06-058180-0(8) , Harper Trophy); 2001. 19.95 (978-0-06-029647-6(X)); 2007. 19.99 ***(*978-0-06-128980-4(9))*** HarperCollins Pubs.

—Little House in the Big Woods. Williams, Garth, illus. l.t. ed. 2000. (Little House Ser.). 244p. (J). (gr. 3-6). lib. bdg. 28.95 (978-1-58118-078-7(0) , 24070) LRS.

—Little House in the Big Woods A Special Read Aloud Edition. Williams, Garth, illus. 2001. (Little House Ser.). 256p. (J). (gr. 3-5). 19.89 (978-0-06-029648-3(8)) HarperCollins Pubs.

—Little House on the Prairie. 2007. (Little House Ser.). 336p. (J). pap. 6.99 (978-0-06-088539-7(4) , Harper Trophy) HarperCollins Pubs.

—The Little House Treasury. Sewell, Helen & Boyle, Mildred, illus. 2004. 239p. (J). (978-0-06-053979-5(8) , HarperCollins) HarperCollins Pubs.

—The Little House Treasury. Sewell, Helen, illus. 1998. (Little House Ser.). 640p. (J). (gr. 3 up). 5.00 (978-0-06-028238-7(X)) HarperCollins Pubs.

—A Little Prairie House. Graef, Renée, illus. 1999. (My First Little House Bks.). 32p. (J). (ps-3). pap. 6.99 (978-0-06-443526-0(1) , Harper Trophy) HarperCollins Pubs.

—A Little Prairie House. Graef, Renee, illus. adapted ed. 1998. (Little House Picture Bks.). 40p. (J). (ps-3). 13.89 (978-0-06-025908-2(6)) HarperCollins Pubs.

—Little Town on the Prairie. 2007. (Little House Ser.). 320p. (J). pap. 6.99 (978-0-06-088543-4(2) , Harper Trophy) HarperCollins Pubs.

—The Long Winter. 2007. (Little House Ser.). 352p. (J). pap. 6.99 (978-0-06-088542-7(4) , Harper Trophy) HarperCollins Pubs.

—The Long Winter. Williams, Garth, illus. 2004. (Little House Ser.). 352p. (J). pap. 8.99 (978-0-06-058185-5(9) , Harper Trophy) HarperCollins Pubs.

—The Long Winter. Williams, Garth, illus. l.t. ed. 2002. (LRS Large Print Cornerstone Ser.). (J). lib. bdg. 35.95 (978-1-58118-100-5(0)) LRS.

—My Little House Book of Family. Graef, Renee, illus. 1998. (My First Little House Bks.). (J). (ps). lib. bdg. (978-0-06-025989-1(2)) HarperCollins Pubs.

—On the Banks of Plum Creek. 2007. (Little House Ser.). 384p. (J). pap. 6.99 (978-0-06-088540-3(8) , Harper Trophy) HarperCollins Pubs.

—Santa Comes to Little House. Graef, Renee, illus. 2004. (Little House Ser.). 32p. (J). (ps-3). pap. 5.99 (978-0-06-058694-2(X) , Harper Trophy) HarperCollins Pubs.

—These Happy Golden Years. 2007. (Little House Ser.). 304p. (J). pap. 6.99 (978-0-06-088544-1(0) , Harper Trophy) HarperCollins Pubs.

Wilder, Rae. Soccer Girls. 2000. 252p. (J). (gr. 4-7). pap. 13.95 (978-0-595-00566-6(7)) iUniverse, Inc.

Wildner, Martina & Skofield, James. Shooting Stars Everywhere. 2006. 192p. (J). (gr. 7). 15.95 (978-0-385-73250-5(3) , Delacorte Bks. for Young Readers) Random Hse. Children's Bks.

Wiles, Deborah. Each Little Bird That Sings. (Illus.). (J). 2005. 272p. 16.00 (978-0-15-205113-6(9)); 2006. 276p. reprint ed. pap. 5.95 (978-0-15-205657-5(2) , Harcourt Paperbacks) Harcourt Children's Bks.

Wiley, Melissa. Across the Puddingstone Dam. Andreasen, Dan, illus. 2004. (Little House Ser.). 224p. (J). pap. 6.99 (978-0-06-440740-3(3)) HarperCollins Pubs.

—The Far Side of the Loch. Graef, Renee, illus. (Little House). (J). (gr. 3-6). 2001. lib. bdg. (978-0-06-028556-2(7)); 2000. 256p. pap. 6.99 (978-0-06-440713-7(6) , Harper Trophy); 2000. 256p. 15.89 (978-0-06-028203-5(7)); 2000. 256p. 15.95 (978-0-06-027984-4(2)) HarperCollins Pubs.

—The Far Side of the Loch. 2000. (Little House Ser.). (Illus.). (J). 12.64 (978-0-606-18689-6(1)) Tandem Library Bks.

—Far Side of the Loch. 2000. (gr. 3-6). lib. bdg. 14.15 (978-0-613-25131-0(8)) Tandem Library Bks.

—The Far Side of the Loch Bk. 2: The Martha Years. 2007. (Little House Ser.). 160p. (J). pap. 5.99 ***(*978-0-06-114818-7(0)*** , Harper Trophy) HarperCollins Pubs.

—Little House by Boston Bay. 2007. (Little House Ser.). 160p. (J). pap. 5.99 ***(*978-0-06-114828-6(8)*** , Harper Trophy) HarperCollins Pubs.

—Little House by Boston Bay. Andreasen, Dan, illus. 1999. (Little House Ser.). 195p. lib. bdg. 13.04 (978-0-606-16684-3(X)) Tandem Library Bks.

—Little House Chapter Book, No. 26. 2001. (J). pap. (978-0-06-442112-6(0) , Harper Trophy) HarperCollins Pubs.

—Little House in the Highlands. 2007. (Little House Ser.). 144p. (J). pap. 5.99 ***(*978-0-06-114817-0(2)*** , Harper Trophy) HarperCollins Pubs.

—Little House in the Highlands. Andreasen, Dan & Graef, Renee, illus. 1999. (Little House Ser.). 288p. (J). (gr. 3-7). pap. 6.99 (978-0-06-440712-0(8) , Harper Trophy) HarperCollins Pubs.

—Little House in the Highlands. Graef, Renee, illus. 1999. (Little House). 271p. (J). (gr. 4-7). 15.89 (978-0-06-028202-8(9)) HarperCollins Pubs.

—Little House in the Highlands. 1999. (Little House Ser.). 271p. (J). (978-0-606-15838-1(3)); (gr. 3-6). lib. bdg. 14.15 (978-0-613-11795-1(6)) Tandem Library Bks.

—On Tide Mill Lane. 2007. (Little House Ser.). 176p. (J). pap. 5.99 ***(*978-0-06-114829-3(6)*** , Harper Trophy) HarperCollins Pubs.

—On Tide Mill Lane, No. 2. Andreasen, Dan, illus. 2001. (Little House Ser.). 272p. (J). (gr. k-4). 16.95 (978-0-06-027013-1(6)); (gr. 3-7). 16.89 (978-0-06-027014-8(4)) HarperCollins Pubs.

—The Road from Roxbury. 2002. (Little House Ser.). (Illus.). 256p. (J). 16.99 (978-0-06-027019-3(5)); 18.89 (978-0-06-027020-9(9)) HarperCollins Pubs.

Wiley, Melissa. Road from Roxbury. 2008. (Little House Ser.). 176p. (J). pap. 5.99 ***(*978-0-06-114830-9(X)*** , Harper Trophy) HarperCollins Pubs.

Wiley, Melissa, et al. Little House in the Highlands. Graef, Renee, illus. 1999. (Little House Ser.). 288p. (J). (gr. 3-7). 16.95 (978-0-06-027983-7(4)) HarperCollins Pubs.

Wilhelm, Doug. Falling. 2007. 256p. (YA). (gr. 9 up). 17.00 (978-0-374-32251-9(1)) Farrar, Straus & Giroux.

Wilkes, Maria. Little Clearing in the Woods. 2008. (Little House Ser.). 160p. (J). pap. 5.99 ***(*978-0-06-114823-1(7)*** , Harper Trophy) HarperCollins Pubs.

Wilkes, Maria D. Little Clearing in the Woods. Andreasen, Dan, illus. 1998. (Little House Ser.). 336p. (J). (gr. 3-7). 15.95 (978-0-06-026997-5(9)); 15.89 (978-0-06-026998-2(7)) HarperCollins Pubs.

—Little House in Brookfield. 2007. (Little House Ser.). 144p. (J). pap. 5.99 ***(*978-0-06-114821-7(0)*** , Harper Trophy) HarperCollins Pubs.

Wilkes, Maria D. On Top of Concord Hill. Andreasen, Dan, illus. 2000. (Little House Ser.). 288p. (J). (gr. 3-7). 15.89 (978-0-06-027003-2(9)) HarperCollins Pubs.

Williams, Barbara. Michi y Su Nueva Familia. 1998. (SPA.). 136p. (gr. 6-8). (978-84-239-7127-5(9)) Espasa Calpe, S.A.

Williams, Karen Lynn. One Thing I'm Good At. 1999. 137p. (J). (gr. 3-7). 14.95 (978-0-688-16846-9(9)) HarperCollins Pubs.

Williams, Kashamba. Dymond in the Rough: Platinum Teen Series. Smith, Joanie & Ross, Jahmya, eds. 2005. 128p. (YA). per. 6.99 (978-0-9729325-2-3(6)) Precioustymes Entertainment, LLC.

Williams, Kathy B. The Can Family. Newton, Beulah & Hargrove, Fred, eds. Williams, Kathy B., illus. 1998. (Illus.). iii, 15p. (J). (gr. 1-3). pap. 6.95 (978-0-9665043-0-9(5)) Can Family, The.

Williams, Lori Aurelia. Shayla's Double Brown Baby Blues. 2003. (Illus.). 304p. (YA). pap. 7.99 (978-0-689-85670-9(9) , Simon Pulse) Simon & Schuster Children's Publishing.

—Shayla's Double Brown Baby Blues. 2003. 300p. (gr. 7-12). lib. bdg. 16.45 (978-0-613-61815-1(7)) Tandem Library Bks.

—When Kambia Elaine Flew in from Neptune. unabr. ed. 2004. 246p. (J). (gr. 7 up). pap. 50.00 incl. audio (978-0-8072-8851-1(9) , Listening Library) Random Hse. Audio Publishing Group.

—When Kambia Elaine Flew in from Neptune. Louth, Jack, illus. 2001. 256p. (YA). pap. 10.00 (978-0-689-84593-2(6) , Simon Pulse) Simon & Schuster Children's Publishing.

—When Kambia Elaine Flew in from Neptune. 2002. (978-0-606-22109-2(3)); 2001. (gr. 7-12). lib. bdg. 18.80 (978-0-613-73307-6(X)) Tandem Library Bks.

Williams, Sherley Anne. Working Cotton. Byard, Carole, illus. 2002. (J). 14.04 (978-0-7587-0168-8(3)) Book Wholesalers, Inc.

Williams, Vera B. Algo Especial Para Mi. Williams, Vera B., illus. 2006. (SPA.). 32p. (J). pap. 6.99 (978-0-06-088707-0(9)) HarperCollins Pubs.

—A Chair for My Mother: Ib Lub Rooj Rua Kuv Nam/Ib Lub Rooj Rau Kuv Niam. Williams, Vera B., illus. 2001. 32p. (J). pap. 6.95 (978-1-931016-03-2(8) , MHC-03-8) Minnesota Humanities Commission.

Willis, Meredith Sue. Billie of Fish House Lane. 2006. (J). pap. 12.95 (978-1-932727-02-9(7)) Montemayor Pr.

Wilson, Budge. A Fiddle for Angus. Tooke, Susan, illus. 2006. 32p. (J). (gr. 1-4). pap. 9.95 (978-0-88776-785-2(0) , Random Hse. Puzzles & Games) Random Hse. Information Group.

Wilson, Diane Lee. Firehorse. 2006. 336p. (J). (gr. 7 up). 16.95 (978-1-4169-1551-5(6) , McElderry, Margaret K.) Simon & Schuster Children's Publishing.

Wilson, Henry. Do Goldfish Play the Violin? Scheffler, Axel, illus. unabr. ed. 2000. (Read-Along Ser.). 136p. (J). pap. 24.95 incl. audio (978-0-7540-6220-2(1) , RA021, Chivers Children's Audio Bks.) BBC Audiobooks America.

Wilson, Jacqueline. The Bed & Breakfast Star. Sharratt, Nick, illus. l.t. ed. 2000. 255p. (J). pap. (978-0-7540-6090-1(X) , CLP 292) BBC Audio.

—The Bed & Breakfast Star. Sharratt, Nick, illus. unabr. ed. 2000. (Read-Along Ser.). 242p. (J). pap. 29.95 incl. audio (978-0-7540-6231-8(7) , RA032, Chivers Children's Audio Bks.) BBC Audiobooks America.

—The Bed & Breakfast Star. Sharratt, Nick, illus. 2001. (Yearling Book Ser.). 32p. pap. 9.99 (978-0-440-86324-3(4) , Corgi) Transworld Publishers Ltd. GBR. *Dist:* Trafalgar Square Publishing.

—Best Friends. 2008. (J). ***(*978-1-59643-278-9(0))*** Roaring Brook Pr.

—Double Act. 1999. (J). (978-0-606-16442-9(1)); (gr. 3-6). lib. bdg. 12.40 (978-0-613-16097-1(5)) Tandem Library Bks.

—Double Act. 2001. (Corgi Yearling Ser.). (Illus.). 32p. 9.99 (978-0-440-86334-2(1) , Corgi) Transworld Publishers Ltd. GBR. *Dist:* Trafalgar Square Publishing.

—Girls in Tears. 176p. (YA). (gr. 7). 2004. (Girls Quartet: Bk. 4). mass mkt. 4.99 (978-0-440-23807-2(2) , Laurel Leaf); 2003. lib. bdg. 11.99 (978-0-385-90104-8(6) , Delacorte Bks. for Young Readers) Random Hse. Children's Bks.

—Girls in Tears. 2004. (gr. 7-12). lib. bdg. 13.00 (978-0-613-72253-7(1)) Tandem Library Bks.

—Girls Out Late. 2003. 224p. (YA). (gr. 7). mass mkt. 5.50 (978-0-440-22959-9(6) , Laurel Leaf) Random Hse. Children's Bks.

—Girls Out Late. Sharratt, Nick, illus. 2003. 192p. (YA). mass mkt. (978-0-552-54523-5(6) , Corgi) Transworld Publishers Ltd. GBR. *Dist:* Random Hse. of Canada, Ltd.

Wilson, John. Adrift in Time. 2005. 134p. (J). pap. 9.95 (978-1-55380-007-1(9)) Ronsdale Pr. CAN. *Dist:* Literary Pr. Group of Canada.

Wilson, N. D. 100 Cupboards. 2007. (J). pap. ***(*978-0-375-83882-8(1));*** 304p. lib. bdg. ***(*978-0-375-93881-8(8));*** 304p. (gr. 3-7). 16.99 ***(*978-0-375-83881-1(3))*** Random Hse., Inc.

Winkler, Henry & Oliver, Lin. Who Ordered This Baby Brother? Definitely Not Me! Watson, Jesse Joshua, illus. 2007. (Hank Zipzer Ser.: No. 13). 160p. (J). (gr. 3-7). 13.99 ***(*978-0-448-44375-1(9));*** pap. 4.99 ***(*978-0-448-44374-4(0))*** Penguin Group (USA) Inc. (Grosset & Dunlap).

Winters, Susan. Yo Tambien. 1999. (Jardin de los Ninos Ser.). (SPA., Illus.). 24p. (J). (ps-1). pap. 6.99 (978-980-257-231-1(4)) Ekare, Ediciones VEN. *Dist:* Kane/Miller Bk. Pubs., Inc., Lectorum Pubns., Inc.

Wittlinger, Ellen. Blind Faith. (YA). 2007. 304p. pap. 8.99 ***(*978-1-4169-4906-0(2)*** , Simon Pulse); 2006. 288p. (gr. 7 up). 16.99 (978-1-4169-0273-7(2) , Simon & Schuster Children's Publishing) Simon & Schuster Children's Publishing.

—Gracie's Girl. 2002. (Illus.). 192p. (J). (gr. 4-7). pap. 4.99 (978-0-689-84960-2(5) , Aladdin) Simon & Schuster Children's Publishing.

—Gracie's Girl. Hamlin, Janet, illus. 2000. 192p. (J). (gr. 3-7). 16.95 (978-0-689-82249-0(9)) Simon & Schuster Children's Publishing.

—Gracie's Girl. 2002. (gr. 3-6). lib. bdg. 13.00 (978-0-613-53441-3(7)) Tandem Library Bks.

—Gracie's Girl. l.t. ed. 2002. 224p. (J). 22.95 (978-0-7862-3761-6(9)) Thomson Gale.

—Heart on My Sleeve. 2005. (Illus.). 240p. (YA). reprint ed. pap. 6.99 (978-0-689-84999-2(0) , Simon Pulse) Simon & Schuster Children's Publishing.

—Parrotfish. 2007. 304p. (YA). (gr. 7 up). 16.99 (978-1-4169-1622-2(9) , Simon & Schuster Children's Publishing) Simon & Schuster Children's Publishing.

Wolf, Jake. Daddy, Could I Have an Elephant? 1998. (Picture Puffin Ser.). (J). (978-0-606-13303-6(8)) Tandem Library Bks.

Wollman, Jessica. Bunches of Fun. MacNeil, Chris, illus. 2006. (Penelope Fritter Ser.). (J). 160p. pap. 4.99 (978-1-4169-0091-7(8)); 149p. ***(*978-1-4156-5003-5(9))*** Simon & Schuster Children's Publishing. (Aladdin).

—The Chipster's Sister. MacNeil, Chris, illus. 2005. (Penelope Fritter, Super-Sitter Ser.). 128p. (J). pap. 4.99 (978-1-4169-0089-4(6) , Aladdin) Simon & Schuster Children's Publishing.

Won, Kim Kang. I.N.V.U., Book 3, Vol. 3. rev. ed. 2003. (Illus.). 192p. (gr. 8 up). pap. 9.99 (978-1-59182-062-8(6) , Tokyopop Adult) TOKYOPOP, Inc.

Wong, Janet S. The Trip Back Home. Jia, Bo, illus. 2000. 32p. (J). (ps-2). 17.00 (978-0-15-200784-3(9)) Harcourt Children's Bks.

Wong, Joyce Lee. Seeing Emily. 2005. (Illus.). 288p. (J). (gr. 7-11). 16.95 (978-0-8109-5757-2(4) , Abrams Bks. for Young Readers) Abrams, Harry N. , Inc.

Wood, Douglas. What Dads Can't Do. ed. 2004. (Illus.). (J). (gr. k-3). spiral bd. (978-0-616-07247-9(3)) Canadian National Institute for the Blind/Institut National Canadien pour les Aveugles.

—What Dads Can't Do. Cushman, Doug, illus. ed. 2005. 24p. (J). 6.95 (978-1-4169-0197-6(3)) Simon & Schuster Children's Publishing.

Wood, June Rae. Turtle on a Fence Post. 2001. 264p. (J). (gr. k-9). per. 15.30 (978-0-613-44424-8(8)) Tandem Library Bks.

Wood, Lena. Elijah Creek & the Armor of Gift Set. 2006. 576p. (J). Bks. 1-3. 17.99 (978-0-7847-1966-4(7)); Bks. 4-6. 17.99 (978-0-7847-1967-1(5)) Standard Publishing.

—The Raven's Curse. 2006. 192p. (J). pap. 6.99 (978-0-7847-1592-5(0) , 42153) Standard Publishing.

Woodruff, Elvira. Small Beauties: The Journey of Darcy Heart O'Hara. Rex, Adam, illus. 2006. 40p. (J). (gr. 1-4). 15.95 (978-0-375-82686-3(6)); lib. bdg. 17.99 (978-0-375-92686-0(0)) Random Hse. Children's Bks. (Knopf Bks. for Young Readers).

Woodson, Jacqueline. Feathers. 2007. 128p. (J). (gr. 3-7). 15.99 (978-0-399-23989-2(8) , Putnam Juvenile) Penguin Group (USA) Inc.

—If You Come Softly. (gr. 5). 2006. 192p. (YA). pap. 5.99 (978-0-14-240601-4(5) , Puffin); 1998. 1p. (J). 16.99 (978-0-399-23112-4(9) , Putnam Juvenile) Penguin Group (USA) Inc.

—If You Come Softly. 2000. 12.64 (978-0-606-17863-1(5)) Tandem Library Bks.

—Miracle's Boys. 2002. (Illus.). 13.19 (978-1-4046-0953-2(9)) Book Wholesalers, Inc.

—Miracle's Boys. 2006. 144p. (J). (gr. 5). pap. 5.99 (978-0-14-240602-1(3) , Puffin) Penguin Group (USA) Inc.

—Miracle's Boys. unabr. ed. 2004. 192p. (J). (gr. 7 up). pap. 29.00 incl. audio (978-0-8072-0789-5(6) , LYA 322 SP, Listening Library) Random Hse. Audio Publishing Group.

—We Had a Picnic This Sunday Past. Greenseid, Diane, illus. 1998. 32p. (ps-3). 14.95 (978-0-7868-0242-5(1)) Hyperion Bks. for Children.

Woodworth, Chris. When Ratboy Lived Next Door. 2005. (Illus.). 192p. (J). 16.00 (978-0-374-34677-5(1) , Farrar, Straus & Giroux (BYR)) Farrar, Straus & Giroux.

Wrede, Patricia C. & Stevermer, Caroline. The Grand Tour: Being a Revelation of Matters of High Confidentiality & Greatest Importance, Including Extracts from the Intimate Diary of a Noblewoman & the Sworn Testimony of a Lady of Quality. 2004. (Illus.). 480p. (YA). 17.00 (978-0-15-204616-3(X)) Harcourt Children's Bks.

Wright, Betty Ren. Crandall's Castle. 2005. 184p. (YA). (gr. 4-6). tchr. ed. 16.95 (978-0-8234-1726-1(3)) Holiday Hse., Inc.

Wright, Bill. Sunday You Learn to Box. 2000. (gr. 7-12). lib. bdg. 21.10 (978-0-613-33972-8(X)) Tandem Library Bks.

Wright, Nina. Homefree. 2006. 240p. (J). pap. 8.95 (978-0-7387-0927-7(1) , Flux) Llewellyn Pubns.

Wyatt, Leslie J. Poor Is Just a Starting Place. 2005. 192p. (J). (gr. 6-17). 16.95 (978-0-8234-1884-8(7)) Holiday Hse., Inc.

Wyeth, Sharon Dennis. Orphea Proud. 2006. 208p. (YA). (gr. 9). pap. 5.99 (978-0-440-22706-9(2) , Laurel Leaf) Random Hse. Children's Bks.

Wynne-Jones, Tim. Rex Zero & the End of the World. 2007. (Illus.). 192p. (J). (gr. 3-7). 16.00 (978-0-374-33467-3(6)) Farrar, Straus & Giroux.

—Rex Zero, the King of Nothing. 2008. 224p. (J). 16.95 (***978-0-374-36259-1(9)***) Farrar, Straus & Giroux.

—Stephen Fair. (J). pap. 6.95 (978-0-88899-360-1(9)); 1998. 192p. (YA). (gr. 7-10). pap. (978-0-88899-295-6(5)) Groundwood Bks. CAN. *Dist:* Transition Vendor.

—Stephen Fair. 2000. (978-0-606-18905-7(X)) Tandem Library Bks.

—A Thief in the House of Memory. 2005. 224p. (YA). 17.00 (978-0-374-37478-5(3) , Nelanie Kroupa Bks.) Farrar, Straus & Giroux.

—A Thief in the House of Memory. l.t. ed. 2006. 235p. (YA). 21.95 (978-0-7862-9022-2(6)) Thorndike Pr.

Wyss, Johann. The Swiss Family Robinson. 2006. (Illus.). 61p. (J). lib. bdg. 30.77 (***978-1-4242-1334-4(7)***) Fitzgerald Bks.

Wyss, Johann David. The Swiss Family Robinson. unabr. ed. 2001. (Dover Juvenile Classics Ser.). 336p. (J). (gr. 4-7). pap. 3.50 (978-0-486-41660-1(7)) Dover Pubns., Inc.

—The Swiss Family Robinson. rev. ed. 2004. 352p. (gr. 12). pap. 4.95 (978-0-451-52961-9(8) , Signet Classics) Penguin Group (USA) Inc.

—The Swiss Family Robinson. McKowen, Scott, illus. 2006. (Unabridged Classics Ser.). 352p. 9.95 (978-1-4027-2602-6(3)) Sterling Publishing Co., Inc.

—Swiss Family Robinson: A Classic Story about Initiative. 2003. (Illus.). 32p. per. 3.95 (978-0-9747133-3-5(3) , Values to Live By Classic Stories) Thomas, Frederic Inc.

—The Swiss Family Robinson: Critical Reading Series. 2002. (Great Illustrated Classics Ser.). (Illus.). 240p. (J). (gr. 3-8). 21.35 (978-1-57765-801-6(9) , ABDO & Daughters) ABDO Publishing Co.

—The Swiss Family Robinson: Critical Reading Series. 1999. 336p. (J). (gr. 5-7). pap. 6.50 (978-0-440-41594-7(2) , Yearling) Random Hse. Children's Bks.

—Swiss Family Robinson: With a Discussion of Teamwork. Butterfield, Ned, illus. 2003. (Values in Action Illustrated Classics Ser.). 191p. (J). (978-1-59203-036-1(X)) Learning Challenge, Inc.

Wyss, Johann David, illus. The Swiss Family Robinson. 2004. reprint ed. pap. 30.95 (978-1-4191-5012-8(X)); pap. 1.99 (978-1-4192-5012-5(4)) Kessinger Publishing, LLC.

Wyss, Johann David & McGraw-Hill - Jamestown Education Staff. The Swiss Family Robinson: Critical Reading Series. unabr. ed. 1999. (Wordsworth Classics Ser.). (gr. 6-12). pap. 16.64 (978-0-89061-111-1(4) , 9780890611111) Jamestown.

Wyss, Johann Rudolf. Swiss Family Robinson. 1999. (gr. 5-8). lib. bdg. 13.00 (978-0-613-86235-6(X)) Tandem Library Bks.

Yaccarino, Dan. Where the 4 Winds Blow. 2000. mass mkt. 6.95 (978-0-06-443841-4(4)) HarperCollins Pubs.

—Where the Four Winds Blow. Yaccarino, Dan, illus. 2003. (Illus.). 104p. (J). 17.89 (978-0-06-623627-8(4) , Cotler, Joanna Books) HarperCollins Pubs.

Yates, Alma J. Sammy's Song: A Novel. 2005. 272p. (J). (***978-1-59156-945-9(1)***) Covenant Communications.

Ye, Ting-Xing. Throwaway Daughter. 2003. (Illus.). 240p. (YA). (gr. 7 up). pap. 19.95 (978-0-385-65952-9(0) , Doubleday Can) Doubleday Canada, Ltd. CAN. *Dist:* Random Hse. of Canada, Ltd., Random Hse., Inc.

Yee, Lisa. Stanford Wong Flunks Big Time. (Illus.). (J). 2007. 320p. pap. 5.99 (978-0-439-62248-6(4)); 2005. 304p. (gr. 5-7). pap. 16.99 (978-0-439-62247-9(6)) Scholastic, Inc. (Levine, Arthur A. Bks.).

Yee, Paul. Bamboo. Wang, Shaoli, illus. 2006. 32p. (J). 16.95 (978-1-894965-53-8(1)) Simply Read Bks. CAN. *Dist:* Perseus Distribution.

—The Jade Necklace. Lin, Grace, illus. 2006. 29p. (J). (gr. 4-8). reprint ed. 16.00 (978-1-4223-5135-2(1)) DIANE Publishing Co.

—The Jade Necklace. Lin, Grace, illus. 2002. 32p. (J). (ps-3). 15.95 (978-1-56656-455-7(7) , Crocodile Bks.) Interlink Publishing Group, Inc.

Yeomans, Ellen. Rubber Houses. 2007. 160p. (J). (gr. 7-17). 15.99 (978-0-316-10647-4(X)) Little Brown & Co.

Ylvisaker, Anne. Dear Papa. (Illus.). 192p. (J). (gr. 4). 2007. pap. 5.99 (***978-0-7636-3402-5(6)***); 2002. 15.99 (978-0-7636-1618-2(4)) Candlewick Pr.

Yoon, Salina. Count My Blessings 1 Through 10. Yoon, Salina, illus. 2008. 24p. (J). (ps-ps). bds. 6.99 (***978-0-399-25069-9(7)*** , Putnam Juvenile) Penguin Group (USA) Inc.

Young, Ed. I, Doko: The Tale of a Basket. Young, Ed, illus. 2004. (Illus.). 32p. (J). (ps-3). 16.99 (978-0-399-23625-9(2) , Philomel) Penguin Group (USA) Inc.

Young, Karen Romano. The Beetle & Me: A Love Story. 2001. (Illus.). (J). 12.60 (978-0-606-21054-6(7)) Tandem Library Bks.

Young, Kathy Chase. The Gift. ed. 2005. (Illus.). 32p. (J). pap. 16.99 (978-0-9768861-0-5(3) , 1001) Tishomingo Tree Pr., The.

Young, Ronder Thomas. Moving Mama to Town: Class Set. unabr. ed. 1998. (J). pap. 106.70 incl. audio (978-0-7887-2560-9(2) , 46730) Recorded Bks., LLC.

—Moving Mama to Town: Homework Set. unabr. ed. 1998. (J). 58.24 incl. audio (978-0-7887-1936-3(X) , 40643) Recorded Bks., LLC.

Zalben, Jane Breskin. Baby Babka, the Gorgeous Genius. Chess, Victoria, illus. 2004. 40p. (J). (gr. k-3). tchr. ed. 15.00 (978-0-618-23489-9(6) , Clarion Bks.) Houghton Mifflin Co. Trade & Reference Div.

Zamorano, Ana. A Comer! 1999. Tr. of Let's Eat!. (J). (978-0-606-16653-9(X)) Tandem Library Bks.

—Let's Eat! Vivas, Julie, illus. 1999. 32p. (J). (ps-ps). pap. 5.99 (978-0-439-06758-4(8) , SO1095) Scholastic, Inc.

—Let's Eat! 1999. (J). lib. bdg. (978-0-606-16652-2(1)); lib. bdg. 14.15 (978-0-613-18318-5(5)) Tandem Library Bks.

Zanimo & Perkes, Carolyn. My Day. 2000. (Maki's Words Ser.). (Illus.). 24p. (J). (ps-k). pap. (978-1-894363-54-9(X)) Dominique & Friends.

Zarr, Sara. Story of a Girl. 2007. 208p. (J). (gr. 7-17). 16.99 (978-0-316-01453-3(2)) Little Brown & Co.

Zatz, Lia. Mamita Monstruo. Guevara, Angeles Godinez, tr. Furnari, Eva, illus. 2003. (ENG & SPA.). 32p. pap. 6.95 (978-85-7416-173-0(X)) Callis Editora Ltda BRA. *Dist:* Independent Pubs. Group.

Ziefert, Harriet. When Daddy Travels. Bolam, Emily, illus. 2007. 16p. (J). pap. 5.95 (***978-1-4027-4802-8(7)***) Sterling Publishing Co., Inc.

—When Mommy Travels. Bolam, Emily, illus. 2007. 16p. (J). pap. 5.95 (***978-1-4027-4803-5(5)***) Sterling Publishing Co., Inc.

Zink, Rui. The Boy Who Did Not Like Television. Dreher, Patrick, tr. from POR. Ramos, Manuel Joao, illus. 2004. (J). 14.95 (978-1-931561-96-9(6)) MacAdam/Cage Publishing, Inc.

Zweibel, Alan. Our Tree Named Steve. Catrow, David, illus. 2005. 32p. (J). (ps-3). 15.99 (978-0-399-23722-5(4) , Putnam Juvenile) Penguin Group (USA) Inc.

—Our Tree Named Steve. Catrow, David, illus. 2007. 32p. (J). pap. 5.99 (978-0-14-240743-1(7) , Puffin) Penguin Group (USA) Inc.

FAMILY LIFE EDUCATION

Amidei, Kathie & Osep, Mary. Family Crises. Cannizzo, Karen A., ed. 2000. (Conversations with Teens Ser.). 16p. (YA). pap. 7.95 (978-0-937997-67-3(6)) Pflaum Publishing Group.

Johnson, Leona. Strengthening Family & Self. 2005. 750p. (J). (978-1-59070-495-0(9)) Goodheart-Willcox Pub.

—Strengthening Family & Self: Teaching Package Teacher's Annotated Edition. annot. ed. 845p. (gr. 9-12). tchr. ed. 69.00 (978-1-59070-123-2(2)) Goodheart-Willcox Pub.

—Strengthening Family & Self: Teaching Package Teacher's Resource Guide. 424p. (gr. 9-12). tchr. ed. 64.00 (978-1-59070-125-6(9)) Goodheart-Willcox Pub.

—Strengthening Family & Self: Teaching Package Teacher's Resource Portfolio. 460p. (gr. 9-12). tchr. ed. 136.00 (978-1-59070-126-3(7)) Goodheart-Willcox Pub.

FAMILY PLANNING

see Birth Control

FAMILY RELATIONS

see Domestic Relations

FAMINE

Allan, Tony. The Irish Famine: The Birth of Irish America. (Point of Impact Ser.). 32p. pap. 7.50 (978-1-4034-4113-3(8)); 2001. (Illus.). (J). (gr. 5-7). lib. bdg. 24.22 (978-1-58810-077-1(4)) Heinemann Library.

Bennett, Paul. Famine. 1999. (World Reacts Ser.). (Illus.). 32p. (J). (gr. 2-5). lib. bdg. 16.95 (978-1-887068-88-8(0)) Smart Apple Media.

Connolly, Sean. Famines & Droughts. 2003. (J). lib. bdg. 27.10 (978-1-58340-389-1(2)) Smart Apple Media.

Crosbie, Duncan. Life on a Famine Ship: A Journal of the Irish Famine 1845-1850. Lee, Brian & Peter Bull Art Studio Staff, illus. 2006. 26p. (J). 16.99 (978-0-7641-6004-2(4)) Barron's Educational Series, Inc.

Dolan, Edward F., Jr. The Irish Potato Famine: The Story of Irish-American Immigration. 2002. (Great Journeys Ser.). (Illus.). 109p. (J). 32.79 (978-0-7614-1323-3(5) , Benchmark Bks.) Cavendish, Marshall Corp.

Gallagher, Carole S. The Irish Potato Famine. 2001. (Great Disasters, Reforms & Ramifications Ser.). (Illus.). 112p. (J). 30.00 (978-0-7910-5788-9(7) , Chelsea Hse.) Facts On File, Inc.

Glaser, Elizabeth & Biel, Timothy Levi. The Ethiopian Famine. 2002. (World Disasters Ser.). (Illus.). 64p. (YA). (gr. 4-12). lib. bdg. 26.20 (978-1-56006-014-7(X) , Lucent Bks.) Thomson Gale.

Thornton, Jeremy. The Irish Potato Famine: Irish Immigrants Come to America (1845-1850) 2004. (Primary Sources of Immigration & Migration in America Ser.). (Illus.). 24p. (J). lib. bdg. 19.95 (978-0-8239-6831-2(6) , PowerKids Pr.) Rosen Publishing Group, Inc., The.

—The Irish Potato Famine: Irish Immigrants Come to America, 1845-1850. 2004. (Primary Sources of Immigration & Migration in America Ser.). (Illus.). 24p. (J). lib. bdg. (978-0-8239-8957-7(7) , PowerKids Pr.) Rosen Publishing Group, Inc., The.

Walker, Jane. Famine, Drought, & Plagues. 2004. (Natural Disasters Ser.). (J). lib. bdg. 27.10 (978-1-932799-08-8(7)) Stargazer Bks.

Witherick, Michael. Farming, Food & Famine. 2001. (Epics Ser.). (Illus.). 104p. (YA). (gr. 11 up). pap. 26.50 (978-0-7487-5819-7(4)) Nelson Thornes Ltd. GBR. *Dist:* Trans-Atlantic Pubns., Inc.

FANTASTIC FICTION

see Fantasy Fiction

FANTASY

see Fantasy Fiction

FANTASY FICTION

see also Ghost Stories; Science Fiction

Aaron, Chester. Home to the Sea, 2005. (Illus.). 144p. (J). pap. 10.95 (978-0-9746481-2-5(4)) Brown Barn Bks.

Abalos, Rafael. Bufo Sonador en la Galazia de la Tristeza. 2000. (SPA., Illus.). 240p. 19.95 (978-84-8306-356-9(5)) Debate, Editorial ESP. *Dist:* Libros Sin Fronteras.

Abalos, Rafael & Baca Castex, Noël. Grimpow: The Invisible Road. 2007. 512p. (J). (gr. 7). 17.99 (***978-0-385-73374-8(7)***); lib. bdg. 20.99 (***978-0-385-90389-9(8)***) Random Hse. Children's Bks. (Delacorte Bks. for Young Readers).

Abbot, Jax. SuperWhat? 2004. (YA). mass mkt. 5.99 (978-0-8439-5385-5(3)) Dorchester Publishing Co., Inc.

Abbott, Candy. Gavin Goodfellow: The Lure of Burnt Swamp. 2007. 368p. pap. 14.95 (***978-1-886068-03-2(8)***) Fruitbearer Publishing.

Abbott, Charles R. Patches & Leif. 2003. pap. 9.00 (978-0-8059-6077-8(5)) Dorrance Publishing Co., Inc.

Abbott, Tony. Chariot of Queen Zara. Merrell, David, illus. 2006. 124p. (J). lib. bdg. 15.38 (***978-1-4242-0308-6(2)***) Fitzgerald Bks.

—City in the Clouds. Jessell, Tim, illus. 1999. (Secrets of Droon Ser.: No. 4). 96p. (J). (gr. 2-5). pap. 3.99 (978-0-590-10842-3(5)) Scholastic, Inc.

—City in the Clouds. 1999. (gr. 3-6). lib. bdg. 11.80 (978-0-613-21354-7(8)) Tandem Library Bks.

—The Coiled Viper. Jessell, Tim, illus. 2003. (Secrets of Droon Ser.: Vol. 19). 128p. (J). (gr. 2-5). pap. 4.99 (978-0-439-42080-8(6)) Scholastic, Inc.

—Dream Thief. Merrell, David, illus. 2003. (Secrets of Droon Ser.: No. 17). 128p. (J). (gr. 2-5). pap. 4.99 (978-0-439-42078-5(4) , Scholastic Paperbacks) Scholastic, Inc.

—Dream Thief. 2003. (gr. k-3). lib. bdg. 11.80 (978-0-613-58148-6(2)) Tandem Library Bks.

—Flight of the Genie. Jessell, Tim, illus. 2004. 122p. (J). lib. bdg. 15.38 (***978-1-4242-0314-7(7)***) Fitzgerald Bks.

—Fortress of the Treasure Queen. Merrell, David, illus. 2004. 115p. (J). lib. bdg. 15.38 (***978-1-4242-0312-3(0)***) Fitzgerald Bks.

—Golden Wasp. Jessell, Tim, illus. 2000. (Secrets of Droon Ser.: No. 8). 112p. (J). (gr. 2-5). pap. 4.99 (978-0-439-18298-0(0)) Scholastic, Inc.

—Golden Wasp. 2000. (gr. 3-6). lib. bdg. 11.80 (978-0-613-25348-2(5)) Tandem Library Bks.

—The Great Ice Battle. 1999. (gr. 3-6). lib. bdg. 11.80 (978-0-613-21639-5(3)) Tandem Library Bks.

—The Hawk Bandits of Tarkoom. Jessell, Tim, illus. 2001. (Secrets of Droon Ser.: No. 11). 128p. (J). (gr. 2-5). pap. 3.99 (978-0-439-20785-0(1)) Scholastic, Inc.

—The Hawk Bandits of Tarkoom. 2001. (gr. 3-6). lib. bdg. 11.80 (978-0-613-32634-6(2)) Tandem Library Bks.

—Hidden Stairs & the Magic Carpet. 1999. (gr. 3-6). lib. bdg. 11.80 (978-0-613-16947-9(6)) Tandem Library Bks.

—The Hidden Stairs & the Magic Carpet. 2007. (Secrets of Droon Ser.: No. 1). 96p. (J). pap. 2.99 (***978-0-545-01038-2(1)***) Scholastic, Inc.

—The Knights of Silversnow. Jessell, Tim, illus. 2002. (Secrets of Droon Ser.: no. 16). 128p. (J). pap. 4.99 (978-0-439-30609-6(4) , Scholastic Paperbacks) Scholastic, Inc.

—The Magic Escapes. ed. 2002. (Secrets of Droon Ser.: Bk. 1). (Illus.). 176p. (J). pap. 5.99 (978-0-439-42077-8(6) , Scholastic Paperbacks) Scholastic, Inc.

—The Mask of Maliban. Jessell, Tim, illus. 2001. (Secrets of Droon Ser.: No. 13). 128p. (J). (gr. 2-5). pap. 3.99 (978-0-439-30606-5(X) , Scholastic Paperbacks) Scholastic, Inc.

—The Mask of Maliban. 2001. (gr. 3-6). lib. bdg. 11.80 (978-0-613-35785-2(X)) Tandem Library Bks.

—The Moon Dragon. Merrell, David, illus. 2006. (Little Apple Ser.). 121p. (J). (978-1-4156-4703-5(8)) Scholastic, Inc.

—Moon Dragon. Merrell, David, illus. 2006. 121p. (J). lib. bdg. 15.38 (***978-1-4242-0309-3(0)***) Fitzgerald Bks.

—Queen of Shadowthorn. 2007. (Secrets of Droon Ser.). 128p. (J). pap. 4.99 (***978-0-439-90252-6(5)*** , Scholastic Paperbacks) Scholastic, Inc.

—Quest for the Queen, No. 10. Merrell, David, illus. 2000. (Secrets of Droon Ser.: No. 10). 112p. (gr. 2-5). pap. 3.99 (978-0-439-20784-3(3)) Scholastic, Inc.

—Quest for the Queen. 2000. (gr. 3-6). lib. bdg. 11.80 (978-0-613-32973-6(2)) Tandem Library Bks.

—The Riddle of Zorfendorf Castle. Merrell, David, illus. 2005. 124p. (J). (ps-k). lib. bdg. 10.79 (978-0-606-33298-9(7)) Tandem Library Bks.

—Riddle of Zorfendorf Castle. Merrell, David, illus. 2005. 124p. (J). lib. bdg. 15.38 (***978-1-4242-0310-9(4)***) Fitzgerald Bks.

—Search for the Dragon Ship. Jessell, Tim, illus. 2003. (Secrets of Droon Ser.: Vol. 18). 128p. (gr. 2-5). pap. 3.99 (978-0-439-42079-2(2) , Scholastic Paperbacks) Scholastic, Inc.

—Search for the Dragon Ship. 2003. (gr. 3-6). lib. bdg. 11.80 (978-0-613-66379-3(9)) Tandem Library Bks.

—The Secrets of Droon. 2005. 389p. (J). (978-0-7607-9540-8(1)) Scholastic, Inc.

—The Secrets of Droon: The Isle of Mists. Merrell, David, illus. 2004. (Secrets of Droon Ser.). 112p. (J). 3.99 (978-0-439-56048-1(9)) Scholastic, Inc.

—Sleeping Giant of Goll. 2000. (gr. 3-6). lib. bdg. 11.80 (978-0-613-22389-8(6)) Tandem Library Bks.

—Sorcerer. 2006. (J). (Illus.). 112p. pap. 3.99 (978-0-439-67175-0(2)); (Secrets of Droon Ser.: No. 4). 176p. pap. 5.99 (978-0-439-67178-1(7)) Scholastic, Inc. (Scholastic Paperbacks).

—The Tower of the Elf King. 2000. (gr. 3-6). lib. bdg. 11.80 (978-0-613-33156-2(7)) Tandem Library Bks.

—Under the Serpent Sea. Jessell, Tim, illus. 2001. (Secrets of Droon Ser.: No. 12). 128p. (gr. 2-5). pap. 3.99 (978-0-439-20786-7(X)) Scholastic, Inc.

—Under the Serpent Sea. 2001. (gr. 3-6). lib. bdg. 11.80 (978-0-613-35758-6(2)) Tandem Library Bks.

Abbott, Tony & Jessell, Tim. The Moon Scroll. 2002. (Secrets of Droon Ser.: No. 15). (Illus.). 144p. (J). (gr. 2-5). pap. 3.99 (978-0-439-30608-9(6)) Scholastic, Inc.

Abbott, Tony & Reeves, Linda. Into the Land of the Lost. Jessell, Tim, illus. 2000. (Secrets of Droon Ser.: No. 7). 112p. (J). (gr. 2-5). pap. 3.99 (978-0-439-18297-3(2)) Scholastic, Inc.

Abouzeid, Chris. Anatopsis. 2006. 336p. (J). (gr. 5). 16.99 (978-0-525-47583-5(4) , Dutton Juvenile) Penguin Group (USA) Inc.

Acquaire, M. T. Marty Boggs & the Curse of Kutkara's Tomb. 2006. 328p. (YA). 28.99 (978-1-59507-112-5(1) , ArcheBooks) ArcheBooks Publishing.

Ada, Alma Flor. Alla Donde Florecen los Framboyanes. Martorell, Antonio, illus. (SPA.). 80p. (J). (gr. 5-8). 15.95 (978-1-58105-658-7(3)) Santillana USA Publishing Co., Inc.

—Extra! Extra! Fairy-Tale News from Hidden Forest. Tryon, Leslie, illus. 2001. 32p. (J). (gr. k-3). 16.99 (978-0-689-82582-8(X) , Atheneum) Simon & Schuster Children's Publishing.

—Una Extrana Visita. (Libros para Contar Ser.). (SPA., Illus.). 16p. (J). (gr. k-3). pap. 6.95 (978-1-58105-192-6(1)) Santillana USA Publishing Co., Inc.

—Una Extrana Visita. 2000. (SPA.). (gr. k-3). lib. bdg. 15.25 (978-0-613-79378-0(1)) Tandem Library Bks.

Adamchuk, Rachelle G. Disappearance: The First Part of Trickery & Honest Deception. 2006. 169p. pap. (***978-1-4120-8991-3(3)***) Trafford Publishing.

Adams, Ann. The Silver Boat. Elbo, Max, illus. 2000. iv, 34p. (J). pap. 12.95 (978-0-9678498-0-5(2)) Silver Boat Productions.

Adams, George. Cuentame un Cuento. Utton, Peter, illus. 2001. (SPA.). 96p. (J). (gr. k-3). (978-84-480-1081-2(7) , TM7572) Timun Mas, Editorial S.A. ESP. *Dist:* Lectorum Pubns., Inc.

Adams, Richard. Watership Down. 2001. (Perennial Classics Ser.). (Illus.). 512p. pap. 13.00 (978-0-06-093545-0(6)) HarperCollins Pubs.

Adams, W. Royce. The Computer's Nerd. (J). 2004. 136p. pap. 9.95 (978-0-9712206-4-5(6)); 2002. 128p. (gr. 4 up). 17.95 (978-0-9712206-2-1(X)) Rairarubia Bks.

—Rairarubia. 1999. (Rairarubia Tales Ser.: Bk. 1). (Illus.). 138p. (J). (gr. 3-7). pap. 10.95 (978-1-882897-36-0(6)) Lost Coast Pr.

—Return to Rairarubia. 2000. (Rairarubia Tales Ser.: Bk. 2). 138p. (J). (gr. 3-7). pap. 10.95 (978-1-882897-44-5(7)) Lost Coast Pr.

—Return to Rairarubia. 2000. (gr. 3-6). lib. bdg. 19.90 (978-0-613-86348-3(8)) Tandem Library Bks.

—Revenge on Rairarubia. 2001. (Rairarubia Tales Ser.: Vol. 4). (Illus.). 134p. (J). (gr. 4-6). pap. 10.95 (978-0-9712206-0-7(3)) Rairarubia Bks.

—The Ring from Rairarubia. 2003. (Rairarubia Tales Ser.: Bk. 5). (Illus.). 126p. (J). (gr. 5 up). pap. 10.95 (978-0-9712206-3-8(8)) Rairarubia Bks.

Adamson, Bobby R. The Field Mice of Deer Park. 2002. 96p. (YA). (gr. 7-12). 6.95 (978-0-9720631-0-4(2)) Adamson, Bobby R.

Aguirre-Sacasa, Roberto. Wolf at the Door. 2004. (Fantastic Four Ser.: Vol. 1). (Illus.). 168p. (YA). 16.99 (978-0-7851-1471-0(8)) Marvel Enterprises, Inc.

Aguirre-Sacasa, Roberto & Muniz, Jim. Marvel Holiday Special TPB, Vol. 2. 2005. (Fantastic Four Ser.). (Illus.). 120p. pap. 13.99 (978-0-7851-1472-7(6)) Marvel Enterprises, Inc.

Aiken, Joan. The Cockatrice Boys. 2002. (gr. 5-8). lib. bdg. 14.15 (978-0-613-57501-0(6)) Tandem Library Bks.

Aisaka (Character Designs), Koji, et al, illus. Lost War Chronicles, Vol. 2. 2nd rev. ed. 2006. (Mobile Suit Gundam Ser.). pap. 9.99 (978-1-59816-214-1(4) , Tokyopop Kids) TOKYOPOP, Inc.

Akimine, Kamijyo. Samurai Deeper Kyo, Vol. 12. Akimine, Kamijyo, illus. 12th rev. ed. 2005. (Illus.). 192p. pap. 9.99 (978-1-59532-452-8(6) , Tokyopop Adult) TOKYOPOP, Inc.

Akimoto, Nami. Miracle Girls, 9 vols. (Illus.). (gr. 7-12). Vol. 1. 2000. 184p. pap. 9.99 (978-1-892213-64-8(8)); Vol. 2. 2nd rev. ed. 2001. 194p. pap. 9.99 (978-1-892213-69-3(9)) TOKYOPOP, Inc.

Akira, Shouko. Times Two. Akira, Shouko, illus. 2005. (Times Two Ser.). (Illus.). 200p. (YA). pap. 9.99 (978-1-59116-736-5(1)) Viz Media.

Akita, Yoshinobu. Orphen, Vol. 5. 2006. (Illus.). 168p. (YA). pap. (978-1-4139-0270-9(7)) ADV Manga.

—Orphen Volume 6. 2006. (Illus.). 168p. (YA). pap. (978-1-4139-0271-6(5)) ADV Manga.

E F G

Akiyama, Tamayo. Mouryo-Kiden: Legend of the Nymphs, 3 vols., Vol. 1. 2004. (Illus.). 208p. pap. 9.99 (978-1-59532-245-6(0) , Tokyopop Adult) TOKYOPOP, Inc.

Aladino. 2001. Tr. of Aladdin. (978-84-305-7555-8(3)) Lectorum Pubns., Inc.

Albee, Sarah. Elmo Says Achoo! Brannon, Tom, illus. 2000. (Step into Reading Ser.). 32p. (J). (ps-1). lib. bdg. 11.99 (978-0-375-90311-3(9) , Random Hse. Bks. for Young Readers) Random Hse. Children's Bks.

—Elmo Says Achoo! 2000. (ps-2). lib. bdg. 21.10 (978-0-613-25013-9(3)) Tandem Library Bks.

Albee, Sarah & Wilson, Sarah. Elmo Says Achoo! Brannon, Tom, illus. 2000. (Early Step into Reading Ser.). 32p. (J). (ps-1). pap. 3.99 (978-0-375-80311-6(4) , Random Hse. Bks. for Young Readers) Random Hse. Children's Bks.

Alberti, Robert. Mitlanyal: The Gods of Stability, Vol. 1. 10th ed. 2004. (Illus.). 152p. (YA). pap. 19.95 (978-0-9725880-2-7(7) , mit1) Zottola Publishing, Inc.

—Mitlanyal: The Gods of Change, Vol. 2. 10th ed. 2004. (Illus.). 184p. (YA). pap. 19.95 (978-0-9725880-3-4(5) , mit2) Zottola Publishing, Inc.

Alden, Paul. Dungeon Siege: The Battle for Aranna. 2005. (Illus.). 88p. (YA). pap. 6.95 (978-1-59307-425-8(5)) Dark Horse Comics.

Aldovini, Giulia & Miceli, Monica. El Pequeno Celestino. Brignole, Giancarla, tr. rev. ed. 2002. (Fabulas De Familia Ser.). (SPA.). 32p. (J). pap. 6.95 (978-970-20-0272-7(9)) Castillo, Ediciones, S. A. de C. V. MEX. *Dist:* Macmillan.

Alessandra, Joseph R. 13 Eyes. Alessandra, Lee, ed. Alessandra, Joseph R., illus. 1999. 113p. (YA). (gr. 10 up). pap. 5.95 (978-0-9671255-0-3(2)) Netherfield Creations, Inc.

Alexander, Alma. Gift of the Unmage. 2007. (Worldweavers Ser.: Bk. 1). 400p. (YA). (gr. 7 up). 16.99 (978-0-06-083955-0(4)); lib. bdg. 17.89 (978-0-06-083956-7(2)) HarperCollins Pubs.

—Spellspam. 2008. (Worldweavers Ser.). 448p. (J). 17.99 (***978-0-06-083958-1(9));*** lib. bdg. 18.89 (***978-0-06-083959-8(7))*** HarperCollins Pubs. (Eos).

—Worldweavers: Gift of the Unmage. 2008. (Worldweavers Ser.). 416p. (J). pap. 7.99 (***978-0-06-083957-4(0)*** , Eos) HarperCollins Pubs.

Alexander, Lloyd. The Arkadians. 272p. (gr. 5 up). (YA). pap. 4.99 (978-0-8072-1527-2(9)); 1998. (J). pap. 37.00 incl. audio (978-0-8072-8022-5(4) , YA969SP) Random Hse. Audio Publishing Group. (Listening Library).

—The Beggar Queen. 2002. (Westmark Trilogy: Vol. 3). (Illus.). 256p. (J). (gr. 7). pap. 6.99 (978-0-14-131070-1(7) , Puffin) Penguin Group (USA) Inc.

—The Black Cauldron. 2002. (Chronicles of Prydain Ser.: Bk. 2). (YA). (gr. 5 up). 14.47 (978-0-7587-6755-4(2)) Book Wholesalers, Inc.

—The Black Cauldron. (Chronicles of Prydain Ser.: Bk. 2). (J). (gr. 3-7). rev. ed. 1999. (Illus.). 224p. 19.95 (978-0-8050-6131-4(2)); 2nd rev. ed. 2006. 208p. pap. 5.99 (978-0-8050-8049-0(X)) Holt, Henry & Co. (Holt, Henry & Co. Bks. For Young Readers).

—The Black Cauldron. 2004. (Chronicles of Prydain Ser.: Bk. 2). 240p. (J). (gr. 4-7). pap. 38.00 incl. audio (978-1-4000-8636-8(1) , Listening Library) Random Hse. Audio Publishing Group.

—The Book of Three. 2006. (Chronicles of Prydain Ser.: Bk. 1). 224p. (J). (gr. 3-7). pap. 5.99 (978-0-8050-8048-3(1) , Holt, Henry & Co. Bks. For Young Readers) Holt, Henry & Co.

—The Castle of Llyr. (Chronicles of Prydain Ser.: Bk. 3). (J). rev. ed. 1999. (Illus.). 204p. (gr. 3-7). 21.95 (978-0-8050-6133-8(9)); 3rd rev. ed. 2006. 208p. (gr. 5 up). pap. 5.99 (978-0-8050-8050-6(3)) Holt, Henry & Co. (Holt, Henry & Co. Bks. For Young Readers).

—The Castle of Llyr. 2004. (Chronicles of Prydain Ser.: Bk. 3). 208p. (J). (gr. 4-7). pap. 36.00 incl. audio (978-1-4000-9019-8(9) , Listening Library) Random Hse. Audio Publishing Group.

—The Chronicles of Prydain. rev. ed. 1999. (Chronicles of Prydain Ser.: Bk. 3). (Illus.). 224p. (J). (gr. 3-7). 19.95 (978-0-8050-6132-1(0) , Holt, Henry & Co. Bks. For Young Readers) Holt, Henry & Co.

—The First Two Lives of Lukas-Kasha. 1998. (Puffin Novel Ser.). 12.64 (978-0-606-13389-0(5)) Tandem Library Bks.

—The Foundling: And Other Tales of Prydain. 6th rev. ed. 2006. (Chronicles of Prydain Ser.). 128p. (J). (gr. 3-7). pap. 5.99 (978-0-8050-8053-7(8) , Holt, Henry & Co. Bks. For Young Readers) Holt, Henry & Co.

—The Golden Dream of Carlo Chuchio. 2007. 320p. (J). (gr. 5 up). 18.95 (***978-0-8050-8333-0(2)*** , Holt, Henry & Co. Bks. For Young Readers) Holt, Henry & Co.

—Gypsy Rizka. 2000. (Illus.). 208p. (J). (gr. 3-7). pap. 5.99 (978-0-14-130980-4(6) , Puffin) Penguin Group (USA) Inc.

—Gypsy Rizka. unabr. ed. 2000. (YA). pap. 58.99 incl. audio (978-0-7887-3954-5(9) , 41059X4) Recorded Bks., LLC.

—Gypsy Rizka. 2000. (gr. 3-6). lib. bdg. 14.15 (978-0-613-30458-0(6)) Tandem Library Bks.

—The High King. (Chronicles of Prydain Ser.: Bk. 5). (J). (gr. 3-7). rev. ed. 1999. (Illus.). 288p. 19.95 (978-0-8050-6135-2(5)); 5th rev. ed. 2006. 272p. pap. 5.99 (978-0-8050-8052-0(X)) Holt, Henry & Co. (Holt, Henry & Co. Bks. For Young Readers).

—The Illyrian Adventure. 2000. (Vesper Holly Ser.). (Illus.). 144p. (J). (gr. 5-9). pap. 5.99 (978-0-14-130313-0(1) , Puffin) Penguin Group (USA) Inc.

—The Illyrian Adventure. 1999. (Vesper Holly Ser.). (YA). (gr. 7 up). 12.64 (978-0-606-16832-8(X)) Tandem Library Bks.

—The Iron Ring. 1999. (Illus.). 304p. (J). (gr. 5-9). pap. 6.99 (978-0-14-130348-2(4) , Puffin) Penguin Group (USA) Inc.

—The Iron Ring. unabr. ed. 1998. (J). Class Set. 133.70 incl. audio (978-0-7887-2555-5(6) , 46725); Homework Set. 76.24 incl. audio (978-0-7887-2251-6(4) , 40735) Recorded Bks., LLC.

—The Iron Ring. 1999. (gr. 5-8). lib. bdg. 14.15 (978-0-613-18257-7(X)) Tandem Library Bks.

—The Kestrel. 2002. (Westmark Trilogy: Vol. 2). (YA). (gr. 5-8). lib. bdg. 14.15 (978-0-613-63956-9(1)) Tandem Library Bks.

—The Remarkable Journey of Prince Jen. l.t. ed. 2002. (LRS Large Print Cornerstone Ser.). (J). lib. bdg. 32.95 (978-1-58118-104-3(3) , 25787) LRS.

—The Remarkable Journey of Prince Jen. 2004. (Illus.). 288p. (J). (gr. 5). pap. 6.99 (978-0-14-240225-2(7) , Puffin) Penguin Group (USA) Inc.

—Taran Wanderer. (Chronicles of Prydain Ser.: Bk. 4). 256p. (J). rev. ed. 1999. (gr. 3-7). 19.95 (978-0-8050-6134-5(7)); 4th rev. ed. 2006. pap. 5.99 (978-0-8050-8051-3(1)) Holt, Henry & Co. (Holt, Henry & Co. Bks. For Young Readers).

Alexander, Lloyd, et al. Firebirds: An Anthology of Original Fantasy & Science Fiction. Vess, Charles, illus. 2005. 432p. (YA). (gr. 6-11). pap. 8.99 (978-0-14-240320-4(2) , Puffin) Penguin Group (USA) Inc.

Alexander, Martha. You're a Genius, Blackboard Bear. Alexander, Martha, illus. 2002. (Blackboard Bear Ser.). (Illus.). (J). 11.91 (978-0-7587-4064-9(6)) Book Wholesalers, Inc.

Alexander, R. W. Born in an Eggshell. 2004. 135p. (YA). pap. 12.95 (978-0-7414-2241-5(7)) Infinity Publishing.

Alexander, Wilma E. The William Ghost. 2001. (Illus.). 120p. (J). (gr. 3-7). pap. 6.95 (978-1-896184-92-0(8)) Roussan Pubs., Inc./Roussan Editeur, Inc. CAN. *Dist:* Orca Bk. Pubs. USA.

Alfonseca, Manuel. The Journey of Tivo the Dauntless. 2000. 108p. (YA). pap. 9.95 (978-0-595-14869-1(7)) iUniverse, Inc.

Algozin, Bruce. Claw of the Dragon. 2008. (Endless Quest Ser.). 192p. (J). (gr. 3-7). 5.99 (***978-0-7869-4719-5(5)*** , Mirrorstone) Wizards of the Coast.

Alice in Wonderland. 2003. (J). 12.99 (978-0-7868-3476-1(5)) Disney Pr.

Alice in Wonderland. 2006. 64p. (J). 8.99 (978-0-7945-1239-2(9) , Usborne) EDC Publishing.

Alice in Wonderland. 2003. (Illus.). 288p. (J). 9.98 (978-1-4054-1674-0(2)) Parragon, Inc.

Alice in Wonderland Read Along. 1999. (J). (ps-3). pap. 6.98 incl. audio (978-0-7634-0589-2(2)) Walt Disney Records.

Aliseda, Francisco. Melon King: The Magic Horse Collection. 1999. (J). 20.00 (978-1-883816-01-8(7) , Alif Publishing Corp.) Tractus Bks.

Allen, John. Esidarap. 2002. 127p. (YA). pap. 10.95 (978-0-595-22140-0(8) , Writers Club Pr.) iUniverse, Inc.

Allen, Will. Swords for Hire: Two of the Most Unlikely Heroes you'll ever Meet. Beck, David Michael, illus. 2003. 168p. (gr. 3 up). pap. 6.95 (978-0-9724882-0-4(0)) Centerpunch Pr.

Allende, Isabel. Kingdom of the Golden Dragon. Peden, Margaret Sayers, tr. from SPA. 2005. 464p. (J). (gr. 7-12). pap. 7.99 (978-0-06-058944-8(2) , Rayo) HarperCollins Pubs.

—Kingdom of the Golden Dragon. 2004. (Illus.). 448p. (J). (gr. 5 up). 19.99 (978-0-06-058942-4(6)) HarperCollins Pubs.

—Kingdom of the Golden Dragon. Peden, Margaret Sayers, tr. from SPA. 2004. (Illus.). 448p. (J). (gr. 5 up). lib. bdg. 20.89 (978-0-06-058943-1(4)) HarperCollins Pubs.

—Kingdom of the Golden Dragon. l.t. ed. 2004. 416p. (J). pap. 19.99 (978-0-06-059474-9(8)) HarperCollins Pubs.

—El Reino del Dragon de Oro. 2003. (SPA.). 432p. 19.99 (978-0-06-059170-0(6)) HarperCollins Pubs.

Allred, Alexandra Powe. The Code. 2002. 167p. (J). pap. 5.95 (978-0-7569-0692-4(X)); (gr. 3-6). lib. bdg. 13.95 (978-0-7569-0693-1(8)) Perfection Learning Corp.

Alonso, Fernando. Ennia. 2002. Tr. of Ennia. (SPA.). (gr. 3-6). lib. bdg. 17.05 (978-0-613-80660-2(3)) Tandem Library Bks.

—La Historia de un Hombrecillo de Papel. (Leer Es Vivir Serie Teatro). (SPA.). 96p. (J). (gr. 3-5). 6.36 (978-84-241-7711-9(8)) Everest de Ediciones y Distribucion, S.L. ESP. *Dist:* Lectorum Pubns., Inc.

Alonso, Manuel L. Extrano, Muy Extrano. Schubert, Karin, illus. 2003. (SPA.). 124p. (J). (gr. 3-5). pap. 10.95 (978-84-204-4906-7(7)) Santillana USA Publishing Co., Inc.

Alonzo, Debra. To the Moon & Back. 2001. (J). pap. 10.00 (978-0-8059-5297-1(7)) Dorrance Publishing Co., Inc.

Alpha Blox. (J). pap. 9.95 (978-1-886647-07-7(0)) ALPI International, Ltd.

Alston, E. B. The Last Voyage of the Dan-D. Garrett, Toni, illus. l.t. ed. 2003. 47p. (J). per. 6.99 (978-0-9747735-0-6(6)) Righter Publishing Co., Inc.

Aluris: The Book of Annua, 1, 4. 2006. (Illus.). 320p. (YA). per. 20.00 (978-0-9786177-0-7(3)) Michalek, Curtis.

Alvarez, Tom. Master of Magic: Shadows of Time. Payne, Michael, ed. 2002. (Illus.). 350p. (Orig.). (YA). (gr. 9-12). pap. 6.95 (978-1-880852-00-2(4)) Magical Pubns.

Amakawa, Sumiko. Cross, 5 vols., Vol. 1. 2004. (Graphic Novel-Manga Ser.). (Illus.). 192p. pap. 9.99 (978-1-59532-227-2(2) , Tokyopop Adult) TOKYOPOP, Inc.

—Cross, Vol. 2. Amakawa, Sumiko, illus. rev. ed. 2005. (Illus.). 192p. pap. 9.99 (978-1-59532-228-9(0) , Tokyopop Adult) TOKYOPOP, Inc.

Amakawa, Sumiko, illus. & creator. Cross, Vol. 3. Amakawa, Sumiko, creator. rev. ed. 2005. 200p. pap. 9.99 (978-1-59532-229-6(9) , Tokyopop Adult) TOKYOPOP, Inc.

Amano, Kozue. Aria, Vol. 3. 2004. (Illus.). 188p. pap. (978-1-4139-0089-7(5)) ADV Manga.

Ambrus, Victor G., illus. The Iliad. 2004. (Kingfisher Epics Ser.). 176p. (J). (gr. 3-5). pap. 7.95 (978-0-7534-5722-1(9) , Kingfisher) Houghton Mifflin Co. Trade & Reference Div.

Amma, Jill. The Indaba Tree Odyssey: An African Tale. 2006. 360p. pap. 18.95 (978-0-7414-3172-1(6)) Infinity Publishing.

Amodeo, John, et al. Lost on Aquaria. 2004. (Zenda Ser.: No. 4). (Illus.). 144p. (J). (gr. 5 up). pap. 4.99 (978-0-448-43256-4(0) , Grosset & Dunlap) Penguin Group (USA) Inc.

Anacker, John. The Raven's Ring Pin. Hill, Connie, ed. 2004. (Illus.). 336p. pap. 12.95 (978-0-7387-0433-3(4)) Llewellyn Pubns.

Anasti, Tedd, et al. Reign of the Soul Eater. 2006. (Spider Riders Ser.). (Illus.). 224p. (YA). pap. 5.99 (978-1-55704-728-1(6)) Newmarket Pr.

Andersen, Hans Christian. The Emperor's New Clothes. Hall, Francois, illus. 2006. (First Fairy Tales Ser.). 30p. (J). (978-1-59771-071-8(7) , 1262700) Sea-To-Sea Pubns.

—The Little Match Girl. 2002. (Illus.). (J). (ps-3). lib. bdg. 15.30 (978-0-613-83546-6(8)) Tandem Library Bks.

Anderson, Jodi Lynn. May Bird among the Stars, Bk. 2. 272p. (J). 2007. pap. 5.99 (978-1-4169-0608-7(8) , Aladdin); 2006. 16.95 (978-0-689-86924-2(X) , Atheneum) Simon & Schuster Children's Publishing.

—May Bird & the Ever After, Bk. 1. Gore, Leonid, illus. (J). (gr. 5-7). 2005. 336p. 15.95 (978-0-689-86923-5(1) , Atheneum); 2006. 352p. reprint ed. pap. 5.99 (978-1-4169-0607-0(X) , Aladdin) Simon & Schuster Children's Publishing.

Anderson, Jodi Lynn. May Bird, Warrior Princess, Bk. 3. 2007. 256p. (J). (gr. 5-9). 16.99 (***978-0-689-86925-9(8)*** , Atheneum) Simon & Schuster Children's Publishing.

Anderson, Kevin J. & Moesta, Rebecca. Crystal Doors, No. 1. 2006. 304p. (J). (gr. 7-17). 15.99 (978-0-316-01055-9(3)) Little Brown & Co.

—Island Realm. 2007. (Crystal Door Ser.: No. 1). 304p. (J). (gr. 7-17). 7.99 (***978-0-316-11295-6(X))*** Little, Brown Bks. for Young Readers.

—Ocean Realm. 2nd ed. 2007. (Crystal Doors Ser.: No. 2). 304p. (J). (gr. 5-8). 16.99 (***978-0-316-01056-6(1))*** Little, Brown Bks. for Young Readers.

Anderson, Leone Castell. Sean's Quest. Welch, Sheila Kelly, illus. 2003. 162p. pap. 10.95 (978-0-9638819-7-7(3)); (J). 16.95 (978-0-9638819-6-0(5)) ShadowPlay Pr.

Anderson, M. T. The Clue of the Linoleum Lederhosen: M. T. Anderson's Thrilling Tales. Cyrus, Kurt, illus. 2006. (M. T. Anderson's Thrilling Tales Ser.). 272p. (J). 15.00 (978-0-15-205352-9(2)) Harcourt Children's Bks.

Anderson, Paris. The Sisters Kennington. 2004. 140p. (J). per. 16.00 (978-1-58982-195-8(5) , Millennial Mind Publishing) American Bk. Publishing Group.

Andrews, Ted. Dreamsong of the Eagle. Hayner, Deborah, illus. 2002. 48p. (J). 16.95 (978-1-57174-294-0(8)) Hampton Roads Publishing Co., Inc.

Anjelae, Samara. Wonder Windows: My Guardian Angel, My Fairy Godmother, My Magical Mermaid. 2002. 42.95 (978-0-9708754-0-2(1) , BelleTress Bks.) Red Wheel/Weiser.

Anna, Jennifer. Year of the Dragon. 2nd ed. 2007. (Illus.). 56p. (J). pap. 24.99 (***978-1-59092-155-5(0)*** , Blue Works) Windstorm Creative.

Anthony, David & David, Charles. Cauldron Cooker's Night No. 1: Knightscares. 2003. (Illus.). 200p. (J). per. 5.99 (978-0-9728461-0-3(7)) Sigil Publishing.

—Voyage to Silvermight: Knightscares #4. 2004. (Illus.). 208p. (J). per. 5.99 (978-0-9728461-3-4(1)) Sigil Publishing.

Anthony, Piers. Key to Chroma. 2003. (ChroMagic Ser.: Bk. 2). 550p. (J). 34.99 (978-1-59426-017-9(6)); 554p. per. 22.50 (978-1-59426-018-6(4)) Mundania Pr.

—Key to Havoc. 2003. (ChroMagic Ser.: Bk. 1). 496p. 29.00 (978-0-9723670-7-3(1) , khhb01) Mundania Pr.

—Vale of the Vole. 2000. (Xanth Ser.: Vol. 10). (978-0-606-18660-5(3)) Tandem Library Bks.

Anton, Robert & Marie, Madeline. Flames of Fortune: Dragonia, Tales of the Golden Talon, 1 bk. 2004. (Illus.). 308p. (YA). per. 19.95 (978-0-9742460-2-4(6)) Timtu Ink.

—The Hope for Zargahn: Dragonia, Tales of the Golden Talon. 2004. (Illus.). 308p. (YA). per. 19.95 (978-0-9742460-3-1(4)) Timtu Ink.

Anton, Robert Wayne & Anton, Madeline Marie. A Portal in the Storm: Dragonia, Tales of the Golden Talon. 2004. (Illus.). 350p. (YA). per. 19.95 (978-0-9742460-1-7(8)) Timtu Ink.

Anzai, Nobuyuki. Flame of Recca, Vol. 14. Anzai, Nobuyuki, illus. 2005. (Flame of Recca Ser.). 184p. (YA). pap. 9.99 (978-1-4215-0014-0(0)) Viz Media.

—Flame of Recca. (Flame of Recca Ser.). (YA). Vol. 15. 2005. (Illus.). 200p. pap. 9.99 (978-1-4215-0131-4(7)); Vol. 16. 2006. 208p. pap. 9.99 (978-1-4215-0250-2(X)); Vol. 17. 2006. 208p. pap. 9.99 (978-1-4215-0381-3(6)); Vol. 18. 2006. 208p. pap. 9.99 (978-1-4215-0454-4(5)); Vol. 19. 2006. 208p. pap. 9.99 (978-1-4215-0455-1(3)) Viz Media.

Applegate, Katherine. The Absolute. 2001. (Animorphs Ser.: No. 51). (Illus.). (J). (978-0-606-21582-4(4)) Tandem Library Bks.

—Animorphs Boxed Set: The Undergound; The Decision; The Departure; The Discovery, No. 5. 2001. (Animorphs Ser.). (J). (gr. 3-7). 19.96 (978-0-590-28497-4(5) , Scholastic Paperbacks) Scholastic, Inc.

—The Answer. 2001. (Animorphs Ser.: No. 53). (Illus.). (J). 11.64 (978-0-606-21035-5(0)) Tandem Library Bks.

—The Beginning. 2001. (Animorphs Ser.: No. 54). (Illus.). (J). 11.64 (978-0-606-21036-2(9)) Tandem Library Bks.

—Destination Unknown. 2001. (Remnant Ser.: No. 2). (Illus.). (J). 11.64 (978-0-606-21399-8(6)) Tandem Library Bks.

—The Diversion. 2001. (Animorphs Ser.: No. 49). 160p. (J). (gr. 9). pap. 4.99 (978-0-439-11523-0(X)) Scholastic, Inc.

—The Diversion. 2000. (Animorphs Ser.: No. 49). (J). (gr. 3-7). (978-0-606-19532-4(7)) Tandem Library Bks.

—Elfangor's Secret. 1999. (Animorphs Ser.: No. 3). (J). (gr. 3-7). 12.64 (978-0-606-16619-5(X)) Tandem Library Bks.

—The Mayflower Project. 2001. (Remnant Ser.: No. 1). (Illus.). (J). (978-0-606-21398-1(8)) Tandem Library Bks.

—The Return. 2000. (Animorphs Ser.: No. 48). (Illus.). 160p. (J). (gr. 3-7). pap. 4.99 (978-0-439-11522-3(1)) Scholastic, Inc.

—The Return. 2000. (Animorphs Ser.: No. 48). (J). (gr. 3-7). (978-0-606-19531-7(9)) Tandem Library Bks.

—The Sacrifice. 2001. (Animorphs Ser.: No. 52). (Illus.). (J). (978-0-606-21034-8(2)) Tandem Library Bks.

—Survival. 2003. (Remnants Ser.: No. 13). (gr. 3-6). lib. bdg. 13.00 (978-0-613-66387-8(X)) Tandem Library Bks.

—The Threat. 1998. (Animorphs Ser.: No. 21). 158p. (J). (gr. 3-7). pap. 4.99 (978-0-590-76254-0(0) , Scholastic Paperbacks) Scholastic, Inc.

—The Ultimate. 2000. (Animorphs Ser.: No. 50). (J). (gr. 3-7). (978-0-606-19910-0(1)) Tandem Library Bks.

Appleton, Victor. Tom Swift & His Electric Rifle. 2004. (J). 21.95 (978-0-8488-2725-0(2)) Amereon LTD.

Aranha, Marc. The Queen of Spiders. 2003. 210p. pap. 14.95 (978-0-595-29275-2(5)) iUniverse, Inc.

Arbuthnott, Gill. The Chaos Clock. 2003. (Kelpies Ser.). 160p. pap. 10.00 (978-0-86315-422-5(0)) Floris Bks. GBR. *Dist:* SteinerBooks, Inc.

Arengo, Sue. The Fisherman & His Wife: Beginner Level 2. 2001. (Illus.). 24p. (J). 5.50 (978-0-19-422057-6(5)) Oxford Univ. Pr., Inc.

Arevalo, Luis Paquime. Juan & the Magic Shoes. 2005. (J). per. 3.99 (978-0-9748598-1-1(8)) L. A. Eng Bks.

Argiento, Cindy. Doris in Dreamland. 2007. pap. 8.00 (***978-0-8059-7461-4(X))*** Dorrance Publishing Co., Inc.

Armentrout, James & Macon, Steven, eds. Alien Alerts Journal Winter 2003, 2004. (Illus.). 64p. pap. 5.00 (978-1-57688-038-8(9) , 80389, Otherworlds Sci-Fi) Branch & Vine Pubs., LLC.

Armson, Michelle. A Pair of Snaphaunce Locks. 2002. 114p. pap. 9.95 (978-0-595-24641-0(9) , Writers Club Pr.) iUniverse, Inc.

Arraras, Maria Celeste. Dogs. 2007. 32p. (J). pap. 16.99 (***978-0-545-01912-5(5))*** Scholastic, Inc.

Arthur, Anne. The Pigeon with the Sticky Stuck Neck. Liebman, Simean, illus. 2004. (J). per. 7.99 (978-0-9753320-0-9(7)) Riverbank Publishing.

Artifact Group. The Mighty Egg Sitters. 2008. (Backyardigans Ser.). 24p. (J). pap. 3.99 (***978-1-4169-5039-4(7)*** , Simon Spotlight/Nickelodeon) Simon & Schuster Children's Publishing.

Arvidson, Douglas N. The Eye of the Stallion Bk. 1: The Face in Amber. 2006. 237p. (YA). pap. 14.95 (978-1-890109-81-3(9) , Cross Time) Crossquarter Publishing Group.

Asamiya, Kia. Silent Mobius, Vol. 8. Asamiya, Kia, illus. 2002. (Silent Mobius Ser.: Vol. 8). (Illus.). 192p. (YA). pap. 15.95 (978-1-56931-743-3(7)) Viz Media.

Asano, Rin. Tengai-Retrogical, Vol. 1. 2004. (Illus.). 184p. (YA). pap. (978-1-4139-0208-2(1)) ADV Manga.

Asare, Meshack. L' Appel de Sosu (Sosu's Call) Keita, Fatou, tr. 2003. (Illus.). 37p. pap. (978-9988-550-48-6(0)) Sub-Saharan Pubs. & Traders.

Ashe, Gregory. The Imagineer (Fire Eye Edition) A Book of Miracles. Whittaker, Kay, illus. 3rd ed. 2005. 198p. pap. (978-1-905532-01-8(6) , Whitenoise) Humdrumming, Ltd.

—The Imagineer (Snow Scene Edition) A Book of Miracles. Whittaker, Kay, illus. 2nd ed. 2005. 198p. (YA). pap. (978-1-905532-00-1(8) , Whitenoise) Humdrumming, Ltd.

Ashworth, Sherry. Dream Travellers. 2004. 336p. (YA). pap. 9.99 (978-0-689-83756-2(9)) Simon & Schuster, Ltd. GBR. *Dist:* Independent Pubs. Group.

Askegren, Pierce. Afterimage. 2006. (Buffy the Vampire Slayer Ser.). 272p. (YA). pap. 6.99 (978-1-4169-1181-4(2) , Simon Spotlight Entertainment) Simon & Schuster.

Askounis, Christina. The Dream of the Stone. 2007. 304p. (YA). 17.99 (978-1-4169-3568-1(1) , Atheneum); pap. 8.99 (978-1-4169-1187-6(1)) Simon & Schuster Children's Publishing.

Asprin, Robert. M. Y. T. H. Inc. Link. 2006. 176p. (gr. 12). mass mkt. 6.99 (978-0-441-01449-1(6) , Ace Bks.) Penguin Group (USA) Inc.

—Myth-ing Persons. 2002. (gr. 7-12). lib. bdg. 16.45 (978-0-613-57628-4(4)) Tandem Library Bks.

Atkins, Darrin E. Cooked Chickens Falling from the Sky: And Other Illustrated Children's Stories. Durr, Michael, illus. 2002. 148p. (J). pap. 11.95 (978-0-595-21988-9(8) , Writers Club Pr.) iUniverse, Inc.

Atkinson, Robert. Daddy Monster Eats (Around) the World! Atkinson, Robert, illus. 2001. (J). spiral bd. 16.95 (978-0-9717868-5-1(2)) WordWright.biz, Inc.

—Daddy Monster Tells the Tale of the Teddy Bear. Atkinson, Robert, illus. 2001. (J). spiral bd. 16.95 (978-0-9717868-6-8(0)) WordWright.biz, Inc.

Atnip, Linda. Miranda's Magic Garden. 2004. cd-rom 15.98 (978-1-885394-25-5(X)) Amber Lotus Publishing.

—Miranda's Magic Garden. Rothan, Ann, illus. 2004. 32p. (ps-7). 19.95 (978-1-885394-21-7(7)) Amber Lotus Publishing.

E F G

Atwater-Rhodes, Amelia. Falcondance. 2005. 192p. (YA). (gr. 7-12). lib. bdg. 16.99 (978-0-385-90334-9(0), Delacorte Bks. for Young Readers) Random Hse. Children's Bks.

—Falcondance Vol. III: The Kiesha'ra. 2007. 208p. (YA). (gr. 7). pap. 7.99 (978-0-440-23885-0(4), Delacorte Bks. for Young Readers) Random Hse. Children's Bks.

—Falcondance Vol. 3: The Kiesha'ra. 2005. 192p. (YA). (gr. 7-12). 14.95 (978-0-385-73194-2(9), Delacorte Bks. for Young Readers) Random Hse. Children's Bks.

—Hawksong. l.t. ed. 2005. 248p. 21.95 (978-0-7862-7179-5(5)) Thorndike Pr.

—Snakecharm. 2006. 176p. (YA). (gr. 7-11). mass mkt. 5.99 (978-0-440-23804-1(8), Laurel Leaf) Random Hse. Children's Bks.

—Snakecharm Vol. 2: The Kiesha'ra. 176p. (YA). (gr. 7). 2007. pap. 7.99 (978-0-385-73493-6(X)); 2004. (Illus.). 14.95 (978-0-385-73072-3(1)) Random Hse. Children's Bks. (Delacorte Bks. for Young Readers).

—Wolfcry. 2008. 208p. (YA). (gr. 9). pap. 7.99 (***978-0-440-23886-7(2)***, Delacorte Bks. for Young Readers) Random Hse. Children's Bks.

—Wolfcry Vol. 4: The Kiesha'ra. 2006. (Illus.). 208p. (YA). (gr. 7). 14.95 (978-0-385-73195-9(7)); lib. bdg. 16.99 (978-0-385-90354-7(5)) Random Hse. Children's Bks. (Delacorte Bks. for Young Readers).

Atwater-Rhodes, Amelia. Wyvernhail Vol. 5: The Kiesha'ra. 2007. (Kiesha'ra Ser.: Vol. 5). 192p. (YA). (gr. 7 up). 14.99 (***978-0-385-73436-3(0)***); lib. bdg. 17.99 (***978-0-385-90442-1(8)***) Random Hse. Children's Bks. (Delacorte Bks. for Young Readers).

Auerbach, Annie. Fiona's Fairy-Tale Five. 2007. (Shrek the Third Ser.). 24p. (J). pap. 3.99 (978-0-06-122862-9(1), Harper Entertainment) HarperCollins Pubs.

—Royally Wrong. 2007. (Shrek 3 Ser.). 24p. (J). pap. 3.99 (978-0-06-122861-2(3), Harper Entertainment) HarperCollins Pubs.

Augarde, Steve. The Various. 2005. 448p. (J). (gr. 5). reprint ed. 6.99 (978-0-440-42029-3(6), Yearling) Random Hse. Children's Bks.

Auger, Dale. Mwakwa Talks to the Loon: A Cree Story for Children. 2007. (Illus.). 32p. (J). pap. 9.95 (***978-1-894974-32-5(8)***) Heritage Hse. Publishing Co., Ltd. CAN. *Dist:* Midpoint Trade Bks., Inc.

Augustin, Lucus. Traeh: The Portal. 2007. 208p. per. 14.95 (***978-0-595-45890-5(4)***) iUniverse, Inc.

Avery, Fiona & Brooks, Mark. Arana: The Heart of the Spider. 2005. (Spider-Man Ser.). (Illus.). 144p. pap. 7.99 (978-0-7851-1506-9(4)) Marvel Enterprises, Inc.

Avi. Avi Mid Grade 2. 2008. 208p. (J). 16.99 (***978-0-06-000015-8(5)***); lib. bdg. 17.89 (***978-0-06-000016-5(3)***) HarperCollins Pubs.

—The Book Without Words: A Fable of Medieval Magic. 2005. 208p. (gr. 5-9). 15.99 (978-0-7868-0829-8(2)) Hyperion Bks. for Children.

—City of Light, City of Dark. Floca, Brian, illus. 2004. (Comic-Book Ser.). 192p. (J). (ps up). pap. 8.99 (978-0-531-07058-1(1), Orchard Bks.) Scholastic, Inc.

—Lord Kirkle's Money, 2. 1998. (Beyond the Western Sea Ser.). (J). (978-0-606-13200-8(7)) Tandem Library Bks.

—Perloo the Bold. Reed, Marcy, illus. 1999. 240p. (J). (gr. 3-7). pap. 4.99 (978-0-590-11003-7(9), Scholastic Paperbacks) Scholastic, Inc.

—Poppy's Return. Floca, Brian, illus. (Poppy Stories Ser.). (J). 2006. 256p. pap. 5.99 (978-0-06-000014-1(7), Harper Trophy); 2005. 240p. 15.99 (978-0-06-000012-7(0)); 2005. 240p. lib. bdg. 16.89 (978-0-06-000013-4(9)) HarperCollins Pubs.

AWRP Meet Superkids. (J). pap., stu. ed. (978-0-201-21600-4(0)) Addison-Wesley Longman, Inc.

Ayamine, Rando, illus. Getbackers, Vol. 8. 8th rev. ed. 2005. (JPN & ENG.). 200p. pap. 9.99 (978-1-59182-970-6(4), Tokyopop Adult) TOKYOPOP, Inc.

Ayers, Linda. The Time Bridge Travelers, 3 bks., Bk. 1. Ayers, Ryan, illus. 56p. (J). 2006. 13.95 (978-0-9760505-8-2(7)); 2004. per. 7.95 (978-0-9760505-0-6(1)) Blue Thistle Pr.

—The Time Bridge Travelers & the Mysterious Map, 3 bks., Bk. 2. Ayers, Ryan, illus. l.t. ed. (Time Bridge Travelers Ser.: 2). 80p. (J). 2006. 13.95 (978-0-9760505-6-8(0)); 2005. per. 7.95 (978-0-9760505-3-7(6)) Blue Thistle Pr.

Azuma, Kiyohiko. Azumanga Daioh, Vol. 3. 2004. (Illus.). 172p. (YA). pap. 9.99 (978-1-4139-0030-9(5)) ADV Manga.

—Azumanga Daioh: The Manga, Vol. 2. 2003. (Illus.). 168p. (YA). pap. (978-1-4139-0023-1(2)) ADV Manga.

Babbitt, Natalie. The Search for Delicious. 167p. (J). pap. 3.95 (978-0-8072-1481-7(7), Listening Library) Random Hse. Audio Publishing Group.

—The Search for Delicious. 2007. (Illus.). 176p. (J). pap. 6.99 (***978-0-312-36982-8(4)***) Square Fish.

Babbitt, Natalie. Tuck Everlasting. l.t. ed. 2003. 248p. (J). 16.95 (978-0-7540-7847-0(7), Galaxy Children's Large Print) BBC Audiobooks America.

—Tuck Everlasting. Babbitt, Natalie, illus. 2002. (Illus.). (J). 14.43 (978-0-7587-6382-2(4)) Book Wholesalers, Inc.

—Tuck Everlasting. 139p. (J). (gr. 4-6). pap. 4.95 (978-0-8072-1385-8(3), Listening Library) Random Hse. Audio Publishing Group.

—Tuck Everlasting. 2003. 152p. (J). 25.95 (978-0-7862-5181-0(6)) Thorndike Pr.

Baca, Ana. Benito's Bizcochitos. Castilla, Julia Mercedes, tr. Accardo, Anthony, illus. 1999. Tr. of Bizcochitos de Benito. (ENG & SPA.). 32p. (J). (ps-3). 14.95 (978-1-55885-264-8(6), Piñata Books) Arte Publico Pr.

Badalian, Lucy. George the Dragonslayer & His Friends: On Earth. Badalian, Lucy, illus. 2003. (Illus.). 312p. (YA). per. 18.95 (978-0-9725344-0-6(7), 9725344) Millennium Workshop Production.

Bailey, Helen. Takes a Break. 2007. (Topaz Ser.: Vol. 4). (Illus.). 144p. pap. 7.95 (***978-0-340-91733-6(4)***) Hodder Children's Division GBR. *Dist:* Independent Pubs. Group.

Bailey, J. L. Children's Gate. 2005. 292p. 21.95 (978-1-58939-814-6(9)) Virtualbookworm.com Publishing, Inc.

Bailey, Len. Clabbernappers. 2005. (Illus.). 224p. (J). 17.95 (978-0-7653-0981-5(5), Tor Bks.) Doherty, Tom Assocs., LLC.

Bailey-Peiffer, Stefanie & Bailey-Yarbrough, Caroline. Modie & the Power of the BellKeys. 2004. pap. 8.95 (978-0-9762502-0-3(9)) Hudson Bks.

Baird, Alison. The Warding of Willowmere. 2005. 224p. (YA). pap. 15.00 (978-0-14-301529-1(X), Penguin Global) Penguin Group (USA) Inc.

Baker, E. D. Dragon's Breath. 2005. (Tales of the Frog Princess Ser.: Bk. 2). (Illus.). 304p. (J). (gr. 3-7). reprint ed. pap. 6.95 (978-1-58234-666-3(6), Bloomsbury Children) Bloomsbury Publishing.

Baker, Jennifer. Jack Frost Digest. 1998. (Illus.). 128p. (gr. 3-7). pap. 3.99 (978-0-590-63983-5(8)) Scholastic, Inc.

Balch, Betty Neff & Poythress, Jean Hill. Tales of the Cinnamon Dragon Book I: Adventures in Farr Elvenhome. Balch, Betty Neff, illus. 2004. (Illus.). 152p. (J). lib. bdg. 16.95 (978-1-930580-46-6(0), Luminary Media Group) Pine Orchard, Inc.

Baldry, Cherith. The Emerald Throne. Wyatt, David, illus. 2003. (J). 144p. 15.95 (978-1-59034-584-9(3)); 141p. pap. (978-1-59034-585-6(1)) Mondo Publishing.

—The Lake of Darkness. Wyatt, David, illus. 2004. 144p. (J). 15.95 (978-1-59034-586-3(X)); pap. (978-1-59034-587-0(8)) Mondo Publishing.

—The Silver Horn. 2002. (Eaglesmount Ser.). (Illus.). 132p. (J). (gr. 3-6). 15.95 (978-1-59034-475-0(8)) Mondo Publishing.

—The Silver Horn. Wyatt, David, illus. 2002. 141p. (J). pap. 15.95 (978-1-59034-490-3(1)) Mondo Publishing.

Baldwin, James. The Story of Siegfried. 2005. 256p. pap. 13.95 (978-1-4218-1152-9(9), 1st World Library - Literary Society) 1st World Publishing, Inc.

—The Story of Siegfried. 2006. 224p. (J). (gr. 4). pap. 9.95 (978-0-486-44574-8(7)) Dover Pubns., Inc.

—The Story of Siegfried. 2004. reprint ed. pap. 22.95 (978-1-4191-8401-7(6)); pap. 1.99 (978-1-4192-8401-4(0)) Kessinger Publishing, LLC.

Baldwin, Stephen. Spirit Warriors: A Graphic Novel. 2006. Vol. 1. (Illus.). 208p. (YA). pap. 9.99 (978-0-8054-4357-8(6)) B&H Publishing Grp.

—Spirit Warriors: Number Three. Simko, Joe et al, illus. 2007. 208p. (YA). pap. 9.99 (978-0-8054-4356-1(8)) B&H Publishing Grp.

Ballesta, Juan. Tommy y el Elefante. (SPA., Illus.). 28p. (J). (gr. k-3). (978-84-264-3578-1(5), LM1605) Editorial Lumen ESP. *Dist:* Lectorum Pubns., Inc.

Banerjee, Anjali. The Silver Spell. Fiegenshuh, Emily, illus. 2005. (Knights of the Silver Dragon Ser.: Bk. 8). 174p. (J). (***978-1-4156-1645-1(0)***, Mirrorstone) Wizards of the Coast.

Banks, Lynne Reid. The Fairy Rebel. 2004. (Illus.). 128p. (gr. 4-7). 5.50 (978-0-440-41925-9(5), Yearling) Random Hse. Children's Bks.

—The Fairy Rebel. Geldart, William, illus. 2003. 128p. (gr. 4-7). reprint ed. 15.95 (978-0-385-73076-1(4), Delacorte Bks. for Young Readers) Random Hse. Children's Bks.

—The Farthest-Away Mountain. 2004. 160p. (gr. 4-7). pap. 4.99 (978-0-440-41926-6(3), Yearling) Random Hse. Children's Bks.

—I, Houdini: The Amazing Story of an Escape-Artist Hamster. 127p. (J). (gr. 4-5). pap. 4.99 (978-0-8072-1493-0(0), Listening Library) Random Hse. Audio Publishing Group.

—The Indian in the Cupboard. 1999. (Indian in the Cupboard Ser.: No. 1). (J). (gr. 4-7). pap. 4.95 (978-5-553-81211-9(9)) HarperCollins Pubs.

—The Indian in the Cupboard. 181p. (J). (Indian in the Cupboard Ser.: No. 1). (gr. 4-7). pap. 4.99 (978-0-8072-1433-6(7)); 2004. (Indian in the Cupboard Ser.). (gr. 3-7). pap. 36.00 incl. audio (978-0-8072-7308-1(2), YA809SP) Random Hse. Audio Publishing Group. (Listening Library).

—The Key to the Indian. Watling, James, illus. 1999. (Indian in the Cupboard Ser.: No. 5). 288p. (J). (gr. 4 up). pap. 6.99 (978-0-380-80373-6(9)) HarperCollins Pubs.

—The Key to the Indian. 1998. (Indian in the Cupboard Ser.: No. 5). 240p. (J). (gr. 4-7). 16.00 (978-0-380-97717-8(6)) HarperCollins Pubs.

—The Key to the Indian. (Indian in the Cupboard Ser.: No. 5). 240p. (J). (gr. 4-7). pap. 4.99 (978-0-8072-1551-7(1), Listening Library) Random Hse. Audio Publishing Group.

—The Return of the Indian. (Indian in the Cupboard Ser.: No. 2). 189p. (J). (gr. 4-7). pap. 4.99 (978-0-8072-1434-3(5), Listening Library) Random Hse. Audio Publishing Group.

Banks, Sara Harrell. Under the Shadow of Wings. 1999. (978-0-606-16296-8(8)) Tandem Library Bks.

Banner, Catherine. The Eyes of a King. 2008. 480p. (J). lib. bdg. 19.99 (***978-0-375-93875-7(3)***); (gr. 7-11). 16.99 (***978-0-375-83875-0(9)***) Random Hse. Children's Bks. (Random Hse. Bks. for Young Readers).

Banyai, Istvan. Zoom. 1998. (J). (978-0-606-13944-1(3)) Tandem Library Bks.

Barbie of Swan Lake. 10p. 9.98 (978-0-7853-9372-6(2)) Publications International, Ltd.

Barbot, Daniel. El Auto del Sr. Pulga. Mas, Maribel, illus. 2004. (SPA.). 28p. (J). pap. 6.99 (978-980-257-260-1(8)) Ekare, Ediciones VEN. *Dist:* Lectorum Pubns., Inc.

BareBones Publishing. The Legend of CaseyRock. 2007. (Illus.). 40p. (J). per. 12.00 (***978-0-9779601-2-5(9)***) BareBones Publishing.

Barker, Cicely Mary. How to Find Flower Fairies. 2007. (Flower Fairies Ser.). 24p. (J). (gr. 2). 19.99 (***978-0-7232-5890-2(2)***, Warne) Penguin Group (USA) Inc.

—Willow's Underwater World. 2008. (Flower Fairies Ser.). 80p. 3.99 (***978-0-7232-5952-7(6)***, Warne) Penguin Group (USA) Inc.

Barker, Cicely Mary & Swain-Smith, Justine. Return to Fairyopolis. 2008. 24p. (J). (gr. k). 19.99 (***978-0-7232-5996-1(8)***, Warne) Penguin Group (USA) Inc.

Barker, Clive. Abarat. 119.90 (978-0-06-056894-8(1)) HarperCollins Pubs.

—Abarat. Barker, Clive, illus. (Abarat Ser.). (Illus.). (J). 2002. 432p. 24.99 (978-0-06-028092-5(1), Cotler, Joanna Books); 2002. 432p. lib. bdg. 26.89 (978-0-06-051084-8(6), Cotler, Joanna Books); 2004. 496p. reprint ed. pap. 6.99 (978-0-06-059637-8(6)) HarperCollins Pubs.

—Abarat. 2002. (gr. 7-12). lib. bdg. 21.10 (978-0-613-68396-8(X)) Tandem Library Bks.

—Days of Magic, Nights of War. Barker, Clive, illus. (Abarat Ser.). 512p. (J). 2005. pap. 11.99 (978-0-06-440932-2(5), Harper Trophy); 2004. (Illus.). 24.99 (978-0-06-029170-9(2), Cotler, Joanna Books) HarperCollins Pubs.

—The Thief of Always. 2002. 224p. (J). (gr. 5 up). reprint ed. pap. 5.99 (978-0-06-440994-0(5), Harper Trophy) HarperCollins Pubs.

Barker, Laraine Anne. Lord of Obsidian: Quest for Earthlight Trilogy. 2004. (Quest for Earthlight Trilogy: 2). 184p. (YA). pap. 10.95 (978-0-7599-0502-3(9)) Hard Shell Word Factory.

Barker, M. A. R. Prince of Skulls. 2002. (Illus.). 204p. (YA). per. 19.95 (978-0-9725880-0-3(0), 1) Zottola Publishing, Inc.

Barkow, Henriette. Buri & the Marrow. Finlay, Lizzie, illus. 2004. (ENG & URD.). 24p. (J). pap. (978-1-85269-592-7(7)); pap. (978-1-85269-705-1(9)) Mantra Publishing, Ltd.

—Pandora's Box: A Greek Myth. Mayo, Diana, illus. 2004. 32p. (J). (TAM, CZE, VIE, SPA & GUJ.). (978-1-85269-809-6(8)); (TAM, CZE, VIE, SPA & GUJ.). (978-1-85269-814-0(4)); (TAM, CZE, VIE, SPA & GUJ.). (978-1-85269-819-5(5)); (TAM, CZE, VIE, SPA & GUJ.). (978-1-85269-824-9(1)); (TAM, CZE, VIE, SPA & GUJ.). (978-1-85269-829-4(2)); (TAM, CZE, VIE, SPA & GUJ.). (978-1-85269-834-8(9)); (TAM, CZE, VIE, SPA & GUJ.). (978-1-85269-839-3(X)); (TAM, CZE, VIE, SPA & GUJ.). (978-1-85269-844-7(6)); (TAM, CZE, VIE, SPA & GUJ.). (978-1-85269-849-2(7)); (TAM, CZE, VIE, SPA & GUJ.). (978-1-85269-854-6(3)); (TAM, CZE, VIE, SPA & GUJ.). (978-1-85269-859-1(4)); (TAM, CZE, VIE, SPA & GUJ.). (978-1-85269-864-5(0)); (TAM, CZE, VIE, SPA & GUJ.). (978-1-85269-869-0(1)); (TAM, CZE, VIE, SPA & GUJ.). (978-1-85269-874-4(8)); (TAM, CZE, VIE, SPA & GUJ.). (978-1-85269-879-9(9)); (CZE, TAM, VIE, SPA & GUJ.). (978-1-85269-884-3(5)); (TAM, CZE, VIE, SPA & GUJ.). (978-1-85269-889-8(6)); (TAM, CZE, VIE, SPA & GUJ.). (978-1-85269-893-5(4)); (TAM, CZE, VIE, SPA & GUJ.). (978-1-85269-894-2(2)); (TAM, CZE, VIE, SPA & GUJ.). (978-1-85269-898-0(5)); (TAM, CZE, SPA, VIE & GUJ.). (978-1-85269-899-7(3)) Mantra Publishing, Ltd.

Barkow, Henriette & Reed, Nathan, illus. The Buskers of Bremen: Les Chanteurs de Rues de Bremen. 2004. (TAM, CZE, VIE, SPA & GUJ.). 24p. (J). pap. (978-1-85269-769-3(5)) Mantra Publishing, Ltd.

Barlow, Dave. The Forgotten Armory. 2002. (Illus.). 12p. 8.99 (978-0-9725230-1-1(4)) Wandering Sage Bookstore & More, LLC.

Barlow, Steve & Skidmore, Steve. Stone Me! Ross, Tony, illus. 2005. (Mad Myths Ser.). 122p. (J). pap. 5.95 (978-1-903015-43-8(X)) Barn Owl Bks, London GBR. *Dist:* Independent Pubs. Group.

—Tales of Dark Forest Trilogy. 3rd ed. 2003. (Tales of the Dark Forest Ser.). (Illus.). 192p. (J). pap. 10.99 (978-0-00-710865-7(6)) HarperCollins Pubs. Ltd. GBR. *Dist:* Independent Pubs. Group.

—Whizzard. 2002. (Tales of the Dark Forest Ser.). (Illus.). 256p. pap. 11.00 (978-0-00-710864-0(8)) HarperCollins Pubs. Ltd. GBR. *Dist:* Independent Pubs. Group.

Barnes, Susan. Kelly Karate: Encounters the Moon Princess. 2001. 160p. (J). (gr. 4-8). pap. 10.50 (978-0-9705777-2-6(9)) McBook Pubs., LLC.

Barnett, Gary W. Princess of the Lights: Fantasy Adventure. 2007. 324p. 29.95 (***978-0-595-68957-6(4)***); per. 19.95 (***978-0-595-44705-3(8)***) iUniverse, Inc.

Barrera, F. M. Tales of the Blue Wizard: The Children of Jamomere. Barrera, F. M., illus. 2005. (Illus.). 180p. (YA). (gr. 4-9). per. 12.95 (978-0-9670848-1-7(4)) Talisman Pr.

Barrera, J. Mario. Nine Moons. 2005. (ENG & SPA., Illus.). (YA). cd-rom 21.99 (978-0-9752725-2-7(7)) Orion-Cosmos.

Barrie, J. M. Peter Pan. Davis, Allen, illus. 2002. (Great Illustrated Classics Ser.). 240p. (J). (gr. 3-8). 21.35 (978-1-57765-820-7(5), ABDO & Daughters) ABDO Publishing Co.

—Peter Pan. (SPA.). 191p. 15.95 (978-84-206-3689-4(4)) Alianza Editorial, S. A. ESP. *Dist:* Distribooks, Inc.

—Peter Pan. Vess, Charles, illus. rev. ed. 2003. 224p. (J). 15.95 (978-0-7653-0809-2(6), Starscape) Doherty, Tom Assocs., LLC.

—Peter Pan. 2000. (Charming Classics). 240p. (J). (gr. 4-7). pap. 6.99 (978-0-694-01318-0(8), Harper Festival) HarperCollins Pubs.

—Peter Pan. (J). pap. (978-0-340-71498-0(0), Hodder & Stoughton) Hodder General Publishing Division.

—Peter Pan. 2006. (Scholastic Classics Ser.). (Illus.). v, 140p. (J). (gr. 9-12). 25.00 (978-0-531-16993-3(6), Watts, Franklin) Scholastic Library Publishing.

—Peter Pan. 2003. (Aladdin Classics Ser.). 256p. (J). (gr. 3-7). pap. 4.99 (978-0-689-86691-3(7), Aladdin) Simon & Schuster Children's Publishing.

—Peter Pan. 2000. (Illus.). 134p. (J). 24.95 (978-1-58479-029-7(6)) Stewart, Tabori & Chang.

—Peter Pan. 2003. (gr. 3-6). lib. bdg. 14.15 (978-0-613-85653-9(8)) Tandem Library Bks.

—Peter Pan: Peter & Wendy & Peter Pan in Kensington Gardens. 2004. (Illus.). 272p. (gr. 12). pap. 9.00 (978-0-14-243793-3(X), Penguin Classics) Penguin Group (USA) Inc.

—Peter Pan: The Original Story. 2003. (gr. 3-6). lib. bdg. 13.00 (978-0-613-71839-4(9)) Tandem Library Bks.

—Peter Pan: The Original Tale of Neverland. Jaramillo, Raquel, illus. Jaramillo, Raquel, photos by. unabr. ed. 2003. 135p. (YA). (gr. 5-8). reprint ed. 25.00 (978-0-7567-6883-6(7)) DIANE Publishing Co.

—Peter Pan & Other Plays: The Admirable Crichton; Peter Pan; When Wendy Grew Up; What Every Woman Knows; Mary Rose. Hollindale, Peter, ed. 1999. (Oxford World's Classics Ser.). (Illus.). 384p. 14.95 (978-0-19-283919-0(5)) Oxford Univ. Pr., Inc.

—Peter Pan & Other Plays Vol. 10: The Admirable Crichton; Peter Pan; When Wendy Grew Up; What Every Woman Knows; Mary Rose. (J). reprint ed. 57.50 (978-0-404-08790-6(6)) AMS Pr., Inc.

—Peter Pan & Wendy. Foreman, Michael, illus. 1999. (Abbeville Classics Ser.). 176p. (J). 12.95 (978-0-7892-0560-5(2)); pap. 7.95 (978-0-7892-0550-6(5)) Abbeville Pr., Inc. (Abbeville Kids).

—Peter Pan & Wendy. Foreman, Michael, illus. 2000. 176p. (J). pap. 8.99 (978-1-85793-909-5(3), Pavilion Bks., Ltd.) Anova Bks. GBR. *Dist:* Trafalgar Square Publishing.

—Peter Pan & Wendy. Foreman, Michael, illus. 2003. (Chrysalis Children's Classics Ser.). 176p. (YA). pap. (978-1-84365-039-3(8)) Chrysalis Children's Bks.

—Peter Pan & Wendy. Carruth, Jane, ed. Johnstone, Anne G., illus. 2000. 92p. (J). (gr. 4-6). reprint ed. 25.00 (978-0-7881-9230-2(2)) DIANE Publishing Co.

—Peter Pan & Wendy. 2004. (Illus.). 96p. (J). 9.99 (978-0-517-22366-6(X), Gramercy) Random Hse. Value Publishing.

—Peter Pan & Wendy: Centenary Edition. Ingpen, Robert R., illus. 2004. 216p. (J). (978-1-897035-12-2(8), Blue Heron Bks.) Raincoast Bk. Distribution.

—Peter Pan in Kensington Gardens. (J). 18.95 (978-0-8488-0427-5(9)) Amereon LTD.

—Peter Pan in Kensington Gardens. 2006. pap. (***978-1-4065-0950-2(7)***) Dodo Pr.

—Peter Pan in Kensington Gardens & Peter & Wendy. Hollindale, Peter, ed. 1999. (Oxford World's Classics Ser.). (Illus.). 288p. 9.95 (978-0-19-283929-9(2)) Oxford Univ. Pr., Inc.

—The Story of Peter Pan. Woodward, Alice B., illus. unabr. ed. 1998. (Dover Children's Thrift Classics Ser.). 96p. (J). (gr. 3-6). reprint ed. pap. 1.50 (978-0-486-27294-8(X)) Dover Pubns., Inc.

Barrie, J. M., ed. Peter Pan: Juvenile Classic. 2004. (Great Classics for Children Ser.). (Illus.). 179p. (J). 5.99 (978-1-4037-0795-6(2)) Dalmatian Pr.

Barrie, J. M. & Hyman, Trina Schart. Peter Pan. 2001. (Scribner Illustrated Classics Ser.). (Illus.). 208p. (J). 27.00 (978-0-689-83078-5(5), Atheneum) Simon & Schuster Children's Publishing.

Barrie, J. M., et al. Peter Pan. 2000. (Illus.). 176p. (J). (gr. 4-7). 19.95 (978-0-8118-2297-8(4)) Chronicle Bks. LLC.

Barron, T. A. The Ancient One. 2003. 320p. (gr. 12). mass mkt. 6.99 (978-0-441-01032-5(6), Ace Bks.) Penguin Group (USA) Inc.

—Child of the Dark Prophecy. 2004. (Great Tree of Avalon Trilogy: Bk. 1). 432p. (YA). (gr. 5-6). 19.99 (978-0-399-23763-8(1), Philomel) Penguin Group (USA) Inc.

—The Eternal Flame. 2006. (Great Tree of Avalon Trilogy: Bk. 3). (Illus.). 400p. (YA). (gr. 5). 19.99 (978-0-399-24213-7(9), Philomel) Penguin Group (USA) Inc.

—The Fires of Merlin. (J). (gr. 5-7). 2007. (Lost Years of Merlin (Hardcover) Ser.). 261p. 10.99 (***978-0-399-25022-4(0)***); 1998. (Lost Years of Merlin Ser.: Vol. 3). (Illus.). 272p. 20.99 (978-0-399-23020-2(3)) Penguin Group (USA) Inc. (Philomel).

—The Fires of Merlin. 2000. (J). 13.64 (978-0-606-19239-2(5)) Tandem Library Bks.

—Fires of Merlin. (gr. 3-6). 2002. lib. bdg. 14.15 (978-0-613-89067-0(1)); 2000. lib. bdg. 15.30 (978-0-613-81176-7(3)) Tandem Library Bks.

—The Fires of Merlin Bk. 3. 2000. (Lost Years of Merlin Ser.: Vol. 3). (Illus.). 304p. (gr. 4-7). reprint ed. mass mkt. 6.99 (978-0-441-00713-4(9), Ace Bks.) Penguin Group (USA) Inc.

—Heartlight. 2003. 256p. (gr. 12). mass mkt. 6.99 (978-0-441-01036-3(9), Ace Bks.) Penguin Group (USA) Inc.

—Heartlight. 2003. (gr. 3-6). lib. bdg. 15.30 (978-0-613-83897-9(1)) Tandem Library Bks.

—Lost Years of Merlin. (gr. 3-6). 2002. lib. bdg. 14.15 (978-0-613-83896-2(3)); 1999. lib. bdg. 15.30 (978-0-613-23013-1(2)) Tandem Library Bks.

—The Lost Years of Merlin, Bk. 1. 1999. (Lost Years of Merlin Ser.). (Illus.). 304p. (gr. 4-7). reprint ed. mass mkt. 6.99 (978-0-441-00668-7(X), Ace Bks.) Penguin Group (USA) Inc.

—Mirror of Merlin. Wimmer, Mike, illus. 1999. (Lost Years of Merlin Ser.: Vol. 4). 256p. (J). (gr. 5-9). 19.99 (978-0-399-23455-2(1), Philomel) Penguin Group (USA) Inc.

—Mirror of Merlin. 2002. (gr. 3-6). lib. bdg. 14.15 (978-0-613-81728-8(1)); 2001. (gr. 5-8). lib. bdg. 15.30 (978-0-613-44404-0(3)) Tandem Library Bks.

—Seven Songs of Merlin. 2002. (gr. 7-12). lib. bdg. 14.15 (978-0-613-81177-4(1)); 2000. (978-0-606-17833-4(3)); 2000. (gr. 5-8). lib. bdg. 15.30 (978-0-613-28637-4(5)) Tandem Library Bks.

—The Seven Songs of Merlin. 2000. (Lost Years of Merlin Ser.: Vol. 2). (Illus.). 1p. (gr. 5-9). reprint ed. mass mkt. 6.99 (978-0-441-00701-1(5) , Ace Bks.) Penguin Group (USA) Inc.

—Shadows on the Stars. (Great Tree of Avalon Trilogy: Bk. 2). 2006. 384p. (gr. 12). mass mkt. 7.99 (978-0-441-01447-7(X) , Ace Bks.); 2005. (Illus.). 432p. (YA). (gr. 5 up). 19.99 (978-0-399-23764-5(X) , Philomel) Penguin Group (USA) Inc.

—Tree Girl. 2002. 144p. reprint ed. mass mkt. 6.99 (978-0-441-00994-7(8) , Ace Bks.) Penguin Group (USA) Inc.

—Tree Girl. 2002. (gr. 3-6). lib. bdg. 14.15 (978-0-613-81179-8(8)) Tandem Library Bks.

—Wings of Merlin. 2000. (Lost Years of Merlin Ser.: Vol. 5). (Illus.). 272p. (J). (gr. 6-9). 19.99 (978-0-399-23456-9(X) , Philomel) Penguin Group (USA) Inc.

—Wings of Merlin. (gr. 3-6). 2003. lib. bdg. 14.15 (978-0-613-81180-4(1)); 2002. lib. bdg. 15.30 (978-0-613-81178-1(X)) Tandem Library Bks.

Barthelme, Donald. The Slightly Irregular Fire Engine: Or, The Hithering, Thithering Djinn. 2006. (Illus.). 32p. (J). 19.95 (978-1-58567-828-0(7)) Overlook Pr., The.

Barwin, Gary. The Magic Mustache. Jorisch, Stephane, illus. 1999. 32p. (J). (ps-2). lib. bdg. 17.95 (978-1-55037-607-4(1)) Annick Pr., Ltd. CAN. *Dist:* Firefly Bks., Ltd.

Base, Graeme. Truckdogs: A Novel in Four Bites. (J). (gr. 3-7). 2005. 160p. pap. 7.95 (978-0-8109-8789-0(9)); 2004. (Illus.). 158p. 16.95 (978-0-8109-5031-3(6)) Abrams, Harry N. , Inc.

Bass, L. G. The Outlaws of Moonshadow Marsh No. 1, Bk.1: The Sign of Qin. 2004. (Illus.). 400p. (gr. 5-17). 17.99 (978-0-7868-1918-8(9)) Hyperion Bks. for Children.

—The Outlaws of Moonshadow Marsh the Sign of Qin, Bk. 1. 2006. 400p. (gr. 5-17). reprint ed. pap. 7.99 (978-0-7868-5566-7(5)) Hyperion Pr.

—Sign of the Qin. l.t. ed. 2004. 513p. 23.95 (978-0-7862-6772-9(0) , Large Print Pr.) Thorndike Pr.

Batchler, Darla. If I Were a Monkey. Parris, Kitty, illus. 2005. 24p. (J). bds. 12.95 (978-0-9746959-2-1(0)) Falcon Publishing LTD.

Bates, Martine. The Taker's Key, Vol. 3. 1998. (Praise for the Marmawell Ser.). 208p. (J). pap. 8.95 (978-0-88995-184-6(5)) Red Deer Pr. CAN. *Dist:* Fitzhenry & Whiteside, Ltd.

Bateson-Hill, Margaret. Chanda & the Mirror of Moonlight. Littlewood, Karin, illus. 2003. (Folk Tales Series Ser.). 32p. (J). (gr. 3-4). (978-1-84089-217-8(X) , Zero to Ten, Limited) Evans Publishing Group.

—Lao Lao of Dragon Mountain. Pelizzoli, Francesca, illus. 1998. (Folk Tales Series Ser.). 32p. (J). (ps-3). 14.95 (978-1-84089-035-8(5)); pap. 7.95 (978-1-84089-011-2(8)) Evans Publishing Group GBR. (Zero to Ten, Limited). *Dist:* Independent Pubs. Group.

—Masha & the Firebird. Wilson, Anne, illus. (Folk Tales Ser.). (RUS & ENG.). 32p. (J). 2005. pap. 7.99 (978-1-84089-201-7(3)); 2000. 17.95 (978-1-84089-134-8(3)) Evans Publishing Group GBR. (Zero to Ten, Limited). *Dist:* Independent Pubs. Group.

Bath, K. P. Escape from Castle Cant. 2006. (Illus.). 304p. (J). (gr. 3-7). 16.99 (978-0-316-10857-7(X)) Little Brown & Co.

—The Secret of Castle Cant. 2006. 304p. (J). (gr. 3-7). reprint ed. pap. 6.99 (978-0-316-05991-6(9)) Little Brown & Co.

Batory, Edward A. Bo's Paradise Lost. 2002. 223p. (J). pap. 14.95 (978-0-595-21857-8(1) , Writers Club Pr.) iUniverse, Inc.

Batson, Wayne Thomas. The Door Within. 2005. (Door Within Trilogy: Bk. 1). (Illus.). 320p. (J). 16.99 (978-1-4003-0659-6(0)) Nelson, Thomas Inc.

—The Door Within: The Door Within Trilogy - Book One. 2007. 336p. (J). pap. 9.99 (***978-1-4003-1011-1(3)***) Nelson, Thomas Inc.

—The Final Storm. 2006. (Door Within Trilogy: Bk. 3). (Illus.). 320p. (J). 16.99 (978-1-4003-0783-8(X)) Nelson, Thomas Inc.

Batson, Wayne Thomas. The Rise of the Wyrm Lord: The Door Within Trilogy - Book Two. 2007. 336p. (J). pap. 9.99 (***978-1-4003-1012-8(1)***) Nelson, Thomas Inc.

Baum, L. Frank. Dorothy & the Wizard in Oz. 2006. pap. 26.99 (***978-1-4219-7695-2(1)***) IndyPublish.com.

—Dorothy & the Wizard of Oz. 2004. (Twelve-Point Ser.). lib. bdg. 24.00 (978-1-58287-273-5(2)) North Bks.

—The Emerald City if Oz. 2005. 256p. pap. 13.95 (978-1-4218-0464-4(6) , 1st World Library - Literary Society) 1st World Publishing, Inc.

—The Emerald City of Oz. (Oz Ser.). (YA). (gr. 5-8). 21.95 (978-0-8488-0733-7(2)) Amereon LTD.

—The Emerald City of Oz. 2002. (Illus.). 294p. (J). per. (978-1-58726-023-0(9) , Mundus) Ann Arbor Media Group, LLC.

—The Emerald City of Oz. Neill, John R., illus. 2002. 296p. (YA). pap. 17.00 (978-0-7567-6271-1(5)) DIANE Publishing Co.

—The Emerald City of Oz. 2003. (Twelve-Point Ser.). lib. bdg. 24.00 (978-1-58287-254-4(6)) North Bks.

—The Enchanted Island of Yew. (Twelve-Point Ser.). 2003. (J). lib. bdg. 24.00 (978-1-58287-253-7(8)); 2004. 207p. 25.00 (978-1-58287-737-2(8)) North Bks.

—Glinda of Oz. rev. ed. 2006. 184p. 26.95 (978-1-4218-1786-6(1)); pap. 11.95 (978-1-4218-1886-3(8)) 1st World Publishing, Inc. (1st World Library - Literary Society).

—Glinda of Oz. (Oz Ser.). (YA). (gr. 5-8). 21.95 (978-0-8488-0784-9(7)) Amereon LTD.

—Glinda of Oz. 2002. (Illus.). 276p. (J). per. (978-1-58726-024-7(7) , Mundus) Ann Arbor Media Group, LLC.

—Glinda of Oz. Neill, John R., illus. 2000. (Oz Ser.). 288p. (J). (gr. 4-7). pap. 7.95 (978-0-486-41018-0(8)) Dover Pubns., Inc.

—Glinda of Oz. (Twelve-Point Ser.). 2003. lib. bdg. 24.00 (978-1-58287-256-8(2)); 2004. 210p. 25.00 (978-1-58287-740-2(8)) North Bks.

—The Land of Oz. 1999. (Oz Ser.). (Illus.). 320p. (YA). (gr. 5-8). reprint ed. 12.95 (978-1-56852-226-5(6) , Konecky & Konecky) Konecky, William S. Assocs., Inc.

—The Land of Oz. 2001. (Illus.). 288p. pap. 14.95 (978-0-7434-2399-1(2)) ibooks, Inc.

—The Lost Princess of Oz. 208p. 2005. 27.95 (978-1-4218-0647-1(9) , 1st World Library - Literary Society); 2004. per. 12.95 (978-1-59540-047-5(8)) 1st World Publishing, Inc.

—The Lost Princess of Oz. (Oz Ser.). (YA). (gr. 5-8). 22.95 (978-0-8488-0786-3(3)) Amereon LTD.

—The Lost Princess of Oz. 2002. (Illus.). 302p. (J). per. (978-1-58726-022-3(0) , Mundus) Ann Arbor Media Group, LLC.

—The Lost Princess of Oz. Neill, John R., illus. 2002. 312p. (J). (gr. 3-6). pap. 17.00 (978-0-7567-6273-5(1)) DIANE Publishing Co.

—The Lost Princess of Oz. Neill, John R., illus. unabr. ed. 1998. (Oz Ser.). 332p. (J). (gr. 4-7). pap. 9.95 (978-0-486-40344-1(0)) Dover Pubns., Inc.

—The Lost Princess of Oz. 2004. reprint ed. pap. 20.95 (978-1-4191-7079-9(1)); pap. 1.99 (978-1-4192-7079-6(6)) Kessinger Publishing, LLC.

—The Lost Princess of Oz. (Twelve-Point Ser.). 2003. lib. bdg. 24.00 (978-1-58287-255-1(4)); 2004. 241p. 25.00 (978-1-58287-739-6(4)) North Bks.

—The Magic of Oz. 184p. 2005. 26.95 (978-1-4218-0651-8(7)); 2004. pap. 11.95 (978-1-59540-101-4(6)) 1st World Publishing, Inc. (1st World Library - Literary Society).

—The Magic of Oz. 2004. (Twelve-Point Ser.). lib. bdg. 24.00 (978-1-58287-279-7(1)) North Bks.

—Magic of Oz. 2006. pap. 12.99 (***978-1-4280-2747-3(5)***) IndyPublish.com.

—The Magic of Oz. 2004. reprint ed. pap. 19.95 (978-1-4191-7118-5(6)); pap. 1.99 (978-1-4192-7118-2(0)) Kessinger Publishing, LLC.

—The Magic of Oz. l.t. ed. 2004. (Large Print Ser.). lib. bdg. 25.00 (978-1-58287-775-4(0)) North Bks.

—El Maravilloso Mago de Oz. (Oz Ser.). (SPA., Illus.). 160p. (YA). (gr. 5-8). 14.95 (978-84-7281-184-3(0) , AF1184) Auriga, Ediciones S.A. ESP. *Dist:* Continental Bk. Co., Inc.

—El Maravilloso Mago de Oz. 3rd ed. 2002. (Clover Ser.). (SPA., Illus.). 264p. (YA). 11.50 (978-84-392-8002-6(5) , EV3454) Lectorum Pubns., Inc.

—The Marvelous Land of Oz. 2004. 208p. per. 12.95 (978-1-59540-100-7(8)) 1st World Publishing, Inc.

—The Marvelous Land of Oz. Neill, John R., illus. 2001. (Books of Wonder). 320p. (J). (gr. 3 up). pap. 7.99 (978-0-06-440963-6(5) , Harper Trophy) HarperCollins Pubs.

—The Marvelous Land of Oz. 2004. reprint ed. pap. 21.95 (978-1-4191-7194-9(1)); pap. 1.99 (978-1-4192-7194-6(6)) Kessinger Publishing, LLC.

—The Marvelous Land of Oz. 2004. (Twelve-Point Ser.). lib. bdg. 24.00 (978-1-58287-272-8(4)); lib. bdg. 25.00 (978-1-58287-768-6(8)) North Bks.

—Master Key. 2006. 18.99 (***978-1-4280-2748-0(3)***) IndyPublish.com.

—The Master Key. 2004. reprint ed. pap. 15.95 (978-1-4191-7199-4(2)); pap. 1.99 (978-1-4192-7199-1(7)) Kessinger Publishing, LLC.

—Ozma of Oz. 2003. pap. 14.95 (978-1-58726-035-3(2) , For Your Knowledge) Ann Arbor Media Group, LLC.

—Ozma of Oz. Neill, John R., illus. 2001. (Books of Wonder). 272p. (J). (gr. 3 up). pap. 7.99 (978-0-06-440962-9(7) , Harper Trophy) HarperCollins Pubs.

—Ozma of Oz. 2006. pap. 44.99 (***978-1-4219-7955-7(1)***) IndyPublish.com.

—Ozma of Oz. (Twelve-Point Ser.). 2003. lib. bdg. 24.00 (978-1-58287-252-0(X)); 2004. 210p. 25.00 (978-1-58287-736-5(X)) North Bks.

—Ozma of Oz. l.t. ed. 2003. (Perennial Bestsellers Ser.). 288p. (J). 29.95 (978-0-7862-5888-8(8)) Thorndike Pr.

—The Patchwork Girl of Oz. (Oz Ser.).Tr. of 220. (YA). (gr. 5-8). 25.95 (978-0-8488-0705-4(7)) Amereon LTD.

—The Patchwork Girl of Oz. 2003. Tr. of 220. (Illus.). 342p. pap. 14.95 (978-1-58726-038-4(7) , For Your Knowledge) Ann Arbor Media Group, LLC.

—The Patchwork Girl of Oz. Neill, John R., illus. l.t. ed. 2005. (Thorndike Press Large Print Classics Ser.).Tr. of 220. 476p. (J). 20.95 (978-0-7862-8208-1(8)) Thorndike Pr.

—The Patchwork Girl of OZ. l.t. ed. 2004. (Large Print Ser.). lib. bdg. 25.00 (978-1-58287-771-6(8)) North Bks.

—Rinkitink in Oz. rev. ed. 2006. 216p. 27.95 (978-1-4218-1791-0(8)); pap. 12.95 (978-1-4218-1891-7(4)) 1st World Publishing, Inc. (1st World Library - Literary Society).

—Rinkitink in Oz. (Oz Ser.). (YA). (gr. 5-8). 22.95 (978-0-8488-0735-1(9)) Amereon LTD.

—Rinkitink in Oz. Neill, John R., illus. 1998. (Oz Ser.). 352p. (gr. 5-8). 24.99 (978-0-688-14720-4(8)) HarperCollins Pubs.

—Rinkitink in Oz. 2004. reprint ed. pap. 20.95 (978-1-4191-6718-8(9)); pap. 1.99 (978-1-4192-6718-5(3)) Kessinger Publishing, LLC.

—Rinkitink in Oz. 2004. (Twelve-Point Ser.). lib. bdg. 24.00 (978-1-58287-278-0(3)); lib. bdg. 25.00 (978-1-58287-774-7(2)) North Bks.

—The Road to Oz. 2005. 192p. pap. 11.95 (978-1-4218-0165-0(5)); 26.95 (978-1-4218-0065-3(9)) 1st World Publishing, Inc. (1st World Library - Literary Society).

—The Road to Oz. (Oz Ser.). (YA). (gr. 5-8). 20.95 (978-0-8488-0788-7(X)) Amereon LTD.

—The Road to Oz. 2004. reprint ed. pap. 20.95 (978-1-4191-8077-4(0)); pap. 1.99 (978-1-4192-8077-1(5)) Kessinger Publishing, LLC.

—The Road to Oz. 2004. (Twelve-Point Ser.). lib. bdg. 24.00 (978-1-58287-274-2(0)); lib. bdg. 25.00 (978-1-58287-770-9(X)) North Bks.

—The Royal Book of Oz. 2000. (YA). 26.95 (978-0-8488-2914-8(X)) Amereon LTD.

—The Royal Book of Oz. Thompson, Ruth Plumly, ed. enl. ed. 2001. (Oz Ser.). (Illus.). 320p. (J). (gr. 4-7). pap. 9.95 (978-0-486-41766-0(2)) Dover Pubns., Inc.

—The Scarecrow of Oz. rev. ed. 2006. 208p. 27.95 (978-1-4218-1790-3(X)); pap. 12.95 (978-1-4218-1890-0(6)) 1st World Publishing, Inc. (1st World Library - Literary Society).

—The Scarecrow of Oz. (Oz Ser.). (YA). (gr. 5-8). 20.95 (978-0-8488-0707-8(3)) Amereon LTD.

—The Scarecrow of Oz. Neill, John R., illus. 1998. (Oz Ser.). 304p. (J). (gr. 4-7). pap. 9.95 (978-0-486-40548-3(6)) Dover Pubns., Inc.

—The Scarecrow of Oz. 2004. reprint ed. pap. 20.95 (978-1-4191-8147-4(5)); pap. 1.99 (978-1-4192-8147-1(X)) Kessinger Publishing, LLC.

—The Scarecrow of Oz. 2004. (Twelve-Point Ser.). lib. bdg. 24.00 (978-1-58287-277-3(5)); lib. bdg. 25.00 (978-1-58287-773-0(4)) North Bks.

—The Sea Fairies. rev. ed. 2006. 192p. 26.95 (978-1-4218-1788-0(8)); pap. 11.95 (978-1-4218-1888-7(4)) 1st World Publishing, Inc. (1st World Library - Literary Society).

—The Sea Fairies. Neill, John R., illus. 1998. 240p. (J). (gr. 4-7). pap. 9.95 (978-0-486-40182-9(0)) Dover Pubns., Inc.

—The Sea Fairies. 2006. pap. 45.99 (***978-1-4219-8091-1(6)***) IndyPublish.com.

—The Sea Fairies. 2004. reprint ed. pap. 20.95 (978-1-4191-8165-8(3)); pap. 1.99 (978-1-4192-8165-5(8)) Kessinger Publishing, LLC.

—The Sea Fairies. l.t. ed. 2004. (Large Print Ser.). lib. bdg. 25.00 (978-1-58287-793-8(9)) North Bks.

—Sky Island. 2002. (Illus.). 300p. (J). (gr. 4-7). pap. 9.95 (978-0-486-42360-9(3)) Dover Pubns., Inc.

—Sky Island. 2004. (Twelve-Point Ser.). lib. bdg. 24.00 (978-1-58287-280-3(5)); lib. bdg. 25.00 (978-1-58287-792-1(0)) North Bks.

—Sky Island (Being the Further Exciting A. 2006. pap. 45.99 (***978-1-4219-8094-2(0)***) IndyPublish.com.

—Tik-Tok of Oz. rev. ed. 2006. 232p. 27.95 (978-1-4218-1792-7(6)); pap. 12.95 (978-1-4218-1892-4(2)) 1st World Publishing, Inc. (1st World Library - Literary Society).

—Tik-Tok of Oz. 2004. (Twelve-Point Ser.). lib. bdg. 24.00 (978-1-58287-276-6(7)); lib. bdg. 25.00 (978-1-58287-772-3(6)) North Bks.

—The Tin Woodman of Oz. (J). 20.95 (978-0-8488-0709-2(X)) Amereon LTD.

—The Tin Woodman of Oz. 2000. (Oz Ser.). (Illus.). 288p. (J). (gr. 4-7). pap. 8.95 (978-0-486-41302-0(0)) Dover Pubns., Inc.

—The Tin Woodman of Oz. Neill, John R., illus. 1999. (Books of Wonder). 336p. (gr. 5). 25.99 (978-0-688-14976-5(6)) HarperCollins Pubs.

—The Tin Woodman of Oz. (Twelve-Point Ser.). 2003. lib. bdg. 24.00 (978-1-58287-257-5(0)); 2004. 230p. 25.00 (978-1-58287-741-9(6)) North Bks.

—The Wizard of Oz. 2002. (Great Illustrated Classics Ser.). (Illus.). 240p. (J). (gr. 3-8). 21.35 (978-1-57765-807-8(8) , ABDO & Daughters) ABDO Publishing Co.

—The Wizard of Oz. Denslow, W. W., illus. 2002. 208p. (J). (gr. 5-7). 25.00 (978-0-7567-5917-9(X)) DIANE Publishing Co.

—The Wizard of Oz. Zwerger, Lisbeth, illus. 2004. 103p. (J). (gr. 4-8). reprint ed. 20.00 (978-0-7567-7708-1(9)) DIANE Publishing Co.

—The Wizard of Oz. 2004. (Great Classics for Children Ser.). (Illus.). 192p. (J). 5.99 (978-1-4037-0601-0(8)) Dalmatian Pr.

—The Wizard of Oz. 2004. reprint ed. pap. 19.95 (978-1-4191-8832-9(1)) Kessinger Publishing, LLC.

—The Wizard of Oz. 1999. (Illus.). 272p. (YA). (gr. 3 up). reprint ed. 12.95 (978-1-56852-225-8(8) , Konecky & Konecky) Konecky, William S. Assocs., Inc.

—The Wizard of Oz. Kilgras, Heidi, ed. Santore, Charles, illus. 100th anniv. ed. 2000. 96p. (J). (ps-3). 21.95 (978-0-375-81137-1(0) , Random Hse. Bks. for Young Readers) Random Hse. Children's Bks.

—The Wizard of Oz. (SPA.). 256p. (J). 9.95 (978-84-204-3509-1(0)) Santillana USA Publishing Co., Inc.

—The Wizard of Oz. Granger, Paul, illus. 2001. 160p. (J). pap. 3.99 (978-0-439-23641-6(X)) Scholastic, Inc.

—The Wizard of Oz. 1999. (Aladdin Classics Ser.). 224p. (gr. 4-7). mass mkt. 4.99 (978-0-689-83142-3(0) , Aladdin) Simon & Schuster Children's Publishing.

—The Wizard of Oz. 1999. (978-0-606-17516-6(4)); (gr. 3-6). lib. bdg. 11.80 (978-0-613-63243-0(5)) Tandem Library Bks.

—The Wizard of Oz. 1998. (Children's Classics). (ENG., Illus.). 144p. (J). (gr. 4-7). pap. (978-1-85326-112-1(2) , 1122WW) Wordsworth Editions, Ltd.

—The Wizard of Oz Book & Charm. (Charming Classics). 208p. (J). 1999. (Illus.). (gr. 3-7). pap. 6.99 (978-0-694-01319-7(6)); 2005. 9.99 (978-0-06-075772-4(8) , Harper Festival) HarperCollins Pubs.

—A Wonderful Welcome to Oz: The Marvelous Land of Oz, Ozma of Oz, & the Emerald City of Oz. Maguire, Gregory, ed. Neill, John R., illus. 2006. (Modern Library Classics). 624p. 15.95 (978-0-8129-7494-2(8) , Modern Library) Random House Publishing Group.

—The Wonderful Wizard of Oz. 2004. 180p. pap. 11.95 (978-1-59540-102-1(4) , 1st World Library - Literary Society) 1st World Publishing, Inc.

—The Wonderful Wizard of Oz. 2000. 129p. reprint ed. pap. 9.95 (978-1-4021-9983-7(X) , Elibron Classics) Adamant Media.

—The Wonderful Wizard of Oz. (Oz Ser.). (YA). (gr. 5-8). 20.95 (978-0-88411-772-8(3)) Amereon LTD.

—The Wonderful Wizard of Oz. 2003. (Illus.). 268p. pap. 14.95 (978-1-58726-034-6(4) , For Your Knowledge) Ann Arbor Media Group, LLC.

—The Wonderful Wizard of Oz. l.t. unabr. ed. 2002. (Dover Large Print Classics Ser.). (Illus.). 256p. pap. 9.95 (978-0-486-42248-0(8)) Dover Pubns., Inc.

—The Wonderful Wizard of Oz. Denslow, W. W., illus. (Books of Wonder). 2001. 320p. (J). pap. 7.99 (978-0-688-16677-9(6) , Harper Trophy); 100th anniv. ed. 2000. 272p. (gr. 5-8). 24.99 (978-0-06-029323-9(3)) HarperCollins Pubs.

—The Wonderful Wizard of Oz. 2003. (ENG.). 136p. 23.99 (***978-1-4043-4042-8(4)***) IndyPublish.com.

—The Wonderful Wizard of Oz. Wolstenholme, Susan, ed. 2000. (Oz Ser.). (Illus.). 336p. (gr. 5-8). 13.95 (978-0-19-283930-5(6)) Oxford Univ. Pr., Inc.

—The Wonderful Wizard of Oz. 2003. (Modern Library Classics Ser.). (Illus.). 224p. pap. 11.95 (978-0-8129-7011-1(X) , Modern Library) Random House Publishing Group.

—The Wonderful Wizard of Oz. Hildebrandt, Greg, illus. 2003. 64p. (J). 9.98 (978-0-7624-1628-8(9) , Courage Bks.) Running Pr. Bk. Pubs.

—The Wonderful Wizard of Oz. Sabuda, Robert, illus. 2000. (Classic Collectible Pop-Up Ser.). 16p. (J). (ps-3). pap. 26.99 (978-0-689-81751-9(7) , Little Simon) Simon & Schuster Children's Publishing.

—The Wonderful Wizard of Oz. Foreman, Michael, illus. 2005. 176p. (J). (gr. 2-7). 12.95 (978-1-4027-2535-7(3)) Sterling Publishing Co., Inc.

—Wonderful Wizard of Oz: A Classic Story about Cooperation. 2003. (Illus.). 32p. per. 3.95 (978-0-9747133-5-9(X) , Values to Live By Classic Stories) Thomas, Frederic Inc.

—The Wonderful Wizard of Oz: The Centennial Edition. Foreman, Michael, illus. 2002. (Oz Ser.). 160p. (J). (gr. 5-8). 29.99 (978-1-86205-343-4(X) , Pavilion Bks., Ltd.) Anova Bks. GBR. *Dist:* Independent Pubs. Group.

—The Wonderful Wizard of Oz: The Kansas Centennial Edition. McCurdy, Michael, illus. deluxe collector's ed. 2001. (Oz Ser.). 212p. (gr. 5-8). pap. 12.95 (978-0-7006-1151-5(7)) Univ. Pr. of Kansas.

—The Wonderful World of Oz: The Wizard of Oz, The Emerald City of Oz & Glinda of Oz. Zipes, Jack D., ed. 1998. (Illus.). 389p. (YA). pap. 14.00 (978-0-7567-6039-7(9)) DIANE Publishing Co.

—The Wonderful World of Oz: The Wizard of Oz, the Emerald City of Oz & Glinda of Oz. Denslow, W. W., illus. 1998. (Twentieth Century Classics Ser.). 368p. pap. 13.95 (978-0-14-118085-4(4) , Penguin Classics) Penguin Group (USA) Inc.

Baum, L. Frank, told to. The Emerald City of Oz. l.t. ed. 2004. (Large Print Ser.). 285p. 25.00 (978-1-58287-738-9(6)) North Bks.

Baum, L. Frank & Denslow, W. W. Oz-Story 5. Maxine, David, ed. Shanower, Eric & Denslow, W. W., illus. 1999. (Oz Ser.:). 128p. (Orig.). (YA). (gr. 5-8). pap. 14.95 (978-1-929527-00-7(4)) Hungry Tiger Pr.

Baum, L. Frank & Dickins, Rosie. Wizard of Oz. 2007. 64p. (J). 8.99 (978-0-7945-1457-0(X) , Usborne) EDC Publishing.

Baum, L. Frank & Glassman, Peter. Glinda of Oz. Neill, John R., illus. 2000. (Books of Wonder). 304p. (gr. 5-8). 25.99 (978-0-688-14978-9(2)) HarperCollins Pubs.

—The Lost Princess of Oz. Neill, John R., illus. 1998. (Books of Wonder). 352p. (gr. 5-8). 24.99 (978-0-688-14975-8(8)) HarperCollins Pubs.

—The Magic of Oz. Neill, John R., illus. 1999. (Books of Wonder). 292p. (gr. 5-8). 25.99 (978-0-688-14977-2(4)) HarperCollins Pubs.

Baum, L. Frank, et al. Oz-Story 4. Maxine, David, ed. Shanower, Eric, illus. 1998. (Oz Ser.). 128p. (Orig.). (YA). (gr. 5-8). pap. 14.95 (978-0-9644988-7-7(1)) Hungry Tiger Pr.

—Oz-Story 6. 2000. (Oz Ser.). (Illus.). 224p. (YA). (gr. 5-8). pap. 19.95 (978-1-929527-02-1(0)) Hungry Tiger Pr.

Baum, Roger S. The Green Star of Oz: A Special Oz Story. Seitzinger, Victoria, illus. 2000. 102p. (J). (ps-3). 24.95 (978-1-57072-161-8(0)) Overmountain Pr.

—The Lion of Oz & the Badge of Courage. Coons, Dean, illus. 2nd ed. 2003. 247p. (J). 24.95 (978-1-57072-255-4(2)) Overmountain Pr.

—The Oz Odyssey. Seitzinger, Victoria, illus. 2006. 176p. (J). 19.95 (978-1-57072-299-8(4)) Overmountain Pr.

Baun, Frank L. The Wonderful Wizard of Oz: Juvenile Classic. 2005. (Illus.). 192p. (J). 5.99 (978-1-4037-1385-8(5)) Dalmatian Pr.

Beahm, George. Fact, Fiction, & Folklore in Harry Potter's World: An Unofficial Guide. Kirk, Tim & McDaniel, Britton, illus. 2005. 256p. (J). (gr. k-10). pap. 16.95 (978-1-57174-440-1(1)) Hampton Roads Publishing Co., Inc.

—Passport to Narnia: The Unofficial Giude. Kirk, Tim, illus. 2005. (J). lib. bdg. 15.95 (978-1-57174-481-4(9)) Hampton Roads Publishing Co., Inc.

Beardsley, Martyn. Sir Gadabout Does His Best. Ross, Tony, illus. 2007. (Sir Gadabout Ser.). 96p. (J). pap. 6.95 (***978-1-85881-892-4(3)***) Orion Publishing Group, Ltd. GBR. *Dist:* Independent Pubs. Group.

—Sir Gadabout Goes to Knight School, Bk. 8. 2007. (Sir Gadabout Ser.). (Illus.). 96p. (J). pap. 6.95 ***(978-1-84255-276-6(7))*** Orion Publishing Group, Ltd. GBR. *Dist:* Independent Pubs. Group.

Beatty, Scott. Batman Begins: The Visual Guide. 2005. (Illus.). 64p. (J). (ps-7). 19.99 (978-0-7566-1233-7(0)) Dorling Kindersley Publishing, Inc.

Beauty & the Boy: An old man's story for a dying Boy. 2006. (Illus.). 270p. (YA). per. 19.95 (978-0-9759902-0-9(9)) Before Christmas Pr.

Beck, Carolyn. The Waiting Dog. Beck, Andrea, illus. 2004. 32p. (J). (gr. 4-6). (978-1-55337-006-2(6)) Kids Can Pr., Ltd.

Beckerman, Menucha. The Crying Clown. 2003. (My Little World Ser.: Vol. 2). (Illus.). 34p. (J). (gr. k-5). 5.95 (978-1-931681-07-0(4)) Israel Bk. Shop.

—Dina-dee Is a Goody. Gaash, Elisheva, illus. 2003. (My Middos World Ser.: Vol. 4). 24p. (J). (gr. k-5). 11.95 (978-1-931681-03-2(1)) Israel Bk. Shop.

—Dina-dee Loves Shabbos. Gaash, Elisheva, illus. 2003. (My Middos World Ser.: Vol. 5). 24p. (J). (gr. k-5). 11.95 (978-1-931681-04-9(X)) Israel Bk. Shop.

—Gitty's Dream Comes True. 2003. (My Little World Ser.: Vol. 1). (Illus.). (J). (gr. k-5). 5.95 (978-1-931681-06-3(6)) Israel Bk. Shop.

—Hurray! Michael Is Big. 2003. (My Middos World Ser.: Vol. 3). (Illus.). 24p. (J). (gr. k-5). 11.95 (978-1-931681-02-5(3)) Israel Bk. Shop.

—Michael & the Raindrops. 2003. (My Middos World Ser.: Vol. 7). (Illus.). 24p. (J). (gr. k-5). 11.95 (978-1-931681-17-9(1)) Israel Bk. Shop.

—Michael & the Secret of Making Friends. 2003. (My Middos World Ser.: Vol. 9). (Illus.). 24p. (J). (gr. k-5). 11.95 (978-1-931681-15-5(5)) Israel Bk. Shop.

—Michael Wants Patience. 2003. (My Middos World Ser.: Vol. 2). (Illus.). 24p. (J). (gr. k-5). 11.95 (978-1-931681-01-8(5)) Israel Bk. Shop.

—That's All! I Want to be Small. 2000. (My Little World Ser.: Vol. 8). (Illus.). 34p. (J). (gr. k-5). 5.95 (978-1-931681-13-1(9)) Israel Bk. Shop.

Beckham, David. Charlie Barker & the Secret of the Deep Dark Woods. 2006. 570p. pap. ***(978-1-4120-9264-7(7))*** Trafford Publishing.

Beckwith, Agnes. Zar Meets Rahbue: From the Land of Senga. 1998. (Illus.). 16p. (J). (gr. 3-6). pap. 6.00 (978-0-8059-4263-7(7)) Dorrance Publishing Co., Inc.

Bedard, Michael. Stained Glass. 2001. (gr. 7-12). lib. bdg. 17.60 (978-0-613-57923-0(2)) Tandem Library Bks.

—Stained Glass. 2002. 312p. (J). (gr. 6). pap. 8.95 (978-0-88776-602-2(1)) Tundra Bks., Inc./Livres Toundra, Inc. CAN. *Dist:* Random Hse., Inc.

Bedard, Tony. Mystic: The Mathemagician, Vol. 6. Lopresti, Aaron et al, illus. 2004. (Mystic Ser.). 160p. (YA). pap. 15.95 (978-1-59314-039-7(8)) CrossGeneration Comics, Inc.

Beddor, Frank. The Looking Glass Wars. (Looking Glass Wars Trilogy: Bk. 1). (J). (gr. 5 up). 2007. 400p. 8.99 ***(978-0-14-240941-1(3)*** , Puffin); 2006. (Illus.). 384p. 17.99 (978-0-8037-3153-0(1) , Dial) Penguin Group (USA) Inc.

—Princess Alyss of Wonderland. Chien, Catia, illus. 2007. 30p. (J). (gr. 4). 19.99 ***(978-0-8037-3251-3(1)*** , Dial) Penguin Group (USA) Inc.

—Seeing Redd. 2007. (Looking Glass Wars Trilogy: Bk. 2). 384p. (YA). (gr. 6 up). 17.99 ***(978-0-8037-3155-4(8)*** , Dial) Penguin Group (USA) Inc.

Beekman, Kelley Lee. Sir Eli & the Halloween Dragon: The Legend of the Toasted Marshmallow. 2006. 55p. pap. 12.95 ***(978-1-4241-4047-3(1))*** PublishAmerica, Inc.

Begamudre, Ven. The Phantom Queen. 2005. (Illus.). 320p. (J). 10.95 (978-1-55050-200-8(X)) Coteau Bks. CAN. *Dist:* Fitzhenry & Whiteside, Ltd.

Bell, Cindy. Flutter By. 2004. 85p. pap. 14.95 (978-1-4137-1318-3(1)) PublishAmerica, Inc.

Bell, Clare. Clan Ground. 2007. 272p. (YA). (gr. 7). pap. 7.99 (978-0-14-240812-4(3) , Puffin) Penguin Group (USA) Inc.

—Ratha & Thistle-Chaser: The Third Book of the Named. 2007. 272p. (YA). (gr. 7). 8.99 ***(978-0-14-240944-2(8)*** , Puffin) Penguin Group (USA) Inc.

—Ratha's Challenge: The Fourth Book of the Named. 2007. 272p. (YA). (gr. 7). 8.99 ***(978-0-14-240915-2(4)*** , Puffin) Penguin Group (USA) Inc.

—Ratha's Courage. 2007. 256p. (J). (gr. 7). 18.99 ***(978-0-670-06170-9(0)*** , Viking Juvenile) Penguin Group (USA) Inc.

Bell, David. Dawn Grays Cosmic Adventure 1. 2007. (Dawn Gray Trilogy Ser.). (Illus.). 260p. pap. 11.95 ***(978-1-84167-558-9(X))*** Ransom Publishing Ltd. GBR. *Dist:* International Publishers Marketing.

—Pink Alert! 2007. (Dawn Gray Trilogy Ser.). 260p. pap. 11.95 ***(978-1-84167-581-7(4))*** Ransom Publishing Ltd. GBR. *Dist:* International Publishers Marketing.

—Pyjamas in Space. 2007. (Dawn Gray Trilogy Ser.). 260p. pap. 11.95 ***(978-1-84167-580-0(6))*** Ransom Publishing Ltd. GBR. *Dist:* International Publishers Marketing.

Bell, Frank. Panda Patrol to the Rescue. Seaman, Paul, illus. 2004. 24p. pap. 7.00 (978-1-84161-068-9(2)) Ravette Publishing, Ltd. GBR. *Dist:* Parkwest Pubns., Inc.

Bell, Hilari. Fall of a Kingdom. 2005. (Farsala Trilogy Ser.). 448p. (YA). pap. 6.99 (978-0-689-85414-9(5) , Simon Pulse) Simon & Schuster Children's Publishing.

—Fall of a Kingdom. 2005. 422p. (YA). (gr. 7-12). per. 14.45 (978-1-4176-5288-4(8)) Tandem Library Bks.

—Forging the Sword. (Farsala Trilogy Ser.: No. 3). (YA). 2007. 624p. mass mkt. 6.99 (978-0-689-85418-7(8) , Simon & Schuster Children's Publishing); 2006. 512p. 17.99 (978-0-689-85416-3(1)) Simon & Schuster Children's Publishing.

—The Last Knight. 2007. (Knight & Rogue Ser.). 368p. (YA). (gr. 7 up). 16.99 ***(978-0-06-082503-4(0));*** lib. bdg. 17.89 ***(978-0-06-082504-1(9))*** HarperCollins Pubs. (Eos).

—Rise of a Hero. 2005. (Book of Sorahb Ser.: No. 2). (Illus.). 480p. (YA). 17.95 (978-0-689-85415-6(3)) Simon & Schuster Children's Publishing.

—Shield of Stars. 2007. (Shield, Sword, & Crown Ser.). (Illus.). 272p. (J). 16.99 (978-1-4169-0594-3(4) , Simon & Schuster Children's Publishing) Simon & Schuster Children's Publishing.

—The Wizard Test. 176p. (J). 2006. pap. 5.99 (978-0-06-059942-3(1)); 2005. (gr. 5 up). 15.99 (978-0-06-059940-9(5)); 2005. (gr. 5 up). lib. bdg. 16.89 (978-0-06-059941-6(3)) HarperCollins Pubs.

Bellairs, John. The Face in the Frost. 2000. 176p. (J). pap. 14.95 (978-1-58754-105-6(X) , Olmstead Pr.) Moyer Bell.

—The Face in the Frost. 2002. (J). pap. 6.99 (978-1-58586-035-7(2)) ereads.com.

—The Mansion in the Mist. Gorey, Edward, illus. 2004. (Anthony Monday Ser.). 176p. (J). pap. 5.99 (978-0-14-240262-7(1) , Puffin) Penguin Group (USA) Inc.

Bendis, Brian Michael & Finch, David. The Avengers: Disassembled. (Illus.). 176p. pap. 15.99 (978-0-7851-1482-6(3)) Marvel Enterprises, Inc.

—Ultimate X-Men, Vol. 4. 2005. (X-Men Ser.). (Illus.). 304p. 29.99 (978-0-7851-1251-8(0)) Marvel Enterprises, Inc.

Bendis, Brian Michael, et al. What If... ? Why Not?, Vol. 1. 2005. (Marvel Heroes Ser.). (Illus.). 152p. pap. 16.99 (978-0-7851-1593-9(5)) Marvel Enterprises, Inc.

Benesch, Walter. Adam Cox Meets the CrackleCrunch for Lunch. Jamieson, Sandy, illus. 2004. 32p. (J). 24.95 (978-1-932053-09-8(3)) Nonetheless Pr.

Benjamin, A. H. Shamwood. 2006. 140p. pap. 19.95 (978-1-4137-9193-8(X)) PublishAmerica, Inc.

Bennett, Holly. The Bonemender's Oath. 2006. 176p. (YA). (gr. 7 up). pap. 8.95 (978-1-55143-443-8(1)) Orca Bk. Pubs. USA.

Bennett, Steven. The Adventures of Super Dad: Colossal Encounters (Book #1) 2005. 98p. pap. 10.49 (978-1-4116-5947-6(3)) Lulu.com.

Beobi & the Magic Coloring Book A Visit to the Doctor. 2005. (J). 3.99 (978-0-9743847-3-3(9)) Cohn, Tricia.

Beop-Ryong, Yuy. Chronicles of the Cursed Sword, 10 vols. Hui-Jin, Park, illus. 2004. 176p. Vol. 4. rev. ed. pap. 9.99 (978-1-59182-421-3(4)); Vol. 5. 5th rev. ed. pap. 9.99 (978-1-59182-422-0(2)) TOKYOPOP, Inc. (Tokyopop Adult).

Bergen, Lara Rice. Into the Woods. 2000. (Back to Sherwood Ser.: 1). 176p. (J). (gr. 5-9). pap. 3.99 (978-0-440-22853-0(0) , Laurel Leaf) Random Hse. Children's Bks.

—The Trouble with Brenan. 2000. (Back to Sherwood Ser.: 2). (J). (gr. 5-9). pap. 3.99 (978-0-440-22856-1(5) , Laurel Leaf) Random Hse. Children's Bks.

Berger, Barbara Helen. Lot of Otters. 2000. (ps-2). lib. bdg. 15.30 (978-0-613-28563-6(8)) Tandem Library Bks.

Berger, Thomas. Stan Bolivan & the Dragon. (Illus.). 30p. (J). 17.95 (978-0-86315-152-1(3) , 1585) Floris Bks. GBR. *Dist:* Gryphon Hse., Inc., SteinerBooks, Inc.

Bergsma, Jody Lynn. Faerie. 2002. (Illus.). 40p. (J). 15.95 (978-0-9717117-0-9(4)) Gallery Press Publishing, Inc.

Bergsma, Jody Lynn, et al. Dragon. Bergsma, Jody Lynn, illus. 1999. (Illus.). 32p. (ps-7). 15.95 (978-0-935699-17-3(1)) Illumination Arts Publishing Co., Inc.

Berman, Steve, ed. Magic in the Mirrorstone: Tales of Fantasy. 2008. 304p. (J). (gr. 3-7). 14.95 ***(978-0-7869-4732-4(2)*** , Mirrorstone) Wizards of the Coast.

Bernhardt, William. Princess Alice & the Dreadful Dragon. McGhee, Kerry, illus. 2007. 36p. (J). 19.95 ***(978-1-930709-65-2(X))*** HAWK Publishing Group.

Berryhill, Shane. Chance Fortune & the Outlaws. 2006. (Adventures of Chance Fortune Ser.). 272p. (J). (gr. 5-8). 17.95 (978-0-7653-1468-0(1) , Starscape) Doherty, Tom Assocs., LLC.

Bessen, Luc. Arthur & the Minimoys. Sowchek, Ellen, tr. from FRE. 2005. 240p. (J). 15.99 (978-0-06-059623-1(6)) HarperCollins Pubs.

Besson, Luc. Arthur & the Invisibles. movie tie-in ed. 2006. 416p. (J). pap. 7.99 (978-0-06-122726-4(9)) HarperCollins Pubs.

—Arthur & the Minimoys. (Illus.). (J). 2006. 256p. pap. 6.99 (978-0-06-059625-5(2) , Harper Trophy); 2005. 240p. lib. bdg. 16.89 (978-0-06-059624-8(4)) HarperCollins Pubs.

BeSwitched. 2004. (YA). mass mkt. 7.99 (978-0-9759784-0-5(3)) Joseph's Coat Publishing.

Bethea, Steve. True to That, Earth's Last Days in the Hood: A Novel of the Earth's Last Days in the Hood. rev. ed. 2007. 303p. (gr. 12 up). pap. 14.99 (978-0-9727010-0-6(1)) Satellite Dynamica Pub., Inc.

Between Light & Dark. rev. ed. 2006. (W. I. T. C. H. Graphic Novels Ser.: Bk. 4). (Illus.). 128p. (gr. 3-7). pap. 4.99 (978-0-7868-3656-7(3) , Volo) Hyperion Bks. for Children.

Billingsley, Franny. The Folk Keeper. unabr. ed. 2004. 176p. (J). (gr. 5-9). pap. 36.00 incl. audio (978-0-8072-0662-1(8) , Listening Library) Random Hse. Audio Publishing Group.

—The Folk Keeper. Gore, Leonid, illus. 2001. 176p. (J). pap. 4.99 (978-0-689-84461-4(1) , Aladdin) Simon & Schuster Children's Publishing.

—The Folk Keeper. 2001. 11.64 (978-0-606-22111-5(5)); (gr. 5-8). lib. bdg. 13.00 (978-0-613-60640-0(X)) Tandem Library Bks.

—The Folk Keeper. l.t. ed. 2000. 224p. (YA). (gr. 5-9). 20.95 (978-0-7862-2461-6(4)) Thorndike Pr.

—Well Wished. Gore, Leonid, illus. 2000. 176p. (J). (gr. 3-7). pap. 9.95 (978-0-689-83255-0(9) , Aladdin) Simon & Schuster Children's Publishing.

—Well Wished. 2000. (978-0-606-17941-6(0)); (gr. 3-6). lib. bdg. 13.00 (978-0-613-28693-0(6)) Tandem Library Bks.

—Well Wished. l.t. ed. 2001. (Illus.). 197p. (J). (gr. 4-7). 21.95 (978-0-7862-3106-5(8)) Thorndike Pr.

Billingsley, Franny & Gore, Leonid. The Folk Keeper. 1999. (Illus.). 176p. (YA). (gr. 5-9). 16.95 (978-0-689-82876-8(4) , Atheneum) Simon & Schuster Children's Publishing.

Birdsall, Jeanne. The Penderwicks on Gardam Street. 2008. 320p. (J). (gr. 3-7). 15.99 ***(978-0-375-84090-6(7)*** , Knopf Bks. for Young Readers) Random Hse. Children's Bks.

Bishop, Debbie. The Fairies of Bladderwhack Pond. Park, Andy, illus. 2007. (Fairies of Bladderwhack Pond Ser.: Vol. 1). 152p. 19.99 (978-1-932431-01-8(2) , Angel Gate) Left Field Ink.

Bishop, Rose. Arielle's Pursuit. 2007. 100p. pap. 10.95 ***(978-0-7414-3804-1(6))*** Infinity Publishing.

Bittner, Wolfgang. Despierta, Osogris! 1999. (gr. k-3). (SPA.). lib. bdg. 15.25 (978-0-613-73509-4(9)); 13.75 (978-0-606-17635-4(7)) Tandem Library Bks.

Blacker, Terence. Power Crazy Ms. Wiz. (Illus.). 57p. (J). pap. 6.99 (978-0-330-34872-0(8) , Pan) Pan Macmillan GBR. *Dist:* Trafalgar Square Publishing.

Blackman, Malorie. Whizziwig. Lee, Stephen, illus. l.t. ed. 1998. 120p. (J). pap. (978-0-7540-6026-0(8) , CLP 227) BBC Audio.

Blackwood, Algernon. The Extra Day. 2002. 296p. 32.95 (978-1-59224-817-9(9)) Wildside Pr.

Blair, Eric. Rumpelstiskin: Version del Cuento de los Hermanos Grimm. Shaw, David, illus. 2006. (Read-It! Readers en Espanol Ser.).Tr. of Rumpelstiltskin: A Retelling of the Grimm's Fairy Tale. (SPA.). 32p. (J). (ps-3). 19.95 (978-1-4048-1637-4(2)) Picture Window Bks.

Blair, Thomas L. The Sabatini Prophecy. 2006. 480p. (YA). 22.95 (978-0-9760237-1-5(7)) Axiom Hse.

Blankenship, Paula. We Both Read-Lulu's Lost Shoes Big Book: Lulu's Lost Shoes Big Book. Reinhart, Larry, illus. 2005. 44p. (J). (gr. k-1). 29.95 (978-1-891327-90-2(9)) Treasure Bay, Inc.

Bliss, Bob, illus. The Hardest Lessons: The Lost Babies Series #3. 2007. 118p. (J). per. 5.99 ***(978-0-9792499-2-1(9))*** Howell, M Kay.

—The Ruby Hind: The Lost Babies Series #1. 2007. 116p. (J). per. 5.99 ***(978-0-9792499-0-7(2))*** Howell, M Kay.

—Too Many Parents: The Lost Babies Series #2. 2007. 109p. (J). per. 5.99 ***(978-0-9792499-1-4(0))*** Howell, M Kay.

Block, Francesca Lia. Ecstasia. 2004. (Illus.). 208p. (Orig.). (YA). (gr. 5-7). pap. 6.99 (978-0-14-240037-1(8) , Puffin) Penguin Group (USA) Inc.

—I Was a Teenage Fairy. 192p. (J). (gr. 7 up). 1998. 14.89 (978-0-06-027748-2(3)); 2000. reprint ed. pap. 7.99 (978-0-06-440862-2(0) , Cotler, Joanna Books) HarperCollins Pubs.

—I Was a Teenage Fairy. 2000. (gr. 7-12). lib. bdg. 16.45 (978-0-613-28529-2(8)); (Illus.). (J). 14.64 (978-0-606-18903-3(3)) Tandem Library Bks.

—Primavera. 2004. 208p. (Orig.). (YA). pap. 6.99 (978-0-14-240067-8(X) , Puffin) Penguin Group (USA) Inc.

—Primavera. 2004. (Orig.). (gr. 7-12). lib. bdg. 15.30 (978-0-613-71572-0(1)) Tandem Library Bks.

Block, Francesca Lia, et al. Firebirds Rising: An Anthology of Original Science Fiction & Fantasy. November, Sharyn, ed. 2006. (Firebird Ser.). 544p. (YA). (gr. 7). 19.99 (978-0-14-240549-9(3) , Puffin) Penguin Group (USA) Inc.

Bloom, Harold. The Chronicles of Narnia. 2006. (Bloom's Modern Critical Interpretations Ser.). 248p. (gr. 9). 45.00 (978-0-7910-9310-8(7) , Chelsea Hse.) Facts On File, Inc.

Bloom, Janice Stitziel. A Grateful Heart under My Bed. Woodcock, Marcy, illus. 2007. 36p. (J). per. 15.99 ***(978-1-934643-06-8(8))*** Villager Bk. Publishing.

—Wonderfully Made under My Bed. Woodcock, Marcy, illus. 2007. 36p. (J). per. 15.99 ***(978-1-934643-00-6(9))*** Villager Bk. Publishing.

Blume, Rebecca. When the World Was Green! Blume, Rebecca, illus. 2007. (Illus.). 32p. (J). per. 14.00 ***(978-0-9785427-1-9(1))*** Liberty Artists Management.

Blythe, William. Solar Element Saga: The Legacy of Mirgard. 2004. 175p. pap. 19.95 (978-1-4137-2460-8(4)) PublishAmerica, Inc.

Bode, Mark & McCormick, Carlo. The Lizard of Oz. 2004. (Illus.). 64p. 12.95 (978-1-56097-595-3(4)) Fantagraphics Bks.

Bodecker, N. M. The Mushroom Center Disaster. Blegvad, Erik & Starr, Branka, illus. 2004. 48p. (J). reprint ed. 14.95 (978-1-931561-98-3(2)) MacAdam/Cage Publishing, Inc.

—Quimble Wood. Starr, Branka, illus. 2004. 32p. (J). reprint ed. 14.95 (978-1-931561-97-6(4)) MacAdam/Cage Publishing, Inc.

Boelts, Maribeth. Big Daddy, Frog Wrestler. Huang, Benrei, illus. 2000. 32p. (J). (ps-3). lib. bdg. 14.95 (978-0-8075-0717-9(2)) Whitman, Albert & Co.

Bogardus, Ray & Bogardus, Karin. Hannah the Magic Shelter Dog. Seltzer, Jerry, illus. 2005. 143p. (J). pap. 14.99 ***(978-1-932864-30-4(X))*** Masthof Pr.

Bogumill, Mark P. KingMaker: The Swamp Crusade, 4 vols. 2003. 310p. (YA). bds. 25.00 (978-0-9744870-0-7(7)) KingMaker Bks. LLC.

Bollers, Karl. Bloom Digest, Vol. 3. 2005. (X-Men Ser.). (Illus.). 144p. (YA). pap. 7.99 (978-0-7851-1473-4(4)) Marvel Enterprises, Inc.

Bonniol, Magali. El Ogro De Mariuchi. 2003. (SPA.). 40p. (978-84-8470-112-5(3)) Corimbo, Editorial S.L.

Bontempelli, Massimo. The Chess Set in the Mirror. Gilson, Estelle, tr. from ITA. 2007. (Illus.). 120p. (YA). (gr. 5 up). pap. 9.95 (978-1-58988-031-3(5)) Dry, Paul Bks., Inc.

Booth, Richard A. The Valley of Gillhista. 2003. (Valley Ser.: Bk. 4). 145p. (YA). pap. 9.95 (978-1-885813-11-4(2)) B&B Publishing.

Borrowers. 1999. (J). 9.95 (978-1-56137-069-6(X)) Novel Units, Inc.

Bosch, Pseudonymous. The Name of This Book Is Secret. Ford, Gilbert, illus. rev. ed. 2007. 384p. (J). (gr. 3-7). 16.99 ***(978-0-316-11366-3(2))*** Little, Brown Bks. for Young Readers.

Bostock, Mike. Louie & Bloop & the Swapped Shopping. 2002. (Illus.). 32p. (J). pap. 8.99 (978-1-4052-0080-6(4)) Egmont Bks., Ltd. GBR. *Dist:* Independent Pubs. Group.

Boston, Lucy M. Enemy at Green Knowe. 2002. (gr. 3-6). lib. bdg. 14.15 (978-0-613-54436-8(6)) Tandem Library Bks.

Boswell, Sharon. Hank-Willy. Chappell, Steve, illus. 1999. x, 155p. (J). (ps-6). pap. 12.99 (978-0-9668894-0-6(1)) Lorgnette Bks.

Bova, Louise. Harry Potter & the Sorcerer's Stone: Stationery Kit. 2000. (Illus.). (J). (gr. 1-5). 10.95 (978-0-439-23658-4(4)) Scholastic, Inc.

Bow, James. Fathom Five: A Rosemary & Time Book. 2007. 232p. (YA). pap. 12.99 ***(978-1-55002-692-4(5)*** , Boardwalk Bks.) Dundurn Group, The CAN. *Dist:* Univ. of Toronto Pr.

Bowler, Tim. Midget. 2000. (978-0-606-17929-4(1)) Tandem Library Bks.

Bowman, Alice W. Twinkle-Dust. rev. ed. 1998. 24p. (J). (gr. k-6). pap. 7.95 (978-0-9645870-6-9(8)) Big Foot Publishing.

Bowman, Todd A. Give it a Chance. 2004. 47p. (J). pap. 19.95 (978-1-4137-1293-3(2)) PublishAmerica, Inc.

Bowyer, Clifford. The Spread of Darkness: The Imperium Saga: the Adventures of Kyria. 2007. (Adventures of Kyria: 7). 168p. (YA). pap. 5.99 ***(978-0-9787782-1-7(9)*** , BK0022) Silver Leaf Bks., LLC.

Bowyer, Clifford B. The Apprentice of Zoldex: The Imperium Saga: the Adventures of Kyria. 2008. (Adventures of Kyria: 8). 208p. (YA). pap. 5.99 ***(978-0-9787782-2-4(7)*** , BK0023) Silver Leaf Bks., LLC.

—The Awakening: The Imperium Saga: the Adventures of Kyria. 2004. (Adventures of Kyria: Bk. 2). 192p. (J). pap. 5.99 (978-0-9744354-1-1(4) , BK0004) Silver Leaf Bks., LLC.

—The Child of Prophecy: The Imperium Saga: the Adventures of Kyria. 2004. (Adventures of Kyria: Bk. 1). 192p. (YA). pap. 5.99 (978-0-9744354-0-4(6) , BK0002) Silver Leaf Bks., LLC.

—The Mage's Council: The Imperium Saga: the Adventures of Kyria. 2005. (Adventures of Kyria: Vol. 3). 192p. (J). pap. 5.99 (978-0-9744354-2-8(2) , BK0006) Silver Leaf Bks., LLC.

—Quest for the Shard: The Imperium Saga: the Adventures of Kyria. 2007. (Adventures of Kyria: 6). 176p. (YA). pap. 5.99 (978-0-9744354-8-0(1) , BK0020) Silver Leaf Bks., LLC.

—Trapped in Time: The Imperium Saga: the Adventures of Kyria. 2006. (Adventures of Kyria: 5). 160p. (YA). pap. 5.99 (978-0-9744354-7-3(3) , BK0008) Silver Leaf Bks., LLC.

Boyd, David. Khan of Khans: An Adventure with Genghis Khan. 2003. (Milo the Wonderdog Adventures Ser.). 64p. pap. 4.95 (978-0-921156-90-1(1)) Rubicon Publishing, Inc. CAN. *Dist:* International Publishers Marketing.

—Spellbound. 2002. (gr. 3-6). lib. bdg. 12.95 (978-0-613-77599-1(6)) Tandem Library Bks.

Boyd, Johnny. First Tracks. 2004. 32p. 17.95 (978-0-9760187-0-4(5)) PTO Pr.

Bradbury, Ray. Death Is a Lonely Business. 1999. (gr. 7-12). lib. bdg. 22.20 (978-0-613-17166-3(7)) Tandem Library Bks.

Bradfield, Roger. The Flying Hockey Stick. Bradfield, Roger, illus. 2006. (J). 18.95 (978-1-930900-31-8(7)) Purple Hse. Pr.

Bradford, Emma. Kat the Time Explorer. Sano, Kazuhiko, illus. 1998. (Stardust Classics). 117p. (J). (gr. 2-6). 12.95 (978-1-889514-11-6(X)); pap. 5.95 (978-1-889514-12-3(8)) Dolls Corp.

Bradley, Marion Zimmer. Traitor's Sun. 2000. (gr. 7-12). lib. bdg. 16.45 (978-0-613-28110-2(1)) Tandem Library Bks.

Bramscher, Cynthia. Night of the Corn Maiden. 2003. 211p. pap. 19.95 (978-1-59286-704-2(9)) PublishAmerica, Inc.

Branson, Terri. Tyler on the Moon. Taylor, Chet, illus. l.t. ed. 2004. 24p. (J). 18.99 (978-0-9755888-2-6(6)) Dragonfly Publishing, Inc.

Braver, Gary. Elixir. 2001. (978-0-606-21174-1(8)) Tandem Library Bks.

Breckenridge, Trula & Breckenridge, Scott. Squiggly the Roach. Breckenridge, Trula & Breckenridge, Scott, illus. 2004. (J). per. (978-0-9749480-6-5(3) , MSPpress) Mama Specific Productions.

Breckenridge, Trula & Palmore, Iyende. FiFi the Leaf. Breckenridge, Trula & Palmore, Iyende, illus. 2004. (J). per. (978-0-9749480-7-2(1) , MSPpress) Mama Specific Productions.

Brege K. B. Mick Morris Myth Solver All Isn't Well in Roswell! No. 1. 2005. (Mick Morris Myth Solver Ser.: No. 1). (Illus.). 188p. (J). pap. 6.99 (978-0-9774119-0-0(7)) Team B Creative LLC.

Brennan, Herbie. Faerie Wars. 2004. 368p. (J). reprint ed. pap. 8.95 (978-1-58234-943-5(6) , Bloomsbury Children) Bloomsbury Publishing.

—Nuff Said. 2002. (gr. 3-6). lib. bdg. 15.25 (978-0-613-85268-5(0)) Tandem Library Bks.

Brennan, Michael. Electric Girl. Vol. 1. 2001. 172p. pap. 9.95 (978-0-9703555-0-8(5)); Vol. 2. 2002. (Illus.). 160p. (gr. 6-9). pap. 13.95 (978-0-9703555-1-5(3)) Diamond Bk. Distributors.

Brenner, Barbara. The Plant That Kept on Growing. Sweet, Melissa, illus. 1999. (Bank Street Reader Collection). 48p. (J). (ps-2). lib. bdg. (978-0-8368-1776-8(1)) Stevens, Gareth Inc.

Brent-Dyer, Elinor M. The Chalet School & the Lintons. 2001. (Chalet School Ser.). (Illus.). 300p. pap. 5.95 (978-0-00-690515-8(3)) HarperCollins Pubs. Ltd. GBR. *Dist:* Trafalgar Square Publishing.

—Exploits of the Chalet Girls. 2001. (Chalet School Ser.). 300p. (J). pap. 5.99 (978-0-00-692518-7(9)) HarperCollins Pubs. Ltd. GBR. *Dist:* Independent Pubs. Group.

—The Princess of the Chalet School. 2001. (Chalet School Ser.). (Illus.). 300p. pap. 5.99 (978-0-00-690601-8(X)) Zondervan.

—Rivals of the Chalet School. 2001. (Chalet School Ser.). (Illus.). 300p. (J). pap. 5.95 (978-0-00-690723-7(7)) HarperCollins Pubs. Ltd. GBR. *Dist:* Independent Pubs. Group.

Breslin, Theresa. The Dream Master. l.t. ed. 1999. 216p. (J). pap. (978-0-7540-6070-3(5), CLP 272) BBC Audio.

—Gladiator. 2004. (J). pap. 29.95 incl. audio (978-0-7540-6277-6(5), Chivers Children's Audio Bks.) BBC Audiobooks America.

Brett, Jan. Gingerbread Baby. 1999. (Illus.). 32p. (J). (ps-3). 16.99 (978-0-399-23444-6(6), Putnam Juvenile) Penguin Group (USA) Inc.

—The Trouble with Trolls. Brett, Jan, illus. 1999. (Illus.). 32p. (J). (ps-3). pap. 6.99 (978-0-698-11791-4(3), Putnam Juvenile) Penguin Group (USA) Inc.

—The Trouble with Trolls. 1999. (978-0-606-17433-6(8)) Tandem Library Bks.

Brewer, Heather. The Chronicles of Vladimir Tod: Eighth Grade Bites. 2007. 192p. (YA). (gr. 5 up). 16.99 (978-0-525-47811-9(6), Dutton Juvenile) Penguin Group (USA) Inc.

Bright, J. E. Dark Rings Attack! 2001. (Digimon 2nd Season Ultimate Adventures Ser.: No. 3). 96p. (gr. 1-4). 4.50 (978-0-06-107207-9(9), Harper Entertainment) HarperCollins Pubs.

Brightwood, Laura, illus. The House That Talked to Itself. 2006. (J). (978-0-9779290-3-0(5)) 3-C Institute for Social Development.

Brignole, Giancarla, tr. El Gigante y el Mar. Gazzaneo, Lucia, illus. (Fabulas De Familia Ser.). (SPA.). 32p. (978-970-20-0268-0(0)) Castillo, Ediciones, S. A. de C. V.

Brin, Susannah. Rabbit Tattoo. 2001. (gr. 5-8). lib. bdg. 11.80 (978-0-613-57864-6(3)) Tandem Library Bks.

—Under the Waterfall. 2001. (gr. 5-8). lib. bdg. 11.80 (978-0-613-63136-5(6)) Tandem Library Bks.

Brinkerhoff, Phillip. To the Magical Pond. 2004. 116p. (YA). pap. 11.95 (978-0-7414-1982-8(3)) Infinity Publishing.

Britton, Susan. The Treekeepers. 2003. 256p. (J). (gr. 4-7). 16.99 (978-0-525-46944-5(3), Dutton Juvenile) Penguin Group (USA) Inc.

Brocato, Bert & Brocato, Tim. QuizQuester & the Captive of the Illusionist. 2002. (Illus.). 181p. pap. 8.95 (978-0-9718432-0-2(1)) QuizQuester Pr. LLC.

Bromden, David. A Gathering in the Mist. 2006. 280p. (YA). pap. 14.99 (978-1-59092-341-2(3)) Windstorm Creative.

Brookes, Diane. Su Lin & the Dragon. Carrareto, Mary-Lynn, illus. 1999. 24p. (J). (ps-3). pap. (978-0-9683640-0-0(4)) Raven Rock Publishing.

Brookes, Diane & Dahl, Roald. A Novel Study for Grades One & Two Based on the Twits. Blake, Quentin, illus. 1998. (J). pap., tchr. ed. (978-0-9683449-6-5(8)) Raven Rock Publishing.

—A Novel Study for Grades Two & Three Based on the Magic Finger. Blake, Quentin, illus. 1998. (J). pap., tchr. ed. (978-0-9683449-4-1(1)) Raven Rock Publishing.

Brooks, Bruce. Throwing Smoke. 2000. (Illus.). 144p. (J). (gr. 5 up). 15.95 (978-0-06-028972-0(4), Geringer, Laura Book) HarperCollins Pubs.

—Throwing Smoke. 2002. (gr. 3-6). lib. bdg. 14.10 (978-0-613-68470-5(2)) Tandem Library Bks.

Brooks, Kevin. Being. 2007. 336p. (J). (gr. 7 up). pap. 16.99 (978-0-439-89973-4(7), Chicken Hse., The) Scholastic, Inc.

Brooks, Stephen J. Alexander Asenby's Great Adventure. Rajesh, illus. 2006. 32p. (J). 16.96 (978-0-9769017-2-3(2)) Purple Sky Publishing.

Brooks, Terry. A Knight of the Word. 1999. (Word & the Void Ser.: Bk. 2). (gr. 7-12). lib. bdg. 15.30 (978-0-613-21872-6(8)) Tandem Library Bks.

—Morgawr. 2003. (Voyage of the Jerle Shannara Ser.: Bk. 3). lib. bdg. 16.45 (978-0-613-66596-4(1)) Tandem Library Bks.

Brothers Grimm Staff. Rumpelstiltskin. 2004. (Illus.). (J). (978-1-933530-17-8(0)) Bingo Bks., Inc.

Brouillet, Chrystine. Les Chevaux Enchantes. 2002. (Roman Jeunesse Ser.). (FRE.). 96p. (YA). (gr. 4-7). pap. (978-2-89021-221-3(1)) Diffusion du livre Mirabel.

—La Veuve Noire. 2002. (Roman Jeunesse Ser.). (FRE., Illus.). 96p. (YA). (gr. 4-7). pap. (978-2-89021-237-4(8)) Diffusion du livre Mirabel.

Brown, Farwell Abbie. John of the Woods. 2006. 32.99 (***978-1-4280-1771-9(2)***) IndyPublish.com.

Brown, Kevin. In a Field of Sunflowers. 2006. pap. 9.00 (978-0-8059-6921-4(7)) Dorrance Publishing Co., Inc.

Brown, Marc. Arthur & the Cootie-Catcher. Brown, Marc, illus. 15th ed. 1999. (Arthur Chapter Bks.: Bk. 15). (Illus.). 64p. (J). (gr. 2-4). pap. 4.25 (978-0-316-12266-5(1)) Little, Brown Bks. for Young Readers.

—Buster's Dino Dilemma. 7th ed. 1998. (Arthur Chapter Bks.: Bk. 7). (Illus.). 64p. (J). (gr. 2-4). pap. 4.25 (978-0-316-11560-5(6)); 13.95 (978-0-316-11559-9(2)) Little, Brown Bks. for Young Readers.

Brown, Michele. New Tales From Alice's Wonderland: Collection One. 2000. (Illus.). 96p. (J). pap. 13.99 (978-0-233-99610-3(9)) Andre Deutsch GBR. *Dist:* Independent Pubs. Group.

—New Tales from Alice's Wonderland: The March Hare's Big Secret. Martyr, Paula, illus. 1999. 24p. (J). pap. 7.99 (978-0-233-99537-3(4)) Andre Deutsch GBR. *Dist:* Independent Pubs. Group.

Brown, Sharon. Kit's Indian Summer. 2004. 68p. pap. 14.95 (978-1-4137-3956-5(3)) PublishAmerica, Inc.

Brown, Stan. Dragon Day. Rams, Vinod, illus. 2005. (Dragonlance Ser.: Vol. 6). 256p. (YA). pap. 5.99 (978-0-7869-3622-9(3)) Wizards of the Coast.

Browne, N. M. Basilisk. 2006. 320p. (YA). pap. 7.95 (978-1-58234-910-7(X), Bloomsbury Children) Bloomsbury Publishing.

—Hunted. 2004. 336p. (J). (gr. 5 up). reprint ed. pap. 7.95 (978-1-58234-903-9(7), Bloomsbury Children) Bloomsbury Publishing.

—Silverboy. 2007. (Illus.). 240p. (YA). 16.95 (978-1-58234-780-6(8), Bloomsbury Children) Bloomsbury Publishing.

Bruce, Karl. Annie Apple & the Teleportation Phantoms from Outer Space. 2006. (YA). pap. 16.00 (978-0-8059-7156-9(4)) Dorrance Publishing Co., Inc.

Bruchac, Joseph. Heroes & Heroines, Monsters & Magic: Native American Legends & Folktales. Burgevin, Daniel, illus. 2004. 200p. (gr. 3-7). reprint ed. pap. 12.95 (978-0-89594-995-0(4), Crossing Pr., Inc.) Ten Speed Pr.

Brundage, Frances, illus. Cinderella: A Fairy Story. 2004. reprint ed. pap. 15.95 (978-1-4179-8713-9(8)) Kessinger Publishing, LLC.

Buffie, Margaret. The Finder. 2005. (Watcher's Quest Ser.). (Illus.). (YA). 406p. (gr. 7-12). (978-1-55337-672-9(2)); 416p. (gr. 5-9). (978-1-55337-671-2(4)) Kids Can Pr., Ltd.

—The Seeker. 2004. (Watcher's Quest Ser.). (Illus.). 384p. (YA). (gr. 13 up). (978-1-55337-359-9(6)); (978-1-55337-358-2(8)) Kids Can Pr., Ltd.

—Seeker. 2002. (gr. 7-12). lib. bdg. 15.25 (978-0-613-70772-5(9)) Tandem Library Bks.

—The Watcher. 2004. (Watcher's Quest Ser.). (Illus.). 264p. (YA). (gr. 13 up). (978-1-55074-829-1(7)) Kids Can Pr., Ltd.

—Watcher. 2000. (gr. 7-12). lib. bdg. 15.25 (978-0-613-44540-5(6)) Tandem Library Bks.

Bujor, Flavia. The Prophecy of the Stones: A Novel. Coverdale, Linda, tr. 2005. Tr. of Prophetie des Pierres. 400p. (J). (gr. 5-17). reprint ed. pap. 7.99 (978-0-7868-5655-8(6)) Hyperion Bks. for Children.

Bull, Emma, et al. Firebirds: An Anthology of Original Fantasy & Science Fiction. Vess, Charles, illus. 2003. (Firebird Ser.). 432p. (YA). (gr. 6-11). 19.99 (978-0-14-250142-9(5), Puffin) Penguin Group (USA) Inc.

Bulla, Lynda. Katydid. 2003. (Illus.). 20p. (J). lib. bdg. 17.99 (978-0-9724272-1-0(X)) Katydid Publishing LLC.

Bulow, Wayde. Mystical Land: Short Stories for Children. 2001. 112p. pap. 9.95 (978-0-595-18550-4(9), Writers Club Pr.) iUniverse, Inc.

Bundy, Kim. Aiko. Less, Sally, illus. 2000. 32p. (J). 7.95 net. (978-0-9706654-0-9(7)) Sprite Pr.

Burch, Steve, et al. Mercury's Fire. 2001. (Pendragon Tales Ser.: Vol. 2). 317p. (YA). pap. 13.99 (978-0-9708834-1-4(2)) SPYMYTHS, Inc.

Burchell, Graham. The Ice Spells of Krollinad. 2005. 213p. pap. 11.99 (978-1-4116-5258-3(4)) Lulu.com.

—Wumpleberries & Grонglenuts. 2005. 242p. pap. 11.99 (978-1-4116-5399-3(8)) Lulu.com.

Burgess, Thornton W. Tommy & the Wishing Stone. (J). 19.95 (978-0-8488-0932-4(7)) Amereon LTD.

—Tommy's Change of Heart. (J). 19.95 (978-0-8488-1418-2(5)) Amereon LTD.

—Tommy's Wishes Come True. (J). 19.95 (978-0-8488-1419-9(3)) Amereon LTD.

—While the Story-Log Burns. (J). 18.95 (978-0-8488-0401-5(5)) Amereon LTD.

Burke, Anne. Crystal Forest of the Green Goddess. 2000. (Illus.). 20p. (J). (ps-3). pap. (978-0-7880-1440-6(4)) CSS Publishing Co.

Burnett, Frances Hodgson. The Secret Garden: A Young Reader's Edition of the Classic Story. 1999. (Aladdin Classics Ser.). (Illus.). 416p. (J). (gr. 4-7). pap. 5.99 (978-0-689-83141-6(2), Aladdin) Simon & Schuster Children's Publishing.

Burningham, John. La Cama Magica. 2004. (SPA., Illus.). (J). 19.99 (978-84-88342-46-1(2)) S.A. Kokinos ESP. *Dist:* Lectorum Pubns., Inc.

Burningham, John. Cloudland. 2007. (Illus.). 48p. (J). pap. 9.95 (***978-0-09-971161-2(3)***, Red Fox) Random Hse. Children's Bks. GBR. *Dist:* Independent Pubs. Group.

Burns Knight, Margy. Talking Walls. unabr. ed. 1999. (Illus.). (J). (gr. 1-4). audio 15.95 (978-1-883332-33-4(8)) Tilbury Hse. Pubs.

Burroughs, Edgar Rice. Minidoka. 1998. (937th Earl of One Mile Series). (Illus.). 64p. (YA). (gr. 7 up). 14.95 (978-1-56971-280-1(8)) Dark Horse Comics.

Burt, Steven E. The Star in the Apple. 2002. (J). pap. (978-0-9649283-8-1(8)) Burt Creations.

Burt, William. The King of the Trees. 2nd rev. ed. 2004. (Illus.). 224p. (J). (gr. 4-7). pap. 11.99 (978-1-57921-090-8(2)) WinePress Publishing.

Burt, William D. The Golden Wood: The King of the Trees, Bk. III. 2002. 288p. per. 14.95 (978-1-57921-466-1(5)) WinePress Publishing.

Burton, Martin Nelson. Fooling the Tooth Fairy. Hansen, Clint, illus. Tanner, Dean, photos by. 2005. 32p. (J). 17.00 (978-0-9666490-2-4(8)) London Town Pr.

Bush, Randall B. Gabriel's Magic Ornament. Schunemann, Ryan, illus. 2003. 120p. (gr. 5-8). pap. 11.95 (978-0-9716633-0-5(0)) Pristine Pubs., Inc.

Bustard, Ned. A Tale of Sir Galahad. Bustard, Ned, illus. 2000. per. 3.00 (978-1-930710-40-5(2)) Veritas Pr., Inc.

But I Knew Better: Individual Title, 6 pack. (gr. k-1). 23.00 (978-0-7635-9033-8(9)) Rigby Education.

Butcher, Kristin. The Tomorrow Tunnel. 2004. 188p. pap. (978-1-895449-90-7(1)) Thistledown Pr., Ltd.

Butler, Berwyn. Dinky the Doorknob: The Adventures of Sir Dinkum Wilhelm, the Third Earl of Surridge. 2005. (J). per. 11.99 (***978-1-933732-02-2(4)***, Round Rock Chapter Bks.) MidAmerica Publishing Co.

Butler, Berwyn & McClean, Shorty. Dinky the Doorknob. 2006. (J). lib. bdg. 21.95 (***978-1-933732-04-6(0)***, Round Rock Chapter Bks.) MidAmerica Publishing Co.

Butler, Charles. The Fetch of Mardy Watt. 2004. 222p. (Orig.). (J). pap. 9.99 (978-0-00-712857-0(6)) HarperCollins Pubs. Ltd. GBR. *Dist:* Independent Pubs. Group.

Butler, Susan. The Hermit Thrush Sings. 2001. (J). 12.15 (978-0-606-20414-9(8)) Tandem Library Bks.

Byars, Betsy. Burbujas, el Pez de una Tonelada. 2003. (SPA., Illus.). 160p. (YA). (gr. 5-8). 6.80 (978-84-279-3191-6(3), NG3953) Noguer y Caralt Editores, S. A. ESP. *Dist:* Lectorum Pubns., Inc.

Byers, Carla Rae. Finding My Star Shoes: Rainbow Journeys. Kepler, Kit, ed. l.t. ed. 2000. Vol. 4. (Illus.). 18p. (gr. 1 up). spiral bd. 7.95 (978-0-9656124-9-4(X)) Heyokah Publishing Co.

Byng, Georgia. Molly Moon Detiene el Mundo. 2004. (SPA.). 358p. (gr. 5-8). 18.99 (978-84-348-9610-9(9)) SM Ediciones ESP. *Dist:* Lectorum Pubns., Inc.

—Molly Moon, Micky Minus, & the Mind Machine. 2007. 416p. (J). (gr. 3-7). 16.99 (***978-0-06-075036-7(7)***); lib. bdg. 17.89 (***978-0-06-075037-4(5)***) HarperCollins Pubs.

—Molly Moon Stops the World. 2005. 416p. (J). (ps-7). reprint ed. pap. 7.99 (978-0-06-051415-0(9), Harper Trophy) HarperCollins Pubs.

—Molly Moon's Incredible Book of Hypnotism. 2nd ed. 2005. 432p. (J). (gr. 7 up). pap. 6.99 (978-0-06-075976-6(3), Harper Trophy) HarperCollins Pubs.

Byrd, Robert. The Hero & the Minotaur: The Fantastic Adventures of Theseus. Byrd, Robert, illus. 2005. (Illus.). 40p. (J). (gr. 1-ps). 17.99 (978-0-525-47391-6(2), Dutton Juvenile) Penguin Group (USA) Inc.

Byrne, John William. Jonnie & the Magic Whistle. 2007. 172p. per. (***978-1-84685-675-4(2)***, Exposure Publishing) Meadow Bks.

Cabot, Meg. Haunted. 2005. (Mediator Ser.: Bk. 5). 288p. (J). (gr. 7 up). pap. 6.99 (978-0-06-075164-7(9)) HarperCollins Pubs.

—Missing You. 2007. (1-800-Where-R-You Ser.: No. 5). 288p. (J). pap. 6.99 (978-0-06-087430-8(9), HarperTeen) HarperCollins Pubs.

Cadnum, Michael. Phaeton & the Chariot of the Sun. 2004. (Starfall Ser.). 128p. (J). (gr. 4-7). pap. 16.95 (978-0-439-54533-4(1), Orchard Bks.) Scholastic, Inc.

Calderwood, David & Retlin, Stieg. The Dragonslayer's Apprentice. 1998. (Point Fantasy Ser.). (Illus.). 160p. (YA). (gr. 6-12). pap. 4.50 (978-0-590-63093-1(8)) Scholastic, Inc.

Caldwell, Walter, text. The Tree in the Field of Mathingamy Thame. ltd. ed. 2002. (Stories of Mathingamy Thame Ser.). 30p. 18.95 (978-1-930729-02-5(2)) What's Inside Pr.

Calhoun, Dia. Aria of the Sea. 2003. 272p. (J). pap. 7.95 (978-0-374-40454-3(2), Sunburst) Farrar, Straus & Giroux.

—Aria of the Sea. 2003. (gr. 5-8). lib. bdg. 16.40 (978-0-613-59572-8(6)) Tandem Library Bks.

—Aria of the Sea. (Illus.). (gr. 5-9). 2002. 340p. (YA). pap. 5.95 (978-1-58837-019-8(4)); 2000. 264p. (J). 15.95 (978-1-890817-25-1(2)) Winslow Pr.

—Avielle of Rhia. 2006. 400p. (J). 16.99 (978-0-7614-5320-8(2)) Cavendish, Marshall Corp.

—Firegold. 2003. 304p. (YA). pap. 8.95 (978-0-374-42311-7(3), Sunburst) Farrar, Straus & Giroux.

—Firegold. (YA). 2003. 285p. (gr. 8-12). per. 17.60 (978-0-613-59617-6(X)); 1999. (Illus.). (gr. 6 up). (978-0-606-18341-3(8)) Tandem Library Bks.

—Firegold. l.t. ed. 2005. 415p. (YA). (gr. 7-12). per. 21.95 (978-0-7862-7696-7(7), Large Print Pr.) Thorndike Pr.

—Firegold. 2001. 352p. (J). (gr. 7-12). pap. 5.95 (978-1-58837-003-7(8)) Winslow Pr.

—Firegold. Blondon, Herve, illus. 1999. (J). (gr. 7-12). 285p. 15.95 (978-1-890817-10-7(4)); 286p. pap. 9.95 (978-1-890817-28-2(7)) Winslow Pr.

Calhoun, Terry. The Muggwapps. 2007. (J). pap. 8.00 (***978-0-8059-7223-8(4)***) Dorrance Publishing Co., Inc.

Cameron-Anasti, Patsy, et al, contrib. by. Spider Riders Bk. 1: Shards of the Oracle. movie tie-in ed. 2005. (Illus.). 224p. (J). 15.00 (978-1-55704-653-6(0)); pap. 5.99 (978-1-55704-652-9(2)) Newmarket Pr.

Cameron, Anne. Dreamspeaker. unabr. ed. 2005. 128p. pap. 9.95 (978-1-55017-364-2(2)) Harbour Publishing Co., Ltd. CAN. *Dist:* Graphic Arts Ctr. Publishing Co.

—Dreamspeaker. 2000. 128p. (YA). (gr. 7-9). mass mkt. 5.95 (978-0-7736-7482-0(9)) Stoddart Kids CAN. *Dist:* Fitzhenry & Whiteside, Ltd.

Campbell, Charles K. La Magic Coin. 2004. (YA). (gr. 3 up). per. 15.00 (978-0-9742064-3-1(1)) Unmistakably C K C.

Cañas, José. El Gato Que Quiso Volar Alto. (SPA.). 84p. (J). (gr. 3-5). 9.50 (978-84-241-3370-2(6)) Everest de Ediciones y Distribucion, S.L. ESP. *Dist:* Lectorum Pubns., Inc.

Cannizzaro, Debbie. We Live in Mandeville: 0. l.t. ed. 2005. (Illus.). 32p. (J). lib. bdg. 9.99 (978-0-9762262-0-8(0)) DeCa Communications, LLC.

Cannon, Ann. The Guardian Lepraclone. Sincak, Tom, illus. 1998. 32p. (J). (gr. 1-4). lib. bdg. 14.95 (978-0-9649539-1-8(9)) Star Chaser Pr.

—The Legend of the Lepraclone. Williamson, Melissa, illus. 1998. 32p. (J). (ps-3). lib. bdg. 14.95 (978-0-9649539-0-1(0)) Star Chaser Pr.

Cannon, Janell. Trupp: A Fuzzhead Tale. 1998. (Illus.). 48p. (J). pap. 7.00 (978-0-15-201695-1(3), Harcourt Paperbacks) Harcourt Children's Bks.

—Trupp: A Fuzzhead Tale. 1998. (J). (978-0-606-13876-5(5)) Tandem Library Bks.

Capeci, Anne. Insect Invaders. 2001. (gr. 3-6). lib. bdg. 11.80 (978-0-613-63304-8(0)) Tandem Library Bks.

Capeci, Anne & Speirs, John. Insect Invaders. 2001. 87p. (J). pap. (978-0-439-26551-5(7)) Scholastic, Inc.

Capone, Deb. Tooth Fairy Tales. 2005. (J). 14.95 (***978-0-9728666-7-5(1)***) As Simple As That Publishing.

Carbajal, Xavier Joseph. Captain Nemo, Set. abr. ed. 1999. (Captain Nemo Legacy Ser.: Vol. 13). (YA). (gr. 6 up). pap. 18.95 incl. audio (978-0-9654507-7-5(5), 97-92534) New Future Publishing.

Card, Orson Scott, ed. Future on Ice. rev. ed. 1998. 432p. (YA). (gr. 7 up). 24.95 (978-0-312-86694-5(1), Tor Bks.) Doherty, Tom Assocs., LLC.

Cardosi, Calesse. The Gifts. 2007. 192p. (YA). 16.95 (***978-0-9776281-3-1(2)***) HPH Publishing.

Cardwell, Helen. Amber Janusson & the Battle for the Magic Lands. 2004. 124p. (YA). pap. 10.95 (978-0-595-33006-5(1)) iUniverse, Inc.

Carey, Janet Lee. The Beast of Noor. 2006. 512p. (J). 16.95 (978-0-689-87644-8(0)) Simon & Schuster Children's Publishing.

Carle, Eric. The Mixed-up Chameleon. Carle, Eric, illus. 1998. (Illus.). 32p. (J). (ps up). 7.99 (978-0-694-01147-6(9), Harper Festival) HarperCollins Pubs.

Carlson, Lavelle. Rocks in My Socks & Rainbows Too, 10 vols. Adams, Lucas, illus. 2003. 32p. (J). per. 16.95 (978-0-9725803-2-8(8)) Children's Publishing.

Carman, Patrick. Atherton. 2nd ed. 2008. 304p. 16.99 (***978-0-316-16672-0(3)***) Little Brown & Co.

Carman, Patrick. The Dark Hills Divide. 2003. (Land of Elyon Ser.: Bk. 1). 200p. (J). pap. 11.95 (978-0-9742287-0-9(2)) Amped Media.

Carmi, Daniella. Samir y Jonatan en el Planeta Marte. 2002. (Joven Coleccion Ser.). (SPA.). 144p. (YA). (gr. 5-8). (978-84-85334-95-7(7), LG7474) Loguez Ediciones ESP. *Dist:* Lectorum Pubns., Inc.

Carmody, Isobelle. Dreamwalker. Woolman, Steven, illus. 2002. 48p. (YA). (978-0-7344-0007-9(1), Lothian Bks.) Hachette Livre Australia.

—A Fox Called Sorrow. (Little Fur Ser.). (Illus.). (J). (gr. 1-7). 2008. 272p. 5.99 (978-0-375-83857-6(0)); 2007. 256p. 14.99 (978-0-375-83856-9(2), Random Hse. Bks. for Young Readers); 2007. 256p. lib. bdg. 16.99 (978-0-375-93856-6(7), Random Hse. Bks. for Young Readers) Random Hse. Children's Bks.

—The Legend Begins. 2006. (Illus.). 208p. (J). (gr. 1-7). 12.95 (978-0-375-83854-5(6)); (gr. 3-7). lib. bdg. 14.99 (978-0-375-93854-2(0)) Random Hse. Children's Bks. (Random Hse. Bks. for Young Readers).

—Little Fur: The Legend Begins. 2006. (Illus.). 272p. (J). (978-0-375-83855-2(4)) Random Hse., Inc.

—A Mystery of Wolves: Little Fur #3. 2008. (J). pap. (***978-0-375-83859-0(7)***); (Little Fur: 3). 12.99 (***978-0-375-83858-3(9)***); (Little Fur: 3). lib. bdg. 15.99 (***978-0-375-93858-0(3)***) Random Hse., Inc.

—Night Gate. 2006. 272p. (gr. 4-7). 6.50 (978-0-375-83017-4(0), Yearling) Random Hse. Children's Bks.

—Winter Door. (Gateway Trilogy Ser.). 336p. (J). (gr. 3-5). 2007. 5.99 (978-0-375-83019-8(7), Yearling); 2006. 16.95 (978-0-375-83018-1(9), Random Hse. Bks. for Young Readers); 2006. lib. bdg. 18.99 (978-0-375-93018-8(3), Random Hse. Bks. for Young Readers) Random Hse. Children's Bks.

Carothers, Daniella. Over the Valley. 2007. 148p. pap. 17.95 (***978-1-59299-291-1(9)***) Inkwater Pr.

Carpenter, Nancy Sippel. The Land of Unicorns. 1999. (Sticker Stories Ser.). (Illus.). 16p. (J). (ps-1). pap. 4.99 (978-0-448-41984-8(X), Grosset & Dunlap) Penguin Group (USA) Inc.

Carrol, Jacqueline. Strongest Evil. 2003. (gr. 3-6). lib. bdg. 13.00 (978-0-613-72477-7(1)) Tandem Library Bks.

Carroll, Jenny, pseud. Reunion. 2005. (Mediator Ser.: Bk. 3). 304p. (YA). (gr. 7 up). pap. 7.99 (978-0-06-072513-6(3)) HarperCollins Pubs.

Carroll, Lewis, pseud. Alice im Wunderland. 1999. Tr. of Alice in Wonderland. (GER., Illus.). (J). (ps up). 12.95 (978-3-499-20733-4(8)) Rowohlt Taschenbuch Verlag GmbH DEU. *Dist:* Distribooks, Inc.

—Alice in Wonderland. 2007. 228p. 12.99 (***978-1-58726-532-7(X)***) Ann Arbor Media Group, LLC.

—Alice in Wonderland. Tenniel, John, illus. 2007. 204p. 24.95 (***978-1-58218-791-4(6)***); per. 14.95 (***978-1-58218-790-7(8)***) Digital Scanning, Inc.

—Alice in Wonderland. Zwerger, Lisbeth, illus. 2007. 103p. (J). (ps). 24.99 (***978-0-698-40052-8(6)***, Minedition) Penguin Group (USA) Inc.

—Alice in Wonderland. 2004. (Illus.). 96p. (J). 9.99 (978-0-517-22362-8(7), Gramercy) Random Hse. Value Publishing.

—Alice in Wonderland Jigsaw Book. Tenniel, John, illus. 1999. 16p. (J). 19.99 (978-0-333-76291-2(6)) Macmillan Publishers Ltd. GBR. *Dist:* Independent Pubs. Group.

—Alice Through the Looking-Glass. Oxenbury, Helen, illus. 2005. 208p. (J). (gr. 3-7). 24.99 (978-0-7636-2892-5(1)) Candlewick Pr.

—Alice Through the Looking-Glass. Reed, Jeremy, ed. Brown, Trevor R., illus. 2000. (Classic Portables Ser.). 192p. (J). reprint ed. 10.95 (978-1-84068-021-8(0)) Creation Bks. GBR. *Dist:* Subterranean Co.

—Alice's Adventures in Wonderland. Date not set. (J). lib. bdg. 16.95 (978-0-8488-1262-1(X)) Amereon LTD.

—Alice's Adventures in Wonderland. Tenniel, John, illus. Date not set. 248p. (YA). 14.95 (978-1-884807-19-0(4)) Blushing Rose Publishing.
—Alice's Adventures in Wonderland. Oxenbury, Helen, illus. 2003. 208p. (J). (gr. 3). pap. 12.99 (978-0-7636-2049-3(1)) Candlewick Pr.
—Alice's Adventures in Wonderland. Carruth, Jane, ed. Cloke, Rene, illus. 2000. 93p. (J). (gr. 4-6). reprint ed. 25.00 (978-0-7881-9229-6(9)) DIANE Publishing Co.
—Alice's Adventures in Wonderland. 1998. (Illus.). 192p. (J). (gr. 3-5). pap. 3.99 (978-0-87406-864-1(9) , Silver Elm Classic) Darby Creek Publishing.
—Alice's Adventures in Wonderland. Noble, Marty, illus. 1998. (Dover Children's Thrift Classics Ser.). 80p. (J). pap. 1.00 (978-0-486-40345-8(9)) Dover Pubns., Inc.
—Alice's Adventures in Wonderland. unabr. ed. 2001. (Dover Juvenile Classics Ser.). (Illus.). 160p. (J). (gr. 4-7). pap. 3.00 (978-0-486-41658-8(5)) Dover Pubns., Inc.
—Alice's Adventures in Wonderland. Steadman, Ralph, illus. 2006. 128p. pap. 19.95 (978-1-55407-203-3(4)) Firefly Bks., Ltd.
—Alice's Adventures in Wonderland, Vol. 1. Ewing, Carolyn, illus. 1999. (Selected Classic Fairy Tales Ser.). 20p. (J). (gr. k-7). lib. bdg. 13.95 (978-1-56674-220-7(X)) Forest Hse. Publishing Co., Inc.
—Alice's Adventures in Wonderland. Date not set. 192p. (YA). (gr. 3 up). mass mkt. 8.99 (978-0-06-440929-2(5)); (Illus.). 176p. (J). 14.95 (978-0-06-095770-4(0)) HarperCollins Pubs.
—Alice's Adventures in Wonderland, Level 2. 2nd abr. ed. 2000. (Bookworms Ser.). (Illus.). 64p. 6.50 (978-0-19-422964-7(5)) Oxford Univ. Pr., Inc.
—Alice's Adventures in Wonderland, Level 2. 2001. (Illus.). 48p. (C). pap. 9.00 (978-0-582-42123-3(3)) Pearson ESL.
—Alice's Adventures in Wonderland. rev. ed. 2002. (Illus.). 160p. (J). (gr. 2). pap. 3.99 (978-0-439-29149-1(6)) Scholastic, Inc.
—Alice's Adventures in Wonderland. 2000. (Aladdin Classics Ser.). (Illus.). 176p. (J). (gr. 3-7). pap. 3.99 (978-0-689-83375-5(X) , Aladdin) Simon & Schuster Children's Publishing.
—Alice's Adventures in Wonderland. Ghiuselev, Iassen, illus. 2003. 120p. 29.95 (978-1-894965-00-2(0)) Simply Read Bks. CAN. *Dist:* Perseus Distribution.
—Alice's Adventures in Wonderland. Oxenbury, Helen, illus. 2003. 207p. (J). (gr. 4-7). per. 22.25 (978-0-613-60270-9(6)) Tandem Library Bks.
—Alice's Adventures in Wonderland. (gr. 3-6). 2001. lib. bdg. 11.80 (978-0-613-66612-1(7)); 2000. lib. bdg. 11.80 (978-0-613-63173-0(0)) Tandem Library Bks.
—Alice's Adventures in Wonderland. (Children's Classics). (ENG., Illus.). 2001. 272p. (J). pap. (978-1-85326-118-3(1)); 1998. 288p. pap. (978-1-85326-002-5(9) , 0029WW) Wordsworth Editions, Ltd.
—Alice's Adventures in Wonderland: A Classic Illustrated Edition. 2000. (Illus.). 152p. (J). (gr. 4-7). 19.95 (978-0-8118-2274-9(5)) Chronicle Bks. LLC.
—Alice's Adventures in Wonderland: With a Discussion of Imagination. Schneider, Rex, tr. Schneider, Rex, illus. 2003. (J). (978-1-59203-046-0(7)) Learning Challenge, Inc.
—Alice's Adventures in Wonderland & Through the Looking-Glass. Tenniel, John, illus. 1998. (Puffin Bks.). 336p. (J). (gr. 3-7). 4.99 (978-0-14-038351-5(4) , Puffin) Penguin Group (USA) Inc.
—Alice's Adventures in Wonderland & Through the Looking-Glass: And What Alice Found There. Haughton, Hugh, ed. rev. ed. 2003. (Illus.). 400p. (YA). (gr. 12). pap. 9.00 (978-0-14-143976-1(9) , Penguin Classics) Penguin Group (USA) Inc.
—Alice's Adventures in Wonderland & Through the Looking-Glass: The Classic Collection. 2005. 256p. (J). pap. 7.99 (978-1-4003-0753-1(8)) Nelson, Thomas Inc.
—Alice's Adventures under Ground. 1999. (Illus.). 120p. (J). 17.95 (978-1-85145-471-6(3) , Pavilion Bks., Ltd.) Anova Bks. GBR. *Dist:* Trafalgar Square Publishing.
—Alice's Adventures under Ground. Deitch, Kim, illus. 2000. (Cottage Classics). 88p. (YA). (gr. 3-12). 29.95 (978-1-892847-00-3(0)) Word Play Pubns.
—Alicia en el Pais de las Maravillas. (SPA.). 152p. 24.95 (978-84-261-2700-6(2)) Juventud, Editorial ESP. *Dist:* Distribooks, Inc.
—Alicia en el Pais de las Maravillas. (SPA.). pap. 11.95 (978-84-95311-04-7(6)) Mestas, Jorge A. Ediciones Escolares La Escuela Nueva y Alinorma, S.L. ESP. *Dist:* Distribooks, Inc.
—Las Aventuras de Alicia. (Coleccion Clasicos de la Juventud). (SPA., Illus.). 240p. (J). 12.95 (978-84-7189-060-3(7) , ORT308) Ortells, Alfredo Editorial S.L. ESP. *Dist:* Continental Bk. Co., Inc.
—The Best of Lewis Carroll. Tenniel, John & Holiday, Henry, illus. 2001. 480p. (gr. 4-7). pap. 7.99 (978-0-7858-1326-2(8)) Book Sales, Inc.
—Jabberwocky. Stewart, Joel, illus. 2003. 32p. (J). (ps-2). 15.99 (978-0-7636-2018-9(1)) Candlewick Pr.
—The Story of Sylvie & Bruno. 2005. pap. 31.95 (978-0-7661-9697-1(6)) Kessinger Publishing, LLC.
—Through the Looking Glass. Date not set. 176p. (J). 19.95 (978-0-8488-2629-1(9)) Amereon LTD.
—Through the Looking-Glass. 1999. (gr. 7-12). lib. bdg. 9.50 (978-0-613-82766-9(X)) Tandem Library Bks.
—Through the Looking Glass: And What Alice Found There. 1999. (Thrift Edition Ser.). 128p. (gr. 6). pap. 2.00 (978-0-486-40878-1(7)) Dover Pubns., Inc.
—Through the LookingGlass. l.t. ed. 2006. 176p. pap. (978-1-84637-329-9(8)) Echo Library.
—A Traves del Espejo. 2002. (Clover Ser.). (SPA., Illus.). 204p. (YA). 11.50 (978-84-392-8028-6(9) , EV5540) Lectorum Pubns., Inc.
Carroll, Lewis, pseud & Baker, Kyle. Through the Looking Glass. (Classics Illustrated Ser.). (Illus.). 52p. (YA). pap. 4.95 (978-1-57209-002-6(2)) Classics International Entertainment, Inc.
Carroll, Lewis, pseud & Hedge, Tricia. Through the Looking Glass: And What Alice Found There, Level 3. 2nd abr. ed. 2000. (Bookworms Ser.). (Illus.). 80p. 6.50 (978-0-19-423019-3(8)) Oxford Univ. Pr., Inc.
Carroll, Lewis, pseud & Kipling, Rudyard. Alice's Adventures in Wonderland. 2003. (J). cd-rom (978-0-9724995-2-1(0)) Alcazar AudioWorks.
Carroll, Lewis, pseud & Sabuda, Robert. Alice's Adventures in Wonderland. 2003. (Classic Collectible Pop-Up Ser.). (Illus.). 12p. (J). 26.99 (978-0-689-84743-1(2) , Little Simon) Simon & Schuster Children's Publishing.
Carroll, Lewis, pseud, et al. Alice's Adventures in Wonderland. 2002. (Illus.). 208p. (J). 19.95 (978-1-58717-152-9(X) , SeaStar Bks.) Chronicle Bks. LLC.
Cart, Michael. Tomorrowland: Ten Stories about the Future. 2001. 208p. (YA). (gr. 6 up). pap. 4.99 (978-0-590-37679-2(9)) Scholastic, Inc.
Carter, Anne. The Girl on Evangeline Beach. 2001. (Illus.). 253p. (YA). (gr. 7-9). pap. 7.95 (978-0-7737-6139-1(X)) Stoddart Kids CAN. *Dist:* Fitzhenry & Whiteside, Ltd.
Carter, David & Carter, Noelle. The Nutcracker: A Pop-Up Adaptation of E. T. A. Hoffmann's Original Tale. Carter, David & Carter, Noelle, illus. 2004. (Illus.). 16p. (J). (gr. k-4). reprint ed. 20.00 (978-0-7567-8231-3(7)) DIANE Publishing Co.
Carter, R. J. Alices Journey Beyond Moon. Wright, Lucy, illus. 2004. 98p. (978-1-903889-76-3(6)) Telos Publishing, Ltd. GBR. *Dist:* Fitzhenry & Whiteside, Ltd.
Carter, Timothy. Epoch. 2007. 312p. (J). (gr. 7 up). pap. 8.95 (***978-0-7387-1066-2(0)***) Llewellyn Pubns.
Casado, Dami. Como Comes Tu? (SPA.). 8p. 9.95 (978-84-272-8325-1(3)) Molino, Editorial ESP. *Dist:* Distribooks, Inc.
—Como Te Lavas? (SPA.). 8p. 9.95 (978-84-272-8326-8(1)) Molino, Editorial ESP. *Dist:* Distribooks, Inc.
—Como Te Vistes? (SPA.). 8p. 9.95 (978-84-272-8328-2(8)) Molino, Editorial ESP. *Dist:* Distribooks, Inc.
Casaro, Jesus M. Las Sombras de la Caverna. 1998. Tr. of Cavern's Shadow. (SPA., Illus.). 120p. (gr. 4-7). 11.95 (978-84-204-4801-5(X)) Santillana USA Publishing Co., Inc.
Casey, C. A. Dragon Drool. 2005. (J). 21.95 (978-0-9759555-0-5(0)); per. 9.95 (978-0-9759555-1-2(9)) Bedazzled Ink Publishing Co.
Caso, George R. The Mission. Caso, George R., illus. 2003. (Illus.). 16p. (J). (ps-6). pap. 4.95 (978-0-9719290-1-2(7)) Caso, George R.
Castilla, Julia Mercedes. El Tesoro de la Pordiosera. Diaz, Carlos Manuel, illus. 2002. (SPA.). 118p. pap. 5.30 (978-958-04-6889-9(3)) Norma S.A. COL. *Dist:* Lectorum Pubns., Inc.
The Castle in the Attic. 1999. (J). 11.95 (978-1-56137-830-2(5)) Novel Units, Inc.
Castro, Griselda. De Como Nacieron las Sirenas. Roldan, Gustavo, illus. 2000. (Tren Azul Ser.). (SPA.). 32p. (J). (ps-2). (978-84-236-5492-5(3)) Edebé ESP. *Dist:* Baker & Taylor Bks., Lectorum Pubns., Inc.
Catanese, P. W. The Riddle of the Gnome. 2007. 256p. (J). pap. 5.99 (978-1-4169-1252-1(5) , Aladdin) Simon & Schuster Children's Publishing.
Catran, Ken. Voyage with Jason. 2005. 208p. pap. (978-0-7344-0151-9(5) , Lothian Bks.) Hachette Livre Australia.
Cattell, James. Albuman's Quest. Davidson, Dorelle, illus. 2002. 32p. (J). (978-0-7344-0166-3(3) , Lothian Bks.) Hachette Livre Australia.
Cauldwell, E. S. Alma Mae & the Golden Treasure. Myers, Shari, illus. 2007. (J). per. 19.95 (***978-0-9788985-8-8(3)***) A Better Be Write Pub.
Chabon, Michael. Summerland. 2004. (gr. 3-6). lib. bdg. 17.60 (978-0-613-90441-4(9)) Tandem Library Bks.
—Summerland. l.t. ed. 2003. 615p. (J). 25.95 (978-0-7862-5143-8(3)) Thorndike Pr.
—Summerland: A Novel. 2004. 512p. (J). (ps-17). reprint ed. pap. 8.95 (978-0-7868-1615-6(5)) Miramax Bks.
Chan, San Wei, illus. Spear & Shield. (978-0-9744905-0-2(4)) Santoon Bks.
Chananie, Gloria. Fearful Frannie's African Safari. 2006. 95p. pap. 14.95 (978-1-4241-2617-0(7)) PublishAmerica, Inc.
Chandler, Elizabeth. The Deep End of Fear. 2003. (gr. 7-12). lib. bdg. 13.00 (978-0-613-61757-4(6)) Tandem Library Bks.
Chapman, Linda. Dreams Come True. 2006. (My Secret Unicorn Ser.: No. 2). (Illus.). 128p. (J). pap. 4.99 (978-0-439-81383-9(2) , Scholastic Paperbacks) Scholastic, Inc.
—Dreams Come True. Hull, Biz, illus. 2002. 120p. (J). (978-0-439-60010-1(3)) Scholastic, Inc.
—Flying High. 2006. (My Secret Unicorn Ser.). 144p. (J). pap. 4.99 (978-0-439-81384-6(0) , Scholastic Paperbacks) Scholastic, Inc.
—The Magic Spell. Hull, Biz, illus. 2003. 136p. (J). (978-0-439-60009-5(X)) Scholastic, Inc.
—Magic Spell. 2006. (My Secret Unicorn Ser.: No. 1). (Illus.). 128p. (J). pap. 4.99 (978-0-439-81382-2(4) , Scholastic Paperbacks) Scholastic, Inc.
Chariton, Dan & Weiss, Stacy. Silver Surfer, Vol. 2. 2005. (Silver Surfer Ser.: Vol. 2). (Illus.). 192p. (YA). pap. 19.99 (978-0-7851-1575-5(7)) Marvel Enterprises, Inc.
Charlesworth, Liza. Word Family Tales: Dine with Nine Messy Monsters. Phillips, Matt, illus. 2002. (Word Family Tales Ser.). 16p. (ps-2). pap. 2.95 (978-0-439-26250-7(X)) Scholastic, Inc.
Charlie & Champ. 2nd ed. 2004. (J). 4.95 (978-0-943864-57-0(7)) Davenport, May Pubs.
Chastain, Sandra. Kaseybelle: The Tiniest Fairy in the Kingdom, 1 bk. Chadwick, Cindy, illus. 2004. 32p. (J). 14.95 (978-0-9673035-6-7(7) , 24) BelleBks.
Cherie, J. Speed. 2003. (gr. 7-12). lib. bdg. 14.15 (978-0-613-61675-1(8)) Tandem Library Bks.
Cherryh, C. J. Faded Sun. 2000. (gr. 7-12). lib. bdg. 16.45 (978-0-613-21517-6(6)) Tandem Library Bks.
—Fortress of Owls. 2000. (gr. 7-12). lib. bdg. 15.90 (978-0-613-27832-4(1)) Tandem Library Bks.
Chetwin, Grace. The Foundling of Snawbyr Crygg: Part 2 of the Lords of Aelyth-kintalyn. 2003. (Ulm Ser.: 3). (Illus.). 140p. (YA). pap. 15.00 net. (978-1-930094-13-0(2) , Rivet Bks.) Feral Pr., Inc.
—Jason's Wonderful Week of Fabulous Night Rides. 2003. Orig. Title: Jason's Seven Magical Night Rides. (Illus.). 116p. (J). pap. 25.00 net. (978-1-930094-12-3(4) , Rivet Bks.) Feral Pr., Inc.
Chew, E. B. Daniel & the Grubby Old Book. 2007. 196p. per. 14.95 (***978-0-595-34880-0(7)***) iUniverse, Inc.
Chiang, Dean. The Yearning. 2000. (Illus.). 96p. (YA). pap. 10.95 (978-0-943151-11-3(2)) Slave Labor Bks.
Chic, Suzy & Touvay, Monique. Watching. 2007. 48p. (J). 12.00 (***978-1-905341-07-8(5)***) WingedChariot Pr. GBR. *Dist:* Independent Pubs. Group.
Child, Lauren. I Can Do Anything That's Everything All on My Own. 2008. (Charlie & Lola Ser.). 24p. (J). (ps-1). 3.99 (***978-0-448-44792-6(4)***, Grosset & Dunlap) Penguin Group (USA) Inc.
Childress, Jenna Lynn. Dragon Soul: Book One of the Triune Jewels. 2003. 262p. (YA). per. 8.00 (978-0-9704006-2-8(4)) Bound & Determined Pubs.
Chima, Cinda Williams. The Warrior Heir. 2007. 448p. (gr. 7-17). pap. 8.99 (***978-0-7868-3917-9(1)***) Hyperion Pr.
Chinery, Michael. Enciclopedia de los Animales Salvajes, 8 vols.Tr. of Wild World of Animals. (SPA.). 346p. (J). (gr. 3-5). 100.00 (978-84-241-2059-7(0)) Everest de Ediciones y Distribucion, S.L. ESP. *Dist:* Lectorum Pubns., Inc.
Chiu, Harry. Enve Lopt Unfolded. 2007. 268p. per. 17.95 (***978-0-595-44707-7(4)***) iUniverse, Inc.
Chizuru, Mio. The Pirate & the Princess Volume 1: the Timelight Stone: The Timelight Stone. 2007. 110p. (J). pap. 5.99 (***978-1-933164-43-4(3)***) Seven Seas Entertainment, LLC.
—The Pirate & the Princess Volume 2: the Red Crystal: The Red Crystal. 2007. 110p. (J). pap. 5.99 (***978-1-933164-44-1(1)***) Seven Seas Entertainment, LLC.
Cho, Jerry, et al. Stray Little Devil. 2006. (Illus.). 200p. (YA). pap. 9.95 (978-1-59796-043-4(8)) DrMaster Pubns. Inc.
Chomiak, Joseph N. & Swanson, Matt. Mookie: A Girl in Maximsubornia. Tremlin, Nathan A., illus. 2000. 48p. (J). 17.95 (978-0-9676688-0-2(8)) Tremiak Publishing.
Christensen, James C., et al. Voyage of the Basset. 2003. (Illus.). 168p. (J). (gr. 4-7). tchr. ed. 29.95 (978-1-885183-58-3(5)) Artisan.
Christensen, Margaret Kate. The Hollyhock Fairies. 2004. 48p. per. (978-1-932077-85-8(5)) Athena Pr.
Christopher, Evans. Dreamtime Spiritfeather. (Illus.). 119p. (J). pap. 8.99 (978-1-85881-710-1(2)) Orion Bks. Ltd. GBR. *Dist:* Trafalgar Square Publishing.
Christopher, John. When the Tripods Came. 2003. (Tripods Ser.). (Illus.). 160p. (YA). mass mkt. 5.99 (978-0-689-85762-1(4) , Simon Pulse) Simon & Schuster Children's Publishing.
—When the Tripods Came. 2003. (gr. 7-12). lib. bdg. 13.00 (978-0-613-61829-8(7)) Tandem Library Bks.
Chrono, Nanae. Peacemaker Kurogane, Vol. 1. Forsyth, Amy, tr. 2004. (Illus.). 194p. (YA). pap. (978-1-4139-0161-0(1)) ADV Manga.
—Peacemaker Kurogane, Vol. 2. 2004. (Illus.). 184p. (YA). pap. (978-1-4139-0192-4(1)) ADV Manga.
Ciencin, Scott. Jurassic Park Adventures, Bk. 1. 2001. (Step into Reading Ser.). (Illus.). (J). (978-0-606-21274-8(4)) Tandem Library Bks.
—Sky Dance. 1999. (Dinotopia Ser.: No. 10). (Illus.). 264p. (J). (gr. 3-6). pap. 4.99 (978-0-679-80417-8(X)) Random Hse., Inc.
—Sky Dance. 1999. (Dinotopia Ser.). (Illus.). (J). (978-0-606-20468-2(7)) Tandem Library Bks.
Ciencin, Scott & Burge, Constance M. Luck Be a Lady. 2004. (Charmed Ser.). (Illus.). 224p. (YA). mass mkt. 11.95 (978-0-689-85793-5(4) , Simon & Schuster Children's Publishing) Simon & Schuster Children's Publishing.
Ciencin, Scott & Ciencin, Denise. Mortal Fear. 2003. (Buffy the Vampire Slayer Ser.). (Illus.). 496p. (YA). pap. 21.95 (978-0-7434-2771-5(8) , Simon Pulse) Simon & Schuster Children's Publishing.
Circle of Friends: The Camelot Rabbitry Serires - Volume Three. 2006. (Camelot Rabbitry Ser.: 3). (Illus.). 98p. (J). per. 9.95 (978-0-9672375-3-4(X)) Camelot Tales.
Clairday, Robynn. Tell Me This Isn't Happening!, 1 vol. 1999. 144p. (gr. 3-7). pap. 4.50 (978-0-439-09502-0(6)) Scholastic, Inc.
Clamp. CardCaptor Sakura, Vol. 3. 3rd rev. ed. 2004. (Juvenile Favorite Ser.). (Illus.). (J). pap. 9.99 (978-1-59182-880-8(5) , Tokyopop Kids) TOKYOPOP, Inc.
—CardCaptor Sakura, Vol. 4. Clamp, illus. rev. ed. 2005. (Illus.). 200p. pap. 9.99 (978-1-59182-881-5(3) , Tokyopop Kids) TOKYOPOP, Inc.
—Cardcaptor Sakura: Master of the Clow, 6 vols. (Illus.). 192p. (gr. 2-6). Vol. 1. 2002. pap. 9.99 (978-1-892213-75-4(3)); Vol. 3. 2003. pap. 9.99 (978-1-892213-77-8(X)); Vol. 4. 2003. pap. 9.99 (978-1-892213-78-5(8)) TOKYOPOP, Inc. (Tokyopop Kids).
—Cardcaptor Sakura Vol. 6, 6 vols. 6th rev. ed. 2003. (Master of the Clow Ser.). (Illus.). (gr. 2 up). pap. 9.99 (978-1-892213-80-8(X) , Tokyopop Kids) TOKYOPOP, Inc.
—Fugue. Olsen, Lillian, tr. 2002. (X/1999 Ser.: Vol. 10). (Illus.). 180p. (YA). pap. 9.95 (978-1-56931-896-6(4)) Viz Media.
—Magic Knight Rayearth, 3 vols., Vol. 1. 2003. (Illus.). 192p. (gr. 2 up). pap. 9.99 (978-1-59182-082-6(0) , Tokyopop Kids) TOKYOPOP, Inc.
—Magic Knight Rayearth, 6 vols., Vol. 2. Sengupta, Anita, tr. from JPN. rev. ed. 2003. (Illus.). 208p. pap. 9.99 (978-1-59182-083-3(9) , Tokyopop Kids) TOKYOPOP, Inc.
—Magic Knight Rayearth, 2 vols., Vol. 2, Set. 2003. (Illus.). 650p. (gr. 2 up). pap. 29.99 (978-1-59182-091-8(X)) TOKYOPOP, Inc.
—Magic Knight Rayearth II, 3 vols., Vol. 3. rev. ed. 2004. (Illus.). 192p. pap. 9.99 (978-1-59182-268-4(8) , Tokyopop Kids) TOKYOPOP, Inc.
—Master of the Clow 5. 2003. (gr. 3-6). lib. bdg. 18.80 (978-0-613-80317-5(5)) Tandem Library Bks.
—Waltz, Vol. 15. Clamp, illus. 2004. (X/1999 Ser.). (Illus.). 200p. (YA). pap. 9.95 (978-1-59116-349-7(8)) Viz Media.
—X/1999 Vol. 16: Nocturne. Clamp, illus. 2004. (X/1999 Ser.). (Illus.). 184p. (YA). pap. 9.95 (978-1-59116-596-5(2)) Viz Media.
Clamp, creator. CardCaptor Sakura, 6 vols., Vol. 5. 2001. 184p. pap. 9.99 (978-1-892213-73-0(7)) TOKYOPOP, Inc.
Clamp, ed. Magic Knight Rayearth, 6 vols., 3. rev. ed. 2003. (Illus.). 208p. pap. 9.99 (978-1-59182-084-0(7) , Tokyopop Kids) TOKYOPOP, Inc.
—Magic Knight Rayearth II, 3 vols., Vol. 1. 2004. (Illus.). 192p. pap. 9.99 (978-1-59182-266-0(1) , Tokyopop Kids) TOKYOPOP, Inc.
Clamp, illus. & creator. Rg Veda. Clamp, creator. 2005. pap. 9.99 (978-1-59532-484-9(4) , Tokyopop Adult) TOKYOPOP, Inc.
—Tokyo Babylon, Vol. 7. Clamp, creator. rev. ed. 2005. 160p. pap. 9.99 (978-1-59532-051-3(2) , Tokyopop Adult) TOKYOPOP, Inc.
Clamp, et al. Cardcaptor Sakura: Master of the Clow, 6 vols., Vol. 2. rev. ed. 2002. (Illus.). 192p. (gr. 2-6). pap. 9.99 (978-1-892213-76-1(1) , Tokyopop Kids) TOKYOPOP, Inc.
Clanahan, Mary. Nama Kwa's Garden. Taylor, Jacqui, illus. 2005. 72p. (J). (ps-7). 12.95 (978-1-77007-025-7(7)) Struik Pubs. ZAF. *Dist:* International Publishers Marketing.
Clancy, Kaycee. Sky Painters. 2007. (J). per. 11.95 (***978-0-9776777-8-8(8)***) Legacy Publishing Services, Inc.
Clarizio, Laura. If i Had a Magic Carpet. 2005. 48p. pap. 12.95 (978-1-4137-8557-9(3)) PublishAmerica, Inc.
Clark, Catherine A. The Golden Pine Cone. Guzek, Greta, illus. 2nd unabr. ed. 192p. (Orig.). (J). pap. (978-1-55017-085-6(6)) Harbour Publishing Co., Ltd.
Clark, Malcolm. Bounty's Cave. 2007. (ENG.). 156p. per. 19.95 (***978-1-932762-82-2(5)***) Elderberry Press, Inc.
Clausen, Andrew. Prince Caspian. 2003. stu. ed., ring bd. 14.99 (978-1-58609-195-8(6)) Progeny Pr.
Clement-Davies, David. Fell. 2007. 432p. (YA). pap. 19.95 (***978-0-8109-9470-6(4)***) Abrams, Harry N. , Inc.
Clement, Maryceleste. Mr. Tootles & the Polka-Dot Lollypops. Schexnayder, Paul, illus. 2004. (Tootle Tales Ser.: Vol. 2). 32p. (J). 14.95 (978-0-9721706-1-1(8)) Tootle Time Publishing Co.
Clish, Marian L. You Choose the Way: A Book That Reads Like a Game - Mazash the Wizard. Anderson, Jan, illus. l.t. ed. 1999. (J). (gr. k-5). 56p. pap. 7.95 (978-1-928632-07-8(6)); pap. 14.95 incl. audio compact disk (978-1-928632-09-2(2)) Writers Marketplace:Consulting, Critiquing & Publishing.
—You Choose the Way: A Book That Reads Like a Game: Mazash the Wizard. 1999. (J). (gr. 2-7). 22.95 incl. cd-rom (978-1-928632-25-2(4)) Writers Marketplace:Consulting, Critiquing & Publishing.
—You Choose the Way: A Book That Reads Like a Game: Mazash the Wizard. Anderson, Jan, illus. unabr. ed. 1999. (J). (gr. 3-5). 15.95 (978-1-928632-23-8(8)) Writers Marketplace:Consulting, Critiquing & Publishing.
Clone of My Own 7. 1999. (J). (gr. 4-6). per. 3.99 (978-0-689-82857-7(8) , Aladdin) Simon & Schuster Children's Publishing.
Clone of My Own 8. 1999. (J). (gr. 4-6). per. 3.99 (978-0-689-82858-4(6) , Aladdin) Simon & Schuster Children's Publishing.
Clone of My Own 9. 1999. (J). (gr. 4-6). per. 3.99 (978-0-689-82859-1(4) , Aladdin) Simon & Schuster Children's Publishing.
Coates, Theresa. Imaginary Time of Life. 2007. 102p. pap. 10.95 (***978-0-7414-4067-9(9)***) Infinity Publishing.
Cofer, Amadeus. Aloha Adventure: The Magic of Imagination on a Rainy Day. l.t. ed. 2004. (Illus.). 36p. (J). 14.00 (978-1-932957-01-3(4)) Legacy Pubs.
Coffin, Bill & Siembieda, Kevin. Systems Failure. Marciniszyn, Alex et al, eds. Wilson, Michael et al, illus. 1999. 144p. (YA). (gr. 8 up). pap. 12.95 (978-1-57457-038-0(2)) Palladium Bks., Inc.
Cohen, Daniel. Prophets of Doom: Millennium Edition. 1999. (Single Titles Ser.: up). (Illus.). 160p. (gr. 7-12). lib. bdg. 24.90 (978-0-7613-1317-5(6) , Millbrook Pr.) Lerner Publishing Group.
Cohen, Elly, illus. Peg Bearskin. 2003. (J). pap. (978-0-9688712-7-0(5)) Running the Goat.
Cohen, Warren Lee. Dragon Baked Bread. Ssebulime, John, illus. 2005. 32p. (J). (978-1-902636-70-2(8)) Clairview Bks.
Coia, Kristina. Lymeria. 2007. 120p. (YA). 20.95 (***978-0-595-69347-4(4)***); per. 10.95 (***978-0-595-45268-2(X)***) iUniverse, Inc.
Cola, Arthur. Papa & the Gingerbread Man. 2006. 14.95 (***978-0-9789423-0-4(2)***) Cola, Arthur.

E F G

Colbert, Norman. Norman Okay, Not Today. 2001. 109p. pap. 10.95 (978-0-7414-0674-3(8)) Infinity Publishing.

Cole, Myke. The Wildsidhe Chronicles Bk. 6: Car Trouble. 2003. (J). pap. 7.99 (978-1-890096-18-2(0)) Padwolf Publishing, Inc.

Cole, Stephen. Resurrection, No. 3. 2005. (Wereling Ser.). 272p. (YA). (gr. 7-12). mass mkt. 5.99 (978-1-59514-043-2(3) , Razorbill) Penguin Group (USA) Inc.

Colfer, Eoin. The Eternity Code. 2003. (Artemis Fowl Ser.: Bk. 3). (Illus.). 320p. (J). pap. 7.99 (978-0-7868-1815-0(8)) Hyperion Bks. for Children.

—The Legend of Captain Crow's Teeth. McCoy, Glenn, illus. 2005. 112p. (J). (gr. 2-6). 12.95 (978-0-7868-5502-5(9)) Miramax Bks.

—The Supernaturalist. (gr. 5-17). 2005. 267p. (YA). pap. 7.99 (978-0-7868-5149-2(X)); 2004. (Illus.). 272p. 16.95 (978-0-7868-5148-5(1)) Hyperion Bks. for Children.

—The Wish List. 2003. (Illus.). 256p. (gr. 7-17). 16.95 (978-0-7868-1863-1(8) , Disney Editions) Disney Pr.

—The Wish List. l.t. ed. 2004. 274p. 23.95 (978-0-7862-6383-7(0)) Thorndike Pr.

Collins, Anthony. Rip Power: Reading gave him the strength to fight Back! 2006. 178p. per. 12.99 (978-1-59886-469-4(6)) Tate Publishing & Enterprises, L.L.C.

Collins, Craig, et al. Visitors. 1999. (Buffy the Vampire Slayer Ser.: No. 9). 176p. (YA). (gr. 7 up). pap. 5.99 (978-0-671-02628-8(3) , Simon Pulse) Simon & Schuster Children's Publishing.

Collins, Max Allan. Jax Epoch & the Quicken Forbidden Vol. 1: Borrowed Magic. Beatty, Terry, illus. 2003. 156p. (gr. 8 up). pap. 14.95 (978-1-932051-11-7(2)) A i T/Planet Lar.

Collins, Paul. The Great Ferret Race. 2002. (Illus.). 160p. (YA). pap. (978-0-7344-0272-1(4) , Lothian Bks.) Hachette Livre Australia.

—Slaves of Quentaris. (Illus.). 160p. pap. (978-0-7344-0557-9(X) , Lothian Bks.) Hachette Livre Australia.

—Swords of Quentaris. 2005. 160p. pap. (978-0-7344-0470-1(0) , Lothian Bks.) Hachette Livre Australia.

Collins, Suzanne. Gregor & the Code of Claw. 2007. (Underland Chronicles). 416p. (YA). (gr. 5-9). pap. 17.99 (*978-0-439-79143-4(X) , Scholastic Pr.) Scholastic, Inc.

—Gregor & the Curse of the Warmbloods. 368p. 2006. (J). pap. 6.99 (978-0-439-65624-5(9) , Scholastic Paperbacks); 2005. (Underland Chronicles: Bk. 3). pap. 16.95 (978-0-439-65623-8(0) , Scholastic Pr.) Scholastic, Inc.

—Gregor & the Curse of the Warmbloods. l.t. ed. 2006. 297p. (J). 23.95 (978-0-7862-8083-4(2)) Thorndike Pr.

—Gregor & the Marks of Secret. 352p. (J). 2007. pap. 6.99 (*978-0-439-79146-5(4) , Scholastic Paperbacks); Vol. 4. 2006. pap. 16.99 (978-0-439-79145-8(6) , Scholastic Pr.) Scholastic, Inc.

—Gregor & the Marks of Secret. rev. l.t. ed. 2007. (Underland Chronicles Ser.). 343p. (YA). 23.95 (*978-0-7862-9553-1(8)) Thorndike Pr.

Collins, Suzanne. Gregor & the Prophecy of Bane. (J). (gr. 3-6). 2005. (Underland Chronicles: Bk. 2). 304p. 6.99 (978-0-439-65076-2(3)); 2004. (Underland Chronicles: Bk. 2). 320p. 16.95 (978-0-439-65075-5(5) , Scholastic Pr.); 2003. 320p. 16.95 (978-0-439-43536-9(6)) Scholastic, Inc.

—Gregor & the Prophecy of Bane. l.t. ed. 2006. 297p. 23.95 (978-0-7862-8084-1(0)) Thorndike Pr.

Come Away from the Water, Shirley. 2004. (J). pap. 14.95 incl. audio (978-1-56008-183-8(X)) Weston Woods Studios, Inc.

Come Away from the Water Shirley, 2004. (J). 24.95 incl. audio (978-1-56008-182-1(1)) Weston Woods Studios, Inc.

Comella, Maria Angeles. Donde Esta la Reina? Comella, Maria Angeles, illus. 2001. (CAT., Illus.). 32p. (J). (gr. k-4). 14.95 (978-84-8488-001-1(X)) Serres, Ediciones, S. L. ESP. *Dist:* Lectorum Pubns., Inc.

—Donde Esta la Reina? Comella, Maria Angeles, illus. Dominguez, Juan Manuel, photos by. 2001. (SPA., Illus.). 126p. (J). (gr. k-4). 14.95 (978-84-95040-98-5(0)) Serres, Ediciones, S. L. ESP. *Dist:* Lectorum Pubns., Inc.

Coniglio, Michael. Two Times, One: Traveling the Time Fanta. 2005. 233p. pap. 19.95 (978-1-4137-6402-4(9)) PublishAmerica, Inc.

Conover, Chris. Lion's Share. 2003. (gr. k-3). lib. bdg. 15.25 (978-0-613-71866-0(6)) Tandem Library Bks.

Conrad, Pam. The Tub People. Egielski, Richard, illus. 2002. (J). 15.49 (978-0-7587-3869-1(2)) Book Wholesalers, Inc.

Constable, Kate. The Tenth Power. (Chanters of Tremaris Trilogy Ser.: Bk. 3). (Illus.). 320p. (J). 2007. pap. 5.99 (978-0-439-55483-1(7)); 2006. (gr. 7 up). pap. 16.99 (978-0-439-55482-4(9)) Scholastic, Inc. (Levine, Arthur A. Bks.).

—The Waterless Sea, Bk. 2. 2006. (Chanters of Tremaris Trilogy Ser.: Bk. 2). (Illus.). 336p. (J). pap. 5.99 (978-0-439-55481-7(0) , Levine, Arthur A. Bks.) Scholastic, Inc.

—The Waterless Sea Bk. 2: Chanters of Tremaris. 2005. (Illus.). 320p. (J). pap. 16.95 (978-0-439-55480-0(2) , Levine, Arthur A. Bks.) Scholastic, Inc.

Cooney, Caroline B. Goddess of Yesterday. 2003. 272p. (YA). (gr. 7). pap. 6.50 (978-0-440-22930-8(8) , Laurel Leaf) Random Hse. Children's Bks.

—Prisoner of Time. 1999. 224p. (YA). (gr. 7-12). pap. 5.50 (978-0-440-22019-0(X) , Laurel Leaf) Random Hse. Children's Bks.

Cooper, Clare. One Day on Morfa. 2001. 112p. pap. 12.95 (978-1-85902-946-6(9)) Beekman Bks., Inc.

—Time Ball. 2003. 72p. pap. 11.95 (978-1-84323-255-1(3)) Beekman Bks., Inc.

Cooper, Louise. Creatures: Once I Caught a Fish Alive. unabr. ed. 2000. (Read-Along Ser.). 152p. (J). pap. incl. audio (978-0-7540-6225-7(2) , RA026, Chivers Children's Audio Bks.) BBC Audiobooks America.

Cooper, Paul Fenimore. Tal, His Marvelous Adventures with Noom-Zor-Noom. Reeves, Ruth, illus. 2001. 320p. (J). (gr. 3-7). 20.00 (978-1-930900-08-0(2)) Purple Hse. Pr.

Cooper, Susan. The Boggart. Rayyan, Omar, illus. 2004. 208p. (J). pap. 5.99 (978-0-689-86930-3(4) , Aladdin) Simon & Schuster Children's Publishing.

—The Boggart & the Monster. Rayyan, Omar, illus. 2004. 192p. (J). pap. 5.99 (978-0-689-86931-0(2) , Aladdin) Simon & Schuster Children's Publishing.

—The Dark Is Rising. (Dark Is Rising Sequence Ser.). 244p. (YA). (gr. 5 up). pap. 4.99 (978-0-8072-1533-3(3) , Listening Library) Random Hse. Audio Publishing Group.

—The Dark Is Rising. (Dark Is Rising Sequence Ser.). 2007. 272p. (YA). pap. 8.99 (*978-1-4169-4965-7(8) , Simon Pulse); 2005. 232p. pap. 2.99 (978-1-4169-0528-8(6) , Aladdin); 1999. 232p. (J). (gr. 7 up). pap. 5.99 (978-0-689-82983-3(3) , Aladdin); 2007. 256p. (J). (gr. 4-8). pap. 6.99 (*978-1-4169-4995-4(X) , Aladdin); 2007. 272p. (YA). (gr. 7). pap. 8.99 (*978-1-4169-4969-5(0) , Simon Pulse) Simon & Schuster Children's Publishing.

—The Dark Is Rising. 1999. (Dark Is Rising Sequence Ser.). (gr. 5-8). lib. bdg. 13.00 (978-0-613-90606-7(3)) Tandem Library Bks.

—The Dark Is Rising. l.t. ed. 2001. (Dark Is Rising Sequence Ser.). 395p. (J). (gr. 4-7). 21.95 (978-0-7862-2920-8(9)) Thorndike Pr.

—The Dark Is Rising Boxed Set: The Dark Is Rising, Greenwitch, over Sea, under Stone, Silver on the Tree, the Grey King. 2007. (Dark Is Rising Sequence Ser.). 1088p. (J). pap., pap. 29.99 (*978-1-4169-4996-1(8) , Aladdin) Simon & Schuster Children's Publishing.

—Green Boy. 2003. (Illus.). 208p. (J). pap. 5.99 (978-0-689-84760-8(2) , Aladdin) Simon & Schuster Children's Publishing.

—Greenwitch. (Dark Is Rising Sequence Ser.). 2007. 176p. (YA). pap. 8.99 (*978-1-4169-4966-4(6) , Simon Pulse); 2000. 144p. (J). (gr. 4-7). pap. 5.99 (978-0-689-84034-0(9) , Aladdin) Simon & Schuster Children's Publishing.

—Greenwitch. 2000. (Dark Is Rising Sequence Ser.). (J). 11.64 (978-0-606-19710-6(9)); (gr. 3-6). lib. bdg. 13.00 (978-0-613-29971-8(X)) Tandem Library Bks.

—Greenwitch. l.t. ed. 2001. (Dark Is Rising Sequence Ser.). 131p. (J). 21.95 (978-0-7862-2923-9(3)) Thorndike Pr.

—The Grey King. 2002. (Dark Is Rising Sequence Ser.). (Illus.). (J). 13.40 (978-0-7587-0188-6(8)) Book Wholesalers, Inc.

—The Grey King. (Dark Is Rising Sequence Ser.). 2007. 192p. (YA). pap. 8.99 (*978-1-4169-4967-1(4) , Simon Pulse); 1999. 176p. (J). (gr. 4-7). pap. 5.99 (978-0-689-82984-0(1) , Aladdin) Simon & Schuster Children's Publishing.

—The Grey King. 1999. (Dark Is Rising Sequence Ser.). (gr. 5-8). lib. bdg. 13.00 (978-0-613-73286-4(3)) Tandem Library Bks.

—The Grey King. l.t. ed. 2002. (Dark Is Rising Sequence Ser.). 262p. (J). 21.95 (978-0-7862-2919-2(5)) Thomson Gale.

—King of Shadows. unabr. ed. 2004. 192p. (J). (gr. 5-9). pap. 36.00 incl. audio (978-0-8072-8388-2(6) , Listening Library) Random Hse. Audio Publishing Group.

—King of Shadows. 2001. (J). (978-0-606-21281-6(7)) Tandem Library Bks.

—Over Sea, under Stone. 2002. (Dark Is Rising Sequence Ser.). (Illus.). (J). 13.40 (978-0-7587-5635-0(6)) Book Wholesalers, Inc.

—Over Sea, under Stone. 2007. (Dark Is Rising Sequence Ser.). 224p. (YA). pap. 8.99 (*978-1-4169-4964-0(X) , Simon Pulse) Simon & Schuster Children's Publishing.

—Over Sea, under Stone. Wiesner, David, illus. 2000. (Dark Is Rising Sequence Ser.). 208p. (J). (gr. 4-7). pap. 5.99 (978-0-689-84035-7(7) , Aladdin) Simon & Schuster Children's Publishing.

—Over Sea, under Stone. 2000. (Dark Is Rising Sequence Ser.). (gr. 7-12). lib. bdg. 13.00 (978-0-613-30082-7(3)) Tandem Library Bks.

—Over Sea, under Stone. l.t. ed. 2000. (Dark Is Rising Sequence Ser.). 332p. (J). (gr. 4-7). 22.95 (978-0-7862-2918-5(7)) Thorndike Pr.

Cooper, Susan. Silver on the Tree. 2002. (Dark Is Rising Sequence Ser.). (Illus.). (J). 13.40 (978-0-7587-5639-8(9)) Book Wholesalers, Inc.

—Silver on the Tree. (Dark Is Rising Sequence Ser.). 288p. 2007. (YA). pap. 8.99 (*978-1-4169-4968-8(2) , Simon Pulse); 2000. (J). (gr. 4-7). pap. 5.99 (978-0-689-84033-3(0) , Aladdin) Simon & Schuster Children's Publishing.

—Silver on the Tree. 2000. (Dark Is Rising Sequence Ser.). (gr. 5-8). lib. bdg. 13.00 (978-0-613-30127-5(7)) Tandem Library Bks.

—Silver on the Tree. l.t. ed. 2002. (Dark Is Rising Sequence Ser.). (Illus.). 430p. (J). 23.95 (978-0-7862-2921-5(7)) Thomson Gale.

Corbett, Sue. 12 Again. 2002. (Illus.). 160p. (J). (gr. 5-9). 16.99 (978-0-525-46899-8(4) , Dutton Juvenile) Penguin Group (USA) Inc.

Corbett, W. J. Quest for the End of the Tail. 2002. (Ark of the People Ser.: Vol. 2). (Illus.). (J). (gr. 4-7). mass mkt. 11.99 (978-0-340-77340-6(5) , Hodder & Stoughton) Hodder General Publishing Division GBR. *Dist:* Trafalgar Square Publishing.

—Spell to Save the Golden Snake. 2003. (Ark of the People Ser.: Vol. 3). (Illus.). (J). (gr. 4-7). mass mkt. 11.99 (978-0-340-85064-0(7) , Hodder & Stoughton) Hodder General Publishing Division GBR. *Dist:* Trafalgar Square Publishing.

Corder, Zizou. Lionboy: The Chase. 2005. (Lionboy Trilogy : Bk. 2). (Illus.). 288p. (J). (gr. 3-7). pap. 6.99 (978-0-14-240454-6(3) , Puffin) Penguin Group (USA) Inc.

—Lionboy: The Chase. Van Deelen, Fred, illus. 2004. (Lionboy Trilogy Ser.: Bk. 2). 272p. (J). (gr. 5). 15.99 (978-0-8037-2984-1(7) , Dial) Penguin Group (USA) Inc.

—Truth. 2005. (Lionboy Trilogy : Bk. 3). (Illus.). 240p. (J). (gr. 5). 16.99 (978-0-8037-2985-8(5) , Dial) Penguin Group (USA) Inc.

Cordero, Silvia Jaeger. El Huevo Azul. Sunset Producciones Staff, illus. rev. ed. 2004. (Castillo de la Lectura Verde Ser.). (SPA.). 136p. (J). (gr. 4-6). pap. 7.95 (978-970-20-0127-0(7)) Castillo, Ediciones, S. A. de C. V. MEX. *Dist:* Macmillan.

Corduroy. 2004. (J). pap. 32.75 incl. audio (978-1-55592-210-8(4)); pap. 32.75 incl. audio (978-1-55592-211-5(2)); pap. 14.95 incl. audio (978-0-7882-0677-1(X)); pap. 14.95 incl. audio (978-1-55592-655-7(X)) Weston Woods Studios, Inc.

Corlett, William. The Bridge in the Clouds. 2003. 20.25 (978-0-8446-7239-7(4)) Smith, Peter Pub., Inc.

—The Door in the Tree. 2000. (Magician's House Quartet Ser.: Vol. 2). (Illus.). 304p. (YA). (gr. 7-12). mass mkt. 4.99 (978-0-7434-1002-1(5) , Simon Pulse) Simon & Schuster Children's Publishing.

—The Door in the Tree. 2000. (978-0-606-20635-8(3)) Tandem Library Bks.

—The Tunnel Behind the Waterfall. 2001. (gr. 7-12). lib. bdg. 13.00 (978-0-613-74172-9(2)) Tandem Library Bks.

Corman, Dick. Fountain of Age. 2006. 185p. (YA). pap. 12.95 (*978-0-9655749-2-1(X)) Corman Productions.

Cormier, Shawn P. Nomadin. 2003. 296p. (YA). per. 12.95 (978-0-9740151-0-1(5)) Pine View Pr.

Cornish, D. M. Foundling, Bk. 1. 2007. (Monster Blood Tattoo Ser.). 448p. (YA). (gr. 7 up). 8.99 (*978-0-14-240913-8(8) , Puffin) Penguin Group (USA) Inc.

—Lamplighter: Monster Blood Tattoo, Book 2: Monster Blood Tattoo, Book 2. 2008. 400p. (YA). (gr. 7). 18.99 (*978-0-399-24639-5(8) , Putnam Juvenile) Penguin Group (USA) Inc.

Cornish, D. M. Monster Blood Tattoo: Foundling. 2006. 404p. (YA). (gr. 4 up). 18.99 (978-0-399-24638-8(X) , Putnam Juvenile) Penguin Group (USA) Inc.

Coronado, Jinky. Banzai Girl: Manga TPB. 2006. (YA). 9.95 (978-0-9763095-2-9(1)) Arcana Studio, Inc.

Corrie, Chad. Gambit's End. 2007. (Divine Gambit Trilogy Ser.: Bk. 3). (Illus.). 492p. pap. 15.99 (*978-0-9776043-5-7(7)) Aspirations Media, Inc.

Corwin, Susan Simon. The Cryptic Cat. Corwin, Stuart, illus. 2006. 99p. (YA). (*978-0-9790632-0-6(5)) Lucky Duck Designs.

Cosby, Andrew. Mary Scary. 2007. 56p. (YA). 9.95 (978-1-59307-730-3(0)) Dark Horse Comics.

Cosgrove, Stephen. Gnome from Nome. James, Robin, illus. 2003. (Serendipity Bks.). 32p. (J). (gr. k-3). pap. 4.99 (978-0-8431-0585-8(2) , Price Stern Sloan) Penguin Group (USA) Inc.

—Gnome from Nome. 2003. (gr. k-3). lib. bdg. 13.00 (978-0-613-70763-3(X)) Tandem Library Bks.

—Nitter Pitter. 2002. (gr. k-3). lib. bdg. 13.00 (978-0-613-57629-1(2)) Tandem Library Bks.

—Wheedle on the Needle. James, Robin, illus. ed. 2002. (Serendipity Ser.). 32p. (J). reprint ed. pap. 4.99 (978-0-8431-4872-5(1) , Price Stern Sloan) Penguin Group (USA) Inc.

Cosmic, Debris & Reger, Rob. Emily's Good Nightmares. 2005. (Illus.). 64p. (J). 12.95 (978-0-8118-4771-1(3)) Chronicle Bks. LLC.

Cote, Denis. L' Arrivee des Inactifs. 2002. (Roman Plus Ser.). (FRE.). 160p. (YA). (gr. 8 up). pap. (978-2-89021-191-9(6)) Diffusion du livre Mirabel.

—Les Chemins de Mirlande. 2003. (Roman + Ser.). 160p. (YA). (gr. 8 up). pap. (978-2-89021-310-4(2)) Diffusion du livre Mirabel.

Coté, Denis. La Forêt aux Mille et un Périls, Tome 2. Poulin, Stephane, illus. 2004. (Roman Jeunesse Ser.). (FRE.). 96p. (J). (gr. 4-7). pap. (978-2-89021-696-9(9)) Diffusion du livre Mirabel.

—La Machination du Scorpion Noir. 2004. (Mon Roman Ser.). (FRE.). 160p. (J). (gr. 2). pap. (978-2-89021-667-9(5)) Diffusion du livre Mirabel.

Coursen, H. R. Return to Archerland: Sequel to the Search for Archerland. 1999. 224p. pap. 16.95 (978-0-918606-14-3(4)) Heidelberg Graphics.

Coville, Bruce. The Attack of the Two-Inch Teacher. unabr. ed. 2000. (I Was a Sixth Grade Alien Ser.). 165p. (J). (gr. 3-5). pap. 28.00 incl. audio (978-0-8072-8354-7(1) , YA170SP, Listening Library) Random Hse. Audio Publishing Group.

—The Attack of the Two-Inch Teacher. 1999. (I Was a Sixth Grade Alien Ser.). (Illus.). (J). 10.64 (978-0-606-18374-1(4)) Tandem Library Bks.

—A Glory of Unicorns. 1998. (J). pap. (978-0-590-95582-9(9)) Scholastic, Inc.

—Into the Land of the Unicorns. (Unicorn Chronicles: Bk. 1). 159p. (J). (gr. 4-7). pap. 4.50 (978-0-8072-1518-0(X) , Listening Library) Random Hse. Audio Publishing Group.

—Into the Land of the Unicorns. rev. ed. 1999. (Unicorn Chronicles: Vol. 1). 176p. (J). (gr. 4-7). pap. 4.99 (978-0-439-10838-6(1)) Scholastic, Inc.

—Into the Land of the Unicorns. 1999. (Unicorn Chronicles: Bk. 1). (Illus.). (J). (gr. 4-7). 11.64 (978-0-606-21863-4(7)) Tandem Library Bks.

—The Skull of Truth. Lippincott, Gary A., illus. 2002. (Magic Shop Bks.). 208p. (YA). (gr. 3-7). 17.00 (978-0-15-204612-5(7)) Harcourt Children's Bks.

—Song of the Wanderer. 2001. (Unicorn Chronicles: Bk. 2). (978-0-606-22215-0(4)); 2000. (gr. 3-6). lib. bdg. 12.40 (978-0-613-44369-2(1)) Tandem Library Bks.

—Thor's Wedding Day: By Thialfi, the Goat Boy. Cogswell, Matthew, illus. 2005. 144p. (J). (ps-7). 15.00 (978-0-15-201455-1(1)) Harcourt Children's Bks.

Cowan, Catherine. My Life with Wave. Buehner, Mark, illus. ed. 2004. (J). (gr. k-3). spiral bd. (978-0-616-11863-4(5)) Canadian National Institute for the Blind/Institut National Canadien pour les Aveugles.

Cowell, Cressida. Heroic Misadventures of Hiccup the Viking, the: the First Collection Boxed Set. 2007. (gr. 3-7). 28.99 (*978-0-316-00592-0(4)) Little, Brown Bks. for Young Readers.

Cowley, Joy. Starbright & the Dream Eater. 208p. (gr. 4 up). Date not set. (J). pap. 4.99 (978-0-06-440791-5(8)); 2000. (Illus.). (YA). 14.89 (978-0-06-028420-6(X)); 2000. (Illus.). (YA). 14.95 (978-0-06-028419-0(6)) HarperCollins Pubs.

Craig, Janet. Good Luck Clover. 1999. (gr. k-3). lib. bdg. 10.10 (978-0-613-76296-0(7)) Tandem Library Bks.

Crew, Gary. Gothic Hospital. 2002. (Illus.). 160p. (YA). pap. (978-0-7344-0232-5(5) , Lothian Bks.) Hachette Livre Australia.

Crilley, Mark. Creatch Battler. 2006. (Illus.). 272p. (J). (gr. 4-7). 5.99 (978-0-440-41953-2(0) , Yearling) Random Hse. Children's Bks.

—Rogmasher Rampage. 2005. (Illus.). 224p. (J). (gr. 4-7). 10.95 (978-0-385-73112-6(4)); lib. bdg. 12.99 (978-0-385-90137-6(2)) Random Hse. Children's Bks. (Delacorte Bks. for Young Readers).

Croggon, Alison. The Crow. 2007. (Pellinor Ser.: Bk. 3). (Illus.). 528p. (YA). (gr. 7 up). 18.99 (*978-0-7636-3409-4(3)) Candlewick Pr.

—The Naming. 2006. (Pellinor Ser.: Bk. 1). 528p. (YA). (gr. 7). pap. 8.99 (978-0-7636-3162-8(0)) Candlewick Pr.

—The Riddle. (Pellinor Ser.: Bk. 2). (Illus.). (YA). (gr. 7). 2007. 528p. pap. 8.99 (*978-0-7636-3414-8(X)); 2006. 512p. 17.99 (978-0-7636-3015-7(2)) Candlewick Pr.

Croggon, Allison. Naming: The First Book of Pellinor, No. 1. 2005. 528p. (YA). (gr. 7 up). 17.99 (978-0-7636-2639-6(2)) Candlewick Pr.

Cross, Frances. Boy the Witch & the Blobber 1. 2007. (Blobber Trilogy Ser.). (Illus.). 96p. pap. 7.95 (*978-1-84167-560-2(1)) Ransom Publishing Ltd. GBR. *Dist:* International Publishers Marketing.

Cross, Gillian. The Dark Ground, Bk. 1. 2004. (Dark Ground Ser.). 272p. (J). (gr. 5). 15.99 (978-0-525-47350-3(5) , Dutton Juvenile) Penguin Group (USA) Inc.

—Gobbo the Great. l.t. ed. 2000. 192p. (J). pap. (978-0-7540-6123-6(X) , CLP 315) BBC Audio.

—Gobbo the Great. unabr. l.t. ed. 2003. (Read-Along Ser.). 176p. (J). 24.95 incl. audio (978-0-7540-6241-7(4) , RA042, Galaxy Children's Large Print) BBC Audiobooks America.

—Pictures in the Dark. 1998. (978-0-606-13703-4(3)) Tandem Library Bks.

Croteau, Marie-Danielle & St. Aubin, Bruno. Des Fantomes Sous la Mer. 2003. (Roman Jeunesse Ser.). (FRE., Illus.). 96p. (J). (gr. 4-7). pap. (978-2-89021-610-5(1)) Diffusion du livre Mirabel.

Crow, Gary & Crow, Brock. JimJim Meets PosterGuy. 2006. 100p. (J). pap. 14.95 (978-0-9759621-5-2(9)) Koenisha Pubns.

Crowe, Carole. Sharp Horns on the Moon. 2003. 128p. (YA). (gr. 4-6). 14.95 (978-1-56397-671-1(4)) Boyds Mills Pr.

Crum, Shutta & Beder, John. TCick. 2004. (Illus.). 24p. pap. (978-1-55005-079-0(6)) Fitzhenry & Whiteside, Ltd.

Cue, Ian J. The Renewal: First Encounter. 2003. 192p. (YA). per. 9.95 (978-0-9741989-0-3(0)) Mill Creek Metro Publishing.

Cunningham, Mary. Cynthia's Attic: The Missing Locket. 2005. (J). pap. 9.99 (978-1-59080-441-4(4)) Echelon Press Publishing.

Curley, Marianne. The Key. (J). 2006. 416p. pap. 8.95 (978-1-59990-001-8(7)); 2005. 250p. 16.95 (978-1-58234-953-4(3)) Bloomsbury Publishing. (Bloomsbury Children).

—The Named. (J). 2002. 332p. (gr. 5 up). 16.95 (978-1-58234-779-0(4)); 2005. 336p. reprint ed. pap. 8.95 (978-1-58234-913-8(4)) Bloomsbury Publishing. (Bloomsbury Children).

Curran, Steven Earl. Whales used to Fly in the Sky. 2005. 9.00 (978-0-8059-8086-8(5)) Dorrance Publishing Co., Inc.

Curry, Don, ed. The Legend of Shrek. 2007. 32p. (J). 19.99 (*978-0-696-23934-2(5)) Meredith Bks.

Curry, Kenneth. The Legend of the Dancing Trees: An African American Folk Tale. 2007. 111p. (J). per. 14.95 (*978-0-9798364-0-4(9)) Curry Brothers Publishing.

Curry, Kenneth, et al. The Legend of the Dancing Tees Teachers Resource: The Legend of the Dancing Trees. 2007. Tr. of Teachers Resource. per. 19.95 (*978-0-9798364-1-1(7)) Curry Brothers Publishing.

Curtis, Philip. El Senor Browser y los Afilacerebros. Ross, Tony, illus. (SPA.). 112p. (YA). (gr. 5-8). (978-84-239-2754-8(7) , EC2750) Espasa Calpe, S.A. ESP. *Dist:* Lectorum Pubns., Inc.

Cutler, Ivor. El Desayuno de Tomas. (SPA., Illus.). 30p. (J). (gr. k-3). pap. 8.95 (978-1-56014-162-4(X)) Aguilar Editorial MEX. *Dist:* Santillana USA Publishing Co., Inc.

—El Desayuno de Tomas. Oxenbury, Helen, illus. (SPA.). 30p. (J). (gr. k-3). pap. 6.95 (978-1-56014-629-2(X)) Santillana USA Publishing Co., Inc.

Cyber. The Transdimensional War Series. 2006. 67p. pap. 14.95 (978-1-4241-2778-8(5)) PublishAmerica, Inc.

Dadey, Debbie & Jones, Marcia Thornton. Genies Don't Ride Bicycles. (Adventures of the Bailey School Kids Ser.: No. 8). (FRE., Illus.). (J). (gr. 2-4). pap. 5.99 (978-0-590-24377-3(2)) Scholastic, Inc.

—Goblins Don't Play Video Games. Gurney, John Steven, illus. 1999. (Adventures of the Bailey School Kids Ser.: No. 37). 96p. (J). (gr. 2-4). pap. 3.99 (978-0-439-04397-7(2)) Scholastic, Inc.

—Goblins Don't Play Video Games. 1999. (Adventures of the Bailey School Kids Ser.: No. 37). (J). (gr. 2-4). 10.79 (978-0-606-17276-9(9)) Tandem Library Bks.

Daffern, Brian. Prince Albert Bk. 2: The Beast School. 2005. 160p. (YA). per. 10.95 (978-0-9709104-6-2(0)) Hickory Tales Publishing.

—Prince Albert in a Can, Bk. 1. 2004. 256p. (YA). per. 13.95 (978-0-9709104-5-5(2)) Hickory Tales Publishing.

Dahl, Michael. Attack of the Paperbats. Garvey, Brann, illus. 2007. (J). 40p. (***978-1-59889-325-0(4)***); 33p. pap. (***978-1-59889-420-2(X)***) Stone Arch Bks.

—The Beast Beneath the Stairs. Garvey, Brann, illus. 2007. (J). 40p. (***978-1-59889-323-6(8)***); 33p. pap. (***978-1-59889-418-9(8)***) Stone Arch Bks.

—The Book That Dripped Blood. Kendall, Bradford, illus. 2007. (J). 40p. (***978-1-59889-324-3(6)***); 33p. pap. (***978-1-59889-419-6(6)***) Stone Arch Bks.

—The Eye in the Graveyard. Garvey, Brann, illus. 2007. (J). 40p. (***978-1-59889-328-1(9)***); 33p. pap. (***978-1-59889-423-3(4)***) Stone Arch Bks.

—Poison Pages. Garvey, Brann, illus. 2007. (J). 40p. (***978-1-59889-327-4(0)***); 33p. pap. (***978-1-59889-422-6(6)***) Stone Arch Bks.

—The Smashing Scroll. Kendall, Bradford, illus. 2007. (J). 40p. (***978-1-59889-326-7(2)***); 33p. pap. (***978-1-59889-421-9(8)***) Stone Arch Bks.

Dahl, Roald. Charlie & the Chocolate Factory. Blake, Quentin, illus. 2004. (Puffin Modern Classics Ser.). 176p. (J). (gr. 3-6). pap. 6.99 (978-0-14-240108-8(0), Puffin) Penguin Group (USA) Inc.

—Charlie & the Chocolate Factory. Blake, Quentin, illus. 40th anniv. movie tie-in ed. 2004. 160p. (J). (gr. k). 22.95 (978-0-375-83197-3(5), Knopf Bks. for Young Readers) Random Hse. Children's Bks.

—Charlie et le Grand Ascenseur de Verre. 3rd ed. 1998. Tr. of Charlie & the Great Glass Elevator. (FRE., Illus.). (J). (gr. 4-7). pap. 16.95 (978-2-07-051517-2(6)) Gallimard, Editions FRA. *Dist:* Distribooks, Inc.

—Charlie y la Fabrica de Chocolate. (SPA.). (J). pap. (978-84-204-5999-8(2), KZ992) Alfaguara, Ediciones, S.A.-Grupo Santillana.

—Charlie y la Fabrica de Chocolate. Jacques, Faith, illus. 2003. (FRE & SPA.). 176p. (J). (gr. 4-7). (978-84-204-4771-1(4), AF0153) Alfaguara, Ediciones, S.A.- Grupo Santillana.

—Charlie y la Fabrica de Chocolate. Sanz, Jesus, tr. Sanz, Jesus, illus. 51st ed. (SPA.). 172p. (J). (gr. 5-8). pap. 9.95 (978-84-204-6450-3(3)) Santillana USA Publishing Co., Inc.

—Esio Trot. Blake, Quentin, illus. 1999. 64p. (J). (gr. 2-6). pap. 5.99 (978-0-14-130464-9(2), Puffin) Penguin Group (USA) Inc.

—Esio Trot. 1999. (Illus.). (J). 12.79 (978-0-606-18402-1(3)) Tandem Library Bks.

—James & the Giant Peach. 1999. (J). 11.95 (978-1-56137-487-8(3)) Novel Units, Inc.

—James & the Giant Peach. Blake, Quentin, illus. 2002. 160p. (J). (gr. 3-7). 15.95 (978-0-375-81424-2(8), Knopf Bks. for Young Readers) Random Hse. Children's Bks.

—James & the Giant Peach. 2000. (J). (gr. 3-7). 22.00 (978-0-8446-7142-0(8)) Smith, Peter Pub., Inc.

—James et la Grosse Peche.Tr. of James & the Giant Peach. (FRE.). (J). pap. 17.95 (978-2-07-051374-1(2)) Gallimard, Editions FRA. *Dist:* Distribooks, Inc.

—James und der Riesenpfirsich.Tr. of James & the Giant Peach. pap. 17.95 (978-3-499-21183-6(1)) Rowohlt Taschenbuch Verlag GmbH DEU. *Dist:* Distribooks, Inc.

—James y el Melocoton Gigante. Blake, Quentin, illus. 2003. (SPA.). 184p. pap. 9.95 (978-968-19-0625-2(X)) Aguilar, Altea, Taurus, Alfaguara, S.A. de C.V MEX. *Dist:* Santillana USA Publishing Co., Inc.

—James y el Melocoton Gigante. (SPA., Illus.). (YA). (gr. 5-8). 7.96 net. (978-1-56137-543-1(8), NU5724) Novel Units, Inc.

—The Magic Finger. Blake, Quentin, illus. 1998. 64p. (J). (gr. 2-6). pap. 5.99 (978-0-14-130229-4(1), Puffin) Penguin Group (USA) Inc.

—La Potion Magique de Georges Bouillon. (FRE.). (J). pap. 17.95 (978-2-07-051340-6(8)) Gallimard, Editions FRA. *Dist:* Distribooks, Inc.

Dalmatian Press Staff. Disney Alice in Wonderland. 2006. 72p. (J). 9.99 (978-1-4037-2185-3(8)) Dalmatian Pr.

—There's No I in Team: Ninja Storm. 2003. (Power Rangers Ninja Storm Ser.). 24p. (J). pap. 2.99 (978-1-4037-0354-5(X)) Dalmatian Pr.

Dalmatian Press Staff, adapted by. Alice's Adventures in Wonderland. 2002. (Spot the Classics Ser.). (Illus.). 192p. (J). (gr. k-5). 4.99 (978-1-57759-550-2(5)) Dalmatian Pr.

Dalton, Andrew. Temples of Malplaquet. 2005. 192p. (YA). 14.50 (978-0-7188-3046-5(6)); pap. 7.50 (978-0-7188-3047-2(4)) Lutherworth Pr., The GBR. *Dist:* Parkwest Pubns., Inc.

Dalton, Annie. Mel Beeby, Agent Angel - Flying High. 2008. 144p. (J). pap. 6.95 (***978-0-00-720473-1(6)***) HarperCollins Pubs. Ltd. GBR. *Dist:* Independent Pubs. Group.

—Mel Beeby, Agent Angel - Losing the Plot. 2008. 160p. (J). pap. 6.95 (***978-0-00-720472-4(8)***) HarperCollins Pubs. Ltd. GBR. *Dist:* Independent Pubs. Group.

—Mel Beeby, Agent Angel - Winging It. 2008. 144p. pap. 6.95 (***978-0-00-720471-7(X)***) HarperCollins Pubs. Ltd. GBR. *Dist:* Independent Pubs. Group.

Danson, Lesley, et al, illus. Snow White. 2006. 24p. pap. 5.99 (978-1-84643-023-7(2)) Child's Play-International.

Danvers, Dennis. The Watch. 2003. 356p. (YA). (gr. 8-12). per. 25.70 (978-0-613-58394-7(9)) Tandem Library Bks.

Danziger, Paula. This Place Has No Atmosphere. 1999. (978-0-606-16860-1(5)) Tandem Library Bks.

Darden, Amy. Yesterday Once Again: Guenevere's Quest. 2003. (J). pap. 11.00 (978-0-8059-9238-0(3), RoseDog Bks.) Dorrance Publishing Co., Inc.

Dark Horse Comics Staff & Fujishima, Kosuke. The Adventures of the Mini-Goddesses. 2000. (Oh My Goddess! Ser.). (Illus.). 88p. (J). (gr. 3 up). pap. 9.95 (978-1-56971-421-8(5)) Dark Horse Comics.

The Dark Is Rising. 2002. (Dark Is Rising Sequence Ser.). (J). 13.40 (978-0-7587-0253-1(1)) Book Wholesalers, Inc.

Darling, Fiona. The Horse's Curse. 2003. 144p. (J). pap. 7.95 (978-0-86327-904-1(X)) Wolfhound Pr. IRL. *Dist:* Interlink Publishing Group, Inc.

Dart-Thornton, Cecilia. Lady of the Sorrows. 2003. (gr. 7-12). lib. bdg. 15.30 (978-0-613-61841-0(6)) Tandem Library Bks.

Datlow, Ellen & Windling, Terri, eds. The Coyote Road: Trickster Tales. Vess, Charles, illus. 2007. 384p. (YA). (gr. 7 up). 19.99 (978-0-670-06194-5(8), Viking Juvenile) Penguin Group (USA) Inc.

David. Runelords. 1999. (978-0-606-16883-0(4)) Tandem Library Bks.

David, Beth. Zorena: And the Medallion of Corandu. 2003. (Illus.). 238p. (YA). per. 13.99 (978-0-9740170-0-6(0), 0-9740170-0-0) David, Elizabeth A.

Davids, Paul. The Fountain of Youth. Davids, Paul, photos by. (Illus.). 56p. (Orig.). (YA). (gr. 5-9). pap. 9.95 (978-0-939031-01-6(9)) Pictorial Legends.

Davie, Jan. The Nexus Facilitator. 2006. 96p. pap. (***978-1-84401-798-0(2)***) Athena Pr.

Davies, Michael J. Mashu & the Mystery of the Missing Image. 2005. (YA). pap. 13.95 (978-1-59088-611-3(9)) Wings ePress, Inc.

Davies, Nicola. Shampoo & Seawater. 1998. (J). pap. 29.95 (978-0-8464-4913-3(7)) Beekman Bks., Inc.

Davis, Aubrey. Bone Button Borscht. Petricic, Dusan, illus. 2002. 32p. (J). (gr. k-3). (978-1-55074-326-5(0)) Kids Can Pr., Ltd.

—La Grosse Patate. ed. 2004. Tr. of Enormous Potato. (FRE., Illus.). (J). (gr. k-3). spiral bd. (978-0-616-14598-2(5)) Canadian National Institute for the Blind/Institut National Canadien pour les Aveugles.

Davis, Bryan. The Tears of a Dragon, 2005. (Dragons in Our Midst Ser.: 4). 363p. (J). (gr. 7-12). pap. 12.99 (978-0-89957-173-7(5)) AMG Pubs.

Davis, Buddy. When Dragons' Hearts Were Good. 1999. (Illus.). 40p. (J). (ps-3). 12.99 (978-0-89051-259-3(0), 303-087) Master Bks.

Davis, Darren. Atlas - ABC's for Superheroes: ABC's for Superheroes. l.t. ed. 2004. (Illus.). 16p. (J). bds. 5.99 (978-1-59559-110-4(9), Angel Gate) Left Field Ink.

Davis, Katie. Quien Salta? Campoy, F. Isabel, tr. 2005. Tr. of Who Hops?. (SPA., Illus.). 34p. (J). (ps-ps). bds. 6.95 (978-0-15-205602-5(5), Red Wagon Bks.) Harcourt Children's Bks.

Davis, Linda. A Chanukah Story. Taub, Udi, illus. 24p. 13.99 (978-1-58330-652-9(8)) Feldheim Pubs.

Dawn, Thomas F. The Crystal Dream. 2007. 188p. (YA). (gr. 8 up). pap. 9.95 (978-1-56315-377-8(7), Blue Imp Bks.) SterlingHouse Pubs., Inc.

Dawson, Janine, illus. Lily Quench 6 Hand of Manuelo, Vol. 6. 2004. 176p. (J). pap. 4.99 (978-0-14-240222-1(2), Puffin) Penguin Group (USA) Inc.

Daynes, Katie. Aladdin & His Magical Lamp. 2004. (Young Reading Ser.: Vol. 1). 48p. (J). (gr. 2 up). lib. bdg. 13.95 (978-1-58086-559-3(3), Usborne) EDC Publishing.

DC Comics Staff. Wonder Woman Morphing Journal. 2004. (Illus.). 128p. 10.95 (978-0-8118-4197-9(9)) Chronicle Bks. LLC.

DC Comics Staff, et al. See No Evil. 2nd ed. 2002. (Smallville Ser.: No. 2). 192p. (J). (gr. 7-17). mass mkt. 5.99 (978-0-316-17301-8(0)) Little, Brown Bks. for Young Readers.

De Bie, Erik Scott. Ghostwalker. 2005. (Fighters Ser.). 318p. (978-1-4156-3838-5(1)) Wizards of the Coast.

De Lint, Charles. The Blue Girl. 2004. 368p. (YA). (gr. 7). 17.99 (978-0-670-05924-9(2), Viking Juvenile) Penguin Group (USA) Inc.

—Dingo. 2008. 192p. (YA). (gr. 7). 11.99 (***978-0-14-240816-2(6)***, Puffin) Penguin Group (USA) Inc.

—Little (Grrl) Lost. 2007. 288p. (YA). (gr. 7 up). 17.99 (***978-0-670-06144-0(1)***, Viking Juvenile) Penguin Group (USA) Inc.

—The Riddle of the Wren. 2002. (gr. 7-12). lib. bdg. 15.30 (978-0-613-56586-8(X)) Tandem Library Bks.

—Wolf Moon. 2004. (Orig.). (gr. 7-12). lib. bdg. 15.30 (978-0-613-71569-0(1)) Tandem Library Bks.

De Long, Robert & De Long, Janice. Redwall Study Guide. 2003. ring bd. 14.99 (978-1-58609-196-5(4)) Progeny Pr.

De Mari, Silvana. The Last Dragon. Whiteside, Shaun, tr. from ITA. 2006. (Illus.). 368p. (gr. 5 up). 16.95 (978-0-7868-3636-9(9)) Miramax Bks.

de Saint-Exupery, Antoine. The Little Prince. l.t. ed. 2005. 100p. pap. 10.95 (978-0-7862-7539-7(1)) Thorndike Pr.

Dean, Pamela. Hidden Land. 2003. (gr. 7-12). lib. bdg. 15.30 (978-0-613-71575-1(6)) Tandem Library Bks.

—The Secret Country. 2003. (Secret Country Trilogy). 384p. (YA). pap. 7.99 (978-0-14-250153-5(0), Puffin) Penguin Group (USA) Inc.

—The Whim of the Dragon. 2003. (Secret Country Trilogy). 400p. (YA). pap. 6.99 (978-0-14-250161-0(1), Puffin) Penguin Group (USA) Inc.

DeAndrea, William L. & DeAndrea, Matthew. The Pizza That Time Forgot. 1999. (J). (gr. 3-7). pap. 3.99 (978-0-380-79155-2(2)) HarperCollins Pubs.

DeArmond, Dale. The Raven Charm. 1998. (Illus.). 51p. (J). (gr. k-4). 12.95 (978-0-9641998-6-6(6)) Lapcat Pubns.

Deary, Terry. The Fire Thief. 256p. (J). (gr. 5). 2007. pap. 5.95 (***978-0-7534-6118-1(8)***); 2005. per. 9.95 (978-0-7534-5818-1(7)) Houghton Mifflin Co. Trade & Reference Div. (Kingfisher).

Deaver, Julie Reece. Webb. 2002. (YA). (978-0-7434-3978-7(3), Simon Pulse) Simon & Schuster Children's Publishing.

Decker, Wendy. The Bedazzling Bowl. 2006. pap. 13.99 (***978-1-60034-468-8(2)***) Xulon Pr., Inc.

DeFalco, Tom. Avenging Allies, Vol. 3. 2005. (Spider-Man Ser.: Vol. 3). (Illus.). 152p. pap. 7.99 (978-0-7851-1658-5(3)) Marvel Enterprises, Inc.

Degen, Bruce, illus. Commander Toad & the Space Pirates. 2002. (Commander Toad Ser.). (J). 13.19 (978-0-7587-1080-2(1)) Book Wholesalers, Inc.

—Commander Toad & the Voyage Home. 2002. (Commander Toad Ser.). (J). 13.19 (978-0-7587-1077-2(1)) Book Wholesalers, Inc.

Deisher, Kathleen E. Beyond the Gloesmur: In the Gloesmur Scrolls. Deisher, Kathleen E., illus. 2003. (Gloesmur Scrolls Ser.: Bk. 1). (Illus.). 270p. (J). pap. 13.95 (978-1-892135-00-1(0)) Lamp Post Publishing, Inc.

Deiss, A. G. & Emi. The Sad Tale of Emmaline Austin, Monkey-Girl. 2005. 23p. 10.67 (978-1-4116-5439-6(0)) Lulu.com.

DeJesus, Melissa, illus. Sokora Refugees, Vol. 1. 2005. (YA). pap. 9.99 (978-1-59532-736-9(3), Tokyopop Adult) TOKYOPOP, Inc.

Del Vecchio, Gene. The Pearl of Anton. 2004. (Illus.). 256p. (J). (gr. 5-9). pap. 16.95 (978-1-58980-172-1(5)) Pelican Publishing Co., Inc.

—The Sword of Anton. 2006. (Illus.). 256p. (YA). 16.95 (978-1-58980-304-6(3)) Pelican Publishing Co., Inc.

Delaney, Joseph. The Last Apprentice: Attack of the Fiend. Arrasmith, Patrick, illus. 2008. (Last Apprentice Ser.). 560p. (J). 16.99 (***978-0-06-089127-5(0)***); lib. bdg. 17.89 (***978-0-06-089128-2(9)***) HarperCollins Pubs. (Greenwillow Bks.).

Dem Bones. 2004. 24.95 incl. audio (978-1-55592-692-2(4)); 29.95 incl. cd-rom (978-1-55592-702-8(5)) Weston Woods Studios, Inc.

Demarest, Chris L. Supertwins Meet the Bad Dogs from Space. 2003. (gr. k-3). lib. bdg. 11.80 (978-0-613-72178-3(0)) Tandem Library Bks.

Dematteis, J. M. The Dream Thief. Ploog, Mike, illus. 2nd rev. ed. 2006. (Abadazad Ser.: Bk. 2). 144p. (gr. 4-7). 9.99 (978-1-4231-0064-5(6)) Hyperion Pr.

DeMatteis, J. M. & Ploog, Mike. The Road to Inconceivable. Ploog, Mike, illus. 2006. (Abadazad Ser.: Bk. 1). (Illus.). 144p. (gr. 4-7). 9.99 (978-1-4231-0062-1(X)) Hyperion Pr.

DeMatteis, J.M. Stardust Kid. 2008. (Stardust Kind Ser. : Ser.). (Illus.). 128p. pap. 14.99 (***978-1-934506-04-2(4)***) Boom! Studios.

Demers, Dominique, et al. Old Thomas & the Little Fairy. Poulin, Stephane, illus. 2001. 29p. (J). (ps-3). pap. (978-1-894363-45-7(0)) Dominique & Friends.

Dent, Sue. Never Ceese: Can Two Who Were Wronged Make It Right? 2006. 336p. (YA). lib. bdg. 17.99 (978-1-59958-017-3(9)) Journey Stone Creations, LLC.

Desrosiers, Sylvie. Aimez-Vous la Musique? Sylvestre, Daniel, illus. 2004. (Roman Jeunesse Ser.). (FRE.). 96p. (J). (gr. 4-7). pap. (978-2-89021-709-6(4)) Diffusion du livre Mirabel.

—Ma Mère Est un Extraterrestre. Franson, Leanne, illus. 2002. (Premier Roman Ser.). (FRE.). 64p. (J). (gr. 1-4). pap. (978-2-89021-561-0(X)) Diffusion du livre Mirabel.

Dessen, Sarah. Dreamland. ed. 2004. 256p. (YA). (gr. 6-11). pap. 7.99 (978-0-14-240175-0(7), Puffin) Penguin Group (USA) Inc.

Devaney, Patrick. The Psychic Edge. 2000. 137p. (YA). (gr. 5-9). per. (978-1-84210-020-2(3)) Mentor Bks.

Devers, Joe. Dungeons of Torgar. (Illus.). (J). (gr. k-6). 5.95 (978-0-09-951250-9(5)) Random Hse. GBR. *Dist:* Trafalgar Square Publishing.

DeVita, James. The Silenced. 2007. 512p. (YA). (gr. 7 up). 17.99 (978-0-06-078462-1(8)); lib. bdg. 18.89 (978-0-06-078464-5(4)) HarperCollins Pubs.

Dewin, Howie. Sleeping Ugly. 2004. (Shrek 2 Ser.). 64p. (J). 3.99 (978-0-439-59716-6(1)) Scholastic, Inc.

Dharmarajan, Geeta. The Magic Raindrop. Bist, Vandana, illus. 2002. 32p. (J). (978-81-87649-60-1(7)) Katha.

Diablo - Race Against Time. 2006. (J). (978-1-933343-29-7(X), PONY) Stabenfeldt Inc.

Dickens, Charles. A Christmas Carol. Lynch, P. J., illus. 2006. 160p. (J). (gr. 5). 19.99 (978-0-7636-3120-8(5)) Candlewick Pr.

Dickins, Rosie. Emperor & the Nightingale. Philpot, Graham, illus. 2007. (First Reading Level 4 Ser.). 48p. (J). 8.99 (***978-0-7945-1614-7(9)***, Usborne) EDC Publishing.

Dickinson, John. The Cup of the World. 432p. (YA). (gr. 7-11). 2007. mass mkt. 6.99 (978-0-553-49489-1(9), Laurel Leaf); 2004. (Illus.). 15.95 (978-0-385-75025-7(0), Fickling, David Bks.) Random Hse. Children's Bks.

—The Widow & the King. 624p. (YA). (gr. 7-11). 2007. mass mkt. 7.99 (978-0-553-49503-4(8), Laurel Leaf); 2005. (Illus.). 18.95 (978-0-385-75084-4(6), Fickling, David Bks.) Random Hse. Children's Bks.

Dickinson, Peter. Angel Isle. 2007. 512p. (gr. 9). (J). lib. bdg. 20.99 (***978-0-385-90928-0(4)***); (YA). 17.99 (***978-0-385-74690-8(3)***) Random Hse. Children's Bks. (Lamb, Wendy).

—Healer. 2001. 188p. (YA). (gr. 4-7). pap. 12.00 (978-0-375-89511-1(6), Laurel Leaf) Random Hse. Children's Bks.

—Mana's Story. 1999. (Kin Ser.). (978-0-606-17678-1(0)) Tandem Library Bks.

—Po's Story. Jakesevic, Nenad, illus. 1999. (Peter Dickinson's The Kin Ser.). 1p. (J). (gr. 5-9). pap. 3.99 (978-0-448-41711-0(1), Grosset & Dunlap) Penguin Group (USA) Inc.

—The Ropemaker. 2003. 384p. (YA). (gr. 7). pap. 7.95 (978-0-385-73063-1(2), Delacorte Bks. for Young Readers) Random Hse. Children's Bks.

Dickinson, Peter & Dickinson, Peter. Suth's Story. 2003. 640p. (YA). (gr. 8-12). pap. 8.99 (978-0-14-250120-7(4), Puffin) Penguin Group (USA) Inc.

DiGenti, Victor. Windrusher. 2006. 292p. per. 15.95 (978-0-9767291-4-3(8)) Ocean Publishing.

DiGerolamo, Tony. The Wildsidhe Chronicles Bk. 5: The Undercover Dragon. 2003. (J). pap. 7.99 (978-1-890096-17-5(2)) Padwolf Publishing, Inc.

Dillon, Jana. Lucky O'Leprechaun. 1998. (Illus.). 32p. (J). (gr. k-3). 15.95 (978-1-56554-333-1(5)) Pelican Publishing Co., Inc.

—Lucky O'Leprechaun Comes to America. 2001. (Illus.). 32p. (J). (ps-1). pap. 15.95 (978-1-56554-816-9(7)) Pelican Publishing Co., Inc.

Dillon, Sally Pierson. Exile of the Chosen: God's Heroes from Solomon to Malachi. 2003. 223p. (J). pap. 10.99 (978-0-8280-1703-9(4), 58-710) Review & Herald Publishing Assn.

Dinsdale, Christopher. Broken Circle. 2004. 98p. (J). pap. 7.95 (978-1-894917-15-5(4)) Napoleon Publishing/Rendezvous Pr. CAN. *Dist:* AtlasBooks Distribution.

DiPucchio, Kelly S. Liberty's Journey. Egielski, Richard, illus. 2004. 32p. (ps-2). 15.99 (978-0-7868-1876-1(X)) Hyperion Bks. for Children.

Disney Book Club Staff. Aladdin & the Wonderful Lamp. 1999. (J). lib. bdg. (978-0-394-93937-7(9), Random Hse. Bks. for Young Readers) Random Hse. Children's Bks.

Disney Classics: My First Library. 2004. (J). bds. (978-1-4127-0314-7(X), 7217800) Publications International, Ltd.

Disney Press Staff. Fight for Your Right. 2001. (gr. 3-6). lib. bdg. 13.00 (978-0-613-75081-3(0)) Tandem Library Bks.

Disney Staff. Fight for Your Right. 2001. (Jersey Ser.). (Illus.). (J). 11.64 (978-0-606-21265-6(5)) Tandem Library Bks.

—Head over Heels. 2001. (Jersey Ser.). (Illus.). (J). 11.64 (978-0-606-21264-9(7)) Tandem Library Bks.

—Team Player. 2001. (Jersey Ser.). (Illus.). (J). (978-0-606-21263-2(9)) Tandem Library Bks.

Disneys Cinderella Palace. 2004. (Illus.). 10p. (J). bds. 9.98 (978-1-4127-3349-6(9), 7249700) Publications International, Ltd.

Distler, Christine A. Pegasus: The Introduction. 2005. 84p. pap. 11.95 (978-1-59113-763-4(2)) Booklocker.com, Inc.

Ditama, Bow, illus. Mahoromatic, Vol. 5. rev. ed. 2005. 184p. pap. 9.99 (978-1-59182-915-7(1), Tokyopop Adult) TOKYOPOP, Inc.

DiTerlizzi, Tony. Moon Pie Adventure. DiTerlizzi, Tony, illus. 2000. (Illus.). 40p. (J). (gr. k-3). 17.99 (978-0-689-82215-5(4)) Simon & Schuster Children's Publishing.

DiTerlizzi, Tony & Black, Holly. El Anteojo Asombroso. Abreu Fetter, Carlos, tr. 2005. (Escritura desatada Ser.). (SPA., Illus.). 128p. (J). 12.95 (978-84-666-1280-7(7)) Ediciones B ESP. *Dist:* Independent Pubs. Group.

—Arthur Spiderwick's Field Guide to the Fantastical World Around You. DiTerlizzi, Tony, illus. 2005. (Spiderwick Chronicles). (Illus.). 142p. (J). 24.95 (978-0-689-85941-0(4)) Simon & Schuster Children's Publishing.

—El Libro Fantastico. Abreu, Carlos, tr. 2005. (Escritura desatada Ser.). (SPA., Illus.). 128p. (J). (gr. 4-7). 12.95 (978-84-666-1279-1(3)) Ediciones B ESP. *Dist:* Independent Pubs. Group.

—Lucinda's Secret, Bk. 3. DiTerlizzi, Tony, illus. 2003. (Spiderwick Chronicles: Bk. 3). (Illus.). 128p. (YA). 10.99 (978-0-689-85938-0(4)) Simon & Schuster Children's Publishing.

—The Spiderwick Chronicles Boxed Set: The Field Guide; The Seeing Stone; Lucinda's Secret; The Ironwood Tree; The Wrath of Mulgrath, Vol. 1-5. DiTerlizzi, Tony & Black, Holly, illus. 2004. (Spiderwick Chronicles). (Illus.). 672p. (J). 49.99 (978-0-689-04034-4(2)) Simon & Schuster Children's Publishing.

DiTocco, Robyn & DiTocco, Tony. Atlas' Revenge: Another Mad Myth Mystery. 2005. 234p. 19.95 (978-0-9723429-2-6(3)); pap. 11.95 (978-0-9723429-3-3(1)) Brainstorm Pubns., Inc.

—The Hero Perseus: A Mad Myth Mystery. 2004. 220p. (gr. 3-12). 19.95 (978-0-9723429-0-2(7)); pap. 11.95 (978-0-9723429-1-9(5)) Brainstorm Pubns., Inc.

Divakaruni, Chitra Banerjee. The Conch Bearer. rev. ed. 2003. (Illus.). 272p. (J). (gr. 3 up). 16.95 (978-0-7613-1935-1(2)) Roaring Brook Pr.

—The Conch Bearer. 2005. 272p. (J). reprint ed. pap. 5.99 (978-0-689-87242-6(9), Aladdin) Simon & Schuster Children's Publishing.

Dixon, Andy. Dragon Quest. Brooks, Felicity, ed. Harris, Nick, illus. rev. ed. 2005. 32p. (J). (ps-7). pap. 7.99 (978-0-7945-1098-5(1), Usborne) EDC Publishing.

—Sword Quest. Brooks, Felicity, ed. Boni, Simone, illus. rev. ed. 2005. 31p. (J). (ps-7). pap. 7.95 (978-0-7945-1096-1(5), Usborne) EDC Publishing.

Dixon, Chuck. Old Friends, New Enemies. Land, Greg, illus. rev. ed. 2003. (Birds of Prey Ser.: Vol. 2). 224p. pap. 17.95 (978-1-56389-939-3(6)) DC Comics.

DK Publishing. The Wise Dragon. 2008. 12p. (J). (ps-k). 12.99 (***978-0-7566-3811-5(9)***) Dorling Kindersley Publishing, Inc.

E F G

DK Publishing Staff. Magic Toy Shop. 2007. 12p. (J). (ps-3). 14.99 (***978-0-7566-3179-6(3)***) Dorling Kindersley Publishing, Inc.

Dobkin, Bonnie. Dream Spinner. 2006. 288p. pap. 8.95 (978-0-7387-0919-2(0) , Flux) Llewellyn Pubns.

Dodd, Emma. Yellow, Blue, & Bunny, Too! A Changing Picture Book of Colors. Dodd, Emma, illus. 2004. (Illus.). 16p. (J). (gr. k-3). reprint ed. 12.00 (978-0-7567-7267-3(2)) DIANE Publishing Co.

Dodd, Lynley. Hairy Maclary from Donaldson's Dairy. 2001. (gr. k-3). lib. bdg. 14.10 (978-0-613-50130-9(6)) Tandem Library Bks.

Doherty, B. Jack the Giant Killer. (Illus.). 139p. pap. 8.99 (978-0-340-76452-7(X) , Hodder & Stoughton) Hodder General Publishing Division GBR. *Dist:* Trafalgar Square Publishing.

Doherty, Berlie. Famous Adventures of Jack. l.t. ed. 2005. (Illus.). 152p. (J). pap. (978-0-7540-6140-3(X) , CLP 332) BBC Audio.

Dokey, Cameron. Beauty Sleep: A Retelling of Sleeping Beauty. 2006. (Once upon a Time Ser.). 208p. (YA). pap. 5.99 (978-1-4169-4014-2(6) , Simon Pulse) Simon & Schuster Children's Publishing.

—The Crimson Spell. 2000. (gr. 7-12). lib. bdg. 14.15 (978-0-613-27780-8(5)) Tandem Library Bks.

—Sunlight & Shadow. 2004. (Once upon a Time Ser.). 192p. (YA). pap. 5.99 (978-0-689-86999-0(1) , Simon Pulse) Simon & Schuster Children's Publishing.

Dolbeck, Andrew. Fever Jenny, Bk. 1. 2006. 120p. pap. 10.99 (978-1-59092-324-5(3)) Windstorm Creative.

Dollinger, Renate. The Rabbi Who Flew: A Grandma Hanne Sheyne Story. Dollinger, Renate, illus. 2000. (Illus.). 40p. (J). (ps-3). 18.00 (978-0-945585-20-6(9)) Booksmythe.

Donaldson, Julia. The Giants & the Joneses. Swearingen, Greg, illus. 2005. 224p. (J). (gr. 3-5). 14.95 (978-0-8050-7805-3(3)) Holt, Henry & Co.

—The Giants & the Joneses. Swearingen, Greg, illus. 2008. 240p. (J). pap. 6.99 (***978-0-312-37961-2(7)***) Square Fish.

Donaldson, Julia. Princess Mirror-Belle. l.t. ed. 2005. (J). pap. (978-0-7540-7890-6(6) , CLP 463) BBC Audio.

Donnelly, Michael. Awakening Curry Buckle. 2005. (ALB.). 380p. (YA). pap. 14.99 (978-1-59092-226-2(3) , Blue Works) Windstorm Creative.

Doolittle, Benjamin R. The Grundilini: From the Chronicles of Audelae. Kabak, Carrie, illus. 2002. 208p. pap. 12.95 (978-1-889658-24-7(3)) New Canaan Publishing Co. LLC.

Dorling Kindersley Publishing Staff. Transformers Energon Ultimate Glow in the Dark Sticker Book. 2005. (Ultimate sticker Bks.). (Illus.). 16p. (J). (ps-ps). pap. 6.99 (978-0-7566-1148-4(2)) Dorling Kindersley Publishing, Inc.

Dorn, Patrick Rainville. The Gingerbread Man: Comedy for the Stage. 1999. 40p. (YA). (gr. 1-12). pap. 4.00 (978-0-88680-462-6(0)) Clark, I. E. Pubns.

Dotson, Kyt. The Specter in the Spectacles. 2003. 126p. pap. 10.95 (978-0-595-28251-7(2)) iUniverse, Inc.

Dougherty, Terri. The Traveling Shoes. Haugen, Ryan, illus. 2006. (Read-It! Readers Ser.). 24p. (J). (ps-3). 18.60 (978-1-4048-1588-9(0)) Picture Window Bks.

Douglas, Vincent & School Specialty Publishing Staff. Rumpelstiltskin. 2004. (Handle Book with CD Ser.). (Illus.). 24p. (J). 3.99 (978-1-58845-727-1(3)) School Specialty Publishing.

Dower, Laura. Bubble Trouble. 2000. (gr. k-3). lib. bdg. 11.25 (978-0-613-24426-8(5)) Tandem Library Bks.

—Forget Me Not. 21st rev. ed. 2006. (From the Files of Madison Finn Ser.: Bk. 21). 176p. (gr. 3-7). pap. 4.99 (978-0-7868-3768-7(3) , Volo) Hyperion Bks. for Children.

Downer, Ann. Hatching Magic. 2006. 256p. (J). pap. 2.99 (978-1-4169-2497-5(3) , Aladdin) Simon & Schuster Children's Publishing.

Doyle, Arthur Conan. The Lost World & Other Thrilling Tales. 2001. (gr. 7-12). lib. bdg. 17.65 (978-0-613-64299-6(6)) Tandem Library Bks.

Doyle, Debra. The Wizard's Castle, Bk. 5. 2001. (Circle of Magic Ser.). (Illus.). (Orig.). (J). (978-0-606-20998-4(0)) Tandem Library Bks.

Doyle, Malachy. Hair Scare. Allen, Jonathan, illus. 2005. 24p. (J). lib. bdg. 22.65 (***978-1-59646-724-8(X)***) Dingles & Co.

Doyle, Richard & Lang, Andrew. Princess Nobody: A Tale of Fairyland. 2000. (Illus.). 64p. (J). (gr. 4-7). pap. 9.95 (978-0-486-41020-3(X)) Dover Pubns., Inc.

Dragon: Enter the Realm. 2007. (YA). per. (***978-1-934345-43-6(1)***) SouthWest Pubns.

Dragon: The Fantasy Continues. 2007. (YA). per. (***978-1-934345-44-3(X)***) SouthWest Pubns.

Dragons, Phantoms, & Secrets: The Best New Fantasy from Arrow Writers. 2005. 63p. (J). (***978-0-439-74432-4(6)***) Scholastic, Inc.

Drake, David. Tommy Powers & the Replicator of Rio Azul. 2005. 210p. (YA). pap. 14.99 (978-1-885631-93-0(6)) Hutchison, G.F. Pr.

—Tommy Powers & the Sorcerer of Akmindo Teeki. 2005. 213p. (J). pap. 14.95 (978-1-885631-92-3(8) , Family Of Man Pr., The) Hutchison, G.F. Pr.

Drake, Emily. Curse of Arkady. 2003. 384p. (gr. 12). mass mkt. 6.99 (978-0-7564-0103-0(8) , D A W Bks., Inc.) Penguin Group (USA) Inc.

—Magickers. 2002. (gr. 5-8). lib. bdg. 15.30 (978-0-613-67340-2(9)) Tandem Library Bks.

Drake, Salamanda. Dragonsdale. Marklew, Gilly, illus. 2007. 288p. (J). (gr. 4-7). pap. 16.99 (***978-0-439-87173-0(5)*** , Chicken Hse., The) Scholastic, Inc.

Dravis, Betty. The Toonies Invade Silicon Valley. 2005. (Illus.). 168p. (J). per. 14.95 (978-1-932586-29-9(6) , Just My Bk., Inc.) Just My Best Bk. Publishing Co.

Driggs, Scout. The Lion, the Witch & the Wardrobe: The Creatures of Narnia. Sweet, Justin, illus. movie tie-in ed. 2005. (Chronicles of Narnia Ser.). 24p. (J). pap. 3.99 (978-0-06-076563-7(1)) HarperCollins Pubs.

Drouin, Véronique. L' Ile D'Aurélie. 2004. (Mon Roman Ser.). (FRE.). 304p. (J). (gr. 2). pap. (978-2-89021-690-7(X)) Diffusion du livre Mirabel.

Duane, Diane. Deep Wizardry. (Young Wizards Ser.: Bk. 2). 384p. (YA). 2003. (Illus.). pap. 6.95 (978-0-15-204942-3(8)); 2001. (gr. 5 up). pap. 6.95 (978-0-15-216257-3(7)) Harcourt Children's Bks. (Magic Carpet Bks.).

—Deep Wizardry. 2003. (gr. 3-6). lib. bdg. 15.25 (978-0-613-71628-4(0)); 2001. (gr. 5-8). lib. bdg. 15.25 (978-0-613-36059-3(1)) Tandem Library Bks.

—High Wizardry. (Young Wizards Ser.: Bk. 3). (YA). 2003. 372p. (ps-7). pap. 6.95 (978-0-15-204941-6(X)); 2001. 368p. (gr. 5 up). pap. 6.95 (978-0-15-216244-3(5)) Harcourt Children's Bks. (Magic Carpet Bks.).

—High Wizardry. 2000. (YA). (gr. 5 up). pap. 58.25 incl. audio (978-0-7887-3799-2(6) , 41043) Recorded Bks., LLC.

—High Wizardry. 2003. (gr. 3-6). lib. bdg. 15.25 (978-0-613-71634-5(5)); 2001. (gr. 5-8). lib. bdg. 15.25 (978-0-613-36065-4(6)) Tandem Library Bks.

—So You Want to Be a Wizard. (Young Wizards Ser.). (YA). 2003. 408p. pap. 6.95 (978-0-15-204940-9(1) , Magic Carpet Bks.); 2001. 400p. (gr. 5 up). pap. 6.95 (978-0-15-216250-4(X) , Magic Carpet Bks.); 20th anniv. ed. 2003. (Illus.). 336p. 16.95 (978-0-15-204738-2(7)) Harcourt Children's Bks.

—So You Want to Be a Wizard. 2003. (gr. 3-6). lib. bdg. 15.25 (978-0-613-71630-7(2)); 2001. (gr. 5-8). lib. bdg. 15.25 (978-0-613-36077-7(X)) Tandem Library Bks.

—A Wizard Abroad. 2001. (Young Wizards Ser.: Bk. 4). 368p. (YA). (gr. 5 up). pap. 6.95 (978-0-15-216238-2(0) , Magic Carpet Bks.) Harcourt Children's Bks.

—A Wizard Abroad. 2001. (gr. 5-8). lib. bdg. 14.75 (978-0-613-36083-8(4)) Tandem Library Bks.

—A Wizard Alone. (Young Wizards Ser.: Bk. 6). (YA). 2003. 352p. pap. 6.95 (978-0-15-204911-9(8) , Magic Carpet Bks.); 2002. (Illus.). 336p. (gr. 7 up). 17.00 (978-0-15-204562-3(7)) Harcourt Children's Bks.

—Wizards at War: The Eighth Book in the Young Wizards Series. 2007. (Young Wizards Ser.). (Illus.). 560p. (YA). pap. 6.95 (978-0-15-205223-2(2) , Magic Carpet Bks.) Harcourt Children's Bks.

—The Wizard's Dilemma. 2002. (Young Wizards Ser.: Bk. 5). 432p. (YA). (gr. 7 up). pap. 6.95 (978-0-15-202460-4(3) , Magic Carpet Bks.) Harcourt Children's Bks.

—The Wizard's Dilemma. 2002. (gr. 5-8). lib. bdg. 15.25 (978-0-613-55225-7(3)) Tandem Library Bks.

Dubrovin, Barbara. Fantasy Fair: Bright Stories of Imagination. Dubrovin, Barbara, illus. 2007. (Illus.). 128p. (J). pap. 17.50 (978-0-9638339-6-9(0)) Storycraft Publishing.

Dubya, Jay. Pot of Gold. 2001. 182p. pap. 16.95 (978-1-58909-174-0(4)) Bookstand Publishing.

—Space Bugs, Earth Invasion. 2001. 216p. pap. 16.95 (978-1-58909-172-6(8)) Bookstand Publishing.

Duce, Gillian. Magic & Mayhem. 2006. 208p. per. (***978-1-894936-64-4(7)***) Saga Bks.

Duey, Kathleen. Castle Avamir. 2003. (gr. 3-6). lib. bdg. 11.80 (978-0-613-66482-0(5)) Tandem Library Bks.

—Mountains of the Moon. 2002. (gr. 3-6). lib. bdg. 11.80 (978-0-613-58375-6(2)) Tandem Library Bks.

—Silver Bracelet. 2002. (gr. 3-6). lib. bdg. 11.80 (978-0-613-58388-6(4)) Tandem Library Bks.

—Skin Hunger. Rayyan, Sheila, illus. 2007. (Resurrection of Magic Ser.). 368p. (YA). (gr. 7 up). 17.99 (***978-0-689-84093-7(4)***) Simon & Schuster Children's Publishing.

—Sunset Gates. 2002. (gr. 3-6). lib. bdg. 11.80 (978-0-613-57584-3(9)) Tandem Library Bks.

—True Heart. Rayyan, Omar, illus. ed. 2005. 76p. (J). lib. bdg. 15.00 (978-1-59054-920-9(1)) Fitzgerald Bks.

—Unicorn Secret 5. Rayyan, Omar, illus. 2002. 80p. (J). mass mkt. 3.99 (978-0-689-85368-5(8) , Aladdin) Simon & Schuster Children's Publishing.

DuFalla, Anita, illus. Sumac & the Magic Lake: Levels F-M (9-28) ed. 2004. (Reader's Theater Ser.). 16p. (J). pap. 22.00 (978-1-4108-2291-8(5) , A22915) Benchmark Education Co.

Duggan, Matt. The Royal Woods. rev. ed. 2007. 244p. (gr. 7-12). 12.95 (***978-1-55263-826-2(X)***) Key Porter Bks. CAN. *Dist:* Perseus Distribution.

Duncan, Dave. The Crooked House. 2000. (King's Daggers Ser.: Vol. 2). (Illus.). 256p. (J). (gr. 7 up). pap. 5.99 (978-0-380-80099-5(3)) HarperCollins Pubs.

—Silvercloak. 2001. (King's Daggers Ser.: Bk. 3). (Illus.). 288p. (J). (gr. 7 up). pap. 5.99 (978-0-380-80100-8(0) , Avon) HarperCollins Pubs.

Duncan, Lois. The Magic of Spider Woman. Begay, Shonto W., illus. 2000. 32p. (J). (gr. k-3). pap. 5.99 (978-0-590-46156-6(7)) Scholastic, Inc.

—Stranger with My Face. 2002. (Illus.). (J). 13.40 (978-0-7587-4793-8(4)) Book Wholesalers, Inc.

—Stranger with My Face. 235p. (YA). (gr. 7 up). pap. 4.99 (978-0-8072-1371-1(3) , Listening Library) Random Hse. Audio Publishing Group.

Dunmore, Helen. Ingo. 2006. 336p. (J). 16.99 (978-0-06-081852-4(2)) ; lib. bdg. 17.89 (978-0-06-081853-1(0)) HarperCollins Pubs.

Dunn, Ben. The Agents Pocket Manga. 2004. 136p. (YA). pap. 9.99 (978-1-932453-64-5(4)) Antarctic Pr., Inc.

Dunn, Matthew. Day One. 2007. 192p. (YA). per. 15.00 (***978-0-9794908-0-4(4)***) Onondaga Hill Publishing.

Dunsany, Lord. Charwoman's Shadow. 1999. (gr. 7-12). lib. bdg. 21.10 (978-0-613-21324-0(6)) Tandem Library Bks.

—The King of Elfland's Daughter. 1999. (gr. 7-12). lib. bdg. 22.20 (978-0-613-21863-4(9)) Tandem Library Bks.

DuPrau, Jeanne. The City of Ember. 2003. (Books of Ember Ser.). 288p. (J). (gr. 5-8). 16.99 (978-0-375-82273-5(9)) ; lib. bdg. 17.99 (978-0-375-92274-9(1)) Random Hse. Children's Bks. (Random Hse. Bks. for Young Readers).

Duprau, Jeanne. The City of Ember. 2004. 288p. (J). (gr. 5-8). pap. 5.99 (978-0-375-82274-2(7) , Yearling) Random Hse. Children's Bks.

DuPrau, Jeanne. People of Sparks. 2005. 338p. (J). (gr. k-8). per. 12.64 (978-0-606-33727-4(X)) Tandem Library Bks.

—The People of Sparks. 2005. (Books of Ember Ser.). 352p. (J). (gr. 5-8). reprint ed. 5.99 (978-0-375-82825-6(7) , Yearling) Random Hse. Children's Bks.

—The Prophet of Yonwood. 2006. 304p. (J). (gr. 4-8). lib. bdg. 17.99 (978-0-375-97526-4(8)) ; (Books of Ember Ser.: Bk. 3). 15.95 (978-0-375-87526-7(3)) Random Hse. Children's Bks. (Random Hse. Bks. for Young Readers).

—Prophet of Yonwood. 2007. (Books of Ember Ser.: Bk. 3). 304p. (J). (gr. 4-7). 6.50 (978-0-440-42124-5(1) , Yearling) Random Hse. Children's Bks.

Durrell, Gerald. The Fantastic Flying Journey. Percy, Graham, illus. 2001. 160p. 19.95 (978-0-7551-0436-9(6)) ; 156p. 9.95 (978-0-7551-1336-1(5)) House of Stratus, Inc. GBR. *Dist:* Midpoint Trade Bks., Inc.

Durst, Sarah. Into the Wild. 2007. 272p. (J). (gr. 5-7). 15.99 (978-1-59514-156-9(1) , Razorbill) Penguin Group (USA) Inc.

Dutton, John. Tiger's Island. Dutton, John, illus. unabr. ed. Date not set. (Dreamguard Trilogy Ser.: Vol. 2). (Illus.). viii, 245p. (J). pap. 12.95 (978-0-9577556-1-1(9)) Samara Pr.

Dyan, Penelope. The Warrior Mouse of Forest Hollow. 2005. (J). per. 5.95 (978-0-9771916-5-9(6)) Bellissima Publishing, LLC.

Dyer, Sarah, tr. Snow Drop, 12 vols., Vol. 6. rev. ed. 2004. (Teen Ser.). (Illus.). 192p. (gr. 11 up). pap. 9.99 (978-1-59182-689-7(6) , Tokyopop Adult) TOKYOPOP, Inc.

Eager, Edward. Half Magic. Bodecker, N. M., illus. 1999. 208p. (YA). (gr. 3-6). pap. 6.00 (978-0-15-202068-2(3) , Odyssey Classics) Harcourt Children's Bks.

—Knight's Castle. Bodecker, N. M., illus. 1999. 208p. pap. 6.00 (978-0-15-202073-6(X) , Odyssey Classics) Harcourt Children's Bks.

—Magic by the Lake. Bodecker, N. M., illus. 1999. 208p. (YA). pap. 6.00 (978-0-15-202076-7(4) , Odyssey Classics) Harcourt Children's Bks.

—Magic or Not? 1999. (gr. 3-6). lib. bdg. 14.15 (978-0-613-21946-4(5)) Tandem Library Bks.

—The Time Garden. Bodecker, N. M., illus. 1999. 208p. (YA). pap. 6.00 (978-0-15-202070-5(5) , Odyssey Classics) Harcourt Children's Bks.

Eagle, Kin. Humpty Dumpty. Gilbert, Rob, illus. 2004. (Nursery Rhyme Ser.). 32p. (J). (ps-3). 15.95 (978-1-58089-019-9(9)) Charlesbridge Publishing, Inc.

Eastwood, J. G. Dragon the Fantasy Continues. 2006. pap. 33.49 (***978-1-4259-7068-0(0)***) AuthorHouse.

Eaton, Anthony. Nightpeople. 2005. (Darklands Trilogy Ser.: Bk. 1). 400p. (Orig.). (YA). pap. 18.95 (978-0-7022-3494-1(X)) Univ. of Queensland Pr. AUS. *Dist:* International Specialized Bk. Services.

Ebert, Marie-Francine & Germain, Philippe. Un Dragon dans les Pattes. 2002. (Premier Roman Ser.). 64p. (J). (gr. 2-5). pap. (978-2-89021-296-1(3)) Diffusion du livre Mirabel.

Eckert, Allan W. The Dark Green Tunnel. 2000. 168p. (gr. 4-7). pap. 13.95 (978-0-595-08962-8(3)) iUniverse, Inc.

—The Wand: The Return to Mesmeria. 2001. 168p. (gr. 4-7). pap. 13.95 (978-0-595-18325-8(5)) iUniverse, Inc.

Edwards, Mark. The Gang Book 1 the Saint's Bones. 2004. (YA). per. 10.95 (978-0-9755704-0-1(4)) New Classics Pr.

Edwards, Stuart. Dragon Jack. 2006. 42p. 15.99 (978-1-4116-7499-8(5)) Lulu.com.

Egan, Kate, adapted by. The Darkest Dream. 17th rev. ed. 2005. (W. I. T. C. H. Ser.: Bk. 17). (Illus.). 144p. (gr. 3-7). pap. 4.99 (978-0-7868-5278-9(X) , Volo) Hyperion Bks. for Children.

Egielski, Richard. The Gingerbread Boy. Egielski, Richard, illus. 2002. (Illus.). (J). 25.04 (978-0-7587-2595-0(7)) Book Wholesalers, Inc.

—The Gingerbread Boy. Egielski, Richard, illus. 2000. (Illus.). 32p. (J). (ps-2). pap. 6.99 (978-0-06-443708-0(6) , Harper Trophy) HarperCollins Pubs.

—The Gingerbread Boy. 2000. (J). 12.79 (978-0-606-19975-9(6)) Tandem Library Bks.

Einhorn, Edward. The Living House of Oz. Shanower, Eric, illus. 2005. 239p. (J). 27.95 (978-1-929527-08-3(X)) Hungry Tiger Pr.

Einhorn, Edward A. Paradox in Oz. Shanower, Eric, illus. 2000. 238p. (J). (gr. 3 up). 24.95 (978-1-929527-01-4(2)) Hungry Tiger Pr.

Ekaitis, Joe. Collinsfort Village. 2005. (Illus.). 161p. (J). per. 9.95 (978-1-886249-21-9(0)) WindRiver Publishing.

Elkins, Tilke. Jakes & Dustin Take Off. 2001. (Illus.). 96p. (978-0-9688648-0-7(5)) Parkhurst Publishing, Ltd. CAN. *Dist:* Words Distributing Co.

Ellerton, Sarah. Inverloch, Vol. 1. 2006. (Illus.). 160p. pap. 14.99 (978-1-933164-13-7(1)) Seven Seas Entertainment, LLC.

Elliot, Greg & Burge, Constance M. Demon Doppelgangers. 2005. (Charmed Ser.). 256p. (YA). pap. 5.99 (978-1-4169-0026-9(8) , Simon Spotlight Entertainment) Simon & Schuster.

Elliot, Patricia. Murkmere. 2006. 344p. (J). 16.99 (978-0-316-01365-9(X)) Little Brown & Co.

Elliott, David. The Transmogrification of Roscoe Wizzle. 2004. (Illus.). 128p. (J). (gr. 2-5). reprint ed. pap. 5.99 (978-0-7636-1880-3(2)) Candlewick Pr.

Elliott, Patricia. Ambergate. 2007. 400p. (J). (gr. 7-17). 16.99 (978-0-316-01060-3(X)) Little Brown & Co.

—Murkmere. 2007. 352p. (J). (gr. 7-17). pap. 7.99 (978-0-316-01044-3(8)) Little Brown & Co.

Ellis, Warren & Hairsine, Trevor. Ultimate Galactus: Nightmare. 2005. (Ultimate Galactus: Vol. 1). (Illus.). 120p. pap. 12.99 (978-0-7851-1497-0(1)) Marvel Enterprises, Inc.

Ellis, Warren & Immonen, Stuart. Doom, Vol. 2. 2004. (Fantastic Four Ser.). (Illus.). 144p. pap. 12.99 (978-0-7851-1457-4(2)) Marvel Enterprises, Inc.

Elmo Can Taste Touch Smell See. 2001. (J). 1.99 (978-0-375-80443-4(9) , Random Hse. Bks. for Young Readers) Random Hse. Children's Bks.

Elves & the Shoemaker. 2005. (J). bds. 3.99 (978-1-933200-07-1(3)) Family Bks. at Home.

The Elves & the Shoemaker. 2005. (J). (978-1-58453-304-7(8)) Pioneer Valley Educational Pr., Inc.

The Elves & the Shoemaker. 2004. 29.95 incl. cd-rom (978-0-7882-0547-7(1)) ; 24.95 incl. audio (978-0-7882-0546-0(3)) Weston Woods Studios, Inc.

Elwell, Sharon. Jeremy & the Wappo. Gentry, Debra, illus. 126p. (Orig.). (J). (gr. 3-4). pap. 10.50 (978-0-9626210-0-0(5)) Rattle OK Pubns.

Emesse, Tea. Nova Rocks. 2005. (Star Sisterz Ser.: Bk. 1). (Illus.). 192p. (J). pap. 5.99 (978-0-7869-3625-0(8)) Wizards of the Coast.

The Emperor's Fruits. 2002. (YA). pap. 14.00 (978-1-59268-004-7(6)) GMA Publishing & Inspiration Pr.

Emshwiller, Carol. Mister Boots. 2007. (Firebird Ser.). 192p. (YA). pap. 6.99 (978-0-14-240770-7(4) , Puffin) Penguin Group (USA) Inc.

Ende, Michael. La Historia Interminable. (SPA.). 432p. (YA). (gr. 5-8). 13.95 (978-84-204-2522-1(2) , LEC5222) Alfaguara, Ediciones, S.A.- Grupo Santillana ESP. *Dist:* Lectorum Pubns., Inc.

—La Historia Interminable. Quadflieg, Roswitha & Saenz, Miguel, trs. Quadflieg, Roswitha, illus. (SPA.). 424p. (J). 9.95 (978-84-204-3226-7(1)) Alfaguara, Ediciones, S.A.- Grupo Santillana ESP. *Dist:* Santillana USA Publishing Co., Inc.

—La Historia Interminable. 2003. (SPA., Illus.). 420p. (J). (gr. 5-8). pap. 12.95 (978-968-19-0254-4(8)) Santillana USA Publishing Co., Inc.

Endoh, Minari. Dazzle, Vol. 4. 3rd rev. ed. 2006. pap. 9.99 (978-1-59816-094-9(X) , Tokyopop Kids) TOKYOPOP, Inc.

Engelbrecht, Carla. Professor Dalrymple's Deluxe Patented Fairy Catching System. 2007. (Illus.). 32p. (J). (ps up). pap. 12.95 (***978-0-7624-2995-0(X)*** , Running Pr. Kids) Running Pr. Bk. Pubs.

Engler, L. E. The Forgotten Isle. 2004. 108p. pap. 16.95 (978-1-4137-1941-3(4)) PublishAmerica, Inc.

Eno, Paul F. The Kitleys & the Gate of the Poltergeist. 2006. (ENG.). (YA). pap. 12.95 (978-1-891724-04-6(5) , 5,000) New River Pr.

Enormous Egg. 1999. (J). 9.95 (978-1-56137-256-0(0)) Novel Units, Inc.

Ensor, Barbara. Cinderella (As If You Didn't Already Know the Story) Ensor, Barbara, illus. 2006. (Illus.). 128p. (J). (gr. 2-5). lib. bdg. 14.99 (978-0-375-93620-3(3) , Schwartz & Wade Bks.) Random Hse. Children's Bks.

Ensor, Rod. Getting It. 2007. 216p. per. 14.95 (***978-0-595-44800-5(3)***) iUniverse, Inc.

Eon Isle Chronicles. 2001. 160p. (J). 24.95 (978-1-890306-30-4(4)) Warwick Hse. Publishing.

Epstein, Dwayne. Cooler King. 2001. (gr. 5-8). lib. bdg. 11.80 (978-0-613-63100-6(5)) Tandem Library Bks.

Erickson, Lori. The Adventures of Sandy Clown Bk. 1: The Journey Home. 2002. (Illus.). 144p. (J). 14.95 (978-1-58930-076-7(9)) Selah Publishing Group, LLC.

Escott, John & Falkner, John Meade. Moonfleet. Date not set. (Nelson Readers Ser.). (Illus.). 47p. (J). pap. (978-0-17-557052-2(3)) Addison-Wesley Longman, Inc.

Estes, Rose. Dragon of Doom. 2008. (Endless Quest Ser.). 192p. (J). (gr. 3-7). 5.99 (***978-0-7869-4717-1(9)*** , Mirrorstone) Wizards of the Coast.

Etchemendy, Nancy. The Power of UN. 2002. 160p. (J). pap. 4.99 (978-0-439-31331-5(7)) Scholastic, Inc.

Etchison, Craig. The Golden Key. 2004. 250p. pap. 16.95 (978-0-595-30614-5(4)) iUniverse, Inc.

Ettwein, George. Edgar the Fish. Jansen, Kristen, illus. 2002. 38p. (J). pap. 12.95 (978-1-889276-02-1(2)) Animal Sounds.

Eun-Ah, Park. Sweet & Sensitive, Vol. 2. 2004. 208p. pap. (978-1-4139-0095-8(X)) ADV Manga.

Evans, Chris. Dreamtime Icetower. 119p. pap. 8.99 (978-1-85881-709-5(9)) Orion Bks. Ltd. GBR. *Dist:* Trafalgar Square Publishing.

Evans, Hubert. Silversides: The Life of a Sockeye. LaFave, Kim, illus. unabr. ed. 32p. (Orig.). (J). (978-0-88971-152-5(6)) Harbour Publishing Co., Ltd.

Evans, Margaret. The Tale of Rainbow's End. 2007. pap. 11.00 (***978-0-8059-8716-4(9)***) Dorrance Publishing Co., Inc.

Evslin, Bernard. The Adventures of Ulysses. 2000. (YA). pap. 39.75 incl. audio (978-0-7887-4155-5(1) , 41117) Recorded Bks., LLC.

Ewan, Ann. Firedrake. 2005. 520p. pap. 10.95 (978-1-894345-45-3(2)) Thistledown Pr., Ltd. CAN. *Dist:* Literary Pr. Group of Canada.

Ewing, Juliana Horatia. Old-Fashioned Fairy Tales. 2006. 77.99 (***978-1-4280-4762-4(X)***); pap. 70.99 (***978-1-4280-4770-9(0)***) IndyPublish.com.

Ewing, Lynne. Moon Demon, Bk. 7. rev. ed. 2002. (Daughters of the Moon Ser.: No. 7). 289p. (J). (gr. 7-17). 9.99 (978-0-7868-0849-6(7) , Volo) Hyperion Bks. for Children.

—Night Sun. 4th rev. ed. 2005. (Sons of the Dark Ser.: Bk. 4). 272p. (gr. 7-17). 9.99 (978-0-7868-1814-3(X) , Volo) Hyperion Bks. for Children.

—Outcast. rev. ed. 2005. (Sons of the Dark Ser.: Bk. 3). 272p. (J). (gr. 7-17). 9.99 (978-0-7868-1813-6(1) , Volo) Hyperion Bks. for Children.

—The Talisman, Bk. 10. 2003. (Daughters of the Moon Ser.: No. 10). 288p. (J). (gr. 8-17). 9.99 (978-0-7868-1878-5(6) , Volo) Hyperion Bks. for Children.

Exony's Excursion. (Tales of Planet Artembo Ser.: Bk. 6). (Illus.). 56p. (J). (gr. 5-7). pap. 20.00 (978-0-9600792-7-8(0)) Rymer Bks.

Fagan, Cary. The Fortress of Kaspar Snit. 2004. (gr. 3-6). lib. bdg. 18.75 (978-0-613-77346-1(2)) Tandem Library Bks.

Fairy Tale Digest Novel 1. 1998. (J). pap. (978-0-679-88813-0(6) , Random Hse. Bks. for Young Readers) Random Hse. Children's Bks.

Fairy Tale Digest Novel 2. 1998. (J). pap. (978-0-679-88814-7(4) , Random Hse. Bks. for Young Readers) Random Hse. Children's Bks.

Fairy Tales. (J). 2.29 (978-1-59445-060-0(9)) Dogs in Hats Children's Publishing Co.

Fairy Tales. 2003. (J). per. (978-1-57657-912-1(3)); per. (978-1-57657-913-8(1)) Paradise Pr., Inc.

Fairy Tales. (Little Lift-A-Flaps Ser.). (J). bds. (978-1-4127-3441-7(X) , 3910601) Publications International, Ltd.

Fake, Vol. 8. 2004. (YA). pap. 9.99 (978-1-59182-454-1(0)) TOKYOPOP, Inc.

The Fall of Aelyth-kintalyn: Part One of the Lords of Aelyth Kintalyn in Tales of Ulm from Hesta's Hearth. 2002. (Ulm Ser.: Vol. 2). pap. 15.00 (978-1-930094-11-6(6) , Rivet Bks.) Feral Pr., Inc.

Fan, Nancy Yi. Swordbird. Zug, Mark, illus. 2008. 256p. (J). pap. 6.99 (***978-0-06-113101-1(6)*** , Harper Trophy) HarperCollins Pubs.

Fancher, Joseph. Sydney's Travels Through Dreamland Part. 2006. 48p. pap. 12.95 (978-1-4241-3690-2(3)) PublishAmerica, Inc.

Fantasy Collection. (Fiction Collections). 184.69 (978-1-59889-040-2(9)) Stone Arch Bks.

Farhadi, Hamid. Ghooch-Ali & the Story of Love. 2004. pap. 14.95 (978-0-533-14217-0(2)) Vantage Pr., Inc.

Farley, Steven. South Wind Spring. 2000. (Young Black Stallion Ser.: No. 7). (Illus.). 144p. (J). (gr. 4-6). pap. 3.99 (978-0-375-80139-6(1) , Random Hse. Bks. for Young Readers) Random Hse. Children's Bks.

Farley, Terri. Golden Ghost. 2003. (Phantom Stallion Ser.: No. 8). (Illus.). 224p. (gr. 5 up). pap. 4.99 (978-0-06-053726-5(4)) HarperCollins Pubs.

—Golden Ghost. 2003. (gr. 5-8). lib. bdg. 13.00 (978-0-613-67623-6(8)) Tandem Library Bks.

—Moonrise, Vol. 14. 2005. (Phantom Stallion Ser.). (Illus.). 208p. (gr. 5 up). pap. 4.99 (978-0-06-058315-6(0)) HarperCollins Pubs.

Farley, Terri. The Shining Stallion. 2007. (Phantom Stallion: Wild Horse Island Ser.: No. 2). 224p. (J). (gr. 5 up). pap. 4.99 (***978-0-06-081543-1(4)*** , Harper Trophy) HarperCollins Pubs.

Farooqi, Imran A. The Spell of the Witch-Queen. 2006. (Illus.). 60p. pap. (***978-1-84401-816-1(4))*** Athena Pr.

Farrell, Patricia. Jessicah the Mountain Slayer. 1999. 92p. pap. (978-1-77901-095-7(8)) Zimbabwe Publishing House Ltd, Zimbabwe.

Farrell, Samantha. Return of the Boomerang. 2004. (Illus.). 46p. (J). pap. 12.95 (978-1-932373-68-4(3) , Cedar Hill Pr.) Cedar Hill Publishing.

Farrow, Edward Georg. The Mysterious Shin Shira. 2006. 40.99 (***978-1-4280-1467-1(5));*** pap. 34.99 (***978-1-4280-1471-8(3))*** IndyPublish.com.

Farshtey, Greg. Bionicle World, Vol. 5. 2007. (Bionicle Ser.). 96p. (J). pap. 6.99 (978-0-439-78796-3(3)) Scholastic, Inc.

—Dark Destiny. 2006. 128p. (J). pap. 4.99 (978-0-439-78795-6(5)) Scholastic, Inc.

—Downfall. 2008. (Bionicle Legends Ser.: No. 8). 128p. (J). pap. 4.99 (***978-0-439-89037-3(3))*** Scholastic, Inc.

—Maze of Shadows. 2004. (Bionicle Ser.). 128p. (J). (gr. 4-7). 4.99 (978-0-439-68023-3(9)) Scholastic, Inc.

—Prisoners of the Pit. 2007. (Bionicle Legends Ser.: No. 7). 144p. (J). pap. 4.99 (***978-0-439-89034-2(9))*** Scholastic, Inc.

—Shadows in the Sky. 2008. (Bionicle Legends Ser.). 128p. (J). 4.99 (***978-0-439-91641-7(0)*** , Scholastic) Scholastic, Inc.

—Time Trap. 2005. 137p. (J). (***978-1-4156-3150-8(6))*** Scholastic, Inc.

Farshtey, Greg. Web of Shadows. 2005. 139p. (J). (978-1-4156-0699-5(4)) Scholastic, Inc.

Faucher, W. Thomas. Candy Cane Cottage & the Cloud of Nica. Hamilton, Barbara Small, illus. 1998. 136p. (J). (gr. 3-6). pap. 12.95 (978-0-9664787-0-9(3)) Kern-O'Neil Pubns.

Feiffer, Jules. Bark, George. 2004. 24.95 incl. audio (978-1-55592-690-8(8)); 29.95 incl. cd-rom (978-1-55592-700-4(9)); pap. 14.95 incl. audio (978-1-55592-696-0(7)); pap. 18.95 incl. audio compact disk (978-1-55592-706-6(8)) Weston Woods Studios, Inc.

Fénelon, Marie Jirlande. The Two Best Friends & the Old Lady. 2004. (Illus.). 28p. (J). bds. 19.00 (978-1-58432-128-6(8)) Educa Vision.

Fenoglio, Paulette. If Wishes Were Brooms. Dudley, Theresa, illus. 2000. 32p. (J). (gr. 3-5). 12.95 (978-0-615-11216-9(1)) Aurelia Pr.

Fequiere, Marie A. Devil Rain & the Bearded Child of the Desert. 2007. (J). pap. 8.00 (***978-0-8059-7366-2(4))*** Dorrance Publishing Co., Inc.

Ferreiro-Esteban, Carmen. Two Moon Princess. 2007. 300p. (gr. 5 up). 15.95 (***978-1-933718-12-5(9))*** Tanglewood Pr.

Ferriss, Gregory. A Second Seer. 2002. 162p. pap. 12.95 (978-0-595-22222-3(6) , Writers Club Pr.) iUniverse, Inc.

Field, Eugene. Wynken, Blynken, & Nod. Westerman, Johanna, illus. 1998. 32p. (J). (gr. k-3). pap. 6.95 (978-1-55858-998-8(8)) North-South Bks., Inc.

Fienberg. Power to Burn. 167p. (J). pap. (978-0-340-70930-6(8) , Hodder & Stoughton) Hodder General Publishing Division.

Fienberg, Anna. Big Big Big Book of Tashi. 2002. (gr. 3-6). lib. bdg. 21.05 (978-0-613-54979-0(1)) Tandem Library Bks.

Fienberg, Anna & Fienberg, Barbara. Tashi & the Demons. Gamble, Kim, illus. 2000. 64p. (Orig.). (J). pap. 5.95 (978-1-86508-084-0(5)) Allen & Unwin AUS. *Dist:* Independent Pubs. Group.

Fienberg, Anna & Fienberg, Barbara. Tashi & the Royal Tomb. Gamble, Kim, illus. (Tashi Ser.). 64p. (Orig.). (J). (gr. k-2). 2007. pap. 5.95 (***978-1-74114-973-9(8));*** Vol. 10. 2004. pap. 5.95 (978-1-74114-090-3(0)) Allen & Unwin AUS. *Dist:* Independent Pubs. Group.

Filaretos, William. The Potion of Time: A Story of Demetrios. 2006. per. 12.95 (978-0-9724520-0-7(1)) Filaretos, William.

Findlay, Jamieson. The Blue Roan Girl. 2004. (Illus.). 272p. (J). 16.95 (978-0-439-62752-8(4)) Scholastic, Inc.

Findon, Joanne. When Night Eats the Moon. 2004. 175p. (YA). (gr. 7-12). per. 16.60 (978-0-613-93942-3(5)) Tandem Library Bks.

Fine, Anne. Goldnebel. Koesters-Roth, Ursula, tr. from ENG. Kernke, Gabriele, photos by. 1999. Orig. Title: A Sudden Glow of Gold. (GER., Illus.). 64p. (J). pap. (978-3-257-00853-1(8)) Diogenes Verlag AG CHE. *Dist:* International Bk. Import Service, Inc.

Fink. Future Fantastic. 2000. (Fink, Inc. Presents Ser.). 32p. (J). 3.50 (978-1-930281-03-5(X)) FINK, Inc.

Finlay, Lizzie, illus. Buri & the Marrow. 2004. (TAM, VIE, SPA, GUJ & PER.). 24p. (J). pap. (978-1-85269-579-8(X)); pap. (978-1-85269-581-1(1)); pap. (978-1-85269-582-8(X)); pap. (978-1-85269-584-2(6)); pap. (978-1-85269-585-9(4)); pap. (978-1-85269-587-3(0)); pap. (978-1-85269-588-0(9)); pap. (978-1-85269-589-7(7)); pap. (978-1-85269-590-3(0)); pap. (978-1-85269-591-0(9)) Mantra Publishing, Ltd.

Fiona, Simpson, ed. Harry Potter & the Goblet of Fire: Book of Creatures, Create & Trace. 2005. (Harry Potter Ser.). (Illus.). 32p. (J). (gr. 2-5). pap. 3.99 (978-0-439-63296-6(X) , Levine, Arthur A. Bks.) Scholastic, Inc.

—Harry Potter & the Goblet of Fire: Coloring Book. 2005. (Harry Potter Ser.). (Illus.). 48p. (J). (gr. 2-5). pap. 3.99 (978-0-439-63295-9(1) , Levine, Arthur A. Bks.) Scholastic, Inc.

Fisher, Catherine. Darkhenge. 2006. 352p. (J). 15.99 (978-0-06-078582-6(9)); lib. bdg. 16.89 (978-0-06-078583-3(7)) HarperCollins Pubs.

—Day of the Scarab. (Oracle Prophecies Ser.: Bk. 3). (J). 2007. 400p. pap. 7.99 (978-0-06-057165-8(9)); 2006. 416p. 16.99 (978-0-06-057163-4(2)); 2006. 416p. lib. bdg. 18.89 (978-0-06-057164-1(0)) HarperCollins Pubs.

—Lammas Field. 2003. 240p. pap. (978-0-340-73699-9(2) , Hodder Children's Books) Hodder Children's Division.

—The Oracle Betrayed. (Oracle Prophecies Ser.: Bk. 1). 352p. (J). (gr. 7 up). 2004. 16.99 (978-0-06-057157-3(8)); 2004. lib. bdg. 17.89 (978-0-06-057158-0(6)); 2005. reprint ed. pap. 6.99 (978-0-06-057159-7(4)) HarperCollins Pubs.

—Snow-Walker. 2004. 512p. (J). (gr. 5 up). 17.99 (978-0-06-072474-0(9)) HarperCollins Pubs.

—The Sphere of Secrets. (Oracle Prophecies Ser.: Bk. 2). (J). 2006. 368p. pap. 6.99 (978-0-06-057160-3(8)); 2005. 384p. (gr. 5 up). 16.99 (978-0-06-057161-0(6)); 2005. 384p. (gr. 5 up). lib. bdg. 18.89 (978-0-06-057162-7(4)) HarperCollins Pubs.

Fisher, Jude. El Senor de los Anillos: Las Dos Torres. Torres, Estela Gutierrez, tr. 2003. (Lord of the Rings Ser.). (SPA., Illus.). 67p. (J). 14.95 (978-84-450-7413-8(X)) Minotauro Ediciones ESP. *Dist:* Planeta Publishing Corp.

Fisk, N. Flip Side. 140p. pap. 8.99 (978-0-340-71019-7(5) , Hodder & Stoughton) Hodder General Publishing Division GBR. *Dist:* Trafalgar Square Publishing.

Fitzgerald, Gyleen Xavier. The Dream: A Magical Journey in Colourful Stitches. 2006. (Illus.). 96p. (J). 29.95 (978-0-9768215-1-9(6)) FPI Publishing.

Flanagan, John. The Burning Bridge. 2007. (Ranger's Apprentice Ser.: Bk. 2). 288p. (J). (gr. 5 up). pap. 7.99 (978-0-14-240842-1(5) , Puffin) Penguin Group (USA) Inc.

—The Icebound Land. (Ranger's Apprentice Ser.: Bk. 3). (J). (gr. 5). 2008. 288p. 7.99 (***978-0-14-241075-2(6)*** , Puffin); 2007. 260p. 16.99 (978-0-399-24456-8(5) , Philomel) Penguin Group (USA) Inc.

Flanagan, John. The Ruins of Gorlan. 2006. (Ranger's Apprentice Ser.: Bk. 1). 272p. (J). (gr. 5). pap. 6.99 (978-0-14-240663-2(5) , Puffin) Penguin Group (USA) Inc.

Fleischman, Sid. Here Comes McBroom! Three More Tall Tales. Blake, Quentin, illus. 1998. 80p. (J). (gr. 2-5). reprint ed. pap. 4.99 (978-0-688-16364-8(5)) HarperCollins Pubs.

Fleissner, Else. The Magic Key: A Story for Mothers & Children. Fleissner, Robert F., ed. Zalewski, Jennifer, illus. 1999. 64p. (gr. 3-6). pap. 15.00 (978-1-887196-05-5(6)) Wells College Pr.

Fletcher, Susan. Dadblamed Union Army Cow. Root, Kimberly Bulcken, illus. 2007. 32p. (J). (gr. k-2). 16.99 (978-0-7636-2263-3(X)) Candlewick Pr.

Flexer, Michael. Lucy's Adventure. 2005. 2005p. (J). lib. bdg. 15.00 (***978-1-4242-0760-2(6))*** Fitzgerald Bks.

Fodi, Lee Edward. Kendra Kandlestar & the Box of Whispers. Fodi, Lee Edward, illus. 2005. (Illus.). 225p. (J). 16.95 (978-1-933285-10-8(9)); per. 8.95 (978-1-933285-11-5(7)) Brown Bks. Publishing Group.

Fonseca, Mireya (Adaptacion). NEREO -el anciano del Mar. 2005. 32p. pap. (978-958-30-1909-8(7)) Panamericana Editorial.

Fontes, Ron & Fontes, Justine. Rex to the Rescue! 1999. (Disney Chapters Ser.). (Illus.). 46p. (J). (gr. 2-4). pap. 3.99 (978-0-7868-4288-9(1)) Disney Pr.

Foon, Dennis. The Dirt Eaters. 2003. (Longlight Legacy Ser.). 320p. (YA). (gr. 8). 19.95 (978-1-55037-807-8(4)); pap. 9.95 (978-1-55037-806-1(6)) Annick Pr., Ltd. CAN. *Dist:* Firefly Bks., Ltd.

—Freewalker. 2004. (Longlight Legacy Ser.). 320p. (YA). (gr. 6). 19.95 (978-1-55037-885-6(6)); pap. 9.95 (978-1-55037-884-9(8)) Annick Pr., Ltd. CAN. *Dist:* Firefly Bks., Ltd.

Forbeck, Matt. The Dragons Revealed, Pt. 2. ed. 2006. (Illus.). 192p. (YA). pap. 5.99 (978-0-7869-4032-5(8) , Mirrorstone) Wizards of the Coast.

—Prophecy of the Dragons, Pt. 1. ed. 2006. 192p. (YA). pap. 5.99 (978-0-7869-4031-8(X) , Mirrorstone) Wizards of the Coast.

—Secret of the Spiritkeeper. 2004. (Dungeons & Dragons Ser.). (Illus.). 192p. (J). (gr. 3-7). pap. 5.99 (978-0-7869-3143-9(4)) Wizards of the Coast.

Forbes, Anne. Dragonfire. 2006. 256p. (YA). pap. 11.95 (978-0-86315-552-9(9)) Floris Bks. GBR. *Dist:* Steiner-Books, Inc.

The Forest of the Frendibles. 2006. (J). mass mkt. (***978-0-9791982-0-5(8))*** Donnellan, Martha.

Forgey, Winchester. Chronicle of the Bent Nail. 2004. (J). per. (978-0-9666572-7-2(6)) Acacia Publishing, Inc.

Forrestal, Elaine. Watching Lake. 2002. 104p. reprint ed. pap. 12.95 (978-1-86368-360-9(7)) Fremantle Pr. AUS. *Dist:* International Specialized Bk. Services.

Forst, Arthur & Patterson, Renee. Pippin & Peanut: The Adventure Begins. 2000. 108p. (J). (gr. 4-7). pap. 9.95 (978-0-595-14537-9(X)) iUniverse, Inc.

Forward, Toby. Travelling Backwards. 2003. (Illus.). 128p. (J). 9.99 (978-1-84270-293-2(9)) Andersen GBR. *Dist:* Independent Pubs. Group.

Foster, Alan Dean. The Hand of Dinotopia. Gurney, James, illus. 1999. (Dinotopia Ser.). 416p. (J). (gr. 5 up). 22.99 (978-0-06-028005-5(0)) HarperCollins Pubs.

—Hand of Dinotopia. 2002. (Dinotopia Ser.). (Illus.). 416p. (J). (gr. 5 up). pap. 7.99 (978-0-06-051851-6(0)) HarperCollins Pubs.

Fowler, Zinita. In Search of Three Sillies: A One-Act Comedy. 1998. (Illus.). 12p. pap. 3.00 (978-0-88680-448-0(5) , C448-5) Clark, I. E. Pubns.

Fowles, Shelley, illus. The Seven Voyages of Sinbad. 2008. 64p. (J). 18.95 (***978-1-84507-531-6(5))*** Lincoln, Frances Ltd. GBR. *Dist:* Perseus Distribution.

Fox, Gardner. All Star Comics. Kubert, Joe et al, illus. rev. ed. 2001. (Archives Ser.: Vol. 7). 216p. 49.95 (978-1-56389-720-7(2)) DC Comics.

—All Star Comics. rev. ed. (Illus.). 2000. (Archives Ser.: Vol. 6). 240p. 49.95 (978-1-56389-636-1(2)); Vol. 5. 1999. 224p. 49.95 (978-1-56389-497-8(1)) DC Comics.

Fox, Gardner, et al. All Star Comics, Vol. 8. Infantino, Carmine & Irwin, H., illus. rev. ed. 2002. 228p. 49.95 (978-1-56389-812-9(8)) DC Comics.

Fox, Lee White. Toby Erdrich & the Golden Eclipse. Selyov, Trebor E., ed. 2005. 170p. (YA). (gr. 7-12). pap. 11.95 (978-0-9665055-7-3(3) , 5) Hallmark Emporium.

Frantz, Jennifer. Chronicles of Narnia: Prince Caspian. 2008. (I Can Read Bks.). 32p. (J). pap. 3.99 (978-0-06-123162-9(2) , Harper Trophy) HarperCollins Pubs.

Frantz, Jennifer, adapted by. Narnia: Tea with Mr Tumnus. 2005. (Illus.). 32p. (J). lib. bdg. 13.85 (***978-1-4242-0616-2(2))*** Fitzgerald Bks.

—Narnia: Welcome to Narnia. 2005. (Illus.). 32p. (J). lib. bdg. 13.85 (***978-1-4242-0617-9(0))*** Fitzgerald Bks.

Frantz, Jennifer & Zondervan. The Lion, the Witch & the Wardrobe: Welcome to Narnia. movie tie-in ed. 2005. (Chronicles of Narnia Ser.). (Illus.). 32p. (J). pap. 3.99 (978-0-06-076560-6(7) , Harper Trophy) HarperCollins Pubs.

Freeman, Don. Corduroy. Freeman, Don, illus. 2004. (Illus.). (J). pap. 18.95 incl. audio compact disk (978-1-59112-789-5(0)) Live Oak Media.

Freeman, Greg. The Legend of Booga Bearia: Land of the. 2005. 128p. pap. 17.95 (978-1-4137-8411-4(9)) PublishAmerica, Inc.

Freeman, R. Gregory. A Carpenter¿s Tale: The Mystery of Kidron Valley. 2006. (Illus.). 44p. (J). per. 10.95 (978-1-60002-118-3(2) , 3901, Airleaf Publishing) Airleaf Publishing & Bookselling.

Freeman, Richard. The Legend of Booga Bearia. 2004. 117p. pap. 16.95 (978-1-4137-2016-7(1)) PublishAmerica, Inc.

Frei, Greg & Frei, Greg. Discovery. 2006. 44p. (J). 10.99 (978-1-59092-253-8(0) , Little Blue Works) Windstorm Creative.

French, Fiona. Anancy & Mr. Dry-Bone. 1999. (Illus.). 32p. (J). pap. (978-0-7112-0787-5(9)) Lincoln, Frances Ltd. GBR. *Dist:* Transition Vendor.

French, Vivian. Capitana Jennifer - Aguamala Jones. Solana, Maria T., tr. Ortega, Damian, illus. 1998. (SPA.). 48p. (J). (ps-ps). pap. 5.99 (978-968-16-5435-1(8)) Fondo de Cultura Economica MEX. *Dist:* Continental Bk. Co., Inc.

—I Wish I Were an Alien. Williams, Lisa, illus. 2005. (Lightning Readers Ser.). 32p. (J). (ps-ps). pap., pap. 3.95 (978-0-7696-4020-4(6) , Gingham Dog Pr.) School Specialty Publishing.

—Ojala fuera un Extraterrestre. Williams, Lisa, illus. 2005. (Lightning Readers Ser.). (SPA.). 32p. (J). (gr. k-1). pap. 3.95 (978-0-7696-4060-0(5) , Gingham Dog Pr.) School Specialty Publishing.

—Space Dog Visits Planet Earth. Heap, Sue, illus. 2000. (Space Dog Ser.: No. 4). 64p. (J). (ps-3). pap. 3.99 (978-0-439-13086-8(7) , Scholastic Paperbacks) Scholastic, Inc.

—The Tiara Club at Ruby Mansions 3: Princess Georgia & the Shimmering Pearl. Gibb, Sarah, illus. 2008. (Tiara Club Ser.). 80p. (J). pap. 3.99 (***978-0-06-143486-0(8)*** , Harper Trophy) HarperCollins Pubs.

—The Tiara Club at Ruby Mansions 4: Princess Olivia & the Velvet Cape. Gibb, Sarah, illus. 2008. (Tiara Club Ser.). 80p. (J). pap. 3.99 (***978-0-06-143487-7(6)*** , Harper Trophy) HarperCollins Pubs.

French, Vivian & McDonald, Ronald L. Once upon a Time. Prater, John, illus. 1999. (Read & Share Ser.). 32p. (J). (ps). pap. 3.99 (978-0-7636-0858-3(0)) Candlewick Pr.

Freymann, Saxton & Elffers, Joost. How Are You Peeling? Foods with Moods. 1999. (Illus.). 48p. (J). (ps-3). pap. 16.95 (978-0-439-10431-9(9) , Levine, Arthur A. Bks.) Scholastic, Inc.

Fridman, Sashi. When I Fell into My Kiddush Cup. Kranz, Sarah, illus. 1999. 32p. (J). (ps-1). 12.95 (978-0-8266-0026-4(3)) Merkos L'Inyonei Chinuch.

Frie, Robert R. & Zahradnik, Kristen M. Windy Wildwood: The Secret in the Attic. 2004. 103p. (J). per. 9.95 (978-0-9753641-0-9(3)) Zahrob Publishing Co.

Friel, Maeve. Charming or What?, Vol. 2. 2003. (Witch-in-Training Ser.). (Illus.). 96p. pap. 7.50 (978-0-00-713342-0(1)) HarperCollins Pubs. Ltd. GBR. *Dist:* Independent Pubs. Group.

Friend, Catherine. When Night & Day Meet. 2005. 32p. (J). (978-0-7868-0112-1(3)) Hyperion Pr.

Friesner, Esther M. Nobody's Princess. 2008. 336p. (J). (gr. 7-11). pap. 7.99 (978-0-375-87529-8(8) , Random Hse. Bks. for Young Readers) Random Hse. Children's Bks.

Frontiera, Deborah K. Eric & the Enchanted Leaf / Eric y la Hoja Encantada: A Visit with Canis Lupis / una Visita con Canis Lupis. Santillan-Cruz, Silvia R., tr. Scott, Korey, illus. 2nd l.t. ed. 2005. (SPA & ENG.). 32p. (J). lib. bdg. 16.95 (978-0-9663629-8-5(5)) By Grace Enterprises.

Frost-Snyder, M. G. The Hallu Realm. 2001. (Illus.). 80p. (J). pap. 9.00 (978-0-8059-5418-0(X)) Dorrance Publishing Co., Inc.

Fry, Sonali. Let's Catch Stars! Aikins, Dave, illus. 2004. (Dora the Explorer Ser.). 14p. (J). bds. 6.99 (978-0-689-86454-4(X) , Simon Spotlight/Nickelodeon) Simon & Schuster Children's Publishing.

Fujima, Takuya, creator. Deus Vitae, 3 vols., Vol. 3. 3rd rev. ed. 2004. (Illus.). 264p. pap. 9.99 (978-1-59182-771-9(X) , Tokyopop Adult) TOKYOPOP, Inc.

Fujino, Moyamu. The First King Adventure, Vol 1. 2004. (Illus.). 184p. (YA). pap. (978-1-4139-0194-8(8)) ADV Manga.

Fujisawa, Tohru. GTO Vol. 1: Great Teacher Onizuka, 25 vols. Papia, Dan, tr. rev. ed. 2004. (Illus.). 192p. pap. 9.99 (978-1-59182-142-7(8) , Tokyopop Adult) TOKYOPOP, Inc.

Fujisawa, Tohru, illus. & compiled by. GTO: Great Teacher Onizuka, 25 vols. Fujisawa, Tohru, compiled by. Vol. 8. 8th rev. ed. 2002. 192p. pap. 9.99 (978-1-59182-032-1(4)); Vol. 9. rev. ed. 2003. 192p. (gr. 11 up). pap. 9.99 (978-1-59182-070-3(7)); Vol. 10. rev. ed. 2003. 192p. (gr. 11 up). pap. 9.99 (978-1-59182-106-9(1)); Vol. 11. rev. ed. 2003. 192p. (gr. 11 up). pap. 9.99 (978-1-59182-135-9(5)); Vol. 12. rev. ed. 2003. 192p. (gr. 11 up). pap. 9.99 (978-1-59182-136-6(3)); Vol. 13. 13th rev. ed. 2003. 192p. (gr. 11 up). pap. 9.99 (978-1-59182-137-3(1)); Vol. 14. rev. ed. 2003. 192p. (gr. 11 up). pap. 9.99 (978-1-59182-138-0(X)); Vol. 15. rev. ed. 2003. 200p. pap. 9.99 (978-1-59182-139-7(8)); Vol. 16. rev. ed. 2004. 192p. pap. 9.99 (978-1-59182-140-3(1)); Vol. 17. rev. ed. 2004. 192p. pap. 9.99 (978-1-59182-141-0(X)); Vol. 19. rev. ed. 2004. 192p. pap. 9.99 (978-1-59182-143-4(6)); Vol. 21. rev. ed. 2004. 192p. pap. 9.99 (978-1-59182-455-8(9)) TOKYOPOP, Inc. (Tokyopop Adult).

Fujishima, Kosuke. The Devil in Miss Urd. 2001. (Oh My Goddess! Ser.: Vol. 11). (Illus.). 176p. (J). (gr. 5 up). pap. 14.95 (978-1-56971-540-6(8)) Dark Horse Comics.

—Oh My Goddess!, Vol. 25. 2007. 176p. (J). pap. 10.95 (978-1-59307-644-3(4)) Dark Horse Comics.

—Oh My Goddess! Childhood's End. 2002. (gr. 7-12). lib. bdg. 25.70 (978-0-613-55151-9(6)) Tandem Library Bks.

—Oh My Goddess! Devil in Miss Urd. 2001. (gr. 7-12). lib. bdg. 24.55 (978-0-613-55156-4(7)) Tandem Library Bks.

—Oh My Goddess! Fourth Goddess. 2001. (gr. 7-12). lib. bdg. 29.20 (978-0-613-55165-6(6)) Tandem Library Bks.

—The Queen of Vengeance. 1999. (Oh My Goddess! Ser.: Vol. 7). (Illus.). 152p. (J). (gr. 3 up). pap. 13.95 (978-1-56971-431-7(2)) Dark Horse Comics.

Fujita, Maki, illus. & creator. Platinum Garden. Fujita, Maki, creator. 2006. (YA). pap. 9.99 (978-1-59816-361-2(2) , Tokyopop Kids) TOKYOPOP, Inc.

Fumiya, Sato, illus. The Kindaichi Case Files Vol. 13, Pt. 2: Playing the Fool. 2006. 312p. pap. 9.99 (978-1-59532-697-3(9) , Tokyopop Kids) TOKYOPOP, Inc.

Funke, Cornelia. Dragon Rider. Bell, Anthea, tr. from GER. 2004. Orig. Title: Drachenreiter. (Illus.). 528p. (J). (gr. 3-6). pap. 14.99 (978-0-439-45695-1(9) , Chicken Hse., The) Scholastic, Inc.

—Dragon Rider. collector's ed. 2004. Orig. Title: Drachenreiter. 528p. (J). 100.00 (978-0-439-74336-5(2)) Scholastic, Inc.

Funke, Cornelia. Igraine the Brave. Bell, Anthea, tr. from GER. 2007. 224p. (J). (gr. 4-7). pap. 16.99 (***978-0-439-90379-0(3)*** , Chicken Hse., The) Scholastic, Inc.

Funny Faces. 2002. (Tap My Nose Ser.). (J). (ps-k). 4.98 (978-0-7525-8727-1(7)) Parragon, Inc.

Funny Faces. 120p. 19.99 (978-1-58279-127-2(9) , 92) Trident Pr. International.

E F G

Fuqua, Jonathon Scott. Medusas Daughter: A Graphic Novel. Parke, Steven, illus. 2007. (Narrative, Ink Ser.). 128p. (YA). (gr. 10 up). pap. 17.95 (*978-1-933368-92-4(6)) Counterpoint.

—Medusas Daughter Graphic Novella. Parke, Steven, illus. 2007. (Narrative, Ink Ser.). 64p. (J). (*978-1-933368-93-1(4)) Counterpoint.

—Medusas Daughter Novel. 2007. (Narrative, Ink Ser.). 192p. (J). (*978-1-933368-91-7(8)) Counterpoint.

Furuya, Usamaru. Short Cuts, Vol. 1. Furuya, Usamaru, illus. 2002. (Short Cuts Ser.). (Illus.). 136p. (YA). pap. 12.95 (978-1-59116-031-1(6)) Viz Media.

Gackenbach, Dick. Harry y el Terrible Quiensabeque. Palacios, Argentina, tr. 2000. (SPA., Illus.). (J). (ps-3). pap. 4.99 (978-0-590-41820-1(3) , SO2845) Scholastic, Inc.

—Harry y el Terrible Quiensabeque. 2000. (SPA., Illus.). (J). (978-0-606-21809-2(2)) Tandem Library Bks.

Gaetz, Dayle Campbell. Living Freight. 1998. (On Time's Wing Ser.). 176p. (J). (gr. 4-7). pap. 8.95 (978-1-896184-32-6(4)) Roussan Pubs., Inc./Roussan Editeur, Inc. CAN. *Dist:* Orca Bk. Pubs. USA.

Gaiman, Neil. Coraline, 12 Copies. 2003. (J). pap. 71.88 (978-0-06-056895-5(X)); pap. 71.88 (978-0-06-057152-8(7)) HarperCollins Pubs.

—Coraline. McKean, Dave, tr. McKean, Dave, illus. l.t. ed. 2003. 181p. (J). 25.95 (978-0-7862-5542-9(0)) Thorndike Pr.

—Gaiman Mid Grade Novel. 2005. 176p. (J). 15.99 (978-0-06-088123-8(2)); pap. 5.99 (978-0-06-088125-2(9) , Harper Trophy); lib. bdg. 16.89 (978-0-06-088124-5(0)) HarperCollins Pubs.

—InterWorld. 2007. 256p. (J). lib. bdg. 17.89 (*978-0-06-123897-0(X) , Eos) HarperCollins Pubs.

Gaiman, Neil. Stardust. 2005. (Single Volume Ser.). (SPA., Illus.). 210p. pap. 16.95 (978-1-59497-097-9(1)) Public Square Bks.

Gaiman, Neil & Reaves, Michael. InterWorld. 2007. 256p. (J). (gr. 5 up). 16.99 (*978-0-06-123896-3(1) , Eos) HarperCollins Pubs.

Gainax. FLCL, Vol. 2. Yoshimoto, Ray, tr. from JPN. Ueda, Hajime, illus. rev. ed. 2003. (ENG.). 204p. (YA). pap. 9.99 (978-1-59182-397-1(8) , Tokyopop Adult) TOKYOPOP, Inc.

Galdone, Paul. The Gingerbread Boy. Galdone, Paul, illus. 2002. (Illus.). (J). 14.74 (978-0-7587-2594-3(9)) Book Wholesalers, Inc.

Gallagher, Diana. Dark Vengeance. 2002. 202p. (YA). (gr. 7-12). lib. bdg. 14.15 (978-0-613-73371-7(1)) Tandem Library Bks.

Gallagher, Diana G. Dark Vengeance. 2002. (Charmed Ser.). 208p. (YA). pap. 5.99 (978-0-689-85079-0(4) , Simon Pulse) Simon & Schuster Children's Publishing.

—Mist & Stone. 2003. (gr. 7-12). lib. bdg. 14.15 (978-0-613-66520-9(1)) Tandem Library Bks.

Gallagher, Diana G. & Burge, Constance M. Mystic Knoll. 2005. (Charmed Ser.). 224p. (YA). pap. 6.99 (978-0-689-86854-2(5) , Simon Spotlight Entertainment) Simon & Schuster.

Gallagher, Diana G. & Burge, Constance M. Trickery Treat. 2008. (Charmed Ser.). 208p. (YA). mass mkt. 6.99 (*978-1-4169-3670-1(X) , Simon Spotlight Entertainment) Simon & Schuster.

Gallagher, Michael. X-Men, Scourge of the Savage Land. Severin, Marie, illus. 24p. (YA). (gr. k up). 12.95 (978-0-9627001-7-0(7)) Futech Educational Products, Inc.

Gallardo, Adam. Grunts Vol 1, Vol. 1. Demong, Todd, illus. 2008. (YA). 17.95 (978-0-9763095-3-6(X)) Arcana Studio, Inc.

Gallop to the Sea. 2005. (J). (978-1-933343-12-9(5)) Stabenfeldt Inc.

Ganguli, Taraknath & Gangapadhyay, Narayan. 4 Heroes & a Green Beard. Bhattacharjee, Swati, tr. from BEN. 1999. (Translations from Indian Languages Ser.). (Illus.). 92p. (J). pap. (978-81-86211-52-6(7)) Tara Publishing.

Gannett, Ruth Stiles. The Dragons of Blueland. Gannett, Ruth Chrisman, illus. 2002. 14.47 (978-0-7587-9533-5(5)) Book Wholesalers, Inc.

—The Dragons of Blueland. Gannett, Ruth Chrisman, illus. (Tales of My Father's Dragon Ser.: Bk. 3). 88p. (J). (gr. 3-6). pap. 4.99 incl. audio (978-0-8072-1287-5(3) , Listening Library) Random Hse. Audio Publishing Group.

—Elmer & the Dragon. Gannett, Ruth Chrisman, illus. 2002. (J). 14.47 (978-0-7587-9151-1(8)) Book Wholesalers, Inc.

—Elmer & the Dragon. Gannett, Ruth Chrisman, illus. (Tales of My Father's Dragon Ser.: Bk. 2). 87p. (J). (gr. 3-6). pap. 4.99 incl. audio (978-0-8072-1288-2(1) , Listening Library) Random Hse. Audio Publishing Group.

Garcia, Belinda. Alyson's Adventures in Computer Land. 2005. 184p. (J). pap. 15.95 (978-1-58736-484-6(0) , Hats Off Bks.) Wheatmark.

García Marquez, Gabriel. Un Senor muy Viejo con unas Alas Enormes.Tr. of Very Old Man with Large Wings. 10.50 (978-958-04-5570-7(8)) Norma S.A. COL. *Dist:* AIMS International Bks., Inc., Distribuidora Norma, Inc.

Gardner, Hugh. Tales from the Marble Mountain. 2005. pap. 26.95 (978-1-4191-1589-9(8)) Kessinger Publishing, LLC.

Gardner, Lyn. Into the Woods. Grey, Mini, illus. 2007. 488p. (J). (gr. 3-7). 16.99 (978-0-385-75115-5(X)); lib. bdg. 19.99 (978-0-385-75116-2(8)) Random Hse. Children's Bks. (Fickling, David Bks.).

Gardner, Sally. I, Coriander. 2005. (Illus.). 288p. (YA). (gr. 5). 16.99 (978-0-8037-3099-1(3) , Dial) Penguin Group (USA) Inc.

Garner, Alan. Elidor. 192p. (YA). (gr. 5 up). pap. 6.00 (978-0-8072-1545-6(7) , Listening Library) Random Hse. Audio Publishing Group.

—The Moon of Gomrath: A Tale of Alderley. Call, Greg, illus. 2006. 216p. (J). pap. 6.95 (978-0-15-205630-8(0) , Odyssey Classics) Harcourt Children's Bks.

—The Weirdstone of Brisingamen: A Tale of Alderley. Call, Greg, illus. 2006. 288p. (J). pap. 6.95 (978-0-15-205636-0(X) , Odyssey Classics) Harcourt Children's Bks.

Garrido, Pedro Gelabert. El Libro del Abuelo: Un Mundo de Aventuras Entre la Realidad y la Fantasma. Velert, Miriam, illus. 2003. (Ficcion Interactiva Series Ser.). (SPA.). 160p. pap. 14.95 (978-84-89984-11-0(5)) Recursos, Ediciones ESP. *Dist:* Independent Pubs. Group.

Garrison, Terie. AutumnQuest. 2006. 192p. (YA). (gr. 7-9). pap. 8.95 (978-0-7387-0926-0(3) , Flux) Llewellyn Pubns.

—SpringFire. 2007. (DragonSpawn Cycle Ser.: Bk. 3). 240p. (J). pap. 8.95 (978-0-7387-1096-9(2) , Flux) Llewellyn Pubns.

Garrison, Victoria. Bean. 2004. 48p. pap. 12.95 (978-1-4137-2735-7(2)) PublishAmerica, Inc.

Gates, Josephine Scribner. The April fool Doll. Keep, Virginia, illus. 2007. 152p. (J). lib. bdg. 59.00 (*978-1-60304-009-9(9)) Dollworks.

—Captain Billie: Leads the way to the land of I don't want To. Sichel, Harold, illus. 2007. 96p. (J). lib. bdg. 59.00 (*978-1-60304-019-8(6)) Dollworks.

—The dolls in Fairyland. Keep, Virginia, illus. 2007. 136p. (J). lib. bdg. 59.00 (*978-1-60304-013-6(7)) Dollworks.

—Little girl Blue: Lives in the woods till she learns to say Please. Keep, Virginia, illus. 2007. 54p. (J). lib. bdg. 59.00 (*978-1-60304-012-9(9)) Dollworks.

—Little Girl Blue plays I Spy. 2007. (Illus.). 64p. (J). lib. bdg. 59.00 (*978-1-60304-017-4(X)) Dollworks.

—Little red white & Blue. Keep, Virginia, illus. 2007. 118p. (J). lib. bdg. 59.00 (*978-1-60304-006-8(4)) Dollworks.

—The live dolls' busy Days. Keep, Virginia, illus. 2007. 106p. (J). lib. bdg. 59.00 (*978-1-60304-007-5(2)) Dollworks.

—The live dolls' house Party. Keep, Virginia, illus. 2007. 104p. (J). lib. bdg. 59.00 (*978-1-60304-005-1(6)) Dollworks.

—The live dolls in Wonderland. Keep, Virginia, illus. 2007. 150p. (J). lib. bdg. 59.00 (*978-1-60304-015-0(3)) Dollworks.

—The live dolls' play Days. Keep, Virginia, illus. 2007. 110p. (J). lib. bdg. 59.00 (*978-1-60304-008-2(0)) Dollworks.

—More about live Dolls. Keep, Virginia, illus. 2007. 106p. (J). lib. bdg. 59.00 (*978-1-60304-002-0(1)) Dollworks.

—Nannette & the baby Monkey. 2007. (Illus.). 50p. (J). lib. bdg. 59.00 (*978-1-60304-020-4(X)) Dollworks.

—Nannette goes to visit her Grandmother. 2007. (J). lib. bdg. 59.00 (*978-1-60304-021-1(8)) Dollworks.

—One day in Betty,s Life. Stuart, B. S., illus. 2007. 58p. (J). lib. bdg. 59.00 (*978-1-60304-018-1(8)) Dollworks.

—The secret of the live Dolls. Archibald, A. L., illus. 2007. (J). lib. bdg. 59.00 (*978-1-60304-024-2(2)) Dollworks.

—The Story of Live Dolls: Being an account by Josephine Scribner Gates of how, on a certian June morning, all of the dolls in the Cloverdale came Alive. Keep, Virginia, illus. 2007. 102p. (J). lib. bdg. 59.00 (*978-1-60304-001-3(3)) Dollworks.

—The story of the lost Doll. Keep, Virginia, illus. 2007. 108p. (J). lib. bdg. 59.00 (*978-1-60304-003-7(X)) Dollworks.

—The Story of the three Dolls. Keep, Virginia, illus. 2007. 148p. (J). lib. bdg. 59.00 (*978-1-60304-004-4(8)) Dollworks.

—Sunshine Annie. Cory, Fanny Y., illus. 2007. 148p. (J). lib. bdg. 59.00 (*978-1-60304-011-2(0)) Dollworks.

—Tommy Sweet-Tooth & Little girl Blue. Churbuck, Esther V., illus. 2007. 64p. (J). lib. bdg. 59.00 (*978-1-60304-014-3(5)) Dollworks.

—The Turkey Doll. Flass, E. C., illus. 2007. 62p. (J). lib. bdg. 59.00 (*978-1-60304-016-7(1)) Dollworks.

Gauthier, Bertrand. Panique au Cimetiere. 2002. (Roman Jeunesse Ser.). (FRE.). 96p. (YA). (gr. 4-7). pap. (978-2-89021-169-8(X)) Diffusion du livre Mirabel.

Gavioli, Gino. Candido, el Limpiador de Chimeneas. Brignole, Giancarla, tr. Gavioli, Gino, illus. rev. ed. 2006. (Fabulas De Familia Ser.). (SPA., Illus.). 32p. (J). pap. 6.95 (978-970-20-0264-2(8)) Castillo, Ediciones, S. A. de C. V. MEX. *Dist:* Macmillan.

Gay, Marie-Louise. Stella, Princess of the Sky. 2004. (Stella Ser.). (Illus.). 32p. (J). 15.95 (978-0-88899-601-5(2)) Groundwood Bks. CAN. *Dist:* Perseus Distribution.

Gébler, Carlo. The Bull Raid. 2006. 402p. (J). (gr. 7-9). 22.95 (978-1-4052-1255-7(1)) Egmont Bks., Ltd. GBR. *Dist:* Independent Pubs. Group.

Geissen, Steve. Willie & the World Wide Web. Kuon, Vuthy, illus. 1998. 40p. (J). (gr. 1-7). lib. bdg. 15.95 (978-0-9661974-0-2(2)) Three Leaves Publishing.

Gell, Jay & McMahan, Virginia. Where the Mushgnomes Live. 2nd ed. 2003. (J). per. 11.15 (978-1-4116-0221-2(8)) Lulu.com.

Geras, Adele. The Tower Room. 1998. (Egerton Hall Trilogy: Vol. 1). (J). (978-0-606-13860-4(9)) Tandem Library Bks.

Gershon, Neil. The Other Side of the Frame. 2007. 184p. (J). per. 13.95 (*978-0-595-40618-0(1)) iUniverse, Inc.

Gerstein, Sherry. Brainbenders from the Four Nations. 2008. (Avatar Ser.). 48p. (J). pap. 3.99 (*978-1-4169-5350-0(7) , Simon Spotlight) Simon & Schuster Children's Publishing.

Ghoshal, Taposhi, illus. The Walking Mountain. 2002. 32p. (J). (978-81-87649-59-5(3)) Katha.

Gideon, Melanie. Pucker. 2006. 288p. (YA). (gr. 7-12). 16.99 (978-1-59514-055-5(7) , Razorbill) Penguin Group (USA) Inc.

Gili, Phillida. Cinderella: A Pop-up Book. Gili, Phillida, illus. 2007. (Illus.). 12p. (J). 25.00 (*978-1-4223-9031-3(4)) DIANE Publishing Co.

Gill, Margaret. The Brain Changers. 2004. 160p. (YA). pap. 12.95 (978-0-595-31161-3(X)) iUniverse, Inc.

Gill, Paul. The Centaurs: An Adventure Fantasy. 2003. 54p. pap. 8.95 (978-0-595-30260-4(2)) iUniverse, Inc.

Gilmore, Rachna. The Sower of Tales. 2007. 348p. (YA). (gr. 6-8). pap. (*978-1-55041-590-2(5)) Fitzhenry & Whiteside, Ltd.

Giovanni, Nikki. The Genie in the Jar. Raschka, Chris, illus. rev. ed. 1998. 32p. (J). (gr. k up). pap. 8.95 (978-0-8050-6076-8(6) , Holt, Henry & Co. Bks. For Young Readers) Holt, Henry & Co.

Givens, Lisa. Meet the Blue Sky Nuts. 2001. (Illus.). 36p. (J). (ps-4). mass mkt. 5.99 (978-0-9705347-0-5(1)) Kookla KooksToy Co.

Glass Menagerie. 1999. (YA). 11.95 (978-1-56137-337-6(0)) Novel Units, Inc.

Glassman, Peter. The Magical Land of Noom. 1998. (Books of Wonder). (Illus.). 192p. (J). (gr. 3-7). reprint ed. 22.00 (978-0-688-14117-2(X)) HarperCollins Pubs.

Glassman, Peter, ed. Oz: The Hundredth Anniversary Celebration. 2000. (Illus.). 55p. (YA). reprint ed. 25.00 (978-0-7567-5499-0(2)) DIANE Publishing Co.

Gloden, et al. Tales of the Slayer, Vol. 3. Simon and Schuster Children's Staff, ed. 2003. (Buffy the Vampire Slayer Ser.). (Illus.). 336p. (YA). pap. 9.99 (978-0-689-86436-0(1) , Simon Pulse) Simon & Schuster Children's Publishing.

Glur, D. L' Empire Contre Attaque.Tr. of Empire Strikes Back. (FRE.). (J). pap. 11.95 (978-2-265-06729-5(6)) Fleuve Noir FRA. *Dist:* Distribooks, Inc.

Godwin, Patricia. I Feel Orange Today. Macaulay, Kitty, illus. 24p. (J). (ps-k). 2001. pap. 5.95 (978-1-55037-285-4(8)); 2000. pap. 1.25 (978-1-55037-640-1(3)) Annick Pr., Ltd. CAN. *Dist:* Firefly Bks., Ltd.

Gokurakuin, Sakurako. Aquarian Age: Juvenile Orion, 5 vols., Vol. 2. Yamashita, Satsuki, ed. Gokurakuin, Sakurako, illus. 2004. (Aquarian Age - Juvenile Orion Ser.). Orig. Title: Aquarian Age - Orion No Shonen. (Illus.). 208p. (YA). pap. 9.99 (978-1-932480-10-8(2) , Broccoli Bks. Deluxe) Broccoli International USA, Inc.

Gold, Bernice. My Four Lions. Stanbridge, Joanne, illus. 1999. 24p. (J). (ps-1). lib. bdg. 17.95 (978-1-55037-603-6(9)) Annick Pr., Ltd. CAN. *Dist:* Firefly Bks., Ltd.

—My Four Lions. 1999. (978-0-606-18141-9(5)) Tandem Library Bks.

Goldberg, Dennis. Double Bubble Trouble. 2007. (J). 14.95 (*978-1-933769-19-6(X)) Level 4 Press, Inc.

Golden Bks Staff. Enchanted. Akyaka, Sarl, illus. 2007. 48p. (J). (ps-2). pap. 6.99 (*978-0-7364-2482-0(2) , Bolder Bks.) Random Hse. Children's Bks.

Golden Books Staff. Kingdom in the Sun: Coloring Book. 2000. (Illus.). 70p. (J). (ps-3). pap. 2.99 (978-0-307-33763-4(4) , 33763, Golden Bks.) Random Hse. Children's Bks.

—A Superhero Day. 2000. (Illus.). 10p. (J). (ps-2). 7.99 (978-0-307-10148-8(7) , 10148, Golden Bks.) Random Hse. Children's Bks.

The Golden Compass. 2002. (His Dark Materials Ser.). (Illus.). 19.53 (978-1-4046-1654-7(3)) Book Wholesalers, Inc.

Goldman, Leslie. The Onliest Tigger. 2000. (Illus.). 64p. (J). (gr. 2-5). pap. 4.99 (978-0-7868-4416-6(7)) Disney Pr.

Goldwell, Bruce. Dragon Keepers. 2005. (Illus.). (YA). (978-1-894936-43-9(4)) Saga Bks.

Gonzalez, Julie. Wings. 2005. 208p. (YA). (gr. 7). lib. bdg. 17.99 (978-0-385-90253-3(0) , Delacorte Bks. for Young Readers) Random Hse. Children's Bks.

Gonzalez, Mary. The Ferry That Was. 2005. 48p. pap. 12.95 (978-1-4137-4758-4(2)) PublishAmerica, Inc.

—The House That Was. 2003. 49p. pap. 12.95 (978-1-4137-0872-1(2)) PublishAmerica, Inc.

Goode, Jeff. The American Dragon Bk.1: The Dragon Hunter. 2004. (American Dragon Ser.: Vol. 1). (Illus.). 112p. (J). 8.99 (978-0-7868-1926-3(X)) Hyperion Paperbacks for Children.

—The Gnome Eater. 2003. (American Dragon Ser.: Vol. 2). (Illus.). 112p. (J). 8.99 (978-0-7868-1927-0(8)) Hyperion Paperbacks for Children.

Goode, Suzi. The Lost Wizard Series Bk 1. 2007. pap. 11.95 (*978-1-59374-817-3(5)) Whiskey Creek Pr., LLC.

Goodin, Carolyn M. Candy Land. Goodin, Carolyn M., illus. 2007. (Illus.). 38p. (J). per. 14.99 (*978-0-9797879-1-1(2)) Family Legacy Ministries.

Goodman, Gordon. The King of the Northern Lights. 2000. 60p. (J). (gr. 3-8). pap. 19.95 incl. cd-rom (978-1-58569-100-0(0)) Book-On-Disc.Com.

Goodman-Pollack, Suzy. Life on a Lucky Star. 2000. 32p. (J). (ps-3). 19.90 incl. cd-rom (978-0-9672063-0-1(8)) Dandy Productions.

Gopnik, Adam. The King in the Window. 2005. (Illus.). 416p. (gr. 5-17). 19.95 (978-0-7868-1862-4(X)) Hyperion Bks. for Children.

—The King in the Window. Rayyan, Omar, illus. 2006. 416p. (gr. 5-17). reprint ed. pap. 9.99 (978-0-7868-3894-3(9)) Miramax Bks.

Gorbachev, Valeri, illus. & retold by. Fool of the World & the Flying Ship. Gorbachev, Valeri, retold by. 1998. 32p. (J). (ps-3). 15.95 (978-1-887734-19-6(8)) Star Bright Bks., Inc.

Gordon, Amy. When JFK Was My Father. 2001. (J). (978-0-606-21520-6(4)) Tandem Library Bks.

Gorham, C. J. Alice's Adventures in Wonderland. 2007. (ENG.). 76p. per. 87.99 (*978-1-4280-7448-4(1)) Indy-Publish.com.

Goscinny, René & Uderzo, Albert. Asterix et Cleopatre. 1999. (FRE.). pap. 21.95 (978-2-01-210006-0(6)) Hachette Groupe Livre FRA. *Dist:* Distribooks, Inc.

Gostick, Adrian & Elton, Chester. Demonstrado: La Zanahoria Funciona. Roig, Esther, tr. 2005. (SPA.). 128p. (J). pap. (978-0-307-27386-4(5)) Grijalbo Mondadori, S.A.-Junior.

Goto, Hiromi. The Water of Possibility. Cheung, Aries, illus. 2005. (In the Same Boat Ser.: No. 1). 256p. (J). (gr. 4-6). pap. 8.95 (978-1-55050-183-4(6)) Coteau Bks. CAN. *Dist:* Fitzhenry & Whiteside, Ltd.

Gouveia, Keith. Children of the Dragon. 2005. (ENG.). 174p. pap. (*978-1-897217-03-0(X)) Coscom Entertainment.

Gow, Kailin. Reborn #1: Queen B Superheroine Series. 2005. 168p. (YA). per. 7.99 (978-1-59748-855-6(0)) Sparklesoup Studios, Inc.

Gownley, Jimmy. Amelia Rules! Vol. 3: Superheroes. 2006. (Illus.). 176p. (J). pap. (978-0-9712169-6-9(7)) Renaissance Pr.

—Amelia Rules! Superheroes. 2006. 176p. (J). (978-0-9712169-7-6(5)) Renaissance Pr.

Graham, Craig. Peter's Destiny. 2005. 71p. (J). lib. bdg. 15.00 (*978-1-4242-0761-9(4)) Fitzgerald Bks.

Graham, Craig. Peter's Destiny: The Battle for Narnia. Baynes, Pauline, illus. 2006. (Narnia Ser.). 96p. (J). 14.99 (978-0-06-085236-8(4)) HarperCollins Pubs.

Graham, L. B. Beyond the Summerland. 2004. (Binding of the Blade Ser.: 1). (Illus.). 608p. (J). per. 16.99 (978-0-87552-720-8(5) , 5000) P & R Publishing.

Graham, L. B. Father of Dragons. 2007. (Binding of the Blade Ser.). (YA). pap. 16.99 (*978-0-87552-723-9(X)) P & R Publishing.

Graham, Lisa Faire. Olly Oliver & Rap Jack: The Endangered Journey. 2004. 58p. pap. 12.95 (978-1-4137-2533-9(3)) PublishAmerica, Inc.

Graham, Richard. Jack y el Monstruo. Varley, Susan, illus. (Cotton Cloud Ser.). (SPA.). 32p. (J). (gr. 1-3). (978-84-7722-680-2(6)) Timun Mas, Editorial S.A. ESP. *Dist:* Lectorum Pubns., Inc.

Grannis, Greg. Lottie Bright & the Starmaker's Universe. Vargas, Robert, illus. 2006. (ENG.). 272p. (J). pap. (*978-0-9778205-9-7(9)) Helm Publishing.

Grant, Crystal. Warrior Boy. 2007. (ENG.). 92p. per. 14.95 (*978-1-4241-3978-1(3)) PublishAmerica, Inc.

Graves, Damien. Voices. 2007. (Midnight Library: No. 1). 176p. (J). mass mkt. 2.99 (*978-0-545-01035-1(7)) Scholastic, Inc.

Graves, Robert. El Gran Libro Verde. Sendak, Maurice, illus. 2001. (SPA.). 66p. (J). (gr. 3-5). 9.56 (978-84-264-3580-4(7)) Editorial Lumen ESP. *Dist:* Lectorum Pubns., Inc.

Gray, Keith. The Fearful. 2005. 256p. (J). (978-0-370-32836-2(1)) Random Hse.

Grban, Tanguy. Sarah So Small. 2004. 32p. (978-1-59687-179-3(2) , Milk & Cookies) ibooks, Inc.

Green, Richard G. Skywoman's Granddaughter. 1998. (Darrin Captain Ser.). 128p. (J). (gr. 7 up). pap. 12.95 (978-0-911737-04-2(9)) Ricara Features.

Greenberg, Martin H. & Hoyt, Sarah, eds. Something Magic This Way Comes. 2008. 320p. (gr. 12). mass mkt. 7.99 (*978-0-7564-0472-7(X) , D A W Bks., Inc.) Penguin Group (USA) Inc.

Greenburg, Dan. Elvis, the Turnip...and Me, Vol. 14. Davis, Jack E., illus. 1998. (Zack Files Ser.: No. 14). 64p. (J). (gr. 2-5). pap. 4.99 (978-0-448-41749-3(9) , Grosset & Dunlap) Penguin Group (USA) Inc.

—Hang a Left at Venus. Davis, Jack E., illus. 1999. (Zack Files Ser.: No. 15). 64p. (J). (gr. 2-5). pap. 4.99 (978-0-448-41875-9(4) , Grosset & Dunlap) Penguin Group (USA) Inc.

—Hang a Left at Venus. 1999. (gr. 3-6). lib. bdg. 13.00 (978-0-613-14785-9(5)); (Zack Files Ser.: No. 15). (J). (gr. 2-5). 11.79 (978-0-606-17781-8(7)) Tandem Library Bks.

—How I Fixed the Year 1000 Problem. Davis, Jack E., illus. 1999. (Zack Files Ser.: No. 18). 32p. (J). (gr. 2-5). pap. 4.99 (978-0-448-42034-9(1) , Grosset & Dunlap) Penguin Group (USA) Inc.

—How I Fixed the Year 1000 Problem. 1999. (Zack Files Ser.: No. 18). (J). (gr. 2-5). 11.79 (978-0-606-17784-9(1)) Tandem Library Bks.

—The Misfortune Cookie. Davis, Jack E., illus. 1998. (Zack Files Ser.: No. 13). 64p. (J). (gr. 2-5). pap. 4.99 (978-0-448-41748-6(0) , Grosset & Dunlap) Penguin Group (USA) Inc.

—Now You See Me... Now You Don't. 1998. (Zack Files Ser.: No. 12). (J). (gr. 2-5). (978-0-606-12852-0(2)) Tandem Library Bks.

—The Onts. Fischer, Scott M., illus. 2005. (Secrets of Dripping Fang Ser.: Bk. 1). 144p. (J). (gr. 3-7). 9.95 (978-0-15-205457-1(X)) Harcourt Children's Bks.

—Superhero... Or Super Thief? 2001. (Maximum Boy Ser.). (Illus.). (J). (978-0-606-21321-9(X)) Tandem Library Bks.

Greene, Janice. Gulliver's Travels. abr. ed. 2001. (gr. 7-12). lib. bdg. 15.25 (978-0-613-36384-6(1)) Tandem Library Bks.

Greenwood, Kerry. Alien Invasions. 2005. (Thrillogy Ser.). (Illus.). 48p. (gr. 4-8). 17.50 (978-0-7910-8865-4(0)) Facts On File, Inc.

Gregory, Dave & Puls, Grace. Theodore Was Here Again! Dudley, Dan, illus. 2001. 28p. (J). 15.95 (978-0-9653798-2-3(5)) Theodore Publishing, Inc.

Gregory, David. Visions of Reality. 2007. 236p. per. 15.95 (*978-0-595-44969-9(7)) iUniverse, Inc.

Gregory, Jillian Louise. Dobbs Dog Detective: Operation Fido & Fifi. 2003. 67p. pap. 11.95 (978-1-4137-0644-4(4)) PublishAmerica, Inc.

Gregory, Manju & Le, Guo, illus. The Dragon's Tears: Les Larmes du Dragon. 2004. (TAM, CZE, VIE, SPA & GUJ.). 24p. (J). pap. (978-1-85269-689-4(3)) Mantra Publishing, Ltd.

Gresh, Lois. The Ultimate Eragon Guide: The Hidden Facts Behind the World of Alagaesia. 2006. 176p. (J). pap. 11.95 (978-0-312-35792-4(3) , St. Martin's Griffin) St. Martin's Pr.

Gresham, P. A. Anything Could Be Any Thing. 2005. 128p. pap. 12.95 (978-1-4116-4353-6(4)) Lulu.com.

Griggs, Terry. Invisible Ink. Nugent, Cynthia, illus. 2006. (Cat's Eye Corner Ser.). 256p. pap. 7.95 (978-1-55192-833-3(7)) Raincoast Bk. Distribution CAN. *Dist:* Perseus Distribution.

Grimes, Linda. Jiggery-Jee's Eden Valley Stories. 2004. 84p. pap. 14.95 (978-1-4137-0677-2(0)) PublishAmerica, Inc.

Grimm, Jacob W. Cinderella/Cenicienta. 2004. (Illus.). (J). (978-1-933530-13-0(8)) Bingo Bks., Inc.

—Cinderella/Cenicienta Take Home Version. 2004. (Illus.). (J). cd-rom (978-1-933530-39-0(1)) Bingo Bks., Inc.

Grimm, Jacob W. Grimm's Fairy Stories. 2006. pap. 26.99 (***978-1-4280-4819-5(7)***) IndyPublish.com.

Grimm, Jacob W. & Grimm, Wilhelm K. Grimm's Fairy Tales. 2007. (Thrift Edition Ser.). (Illus.). 208p. pap. 3.95 (***978-0-486-45656-0(0)***) Dover Pubns., Inc.

Grolla, Daniel. A Tolkien Treasury. 2001. (Irresistible Miniature Editionstm Ser.). (Illus.). 128p. 4.95 (978-0-7624-0980-8(0) , Running Pr. Minature Editions) Running Pr. Bk. Pubs.

Gruelle, Johnny. Raggedy Ann in Cookie Land. Gruelle, Johnny, illus. 2002. (Classic Edition Ser.). (Illus.). 96p. (J). 17.95 (978-0-689-85096-7(4)) Simon & Schuster Children's Publishing.

Gruler, Monica. The Secret of the Cottage Elves. 2001. (Illus.). 64p. (J). per. 8.95 (978-0-9711111-0-3(3)) Gruler, Monica.

Guardians of Ga'hoole Staff & Lasky, Kathryn. The Coming of Hoole. 2006. (Guardians of Ga'Hoole Ser.: Bk. 10). (Illus.). 224p. (J). (gr. 4-7). pap. 5.99 (978-0-439-79569-2(9) , Scholastic Paperbacks) Scholastic, Inc.

Guilin, Peadar O. The Inferior. 2008. 448p. (J). (gr. 7). lib. bdg. 19.99 (***978-0-385-75146-9(X)*** , Fickling, David Bks.) Random Hse. Children's Bks.

Guillain, Adam. Bella Balistica & the Temple of Tikal. 2004. (Bella Balistica Ser.). (Illus.). 288p. (J). pap. 9.95 (978-1-84059-394-5(6)) Milet Publishing.

Guillen, Michael. Dr. Universe, Vol. 3. 2000. (J). pap. 10.00 (978-0-517-88563-5(8)); lib. bdg. 16.99 (978-0-517-88564-2(6)) Random Hse. Children's Bks. (Random Hse. Bks. for Young Readers).

Gunderson, Jeff. The Magic. 2007. pap. 7.95 (***978-0-533-15572-9(X)***) Vantage Pr., Inc.

Gunson, Jonathan. The Divine Calling. 2006. 289p. 24.30 (978-1-4116-7790-6(0)) Lulu.com.

Guptara, Suresh & Guptara, Jyoti. The Conspiracy of Calaspia. 2007. 226p. pap. 13.95 (***978-81-8386-026-0(5)***) India Research Pr. IND. *Dist:* Independent Pubs. Group.

Gurney, James. Dinotopia: Journey to Chandara. 2007. (Illus.). 160p. 29.95 (***978-0-7407-6431-8(4)***) Andrews McMeel Publishing.

—A Land Apart from Time. Gurney, James, illus. 2003. (Dinotopia Ser.). (Illus.). 160p. (J). pap. 21.99 (978-0-06-053064-8(2)) HarperCollins Pubs.

—Land Apart from Time. 2003. (gr. 3-6). lib. bdg. 30.40 (978-0-613-85748-2(8)) Tandem Library Bks.

Gutman, Dan. Funny Boy Versus the Bubble-Brained Barbers from the Big Bang. 2000. (L.A.F. Ser.). 122p. (J). (gr. 4-7). 14.49 (978-0-7868-2570-7(7)) Hyperion Bks. for Children.

Gutsche, Brigitte. Stardust & Moonbeams, Vol. 5. 2001. (Holt's Friends Ser.: Vol. 5). 126p. (J). (ps-7). pap. 9.99 (978-0-88092-518-1(3) , 5183) Royal Fireworks Publishing Co.

Gwinna. (J). (978-0-399-22454-6(8) , Philomel) Penguin Group (USA) Inc.

Haas, Jessie. Runaway Radish. Apple, Margot, illus. 2001. 56p. (J). (gr. 2 up). 15.99 (978-0-688-16688-5(1)) HarperCollins Pubs.

Haberlin, Brian. Manhunter Project Vol. 1. 2003. (Illus.). 240p. (gr. 11 up). pap. 19.95 (978-1-58240-303-8(1)) Image Comics.

Habiger-Doxon, Lydia, et al. The World Upside Down. Norcross, Terry, illus. 2007. (J). 12.95 (978-1-932926-97-2(6) , Kinkajou Pr.) Artemesia Publishing, LLC.

Haddix, Margaret Peterson. Among the Hidden. 1998. (Shadow Children Ser.). 160p. (J). (gr. 3-7). 16.95 (978-0-689-81700-7(2)) Simon & Schuster Children's Publishing.

—Running Out of Time. 2005. 192p. (J). pap. 2.99 (978-1-4169-0531-8(6) , Aladdin) Simon & Schuster Children's Publishing.

Hadley, Amy. Fool's Gold. 2006. (Illus.). pap. 9.99 (978-1-59816-585-2(2) , Tokyopop Adult) TOKYOPOP, Inc.

Hadnot, Victor. The Wheels of God. 2003. 140p. (YA). pap. 11.95 (978-0-595-27507-6(9)) iUniverse, Inc.

Haesche, Richard P., Sr. Jason & the Money Tree. Switzer, Cheryle, illus. aut. ed. 2000. 170p. (J). pap. 11.99 (978-1-929381-71-5(9) , Third Millennium Publishing) Sci Fi-Arizona, Inc.

Hague, Michael. The Book of Dragons. Hague, Michael, illus. 2005. (Illus.). 160p. (J). (ps-7). pap., pap. 9.99 (978-0-06-075968-1(2) , Harper Trophy) HarperCollins Pubs.

Hahn, Mary Downing. The Doll in the Garden: A Ghost Story. 2007. 144p. (J). (gr. 4-6). pap. 5.95 (***978-0-618-87315-9(5)*** , Clarion Bks.) Houghton Mifflin Co. Trade & Reference Div.

Haigh, Liz. The Dragon's Ring. 2002. (Illus.). 80p. pap. 11.95 (978-1-85902-724-0(5)) Beekman Bks., Inc.

Haining, Peter, ed. Magician's Circle: More Spellbinding Stories of Wizards & Wizardry. 2004. (Illus.). 256p. (J). 19.95 (978-0-285-63681-1(2)) Souvenir Pr. Ltd. GBR. *Dist:* Independent Pubs. Group.

Haining, Peter & Strings Magazine Staff. The Wizard's Den: Spellbinding Stories of Magic & Magicians. 2003. (Illus.). 320p. (J). 22.95 (978-0-285-63628-6(6)) Souvenir Pr. Ltd. GBR. *Dist:* Independent Pubs. Group.

Hakase, Mizuki. The Demon Ororon, 4 vols. 2004. (Illus.). Vol. 1. 232p. pap. 9.99 (978-1-59182-725-2(6)); Vol. 3. 200p. pap. 9.99 (978-1-59182-727-6(2)) TOKYOPOP, Inc. (Tokyopop Adult).

Hakase, Mizuki, creator. Demon Ororon, 4 vols., Vol. 4. 4th rev. ed. 2004. (Illus.). 192p. (YA). pap. 9.99 (978-1-59182-728-3(0) , Tokyopop Adult) TOKYOPOP, Inc.

Hakoda, Maki. R2, Vol. 1. 2004. (Illus.). 184p. (YA). pap. (978-1-4139-0056-9(9)) ADV Manga.

Halam, Ann. Siberia: A Novel. 2005. (J). (gr. 7). 272p. 16.95 (978-0-385-74650-2(4)); 262p. lib. bdg. 18.99 (978-0-385-90885-6(7)) Random Hse. Children's Bks. (Lamb, Wendy).

Halam, Ann. Snakehead. 2008. 272p. (YA). (gr. 7). 16.99 (***978-0-375-84108-8(3)***); lib. bdg. 19.99 (***978-0-375-94108-5(8)***) Random Hse. Children's Bks. (Lamb, Wendy).

Hale, Shannon & Smith, James Noel. Book of a Thousand Days. 2007. (Illus.). 320p. (YA). (gr. 7 up). 17.95 (***978-1-59990-051-3(3)***) Bloomsbury Publishing.

Hall, John & Gilpin, Stephen. If the Earth Had a Zipper. 2006. (Illus.). 48p. 15.99 (978-1-59379-069-1(4)) White Stone Bks.

Hallam, Gwion. Creadyn: Neu, Huw Dafis A'r Draenog Wnaeth Gnoi at y Gwaed, A'r Corryn Sy'n Crwydro'i Hunllefau. 2005. (WEL.). 171p. 5.99 (978-1-84323-247-6(2)) Gomer Pr. GBR. *Dist:* Gomer Pr.

Hamazaki, Tatsuya. . hack //Legend of the Twilight, Volume 1: Kaplan SAT/ACT Vocabulary-Building Manga. Izumi, Rei, illus. 2007. (Kaplan SAT/ACT Score-Raising Manga Ser.). 192p. pap. 9.99 (***978-1-4277-5497-4(7)***) Kaplan Bks.

Hamel, Mike. Dragon's Lair: Matterhorn, the Brave Series, 5. 2007. 192p. (J). pap. 12.99 (***978-0-89957-837-8(3)***) AMG Pubs.

—Rylan the Renegade: Matterhorn, the Brave Series, 6. 2007. 192p. (J). pap. 12.99 (***978-0-89957-838-5(1)***) AMG Pubs.

Hamel, William T. Sam Whitton & the Angels' Prophecy. 2006. 283p. pap. 16.95 (978-0-9759818-7-0(0) , 349-020) High-Pitched Hum Inc.

Hamilton, C. After Ever Happily. 2006. 80p. pap. 14.95 (978-1-4241-3190-7(1)) PublishAmerica, Inc.

Hamilton, Tisha. All That Glitters. Noel, Aragon & Hwan, Choi Sung, illus. 2006. (Trollz Ser.). 80p. (J). pap. 3.99 (978-0-439-75309-8(0)) Scholastic, Inc.

—Five Times the Trouble. 2006. (Trollz Ser.). (Illus.). 32p. (J). pap. 3.99 (978-0-439-82825-3(2)) Scholastic, Inc.

Hamilton, Virginia. Dustland. 1998. (Justice Cycle Ser.: Bk. 2). 214p. (YA). (gr. 6-12). pap. 4.50 (978-0-590-36217-7(8)) Scholastic, Inc.

—Dustland. 1998. (Justice Cycle Ser.). (978-0-606-12927-5(8)) Tandem Library Bks.

—The Gathering. 1998. (Justice Cycle Ser.: Bk. 3). 214p. (J). (gr. 6-12). mass mkt. 4.50 (978-0-590-36216-0(X)) Scholastic, Inc.

—The Gathering. 1998. (Justice Cycle Ser.). (978-0-606-13414-9(X)) Tandem Library Bks.

Hamley, Dennis. Pageants of Despair. 2006. 245p. pap. 9.95 (978-1-58988-028-3(5)) Consortium Bk. Sales & Distribution.

Hammond, John, as told by. Lucky in Life. 2003. 150p. (YA). per. 13.95 (978-1-885631-76-3(6)) Hutchison, G.F. Pr.

Hancock, Niel. Calix Stay. 3rd rev. ed. 2004. (Circle of Light Ser.). (Illus.). 256p. (J). 5.99 (978-0-7653-4617-9(6) , Tor Bks.) Doherty, Tom Assocs., LLC.

—Squaring the Circle. 4th rev. ed. 2004. (Circle of Light Ser.: Vol. 4). (Illus.). 368p. (J). 5.99 (978-0-7653-4618-6(4) , Tor Bks.) Doherty, Tom Assocs., LLC.

Hanft, Joshua E., et al. Alice in Wonderland. Kaster, Lea, illus. 2005. (Great Illustrated Classics Ser.). 238p. (J). (gr. 3-8). 21.35 (978-1-59679-235-7(3) , ABDO & Daughters) ABDO Publishing Co.

Hanley, Victoria. The Healer's Keep. 2002. (Illus.). 384p. (J). (gr. 7 up). tchr. ed. 17.95 (978-0-8234-1760-5(3)) Holiday Hse., Inc.

—The Healer's Keep. 2005. 384p. (YA). (gr. 7). pap. 6.50 (978-0-553-49435-8(X) , Laurel Leaf); 2002. (J). 15.95 (978-0-385-75010-3(2) , Delacorte Bks. for Young Readers) Random Hse. Children's Bks.

—The Light of the Oracle. 2005. 320p. (YA). (gr. 7). 15.95 (978-0-385-75086-8(2) , Fickling, David Bks.) Random Hse. Children's Bks.

—Light of the Oracle. 2006. 320p. (YA). (gr. 7). mass mkt. 6.50 (978-0-553-49502-7(X) , Laurel Leaf) Random Hse. Children's Bks.

—The Seer & the Sword. 2000. 352p. (YA). (gr. 7 up). tchr. ed. 17.95 (978-0-8234-1532-8(5)) Holiday Hse., Inc.

—The Seer & the Sword. 2003. (Illus.). 352p. (YA). (gr. 7). pap. 6.50 (978-0-440-22977-3(4) , Laurel Leaf) Random Hse. Children's Bks.

—The Seer & the Sword. 2003. (gr. 7-12). lib. bdg. 14.75 (978-0-613-65095-3(6)) Tandem Library Bks.

Hanley, Victoria & Said, S. F. The Outlaw Varjak Paw. 2006. (Illus.). 272p. (J). (gr. 3-7). lib. bdg. 18.99 (978-0-385-75042-4(0) , Fickling, David Bks.) Random Hse. Children's Bks.

Hanson, Ann. Flicker's Round Trip. 2003. (Illus.). per. 12.95 (978-1-888345-51-3(9)) Paper Jam Publishing.

Hapka, Cathy. Add a Little Magic - Gift Box: Words of Inspiration from Disney. 2005. 224p. (J). pap. (978-0-7868-4350-3(0)) Disney Pr.

—Oasis. 2002. (Dinotopia Ser.: Vol. 16). 208p. (J). (gr. 3-8). pap. 3.99 (978-0-375-82295-7(X) , Random Hse. Bks. for Young Readers) Random Hse. Children's Bks.

—Sparkle Purse. Schwaner, Lynne, illus. Date not set. 10p. (J). 5.99 (978-0-9986300-7-6(1)) Playhouse Publishing.

Hapka, Cathy, et al. Makuta's Revenge. 2003. (Bionicle Chronicles: Bk. 3). 96p. (J). 4.99 (978-0-439-50119-4(9)) Scholastic, Inc.

Haptie, Charlotte. Otto & the Bird Charmers: The Second Book of the Karmidee. 2005. (Illus.). 417p. (J). 17.95 (978-0-8234-1883-1(9)) Holiday Hse., Inc.

Harcourt School Publishers Staff. The Crayon Box That Talked: Library Book. 3rd ed. 2002. (Trophies Reading Program Ser.). (Illus.). pap. 13.50 (978-0-15-326527-3(2)) Harcourt Schl. Pubs.

—How to Write a Play On Level. 3rd ed. 2002. (Trophies Reading Program Ser.). (Illus.). pap. 5.10 (978-0-15-323269-5(2)) Harcourt Schl. Pubs.

—I Have a Pal: Independent Reader. 3rd ed. 2002. (Trophies Reading Program Ser.). (Illus.). (J). pap. 2.90 (978-0-15-325470-3(X)) Harcourt Schl. Pubs.

—The Ice Cream House: Take-Home Book. 1999. (Illus.). (J). pap. 1.90 (978-0-15-313872-0(6)) Harcourt Schl. Pubs.

—Jenny's Wish: Take-Home Book. 1999. (Collections Ser.). (Illus.). (J). pap. 1.90 (978-0-15-317221-2(5)) Harcourt Schl. Pubs.

—Jill & the Giant: Take-Home Book. 1999. (Collections Ser.). (Illus.). (J). pap. 1.90 (978-0-15-317223-6(1)) Harcourt Schl. Pubs.

—Jill & the Giant Below Level. 3rd ed. 2002. (Trophies Reading Program Ser.). (Illus.). pap. 5.10 (978-0-15-323046-2(0)) Harcourt Schl. Pubs.

—The Lad Who Went with the North Wind On Level. 3rd ed. 2002. (Illus.). pap. 5.10 (978-0-15-323268-8(4)) Harcourt Schl. Pubs.

—Mama Provi's Pot: Library Edition. 1999. (Collections Ser.). (Illus.). (J). 4.70 (978-0-15-314325-0(8)) Harcourt Schl. Pubs.

—Silly Sandwich: A Reader. 1999. (Collections Ser.). (Illus.). (J). pap. 2.10 (978-0-15-313443-2(7)) Harcourt Schl. Pubs.

—Trapped in the Future Advanced Level. 3rd ed. 2002. (Trophies Reading Program Ser.). (Illus.). pap. 5.10 (978-0-15-323395-1(8)) Harcourt Schl. Pubs.

—What Jason's Mom Didn't See Advanced Level. 3rd ed. 2002. (Trophies Reading Program Ser.). (Illus.). pap. 5.10 (978-0-15-323117-9(3)) Harcourt Schl. Pubs.

Hardinge, Frances. Fly by Night. (J). 2008. 512p. pap. 7.99 (***978-0-06-087630-2(1)*** , Harper Trophy); 2006. 496p. (gr. 5-9). 16.99 (978-0-06-087627-2(1)); 2006. 496p. (gr. 5-9). lib. bdg. 17.89 (978-0-06-087629-6(8)) HarperCollins Pubs.

Hargreaves, Roger. Little Miss Naughty. Hargreaves, Roger, illus. 1998. (Mr. Men & Little Miss Ser.). (Illus.). 32p. (J). (gr. k-3). pap. 3.99 (978-0-8431-7842-5(6) , Price Stern Sloan) Penguin Group (USA) Inc.

—Little Miss Neat. Hargreaves, Roger, illus. 1998. (Mr. Men & Little Miss Ser.). (Illus.). 32p. (J). (gr. k-3). pap. 3.99 (978-0-8431-7843-2(4) , Price Stern Sloan) Penguin Group (USA) Inc.

—Little Miss Scatterbrain. Hargreaves, Roger, illus. 1998. (Mr. Men & Little Miss Ser.). (Illus.). 32p. (J). (gr. k-3). pap. 3.99 (978-0-8431-7845-6(0) , Price Stern Sloan) Penguin Group (USA) Inc.

—Mr. Bump. Hargreaves, Roger, illus. 1998. (Mr. Men & Little Miss Ser.). (Illus.). 32p. (J). (gr. 1 up). pap. 3.99 (978-0-8431-7838-8(8) , Price Stern Sloan) Penguin Group (USA) Inc.

—Mr. Greedy. Hargreaves, Roger, illus. 1998. (Mr. Men & Little Miss Ser.). (Illus.). 32p. (J). (gr. k-3). pap. 3.99 (978-0-8431-7840-1(X) , Price Stern Sloan) Penguin Group (USA) Inc.

—Mr. Grumpy. rev. ed. 1999. (Mr. Men & Little Miss Ser.). (Illus.). 32p. (J). (gr. k-3). pap. 3.99 (978-0-8431-7477-9(3) , Price Stern Sloan) Penguin Group (USA) Inc.

—Mr. Nonsense. Hargreaves, Roger, illus. rev. ed. 1998. (Mr. Men & Little Miss Ser.). (Illus.). 32p. (J). (gr. k-3). pap. 3.99 (978-0-8431-7839-5(6) , Price Stern Sloan) Penguin Group (USA) Inc.

—Mr. Rush. Hargreaves, Roger, illus. 1998. (Mr. Men & Little Miss Ser.). (Illus.). 32p. (J). (gr. k-3). pap. 2.99 (978-0-8431-7841-8(8) , Price Stern Sloan) Penguin Group (USA) Inc.

—Mr Skinny. 2001. (gr. k-3). lib. bdg. 10.65 (978-0-613-31490-9(5)) Tandem Library Bks.

Harold & the Purple Crayon. 2004. (J). 24.95 incl. audio (978-1-56008-236-1(4)); pap. 14.95 incl. audio (978-0-7882-0602-3(8)) Weston Woods Studios, Inc.

Harold's Fairy Tale. 2004. (J). pap. 14.95 incl. audio (978-0-7882-0686-3(9)) Weston Woods Studios, Inc.

HarperCollins Children's Books. Fairy Tales. 2007. (Word Play Ser.). 208p. (J). pap. 5.95 (***978-0-00-724336-5(7)***) HarperCollins Pubs. Ltd. GBR. *Dist:* Independent Pubs. Group.

HarperCollins Staff & Auerbach, Annie. Royally Wrong. 2007. (Shrek 3 Ser.). (SPA.). 24p. (J). pap. 3.99 (978-0-06-122863-6(X) , Harper Entertainment) HarperCollins Pubs.

Harperfestival. Hulk: The Beast Within. 2003. (gr. 3-6). lib. bdg. 13.00 (978-0-613-85980-6(4)) Tandem Library Bks.

—Hulk: The Hulk Escapes. 2003. (ps-2). lib. bdg. 11.80 (978-0-613-81693-9(5)) Tandem Library Bks.

—Hulk: The Hulk Fights Back. 2003. (gr. 3-6). lib. bdg. 13.00 (978-0-613-81692-2(7)) Tandem Library Bks.

Harris, Ann Marie, ed. Teen Titans: Calm Before the Storm. 2006. (Teen Titans Ser.). 48p. (J). pap. 3.99 (978-0-439-78962-2(1)) Scholastic, Inc.

—Teen Titans: How to Draw. 2006. (Teen Titans Ser.). 32p. (J). pap. 4.99 (978-0-439-78963-9(X)) Scholastic, Inc.

Harris, Joanne. Runemarks. 2008. 544p. (J). (gr. 5). 18.99 (***978-0-375-84444-7(9)*** , Knopf Bks. for Young Readers) Random Hse. Children's Bks.

Harris, Robert & Yolen, Jane. Girl in a Cage. 2004. 240p. (J). (gr. 5 up). pap. 6.99 (978-0-14-240132-3(3) , Puffin) Penguin Group (USA) Inc.

Harris, Terry. The Lonliest Leprechaun. 2002. pap. 10.95 (978-0-7414-0930-0(5)) Infinity Publishing.

Harrison, Cora. The Famine Secret. 1998. (Drumshee Timeline Ser.: Bk. 5). (Illus.). 128p. (J). (gr. 4-8). pap. 6.95 (978-0-86327-649-1(0)) Wolfhound Pr. IRL. *Dist:* Irish American Bk. Co.

—Nuala & Her Secret Wolf. 1998. (Drumshee Timeline Ser.: Bk. 1). (Illus.). 128p. (J). (gr. 4-8). pap. 6.95 (978-0-86327-585-2(0)) Wolfhound Pr. IRL. *Dist:* Irish American Bk. Co.

—The Secret of 1798. 1998. (Drumshee Timeline Ser.: Bk. 4). (Illus.). 128p. (J). (gr. 4-8). pap. 6.95 (978-0-86327-638-5(5)) Wolfhound Pr. IRL. *Dist:* Irish American Bk. Co.

—The Secret of Drumshee Castle. 1998. (Drumshee Timeline Ser.: Bk. 3). (Illus.). 128p. (J). (gr. 3-9). pap. 6.95 (978-0-86327-632-3(6)) Wolfhound Pr. IRL. *Dist:* Interlink Publishing Group, Inc., Irish American Bk. Co.

—The Secret of the Seven Crosses. 1998. (Drumshee Timeline Ser.: Bk. 2). (Illus.). 128p. (J). (gr. 4-8). pap. 6.95 (978-0-86327-616-3(4)) Wolfhound Pr. IRL. *Dist:* Irish American Bk. Co.

Harrison, Emma. Moving On. 2004. (Everwood Ser.). 240p. (YA). mass mkt. 5.99 (978-0-689-87083-5(3) , Simon Spotlight Entertainment) Simon & Schuster.

—A Tale of Two Pipers. 2004. (Charmed Ser.). 208p. (YA). mass mkt. 6.99 (978-0-689-86850-4(2) , Simon Spotlight Entertainment) Simon & Schuster.

Harrison, Troon. The Dream Collector. Daniel, Alan & Daniel, Lea, illus. 2001. 32p. (J). (gr. k-3). (978-1-55074-915-1(3)) Kids Can Pr., Ltd.

—Dream Collector. 2001. (gr. k-3). lib. bdg. 14.10 (978-0-613-83950-1(1)) Tandem Library Bks.

—The Dream Collector. ed. 2004. (Illus.). (J). (gr. k-3). spiral bd. (978-0-616-01671-8(9)) Canadian National Institute for the Blind/Institut National Canadien pour les Aveugles.

—The Dream Collector. Daniel, Alan & Daniel, Lea, illus. unabr. ed. 1999. 32p. (J). (gr. k-3). (978-1-55074-437-8(2)) Kids Can Pr., Ltd.

Harrison, Troon. The Twilight Box: Tales of Terre II. 2007. (Tales of Terre Ser.: 2). 376p. (YA). per. 10.95 (***978-0-9768126-7-8(3)***) Brown Barn Bks.

Harry Potter & the Chamber of Secrets. 2002. (Harry Potter Ser.). (Illus.). (J). 15.23 (978-0-7587-4426-5(9)) Book Wholesalers, Inc.

Harry Potter & the Sorcerer's Stone. 2002. (Harry Potter Ser.). (Illus.). (J). 15.23 (978-0-7587-0016-2(4)) Book Wholesalers, Inc.

Hart, Lenore. The Treasure of Savage Island. 2005. 288p. (J). (gr. 5-9). 17.99 (978-0-525-47092-2(1) , Dutton Juvenile) Penguin Group (USA) Inc.

Hartman, Rachel. Amy Unbounded: Belondweg Blossoming. 2002. 208p. (J). pap. 16.95 (978-0-9717900-0-1(0)) Pug House Pr.

Harvey, Ken. Brothers of the Storm: A Tale of Boys Born to Fight. 2007. per. 10.99 (***978-1-59886-676-6(1)***) Tate Publishing & Enterprises, L.L.C.

Harwood, Chuck. Bowled Over: The Case of the Gravity Goof-Up. 1998. (Kinetic City Super Crew Ser.: No. 13). (Illus.). 160p. (C). (gr. 4-7). pap. 4.25 (978-0-07-007055-4(5) , 9780070070554) McGraw-Hill Cos., The.

Hatton, Sandy. Vale of Ickybodd. 2004. 64p. pap. 12.95 (978-1-4137-3928-2(8)) PublishAmerica, Inc.

Hauck, Phillip E. A Timeless Journey Told by Mr. Walnut. Folchi, Robert A., ed. Arena, Audrey R., illus. 2000. 32p. (J). (gr. 2-6). 15.00 (978-0-9662228-7-6(3)) Dab Publishing Co.

A Haunting Melody. 80p. (YA). (gr. 6-12). pap. 10.95 (978-0-8224-3943-1(3)) Globe Fearon Educational Publishing.

Haviland, C. S. Faith & Fairies. (YA). 2004. 258p. pap. 14.95 (978-0-9759355-0-7(X)); 2005. reprint ed. pap. 14.95 (978-0-9759355-1-4(8)) LegendMaker Scriptoria.

Hawkins, Linda J. Alexander & the Great Vegetable Feud. Bowles, Jennifer, illus. 2004. 40p. (J). (gr. k-5). 19.99 (978-0-9742806-1-5(5)) Heart to Heart Publishing.

Hawthorn, P. Little Book of Fairy Stories. 2004. (Mini Storybooks Ser.). (Illus.). 96p. (J). 7.95 (978-0-7945-0297-3(0) , Usborne) EDC Publishing.

Haydon, Elizabeth. The Floating Island, No. 1. Helquist, Brett, illus. 2006. (Lost Journals of Ven Polypheme Ser.). 368p. (J). 17.95 (978-0-7653-0867-2(3) , Tor Bks.) Doherty, Tom Assocs., LLC.

Hayes, Drew & Davidsen, Keith. Poison Elves Ventures 1: Hyena. 2006. (Illus.). 128p. pap. 14.95 (978-1-57989-084-1(9)) Diamond Bk. Distributors.

Hayes, Joe. Little Gold Star: A Cinderella Cuento. 2002. (gr. k-3). lib. bdg. 16.40 (978-0-613-77773-5(5)) Tandem Library Bks.

Hayes, Joe & Castro Leal, Antonio. Pajaro Verde. 2005. (SPA.). 40p. pap. 8.95 (978-0-938317-90-6(3)) Cinco Puntos Pr.

Hayes, Malcolm. The Dreamcatchers. 2006. 282p. pap. (***978-1-4120-8320-1(6)***) Trafford Publishing.

Hayes, Rosemary. The Amazing Mr Mulch. 2005. (Cambridge Storybooks Ser.). (Illus.). 32p. pap. 7.00 (978-0-521-67479-9(4)) Cambridge Univ. Pr.

—The Magic Sword. 2005. (Cambridge Storybooks Ser.). 32p. pap. 7.00 (978-0-521-67475-1(1)) Cambridge Univ. Pr.

—The Peace Ring. 2005. (Cambridge Storybooks Ser.). 32p. pap. 7.00 (978-0-521-67478-2(6)) Cambridge Univ. Pr.

Haynes, Cate. Groovy Granny. Tholen, Shane, illus. 2003. 32p. (J). pap. 13.50 (978-1-86388-332-6(1)) Fremantle Pr. AUS. *Dist:* International Specialized Bk. Services.

Hays, Steve. Beauty & the Boy: An Old Man's Story for a Dying Boy. 2006. (YA). 24.95 (978-0-9759902-1-6(7)) Before Christmas Pr.

Hearn, Julie & Yankus, Marc. Sign of the Raven. 2005. (Illus.). 336p. (YA). 16.95 (978-0-689-85734-8(9) , Atheneum) Simon & Schuster Children's Publishing.

Hecker, Howard. Mike McGill, Wizard. Falkey, Mark, illus. 2000. 240p. (YA). (gr. 6-11). pap. 5.99 (978-0-9676870-2-5(0)) Chesire Pr.

Heddle, Rebecca. Puzzle Journey through Time. Spenceley, Annabel, illus. 2003. 32p. (J). pap. 6.95 (978-0-7945-0440-3(X) , Usborne) EDC Publishing.

Hee-Joon, Son. PhD Vol. 3: Phantasy Degree. Hee-Joon, Son, illus. 2005. (Illus.). pap. 9.99 (978-1-59532-319-4(8) , Tokyopop Adult) TOKYOPOP, Inc.

Hee-Joon, Son, illus. & creator. PHD: Phantasy Degree, Vol. 2. Hee-Joon, Son, creator. rev. ed. 2005. 192p. pap. 9.99 (978-1-59532-320-0(1) , Tokyopop Adult) TOKYOPOP, Inc.

Hee, Lee Yun. Demon Diary, Vol. 3. Na, Lauren, tr. from KOR. Kara, illus. rev. ed. 2003. 192p. pap. 9.99 (978-1-59182-156-4(8) , Tokyopop Adult) TOKYOPOP, Inc.

Heil, Christopher. Wish Rings: A Second Beginning. 2003. 196p. pap. 14.95 (978-0-595-29582-1(7)) iUniverse, Inc.

The Heir of King Meldh: Book One of the Geometry of Power. 2004. (YA). per. 10.95 (978-0-9747441-0-0(7)) Brainerd Enterprises.

Helgerson, Joseph. Horns & Wrinkles. Ceccoli, Nicoletta, illus. 2008. 240p. (J). (gr. 5-9). pap. 4.95 (***978-0-618-98178-6(0)***) Houghton Mifflin Co. Trade & Reference Div.

Helldorfer, Mary C. Night of the White Stag. 2001. (978-0-606-22408-6(4)) Tandem Library Bks.

Heller, Andrew. Turn Your Heart On. Burgos, Javier Gonzalez, illus. 2005. (ENG.). 40p. (J). (ps-3). per. 23.00 (978-1-4208-1866-6(X)) AuthorHouse.

Helliwell, Sheila. Hoonraki Moon: The Murphy Stories. 2006. (J). pap. 9.00 (978-0-8059-7027-2(4)) Dorrance Publishing Co., Inc.

Henham, R. D. Red Dragon Codex. 2008. 256p. (J). bds. (***978-0-7869-4925-0(2)***) Wizards of the Coast.

Henighan, Tom. Demon in My View. 2007. 176p. (J). pap. 12.99 (***978-1-55002-656-6(9)*** , Boardwalk Bks.) Dundurn Group, The CAN. *Dist:* Univ. of Toronto Pr.

Henkes, Kevin. Oh! Dronzek, Laura, illus. 1999. 24p. (J). (ps-k). 14.89 (978-0-688-17054-7(4)) HarperCollins Pubs.

—Wemberly's Ice-Cream Star. Henkes, Kevin, illus. 2003. (Illus.). 24p. (J). 6.99 (978-0-06-050405-2(6)) HarperCollins Pubs.

Herman, Gail. Mixed-Up Magic. 1999. (Fairy School Ser.). (J). (978-0-606-19281-1(6)) Tandem Library Bks.

—Toys R Us's Be Good Gertie. 2002. (Illus.). (J). 9.95 (978-0-689-85208-4(8) , Simon Spotlight) Simon & Schuster Children's Publishing.

—The Wizard of Oz Movie Storybook. 1998. (Illus.). 48p. (J). (ps-3). pap. 6.99 (978-0-590-63268-3(X)) Scholastic, Inc.

Herrera, Joaquin. Horris, Little Eli & the Lens of Truth. 2007. (DreamFever Chronicles Ser.: Bk. 1). 208p. (978-1-59258-245-7(1)) Hylas Publishing.

Herrick, Steven. The Spangled Drongo. 1999. (UQP Storybridge Ser.). (Illus.). 152p. (J). pap. 13.95 (978-0-7022-3095-0(2)) Univ. of Queensland Pr. AUS. *Dist:* International Specialized Bk. Services.

Herskowitz, Sol. The Horrible Happening. 2004. (J). per. (978-1-932203-66-0(4)) Sundog, Ltd.

Hess, Brian F. Lynquest & the Search for Greatness. 2006. (ENG.). 116p. per. 16.95 (978-1-4241-4503-4(1)) PublishAmerica, Inc.

Hibbett, Myles. Zephyr: Spheres & the Sword of Wonders. 2001. 200p. pap. 14.95 (978-0-595-17452-2(3) , Writer's Showcase Pr.) iUniverse, Inc.

Higgins, F. E. The Black Book of Secrets. 2007. 288p. (J). (gr. 4-7). 14.95 (***978-0-312-36844-9(5)***) Feiwel & Friends.

Higgins, James E. Little Prince. Date not set. 136p. (J). 17.00 (978-0-8488-2801-1(1)) Amereon LTD.

Higuri, You. Seimaden, Vol. 2. 2005. 180p. (YA). pap. 9.99 (978-1-4012-0700-7(6)) DC Comics.

Hikawa, Kyoko. From Far Away. Hikawa, Kyoko, illus. (From Far Away Ser.). (Illus.). (YA). 1. 2004. 200p. pap. 9.99 (978-1-59116-599-6(7)); Vol. 2. 2005. 184p. pap. 9.99 (978-1-59116-601-6(2)) Viz Media.

Hildebrandt, Greg. Magical Storybook Treasury. 2006. (Illus.). 184p. 14.98 (978-0-7624-2837-3(6) , Running Pr.) Running Pr. Bk. Pubs.

Hill, Douglas. The Dragon Charmer. Melnyczuk, Peter, illus. 2005. 151p. (J). (ps-k). pap. 4.95 (978-1-903015-36-0(7)) Barn Owl Bks, London GBR. *Dist:* Independent Pubs. Group.

—Warriors Wasteland: The Huntsmen. 122p. pap. (978-0-330-35384-7(5)) Pan Macmillan.

Hill, Stephen W., ed. Magic of Kokopelli. 2001. (J). (ps-3). 12.95 (978-1-885772-12-1(2)) Kiva Publishing, Inc.

Hill, Stuart. Blade of Fire: Icemark Chronicles #2. 2008. (Blade of Fire Ser.). 592p. (J). pap. 8.99 (***978-0-439-87327-7(4)*** , Scholastic Paperbacks) Scholastic, Inc.

—The Cry of the Icemark. 2006. 496p. (J). pap. 8.99 (978-0-439-68627-3(X) , Scholastic Paperbacks); 2005. 480p. (YA). pap. 18.95 (978-0-439-68626-6(1) , Chicken Hse., The); 2006. (J). 44.95 (978-0-439-87591-2(9)) Scholastic, Inc.

—The Cry of the Icemark. l.t. ed. 2005. 611p. (YA). 22.95 (978-0-7862-8089-6(1)) Thorndike Pr.

—Cry of the Icemark (library Edition) 2006. (J). 99.95 (978-0-439-87914-9(0)) Scholastic, Inc.

Hill, William. Chasing Time, Vol. X. 381p. (YA). (gr. 4-10). 2004. 22.95 (978-1-890611-06-4(9)); 1999. pap. 14.95 (978-1-890611-03-3(4)) Otter Creek Pr., Inc.

—Chasing Time. 1999. (gr. 3-6). lib. bdg. 24.55 (978-0-613-43741-7(1)) Tandem Library Bks.

—The Vampire Hunters Stalked. 2006. 350p. (J). 24.95 (***978-1-890611-41-5(7)***) Otter Creek Pr., Inc.

Hill, William. Vampires Stalked. 2006. (Illus.). 331p. (J). pap. 14.95 (978-1-890611-42-2(5)) Otter Creek Pr., Inc.

Hillenburg, Steven. Gone Jellyfishin', Vol. 7. 2005. (Spongebob Squarepants Ser.). (Illus.). pap. 7.99 (978-1-59532-678-2(2) , Tokyopop Kids) TOKYOPOP, Inc.

—SpongeBob Box Set. 2004. (Illus.). pap. 19.99 (978-1-59532-476-4(3) , Tokyopop Kids) TOKYOPOP, Inc.

Hillenburg, Steven, creator. Spongebob Squarepants Vol. 8: Saves the Day. 2005. (Nickelodeon Ser.). (Illus.). pap. 7.99 (978-1-59532-679-9(0) , Tokyopop Kids) TOKYOPOP, Inc.

Hillman, Jack. There Are Giants in This Valley. 2005. 256p. (YA). 26.99 (978-1-59507-096-8(6) , ArcheBooks) ArcheBooks Publishing.

Himler, Ronald. The Girl on the Yellow Giraffe. Himler, Ronald, illus. 2004. (Illus.). 40p. (J). 15.95 (978-1-932065-93-0(8)) Star Bright Bks., Inc.

Hinchliffe, Polly. Trio Theo in the Grip of Terror. 2003. 150p. pap. 12.95 (978-0-595-28727-7(1)) iUniverse, Inc.

Hine, David. Mr. M. 2005. (X-Men Ser.: Vol. 1). (Illus.). 144p. (YA). pap. 14.99 (978-0-7851-1444-4(0)) Marvel Enterprises, Inc.

Hinker Books. Disney Pixar Storybook: Finding Nemo: Monsters, Inc.: A Bug's Life: Toy Story. rev. ed. 2004. (Disney CD Storybooks Ser.). (Illus.). 128p. (J). (gr. 4-12). 14.95 incl. cd-rom (978-1-86515-517-3(9)) Hinkler Bks. Pty. Ltd. AUS. *Dist:* Penton Overseas, Inc.

Hiroyuki, Tamakoshi, illus. Boys Be Vol. 4: Second Season. rev. ed. 2005. 208p. pap. 9.99 (978-1-59532-102-2(0) , Tokyopop Adult) TOKYOPOP, Inc.

Hiwatari, Saki. Please Save My Earth, Vol. 17. Hiwatari, Saki, illus. 2006. (Please Save My Earth Ser.). 208p. (YA). pap. 9.99 (978-1-4215-0550-3(9)) Viz Media.

—Please Save My Earth, Vol. 18. 2006. (Please Save My Earth Ser.). 208p. (YA). pap. 9.99 (978-1-4215-0551-0(7)) Viz Media.

Ho-Kyung, Yeo. Honey Mustard, 2 vols. 2005. (Illus.). 176p. pap. 9.99 (978-1-59532-239-5(6) , Tokyopop Adult) TOKYOPOP, Inc.

Ho, Sohn Eun. Quamtum Mistake, Vol. 1. 2004. 192p. (YA). pap. (978-1-4139-0149-8(2)) ADV Manga.

Hoepfner, John. The Tale of Magic Pixie Dust. 2003. (J). pap. 9.00 (978-0-8059-9273-1(1) , RoseDog Bks.) Dorrance Publishing Co., Inc.

Hoffman, Mary. City of Flowers. 2005. (Illus.). 250p. (YA). (gr. 7-12). 17.95 (978-1-58234-887-2(1) , Bloomsbury Children) Bloomsbury Publishing.

—City of Stars. 2005. (Illus.). 464p. (YA). (ps-17). reprint ed. pap. 7.95 (978-1-58234-982-4(7) , Bloomsbury Children) Bloomsbury Publishing.

—City of Stars. 2005. (Illus.). 457p. (J). (ps-7). per. 15.00 (978-0-606-33760-1(1)) Tandem Library Bks.

Hoffmann, E. T. A. The Nutcracker: The Untold Story. (Illus.). 12p. (J). 4.95 (978-1-58989-100-5(7)) Thurman Hse., LLC.

Hofmeyr, Dianne. The Stone: A Persian Legend of the Magi. Daly, Jude, illus. 2005. 32p. (J). (ps-ps). pap., pap. 7.95 (978-1-84507-446-3(7)) Lincoln, Frances Ltd. GBR. *Dist:* Perseus Distribution.

Holder, Nancy. Spirited. 2004. (Once upon a Time Ser.). 272p. (YA). pap. 13.95 (978-0-689-87063-7(9) , Simon Pulse) Simon & Schuster Children's Publishing.

—Up, up, & Away. 1999. (gr. 3-6). lib. bdg. 12.40 (978-0-613-22556-4(2)) Tandem Library Bks.

Holder, Nancy & Matsuda, Jeff. Keep Me in Mind. 2005. (Buffy the Vampire Slayer Ser.). 256p. (YA). pap. 6.99 (978-0-689-86956-3(8) , Simon Spotlight Entertainment) Simon & Schuster.

Holl, Kristi D. Invisible Alex. 126p. (J). (gr. 3-7). pap. 9.99 (978-0-88092-340-8(7)) Royal Fireworks Publishing Co.

Holland, Janice R. Tom Bear & the Purple-Stripped, Orange-Dotted Dragon. 1999. (Illus.). 33p. (J). (ps-6). 9.00 (978-0-9672199-1-2(4)) Bloomin' Tulip Studios.

Hollaway, David. Quigley Mccormick: And the Curse of the Polka Dotted Pig, 3 vols. l.t. ed. 2005. (Illus.). 156p. (J). per. 15.95 (978-1-933211-54-1(7)) Quackenworth Publishing.

Holman, Doris Anne. Edre the Great Egret. Holman, Doris Anne, illus. 1999. (Illus.). 33p. (J). (gr. k-3). pap. 12.95 (978-0-9667192-1-5(2)) Holman, Doris Anne.

Holman, Felice. The Cricket Winter. Thomas, Robyn, illus. 2006. 96p. (J). 15.00 (978-0-8028-5289-2(0) , Eerdmans Bks For Young Readers) Eerdmans, William B. Publishing Co.

Holston-Holloway, Angela M. The Apple Pie Kids. 2006. (J). pap. 8.00 (***978-0-8059-6899-6(7)***) Dorrance Publishing Co., Inc.

Holt, Rinehart and Winston Staff. Searching for Dragons. 2nd ed. 2002. (Illus.). (J). pap. 4.74 (978-0-03-073834-0(2)) Holt, Rinehart & Winston of Canada, Ltd. CAN. *Dist:* Harcourt Canada, Ltd.

Holub, Joan. Jack & the Jellybeanstalk. 2002. (gr. k-3). lib. bdg. 11.25 (978-0-613-72447-0(X)) Tandem Library Bks.

Hondo. Dream World Tales. 2005. pap. 9.99 (978-0-9773016-0-7(5)) Capital Publishing.

The Honey Tree, 6 Packs. (Literatura 2000 Ser.). (gr. 2-3). 33.00 (978-0-7635-0262-1(6)) Rigby Education.

Hong, Jihae, tr. Threads of Time, Vol. 5. Young Noh, Mi, illus. rev. ed. 2005. 192p. pap. 9.99 (978-1-59532-036-0(9) , Tokyopop Adult) TOKYOPOP, Inc.

Hoover, H. M. Another Heaven, Another Earth. 2002. (gr. 7-12). lib. bdg. 14.15 (978-0-613-70761-9(3)) Tandem Library Bks.

Hopkins, Cathy. Recipe for Rebellion: Big Mouth. 2007. (Zodiac Girls Ser.). 192p. (J). (gr. 4-6). pap. 5.95 (978-0-7534-5896-9(9) , Kingfisher) Houghton Mifflin Co. Trade & Reference Div.

Hopton, Stan. To Dance Beneath a Diamond Sky. 2005. 118p. pap. 16.95 (978-1-4241-0032-3(1)) PublishAmerica, Inc.

Horner, Dwana. Amanda's Toybox. 2001. 21p. pap. 9.95 (978-0-7414-0793-1(0)) Infinity Publishing.

Horowitz, Alena Netia. The Tlytiettlym Tree. Horowitz, Alena Netia & De La Fuente, Mary, illus. l.t. ed. 2003. 64p. (J). per. 12.95 (978-0-923550-42-4(9)) Tetrahedron Publishing LLC.

Horton, Randy. The Great UFO Frame-Up. Taylor, Marjorie, illus. rev. ed. 1999. (Take Ten Ser.). 46p. (YA). (gr. 4-12). pap. 3.95 (978-1-58659-012-3(X)) Artesian Pr.

Horwitz, Elinor Lander. When the Sky Is Like Lace. Cooney, Barbara, illus. 2004. 32p. (J). (ps-3). reprint ed. 16.99 (978-0-670-05909-6(9) , Viking Juvenile) Penguin Group (USA) Inc.

Houghton, John. A Closer Look at Harry Potter. 2001. 92p. pap., pap. 7.99 (978-0-85476-941-4(2) , 0854769412) Cook, David C. Publishing Co.

House, David James. The Key to Space. 2006. (ENM.). 364p. (YA). 24.95 (978-0-9777086-0-4(8)) House, David.

Houston, James A. James Houston's Treasury of Inuit Legends. 2006. (Illus.). 304p. (J). 18.00 (978-0-15-205924-8(5) , Harcourt Young Classics); (YA). pap. 8.95 (978-0-15-205930-9(X) , Odyssey Classics) Harcourt Children's Bks.

Howard, Peggy Ann. Zorees: Land of Dreams. 2007. (YA). per. 16.95 (***978-0-9795519-0-1(0)***) Dream Scape Publishing.

Howe, James. Screaming Mummies of the Pharaoh's Tomb II. Helquist, Brett, illus. 2003. (Tales from the House of Bunnicula Ser.). 112p. (J). pap. 3.99 (978-0-689-83954-2(5) , Aladdin) Simon & Schuster Children's Publishing.

Howe, Tina Field. Alysa of the Fields: Book One in the Tellings of Xunar-kun. 2006. (Illus.). 320p. (YA). pap. 16.95 (978-0-9768585-1-5(7) , 002) Howe, Tina Field.

Howe, Tom. Stonebringer: A Novel of Individuation. 2004. (Illus.). (YA). pap. 16.69 (978-0-9717280-5-9(4)) Roundsquare Pr.

Howell, David. Swan Songs-in Search of the Staffstone. 2005. per. 13.99 (978-1-59781-002-9(9)) Xulon Pr., Inc.

Howell, Robert. Third Times the Charm. 2007. 224p. (J). (gr. 1-7). pap. 10.95 (***978-1-897235-20-1(8)***) Thistledown Pr., Ltd. CAN. *Dist:* Fitzhenry & Whiteside, Ltd.

Howell, Trisha Adelena. Talia & the Great Sapphire of Knowledge. Hohn, David, illus. 2005. 128p. (J). pap. 11.95 (978-1-931210-11-9(X)) Howell Canyon Pr.

Howells, Andrea. Finding Peace & the True Soul. 2006. 60p. (J). per. 11.95 (978-0-9765072-4-6(2)) Tribute Bks.

Hoylie, Gerry. Byron Unleashed. 2005. 60p. pap. 14.95 (978-1-59113-670-5(9)) Booklocker.com, Inc.

Huband, Sue. Arabellas Stories. 2006. pap. 14.49 (***978-1-4259-6597-6(0)***) AuthorHouse.

Hudson, Margaret Parker. The Blue Umbrella. 2005. (Illus.). (J). 15.95 (978-0-9771301-0-8(X)) FayRe Pr.

Hughes, Carol. Dirty Magic. 2006. (Illus.). 432p. (J). (gr. 4-9). 17.95 (978-0-375-83187-4(8)); (gr. 5-8). lib. bdg. 19.99 (978-0-375-93187-1(2)) Random Hse. Children's Bks. (Random Hse. Bks. for Young Readers).

—Dirty Magic. 2008. (Illus.). 432p. (J). (gr. 5-9). 5.99 (978-0-375-83188-1(6)) Random Hse., Inc.

Hughes, Frieda. Tall Story. Riddell, Chris, illus. 2003. pap. (978-0-340-86578-1(4) , Hodder Children's Books) Hodder Children's Division.

Hughes, Ted. The Iron Giant: A Story in Five Nights. Davidson, Andrew, illus. 1999. 79p. (J). (ps-7). per. 13.00 (978-0-613-21772-9(1)) Tandem Library Bks.

Hundal, Nancy. Twilight Fairies. Kilby, Don, illus. 2002. 32p. (J). (gr. k-3). (978-1-55041-645-9(6)) Fitzhenry & Whiteside, Ltd.

—Twilight Fairies. Kilby, Don, illus. 2006. 32p. pap. 7.95 (978-1-55041-961-0(7)) Fitzhenry & Whiteside, Ltd. CAN. *Dist:* F & W Pubns., Inc.

Hunter, Erin. A Dangerous Path. 2004. (Warriors Ser.: Bk. 5). 336p. (J). (gr. 5 up). 16.99 (978-0-06-000006-6(6)) HarperCollins Pubs.

—Dark River. 2008. (Warriors Ser.: Bk. 2). 352p. (J). (gr. 5 up). 16.99 (***978-0-06-089205-0(6)***) HarperCollins Pubs.

—The Darkest Hour. (Warriors Ser.: Bk. 6). (Illus.). (J). 2006. 315p. (***978-1-4156-2257-5(4)*** , Avon Bks.); 2005. 336p. pap. 6.99 (978-0-06-052585-9(1)); 2004. 336p. (gr. 5 up). 15.99 (978-0-06-000007-3(4)); 2004. 336p. (gr. 5 up). lib. bdg. 17.89 (978-0-06-052584-2(3)) HarperCollins Pubs.

—Dawn. 2006. (Warriors Ser.: Bk. 3). 352p. (J). pap. 6.99 (978-0-06-074457-1(X) , Harper Trophy); (Illus.). 15.99 (978-0-06-074455-7(3)); (Illus.). lib. bdg. 17.89 (978-0-06-074456-4(1)) HarperCollins Pubs.

—Fire & Ice. (Warriors Ser.: Bk. 2). 336p. (gr. 5 up). 2004. (Illus.). pap. 6.99 (978-0-06-052559-0(2)); 2003. (J). 16.99 (978-0-06-000003-5(1)); 2003. (J). lib. bdg. 17.89 (978-0-06-052556-9(8)) HarperCollins Pubs.

—Firestar's Quest. 2008. (Warriors Ser.). 544p. (J). pap. 7.99 (***978-0-06-113167-7(9)***) HarperCollins Pubs.

—Firestar's Quest. Chalk, Gary, illus. 2007. (Warriors Ser.). 528p. (J). (gr. 5 up). lib. bdg. 18.89 (***978-0-06-113166-0(0)***); 17.99 (***978-0-06-113164-6(4)***) HarperCollins Pubs.

—Forest of Secrets. 2003. (Warriors Ser.: Bk. 3). (Illus.). 336p. (J). (gr. 5 up). lib. bdg. 17.89 (978-0-06-052560-6(6)) HarperCollins Pubs.

—Into the Wild. 2003. (Warriors Ser.: Bk. 1). 288p. (J). (gr. 5 up). 16.99 (978-0-06-000002-8(3)) HarperCollins Pubs.

—Midnight. 2005. (Warriors Ser.: Bk. 1). (Illus.). 320p. (J). (gr. 5 up). lib. bdg. 16.89 (978-0-06-074450-2(2)); 16.99 (978-0-06-074449-6(9)) HarperCollins Pubs.

—Rising Storm. (Warriors Ser.: Bk. 4). 336p. (J). (gr. 5 up). 2005. pap. 6.99 (978-0-06-052563-7(0)); 2004. lib. bdg. 17.89 (978-0-06-052562-0(2)); 4. 2004. 16.99 (978-0-06-000005-9(8)) HarperCollins Pubs.

—Rising Storm. 2005. (Warriors Ser.: Bk. 4). (Illus.). 315p. (J). (gr. 5-9). lib. bdg. 13.04 (978-0-606-33340-5(1)) Tandem Library Bks.

—Starlight. (Warriors Ser.: Bk. 4). (J). 2007. 320p. pap. 6.99 (978-0-06-082762-5(9) , Harper Trophy); 2006. 336p. 16.99 (978-0-06-082758-8(0)); 2006. 336p. lib. bdg. 17.89 (978-0-06-082760-1(2)) HarperCollins Pubs.

—Sunset. 2007. (Warriors Ser.: Bk. 6). (Illus.). 303p. (J). (gr. 5-9). per. 6.99 (***978-0-06-082771-7(8)*** , Harper Trophy) HarperCollins Pubs.

—Twilight. 2006. (Warriors Ser.: Bk. 5). (Illus.). 336p. (J). 16.99 (978-0-06-082764-9(5)); lib. bdg. 16.89 (978-0-06-082766-3(1)) HarperCollins Pubs.

Hunter, Erin. Warriors Boxed Set: Rising Storm; A Dangerous Path; The Darkest Hour. 2007. (Warriors Ser.: Bks. 4-6). (J). pap. 19.99 (***978-0-06-128452-6(1)*** , Harper Trophy) HarperCollins Pubs.

Hunter, Melanie. Dorsello's Key. 2005. 131p. pap. 19.95 (978-1-4137-6294-5(8)) PublishAmerica, Inc.

Hutchins, Hazel J. The Sidewalk Rescue. Ohi, Ruth, illus. 2004. 32p. (J). (ps-1). pap. 7.95 (978-1-55037-830-6(9)); lib. bdg. 19.95 (978-1-55037-831-3(7)) Annick Pr., Ltd. CAN. *Dist:* Firefly Bks., Ltd.

Hutsell-Manning, Linda. Jason & the Wonder Horn. Gardos, Susan, illus. 2005. (In the Same Boat Ser.). 328p. (J). 8.95 (978-1-55050-214-5(X)) Coteau Bks. CAN. *Dist:* Fitzhenry & Whiteside, Ltd.

Hwang, Mina. Redmoon, Vol. 2. 2001. 200p. (YA). pap. 11.95 (978-1-58899-094-5(X)) ComicsOne Corp./Dr. Masters.

Hyong, Lee Chi. Demon Diary. Kara, illus. 2003. 192p. (gr. 8 up). pap. 9.99 (978-1-59182-154-0(1) , Tokyopop Adult) TOKYOPOP, Inc.

Hyperion, ed. An Unexpected Return - #8: W. I. T. C. H. Graphic Novel. 8th rev. ed. 2007. 128p. (gr. 3-7). pap. 4.99 (***978-1-4231-0903-7(1)***) Hyperion Pr.

Hyperion Staff. A Choice Is Made. rev. ed. 2006. (W. I. T. C. H. Ser.: Bk. 22). 144p. (gr. 3-7). pap. 4.99 (978-0-7868-4878-2(2)) Hyperion Pr.

—Enchanted Music. rev. ed. 2006. (W. I. T. C. H. Adventures Ser. : Bk. 5). 112p. (J). pap. 4.99 (978-0-7868-0978-3(7) , Volo) Hyperion Bks. for Children.

Hyun, You. Faeries' Landing, 13 vols. 2004. (Illus.). Vol. 2. rev. ed. 192p. pap. 9.99 (978-1-59182-610-1(1)); Vol. 3. 3rd rev. ed. pap. 9.99 (978-1-59182-611-8(X)); Vol. 4. rev. ed. 192p. pap. 9.99 (978-1-59182-612-5(8)) TOKYOPOP, Inc. (Tokyopop Adult).

Hyun, You, illus. & creator. Faeries' Landing, Vol. 8. Hyun, You, creator. rev. ed. 2005. 192p. pap. 9.99 (978-1-59532-396-5(1) , Tokyopop Adult) TOKYOPOP, Inc.

Hyung, Kang-Suk & Ah, Shin. Sky Blade Sword of the Heavens, Vol. 1. 2004. 184p. pap. (978-1-4139-0081-1(X)) ADV Manga.

Hyung, Kang Suk & Ah, Shin. Sky Blade Sword of the Heavens, Vol. 2. 2004. 184p. pap. (978-1-4139-0102-3(6)) ADV Manga.

Hyung Kim, Tae, illus. & creator. Planet Blood, Vol. 2. Hyung Kim, Tae, creator. rev. ed. 2005. 200p. pap. 9.99 (978-1-59532-538-9(7) , Tokyopop Adult) TOKYOPOP, Inc.

Hyung, Min-Woo. Priest, Vol. 15. 2006. 224p. pap. 9.99 (978-1-59182-516-6(4) , Tokyopop Adult) TOKYOPOP, Inc.

—Priest: Stygian Mode, Vol. 14. rev. ed. 2005. (Illus.). 176p. pap. 9.99 (978-1-59182-515-9(6) , Tokyopop Adult) TOKYOPOP, Inc.

Hyung, Min-Woo, creator. Priest Vol. 13: Strain of the Dispossessed. 13th rev. ed. 2004. (Illus.). 192p. pap. 9.99 (978-1-59182-514-2(8) , Tokyopop Adult) TOKYOPOP, Inc.

Ikumi, Mia. Tokyo Mew Mew, 7 vols. Yoshida, Reiko, illus. 176p. Vol. 2. rev. ed. 2003. (gr. 2 up). pap. 9.99 (978-1-59182-237-0(8)); Vol. 7. 7th rev. ed. 2004. (J). pap. 9.99 (978-1-59182-550-0(4)) TOKYOPOP, Inc. (Tokyopop Kids).

Ikumi, Mia & Yoshida, Raiko. Tokyo Mew Mew, 10 vols., Vol. 5. rev. ed. 2004. (Illus.). 192p. pap. 9.99 (978-1-59182-548-7(2) , Tokyopop Kids) TOKYOPOP, Inc.

Ikumi, Mia & Yoshida, Reiko. Tokyo Mew Mew, 7 vols. 2003. (Illus.). (gr. 2 up). Vol. 1. 176p. (J). pap. 9.99 (978-1-59182-236-3(X)); Vol. 3. 3rd rev. ed. pap. 9.99 (978-1-59182-238-7(6)) TOKYOPOP, Inc. (Tokyopop Kids).

—Tokyo Mew Mew, 10 vols., Vol. 6. Hiroe, Ikoi, tr. from JPN. rev. ed. 2004. (Illus.). 176p. pap. 9.99 (978-1-59182-549-4(0) , Tokyopop Kids) TOKYOPOP, Inc.

Im, Hye-Young, tr. Dragon Hunter, Vol. 12. Seock Seo, Hong, illus. rev. ed. 2005. 176p. pap. 9.99 (978-1-59182-960-7(7) , Tokyopop Adult) TOKYOPOP, Inc.

Im, Jae Won. The Boss. 2004. 184p. (YA). Vol. 1. pap. (978-1-4139-0069-9(0)); Vol. 2. pap. (978-1-4139-0075-0(5)) ADV Manga.

Impey, Rose & Huws, Emily. Dymuniad Mewn Eiliad. 2005. (WEL., Illus.). 64p. (978-0-86381-912-4(5)) Gwasg Carreg Gwalch.

In-Soo, Ra. King of Hell, 8 vols., Vol. 8. Jae-Hwan, Kim, illus. rev. ed. 2005. Tr. of Ma-Je. 200p. pap. 9.99 (978-1-59182-914-0(3) , Tokyopop Adult) TOKYOPOP, Inc.

Inches, Alison. Big Sister Dora. 2006. (Illus.). (J). (ps-2). 21.35 (978-1-59961-067-2(1)) Spotlight.

Ingpen, Robert R. & Lawrence, Michael. Los Manuscritos de la Tetera: El Intrepido Viaje al Extremo del Mundo. 2002. (SPA., Illus.). 120p. (J). (gr. 4-7). 19.95 (978-84-89396-79-1(5)) Blume ESP. *Dist:* Independent Pubs. Group.

Ingram, Richard. Land of the Giddiwonks. 2004. (J). pap. 12.50 net. (978-0-9745741-1-0(2)) Quality Publishing Inc.

Inns, Christopher. What Will I Be? 2005. (Mirror, Mirror Ser.). (Illus.). 12p. (J). (ps-k). bds. 5.95 (978-0-7534-5893-8(4) , Kingfisher) Houghton Mifflin Co. Trade & Reference Div.

Irwin, Jacqueline. Secrets of Seacrest School. 2005. 85p. pap. 14.95 (978-1-4137-6363-8(4)) PublishAmerica, Inc.

Izubuchi, Yukaka. RahXephon Bible. 2003. (JPN & ENG., Illus.). 100p. pap. 19.98 (978-1-4139-0026-2(7)) A. D. Vision, Inc.

Jablonski, Carla. The Gypsy Enchantment. 2001. 181p. (YA). (gr. 7-12). lib. bdg. 14.15 (978-0-613-74199-6(4)) Tandem Library Bks.

Jablonsky, Alice. Mane Event. 2002. (gr. k-3). lib. bdg. 11.25 (978-0-613-50466-9(6)) Tandem Library Bks.

Jackson, Marjorie. Los Pies del Dragon. Romo, Alberto, tr. Mitchell, Mark, illus. 1998. (Books for Young Learners).Tr. of Dragon Feet. (SPA.). 16p. (J). (gr. k-2). pap. 5.00 (978-1-57274-199-7(6) , A2890) Owen, Richard C. Pubs., Inc.

Jackson, Stephen. Mundoespejo. Abreu, Carlos, tr. 2005. (SPA., Illus.). 28p. (J). (gr. 2-4). 15.95 (978-84-666-1495-5(8)) Ediciones B ESP. *Dist:* Independent Pubs. Group.

Jackson, Steve. The Citadel of Chaos. 2003. 208p. pap. (978-0-7434-7510-5(0)) ibooks, Inc.

Jackson, Steve & Livingstone, Ian. The Worlock of Firetop Mountain. 2003. 192p. pap. 6.99 (978-0-7434-7511-2(9)) ibooks, Inc.

Jacobs, Deborah Lynn. Powers. 2006. 192p. (YA). 16.95 (978-1-59643-112-6(1)) Roaring Brook Pr.

Jacobsen, Allan. To End All Wars, Vol. 1. Lucas, Jorge, illus. 2005. (Marvel Heroes Ser.). 216p. (YA). pap. 19.99 (978-0-7851-1449-9(1)) Marvel Enterprises, Inc.

Jacques, Brian. Badgers. Baker, Chris, illus. 2002. (YA). 8.99 (978-0-399-23852-9(2) , Philomel) Penguin Group (USA) Inc.

—Castaways of the Flying Dutchman. Schoenherr, Ian, illus. 2003. (Castaways of the Flying Dutchman Ser.: No. 1). 336p. (J). (gr. 3-6). pap. 7.99 (978-0-14-250118-4(2) , Puffin) Penguin Group (USA) Inc.

—Eulalia! 2007. (Redwall Ser.). 400p. (J). (gr. 5). 23.99 (***978-0-399-24209-0(0)*** , Philomel) Penguin Group (USA) Inc.

—Friend & Foe. 2000. (Redwall Ser.). (Illus.). 16p. (J). (gr. 4-7). 8.99 (978-0-399-23589-4(2) , Philomel) Penguin Group (USA) Inc.

—The Great Redwall Feast. Denise, Christopher, illus. 2000. (Redwall Ser.). 64p. (J). (gr. 4-8). pap. 6.99 (978-0-698-11876-8(6) , Putnam Juvenile) Penguin Group (USA) Inc.

—The Great Redwall Feast. Denise, Christopher, illus. 2000. (Redwall Ser.). 64p. (J). (ps-3). lib. bdg. 13.79 (978-0-606-20360-9(5)) Tandem Library Bks.

—The Great Redwall Feast. 2000. (Redwall Ser.). (J). (gr. 4-8). (978-0-606-20236-7(6)) Tandem Library Bks.

—High Rhulain. (Redwall Ser.). 2008. 352p. (YA). (gr. 7). 8.99 (***978-0-14-240938-1(3)*** , Puffin); 2007. 336p. mass mkt. 7.99 (978-0-441-01436-1(4) , Ace Bks.) Penguin Group (USA) Inc.

—The Legend of Luke. 2005. (Redwall Ser.). (Illus.). 384p. (YA). (gr. k-3). pap. 7.99 (978-0-14-250109-2(3) , Puffin) Penguin Group (USA) Inc.

—The Legend of Luke. Baker, Chris, illus. (Redwall Ser.). (gr. 4-8). 2000. 384p. (J). 23.99 (978-0-399-23490-3(X) , Philomel); 2001. 368p. reprint ed. mass mkt. 7.99 (978-0-441-00773-8(2) , Ace Bks.) Penguin Group (USA) Inc.

—Loamhedge. Elliot, David, illus. (Redwall Ser.). 2005. 464p. (J). (gr. 5). pap. 8.99 (978-0-14-240377-8(6) , Puffin); 2003. 432p. (YA). (gr. 3-6). 23.99 (978-0-399-23724-9(0) , Philomel) Penguin Group (USA) Inc.

—The Long Patrol. Curless, Allan, illus. 1998. (Redwall Ser.). 352p. (J). (gr. 4-8). 23.99 (978-0-399-23165-0(X) , Philomel) Penguin Group (USA) Inc.

—The Long Patrol. 1999. (Redwall Ser.). (J). (gr. 4-8). (978-0-606-15882-4(0)); (gr. 5-8). lib. bdg. 15.30 (978-0-613-13199-5(1)) Tandem Library Bks.

—Lord Brocktree. 2002. (Redwall Ser.). 15.23 (978-1-4046-1587-8(3)) Book Wholesalers, Inc.

—Lord Brocktree. Fangorn, illus. 2005. (Redwall Ser.). 384p. (YA). (gr. 7). pap. 7.99 (978-0-14-250110-8(7) , Puffin) Penguin Group (USA) Inc.

—Lord Brocktree. 2000. (Redwall Ser.). (Illus.). 384p. (J). (gr. 4-8). 23.99 (978-0-399-23590-0(6) , Philomel) Penguin Group (USA) Inc.

—Lord Brocktree. 2001. (Redwall Ser.). (gr. 5-8). lib. bdg. 15.30 (978-0-613-44230-5(X)) Tandem Library Bks.

—Mariel of Redwall. Chalk, Gary, illus. 2003. (Redwall Ser.). 400p. (YA). (gr. 5). pap. 8.99 (978-0-14-230239-2(2) , Puffin) Penguin Group (USA) Inc.

—Mariel of Redwall. 2000. (Redwall Ser.). (Illus.). 384p. (gr. 4-8). mass mkt. 7.99 (978-0-441-00694-6(9) , Ace Bks.) Penguin Group (USA) Inc.

—Mariel of Redwall. 2003. (Redwall Ser.). (gr. 5-8). lib. bdg. 16.45 (978-0-613-59976-4(4)) Tandem Library Bks.

—Marlfox. Baker, Chris, illus. 1998. (Redwall Ser.). 400p. (J). (gr. 4-8). 22.99 (978-0-399-23307-4(5) , Philomel) Penguin Group (USA) Inc.

—Marlfox. 2005. (Redwall Ser.). 400p. (J). (gr. 5). reprint ed. pap. 8.99 (978-0-14-250108-5(5)) Penguin Group (USA) Inc.

—Marlfox. 2000. (Redwall Ser.). (gr. 5-8). lib. bdg. 15.30 (978-0-613-23017-9(5)) Tandem Library Bks.

—Martin the Warrior. Chalk, Gary, illus. 2004. (Redwall Ser.). 376p. (YA). 8.99 (978-0-14-240055-5(6) , Puffin) Penguin Group (USA) Inc.

—Martin the Warrior. 2004. (Redwall Ser.). (gr. 3-6). lib. bdg. 16.45 (978-0-613-71583-6(7)) Tandem Library Bks.

—Mattimeo. Chalk, Gary, illus. 2003. (Redwall Ser.). 448p. (J). pap. 8.99 (978-0-14-230240-8(6) , Puffin) Penguin Group (USA) Inc.

—Mattimeo. 1999. (Redwall Ser.). (Illus.). 448p. (gr. 4-8). mass mkt. 7.99 (978-0-441-00610-6(8) , Ace Bks.) Penguin Group (USA) Inc.

—Mattimeo. (Redwall Ser.). (gr. 5-8). 2003. lib. bdg. 16.45 (978-0-613-64193-7(0)); 1999. lib. bdg. 15.30 (978-0-8335-8134-1(1)) Tandem Library Bks.

—Mossflower. 1998. (Redwall Ser.). (Illus.). 384p. (gr. 4-8). reprint ed. mass mkt. 7.99 (978-0-441-00576-5(4) , Ace Bks.) Penguin Group (USA) Inc.

—Pearls of Lutra. (Redwall Ser.). (Illus.). 2004. 416p. (J). (gr. 5 up). pap. 8.99 (978-0-14-240144-6(7) , Puffin); 1998. 368p. (gr. 4-8). mass mkt. 7.99 (978-0-441-00508-6(X) , Ace Bks.) Penguin Group (USA) Inc.

—Pearls of Lutra. 1998. (Redwall Ser.). (J). (gr. 4-8). (978-0-606-13015-8(2)) Tandem Library Bks.

—Rakkety Tam. David, Elliot, illus. 2006. (Redwall Ser.). 384p. (J). (gr. 5). pap. 8.99 (978-0-14-240683-0(X) , Puffin) Penguin Group (USA) Inc.

—Rakkety Tam. 2005. (Redwall Ser.). 384p. (gr. 12). mass mkt. 7.99 (978-0-441-01318-0(X) , Ace Bks.) Penguin Group (USA) Inc.

—Rakkety Tam. Elliot, David, illus. 2004. (Redwall Ser.). 432p. (YA). (gr. 4-6). 23.99 (978-0-399-23725-6(9) , Philomel) Penguin Group (USA) Inc.

—Redwall. 2002. (Redwall Ser.). (Illus.). 352p. (J). pap. 8.99 (978-0-14-230237-8(6) , Puffin) Penguin Group (USA) Inc.

—Redwall. Howell, Troy, illus. 2000. (Redwall Ser.). 352p. (J). (gr. 4-8). pap. 12.99 (978-0-399-23629-7(5) , Philomel) Penguin Group (USA) Inc.

—Redwall. (Redwall Ser.). 352p. 10th anniv. ed. 1998. (Illus.). (gr. 4-8). mass mkt. 7.99 (978-0-441-00548-2(9) , Ace Bks.); 20th anniv. ed. 2007. (YA). (gr. 5). 23.99 (***978-0-399-24794-1(7)*** , Philomel) Penguin Group (USA) Inc.

—Redwall. (Redwall Ser.). 2002. (gr. 3-6). lib. bdg. 16.45 (978-0-613-71581-2(0)); 2000. (gr. 3-6). lib. bdg. 22.25 (978-0-613-89563-7(0)); 1998. (J). (gr. 4-8). (978-0-606-13734-8(3)) Tandem Library Bks.

—Redwall. Chalk, Gary, illus. l.t. ed. 2002. (Redwall Ser). (J). 25.95 (978-0-7862-3858-3(5)) Thomson Gale.

—Redwall: The Graphic Novel. Blevins, Bret, illus. 2007. (Redwall Ser.). 148p. (YA). (gr. 3 up). 12.99 (***978-0-399-24481-0(6)*** , Philomel) Penguin Group (USA) Inc.

—Redwall Map & Riddle Book: Includes the Redwall Riddler! Baker, Chris & Curless, Allan, illus. 1998. (Redwall Ser.). (J). (gr. 4-8). 9.99 (978-0-399-23248-0(6) , Philomel) Penguin Group (USA) Inc.

—A Redwall Winter's Tale. Denise, Christopher, illus. (Redwall Ser.). (J). 2004. 72p. (gr. 6). pap. 7.99 (978-0-14-240198-9(6) , Puffin); 2001. 80p. (gr. 4-8). 18.99 (978-0-399-23346-3(6) , Philomel) Penguin Group (USA) Inc.

—Salamandastron. Chalk, Gary, illus. 2003. (Redwall Ser.). 400p. (YA). pap. 8.99 (978-0-14-250152-8(2) , Puffin) Penguin Group (USA) Inc.

—Salamandastron. 2003. (Redwall Ser.). (gr. 5-8). lib. bdg. 16.45 (978-0-613-71576-8(4)) Tandem Library Bks.

—Seven Strange & Ghostly Tales. 1999. (Illus.). 144p. (J). (gr. 4-7). pap. 5.99 (978-0-698-11808-9(1) , Putnam Juvenile) Penguin Group (USA) Inc.

—The Taggerung. Standley, Peter, illus. (Redwall Ser.). 448p. 2003. pap. 8.99 (978-0-14-250154-2(9) , Puffin); 2001. (J). (gr. 3-6). 23.99 (978-0-399-23720-1(8) , Philomel) Penguin Group (USA) Inc.

—The Taggerung. 2002. (Redwall Ser.). (Illus.). 416p. reprint ed. mass mkt. 7.99 (978-0-441-00968-8(9) , Ace Bks.) Penguin Group (USA) Inc.

—The Taggerung. 2001. (Redwall Ser.). (Illus.). 384p. (J). (978-0-09-176928-4(0) , Hutchinson) Random Hse.

—The Taggerung. Standley, Peter, illus. l.t. ed. 2002. (Redwall Ser). 683p. (J). 25.95 (978-0-7862-4014-2(8)) Thomson Gale.

—Triss. Elliot, David, illus. (Redwall Ser.). (YA). 2004. 400p. (gr. 7). pap. 7.99 (978-0-14-240248-1(6) , Puffin); 2002. 432p. 23.99 (978-0-399-23723-2(2) , Philomel) Penguin Group (USA) Inc.

—Triss. l.t. ed. 2004. (Redwall Ser.). 596p. (J). 23.95 (978-0-7862-6207-6(9)) Thorndike Pr.

Jae Hoo, Yoon, creator. In Dream World. 2005. (Illus.). pap. 9.99 (978-1-59532-516-7(6) , Tokyopop Adult) TOKYOPOP, Inc.

Jae-Hwan, Kim. King of Hell, 6 vols., Vol. 6. Na, Lauren, tr. from KOR. In-Soo, Ra, illus. rev. ed. 2004. 216p. pap. 9.99 (978-1-59182-484-8(2) , Tokyopop Adult) TOKYOPOP, Inc.

Jaffe, Nina. The Journey Begins. Caldwell, Ben, illus. 2004. (Wonder Woman Ser.). 64p. (J). pap. 4.99 (978-0-06-056521-3(7) , Harper Festival) HarperCollins Pubs.

—Wonder Woman: Amazon Princess. 2004. (gr. 3-6). lib. bdg. 13.00 (978-0-613-71471-6(7)) Tandem Library Bks.

—Wonder Woman: The Contest. 2004. (ps-2). lib. bdg. 11.80 (978-0-613-71841-7(0)) Tandem Library Bks.

—Wonder Woman: The Journey Begins. 2004. (gr. 3-6). lib. bdg. 13.00 (978-0-613-71470-9(9)) Tandem Library Bks.

James, B. J. Supertwins Meet the Dangerous Dino-Robots. 2003. (gr. k-3). lib. bdg. 11.80 (978-0-613-72179-0(9)) Tandem Library Bks.

James, Betsy. Dark Heart. 2005. (Seeker Chronicles Ser.). 272p. (YA). pap. 5.99 (978-0-689-85070-7(0) , Simon Pulse) Simon & Schuster Children's Publishing.

James, Betsy. Listening at the Gate. 2007. (Seeker Chronicles Ser.). 512p. (YA). pap. 8.99 (***978-0-689-85069-1(7)*** , Simon Pulse) Simon & Schuster Children's Publishing.

—Listening at the Gate. James, Betsy, illus. 2006. (Seeker Chronicles Ser.). (Illus.). 512p. (YA). (gr. 7 up). 16.95 (978-0-689-85068-4(9) , Atheneum) Simon & Schuster Children's Publishing.

James, Gill. Nick's Gallery. 2004. 149p. pap. 19.95 (978-1-4137-2186-7(9)) PublishAmerica, Inc.

James, Margaret. Counting on Dreams. James, Margaret, illus. 2002. (978-0-9720825-6-3(5)) Toy Box Pr., The.

Jane, Pamela. Winky Blue Forever. Tilley, Debbie, illus. 1999. 56p. (J). (gr. 2-6). pap. 3.95 (978-1-57255-624-9(2)) Mondo Publishing.

Janicke, Gregory. Attack of the Shadow Beasts. 2007. 280p. (YA). (***978-983-3318-64-3(9)***) Cavendish, Marshall Corp.

—The Dark Mystery of the Shadow Beasts. 2004. (Illus.). 168p. (978-983-58-0993-4(3)) Times Edition.

—Lost & Found. 2008. (YA). (***978-0-7614-5426-7(8)***) Cavendish, Marshall Corp.

—The Shadow Beasts. 2007. (Outcasts Ser.: Bk. 1). 276p. (YA). (gr. 5 up). pap. 6.99 (***978-0-7614-5364-2(4)***) Cavendish, Marshall Corp.

—The Survivors. 2007. (Outcasts Ser.: Bk. 2). 276p. (YA). (gr. 5 up). 6.99 (***978-0-7614-5365-9(2)***) Cavendish, Marshall Corp.

Janik, Dan. Sourdough Scott's Bedtime Fairy Tales from Alaska. 2005. (J). per. 12.95 net. (978-1-59433-031-5(X)) Publication Consultants.

Jansson, Tove. Moominvalley in November. Hart, Kingsley, tr. from SWE. Jansson, Tove, illus. 2003. (Moomintrolls Ser.). (Illus.). 176p. (J). pap. 6.95 (978-0-374-45309-1(8) , Sunburst) Farrar, Straus & Giroux.

Jarvis, Robin. The Alchemist's Cat. 2006. 304p. (YA). pap. 6.95 (978-0-8118-5450-4(7)) Chronicle Bks. LLC.

—Thorn Ogres of Hagwood. 2002. (Hagwood Books: Bk. 1). (Illus.). 256p. (YA). (gr. 5 up). 16.00 (978-0-15-216752-3(8) , Silver Whistle) Harcourt Trade Pubs.

Jarvis, Robin & Jarvis, Robert M. The Alchemist's Cat. 2004. 320p. (YA). 17.95 (978-1-58717-257-1(7) , Sea-Star Bks.) Chronicle Bks. LLC.

Jea-Eun, Kim, illus. Soul to Seoul, Vol. 2. 2nd rev. ed. 2005. 200p. pap. 9.99 (978-1-59532-313-2(9) , Tokyopop Adult) TOKYOPOP, Inc.

Jenkins, Gloria. Storm: The Peace Maker. 2006. (J). pap. 8.00 (***978-0-8059-7116-3(5)***) Dorrance Publishing Co., Inc.

Jenkins, Jerry B. & Fabry, Chris. The Sword of the Wormling. 2007. (Wormling Ser.). 336p. (J). (gr. 5-9). pap. 7.99 (***978-1-4143-0156-3(1)***) Tyndale Hse. Pubs.

Jenkins, Jerry B. & LaHaye, Tim. Battling the Commander: The Hidden Cave. 2001. (Left Behind Ser.: Bk. 15). (gr. 5-8). lib. bdg. 14.15 (978-0-613-57389-4(7)) Tandem Library Bks.

—Darkening Skies: Judgment of Ice. 2001. (Left Behind Ser.: Bk. 18). (gr. 5-8). lib. bdg. 14.15 (978-0-613-57402-0(8)) Tandem Library Bks.

—Death Strike: The Young Trib Force Faces War. 2000. (Left Behind Ser.: Bk. 8). (gr. 5-8). lib. bdg. 14.15 (978-0-613-33289-7(X)) Tandem Library Bks.

—Fire from Heaven: Deceiving the Enemy. 2001. (Left Behind Ser.: Bk. 16). (gr. 5-8). lib. bdg. 14.15 (978-0-613-57411-2(7)) Tandem Library Bks.

—Into the Storm: The Search for Secret Documents. 2000. (Left Behind Ser.: Bk. 11). (gr. 5-8). lib. bdg. 14.15 (978-0-613-33301-6(2)) Tandem Library Bks.

—On the Run: The Kids Are on the Run. 2000. (Left Behind Ser.: Bk. 10). (gr. 5-8). lib. bdg. 14.15 (978-0-613-33310-8(1)) Tandem Library Bks.

—The Search: The Struggle to Survive. 2000. (Left Behind Ser.: Bk. 9). 159p. (J). (gr. k-9). lib. bdg. 12.64 (978-0-606-21869-6(6)) Tandem Library Bks.

—Secrets of New Babylon: The Search for an Impostor. 2002. (Left Behind Ser.: Bk. 21). (gr. 3-6). lib. bdg. 14.15 (978-0-613-59360-1(X)) Tandem Library Bks.

—The Showdown: Behind Enemy Lines. 2001. (Left Behind Ser.: Bk. 13). (gr. 5-8). lib. bdg. 14.15 (978-0-613-33316-0(0)) Tandem Library Bks.

—Terror in the Stadium: Witnesses under Fire. 2001. (Left Behind Ser.: Bk. 17). (gr. 5-8). lib. bdg. 14.15 (978-0-613-57449-5(4)) Tandem Library Bks.

Jenna of Erdovon: The Philosopher's Egg. 2007. (Illus.). 220p. (J). (gr. 4-7). per. 19.95 (978-1-929084-14-2(5)) Malibu Bks. for Children.

Jennings, Paul. Uncanny! Even More Surprising Stories. l.t. ed. 2000. 258p. (J). pap. (978-0-7540-6114-4(0) , CLP 309) BBC Audio.

Jeon, Kook Jin. Ruler of the Land, Vol. 2. 2004. 200p. (YA). pap. (978-1-4139-0037-8(2)) ADV Manga.

Jeon, Kook Jin & Yang, Jae Hyun. Ruler of the Land, Vol. 3. 2004. 200p. (YA). pap. (978-1-4139-0057-6(7)) ADV Manga.

Jocelyn, Marthe. Earthly Astonishments: A Novel. 2003. 192p. (J). (gr. 3-7). pap. 7.95 (978-0-88776-628-2(5)) Tundra Bks., Inc./Livres Toundra, Inc. CAN. *Dist:* Random Hse., Inc.

—The Invisible Harry. Carter, Abby, illus. 2000. 160p. (J). (gr. 3-7). pap. 6.99 (978-0-88776-512-4(2)) Tundra Bks., Inc./Livres Toundra, Inc. CAN. *Dist:* Random Hse., Inc.

—The Invisible Harry. Carter, Abby, illus. 1999. 144p. (J). (gr. 4-7). 14.99 (978-0-88776-467-7(3)) Tundra Pubns.

Johansen, K. V. Nightwalker. 2007. (Warlocks of Talverdin Ser.: Bk. 1). 208p. (YA). (gr. 7 up). pap. (***978-1-55143-481-0(4)***) Orca Bk. Pubs.

Johansen, K. V. The Serpent Bride: Stories from Medieval Danish Ballads. 1998. 192p. pap. (978-1-895449-82-2(0)) Thistledown Pr., Ltd.

Johns, Geoff. Rogues. rev. ed. 2003. (Flash Ser.). (Illus.). 144p. pap. 14.99 (978-1-56389-950-8(7)) DC Comics.

Johns, Linda. Carmen Dives In. 2005. (Star Sisterz Ser.: Bk. 2). (Illus.). 192p. (J). pap. 5.99 (978-0-7869-3714-1(9)) Wizards of the Coast.

Johnson, Bob. The Squatland Chronicles: Book 5 - the Dreaded Swamp of the Bubble Dragon. 2005. (Illus.). 56p. (J). per. 11.00 (978-1-59453-853-7(0) , Airleaf Publishing) Airleaf Publishing & Bookselling.

Johnson, Bob. The Squatland Chronicles: The Lost Mine of the Mechanical Spider. 2006. (Illus.). 56p. (J). per. 11.00 (***978-1-60002-185-5(9)*** , 3977, Airleaf Publishing) Airleaf Publishing & Bookselling.

Johnson, Cheryl. Marllow. Ciesinki, Izabela, illus. 2007. 27p. (J). 14.95 (***978-0-9785728-4-6(X)***) Entry Way Marketing & Publishing.

Johnson, Crockett. Magic Beach. 2005. (Illus.). 64p. (J). 18.95 (978-1-932425-27-7(6) , Lemniscaat) Boyds Mills Pr.

Johnson, Jane. The Secret Country. Stower, Adam, illus. 336p. (J). 2007. (Eidolon Chronicles Ser.). pap. 5.99 (***978-1-4169-3815-6(X)*** , Aladdin); 2006. (Chronicles of Eidolon Ser.: Bk. 1). (gr. 3-7). 14.95 (978-1-4169-0712-1(2)) Simon & Schuster Children's Publishing.

Johnson, Kathleen Jeffrie. A Fast & Brutal Wing. unabr. ed. 2005. (YA). 46.70 incl. audio (978-1-4193-3247-0(3) , 42029) Recorded Bks., LLC.

—A Fast & Brutal Wing. rev. ed. 2004. 192p. (YA). 16.95 (978-1-59643-013-6(3)) Roaring Brook Pr.

Johnson, Pete. My Friend's a Werewolf. 2000. (Corgi Yearling Ser.). (Illus.). 128p. (J). pap. 8.99 (978-0-440-86342-7(2)) Transworld Publishers Ltd. GBR. *Dist:* Trafalgar Square Publishing.

Johnson, Shelli Wright. The Story of Bes. 2000. 99p. (J). pap. 12.95 (978-1-58851-428-8(5)) PublishAmerica, Inc.

Johnson, Suzanne C. Fribbity Ribbit. 1999. (J). lib. bdg. 17.99 (978-0-517-70983-2(X)) Crown Publishing Group.

Johnson, William Crow. The Adventures of Sara Springborn & Mr. Wollo Bushtail. 2001. 208p. (gr. 7). pap. 14.95 (978-0-595-17616-8(5)) iUniverse, Inc.

Johnson, Yuki N., tr. from JPN. Tramps Like Us, 7 vols., Vol. 2. rev. ed. 2004. (Teen Ser.). (Illus.). 200p. pap. 9.99 (978-1-59532-140-4(3) , Tokyopop Adult) TOKYOPOP, Inc.

Johnston, Annie Fellows. The Giant Scissors. Barry, Ethelred B., illus. 2005. reprint ed. pap. 22.95 (978-1-4179-0341-2(4)) Kessinger Publishing, LLC.

Johnston, Karen Ann. Mr. Bob's Magic Ride in the Sky. Johnston, Karen Ann, illus. 2002. (Illus.). 32p. (J). (ps-2). 14.95 (978-1-55285-393-1(4)) Whitecap Bks., Ltd. CAN. *Dist:* Firefly Bks., Ltd.

Johse, Jill Taylor. Beyond the Third Floor. 2003. (gr. 7-12). lib. bdg. 22.20 (978-0-613-86202-8(3)) Tandem Library Bks.

—Beyond the Third Floor. 2003. 166p. (YA). pap. 12.95 (978-0-595-28006-3(4)) iUniverse, Inc.

Jones, Anne Marie. Mother Hen's Family Time Rhymes for Thought Book II. 2004. (YA). per. (978-1-4134-5837-4(8)) Borders Personal Publishing.

Jones, Bruce. Hulk & Thing: Hard Knocks. Lee, Jae, illus. 2005. (Hulk Ser.). 120p. pap. 13.99 (978-0-7851-1576-2(5)) Marvel Enterprises, Inc.

Jones, Claudia. Riding Out the Storm. 2006. 264p. pap. 8.95 (978-0-7387-0867-6(4)) Llewellyn Pubns.

Jones, Diana, ed. Spellbound: Fantasy Stories. 2007. 280p. (J). (gr. 4-7). pap. 6.95 (***978-0-7534-6144-0(7)*** , Kingfisher) Houghton Mifflin Co. Trade & Reference Div.

Jones, Diana Wynn. The Game. 2007. (Firebird Ser.). 192p. (YA). (gr. 7 up). 11.99 (978-0-14-240718-9(6) , Puffin) Penguin Group (USA) Inc.

Jones, Diana Wynne. Cart & Cwidder & Drowned Ammet, Vol. 1. 2005. (Dalemark Quartet Ser.). (Illus.). 560p. (J). (gr. 7 up). reprint ed. pap. 7.99 (978-0-06-076369-5(8)) HarperCollins Pubs.

—Castle in the Air. 2001. 304p. (J). (gr. 7 up). pap. 6.99 (978-0-06-447345-3(7) , Harper Trophy) HarperCollins Pubs.

—Castle in the Air. 2001. (gr. 5-8). lib. bdg. 15.25 (978-0-613-46238-9(6)) Tandem Library Bks.

—Charmed Life. l.t. ed. 2005. 360p. (J). pap. (978-0-7540-6139-7(6) , CLP 334) BBC Audio.

—Charmed Life. 1998. (Chrestomanci Quartet Ser.). (Illus.). 224p. (J). (gr. 5 up). pap. 6.99 (978-0-688-15546-9(4) , Harper Trophy) HarperCollins Pubs.

—The Chronicles of Chrestomanci, 2 vols. 2001. (Chronicles of Chrestomanci Ser.: Vol. I). (J). (gr. 7-12). Vol. I. 608p. pap. 7.99 (978-0-06-447268-5(X) , Harper Trophy); Vol. II. 560p. pap. 7.99 (978-0-06-447269-2(8)) HarperCollins Pubs.

—Chronicles of Chrestomanci: Lives of Christopher Chant & Charmed Life. 2001. (gr. 5-8). lib. bdg. 15.30 (978-0-613-31070-3(5)) Tandem Library Bks.

—Chronicles of Chrestomanci: Magicians of Caprona & Witch Week. 2001. (gr. 5-8). lib. bdg. 15.30 (978-0-613-31071-0(3)) Tandem Library Bks.

—Conrad's Fate. (J). 2006. 400p. pap. 6.99 (978-0-06-074745-9(5)); 2005. 384p. (gr. k-17). lib. bdg. 17.89 (978-0-06-074744-2(7)); 2005. 384p. (gr. 5 up). 16.99 (978-0-06-074743-5(9)) HarperCollins Pubs.

—Conrad's Fate: Read-Along/Homework Pack. 2005. (Chrestomanci Ser.). (YA). (gr. 5-8). 102.74 incl. audio (978-1-4193-3551-8(0) , 42039) Recorded Bks., LLC.

—Dark Lord of Derkholm. 2001. (gr. 7-12). lib. bdg. 15.30 (978-0-613-35925-2(9)) Tandem Library Bks.

—Drowned Ammet. 2001. (gr. 7-12). lib. bdg. 15.25 (978-0-613-35940-5(2)) Tandem Library Bks.

—Fantasy Stories. 2003. (gr. 5-8). lib. bdg. 15.25 (978-0-613-67405-8(7)) Tandem Library Bks.

—Fire & Hemlock. 2002. 432p. (J). (gr. 7 up). pap. 7.99 (978-0-06-447352-1(X)) HarperCollins Pubs.

E
F
G

—Fire & Hemlock. 2002. (gr. 7-12). lib. bdg. 15.25 (978-0-613-62617-0(6)) Tandem Library Bks.

—Homeward Bounders. 2002. (gr. 7-12). lib. bdg. 14.10 (978-0-613-59311-3(1)) Tandem Library Bks.

—Howl's Moving Castle. 2001. (gr. 5-8). lib. bdg. 15.30 (978-0-613-37151-3(8)) Tandem Library Bks.

—The Lives of Christopher Chant. l.t. ed. 2005. 360p. (J). pap. (978-0-7540-6163-2(9) , CLP 359) BBC Audio.

—The Magicians of Caprona. 1999. (978-0-606-22058-3(5)) Tandem Library Bks.

—Magicians of Caprona. Stevens, Tim, illus. l.t. ed. 2005. 288p. (J). pap. (978-0-7540-6151-9(5) , CLP 345) BBC Audio.

—Magicians of Caprona. 1999. (gr. 5-8). lib. bdg. 14.15 (978-0-613-16750-5(3)) Tandem Library Bks.

—The Merlin Conspiracy. 480p. (J). (gr. 5 up). 2004. pap. 6.99 (978-0-06-052320-6(4) , Harper Trophy); 2003. 17.89 (978-0-06-052319-0(0)); 2003. 16.99 (978-0-06-052318-3(2)) HarperCollins Pubs.

—Mixed Magics: Four Tales of Chrestomanci. 2001. (Chronicles of Chrestomanci Ser.: Bk. 4). 144p. (J). (gr. 5 up). 15.89 (978-0-06-029706-0(9)) HarperCollins Pubs.

—Mixed Magics: Four Tales of Chrestomanci. 2003. 193p. (J). (ps-7). lib. bdg. 14.15 (978-0-613-68452-1(4)) Tandem Library Bks.

—Ogre Downstairs. 2002. (gr. 3-6). lib. bdg. 14.10 (978-0-613-68455-2(9)) Tandem Library Bks.

—The Pinhoe Egg: A Chrestomanci Book. (J). 2007. 480p. pap. 7.99 (***978-0-06-113126-4(1)*** , Eos); 2006. 528p. 17.99 (978-0-06-113124-0(5) , Greenwillow Bks.); 2006. 528p. lib. bdg. 18.89 (978-0-06-113125-7(3)) HarperCollins Pubs.

—Power of Three. 2003. (gr. 5-8). lib. bdg. 14.15 (978-0-613-68376-0(5)) Tandem Library Bks.

—Spellcoats. 2001. (gr. 7-12). lib. bdg. 15.25 (978-0-613-36015-9(X)) Tandem Library Bks.

—Unexpected Magic: Collected Stories. (J). 2006. 608p. pap. 7.99 (978-0-06-055535-1(1)); 2004. 512p. (gr. 5 up). 16.99 (978-0-06-055533-7(5)); 2004. 512p. (gr. 5 up). lib. bdg. 17.89 (978-0-06-055534-4(3)) HarperCollins Pubs.

—Year of the Griffin. (J). 2001. 400p. (gr. 7 up). pap. 7.99 (978-0-06-447335-4(X) , Harper Trophy); 2000. 272p. (gr. 5 up). 15.89 (978-0-06-029158-7(3)) HarperCollins Pubs.

—Year of the Griffin. 2001. (J). (978-0-606-21708-8(8)); (gr. 5-8). lib. bdg. 15.30 (978-0-613-44275-6(X)) Tandem Library Bks.

Jones, Frewin. The Faerie Path. (Faerie Path Ser.: Bk. 1). (J). 2008. 336p. pap. 8.99 (***978-0-06-087104-8(0)*** , Eos); 2007. 320p. 16.99 (978-0-06-087102-4(4)); 2007. 320p. lib. bdg. 17.89 (978-0-06-087103-1(2)) HarperCollins Pubs.

—The Lost Queen. 2007. (Faerie Path Ser.: Bk. 2). 352p. (J). lib. bdg. 17.89 (***978-0-06-087106-2(7));*** 335p. (YA). (gr. 7 up). 16.99 (***978-0-06-087105-5(9))*** HarperCollins Pubs. (Eos).

—The Sorcerer King. 2008. (Faerie Path Ser.: Bk. 3). 336p. (J). 16.99 (***978-0-06-087108-6(3));*** lib. bdg. 17.89 (***978-0-06-087109-3(1))*** HarperCollins Pubs. (Eos).

Jones, Heulwen. O'Grady's Well. 2005. (Illus.). 96p. pap. (***978-1-84401-578-8(5))*** Athena Pr.

Jones, Jasmine, adapted by. Tell It Like It Is, Vol. 7. rev. ed. 2005. (That's So Raven Ser.: Bk. 7). (Illus.). 128p. (J). (gr. 3-7). pap. 4.99 (978-0-7868-4684-9(4)) Disney Pr.

Jones, Marcia Thornton & Dadey, Debbie. The Hauntlys' Hairy Surprise. 1999. (Bailey City Monsters Super Special Ser.: No. 1). (Illus.). 112p. (J). (gr. 2-4). pap. 3.99 (978-0-590-04302-1(1)) Scholastic, Inc.

—The Hauntlys' Hairy Surprise. 1999. (Bailey City Monsters Super Special Ser.: No. 1). (J). (gr. 2-4). (978-0-606-19911-7(X)) Tandem Library Bks.

Jones, Michael. Finding Imagine Nation. 2007. (YA). per. 10.95 (***978-0-9789386-4-2(X))*** Lucy Rose Publishing LLC.

Jones, Miranda. Make a Wish. 2005. 128p. (J). (gr. 1-3). pap. 4.99 (978-0-440-41973-0(5) , Yearling) Random Hse. Children's Bks.

Jones, Stephen M. Charlemagne Mack: Rise of the Queen, Personal Journal #1. 2007. 178p. (J). (gr. 4-7). per. 14.95 (***978-1-933002-41-5(7))*** PublishingWorks.

Jones, T. W. Derth. 2006. 165p. pap. 19.95 (978-1-4241-0806-0(3)) PublishAmerica, Inc.

Jopling, John Perry & Jopling, Hazel Joan. John, the Airport Kid: A Magical Adventure. 2007. (YA). per. (***978-0-9778070-4-8(5))*** SilverBear.

Jordan, Robert. From the Two Rivers. 2002. (gr. 7-12). lib. bdg. 14.15 (978-0-613-62621-7(4)) Tandem Library Bks.

—The Path of Daggers. 1999. (Wheel of Time Ser.: Bk. 8). (978-0-606-18661-2(1)) Tandem Library Bks.

—To the Blight. 2002. (gr. 7-12). lib. bdg. 14.15 (978-0-613-62655-2(9)) Tandem Library Bks.

—Winter's Heart. 2002. (Wheel of Time Ser.: Bk. 9). (gr. 7-12). lib. bdg. 16.45 (978-0-613-61150-3(0)) Tandem Library Bks.

Joyce, Graham. T. W. O. C. Taken Without Owner's Consent. 2007. 224p. (YA). (gr. 8 up). 16.99 (978-0-670-06090-0(9) , Viking Juvenile) Penguin Group (USA) Inc.

Joyce, William. George Shrinks. 2003. (ps-2). lib. bdg. 15.30 (978-0-613-89298-8(4)) Tandem Library Bks.

—The Leaf Men & the Brave Good Bugs. Joyce, William, illus. 2001. (Harper Trophy Bks.). (Illus.). 40p. (J). (ps-3). reprint ed. pap. 7.99 (978-0-06-443817-9(1) , Harper Trophy) HarperCollins Pubs.

Jubert, Hervé. Dance of the Assassins. Bell, Anthea, tr. from FRE. 2005. (Devil's Dances Trilogy Ser.: Bk. 1). 400p. (J). (gr. 9 up). lib. bdg. 17.89 (978-0-06-077718-0(4)) HarperCollins Pubs.

—Devil's Tango. Bell, Anthea, tr. from FRE. 2006. (Devil's Dances Trilogy Ser.). 384p. (J). (gr. 7 up). 16.99 (978-0-06-077720-3(6) , Eos); lib. bdg. 17.89 (978-0-06-077721-0(4)) HarperCollins Pubs.

Juckes, Deborah Sioux. Meesha, Guardian of Grand Mountain: Book One of the Guardian Series. McCleary, Twila, illus. 2005. (YA). 18.95 (978-0-9767748-1-5(X)) Red Earth Publishing.

Judal. Vampire Game, 12, 5. Hiroe, Ikoi, tr. from JPN. rev. ed. 2004. (Graphic Novel-Manga Ser.). (Illus.). 192p. (YA). pap. 9.99 (978-1-59182-557-9(1) , Tokyopop Adult) TOKYOPOP, Inc.

—Vampire Game, 3 vols. rev. ed. 2003. (Graphic Novel-Manga Ser.). (Illus.). 192p. Vol. 2. (gr. 8 up). pap. 9.99 (978-1-59182-370-4(6)); Vol. 3. pap. 9.99 (978-1-59182-371-1(4)) TOKYOPOP, Inc. (Tokyopop Adult).

—Vampire Game, 12 vols., Vol. 6. Hiroe, Ikoi, tr. from JPN. rev. ed. 2004. (Graphic Novel-Manga Ser.). (Illus.). 192p. pap. 9.99 (978-1-59182-558-6(X) , Tokyopop Adult) TOKYOPOP, Inc.

—Vampire Game, 12 vols., Vol. 7. Coffman, Patrick, tr. from JPN. rev. ed. 2004. (Graphic Novel-Manga Ser.). (Illus.). 192p. pap. 9.99 (978-1-59182-559-3(8) , Tokyopop Adult) TOKYOPOP, Inc.

Julian, B. T. Mirror Me This. 2006. 172p. per. 12.95 (978-1-59886-056-6(9)) Tate Publishing & Enterprises, L.L.C.

Jumanji. 1999. (J). 9.95 (978-1-56137-331-4(1)) Novel Units, Inc.

Just, Rick. Wizard Chase. 2000. 296p. (J). (gr. 5 up). pap. 13.95 (978-0-9653539-5-3(8)) Cedar Creek Pr.

Juster, Norton. The Phantom Tollbooth. 2003. (Illus.). (J). mass mkt. 5.99 (978-0-440-23808-9(0) , Laurel) Dell Publishing.

—Phantom Toolbooth. Feiffer, Jules, illus. 256p. (J). pap. 4.99 (978-0-8072-1400-8(0) , Listening Library) Random Hse. Audio Publishing Group.

Kaaberbol, Lene. The Serpent Gift. 3rd ed. 2007. (Shamer Chronicles Ser.). Orig. Title: Slangens Gave. 377p. (J). pap. 9.95 (***978-0-8050-8655-3(2)*** , Holt, Henry & Co. Bks. For Young Readers) Holt, Henry & Co.

—The Shamer's Daughter. (Shamer Chronicles Ser.). 240p. (J). 2006. pap. 7.95 (978-0-8050-8111-4(9)); 2004. (Illus.). 16.95 (978-0-8050-7541-0(0)) Holt, Henry & Co. (Holt, Henry & Co. Bks. For Young Readers).

Kaaberbol, Lene. The Shamer's Signet. 2nd rev. ed. (Shamer Chronicles Ser.). 320p. 2007. (YA). pap. 8.95 (***978-0-8050-8217-3(4));*** 2005. (J). 16.95 (978-0-8050-7542-7(9)) Holt, Henry & Co. (Holt, Henry & Co. Bks. For Young Readers).

Kadokawa. Steel Angel Kurumi, Vol. 3. 2004. 172p. pap. (978-1-4139-0013-2(5)) ADV Manga.

Kaesshaefer, Charles. The Lost Princess. 2004. (J). mass mkt. 10.00 (978-0-9744407-0-5(1)) Shelbykay Pubilshing Co.

Kahn, J. Le Retour du Jedi, Vol. II.Tr. of Return of the Jedi. (FRE.). (J). pap. 11.95 (978-2-265-06728-8(8)) Fleuve Noir FRA. *Dist:* Distribooks, Inc.

Kaishaku. Steel Angel Kurumi. 2004. Vol. 5. (Illus.). 176p. (YA). pap. (978-1-4139-0078-1(X)); Vol. 6. 192p. pap. (978-1-4139-0099-6(2)); Vol. 8. 184p. pap. (978-1-4139-0152-8(2)) ADV Manga.

Kaisyaku. Steel Angel Kurumi, Vol. 1. 2003. 176p. pap. (978-1-4139-0011-8(9)) ADV Manga.

—Steel Angel Kurumi, Vol. 2. Bertrand, Kay, tr. from JPN. 2004. (Illus.). 172p. (YA). pap. (978-1-4139-0012-5(7)) ADV Manga.

—Steel Angel Kurumi. 2004. (Illus.). (YA). Vol. 7. 180p. pap. (978-1-4139-0117-7(4)); Vol. 9. 188p. pap. (978-1-4139-0153-5(0)) ADV Manga.

Kanan. Galaxy Angel Party, Vol. 1. 2005. (Galaxy Angel Ser.). Orig. Title: Galaxy Angel Anthology. (Illus.). 208p. pap. 9.99 (978-1-932480-26-9(9) , Broccoli Bks.) Broccoli International USA, Inc.

Kane, James. Ellie's Magic Kingdom. 2005. 73p. pap. 14.95 (978-1-4137-6420-8(7)) PublishAmerica, Inc.

Kaneko, Shinya. Culdcept, Vol. 3. 3rd rev. ed. 2004. (Illus.). pap. 9.99 (978-1-59182-954-6(2) , Tokyopop Adult) TOKYOPOP, Inc.

—Culdcept, Vol. 4. Kaneko, Shinya, illus. rev. ed. 2005. (Illus.). 234p. pap. 9.99 (978-1-59532-447-4(X) , Tokyopop Adult) TOKYOPOP, Inc.

Kaneko, Shinya, creator. Culdcept, Vol. 2. rev. ed. 2004. (Illus.). 210p. pap. 9.99 (978-1-59182-783-2(3) , Tokyopop Adult) TOKYOPOP, Inc.

Kanemaki, Tomoco. Kingdom Hearts: Darkness Within. Disney Press Staff, ed. Amano, Shiro, illus. 2nd rev. ed. 2008. 224p. (J). (gr. 4-7). pap. 5.99 (***978-1-4231-0396-7(3))*** Disney Pr.

—Kingdom Hearts: The First Door. Disney Press Staff, ed. Amano, Shiro, illus. 2008. 224p. (J). (gr. 4-7). pap. 5.99 (***978-1-4231-0395-0(5))*** Disney Pr.

Kang Won, Kim, illus. & creator. The Queen's Knight. Kang Won, Kim, creator. 2005. Vol. 3. 3rd rev. ed. pap. 9.99 (978-1-59532-259-3(0)); Vol. 4. rev. ed. 208p. pap. 9.99 (978-1-59532-260-9(4)) TOKYOPOP, Inc. (Tokyopop Kids).

Kanietzko, Bryan. Avatar Volume 6. 2007. 192p. pap. 7.99 (***978-1-59816-930-0(0)*** , Tokyopop Kids) TOKYOPOP, Inc.

Kanietzko, Bryan & Dimartino, Michael Dante. Avatar. 2007. (Illus.). pap. 7.99 (***978-1-59816-929-4(7));*** 96p. pap. 7.99 (***978-1-59816-928-7(9))*** TOKYOPOP, Inc. (Tokyopop Kids).

Kanzaka, Hajime & Yoshinaka, Shoko. Slayers Super-Explosive Demon Story 4: Return, Vol. 4. 2004. Orig. Title: Slayers: Super Explosive Magic Story Book 4. (Illus.). 136p. pap. 9.99 (978-1-58664-914-2(0) , CMX 64604G, CPM Manga) Central Park Media Corp.

Karandeev, Oleg. Dmitri: The Kind Storyteller Book One of Five. Ciesinska, Izabela, illus. 2006. 76p. (YA). per. 15.95 (***978-0-9785728-9-1(0))*** Entry Way Marketing & Publishing.

Karesh, Tracy Ann. Brave Little Soldier. 2005. (J). pap. 15.00 (978-0-8059-6742-5(7)) Dorrance Publishing Co., Inc.

Karlskin, Lisa. Pepino. 2001. (J). pap. 8.00 (978-0-8059-5243-8(8)) Dorrance Publishing Co., Inc.

Kasamatsu, Shiro. Inch-High Samurai. 2000. (Kodansha Children's Bilingual Classics Ser.). (Illus.). 48p. (gr. 4-7). 9.95 (978-4-7700-2101-4(1)) Kodansha International JPN. *Dist:* Oxford Univ. Pr., Inc.

Kastigar, Jessica. The King of Hearts. 2006. 49p. pap. 12.95 (978-1-4241-3875-3(2)) PublishAmerica, Inc.

Katsura, Masakazu. Off-Line. Katsura, Masakazu, illus. 2nd ed. 2004. (Video Girl Ai Ser.). 200p. (YA). pap. 9.99 (978-1-59116-104-2(5)) Viz Media.

—Recall Vol. 3. Katsura, Masakazu, illus. 2nd ed. 2004. (Video Girl Ai Ser.). 184p. (YA). pap. 9.99 (978-1-59116-103-5(7)) Viz Media.

—Shadow Lady: The Awakening. 2000. (Illus.). 184p. (gr. 11 up). pap. 15.95 (978-1-56971-446-1(0)) Dark Horse Comics.

—Spinoff, Vol. 5. Katsura, Masakazu, illus. 2004. (Video Girl Ai Ser.). (Illus.). 200p. (YA). pap. 9.99 (978-1-59116-146-2(0)) Viz Media.

Katz, Alan & Slack, Michael. The Flim-Flam Fairies. 2008. (Illus.). 32p. (J). 14.95 (***978-0-7624-2996-7(8)*** , Running Pr. Kids) Running Pr. Bk. Pubs.

Katz, S. Natives. 2002. (Larbu & Tia Adventures Ser.). (Illus.). 88p. (YA). (gr. 2-10). pap. 16.00 (978-0-9648834-1-3(4)) Really Alive Bks.

Katz, Welwyn W. False Face. 2001. 155p. (J). (gr. 5-9). pap. 5.95 (978-0-88899-082-2(0)) Groundwood Bks. CAN. *Dist:* Perseus Distribution.

—The Third Magic. 2nd ed. 2000. (Illus.). 218p. (J). (gr. 4-7). pap. 6.95 (978-0-88899-385-4(4) , Libros Tigrillo) Groundwood Bks. CAN. *Dist:* Perseus Distribution.

Kaufman, Dan. Red Flags & Pixies. 2004. 81p. pap. 14.95 (978-1-4137-0244-6(9)) PublishAmerica, Inc.

Kavanagh, Terry & Felder, James. Rise of Apocalypse. Pollina, Adam & Morales, Mark, illus. 1998. 160p. (J). (gr. 5-12). pap. 15.99 (978-0-7851-0586-2(7)) Marvel Enterprises, Inc.

Kawahara, Yumiko. Dolls, 1. Kawahara, Yumiko, illus. 2004. (Dolls Ser.). (Illus.). 200p. (YA). pap. 9.99 (978-1-59116-508-8(3)) Viz Media.

Kay, Elizabeth. Divide. 2007. 320p. (J). pap. 6.99 (***978-0-439-54343-9(6)*** , Chicken Hse., The) Scholastic, Inc.

Kay, Elizabeth, et al. The Divide. 2003. 320p. (J). (gr. 3-6). pap. 15.95 (978-0-439-45696-8(7) , Chicken Hse., The) Scholastic, Inc.

Kaye, David. Dream Catcher. 2000. 32p. (J). pap. 7.00 (978-1-58193-186-0(7)) Brown Bag Productions.

Kaye, Steven. The Narrow Road. 2002. 341p. per. 15.95 (978-0-9674467-1-4(6)) Creative Passages, Inc.

Kazenbroot, Nelly. Down the Chimney with Googol & Googolplex. Kazenbroot, Nelly, illus. 2004. (Orca Echoes Ser.). (Illus.). 64p. (J). (gr. 2-3). pap. 4.99 (978-1-55143-290-8(0) , 1234537) Orca Bk. Pubs. USA.

Keegan, Shannon. Legend of the Sea Fairies. 2006. (J). per. 14.99 (978-0-9773433-0-0(8)) Bixie Gate Publishing.

Kellogg, Steven. The Island of the Skog. Kellogg, Steven, illus. 2002. (Illus.). (J). 14.04 (978-0-7587-2870-8(0)) Book Wholesalers, Inc.

Kelly, Joe. Golden Perfect. rev. ed. 2003. (Justice League Adventures Ser.: Vol. 10). (Illus.). 128p. pap. 14.99 (978-1-56389-941-6(8)) DC Comics.

—Justice League Elite, Vol. 1. rev. ed. 2005. (Illus.). 208p. pap. 19.99 (978-1-4012-0481-5(3)) DC Comics.

Kenah, Katharine & Lithgow, John. Pockets That Hop, Level 4: An Animal Adventure. 2005. (Lithgow Palooza Readers Ser.). (Illus.). 32p. (J). (gr. 2-3). pap. 3.95 (978-0-7696-4274-1(8)) School Specialty Publishing.

Kendall, Carol. The Gammage Cup. Blegvad, Erik, illus. 2000. (Carol Kendall's Tales of the Minnipins Ser.). 288p. (YA). (gr. 3-7). pap. 6.95 (978-0-15-202493-2(X) , Odyssey Classics) Harcourt Children's Bks.

—The Gammage Cup. 2000. (YA). pap. 51.25 incl. audio (978-0-7887-4333-7(3) , 41128) Recorded Bks., LLC.

—Gammage Cup. 2000. (gr. 3-6). lib. bdg. 14.15 (978-0-613-57213-2(0)) Tandem Library Bks.

—The Whisper of Glocken. Gobbato, Imero, illus. 2000. (Carol Kendall's Tales of the Minnipins Ser.). 320p. (Orig.). (YA). (gr. 3-7). pap. 6.00 (978-0-15-202517-5(0) , Odyssey Classics) Harcourt Children's Bks.

—Whisper of Glocken. 2000. (978-0-606-18196-9(2)); (gr. 3-6). lib. bdg. 14.15 (978-0-613-27550-7(0)) Tandem Library Bks.

Kendall, Cassie. Laurel. 1999. (Stardust Classics). (J). 16.95 (978-1-889514-22-2(5)) Dolls Corp.

Kendrick, Rosalyn. Bride of the Nile. 1998. 176p. (YA). (gr. 9 up). pap. 6.95 (978-0-86327-622-4(9)) Wolfhound Pr. IRL. *Dist:* Irish American Bk. Co.

Kennedy Tosten, S. Troy's Amazing Universe: A for Aliens. 2005. 124p. pap. 12.95 (978-1-59113-672-9(5)) Booklocker.com, Inc.

Kenner, Julie, et al. Fendi, Ferragamo, & Fangs. 2007. 288p. (YA). (gr. 6 up). pap. 9.99 (***978-0-425-21539-5(3)*** , Berkley Trade) Penguin Group (USA) Inc.

Kernaghan, Eileen. The Alchemist's Daughter. 2005. (Illus.). 192p. (YA). pap. 13.95 (978-1-894345-79-8(7)) Thistledown Pr., Ltd. CAN. *Dist:* Literary Pr. Group of Canada.

—The Snow Queen. 2005. 160p. mass mkt. 12.95 (978-1-894345-14-9(2)) Thistledown Pr., Ltd. CAN. *Dist:* Literary Pr. Group of Canada.

Kerr, Katharine. The Black Raven. 1999. (Dragon Mage Ser.: Bk. 2). (gr. 7-12). lib. bdg. 15.30 (978-0-613-63018-4(1)) Tandem Library Bks.

Kerr, P. B. The Akhenaten Adventure. 2005. (Children of the Lamp Ser.: 1). (Illus.). 384p. mass mkt. 2.99 (978-0-439-77135-1(8)) Scholastic, Inc.

—Blue Djinn of Baby. 2006. (Children of the Lamp Ser.: No. 2). 384p. (J). pap. 6.99 (978-0-439-67022-7(5)) Scholastic, Inc.

—The Blue Djinn of Babylon. 2006. (Children of the Lamp Ser.: Bk. 2). 384p. (J). (gr. 4-7). pap. 16.99 (978-0-439-67021-0(7) , Orchard Bks.) Scholastic, Inc.

Kessler, Liz. Emily Windsnap & the Monster from the Deep. Gibb, Sarah, illus. 2006. (Emily Windsnap Ser.). 224p. (J). (gr. 3-7). 15.99 (978-0-7636-2504-7(3)) Candlewick Pr.

—The Tail of Emily Windsnap. Gibb, Sarah, illus. (Emily Windsnap Ser.). 224p. (J). (gr. 3-7). 2004. 15.99 (978-0-7636-2483-5(7)); 2006. reprint ed. 5.99 (978-0-7636-2811-6(5)) Candlewick Pr.

Keyes, Pamela. Legend of Zamiel Zimbalist: Book Two of the Connedim Series. 2005. 280p. (YA). pap. 14.99 (978-1-59092-062-6(7) , Blue Works) Windstorm Creative.

—Rune of Zachary Zimbalist: Book One of the Connedim Series. 2005. 280p. (YA). pap. 14.99 (978-1-59092-131-9(3) , Blue Works) Windstorm Creative.

Kikuchi, Hideyuki. Azumanga Daioh Vol. 4: The Manga. 2004. (Illus.). 198p. (YA). pap. (978-1-4139-0048-4(8)) ADV Manga.

—Steel Angel Kurumi, Vol. 4. 2004. 172p. pap. (978-1-4139-0059-0(3)) ADV Manga.

Kilworth, Garry. Attica. 2006. 352p. (YA). pap. 17.95 (***978-1-904233-81-7(3))*** Little, Brown Bk. Group Ltd. GBR. *Dist:* Independent Pubs. Group.

Kilworth, Garry. The Castle Storm. 1998. (Welkin Weasels Ser.: No. 2). 388p. (YA). (gr. 9). pap. 11.99 (978-0-552-54547-1(3) , Corgi) Transworld Publishers Ltd. GBR. *Dist:* Independent Pubs. Group.

Kim, Kang Won. The Queen's Knight, 14 vols. 2004. (Illus.). pap. 9.99 (978-1-59532-257-9(4) , Tokyopop Kids) TOKYOPOP, Inc.

Kim, Mi-Kyung. 11th Cat, Vol. 2. 2006. (Illus.). 200p. (YA). pap. 10.95 (***978-89-527-4473-9(X))*** ICE Kunion KOR. *Dist:* Diamond Bk. Distributors.

—11th Cat, Vol. 3. 2006. (Illus.). 200p. (YA). pap. 10.95 (***978-89-527-4481-4(0))*** ICE Kunion KOR. *Dist:* Diamond Bk. Distributors.

—11th Cat, Vol. 4. 2006. (Illus.). 200p. (YA). pap. 10.95 (***978-89-527-4500-2(0))*** ICE Kunion KOR. *Dist:* Diamond Bk. Distributors.

Kim, Mikyung. 11th Cat: Vol. 1. 2005. (Illus.). 180p. (YA). pap. 10.95 (978-89-527-4461-6(6)) Diamond Bk. Distributors.

Kim, Raeshin. The Legend of Goo-Shu: Journal 1. 2003. (Illus.). 179p. (YA). per. 17.95 net. (978-0-9743775-0-6(3)) RK Enterprises, Inc.

Kim, Wu-kyung. Su-il vs. Su-il. Park, Jung-eun, tr. from KOR. Kwon, Sawoo, illus. 2005. 164p. (J). pap. 20.00 (978-0-89581-839-3(6)) Jain Publishing Company, Inc.

Kindergarden: El Jardin del Arco Iris, 3 vols. 2002. Tr. of Kindergarden: El Jardin del Arco Iris. (SPA., Illus.). 192p. 50.00 incl. audio compact disk (978-84-494-2025-2(3) , GML07104-186055) Oceano Grupo Editoria, S.A. ESP. *Dist:* Thomson Gale.

Kinefield, David. Little Angel. Lawson, Peter, illus. 2004. 12p. (J). bds. 5.99 (978-0-689-86734-7(4) , Little Simon) Simon & Schuster Children's Publishing.

King, J. R. Arianna Kelt & the Wizards of Skyhall. 2006. (Illus.). (J). 200p. pap. 11.95 (978-1-57545-115-2(8)); 148p. per. 18.95 (978-1-57545-106-0(9) , Reagent Pr. Echo) Reagent Pr.

King-Smith, Dick. The Merman. unabr. ed. 2004. 102p. (J). (gr. 3-7). pap. 29.00 incl. audio (978-0-8072-8132-1(8) , Listening Library) Random Hse. Audio Publishing Group.

—The Merman. 2001. (J). (978-0-606-21328-8(7)) Tandem Library Bks.

—Water Horse. 2000. (gr. 3-6). lib. bdg. 13.00 (978-0-613-24003-1(0)) Tandem Library Bks.

King, Steve. The Stone Dragon. 2005. 80p. pap. 14.95 (978-1-4137-9628-5(1)) PublishAmerica, Inc.

Kingfisher Editors, ed. Marvelous Magical Stories. 2007. (Super Shorts Ser.). 160p. (J). (gr. k-3). pap. 6.95 (978-0-7534-6072-6(6) , Kingfisher) Houghton Mifflin Co. Trade & Reference Div.

Kingsley, Kaza. Erec Rex: The Dragon's Eye. Payne, John, ed. 2007. 343p. (J). pap. 9.99 (***978-0-9786555-3-2(2))*** Firelight Press, Inc.

—Erec Rex: The Dragon's Eye. Payne, John, ed. Grant, Melvyn, illus. 2006. 360p. (J). 17.99 (978-0-9786555-6-3(7)) Firelight Press, Inc.

Kingsley, Kaza. Erec Rex: The Monsters of Otherness. Payne, John, ed. 2007. 350p. (J). 18.99 (***978-0-9786555-7-0(5))*** Firelight Press, Inc.

Kiriga, Yuki. Di Gi Charat Theater: Dejiko's Adventure, Volume 1. Kiriga, Yuki, illus. 2004. (Di Gi Charat Theater Ser.). Orig. Title: Dejiko's Adventure. (Illus.). 192p. (YA). pap. 9.99 (978-1-932480-14-6(5) , Broccoli Bks. Deluxe) Broccoli International USA, Inc.

Kirkman, Robert. Marvel Knights 2099. 2005. (Marvel Heroes Ser.). (Illus.). 120p. (YA). pap. 13.99 (978-0-7851-1613-4(3)) Marvel Enterprises, Inc.

Kirkpatrick, Katherine. Trouble's Daughter: The Story of Susanna Hutchinson, Indian Captive. 2000. (978-0-606-17896-9(1)) Tandem Library Bks.

Kiser, Kevin. Buzzy Widget. O'Brien, John, illus. 1999. (Accelerated Reader Bks.). 32p. (J). (gr. k-3). 15.95 (978-0-7614-5057-3(2) , Cavendish Children's Bks.) Cavendish, Marshall Corp.

Kishimoto, Masashi. Naruto. Kishimoto, Masashi, illus. 2004. (Naruto Ser.). (Illus.). 200p. (YA). Vol. 4. pap. 7.95 (978-1-59116-358-9(7)); Vol. 5. pap. 7.95 (978-1-59116-359-6(5)) Viz Media.

Kishiro, Yukito. Angel of the Innocents, Vol. 2. 2003. (Battle Angel Alita Last Order Ser.). (Illus.). 208p. (YA). pap. 9.95 (978-1-56931-976-5(6)) Viz Media.

Kitamura, Satoshi. Stone Age Boy. Kitamura, Satoshi, illus. 2007. (Illus.). 40p. (J). (ps-3). 15.99 ***(978-0-7636-3474-2(3))*** Candlewick Pr.

Kitamura, Satoshi. Yo y Mi Gato? (Los Especiales de A la Orilla Del Viento Ser.). (SPA., Illus.). 36p. (J). (gr. k-3). 13.99 (978-968-16-6234-9(2) , FC30958) Fondo de Cultura Economica USA.

Kitoh, Mohiro. Nothing but Truth. 2003. (Shadow Star Ser.: Vol. 4). (Illus.). 160p. (YA). (gr. 8 up). pap. 14.95 (978-1-56971-920-6(9)) Dark Horse Comics.

Kladstrup, Kristin. The Book of Story Beginnings. 2006. 368p. (J). (gr. 5-8). 15.99 (978-0-7636-2609-9(0)) Candlewick Pr.

Klett, David E. Rachel & the Wizard of Lake Lure: The Lake Lure Chronicles - Book 2. 2006. (J). lib. bdg. 17.95 ***(*978-0-9779325-1-1(6))*** Five Oaks Pr.

Kline, Suzy. Horrible Harry & the Green Slime. Remkiewicz, Frank, illus. 1998. (Horrible Harry Ser.: No. 3). 64p. (gr. 2-4). pap. 3.99 (978-0-14-038970-8(9) , Puffin) Penguin Group (USA) Inc.

—Horrible Harry & the Mud Gremlins. Remkiewicz, Frank, illus. 2004. 64p. (J). (gr. 2 up). pap. 3.99 (978-0-14-240123-1(4) , Puffin) Penguin Group (USA) Inc.

—Orp. 1999. (978-0-606-17423-7(0)) Tandem Library Bks.

Kluepfel, Brian. Anatoly of the Gomdars. 2001. 120p. (J). pap. 5.95 (978-0-7891-5516-0(8)); lib. bdg. 11.95 (978-0-7569-0296-4(7)) Perfection Learning Corp.

Kluger, Jeffrey. Nacky Patcher & the Curse of the Dry-Land Boats. Elliot, David, illus. 2007. 384p. (YA). (gr. 4 up). 18.99 (978-0-399-24604-3(5) , Philomel) Penguin Group (USA) Inc.

K.M. Mohr, John Kelley and. Waking Dalifi. 2005. 72p. pap. 9.95 (978-1-4116-6364-0(0)) Lulu.com.

Knaak, Richard A. & Kim, Jae-Hwan. Warcraft Vol. 1: Dragon Hunt : SAT/ACT Vocabulary-Building Manga. 2007. (Kaplan SAT/ACT Score-Raising Manga Ser.). 160p. pap. 9.99 ***(*978-1-4277-5495-0(0))*** Kaplan Publishing.

Knight, Caitlyn. Anastasia: the Tapestry of the Silver Unicorns. 2007. 386p. pap. 19.98 ***(*978-0-615-15145-8(0))*** Neugard, S.L.

Knight, Ernest C. Bean Head & the Imagination Machine. l.t. ed. 2002. (Illus.). 42p. per. 12.99 (978-0-9724680-7-7(2)) Lifevest Publishing, Inc.

Knoos, Sara Marie. A Fairy's Tail. Van Eps, Ann, illus. 2002. 29p. (J). (ps-6). pap. 14.99 (978-0-9721276-0-8(7)) Mermaid Utopia, Inc.

Knox, Elizabeth. Dreamhunter. 2006. (Dreamhunter Duet Ser.: Bk. 1). (Illus.). 384p. (YA). (gr. 7 up). 19.00 (978-0-374-31853-6(0)) Farrar, Straus & Giroux.

—Dreamquake. 2007. (Dreamhunter Duet Ser.: Bk. 2). (Illus.). 464p. (YA). (gr. 7 up). 19.00 (978-0-374-31854-3(9)) Farrar, Straus & Giroux.

Knox, Elizabeth. Dreamquake: Book Two of the Dreamhunter Duet. 2007. (Illus.). 449p. (J). ***(*978-1-4287-3321-3(3))*** Farrar, Straus & Giroux.

Koge-Donbo. Di Gi Charat Theater, Vol. 1. 2004. (Illus.). pap. (978-1-932480-25-2(0) , Broccoli Bks.) Broccoli International USA, Inc.

—Di Gi Charat Theater - Dejiko's Summer Vacation. Yamashita, Saki, ed. Hina., illus. 2003. (Di Gi Charat Theater Ser.). 176p. pap. 9.99 (978-1-932480-07-8(2) , Broccoli Bks.) Broccoli International USA, Inc.

—Kamichama Karin, Vol. 5. 5th rev. ed. 2006. pap. 9.99 (978-1-59816-186-1(5) , Tokyopop Kids) TOKYOPOP, Inc.

Koller, Jackie French. The Dragonling, 3 bks., Vol. 1. collector's ed. 2000. (Dragonling Ser.). 224p. (J). (gr. 2-5). pap. 11.95 (978-0-7434-1019-9(X) , Aladdin) Simon & Schuster Children's Publishing.

—The Dragonling. 2000. (J). 12.64 (978-0-606-19872-1(5)) Tandem Library Bks.

Komorn, Julie, adapted by. Out of the Dark. 2004. (W. I. T. C. H. Ser.: Bk. 8). (Illus.). 128p. (J). lib. bdg. 16.92 ***(*978-1-4242-0789-3(4))*** Fitzgerald Bks.

Komorn, Julie & Lenhard, Elizabeth, adapted by. The Light of Meridian. 2004. (W. I. T. C. H. Ser.: Bk. 7). (Illus.). 144p. (J). lib. bdg. 16.92 ***(*978-1-4242-0794-7(0))*** Fitzgerald Bks.

Koontz, Dean. The Paper Doorway: Funny Verse & Nothing Worse. Parks, Phil, illus. 2003. 160p. (J). pap. 9.99 (978-0-06-440984-1(8)) HarperCollins Pubs.

Koralek, Jenny. War Games. 216p. (J). pap. 8.99 (978-1-4052-0074-5(X)) Egmont Bks., Ltd. GBR. *Dist:* Trafalgar Square Publishing.

Kostick, Conor. Saga. 2008. 368p. (YA). (gr. 7). 18.99 ***(*978-0-670-06280-5(4)*** , Viking Juvenile) Penguin Group (USA) Inc.

Kovac, Tommy. Wonderland #1. 2006. (Illus.). 24p. (YA). pap. 3.50 (978-1-59362-039-4(X) , Slave Labor Graphics) Slave Labor Bks.

Kraft, Erik P. Chocolatina. Brunkus, Denise, illus. 2004. 32p. (J). pap. 5.99 (978-0-439-63592-9(6)) Scholastic, Inc.

Krahn, Fernando. La Familia Numerozzi. 2000. (SPA., Illus.). 28p. (J). (ps-3). pap. 6.99 (978-980-257-247-2(0)) Ekare, Ediciones VEN. *Dist:* Kane/Miller Bk. Pubs., Inc., Lectorum Pubns., Inc.

Kress, Adrienne. Alex & the Ironic Gentleman. 2007. 320p. (YA). (gr. 3-7). 16.95 ***(*978-1-60286-005-6(X))*** Weinstein Bks.

Kret, Itzah C. The Man with the Sneezes. 2003. per. 16.99 (978-1-4134-2895-7(9)) Xlibris Corp.

Kretzer-Malvehy, Terry. Passage to Little Bighorn. 1999. (978-0-606-18313-0(2)) Tandem Library Bks.

Krohn, Genendel. I Wish I Were a King. Pelleg, Tirtsa, illus. 50p. 13.95 (978-1-58330-590-4(4)) Feldheim Pubs.

Krulik, Nancy E. Katie Kazoo, Switcheroo Keepsake, Set. 2005. (Katie Kazoo, Switcheroo Ser.). 80p. (J). lthr. 19.96 (978-0-448-43978-5(6) , Grosset & Dunlap) Penguin Group (USA) Inc.

—My Pops Is Tops!, No. 25. John and Wendy Staff, illus. 2007. (Katie Kazoo, Switcheroo Ser.: No. 25). 80p. (J). pap. 3.99 (978-0-448-44441-3(0) , Grosset & Dunlap) Penguin Group (USA) Inc.

Krulik, Nancy E. Super Special on Thin Ice. John and Wendy Staff, illus. 2007. (Katie Kazoo, Switcheroo Ser.). 160p. (J). (gr. 2-5). pap. 4.99 ***(*978-0-448-44447-5(X)*** , Grosset & Dunlap) Penguin Group (USA) Inc.

Kuehl, Karen. Hickson. 2004. 125p. pap. 17.95 (978-1-4137-3772-1(2)) PublishAmerica, Inc.

Kumakura, Yuichi. Jing, 7 vols., Vol. 3. Kumakura, Yuichi, illus. 3rd rev. ed. 2003. (Illus.). 216p. pap. 9.99 (978-1-59182-178-6(9) , Tokyopop Kids) TOKYOPOP, Inc.

—Jing Vol. 6: King of Bandits, 7 vols. rev. ed. 2004. (Illus.). 216p. pap. 9.99 (978-1-59182-467-1(2) , Tokyopop Kids) TOKYOPOP, Inc.

—Jing Vol. 6: King of Bandits, 7 vols. Kumakura, Yuichi, illus. rev. ed. 2004. (Illus.). Vol. 4. 216p. pap. 9.99 (978-1-59182-179-3(7)); Vol. 5. 192p. pap. 9.99 (978-1-59182-466-4(4)) TOKYOPOP, Inc. (Tokyopop Kids).

Kunhardt, Dorothy, ed. Pinocchio. deluxe ed. 1999. (J). 100.00 (978-1-55709-341-7(5)) Applewood Bks.

Kupperberg, Paul. Superman's World of Krypton. 2001. (Illus.). 32p. (J). (gr. 3 up). pap. 14.95 (978-0-312-49017-1(8) , Priddy Bks.) St. Martin's Pr.

Kuroda, Yosuke & Hayashiya, Shizuru. Onegai Teacher. 2003. No. 2. 120p. pap. 9.95 (978-1-58899-179-9(2)); Vol. 1. (Illus.). 200p. (YA). 9.95 (978-1-58899-196-6(2)) ComicsOne Corp./Dr. Masters.

Kurty, G. Thomas the Treemaker: a Short Story about a Tall Tale. 2007. (ENG.). 76p. per. 14.95 ***(*978-1-4241-6219-2(X))*** PublishAmerica, Inc.

Kurumada, Masami. Knights of the Zodiac. Kurumada, Masami, illus. (Knights of the Zodiac (Saint Seiya) Ser.). 200p. (YA). 2004. (Illus.). pap. 7.95 (978-1-59116-525-5(3)); Vol. 5. 2004. pap. 7.95 (978-1-59116-470-8(2)); Vol. 7. 2005. (Illus.). pap. 7.95 (978-1-59116-616-0(0)) Viz Media.

—Knights of the Zodiac, Vol. 17. 2006. (Knights of the Zodiac Ser.). 208p. (YA). pap. 7.95 (978-1-4215-0660-9(2)) Viz Media.

Kusaka, Hidenori. Pokemon Yellow Caballero: Blue Returns. MATO Staff, illus. 2002. (Pokemon Adventures Ser.). 54p. (YA). (gr. 4-7). pap. 4.95 (978-1-56931-564-4(7)) Viz Media.

—Pokemon Yellow Caballero: The Gym Leader's Alliance. MATO Staff, illus. 2002. (Pokemon Adventures Ser.). 53p. (YA). (gr. 4-7). pap. 4.95 (978-1-56931-563-7(9)) Viz Media.

—Saffron City Siege. MATO Staff, illus. 2001. (Pokemon Adventures Ser.: Vol. 3). 224p. (YA). (gr. 4-7). pap. 13.95 (978-1-56931-560-6(4)) Viz Media.

—Yellow Caballero: Making Waves. MATO Staff, illus. 1999. (Pokemon Adventures Ser.: Vol. 5). 192p. (YA). pap. 13.95 (978-1-59116-027-4(8)) Viz Media.

Kusube, Aya & Toda, Akihito. Onix Underground, Vol. 20. Himeno, Kagemaru, illus. 2001. (Pokemon Tales Ser.: Vol. 20). 18p. (YA). (ps-k). 4.95 (978-1-56931-571-2(X)) Viz Media.

Kusugak, Michael Arvaarluk. Who Wants Rocks? Krykorka, Vladyana Langer, illus. 1999. 24p. (J). (ps-2). lib. bdg. 17.95 (978-1-55037-589-3(X)) Annick Pr., Ltd. CAN. *Dist:* Firefly Bks., Ltd.

—Who Wants Rocks? 1999. (gr. k-3). lib. bdg. 15.25 (978-0-613-27556-9(X)) Tandem Library Bks.

Kusunoki, Kei & Ohashi, Kaoru. Diabolo. 2004. (Graphic Novel-Manga Ser.). (Illus.). 208p. pap. 9.99 (978-1-59532-232-6(9)); Vol. 2. 192p. pap. 9.99 (978-1-59532-233-3(7)) TOKYOPOP, Inc. (Tokyopop Adult).

Kuyper, Sjoerd & Crampton, Patricia. The Swan's Child. Jutte, Jan, illus. 2005. 128p. (J). 16.95 (978-0-8234-1861-9(8)) Holiday Hse., Inc.

Kyber, Manifred. Fables & Fairytales to Delight All Ages Book Two: Gossamer Kingdoms. 2007. 140p. per. ***(*978-1-84401-985-4(3))*** Athena Pr.

Kyung-ah, Choi, illus. & creator. Snow Drop. Kyung-ah, Choi, creator. 2005. Vol. 8. rev. ed. 208p. pap. 9.99 (978-1-59532-044-5(X)); Vol. 9. 9th rev. ed. 192p. pap. 9.99 (978-1-59532-045-2(8)) TOKYOPOP, Inc. (Tokyopop Adult).

La Fevers, R. L. The True Blade of Power. 2006. (Lowthar's Blade Ser.: Bk. 3). 160p. (J). (gr. 2). pap. 5.99 (978-0-14-240559-8(0) , Puffin) Penguin Group (USA) Inc.

La Fevers, Robin. The Forging of the Blade. 2006. (Lowthar's Blade Ser.: Bk. 1). 144p. (J). (gr. 2). pap. 5.99 (978-0-14-240557-4(4) , Puffin) Penguin Group (USA) Inc.

—The True Blade of Power. 2005. (Lowthar's Blade Ser.: No. 3). (Illus.). 128p. (J). (gr. 2-5). 15.99 (978-0-525-47431-9(5) , Dutton Juvenile) Penguin Group (USA) Inc.

Lachtman, Ofelia Dumas. The Truth about las Mariposas. 2007. 144p. (YA). (gr. 6 up). pap. 9.95 ***(*978-1-55885-494-9(0)*** , Piñata Books) Arte Publico Pr.

Lackey, Mercedes. The Black Swan. 1999. (gr. 7-12). lib. bdg. 15.30 (978-0-613-27746-4(5)) Tandem Library Bks.

—Take a Thief. 2002. (Heralds of Valdemar Ser.). (gr. 7-12). lib. bdg. 15.30 (978-0-613-63081-8(5)) Tandem Library Bks.

Lacy, Kendra. The Stone Garden. 2004. 72p. (YA). pap. 8.95 (978-0-595-30719-7(1)) iUniverse, Inc.

Lagerlof, Selma. The Wonderful Adventures of Nils. 2004. reprint ed. pap. 34.95 (978-1-4191-8845-9(3)); pap. 1.99 (978-1-4192-8845-6(8)) Kessinger Publishing, LLC.

LaHaye, Tim & Jenkins, Jerry B. Apollyon: The Destroyer Is Unleashed. 1999. (Left Behind Ser.: Bk. 5). (gr. 7-12). lib. bdg. 24.60 (978-0-613-23100-8(7)) Tandem Library Bks.

—Attack of Apollyon: Revenge of the Locusts. 2002. (Left Behind Ser.: Bk. 19). (gr. 5-8). lib. bdg. 14.15 (978-0-613-57388-7(9)) Tandem Library Bks.

—The Remnant: On the Brink of Armageddon. 2002. (Left Behind Ser.: Bk. 10). (gr. 7-12). lib. bdg. 24.60 (978-0-613-59820-0(2)) Tandem Library Bks.

Laird, Christa. But Can the Phoenix Sing? 1998. (978-0-606-13232-9(5)) Tandem Library Bks.

Lake, A. J. The Coming of Dragons. 2006. (Darkest Age Ser.: Bk. 1). (Illus.). 250p. (J). 16.95 (978-1-58234-965-7(7) , Bloomsbury Children) Bloomsbury Publishing.

—The Coming of Dragons Bk. 1: Darkest Age I. 2007. (Illus.). 240p. (YA). pap. 6.95 (978-1-58234-902-2(9) , Bloomsbury Children) Bloomsbury Publishing.

Lakeshore Learning Materials Staff, contrib. by. Jack & the Beanstalk Packet. 2000. (J). pap. 19.95 (978-1-929255-29-0(2)) Lakeshore Learning Materials.

—Rumpelstiltskin Packet. 2000. (J). pap. 19.95 (978-1-929255-27-6(6)) Lakeshore Learning Materials.

Lambrou, M. A. Kokos. WWWWings: Anything Is Possible When You Believe. 2004. 128p. pap. 9.95 (978-1-932047-16-5(6) , Llumina Pr.) Media Creations, Inc.

Lamere, Jill. The King's Crown. 2007. (Illus.). 5p. (J). 14.95 ***(*978-0-9772320-2-4(6))*** Minikin Pr.

Lamont, Jess. Peter's Garden. 2003. 230p. (YA). pap. 14.95 (978-0-9740319-0-3(9)) Added Upon, Inc.

Lampman, Annette. Nicole's Wish. 2006. 23.00 ***(*978-0-8059-9146-8(8))*** Dorrance Publishing Co., Inc.

Lancaster, Janie. Julie & the Lost Fairy Tale. 2006. (Illus.). 116p. (J). per. 10.95 ***(*978-1-932993-60-8(6))*** Star Publish LLC.

Lancaster, Susan. Caves & the Skull. 2003. (gr. 7-12). lib. bdg. 22.20 (978-0-613-83368-4(6)) Tandem Library Bks.

Land of Dawny Dusk: Fruit. 2003. (978-0-9720334-0-4(8)) Nicewood Imagined.

Land of the Dawny Dusk: Seashell. 2003. (978-0-9720334-1-1(6)) Nicewood Imagined.

Landis, Leanne. A Curious Breeze. 2002. 32p. (J). (ps-5). pap. 12.95 (978-0-9723707-0-7(6) , CBPB01) White Door Publishing.

Landry, Leo. The Snow Ghosts. Landry, Leo, illus. 2003. (Illus.). 32p. (J). (ps-3). tchr. ed. 9.95 (978-0-618-19655-5(2)) Houghton Mifflin Co. Trade & Reference Div.

Landy, Derek. Skulduggery Pleasant. (Skulduggery Pleasant Ser.). (J). 2008. 416p. pap. 7.99 ***(*978-0-06-123117-9(7)*** , Harper Trophy); 2007. 400p. (gr. 3-7). 17.99 ***(*978-0-06-123115-5(0));*** 2007. 400p. (gr. 5 up). lib. bdg. 18.89 ***(*978-0-06-123116-2(9))*** HarperCollins Pubs.

Lang, Andrew. The Lilac Fairy Book. l.t. ed. 2005. 508p. pap. (978-1-84637-149-3(X)) Echo Library.

Lang, Andrew. The Rainbow Fairy Book. 2007. (Illus.). 224p. (J). pap. 12.95 ***(*978-0-486-45455-9(X))*** Dover Pubns., Inc.

Langdon, Mary LaFleur. Pancake Girl. 2003. 37p. pap. 17.95 (978-1-4137-1610-8(5)) PublishAmerica, Inc.

Langley, Kimberley. Another Time. 2004. 187p. pap. 19.95 (978-1-4137-3717-2(X)) PublishAmerica, Inc.

Langlois, Annie. Victorine et la Pièce D'or. Beshwaty, Steve, tr. 2003. (Picture Bks.). (FRE., Illus.). 32p. (J). (ps). pap. (978-2-89021-658-7(6)) Diffusion du livre Mirabel.

Lantz, Francess L. The Day Joanie Frankenhauser Became a Boy. 2005. 208p. (J). (gr. 3-6). 16.99 (978-0-525-47437-1(4) , Dutton Juvenile) Penguin Group (USA) Inc.

Lanza, Barbara. Time to Fly: A Fairy Lane Book. Lanza, Barbara, illus. 2005. (Illus.). 32p. 19.95 (978-0-9724853-7-1(6)) Keene Publishing.

Larry's Adventure (a Carpet Dweller's Tale) 2002. (J). per. 9.97 (978-0-9723929-0-7(4)) MTW Investments.

Larsen, C. S. The Chronicles of Marvin Archibald Trekker: Boy Magician Book 1 - Penguins of Choice. l.t. ed. 2006. (Illus.). 163p. (YA). per. 5.99 (978-0-9779844-1-1(9)) KnowledgeGain Inc.

Larson, Erik. A Force to Be Reckoned With. Larson, Erik, illus. (Savage Dragon Ser.: Vol. 2). (Illus.). 144p. pap. 14.95 (978-1-887279-12-3(1)) Image Comics.

Lascuráin, Anna. Apollo in the Moon House. 2006. Orig. Title: The Moonboy. (J). per. 7.99 (978-0-9769612-3-9(7) , Pixiefire) Darker Intentiona Pr.

Lasky, Kathryn. Guardians of Ga'Hoole #14 Exile. 2008. 224p. pap. 5.99 ***(*978-0-439-88808-0(5)*** , Scholastic Paperbacks) Scholastic, Inc.

—The Hatchling. 2005. (Guardians of Ga'Hoole Ser.: Bk. 7). 222p. (J). (ps-7). per. 12.04 (978-0-606-33802-8(0)) Tandem Library Bks.

—The Journey. 2003. (Guardians of Ga'Hoole Ser.: Bk. 2). 256p. (J). (gr. 3-7). mass mkt. 4.99 (978-0-439-40558-4(0) , Scholastic Paperbacks) Scholastic, Inc.

—The Journey. 2003. (Guardians of Ga'Hoole Ser.: Bk. 2). (J). (gr. 3-6). lib. bdg. 13.00 (978-0-613-72135-6(7)) Tandem Library Bks.

—The Outcast. 2005. (Guardians of Ga'Hoole Ser.: Bk. 8). 209p. (J). (gr. 4-7). per. 12.04 (978-0-606-34177-6(3)) Tandem Library Bks.

Lau, Ding King. Story of the Tao, Vol. 4. 2003. (Illus.). 120p. (YA). (gr. 8 up). pap. 13.95 (978-1-58899-278-9(0)) ComicsOne Corp./Dr. Masters.

Laura & the Leprechauns. 2007. (J). 19.95 ***(*978-0-9795933-0-7(1))*** Chrysalis Pr.

Laurence, Margaret. The Olden Days Coat. Wood, Muriel, illus. 2004. 32p. (J). (gr. 2-5). pap. 8.95 (978-0-88776-704-3(4)) Tundra Bks., Inc./Livres Toundra, Inc. CAN. *Dist:* Random Hse., Inc.

Lawler, Rick. Majesty Blake in Queen of the Trillis. 2001. (J). pap. 8.50 (978-1-930322-02-8(X) , 193032202X) MinRef Pr.

Lawrence, Ann. Between the Forest & the Hills. 1999. (Adventure Library). (Illus.). 264p. (J). (gr. 9-12). reprint ed. pap. 12.95 (978-1-883937-39-3(6) , 39-6) Bethlehem Bks.

Lawrence, David. El Niño Escarabajo. 2004. (SPA.). 32p. (978-84-7720-794-8(1)) Obelisco, Ediciones S.A.

Lawrence, R. R. The Starsword. 2005. 416p. pap. 12.99 (978-0-9742549-0-6(8)) nightwares Bks.

Lawrie, Robin, illus. Fantasy Stories. 2003. (Red Hot Reads Ser.). 256p. (J). (gr. 4-8). pap. 6.95 (978-0-7534-5637-8(0) , Kingfisher) Houghton Mifflin Co. Trade & Reference Div.

Layden, Joseph Lyon. The Other Side of Yore. 2007. 156p. pap. 14.95 ***(*978-1-60145-122-4(9))*** Booklocker.com, Inc.

Layne, Steven L. This Side of Paradise. 2005. 224p. (YA). (gr. 5-9). pap. 9.95 (978-1-58980-254-4(3)) Pelican Publishing Co., Inc.

Layton, Dan. Adventures in the Kingdom, the Dreamer. 2004. 64p. pap. 5.99 (978-0-9707919-4-8(1)) Mercy Place, Inc.

Le Guin, Ursula K. The Beginning Place. 2005. 240p. (YA). 6.99 (978-0-7653-4625-4(7) , Tor Bks.) Doherty, Tom Assocs., LLC.

—Catwings. Schindler, S. D., illus. 1999. (Catwings Ser.: No. 1). 39p. (J). (gr. 1-4). pap. 3.95 (978-0-531-07110-6(3) , Orchard Bks.) Scholastic, Inc.

—Catwings. 2003. (Catwings Ser.: No. 1). (gr. 3-6). lib. bdg. 11.80 (978-0-613-70842-5(3)) Tandem Library Bks.

—Catwings Return. 2003. (Catwings Ser.: No. 2). (gr. 3-6). lib. bdg. 11.80 (978-0-613-65072-4(7)) Tandem Library Bks.

—The Farthest Shore. 2001. (Earthsea Ser.: Vol. 3). (YA). lib. bdg. 13.00 (978-0-613-88305-4(5)); lib. bdg. 15.30 (978-0-613-73333-5(9)) Tandem Library Bks.

—Gifts. (Chronicles of the Western Shore Ser.: No. 1). (Illus.). (YA). 2004. 288p. 17.00 (978-0-15-205123-5(6)); 2006. 300p. reprint ed. pap. 7.95 (978-0-15-205124-2(4) , Harcourt Paperbacks) Harcourt Children's Bks.

—Jane on Her Own. Schindler, S. D., illus. 1999. (Catwings Ser.: No. 4). 48p. (J). (gr. 1-4). 15.99 (978-0-531-33133-0(4) , Orchard Bks.) Scholastic, Inc.

—Jane on Her Own. 2003. (Catwings Ser.: No. 4). (gr. k-3). lib. bdg. 11.80 (978-0-613-85117-6(X)) Tandem Library Bks.

—The Other Wind. 2003. (Earthsea Ser.: Vol. 5). (gr. 7-12). lib. bdg. 23.40 (978-0-613-55509-8(0)) Tandem Library Bks.

—Powers. 2007. (Chronicles of the Western Shore Ser.: No. 3). (Illus.). 512p. (YA). (gr. 9 up). 17.00 (978-0-15-205770-1(6)) Harcourt Trade Pubs.

—Tehanu. 2001. (Earthsea Ser.: Vol. 4). (gr. 7-12). lib. bdg. 15.30 (978-0-613-49527-1(6)) Tandem Library Bks.

—The Tombs of Atuan. 2001. (Earthsea Ser.: Vol. 2). (gr. 7-12). lib. bdg. 15.30 (978-0-613-73334-2(7)); (YA). lib. bdg. 13.00 (978-0-613-55910-2(X)) Tandem Library Bks.

—Voices. (Illus.). (YA). 2008. (Annals of the Western Shore Ser.). 360p. pap. 7.95 ***(*978-0-15-206242-2(4)*** , Harcourt Paperbacks); 2006. (Chronicles of the Western Shore Ser.: No. 2). 352p. 17.00 (978-0-15-205678-0(5)) Harcourt Children's Bks.

Le Guin, Ursula K. Wonderful Alexander & the Catwings. 2003. (Catwings Ser.: No. 3). (gr. k-3). lib. bdg. 11.80 (978-0-613-85116-9(1)) Tandem Library Bks.

Le, Guo, illus. The Dragon's Tears. 2004. 24p. (J). (TAM, CZE, VIE, SPA & GUJ.). pap. (978-1-85269-686-3(9)); (TAM, CZE, VIE, SPA & GUJ.). pap. (978-1-85269-687-0(7)); (TAM, CZE, VIE, SPA & GUJ.). pap. (978-1-85269-688-7(5)); (TAM, CZE, VIE, SPA & GUJ.). pap. (978-1-85269-691-7(5)); (TAM, CZE, VIE, SPA & GUJ.). pap. (978-1-85269-692-4(3)); (TAM, CZE, VIE, SPA & GUJ.). pap. (978-1-85269-693-1(1)); (TAM, CZE, VIE, SPA & GUJ.). pap. (978-1-85269-694-8(X)); (TAM, CZE, VIE, SPA & GUJ.). pap. (978-1-85269-695-5(8)); (CZE, TAM, VIE, SPA & GUJ.). pap. (978-1-85269-696-2(6)); (TAM, CZE, VIE, SPA & GUJ.). pap. (978-1-85269-697-9(4)); (TAM, CZE, VIE, SPA & GUJ.). pap. (978-1-85269-698-6(2)); (TAM, CZE, VIE, SPA & GUJ.). pap. (978-1-85269-699-3(0)); (TAM, CZE, SPA, VIE & GUJ.). pap. (978-1-85269-700-6(8)); (TAM, CZE, VIE, SPA & GUJ.). pap. (978-1-85269-787-7(3)); (TAM, CZE, VIE, SPA & GUJ.). pap. (978-1-85269-805-8(5)); (TAM, CZE, VIE, SPA & GUJ.). pap. (978-1-85269-810-2(1)) Mantra Publishing, Ltd.

LeapFrog Staff, compiled by. Classic Fairy Tales. 2001. (J). spiral bd. 14.99 (978-1-58605-048-1(6)) LeapFrog Enterprises, Inc.

Leaves: Look & Find. 2004. (J). pap. 12.95 (978-1-932762-03-7(5)) Elderberry Press, Inc.

Leblanc, Louise. Le Bon, la Brute et le Vampire. 2003. (Premier Roman Ser.). (FRE., Illus.). 64p. (J). (gr. 2-5). pap. (978-2-89021-365-4(X)) Diffusion du livre Mirabel.

—Maddie's Millionaire Dreams. Cummins, Sarah, tr. from FRE. Gay, Marie-Louise, illus. 2002. (First Novel Ser.). 64p. (J). ***(*978-0-88780-579-0(5));*** (gr. 1-5). 4.95 (978-0-88780-578-3(7)) Formac Publishing Co., Ltd. CAN. *Dist:* Casemate Pubs. & Bk. Distributors, LLC.

—Maddie's Millionaire Dreams. 2003. (gr. k-3). lib. bdg. 11.80 (978-0-613-90975-4(5)) Tandem Library Bks.

LeClair, Victor. Nick Faber's Touch. 2003. 113p. pap. 16.95 (978-1-59286-545-1(3)) PublishAmerica, Inc.

Lee, Chad. Familiar Ends. 2003. 219p. (J). pap. 19.95 (978-1-59129-672-0(2)) PublishAmerica, Inc.

Lee, Imani K., illus. Clever! Clever! & the Book of Forever. 2005. 17p. (YA). per. 9.99 (978-0-9764829-2-7(0)) Genius In A Bottle Technology Corp.

Lee, Jee-Hyung. Demon Diary. Lim, Kara, illus. rev. ed. 192p. Vol. 2. 2003. (gr. 8 up). pap. 9.99 (978-1-59182-155-7(X)); Vol. 4. 2003. pap. 9.99 (978-1-59182-157-1(6)); Vol. 5. 2004. pap. 9.99 (978-1-59182-430-5(3)); Vol. 6. 2004. pap. 9.99 (978-1-59182-431-2(1)) TOKYOPOP, Inc. (Tokyopop Adult).

Lee, Jong-Kyu. Evil's Return, 4 vols., Vol. 2. Shin, Hwan, illus. 2nd rev. ed. 2004. 184p. pap. 9.99 (978-1-59182-785-6(X) , Tokyopop Adult) TOKYOPOP, Inc.

Lee, Myung-Jin, creator. Ragnarok: Memories of Shadow, Vol. 10. rev. ed. 2004. (Illus.). 192p. pap. 9.99 (978-1-59182-209-7(2) , Tokyopop Adult) TOKYOPOP, Inc.

Lee, Quinlan B. Twink & the Sprites. Langer, Jutta, illus. 2004. (Rainbow Brite Ser.). 33p. (J). (ps-3). pap. 3.99 (978-0-439-68114-8(6)) Scholastic, Inc.

Lee, Shi Young. Fantasy Land, Vol. 1. 2004. 192p. (YA). pap. (978-1-4139-0066-8(6)) ADV Manga.

Lee, So-Young, illus. & creator. Arcana, Vol. 4. Lee, So-Young, creator. 4th rev. ed. 2006. pap. 9.99 (978-1-59816-200-4(4) , Tokyopop Kids) TOKYOPOP, Inc.

Lee, Stan. Essential Fantastic Four, Vol. II. Kirby, Jack, illus. 1999. 528p. 14.95 (978-0-7851-0731-6(2) , Essential Series, The) Marvel Enterprises, Inc.

Lee, Tanith. Black Unicorn. 2005. (Illus.). 138p. pap. 12.00 (978-1-59687-162-5(8)) ibooks, Inc.

—Indigara: Firebird Novella. 2007. 192p. (YA). (gr. 7 up). 11.99 (*978-0-14-240922-0(7)* , Puffin) Penguin Group (USA) Inc.

—Red Unicorn. 2003. (gr. 5-8). lib. bdg. 14.15 (978-0-613-82914-4(X)) Tandem Library Bks.

—Wolf Queen. 2003. (Claidi Journals: Bk. 3). 240p. (YA). (gr. 5-8). pap. 6.99 (978-0-14-250187-0(5) , Puffin) Penguin Group (USA) Inc.

—Wolf Star. 2002. (Claidi Journals: Bk. 2). (gr. 7-12). lib. bdg. 14.15 (978-0-613-53584-7(7)) Tandem Library Bks.

—Wolf Tower. 2001. (Claiddi Journals: Bk. 1). (Illus.). 240p. (J). pap. 6.99 (978-0-14-230030-5(6) , Puffin) Penguin Group (USA) Inc.

—Wolf Tower. 2001. (Claidi Journals: Bk. 1). (gr. 7-12). lib. bdg. 15.30 (978-0-613-44433-0(7)) Tandem Library Bks.

Lee, Vin, creator. Crazy Love Story, 5 vols. (Teen Ser.). (Illus.). Vol. 1. 2004. 192p. pap. 9.99 (978-1-59182-772-6(8)); Vol. 2. 2005. 208p. pap. 9.99 (978-1-59182-773-3(6)) TOKYOPOP, Inc. (Tokyopop Kids).

Lee, Young Yuu, creator. Kill Me, Kiss Me, 5 vols., Vol. 4. 4th rev. ed. 2004. (Teen Ser.). (Illus.). 192p. pap. 9.99 (978-1-59182-596-8(2) , Tokyopop Kids) TOKYOPOP, Inc.

LeFaucheur, Sandi. The Secret Shelter. 2005. (Illus.). 144p. (J). pap. 12.95 (978-0-9746481-4-9(0)) Brown Barn Bks.

Lehman, Barbara. The Red Book. Lehman, Barbara, illus. 2004. (Illus.). 32p. (J). (gr. k-3). 12.95 (978-0-618-42858-8(5)) Houghton Mifflin Co. Trade & Reference Div.

Lehman, Seth. The Color Pets. 2006. (Illus.). 52p. (J). 7.00 net. (*978-0-9787986-0-4(0)*) 4All Ages LLC.

Lehmann, Christian. El Cocodrilo de la Tina. (la Orilla Del Viento Ser.). (SPA., Illus.). 40p. (J). reprint ed. 6.99 (978-968-16-5835-9(3) , 114) Fondo de Cultura Economica USA.

Lehmann, Christian & Rodarmor, William. Ultimate Game. 2002. 192p. pap. 10.95 (978-1-56792-215-8(5)) Godine, David R. Pub.

Leigh, Tina. Miss Maplewood Mooves. Leigh, Tina, illus. 2002. (Illus.). 24p. (J). pap. 10.95 (978-0-9715673-1-3(X)) Leigh, Tina Illustrator.

Leininger, Tracy M. The Land Beyond the Setting Sun: The Story of Sacagewea. Pulley, Kelly & Reed, Lisa, illus. 2000. 61p. (J). 16.00 (978-1-929241-19-4(4)) Vision Forum, Inc., The.

Leithart, Peters. Wise Words: Family Stories That Bring the Proverbs to Life. 2006. cd-rom 20.00 (*978-1-59128-585-4(2)*) Canon Pr.

L'Engle, Madeleine. Many Waters. 2002. (Illus.). (J). 15.00 (978-0-7587-9605-9(6)) Book Wholesalers, Inc.

—Many Waters. Sis, Peter & Nelson, Cliff, illus. anniv. rev. ed. 1998. 336p. (J). (gr. 5-8). pap. 5.99 (978-0-440-22770-0(4) , Laurel Leaf) Random Hse. Children's Bks.

—Many Waters. 2007. 224p. (J). 6.99 (978-0-312-36861-6(5)); pap. 6.99 (978-0-312-36857-9(7)) Square Fish.

—Many Waters. 1998. (J). (978-0-606-13596-2(0)); (gr. 5-8). lib. bdg. 14.15 (978-0-613-72320-6(1)) Tandem Library Bks.

—Meet the Austins. 2002. (Austin Family Ser.: No. 1). (Illus.). (J). 13.94 (978-0-7587-8955-6(6)) Book Wholesalers, Inc.

—A Swiftly Tilting Planet. 228p. (YA). (gr. 5 up). pap. 5.50 (978-0-8072-1495-4(7) , Listening Library) Random Hse. Audio Publishing Group.

—A Swiftly Tilting Planet. 2007. 224p. (J). 6.99 (978-0-312-36860-9(7)); pap. 6.99 (978-0-312-36856-2(9)) Square Fish.

—A Swiftly Tilting Planet. 1998. (978-0-606-13831-4(5)) Tandem Library Bks.

—A Wind in the Door. 211p. (YA). (gr. 5 up). pap. 5.50 (978-0-8072-1466-4(3) , Listening Library) Random Hse. Audio Publishing Group.

—A Wind in the Door. 2007. 224p. (J). 6.99 (978-0-312-36859-3(3)); pap. 6.99 (978-0-312-36854-8(2)) Square Fish.

—A Wrinkle in Time. 2002. (J). 15.00 (978-0-7587-6754-7(4)) Book Wholesalers, Inc.

—A Wrinkle in Time, 2 vols., Set. 20.00 (978-0-89064-014-2(9)) National Assn. for Visually Handicapped.

—A Wrinkle in Time. 211p. (YA). (gr. 5 up). pap. 5.99 (978-0-8072-1460-2(4) , Listening Library) Random Hse. Audio Publishing Group.

—A Wrinkle in Time. l.t. ed. 2005. 273p. pap. 10.95 (978-0-7862-7335-5(6) , Large Print Pr.); 1998. 208p. (J). (gr. 4-7). 24.95 (978-0-7838-8371-7(4)) Thorndike Pr.

Lenhard, Elizabeth. A Bridge Between Worlds. 2004. (W. I. T. C. H. Ser.: Bk. 10). 158p. (J). lib. bdg. 16.92 (*978-1-4242-0796-1(7)*) Fitzgerald Bks.

—The Disappearance. 2004. (W. I. T. C. H. Ser.: Bk. 2). 158p. (J). lib. bdg. 16.92 (*978-1-4242-0799-2(1)*) Fitzgerald Bks.

—Finding Meridian. 2004. (W. I. T. C. H. Ser.: Bk. 3). 158p. (J). lib. bdg. 16.92 (*978-1-4242-0801-2(7)*) Fitzgerald Bks.

Lenhard, Elizabeth, adapted by. The Crown of Light, Bk. 11. rev. ed. 2004. (W. I. T. C. H. Ser.: Bk. 11). (Illus.). 160p. (J). (gr. 3-7). pap. 4.99 (978-0-7868-5139-3(2) , Volo) Hyperion Bks. for Children.

—The Light of Meridian. 7th rev. ed. 2004. (W. I. T. C. H. Ser.: Bk. 7). (Illus.). 144p. (gr. 3-7). pap. 4.99 (978-0-7868-1796-2(8) , Disney Editions) Disney Pr.

leo, domenic. The Messengers: The Secret of the Orbs. 2007. 324p. per. 19.95 (*978-0-595-42668-3(9)*) iUniverse, Inc.

Leone, Jason, illus. the Enchantress of Caratunk. Manna, Elizabeth, photos by. 2003. 30p. (J). (gr. 1-5). pap. 9.95 (978-0-9729807-0-8(9)) Murray, David M.

Lethcoe, Jason. Wishing Well. Damkoehler, Katrina, illus. 2007. (Benjamin Bartholomew Piff Ser.: No. 3). 224p. (J). (gr. 3-7). 9.99 (*978-0-448-44498-7(4)* , Grosset & Dunlap) Penguin Group (USA) Inc.

Let's Go! A Snap-Back Book. (Illus.). (J). 4.00 net. (978-1-56021-383-3(3)) W.J. Fantasy, Inc.

Levin, Betty. The Banished. 1999. (Illus.). 160p. (J). (gr. 5 up). 16.00 (978-0-688-16602-1(4)) HarperCollins Pubs.

—Thorn. 2005. 176p. (J). (gr. 5). 16.95 (978-1-932425-46-8(2) , Lemniscaat) Boyds Mills Pr.

Levine, Gail Carson. Ella Enchanted. 1998. 240p. (J). (gr. 3 up). pap. 6.99 (978-0-06-440705-2(5) , Harper Trophy) HarperCollins Pubs.

—Ella Enchanted. unabr. ed. 2004. 232p. (J). (gr. 4-7). pap. 38.00 incl. audio (978-0-8072-8694-4(X) , YA238SP, Listening Library) Random Hse. Audio Publishing Group.

—Ella Enchanted. 1998. (J). 13.15 (978-0-606-13099-8(3)) Tandem Library Bks.

—Ella Enchanted. l.t. ed. 2000. (Juvenile Ser.). (Illus.). 294p. (J). (gr. 4-7). 21.95 (978-0-7862-2743-3(5)) Thorndike Pr.

Levitin, Sonia. The Cure. 2000. (J). 12.64 (978-0-606-19967-4(5)) Tandem Library Bks.

Lewis, C. S. L' Armoire Magique. 6th ed. 1999. Orig. Title: The Lion, the Witch & the Wardrobe. (FRE.). (J). (gr. 4-7). pap. 12.95 (978-2-08-164414-4(2)) Distribooks, Inc.

—L' Armoire Magique. Orig. Title: The Lion, the Witch & the Wardrobe. (FRE.). pap. 12.95 (978-2-08-161994-4(6)) Flammarion et Cie FRA. *Dist:* Distribooks, Inc.

—Aslan's Triumph. 1999. (Illus.). (J). (978-0-606-18675-9(1)) Tandem Library Bks.

—The Chronicles of Narnia. Baynes, Pauline, illus. ed. (Narnia Ser.). (J). 2004. 784p. 32.99 (978-0-06-059824-2(7)); 2005. 768p. pap. 21.99 (978-0-06-076545-3(3)); Set. 2000. (gr. 3 up). pap., pap. 59.99 (978-0-06-440939-1(2)) HarperCollins Pubs.

—The Chronicles of Narnia. Baynes, Pauline, illus. (Narnia Ser.). (J). 2001. 768p. pap. 21.99 (978-0-06-623850-0(1)); Set. 2005. (gr. 3-7). pap., pap. 45.00 (978-0-06-076550-7(X)) Zonderkidz.

—Chronicles of Narnia: The Lion, the Witch & the Wardrobe Chapter Book. 2006. (Narnia Ser.). 384p. (J). pap. 14.99 (978-0-06-117453-7(X)) HarperCollins Pubs.

—The Chronicles of Narnia Book & Audio Box Set. Baynes, Pauline, illus. 2008. (Narnia Ser.). 768p. (J). pap. 99.99 (*978-0-06-076552-1(6)*) HarperCollins Pubs.

—The Chronicles of Narnia Box Set: The Magician's Nephew; The Lion, the Witch & the Wardrobe; The Hourse & His Boy; Prince Caspian; The Voyage of the Dawn Treader; The Silver Chair; The Last Battle, Books 1-7. Baynes, Pauline, illus. 2005. (Chronicles of Narnia Ser.: Bks. 1-7). (gr. 3 up). pap. 45.00 (978-0-06-447119-0(5)) Zonderkidz.

—The Complete Chronicles of Narnia. 2002. (Chronicles of Narnia Ser.). pap. 29.99 (978-0-06-051758-8(1)) HarperCollins Pubs.

—The Complete Chronicles of Narnia. Baynes, Pauline, illus. deluxe ed. 1998. (Chronicles of Narnia Ser.). 528p. (J). (gr. 3 up). 50.00 (978-0-06-028137-3(5)) HarperCollins Pubs.

—Las Cronicas de Narnia. 2006. (SPA.). 816p. pap. 19.99 (978-0-06-119900-4(1) , Rayo) HarperCollins Pubs.

—The Horse & His Boy. Baynes, Pauline, illus. 240p. 2006. (Narnia Ser.). (J). 11.99 (978-0-06-112524-9(5)); 2000. (Chronicles of Narnia Ser.: Bk. 5). (YA). (gr. 3 up). pap. 8.99 (978-0-06-440940-7(6) , Harper Trophy) HarperCollins Pubs.

—The Horse & His Boy. 2000. (Chronicles of Narnia Ser.: Bk.5). (J). (gr. 4-8). (978-0-606-19976-6(4)) Tandem Library Bks.

—The Horse & His Boy. Baynes, Pauline, illus. l.t. ed. 2000. (Chronicles of Narnia Ser.: Bk. 5). 253p. (J). (gr. 4-8). 21.95 (978-0-7862-2233-9(6)) Thorndike Pr.

—The Last Battle. Baynes, Pauline, illus. 224p. 2006. (Narnia Ser.). (J). 11.99 (978-0-06-112529-4(6)); 2000. (Chronicles of Narnia Ser.: Bk. 7). (YA). (gr. 3 up). pap. 8.99 (978-0-06-440941-4(4) , Harper Trophy) HarperCollins Pubs.

—El Leon, la Bruja y el Ropera. 2000. (978-0-606-22688-2(5)) Tandem Library Bks.

—El Leon, la Bruja y el Ropero. 2005. (ESP & SPA.). 208p. pap. 9.95 (978-0-06-084253-6(9) , Rayo) HarperCollins Pubs.

—The Lion, the Witch & the Wardrobe. Baynes, Pauline, illus. movie tie-in ed. 2005. (Chronicles of Narnia Ser.). (J). 208p. pap. 7.99 (978-0-06-076546-0(1)); 224p. pap. 6.99 (978-0-06-076548-4(8)) HarperCollins Pubs.

—The Lion, the Witch & the Wardrobe. 1999. (Chronicles of Narnia Ser.: Bk.1). (gr. 4-8). pap. 10.95 (978-1-84002-049-6(0)) Theatre Communications Group, Inc.

—The Lion, the Witch & the Wardrobe. Baynes, Pauline, illus. l.t. ed. 2000. (Chronicles of Narnia Ser.: Bk.1). 208p. (J). (gr. 4-8). 21.95 (978-0-7862-2232-2(8)) Thorndike Pr.

—The Magician's Nephew. Baynes, Pauline, illus. (J). 2006. (Narnia Ser.). 208p. 11.99 (978-0-06-112526-3(1)); 2000. (Chronicles of Narnia Ser.: Bk.6). 208p. (gr. 3 up). pap. 8.99 (978-0-06-440943-8(0) , Harper Trophy); 2004. (Narnia Ser.). 208p. (gr. 3 up). pap., pap. 29.99 incl. audio compact disk (978-0-06-059501-2(9)); 2003. (Narnia Ser.). 112p. (gr. 3 up). 19.99 (978-0-06-053084-6(7)) HarperCollins Pubs.

—The Magician's Nephew. l.t. ed. 2000. (Chronicles of Narnia Ser.: Bk.6). 224p. (J). (gr. 4-8). 21.95 (978-0-7862-2231-5(X)) Thorndike Pr.

—The Magician's Nephew Read-Aloud Edition. Baynes, Pauline, illus. 2006. (Narnia Ser.). 208p. (J). 15.99 (978-0-06-087588-6(7)) HarperCollins Pubs.

—Prince Caspian. Armstrong, Matthew S., illus. 2007. (Narnia Ser.). 32p. (J). 16.99 (*978-0-06-117327-1(4)*); lib. bdg. 17.89 (*978-0-06-117328-8(2)*) HarperCollins Pubs.

—Prince Caspian. Baynes, Pauline, illus. 2000. (Chronicles of Narnia Ser.: Bk.2). 240p. (YA). (gr. 3 up). pap. 8.99 (978-0-06-440944-5(9) , Harper Trophy) HarperCollins Pubs.

—Prince Caspian. 2000. (Chronicles of Narnia Ser.: Bk.2). (J). (gr. 4-8). (978-0-606-19995-7(0)) Tandem Library Bks.

—Prince Caspian. Baynes, Pauline, illus. l.t. ed. 2000. (Chronicles of Narnia Ser.: Bk. 2). 262p. (J). (gr. 4-8). 21.95 (978-0-7862-2234-6(4)) Thorndike Pr.

—Prince Caspian. 1998. (Chronicles of Narnia Ser.: Bk. 2). (J). (gr. 4-8). lib. bdg. 18.95 (978-1-56723-072-7(5)) Yestermorrow, Inc.

—Prince Caspian (paper-over-board) The Return to Narnia. Baynes, Pauline, illus. 2006. (Narnia Ser.). 240p. (J). 11.99 (978-0-06-112525-6(3)) HarperCollins Pubs.

—Prince Caspian Read-Aloud Edition: The Return to Narnia. Baynes, Pauline, illus. 2008. (Narnia Ser.). 240p. (J). 17.99 (*978-0-06-122764-6(1)*) HarperCollins Pubs.

—La Silla de Plata. 2005. (ESP & SPA.). 304p. pap. 9.95 (978-0-06-088430-7(4) , Rayo) HarperCollins Pubs.

—La Silla de Plata. 2001. (978-0-606-22694-3(X)) Tandem Library Bks.

—The Silver Chair. Baynes, Pauline, illus. 256p. 2006. (Narnia Ser.). (J). 11.99 (978-0-06-112528-7(8)); 2000. (Chronicles of Narnia Ser.: Bk.6). (YA). (gr. 3 up). pap. 8.99 (978-0-06-440945-2(7) , Harper Trophy) HarperCollins Pubs.

—The Silver Chair. 2000. (Chronicles of Narnia Ser.: Bk.4). (J). (gr. 4-8). (978-0-606-19997-1(7)) Tandem Library Bks.

—Travesia del "Explorador del Amencer" 2001. Tr. of Voyage of the Dawn Treader. (978-0-606-22700-1(8)) Tandem Library Bks.

—The Voyage of the Dawn Treader. Baynes, Pauline, illus. 256p. 2006. (Narnia Ser.). (J). 11.99 (978-0-06-112527-0(X)); 2000. (Chronicles of Narnia Ser.: Bk.3). (YA). (gr. 3 up). pap. 8.99 (978-0-06-440946-9(5) , Harper Trophy) HarperCollins Pubs.

—The Wood Between the Worlds. 2000. (978-0-606-18732-9(4)) Tandem Library Bks.

Lewis, Jody M. Finding April Hollow. 2006. per. 15.00 (978-0-9772115-1-7(7) , WCP) White Canoe Productions.

Lewis, Omar. Myat & the Sea Queen, Vol. 2. Lewis, Omar, illus. 2001. (J). 5.99 (978-1-886433-88-5(7)) A & B Distributors & Pubs. Group.

Lewis, Steven & Parker, Shelley. Return to Allapatria. 2006. 395p. (J). pap. 12.95 (978-0-9547092-9-7(2)) Accent Pr. GBR. *Dist:* Dufour Editions, Inc.

Leyland, Mark. Slate Mountain. (J). mass mkt. 8.99 (978-0-340-71607-6(X) , Hodder & Stoughton) Hodder General Publishing Division GBR. *Dist:* Trafalgar Square Publishing.

L'Homme, Erik. Face of the Shadow. 2006. (Illus.). 288p. (J). pap. 5.99 (978-0-439-65666-5(4)) Scholastic, Inc.

Lieshout, Ted van. Uncle Gus's Magic Box. Sideri, Simona, tr. from DUT. Hopman, Philip, illus. 2005. 60p. (J). (gr. 2-4). 18.95 (978-1-55037-935-8(6)) Annick Pr., Ltd. CAN. *Dist:* Firefly Bks., Ltd.

Lijewski, Christy. Next Exit, Vol. 1. 2006. (Illus.). 168p. (YA). pap. 12.95 (978-1-59362-037-0(3)) Slave Labor Bks.

Limb, Sue. You're Amazing, Mr. Jupiter. l.t. ed. 2005. (J). pap. (978-1-4056-6021-1(X)) BBC Audio.

Lin, Grace. Red Thread: An Adoption Fairy Tale. Lin, Grace, illus. 2007. (Illus.). 32p. (J). (ps-3). 16.95 (*978-0-8075-6922-1(4)*) Whitman, Albert & Co.

Lindbergh, Anne M. People in Pineapple Place. 2003. (gr. 3-6). lib. bdg. 14.15 (978-0-613-70998-9(5)) Tandem Library Bks.

Lindgren, Astrid. Pippi's Extraordinary Ordinary Day. 1999. (Pippi Longstocking Storybooks). (Illus.). 64p. (J). (gr. k-2). 14.99 (978-0-670-88073-7(6) , Viking Juvenile) Penguin Group (USA) Inc.

Lindner, Simone. Gobulus the Earth Fairy. Unzner, Christa, illus. 2008. 32p. (J). (ps). 9.99 (*978-0-698-40072-6(0)* , Minedition) Penguin Group (USA) Inc.

—Tara the Air Fairy. Unzner, Christa, illus. 2008. 32p. (J). (ps). 9.99 (*978-0-698-40069-6(0)* , Minedition) Penguin Group (USA) Inc.

Lindsay, Elizabeth. Annie to the Rescue. Kavanagh, Peter, illus. 2003. 94p. (J). (978-0-439-56006-1(3)) Scholastic, Inc.

—The Lucky Bunny. Eastwood, John, illus. 2004. 92p. (J). (978-0-439-56007-8(1)) Scholastic, Inc.

Lindsay, Norman. The Magic Pudding. 2006. (Illus.). 144p. (J). pap. 7.95 (978-0-486-45281-4(6)) Dover Pubns., Inc.

—The Magic Pudding. 2006. 77.99 (*978-1-4280-3115-9(4)*); 2005. (ENG.). pap. 70.99 (*978-1-4219-2134-1(0)*) IndyPublish.com.

—The Magic Pudding. 2004. reprint ed. pap. 15.95 (978-1-4191-7119-2(4)); pap. 1.99 (978-1-4192-7119-9(9)) Kessinger Publishing, LLC.

—The Magic Pudding. Lindsay, Norman, illus. 2004. (New York Review Children's Collection). (Illus.). 184p. (J). (gr. 3-6). pap. 16.95 (978-1-59017-101-1(2) , NYR Children's Collection) New York Review of Bks., Inc., The.

Lindskold, Jane. Through Wolf's Eyes. 2002. (gr. 5-8). lib. bdg. 16.45 (978-0-613-64450-1(6)) Tandem Library Bks.

Lininger, Dianne. The Kingdom of Cydinah. 2006. (J). (*978-0-9790337-0-4(5)*) Crosam Pr.

Lipson, Susan L. Knock on Wood. Crittenden Communications Staff & Twining, Miki, illus. 2000. 135p. (J). (gr. 3-6). pap. 12.95 (978-0-9677902-0-6(4)) Leba Hse. Pubs.

Lisle, Holly. Vengeance of Dragons. 2000. (gr. 7-12). lib. bdg. 15.30 (978-0-613-29378-5(9)) Tandem Library Bks.

List, Lynn M. Little Green Friend. 1998. (Illus.). 36p. (J). (gr. k-5). 14.95 (978-0-9662900-0-4(3)) Skinny Lamb Publishing.

Literature Connections English: A Midsummer Night's Dream. 2004. (gr. 6-12). (978-0-395-77543-1(4) , 2-80112) McDougal Littell Inc.

Literature Connections English: Tuck Everlasting. 2004. (gr. 6-12). (978-0-395-77522-6(1) , 2-80091) McDougal Littell Inc.

Literature Connections Spanish: Tuck para Siempre (Tuck Everlasting) 2004. (gr. 6-12). (978-0-395-80046-1(3) , 2-70465) McDougal Littell Inc.

Little, Berta. Nights in Nemra. 2003. 137 p. pap. 19.95 (978-1-4137-0511-9(1)) PublishAmerica, Inc.

Little Golden Books Staff. Peter Pan. 2000. (Disney Ser.). (Illus.). 24p. (J). (ps-2). bds. 2.99 (978-0-307-00104-7(0) , 98065, Golden Bks.) Random Hse. Children's Bks.

The Littles. 2002. (Littles Ser.). (J). 12.17 (978-0-7587-5710-4(7)) Book Wholesalers, Inc.

The Littles & the Great Halloween Scare. 2002. (Littles Ser.). (Illus.). (J). 12.17 (978-0-7587-8434-6(1)) Book Wholesalers, Inc.

The Littles & the Lost Children. 2002. (Littles Ser.). 12.17 (978-0-7587-8428-5(7)) Book Wholesalers, Inc.

The Littles & the Trash Tinies. 2002. (Littles Ser.). (Illus.). (J). 12.17 (978-0-7587-8430-8(9)) Book Wholesalers, Inc.

The Littles Gave a Party. 2002. (Littles Ser.). (Illus.). (J). 12.17 (978-0-7587-8433-9(3)) Book Wholesalers, Inc.

The Littles Go Exploring. 2002. (Littles Ser.). (Illus.). (J). 12.17 (978-0-7587-8432-2(5)) Book Wholesalers, Inc.

The Littles Go to School. 2002. (Littles Ser.). (Illus.). (J). 12.17 (978-0-7587-4769-3(1)) Book Wholesalers, Inc.

The Littles Have a Wedding. 2002. (Littles Ser.). (Illus.). (J). 12.17 (978-0-7587-8431-5(7)) Book Wholesalers, Inc.

The Littles Take a Trip. 2002. (Littles Ser.). (Illus.). (J). 12.17 (978-0-7587-6978-7(4)) Book Wholesalers, Inc.

The Littles to the Rescue. 2002. (Littles Ser.). (J). 12.17 (978-0-7587-8429-2(5)) Book Wholesalers, Inc.

The live dolls' party Days. 2007. (Illus.). 160p. (J). lib. bdg. 59.00 (*978-1-60304-010-5(2)*) Dollworks.

Living Books, Inc. Staff. Dr. Seuss Library. 1998. (J). cd-rom 119.95 net. (978-1-57404-435-5(4)) Broderbund Software, Inc.

Livingstone, Ian. Deathtrap Dungeon. 2003. 224p. pap. 6.99 (978-0-7434-7967-7(X)) ibooks, Inc.

Lloyd, Megan, illus. The Gingerbread Man. 2004. (J). (gr. k-3). pap. 16.95 incl. audio (978-0-87499-318-9(0)) Live Oak Media.

Lobdell, Scott. Flesh & Blood, 3. 5. (Illus.). 464p. (Orig.). pap. 24.99 (978-1-58240-538-4(7)) Image Comics.

Lobdell, Scott, et al. X-Men: Dreams End. 2004. (X-Men Ser.). (Illus.). 192p. pap. 17.99 (978-0-7851-1551-9(X)) Marvel Enterprises, Inc.

Lobel, Arnold. Ming Lo Moves the Mountain. 2001. (J). (gr. k-3). pap. 16.90 incl. audio (978-0-8045-6846-3(4) , 6846) Spoken Arts, Inc.

Locke, Pamela K. The Young Writers Series: Centaur's Door. 2007. (YA). pap. 5.99 (*978-1-58158-111-9(4)*) McDougal Publishing Co.

Loehr, Mallory. Earth Magic. 1999. (Magic Elements Quartet Ser.: Vol. 2). (Illus.). 112p. (J). (gr. 3-5). pap. 3.99 (978-0-679-89218-2(4) , Random Hse. Bks. for Young Readers) Random Hse. Children's Bks.

—Earth Magic. 1999. (J). 10.64 (978-0-606-19081-7(3)); (gr. 3-6). lib. bdg. 11.80 (978-0-613-21473-5(0)) Tandem Library Bks.

—Water Wishes. 1999. (Magic Elements Quartet Ser.: Vol. 1). 128p. (J). (gr. k-3). pap. 3.99 (978-0-679-89216-8(8) , Random Hse. Bks. for Young Readers) Random Hse. Children's Bks.

—Water Wishes. 1999. (J). (978-0-606-19085-5(6)); (gr. 3-6). lib. bdg. 11.80 (978-0-613-16234-0(X)) Tandem Library Bks.

Lofting, Hugh. The Story of Doctor Dolittle. 2005. 128p. pap. 10.95 (978-1-4218-0147-6(7) , 1st World Library - Literary Society) 1st World Publishing, Inc.

—The Story of Doctor Dolittle. 2005. 96p. per. 4.95 (978-1-4209-2544-9(X)) Digireads.com.

—The Story of Doctor Dolittle. Exams Unlimited, Inc. Staff, ed. 2001. 116p. (J). reprint ed. cd-rom 5.95 (978-1-885343-94-9(9)) Exams Unlimited, Inc.

—The Story of Doctor Dolittle. 2004. reprint ed. pap. 15.95 (978-1-4191-8383-6(4)); pap. 1.99 (978-1-4192-8383-3(9)) Kessinger Publishing, LLC.

—The Voyages of Doctor Dolittle. 2005. 340p. pap. 14.95 (978-1-4218-0148-3(5) , 1st World Library - Literary Society) 1st World Publishing, Inc.

—The Voyages of Doctor Dolittle. Hague, Michael, illus. 2001. (Doctor Dolittle Ser.). 368p. (J). (gr. 4-6). 28.99 (978-0-688-14002-1(5)) HarperCollins Pubs.

—The Voyages of Doctor Dolittle. 2000. (Doctor Dolittle Ser.). (Illus.). 272p. (gr. 4-6). mass mkt. 4.95 (978-0-451-52769-1(0) , Signet Classics) Penguin Group (USA) Inc.

—The Voyages of Doctor Dolittle. Lamut, Sonja, illus. 1998. (Doctor Dolittle Ser.). 288p. (J). (gr. 1-6). 16.99 (978-0-448-41863-6(0) , Grosset & Dunlap) Penguin Group (USA) Inc.

—Voyages of Doctor Dolittle. 2006. 53.99 (***978-1-4280-2312-3(7)***) IndyPublish.com.

—The Voyages of Doctor Dolittle. Corvino, Lucy, illus. 2008. (Classic Starts Ser.). 160p. (J). 5.95 (***978-1-4027-4574-4(5)***) Sterling Publishing Co., Inc.

Lofting, Hugh. Voyages of Dr Dolittle. 2000. (gr. 5-8). lib. bdg. 12.95 (978-0-613-27681-8(7)) Tandem Library Bks.

Logston, Anne. Waterdance. 1999. (978-0-606-17898-3(8)) Tandem Library Bks.

Lombardo, G. Where the Trees Grow Gumballs. 2006. 57p. pap. 12.95 (978-1-4241-2978-2(8)) PublishAmerica, Inc.

London, Victoria. Emily Cobbs & the Naked Painting. 2002. (Gifted Girls Ser.: Bk. 1). (Illus.). 64p. (J). (gr. 2-7). pap. 6.95 (978-0-9714776-2-9(0) , 083-003) Sparklesoup Studios, Inc.

—Lucy & the Beauty Queen. 2002. (Gifted Girls Ser.). 64p. (J). (gr. 2-7). per. 6.95 (978-0-9714776-1-2(2)) Sparklesoup Studios, Inc.

—Lucy & the Liberty Quilt. collector's ed. 2001. (Gifted Girls Ser.: Bk. 1). 64p. (J). (gr. 2-7). per. 7.95 (978-0-9714776-0-5(4)) Sparklesoup Studios, Inc.

Longoria, Eugene R., Jr. Junior y la Llorona en la Montana de Nieve. 2006. (SPA., Illus.). 40p. (J). 12.00 (***978-0-9796818-0-6(4)***) Longoria, Eugene R.

Lovhaug, Lewis J. Angel Armor: Just a Boy. 2003. (gr. 7-12). lib. bdg. 25.70 (978-0-613-86197-7(3)) Tandem Library Bks.

—Angel Armor: Just a Boy. 2003. 224p. (YA). pap. 15.95 (978-0-595-28475-7(2)) iUniverse, Inc.

Lowe, Wesley. The Griffin's Gauntlet. 2003. (Illus.). (YA). per. 14.95 (978-0-9723011-2-1(7)) Helm Publishing.

—The Griffin's Gauntlet. 2003. (YA). per. 14.95 (978-1-59453-013-5(0) , 1171) Airleaf Publishing & Bookselling.

Lowell, Susan. The Bootmaker & the Elves. Curry, Tom, illus. 1999. 32p. (J). (ps-3). pap. 6.95 (978-0-531-07138-0(3) , Orchard Bks.) Scholastic, Inc.

Lower, Joseph N. Cry from the Blue. 2005. pap. 9.00 (978-0-8059-6971-9(3)) Dorrance Publishing Co., Inc.

Lubbert, Constance L. True Colors. 2000. 328p. (YA). pap. 15.95 (978-0-595-14530-0(2)) iUniverse, Inc.

Luberto, Bradley. Clide & Druce: A Repulsive Tale of Trolls & Tax Money. 2006. (ENG.). 48p. per. 12.95 (***978-1-4241-5012-0(4)***) PublishAmerica, Inc.

Lucas, George. La Guerre des Etoiles, Tome 1.Tr. of Star Wars. (FRE.). (J). pap. 11.95 (978-2-265-06730-1(X)) Fleuve Noir FRA. *Dist:* Distribooks, Inc.

Lum, Kate. Princesses Are Not Quitters! Hellard, Sue, illus. 2005. 32p. (J). (ps-7). pap. 6.95 (978-1-58234-987-9(8) , Bloomsbury Children) Bloomsbury Publishing.

Lupin III 2nd Series, Vol. 2. 2004. (YA). pap. 9.99 (978-1-59182-494-7(X)) TOKYOPOP, Inc.

Lupin III Series 2. 2004. (YA). pap. 9.99 (978-1-59182-493-0(1)) TOKYOPOP, Inc.

Lupton, Hugh. The Gingerbread Man. Mayo, Diana, illus. 2003. 24p. (J). (gr. k-3). 14.99 (978-1-84148-056-5(8)) Barefoot Bks., Inc.

Lying as Still as I Can: Six-Pack. (Greetings Ser.: Vol. 3). (gr. 2-3). 31.00 (978-0-7635-9433-6(4)) Rigby Education.

Lynn, Erin. Demon Envy. 2007. 192p. (gr. 12 up). 9.99 (***978-0-425-21737-5(X)*** , Berkley Trade) Penguin Group (USA) Inc.

Lynn, Tracy. Snow. Craft, Kinuko Y., illus. 2005. 224p. (YA). mass mkt. 3.99 (978-1-4169-0518-9(9) , Simon Pulse) Simon & Schuster Children's Publishing.

Lyon, Steve. The Gift Moves. 2006. 240p. (YA). (gr. 7). mass mkt. 6.50 (978-0-553-49494-5(5) , Laurel Leaf) Random Hse. Children's Bks.

Lyrrek, E. Dawne. A Page Turns 12 & Comes of Age. 2004. (J). 8.95 (978-1-59590-009-8(8)) Books2Go.

Ma, Wing Shing. Black Leopard, Vol. 1. 2005. (Illus.). 160p. (YA). pap. 14.95 (978-1-58899-333-5(7)) ComicsOne Corp./Dr. Masters.

Macaw, Grant. Vigil's End: Book One of the Ninth Day of Man. 2005. 310p. (YA). (gr. 7). pap. 11.95 (978-1-933255-13-2(7)) DNA Pr.

MacDonald, Betty. Mrs. Piggle-Wiggle's Magic. Boiger, Alexandra, illus. 2007. 192p. (J). lib. bdg. 16.89 (***978-0-06-125125-2(9)***) HarperCollins Pubs.

MacDonald, George. At the Back of the North Wind. 1998. (Twelve-Point Ser.). 280p. reprint ed. lib. bdg. 25.00 (978-1-58287-015-1(2)) North Bks.

—The Boyhood of Ranald Bannerman: With Colour Plates. Wheelhouse, A. V. & Hughes, Arthur, illus. unabr. ed. 1999. (George MacDonald Original Works Ser.: Series III). 335p. (J). (gr. 5 up). reprint ed. lib. bdg. 28.00 (978-1-881084-13-6(2)) Johannesen Printing & Publishing.

—Lilith a & Lilith 1896. unabr. ed. 1998. (George MacDonald Original Works Ser.: Series IV). 388p. reprint ed. lib. bdg. 26.00 (978-1-881084-27-3(2)) Johannesen Printing & Publishing.

—The Princess & Curdie. l.t. ed. 2005. 320p. pap. (978-1-84637-020-5(5)) Echo Library.

MacHado, Ana Maria. Del Tamano Justo. Vasco, Irene, tr. Violi, Daniela, illus. 2001. (Torre de Papel Ser.). (SPA.). 88p. (J). 7.95 (978-958-04-6265-1(8)) Norma S.A. COL. *Dist:* Distribuidora Norma, Inc.

MacHale, D. J. Black Water. 2004. (Pendragon Ser. : Bk. 5). 200p. (J). (gr. k-9). lib. bdg. 14.30 (978-1-4176-2874-2(X)) Tandem Library Bks.

—The Lost City of Faar. 2003. (Pendragon Ser.: Bk. 2). 400p. (J). (gr. 5 up). pap. 6.99 (978-0-7434-3732-5(2) , Aladdin) Simon & Schuster Children's Publishing.

—The Lost City of Faar. 2003. (Pendragon Ser. : Bk. 2). 384p. (J). (gr. 4-7). per. 14.15 (978-0-613-61640-9(5)) Tandem Library Bks.

—The Merchant of Death. (Pendragon Ser.: Bk. 1). (J). 2006. 400p. pap. 2.99 (978-1-4169-2495-1(7)); 2002. 384p. (gr. 5-8). pap. 7.99 (978-0-7434-3731-8(4)) Simon & Schuster Children's Publishing. (Aladdin).

—The Merchant of Death. 2002. (Pendragon Ser. : Bk. 1). (gr. 5-8). lib. bdg. 14.15 (978-0-613-52144-4(7)) Tandem Library Bks.

—The Merchant of Death & The Lost City of Faar: Journal of an Adventure through Time & Space. 2005. (Pendragon Ser.: Bks. 1-2). 758p. (YA). 9.99 (978-0-681-05434-9(4)) Borders Pr.

—The Never War. 2003. (Pendragon Ser. : Bk. 3). 336p. (J). (gr. 4-7). per. 14.15 (978-0-613-66526-1(0)) Tandem Library Bks.

—Pendragon: The Merchant of Death; the Lost City of Faar; the Never War. 2004. (Pendragon Ser.: Bks. 1-3). (Illus.). 1136p. (J). 15.95 (978-0-689-03808-2(9) , Aladdin) Simon & Schuster Children's Publishing.

—The Pilgrims of Rayne. 2007. (Pendragon Ser.: Bk. 8). 560p. (J). 16.99 (978-1-4169-1416-7(1)) Simon & Schuster Children's Publishing.

—The Quillan Games. 2007. (Pendragon Ser.: Bk. 7). 496p. (J). pap. 8.99 (***978-0-689-86913-6(4)*** , Aladdin) Simon & Schuster Children's Publishing.

MacHale, D. J. The Rivers of Zadaa. (Pendragon Ser.: Bk. 6). 416p. (J). 2006. pap. 6.99 (978-0-689-86912-9(6) , Aladdin); 2005. 14.95 (978-1-4169-0710-7(6)) Simon & Schuster Children's Publishing.

MacInnis, Katherine Grace. Kelsar. 2006. 140p. 19.95 (978-1-58939-877-1(7)) Virtualbookworm.com Publishing, Inc.

MacInnis, Ron. The Quest for the Magic Apple Tree. Cupido, Matthew, illus. 1999. 328p. pap., pap. (978-1-894031-15-8(6)) Gaspereau Pr.

MacKall, Dandi Daley. Little Shepherds First Christm. 2004. 32p. (J). 6.99 (978-0-7586-0324-1(X)) Concordia Publishing Hse.

MacLeish, Roderick. Prince Ombra. 2002. (Illus.). 384p. (J). 5.99 (978-0-7653-4244-7(8) , Starscape) Doherty, Tom Assocs., LLC.

—Prince Ombra. 2002. (gr. 5-8). lib. bdg. 14.15 (978-0-613-70769-5(9)) Tandem Library Bks.

Maconie, Robin. Alice & Her Fabulous Teeth! Fruisen, Catherine Myler, illus. 2004. 32p. (J). per. (978-1-893974-21-0(9) , Design Pr. Bks.) Savannah College of Art & Design.

Maddux, Marlaine. The Loch Pt. 3: Discovery, 3 vols. Harman, Michelle, ed. Huddleston, Courtney, illus. 2002. (Mythics Ser.). 71p. (J). (gr. 3-6). (978-0-9673683-5-1(9)) Penny-Farthing Pr., Inc.

—Loch Trilogy, 3 vols. Harman, Michelle, ed. Huddleston, Courtney, illus. 2002. (Mythics Ser.). (J). (gr. 2-6). 49.00 (978-0-9673683-7-5(5)) Penny-Farthing Pr., Inc.

—The Loch Trilogy Slipcase. Huddleston, Courtney, illus. 2002. (Mythics Ser.). (J). 10.00 (978-0-9673683-6-8(7)) Penny-Farthing Pr., Inc.

Madigan, Leo. The Weka-Feather Cloak: A New Zealand Fantasy. 2002. (Morning Gate Bks.). 270p. (J). pap. 12.95 (978-1-883937-68-3(X) , 68-X) Bethlehem Bks.

Madiwale, Frances. Special Creatures. 2005. (Illus.). 20p. (J). per. 9.99 (978-1-59879-011-5(0)) Lifevest Publishing, Inc.

Madsen, Ross Martin. Perrywinkle's Magic Match. 1999. (978-0-606-17424-4(9)) Tandem Library Bks.

Magee, Massimo. The Shell Maker. 2005. (YA). per. (978-1-921005-38-1(6)) Zeus Pubns.

—The Sword the Axe & the Bow. 2005. 254p. (YA). per. (978-1-921005-37-4(8)) Zeus Pubns.

Magness, Lee. Silver Dasher. 2003. 164p. pap. 12.95 (978-0-595-29043-7(4)) iUniverse, Inc.

Magnificent Staff. The Road to Paradise. Clouche, Armelle, ed. Heyer, Marilee, illus. 2000. 88p. (J). (gr. 4-7). 16.95 (978-0-615-11546-7(2)) Armelle Prod.

Mahy, Margaret. Maddigan's Fantasia. 2007. 512p. (J). (gr. 5 up). 17.99 (978-1-4169-1812-7(4) , McElderry, Margaret K.) Simon & Schuster Children's Publishing.

—A Villain's Night Out. Horse, Harry, illus. unabr. l.t. ed. 2003. (Read-Along Ser.). 184p. (J). pap. 24.95 incl. audio (978-0-7540-6224-0(4) , RA025, Galaxy Children's Large Print) BBC Audiobooks America.

Mallory, James. Merlin 1: Old Magic. 1999. (978-0-606-18745-9(6)) Tandem Library Bks.

Man-Kong, Mary. Barbie & the Magic of Pegasus. 2006. (Illus.). 22p. (J). (gr. k-ps). bds. 4.99 (978-0-375-83539-1(3) , Golden Bks.) Random Hse. Children's Bks.

Manatee Moon. 2006. (J). per. 9.95 (978-0-9766620-3-7(5)) Avery Goode-Reid Pubs.

Mancebo, pseud. Cecil, the Nearsighted Dragon. Phillips, Christina, illus. 1998. 32p. (J). (ps-3). pap. 14.95 (978-0-9626993-4-4(9)) Armadillo Niche.

Mangels, Andy. Dragon's Lair. 2007. (Illus.). 140p. (YA). per. 19.95 (978-0-9763095-5-0(6)) Arcana Studio, Inc.

Manjula Padmanabhan, illus. Unprincess! 2005. 98p. (J). (***978-0-14-333495-8(6)*** , Puffin) Penguin Group (USA) Inc.

Mann, Emma. Amelia's Star. 2006. 110p. pap. 16.95 (978-1-4241-2363-6(1)) PublishAmerica, Inc.

Manners, Richard. Girl Child Saturday: A Children's Fantasy. 2000. 152p. (J). (gr. 1-7). pap. 9.95 (978-0-595-12673-6(1)) iUniverse, Inc.

Manuel, Lynn. The Lickety-Split Princess. 2005. (Illus.). 96p. (J). pap. 6.95 (978-1-55050-178-0(X)) Coteau Bks. CAN. *Dist:* Fitzhenry & Whiteside, Ltd.

Marillier, Juliet. Wildwood Dancing. 2007. 416p. (J). (gr. 7). 16.99 (978-0-375-83364-9(1)); lib. bdg. 19.99 (978-0-375-93364-6(6)) Random Hse. Children's Bks. (Knopf Bks. for Young Readers).

Marini, Enrico & Dufaux, Jean. Rapaces, Vol. 4. 2005. (SPA., Illus.). 56p. pap. 17.95 (978-1-59497-107-5(2)) Public Square Bks.

Mariotte, Jeff. Sanctuary. 2003. (gr. 7-12). lib. bdg. 14.15 (978-0-613-61812-0(2)) Tandem Library Bks.

Mark, Jan. Useful Idiots. 2004. 416p. (YA). (gr. 7). 17.99 (978-0-385-75023-3(4) , Fickling, David Bks.) Random Hse. Children's Bks.

Mark, Yudel. The Jewish Pope: A Yiddish Tale. Goodman, Ruth Fisher, tr. from YID. 2006. (Illus.). 128p. (YA). pap. 10.00 (978-1-56474-459-3(0)) Fithian Pr.

Markes, Julie. Sidewalk 123. Markes, Jennifer, illus. 2001. 24p. (J). (ps-k). 8.95 (978-0-694-01500-9(8) , Harper Festival) HarperCollins Pubs.

Marley, Louise. Singer in the Snow. 2005. 304p. (J). (gr. 7). 16.99 (978-0-670-05965-2(X) , Viking Juvenile) Penguin Group (USA) Inc.

Marlowe, Pete. Mallory & the Power Boy. Revell, Cindy, illus. 2001. 32p. (J). (gr. k-3). pap. 6.95 (978-1-55037-688-3(8)); lib. bdg. 19.95 (978-1-55037-689-0(6)) Annick Pr., Ltd. CAN. *Dist:* Firefly Bks., Ltd.

—One Arabian Morning. Bell, Charles, illus. 2000. 32p. (J). (gr. k-3). lib. bdg. 19.95 (978-1-55037-659-3(4)) Annick Pr., Ltd. CAN. *Dist:* Firefly Bks., Ltd.

—The Trailer Park Princesses. Franson, Leanne, illus. 2000. 32p. (J). (gr. k-2). pap. 6.95 (978-1-55037-616-6(0)); lib. bdg. 17.95 (978-1-55037-617-3(9)) Annick Pr., Ltd. CAN. *Dist:* Firefly Bks., Ltd.

Marney, Dean. How to Drive Your Family Crazy on Valentine's Day. 2001. (gr. 3-6). lib. bdg. 12.40 (978-0-613-84121-4(2)) Tandem Library Bks.

Marriotte, Jeff. Door to Alternity. 2001. (gr. 7-12). lib. bdg. 15.30 (978-0-613-63279-9(6)) Tandem Library Bks.

Marsh, Carole. To the Eight Wonders of the World. 2007. 128p. pap. 5.99 (***978-0-635-06335-9(2)***) Gallopade International.

—To the Planet Mars! 2007. 128p. pap. 5.99 (***978-0-635-06336-6(0)***) Gallopade International.

Marshall, James. George & Martha: Round & Round Early Reader #3. 2008. 32p. (J). (ps-3). 15.00 (***978-0-618-98505-0(0)***) Houghton Mifflin Co. Trade & Reference Div.

Marsoli, Lisa Ann. Harold Takes a Trip: Harold & the Purple Crayon. Chiang, Andy, illus. 2005. 10p. (J). 7.95 (978-1-58117-262-1(1) , Intervisual/Piggy Toes) Dalmatian Pr.

Martin, Cynthia Bloom. Tryloc: The Quest. ed. 2006. (J). per. 22.95 (978-0-9787015-0-5(X)) T.C. McSears Publishing.

Martin, Dick. The Ozmapolitan of Oz. 2006. (J). 24.95 (978-1-930764-11-8(1)) International Wizard of Oz Club, The.

Martin, George R. R. The Ice Dragon. 2007. 112p. (J). 5.99 (***978-0-7653-5539-3(6)*** , Starscape) Doherty, Tom Assocs., LLC.

Martin, JoElle. A Bridge in the Forest, Pt. 1. 2007. 280p. (YA). pap. 14.99 (978-1-59092-372-6(3) , Blue Works) Windstorm Creative.

—A Promise in the Forest, Vol. 2. 2008. 280p. (YA). pap. 16.99 (978-1-59092-541-6(6) , Blue Works) Windstorm Creative.

Martin, Nicole. The Werewolf. 2006. 146p. pap. (***978-1-4120-8802-2(X)***) Trafford Publishing.

Martin, S. R. Tankworld. 2000. 112p. (J). (gr. 7-12). pap. 4.50 (978-0-439-10567-5(6)) Scholastic, Inc.

—Vanish. 1999. (Insomniacs Ser.: No. 6). 80p. (YA). (gr 7-12). pap. 2.99 (978-0-439-04426-4(X)) Scholastic, Inc.

Martin, W. Lyon. An Ordinary Girl, A Magical Child. Martin, W. Lyon, illus. 2008. (Illus.). 48p. (J). lib. bdg. 16.95 (***978-0-9796834-3-5(2)***) Shades of White.

Martinez, Shawna Joy. Lemur's Legacy: A Savior Is Born. l.t. ed. 2003. (Illus.). 176p. (YA). per. 11.00 (978-0-9729057-0-1(7)) Training Grounds.

—Lemur's Legacy: The Final Outcome. l.t. ed. 2003. (Illus.). 176p. (YA). per. 11.00 (978-0-9729057-2-5(3)) Training Grounds.

—Lemur's Legacy: The Training Begins. l.t. ed. 2003. (Illus.). 176p. (YA). per. 11.00 (978-0-9729057-1-8(5)) Training Grounds.

Marvel & Kiefer, Kit. Marvel Encyclopedia Vol. 6: Fantastic Four. 2004. (Fantastic Four Ser.). (Illus.). 240p. 29.99 (978-0-7851-1480-2(7)) Marvel Enterprises, Inc.

Marvel Characters, Inc Staff. X-Men Pop-Up: Marvel True Believers Retro Collection. Repchuck, Caroline, ed. 2007. (Marvel True Believers Ser.). (Illus.). 16p. (J). (gr. k). 24.99 (***978-0-7636-3462-9(X)***) Candlewick Pr.

Marz, Ron. Mystic Traveler: The Demon Queen, Vol. 2. Peterson, Brandon et al, illus. 2004. (Mystic Traveler Ser.). 160p. (YA). pap. 9.95 (978-1-59314-037-3(1)) CrossGeneration Comics, Inc.

—Scion Vol. 6: The Royal Wedding. Cheung, Jim et al, illus. 2004. (Scion Ser.). 160p. (YA). pap. 15.95 (978-1-59314-034-2(7)) CrossGeneration Comics, Inc.

Masashi, Kishimoto. Zatch Bell. 2004. 192p. pap. 9.95 (978-1-59116-679-5(9)) Viz Media.

Masefield, John. The Box of Delights. 2007. (Illus.). 320p. (J). (gr. 4-9). 17.95 (***978-1-59017-251-3(5)*** , NYR Children's Collection) New York Review of Bks., Inc., The.

Mashima, Hiro. Rave Master, 8 vols. Mashima, Hiro, illus. 2003. (Illus.). Vol. 5. 5th rev. ed. pap. 9.99 (978-1-59182-212-7(2)); Vol. 6. rev. ed. 192p. pap. 9.99 (978-1-59182-213-4(0)) TOKYOPOP, Inc. (Tokyopop Kids).

—Rave Master, 18 vols., Vol. 7. Dunn, Brian, tr. from JPN. Mashima, Hiro, illus. rev. ed. 2004. (Illus.). 200p. pap. 9.99 (978-1-59182-517-3(2) , Tokyopop Kids) TOKYOPOP, Inc.

—Rave Master, 18 vols., Vol. 8. Dunn, Brian, tr. from JPN. rev. ed. 2004. (Illus.). 200p. pap. 9.99 (978-1-59182-518-0(0) , Tokyopop Kids) TOKYOPOP, Inc.

—Rave Master, 18 vols., Vol. 9. rev. ed. 2004. (Illus.). 192p. pap. 9.99 (978-1-59182-519-7(9) , Tokyopop Kids) TOKYOPOP, Inc.

—Rave Master, 18 vols., Vol. 10. Dunn, Brian, tr. from JPN. rev. ed. 2004. (Illus.). 192p. pap. 9.99 (978-1-59182-520-3(2) , Tokyopop Kids) TOKYOPOP, Inc.

—Rave Master, 21 vols., Vol. 11. Bourque, Jeremiah, tr. from JPN. Mashima, Hiro, illus. rev. ed. 2004. (Illus.). 192p. pap. 9.99 (978-1-59182-521-0(0) , Tokyopop Kids) TOKYOPOP, Inc.

—Rave Master. Mashima, Hiro, illus. rev. ed. 2005. (Illus.). 192p. Vol. 13. pap. 9.99 (978-1-59532-018-6(0)); Vol. 15. pap. 9.99 (978-1-59532-020-9(2)) TOKYOPOP, Inc. (Tokyopop Kids).

Mashima, Hiro, creator. Rave Master, 21 vols., Vol. 12. rev. ed. 2004. (Teen Ser.). (Illus.). 192p. pap. 9.99 (978-1-59182-522-7(9) , Tokyopop Kids) TOKYOPOP, Inc.

Mashima, Hiro, illus. Rave Master, Vol. 14. rev. ed. 2005. 200p. pap. 9.99 (978-1-59532-019-3(9) , Tokyopop Kids) TOKYOPOP, Inc.

Mason, Jane. Jack Frost Movie Storybook. 1998. (Illus.). 48p. (gr. 1-5). pap. 5.99 (978-0-590-66070-9(5)) Scholastic, Inc.

—Legend of Sleepy Hollow. 2002. (gr. 3-6). lib. bdg. 11.80 (978-0-613-71993-3(X)) Tandem Library Bks.

Mason, Tom & Danko, Dan. Shrek 2: The Movie Storybook. Koelsch Studios Staff, illus. movie tie-in ed. 2004. (Shrek 2 Ser.). 56p. (J). (gr. 3-6). pap. 8.99 (978-0-439-53849-7(1)) Scholastic, Inc.

Mason, Tom & Danko, Dan. The Ultimate Pocket Guide. 2007. (Avatar Ser.). 48p. (J). pap. 3.99 (***978-1-4169-4736-3(1)*** , Simon Spotlight) Simon & Schuster Children's Publishing.

Masson, Sophie. Snow, Fire, Sword. 2006. 368p. (J). 15.99 (978-0-06-079091-2(1)); lib. bdg. 16.89 (978-0-06-079092-9(X)) HarperCollins Pubs.

Matens, Margaret H. The Wisdom of Fishing. Matens, Margaret H., illus. 2004. (Wisdom Ser.). (Illus.). 160p. pap. 7.00 (978-1-882959-53-2(1)) Foxglove Pr.

Mathson, Brent V. If I Could Be Anything I Wanted to Be. Maval Publishing Inc. Staff, illus. 2001. 32p. (J). (ps-3). pap. 7.50 (978-1-884083-66-2(8)) Maval Publishing, Inc.

—Si yo Pudiera Ser... Maval Publishing Inc. Staff, illus. 2001. Tr. of If I Could Be Anything I Wanted to Be. (SPA.). 32p. (J). (gr. k-3). pap. 7.50 (978-1-59134-009-6(8)); pap. 7.50 (978-1-884083-79-2(X)) Maval Publishing, Inc.

Matott, J. P. & Baker, Margaret. When I Was a Girl ... I Dreamed. Ludy, Mark, illus. 2005. 32p. (J). 16.95 (978-0-9664276-3-9(7)) Green Pastures Publishing, Inc.

Matott, Justin. When I Was a Boy... I Dreamed. Ludy, Mark, illus. 2004. 32p. (J). 17.00 (978-0-9664276-2-2(9)) Green Pastures Publishing, Inc.

Matsubara, Hiroaki. More Starlight to Your Heart, Vol 1. 2004. (Illus.). 184p. (YA). pap. (978-1-4139-0206-8(5)) ADV Manga.

Matsushita, Yoko. Yami No Matsuei, 2. Matsushita, Yoko, illus. 2004. (Descendants of Darkness Ser.). (Illus.). 208p. (YA). pap. 9.99 (978-1-59116-597-2(0)) Viz Media.

Maxwell, Marc C. B. The Wallace Dream: The Adventures of the Baby Seekers. 2006. 148p. pap. 12.95 (978-1-59113-933-1(3)) Booklocker.com, Inc.

Mayer. Si Javais Gorille. (FRE.). (J). pap. (978-2-07-050613-2(4)) Gallimard, Editions FRA. *Dist:* Distribooks, Inc.

Mayer, Gina. Walt Disney's Peter Pan. 2002. (J). spiral bd. (978-0-9720651-1-5(3)) Story Reader, Inc.

Mayes, Walter M. Walter the Giant Storyteller's Giant Book of Giant Stories. O'Malley, Kevin, illus. 2005. 48p. (J). (gr. 1-5). 19.85 (978-0-8027-8975-4(7)) Walker & Co.

Mazurowski, Jeff. Aurora & Boris Touch the Sky. Lesniewicz, Kerry, illus. 1998. 22p. (J). (gr. k-5). pap. 9.95 (978-0-9662153-1-1(1)) My World Pr.

Mazzola, Lori. Tales of the Tree People to Tree... or. 2006. 48p. pap. 12.95 (***978-1-4241-5065-6(5)***) PublishAmerica, Inc.

Mc Collin, Alethea. The Cloud Catcher. 2005. (J). per. 3.99 (978-0-9764163-0-2(1)) Bookmark Bks., LLC.

McAllister, M. I. Mistmantle Chronicles, the: Urchin & the Heartstone - Book #2. Rayyan, Omar, illus. 2nd rev. ed. 2007. 304p. (gr. 3-7). pap. 7.99 (***978-0-7868-5489-9(8)***) Miramax Bks.

McAllister, M. I. Urchin of the Riding Stars. Rayyan, Omar, illus. 2006. (Mistmantle Chronicles Ser.: Bk. 1). 288p. (gr. 3-7). pap. 7.99 (978-0-7868-5487-5(1)) Hyperion Bks. for Children.

McBride, A. W. The Story of the Forest People: A Forever Fantasy for All of Us. Pioneer Heritage Staff, illus. 2001. 20p. (J). (ps-1). pap. 6.95 (978-0-9708289-0-3(X)) Pioneer Heritage.

McBride, Earvin, Jr. Earvin MacBride's Amazing Sci-Fi & Adventure Heroes, 7 vols. McBride, Earvin, Jr., illus. 2nd unabr. ed. 2003. (Illus.). (J). (gr. 7-12). pap. 25.95 (978-1-892511-05-8(3)) MacBride, E. J. Pubn., Inc.

McCaffrey, Anne. Acorna: The Unicorn Girl. 2001. (Acorna Ser.). lib. bdg. 15.90 (978-0-613-55549-4(X)) Tandem Library Bks.

—Acorna's World. 2001. (Acorna Ser.). lib. bdg. 15.30 (978-0-613-55395-7(0)) Tandem Library Bks.

E F G

—The Coelura. 2000. (978-0-606-20611-2(6)) Tandem Library Bks.

—Dragondrums. 2003. (Harper Hall Trilogy: Vol. 3). (J). (gr. 5-8). lib. bdg. 14.15 (978-0-613-91041-5(9)); (gr. 7-12). lib. bdg. 15.30 (978-0-613-66493-6(0)) Tandem Library Bks.

—Dragonsinger. 2003. (Harper Hall Trilogy: Vol. 2). (gr. 5-8). lib. bdg. 14.15 (978-0-613-73345-8(2)) Tandem Library Bks.

—Dragonsong. 2003. (Harper Hall Trilogy: Vol. 1). (J). (gr. 5-8). lib. bdg. 14.15 (978-0-613-91042-2(7)) Tandem Library Bks.

McCaffrey, Laura Williams. Water Shaper. 2006. 224p. (J). (gr. 5-9). 16.00 (978-0-618-61489-9(3) , Clarion Bks.) Houghton Mifflin Co. Trade & Reference Div.

McCarthy, Bairbre. Irish Leprechaun Stories. 1998. 93p. (J). (gr. 3 up). pap. 7.95 (978-1-85635-229-1(3)) Irish Bks. & Media, Inc.

McCarthy, Ingrid. The Black Pearl of Osis. 2004. 158p. pap. 19.95 (978-1-4137-3719-6(6)) PublishAmerica, Inc.

McCarthy, Ralph F. Moon Princess. Oda, Kancho, illus. 2000. (Kodansha Children's Bilingual Classics Ser.). 48p. (ps-3). 9.95 (978-4-7700-2099-4(6)) Kodansha International JPN. *Dist:* Oxford Univ. Pr., Inc.

—Urashima & the Kingdom Beneath the Sea. Kasamatsu, Shiro, illus. 2000. (Kodansha Children's Classics Ser.). 48p. (gr. 4-7). 9.95 (978-4-7700-2100-7(3)) Kodansha International JPN. *Dist:* Oxford Univ. Pr., Inc.

McCarty, Marty. Hard Girl Goes to a Scary Movie. 2004. (J). 7.99 (978-0-9748712-0-2(6)) hard girl bk. club.

McCaughrean, Geraldine. Peter Pan. 2006. 232p. pap. 17.95 (**978-958-704-467-6(3)*) Alfaguara, Ediciones, S.A.- Grupo Santillana ESP. *Dist:* Santillana USA Publishing Co., Inc.

—The Stones Are Hatching. 2000. (Illus.). 240p. (J). (gr. 5 up). 15.95 (978-0-06-028765-8(9)) HarperCollins Pubs.

—Stones Are Hatching. 2002. (gr. 7-12). lib. bdg. 14.10 (978-0-613-33496-9(5)) Tandem Library Bks.

—The Stones Are Hatching. unabr. ed. 2004. 240p. (J). (gr. 5-9). pap. 38.00 incl. audio (978-0-8072-0866-3(3) , LYA 318 SP, Listening Library) Random Hse. Audio Publishing Group.

McClear, Preston. Old Man Brown & His Magic Bike. Dollak, Nicholas, illus. 1999. 30p. (J). (gr. k-5). 16.95 (978-1-929084-06-7(4)); pap. 12.95 (978-1-929084-07-4(2)) Malibu Bks. for Children.

McCracken, Craig. Buttercup Keychain Book. Romano, Lou, illus. 2001. (Golden Book Ser.). 48p. (J). (ps-3). pap. 3.99 (978-0-307-10242-3(4) , Golden Bks.) Random Hse. Children's Bks.

McCray, Ed. Jill Chill & the Baron of Glacier Mountain: Wonder Tales from the Book of Ed. Brewer, Tammy & Harms, Cathy, eds. McCray, Ed, illus. 2003. (Illus.). 150p. (J). mass mkt. 14.95 (978-1-929515-26-4(X) , Solovisions) Comic Library International.

McCurdy, J. Fitzgerald. The Serpent's Egg. 2001. (Illus.). 280p. (J). (gr. 9-13). (978-0-9688713-0-0(5)) Saratime, Inc.

McCutchen, Heather L. LightLand. (Illus.). 240p. (J). 2002. (gr. 3-7). pap. 16.95 (978-0-439-39565-6(8)); 2004. reprint ed. pap. 4.99 (978-0-439-39566-3(6)) Scholastic, Inc. (Orchard Bks.).

McDermott, Gerald. Arrow to the Sun. 30th anniv. ed. 2004. 48p. (J). (gr. k). 16.99 (978-0-670-05938-6(2) , Viking Juvenile) Penguin Group (USA) Inc.

McFann, Jennifer. Laveidem. 2004. 192p. (J). (gr. 5 up). pap. 9.95 (978-0-439-63987-3(5)) Scholastic, Inc.

McGauley, Patrick. Mazral & Derisa: An Easter Story. l.t. ed. 2004. (Illus.). 40p. (J). pap. 17.99 (978-0-9724209-9-0(1)) McGauley, Patrick.

McGee, D. M. The Jollys & the Cross. 2007. 164p. per. (**978-1-84685-674-7(4)* , Exposure Publishing) Meadow Bks.

McGee, Warner, illus. Hide & Go Boo! 2006. (Backyardigans Ser.). 16p. (J). pap. 5.99 (978-1-4169-1229-3(0) , Simon Spotlight/Nickelodeon) Simon & Schuster Children's Publishing.

McGraw, Eloise Jarvis & McGraw, Lauren Lynn. The Forbidden Fountain of Oz. 2006. (J). 24.95 (978-1-930764-12-5(X)) International Wizard of Oz Club, The.

McGraw-Hill Staff. Rapunzel. 2001. (gr. k-3). lib. bdg. 11.80 (978-0-613-87941-5(4)) Tandem Library Bks.

McKay, Sindy. We Both Read-the New Red Bed. Mauterer, Erin Marie, illus. 1999. (We Both Read Ser.). 44p. (J). (gr. 1 up). 7.99 (978-1-891327-12-4(7)); pap. 3.99 (978-1-891327-16-2(X)) Treasure Bay, Inc.

McKillip, Patricia A. The Changeling Sea. 2003. (Firebird Ser.). (Illus.). 144p. (YA). (gr. 7). pap. 5.99 (978-0-14-131262-0(9) , Puffin) Penguin Group (USA) Inc.

—Changeling Sea. 2003. (gr. 7-12). lib. bdg. 14.15 (978-0-613-61615-7(4)) Tandem Library Bks.

—The Forgotten Beasts of Eld. 2006. 352p. (YA). pap. 6.95 (978-0-15-205536-3(3) , Magic Carpet Bks.) Harcourt Children's Bks.

McKinley, Robin. Beauty: A Retelling of the Story of Beauty & the Beast. 2005. 336p. (YA). (gr. 7 up). pap. 6.99 (978-0-06-075310-8(2)) HarperCollins Pubs.

—Blue Sword. 2001. (Illus.). 288p. (J). (gr. 3-7). pap. (978-0-14-131188-3(6) , Puffin) Penguin Group (USA) Inc.

—Door in the Hedge. 2003. (gr. 7-12). lib. bdg. 15.30 (978-0-613-73478-3(5)) Tandem Library Bks.

—Hero & the Crown. 2000. 13.64 (978-0-606-20361-6(3)); (gr. 7-12). lib. bdg. 15.30 (978-0-613-33703-8(4)) Tandem Library Bks.

—The Spindle's End. 2001. 368p. (gr. 8-12). reprint ed. mass mkt. 6.99 (978-0-441-00865-0(8) , Ace Bks.) Penguin Group (USA) Inc.

—The Spindle's End. 2001. (Illus.). (J). (978-0-606-21447-6(X)) Tandem Library Bks.

McKinty, Adrian. The Lighthouse Land. 2006. (Illus.). 200p. (YA). (gr. 6-10). 16.95 (978-0-8109-5480-9(X)) Abrams, Harry N. , Inc.

McLean, Wendy & Book Company Staff. Follow an Elf. Worthington, Leonie, illus. 2003. (Sparkle Bks.). 10p. (J). bds. 8.95 (978-1-74047-314-9(0)) Book Co. Publishing Pty, Ltd., The AUS. *Dist:* Penton Overseas, Inc.

McMillan, Matthew G. The Dreamer. 2002. 192p. (YA). per. 16.95 (978-0-9708053-1-7(4)) Authors & Artists Publishers of New York, Inc.

McMillion, Gloria. Whirlwinds Whirl Around. 2007. 136p. per. 11.95 (**978-0-595-42248-7(9)*) iUniverse, Inc.

McMullan, Kate. Dragon Slayers' Academy. Basso, Bill, illus. 2005. (Dragon Slayers' Academy Ser.). 112p. (J). lthr. 19.96 (978-0-448-43976-1(X) , Grosset & Dunlap) Penguin Group (USA) Inc.

—The Ghost of Sir Herbert Dungeonstone, Vol. 12. Basso, Bill, illus. 2004. (Dragon Slayers' Academy Ser.: No. 12). 112p. (J). (gr. 2-5). pap. 4.99 (978-0-448-43530-5(6) , Grosset & Dunlap) Penguin Group (USA) Inc.

—Stop That Bull, Theseus! LaFleur, David, illus. 2003. (Myth-o-Mania Ser.: Bk. 5). 160p. (J). (gr. 3-7). 9.99 (978-0-7868-0861-8(6)) Hyperion Bks. for Children.

—A Wedding for Wiglaf?, Vol. 4. Basso, Bill, illus. 2003. (Dragon Slayers' Academy Ser.: No. 4). 112p. (gr. 1-4). pap. 4.99 (978-0-448-43111-6(4) , Grosset & Dunlap) Penguin Group (USA) Inc.

McMullan, Kate. Wheel of Misfortune. 2007. (Dragon Slayers' Academy Ser.: No. 7). 112p. (J). (gr. 1-6). 24.21 (**978-1-59961-381-9(6)*) Spotlight.

McNair, Ed. Indigo Star. 2002. 132p. (YA). pap. 10.95 (978-0-595-21441-9(X) , Writers Club Pr.) iUniverse, Inc.

McNamee, Eoin. The Navigator. (gr. 4-7). 2008. 252p. (J). 6.99 (**978-0-385-73554-4(5)* , Yearling); 2007. (Illus.). 352p. (YA). 15.99 (978-0-375-83910-8(0) , Lamb, Wendy) Random Hse. Children's Bks.

McNaughton, Janet. An Earthly Knight. 2004. 272p. (YA). (gr. 7 up). 15.99 (978-0-06-008992-4(X)) HarperCollins Pubs.

McNish, Cliff. The Silver Child. 192p. (J). (gr. 4-6). 2006. pap. 6.95 (978-0-8225-6503-1(X) , First Avenue Editions); 2005. (Silver Sequence: Book 1). 15.95 (978-1-57505-825-2(1)) Lerner Publishing Group.

—Silver City. 2007. (Exceptional Reading & Language Arts Titles for Intermediate Grades Ser.). 256p. (J). (gr. 4-8). pap. 6.95 (**978-0-8225-6780-6(6)* , First Avenue Editions) Lerner Publishing Group.

McNish, Cliff. Silver World. 2007. (Silver Sequence Ser.). 248p. (J). (gr. 4-8). 15.95 (978-1-57505-897-9(9) , Carolrhoda Bks.) Lerner Publishing Group.

McOmber, Rachel B., ed. McOmber Phonics Storybooks: Robin Hood's Cook. rev. ed. (Illus.). (J). (978-0-944991-64-0(5)) Swift Learning Resources.

—McOmber Phonics Storybooks: Under the Rainbow. rev. ed. (Illus.). (J). (978-0-944991-81-7(5)) Swift Learning Resources.

McPartland, Dorothy. Wishing Stars. McPartland, Dorothy, illus. 2004. (Illus.). 34p. (J). bds. 15.95 (978-0-9755374-0-4(7)) Little Light Pr.

McPhail, David M. In the Summer I Go Fishing. pap. 5.00 (978-0-201-04612-0(1)) Addison-Wesley Longman, Inc.

Mead. Crossing Starlight Bridge. 1998. (J). pap. 3.95 (978-0-87628-343-1(1)) Ctr. for Applied Research in Education, The.

Mead, David. Fairy Magic: An Enchanted Journey of Discovery. Byers, Brian, illus. 2006. 22p. (J). (gr. 3-12). bds. 10.95 (978-1-59125-555-0(4)) Penton Overseas, Inc.

Meadows, Daisy. Heather the Violet Fairy. 2005. 71p. (J). (978-0-439-69192-5(3)) Scholastic, Inc.

—Inky the Indigo Fairy. 2005. 67p. (J). (978-0-439-69193-2(1)) Scholastic, Inc.

—Weather Fairies: Crystal the Snow Fairy. Ripper, Georgie, illus. 2006. 80p. (J). pap. 4.99 (978-0-439-81387-7(5) , Scholastic Paperbacks) Scholastic, Inc.

Mebus, Scott. Gods of Manhattan: the Hidden Light: The Hidden Light. 2008. 272p. (YA). (gr. 5). 17.99 (**978-0-525-47955-0(4)* , Dutton Juvenile) Penguin Group (USA) Inc.

Meehan, William. Amulets of Acacia. 2003. 184p. 23.95 (978-0-595-74755-9(8)); pap. 13.95 (978-0-595-27163-4(4)) iUniverse, Inc.

Meganck, Glenn & Ward, Jon, illus. Big Deal & the Fountain of Youth. 2000. (J). pap. (978-1-892339-06-5(4)) Beachfront Publishing.

Memoirs of Gulis: Growing Up. l.t. ed. 2005. (Illus.). 28p. (J). pap. 14.95 (978-0-9768752-1-5(7)) Open Spaces Publishing (Rupen), LLC.

Menchen, Antonio Martinez. Fosco. (SPA.). 104p. (YA). (gr. 5-8). (978-84-204-4101-6(5) , AF1750) Alfaguara, Ediciones, S.A.- Grupo Santillana ESP. *Dist:* Lectorum Pubns., Inc.

Menchu, Rigoberta. The Honey Jar. Domi, illus. 2006. 56p. (J). 16.95 (978-0-88899-670-1(5)) Groundwood Bks. CAN. *Dist:* Perseus Distribution.

Mendo, Miguel Angel, contrib. by. The Old Princess Armonia. 2002. (Illus.). 56p. 16.00 (978-88-7757-141-0(1)) Hopefulmonster Editore ITA. *Dist:* D.A.P./Distributed Art Pubs.

Mendo, Miguel Angel, tr. Blancanieves. Barrett, Angela, illus. 2007. (SPA.). (J). (gr. 2-5). 24.95 (**978-84-96629-17-2(1)*) S.A. Kokinos ESP. *Dist:* Lectorum Pubns., Inc.

Merce Company Staff. Don Gil y el Paraguas Magico. (Barril Sin Fondo Ser.). (SPA.). (J). (gr. 3-5). pap. (978-968-6465-02-0(2)) Casa de Estudios de Literatura y Talleres Artisticos Amaquemecan A.C. MEX. *Dist:* Lectorum Pubns., Inc.

Meredith Books Staff. Shrek the Third. Marshall, Paula, ed. 2007. (I Can Find It Ser.). 24p. (J). pap. 4.99 (**978-0-696-23729-4(6)*) Meredith Bks.

Meredith Books Staff & Forlini, Victoria, eds. The Sweet Treats Contest: Deluxe Sound Storybook. 2004. (Strawberry Shortcake Ser.). (ENG., Illus.). 22p. (J). (gr. k-3). 15.95 (978-0-696-22242-9(6)) Meredith Bks.

Merlin, Master. Wizardology: The Book of the Secrets of Merlin. Steer, Dugald, ed. Gilbert, Anne Yvonne et al, illus. gif. ed. 2005. (Ologies Ser.). 32p. (J). (gr. 3 up). 19.99 (978-0-7636-2895-6(6)) Candlewick Pr.

Merritt, Gail. Silver Mantle. 2002. (Illus.). 160p. (YA). pap. (978-0-7344-0177-9(9) , Lothian Bks.) Hachette Livre Australia.

—Silver Mantle. 2001. (gr. 7-12). lib. bdg. 22.20 (978-0-613-90916-7(X)) Tandem Library Bks.

Metaxas, Eric. The Fool & the Flying Ship. Drescher, Henrik, illus. 2007. (J). 25.65 (978-1-59961-308-6(5)) ABDO Publishing Co.

Metroid, 2 vols., Vol. 1. 2005. (Illus.). 192p. (YA). pap. 9.99 (978-1-59182-738-2(8)) TOKYOPOP, Inc.

Metz, Diana. Talon & the Dragons of Crinnelia. Metz, Dave, illus. 2002. 280p. (J). per. 6.95 (978-0-9718431-1-0(2)) M.O.T.H.E.R. Publishing Co., Inc., The.

Meyer, Eleanor Walsh. The Keeper of Ugly Sounds. Guzner, Vlad, illus. 1998. 32p. (J). (gr. k-3). 16.95 (978-1-890817-02-2(3)) Winslow Pr.

Meyer, Kai. The Glass Word. Crawford, Elizabeth D., tr. from GER. 2008. (Dark Reflections Trilogy Ser.). 288p. (YA). (gr. 7 up). 16.99 (**978-0-689-87791-9(9)* , McElderry, Margaret K.) Simon & Schuster Children's Publishing.

—Pirate Curse. Crawford, Elizabeth D., tr. from GER. 2006. (Wave Walkers Ser.). 336p. (J). (gr. 5-9). 15.95 (978-1-4169-2421-0(3) , McElderry, Margaret K.) Simon & Schuster Children's Publishing.

—The Stone Light. Crawford, Elizabeth D., tr. (Dark Reflections Trilogy Ser.). (YA). 2007. 384p. pap. 8.99 (**978-0-689-87790-2(0)* , Simon Pulse); 2006. 368p. (gr. 7 up). 16.95 (978-0-689-87789-6(7) , McElderry, Margaret K.) Simon & Schuster Children's Publishing.

Meyer, Kai. The Water Mirror. Crawford, Elizabeth D., tr. 2006. (Dark Reflections Trilogy Ser.). 272p. (YA). pap. 7.99 (978-0-689-87788-9(9) , Simon Pulse); 2005. (Dark Reflections Ser.: Bk. 1). 256p. (J). (gr. 7 up). 15.95 (978-0-689-87787-2(0) , McElderry, Margaret K.) Simon & Schuster Children's Publishing.

—The Water Mirror. l.t. ed. 2006. 260p. (YA). 22.95 (978-0-7862-8288-3(6)) Thorndike Pr.

Meyer, Kai & Crawford, Elizabeth D. The Water Mirror. 2005. (J). (978-978-068-987-2(7) , McElderry, Margaret K.) Simon & Schuster Children's Publishing.

Meyer, Stephenie. New Moon. 2006. (Twilight Saga Ser.). 608p. (J). (gr. 7 up). 18.99 (978-0-316-16019-3(9) , Tingley, Megan Bks.) Little, Brown Bks. for Young Readers.

Mhlophe, Gcina. Our Story Magic. 2006. 100p. 29.95 (**978-1-86914-111-0(3)*) Univ. of Natal Pr. ZAF. *Dist:* International Specialized Bk. Services.

Michael, Livi. City of Dogs. 2007. 250p. (J). (gr. 5). 16.99 (**978-0-399-24356-1(9)* , Putnam Juvenile) Penguin Group (USA) Inc.

Michel, Pauline. Frissons D'enfants: Nouvelles. 2006. (ENG & FRE.). 94p. (J). (978-2-89261-460-2(0)); (978-1-894852-21-0(4)) X Y Z Publishing.

Mieville, China. Un Lun Dun. 2007. (Illus.). 448p. (J). (gr. 5-9). 17.95 (978-0-345-49516-7(0) , Del Rey) Random House Publishing Group.

Miglis Sandvik, Jenny. Midnight Mayhem No. 4: Color Activity Book with Iron-On Transfer. Karl, Linda, illus. 2004. (Shrek 2 Ser.). 32p. (J). act. bk. ed. 3.99 (978-0-439-57635-2(0)) Scholastic, Inc.

—Smellyweds. Bahr, Beth Lazor, illus. 2004. (Shrek 2 Ser.). 32p. (J). 4.99 (978-0-439-63402-1(4)) Scholastic, Inc.

Mignola, Mike, et al. Odd Jobs. (Hellboy Ser.). (Illus.). 216p. (gr. 11 up). pap. 14.95 (978-1-56971-440-9(1)) Dark Horse Comics.

Mihara, Mitsukazu, creator. Doll, 6 vols., Vol. 3. rev. ed. 2005. (Illus.). 192p. pap. 9.99 (978-1-59182-888-4(0) , Tokyopop Adult) TOKYOPOP, Inc.

Mihara, Mitsukazu, illus. & creator. Doll, Vol. 4. Mihara, Mitsukazu, creator. rev. ed. 2005. 192p. pap. 9.99 (978-1-59532-390-3(2) , Tokyopop Adult) TOKYOPOP, Inc.

Milky, D. J. Treasure Chess. 2004. (Illus.). 200p. (YA). pap. 9.99 (978-1-59182-658-3(6)) TOKYOPOP, Inc.

Miller, Deanna. Sky Bounce. 2003. (Illus.). 210p. (YA). per. 7.99 (978-0-9725424-1-8(8)) Miller, Deanna.

Miller, Dorothy Anne. Stories to Read 'Round the Campfire. 2006. pap. 12.95 (978-1-4137-7554-9(3)) PublishAmerica, Inc.

Miller, Frank. Daredevil Visionaries Vol. 2: Frank Miller. 2001. 368p. (YA). (gr. 4-7). 24.95 (978-0-7851-0771-2(1) , Visionaries) Marvel Enterprises, Inc.

Miller, Leslie A. Annie's Second Chance: A Second Chance at Life Offers a Second Chance at Love. Hutchinson, Nancy, illus. 2000. 48p. (J). (gr. 3-6). 17.95 (978-1-929407-00-2(9)) Treasure Text Pubns.

Miller, Walter. Saint Leibowitz & the Wild Horse Woman. 2000. (gr. 7-12). lib. bdg. 24.55 (978-0-613-22295-2(4)) Tandem Library Bks.

Millin, Christopher. The King of Arugula. 2007. 208p. (J). (gr. 1-7). pap. 10.95 (**978-1-897235-21-8(6)*) Thistledown Pr., Ltd. CAN. *Dist:* Fitzhenry & Whiteside, Ltd.

Mills, Judith. The Book of the Sage. 3rd rev. ed. 2004. (Goodfellow Chronicles Ser.). (Illus.). 304p. (J). pap. 9.95 (**978-1-55263-559-9(7)*) Key Porter Bks. CAN. *Dist:* Perseus Distribution.

—The Messengers, Vol. 2. 2nd rev. ed. 2002. (Goodfellow Chronicles Ser.). (Illus.). 296p. (J). pap. 9.95 (**978-1-55263-551-3(1)*) Key Porter Bks. CAN. *Dist:* Perseus Distribution.

—A Sacred Seal. rev. ed. 2001. (Goodfellow Chronicles Ser.). (Illus.). 304p. (J). pap. 9.95 (**978-1-55263-328-1(4)*) Key Porter Bks. CAN. *Dist:* Perseus Distribution.

Mills, Lauren A. Fairy Wings. 2001. (J). 13.54 (978-0-606-20656-3(6)) Tandem Library Bks.

Milson, Matthew R. Young Arcan & the Garden of Loc. 2007. 240p. pap. 14.95 (**978-1-933770-03-1(1)*) Avari Press.

Mindler, Jason. Giralon. 2003. 122p. (YA). 20.95 (978-0-595-74854-9(6)); pap. 10.95 (978-0-595-28581-5(3)) iUniverse, Inc. (Writers Club Pr.).

Minsky, Terri. Mom's Best Friend & Movin' on Up, 7 vols. (Lizzie McGuire Ser.). (Illus.). 96p. Vol. 6. 2004. pap. 7.99 (978-1-59182-572-2(5)); Vol. 7. 2004. pap. 7.99 (978-1-59182-573-9(3)); Vol. 10. 2005. pap. 7.99 (978-1-59532-281-4(7)) TOKYOPOP, Inc. (Tokyopop Kids).

Minsky, Terri, creator. Lizzie Mcguire Box 1. 2005. (Illus.). 384p. pap. 19.99 (978-1-59816-063-5(X) , Tokyopop Kids) TOKYOPOP, Inc.

—Lizzie Mcguire Cine-Manga Vol. 11: In Miranda, Lizzie Does Not Trust & the Longest Yard. 2005. (Illus.). 192p. pap. 7.99 (978-1-59532-282-1(5) , Tokyopop Kids) TOKYOPOP, Inc.

Miraglia, Matthew. Maria & the Carrot Patch. 2007. (J). per. 17.99 (**978-1-59886-984-2(1)*) Tate Publishing & Enterprises, L.L.C.

The Mission. 2nd ed. 2003. 200p. (YA). per. 10.95 (978-0-9713292-2-5(2)) Aim Higher Bks.

Mitchell, Chris. The Realm Legends. 2006. pap. 40.99 (**978-1-4208-9129-4(4)*) AuthorHouse.

Mitchell, Joni. Chelsea Morning. Froud, Brian, illus. 2004. 32p. 17.95 (978-1-59687-178-6(4) , Milk & Cookies) ibooks, Inc.

Mitchell, Malinda. Kon-Reah's Dream Guy. 2005. 50p. pap. 12.95 (978-1-4137-5317-2(5)) PublishAmerica, Inc.

Mitchell, Mark E. The Curious Courtship of King George, 5 vols. 1998. (Chronicles of the House of Chax Ser.: Bk. 4). 84p. (J). (ps-k). pap. 9.99 (978-0-88092-351-4(2) , 3512) Royal Fireworks Publishing Co.

—The Curious Flame of King Pellimore, 5 vols. 1998. (Chronicles of the House of Chax Ser.: Bk. 5). 88p. (J). (ps-k). pap. 9.99 (978-0-88092-353-8(9) , 3539) Royal Fireworks Publishing Co.

Mitchell, N. J. W. Fuzbud & the Wizard: A Sequel to the Adventures of Princess Nightshade. 2001. 168p. (J). pap. 12.95 (978-0-595-19111-6(8)) iUniverse, Inc.

—Hannah, the Witch, & the Unicorn: A Sequel to the Adventures of Princess Nightshade & Fuzbud & the Wizard. 2002. 154p. (J). pap. 11.95 (978-0-595-21186-9(0) , Writer's Showcase Pr.) iUniverse, Inc.

Miyasaka, Kaho. Kare First Love. Watanabe, Akira, tr. Miyasaka, Kaho, illus. 2004. (Kare First Love Ser.: Vol. 1). (Illus.). 200p. (YA). pap. 9.95 (978-1-59116-394-7(3)) Viz Media.

—Kare First Love. Miyasaka, Kaho, illus. (Kare First Love Ser.). (Illus.). (YA). Vol. 2. 2004. 200p. pap. 9.95 (978-1-59116-395-4(1)); Vol. 3. 2005. 192p. pap. 9.99 (978-1-59116-701-3(9)) Viz Media.

Miyazaki, Hayao. Miyazaki's Spirited Away. Miyazaki, Hayao, illus. 2002. (Spirited Away Ser.). (Illus.). 17.51 (978-1-4046-2807-6(X)); 17.51 (978-1-4046-2808-3(8)); 17.51 (978-1-4046-2809-0(6)); 17.51 (978-1-4046-2789-5(8)); 17.51 (978-1-4046-2587-7(9)) Book Wholesalers, Inc.

—Nausicaa of the Valley of the Wind. Miyazaki, Hayao, illus. 2nd ed. 2004. (Nausicaa of the Valley of the Wind Ser.). (YA). Vol. 6. 168p. pap. 9.95 (978-1-59116-354-1(4)); Vol. 7. 232p. pap. 9.95 (978-1-59116-355-8(2)) Viz Media.

—Spirited Away. Orig. Title: Sen to Chihiro no kamikakushi. (gr. 3-6). 2003. lib. bdg. 18.75 (978-0-613-79014-7(6)); 2002. lib. bdg. 18.75 (978-0-613-79012-3(X)); 2002. lib. bdg. 18.75 (978-0-613-79013-0(8)); 2002. lib. bdg. 18.75 (978-0-613-79011-6(1)) Tandem Library Bks.

—Spirited Away. Miyazaki, Hayao, illus. (Spirited Away Ser.). Orig. Title: Sen to Chihiro no kamikakushi. (Illus.). 172p. (YA). Vol. 1. 2002. pap. 9.95 (978-1-56931-791-4(7)); Vol. 2. 2002. pap. 9.95 (978-1-56931-792-1(5)); Vol. 3. 2003. pap. 9.95 (978-1-56931-793-8(3)) Viz Media.

Mizuki, Hakase. The Demon Ororon, 4 vols., Vol. 2. rev. ed. 2004. (Illus.). 208p. pap. 9.99 (978-1-59182-726-9(4) , Tokyopop Adult) TOKYOPOP, Inc.

Mizuno, Ryou & Sasameyuki, Jun. Louie the Rune Soldier, Vol. 2. 2004. (Illus.). 168p. (YA). pap. (978-1-4139-0105-4(0)) ADV Manga.

Modesitt, L. E., Jr. The Spellsong War. 1999. (Spellsong Cycle Ser.: Bk. 2). (gr. 7-12). lib. bdg. 15.30 (978-0-613-22421-5(3)) Tandem Library Bks.

Moerbeck, Kees, illus. & des. Cinderella. Moerbeck, Kees, des. 2006. 9.99 (978-1-84643-019-0(4)) Child's Play-International.

Moloney, James. The Book of Lies. 2007. 368p. (J). (gr. 4-8). 16.99 (978-0-06-057842-8(4)); lib. bdg. 17.89 (978-0-06-057843-5(2)) HarperCollins Pubs.

Monesson, Harry S. Berry Patch Tales: A Collection of Stories. 2000. (gr. 3-6). lib. bdg. 28.45 (978-0-613-79688-0(8)) Tandem Library Bks.

Montgomery, L. M. Ana la de Alamos Ventosos. (SPA.). 288p. (YA). (gr. 5-8). (978-84-7888-636-4(2) , SAL3944) Emece Editores ESP. *Dist:* Lectorum Pubns., Inc.

Moon, Adam. The Fuzzle. 2007. (J). per. 7.95 (**978-1-934345-28-3(8)*) SouthWest Pubns.

Mooney, Jane-Marie. Wings in Dragon Dance. 2007. (ENG.). 168p. pe. (**978-1-84685-551-1(9)* , Exposure Publishing) Meadow Bks.

Mooney, Margaret. Sour Grapes. 2001. (gr. k-3). lib. bdg. 11.65 (978-0-613-33434-1(5)) Tandem Library Bks.

Moore, Alan. Watchmen: The Absolute Edition. Gibbons, David, illus. 2002. 27.19 (978-1-4046-0914-3(8)) Book Wholesalers, Inc.

Moore, Ishbel. Xanthe's Pyramid. 1998. 120p. (YA). (gr. 7-12). pap. 6.95 (978-1-896184-34-0(0)) Roussan Pubs., Inc./Roussan Editeur, Inc. CAN. *Dist:* Orca Bk. Pubs. USA.

Moore, James. Chaos Bleeds. 2003. (gr. 7-12). lib. bdg. 15.30 (978-0-613-66483-7(3)) Tandem Library Bks.

Moore, Perry. Hero. rev. ed. 2007. 432p. (gr. 8 up). 16.99 ***(978-1-4231-0195-6(2))*** Hyperion Pr.

Morano, John. Makoona. 2nd rev. ed. 2005. (Morano Eco-Adventure Ser.: 2). 280p. (YA). (gr. 8-12). pap. 14.99 (978-1-59092-111-1(9) , Blue Works) Windstorm Creative.

Morden, Simon. The Lost Art. 2008. 528p. (J). (gr. 7). lib. bdg. 19.99 (***978-0-385-75148-3(6)*** , Fickling, David Bks.) Random Hse. Children's Bks.

Moredun, P. R. The World of Eldaterra Vol. 1: The Dragon Conspiracy. 2005. (World of Eldaterra Ser.). (Illus.). 304p. (J). (gr. 7 up). lib. bdg. 17.89 (978-0-06-076664-1(6)) HarperCollins Pubs.

Moredun, P.R. The World of Eldaterra: The Dragon Conspiracy, Vol. 1. 2005. (World of Eldaterra Ser.). 304p. (J). (gr. 7 up). 16.99 (978-0-06-076663-4(8)) HarperCollins Pubs.

Morena - di Palma, Alicia. One Dampy Dawn. 2004. (J). 5.95 (978-0-9729454-1-7(5) , MomGeek.com) Wood Designs, Inc.

Morgan, Allen. Matthew & the Midnight Tow Truck. Martchenko, Michael, illus. 2003. (Annikins Ser.: Vol. 11). 32p. (J). (ps-2). pap. 1.25 (978-1-55037-192-5(4)) Annick Pr., Ltd. CAN. *Dist:* Firefly Bks., Ltd.

—Matthew & the Midnight Turkeys. Martchenko, Michael, illus. 2003. 24p. (J). (ps-2). pap. 5.95 (978-0-920303-37-5(4)); (Annikins Ser.: Vol. 11). pap. 0.99 (978-1-55037-193-2(2)) Annick Pr., Ltd. CAN. *Dist:* Firefly Bks., Ltd.

—Matthew & the Midnight Wrecker. ed. 2004. (Illus.). (J). (gr. k-3). spiral bd. (978-0-616-11123-9(1)) Canadian National Institute for the Blind/Institut National Canadien pour les Aveugles.

—Matthew & the Midnight Wrecker. Martchenko, Michael, illus. 2001. (Matthew's Midnight Adventures Ser.). 32p. (J). 6.99 (978-0-7737-3295-7(0)) Stoddart Kids CAN. *Dist:* Fitzhenry & Whiteside, Ltd.

—Matthew & the Midnight Wrestlers. 2000. (gr. k-3). lib. bdg. 15.30 (978-0-613-84051-4(8)) Tandem Library Bks.

—Matthew's Midnight Adventures. Martchenko, Michael, illus. 2001. 80p. (J). (ps-2). 19.95 (978-1-55037-699-9(3)) Annick Pr., Ltd. CAN. *Dist:* Firefly Bks., Ltd.

Morgan, Allen & Martchenko, Michael. Matthew & the Midnight Wrestlers. 2000. (Matthew's Midnight Adventures Ser.). (Illus.). 32p. (J). (ps-3). 6.99 (978-0-7737-6053-0(9)) Stoddart Kids CAN. *Dist:* Fitzhenry & Whiteside, Ltd.

Morgan, C. M. Silver Doorway #1: A Gnome Away from Home. 2003. 104p. (J). pap. 6.99 (978-0-9702189-2-6(2)) Sabledrake Enterprises.

—Silver Doorway #3: An Elf's Adventure. 2004. 104p. (J). pap. 6.99 (978-0-9702189-4-0(X)) Sabledrake Enterprises.

MOrgan, C. M. Silver Doorway #4: Dragon on the Loose. 2004. 104p. (J). pap. 6.99 (978-0-9702189-7-1(4)) Sabledrake Enterprises.

Morgan, C. M. Silver Doorway #5: Orcs Ahoy! 2005. 104p. (J). pap. 6.99 (978-0-9702189-8-8(2)) Sabledrake Enterprises.

Morgan, Jill. Afton of Castlethorpe. 1999. (J). pap. 3.99 (978-0-679-88838-3(1) , Random Hse. Bks. for Young Readers) Random Hse. Children's Bks.

—Nora of Skye Aerie. 1999. (J). pap. 3.99 (978-0-679-88837-6(3) , Random Hse. Bks. for Young Readers) Random Hse. Children's Bks.

Morgan, Nikki. Mithendrove: Escaping Callendae. 2003. 110p. (YA). pap. 9.95 (978-0-595-27138-2(3)) iUniverse, Inc.

Mori, Kotaro. Stray Little Devil. 2006. (Illus.). 200p. (YA). Vol. 2. pap. 9.95 (***978-1-59796-044-1(6));*** Vol. 3. pap. 9.95 (***978-1-59796-045-8(4)***) DrMaster Pubns. Inc.

—Stray Little Devil Volume 4. 2007. (Illus.). 200p. (YA). pap. 9.95 (***978-1-59796-046-5(2)***) DrMaster Pubns. Inc.

Morin, James F. Rothshield Chasing Shadows. 2006. pap. 14.95 (***978-1-59330-422-5(6)***) Aventine Pr.

Morinaga, Ai. Your & My Secret, Vol.1. 2004. (Illus.). 184p. (YA). pap. (978-1-4139-0143-6(3)) ADV Manga.

Moriyama, Daisuke. Chrono Crusade. 2004. (Illus.). (YA). Vol. 2. 200p. pap. (978-1-4139-0104-7(2)); Vol. 3. 198p. pap. (978-1-4139-0045-3(3)) ADV Manga.

Morpurgo, Michael & Richards, Lucy. Mairi's Mermaid. 2006. (Blue Bananas Ser.). (Illus.). 48p. (J). pap. (978-0-7787-0897-1(7)) Crabtree Publishing Co.

Morris, Dave. Kingdom Dream. (Chronicles of Magi Ser.: No. 2). (Illus.). 198p. (J). (gr. k-6). pap. (978-0-340-67299-0(4) , Hodder & Stoughton) Hodder General Publishing Division.

Morris, Gilbert. City of the Cyborgs. 2000. (gr. 7-12). lib. bdg. 14.15 (978-0-613-88613-0(5)) Tandem Library Bks.

—The Spell of the Crystal Chair. 2000. (Seven Sleepers the Lost Chronicles Ser.: Vol. 1). (Illus.). 160p. (J). (gr. 7-12). pap. 5.99 (978-0-8024-3667-2(6)) Moody Pubs.

—Spell of the Crystal Chair. 2000. (gr. 7-12). lib. bdg. 14.15 (978-0-613-88611-6(9)) Tandem Library Bks.

—Strange Creatures of Dr Korbo. 2000. (gr. 7-12). lib. bdg. 14.15 (978-0-613-88022-0(6)) Tandem Library Bks.

—Strange Creatures of Dr. Korbo, Vol. 3. 2000. (Seven Sleepers the Lost Chronicles Ser.: Vol. 3). (Illus.). 144p. (J). (gr. 7-12). pap. 5.99 (978-0-8024-3669-6(2)) Moody Pubs.

Morris, Rooster. The Gate of No Return. Cummins, Scott, illus. 2004. (J). per. 7.95 (978-0-9755895-1-9(2) , 0-9755895-1-2) Axle Publishing Co., Inc.

Mortenson, R. K. Landon Snow & the Auctor's Riddle. 2005. (Landon Now Ser.). (Illus.). 224p. (J). (gr. 4-7). 9.97 (978-1-59310-881-6(8)) Barbour Publishing, Inc.

—Landon Snow & the Igneus Forest. 2007. 224p. (J). 9.97 (978-1-59789-296-4(3) , Barbour Bks.) Barbour Publishing, Inc.

—Landon Snow & the Shadows of Malus Quidam. 2006. (Landon Now Ser.). 208p. (J). 9.97 (978-1-59789-044-1(8)) Barbour Publishing, Inc.

Mortimer, Roger. Ruby of Carminel. 2002. 240p. (J). pap. 8.99 (978-0-7497-4638-4(6)) Egmont Bks., Ltd. GBR. *Dist:* Independent Pubs. Group.

Moshonas, Spyridon. Escape from Argopoli. 2002. 108p. pap. 16.95 (978-1-59129-661-4(7)) PublishAmerica, Inc.

Mouse Works Staff. Aladdin - Peter Pan, 2. 75th anniv. ed. 1998. (Illus.). (ps-3). 9.99 (978-0-7364-0086-2(9)) Mouse Works.

—Alice in Wonderland. 2002. (Classic Storybook Ser.). (J). 7.99 (978-1-57082-976-5(4)) Mouse Works.

—La Bella y la Bestia: Read Aloud Storybook Classic. 1999. (SPA., Illus.). 64p. (J). 6.99 (978-0-7364-0141-8(5)) Disney Pr.

—Mulan - Lady & the Tramp, 2. 75th anniv. ed. 1998. (Illus.). (ps-3). (978-0-7364-0089-3(3)) Mouse Works.

—Peter Pan. 1999. (J). 4.99 (978-0-7364-0045-9(1)) Mouse Works.

—Pinocchio - Toy Story, 2. 75th anniv. ed. 1998. 9.99 (978-0-7364-0088-6(5)) Mouse Works.

Mowll, Joshua. Operation Typhoon Shore. Mowll, Joshua et al, illus. 2006. (Guild of Specialists Ser.). 288p. (YA). (gr. 5 up). 15.99 (978-0-7636-3122-2(1)) Candlewick Pr.

Mudenda, Duly & Nagunga, Kansi. Syankombo. 2004. (Illus.). 20p. 16.95 (978-1-77936-005-2(3)) Africa Community Publishing & Development Trust ZWE. *Dist:* Michigan State Univ. Pr.

Muller, Ann. The Elfree Stories. 2002. (Illus.). 64p. (J). (gr. 1-5). pap. 8.95 (978-1-903464-05-2(6)) Collins Pr., The IRL. *Dist:* Dufour Editions, Inc.

Mulligan, Glori. The Challenge of the Dragons: Book Two of the Trilogy of the Dragons. 2007. (Illus.). 48p. (J). per. 19.95 (***978-1-933324-73-9(2)***) Cedar Hill Publishing.

Munch a Lunch with Wakko, Bk. 3. 1999. (McGraw-Hill Junior Academic Ser.). (Illus.). 16p. (J). (gr. 2). pap. 2.99 (978-1-57768-532-6(6)) School Specialty Publishing.

Munroe, Jim. Flyboy Action Figure Comes with Gasmask. 1999. 256p. pap. 13.50 (978-0-380-81043-7(3)) HarperCollins Pubs.

—Flyboy Action Figure Comes with Gasmask. 1999. (gr. 7-12). lib. bdg. 21.70 (978-0-613-25209-6(8)) Tandem Library Bks.

Murakami, Maki. Gamerz Heaven, Vol. 1. 2004. (Illus.). 184p. (YA). pap. (978-1-4139-0202-0(2)) ADV Manga.

—Gravitation, Vol. 11. Murakami, Maki, illus. rev. ed. 2005. (Illus.). 176p. pap. 9.99 (978-1-59532-414-6(3) , Tokyopop Adult) TOKYOPOP, Inc.

Murayama, Wataru. Desert Coral, Vol. 1. Spencer, Tomoe, tr. 2004. (Illus.). 200p. (YA). pap. (978-1-4139-0050-7(X)) ADV Manga.

—Desert Coral, Vol. 2. 2004. (Illus.). 186p. (YA). pap. (978-1-4139-0088-0(7)) ADV Manga.

—Kagerou-Nostalgia, Vol. 1. 2004. 186p. pap. (978-1-4139-0053-8(4)) ADV Manga.

My Monsters Pop-Up Boggle Eyes. 2001. (Illus.). 10p. (J). (ps-k). 2.99 (978-0-307-20043-3(4) , Golden Bks.) Random Hse. Children's Bks.

My Time on Nantucket. 2005. (J). cd-rom 11.95 (978-0-9755078-2-7(6)) Sweet Punkin Pr.

Mystical World of Nebe: Sky of Dreams. 2006. (YA). 14.95 (978-0-9779369-0-8(2)) Adamson, Mac.

Naifeh, Ted. Courtney Crumrin & the Night Things. Jones, James Lucas, ed. 2005. (Illus.). 120p. lib. bdg. 19.00 (978-0-606-33365-8(7)) Tandem Library Bks.

Nakazaki, Tow. Et Cetera, Vol. 4. Nakazaki, Tow, illus. rev. ed. 2005. (Illus.). 200p. pap. 9.99 (978-1-59532-133-6(0) , Tokyopop Kids) TOKYOPOP, Inc.

Nakazaki, Tow, creator. Et Cetera, 9 vols. rev. ed. 2004. (Illus.). 192p. Vol. 2. pap. 9.99 (978-1-59532-131-2(4)); Vol. 3. pap. 9.99 (978-1-59532-132-9(2)) TOKYOPOP, Inc. (Tokyopop Kids).

Nakazaki, Tow, illus. & creator. Et Cetera, Vol. 5. Nakazaki, Tow, creator. 5th rev. ed. 2005. 208p. pap. 9.99 (978-1-59532-134-3(9) , Tokyopop Kids) TOKYOPOP, Inc.

Namjoshi, Suniti & Jain, Shefalee. Aditi & the Marine Sage. 2004. (Simply a Story Ser.). (Illus.). 80p. (J). (978-81-8146-040-0(5)) Tulika Pubs.

Napoli, Donna Jo. Spinners. 2001. (978-0-606-20924-3(7)) Tandem Library Bks.

Narsimhan, Mahtab. The Third Eye. 2007. 240p. (YA). pap. 11.99 (***978-1-55002-750-1(6)*** , Boardwalk Bks.) Dundurn Group, The CAN. *Dist:* Univ. of Toronto Pr.

Naruse, Kaori. Pretear Vol. 2: The New Legend of Snow White. 2004. (Illus.). 198p. (YA). pap. (978-1-4139-0145-0(X)) ADV Manga.

Narvick, the Whark (or a Shwale) 2003. (J). 8.95 (978-0-9729703-1-0(2)) Kidderature Publishing.

Nasu, Yukie. Here Is Greenwood. Nasu, Yukie, illus. 2005. (Here Is Greenwood Ser.). (Illus.). (YA). Vol. 2. 216p. pap. 9.99 (978-1-59116-605-4(5)); Vol. 3. 200p. pap. 9.99 (978-1-59116-606-1(3)) Viz Media.

Nasu, Yukie & Smith, Joe. Here Is Greenwood, 1. Nasu, Yukie, illus. 2004. (Here Is Greenwood Ser.). (Illus.). 208p. (YA). pap. 9.99 (978-1-59116-604-7(7)) Viz Media.

Naylor, Phyllis Reynolds. Sang Spell. unabr. ed. 2000. 224p. (YA). (gr. 5 up). pap. 35.00 incl. audio (978-0-8072-8293-9(6) , YYA153SP, Listening Library) Random Hse. Audio Publishing Group.

—Sang Spell. 2000. (978-0-606-17828-0(7)); (gr. 5-8). lib. bdg. 13.00 (978-0-613-28632-9(4)) Tandem Library Bks.

Nazemi, Mary. Kaveh, Jolly & the Super Giant. 2006. (J). pap. 15.00 (978-0-8059-7001-2(0)) Dorrance Publishing Co., Inc.

Nelson, Blake. They Came from Below. 2007. 304p. (YA). (gr. 8 up). 17.95 (***978-0-7653-1423-9(1)*** , Tor Teen) Doherty, Tom Assocs., LLC.

Nesbit, E. Enchanted Castle. 2006. pap. (***978-1-4068-3500-7(5)***) Echo Library.

—Five Children & IT. 207p. 20.95 (978-0-8488-2523-2(3)) Amereon LTD.

—Five Children & It. 2006. pap. (***978-1-4068-3501-4(3));*** 2005. 296p. pap. (978-1-84637-200-1(3)) Echo Library.

—The Magic City. 2000. (J). (978-0-606-19471-6(1)) Tandem Library Bks.

—Magic City. 2000. 212p. (gr. 3-6). lib. bdg. 18.75 (978-0-613-32808-1(6)) Tandem Library Bks.

—The Phoenix & the Carpet. 2003. (Children's Classics). (ENG., Illus.). 224p. (J). (gr. 3-6). pap. (978-1-85326-155-8(6)) Wordsworth Editions, Ltd.

Nesbit, E. & Millar, H. R. The Magic City. 2000. (Illus.). 224p. (J). (gr. 4-7). pap. 9.95 (978-1-58717-025-6(6) , SeaStar Bks.) Chronicle Bks. LLC.

Netcomics. Kingdom of the Winds, Vol. 1. 2007. (Kingdom of the Winds Ser.). (Illus.). 216p. per. 9.99 (***978-1-60009-251-0(9)***) Netcomics.

Netcomics & Lee, Youngran. Click, Vol. 4. 2007. (Click (Netcomics) Ser.). (Illus.). 184p. per. 9.99 (***978-1-60009-204-6(7)***) Netcomics.

Nettrour, Nelani. Banshees Bk. 2; Dragon Lands. Nettrour, Heather, illus. l.t. ed. 2003. 114p. (J). pap. 11.95 (978-1-932657-03-6(7)) Third Millennium Pubns.

—Nunkey's Adventures, Bk. 1. Nettrour, Autumn, illus. 2003. 70p. (J). pap. 11.95 (978-1-929381-17-3(4) , Third Millennium Publishing) Sci Fi-Arizona, Inc.

Neuhaus, Eve. Journey to Mythaca. 2006. 347p. (YA). per. 16.95 (***978-1-59594-101-5(0)*** , Wingspan Pr.) WingSpan Publishing.

Newsom, Carol, illus. The Wizard of Oz. 1998. 32p. (J). (ps-1). 12.99 (978-1-929174-02-7(0)) Oshkosh B'Gosh, Inc.

Nicholls, Stan. The Book of Shadows. l.t. ed. 2000. (Illus.). 344p. 18.99 (978-0-7089-9526-6(8)) Ulverscroft Large Print Bks. GBR. *Dist:* Ulverscroft Large Print Bks., Ltd.

Nicholson, William. Firesong. 2002. (Wind on Fire Trilogy: Bk. 3). (YA). (gr. 7-12). lib. bdg. 21.10 (978-0-613-68232-9(7)) Tandem Library Bks.

—Jango. 2007. (YA). (Noble Warriors Trilogy: Bk. 2). (Illus.). 432p. (gr. 7 up). 17.00 (978-0-15-206011-4(1)); 409p. (***978-1-4287-4812-5(1)***) Harcourt Trade Pubs.

—Jango: Book Two of the Noble Warriors. 2008. (Noble Warriors Ser.). (Illus.). 448p. (YA). pap. 7.95 (***978-0-15-206160-9(6)*** , Harcourt Paperbacks) Harcourt Children's Bks.

—Noman. 2008. (YA). (***978-0-15-206005-3(7)***) Harcourt Trade Pubs.

—Seeker. 2007. (Noble Warriors Trilogy Ser.: Bk. 1). (Illus.). 448p. (YA). (gr. 7 up). pap. 7.95 (978-0-15-205866-1(4) , Harcourt Paperbacks) Harcourt Children's Bks.

—Seeker. 2006. (Noble Warriors Trilogy Ser.: Bk. 1). (Illus.). 432p. (YA). 17.00 (978-0-15-205768-8(4)) Harcourt Trade Pubs.

—Slaves of the Mastery. Sis, Peter, illus. 2001. (Wind on Fire Trilogy: Bk. 2). 448p. (gr. 5-9). 17.99 (978-0-7868-0570-9(6)) Hyperion Bks. for Children.

—The Wind on Fire Trilogy, Bk.1. Sis, Peter, illus. 2004. (Wind on Fire Trilogy). 486p. (J). (gr. 5-17). mass mkt. 7.99 (978-0-7868-1826-6(3)) Hyperion Bks. for Children.

—The Wind Singer. 2000. (Wind on Fire Trilogy: Bk. 1). 368p. (gr. 5-9). 17.99 (978-0-7868-2494-6(8)) Hyperion Bks. for Children.

—The Wind Singer. 2003. (Wind on Fire Trilogy: Bk. 1). 384p. (gr. 5-17). pap. 11.99 (978-0-7868-1799-3(2)) Hyperion Pr.

—The Wind Singer. (Wind on Fire Trilogy: Bk. 1). (YA). (gr. 5 up). 2004. lib. bdg. 16.45 (978-0-613-75034-9(9)); 2003. lib. bdg. 21.10 (978-0-613-74958-9(8)) Tandem Library Bks.

Night of the Living Dummy II. 2004. 120p. (J). (gr. 4-7). lib. bdg. 12.04 (978-0-606-30596-9(3)) Tandem Library Bks.

The Night Toys Came to Life. 2001. (J). (POL.). bds. (978-1-58805-156-1(0)); (FRE.). bds. (978-1-58805-157-8(9)) DS-Max USA, Inc.

Nimmo, Jenny. Charlie Bone & the Beast. 2007. (Children of the Red King Ser.: Bk. 6). 464p. (J). 10.99 (***978-0-439-84665-3(X)*** , Orchard Bks.) Scholastic, Inc.

—Charlie Bone & the Hidden King. 2006. (Children of the Red King Ser.: Bk. 5). xx, 441p. (J). (***978-1-4156-7832-9(4)*** , Orchard Bks.) Scholastic, Inc.

—Charlie Bone & the Invisible Boy. 2004. (Children of the Red King Ser.: Bk. 3). (Illus.). 432p. (J). 9.95 (978-0-439-54526-6(9) , Orchard Bks.) Scholastic, Inc.

—Emlyn's Moon. 2007. (Snow Spider Trilogy: Bk. 2). 176p. (J). (gr. 4-7). 9.99 (978-0-439-84676-9(5) , Orchard Bks.) Scholastic, Inc.

—Midnight for Charlie Bone. 2003. (Children of the Red King Ser.: Bk. 1). (J). (gr. 2-6). per. 4.99 (978-0-439-48839-6(7)) Scholastic, Inc.

Nishida, Ryoko. Pokemon Origami: Gold & Silver. Aoyama, Minami, illus. 2001. (Pokemon Ser.). 80p. (YA). pap. 9.95 (978-1-56931-655-9(4)) Viz Media.

Nishiyama, Yukio. Dragon Voice, Vol. 3. Nishiyama, Yukio, illus. rev. ed. 2005. (Illus.). 208p. pap. 9.99 (978-1-59532-121-3(7) , Tokyopop Adult) TOKYOPOP, Inc.

Nishiyama, Yukio, creator. Dragon Voice. 2004. (Teen Ser.). (Illus.). Vol. 1. 208p. pap. 9.99 (978-1-59532-119-0(5)); Vol. 2. 192p. pap. 9.99 (978-1-59532-120-6(9)) TOKYOPOP, Inc. (Tokyopop Adult).

Nishiyama, Yurik. Rebound, Vol. 12. Nishiyama, Yurik, illus. rev. ed. 2005. (Illus.). 200p. pap. 9.99 (978-1-59532-617-1(0) , Tokyopop Adult) TOKYOPOP, Inc.

Nishiyama, Yuriko, illus. & creator. Dragon Voice, Vol. 4. Nishiyama, Yuriko, creator. rev. ed. 2005. 192p. pap. 9.99 (978-1-59532-122-0(5) , Tokyopop Adult) TOKYOPOP, Inc.

—Rebound, Vol. 13. Nishiyama, Yuriko, creator. rev. ed. 2005. 192p. pap. 9.99 (978-1-59532-618-8(9) , Tokyopop Adult) TOKYOPOP, Inc.

Nix, Garth. Abhorsen. 2004. (Old Kingdom Ser.: No. 3). (J). 528p. (gr. 7 up). pap. 7.99 (978-0-06-052873-7(7)); 352p. pap. 12.99 (978-0-06-059498-5(5)) HarperCollins Pubs.

—Abhorsen. Filipetto, Celia, tr. 2006. (Old Kingdom Ser.: No. 3). (SPA.). 315p. (J). 25.99 (***978-84-7871-508-4(8)***) RBA Libros, S.A. ESP. *Dist:* Santillana USA Publishing Co., Inc.

—Abhorsen. 2004. (Old Kingdom Ser.: No. 3). 528p. (J). (gr. 7 up). pap. 54.00 incl. audio (978-1-4000-9011-2(3) , Listening Library) Random Hse. Audio Publishing Group.

—Abhorsen. 2004. (Old Kingdom Ser.: No. 3). (gr. 7-12). lib. bdg. 16.45 (978-0-613-83572-5(7)) Tandem Library Bks.

—Abhorsen Trilogy Set: Sabriel; Lirael; Abhorsen. 2005. (Old Kingdom Ser.: Nos. 1-3). (J). pap. 23.99 (978-0-06-073419-0(1)) HarperCollins Pubs.

—Across the Wall: A Tale of the Abhorsen & Other Stories. 2006. 432p. (J). pap. 7.99 (978-0-06-074715-2(3)) HarperCollins Pubs.

—Aenir. 2001. (Seventh Tower Ser.: Bk. 3). 240p. (J). (ps-7). mass mkt. 5.99 (978-0-439-17684-2(0)) Scholastic, Inc.

—Aenir. 2001. (Seventh Tower Ser.: Bk. 3). 233p. (gr. 3-6). lib. bdg. 13.00 (978-0-613-32247-8(9)) Tandem Library Bks.

—Castle. Rawlings, Steve, illus. 2007. (Seventh Tower Ser.: Bk. 2). 224p. (J). (gr. 3-7). pap. 4.99 (978-0-439-17683-5(2)) Scholastic, Inc.

—The Fall. 2007. (Seventh Tower Ser.: Bk. 1). 208p. (J). (gr. 4-7). pap. 4.99 (978-0-439-17682-8(4)) Scholastic, Inc.

—The Fall. 2000. (Seventh Tower Ser.: Bk. 1). 11.64 (978-0-606-18889-0(4)); (gr. 5-8). lib. bdg. 13.00 (978-0-613-26900-1(4)) Tandem Library Bks.

—Into Battle. 2000. (Seventh Tower Ser.: Bk. 5). (Illus.). (J). 11.64 (978-0-606-21427-8(5)) Tandem Library Bks.

—The Keys to the Kingdom, 3 bks., Set. Incl. Drowned Wednesday. 400p. pap. 15.95 (978-0-439-70086-3(8)); Grim Tuesday. 336p. pap. 15.95 (978-0-439-70370-3(0) , Scholastic Pr.); (J). (gr. 4-7). 2005. 2006. 47.85 (978-0-439-78080-3(2) , Scholastic Pr.) Scholastic, Inc.

—Lirael: Daughter of the Clayr. (Old Kingdom Ser.: No. 2). 2002. 720p. (gr. 7 up). pap. 7.99 (978-0-06-000542-9(4) , Harper Trophy); 2001. (Illus.). 496p. (YA). (gr. 7 up). 18.99 (978-0-06-027823-6(4)); 2004. 480p. (J). pap. 12.99 (978-0-06-059016-1(5)) HarperCollins Pubs.

—Lirael: Daughter of the Clayr. 2002. (Old Kingdom Ser.: No. 2). (gr. 7-12). lib. bdg. 15.30 (978-0-613-62468-8(8)) Tandem Library Bks.

—One Beastly Beast: Two Aliens, Three Inventors, Four Fantastic Tales. Biggs, Brian, illus. 2007. 176p. (J). (gr. 2-6). 15.99 (***978-0-06-084319-9(5));*** lib. bdg. 16.89 (***978-0-06-084320-5(9)***) HarperCollins Pubs. (Eos).

—The Ragwitch. 2004. (gr. 7-12). lib. bdg. 15.30 (978-0-613-71441-9(5)) Tandem Library Bks.

—Sabriel. unabr. ed. 2004. (Old Kingdom Ser.: No. 1). 491p. (J). (gr. 7 up). pap. 54.00 incl. audio (978-0-8072-0794-9(2) , S YA 351 SP, Listening Library) Random Hse. Audio Publishing Group.

—Sabriel. (Old Kingdom Ser.: No. 1). (gr. 7-12). lib. bdg. 15.30 (978-0-613-03597-2(6)) Tandem Library Bks.

—Sir Thursday. (Keys to the Kingdom Ser.: No. 4). 352p. (J). 2007. pap. 6.99 (***978-0-439-43657-1(5)*** , Scholastic Paperbacks); 2006. (gr. 4-7). pap. 16.99 (978-0-439-70087-0(6) , Scholastic Pr.) Scholastic, Inc.

Nix, Garth. The Violet Keystone. 2001. (Seventh Tower Ser.: Bk. 6). 240p. (J). pap. 5.99 (978-0-439-17687-3(5)) Scholastic, Inc.

—The Violet Keystone. 2001. (Seventh Tower Ser.: Bk. 6). 233p. (gr. 3-6). lib. bdg. 13.00 (978-0-613-43905-3(8)) Tandem Library Bks.

No, Yi-Jung, illus. & creator. Visitor. No, Yi-Jung, creator. 2005. 192p. (YA). pap. 9.99 (978-1-59532-342-2(2) , Tokyopop Adult) TOKYOPOP, Inc.

Noble, Marty. Alice in Wonderland Sticker Activity Book. 1998. 4p. (J). pap. 1.50 (978-0-486-40314-4(9)) Dover Pubns., Inc.

Nolan, Lucy. The Lizard Man of Crabtree County. Kastner, Jill, illus. 32p. (J). 2005. pap. 5.95 (978-0-7614-5144-0(7)); 1999. 15.95 (978-0-7614-5049-8(1) , Cavendish Children's Bks.) Cavendish, Marshall Corp.

Noland, Charles. The Adventures of Drew & Ellie: The Daring Rescue. Moyer, Tom, illus. 2nd ed. 2006. (J). per. 7.95 (***978-0-9789297-2-5(1)***) TMD Enterprises.

Norfolk. In the Shape of a Boar. 2002. 336p. pap. 13.00 (978-0-8021-3967-2(1)) Grove/Atlantic, Inc.

Norris, Christine. Talisman of Zandria, 1. Nagy, Robert, illus. 2005. 187p. (YA). pap. 14.95 (978-1-885093-44-8(6) , LBF/Hadrosaur) Hadrosaur Pr.

Norton, Andre. Fur Magic: The Magic Books #3. 2006. (Magic Bks.). 160p. (J). 5.99 (978-0-7653-5299-6(0) , Starscape) Doherty, Tom Assocs., LLC.

—Octagon Magic. 2005. (Magic Bks.: No. 2). 192p. (J). (gr. 5). 5.99 (978-0-7653-5298-9(2) , Starscape) Doherty, Tom Assocs., LLC.

Norton, Jack, Jr. Natasha Goes to the Brush Dance. 2000. pap. 16.50 (978-0-9740071-1-3(0)) Ctr. for the Affirmation of Responsible Education.

Norton, Mary. The Borrowers. Krush, Beth & Krush, Joe, illus. 2003. (Borrowers Ser.). 192p. (J). pap. 5.95 (978-0-15-204737-5(9) , Odyssey Classics) Harcourt Children's Bks.

—The Borrowers. Krush, Beth & Krush, Joe, illus. 2003. 180p. (J). (ps-7). per. 14.10 (978-0-613-63581-3(7)) Tandem Library Bks.

—The Borrowers. Krush, Beth & Krush, Joe, illus. l.t. ed. 2005. 215p. (J). (gr. 3). pap. 10.95 (978-0-7862-7954-8(0)) Thorndike Pr.

—Borrowers. 50th anniv. ed. 2003. (Illus.). (YA). (978-0-15-204768-9(9) , Harcourt Children's Bks) Harcourt Children's Bks.

—The Borrowers. Stanley, Diana, illus. 50th anniv. gif. ed. 2003. (Borrowers Ser.). 176p. (J). 19.95 (978-0-15-204928-7(2)) Harcourt Children's Bks.

—Borrower's Afield. 2003. (gr. 3-6). lib. bdg. 14.10 (978-0-613-70976-7(4)) Tandem Library Bks.

—The Borrowers Afield. Krush, Beth & Krush, Joe, illus. 50th anniv. ed. 2003. (Borrowers Ser.). 224p. (J). pap. 5.95 (978-0-15-204732-0(8) , Odyssey Classics) Harcourt Children's Bks.

—The Borrowers Afloat. Krush, Beth & Krush, Joe, illus. 2003. (Borrowers Ser.). 192p. (J). pap. 5.95 (978-0-15-204733-7(6) , Odyssey Classics) Harcourt Children's Bks.

—The Borrowers Avenged. Krush, Joe & Krush, Beth, illus. 50th anniv. ed. 2003. (Borrowers Ser.). 304p. (J). pap. 5.95 (978-0-15-204731-3(X) , Odyssey Classics) Harcourt Children's Bks.

Nosov, Nikolai. The Adventures of Dunno & His Friends. Kay, Nicole, tr. from ENG. 2006. (RUS.). (J). (978-0-9754433-2-3(1) , Language Transformer Bks.) Velichko, Vera.

Noyes, Deborah. Angel & the Apostle. 2006. 304p. pap. 14.95 (978-1-932961-29-4(1)) Unbridled Bks.

Nuckols, Frank J. The Ghost, the Gold & the Whippoorwill. Nuckols, Alex, illus. 1998. 157p. (J). (gr. 4-6). pap. 8.95 (978-0-943864-91-4(7)) Davenport, May Pubs.

Nunes, Lygia Bojunga. La Cuerda Floja. (SPA.). 136p. (YA). (gr. 5-8). (978-84-204-3122-2(2) , AF1749) Alfaguara, Ediciones, S.A.- Grupo Santillana ESP. *Dist:* Lectorum Pubns., Inc.

Nygren, Kelsie. The Young Writers Series: The Line Between. 2007. (YA). pap. 5.99 (*978-1-58158-109-6(2)) McDougal Publishing Co.

Oberne, Sharon. Kelsey. 2006. 88p. (YA). pap. 13.95 (978-1-58909-340-9(2)) Bookstand Publishing.

O'Brien, John. Poof! O'Brien, John, illus. 2003. (Illus.). 32p. (J). (gr. k-2). 16.95 (978-1-56397-815-9(6)) Boyds Mills Pr.

O'Brien, Patrick. Megatooth. rev. ed. 2001. (Illus.). 32p. (J). (ps-3). 17.95 (978-0-8050-6214-4(9) , Holt, Henry & Co. Bks. For Young Readers) Holt, Henry & Co.

O'Brien, Robert C. Mrs. Frisby & the Rats of Nimh. Bernstein, Zena, illus. 2002. (J). 13.94 (978-0-7587-0205-0(1)) Book Wholesalers, Inc.

—The Silver Crown. Bowers, David M., illus. 2001. (Fantasy Ser.). 272p. (J). pap. 5.99 (978-0-689-84111-8(6) , Aladdin) Simon & Schuster Children's Publishing.

—The Silver Crown. 2001. (gr. 5-8). lib. bdg. 13.00 (978-0-613-37168-1(2)) Tandem Library Bks.

Ocampo, Silvina. La Torre Sin Fin. 1998. Tr. of Tower of No End. (SPA.). 80p. (J). (gr. 4-7). 9.95 (978-84-204-4502-1(9)) Santillana USA Publishing Co., Inc.

Ocelot, Michel. Kirikou et la Soriciere. pap. 14.95 (978-2-01-321877-1(X)) Hachette Groupe Livre FRA. *Dist:* Distribooks, Inc.

Ochiltree, Dianne. Bart's Amazing Charts. Lemelman, Martin, illus. 2001. (Hello Reader! Math Ser.). 32p. (J). (gr. 6). pap. 3.99 (978-0-439-09953-0(6)) Scholastic, Inc.

—Bart's Amazing Charts. 2000. (Hello Reader! Math Ser.). (J). (978-0-606-19538-6(6)) Tandem Library Bks.

Odgers, Sally. Boy down Under. 2004. (YA). mass mkt. 5.99 (978-0-8439-5453-1(1)) Dorchester Publishing Co., Inc.

Odom, Keith C. Mervin the Purple Three-Toed Schmoo. 1999. (Illus.). (J). pap. (978-1-886021-32-7(5)) Wood, Judy W.

Odom, Mel. Cursed. 2003. (Buffy the Vampire Slayer & Angel Crossover Ser.). 448p. mass mkt. 7.99 (978-0-689-86437-7(X) , Simon Pulse) Simon & Schuster Children's Publishing.

O'Dwyer, Bridget. A Celtic Night: A fifteen-year old girl's modern retelling of Shakespeare's A Midsummer Night's Dream. 2006. 160p. (J). pap. 5.95 (978-1-932802-94-8(0) , Holy Macro! Bks.) MrExcel.com Publishing.

Offley, Nancy. The Story of Snickers. 2004. (Illus.). 40p. (J). pap. 9.95 (978-0-9748081-0-9(5)) Classroom Enrichment Assocs.

O'Flatharta, Antoine. The Prairie Train. Rohmann, Eric, illus. 2004. 40p. (J). (ps-3). reprint ed. pap. 6.99 (978-0-553-11334-1(8) , Dragonfly Bks.) Random Hse. Children's Bks.

Ogawa, Yayoi, creator. Tramps Like Us, 7 vols., Vol. 3. rev. ed. 2004. (Illus.). 192p. pap. 9.99 (978-1-59532-141-1(1) , Tokyopop Adult) TOKYOPOP, Inc.

Ogilvy, Ian. Measle & the Dragodon. 2005. 352p. (J). (ps-8). 15.99 (978-0-06-058688-1(5)) HarperCollins Pubs.

O'Hare, Jeff. Dragon Ball Z Extreme. 2003. (Dragonball Z Ser.). (Illus.). 32p. (J). pap. 5.99 (978-0-439-43722-6(9)) Scholastic, Inc.

Ohashi, Kaoru & Kusunoki, Kei. Diabolo, Vol. 3. rev. ed. 2005. (Illus.). 216p. pap. 9.99 (978-1-59532-594-5(8) , Tokyopop Adult) TOKYOPOP, Inc.

Ohkami, Mineko. Dragon Knights. (Graphic Novel-Manga Ser.). (Illus.). Vol. 2. 2nd rev. ed. 2002. 200p. pap. 9.99 (978-1-931514-41-5(0) , Tokyopop Adult); Vol. 3. rev. ed. 2002. 208p. pap. 9.99 (978-1-931514-42-2(9) , TOKYOPOP Manga); Vol. 4. 4th rev. ed. 2002. 200p. pap. 9.99 (978-1-931514-43-9(7) , Tokyopop Adult); Vol. 5. 5th rev. ed. 2002. 208p. pap. 9.99 (978-1-59182-069-7(3) , Tokyopop Adult); Vol. 6. 6th rev. ed. 2003. 208p. pap. 9.99 (978-1-59182-102-1(9) , Tokyopop Adult) TOKYOPOP, Inc.

—Dragon Knights, 17 vols., Vol. 7. Yoshida, Agnes, tr. from JPN. Ohkami, Mineko, illus. rev. ed. 2003. (Graphic Novel-Manga Ser.). (Illus.). 208p. (gr. 8 up). pap. 9.99 (978-1-59182-111-3(8) , Tokyopop Adult) TOKYOPOP, Inc.

—Dragon Knights, 17 vols. 2003. (Graphic Novel-Manga Ser.). (Illus.). 192p. (gr. 8 up). Vol. 8. 8th rev. ed. pap. 9.99 (978-1-59182-112-0(6)); Vol. 9. rev. ed. pap. 9.99 (978-1-59182-113-7(4)) TOKYOPOP, Inc. (Tokyopop Adult).

—Dragon Knights, 17 vols. Ohkami, Mineko, illus. rev. ed. 2003. (Graphic Novel-Manga Ser.). (Illus.). 192p. Vol. 10. pap. 9.99 (978-1-59182-114-4(2)); Vol. 11. pap. 9.99 (978-1-59182-115-1(0)) TOKYOPOP, Inc. (Tokyopop Adult).

—Dragon Knights, 17 vols., Vol. 12. Nakamura, Yuki, tr. from JPN. Ohkami, Mineko, illus. rev. ed. 2004. (Graphic Novel-Manga Ser.). (Illus.). 200p. pap. 9.99 (978-1-59182-440-4(0) , Tokyopop Adult) TOKYOPOP, Inc.

—Dragon Knights, 17 vols. 2004. (Graphic Novel-Manga Ser.). (Illus.). 200p. Vol. 13. rev. ed. pap. 9.99 (978-1-59182-441-1(9)); Vol. 14. 14th rev. ed. pap. 9.99 (978-1-59182-442-8(7)) TOKYOPOP, Inc. (Tokyopop Adult).

—Dragon Knights, 17 vols., Vol. 15. Johnson, Yuki, tr. rev. ed. 2004. (Graphic Novel-Manga Ser.). (Illus.). 200p. pap. 9.99 (978-1-59182-443-5(5) , Tokyopop Adult) TOKYOPOP, Inc.

—Dragon Knights, 20 vols., Vol. 17. rev. ed. 2004. (Graphic Novel-Manga Ser.). (Illus.). 200p. pap. 9.99 (978-1-59182-445-9(1) , Tokyopop Adult) TOKYOPOP, Inc.

Ohkami, Mineko, illus. & creator. Dragon Knights, Vol. 19. Ohkami, Mineko, creator. 19th rev. ed. 2005. 192p. pap. 9.99 (978-1-59182-962-1(3) , Tokyopop Adult) TOKYOPOP, Inc.

Okorafor-Mbachu, Nnedi. The Shadow Speaker. rev. ed. 2007. 336p. (gr. 7 up). 16.99 (*978-1-4231-0033-1(6) , Jump at the Sun) Hyperion Bks. for Children.

Okorafor-Mbachu, Nnedi. Zahrah the Windseeker. Cooper, Stephanie & Hall, Amanda, illus. 2005. 320p. (YA). (gr. 5-7). 16.00 (978-0-618-34090-3(4)) Houghton Mifflin Co. Trade & Reference Div.

Okudo, Hitoshi. The All-New Tenchi Muyo!, Vol. 6. Okudo, Hitoshi, illus. 2005. (All New Tenchi Muyo! Ser.). (Illus.). 184p. (YA). (gr. 8-8). pap. 8.95 (978-1-4215-0011-9(6)) Viz Media.

Oldfield, J. Silver Cloud. 2002. (Illus.). 229p. pap. (978-0-340-85108-1(2) , Hodder & Stoughton) Hodder General Publishing Division.

Oliver, Andrew. Beyond the Enchanted Bridge: A Visit to Scarecrow Land. Oliver, Andrew, photos by. 2002. (Illus.). 136p. (J). (gr. 4-8). pap. 14.95 (978-0-9661009-3-8(X)) Adams-Pomeroy Pr.

Olshan, Matthew. The Flown Sky, 1. 2007. (Illus.). 352p. 19.95 (978-0-9789391-0-6(7)) Chacmool Pr.

Olson, Kevin Noel. Eerey Tocsin in the Cryptoid Zoo. Hammack, Debi, illus. 2006. (YA). per. 15.95 (*978-1-887560-17-7(3) , Cornerstone Bk. Publishers) Poll, Michael Publishing.

Omishi, Ray, illus. Sorcerer Hunters Vol. 2: Authentic Relaunch. rev. ed. 2005. 192p. pap. 9.99 (978-1-59532-495-5(X) , Tokyopop Adult) TOKYOPOP, Inc.

—Sorcerer Hunters Authentic Relaunch. 2005. Vol. 1. 208p. pap. 9.99 (978-1-59532-494-8(1)); Vol. 3. 192p. pap. 9.99 (978-1-59532-496-2(8)) TOKYOPOP, Inc. (Tokyopop Adult).

Once upon a Time- Fantasy Flight. 2005. (J). bds. (978-1-4194-0095-7(9)) Paradise Pr., Inc.

O'Neill, Alexis. Liam McLafferty's Choice. 2006. (J). (978-0-8028-5281-6(5) , Eerdmans Bks For Young Readers) Eerdmans, William B. Publishing Co.

O'Neill, Katrina. Racing for the Birdman. Cantell, Brenda, illus. 2005. (Treasure Trackers Ser.). 80p. (gr. 5-9). 19.00 (978-0-7910-8877-7(4)) Facts On File, Inc.

Oppel, Kenneth. Airborn. (J). 2004. 368p. (gr. 7 up). lib. bdg. 17.89 (978-0-06-053181-2(9)); 2004. (Illus.). 368p. (gr. 7 up). 16.99 (978-0-06-053180-5(0)); 2005. (Illus.). 544p. reprint ed. pap. 7.99 (978-0-06-053182-9(7)) HarperCollins Pubs.

—Airborn. l.t. ed. 2004. 525p. 22.95 (978-0-7862-7035-4(7) , Large Print Pr.) Thorndike Pr.

—Firewing. 2008. 320p. (J). pap. 6.99 (*978-1-4169-4999-2(2) , Aladdin) Simon & Schuster Children's Publishing.

Oppel, Kenneth. Skybreaker. (J). 2007. 560p. (gr. 7 up). pap. 6.99 (978-0-06-053229-1(7)); 2005. (Illus.). 384p. (gr. 6-10). 16.99 (978-0-06-053227-7(0)); 2005. (Illus.). 384p. (gr. 6-10). lib. bdg. 17.89 (978-0-06-053228-4(9)) HarperCollins Pubs.

Oppenheim, Joanne. Could It Be? Schindler, S. D., illus. 1998. (Bank Street Reader Collection). 48p. (J). (gr. 1-3). lib. bdg. 22.60 (978-0-8368-1770-6(2)) Stevens, Gareth Inc.

Oram, Hiawyn. The Giant Surprise: A Narnia Story. Humphries, Tudor, illus. 2005. (Step into Narnia Ser.). 40p. (J). (ps-2). lib. bdg. 16.89 (978-0-06-001360-8(5)) HarperCollins Pubs.

Oram, Hiawyn & Lewis, C. S. The Giant Surprise: A Narnia Story. Humphries, Tudor, illus. 2005. (Step into Narnia Ser.). 40p. (J). (ps-2). 15.99 (978-0-06-008361-8(1)) HarperCollins Pubs.

O'Reilly, Sean. Ezra: Egyptian Exchange. 2005. (YA). 9.95 (978-0-9763095-4-3(8)) Arcana Studio, Inc.

—Kade: Identity. 2005. (YA). 9.95 (978-0-9763095-1-2(3)) Arcana Studio, Inc.

Ormondroyd, Edward. David & the Phoenix. 2002. (J). lib. bdg. 20.00 incl. audio (978-1-932076-04-2(2) , 02007A) Full Cast Audio.

—David & the Phoenix. Rayso, Joan, illus. 2001. 176p. (J). 16.95 (978-1-930900-13-4(9)) Purple Hse. Pr.

—David & the Phoenix. Raysor, Joan, illus. 2001. 173p. (J). (gr. 4-7). pap. 8.99 (978-1-930900-01-1(5)) Purple Hse. Pr.

Orndorff, John C. Prince Michael & the Dragon (A True Story) Morris-Orndorff, Debora, illus. 1998. vi, 87p. (J). (gr. 5-8). pap. 5.95 (978-1-893213-00-5(5)) Pensive Bks.

Orr, Judith A. A Fairy Walk. 2004. 47p. (J). (gr. k-9). pap. 18.95 (978-1-930002-66-1(1)) I & L Publishing.

Ortiz, Kerri L. No-it-at-er... What? & the Tale of the Misplaced Mermaids. 2005. 48p. pap. 12.95 (978-1-4137-4938-0(0)) PublishAmerica, Inc.

Osborne, Mary Pope. Buffalo Before Breakfast. 2004. (Magic Tree House Ser. : No. 18). 72p. (J). (gr. k-3). pap. 17.00 incl. audio (978-0-8072-0927-1(9) , Listening Library) Random Hse. Audio Publishing Group.

—Buffalo Before Breakfast. Murdocca, Sal, illus. 1999. (Magic Tree House Ser.: No. 18). (J). (gr. k-3). 20.00 (978-0-375-80041-2(7)); 96p. lib. bdg. 11.99 (978-0-679-99064-2(X)); Vol. 18. 96p. mass mkt. 3.99 (978-0-679-89064-5(5)) Random Hse. Children's Bks. (Random Hse. Bks. for Young Readers).

—Buffalo Before Breakfast. Murdocca, Salvatore, illus. 1999. (Magic Tree House Ser. : No. 18). 72p. (J). (gr. k-3). lib. bdg. 11.80 (978-0-613-16067-4(3)) Tandem Library Bks.

—Buffalo Before Breakfast. 1999. (Magic Tree House Ser. : No. 18). (J). (gr. k-3). lib. bdg. 10.79 (978-0-606-16841-0(9)) Tandem Library Bks.

—Civil War on Sunday, Vol. 21. unabr. ed. 2004. (Magic Tree House Ser.: No. 21). 76p. (J). (gr. k-3). pap. 17.00 incl. audio (978-0-8072-0930-1(9) , S FTR 253 SP, Listening Library) Random Hse. Audio Publishing Group.

—Civil War on Sunday. Murdocca, Sal, illus. 2000. (Magic Tree House Ser.: No. 21). 96p. (J). (gr. k-3). lib. bdg. 11.99 (978-0-679-99067-3(4)); mass mkt. 3.99 (978-0-679-89067-6(X)) Random Hse. Children's Bks. (Random Hse. Bks. for Young Readers).

—Civil War on Sunday. 2000. (Magic Tree House Ser. : No. 21). (J). (gr. k-3). lib. bdg. 11.80 (978-0-613-24596-8(2)); (Illus.). 10.79 (978-0-606-18852-4(5)) Tandem Library Bks.

—Day of the Dragon King, Vol. 14. unabr. ed. 2004. (Magic Tree House Ser. : No. 14). 68p. (J). (gr. k-3). pap. 17.00 incl. audio (978-0-8072-0783-3(7) , S FTR 242 SP, Listening Library) Random Hse. Audio Publishing Group.

—Day of the Dragon King. Murdocca, Sal, illus. 1998. (Magic Tree House Ser.: No. 14). 96p. (J). (gr. k-3). lib. bdg. 11.99 (978-0-679-99051-2(8)); 14th ed. pap. 3.99 (978-0-679-89051-5(3)) Random Hse. Children's Bks. (Random Hse. Bks. for Young Readers).

—Day of the Dragon King. Murdocca, Sal, illus. 1998. (Magic Tree House Ser. : No. 14). (J). (gr. k-3). 10.79 (978-0-606-13958-8(3)) Tandem Library Bks.

—Dinosaurios al Atardecer. 2003. (SPA.). (gr. 3-6). lib. bdg. 12.95 (978-0-613-64486-0(7)) Tandem Library Bks.

—Dinosaurs Before Dark. unabr. ed. 2004. (Magic Tree House Ser. : No. 1). 68p. (J). (gr. k-5). pap. 17.00 incl. audio (978-0-8072-0330-9(0) , FTR208SP, Listening Library) Random Hse. Audio Publishing Group.

—The Gray-Eyed Goddess. Howell, Troy, illus. 4th rev. ed. 2003. 128p. (gr. 3-6). (Tales from the Odyssey Ser.: No. 4). pap. 4.99 (978-0-7868-0931-8(0)); (Odyssey Ser.: Vol. 4). 9.99 (978-0-7868-0773-4(3)) Hyperion Bks. for Children.

—Haunted Waters. 2006. 160p. (J). (gr. 7). 14.99 (978-0-7636-2995-3(2)) Candlewick Pr.

—Hour of the Olympics. Murdocca, Sal, illus. 1998. (Magic Tree House Ser.: No. 16). 96p. (J). (gr. k-3). lib. bdg. 11.99 (978-0-679-99062-8(3)); mass mkt. 3.99 (978-0-679-89062-1(9)) Random Hse. Children's Bks. (Random Hse. Bks. for Young Readers).

—The Knight at Dawn. unabr. ed. 2004. (Magic Tree House Ser. : No. 2). 66p. (J). (gr. k-3). pap. 17.00 incl. audio (978-0-8072-0331-6(9) , Listening Library) Random Hse. Audio Publishing Group.

—Medianoche en la Luna. 2004. (Coleccion la Casa Del Arbol the Magic Tree House Ser.).Tr. of Midnight on the Moon. (SPA.). (J). pap. 4.95 (978-1-930332-69-0(6)) Lectorum Pubns., Inc.

—The One-Eyed Giant. Howell, Troy, illus. 2003. (Odyssey Ser.: Bk. 1). 112p. (gr. 3-6). pap. 4.99 (978-0-7868-0928-8(0)) Hyperion Bks. for Children.

—Sirens & Sea Monsters. Howell, Troy, illus. 3rd rev. ed. 2003. (Odyssey Ser.: No. 3). 112p. (gr. 3-6). pap. 4.99 (978-0-7868-0930-1(2)) Hyperion Bks. for Children.

—Sirens & Sea Monsters. 2003. (gr. 3-6). lib. bdg. 13.00 (978-0-613-68286-2(6)) Tandem Library Bks.

—Winter of the Ice Wizard. Murdocca, Sal, illus. 2004. (Magic Tree House Ser.: No. 32). 128p. (J). (gr. 1-4). 11.95 (978-0-375-82736-5(6)); lib. bdg. 13.99 (978-0-375-92736-2(0)) Random Hse. Children's Bks. (Random Hse. Bks. for Young Readers).

Osburn, Tracy. Gorp's Gift. 1999. (J). pap., tchr. ed. 7.95 (978-0-9642160-1-3(9)) Round Top Pr.

Osterweil, Adam. The Lost Treasure of Talus Scree. 2005. (Illus.). 152p. (J). (gr. 3-7). 16.95 (978-1-932425-30-7(6) , Lemniscaat) Boyds Mills Pr.

Ostow, Micol. Changeling Places. 2005. (Charmed Ser.). 176p. (YA). pap. 5.99 (978-0-689-87852-7(4) , Simon Spotlight Entertainment) Simon & Schuster.

Osu Library Fund Staff. Fati et l'Arbre a Miel (Fati & the Honey Tree) Keita, Fatou, tr. 2002. (Illus.). 28p. pap. (978-9988-550-42-4(1)) Sub-Saharan Pubs. & Traders.

Otoshi, Kathryn. What Emily Saw. Otoshi, Kathryn, illus. 2004. (Illus.). 36p. (J). (ps-12). 16.95 (978-0-9723946-0-4(5)) KO Kids Bks.

Owen, James A. Here, There Be Dragons. Owen, James A., illus. (Chronicles of the Imaginarium Geographica Ser.). (YA). 2007. 352p. pap. 9.99 (*978-1-4169-1228-6(2) , Simon Pulse); 2006. 336p. 17.95 (978-1-4169-1227-9(4)) Simon & Schuster Children's Publishing.

—The Search for the Red Dragon. Owen, James A., illus. 2008. (Chronicles of the Imaginarium Geographica Ser.). 384p. (YA). (gr. 7 up). 17.99 (*978-1-4169-4850-6(3)) Simon & Schuster Children's Publishing.

Packard, Albert. Cavern of Babel. Boyles, Shawn, illus. 2006. (J). per. 14.95 (*978-0-9790652-0-0(8)) Diamond Triple C Ranch.

Packard, Edward. The Dragon's Den. 1999. (Illus.). 116p. mass mkt. (978-0-553-24249-2(0)) Bantam Bks.

—Mountain Survival. 1999. mass mkt. (978-0-553-23868-6(X)) Bantam Bks.

Page, Nick & Page, Claire. The Summer Queen. 2006. (Read with Me (Make Believe Ideas) Ser.). (Illus.). 31p. (J). (gr. k-2). 3.95 (978-1-84610-170-0(0)) Make Believe Ideas GBR. *Dist:* Ingram Pub. Services.

Pakkins' Land: Quest For Kings, 3 vols., 2. 2001. 128p. (J). pap. 15.95 (978-0-9700241-2-1(6)) Pakkins Presents.

Palmer Preiss, Leah, illus. Escape from Castle Cant. rev. ed. 2007. 287p. (J). (gr. 3-7). per. 6.99 (*978-0-316-15436-9(9)) Little, Brown Bks. for Young Readers.

Panev, Aleksandar. Queen Nzinga. Stefflbauer, Thomas, illus. 2007. 48p. (J). lib. bdg. 23.08 (*978-1-4242-1641-3(9)) Fitzgerald Bks.

Paolini, Christopher. Eldest. (Inheritance Trilogy: Bk. 2). (gr. 7 up). 2007. 704p. (YA). pap. 12.99 (978-0-375-84040-1(0)); 2005. (Illus.). 704p. (YA). lib. bdg. 24.99 (978-0-375-92670-9(4)); 2006. 736p. (J). 24.00 (978-0-375-84060-9(5)); 2006. 736p. (J). lib. bdg. 27.99 (978-0-375-94060-6(X)) Random Hse. Children's Bks. (Knopf Bks. for Young Readers).

—Eldest: Inheritance. 2005. (Inheritance Trilogy: Bk. 2). (Illus.). 704p. (YA). (gr. 7 up). 21.00 (978-0-375-82670-2(X) , Knopf Bks. for Young Readers) Random Hse. Children's Bks.

—Eragon. 2006. (Inheritance Trilogy: Bk. 1). (YA). cd-rom 39.99 (978-1-59895-406-7(7)) Findaway World, LLC.

—Eragon. 2006. (Inheritance Trilogy: Bk. 1). (Illus.). 503p. (YA). (gr. 7 up). (*978-1-4287-0954-6(1)) Knopf, Alfred A. Inc.

—Eragon. (Inheritance Trilogy: Bk. 1). (gr. 7 up). 2007. 768p. (YA). mass mkt. 6.99 (*978-0-440-24073-0(5) , Laurel Leaf); 2006. 768p. (YA). mass mkt. 6.99 (978-0-440-23848-5(X) , Laurel Leaf); 2003. (Illus.). 544p. (J). lib. bdg. 20.99 (978-0-375-92668-6(2) , Knopf Bks. for Young Readers); 2003. (Illus.). 544p. (YA). 18.95 (978-0-375-82668-9(8) , Knopf Bks. for Young Readers); 2005. 528p. (J). reprint ed. pap. 10.95 (978-0-375-82669-6(6) , Knopf Bks. for Young Readers) Random Hse. Children's Bks.

—Eragon. (Inheritance Trilogy: Bk. 1). (SPA.). (YA). pap. (978-84-96284-44-9(1)) Roca Editorial De Libros.

—Eragon. 2005. (Inheritance Trilogy: Bk. 1). 503p. (YA). (gr. 7 up). per. 16.60 (978-0-606-33728-1(8)) Tandem Library Bks.

Papademetriou, Lisa. Ultimate Adventures Digiarmor Engergize! 2001. 96p. (gr. 4-7). pap. 4.50 (978-0-06-107204-8(4)) HarperCollins Pubs.

Papademetriou, Lisa & Jones, Jasmine. The Lion, the Witch & the Wardrobe: The Quest for Aslan. movie tie-in ed. 2005. (Chronicles of Narnia Ser.). (Illus.). 64p. (J). pap. 4.99 (978-0-06-076554-5(2)) HarperCollins Pubs.

Papineau, Lucie, et al. Baby Vampire, Gulp! Constantin, Pascale, illus. 1999. (Monster Country Ser.). 32p. (J). pap. (978-1-894363-21-1(3)) Dominique & Friends.

Parent, Nancy. Putt-Putt Lost in Time! Yee, Josie, illus. 2001. (Humongous Ser.). 24p. (J). (ps-3). pap. 3.99 (978-1-58668-060-2(9)) Lyrick Studios.

Park, Sang-Sun, creator. The Tarot Cafe, Vol. 1. 2005. (Illus.). 184p. (YA). pap. 9.99 (978-1-59532-555-6(7) , Tokyopop Adult) TOKYOPOP, Inc.

Parker, John. Gwoppy. 2003. 79 p. pap. 14.95 (978-1-4137-0795-3(5)) PublishAmerica, Inc.

Parker, John F. Rosezinda: Riding Rainbows. 2003. 148p. pap. 11.95 (978-0-595-28042-1(0)) iUniverse, Inc.

Pass, Erica. Big SuperHero Wish! Goldberg, Barry, illus. ed. 2005. (Fairly Odd Parents Ser.: 6). 24p. (J). lib. bdg. 15.00 (978-1-59054-801-1(9)) Fitzgerald Bks.

Paterson, Judy. Thomas the Rhymer. Collins, Sally J., illus. 1999. 32p. (J). (gr. k-4). pap. (978-1-871512-60-1(3)) Glowworm Bks., Ltd.

Paterson, Katherine. The Angel & the Donkey. 2003. (gr. k-3). lib. bdg. 14.10 (978-0-613-70991-0(8)) Tandem Library Bks.

Patrick, James. Osmosis Jones: Novelization. 2001. (J). (978-0-606-21957-0(9)) Tandem Library Bks.

Patrick, Ruthven. Prisoners under Glass. 2005. (YA). per. (978-0-9735422-2-6(5)) Scroll Pr.

Patterson, Christine. Conversation in the Crayon Box. 2004. 12p. (J). per. 9.33 (978-1-4116-0672-2(8)) Lulu.com.

Patton, Rick E. The Warlock Crystal: An Unexpected Journey. 2002. 116p. pap. 9.95 (978-0-595-26076-8(4) , Writers Club Pr.) iUniverse, Inc.

—Warlock Crystal: An Unexpected Journey. 2002. lib. bdg. 18.75 (978-0-613-81385-3(5)) Tandem Library Bks.

Patton, Rick E. & Patton, Katrina. A Journey into Imagination: The Adventure Begins. 2002. 364p. pap. 18.95 (978-0-595-19838-2(4) , Writers Club Pr.) iUniverse, Inc.

Paulson Sternlight, Phyllis. Journey to the Dark Edge of Time. Anderson, Gunn, illus. 1999. 29p. (J). (gr. 4-7). 9.95 (978-0-9673505-0-9(6)) Sternlight, Phyllis Paulson.

Pausacker, Jenny. The Perfect Princess. 2006. (Illus.). 160p. pap. (978-0-7344-0586-9(3) , Lothian Bks.) Hachette Livre Australia.

Pavlova, Elena. Adventures at Tall Oaks: New Friends. 2004. (Illus.). 80p. (J). 19.95 (978-0-9755839-0-6(5)) Read 2 Children.

Pavon, Maria del Mar. Selena, Seleeena! 2005. (Caballo alado series-Al Galope Ser.). (SPA., Illus.). 24p. (J). pap. 4.95 (978-84-7864-885-6(2)) Combel Editorial, S.A. ESP. *Dist:* Independent Pubs. Group.

Paxton, Tom. The Story of the Tooth Fairy. Sauber, Robert G., illus. 2000. 32p. (YA). (ps-3). pap. 5.95 (978-0-688-17523-8(6) , Harper Trophy) HarperCollins Pubs.

Peabody, Richard. Alice Redux: New Stories of Alice, Lewis, & Wonderland. 2006. (Illus.). xvi, 319p. pap. (***978-0-931181-22-1(4)***) Paycock Pr.

Peach-Pit. Dear's, Vol. 2. Peach-Pit & Peach-Pit, illus. Peach-Pit, illus. 2nd rev. ed. 2005. (Illus.). pap. 9.99 (978-1-59532-309-5(0) , Tokyopop Adult) TOKYOPOP, Inc.

—DearS. 2006. Vol. 7. 7th rev. ed. (Illus.). pap. 9.99 (978-1-59816-185-4(7)); Vol. 8. 8th rev. ed. pap. 9.99 (978-1-59816-861-7(4)) TOKYOPOP, Inc. (Tokyopop Adult).

PEACH-PIT. DearS Official Fan Book. 2006. (Illus.). 192p. pap. 9.99 (978-1-59816-493-0(7) , Tokyopop Adult) TOKYOPOP, Inc.

Peacock, Ann & Lewis, C. S. The Chronicles of Narnia. Barbera, Tony et al, illus. Barbera, Tony et al, photos by. 2005. (Narnia Ser.). 64p. (J). (***978-1-4156-3678-7(8)***) HarperCollins Pubs.

—Welcome to Narnia. 2005. (Illus.). 32p. (J). (***978-1-4156-2261-2(2)***) HarperCollins Pubs.

Peak, Danielle. The Enchanted Conquest. 2003. 145p. pap. 13.95 (978-0-7414-1355-0(8)) Infinity Publishing.

Peake, Mervyn. Letters from a Lost Uncle. 2004. (Illus.). 19.95 (978-0-413-74590-3(2)) Methuen Publishing Ltd. GBR. *Dist:* Consortium Bk. Sales & Distribution.

Pearson, Kit. A Handful of Time. 2003. (Illus.). 208p. (gr. 3-7). pap. 6.99 (978-0-14-032268-2(X) , Penguin Global) Penguin Group (USA) Inc.

Pearson, Ridley. The Kingdom Keepers. 2005. 336p. (gr. 5-17). 17.99 (978-0-7868-5444-8(8) , Disney Editions) Disney Pr.

Pearson, Ridley. Kingdom Keepers: Disney after Dark. 2007. 336p. (gr. 5-17). pap. 8.99 (***978-1-4231-0545-9(1)*** , Disney Editions) Disney Pr.

Pedro y el Lobo. 2004. (SPA., Illus.). (J). (978-1-84458-109-2(8)) Chrysalis Children's Bks.

Peel, John. Book of Doom. 2006. 168p. pap. 4.99 (978-0-7387-0842-3(9) , 1254725) Llewellyn Pubns.

—Book of Magic, Vol. 3. Karre, Andrew, ed. 2004. (Diadem Worlds of Magic Ser.). 208p. pap. 4.99 (978-0-7387-0615-3(9)) Llewellyn Pubns.

—Book of Names. Karre, Andrew, ed. 2004. (Diadem Worlds of Magic Ser.). 208p. pap. 6.99 (978-0-7387-0617-7(5)) Llewellyn Pubns.

—Book of Oceans. 2005. 216p. (ps-7). pap. 4.99 (978-0-7387-0748-8(1)) Llewellyn Pubns.

—Book of Reality. 2006. 216p. pap. 4.99 (978-0-7387-0843-0(7)) Llewellyn Pubns.

—Book of Signs, Vol. 2. Karre, Andrew, ed. 2004. (Diadem Worlds of Magic Ser.). (Illus.). 208p. pap. 5.99 (978-0-7387-0616-0(7)) Llewellyn Pubns.

—Book of War. 2005. (Diadem: Worlds of Magic Ser.: Book 7). 264p. pap. 4.99 (978-0-7387-0611-5(6)) Llewellyn Pubns.

—Double Disaster! 2002. (gr. 3-6). lib. bdg. 13.00 (978-0-613-70890-6(3)) Tandem Library Bks.

—Firestorm. 2000. (Twenty Ninety-Nine Ser.: Bk. 6). (Illus.). 160p. (J). (gr. 3-7). pap. 4.99 (978-0-439-06035-6(4)) Scholastic, Inc.

—Secret of Dragonhome. 1998. (YA). pap. 4.99 (978-0-590-59680-0(2)) Scholastic, Inc.

Peel, John & Peel, John. Suddenly Twins! 2001. 162p. (J). (gr. 3-6). per. 13.00 (978-0-613-70902-6(0)) Tandem Library Bks.

Pelelo-Ray, Sam. Athenrei. 2006. 56p. pap. 12.95 (978-1-4137-9946-0(9)) PublishAmerica, Inc.

Pemberton, Bonnie. The Cat Master. 2007. 259p. (YA). (gr. 5-9). 16.99 (***978-0-7614-5340-6(7)***) Cavendish, Marshall Corp.

Pendziwol, Jean. No dragons for tea: Fire safety for kids (and dragons) Gourbault, Martine, illus. unabr. ed. 1999. 32p. (J). (gr. k-3). (978-1-55074-569-6(7)) Kids Can Pr., Ltd.

Penick Phillips-Cermak, Mosetta. The Wishing Flower. 2007. 24p. 16.50 (***978-0-615-15573-9(1)***) PM Moon Pubs.

Peretti, Frank E. Escape from the Island of Aquarius. 2004. (Cooper Kids Adventure Ser.: No. 2). 160p. (gr. 4-7). 5.99 (978-0-89107-592-9(5)) Crossway Bks.

Peretti, Frank E., et al. The Door in the Dragon's Throat. 2004. (Cooper Kids Adventures Ser.: No. 1). 125p. (YA). (gr. 4-7). 5.99 (978-0-89107-591-2(7)) Crossway Bks.

Perez, Lana. Figure in the Frost: Knights of the Silver Dragon, Book 5. Fiegenschuh, Emily, illus. 2005. (Dungeons & Dragons Ser.). 192p. (YA). pap. 5.99 (978-0-7869-3587-1(1)) Wizards of the Coast.

Perloo the Bold. 2002. (Avi Ser.). (Illus.). (J). 13.19 (978-0-7587-6522-2(3)) Book Wholesalers, Inc.

Perrault, Charles. Cenicienta. 2002. (SPA.). (gr. k-3). lib. bdg. 15.25 (978-0-613-73572-8(2)) Tandem Library Bks.

Perret, Gene. Clean Underwear. 2003. (978-1-893860-88-9(4)) Arizona Highways.

Peter Pan. 2003. (Illus.). 12.99 (978-0-7868-3479-2(X)) Disney Pr.

Peter Pan II: Return to Neverland. 2002. (Illus.). (J). 15.95 (978-0-7853-6003-2(4)) Publications International, Ltd.

Peter Pantm. 2003. (J). 173.68 (978-0-06-056911-2(5)) HarperCollins Pubs.

Peterson, Brandon & Brereton, Dan. Giant Killer. 2006. (Illus.). 128p. (YA). pap. 14.99 (978-1-58240-539-1(5)) Image Comics.

Peterson, Joel. The Littles & the Perfect Christmas. Rogers, Jacqueline, illus. 2004. (Little Apple Ser.). 91p. (J). (978-0-439-68703-4(9)) Scholastic, Inc.

Peterson, John. The Littles. Clark, Roberta C., illus. rev. ed. 2007. (Littles Ser.). 80p. (J). (gr. 1-5). pap. 3.99 (978-0-590-46225-9(3)) Scholastic, Inc.

—Littles & the Big Blizzard. 2001. (Littles Ser.). (Illus.). (J). (978-0-606-20390-6(7)) Tandem Library Bks.

—Littles & Their Amazing New Friend. 1999. (gr. 3-6). lib. bdg. 11.80 (978-0-613-16970-7(0)); (Illus.). (J). (978-0-606-21811-5(4)) Tandem Library Bks.

—The Littles Get Trapped. 2001. (Littles Ser.). (Illus.). (J). (978-0-606-21303-5(1)) Tandem Library Bks.

—The Littles Go Around the World, No. 2. Rogers, Jacqueline, illus. 2000. (Littles Ser.). 32p. (J). (gr. 1-5). pap. 3.99 (978-0-439-20300-5(7)) Scholastic, Inc.

—The Littles Have a Wedding. Clark, Roberta C., illus. 2007. (Littles Ser.). 96p. (J). (gr. 1-5). pap. 3.99 (978-0-590-46224-2(5)) Scholastic, Inc.

—The Littles Ready-to-Go. 1998. (J). pap. 3.95 (978-0-439-04450-9(2)) Scholastic, Inc.

—The Littles to the Rescue. Clark, Roberta C., illus. rev. ed. 2007. (Littles Ser.). 96p. (J). (gr. 1-5). pap. 3.99 (978-0-590-46223-5(7)) Scholastic, Inc.

Peterson, Wendy M. The Tail of the Sea Witch. Scott, Ardy M., illus. 2002. (YA). cd-rom 14.95 (978-1-931201-89-6(7)) Twilight Times Bks.

Petri, Michelle. The Fvantom: Omegapocalypse. 2007. 212p. per. 14.95 (***978-0-595-45723-6(1)***) iUniverse, Inc.

Petti, Ken. Zenda 09 Trapped in Time. 2007. 144p. (J). pap. (***978-0-448-44343-0(0)*** , Grosset & Dunlap) Penguin Group (USA) Inc.

Philbrick, Rodman. REM World. 2000. (Illus.). 176p. (J). (gr. 4-7). pap. 16.95 (978-0-439-08362-1(1) , Blue Sky Pr., The) Scholastic, Inc.

Philips, Dana. Blacksmith's Tale, or Once Upon a Flower. 2000. (J). (gr. 4-6). 24.95 (978-1-889274-07-2(0)) Posterity Pr., Inc.

Philpot, Graham. Troglobytes. 1998. (Illus.). 32p. (J). pap. 11.99 (978-1-85881-621-0(1)) Orion Children's Bks. GBR. *Dist:* Independent Pubs. Group.

Picouly, Daniel. Thumbelina of Toulaba. Bedrick, Claudia Zoe, tr. Tallac, Olivier, illus. 2007. 32p. (J). (ps-3). 16.95 (***978-1-59270-069-1(1)***) Enchanted Lion Bks., LLC.

A Picture for Harold's Room. 2004. (J). pap. 14.95 incl. audio (978-0-7882-0624-5(9)) Weston Woods Studios, Inc.

Pierce, Meredith. Woman Who Loved Reindeer. 2000. (gr. 7-12). lib. bdg. 14.15 (978-0-7857-1642-6(4)) Tandem Library Bks.

Pierce, Meredith Ann. The Birth of the Firebringer, Vol. 1. 2003. (Firebird Ser.). 208p. pap. 6.99 (978-0-14-250053-8(4) , Puffin) Penguin Group (USA) Inc.

—The Dark Moon. 2003. (Firebird Ser.). 256p. (YA). (gr. 7-11). pap. 6.99 (978-0-14-250057-6(7) , Puffin) Penguin Group (USA) Inc.

—Dark Moon. 2003. (gr. 7-12). lib. bdg. 15.30 (978-0-613-67448-5(0)) Tandem Library Bks.

—The Darkangel, Vol. 1. 1998. (Darkangel Trilogy Ser.). 12.65 (978-0-606-13316-6(X)) Tandem Library Bks.

—A Gathering of Gargoyles. rev. ed. 2007. (Darkangel Trilogy Ser.). 284p. (YA). (gr. 7-12). per. 7.99 (***978-0-316-06725-6(3)***) Little, Brown Bks. for Young Readers.

—The Pearl of the Soul of the World. 2008. (Darkangel Trilogy Ser.). 256p. (YA). (gr. 7-17). pap. 7.99 (***978-0-316-06724-9(5)***) Little, Brown Bks. for Young Readers.

—The Pearl of the Soul of the World. 1999. (Darkangel Trilogy Ser.). (978-0-606-16526-6(6)) Tandem Library Bks.

—Pearl of the Soul of the World. 1999. (gr. 7-12). lib. bdg. 14.15 (978-0-613-15938-8(1)) Tandem Library Bks.

—Son of Summer Stars. 2003. (gr. 7-12). lib. bdg. 15.30 (978-0-613-67474-4(X)) Tandem Library Bks.

—The Son of Summer Stars, Vol. 3. 2003. (Firebird Ser.). 256p. (YA). (gr. 7). pap. 6.99 (978-0-14-250074-3(7) , Puffin) Penguin Group (USA) Inc.

—The Woman Who Loved Reindeer. 2000. 256p. (YA). (gr. 7-12). pap. 6.95 (978-0-15-201799-6(2) , Magic Carpet Bks.) Harcourt Children's Bks.

—Woman Who Loved Reindeer. 2000. (978-0-606-18808-1(8)) Tandem Library Bks.

Pierce, Tamora. Alanna: The First Adventure. unabr. ed. 2004. (Song of the Lioness Ser.: Bk. 1). 216p. (J). (gr. 6 up). pap. 36.00 incl. audio (978-0-8072-8772-9(5) , YA263SP, Listening Library) Random Hse. Audio Publishing Group.

—Alanna: The First Adventure. 2005. (Song of the Lioness Ser.: Bk. 1). (Illus.). 304p. (YA). pap. 6.99 (978-0-689-87855-8(9) , Simon Pulse) Simon & Schuster Children's Publishing.

—Alanna: The First Adventure. 1999. (Song of the Lioness Ser.: Bk. 1). (J). (gr. 5 up). 20.50 (978-0-8446-7002-7(2)) Smith, Peter Pub., Inc.

—Bloodhound. 2008. (Beka Cooper Ser.: No. 2). 240p. (J). (gr. 7-11). 18.99 (***978-0-375-81469-3(8)***); lib. bdg. 21.99 (***978-0-375-91469-0(2)***) Random Hse. Children's Bks. (Random Hse. Bks. for Young Readers).

—Briar's Book. (Circle of Magic Ser.: No. 4). (Illus.). 272p. (J). 2000. 5.99 (978-0-590-55411-4(5) , Scholastic Paperbacks); 1999. (gr. 6-12). pap. 15.95 (978-0-590-55359-9(3)) Scholastic, Inc.

—Briar's Book. (Circle of Magic Ser.: No. 4). 2000. (gr. 5-8). lib. bdg. 13.00 (978-0-613-24415-2(X)); 1999. (J). 11.64 (978-0-606-19550-8(5)) Tandem Library Bks.

—Cold Fire. (Circle Opens Ser.: No. 3). (J). 2003. 384p. 5.99 (978-0-590-39656-1(0) , Scholastic Paperbacks); 2002. (Illus.). 368p. (gr. 5 up). pap. 16.95 (978-0-590-39655-4(2) , Scholastic Pr.) Scholastic, Inc.

—Cold Fire. 2003. (Circle Opens Ser.: No. 3). (gr. 7-12). lib. bdg. 14.15 (978-0-613-72894-2(7)) Tandem Library Bks.

—Daja's Book. (Circle of Magic Ser.: No. 3). (Illus.). 240p. (J). 2000. 5.99 (978-0-590-55410-7(7) , Scholastic Paperbacks); 1998. (gr. 6-12). pap. 15.95 (978-0-590-55358-2(5)) Scholastic, Inc.

—Daja's Book. 2000. (Circle of Magic Ser.: No. 3). (gr. 5-8). lib. bdg. 13.00 (978-0-613-28460-8(7)) Tandem Library Bks.

—Emperor Mage. 2005. (Immortals Ser.: No. 2). 384p. (YA). pap. 6.99 (978-1-4169-0337-6(2) , Simon Pulse) Simon & Schuster Children's Publishing.

—First Test. (Protector of the Small Ser.: No. 1). (YA). (gr. 7). 2004. 240p. pap. 8.95 (978-0-375-82905-5(9) , Random Hse. Bks. for Young Readers); 2000. (Illus.). 256p. mass mkt. 6.50 (978-0-679-88917-5(5) , Laurel Leaf) Random Hse. Children's Bks.

—First Test. 2000. (Protector of the Small Ser.: No. 1). (gr. 5-8). lib. bdg. 14.15 (978-0-613-25184-6(9)) Tandem Library Bks.

—In the Hand of the Goddess. unabr. ed. 2004. (Song of the Lioness Ser.: Bk. 2). 206p. (J). (gr. 6 up). pap. 36.00 incl. audio (978-0-8072-0665-2(2) , S YA 338 SP, Listening Library) Random Hse. Audio Publishing Group.

—In the Hand of the Goddess. 2005. (Song of the Lioness Ser.: Bk. 2). 288p. (YA). mass mkt. 6.99 (978-0-689-87856-5(7) , Simon Pulse) Simon & Schuster Children's Publishing.

—In the Hand of the Goddess. Heyer, Marilee, illus. 2002. (Song of the Lioness Ser.: Bk. 2). 240p. (J). 11.99 (978-0-689-85324-1(6) , Atheneum) Simon & Schuster Children's Publishing.

—In the Hand of the Goddess. 1999. (Song of the Lioness Ser.: Bk. 2). (J). (gr. 5 up). 20.75 (978-0-8446-7003-4(0)) Smith, Peter Pub., Inc.

—Lady Knight. (Protector of the Small Ser.: No. 4). (YA). (gr. 7-12). 2004. 464p. pap. 8.95 (978-0-375-82908-6(3) , Random Hse. Bks. for Young Readers); 2003. (Illus.). 448p. mass mkt. 6.50 (978-0-375-81471-6(X) , Laurel Leaf); 2002. 448p. 16.95 (978-0-375-81465-5(5) , Random Hse. Bks. for Young Readers) Random Hse. Children's Bks.

—Lady Knight. 2003. (Protector of the Small Ser.: No. 4). (gr. 7-12). lib. bdg. 14.15 (978-0-613-88335-1(7)) Tandem Library Bks.

—Lady Knight. l.t. ed. 2003. (Protector of the Small Ser.: No. 4). (J). (gr. 3-6). 23.95 (978-0-7862-5217-6(0)) Thorndike Pr.

—Lioness Rampant. unabr. ed. 2004. (Song of the Lioness Ser.: Bk. 4). 308p. (J). (gr. 6 up). pap. 38.00 incl. audio (978-0-8072-0985-1(6) , S YA 388 SP, Listening Library) Random Hse. Audio Publishing Group.

—Lioness Rampant. (Song of the Lioness Ser.: Bk. 4). (YA). 2005. 400p. mass mkt. 6.99 (978-0-689-87857-2(5) , Simon Pulse); 2003. (Illus.). 320p. 11.99 (978-0-689-85430-9(7) , Atheneum) Simon & Schuster Children's Publishing.

—Magic Steps. (Circle Opens Ser.: No. 1). 272p. (J). 2000. (Illus.). (gr. 4-7). pap. 16.95 (978-0-590-39588-5(2) , Scholastic Pr.); 2001. (gr. 6-12). pap. 5.99 (978-0-590-39605-9(6)) Scholastic, Inc.

—Magic Steps. (Circle Opens Ser.: No. 1). 2001. (gr. 5-8). lib. bdg. 13.00 (978-0-613-35738-8(8)); 2000. (Illus.). (J). (978-0-606-21109-3(8)) Tandem Library Bks.

—Page. (Protector of the Small Ser.: No. 2). 2004. 288p. (YA). (gr. 7). pap. 8.95 (978-0-375-82907-9(5) , Random Hse. Bks. for Young Readers); 2001. 288p. (YA). (gr. 7-11). mass mkt. 6.50 (978-0-679-88918-2(3) , Laurel Leaf); 2000. (Illus.). 272p. (gr. 5-9). lib. bdg. 17.99 (978-0-679-98915-8(3) , Random Hse. Bks. for Young Readers) Random Hse. Children's Bks.

—Page. 2001. (Protector of the Small Ser.: No. 2). (gr. 5-8). lib. bdg. 13.55 (978-0-613-50483-6(6)) Tandem Library Bks.

—Sandry's Book. 1999. (Circle of Magic Ser.: No. 1). 272p. (YA). (gr. 6-12). mass mkt. 6.99 (978-0-590-55408-4(5)) Scholastic, Inc.

—Sandry's Book. 1999. (Circle of Magic Ser.: No. 1). (gr. 5-8). lib. bdg. 13.00 (978-0-613-17935-5(8)) Tandem Library Bks.

—Shatterglass. (Circle Opens Ser.: No. 4). 368p. (J). 2004. pap. 5.99 (978-0-590-39696-7(X) , Scholastic Paperbacks); 2003. pap. 16.95 (978-0-590-39683-7(8)) Scholastic, Inc.

—Squire. (Protector of the Small Ser.: No. 3). 432p. (YA). (gr. 7). 2004. pap. 8.95 (978-0-375-82906-2(7) , Random Hse. Bks. for Young Readers); 2002. mass mkt. 6.50 (978-0-679-88919-9(1) , Laurel Leaf) Random Hse. Children's Bks.

—Squire. 2002. (Protector of the Small Ser.: No. 3). (gr. 5-8). lib. bdg. 14.15 (978-0-613-49349-9(4)) Tandem Library Bks.

—Street Magic. (Circle Opens Ser.: No. 2). (J). 2001. 304p. pap. 16.95 (978-0-590-39628-8(5)); 2002. (Illus.). 312p. pap. 6.99 (978-0-590-39643-1(9)) Scholastic, Inc.

—Street Magic. 2002. (Circle Opens Ser.: No. 2). (gr. 5-8). lib. bdg. 13.00 (978-0-613-53870-1(6)) Tandem Library Bks.

—Terrier. (Beka Cooper Ser.: No. 1). 2007. 608p. (YA). (gr. 7-11). pap. 9.99 (***978-0-375-83816-3(3)***); 2006. (Illus.). 592p. (J). (gr. 5-8). 18.95 (978-0-375-81468-6(X)) Random Hse. Children's Bks. (Random Hse. Bks. for Young Readers).

—Trickster's Choice. (Daughter of the Lioness Ser.: Bk. 1). (Illus.). 2003. 432p. (J). (gr. 5-8). lib. bdg. 19.99 (978-0-375-91466-9(8)); 2003. 432p. (YA). (gr. 7-8). 17.95 (978-0-375-81466-2(3)); 2004. 448p. (YA). (gr. 7). reprint ed. pap. 8.95 (978-0-375-82879-9(6)) Random Hse. Children's Bks. (Random Hse. Bks. for Young Readers).

—Trickster's Choice. 2003. (Daughter of the Lioness Ser.: Bk. 1). (Illus.). 422p. (J). pap. (978-0-375-81472-3(8)) Random Hse., Inc.

—Trickster's Queen. (Daughter of the Lioness Ser.: Bk. 2). (Illus.). 480p. (gr. 7-12). 2005. (YA). pap. 8.95 (978-0-375-82878-2(8)); 2004. (J). lib. bdg. 19.99 (978-0-375-91467-6(6)); 2004. (YA). 17.95 (978-0-375-81467-9(1)) Random Hse. Children's Bks. (Random Hse. Bks. for Young Readers).

—Tris's Book. 1999. (Circle of Magic Ser.: No. 2 2). 272p. (YA). (gr. 6-12). mass mkt. 5.99 (978-0-590-55409-1(3)) Scholastic, Inc.

—Wild Magic. 2003. (Immortals Ser.: No. 1). (Illus.). 320p. (YA). 11.99 (978-0-689-85611-2(3) , Atheneum) Simon & Schuster Children's Publishing.

—The Will of the Empress. (Circle Reforged Ser.: Bk. 1). 560p. (J). 2006. pap. 8.99 (978-0-439-44172-8(2)); 2005. (Illus.). (gr. 9-12). pap. 17.99 (978-0-439-44171-1(4) , Scholastic Pr.) Scholastic, Inc.

—Wolf-Speaker. 2003. (Immortals Ser.: No. 2). (Illus.). 304p. (YA). 10.95 (978-0-689-85612-9(1) , Atheneum) Simon & Schuster Children's Publishing.

—The Woman Who Rides Like a Man. unabr. ed. 2004. (Song of the Lioness Ser.: Bk. 3). 228p. (J). (gr. 6 up). pap. 38.00 incl. audio (978-0-8072-0797-0(7) , LYA 357 SP, Listening Library) Random Hse. Audio Publishing Group.

—The Woman Who Rides Like a Man. (Song of the Lioness Ser.: Bk. 3). (Illus.). (YA). 2005. 304p. mass mkt. 6.99 (978-0-689-87858-9(3) , Simon Pulse); 2003. 256p. 11.99 (978-0-689-85429-3(3) , Atheneum) Simon & Schuster Children's Publishing.

—The Woman Who Rides Like a Man. 2002. (Song of the Lioness Ser.: Bk. 3). (J). (gr. 5 up). 20.50 (978-0-8446-7228-1(9)) Smith, Peter Pub., Inc.

Pierce, Tamora & Sherman, Josepha. Young Warriors: Stories of Strength. 2006. 336p. (J). (gr. 7-11). pap. 8.95 (978-0-375-82963-5(6) , Random Hse. Bks. for Young Readers) Random Hse. Children's Bks.

Pierce, Walter. Dreams Unseen: The Dragon of Mists. 2007. 260p. (YA). per. 16.95 (***978-0-595-45171-5(3)***) iUniverse, Inc.

Pike, Christopher, pseud. The Shaktra. 2006. (Alosha Trilogy: No. 2). 336p. (YA). 6.99 (978-0-7653-4961-3(2) , Tor Bks.) Doherty, Tom Assocs., LLC.

—The Yanti. 2006. (Alosha Trilogy: No. 3). 400p. (YA). (gr. 8 up). 18.95 (978-0-7653-1100-9(3) , Tor Bks.) Doherty, Tom Assocs., LLC.

Pilkey, Dav. El Capitan Calzoncillos y la Feroz Batalla Contra el Nino Mocobionico Vol. 1: La Noche de los Mocos Vivientes. Pilkey, Dav, illus. 2005. (Captain Underpants Ser.: Bk. 6). Orig. Title: Captain Underpants & the Big, Bad Battle of the Bionic Booger Boy: The Night of the Nasty Nostril Nuggets. (SPA., Illus.). 176p. mass mkt. 4.99 (978-0-439-66204-8(4) , Scholastic en Espanol) Scholastic, Inc.

—Ricky Ricotta Y el Poderoso Robot Contra Los Mecamonos de Marte. 2002. (Ricky Ricotta Ser.: No. 4). (978-0-606-22263-1(4)) Tandem Library Bks.

—Ricky Ricotta's Mighty Robot vs. the Voodoo Vultures from Venus. Ontiveros, Martin, illus. 2001. (Ricky Ricotta Ser.: No. 3). 128p. (J). (ps-3). pap. 3.99 (978-0-439-23625-6(8)) Scholastic, Inc.

Pinkney, Gloria Jean. Back Home. Pinkney, Jerry, illus. 1999. 40p. (J). (ps-3). pap. 6.99 (978-0-14-056547-8(7) , Puffin) Penguin Group (USA) Inc.

Pinkwater, Daniel M. The Lunchroom of Doom. Pinkwater, Jill, illus. 2000. (Werewolf Club Ready for Chapters Ser.: Vol. 2). 64p. (J). (gr. 4-7). pap. 3.99 (978-0-689-83845-3(X) , Aladdin) Simon & Schuster Children's Publishing.

—The Lunchroom of Doom. Pinkwater, Jill, illus. 2000. (Werewolf Club Ser.). (J). (978-0-606-19733-5(8)) Tandem Library Bks.

—4: Fantastic Novels. 2000. (gr. 3-6). lib. bdg. 18.80 (978-0-613-25238-6(1)) Tandem Library Bks.

Pinocchio & Peter Pan. 2004. (Classics to Color with Stickers Ser.). 80p. (J). pap. 2.49 (978-1-4037-0736-9(7)) Dalmatian Pr.

Pinocho: The Human Body, Sea Life, the Bedroom. 1999. Tr. of Pinocchio. (SPA & ENG., Illus.). (J). (ps-5). pap. 7.95 (978-88-8148-253-5(3)) European Language Institute ITA. *Dist:* Distribooks, Inc., Midwest European Pubns.

Piraino, Joseph. The Five Keys of the Sphinx. 2006. 168p. pap. (***978-1-84549-157-4(2)***) arima publishing.

Pitcher. Pitcher - Cloud Cat Quartet Bind-up. 2008. 320p. (YA). pap. 9.95 (***978-1-4052-0851-2(1)***) Egmont Bks., Ltd. GBR. *Dist:* Independent Pubs. Group.

Pitcher, Caroline. Cloud Cat. 2005. 160p. (J). pap. 9.99 (***978-1-4052-0849-9(X)***) Egmont Bks., Ltd. GBR. *Dist:* Independent Pubs. Group.

—Sky Shifter. 2005. 160p. (J). pap. 8.99 (***978-1-4052-0850-5(3)***) Egmont Bks., Ltd. GBR. *Dist:* Independent Pubs. Group.

Pitcher, Caroline. The Winter Dragon. Williams, Sophy, illus. 2004. 36p. (J). (ps-2). 15.95 (978-1-84507-322-0(3)) Lincoln, Frances Ltd. GBR. *Dist:* Perseus Distribution.

Pittman, Helena Clare. The Gift of the Willows. Pittman, Helena Clare, illus. 1999. 32p. (J). (gr. 1-4). pap. 7.95 (978-0-930545-19-2(2)) Maple Hill Pr., Ltd.

Plant, Timothy. Beyond the Wall. 2005. (Illus.). 192p. pap. 8.95 (978-1-56315-368-6(8)) SterlingHouse Pubs., Inc.

Plante, Raymond. Le Monde de Xéros. Delezenne, Christine, illus. 2004. (Roman Jeunesse Ser.). (FRE.). 96p. (J). (gr. 4-7). pap. (978-2-89021-615-0(2)) Diffusion du livre Mirabel.

Pocket Books Staff. Errata: Final Fantasy. (Illus.). (YA). mass mkt. (978-0-7434-4646-4(1) , Aladdin) Simon & Schuster Children's Publishing.

Poe, Edgar Allan. The Raven & Other Writings. 2003. (Aladdin Classics Ser.). 448p. pap. 4.99 (978-0-689-86352-3(7) , Aladdin) Simon & Schuster Children's Publishing.

Polacco, Patricia. Meteor! 2001. (J). (gr. k-4). pap. 17.95 incl. audio (978-0-8045-6857-9(X) , 6857) Spoken Arts, Inc.

Pomaska, Anna. Scruffy & Muffin in the Land of Enchantment: A Dot-to-Dot Story Book. 2004. (Dover Coloring Bks.). 32p. (J). pap. 3.95 (978-0-486-43566-4(0)) Dover Pubns., Inc.

Pooh Please & Thank You. 2002. (Illus.). (J). 7.98 (978-0-7853-6038-4(7)) Publications International, Ltd.

Poole, Richard. The Brass Key. 2007. (Book of Lowmoor Ser.). (Illus.). 403p. (J). pap. 11.95 (***978-0-689-87549-6(5)***) Simon & Schuster, Ltd. GBR. *Dist:* Independent Pubs. Group.

—Jewel & Thorn. 2007. (Book of Lowmoor Ser.). (Illus.). 391p. (YA). (gr. 7 up). per. 11.95 (***978-0-689-87290-7(9)***) Simon & Schuster, Ltd. GBR. *Dist:* Independent Pubs. Group.

Popcorn. 2004. (YA). spiral bd. (978-0-9754913-2-4(6) , Gap Tooth Publishing) Charles River Pr.

Pope, Elizabeth Marie. The Sherwood Ring. 2001. 272p. (YA). (gr. 5-9). pap. 5.95 (978-0-618-15074-8(9)); (Illus.). tchr. ed. 18.00 (978-0-618-17737-0(X)) Houghton Mifflin Co. Trade & Reference Div.

Porter, Todd. Firefly Fred. 2004. (Illus.). 36p. (J). 19.95 (978-1-932278-00-2(1)) Mayhaven Publishing.

Posadas, Carmen. Dorilda. 2003. (SPA., Illus.). 127p. (J). (gr. 3-5). pap. 13.95 (978-84-204-5800-7(7)) Santillana USA Publishing Co., Inc.

Pottle, Bill T. DreamQuest. 2003. 274p. (YA). pap. 16.95 (978-0-595-26804-7(8) , Writers Club Pr.) iUniverse, Inc.

Prachett, Terry. Men at Arms. 2000. (gr. 7-12). lib. bdg. 15.30 (978-0-613-34006-9(X)) Tandem Library Bks.

Pratchett, Terry. Carpe Jugulum. 2000. (gr. 7-12). lib. bdg. 15.30 (978-0-613-27761-7(9)) Tandem Library Bks.

—Eric. 2002. (gr. 5-8). lib. bdg. 15.30 (978-0-613-57205-7(X)) Tandem Library Bks.

—Guards! Guards! 2001. (gr. 5-8). lib. bdg. 15.30 (978-0-613-57217-0(3)) Tandem Library Bks.

—The Light Fantastic. 2000. (gr. 7-12). lib. bdg. 15.30 (978-0-613-27938-3(7)) Tandem Library Bks.

—Lords & Ladies. 2002. (gr. 5-8). lib. bdg. 15.30 (978-0-613-57242-2(4)) Tandem Library Bks.

—Sourcery. 2001. (gr. 5-8). lib. bdg. 15.30 (978-0-613-57278-1(5)) Tandem Library Bks.

—The Truth. 2001. (gr. 5-8). lib. bdg. 15.30 (978-0-613-57290-3(4)) Tandem Library Bks.

—Where's My Cow? 2005. (Illus.). 32p. 16.95 (978-0-06-087267-0(5)) HarperCollins Pubs.

Priest, Christopher. Brothers & Keepers. 2005. (Captain America & the Falcon Ser.: Vol. 2). (Illus.). 168p. (YA). pap. 17.99 (978-0-7851-1568-7(4)) Marvel Enterprises, Inc.

Priestley, Chris. Billy Wizard. 2005. (Young Corgi Ser.). 90p. (J). (gr. 4-6). pap. 6.99 (978-0-552-54689-8(5) , Corgi) Transworld Publishers Ltd. GBR. *Dist:* Independent Pubs. Group.

Primavera, Elise. Secret Order Gumm Street Girl, No. 2. 2006. (978-0-06-056949-5(2)); (978-0-06-056950-1(6)) HarperCollins Canada, Ltd.

—The Secret Order of the Gumm Street Girls, No. 1. Primavera, Elise, illus. 2006. (Illus.). 464p. (J). 16.99 (978-0-06-056946-4(8)); lib. bdg. 17.89 (978-0-06-056947-1(6)) HarperCollins Pubs.

Princeler, Don C. Bodywork: And Other Adventures of Skippy Redcap. Johnson, Rita, illus. Princeler, Cynthia, photos by. 2001. 183p. (J). pap. 12.00 (978-1-884687-30-3(X)) New Horizons Publishing Co.

Principe, Hilda. My Red Hat Grandma & Me. 2007. 24p. (J). pap. 8.99 (***978-1-59886-990-3(6)***) Tate Publishing & Enterprises, L.L.C.

The Priness Who Lost Her Smile. 2006. (J). 19.95 (***978-0-9790682-0-1(7)***) Clear Braces L.L.C.

Prior, Natalie. Lily Quench & the Dragon of Ashby. Janine, Dawson, illus. 2004. 160p. (YA). (gr. 3 up). pap. 5.99 (978-0-14-240020-3(3) , Puffin) Penguin Group (USA) Inc.

Prior, Natalie Jane. The Search for King Dragon. Dawson, Janine, illus. 2005. (Lily Quench Ser.: Vol. 7). 192p. (J). (gr. 3). pap. 4.99 (978-0-14-240267-2(2) , Puffin) Penguin Group (USA) Inc.

Prior, Natalie Jane, contrib. by. Lily Quench & the Black Mountains, Vol. 2. 2004. (Illus.). 160p. (YA). (gr. 3 up). pap. 4.99 (978-0-14-240021-0(1) , Puffin) Penguin Group (USA) Inc.

Pritchard, Jeff. The Secret Treasures of Oak Island. 2002. 208p. (gr. 4-9). 6.95 (978-0-88780-582-0(5)) Formac Publishing Co., Ltd. CAN. *Dist:* Casemate Pubs. & Bk. Distributors, LLC.

Pryor, Michael. Beneath Quentaris. (Illus.). 160p. pap. (978-0-7344-0556-2(1) , Lothian Bks.) Hachette Livre Australia.

—Quentaris in Flames. 2005. (Illus.). 160p. pap. (978-0-7344-0469-5(7) , Lothian Bks.) Hachette Livre Australia.

Puffy: The Cloud That Couldn't Rain. 2005. (J). 8.95 (978-0-9755348-0-9(7)) Kids Life Pr.

Pullman, Philip. The Amber Spyglass. 2002. (His Dark Materials Ser.: Bk. 3). (Illus.). (YA). (gr. 7-12). 19.53 (978-1-4046-1653-0(5)) Book Wholesalers, Inc.

—The Amber Spyglass. unabr. ed. 2004. (His Dark Materials Ser.: Bk. 3). 465p. (YA). (gr. 7 up). pap. 63.00 incl. audio (978-0-8072-1593-7(7) , S YA 169 SP, Listening Library) Random Hse. Audio Publishing Group.

—The Amber Spyglass. (His Dark Materials Ser.: Bk. 3). (gr. 7-12). 2003. 480p. (YA). mass mkt. 7.50 (978-0-440-23815-7(3) , Laurel Leaf); 2003. (Illus.). 544p. pap. 7.50 (978-0-440-41856-6(9) , Yearling); 2002. (Illus.). 544p. (YA). pap. 11.95 (978-0-375-82335-0(2) , Knopf Bks. for Young Readers); 2000. 544p. (YA). 20.00 (978-0-679-87926-8(9) , Knopf Bks. for Young Readers); 2007. 560p. (YA). 22.99 (***978-0-375-84673-1(5)*** , Knopf Bks. for Young Readers); 2007. 560p. (YA). lib. bdg. 25.99 (***978-0-375-94673-8(X)*** , Knopf Bks. for Young Readers) Random Hse. Children's Bks.

—The Amber Spyglass. (His Dark Materials Ser.: Bk. 3). (YA). (gr. 7-12). 2003. lib. bdg. 15.30 (978-0-613-72258-2(2)); 2002. lib. bdg. 21.05 (978-0-613-71927-8(1)) Tandem Library Bks.

—The Amber Spyglass. l.t. ed. 2003. (His Dark Materials Ser.: Bk. 3). 686p. (YA). (gr. 7-12). 25.95 (978-0-7862-4122-4(5)) Thorndike Pr.

—La Daga. Gallart Iglesias, Maria Dolores, tr. 7th ed. 2005. (Escritura desatada Ser.). (SPA., Illus.). 288p. (YA). (gr. 7-11). 13.95 (978-84-406-8409-7(6)) Ediciones B ESP. *Dist:* Independent Pubs. Group.

—La Daga. (SPA.). 448p. 18.95 (978-84-663-0742-0(7)) Suma de Letras, S.L. ESP. *Dist:* Distribooks, Inc.

—The Firework-Maker's Daughter. 2001. 11.64 (978-0-606-21186-4(1)) Tandem Library Bks.

—The Golden Compass. (His Dark Materials Ser.: Bk. 1). (YA). (gr. 7-12). 1999. mass mkt. 5.99 (978-0-345-91640-2(9)); 1998. mass mkt. 5.99 (978-0-345-91365-4(5)) Random House Publishing Group.

—The Golden Compass. unabr. ed. 1999. (His Dark Materials Ser.: Bk. 1). 399p. (J). (gr. 7 up). pap. 58.00 incl. audio (978-0-8072-8063-8(1) , S YA 001 SP, Listening Library) Random Hse. Audio Publishing Group.

—The Golden Compass. (His Dark Materials Ser.: Bk. 1). (YA). (gr. 7-12). 2003. 368p. pap. 7.50 (978-0-440-23813-3(7) , Laurel Leaf); 2002. 416p. pap. 11.95 (978-0-375-82345-9(X) , Knopf Bks. for Young Readers) Random Hse. Children's Bks.

—The Golden Compass. Beck, Ian, illus. 10th deluxe ed. 2006. (His Dark Materials Ser.: Bk. 1). 432p. (J). (gr. 7-12). 22.95 (978-0-375-83830-9(9) , Knopf Bks. for Young Readers) Random Hse. Children's Bks.

—The Golden Compass. (His Dark Materials Ser.: Bk. 1). (YA). (gr. 7-12). 2003. lib. bdg. 15.30 (978-0-613-81036-4(8)); 2002. lib. bdg. 21.05 (978-0-613-71928-5(X)) Tandem Library Bks.

—The Golden Compass. l.t. ed. 2002. (His Dark Materials Ser.: Bk. 1). 550p. (YA). (gr. 7-12). 25.95 (978-0-7862-4123-1(3)) Thorndike Pr.

—Golden Compass. Beck, Ian, illus. 10th deluxe ed. 2006. (His Dark Materials Ser.: Bk. 1). 432p. (YA). (gr. 7-12). lib. bdg. 24.99 (978-0-375-93830-6(3) , Knopf Bks. for Young Readers) Random Hse. Children's Bks.

—The Golden Compass, Bk. 1. 2001. (His Dark Materials Ser.: Bk. 1). 416p. (YA). (gr. 7-12). pap. 7.50 (978-0-440-41832-0(1) , Yearling) Random Hse. Children's Bks.

—His Dark Materials (Laurel-Leaf) 2003. (His Dark Materials Ser.: Bks. 1-3). (YA). pap. 22.50 (978-0-440-23860-7(9) , Laurel Leaf) Random Hse. Children's Bks.

—His Dark Materials Omnibus. 2007. (His Dark Materials Ser.: Bks. 1-3). 944p. (YA). (gr. 7-12). pap. 21.99 (***978-0-375-84722-6(7)***); lib. bdg. 26.99 (***978-0-375-94722-3(1)***) Random Hse. Children's Bks. (Knopf Bks. for Young Readers).

—Lyra's Oxford. Lawrence, John, illus. 64p. (gr. 7-12). 2007. (YA). per. 6.99 (***978-0-375-84369-3(8)***); 2003. 12.99 (978-0-375-82819-5(2)) Random Hse. Children's Bks. (Knopf Bks. for Young Readers).

—Lyra's Oxford: A Novel. Lawrence, John, illus. 2006. 49p. (YA). reprint ed. 11.00 (978-1-4223-5410-0(5)) DIANE Publishing Co.

—Le Miroir d'Ambre. (FRE.). pap. 18.95 (978-2-07-054376-2(5)) Gallimard, Editions FRA. *Dist:* Distribooks, Inc.

—Once Upon a Time in the North. 2008. 112p. (J). (gr. 7). 12.99 (***978-0-375-84510-9(0)*** , Knopf Bks. for Young Readers) Random Hse. Children's Bks.

—Les Royaumes du Nord. (FRE.). pap. 19.95 (978-2-07-054188-1(6)) Gallimard, Editions FRA. *Dist:* Distribooks, Inc.

—The Subtle Knife. 1999. (His Dark Materials Ser.: Bk. 2). (YA). (gr. 7-12). mass mkt. 5.99 (978-0-345-91641-9(7)) Random House Publishing Group.

—The Subtle Knife, Vol. 2. unabr. ed. 2004. (His Dark Materials Ser.: Bk. 2). 326p. (J). (gr. 7 up). pap. 58.00 incl. audio (978-0-8072-0567-9(2) , S YA 136 SP, Listening Library) Random Hse. Audio Publishing Group.

—The Subtle Knife. (His Dark Materials Ser.: Bk. 2). 2003. 304p. (YA). (gr. 7-12). mass mkt. 7.50 (978-0-440-23814-0(5) , Laurel Leaf); 2002. 352p. (J). (gr. 7-12). pap. 11.95 (978-0-375-82346-6(8) , Knopf Bks. for Young Readers); 2001. 352p. (gr. 5-12). 7.50 (978-0-440-41833-7(X) , Yearling); 2007. 368p. (YA). (gr. 7-12). 22.99 (***978-0-375-84672-4(7)*** , Knopf Bks. for Young Readers); 2007. 368p. (YA). (gr. 7-12). lib. bdg. 25.99 (***978-0-375-94672-1(1)*** , Knopf Bks. for Young Readers) Random Hse. Children's Bks.

—The Subtle Knife. 1998. (His Dark Materials Ser.: Bk. 2). (YA). (gr. 7-12). (978-0-606-13822-2(6)) Tandem Library Bks.

—The Subtle Knife. l.t. ed. 2002. (His Dark Materials Ser.: Bk. 2). 490p. (YA). (gr. 7-12). 25.95 (978-0-7862-4124-8(1)) Thorndike Pr.

—La Tour des Anges. (FRE.). pap. 19.95 (978-2-07-054189-8(4)) Gallimard, Editions FRA. *Dist:* Distribooks, Inc.

Punch, Monkey, creator. Lupin III Vol. 2: World's Most Wanted. 2nd rev. ed. 2004. (Illus.). 192p. pap. 9.99 (978-1-59532-071-1(7) , Tokyopop Adult) TOKYOPOP, Inc.

Pyle, Howard. The Garden Behind the Moon. 2005. (Illus.). 128p. pap. 7.95 (978-0-486-44073-6(7)) Dover Pubns., Inc.

—The Garden Behind the Moon. 2002. (gr. 3-6). lib. bdg. 14.15 (978-0-613-57052-7(9)) Tandem Library Bks.

—Twilight Land. 2006. 192p. pap. 11.99 (978-1-4264-0425-2(5)) BiblioBazaar.

—Twilight Land. 2004. reprint ed. pap. 1.99 (978-1-4192-9142-5(4)) Kessinger Publishing, LLC.

—The Wonder Clock: Or Four & Twenty Marvelous Tales, Being One for Each Hour of the Day. Exams Unlimited, Inc. Staff, ed. Pyle, Katharine, illus. 2001. 373p. (J). reprint ed. cd-rom 6.75 (978-1-885343-14-7(0)) Exams Unlimited, Inc.

Pyne, Erin A. A Fandom of Magical Proportions: S: an Unauthorized History of the Harry Potter Phenomenon. 2007. (Illus.). 84p. (J). per. 8.36 (***978-0-9788138-8-8(X)***) Nimble Bks. LLC.

Quest for a Moose: An Alaska Tale of Searching for an Animal that Doesn't Exist — until it Is Found. 2005. 12.95 (978-1-59433-019-3(0)) Publication Consultants.

Quidditch Through the Ages. 2002. (Harry Potter Ser.). (Illus.). (J). 12.17 (978-0-7587-5135-5(4)) Book Wholesalers, Inc.

Quinones, Juan Carlos. The Gang under the Tree. Montanez, Nivea Ortiz, illus. 2004. (Purple Ser.). (SPA.). 44p. (J). (gr. 3-5). pap. 5.95 (978-1-57581-439-1(0)) Santillana USA Publishing Co., Inc.

Ra, In-Soo. King of Hell, 8 vols., Vol. 7. Jae-Hwan, Kim, illus. 7th rev. ed. 2004. pap. 9.99 (978-1-59182-867-9(8) , Tokyopop Adult) TOKYOPOP, Inc.

Radcliffe, Wil. Noggle Stones. 2003. 236p. (YA). pap. 15.95 (978-0-595-28274-6(1)) iUniverse, Inc.

Rahm, Janene Elizabeth. Mason's Mountain Adventures. 2002. 108p. pap. 16.95 (978-1-59129-626-3(9)) PublishAmerica, Inc.

Raiku, Makoto. Zatch Bell! Raiku, Makoto, illus. 2005. (Zatch Bell Ser.). (Illus.). (YA). Vol. 1. 192p. pap. 9.99 (978-1-59116-586-6(5)); Vol. 2. 192p. pap. 9.99 (978-1-59116-588-0(1)); Vol. 3. 200p. pap. 9.99 (978-1-59116-590-3(3)) Viz Media.

Raine, Bonnie. Islands. MacMenamin, John, illus. 2003. 48p. (J). per. (978-1-931456-74-6(7)) Athena Pr.

Raintree Steck-Vaughn Staff. La Luna Adormecedora. 1999. (SPA.). (J). pap., stu. ed. 31.05 (978-0-7398-0761-3(7)) Steck-Vaughn.

Ralles, H. J. Keeper of the Empire, Vol. 3. 2004. (Illus.). 235p. (J). pap. 9.95 (978-1-929976-25-6(9)) Top Pubns., Ltd.

Ramakar, Ram. Little Crow Feather. 2006. (ENG.). 48p. per. 12.95 (***978-1-4241-5134-9(1)***) PublishAmerica, Inc.

Ramsby, H. S. Neverlore. Velario, Jackie, illus. 2005. (YA). 16.95 (978-0-9785075-6-5(8) , Ferne Pr.) Nelson Publishing & Marketing.

Ramsey, John Charles & McGuire, Deborah. The Rose Princess: A Fable for Our Time. 1999. (Illus.). 87p. (YA). pap. (978-0-9670129-0-2(2)) Birthwrite Publishing.

Rancourt, Heather & Gauches, Claudia. The Fossibles - Bursting from Extinction to Distinction. 2007. (J). per. 8.85 (***978-0-9702654-4-9(1)***) 360 Marketing, LLC.

Rand, Johnathan. American Chillers: Nebraska Night Crawlers, 15. 2004. (American Chillers Ser.: 15). 208p. (J). pap. 5.99 (978-1-893699-67-0(6)) AudioCraft Publishing, Inc.

—Freddie Fernortner: Fearless First Grader. 2005. 89p. (J). pap. 4.99 (978-1-893699-78-6(1)) AudioCraft Publishing, Inc.

Rand, Jonathan. Ogres of Ohio. 2002. (American Chillers Ser.: No. 2). (J). (gr. 4-7). pap. 5.99 (978-1-893699-21-2(8)) AudioCraft Publishing, Inc.

Randall, David. Chandlefort: In the Shadow of the Bear. 2006. 304p. (YA). (gr. 7 up). 16.95 (978-0-689-87870-1(2) , McElderry, Margaret K.) Simon & Schuster Children's Publishing.

—Clovermead. l.t. ed. 2004. (Illus.). 365p. (J). 21.95 (978-0-7862-7071-2(3)) Thorndike Pr.

—Clovermead: In the Shadow of the Bear. (YA). 2005. 432p. mass mkt. 5.99 (978-1-4169-0715-2(7) , Simon Pulse); 2004. (Illus.). 304p. 15.95 (978-0-689-86639-5(9) , McElderry, Margaret K.) Simon & Schuster Children's Publishing.

Randall, David. Sorrel. 2007. 304p. (YA). (gr. 7 up). 16.99 (***978-0-689-87872-5(9)*** , McElderry, Margaret K.) Simon & Schuster Children's Publishing.

Random House Disney Staff. Beauty & the Beast. 2004. (Illus.). 24p. (J). (gr. k-k). bds. 4.99 (978-0-7364-2248-2(X) , RH/Disney) Random Hse. Children's Bks.

—Smash Trash! 2008. (Step into Reading Ser.). 32p. (J). (ps-1). pap. 3.99 (***978-0-7364-2515-5(2)***); lib. bdg. 11.99 (***978-0-7364-8058-1(7)***) Random Hse. Children's Bks. (RH/Disney).

—Space Chase. 2008. (Holographic Sticker Book Ser.). 48p. (J). (ps-2). pap. 3.99 (***978-0-7364-2522-3(5)*** , Golden/Disney) Random Hse. Children's Bks.

Random House Value Publishing Staff & Burnett, Frances Hodgson. Secret Garden. 1998. (Children's Classics Ser.). 288p. (J). (gr. 5-9). 5.99 (978-0-517-18960-3(7) , Children's Classics) Random Hse. Value Publishing.

Rankin, Robert. The Greatest Show off Earth. 2000. 320p. (J). pap. 10.95 (978-0-552-13924-3(6)) Transworld Publishers Ltd. GBR. *Dist:* Trafalgar Square Publishing.

Ransom, Candice. Giant in the Garden. 2007. (Time Spies Ser.: Bk. 3). (Illus.). 128p. (J). (gr. 1-5). pap. 4.99 (978-0-7869-4074-5(3) , Mirrorstone) Wizards of the Coast.

—Rider in the Night: A Tale of Sleepy Hollow. 2007. 128p. (J). (gr. 1-5). pap. 4.99 (***978-0-7869-4354-8(8)*** , Mirrorstone) Wizards of the Coast.

Ransom, Candice. Secret in the Tower. Call, Greg, illus. 2006. 128p. (J). (gr. 2-4). pap. 4.99 (978-0-7869-4027-1(1) , Mirrorstone) Wizards of the Coast.

Ransom, Candice F. Key to the Griffon's Lair. Fiegenshuh, Emily, illus. 2005. (Knights of the Silver Dragon Ser.: Bk. 9). 182p. (J). (***978-1-4156-3032-7(1)*** , Mirrorstone) Wizards of the Coast.

Rash, Brett. The Dragon Lords. 2007. 160p. per. 12.95 (***978-0-595-43842-6(3)***) iUniverse, Inc.

Raskin, Ellen. Figgs & Phantoms. 2000. (J). (gr. 4-8). 20.75 (978-0-8446-7153-6(3)) Smith, Peter Pub., Inc.

Rauzon, Mark. The Sky's the Limit: All about the Atmosphere. 1999. (Our World Ser.). (Illus.). 32p. (gr. 2-4). lib. bdg. 22.90 (978-0-7613-1263-5(3) , Millbrook Pr.) Lerner Publishing Group.

Ravishankar, Anushka. Today Is My Day. 2005. (Illus.). 40p. 14.95 (978-81-86211-76-2(4)) Tara Publishing IND. *Dist:* Consortium Bk. Sales & Distribution.

Rawson, Christopher. Gnomes & Goblins. Cartwright, Stephen, illus. 2004. (Young Reading Series One Ser.). 48p. (J). (gr. 2 up). pap. 5.95 (978-0-7945-0407-6(8) , Usborne) EDC Publishing.

Ray, Belinda. Fairy: Blinda Ray. 2004. 136p. (J). (978-0-439-56013-9(6)) Scholastic, Inc.

—Unicorn. 2003. 131p. (J). (978-0-439-56012-2(8)) Scholastic, Inc.

Raymond, Ruth A. The Day the Earth Went Flat. 1999. (Illus.). 58p. (J). (gr. 6-8). pap. 19.95 (978-0-9659533-2-0(7)) Osmer, Harold L. Publishing.

Read Magazine Editorial Staff. Read into the Millennium: Stories of the Future. 1999. (Best of READ Ser.). 160p. (gr. 5 up). lib. bdg. 24.90 (978-0-7613-0962-8(4) , Millbrook Pr.) Lerner Publishing Group.

Redman, Rich. Spider-Man: Mysterio's Ways. rev. ed. 2000. (Marvel Super Heroes Adventures Ser.). (Illus.). 32p. pap. 4.95 (978-0-7869-1669-6(9)) Wizards of the Coast.

Reed, W. F. Andy & Mark & the Time Machine: Pickett's Charge at Gettysburg. 2000. 144p. (YA). pap. 10.95 (978-0-595-12885-3(8)) iUniverse, Inc.

Reed, Wilfred. Andy & Mark & the Time Machine: Custer's Last Stand. 2003. 240p. (YA). pap. 15.95 (978-0-595-26496-4(4) , Writers Club Pr.) iUniverse, Inc.

Rees, Gwyneth. Fairy Dust. l.t. ed. 2005. 176p. (J). pap. (978-0-7540-7929-3(5) , CLP 480) BBC Audio.

Regan, Dian Curtis. Cam's Quest: The Continuing Story of Princess Nevermore & the Wizard's Apprentice. 2007. 256p. (J). (gr. 4-8). 17.95 (***978-1-58196-056-3(5)***) Darby Creek Publishing.

—Princess Nevermore. rev. ed. 2007. (J). 17.95 (***978-1-58196-055-6(7)***) Darby Creek Publishing.

Reilly, Matthew. Full Throttle. Raimondi, Pablo, illus. 2007. (Hover Car Racer Ser.). 224p. (J). 9.95 (978-1-4169-0227-0(9)) Simon & Schuster Children's Publishing.

Rennie, Gordon, et al. Starship Troopers. 1998. (Illus.). 152p. (YA). pap. 14.95 (978-1-56971-314-3(6)) Dark Horse Comics.

Revenson, Jody. Popping up Around Walt Disney World. Arkush, Bez, illus. 2004. 5p. (ps-17). 24.95 (978-0-7868-5423-3(5) , Disney Editions) Disney Pr.

Reverman, Ardys. All about the Whole You Vol. 4: The Riddle of Me at the Heart-Wood Tree. Lewis, Charlotte, illus. 1998. (Friendly Universe Collection). 196p. pap. 9.95 incl. audio (978-0-9625385-5-1(8)) Friendly Universe Pr.

Reynolds, Jean. Gwen & the Talking Napkin. 2007. (Grandma Ser.: 4). (J). per. 7.99 (***978-1-59872-897-2(0)***) Instantpublisher.com.

Rhea, Herbert. Harold McRhea & the Magical Pot. 2003. 215p. pap. 19.95 (978-1-59286-731-8(6)) PublishAmerica, Inc.

Richards, Maxwell J. George & the Dragon. 2000. 268p. (J). pap. 13.95 (978-1-891929-36-6(4)) Four Seasons Pubs.

Richardson, Bill. After Hamelin. 2000. 144p. (J). (gr. 5-8). 19.95 (978-1-55037-629-6(2)); pap. 8.95 (978-1-55037-628-9(4)) Annick Pr., Ltd. CAN. *Dist:* Firefly Bks., Ltd.

—After Hamelin. 2000. (gr. 5-8). lib. bdg. 17.60 (978-0-613-46188-7(6)) Tandem Library Bks.

Richardville, Carol. Beau Bandit's Tale. Davis, Kaley, illus. 2004. (J). per. 16.99 (978-1-932503-23-4(4)) Insight Publishing Group.

Richler, Mordecai. Jacob Two-Two & the Dinosaur. Eyolfson, Norman, illus. 2004. 96p. (J). (gr. 3-7). pap. 6.95 (978-0-88776-712-8(5)) Tundra Bks., Inc./Livres Toundra, Inc. CAN. *Dist:* Random Hse., Inc.

Richmond, John. Three & Many Wishes of Jason Reid. 2000. (gr. 3-6). lib. bdg. 15.25 (978-0-613-78404-7(9)) Tandem Library Bks.

Ricketts, Mark & Harris, Tony. The Invincible Iron Man': Disassembled. (Illus.). 144p. pap. 14.99 (978-0-7851-1653-0(2)) Marvel Enterprises, Inc.

Ridley, R. W. Dèlon City: Book Two of the Oz Chronicles. 2006. (YA). per. 14.99 (***978-0-9792067-0-2(7)***) Middleburry Hse. Publishing.

Rigby Education Staff. Rumpelstiltskin: Jumbled Tumble. (gr. k-2). 26.00 (978-0-7635-2421-0(2)) Rigby Education.

Rika, Tanaka. Kilala Princess. 20th rev. ed. 2007. (Illus.). pap. 5.99 (***978-1-59816-768-9(5)*** , Tokyopop Kids) TOKYOPOP, Inc.

Rinaldo, Jessica. Key to the Gate Book 1. 2005. 324p. (YA). pap. 14.98 (978-1-4116-5262-0(2)) Lulu.com.

Ring, Vicky L. Who's There? 2001. (gr. 7-12). lib. bdg. 31.55 (978-0-613-78009-4(4)) Tandem Library Bks.

Riordan, Rick. The Sea of Monsters. 2nd rev. ed. 2006. (Percy Jackson & the Olympian Ser.: Bk. 2). 288p. (gr. 5-17). 17.95 (978-0-7868-5686-2(6)) Miramax Bks.

—The Sea of Monsters. l.t. ed. 2006. (Percy Jackson & the Olympians Ser.: Bk. 2). (YA). (gr. 5 up). 22.95 (978-0-7862-9074-1(9)) Thorndike Pr.

Ripley, Virginia. The Little Troll's Big Adventure. Dintzer, Josh, illus. 1999. 32p. (J). (gr. k-2). pap. 12.00 (978-0-9674612-0-5(0)) Strike Publishing.

Risso, Eduardo. Los misterios de la Luna Roja Vol. 1: Mysteries of the Red Moon. 2006. (SPA.). 48p. pap. 16.95 (978-1-59497-162-4(5)) Public Square Bks.

—Mysteries of the Red Moon, Vol. 3. 2006. (SPA.). 48p. pap. 16.95 (978-1-59497-163-1(3)) Public Square Bks.

Ritchie, Thelma. Terra Nova: Settling the Red Planet. 2005. 208p. pap. 16.95 (978-1-933148-25-0(X)) Tate Publishing & Enterprises, L.L.C.

Riva, Jim. Marvin Mallard & the Magic Medallion. Steinmark, Sharyl, illus. 2004. 64p. (YA). pap. 14.95 (978-1-891262-03-6(3)) Soaring Sparrow Pr.

Rivers, Karen. Dream Water. 2000. 176p. (J). (gr. 7-10). lib. bdg. 14.95 (978-1-55143-160-4(2)) Orca Bk. Pubs. USA.

Robbins, Judith. American Spirits: The Sugar Creek Anthologies of Jesse Freedom. 2002. 274p. pap. 15.95 (978-0-595-22460-9(1) , Writers Club Pr.) iUniverse, Inc.

Robert, Naima Bint & Mistry, Nilesh, trs. The Swirling Hijaab: Percja Valezuese. 2004. (TAM, CZE, VIE, SPA & GUJ., Illus.). 24p. (J). (978-1-85269-105-9(0)) Mantra Publishing, Ltd.

Roberts, Bethany. May Belle & the Ogre. Winborn, Marsha, illus. 2003. (Dutton Easy Reader Ser.). 48p. (J). (gr. 1-3). 14.99 (978-0-525-46855-4(2) , Dutton Juvenile) Penguin Group (USA) Inc.

Roberts, Katherine. The Babylon Game. 2002. (Seven Fabulous Wonders Ser.). (Illus.). 310p. pap. 11.00 (978-0-00-711279-1(3)) HarperCollins Pubs. Ltd. GBR. *Dist:* Independent Pubs. Group.

—The Cleopatra Curse. 2006. (Seven Fabulous Wonders Ser.). (Illus.). 288p. (J). pap. 11.99 (978-0-00-711284-5(X) , HarperCollins Children's Bks.) HarperCollins Pubs. Ltd. GBR. *Dist:* Independent Pubs. Group.

—Crystal Mask. 2003. 272p. (J). (Echorium Sequence). 5.99 (978-0-439-44083-7(1) , Chicken Hse., The); Vol. 2. (Echorium Sequence Ser.: Vol. 2). pap. 4.99 (978-0-439-51147-6(X)) Scholastic, Inc.

—Crystal Mask, Vol. 2. Ontiveros, Martin & Down, Chris, illus. 2002. (Echorium Sequence Ser.: Vol. 2). 256p. (J). (gr. 4 up). pap. 15.95 (978-0-439-33864-6(6) , Chicken Hse., The) Scholastic, Inc.

—Crystal Mask. 2003. (gr. 3-6). lib. bdg. 13.00 (978-0-613-82493-4(8)) Tandem Library Bks.

—Dark Quetzal, Bk. 3. 2003. (Echorium Sequence Ser.: Vol. 3). 256p. (J). pap. 15.95 (978-0-439-45697-5(5) , Chicken Hse., The) Scholastic, Inc.

—The Olympic Conspiracy. 2004. (Seven Fabulous Wonders Ser.). (Illus.). 300p. (J). pap. 11.99 (978-0-00-711282-1(3)) HarperCollins Pubs. Ltd. GBR. *Dist:* Independent Pubs. Group.

—Seven Fabulous Wonders Colossu. 2005. (Seven Fabulous Wonders Ser.). 320p. (J). pap. 11.00 (978-0-00-711283-8(1)) HarperCollins Pubs. Ltd. GBR. *Dist:* Independent Pubs. Group.

—Seven Fabulous Wonders Great. 2001. (Seven Fabulous Wonders Ser.). (Illus.). 298p. (J). pap. 11.00 (978-0-00-711278-4(5)) HarperCollins Pubs. Ltd. GBR. *Dist:* Trafalgar Square Publishing.

—Seven Fabulous Wonders Temple. 2002. (Seven Fabulous Wonders Ser.). (Illus.). 298p. (J). pap. 11.00 (978-0-00-711280-7(7)) HarperCollins Pubs. Ltd. GBR. *Dist:* Trafalgar Square Publishing.

—Song Quest. (Illus.). (J). (gr. 5 up). 2000. 240p. pap. 5.95 (978-1-902618-94-4(7)); 1999. 236p. 16.95 (978-1-902618-28-9(9)) Element Children's Bks.

—Song Quest, Vol. 1. 2002. (Echorium Sequence Ser.: Vol. 1). 272p. (J). (gr. 4 up). pap. 5.99 (978-0-439-33892-9(1) , Chicken Hse., The) Scholastic, Inc.

—Song Quest. 2002. lib. bdg. 13.00 (978-0-613-54676-8(8)); (Illus.). 271p. (J). lib. bdg. 13.04 (978-0-606-24222-6(8)) Tandem Library Bks.

Roberts, Kerry Daniel. Dagger of Doom. 2005. (Dungeons & Dragons Ser.: Bk. 6). (Illus.). 192p. (J). pap. 5.99 (978-0-7869-3631-1(2)) Wizards of the Coast.

—Room of the Eyes. 2006. (Knights of the Silver Dragon Ser.). 192p. (YA). pap. 4.99 (978-0-7869-4185-8(5) , Mirrorstone) Wizards of the Coast.

Roberts, Rachel. All That Glitters. 2007. (Avalon Ser.: Bk. 2). 175p. (J). (gr. 3-7). 9.99 ***(*978-1-933164-65-6(4))*** Seven Seas Entertainment, LLC.

—All's Fairy in Love & War. 2003. (Avalon Ser.: Vol. 2). 200p. (J). pap. 4.99 (978-1-59315-011-2(3)) Perseus Bks. Group.

—All's Fairy in Love & War. 2003. (gr. 3-6). lib. bdg. 13.00 (978-0-613-79959-1(3)) Tandem Library Bks.

—Cry of the Wolf. 2001. (Avalon Ser.: Bk. 3). (J). (gr. 3-7). (978-0-606-22236-5(7)) Tandem Library Bks.

—The Dark Mage: Avalon Quest for Magic. 2006. (Avalon Ser.: Vol. 5). 224p. (J). pap. 5.99 (978-1-59315-014-3(8)) Vanguard Pr.

—Trial by Fire. 2003. (Avalon Ser.: Bk. 6). 176p. (YA). (gr. 3-7). pap. 4.99 (978-1-59315-008-2(3)) Perseus Bks. Group.

Robertson, Ivan T. Jack & the Leprechaun. Bratun, Katy, illus. 2000. (Pictureback Ser.). 24p. (J). (gr. k-3). pap. 3.99 (978-0-375-80328-4(9) , Random Hse. Bks. for Young Readers) Random Hse. Children's Bks.

Robertson, M. P. The Egg. 2004. (Illus.). 32p. (J). pap. 6.99 (978-0-14-240038-8(6) , Puffin) Penguin Group (USA) Inc.

Robertson, Mark. Dragon Snatcher. 2005. (Illus.). 32p. (J). ***(*978-1-84507-398-5(3))*** Lincoln, Frances Ltd.

Robinson, Fay. Fish Wish. 2005. (Illus.). 32p. (J). ***(*978-1-84011-605-2(6))*** Templar Publishing, Dorking.

Rockhill, Dennis. Polar Slumber/Sueño Polar. Raven Tree Press Staff, ed. de la Vega, Eida, tr. Rockhill, Dennis, illus. 2004. Tr. of Sueño Polar. (SPA & ENG., Illus.). 32p. (J). (ps-3). 16.95 (978-0-9724973-1-2(5) , 1234791) Raven Tree Pr.

Rodda, Emily. Cavern of the Fear. McBride, Marc, illus. 2002. (Deltora Quest Ser.: No. 1). 144p. (J). (gr. 3-7). pap. 5.99 (978-0-439-39491-8(0)) Scholastic, Inc.

—Cavern of the Fear. 2002. (gr. 3-6). lib. bdg. 13.00 (978-0-613-50594-9(8)) Tandem Library Bks.

—City of the Rats. 2001. (Deltora Quest Ser.: No. 3). (Illus.). 144p. (J). (gr. 3-7). pap. 5.99 (978-0-439-25325-3(X)) Scholastic, Inc.

—City of the Rats. 2001. (gr. 5-8). lib. bdg. 13.00 (978-0-613-36052-4(4)) Tandem Library Bks.

—The Flower Fairies. Vitale, Raoul, illus. 2007. (Fairy Realm Ser.). 128p. (J). (gr. 3-6). 25.65 (978-1-59961-324-6(7)) Spotlight.

—The Forests of Silence. (Deltora Quest Ser.: No. 1). 144p. (J). 2007. pap. 2.99 ***(*978-0-545-01031-3(4));*** 2001. (Illus.). (gr. 3-7). pap. 5.99 (978-0-439-25323-9(3)) Scholastic, Inc.

—The Forests of Silence. 2001. (gr. 5-8). lib. bdg. 13.00 (978-0-613-35718-0(3)) Tandem Library Bks.

—The Isle of Illusion. 2002. (Deltora Quest Ser.: No. 2). (Illus.). 160p. (J). pap. 4.99 (978-0-439-39492-5(9) , Scholastic Paperbacks) Scholastic, Inc.

—The Isle of Illusion. 2002. (gr. 3-6). lib. bdg. 13.00 (978-0-613-50624-3(3)) Tandem Library Bks.

—Isle of the Dead. 2004. 195p. (J). lib. bdg. 16.92 ***(*978-1-4242-0273-7(6))*** Fitzgerald Bks.

—Isle of the Dead. McBride, Marc, illus. 2004. (Deltora Ser.). 144p. (J). (gr. 4-7). 4.99 (978-0-439-63375-8(3) , Scholastic Paperbacks) Scholastic, Inc.

—The Lake of Tears. 2001. (Deltora Quest Ser.: No. 2). (Illus.). 144p. (J). (gr. 3-7). pap. 4.99 (978-0-439-25324-6(1)) Scholastic, Inc.

—The Lake of Tears. 2001. (gr. 5-8). lib. bdg. 13.00 (978-0-613-35736-4(1)) Tandem Library Bks.

—The Last Fairy-Apple Tree. Vitale, Raoul, illus. 2007. (Fairy Realm Ser.). 128p. (J). (gr. 3-6). 25.65 (978-1-59961-326-0(3)) Spotlight.

—The Peskie Spell. Vitale, Raoul, illus. 2007. (Fairy Realm Ser.). 128p. (J). (gr. 3-6). 25.65 (978-1-59961-331-4(X)) Spotlight.

—Rowan & the Ice Creepers. 2003. (Rowan of Rin Ser.). 272p. (J). (gr. 3 up). 15.99 (978-0-06-029780-0(8)) HarperCollins Pubs.

—Rowan & the Ice Creepers. 2004. 262p. (J). (gr. 3-7). lib. bdg. 13.04 (978-0-606-32643-8(X)) Tandem Library Bks.

—Rowan & the Keeper of the Crystal. (Rowan of Rin Ser.). 2004. 224p. (gr. 3 up). pap. 5.99 (978-0-06-056073-7(8)); 2002. 208p. (J). (gr. 2 up). pap. 5.99 (978-0-06-441025-0(0)); 2002. 208p. (J). (gr. 2 up). 15.99 (978-0-06-029776-3(X)); 2002. (Illus.). 208p. (J). (gr. 2 up). lib. bdg. 16.89 (978-0-06-029777-0(8)) HarperCollins Pubs.

—Rowan & the Travelers. (Rowan of Rin Ser.). 2004. 192p. (gr. 3 up). pap. 5.99 (978-0-06-056072-0(X)); 2002. 176p. (J). (gr. 2 up). pap. 5.95 (978-0-06-441026-7(9) , Harper Trophy) HarperCollins Pubs.

—Rowan & the Zebak. (Rowan of Rin Ser.). (J). 2004. 224p. (gr. 3 up). pap. 5.99 (978-0-06-056074-4(6)); 2003. (Illus.). 208p. (gr. 2 up). pap. 5.99 (978-0-06-441024-3(2) , Harper Trophy); 2002. 208p. (gr. 2 up). 15.99 (978-0-06-029778-7(6)) HarperCollins Pubs.

—Rowan of Rin. (Rowan of Rin Ser.). (J). 2004. (Illus.). 176p. (gr. 3 up). pap. 5.99 (978-0-06-056071-3(1)); 2002. (gr. 2 up). pap. 5.95 (978-0-06-441019-9(6) , Harper Trophy) HarperCollins Pubs.

—Shadowgate. 2004. 195p. (J). lib. bdg. 16.92 ***(*978-1-4242-0274-4(4))*** Fitzgerald Bks.

—The Shadowlands. McBride, Marc, illus. 2002. (Deltora Quest Ser.: No. 3). 160p. (J). (gr. 4-9). pap. 4.99 (978-0-439-39493-2(7) , Scholastic Paperbacks) Scholastic, Inc.

—The Shadowlands. 2002. (gr. 3-6). lib. bdg. 13.00 (978-0-613-50643-4(X)) Tandem Library Bks.

—The Shifting Sands. 2001. (Deltora Quest Ser.: No. 4). (Illus.). 144p. (J). (gr. 4-7). pap. 4.99 (978 0 439 25326-0(8)) Scholastic, Inc.

—Sister of the South. 2004. 205p. (J). lib. bdg. 16.92 ***(*978-1-4242-0275-1(2))*** Fitzgerald Bks.

—The Star Cloak. Vitale, Raoul, illus. 2007. (Fairy Realm Ser.). 128p. (J). (gr. 3-6). 25.65 (978-1-59961-329-1(8)) Spotlight.

—Tales of Deltora. 2006. (Illus.). 176p. (J). pap. 14.99 (978-0-439-87785-5(7)) Scholastic, Inc.

—The Third Wish. Vitale, Raoul, illus. 2007. (Fairy Realm Ser.). 128p. (J). (gr. 3-6). 25.65 (978-1-59961-325-3(5)) Spotlight.

—The Unicorn. Vitale, Raoul, illus. 2007. (Fairy Realm Ser.). 112p. (J). (gr. 3-6). 25.65 (978-1-59961-328-4(X)) Spotlight.

—The Valley of the Lost. 2001. (gr. 5-8). lib. bdg. 13.00 (978-0-613-43903-9(1)) Tandem Library Bks.

—The Water Sprites. Vitale, Raoul, illus. 2005. (Fairy Realm Ser.). 128p. (J). lib. bdg. 14.89 (978-0-06-077762-3(1)); 8.99 (978-0-06-077761-6(3)) HarperCollins Pubs.

—The Water Sprites. Vitale, Raoul, illus. 2007. (Fairy Realm Ser.). 128p. (J). (gr. 3-6). 25.65 (978-1-59961-330-7(1)) Spotlight.

Rodi, Robert & Higgins, John. Identity Disc. 2005. (Marvel Heroes Ser.). (Illus.). 120p. pap. 13.99 (978-0-7851-1567-0(6)) Marvel Enterprises, Inc.

Rodi, Robert & Richards, Cliff. Rogue: Going Rogue. 2005. (X-Men Ser.). (Illus.). 144p. pap. 14.99 (978-0-7851-1336-2(3)) Marvel Enterprises, Inc.

Rodowsky, Colby. Remembering Mog. 1998. (978-0-606-13736-2(X)) Tandem Library Bks.

Rogers, Joe. The War of the Elves (Book Two of the Changeling) 2006. 221p. pap. (978-1-84685-164-3(5) , Exposure Publishing) Meadow Bks.

Rogers, Jonathan. The Bark of the Bog Owl. 2005. (Wilderking Trilogy: Bk. 1). (Illus.). 240p. pap. 9.97 (978-0-8054-3131-5(4)) B&H Publishing Grp.

—The Secret of the Swamp King 2: The Wilderking Trilogy. 2005. 240p. pap. 9.97 (978-0-8054-3132-2(2)) B&H Publishing Grp.

—The Way of the Wilderking. 2006. (Wilderking Trilogy: Vol. 3). 24p. (J). 9.97 (978-0-8054-3133-9(0)) B&H Publishing Grp.

Romey, Elizabeth A. Dragon Magic. (YA). pap. 9.99 (978-0-88092-625-6(2)) Royal Fireworks Publishing Co.

Rose, Alice. Maria Dracula: A Fantasy Novel for Children. 2007. (Illus.). 191p. pap. 13.50 ***(*978-0-615-15099-4(3))*** DUENDE Bks.

Rose, Lynda J. Assignment Earth. 2008. 160p. (J). pap. 8.95 ***(*978-0-7459-6063-0(4))*** Lion Hudson plc GBR. *Dist:* Independent Pubs. Group.

Rose, Simon. The Emerald Curse. Nugent, Cynthia, illus. 2006. 96p. (J). (gr. 3-7). 7.95 (978-1-896580-90-6(4)) Tradewind Bks. CAN. *Dist:* Orca Bk. Pubs. USA.

—The Sorcerer's Letterbox. 2006. 116p. (J). 7.95 (978-1-896580-52-4(1)) Tradewind Bks. CAN. *Dist:* Orca Bk. Pubs. USA.

Rosell, Joel Franz. Vuela, Ertico, Vuela. (SPA.). 64p. (J). (978-84-348-5268-6(3)) SM Ediciones ESP. *Dist:* Lectorum Pubns., Inc.

Ross, Dev. We Both Read-Fox's Best Trick Ever. Reinhart, Larry, illus. 2006. (We Both Read Ser.). 48p. (J). 7.99 (978-1-891327-69-8(0)) Treasure Bay, Inc.

Ross, Jillian. Alissa & the Dungeons of Grimrock. Backes, Nick, illus. 1998. (Stardust Classics). 106p. (J). (gr. 2-6). 12.95 (978-1-889514-15-4(2)) Dolls Corp.

Ross, Tony. I Want My Pacifier. Ross, Tony, illus. 2004. (Illus.). 28p. (J). pap. 4.95 (978-1-929132-65-2(4)) Kane/Miller Bk. Pubs., Inc.

Rousseau, Paul & Mongeau, Marc. Une Panthère dans la Litière. 2002. (Roman Jeunesse Ser.). (FRE.). 96p. (J). (gr. 4-7). pap. (978-2-89021-564-1(4)) Diffusion du livre Mirabel.

Rowe, John A., illus. The Gingerbread Man: An Old English Folktale. 1998. 32p. (J). (ps-1). pap. 6.95 (978-1-55858-906-3(6) , Michael Neugebauer Bks.) North-South Bks., Inc.

Rowling, J. K. Les Animaux Fantastiques et Ou les Trouver. 2001. (FRE.). 96p. pap. 16.95 (978-0-320-04844-9(6)) French & European Pubns., Inc.

—Harri Potter Maen yr Athronydd. 2003. (WEL.). 300p. (J). 21.95 (978-1-58234-827-8(8) , Bloomsbury Children) Bloomsbury Publishing.

—Harrius Potter et Philosophi Lapis. Needham, Peter, tr. from ENG. 2003. (Harry Potter Ser.: Year 1). Orig. Title: Harry Potter & the Philosopher's Stone. (LAT., Illus.). 300p. (J). 23.95 (978-1-58234-825-4(1) , Bloomsbury Children) Bloomsbury Publishing.

—Harry Potter agus an Orebloch. 2004. (GAE.). 300p. (J). (gr. 5 up). 21.95 (978-1-58234-828-5(6) , Bloomsbury Children) Bloomsbury Publishing.

—Harry Potter & the Chamber of Secrets. braille ed. 1999. (Harry Potter Ser.: Year 2). 520p. (YA). (gr. 3 up). pap. 17.99 (978-0-939173-35-8(2)) National Braille Pr.

—Harry Potter & the Chamber of Secrets. 2003. 203p. 23.95 (978-7-02-003344-7(X) , HAP02) People's Literature Publishing Hse. CHN. *Dist:* China Bks. & Periodicals, Inc.

—Harry Potter & the Chamber of Secrets. unabr. ed. 2004. (Harry Potter Ser.: Year 2). 352p. (J). (gr. 3 up). pap. 46.00 incl. audio (978-0-8072-8207-6(3) , S YA 137 SP, Listening Library) Random Hse. Audio Publishing Group.

—Harry Potter & the Chamber of Secrets. (RUS., Illus.). 28.95 (978-5-8451-0947-7(7)) Rosmen-Izdat RUS. *Dist:* Distribooks, Inc.

—Harry Potter & the Chamber of Secrets. 2003. (Harry Potter Ser.: Year 2). 352p. (J). 24.95 (978-0-439-55489-3(6) , Levine, Arthur A. Bks.) Scholastic, Inc.

—Harry Potter & the Chamber of Secrets. GrandPré, Mary, illus. (Harry Potter Ser.: Year 2). (J). 2002. 448p. mass mkt. 6.99 (978-0-439-42010-5(5) , Levine, Arthur A. Bks.); 2000. 352p. (gr. 3 up). mass mkt. 8.99 (978-0-439-06487-3(2)); 1999. 352p. (gr. 3 up). 22.99 (978-0-439-06486-6(4) , Levine, Arthur A. Bks.); 2002. 352p. 75.00 (978-0-439-20353-1(8) , Levine, Arthur A. Bks.) Scholastic, Inc.

—Harry Potter & the Chamber of Secrets. GrandPré, Mary, illus. l.t. ed. 2000. (Harry Potter Ser.: Year 2). 464p. (gr. 3 up). 24.95 (978-0-7862-2273-5(5) , Large Print Pr.) Thorndike Pr.

—Harry Potter & the Deathly Hallows. braille ed. 2007. (Harry Potter Ser.: Year 7). 34.99 ***(*978-0-939173-57-0(3))*** National Braille Pr.

—Harry Potter & the Deathly Hallows. GrandPré, Mary, illus. 2007. (Harry Potter Ser.: Year 7). 784p. (J). (gr. 4-7). 34.99 ***(*978-0-545-01022-1(5));*** 784p. (YA). (gr. 6 up). 39.99 ***(*978-0-545-02936-0(8));*** 816p. (J). 65.00 ***(*978-0-545-02937-7(6))*** Scholastic, Inc. (Levine, Arthur A. Bks.).

—Harry Potter & the Deathly Hallows. l.t. ed. 2007. (Harry Potter Ser.: Year 7). (YA). 34.95 ***(*978-0-7862-9665-1(8))*** Thorndike Pr.

—Harry Potter & the Goblet of Fire. 2003. 433p. 19.95 (978-7-02-003463-5(2) , HAP04) People's Literature Publishing Hse. CHN. *Dist:* China Bks. & Periodicals, Inc.

—Harry Potter & the Goblet of Fire. 2003. (Harry Potter Ser.: Year 4). 752p. (J). 30.95 (978-0-439-55490-9(X) , Levine, Arthur A. Bks.) Scholastic, Inc.

—Harry Potter & the Goblet of Fire. GrandPré, Mary, illus. (Harry Potter Ser.: Year 4). 752p. (J). (gr. 3 up). 2002. mass mkt. 9.99 (978-0-439-13960-1(0)); 2000. 29.99 (978-0-439-13959-5(7)) Scholastic, Inc. (Levine, Arthur A. Bks.).

—Harry Potter & the Goblet of Fire. 2002. (gr. 3-6). lib. bdg. 17.60 (978-0-613-49674-2(4)) Tandem Library Bks.

—Harry Potter & the Goblet of Fire. GrandPré, Mary, illus. l.t. ed. 2000. (Harry Potter Ser.: Year 4). 936p. (gr. 3 up). 25.95 (978-0-7862-2927-7(6) , Large Print Pr.) Thorndike Pr.

—Harry Potter & the Half-Blood Prince, 9 vols. braille ed. 2005. (Harry Potter Ser.: 6). (YA). 29.99 (978-0-939173-39-6(5) , HALF) National Braille Pr.

—Harry Potter & the Half-Blood Prince. 2003. (Harry Potter Ser.). 496p. 24.95 ***(*978-7-02-005323-0(8)*** , HAP06) People's Literature Publishing Hse. CHN. *Dist:* China Bks. & Periodicals, Inc.

—Harry Potter & the Half-Blood Prince. GrandPré, Mary, illus. (J). 2005. (Harry Potter Ser.: Year 6). 672p. 34.99 (978-0-439-78677-5(0)); 2005. (Harry Potter Ser.: Year 6). 672p. 29.99 (978-0-439-78454-2(9)); 2005. (Harry Potter Ser.: Year 6). 704p. 60.00 (978-0-439-79132-8(4)); 2006. 672p. reprint ed. pap. 9.99 (978-0-439-78596-9(0)) Scholastic, Inc. (Levine, Arthur A. Bks.).

—Harry Potter & the Half-Blood Prince. l.t. ed. 2005. (Harry Potter Ser.: Year 6). 832p. 29.95 (978-0-7862-7745-2(9) , Large Print Pr.) Thorndike Pr.

—Harry Potter & the Order of the Phoenix, 13 vols. braille ed. 2003. (Harry Potter Ser.: Year 5). (YA). 29.99 (978-0-939173-38-9(7)) National Braille Pr.

—Harry Potter & the Order of the Phoenix. GrandPré, Mary, illus. (Harry Potter Ser.: Year 5). (J). 2004. 896p. (gr. 4-7). mass mkt. 9.99 (978-0-439-35807-1(8) , Scholastic Paperbacks); 2003. 896p. (gr. 3-6). 34.99 (978-0-439-56761-9(0)); 2003. 870p. (gr. 3-6). 29.99 (978-0-439-35806-4(X)); 2003. 896p. (gr. 3-6). 60.00 (978-0-439-56762-6(9)) Scholastic, Inc.

—Harry Potter & the Order of the Phoenix. l.t. ed. 2003. (Harry Potter Ser.: Year 5). 1093p. 29.95 (978-0-7862-5778-2(4) , Large Print Pr.) Thorndike Pr.

—Harry Potter & the Philosopher's Stone. 2004. (GRE & GEC.). 300p. (J). (gr. 3-6). 21.95 (978-1-58234-826-1(X) , Bloomsbury Children) Bloomsbury Publishing.

—Harry Potter & the Prisoner of Azkaban. 2002. (Harry Potter Ser.). (Illus.). (YA). 16.26 (978-0-7587-5662-6(3)) Book Wholesalers, Inc.

—Harry Potter & the Prisoner of Azkaban. braille ed. 1999. (Harry Potter Ser.: Year 3). (YA). (gr. 3 up). pap. 19.95 (978-0-939173-36-5(0)) National Braille Pr.

—Harry Potter & the Prisoner of Azkaban. 2000. (J). tchr. ed. 9.95 (978-1-58130-656-9(3)); stu. ed. 11.95 (978-1-58130-657-6(1)) Novel Units, Inc.

—Harry Potter & the Prisoner of Azkaban. 2003. 260p. 15.95 (978-7-02-003345-4(8) , HAP03) People's Literature Publishing Hse. CHN. *Dist:* China Bks. & Periodicals, Inc.

—Harry Potter & the Prisoner of Azkaban. 2004. (Harry Potter Ser.: Year 3). 560p. mass mkt. 7.99 (978-0-439-65548-4(X) , Scholastic Paperbacks) Scholastic, Inc.

—Harry Potter & the Prisoner of Azkaban. GrandPré, Mary, illus. 2001. (Harry Potter Ser.: Year 3). 448p. (YA). (gr. 3 up). mass mkt. 8.99 (978-0-439-13636-5(9) , Levine, Arthur A. Bks.) Scholastic, Inc.

—Harry Potter & the Prisoner of Azkaban. 2001. (gr. 3-6). lib. bdg. 16.45 (978-0-613-37106-3(2)) Tandem Library Bks.

—Harry Potter & the Prisoner of Azkaban. GrandPré, Mary, illus. l.t. ed. 2000. (Harry Potter Ser.: Year 3). 592p. (gr. 3 up). 24.95 (978-0-7862-2274-2(3) , Large Print Pr.) Thorndike Pr.

—Harry Potter & the Sorcerer's Stone. 2003. (CHI.). 191p. 13.95 (978-7-02-003343-0(1) , HAP01) People's Literature Publishing Hse. CHN. *Dist:* China Bks. & Periodicals, Inc.

—Harry Potter & the Sorcerer's Stone. unabr. ed. (Harry Potter Ser.: Year 1). 320p. (gr. 3 up). (YA). pap. 62.00 incl. audio (978-0-8072-1547-0(3)); 2004. (J). pap. 46.00 incl. audio (978-0-8072-8119-2(0) , S YA 108 SP) Random Hse. Audio Publishing Group. (Listening Library).

—Harry Potter & the Sorcerer's Stone. GrandPré, Mary, illus. (Harry Potter Ser.: Year 1). (gr. 3 up). 2001. 400p. (J). mass mkt. 6.99 (978-0-439-36213-9(X)); 1999. 320p. (YA). mass mkt. 8.99 (978-0-590-35342-7(X)); 1998. 320p. (J). pap. 22.99 (978-0-590-35340-3(3) , Levine, Arthur A. Bks.) Scholastic, Inc.

—Harry Potter & the Sorcerer's Stone. collector's ed. 2000. (Harry Potter Ser.: Year 1). 320p. (YA). (gr. 3 up). 75.00 (978-0-439-20352-4(X)) Scholastic, Inc.

—Harry Potter & the Sorcerer's Stone. GrandPré, Mary, illus. l.t. ed. 1999. (Harry Potter Ser.: Year 1). 422p. (gr. 3 up). 24.95 (978-0-7862-2272-8(7) , Large Print Pr.) Thorndike Pr.

—Harry Potter Boxed Set, Bks. 1-7. 2007. (Harry Potter Ser.: Years 1-7). (J). 195.00 ***(*978-0-545-04425-7(1)*** , Levine, Arthur A. Bks.) Scholastic, Inc.

—Harry Potter Boxed Set: Harry Potter & the Sorcerer's Stone; Harry Potter & the Chamber of Secrets; Harry Potter & the Prisoner of Azkaban, 3 vols. GrandPré, Mary, illus. (Harry Potter Ser.: Years 1-3). (YA). 2002. pap. 21.97 (978-0-439-32466-3(1)); 1999. (gr. 3 up). 55.85 (978-0-439-13316-6(5)) Scholastic, Inc. (Levine, Arthur A. Bks.).

—Harry Potter Boxed Set: Harry Potter & the Sorcerer's Stone; Harry Potter & the Chamber of Secrets; Harry Potter & the Prisoner of Azkaban; Harry Potter & the Goblet of Fire, 4 vols. GrandPré, Mary, illus. 2000. (Harry Potter Ser.: Years 1-4). (YA). (gr. 3 up). 85.80 (978-0-641-06631-3(7) , Levine, Arthur A. Bks.) Scholastic, Inc.

—Harry Potter Coffret: Harry Potter a l'Ecole des Sorciers; Harry Potter et la Chambre des Secrets; Harry Potter et le Prisonnier d'Azkaban. 1999. (Harry Potter Ser.: Years 1-3). Tr. of Harry Potter Boxed Set: Harry Potter & the

Chamber of Secrets; Harry Potter & the Sorcerer's Stone; Harry Potter & the Prisoner of Azkaban. (FRE.). (YA). (gr. 3 up). pap. 43.95 (978-2-07-052929-2(0)) Gallimard, Editions FRA. *Dist:* Distribooks, Inc.

—Harry Potter Coffret: Harry Potter a l'Ecole des Sorciers; Harry Potter et la Chambre des Secrets; Harry Potter et le Prisonnier d'Azkaban; Harry Potter et la Coupe de Feu. 1999. (Harry Potter Ser.: Years 1-3). Tr. of Harry Potter Boxed Set: Harry Potter & the Chamber of Secrets; Harry Potter & the Sorcerer's Stone; Harry Potter & the Prisoner of Azkaban; Harry Potter et la COupe de Feu. (FRE.). 1400p. (YA). (gr. 3 up). pap. 34.95 (978-0-320-03843-3(2)) French & European Pubns., Inc.

—Harry Potter e la Camera dei Segreti. (ITA.). pap. 32.95 (978-88-7782-703-6(3)) Salani ITA. *Dist:* Distribooks, Inc.

—Harry Potter e la Pietra Filosofale. (ITA.). pap. 32.95 (978-88-7782-702-9(5)) Salani ITA. *Dist:* Distribooks, Inc.

—Harry Potter et la Chambre des Secrets. 1999. (Harry Potter Ser.: Year 2). Tr. of Harry Potter & the Chamber of Secrets. (FRE.). (YA). (gr. 3 up). pap. 13.95 (978-0-320-03778-8(9)) French & European Pubns., Inc.

—Harry Potter et la Chambre des Secrets. 1999. (Harry Potter Ser.: Year 2). Tr. of Harry Potter & the Chamber of Secrets. (FRE., Illus.). 358p. (YA). (gr. 3 up). pap. 16.95 (978-2-07-052455-6(8)) Gallimard, Editions FRA. *Dist:* Distribooks, Inc.

—Harry Potter et la Coupe de Feu. 2001. Tr. of Harry Potter & the Goblet of Fire. 1173p. pap. 19.95 (978-0-320-04838-8(1)) French & European Pubns., Inc.

—Harry Potter et le Prisonnier d'Azkaban. 1999. (Harry Potter Ser.: Year 3). Tr. of Harry Potter & the Prisoner of Azkaban. (FRE.). 465p. (YA). (gr. 3 up). pap. 16.95 (978-2-07-052818-9(9)) Gallimard, Editions FRA. *Dist:* Distribooks, Inc.

—Harry Potter et l'Ecole des Sorciers. 3rd ed. 1998. (Harry Potter Ser.: Year 1). Tr. of Harry Potter & the Sorcerer's Stone. (FRE., Illus.). (YA). (gr. 3 up). pap. 14.95 (978-2-07-050142-7(6)) Distribooks, Inc.

—Harry Potter et l'Ecole des Sorciers. 1999. (Harry Potter Ser.: Year 1). Tr. of Harry Potter & the Sorcerer's Stone. (FRE.). (YA). (gr. 3 up). pap. 16.95 (978-0-320-03780-1(0)) French & European Pubns., Inc.

—Harry Potter et l'Ecole des Sorciers.Tr. of Harry Potter & the Sorcerer's Stone. 2007. 311p. pap. 14.95 ***(978-2-07-061236-9(8));*** 2000. (FRE.). (J). pap. 14.95 (978-2-07-051426-7(9)) Gallimard, Editions FRA. *Dist:* Distribooks, Inc.

—Harry Potter et l'Ordre du Phenix. 2003. 975p. pap. 75.00 (978-0-320-04839-5(X)) French & European Pubns., Inc.

—Harry Potter und der Gefangene von Azkaban. 1999. (Harry Potter Ser.: Year 3). Tr. of Harry Potter & the Prisoner of Azkaban. (GER.). (YA). (gr. 3 up). pap. 34.95 (978-3-551-55169-6(3)) Carlsen Verlag DEU. *Dist:* Distribooks, Inc.

—Harry Potter und der Stein der Weisen. 1999. (Harry Potter Ser.: Year 1). (GER.). 335p. (YA). (gr. 3 up). pap. 34.95 (978-3-551-55167-2(7)) Carlsen Verlag DEU. *Dist:* Distribooks, Inc.

—Harry Potter und die Kammer des Schreckens. 1999. (Harry Potter Ser.: Year 2). Tr. of Harry Potter & Chamber of Secrets. (GER.). (YA). (gr. 3 up). pap. 36.95 (978-3-551-55168-9(5)) Carlsen Verlag DEU. *Dist:* Distribooks, Inc.

—Harry Potter y el Caliz de Fuego. 2004. (Harry Potter Ser.). (SPA., Illus.). 240p. (YA). 19.95 (978-84-7888-645-6(1), SAL30169) Emece Editores ESP. *Dist:* Lectorum Pubns., Inc.

—Harry Potter y el Caliz de Fuego. 2000. 636p. 39.95 (978-0-320-04849-4(7)) French & European Pubns., Inc.

—Harry Potter y el Caliz de Fuego. 2001. (SPA.). (gr. 3-6). lib. bdg. 26.35 (978-0-613-35957-3(7)); (Illus.). (J). 23.15 (978-0-606-21227-4(2)) Tandem Library Bks.

—Harry Potter y el Misterio del Principe. Ortega, Gemma Rovira, tr. (SPA.). 2006. 670p. (YA). pap. 15.99 (978-84-7888-996-9(5)); 2005. 602p. (J). 19.99 (978-84-7888-993-8(0)) Publicaciones y Ediciones Salamandra, S.A. ESP. *Dist:* Ediciones Universal, Lectorum Pubns., Inc., Lectorum Pubns., Inc.

—Harry Potter y el Prisionero de Azkaban. (SPA.). 2002. 362p. (978-84-7888-761-3(X), 1950); 2000. 360p. (978-84-7888-615-9(X), 1950) Emece Editores.

—Harry Potter y el Prisionero de Azkaban. 2004. (Harry Potter Ser.). (SPA.). 359p. pap. 12.00 (978-84-7888-655-5(9), SAL30174); (Illus.). 360p. (gr. 3 up). 17.95 (978-84-7888-519-0(6), SAL1889) Emece Editores ESP. *Dist:* Lectorum Pubns., Inc.

—Harry Potter y el Prisionero de Azkaban. 2000. (Harry Potter Ser.: Year 3). (SPA.). (YA). (gr. 3 up). 16.95 (978-0-320-03783-2(5)); 360p. 29.95 (978-0-320-04846-3(2)) French & European Pubns., Inc.

—Harry Potter y el Prisionero de Azkaban. 2001. (SPA.). (gr. 3-6). lib. bdg. 21.10 (978-0-613-35958-0(5)) Tandem Library Bks.

—Harry Potter y la Camara Secreta. 2000. (SPA.). 288p. (978-84-7888-614-2(1), 1950) Emece Editores.

—Harry Potter y la Camara Secreta. 2004. (Harry Potter Ser.). (SPA.). (YA). 286p. pap. 9.99 (978-84-7888-656-2(7), SAL30173); (Illus.). 288p. (gr. 3 up). 15.95 (978-84-7888-495-7(5), SAL4595) Emece Editores ESP. *Dist:* Lectorum Pubns., Inc.

—Harry Potter y la Camara Secreta. 2000. (SPA.). 290p. (YA). (gr. 7 up). 15.95 (978-950-04-2068-6(6)) Emecé Editores S.A. ARG. *Dist:* Libros Sin Fronteras.

—Harry Potter y la Camara Secreta. 1999. (Harry Potter Ser.: Year 2). (SPA.). (YA). (gr. 3 up). 14.95 (978-0-320-03781-8(9)) French & European Pubns., Inc.

—Harry Potter y la Orden del Fenix. 2004. (Harry Potter Ser.). (SPA.). 893p. (YA). 23.99 (978-84-7888-901-3(9)) Emece Editores ESP. *Dist:* Lectorum Pubns., Inc.

—Harry Potter y la Orden del Fenix. Ortega, Gemma Rovira, tr. 2004. (Harry Potter Ser.). (SPA.). 893p. (YA). pap. 17.99 (978-84-7888-884-9(5)) Emece Editores ESP. *Dist:* Lectorum Pubns., Inc.

—Harry Potter y la Piedra Filosofal. (SPA.). 2002. 258p. (978-84-7888-759-0(8), 1950); 2000. 256p. (978-84-7888-612-8(5), 1950) Emece Editores.

—Harry Potter y la Piedra Filosofal. 2004. (Harry Potter Ser.: Bk. 1). (SPA., Illus.). 256p. (YA). (gr. 7 up). 15.95 (978-84-7888-445-2(9), SAL2819) Emece Editores ESP. *Dist:* Lectorum Pubns., Inc.

—Harry Potter y la Piedra Filosofal. 2000. 254p. 29.95 (978-0-320-04848-7(9)); 1999. (Harry Potter Ser.: Year 1). (SPA.). (YA). (gr. 3 up). 14.95 (978-0-320-03782-5(7)) French & European Pubns., Inc.

—Harry Potter y la Piedra Filosofal. 2001. (SPA.). (gr. 3-6). lib. bdg. 18.80 (978-0-613-35960-3(7)) Tandem Library Bks.

—Le Quidditch a Travers les Ages. 2001. 96p. pap. 16.95 (978-0-320-04845-6(4)) French & European Pubns., Inc.

Rowling, J. K. & Dale, Jim. Harry Potter & the Goblet of Fire. unabr. ed. 2004. (Harry Potter Ser.). 752p. (J). pap. 65.00 incl. audio (978-0-8072-1196-0(6), S YA 270 SP, Listening Library) Random Hse. Audio Publishing Group.

Ruble, Kam. Princess Annado Tandy's Versery-Rhymes. McMullen, T. C., illus. 2007. (J). per. ***(978-0-9779680-4-6(9))*** Global Authors Pubns.

Ruby, Anne. Children of the Sea. Meier, Ty, illus. 2007. (YA). per. (978-0-9787881-0-0(9)) Seachild.

Ruby, Laura. The Chaos King. 2007. 336p. (J). lib. bdg. 17.89 ***(978-0-06-075259-0(9));*** (gr. 5 up). 16.99 ***(978-0-06-075258-3(0))*** HarperCollins Pubs. (Eos).

Ruby, Laura. The Wall & the Wing. 2006. 336p. (J). 16.99 (978-0-06-075255-2(6)) HarperCollins Pubs.

Ruditis, Paul. The Brewing Storm. 2004. (Charmed Ser.). 240p. (YA). mass mkt. 6.99 (978-0-689-86851-1(0), Simon Spotlight Entertainment) Simon & Schuster.

—Ready to Glow. Choi Sung Hwan, Aragon Noel, illus. 2005. (Trollz Ser.). 80p. (J). pap. 5.99 (978-0-439-80313-7(6)) Scholastic, Inc.

Rue, Nancy N. The Trick. 1999. (Christian Heritage Ser.). (Illus.). 208p. (J). (gr. 3-7). pap. (978-1-56179-734-9(0)) Focus on the Family Publishing.

Rumpelstiltskin: 6 Small Books. (gr. k-2). 23.00 (978-0-7635-8515-0(7)) Rigby Education.

Rumpelstiltskin: Individual Title Six-Packs. 32p. (gr. 2 up). 37.00 (978-0-7635-9402-2(4)) Rigby Education.

Running Press Staff. Harry Potter Golden Snitch. 2006. 16p. pap. 8.95 (978-0-7624-2821-2(X), Running Pr.) Running Pr. Bk. Pubs.

Rupp, Rebecca. The Dragon of Lonely Island. ed. 2006. 192p. (J). (gr. 3-6). pap. 5.99 (978-0-7636-2805-5(0)) Candlewick Pr.

—Journey to the Blue Moon: In Which Time Is Lost & Then Found Again. 2006. 272p. (J). (gr. 5). 15.99 (978-0-7636-2544-3(2)) Candlewick Pr.

Rushdie, Salman. Haroun & the Sea of Stories. 1999. 96p. 13.00 (978-0-571-19693-7(4)) Faber & Faber, Inc.

Ruth, Nick. The Dark Dreamweaver. Concannon, Sue, illus. 2007. (Remin Chronicles: 1). 256p. (J). per. 11.95 ***(978-0-9745603-5-9(9))*** Imaginator Pr.

Ryan, Kris. Spoon. 2005. 201p. pap. 19.95 (978-1-4137-7229-6(3)) PublishAmerica, Inc.

Ryder, Joanne. Earthdance. Gorbaty, Norman, illus. rev. ed. 1999. 32p. (J). (ps-2). pap. 7.95 (978-0-8050-6231-1(9), Holt, Henry & Co. Bks. For Young Readers) Holt, Henry & Co.

—Earthdance. 1999. (gr. k-3). lib. bdg. 15.25 (978-0-613-16666-9(3)) Tandem Library Bks.

Rylant, Cynthia. The Wonderful Happens. Dowley, Coco, illus. 40p. (J). 2003. pap. 7.99 (978-0-689-86355-4(1), Aladdin); 2000. 16.95 (978-0-689-83177-5(3)) Simon & Schuster Children's Publishing.

Sabin, E. Rose. School for Sorcery. 2003. (gr. 5-8). lib. bdg. 14.15 (978-0-613-67854-4(0)) Tandem Library Bks.

—A School for Sorcery. rev. ed. 2002. 318p. 17.95 (978-0-7653-0289-2(6), Forge Bks.) Doherty, Tom Assocs., LLC.

Sabuda, Robert, illus. The Wonderful Wizard of Oz. 2000. (Oz Ser.). (YA). (gr. 5-8). 175.00 (978-0-689-84207-8(4), Little Simon) Simon & Schuster Children's Publishing.

Sagar, Marie. Jimmy's Adventures: I'm Bored & Mr. Gray Bat. 2007. 20p. (J). 7.00 ***(978-0-8059-7494-2(6))*** Dorrance Publishing Co., Inc.

Sage, Alison. Susan's Journey. 2005. 82p. (J). lib. bdg. 15.00 ***(978-1-4242-0762-6(2))*** Fitzgerald Bks.

Sage, Angie. Flyte. Zug, Mark, illus. (Septimus Heap Ser.: Bk. 2). 544p. (J). (gr. 4 up). 2007. pap. 7.99 (978-0-06-057736-0(3), Harper Trophy); 2006. lib. bdg. 18.89 (978-0-06-057735-3(5)); 2006. 17.99 (978-0-06-057734-6(7), Tegen, Katherine Bks) HarperCollins Pubs.

—Magyk. Zug, Mark, illus. (Septimus Heap Ser.: Bk. 1). (J). (gr. 4 up). 2005. 576p. 17.99 (978-0-06-057731-5(2), Tegen, Katherine Bks); 2005. 576p. lib. bdg. 18.89 (978-0-06-057732-2(0)); 2006. 608p. reprint ed. pap. 7.99 (978-0-06-057733-9(9), Harper Trophy); Bk. 1. 2006. (SPA.). 496p. pap. 7.99 (978-0-06-084979-5(7), Rayo) HarperCollins Pubs.

Sage, Angie. Physik. Zug, Mark, illus. (Septimus Heap Ser.: Bk. 3). 560p. (J). (gr. 4-6). 2008. pap. 7.99 ***(978-0-06-057739-1(8)***, Harper Trophy); 2007. 17.99 (978-0-06-057737-7(1), Tegen, Katherine Bks); 2007. lib. bdg. 18.89 (978-0-06-057738-4(X), Tegen, Katherine Bks) HarperCollins Pubs.

Said, S. F. The Outlaw Varjak Paw. McKean, Dave, illus. 2006. 272p. (J). 16.95 (978-0-385-75044-8(7), Fickling, David Bks.) Random Hse. Children's Bks.

Saint-Exupéry, Antoine de. The Little Prince. 2000. (Illus.). (J). (978-0-606-18806-7(1)) Tandem Library Bks.

—The Little Prince. 1998. (Children's Library). (J). pap. 3.95 Wordsworth Editions, Ltd. GBR. *Dist:* Combined Publishing.

Saito, Chiho. Revolutionary Girl Utena: The Adolesence of Utena. Saito, Chiho, illus. 2004. (Revolutionary Girl Utena Ser.). (Illus.). 192p. (YA). pap. 9.95 (978-1-59116-500-2(8)) Viz Media.

Salvatore, R. A. Canticle. 2000. (gr. 7-12). lib. bdg. 15.30 (978-0-613-23606-5(8)) Tandem Library Bks.

—Road of the Patriarch. 2007. (Forgotten Realms Ser.: No. 3). 384p. pap. 7.99 ***(978-0-7869-4277-0(0))*** Wizards of the Coast.

Salvatore, R. A. Vector Prime. 2000. (Star Wars Ser.: Bk. 1). (gr. 7-12). lib. bdg. 15.90 (978-0-613-29377-8(0)) Tandem Library Bks.

Salvatore, R. A. & Dabb, Andrew. Demonwars, Vol. 1. 2007. (Illus.). 144p. (YA). pap. 18.99 ***(978-1-932796-89-6(4))*** Devil's Due Publishing, Inc.

Sampson, Fay. Pangur Ban, the White Cat, Vol. 2. 2002. 160p. (J). (gr. 5-8). pap. 7.99 (978-0-7459-4763-1(8), Lion) Lion Hudson plc GBR. *Dist:* Independent Pubs. Group.

—Shape-Shifter: The Naming of Pangur Ban. 2002. (Illus.). 160p. (J). (gr. 5-8). pap. 7.99 (978-0-7459-4762-4(X), Lion) Lion Hudson plc GBR. *Dist:* Independent Pubs. Group.

—The Sorcerer's Daughter. 2007. 224p. (J). (gr. 4-7). pap. 9.95 ***(978-0-7459-6072-2(3))*** Lion Hudson plc GBR. *Dist:* Independent Pubs. Group.

—Sorcerers Trap. 2005. 224p. (J). pap. 9.99 (978-0-7459-4985-7(1)) Lion Hudson plc GBR. *Dist:* Independent Pubs. Group.

—Them. 2003. 256p. (J). (gr. 3-8). pap. 8.99 (978-0-7459-4670-2(4), Lion) Lion Hudson plc GBR. *Dist:* Independent Pubs. Group.

Sampson, Jeff. The Ebony Eye. 2007. (Suncatcher Trilogy Ser.: Vol. 2). 256p. (YA). pap. 5.99 (978-0-7869-4255-8(X), Mirrorstone) Wizards of the Coast.

—The Stolen Sun. 2007. (Suncatcher Trilogy Ser.: Vol. 3). (J). (gr. 5-9). pap. 5.99 ***(978-0-7869-4291-6(6)***, Mirrorstone) Wizards of the Coast.

—Wizard's Betrayal. 2006. (New Adventures Ser.). (Illus.). 241p. (J). ***(978-1-4156-4798-1(4)***, Mirrorstone) Wizards of the Coast.

Samuels, Vallerie. The Village of Time. 2005. 9.00 (978-0-8059-9709-5(1)) Dorrance Publishing Co., Inc.

San Souci, Robert D. Little Gold Star: A Spanish American Cinderella Story. Martinez, Sergio, illus. 2000. 32p. (J). (gr. k-3). lib. bdg. 17.89 (978-0-688-14781-5(X)) HarperCollins Pubs.

—Little Gold Star: A Spanish American Cinderella Tale. Martinez, Sergio, illus. 2000. 32p. (J). (gr. k-3). 16.99 (978-0-688-14780-8(1)) HarperCollins Pubs.

San Souci, Robert Daniel. Cendrillon: A Caribbean Cinderella. Pinkney, Brian, illus. 1998. 40p. (J). (ps-3). 17.00 (978-0-689-80668-1(X)) Simon & Schuster Children's Publishing.

Sanchez, Juanvi. Cero. (SPA.). 12p. (J). (978-84-348-7852-5(6)) SM Ediciones ESP. *Dist:* Lectorum Pubns., Inc.

—Cinco. (SPA.). 16p. (J). (978-84-348-7183-0(1)) SM Ediciones ESP. *Dist:* Lectorum Pubns., Inc.

—Cuatro. (SPA.). 16p. (J). (978-84-348-7182-3(3)) SM Ediciones ESP. *Dist:* Lectorum Pubns., Inc.

—Un Dos Con Lunares. (SPA.). 16p. (J). (978-84-348-7180-9(7)) SM Ediciones ESP. *Dist:* Lectorum Pubns., Inc.

—Seis. (SPA.). (J). bds. (978-84-348-7184-7(X)) SM Ediciones ESP. *Dist:* Lectorum Pubns., Inc.

—Siete. (SPA.). (J). bds. (978-84-348-7850-1(X)) SM Ediciones ESP. *Dist:* Lectorum Pubns., Inc.

—El Tres de Lunares. (SPA.). 16p. (J). (978-84-348-7181-6(5)) SM Ediciones ESP. *Dist:* Lectorum Pubns., Inc.

—Uno. (SPA.). 16p. (J). (978-84-348-7179-3(3)) SM Ediciones ESP. *Dist:* Lectorum Pubns., Inc.

Sanders, Scott Russell. The Floating House. 1999. (J). (978-0-606-17316-2(1)) Tandem Library Bks.

Sanderson, Brandon. Alcatraz Versus the Evil Librarians. 2007. (Alcatraz Versus the Evil Librarians Ser.). 320p. (J). pap. 16.99 ***(978-0-439-92550-1(9)***, Scholastic Pr.) Scholastic, Inc.

Sanjo, Riku. Beet the Vandel Buster. Inada, Koji, illus. 2004. (Beet the Vandel Buster Ser.). 200p. (YA). pap. 7.99 (978-1-59116-690-0(X)) Viz Media.

Sanschagrin, Joceline. La Marque du Dragon. 2002. (Roman Jeunesse Ser.). (Illus.). 96p. (YA). (gr. 4-7). pap. (978-2-89021-355-5(2)) Diffusion du livre Mirabel.

—Le Visage Masqué. Brignaud, Pierre, illus. 2004. (Mon Roman Ser.). (FRE.). 160p. (J). (gr. 2). pap. (978-2-89021-651-8(9)) Diffusion du livre Mirabel.

Sarfati, Sonia. Le Manuscrit Envole. 1999. (Roman Jeunesse Ser.). (Illus.). 96p. (YA). (gr. 4-7). pap. (978-2-89021-346-3(3)) Diffusion du livre Mirabel.

Sargent, Daina. Arkansas: Dream Big. Lenoir, Jane, illus. l.t. ed. 2004. (Double Trouble Ser.). 48p. (J). pap. 6.95 (978-1-59381-123-5(3)); lib. bdg. (978-1-59381-122-8(5)) Ozark Publishing.

Sargent, Dave & Sargent, Pat. Bo Bo's Big Imagination/la Gran Imaginacion de Bo Bo, 10, 13. Robinson, Laura, illus. 2004. (Learn to Read Ser.: 10). (ENG & SPA.). 18p. (J). pap. 9.95 (978-1-56763-986-5(0)) Ozark Publishing.

Sargent, Dave, et al. Counting Cup Vol. 4: (Cheyenne) Be Proud, 20. l.t. ed. 2003. (Story Keeper Ser.). (Illus.). 42p. (J). pap. 6.95 (978-1-56763-910-0(0)) Ozark Publishing.

Sastrias, Marta. Cuentos de Todo y de Nada. Martinez y Luis San Vicente, Enrique, illus. 2003. (SPA.). 82p. (J). (gr. 3-5). (978-968-19-0551-4(2)) Aguilar, Altea, Taurus, Alfaguara, S.A. de C.V.

Sautereau, Francois. La Extrana Navidad de Jonas.Tr. of Jonas's Extraordinary Christmas. (SPA.). 92p. (YA). (gr. 5-8). (978-84-279-3163-3(8), NG3472) Noguer y Caralt Editores, S. A. ESP. *Dist:* Lectorum Pubns., Inc.

—La Extrana Navidad de Jonas. 2000. Tr. of Jonas's Extraordinary Christmas. (SPA.). (gr. 5-8). lib. bdg. 18.20 (978-0-613-80653-4(0)) Tandem Library Bks.

Sava, Scott Christian. The Dreamland Chronicles: Collecting the first four issues of the critically acclaimed comic series. : Book One, 6. 2006. (Illus.). 300p. (YA). per. 19.99 net. (978-0-9789168-0-0(8)) Blue Dream Studios.

Sawada, Hijime & Akita, Yoshinobu. Orphen, Vol. 4. 2006. (Illus.). 168p. (YA). pap. (978-1-4139-0269-3(3)) ADV Manga.

Sawyer, Ruth. The Primrose Ring. 2006. 77.99 ***(978-1-4280-4665-8(8));*** pap. 70.99 ***(978-1-4280-4664-1(X))*** IndyPublish.com.

Saxon, Victoria. Family of Tiggers. 2000. (Winnie the Pooh Ser.). (Illus.). 32p. (J). (ps-3). 12.99 (978-0-7868-3264-4(9)) Disney Pr.

Say, Allen, illus. Stranger in the Mirror. 1998. 32p. (J). (gr. 4-6). pap. 6.95 (978-0-395-93883-6(X), Walter Lorraine) Houghton Mifflin Co. Trade & Reference Div.

Schaefer, Lola M. Zap! Smith, Shane, illus. 1998. 8p. (J). (ps-2). 3.75 (978-1-880612-83-5(6), Seedling Pubns.) Continental Pr., Inc.

Scharf, J. L. Grace & the Ice Prince. 2007. 262p. pap. 15.95 ***(978-1-897235-09-6(7))*** Thistledown Pr., Ltd. CAN. *Dist:* Fitzhenry & Whiteside, Ltd.

Schend, Steven E. Blackstaff. 2006. (Wizards Ser.). 320p. pap. 6.99 (978-0-7869-4016-5(6)) Wizards of the Coast.

Schick, Doris. The Summer of Missandra. Schulte, Mary K., illus. 1998. 208p. (Orig.). (J). (gr. 5-9). pap. 12.95 (978-1-880090-35-0(X)) Galde Pr., Inc.

Schilling, Katherine, tr. Boys Be, Vol. 3. Tamakoshi, Hiroyuki, illus. rev. ed. 2005. 208p. pap. 9.99 (978-1-59532-101-5(2), Tokyopop Adult) TOKYOPOP, Inc.

Schirado, William C. Creatures, Vol. 1. Assenzo, Teresa M., illus. 18th l.t. ed. 1998. 128p. (J). (gr. k-6). 21.95 (978-0-9660166-1-1(0)) TW Publishing.

Schizas, Lea. The Rock of Realm. 2005. 244p. (YA). per. 12.95 (978-1-932993-08-0(8)) Star Publish LLC.

Schlegel, Paige. Que Desorden. Schlegel, Paige, illus. 2001. Tr. of What a Mess. (SPA., Illus.). 32p. (J). (ps-3). pap. 7.50 (978-1-884083-20-4(X)) Maval Publishing, Inc.

Schmidt, Jonathan. Lost Lagoon. 1999. (Roxbury Park Bks.). 160p. (gr. 3-7). (978-0-7373-0116-8(3)); pap. (978-0-7373-0117-5(1)) Lowell Hse.

Schmidt, Scott. The Hobogoblin of the Redwoods. 2004. 80p. pap. 14.95 (978-1-4137-1236-0(3)) PublishAmerica, Inc.

Schnitzius, Ron. Timecastle. unabr. ed. 2002. 191p. (YA). (gr. 7-12). pap. 8.95 (978-0-9718411-0-9(1)) JumpRope Bks.

Scholastic, Inc. Staff. Are We There Yet? Hult, Gene, ed. 2004. (Shrek 2 Ser.). 80p. (J). 3.99 (978-0-439-57634-5(2)) Scholastic, Inc.

—Bionicle Chronicles: Box Set 1-4: Tales of the Masks; Makuta's Revenge; Beware the Bohrok; Tale of the Toa. 2004. (Bionicle Ser.). (Illus.). 620p. (J). (gr. 4-7). 19.96 (978-0-439-69053-9(6)) Scholastic, Inc.

—World of Rainbow Brite. Swendsen, Silje, ed. 2004. (Rainbow Brite Ser.). (Illus.). 17p. (J). (ps-3). pap. 5.99 (978-0-439-65937-6(X)) Scholastic, Inc.

Scholastic, Inc. Staff & Dewin, Howie. Sleeping Ugly. 2004. (Shrek Ser.). (SPA., Illus.). 64p. (J). pap. 3.99 (978-0-439-63199-0(8), Scholastic en Espanol) Scholastic, Inc.

Scholastic, Inc. Staff & Farshtey, Greg. Trial by Fire. 2004. (Bionicle Ser.). (Illus.). 96p. (J). 4.99 (978-0-439-60732-2(9), Scholastic Paperbacks) Scholastic, Inc.

Scholtz, Pieter. Tales of the Tokoloshe. Treweek, Cherie, illus. 2005. 144p. (J). pap. 12.95 (978-1-86872-970-8(2)) Struik Pubs. ZAF. *Dist:* International Publishers Marketing.

Schoop, Bernice F. The Legend of Moon-Goblin Town. 2003. pap. 8.95 (978-0-533-14342-9(X)) Vantage Pr., Inc.

Schraff, Anne. Wishstone. 2001. (gr. 5-8). lib. bdg. 11.80 (978-0-613-63145-7(5)) Tandem Library Bks.

Schuler, Betty Jo. Brainman. Cummins, Sandy, ed. 2002. 55p. (J). mass mkt. (978-1-876962-67-8(4)) Writers Exchange E-Publishing Australia.

Schulz, Charles M. Necesito Todos los Amigos Que Pueda Tener. (SPA.). (J). 7.00 (978-84-7655-665-8(9), PI3928) Plaza Joven, S.A. ESP. *Dist:* Lectorum Pubns., Inc.

Schusterman, Neal. The Dark Side of Nowhere. unabr. ed. 2004. 192p. (J). (gr. 4-7). pap. 36.00 incl. audio (978-0-8072-8757-6(1), YA258SP, Listening Library) Random Hse. Audio Publishing Group.

Schuyler, Bull. The Nutcracker. Smath, Jerry, illus. 1998. (Jewel Sticker Stories Ser.). 24p. (J). (ps-2). 3.99 (978-0-448-41852-0(5), Grosset & Dunlap) Penguin Group (USA) Inc.

Scieszka, Jon. Baloney (Henry P.) Smith, Lane, illus. 2005. 40p. (J). (gr. k-3). pap. 5.99 (978-0-14-240430-0(6), Puffin) Penguin Group (USA) Inc.

—Hey Kid, Want to Buy a Bridge? McCauley, Adam, illus. 2002. (Time Warp Trio Ser.: No. 11). 80p. (J). (gr. 3-5). 15.99 (978-0-670-89916-6(X), Viking Juvenile) Penguin Group (USA) Inc.

Scott, Deborah. The California Kid Fights Back. 1998. (J). (gr. 3-7). pap. 3.99 (978-0-380-72851-0(6)) HarperCollins Pubs.

Scott, Mark. Nell of the Seas. Bayley, Ruth, illus. 2002. 160p. (YA). 32.50 (978-1-85776-680-6(6)) Book Guild, Ltd. GBR. *Dist:* Trans-Atlantic Pubns., Inc.

Scrimger, Richard. The Nose from Jupiter. 1998. 160p. (J). (gr. 3-7). pap. 7.95 (978-0-88776-428-8(2)) Tundra Bks., Inc./Livres Toundra, Inc. CAN. *Dist:* Random Hse., Inc.

Searle, Michael. Civilizations. 2005. (Duel Masters Ser.). 80p. (J). pap. 6.99 (978-0-439-73382-3(0)) Scholastic, Inc.

Secrets Of Droon #28 Staff & Abbott, Tony. In the Shadow of Goll. 2006. (Secrets of Droon Ser.: No. 28). (Illus.). 112p. (J). pap. 3.99 (978-0-439-67176-7(0) , Scholastic Paperbacks) Scholastic, Inc.

Seibold, J. Otto & Carroll, Lewis. Alice's Adventures in Wonderland. Seibold, J. Otto, illus. 2003. (Illus.). 6p. (J). (gr. k-3). bds. 19.95 (978-0-439-41184-4(X) , Orchard Bks.) Scholastic, Inc.

Seidman, David & Marvel Comics Staff. A Great Day. Curry, Don & Meredith Books Staff, eds. Stewart, Scott, illus. 2005. (Spider-Man Ser.). 24p. (J). pap. 3.99 (978-0-696-22515-4(8)) Meredith Bks.

Sendak, Maurice. Bumble Ardy. 2000. (Illus.). (J). 15.95 (978-0-06-205198-1(9)) HarperCollins Pubs.

—Donde Viven los Monstruos. Mlawer, Teresa, tr. 2001. (SPA., Illus.). (J). 7.96 net. (978-1-56137-544-8(6) , NU5725) Novel Units, Inc.

—Where the Wild Things Are. Sendak, Maurice, illus. 2002. (Illus.). (J). 16.60 (978-0-7587-0028-5(8)) Book Wholesalers, Inc.

—Where the Wild Things Are. 1998. (J). 16.95 (978-0-06-028223-3(1)) HarperCollins Pubs.

—Where the Wild Things Are. 1999. (J). 9.95 (978-1-56137-022-1(3)) Novel Units, Inc.

—Where the Wild Things Are. (J). pap. 12.95 incl. audio Weston Woods Studios, Inc.

Sengupta, Anita, tr. from JPN. Magic Knight Rayearth II, 3 vols., Vol. 2. rev. ed. 2004. (Illus.). 221p. pap. 9.99 (978-1-59182-267-7(X) , Tokyopop Kids) TOKYOPOP, Inc.

Seock Seo, Hong. Dragon Hunter. (Illus.). 192p. Vol. 3. rev. ed. 2003. pap. 9.99 (978-1-59182-163-2(0)); Vol. 4. rev. ed. 2004. pap. 9.99 (978-1-59182-434-3(6)); Vol. 5. 5th rev. ed. 2004. pap. 9.99 (978-1-59182-435-0(4)); Vol. 6. 6th rev. ed. 2004. pap. 9.99 (978-1-59182-436-7(2)); Vol. 7. 7th rev. ed. 2004. pap. 9.99 (978-1-59182-437-4(0)) TOKYOPOP, Inc. (Tokyopop Adult).

Seow, David. Monkey: The Journey Begins. 2005. (Illus.). 32p. 15.95 (978-0-8048-3517-6(9)) Tuttle Publishing.

Serna, Ana. Una Estrella Muy Especial. 4th ed. 2000. (Cuentos de Ahora Ser.).Tr. of Very Special Star. (SPA., Illus.). 32p. (J). 12.95 (978-84-348-5159-7(8)) SM Ediciones ESP. *Dist:* Distribooks, Inc.

Service, Pamela F. Tomorrow's Magic. 2007. 448p. (J). (gr. 3-7). 15.99 (978-0-375-84087-6(7)); (gr. 4-9). lib. bdg. 18.99 (978-0-375-94087-3(1)) Random Hse. Children's Bks. (Random Hse. Bks. for Young Readers).

—Tomorrow's Magic. 2007. (J). pap. (978-0-375-84088-3(5)) Random Hse., Inc.

Seuss, Dr. Horton Escucha a Quien. Canetti, Yanitzia, tr. from SPA. 2002. (SPA & ENG., Illus.). (J). (gr. k-2). 16.00 (978-1-930332-35-5(1) , LC7301) Lectorum Pubns., Inc.

—Hunches in Bunches. Seuss, Dr., illus. 2002. (Illus.). (J). 22.40 (978-0-7587-2784-8(4)) Book Wholesalers, Inc.

—I Had Trouble in Getting to Solla Sollew. Seuss, Dr., illus. 2002. (Illus.). (J). 22.40 (978-0-7587-2799-2(2)) Book Wholesalers, Inc.

—Oh, the Places You'll Pop-Up! 2003. (Illus.). (J). bds. 6.99 (978-0-375-82310-7(7)) Random Hse. Children's Bks.

—Scrambled Eggs Super! Seuss, Dr., illus. 2002. (Illus.). (J). 22.40 (978-0-7587-3580-5(4)) Book Wholesalers, Inc.

—The Simplifier. 1998. 14.00 (978-0-679-88612-9(5) , Random Hse. Bks. for Young Readers) Random Hse. Children's Bks.

Shahan, Sherry. Fountain of Weird. 2003. (Illus.). 117p. (J). mass mkt. 6.99 (978-0-330-37072-1(3) , Pan) Pan Macmillan GBR. *Dist:* Trafalgar Square Publishing.

Shannon & Morgan, Christopher. Invisible Crying Tree. 2000. (Illus.). 199p. (J). 22.99 (978-0-385-40767-0(X)) Transworld Publishers Ltd. GBR. *Dist:* Trafalgar Square Publishing.

Shannon, Ronnie Jay. Samurai Force: the Final Hope: The Junior Novel. 2007. (ENG.). 76p. per. 14.95 (***978-1-4241-6528-5(8)***) PublishAmerica, Inc.

Sharpe, Gerald. What Lies Beneath the Bed: Parade of Lights. 2007. 496p. (YA). pap. 11.00 (***978-1-933894-01-0(6)***) IJN Publishing, Inc.

Sharpe, Gerald. What Lies Beneath the Bed: Tommy's Tales. 2006. 304p. (YA). pap. 7.00 (978-1-933894-00-3(8)) IJN Publishing, Inc.

Shasha, Mark. Night of the Moonjellies. Shasha, Mark, illus. 10th anniv. ed. 2002. 32p. (J). 17.95 (978-1-930900-16-5(3)) Purple Hse. Pr.

Shaw, Esther. The Winter Mare. 2005. (ENG., Illus.). 198p. pap. (***978-1-84401-447-7(9)***) Athena Pr.

Shaw, Heather. Smallfish Clover. 2007. 368p. (J). pap. 20.00 (***978-1-4243-4242-6(2)***) Independent Publisher Services.

Shaw, Tucker. Flavor of the Week. 2005. 224p. (gr. 7-17). pap. 5.99 (978-0-7868-5698-5(X)) Hyperion Bks. for Children.

Shearer, Alex. The Great Blue Yonder. 2004. 192p. (J). (ps-7). mass mkt. 4.99 (978-0-439-56127-3(2) , Scholastic Paperbacks) Scholastic, Inc.

Shearer, Tony. The Praying Flute: Song of the Earth Mother. rev. ed. 2006. (Illus.). 96p. pap. 16.95 (978-0-87961-268-9(1)) Naturegraph Pubs., Inc.

Shepard, Aaron. The Magic Flyswatter: A Superhero Tale of Africa, Retold from the Mwindo Epic. 2008. (Ancient Fantasy Ser.: 3). 44p. (J). pap. 6.00 (***978-0-938497-39-4(1)***); lib. bdg. 15.00 (***978-0-938497-38-7(3)***) Shepard Pubns. (Skyhook Pr.).

—Monkey: A Superhero Tale of China, Retold from the Journey to the West. 2005. 48p. (J). lib. bdg. 15.00 (978-0-938497-25-7(1)); (YA). pap. 6.00 (978-0-938497-26-4(X)) Shepard Pubns. (Skyhook Pr.).

—The Monkey King: A Superhero Tale of China, Retold from the Journey to the West. 2008. (Ancient Fantasy Ser.: 4). 50p. (J). lib. bdg. 15.00 (***978-0-938497-40-0(5)***); lib. bdg. 6.00 (***978-0-938497-41-7(3)***) Shepard Pubns. (Skyhook Pr.).

—The Mountain of Marvels: A Celtic Tale of Magic, Retold from the Mabinogion. 2007. (Ancient Fantasy Ser.: 1). 46p. (J). pap. 6.00 (978-0-938497-36-3(7)); lib. bdg. 15.00 (978-0-938497-34-9(0)) Shepard Pubns. (Skyhook Pr.).

—The Sea King's Daughter: A Russian Legend. 1999. (Illus.). 28p. (J). (gr. k-3). per. 17.00 (978-0-689-82743-3(1) , Simon & Schuster Children's Publishing) Simon & Schuster Children's Publishing.

—The Songs of Power: A Finnish Tale of Magic, Retold from the Kalevala. 2007. (Ancient Fantasy Ser.: 2). 54p. (J). lib. bdg. 15.00 (978-0-938497-35-6(9)); lib. bdg. 6.00 (978-0-938497-37-0(5)) Shepard Pubns. (Skyhook Pr.).

Shepherd, Deanna. Lil' Winkie & His Adventure. 2002. (Illus.). 46p. (J). per. (978-1-931456-28-9(3)) Athena Pr.

Shepherd, JaiLeen. Anan: Lea's Special Friend—Part II of the Lea Trilogy. 2006. (J). per. 15.95 (978-1-889743-55-4(0)) Robbie Dean Pr.

Sherman, Deborah. Triple Chocolate Brownie Genius. 2007. 120p. (J). (gr. 4-6). pap. (***978-1-55455-035-7(1)***) Fitzhenry & Whiteside, Ltd.

Sherman, Delia. Changeling. 2008. 304p. (J). (gr. 4-6). pap. 8.99 (***978-0-14-241188-9(4)*** , Puffin); 2006. (Illus.). 256p. (YA). (gr. 7). 16.99 (978-0-670-05967-6(6) , Viking Juvenile) Penguin Group (USA) Inc.

Shetterly, Will. Elsewhere. 2004. 264p. (YA). pap. 6.95 (978-0-15-205209-6(7) , Magic Carpet Bks.) Harcourt Children's Bks.

—Never Never. 2004. 240p. (YA). pap. 6.95 (978-0-15-205210-2(0) , Magic Carpet Bks.) Harcourt Children's Bks.

—Nevernever. 2004. 226p. (YA). (gr. 9-12). lib. bdg. 13.60 (978-0-606-33013-8(5)) Tandem Library Bks.

Shi, Sharon. Mr. Scotts Magical Farm. Hernandez, Alaena, illus. rev. ed. 2000. 24p. (J). mass mkt. 4.99 (978-0-9678636-7-2(8) , B008, Tattootles Bks.) Tattoo Manufacturing.

Shickman, Allan Richard. Zan-Gah: A Prehistoric Adventure. 2007. 160p. pap. 9.95 (***978-0-9790357-0-8(8)***) Earthshaker Bks.

Shields, Carol Diggory. Wish My Brother Was a Dog. 1999. 13.79 (978-0-606-17435-0(4)) Tandem Library Bks.

Shinn, Sharon. The Dream-Maker's Magic. 2008. 272p. (YA). (gr. 7). pap. 7.99 (***978-0-14-241096-7(9)*** , Puffin) Penguin Group (USA) Inc.

Shiozu, Shuri, creator. Eerie Queerie!, 4 vols., Vol. 4. rev. ed. 2004. (Illus.). 200p. pap. 9.99 (978-1-59182-861-7(9) , Tokyopop Adult) TOKYOPOP, Inc.

Shipley, Jocelyn. Seraphina's Circle: A Young Adult Novel. 2006. 144p. (YA). (gr. 6-9). pap. 9.95 (978-1-894549-51-6(1)) Sumach Pr. CAN. *Dist:* Orca Bk. Pubs. USA.

Shipman, Gary. Pakkins' Land: Paul's Adventure, 3 vols., Vol. 1. Shipman, Rhoda, ed. Shipman, Gary, illus. rev. ed. 2000. (Illus.). 128p. (J). pap. 15.95 (978-0-9700241-1-4(8)) Pakkins Presents.

Shook, Karl. The Family Thing. 2004. 166p. (YA). pap. 12.95 (978-0-595-31121-7(0)) iUniverse, Inc.

Shortall, Leonard, illus. Encyclopedia Brown Keeps the Peace. 2002. (Encyclopedia Brown Ser.: No. 6). (J). 12.87 (978-0-7587-0848-9(3)) Book Wholesalers, Inc.

—Encyclopedia Brown Saves the Day. 2002. (Encyclopedia Brown Ser.). (J). 12.87 (978-0-7587-0850-2(5)) Book Wholesalers, Inc.

—Encyclopedia Brown Solves Them All. 2002. (Encyclopedia Brown Ser.: No. 5). (J). 12.87 (978-0-7587-0862-5(9)) Book Wholesalers, Inc.

Shoujo Pocket Manga #1. 2004. 128p. (YA). pap. 9.99 (978-1-932453-46-1(6)) Antarctic Pr., Inc.

Showalter, Gena. Oh My Goth. 2006. 256p. pap. 9.95 (978-1-4165-2474-8(6) , MTV) Simon & Schuster.

Shusterman, Neal. Downsiders. 2001. (YA). 11.64 (978-0-606-20637-2(X)); (gr. 5-8). lib. bdg. 13.00 (978-0-613-33694-9(1)) Tandem Library Bks.

—The Eyes of Kid Midas. 2004. 192p. (YA). mass mkt. 4.99 (978-0-689-87349-2(2) , Simon Pulse) Simon & Schuster Children's Publishing.

—Mindquakes: Stories to Blow Your Mind. 2002. (gr. 7-12). lib. bdg. 14.15 (978-0-613-74855-1(7)) Tandem Library Bks.

Sias, Bobby & Sias, Sybil. Three Wishes for a Little Old Man. 2005. 108p. (J). pap. 11.95 (978-1-58736-393-1(3) , Iceni Bks.) Wheatmark.

Siembieda, Kevin. Heros Unlimited G. M. Guide. Marciniszyn, Alex et al, eds. Zeleznik, John et al, illus. 1999. (Heroes Unlimited Ser.). 224p. (YA). (gr. 8 up). pap. 20.95 (978-1-57457-035-9(8)) Palladium Bks., Inc.

—Rifter, No. 8. Smith, Wayne & Osten, James, eds. Brom, Gerald et al, illus. 1999. (Rifter Ser.: Vol. 8). 112p. (YA). (gr. 8 up). pap. 7.95 (978-1-57457-036-6(6)) Palladium Bks., Inc.

—Rifts Dark Conversions. Breaux, Wayne, Jr. et al, illus. 2002. (Rifts Conversion Bks.). (YA). per. 22.95 (978-1-57457-079-3(X)) Palladium Bks., Inc.

Siembieda, Kevin & Thompson, Eric. Rifts Canada. Marciniszyn, Alex et al, eds. Perez, Ramon et al, illus. 1999. (Rifts Worldbook Ser.: Vol. 20). 192p. (YA). (gr. 8 up). pap. 20.95 (978-1-57457-025-0(0)) Palladium Bks., Inc.

—Rifts Xiticix Invasion. Marciniszyn, Alex et al, eds. Perez, Ramon et al, illus. 1999. (Rifts Worldbook Ser.: Vol. 23). 160p. (YA). (gr. 8 up). pap. 16.95 (978-1-57457-031-1(5)) Palladium Bks., Inc.

Siert, Kara Grace ManJian. Tales of Cunburra & Other Stories. 2006. 240p. pap. (***978-1-84549-114-7(9)***) arima publishing.

Silver Dolphin en Español Editors. Caritas felices: Cenicienta: Happy faces: Cinderella, Spanish-Language Edition. 2007. (Illus.). 8p. (J). bds. 7.95 (***978-970-718-390-2(X)*** , Silver Dolphin en Español) Advanced Marketing, S. de R. L. de C. V. MEX. *Dist:* Perseus Distribution.

Simard, Remy. Mister Once-upon-A-Time. 2000. (ps-2). lib. bdg. 15.25 (978-0-613-26235-4(2)) Tandem Library Bks.

Simcox, Helen E. Four Little Blobs. Weinberger, Jane, ed. Simcox, Helen E., illus. 1998. (Illus.). 46p. (J). (ps-3). pap. 8.00 (978-1-883650-46-9(1)) Windswept Hse. Pubs.

Simmons, Steven J. Alicia y Greta: Un Cuento de Dos Brujas. Mlawer, Teresa, tr. Moore, Cyd, illus. 2004. Tr. of Alice & Greta. (SPA.). 32p. (J). (gr. k-2). pap. 7.95 (978-0-88106-133-8(6) , CH5119) Charlesbridge Publishing, Inc.

Simms, Mattie. Q. 2006. (J). pap. 2.99 (***978-0-9772077-1-8(4)***) Kanlearn, Inc.

Simon & Schuster, eds. Millennium Madness. 2000. (gr. 3-6). lib. bdg. 14.15 (978-0-613-22002-6(1)) Tandem Library Bks.

Simon, Jay. Deep Freeze. 2004. 255p. (YA). per. 7.99 (978-0-931764-17-2(3)) Roberts Publishing Co.

Simon, Morris. Wizards Keep. 2007. 124p. pap. 4.99 (***978-1-931567-67-1(0)***) Sovereign Pr.

Sinclair, Lynn. Key to Aten: The First Chronicle of Aten, 2005. 190p. (YA). pap. 8.95 (978-0-9746481-7-0(5)) Brown Barn Bks.

Singer, Marilyn. Deal with a Ghost. 1999. 192p. (J). pap. 6.99 (978-0-380-73183-1(5) , HarperTeen) HarperCollins Pubs.

Singleton, Linda Joy. Sword Play. 2006. 288p. pap. 6.99 (978-0-7387-0880-5(1)) Llewellyn Pubns.

Sinke, Janet Mary. Priscilla McdoodleNutMcDoodleMcMae Asks Why. Penington, Craig, illus. 2007. 40p. (J). 17.95 (978-0-9742732-8-0(7)) My Grandma & Me Pubs.

Skelton, Matthew. Endymion Spring. 2006. (Illus.). 400p. (J). (gr. 7). 17.95 (978-0-385-73380-9(1)); lib. bdg. 19.99 (978-0-385-90397-4(9)) Random Hse. Children's Bks. (Delacorte Bks. for Young Readers).

Skorseth, Theresa. The Birds of Storm Hill. 2000. 144p. (J). (gr. 5 up). 2.50 (978-0-687-03547-2(3)) Abingdon Pr.

Skretteberg, James. A New M/Age Dawns, . 2005. 268p. (YA). per. 16.95 (978-0-9766449-8-9(3)) Global Authors Pubns.

Skurzynski, Gloria. Virtual War. 2003. (Virtual War Chronologs Ser.: Bk. 1). 160p. (YA). mass mkt. 5.99 (978-0-689-86785-9(9) , Simon Pulse) Simon & Schuster Children's Publishing.

—Virtual War. 1999. (Virtual War Chronologs Ser.: Bk. 1). (978-0-606-15926-5(6)) Tandem Library Bks.

Skye, Obert. Leven Thumps & the Eyes of the Want. 2007. (Leven Thumps Ser.: Bk. 3). (Illus.). 406p. (J). (gr. 5 up). 18.95 (***978-1-59038-800-6(3)*** , Shadow Mountain) Deseret Bk. Co.

—Leven Thumps & the Gateway to Foo. 2005. (Leven Thumps Ser.: Bk. 1). (Illus.). 384p. (J). 17.95 (978-1-59038-369-8(9) , Shadow Mountain) Deseret Bk. Co.

—Leven Thumps & the Gateway to Foo. Sowards, Ben, illus. 2006. (Leven Thumps Ser.: Bk. 1). 400p. (J). (gr. 4 up). pap. 7.99 (978-1-4169-2806-5(5) , Aladdin) Simon & Schuster Children's Publishing.

—Leven Thumps & the Whispered Secret. Sowards, Ben, illus. 2007. (Leven Thumps Ser.: Bk. 2). 433p. (J). (gr. 3-7). per. 8.99 (***978-1-4169-4718-9(3)*** , Aladdin) Simon & Schuster Children's Publishing.

—Professor Winsnicker's Book of Proper Etiquette for Well-Mannered Sycophants. 2007. 167p. (J). (***978-1-59038-716-0(3)*** , Shadow Mountain) Deseret Bk. Co.

Slade, Arthur G. Return of the Grudstone Ghosts. 2005. 150p. (J). pap. 6.95 (978-1-55050-212-1(3)) Coteau Bks. CAN. *Dist:* Fitzhenry & Whiteside, Ltd.

Slater, Teddy. Beauty & the Beast. Dias, Ron & Gonzaelz, Ric, illus. 2004. (Little Golden Book Ser.). 24p. (J). (gr. k-k). 2.99 (978-0-7364-2197-3(1) , Golden/Disney) Random Hse. Children's Bks.

—Littles Go on a Hike. 2002. (gr. 3-6). lib. bdg. 11.80 (978-0-613-50462-1(3)) Tandem Library Bks.

Sleator, William. The Boy Who Reversed Himself. 1998. 12.64 (978-0-606-12896-4(4)) Tandem Library Bks.

—The Duplicate. 1999. (Illus.). 160p. (J). (gr. 7-12). pap. 5.99 (978-0-14-130431-1(6) , Puffin) Penguin Group (USA) Inc.

Sloat, Teri & Huffmon, Betty. Berry Magic. 2005. (Illus.). 32p. 15.95 (978-0-88240-575-9(6)); pap. 8.95 (978-0-88240-576-6(4)) Graphic Arts Ctr. Publishing Co.

Slote, Alfred. My Trip to Alpha I. 96p. (J). (gr. 3-5). pap. 96.00 (978-0-8072-1402-2(7) , Listening Library) Random Hse. Audio Publishing Group.

Smalldige, Heidi. Dirt Fairies. l.t. ed. 2006. (ENG., Illus.). 28p. (J). per. 4.95 (978-1-933300-10-8(8)) Wandering Sage Bookstore & More, LLC.

Smiles from the Deep. 2004. (Illus.). 50p. (J). per. 12.00 (978-0-9745249-0-0(5)) Calliope Pubns.

Smith. The Ring, Level 3. 2001. (Illus.). v, 54p. (C). pap. 9.00 (978-0-582-42737-2(1)) Longman Publishing Group.

Smith, A. Valentine. A Circle of Three: Book of Newport. Smith, Frederick J. & Davis, Cynthia, eds. 2003. 464p. (YA). pap. 16.98 (978-0-9727309-4-5(X) , 097273094X) Alien Time Treasure.

Smith, Bryon. Night Visions Bk. 5: The Adventures of Megan Martin. 2003. 524p. (YA). pap. 20.00 (978-0-9745434-1-3(1)) Sweetgrass Pr., L.L.C.

Smith, Jeff. Bone: Out from Boneville. Hamaker, Steve, illus. 2005. (Bone Ser.). 144p. (J). 9.99 (978-0-439-70640-7(8) , Graphix) Scholastic, Inc.

—Bone: Out from Boneville. Smith, Jeff & Hamaker, Steve, illus. 2005. 138p. (J). (gr. 4-7). lib. bdg. 17.94 (978-0-606-33282-8(0)) Tandem Library Bks.

—The Ghost Circles. 2008. 160p. pap. 19.99 (***978-0-439-70629-2(7)*** , Graphix) Scholastic, Inc.

—The Great Cow Race. Hamaker, Steve, illus. 2005. (Bone Ser.: No. 2). 144p. (ps-7). pap. 9.99 (978-0-439-70639-1(4) , Graphix) Scholastic, Inc.

—Out from Boneville. 2005. (Bone Ser.: No. 1). (Illus.). 144p. (J). pap. 18.95 (978-0-439-70623-0(8) , Graphix) Scholastic, Inc.

Smith, Joe & Matsumoto, Taiyo. Blue Spring, Vol. 1. Smith, Joe, illus. 2004. (Blue Spring Ser.). 216p. pap. 9.99 (978-1-59116-645-0(4)) Viz Media.

Smith, L. J. The Awakening. 1999. (Vampire Diaries: No. 1). 320p. (gr. 7-12). mass mkt. 5.99 (978-0-06-102000-1(1)) HarperCollins Pubs.

Smith, Linda. Mrs. Biddlebox. Frazee, Marla, illus. 2002. 32p. (J). (ps-3). 15.99 (978-0-06-028690-3(3)); lib. bdg. 17.89 (978-0-06-029782-4(4)) HarperCollins Pubs.

—Talisa's Song. 2006. 272p. (YA). pap. 8.95 (978-1-55050-327-2(8)) Coteau Bks. CAN. *Dist:* F & W Pubns., Inc.

—The Turning Time. 2005. (Illus.). 352p. mass mkt. 7.95 (978-1-894345-26-2(6)) Thistledown Pr., Ltd. CAN. *Dist:* Literary Pr. Group of Canada.

Smith, M. J. Kevin Murphy Takes on the Father of Lies. 2005. (Illus.). 311p. (J). (gr. 4-8). pap. 10.95 (978-0-9765066-0-7(2)) B & S Publishing Corp.

Smith, Sherwood. Crown Duel. 2002. (Firebird Ser.). (Illus.). 480p. (YA). pap. 7.99 (978-0-14-230151-7(5) , Puffin) Penguin Group (USA) Inc.

—Crown Duel. 2002. (gr. 5-8). lib. bdg. 16.45 (978-0-613-45255-7(0)) Tandem Library Bks.

—Emerald Wand of Oz. Stout, William, illus. 2005. 272p. (J). (gr. 3 up). lib. bdg. 17.89 (978-0-06-029608-7(9)) HarperCollins Pubs.

—The Emerald Wand of Oz. Stout, William, illus. 2007. 262p. (J). 17.00 (***978-1-4223-6710-0(X)***) DIANE Publishing Co.

—The Emerald Wand of Oz. Stout, William, illus. 2005. 262p. (J). (ps-17). 16.99 (978-0-06-029607-0(0)) HarperCollins Pubs.

—Wren to the Rescue. 2004. (Illus.). 224p. (YA). (gr. 5 up). pap. 6.99 (978-0-14-240160-6(9) , Puffin) Penguin Group (USA) Inc.

—Wren's Quest, Vol. 2. 2004. (Illus.). 208p. (YA). (gr. 5 up). pap. 6.99 (978-0-14-240161-3(7) , Puffin) Penguin Group (USA) Inc.

Snead, Shawn A. Dragon's Egg. 2002. 220p. pap. 14.95 (978-0-595-20964-4(5) , Writers Club Pr.) iUniverse, Inc.

Sneeden, Amy. The Earth Explorer. 2004. 48p. pap. 12.95 (978-1-4137-3735-6(8)) PublishAmerica, Inc.

Snelson, Brian & Sellars, Rodney. Shaturanga: The Story of Onus. 2003. 244p. (YA). 26.95 (978-0-595-66019-3(3)) iUniverse, Inc.

Sniegoski, Thomas E. Reckoning. 2004. (Fallen Ser.). (Illus.). 272p. (YA). pap. 5.99 (978-0-689-85308-1(4) , Simon Pulse) Simon & Schuster Children's Publishing.

Snow, Alan. Here Be Monsters! Snow, Alan, illus. (Ratbridge Chronicles Ser.). 544p. (J). (gr. 3-9). 2007. pap. 8.99 (978-0-689-87048-4(5) , Aladdin); 2006. (Illus.). 17.95 (978-0-689-87047-7(7) , Atheneum) Simon & Schuster Children's Publishing.

Snow White & the Seven Dwarfs: Individual Title Six-Packs. 32p. (gr. 2 up). 37.00 (978-0-7635-9401-5(6)) Rigby Education.

Snyder, Midori. New Moon. 2005. (Queen's Quarter Ser.: Bk. 1). 288p. (YA). (gr. 7). pap. 7.99 (978-0-14-240349-5(0) , Puffin) Penguin Group (USA) Inc.

—Sadar's Keep. 2005. (Queen's Quarter Ser.: Bk. 2). 352p. (YA). (gr. 7). pap. 7.99 (978-0-14-240345-7(8) , Puffin) Penguin Group (USA) Inc.

Snyder, Zilpha Keatley. The Unseen. 2005. 208p. 5.99 (978-0-440-41930-3(1) , Yearling) Random Hse. Children's Bks.

So-Young, Lee. Model, Vol. 6. rev. ed. 2005. (Illus.). 200p. pap. 9.99 (978-1-59532-008-7(3) , Tokyopop Adult) TOKYOPOP, Inc.

Soesbee, Ree. Dragon Sword: Dragonlance: the New Adventures, Vol. 5. Rams, Vinod, illus. 2005. (Dragonlance Ser.). 256p. (YA). pap. 5.99 (978-0-7869-3578-9(2)) Wizards of the Coast.

—Pillar of Flame. 2007. (Elements Ser.: Vol. 1). (Illus.). 256p. (J). (gr. 5-9). pap. 5.99 (978-0-7869-4248-0(7) , Mirrorstone) Wizards of the Coast.

—Riddle in Stone. Fiegenshuh, Emily, illus. 2004. (Dungeons & Dragons Ser.). 192p. (YA). pap. 5.99 (978-0-7869-3211-5(2)) Wizards of the Coast.

Soloman, Ms Debra. Jasper & his magical Tail. 2006. 21p. (J). 10.00 (978-1-4116-3963-8(4)) Lulu.com.

Soundprints. Fairy Tales. 2005. (Studio Mouse Ser.). (Illus.). 256p. (J). (ps-2). 14.95 (978-1-59069-229-5(2)) Studio Mouse LLC.

—Pat-a-Cake: And Othe Favorites. 2005. (Meet Mother Goose Ser.). (Illus.). 36p. (J). bds. 14.95 incl. audio compact disk (978-1-931465-48-9(7) , MPD1104) Soundprints.

—Pat-a-Cake: And Other Favorites. 2005. (Meet Mother Goose Ser.). (Illus.). 36p. (J). bds. 10.95 incl. audio compact disk (978-1-931465-28-1(2) , MD1104) Soundprints.

Spalding, Andrea. Behind the Sorcerer's Cloak. 2006. 192p. (J). pap. 8.95 (978-1-55143-627-2(2)) Orca Bk. Pubs. USA.

—Dance of the Stones. 2003. (gr. 3-6). lib. bdg. 16.40 (978-0-613-70937-8(3)) Tandem Library Bks.

—The White Horse Talisman. 2002. (Summer of Magic Quartet Ser.: Bk. 1). 192p. (J). (gr. 3-7). pap. 6.95 (978-1-55143-222-9(6)) Orca Bk. Pubs. USA.

—White Horse Talisman. 2003. (gr. 5-8). lib. bdg. 15.25 (978-0-613-70942-2(X)) Tandem Library Bks.

Spalding, Robert, Jr. The Kingdom of Fu Fu. Lyle, Chris, illus. l.t. ed. 2001. 32p. (J). (ps-4). 15.95 (978-0-9711068-0-2(0) , FU001) Chattanooga FuFu Factory.

Spalenka, Greg & Sniegoski, Thomas E. Aerie. 2003. (Fallen Ser.). (Illus.). 320p. (YA). pap. 5.99 (978-0-689-85307-4(6) , Simon Pulse) Simon & Schuster Children's Publishing.

Spaziante, Patrick, illus. Meet Leatherhead. 2005. (Teenage Mutant Ninja Turtles Ser.). 24p. pap. 3.99 (978-0-689-87711-7(0) , Simon Spotlight) Simon & Schuster Children's Publishing.

Speaker-Yuan, Margaret & Yuan, Margaret Speaker. Phillip Pullman. 2005. (Who Wrote That? Ser.). (Illus.). 118p. (J). (gr. 6-12). lib. bdg. 30.00 (978-0-7910-8658-2(5) , Chelsea Hse.) Facts On File, Inc.

Speicher, Diane Carty. Brighton One Star's Journey to Shine. Robinson, Lenord, illus. 2005. 84p. (J). 19.95 (978-0-9749806-0-7(9)) Shine On Pubns.

Spence, Craig. Josh & the Magic Vial. 2007. 396p. pap. 16.95 (***978-1-897235-10-2(0)***) Thistledown Pr., Ltd. CAN. *Dist:* Fitzhenry & Whiteside, Ltd.

Spendlove, Owen. Stanley Brambles & the Pirate's Treasure. 2007. 320p. per. 18.95 (***978-0-595-43792-4(3)***) iUniverse, Inc.

Spiegler, Louise. The Amethyst Road. 2005. 336p. (YA). (gr. 7-12). 16.00 (978-0-618-48572-7(4) , Clarion Bks.) Houghton Mifflin Co. Trade & Reference Div.

Spika, Jana. Locket & the Mask. 2004. 12.99 (978-0-9727103-0-5(2)) Tree of Life Pr.

Spilny, Yuri. River of Fire. Schreiber, Catherine, ed. Balzhak, Anna & Balzhak, Nadezhda, illus. 1998. (Incredible Adventures of Kitto Ser.: Vol. 3). 52p. (J). (gr. 3-6). pap. 12.95 (978-1-892316-02-8(1)) Rama Pr., Inc.

—Sorceress's Spell. Schreiber, Catherine, ed. Balzhak, Anna & Balzhak, Nadezhda, illus. 1998. (Incredible Adventures of Kitto Ser.: Vol. 1). 48p. (J). (gr. 3-6). pap. 12.95 (978-1-892316-00-4(5)) Rama Pr., Inc.

—The Toynapers. Schreiber, Catherine, ed. Balzhak, Anna & Balzhak, Nadezhda, illus. 1998. (Incredible Adventures of Kitto Ser.: Vol. 2). 52p. (J). (gr. 3-6). pap. 12.95 (978-1-892316-01-1(3)) Rama Pr., Inc.

Spinner, Stephanie. Monster in the Maze: The Story of the Minotaur. 2000. (All Aboard Reading Ser.). (Illus.). (J). (978-0-606-20404-0(0)) Tandem Library Bks.

Spitzer, Linda & Myers, Sarah. Tales of the Paper Bag Fairies/Color Version. 2005. 54p. (J). pap. 14.95 (978-1-4116-4095-5(0)) Lulu.com.

Spizman, Robyn F. Lollipop Grapes & Clothespin Critters: Quick on the Spot Remedies for Restless Children. (J). pap. 89.50 (978-0-201-57753-2(4)) Addison-Wesley Longman, Inc.

Springer, Nancy. Lionclaw. 2004. (Tales of Rowan Hood Ser.: No. 2). 128p. (J). pap. 5.99 (978-0-14-240053-1(X) , Puffin) Penguin Group (USA) Inc.

Springham, James. Earth-n-Bones: Blue Things. 2006. 54p. pap. 12.95 (978-1-4137-9738-1(5)) PublishAmerica, Inc.

St. Jean, Alan. Aidan of Oren: The Journey Begins. Friedman, Judith, illus. 2004. 208p. 19.95 (978-0-9724853-5-7(X)) Keene Publishing.

Stadther, Michael. Official Solution Book to A Treasure's Trove. Stadther, Michael, illus. 2005. (Treasure's Trove Ser.). (Illus.). 96p. (J). 14.99 (978-0-9760618-5-4(6)) Simon & Schuster, Inc.

Stafford, Liliana. Just Dragon. Fordyce, R. Ewan & Mark, Alan, eds. Power, Margaret, illus. 2000. 32p. (J). (gr. k-3). 9.95 (978-1-876268-02-2(6)) Univ. of Western Australia Pr. AUS. *Dist:* International Specialized Bk. Services.

Stairs-Oberlick, Anita Ruth. Helen the Transartist. 2004. (Illus.). 256p. (J). per. 15.95 (978-0-9759738-0-6(0)) Carleton Bks.

Stamper, Judith Bauer. Three Wishes. 1998. (J). (gr. 1-2). (978-0-606-13409-5(3)) Tandem Library Bks.

Stamper, Judith Bauer & Keenan. Hercules & the Maze of the Minotaur. 1998. (Disney's First Readers Ser.: Vol. 3). 40p. (J). (gr. 2-4). pap. 3.50 (978-0-7868-4171-4(0)) Disney Pr.

Stamper, Judith Bauer & Sol Studios Staff. Hercules & the Maze of the Minotaur. 1999. (Illus.). (J). (978-0-590-39387-4(1)) Scholastic, Inc.

Stampfl, J. R. The Moon Key. 2005. (YA). (gr. 8-12). mass mkt. 5.99 (978-0-8439-5619-1(4) , SMOOCH) Dorchester Publishing Co., Inc.

Standiford, Natalie. Space Dog & Roy. Howell, Kathleen C., illus. 1998. (Space Dog Ser.). (J). (gr. k-3). (978-0-606-13035-6(7)) Tandem Library Bks.

Stanek, Robert. The Elf Queen & the King. (Ruin Mist Chronicles: Bk. 1). (YA). 2003. pap. 23.50 (978-1-57545-076-6(3)); 2002. 300p. pap. 15.00 (978-1-57545-061-2(5)) Reagent Pr.

—The Elf Queen & the King II. (Ruin Mist Chronicles). (YA). 2003. 23.50 (978-1-57545-077-3(1)); 2002. 300p. pap. 15.00 (978-1-57545-062-9(3)) Reagent Pr.

—The Elf Queen & the King III. 2007. 232p. (YA). pap. 15.00 (978-1-57545-086-5(0)) Reagent Pr.

—The Elf Queen & the King IV. 2008. 238p. (YA). pap. 15.00 (978-1-57545-087-2(9)) Reagent Pr.

—In the Service of Dragons. 2005. 220p. (YA). (gr. 4-9). pap. 14.00 (978-1-57545-089-6(5)) Reagent Pr.

—In the Service of Dragons II. 2005. (Illus.). 220p. (YA). (gr. 4-9). pap. 14.00 (978-1-57545-090-2(9)) Reagent Pr.

—In the Service of Dragons III. 2005. (Illus.). 240p. (J). (ps-7). pap. 14.00 (978-1-57545-093-3(3)) Reagent Pr.

—In the Service of Dragons IV. 2005. 240p. (YA). pap. 14.00 (978-1-57545-094-0(1)) Reagent Pr.

—Into the Stone Land. 2006. (Best Fantasy Ser.: Bk. 2). 152p. (J). pap. 11.00 (978-1-57545-092-6(5)) Reagent Pr.

—Journey Beyond the Beyond: Magic Lands Book #1. ed. 2006. (Illus.). 112p. (J). pap. 18.95 (978-1-57545-108-4(5)) Reagent Pr.

—The Kingdoms & the Elves of the Reaches. (Keeper Martin's Tales Ser.: Bk. 1). 2002. (YA). 22.95 (978-1-57545-073-5(9)); 2005. (Illus.). 240p. (J). pap. 14.00 (978-1-57545-059-9(3)) Reagent Pr.

—Kingdoms & the Elves of the Reaches, Bk. 3. 2002. (gr. 3-6). lib. bdg. 22.85 (978-0-613-79224-0(6)) Tandem Library Bks.

—The Kingdoms & the Elves of the Reaches Bk. 1: Keeper Martin's Tales. Stanek, Robert, illus. alt. gif. ed. 2004. (Illus.). 176p. (YA). pap. 10.99 (978-1-57545-501-3(3) , Reagent Pr. Echo) Reagent Pr.

—The Kingdoms & the Elves of the Reaches II. (Keeper Martin's Tales Ser.: No. 2). 2002. (YA). 22.95 (978-1-57545-074-2(7)); 2005. (Illus.). 240p. (J). pap. 14.00 (978-1-57545-060-5(7)) Reagent Pr.

—The Kingdoms & the Elves of the Reaches II Bk. 2: Keeper Martin's Tales. Stanek, Robert, illus. alt. gif. ed. 2004. 180p. (YA). pap. 10.99 (978-1-57545-502-0(1) , Reagent Pr. Echo) Reagent Pr.

—The Kingdoms & the Elves of the Reaches II (Special Illustrated Edition) 2007. (Keeper Martin's Tales Ser.: Bk. 2). (Illus.). 260p. (YA). pap. 18.95 (978-1-57545-506-8(4) , Reagent Pr. Signature Editions) Reagent Pr.

—The Kingdoms & the Elves of the Reaches III. (Keeper Martin's Tales Ser.: No. 3). 2003. (YA). 22.50 (978-1-57545-080-3(1)); 2005. (Illus.). 240p. (J). pap. 14.00 (978-1-57545-063-6(1)) Reagent Pr.

—The Kingdoms & the Elves of the Reaches III Bk. 3: Keeper Martin's Tales. Stanek, Robert, illus. alt. gif. ed. 2004. 172p. (YA). pap. 10.99 (978-1-57545-503-7(X) , Reagent Pr. Echo) Reagent Pr.

—The Kingdoms & the Elves of the Reaches III (Special Illustrated Edition) 2008. (Keeper Martin's Tales Ser.: Bk. 3). (Illus.). 252p. (YA). pap. 18.95 (978-1-57545-507-5(2) , Reagent Pr. Signature Editions) Reagent Pr.

—The Kingdoms & the Elves of the Reaches IV. 2003. (Keeper Martin's Tales Ser.: No. 4). (YA). 22.50 (978-1-57545-081-0(X)) Reagent Pr.

—Kingdoms & the Elves of the Reaches IV. 2003. (gr. 3-6). lib. bdg. 23.45 (978-0-613-79227-1(0)) Tandem Library Bks.

—The Kingdoms & the Elves of the Reaches IV. deluxe ed. 2005. (Keeper Martin's Tales Ser.: Vol. 4). (Illus.). 240p. (YA). pap. 14.00 (978-1-57545-065-0(8)) Reagent Pr.

—The Kingdoms & the Elves of the Reaches IV Bk. 4: Keeper Martin's Tales. Stanek, Robert, illus. alt. gif. ed. 2005. 172p. (YA). pap. 10.99 (978-1-57545-504-4(8) , Reagent Pr. Echo) Reagent Pr.

—The Kingdoms & the Elves of the Reaches IV (Special Illustrated Edition) 2009. (Keeper Martin's Tales Ser.: Bk. 4). (Illus.). 256p. (YA). pap. 18.95 (978-1-57545-508-2(0) , Reagent Pr. Signature Editions) Reagent Pr.

—The Kingdoms & the Elves of the Reaches (Special Illustrated Edition) 2006. (Keeper Martin's Tales Ser.: Bk. 1). (Illus.). 256p. (YA). pap. 18.95 (978-1-57545-505-1(6) , Reagent Pr. Signature Editions) Reagent Pr.

—Ruin Mist Heroes, Legends & Beyond Vol. I: Companion. 2002. (Illus.). 200p. (YA). pap. 15.00 (978-1-57545-067-4(4)) Reagent Pr.

Stanek, Robert & Ruin Mist Publications Staff. The Magic of Ruin Mist: A Candid Look at Robert Stanek's Life, Work & Books. 2003. 150p. pap. 15.00 (978-1-57545-031-5(3) , Ruin Mist Pubns.) Reagent Pr.

Stanley, Diane. Rumpelstiltskin's Daughter. Stanley, Diane, illus. 2002. (Illus.). 32p. (J). (gr. k-4). pap. 6.99 (978-0-06-441095-3(1) , Harper Trophy) HarperCollins Pubs.

—The Trouble with Wishes. Stanley, Diane, illus. 2007. (Illus.). 32p. (J). (gr. 2-4). 16.99 (978-0-06-055451-4(7) , HarperCollins); lib. bdg. 17.89 (978-0-06-055452-1(5)) HarperCollins Pubs.

Stanton, Andy. You're a Bad Man, Mr. Gum! Dezern, Chad, illus. 2008. 144p. (J). 9.99 (***978-0-06-115240-5(4));*** lib. bdg. 14.89 (***978-0-06-115243-6(9)***) HarperCollins Pubs.

Stanton, Mary. Night of the Shifter's Moon. 2000. (Unicorns of Balinor Ser.: Vol. 7). (Illus.). 144p. (J). (gr. 3-7). pap. 4.50 (978-0-439-16786-4(8)) Scholastic, Inc.

—Shadows over Balinor. 2000. (Unicorns of Balinor Ser.: Bk. 8). (Illus.). 128p. (J). (gr. 4-7). pap. 4.50 (978-0-439-16787-1(6)) Scholastic, Inc.

—Shadows over Balinor. 2000. (gr. 3-6). lib. bdg. 12.40 (978-0-613-26902-5(0)) Tandem Library Bks.

—Valley of Fear. 1999. (Unicorns of Balinor Ser.: No. 3). 144p. (J). (gr. 3-7). pap. 4.50 (978-0-439-06282-4(9)) Scholastic, Inc.

—Valley of Fear. 1999. (Unicorns of Balinor Ser.: No. 3). (978-0-606-17552-4(0)) Tandem Library Bks.

Stasheff, Christopher. The Oathbound Wizard. 2004. (Wizard in Rhyme Ser.: Bk. 2). 408p. lib. bdg. 14.04 (978-0-606-30694-2(3)) Tandem Library Bks.

Steadman, Ralph. The Little Red Computer. 2004. (Illus.). 46p. 100.00 (978-0-9673004-9-8(5)) Sylph Pubns.

Steele, Martin Bernard. Wiz World: A Wish from the Heart. Steele, Robert & Stehr, Barbara, eds. Steele, Martin Bernard et al, illus. 2002. 34p. (YA). 14.95 (978-0-9716311-0-6(7)) Sun Star Magic Entertainment.

Steele, Michael Anthony. Fire & Ice. 2006. (Winx Club Ser.). (Illus.). 152p. (J). pap. 4.99 (978-0-439-78781-9(5)) Scholastic, Inc.

—Winx Club: Secret Powers. 2005. (Winx Club Ser.). (Illus.). 120p. (J). 4.99 (978-0-439-68511-5(7)) Scholastic, Inc.

Steers, Billy. Tractor Mac Learns to Fly. 24p. (J). pap. 3.29 (978-1-59445-043-3(9)) Dogs in Hats Children's Publishing Co.

Steig, William. Sylvester & the Magic Pebble. Steig, William, illus. 2002. (Illus.). (J). 15.53 (978-0-7587-0077-3(6)) Book Wholesalers, Inc.

—Sylvester & the Magic Pebble. Steig, William, illus. 2002. 32p. (J). mass mkt. 1.00 (978-0-689-85526-9(5) , Aladdin) Simon & Schuster Children's Publishing.

Stein, Erin, ed. Duel Masters Vol. 5: Goblin Gone Wild. Matsumoto, Shigenobu, illus. 2005. 96p. (J). (ps-7). pap. 7.99 (978-1-59532-675-1(8) , Tokyopop Kids) TOKYOPOP, Inc.

Stephens, Ann Marie. Stella Eats Out. Bolan, Michael, illus. 2004. 32p. (J). per. 12.95 (978-0-9729285-2-6(9) , 2-9) Kinkachoo Pr., The.

Stephenson, Larry K. & Weinbrenner, Patti. The Butterfly King: A Legend for the New Millennium. Stephenson, Larry K., illus. 1999. (Illus.). v, 45p. (J). (gr. 4). 19.95 (978-0-9672202-0-8(3)) Jewel Box & Friends.

Stern, Roger. Spider-Man: Hobgoblin Lives. Frenz, Ron et al, illus. 1998. 112p. (YA). (gr. 5-12). pap. 14.95 (978-0-7851-0585-5(9)) Marvel Enterprises, Inc.

Stevens, Terry. Tommy, the Wizard & the Magic Umbrella. 2006. 60p. pap. (***978-1-84401-752-2(4)***) Athena Pr.

Stevermer, Caroline. A College of Magics. 2002. 468p. (gr. 7-12). per. 14.15 (978-0-613-62606-4(0)) Tandem Library Bks.

Stevermer, Caroline & Wrede, Patricia C. Sorcery & Cecelia or the Enchanted Chocolate Pot: Being the Correspondence of Two Young Ladies of Quality Regarding Various Magical Scandals in London & the Country. 2004. (Illus.). 336p. (YA). pap. 6.95 (978-0-15-205300-0(X) , Magic Carpet Bks.) Harcourt Children's Bks.

Stewart, Mary. The Last Enchantment. 2003. (gr. 7-12). lib. bdg. 24.55 (978-0-613-66978-8(9)) Tandem Library Bks.

Stewart, Paul. Muddle Earth. Riddell, Chris, illus. 2007. 464p. (gr. 5). (J). lib. bdg. 19.99 (***978-0-385-90335-6(9));*** (YA). 16.99 (***978-0-385-73316-8(X)***) Random Hse. Children's Bks. (Delacorte Bks. for Young Readers).

Stewart, Paul & Riddell, Chris. Beyond the Deepwoods. 2004. (Edge Chronicles Ser.: Bk. 1). (Illus.). 288p. (J). (gr. 5-7). 12.95 (978-0-385-75068-4(4) , Fickling, David Bks.) Random Hse. Children's Bks.

—Clash of the Sky Galleons. 2007. (Edge Chronicles Ser.). (J). (gr. 5-7). 432p. 12.99 (***978-0-375-83742-5(6));*** 400p. lib. bdg. 15.99 (***978-0-375-93742-2(0)***) Random Hse. Children's Bks. (Fickling, David Bks.).

—The Curse of the Gloamglozer. 2005. (Edge Chronicles Ser.: Bk. 4). (Illus.). 384p. (J). (gr. 5-7). 12.95 (978-0-385-75076-9(5)); lib. bdg. 14.99 (978-0-385-75077-6(3)) Random Hse. Children's Bks. (Fickling, David Bks.).

—Edge Chronicles 1: Beyond the Deepwoods. 2008. (Edge Chronicles Ser.). 288p. (J). (gr. 5-7). 6.99 (***978-0-440-42087-3(3)*** , Yearling) Random Hse. Children's Bks.

—Edge Chronicles 2: Stormchaser. 2008. (Edge Chronicles Ser.). 400p. (gr. 5-7). 6.99 (***978-0-440-42088-0(1)*** , Yearling) Random Hse. Children's Bks.

—Freeglader. 2006. (Edge Chronicles Ser.: Bk. 7). (Illus.). 416p. (J). (gr. 5-7). 12.95 (978-0-385-75082-0(X)); lib. bdg. 14.99 (978-0-385-75083-7(8)) Random Hse. Children's Bks. (Fickling, David Bks.).

—Hugo Pepper. 2007. (Far-Flung Adventures Ser.). (Illus.). 272p. (J). (gr. 3-7). 14.99 (978-0-385-75092-9(7)); lib. bdg. 16.99 (978-0-385-75093-6(5)) Random Hse. Children's Bks. (Fickling, David Bks.).

—The Last of the Sky Pirates. 2005. (Edge Chronicles Ser.: Bk. 5). (Illus.). 384p. (gr. 5-7). (J). lib. bdg. 14.99 (978-0-385-75079-0(X)); 12.95 (978-0-385-75078-3(1)) Random Hse. Children's Bks. (Fickling, David Bks.).

—Midnight over Sanctaphrax. 2004. (Edge Chronicles Ser.: Bk. 3). (Illus.). 368p. (J). (gr. 5-7). 12.95 (978-0-385-75072-1(2)); lib. bdg. 14.99 (978-0-385-75073-8(0)) Random Hse. Children's Bks. (Fickling, David Bks.).

—Vox. 2005. (Edge Chronicles Ser.: Bk. 6). (Illus.). 400p. (J). (gr. 5-7). 12.95 (978-0-385-75080-6(3)); lib. bdg. 14.99 (978-0-385-75081-3(1)) Random Hse. Children's Bks. (Fickling, David Bks.).

—The Winter Knights. 2007. (Edge Chronicles Ser.: No. 8). (Illus.). 400p. (J). (gr. 5-7). 12.99 (978-0-375-83741-8(8)); lib. bdg. 14.99 (978-0-375-93741-5(2)) Random Hse. Children's Bks. (Fickling, David Bks.).

Stewart, Sharon. Raven Quest. 2005. 320p. (J). (gr. 3-7). per. 15.95 (978-1-57505-894-8(4) , Carolrhoda Bks.) Lerner Publishing Group.

Stillman, William & Scarfone, Jay. The Wizard of Oz: The Film Classic Comes to Life with Music & Stunning 3-Dimension! 2000. (Illus.). 10p. (J). (gr. 4-7). 24.95 (978-1-58117-058-0(0) , Intervisual/Piggy Toes) Dalmatian Pr.

Stims, Robert. The Chain of Wisdom. Bk. I. 2003. 166p. (YA). pap. 12.95 (978-0-595-29235-6(6)) iUniverse, Inc.

Stine, Megan. Power of the Rat. 2002. (gr. 3-6). lib. bdg. 13.00 (978-0-613-72454-8(2)) Tandem Library Bks.

Stine, R. L. The Blob That Ate Everyone. 2006. (Goosebumps Ser.). 144p. (J). pap. 4.99 (978-0-439-79619-4(9) , Scholastic Paperbacks) Scholastic, Inc.

—Deep Trouble II, Vol. 2. rev. ed. 2006. (Goosebumps Ser.). 144p. (J). pap. 4.99 (978-0-439-83780-4(4) , Scholastic Paperbacks) Scholastic, Inc.

—Monster Blood II. 2004. 121p. (J). (ps-7). lib. bdg. 11.64 (978-0-606-32488-5(7)) Tandem Library Bks.

—Monster Blood III. 2007. (Goosebumps Ser.). 144p. (J). pap. 4.99 (978-0-439-89112-7(4)) Scholastic, Inc.

STINE, R. L. My Best Friend Is Invisible. 2007. (Goosebumps Ser.). 144p. (J). pap. 4.99 (***978-0-439-92220-3(8)***) Scholastic, Inc.

Stine, R. L. My Hairiest Adventure. 2006. (Goosebumps Ser.). 144p. (J). pap. 4.99 (978-0-439-86394-0(5) , Scholastic Paperbacks) Scholastic, Inc.

—Nightmare Hour. 2000. (Illus.). 160p. (J). (gr. 5 up). pap. 5.99 (978-0-06-440842-4(6) , Avon) HarperCollins Pubs.

—Nightmare Hour: Time for Terror. 1999. (Illus.). 160p. (J). (gr. 3 up). 16.99 (978-0-06-028688-0(1)) HarperCollins Pubs.

—Nightmare Hour: Time for Terror. 2000. (gr. 5-8). lib. bdg. 14.15 (978-0-613-71481-5(4)) Tandem Library Bks.

—One Day at HorrorLand. 2003. (gr. 5-8). lib. bdg. 13.00 (978-0-613-70771-8(0)) Tandem Library Bks.

—Return of the Mummy. rev. ed. 2006. (Goosebumps Ser.). 144p. (J). pap. 4.99 (978-0-439-83778-1(2) , Scholastic Paperbacks) Scholastic, Inc.

Stinson, Kathy. Those Green Things. Betteridge, Deirdre, illus. 2003. 32p. (J). (ps-1). pap. 4.95 (978-1-55037-376-9(5)) Annick Pr., Ltd. CAN. *Dist:* Firefly Bks., Ltd.

Stockton, Frank Richard. The Bee-Man of Orn: And Other Fanciful Tales. 2007. 140p. pap. 10.99 (***978-1-4264-5788-3(X));*** 154p. pap. 14.99 (***978-1-4264-5848-4(7)***) BiblioBazaar.

Stockton, Frank Richard. The Bee Man of Orn & Other Fanciful Tales. 2004. reprint ed. pap. 20.95 (978-1-4191-5383-9(8)); pap. 1.99 (978-1-4192-5383-6(2)) Kessinger Publishing, LLC.

Stone, David Lee. Illmore Chronicles,the: the Shadewell Shenangans - Book Three. 3rd rev. ed. 2007. 320p. (gr. 2-7). pap. 7.99 (***978-0-7868-3796-0(9)***) Hyperion Pr.

—The Ratastrophe Catastrophe. 2006. (Illmore Chronicles: Bk. 1). 288p. (gr. 5-9). reprint ed. pap. 6.99 (978-0-7868-5129-4(5)) Hyperion Pr.

—The Yowler Foul-Up. 2nd rev. ed. 2006. 304p. (gr. 5-9). pap. 6.99 (978-0-7868-5598-8(3)); (Illmore Chronicles Ser.: Bk. 2). 16.99 (978-0-7868-5597-1(5)) Hyperion Pr.

Stone, Kelsey. The Predahil Chronicles. 2005. (YA). per. 6.49 (978-1-59196-995-2(6)) Instantpublisher.com.

Story Lady. The Master Toy Maker. 2001. 128p. pap. 10.95 (978-0-595-20708-4(1) , Writers Club Pr.) iUniverse, Inc.

The Story of the Incredible Hulk. 2003. (Dk Readers Ser.). (J). pap. 3.99 (978-0-7894-3974-1(3)) Dorling Kindersley Publishing, Inc.

Stover, Anne Long. Cloudy. Spears, Ashley E., illus. 2005. 20p. (J). (978-0-9762389-0-4(X)) Trent's Prints.

Straczynski, J. Michael. Sins Past. Deodato, Mike, Jr., illus. 2005. (Spider-Man Ser.: Vol. 8). 144p. (YA). pap. 12.99 (978-0-7851-1509-0(9)) Marvel Enterprises, Inc.

Strega Nona. 2005. (J). (978-1-59564-834-1(8)) Steps To Literacy, LLC.

Strickland, Brad. Grimoire: Curse of the Midions. 2006. 240p. (J). (gr. 4). 11.99 (978-0-8037-3060-1(8) , Dial) Penguin Group (USA) Inc.

—Grimoire: Tracked by Terror. 2007. 192p. (J). (gr. 4-3). 15.99 (***978-0-8037-3061-8(6)*** , Dial) Penguin Group (USA) Inc.

Strickland, Brad. Survive! 2001. (Dinotopia Ser.). (Illus.). (J). (978-0-606-21475-9(5)) Tandem Library Bks.

Strickland, Brad & Fuller, Thomas E. Marsquake! 2005. (Mars Year One Ser.). (Illus.). 192p. (J). pap. 4.99 (978-0-689-86402-5(7) , Aladdin) Simon & Schuster Children's Publishing.

—Missing! 2004. (Mars Year One Ser.: No. 2). (Illus.). 176p. (J). pap. 4.99 (978-0-689-86401-8(9) , Aladdin) Simon & Schuster Children's Publishing.

Strickler, Ashley. Once upon A Time. 2007. 212p. pap. 12.95 (***978-1-4327-0207-6(6)***) Outskirts Press, Inc.

Strohm, Keith Francis. Bladesinger. 2006. (Fighters Ser.). (Illus.). 312p. (978-1-4156-6627-2(X)) Wizards of the Coast.

Stroud, Jonathan. The Amulet of Samarkand. 2003. (Bartimaeus Trilogy: Bk. 1). (J). pap. 14.00 (978-0-7868-5143-0(0)) Hyperion Bks. for Children.

—The Amulet of Samarkand. 2004. (Bartimaeus Trilogy Ser.: Bk. 1). 480p. (gr. 5-17). reprint ed. pap. 7.99 (978-0-7868-5255-0(0)) Miramax Bks.

—Ptolemy's Gate. 3rd rev. ed. 2007. (Bartimaeus Trilogy Ser.: Bk. 3). 512p. (gr. 5-17). pap. 8.99 (978-0-7868-3868-4(X)) Miramax Bks.

Suarez de la Prida, Isabel. Los Diminutos. Bouchain, Nava, illus. 2003. (SPA.). 32p. (J). (gr. k-3). pap. 6.95 (978-968-19-0631-3(4)) Santillana USA Publishing Co., Inc.

The Subtle Knife. 2002. (His Dark Materials Ser.). (Illus.). 19.53 (978-1-4046-1655-4(1)) Book Wholesalers, Inc.

Sudduth, Brent, et al. The Sea Monster. Curry, Don, ed. Mangaworx Staff, illus. 2005. (Fantastic Four Ser.). 24p. (J). (ps-ps). pap. 3.99 (978-0-696-22509-3(3)) Meredith Bks.

Sudduth, Brent H., et al. Imagination Ring. Curry, Don, ed. Mangaworx Staff, illus. 2005. (Fantastic Four Ser.). 24p. (J). pap. 3.99 (978-0-696-22508-6(5)) Meredith Bks.

Sugisaki, Yukiru. The Candidate for Goddess, 5 vols. 2004. (Illus.). 192p. Vol. 1. pap. 9.99 (978-1-59182-747-4(7)); Vol. 2. pap. 9.99 (978-1-59182-748-1(5)); Vol. 3. pap. 9.99 (978-1-59182-749-8(3)) TOKYOPOP, Inc. (Tokyopop Adult).

Sugisaki, Yukiru, creator. The Candidate for Goddess, 5 vols., Vol. 4. rev. ed. 2004. (Illus.). 192p. pap. 9.99 (978-1-59182-750-4(7) , Tokyopop Adult) TOKYOPOP, Inc.

—Candidate for Goddess, 5 vols., Vol. 5. rev. ed. 2004. (Illus.). 192p. pap. 9.99 (978-1-59182-751-1(5) , Tokyopop Adult) TOKYOPOP, Inc.

Suhay, Lisa. Our Fantasy Island. 2006. 30p. (J). pap. 8.00 (***978-0-9766628-0-8(9)***) Fantasy Island Pr.

Suhay, Lisa. There Goes a Mermaid - A NorFolktale. Sam, Hundley, illus. 2004. 32p. (J). pap. 7.95 (978-0-9648308-2-0(5)) Virginian Pilot.

Sullivan, Jenny. The Back End of Nowhere. 1998. (J). (gr. 4-8). pap. 14.95 (978-0-8464-4598-2(0)) Beekman Bks., Inc.

—Nowhere Again. 2004. 228p. pap. 13.95 (978-1-84323-297-1(9)) Beekman Bks., Inc.

Sullivan, Stephen D. Warrior's Blood. 2007. (Goodlund Trilogy Ser.: Vol. 2). 256p. (YA). pap. 5.99 (978-0-7869-4300-5(9) , Mirrorstone) Wizards of the Coast.

Sullivan, Steve. Warrior's Heart. 2006. (Illus.). 256p. (J). (gr. 5). pap. 5.99 (978-0-7869-4187-2(1) , Mirrorstone) Wizards of the Coast.

Sumerak, Marc, et al. The Return of Doom, Vol. 3. Doddridge, Joseph, illus. 2005. (Fantastic Four Ser.). 96p. pap. 5.99 (978-0-7851-1622-6(2)) Marvel Enterprises, Inc.

Sumimoto, Mark & Siembieda, Kevin. Rifts Splynn Dimensional Market. Marciniszyn, Alex et al, eds. Perez, Ramon et al, illus. 1999. (Rifts Worldbook Ser.: Vol. 21). 192p. (YA). (gr. 8 up). pap. 20.95 (978-1-57457-027-4(7)) Palladium Bks., Inc.

Summers, Gillian. Into the Wildewood. 2008. 312p. (J). pap. 9.95 (***978-0-7387-1332-8(5)*** , Flux) Llewellyn Pubns.

Suplicki, Mark J. Mirthburdz: The Discovery. 2004. (Illus.). 51p. (J). 19.95 (978-0-9764385-0-2(X) , 00B1) Jon'taar Graphxs.

Sussex, Lucy. The Revognase. 2005. (Illus.). 160p. pap. (978-0-7344-0495-4(6) , Lothian Bks.) Hachette Livre Australia.

Sutherland, Paul H. Finding Utopia. Gibbons, Timothy M., illus. 2006. 48p. (J). bds. 20.00 (978-0-9661060-4-6(0)) Utopia Pr.

Sutton, Scott E. The Family of Ree. Sutton, Scott E., illus. rev. ed. 2001. (Family of Ree Ser.). (Illus.). 60p. (gr. 1-5). 14.95 (978-1-888045-12-3(4)) Action Publishing, LLC.

—The Legend of Snow Pookas. Sutton, Scott E., illus. rev. ed. 2001. (Family of Ree Ser.). (Illus.). 48p. (gr. 1-5). 14.95 (978-1-888045-14-7(0)) Action Publishing, LLC.

Swanson, Stan. The Misadventures of Hobart Hucklebuck. 2007. (J). 16.95 (***978-0-9787925-3-4(X)***); per. 9.95 (***978-0-9787925-2-7(1)***) Stony Meadow Publishing.

Swift, Jonathan. Gulliver's Travels. Marcos, Pablo, illus. 2002. (Great Illustrated Classics Ser.). 240p. (J). (gr. 3-8). 21.35 (978-1-57765-818-4(3) , ABDO & Daughters) ABDO Publishing Co.

—Gulliver's Travels. 1999. (YA). 11.95 (978-1-56137-922-4(0)); 9.95 (978-1-56137-921-7(2)) Novel Units, Inc.

—Gulliver's Travels. Akib, Jamel, illus. 2006. (Classic Starts Ser.). 160p. 4.95 (978-1-4027-2662-0(7)) Sterling Publishing Co., Inc.

—Gulliver's Travels. Riddell, Chris, illus. abr. ed. 2005. 144p. (J). (gr. 2 up). 19.99 (978-0-7636-2409-5(8)) Candlewick Pr.

—Gulliver's Travels, Level 4. 2nd abr. ed. 2000. (Bookworms Ser.). (Illus.). 96p. pap. 6.50 (978-0-19-423034-6(1)) Oxford Univ. Pr., Inc.

—Gulliver's Travels: And A Discussion of Tolerance. Clift, Eva, illus. 2003. (Values in Action Illustrated Classics Ser.). 191p. (J). (978-1-59203-029-3(7)) Learning Challenge, Inc.

—Los Viajes de Gulliver. (SPA., Illus.). 144p. (YA). 14.95 (978-84-7281-080-8(1) , AF1080) Auriga, Ediciones S.A. ESP. *Dist:* Continental Bk. Co., Inc.

—Los Viajes de Gulliver. (Coleccion Clasicos de la Juventud). (SPA., Illus.). 204p. (J). 12.95 (978-84-7189-062-7(3) , ORT322) Ortells, Alfredo Editorial S.L. ESP. *Dist:* Continental Bk. Co., Inc.

—Viajes de Gulliver. 2003. (Advanced Reading Ser.). (SPA.). 344p. (J). 11.95 (978-84-670-0095-5(3)) Espasa Calpe, S.A. ESP. *Dist:* Planeta Publishing Corp.

Swindells, Robert. In the Nick of Time. 2008. 224p. (YA). pap. 9.95 (***978-0-552-55585-2(1)***) Transworld Publishers Ltd. GBR. *Dist:* Independent Pubs. Group.

Swope, Sam. The Krazees. Brace, Eric, illus. 2003. 32p. (J). pap. 6.95 (978-0-374-44090-9(5) , Sunburst) Farrar, Straus & Giroux.

Szekeres, Cyndy. Cyndy Szekeres Mixed Display. 1999. (J). 111.20 (978-0-439-04657-2(2)) Scholastic, Inc.

Tachikawa, Megumi, creator. Dream Saga, Vol. 4. rev. ed. 2005. (Illus.). 208p. pap. 9.99 (978-1-59532-210-4(8) , Tokyopop Kids) TOKYOPOP, Inc.

Takahashi, Rumiko. Inu-Yasha. Takahashi, Rumiko, illus. (Inuyasha Ser.). (Illus.). (YA) Vol. 13. 2003. 192p. pap. 8.95 (978-1-56931-808-9(5)); Vol. 19. 2004. 200p. pap. 8.95 (978-1-59116-678-8(0)) Viz Media.

—Inu-Yasha: Anime/Manga Box Set. Takahashi, Rumiko, illus. 2003. (Inuyasha Ser.). 200p. (YA). pap. 39.98 (978-1-59116-235-3(1) , Viz Comics) Viz Media.

—Inu Yasha Animanga. (Inuyasha Ser.). (YA). Vol. 15. 2006. 208p. pap. 11.99 (978-1-4215-0482-7(0)); Vol. 16. 2006. 208p. pap. 11.99 (978-1-4215-0483-4(9)); Vol. 19. 2007. 216p. pap. 11.99 (978-1-4215-0903-7(2)); Vol. 20. 2007. 216p. pap. 11.99 (978-1-4215-0904-4(0)) Viz Media.

—Inuyasha, Vol. 20. Takahashi, Rumiko, illus. 2004. (Inuyasha Ser.). (Illus.). 200p. (YA). pap. 8.95 (978-1-59116-626-9(8)) Viz Media.

—Inuyasha Vol. 19: Demon Box Set. 2004. (Inuyasha Ser.). (Illus.). 192p. pap. 24.99 (978-1-59116-725-9(6)) Viz Media.

—Mermaid Saga. Takahashi, Rumiko, illus. 2004. (Mermaid Saga Ser.). (Illus.). (YA). 3. 176p. pap. 9.99 (978-1-59116-483-8(4)); Vol. 2. 2nd ed. 208p. pap. 9.99 (978-1-59116-484-5(2)); Vol. 4. 2nd ed. 192p. pap. 9.99 (978-1-59116-482-1(6)) Viz Media.

Takao, Ukyou. To Heart. 2004. (Illus.). (YA). Vol. 2. 178p. pap. (978-1-4139-0070-5(4)); Vol. 3. 186p. pap. (978-1-4139-0087-3(9)) ADV Manga.

Takaya, Natsuki. Fruits Basket, 5 vols., Vol. 5. 5th rev. ed. 2004. (Graphic Novel-Manga Ser.). (Illus.). pap. 9.99 (978-1-59182-607-1(1) , Tokyopop Adult) TOKYOPOP, Inc.

Takeuchi, Naoko. Sailor Moon, 11 vols. (Illus.). 184p. (gr. 7-12). Vol. 2. 2nd rev. ed. 1998. (Sailor Moon Ser.: Vol. 2). pap. 9.99 (978-1-892213-05-1(2)); Vol. 3. 3rd rev. ed. 1999. pap. 9.99 (978-1-892213-06-8(0)) TOKYOPOP, Inc.

—Sailor Moon Stars, Vol. 2. 2nd rev. ed. 2001. (Sailor Moon Stars Ser.: Vol. 2). (Illus.). 176p. (gr. 7-12). pap. 9.99 (978-1-892213-70-9(2)) TOKYOPOP, Inc.

—Sailor Moon Supers, Vol. 3. 3rd rev. ed. 2000. (Illus.). 160p. (gr. 7-12). pap. 9.99 (978-1-892213-26-6(5)) TOKYOPOP, Inc.

Talbott, Hudson. O'Sullivan Stew. Talbott, Hudson, illus. 2001. (Illus.). 48p. (J). (ps-3). pap. 6.99 (978-0-698-11889-8(8) , Putnam Juvenile) Penguin Group (USA) Inc.

Tamura, Yumi. Wild Com. Tamura, Yumi, illus. 2004. (Wild Com Ser.). (Illus.). 192p. (YA). pap. 9.95 (978-1-59116-559-0(8)) Viz Media.

Tanabe, Yellow. Kekkaishi, Vol. 6. 2006. (Kekkaishi Ser.). (Illus.). 208p. (YA). pap. 9.99 (978-1-4215-0487-2(1)) Viz Media.

Tanemura, Arina. O Sagashite. Tanemura, Arina, illus. 2006. (Full Moon o Sagashite Ser.). 200p. (YA). pap. 8.99 (978-1-4215-0397-4(2)) Viz Media.

Tashiro, Takuyo. Najica Blitz Tactics, Vol. 1. 2004. (Illus.). 200p. (YA). pap. (978-1-4139-0018-7(6)) ADV Manga.

Tasker, Rod. Jack's Book. 2003. 60p. pap. 9.95 (978-1-59286-966-4(1)) PublishAmerica, Inc.

Tate, Nikki. Cave of Departure. 2002. (Illus.). 239p. (J). (gr. 5-9). pap. 6.95 (978-1-55039-119-0(4)) Sono Nis Pr. CAN. *Dist:* Orca Bk. Pubs. USA.

—Cave of Departure. 2002. (gr. 5-8). lib. bdg. 15.25 (978-0-613-78607-2(6)) Tandem Library Bks.

Taylor, Cora. On Wings of a Dragon. (YA). 2001. 288p. (gr. 7-10). (978-1-55041-674-9(X)); 2nd ed. 2002. 256p. pap. (978-1-55041-782-1(7)) Fitzhenry & Whiteside, Ltd.

—On Wings of a Dragon. 2002. (gr. 7-12). lib. bdg. 16.40 (978-0-613-55507-4(4)) Tandem Library Bks.

—On Wings of Evil. 2005. 250p. (J). (gr. k-17). (978-1-55041-929-0(3)) Fitzhenry & Whiteside, Ltd.

Taylor, G. P. El Hechicero de las Sombras. Attrache, Ismael, tr. 2005. (SPA.). 328p. pap. 9.95 (978-950-511-910-3(0)) Santillana USA Publishing Co., Inc.

—Shadowmancer. (YA). 2005. 288p. (gr. 7). pap. 7.99 (978-0-14-240341-9(5) , Puffin); 2004. 304p. (gr. 4 up). 16.99 (978-0-399-24256-4(2) , Putnam Juvenile) Penguin Group (USA) Inc.

—Shadowmancer. 2004. (Illus.). 280p. 16.99 (978-1-59185-613-9(2)) Strang Communications Co.

—The Shadowmancer Returns: The Curse of Salamander Street. 2007. 272p. (YA). (gr. 7 up). 17.99 (978-0-399-24346-2(1) , Putnam Juvenile) Penguin Group (USA) Inc.

—Tersias. 2005. (Illus.). 336p. (J). (***978-0-571-22152-3(1)***); pap. (***978-0-571-22979-6(4)***) Faber & Faber, Ltd.

—The Tizzle Sisters & Erik. 2007. 188p. (***978-1-905692-22-4(6)***) Markosia Enterprises Ltd.

Taylor, Keith. Dragon Tales. 2000. (gr. 7-12). lib. bdg. 12.10 (978-0-613-28824-8(6)) Tandem Library Bks.

Taylor, Laini. Blackbringer. 2007. (Faeries of Dreamdark Ser.). 368p. (J). (gr. 5 up). 17.99 (978-0-399-24630-2(4) , Putnam Juvenile) Penguin Group (USA) Inc.

Taylor, Lori. Lissy-Lost! 2003. 113p. pap. 13.95 (978-1-59286-964-0(5)) PublishAmerica, Inc.

Taylor, Shane. The Magic of Mortals. 2006. (YA). pap. 11.95 (978-1-58736-542-3(1) , Starbound Bks.) Wheatmark.

Tbd. Prince Caspian: Chapter Book. 2006. (Narnia Ser.: No. 4). 96p. (J). pap. 3.99 (978-0-06-124065-2(6) , Harper Entertainment) HarperCollins Pubs.

—Prince Caspian Chapter Book #1. 2008. (Narnia Ser.). 96p. (J). pap. 3.99 (***978-0-06-147260-2(3)*** , Harper Trophy) HarperCollins Pubs.

—Prince Caspian Chapter Book #2. 2008. (Narnia Ser.). 96p. (J). pap. 3.99 (***978-0-06-147261-9(1)*** , Harper Trophy) HarperCollins Pubs.

—Prince Caspian Chapter Book #3. 2008. (Narnia Ser.). 96p. (J). pap. 3.99 (***978-0-06-147262-6(X)*** , Harper Trophy) HarperCollins Pubs.

—Prince Caspian Chapter Book #4. 2008. (Narnia Ser.). 96p. (J). pap. 3.99 (***978-0-06-147263-3(8)*** , Harper Trophy) HarperCollins Pubs.

Ted's Red Ball: Set B Individual Title, 6 packs. (gr. k-3). 29.00 (978-0-7635-0538-7(2)) Rigby Education.

Teitelbaum, Michael. The Earth Kingdom Chronicles: The Tale of Sokka. Spaziante, Patrick, illus. 2007. (Avatar Ser.). 96p. (J). (gr. 2-6). pap. 5.99 (***978-1-4169-3829-3(X)*** , Simon Spotlight) Simon & Schuster Children's Publishing.

—The Earth Kingdom Chronicles: The Tale of Toph. Spaziante, Patrick, illus. 2007. (Avatar Ser.). 96p. (J). (gr. 2-6). pap. 5.99 (***978-1-4169-3797-5(8)*** , Simon Spotlight) Simon & Schuster Children's Publishing.

Teitelbaum, Michael. Sleeping Beauty. DiCicco, Sue, illus. 2004. (Little Golden Book Ser.). 24p. (J). (gr. k-k). 2.99 (978-0-7364-2198-0(X) , Golden/Disney) Random Hse. Children's Bks.

Tello, Jorge. Here Come the Blobbies. Tello, Jorge, illus. 2004. (Illus.). 32p. (J). pap. 15.89 incl. audio compact disk (978-1-932179-32-3(1)) Pers Publishing.

Teply, George. The Lost Crown of Meleor. Teply, George, illus. 2000. (Illus.). 32p. (J). (ps-2). pap. 6.95 (978-1-55037-600-5(4)) Annick Pr., Ltd. CAN. *Dist:* Firefly Bks., Ltd.

Teys, Jo-Anne. I Wish I Was... Lahdensuo, Debbie, illus. 2005. 36p. (J). pap. 17.50 (978-0-9757001-1-2(1)) Love Song Publishing AUS. *Dist:* AtlasBooks Distribution.

Tezuka, Osamu. A Tale of the Future. Tezuka, Osamu, illus. 2nd ed. 2004. (Phoenix Ser.). 200p. (YA). pap. 15.95 (978-1-59116-608-5(X)) Viz Media.

Thesman, Jean. Singer. l.t. ed. 2005. 384p. (YA). (gr. 8-12). 22.95 (978-0-7862-7919-7(2) , Large Print Pr.) Thorndike Pr.

Thomas, Brook. The Snu & the Greed Seed. Thomas, Brook, illus. 1998. (Illus.). i, 16p. (J). (ps-7). pap. 3.95 (978-0-9662634-1-1(3)) Marketing by Design.

Thomas, John & Rowe, Susan. Mynydd y Brain. 2005. (WEL., Illus.). 32p. pap. (978-1-85596-221-7(7)) Dref Wen.

Thomas, Joyce Carol. The Gospel Cinderella. Diaz, David, illus. 2004. 40p. (J). (gr. k-5). 15.99 (978-0-06-025387-5(8) , Amistad) HarperCollins Pubs.

Thomas, Patrick. The Wildsidhe Chronicles Bk. 1: Welcome to the Wildsidhe. 2002. (J). pap. 7.99 (978-1-890096-12-0(1)) Padwolf Publishing, Inc.

—The Wildsidhe Chronicles Bk. 2: Double Cross. 2002. (J). pap. 7.99 (978-1-890096-14-4(8)) Padwolf Publishing, Inc.

Thompson, Colin. Castles. 2007. (Illus.). 32p. (J). pap. 9.99 (***978-0-09-943942-4(5)*** , Red Fox) Random Hse. Children's Bks. GBR. *Dist:* Independent Pubs. Group.

Thompson, D. R. The Big Ocean: An Underwater Naptime Adventure. Thompson, D. R. & Thompson, Dave, illus. 2004. (Naptime Adventure Ser.: Vol. 2). 32p. (J). (ps-3). 14.95 (978-0-9723252-2-6(0)) This New World Publishing, LLC.

Thompson, Jill, illus. Magic Trixie. 2008. 96p. (J). pap. 7.99 (***978-0-06-117045-4(3)*** , Harper Trophy) HarperCollins Pubs.

Thompson, Kate. Beguilers. 2003. (gr. 3-6). lib. bdg. 15.30 (978-0-613-71574-4(8)) Tandem Library Bks.

—Fourth World. 2005. 316p. (YA). (ps-7). 16.95 (978-1-58234-650-2(X) , Bloomsbury Children) Bloomsbury Publishing.

Thompson, Kate. The New Policeman. 2005. (Illus.). (J). 279p. (***978-0-370-32878-2(7)***); 160p. (***978-0-370-32823-2(X)***) Random Hse. Children's Bks. (Bodley Head).

Thompson, Roy. The Goblins' Ball. 2005. (ENG., Illus.). 84p. pap. (***978-1-84401-362-3(6)***) Athena Pr.

Thompson, Ruth Plumly. The Enchanted Island of Oz. 2006. (J). 24.95 (978-1-930764-10-1(3)) International Wizard of Oz Club, The.

—The Royal Book of Oz. 2004. reprint ed. pap. 20.95 (978-1-4191-8123-8(8)); pap. 1.99 (978-1-4192-8123-5(2)) Kessinger Publishing, LLC.

—Sissajig & Other Surprises. 2003. 25.00 (978-1-930764-05-7(7)); pap. 12.00 (978-1-930764-06-4(5)) International Wizard of Oz Club, The.

—The Wonder Book. 2006. (J). 24.95 (978-1-930764-15-6(4)) International Wizard of Oz Club, The.

—Yankee in Oz. 2006. (J). 24.95 (978-1-930764-13-2(8)) International Wizard of Oz Club, The.

Thomson, Emma. Felicity Wishes: Snowflakes & Sparkle-dust. 2004. 40p. (J). (ps). 14.99 (978-0-670-05935-5(8) , Viking Juvenile) Penguin Group (USA) Inc.

Thomson, John. A Small Boat at the Bottom of the Sea. 2005. (Illus.). (J). (ps-7). 152p. 16.95 (978-1-57131-657-8(4)); 156p. pap. 6.95 (978-1-57131-656-1(6)) Milkweed Editions.

Thomson, Kate. Wild Blood. unabr. ed. 2004. (Switchers Ser.: Vol. 3). 240p. (J). (gr. 5-9). pap. 36.00 incl. audio (978-0-8072-8853-5(5) , LYA 276 SP, Listening Library) Random Hse. Audio Publishing Group.

Thomson, Sarah L. Dragon's Egg. 2007. 272p. (J). (gr. 3-7). 16.99 (***978-0-06-128848-7(9)***); lib. bdg. 17.89 (***978-0-06-128847-0(0)***) HarperCollins Pubs. (Greenwillow Bks.).

Thorn, Nikki. A Shadow of My Own. 2002. 115p. (J). pap. 9.95 (978-0-595-21887-5(3) , Writers Club Pr.) iUniverse, Inc.

Thornewell, Danielle. The Mems. 2007. (ENG.). 52p. per. 12.95 (***978-1-4241-6106-5(1)***) PublishAmerica, Inc.

Thornhill, Gail. The Secret Life of Truly Jones. 2003. 196p. (J). pap. 12.99 (978-1-58832-081-0(2)) Unlimited Publishing LLC.

Thornton, Duncan. Kalifax. Noblet, Yves, illus. 1999. 184p. (J). (gr. 5-9). 8.95 (978-1-55050-152-0(6)) Coteau Bks. CAN. *Dist:* Fitzhenry & Whiteside, Ltd.

—The Star-Glass: The Return of Kalifax & Captain Jenny. Noblet, Yves, illus. 2003. (Kalifax Trilogy Ser.). 432p. (J). (gr. 5-7). pap. 10.95 (978-1-55050-269-5(7)) Coteau Bks. CAN. *Dist:* Fitzhenry & Whiteside, Ltd.

Thorpe, Kiki. Treasure Planet: Jim's Journal. 2002. (ps-2). lib. bdg. 11.80 (978-0-613-50576-5(X)) Tandem Library Bks.

Thrillogy. 2006. (Illus.). (gr. 4-8). 77.70 (978-0-7910-9071-8(X)) Facts On File, Inc.

Through the Looking Glass. (Read-Along Ser.). (YA). pap., stu. ed. 34.95 incl. audio (978-0-88432-971-8(2) , S23946) Norton, Jeffrey Pubs., Inc.

Tibo, Gilles. Le Gardien du Sommeil. Jorisch, Stephane, illus. 2004. (Mon Roman Ser.). (FRE.). 64p. (J). (gr. 2). pap. (978-2-89021-691-4(8)) Diffusion du livre Mirabel.

—Noches de Papel. (Barril Sin Fondo Ser.). (SPA.). (J). (gr. 3-5). pap. (978-968-6465-32-7(4)) Casa de Estudios de Literatura y Talleres Artisticos Amaquemecan A.C. MEX. *Dist:* Lectorum Pubns., Inc.

Tiernan, Cate. Book of Shadows, Bk. 1. 2007. (Sweep Ser.). 192p. (YA). pap. 6.99 (***978-0-14-240986-2(3)*** , Puffin) Penguin Group (USA) Inc.

—Book of Shadows. 2001. (gr. 7-12). lib. bdg. 13.00 (978-0-613-31016-1(0)) Tandem Library Bks.

—Changeling. 2001. (gr. 7-12). lib. bdg. 13.00 (978-0-613-64031-2(4)) Tandem Library Bks.

—Changeling: Book Eight. 2008. (Sweep Ser.). 192p. (YA). (gr. 7). 6.99 (***978-0-14-241023-3(3)*** , Puffin) Penguin Group (USA) Inc.

—The Coven, Bk. 2. 2007. (Sweep Ser.). 192p. (YA). pap. 6.99 (***978-0-14-240987-9(1)*** , Puffin) Penguin Group (USA) Inc.

—Full Circle. 2002. (Sweep Ser.: Vol. 14). 192p. (YA). pap. 6.99 (978-0-14-230182-1(5) , Puffin) Penguin Group (USA) Inc.

—Full Circle. 2002. (gr. 7-12). lib. bdg. 13.00 (978-0-613-64042-8(X)) Tandem Library Bks.

—Moira's Story. 2003. (gr. 7-12). lib. bdg. 15.30 (978-0-613-66595-7(3)) Tandem Library Bks.

—Night's Child Vol. 15: Moira's Story. 2003. (Sweep Ser.). 320p. pap. 6.99 (978-0-14-250119-1(0) , Puffin) Penguin Group (USA) Inc.

Tiernan, Cate. Spellbound. 2007. (Sweep Ser.: Bk. 6). 192p. (YA). pap. 6.99 (***978-0-14-241021-9(7)*** , Puffin) Penguin Group (USA) Inc.

Tilley, Lawrence. Animal Retreat. 2004. 49p. pap. 14.95 (978-1-4137-1136-3(7)) PublishAmerica, Inc.

Timmers, Leo. Happy with Me. 2002. (Illus.). 32p. (J). 16.95 (978-1-931290-08-1(3)) Tallfellow Pr.

Titlebaum, Ellen. Alice in Wonderland Read Aloud: Storybook. 2000. 64p. (J). 6.99 (978-0-7364-1051-9(1)) Hyperion Bks. for Children.

TK (Children's). Clone of My Own #6, No. 6. 1999. (J). (gr. 4-6). pap. 3.99 (978-0-689-82856-0(X) , Aladdin) Simon & Schuster Children's Publishing.

Toda, Akihito. Pokemon Gold & Silver Tales: Corsola's Brave New World. Kizuki, Sumiyashi, illus. 2002. (Pokemon Gold & Silver Tales Ser.). 18p. (YA). 5.50 (978-1-56931-762-4(3)) Viz Media.

Toda, Akihito & Wada, Junko. Don't Laugh Charizard. Kimura, Naoyo et al, illus. 2001. (Pokemon Tales Ser.: Vol. 19). 18p. (YA). (ps-k). 4.95 (978-1-56931-570-5(1)) Viz Media.

Toda, Yasunari, illus. Gundam Seed Astray R, Vol. 2. 2nd rev. ed. 2005. pap. 9.99 (978-1-59532-577-8(8) , Tokyopop Adult) TOKYOPOP, Inc.

Todd, Barbara. The Rainmaker. Roge, illus. 2003. 32p. (J). (ps-2). pap. 5.95 (978-1-55037-774-3(4)) Annick Pr., Ltd. CAN. *Dist:* Firefly Bks., Ltd.

—Roger Gets Carried Away. Roge, illus. 2005. 32p. (J). (ps-2). pap. 7.95 (978-1-55037-898-6(8)); lib. bdg. 19.95 (978-1-55037-899-3(6)) Annick Pr., Ltd. CAN. *Dist:* Firefly Bks., Ltd.

Toksvig, Sandi. If I Didn't Have Elbows. 1998. (Illus.). 32p. (J). (gr. 1-4). pap. (978-1-84089-016-7(9) , Zero to Ten, Limited) Evans Publishing Group.

Tokyopop Staff, creator. Contents under Pressure, Vol. 3. 2005. (Lilo & Stitch Ser.). (Illus.). 89p. (gr. 3-7). pap., pap. 7.99 (978-1-59532-069-8(5) , Tokyopop Kids) TOKYOPOP, Inc.

—Rising Stars of Manga - Uk & Ireland Edition. 2006. (Illus.). 192p. pap. 9.99 (978-1-59816-464-0(3) , Tokyopop Adult) TOKYOPOP, Inc.

Tokyopop Staff, illus. Rave Master: The Sound of Thunder, Vol. 3. 2005. 96p. (J). pap. 7.99 (978-1-59532-791-8(6)) TOKYOPOP, Inc.

Tolan, Stephanie S. Welcome to the Ark. 1998. 256p. (YA). (gr. 5 up). pap. 4.95 (978-0-688-15861-3(7)) HarperCollins Pubs.

Tolkien, J. R. R. Bilbo, le Hobbit. 2000. Tr. of Hobbit. (FRE.). (J). pap. 16.95 (978-2-01-019907-3(3)) Istra FRA. *Dist:* Distribooks, Inc.

—Farmer Giles of Ham. Hammond, Wayne G., ed. 50th anniv. ed. 1999. (Illus.). 128p. 18.00 (978-0-618-00936-7(1)) Houghton Mifflin Co. Trade & Reference Div.

—The Hobbit. 2002. 16.60 (978-0-7587-7961-8(5)) Book Wholesalers, Inc.

—The Hobbit. 1999. (YA). 9.95 (978-1-56137-253-9(6)) Novel Units, Inc.

—The Hobbit. 2001. (gr. 7-12). lib. bdg. 18.80 (978-0-613-88165-4(6)); (J). 23.50 (978-0-606-21234-2(5)) Tandem Library Bks.

—Hobbit: An Illustrated Edition of the Fantasy Classic. Wenzel, David, illus. 2001. 144p. reprint ed. pap. 17.95 (978-0-345-44560-5(0) , Del Rey) Random House Publishing Group.

—Hobbit: An Illustrated Edition of the Fantasy Classic. abr. ed. 2001. (gr. 5-8). lib. bdg. 24.60 (978-0-613-53684-4(3)) Tandem Library Bks.

—Hobbit: Or There & Back Again. 1999. (gr. 3-6). lib. bdg. 21.10 (978-0-613-87066-5(2)) Tandem Library Bks.

—The Hobbit: Or There & Back Again. 2002. (Illus.). 365p. (YA). (gr. 5). pap. 10.00 (978-0-618-26030-0(7)) Houghton Mifflin Co. Trade & Reference Div.

—The Hobbit: Or There & Back Again. Sis, Peter, illus. 2001. 320p. (YA). (gr. 7 up). pap. 10.00 (978-0-618-15082-3(X)) Houghton Mifflin Co. Trade & Reference Div.

—The Hobbit: Or There & Back Again. 1999. (Illus.). 320p. pap. 12.00 (978-0-618-00221-4(9)) Houghton Mifflin Co. Trade & Reference Div.

—The Hobbit: Or, There & Back Again. 2001. (Illus.). 330p. (YA). (gr. 7 up). 18.00 (978-0-618-16221-5(6)) Houghton Mifflin Co. Trade & Reference Div.

—Hobbit, or, There & Back Again. 2002. (gr. 5-8). lib. bdg. 18.80 (978-0-613-90725-5(6)) Tandem Library Bks.

—The Return of the King. 2002. (J). 16.60 (978-0-7587-5212-3(1)) Book Wholesalers, Inc.

—Roverandom. Scull, Christina & Hammond, Wayne G., eds. (Illus.). 1999. 106p. pap. 12.00 (978-0-395-95799-8(0)); 1998. 128p. (gr. 3-5). 17.00 (978-0-395-89871-0(4)) Houghton Mifflin Co. Trade & Reference Div.

—Senhor dos Aneis. pap. 36.95 (978-85-336-1337-9(7)) Livraria Martins Editora BRA. *Dist:* Distribooks, Inc.

Tolkien, J. R. R., et al. Roverandom. Scull, Christina & Hammond, Wayne G., eds. 783rd l.t. ed. 1998. (Illus.). 191p. (J). 25.95 (978-0-7838-0299-2(4)) Thorndike Pr.

Tolstoy, Alexei. The Gigantic Turnip. Sharkey, Niamh, illus. 2000. 40p. (J). (ps-1). pap. 6.99 (978-1-84148-157-9(2)) Barefoot Bks., Inc.

Tomita, Sukehiro. Young Love, Vol. 7. Yazawa, Nao, illus. 2004. (Wedding Peach Ser.). 200p. (YA). pap. 9.95 (978-1-59116-450-0(8)) Viz Media.

Tomizawa, Hitoshi. Alien Nine: Emulators. Pannone, Frank, ed. Jackson, Laura & Kobayashi, Yoko, trs. from JPN. Tomizawa, Hitoshi, illus. 2004. (Illus.). 248p. pap. 9.99 (978-1-58664-924-1(8) , CMX 65004G, CPM Manga) Central Park Media Corp.

E F G

Tomos, Angharad. Cosyn. 2005. (WEL., Illus.). 24p. pap. (978-0-86243-566-0(8)) Y Lolfa.

Top That Publishing Editors, ed. Beastly Ballons. Dahl, Roald, illus. 2005. 24p. (J). pap. (978-1-905359-55-4(1)) Top That! Publishing PLC.

Toriyama, Akira. Dragon Ball. Toriyama, Akira, illus. 2003. (Dragon Ball Ser.). (Illus.). (Orig.). (YA). 2. 200p. pap. 7.95 (978-1-56931-921-5(9)); Vol. 1. 192p. pap. 7.95 (978-1-56931-920-8(0)) Viz Media.

—Dragon Ball, Vol. 3. Morimoto, Mari, tr. from JPN. Toriyama, Akira, illus. 2nd ed. 2003. (Dragon Ball Ser.: Vol. 3). (Illus.). 192p. (Orig.). (YA). pap. 7.95 (978-1-56931-922-2(7)) Viz Media.

—Dragon Ball. Toriyama, Akira, illus. 2nd ed. 2003. (Dragon Ball Ser.). (Illus.). 192p. (Orig.). (YA). Vol. 4. pap. 7.95 (978-1-56931-923-9(5)); Vol. 5. pap. 7.95 (978-1-56931-924-6(3)) Viz Media.

—Dragon Ball. Morimoto, Mari, tr. from JPN. Toriyama, Akira, illus. 2nd ed. 2003. (Dragon Ball Ser.: Vol. 6). (Illus.). 192p. (Orig.). (YA). Vol. 6. pap. 7.95 (978-1-56931-925-3(1)); Vol. 7. pap. 7.95 (978-1-56931-926-0(X)) Viz Media.

—Dragon Ball. Toriyama, Akira, illus. 2003. (Dragon Ball Ser.). (Illus.). 192p. (Orig.). (YA). Vol. 8. 2nd ed. pap. 7.95 (978-1-56931-927-7(8)); Vol. 9. pap. 7.95 (978-1-56931-928-4(6)) Viz Media.

—Dragon Ball, Vol. 11. Morimoto, Mari, tr. from JPN. 2003. (Dragon Ball Ser.). (Illus.). 192p. (Orig.). (YA). pap. 7.95 (978-1-56931-919-2(7)) Viz Media.

Torrey, Michele. Bottles of Eight & Pieces of Rum. 1998. 138p. (J). (ps-7). pap. 9.99 (978-0-88092-321-7(0), 3210) Royal Fireworks Publishing Co.

Town, Nathan. Ned Stapleton & the Wrath of the Death Gods. 2006. 174p. (YA). (*978-0-9781040-0-9(5)) Emerald City Storytellers.

Townsend, Tom. The Dragon Trader, 8 vols., Vol. 3. Lewis, Jason, illus. 2000. (Fairie Ring Ser.: No. 3). 158p. (YA). (gr. 6-12). 9.99 (978-0-88092-527-3(2), 5272) Royal Fireworks Publishing Co.

—Shadow Kiss, Vol. 4. 2001. (Fairie Ring Ser.: Vol. 4). 140p. (J). (ps-7). pap. 9.99 (978-0-88092-528-0(0)) Royal Fireworks Publishing Co.

—The Trouble with an Elf. Kemnitz, Myrna, ed. 1999. (Fairie Ring Ser.: Vol. 1). 158p. (YA). (gr. 5-8). 9.99 (978-0-88092-525-9(6)) Royal Fireworks Publishing Co.

Toy Box Productions Staff, Box, creator. Disney's Instant Classics: Chicken Little/Lilo & Stitch/Brother Bear. unabr. abr. ed. 2005. (Disney's Read along Collection). (Illus.). (J). audio compact disk 14.99 (978-0-7634-1148-0(5)) Walt Disney Records.

Tracy, Judith. The Wildsidhe Chronicles Bk. 3: Dark Proposal. 2003. (J). pap. 7.99 (978-1-890096-15-1(6)) Padwolf Publishing, Inc.

—The Wildsidhe Chronicles Bk. 4: Legacy. 2002. (J). pap. 7.99 (978-1-890096-16-8(4)) Padwolf Publishing, Inc.

The Trail. 2nd ed. 2002. (Illus.). 120p. (YA). per. 10.95 net. (978-0-9713292-1-8(4)) Aim Higher Bks.

Travers, P. L. Mary Poppins. Shepard, Mary, illus. 2006. 224p. (J). 12.95 (978-0-15-205810-4(9), Harcourt Young Classics) Harcourt Children's Bks.

—Mary Poppins & Mary Poppins Comes Back. Shepard, Mary, illus. 2007. 368p. (J). 19.95 (978-0-15-205922-4(9)) Harcourt Children's Bks.

—Mary Poppins Comes Back. Shepard, Mary, illus. 2006. 336p. (J). 12.95 (978-0-15-205816-6(8), Harcourt Young Classics) Harcourt Children's Bks.

—Mary Poppins from A to Z. Shepard, Mary, illus. 2006. 64p. (J). 14.00 (978-0-15-205834-0(6)) Harcourt Children's Bks.

—Mary Poppins in the Park. Shepard, Mary, illus. 2006. 304p. (J). 12.95 (978-0-15-205828-9(1), Harcourt Young Classics) Harcourt Children's Bks.

—Mary Poppins Opens the Door. Shepard, Mary & Sims, Agnes, illus. 2006. 288p. (J). 12.95 (978-0-15-205822-7(2), Harcourt Young Classics) Harcourt Children's Bks.

—Mary Poppins Vintage Boxed Set: Three Enchanting Classics: Mary Poppins, Mary Poppins Comes Back, & Mary Poppins Opens the Door. 2007. (Illus.). (J). 38.85 (978-0-15-205858-6(3)) Harcourt Children's Bks.

Travers, Pamela L. Mary Poppins. 202p. (J). (gr. 3-5). pap. 6.00 (978-0-8072-1536-4(8), Listening Library) Random Hse. Audio Publishing Group.

La Travesia del "Explorador del Amanecer"Tr. of Voyage of the Dawn Treader. (SPA.). pap. (978-956-13-1671-3(4)) Bello, Andres CHL. *Dist:* Lectorum Pubns., Inc.

Trayer, Edward. The Struggles of Felicity Brady. 2004. (YA). per. 14.95 (978-1-59571-043-7(4)) Word Association Pubs.

Trembath, Don. Hypnotized. 2007. (Orca Currents Ser.). 112p. (J). pap. (*978-1-55143-705-7(8)); lib. bdg. (*978-1-55143-707-1(4)) Orca Bk. Pubs.

Trent, Tiffany. In the Serpent's Coils. 2007. (Hallowmere Ser.). 312p. (YA). (gr. 7-11). 8.95 (*978-0-7869-4229-9(0), Mirrorstone) Wizards of the Coast.

Trottier, Maxine. Sister of the Wolf. 2005. (Illus.). 352p. (YA). (gr. 5-9). (978-1-55337-519-7(X)) Kids Can Pr., Ltd.

—Sister of the Wolf. 2006. (Illus.). 352p. 6.95 (978-1-55337-520-3(3)) Kids Can Pr., Ltd. CAN. *Dist:* Wybel Marketing Group.

Troughton, Ruth. The Invisible Ones. 2003. 88p. pap. 9.95 (978-0-595-29592-0(4)) iUniverse, Inc.

Troulis, Jennifer. Penelope & Priscilla & the City of the Banished. 2007. (J). per. 14.95 (*978-0-9768602-1-1(X)) Twin Monkeys Pr.

Trumbauer, Lisa. The Hidden Dragon. Fiegenschuh, Emily, illus. 2005. (Dungeons & Dragons Ser.: Bk. 7). 192p. (J). (ps-7). pap. 5.99 (978-0-7869-3748-6(3)) Wizards of the Coast.

—The Hidden Dragon. Fiegenshuh, Emily, illus. 2005. (Knights of the Silver Dragon Ser.: Bk. 7). 178p. (J). (*978-1-4156-0424-3(X), Mirrorstone) Wizards of the Coast.

Trumbauer, Lisa & Suncatcher, Sindri. A Practical Guide to Dragons. 2006. (Illus.). 80p. (J). (gr. 3-7). pap. 12.95 (978-0-7869-4164-3(2), Mirrorstone) Wizards of the Coast.

Trumbore, Cindy. The Genie in the Book. Alley, R. W., illus. 2004. 120p. (J). (gr. 3-6). 15.95 (978-1-59354-042-5(6)) Handprint Bks.

Tsuda, Masami, illus. & creator. Kare Kano, Vol. 15. Tsuda, Masami, creator. rev. ed. 2005. Tr. of Kareshi Kanojo No Jijo. 200p. pap. 9.99 (978-1-59532-589-1(1), Tokyopop Kids) TOKYOPOP, Inc.

Tsukirino, Yumi. Incredible Shrinking Hazel, Pt. 4. Tsukirino, Yumi, illus. 2001. (Magical Pokemon Journey Ser.: Pt. 4, No. 3). (Illus.). 40p. (YA). pap. 4.95 (978-1-56931-676-4(7)) Viz Media.

—Magical Pokemon Journey Vol. 4: Kadabra's Magic Show. Tsukirino, Yumi, illus. 2001. (Magical Pokemon Journey, Part 3 Ser.: No. 4). (Illus.). 40p. (YA). (ps-3). pap. 4.95 (978-1-56931-557-6(4)) Viz Media.

—Passionate Primeape. 2000. (gr. 3-6). lib. bdg. 12.95 (978-0-613-35649-7(7)) Tandem Library Bks.

—Passionate Primeape Vol. 3, Pt. 3, Pt. 3. Tsukirino, Yumi, illus. 2001. (Magical Pokemon Journey, Part 3 Ser.: No. 3). (Illus.). 40p. (YA). (ps-3). pap. 4.95 (978-1-56931-556-9(6)) Viz Media.

Tuato'o, Jackie. Our Mom, the Human. 2004. (Illus.). 20p. (J). per. 19.95 (978-1-932373-89-9(6)) Cedar Hill Publishing.

Tucker, Kathy. Leprechaun in the Basement. 2002. (gr. k-3). lib. bdg. 15.25 (978-0-613-75744-7(0)) Tandem Library Bks.

Tulloch, Richard. Weird Stuff. 2006. (Illus.). 208p. (J). 16.95 (978-0-8027-8058-4(X)) Walker & Co.

Tunasima, Sirou. Jinki: Extend. 2004. Vol. 1. (Illus.). 186p. pap. (978-1-4139-0052-1(6)); Vol. 2. 184p. pap. (978-1-4139-0090-3(9)) ADV Manga.

Tunnell, Michael O. Moon Without Magic. 2007. 240p. (YA). (gr. 7). 17.99 (*978-0-525-47729-7(2), Dutton Juvenile) Penguin Group (USA) Inc.

Turin, Adela. Las Hierbas Magicas. 1998. (SPA.). 40p. 14.95 (978-84-264-3550-7(5)) Lectorum Pubns., Inc.

Turnbull, Ann & Foreman, Michael. Sandhorse. 2002. (Illus.). 32p. (J). pap. 11.00 (978-1-84270-099-0(5)) Andersen GBR. *Dist:* Trafalgar Square Publishing.

Turner, Deborah & Mohler, Diana. How Willy Got His Wings: The Continuing Adventures of Wheely Willy. Ahrends, Susan, illus. 2003. 30p. 15.95 (978-0-944875-88-9(2)) Doral Publishing, Inc.

Turner, Jessie E. Moon in the Day Sky. 2006. 19p. (YA). pap. 19.95 (*978-1-59299-238-6(2)) Inkwater Pr.

Turner, Julie Anne. A Tale of Summerland. 2007. (Illus.). 72p. pap. (*978-1-84401-902-1(0)) Athena Pr.

Turner, Megan Whalen. The Queen of Attolia. 2000. 288p. (J). (gr. 5 up). 15.95 (978-0-688-17423-1(X)) HarperCollins Pubs.

—Queen of Attolia. 2006. 368p. (J). pap. 6.99 (978-0-06-084182-9(6)) HarperCollins Pubs.

—The Thief. 2006. 304p. (J). reprint ed. pap. 6.99 (978-0-06-082497-6(2)) HarperCollins Pubs.

Turtledove, Harry. Between the Rivers. 1999. (J). (978-0-606-16884-7(2)) Tandem Library Bks.

—Into the Darkness. 2000. (gr. 7-12). lib. bdg. 16.45 (978-0-613-27901-7(8)) Tandem Library Bks.

Tyler, Marchele E. Rebirth of the Druids. 2001. 198p. (YA). pap. 13.95 (978-0-595-21042-8(2), Writers Club Pr.) iUniverse, Inc.

Ueda, Miwa, illus. & creator. Peach Girl Authentic, Vol. 4. Ueda, Miwa, creator. 4th rev. ed. 2005. 192p. pap. 9.99 (978-1-59532-174-9(8), Tokyopop Kids) TOKYOPOP, Inc.

Ueyama, Michiro. Chaotic Century. Ueyama, Michiro, illus. (Zoids Ser.). (Illus.). (YA). Vol. 11. 2004. 82p. pap. 5.95 (978-1-56931-858-4(1)); Vol. 12. 2003. 72p. pap. 5.95 (978-1-56931-867-6(0)) Viz Media.

Umansky, Kaye. Pongwiffy & the Goblin's Revenge. Smedley, Chris, illus. 2002. 160p. (J). pap. 4.50 (978-0-7434-1913-0(8), Aladdin) Simon & Schuster Children's Publishing.

—Pongwiffy & the Goblin's Revenge. 2002. (gr. 3-6). lib. bdg. 12.40 (978-0-613-62534-0(X)) Tandem Library Bks.

Uncle Ernie's Tall Tales: Little Blue Guys. 2006. (Illus.). 110p. (YA). per. 7.95 (*978-0-9760607-1-0(X), ON-E-1) Sanpitch Pr.

Ungerer, Tomi. El Hombre de la Luna. (SPA., Illus.). 40p. (J). (gr. k-2). 7.95 (978-84-204-3746-0(8), AF0456) Santillana USA Publishing Co., Inc.

—El Hombre de la Luna. Ungerer, Tomi, illus. 2003. (Picture Books Collection). (SPA., Illus.). 40p. (J). (gr. k-3). pap. 10.95 (978-968-19-0661-0(6)) Santillana USA Publishing Co., Inc.

Ursu, Anne. The Shadow Thieves. Fortune, Eric, illus. (Cronus Chronicles Ser.). 432p. (J). (gr. 3-7). 2007. pap. 6.99 (978-1-4169-0588-2(X), Aladdin); 2006. 16.95 (978-1-4169-0587-5(1), Atheneum) Simon & Schuster Children's Publishing.

—Spilling Clarence: A Novel. 2003. 304p. pap. 12.95 (978-0-7868-8662-3(5)) Hyperion Pr.

Utatane, Hiroyuki. Target Zone. 2003. (Seraphic Feather Ser.: Vol. 3). (Illus.). 240p. (gr. 11 up). pap. 17.95 (978-1-56971-912-1(8)) Dark Horse Comics.

Valdés, Zoé. Los Aretes de la Luna. 2nd ed. 2000. (SPA., Illus.). 72p. (J). (gr. 3-5). 6.36 net. (978-84-241-7888-8(2)) Lectorum Pubns., Inc.

Valle-Inclan, Ramon del. La Cabeza del Dragon. 1998. Tr. of Head of the Dragon. (SPA.). (gr. 5-8). lib. bdg. 17.60 (978-0-613-86339-1(9)) Tandem Library Bks.

Van Allsburg, Chris. Jumanji. Van Allsburg, Chris, illus. 2002. (Illus.). (J). 25.28 (978-0-7587-6813-1(3)) Book Wholesalers, Inc.

van Gosen, Ryan O'Dell, IV. Ray Conka & the Sortian Jewell. Maximilian Staff, ed. Walker, John, photos by. unabr. ed. 2004. (Illus.). 128p. (YA). lib. bdg. 12.50 (978-1-930211-55-1(4)) Maximilian Pr. Pubs.

Van Lieshout, Ted. Uncle Gus's Magic Box. Sideri, Simona, tr. from DUT. Hopman, Philip, illus. 2005. 60p. (J). (gr. 2-4). pap. 5.95 (978-1-55037-934-1(8)) Annick Pr., Ltd. CAN. *Dist:* Firefly Bks., Ltd.

Van Loon, Michelle. Fairy Tale Academy. 2000. 35p. (J). (gr. k-6). pap. 4.00 (978-1-58193-190-7(5)) Brown Bag Productions.

Van Pelt, James. Strangers & Beggars: Stories. 2002. (gr. 7-12). lib. bdg. 28.05 (978-0-613-60619-6(1)) Tandem Library Bks.

Van Sickle, Lisa. Secret Little City. 2000. 230p. (YA). (gr. 5-8). 15.95 (978-1-930167-11-7(3)) Palmae Publishing.

Vande Velde, Vivian. Dragon's Bait. 2003. (Illus.). 208p. (YA). pap. 5.95 (978-0-15-216663-2(7), Magic Carpet Bks.) Harcourt Children's Bks.

—Dragon's Bait. 2003. (gr. 7-12). lib. bdg. 14.10 (978-0-613-59892-7(X)) Tandem Library Bks.

—Now You See It... 2005. (Illus.). 288p. (YA). 17.00 (978-0-15-205311-6(5)) Harcourt Children's Bks.

—Smart Dog. 2007. (Illus.). 160p. (J). pap. 5.95 (*978-0-15-206172-2(X), Magic Carpet Bks.) Harcourt Children's Bks.

—Smart Dog. 2000. (gr. 3-6). lib. bdg. 12.40 (978-0-613-28646-6(4)) Tandem Library Bks.

—User Unfriendly. 2001. 244p. (YA). (gr. 8-12). lib. bdg. 14.15 (978-0-613-57486-0(9)) Tandem Library Bks.

Vande Velde, Vivian & Nielsen, Cliff. A Well-Timed Enchantment. 2006. (Illus.). 240p. (YA). pap. 6.95 (978-0-15-204919-5(3), Magic Carpet Bks.) Harcourt Children's Bks.

Vargas, George. The Prophecy of the Ages: Of War & Choices. 2004. 458p. (YA). pap. 24.95 (978-0-595-29607-1(6)) iUniverse, Inc.

Varsell, Linda. Ends of Rainbow. Curtis, E., illus. 2003. 260p. (J). per. 8.00 (978-0-9725479-5-6(9)) Rainbow Communications.

—The Humane Touch. Curtis, E., illus. 2003. 316p. per. 10.00 (978-0-9728737-0-3(8)) Rainbow Communications.

—A Journey for Rainbows. Curtis, E., illus. 2003. 166p. (YA). per. 6.00 (978-0-9725479-1-8(6)) Rainbow Communications.

—The Rainbow Breakers. Curtis, E., illus. 2003. 232p. per. 7.00 (978-0-9725479-3-2(2)) Rainbow Communications.

—The Rainbow Circle. Curtis, E., illus. 2003. 428p. (J). per. 10.00 (978-0-9725479-9-4(1)) Rainbow Communications.

—The Rainbow Dreamers. Curtis, E., illus. 2003. 262p. per. 8.00 (978-0-9725479-4-9(0)) Rainbow Communications.

—The Rainbow Makers. Curtis, E., illus. 2003. 148p. per. 6.00 (978-0-9725479-2-5(4)) Rainbow Communications.

—The Rainbow Planet. Curtis, E., illus. 2003. 162p. (J). per. 6.00 (978-0-9725479-7-0(5)) Rainbow Communications.

—The Rainbow Remnants. Curtis, E., illus. 2003. 204p. (J). per. 7.00 (978-0-9725479-8-7(3)) Rainbow Communications.

—The Rainbow Rescue. Curtis, E., illus. 2003. 200p. (J). per. 7.00 (978-0-9725479-6-3(7)) Rainbow Communications.

—With a Human Touch. Curtis, E., illus. 2003. 178p. per. 6.00 (978-0-9725479-0-1(8)) Rainbow Communications.

Vaughan, Brian K. & Kubert, Andy. Cry Wolf, Vol. 10. 2005. (X-Men Ser.). (Illus.). 96p. pap. 8.99 (978-0-7851-1405-5(X)) Marvel Enterprises, Inc.

Vazov, George D. The Other Side of the Mushroom. 2006. 12.00 (978-0-8059-9018-8(6)) Dorrance Publishing Co., Inc.

Vega, Michael, illus. Dark Moon Diary. 2007. 192p. pap. 9.99 (978-1-59532-844-1(0), Tokyopop Kids) TOKYOPOP, Inc.

Veillon, A. M. Shelby & the Shifting Rings: Book One—Defender of Time Series, 1. 2005. (Defender of Time Ser.: Bk. 1). (Illus.). 167p. (J). (gr. 5-7). 18.95 (978-0-9762015-4-0(2)) Parity Pr.

—Shelby & the Shifting Rings Bk. 1: Defender of Time Series. 2005. (Illus.). 167p. (J). per. 9.95 (978-0-9762015-5-7(0)) Parity Pr.

Velde, Vivian Vande. Now You See It.... 2006. (Illus.). 288p. (J). pap. 6.95 (978-0-15-205461-8(8)) Harcourt Children's Bks.

Velveteen Rabbit. 1999. (J). 9.95 (978-1-56137-179-2(3)) Novel Units, Inc.

Venokur, Ross. The Amazing Frecktacle. 1999. (YA). pap. 40.95 incl. audio (978-0-7887-3182-2(3), 40917) Recorded Bks., LLC.

—The Amazing Frecktacle. 2000. (978-0-606-17612-5(8)) Tandem Library Bks.

Verne, Jules. Viaje al Centro de la Tierra. Orig. Title: Journey to the Center of the Earth. (SPA., Illus.). 160p. (YA). 11.95 (978-84-7281-084-6(4), AF1084) Auriga, Ediciones S.A. ESP. *Dist:* Continental Bk. Co., Inc.

—Viaje al Centro de la Tierra. 1999. (Coleccion "Clasicos Juveniles" Ser.). Orig. Title: Journey to the Center of the Earth. (SPA & ENG.). 192p. (gr. 4-7). pap. 10.95 (978-1-58348-780-8(8)) iUniverse, Inc.

—20,000 Leagues under the Sea. Gambog, Romie, illus. 2nd ed. 1998. (Illustrated Classic Book Ser.). 61p. (J). (gr. 3 up). reprint ed. pap. 4.95 (978-1-56767-243-5(4)) Educational Insights, Inc.

Verrillo, Erica F. Elissa's Quest. 2007. (Phoenix Rising Trilogy Ser.). 352p. (J). (gr. 4-7). 16.99 (978-0-375-83946-7(1)); lib. bdg. 19.99 (978-0-375-93946-4(6)) Random Hse. Children's Bks. (Random Hse. Bks. for Young Readers).

—Elissa's Quest. 2007. (J). pap. (978-0-375-83947-4(X)) Random Hse., Inc.

Vick, Helen Hughes. Walker of Time. 1999. (Illus.). 214p. (gr. 7-12). pap. 13.95 (978-0-943173-80-1(9)) Rinehart, Roberts Pubs.

Viguie, Debbie. Midnight Pearls: A Retelling of the Little Mermaid. 2006. (Once upon a Time Ser.). 208p. (YA). pap. 5.99 (978-1-4169-4016-6(2), Simon Pulse) Simon & Schuster Children's Publishing.

—Scarlet Moon. 176p. (YA). 2005. mass mkt. 3.99 (978-1-4169-1150-0(2)); 2004. pap. 5.99 (978-0-689-86716-3(6)) Simon & Schuster Children's Publishing. (Simon Pulse).

—Scarlet Moon. 2004. (gr. 7-12). lib. bdg. 14.15 (978-0-613-73425-7(4)) Tandem Library Bks.

Viguie, Debbie & Speregen, Devra. Miss O & Friends: Room for One More. 2006. (Miss O & Friends Ser.). (Illus.). 112p. (J). pap. 5.99 (978-0-8230-2947-1(6)) Watson-Guptill Pubns., Inc.

Villafane, Javier. El Hombre Que Debia Adivinarle la Edad Al Diablo. 2002. (SPA.). 64p. (J). pap. 6.95 (978-1-4000-0063-0(7)) Random Hse., Inc.

Villarreal Elizondo, Cesar. La Tierra de las Adivinanzas. Garcia, Nasario, tr. from SPA. Accardo, Anthony, illus. 2002. Tr. of Land of the Riddles. (ENG & SPA.). 32p. (J). (gr. 2-3). 14.95 (978-1-55885-352-2(9), Piñata Books) Arte Publico Pr.

Vivekanand, Jennifer. Zakkary Kay & the King of the Asparagus. 2004. 48p. pap. 12.95 (978-1-4137-2242-0(3)) PublishAmerica, Inc.

Viz Media Staff. The Year's Best Articles, 2003. 2003. (Best of Animerica Ser.). (Illus.). 96p. (YA). pap. 12.95 (978-1-56931-899-7(9)) Viz Media.

Voake, Steve. The Dreamwalker's Child. (Illus.). 320p. (YA). 2007. pap. 7.95 (978-1-59990-038-4(6)); 2006. 16.95 (978-1-58234-661-8(5)) Bloomsbury Publishing. (Bloomsbury Children).

Voake, Steve & Voake, Steven. The Web of Fire. Watkinson, Mark, illus. 2007. 336p. (YA). (gr. 5-8). 17.95 (978-1-58234-737-0(9), Bloomsbury Children) Bloomsbury Publishing.

Voigt, Brian Jeffrey. Guardian of the Zercons. 2003. (Illus.). 360p. (YA). 21.95 (978-1-932545-18-0(2)) Blue Pig Productions.

Voigt, Cynthia. Elske: A Novel of the Kingdom. Vermeer, Jan, illus. (Kingdom Ser.). (YA). 2003. 320p. mass mkt. 5.99 (978-0-689-86438-4(8)); 2001. 256p. pap. 10.00 (978-0-689-84444-7(1)) Simon & Schuster Children's Publishing. (Simon Pulse).

—Elske: A Novel of the Kingdom. (Kingdom Ser.). 2003. (gr. 7-12). lib. bdg. 14.15 (978-0-613-73442-4(4)); 2001. (gr. 7-12). lib. bdg. 18.80 (978-0-613-73327-4(4)); 2001. (YA). 16.65 (978-0-606-21175-8(6)) Tandem Library Bks.

Voll, Donna G. Tell Me, Could a Bad Thing Happen to Me? Voll, Donna G. & Voll, Dudley J., eds. 2002. (Illus.). 26p. (J). (ps-3). 12.95 (978-0-9726662-0-6(6)) Golden Words Publishing.

Von Sholly, Peter. Dinosaur Circus. 2001. (Illus.). 32p. (Orig.). (J). (gr. 2-6). pap. 9.95 (978-0-9709368-0-6(X)) Vonshollywood.

Vornholt, John. Dolphin Watch. 2002. (gr. 5-8). lib. bdg. 11.80 (978-0-613-70888-3(1)) Tandem Library Bks.

—The Troll King. 2003. 272p. (J). 22.95 (978-0-7862-5049-3(6)) Thorndike Pr.

—Troll King. 2002. (gr. 5-8). lib. bdg. 13.00 (978-0-613-70774-9(5)) Tandem Library Bks.

—Troll Queen. 2003. (gr. 5-8). lib. bdg. 13.00 (978-0-613-66551-3(1)) Tandem Library Bks.

Vornholt, John & Rayyan, Omar. The Troll Treasure. 2003. (Illus.). 160p. (J). pap. 4.99 (978-0-689-85834-5(5), Aladdin) Simon & Schuster Children's Publishing.

Wagner, Jerri. The Adventures of "Jako", the Florida Troll. 1999. 53p. (J). pap. 9.95 (978-0-7414-0111-3(8)) Infinity Publishing.

Wagoner, Timothy Allen. The Adventures of Jacque & Wanderwan Bk. 1: Naoo. 2005. (J). pap. (978-0-9761739-2-2(1)) Grandoc Publishing.

Waite, Judy. Forbidden. 2006. 256p. (YA). 16.95 (978-0-689-87642-4(4), Atheneum) Simon & Schuster Children's Publishing.

Walburg, Lori. The Legend of the Candy Cane. Bernardin, James, illus. 2002. 28p. (J). bds. 6.99 (978-0-310-70447-8(2)) Zonderkidz.

Walker, Craig, ed. Fantastic Tales for Boys. 2006. 736p. (J). pap. 5.99 (978-0-439-85862-5(3), Scholastic) Scholastic, Inc.

—Fantasy Tales for Girls Bind-Up. 2006. 416p. (J). pap. 5.99 (978-0-439-85857-1(7), Scholastic) Scholastic, Inc.

Walker, E. G. Mario & the Flying Fish. Graffam, Jennifer, illus. 2001. 50p. (J). (gr. 5-12). pap. 6.95 (978-0-9716071-0-1(9)) Walker, Esther.

—Mario & the Tarantula. Leigh, Chris, illus. 1999. 46p. (ps-5). pap. 6.95 (978-0-7392-0268-5(5), PO3351) Morris Publishing.

Walker, Victoria. The Winter of Enchantment. 2007. (J). (*978-1-930900-33-2(3)) Purple Hse. Pr.

Wallace, Barbara Brooks. The Interesting Thing That Happened at Perfect Acres, Inc. 2007. 148p. per. 11.95 (*978-0-595-45763-2(0), Backinprint.com) iUniverse, Inc.

Wallace, Carol & Wallace, Bill. The Flying Flea, Callie & Me. 1999. (Gray Cat Ser.: Vol. 1). 96p. (J). (gr. 3-6). pap. 4.99 (978-0-671-03968-4(7), Aladdin) Simon & Schuster Children's Publishing.

—The Flying Flea, Callie & Me. 1999. (Illus.). (J). 11.79 (978-0-606-18368-0(X)) Tandem Library Bks.

Wallace, Paula S. Rick & Rocky. Fruisen, Catherine Myler, illus. 2004. 32p. (J). pap. (978-1-893974-22-7(7), Design Pr. Bks.) Savannah College of Art & Design.

Walsh, Ellen Stoll. Pip's Magic. 1999. (978-0-606-16520-4(7)) Tandem Library Bks.
Walsh, Maria Elena. La Nube Traicionera. Fiorini, Nancy, illus. 2003. (SPA.). 88p. (YA). (gr. 5-8). 14.95 (978-950-511-616-4(0)) Alfaguara S.A. de Ediciones ARG. *Dist:* Santillana USA Publishing Co., Inc.
Walton, Jo. King's Peace. 2000. (gr. 5-8). lib. bdg. 16.45 (978-0-613-62634-7(6)) Tandem Library Bks.
Ward, Nick. The Ice Child. Bailey, Peter, illus. 2004. 32p. (J). (978-1-84458-038-5(5)) Chrysalis Children's Bks.
Warner Brothers Staff. Quest for Camelot. 1998. (Quest for Camelot Ser.). (J). pap. 3.98 (978-0-590-12062-3(X)) Scholastic, Inc.
Warner, James. An Alien Adventure - The Magic Sled. Holder, Harry, illus. 1999. 107p. (YA). (gr. 5-8). pap. 14.95 (978-1-890549-08-4(8)) Alpha Publishing Group.
Warren, Adam. Meanwhile. 2003. (Gen 13 Ser.). (Illus.). 160p. pap. 17.95 (978-1-4012-0062-6(1)) DC Comics.
Wartik, David J. The Vonnesta Project. 2006. 140p. (J). (gr. 3-6). pap. 12.95 (978-1-59113-938-6(4)) Booklocker-.com, Inc.
Warwaruk, Larry. Andrei & the Snow Walker. Gardos, Susan, illus. 2002. (In the Same Boat Ser.). 202p. (J). (gr. 4-6). pap. 8.95 (978-1-55050-213-8(1)) Coteau Bks. CAN. *Dist:* Fitzhenry & Whiteside, Ltd.
Washer, S. N. The Wingate Adventures: Our New Friends. 2006. 164p. pap. 11.95 (978-1-59800-510-3(3)) Outskirts Press, Inc.
Wasson, Christopher. Quest for Adlaremzee Molair Nopeeoh. 2003. 120p. pap. 14.95 (978-1-4137-0117-3(5)) PublishAmerica, Inc.
Watase, Yu. Enemy, Vol. 10. Watase, Yu, illus. 2004. (Illus.). 200p. lib. bdg. 20.85 (978-1-4176-5241-9(1)) Tandem Library Bks.
—Imadoki: Nowadays. Watase, Yu, illus. 2004. (Imadoki Ser.). (Illus.). 200p. (YA). Vol. 2. pap. 9.95 (978-1-59116-469-2(9)); Vol. 4. pap. 9.95 (978-1-59116-618-4(7)) Viz Media.
Watase, Yuu. Genbu Kaiden, Vol. 4. Watase, Yuu, illus. 2006. (Fushigi Yugi Ser.). 208p. (YA). pap. 8.99 (978-1-4215-0579-4(7)) Viz Media.
—Nowadays. Watase, Yuu, illus. 2005. (Imadoki Ser.: No. 5). 200p. (YA). pap. 9.95 (978-1-59116-619-1(5)) Viz Media.
Watson-Dubisch, Carolyn. Andy! & the Magician's Horn, 1. l.t. ed. 2006. (Illus.). 32p. (J). per. 9.95 (978-0-9779295-0-4(7)) Medusa Road Pr.
—Night of the Armadillos, 1. Watson-Dubisch, Carolyn, illus. l.t. ed. 2006. (Illus.). 32p. (J). per. 9.95 (978-0-9779295-2-8(3)) Medusa Road Pr.
Watson, Jude. Anakin Skywalker. 1999. (978-0-606-17549-4(0)) Tandem Library Bks.
—The Day of Reckoning. 2000. (Star Wars Ser.: Bk. 8). (J). (gr. 4-7). 12.64 (978-0-606-19620-8(X)) Tandem Library Bks.
—The School of Fear. 2003. (Star Wars Ser.: No. 5). (gr. 3-6). lib. bdg. 13.00 (978-0-613-58164-6(4)) Tandem Library Bks.
—Underworld. 3rd ed. 2005. (Star Wars Ser.: No. 3). 137p. (J). (gr. 4-7). pap. 5.99 (978-0-439-68136-0(7)) Scholastic, Inc.
Watsuki, Nobuhiro. Rurouni Kenshin. Watsuki, Nobuhiro, illus. (Rurouni Kenshin Ser.). (Illus.). (YA). 9. 2004. 200p. pap. 7.95 (978-1-59116-669-6(1)); Vol. 6. 2004. 200p. pap. 7.95 (978-1-59116-356-5(0)); Vol. 7. 2004. 200p. pap. 7.95 (978-1-59116-357-2(9)); Vol. 10. 2005. 192p. pap. 7.95 (978-1-59116-703-7(5)) Viz Media.
—Rurouni Kenshin: A Beautiful Night, Vol. 13. Watsuki, Nobuhiro, illus. 2005. (Rurouni Kenshin Ser.). (Illus.). 192p. (YA). pap. 7.95 (978-1-59116-713-6(2)) Viz Media.
Watt, Fiona. (Fairies Luxury Touchy-Feely) - Spanish. 2006. 12p. (J). bds. 15.99 (978-0-7460-7405-3(0) , Usborne) EDC Publishing.
Wax, Wendy. A Royal Valentine. Hall, Susan, illus. 2005. (Backyardigans Ser.). 24p. (J). pap. 3.99 (978-1-4169-0801-2(3) , Simon Spotlight/Nickelodeon) Simon & Schuster Children's Publishing.
Way, Daniel. Ghost Rider Vicious Cycl, Vol. 1. 2007. (Illus.). 120p. pap. 13.99 (978-0-7851-2296-8(6)) Marvel Enterprises, Inc.
—Sabretooth: Open Season. Sears, Bart, illus. 2005. (Wolverine Ser.). 96p. pap. 9.99 (978-0-7851-1507-6(2)) Marvel Enterprises, Inc.
Weatherill, Cat. Barkbelly. 2008. 320p. (J). (gr. 3-7). 6.99 ***(*978-0-440-42077-4(6)*** , Yearling) Random Hse. Children's Bks.
—Barkbelly. Brown, Peter, illus. 2006. 320p. (J). (gr. 3-7). 15.95 (978-0-375-83327-4(7)); lib. bdg. 17.99 (978-0-375-93327-1(1)) Random Hse. Children's Bks. (Knopf Bks. for Young Readers).
—Snowbone. Brown, Peter, illus. 2007. 336p. (J). (gr. 3-7). 15.99 (978-0-375-83328-1(5)); lib. bdg. 18.99 (978-0-375-93328-8(X)) Random Hse. Children's Bks. (Knopf Bks. for Young Readers).
Webb, Beth. The Dragons of Kilve. 2004. (Illus.). 128p. (J). pap. 8.99 (978-0-7459-4881-2(2) , Lion) Lion Hudson plc GBR. *Dist:* Independent Pubs. Group.
—Fleabag & the Ring's End. 2000. (Fleabag Ser.). 208p. (J). pap. 8.99 (978-0-7459-4411-1(6) , Lion) Lion Hudson plc GBR. *Dist:* Independent Pubs. Group.
—Fleabag Trilogy. 2005. 640p. (J). pap. 14.00 (978-0-7459-4977-2(0) , Lion) Lion Hudson plc GBR. *Dist:* Trafalgar Square Publishing.
—Magic in the Pool of Making. 1998. (Illus.). 192p. (J). pap. 7.99 (978-0-7459-2234-8(1) , Lion) Lion Hudson plc GBR. *Dist:* Independent Pubs. Group.
Webb, Catherine. Mirror Dreams. 2005. 320p. (Orig.). (J). (gr. 6-17). pap. 9.99 (978-1-904233-00-8(7) , Atom Books) Little, Brown Bk. Group Ltd. GBR. *Dist:* Trafalgar Square Publishing.
—Timekeepers. 2005. 320p. (J). 9.99 (978-1-904233-43-5(0) , Atom Books) Little, Brown Bk. Group Ltd. GBR. *Dist:* Trafalgar Square Publishing.
—Waywalkers. 2005. 320p. (J). 9.99 (978-1-904233-21-3(X) , Atom Books) Little, Brown Bk. Group Ltd. GBR. *Dist:* Trafalgar Square Publishing.
Webb, M. St. John. Knock Three Times. 2003. (Children's Classics). (ENG.). 288p. (J). (gr. 3-6). pap. (978-1-85326-132-9(7)) Wordsworth Editions, Ltd.
Webb, Mack Henry, Jr. Webb's Wondrous Tales Book 1. Webb, Celia, illus. 2006. 184p. (YA). per. 14.95 (978-0-9779576-1-3(6)) Pilinut Pr., Inc.
Webb, Margot & Chorpash, Marci. My Grandmommy Is Shrinking. 2003. 60p. pap. 8.95 (978-0-595-29143-4(0)) iUniverse, Inc.
Webber, Vanessa. Glitterbug. 2005. (Illus.). 4p. (J). bds. 5.95 (978-1-59354-083-8(3)) Handprint Bks.
Weber, Jane. The Riches of Rangoberra/Las riquezas de Rangoberra. de la Vega, Eida, tr. Saari, Rijalynne, illus. 2002. Tr. of Las riquezas de Rangoberra. (SPA & ENG.). 32p. (J). (gr. 4-6). 16.95 (978-0-9720192-1-7(9) , 626999) Raven Tree Pr.
Weber, Jen Funk. Hogsqueal's Activity Book. 2008. (Spiderwick Chronicles). 64p. 4.99 ***(*978-1-4169-4951-0(8)*** , Simon Scribbles) Simon & Schuster Children's Publishing.
Wein, Elizabeth. The Sunbird. 2004. (Illus.). 224p. (YA). (gr. 7 up). 16.99 (978-0-670-03691-2(9) , Viking Juvenile) Penguin Group (USA) Inc.
Weinbach, Shaindel. Shimmee & the Taste-Me Tree. Backman, Aidel, illus. Date not set. (J). (ps-2). 2.95 (978-0-87306-305-0(8)) Feldheim Pubs.
Weis, Margaret. Dragons of Autumn Twilight. 2000. (gr. 7-12). lib. bdg. 16.45 (978-0-8335-3164-3(6)) Tandem Library Bks.
Weis, Margaret & Hickman, Tracy. Dragons of Spring Dawning. 1999. (gr. 7-12). lib. bdg. 16.45 (978-0-8335-3165-0(4)) Tandem Library Bks.
—Dragons of Winter Night. 2000. (gr. 7-12). lib. bdg. 16.45 (978-0-8335-3166-7(2)) Tandem Library Bks.
—The Nightmare Lands. 2003. (Dragonlance Chronicles : Pt. 3). (Illus.). 256p. (YA). pap. 5.99 (978-0-7869-3093-7(4)) Wizards of the Coast.
Weiss, Ellen. Shrek: Junior Novelization. 2001. (Illus.). (J). (978-0-606-22048-4(8)) Tandem Library Bks.
Weiss, Ellen & Cooke, Tom. Bye-Bye, Bottle. 1998. (Muppets Ser.). 14p. (J). (ps). bds. 3.49 (978-0-307-13469-1(5) , 13469, Golden Bks.) Random Hse. Children's Bks.
Weiss, M. Jerry & Weiss, Helen S. Dreams & Visions. 256p. (J). 2007. 5.99 (978-0-7653-5107-4(2)); 2006. 19.95 (978-0-7653-1249-5(2)) Doherty, Tom Assocs., LLC. (Starscape).
Weissmann, Joe, illus. The Gingerbread Man. 2005. (J). 7.95 (978-0-9770473-0-7(X)) Heersink, Roland.
—Three Tales of Adventure. 2005. (Once-upon-a-Time Ser.). 32p. (J). (gr. k-3). (978-1-55074-945-8(5)) Kids Can Pr., Ltd.
Wellander, J. D. Tales Written in a Forest. 2000. 108p. (J). pap. 9.95 (978-0-595-13336-9(3)) iUniverse, Inc.
Welles, Lee. Gaia Girls Enter the Earth. Hameister, Ann, illus. 2007. (Gaia Girls Ser.). 336p. (YA). pap. 12.95 ***(*978-1-933609-01-0(X))*** Daisyworld Pr.
—Gaia Girls Way of Water. Hameister, Ann, illus. 2007. (Gaia Girls Ser.). 336p. (J). 18.95 ***(*978-1-933609-02-7(8))*** Daisyworld Pr.
Wells, H. G. H. G. Wells: Graphic Classics. Steine, Kent, illus. 2005. 144p. (J). lib. bdg. 30.77 ***(*978-1-4242-1821-9(7))*** Fitzgerald Bks.
Wells, Rosemary. Max & Ruby in Pandora's Box. 1998. (Max & Ruby Ser.). (J). (gr. k-2). (978-0-606-13601-3(0)) Tandem Library Bks.
—Max's Dragon Shirt. Wells, Rosemary, illus. 2002. (Max the Bunny Ser.). (Illus.). (J). 13.19 (978-0-7587-4425-8(0)) Book Wholesalers, Inc.
—Max's Dragon Shirt. 2000. (Max & Ruby Ser.). (Illus.). 32p. (J). (gr. k-2). pap. 5.99 (978-0-14-056727-4(5) , Puffin) Penguin Group (USA) Inc.
Wells, Susan. The Rainbow Dragon/ the Sorcerer's Race. 2004. (Illus.). 60p. (YA). 6.95 (978-0-9741726-1-3(8)) Dreamtime Publishing.
—Rock Parables. 2004. (Illus.). 62p. (YA). 6.95 (978-0-9741726-2-0(6)) Dreamtime Publishing.
Wenke, Christine. Willa's Secret. 2005. 160p. (Orig.). pap. (978-0-7344-0675-0(4) , Lothian Bks.) Hachette Livre Australia.
West, Cathy. Paramount's Rugrats: All Growed Up. Durk, illus. 2001. 32p. (J). mass mkt. 5.99 (978-0-689-84752-3(1) , Simon Spotlight/Nickelodeon) Simon & Schuster Children's Publishing.
West, Tracey. Lord of the Unknown Tower. novel movie tie-in ed. 2001. (Pokemon Ser.). (Illus.). 96p. (gr. 1-3). mass mkt. 4.99 (978-0-439-29487-4(8)) Scholastic, Inc.
—Mayor Is Missing. 2003. (gr. 3-6). lib. bdg. 11.80 (978-0-613-58159-2(8)) Tandem Library Bks.
—Prepare for Trouble. 2001. (Pokemon Chapter Bks.: Vol. 19). (Illus.). 96p. (J). (gr. 2-7). pap. 4.50 (978-0-439-22033-0(5)) Scholastic, Inc.
—Roxy Hunter & the Mystery of the Moody Ghost. 2007. 128p. (J). (gr. 2-5). 4.99 ***(*978-0-8431-2663-1(9)*** , Price Stern Sloan) Penguin Group (USA) Inc.
—Sporty Sprite. 2001. (gr. 3-6). lib. bdg. 11.80 (978-0-613-33086-2(2)) Tandem Library Bks.
—Sprite's Secret. 2006. (Pixie Tricks Ser.: No. 1). (Illus.). 112p. (J). (gr. 1-4). pap. 3.99 (978-0-439-17218-9(7) , Scholastic Paperbacks) Scholastic, Inc.
—Sprite's Secret. 2000. (gr. 3-6). lib. bdg. 11.80 (978-0-613-27048-9(7)) Tandem Library Bks.
—Thundershock in Kanujitsu Stadium. 2001. (Pokemon Chapter Bks.: Vol. 16). (Illus.). 96p. (J). (gr. 2-7). pap. 4.50 (978-0-439-20092-9(X)) Scholastic, Inc.
West, Tracey. Welcome to Sinnoh. 2008. (Pokemon Ser.). 32p. (J). pap. 3.99 ***(*978-0-545-01414-4(X))*** Scholastic, Inc.
Westerfeld, Scott. The Secret Hour. 2004. (Midnighters Ser.: No. 1). 304p. (YA). (gr. 7 up). 16.99 (978-0-06-051951-3(7)) HarperCollins Pubs.
Weyn, Suzanne. The Night Dance. 2005. (Illus.). 208p. (YA). (gr. 9-12). pap. 5.99 (978-1-4169-0579-0(0) , Simon Pulse) Simon & Schuster Children's Publishing.
Wheatley, Marylou. Calypso & Strange Lands. 2004. 119p. pap. 16.95 (978-1-4137-1012-0(3)) PublishAmerica, Inc.
Whedon, Joss. Astonishing X-Men, Vol.1. gif. ed. (Illus.). 152p. (YA). pap. 14.99 (978-0-7851-1531-1(5)) Marvel Enterprises, Inc.
When Kids Dream & Trucks Fly. 2007. per. 14.99 ***(*978-0-9792258-6-4(8))*** Bezalel Bks.
White, E. B. Charlotte's Web. Williams, Garth, illus. movie tie-in ed. 2006. (Charlotte's Web Ser.). (J). 192p. mass mkt. 7.99 (978-0-06-122874-2(5) , Harper Trophy); Set. 50.99 (978-0-06-121501-8(5)); Set. pap. 19.99 (978-0-06-121502-5(3)) HarperCollins Pubs.
—La telarana de Carlota. Williams, Garth, illus. 2005. (SPA.). 224p. (J). pap. 7.99 (978-0-06-075740-3(X) , Rayo) HarperCollins Pubs.
—The Telarana of Carlota (La Telarana de Carlota) Williams, Garth, illus. 2005. (Charlotte's Web Ser.). (SPA.). 224p. (J). 16.99 (978-0-06-075739-7(6) , Rayo) HarperCollins Pubs.
White, John, et al. The Dark Lord's Demise: Archives of Anthropos, Vol. 6. 2001. (Archives of Anthropos Ser.: Vol. 6). (Illus.). 296p. pap. 16.00 (978-0-87784-521-8(2)) InterVarsity Pr.
Whitebeach, Terry. Watersky. 1998. 224p. (YA). pap. 12.95 (978-1-86368-213-8(9)) Fremantle Pr. AUS. *Dist:* International Specialized Bk. Services.
Whitlock, Dean. Raven. 2007. (Illus.). 240p. (J). (gr. 5-9). 16.00 ***(*978-0-618-70224-4(5)*** , Clarion Bks.) Houghton Mifflin Co. Trade & Reference Div.
Whitlock, Dean. Sky Carver. 2005. 256p. (YA). (gr. 5-9). 16.00 (978-0-618-44393-2(2) , Clarion Bks.) Houghton Mifflin Co. Trade & Reference Div.
Whittemore, JoAnne. Curse of Arastold. 2006. 312p. (J). pap. 8.95 (978-0-7387-0917-8(4)) Llewellyn Pubns.
—Escape from Arylon. 2006. 360p. pap. 8.95 (978-0-7387-0869-0(0)) Llewellyn Pubns.
—Onaj's Horn. 2007. 312p. pap. 8.95 (978-0-7387-1125-6(X) , Flux) Llewellyn Pubns.
Wick. Elfish Fantasy: The Great Chocolate Caper. 2003. 128p. (YA). pap. 11.95 (978-0-595-29038-3(8)) iUniverse, Inc.
Wickstrom, Lois June & Lorrah, Jean. Nessie & the Viking Gold. Strand, Sara Silvestri, illus. 2002. 104p. per. 10.00 incl. cd-rom (978-0-916176-22-8(3)) Gripper Products.
Wilce, Ysabeau S. Flora Segunda: Being the Magickal Mishaps of a Girl of Spirit, Her Glass-Gazing Sidekick, Two Ominous Butlers (One Blue), a House with Eleven Thousand Rooms, & a Red Dog. 2007. (eTygers of Wrath Ser.: Vol. 1). (Illus.). 448p. (J). 17.00 (978-0-15-205433-5(2)) Harcourt Children's Bks.
—Flora Segunda: The Magickal Mishaps of a Girl of Spirit, Her Glass-Gazing Sidekick, Two Ominous Butlers (One Blue), a House with Eleven Thousand Rooms, & a Red Dog. 2008. 448p. (J). pap. 7.95 (978-0-15-205439-7(1)) Harcourt Trade Pubs.
Wilde, Oscar. The Happy Prince & Other Tales. 2006. 56p. per. 4.99 (978-1-4209-2736-8(1)) Digireads.com.
—The Happy Prince & Other Tales. 2004. reprint ed. pap. 15.95 (978-1-4191-6538-2(0)); pap. 1.99 (978-1-4192-6538-9(5)) Kessinger Publishing, LLC.
—The Happy Prince & Other Tales. 2006. per. 4.95 (978-1-57646-987-3(5)) Quiet Vision Publishing.
—The Happy Prince & Other Tales. 2005. pap. 9.95 (978-1-55742-431-0(4)) Wildside Pr.
—The Picture of Dorian Gray. 2003. (gr. 7-12). lib. bdg. 16.45 (978-0-613-64313-9(5)); 1999. 240p. (YA). (gr. 8-12). per. 11.80 (978-0-613-17431-3(8)) Tandem Library Bks.
Wilde, Oscar & Irving, Washington. Narraciones Fantasticas. 2000. (SPA.). (J). (gr. 9-12). pap. (978-968-19-0444-9(3)) Aguilar Editorial.
Wilkey, David. Through the Black Hole: The Incredible Adventures of Justin Hart. 2003. 154p. pap. 12.95 (978-0-595-29497-8(9)) iUniverse, Inc.
Wilkins, Kim. Ghost Ship: Sunken Kingdom #1. Cornish, D. M., illus. 2008. 96p. (J). (gr. 4-7). pap. 5.99 ***(*978-0-375-84806-3(1)*** , Random Hse. Bks. for Young Readers) Random Hse. Children's Bks.
—Ghost Ship: Sunken Kingdom #1. Cornish, D. M., illus. 2008. 96p. (J). (gr. 4-7). lib. bdg. 11.99 ***(*978-0-375-94806-0(6)*** , Random Hse. Bks. for Young Readers) Random Hse. Children's Bks.
Willard, Eliza. Power of Three. 1999. (gr. 5-8). lib. bdg. 14.15 (978-0-613-22213-6(X)) Tandem Library Bks.
—Revenge of the Dark Hand with Cards. 2002. (gr. 3-6). lib. bdg. 13.00 (978-0-613-72453-1(4)) Tandem Library Bks.
Willett, Edward. The Dark Unicorn. 18th ed. 1998. 158p. (YA). (gr. 6 up). 9.99 (978-0-88092-414-6(4) , 4144) Royal Fireworks Publishing Co.
Williams, Arlene L. How to Be a Dragon? Without Burning Your Tongue. 2002. 352p. (YA). pap. 16.95 (978-0-9605444-9-3(6)) Waking Light Pr., The.
Williams, Brenda Gail. Little Mo Weep. 2004. (J). per. 7.95 (978-1-59427-027-7(9)) Aglob Publishing.
Williams, Christopher. Kerby "The Cable Car" Garcia, Arturo Lara, photos by. l.t. ed. 1999. (Illus.). 40p. (J). (gr. 3-7). pap. 9.50 (978-0-9676139-9-4(X)) Destiny's Pr.
Williams, Diane. Annie Mae Jumps the Broom. Riphahn, Anna, illus. 1999. 32p. (J). (gr. 3-8). 17.95 (978-1-892455-03-1(X)) Desk Top Pubs., Inc.
Williams, Margery, adapted by. The Velveteen Rabbit. 2006. (Illus.). 20p. (J). bds. 10.99 (978-0-7944-0948-7(2)) Reader's Digest Assn., Inc., The.
Williams, Rozanne Lanczak. The Purple Snerd. GrandPré, Mary, illus. 2003. (Green Light Readers Level 2 Ser.). 24p. (J). 11.95 (978-0-15-204866-2(9)); pap. 3.95 (978-0-15-204826-6(X)) Harcourt Children's Bks. (Green Light Readers).
—The Purple Snerd. 2000. (Green Light Readers Ser.). (J). (978-0-606-20171-1(8)) Tandem Library Bks.
Willis & Ross. Dr Xargle's Book of Earth Hounds. 2003. (Illus.). 32p. (J). pap. 9.95 (978-0-86264-249-5(3)) Random Hse. GBR. *Dist:* Trafalgar Square Publishing.
Willis, Dan. Wizard's Return. 2006. (Dragonlance Ser.: Vol. 3). (Illus.). 256p. (J). pap. 5.99 (978-0-7869-4025-7(5) , Mirrorstone) Wizards of the Coast.
Willson, Sarah. What's Next. Oxley, Jennifer, illus. 2000. (Blue's Clues Ser.). 10p. (J). (ps-k). bds. 4.99 (978-0-689-83226-0(5) , Simon Spotlight/Nickelodeon) Simon & Schuster Children's Publishing.
Wilson, David Henry. Castle of Inside Out. Riddell, Chris, illus. l.t. ed. 2005. 216p. (J). pap. (978-0-7540-6193-9(0) , CLP 387) BBC Audio.
—The Castle of Inside Out. unabr. ed. 2003. (Read-Along Ser.). (J). pap. 24.95 incl. audio (978-0-7540-6249-3(X) , Galaxy Children's Large Print) BBC Audiobooks America.
Wilson, Douglas, reader. What I Learned in Narnia. 2004. cd-rom 35.00 ***(*978-1-59128-438-3(4))*** Canon Pr.
Wilson, Lynda. The Virtual Zone: In Search of Klondike Gold. 2001. (On Time's Wing Ser.). (Illus.). 72p. (J). (gr. 3-7). pap. (978-1-896184-70-8(7)) Roussan Pubs., Inc./Roussan Editeur, Inc.
Winker, Michael & Ashley. One Good Quest Deserves Another: A Crown of Amaranth Story. 2007. 232p. 25.95 ***(*978-0-595-68779-4(2));*** per. 15.95 ***(*978-0-595-43799-3(0))*** iUniverse, Inc.
Winn, Christine M. & Walsh, David. Clover's Secret. Winn, Christine M., illus. 2004. (Illus.). 28p. (J). (gr. k-4). reprint ed. 15.00 (978-0-7567-7653-4(8)) DIANE Publishing Co.
Winn, L. B. Butterpod Jerome & the Planet of Gabool. Winn, L. B., illus. 2007. (J). pap. 18.95 ***(*978-0-9791884-0-4(7))*** Winn, Lynnette.
Winter, Barbara. Anaconda Antics. 2002. (Amazing Dictionary Ser.). (Illus.). 64p. pap. 4.95 ***(*978-0-921156-95-6(2))*** Rubicon Publishing, Inc. CAN. *Dist:* International Publishers Marketing.
Winter, David. Master-Haunter. Young, Sarah, illus. 1998. 256p. pap. 32.50 (978-0-7459-3795-3(0) , Lion) Lion Hudson plc GBR. *Dist:* Independent Pubs. Group.
Winters, Jeffrey. Mystic Uncle & the Magical Bridge. 2005. (J). pap. (978-1-59526-167-0(2) , Llumina Pr.) Media Creations, Inc.
Wishinsky, Frieda. A Noodle up Your Nose. Laliberte, Louise-Andree, illus. 2004. (Orca Echoes Ser.). 64p. (J). (gr. 2-4). pap. 4.99 (978-1-55143-294-6(3)) Orca Bk. Pubs. USA.
Withrow, Sarah. Bat Summer. 2000. 174p. (J). (gr. 4-7). pap. 5.95 (978-0-88899-352-6(8) , Libros Tigrillo) Groundwood Bks. CAN. *Dist:* Perseus Distribution.
Witschen, Kay. Clinker's Christmas Star. Witschen, Kay, illus. 2004. (Illus.). 24p. (J). 6.95 (978-0-9741352-1-2(6)) Dwitt Publishing.
Wizards of the Coast Staff. Duel Masters, Vol. 4. 2005. (Illus.). 96p. (J). pap. 7.99 (978-1-59532-674-4(X) , Tokyopop Kids) TOKYOPOP, Inc.
Wohl, David, et al. Top Cows Best of Michael Turner. 2005. (Illus.). 240p. (YA). pap. 24.99 (978-1-58240-544-5(1)) Image Comics.
Wolf, B. J. Eagles Disobey: The Case for Inca City, Mars. 1998. (Illus.). 299p. pap. 21.95 (978-0-9648090-2-4(8)) Candlelight Publishing.
Wolf, Ema. La Nave de los Brujos. 2002. (SPA.). 64p. (J). pap. 7.95 (978-1-4000-0066-1(1)) Random Hse., Inc.
Wolfel, Ursula. Abecedario Fantastico. (SPA). 128p. (YA). (gr. 5-8). (978-84-279-3357-6(6) , NG3950) Noguer y Caralt Editores, S. A. ESP. *Dist:* Lectorum Pubns., Inc.
Wolfman, Marv. 10th Muse Round Two. Cruz, Roger, illus. 2005. (10th Muse Ser.). 112p. pap. 14.99 (978-1-932431-05-6(5) , Angel Gate) Left Field Ink.
Won, Im Jae. The Boss, Vol. 3. 2004. 184p. (YA). pap. (978-1-4139-0083-5(6)) ADV Manga.
The Wonderful Wizard of Oz & Doctor Doolittle. 2004. (Classics to Color with Stickers Ser.). 80p. (J). pap. 2.49 (978-1-4037-0729-1(4)) Dalmatian Pr.
Wong, Tony. Weapons of the Gods, Vol. 6. 2003. (Illus.). 120p. (YA). (gr. 8 up). pap. 13.95 (978-1-58899-206-2(3)) ComicsOne Corp./Dr. Masters.
WOO, illus. & creator. Rebirth, Vol. 13. WOO, creator. rev. ed. 2005. 200p. pap. 9.99 (978-1-59532-028-5(8) , Tokyopop Adult) TOKYOPOP, Inc.
Woo, Soo Jung. Legend Volume 3. 2007. (Illus.). 200p. (YA). pap. 10.95 ***(*978-89-527-4712-9(7))*** ICE Kunion KOR. *Dist:* Diamond Bk. Distributors.
—Legend Volume 4. 2007. 200p. (YA). pap. 10.95 ***(*978-89-527-4871-3(9))*** ICE Kunion KOR. *Dist:* Diamond Bk. Distributors.
—Legend Volume 5. 2007. 200p. (YA). pap. 10.95 ***(*978-89-527-4883-6(2))*** ICE Kunion KOR. *Dist:* Diamond Bk. Distributors.
Wood, Audrey. Balloonia & Magic Shoelaces. (J). audio 10.97 (978-0-85953-373-7(5)) Child's Play-International.
—Presto Change-O. Wood, Audrey, illus. 2005. (Illus.). 32p. (J). pap. 7.99 (978-1-904550-52-5(5)) Child's Play-International.
—Sweet Dream Pie. Teague, Mark, illus. 2002. 32p. (J). (ps-4). pap. 5.99 (978-0-439-39472-7(4)) Scholastic, Inc.
Wood, D. K. Nightmare at Indian Cave. 2006. pap. 10.00 ***(*978-1-4257-1640-0(7))*** Xlibris Corp.

E
F
G

Wood, Frances M. Becoming Rosemary. 2001. 256p. (gr. 5-9). pap. 12.00 (978-0-375-89504-3(3) , Delacorte Bks. for Young Readers) Random Hse. Children's Bks.

Wood, Francis. The SnowPeople. Larsen, Dan, illus. 2003. 96p. (YA). per. 14.95 (978-0-9746372-0-4(3)) Tip-Of-The-Moon Publishing Co.

Wood, Francis Eugene. Return to Winterville. Pickett, Elizabeth & Dean, Tina, eds. Larsen, Dan, illus. 2004. 96p. (YA). per. 14.95 net. (978-0-9746372-1-1(1)) Tip-Of-The-Moon Publishing Co.

Wood, John. Finnegan's Wind. 2001. 140p. (J). pap. 6.95 (978-0-86327-831-0(0)) Interlink Publishing Group, Inc.

Wood, Maggie L. The Princess Pawn. 2004. 299p. (J). pap. 9.95 (978-1-894549-29-5(5)) Sumach Pr. CAN. *Dist:* Orca Bk. Pubs. USA.

Wood, Maryrose. Why I Let My Hair Grow Out. 2007. 272p. (J). pap. 9.99 (978-0-425-21380-3(3) , Berkley Trade) Penguin Group (USA) Inc.

Wooding, Chris. Poison. 288p. (J). 2006. pap. 7.99 (978-0-439-75571-9(9) , Scholastic Paperbacks); 2005. (gr. 7 up). pap. 16.99 (978-0-439-75570-2(0) , Orchard Bks.) Scholastic, Inc.

Woods, Shirley. The Magical Mystery. 2005. (Illus.). 102p. (J). per. 11.95 (978-1-59453-100-2(5) , 3679) Airleaf Publishing & Bookselling.

Woods, Shirley E. Jack: The Story of a Beaver. Godkin, Celia, illus. 2002. 96p. (J). (gr. 3-6). (978-1-55041-733-3(9)) Fitzhenry & Whiteside, Ltd.

Woodward, J. Howland. A Moment in Time. 2006. 55p. pap. 12.95 (978-1-4241-1334-7(2)) PublishAmerica, Inc.

Woolf, Virginia. Nurse Lugton's Curtain. Vivas, Julie, illus. ed. 2004. 32p. (J). 16.00 (978-0-15-205048-1(5) , Gulliver Bks.) Harcourt Children's Bks.

Woolfson, Malcolm. Bushveld Bibble-Babble. 2000. (J). (gr. 1-8). pap. 6.50 (978-0-87602-375-4(8)) Anchorage Pr.

World of Fairy Tales. unabr. ed. 2004. (Chrysalis Children's Classics Ser.). (Illus.). (YA). pap. (978-1-84365-064-5(9)) Chrysalis Children's Bks.

Wrede, Patricia C. Calling on Dragons. 2003. (Enchanted Forest Chronicles: Bk. 3). (Illus.). 272p. (YA). pap. 5.95 (978-0-15-204692-7(5) , Magic Carpet Bks.) Harcourt Children's Bks.

—Calling on Dragons. unabr. ed. 2004. (Enchanted Forest Ser.: Vol 3). 244p. (J). (gr 6 up). pap. 38.00 incl. audio (978-0-8072-0792-5(6) , LYA 347 SP, Listening Library) Random Hse. Audio Publishing Group.

—Calling on Dragons. 2003. (gr. 7-12). lib. bdg. 14.10 (978-0-613-59887-3(3)) Tandem Library Bks.

—Mairelon the Magician. 2002. (Magician Ser.). 288p. (J). 5.99 (978-0-7653-4232-4(4) , Starscape) Doherty, Tom Assocs., LLC.

—Mairelon the Magician. 2002. (gr. 7-12). lib. bdg. 14.15 (978-0-613-58076-2(1)) Tandem Library Bks.

—Searching for Dragons. 2002. (Enchanted Forest Chronicles: Bk. 2). (Illus.). 272p. (YA). (gr. 5 up). pap. 5.95 (978-0-15-204565-4(1) , Magic Carpet Bks.) Harcourt Children's Bks.

—Searching for Dragons. unabr. ed. 2004. (Enchanted Forest Chronicles Ser.). 242p. (J). (gr. 5 up). pap. 38.00 incl. audio (978-0-8072-0670-6(9) , Listening Library) Random Hse. Audio Publishing Group.

—Searching for Dragons. 2002. 242p. (J). (ps-ps). per. 14.10 (978-0-613-55189-2(3)) Tandem Library Bks.

Wriede, Marilyn. Windows to the Worlds: Azra. Wriede, Valerie, illus. 2001. 160p. (J). (gr. 3-6). pap. 6.95 (978-0-9710098-0-6(5)) Wriede, Peter.

Wright, Joshua. Goom. 2005. (Illus.). 168p. (J). (ps-7). pap. 6.95 (978-1-74114-435-2(3)) Allen & Unwin AUS. *Dist:* Independent Pubs. Group.

Wright, Sean. Jesse Jameson & the Golden Glow, Bk.1. Wright, Trisha & Cole, Patricia Natalie, eds. 2003. (ENG., Illus.). 182p. pap. ***(*978-0-9544374-0-4(3))*** Crowswing Bks.

Wyatt, Valerie. Earthlings Inside & Out. 1999. (gr. 3-6). lib. bdg. 15.25 (978-0-613-16346-0(X)) Tandem Library Bks.

Wyatt, W. Joseph. The Millennium Man. 1999. 196p. (YA). (gr. 8-12). pap. 12.00 (978-0-9663622-0-6(9)) Third Millennium Pr.

Wyke-Smith, E. A. The Marvellous Land of Snergs. Morrow, George, illus. 2006. 224p. (J). pap. 9.95 (978-0-486-45255-5(7)) Dover Pubns., Inc.

Wynn, Thad & Wynn, Juliette. The Tale of a Dragon. 2004. (Illus.). 85p. (gr. k-4). 15.95 (978-1-57197-140-1(8)) Pentland Pr., Inc.

Wynne-Jones, Tim. I'll Make You Small. (J). pap. 15.95 (978-0-88899-045-7(6)); pap. 4.95 (978-0-88899-105-8(3)) Groundwood Bks. CAN. *Dist:* Transition Vendor.

—The Maestro. 2004. 224p. (J). pap. 6.95 (978-0-88899-637-4(3)) Groundwood Bks. CAN. *Dist:* Perseus Distribution.

—Zoom Upstream. (J). pap. 5.95 (978-0-88899-188-1(6)) Groundwood Bks. CAN. *Dist:* Transition Vendor.

Wyss, Tyan. The Solitaire Prince. 2006. 168p. (YA). 12.95 (978-1-58939-907-5(2)); per. 12.95 (978-1-58939-906-8(4)) Virtualbookworm.com Publishing, Inc.

Yaccarino, Dan. Where the 4 Winds Blow. 2000. mass mkt. 6.95 (978-0-06-443841-4(4)) HarperCollins Pubs.

Yagami, Yu. Those Who Hunt Elves, Vol. 1. McGregor, Eiko, tr. 2003. (Illus.). 216p. (YA). pap. (978-1-4139-0014-9(3)) ADV Manga.

—Those Who Hunt Elves. 2004. (YA). Vol. 3 (Illus.). 202p. pap. (978-1-4139-0034-7(8)); Vol. 4. 200p. pap. (978-1-4139-0063-7(1)); Vol. 5. (Illus.). 202p. pap. (978-1-4139-0077-4(1)); Vol. 6. 202p. pap. (978-1-4139-0098-9(4)); Vol. 7. (Illus.). 200p. pap. (978-1-4139-0116-0(6)) ADV Manga.

Yakowicz, Susie. Fire Runner. 2004. (J). per. 12.95 (978-0-9652546-3-2(1)) JESSPress.

Yamashita, Ray, tr. Lupin III Vol. 1: World's Most Wanted. 2004. (Illus.). 240p. pap. 9.99 (978-1-59532-070-4(9) , Tokyopop Adult) TOKYOPOP, Inc.

Yang, Gene. Gordon Yamamoto & the King of the Geeks. 2004. (Illus.). 104p. (gr. 3 up). pap. 9.95 (978-0-943151-95-3(3) , Amaze Ink) Slave Labor Bks.

Yang, Yuh Jin. Saint Marie, Vol. 1. 2004. (Illus.). 190p. (YA). pap. (978-1-4139-0065-1(8)) ADV Manga.

Yazdani, Nanolla. A Fly on the Wall. 2001. 95p. (J). pap. 10.00 (978-0-8059-5188-2(1)) Dorrance Publishing Co., Inc.

Yeo, Ho-Kyung. Honey Mustard, Vol. 4. 4th rev. ed. 2006. (Illus.). pap. 9.99 (978-1-59816-208-0(X) , Tokyopop Adult) TOKYOPOP, Inc.

Yeo-Jin, Yang. Saint Marie, Vol. 2. 2004. 184p. (YA). pap. (978-1-4139-0080-4(1)) ADV Manga.

Yeoman. Princes' Gift Magic Folk Tales. (Illus.). 128p. (YA). (gr. 1 up). 19.99 (978-1-85793-879-1(8) , Pavilion Bks., Ltd.) Anova Bks. GBR. *Dist:* Trafalgar Square Publishing.

Yi Fan, Nancy. Swordbird. Zug, Mark, illus. 2007. 240p. (J). (gr. k-7). 15.99 (978-0-06-113099-1(0) , HarperCollins); lib. bdg. 16.89 (978-0-06-113100-4(8)) HarperCollins Pubs.

YKids Staff. Gulliver's Travels. 2007. (Manga Literary Classics Ser.). 148p. (J). (gr. 4-7). pap. 14.95 ***(*978-981-05-4941-1(5))*** Youngjin (Singapore) Pte Ltd. SGP. *Dist:* Independent Pubs. Group.

Yolen, Jane. Briar Rose. 2002. (gr. 7-12). lib. bdg. 15.30 (978-0-613-46051-4(0)) Tandem Library Bks.

—The Dragon's Boy: A Tale of Young King Arthur. 2001. (Illus.). (J). 11.64 (978-0-606-21161-1(6)) Tandem Library Bks.

—Here There Be Dragons. Wilgus, David, illus. 1998. 160p. (YA). (gr. 5-9). pap. 13.00 (978-0-15-201705-7(4) , Harcourt Paperbacks) Harcourt Children's Bks.

—The Hobby. 1998. (Young Merlin Trilogy Ser.: No. 2). 90p. (J). (gr. 3-9). pap. 3.50 (978-0-590-37118-6(5) , Scholastic Paperbacks) Scholastic, Inc.

—The Hobby. 1998. (Young Merlin Trilogy Ser.). (978-0-606-13939-7(7)) Tandem Library Bks.

—Merlin. 1998. (Young Merlin Trilogy Ser.). 91p. (J). pap. 3.50 (978-0-590-37119-3(3) , Scholastic Paperbacks) Scholastic, Inc.

—Merlin. 1998. (Young Merlin Trilogy Ser.). (J). (978-0-606-13940-3(0)) Tandem Library Bks.

—Merlin & the Dragons. Ming, Li, illus. 1998. 40p. (J). (gr. k-3). pap. 6.99 (978-0-14-055891-3(8) , Puffin) Penguin Group (USA) Inc.

—The Passenger. 1998. (Young Merlin Trilogy Ser.). 76p. (J). pap. 4.50 (978-0-590-37073-8(1) , Scholastic Paperbacks) Scholastic, Inc.

—The Pictish Child. (Tartan Magic Ser.: Bk. 2). (YA). 2002. 156p. pap. 5.95 (978-0-15-216359-4(X) , Magic Carpet Bks.); 1999. 144p. (gr. 3-7). 16.00 (978-0-15-202261-7(9)) Harcourt Children's Bks.

—Pictish Child. 2002. (gr. 3-6). lib. bdg. 14.10 (978-0-613-53854-1(4)) Tandem Library Bks.

—Sister Light, Sister Dark. 2003. (Books of Great Alta Ser.). (Illus.). 256p. (YA). (gr. 7 up). 6.99 (978-0-7653-4357-4(6) , Tor Teen) Doherty, Tom Assocs., LLC.

—Twelve Impossible Things Before Breakfast. 2001. (978-0-606-21496-4(8)) Tandem Library Bks.

—White Jenna. 2nd rev. ed. 2004. (Great Alta Saga Ser.). (Illus.). 272p. (YA). 6.99 (978-0-7653-4358-1(4) , Tor Teen) Doherty, Tom Assocs., LLC.

—White Jenna. 2004. (gr. 3-6). lib. bdg. 15.30 (978-0-613-74859-9(X)) Tandem Library Bks.

—Wizard's Hall. 1999. 144p. (YA). pap. 6.95 (978-0-15-202085-9(3) , Magic Carpet Bks.) Harcourt Children's Bks.

—Wizard's Hall. 144p. (J). (gr. 3-5). pap. 6.00 (978-0-8072-1544-9(9) , Listening Library) Random Hse. Audio Publishing Group.

—Wizard's Hall. 1999. (978-0-606-16528-0(2)); (gr. 3-6). lib. bdg. 14.15 (978-0-7857-1069-1(8)) Tandem Library Bks.

Yolen, Jane & Harris, Robert J. Hippolyta & the Curse of the Amazons. 2002. (Young Heroes Ser.: Bk. 2). 256p. (J). (gr. 3-7). 15.95 (978-0-06-028736-8(5)) HarperCollins Pubs.

Yolen, Jane & Nielsen Hayden, Patrick. The Year's Best Science Fiction & Fantasy for Teens: First Annual Collection. 2005. 288p. (YA). 17.95 (978-0-7653-1383-6(9) , Tor Teen) Doherty, Tom Assocs., LLC.

Yolen, Jane & Stemple, Adam. Pay the Piper: A Rock 'n' Roll Fairy Tale. (J). 2006. 192p. 5.99 (978-0-7653-5041-1(6)); 2005. 176p. 16.95 (978-0-7653-1158-0(5)) Doherty, Tom Assocs., LLC. (Starscape).

—Troll Bridge. 2006. 240p. (J). 16.95 (978-0-7653-1426-0(6) , Starscape) Doherty, Tom Assocs., LLC.

Yoon, Salina. Fire Truck. Yoon, Salina, illus. 2005. (Illus.). 10p. (J). (ps-1). bds. 5.99 (978-0-8431-1395-2(2) , Price Stern Sloan) Penguin Group (USA) Inc.

Yorinks, Arthur. Company's Coming. Small, David, illus. 2001. (J). incl. audio Spoken Arts, Inc.

—The Invisible Man. Date not set. (J). 14.99 (978-0-06-205092-2(3)); lib. bdg. 15.89 (978-0-06-205093-9(1)) HarperCollins Pubs.

—The Nose. 2000. 64p. (J). 14.99 (978-0-7868-0499-3(8)) Hyperion Bks. for Children.

—The Nose. 2020. 64p. (J). pap. 5.99 (978-0-7868-1342-1(3)) Hyperion Paperbacks for Children.

—Tomatoes from Mars. Drucker, Mort, illus. 1999. (Michael di Capua Bks.). 32p. (J). (ps-3). 14.95 (978-0-06-205070-0(2)) HarperCollins Pubs.

Yoshida, Akira. Elektra: The Hand. Gossett, Christian, illus. 2005. (Elektra Ser.). 120p. pap. 13.99 (978-0-7851-1594-6(3)) Marvel Enterprises, Inc.

Yoshimoto, Ray, tr. from JPN. Tokyo Babylon, Vol. 6. Clamp, illus. rev. ed. 2005. 176p. pap. 9.99 (978-1-59532-050-6(4) , Tokyopop Adult) TOKYOPOP, Inc.

Yoshimura, Natsuki. Mystical Prince Yoshida-Kun!, Vol. 1. 2004. (Illus.). 184p. (YA). pap. (978-1-4139-0207-5(3)) ADV Manga.

Yoshizaki, Mine, illus. & creator. Sgt. Frog. Yoshizaki, Mine, creator. rev. ed. 2005. 192p. Vol. 7. pap. 9.99 (978-1-59532-448-1(8)); Vol. 8. pap. 9.99 (978-1-59532-449-8(6)) TOKYOPOP, Inc. (Tokyopop Adult).

Young Noh, Mi, illus. & creator. Threads of Time, Vol. 4. Young Noh, Mi, creator. rev. ed. 2005. 192p. pap. 9.99 (978-1-59532-035-3(0) , Tokyopop Adult) TOKYOPOP, Inc.

Yourzek, Tammy. Dragons of the Soul. 2006. 192p. (YA). pap. 9.95 (978-1-56315-382-2(3)) SterlingHouse Pubs., Inc.

YoYo Books. Princess Charlotte Becomes a Magician. 2005. 32p. 9.95 (978-90-5843-459-3(1)) YoYo Bks. BEL. *Dist:* National Bk. Network.

Yoyo Books Staff. Fantasy Stories: One Minute Goodnight Stories. 2004. 40p. bds. 12.95 (978-90-5843-581-1(4)) YoYo Bks. BEL. *Dist:* National Bk. Network.

Yozaburo, Kanari. Playing the Fool, Vol. 12. Fumiya, Sato, illus. 12th rev. ed. 2005. 192p. pap. 9.99 (978-1-59532-696-6(0) , Tokyopop Kids) TOKYOPOP, Inc.

Yu, Li, et al. The Holy Spark: Rogel & the Goddess of Liberty. 2006. (J). (978-1-931907-42-2(0)) Homa & Sekey Bks.

Yutenji, Ako, illus. & creator. Liling-PO, Vol. 2. Yutenji, Ako, creator. rev. ed. 2005. 200p. pap. 9.99 (978-1-59532-520-4(4) , Tokyopop Adult) TOKYOPOP, Inc.

Zdenek, Joseph. Heart of Courage: The Narscix War. 2007. 372p. (ps-7). per. 20.95 ***(*978-0-595-43187-8(9))*** iUniverse, Inc.

Zhang, Song Nan. A Time of Golden Dragons. ed. 2004. (J). (gr. 3-5). spiral bd. (978-0-616-07258-5(9)) Canadian National Institute for the Blind/Institut National Canadien pour les Aveugles.

Ziarko, Greg. The Waylaid: Asheth. ed. 2007. 280p. (YA). ***(*978-0-9792694-0-0(7))*** gaZko Entertainment.

Ziefert, Harriet. What's Pretend? Brown, Rick & Brown, Richard, illus. 2004. 20p. (J). pap. 6.95 (978-1-4027-1791-8(1)) Sterling Publishing Co., Inc.

Zimmerman, Diana S. Kandide Veil of the Mysts: The Calabiyau Chronicles. 2007. (Illus.). 256p. (YA). per. 24.99 ***(*978-0-9794328-1-1(2))*** Noesis Publishing.

Zimmerman, W. Frederick. Unauthorized Harry Potter & the Alchemist's Cell News: Half-Blood Prince Analysis & Speculation. 2006. 160p. per. 14.94 (978-0-9777424-7-9(4)) Nimble Bks. LLC.

—Unauthorized Harry Potter & the Chariots of Light News: Half-Blood Prince Analysis & Speculation. 2006. 160p. per. 14.94 (978-0-9777424-8-6(2)) Nimble Bks. LLC.

Zoe at the Fancy Dress Ball, 6 Packs. (Literatura 2000 Ser.). (gr. 2-3). 33.00 (978-0-7578-5601-3(2)) Rigby Education.

Zondervan. Bob, el Tomate. 2004. (SPA.). 18p. (J). 3.99 (978-0-8297-4415-6(0)) Zondervan.

FANTASY FICTION—HISTORY AND CRITICISM

Una Arruga en el Tiempo. 1999. (SPA.). (YA). 9.95 (978-1-56137-542-4(X) , NU5723) Novel Units, Inc.

Datnow, Claire L. American Science Fiction & Fantasy Writers. 1999. (Collective Biographies Ser.). (Illus.). 128p. (YA). (gr. 6-12). lib. bdg. 26.60 (978-0-7660-1090-1(2)) Enslow Pubs., Inc.

Frost, Laurie. Philip Pullman's His Dark Materials: The Definitive Guide. 2006. (Illus.). 400p. (YA). 44.95 (978-0-9759430-0-7(6)); pap. 24.95 (978-0-9759430-1-4(4)) Fell Pr., The.

Gifford, Clive. So You Think You Know His Dark Materials? 2006. (Orig.). (YA). (gr. 2-3). pap. 8.95 (978-0-340-91186-0(7)) Hodder General Publishing Division GBR. *Dist:* Independent Pubs. Group.

—So You Think You Know Narnia? 2006. (YA). (gr. 4-7). pap. 8.95 (978-0-340-89392-0(3)) Hodder General Publishing Division GBR. *Dist:* Independent Pubs. Group.

Glassman, Peter. Oz: The Hundredth Anniversary Celebration. 2000. (J). lib. bdg. 19.89 (978-0-06-029219-5(9)) HarperCollins Pubs.

Gresh, Lois. The Fan's Guide to the Spiderwick Chronicle: Unauthorized Fun with Fairies, Ogres, Brownies, Boggarts & More! 2008. (Illus.). 160p. (J). 9.95 (978-0-312-35153-3(4) , St. Martin's Griffin) St. Martin's Pr.

Gribbin, Mary & Gribbin, John. The Science of Philip Pullman's His Dark Materials. 2005. (Illus.). 224p. (J). (gr. 7). 15.95 (978-0-375-83144-7(4) , Knopf Bks. for Young Readers) Random Hse. Children's Bks.

—The Science of Philip Pullman's "His Dark Materials" 2005. 224p. (J). (gr. 7). lib. bdg. 17.99 (978-0-375-93144-4(9) , Knopf Bks. for Young Readers) Random Hse. Children's Bks.

Hamilton, John. Weapons of Fantasy & Folkore. 2005. (Illus.). 32p. (J). (gr. 4-8). lib. bdg. 24.21 (978-1-59679-340-8(6) , ABDO & Daughters) ABDO Publishing Co.

Jones, Diana Wynne. Year of the Griffin Reading Group Guide. 2000. (J). (978-0-06-029311-6(X)) HarperCollins Pubs.

Kirk, E. J. Step into Narnia: A Journey Through the Lion, the Witch & the Wardrobe. 2005. (Narnia Ser.). (Illus.). 64p. (J). lib. bdg. 20.89 (978-0-06-074234-8(8)) HarperCollins Pubs.

Nardo, Don. Understanding the Lord of the Rings. 2003. (Understanding Great Literature Ser.). (Illus.). 96p. (J). (gr. 8-11). lib. bdg. 29.95 (978-1-59018-234-5(0) , Lucent Bks.) Thomson Gale.

Neimark, Anne E. Myth Maker: J. R. R. Tolkien. Newbold, Greg, illus. 1998. 128p. (J). (gr. 5-9). pap. 4.95 (978-0-688-15741-8(6) , Harper Trophy) HarperCollins Pubs.

—Myth Maker: J. R. R. Tolkien. 1998. (J). (978-0-606-13639-6(8)) Tandem Library Bks.

Parker, Victoria. J.R.R. Tolkien. 2006. (Illus.). 48p. (J). pap. (978-1-4034-7338-7(2)); lib. bdg. (978-1-4034-7335-6(8)) Heinemann Library.

Poteet, Michael. The Hobbit: Study Guide. 2000. 72p. (YA). (gr. 8-12). stu. ed., ring bd. 14.99 (978-1-58609-173-6(5)) Progeny Pr.

Sage, Alison & Tolkien, J. R. R. The Lord of the Rings: The Fellowship of the Ring Photo Guide. 2001. (Illus.). 48p. (J). (gr. 4-6). pap. 9.95 (978-0-618-19558-9(0)) Houghton Mifflin Co. Trade & Reference Div.

Sibley, Brian & Tolkien, J. R. R. The Lord of the Rings: The Fellowship of the Ring Insider's Guide. 2001. (Illus.). 80p. (J). (gr. 4-6). pap. 6.95 (978-0-618-19559-6(9)) Houghton Mifflin Co. Trade & Reference Div.

Stouffer, Tere. The World of Harry Potter. 2007. (Complete Idiot's Guides (Lifestyle Paperback) Ser.). (Illus.). 249p. (gr. 12). per. 16.95 ***(*978-1-59257-599-2(4)*** , Alpha Bks.) Penguin Group (USA) Inc.

Waters, Galadriel & Mithrandir, Astre. New Clues to Harry Potter: Hints from the Ultimate Unofficial Guide to the Mysteries of Harry Potter, Vol. 5. Waters, Galadriel, illus. 2003. (Illus.). 134p. (gr. 3-6). 10.95 (978-0-9723936-2-1(5) , 1230146) Wizarding World Pr.

—Ultimate Unofficial Guide to the Mysteries of Harry Potter: Analysis of Books 1-4, 4 vols. Waters, Galadriel, illus. 2003. 444p. (gr. 3-6). 24.95 (978-0-9723936-1-4(7) , 1230146); 2002. 414p. per. 24.99 (978-0-9723936-0-7(9)) Wizarding World Pr.

Willett, Edward. J. R. R. Tolkien: Master of Imaginary Worlds. 2004. (Authors Teens Love Ser.). (Illus.). 128p. (J). lib. bdg. 26.60 (978-0-7660-2246-1(3)) Enslow Pubs., Inc.

A Wrinkle in Time. 1998. 44p. (YA). 11.95 (978-1-56137-498-4(9) , NU4989SP) Novel Units, Inc.

FAR EAST

see East Asia

FARADAY, MICHAEL, 1791-1867

Fullick, Ann. Michael Faraday. (Groundbreakers Ser.). (Illus.). 48p. (J). (gr. 5-7). 2002. pap. 8.50 (978-1-58810-995-8(X) , 91470); 2000. lib. bdg. 25.64 (978-1-57572-375-4(1)) Heinemann Library.

Ganeri, Anita. Michael Faraday. 2000. (What Would You Ask...? Ser.). (Illus.). 32p. (J). (gr. 2-6). lib. bdg. 16.95 (978-1-929298-77-8(3)) Chrysalis Education.

Ross, Stewart. Michael Faraday. 2002. (Scientists Who Made History Ser.). (Illus.). 48p. (J). lib. bdg. 27.12 (978-0-7398-5224-8(8)) Raintree.

Williams, Brian. Faraday: Pioneer of Electricity. Antram, David, illus. 2003. (Explosion Zone Ser.). 32p. (J). pap. 6.95 (978-0-7641-2592-8(3)) Barron's Educational Series, Inc.

Zannos, Susan. Michael Faraday & the Discovery of Electromagnetism. 2004. (Uncharted, Unexplored, & Unexplained Ser.). (Illus.). 48p. (J). (gr. 4-8). lib. bdg. 29.95 (978-1-58415-307-8(5)) Mitchell Lane Pubs., Inc.

FARM ANIMALS

see Domestic Animals; Livestock

FARM CROPS

see Farm Produce

FARM IMPLEMENTS

see Agricultural Machinery

FARM LABORERS

see Agricultural Laborers

FARM LIFE

see also Country Life; Ranch Life

Alphabet Farm. 1998. (Fisher-Price Little People Concept Bks.: Vol. 1). (Illus.). 24p. (J). (978-0-7666-0319-6(9) , 19615) Modern Publishing.

Balfour, Sandy & Dorling Kindersley Publishing Staff. My First Farm Board Book. 2003. (My First Board Books (Bilingual) Ser.). (Illus.). 36p. (J). bds. 6.99 (978-0-7894-9522-8(8)) Dorling Kindersley Publishing, Inc.

Benjamin, Rachel. Take a Trip. 2003. (Compass Point Phonics Readers Ser.). (Illus.). 16p. (J). (gr. 1 up). 13.26 (978-0-7565-0526-4(7)) Compass Point Bks.

BHB International Staff. Farm. 1998. (Here We Go Round Ser.). (J). (ps). (978-2-215-06176-2(6)) Editions Fleurus.

Blevins, Wiley. Farm Animals. 2006. (Let's Find Out Ser.). (Illus.). 24p. (J). pap. 8.99 (978-0-439-72604-7(2) , Cartwheel Bks.) Scholastic, Inc.

Brighter Vision Publishing Staff. About the Farm. 2000. (My Discovery Bks.). (Illus.). 20p. (J). (ps). pap. 2.95 (978-1-55254-202-6(5)) Brighter Vision Pubns.

Brooks, Felicity. Farms lift & Look. Litchfield, Jo, illus. 2005. 12p. (J). 9.95 (978-0-7945-0932-3(0) , Usborne) EDC Publishing.

—Frank the Farmer. Litchfield, Jo, illus. 2005. (Jobs People Do Ser.). 23p. (J). (ps-7). pap. 6.95 (978-0-7945-0723-7(9) , Usborne) EDC Publishing.

—La Granja Minilibros Usborne. Litchfield, Jo, illus. 2005. (SPA.). 10p. (J). 4.95 (978-0-7460-6110-7(2) , Usborne) EDC Publishing.

Bryant-Mole, Karen. On the Farm. 1999. (Picture This! Places Ser.). (Illus.). 24p. (J). (ps-1). lib. bdg. 18.50 (978-1-57572-901-5(6)) Heinemann Library.

Bulla, Clyde Robert. A Grain of Wheat: A Writer Begins. 2004. (Illus.). 56p. (J). pap. 10.95 (978-1-59078-333-7(6)) Boyds Mills Pr.

Burton, Margie, et al. Life on a Farm. Evento, Susan, ed. 1998. (Early Connections Ser.). 16p. (J). (gr. k-2). pap. 4.25 (978-1-892393-55-5(7)) Benchmark Education Co.

Campbell, Rod. Farm Friends. 2003. (Illus.). 12p. (J). 3.99 (978-1-85292-225-2(7) , Campbell Bks.) Pan Macmillan GBR. *Dist:* Trafalgar Square Publishing.

Can Press Staff, ed. This Is Daniel Cook at the Farm. 2006. (Illus.). 28p. (J). (978-1-55453-078-6(4)); (978-1-55453-077-9(6)) Kids Can Pr., Ltd.

Canizares, Susan & Waugh, Betsey. On a Farm. 2000. (Scholastic Placebook Ser.). (Illus.). (J). pap. (978-0-439-15371-3(9)) Scholastic, Inc.

Carney, Margaret. At Grandpa's Sugar Bush. Wilson, Janet, illus. 1998. 32p. (J). (gr. k-3). (978-1-55074-341-8(4)) Kids Can Pr., Ltd.

Connell, Kate. Dust Bowl Days: Hard Times for Farmers. 2004. (Illus.). 40p. (J). pap. (978-0-7922-4557-5(1)) National Geographic Society.

—Hoping for Rain: The Dust Bowl Adventures of Patty & Earl Buckler. 2004. (I Am American Ser.). (Illus.). 40p. (J). (gr. 3-7). pap. 6.99 (978-0-7922-6903-8(9) , National Geographic Children's Bks.) National Geographic Society.

Curley, Andrea, ed. My First Farm Board Book. 2004. (Illus.), 36p. (J). bds. 5.99 (978-0-7894-9902-8(9)) Dorling Kindersley Publishing, Inc.

Dean, Carol. The Hen House: A True Story of Growing up on a Maine Farm. Dunn, Sandy, illus. 2003. 32p. 15.95 (978-0-89272-609-7(1)) Down East Bks.

Diekman, Diane. A Farm in the Hidewood: My South Dakota Home. 2001. 84p. pap. 6.00 (978-0-9708201-0-5(0)) Altruria Publishing Co.

DK Publishing. Down on the Farm. 2007. 16p. (J). (gr. k-5). pap. 2.49 (***978-0-7566-3320-2(6)***) Dorling Kindersley Publishing, Inc.

—Farm 1-2-3. 2008. 12p. (J). 8.99 (***978-0-7566-3525-1(X)***) Dorling Kindersley Publishing, Inc.

—Toddler on the Move: Farm: Activity Pack. 2008. 75p. (J). (ps-k). 9.99 (***978-0-7566-3808-5(9)***) Dorling Kindersley Publishing, Inc.

DK Publishing Staff. All Around the Farm. 2007. 64p. (J). (ps-3). pap. 12.99 (978-0-7566-2977-9(2)) Dorling Kindersley Publishing, Inc.

Doherty, Gillian. 1001 Things to Spot on the Farm. 1999. (gr. k-3). lib. bdg. 15.25 (978-0-613-88990-2(8)) Tandem Library Bks.

Doherty, Gillian, ed. 1001 Things to Spot on the Farm. 1998. (One Thousand One Things to Spot Ser.). (SPA., Illus.). 32p. (J). (ps-3). pap. 6.95 (978-0-7460-2955-8(1)); lib. bdg. 14.95 (978-1-58086-152-6(0)) EDC Publishing.

Durden-Nelson, Mae. I Just Called Her Momma. 2003. (Illus.), xii, 162p. (J). 18.95 (978-1-57168-714-2(9)) Eakin Pr.

Einhorn, Kama. Sesame Subjects: My First Book about Farms. Moroney, Christopher, illus. 2006. 24p. (J). (gr. k-k). 7.99 (978-0-375-83684-8(5) , Random Hse. Bks. for Young Readers) Random Hse. Children's Bks.

Farm Fun Crafts for Kids. 16.99 (978-0-8307-2990-6(9) , Gospel Light) Gospel Light Pubns.

Farmers, 6 vols. (gr. 2-5). 36.95 (978-0-7368-8469-3(6)) Red Brick Learning.

Ferri, Francesca, illus. My Farm. 2004. 12p. (J). 19.95 (978-0-7641-2812-7(4)) Barron's Educational Series, Inc.

Flanagan, Alice K. Raising Cows on the Koebels' Farm. 1999. (gr. k-3). lib. bdg. 15.25 (978-0-613-54316-3(5)) Tandem Library Bks.

Fowler, Allan. Living on Farms. 2001. (Rookie Read-About Geography Ser.). (Illus.). 32p. (J). (gr. 1-2). pap. 5.95 (978-0-516-27085-2(0) , Children's Pr.) Scholastic Library Publishing.

—Living on Farms. 2000. (gr. k-3). lib. bdg. 14.10 (978-0-613-54737-6(3)) Tandem Library Bks.

Fryer, George. On the Farm. 2000. (Find & Fit Ser.). (Illus.). 10p. (J). (ps-k). bds. 14.95 (978-1-57145-432-4(2) , Silver Dolphin Bks.) Advantage Pubs. Group.

Fun Farm. (Flip Flap Fun Book Ser.). 10p. (J). bds. (978-2-89393-819-6(1)) Phidal Publishing, Inc./Editions Phidal, Inc.

Geisert, Bonnie. Haystack. Geisert, Arthur, illus. 2003. 32p. (J). pap. 5.95 (978-0-618-33522-0(6) , Walter Lorraine) Houghton Mifflin Co. Trade & Reference Div.

Gillis, Jennifer Blizin. Farm Life. 2004. (Let's See Ser.). (Illus.). 24p. (J). (gr. 1 up). lib. bdg. 19.93 (978-0-7565-0673-5(5)) Compass Point Bks.

—Farms Long Ago. 2004. (Let's See Ser.). (Illus.). 24p. (J). (gr. 1 up). lib. bdg. 19.93 (978-0-7565-0671-1(9)) Compass Point Bks.

Gordon, Sharon. At Home on the Farm. 2005. (Bookworms Ser.). (ENG & SPA., Illus.). 32p. (J). (gr. 3-7). lib. bdg. (978-0-7614-1958-7(6) , Benchmark Bks.) Cavendish, Marshall Corp.

—At Home on the Farm (Mi Casa en la Granja) 2006. (Bookworms Ser.). (ENG & SPA., Illus.). 32p. (J). lib. bdg. 22.79 (978-0-7614-2454-3(7)) Cavendish, Marshall Corp.

—Mi Casa en la Granja. 2006. (Bookworms Ser.). (SPA & ENG., Illus.). 32p. (J). lib. bdg. 22.79 (978-0-7614-2375-1(3)) Cavendish, Marshall Corp.

Guin, Valerie. In the Country. 2005. (Illus.). 30p. (J). (gr. 3-7). lib. bdg. 27.10 (978-1-58340-695-3(6)) Smart Apple Media.

Hahn, Beverly. Twenty Acres of Love: Irrigation Time. Hahn, Beverly, illus. 2003. (Illus.). v, 65p. (J). (ps-6). spiral bd. 12.95 (978-0-9722494-0-9(0)) Hahn, Beverly.

—Twenty Acres of Love: Little Bit, 8 vols. Hahn, Beverly & Silva, Tom, illus. 2003. (J). (gr. k-6). 12.95 (978-0-9722494-1-6(9)) Hahn, Beverly.

Halley, Ned B. Farm. 2000. (Eyewitness Bks.). (Illus.). 64p. (J). (gr. 4-7). 15.99 (978-0-7894-6040-0(8)) Dorling Kindersley Publishing, Inc.

Harding, Sandy Bacon. Do Tell... What's That Smell. 2000. (Farm Adventures Ser.: Vol. 3). (Illus.). 80p. (J). (gr. k-5). pap. 6.95 (978-1-890609-07-8(2) , Lion's Paw Bks.) Coronet Bks. & Prints.

Hinds, Kathryn. The Countryside. 2007. (Life in Elizabethan England Ser.). 80p. (J). lib. bdg. 32.79 (***978-0-7614-2543-4(8)*** , Benchmark Bks.) Cavendish, Marshall Corp.

Hinkler Books Staff. Farm Lift the Flap. Penton Overseas, Inc. Staff, ed. rev. ed. 2006. (Illus.). 10p. (J). (gr. 3-6). bds. 5.95 (978-1-74157-932-1(5)) Hinkler Bks. Pty, Ltd. AUS. *Dist:* Penton Overseas, Inc.

Holland, Gini. I Live in the Country. 2004. (Weekly Reader Early Learning Library). (Illus.). 24p. (gr. k up). (J). pap. (978-0-8368-4086-5(0)); (YA). lib. bdg. 19.33 (978-0-8368-4079-7(8)) Stevens, Gareth Inc. (Weekly Reader Early Learning Library).

—I Live in the Country/Vivo en el Campo. Coffey, Colleen & Carrillo, Consuelo, trs. 2004. (Weekly Reader Early Learning Library). (Illus.). 24p. (J). (gr. k up). (ENG & SPA.). pap. 5.95 (978-0-8368-4134-3(4)); (SPA & ENG., lib. bdg. 19.33 (978-0-8368-4127-5(1)) Stevens, Gareth Inc. (Weekly Reader Early Learning Library).

Howard, Pam. Farmer Sam. Linke, Don, Jr., illus. l.t. ed. 2000. (Little Bks.). 8p. (J). (ps-k). pap. 10.95 (978-1-57332-149-5(4)); pap. 10.95 (978-1-57332-150-1(8)) HighReach Learning, Inc.

Hughes, Sarah. My Dad Works on a Farm. (Welcome Bks.). (Illus.). 24p. (J). (ps-2). 2001. 17.00 (978-0-516-23178-5(2)); 2000. lib. bdg. (978-0-516-23281-2(9)) Scholastic Library Publishing. (Children's Pr.).

Hutchings, Amy & Hutchings, Richard. Growing Apples & Pumpkins. 2001. (Illus.). (J). (978-0-439-22352-2(0)) Scholastic, Inc.

—Vamos a Rocoger Manzanas y Calabazas. Hutchings, Richard, illus. 2002. (SPA., Illus.). 32p. (J). (gr. 1-3). pap. 3.50 (978-0-439-31739-9(8) , Scholastic en Espanol) Scholastic, Inc.

Imperato, Teresa. On the Farm: A Barnyard Book. Rayner, Olivia, illus. 2005. 10p. (J). 7.95 (978-1-58117-270-6(2) , Intervisual/Piggy Toes) Dalmatian Pr.

Isaacs, Sally Senzell. Life in the Dust Bowl. (Picture the Past Ser.). (Illus.). 32p. (J). 2002. (gr. k-3). 7.50 (978-1-58810-413-7(3) , 91186); 2001. (gr. 2-4). lib. bdg. (978-1-58810-248-5(3)) Heinemann Library.

—Life in the Dust Bowl. 2002. (gr. k-3). lib. bdg. 15.90 (978-0-613-84255-6(3)) Tandem Library Bks.

Jackson, Woody. A Cow's Alfalfa-Bet. 2003. (Illus.). 32p. (J). (gr. k-ps). tchr. ed. 15.00 (978-0-618-16599-5(1)) Houghton Mifflin Co. Trade & Reference Div.

James, Diane. On the Farm. Lynn, Sara, illus. rev. ed. 2004. (My First Look at Animals Ser.). (SPA.). 24p. (J). (ps-2). pap. 5.95 (978-1-58728-862-3(1) , Two Can Publishing) T&N Children's Publishing.

Jeunesse, Gallimard. On the Farm. Galeron, Henri, illus. 2003. (First Discovery Look-and-Learn Bks.). 24p. (J). bds. 6.95 (978-0-439-33634-5(1) , Cartwheel Bks.) Scholastic, Inc.

Kalman, Bobbie. Life on the Ranch. 1998. (Life in the Old West Ser.). (Illus.). 32p. (J). (gr. 3-4). lib. bdg. (978-0-7787-0071-5(2)) Crabtree Publishing Co.

—Life on the Ranch. 1999. (gr. 3-6). lib. bdg. 16.40 (978-0-613-11778-4(6)) Tandem Library Bks.

Kehoe, Stasia Ward. I Live on a Farm. 2000. (Kids in Their Communities Ser.). (Illus.). 24p. (J). (gr. 3). lib. bdg. 18.75 (978-0-8239-5438-4(2) , PowerKids Pr.) Rosen Publishing Group, Inc., The.

King-Smith, Dick. Chewing the Cud: An Extraordinary Life Remembered by the Author of Babe: the Gallant Pig. Horse, Harry, illus. 2002. 208p. (J). (gr. 5 up). 16.95 (978-0-375-81459-4(0) , Knopf Bks. for Young Readers) Random Hse. Children's Bks.

Kortes-Erkkila, Helmi. Before Modern Conveniences: One Finnish Farm Family 1917-1927. Meier, Lynne, illus. 2004. 176p. (J). pap. 14.95 (978-1-58736-271-2(6) , Hats Off Bks.) Wheatmark.

Lester, Alison. My Farm. Lester, Alison, illus. 1999. (Illus.). (J). (ps-ps). lib. bdg. 14.10 (978-0-613-17832-7(7)) Tandem Library Bks.

—My Farm. 1999. (978-0-606-17719-1(1)) Tandem Library Bks.

Litchfield, Jo. Farm. 2004. (Look & Say Board Books Ser.). (Illus.). 10p. (J). 7.95 (978-0-7945-0702-2(6) , Usborne) EDC Publishing.

Longhurst, Terry. I Can Draw on the Farm. 2002. (I Can Draw Ser.). 32p. (J). 9.95 (978-0-7525-7278-9(4)) Parragon, Inc.

Look Who's Popping Up: On the Farm. 2003. (J). (ps-k). 4.98 (978-0-7525-8903-9(2)) Parragon, Inc.

Marks, Anthony. The Usborne Farmyard Tales Songbook. Tyler, Jenny, ed. Cartwright, Stephen, illus. 2005. 31p. (J). (ps-7). per. 6.95 (978-0-7945-0918-7(5) , Usborne) EDC Publishing.

McFarlane, Sheryl. On the Farm. LaFave, Kim, tr. LaFave, Kim, illus. 2004. (What's That Sound? Ser.). 20p. (J). (ps up). bds. (978-1-55041-814-9(9)) Fitzhenry & Whiteside, Ltd.

McKinley, Fred B. Chinqua Where? The Spirit of Rural America, 1947-1955. Blassingame, Calvin, illus. 2003. 319p. 24.95 (978-0-9729655-0-7(5)) Willow Creel Publishing Co.

Michelson, Richard. Tuttle's Red Barn: The Story of America's Oldest Family Farm. Azarian, Mary, illus. 2007. 40p. (J). (gr. k up). 16.99 (***978-0-399-24354-7(2)*** , Putnam Juvenile) Penguin Group (USA) Inc.

Milbourne, Anna. Farmyard Tales Things to Make & Do. 2005. (Activity Books Ser.). 32p. (J). pap. 8.95 (978-0-7945-0940-8(1) , Usborne) EDC Publishing.

—On the Farm. 2006. 24p. (J). 9.99 (978-0-7945-1282-8(8) , Usborne) EDC Publishing.

Millard, Anne, et al. My First Farm Touch & Feel. 2002. (My First Ser.). (Illus.). 12p. (J). (ps-k). bds. 9.99 (978-0-7894-8524-3(9)) Dorling Kindersley Publishing, Inc.

Miller, Jake. Who's Who in a Rural Community. 2005. (Communities at Work Ser.). (Illus.). 24p. (J). (gr. 2-4). lib. bdg. 19.95 (978-1-4042-2787-3(3) , PowerKids Pr.) Rosen Publishing Group, Inc., The.

Murray. Fun at the Farm. rev. ed. (Key Words Readers Ser.: B Series, No. 641-4b). (Illus.). 56p. (J). (ps-5). 3.50 (978-0-7214-0478-3(2) , Dutton Juvenile) Penguin Group (USA) Inc.

Nicholson, Sue & Dorling Kindersley Publishing Staff. A Day at Greenhill Farm. 1999. (Eyewitness Readers). (Illus.). 32p. (J). (ps-1). 14.99 (978-0-7894-4251-2(5)) Dorling Kindersley Publishing, Inc.

O'Hara, Megan. Pioneer Farm: A Farm on the Prairie in the 1880s. 1998. 32p. (J). pap. 21.00 (978-0-516-21253-1(2) , Children's Pr.) Scholastic Library Publishing.

On the Farm II Set. (gr. k-2). 114.95 (978-0-7368-9386-2(5)) Red Brick Learning.

On the Farm Set. (gr. k-2). 114.95 (978-0-7368-9233-9(8)) Red Brick Learning.

One Farm. 2000. (Illus.). (J). pap. 3.21 (978-0-7398-4478-6(4)) Steck-Vaughn.

Pancella, Peggy. Comunidades Agrícolas. 2005. (SPA & ENG., Illus.). 32p. (J). (978-1-4034-6233-6(X)); pap. (978-1-4034-6239-8(9)) Heinemann Library.

—Farm Community. 2005. (Illus.). 32p. (J). pap. (978-1-4034-6222-0(4)); lib. bdg. 25.36 (978-1-4034-6216-9(X)) Heinemann Library.

Parker, Francis W. Uncle Robert's Geography (Uncle Robert's Visit, V. 3) 2006. 84p. pap. (978-1-84702-205-9(7)) Echo Library.

Peterson, Cris. Century Farm: One Hundred Years on a Family Farm. Upitis, Alvis, photos by. 2003. (Illus.). 32p. (YA). (gr. k-2). 17.95 (978-1-56397-710-7(9)) Boyds Mills Pr.

Pfloog, Jan. The Farm Book. Pfloog, Jan, illus. 1999. (Golden Super Shape Book Ser.). (Illus.). 24p. (J). (gr. k-ps). pap. 3.99 (978-0-307-58117-4(9) , 10059, Golden Bks.) Random Hse. Children's Bks.

Pirulino. On the Farm. Ferri, Francesca, illus. 2004. 10p. (J). 16.95 (978-0-7641-2947-6(3)) Barron's Educational Series, Inc.

Pluckrose, Henry Arthur. On the Farm. 1999. (Machines at Work Ser.). (Illus.). 32p. (J). (gr. k-2). pap. 6.95 (978-0-531-15352-9(5) , Watts, Franklin) Scholastic Library Publishing.

Priddy, Roger & Priddy Books Staff. Sticker Activity Fun on the Farm: Play & Learn. rev. ed. 2006. 48p. (J). bds. 3.47 (978-0-312-49798-9(9) , Priddy Bks.) St. Martin's Pr.

Provensen, Alice. Year at Maple Hill Farm. 2001. (ps-2). lib. bdg. 15.30 (978-0-613-90198-7(3)) Tandem Library Bks.

Remson, Billie. A Mississippi Summer on Bluebird Hill: A True Story about Our Little Farm in the Hills of Southern Mississippi. Garraway, Kym, illus. 2005. (J). pap. 12.95 (978-1-59571-073-4(6)) Word Association Pubs.

Rendon, Marcie R. & Bellville, Cheryl Walsh. Farmer's Market: Families Working Together. 2001. (Photo Bks.). (Illus.). 48p. (J). (gr. 3-5). lib. bdg. 23.93 (978-1-57505-462-9(0) , Carolrhoda Bks.) Lerner Publishing Group.

Richardson, Adele D. Farms. 1999. (Let's Investigate Ser.). (Illus.). 32p. (J). (gr. 1-4). lib. bdg. (978-0-88682-353-5(6) , Creative Education) Creative Co., The.

Riggott, Dean. Life on the Farm: A Pictorial Journey of Minnesota's Farmland & Its People. 100th l.t. ed. 2001. 124p. pap. 24.95 (978-0-9659875-2-3(3)) Riggott, Dean Photography.

Roop, Peter & Roop, Connie. A Farm Album. 1999. (Long Ago & Today Ser.). (Illus.). 24p. (J). (gr. 1-3). lib. bdg. 19.92 (978-1-57572-601-4(7)) Heinemann Library.

Roy, Jennifer Rozines & Roy, Gregory. Multiplication on the Farm. 2006. (Math All Around Ser.). (Illus.). 32p. (J). lib. bdg. 28.50 (978-0-7614-2268-6(4) , Benchmark Bks.) Cavendish, Marshall Corp.

Saunders-Smith, Gail. The Farm. 1998. (Field Trips Ser.). 24p. (J). (ps-2). pap. 13.25 (978-0-516-21319-4(9) , Children's Pr.) Scholastic Library Publishing.

Scarry, Huck. Life on a Farm: A Sketchbook. (J). 16.95 (978-0-945912-32-3(3)) Pippin Pr.

Scholastic Editorial Staff. Learn with Lego: Farm. 2007. (Lego Ser.). 24p (J) pap. 4.99 (***978-0-439-91545-8(7)***) Scholastic, Inc.

Schuh, Mari C. Dogs on the Farm. 2002. (On the Farm Ser.). (Illus.). 24p. (J). (gr. k-1). lib. bdg. 15.93 (978-0-7368-1187-3(7) , Pebble Bks.) Capstone Pr., Inc.

—Dogs on the Farm. (On the Farm Ser.). 24p. (J). pap. 5.95 (978-0-7368-9378-7(4)) Capstone Pr., Inc.

—Ducks on the Farm. (On the Farm Ser.). 24p. (J). pap. 5.95 (978-0-7368-3423-0(0)) Capstone Pr., Inc.

—Pigs on the Farm. (On the Farm Ser.). 24p. (J). pap. 5.95 (978-0-7368-9144-8(7)) Capstone Pr., Inc.

—Rabbits on the Farm. (On the Farm Ser.). 24p. (J). pap. 5.95 (978-0-7368-3425-4(7)) Capstone Pr., Inc.

Sieling, Peter. Growing up on a Farm: Responsibilities & Issues. 2007. (Youth in Rural North America Ser.). (J). (978-1-4222-0012-4(4)) Mason Crest Pubs.

Silver Dolphin en Español Editors. Que? Como? Por que? la Granja: What? How? Why? The Farm. 2006. (SPA., Illus.). 12p. (J). 9.95 (978-970-718-345-2(4)) Advantage Pubs. Group.

Sirett, Dawn & Dorling Kindersley Publishing Staff. Farmer for A Day. 2004. (Illus.). 12p. (J). bds. 12.99 (978-0-7566-0211-6(4)) Dorling Kindersley Publishing, Inc.

Smith, Alastair. On the Farm Lift-the-Flap. Torode, Justine, illus. 2004. (Luxury Lift-the-Flap Ser.). 16p. (J). (gr. 1 up). 11.95 (978-0-7945-0508-0(2) , Usborne) EDC Publishing.

Splear, Elsie L. & Pratt, Carolyn. Growing Seasons. Stark, Ken, illus. 2000. 1p. (J). (ps-3). 16.99 (978-0-399-23460-6(8) , Putnam Juvenile) Penguin Group (USA) Inc.

Stanley, Mandy. Vamos a la Granja. 2003. (SPA & ENG., Illus.). 12p. (J). (ps-k). 4.95 (978-0-7534-5691-0(5) , Kingfisher) Houghton Mifflin Co. Trade & Reference Div.

Stewart, Pat L. Old Macdonald's Farm Stickers. 2003. (Dover Little Activity Bks.). (Illus.). 4p. (J). pap. 1.50 (978-0-486-43010-2(3)) Dover Pubns., Inc.

Stone, Lynn M. Animales de la Granja. Sarfatti, Esther & de la Vega, Eida, trs. (Vida en la Granja (Life on the Farm) Ser.).Tr. of Farm Animals. (SPA., Illus.). 24p. (J). 2002. mass mkt. 5.95 (978-1-58952-240-4(0) , RK31456); 2001. (gr. 1-3). lib. bdg. 19.27 (978-1-58952-181-0(1)) Rourke Publishing, LLC.

—Crecer en una Granja. Sarfatti, Esther & de la Vega, Eida, trs. (Vida en la Granja (Life on the Farm) Ser.).Tr. of Growing Up on a Farm. (SPA., Illus.). 24p. (J). 2002. mass mkt. 5.95 (978-1-58952-245-9(1) , RK31461); 2001. (gr. 1-3). lib. bdg. 19.27 (978-1-58952-186-5(2) , RK3040) Rourke Publishing, LLC.

—Growing up on a Farm. 2002. (Life on the Farm Ser.). (Illus.). 24p. (J). (gr. 1-4). 14.95 (978-1-58952-095-0(5)) Rourke Publishing, LLC.

Weber, Lou, ed. Little People on the Farm My First Look & Find. 2005. 18p. (J). bds. 7.98 (978-1-4127-3315-1(4) , 7241600) Publications International, Ltd.

Weeks, Sarah. Little Farmer. Date not set. 24p. (J). (ps up). 9.99 (978-0-694-01203-9(3)) HarperCollins Pubs.

White, Joseph C. Forged in a Country Crucible. 2003. (Illus.). 278p. per. 19.95 (978-0-9726095-1-7(2) , FCC2003) Crossing Trails Pubns.

Willard, Nancy. Cracked Corn & Snow Ice Cream: A Family Almanac. Dyer, Jane, illus. 2005. 56p. (YA). (gr. 4-8). 18.00 (978-0-7567-8835-3(8)) DIANE Publishing Co.

Williams, Dave. Windgalore Farm. 2005. (Illus.). 182p. pap. 21.95 (978-0-937921-56-2(4)) Acorn Publishing.

Wolfman, Judy. Life on a Cattle Farm. Winston, David Lorenz, photos by. 2005. (Life on a Farm Ser.). (Illus.). 48p. (gr. 2-5). lib. bdg. 23.93 (978-1-57505-516-9(3)) Lerner Publishing Group.

—Life on a Chicken Farm. Winston, David Lorenz, illus. Winston, David Lorenz, photos by. 2004. (Life on a Farm Ser.). 48p. (J). (gr. 2-5). lib. bdg. 23.93 (978-1-57505-191-8(5)) Lerner Publishing Group.

—Life on a Dairy Farm. Winston, David Lorenz, illus. Winston, David Lorenz, photos by. 2004. (Life on a Farm Ser.). 48p. (J). (gr. 2-5). lib. bdg. 23.93 (978-1-57505-190-1(7)) Lerner Publishing Group.

—Life on a Goat Farm. Winston, David Lorenz, photos by. 2005. (Life on a Farm Ser.). (Illus.). 48p. (gr. 2-5). lib. bdg. 23.93 (978-1-57505-515-2(5)) Lerner Publishing Group.

—Life on a Horse Farm. Winston, David Lorenz, photos by. 2005. (Life on a Farm Ser.). (Illus.). 48p. (gr. 2-5). lib. bdg. 23.93 (978-1-57505-517-6(1)) Lerner Publishing Group.

—Life on a Pig Farm. Winston, David L., illus. 1998. (Carolrhoda Photo Bks.). 48p. (J). (gr. k-4). lib. bdg. 23.93 (978-1-57505-237-3(7) , Carolrhoda Bks.) Lerner Publishing Group.

—Life on a Pig Farm. Winston, David Lorenz, photos by. 2nd ed. 2005. (Life on a Farm Ser.). (Illus.). 48p. (gr. 2-5). lib. bdg. 23.93 (978-1-57505-236-6(9)) Lerner Publishing Group.

—Life on a Sheep Farm. Winston, David Lorenz, illus. Winston, David Lorenz, photos by. 2004. (Life on a Farm Ser.). 48p. (J). (gr. 2-5). lib. bdg. 23.93 (978-1-57505-192-5(3)) Lerner Publishing Group.

—Life on an Apple Orchard. Winston, David Lorenz, illus. Winston, David Lorenz, photos by. 2004. (Life on a Farm Ser.). 48p. (J). (gr. 2-5). lib. bdg. 23.93 (978-1-57505-193-2(1)) Lerner Publishing Group.

FARM LIFE—FICTION

Abbott, Jacob. Jonas on a Farm in Winter (Illustrated E. 2006. pap. (***978-1-4065-0358-6(4)***) Dodo Pr.

—Rollo at Work & Rollo at Play. 2006. (Illus.). pap. 34.95 (***978-1-4286-4095-5(9)***) Kessinger Publishing, LLC.

Abraham, Susan Gonzales & Abraham, Denise Gonzales. Cecilia's Year. 2007. (Latino Fiction for Young Adults Ser.). 210p. (J). pap. 11.95 (978-1-933693-02-6(9)) Cinco Puntos Pr.

—Surprising Cecilia. 2005. (Latino Fiction for Young Adults Ser.). 216p. (YA). 16.95 (978-0-938317-96-8(2)) Cinco Puntos Pr.

Adams, Pam, illus. Old Macdonald Had a Farm. 2000. 16p. (J). (ps-k). bds. 5.99 (978-0-85953-662-2(9)) Child's Play-International.

—Old Macdonald Storysack. (J). 65.00 (978-0-85953-083-5(3)) Child's Play-International.

Adams, Pam, tr. & illus. Old Macdonald Had a Farm. Adams, Pam, illus. 2003. (Classic Books with Holes). (J). (978-0-85953-135-1(X)) Child's Play-International.

Aiken, Joan. Nightbirds on Nantucket. 1999. (978-0-606-21728-6(2)) Tandem Library Bks.

Alarcon, Karen Beaumont. Louella Mae, She's Run Away! Litzinger, Rosanne, illus. rev. ed. 2002. 32p. (J). (ps-1). pap. 7.95 (978-0-8050-6830-6(9) , Holt, Henry & Co. Bks. For Young Readers) Holt, Henry & Co.

—Louella Mae, She's Run Away! 2002. (ps-2). lib. bdg. 15.25 (978-0-613-75399-9(2)) Tandem Library Bks.

Alex Toys Staff. Farm Fun: Bath Book & Squirting Tub Toy. Silver-Thompson, Pattie, illus. 2007. (Little Squirts Ser.). 8p. (J). (ps-17). 7.99 (***978-0-316-06525-2(0)***) Little, Brown Bks. for Young Readers.

Alger, Horatio. Frank's Campaign: Or, The Farm & the Camp. 2006. 196p. pap. 11.99 (978-1-4264-0484-9(0)); 188p. pap. 14.99 (978-1-4264-0527-3(8)) BiblioBazaar.

—Frank's Campaign: Or, The Farm & the Camp. 2006. pap. (***978-1-4065-0705-8(9)***) Dodo Pr.

Alger, Horatio. Frank's Campaign: Or, What Boys Can Do on the Farm for the Camp. unabr. ed. 2002. (Polyglot Press Alger Ser.). (Illus.). (J). pap. 17.95 (978-1-4115-0000-6(8)) Polyglot Pr., Inc.

Alger Jr. Horatio Staff. Frank's Campaign. rev. ed. 2006. 300p. 29.95 (978-1-4218-1761-3(6)); pap. 14.95 (978-1-4218-1861-0(2)) 1st World Publishing, Inc. (1st World Library - Literary Society).

Allen, Nancy K. Once upon a Dime: A Math Adventure. Doyle, Adam, illus. 2004. (Math Adventures Ser.). 32p. (J). pap. 6.95 (978-1-57091-161-3(4)) Charlesbridge Publishing, Inc.

Amery, H. The Complete Book of Farmyard Tales. 2004. (Farmyard Tales Readers Ser.). 320p. (J). 24.95 (978-0-7945-0902-6(9) , Usborne) EDC Publishing.

—Where's Curly? Cartwright, Stephen, illus. 2004. (Treasury of Farmyard Tales Ser.). 16p. (J). (gr. 1 up). lib. bdg. 15.95 (978-1-58086-563-0(1)) EDC Publishing.

—Where's Woolly? Cartwright, Stephen, illus. 2004. (Treasury of Farmyard Tales Ser.). 16p. (J). (gr. 1 up). lib. bdg. 15.95 (978-1-58086-531-9(3)) EDC Publishing.

Amery, Heather. Farmyard Tales Christmas. 24p. 14.95 incl. audio (978-0-7945-0218-8(0)) EDC Publishing.

—Farmyard Tales Christmas Flap Bk And. 2006. 24p. 12.99 (978-0-7945-0556-1(2) , Usborne) EDC Publishing.

—Farmyard Tales Storybook. 2004. (Treasury of Farmyard Tales Ser.). (Illus.). 128p. (J). 7.95 (978-0-7945-0270-6(9) , Usborne) EDC Publishing.

—Farmyard Tales Treasury - Internet Referenced. Cartwright, Stephen, illus. 2007. 96p. (J). 19.99 (978-0-7945-1440-2(5) , Usborne) EDC Publishing.

—Old Steam Train. rev. ed. 2007. 16p. (J). pap. 5.99 (***978-0-7945-0804-3(9)*** , Usborne) EDC Publishing.

—Surprise Visitors. Cartwright, Stephen, illus. 2004. 16p. (J). pap. 5.95 (978-0-7945-0784-8(0) , Usborne) EDC Publishing.

—Where's Curly? Cartwright, Stephen, illus. 1998. (Farmyard Tales Ser.). 16p. (J). (ps-k). pap. 7.95 (978-0-7460-3011-0(8)) EDC Publishing.

Andersen, C. B. The Book of Mormon Sleuth. 2000. v, 279p. (J). pap. 9.95 (978-1-57345-664-7(0)) Deseret Bk. Co.

Anderson, Jodi. Peaches. 2005. 320p. (J). (gr. 7 up). lib. bdg. 16.89 (978-0-06-073306-3(3)) HarperCollins Pubs.

Anderson, Jodi & Anderson, Jodi Lynn. Peaches. 2005. 320p. (YA). (gr. 7-12). 15.99 (978-0-06-073305-6(5)) HarperCollins Pubs.

Angle, Kimberly Greene. Hummingbird. 2008. 256p. (J). 16.95 (***978-0-374-33376-8(9)***) Farrar, Straus & Giroux.

Animal Farm. 1999. (YA). 11.95 (978-1-56137-306-2(0)) Novel Units, Inc.

Arena, Felice & Kettle, Phil. Bull Riding. Cox, David, illus. 2004. (J). pap. (978-1-59336-370-3(2)) Mondo Publishing.

—On the Farm/By Felice Arena & Phil Kettle ; Illustrated by Susy Boyer. Boyer, Susy, illus. 2004. (J). pap. (978-1-59336-363-5(X)) Mondo Publishing.

Artley, Bob. Christmas on the Farm. Artley, Bob, illus. 2003. (Illus.). 96p. (YA). pap. 20.00 (978-1-58980-108-0(3)) Pelican Publishing Co., Inc.

Ashforth, Camilla. Willow at Christmas. Ashforth, Camilla, illus. 2005. (Illus.). 32p. (J). (ps-1). pap. 3.99 (978-0-7636-2927-4(8)) Candlewick Pr.

Attema, Martha. Hero. 2003. (Orca Young Readers Ser.). (Illus.). 144p. (J). (gr. 3-6). pap. 5.95 (978-1-55143-251-9(X)) Orca Bk. Pubs. USA.

Auerbach, Annie. A Day at the Barn. Giarrano, Vincent, illus. 2001. (Bob the Builder Ser.). 12p. (J). 5.99 (978-0-689-84380-8(1) , Simon Spotlight) Simon & Schuster Children's Publishing.

—Lego's a Day at the Barn. Giarrano, Vincent, illus. 2001. (Bob the Builder Ser.). 12p. (J). bds. 7.99 (978-0-689-84929-9(X) , Simon Spotlight) Simon & Schuster Children's Publishing.

Augarde, Steve. Celandine. 496p. (J). (gr. 5). 2008. 6.99 (***978-0-440-42216-7(7)*** , Yearling); 2006. 16.95 (978-0-385-75048-6(X) , Fickling, David Bks.); 2006. lib. bdg. 18.99 (978-0-385-75049-3(8) , Fickling, David Bks.) Random Hse. Children's Bks.

Bailey, Arthur Scott. Sleepy-Time Tales: The Tale of Fatty Coo. 2006. pap. (***978-1-4065-0446-0(7)***) Dodo Pr.

Bailey, Linda. The Farm Team. Slavin, Bill, illus. 2006. 32p. (J). (978-1-55337-850-1(4)) Kids Can Pr., Ltd.

Baker, Alan. Little Rabbits First Farm Book. 2001. (Little Rabbit Bks.). (Illus.). 32p. (J). (ps-k). tchr. ed. 11.95 (978-0-7534-5352-0(5) , Kingfisher) Houghton Mifflin Co. Trade & Reference Div.

—Little Rabbits' First Farm Book. 2003. (Little Rabbit Bks.). 32p. (J). (ps up). pap. 5.95 (978-0-7534-5594-4(3) , Kingfisher) Houghton Mifflin Co. Trade & Reference Div.

Balian, Lorna. A Garden for Groundhog. 2004. (Illus.). 40p. (J). 15.95 (978-1-932065-38-1(5)) Star Bright Bks., Inc.

Balloon Books Staff, ed. A Visit to the Farm: Sticker Story Time. 2003. (Sticker Bks.). (Illus.). 16p. (J). (ps-1). pap. 4.95 (978-0-8069-2260-7(5) , Balloon Bks.) Sterling Publishing Co., Inc.

Banicki, Patsy & Staige, Pat. Farmer Carpenter's Barn & the Cow's Saturday Night Dance. Staige, Pat & Stanton, Janet, illus. Date not set. (Orig.). (J). (gr. k-4). pap. (978-0-9641375-1-6(8)) Staige Productions.

Barnes, Emma. The Thief of Bracken Farm. 2007. (J). lib. bdg. 16.95 (***978-1-59566-338-2(X)***) QEB Publishing Inc.

Barrett, Anna Pearl. Dreaming of a Neecie Christmas, 4 vols., Vol. 4. Weston, Eunice & Waters, Linda, eds. Peguero, Phillip, illus. 2000. (Neecie Bks.). 60p. (J). (gr. 2-9). pap. 7.95 (978-0-9661330-4-2(8)) Over the Rainbow Productions.

—Neecie & the Freedom Celebration, 4 vols., Vol. 3. Edwards, Lana C. & Waters, Linda, eds. Peguero, Phillip, illus. 1999. (Neecie Bks.). 73p. (J). (gr. 2-5). pap. 10.95 (978-0-9661330-2-8(1)) Over the Rainbow Productions.

—Neecie & the Sparkling Spring. Weston, Eunice Guy, ed. Peguero, Phillip, illus. 2004. (Neecie Bks.: Vol. 5). 70p. (J). (gr. 1-6). 7.95 (978-0-9661330-5-9(6)) Over the Rainbow Productions.

Barrett, Anna Pearl, et al. Neecie & the Sparkling Spring. Pequero, Phillip, ed. 2002. (Illus.). 70p. (YA). (gr. 4-8). pap. 12.95 (978-0-9661330-6-6(4)) Over the Rainbow Productions.

Bateman, Teresa. April Foolishness. Westcott, Nadine Bernard, illus. 32p. (J). 2007. pap. 6.95 (***978-0-8075-0405-5(X)***); 2004. 16.95 (978-0-8075-0404-8(1)) Whitman, Albert & Co.

Bateman, Teresa. Farm Flu. Westcott, Nadine Bernard, illus. 2001. 32p. (J). (ps-2). pap. 7.95 (978-0-8075-2275-2(9)) Whitman, Albert & Co.

Beaton, Clare. There's a Cow in the Cabbage Patch. 2001. 32p. (J). pap. 5.99 (978-1-84148-335-1(4)) Barefoot Bks., Inc.

Beck, Sunny. In the Children's Meadow. 2004. (Illus.). (J). (978-1-59404-013-9(3)) Peanut Butter Publishing.

Beckerman, Menucha. Avi & Chavi Visit the Farm. Peleg, Tirza, illus. 2002. (My Middos World Ser.: 10). 24p. (J). 11.95 (978-1-931681-27-8(9)) Israel Bk. Shop.

—Friends on the Farm. 2004. (My Smiling World Ser.: No. 1). (Illus.). 32p. (J). 11.95 (978-1-931681-53-7(8)) Israel Bk. Shop.

Beiler, Edna. Mattie Mae. Graber, Esther Rose, illus. 2nd ed. 2000. 112p. (J). (ps-4). pap. 6.99 (978-0-8361-9141-7(2)) Herald Pr.

Belser, Maud Corier, illus. Grace & Marie's Little Farm on the Hill. 2007. 32p. (J). bds. 18.00 (***978-0-9791076-0-3(1)***) WebbWorks.

Bender, Carrie. Hemlock Hill Hideaway. 2000. (Whispering Brook Ser.: Bk. 4). (Illus.). 168p. (J). (gr. 4-8). pap. 8.99 (978-0-8361-9128-8(5)) Herald Pr.

—Hemlock Hill Hideaway: Whispering Brook Series #4. 2007. (Illus.). 168p. pap. 8.99 (***978-1-60126-022-2(9)***) Masthof Pr.

—Summerville Days. 2001. (Whispering Brook Ser.). (Illus.). 183p. (J). 25.95 (978-0-7862-3081-5(9) , Five Star) Thomson Gale.

—Summerville Days: Whispering Brook Series #2. 2007. (Illus.). 224p. pap. 8.99 (***978-1-60126-023-9(7)***) Masthof Pr.

Bender, Carrie. Timber Lane Cove. 2003. (Whispering Brook Ser.: Bk. 6). 144p. (YA). pap. 8.99 (978-0-8361-9202-5(8)) Herald Pr.

Benjamin, A. H. Baa! Moo! What Will We Do? Chapman, Jane, tr. Chapman, Jane, illus. 2003. 32p. (J). pap. 6.95 (978-1-58925-381-0(7) , tiger tales) ME Media LLC.

—Un Canguro en la Granja? Chapman, Jane, illus. 2002. (SPA.). (J). (gr. k-2). pap. 14.95 (978-84-488-0936-2(X) , BS30628) Beascoa, Ediciones S.A. ESP. *Dist:* Lectorum Pubns., Inc.

Berenstain, Stan & Berenstain, Jan. The Berenstain Bear Scouts & the Stinky Milk Mystery. 1999. (Berenstain Bear Scouts Ser.). (Illus.). 32p. (J). (gr. 3-6). pap. 3.50 (978-0-590-56524-0(9) , Cartwheel Bks.) Scholastic, Inc.

—The Berenstain Bear Scouts & the Stinky Milk Mystery. 1999. (Berenstain Bear Scouts Ser.). (J). (gr. 3-6). (978-0-606-16597-6(5)) Tandem Library Bks.

—The Berenstain Bears down on the Farm. Berenstain, Stan & Berenstain, Jan, illus. 2006. (Berenstain Bears Ser.). (Illus.). 32p. (J). 15.99 (978-0-06-058350-7(9)) HarperCollins Pubs.

—The Berenstain Bears down on the Farm. 2006. (Berenstain Bears Ser.). (Illus.). 32p. (J). pap. 3.99 (978-0-06-058351-4(7) , Harper Trophy); (***978-1-4156-8342-2(5)***) HarperCollins Pubs.

Berenstain, Stan & Berenstain, Jan. Berenstain Bears down on the Farm. 2006. (Illus.). 32p. (J). lib. bdg. 15.00 (***978-1-4242-1537-9(4)***) Fitzgerald Bks.

Berg, Idabelle L. Adventures of a Cool Cat: More Journals of Blackie "Ice" Berg. Berg, Idabelle L., illus. 2001. (Illus.). 192p. (J). (gr. 6 up). 22.95 (978-0-9677583-4-3(3)) Quixote Pubns.

Bergen, Lara Rice. Visit to the Farm. 2004. (gr. k-3). lib. bdg. 11.25 (978-0-613-73457-8(2)) Tandem Library Bks.

Betz, Adrienne. A Deal Is a Deal. Andriani, Vincent, illus. 1999. (Scholastic At-Home Phonics Reading Program Ser.: Vol. 33). 24p. (J). pap. (978-0-590-68782-9(4)) Scholastic, Inc.

Beylon, Cathy. Old MacDonald's Farm Coloring Book. 2003. (Illus.). 32p. (J). pap. 2.95 (978-0-486-43034-8(0)) Dover Pubns., Inc.

Blackstone, Stella. There's a Cow in the Cabbage Patch. Beaton, Clare, illus. 2001. 32p. (J). (ps). 14.99 (978-1-84148-333-7(8)) Barefoot Bks., Inc.

Blier, Gloria. The Brook That Held Many Secrets. 2004. 144p. pap. 19.95 (978-1-4137-3639-7(4)) PublishAmerica, Inc.

Bloom, Suzanne. We Keep a Pig in the Parlor. 2004. (Illus.). 24p. (J). (gr. k-2). reprint ed. pap. 7.95 (978-1-59078-084-8(1)) Boyds Mills Pr.

Blos, Joan. A Gathering of Days: A New England Girl's Journal, 1830-1832. Blos, Joan, illus. 2002. (Illus.). 13.40 (978-0-7587-0184-8(5)) Book Wholesalers, Inc.

Bluedorn, Johannah. My Mommy, My Teacher. Bluedorn, Johannah, illus. 2002. (Illus.). 53p. (J). per. 12.00 (978-0-9743616-5-9(8)) Trivium Pursuit.

Blyton, Enid. Five on Finniston Farm. 1999. 167p. (J). 16.95 (978-0-7540-6065-9(9) , Galaxy Children's Large Print) BBC Audiobooks America.

Bock, Lee. Oh Crumps/ Ay, Caramba. de la Vega, Eida, tr. Midgett, Morgan, illus. 2006. (SPA.). (J). 4.99 (978-0-9770906-3-1(9)) Raven Tree Pr.

Boeve, Eunice. The Summer of the Crow. 2000. 224p. (J). pap. 12.95 (978-1-58597-059-9(X)) Leathers Publishing.

Bonk, John J. Dustin Grubbs: Take Two! 2006. 256p. (J). (gr. 3-7). 15.99 (978-0-316-15637-0(X)) Little Brown & Co.

Book, Rick. Necking with Louise. 2004. 168p. (gr. 9 up). pap. 7.95 (978-0-88995-194-5(2)) Red Deer Pr. CAN. *Dist:* Fitzhenry & Whiteside, Ltd.

Booth, David. The Dust Bowl. Reczuch, Karen, illus. 2002. 32p. (J). (gr. k-3). (978-1-55074-746-1(0)) Kids Can Pr., Ltd.

Borgo, Lacy Finn. Big Mama's Baby. Cote, Nancy, illus. 2007. (J). (gr. k-2). 15.95 (***978-1-59078-187-6(2)***) Boyds Mills Pr.

Borntrager, Mary Christner. Daniel. l.t. ed. 2000. (Christian Fiction Ser.). 191p. 23.95 (978-0-7862-2859-1(8)) Thorndike Pr.

Bradby, Marie. Once upon a Farm. Rand, Ted, illus. 2002. 32p. (J). (ps-2). pap. 16.95 (978-0-439-31766-5(5) , Orchard Bks.) Scholastic, Inc.

Brammer, Deb. Two Sides to Everything. 2003. (Illus.). 151p. (J). (978-1-59166-166-5(8)) Jones, Bob Univ. Pr.

Brandeis, Batsheva. Faiga Finds the Way. Levitas, Alexander, illus. 2005. (Fun to Read Book Ser.). 120p. (J). pap. 8.95 (978-1-929628-28-5(5)) Hachai Publishing.

Brett, Jan. Armadillo Rodeo. Brett, Jan, illus. 2004. (Illus.). 32p. (J). (ps-1). pap. 6.99 (978-0-14-240125-5(0) , Puffin) Penguin Group (USA) Inc.

Brooke, Peggy. Jake's Orphan. 2001. 11.64 (978-0-606-22137-5(9)) Tandem Library Bks.

Brookins, Cara. Doris Free. Barrow, Ann, illus. 2006. 127p. (J). pap. (978-1-59336-333-8(8)) Mondo Publishing.

Brooks, Felicity. Frank the Farmer. rev. ed. 2007. 24p. (J). pap. 6.99 (978-0-7945-1621-5(1) , Usborne) EDC Publishing.

Brooks, Walter R. Freddy Rides Again. Wiese, Kurt, illus. 2002. 240p. (J). 23.95 (978-1-58567-268-4(8)) Overlook Pr., The.

Brown, Celease N. & Mubarak, Enoch. The Color Orange. 2004. (Illus.). 32p. (978-1-55306-742-9(8) , Guardian Bks.) Essence Publishing.

Brown, Marc. Buster on the Farm. 2005. (Postcards from Buster Ser.). (Illus.). 32p. (J). (gr. 1-4). pap. 3.99 (978-0-316-00108-3(2)) Little, Brown Bks. for Young Readers.

—Buster on the Town. 2005. (Postcards from Buster Ser.). (Illus.). 32p. (J). (gr. 1-4). 14.99 (978-0-316-15882-4(8)) Little, Brown Bks. for Young Readers.

Brown, Margaret Wise. Big Red Barn. 2002. (Illus.). (J). 25.11 (978-0-7587-2100-6(5)) Book Wholesalers, Inc.

—El Gran Granero Rojo. Bond, Felicia, illus. 2003. (SPA.). 34p. (J). (ps-1). bds. 7.99 (978-0-06-009107-1(X)) HarperCollins Pubs.

Brumett, Jonas O. The Weavus Family Storybook. Matera, Francis, illus. l.t. ed. 1999. 64p. (J). (gr. k-2). pap. 16.95 incl. audio compact disk (978-1-892812-50-6(9)) Froginhood & Friends, Inc.

Bruna, Dick. Farmer John's Seeds. 2004. (Illus.). 12p. pap. 5.99 (978-1-59226-191-8(4)) Big Tent Entertainment, Inc.

Bruzzone, Catherine. Lucy the Cat at the Farm: La Gatita Lucia en la Granja. Martin, Rosa Maria, tr. from ENG. Beaton, Clare, illus. 2005. (Bilingual Picture Strip Bks.). (SPA & ENG.). 24p. (J). pap. 4.95 (978-0-7641-3150-9(8)) Barron's Educational Series, Inc.

—Lucy the Cat in Town: La Gatita Lucia en la Cuidad. Martin, Rosa Maria, tr. Beaton, Clare, illus. 2005. (Bilingual Picture Strip Bks.). (SPA & ENG.). 24p. (J). pap. 4.95 (978-0-7641-3149-3(4)) Barron's Educational Series, Inc.

Buchanan, Jane. The Berry-Picking Man. Bowman, Leslie, illus. 2003. 96p. (J). 16.00 (978-0-374-40610-3(3) , Farrar, Straus & Giroux (BYR)) Farrar, Straus & Giroux.

Buck, Pearl S. Christmas Day in the Morning. Buehner, Mark, illus. 2002. 40p. (J). 16.99 (978-0-688-16267-2(3)) HarperCollins Pubs.

Buehner, Caralyn. Fanny's Dream. 2003. (gr. k-3). lib. bdg. 15.30 (978-0-613-67452-2(9)) Tandem Library Bks.

Buehner, Caralyn & Buehner, Mark. Fanny's Dream. Buehner, Caralyn & Buehner, Mark, illus. 2003. (Illus.). 32p. (J). (gr. k-3). pap. 6.99 (978-0-14-250060-6(7) , Puffin) Penguin Group (USA) Inc.

Buffie, Margaret. The Watcher. unabr. ed. 2004. (Watcher's Quest Ser.). (Illus.). 264p. (YA). (gr. 13 up). (978-1-55074-831-4(9)) Kids Can Pr., Ltd.

Burg, Sara Emmanuelle. One More Egg. 2005. (Illus.). 32p. (J). (ps up). 16.50 (978-0-7358-2002-9(3)) North-South Bks., Inc.

Burg, Sarah Emmanuelle. One More Egg. 2005. (Illus.). 32p. (J). (ps up). 15.95 (978-0-7358-2001-2(5)) North-South Bks., Inc.

The Butterfly Farm Burglar, 6 vols., Vol. 3. (Woodland Mysteriestm Ser.). 133p. (gr. 3-7). 42.50 (978-0-322-02374-1(2)) Wright Group, The.

Byars, Betsy. The Midnight Fox. 1999. (J). 9.95 (978-1-56137-667-4(1)) Novel Units, Inc.

—La Zorra Negra. (SPA.). 102p. (YA). (gr. 5-8). 6.80 (978-84-279-3247-0(2) , NG2893) Noguer y Caralt Editores, S. A. ESP. *Dist:* Lectorum Pubns., Inc.

Caldwell, Lise. God's Animals on the Farm. Julien, Terry, illus. 1999. 28p. (J). (ps-2). pap. 3.49 (978-0-7847-1092-0(9) , 22076) Standard Publishing.

Capucilli, Alyssa Satin. Biscuit Visits the Pumpkin Patch. Schories, Pat, illus. 2004. 16p. (J). (ps-1). 4.99 (978-0-06-009466-9(4) , Harper Festival) HarperCollins Pubs.

—Biscuit's Day at the Farm. Schories, Pat, illus. (My First I Can Read Bks.). 32p. (J). 2008. pap. 3.99 (***978-0-06-074169-3(4)*** , Harper Trophy); 2007. 15.99 (978-0-06-074167-9(8)); 2007. lib. bdg. 16.89 (978-0-06-074168-6(6)) HarperCollins Pubs.

Carle, Eric. Dream Snow. Gauch, Patricia Lee, ed. Carle, Eric, illus. 2000. (Illus.). 32p. (J). (ps-1). 21.99 (978-0-399-23579-5(5) , Philomel) Penguin Group (USA) Inc.

Carlstrom, Nancy White. The Way to Wyatt's House. Morgan, Mary, illus. 2000. 32p. (J). (gr. k-3). lib. bdg. 16.85 (978-0-8027-8742-2(8)); 15.95 (978-0-8027-8740-8(1)) Walker & Co.

Carpenter, Dimitrea. Together. 2006. 24p. (J). pap. 8.99 (978-0-439-80323-6(3) , Orchard Bks.) Scholastic, Inc.

Carter, Don. Old MacDonald Drives a Tractor. 2007. (Illus.). 24p. (J). (ps-2). 14.95 (978-1-59643-023-5(0)) Roaring Brook Pr.

Cartwright, Stephen. Where's Curly? Amery, Heather, illus. 1998. (Usborne Farmyard Tales Ser.). 16p. (J). (ps up). lib. bdg. 15.95 (978-1-58086-150-2(4)) EDC Publishing.

Cassidy, Anne. Naughty Nancy. Guicciardini, Desideria, illus. 2004. (Read-It! Readers Ser.). 32p. (J). (gr. k-3). 18.60 (978-1-4048-0558-3(3)) Picture Window Bks.

Cazet, Denys. Minnie & Moo: Minnie & Moo Go Dancing. Cazet, Denys, illus. 2001. (Live Oak Readalong Ser.). (Illus.). (J). pap. 18.95 incl. audio compact disk (978-1-59112-390-3(9)) Live Oak Media.

—Minnie & Moo: Minnie & Moo Go to the Moon. Cazet, Denys, illus. (Live Oak Readalong Ser.). (Illus.). (J). 18.95 incl. audio compact disk (978-1-59112-392-7(5)) Live Oak Media.

—Minnie & Moo: Minnie & Moo: Will You Be My Valentine? Cazet, Denys, illus. 2005. (Live Oak Readalong Ser.). (Illus.). (J). pap. 16.95 incl. audio (978-1-59112-891-5(9)) Live Oak Media.

—Minnie & Moo: Will You Be My Valentine? Cazet, Denys, illus. 2002. (I Can Read Bks.). (Illus.). 48p. (J). (gr. k-3). 15.99 (978-0-06-623754-1(8)); lib. bdg. 16.89 (978-0-06-623755-8(6)) HarperCollins Pubs.

—Minnie & Moo & the Haunted Sweater. Cazet, Denys, illus. 2007. (I Can Read Bks.). 48p. (J). (ps-3). 15.99 (***978-0-06-073016-1(1)***); lib. bdg. 16.89 (***978-0-06-073017-8(X)***) HarperCollins Pubs.

—Minnie & Moo & the Seven Wonders of the World. Cazet, Denys, illus. 2003. (Illus.). 144p. (J). 16.95 (978-0-689-85330-2(0) , Atheneum/Richard Jackson Bks.) Simon & Schuster Children's Publishing.

—Minnie & Moo Go Dancing. Cazet, Denys, illus. 2001. (Illus.). 25.95 incl. audio (978-0-87499-722-4(4)); 28.95 incl. audio compact disk (978-1-59112-591-4(X)); pap. 29.95 incl. audio (978-0-87499-723-1(2)); pap. 31.95 incl. audio compact disk (978-1-59112-590-7(1)) Live Oak Media.

—Minnie & Moo Go to the Moon. Cazet, Denys, illus. 2001. (Illus.). 25.95 incl. audio (978-0-87499-718-7(6)); pap. 29.95 incl. audio (978-0-87499-719-4(4)); pap. 31.95 incl. audio compact disk (978-1-59112-592-1(8)); pap. 18.95 incl. audio compact disk (978-1-59112-593-8(6)) Live Oak Media.

Cazet, Denys, reader. Minnie & Moo: Will You Be My Valentine? (Read-Alongs for Beginning Readers Ser.). (Illus.). (J). (ps-3). 2005. pap. 18.95 incl. audio compact disk (978-1-59112-895-3(1)); 2004. 25.95 incl. audio (978-1-59112-892-2(7)); 2004. pap. 31.95 incl. audio compact disk (978-1-59112-897-7(8)); 2004. pap. 29.95 incl. audio (978-1-59112-893-9(5)) Live Oak Media.

Cazet, Denys & Dorling Kindersley Publishing Staff. Minnie & Moo Go Dancing. 1998. (Minnie & Moo Ser.: Vol. 2). (Illus.). 48p. (J). (gr. 1-3). 12.99 (978-0-7894-2515-7(7)) Dorling Kindersley Publishing, Inc.

—Minnie & Moo Go to the Moon. 1998. (Minnie & Moo Ser.: Vol. 1). (Illus.). 48p. (J). (gr. 1-3). 12.99 (978-0-7894-2516-4(5)) Dorling Kindersley Publishing, Inc.

Chaconas, Dori. Coriander the Contrary Hen. Carrington, Marsha Gray, illus. 2007. 32p. (J). (gr. k-4). spiral bd. 15.95 (978-1-57505-749-1(2) , Carolrhoda Bks.) Lerner Publishing Group.

Chan, Gillian. The Carved Box. Fernandez, Laura, illus. 232p. (YA). (gr. 13 up). 2004. (978-1-55337-016-1(3)); 2001. (978-1-55074-895-6(5)) Kids Can Pr., Ltd.

Chapman, Cynthia. Dog Gone. 2008. 224p. (J). 16.95 (***978-0-312-37123-4(3)***) Feiwel & Friends.

Cheek, Roland. Lincoln County Crucible, 6 vols. 2003. 288p. pap. 14.95 (978-0-918981-10-3(7) , 3) Skyline Publishing.

Chitwood, Suzanne. Wake Up, Big Barn. Chitwood, Suzanne, illus. 2002. (Illus.). 40p. (J). (ps-2). pap. 15.95 (978-0-439-26627-7(0) , Cartwheel Bks.) Scholastic, Inc.

Choukas, Nita & Tyler, Gillian. Bayberry & Beau. 2006. (Illus.). 112p. (J). 15.95 (978-1-933392-35-6(5)) Chelsea Green Publishing.

Clarissa - Evaluation Guide: Evaluation Guide. 2006. (J). (978-1-55942-402-8(8)) Marsh Media.

Clark, Eleanor. Eleanor Jo: The Farmer's Daughter. 2007. (Eleanor Jo Ser.). (J). pap. 14.99 (978-0-9788726-1-8(4)) HonorNet.

Cleary, Beverly. Emily's Runaway Imagination. 2002. (J). 13.83 (978-0-7587-9141-2(0)) Book Wholesalers, Inc.

—Emily's Runaway Imagination. 221p. (J). (gr. 2-4). pap. 4.95 (978-0-8072-1416-9(7) , Listening Library) Random Hse. Audio Publishing Group.

—The Hullabaloo ABC. 2000. pap. (978-0-688-17715-7(8)) HarperCollins Pubs.

Clinton, Cathryn. Simeon's Fire. 128p. (J). 2007. (gr. 3-7). pap. 5.99 (978-0-7636-3294-6(5)); 2005. (gr. 5-9). 15.99 (978-0-7636-2707-2(0)) Candlewick Pr.

Coatsworth, Elizabeth. Five Bushel Farm. 2004. (Illus.). 160p. (J). pap. 10.95 (978-1-883937-84-3(1)) Bethlehem Bks.

Cochran, Jean M. Farmer Brown & His Little Red Truck. Enos, Daryl, illus. 2008. 32p. (J). 16.95 (***978-0-9792035-0-3(3)***) Pleasant St. Pr.

Cohen, Caron Lee. Digger Pig & the Turnip: Marranita Poco Rabo y el Nabo. Denise, Christopher, illus. 2008. (Green Light Readers Level 2 Ser.). (SPA & ENG.). 28p. (J). 12.95 (***978-0-15-206249-1(1)***) Harcourt Trade Pubs.

Cohen, Caron Lee & Douglas, Erin. Digger Pig & the Turnip: Marranita Poco Rabo y el Nabo. Denise, Christopher, illus. 2008. (Green Light Readers Level 2 Ser.). (SPA & ENG.). 28p. (J). 12.95 (*978-0-15-206263-7(7)) Harcourt Trade Pubs.

Coker, Deborah Connor. Aunt Mattie's Present. Joysmith, Brenda, illus. 1998. (J). (978-0-316-23498-6(2)) Little Brown & Co.

Cony, Frances. Old MacDonald Had a Farm. Smyth, Iain, illus. 2002. 12p. (J). (ps-k). bds. 10.95 (978-0-531-30129-6(X) , Orchard Bks.) Scholastic, Inc.

Cooling, Wendy. Farmyard Tales from Far & Wide. Moran, Rosslyn, illus. 1998. (Barefoot Beginners Ser.). 48p. (J). (ps-2). 15.95 (978-1-901223-38-5(8)) Barefoot Bks., Inc.

Coons, Mary, illus. Donnie, Lost in the Cornfield. 2001. 15p. (J). pap. 6.50 (978-0-9713926-0-1(9)) Amicus Vitae Pr.

Copeland, Colene. My Favorite Hobo. 2001. (Priscilla Pig Ser.: 8). 172p. (J). per. 4.95 (978-0-939810-25-3(5) , M) Jordan Valley Heritage Hse.

Corey, Shana. Babe the Brave. 1999. (Illus.). (J). (978-0-606-18482-3(1)) Tandem Library Bks.

Couloumbis, Audrey. Summer's End. 2007. 192p. (YA). (gr. 7 up). pap. 5.99 (978-0-14-240783-7(6) , Puffin) Penguin Group (USA) Inc.

Courtin, Thierry. Decouvre les petits de la Ferme. 15.95 (978-2-09-202273-3(3)) Nathan, Fernand FRA. *Dist:* Distribooks, Inc.

Cousins, Lucy. Maisy's Morning on the Farm. Cousins, Lucy, illus. 2001. (Maisy Bks.). (Illus.). 24p. (J). (gr. k-k). pap. 3.99 (978-0-7636-1611-3(7)) Candlewick Pr.

—Maisy's Morning on the Farm. 2001. (ps-2). lib. bdg. 11.00 (978-0-613-74782-0(8)) Tandem Library Bks.

Cowley, Joy. Mrs. Wishy-Washy's Farm. Fuller, Elizabeth, illus. 32p. (J). (ps). 2006. pap. 5.99 (978-0-14-240299-3(0) , Puffin); 2003. 15.99 (978-0-399-23872-7(7) , Philomel) Penguin Group (USA) Inc.

—The Rusty, Trusty Tractor. Dunrea, Olivier, illus. 2003. 32p. (J). (gr. k-2). 15.95 (978-1-56397-565-3(3)) Boyds Mills Pr.

Cox, Phil Roxbee. Curly's Friends. Cartwright, Stephen, illus. rev. ed. 2005. 10p. (J). bds. 7.95 (978-0-7945-1180-7(5) , Usborne) EDC Publishing.

Cox, Phil Roxbee & Cartwright, S. Wolly's Walk. 2004. (Farmyard Tales Touchy Feely Board Bks.). (Illus.). 10p. (J). 7.95 (978-0-7945-0039-9(0) , Usborne) EDC Publishing.

Coxe, Molly. Hot Dog. Coxe, Molly, illus. 1998. (Road to Reading Ser.). (Illus.). 32p. (J). (ps-1). pap. 3.99 (978-0-307-26101-4(8) , 26101, Random Hse. Bks. for Young Readers) Random Hse. Children's Bks.

—Hot Dog. (Road to Reading Ser.). 1999. (Illus.). (J). 10.79 (978-0-606-16255-5(0)); 1998. lib. bdg. 11.80 (978-0-613-71623-9(X)) Tandem Library Bks.

Crandall, Janet. Winter on the Farm. 2006. (J). per. 9.95 (978-1-59872-612-1(9)) Instantpublisher.com.

Craven, Tracy Leininger. Kathleen's Unforgettable Winter. 2006. (Life of Faith': Kathleen Mckenzie Ser.). 160p. (YA). pap. 6.99 (978-1-928749-26-4(7)) Zonderkidz.

—Life of Faith/Kathleens/Battle. 2007. (Life of Faith': Kathleen Mckenzie Ser.). 160p. (YA). pap. 6.99 (978-1-928749-28-8(3)) Mission City Pr., Inc.

Crist-Evans, Craig. North of Everything. 2004. (Illus.). 80p. (J). (gr. 5-9). 14.99 (978-0-7636-2098-1(X)) Candlewick Pr.

Crossley, David, illus. On the Farm. 2004. (Baby's First Learning Ser.). 12p. (J). bds. 4.99 (978-1-85854-893-7(4)) Brimax Books Ltd. GBR. *Dist:* Byeway Bks.

Crowson, Andrew. Flip Flap Farm. 2003. (Illus.). 12p. bds. (978-1-85602-430-3(X)) Chrysalis Children's Bks.

Crum, Shutta. My Mountain Song. 2007. (Illus.). 32p. (J). 16.00 (*978-1-4223-6590-8(5)) DIANE Publishing Co.

—My Mountain Song. Rand, Ted, tr. Rand, Ted, illus. 2004. 32p. (J). (gr. k-3). tchr. ed. 16.00 (978-0-618-15970-3(3) , Clarion Bks.) Houghton Mifflin Co. Trade & Reference Div.

Crunk, Tony. Grandpa's Overall. Nash, Scott, illus. 2001. 32p. (J). (ps). pap. 15.95 (978-0-531-30321-4(7) , Orchard Bks.) Scholastic, Inc.

—Grandpa's Overalls. Nash, Scott, illus. 2001. (J). lib. bdg. (978-0-531-33321-1(3) , Orchard Bks.) Scholastic, Inc.

Cummins, Julie. Country Kid, City Kid. Rand, Ted, illus. rev. ed. 2002. 32p. (J). (ps-1). 17.95 (978-0-8050-6467-4(2) , Holt, Henry & Co. Bks. For Young Readers) Holt, Henry & Co.

Curry, Peter. Farmer Doogie. 2001. (Illus.). 28p. (J). pap. 9.99 (978-0-00-664741-6(3) , HarperSport) HarperCollins Pubs. Ltd. GBR. *Dist:* Independent Pubs. Group.

Dale, Jenny. Nell the Naughty Kitten, No. 4. 2001. (Kitten Friends Ser.). (Illus.). (J). (978-0-606-20754-6(6)) Tandem Library Bks.

Dallas, Sandra. Alice's Tulips. 2000. (gr. 7-12). lib. bdg. 22.20 (978-0-613-42657-2(6)) Tandem Library Bks.

Dalmatian Press Staff. Farm Fun: Board Book Set, 4 bks., Set. 2003. (Illus.). 20p. (J). bds. 7.99 (978-1-57759-653-0(6)) Dalmatian Pr.

—Happy on the Farm: Happy Tale. 2005. (Illus.). 24p. (J). bds. 2.99 (978-1-4037-1268-4(9)) Dalmatian Pr.

Davis, Rebecca. Jake Riley: Irreparably Damaged. 2003. 240p. (J). 16.89 (978-0-06-051838-7(3)) HarperCollins Pubs.

Dayton, Dorothy. The Legend of Farmer Will. 2006. 70p. pap. 14.95 (978-1-4241-0985-2(X)) PublishAmerica, Inc.

De Angeli, Marguerite. Henner's Lydia. 1998. (Illus.). 74p. (YA). (ps-3). 15.99 (978-0-8361-9093-9(9)) Herald Pr.

de Brunhoff, Laurent. Babar et ses Amis a la Ferme. (Babar Ser.). (FRE., Illus.). 48p. (J). (ps-3). 19.95 (978-0-7859-8805-2(X)) French & European Pubns., Inc.

de Mariscal, Blanca Lopez. The Harvest Birds. 2001. (gr. k-3). lib. bdg. 16.40 (978-0-613-90839-9(2)) Tandem Library Bks.

Dean, Carol S. The Live Bale of Hay: A Real Maine Adventure. Dunn, Sandra, illus. 2005. 32p. (ps-ps). 15.95 (978-0-89272-674-5(1)) Down East Bks.

DeFelice, Cynthia C. Under the Same Sky. 2005. 224p. (J). pap. 5.95 (978-0-374-48065-3(6) , Sunburst) Farrar, Straus & Giroux.

Di Maggio, Joyce. Out on a Farm. 1999. (Illus.). 24p. (J). (ps-1). pap. 5.00 (978-1-928970-10-1(9)) GWR Pr.

Dixon, Franklin W. Farming Fear. ed. 2005. (Hardy Boys II Ser.: No. 188). 154p. (J). lib. bdg. 15.00 (978-1-59054-839-4(6)) Fitzgerald Bks.

DK Publishing Staff. Fun on the Farm Activity Book. 2007. 28p. (J). (ps-1). pap. 19.99 (*978-0-7566-3212-0(9)) Dorling Kindersley Publishing, Inc.

Dodds, Dayle Ann. Minnie's Diner: A Multiplying Menu. Manders, John, illus. 2004. 40p. (J). (gr. k-3). 16.99 (978-0-7636-1736-3(9)) Candlewick Pr.

—Minnie's Diner: A Multiplying Menu. Manders, John, illus. 2007. 40p. (J). (gr. k-3). pap. 6.99 (978-0-7636-3313-4(5)) Candlewick Pr.

Donnelly, Jennifer. A Northern Light. (YA). 2003. (Illus.). 400p. (gr. 9 up). 17.00 (978-0-15-216705-9(6)); 2004. 408p. reprint ed. pap. 8.95 (978-0-15-205310-9(7) , Harcourt Paperbacks) Harcourt Children's Bks.

Douglas, Erin. Get That Pest! 2000. (gr. k-3). lib. bdg. 11.80 (978-0-613-63287-4(7)); (Illus.). (J). (978-0-606-18174-7(1)) Tandem Library Bks.

—Get That Pest! Yee, Wong Herbert, illus. 2003. (Green Light Readers Level 2 Ser.). 24p. (J). 11.95 (978-0-15-204873-0(1)); pap. 3.95 (978-0-15-204833-4(2)) Harcourt Children's Bks. (Green Light Readers).

Douglas, Erin. Get That Pest! Agarren a ése! Yee, Wong Herbert, illus. 2008. (Green Light Readers Level 2 Ser.). (SPA & ENG.). 28p. (J). pap. 3.95 (*978-0-15-206269-9(6)) Harcourt Trade Pubs.

Douglas, Vincent & School Specialty Publishing Staff. Who Lives on the Farm? 2004. (Book & Play Mat Kits Ser.). (Illus.). 10p. (J). bds. 12.95 (978-1-58845-622-9(6) , Brighter Child) School Specialty Publishing.

Dow, Jill. Bridget's Secret. 2001. (Windy Edge Farm Ser.). (Illus.). 32p. (J). (ps-3). pap. 7.99 (978-0-7112-1780-5(7)) Lincoln, Frances Ltd. GBR. *Dist:* Transition Vendor.

—Hazel & Clover's Great Escape. 1999. (Windy Edge Farm Ser.). (Illus.). 32p. (J). (ps-2). pap. 7.99 (978-0-7112-0732-5(1)) Lincoln, Frances Ltd. GBR. *Dist:* Transition Vendor.

—Hepzibah's Woolly Fleece. 1999. (Windy Edge Farm Ser.). (Illus.). 32p. (J). (ps-2). pap. 7.99 (978-0-7112-0616-8(3)) Lincoln, Frances Ltd. GBR. *Dist:* Transition Vendor.

—Maggie's Holiday. (Windy Edge Farm Ser.). (Illus.). 32p. (J). (ps-3). 2001. pap. (978-0-7112-1778-2(5)); 1999. pap. 7.99 (978-0-7112-0852-0(2)) Lincoln, Frances Ltd. GBR. *Dist:* Transition Vendor, Antique Collectors' Club.

—Molly's Supper. 2001. (Windy Edge Farm Ser.). (Illus.). 32p. (J). (ps-3). pap. (978-0-7112-1776-8(9)) Lincoln, Frances Ltd. GBR. *Dist:* Transition Vendor.

—Webster's Walk. 2001. (Windy Edge Farm Ser.). (Illus.). 32p. (J). (ps-3). pap. 7.99 (978-0-7112-1777-5(7)) Lincoln, Frances Ltd. GBR. *Dist:* Transition Vendor.

Down on Piggy Farm. 2005. (J). bds. 12.95 (978-0-9764114-2-0(3)) Little People Bks.

Doyle, Eugenie. Stray Voltage. 1998. 128p. (YA). (gr. 5-7). 16.95 (978-1-886910-86-7(3) , Lemniscaat) Boyds Mills Pr.

Drake, Jane & Love, Ann. Farming. Cupples, Pat, illus. 2002. (America at Work Ser.). 32p. (J). (gr. k-3). (978-1-55074-451-4(8)) Kids Can Pr., Ltd.

Duey, Kathleen. Katie & the Mustang. 2004. 132p. (J). (ps-k). per. 11.64 (978-0-606-32524-0(7)) Tandem Library Bks.

Duffield, Katy. Farmer McPeepers' Milk Cows. Gray, Steve, illus. 2003. 32p. (gr. k-4). 15.95 (978-0-87358-825-6(8) , Rising Moon Bks. for Young Readers) Northland Publishing.

Duncan, Jane. Herself & Janet Reachfar. Hedderwick, Mairi, illus. 2002. 32p. (J). (gr. k-3). pap. 7.95 (978-1-84158-209-2(3)) Birlinn, Ltd. GBR. *Dist:* Interlink Publishing Group, Inc.

—Jane Reachfar & Chickabird. Hedderwick, Mairi, illus. 2002. 32p. (J). (gr. k-3). pap. 7.95 (978-1-84158-208-5(5)) Birlinn, Ltd. GBR. *Dist:* Interlink Publishing Group, Inc.

Dunrea, Olivier. Hanne's Quest. 2006. (Illus.). 96p. (J). (gr. 3). 16.99 (978-0-399-24216-8(3) , Philomel) Penguin Group (USA) Inc.

Duvoisin, Roger. Veronica on Petunia's Farm. 2008. 40p. (J). (gr. k-3). 16.99 (*978-0-375-85211-4(5) , Knopf Bks. for Young Readers) Random Hse. Children's Bks.

Eaglehouse, Carolyn. The Magic of Milky Way Farm. l.t. ed. 2005. (Illus.). 24p. (J). pap. 10.00 (978-0-9773263-0-3(6)) Eaglehouse, Carolyn.

Easton, Richard. A Real American. 2002. 160p. (J). (gr. 4-6). 15.00 (978-0-618-13339-0(9) , Clarion Bks.) Houghton Mifflin Co. Trade & Reference Div.

Edwards, Frank B. A Crowded Ride in the Countryside. 1999. (New Reader Ser.). (Illus.). (J). 11.75 (978-0-606-22028-6(3)) Tandem Library Bks.

—Crowded Ride in the Countryside. 1999. (ps-2). lib. bdg. 12.95 (978-0-613-80351-9(5)) Tandem Library Bks.

Edwards, Julie Andrews & Hamilton, Emma Walton. Dumpy the Dumptruck. Walton, Tony, illus. 2000. (Dumpy Ser.). 32p. (ps-2). 15.99 (978-0-7868-0609-6(5)) Hyperion Bks. for Children.

—Dumpy to the Rescue! Walton, Tony, illus. 2004. (My First I Can Read Bks.). 32p. (J). (ps up). 14.99 (978-0-06-052689-4(0)); pap. 3.99 (978-0-06-052691-7(2)); lib. bdg. 15.89 (978-0-06-052690-0(4)) HarperCollins Pubs.

Edwards, Julie Andrews & Hamilton, Emma Walton. Dumpy to the Rescue. Walton, Tony, illus. 2004. 24p. (J). lib. bdg. 13.85 (*978-1-4242-0707-7(X)) Fitzgerald Bks.

Edwards, Pamela Duncan. Mcgillycuddy Could. Date not set. 32p. (J). (ps-1). pap. 5.99 (978-0-06-443688-5(8)) HarperCollins Pubs.

—McGillycuddy Could! Porter, Sue, illus. 2005. 32p. (J). (ps-1). 14.99 (978-0-06-029001-6(3)); lib. bdg. 15.89 (978-0-06-029002-3(1)) HarperCollins Pubs.

Egan, Tim. Serious Farm. 2006. (Illus.). 32p. (J). (gr. k-3). 6.95 (978-0-618-73745-1(6)) Houghton Mifflin Co. Trade & Reference Div.

—Serious Farm. Egan, Tim, illus. 2003. (Illus.). 32p. (J). (gr. k-3). 15.00 (978-0-618-22694-8(X)) Houghton Mifflin Co. Trade & Reference Div.

Ehlert, Lois. Dia de Mercado: Una Historia Contado a Traves del Arte Popular. Campoy, F. Isabel & Ada, Alma Flor, trs. 2003. (SPA., Illus.). 36p. (J). pap. 7.00 (978-0-15-216814-8(1) , Voyager Bks./Libros Viajeros) Harcourt Children's Bks.

—Market Day: A Story Told with Folk Art. Ehlert, Lois, illus. 2002. (Illus.). (J). 23.40 (978-0-7587-4281-0(9)) Book Wholesalers, Inc.

—Market Day: A Story Told with Folk Art. (Illus.). 36p. (J). (gr. k-2). 2002. pap. 7.00 (978-0-15-216820-9(6) , Voyager Bks./Libros Viajeros); 2000. 16.00 (978-0-15-202158-0(2)) Harcourt Children's Bks.

—Market Day: A Story Told with Folk Art. 2002. (gr. k-3). lib. bdg. 14.15 (978-0-613-53833-6(1)) Tandem Library Bks.

Ehrlich, Gretel. A Blizzard Year: Timmy's Almanac of the Seasons. 2001. (gr. 3-6). lib. bdg. 14.15 (978-0-613-62598-2(6)) Tandem Library Bks.

Ellis, Tacy. Goat Tales: Stories of Izzy & Her Friends. Collins, Don, illus. 2006. 128p. (J). 17.95 (978-1-931721-78-3(5)) Bright Sky Pr.

Enright, Elizabeth. Thimble Summer. unabr. ed. 2004. 136p. (J). (gr. 3-7). pap. 36.00 incl. audio (978-0-8072-0671-3(7) , Listening Library) Random Hse. Audio Publishing Group.

—Thimble Summer. 2006. 21.75 (978-0-8446-7281-6(5)) Smith, Peter Pub., Inc.

—Thimble Summer. 2008. (Illus.). 124p. (J). pap. 6.99 (*978-0-312-38002-1(X)) Square Fish.

Enriquez, Jose. Saving the Mango Farm. 2006. 23p. (J). 10.98 (978-1-4116-5917-9(1)) Lulu.com.

Entara Ltd. Staff, photos by. The Lost Shamrock. 2007. (Jakers! Ser.). 24p. (J). pap. 3.99 (978-1-4169-4067-8(7) , Simon Spotlight) Simon & Schuster Children's Publishing.

Erickson, John R. The Case of the Deadly Ha-Ha Game. Holmes, Gerald L., illus. 2001. (Hank the Cowdog Ser.: No. 37). 144p. (J). (gr. 2-5). 14.99 (978-0-670-89640-0(3) , Viking Juvenile) Penguin Group (USA) Inc.

—The Case of the Deadly Ha-Ha Game, Vol. 37. Gilson, K., ed. Holmes, Gerald L., illus. 2001. (Hank the Cowdog Ser.: No. 37). 144p. (J). (gr. 2-5). pap. 4.99 (978-0-14-131048-0(0) , Puffin) Penguin Group (USA) Inc.

Esbaum, Jill. Stink Soup. Roth, Roger, illus. 2004. 32p. (J). 16.00 (978-0-374-37252-1(7) , Farrar, Straus & Giroux (BYR)) Farrar, Straus & Giroux.

Ewart, Claire. The Giant. Ewart, Claire, illus. 2003. (Illus.). 32p. (J). (ps-3). 16.95 (978-0-8027-8835-1(1)) Walker & Co.

Fairless, Caroline. Hambone. Edelson, Wendy, illus. 2001. 48p. (J). pap. 10.95 (978-0-89869-361-4(6)) Church Publishing, Inc.

Falcone, Karen. Tales from Falmac Farm. Frake, Barbara, illus. 2005. (J). per. 14.00 (978-1-933002-08-8(5)) PublishingWorks.

Farm Chores. 2000. (J). (978-1-58453-125-8(8)) Pioneer Valley Educational Pr., Inc.

Farmer Bob on the Farm Series. 2001. (978-1-883772-87-1(7)) Flying Rhinoceros, Inc.

Farmer Chuck. 1998. (Fisher-Price Phonics Storybooks Ser.: Vol. 3). (Illus.). (J). pap. (978-0-7666-0171-0(4) , Honey Bear Bks.) Modern Publishing.

Farmer Fred & the Farm Show. 2002. 32p. (J). 5.98 (978-0-7525-8180-4(5)) Parragon, Inc.

Farmer Fred & the Naughty Crows. 2002. 32p. (J). 5.98 (978-0-7525-8181-1(3)) Parragon, Inc.

Farmer Fred's: Baby Animals. 2002. bds. 3.98 (978-0-7525-8174-3(0)) Parragon, Inc.

Farmer Fred's: Noisy Animals. 2002. bds. 3.98 (978-0-7525-8175-0(9)) Parragon, Inc.

Farmer Says. 2005. (J). bds. (978-1-4194-0050-6(9)) Paradise Pr., Inc.

Faulkner, Keith. Surprise on the Farm. Clucas, Philip, illus. 2000. (J). (978-0-439-21059-1(3)) Scholastic, Inc.

Felcoski, Victoria. Secret of the Scotchpottle Farm. 2006. 21.99 (*978-1-4259-8117-4(8)); pap. 12.99 (*978-1-4259-8118-1(6)) AuthorHouse.

Feldman, Thea. A Visit to the Farm. 2006. 3p. 5.99 (978-1-932915-32-7(X)) Sandvik Publishing.

Fite, Anna. Ada y Max Visitan Una Granja. 2002. (Ada y Max Ser.). (SPA & ENG.). 10p. 4.95 (978-84-7864-332-5(X)) Combel Editorial, S.A. ESP. *Dist:* Independent Pubs. Group.

Fitz-Gibbon, Sally. En la Granja del Tio Juan. Deines, Brian, illus. 2003. (SPA.). 32p. (J). (978-1-55041-878-1(5)) Fitzhenry & Whiteside, Ltd.

—On Uncle John's Farm. Deines, Brian, tr. Deines, Brian, illus. 2005. 32p. (J). (gr. 1-3). pap. (978-1-55041-886-6(6)) Fitzhenry & Whiteside, Ltd.

—On Uncle John's Farm. Deines, Brian, illus. 2004. 32p. (J). (gr. k-2). (978-1-55041-691-6(X)) Fitzhenry & Whiteside, Ltd.

Fitz-Gibbon, Sally & Deines, Brian. En la granja del tio Juan. 2003. (SPA., Illus.). 32p. pap. (978-1-55041-883-5(1)) Fitzhenry & Whiteside, Ltd.

Fleischman, Sid. McBroom Tells a Lie. Wummer, Amy, illus. 1999. (Adventures of McBroom Ser.). 64p. (J). (gr. 2-6). pap. 4.99 (978-0-8431-7497-7(8) , Price Stern Sloan) Penguin Group (USA) Inc.

—McBroom Tells a Lie. 1999. (J). (978-0-606-19073-2(2)); (gr. 3-6). lib. bdg. 13.00 (978-0-613-14983-9(1)) Tandem Library Bks.

—McBroom the Rainmaker. 1999. (J). (978-0-606-19074-9(0)) Tandem Library Bks.

—McBroom's Ghost. Wummer, Amy, illus. 1998. 62p. lib. bdg. 11.79 (978-0-606-15963-0(0)) Tandem Library Bks.

Fleming, Denise. Barnyard Banter. Fleming, Denise, illus. 2002. (Illus.). (J). 15.49 (978-0-7587-2039-9(4)) Book Wholesalers, Inc.

—Barnyard Banter. Fleming, Denise, illus. rev. ed. 2001. (Illus.). 30p. (J). (ps-k). bds. 6.95 (978-0-8050-6594-7(6) , Holt, Henry & Co. Bks. For Young Readers) Holt, Henry & Co.

Foreman, Michael. Rock-a-Doodle-Do! 2001. (Illus.). 32p. (J). pap. 9.99 (978-0-09-940763-8(9) , Red Fox) Random Hse. Children's Bks. GBR. *Dist:* Trafalgar Square Publishing.

Forrester, Izola. Kit of Greenacre Farm. 2006. 33.99 (*978-1-4280-3401-3(3)); pap. 26.99 (*978-1-4280-3376-4(9)) IndyPublish.com.

Forrester, Izola L. Kit of Greenacre Farm. 2007. 158p. pap. 11.99 (*978-1-4264-8431-5(3)); 174p. pap. 14.99 (*978-1-4264-8489-6(5)) BiblioBazaar.

Franco, Betsy. Going to Grandma's Farm. 2004. (Rookie Reader Espanol Ser.). (Illus.). 23p. (J). (gr. k-2). pap. 4.95 (978-0-516-27787-5(1) , Children's Pr.) Scholastic Library Publishing.

—Going to Grandma's Farm. Rueda, Claudia, illus. 2003. (Rookie Reader Ser.). 24p. (J). 19.50 (978-0-516-22875-4(7) , Children's Pr.) Scholastic Library Publishing.

—Going to Grandma's Farm. Rueda, Claudia, illus. 2004. 24p. (ps-ps). lib. bdg. 11.75 (978-0-606-30159-6(3)) Tandem Library Bks.

—Vamos a la Granja de la Abuela. Rueda, Claudia, illus. 2003. (Rookie Reader Espanol Ser.). (SPA.). (J). 19.50 (978-0-516-25889-8(3) , Children's Pr.) Scholastic Library Publishing.

French, Vivian. Oliver's Milk Shake. Bartlett, Alison, illus. 2001. 32p. (J). (ps-1). 15.95 (978-0-531-30304-7(7) , Orchard Bks.) Scholastic, Inc.

Friedrich, Elizabeth. Leah's Pony. 1999. (gr. k-3). lib. bdg. 17.60 (978-0-613-78901-1(6)); (J). (978-0-606-17333-9(1)) Tandem Library Bks.

Friedrich, Elizabeth & Boyds Mills Press Staff. Leah's Pony. Garland, Michael, illus. 2003. 32p. (J). (gr. 2-4). pap. 9.95 (978-1-56397-828-9(8)) Boyds Mills Pr.

Friend, R. Down on Friendly Acres Set 1: Books #1-4, 4. 2007. (Illus.). (J). (*978-0-9743627-8-6(6)) Sunflower Seeds Pr.

Galvin, Kim. RJ's Farm. 2000. 208p. (J). (gr. 4-7). pap. 12.95 (978-0-595-13989-7(2) , Writers Club Pr.) iUniverse, Inc.

Gansle, Sherry. Oops, a Curious Horse Big Book. Light, Carol, illus. 2003. 56p. (J). (978-0-9745803-6-4(8)) Little Big Tomes.

—Oops, a Curious Horse Little Book. Light, Carol, illus. 2003. 52p. (J). (978-0-9745803-7-1(6)) Little Big Tomes.

—Oops, a Curious Horse Story Book Reader. Light, Carol, illus. 2003. 58p. (J). (978-0-9745803-5-7(X)) Little Big Tomes.

Garis, Howard Roger. Uncle Wiggily on the Farm. Date not set. 192p. (J). 20.95 (978-0-8488-2275-0(7)) Amereon LTD.

Garson, Cindy. Welcome to Kristy's Farm: Book I (Black & White Version) 2007. (ENG.). 56p. per. 21.80 (*978-1-84728-321-4(7)) Lulu.com.

Gavin, Jamila. Fine Feathered Friend. Williams, Dan, illus. 2002. (Yellow Bananas Ser.). 48p. (J). (gr. 3-4). pap. (978-0-7787-0985-5(X)); lib. bdg. (978-0-7787-0939-8(6)) Crabtree Publishing Co.

—Fine Feathered Friend. 2002. (gr. 3-6). lib. bdg. 12.95 (978-0-613-52842-9(5)) Tandem Library Bks.

Geisert, Arthur. Nursery Crimes. 2007. (Illus.). 32p. (J). (ps-3). 6.95 (*978-0-618-95671-5(9)) Houghton Mifflin Co. Trade & Reference Div.

Geisert, Bonnie. Lessons. 2005. 192p. (J). (gr. 4-6). 15.00 (978-0-618-47899-6(X) , Walter Lorraine) Houghton Mifflin Co. Trade & Reference Div.

Gernhart, Cyndi. Gertrude Sees... On the Farm. Gernhart, Cyndi et al, illus. l.t. ed. 2006. 20p. (J). 8.00 (978-0-9778240-0-7(4)) Prairie Winds Publishing.

Gibbons, Faye. The Day the Picture Man Came. Meidell, Sherry, illus. 2003. 32p. (YA). (gr. k-2). 16.95 (978-1-56397-161-7(5)) Boyds Mills Pr.

Gilge-Barnes, Jeanette. Growing-Up Summer. Hauge, Carl, illus. 2000. (J). (gr. 5-7). pap. 9.99 (978-0-9679371-8-2(3)) WinePress Publishing.

Glasscock, Sarah. My Prairie Summer. 2001. lib. bdg. 13.00 (978-0-613-76467-4(6)) Tandem Library Bks.

Golden Books Staff. Farm Tales. 2007. (Little Golden Book Ser.). (Illus.). 224p. (J). (ps-k). 10.99 (978-0-375-83942-9(9) , Golden Bks.) Random Hse. Children's Bks.

Good, Phyllis Pellman. Plain Pig's ABC's: A Day on Plain Pig's Amish Farm. Benner, Cheryl A., illus. 1998. 24p. (J). (ps-1). 14.95 (978-1-56148-251-1(X)) Good Bks.

Goodhart, Pippa & Paine, Colin. Arthur's Tractor: A Fairy Tale with Mechanical Parts. 2003. (Illus.). 32p. (J). (ps-3). 15.95 (978-1-58234-847-6(2) , Bloomsbury Children) Bloomsbury Publishing.

Goodman, Susan E. What Do You Do... at the Farm? 2002. 2. (Illus.). 32p. (J). (gr. k-2). pap. 4.99 (978-0-7613-1786-9(4) , Millbrook Pr.) Lerner Publishing Group.

Goodspeed, J. Fun on the Farm. 2006. (J). pap. 4.99 (978-0-448-43882-5(8) , Grosset & Dunlap) Penguin Group (USA) Inc.

Graef, Renee, illus. Farmer Boy Days. 1998. (Little House Chapter Bks.: No. 6). (J). (gr. 3-6). 11.05 (978-0-606-12929-9(4)) Tandem Library Bks.

Graff, Nancy Price. Taking Wing. Minor, Wendell, illus. 2005. 224p. (YA). (gr. 5-9). 15.00 (978-0-618-53591-0(8) , Clarion Bks.) Houghton Mifflin Co. Trade & Reference Div.

Gray, Dianne. Holding up the Earth. 2006. 224p. (J). (gr. 5-9). pap. 6.95 (978-0-618-73747-5(2)) Houghton Mifflin Co. Trade & Reference Div.

Gray, Dianne E. Holding up the Earth. 2000. 224p. (J). (gr. 5-9). tchr. ed. 15.00 (978-0-618-00703-5(2)) Houghton Mifflin Co. Trade & Reference Div.

—Holding up the Earth. l.t. ed. 2002. 198p. (J). 22.95 (978-0-7862-3889-7(5)) Thomson Gale.

Gray, Kes. Cluck O'Clock. McQuillan, Mary, tr. McQuillan, Mary, illus. 2004. 32p. (J). (gr. k-3). tchr. ed. 16.95 (978-0-8234-1809-1(X)) Holiday Hse., Inc.

Greenwald, Sheila. Rosy Cole's Worst Ever, Best yet Tour of New York City. Greenwald, Sheila, illus. 2003. (Rosie Cole Ser.). (Illus.). 128p. (J). 16.00 (978-0-374-36349-9(8) , Farrar, Straus & Giroux (BYR)) Farrar, Straus & Giroux.

Griffith, Helen V. Grandaddy & Janetta Together: The Three Stories in One Book. Stevenson, James, illus. 2001. 80p. (gr. 2 up). (YA). 15.95 (978-0-06-029148-8(6)); (J). 15.89 (978-0-06-029238-6(5)) HarperCollins Pubs.

Grisham, John. A Painted House. 2002. (gr. 5-8). lib. bdg. 16.45 (978-0-613-49451-9(2)) Tandem Library Bks.

Grosgebauer, Clare Ham. Snickerdoodle's Star-Spangled Fourth of July! Rissing, Karen, illus. 4th ed. 2005. 36p. 12.99 (978-0-9741888-6-7(7)) Small Wonders Enterprises.

Haf, Eurgain & Wen, Dref. Fferm Ffion. 2005. (WEL., Illus.). 142p. (978-1-85596-674-1(3)) Dref Wen.

Hahn, Mary Downing. Anna on the Farm. deGroat, Diane, illus. 2001. 160p. (J). (gr. 4-6). tchr. ed. 15.00 (978-0-618-03605-9(9) , Clarion Bks.) Houghton Mifflin Co. Trade & Reference Div.

—Anna on the Farm. 2001. lib. bdg. 14.15 (978-0-613-68401-9(X)) Tandem Library Bks.

Hall, Barbara. Dixie Storms. 2006. (Illus.). 224p. (J). pap. 6.95 (978-0-15-205756-5(0) , Harcourt Paperbacks) Harcourt Children's Bks.

Hall, Kirsten. On the Farm. Gurney, John Steven, illus. 2005. (My First Reader Ser.). 32p. (J). (gr. k-1). pap. 3.95 (978-0-516-25115-8(5) , Children's Pr.) Scholastic Library Publishing.

—On the Farm. Gurney, John, illus. 2004. (My First Reader Ser.). 31p. (J). 18.50 (978-0-516-24680-2(1) , Children's Pr.) Scholastic Library Publishing.

Hallmark, Hazel. A Little White Hen Called "RolyPoly" 1999. (Illus.). 15p. (J). pap. 8.00 (978-1-930002-01-2(7)) I & L Publishing.

Hamilton, Virginia. Zeely. 1998. (C). pap. 3.95 (978-0-87628-345-5(8)) Simon & Schuster.

Happy on the Farm. 2002. (Illus.). 24p. (J). (gr. k-5). pap. 2.99 (978-1-57759-376-8(6)) Dalmatian Pr.

Harcourt School Publishers Staff. At Summer's End. 3rd ed. 2002. (Trophies English Language Learners Ser.). pap. 5.10 (978-0-15-327761-0(0)) Harcourt Schl. Pubs.

—Bess & Tess: On Level. 3rd ed. 2002. (Trophies Reading Program Ser.). (Illus.). (J). pap. 4.10 (978-0-15-322986-2(1)) Harcourt Schl. Pubs.

—Bess & Tess 5-Pack, On Level. 3rd ed. 2002. (Trophies Reading Program Ser.). (Illus.). (gr. 1). pap. 20.10 (978-0-15-326836-6(0)) Harcourt Schl. Pubs.

—A Family Farm: A Reader. 1999. (Collections Ser.). (Illus.). (J). pap. 2.10 (978-0-15-313446-3(1)) Harcourt Schl. Pubs.

—Never Bored on the Farm Below Level. 3rd ed. 2002. (Trophies Reading Program Ser.). (Illus.). pap. 5.10 (978-0-15-323056-1(8)) Harcourt Schl. Pubs.

—Stone Wall Secrets Level D: Library Edition. 2001. (Collections Ser.). (Illus.). (J). 5.90 (978-0-15-314412-7(2)) Harcourt Schl. Pubs.

—Trofeos On Level: Melaza y Cereza. 3rd ed. 2002. (SPA., Illus.). pap. 5.50 (978-0-15-323897-0(6)) Harcourt Schl. Pubs.

Harding, Sandy Bacon. Hand It to the Bandit. Mickelson, Brenda, illus. 2001. (Farm Adventures Ser.). 80p. (J). (gr. 1-6). pap. 6.95 (978-1-890609-09-2(9) , Lion's Paw Bks.) Coronet Bks. & Pubns.

—A Stick, a Stone & a Bone. Mickelson, Brenda, illus. 1999. (Farm Adventures Ser.: Vol. 2). 79p. (J). (gr. 1-6). pap. 6.95 (978-1-890609-08-5(0) , Lion's Paw Bks.) Coronet Bks. & Pubns.

HarperCollins Staff, ed. Home on the Range. 2001. 40p. (J). (ps-3). lib. bdg. 15.89 (978-0-06-028372-8(6)) HarperCollins Pubs.

Harrison, Troon. Bushel of Light. 2001. (gr. 5-8). lib. bdg. 16.40 (978-0-613-44633-4(X)) Tandem Library Bks.

Hartnett, Sonya. Thursday's Child. 272p. (YA). (gr. 9). 2003. (Illus.). pap. 7.99 (978-0-7636-2203-9(6)); 2002. 15.99 (978-0-7636-1620-5(6)) Candlewick Pr.

—Thursday's Child. 2000. 240p. pap. (978-0-14-029732-4(4)) Penguin Group (USA) Inc.

—Thursday's Child. 2002. (gr. 7-12). lib. bdg. 16.45 (978-0-613-69466-7(X)) Tandem Library Bks.

Hawes, Alison. School Trip. Mould, Chris, illus. 2004. 24p. (J). lib. bdg. 22.65 ***(978-1-59646-694-4(4))*** Dingles & Co.

Hawkins, Colin & Hawkins, Jacqui. Old MacDonald Had a Farm. 2004. (Illus.). 24p. (J). pap. 9.99 (978-1-4052-0681-5(0)) Egmont Bks., Ltd. GBR. *Dist:* Trafalgar Square Publishing.

Hawksley, Gerald. Mommies & Babies on the Farm. Calitri, Susan, illus. 2004. (J). bds. 11.99 (978-1-890647-11-7(X)) RC2 Corp.

Haydon, Julie. Farm: Lift-A-Flap. (Illus.). 10p. (J). bds. (978-1-74121-413-0(0)) Hinkler Bks. Pty, Ltd.

Hazlett, V. Jake's Junction: Henry's Listening Ears. Tucker, E., illus. 2006. (ENG.). 28p. per. 11.95 (978-1-59800-628-5(2)) Outskirts Press, Inc.

Healy, Nick. Fawn Braun's Big City Blues. Erkocak, Sahin, illus. 2007. (Pfeffernut County Ser.). 32p. (J). (gr. k-2). lib. bdg. 23.93 ***(978-1-4048-3696-9(9))*** Picture Window Bks.

—Louie the Layabout. Erkocak, Sahin, illus. 2007. (Pfeffernut County Ser.). 32p. (J). (gr. k-2). lib. bdg. 23.93 ***(978-1-4048-3697-6(7))*** Picture Window Bks.

Hedderwick, Mairi. Walk with Grannie. 2003. (Illus.). 32p. (J). 19.99 (978-0-340-86642-9(X) , Hodder & Stoughton) Hodder General Publishing Division GBR. *Dist:* Trafalgar Square Publishing.

—A Walk with Grannie. Date not set. (Illus.). pap. (978-0-340-87353-3(1) , Hodder Children's Books) Hodder Children's Division.

Heinlein, Robert A. & Briggs, Anita. Hobart. Rayner, Mary, illus. 2002. 64p. (J). (gr. 3-7). 14.00 (978-0-689-84129-3(9)) Simon & Schuster Children's Publishing.

Heinz, Brian J. The Barnyard Cat. Blair, June H., illus. 2000. 32p. (J). (gr. k-4). 14.95 (978-0-936335-04-9(1)) Ballyhoo BookWorks, Inc.

—The Barnyard Cat. l.t. ed. 2003. (Illus.). 32p. (J). pap. 6.96 (978-0-936335-07-0(6)) Ballyhoo BookWorks, Inc.

—Red Fox at McCloskey's Farm. Sheban, Chris, illus. 2006. 32p. (J). 17.95 (978-1-56846-195-3(X) , Creative Editions) Creative Co., The.

Heitzmann, Kristen. Chestnut Ridge Acres. 2001. 220p. (J). 25.95 (978-0-7862-3415-8(6) , Five Star) Thomson Gale.

Henning, Ann. Cow Patty Patti. 2004. 47p. pap. 19.95 (978-1-4137-3456-0(1)) PublishAmerica, Inc.

Hensley, Sarah M. Farmer Sam's Busy Day. 2006. (J). pap. (978-1-57332-396-3(9)) HighReach Learning, Inc.

—Farmer Sam's Busy Day. Teeple, Jackie, illus. 2006. (J). (978-1-57332-395-6(0)) HighReach Learning, Inc.

Henson, Heather & Wilkins, Celia. A Little House of Their Own. Andreasen, Dan, illus. 2005. (Little House Ser.). 320p. (J). 16.99 (978-0-06-027009-4(8)) HarperCollins Pubs.

Hercules's Spring Adventure Pack. 2001. (978-1-883772-01-7(X)) Flying Rhinoceros, Inc.

Hernandez, Elaine. Welcome to Humming Meadow Ranch. Hernandez, Stacy, illus. 2005. 28p. (J). lib. bdg 16.95 (978-0-9766431-0-4(3)) Humming Meadow Ranch.

Hershberger, Noah. Salamonie Farm. Koehler, Chris, illus. 1998. 240p. pap. 12.95 (978-1-879863-53-8(7)) Goosefoot Acres Pr.

Hesse, Karen. Out of the Dust. 2002. (Illus.). (J). 13.19 (978-0-7587-0207-4(8)) Book Wholesalers, Inc.

—Out of the Dust. 240p. (gr. 5 up). (YA). pap. 4.99 (978-0-8072-1526-5(0)) ; 1998. (J). pap. 29.00 incl. audio (978-0-8072-8013-3(5) , YA967SP) Random Hse. Audio Publishing Group. (Listening Library).

—Out of the Dust. 1999. (Apple Signature Edition Ser.). 240p. (gr. 4-7). mass mkt. 5.99 (978-0-590-37125-4(8)) Scholastic, Inc.

—Out of the Dust. 1999. (978-0-606-15665-3(8)); (gr. 5-8). lib. bdg. 13.00 (978-0-613-11953-5(3)) Tandem Library Bks.

—Out of the Dust. l.t. ed. 2004. 180p. 22.95 (978-0-7862-7006-4(3) , Large Print Pr.) Thorndike Pr.

Heurtelou, Maude. Makso's Farm. Vilsaint, Fequiere, ed. Date not set. (ENG & CRP.). 20p. (J). (gr. 1-3). pap. 12.00 (978-1-881839-68-2(0)) Educa Vision.

Heynen, Jim. Cosmos Coyote & William the Nice. 2002. (gr. 7-12). lib. bdg. 16.45 (978-0-613-71513-3(6)) Tandem Library Bks.

Higgenson, Hadley. Keeker & the Sugar Shack. Andersen, Maja, illus. 2006. (Sneaky Pony Ser.: Bk. 3). 48p. (J). pap. 3.95 (978-0-8118-5456-6(6)) Chronicle Bks. LLC.

Higginson, Hadley. Keeker & Springtime Surprise. Parrett, Lisa, illus. 2007. (Sneaky Pony Ser.: No. 4). 56p. (J). 15.50 (978-0-8118-5598-3(8)) Chronicle Bks. LLC.

—Keeker & Springtime Surprise. Perrett, Lisa, illus. 2007. (Sneaky Pony Ser.: No. 4). 56p. (J). pap. 3.95 (978-0-8118-5599-0(6)) Chronicle Bks. LLC.

—Keeker & the Sugar Shack, Bk. 3. Andersen, Maja, illus. 2006. 48p. (J). 15.50 (978-0-8118-5455-9(8)) Chronicle Bks. LLC.

Hill, Eric. Spot en la Granja. (SPA.). pap. 4.95 (978-950-07-1966-7(5)) Editorial Sudamericana S.A. ARG. *Dist:* Distribooks, Inc.

—Spot Goes to the Farm. Hill, Eric, illus. 2006. 22p. (J). (ps-k). bds. 12.99 (978-0-399-24614-2(2) , Putnam Juvenile) Penguin Group (USA) Inc.

—Spot's Little Book of Fun at the Farm. Hill, Eric, illus. 2003. (Spots Little Book of Fun Ser.). (Illus.). 10p. (J). (ps-k). 5.99 (978-0-399-23893-2(X) , Putnam Juvenile) Penguin Group (USA) Inc.

Hill, Sandi. Barnyard Math, Vol. 4466. Kupperstein, Joel, ed. Cochrane, Tom, illus. 1998. (Learn to Read Math Ser.). 16p. (J). pap. 2.99 (978-1-57471-373-2(6) , 4466) Creative Teaching Pr., Inc.

Hillert, Margaret. Dragon Goes to the Farm. 2005. (J). (978-1-59577-034-9(8)); (978-1-59577-032-5(1)) Starfall Education.

Hite, Sid. A Hole in the World. 208p. (J). 2001. (Illus.). pap. 16.95 (978-0-439-09830-4(0)); 2004. (gr. 5 up). reprint ed. pap. 5.99 (978-0-439-09831-1(9) , Scholastic Pr.) Scholastic, Inc.

Hoberman, Mary Ann. Skip to My Lou. Westcott, Nadine Bernard, illus. 2006. 32p. (J). (ps-1). pap. 6.99 (978-0-316-73405-9(5)) Little Brown & Co.

Hodges, Meredith. Jasper: The Story of a Mule. Shields, Bonnie, illus. 2003. 245p. (J). (gr. k-7). 39.95 (978-0-9702309-8-0(2)) Lucky 3 Ranch, Inc.

Hoffman, Emily Allen. A Friend of the Enemy. 2003. 108p. (J). pap. 7.95 (978-1-57249-312-4(7) , White Mane Kids) White Mane Publishing Co., Inc.

Hoffmire, A. B. The Ogre Bully. 2007. 32p. (J). pap. 3.95 ***(978-0-87483-803-9(7))*** August Hse. Pubs., Inc.

Holt, Rinehart and Winston Staff. And Now Miguel. 3rd ed. 2003. (Illus.). 16.80 (978-0-03-035916-3(3)) Holt, Rinehart & Winston.

Hope, Laura Lee. Bunny Brown & His Sister Sue on Grandpa's Farm. 2007. (ENG.). 164p. 95.99 ***(978-1-4280-7438-5(4))***; per. 89.99 ***(978-1-4280-7440-8(6))*** IndyPublish.com.

Hopkinson, Deborah. Bluebird Summer. Andersen, Bethanne, illus. 2001. 32p. (J). (gr. 1 up). 15.95 (978-0-688-17398-2(5)) HarperCollins Pubs.

Hudspeth, Elly Shafter & Peyton, Barbara. Colt Revolt: Memoirs of Three Mischievous, but Adorable Equine Siblings. Wilkins, Rhett, illus. 2007. 140p. pap. 12.95 ***(978-1-60145-223-8(3))*** Booklocker.com, Inc.

Hughes, Dawn Marie. Oakley Farm Friends. 2006. 83p. pap. 14.95 (978-1-4241-2094-9(2)) PublishAmerica, Inc.

Huneck, Stephen. Sally Goes to the Farm. Huneck, Stephen, illus. 2002. (Illus.). 40p. (J). (ps-3). 17.95 (978-0-8109-4498-5(7)) Abrams, Harry N. , Inc.

Hunt, Darleen L. Farm Pizza. Hoskin, Tom, ed. Komarck, Michael, illus. l.t. ed. 1999. (Readers Ser.). 8p. (J). (ps-2). pap. 15.00 (978-1-929591-51-0(9)) Reading Rock, Inc.

—Farm Pizza: Little Book. Hoskin, Tom, ed. Komarck, Michael, illus. l.t. ed. 1999. (Readers Ser.). 8p. (J). (ps-2). pap. 4.00 (978-1-929591-50-3(0)) Reading Rock, Inc.

Hunt, Irene. Across Five Aprils. 2002. 224p. (gr. 12). pap. 4.99 (978-0-425-18278-9(9) , Berkley) Penguin Group (USA) Inc.

—Across Five Aprils. 1999. (J). pap. 1.95 (978-0-590-05178-1(4)) Scholastic, Inc.

Huntington, Amy. One Monday. Huntington, Amy, illus. 2002. (Illus.). 32p. (J). (ps-1). pap. 16.95 (978-0-439-29304-4(9) , Orchard Bks.) Scholastic, Inc.

Hurst, Carol Otis. In Plain Sight. 2002. 160p. (YA). (gr. 5-9). 15.00 (978-0-618-19699-9(4) , Walter Lorraine) Houghton Mifflin Co. Trade & Reference Div.

Hurwitz, Johanna. The Unsigned Valentine: And Other Events in the Life of Emma Meade. Azarian, Mary, illus. 2006. 176p. (J). 15.99 (978-0-06-056053-9(3)); lib. bdg. 16.89 (978-0-06-056054-6(1)) HarperCollins Pubs.

Hutchins, Hazel J. One Duck. 1999. (gr. k-3). lib. bdg. 15.25 (978-0-613-26478-5(9)) Tandem Library Bks.

Hutchins, Pat. Bumpety Bump! Hutchins, Pat, illus. 2006. (Illus.). 32p. (J). 15.99 (978-0-06-055999-1(3)); lib. bdg. 16.89 (978-0-06-056000-3(2)) HarperCollins Pubs.

Hysen, Sylvia. A Very Dairy Christmas. 2005. 312p. (YA). 24.95 (978-0-9763365-6-3(1)) 1st Impression Publishing.

Inteli, Nancy. Farm Faces. 2008. 10p. (J). (ps-k). bds. 8.99 ***(978-0-618-91959-8(7))*** Houghton Mifflin Co. Trade & Reference Div.

Jackson, Chris. Edmund & Washable: A Tale from China Plate Farm. 2000. (Illus.). 24p. (J). 12.00 (978-0-00-224558-6(2)) HarperCollins Pubs.

Jackson, Dave & Jackson, Neta. The Forty-Acre Swindle: George Washington Carver. McLaughlin, Catherine R., illus. 2000. (Trailblazer Bks.: Vol. 31). 144p. (J). (gr. 3-7). pap. 6.99 (978-0-7642-2264-1(3)) Bethany Hse. Pubs.

Jacobs, E. Caroline. The S. W. F. Club. 2006. 77.99 ***(978-1-4280-4783-9(2))***; pap. 71.99 ***(978-1-4280-4779-2(4))*** IndyPublish.com.

Jahn-Clough, Lisa. Country Girl, City Girl. 2004. 192p. (YA). (gr. 5). tchr. ed. 15.00 (978-0-618-44791-6(1) , Walter Lorraine) Houghton Mifflin Co. Trade & Reference Div.

Jam, Teddy. The Stoneboat. Zhang, Ange, illus. 2nd ed. 1999. 32p. (J). (ps-2). 15.95 (978-0-88899-368-7(4) , Libros Tigrillo) Groundwood Bks. CAN. *Dist:* Perseus Distribution.

Janke, Katelan. Survival in the Storm: The Dust Bowl Diary of Grace Edwards. 2002. (Dear America Ser.). (Illus.). 192p. (J). (gr. 4-9). pap. 10.95 (978-0-439-21599-2(4)) Scholastic, Inc.

Jaspersohn, William. The Two Brothers. Donato, Michael A., illus. 2005. (Family Heritage Ser.). 36p. (J). (gr. 1-5). 15.95 (978-0-916718-16-9(6)) Vermont Folklife Ctr.

Jennings, Patrick. The Ears of Corn: An Ike & Mem Story. Alter, Anna, illus. 2003. 64p. (J). (gr. k-3). tchr. ed. 15.95 (978-0-8234-1770-4(0)) Holiday Hse., Inc.

—The Weeping Willow. Alter, Anna, illus. 2002. (Ike & Mem Story Ser.: No. 3). 56p. (J). (gr. k-3). tchr. ed. 15.95 (978-0-8234-1671-4(2)) Holiday Hse., Inc.

Johansen, Hanna. Henrietta & the Golden Egg. Barrett, John S., tr. from GER. Bhend-Zaugg, Kathi, illus. 2002. Tr. of Vom Huhnchen das Goldene Eier Legen Wollte. 64p. (J). 16.95 (978-1-56792-210-3(4)) Godine, David R. Pub.

Johnson, D. B., illus. Four Legs Bad, Two Legs Good! 2007. 32p. (J). (gr. 3-5). 16.00 ***(978-0-618-80909-7(0))*** Houghton Mifflin Co.

Johnston, Annie Fell. The Little Colonel. 2005. reprint ed. pap. 21.95 (978-0-7661-9402-1(7)) Kessinger Publishing, LLC.

Johnston, Annie Fell. The Little Colonel (Illustrated Edition) 2006. pap. ***(978-1-4065-1132-1(3))*** Dodo Pr.

Johnston, Annie Fellows. The Little Colonel. Barry, Etheldred B., illus. 2004. (Little Colonel Ser.). 128p. (J). (gr. 4-7). reprint ed. per. 12.95 (978-1-55709-315-8(6)) Applewood Bks.

Johnston, Fellows Annie. Little Colonel. 2006. pap. 18.99 ***(978-1-4280-3283-5(5))*** IndyPublish.com.

Johnston, Tony. Boo! Croll, Carolyn, illus. 1998. (Hello Reader! Ser.). (J). 3.99 (978-0-590-37998-4(4)) Scholastic, Inc.

Jones, Karen. Stories from the Television Show Imagination Way. 2006. 10.00 (978-0-8059-8195-7(0)) Dorrance Publishing Co., Inc.

Jones, Lara. Fun on the Farm. Jones, Lara, illus. 2003. (Lola & Binky Bks.). (Illus.). 8p. (J). bds. 5.95 (978-0-7641-5688-5(8)) Barron's Educational Series, Inc.

Kalz, Jill. Farmer Cap. Erkocak, Sahin, illus. 2007. (Pfeffernut County Ser.). 26p. (J). (gr. k-2). lib. bdg. 23.93 ***(978-1-4048-3139-1(8))*** Picture Window Bks.

Karim, Roberta. Mandy Sue Day. Ritz, Karen, illus. 2003. 32p. (J). 5.95 (978-0-618-31675-5(2) , Clarion Bks.) Houghton Mifflin Co. Trade & Reference Div.

Kay, Verla. Homespun Sarah. Rand, Ted, illus. 2003. 32p. (J). (ps-3). 16.99 (978-0-399-23417-0(9) , Putnam Juvenile) Penguin Group (USA) Inc.

Kelly, Mij. Where's My Darling Daughter? McEwen, Katharine, illus. 2006. 28p. (J). 16.00 (978-1-56148-537-6(3)) Good Bks.

Kennedy, Fran. The Pickle Patch Bathtub. Aldridge, Sheila, illus. 2004. 32p. (J). 14.95 (978-1-58246-112-0(0) , Tricycle Pr.) Ten Speed Pr.

Ketteman, Helen. Heat Wave! 2000. (J). 13.75 (978-0-606-19679-6(X)) Tandem Library Bks.

—Heat Wave! Goto, Scott, illus. 1998. 32p. (J). (gr. k-3). 15.95 (978-0-8027-8644-9(8)); lib. bdg. 16.85 (978-0-8027-8645-6(6)) Walker & Co.

Kimmel, Haven. Orville: A Dog Story. Parker, Robert Andrew, illus. 2003. 32p. (J). (gr. k-3). 15.00 (978-0-618-15955-0(X) , Clarion Bks.) Houghton Mifflin Co. Trade & Reference Div.

King, Bob & Slavin, Bill. Chantons a la Ferme. (FRE.). (J). pap. 7.99 (978-0-590-73949-8(2)) Scholastic, Inc.

King-Smith, Dick. The Crowstarver. l.t. ed. 2000. (J). (Illus.). 243p. pap. (978-0-7540-6095-6(0) , Galaxy Children's Large Print); 216p. pap. incl. audio (978-0-7540-6228-8(7) , RA029, Chivers Children's Audio Bks.) BBC Audiobooks America.

—The Golden Goose. 2006. 128p. (J). (gr. 4-7). 5.50 (978-0-440-42030-9(X) , Yearling) Random Hse. Children's Bks.

—The Golden Goose. Kronheimer, Ann, illus. 2005. 128p. (J). (gr. 3-7). 15.95 (978-0-375-82984-0(9) , Knopf Bks. for Young Readers) Random Hse. Children's Bks.

Kingsolver, Barbara. Prodigal Summer. 2001. (gr. 7-12). lib. bdg. 23.45 (978-0-613-64446-4(8)) Tandem Library Bks.

Kinsey-Warnock, Natalie. As Long As There Are Mountains. 2001. (gr. 5-8). lib. bdg. 13.00 (978-0-613-35902-3(X)) Tandem Library Bks.

—Canada Geese Quilt. 2000. 11.79 (978-0-606-20354-8(0)) Tandem Library Bks.

—A Christmas Like Helen's. Azarian, Mary, illus. 2004. 32p. (J). (gr. k-3). tchr. ed. 16.00 (978-0-618-23137-9(4)) Houghton Mifflin Co. Trade & Reference Div.

—From Dawn till Dusk. Azarian, Mary, illus. 2002. 40p. (J). (gr. k-3). tchr. ed. 16.00 (978-0-618-18655-6(7)) Houghton Mifflin Co. Trade & Reference Div.

—From Dawn till Dusk. Azarian, Mary, illus. 2006. 40p. (J). (gr. k-3). reprint ed. pap. 6.95 (978-0-618-73750-5(2)) Houghton Mifflin Co. Trade & Reference Div.

—The Night the Bells Rang. 2001. (gr. 1-5). 20.50 (978-0-8446-7180-2(0)) Smith, Peter Pub., Inc.

—The Night the Bells Rang. 2000. (978-0-606-20367-8(2)) Tandem Library Bks.

—The Night the Bells Rang. Bowman, Leslie, illus. 2000. (Puffin Chapters Ser.). 80p. (J). (gr. 2-5). pap. 4.99 (978-0-14-130986-6(5) , Puffin) Penguin Group (USA) Inc.

—Night the Bells Rang. 2000. (gr. 3-6). lib. bdg. 13.00 (978-0-613-30071-1(8)) Tandem Library Bks.

Kjellberg, B. Abe: A Farm Boy. 2006. (J). per. (978-0-912868-07-3(4)) Kjellberg, Inc.

—Apple Acres: The Farm. 2006. (J). per. 7.95 ***(978-0-912868-10-3(4))*** Kjellberg, Inc.

—Courtnee: A Farm Girl. 2005. (Illus.). 84p. (J). per. 7.95 (978-0-912868-06-6(6)) Kjellberg, Inc.

—Sandy: A City Girl. 2005. (Illus.). 94p. (J). per. 7.95 (978-0-912868-08-0(2) , 8080) Kjellberg, Inc.

Klein, Adria F. Max Goes to the Farm. Gallagher-Cole, Mernie, illus. 2007. (J). lib. bdg. ***(978-1-4048-3678-5(0))*** Picture Window Bks.

Korbel, Wendy. Gus: Adventures on the Farm. 2007. 24p. (J). pap. 8.99 ***(978-1-59886-999-6(X))*** Tate Publishing & Enterprises, L.L.C.

Koury, Jen. Big John on the Big Farm. Linden, Pat & Hilko, Steve, eds. Koury, Jen, illus. 1999. (Johnny Tractor Toybooks Ser.). (Illus.). 10p. (J). (ps-1). (978-1-887327-23-7(1)) Ertl Co., Inc.

—Billy Baler's Hay Day. Linden, Pat & Hilko, Steve, eds. Koury, Jen, illus. 1999. (Johnny Tractor Toybooks Ser.). (Illus.). 10p. (J). (ps-1). (978-1-887327-22-0(3)) Ertl Co., Inc.

—Wally Wagon's Big Harvest. Torgerson, Dell & Reyner, Mark, eds. Koury, Jen, illus. 1999. (John Deere Kids Toybook Ser.). (Illus.). 10p. (J). (ps up). mass mkt. 9.99 (978-1-887327-28-2(2)) Ertl Co., Inc.

Kovalski, Maryann. Queen Nadine. Kovalski, Maryann, illus. 2000. (Illus.). 32p. (J). (ps-2). 14.95 (978-1-55143-093-5(2)); 6.95 (978-1-55143-095-9(9)) Orca Bk. Pubs. USA.

E F G

—Queen Nadine. 2000. lib. bdg. 15.25 (978-0-613-54850-2(7)) Tandem Library Bks.

Krauss, Ruth. The Carrot Seed. 2005. (Illus.). (J). pap. 18.95 incl. audio compact disk (978-1-59112-705-5(X)) Live Oak Media.

Krosoczka, Jarrett J. Punk Farm. 2005. (Illus.). 40p. (J). (gr. k-3). 15.95 (978-0-375-82429-6(4)); lib. bdg. 17.99 (978-0-375-92429-3(9)) Random Hse. Children's Bks. (Knopf Bks. for Young Readers).

Krupinski, Loretta. Pirate Treasure. Krupinski, Loretta, illus. 2006. (Illus.). 32p. (J). (gr. k). 15.99 (978-0-525-47579-8(6) , Dutton Juvenile) Penguin Group (USA) Inc.

Kueffner, Sue. Discovery Farm. 1999. (Lamaze Ser.). (Illus.). 12p. (J). (ps-k). 12.99 (978-1-56799-891-7(7) , Friedman-Fairfax) Friedman, Michael Publishing Group, Inc.

Lasky, Kathryn. Sugaring Time. 2003. (Illus.). 21.25 (978-0-8446-7248-9(3)) Smith, Peter Pub., Inc.

Leaf, Munro, et al. Ferdinandus Taurus. 2000. (Illus.). 80p. reprint ed. pap. 17.95 (978-1-56792-127-4(2)) Godine, David R. Pub.

LeapFrog Staff, compiled by. Tad's Counting Day on the Farm. 2001. (YA). (ps up). spiral bd. 9.99 (978-1-58605-096-2(6)) LeapFrog Enterprises, Inc.

Leatherman, Diane. Abigail Before the Revolution. 2005. (Illus.). 64p. (J). ***978-0-9665861-2-1(3)*** Bounty Project, The.

Leatherman, Diane. Rebecca, a Maryland Farm Girl. 2002. (J). (gr. 3-7). per. 7.95 (978-0-9665861-1-4(5)) Bounty Project, The.

Leininger Craven, Tracy. Kathleen's Dreadful Drought. 2006. 12.99 (978-1-928749-90-5(9)) Mission City Pr., Inc.

Lewis, Alan K. I Grew up on a Farm. Fletcher, Bob, illus. 2005. 32p. (J). (ps-3). 19.95 (978-0-9766805-2-9(1) , Moo Pr.) Keene Publishing.

Lewis, Beverly. Just Like Mama. Bladholm, Cheri, illus. 2002. 32p. (J). 14.99 (978-0-7642-2507-9(3)) Bethany Hse. Pubs.

Lewis, Kim. Quilt for Baby. Lewis, Kim, illus. 2002. (Illus.). 32p. (J). (gr. k-k). 15.99 (978-0-7636-1925-1(6)) Candlewick Pr.

Light, Carol. Chickensing Big Book. Light, Carol, illus. 2003. (Illus.). (J). (978-0-9745803-2-6(5)) Little Big Tomes.

—Chickensing Little Book. Light, Carol, illus. 2003. (Illus.). 108p. (J). (978-0-9745803-3-3(3)) Little Big Tomes.

—Chickensing Story Book Reader. Light, Carol, illus. 2003. (Illus.). 60p. (J). (978-0-9745803-1-9(7)) Little Big Tomes.

Light, Carol, illus. Oops, a Curious Horse Story Telling Board. 2003. (J). (978-0-9745803-4-0(1)) Little Big Tomes.

Lindsey, Kathleen D. Sweet Potato Pie. Riley-Webb, Charlotte, illus. 2003. (J). 16.95 (978-1-58430-061-8(2)) Lee & Low Bks., Inc.

Lipe, Riki. Sooty. Spears-Stewart, Reta, ed. 1998. (Illus.). 34p. (J). (ps-6). 10.00 (978-0-9659381-3-6(1)) Hoot N' Cackle Pr.

Literature Connections English: Where the Red Fern Grows. 2004. (gr. 6-12). (978-0-395-77528-8(0) , 2-80097) McDougal Littell Inc.

Little Engine- on the Farm. 2005. (J). (978-1-4194-0006-3(1)) Paradise Pr., Inc.

Little Engine AV on the Farm. 2005. (J). (978-1-4194-0009-4(6)) Paradise Pr., Inc.

Little Farm down the Lane, Bk. III. 2005. pap. 10.99 (978-1-59781-702-8(3)) Xulon Pr., Inc.

Loughead, Deb. Time & Again. 2005. 192p. (J). pap. 9.95 (978-1-894549-39-4(2)) Sumach Pr. CAN. *Dist:* Orca Bk. Pubs. USA.

Ludy, Mark. The Farmer. Farabaugh, Sue-Kyung Y., ed. Ludy, Mark, illus. 1999. (Illus.). 64p. (J). (ps-6). 18.95 (978-0-9664276-0-8(2)) Green Pastures Publishing, Inc.

Luna Rising Staff, ed. Elmo's Big Word Book. 2006. (Elmo's World Ser.). (SPA & ENG., Illus.). 12p. (J). 6.95 (978-0-87358-906-2(8) , Luna Rising) Northland Publishing.

MacBride, Roger Lea. Rose & Alva. 1999. (Little House Chapter Bks.). (J). (gr. 2-5). (978-0-606-18718-3(9)) Tandem Library Bks.

MacBride, Roger Lea & Ettlinger, Doris, illus. Rose & Alva. 2000. (Little House Chapter Bks.: No. 3). 80p. (J). (gr. 2-5). 14.89 (978-0-06-028158-8(8)) HarperCollins Pubs.

MacDonald, Betty Bard. Hello, Mrs. Piggle-Wiggle. 2000. (YA). pap. 40.20 incl. audio (978-0-7887-4171-5(3) , 41089) Recorded Bks., LLC.

—Mrs. Piggle-Wiggle. Knight, Hilary, illus. 2002. (J). 13.40 (978-0-7587-6605-2(X)) Book Wholesalers, Inc.

MacDonald, Betty Bard, ed. Mrs. Piggle-Wiggle's Bad Table-Manners Cure. Whatley, Bruce, illus. 2000. (Mrs. Piggle-Wiggle Adventure Ser.). (J). 12.95 (978-0-06-027632-4(0)); 12.89 (978-0-06-027633-1(9)) HarperCollins Pubs.

MacDonald, Betty Bard & Canham, Anne Macdonald. Mrs. Piggle-Wiggle. Boiger, Alexandra, illus. 2007. 208p. (J). lib. bdg. 16.89 ***978-0-06-072813-7(2)*** HarperCollins Pubs.

Maclean, Christine. Mary Margaret Meets Her Match. 2007. 176p. (J). (gr. 3-5). 15.99 (978-0-525-47775-4(6) , Dutton Juvenile) Penguin Group (USA) Inc.

Macuga, Linda. Harvest of Hope. 1999. 414p. (J). (ps-3). pap. 15.95 (978-1-891929-29-8(1)) Four Seasons Pubs.

Madison, Mike. No Time to Nap. Peterson, Mary, illus. 2007. (J). (978-1-59714-046-1(5)) Heyday Bks.

Maguire, Gregory. Crabby Cratchitt. Glass, Andrew, illus. 2000. 32p. (J). (gr. k-3). tchr. ed. 15.00 (978-0-395-60485-4(0) , Clarion Bks.) Houghton Mifflin Co. Trade & Reference Div.

Maizels, Jennie. The Picnic at Jigsaw Farm. 1999. (Jigsaw Bks.). (Illus.). 14p. (J). (ps-k). bds. 10.95 (978-1-86233-068-9(9)) Sterling Publishing Co., Inc.

Man-Kong, Mary. At the Farm: Create It All with Play-Doh Colors & Stencil. 2003. (Play-Doh Ser.). (Illus.). 12p. (J). 9.95 (978-0-7624-1562-5(2) , Running Pr. Kids) Running Pr. Bk. Pubs.

Martelli, Dawn. Like Me. Wharton, Jennifer Heyd, illus. 2004. (J). (978-1-893516-01-4(6)) Our Child Pr.

Martin, Jacqueline Briggs. Chicken Joy on Redbean Road: A Bayou Country Romp. Sweet, Melissa, illus. 2007. 32p. (J). (gr. 3-5). 17.00 (978-0-618-50759-7(0)) Houghton Mifflin Co.

Martin, Terri L. A Family Trait. 1999. 160p. (J). (gr. 4-6). tchr. ed. 15.95 (978-0-8234-1467-3(1)) Holiday Hse., Inc.

Martínez, Arturo O. Pedrito's World. 2007. (Illus.). 160p. (J). 16.95 ***978-0-89672-600-0(2)*** Texas Tech Univ. Pr.

Martyn, Eve. Killer McKenzie. 2002. 352p. pap. (978-0-7344-0263-9(5) , Lothian Bks.) Hachette Livre Australia.

Mason, Tom & Danko, Dan, adapted by. Barnyard: The Original Party Animals. 2006. (Barnyard Ser.). (Illus.). 128p. (J). pap. 4.99 (978-1-4169-0722-0(X) , Simon Spotlight) Simon & Schuster Children's Publishing.

Masurel, C. & Halpern, S. No Tito No!/No No Titus! 2006. (Illus.). 32p. (J). 16.50 (978-0-7358-2074-6(0)); pap. 6.95 (978-0-7358-2075-3(9)) North-South Bks., Inc.

Masurel, Claire. No, Tito, No! No, No, Titus! Lasconi, Diego, tr. Halpern, Shari, illus. 1999. (SPA.). 32p. (J). (ps-1). 15.95 (978-0-7358-1208-6(X) , NS3699); pap. 6.95 (978-0-7358-1209-3(8) , NS3707) North-South Bks., Inc.

Mather, Melissa. One Summer in Between. 2000. 228p. (YA). pap. 14.95 (978-0-595-09384-7(1) , Backinprint-.com) iUniverse, Inc.

Matteson, Rosemary. Tommy's Circle of Friends at Meadowview Farm. 2002. (Illus.). (J). (ps-5). 21.95 (978-1-881636-64-9(X)) Windsor Hse. Publishing Group, The.

Mayer, Mercer. Harvest Time, Vol. 3. 2003. (Little Critter Ser.). (Illus.). 24p. (J). (gr. 1-2). pap. 3.95 (978-1-57768-578-4(4)) School Specialty Publishing.

—Harvest Time. 2003. (gr. k-3). lib. bdg. 11.80 (978-0-613-86837-2(4)) Tandem Library Bks.

—My Trip to the Farm, Vol. 3. 2002. (Little Critter First Readers Ser.). (Illus.). 24p. (J). (gr. 1-2). pap. 3.95 (978-1-57768-817-4(1)) School Specialty Publishing.

—My Trip to the Farm. 2000. (gr. k-3). lib. bdg. 11.80 (978-0-613-67647-2(5)) Tandem Library Bks.

Mayo, Diana, illus. The House That Jack Built. 24p. (J). pap. 6.99 (978-1-84148-253-8(6)); 2001. 15.99 (978-1-84148-251-4(X)) Barefoot Bks., Inc.

Mayr, Diane. Run, Turkey Run. Rader, Laura, illus. 2007. 32p. (J). (ps-2). 15.95 ***978-0-8027-9630-1(3)*** Walker & Co.

Mayr, Diane & Rader, Laura. Run, Turkey Run. 2007. (Illus.). 32p. (J). 16.85 ***978-0-8027-9631-8(1)*** Walker & Co.

McColley, Kevin. Pecking Order. 2000. 224p. (YA). (gr. 12 up). pap. 4.95 (978-0-06-440516-4(8)) HarperCollins Pubs.

McDonald, Ronald L. Old MacDonald Had a Farm. Chapman, Jane, illus. 1999. (Reading Together Ser.). 24p. (J). (ps). pap. 3.99 (978-0-7636-0854-5(8)) Candlewick Pr.

McGee, Marni. The Noisy Farm. Shearing, Leonie, tr. Shearing, Leonie, illus. 2004. 32p. (J). (ps-1). 15.95 (978-1-58234-879-7(0) , Bloomsbury Children) Bloomsbury Publishing.

McGill, Alice & Soentpiet, Chris K. Molly Bannaky. 1999. (Illus.). 32p. (J). (gr. k-3). tchr. ed. 17.00 (978-0-395-72287-9(X)) Houghton Mifflin Co. Trade & Reference Div.

McJunkin, Jehu David & Wethern, Amelia A. Back on the Farm. l.t. ed. 2006. (Illus.). 100p. (J). 14.95 (978-0-9766124-1-4(0)) Ap Amelia Pr.

McMahon, Kate & Myler, Terry. Timber Twig. 1998. 142p. pap. 10.95 (978-1-901737-01-1(2)) Anvil Bks., Ltd. IRL. *Dist:* Dufour Editions, Inc.

McMullan, Margaret. When I Crossed No-Bob. 2007. 224p. (J). (gr. 5-9). 16.00 ***978-0-618-71715-6(3)*** Houghton Mifflin Co. Trade & Reference Div.

McOmber, Rachel B., ed. McOmber Phonics Storybooks: In the Dell. rev. ed. (Illus.). (J). (978-0-944991-32-9(7)) Swift Learning Resources.

Mi Abuelita. 2001. (SPA.). (J). pap. 14.95 (978-0-9630310-5-1(8)) Will Hall Bks.

Mikesell, Janice H. Some People Don't Know That Barns Have Faces: A Book for Prairie Children. Lindemann, Chad, illus. Mikesell, Janice H., photos by. 1999. 40p. (J). (gr. k-4). pap. 10.00 (978-0-9621112-4-2(4)) Smith, Hilary.

Milgrim, David. Young McDonald. Milgrim, David, illus. 2006. (Illus.). 32p. (J). (gr. k). 12.99 (978-0-525-47570-5(2) , Dutton Juvenile) Penguin Group (USA) Inc.

Millard, Anne. Rose's Farm. 2001. (Illus.). (J). (ps-3). bds. 12.95 (978-0-7894-6896-3(4)) Dorling Kindersley Publishing, Inc.

Miller Cormier, Susan. Life on the Farm. 2007. (Illus.). 28p. (J). pap. ***978-1-4251-1913-3(1)*** Trafford Publishing.

Miller, Ruth. I Went to the Farm. Gurth, Per-Henrik, illus. 2000. 24p. (J). (gr. k-3). (978-1-55074-705-8(3)) Kids Can Pr., Ltd.

—I Went to the Farm. Guerth, Per-Henrik, illus. unabr. ed. 2002. 24p. (J). (gr. k-3). (978-1-55074-709-6(6)) Kids Can Pr., Ltd.

Milord, Susan. The Ghost on the Hearth. Dabcovich, Lydia, illus. 2003. (Family Heritage Ser.). 36p. (J). (gr. 1-5). 15.95 (978-0-916718-18-3(2)) Vermont Folklife Ctr.

Mitzo Thompson, Kim. Early Learning, 2 Packs. 2006. (Read & Sing along Board Books with CDs Ser.). 36p. (J). bds. 14.98 (978-0-7696-4594-0(1)) School Specialty Publishing.

Molly's Magic: Evaluation Guide. 2006. (J). (978-1-55942-417-2(6)) Marsh Media.

Moranville, Sharelle Byars. Over the River. rev. ed. 2002. 240p. (J). (gr. 4-9). 16.95 (978-0-8050-7049-1(4) , Holt, Henry & Co. Bks. For Young Readers) Holt, Henry & Co.

—Over the River. 2004. 240p. (gr. 5). 5.99 (978-0-440-41977-8(8) , Yearling) Random Hse. Children's Bks.

Morganstern, Mimi. The House at Hemlock Farms. Morganstern, Mimi, illus. 2000. (Illus.). vi, 54p. (J). (gr. 3-6). pap. 6.95 (978-0-9700522-3-0(5)) Morganstern, Mimi.

—The House at Hemlock Farms-"Read-Along with Mimi" A Cool Chapterbook-Package. Morganstern, Mimi, illus. 2000. (Illus.). vi, 54p. (J). (gr. 3-6). per. 9.99 incl. audio (978-0-9700522-4-7(3)) Morganstern, Mimi.

Morpurgo, Michael. Farm Boy. Foreman, Michael, illus. 1999. 74p. (YA). pap. 16.99 (978-1-86205-192-8(5) , Pavilion Bks., Ltd.) Anova Bks. GBR. *Dist:* Trafalgar Square Publishing.

—It's a Dog's Life. Allibone, Judith, illus. 2007. (J). ***978-0-374-33620-2(2)*** Farrar, Straus & Giroux.

Morpurgo, Michael. Out of the Ashes. Foreman, Michael, illus. l.t. ed. 2005. 144p. (J). pap. (978-0-7540-6190-8(6) , CLP 382) BBC Audio.

—Out of the Ashes. 2003. (Illus.). 128p. (J). pap. 9.99 (978-0-330-40017-6(7) , Macmillan Children's Bks.) Pan Macmillan GBR. *Dist:* Trafalgar Square Publishing.

Mortensen, Denise Dowling. Ohio Thunder. Kiesler, Kate, illus. 2006. 32p. (J). (gr. k-3). 16.00 (978-0-618-59542-6(2) , Clarion Bks.) Houghton Mifflin Co. Trade & Reference Div.

Morton, Christine. Picnic Farm. Barringer, Sarah, illus. 1998. 32p. (J). (ps-k). 15.95 (978-0-8234-1332-4(2)) Holiday Hse., Inc.

Moss, Marissa. Rose's Journal: The Story of a Girl in the Great Depression. 2003. (Young American Voices Ser.). (Illus.). 56p. (J). pap. 7.00 (978-0-15-204605-7(4) , Silver Whistle) Harcourt Trade Pubs.

—Rose's Journal: The Story of a Girl in the Great Depression. Moss, Marissa, illus. 2001. (Young American Voices Ser.). (Illus.). 56p. (YA). (gr. 3-7). 15.00 (978-0-15-202423-9(9) , Silver Whistle) Harcourt Trade Pubs.

Muhammad, Shahid. The Adventures of the Math Doctor: Book One: King Jafiz & the Evil Farmer Nimra. 2007. (J). per. 7.95 ***978-1-59872-778-4(8)*** Instantpublisher-.com.

Mullican, Judy. Fall on the Farm. Gray, Stacy A., illus. l.t. ed. 2005. (Hrl Boand Book Ser.). (J). (ps-k). pap. 10.95 (978-1-57332-323-9(3)) HighReach Learning, Inc.

—Inside the Big Red Barn. Metzger, Jeanne, illus. l.t. ed. 1999. (Children's Bks.). 8p. (J). (ps-k). pap. 10.95 (978-1-57332-136-5(2)); pap. 10.95 (978-1-57332-135-8(4)) HighReach Learning, Inc.

—Springtime on the Farm. Cress, Michelle H., illus. l.t. ed. 1998. (Big Bks.). 8p. (J). (ps-k). pap. 10.95 (978-1-57332-120-4(6)); pap. 10.95 (978-1-57332-121-1(4)) HighReach Learning, Inc.

Mullican, Judy. The Tod Squad Can Go to the Farm. 2007. (J). bds. ***978-1-57332-445-8(0)*** HighReach Learning, Inc.

Mullins, Norman D. Mountain Boy: The Adventures of Orion Saddler. 2004. 104p. (YA). per. 9.95 (978-0-9724867-4-3(7)) Woodland Pr. LLC.

Murdock, Catherine Gilbert. Dairy Queen: A Novel. 2006. 288p. (YA). (gr. 7-10). 16.00 (978-0-618-68307-9(0)) Houghton Mifflin Co.

—Dairy Queen: A Novel. 2007. 288p. (YA). (gr. 7 up). pap. 8.99 ***978-0-618-86335-8(4)*** , Graphia) Houghton Mifflin Co. Trade & Reference Div.

—The Off Season. 2007. 288p. (YA). (gr. 7-10). 16.00 ***978-0-618-68695-7(9)*** Houghton Mifflin Co. Trade & Reference Div.

Murphy, Bonnie. Can A Rooster Drive A Tractor? Richardson, Shelley, illus. 2001. 32p. (J). 14.95 (978-0-9714419-0-3(1)) Alabama Farmers Federation.

Murphy, Mary. How Kind! Murphy, Mary, illus. 2004. (Illus.). 24p. (J). (gr. k-k). bds. 6.99 (978-0-7636-2307-4(5)) Candlewick Pr.

Murray, Anna. Sarah's Page. 1998. (Illus.). 144p. (J). (gr. 4-7). 14.00 (978-1-886947-58-0(9)) Sleeping Bear Pr.

My Very Own Farm Play Set. 2004. (J). (978-1-59292-005-1(5)) SoftPlay, Inc.

Nash, Margaret. Hetty's New Hat. Impey, Martin, illus. 2005. (Reading Corner Ser.). 24p. (J). (gr. k-3). lib. bdg. 22.80 (978-1-59771-007-7(5)) Sea-To-Sea Pubns.

Naylor, Phyllis Reynolds. Ice. 1998. 256p. (YA). (gr. 7-12). mass mkt. 12.95 (978-0-689-81872-1(6) , Simon Pulse) Simon & Schuster Children's Publishing.

—Ice. 1998. (J). 11.64 (978-0-606-12970-1(7)) Tandem Library Bks.

—Walker's Crossing. 2001. (J). (978-0-606-21506-0(9)); (gr. 7-12). lib. bdg. 13.00 (978-0-613-35030-3(8)) Tandem Library Bks.

Nelson, Ray & Mohr-Hansen, Julie. On the Farm, 5 bks. Holveck, Kyle & Peeples, Aaron, illus. 2000. (J). (gr. k-2). pap. 60.00 (978-1-883772-79-6(6)) Flying Rhinoceros, Inc.

Neusner, Dena. Fun at the County Fair. Carbajal, Richard & Stubbs, Tommy, illus. 2005. (John Deere Lift the Flap Bks.: No. 3). 10p. (J). (ps-1). pap. 11.95 (978-0-7624-2370-5(6) , Running Pr. Kids) Running Pr. Bk. Pubs.

Nikola-Lisa, W. Summer Sun Risin' Tate, Don, illus. 32p. (J). (ps-ps). 2005. pap. 7.95 (978-1-58430-252-0(6)); 2002. 16.95 (978-1-58430-034-2(5)) Lee & Low Bks., Inc.

Nixon-Weaver, Elizabeth. Rooster. 2001. (Illus.). 320p. (J). (gr. 7 up). 16.95 (978-1-58837-001-3(1)) Winslow Pr.

Noble, Trinka Hakes. Apple Tree Christmas. Noble, Trinka Hakes, illus. 2005. (Illus.). 32p. (J). (ps-3). 16.95 (978-1-58536-270-7(0)) Sleeping Bear Pr.

Nolen, Jerdine. Harvey Potter's Balloon Farm. Buehner, Mark, illus. 1998. 32p. (J). (ps-3). pap. 6.99 (978-0-688-15845-3(5) , Harper Trophy) HarperCollins Pubs.

—Harvey Potter's Balloon Farm. 1998. (J). 12.75 (978-0-606-13100-1(0)) Tandem Library Bks.

—Raising Dragons. Primavera, Elise, illus. 2002. (J). 21.70 (978-0-7587-3493-8(X)) Book Wholesalers, Inc.

—Raising Dragons. Primavera, Elise, illus. 40p. (J). 2002. (gr. 1-4). pap. 7.00 (978-0-15-216536-9(3) , Voyager Bks./Libros Viajeros); 1998. (ps-3). 16.00 (978-0-15-201288-5(5)) Harcourt Children's Bks.

—Raising Dragons. 2002. (ps-2). lib. bdg. 14.15 (978-0-613-53857-2(9)) Tandem Library Bks.

O'Brien, John. The Farmer in the Dell. O'Brien, John, illus. 2003. (Illus.). 32p. (YA). (gr. k-2). 14.95 (978-1-56397-775-6(3)) Boyds Mills Pr.

O'Donnell, Liam. Daisy on the Farm. (Pet Tales Ser.). (Illus.). 32p. (J). (ps-2). 9.95 (978-1-59249-452-1(8) , 1B037) Soundprints.

—Daisy on the Farm. Hatala, Dan, illus. 2005. (Pet Tales Ser.). 32p. (J). (ps-2). 2.95 (978-1-59249-451-4(X) , 1B036) Soundprints.

—Daisy the Farm Pony. Hatala, Dan, illus. 2005. (Pet Tales Ser.). 32p. (J). (ps-ps). pap. 4.95 (978-1-59249-450-7(1) , 1B035) Soundprints.

Oke, Janette. Maury Had a Little Lamb. Munger, Nancy, illus. rev. ed. 2001. (Janette Oke's Animal Friends Ser.). 80p. (Orig.). (J). (gr. 1-5). pap. 6.99 (978-0-7642-2457-7(3)) Bethany Hse. Pubs.

—Maury Had a Little Lamb. 2001. (Orig.). (gr. 3-6). lib. bdg. 14.15 (978-0-613-82431-6(8)) Tandem Library Bks.

—This Little Pig. Munger, Nancy, illus. 2001. (Animal Friends Ser.: Vol. 4). 80p. (Orig.). (J). (ps-3). pap. 6.99 (978-0-7642-2448-5(4)) Bethany Hse. Pubs.

—This Little Pig. 2001. (Orig.). (gr. k-3). lib. bdg. 14.15 (978-0-613-85065-0(3)) Tandem Library Bks.

Olasky, Susan. Will Northaway & the Gathering Storm. 2005. (Young American Patriots Ser.: No. 4). 96p. (J). (ps-7). pap. 5.99 (978-1-58134-478-3(3) , Crossway Bibles) Crossway Bks.

Old MacDonald's Farm. 2005. (J). bds. 6.99 (978-0-9753127-6-6(6)) Family Bks. at Home.

Old MacDonald's Farmyard Tales. (Little Treasures Ser.). 256p. (J). 2002. 5.98 (978-0-7525-7689-3(5)); 2000. 25.95 (978-0-7525-3758-0(X)) Parragon, Inc.

Old MacDonald's Hens. 2002. 16p. (J). pap. 2.98 (978-0-7525-7059-4(5)) Parragon, Inc.

Oldfield, J. Skye Champion, Bk. 13. (Illus.). 122p. (J). pap. 7.99 (978-0-340-69985-0(X) , Hodder & Stoughton) Hodder General Publishing Division GBR. *Dist:* Trafalgar Square Publishing.

—Sultan Patient, Vol. 2. (Illus.). 119p. (J). pap. 7.99 (978-0-340-69983-6(3) , Hodder & Stoughton) Hodder General Publishing Division GBR. *Dist:* Trafalgar Square Publishing.

Oldfield, Jenny. Sorrel Substitute, Bk. 12. (Illus.). 120p. (J). pap. 7.99 (978-0-340-69984-3(1) , Hodder & Stoughton) Hodder General Publishing Division GBR. *Dist:* Trafalgar Square Publishing.

—Stevie the Rebel. (Home Farm Twins Ser.: Vol. 9). (Illus.). 128p. (J). pap. 7.99 (978-0-340-68992-9(7) , Hodder & Stoughton) Hodder General Publishing Division GBR. *Dist:* Trafalgar Square Publishing.

Oliver, Andrew. Scrambled. 2007. 288p. (J). per. 12.95 ***978-0-9661009-8-3(0)*** Adams-Pomeroy Pr.

Oller, Erika. The Cabbage Soup Solution. Oller, Erika, illus. 2004. (Illus.). 32p. (J). (ps-1). 15.99 (978-0-525-47005-2(0) , Dutton Juvenile) Penguin Group (USA) Inc.

On the Farm. 2004. (Out & about Ser.). 12p. (J). bds. 4.99 (978-1-85997-805-4(3)) Byeway Bks.

On the Farm. 2000. (Learning Fun for Little Ones Ser.). (Illus.). 64p. (ps-1). pap. 8.99 (978-0-88724-573-2(0) , CD-6405) Carson-Dellosa Publishing Co., Inc.

On the Farm. (Make Your Own Emergent Readers Ser.). 48p. (gr. k-2). 8.99 (978-0-7682-0013-3(X) , FS69001) Schaffer, Frank Pubns.

Onish, Liane. The Alphabet Eurps on the Farm. 1999. (Illus.). (J). 7.95 (978-1-892522-07-8(1)) Eurpsville USA, Inc.

Parkinson, Siobhan. Cows Are Vegetarians. 2002. (Red Flag Ser.: Vol. 3). (Illus.). 80p. (J). pap. 8.95 (978-0-86278-694-6(0)) O'Brien Pr., Ltd., The IRL. *Dist:* Independent Pubs. Group.

Parks, Carmen. Farmers Market. Martinez, Edward, illus. 2003. (Green Light Readers Level 2 Ser.). 24p. (J). 11.95 (978-0-15-204881-5(2)); pap. 3.95 (978-0-15-204841-9(3)) Harcourt Children's Bks. (Green Light Readers).

—Farmers Market. 2002. (gr. k-3). lib. bdg. 11.80 (978-0-613-64496-9(4)) Tandem Library Bks.

Paterson, Katherine. The Smallest Cow in the World. Brown, Jane Clark, illus. 2002. (J). 12.34 (978-0-7587-1673-6(7)) Book Wholesalers, Inc.

Paulsen, Gary. Alida's Song. 2001. 96p. (J). (gr. 5 up). 5.50 (978-0-440-41474-2(1) , Yearling) Random Hse. Children's Bks.

—Alida's Song. 2001. (J). 12.30 (978-0-606-21019-5(9)); (gr. 5-8). lib. bdg. 13.55 (978-0-613-33744-1(1)) Tandem Library Bks.

—Harris & Me: A Summer Remembered. 2007. (Illus.). 168p. (J). (gr. 4-7). pap. 5.95 (978-0-15-205880-7(X) , Harcourt Paperbacks) Harcourt Children's Bks.

—Haymeadow. unabr. ed. 2004. 195p. (J). (gr. 5-9). pap. 36.00 incl. audio (978-0-8072-0452-8(8) , Listening Library) Random Hse. Audio Publishing Group.

—The Winter Room. l.t. ed. 2005. 105p. pap. 10.95 (978-0-7862-7251-8(1) , Large Print Pr.) Thorndike Pr.

Peck, Robert Newton. Weeds in Bloom: Autobiography of an Ordinary Man. 2007. (Illus.). 224p. (YA). (gr. 7-11). mass mkt. 6.50 (978-0-375-82802-7(8) , Laurel Leaf) Random Hse. Children's Bks.

Perera, Hilda. Pepin y el Abuelo.Tr. of Pepin & His Grandfather. (SPA., Illus.). 60p. (J). (gr. 2). 7.50 (978-84-241-3271-2(8)) Everest de Ediciones y Distribucion, S.L. ESP. *Dist:* Lectorum Pubns., Inc.

—Pepin y el Abuelo. 2000. Tr. of Pepin & His Grandfather. (SPA.). (gr. k-3). lib. bdg. 16.40 (978-0-613-80619-0(0)) Tandem Library Bks.

Pienkowski, Jan. Ferme. (Folio Ser.). (FRE.). (J). 5.95 (978-2-07-056307-4(3)) Schoenhof's Foreign Bks., Inc.

Pilney, Dovie. Charlie, the Cocky Rooster. 2007. (ENG., Illus.). 28p. (J). per. 15.95 (***978-1-4327-0220-5(3)***) Outskirts Press, Inc.

Pinkney, Gloria Jean. Back Home. 1999. (J). 13.79 (978-0-606-16773-4(0)); lib. bdg. 15.30 (978-0-613-18238-6(3)) Tandem Library Bks.

Pixley, Marcella. Freak. 2007. 144p. (YA). (gr. 7 up). 16.00 (***978-0-374-32453-7(0)***) Farrar, Straus & Giroux.

Pochocki, Ethel. A Penny for a Hundred. Owens, Mary Beth, illus. 2005. 32p. (J). pap. 9.95 (978-1-883937-52-2(3)) Bethlehem Bks.

Popp, Monika. Farm Year. Popp, Monika & Schmuck, Regine Frick-von, illus. 2002. 48p. (J). (gr. k-3). 18.95 (978-0-88899-452-3(4)) Groundwood Bks. CAN. *Dist:* Perseus Distribution.

Popper, Garry. High Noon in Didley Pidley. Forshaw, John, illus. 2004. (Bret the Vet Ser.). 40p. 7.00 (978-1-84161-013-9(5)) Ravette Publishing, Ltd. GBR. *Dist:* Parkwest Pubns., Inc.

Porter, James G. Edge of the Rainforest. (Illus.). 180p. pap. 11.95 (978-0-7022-2350-1(6)) Univ. of Queensland Pr. AUS. *Dist:* International Specialized Bk. Services.

Porter, Pamela. The Crazy Man. 2005. 176p. (J). (gr. 4-7). 15.95 (978-0-88899-694-7(2)) Groundwood Bks. CAN. *Dist:* Perseus Distribution.

Prigger, Mary Skillings. Aunt Minnie & the Twister. Lewin, Betsy, illus. 2002. 40p. (J). (gr. k-3). 15.00 (978-0-618-11136-7(0) , Clarion Bks.) Houghton Mifflin Co. Trade & Reference Div.

Provensen, Alice. A Day in the Life of Murphy. Provensen, Alice, illus. unabr. rev. ed. 2005. (Illus.). (J). 25.95 incl. audio (978-1-59519-534-0(3)); 28.95 incl. audio compact disk (978-1-59519-538-8(6)) Live Oak Media.

—A Day in the Life of Murphy. Provensen, Alice, illus. 40p. (J). (ps-2). 2003. (Illus.). 16.95 (978-0-689-84884-1(6)); 2006. reprint ed. pap. 6.99 (978-1-4169-1800-4(0) , Aladdin) Simon & Schuster Children's Publishing.

Provensen, Alice & Provensen, Martin. Our Animal Friends at Maple Hill Farm. 2001. (Illus.). 64p. (J). 7.99 (978-0-689-84499-7(9) , Aladdin) Simon & Schuster Children's Publishing.

—The Year at Maple Hill Farm. 2001. (Illus.). 32p. (J). 7.99 (978-0-689-84500-0(6) , Aladdin) Simon & Schuster Children's Publishing.

Prowense, Mary J. Amy Goes Country. 2007. (ENG.). 136p. per. 19.95 (***978-1-4241-5519-4(3)***) PublishAmerica, Inc.

Puckett, Annie Marie. Pedro Learns about Salvation. 2006. 56p. per. 9.95 (***978-1-57258-453-2(X)*** , 945-6314) TEACH Services, Inc.

Purmell, Ann. The Apple Cider Making Days. Friar, Joanne, illus. 2002. 32p. (J). (gr. k-2). 14.95 (978-0-7613-2364-8(3) , Millbrook Pr.) Lerner Publishing Group.

Radtke, Becky. Invisible Old MacDonald's Farm Magic Picture Book. 2004. 32p. (J). pap. 1.50 (978-0-486-43421-6(4)) Dover Pubns., Inc.

Ransom, Candice F. Tractor Day. Bryant, Laura J., illus. 2007. 32p. (J). (ps). 17.85 (978-0-8027-8091-1(1)) Walker & Co.

Ransom, Candice F. & Bryant, Laura. Tractor Day. Bryant, Laura, illus. 2007. (Illus.). 32p. (J). (ps). 16.95 (978-0-8027-8090-4(3)) Walker & Co.

Rau, Dana Meachen. On a Farm. 2007. (Fun Time Ser.). 24p. (J). lib. bdg. 22.79 (***978-0-7614-2605-9(1)*** , Benchmark Bks.) Cavendish, Marshall Corp.

Rawlings, Marjorie Kinnan. The Yearling. 1999. (Illus.). 444p. (J). 17.90 (978-0-03-054778-2(4)) Holt, Rinehart & Winston.

—The Yearling. 2002. 480p. pap. 15.00 (978-0-7432-2525-0(2) , Scribner) Simon & Schuster.

—The Yearling. 2001. (Aladdin Classics Ser.). 528p. mass mkt. 5.99 (978-0-689-84623-6(1) , Aladdin) Simon & Schuster Children's Publishing.

—Yearling. 2001. (gr. 3-6). lib. bdg. 14.15 (978-0-613-90195-6(9)) Tandem Library Bks.

—The Yearling, Level 3. 2001. 64p. (C). pap. 9.00 (978-0-582-34439-6(5)) Pearson ESL.

Ray, Mike. The Farm: A Little Boy's Memory. 2001. (Illus.). 80p. (J). (gr. 1-8). pap. 19.95 (978-0-936283-08-1(4)) Univ. of Temecula Pr., Inc.

Reed, Lynn Rowe. Thelonius Turkey Lives! 2005. (Illus.). 40p. (J). (gr. k-3). 15.95 (978-0-375-83126-3(6) , Knopf Bks. for Young Readers) Random Hse. Children's Bks.

Rees, Shirley. Hannah Stands Tall. 2002. 130p. (J). pap. 10.95 (978-1-55517-652-5(6) , 76526, Bonneville Bks.) Cedar Fort, Inc./CFI Distribution.

Reynolds, Aaron. Chicks & Salsa. Bogan, Paulette, illus. 2007. 32p. (J). (ps-3). pap. 6.95 (***978-1-59990-099-5(8)*** , Bloomsbury Children) Bloomsbury Publishing.

Reynolds, Adrian. Pete & Polo's Farmyard Adventure. Reynolds, Adrian, illus. 2002. (Illus.). 32p. (J). (ps-1). pap. 16.95 (978-0-439-30913-4(1) , Orchard Bks.) Scholastic, Inc.

Richards, Laura E. Marie. 2004. reprint ed. pap. 15.95 (978-1-4179-3794-3(7)) Kessinger Publishing, LLC.

Richards, Lucy. Little Farm. 2007. (Illus.). 10p. (J). bds. 4.99 (***978-1-84458-362-1(7)***) Anova Bks. GBR. *Dist:* Independent Pubs. Group.

Richardson, Steve. Billy's Mountain. Leonhard, Herb, illus. 2007. 52p. 14.95 (***978-0-9786422-0-4(1)***) Impossible Dreams Publishing Co.

Riddle of Penncroft Farm. 2000. (YA). 9.95 (978-1-56137-597-4(7)) Novel Units, Inc.

Robbins, Sandra. Tobias Turkey: A Thanksgiving Tale. Oseki, Iku, illus. 1998. (See-More's Stories Ser.). 32p. (J). (ps-3). pap. 6.95 (978-1-882601-26-4(2)); pap. 11.95 incl. audio (978-1-882601-28-8(9)) See-More's Workshop.

Roberts, Pauline J. Girls Crying. 2007. 9.00 (***978-0-8059-8863-5(7)***) Dorrance Publishing Co., Inc.

Robinson, Anne. Tom Turkey. 2001. (J). cd-rom 9.95 (978-1-58338-357-5(3)) CrossroadsPub.com.

Robinson, Sue. Bear in the Barnyard. Morris, Tony, illus. 2004. 28p. (J). 16.00 (978-1-56148-430-0(X)) Good Bks.

Romain, Trevor. The Boy Who Swallowed a Rainbow. 2003. (Illus.). 32p. (J). (gr. k-2). 15.95 (978-1-56397-920-0(9)) Boyds Mills Pr.

Rosa-Mendoza, Gladys. Animals at the Farm/Animales de la Granja. Wolff, Jason, illus. 2004. (English-Spanish Foundations Ser.). (SPA & ENG.). 20p. (J). (ps). bds. 6.95 (978-1-931398-13-8(5)) Me+Mi Publishing.

Rosen, Michael J. Don't Shoot! Chase R's Top Ten Reasons NOT to Move to the Country. 2007. (Illus.). 160p. (YA). (gr. 7). pap. 6.99 (***978-0-7636-2088-2(2)*** Candlewick Pr.

Rosoff, Meg. How I Live Now. (YA). (gr. 7). 2004. 208p. 16.95 (978-0-385-74677-9(6)); 2006. 224p. reprint ed. pap. 7.99 (978-0-553-37605-0(5)) Random Hse. Children's Bks. (Lamb, Wendy).

—How I Live Now. 2006. 250p. (YA). 23.95 (978-0-7862-8878-6(7)) Thorndike Pr.

Rostoker-Gruber, Karen. Rooster Can't Cock-a-Doodle-Doo. Ratz de Tagyos, Paul, illus. 32p. (J). (ps). 2006. pap. 5.99 (978-0-14-240646-5(5) , Puffin); 2004. 15.99 (978-0-8037-2877-6(8) , Dial) Penguin Group (USA) Inc.

Ruiz, Joseph J. Manuel & the Magic Ring. 2003. (SPA & ENG., Illus.). 108p. (J). pap. 12.95 (978-0-86534-399-3(3)) Sunstone Pr.

Russell, Lisa. The Farm Puppy. 2007. 16p. (J). per. 9.99 (***978-1-59886-810-4(1)***) Tate Publishing & Enterprises, L.L.C.

Russell, Naomi. Guess Who's on the Farm. Russell, Naomi, illus. 2nd ed. 1999. (Flip-the-Flap Book Ser.). (Illus.). 32p. (J). (gr. k-ps). pap. 3.99 (978-0-7636-0689-3(8)) Candlewick Pr.

Rylant, Cynthia. Henry & Mudge & the Wild Goose Chase. Bracken, Carolyn, illus. 2004. (Henry & Mudge Ser.). 40p. (J). pap. 3.99 (978-0-689-83450-9(0) , Aladdin) Simon & Schuster Children's Publishing.

—Henry & Mudge & the Wild Goose Chase. Bracken, Carolyn, illus. 2004. (Henry & Mudge Ser.). 40p. (J). (gr. k-2). lib. bdg. 12.10 (978-1-4176-4340-0(4)) Tandem Library Bks.

Rylant, Cynthia & Bracken, Carolyn. Henry & Mudge & the Wild Goose Chase. 2003. (Henry & Mudge Ser.). (Illus.). 40p. (J). (gr. k-3). 14.95 (978-0-689-81172-2(1)) Simon & Schuster Children's Publishing.

Sadler, Judy Ann. Sandwiches for Duke. Bennett, Lorna, illus. 2007. 32p. (J). pap. (978-1-55005-062-2(1)) Fitzhenry & Whiteside, Ltd.

—Sandwiches for Duke. Bennett, Lorna, illus. 2002. 30p. (ps-3). 15.95 (978-0-7737-3313-8(2)) Stoddart Kids CAN. *Dist:* Fitzhenry & Whiteside, Ltd.

Salas, Macarena, ed. Disney Babies at the Farm / Los Bebes Disney en la Granja: A Book About Farm Words / Un Libro Sobre Palabras de la Granja. 2005. (SPA & ENG., Illus.). 6p. (J). bds. 3.99 (978-0-439-66359-5(8) , Scholastic) Scholastic, Inc.

Santa Claus & the Kids on the Farm. 2004. (J). per. 15.99 (978-0-9753533-0-1(6)) Golden Eagle Publishing Hse., Inc.

Santillo, LuAnn. Down on the Farm, 6 vols. Santillo, LuAnn, ed. 2003. (Half-Pint Kids Readers Ser.). (Illus.). 42p. (J). (ps-1). pap. 6.99 (978-1-59256-056-1(3)) Half-Pint Kids, Inc.

—Six Jobs. Santillo, LuAnn, ed. 2003. (Half-Pint Kids Readers Ser.). (Illus.). 7p. (J). (ps-1). pap. (978-1-59256-058-5(X)) Half-Pint Kids, Inc.

Santomero, Angela C. Blue Skidoos to the Farm A Storybook with 63 Stickers. Speer-Lyon, Tammie, illus. 1998. (Blue's Clues Ser.). 24p. (J). (ps-k). pap. 3.99 (978-0-689-81698-7(7) , Simon Spotlight/Nickelodeon) Simon & Schuster Children's Publishing.

Santoro, Scott. Farm-Fresh Cats. Santoro, Scott, illus. 2006. (Illus.). 32p. (J). 15.99 (978-0-06-078178-1(5)); lib. bdg. 16.89 (978-0-06-078179-8(3)) HarperCollins Pubs.

Sargent, Dave & Sargent, David J., Jr. Sandy Sea Gull: Making Friends, 20, 16. Lenoir, Jane, illus. 2003. (Feather Tales Ser.: 16). 42p. (J). pap. 6.95 (978-1-56763-750-2(7)) Ozark Publishing.

Sargent, Dave & Sargent, David M., Jr. Speedy Roadrunner: Helping Others, 19, 17. Lenoir, Jane, illus. 2003. (Feather Tales Ser.: 17). 42p. (J). pap. 6.95 (978-1-56763-752-6(3)) Ozark Publishing.

Sargent, Dave & Sargent, Pat. Young Brutus: Show Respect!, 4. Woodward, Elaine, illus. 2003. (Young Animal Pride Ser.: 4). 24p. (J). pap. 6.95 (978-1-56763-870-7(8)); lib. bdg. 19.95 (978-1-56763-869-1(4)) Ozark Publishing.

Sargent, Pat. Cougar Holler. Lenoir, Jane, illus. 2000. (J). lib. bdg. 19.95 (978-1-56763-563-8(6)); pap. 6.95 (978-1-56763-564-5(4)) Ozark Publishing.

—Cougar Holler, 8, Vol. 4. Lenoir, Jane, illus. 2004. (Barney the Bear Killer Ser.: 6). (J). lib. bdg. 25.25 (978-1-56763-969-8(0)) Ozark Publishing.

Sargent, Pat L. The Grizzly, 8, Vol. 1. Lenoir, Jane, illus. l.t. ed. 2004. (Barney the Bear Killer Ser.: No. 1). 129p. (YA). lib. bdg. 25.25 (978-1-56763-963-6(1)) Ozark Publishing.

Sargent, Pat L. Jaguar #8 (PB), 6 vols. 2007. (Barney the Bear Killer Ser.: 8). (YA). pap. 9.95 (***978-1-59381-425-0(9)***) Ozark Publishing.

Scarry, Richard. The Worst Helper Ever. Scarry, Richard, illus. 2004. 32p. (J). (ps-2). lib. bdg. 11.99 (978-0-375-99990-1(6) , Random Hse. Bks. for Young Readers) Random Hse. Children's Bks.

—The Worst Helper Ever. 1998. (Road to Reading Ser.). (Illus.). 32p. (J). (ps-2). pap. 3.99 (978-0-307-26100-7(X) , 26100, Random Hse. Bks. for Young Readers) Random Hse. Children's Bks.

Scheer, Julian. A Thanksgiving Turkey. Himler, Ronald, illus. 2001. 32p. (J). (gr. k-3). tchr. ed. 16.95 (978-0-8234-1674-5(7)) Holiday Hse., Inc.

Schmidt, Gary. First Boy. 2007. 224p. (YA). pap. 6.99 (***978-0-312-37149-4(7)***) Square Fish.

Schmidt, Gary D. First Boy. rev. ed. 2005. 208p. (YA). (gr. 6). 17.95 (978-0-8050-7859-6(2)) Holt, Henry & Co.

Scholastic, Inc. Staff. Let's Go to the Farm & the Zoo. 2007. (Barney Ser.). 48p. (J). pap. 4.99 (***978-0-439-92724-6(2)***) Scholastic, Inc.

School Specialty Publishing. Learning Letters. 2004. (Kindergarten Standards Ser.). 144p. (C). pap. 16.99 (978-0-7682-2820-5(4) , FS99276) Schaffer, Frank Pubns.

Seawall: Individual Chapter Book Title Six-Packs. Vol. 27. 32p. (gr. 4 up). 44.00 (978-0-7635-4494-2(9)) Rigby Education.

Shah, Idries. The Farmer's Wife. Santiago, Rose Mary, illus. 2005. 32p. (J). (ps-up). pap. 6.99 (978-1-883536-49-7(9) , Hoopoe Bks.) ISHK.

—The Farmer's Wife (La Esposa del Granjero) Santiago, Rose Mary, illus. 2005. (ENG & SPA.). (J). (ps up). 28.95 incl. audio compact disk (978-1-883536-69-5(3) , FAWCB3); pap. 18.95 incl. audio compact disk (978-1-883536-70-1(7) , FAWCB4) ISHK. (Hoopoe Bks.).

Shannon, George. Wise Acres. Zemke, Deborah, illus. 2004. 40p. (J). 15.95 (978-1-59354-041-8(8)) Handprint Bks.

Shepherd, Jodie. Farm Friends. Ovresat, Laura, illus. 2006. (Guess Who? Ser.). 12p. (J). pap. 7.99 (978-0-7944-1048-3(0)) Reader's Digest Assn., Inc., The.

Siegrist, Bonnie. Little Farm down the Lane -Book IV. 2007. pap. 10.99 (***978-1-60034-912-6(9)***) Xulon Pr., Inc.

Silver Dolphin en Español Editors. Un Dia en la Granja. 2003. (SPA.). 60p. 9.95 (978-970-718-110-6(9) , Silver Dolphin en Español) Advanced Marketing, S. de R. L. de C. V. MEX. *Dist:* Bilingual Pubns. Co., The.

Silver, Pattie, illus. Kitty's Barn. 2005. 12p. (J). bds. 9.95 (978-1-58117-385-7(7) , Intervisual/Piggy Toes) Dalmatian Pr.

Simmons, Lynn Sheffield. Sugar Lump, the Orphan Calf. 2004. (Illus.). 50p. (YA). pap. 8.95 (978-1-58980-216-2(0)) Pelican Publishing Co., Inc.

Skyscrapers & Farms. 2005. (J). per. 5.00 (978-1-59872-020-4(1)) Instantpublisher.com.

Sloat, Teri. Farmer Brown Goes Round & Round. Westcott, Nadine Bernard, illus. 24p. (J). pap. 4.95 (978-0-7513-5237-5(3)) Dorling Kindersley Publishing, Inc.

—Farmer Brown Goes Round & Round. 2001. (978-0-606-22359-1(2)) Tandem Library Bks.

—The Thing That Bothered Farmer Brown. Westcott, Nadine Bernard, illus. 2001. 32p. (J). (ps-2). pap. 5.95 (978-0-531-07183-0(9) , Orchard Bks.) Scholastic, Inc.

Smith, Debra West. Hattie Marshall & the Prowling Panther. 2005. 144p. (J). 6.95 (978-1-56554-940-1(6)) Pelican Publishing Co., Inc.

Smith, George Harmon. Wanderers of the Field. 2000. 220p. (YA). (gr. 7-12). pap. 12.95 (978-0-595-00757-8(0) , Writer's Showcase Pr.) iUniverse, Inc.

Solomon, Heather, illus. Willa & the Wind. 2005. 40p. (J). (gr. 1-4). 16.95 (978-0-7614-5232-4(X)) Cavendish, Marshall Corp.

Spinelli, Eileen. The Best Time of Day. Langdo, Bryan, illus. 2007. 32p. (J). pap. 6.00 (978-0-15-205862-3(1) , Voyager Bks./Libros Viajeros) Harcourt Children's Bks.

—The Best Time of Day. Langdo, Bryan, illus. 2005. 32p. (J). (ps-ps). 16.00 (978-0-15-205051-1(5)) Harcourt Trade Pubs.

Spinelli, Jerry. Blue Ribbon Blues. Nelson, Donna, illus. 1998. (Stepping Stone Books 2: Vol. 2). 80p. (gr. 2-5). lib. bdg. 11.99 (978-0-679-98753-6(3) , Random Hse. Bks. for Young Readers) Random Hse. Children's Bks.

—Blue Ribbon Blues: A Tooter Tale. Nelson, Donna, illus. 1998. (Tooter Tale Ser.: Vol. 2). 80p. (J). (gr. 1-4). pap. 3.99 (978-0-679-88753-9(9) , Random Hse. Bks. for Young Readers) Random Hse. Children's Bks.

Staake, Bob. The Red Lemon. 2006. (Deluxe Golden Book Ser.). (Illus.). 40p. (J). (ps-3). lib. bdg. 16.99 (978-0-375-93593-0(2) , Golden Bks.) Random Hse. Children's Bks.

Stahler, David, Jr. Gathering of Shades. 2006. pap. (978-0-06-052296-4(8)) HarperCollins Canada, Ltd.

—A Gathering of Shades. 2005. 304p. (J). 15.99 (978-0-06-052294-0(1)); lib. bdg. 16.89 (978-0-06-052295-7(X)) HarperCollins Pubs. (HarperTeen).

Stanley, Robin. Fun on the Farm. Julien, Terry, illus. 2006. (Happy Day Summer Titles Ser.). 16p. (J). pap. 1.99 (978-0-7847-1807-0(5) , 04189) Standard Publishing.

Steers, Billy. Tractor Mac Arrives at the Farm. Steers, Billy, illus. 2004. (Illus.). 24p. (J). (ps-ps). pap. 3.29 (978-1-59445-042-6(0)) Dogs in Hats Children's Publishing Co.

—Tractor Mac Builds a Barn. 2004. (Illus.). 24p. (J). (ps-ps). pap. 3.29 (978-1-59445-075-4(7)) Dogs in Hats Children's Publishing Co.

Stem, Jacqueline. The Secret of Little Creek Farm, Vol. 2. 1999. (Hollow Tree Mystery Ser.). (Illus.). 136p. 14.95 (978-1-57168-293-2(7)) Eakin Pr.

Stemple, David. High Ridge Gobbler: A Story of the American Wild Turkey. 2003. (Illus.). 48p. (YA). (gr. 2-4). pap. 10.95 (978-1-56397-933-0(0)) Boyds Mills Pr.

Stevens, Jan Romero. Carlos & the Cornfield. 1999. Tr. of Carlos y la Milpa de Maiz. (SPA & ENG., Illus.). 32p. (J). (gr. k-3). 7.95 (978-0-87358-735-8(9) , Rising Moon Bks. for Young Readers) Northland Publishing.

—Carlos & the Skunk (Carlos y el Zorrillo) Arnold, Jeanne, illus. 2001. (SPA & ENG.). 32p. (J). (gr. 2-3). 7.95 (978-0-87358-779-2(0) , Rising Moon Bks. for Young Readers) Northland Publishing.

—Carlos y el Zorrillo. Arnold, Jeanne, illus. 2001. (SPA.). (J). (ps-ps). lib. bdg. 16.40 (978-0-613-36036-4(2)) Tandem Library Bks.

Stewart, Diane. The Gift of the Sun. Daly, Jude, illus. 2007. 32p. (J). pap. 7.95 (***978-1-84507-787-7(3)***) Lincoln, Frances Ltd. GBR. *Dist:* Perseus Distribution.

Stoeke, Janet Morgan. Minerva Louise & Her Barnyard Friends. Stoeke, Janet Morgan, illus. 2nd ed. 2002. (Illus.). (978-0-525-46877-6(3) , Dutton Juvenile) Penguin Group (USA) Inc.

Stohner, Anu & Wilson, Henrike. Brave Charlotte. Cole, Alyson, tr. from GER. 2005. (Illus.). 32p. (J). (ps-3). 16.95 (978-1-58234-690-8(9) , Bloomsbury Children) Bloomsbury Publishing.

Stratton-Porter. At the Foot of the Rainbow. 2006. 19.99 (***978-1-4219-7512-2(2)***) IndyPublish.com.

Stratton Porter, Gene. At the Foot of the Rainbow. 2007. 180p. 18.95 (***978-1-934169-52-0(8)***); pap. 7.95 (***978-1-934169-53-7(6)***) Norilana Bks.

—A Daughter of the Land. 2007. 340p. 22.95 (***978-1-934169-46-9(3)***); pap. 11.95 (***978-1-934169-47-6(1)***) Norilana Bks.

Strickland, Brad. When Mack Came Back. 2003. (Illus.). 112p. (J). (gr. 3-7). pap. 5.99 (978-0-14-230075-6(6) , Puffin) Penguin Group (USA) Inc.

—When Mack Came Back. 2003. (gr. 3-6). lib. bdg. 14.15 (978-0-613-85719-2(4)) Tandem Library Bks.

Stroud, Bettye. Dance Y'All. Van Wright, Cornelius & Hu, Ying-Hwa, illus. 2001. 32p. (J). (gr. k-3). 15.95 (978-0-7614-5065-8(3) , Cavendish Children's Bks.) Cavendish, Marshall Corp.

Studio Mouse. Sesame Street My First Trip to the Farm: Book & CD. rev. ed. 2007. 24p. 4.99 (***978-1-59069-561-6(5)***) Studio Mouse LLC.

Sullivan, Anne. The Adventures of Dino & Spike: Grandpa's Farm. 2006. (ENG.). 36p. per. 16.49 (***978-1-4259-3885-7(X)***) AuthorHouse.

Swan, Michelle. Old MacDonald Had a Farm. 2007. 12p. (J). bds. 5.99 (***978-0-439-85307-1(9)***) Scholastic, Inc.

Swoish, Tammy. Hot Scots, Castles, & Kilts. 2008. (YA). (gr. 7). 208p. pap. 7.99 (***978-0-385-73447-9(6)***); 224p. lib. bdg. 10.99 (***978-0-385-90450-6(9)***) Random Hse. Children's Bks. (Delacorte Bks. for Young Readers).

Sykes, Julie. That Pesky Dragon. Williamson, Melanie, illus. 2007. 32p. (J). (ps-2). 15.95 (***978-1-58925-069-7(9)*** , tiger tales) ME Media LLC.

Tafuri, Nancy. Blue Goose. Tafuri, Nancy, illus. 2008. 32p. (J). 15.99 (***978-1-4169-2834-8(0)*** , Simon & Schuster Children's Publishing) Simon & Schuster Children's Publishing.

The Tales of the Farm. 1998. (Illus.). 24p. (J). pap. 14.98 (978-1-58048-038-3(1)) Sandvik Publishing.

Thermes, Jennifer. Sam Bennett's New Shoes. 2006. (Illus.). (J). 15.95 (978-1-57505-822-1(7) , Carolrhoda Bks.) Lerner Publishing Group.

Thompson, Karen & Mitzo Thompson, Kim. At the Farm. 2006. (Read & Sing along Board Books with CDs Ser.). (Illus.). 18p. (J). bds. 7.49 (978-0-7696-4582-7(8)) School Specialty Publishing.

Thorson, Kristine & Thorson, Robert. Stone Wall Secrets. Moore, Gustav, illus. 2003. (J). (gr. 4-7). lib. bdg. 16.40 (978-0-613-43779-0(9)) Tandem Library Bks.

—Stone Wall Secrets. Moore, Gustav, illus. 2005. 40p. (J). (gr. 3-7). 7.95 (978-0-88448-229-1(4)) Tilbury Hse. Pubs.

Tjornin, Gerta. Ladies & Gentlemen Presenting Gertas B. 2006. pap. 28.00 (***978-1-4259-5915-9(6)***) AuthorHouse.

Tokunbo, Dimitrea. Together. Oliver, Jennifer, illus. 2005. (J). pap. (978-0-439-79654-5(7)) Scholastic, Inc.

Tolstoy, Alexei. The Gigantic Turnip. Sharkey, Niamh, illus. 2000. (Barefoot Beginner Ser.). 40p. (J). (ps-3). 15.95 (978-1-902283-12-8(0)) Barefoot Bks., Inc.

Tolstoy, Alexei & Daynes, Katie. Enormous Turnip. 2006. 48p. (J). 8.99 (978-0-7945-1376-4(X) , Usborne) EDC Publishing.

Tomaselli, Doris. My Little People Farm. Thompson Brothers Staff, illus. 2003. (Fisher-Price Lift-The-Flap Playbook Ser.). (ENG & SPA.). 5p. (J). 8.99 (978-0-7944-0213-6(5) , Reader's Digest Children's Bks.) Reader's Digest Children's Publishing, Inc.

Tomlinson, Sylvia. Maddie. Cartmell, Ginny, illus. 2002. 124p. (J). (gr. 3-7). 12.95 (978-0-9720293-0-8(3)) Redbud Publishing Co.

Tompkins, Robyn Lee. Miss Molly's Adventure on the Farm: Another great adventure brought to you by Miss Molly & her dog Reyburn. Carson, Shawn, illus. 2006. (J). per. (***978-0-9741647-7-9(1)***) NRG Pubns.

Townsend, Una Belle. Grady's in the Silo. Artley, Bob, illus. 2003. 32p. (J). 15.95 (978-1-58980-098-4(2)) Pelican Publishing Co., Inc.

Trotter, Deborah W. How Do You Know? Downing, Julie, illus. 2006. 32p. (J). (ps-k). 16.00 (978-0-618-46343-5(7) , Clarion Bks.) Houghton Mifflin Co. Trade & Reference Div.

Tub Tales: The Farm. 2003. (Illus.). 10p. (J). 6.00 (978-0-9713507-3-1(6) , 844) Panline U.S.A., Inc.

Tudor, Tasha. Pumpkin Moonshine. 1998. (Illus.). 46p. (J). 6.95 (978-0-446-91246-4(8)) Grand Central Publishing.

—Pumpkin Moonshine. Tudor, Tasha, illus. 2000. (Illus.). 40p. (J). (ps-3). 13.95 (978-0-689-82846-1(2)) Simon & Schuster Children's Publishing.

Uchida, Yoshiko. Samurai of Gold Hill. Forberg, Ati, illus. 2005. 119p. (J). (gr. 2). pap. 8.95 (978-1-59714-015-7(5)) Heyday Bks.

Unknown. Corduroy Visits the Farm! 2008. 16p. (J). (ps-1). pap. 5.99 (***978-0-448-44786-5(X)*** , Grosset & Dunlap) Penguin Group (USA) Inc.

Van Dyne, Edith. Aunt Jane's Nieces & Uncle John. 2006. 95.99 (***978-1-4219-7416-3(9)***); pap. 88.99 (***978-1-4219-7434-7(7)***) IndyPublish.com.

—Aunt Jane's Nieces at Millville. 2006. 95.99 (***978-1-4219-7454-5(1)***); pap. 89.99 (***978-1-4219-7453-8(3)***) IndyPublish.com.

—Aunt Jane's Nieces at Work. 2006. 78.99 (***978-1-4142-5888-1(7)***); pap. 71.99 (***978-1-4142-5882-9(8)***) IndyPublish.com.

—Aunt Jane's Nieces in Society. 2006. 41.99 (***978-1-4280-0211-1(1)***); pap. 35.99 (***978-1-4280-0196-1(4)***) IndyPublish.com.

—Aunt Jane's Nieces on Vacation. 2006. 95.99 (***978-1-4219-7507-8(6)***) IndyPublish.com.

—Aunt Jane's Nieces Out West. 2006. 42.99 (***978-1-4280-0248-7(0)***); pap. 35.99 (***978-1-4280-0254-8(5)***) IndyPublish.com.

Van Frankenhuyzen, Robbyn Smith. Kelly of Hazel Ridge. van Frankenhuyzen, Gijsbert, illus. 3rd rev. ed. 2006. 48p. (J). (gr. k-5). 17.95 (978-1-58536-268-4(9)) Sleeping Bear Pr.

van Kampen, Vlasta. It Couldn't Be Worse. 2003. (gr. k-3). lib. bdg. 15.25 (978-0-613-70723-7(0)) Tandem Library Bks.

Vanderwerff, Corrine. Lucy, the Curiously Comical Cow. 1998. (Julius & Friends Ser.: Vol. 5). (J). 6.99 (978-0-8163-1582-6(5)) Pacific Pr. Publishing Assn.

Voigt, Cynthia. Angus & Sadie. Leigh, Tom, illus. 2005. 208p. (J). lib. bdg. 16.89 (978-0-06-074583-7(5)); 15.99 (978-0-06-074582-0(7)) HarperCollins Pubs.

Waddell, Martin. Farmer Duck. 2002. (Illus.). (J). 13.83 (978-0-7587-2481-6(0)) Book Wholesalers, Inc.

—Farmer Duck. Oxenbury, Helen, illus. 2002. 26p. (J). (ps). bds. 6.99 (978-0-7636-2167-4(6)) Candlewick Pr.

Wallace, Bill. Beauty. 2007. 192p. (J). pap. 5.99 (***978-1-4169-4942-8(9)*** , Aladdin) Simon & Schuster Children's Publishing.

Wallace, Patricia H. Cottontale Christmas & the Cottontail Farm. deluxe unabr. ed. 2000. (J). bdg. 12.00 incl. audio (978-0-932079-03-9(2)) TimeFare AudioBooks.

Walton, Rick. Herd of Cows! Flock of Sheep! Olson, Julie Hansen, illus. 2002. 32p. (J). 15.95 (978-1-58685-153-8(5)) Gibbs Smith, Publisher.

Waltz, Dan. Kornstalkers: Corn Maze Massacre. Waltz, Dan, illus. l.t. ed. 2005. (Chilled to the Bone! Ser.: No. 1). (Illus.). 120p. (J). per. 6.99 (978-0-9741774-3-4(1)) D. W. Publishing.

Wangerin, Walter, Jr. I Am My Grandpa's Enkelin. Tate, Don, illus. 2007. (J). (gr. 2-6). 18.95 (***978-1-55725-468-9(0)***) Paraclete Pr., Inc.

Warburton, Carol. Edge of Night: A Novel. 2004. (Illus.). 278p. pap. 14.95 (978-1-59156-013-5(6)) Covenant Communications, Inc.

Ward, Nick. Farmer George & the Hedgehogs. 2001. (Illus.). 32p. (YA). (gr. k up). pap. 14.95 (978-1-86205-441-7(X) , Pavilion Bks., Ltd.) Anova Bks. GBR. *Dist:* Trafalgar Square Publishing.

—Farmer George & the Hungry Guests. 2001. (Illus.). (gr. k up). 32p. (YA). pap. 14.95 (978-1-86205-436-3(3)); 23p. (J). reprint ed. pap. 8.99 (978-1-86205-531-5(9)) Anova Bks. GBR. (Pavilion Bks., Ltd.). *Dist:* Trafalgar Square Publishing, Independent Pubs. Group.

—Farmer George & the New Piglet. 2002. (Illus.). 32p. (J). 13.99 (978-1-86205-521-6(1) , Pavilion Bks., Ltd.) Anova Bks. GBR. *Dist:* Trafalgar Square Publishing.

—Farmer George & the Snowstorm. 2002. (Illus.). 32p. 13.99 (978-1-86205-516-2(5) , Pavilion Bks., Ltd.) Anova Bks. GBR. *Dist:* Trafalgar Square Publishing.

Warnock, Natalie Kinsey. As Long as There Are Mountains. Bonnell, J., ed. 2001. 144p. (J). (gr. 4-7). pap. 4.99 (978-0-14-130360-4(3) , Puffin) Penguin Group (USA) Inc.

Watkins, Dawn L. Jenny Wren. 2000. (J). (gr. 3-7). pap. 14.98 incl. audio (978-0-89084-909-5(9) , 100065) Jones, Bob Univ. Pr.

Watson, Gayle. Catie Corn & the Corn Cops. Fautsch, Jackie, illus. l.t. ed. 22p. (J). 2006. 15.99 (978-1-59879-098-6(6)); 2005. per. 9.99 (978-1-59879-079-5(X)) Lifevest Publishing, Inc.

Watt, Fiona. Mini Farmyard Tales Children's Cookbook. Cartwright, Stephen, illus. 2006. 48p. (J). 6.99 (978-0-7945-1418-1(9) , Usborne) EDC Publishing.

Weaver, Elizabeth Nixon. Rooster. 2005. 208p. (J). reprint ed. pap. 5.95 (978-0-7614-5218-8(4)) Cavendish, Marshall Corp.

Weaver, Will. Defect. 2007. 208p. (YA). (gr. 7 up). 16.00 (***978-0-374-31725-6(9)*** , Farrar, Straus & Giroux (BYR)) Farrar, Straus & Giroux.

—Full Service. 2005. 240p. (YA). (gr. 9). 17.00 (978-0-374-32485-8(9) , Farrar, Straus & Giroux (BYR)) Farrar, Straus & Giroux.

—Hard Ball. (gr. 6 up). 1999. 256p. (J). pap. 5.99 (978-0-06-447208-1(6) , Harper Trophy); 1998. 240p. (YA). 15.89 (978-0-06-027122-0(1)); 1998. 240p. (YA). 15.95 (978-0-06-027121-3(3)) HarperCollins Pubs.

—Hard Ball. 1999. (J). 12.64 (978-0-606-16706-2(4)); (gr. 7-12). lib. bdg. 14.15 (978-0-613-18254-6(5)) Tandem Library Bks.

—Hard Ball: A Billy Baggs Novel. l.t. ed. 2000. (Illus.). 270p. (YA). (gr. 8-12). 20.95 (978-0-7862-2752-5(4)) Thorndike Pr.

Wellington, Monica. Apple Farmer Annie. Wellington, Monica, illus. 2004. (Illus.). 32p. (J). (ps-1). pap. 5.99 (978-0-14-240124-8(2) , Puffin) Penguin Group (USA) Inc.

—Apple Farmer Annie/ Anna Cultiva Manzanas. Del Risco, Eida, tr. Wellington, Monica, illus. 2004. (ENG & SPA., Illus.). 32p. (J). (ps). 10.99 (978-0-525-47252-0(5) , Dutton Juvenile) Penguin Group (USA) Inc.

Wells, Rosemary. Old MacDonald. Wells, Rosemary, illus. 1998. (Bruno & Boots Book Ser.). (Illus.). 18p. (J). (ps-k). bds. 5.99 (978-0-590-76985-3(5)) Scholastic, Inc.

Wharton, Edith. Ethan Frome, Level 3. 2nd abr. ed. 2000. (Bookworms Ser.). (Illus.). 80p. 6.50 (978-0-19-423002-5(3)) Oxford Univ. Pr., Inc.

Whelan, Gloria. Farewell to the Island. 1998. 208p. (J). (gr. 4 up). 16.95 (978-0-06-027751-2(3)) HarperCollins Pubs.

—Farewell to the Island. 1999. (J). (978-0-606-17462-6(1)) Tandem Library Bks.

—Farewell to the Island. 2004. 200p. (J). (ps-7). pap. 7.95 (978-1-882376-92-6(7)) Thunder Bay Pr.

—Friend on Freedom River. van Frankenhuyzen, Gijsbert, illus. 2004. 48p. (J). 16.95 (978-1-58536-222-6(0)) Sleeping Bear Pr.

White, E. B. Charlotte's Web. Williams, Garth, illus. movie tie-in ed. 2006. (Charlotte's Web Ser.). (J). 192p. mass mkt. 7.99 (978-0-06-122874-2(5) , Harper Trophy); Set. 50.99 (978-0-06-121501-8(5)); Set. pap. 19.99 (978-0-06-121502-5(3)) HarperCollins Pubs.

—Some Pig! A Charlotte's Web Picture Book. Kneen, Maggie, illus. 2006. (Charlotte's Web Ser.). 32p. (J). 16.99 (978-0-06-078161-3(0)); lib. bdg. 17.89 (978-0-06-078162-0(9)) HarperCollins Pubs.

—Wilbur's Adventure. Kneen, Maggie, illus. 2008. (Charlotte's Web Ser.). 32p. (J). (gr. k-2). 16.99 (***978-0-06-078164-4(5)***) HarperCollins Pubs.

—Wilbur's Adventure: A Charlotte's Web Picture Book. Kneen, Maggie, illus. 2008. (Charlotte's Web Ser.). 32p. (J). 17.89 (***978-0-06-078165-1(3)***) HarperCollins Pubs.

Whybrow, Ian & Ayliffe, Alex. Faraway Farm. 2006. (Illus.). 32p. (J). 14.95 (978-1-57505-938-9(X) , Carolrhoda Bks.) Lerner Publishing Group.

Wild, Margaret. Piglet & Mama. King, Stephen Michael, illus. 2005. 32p. (J). (ps-1). 14.95 (978-0-8109-5869-2(4)) Abrams, Harry N. , Inc.

—Piglet & Papa. King, Stephen Michael, illus. 2007. (J). (ps-3). 32p. 14.95 (978-0-8109-1476-6(X)); (***978-1-4287-4648-0(X)***) Abrams, Harry N. , Inc. (Abrams Bks. for Young Readers).

Wilder, Laura Ingalls. Farmer Boy. 2007. (Little House Ser.). 384p. (J). pap. 6.99 (978-0-06-088538-0(6) , Harper Trophy) HarperCollins Pubs.

—Farmer Boy. Williams, Garth, illus. 2004. (Little House Ser.). 384p. (J). pap. 8.99 (978-0-06-058182-4(4) , Harper Trophy) HarperCollins Pubs.

—Farmer Boy. Williams, Garth, illus. l.t. ed. 2000. (Little House Ser.). 400p. (J). (gr. 3-6). lib. bdg. 33.95 (978-1-58118-079-4(9) , 24071) LRS.

—A Farmer Boy Birthday. 1999. (My First Little House Bks.). (Illus.). 32p. (J). (ps-3). pap. 5.95 (978-0-06-443570-3(9)) HarperCollins Pubs.

—A Farmer Boy Birthday. Wheeler, Jody, illus. 1998. (My First Little House Bks.). 40p. (J). (ps-3). lib. bdg. 16.89 (978-0-06-027477-1(8)) HarperCollins Pubs.

—The First Four Years. Williams, Garth, illus. (Little House Ser.). (J). 2004. 160p. pap. 8.99 (978-0-06-058188-6(3) , Harper Trophy); 2003. 144p. pap. 5.99 (978-0-06-052243-6(7)) HarperCollins Pubs.

—The First Four Years. Williams, Garth, illus. l.t. ed. 2002. (LRS Large Print Cornerstone Ser.). (J). lib. bdg. 27.95 (978-1-58118-103-6(5) , 25535) LRS.

Wilkins, Celia. A Little House of Their Own. Andreasen, Dan, illus. 2005. (Little House Ser.). 320p. (J). pap. 6.99 (978-0-06-440736-6(5)) HarperCollins Pubs.

Williams, Jeanne. To Buy a Dream. 2001. 164p. (YA). pap. 11.95 (978-0-595-16527-8(3) , Backinprint.com) iUniverse, Inc.

Williams, Sue. I Went Walking. Vivas, Julie, illus. 2000. (J). pap., tchr. ed. 37.95 incl. audio (978-0-87499-665-4(1)); pap. 16.95 incl. audio (978-0-87499-663-0(5)) Live Oak Media.

Williamson, Stafford. Puppy Goes to Lambergarten. 2005. 11p. 11.18 (978-1-4116-3854-9(9)) Lulu.com.

Wilson, Mary. Paper Dragonfly. 2007. 32p. 15.95 (***978-0-9726614-3-0(3)***) Shenanigan Bks.

Winnick, Karen B. Barn Sneeze. Winnick, Karen B., illus. 2003. (Illus.). 32p. (J). (gr. k-2). 15.95 (978-1-56397-948-4(9)) Boyds Mills Pr.

Wiskur, Darrell. Really Big Barn on Noah's Farm. 2001. (Illus.). 40p. (J). 11.99 (978-0-89051-353-8(8)) Master Bks.

Wood, Jakki. Never Say Boo to a Goose! Beaton, Clare, illus. 2002. 24p. (J). (gr. k-2). 14.99 (978-1-84148-255-2(2)) Barefoot Bks., Inc.

Woods, Noah. Tom Cat. 2004. (Illus.). 32p. (J). (ps-2). lib. bdg. 16.99 (978-0-375-92497-2(3) , Random Hse. Bks. for Young Readers) Random Hse. Children's Bks.

Wright, Randall. The Silver Penny. rev. ed. 2005. 208p. (J). 16.95 (978-0-8050-7391-1(4) , Holt, Henry & Co. Bks. For Young Readers) Holt, Henry & Co.

Wu, Liz. Rosa Farm. Phelan, Matt, illus. 2006. 144p. (J). (gr. 2-7). 15.95 (978-0-375-83681-7(0)); lib. bdg. 17.99 (978-0-375-93681-4(5)) Random Hse. Children's Bks. (Knopf Bks. for Young Readers).

Yocum, Randi. Cowpie Corgi: A Dog's Tale. Yocum, Sam, 2nd, photos by. 2007. 32p. (J). lib. bdg. 16.98 (978-0-9663629-3-0(4)) By Grace Enterprises.

Yolen, Jane. Raising Yoder's Barn. Fuchs, Bernie, illus. 2002. 32p. (J). (ps-3). pap. 6.99 (978-0-316-07593-0(0)) Little, Brown Bks. for Young Readers.

—Raising Yoder's Barn. 2002. (gr. k-3). lib. bdg. 14.10 (978-0-613-71603-1(5)) Tandem Library Bks.

Yorinks, Arthur. The Floating Cow & Other Stories. 2000. (J). (978-0-439-09255-5(8)) Scholastic, Inc.

Young, Pippa, illus. On the Farm. (Match & Twist Ser.). (J). 11.99 (978-0-525-47054-0(9) , Dutton Juvenile) Penguin Group (USA) Inc.

Yoyo Books Staff. On the Farm: Learning Words Series. 2005. 12p. bds. 12.95 (978-90-5843-605-4(5)) YoYo Bks. BEL. *Dist:* National Bk. Network.

—On the Farm: One Minute Goodnight Stories. 2004. 40p. bds. 12.95 (978-90-5843-580-4(6)) YoYo Bks. BEL. *Dist:* National Bk. Network.

Zarley, Jacqualynn R. Adventures with Lucy the Llama Book Two: Shung the Trickster. 2006. 54p. pap. 12.95 (978-1-4137-5996-9(3)) PublishAmerica, Inc.

Zerbst, Elizabeth Lipiec. Dairy Farm Friends. Begley, Melinda J. & Schuyler, Doris E., eds. Zerbst, Elizabeth Lipiec, illus. 1999. (Illus.). 28p. (J). (gr. k-6). pap. 10.00 (978-1-886623-05-7(8)) Canal Side Pubs.

Ziefert, Harriet. Noisy Barn! Taback, Simms, illus. 2003. 14p. 8.95 (978-1-59354-013-5(2)) Blue Apple Bks.

Zoehfeld, Kathleen Weidner. Apples, Apples. Santoro, Christopher, illus. 2004. 20p. (J). (ps up). 5.99 (978-0-06-053787-6(6) , Harper Festival) HarperCollins Pubs.

—Pumpkin Time. Santoro, Christopher, illus. 2004. 20p. (J). (ps up). 5.99 (978-0-06-053788-3(4) , Harper Festival) HarperCollins Pubs.

FARM LIFE—POETRY

Riggott, Gladys Jenkins & Riggott, Ann M., illus. Gilbert & Me. 2006. 30p. (J). 16.95 (978-0-9777641-0-5(9)) Riggott, Ann.

FARM MACHINERY

see Agricultural Machinery

FARM MECHANICS

see Agricultural Machinery

FARM PRODUCE

Capstone Press, contrib. by. Fall Harvest, Vol. 3. 2005. (Our Seasons & Weather Ser.). 24p. (YA). (gr. k-3). pap. (978-1-56065-960-0(2) , Pebble Bks.) Capstone Pr., Inc.

Cobb, Allan B. Scientifically Engineered Foods: The Debate over What's on Your Plate. 2000. (Focus on Science & Society Ser.). (Illus.). 64p. (J). (gr. 4-6). lib. bdg. 26.50 (978-0-8239-3208-5(7) , FSENFO) Rosen Publishing Group, Inc., The.

Farmer, Jacqueline. Bananas! 1999. (gr. k-3). lib. bdg. 15.25 (978-0-613-24034-5(0)) Tandem Library Bks.

Gillis, Jennifer Blizin. Farm Crops. 2004. (Let's See Ser.). (Illus.). 24p. (J). (gr. 1 up). lib. bdg. 19.93 (978-0-7565-0669-8(7)) Compass Point Bks.

—Unusual Farms. 2004. (Let's See Ser.). (Illus.). 24p. (J). (gr. 1 up). lib. bdg. 19.93 (978-0-7565-0668-1(9)) Compass Point Bks.

McEvoy, Paul. Plants as Food. 2003. (Plant Facts Ser.). (Illus.). 24p. (gr. 2-4). 23.00 (978-0-7910-7292-9(4) , Chelsea Hse.) Facts On File, Inc.

Shepard, Daniel. All Kinds of Farms. 2003. (Illus.). 17p. (J). 15.93 (978-0-7368-2912-0(1)); pap. (978-0-7368-2871-0(0)) Yellow Umbrella Pr.

Stone, Lynn M. Farm Crops. 2002. (Life on the Farm Ser.). (Illus.). 24p. (gr. 1-4). 14.95 (978-1-58952-092-9(0)) Rourke Publishing, LLC.

Trumbauer, Lisa. La Cosecha. 2005. Tr. of Harvest Time. (SPA., Illus.). 16p. (J). (gr. 1 up). lib. bdg. 15.93 (978-0-7368-4176-4(8)) Capstone Pr., Inc.

Waters, Jennifer. Harvest Time. 2002. (Spyglass Books). (Illus.). 24p. (J). (gr. 1 up). 18.60 (978-0-7565-0239-3(X)) Compass Point Bks.

Weber, Rebecca. Foods from the Farm. 2004. (Spyglass Books). (Illus.). 24p. (J). (gr. k-1). lib. bdg. 18.60 (978-0-7565-0624-7(7)) Compass Point Bks.

Wolfman, Judy. Life on a Crop Farm. Winston, David Lorenz, photos by. 2005. (Life on a Farm Ser.). (Illus.). 48p. (gr. 2-5). lib. bdg. 23.93 (978-1-57505-518-3(X)) Lerner Publishing Group.

FARM PRODUCE—MARKETING

King, Hazel & Shepard, Tristram. Food Technology for Key Stage 3. 2000. (Design & Make It Ser.). (Illus.). 144p. (J). (gr. 6-9). pap., stu. ed. 22.50 (978-0-7487-4427-5(4)) Nelson Thornes Ltd. GBR. *Dist:* Trans-Atlantic Pubns., Inc.

Linde, Barbara M. Working at the Farmers' Market: Solving Money Problems Involving the Four Math Operations. 2004. (PowerMath Ser.). (Illus.). 24p. (J). lib. bdg. 21.25 (978-0-8239-8975-1(5) , PowerKids Pr.) Rosen Publishing Group, Inc., The.

Randall, Ronne. Do French Fries Come from France? 2003. (What? Where? Why? Ser.). (Illus.). 24p. (J). (gr. 1 up). lib. bdg. 20.67 (978-0-8368-3787-2(8)) Stevens, Gareth Inc.

FARMING

see Agriculture

FARMS

All Kinds of Farms Social Studies, 6 vols. (gr. k-2). 28.95 (978-0-7368-2989-2(X) , Yellow Umbrella Bks.) Capstone Pr., Inc.

Beatty, Sarah. On the Farm (Full-Color) (Prek-K) 2006. pap. 16.99 (978-1-4206-8144-4(3)) Teacher Created Resources, Inc.

Bial, Raymond. The Farms: Building America. 2002. (Building America Ser.). (Illus.). 56p. (J). (gr. 4-7). lib. bdg. 27.07 (978-0-7614-1332-5(4) , Benchmark Bks.) Cavendish, Marshall Corp.

Bodden, Valerie. A Farming Town. 2007. (J). (978-1-58341-513-9(0) , Creative Education) Creative Co., The.

Bracken, Carolyn & Durk, Jim, illus. Early Learning Farm, 8 vols. 2001. (Fisher-Price Little People Ser.). (J). (978-0-7853-4959-4(6)) Publications International, Ltd.

Braidich, Shelby & Roza, Greg. Meet Me on the Farm: Learning the Long E Sound. (PowerPhonics Ser.). (Illus.). (J). 2002. 24p. (gr. 1). lib. bdg. 18.50 (978-0-8239-5920-4(1)); 2001. 23p. pap. 26.40 (978-0-8239-8265-3(3)) Rosen Publishing Group, Inc., The. (PowerKids Pr.).

Brown, Alan. The Story Behind George Orwell's Animal Farm. 2006. (History in Literature Ser.). (Illus.). 56p. (YA). (gr. 6-9). lib. bdg. 32.86 (978-1-4034-8203-7(9)) Heinemann Library.

Bryant, Raymond. On the Farm. 2004. (Funtime Rhymes Ser.). (Illus.). 10p. (J). bds. 4.95 (978-0-7641-5715-8(9)) Barron's Educational Series, Inc.

Campbell, Rod. My Farm. 1998. (Illus.). 6p. (J). 12.50 (978-0-333-65998-4(8)) Macmillan Publishers Ltd. GBR. *Dist:* Independent Pubs. Group.

Can Press Staff, ed. This Is Daniel Cook at the Farm. 2006. (Illus.). 28p. (J). (978-1-55453-078-6(4)); (978-1-55453-077-9(6)) Kids Can Pr., Ltd.

Causley, Charles & Hammond, Andrew. I-Read Year 2 Anthology: Down on the Farm. 2007. (I-read Ser.). (Illus.). 40p. pap. (***978-0-521-70470-0(7)***) Cambridge Univ. Pr.

Color All About: A Giant Coloring Book about Work & Play on the Farm: the Farm. 2004. (SPA & ENG., Illus.). 36p. (J). (978-1-59949-003-8(X)) Food Marketing Consultants, Inc.

Color All About: The Farm: A Giant Coloring Book about Having Fun on a Farm. 2004. (Illus.). (J). (978-0-9763307-5-2(X)) Food Marketing Consultants, Inc.

Coppendale, Jean. Tractors & Farm Vehicles. 2007. (J). lib. bdg. 16.95 (***978-1-59566-340-5(1)***) QEB Publishing Inc.

Cubley, Kathleen. On the Farm. MacMahon, Kelly, illus. 1999. 32p. (J). (ps-k). pap. 3.95 (978-1-57029-257-6(4) , WPH 01109, Totline Pubns.) Schaffer, Frank Pubns.

Dorling Kindersley Publishing Staff. Farm. (Touch & Feel Ser.). (J). 2007. 16p. 9.99 (978-0-7566-1971-8(8)); 2006. (Illus.). 36p. bds. 4.99 (978-0-7566-1750-9(2)); 2003. (Illus.). 16p. pap. 3.99 (978-0-7894-9828-1(6)); 1998. (Illus.). 12p. bds. 6.99 (978-0-7894-2916-2(0)) Dorling Kindersley Publishing, Inc.

—Funny, Fuzzy, Furry Farm. 2006. (Touchables Ser.). (Illus.). 14p. (J). 8.99 (978-0-7566-2021-9(X)) Dorling Kindersley Publishing, Inc.

—My First Farm Sticker Book. 2003. (My First Sticker Board Bks.). (Illus.). 12p. (J). pap. 6.99 (978-0-7894-9542-6(2)) Dorling Kindersley Publishing, Inc.

Dorling Kindersley Publishing Staff, ed. Farm. (Baby Fun Ser.). (J). (ps-3). 2005. (Illus.). 14p. bds. 4.99 (978-0-7566-0987-0(9)); 2004. 16p. pap. 6.99 (978-0-7566-0236-9(X)) Dorling Kindersley Publishing, Inc.

—Farm. 2002. (J). 4.98 (978-0-7525-5236-1(8)) Parragon, Inc.

Dumas, Philippe. A Farm. 1999. (Creative Editions Ser.). (Illus.). 48p. (gr. 6 up). 29.95 (978-1-56846-169-4(0) , Creative Education) Creative Co., The.

Dunn, Mary. My Adventure at a Flower Farm. 2006. 44p. (J). 8.99 (978-1-59092-262-0(X) , Orchard Academy Pr.) Windstorm Creative.

The Farm: Individual Title Six-Packs. (Sails Literacy Ser.). (gr. k up). 16p. 27.00 (978-0-7635-4389-1(6)); 28.00 (978-0-7635-0004-7(6)) Rigby Education.

Farm (Gr. PreK-5) 2003. (J). (978-1-58232-021-2(7)) Bryan Hse. Pubs., Inc.

Farmyard Fun Giant Sticker Shapes. 2002. (Sticker Shapes Ser.). 16p. (J). pap. 5.98 (978-0-7525-7927-6(4)) Parragon, Inc.

Field Trips. 2005. (Transportation Ser.). (YA). (gr. k-3). 118.80 (978-0-7368-4190-0(3) , Pebble Bks.) Capstone Pr., Inc.

Field Trips. (C). 430.74 (978-1-4048-1521-6(X)) Picture Window Bks.

Francis, Dorothy. A Strange Coin. 2007. (ENG.). 90p. (J). per. 10.99 (978-1-59092-409-9(6) , Blue Works) Windstorm Creative.

From Farm to You. 2005. (Illus.). 32p. (gr. 4-8). pap. 168.00 (978-0-7910-7061-1(1) , Chelsea Hse.) Facts On File, Inc.

Galvin, Laura Gates. At the Farm Travel Pack. 2006. 80p. (J). 14.99 (978-1-59069-484-8(8)) Studio Mouse LLC.

Geisert, Arthur. Nursery Crimes. 2001. (Illus.). 32p. (J). (gr. k-3). tchr. ed. 16.00 (978-0-618-06487-8(7) , Walter Lorraine) Houghton Mifflin Co. Trade & Reference Div.

Gillis, Jennifer Blizin. Farms Long Ago. 2004. (Let's See Ser.). (Illus.). 24p. (J). (gr. 1 up). lib. bdg. 19.93 (978-0-7565-0671-1(9)) Compass Point Bks.

Graham, Ian. On the Farm. 2006. (Illus.). 36p. (J). lib. bdg. 16.95 (978-1-59566-189-0(1)) QEB Publishing Inc.

La Granja: Individual Title Six-Packs. (Chiquilibros Ser.). (SPA.). (gr. k-1). 23.00 (978-0-7635-8591-4(2)) Rigby Education.

La Granja: Individual Title Two-Packs. (Chiquilibros Ser.). (SPA.). (ps-1). 12.00 (978-0-7635-8549-5(1)) Rigby Education.

Green, John, illus. Who Lives on the Farm? 2004. (Who Lives... Ser.). 12p. (J). bds. 4.99 (978-1-85854-647-6(8)) Brimax Books Ltd. GBR. *Dist:* Byeway Bks.

Halley, Ned B. & Dorling Kindersley Publishing Staff. Farm. 2000. (Eyewitness Bks.). (Illus.). 64p. (J). (gr. 4-7). lib. bdg. 19.99 (978-0-7894-6615-0(5)) Dorling Kindersley Publishing, Inc.

Hamaguchi, Carla, ed. Farm Stickety-Splits, 12 vols., 0650. Schamber, Kimberly, illus. 2001. 10p. (Orig.). (J). pap. 6.99 (978-1-57471-898-0(3)) Creative Teaching Pr., Inc.

Hoena, B. A. The Farm. 2004. (Pebble Plus, Let's Visit Ser.). (Illus.). 24p. (J). 17.26 (978-0-7368-2390-6(5)) Capstone Pr., Inc.

Hoena, B. A. & Saunders-Smith, Gail. Farm ABC: An Alphabet Book. 2005. (A+ Alphabet Books). 32p. (J). 22.60 (978-0-7368-3664-7(0)) Capstone Pr., Inc.

E F G

Hughes, Monica. We Love the Farm: Individual Title Six-Pack Pouch - Level C. (Lighthouse Ser.). 12p. (gr. k-1). 24.00 (978-0-7578-0822-7(0)) Rigby Education.

Icenoggle, Jodi. 'Til the Cows Come Home. 2004. (Illus.). 32p. (J). (gr. k-2). 15.95 (978-1-56397-987-3(X)) Boyds Mills Pr.

Jacobs, Daniel. Diferentes clases de Granjas. 2005. Tr. of All Kinds of Farms. (SPA., Illus.). 16p. (J). (gr. 1 up). lib. bdg. 15.93 (978-0-7368-4171-9(7)) Capstone Pr., Inc.

Leeper, Angela. The Farm. 2004. (Field Trip! Ser.). (Illus.). 24p. (J). pap. 5.75 (978-1-4034-5167-5(2)) Heinemann Library.

—To a Farm. 2004. (Field Trip! Ser.). (Illus.). 24p. (J). lib. bdg. (978-1-4034-5161-3(3)) Heinemann Library.

The Letter Ff: The Farm, 6 vols. (gr. k-2). 17.50 (978-0-7368-4105-4(9)) Red Brick Learning.

Litchfield, J. & Brooks, F. Farm. 2004. (Illus.). 10p. (J). 4.95 (978-0-7945-0587-5(2)) EDC Publishing.

Mann, Holly, illus. Farm. 2005. 8p. pap. (978-0-7624-2362-0(5)) Running Pr. Bk. Pubs.

Martín Larrañaga, Ana. Family Farm. 2000. (Ana's Animals Bks.). (Illus.). (J). 3.95 (978-1-58646-000-6(5)) Polka Dot Pr.

McCarthy, Edward G. Farm Equipment: How Farmers Get All That Work Done. McCarthy, Edward G. & Sylvester, Carl, illus. 2nd l.t. ed. 1998. 48p. (J). (gr. 1-5). reprint ed. pap. 4.98 (978-0-9664138-0-9(6)) Ed D. Bear Enterprises.

Miller, Heather. My Farm, 6 bks., Set. 2004. (Illus.). 24p. (J). (ps-2). 87.00 (978-0-516-23230-0(4) , Children's Pr.) Scholastic Library Publishing.

Nicholas, Christopher. On the Farm. 1999. (Storyshapes Ser.). (Illus.). 24p. (J). (ps-1). pap. 2.25 (978-0-7681-0134-8(4) , 57042, McClanahan Bk.) Learning Horizons, Inc.

Nieson, Marc. Barns. 2001. (Designing the Future Ser.). (Illus.). 32p. (J). (978-1-58341-189-6(5) , Creative Education) Creative Co., The.

Olson, Nathan. Farm Patterns. 2007. 32p. (J). (978-0-7368-6732-0(5)) Capstone Pr., Inc.

On the Farm: Individual Title Six-Packs. (Literatura 2000 Ser.). (gr. k-1). 28.00 (978-0-7635-0010-8(0)) Rigby Education.

On the Farm: Kindergarten Newcomer Books. (On Our Way to English Ser.). (gr. k up). 23.50 (978-0-7578-7186-3(0)) Rigby Education.

Pfloog, Jan. The Farm Book. Pfloog, Jan, illus. 1999. (Golden Super Shape Book Ser.). (Illus.). 24p. (J). (gr. k-ps). pap. 3.99 (978-0-307-58117-4(9) , 10059, Golden Bks.) Random Hse. Children's Bks.

Pienkowski, Jan, illus. Jan Pienkowski's Farm. 1998. (Animal Action Pops Ser.). 10p. (J). (gr. 2 up). 4.95 (978-1-58117-021-4(1) , Intervisual/Piggy Toes) Dalmatian Pr.

Priddy, Roger. Farm: Picture Pops. 2006. (Illus.). 18p. (J). 12.95 (978-0-312-49677-7(X) , Priddy Bks.) St. Martin's Pr.

—On the Farm. 2005. (Sticker Activity Fun Workbooks). (Illus.). 48p. (J). pap. 3.47 (978-0-312-49663-0(X) , Priddy Bks.) St. Martin's Pr.

Roop, Peter & Roop, Connie. A Farm Album. 1999. (Long Ago & Today Ser.). (Illus.). 24p. (J). (gr. 1-3). lib. bdg. 19.92 (978-1-57572-601-4(7)) Heinemann Library.

Rovin-Murphy, Deborah & Murphy, Frank. Reading - Writing - Learning: All about the Farm. 2004. (Reading - Writing - Learning Ser.). 48p. pap. 11.99 (978-0-439-26585-0(1) , Teaching Resources) Scholastic, Inc.

Rubin, Alan. This Farm. 2006. (Illus.). (J). 16p. (978-0-7368-5986-8(1)); (ENG & SPA., 18p. (978-0-7368-6022-2(3)) Yellow Umbrella Pr.

Running Press Staff & Mann, Holly. Farm. 2005. (Illus.). 8p. (J). pap. 4.95 (978-0-7624-2345-3(5) , Running Pr. Kids) Running Pr. Bk. Pubs.

Schaefer, Lola M. We Need Farmers. Saunders-Smith, Gail, ed. 1999. (Helpers in Our Community Ser.). (Illus.). 24p. (J). (gr. k-1). lib. bdg. 15.93 (978-0-7368-0390-8(4) , Pebble Bks.) Capstone Pr., Inc.

—We Need Farmers. 1999. pap. 13.25 (978-0-516-21903-5(0) , Children's Pr.) Scholastic Library Publishing.

School Specialty Publishing. Learn about the Farm. 2005. (Learn about Coloring Bks.). 32p. (J). (ps-3). pap. 1.99 (978-0-7696-4158-4(X) , Brighter Child) School Specialty Publishing.

Schuh, Mari C. On the Farm, 12 bks. Incl. Cats on the Farm. 2003. lib. bdg. 15.93 (978-0-7368-1660-1(7)); Chickens on the Farm. 2001. lib. bdg. 15.93 (978-0-7368-0991-7(0)); Cows on the Farm. 2001. lib. bdg. 15.93 (978-0-7368-0992-4(9)); Dogs on the Farm. 2002. lib. bdg. 15.93 (978-0-7368-1187-3(7)); Ducks on the Farm. 2003. lib. bdg. 15.93 (978-0-7368-1661-8(5)); Geese on the Farm. 2003. lib. bdg. 15.93 (978-0-7368-1662-5(3)); Goats on the Farm. 2002. lib. bdg. 15.93 (978-0-7368-1188-0(5)); Horses on the Farm. 2002. lib. bdg. 15.93 (978-0-7368-1189-7(3)); Pigs on the Farm. 2001. lib. bdg. 15.93 (978-0-7368-0993-1(7)); Rabbits on the Farm. 2003. lib. bdg. 15.93 (978-0-7368-1663-2(1)); Sheep on the Farm. 2001. lib. bdg. 15.93 (978-0-7368-0994-8(5)); Turkeys on the Farm. 2002. lib. bdg. 15.93 (978-0-7368-1190-3(7)); 24p. (J). (gr. k-1). (Illus.). Set lib. bdg. 191.16 (978-0-7368-1673-1(9) , Pebble Bks.) Capstone Pr., Inc.

Schwartz, David M. At the Farm. Kuhn, Dwight, photos by. 1998. (Springboards into Science Ser.). (Illus.). 24p. (J). (gr. 1 up). lib. bdg. 19.93 (978-0-8368-2221-2(8)) Stevens, Gareth Inc.

Scott, Janine. Farm Friends. 2002. (Spyglass Books). (Illus.). 24p. (J). (gr. 1 up). lib. bdg. 18.60 (978-0-7565-0232-4(2)) Compass Point Bks.

Shepard, Daniel. All Kinds of Farms. 2003. (Illus.). 17p. (J). 15.93 (978-0-7368-2912-0(1)); pap. (978-0-7368-2871-0(0)) Yellow Umbrella Pr.

Sloane, Eric. Eric Sloane's Age of Barns: An Illustrated Review of Classic Barn Styles & Construction. Sloane, Eric, illus. rev. ed. 2005. (Illus.). 94p. (YA). (gr. 10 up). pap. 16.95 (978-0-89658-565-2(4)) Voyageur Pr., Inc.

Stone, Lynn M. Farm Animals. 2001. (Life on the Farm Ser.). (Illus.). 24p. (J). (gr. 1-4). lib. bdg. 20.64 (978-1-58952-090-5(4)) Rourke Publishing, LLC.

—Farm Buildings. 2002. (Life on the Farm Ser.). (Illus.). 24p. (gr. 1-4). 14.95 (978-1-58952-091-2(2)) Rourke Publishing, LLC.

—Farm Machinery. 2002. (Life on the Farm Ser.). (Illus.). 24p. (gr. 1-4). 14.95 (978-1-58952-093-6(9)) Rourke Publishing, LLC.

—Farms Old & New. 2001. (Life on the Farm Ser.). (Illus.). 24p. (J). (gr. 1-4). lib. bdg. 20.64 (978-1-58952-094-3(7)) Rourke Publishing, LLC.

This Farm. 2006. (Yellow Umbrella Social Studies). 8,16p. (J). 6.50 (978-0-7368-1717-2(4)) Red Brick Learning.

Top That!, ed. Alphabet Farm. Parry, Jo, illus. 2007. 10p. (J). (ps). 8.99 (***978-1-84666-272-0(9)*** , Tide Mill Pr.) Top That! Publishing PLC GBR. *Dist:* Random Hse., Inc.

—Counting on the Farm. Sapp, Karen, illus. 2007. 16p. (J). (ps). 14.99 (***978-1-84666-270-6(2)*** , Tide Mill Pr.) Top That! Publishing PLC GBR. *Dist:* Random Hse., Inc.

Welvaert, Scott R. Follow That Crop: From the Farmer's Field to Our Grocery Store. 2003. (From Here to There Ser.). (J). (978-1-58417-194-2(4)); pap. (978-1-58417-195-9(2)) Lake Street Pubs.

Wolfman, Judy. Life on a Crop Farm. Winston, David Lorenz, photos by. 2005. (Life on a Farm Ser.). (Illus.). 48p. (gr. 2-5). lib. bdg. 23.93 (978-1-57505-518-3(X)) Lerner Publishing Group.

FARRAGUT, DAVID GLASGOW, 1801-1870

Roop, Peter & Roop, Connie. Take Command, Captain Farragut! McCurdy, Michael, illus. 2002. 48p. (J). (gr. 3-5). 16.00 (978-0-689-83022-8(X) , Atheneum) Simon & Schuster Children's Publishing.

Stein, R. Conrad. David Farragut: First Admiral of the U. S. Navy. 2005. (Proud Heritage: the Hispanic Library Ser.). (Illus.). 40p. (J). (gr. 3-7). 28.50 (978-1-59296-383-6(8)) Child's World, Inc.

FASCISM—GERMANY

see National Socialism

FASHION

see also Clothing and Dress; Costume; Dressmaking

Barkan, Joanne. Looking Good. 2005. (Real Deal Ser.). (Illus.). 32p. (J). pap. (978-0-7608-9634-1(8)) Sundance/Newbridge Educational Publishing.

Bell, Alison. Fearless Fashion. Mireault, Jerome, illus. 2004. (What's Your Style Ser. ? Ser.). 64p. (J). pap. 14.95 (978-1-894222-86-0(5)) Lobster Pr. CAN. *Dist:* Univ. of Toronto Pr.

Blackman, Cally. The 20s & 30s: Flappers & Vamps. 1999. (Twentieth Century Fashion Ser.). (Illus.). 32p. (J). (gr. 5 up). lib. bdg. 26.00 (978-0-8368-2599-2(3)) Stevens, Gareth Inc.

Bolino, Monika. Fashion. 2002. (Examining Pop Culture Ser.). (Illus.). 176p. (J). 36.20 (978-0-7377-1062-5(4)); (gr. 7-10). pap. 24.95 (978-0-7377-1061-8(6)) Thomson Gale. (Greenhaven Pr., Inc.).

Bratz Fashion Funktivity Books. 2004. (J). 1.49 (978-0-7666-1222-8(8) , 99215); 1.49 (978-0-7666-1223-5(6) , 99215); 1.49 (978-0-7666-1224-2(4) , 99215) Modern Publishing.

Bratz Stylin' Funktivity Box Set. 2004. (J). (978-0-7666-1361-4(5) , 64031) Modern Publishing.

Butterfield, Moira. Wannabes Fashion Queen: For Girls Who Know What They Want to Be. 2004. (Illus.). 128p. (J). pap. (978-1-84458-048-4(2)) Chrysalis Children's Bks.

Daynes, Katie. Fabulous Story of Fashion. Mistry, Nilesh, illus. 2006. 64p. (J). 8.99 (978-0-7945-1263-7(1) , Usborne) EDC Publishing.

Dorling Kindersley Publishing Staff & Spier, Carol. Super Style. 2006. (Illus.). 96p. pap. 8.99 (978-0-7566-1588-8(7)) Dorling Kindersley Publishing, Inc.

Dress Up 'N Get down! 2004. (Bratz Krazy-Kool Sticker Blitz Bks.). (J). (978-0-7666-1228-0(7) , 69580) Modern Publishing.

Erte. Erte Fashions Coloring Book. Noble, Marty, ed. 2003. (Illus.). 32p. (J). pap. 3.95 (978-0-486-43041-6(3)) Dover Pubns., Inc.

Facts on File, Inc. Staff, ed. Fashions of a Decade, 8 Vols., Set. 2006. (Fashions of a Decade Ser.). 64p. (gr. 6-12). 280.00 (978-0-8160-7059-6(8)) Facts On File, Inc.

Fashion. 2001. (Finditquick Ser.). (Illus.). 32p. (J). pap. 6.99 (978-0-307-10538-7(5) , Golden Bks.) Random Hse. Children's Bks.

Fashion Fun: Let's go Shopping! (Girls' Activity Kit Ser.). (J). (978-2-7643-0214-9(2)) Phidal Publishing, Inc./Editions Phidal, Inc.

Fashion Passion. 2004. (Bratz Krazy-Kool Sticker Blitz Bks.). (J). 2.99 (978-0-7666-1229-7(5) , 69580) Modern Publishing.

Flaunt It! 2004. (Bratz). (J). (978-0-7666-1226-6(0) , 65030); (978-0-7666-1227-3(9) , 65030) Modern Publishing.

Focus on Fashion! 2004. (Bratz Ser.). (J). 1.49 (978-0-7666-1225-9(2) , 99215) Modern Publishing.

Friends & Trends. 2004. (Bratz). (J). 2.49 (978-0-7666-1303-4(8) , 49315) Modern Publishing.

Gaines, Ann Graham. Coco Chanel. 2003. (Women in the Arts Ser.). (Illus.). 112p. (gr. 6-12). 30.00 (978-0-7910-7455-8(2) , Chelsea Hse.) Facts On File, Inc.

Gill, Mickey. Glam Slam! 2005. 100p. 12.95 (978-1-892951-28-1(2)) Fine Print Publishing Co.

Gilmour, Sarah. The 70s: Punks, Glam Rockers & New Romantics. 1999. (Twentieth Century Fashion Ser.). (Illus.). 32p. (J). (gr. 5 up). lib. bdg. 26.00 (978-0-8368-2602-9(7)) Stevens, Gareth Inc.

Haberman, Lia. Fashion File Wardrobe Do's & Don'ts. 2005. (Illus.). 48p. (J). (***978-0-439-80298-7(9)***) Scholastic, Inc.

Hangin' with the Girls! 2004. (Bratz). (J). (978-0-7666-1304-1(6) , 49315) Modern Publishing.

Hoobler, Dorothy & Hoobler, Thomas. Vanity Rules: A History of American Fashion & Beauty. 2000. (Single Titles Ser.). (Illus.). 160p. (gr. 7 up). lib. bdg. 28.90 (978-0-7613-1258-1(7) , Millbrook Pr.) Lerner Publishing Group.

J.G. Ferguson Publishing Company Staff, contrib. by. What Can I Do Now? 2007. (What Can I Do Now Ser.). 168p. (J). (gr. 6-12). 29.95 (***978-0-8160-6029-0(0)*** , Ferguson Publishing Co.) Facts On File, Inc.

Jones, Jen. Fashion. 2008. (J). (***978-1-4296-0129-0(9)***) Capstone Pr., Inc.

—Fashion History: Looking Great Through the Ages. 2007. (Illus.). 32p. (J). (978-0-7368-6828-0(3)) Capstone Pr., Inc.

—Fashion Trends: How Popular Style Is Shaped. 2007. (Illus.). 32p. (J). (978-0-7368-6831-0(3) , 1264962) Capstone Pr., Inc.

Jones, Jen. Fashion Trends: How Popular Style Is Shaped. 2007. (Illus.). 32p. (J). (***978-0-7368-7885-2(8)*** , 1264962) Capstone Pr., Inc.

Lomas, Clare. The 80s & 90s: Power Dressing to Sportswear. 1999. (Twentieth Century Fashion Ser.). (Illus.). 32p. (J). (gr. 5 up). lib. bdg. 26.00 (978-0-8368-2603-6(5)) Stevens, Gareth Inc.

Louie, Ai-Ling. Vera Wang Queen of Fashion; Amazing Chinese American: Biographies of Amazing Asian Americans. 2007. (Illus.). 48p. (J). pap. 12.99 (***978-0-9787465-3-7(8)***) Dragoneagle Pr.

Lundsten, Apryl. The Girls' Life Guide to Being a Style Superstar! Parett, Lisa, illus. 2004. 124p. (J). (978-0-439-44984-7(7)) Scholastic, Inc.

Maggio, Viqui. Baby Tease. 2007. 16p. bds. 10.00 (***978-1-933572-08-6(6)***) Centro Bks., LLC.

McAlpine, Margaret. Working in the Fashion Industry. 2005. (My Future Career Ser.). (Illus.). 64p. (J). lib. bdg. 26.00 (978-0-8368-4774-1(1)) Stevens, Gareth Inc.

McGraw-Hill Staff & Weber, Jeanette. Clothing: Fashion, Fabrics & Construction, 2 vols. 4th ed. 2002. 630p. (gr. 9-12). stu. ed. 59.96 (978-0-07-829006-0(6) , 9780078290060) Glencoe/McGraw-Hill.

Mee, Sue. 1900-1920: Linen & Lace. 1999. (Twentieth Century Fashion Ser.). (Illus.). 32p. (J). (gr. 5 up). lib. bdg. 26.00 (978-0-8368-2598-5(5)) Stevens, Gareth Inc.

Noble, Marty. Favorite Fashions. 2002. (Sticker Styles Ser.). (Illus.). (J). mass mkt. 12.95 (978-0-448-42839-0(3) , Planet Dexter) Penguin Group (USA) Inc.

—Victorian Fashions Stained Glass Coloring Book. 2001. (Illus.). 32p. (J). pap. 5.95 (978-0-486-41555-0(4)) Dover Pubns., Inc.

Nunn, Joan. Fashion in Costume 1200-1980. 1999. (gr. 7-12). lib. bdg. 29.20 (978-0-8335-6240-1(1)) Tandem Library Bks.

Orme, David. Fashion. 2008. (Trailblazers Ser.). (Illus.). 36p. pap. 7.95 (***978-1-84167-650-0(0)***) Ransom Publishing Ltd. GBR. *Dist:* International Publishers Marketing.

Peterson, Tiffany. Fashion Design. Westerfield, David, illus. 2003. (Draw It! Ser.). 32p. (J). (gr. 3-5). lib. bdg. 24.22 (978-1-4034-0211-0(6)); pap. 7.50 (978-1-4034-4030-3(1)) Heinemann Library.

Platt, Richard. They Wore What?! The Weird History of Fashion & Beauty. 2007. (J). pap. (***978-1-58728-584-4(3)***); 48p. (***978-1-58728-582-0(7)***) T&N Children's Publishing. (Two Can Publishing).

Powe-Temperley, Kitty. The 60s: Mods & Hippies. 1999. (Twentieth Century Fashion Ser.). (Illus.). 32p. (J). (gr. 5 up). lib. bdg. 26.00 (978-0-8368-2601-2(9)) Stevens, Gareth Inc.

Reynolds, Helen. Dresses & Skirts. 2003. (Fashionable History of Costume Ser.). (Illus.). 32p. (J). lib. bdg. 25.70 (978-1-4109-0031-9(2)) Raintree.

—Jewelry & Accessories. 2003. (Fashionable History of Costume Ser.). (Illus.). 32p. (J). lib. bdg. 25.70 (978-1-4109-0029-6(0)) Raintree.

—The 40s & 50s: Utility to New Look. 1999. (Twentieth Century Fashion Ser.). (Illus.). 32p. (J). (gr. 5 up). lib. bdg. 26.00 (978-0-8368-2600-5(0)) Stevens, Gareth Inc.

Rowland-Warne, L. & Dorling Kindersley Publishing Staff. Costume. 2000. (Eyewitness Bks.). (Illus.). 64p. (J). (gr. 4-7). lib. bdg. 19.99 (978-0-7894-6584-9(1)) Dorling Kindersley Publishing, Inc.

Salmansohn, Karen. Fashion. Stauffer, Brian, illus. 2005. (Petit Connoisseur Ser.). 16p. bds. 6.95 (978-1-58246-105-2(8) , Tricycle Pr.) Ten Speed Pr.

Seventeen Fashion. 2001. (YA). pap. (978-0-06-447244-9(2) , Harper Trophy) HarperCollins Pubs.

Simm, Joanna & Ladybird Books Staff. Friends 4-Ever! 2004. (Lil' Bratz Ser.). (Illus.). 32p. pap. 5.43 (978-1-84422-520-0(8) , Grosset & Dunlap) Penguin Group (USA) Inc.

Sun, Ming-Ju. Chinese Fashions. 2002. (Illus.). 48p. (J). pap. 3.95 (978-0-486-42053-0(1)) Dover Pubns., Inc.

Teen People Magazine Editors. Celebrity Style Guide. rev. ed. 2006. (Teen People Ser.). (Illus.). 160p. pap. 16.95 (978-1-933405-35-3(X) , People Bks.) Time, Inc. Home Entertainment.

Tierney, Tom. Ancient Egyptian Fashions. 1999. 48p. (J). pap. 3.95 (978-0-486-40806-4(X)) Dover Pubns., Inc.

—Cavalier & Puritan Fashions. 2005. (Illus.). 48p. (J). pap. 3.95 (978-0-486-43655-5(1)) Dover Pubns., Inc.

—Italian & Spanish Fashion Designers Paper Dolls. 2004. (Illus.). 32p. pap. 5.95 (978-0-486-43712-5(4)) Dover Pubns., Inc.

—Jacobean & Early Bourbon Fashions. 2004. (Dover Coloring Bks.). (Illus.). 48p. (J). pap. 3.95 (978-0-486-43333-2(1)) Dover Pubns., Inc.

—Renaissance Fashions. 2000. (Dover Coloring Bks.). (Illus.). 48p. (J). pap. 3.95 (978-0-486-41038-8(2)) Dover Pubns., Inc.

Ungs, Tim. Paul McCartney & Stella McCartney. 2004. (Famous Families Ser.). (Illus.). 48p. (J). lib. bdg. 25.25 (978-1-4042-0263-4(3)) Rosen Publishing Group, Inc., The.

Wallis, Jeremy. Coco Chanel. 2001. (Creative Lives Ser.). (Illus.). 64p. (J). (gr. 6-8). lib. bdg. 27.07 (978-1-58810-202-7(5)) Heinemann Library.

Warrick, Leanne. Style Trix for Cool Chix: The One-Stop Guide to Finding Your Perfect Look. 2005. (Illus.). 96p. (J). pap. 9.95 (978-0-8230-4940-0(X)) Watson-Guptill Pubns., Inc.

Wasserman, Robin. So You Want to Be... Unfabulous. 2006. (Teenick Ser.). 48p. (J). pap. 7.99 (978-0-439-83164-2(4)) Scholastic, Inc.

Watson, Linda. Designers A-F. 2000. (Vogue 20th Century Fashion Ser.). (Illus.). (YA). 24.95 (978-0-7910-6194-7(9) , Chelsea Hse.) Facts On File, Inc.

—Designers G-M. 2000. (Vogue 20th Century Fashion Ser.). (Illus.). (YA). 24.95 (978-0-7910-6195-4(7) , Chelsea Hse.) Facts On File, Inc.

—Designers N-Z. 2000. (Vogue 20th Century Fashion Ser.). (Illus.). (J). 24.95 (978-0-7910-6196-1(5) , Chelsea Hse.) Facts On File, Inc.

—Fashions 1900-1949. 2000. (Vogue 20th Century Fashion Ser.). (Illus.). (J). 24.99 (978-0-7910-6192-3(2) , Chelsea Hse.) Facts On File, Inc.

—Fashions 1950-2000. 2000. (Vogue 20th Century Fashion Ser.). (YA). 24.95 (978-0-7910-6193-0(0) , Chelsea Hse.) Facts On File, Inc.

—20th Century Fashion: 100 Years of Style by Decade & Designer, 5 vols., Set. 2000. (Illus.). 48-64p. (YA). (gr. 9 up). 180.00 (978-0-7910-6191-6(4)) Facts On File, Inc.

Weaver, Janice. From Head to Toe: Bound Feet, Bathing Suits, & Other Bizarre & Beautiful Things. Blake, Francis, illus. 2003. 80p. (J). (gr. 5-9). pap. 16.95 (978-0-88776-654-1(4)) Tundra Bks., Inc./Livres Toundra, Inc. CAN. *Dist:* Random Hse., Inc.

Whitty, Helen. Dressing Up. 2001. (Clothing Ser.). (Illus.). 32p. (J). (gr. 4 up). 22.95 (978-0-7910-6576-1(6) , 010402, Chelsea Hse.) Facts On File, Inc.

Xpress Yourself! 2004. (Bratz). (Illus.). 384p. (J). pap. (978-0-7666-1307-2(0) , 11765) Modern Publishing.

20th Century Fashion, 6 bks. Incl. 20s & 30s : Flappers & Vamps. Blackman, Cally. lib. bdg. 26.00 (978-0-8368-2599-2(3)); 40s & 50s : Utility to New Look. Reynolds, Helen. lib. bdg. 26.00 (978-0-8368-2600-5(0)); 60s : Mods & Hippies. Powe-Temperley, Kitty. lib. bdg. 26.00 (978-0-8368-2601-2(9)); 70s : Punks, Glam Rockers & New Romantics. Gilmour, Sarah. lib. bdg. 26.00 (978-0-8368-2602-9(7)); 80s & 90s : Power Dressing to Sportswear. Lomas, Clare. lib. bdg. 26.00 (978-0-8368-2603-6(5)); 1900-1920 : Linen & Lace. Mee, Sue. lib. bdg. 26.00 (978-0-8368-2598-5(5)); 32p. (J). (gr. 5 up). (Illus.). 1999. Set lib. bdg. 104.00 (978-0-8368-2597-8(7)) Stevens, Gareth Inc.

FASHION—FICTION

Barham, Lisa. Accidentally Fabulous. 2008. (Fashion-Forward Adventures of Imogene Ser.). 256p. (YA). pap. 9.99 (***978-1-4169-1445-7(5)*** , Simon Pulse) Simon & Schuster Children's Publishing.

Blacker, Terence. Ms Wiz, Supermodel. Ross, Tony, illus. 2003. 58p. (J). pap. 6.99 (978-0-330-35312-0(8) , Pan) Pan Macmillan GBR. *Dist:* Trafalgar Square Publishing.

Chesterfield, Sadie & S. I. International. Feeling Groovy Art Studio. Cuddy, Robbin, illus. 2007. (Groovy Girls Ser.). 48p. (J). 9.99 (***978-1-4169-3551-3(7)*** , Simon Scribbles) Simon & Schuster Children's Publishing.

Clarke, Nicole. Copycat. 2007. (Flirt Ser.: No. 9). 224p. (J). (gr. 7). pap. 6.99 (978-0-448-44561-8(1) , Grosset & Dunlap) Penguin Group (USA) Inc.

—French Twist. 2007. (Flirt Ser.: Vol. 8). 224p. (YA). pap. 6.99 (978-0-448-44463-5(1) , Grosset & Dunlap) Penguin Group (USA) Inc.

—Issues. 2006. (Flirt Ser.: No. 5). 224p. (J). (gr. 7). pap. 6.99 (978-0-448-44394-2(5) , Grosset & Dunlap) Penguin Group (USA) Inc.

Clarke, Nicole & Henderson, Mel. Write Here, Right Now, No. 1. 2006. (Flirt Ser.: No. 1). 224p. (J). (gr. 7-10). pap. 6.99 (978-0-448-44263-1(9) , Grosset & Dunlap) Penguin Group (USA) Inc.

Get Together Girls - Fashion Show. 2005. (J). bds. (978-1-4194-0086-5(X)) Paradise Pr., Inc.

Golden Books Staff. Fashion Show. 2000. (Illus.). 128p. (J). (ps-2). pap. 0.99 (978-0-307-44332-8(9) , Golden Bks.) Random Hse. Children's Bks.

—Glamour Girl. Harchy, Atelier Philippe, illus. 2004. 32p. (J). (ps-2). 4.99 (978-0-375-82811-9(7) , Golden Bks.) Random Hse. Children's Bks.

Harper, Charise Mericle. Fashion Kitty. 2005. (Illus.). 96p. (gr. 3-7). pap. 8.99 (978-0-7868-5134-8(1)) Hyperion Pr.

Jones, Jasmine. Best Dressed. 2004. 138p. (J). lib. bdg. 16.92 (***978-1-4242-0678-0(2)***) Fitzgerald Bks.

Karasyov, Carrie & Kargman, Jill. Summer Intern. 2007. 192p. (gr. 7 up). (J). lib. bdg. 17.89 (***978-0-06-115376-1(1)***); (YA). 16.99 (***978-0-06-115375-4(3)***) HarperCollins Pubs. (HarperTeen).

Man-Kong, Mary. High Fashion: Cool & Casual, No. 2. 2007. (Illus.). 32p. (J). (ps-2). 4.99 (978-0-375-83548-3(2) , Golden Bks.) Random Hse. Children's Bks.

—High Fashion Glam & Glitz, No. 1. 2007. (Illus.). 32p. (J). (ps-2). 4.99 (978-0-375-83547-6(4) , Golden Bks.) Random Hse. Children's Bks.

Maude, Rachel. Poseur #1. Compai, illus. 2008. 304p. (J). (gr. 7-17). pap. 9.99 (***978-0-316-06583-2(8)*** , Poppy) Little, Brown Bks. for Young Readers.

Neuman, Maria. Style Patrol. Choi Sung Hwan, Aragon Noel, illus. 2005. (Trollz Ser.). 64p. (J). (gr. 4-7). pap. 6.99 (978-0-439-70006-1(X)) Scholastic, Inc.

Oliver, Jasmine. Prada Princesses. 2007. (Project Fashion Ser.). 192p. (YA). pap. 8.99 (***978-1-4169-3812-5(5)*** , Simon Pulse) Simon & Schuster Children's Publishing.

Olsen, Mary-Kate. Make-up, Shake-up. 2002. (gr. k-3). lib. bdg. 12.40 (978-0-613-64746-5(7)) Tandem Library Bks.

Pagliarulo, Antonio. On the Avenue. 2007. (Celebutantes Ser.). 352p. (YA). (gr. 9 up). pap. 9.99 (978-0-385-73404-2(2)); lib. bdg. 12.99 (978-0-385-90415-5(0)) Random Hse. Children's Bks. (Delacorte Bks. for Young Readers).

Whytock, Cherry. My Cup Runneth Over: The Life of Angelica Cookson Potts. Whytock, Cherry, illus. (YA). 2003. (Illus.). 176p. 14.95 (978-0-689-86546-6(5)); 2004. 192p. reprint ed. mass mkt. 5.99 (978-0-689-86551-0(1) , Simon Pulse) Simon & Schuster Children's Publishing.

FASHION—VOCATIONAL GUIDANCE

Beker, Jeanne. Passion for Fashion: Careers in Style. Dion, Nathalie, illus. 2008. 80p. pap. 18.95 (***978-0-88776-800-2(8)***) Tundra Bks., Inc./Livres Toundra, Inc. CAN. *Dist:* Random Hse. of Canada, Ltd.

Fiscus, Jim. Careers in the Fashion Industry. rev. ed. 2005. (Career Resource Library). (Illus.). 192p. (YA). (gr. 7-12). lib. bdg. 26.50 (978-0-8239-4082-0(9)) Rosen Publishing Group, Inc., The.

Giacobello, John. Careers in the Fashion Industry. rev. ed. 1999. (Careers). (Illus.). 122p. (YA). (gr. 7-12). lib. bdg. 18.95 (978-0-8239-2890-3(X) , CAFASH) Rosen Publishing Group, Inc., The.

—Choosing a Career in the Fashion Industry. 2005. (World of Work Ser.). (Illus.). 64p. (YA). (gr. 7-12). lib. bdg. 25.25 (978-0-8239-3296-2(6) , WWFASH) Rosen Publishing Group, Inc., The.

Jones, Jen. Fashion Careers: Finding the Right Fit. 2007. (Illus.). 32p. (J). (978-0-7368-6829-7(1) , 1264957, Capstone Bks.) Capstone Pr., Inc.

—Fashion Careers: Finding the Right Fit. 2007. (Illus.). 32p. (J). (***978-0-7368-7883-8(1)*** , 1264957, Capstone Bks.) Capstone Pr., Inc.

—Fashion Design: The Art of Style. 2007. (Illus.). 32p. (J). (978-0-7368-6827-3(5) , 1264959) Capstone Pr., Inc.

—Fashion Design School: Learning the Skills to Succeed. 2007. (Illus.). 32p. (J). (978-0-7368-6832-7(1) , 1264958) Capstone Pr., Inc.

—Fashion Design School: Learning the Skills to Succeed. 2007. (Illus.). 32p. (J). (***978-0-7368-7886-9(6)*** , 1264958) Capstone Pr., Inc.

—Fashion Design: the Art of Style. 2007. (Illus.). 32p. (J). (***978-0-7368-7881-4(5)*** , 1264959) Capstone Pr., Inc.

O'Donnell, Kerri. Careers in Modeling. 2005. (Career Resource Library). (Illus.). 192p. (YA). (gr. 7-12). lib. bdg. 26.50 (978-0-8239-3183-5(8)) Rosen Publishing Group, Inc., The.

FASTS AND FEASTS

see also Christmas; Easter; Holidays

Allen, Katherine E., illus. Festival of Light: Deepavali Legends from Around India. 2005. 61p. (J). (***978-81-87111-70-2(4)***) Vakils, Feffer & Simons, Ltd.

Andrade, Mary J., photos by. Day of the Dead A Passion for Life: Día de los Muertos Pasion por la Vida. Andrade, Mary J., . 2nd ed. 2007. (SPA.). lib. bdg., stu. ed., tchr.'s training gde. ed. 29.95 (***978-0-9791624-0-4(8)***) La Oferta Publishing Co.

Berger, Samantha & Daniel, Moreton. Celebrations. 1999. (ps-2). lib. bdg. 10.10 (978-0-613-21314-1(9)) Tandem Library Bks.

Berger, Samantha & Moreton, Daniel. Celebrations. 1999. (Social Studies Emergent Readers). (J). 2.50 (978-0-439-04557-5(6)) Scholastic, Inc.

Dineen, Jacqueline. Feasts & Festivals. Wilkinson, Philip, ed. Ingpen, Robert R., illus. 1999. (People & Customs of the World Ser.). 96p. (YA). lib. bdg. 34.02 (978-0-7910-5136-8(6) , Chelsea Hse.) Facts On File, Inc.

Elayne. The Entrance of the Theotokos into the Temple. Gillis, Bonnie, illus. 2003. (Twelve Great Feasts for Children Ser.). 24p. pap. 5.95 (978-1-888212-40-2(3)) Conciliar Pr.

Elliott, Lynne. Food & Feasts in the Middle Ages. 2004. (Medieval World Ser.). (Illus.). 32p. pap. (978-0-7787-1380-7(6)); (J). (978-0-7787-1348-7(2)) Crabtree Publishing Co.

Festivals & Feasts: Individual Title Six-Packs. (Rigby Infoquest Ser.). 32p. (gr. 4 up). 37.00 (978-0-7578-5726-3(4)) Rigby Education.

Fischer, Carl. Celebration Times: Feasts & Seasons of the Church Year. Larkin, Jean, ed. Lynch, Patricia, illus. 1999. (Active Learning for Catholic Kids Ser.). 28p. (J). (gr. 1-3). pap. 7.95 (978-0-937997-49-9(8) , 3400) Pflaum Publishing Group.

Foran, Jill. Buddha Day. 2003. (Celebrating Cultures Ser.). (Illus.). 24p. (J). lib. bdg. 15.95 (978-1-59036-090-3(7)) Weigl Pubs., Inc.

Ganeri, Anita. Buddhist Festivals Through the Year. 2003. (Year of Festivals Ser.). (J). 30p. lib. bdg. 24.25 (978-1-58340-375-4(2)); (Illus.). 32p. (978-0-7496-4801-5(5)) Smart Apple Media.

—Christian Festivals Through the Year. 2003. (Year of Festivals Ser.). 30p. (J). lib. bdg. 24.25 (978-1-58340-370-9(1)) Smart Apple Media.

—Hindu Festivals Through the Year. 2003. (Year of Festivals Ser.). 30p. (J). lib. bdg. 24.25 (978-1-58340-372-3(8)) Smart Apple Media.

—Muslim Festivals Through the Year. 2003. (Year of Festivals Ser.). 30p. (J). lib. bdg. 24.25 (978-1-58340-371-6(X)) Smart Apple Media.

—Religious Food. 1999. (What's Sacred to Me Ser.). (Illus.). 32p. (J). (ps-3). lib. bdg. 25.69 (978-0-7398-2762-8(6)) Raintree.

—Religious Food. 2001. (What's Sacred to Me Ser.). (Illus.). 32p. (J). (ps-3). pap. 10.34 (978-0-7398-3124-3(0)) Steck-Vaughn.

—Religious Food. 2000. (gr. k-3). lib. bdg. 17.60 (978-0-613-74050-0(5)) Tandem Library Bks.

Ganeri, Anita & Saunders, Mary. The First Book of Festivals: A Resource Book. 2005. (Illus.). 80p. (J). pap. 19.95 (978-0-237-52784-6(7) , Evans Brothers, Limited) Evans Publishing Group GBR. *Dist:* Independent Pubs. Group.

Gardeski, Christina Mia. Diwali. 2001. (Rookie Read-About Holidays Ser.). (Illus.). 32p. (J). (gr. 1-2). 19.50 (978-0-516-22372-8(0)); pap. 5.95 (978-0-516-26311-3(0)) Scholastic Library Publishing. (Children's Pr.).

Gillis, Jennifer Blizin & Jordan, Denise M. Diwali. 2002. (Fiestas Con Velas (Candle Time) Ser.). (SPA.). 24p. (J). (ps-1). lib. bdg. 18.50 (978-1-58810-782-4(5)); (Illus.). pap. 5.25 (978-1-58810-829-6(5) , 91588) Heinemann Library.

Gnojewski, Carol. Ramadan: A Muslim Time of Fasting, Prayer, & Celebration. 2004. (Finding Out about Holidays Ser.). (Illus.). 48p. (J). (gr. 2-5). lib. bdg. 23.93 (978-0-7660-2275-1(7)) Enslow Pubs., Inc.

Gustafson, Janie. Advent ABCs: Reproducible Activities. 1999. (God's Gift Ser.). (Illus.). 32p. (J). (gr. k-3). pap. 9.95 (978-1-893757-02-8(1) , 04) Needer, E.T. Publishing.

Haven, Kendall F. New Year's to Kwanzaa: Original Stories of Celebration. 1999. 240p. (gr. 3-8). pap. 16.95 (978-1-55591-962-7(6)) Fulcrum Publishing.

Heiligman, Deborah. Celebrate Ramadan & Eid Al-Fitr: With Prayer, Fasting, & Charity. 2006. (Holidays Around the World Ser.). (Illus.). 32p. (J). (gr. 1-4). 15.95 (978-0-7922-5926-8(2) , National Geographic Children's Bks.) National Geographic Society.

—Celebrate Ramadan & Eid Al-Fitr: With Praying, Fasting, & Charity. 2006. (Holidays Around the World Ser.). (Illus.). 32p. (J). (gr. 1-4). lib. bdg. 23.90 (978-0-7922-5927-5(0) , National Geographic Children's Bks.) National Geographic Society.

Hoyt-Goldsmith, Diane. Celebrating Ramadan. Migdale, Lawrence, illus. Migdale, Lawrence, photos by. 32p. (YA). (gr. 4-6). tchr. ed. 17.95 (978-0-8234-1581-6(3)) Holiday Hse., Inc.

—Celebrating Ramadan. Migdale, Lawrence, photos by. (Illus.). 32p. (J). (gr. 4-6). 6.95 (978-0-8234-1762-9(X)) Holiday Hse., Inc.

Hughes, Monica. My Divali. 2003. (Festivals Ser.). (Illus.). 24p. (J). pap. 5.50 (978-1-4109-0663-2(9)); lib. bdg. 18.56 (978-1-4109-0637-3(X)) Raintree.

—My Id-Ul-Fitr. 2003. (Festivals Ser.). (Illus.). 24p. (J). pap. 5.50 (978-1-4109-0666-3(3)) Raintree.

—My Id-ul-Fitr. 2003. (Festivals Ser.). (Illus.). 24p. (J). lib. bdg. 18.56 (978-1-4109-0640-3(X)) Raintree.

Jeffrey, Laura S. Celebrate Ramadan. 2007. (Celebrate Holidays Ser.). (Illus.). 112p. (J). lib. bdg. 31.93 (978-0-7660-2774-9(0)) Enslow Pubs., Inc.

Jordan, Denise M. Diwali. 2002. (Candle Time Ser.). (Illus.). 24p. (J). (ps-1). pap. 5.25 (978-1-58810-736-7(1) , 91385); lib. bdg. 18.50 (978-1-58810-527-1(X)) Heinemann Library.

Kadela, Natalie. Our Year with God: A Child's Introduction to Catholic Holy Days & the Liturgical Year. Richards, Virginia Helen & Lane, Helen Rita, illus. 1999. 152p. (J). (gr. 3-7). pap. 14.95 (978-0-8198-5436-0(0) , 332-265) Pauline Bks. & Media.

Khan, Farjana. Yippee! Ramadan's over, It's Eid. 2005. (ENG., Illus.). 28p. (J). per. (***978-1-4208-9412-7(9)***) AuthorHouse.

MacMillan, Dianne M. Ramadan & Id Al-Fitr. 2nd ed. 2008. (Best Holiday Books Ser.). 48p. (J). (gr. 3-4). lib. bdg. 23.93 (***978-0-7660-3045-9(8)***) Enslow Pubs., Inc.

Marchant, Kerena. Feasts & Fasting. Sloan, Frank, ed. 2001. (Ceremonies & Celebrations Ser.). (Illus.). 32p. (J). (ps-3). lib. bdg. 25.69 (978-0-7398-3268-4(9)) Raintree.

—Feasts & Fasting. Sloan, Frank, ed. 2001. (Ceremonies & Celebrations Ser.). (Illus.). 32p. (J). (978-0-7502-2803-9(2)) Steck-Vaughn.

—Hindu Festivals. 2001. (Festival Tales Ser.). (Illus.). 32p. (J). (gr. 4-7). lib. bdg. 25.69 (978-0-7398-2734-5(0)) Raintree.

—Id-Ul-Fitr. 1998. (Festivals Ser.). (Illus.). 32p. (gr. 2-4). lib. bdg. 22.90 (978-0-7613-0963-5(2) , Millbrook Pr.) Lerner Publishing Group.

—Muslim Festivals. Barber, Tina, illus. 2001. (Festival Tales Ser.). 32p. (J). (gr. 4-7). lib. bdg. 25.69 (978-0-7398-2735-2(9)) Raintree.

Marx, David F. Ramadan. 2002. (Rookie Read-About Holidays Ser.). (Illus.). 32p. (J). (gr. 1-2). 20.50 (978-0-516-22269-1(4)); pap. 5.95 (978-0-516-27377-8(9)) Scholastic Library Publishing. (Children's Pr.).

—Ramadan. 2002. (gr. k-3). lib. bdg. 14.10 (978-0-613-54317-0(3)) Tandem Library Bks.

Mitchell, Judy & Borst, Donna, eds. The Best of Holidays & Seasonal Celebrations. 2001. 320p. (J). Issues 9-13. (Illus.). (ps-k). pap. 24.95 (978-1-57310-298-8(9)); Issues 22-26. (gr. 1-3). pap. 24.95 (978-1-57310-299-5(7)) Teaching & Learning Co.

Mobin-Uddin, Asma. The Best Eid Ever. Jacobsen, Laura, illus. 2007. 32p. (J). (gr. 2-4). 16.95 (***978-1-59078-431-0(6)***) Boyds Mills Pr.

Moehn, Heather. World Holidays: A Watts Guide for Children. 2000. (Watts Reference Ser.). (Illus.). 124p. (YA). (gr. 4 up). pap. 19.95 (978-0-531-16490-7(X) , Watts, Franklin) Scholastic Library Publishing.

—World Holidays: A Watts Guide for Children. 2000. (gr. 3-6). lib. bdg. 30.35 (978-0-613-72663-4(4)) Tandem Library Bks.

O'Keefe, Kathy Della Torre. Child's Guide to the Holy Days. 2007. (Illus.). 32p. (J). (gr. k-4). 9.95 (978-0-8091-6731-9(X) , 6731-9) Paulist Pr.

Pirotta, Saviour. Id-Ul-Fitr. 2007. (J). lib. bdg. (978-1-4042-3708-7(9) , PowerKids Pr.) Rosen Publishing Group, Inc., The.

Podwal, Mark. A Sweet Year: A Taste of the Jewish Holidays. Podwal, Mark, illus. 2003. (Illus.). 32p. (J). 12.95 (978-0-385-74637-3(7) , Doubleday Bks. for Young Readers) Random Hse. Children's Bks.

Powell, Jillian. Id-Ul-Fitr. 2006. (J). (978-1-58340-943-5(2)) Smart Apple Media.

Reed. What Is Communion? 2006. 32p. pap. 2.00 (978-0-687-49337-1(4)) Abingdon Pr.

Reynolds, Jan. Celebrate! Connections among Cultures. 2006. (Illus.). 32p. (J). (gr. k-3). 16.95 (978-1-58430-253-7(4)) Lee & Low Bks., Inc.

Rocio, Mejia. Celebrando Dia de Muertos: Celebrating Day of the Dead. 2006. (SPA & ENG.). 8.00 (***978-0-9776332-6-5(8)***) Salt City Books.

Senker, Cath. My Buddhist Year. (Illus.). 2005. (J). pap. (978-0-7502-4059-8(8)); 2003. (978-0-7502-4058-1(X)) Hodder Children's Division. (Hodder Wayland).

—My Buddhist Year. 2007. (J). lib. bdg. (***978-1-4042-3730-8(5)*** , PowerKids Pr.) Rosen Publishing Group, Inc., The.

—My Christian Year. 2004. (Illus.). (J). pap. (978-0-7502-4063-5(6) , Hodder Wayland) Hodder Children's Division.

—My Christian Year. 2007. (J). lib. bdg. (***978-1-4042-3729-2(1)*** , PowerKids Pr.) Rosen Publishing Group, Inc., The.

—My Hindu Year. (Illus.). 2004. 32p. (J). pap. (978-0-7502-4057-4(1)); 2003. (978-0-7502-4056-7(3)) Hodder Children's Division. (Hodder Wayland).

—My Hindu Year. 2007. (J). lib. bdg. (***978-1-4042-3731-5(3)*** , PowerKids Pr.) Rosen Publishing Group, Inc., The.

—My Muslim Year. 2004. (Illus.). 32p. (J). pap. (978-0-7502-4053-6(9) , Hodder Wayland) Hodder Children's Division.

—My Muslim Year. 2007. (J). lib. bdg. (***978-1-4042-3728-5(3)*** , PowerKids Pr.) Rosen Publishing Group, Inc., The.

Senker, Cath. My Sikh Year. (Illus.). 2005. (J). pap. (978-0-7502-4055-0(5)); 2003. (978-0-7502-4054-3(7)) Hodder Children's Division. (Hodder Wayland).

—My Sikh Year. 2007. (J). lib. bdg. (***978-1-4042-3733-9(X)*** , PowerKids Pr.) Rosen Publishing Group, Inc., The.

Sievert, Terri. Ramadan: Islamic Holy Month. 2006. (First Facts Ser.). (Illus.). 24p. (J). (978-0-7368-5392-7(8)) Capstone Pr., Inc.

Thompson, Stuart, et al. Chinese Cookbook. 2001. (Holiday Cookbooks from Around the World). (Illus.). 32p. (J). lib. bdg. 25.69 (978-0-7398-3262-2(X)) Raintree.

Tomljanovic, Tatiana. Ramadan. 2006. (J). (978-1-59036-461-1(9)); (978-1-59036-464-2(3)) Weigl Pubs., Inc.

Vaughan, Jenny & Beauchamp, Penny. Festival Foods. 2004. (World of Recipes Ser.). (Illus.). 48p. (J). pap. 8.50 (978-1-4034-6012-7(4)) Heinemann Library.

—Festivals. 2004. (World of Recipes Ser.). (Illus.). 48p. (J). lib. bdg. (978-1-4034-4699-2(7)) Heinemann Library.

Walsh, Kieran. Ramadan. 2002. (Illus.). 24p. (J). lib. bdg. 20.64 (978-1-58952-223-7(0)) Rourke Publishing, LLC.

Ward, Hadley. Saints to Lead Me: Feast Days Through the Year. Larkin, Jean, ed. Barnes, Wendy, illus. 2000. (Active Learning for Catholic Kids Ser.). 28p. (J). (gr. 4-6). pap. 7.95 (978-0-937997-86-4(2)) Pflaum Publishing Group.

Wells, Elisabeth & Trout, Lisa. Seasons of the Church: Intermediate. 2000. (Illus.). 32p. (YA). (gr. 5-8). 9.95 (978-1-893757-21-9(8) , 21-8) Needer, E.T. Publishing.

Winchester, Faith. Muslim Holidays. 1999. (Ethnic Holidays Ser.). (Illus.). 24p. (J). (gr. 2-3). lib. bdg. 18.60 (978-1-56065-459-9(7) , Bridgestone Bks.) Capstone Pr., Inc.

World Book, Inc. Staff, contrib. by. Religious Celebrations. 2003. (World Book's Celebrations & Rituals Around the World Ser.). (Illus.). 46p. (J). (978-0-7166-5015-7(0)) World Bk., Inc.

FASTS AND FEASTS—FICTION

Blitz, Shmuel. Bedtime Stories of Jewish Holidays. 1998. 48p. 14.99 (978-1-57819-174-1(2) , BEDJH) Mesorah Pubns., Ltd.

Cohen, Barbara. Here Come the Purim Players! Mekibel, Shoshana, illus. 1998. (gr. k-3). 13.95 (978-0-8074-0645-8(7) , 101251) URJ Pr.

Emerman, Ellen. Is It Shabbos Yet? Rosenfeld, Dina, ed. Leff, Tova, illus. 2nd ed. 2001. 32p. (J). (ps-k). 9.95 (978-1-929628-02-5(1)) Hachai Publishing.

Estrin, Leibel. Rabbi Riddle Says... Look Who Dropped in for Yom Tov. Sears, Dovid, illus. 2005. (J). 10.95 (***978-1-931681-74-2(0)***) Israel Bk. Shop.

Falwell, Cathryn. Feast for 10. Falwell, Cathryn, illus. 2002. (Illus.). (J). 14.74 (978-0-7587-2485-4(3)) Book Wholesalers, Inc.

—Feast for 10. Falwell, Cathryn, illus. 2003. (Illus.). 28p. (J). (gr. k-ps). bds. 4.95 (978-0-618-38226-2(7) , Clarion Bks.) Houghton Mifflin Co. Trade & Reference Div.

Gerstein, Mordicai. The White Ram: A Story of Abraham & Isaac. Gerstein, Mordicai, illus. 2006. (Illus.). 32p. (J). (gr. 1-5). 16.95 (978-0-8234-1897-8(9)) Holiday Hse., Inc.

Katz, Karen. My First Ramadan. 2007. (Illus.). 32p. (J). (ps-k). 14.95 (***978-0-8050-7894-7(0)***) Holt, Henry & Co.

Kimmelman, Leslie. Sound the Shofar! A Story for Rosh Hashanah & Yom Kippur. Himmelman, John, illus. 1998. 32p. (J). (ps-1). 15.99 (978-0-06-027501-3(4)) HarperCollins Pubs.

Levy, Janice. I Remember Abuelito/Yo Recuerdo a Abuelito: A Day of the Dead Story/Un Cuento del Dia de los Muertos. Arisa, Miguel, tr. Lopez, Loretta, illus. 2007. (Albert Whitman Prairie Paperback Ser.). (SPA & ENG.). 32p. (J). (ps-3). 6.95 (***978-0-8075-3517-2(6)***); 16.95 (***978-0-8075-3516-5(8)***) Whitman, Albert & Co.

Madrigal, Antonio Hernandez. Blanca's Feather. Suzan, Gerardo, illus. 2000. 32p. (gr. k-3). 15.95 (978-0-87358-743-3(X) , Rising Moon Bks. for Young Readers) Northland Publishing.

Matthews, Mary. Magid Fasts for Ramadan. Lewis, E. B., illus. 2000. 48p. (J). (gr. 4-6). 6.95 (978-0-618-04035-3(8) , Clarion Bks.) Houghton Mifflin Co. Trade & Reference Div.

Mejuto, Eva. La Casa de la Mosca Fosca. Mora, Sergio, illus. 2002. (Libros para Soñar Ser.). (SPA.). 28p. (J). (978-84-8464-143-8(0)) Kalandraka Editora, S.L.

Pearl, Sydelle. Elijah's Tears: Stories for the Jewish Holidays. Skortcheva, Rossitza, illus. 2004. 80p. (YA). pap. 14.95 (978-1-58980-178-3(4)) Pelican Publishing Co., Inc.

Ron, Kare. The Adventures of Sir Noodlefish: The Cake Wars. McCracken, Ken, illus. 2000. 32p. (J). (gr. 1-3). pap. (978-1-931179-00-3(X)) Long Hill Productions, Inc.

Rouss, Sylvia A. The Littlest Candlesticks. Hannon, Holly, illus. 2005. (Littlest Ser.). 32p. (J). 14.95 (978-1-930143-48-7(6)); pap. 9.95 (978-1-930143-49-4(4)) Pitspopany Pr. (Devora Publishing).

Samira's Eid. 2004. (ENG & KUR.). (J). (978-1-84444-667-4(0)) Mantra Publishing, Ltd.

Schotter, Roni. Purim Play. Hafner, Marylin, illus. 1998. 32p. (J). (ps-3). 15.95 (978-0-316-77518-2(5)) Little Brown & Co.

Zolkower, Edie Stoltz. Too Many Cooks: A Passover Parable. Kawasaki, Shauna Mooney, illus. 2003. 24p. (J). (ps-3). pap. 5.95 (978-1-58013-063-9(1)) Kar-Ben Publishing.

Zucker, Jonny. It's Party Time! A Purim Story. Cohen, Jan Barger, illus. 2003. (Festival Time! Ser.). 24p. (J). (ps-2). pap. 6.95 (978-0-7641-2268-2(1)) Barron's Educational Series, Inc.

FASTS AND FEASTS—JUDAISM

see also names of individual fasts and feasts, e.g. Yom Kippur, etc.

Bar a Bat Mitzvah: Pecyn Gwybodaeth a Gweithgareddau (CA2) 2005. (978-1-85357-093-3(1)) Welsh National Centre for Religious Education (Canolfan Genedlaethol Addysg Grefyddol).

Berger, Gilda. Celebrate! Stories of the Jewish Holidays. Catalanotto, Peter, illus. 2002. 128p. (J). (gr. k-3). pap. 8.99 (978-0-439-43052-4(6) , Scholastic Paperbacks) Scholastic, Inc.

—Celebrate! Stories of the Jewish Holidays. 2002. (gr. 5-8). lib. bdg. 17.60 (978-0-613-50189-7(6)) Tandem Library Bks.

Brownstein, Rita Milos. Jewish Holiday Style. 1999. (Illus.). 144p. 30.00 (978-0-684-84959-1(3)) Simon & Schuster.

Cardin, Nina Beth & Gevirtz, Gila. Rediscovering the Jewish Holidays: Tradition in a Modern Voice. 2002. (Illus.). 196p. (J). 10.95 (978-0-87441-663-3(9)) Behrman Hse., Inc.

Chanukah: Pecyn Gwybodaeth a Gweithgareddau (CA1/2) 2005. (978-1-85357-094-0(X)) Welsh National Centre for Religious Education (Canolfan Genedlaethol Addysg Grefyddol).

Chwast, Seymour, illus. Had Gadya: A Passover Song. rev. ed. 2005. 32p. (J). 16.95 (978-1-59643-033-4(8)) Roaring Brook Pr.

Cohen, Santiago. It's Hanukkah! 2003. (Illus.). 16p. 8.95 (978-1-59354-021-0(3)) Blue Apple Bks.

Cooper, Ilene. Jewish Holidays All Year Round: A Family Treasury. Savadier, Elivia, illus. 2002. 80p. (J). 19.95 (978-0-8109-0550-4(7)) Abrams, Harry N. , Inc.

Elias, Miriam L. Special Days Are Wonderful: A Guessing Game Book. Leff, Tova, illus. 2nd ed. 1998. 32p. (J). (ps-k). reprint ed. 9.95 (978-0-922613-46-5(X)) Hachai Publishing.

Ferro, Jennifer. Jewish Foods & Culture. 1999. (Festive Foods & Celebrations Ser.). (Illus.). 48p. (J). (gr. 3-6). lib. bdg. 27.93 (978-1-57103-303-1(3)) Rourke Publishing, LLC.

Fishman, Cathy Goldberg. On Rosh Hashanah & Yom Kippur. Hall, Melanie W., illus. 2000. 40p. (J). (ps-3). 6.99 (978-0-689-83892-7(1) , Aladdin) Simon & Schuster Children's Publishing.

—On Rosh Hashanah & Yom Kippur. 2000. (J). (978-0-606-19250-7(6)); (gr. 3-6). lib. bdg. 14.15 (978-0-613-31547-0(2)) Tandem Library Bks.

—On Sukkot & Simchat Torah. Hall, Melanie W., illus. (J). (ps-4). 2006. 32p. lib. bdg. 17.95 (978-1-58013-165-0(4)); 2005. pap. (978-1-58013-166-7(2)) Kar-Ben Publishing.

Fun for Little Hands Series, 7 bks., Set. 2003. (Illus.). (J). 21.33 (978-0-929371-92-4(5)) Kar-Ben Publishing.

Ganeri, Anita. Jewish Festivals Through the Year. 2003. (Year of Festivals Ser.). 30p. (J). lib. bdg. 24.25 (978-1-58340-373-0(6)) Smart Apple Media.

Gellman, Ellie. Tamar's Sukkah. Kawasaki, Shauna Mooney, illus. rev. ed. 1999. 12p. (J). (ps up). pap. 4.95 (978-1-58013-054-7(2)) Kar-Ben Publishing.

Gold-Vukson, Marji. The Shapes of My Jewish Year. Springer, Sally, illus. 2003. 12p. (J). (ps-1). 4.95 (978-1-58013-049-3(6)) Kar-Ben Publishing.

—The Sounds of My Jewish Year. Urban, Suzanne, illus. 2003. 12p. (J). (ps-1). 4.95 (978-1-58013-047-9(X)) Kar-Ben Publishing.

Goodman, L. J. & Silverhardt, Lauryn. Oh Chanukah. Conrad, Liz, illus. 2003. 12p. (J). bds. 5.99 (978-0-8431-0508-7(9) , Price Stern Sloan) Penguin Group (USA) Inc.

Gootel, Rifka. My First Learn & Do Jewish Holiday Book. Rosenberg, Amye, illus. 64p. (J). (gr. k-2). pap. 4.95 (978-0-87441-475-2(X)) Behrman Hse., Inc.

Gordon, Lynn. 52 Activities for Jewish Holidays. 2004. (Illus.). 52p. 6.95 (978-0-8118-4124-5(3)) Chronicle Bks. LLC.

Groffman, Simcha. Simcha's Kinder Torah Presents Awesome Days: Torah Stories & Thoughts for the Yomim Noraim & Succos to Enhance Your Yom Tov Table. 2004. (Illus.). 164p. (J). (978-1-58330-709-0(5)) Feldheim Pubs.

Groner, Judyth Saypol & Wikler, Madeline. All about Sukkot. Kreiswirth, Kinny, illus. 1998. Orig. Title: My Very Own Sukkot. 32p. (J). (gr. k-5). pap. 5.95 (978-1-58013-018-9(6)) Kar-Ben Publishing.

Gross, Judith. Celebrate: A Book of Jewish Holidays. Weissman, Bari, illus. 2005. 32p. (J). (ps-4). pap. 3.99 (978-0-448-44300-3(7) , Grosset & Dunlap) Penguin Group (USA) Inc.

Hildebrandt, Ziporah. This Is Our Seder. Roraback, Robin, illus. 1999. 32p. (J). (gr. k-3). tchr. ed. 15.95 (978-0-8234-1436-9(1)) Holiday Hse., Inc.

Holub, Joan. Apples & Honey: A Rosh Hashanah Story. Pillo-Lassen, Cary, illus. 2003. (Lift-the-Flap, Puffin Ser.). 16p. (J). (ps-k). pap. 6.99 (978-0-14-250136-8(0) , Puffin) Penguin Group (USA) Inc.

Isaacs, Ron. Kids Love Jewish Holiday Games. Horton, Mike, photos by. 2001. (Kids Love Ser.). 128p. (J). spiral bd. 18.95 (978-1-930143-32-6(X)) ; (Illus.). pap. 16.95 (978-1-930143-19-7(2)) Pitspopany Pr.

Kimmelman, Leslie. Dance, Sing, Remember: A Celebration of Jewish Holidays. Eitan, Ora, illus. 2000. 48p. (J). (ps-3). 18.99 (978-0-06-027725-3(4)) HarperCollins Pubs.

Koffsky, Ann D. My Jewish Holiday Fun Book. 2004. (Illus.). 32p. (gr. k-3). pap. 9.95 (978-0-8074-0727-1(5) , 101983) URJ Pr.

Kress, Camille. The High Holy Days. Kress, Camille, illus. 2004. (Illus.). bds. 5.95 (978-0-8074-0776-9(3) , 241856) URJ Pr.

—Purim! Kress, Camille, illus. 2004. (Illus.). 10p. (ps-k). bds. 5.95 (978-0-8074-0654-0(6) , 102555) URJ Pr.

—A Tree Trunk Seder. Kress, Camille, illus. 2004. (Camille Kress Library: Vol. 4). (Illus.). 7p. (ps-k). bds. 5.95 (978-0-8074-0735-6(6) , 101252) URJ Pr.

Kropf, Latifa Berry. It's Seder Time! Cohen, Tod, illus. Cohen, Tod, photos by. 2004. 24p. (J). (ps-1). 12.95 (978-1-58013-092-9(5)) Kar-Ben Publishing.

Margolis, Isidor & Markowitz, Sidney L. Jewish Holidays & Festivals: A Young Person's Guide to the Stories, Practices, & Prayers of Jewish Celebrations. 2002. (Illus.). 124p. pap. 12.95 (978-0-8065-2429-0(4) , Citadel Pr.) Kensington Publishing Corp.

Michels, Dia L. Look What I See! Where Can I Be? at the Synagogue. Bowles, Michael J. N., photos by. 2003. (Look What I See! Where Can I Be? Ser.: Vol. 4). (Illus.). 32p. 16.95 (978-1-930775-16-9(4)); 2002. (J). pap. 9.95 (978-1-930775-14-5(8)) Platypus Media, L.L.C.

Mindel, Rabbi Nissan. The Storyteller Volume 5, Vol. 5. Smechov, Zeli, illus. 1998. 324p. (gr. 4-7). 17.95 (978-0-8266-1313-4(6)) Merkos L'Inyonei Chinuch.

Musleah, Rahel. Why on This Night? A Passover Haggadah for Family Celebration. August, Louise, illus. 2000. 112p. (J). (gr. k-4). pap. 13.99 (978-0-689-83313-7(X) , Simon Pulse) Simon & Schuster Children's Publishing.

O'Hare, Jeff, ed. Hanukkah: Festival of Lights. Friedman, Arthur & Rhinelander, Mary F., illus. 2001. 64p. (J). pap. 7.95 (978-1-56397-907-1(1)) Boyds Mills Pr.

Oren, Rony. The Animated Menorah. 2006. 17.95 (978-965-7108-80-2(2)) Urim Pubns. ISR. *Dist:* Biblio Distribution.

Podwal, Mark H. A Sweet Year: A Taste of the Jewish Holidays. Podwal, Mark H., illus. 2003. (Illus.). 32p. (J). (ps-3). lib. bdg. 14.99 (978-0-385-90869-6(5) , Doubleday Bks. for Young Readers) Random Hse. Children's Bks.

Randall, Ronne. Jewish Cookbook. Mukhida, Zul, illus. 2001. (Holiday Cookbooks from Around the World). 32p. (J). (gr. 4-7). lib. bdg. 25.69 (978-0-7398-3265-3(4)) Raintree.

Rauchwerger, Lisa. Chocolate Chip Challah: And Other Twists on the Jewish Holiday Table. Rauchwerger, Lisa, illus. 2004. (Illus.). 127p. (gr. k-3). pap. 17.95 (978-0-8074-0700-4(3) , 510606) URJ Pr.

—P: Vol. 2: Winter, Spring & Summer Holidays. Rauchwerger, Lisa, illus. 2004. (Illus.). (gr. k-3). pap., act. bk. ed. 9.95 (978-0-8074-0775-2(5) , 104036) URJ Pr.

Ross, Kathy. The Jewish Holiday Craft Book. Levine, Melinda, illus. 2001. 95p. (J). (gr. 5-7). pap. 13.00 (978-0-7567-5122-7(5)) DIANE Publishing Co.

Scharfstein, Sol. Understanding Jewish Holidays & Customs: Historical & Contemporary. 1999. 186p. (YA). (gr. 5-8). 27.50 (978-0-88125-634-5(X)) Ktav Publishing Hse., Inc.

Schilling-Gould, Karen. Shabbat: Forever & Always. Wise, Noreen, ed. Schneider, Rex, illus. 2000. (Book-a-Day Collection). 32p. (YA). (ps up). pap. 5.95 (978-1-58584-383-1(0)) Huckleberry Pr.

Senker, Cath. My Jewish Year. 2004. (Illus.). (J). pap. (978-0-7502-4061-1(X) , Hodder Wayland) Hodder Children's Division.

—My Jewish Year. 2007. lib. bdg. (***978-1-4042-3732-2(1)*** , PowerKids Pr.) Rosen Publishing Group, Inc., The.

Siegel, Bruce H. The Magic of Kol Nidre: A Yom Kippur Story. Haas, Shelly, illus. 1998. 32p. (J). (gr. k-4). 16.95 (978-1-58013-003-5(8)) ; pap. 6.95 (978-1-58013-002-8(X)) Kar-Ben Publishing.

Sokoloff, David. My Alef-Bet Coloring Book. Sokoloff, David, illus. 1998. (Illus.). 24p. (Orig.). (J). (ps-5). pap. 1.00 (978-1-889655-04-8(X)) Jewish Educational Toys.

—My Chanukah. Sokoloff, David, illus. 1998. (Illus.). 24p. (Orig.). (J). (ps-5). pap. 1.00 (978-1-889655-06-2(6)) Jewish Educational Toys.

—My Jewish Holiday. Sokoloff, David, illus. 1998. (Illus.). 24p. (Orig.). (J). (ps-5). pap., act. bk. ed. 1.00 (978-1-889655-09-3(0)) Jewish Educational Toys.

—My Shabbat. Sokoloff, David, illus. 1998. (Illus.). 24p. (Orig.). (J). (ps-5). pap., act. bk. ed. 1.00 (978-1-889655-07-9(4)) Jewish Educational Toys.

—The New Jewish Holiday. 2003. (Illus.). 96p. pap. 6.95 (978-1-56171-949-5(8)) SPI Bks.

Sokoloff, David, illus. My Favorite Jewish Holiday. 1998. 12p. (Orig.). (J). (ps-1). bds. 5.00 (978-1-889655-12-3(0)) Jewish Educational Toys.

Sper, Emily. The Kids' Fun Book of Jewish Time. Sper, Emily, illus. 2006. (HEB & ENG., Illus.). 24p. (J). 16.99 (978-1-58023-311-8(2) , 1260461) Jewish Lights Publishing.

Wark, Mary Ann Barrows. We Tell It to Our Children: The Story of Passover: A Haggadah for Seders with Young Children. Oskow, Craig, illus. 2nd ed. 2002. (HEB.). 116p. spiral bd. 7.95 (978-0-9619880-6-7(1)) ; 136p. spiral bd. 15.95 (978-0-9619880-7-4(X)) Mensch Makers Pr.

Wertheim, Janie-Sue & Shapiro, Kathy. Walk with Y'shua Through the Jewish Year. Rosen, Ruth, ed. Clemons, Carol, illus. 1998. (YA). (gr. 5 up). pap. 6.00 (978-1-881022-40-4(4)) Purple Pomegranate Productions.

Wikler, Madeline. Let's Celebrate Shabbat! Sagasti, Miriam, illus. 1999. 12p. (J). (ps up). 5.95 (978-1-58013-055-4(0)) Kar-Ben Publishing.

Wool, Danny, et al. The Animated Jewish Year. 2006. 88p. 19.95 (978-965-7108-79-6(9)) Urim Pubns. ISR. *Dist:* Biblio Distribution.

FATHER AND CHILD

see also Fathers and Daughters; Fathers and Sons

DK Publishing. Daddy Loves Me. 2007. 16p. (J). pap. 5.99 (***978-0-7566-3464-3(4)***) Dorling Kindersley Publishing, Inc.

Hansen, Holly T. & Johnson, Jennifer Hunt. Remembering Father, 14 vols. 2002. (Illus.). 32p. 9.95 (978-0-9741172-1-8(8) , CMB14) Tapis & Assocs., Inc.

Haskins, Amanda. God Is My Daddy. l.t. ed. 2006. (Illus.). 26p. (J). per. 11.99 (***978-1-59879-279-9(2)***) Lifevest Publishing, Inc.

Heinrichs, Ann. Father's Day. Alley, R. W., illus. 2006. (Holidays, Festivals, & Celebrations Ser.). 32p. (J). (gr. k-4). 22.79 (978-1-59296-575-5(X)) Child's World, Inc.

Liles, Rebecca. My Daddy's a Soldier, 2 bks. 2003. (Illus.). 16p. (J). 4.99 (978-0-9744346-0-5(4)) Rebecca's Bks.

Richmond, Marianne R. I'm Glad You're My Dad. 2005. (Illus.). 40p. (J). 7.95 (978-0-9763101-2-9(0)) Marianne Richmond Studios, Inc.

Saleh, Amal Kamal Ali. Guess Who My Best Friend Is. 2005. (Illus.). 15p. (J). (***978-1-4120-6052-3(4)***) Trafford Publishing.

Schaefer, Lola M. Fathers. 2008. (J). (***978-1-4296-1224-1(X)*** , Pebble Bks.) Capstone Pr., Inc.

FATHER AND CHILD—FICTION

Anderson, Eric B. Alena & the Favorite Thing. 2007. 48p. pap. 23.95 (***978-0-615-15153-3(1)***) EBA Creative.

Bauer, Marion Dane & Wu, Leslie. The Very Best Daddy of All. 2007. 40p. (J). pap. 6.99 (978-1-4169-2736-5(0) , Aladdin) Simon & Schuster Children's Publishing.

Bennett, Leonie. No Problem! Brown, Judy, illus. 2004. 16p. (J). lib. bdg. 22.65 (***978-1-59646-680-7(4)***) Dingles & Co.

Berry, Matt. Up on Daddy's Shoulders. Corvino, Lucy, illus. 2006. 32p. (J). pap. 6.99 (978-0-439-67045-6(4) , Cartwheel Bks.) Scholastic, Inc.

Cohen, Miriam. Mine! A Backpack Baby Story. 2005. (ENG & SPA., Illus.). 12p. (J). (ps-ps). per. 5.95 (978-1-59572-019-1(7)) Star Bright Bks., Inc.

Daddy You're My Hero! 2005. (J). bds. 12.99 (978-0-9729264-4-7(5) , Books for Brats) Little Redhaired Girl Publishing, Inc.

Daley Mackall, Dandi. I Love You Daddy. Lee Schmidt, Karen, illus. 2006. (I Love You Ser.). 20p. (J). bds. 7.99 (978-0-7847-1816-2(4) , 04138) Standard Publishing.

Davis, Terry. Camping with Dad: The Mystery of Valley Gulch. 2006. (ENG.). 148p. per. 19.95 (***978-1-4241-5659-7(9)***) PublishAmerica, Inc.

Dilz, Ric. My Dad Could do Anything! 2006. (Illus.). (J). pap. 6.95 (978-0-9758704-1-9(6)) Rein Designs, Inc.

Easter, Julie. My Military Dad. 2004. (J). pap. 8.00 (978-0-8059-6534-6(3)) Dorrance Publishing Co., Inc.

Finnemore, John. Jack Haydons Quest. 2006. pap. 15.95 (***978-0-8095-0116-8(3)***) Wildside Pr.

Gottleib, Dale, illus. Are We There Yet?, Level 3. 2005. (I'm Going to Read Ser.). 32p. (J). (gr. 1-2). pap. 3.95 (978-1-4027-2713-9(5)) Sterling Publishing Co., Inc.

Griffith, Travis. Your Father Forever. Abreu, Raquel, illus. 2005. 32p. (J). (ps-3). 15.95 (978-0-9740190-3-1(8)) Illumination Arts Publishing Co., Inc.

Grimes, Nikki. A Day with Daddy. Tadgell, Nicole, illus. 2004. 32p. (J). lib. bdg. 15.00 (***978-1-4242-0226-3(4)***) Fitzgerald Bks.

Hallinan, P. K. My Daddy & I. 2006. (Illus.). 32p. (J). pap. 3.95 (978-0-8249-5521-2(8) , Ideals Children's Bks.) Ideals Pubns.

Higgins, Jack & Richards, Justin. Sure Fire. 2007. 256p. (YA). (gr. 7). 16.99 (***978-0-399-24784-2(X)*** , Putnam Juvenile) Penguin Group (USA) Inc.

Howard, Annabelle. A Father, His Son, & Their Donkey: An Aesop's Fable. 2006. spiral bd. 42.00 (***978-1-4108-7154-1(1)***) Benchmark Education Co.

Howe, James. Pinky & Rex & the Double-Dad Weekend. 2006. (J). (gr. 1-4). 24.21 (978-1-59961-075-7(2)) Spotlight.

Huizenga, Pam. My Best Friend. V'in, Anica, illus. 2000. 12p. (J). (ps-k). 7.95 (978-1-929774-00-5(1)) Greenleaf Book Group Pr.

Katz, Karen. Daddy Hugs. Katz, Karen, illus. 2007. (Classic Board Bks.). 32p. (J). 7.99 (978-1-4169-4120-0(7) , Little Simon) Simon & Schuster Children's Publishing.

—Daddy Hugs 1 2 3. Katz, Karen, illus. 2005. (Illus.). 32p. (J). 14.99 (978-0-689-87771-1(4) , McElderry, Margaret K.) Simon & Schuster Children's Publishing.

Kristina Learns about Fishing. 2007. (J). (***978-0-9792728-0-6(7)***) Tracepaper Bks. Inc.

Lawler, Janet. A Father's Song. Corvino, Lucy, illus. 2006. 24p. (J). 12.95 (978-1-4027-2501-2(9)) Sterling Publishing Co., Inc.

Lawson-Miller, Barb. I Love Daddy Because... 2004. (Illus.). 14p. bds. (978-0-9688553-0-0(X)) Barbamel Bks., Inc.

Lee, Day's. The Fragrant Garden. Bellemare, Josee, illus. 2005. 32p. (J). (ps-7). pap. 9.95 (978-1-894917-26-1(X) , Napoleon Publishing) Napoleon Publishing/ Rendezvous Pr. CAN. *Dist:* AtlasBooks Distribution.

Leland, Debbie. Daddy's Love. Rife, Ann Hollis, illus. ed. 2006. (J). 15.95 (978-0-9667086-4-6(4)) Wildflower Run.

Less, Emma. My Day with Daddy. Ledger, Bill, illus. 2006. 14p. bds. 5.95 (978-1-4027-2177-9(3)) Sterling Publishing Co., Inc.

L'Heureux, Christine. Caillou Moves Around. Brignaud, Pierre, illus. rev. ed. 2007. (Caillou Board Bks.). 24p. (J). bds. 7.95 (***978-2-89450-610-3(4)***) Chouette Publishing CAN. *Dist:* Independent Pubs. Group.

Lozano, Neal. Will You Bless Me? Hatke, Ben, illus. 2006. (J). lib. bdg. 14.95 (978-1-883551-32-2(3) , MCP-323, Maple Corners Press) Attic Studio Publishing Hse.

Ltd Daddy Kisses/Daddy Cuddles. 2005. (J). bds. 11.90 (978-0-8118-9933-8(0)) Chronicle Bks. LLC.

Maybank, Roger. The Sun Boat: A Fairytale. 2005. 324p. pap. (***978-1-4120-6452-1(X)***) Trafford Publishing.

Mayer, Mercer. Happy Father's Day. Mayer, Mercer, illus. 2007. (Little Critter Ser.: Bk. 2). (Illus.). 20p. (J). pap. 6.99 (***978-0-06-053965-8(8)*** , Harper Festival) HarperCollins Pubs.

McCafferty, Catherine. Picture Me as Dad's Little Helper. Rasmussen, Wendy, illus. 2001. (Picture Me Ser.). 10p. (J). (ps up). bds. 4.99 (978-1-57151-588-9(7)) Playhouse Publishing.

Murphy, Jill. Mr. Large in Charge. Murphy, Jill, illus. 2007. (Illus.). 40p. (J). (ps-2). 16.99 (978-0-7636-3504-6(9)) Candlewick Pr.

My First Day Lobstering with Dad. 2000. 28p. (J). (978-1-931015-03-5(1)) Distant Waters Publishing & Designs.

Newton, Jill. Peek-a-Boo, Papa! A Peek-under-the Flap Book. 2007. (Illus.). 20p. (ps). bds. 8.95 (***978-1-59354-626-7(2)***) Blue Apple Bks.

Ottolenghi, Carol. Father Loves His Little One. Campanella, Marco, illus. 2006. (Tell Me a Story Ser.). 36p. (J). (gr. k-k). bds. 14.95 (978-0-7696-4813-2(4) , Gingham Dog Pr.) School Specialty Publishing.

Perkins-Stell, Crystal. Never Knew a Father's Love. 2004. 256p. (YA). pap. 14.95 (978-0-9740705-3-7(X)) Perkins-Stell, Crystal.

Plourde, Lynn. Dad Aren't You Glad. Wummer, Amy, illus. 2005. 32p. (J). (gr. 3). 12.99 (978-0-525-47362-6(9) , Dutton Juvenile) Penguin Group (USA) Inc.

Pope, Jerald. Madeleine Claire & the Dinosaur. 2006. (J). 16.00 (978-0-9700125-6-2(X)) Brave Ulysses Bks.

Ransom, Candice F. Tractor Day. Bryant, Laura J., illus. 2007. 32p. (J). (ps). 17.85 (978-0-8027-8091-1(1)) Walker & Co.

Ransom, Candice F. & Bryant, Laura. Tractor Day. Bryant, Laura, illus. 2007. (Illus.). 32p. (J). (ps). 16.95 (978-0-8027-8090-4(3)) Walker & Co.

Skolmoski, Stephanie. A Paper Hug. Bennion, Anneliese, illus. 2006. (J). 6.95 (978-0-9786425-0-1(3)) Design-Ability.

St-Aubin, Bruno, illus. Daddy's a Busy Beaver. 2005. (Read-It! Readers Ser.). 32p. (J). (gr. k-3). 18.60 (978-1-4048-1025-9(0)) Picture Window Bks.

Tunley, Annabel & Tellis, Annabel. If My Dad Were A Dog. 2007. 32p. (J). pap. 16.99 (***978-0-439-91387-4(X)*** , Chicken Hse., The) Scholastic, Inc.

Waite, Lance. A Day with Dad at the Beach. 2008. (J). 15.99 (***978-1-60131-016-3(1)***) Big Tent Bks.

—A Day with My Dad. 2008. (Illus.). 24p. (J). 15.99 (***978-1-60131-015-6(3)***) Big Tent Bks.

Warnes, Tim. Daddy Hug. Chapman, Jane, illus. 2008. 32p. (J). 16.99 (978-0-06-058950-9(7)) ; lib. bdg. 17.89 (978-0-06-058951-6(5)) HarperCollins Pubs.

Webb, Mack H., Jr. Danny & the Detention Demons. Espinola, Nicole & Nealon, Eve, illus. l.t. ed. 2007. 52p. (J). per. 15.95 (***978-0-9779576-2-0(4)***) Pilinut Pr., Inc.

Wild, Margaret. Piglet & Papa. King, Stephen Michael, illus. 2007. (J). (ps-3). 32p. 14.95 (978-0-8109-1476-6(X)) ; (***978-1-4287-4648-0(X)***) Abrams, Harry N. , Inc. (Abrams Bks. for Young Readers).

Yaccarino, Dan. Every Friday. 2007. (Illus.). 32p. (J). (ps-2). 16.95 (978-0-8050-7724-7(3)) Holt, Henry & Co.

Ziefert, Harriet. Are We There Yet? Gottleib, Dale, illus. 2005. (I'm Going to Read Ser.). 32p. (J). (ps-ps). 11.95 (978-1-4027-2714-6(3)) Sterling Publishing Co., Inc.

Ziefert, Harriet. When Daddy Travels. Bolam, Emily, illus. 2007. 16p. (J). pap. 5.95 (***978-1-4027-4802-8(7)***) Sterling Publishing Co., Inc.

FATHERS

Alpert, Lou. You & Your Dad. 1998. (Illus.). 32p. (J). (ps-2). pap. 5.95 (978-1-58089-004-5(0)) Charlesbridge Publishing, Inc.

Apel, Melanie Ann. Let's Talk about Living with Your Single Dad. 2001. (Let's Talk Library). (Illus.). 24p. (J). (gr. 3). lib. bdg. 18.75 (978-0-8239-5619-7(9) , PowerKids Pr.) Rosen Publishing Group, Inc., The.

Arquette, Kerry. Daddy Promises. McCain, Kevin, illus. 32p. 2005. (ENG.). (J). pap. 6.99 (978-0-7586-0905-2(1)); 1999. 12.99 (978-0-570-05554-9(7) , 56-1971) Concordia Publishing Hse.

Auld, Mary. Mi Papa. 2004. (Conoce la Familia Ser.). (SPA., Illus.). 24p. (J). (gr. 1 up). lib. bdg. 20.67 (978-0-8368-3933-3(1)) Stevens, Gareth Inc.

—My Dad. 2004. (Meet the Family Ser.). (Illus.). 24p. (J). (gr. 1 up). lib. bdg. 20.67 (978-0-8368-3925-8(0)) Stevens, Gareth Inc.

Avis, Ed. Come on Dad! 75 Things for Fathers & Sons to Do Together. Despres, Genevieve, illus. 2002. 140p. (J). (ps-3). pap. 9.95 (978-1-894222-72-3(5)) Lobster Pr. CAN. *Dist:* Univ. of Toronto Pr.

Backes, Michel & Brun-Cosme, Nadine. Hoy lo Hace Papa! Ros, Rafael, tr. Backes, Michael, illus. 2003. (SPA.). 164p. (978-84-8470-116-3(6)) Corimbo, Editorial S.L.

Barbara, Diane & Bloch, Serge. Dad & Me: A Special Book for You & Your Dad to Fill in Together & Share with Each Other. 2005. (Illus.). 52p. (J). (gr. k-5). 16.95 (978-0-8109-5881-4(3)) Abrams, Harry N. , Inc.

Baron, Larry. A Day with My Dad. 2002. (PowerPhonics Ser.). (Illus.). 23p. (J). lib. bdg. (978-0-8239-8247-9(5)) Rosen Publishing Group, Inc., The.

—A Day with My Dad: Learning the D Sound. 2002. (PowerPhonics Ser.). (Illus.). 24p. (J). (gr. 1). lib. bdg. 18.00 (978-0-8239-5902-0(3) , PowerKids Pr.) Rosen Publishing Group, Inc., The.

Clayburn, Brenda. Daddy's Gone. 2000. (Illus.). 40p. (J). (ps-3). pap. 7.50 (978-1-892614-25-4(1) , BWP-DG1) Briarwood Pubns.

Dalmatian Press Staff. Daddy Loves Me. (J). 2005. 8p. bds. 4.99 (978-1-4037-1986-7(1)); 2000. (Illus.). 20p. 2.99 (978-1-57759-372-0(3)) Dalmatian Pr.

Dorling Kindersley Publishing Staff, ed. Being a Dad. 2004. (Johnson's Everyday Babycare Ser.). (Illus.). 64p. pap. 8.00 (978-0-7566-0566-7(0)) Dorling Kindersley Publishing, Inc.

Drake, Jane & Love, Ann. My Father & Me. Ritchie, Scot, illus. unabr. ed. 2000. (Memory Scrapbks. for Kids). 32p. (J). (gr. k-3). (978-1-55074-637-2(5)) Kids Can Pr., Ltd.

Endersbe, Julie. Teen Fathers: Getting Involved. 1999. (Perspectives on Healthy Sexuality Ser.). (Illus.). 64p. (J). (gr. 4-6). lib. bdg. 23.93 (978-0-7368-0269-7(X) , LifeMatters Bks.) Capstone Pr., Inc.

Gardella, Tricia. Just Like My Dad. Apple, Margot, illus. 2003. 32p. (J). (gr. k-2). pap. 8.95 (978-1-56397-917-0(9)) Boyds Mills Pr.

—Just Like My Dad. 2000. (gr. k-3). lib. bdg. 17.60 (978-0-613-29998-5(1)) Tandem Library Bks.

Hurtt, Cedric I. I Look up to My Dad. 1999. (Illus.). 32p. (J). pap. 6.95 (978-1-890622-82-4(6)) Leathers Publishing.

Kappler, Samantha, et al. 15 Reasons I Love My Dad. 2002. (Fifteen Reasons Ser.). (Illus.). 48p. (J). (gr. k-6). 14.95 (978-0-9666843-1-5(1)) S B C Publishing.

Mack, Judy B. My Daddy & Me. Levin, Sidney L., illus. 2000. 40p. (Orig.). (J). (gr. k-4). pap. (978-0-9637795-7-1(5)) MinervaPress.

Macmillan Children's Books Staff. The Little Guide to Dads. 2000. (Little Guides Ser.). (Illus.). 18p. (J). (ps-3). (978-0-333-73420-9(3) , Macmillan Children's Bks.) Pan Macmillan.

Marriott, Donna. Celebrating Father's Day: Father's Day is for Special People, No. 4530. Kupperstein, Joel, ed. Motoyama, Keiko, illus. 1999. 16p. (ps-2). pap. 2.99 (978-1-57471-575-0(5)) Creative Teaching Pr., Inc.

McCain, John. Faith of Our Fathers. 2000. (gr. 7-12). lib. bdg. 23.45 (978-0-613-27819-5(4)) Tandem Library Bks.

Mi Papa: Individual Title Six-Packs. (Coleccion Pm Ser.).Tr. of My dad. (SPA.). 16p. (gr. 1 up). 26.00 (978-0-7578-2990-1(2)) Rigby Education.

Numeroff, Laura Joffe. What Mommies Do Best/What Daddies Do Best. Munsinger, Lynn, illus. 2006. (Stories to Go! Ser.). 40p. (J). pap. 4.99 (978-0-689-84218-4(X) , Aladdin) Simon & Schuster Children's Publishing.

Roche, Hannah. My Dads a Wizard. 1998. (Science Made Simple Ser.). (Illus.). 24p. (J). (ps-3). pap. (978-1-84089-013-6(4) , 868236Q, Zero to Ten, Limited) Evans Publishing Group.

Rotner, Shelley. Lots of Dads. 2000. (Illus.). (J). (978-0-606-18422-9(8)) Tandem Library Bks.

Rubin, Howie. Dads. Hastings, Doug, illus. 2001. 32p. (J). (ps-9). 20.00 (978-0-9703971-1-9(9)) Howie Haus Bks.

Ruth, Angie. My Daddy: Early My Adventure. 2007. 44p. (J). 8.99 (978-1-59092-480-8(0) , Orchard Academy Pr.) Windstorm Creative.

—My Step-Dad: Early My Adventure. 2007. 44p. (J). 8.99 (978-1-59092-485-3(1) , Orchard Academy Pr.) Windstorm Creative.

Schaefer, Lola M. Fathers. Saunders-Smith, Gail, ed. 1999. (Families Ser.). (Illus.). 24p. (J). (gr. k-1). lib. bdg. 15.93 (978-0-7368-0256-7(8) , Pebble Bks.) Capstone Pr., Inc.

Sharp, N. L. Today I'm Going Fishing with My Dad. Demarest, Chris L., illus. 2003. 32p. (J). (gr. k-2). pap. 12.50 (978-1-56397-613-1(7)) Boyds Mills Pr.

Waintrub, George. Where Is My Dad? 2000. Tr. of Donde Esta Mi Papa?. (ENG & SPA., Illus.). 48p. (J). (ps-1). (978-1-884083-47-1(1)) Maval Publishing, Inc.

Yep, Laurence. Conversations with My Father. 144p. (J). (gr. 2-5). 2008. lib. bdg. 16.89 (978-0-06-027693-5(2)); 2001. 15.99 (978-0-06-027692-8(4)) HarperCollins Pubs.

FATHERS—FICTION

Agell, Charlotte. Welcome Home or Someplace Like It. rev. ed. 2003. (Illus.). 240p. (J). 16.95 (978-0-8050-7083-5(4) , Holt, Henry & Co. Bks. For Young Readers) Holt, Henry & Co.

 For book reviews, descriptive annotations, tables of contents, cover images, author biographies & additional information, updated daily, subscribe to **www.booksinprint.com**

Aiken, Joan. Dido & Pa. 2002. (Illus.). 304p. (J). (gr. 5). pap. 5.95 (978-0-618-19623-4(4)); 16.00 (978-0-618-19624-1(2)) Houghton Mifflin Co. Trade & Reference Div.

—Dido & Pa. 2003. (gr. 5-8). lib. bdg. 14.10 (978-0-613-57503-4(2)) Tandem Library Bks.

Alcantara, Ignacio, illus. Who's That Crying? 2005. 63p. (J). 17.00 (978-0-9659538-1-8(5)) Soul Vision Works Publishing.

Ames, Adele Z. & Brown, Blake Adele. A Flower for My Papa. 1999. (Illus.). 32p. (J). (gr. 1-6). pap. 7.50 (978-0-9677692-0-2(5)) Butterfly Pr.

Anderson, Laurie Halse. Catalyst. 2002. 240p. (YA). (gr. 7 up). 17.99 (978-0-670-03566-3(1) , Viking Juvenile) Penguin Group (USA) Inc.

Arno, Iris H. I Love You, Dad. 1998. (978-0-606-13507-8(3)) Tandem Library Bks.

Avi. Poppy & Rye. Floca, Brian, illus. (Poppy Bks.). (J). (gr. 3-7). 1999. 240p. pap. 5.99 (978-0-380-79717-2(8) , Harper Trophy); 1998. 192p. 16.99 (978-0-380-97638-6(2)) HarperCollins Pubs.

—Poppy & Rye. unabr. ed. 2000. (J). (gr. 8). pap., stu. ed. 50.24 incl. audio (978-0-7887-3185-3(8) , 40920E5) Recorded Bks., LLC.

—Poppy & Rye. Floca, Brian, illus. 1999. 182p. (J). (ps-7). per. 14.15 (978-0-613-17447-3(X)) Tandem Library Bks.

—Poppy & Rye. 1999. (978-0-606-16352-1(2)) Tandem Library Bks.

Azean, Evon, Sr. Aataq Maktuq. Beaver, Mary Lou, illus. l.t. ed. 1999. Tr. of Father Gets Up. (ESK.). 12p. (J). (gr. k-3). pap. 6.00 (978-1-58084-145-0(7)) Lower Kuskokwim Schl. District.

—At'a Maktur (Father Gets Up) Beaver, Mary Lou, illus. l.t. ed. 1999. (ESK.). 12p. (J). (gr. k-3). pap. 6.00 (978-1-58084-146-7(5)) Lower Kuskokwim Schl. District.

—Father Gets Up. Beaver, Mary Lou, illus. l.t. ed. 1999. 12p. (J). (gr. k-3). pap. 6.00 (978-1-58084-144-3(9)) Lower Kuskokwim Schl. District.

Bache, Ellyn. Daddy & the Pink Flash. Tornatore, Carol, illus. 2003. 32p. 14.95 (978-1-889199-11-5(7)) Banks Channel Bks.

Bailey, Debbie. Mi Papa. Huszar, Susan, photos by. 2003. (Hablemos Ser.). (SPA., Illus.). 14p. (J). (ps). bds. 5.95 (978-1-55037-265-6(3)) Annick Pr., Ltd. CAN. *Dist:* Firefly Bks., Ltd.

Banks, Steven. Pick a Dad, Any Dad! Moore, Harry, illus. ed. 2005. (Fairly Odd Parents Ser.: 7). 24p. (J). lib. bdg. 15.00 (978-1-59054-804-2(3)) Fitzgerald Bks.

Bauer, Marion Dane & Wu, Leslie. The Very Best Daddy of All. 2004. (Illus.). 40p. (J). 12.95 (978-0-689-84178-1(7)) Simon & Schuster Children's Publishing.

Bea, Holly. Good Night, God. Howard, Kim, illus. 2000. 32p. (J). (ps-k). 15.00 (978-0-915811-84-7(7)) Kramer, H.J. Inc.

Bell, Caroline. I Love My Dad. Bell, Caroline, illus. 1999. (Illus.). 18p. (J). (ps-1). (978-0-88902-736-7(6)) Fitzhenry & Whiteside, Ltd.

Berenstain, Stan & Berenstain, Jan. The Berenstain Bears & the Papa's Day Roast. 2003. (Illus.). 32p. (J). (gr. k-3). lib. bdg. 8.99 (978-0-375-91129-3(4) , Random Hse. Bks. for Young Readers) Random Hse. Children's Bks.

—The Berenstain Bears & the Papa's Day Surprise. 2003. (Berenstain Bears First Time Bks.), (Illus.). 32p. (J). (gr. k-3). pap. 3.99 (978-0-375-81129-6(X) , Random Hse. Bks. for Young Readers) Random Hse. Children's Bks.

—The Berenstain Bears Get Their Kicks. 1998. (Berenstain Bears First Time Bks.). (Illus.). 32p. (J). (gr. k-3). pap. 3.25 (978-0-679-88955-7(8) , Random Hse. Bks. for Young Readers) Random Hse. Children's Bks.

—The Berenstain Bears Get Their Kicks. 1998. (Berenstain Bears First Time Bks.). (J). (gr. k-2). 10.05 (978-0-606-13955-7(9)) Tandem Library Bks.

Berry, Carmen Renee & Barrington, Lynn. Daddies & Daughters. 1999. 288p. pap. 11.00 (978-0-684-84993-5(3) , Fireside) Simon & Schuster.

Black, Frank M. A Visit with Daddy. Moses, Robin, photos by. 1999. (Illus.). 20p. (J). pap. 6.95 (978-1-929157-00-6(2)) Inside-OUT Corp.

—Una Visita a Papi. Moses, Robin, photos by. 1999. (SPA., Illus.). 20p. (J). pap. (978-1-929157-02-0(9)) Inside-OUT Corp.

Bluemle, Elizabeth. My Father the Dog. Cecil, Randy, illus. 2006. 32p. (J). (ps-2). 15.99 (978-0-7636-2222-0(2)) Candlewick Pr.

Bodeen, S. A. The Compound. 2008. 256p. (YA). 16.95 (***978-0-312-37015-2(6)***) Feiwel & Friends.

Bongiorno, Patti Lynn. My Dad's Footsteps. Bongiorno, Patti Lynn, illus. 2002. (J). spiral bd. 20.00 (978-0-9715819-8-2(3)) Bongiorno Bks.

Bonk, John J. Dustin Grubbs: Take Two! 2006. 256p. (J). (gr. 3-7). 15.99 (978-0-316-15637-0(X)) Little Brown & Co.

Bostrom, Kathleen Long. Papa's Gift. 2002. 40p. (J). 15.99 (978-0-310-70274-0(7)) Zonderkidz.

—When Pete's Dad Got Sick: A Book about Chronic Illness. Bladholm, Cheri, illus. 2004. (Helping Kids Heal Ser.). 32p. (J). 9.99 (978-0-310-70655-7(6)) Zonderkidz.

Bowler, Tim. Firmament. 2004. (Illus.). 320p. (YA). 16.95 (978-0-689-86161-1(3) , McElderry, Margaret K.) Simon & Schuster Children's Publishing.

Braun, Sebastien. I Love My Daddy. Braun, Sebastien, illus. 2004. (Illus.). 32p. (J). (ps-2). 12.99 (978-0-06-054311-2(6)) HarperCollins Pubs.

Bray, Jeannine D. My Poppie. Kenyatta, Imani, ed. Mitchell, Denise B., illus. 1998. 80p. (J). (gr. k-6). 14.95 (978-1-886580-62-6(6)) Pinnacle-Syatt Pubns.

Briant, Ed. A Day at the Beach. Briant, Ed, illus. 2006. (Illus.). 32p. (J). 16.99 (978-0-06-079981-6(1)); No. 1. lib. bdg. 17.89 (978-0-06-079982-3(X)) HarperCollins Pubs.

Bridges, Margaret Park. If I Were Your Father. Denton, Kady MacDonald, illus. 1999. 32p. (J). (ps-3). 16.00 (978-0-688-15192-8(2)) HarperCollins Pubs.

Bridwell, Norman. Clifford's Day with Dad. Bridwell, Norman, illus. 2003. (Clifford Ser.). 32p. (J). pap. 3.50 (978-0-439-41073-1(8)) Scholastic, Inc.

—Clifford's Day with Dad. 2003. (gr. k-3). lib. bdg. 11.25 (978-0-613-70588-2(2)) Tandem Library Bks.

Britton, Susan. The Treekeepers. 2003. 256p. (J). (gr. 4-7). 16.99 (978-0-525-46944-5(3) , Dutton Juvenile) Penguin Group (USA) Inc.

Brown, Marc. Arthur & the 1,001 Dads. Brown, Marc, illus. 28th ed. 2003. (Arthur Chapter Bks. : Bk. 28). (Illus.). 64p. (J). (gr. 1-4). 14.95 (978-0-316-12516-1(4)); pap. 4.25 (978-0-316-12280-1(7)) Little, Brown Bks. for Young Readers.

—Arthur & the 1,001 Dads. 2003. (Arthur Chapter Bks.: Bk. 28). (Illus.). 57p. (J). (ps). lib. bdg. 12.10 (978-0-613-58311-4(6)) Tandem Library Bks.

Browne, Anthony. My Dad. 2000. (J). (ps-3). 16.00 (978-0-7894-2681-9(1)) Dorling Kindersley Publishing, Inc.

—My Dad. Browne, Anthony, illus. (Illus.). 32p. (J). (ps-3). 2001. 16.00 (978-0-374-35101-4(5)); 2004. 5.95 (978-0-374-35100-7(7)) Farrar, Straus & Giroux. (Farrar, Straus & Giroux (BYR)).

Brugman, Alyssa. Being Bindy. 2006. 208p. (YA). (gr. 7). 15.95 (978-0-385-73294-9(5)); lib. bdg. 17.99 (978-0-385-90315-8(4)) Random Hse. Children's Bks. (Delacorte Bks. for Young Readers).

Burton, Yvette M. A Twinkle in His Eye. Burton, Yvette M., illus. l.t. ed. 2000. (Illus.). 28p. (J). 10.00 (978-0-615-11477-4(6)) Shooting Star Publishing.

Butterworth, Nick. My Dad Is Awesome. Butterworth, Nick, illus. 2003. (Illus.). 32p. (J). (ps-3). 5.99 (978-0-7636-2056-1(4)) Candlewick Pr.

Caletti, Deb. The Queen of Everything. 2002. 384p. (YA). (gr. 9 up). pap. 6.99 (978-0-7434-3684-7(9) , Simon Pulse) Simon & Schuster Children's Publishing.

Canfield, Jack L., et al. Chicken Soup for Little Souls Reader: The Best Night Out with Dad. Dodson, Bert, illus. 2005. 48p. (J). pap. 3.95 (978-0-7573-0281-7(5)) Health Communications, Inc.

Carle, Eric. Mister Seahorse. Carle, Eric, illus. 2004. (Illus.). 32p. (J). (ps-2). 17.99 (978-0-399-24269-4(4) , Philomel) Penguin Group (USA) Inc.

—Papa, Please Get the Moon for Me. Carle, Eric, illus. 1999. (Classic Board Bks.). (Illus.). 32p. (J). (ps-k). 10.99 (978-0-689-82959-8(0) , Little Simon) Simon & Schuster Children's Publishing.

Carter, Anne. From Poppa. Pavanel, Jane, ed. Charko, Kasia, illus. 1999. 32p. (J). (gr. 4-7). 16.95 (978-1-894222-02-0(4)) Lobster Pr. CAN. *Dist:* Univ. of Toronto Pr.

Catalanotto, Peter. The Painter. Catalanotto, Peter, illus. 1999. (Illus.). 32p. (J). (ps-2). pap. 5.95 (978-0-531-07116-8(2) , Orchard Bks.) Scholastic, Inc.

Chambers, Veronica. Marisol & Magdalena. 2001. 176p. (gr. 3-7). pap. 5.99 (978-0-7868-1304-9(0)) Hyperion Bks. for Children.

—Marisol & Magdalena: The Sound of Our Sisterhood. 2001. (gr. 5-8). lib. bdg. 14.15 (978-0-613-60642-4(6)) Tandem Library Bks.

Chethik, Neil. Fatherloss: How Sons of All Ages Come to Terms with the Deaths of Their Dads. 2001. (Illus.). 336p. pap. 14.95 (978-0-7868-8449-0(5)) Hyperion Pr.

Chiappetta, Joe. Silly Daddy: A Death in the Family. unabr. ed. 1999. (Illus.). 96p. pap. 8.00 (978-0-9644323-1-4(5)) Chiappetta, Joe.

Chronicle Books Staff. Papa Do You Love Me Teacher's. 2005. (J). pap. 0.01 (978-0-8118-9927-7(6)) Chronicle Bks. LLC.

Clements, Andrew. The Secret Father's Day Present. Livney, Varda, illus. 2000. (Lift-the-Flap Story Ser.). Orig. Title: Father's Day. 16p. (J). (ps-3). pap. 5.99 (978-0-689-83359-5(8) , Little Simon) Simon & Schuster Children's Publishing.

Colato Lainez, Rene. Waiting for Papa/Esperando a Papa. Accardo, Anthony, illus. Tr. of Esperando a Papa. (ENG & SPA.). 32p. (gr. 1-3). 15.95 (978-1-55885-403-1(7) , Piñata Books) Arte Publico Pr.

Cole, Babette. The Trouble with Dad. 2005. (Illus.). 32p. (J). pap. 3.99 (978-1-4052-1122-2(9)) Egmont Bks., Ltd. GBR. *Dist:* Trafalgar Square Publishing.

Cole, Brock. Buttons. Cole, Brock, illus. (Illus.). 32p. (J). 2004. pap. 6.95 (978-0-374-41013-1(5) , Sunburst); 2000. 16.00 (978-0-374-31001-1(7) , Farrar, Straus & Giroux (BYR)) Farrar, Straus & Giroux.

—Buttons. 2001. (J). (ps-3). 26.90 incl. audio (978-0-8045-6881-4(2) , 6881) Spoken Arts, Inc.

Colfer, Eoin. The Arctic Incident. l.t. ed. 2003. (Artemis Fowl Ser.: Bk. 2). 296p. (J). (gr. 3-6). 16.95 (978-0-7540-7839-5(6) , Galaxy Children's Large Print) BBC Audiobooks America.

—The Arctic Incident. 2002. (Artemis Fowl Ser.: Bk. 2). 288p. (ps-17). 16.95 (978-0-7868-0855-7(1)) Hyperion Bks. for Children.

—The Arctic Incident. l.t. ed. 2003. (Artemis Fowl Ser.: Bk. 2). 313p. (J). (gr. 3-6). 25.95 (978-0-7862-4825-4(4)) Thorndike Pr.

Conly, Jane Leslie. While No One Was Watching. 2000. (978-0-606-18728-2(6)) Tandem Library Bks.

Cooney, Doug. The Beloved Dearly: Requiem for Fluffy. DiTerlizzi, Tony, illus. 2002. 192p. (J). 16.00 (978-0-689-83127-0(7)) Simon & Schuster Children's Publishing.

Cooney, Doug & DiTerlizzi, Tony. The Beloved Dearly. 2003. (Illus.). 192p. (J). pap. 5.99 (978-0-689-86354-7(3) , Aladdin) Simon & Schuster Children's Publishing.

Cosby, Bill. The Day I Saw My Father Cry. 2000. (Little Bill Books for Beginning Readers Ser.). (Illus.). (J). 10.79 (978-0-606-20470-5(9)) Tandem Library Bks.

Cosby, Bill & Honeywood, Varnette P. The Day I Saw My Father Cry. 2000. (Little Bill Books for Beginning Readers Ser.). (Illus.). 40p. (J). (gr. k-3). pap. 15.95 (978-0-590-52197-0(7)) Scholastic, Inc.

Croteau, Marie-Danielle. Le Tresor de Mon Pere. 2003. (Premier Roman Ser.). (FRE., Illus.). 64p. (J). (gr. 2-5). pap. (978-2-89021-246-6(7)) Diffusion du livre Mirabel.

Cullimore, Stan. Killer Sharks. Savage, Paul, illus. 2006. 40p. (J). (gr. 2-3). lib. bdg. (978-1-59889-013-6(1)) Stone Arch Bks.

Curtis, Christopher. Me Llamo Bud, No Buddy. 2003. (SPA.). 248p. (J). 10.99 (978-84-241-8638-8(9)) Everest de Ediciones y Distribucion, S.L. ESP. *Dist:* Lectorum Pubns., Inc.

—Me Llamo Bud, No Buddy. 2002. (SPA.). (gr. 5-8). lib. bdg. 18.75 (978-0-613-64546-1(4)) Tandem Library Bks.

Czech, Jan. Grace Happens. 2007. 160p. (YA). pap. 6.99 (978-0-14-240752-3(6) , Puffin) Penguin Group (USA) Inc.

Dad & I: First Grade Guided Reading Level A. (On Our Way to English Ser.). (gr. 1 up). 27.75 (978-0-7578-7025-5(2)) Rigby Education.

Dad & Me: KinderConcepts, 6 Packs. (Kinderstarters Ser.). 8p. (ps-1). 21.00 (978-0-7635-8735-2(4)) Rigby Education.

Dad & the Bike Race, 6 Packs. (Sails Literacy Ser.). (gr. 1-2). 36.00 (978-0-7578-4003-6(5)) Rigby Education.

Dad at the Beach: Individual Title Six-Packs. (Sails Literacy Ser.). (gr. 1-2). 36.00 (978-0-7578-6714-9(6)) Rigby Education.

Dad at the Fair: Individual Title Six-Packs. (Sails Literacy Ser.). (gr. 1-2). 36.00 (978-0-7578-6719-4(7)) Rigby Education.

Dad cooks Breakfast: Individual Title Six-Packs. (gr. 1-2). 25.00 (978-0-7635-9135-9(1)) Rigby Education.

Dagg, Stephanie. Oh Dad! 1999. (Illus.). 48p. (J). (gr. 1-4). per. (978-1-902586-45-8(X)) Mentor Bks.

Daly, Niki. Papa Lucky's Shadow. 1999. (978-0-606-16283-8(6)) Tandem Library Bks.

Dart, Iris Rainer & Brotman, Joyce. Larry: The King of Rock & Roll. 2007. 176p. (J). (gr. 4-6). 16.99 (978-0-399-24546-6(4) , Putnam Juvenile) Penguin Group (USA) Inc.

Davis, Adda Leah. Caleb's Song. l.t. ed. 2003. (Illus.). 56p. (J). (978-0-9747904-0-4(0)) Golden Harvest Publishing Co.

de Beer, Hans. Just Like Father! 2004. (Little Polar Bear Story Ser.). (Illus.). 22p. (J). bds. 3.95 (978-1-4027-1289-0(8)) Sterling Publishing Co., Inc.

Degen, Bruce. Daddy Is a Doodlebug. Degen, Bruce, illus. (Illus.). 40p. (J). (ps-1). 2002. pap. 7.99 (978-0-06-443578-9(4)); 2000. 15.89 (978-0-06-028416-9(1)) HarperCollins Pubs.

—Daddy Is a Doodlebug. 2002. (ps-2). lib. bdg. 14.10 (978-0-613-55210-3(5)) Tandem Library Bks.

DeStout, Carole. My Dad Wears Striped Pajamas. Heath, Paul Reaves, illus. 2003. (Children's Outreach Ser.). 38p. (J). pap. 5.00 (978-1-880994-83-2(6)) Mount Olive College Pr.

Deuker, Carl. High Heat. 2005. 352p. (J). (gr. 7 up). pap. 6.99 (978-0-06-057248-8(5) , Harper Trophy) HarperCollins Pubs.

—High Heat. 2003. 288p. (J). (gr. 7-9). tchr. ed. 16.00 (978-0-618-31117-0(3)) Houghton Mifflin Co. Trade & Reference Div.

DiCamillo, Kate. The Tiger Rising. 2002. 128p. (YA). (gr. 5-12). pap. 5.99 (978-0-7636-1898-8(5)) Candlewick Pr.

DiTerlizzi, Tony. Ted. DiTerlizzi, Tony, illus. 2001. (Illus.). 40p. (J). (ps-1). 16.95 (978-0-689-83235-2(4)) Simon & Schuster Children's Publishing.

Dowd, Siobhan. A Swift Pure Cry. 2007. 320p. (YA). (gr. 7). 16.99 (978-0-385-75108-7(7)); lib. bdg. 19.99 (978-0-385-75109-4(5)) Random Hse. Children's Bks. (Fickling, David Bks.).

Dr. Seuss Enterprises Staff. Hop on Pop. 2004. (Illus.). 24p. (J). (gr. k-ps). bds. 4.99 (978-0-375-82837-9(0) , Random Hse. Bks. for Young Readers) Random Hse. Children's Bks.

Dragonwagon, Crescent. The Sun Begun. Shaffer, Terea, illus. 1999. (J). 16.00 (978-0-689-81159-3(4) , Atheneum) Simon & Schuster Children's Publishing.

DuCharme, Dede Fox. The Treasure in the Tiny Blue Tin. 1998. (Chaparral Books for Young Readers). 144p. (J). (gr. 5-8). pap. 11.95 (978-0-87565-180-4(1)) Texas Christian Univ. Pr.

Edwards, Michelle. Papa's Latkes. Gustavson, Adam & Schuett, Stacey, illus. 2004. 32p. (J). (gr. k-2). 15.99 (978-0-7636-0779-1(7)) Candlewick Pr.

Edwards, Michelle. Papa's Latkes. Schuett, Stacey, illus. 2007. 32p. (J). (gr. k-2). pap. 6.99 (***978-0-7636-3563-3(4)***) Candlewick Pr.

Ehlert, Lois. Pie in the Sky. 2004. (Illus.). 40p. (J). (ps-2). 16.00 (978-0-15-216584-0(3)) Harcourt Children's Bks.

Eliot, George & West, Clare. Silas Marner: The Weaver of Raveloe, Level 4. 2nd ed. 2000. (Bookworms Ser.). (Illus.). 96p. 6.50 (978-0-19-423044-5(9)) Oxford Univ. Pr., Inc.

Emshwiller, Carol. Mister Boots. 2007. (Firebird Ser.). 192p. (YA). pap. 6.99 (978-0-14-240770-7(4) , Puffin) Penguin Group (USA) Inc.

Evans, Edie. I Love You, Daddy. Fletcher, Rusty, illus. 2001. (Little Golden Bks.). 16p. (J). (gr. k-k). 2.99 (978-0-307-99508-7(9) , Golden Bks.) Random Hse. Children's Bks.

Farnes, Catherine. The Slide. 2003. 128p. (J). 6.49 (978-1-57924-967-0(1)) Jones, Bob Univ. Pr.

Feiffer, Jules. The Daddy Mountain. 2004. (Illus.). 32p. (J). (ps-17). (978-0-7868-0912-7(4)) Hyperion Bks. for Children.

Fischer, Ty & Fischer, Emily. Fathers' Faith. Ream, Todd, illus. 2000. per. 3.00 (978-1-930710-50-4(X)) Veritas Pr., Inc.

Fox, Mem. Zoo-Looking. Love, Judith DuFour & Whitman, Candace, illus. 2001. (J). (ps-2). pap. 6.00 (978-1-57255-011-7(2)) Mondo Publishing.

Fox, Paula. Ivan. 2002. (SPA.). (YA). pap. 8.50 (978-84-279-3245-6(6) , NG31202) Molino, Editorial ESP. *Dist:* Lectorum Pubns., Inc.

Francomano, Alfred. Dilemma: Story of a Father & Two Sons. 1998. 64p. pap. 8.00 (978-0-8059-4431-0(1)) Dorrance Publishing Co., Inc.

Friend, Natasha. Lush. 192p. (J). 2007. (gr. 7 up). pap. 6.99 (***978-0-439-85347-7(8));*** 2006. pap. 16.99 (978-0-439-85346-0(X)) Scholastic, Inc. (Scholastic Paperbacks).

Fuge, Charles. My Dad! (Illus.). (J). 2005. 22p. bds. 5.95 (978-1-4027-2191-5(9)); 2003. 24p. 12.95 (978-1-4027-0707-0(X)) Sterling Publishing Co., Inc.

Fuqua, Jonathon Scott. The Reappearance of Sam Webber. 2001. (978-0-606-21397-4(X)) Tandem Library Bks.

Gaiman, Neil. The Day I Swapped My Dad for Two Goldfish. McKean, Dave, illus. 2004. 64p. (J). 16.99 incl. audio compact disk (978-0-06-058701-7(6)) HarperCollins Pubs.

Garfield, Henry. My Father the Werewolf. 2005. (Illus.). 240p. (J). (gr. 8-12). 17.95 (978-0-689-85180-3(4) , Atheneum) Simon & Schuster Children's Publishing.

Gifaldi, David. One Thing for Sure. 2000. (gr. 3-6). lib. bdg. 22.20 (978-0-613-84089-7(5)) Tandem Library Bks.

—One Thing for Sure. 2000. 184p. (YA). (gr. 4-7). pap. 12.95 (978-0-595-15326-8(7) , Backinprint.com) iUniverse, Inc.

Gikow, Louise. A Day with Daddy. Mazali, Gustavo, illus. 2004. (My First Reader Pb Ser.). 32p. (J). (gr. k-1). pap. 3.95 (978-0-516-25501-9(0) , Children's Pr.) Scholastic Library Publishing.

Glaze, Dave. Waiting for Pelly. 2003. (Pelly Ser.). (Illus.). 240p. (J). (gr. 3-6). pap. 7.95 (978-1-55050-228-2(X)) Coteau Bks. CAN. *Dist:* Fitzhenry & Whiteside, Ltd.

Gomi, Taro. I Lost My Dad! Gomi, Taro, illus. 2001. Orig. Title: Tousan Maigo. (Illus.). 32p. (J). (ps-2). 14.95 (978-1-929132-04-1(2)) Kane/Miller Bk. Pubs., Inc.

Gormley, Greg. Daddy's Day at Work. 2007. (Fantastic Phones Ser.). (Illus.). 12p. (J). 9.99 (***978-0-7475-8378-3(1)***) Bloomsbury Publishing Plc GBR. *Dist:* Independent Pubs. Group.

Graham, Georgia. The Strongest Man This Side of Cremona. Graham, Georgia, illus. 1998. (Illus.). 32p. (J). (ps-3). pap. 15.95 (978-0-88995-182-2(9)) Red Deer Pr. CAN. *Dist:* Fitzhenry & Whiteside, Ltd.

Greene-Alexander, Alesia. Sunflowers & Rainbows for Tia: Saying Goodbye to Daddy. 1999. (Illus.). (J). 7.95 (978-1-56123-128-7(2)) Centering Corp.

Gutman, Anne. Daddy Kisses. Hallensleben, Georg, illus. 2003. 14p. (J). bds. 5.95 (978-0-8118-3914-3(1)) Chronicle Bks. LLC.

Haley, Amanda. 33 Uses for Dad. 2004. (Illus.). 40p. 12.95 (978-1-59354-028-9(0)) Blue Apple Bks.

Haley, Gail E. My father's Beast. Haley, Gail E., illus. 2006. (Illus.). 32p. (J). (978-1-933251-35-6(2)) Parkway Pubs., Inc.

Hallinan, P. K. We're Very Good Friends, My Father & I. 24p. (J). 7.95 (978-0-8249-5375-1(4) , Ideals); 5.95 (978-0-8249-5376-8(2)) Ideals Pubns.

Harcourt School Publishers Staff. Dos Familias On Level. 3rd ed. 2002. (Trofeos Ser.).Tr. of Two Families. (SPA., Illus.). pap. 6.80 (978-0-15-324174-1(8)) Harcourt Schl. Pubs.

—Trofeos On Level: A Pescar! 3rd ed. 2002. (SPA., Illus.). pap. 5.50 (978-0-15-323895-6(X)) Harcourt Schl. Pubs.

Harkrader, L. D. Airball: My Life in Briefs. 2008. 224p. (J). pap. 6.99 (***978-0-312-37382-5(1)***) Square Fish.

Hayes, Alan. Dad's Golf Story: Coloring Book. Hayes, Alan, illus. 2000. (Illus.). 24p. (J). (ps-2). pap. 4.95 (978-0-615-11424-8(5)) A R T L U Publishing.

Hearn, Diane Dawson. Dad's Dinosaur Day. Hearn, Diane Dawson, illus. 1999. (Illus.). 32p. (J). (ps-3). pap. 5.99 (978-0-689-82611-5(7) , 076714005990, Aladdin) Simon & Schuster Children's Publishing.

—Dad's Dinosaur Day. 1999. (J). 12.79 (978-0-606-16309-5(3)); lib. bdg. 14.15 (978-0-613-18246-1(4)) Tandem Library Bks.

Henderson, Malcolm. Katie & Her Friends. Moss, P. Buckley, illus. 1998. 32p. (J). (ps-3). 15.95 (978-0-9665198-0-8(9) , 0998001000) Moss Portfolio, The.

Hesse, Karen. Just Juice. 1999. (gr. 3-6). lib. bdg. 13.00 (978-0-613-23005-6(1)) Tandem Library Bks.

Hiaasen, Carl. Flush. 272p. (J). (gr. 5). 2007. pap. 8.99 (***978-0-375-84185-9(7));*** 2005. lib. bdg. 18.99 (978-0-375-92182-7(6)); 2005. 16.95 (978-0-375-82182-0(1)) Random Hse. Children's Bks. (Knopf Bks. for Young Readers).

—Flush. l.t. ed. 2005. 335p. (YA). 23.95 (978-0-7862-7908-1(7)) Thorndike Pr.

High, Linda Oatman. Barn Savers. Lewin, Ted, illus. 2003. 32p. (J). (gr. 2-4). 15.95 (978-1-56397-403-8(7)) Boyds Mills Pr.

Hilbrecht, Kirk & Hilbrecht, Sharron. My Daddy Is a Guardsman. 2002. (Illus.). 30p. (gr. k-3). pap. 6.95 (978-1-889658-30-8(8)) New Canaan Publishing Co. LLC.

—My Daddy Is a Soldier. Hilbrecht, Kirk & Hilbrecht, Sharron, illus. 2000. (Illus.). 32p. (ps-3). reprint ed. pap. 6.95 (978-1-889658-01-8(4)) New Canaan Publishing Co. LLC.

Hill, Pamela Smith. A Voice from the Border. 2000. (J). (978-0-606-20004-2(5)) Tandem Library Bks.

Hines, Anna Grossnickle. Daddy Makes the Best Spaghetti. Hines, Anna Grossnickle, illus. 2002. (Illus.). (J). 13.79 (978-0-7587-2332-1(6)) Book Wholesalers, Inc.

—Daddy Makes the Best Spaghetti. 1999. (J). (ps-2). lib. bdg. 14.10 (978-0-8335-2786-8(X)) Tandem Library Bks.

Hines, Anna Grossnickle & Rey, Hans Augusto. Daddy Makes the Best Spaghetti. Hines, Anna Grossnickle, illus. 1999. (Illus.). 12p. (J). (gr. k-ps). bds. 5.95 (978-0-395-98036-1(4) , Clarion Bks.) Houghton Mifflin Co. Trade & Reference Div.

Hoese, Ray. My Dad Is an Ironman. Steinbach, Coreen, illus. 2004. 32p. 15.00 (978-1-891369-51-3(2)) Breakaway Bks.

Holmes, Barbara W. Following Fake Man. 2002. (gr. 3-6). lib. bdg. 13.00 (978-0-613-61839-7(4)) Tandem Library Bks.

Holub, Josef. The Robber & Me. 1999. (J). (gr. 4-7). 19.25 (978-0-8446-7007-2(3)) Smith, Peter Pub., Inc.

—The Robber & Me. 1999. (978-0-606-15909-8(6)) Tandem Library Bks.

Horn, Peter. The Best Father of All. James, J. Alison, tr. from GER. Kadmon, Cristina, illus. 2003. 32p. (J). (ps-1). 15.95 (978-0-7358-1679-4(4)) North-South Bks., Inc.

—Best Father of All Spanish Le. 2007. (J). 16.50 (978-0-7358-2116-3(X)) North-South Bks., Inc.

—Best Father of All Spanish PB. 2007. (J). pap. 6.95 (978-0-7358-2117-0(8)) North-South Bks., Inc.

Hornby, Nick. Slam. 2007. 304p. (J). (gr. 6). 19.99 (*978-0-399-25048-4(4) , Putnam Juvenile) Penguin Group (USA) Inc.

Horner, Polly. Polly & the North Star. (Illus.). pap. 11.00 (978-1-84255-281-0(3)); 2003. 32p. 19.99 (978-1-84255-085-4(3)) Orion Children's Bks. GBR. *Dist:* Trafalgar Square Publishing.

Hunter, Terri. One Starry Night. 2000. 32p. (J). 16.95 (978-0-9705974-0-3(1)) Baby Star Productions, LLC.

Hurst, Carol Otis. In Plain Sight. 2002. 160p. (YA). (gr. 5-9). 15.00 (978-0-618-19699-9(4) , Walter Lorraine) Houghton Mifflin Co. Trade & Reference Div.

Hyde, Judith Jensen. Rainy-Day Music. Abbott, Jason, illus. 2006. (Rookie Reader Skill Set Ser.). 32p. (J). (gr. k-2). 19.50 (978-0-516-24983-4(5) , Children's Pr.) Scholastic Library Publishing.

Hyde, Judith Jensen & Abbott, Jason. Rainy-day Music. 2006. (Illus.). 32p. (YA). pap. 4.95 (978-0-516-24998-8(3) , Children's Pr.) Scholastic Library Publishing.

Jacobs, Breena. Daddy's Girl. Austrew, Neva, illus. ed. 2006. 32p. (J). 15.95 (978-0-9749423-2-2(4)) Bookworm Bks.

Jacobson, Jennifer. Winnie (Dancing) on Her Own. Geis, Alissa Imre, illus. 2003. 112p. (J). (gr. 3-5). pap. 5.95 (978-0-618-36921-8(X)) Houghton Mifflin Co. Trade & Reference Div.

Jenck, Heidi Shelton. Gabe's Grocery List. Trover, Zachary, illus. 2006. 32p. (J). (*978-1-4048-3140-7(1)) Picture Window Bks.

Jobling, Curtis. My Daddy: My Daddy Is the Best in the Universe! 2006. (Illus.). 32p. (J). (ps-3). pap., pap. 8.99 (978-0-00-712255-4(1)) HarperCollins Pubs. Ltd. GBR. *Dist:* Independent Pubs. Group.

Johansson, Cecilia, illus. Just Like Daddy. 2006. 16p. (J). bds. 6.99 (978-1-4169-1220-0(7) , Little Simon) Simon & Schuster Children's Publishing.

Johnson, Angela. The First Part Last. l.t. ed. 241p. 2005. pap. 10.95 (978-0-7862-7379-9(8) , Large Print Pr.); 2004. 22.95 (978-0-7862-6510-7(8)) Thorndike Pr.

—Songs of Faith. 1998. (Illus.). 112p. (J). (gr. 3-7). 16.99 (978-0-531-33023-4(0)); pap. 15.95 (978-0-531-30023-7(4)) Scholastic, Inc. (Orchard Bks.).

Johnson, Craig Alan. Wave Watcher. 2005. viii, 139p. (J). pap. (978-0-87743-707-9(6)) Baha'i Publishing Trust, U.S.

Johnson, Pete. Rescuing Dad. Nayler, Sarah, illus. l.t. ed. 2005. 256p. (J). pap. (978-0-7540-7809-8(4) , CLP 401) BBC Audio.

—Rescuing Dad. 2003. (Read-Along Ser.). (J). pap. 29.95 incl. audio (978-0-7540-6254-7(6) , Galaxy Children's Large Print) BBC Audiobooks America.

"Johnson, Vincent L. ". Daddy's Good Cookin' 2007. 32p. (J). 16.95 (978-0-9657033-3-8(9)) Marzetta Bks.

Joosse, Barbara M. & Lavallee, Barbara. Papa Do You Love Me? Lavallee, Barbara, illus. 2005. (Illus.). 36p. (J). 15.95 (978-0-8118-4265-5(7)) Chronicle Bks. LLC.

Joseph, Ronald Rico. Daddy's First Diaper. 2000. (J). (gr. k-1). pap. 10.95 (978-0-533-13227-0(4)) Vantage Pr., Inc.

Jougla, Frederic. Tricked on Halloween: Rina & Jax's Stories. Jougla, Karina, illus. l.t. ed. 2004. 36p. (J). bds. 14.99 (978-0-9754287-0-2(5)) Imagery Pr.

Kaaberbol, Lene. The Serpent Gift. 3rd ed. 2007. (Shamer Chronicles Ser.). Orig. Title: Slangens Gave. 377p. (J). pap. 9.95 (*978-0-8050-8655-3(2) , Holt, Henry & Co. Bks. For Young Readers) Holt, Henry & Co.

Kanevsky, Polly. Sleepy Boy. Anderson, Stephanie, illus. 2006. 32p. (J). (ps-k). 15.95 (978-0-689-86735-4(2) , Atheneum) Simon & Schuster Children's Publishing.

Keats, Ezra Jack. Louie's Search. Keats, Ezra Jack, illus. 2002. (Illus.). (J). 13.19 (978-0-7587-5737-1(9)) Book Wholesalers, Inc.

—Louie's Search. Keats, Ezra Jack, illus. 2001. (Illus.). 40p. (J). (ps-3). pap. 6.99 (978-0-14-056761-8(5) , Puffin) Penguin Group (USA) Inc.

—Louie's Search. 2001. (978-0-606-20775-1(9)); lib. bdg. 15.30 (978-0-613-31436-7(0)) Tandem Library Bks.

Keep, Linda Lowery. Truth & Salsa. 2006. 176p. (J). 14.95 (978-1-56145-366-5(8) , Peachtree Junior) Peachtree Pubs., Ltd.

Kerrett, Etgar. Dad Runs Away with the Circus. Modan, Rutu, illus. 2004. 40p. (J). 16.99 (978-0-7636-2247-3(8)) Candlewick Pr.

Keselman, Gabriela. Cuando Viene Papa? Gusti, illus. 2000. (Tren Azul Ser.).Tr. of When Will Dad Be Back?. (SPA.). 32p. (J). (ps-2). (978-84-236-5493-2(1)) Edebé ESP. *Dist:* Baker & Taylor Bks.

Ketteman, Helen. I Remember Papa. 2001. 13.79 (978-0-606-21244-1(2)); lib. bdg. 15.30 (978-0-613-35961-0(5)) Tandem Library Bks.

Krensky, Stephen. My Dad Can Do Anything. Wohnoutka, Mike, illus. 2004. (Pictureback Bks.). 24p. (J). (ps-2). pap. 3.99 (978-0-375-82627-6(0) , Random Hse. Bks. for Young Readers) Random Hse. Children's Bks.

—My Dad Can Do Anything. 2004. (ps-2). lib. bdg. 11.80 (978-0-613-82988-5(3)) Tandem Library Bks.

Kurtz, Jane. Faraway Home. Lewis, Earl, illus. 2000. 32p. (J). (gr. 1-5). 17.00 (978-0-15-200036-3(4) , Gulliver Bks.) Harcourt Children's Bks.

Landalf, Helen & McConnell, Mary. Getting Used to Candy. 2000. (Illus.). (J). (gr. k-5). 6.95 (978-1-56123-139-3(8)) Centering Corp.

Langley, Karen. Shine! Langley, Jonathan, illus. 2002. 32p. (J). (gr. k-3). 15.95 (978-0-7614-5127-3(7)) Cavendish, Marshall Corp.

Lanthier, Jennifer. The Mystery of the Martello Tower. 2008. 272p. (J). 16.99 (*978-0-06-125712-4(5)); lib. bdg. 17.89 (*978-0-06-125713-1(3)) HarperCollins Pubs. (Geringer, Laura Book).

Leno, Jay & Whitehead, S. B. If Roast Beef Could Fly. 2004. (Illus.). 32p. (J). 17.95 (978-0-689-86767-5(0)) Simon & Schuster Children's Publishing.

Leonard, Marcia. My Camp-Out. Handelman, Dorothy, photos by. 1999. (Real Kids Readers Ser.). (Illus.). 32p. (ps-1). lib. bdg. 18.90 (978-0-7613-2052-4(0)); (J). pap. 4.99 (978-0-7613-2077-7(6)) Lerner Publishing Group. (Millbrook Pr.).

—My Camp-Out. 1999. (J). (978-0-606-19165-4(8)); lib. bdg. 13.00 (978-0-613-16774-1(0)) Tandem Library Bks.

Levine, Abby. Daddies Give You Horsey Rides. Bendall-Brunello, John, illus. 2004. 32p. (J). (ps-k). 16.95 (978-0-8075-1429-0(2)) Whitman, Albert & Co.

Levy, Elizabeth. My Life As a Fifth-Grade Comedian. 1998. 192p. (J). (ps-7). pap. 5.99 (978-0-06-440723-6(3) , Harper Trophy) HarperCollins Pubs.

—My Life As a Fifth-Grade Comedian. 1999. (J). pap., stu. ed. 41.20 incl. audio (978-0-7887-3180-8(7) , 40915) Recorded Bks., LLC.

Levy, Janice. Alley Oops. Decker, Cynthia, illus. 2005. 32p. (J). 15.95 (978-0-9729225-4-8(7)) Flashlight Pr.

Lewis, Beverly. Secret Summer Dreams. rev. ed. 2001. (Holly's Heart Ser.: Bk. 2). 144p. (YA). (gr. 6-9). pap. 6.99 (978-0-7642-2501-7(4)) Bethany Hse. Pubs.

L'Heureux, Christine. Como Papa. 2004. (Caillou Estrella Polar Ser.). (SPA., Illus.). 24p. (J). (ps up). pap. 3.95 (978-1-58728-347-5(6) , Creative Publishing International) Quayside.

Limb, Sue. Girl, (Nearly) 16: Absolute Torture. (Girl, 15 Ser.). 224p. (YA). (gr. 5-11). 2008. mass mkt. 6.50 (*978-0-440-23897-3(8) , Laurel Leaf); 2006. pap. 8.95 (978-0-385-73217-8(1) , Delacorte Bks. for Young Readers) Random Hse. Children's Bks.

London, Jonathan. Giving Thanks. Manchess, Gregory, illus. 2003. 32p. (J). (ps-2). 16.99 (978-0-7636-1680-9(X)) Candlewick Pr.

Loomis, Christine. The Ten Best Things about My Dad. Urbanovic, Jackie, tr. Urbanovic, Jackie, illus. 2004. 32p. (J). (ps-3). pap. 3.99 (978-0-439-57769-4(1) , Cartwheel Bks.) Scholastic, Inc.

Lowenstein, Sallie. Waiting for Eugene. Lowenstein, Sallie, illus. 2005. (Illus.). 208p. (J). 19.00 (978-0-9658486-5-7(5)) Lion Stone Bks.

Luckett, Kathy. Little Library Literacy: Does your Father Snore? Afrikaans. van Heerden, Marjorie, illus. 2007. pap. (*978-0-521-70298-0(4)) Cambridge Univ. Pr.

—Little Library Literacy: Does your Father Snore? Sesotho. van Heerden, Marjorie, illus. 2007. pap. (*978-0-521-70296-6(8)) Cambridge Univ. Pr.

—Little Library Literacy: Does your Father Snore? Setswana. van Heerden, Marjorie, illus. 2007. pap. (*978-0-521-70295-9(X)) Cambridge Univ. Pr.

—Little Library Literacy: Does your Father Snore? Siswati. van Heerden, Marjorie, illus. 2007. pap. (*978-0-521-70294-2(1)) Cambridge Univ. Pr.

—Little Library Literacy: Does your Father Snore? Tsonga. van Heerden, Marjorie, illus. 2007. pap. (*978-0-521-70292-8(5)) Cambridge Univ. Pr.

—Little Library Literacy: Does your Father Snore? Venda. van Heerden, Marjorie, illus. 2007. pap. (*978-0-521-70293-5(3)) Cambridge Univ. Pr.

—Little Library Literacy: Does your Father Snore? Xhosa. van Heerden, Marjorie, illus. 2007. pap. (*978-0-521-70289-8(5)) Cambridge Univ. Pr.

MacNeil, Stephen. Woolies & Worms. 2007. 192p. (J). (gr. 2-5). 16.95 (*978-0-8126-2751-0(2)) Cricket Bks.

Manns, Nick. Dead Negative. 2003. mass mkt. (978-0-340-85566-9(5) , Hodder Children's Books) Hodder Children's Division.

Marriott, Donna. Celebrating Father's Day: Father's Day Is for Special People. 1999. (ps-2). lib. bdg. 10.65 (978-0-613-34120-2(1)) Tandem Library Bks.

Marzollo, Jean. Papa Papa. Regan, Laura, illus. 2000. (Growing Tree Ser.). 14p. (J). (ps up). 5.99 (978-0-694-01246-6(7) , Harper Festival) HarperCollins Pubs.

Masurel, Claire. Emily & Her Daddy. Calitri, Susan, illus. 2003. (Lift-the-Flap Ser.). 16p. (J). (gr. k-1). pap. 6.99 (978-0-14-250080-4(1) , Puffin) Penguin Group (USA) Inc.

Matthews, Kezi. John Riley's Daughter. 2000. 144p. (YA). (gr. 7 up). 16.95 (978-0-8126-2775-6(X)) Cricket Bks.

Mayer, Mercer. Just Me & My Dad. Mayer, Mercer, illus. 2001. (Little Critter Ser.). (Illus.). 24p. (J). (gr. k-k). pap. 3.29 (978-0-307-11839-4(8) , 11839, Random Hse. Bks. for Young Readers) Random Hse. Children's Bks.

Mayfield, Sue. The Four Franks. Parsons, Garry, illus. 2005. (Blue Go Bananas Ser.). 38p. (J). (978-0-7787-2629-6(0)) Crabtree Publishing Co.

Maynard, Joyce. The Cloud Chamber. 288p. (YA). 2006. (gr. 9). pap. 7.99 (978-1-4169-2699-3(2) , Simon Pulse); 2005. (gr. 6-9). 16.95 (978-0-689-87152-8(X) , Atheneum) Simon & Schuster Children's Publishing.

Mazer, Norma Fox. Missing Pieces. 2007. (Illus.). 160p. (YA). pap. 6.95 (978-0-15-206271-2(8) , Harcourt Paperbacks) Harcourt Children's Bks.

McBratney, Sam. Adivina Cuanto Te Quiero. Roehrich-Rubio, Esther, tr. Jeram, Anita, illus. 2001. Tr. of Guess How Much I Love You. (SPA.). 32p. (J). pap. (978-84-88342-15-7(2) , KK7612) S.A. Kokinos ESP. *Dist:* Lectorum Pubns., Inc.

—Guess How Much I Love You. 2002. (Illus.). (J). 23.40 (978-0-7587-2668-1(6)) Book Wholesalers, Inc.

—Guess How Much I Love You. Jeram, Anita, illus. 1999. 24p. (J). (ps). bds. 6.99 (978-0-8499-5971-4(3)) Nelson, Thomas Inc.

McCormick, Wendy. Daddy, Will You Miss Me? 2002. (gr. k-3). lib. bdg. 15.30 (978-0-613-53803-9(X)) Tandem Library Bks.

—Daniel & His Walking Stick. Bergum, Constance Rummel, illus. 2005. 32p. (J). 15.95 (978-1-56145-330-6(7)) Peachtree Pubs., Ltd.

McCreary, Laura & Myers, Mark. The Best Dad. Goldberg, Barry, illus. 2001. (Angela Anaconda Ser.: Vol. 3). 64p. (J). (gr. 2-5). pap. 3.99 (978-0-689-84039-5(X) , Simon Spotlight) Simon & Schuster Children's Publishing.

McKay, Hilary. Permanent Rose. (J). (gr. 3-7). 2005. 240p. 16.99 (978-1-4169-0372-7(0) , McElderry, Margaret K.); 2006. 256p. reprint ed. pap. 5.99 (978-1-4169-2804-1(9) , Aladdin) Simon & Schuster Children's Publishing.

McKissack, Patricia C. & McKissack, Fredrick L., Jr. Let My People Go: Bible Stories Told by a Freeman of Color. Ransome, James E., illus. 1998. 144p. (YA). (gr. 4-7). 21.99 (978-0-689-80856-2(9) , Atheneum/Anne Schwartz Bks.) Simon & Schuster Children's Publishing.

Minarik, Else Holmelund. Father Bear's Special Day. 2003. (gr. k-3). lib. bdg. 11.80 (978-0-613-67193-4(7)) Tandem Library Bks.

Mitchell, Kathy. Daddy Got His Orders. Hergenroeder, Ernie, illus. 2004. 16p. (J). pap. 14.95 (978-0-9760811-0-4(5)) T.J. Publishing.

Montgomery Gibson, Jane. Daddy's Valentine. Montgomery Gibson, Jane, illus. 2005. (J). bds. 8.99 (978-1-4183-0046-3(2)) Christ Inspired, Inc.

Mora, Eddy G. Have You Seen My Daddy? Martin, April, ed. deluxe l.t. ed. 1999. (Toby & Tig Ser.: Vol. 1). (Illus.). 32p. (J). (ps-5). per. 7.99 incl. audio compact disk (978-0-9671753-0-0(5)) Mora Art Studio.

—Toby & Dad at Work. Martin, April, illus. deluxe ed. 2000. (Toby & Tig Ser.). (J). (gr. 3-8). 13.99 (978-0-9671753-1-7(3)) Mora Art Studio.

Morozumi, Atsuko. Un Dia con Papa. 2000. (Coleccion "Conejito" Ser.). (SPA.). (J). (ps-k). bds. (978-958-04-4520-3(6)) Norma S.A. COL. *Dist:* Lectorum Pubns., Inc.

Morrison, Kevin. Stitches. Nixon, John, illus. 2003. 32p. (J). 12.95 (978-1-929039-15-9(8)) Ambassador Bks., Inc.

Moss, Marissa. Amelia's Family Ties. Moss, Marissa, illus. 2007. (Amelia's Notebooks). 40p. (J). (gr. 2-5). 9.99 (*978-1-4169-0914-9(1) , Simon & Schuster/Paula Wiseman Bks.) Simon & Schuster Children's Publishing.

—Amelia's Family Ties. 2000. (Amelia's Notebooks). (Illus.). (J). (gr. 3-5). 12.75 (978-0-606-18352-9(3)) Tandem Library Bks.

Munsch, Robert. David's Father. Martchenko, Michael, illus. 2003. (Annikins Ser.: Vol. 7). 32p. (J). (ps-2). pap. 1.25 (978-1-55037-011-9(1)) Annick Pr., Ltd. CAN. *Dist:* Firefly Bks., Ltd.

My Daddy Is a Giant. 2004. (J). (ALB & ENG.). (978-1-84444-499-1(6)); (ARA & ENG.). (978-1-84444-501-1(1)); (BEN & ENG.). (978-1-84444-502-8(X)); (CHI & ENG.). (978-1-84444-503-5(8)); (CHI & ENG.). (978-1-84444-504-2(6)); (CRO & ENG.). (978-1-84444-505-9(4)); (ENG & PER.). (978-1-84444-506-6(2)); (ENG & FRE.). (978-1-84444-507-3(0)); (ENG & GUJ.). (978-1-84444-509-7(7)); (ENG & HIN.). (978-1-84444-510-3(0)); (ENG & ITA.). (978-1-84444-511-0(9)); (ENG & JPN.). (978-1-84444-512-7(7)); (ENG & KOR.). (978-1-84444-513-4(5)); (ENG & KUR.). (978-1-84444-514-1(3)); (ENG & PAN.). (978-1-84444-515-8(1)); (ENG & POL.). (978-1-84444-516-5(X)); (ENG & POR.). (978-1-84444-517-2(8)); (ENG & RUS.). (978-1-84444-518-9(6)); (ENG & SOM.). (978-1-84444-519-6(4)); (ENG & SPA.). (978-1-84444-520-2(8)); (ENG & TAG.). (978-1-84444-508-0(9)); (ENG & TAM.). (978-1-84444-521-9(6)); (ENG & TUR.). (978-1-84444-522-6(4)); (ENG & URD.). (978-1-84444-523-3(2)); (ENG & VIE.). (978-1-84444-524-0(0)) Mantra Publishing, Ltd.

My Father the Mad Professor: Individual Title Six-Packs. (Action Packs Ser.). 120p. (gr. 3-5). 44.00 (978-0-7635-8424-5(X)) Rigby Education.

Myers, Walter Dean. Somewhere in the Darkness: Un Lugar Entre Las Sombras. Blanco, Osvaldo, tr. 2003. (SPA., Illus.). 224p. (J). (gr. 7-9). mass mkt. 8.50 (978-0-590-47701-7(3) , Scholastic en Espanol) Scholastic, Inc.

Naylor, Phyllis Reynolds. Ice. 1998. 256p. (YA). (gr. 7-12). mass mkt. 12.95 (978-0-689-81872-1(6) , Simon Pulse) Simon & Schuster Children's Publishing.

—Ice. 1998. (J). 11.64 (978-0-606-12970-1(7)) Tandem Library Bks.

Numeroff, Laura Joffe. What Daddies Do Best. Munsinger, Lynn, illus. 2003. (Classic Board Bks.). 22p. (J). bds. 6.99 (978-0-689-85973-1(2) , Little Simon) Simon & Schuster Children's Publishing.

Numeroff, Laura Joffe & Munsinger, Lynn. What Mommies Do Best: What Daddies Do Best. 1998. (Illus.). 40p. (J). (ps-3). 13.95 (978-0-689-80577-6(2)) Simon & Schuster Children's Publishing.

O'Connor, Joe. Where Did Daddy's Hair Go? Payne, Henry, illus. 2006. 40p. (J). (gr. k-3). 14.95 (978-0-375-83571-1(7) , Random Hse. Bks. for Young Readers) Random Hse. Children's Bks.

One Starry Night Gift Box. 2000. 32p. 29.95 (978-0-9705974-1-0(X)) Baby Star Productions, LLC.

One Way Out: A Father's Story. 2002. pap. 12.00 (978-0-9742738-0-8(5)) One Way Out.

Padwe, Phil. Daddy Has A Tattoo (or Two) Padwe, Phil, illus. 2007. (J). 17.95 (*978-0-9770232-5-7(7)) Mommy Has Tattoos.

Papa Piccolo: Evaluation Guide. 2006. (J). 17.95 (978-1-55942-419-6(2)) Marsh Media.

Paradis, Susan. My Daddy. 2007. (Illus.). 30p. (J). (ps-1). 9.95 (978-1-886910-50-8(2) , Lemniscaat) Boyds Mills Pr.

Parkinson, Siobhan. Second Fiddle: Or How to Tell a Blackbird from a Sausage. 2007. 192p. (J). (gr. 6-9). 16.95 (978-1-59643-122-5(9)) Roaring Brook Pr.

Parr, Todd. The Daddy Book. Parr, Todd, illus. 2002. (Illus.). 32p. (J). (ps-3). 15.99 (978-0-316-60799-5(1)) Little, Brown Bks. for Young Readers.

Petersen, P. J. White Water. 1999. (978-0-606-16710-9(2)) Tandem Library Bks.

Pleau-Murissi, Marilyn. Caillou, Spends the Day with Daddy. CINAR Animation Staff, illus. 2004. (Clubhouse Usa Ser.). 24p. (J). (ps up). 3.95 (978-2-89450-523-6(X)) Chouette Publishing CAN. *Dist:* Perseus Distribution.

Polacco, Patricia. My Ol' Man. 1999. (Illus.). 40p. (J). (gr. k-3). pap. 6.99 (978-0-698-11770-9(0) , Putnam Juvenile) Penguin Group (USA) Inc.

—My Ol' Man. 1999. (J). (978-0-606-16791-8(9)); lib. bdg. 15.30 (978-0-613-18268-3(5)) Tandem Library Bks.

Porter-Gaylord, Laurel. I Love My Daddy Because... Wolff, Ashley, illus. 2004. 24p. (J). (ps). bds. 6.99 (978-0-525-47250-6(9) , Dutton Juvenile) Penguin Group (USA) Inc.

—I Love My Daddy Because. Wolff, Ashley, illus. 2004. (SPA.). 24p. (J). bds. 6.99 (978-0-525-47251-3(7) , Dutton Juvenile) Penguin Group (USA) Inc.

Portman, Frank. King Dork. 352p. (YA). (gr. 9). 2007. pap. 8.99 (*978-0-385-73450-9(6)); 2006. (Illus.). 16.95 (978-0-385-73291-8(0)); 2006. (Illus.). lib. bdg. 18.99 (978-0-385-90312-7(X)) Random Hse. Children's Bks. (Delacorte Bks. for Young Readers).

Poupeney, Mollie. Her Father's Daughter. 2002. (gr. 7-12). lib. bdg. 13.55 (978-0-613-49493-9(8)) Tandem Library Bks.

Pow, Tom. Tell Me One Thing, Dad. Andrew, Ian, illus. 2004. 32p. (J). (ps-k). 15.99 (978-0-7636-2474-3(8)) Candlewick Pr.

Reece, Stephen. The Bear in the Air Scare. 1998. (Illus.). 12p. (J). (ps-3). pap. 2.95 (978-1-892388-00-1(6)) Little Trucker Bks.

—My Dad Drives a Big Truck. 1998. (Illus.). 12p. (J). (ps-3). pap. 2.95 (978-1-892388-02-5(2)) Little Trucker Bks.

Reeder, Carolyn. Foster's War. 2000. 272p. (J). (gr. 4-7). pap. 4.99 (978-0-590-09856-4(X)) Scholastic, Inc.

—Foster's War. 2000. (J). 11.15 (978-0-606-19697-0(8)); (gr. 5-8). lib. bdg. 12.40 (978-0-613-29960-2(4)) Tandem Library Bks.

Reynolds, Marilyn. Too Soon for Jeff. 2003. 192p. (gr. 7-12). pap. 8.95 (978-0-930934-91-0(1)); 15.95 (978-0-930934-90-3(3)) Morning Glory Pr., Inc.

Rich, Scharlotte. I Love My Daddy. 2001. 96p. (J). 7.99 (978-0-310-70104-0(X)) Zondervan.

Rigby Education Staff. Kids in the Kitchen. (Sails Literacy Ser.). (Illus.). 16p. (gr. 1-2). 27.00 (978-0-7635-9895-2(X) , 698959C99) Rigby Education.

Robinson, Sharon. Slam Dunk! 2007. 160p. (J). (gr. 4-7). pap. 16.99 (*978-0-439-67199-6(X) , Scholastic Pr.) Scholastic, Inc.

Rockwell, Anne F. Father's Day. Rockwell, Lizzy, illus. 2005. 40p. (J). (ps-1). 14.99 (978-0-06-051377-1(2)); lib. bdg. 15.89 (978-0-06-051378-8(0)) HarperCollins Pubs.

Rottman, S. L. Slalom. 2004. 256p. (YA). (gr. 7). 16.99 (978-0-670-05913-3(7) , Viking Juvenile) Penguin Group (USA) Inc.

Ruel, Francine. Mon Père et Moi. 2001. (Roman + — Special Editions Ser.). (FRE.). 96p. (YA). (gr. 8). pap. (978-2-89021-514-6(8)) Diffusion du livre Mirabel.

Rutledge, Linda Austin. Without Dad: Written & Illustrated by Linda Austin Rutledge. 2002. (gr. 7-12). lib. bdg. 20.50 (978-0-613-74649-6(X)) Tandem Library Bks.

Saenz, Benjamin Alire. He Forgot to Say Good-Bye. 2008. 272p. (YA). (*978-1-4169-4963-3(1) , Simon & Schuster Children's Publishing) Simon & Schuster Children's Publishing.

Salisbury, Graham. Shark Bait. 1999. (978-0-606-16449-8(9)) Tandem Library Bks.

Schmatz, Pat. Circle the Truth. 2007. (Exceptional Reading & Language Arts Titles for Upper Grades Ser.). 192p. (YA). (gr. 8-12). 16.95 (*978-0-8225-7268-8(0) , Carolrhoda Bks.) Lerner Publishing Group.

Schraff, Anne. Terrible Orchid Sky. 2001. (gr. 7-12). lib. bdg. 11.80 (978-0-613-33129-6(X)) Tandem Library Bks.

Sedgwick, Marcus. The Dark Flight Down. 240p. 2008. (YA). (gr. 7). pap. 7.99 (*978-0-553-48784-8(1)); 2005. (J). (gr. 5-7). 15.95 (978-0-385-74645-8(8)) Random Hse. Children's Bks. (Lamb, Wendy).

Seskin Steve & Shamblin Allen. Chance to Shine. 2006. (Illus.). 32p. 16.95 incl. audio compact disk (978-1-58246-167-0(8) , Tricycle Pr.) Ten Speed Pr.

Seuss, Dr. Hop on Pop-Up! 2002. (Illus.). 12p. (J). 6.99 (978-0-375-81547-8(3) , Random Hse. Bks. for Young Readers) Random Hse. Children's Bks.

Sharratt, Nick. Robopop. 2000. (Illus.). 121p. (J). pap. 7.99 (978-0-440-86352-6(X)) Transworld Publishers Ltd. GBR. *Dist:* Trafalgar Square Publishing.

Shelton, Diane & Shelton, Rachelle. Lessons from My Father's Vineyard. Shelton, Diane & Shelton, Rachelle, illus. 2002. (Illus.). 48p. 4.50 (978-0-9719108-1-2(2)) Rumsey Family Ministries.

Shepard. Los Regalos de Wali Dad. 1999. (J). per. 16.00 (978-0-689-80419-9(9) , Atheneum) Simon & Schuster Children's Publishing.

Shreve, Susan. Jonah, the Whale. 1999. 110p. (J). (ps-7). per. 13.00 (978-0-613-06739-3(8)) Tandem Library Bks.

Shreve, Susan Richards. Jonah, the Whale. 1999. 128p. (J). (gr. 3-7). pap. 4.99 (978-0-590-37134-6(7) , Scholastic Paperbacks) Scholastic, Inc.

Sollinger, Emily. Giggles with Daddy. Hathon, Elizabeth, photos by. 2002. (Illus.). 14p. (J). bds. 5.99 (978-0-448-42548-1(3) , Grosset & Dunlap) Penguin Group (USA) Inc.

Spinelli, Eileen. Night Shift Daddy. Iwai, Melissa, illus. 2000. 32p. (ps-2). 14.99 (978-0-7868-0495-5(5)) Hyperion Pr.

St. Aubin, Bruno. Daddy Is a Dinosaur. St. Aubin, Bruno, illus. 1999. (Little Wolf Bks.). (Illus.). 32p. (J). (gr. k-1). pap. (978-1-894363-19-8(1)) Dominique & Friends.

—Daddy's a Busy Beaver. Perkes, Carolyn, tr. from FRE. 2001. (Little Wolf Bks.: Level 1). (Illus.). 32p. (J). (gr. 1 up). pap. (978-1-894363-74-7(4)) Dominique & Friends.

—Daddy's an Alien. St. Aubin, Bruno, illus. 2005. (Read-It! Readers Ser.). (Illus.). 32p. (J). (gr. k-3). 18.60 (978-1-4048-1067-9(6)) Picture Window Bks.

St-Aubin, Bruno, illus. Daddy's a Dinosaur. 2005. (Read-It! Readers Ser.). 32p. (J). (gr. k-3). 18.60 (978-1-4048-1028-0(5)) Picture Window Bks.

Stanley, Diane. A Time Apart. 2001. (J). (978-0-606-21490-2(9)) Tandem Library Bks.

Steadman, Ralph. That's My Dad. 2001. (Illus.). 32p. (J). pap. 8.99 (978-1-84270-011-2(1)) Andersen GBR. *Dist:* Independent Pubs. Group.

Still, Wayne Anthony, illus. Desert Treasure. 1999. (J). 30.00 (978-0-8172-7296-8(8)) Steck-Vaughn.

Stine, R. L. Goosebumps: Night of the Living Dummy III. 2005. (Goosebumps Ser.). 144p. (J). 4.99 (978-0-439-66989-4(8) , Scholastic Paperbacks) Scholastic, Inc.

—Stay Out of the Basement. 2003. (Goosebumps Ser.). 144p. (J). pap. 4.99 (978-0-439-56845-6(5) , 53657972, Scholastic Paperbacks) Scholastic, Inc.

—Stay Out of the Basement. 2003. (gr. 5-8). lib. bdg. 13.00 (978-0-613-70767-1(2)) Tandem Library Bks.

Straight, Susan. The Friskative Dog. 2007. 160p. (J). (gr. 3-7). 14.99 (978-0-375-83777-7(9)); lib. bdg. 17.99 (978-0-375-93777-4(3)) Random Hse. Children's Bks. (Knopf Bks. for Young Readers).

Strauss, Linda Leopold. Really, Truly, Everything's Fine. 2004. 160p. (YA). 15.95 (978-0-7614-5163-1(3)) Cavendish, Marshall Corp.

Strong, Jeremy. Pirate Pendemonium. 2002. (J). pap. 24.95 incl. audio (978-0-7540-6252-3(X)) BBC Audiobooks America.

Supplee, Audra. I Almost Love You, Eddie Clegg. 2004. 192p. (J). (gr. 4-6). 14.95 (978-1-56145-308-5(0)) Peachtree Pubs., Ltd.

Tattum, Stephan. Dad. 2005. (J). 4.95 (978-1-59792-002-5(9)) F.A.S.T. Learning LLLC.

Testa, Maria. Almost Forever. 2007. 80p. (J). (gr. 4-8). pap. 5.99 (978-0-7636-3366-0(6)) Candlewick Pr.

Tyler, Amy J. Best Dad in the Sea. 2003. (Step into Reading Ser.). (Illus.). 32p. (J). (ps-1). pap. 3.99 (978-0-7364-2131-7(9) , RH/Disney) Random Hse. Children's Bks.

Uhlberg, Myron. The Printer. Sorensen, Henri, tr. Sorensen, Henri, illus. 2003. 32p. (J). (gr. 1-5). 16.95 (978-1-56145-221-7(1)) Peachtree Pubs., Ltd.

Valentine, Jenny. Me, the Missing, & the Dead. 2008. 208p. (J). 16.99 (*978-0-06-085068-5(X)); lib. bdg. 17.89 (*978-0-06-085069-2(8)) HarperCollins Pubs.

Valentine, Johnny. One Dad, Two Dads, Brown Dad, Blue Dads. Sarecky, Melody, illus. 2004. (Alyson Wonderland Ser.). 32p. (ps-1). 10.95 (978-1-55583-253-7(9) , Alyson Wonderland) Alyson Pubns.

Vestergaard, Hope. Driving Daddy. Courtin, Thierry, illus. 2003. 20p. (J). (ps). 6.99 (978-0-525-47032-8(8) , Dutton Juvenile) Penguin Group (USA) Inc.

Vogelaar, Alie. A Shot Through the Window. Bazen, Edith, tr. from DUT. Visser, Rino, illus. 2000. Orig. Title: Een Schot Door Het Raam. 107p. lib. bdg. 8.95 (978-0-9670728-1-4(6)) Early Foundations Pubs.

Wallace, John. It's You, Daddy. 2005. (Illus.). 32p. (ps-k). 12.99 (978-0-7868-0958-5(2)) Hyperion Bks. for Children.

Watson, Kim. Just Like Dad. 2001. (Little Bill Books for Beginning Readers Ser.). (Illus.). (J). 12.79 (978-0-606-21276-2(0)) Tandem Library Bks.

Watson Martin, JoAn. Goodnight Mrs. Dinglewall. Sleep Tight! 2006. (YA). per. (978-0-9777996-0-2(3)) Great American Pr.,The.

Waugh, Sylvia. Who Goes Home? 2005. 224p. (gr. 4-7). 5.99 (978-0-440-41839-9(9) , Yearling) Random Hse. Children's Bks.

Weaver, Will. Hard Ball. (gr. 6 up). 1999. 256p. (J). pap. 5.99 (978-0-06-447208-1(6) , Harper Trophy); 1998. 240p. (YA). 15.89 (978-0-06-027122-0(1)); 1998. 240p. (YA). 15.95 (978-0-06-027121-3(3)) HarperCollins Pubs.

—Hard Ball. 1999. (J). 12.64 (978-0-606-16706-2(4)); (gr. 7-12). lib. bdg. 14.15 (978-0-613-18254-6(5)) Tandem Library Bks.

Welch, Willy. Dancing with Daddy. Woodruff, Liza, illus. 2004. 32p. (J). (ps-3). pap. 6.95 (978-1-58089-078-6(4)) Charlesbridge Publishing, Inc.

Wilder, Laura Ingalls. Laura's Pa. 1999. (Little House Chapter Bks.: No. 12). (J). (gr. 3-6). (978-0-606-15840-4(5)) Tandem Library Bks.

Williams, Vicki & Williams, Kathy. Everybody Has a Daddy. Wood, Joe, illus. 2003. 16p. (J). 7.95 (978-0-9747597-0-8(8)) Self-Esteem Adventures Pr.

Wolfgram, Barbara. I Know My Daddy Loves Me. McAuley, Marlene, illus. 1998. 32p. (J). (ps-1). 6.99 (978-0-570-05050-6(2) , 56-1874GJ) Concordia Publishing Hse.

Wood, Douglas. What Dads Can't Do. ed. 2004. (Illus.). (J). (gr. k-3). spiral bd. (978-0-616-07247-9(3)); spiral bd. (978-0-616-07248-6(1)) Canadian National Institute for the Blind/Institut National Canadien pour les Aveugles.

—What Dads Can't Do. Cushman, Doug, illus. (J). (ps-3). 2000. 32p. 14.95 (978-0-689-82620-7(6)); 2005. 24p. 6.95 (978-1-4169-0197-6(3)) Simon & Schuster Children's Publishing.

Woodworth, Chris. Busted.com. 2008. 176p. (YA). 16.00 (*978-0-374-30987-9(6)) Farrar, Straus & Giroux.

Wooldridge, Frosty. Strike Three! Take Your Base. Petri, Freeman, illus. 2001. 160p. (YA). (gr. 6-12). pap. 6.95 (978-1-930093-07-2(1)) Brookfield Reader, Inc., The.

Young, Janet Ruth. The Opposite of Music. 2007. 352p. (YA). 15.99 (978-1-4169-0040-5(3) , Atheneum) Simon & Schuster Children's Publishing.

Ziefert, Harriet. Daddies Are for Catching Butterflies. Jabar, Cynthia, illus. 1999. (Lift-the-Flap Bks.). 16p. (J). (ps-1). pap. 6.99 (978-0-14-056553-9(1) , Puffin) Penguin Group (USA) Inc.

—Just Like Daddy! Brown, Erik, illus. 2005. 16p. (J). bds. 6.95 (978-1-4027-1789-5(X) , 1241731) Sterling Publishing Co., Inc.

Zolotow, Charlotte. A Father Like That. Scribner, Joanne & Pham, LeUyen, illus. 1999. 40p. (J). (ps-3). 16.99 (978-0-06-027864-9(1)); lib. bdg. 17.89 (978-0-06-027865-6(X)) HarperCollins Pubs.

FATHERS—POETRY

Appelt, Kathi. My Father's House. Colon, Raul, illus. 2007. 32p. (J). (gr. 1-4). 16.99 (978-0-670-03669-1(2) , Viking Juvenile) Penguin Group (USA) Inc.

Cook, Annabel. Poems for Dad: A Collection of Poetry. 2005. (Illus.). 239p. (*978-1-84602-213-5(4) , Young Writers) Forward Pr.

Johnson, Angela. In Daddy's Arms, I Am Tall. ed. 2004. (Illus.). (J). (gr. k-3). spiral bd. (978-0-616-03094-3(0)) Canadian National Institute for the Blind/Institut National Canadien pour les Aveugles.

Johnson, Angela & Adedjouma, Davida, contrib. by. In Daddy's Arms, I Am Tall. 2002. (Illus.). (J). (ps). 25.95 incl. audio (978-0-87499-895-5(6)); pap., tchr.'s planning gde. ed. 37.95 incl. audio (978-0-87499-896-2(4)); pap. 16.95 incl. audio (978-0-87499-894-8(8)) Live Oak Media.

Purple Ronnie. Purple Ronnie's Little Book for a Smashing Dad. 2008. 64p. 8.95 (*978-0-7407-7118-7(3)) Andrews McMeel Publishing.

Steptoe, Javaka, illus. In Daddy's Arms I Am Tall: African Americans Celebrating Fathers. 2000. 32p. (J). 15.95 (978-1-880000-31-1(8)) Lee & Low Bks., Inc.

FATHERS AND DAUGHTERS

Linsley, Sonja Paschal. May I Have the First Dance? Linsley, Paul Adam, illus. 2005. (J). per. 19.95 net. (978-0-9766062-0-8(8)) Higher Ground Pr.

FATHERS AND DAUGHTERS—FICTION

Abela, Deborah. Mission: Hollywood. O'Connor, George, illus. 2006. (Spy Force Ser.). 240p. (J). 9.95 (978-0-689-87360-7(3)) Simon & Schuster Children's Publishing.

Abela, Deborah. Mission: Hollywood. O'Connor, George, illus. 2007. (Spy Force Ser.). 240p. (J). pap. 5.99 (*978-1-4169-3969-6(5) , Aladdin) Simon & Schuster Children's Publishing.

Alberts, Nancy Markham & Alley, R. W. Joselina Piggy Goes Out. 2007. (I'm Going to Read Ser.). (Illus.). 32p. (J). pap. 3.95 (978-1-4027-4299-6(1)) Sterling Publishing Co., Inc.

Allison, Jennifer. Gilda Joyce: Psychic Investigator. 2006. 336p. (J). (gr. 5). reprint ed. pap. 6.99 (978-0-14-240698-4(8) , Puffin) Penguin Group (USA) Inc.

Almond, David. My Dad's A Birdman. Dunbar, Polly, illus. 2008. (J). 15.99 (*978-0-7636-3667-8(3)) Candlewick Pr.

Alonso, Manuel L. Rumbo Sur. 2005. (*978-84-263-5948-3(5)) Vives, Luis Editorial (Edelvives).

Amato, Mary. The Naked Mole Rat Letters. 2007. 208p. (J). (gr. 3-7). pap. 6.95 (*978-0-8234-2098-8(1)) Holiday Hse., Inc.

Andersen, D. R. Why the Moon Changes in the Night Sky. 2005. 40.00 (*978-1-4108-4190-2(1)) Benchmark Education Co.

Andracki, Andy. Dear Mother Teresa. 2005. 57p. pap. 12.95 (978-1-4137-7682-9(5)) PublishAmerica, Inc.

Asim, Jabari. Daddy Goes to Work. Boyd, Aaron, illus. 2006. 32p. (J). (ps-3). 15.99 (978-0-316-73575-9(2)) Little Brown & Co.

Azams, Carol. Journey of the Irish Child. 2005. 171p. pap. 19.95 (978-1-4137-8933-1(1)) PublishAmerica, Inc.

Banting, Celia. I Only Said Yes So That They'd Like Me. 2006. 224p. (YA). per. 14.99 (*978-0-9786648-1-7(7)) Wighita Pr.

Baptiste, Tracey. Angel's Grace. 2005. 176p. (J). 15.95 (978-0-689-86773-6(5) , Simon & Schuster/Paula Wiseman Bks.) Simon & Schuster Children's Publishing.

Barron, T. A. The Merlin Effect. 2004. 288p. (gr. 12). mass mkt. 6.99 (978-0-441-01222-0(1) , Ace Bks.) Penguin Group (USA) Inc.

Bates, Sheree. Megan's One Wish. 2006. 124p. (YA). pap. 12.99 (978-1-4141-0555-0(X)) Pleasant Word.

Bauer, Cat. Harley's Ninth. 2007. 208p. (YA). (gr. 9). 15.99 (978-0-375-83736-4(1)); lib. bdg. 18.99 (978-0-375-93736-1(6)) Random Hse. Children's Bks. (Knopf Bks. for Young Readers).

Beth, Hodder. The Ghost of Schafer Meadows. 2007. (J). per. 7.99 (*978-0-9793963-0-4(1)) Grizzly Ridge Publishing.

Boles, Philana Marie. Little Divas. 2006. 176p. (J). 15.99 (978-0-06-073299-8(7) , Amistad); lib. bdg. 16.89 (978-0-06-073300-1(4)) HarperCollins Pubs.

Boyd, Jones Veda. Laura's Victory: End of the Second World War. 2006. 144p. (J). pap. 4.97 (978-1-59789-103-5(7)) Barbour Publishing, Inc.

Bradley, Kimberly Brubaker. The President's Daughter. 2006. 176p. (gr. 4-7). 5.50 (978-0-440-41995-2(6) , Yearling) Random Hse. Children's Bks.

Brooks, Bruce. Midnight Hour Encores. 2000. (978-0-606-19987-2(X)) Tandem Library Bks.

Brown, Petra, illus. Hush, Little Baby. 2007. 24p. (J). 8.95 (*978-1-58925-819-8(3) , tiger tales) ME Media LLC.

Brust, Beth Wagner. The Great Tulip Trade. Mattheson, Jenny, illus. 2005. (Step into Reading Ser.: Vol. 3). 48p. (J). (gr. 1-3). pap. 3.99 (978-0-375-82573-6(8) , Random Hse. Bks. for Young Readers) Random Hse. Children's Bks.

Bryant, Jennifer. Pieces of Georgia. 176p. (J). 2007. (gr. 5-9). 5.99 (*978-0-440-42055-2(5) , Yearling); 2006. (gr. 6-9). 15.95 (978-0-375-83259-8(9) , Knopf Bks. for Young Readers); 2006. (gr. 6-9). lib. bdg. 17.99 (978-0-375-93259-5(3) , Knopf Bks. for Young Readers) Random Hse. Children's Bks.

Bunting, Eve. A Perfect Father's Day. 2002. (Illus.). (J). 13.79 (978-0-7587-3390-0(9)) Book Wholesalers, Inc.

Buske, Jody. Wilderness Awakening. 2006. 108p. pap. 16.95 (978-1-4241-2685-9(1)) PublishAmerica, Inc.

Cabot, Meg. Princess on the Brink. 2008. (Princess Diaries: Vol. 8). (J). 288p. 16.99 (*978-0-06-072461-0(7)); 272p. pap. 7.99 (*978-0-06-072460-3(9) , Harper Trophy) HarperCollins Pubs.

Castellucci, Cecil. Beige. 2007. (Illus.). 304p. (YA). (gr. 9 up). 16.99 (*978-0-7636-3066-9(7)) Candlewick Pr.

Cerullo, Jillian. The Danger of the River. 2005. 36p. pap. 14.99 (978-1-4116-6988-6(6)) Lulu.com.

Cleary, Beverly. Ramona the Brave. Dockray, Tracy, illus. 2006. 176p. (J). lib. bdg. 20.00 (*978-1-4242-0411-3(9)) Fitzgerald Bks.

Cleary, Beverly. Ramona y Su Padre. 10th ed. 2003. (SPA., Illus.). 136p. (J). (gr. 3-5). 15.95 (978-84-239-9020-7(6) , EC1443) Espasa Calpe, S.A. ESP. *Dist:* Distribooks, Inc., Lectorum Pubns., Inc., Planeta Publishing Corp.

Clements, Andrew. Because Your Daddy Loves You. Alley, R. W., tr. Alley, R. W., illus. 2005. 32p. (J). (gr. k-3). 16.00 (978-0-618-00361-7(4) , Clarion Bks.) Houghton Mifflin Co. Trade & Reference Div.

Cohlene, Terri. Won't Papa Be Surprised! Dooling, Michael & Sayles, Elizabeth, illus. 2003. 32p. (J). 16.89 (978-0-688-13094-7(1)) HarperCollins Pubs.

Conway, Celeste. The Melting Season. (YA). (gr. 7). 2008. 224p. mass mkt. 6.50 (*978-0-440-23953-6(2) , Laurel Leaf); 2006. 288p. 15.95 (978-0-385-73339-7(9) , Delacorte Bks. for Young Readers); 2006. 288p. 17.99 (978-0-385-90357-8(X) , Delacorte Bks. for Young Readers) Random Hse. Children's Bks.

Cooley, Judy. I Love You More. 2007. 32p. 9.95 (*978-1-59038-758-0(9)); 2005. (Illus.). 29p. (J). 17.95 (978-1-59038-432-9(6)) Deseret Bk. Co. (Shadow Mountain).

Cooper, Ilene. The Worst Noel: A Novel. 2006. 143p. (J). (gr. 4-8). reprint ed. pap. 4.00 (978-1-4223-5411-7(3)) DIANE Publishing Co.

Corey, Shana. Milly & the Macy's Parade. 2006. 40p. (J). pap. 5.99 (978-0-439-29755-4(9)) Scholastic, Inc.

Coville, Bruce & Shakespeare, William. William Shakespeare's the Winter's Tale. Pham, LeUyen, illus. 2007. 40p. (J). (gr. 3 up). 16.99 (*978-0-8037-2709-0(7) , Dial) Penguin Group (USA) Inc.

Cullen, Lynn. I Am Rembrandt's Daughter. 2007. 320p. (YA). (gr. 7 up). 16.95 (*978-1-59990-046-9(7)) Bloomsbury Publishing.

Daddy! 2005. (J). bds. (978-0-9769910-6-9(3)) Terrific Twins LLC.

Dahl, Lesley. The Problem with Paradise. 2006. 224p. (J). (gr. 3-7). 15.95 (978-0-385-73335-9(6)); lib. bdg. 17.99 (978-0-385-90352-3(9)) Random Hse. Children's Bks. (Delacorte Bks. for Young Readers).

Dean, Zoey. Some Like It Hot. 6th ed. 2006. (A-List Ser.: No. 6). 320p. (J). (gr. 9-17). pap. 9.99 (978-0-316-01093-1(6) , Poppy) Little, Brown Bks. for Young Readers.

Douglas, Eileen. Rachel & the Upside down Heart. 2006. (J). per. 14.95 (978-0-9790041-0-0(1)) Dancing Magic Heart Bk.

Downer, Ann. Hatching Magic. 2005. 256p. (J). pap. 2.99 (978-1-4169-0535-6(9) , Aladdin) Simon & Schuster Children's Publishing.

Doyle, Brian. Hey, Dad! 2006. 112p. (J). pap. 6.95 (978-0-88899-708-1(6)) Groundwood Bks. CAN. *Dist:* Perseus Distribution.

Easley, Maryann. Warriors Daughter. 2007. 150p. pap. 19.95 (*978-1-4241-4875-2(8)) PublishAmerica, Inc.

Ellis-Herrera, Alta. Papa's little Princess. 2006. pap. 7.95 (*978-0-533-15566-8(5)) Vantage Pr., Inc.

Ephron, Delia. Frannie in Pieces. 2007. 384p. (YA). (gr. 7 up). 16.99 (*978-0-06-074716-9(1) , HarperTeen) HarperCollins Pubs.

—Frannie in Pieces. Beckerman, Chad, illus. 2007. 384p. (YA). (gr. 7 up). lib. bdg. 17.89 (*978-0-06-074717-6(X) , HarperTeen) HarperCollins Pubs.

Fedrau, Noel. A Time for Everything. 2007. (ENG.). 48p. (J). per. 24.99 (*978-1-4141-0827-8(3)) Pleasant Word.

Ferber, Brenda A. Julia's Kitchen. 2006. (Illus.). 160p. (J). 16.00 (978-0-374-39932-0(8)) Farrar, Straus & Giroux.

Ferguson, Alane. The Christopher Killer. (Forensic Mystery Ser.). 288p. (YA). (gr. 7). 2008. pap. 6.99 (978-0-14-240811-7(5) , Puffin); 2006. 15.99 (978-0-670-06008-5(9) , Viking Juvenile) Penguin Group (USA) Inc.

Finley, Martha. Elsie's Impossible Choice, Vol. 2. 2006. (Life of Faith': Elsie Dinsmore Ser.). 224p. (J). pap. 7.99 (978-1-928749-81-3(X)) Zonderkidz.

—Elsie's New Life, Vol. 3. 2006. (Life of Faith': Elsie Dinsmore Ser.). 224p. (J). pap. 7.99 (978-1-928749-82-0(8)) Zonderkidz.

—Elsie's Stolen Heart, Vol. 4. 2006. (Life of Faith': Elsie Dinsmore Ser.). 224p. (J). pap. 7.99 (978-1-928749-83-7(6)) Zonderkidz.

—Elsie's True Love, Vol. 5. 2006. (Life of Faith': Elsie Dinsmore Ser.). 224p. (J). pap. 7.99 (978-1-928749-84-4(4)) Zonderkidz.

Forman, Gayle. Sisters in Sanity. 2007. 304p. (J). lib. bdg. 17.89 (*978-0-06-088748-3(6)); (YA). (gr. 7 up). 16.99 (*978-0-06-088747-6(8)) HarperCollins Pubs. (HarperTeen).

Franklin, Emily. All You Need Is Love: The Principles of Love. 2006. 256p. (gr. 12). pap. 9.99 (978-0-451-21961-9(9) , N A L Trade) Penguin Group (USA) Inc.

French, Jackie. Hitler's Daughter. 2003. 128p. (J). 15.99 (978-0-06-008652-7(1)) HarperCollins Pubs.

Geringer & Czernecki, Stefan. Silverpoint. 1999. 160p. (J). (gr. 5 up). pap. (978-0-06-440432-7(3) , Harper Trophy) HarperCollins Pubs.

Gleitzman, Morris. Sticky Beak. l.t. ed. 2005. 200p. (J). pap. (978-0-7540-6180-9(9) , CLP 374) BBC Audio.

Goodman, Susan E. Cora Frear. Ettlinger, Doris, illus. ed. 2005. 55p. (J). lib. bdg. 15.00 (978-1-59054-901-8(5)) Fitzgerald Bks.

Grab, Daphne. Alive & Well in Prague, NY. 2008. 256p. (J). 16.99 (*978-0-06-125670-7(6)); lib. bdg. 17.89 (*978-0-06-125671-4(4)) HarperCollins Pubs. (Geringer, Laura Book).

Grambling, Lois G. Daddy Will Be There. Kessell, Walter G., illus. 1998. 24p. (J). (ps-3). 15.99 (978-0-688-14983-3(9)) HarperCollins Pubs.

Grimm. Hija del molinero. 2005. incl. cd-rom (978-84-494-2899-9(8)) Oceano Grupo Editoria, S.A.

Grimm, Jacob W. & Grimm, Wilhelm K. Doctor All-Knowing: A Folk Tale from Grimm. Boiger, Alexandra, illus. 2008. (J). (978-1-4169-1246-0(0)) Simon & Schuster Children's Publishing.

Gutman, Dan. Babe Ruth & the Ice Cream Mess. Garvin, Elaine, illus. ed. 2005. (Ready-to-Read Ser. Level 2). 32p. (J). lib. bdg. 15.00 (978-1-59054-940-7(6)) Fitzgerald Bks.

Hacker, Randi. Life As I Knew It. 2006. 240p. (J). pap. 6.99 (978-1-4169-0995-8(8) , Simon Pulse) Simon & Schuster Children's Publishing.

Haddix, Margaret Peterson. Don't You Dare Read This, Mrs. Dunphrey. 2004. 128p. (YA). mass mkt. 4.99 (978-0-689-87102-3(3) , Simon Pulse) Simon & Schuster Children's Publishing.

Hahn, Mary Downing. Witch Catcher. 2006. 240p. (J). (gr. 4-6). 16.00 (978-0-618-50457-2(5) , Clarion Bks.) Houghton Mifflin Co. Trade & Reference Div.

Hall, Barbara. The Noah Confessions. 2007. 224p. (YA). (gr. 7). lib. bdg. 18.99 (978-0-385-90346-2(4)); 15.99 (978-0-385-73328-1(3)) Random Hse. Children's Bks. (Delacorte Bks. for Young Readers).

Hamilton, Harriet. Ribbons of the Sun. 2006. (YA). pap. 8.95 (978-0-9768126-2-3(2)) Brown Barn Bks.

Hamilton, Virginia. Plain City. (Barco de Vapor). (SPA.). 176p. (YA). (gr. 5-8). 6.95 (978-84-348-4686-9(1) , LEC6861) SM Ediciones ESP. *Dist:* Continental Bk. Co., Inc.

—Plain City. 2003. 208p. (J). (gr. 4-7). pap. 5.99 (978-0-590-47365-1(4) , Scholastic Paperbacks) Scholastic, Inc.

Harmel, Kristin. When You Wish. 2008. 288p. (J). (*978-0-385-73475-2(1) , Delacorte Pr.) Dell Publishing.

Harper, Jo & Harper, Josephine. Prairie Dog Pioneers. Spearing, Craig, illus. 48p. (J). (ps-3). 2000. pap. 8.95 (978-1-890515-23-2(X)); 1998. (SPA.). 16.95 (978-1-890515-10-2(8)) Turtle Bks.

Harper, Jo & Harper, Josephine L. Prairie Dog Pioneers. Spearing, Craig, illus. 2000. 44p. (J). (ps-3). lib. bdg. 17.60 (978-0-613-32966-8(X)) Tandem Library Bks.

Henkes, Kevin. Protecting Marie. 2007. 208p. (J). pap. 5.99 (*978-0-06-128876-0(4) , Harper Trophy) HarperCollins Pubs.

Hermes, Patricia. Calling Me Home. (J). 1999. 448p. pap. 3.99 (978-0-380-79100-2(5) , Harper Trophy); 1998. 144p. (gr. 4-7). 15.00 (978-0-380-97451-1(7)) HarperCollins Pubs.

—Calling Me Home. 1999. (Illus.). (J). (978-0-606-17961-4(5)) Tandem Library Bks.

Herrick, Steven. The Wolf. 2007. 214p. (YA). (gr. 7 up). 17.95 (978-1-932425-75-8(6) , Front Street) Boyds Mills Pr.

Hesse, Karen. Sable. Sewall, Marcia, illus. rev. ed. 1998. 96p. (J). (gr. 4 up). pap. 7.95 (978-0-8050-5772-0(2) , Holt, Henry & Co. Bks. For Young Readers) Holt, Henry & Co.

—Sable. 1998. (YA). (gr. 4 up). (978-0-606-13755-3(6)) Tandem Library Bks.

E F G

—Sable. Sewall, Marcia, illus. 1998. 81p. (J). (ps-k). lib. bdg. 16.40 (978-0-613-08689-9(9)) Tandem Library Bks.

Hodgson, Miriam. Love from Dad: Stories about Fathers & Daughters. 160p. (J). pap. 8.99 (978-0-7497-4330-7(1)) Egmont Bks., Ltd. GBR. *Dist:* Trafalgar Square Publishing.

Holmes, Sarah. Letters from Rapunzel. 2007. 192p. (J). (gr. 5-8). 15.99 (978-0-06-078073-9(8)); lib. bdg. 16.89 (978-0-06-078074-6(6)) HarperCollins Pubs.

Hurst, Rich. The Goodnight Thing. 2006. 10.99 (*978-0-9763770-1-6(2)) Red Door Pr.

If You're So Smart, How Come You Can't Spell Mississippi? 2007. (J). 16.99 (*978-1-60336-448-5(X)) Mainstream Connections, Inc.

Inches, Alison. I Love My Papi! Aikins, Dave, illus. 2004. 24p. (J). (ps-1). lib. bdg. 12.10 (978-1-4176-2901-5(0)) Tandem Library Bks.

Irwin, Inez. Maida's Little Shop. 2006. 41.99 (*978-1-4219-7069-1(4)) IndyPublish.com.

Johnston, Tony. The Spoon in the Bathroom Wall. 2006. (Illus.). 144p. (J). pap. 5.95 (978-0-15-205625-4(4) , Harcourt Paperbacks) Harcourt Children's Bks.

Johnston, Tony & Johnston, Tony. The Spoon in the Bathroom Wall. 2005. 144p. (J). (ps-7). 16.00 (978-0-15-205292-8(5)) Harcourt Trade Pubs.

Jones, Christianne C. Emma's New Look. 2007. (Illus.). 24p. (J). (*978-1-4048-1230-7(X)) Picture Window Bks.

—Emma's New Look. Yilmaz, Necdet, illus. 2006. (Read It! Readers Ser.). 32p. (J). (gr. 1-2). 19.93 (*978-1-4048-3138-4(X)) Picture Window Bks.

Kaplow, Julie B. & Pincus, Donna. Samantha Jane's Missing Smile: A Story about Coping with the Loss of a Parent. Spiegel, Beth, illus. 2007. 32p. (J). (ps-3). 14.95 (*978-1-59147-808-9(1)); pap. 8.95 (*978-1-59147-809-6(X)) American Psychological Assn. (Magination Pr.).

Karwoski, Gail Langer. Julie the Rockhound. Downey, Lisa, illus. 2007. 32p. (J). (gr. k-4). 15.95 (978-0-9764943-7-9(X)) Sylvan Dell Pubng.

Kaslik, Ibi. Skinny. 2006. (YA). 256p. 16.95 (978-0-8027-9608-0(7)); viii, 244p. (*978-1-4287-0474-9(4)) Walker & Co.

Kerr, M. E. Someone Like Summer. 2007. 272p. (J). lib. bdg. 17.89 (*978-0-06-114100-3(3)); (YA). (gr. 7 up). 16.99 (*978-0-06-114099-0(6)) HarperCollins Pubs. (HarperTeen).

Kidd, Ronald. Monkey Town: The Summer of the Scopes Trial. 2006. (Illus.). 272p. (YA). 16.99 (978-1-4169-0572-1(3)) Simon & Schuster Children's Publishing.

—Monkey Town, the Summer of the Scopes Trial. l.t. ed. 2006. 320p. (YA). 22.95 (978-0-7862-9080-2(3)) Thorndike Pr.

Kimmel, Elizabeth Cody. The Top Job. Neubecker, Robert, illus. 2007. 32p. (J). (gr. 1-4). 16.99 (978-0-525-47789-1(6) , Dutton Juvenile) Penguin Group (USA) Inc.

Komaiko, Leah. Just My Dad & Me. Greene, Jeffrey, illus. 1999. (Trophy Picture Bk.). 32p. (J). (ps-2). pap. 5.95 (978-0-06-443562-8(8) , Harper Trophy) HarperCollins Pubs.

—Just My Dad & Me. 1999. (J). (978-0-606-16691-1(2)); lib. bdg. 14.10 (978-0-613-18259-1(6)) Tandem Library Bks.

Krisher, Trudy B. Kinship. 1999. (J). (978-0-606-16170-1(8)) Tandem Library Bks.

Lakin, Patricia. Hurricane! Lubach, Vanessa, illus. 2000. (Our World Ser.). 32p. (gr. k-4). lib. bdg. (978-0-7613-1616-9(7) , Millbrook Pr.) Lerner Publishing Group.

Lamb, Charles & Lamb, Mary. Tales from Shakespeare: "King Lear" Strang, Kay, ed. Andrews, Gary, illus. rev. ed. 2005. 40p. pap. 4.95 (978-0-9542905-6-6(9)) Capercaillie Bks., Ltd GBR. *Dist:* Wilson & Assocs.

Lavender, William. Aftershocks. 2006. (Illus.). 352p. (YA). 17.00 (978-0-15-205882-1(6)) Harcourt Children's Bks.

L'Engle, Madeleine. A Wrinkle in Time. 2007. 224p. (J). 6.99 (978-0-312-36755-8(4)); pap. 6.99 (978-0-312-36754-1(6)) Square Fish.

Leonard, Marcia. The Tin Can Man. Handelman, Dorothy, photos by. 1998. (Real Kids Readers Ser.: 1). (Illus.). 32p. (J). (gr. k-1). pap. 4.99 (978-0-7613-2037-1(7) , Millbrook Pr.) Lerner Publishing Group.

Lethcoe, Jason. Amazing Adventures from Zoom's Academy: The Capture of the Crimson Cape. 2006. (Illus.). 144p. (J). pap. 12.95 (978-0-345-48356-0(1) , Ballantine Bks.) Random House Publishing Group.

Levinson, Robin. Reyna & the Jade Star. 2006. (Illus.). (J). per. 12.00 (978-0-9773673-1-3(2)) Gali Girls, Inc.

Levy, Elizabeth. Tackling Dad. 2005. 144p. (J). 16.89 (978-0-06-000050-9(3)); 15.99 (978-0-06-000051-6(1)) HarperCollins Pubs.

Linamen, Karen Scalf. Princess Madison & the Whispering Woods. 2006. (Princess Madison Trilogy Ser.). (Illus.). 32p. 12.99 (978-0-8007-1842-8(9)) Revell.

Lollino, Jessica. Little Lily Mays & the Daddy Dilemma. Kendrick-TaZiyah, Brandi, illus. 2006. (Little Lily Mays Ser.: vol. 1). 32p. (J). per. 20.00 (978-0-9712383-1-2(6)) Culture Connection, The.

Long, Sharon J. Let Me be Me. 2004. 137p. pap. 8.95 (978-1-4116-1734-6(7)) Lulu.com.

Lowenstein, Sallie Claire. Waiting for Eugene. 2006. (Illus.). 201p. (J). (*978-1-4156-6166-6(9)) Book Wholesalers, Inc.

Lucado, Max. The Way Home: A Princess Story. Elwell, Tristan, illus. 2005. 48p. (J). 16.99 (978-1-4003-0554-4(3)) Nelson, Thomas Inc.

Lupica, Mike. Miracle on 49th Street. 256p. (gr. 5). 2007. (J). pap. 7.99 (*978-0-14-240942-8(1) , Puffin); 2006. (YA). 17.99 (978-0-399-24488-9(3) , Philomel) Penguin Group (USA) Inc.

Ly, Many. Home Is East. 2007. 304p. (YA). (gr. 7-11). mass mkt. 6.50 (*978-0-440-23900-0(1) , Laurel Leaf) Random Hse. Children's Bks.

Maccarone, Grace. I Shop with My Daddy. Brunkus, Denise, illus. 2004. 32p. (J). lib. bdg. 15.00 (978-1-59054-659-8(8)) Fitzgerald Bks.

—I Shop with My Daddy. Brunkus, Denise, illus. 1998. (Hello Reader! Ser.). 32p. (J). (ps-1). pap. 3.99 (978-0-590-50196-5(8)) Scholastic, Inc.

—I Shop with My Daddy. 1998. (Hello Reader! Ser.). (J). 10.79 (978-0-606-13510-8(3)) Tandem Library Bks.

Mackall, Dandi Daley. Eva Underground. 2006. (Illus.). 256p. (YA). 17.00 (978-0-15-205462-5(6)) Harcourt Trade Pubs.

Mahy, Margaret. The Catalogue of the Universe. Hopes, illus. 2002. 192p. (YA). pap. 7.99 (978-0-689-85353-1(X) , Simon Pulse) Simon & Schuster Children's Publishing.

Marchetta, Melina. Looking for Alibrandi. 2006. 320p. (YA). (gr. 7). lib. bdg. 17.99 (978-0-375-93694-4(7)); reprint ed. pap. 8.95 (978-0-375-83694-7(2)) Random Hse. Children's Bks. (Knopf Bks. for Young Readers).

Marsh, Carole. The Secret of Skullcracker Swamp. 2006. 128p. (gr. 3-5). pap. 5.99 (*978-0-635-06234-5(8)); (gr. 7-14). 14.95 (*978-0-635-06238-3(0)) Gallopade International.

Mayer, Mercer. Shibumi & the Kitemaker. Mayer, Mercer, illus. 2005. (Illus.). 48p. (J). pap. 5.95 (978-0-7614-5145-7(5)) Cavendish, Marshall Corp.

—Shibumi & the Kitemaker. 1999. (Accelerated Reader Bks.). (Illus.). 48p. (YA). (ps-3). 18.95 (978-0-7614-5054-2(8) , Cavendish Children's Bks.) Cavendish, Marshall Corp.

—Shibumi & the Kitemaker. 2003. (gr. k-3). lib. bdg. 14.10 (978-0-613-87253-9(3)) Tandem Library Bks.

Mazer, Norma Fox. Has Anyone Seen My Emily Greene? Davenier, Christine, illus. 2007. (J). (ps-2). 32p. 15.99 (*978-0-7636-1384-6(3)); (*978-1-4287-4761-6(3)) Candlewick Pr.

McClintock, Barbara. The Fantastic Drawings of Danielle. 2004. (Illus.). 32p. (J). (gr. k-3). pap. 5.95 (978-0-618-43230-1(2)) Houghton Mifflin Co. Trade & Reference Div.

McDaniel, Lurlene. Until Angels Close My Eyes. 1998. (Angels Trilogy: No. 3). 256p. (YA). (gr. 7-12). pap. 5.50 (978-0-553-57115-8(X) , Laurel Leaf) Random Hse. Children's Bks.

—Until Angels Close My Eyes. 1998. (Angels Trilogy: No. 3). (978-0-606-13884-0(6)) Tandem Library Bks.

Mechling, Lauren & Moser, Laura. All Q, No A: More Tales of a 10th-Grade Social Climber. 2006. 288p. (YA). (gr. 7). pap. 7.99 (978-0-618-66378-1(9) , Graphia) Houghton Mifflin Co. Trade & Reference Div.

Mendes, Valerie. Coming of Age. 2004. 224p. (YA). pap. 8.99 (978-0-689-83772-2(0)) Simon & Schuster, Ltd. GBR. *Dist:* Independent Pubs. Group.

Meyer, Stephenie. New Moon. 2006. (Twilight Saga Ser.). 608p. (J). (gr. 7 up). 18.99 (978-0-316-16019-3(9) , Tingley, Megan Bks.) Little, Brown Bks. for Young Readers.

Miller, Mitzi & Millner, Denene. Hotlanta #1. 2008. 288p. (J). 8.99 (*978-0-545-00308-7(3) , Scholastic Paperbacks) Scholastic, Inc.

Modiano, Patrick. Catherine Certitude. (FRE.). pap. 17.95 (978-2-07-051608-7(3)) Gallimard, Editions FRA. *Dist:* Distribooks, Inc.

—Catherine Certitude. Rodarmor, William, tr. from FRE. Sempe, Jean-Jacques, illus. 2001. 58p. (J). (gr. 4 up). reprint ed. 17.95 (978-0-87923-959-6(X)) Godine, David R. Pub.

Moore, Beth. My Child, My Princess: A Parable about the King for Little Girls of All Ages. Warren, Beverly, illus. 2007. 32p. pap. 9.99 (978-0-8054-4455-1(6)) B&H Publishing Grp.

Moranville, Sharelle Byars. Over the River. rev. ed. 2002. 240p. (J). (gr. 4-9). 16.95 (978-0-8050-7049-1(4) , Holt, Henry & Co. Bks. For Young Readers) Holt, Henry & Co.

—Over the River. 2004. 240p. (gr. 5). 5.99 (978-0-440-41977-8(8) , Yearling) Random Hse. Children's Bks.

Morgan, Melissa J. Natalie's Secret, No. 1. 2005. (Camp Confidential Ser.). 160p. (J). (gr. 4-7). mass mkt. 4.99 (978-0-448-43737-8(6) , Grosset & Dunlap) Penguin Group (USA) Inc.

Moss, Marissa. Amelia's Longest, Biggest, Most-Fights-Ever Family Reunion. Moss, Marissa, illus. 2006. (Amelia's Notebooks). (Illus.). 80p. (J). 9.95 (978-0-689-87447-5(2) , Simon & Schuster Children's Publishing) Simon & Schuster Children's Publishing.

Munsil, Janet. Donde Hay Humo. Martchenko, Michael, illus. 2003. (Hablemos Ser.). (SPA.). 24p. (J). (gr. k up). pap. 5.95 (978-1-55037-968-6(2)) Annick Pr., Ltd. CAN. *Dist:* Firefly Bks., Ltd.

Ochiltree, Dianne. It's a Firefly Night. Snyder, Betsy, illus. 2008. (J). (*978-1-55971-991-9(5) , NorthWord Bks. for Young Readers) T&N Children's Publishing.

Orr, Wendy. Nim's Island. Millard, Kerry, illus. (gr. 3-7). 2008. 144p. 5.50 (*978-0-385-73606-0(1)); 2002. 128p. 5.50 (978-0-440-41868-9(2)) Random Hse. Children's Bks. (Yearling).

—Nim's Island. 2002. (gr. 3-6). lib. bdg. 13.00 (978-0-613-46203-7(3)) Tandem Library Bks.

Paradise, Susan. Snow Princess. 2005. (Illus.). 32p. (J). (ps-3). 16.95 (978-1-932425-31-4(4) , Lemniscaat) Boyds Mills Pr.

Paratore, Coleen Murtagh. The Wedding Planner's Daughter. 2006. (Wedding Planner's Daughter Ser.). 208p. (J). reprint ed. pap. 5.99 (978-1-4169-1854-7(X) , Aladdin) Simon & Schuster Children's Publishing.

Pearce, Jonathan. Nobody's Fault: Surprises from the Earth & the Heart. 2006. 234p. (YA). per. (978-0-9765479-3-8(7)) Balona Bks.

Peirce-Bale, Mary. Twinkle, Twinkle Little Girl. 2005. (J). 6.95 (978-0-9743869-9-7(5)) Mother's Hse. Publishing.

Pérez, Alfredo. Sueno de Novela. (SPA.). (J). 8.95 (978-958-04-6870-7(2)) Norma S.A. COL. *Dist:* Distribuidora Norma, Inc.

Perez-Mercado, Mary Margaret. Splat! 2000. (Rookie Reader Espanol Ser.). (Illus.). 24p. (J). (gr. k-2). pap. 4.95 (978-0-516-26543-8(1) , Children's Pr.) Scholastic Library Publishing.

—Splat! Torrey, Richard L., illus. 1999. (Rookie Readers Ser.). 24p. (J). (gr. k-1). 19.50 (978-0-516-21615-7(5) , Children's Pr.) Scholastic Library Publishing.

—Splat! 1999. (gr. k-3). lib. bdg. 12.95 (978-0-613-54858-8(2)) Tandem Library Bks.

Perry, R. W. Kelly Mccabe in Slow Boat to Terror. 2003. 160p. (J). (gr. 3-6). pap. 11.95 (978-0-9745522-0-0(8)) Greenleaf Book Group Pr.

Plummer, Louise. Finding Daddy. 2007. 176p. (YA). (gr. 7). 15.99 (978-0-385-73092-1(6) , Delacorte Bks. for Young Readers) Random Hse. Children's Bks.

Porter, Pamela. The Crazy Man. 2006. 176p. pap. 6.95 (978-0-88899-695-4(0)) Groundwood Bks. CAN. *Dist:* Perseus Distribution.

Poryes, Michael & Sherman, Susan. Showtime! 2005. (That's So Raven Ser.: Vol. 9). (Illus.). 134p. (J). (*978-1-4156-1643-7(4)) Disney Pr.

Powers, Nacole. Push Daddy Push. 2006. (ENG.). 36p. per. 15.95 (*978-1-4259-6963-9(1)) AuthorHouse.

Rahlens, Holly-Jane. Prince William, Maximilian Minsky, & Me. (YA). (gr. 7-11). 2007. 320p. pap. 7.99 (*978-0-7636-3299-1(6)); 2005. 160p. 16.99 (978-0-7636-2704-1(6)) Candlewick Pr.

Ransom, Candice F. Finding Day's Bottom. 2006. 168p. (J). (gr. 4-6). 15.95 (978-1-57505-933-4(9) , Carolrhoda Bks.) Lerner Publishing Group.

Rinaldi, Ann. Mutiny's Daughter. 2005. 224p. (J). (ps-7). pap. 5.99 (978-0-06-441010-6(2) , Harper Trophy) HarperCollins Pubs.

Rosner, Hannah. The Ambulance Club. 2005. 87p. pap. 14.95 (978-1-4137-7492-4(X)) PublishAmerica, Inc.

Russon, Penni. Undine. 2006. (Illus.). 336p. (J). 16.99 (978-0-06-079389-0(9)); lib. bdg. 17.89 (978-0-06-079390-6(2)) HarperCollins Pubs.

Salisbury, Linda G. No Sisters Sisters Club: A Bailey Fish Adventure. Grotke, Christopher A., illus. 2005. 188p. (J). per. 8.95 (978-1-881539-40-7(7)) Tabby Hse. Bks.

Sandoval, Lynda. Who's Your Daddy? 2004. 318p. (YA). (gr. 7). lib. bdg. 15.60 (978-1-4176-4527-5(X)) Tandem Library Bks.

Seelen, Christopher. Daddy Is That the Best You Got? Moen, Tyler, illus. 2005. 36p. (J). 5.97 (978-0-9776385-0-5(2)) JoBen Bks., LLC.

Seward, Angela. Goodnight, Daddy. Ferreiro, Donna, illus. 48p. (J). (ps-3). 2003. 14.95 (978-1-885356-71-0(4)); 2000. pap. 7.95 (978-1-885356-72-7(2)) Morning Glory Pr., Inc.

Siegel, Elizabeth. Taj. Toye, Derek, illus. 2007. 48p. (J). lib. bdg. 23.08 (*978-1-4242-1632-1(X)) Fitzgerald Bks.

Slater, David Michael. Flour Girl: A Recipe for Disaster. Brooks, S. G., illus. 2007. (Missy Swiss & More Ser.). 32p. (J). (ps-4). lib. bdg. 27.07 (*978-1-60270-009-3(5) , Looking Glass Library) Magic Wagon.

Smith, Alexander McCall. The Five Lost Aunts of Harriet Bean. Rankin, Laura, illus. 2006. 96p. (J). 9.95 (978-1-58234-975-6(4) , Bloomsbury Children) Bloomsbury Publishing.

Smith, Jennifer E. The Comeback Season. 2008. 256p. (YA). 15.99 (*978-1-4169-3847-7(8) , Simon & Schuster Children's Publishing) Simon & Schuster Children's Publishing.

Sones, Sonya. One of Those Hideous Books Where the Mother Dies. 272p. (YA). 2004. (Illus.). 16.95 (978-0-689-85820-8(5)); 2005. (gr. 7-12). reprint ed. pap. 6.99 (978-1-4169-0788-6(2) , Simon Pulse) Simon & Schuster Children's Publishing.

Spooner, Michael. Last Child. rev. ed. 2005. 240p. (J). (gr. 3-7). 16.95 (978-0-8050-7739-1(1) , Holt, Henry & Co. Bks. For Young Readers) Holt, Henry & Co.

Stanton, Karen. Papi's Gift. Moreno, Rene King, illus. 2007. 32p. (J). (gr. k-3). 16.95 (978-1-59078-422-8(7)) Boyds Mills Pr.

Summers, Gillian. Into the Wildewood. 2008. 312p. (J). pap. 9.95 (*978-0-7387-1332-8(5) , Flux) Llewellyn Pubns.

—The Tree Shepherd's Daughter: The Faire Folk Trilogy. 2007. 336p. (J). (gr. 4-7). pap. 9.95 (*978-0-7387-1081-5(4) , Flux) Llewellyn Pubns.

Tal, Eve. Double Crossing: A Jewish Immigration Story. 2005. 216p. (gr. 3-7). 16.95 (978-0-938317-94-4(6)) Cinco Puntos Pr.

Taylor, Mary Ann. Traitors: A Gander's Cove Mystery. Casteel, Kay, illus. 2006. (J). mass mkt. 5.99 (*978-0-9753367-9-3(7)) Onstage Publishing, LLC.

Tiffany, Grace. Ariel. 2005. 240p. (J). 16.99 (978-0-06-075327-6(7)); lib. bdg. 17.89 (978-0-06-075328-3(5)) HarperCollins Pubs.

Verrillo, Erica F. Elissa's Quest. 2007. (Phoenix Rising Trilogy Ser.). 352p. (J). (gr. 4-7). 16.99 (978-0-375-83946-7(1)); lib. bdg. 19.99 (978-0-375-93946-4(6)) Random Hse. Children's Bks. (Random Hse. Bks. for Young Readers).

—Elissa's Quest. 2007. (J). pap. (978-0-375-83947-4(X)) Random Hse., Inc.

Vision, David & Vision, Mutiya Sahar, illus. Daddy Loves His Baby Girl. 2005. 32p. (J). 16.00 (978-0-9659538-7-0(4)) Soul Vision Works Publishing.

Waggoner, Sandra. Maggie's Treasure. 2005. (Gatlin Fields Ser.). 107p. (J). per. 6.99 (978-0-9766823-0-1(3)) Sable Creek Pr. LLC.

Watts, Leander. Stonecutter. 2006. 182p. (J). (gr. 5-9). reprint ed. pap. 7.99 (978-0-618-60577-4(0) , Graphia) Houghton Mifflin Co. Trade & Reference Div.

Weatherly, Lee. Kat Got Your Tongue. 2007. 208p. (YA). (gr. 7-9). lib. bdg. 18.99 (978-0-385-75122-3(2)); 15.99 (978-0-385-75117-9(6)) Random Hse. Children's Bks. (Fickling, David Bks.).

Wemmlinger, Raymond. Booth's Daughter. 2007. 210p. (YA). (gr. 7 up). 17.95 (978-1-932425-86-4(1) , Front Street) Boyds Mills Pr.

West, Tracy. Dreamer: Inspired by a True Story. 2005. (Scholastic Reader Ser.). (Illus.). 32p. (J). (ps-3). pap. 3.99 (978-0-439-77495-6(0)) Scholastic, Inc.

Whelan, Gloria. Parade of Shadows. 2007. 304p. (J). (gr. 5 up). 15.99 (*978-0-06-089028-5(2)); lib. bdg. 16.89 (*978-0-06-089029-2(0)) HarperCollins Pubs.

Willems, Mo. Knuffle Bunny Too: A Case of Mistaken Identity. Willems, Mo, illus. rev. ed. 2007. (Illus.). 48p. (J). (ps-1). 16.99 (*978-1-4231-0299-1(1)) Hyperion Pr.

Williams, Laura E. Executioner's Daughter. 2007. 144p. (YA). pap. 6.95 (*978-0-8050-8186-2(0) , Holt, Henry & Co. Bks. For Young Readers) Holt, Henry & Co.

Wilson, Heather Gemmen. Lydia Barnes & the Blood Diamond Treasure. 2007. (J). (*978-0-89827-350-2(1)) Wesleyan Publishing Hse.

Wilson, Jacqueline & Sharratt, Nick. Candyfloss. 2007. (Illus.). 352p. (J). (gr. 4-7). 14.95 (*978-1-59643-241-3(1)) Roaring Brook Pr.

Woodson, Jacqueline. I Hadn't Meant to Tell You This. 2006. (YA). 176p. (gr. 4). 17.99 (978-0-399-24499-5(9) , Putnam Juvenile); 128p. (gr. 7). pap. 5.99 (978-0-14-240555-0(8) , Puffin) Penguin Group (USA) Inc.

Woodworth, Chris. Georgie's Moon. 2006. 176p. (J). 16.00 (978-0-374-33306-5(8)) Farrar, Straus & Giroux.

Yolen, Jane. Owl Moon: 20th Anniversary Edition. Schoenherr, John, illus. 2007. 40p. (J). (ps). 16.99 (*978-0-399-24799-6(8) , Philomel) Penguin Group (USA) Inc.

FATHERS AND SONS

L'Heureux, Christine & Brignaud, Pierre. Caillou: Just Like Daddy. rev. ed. 2006. (Hand in Hand Ser.). (Illus.). 24p. (J). pap. 5.95 (*978-2-89450-587-8(6)) Chouette Publishing CAN. *Dist:* Independent Pubs. Group.

Worthington, Joe. The Mannings: Football's Famous Family. 2005. (High Five Reading Ser.). (J). (Illus.). 64p. (gr. 4-5). lib. bdg. incl. audio (978-0-7368-5751-2(6)); (978-0-7368-5731-4(1)); (978-0-7368-5741-3(9)) Capstone Pr., Inc.

FATHERS AND SONS—FICTION

Abdullah, Patricia Noor. Saving Daddy. Cabri, Alexandra, illus. 2006. 32p. (J). (gr. 2-5). 17.95 (*978-1-933193-16-8(6)) EECI, Inc.

Alphin, Elaine Marie. Picture Perfect. 2003. (Illus.). 252p. (J). (gr. 7 up). 15.95 (978-0-8225-0535-8(5)) Lerner Publishing Group.

Appleton, Victor. Into the Abyss. 2007. (Tom Swift, Young Inventor Ser.). 160p. (J). (gr. 4-7). 27.07 (*978-1-59961-350-5(6)) Spotlight.

Baillie, Allan. Treasure Hunters. 2004. 216p. pap. 6.99 (978-0-14-330007-6(5) , Penguin Global) Penguin Group (USA) Inc.

Banks, Kate. The Night Worker. Hallensleben, Georg, illus. 2007. 40p. (J). pap. 6.95 (978-0-374-40000-2(8) , Farrar, Straus & Giroux (BYR)) Farrar, Straus & Giroux.

Bee, William. Whatever. 2005. (Illus.). 40p. (J). (gr. k-1). 12.99 (978-0-7636-2886-4(7)) Candlewick Pr.

—Whatever: Mini Edition. Bee, William, illus. 2007. (Illus.). 32p. (J). (gr. k). 5.99 (978-0-7636-3431-5(X)) Candlewick Pr.

Bergstrom, Gunilla. Good Night, Alfie Atkins. Dyssegaard, Elisabeth Kallick, tr. from SWE. 2005. (Illus.). 32p. (J). 15.00 (978-91-29-66154-5(4)) R & S Bks. SWE. *Dist:* Macmillan.

Beveridge, Cathy. One on One. 2005. 224p. pap. 7.95 (978-1-894345-80-4(0)) Thistledown Pr., Ltd. CAN. *Dist:* Literary Pr. Group of Canada.

Blackaby, Susan. De Pesca. Haugen, Ryan, illus. 2006. (Read-It! Readers en Espanol Ser.).Tr. of Fishing Trip. (SPA.). 32p. (J). (ps-3). 19.95 (978-1-4048-1684-8(4)) Picture Window Bks.

Bodett, Tom. Norman Tuttle on the Last Frontier. 2006. 208p. (YA). (gr. 7). mass mkt. 5.99 (978-0-553-49493-8(7) , Laurel Leaf) Random Hse. Children's Bks.

Bolam, Emily, illus. Father's Day Is Coming. 2007. (I'm Going to Read Ser.: No. 2). 32p. (J). pap. 3.95 (978-1-4027-4247-7(9)) Sterling Publishing Co., Inc.

Bondoux, Anne-Laure. The Killer's Tears. Maudet, Y., tr. 176p. (YA). (gr. 7). 2007. pap. 8.99 (978-0-385-73384-7(4)); 2006. (Illus.). 15.95 (978-0-385-73293-2(7)); 2006. (Illus.). lib. bdg. 17.99 (978-0-385-90314-1(6)) Random Hse. Children's Bks. (Delacorte Bks. for Young Readers).

Bonnell, Kris. Too Big to Play. 2006. (J). 3.95 (*978-1-933727-35-6(7)) Reading Reading Bks., LLC.

Born to be a Tiger. 2004. (J). per. 18.50 net. (978-0-615-12596-1(4)) Little Band Man Co., LLC, The.

Bowman, Crystal. Jake Goes Fishing. Maizel, Karen, illus. 2007. (I Can Read!). 32p. (J). pap. 3.99 (*978-0-310-71454-5(0)) Zonderkidz.

Bradford, William. Jeremy Mcbright Was Afraid of the Night. 2006. (Illus.). 36p. (J). lib. bdg. 13.95 (978-0-9672585-2-2(9)) CyPress Pubns.

Bradman, Tony, compiled by. My Dad's a Punk: 12 Stories about Boys & Their Fathers. 2006. 240p. (J). (gr. 5-9). pap. 7.95 (978-0-7534-5870-9(5) , Kingfisher) Houghton Mifflin Co. Trade & Reference Div.

Breault, Christie Merriman. Logan West, Printer's Devil. Archambault, Matthew, illus. 2006. 142p. (J). pap. (978-1-59336-762-6(7)) Mondo Publishing.

Brooke, Susan Rich, adapted by. Finding Nemo. 2003. (Interactive Play-A-Sound Ser.). (Illus.). (J). (978-0-7853-8916-3(4)); 24p. 15.98 (978-0-7853-8420-5(0) , 7184400) Publications International, Ltd.

Brown, Marc. Arthur Jumps into Fall. 2006. (Illus.). 24p. (J). (ps-1). mass mkt. 3.99 (978-0-316-05775-2(4)) Little Brown & Co.

Buckley-Archer, Linda. Gideon the Cutpurse. 2006. (Gideon Trilogy Ser.). 416p. (J). (gr. 5 up). 17.95 (978-1-4169-1525-6(7)) Simon & Schuster Children's Publishing.

Bunting, Eve. My Red Balloon. Life, Kay, illus. 2005. 32p. (J). 15.95 (978-1-59078-263-7(1)) Boyds Mills Pr.

—Some Frog! Medlock, Scott, illus. 2002. 48p. (J). (gr. 1-4). pap. 6.00 (978-0-15-216384-6(0) , Voyager Bks./Libros Viajeros) Harcourt Children's Bks.

—Some Frog! 2002. (gr. 3-6). lib. bdg. 14.15 (978-0-613-53865-7(X)) Tandem Library Bks.

Byars, Betsy. Disappearing Acts. 2006. (Herculeah Jones Mystery Ser.). 144p. (J). (gr. 3). pap. 5.99 (978-0-14-240566-6(3) , Puffin) Penguin Group (USA) Inc.

Candido, Jeane Heimberger. Levi: The Smartest Boy in the World. 2nd rev. ed. 2007. 44p. (J). 10.99 (978-1-59092-222-4(0)) Windstorm Creative.

Candlewick Press Staff. Ghmily Ams Ed. 2002. (J). bds. 12.99 (978-0-7636-1820-9(9)) Candlewick Pr.

Chaconas, Dori. Pennies in a Jar. Lewin, Ted, illus. 2007. 32p. (J). (ps-3). 16.95 (***978-1-56145-422-8(2)*** , Peachtree Junior) Peachtree Pubs., Ltd.

Chalifour, Francis. After. 2005. 144p. (J). (gr. 7). pap. 7.95 (978-0-88776-705-0(2)) Tundra Bks., Inc./Livres Toundra, Inc. CAN. *Dist:* Random Hse., Inc.

Chan, Gillian. The Turning. 2005. (Illus.). 200p. (YA). (gr. 7 up). (978-1-55337-576-0(9)); (978-1-55337-575-3(0)) Kids Can Pr., Ltd.

Chbosky, Stacy. Who Owns the Sun? Chbosky, Stacy, illus. 2002. (Illus.). 32p. (J). (gr. 4-7). per. 19.95 (978-0-933849-82-2(6)) Landmark Editions, Inc.

Clements, Andrew. Head of the Class: Frindle; the Landry News; the Janitor's Boy. Selznick, Brian, illus. 2007. 416p. (J). 17.99 (***978-1-4169-4974-9(7)*** , Aladdin) Simon & Schuster Children's Publishing.

Cole, Gina, illus. Adapt. 2005. 40p. (J). 17.00 (978-0-9659538-3-2(1)) Soul Vision Works Publishing.

Comora, Madeleine. Rembrandt & Titus: Father & Son. Locker, Thomas, illus. 2005. 32p. (J). (gr. 2-5). 17.95 (978-1-55591-490-5(X)) Fulcrum Publishing.

Cook, Stephen. Day Out with Daddy. 2006. (Illus.). 32p. (J). 17.85 (978-0-8027-8060-7(1)); 16.95 (978-0-8027-8059-1(8)) Walker & Co.

Coulton, Mia. Danny & Dad Go Shopping. Coulton, Mia, photos by. 2003. (J). 4.95 (978-0-9720295-4-4(0)) Maryruth Bks., Inc.

Coy, John. Crackback. (J). 2007. 224p. pap. 6.99 (***978-0-439-69734-7(4)*** , Scholastic Paperbacks); 2005. 208p. (gr. 7 up). pap. 16.99 (978-0-439-69733-0(6) , Scholastic Pr.) Scholastic, Inc.

Creech, Sharon. Fishing in the Air. Raschka, Chris, illus. 2003. pap. 9.95 incl. audio (978-1-59112-223-4(6)) Live Oak Media.

—Replay. 240p. (J). (gr. 3-7). 2007. pap. 5.99 (978-0-06-054021-0(4) , Harper Trophy); 2005. 15.99 (978-0-06-054019-7(2) , Cotler, Joanna Books); 2005. lib. bdg. 16.89 (978-0-06-054020-3(6) , Cotler, Joanna Books) HarperCollins Pubs.

Crow, E. J. The Eye Pocket: The Fantastic Society of Peculiar Adventurers. 2006. (Illus.). 48p. (J). pap. 7.95 (978-1-933255-17-0(X)) DNA Pr.

Crutcher, Chris. Ironman. 2004. 280p. (YA). (gr. 10). lib. bdg. 14.04 (978-0-606-32640-7(5)) Tandem Library Bks.

Cumberland, Marcie Hoye. The Tree at the Top of the Hill. 2006. 80p. pap. 12.95 (978-1-60145-019-7(2)) Booklocker.com, Inc.

Cummings, John Michael. The Night I Freed John Brown. 2008. 276p. (YA). (gr. 6-9). 17.99 (***978-0-399-25054-5(9)*** , Philomel) Penguin Group (USA) Inc.

Daddy Is a Doodlebug Doodle Pad. 2000. (J). (978-0-06-029068-9(4)) HarperCollins Pubs.

Dahl, Roald. Danny el Campeon del Mundo. Blake, Quentin, illus. (SPA.). 195p. (J). (gr. 5-8). pap. 9.95 (978-968-19-1013-6(3)) Santillana USA Publishing Co., Inc.

Danegu, Danielle. Reader. Cecil, Lauren, ed. 2007. (Firehouse Dog Ser.). 32p. (J). pap. 3.99 (978-0-439-89643-6(6)) Scholastic, Inc.

Daudet, Alphonse. The Siege of Berlin & Other Stories. 2004. reprint ed. pap. 15.95 (978-1-4191-8248-8(X)); pap. 1.99 (978-1-4192-8248-5(4)) Kessinger Publishing, LLC.

Davidson, Dana. Jason & Kyra. 2005. 352p. (gr. 7-17). pap. 5.99 (978-0-7868-3653-6(9) , Jump at the Sun) Hyperion Bks. for Children.

Demers, Dominique. Every Single Night. Debon, Nicolas, illus. 2006. 32p. (J). 17.95 (978-0-88899-699-2(3)) Groundwood Bks. CAN. *Dist:* Perseus Distribution.

Deuker, Carl. Gym Candy. 2007. 320p. (J). (gr. 7 up). 16.00 (***978-0-618-77713-6(X)***) Houghton Mifflin Co. Trade & Reference Div.

DiLorenzo, Michael A. Adventures with Jonny: Let's Go Fishing! Julich, Jenniffer, illus. 2006. 68p. (J). 17.95 (978-0-9777210-0-9(0)) Running Moose Publications.

Dodd, Emma. Just Like You. 2008. 24p. (J). (ps). 10.99 (***978-0-525-47933-8(3)*** , Dutton Juvenile) Penguin Group (USA) Inc.

Dodds, Dayle Ann. Minnie's Diner: A Multiplying Menu. Manders, John, illus. 2007. 40p. (J). (gr. k-3). pap. 6.99 (978-0-7636-3313-4(5)) Candlewick Pr.

Donahue, Jill L. Dad's Shirt. Lee, Jisun, illus. 2006. 32p. (J). (***978-1-4048-3163-6(0)***) Picture Window Bks.

—Dad_s Shirt. 2007. (Illus.). 32p. (J). (***978-1-4048-1228-4(8)***) Picture Window Bks.

Dorfman, Joaquín. Playing It Cool. 2006. 352p. (gr. 7-11). (J). lib. bdg. 17.99 (978-0-375-93641-8(6)); (YA). 15.95 (978-0-375-83641-1(1)) Random Hse. Children's Bks. (Random Hse. Bks. for Young Readers).

Dorfman, Joaquin. Playing it Cool. 2007. 352p. (J). (gr. 7-11). pap. 7.99 (978-0-375-84024-1(9) , Random Hse. Bks. for Young Readers) Random Hse. Children's Bks.

Dorros, Arthur. Papa & Me. Gutierrez, Rudy, illus. 2008. 32p. (J). 16.99 (***978-0-06-058156-5(5)***); lib. bdg. 17.89 (***978-0-06-058157-2(3)***) HarperCollins Pubs.

Doyle, Brian. You Can Pick Me up at Peggy's Cove. 2006. 104p. (J). pap. 6.95 (978-0-88899-709-8(4)) Groundwood Bks. CAN. *Dist:* Perseus Distribution.

Endoh, Minari, illus. & creator. Dazzle, Vol. 2. Endoh, Minari, creator. 2nd rev. ed. 2006. pap. 9.99 (978-1-59816-093-2(1) , Tokyopop Kids) TOKYOPOP, Inc.

Ennis, Scott. Feed My Sheep. 2005. 23p. 7.49 (978-1-4116-6287-2(3)) Lulu.com.

Farmer, Nancy. Clever Ali. De Marcken, Gail, illus. 2006. 40p. (J). pap. 17.99 (978-0-439-37014-1(0) , Orchard Bks.) Scholastic, Inc.

Fickey, Brenda. Whispering Darkness. 2007. (ENG.). 136p. per. 19.95 (***978-1-4241-6932-0(1)***) PublishAmerica, Inc.

Fine, Anne & Trimmer, Tony. Countdown. 2006. (Yellow Bananas Ser.). (Illus.). 44p. (J). (978-0-7787-0958-9(2)) Crabtree Publishing Co.

Fogelin, Adrian. The Real Question. 2006. 240p. (YA). 15.95 (978-1-56145-383-2(8) , Peachtree Junior) Peachtree Pubs., Ltd.

Freeman, Marilyn. Pasquale's Journey. 2003. 49p. pap. 8.95 (978-0-595-30311-3(0)) iUniverse, Inc.

Gantos, Jack. Joey Pigza Loses Control. braille ed. 2003. (J). (gr. 2). spiral bd. (978-0-616-15268-3(X)) Canadian National Institute for the Blind/Institut National Canadien pour les Aveugles.

—Joey Pigza Loses Control. 2000. (Joey Pigza Ser.). 208p. (J). (gr. 4-7). 16.00 (978-0-374-39989-4(1) , Farrar, Straus & Giroux (BYR)) Farrar, Straus & Giroux.

—Joey Pigza Loses Control. 2002. 208p. (J). (gr. 5 up). pap. 5.99 (978-0-06-441022-9(6) , Harper Trophy) HarperCollins Pubs.

—Joey Pigza Loses Control. unabr. ed. 2004. 195p. (J). (gr. 5-9). pap. 36.00 incl. audio (978-0-8072-8726-2(1) , LyA 248 SP, Listening Library) Random Hse. Audio Publishing Group.

—Joey Pigza Loses Control. 2002. (gr. 5-8). lib. bdg. 14.15 (978-0-613-49677-3(9)) Tandem Library Bks.

—Joey Pigza Loses Control. l.t. ed. 2001. 196p. (J). 22.95 (978-0-7862-3425-7(3)) Thorndike Pr.

Gibbons, Alan. Defender. 2006. 192p. (J). pap. 11.99 (***978-1-84255-098-4(5)***) Orion Publishing Group, Ltd. GBR. *Dist:* Independent Pubs. Group.

Gomes, Barbara K. Esau at the Big House. 2006. 76p. pap. 14.95 (978-1-4241-2288-2(0)) PublishAmerica, Inc.

Gould, Robert. Father & Son Read-Aloud Stories. Gurin, Lara, illus. 2006. 56p. (J). 12.95 (978-1-929945-67-2(1)) Big Guy Bks., Inc.

Gratz, Alan. Samurai Shortstop. 2006. 288p. (J). (gr. 6 up). 17.99 (978-0-8037-3075-5(6) , Dial) Penguin Group (USA) Inc.

Gratz, Alan M. Samurai Shortstop. 2008. 288p. (YA). (gr. 6). pap. 7.99 (***978-0-14-241099-8(3)*** , Puffin) Penguin Group (USA) Inc.

Halvorson, Marilyn. Let It Go. 2004. 224p. (YA). (gr. 7-9). (978-1-55005-105-6(9)) Fitzhenry & Whiteside, Ltd.

Hamilton, Tisha. Pirate Island Storybook & Dress up Kit. 2006. (Storybook & Dress-up Kit Ser.). 24p. (J). pap. 18.99 (978-0-7944-1105-3(3)) Reader's Digest Assn., Inc., The.

Harel, Nira. The Key to My Heart. Abulafia, Yossi, illus. 2003. 24p. (J). 15.95 (978-1-929132-40-9(9)) Kane/Miller Bk. Pubs., Inc.

Harmon, Michael B. The Last Exit to Normal. 2008. (YA). (***978-0-375-84098-2(2)***); lib. bdg. (***978-0-375-94098-9(7)***) Knopf, Alfred A. Inc.

Harrar, George. The Trouble with Jeremy Chance. 2007. (Historical Fiction for Young Readers Ser.). 168p. (J). pap. 6.95 (978-1-57131-669-1(8)) Milkweed Editions.

—The Wonder Kid. Winiarski, Anthony, illus. 2006. 256p. (J). (gr. 5). 16.00 (978-0-618-56317-3(2)) Houghton Mifflin Co.

Harris, Kandi. Prince, the Future King: A Father's Example. Wyman, M. C. & Anderson, Bill, illus. 2005. 32p. (J). bds. 19.95 (978-0-9770331-0-2(4)) Harris, K Publishing, Inc.

Hawke, Rosanne. The Keeper. (Illus.). 164p. (J). pap. (978-0-7344-0068-0(3) , Lothian Bks.) Hachette Livre Australia.

Hemphill, Helen. Long Gone Daddy. 2006. 176p. (J). 16.95 (978-1-932425-38-3(1) , Lemniscaat) Boyds Mills Pr.

Hemyng, Bracebridge. Jack Harkaway & His Son's Escape from the Brigand's of Greece. 2006. 342p. pap. 14.99 (978-1-4264-2290-4(3)); 386p. pap. 20.99 (978-1-4264-2325-3(X)) BiblioBazaar.

—Jack Harkaway & His Son's Escape from the Brigands of Greece. 2004. reprint ed. pap. 1.99 (978-1-4192-2705-9(X)) Kessinger Publishing, LLC.

Henighan, Tom. Demon in My View. 2007. 176p. (J). pap. 12.99 (***978-1-55002-656-6(9)*** , Boardwalk Bks.) Dundurn Group, The CAN. *Dist:* Univ. of Toronto Pr.

Hernandez, David. Suckerpunch. 2008. 224p. (J). 16.99 (***978-0-06-117330-1(4)***); lib. bdg. 17.89 (***978-0-06-117331-8(2)***) HarperCollins Pubs. (HarperTeen).

Herrick, Steven. By the River. 2006. 240p. (YA). 16.95 (978-1-932425-72-7(1) , Lemniscaat) Boyds Mills Pr.

Hey Dad, Let's Have a Catch! 2006. (J). 16.95 (978-0-9786584-0-3(X)) Column Hall Concepts, LLC.

Higgins, F. E. The Black Book of Secrets. 2007. 288p. (J). (gr. 4-7). 14.95 (***978-0-312-36844-9(5)***) Feiwel & Friends.

Hightman, Jason. Samurai. 2007. 416p. (J). pap. 6.99 (***978-0-06-054016-6(8)*** , Eos) HarperCollins Pubs.

Hughes, V. I. Aziz the Story Teller. Czernecki, Stefan, illus. 2006. 29p. (J). (gr. k-4). reprint ed. 17.00 (978-1-4223-5298-4(6)) DIANE Publishing Co.

Hunter, Jana Novotny. When Daddy Picks Me Up. Miller, Thomas O., illus. 2004. (J). (gr. k-3). 12.95 (978-0-7696-3169-1(X) , Gingham Dog Pr.) School Specialty Publishing.

—When Daddy's Truck Picks Me Up. Thompson, Carol, illus. 2006. 32p. (J). 15.95 (978-0-8075-8914-4(4)) Whitman, Albert & Co.

Jarnes, Jon Jeffery. Jason Post: Magic at the Downs. 2006. (YA). 19.95 (978-0-9770483-0-4(6)) Speech Publishing Hse.

Jennings, Patrick. Out Standing in My Field. 2006. 176p. (J). pap. 5.99 (978-0-439-48749-8(8) , Scholastic Paperbacks) Scholastic, Inc.

Jennings, Sharon. No Monsters Here. Ohi, Ruth, illus. 2004. 32p. (J). (gr. k-1). (978-1-55041-787-6(8)) Fitzhenry & Whiteside, Ltd.

Johnson, Peter. What Happened. 2007. 133p. (YA). (gr. 9 up). 16.95 (978-1-932425-67-3(5) , Front Street) Boyds Mills Pr.

Johnston, Tony. Bone by Bone by Bone. 2007. 192p. (YA). (gr. 7 up). 17.95 (***978-1-59643-113-3(X)***) Roaring Brook Pr.

Jones, Patrick. Nailed. (YA). 2007. 240p. (gr. 9 up). pap. 7.95 (***978-0-8027-9648-6(6)***); 2006. 224p. 16.95 (978-0-8027-8077-5(6)) Walker & Co.

Kehret, Peg. Abduction! (J). 2006. 224p. (gr. 4). pap. 6.99 (978-0-14-240617-5(1) , Puffin); 2004. 192p. (gr. 5). reprint ed. 16.99 (978-0-525-47294-0(0) , Dutton Juvenile) Penguin Group (USA) Inc.

Kennedy Tosten, S. Troy's Amazing Universe: A for Aliens. 2005. 124p. pap. 12.95 (978-1-59113-672-9(5)) Booklocker.com, Inc.

Kerley, Barbara. Greetings from Planet Earth. 2007. (Illus.). 256p. (J). (gr. 4-7). pap. 16.99 (978-0-439-80203-1(2) , Scholastic Pr.) Scholastic, Inc.

Kimball, Linda Hoffman. Come with Me on Halloween. Reed, Mike, illus. 2005. 32p. (J). (ps-1). 16.95 (978-0-8075-3132-7(4)) Whitman, Albert & Co.

Kirk, Connie Ann. Sky Dancers. Hale, Christy, illus. 2004. (J). (gr. 1-4). 16.95 (978-1-58430-162-2(7)) Lee & Low Bks., Inc.

Korman, Gordon. Born to Rock. 272p. 2008. pap. 8.99 (***978-0-7868-0921-9(3)***); 2006. (gr. 7 up). 15.99 (978-0-7868-0920-2(5)) Hyperion Bks. for Children.

La Fevers, Robin. The Forging of the Blade. 2006. (Lowthar's Blade Ser.: Bk. 1). 144p. (J). (gr. 2). pap. 5.99 (978-0-14-240557-4(4) , Puffin) Penguin Group (USA) Inc.

LaBate, Jim. Mickey Mantle Day in Amsterdam: Another Novella by Jim LaBate. Batemen, Brian, illus. 1999. 61p. (YA). (gr. 7-12). pap. 7.95 (978-0-9662100-7-1(7)) Mohawk River Pr.

Lachenmeyer, Nathaniel. Searching for Sasquatch. Bradley, Vicki, illus. 2007. 32p. 16.95 (***978-1-57061-442-2(3)***) Sasquatch Bks.

LaFaye, A. Worth. unabr. ed. 2006. (Live Oak Histories Ser.). (J). (gr. 3-6). pap. 24.95 incl. audio (***978-1-59519-766-5(4)***); pap. 28.95 incl. audio compact disk (***978-1-59519-767-2(2)***) Live Oak Media.

—Worth. 2006. 160p. (J). (gr. 4-7). reprint ed. pap. 5.99 (978-1-4169-1624-6(5) , Aladdin) Simon & Schuster Children's Publishing.

Laguna, Sofie. Bad Buster: Being Bad Is Not Just for the Dogs! Hobbs, Leigh, illus. 2006. (Nibbles Ser.). 72p. (J). (gr. 1-4). pap. 3.95 (978-0-7624-2626-3(8) , Running Pr. Kids) Running Pr. Bk. Pubs.

LaMarche, Jim. Up. 2006. (Illus.). 32p. (J). 16.95 (978-0-8118-4445-1(5)) Chronicle Bks. LLC.

Lawlor, Laurie. He Will Go Fearless. 2006. 224p. (J). 15.95 (978-0-689-86579-4(1)) Simon & Schuster Children's Publishing.

Lawrence, Iain. The Convicts Book I. The Curse of the Jolly Stone Trilogy. 2006. 208p. (YA). (gr. 7). pap. 5.99 (978-0-440-41932-7(8) , Laurel Leaf) Random Hse. Children's Bks.

Layefsky, Virginia. Impossible Things. 1998. (Accelerated Reader Bks.). 208p. (J). (gr. 5-9). 14.95 (978-0-7614-5038-2(6) , Cavendish Children's Bks.) Cavendish, Marshall Corp.

Lemieux, Jean. Toby Shoots for Infinity. Cummins, Sarah, tr. from FRE. Casson, Sophie, illus. 2005. (First Novel Ser.). 64p. (J). (gr. 2-5). (***978-0-88780-685-8(6)***); 4.95 (978-0-88780-684-1(8)) Formac Publishing Co., Ltd. CAN. *Dist:* Casemate Pubs. & Bk. Distributors, LLC.

Leno, Jay. If Roast Beef Could Fly. Whitehead, S. B., illus. 2005. 30p. (J). (gr. k-4). 18.00 (978-0-7567-9365-4(3)) DIANE Publishing Co.

LeTourneau, Marie. The Mice of Bistrot des Sept Freres. LeTourneau, Marie, illus. 2006. (Illus.). 32p. 15.95 (978-0-9749303-6-7(9)) Tanglewood Pr.

Leuck, Laura. I Love My Pirate Papa. Stone, Kyle M., illus. 2007. 32p. (J). (ps-2). 16.00 (978-0-15-205664-3(5)) Harcourt Trade Pubs.

Lieshout, Ted van. Uncle Gus's Magic Box. Sideri, Simona, tr. from DUT. Hopman, Philip, illus. 2005. 60p. (J). (gr. 2-4). 18.95 (978-1-55037-935-8(6)) Annick Pr., Ltd. CAN. *Dist:* Firefly Bks., Ltd.

Lignell, Kirk. Listen to the Raindrops W/cd. 2007. 32p. 17.95 (***978-1-932399-15-8(1)***) Huron River Pr.

Linhart, Sandra Miller. Daddy's Boots. 2007. 44p. (J). 16.99 (978-1-59092-575-1(0) , Little Blue Works) Windstorm Creative.

London, Jonathan. Froggy Bakes a Cake. Remkiewicz, Frank, illus. 2000. (Reading Railroad Bks.). 32p. (J). (ps-3). pap. 3.99 (978-0-448-42153-7(4) , Grosset & Dunlap) Penguin Group (USA) Inc.

—Froggy Bakes a Cake. 2000. (ps-2). lib. bdg. 11.25 (978-0-613-25269-0(1)); (Illus.). (J). 10.29 (978-0-606-21801-6(7)) Tandem Library Bks.

—Froggy's Day with Dad. Remkiewicz, Frank, illus. 2006. (Froggy Ser.). 32p. (J). (ps). pap. 5.99 (978-0-14-240634-2(1) , Puffin) Penguin Group (USA) Inc.

London, Jonathan & Moore, Margie. Do Your ABCs, Little Brown Bear. 2007. 32p. (J). pap. 5.99 (978-0-14-240713-4(5) , Puffin) Penguin Group (USA) Inc.

Lupica, Mike. Hot Hand. 2007. (Mike Lupica's Comeback Kids Ser.). 165p. (J). (gr. 4-7). 9.99 (***978-0-399-24714-9(9)*** , Philomel) Penguin Group (USA) Inc.

Lupica, Mike. Travel Team. l.t. ed. 2005. 400p. (J). (ps-7). lib. bdg. 23.95 (978-0-7862-7415-4(8)) Thorndike Pr.

MacDonald, Alan. Trolls United! Beech, Mark, illus. 2007. 128p. (J). (gr. 1-5). 14.95 (***978-1-59990-125-1(0)***); pap. 5.95 (***978-1-59990-126-8(9)***) Bloomsbury Publishing.

MacPhail, Catherine. Fugitive. 128p. (J). (gr. k-6). 7.95 (978-0-14-038271-6(2)) Penguin Bks., Ltd. GBR. *Dist:* Trafalgar Square Publishing.

Maier, Inger M. When Fuzzy Was Afraid of Big & Loud Things. Candon, Jennifer, illus. 2005. 32p. (J). 14.95 (978-1-59147-322-0(5)); pap. 8.95 (978-1-59147-323-7(3)) American Psychological Assn. (Magination Pr.).

Mankell, Henning. A Bridge to the Stars. 2007. 176p. (YA). (gr. 7). 15.99 (***978-0-385-73495-0(6)***); lib. bdg. 18.99 (***978-0-385-90489-6(4)***) Random Hse. Children's Bks. (Delacorte Bks. for Young Readers).

Mankell, Henning & Thompson, Laurie. Shadows in the Twilight. 2008. 176p. (J). (***978-0-385-73496-7(4)***); (YA). (gr. 7). lib. bdg. 18.99 (***978-0-385-90490-2(8)***) Dell Publishing. (Delacorte Pr.).

Many, Paul. Dad's Bald Head. O'Malley, Kevin, illus. 2007. 32p. (J). (ps-2). 15.95 (***978-0-8027-9579-3(X)***) Walker & Co.

Many, Paul & O'Malley, Kevin. Dad's Bald Head. O'Malley, Kevin, illus. 2007. (Illus.). 32p. (J). (ps-2). 16.85 (***978-0-8027-9580-9(3)***) Walker & Co.

Martin, Hugo. Pablo's Christmas. Chapman, Lee, illus. 2006. 24p. (J). 14.95 (978-1-4027-2560-9(4)) Sterling Publishing Co., Inc.

Mass, Wendy. Jeremy Fink & the Meaning of Life. 2006. 304p. (J). (gr. 4-7). 15.99 (978-0-316-05829-2(7)) Little Brown & Co.

—Jeremy Fink & the Meaning of Life. 2008. 304p. (J). (gr. 3-7). pap. 6.99 (***978-0-316-05849-0(1)***) Little, Brown Bks. for Young Readers.

Mayfield, Sue. Patterns in the Sand. 2004. 144p. (J). pap. 8.99 (***978-0-7459-4891-1(X)***) Lion Hudson plc GBR. *Dist:* Independent Pubs. Group.

McBratney, Sam. Guess How Much I Love You. Jeram, Anita, illus. 2005. 34p. (J). bds. 19.95 (978-0-9769313-1-7(1)) BrailleInk.

—Guess How Much I Love You & Story Time DVD. Jeram, Anita, illus. 2006. 32p. (J). (ps-3). 15.99 incl. DVD (978-0-7636-3503-9(0)) Candlewick Pr.

McCaughrean, Geraldine. Father & Son: A Nativity Story. Negrin, Fabian, illus. 2006. 40p. (ps-3). 16.99 (978-1-4231-0344-8(0)) Hyperion Pr.

McDaniel, Lurlene. Prey. 2008. 208p. (YA). (***978-0-385-73453-0(0)*** , Delacorte Pr.) Dell Publishing.

Mercier, Johanne & Brignaud, Pierre. Caillou on the Subway. rev. ed. 2006. (Out & about Ser.). (Illus.). 24p. (J). pap. 3.95 (***978-2-89450-584-7(1)***) Chouette Publishing CAN. *Dist:* Independent Pubs. Group.

Michelson, Richard. Happy Feet: The Savoy Ballroom Lindy Hoppers & Me. Lewis, E. B., illus. 2005. 32p. (J). (ps-ps). 16.00 (978-0-15-205057-3(4)) Harcourt Children's Bks.

Montanari, Eva. Go-Cart Number 1. 2005. (Illus.). 31p. (J). lib. bdg. 24.67 (978-0-8368-4478-8(5)) Stevens, Gareth Inc.

Murphy, Barbara Beasley. Ace Flies Like an Eagle. 2003. (Can't Stop Ace Ser.: No. 3). 180p. (J). pap. 16.95 (978-0-86534-409-9(4)) Sunstone Pr.

Neff, Henry H. The Hound of Rowan. 2007. (Tapestry Ser.: Bk. 1). (Illus.). 414p. (J). (gr. 3-7). 17.99 (978-0-375-83894-1(5) , Random Hse. Bks. for Young Readers) Random Hse. Children's Bks.

—The Hound of Rowan. Neff, Henry H., illus. 2007. (Tapestry Ser.: Bk. 1). (Illus.). 414p. (J). (gr. 3-7). lib. bdg. 20.99 (978-0-375-93894-8(X) , Random Hse. Bks. for Young Readers) Random Hse. Children's Bks.

—The Hound of Rowan. 2007. (J). pap. (978-0-375-83895-8(3)) Random Hse., Inc.

Newman, Robert. Lost Treasures Bk. 3: The Teddy Bear Habit. 2001. 184p. (J). 13.49 (978-0-7868-2599-8(5)) Hyperion Pr.

Nimmo, Jenny. The Snow Spider. 2006. (Snow Spider Trilogy: Bk. 1). (J). 39.95 (978-0-439-89844-7(7)); 160p. (gr. 3-7). 9.99 (978-0-439-84675-2(7) , Orchard Bks.) Scholastic, Inc.

Nolan, Janet. A Father's Day Thank You. Ember, Kathi, illus. 2007. 32p. (J). 15.95 (978-0-8075-2291-2(0)) Whitman, Albert & Co.

Nolan, Peggy. The Spy Who Came in from the Sea. 144p. (J). 2001. pap. 8.95 (978-1-56164-245-8(2)); 2000. (gr. 5-9). 14.95 (978-1-56164-186-4(3)) Pineapple Pr., Inc.

Norac, Carl. My Daddy Is a Giant. Godon, Ingrid, illus. 2005. 32p. (J). (ps-k). 16.00 (978-0-618-44399-4(1) , Clarion Bks.) Houghton Mifflin Co. Trade & Reference Div.

—My Daddy Is a Giant. Godon, Ingrid, illus. 2004. (ENG & IRI.). 32p. (J). pap. 12.95 (978-1-84444-719-0(7)) Mantra Lingua GBR. *Dist:* Mantra Publishing, Ltd.

—My Daddy Is a Giant: For Everyone Who Has the Best Daddy in the World. 2004. (Illus.). 32p. (J). (978-1-4050-2167-8(5) , Macmillan Children's Bks.) Pan Macmillan.

E F G

—My Daddy Is a Giant (Pb) Godon, Ingrid, illus. 2004. 32p. (J). pap. (978-1-4050-2168-5(3) , Macmillan Children's Bks.) Pan Macmillan.

Oliver, Merlin. John Laughinghouse. 2007. 20.00 (978-0-8059-7333-4(8)) Dorrance Publishing Co., Inc.

Oppel, Kenneth. Sunwing. 320p. (J). 2008. pap. 6.99 (978-1-4169-4997-8(6)); 2001. (gr. 3-7). pap. 5.99 (978-0-689-83287-1(7)) Simon & Schuster Children's Publishing. (Aladdin).

—Sunwing. 2001. (J). (978-0-606-21473-5(9)); (gr. 3-6). lib. bdg. 13.00 (978-0-613-62080-2(1)) Tandem Library Bks.

Osborn, Kelly. The Green Knight. 2006. 64p. pap. 12.95 (978-1-4241-1741-3(0)) PublishAmerica, Inc.

Paterson, Katherine. Marvin One Too Many. Clark Brown, Jane, illus. 2003. 25.95 incl. audio (978-1-59112-254-8(6)); 28.95 incl. audio compact disk (978-1-59112-635-5(5)); pap. 18.95 incl. audio compact disk (978-1-59112-634-8(7)); pap. 31.95 incl. audio compact disk (978-1-59112-636-2(3)) Live Oak Media.

Paulsen, Gary. The Tent. 2006. (Illus.). 96p. (J). pap. 5.95 (978-0-15-205833-3(8) , Harcourt Paperbacks) Harcourt Children's Bks.

Pearsall, Shelley. All Shook Up. 2008. (J). (978-0-375-83698-5(5)); 256p. lib. bdg. (978-0-375-93698-2(X)) Knopf, Alfred A. Inc.

Philbrick, Rodman. The Young Man & the Sea. 2005. 192p. (J). (ps-7). per. 12.64 (978-0-606-33810-3(1)) Tandem Library Bks.

Polak, Monique. Finding Elmo. 2007. (Orca Currents Ser.). 112p. (YA). (gr. 5 up). pap. (978-1-55143-686-9(8)); lib. bdg. (978-1-55143-688-3(4)) Orca Bk. Pubs.

Posada, Jorge. Play Ball! Colon, Raul, illus. 2006. 32p. (J). (gr. 1-5). 16.95 (978-1-4169-0687-2(8)) Simon & Schuster Children's Publishing.

Powell, Randy. Run If You Dare. 2006. 192p. (YA). pap. 6.95 (978-0-374-46375-5(1)) Macmillan.

Rene, Richard. The Nightmare Tree. 2007. 240p. (YA). (gr. 5-8). 8.95 (978-1-55050-363-0(4)) Coteau Bks. CAN. *Dist:* Fitzhenry & Whiteside, Ltd.

Rex, Michael. You Can Do Anything, Daddy! Rex, Michael, illus. 2007. 32p. (J). (ps). 14.99 (978-0-399-24298-4(8) , Putnam Juvenile) Penguin Group (USA) Inc.

Rich, Francine Poppo. Small, Not Tall. Difilippi, Thomas, illus. 2001. 32p. (J). (ps-3). 16.00 (978-0-9674602-2-2(0)) Blue Marlin Pubns.

Rio, Adam del & Noel III. Teo & the Brick. Rio, Adam del & Noel III, illus. 2006. (SPA & ENG., Illus.). 28p. (978-0-9772852-4-2(3)); (978-0-9772852-5-9(1)) Lectura Bks.

Riordan, Rick. The Lightning Thief. 2006. (Percy Jackson & the Olympians Ser.: Bk. 1). 392p. (gr. 5 up). reprint ed. pap. 7.99 (978-0-7868-3865-3(5)) Miramax Bks.

—The Sea of Monsters. 2nd rev. ed. 2007. (Percy Jackson & the Olympians Ser.: Bk. 2). 304p. (gr. 5 up). pap. 7.99 (978-1-4231-0334-9(3)) Miramax Bks.

—The Sea of Monsters. l.t. ed. 2006. (Percy Jackson & the Olympians Ser.: Bk. 2). (YA). (gr. 5 up). 22.95 (978-0-7862-9074-1(9)) Thorndike Pr.

Ritchie, Alison. Me & My Dad! Edgson, Alison, illus. 2007. 28p. (J). (ps-2). 16.95 (978-1-56148-565-9(9)) Good Bks.

Roman, Steven A. Sunn. Lau, Kevin et al, illus. 2003. 192p. (gr. 7). pap. 9.95 (978-1-59687-814-3(2)) ibooks, Inc.

Rosen, Michael. Michael Rosen's Sad Book. Blake, Quentin, illus. 2005. 32p. (J). 16.99 (978-0-7636-2597-9(3)) Candlewick Pr.

Rosenbloom, Eileen. Stuck Down. 2005. 240p. pap. 8.95 (978-0-7387-0658-0(2)) Llewellyn Pubns.

Rosselson, Leon. Somewhere Else. (Illus.). 121p. (J). pap. 8.99 (978-0-340-72264-0(9) , Hodder & Stoughton) Hodder General Publishing Division GBR. *Dist:* Trafalgar Square Publishing.

Rylant, Cynthia. Henry & Mudge & the Forever Sea. Stevenson, Sucie, illus. 2000. (Henry & Mudge Ser.). 28.95 incl. audio compact disk (978-1-59112-575-4(8)); pap. 31.95 incl. audio compact disk (978-1-59112-574-7(X)) Live Oak Media.

—Henry & Mudge & the Funny Lunch. Bracken, Carolyn, illus. 2005. (Henry & Mudge Ser.). 40p. (J). (gr. k-2). lib. bdg. 12.10 (978-1-4176-7107-6(6)) Tandem Library Bks.

—Henry & Mudge & the Snowman Plan. Stevenson, Sucie, illus. 2002. (Henry & Mudge Ser.). 28.95 incl. audio compact disk (978-1-59112-651-5(7)); pap. 31.95 incl. audio compact disk (978-1-59112-652-2(5)) Live Oak Media.

Salisbury, Graham. House of the Red Fish. 2006. 304p. (gr. 7). (J). 16.95 (978-0-385-73121-8(3)); (YA). lib. bdg. 18.99 (978-0-385-90145-1(3)) Random Hse. Children's Bks. (Lamb, Wendy).

Savadier, Elivia. Time to Get Dressed! Savadier, Elivia, illus. 2006. (Illus.). 32p. (J). 14.95 (978-1-59643-161-4(X)) Roaring Brook Pr.

The Secret Life of Jack O' Lanterns. 2004. 32p. 15.00 (978-1-883211-35-6(2)) Laughing Elephant.

Shahan, Sherry. That's Not How You Play Soccer, Daddy! Mai-Wyss, Tatjana, illus. 2007. 32p. (J). (ps-3). 15.95 (978-1-56145-416-7(8) , Peachtree Junior) Peachtree Pubs., Ltd.

Shaw, Marilyn Bishop. Solomon. 2006. 203p. (J). 14.95 (978-1-56164-349-3(1)) Pineapple Pr., Inc.

Slater, David Michael. Comin' Through. Rooney, Ronnie, illus. 2007. (Missy Swiss & More Ser.). 32p. (J). (ps-4). lib. bdg. 27.07 (978-1-60270-008-6(7) , Looking Glass Library) Magic Wagon.

Spain, Susan Rosson. The Deep Cut. 2006. (Illus.). 224p. (J). 16.99 (978-0-7614-5316-1(4)) Cavendish, Marshall Corp.

Spillebeen, Geert. Kipling's Choice. Edelstein, Terese, tr. 160p. (YA). (gr. 7 up). 2007. pap. 7.99 (978-0-618-80035-3(2) , Graphia); 2005. 16.00 (978-0-618-43124-3(1)) Houghton Mifflin Co. Trade & Reference Div.

Spinelli, Jami. David's Tractor. Margolis, Lois, illus. l.t. ed. 2006. 32p. (J). 20.99 (978-1-59879-242-3(3)); per. 11.99 (978-1-59879-241-6(5)) Lifevest Publishing, Inc.

Spinelli, Jerry. My Daddy & Me. Chwast, Seymour, illus. 2006. 40p. (J). (ps-1). pap. 6.99 (978-0-553-11303-7(8) , Dragonfly Bks.) Random Hse. Children's Bks.

Stead, Rebecca. First Light. 2007. 336p. (J). (gr. 4-7). 15.99 (978-0-375-84017-3(6)); lib. bdg. 18.99 (978-0-375-94017-0(0)) Random Hse. Children's Bks. (Lamb, Wendy).

Steele, Michael Anthony. Movie Novel. Cecil, Lauren, ed. 2007. (Firehouse Dog Ser.). 160p. (J). pap. 4.99 (978-0-439-89642-9(8)) Scholastic, Inc.

Stewart, Paul & Riddell, Chris. Edge Chronicles 2: Stormchaser. 2008. (Edge Chronicles Ser.). 400p. (gr. 5-7). 6.99 (978-0-440-42088-0(1) , Yearling) Random Hse. Children's Bks.

Stier, Roy E. Son of Bunyan & the Sacred Moonstone. 2003. (Illus.). 158p. (J). per. 15.95 (978-1-892264-10-7(2)) Timeless Voyager Pr.

Strasser, Todd. Slide or Die. Phillips, Craig, illus. 2006. (DriftX Ser.). 224p. (YA). (gr. 9 up). pap. 6.99 (978-1-4169-0581-3(2) , Simon Pulse) Simon & Schuster Children's Publishing.

Strong, Jeremy. Chicken School. l.t. ed. 2005. pap. 16.95 (978-1-4056-6037-2(6)) BBC Audio GBR. *Dist:* BBC Audiobooks America.

Stryer, Andrea Stenn. Kami & the Yaks. Dodson, Bert, illus. 2007. 48p. (J). (gr. k-3). 16.95 (978-0-9778961-0-3(2)); pap. 9.95 (978-0-9778961-1-0(0)) Bay Otter Pr.

Tada, Joni Eareckson. A Father's Touch. Nelson, Craig, illus. 2005. 48p. (J). pap. 17.99 (978-1-58134-714-2(6) , Crossway Bibles) Crossway Bks.

Thomas, Jane Resh. Blind Mountain. 2006. 128p. (J). (gr. 4-6). 15.00 (978-0-618-64872-6(0) , Clarion Bks.) Houghton Mifflin Co. Trade & Reference Div.

Thomas, Rob. Rats Saw God. 2007. 208p. (YA). pap. 6.99 (978-1-4169-3897-2(4) , Simon Pulse) Simon & Schuster Children's Publishing.

Tong, Kevin. The Earth Machine. Tong, Kevin, illus. 2007. (Illus.). 32p. (J). 15.95 (978-1-60108-001-1(8)) Red Cygnet Pr.

Trevor, Simeon. I'm Going to Fly SomeDay. 2004. 36p. spiral bd. 13.93 (978-1-4116-2072-8(0)) Lulu.com.

Trueman, Terry. No Right Turn. 2006. 176p. (J). 16.99 (978-0-06-057491-8(7)); lib. bdg. 16.89 (978-0-06-057492-5(5)) HarperCollins Pubs. (HarperTeen).

Turner, Ann. Hard Hit. l.t. ed. 2006. (YA). 21.95 (978-0-7862-8745-1(4)) Thorndike Pr.

Turner, Ann Warren. Hard Hit. 2006. 128p. (J). (gr. 7 up). pap. 16.99 (978-0-439-29680-9(3)) Scholastic, Inc.

Van Lieshout, Ted. Uncle Gus's Magic Box. Sideri, Simona, tr. from DUT. Hopman, Philip, illus. 2005. 60p. (J). (gr. 2-4). pap. 5.95 (978-1-55037-934-1(8)) Annick Pr., Ltd. CAN. *Dist:* Firefly Bks., Ltd.

Villaseñor, Victor. Goodnight, Papito Dios/Buenas Noches, Papito Dios. Ramírez, José, illus. 2007. (SPA & ENG.). 32p. (J). (ps-2). 15.95 (978-1-55885-467-3(3) , Piñata Books) Arte Publico Pr.

Voigt, Cynthia. A Solitary Blue. l.t. ed. 2005. (Tillerman Cycle Ser.: Bk. 3). 359p. (J). pap. 10.95 (978-0-7862-7912-8(5)) Thorndike Pr.

Wallace, Rich. Southpaw. 2006. 105p. (J). lib. bdg. 15.38 (978-1-4242-2166-0(8)) Fitzgerald Bks.

—Southpaw. (Winning Season Ser.: Vol. 6). 128p. (J). 2007. pap. 4.99 (978-0-14-240785-1(2) , Puffin); 2006. (gr. 4). 14.99 (978-0-670-06053-5(4) , Viking Juvenile) Penguin Group (USA) Inc.

Walters, Virginia. Are We There yet, Daddy? Schindler, S. D., illus. 2005. 27p. (J). (gr. k-4). reprint ed. 16.00 (978-0-7567-9708-9(X)) DIANE Publishing Co.

Warwick, J. M. An Open Vein. 2007. (YA). per. 12.95 (978-1-933963-96-9(4)) Grove Creek Publishing, LLC.

Wells, Eva. Wishing I Was Fishing. 2006. 32p. lib. bdg. 16.95 (978-1-59298-168-7(2)) Beaver's Pond Pr., Inc.

Whelan, Gloria. Mackinac Bridge: The Five-Mile Poem. van Frankenhuyzen, Gijsbert, illus. 2006. 40p. (J). 17.95 (978-1-58536-283-7(2)) Sleeping Bear Pr.

Wilhelm, Doug. Raising the Shades. l.t. ed. 2005. 182p. 20.95 (978-0-7862-7812-1(9) , Large Print Pr.) Thorndike Pr.

Williams, John R. Daddy & Me: Children's Story & Coloring Book. 2006. (ENG.). 48p. per. 11.95 (978-1-59800-799-2(8)) Outskirts Press, Inc.

Williams, Mark London. Ancient Fire: Danger Boy Episode 1. 2006. 232p. (J). (gr. 4-8). pap. 4.99 (978-0-7636-3092-8(6)) Candlewick Pr.

Willie Wins. 2007. (J). pap. 7.95 (978-1-60060-237-5(1)) Lee & Low Bks., Inc.

Willson, Sarah. Brand-New Daddy. 2001. lib. bdg. 14.15 (978-0-613-49321-3(X)) Tandem Library Bks.

Wilson, Mary. Paper Dragonfly. 2007. 32p. 15.95 (978-0-9726614-3-0(3)) Shenanigan Bks.

Winfield, Arthur M. The Rover Boys in New York or Saving the. 2004. reprint ed. pap. 22.95 (978-1-4191-8117-7(3)) Kessinger Publishing, LLC.

Winfield, Arthur M. The Rover Boys in New York or Saving Their Father's Honor. 2004. reprint ed. pap. 1.99 (978-1-4192-8117-4(8)) Kessinger Publishing, LLC.

Yee, Lisa. Stanford Wong Flunks Big Time. (Illus.). (J). 2007. 320p. pap. 5.99 (978-0-439-62248-6(4)); 2005. 304p. (gr. 5-7). pap. 16.99 (978-0-439-62247-9(6)) Scholastic, Inc. (Levine, Arthur A. Bks.).

Yoshida, Akimi. Banana Fish. 2007. (Banana Fish Ser.). 192p. (YA). Vol. 18. pap. 9.99 (978-1-4215-0876-4(1)); Vol. 19. pap. 9.99 (978-1-4215-0877-1(X)) Viz Media.

Young, Ronder Thomas. Moving Mama to Town: Class Set. unabr. ed. 1998. (J). pap. 106.70 incl. audio (978-0-7887-2560-9(2) , 46730) Recorded Bks., LLC.

—Moving Mama to Town: Homework Set. unabr. ed. 1998. (J). 58.24 incl. audio (978-0-7887-1936-3(X) , 40643) Recorded Bks., LLC.

FAULKNER, WILLIAM, 1897-1962

Bloom, Harold, ed. & intro. William Faulkner's The Sound & the Fury. Bloom, Harold, intro. 1999. (Bloom's Notes Ser.). 90p. (YA). (gr. 8-12). lib. bdg. 21.95 (978-0-7910-4519-0(6) , Chelsea Hse.) Facts On File, Inc.

Fargnoli, A. Nicholas. William Faulkner A to Z: The Essential Reference to His Life & Work. 2002. (gr. 7-12). lib. bdg. 28.00 (978-0-613-64778-6(5)) Tandem Library Bks.

FAUNA

see Animals; Zoology

FAWKES, GUY, 1570-1606

Ashworth, Leon. Guy Fawkes. (Illus.). 32p. (978-0-7451-5288-2(0) , Cherrytree Books) Evans Publishing Group.

—Guy Fawkes. (British History Makers Ser.). (Illus.). 32p. 2004. (YA). pap. 11.99 (978-1-84234-302-9(5)); 2001. 22.99 (978-1-84234-080-6(8)); 1999. pap. 11.99 (978-0-7540-9011-3(6)) Evans Publishing Group GBR. (Cherrytree Books). *Dist:* Independent Pubs. Group.

FEAR

see also Courage

Adams, Carol J. God Listens When You're Afraid: Prayers for When Animals Scare You. 2006. (J). (978-0-8298-1741-6(7)) Pilgrim Pr., The/United Church Pr.

Arnold, Ellen. Brilliant Brain Battles Bad Guys. Farber, Deborah, illus. 2001. (MI Strategies for Kids Ser.). 32p. (J). (gr. 1-5). pap. 7.00 (978-1-56976-111-3(6) , 1140, Zephyr Pr.) Chicago Review Pr., Inc.

Aunt Darla. There's a Monster under the Captain's Bed!!! Erik's Monster. Petersen, Darla & Shields, Erik P., illus. Date not set. 32p. 16.00 (978-0-9658926-1-2(1)) Poet Tree Pubns.

Berry, Joy. Fear. 2005. (Winning skills series, get over It! Ser.). (Illus.). 48p. (J). 3.95 (978-1-57687-275-8(0) , PowerHouse Kids) powerHouse Cultural Entertainment, Inc.

Berry, Joy Wilt. Fear: Get over It! Bartholomew, illus. rev. ed. 2000. (Winning Skills Ser.: Vol. 1). 48p. (YA). (gr. 4-7). pap. 2.95 (978-1-58634-160-2(X)) Goldstar Publishing, Inc.

—Feeling Afraid. Smith, Maggie, illus. 2001. (J). (978-0-439-34149-3(3)) Scholastic, Inc.

Braithwaite, Althea. Feeling Scared. Jude, Conny, illus. Best, Charlie, photos by. 1998. (Exploring Emotions Ser.). 32p. (J). (gr. 3 up). lib. bdg. 23.33 (978-0-8368-2118-5(1)) Stevens, Gareth Inc.

Cantor, Joanne. Teddy's TV Troubles. Lowes, Tom, illus. 2004. 36p. (J). mass mkt. 16.95 (978-0-9647663-7-2(X)) Goblin Fern Pr., Inc.

Carlson, Melody. Don't Worry about Tomorrow. Regan, Susan, illus. 2004. (Just Like Jesus Said Ser.). 32p. (J). (ps-5). 12.99 (978-0-8054-2386-0(9)) B&H Publishing Grp.

Castillo, Sara, et al. Getting Face to Face with Your Fears: A Kid's Guide to Understanding & Coping with Fears & Phobias. 2000. (Illus.). 230p. (J). pap. 11.95 (978-1-930572-00-3(X)) Educational Media Corp.

Crist, James J. What to Do When You're Scared & Worried: A Guide for Kids. 2004. (Illus.). 128p. (YA). (gr. 4-8). pap. 9.95 (978-1-57542-153-7(4)) Free Spirit Publishing, Inc.

Doudna, Kelly. I Feel Scared. l.t. ed. 1999. (How Do You Feel? Ser.). (Illus.). 24p. (J). (ps-3). lib. bdg. 19.93 (978-1-57765-192-5(8) , SandCastle) ABDO Publishing Co.

Franzen, Lenore. Fear. 2004. (My Feelings Ser.). (Illus.). 24p. (J). lib. bdg. 15.95 (978-1-58341-319-7(7) , Creative Education) Creative Co., The.

Freedom from Fear, Worry & Anxiety. 2002. 5.00 (978-0-9718012-3-3(1)) Fresh Word.

Frost, Helen. Feeling Scared. Saunders-Smith, Gail, ed. 2000. (Emotions Ser.). (Illus.). 24p. (J). (gr. k-1). lib. bdg. 15.93 (978-0-7368-0671-8(7) , Pebble Bks.) Capstone Pr., Inc.

Harpster, Steve, illus. Catherine Finds Her Courage: An Emotional Literacy Book. 2004. (Emotional Literacy Ser.). 44p. (J). (gr. 2 up). 14.95 (978-0-9747789-2-1(3) , 67314) CTC Publishing.

Johanson, Sarah Margaret. Caillou: The Missing Sock. rev. ed. 2003. (Clubhouse Ser.). (Illus.). 24p. (J). pap. 2.50 (978-2-89450-445-1(4)) Chouette Publishing CAN. *Dist:* Independent Pubs. Group.

Johnson, Marion. Caillou, What's That Noise. CINAR Corporation Staff, illus. 2004. (Clubhouse Usa Ser.). 24p. (J). pap. 3.95 (978-2-89450-489-5(6)) Chouette Publishing CAN. *Dist:* Perseus Distribution.

Kahn, Ada P. & Doctor, Ronald M. Phobias. 2003. (Life Balance Ser.). (Illus.). 80p. (J). 20.50 (978-0-531-12256-3(5) , Watts, Franklin) Scholastic Library Publishing.

Kunkel, Jeff, ed. What Scares Me & What I Do about It: Stories & Pictures by Sunday School Kids. 2004. (Illus.). 48p. 12.99 (978-0-8066-4558-2(X) , Augsburg Bks.) Augsburg Fortress, Pubs.

Leonard, Marcia. I Feel Scared. Bartholomew, illus. 2003. 24p. (J). bds. 2.95 (978-0-8249-6525-9(6)) Ideals Pubns.

—Scared. Bartholomew, illus. 2001. (How I Feel Ser.). 24p. (J). lib. bdg. 13.45 (978-1-56674-287-0(0)) Forest Hse. Publishing Co., Inc.

L'Heureux, Christine, et al. Caillou: Good Night! 2006. (Hand in Hand Ser.). (Illus.). 24p. (J). pap. 5.95 (978-2-89450-588-5(4)) Chouette Publishing CAN. *Dist:* Independent Pubs. Group.

Meiners, Cheri J. When I Feel Afraid. 2004. (Learning to Get along Ser.). (Illus.). 40p. (J). (ps-3). pap. 10.95 (978-1-57542-138-4(0)) Free Spirit Publishing, Inc.

Nelson, Robin. Afraid. 2003. (First Step Nonfiction Ser.). (Illus.). 8p. (J). pap. 3.95 (978-0-8225-3886-8(5) , Lerner Pubns.) Lerner Publishing Group.

Newbury, Elizabeth. Art to Make You Scared! 2008. (Illus.). 24p. (J). 15.95 (978-1-84507-584-2(6)) Lincoln, Frances Ltd. GBR. *Dist:* Perseus Distribution.

La Nueva Maestra. (Coleccion Chiquilines). (SPA., Illus.). 24p. (J). 8.50 (978-950-11-0066-2(9) , SGM066) Sigmar ARG. *Dist:* Continental Bk. Co., Inc.

Porter, Daniel. Taming Monster Moments: Turning on Soul Lights to Help Children Handle Fear Anda. 1999. (ps-2). lib. bdg. 14.10 (978-0-613-75754-6(8)) Tandem Library Bks.

El Primer Dia De Clases. (Coleccion Chiquilines). (SPA.). 24p. (J). 8.50 (978-950-11-0359-5(5) , SGM359) Sigmar ARG. *Dist:* Continental Bk. Co., Inc.

Roca, Nuria. Scared? From Fear... to Courage. Curto, Rosa Maria, illus. 2002. (From ... to Ser.). 36p. (J). (ps-1). pap. 6.95 (978-0-7641-2097-8(2)) Barron's Educational Series, Inc.

Shuman, Carol. Jenny Is Scared! When Sad Things Happen in the World. Pillo, Cary, tr. Pillo, Cary, illus. 2003. 32p. (J). (gr. k-3). 14.95 (978-1-59147-002-1(1)); pap. 8.95 (978-1-59147-003-8(X)) American Psychological Assn. (Magination Pr.).

Silverthorne, Sandy. Surviving When You're Home Alone: How to Avoid Being Grounded for Life. Silverthorne, Sandy, illus. 2006. (Illus.). 96p. (YA). (gr. 3-6). pap. 5.99 (978-0-7847-1434-8(7) , 42176) Standard Publishing.

Stewart, Gail. Phobias. 2004. (Understanding Diseases & Disorders Ser.). (Illus.). 48p. (J). (gr. 4-7). 26.20 (978-0-7377-2169-0(3) , Greenhaven Pr., Inc.) Thomson Gale.

Sunderland, Margot & Hancock, Nicky. Helping Children with Fear: A Guidebook, 2 vols. Armstrong, Nicky, tr. (Illus.). 140p. spiral bd. (978-0-86388-464-1(4) , 002-5151) Speechmark Publishing Ltd.

Szpirglas, Jeff. Fear This Book: Your Guide to Fright, Horror, & Things That Go Bump in the Night. Perez, Ramon, illus. 2006. 64p. 21.95 (978-1-897066-66-9(X)) Maple Tree Pr. CAN. *Dist:* Perseus Distribution.

—Fear This Book: Your Guide to Fright, Horror, & Things That Go Bump in the Night. Perez, Ramon & Cho, Michael, illus. 2006. 64p. pap. 9.95 (978-1-897066-67-6(8)) Maple Tree Pr. CAN. *Dist:* Perseus Distribution.

Todt, Teresa. No More Monsters: A Parent & Child Guide to Freedom from Fear. Smith, Jeremy, illus. 2003. 15p. (J). (978-1-55306-647-7(2) , Guardian Bks.) Essence Publishing.

Tubbs, Janet. Fear of the Dark. 2000. (Spud Packs Ser.). 16p. (J). pap. 19.95 (978-1-881185-17-8(6)) Arcadia Pr.

Wigand, Molly. Help Is Here for Facing Fear. Alley, R. W., illus. 2000. (Elf-Help Books for Kids). 32p. (J). (ps-3). pap. 5.95 (978-0-87029-344-3(3)) Abbey Pr.

Williams, Brett. Xaler & the Dragon: A Relaxation Technique for the Anxious/Fearful Child. 2nd ed. 2001. (Illus.). 15p. (J). per. 11.95 (978-0-9761269-1-1(5)) Tapas Pubns.

FEAR—FICTION

The Acorn Story: An Adventure about Change. 2005. (J). 12.95 (978-0-9767769-0-1(1)) Rutigliano, Joe.

Adams, William J. Hate that Thunder. Stiglich, Tom, illus. 2005. 24p. (J). pap. 8.95 (978-0-9772757-0-0(1)) Mandy & Andy Bks., Inc.

Alberts, Katharine O. Boo on the Loose. 2006. (J). 14.00 (978-0-8059-7071-5(1)) Dorrance Publishing Co., Inc.

Alborough, Jez. Watch Out! Big Bro's Coming! Alborough, Jez, illus. 1998. (Illus.). 32p. (J). (ps-3). pap. 6.99 (978-0-7636-0584-1(0)) Candlewick Pr.

Aleman Lascurain, Guadalupe. La Domadora de Miedos. Diseno, Tane Arte y, illus. rev. ed. 2006. (SPA.). 232p. (J). pap. 8.95 (978-970-20-0182-9(X)) Castillo, Ediciones, S. A. de C. V. MEX. *Dist:* Macmillan.

Allen, Kit. Slide, Already! 2005. (Illus.). 48p. (J). (gr. k-3). 12.00 (978-0-618-49643-3(2)) Houghton Mifflin Co. Trade & Reference Div.

Anderson, Laurie Halse. Storm Rescue. 2003. (Wild at Heart Ser.). (Illus.). 105p. (J). (gr. 4 up). lib. bdg. 23.33 (978-0-8368-3260-0(4)) Stevens, Gareth Inc.

—Storm Rescue. 2001. (American Girl Wild at Heart Ser.: Bk. 6). (Illus.). (YA). (978-0-606-21528-2(X)) Tandem Library Bks.

Applegate, Katherine. The Buffalo Storm. Ormerod, Jan, illus. 2007. 32p. (J). (ps-3). 16.00 (978-0-618-53597-2(7) , Clarion Bks.) Houghton Mifflin Co. Trade & Reference Div.

Arnold, Marsha D. The Bravest of Us All. Sneed, Brad, illus. 2000. 32p. (J). (ps-3). 16.99 (978-0-8037-2409-9(8) , Dial) Penguin Group (USA) Inc.

Arnold, Tedd, et al. Five Ugly Monsters. Arnold, Tedd, illus. 2003. 28p. (J). bds. 6.99 (978-0-439-52465-0(2) , Cartwheel Bks.) Scholastic, Inc.

Bader, Bonnie & West, Tracey. First Day Fright. Molnar, Albert, illus. 2000. (Spooky School Ser.). 28p. (J). (978-0-439-21553-4(6)) Scholastic, Inc.

—The 100th Day of School. Molnar, Albert, illus. 2001. (Spooky School Ser.). 26p. (J). (978-0-439-21554-1(4)) Scholastic, Inc.

Bailey, Linda & Bailey, Wendy. When Addie Was Scared. 1999. (Illus.). 32p. (J). (gr. k-3). (978-1-55074-431-6(3)) Kids Can Pr., Ltd.

Bang-Campbell, Monika. Little Rat Rides. Bang, Molly, illus. 2006. (Little Rat Ser.). 48p. (J). pap. 5.95 (978-0-15-205598-1(3) , Harcourt Paperbacks) Harcourt Children's Bks.

—Little Rat Rides. Bang, Molly Garrett, tr. Bang, Molly Garrett, illus. 2004. (Little Rat Ser.). 48p. (J). 15.00 (978-0-15-204667-5(4)) Harcourt Children's Bks.

—Little Rat Sets Sail. Bang, Molly Garrett, illus. (Little Rat Ser.). 48p. (J). 2003. pap. 5.95 (978-0-15-204769-6(7) , Harcourt Paperbacks); 2002. (gr. 1-3). 14.00 (978-0-15-216297-9(6)) Harcourt Children's Bks.

—Little Rat Sets Sail. 2003. (gr. k-3). lib. bdg. 14.10 (978-0-613-70519-6(X)) Tandem Library Bks.

Banks, Steven. The Big Halloween Scare. Martinez, Heather, illus. 2005. (Ready-to-Read Ser. Level 2: 1). 32p. (J). lib. bdg. 15.00 (978-1-59054-987-2(2)) Fitzgerald Bks.

—The Big Halloween Scare. Martinez, Heather, illus. 2003. (SpongeBob SquarePants Ready-To-Read Ser.: Vol. 1). 32p. (J). (gr. k-2). pap. 3.99 (978-0-689-84196-5(5) , Simon Spotlight/Nickelodeon) Simon & Schuster Children's Publishing.

—The Big Halloween Scare. Martinez, Heather, illus. 2003. 32p. (J). (gr. k-2). lib. bdg. 11.80 (978-0-613-73339-7(8)) Tandem Library Bks.

—Spongebob Goes to the Doctor. Saunders, Zina, illus. 2005. 22p. (J). lib. bdg. 15.00 (***978-1-4242-0976-7(5)***) Fitzgerald Bks.

Banks, Steven. Wild River Adventure. 2002. (gr. k-3). lib. bdg. 11.80 (978-0-613-57590-4(3)) Tandem Library Bks.

Banks, Steven & Hillenburg, Stephen. SpongeBob Goes to the Doctor. Saunders, Zina, illus. 2005. (J). (***978-1-4156-3131-7(X)*** , Simon Spotlight/Nickelodeon) Simon & Schuster Children's Publishing.

Baumgart, Klaus. Don't Be Afraid, Tommy. 1998. (Illus.). 28p. (J). (ps-2). 14.95 (978-1-888444-32-2(0) , 21150) Little Tiger Pr.

Beck, Scott. Pepito the Brave. Van Metre, Susan, ed. 2001. (Illus.). 32p. (J). (ps). 12.99 (978-0-525-46524-9(3) , Dutton Juvenile) Penguin Group (USA) Inc.

Bee, Clair. Ten Seconds to Play!, Vol. 12. 1999. (Chip Hilton Sports Ser.). x, 191p. (J). reprint ed. pap. 5.99 (978-0-8054-1994-8(2)) B&H Publishing Grp.

—Ten Seconds to Play! 1999. (gr. 7-12). lib. bdg. 14.15 (978-0-613-90142-0(8)) Tandem Library Bks.

Beechen, Adam. Chuckie's Ghost. Artful Doodlers Limited Staff, illus. 2005. (Ready-To-Read Ser.). 32p. (J). (ps-ps). pap. 3.99 (978-0-689-87723-0(4) , Simon Spotlight/Nickelodeon) Simon & Schuster Children's Publishing.

Beetle Dan & the Big Purple Slide. 2006. 32p. pap. 14.99 (978-1-59185-921-5(2) , Creation Hse.) Strang Communications Co.

Belle, Jennifer. Little Stalker: A Novel. 2007. 352p. (gr. 8). 24.95 (978-1-59448-946-4(7) , Riverhead Bks. (Hardcover)) Penguin Group (USA) Inc.

Berenstain, Stan & Berenstain, Jan. The Berenstain Bears & the Bad Dream. Berenstain, Stan & Berenstain, Jan, illus. 2002. (Berenstain Bears First Time Bks.). (Illus.). (J). 11.19 (978-0-7587-0957-8(9)) Book Wholesalers, Inc.

—The Berenstain Bears & the Bad Dream. ed. 2004. (Berenstain Bears First Time Bks.). (J). (ps-2). spiral bd. (978-0-616-01555-1(0)); spiral bd. (978-0-616-01556-8(9)) Canadian National Institute for the Blind/Institut National Canadien pour les Aveugles.

—The Berenstain Bears Get the Scaredies. Berenstain, Stan & Berenstain, Jan, illus. 1999. (Berenstain Bears Ser.). (Illus.). 24p. (J). (ps-3). lib. bdg. 7.99 (978-0-679-99323-0(1) , Random Hse. Bks. for Young Readers) Random Hse. Children's Bks.

Bergman, Mara. Snip Snap! What's That? Maland, Nick, illus. 2005. 32p. (J). (ps-17). 16.99 (978-0-06-077754-8(0)) HarperCollins Pubs.

Binch, Caroline. The Princess & the Castle. 2005. (Illus.). 32p. (J). pap. 8.99 (978-0-09-943236-4(6) , Red Fox) Random Hse. Children's Bks. GBR. *Dist:* Trafalgar Square Publishing.

Blegvad, Lenore. Ana Banana y Yo. 1999. (SPA., Illus.). (J). (978-0-606-16025-4(6)) Tandem Library Bks.

—Anna Banana & Me. 2005. (Live Oak Readalong Ser.). (J). pap. 18.95 incl. audio compact disk (978-1-59519-295-0(6)) Live Oak Media.

Blegvad, Lenore, et al, trs. Ana Banana y Yo. Blegvad, Erik, illus. 2003. (SPA.). 56p. (J). (gr. k-3). pap. 9.95 (978-84-204-4375-1(1)) Santillana USA Publishing Co., Inc.

Bloor, Thomas. House of Eyes. 2002. 160p. (J). pap. 9.99 (978-0-340-84180-8(X) , Hodder & Stoughton) Hodder General Publishing Division GBR. *Dist:* Trafalgar Square Publishing.

Bly, Stephen A. Danger at Deception Pass. 1998. (gr. 7-12). lib. bdg. 13.00 (978-0-613-77372-0(1)) Tandem Library Bks.

Boelts, Maribeth. Sometimes I'm Afraid: A Book about Fear. Bladholm, Cheri, illus. 2004. (Helping Kids Heal Ser.). 32p. (J). 9.99 (978-0-310-70657-1(2)) Zonderkidz.

Bogacki, Tomek. The Story of a Blue Bird. Bogacki, Tomek, illus. 1998. (Illus.). 32p. (J). (ps-k). 16.00 (978-0-374-37197-5(0) , Farrar, Straus & Giroux (BYR)) Farrar, Straus & Giroux.

Bond, Felicia. Poinsettia & the Firefighters. Bond, Felicia, illus. 2003. (Illus.). (J). (978-0-06-056871-9(2)); 32p. 14.99 (978-0-06-053509-4(1) , Geringer, Laura Book); 32p. lib. bdg. 15.89 (978-0-06-053510-0(5) , Geringer, Laura Book) HarperCollins Pubs.

Bourgeois, Paulette. Franklin & the Thunderstorm. Clark, Brenda, illus. 1998. (Franklin the Turtle Ser.). 32p. (J). (gr. k-3). (978-1-55074-403-3(8)) Kids Can Pr., Ltd.

—Franklin & the Thunderstorm. Clark, Brenda, illus. 1998. (Franklin Ser.). 32p. (J). (ps-3). pap. 4.99 (978-0-590-02635-2(6) , Cartwheel Bks.) Scholastic, Inc.

—Franklin & the Thunderstorm. Clark, Brenda, illus. 1998. (Franklin Ser.). (J). (ps-3). 11.30 (978-0-606-13403-3(4)); lib. bdg. 12.40 (978-0-613-07814-6(4)) Tandem Library Bks.

Bourgeois, Paulette & Clark, Brenda. Franklin Is Lost. 1999. (Franklin Ser.). (Illus.). 162p. (J). (ps-3). (978-1-55074-670-9(7)) Kids Can Pr., Ltd.

Bourgeois, Paulette, et al. Franklin en la Oscuridad. Lopez Varela, Alejandra, tr. from ENG. Clark, Brenda, illus. 1998. (Franklin Ser.). (SPA.). 32p. (J). (ps-3). pap. 5.95 (978-1-880507-43-8(9) , LC7861) Lectorum Pubns., Inc.

Bowdish, Lynea. Thunder Doesn't Scare Me! Wallace, John, illus. 2001. (Rookie Reader Espanol Ser.). 32p. (J). (gr. k-2). pap. 4.95 (978-0-516-27291-7(8) , Children's Pr.) Scholastic Library Publishing.

—Thunder Doesn't Scare Me! 2001. (gr. k-3). lib. bdg. 12.95 (978-0-613-54706-2(3)) Tandem Library Bks.

—Los Truenos No Me Asustan! Wallace, John, illus. 2001. (Rookie Espanol Ser.). (SPA.). 32p. (J). (gr. k-2). 19.50 (978-0-516-22354-4(2) , Children's Pr.) Scholastic Library Publishing.

Bradford, Karleen. Ghost Wolf. Cormack, Allan & Drew-Brook, Deborah, illus. 2005. 59p. (J). lib. bdg. 20.00 (***978-1-4242-1254-5(5)***) Fitzgerald Bks.

Bradford, William. Jeremy Mcbright Was Afraid of the Night. 2006. (Illus.). 36p. (J). lib. bdg. 13.95 (978-0-9672585-2-2(9)) CyPress Pubns.

Bradman, Tony. Flora the Fairy. 2005. (Green Bananas Ser.). (Illus.). 48p. (J). (ps). pap. (978-0-7787-1038-7(6)) Crabtree Publishing Co.

Brandenburg, Claire. Daniel & the Lion. 2002. (Illus.). 32p. pap. 8.95 (978-1-888212-35-8(7) , 005674) Conciliar Pr.

Bravery Soup. 2002. (Albert Whitman Prairie Bks.). (Illus.). 32p. (J). (ps-2). pap. 6.95 (978-0-8075-0871-8(3)) Whitman, Albert & Co.

Bright, Paul. I'm Not Going Out There! Cort, Ben, illus. 2006. 28p. (J). (ps-2). 16.00 (978-1-56148-535-2(7)) Good Bks.

—Under the Bed. Cort, Ben, illus. 2004. 32p. (J). 16.00 (978-1-56148-436-2(9)) Good Bks.

Brisco, Dianna. The Day Marcus Flew. 2007. (J). per. 9.99 (***978-1-60247-024-8(3)***) Tate Publishing & Enterprises, L.L.C.

Brown, J. A. Scaredy Duck. Knight, Paula, illus. 2004. (Funny Faces Ser.). 10p. (J). 3.95 (978-1-58925-716-0(2) , tiger tales) ME Media LLC.

Bruchac, Joseph. Whisper in the Dark. Comport, Sally Wern, illus. 2005. 192p. (J). (gr. 5 up). 15.99 (978-0-06-058087-2(9)); lib. bdg. 16.89 (978-0-06-058088-9(7)) HarperCollins Pubs.

Bunting, Eve. Snowboarding on Monster Mountain. 2003. (Illus.). 64p. (J). 15.95 (978-0-8126-2704-6(0)) Cricket Bks.

Cameron, Ann. Julian's Glorious Summer. 2002. (Illus.). (J). 12.87 (978-0-7587-1354-4(1)) Book Wholesalers, Inc.

Capdevila, Roser & Vendrell, Maria Martinez. El Agua Inquieta. 2003. Tr. of Rough Water. (SPA.). 24p. (J). 7.95 (978-84-233-1742-4(0)) Ediciones Destino ESP. *Dist:* Planeta Publishing Corp.

Carlow, Emma. Flora the Fairy. Carlow, Emma, illus. 2005. (Green Bananas Ser.). (Illus.). 48p. (J). (978-0-7787-1022-6(X)) Crabtree Publishing Co.

Carlson, Nancy. Harriet's Recital. 2006. (J). pap. 6.95 (978-1-57505-929-7(0) , First Avenue Editions) Lerner Publishing Group.

—There's a Big, Beautiful World Out There! Carlson, Nancy, illus. 2004. 32p. (J). pap. 5.99 (978-0-14-240184-2(6) , Puffin) Penguin Group (USA) Inc.

—There's a Big, Beautiful World Out There! 2002. (Illus.). 32p. (J). (ps-3). 15.99 (978-0-670-03580-9(7) , Viking Juvenile) Penguin Group (USA) Inc.

Carlson, Nancy L. Harriet's Recital. 2006. (Illus.). (J). 15.95 (978-1-57505-898-6(7) , Carolrhoda Bks.) Lerner Publishing Group.

Carlstrom, Nancy White. What a Scare. Degen, Bruce, illus. 2002. (Jesse Bear Ser.). 32p. (J). 6.99 (978-0-689-85190-2(1) , Aladdin) Simon & Schuster Children's Publishing.

—What a Scare, Jesse Bear! 2002. (ps-2). lib. bdg. 15.30 (978-0-613-90790-3(6)) Tandem Library Bks.

Catalano, Dominic. Hush! Catalano, Dominic, illus. 2003. (Illus.). 32p. (J). (gr. k-3). 14.95 (978-1-57768-679-8(9) , Gingham Dog Pr) School Specialty Publishing.

Cave, Kathryn & Maland. Brave Little Grork. (Illus.). 30p. (J). (978-0-340-74677-6(7) , Hodder Children's Books) Hodder Children's Division.

Celsi, Teresa. The Fourth Little Pig. (Metro Reading Program Ser.). (J). (gr. k). 2000. 45.95 (978-1-58830-030-0(7)); 1999. 29.95 (978-1-58120-118-5(4)) Metropolitan Teaching & Learning Co.

Chaconas, Dori. Pennies in a Jar. Lewin, Ted, illus. 2007. 32p. (J). (ps-3). 16.95 (***978-1-56145-422-8(2)*** , Peachtree Junior) Peachtree Pubs., Ltd.

Child, Lauren. Boo! Made You Jump! 2007. (Charlie & Lola Ser.). 24p. (J). (ps-1). pap. 3.99 (***978-0-448-44696-7(0)*** , Grosset & Dunlap) Penguin Group (USA) Inc.

Child, Lauren. Can You Maybe Turn the Light On? 2007. 32p. (J). pap. 3.99 (978-0-448-44570-0(0) , Grosset & Dunlap) Penguin Group (USA) Inc.

Childress, H. Lee. The Cane. 2007. pap. 9.00 (***978-0-8059-8453-8(4)***) Dorrance Publishing Co., Inc.

Christopher, Lawrence. The Tickle Fingers: Where Is Pinky? Christopher, Lawrence, illus. 2006. (ENG., Illus.). 24p. (J). (ps up). 9.95 (978-0-9712278-3-5(7)) MF Unlimited.

Christopher, Matt. Football Nightmare. 2001. 128p. (J). (gr. 3-7). 15.95 (978-0-316-14370-7(7)); pap. 4.99 (978-0-316-14307-3(3)) Little, Brown Bks. for Young Readers.

—Football Nightmare. 2001. (gr. 3-6). lib. bdg. 12.40 (978-0-613-44166-7(4)) Tandem Library Bks.

Clark, John T. & Clark, Nicole K. Adventures in Dreamtime. l.t. ed. 1998. (Illus.). 32p. (J). (gr. k-2). 15.95 (978-1-892176-12-7(2)) PremaNations Publishing.

Clarke, Jane. Gilbert in Deep. Fuge, Charles, illus. 2007. 32p. (J). (ps-2). 12.95 (***978-1-4027-5125-7(7)***) Sterling Publishing Co., Inc.

Cole, Brock. Fair Monaco. 2004. (Illus.). 32p. (J). 16.95 (978-1-932425-07-9(1) , Lemniscaat) Boyds Mills Pr.

Cosby, Bill. One Dark & Scary Night. 1999. (Little Bill Books for Beginning Readers Ser.). (J). (gr. k-3). pap. 47.88 (978-0-439-04655-8(6) , Cartwheel Bks.) Scholastic, Inc.

—One Dark & Scary Night. 1999. (Little Bill Books for Beginning Readers Ser.). (J). (gr. k-3). (978-0-606-15831-2(6)) Tandem Library Bks.

—One Dark & Scary Night: Level. 3. Honeywood, Varnette P., illus. 1999. (Little Bill Books for Beginning Readers Ser.: No. 7). 40p. (J). (gr. k-3). pap. 3.99 (978-0-590-51476-7(8) , Cartwheel Bks.) Scholastic, Inc.

Cosby, Bill & Honeywood, Varnette P. One Dark & Scary Night. 1999. (Little Bill Books for Beginning Readers Ser.). (Illus.). (J). (gr. k-3). pap. 13.95 (978-0-590-51475-0(X)) Scholastic, Inc.

Cosgrove, Stephen. Buttermilk. James, Robin, illus. ed. 2003. (Serendipity Ser.). 32p. (J). (gr. k-5). pap. 4.99 (978-0-8431-0487-5(2) , Price Stern Sloan) Penguin Group (USA) Inc.

—Buttermilk. 2003. (gr. k-3). lib. bdg. 13.00 (978-0-613-89165-3(1)) Tandem Library Bks.

Courtney, Richard, illus. The Monster under the Shed. 2001. (Pictureback Bk.). 24p. (J). (ps-3). pap. 3.25 (978-0-375-81371-9(3) , Random Hse. Bks. for Young Readers) Random Hse. Children's Bks.

Cox, Judy. Mean, Mean Maureen Green. Fisher, Cynthia, illus. 1999. 80p. (J). (gr. 1-5). tchr. ed. 15.95 (978-0-8234-1502-1(3)) Holiday Hse., Inc.

Crawford, Deborah. Tyler the Turtle Is Afraid of the Dark. Balzer, Jeremy, illus. 2006. 32p. (J). 14.95 (***978-0-9770516-1-8(7)***) Laffin Minor Pr.

Culver, Dan. My Little Everest: A Story about Dealing with Fear. 2000. (Illus.). 48p. (J). (gr. 3-7). 11.95 (978-1-55039-105-3(4)) Sono Nis Pr. CAN. *Dist:* Orca Bk. Pubs. USA.

Cunningham, Laura Shaine. The Midnight Diary of Zoya Blume. 176p. (J). 2006. pap. 5.99 (978-0-06-072261-6(4) , Harper Trophy); 2005. (gr. 3 up). 15.99 (978-0-06-072259-3(2) , Geringer, Laura Book) HarperCollins Pubs.

Cuyler, Margery. Stop, Drop, & Roll. Howard, Arthur, illus. 2001. (Jessica Worries Ser.). 32p. (J). (ps-2). 17.99 (978-0-689-84355-6(0)) Simon & Schuster Children's Publishing.

D'Agata, Tabatha. Storm Tunes. Lineberger, Judy, illus. 2006. (Yes, I Can Read! Ser.: Bk. 2). 30p. (J). 6.95 (***978-1-934138-02-1(9)***) Bouncing Ball Bks., Inc.

Dahl, Michael. The Tall, Tall Slide. Gray, Sara, illus. 2005. (Read-It! Readers Ser.). 32p. (J). (ps). lib. bdg. 18.60 (978-1-4048-1186-7(9)) Picture Window Bks.

The Daniel & the Lions- Beginner's Biblereg; 2007. 24p. (J). 5.99 (978-0-8297-4938-0(1)) Vida Pubs.

Day, Marie. Quennu & the Cave Bear: A Prehistoric Tale. 1999. (gr. k-3). lib. bdg. 15.25 (978-0-613-26686-4(2)) Tandem Library Bks.

DeSmet, Sara. Scared Silly. DeSmet, Sara, illus. 2006. (Illus.). 32p. (J). 15.95 (978-1-60108-009-7(3)) Red Cygnet Pr.

Dickinson, Peter. Chuck & Danielle. 115p. (J). (gr. 3-5). pap. 3.99 (978-0-8072-1504-3(X) , Listening Library) Random Hse. Audio Publishing Group.

—Chuck & Danielle. 2001. (Illus.). 128p. (gr. 4-7). pap. 12.00 (978-0-375-89505-0(1) , Yearling) Random Hse. Children's Bks.

—Chuck & Danielle. 2001. lib. bdg. 21.10 (978-0-613-87813-5(2)) Tandem Library Bks.

Dongweck, James. The Dragon Cant. Baker, Joe, illus. 2004. 32p. (J). per. 16.95 (978-0-9719632-0-7(7)) Golden Monkey Publishing, LLC.

Drake, Isabelle. La Cancion de Gabriela: Como Me Adapto a un Lugar Nuevo. Burris, Priscilla Garcia, illus. 2007. (SPA.). 32p. (J). (ps-3). 12.99 (***978-0-06-114102-7(X)*** , Rayo) HarperCollins Pubs.

Drouin, Véronique. L' Ile D'Aurélie. 2004. (Mon Roman Ser.). (FRE.). 304p. (J). (gr. 2). pap. (978-2-89021-690-7(X)) Diffusion du livre Mirabel.

East, Jacqueline. Ed the Pup I'm Scared of the Dark. 1999. (Ed the Pup Ser.). (ps-3). (978-1-894155-77-9(7)) Cethial & Bossche Co.

Eaton Deborah. Canciones de monstruos (Monster Songs) 2007. (Lecturas para niños de verdad - Nivel 2 (Real Kids Readers - Level 2) Ser.). (J). pap. 5.95 (***978-0-8225-7803-1(4)*** , Ediciones Lerner) Lerner Publishing Group.

Eaton, Deborah. Monster Songs. Handelman, Dorothy, photos by. 1999. (Real Kids Readers Ser.). (Illus.). 32p. (gr. k-2). (J). pap. 4.99 (978-0-7613-2079-1(2)); lib. bdg. 18.90 (978-0-7613-2054-8(7)) Lerner Publishing Group. (Millbrook Pr.).

—Monster Songs. 1999. (J). (978-0-606-19162-3(3)); lib. bdg. 11.80 (978-0-613-16767-3(8)) Tandem Library Bks.

Egan, Tim. The Experiments of Doctor Vermin. Egan, Tim, illus. 2002. (Illus.). 32p. (J). (gr. k-3). tchr. ed. 15.00 (978-0-618-13224-9(4)) Houghton Mifflin Co. Trade & Reference Div.

Elkins, Stephen. Know God, No Fear. Reisch, Jessie, illus. 2003. 32p. (J). (gr. k-5). 14.99 (978-0-8054-2658-8(2)) B&H Publishing Grp.

Ellis, Sarah. Ben Over Night. LaFave, Kim, illus. 2005. 32p. (J). (978-1-55041-807-1(6)) Fitzhenry & Whiteside, Ltd.

Ellsworth, Mark R. The Quiniela of Angels. 2006. 19p. (YA). per. 8.95 (***978-1-59453-841-4(7)*** , 3319, Airleaf Publishing) Airleaf Publishing & Bookselling.

Emberley, Edward R. Go Away, Big Green Monster! 2005. (Illus.). 32p. (J). (ps-1). reprint ed. 10.99 (978-0-316-23653-9(5)) Little Brown & Co.

Emmett, Jonathan. Terry Takes Off. Rutherford, Peter, illus. 2006. 32p. (J). (***978-1-4048-3132-2(0)***) Picture Window Bks.

Engelbreit, Mary. Queen of Halloween. 2008. 32p. (J). 16.99 (***978-0-06-008190-4(2)***); lib. bdg. 17.89 (***978-0-06-008191-1(0)***) HarperCollins Pubs.

Ernst, Lisa Campbell. Bubba & Trixie. 2000. (J). (978-0-606-20085-1(1)) Tandem Library Bks.

Espinosa, Laura & Espinosa, Leo. Otis & Rae & the Grumbling Splunk. Espinosa, Laura & Espinosa, Leo, illus. 2008. 32p. (J). (ps-3). 12.95 (***978-0-618-98206-6(X)***) Houghton Mifflin Co.

Experiences of Terror. Date not set. (Nelson Readers Ser.: 5). (J). pap. (978-0-17-557038-6(8)) Addison-Wesley Longman, Inc.

Faine, Edward Allan. Little Ned Stories. Waites, Joan C., illus. 1999. 128p. (J). (gr. k-3). pap. 9.99 (978-0-9654651-5-1(2)) IM Pr.

Faulkner, Keith. The Scared Little Bear: A Not Too Scary Pop up Book. Lambert, Jonathan, illus. 2000. 16p. (J). (ps-2). bds. 9.95 (978-0-531-30267-5(9) , Orchard Bks.) Scholastic, Inc.

Fear in Florence, 3 vols. 2002. (Hannah & Niki Mysteries Ser.: 2). 278p. (J). pap. 14.95 (978-0-9717849-0-1(6)) InfoHi Publishing.

The Fearful Fairy. ed. 2007. (Illus.). 40p. (J). 16.95 (***978-0-9793823-0-7(0)***) StonesThrow Publishing LLC.

Fears & Phantoms. 2006. (J). (978-1-933343-20-4(6)) Stabenfeldt Inc.

Feldman, Eve B. Seymour, the Formerly Fearful. 2000. 164p. (J). (gr. 4-7). pap. 11.95 (978-0-595-00391-4(5) , Backinprint.com) iUniverse, Inc.

Figueredo, D. H. Un Mundo Nuevo. de la Vega, Eida, tr. from ENG. Sanchez, Enrique O., illus. 2000. (SPA & ENG.). 32p. (J). (gr. k-2). 15.95 (978-1-58430-006-9(X) , LW2987); pap. 6.95 (978-1-58430-007-6(8) , LW3110) Lee & Low Bks., Inc.

—Un Mundo Nuevo. Sanchez, Enrique O., illus. 2000. (SPA.). (J). (978-0-606-19833-2(4)); (978-0-606-19834-9(2)) Tandem Library Bks.

—When This World Was New. Sanchez, Enrique O., illus. 2003. (J). pap. 6.95 (978-1-58430-173-8(2)); 1999. 32p. (YA). 12.76 (978-1-880000-86-1(5)) Lee & Low Bks., Inc.

—When This World Was New. 2003. (gr. k-3). lib. bdg. 15.25 (978-0-613-83688-3(X)) Tandem Library Bks.

Finley, Martha. Mildred's Boys & Girls, Vol. 6. (Mildred Classics Ser.: Vol. 6). 288p. pap. 6.95 (978-1-58182-232-8(4)) Cumberland Hse. Publishing.

Firth, Barbara, illus. Let's Go Home, Little Bear. 2002. (Little Bear Picture Bks.). (J). 13.83 (978-0-7587-2976-7(6)) Book Wholesalers, Inc.

Fore, S. J. Tiger Can't Sleep. Alley, R. W., illus. 2006. 32p. (J). 15.99 (978-0-670-06078-8(X) , Viking Juvenile) Penguin Group (USA) Inc.

Foreman, Michael. Surprise! Surprise! 2004. (Illus.). 32p. (J). pap. (978-1-84270-379-3(X)) Andersen.

Fox, Sabrina. Who Can Help Me Sleep? Rothan, Ann, illus. 2004. 32p. (ps-3). 16.95 (978-1-885394-36-1(5)) Amber Lotus Publishing.

Friedman, Laurie B. I'm Not Afraid of This Haunted House. Murfin, Teresa, illus. 2005. 32p. (J). (ps-ps). 15.95 (978-1-57505-751-4(4) , Carolrhoda Bks.) Lerner Publishing Group.

Friedman, Rainey L. Monsters in Your Bed... Monsters in Your Head. Dill, Betsy, illus. 1999. 32p. (J). 15.95 (978-0-9666199-1-1(9)) DreamDog Pr.

Froeber, Sarah & Mosher, Kim. Pelican & Pelicant. 2003. (Illus.). 36p. (J). 17.99 (978-0-9744926-0-5(4)) Toucan Pr., Inc.

Fuchs-Rice, Dwayne. Troika. 2007. 248p. per. 16.95 (***978-0-595-45834-9(3)***) iUniverse, Inc.

Fuks, Menuhah & Tager, Gavriella. Smile with Avigayil #2: Avigayil & the Black Cat. Haas, Esti, illus. 2006. (ENG.). 64p. (J). 12.95 (***978-1-932443-58-5(4)***) Judaica Pr., Inc., The.

Fuqua, Jonathon Scott. Reappearance of Sam Webber. 1999. (Illus.). 232p. (YA). pap. 23.95 (978-1-890862-03-9(7)) Bancroft Pr.

—The Reappearance of Sam Webber. 2001. (Illus.). 288p. (J). (gr. 5). reprint ed. pap. 9.99 (978-0-7636-1424-9(6)) Candlewick Pr.

Galbraith, Kathryn Osebold. One Shy Bunny, One Dark Night. Mack, Jeff, illus. 2008. (J). (***978-0-15-216246-7(1)***) Harcourt Trade Pubs.

Gallo, Donald R., compiled by. What Are You Afraid Of? Stories about Phobias. 2006. 208p. (J). (gr. 7). 16.99 (978-0-7636-2654-9(6)) Candlewick Pr.

Gallo, Donald R., ed. What Are You Afraid Of? Stories about Phobias. 2007. (Illus.). 208p. (YA). (gr. 7). pap. 8.99 (***978-0-7636-3417-9(4)***) Candlewick Pr.

Gay, Michel. Zee Is Not Scared. Mianowski, Marie, tr. from FRE. 2004. (Illus.). 32p. (J). (gr. k-ps). tchr. ed. 15.00 (978-0-618-43931-7(5) , Clarion Bks.) Houghton Mifflin Co. Trade & Reference Div.

Genechten, Guido van. Floppy in the Dark. 2004. (Illus.). (J). (TAM, CZE, VIE, SPA & GUJ., 25p. (978-1-85269-238-4(3)); (TAM, CZE, VIE, SPA & GUJ., 25p. (978-1-85269-239-1(1)); (TAM, CZE, VIE, SPA & GUJ., 25p. (978-1-85269-240-7(5)); (TAM, CZE, VIE, SPA & GUJ., 25p. (978-1-85269-241-4(3)); (TAM, CZE, VIE, SPA & GUJ., 25p. (978-1-85269-244-5(8)); (TAM, CZE, VIE, SPA & GUJ., 25p. (978-1-85269-245-2(6)); (TAM, CZE, VIE, SPA & GUJ., 25p. (978-1-85269-247-6(2)); (TAM, CZE, VIE, SPA & GUJ., 25p. (978-1-85269-249-0(9)); (CZE, TAM, VIE, SPA & GUJ., 25p. (978-1-85269-250-6(2)); (TAM, CZE, VIE, SPA & GUJ., 25p. (978-1-85269-251-3(0)); (TAM, CZE, VIE, SPA & GUJ., 25p. (978-1-85269-252-0(9)); (TAM, CZE, SPA, VIE & GUJ., 25p. (978-

E F G

1-85269-253-7(7)); (TAM, CZE, VIE, SPA & GUJ., 25p. (978-1-85269-278-0(2)); (TAM, CZE, VIE, SPA & GUJ., 25p. (978-1-85269-282-7(0)); (ENG & POR., 32p. (978-1-85269-246-9(4)) Mantra Publishing, Ltd.

Genechten, Guido van, tr. from DUT. Floppy in the Dark: Veshllapushi Ne Erresire. 2004. (TAM, CZE, VIE, SPA & GUJ., Illus.). 25p. (J). (978-1-85269-234-6(0)) Mantra Publishing, Ltd.

Geoghegan, Adrienne. There's a Wardrobe in My Monster! Johnson, Adrian, illus. 2003. (Picture Bks.). 32p. (J). (ps-3). 15.95 (978-1-57505-414-8(0) , Carolrhoda Bks.) Lerner Publishing Group.

George, Olivia. The Bravest Girls in the World. DuBurke, Randy, illus. 2004. 32p. (J). lib. bdg. 15.00 (*978-1-4242-0241-6(8)) Fitzgerald Bks.

Goldin, Barbara Diamond. Night Lights: A Sukkot Story. Carmi, Giora, illus. 2004. (gr. k-3). 13.95 (978-0-8074-0803-2(4) , 142687) URJ Pr.

Gollub, Matthew. The Twenty-Five Mixtec Cats. Martinez, Leovigildo, illus. 2004. 32p. (J). pap. 6.95 (978-1-889910-29-1(5)) Tortuga Pr.

Gollub, Matthew W. The Twenty-five Mixtec Cats. Martinez, Leovigildo, illus. rev. ed. 2004. 32p. (J). 15.95 (978-1-889910-28-4(7)) Tortuga Pr.

Gorbachev, Valeri. Dragon Is Coming! 2008. (J). (*978-0-15-205196-9(1)) Harcourt Trade Pubs.

Goss, Leon. By the Light of the Moon. Luo, Shiyin Sean, illus. 2005. (J). pap. (978-1-933156-12-5(0) , Vision-Quest Kids) GSVQ Publishing.

Grant, Vicki. Dead-End Job. 2006. 112p. (YA). lib. bdg. 14.95 (978-1-55143-566-4(7)) Orca Bk. Pubs. USA.

Guilloppe, Antoine. One Scary Night. 2005. (Illus.). 32p. (J). 15.95 (978-0-689-04636-0(7) , Milk & Cookies) ibooks, Inc.

Haddix, Margaret Peterson. Among the Impostors. (Shadow Children Ser.). (J). (gr. 3-7). 2002. 192p. mass mkt. 5.99 (978-0-689-83908-5(1) , Aladdin); 2001. (Illus.). 176p. 16.95 (978-0-689-83904-7(9)) Simon & Schuster Children's Publishing.

—Among the Impostors. 2002. (Shadow Children Ser.). (gr. 3-6). lib. bdg. 13.00 (978-0-613-61844-1(0)) Tandem Library Bks.

Hall, Kirsten. Going Batty. Burnett, Lindy, illus. 2001. (Hello Reader! Ser.). (J). pap. (978-0-439-31706-1(1)) Scholastic, Inc.

—I'm Not Scared. 2004. (My First Reader Ser.). 31p. (J). (gr. k-1). pap. 3.95 (978-0-516-24631-4(3) , Children's Pr.) Scholastic Library Publishing.

—I'm Not Scared. Holub, Joan, illus. 2003. (My First Reader Ser.). 32p. (J). 18.50 (978-0-516-22929-4(X) , Children's Pr.) Scholastic Library Publishing.

—I'm So Scared! Eugenie, illus. 2002. (My First Hello Reader! Ser.). (J). 2.95 (978-0-439-32098-6(4)) Scholastic, Inc.

Hambleton, Laura. I'm Afraid Too! (Illus.). 2002. 24p. 22.95 (978-1-84059-320-4(2)); 2001. 32p. (J). pap. 7.95 (978-1-84059-317-4(2)) Milet Publishing.

Hanson, Regina. A Season for Mangoes. Velasquez, Eric, illus. 2005. 40p. (J). (gr. k-3). 15.00 (978-0-618-15972-7(X) , Clarion Bks.) Houghton Mifflin Co. Trade & Reference Div.

Harcourt School Publishers Staff. Trofeos On Level: La Pieza de Piano. 3rd ed. 2002. (SPA., Illus.). pap. 6.80 (978-0-15-324083-6(0)) Harcourt Schl. Pubs.

Harmon, Lyn. Clyde's Clam Farm. 2001. (Illus.). 132p. (gr. 4-7). pap. 9.95 (978-0-595-16339-7(4) , Backinprint.com) iUniverse, Inc.

Heide, Florence Parry. Some Things Are Scary. Feiffer, Jules, illus. 2000. (J). 0.01 net. (978-0-07-361222-5(7) , Random House) Random House Publishing Group.

—Some Things Are Scary: No Matter How Old You Are. ed. 2003. (Illus.). 40p. (J). 12.00 (978-0-7636-2147-6(1)) Candlewick Pr.

Heiligman, Deborah. Mike Swan, Sink or Swim. 1998. (978-0-606-13610-5(X)) Tandem Library Bks.

Helakoski, Leslie. Big Chickens. Cole, Henry, illus. 2006. 32p. (J). (ps). 15.99 (978-0-525-47575-0(3) , Dutton Juvenile) Penguin Group (USA) Inc.

Helakoski, Leslie. Big chickens Fly the Coop. Cole, Henry, illus. 2008. 32p. (J). (ps). 15.99 (*978-0-525-47915-4(5) , Dutton Juvenile) Penguin Group (USA) Inc.

Hendry, Diana. Very Noisy Night. 2001. (gr. k-3). lib. bdg. 14.15 (978-0-613-44427-9(2)) Tandem Library Bks.

Hendry, Diana. The Very Snowy Christmas. Chapman, Jane, illus. 32p. (J). 2007. pap. 6.95 (*978-1-58925-406-0(6)); 2005. 15.95 (978-1-58925-051-2(6)) ME Media LLC. (tiger tales).

Henkes, Kevin. Words of Stone. 2005. (J). 152p. (*978-1-4156-2647-4(2)); 160p. reprint ed. pap. 5.99 (978-0-06-078230-6(7)) HarperCollins Pubs. (Harper Trophy).

Henry, Panya A. Francis' Fear of Flying. 2006. (ENG.). 40p. per. 24.95 (*978-1-4259-3162-9(6)) AuthorHouse.

Herman, Gail. Spiders Everywhere. Zimmerman, Jerry, illus. 2000. (Hello Reader! Ser.). (J). pap. (978-0-439-20540-5(9)) Scholastic, Inc.

Hest, Amy. Off to School, Baby Duck! Barton, Jill, illus. 2002. (J). 26.15 (978-0-7587-3294-1(5)) Book Wholesalers, Inc.

Hest, Amy. Off to School, Baby Duck! Barton, Jill, illus. 2007. 32p. (J). (ps-1). pap. 6.99 (*978-0-7636-3438-4(7)) Candlewick Pr.

Hicks, Barbara Jean. Jitterbug Jam: A Monster Tale. Deacon, Alexis, illus. 2005. 40p. (J). 16.00 (978-0-374-33685-1(7) , Farrar, Straus & Giroux) Farrar, Straus & Giroux.

Higgs, Liz Curtis. Go Away, Dark Night. Munger, Nancy, illus. 1998. 40p. (J). (ps-3). 9.99 (978-1-57856-129-2(9) , WaterBrook Pr.) WaterBrook Pr.

Holm, Jennifer L. The Creek. 2003. 240p. (J). (gr. 7 up). 15.99 (978-0-06-000133-9(X)); 16.89 (978-0-06-000134-6(8)) HarperCollins Pubs.

—The Creek. l.t. ed. 2003. 303p. (J). 21.95 (978-0-7862-6143-7(9) , Large Print Pr.) Thorndike Pr.

Holm, Jennifer L. & Holm, Matthew. Our Hero. 2005. (Babymouse Ser.). (Illus.). 96p. (J). (gr. 2-5). pap. 5.95 (978-0-375-83230-7(0)); lib. bdg. 12.99 (978-0-375-93230-4(5)) Random Hse. Children's Bks. (Random Hse. Bks. for Young Readers).

Holub, Joan. Scaredy-Pants: A Halloween Story. Terry, Will, illus. 2007. (Ant Hill Ser.). 24p. (J). lib. bdg. 13.89 (*978-1-4169-2561-3(9) , Aladdin) Simon & Schuster Children's Publishing.

—Scaredy-Pants! A Halloween Story. Terry, Will, illus. 2007. (Ant Hill Ser.). 24p. (J). pap. 3.99 (*978-1-4169-0956-9(7) , Aladdin) Simon & Schuster Children's Publishing.

Hornsby, Ashley. Pretty Little Lilly & the Magical Night (Hard Bound) Couch, Greg, illus. 2007. 32p. 15.95 (978-0-9777241-0-9(7)) Cepia LLC.

Hornsby, Ashley Brooke. Pretty Little Lilly & the Magical Night (paperback) 2006. (J). (978-0-9777241-1-6(5)) Cepia LLC.

Howe, James. Pinky & Rex Go to Camp. 1999. (gr. k-3). lib. bdg. 11.80 (978-0-7857-0627-4(5)); (J). (gr. 1-4). (978-0-606-16306-4(9)) Tandem Library Bks.

Howe, James & Sweet, Melissa. Pinky & Rex Go to Camp. 1999. (Pinky & Rex Ser.). (Illus.). 48p. (J). (gr. 1-4). pap. 3.99 (978-0-689-82588-0(9) , 076714003996, Aladdin) Simon & Schuster Children's Publishing.

Hulme, Joy N. Eerie Feary Feeling: A Hairy Scary Pop-up Book. Ely, Paul & Dudley, Dick, illus. 2006. 12p. (J). (gr. k-4). reprint ed. 14.00 (978-1-4223-5171-0(8)) DIANE Publishing Co.

Hunter, Tammy. Tede's Search for his Mom. 2004. 27p. pap. 14.95 (978-1-4137-2854-5(5)) PublishAmerica, Inc.

Impey, Rose. The Ankle Grabber. Kemp, Moira, illus. 1998. (Creepies Ser.). 48p. (J). (gr. 1-3). lib. bdg. 22.60 (978-1-57505-296-0(2) , Carolrhoda Bks.) Lerner Publishing Group.

—Jumble Joan. Kemp, Moira, illus. 1998. (Creepies Ser.). 48p. (J). (gr. 1-3). lib. bdg. (978-1-57505-295-3(4) , Carolrhoda Bks.) Lerner Publishing Group.

—Scare Yourself to Sleep. Kemp, Moira, illus. 1998. (Creepies Ser.). 48p. (J). (gr. 1-3). pap. 6.95 (978-1-57505-316-5(0) , Carolrhoda Bks.) Lerner Publishing Group.

Inches, Alison. Hooray for Polka Dots! Chernichaw, Ian, illus. 2005. (Blue's Clues Ser.: Vol. 10). 24p. (J). pap. 3.99 (978-0-689-87210-5(0) , Simon Spotlight/Nickelodeon) Simon & Schuster Children's Publishing.

It's Dark! 2005. (J). bds. (978-0-9769910-1-4(2)) Terrific Twins LLC.

James, Richard E., III. Adventures of the Elements Vol. 3: Dangerous Games. Lyle, Maryann, ed. Welch, Chad, illus. 2004. 169p. (YA). (gr. 3-12). pap. 5.95 (978-0-9675901-2-7(4)) Three Rivers Council, BSA, Inc.

Jensen, Patricia. I Am Sick. Hantel, Johanna, illus. (J). (gr. k-1). 2006. 32p. pap. 3.95 (978-0-516-24970-4(3)); 2005. 31p. 18.50 (978-0-516-24878-3(2)) Scholastic Library Publishing. (Children's Pr.).

Johnston, Tony. Boo! Croll, Carolyn, illus. 1998. (Hello Reader! Ser.). (J). 3.99 (978-0-590-37998-4(4)) Scholastic, Inc.

Jordan, Apple & Random House Disney Staff. Just Like Me! 2005. (Step into Reading Ser.). (Illus.). 32p. (J). (ps-1). lib. bdg. 11.99 (978-0-7364-8039-0(0) , RH/Disney) Random Hse. Children's Bks.

—Just Like Me. 2005. (Step into Reading Ser.). (Illus.). 32p. (J). (ps-1). pap. 3.99 (978-0-7364-2288-8(9) , RH/Disney) Random Hse. Children's Bks.

Jordan, Mark. Courage the Monkey. 2006. (Illus.). 40p. (J). 13.95 (978-0-9717013-7-3(7)) Decere Publishing.

Keep, Richard. A Thump from Upstairs: Starring Mr. Boo & Max. Keep, Richard, illus. 2005. (Illus.). 36p. (J). (ps-ps). 15.95 (978-1-56145-348-1(X)) Peachtree Pubs., Ltd.

Kehl, Mark. Tournament of Fear: And Other Martial Arts Stories. Artenstein, Michael, ed. 1999. (Sports Shorts Ser.). (Illus.). 95p. (J). (gr. 3-7). pap. 5.95 (978-1-56565-949-0(X) , 09499W, Roxbury Park) Lowell Hse.

Keller, Holly. Brave Horace. 1998. (Illus.). 32p. (J). (ps-3). 14.89 (978-0-688-15408-0(5)) HarperCollins Pubs.

—Help! A Story of Friendship. Keller, Holly, illus. 2007. (Illus.). 32p. (J). (ps-3). 16.99 (*978-0-06-123913-7(5)); lib. bdg. 17.89 (*978-0-06-123914-4(3)) HarperCollins Pubs. (Greenwillow Bks.).

Keller, Holly. Sophie's Window. Keller, Holly, illus. 2005. (Illus.). 32p. (J). 15.99 (978-0-06-056282-3(X)); 16.89 (978-0-06-056283-0(8)) HarperCollins Pubs.

Keselman, Gabriela. Marc Just Couldn't Sleep. Villamuza, Noemi, illus. 2004. 32p. (J). 15.95 (978-1-929132-68-3(9)) Kane/Miller Bk. Pubs., Inc.

Keyes, Eric, 3rd, et al. The Light in the Dark, 1. Marie, Paula Braxton, illus. l.t. ed. 2004. 40p. (J). per. 14.99 (978-0-9722795-5-0(5) , Precious Gems) EbonyEnergy Publishing.

Kido, Yukiko, illus. In a Scary Old House. 2006. (I'm Going to Read Ser.). 24p. (J). pap. 3.95 (978-1-4027-3406-9(9) , 1261644) Sterling Publishing Co., Inc.

Kline, Suzy. Horrible Harry & the Drop of Doom. (Horrible Harry Ser.: No. 9). (Illus.). 64p. (J). (gr. 2-4). 2000. pap. 3.99 (978-0-14-037256-4(3) , Puffin); 1998. 13.99 (978-0-670-85849-1(8) , Viking Juvenile) Penguin Group (USA) Inc.

—Horrible Harry & the Drop of Doom. 2000. (Illus.). (J). 10.79 (978-0-606-17861-7(9)) Tandem Library Bks.

Kline, Suzy & Kline, Suzy. Horrible Harry & the Drop of Doom. Remkiewicz, Frank, illus. 2000. 57p. (J). (gr. 2-5). lib. bdg. 11.80 (978-0-613-28521-6(2)) Tandem Library Bks.

Koller, Jackie. No Such Thing. Lewin, Betsy, illus. 2003. 32p. (J). (gr. k-2). 15.95 (978-1-56397-490-8(8)) Boyds Mills Pr.

Krensky, Stephen. Fraidy Cats. Lewin, Betsy, illus. 2004. 32p. (J). lib. bdg. 15.00 (978-1-59054-383-2(1)) Fitzgerald Bks.

Lagonegro, Melissa. Monsters Get Scared of the Dark, Too. Harchy, Atelier Philippe, illus. 2003. (Disney Books in Pictureback). 16p. (J). (ps-2). pap. 3.99 (978-0-7364-2162-1(9) , 53528995, RH/Disney) Random Hse. Children's Bks.

Lai-Ma. The Monster of Palapala Mountain. 2006. (Illus.). 44p. (J). 17.95 (978-0-9762056-5-4(3)) Heryin Publishing Corp.

Laminack, Lester L. Trevor's Wiggly-Wobbly Tooth. McCord, Kathi Garry, illus. 2002. 32p. (J). pap. 7.95 (978-1-56145-279-8(3)) Peachtree Pubs., Ltd.

—Trevor's Wiggly-Wobbly Tooth. McCord, Kathi G., illus. 1998. 32p. (J). (ps-2). 15.95 (978-1-56145-175-3(4)) Peachtree Pubs., Ltd.

Lamm, Drew. Pirates. Schuett, Stacey, illus. 2001. 40p. (gr. 4-7). 15.99 (978-0-7868-0392-7(4)) Hyperion Bks. for Children.

Larcombe, Jennifer Rees. The Terrible Giant. Bjorkman, Steve, illus. 2004. (Best Bible Stories Ser.). 24p. (ps-3). 2.99 (978-1-58134-054-9(0)) Crossway Bks.

Larsen, Wendy. After Dark. Larsen, Wendy, illus. 1999. (Illus.). (J). (ps-3). pap. 10.99 (978-0-9665699-0-2(3)) Chase Pubns.

Lasky, Kathryn. Show & Tell Bunnies. Hafner, Marylin, illus. 2001. 32p. (J). (ps-3). pap. 5.99 (978-0-7636-1050-0(X)) Candlewick Pr.

—Show & Tell Bunnies. 2001. (ps-2). lib. bdg. 14.15 (978-0-613-44257-2(1)) Tandem Library Bks.

Lawrie, Robin & Lawrie, Christine, illus. Fear 3.1. 2007. 32p. (J). pap. (*978-1-59889-443-1(9)) Stone Arch Bks.

Layne, Steven L. My Brother Dan's Delicious. Galey, Chuck, illus. 2004. 32p. 15.95 (978-1-58980-071-7(0)) Pelican Publishing Co., Inc.

Lemieux, Jean. Toby Shoots for Infinity. Casson, Sophie, illus. 2005. 61p. (J). lib. bdg. 12.00 (*978-1-4242-1201-9(4)) Fitzgerald Bks.

Lenam, Salva. Kiko Dibuja y Pinta. Roman, Santi, illus. 2005. (Kiko Ser.). (SPA.). 10p. (J). 3.95 (978-84-95761-78-1(5)) Ediciones Norte, Inc.

Lester, Helen. Something Might Happen. Munsinger, Lynn, illus. 2003. 32p. (J). (gr. k-3). tchr. ed. 16.00 (978-0-618-25406-4(4) , Walter Lorraine) Houghton Mifflin Co. Trade & Reference Div.

L'Heureux, Christine, et al. Good Night! Lapierre, Claude, illus. rev. ed. 2000. (J). pap. (978-2-89450-176-4(5)) Chouette Publishing.

Life, Kay, illus. Benny's Boxcar Sleepover, Vol. 12. 2004. (Adventures of Benny & Watch: 12). 32p. (J). (gr. 1-3). pap. 3.95 (978-0-8075-0636-3(2)) Whitman, Albert & Co.

Lignell, Kirk. Listen to the Raindrops W/cd. 2007. 32p. 17.95 (*978-1-932399-15-8(1)) Huron River Pr.

Lin, Grace. Olvina Flies. Lin, Grace, illus. rev. ed. 2003. (Illus.). 32p. (J). (ps-2). 15.95 (978-0-8050-6711-8(6) , Holt, Henry & Co. Bks. For Young Readers) Holt, Henry & Co.

—Olvina Swims. rev. ed. 2007. (Illus.). 32p. (J). (ps-2). 16.95 (978-0-8050-7661-5(1)) Holt, Henry & Co.

Linko, G. J. Frank's Fear. 2004. (Seekers Ser.: No. 6). 108p. 5.99 (978-0-8066-4187-4(8) , Augsburg Bks.) Augsburg Fortress, Pubs.

The Lion Who Lost His Roar: A Story about Facing Your Fears. 2000. (Early Prevention Ser.). 53p. (J). pap. 11.50 (978-1-58815-004-2(6)) Childswork/Childsplay.

Listening with Zachary. (J). pap. 13.75 (978-0-8136-4655-8(3)) Modern Curriculum Pr.

Little Is Big. 2006. (Illus.). (J). (978-1-882601-58-5(0)) See-More's Workshop.

Little, Jean. Different Dragons. 2007. (Illus.). 112p. (J). (gr. 3). pap. 5.99 (978-0-14-331230-7(8) , Puffin) Penguin Group (USA) Inc.

Lozano, Neal. Can God See Me in the Dark? Hatke, Ben, illus. 2007. (J). (*978-1-883551-45-2(5) , Maple Corners Press) Attic Studio Publishing Hse.

Lucado, Max & Schmidt, Troy. Webster, the Scaredy Spider. 2005. 32p. (J). pap. 3.99 (978-1-4003-0665-7(5)) Nelson, Thomas Inc.

Lucke, Deb. The Boy Who Wouldn't Swim. 2008. (J). (*978-0-618-91484-5(6) , Clarion Bks.) Houghton Mifflin Co. Trade & Reference Div.

Lyssenko, Taras. Wendy's Fear of Heights. 2003. 14p. (J). (978-0-9740542-0-9(8)) Prairie Shore Creative, Inc.

MacDonald, Alan. Scaredy Mouse. Warnes, Tim, illus. (J). (ps-k). 2007. 18p. bds. 6.95 (*978-1-58925-827-3(4)); 2002. 32p. tchr. ed. 14.95 (978-1-58925-018-5(4)) ME Media LLC. (tiger tales).

Mackall, Dandi Daley. Little Lost Donkey. 2007. 26p. (J). bds. 6.99 (*978-1-4003-1009-8(1)) Nelson, Thomas Inc.

—No, No, Noah! Kucharik, Elena, illus. 2002. (I'm Not Afraid Ser.). 24p. (J). (ps-2). 6.99 (978-0-8499-7750-3(9)) Nelson, Thomas Inc.

Mackall, Dandi Daley. So No Noah! 2007. 26p. (J). bds. 6.99 (*978-1-4003-1007-4(5)) Nelson, Thomas Inc.

MacLean, Kerry Lee. Sophie's Not Afraid! A Bubble-Bug Book. 1999. (Illus.). 32p. (J). (gr. k-4). 16.95 (978-0-9652998-2-4(1)) On the Spot! Bks.

Maier, Inger M. When Fuzzy Was Afraid of Big & Loud Things. Candon, Jennifer, illus. 2005. 32p. (J). 14.95 (978-1-59147-322-0(5)); pap. 8.95 (978-1-59147-323-7(3)) American Psychological Assn. (Magination Pr.).

Maizel, Karen, illus. Jake's Brave Night. 2007. (I Can Read!). 32p. (J). pap. 3.99 (*978-0-310-71456-9(7)) Zonderkidz.

Martin, Jacqueline Briggs. Grandmother Bryant's Pocket. Mathers, Petra, illus. 2000. 48p. (J). (gr. k-3). pap. 5.95 (978-0-618-03309-6(2)) Houghton Mifflin Co. Trade & Reference Div.

—Grandmother Bryant's Pocket. 2000. (Illus.). (J). (978-0-606-18209-6(8)) Tandem Library Bks.

Marvin Redpost: Super Fast, Out of Control! 2002. (Marvin Redpost Ser.). (Illus.). (J). 11.91 (978-0-7587-6199-6(6)) Book Wholesalers, Inc.

Maselli, Christopher P. N. Choke Hold Bk. 7: They Must Not Surrender to Fear's Grip. 2004. 128p. (J). pap. 4.99 (978-0-310-70666-3(1)) Zonderkidz.

—Escape from Jungle Island. 1998. (Commander Kellie & the Superkids' Early Adventures Ser.). (J). pap. (978-1-57562-217-0(3)) Copeland, Kenneth Pubns.

Masurel, Claire. Big Bad Wolf. Iwai, Melissa, illus. 2002. 32p. (J). pap. 12.95 (978-0-439-28243-7(8) , Cartwheel Bks.) Scholastic, Inc.

May, Paul. Billy & the Seagulls. 2004. (Young Corgi Ser.). (Illus.). 229p. pap. 6.95 (978-0-552-55158-8(9) , Corgi) Transworld Publishers Ltd. GBR. *Dist:* Independent Pubs. Group.

Mayer, Mercer. Camping Out. 2002. (Little Critter Ser.). (Illus.). 24p. (J). (ps-k). pap. 3.95 (978-1-57768-806-8(6)) School Specialty Publishing.

—Camping Out. 2001. (ps-2). lib. bdg. 11.80 (978-0-613-79359-9(5)) Tandem Library Bks.

—There Are Monsters Everywhere. 2005. (Illus.). 32p. (YA). (ps-2). 15.99 (978-0-8037-0621-7(9) , Dial) Penguin Group (USA) Inc.

—There's a Nightmare in My Closet. Mayer, Mercer, illus. 2002. (Illus.). (J). 14.04 (978-0-7587-3783-0(1)) Book Wholesalers, Inc.

McConnaughhay, JoDee. Be Brave, Anna! God Helps Me When I'm Afraid. Caldwell, Lise, ed. Dubin, Jill, illus. 1999. (Happy Day Bks.). 24p. (J). (ps-2). 2.49 (978-0-7847-0895-8(9) , 04268, Bean Sprouts) Standard Publishing.

McDonald, Erin Melodie. What Am I Scared Of? Hanrahan, Denise, illus. 2002. 24p. per. 9.95 (978-0-9721427-0-0(3)) Talking Hands, Inc.

McDonald, Megan. Bedbugs. Johnson, Paul Brett, illus. 1999. 32p. (J). (ps-1). 16.99 (978-0-531-33193-4(8) , Orchard Bks.) Scholastic, Inc.

McGhee, Alison. Countdown to Kindergarten. Bliss, Harry, illus. 2006. 32p. (J). reprint ed. pap. 6.00 (978-0-15-205586-8(X) , Voyager Bks./Libros Viajeros) Harcourt Children's Bks.

—Countdown to Kindergarten. Bliss, Harry, illus. 2002. 32p. (J). (ps-2). 16.00 (978-0-15-202516-8(2) , Silver Whistle) Harcourt Trade Pubs.

—Countdown to Kindergarten. Bliss, Harry, illus. pap. 16.95 incl. audio (978-1-59112-467-2(0)); pap. incl. audio compact disk (978-1-59112-469-6(7)); pap. 18.95 incl. audio compact disk (978-1-59112-927-1(3)); pap. incl. audio (978-1-59112-929-5(X)) Live Oak Media.

McKay, Hilary. There's a Dragon Downstairs. Harvey, Amanda, tr. Harvey, Amanda, illus. 2005. 32p. (J). 16.95 (978-0-689-86774-3(3) , McElderry, Margaret K.) Simon & Schuster Children's Publishing.

McKeowen, Sean. Cualquier Cosa Menos la Inyeccion. McKeowen, Sean, illus. 2001. (Illus.). 32p. (J). (ps-3). pap. 7.50 (978-1-884083-34-1(X)) Maval Publishing, Inc.

McNamara, Margaret. First-Grade Bunny. Gordon, Mike, illus. ed. 2005. (Ready-to-Read Ser. Level 1). 32p. (J). lib. bdg. 15.00 (978-1-59054-926-1(0)) Fitzgerald Bks.

—First-Grade Bunny. Gordon, Mike, illus. 2005. (Ready-to-Read Ser.). 32p. (J). pap. 3.99 (978-0-689-86427-8(2)); lib. bdg. 11.89 (978-0-689-86428-5(0)) Simon & Schuster Children's Publishing. (Aladdin).

McNamara, Margaret. Snow Day. Gordon, Mike, illus. 2007. (Robin Hill School Ser.). 32p. (J). lib. bdg. 13.89 (*978-1-4169-3492-9(8)); pap. 3.99 (*978-1-4169-3493-6(6)) Simon & Schuster Children's Publishing. (Aladdin).

McQueen, John Troy. A World Full of Monsters. Brown, Marc, illus. 2001. 32p. (J). (gr. 5 up). 15.89 (978-0-06-029770-1(0)); (ps up). 15.95 (978-0-06-029769-5(7)) HarperCollins Pubs.

Metz, Lorijo. Floridius Bloom & the Planet of Gloom. Phelan, Matt, illus. 2007. 32p. (J). (gr. 1-3). 16.99 (978-0-8037-3084-7(5) , Dial) Penguin Group (USA) Inc.

Metzger, Steve. It's Beach Day! Wilhelm, Hans, illus. 1998. (Dinofours Ser.: No. 9). 32p. (J). (ps-1). pap. 3.25 (978-0-590-03267-4(4)) Scholastic, Inc.

—It's Halloween! Wilhelm, Hans, illus. 1999. (Dinofours Ser.: No. 13). (J). (ps-1). (978-0-439-06326-5(4)) Scholastic, Inc.

Meunier, Sylvain & Lapierre, Steeve. Graindsel et Bretel. Fil et, Julie, illus. 2004. (était une Fois Ser.). (FRE.). 24p. (J). (ps). pap. (978-2-89021-699-0(3)) Diffusion du livre Mirabel.

Michelson, Richard. Oh No, Not Ghosts! McCauley, Adam, illus. 2006. 44p. (J). 16.00 (978-0-15-205186-0(4)) Harcourt Trade Pubs.

Moodie, Fiona. Noko & the Night Monster. Moodie, Fiona, illus. 2001. (Illus.). 32p. (J). (gr. k-3). 15.95 (978-0-7614-5093-1(9) , Cavendish Children's Bks.) Cavendish, Marshall Corp.

Moore, Sean, illus. Always Run up the Stairs. 2004. 32p. 15.95 (978-1-894965-05-7(1)) Simply Read Bks. CAN. *Dist:* Perseus Distribution.

Morgan, Michaela. Silly Sausage & the Spooks. Shulman, Dee, illus. 2006. (Read-It! Chapter Books). (J). 21.26 (978-1-4048-2736-3(6)) Picture Window Bks.

Moss, Miriam. Wiley & Jasper. Bucker, Jutta, tr. Bucker, Jutta, illus. 2003. (J). 25p. pap. (978-1-59336-061-0(4)); 32p. 15.95 (978-1-59336-060-3(6)) Mondo Publishing.

Murphy, Stephen, et al. The Secret. S. I. International Staff & Ostrom, Bob, illus. 2004. (Teenage Mutant Ninja Turtles Ser.). 32p. (J). pap. 3.99 (978-0-689-86965-5(7) , Simon Spotlight) Simon & Schuster Children's Publishing.

E F G

Newmark, Rachel J. Fearless Faith: And the New School. Specialty Publishing Company, illus. 2006. (J). pap. 7.95 (978-0-9755199-4-3(8)) Specialty Publishing Co.

Nickel, Scott. Curse of the Red Scorpion. Harpster, Steve, illus. 2006. (Graphic Sparks Ser.). 33p. (J). 19.93 (978-1-59889-034-1(4)) Stone Arch Bks.

Nivola, Claire A. El Bosque. 2002. (SPA.). 32p. (J). (978-84-261-3255-0(3)) Juventud, Editorial.

Odgers, Darrel & Odgers, Sally. The Awful Pawful: Jack Russell: Dog Detective. Dawson, Janine, illus. 2007. (Jack Russell: Dog Detective Ser.: No. 5). 80p. (J). (gr. 2-6). pap. 4.95 (***978-1-933605-53-1(7)*** Kane/Miller Bk. Pubs., Inc.

Oke, Janette. Pordy's Prickly Problem. Munger, Nancy, illus. rev. ed. 2001. (Animal Friends Ser.). 80p. (J). (gr. 1-5). pap. 6.99 (978-0-7642-2458-4(1)) Bethany Hse. Pubs.

—Pordy's Prickly Problem. 2001. (gr. k-3). lib. bdg. 14.15 (978-0-613-85068-1(8)) Tandem Library Bks.

Ottolenghi, Carol. Tip the Mouse Can't Sleep. Campanella, Marco, illus. 2005. (Tip the Mouse Ser.). 32p. (J). (ps-ps). 10.95 (978-0-7696-4299-4(3) , Gingham Dog Pr.) School Specialty Publishing.

Packard, Mary. The Shy Scarecrow. Huang, Benrei, illus. 2001. (Hello Reader! Ser.). (J). (978-0-439-31704-7(5)) Scholastic, Inc.

Papineau, Lucie. Gilda the Giraffe & Marvin the Marmoset. Sarrazin, Marisol, illus. 2005. (Gilda the Giraffe Ser.). 32p. (J). (ps-3). lib. bdg. 22.60 (978-1-4048-1516-2(3)) Picture Window Bks.

Papineau, Lucie & Fischman, Sheila. Marvin the Strange Little Marmoset. Sarrazin, Marisol, illus. 2001. 32p. (J). (ps up). pap. (978-1-894363-80-8(9)) Dominique & Friends.

Parazette, Joan. Aldo! Nascimbene, Yan, illus. 2006. (J). (978-1-56846-197-7(6) , Creative Editions) Creative Co., The.

Park, Barbara. Junie B. , First Grader Boo... & I Mean It! Brunkus, Denise, illus. 2004. 86p. (J). lib. bdg. 18.46 (***978-1-4242-0359-8(7)***) Fitzgerald Bks.

—Junie B., First Grader: Boo... & I Mean It! Brunkus, Denise, illus. (Junie B. Jones Ser.: No. 24). 96p. (J). (gr. k-3). 2005. pap. 3.99 (978-0-375-82807-2(9)); 2004. 11.95 (978-0-375-82806-5(0)) Random Hse. Children's Bks. (Random Hse. Bks. for Young Readers).

—Junie B., First Grader: Boo... & I Mean It! Brunkus, Denise, illus. 2005. (Junie B. Jones Ser.: No. 24). 86p. (J). (gr. k-3). lib. bdg. 11.04 (978-0-606-33718-2(0)) Tandem Library Bks.

—Junie B. Jones Has a Peep in Her Pocket. Brunkus, Denise, illus. 2000. (Junie B. Jones Ser.: No. 15). 80p. (J). (gr. k-3). lib. bdg. 11.99 (978-0-375-90040-2(3)); pap. 3.99 (978-0-375-80040-5(9)) Random Hse. Children's Bks. (Random Hse. Bks. for Young Readers).

—Junie B. Jones Has a Peep in Her Pocket. 2000. (Junie B. Jones Ser.: No. 15). (J). (gr. k-3). lib. bdg. 11.80 (978-0-613-25835-7(5)); (Illus.). 10.79 (978-0-606-18499-1(6)) Tandem Library Bks.

—Psssst! It's Me... the Bogeyman. Kroninger, Stephen, illus. 1999. 32p. (J). (gr. k-3). per. 16.00 (978-0-689-82742-6(3) , Simon & Schuster Children's Publishing) Simon & Schuster Children's Publishing.

—Psssst! It's Me... the Bogeyman. 2001. (gr. k-3). lib. bdg. 15.30 (978-0-613-73372-4(X)) Tandem Library Bks.

Pascal, Francine. Fearless. 2003. (Fearless Ser.: No. 25). Tr. of Lost. lib. bdg. 14.15 (978-0-613-73397-7(5)) Tandem Library Bks.

—Fearless Nos. 4 & 28: Twisted & Chase. 2003. (Fearless Ser.: No. 4). lib. bdg. 14.15 (978-0-613-68861-1(9)) Tandem Library Bks.

—Gaia Abducted. 2003. (Fearless Super Edition Ser.). (gr. 7-12). lib. bdg. 15.30 (978-0-613-66504-9(X)) Tandem Library Bks.

—Kiss & Lust. 2003. (Fearless Ser.: No. 5). lib. bdg. 14.15 (978-0-613-73413-4(0)) Tandem Library Bks.

Patschke, Steve. The Spooky Book. McElligott, Matthew, illus. 32p. (J). (gr. k-3). 1999. lib. bdg. 16.85 (978-0-8027-8693-7(6)); 2006. reprint ed. pap. 6.95 (978-0-8027-8870-2(X)) Walker & Co.

Paul, Alison. The Crow (A Not So Scary Story) 2007. (Illus.). 40p. (J). (gr. 3-5). 16.00 (***978-0-618-66380-4(0)***) Houghton Mifflin Co.

Peretti, Frank E. Hangman's Curse. movie tie-in ed. 2003. (Veritas Project Ser.). 312p. (YA). pap. 9.99 (978-1-4003-0371-7(0)) Nelson, Thomas Inc.

—Hangman's Curse. 2003. (gr. 3-6). lib. bdg. 18.80 (978-0-613-77934-0(7)) Tandem Library Bks.

—Nightmare Academy. 2003. (Veritas Project Ser.). 320p. (YA). pap. 8.99 (978-1-4003-0340-3(0)) Nelson, Thomas Inc.

—Nightmare Academy. 2003. (gr. 3-6). lib. bdg. 17.60 (978-0-613-77930-2(4)) Tandem Library Bks.

Petersen, P. J. White Water. 1999. (978-0-606-16710-9(2)) Tandem Library Bks.

Peterson, Doug & Kenney, Cindy. Lost in Place: A Lesson in Overcoming Fear. Big Idea Productions Staff, illus. 2005. (VeggieTown Values Ser.: Bk. 4). 32p. pap. 3.99 (978-0-310-70629-8(7)) Zonderkidz.

Pfister, Marcus. Pececitos Miedosos. 2002. Tr. of Scaredy-Cat Fish. (SPA.). (gr. k-3). lib. bdg. 11.80 (978-0-613-87418-2(8)) Tandem Library Bks.

Pitcher, Caroline. The Winter Dragon. Williams, Sophy, illus. 2004. 36p. (J). (ps-2). 15.95 (978-1-84507-322-0(3)) Lincoln, Frances Ltd. GBR. *Dist:* Perseus Distribution.

Pitzer, Susanna. Not Afraid of Dogs. Day, Larry, illus. 2006. 32p. (J). 16.95 (978-0-8027-8067-6(9)) Walker & Co.

Pitzer, Susanna & Day, Larry. Not Afraid of Dogs. 2006. (Illus.). 32p. (J). 17.85 (978-0-8027-8068-3(7)) Walker & Co.

Polisar, Barry Louis. Snakes & the Boy Who Was Afraid of Them. Clark, David, illus. 2003. (Rainbow Morning Music Picture Bks.). 32p. (J). (ps-3). reprint ed. 14.95 (978-0-938663-15-7(1)) Rainbow Morning Music Alternatives.

Pottie, Marjolein & Auzary-Luton, Sylvie. Going Batty! Special Glow-in-the-Dark Surprise Pictures. Auzary-Luton, Sylvie, illus. 2005. (Illus.). 32p. (J). 15.95 (978-0-689-04635-3(9) , Milk & Cookies) ibooks, Inc.

Pringle, Laurence P. Bear Hug. Palmer, Kate Salley, illus. 2003. 32p. (J). (gr. k-2). 15.95 (978-1-56397-876-0(8)) Boyds Mills Pr.

Puckett, Kelley. Batman's Dark Secret. Muth, Jon J., illus. 2000. (Hello Reader! Ser.). 32p. (J). (gr. 1-3). pap. 3.99 (978-0-439-09551-8(4)) Scholastic, Inc.

—Batman's Dark Secret. 2000. (Hello Reader! Ser.). (Illus.). (J). 10.79 (978-0-606-18517-2(8)) Tandem Library Bks.

Pumphrey, Jerome & Pumphrey, Jarrett. Creepy Things Are Scaring Me! Litzinger, Rosanne, illus. 2003. 32p. (J). (ps-3). lib. bdg. 15.89 (978-0-06-028963-8(5)) HarperCollins Pubs.

Pumphrey, W. Jerome. Creepy Things Are Scaring Me! (Illus.). 32p. (J). (ps-3). 5.99 (978-0-06-443680-9(2)) HarperCollins Pubs.

Ramon, Elisa. Aquello Que Tanto Queria Susana. Lavarello, Jose Maria, illus. 2004. Tr. of What Susana Loved Dearly. (SPA.). (J). pap. 7.99 (978-84-236-6702-4(2)) Edebé ESP. *Dist:* Lectorum Pubns., Inc.

Rankin, Joan. Scaredy Cat. 1999. (978-0-606-16292-0(5)) Tandem Library Bks.

Ransom, Candice. Seeing Sky-Blue Pink. 2007. (Exceptional Reading & Language Arts Titles for Intermediate Grades Ser.). 128p. (J). (gr. 3-6). 16.95 (***978-0-8225-7142-1(0)*** , Carolrhoda Bks.) Lerner Publishing Group.

Raschka, Chris. Can't Sleep. Raschka, Chris, illus. 1999. (Illus.). (J). (ps-1). 32p. 15.99 (978-0-531-08779-4(4)); 16p. bds. 6.95 (978-0-531-30201-9(6)); 32p. pap. 14.95 (978-0-531-09479-2(0)) Scholastic, Inc. (Orchard Bks.).

Ratoff, Michael. Silver & Shiny, 3 vols. Painter, Laurie, illus. 2nd l.t. ed. 2001. (Every Thing in an Empty Box Ser.). 56p. (J). (ps-3). lib. bdg. 9.95 (978-0-9627986-2-7(2)) Rebel Butterfly Pr.

Rau, Dana Meachen. Ladies & Gentlemen, Level C. Caputo, Jim, illus. 2001. (Compass Point Early Reader Ser.). 32p. (J). (gr. k up). lib. bdg. 18.60 (978-0-7565-0120-4(2)) Compass Point Bks.

—Yahoo for You, Level B. Pillo, Cary, illus. 2002. (Compass Point Early Reader Ser.). 32p. (J). (gr. k up). lib. bdg. 18.60 (978-0-7565-0177-8(6)) Compass Point Bks.

Ravishankar, Anushka. The Fivetongued, Firefanged, Folkadotted Dragon Snake. Roy, Indrapramit & Ramanathan, Rathna, illus. 1999. 50p. (J). pap. (978-81-86211-26-7(8)) Tara Publishing.

Rector, Rebecca Kraft. Tria & the Great Star Rescue. 2003. (gr. 3-6). lib. bdg. 13.00 (978-0-613-86232-5(5)) Tandem Library Bks.

Remkiewicz, Frank, illus. Froggy Learns to Swim. 2002. (Froggy Ser.). (J). 13.19 (978-0-7587-2553-0(1)) Book Wholesalers, Inc.

—Horrible Harry & the Drop of Doom. 2002. (Horrible Harry Ser.). (J). 11.49 (978-0-7587-0589-1(1)) Book Wholesalers, Inc.

Richards, Chuck. Jungle Gym Jitters. Richards, Chuck, illus. 2004. (Illus.). 32p. (J). 17.85 (978-0-8027-8932-7(3)); 16.95 (978-0-8027-8931-0(5)) Walker & Co.

Richardson, E. E. Devil's Footsteps. 192p. 2006. (YA). (gr. 9). mass mkt. 5.99 (978-0-440-23916-1(8) , Laurel Leaf); 2005. (J). (gr. 7 up). lib. bdg. 17.99 (978-0-385-90279-3(4) , Delacorte Bks. for Young Readers); 2005. (YA). (gr. 7 up). 15.95 (978-0-385-73263-5(5) , Delacorte Bks. for Young Readers) Random Hse. Children's Bks.

River Runners: Individual Title Six-Packs. (Action Packs Ser.). 120p. (gr. 3-5). 44.00 (978-0-7635-8398-9(7)) Rigby Education.

Rivers, Katie. Blown Away. 2002. 101p. (J). (gr. 3-7). per. 6.95 (978-0-9721640-4-7(9)) Whispering Wind Publishing Inc.

Rix, Jamie. Giddy Goat. Chapman, Lynne, illus. 2003. 32p. (J). (gr. k-3). 14.95 (978-0-7696-3161-5(4) , Gingham Dog Pr.) School Specialty Publishing.

Robberecht, Thierry. Sam Is Never Scared. Goossens, Philippe, illus. 2006. 32p. (J). (gr. k-3). 12.00 (978-0-618-73278-4(0) , Clarion Bks.) Houghton Mifflin Co. Trade & Reference Div.

Robbins, Beth. Tom, Ally & the Babysitter. Stuart, Jon, illus. 2001. (It's OK! Ser.). 24p. (J). (ps-k). pap. 3.95 (978-0-7894-7426-1(3) , D K Ink) Dorling Kindersley Publishing, Inc.

—Tom & Ally Visit the Doctor: American Edition. Stuart, Jon, illus. 2001. (It's OK! Ser.). 24p. (J). (ps-k). pap. 3.95 (978-0-7894-7428-5(X) , D K Ink) Dorling Kindersley Publishing, Inc.

—Tom Is Afraid of the Dark. Stuart, Jon, illus. 2001. (It's OK! Ser.). 24p. (J). (ps-k). pap. 3.95 (978-0-7894-7420-9(4) , D K Ink) Dorling Kindersley Publishing, Inc.

Robbins, Beth & Stuart, Jon. Tom's First Haircut. 2001. (It's OK! Ser.). (Illus.). 24p. (J). (ps-k). pap. 3.95 (978-0-7894-7424-7(7) , D K Ink) Dorling Kindersley Publishing, Inc.

Robinson, Hilary. Freddie's Fears. Collins, Ross, illus. 2004. (Read-It! Readers Ser.). 32p. (C). (gr. k-3). 18.60 (978-1-4048-0056-4(5)) Picture Window Bks.

Rockwell, Anne F. Katie Catz Makes a Splash. Meisel, Paul, illus. 2003. (Good Sports Ser.). 40p. (J). (ps-1). 15.99 (978-0-06-028441-1(2)) HarperCollins Pubs.

—Katie Catz Swims at Last. Meisel, Paul, illus. 1999. 32p. (J). (ps-1). pap. 5.95 (978-0-06-446740-7(6)) HarperCollins Pubs.

Rodowsky, Colby. The Next-Door Dogs. Bates, Amy June, illus. 2005. 112p. (J). 15.00 (978-0-374-36410-6(9) , Farrar, Straus & Giroux (BYR)) Farrar, Straus & Giroux.

Rodriguez, Edel. Sergio Makes a Splash. 2008. 40p. 15.99 (***978-0-316-06616-7(8)***) Little Brown & Co.

Rose, Gill. The Scary Video: A Book about Using Good Judgment. Archbold, Tim, illus. 2004. (Making Good Choices Ser.). 24p. (C). (gr. k-3). 22.60 (978-1-4048-0663-4(6)) Picture Window Bks.

Rosoff, Meg. Jumpy Jack & Googily. Blackall, Sophie, illus. 2008. 32p. (J). 16.95 (***978-0-8050-8066-7(X)***) Holt, Henry & Co.

Ross, Dev. We Both Read-Frank & the Giant (Picture Book Edition) Reinhart, Larry, illus. 2007. (We Both Read Ser.). 44p. (J). 14.95 (***978-1-60115-006-6(7)***) Treasure Bay, Inc.

Rudisill, J. J., et al, illus. Scaredy Cats. 1999. (Wimzie's House Bks.). 24p. (J). pap. 3.99 (978-0-88724-518-3(8) , CD-4842) Carson-Dellosa Publishing Co., Inc.

Ruelle, Karen Gray. The Monster in Harry's Backyard. (Holiday House Readers Ser.). (Illus.). 32p. (J). (gr. k-3). 4.95 (978-0-8234-1783-4(2)) Holiday Hse., Inc.

Runnells, Treesha. Afraid of the Dark? Runnells, Treesha, illus. 2005. (Stories to Share Ser.). (Illus.). 14p. (J). (ps-2). 10.95 (978-1-58117-107-5(2) , Intervisual/Piggy Toes) Dalmatian Pr.

Russ, Tim. Bugsters! 2008. (Illus.). 32p. (J). (***978-0-9795131-7-6(0)***) Woods N' Water, Inc.

Russell, Natalie. Hamish the Highland Cow. 2003. (J). 7.99 (978-1-58234-818-6(9)) Bloomsbury Publishing.

Rylant, Cynthia. Henry & Mudge & Annie's Good Move. Stevenson, Sucie, illus. 2002. (Henry & Mudge Ser.). (J). 11.91 (978-0-7587-1260-8(X)) Book Wholesalers, Inc.

—Henry & Mudge & Annie's Good Move. Stevenson, Sucie, illus. 2002. (Henry & Mudge Ser.). 28.95 incl. audio compact disk (978-1-59112-648-5(7)); pap. 31.95 incl. audio compact disk (978-1-59112-647-8(9)) Live Oak Media.

—Henry & Mudge & Annie's Good Move. Stevenson, Sucie, illus. (Henry & Mudge Ser.). (J). (gr. k-3). 2000. 48p. pap. 3.99 (978-0-689-83284-0(2) , Aladdin); 1998. 40p. 15.95 (978-0-689-81174-6(8)) Simon & Schuster Children's Publishing.

Sachar, Louis. Super Fast, Out of Control! Wummer, Amy, illus. 2000. (Marvin Redpost Ser.: No. 7). 96p. (J). (gr. 1-4). lib. bdg. 11.99 (978-0-679-99001-7(1)); 7th ed. pap. 3.99 (978-0-679-89001-0(7)) Random Hse. Children's Bks. (Random Hse. Bks. for Young Readers).

—Super Fast, Out of Control! 2000. (Marvin Redpost Ser.: Bk. 7). (978-0-606-18502-8(X)); (gr. 3-6). lib. bdg. 11.80 (978-0-613-26149-4(6)) Tandem Library Bks.

Salisbury, Graham. Jungle Dogs. unabr. ed. 2000. (YA). (gr. 5 up). pap., stu. ed. 59.95 incl. audio (978-0-7887-4336-8(8) , 41131) Recorded Bks., LLC.

—Jungle Dogs. 1999. 11.64 (978-0-606-17837-2(6)) Tandem Library Bks.

Sand, George. The Wings of Courage. Bloom, Margaret, tr. from FRE. Frasconi, Antonio, illus. 1998. 70p. (gr. 4-7). 12.95 (978-0-8076-1434-1(3)) Braziller, George Inc.

Sanders, Scott Russell. Bad Man Ballad. 2004. (Library of Indiana Classics). 256p. (J). reprint ed. 32.95 (978-0-253-34414-4(X)) Indiana Univ. Pr.

Sardon, Sonya. Young Warren Sings! 2004. pap. 7.95 (978-0-533-14852-3(9)) Vantage Pr., Inc.

Scarabosio, Holly. Happy Thoughts with Sandy D. Dandelion & Friends. 2002. 28p. (J). pap. 13.95 incl. audio compact disk (978-0-9721445-0-6(1)) Dandelion Productions.

Scared at Night. 2001. (J). (978-1-58453-143-2(6)) Pioneer Valley Educational Pr., Inc.

Schaefer, Lola M. Out of the Night. Gilbert, Rob, illus. 1999. 32p. (ps-k). pap. 6.95 (978-1-58089-023-6(7)) Charlesbridge Publishing, Inc.

Schietinger-Cachina, Daryl A. There Is a People under My Bed. Schietinger-Cachina, Daryl A., illus. 1999. (Illus.). 10p. (J). (ps-5). pap. 5.00 (978-1-928641-04-9(0)) Daryl Ann Pubns.

Schneider, Richard H. The Lighthouse Boy: A Story of Courage. Petrov, Anton, illus. 2007. 32p. (J). (ps-3). pap. 8.99 (***978-0-8249-5557-1(9)*** , Guideposts) Ideals Pubns.

Schuurmans, Hilde. Sidney Won't Swim. Schuurmans, Hilde, illus. 2001. (Illus.). 32p. (J). (ps-3). 15.95 (978-1-57091-476-8(1)) Charlesbridge Publishing, Inc.

Schwarz, Viviane. Shark & Lobster's Amazing Undersea Adventure. Stewart, Joel, illus. 2006. 34p. (J). (***978-1-4156-8140-4(6)***) Candlewick Pr.

Scripture Teachers: Solomon & Friends Learn about Trusting God. 2003. pap. (***978-0-9712894-2-0(5)***) Lighthouse Christian Products Co.

Shipton, Paul. Bug Muldoon & the Garden of Fear. 2003. (gr. 3-6). lib. bdg. 14.15 (978-0-613-61608-9(1)) Tandem Library Bks.

Shusterman, Neal. Dread Locks, No. 1. 2006. (Dark Fusion Ser.). 176p. (YA). (gr. 7). pap. 6.99 (978-0-14-240599-4(X) , Puffin) Penguin Group (USA) Inc.

—Dread Locks: Dark Fusion # 1. 2005. 176p. (J). (gr. 6-12). 15.99 (978-0-525-47554-5(0) , Dutton Juvenile) Penguin Group (USA) Inc.

Slyder, Ingrid. Fabulous Flying Fandinis. Slyder, Ingrid, illus. 1999. 32p. (J). pap. 4.99 (978-0-14-056266-8(4) , Puffin) Penguin Group (USA) Inc.

Spelman, Cornelia Maude. When I Feel Scared. Parkinson, Kathy, illus. 2002. (Way I Feel Bks.). 24p. (J). (ps-1). 15.95 (978-0-8075-8890-1(3)); pap. 6.95 (978-0-8075-8900-7(4)) Whitman, Albert & Co.

Spinelli, Eileen. A Safe Place Called Home. Hale, Christy, illus. 2001. 32p. (J). (gr. k-3). 15.95 (978-0-7614-5085-6(8) , Cavendish Children's Bks.) Cavendish, Marshall Corp.

Spohn, Kate. Turtle & Snake at Work. 1999. (Puffin Easy-to-Read Ser.). (978-0-606-16823-6(0)) Tandem Library Bks.

—Turtle & Snake Go Camping. 2000. (Easy-to-Read Ser.). (Illus.). 32p. (J). (ps-2). pap. 3.99 (978-0-14-130670-4(X) , Puffin) Penguin Group (USA) Inc.

—Turtle & Snake Go Camping. 2000. (Puffin Easy-to-Read Ser.). (978-0-606-18460-1(0)); lib. bdg. 11.80 (978-0-613-27346-6(X)) Tandem Library Bks.

Sproul, R. C. The Lightlings. Gerard, Justin, illus. 2006. (J). (***978-1-56769-078-1(5)***) Reformation Pubs.

St-Aubin, Bruno. My Favorite Monster. 2005. (Read-It! Readers Ser.). (Illus.). 32p. (J). (gr. k-3). 18.60 (978-1-4048-1029-7(3)) Picture Window Bks.

Stamper, Judith Bauer. A Squeak, a Squeal, & a Screech! Fisher, Cynthia, illus. 1999. (Scholastic At-Home Phonics Reading Program Ser.: Vol. 31). 24p. (J). (978-0-590-68779-9(4)) Scholastic, Inc.

Steele, Giselle. The off-Limits Watermelon Patch. 2006. (Illus.). 35p. (J). per. 12.95 (978-0-9769949-0-9(9)) Stuart & Weitz Publishing Group.

Stein, Mathilde. Brave Ben. 2006. (Illus.). 32p. (J). 15.95 (978-1-932425-64-2(0) , Lemniscaat) Boyds Mills Pr.

Stephenson, Beth Mitchell. The Angel's Song. unabr. ed. 2002. 106p. (Orig.). pap. 7.95 (978-1-930980-93-8(0) , 80930) Granite Publishing & Distribution.

Stevenson, James. What's under My Bed? 2004. (J). (ps-3). pap. 14.95 incl. audio (978-0-89719-798-4(4) , PRA299) Weston Woods Studios, Inc.

Stine, R. L. Darkest Dawn. 2005. 182p. (YA). (978-1-4156-1459-4(8) , Simon Pulse) Simon & Schuster Children's Publishing.

—The Girl Who Cried Monster. 2005. 137p. (J). (ps-7). 12.04 (978-0-606-33299-6(5)) Tandem Library Bks.

—Invaders from the Big Screen. 1998. (Give Yourself Goosebumps Ser.: No. 29). 137p. (J). (gr. 3-7). pap. 3.99 (978-0-590-40289-7(7) , Scholastic Paperbacks) Scholastic, Inc.

—It Came from the Internet. 1999. (Give Yourself Goosebumps Ser.: No. 33). 144p. (gr. 3-7). pap. 3.99 (978-0-590-51665-5(5)) Scholastic, Inc.

—Monstruos en el Campamento. (Fantasmas de Fear Street Coleccion). (SPA.). (YA). (gr. 5-8). pap. 7.95 (978-950-04-1871-3(1) , EM10012) Emecé Editores S.A. ARG. *Dist:* Lectorum Pubns., Inc., Planeta Publishing Corp.

—Revenge R Us. 1998. (Goosebumps Series 2000: No. 7). 118p. (J). (gr. 3-7). pap. 3.99 (978-0-590-39994-4(2) , Scholastic Paperbacks) Scholastic, Inc.

—What Scares You the Most? 2001. (Nightmare Room Ser.). (Illus.). (J). (978-0-606-21354-7(6)) Tandem Library Bks.

Stine, R.L. Darkest Dawn. 2005. 182p. (YA). lib. bdg. 20.00 (***978-1-4242-0994-1(3)***) Fitzgerald Bks.

Stone Arch Books (Firm : Afton, Minn.) Staff. Fear 3.1. Lawrie, Robin & Lawrie, Christine, illus. 2007. (Ridge Riders Ser.). 40p. (J). (gr. 2-6). lib. bdg. 21.26 (***978-1-59889-348-9(3)***) Stone Arch Bks.

A Stormy Adventure: Facing the Fear of Storms. 2004. (J). 6.99 (978-0-9753870-3-0(0)) Write On!.

Strasser, Todd. Here Comes Heavenly: Pastabilities. 2000. (J). (978-0-606-19054-1(6)) Tandem Library Bks.

Stroud, Bettye. Dance Y'All. Van Wright, Cornelius & Hu, Ying-Hwa, illus. 2001. 32p. (J). (gr. k-3). 15.95 (978-0-7614-5065-8(3) , Cavendish Children's Bks.) Cavendish, Marshall Corp.

Sunderland, Margot & Hancock, Nicky. Teenie Weenie in a Too Big World: A Story for Fearful Children, 2 vols. Armstrong, Nicky, tr. Armstrong, Nicky, illus. 32p. pap. (978-0-86388-460-3(1) , 002-5144) Speechmark Publishing Ltd.

Taulbert, Clifton L. Little Cliff's First Day of School. Taulbert, Clifton L. & Lewis, Earl, illus. 2003. 32p. (J). (gr. k-3). pap. 6.99 (978-0-14-250082-8(8) , Puffin) Penguin Group (USA) Inc.

—Little Cliff's First Day of School. Lewis, Earl, illus. 2001. 32p. (J). (ps-3). 15.99 (978-0-8037-2557-7(4) , Dial) Penguin Group (USA) Inc.

—Little Cliff's First Day of School. 2003. (gr. k-3). lib. bdg. 15.30 (978-0-613-67561-1(4)) Tandem Library Bks.

Teague, Mark. Field Beyond the Outfield. 2006. (Illus.). 40p. (J). pap. 5.99 (978-0-439-81215-3(1) , Scholastic Pr.) Scholastic, Inc.

Thaler, Mike. The Class Pet from the Black Lagoon. Lee, Jared D., illus. 2003. (J). pap. (978-0-439-55718-4(6)) Scholastic, Inc.

—The Custodian from the Black Lagoon. Lee, Jared D., illus. 2001. (Black Lagoon Ser.). 32p. (J). (ps-3). pap. 3.25 (978-0-439-18874-6(1)) Scholastic, Inc.

—Custodian from the Black Lagoon. 2001. (gr. k-3). lib. bdg. 10.95 (978-0-613-35667-1(5)) Tandem Library Bks.

—The Field Day from the Black Lagoon. Lee, Jared D., illus. 2008. (Little Apple Ser.). 64p. (J). 3.99 (***978-0-439-68076-9(X)***) Scholastic, Inc.

—Field Day from the Black Lagoon. Lee, Jared D., illus. 2005. 64p. (J). lib. bdg. 15.00 (***978-1-4242-2261-2(3)***) Fitzgerald Bks.

Thaler, Mike. Teacher from Black Lagoon Read along Library. 2006. (J). 18.95 (978-0-439-87596-7(X)) Scholastic, Inc.

Thiesing, Lisa. A Dark & Noisy Night: A Silly Thriller with Peggy the Pig. 2005. (Dutton Easy Reader Ser.). (Illus.). 32p. (J). (***978-1-4156-1784-7(8)*** , Dutton Juvenile) Penguin Group (USA) Inc.

Time-Life Books Editors. Scaredy Cat: A Book about Being Brave. 1998. (Big Comfy Couch Ser.). (Illus.). 32p. (J). 5.95 (978-0-7370-1000-8(2)) Time-Life Inc.

E F G

Tomlinson, Jill. Owl Who Was Afraid of the Dark. Howard, Paul, illus. 2005. 96p. (J). reprint ed. pap. 6.99 (978-1-4052-1093-5(1)) Egmont Bks., Ltd. GBR. *Dist:* Trafalgar Square Publishing.

Umphenour, Terry. Across a Broken Sky. 2001. 176p. (YA). pap. 12.95 (978-0-595-17949-7(5) , Writer's Showcase Pr.) iUniverse, Inc.

Uttley, Tracy. Molly Mcsholly Conquers Kindergarten. 2004. 32p. (J). bds. 15.95 (978-1-59298-077-2(5)) Beaver's Pond Pr., Inc.

Vail, Rachel & Bjorkman, Steve. Halloween Knight. 2004. (Illus.). (J). (ps-2). lib. bdg. 12.19 (978-0-606-29858-2(4)) Tandem Library Bks.

Walker, Wayne. Henrietta. Powers, Daniel, illus. 1998. (J). (gr. 1-6). pap. 12.95 (978-0-944576-18-2(4)) Rocky River Pubs., LLC.

Wallace, Carol. Flying Flea, Callie & Me. 1999. (gr. 3-6). lib. bdg. 13.00 (978-0-613-84533-5(1)) Tandem Library Bks.

Wallace, Karen. Prince Marvin's Great Moment. Flook, Helen, illus. 2007. (J). lib. bdg. ***978-1-4048-3707-2(8))** Picture Window Bks.

Wallen, Ila. The Moon in My Room. Sauber, Robert, illus. 2002. (Willowbe Woods Campfire Stories Ser.: Bk. 1). 32p. (J). (ps-3). 16.95 (978-0-9710627-0-2(6)) Bent Willow Publishing.

Ward, Nick. Come on, Baby Duck! 2004. (Illus.). 30p. (J). (ps up). 16.00 (978-1-56148-447-8(4)) Good Bks.

Weiss, Ellen. My First Day at Camp. Thornburgh, Rebecca McKillip, illus. 1999. (Bank Street Reader Collection). (J). (ps-2). lib. bdg. 22.60 (978-0-8368-2418-6(0)) Stevens, Gareth Inc.

Weiss, Ellen, et al. Babar & the Scary Day. Gibert, Jean Claude, illus. 2004. 24p. (J). (ps-3). 9.95 (978-0-8109-5019-1(7)) Abrams, Harry N. , Inc.

Wells, Rosemary. Wingwalker. Selznick, Brian, illus. 2002. 80p. (gr. 2-5). 15.99 (978-0-7868-0397-2(5)); 16.49 (978-0-7868-2347-5(X)) Hyperion Bks. for Children.

Wheeler, Lisa. One Dark Night. Bates, Ivan, illus. 2006. 32p. (J). reprint ed. pap. 6.00 (978-0-15-205888-3(5) , Voyager Bks./Libros Viajeros) Harcourt Children's Bks.

Wild, Margaret. Woolvs in the Sitee. Spudvilas, Anne, illus. 2007. 40p. (YA). (gr. 7 up). 17.95 ***978-1-59078-500-3(2)** , Front Street) Boyds Mills Pr.

Willey, Margaret. The Bigger Book of Lydia. 2001. 228p. (YA). pap. 16.95 (978-0-595-17700-4(X) , Backinprint-.com) iUniverse, Inc.

Willis, Jeanne. Monster Bed. 1999. (J). (978-0-606-17392-6(7)) Tandem Library Bks.

—La Tormenta Monstruosa. (Cotton Cloud Ser.). (SPA.). (J). (gr. 1-3). pap. (978-84-480-0180-3(X)) Timun Mas, Editorial S.A. ESP. *Dist:* Lectorum Pubns., Inc.

Willis, Jeanne & Varley, Susan. The Monster Bed. 1999. (Illus.). 32p. (J). (ps-3). mass mkt. 5.95 (978-0-688-16707-3(1) , Harper Trophy) HarperCollins Pubs.

Willner-Pardo, Gina. Jumping into Nothing. Chang, Heidi, illus. 1999. 64p. (J). (gr. 4-6). tchr. ed. 14.00 (978-0-395-84130-3(5) , Clarion Bks.) Houghton Mifflin Co. Trade & Reference Div.

Wilson, Budge. The Fear of Angelina Domino. ed. 2004. (Illus.). (J). (gr. k-3). spiral bd. (978-0-616-07246-2(5)) Canadian National Institute for the Blind/Institut National Canadien pour les Aveugles.

Winton, Tim. The Deep. Louise, Karen, illus. 1998. 32p. (YA). 21.95 (978-1-86368-242-8(2)) Fremantle Pr. AUS. *Dist:* International Specialized Bk. Services.

—The Deep. Louise, Karen, illus. 2004. 32p. (ps-2). 14.95 (978-1-58246-024-6(8) , Tricycle Pr.) Ten Speed Pr.

Winton, Tim & Louise, Karen. The Deep. (Illus.). 32p. (YA). pap. 13.95 (978-1-86368-210-7(4)) Fremantle Pr. AUS. *Dist:* International Specialized Bk. Services.

Wishinsky, Frieda. Give Maggie a Chance. Griffiths, Dean, illus. 2004. 32p. (J). (gr. k-2). pap. (978-1-55041-704-3(5)) Fitzhenry & Whiteside, Ltd.

—Nothing Scares Us. Layton, Neal, illus. (Carolrhoda Picture Books Ser.). 32p. (gr. k-2). 2005. pap. 6.25 (978-1-57505-669-2(0)); 2003. (J). 15.95 (978-1-57505-490-2(6) , Carolrhoda Bks.) Lerner Publishing Group.

Wolkstein, Diane. The Banza: A Haitian Story. Brown, Marc, illus. 33p. (J). (gr. k-2). pap. 5.99 (978-0-8072-1268-4(7) , Listening Library) Random Hse. Audio Publishing Group.

Zagwyn, Deborah Turney. The Pumpkin Blanket. Zagwyn, Deborah Turney, illus. 2004. (Illus.). 32p. (J). (gr. k-3). 7.95 (978-1-883672-59-1(7) , Tricycle Pr.) Ten Speed Pr.

Zimmerman, Erik. Booga-Boo - Coloring Book. 2005. (Illus.). 32p. (J). per. 7.99 (978-1-59879-009-2(9)) Lifevest Publishing, Inc.

Zimmermann, Erik. Booga-Boo. 2002. (Illus.). 32p. per. 8.95 (978-0-9724680-0-8(5)) Lifevest Publishing, Inc.

FEASTS

see Fasts and Feasts

FEDERATION, INTERNATIONAL

see International Organization

FEEDING AND FEEDS

Olsen, Mary. I'm Made of Mama's Milk. 2003. (Illus.). 24p. 8.95 (978-0-9715374-0-8(2)) Olsen, Mary Bks.

Open Court Staff. We Feed Deer. (J). pap. (978-0-8126-1002-4(4) , 61002) Open Court Publishing Co.

FEELING

see Perception; Touch

FEELINGS

see Emotions

FEET

see Foot

FELIDAE

see Cat Family (Mammals)

FELIX THE CAT (FICTITIOUS CHARACTER)—FICTION

The Comic Adventures of Felix the Cat. 2004. (Illus.). 128p. (YA). per. 12.95 (978-0-615-12660-9(X)) Felix Comics, Inc.

FELLOWSHIPS

see Scholarships

FELONY

see Crime and Criminals

FEMINISM

see also Women's Rights

Adhikary, Qiron. Feminist Folktales from India. 2003. (Illus.). 97p. (YA). per. 9.95 (978-0-9714127-3-6(1)) Masalai Pr.

Alter, Judy. Cissie Palmer: Putting Wealth to Work. 1999. (Community Builders Ser.). (Illus.). 48p. (J). (gr. 3-5). pap. 6.95 (978-0-516-26345-8(5) , Children's Pr.) Scholastic Library Publishing.

Archer, Jules. Breaking Barriers: The Feminist Revolution from Susan B. Anthony to Margaret Sanger to Betty Friedan. 2001. (Illus.). 207p. (YA). (gr. 7-9). 20.00 (978-0-7567-5224-8(8)) DIANE Publishing Co.

Attebury, Nancy Garhan. Gloria Steinem: Champion of Women's Rights. 2006. (Signature Lives Ser.). (Illus.). 112p. (J). (gr. 5-7). 30.60 (978-0-7565-1587-4(4)) Compass Point Bks.

Bohannon, Lisa Frederiksen. Woman's Work: The Story of Betty Friedan. 2004. (Illus.). 144p. (YA). (gr. 6-12). 23.95 (978-1-931798-41-9(9)) Reynolds, Morgan Inc.

Bolden, Tonya, ed. 33 Things Every Girl Should Know about Women's History: From Suffragettes to Skirt Lengths to the E.R.A. 2002. (Illus.). 240p. (YA). (gr. 7 up). pap. 12.95 (978-0-375-81122-7(2) , Crown Books For Young Readers) Random Hse. Children's Bks.

Carlson, Dale B. & Carlson, Hannah. Girls Are Equal Too: The Teenage Girls How-to-Survive Book. Nicklaus, Carol, illus. 2nd rev. ed. 2000. (Psychology for Teenagers Ser.: Vol. 1). 231p. (gr. 5-12). pap. 14.95 (978-1-884158-18-6(8)) Bick Publishing Hse.

Gorman, Jacqueline Laks. Gloria Steinem. 2003. (Trailblazers of the Modern World Ser.). (Illus.). 48p. (J). (gr. 5 up). lib. bdg. 30.00 (978-0-8368-5093-2(9)); pap. 14.60 (978-0-8368-5253-0(2)) Stevens, Gareth Inc. (World Almanac Library).

Kendall, Martha E. Failure Is Impossible! The History of American Women's Rights. 3rd ed. 2005. (People's History Ser.). (Illus.). 96p. (gr. 6-12). lib. bdg. 26.60 (978-0-8225-1744-3(2)) Lerner Publishing Group.

McIntosh, Kenneth. Women & Religion: Reinterpreting Scriptures to Find the Sacred Feminine. 2005. (Religion & Modern Culture Ser.). (Illus.). 112p. (J). (gr. 7 up). (978-1-59084-977-4(9)) Mason Crest Pubs.

Miller, Connie Colwell. Elizabeth Cady Stanton: Women's Rights Pioneer. Webb, James, illus. 2006. (Graphic Library). 32p. (J). 25.26 (978-0-7368-4971-5(8)) Capstone Pr., Inc.

Mouser, Barbara K. & Fisher, Priscilla. Five Aspects of Femininity for Young Women: A Biblical Theology of Womanhood. 2000. 164p. (YA). (gr. 7-12). pap. 15.00 (978-1-929656-03-5(3)) International Council for Gender Studies.

Noyed, Robert B. Susan B. Anthony: Reformer. 2002. (Spirit of America: Our People Ser.). (Illus.). 32p. (J). (gr. 2-6). 27.07 (978-1-56766-171-2(8)) Child's World, Inc.

Schomp, Virginia. American Voices from the Women's Movement. 2006. (American Voices Ser.). (Illus.). xix, 138p. (J). lib. bdg. 37.07 (978-0-7614-2171-9(8) , Benchmark Bks.) Cavendish, Marshall Corp.

Stearman, Kaye. Feminism. 2003. (Ideas of the Modern World Ser.). (Illus.). 64p. (J). lib. bdg. 28.56 (978-0-7398-6415-9(7)) Raintree.

Turner, Cherie. Everything You Need to Know about the Riot Grrrl Movement: The Feminism of a New Generation. 2001. (Need to Know Library). (Illus.). 64p. (YA). (gr. 4-6). lib. bdg. 25.25 (978-0-8239-3400-3(4)) Rosen Publishing Group, Inc., The.

Weidt, Maryann N. Fighting for Equal Rights: A Story about Susan B. Anthony. Sartor, Amanda, tr. Sartor, Amanda, illus. 2004. (Creative Minds Biography Ser.). 64p. (J). 22.60 (978-1-57505-181-9(8) , Carolrhoda Bks.) Lerner Publishing Group.

Wheaton, Elizabeth. Ms. The Story of Gloria Steinem. 2004. (Feminist Voices Ser.). (Illus.). 112p. (YA). (gr. 6-12). 23.95 (978-1-883846-82-4(X) , First Biographies) Reynolds, Morgan Inc.

Wheeler, Jill C. Susan B. Anthony. 2003. (Breaking Barriers Ser.). (Illus.). 64p. (J). (gr. 3-8). lib. bdg. 25.65 (978-1-57765-903-7(1)) ABDO Publishing Co.

FENCING

Page, Jason. Combat: Fencing, Judo, Wrestling, Boxing, Taekwondo & Lots, Lots More. 2000. (Zeke's Olympic Pocket Guide Ser.). (Illus.). 32p. (J). pap. 3.95 (978-0-8225-5055-6(5) , LernerSports) Lerner Publishing Group.

Sloan, Peter. Fences & Walls. 1999. (gr. k-3). lib. bdg. 11.80 (978-0-613-30399-6(7)) Tandem Library Bks.

FERMI, ENRICO, 1901-1954

Cooper, Dan. Enrico Fermi: And the Revolutions of Modern Physics. Gingerich, Owen, ed. 1998. (Oxford Portraits in Science Ser.). (Illus.). 120p. (YA). (gr. 7 up). 30.00 (978-0-19-511762-2(X)) Oxford Univ. Pr., Inc.

Golus, Carrie. Enrico Fermi. 2006. (Giants of Science Ser.). (J). (978-1-4103-0578-7(3) , Blackbirch Pr., Inc.) Thomson Gale.

Stux, Erica. Enrico Fermi: Trailblazer in Nuclear Physics. 2004. (Nobel Prize-Winning Scientists Ser.). (Illus.). 128p. (J). lib. bdg. 26.60 (978-0-7660-2177-8(7)) Enslow Pubs., Inc.

FERNS

Fowler, Allan. Ferns. (Rookie Read-About Science Ser.). (Illus.). 32p. (J). (gr. 1-2). 2002. pap. 4.95 (978-0-516-25984-0(9)); 2001. 20.50 (978-0-516-21687-4(2)) Scholastic Library Publishing. (Children's Pr.).

Greenaway, Theresa. Ferns: The Green World. 2000. (Illus.). 47p. (J). (gr. 5-7). 15.00 (978-0-7881-9434-4(8)) DIANE Publishing Co.

Hallowell, Barbara G. & Hallowell, Anne C. Fern Finder: A Guide to Native Ferns of Central & Northeastern United States & Eastern Canada. Hallowell, Anne C., illus. 2nd rev. ed. 2001. (Finders Field Guides Ser.). (Illus.). n/ap. pap. 3.50 (978-0-912550-24-4(4)) Nature Study Guild.

Loves, June. Ferns. 2004. (Plants Ser.). (Illus.). 32p. (J). (gr. 2-4). 23.00 (978-0-7910-8267-6(9) , Chelsea Hse.) Facts On File, Inc.

FERRIES

Hilton, George Woodman. The Great Lakes Car Ferries. 2003. (Illus.). 240p. lib. bdg. 39.95 net. (978-0-9658624-3-1(7)) Montevallo Historical Pr., Inc.

Walker, Pam. Ferry Rides. 2000. (Welcome Bks.). (Illus.). 24p. (J). (ps-2). pap. 4.95 (978-0-516-23026-9(3) , Children's Pr.) Scholastic Library Publishing.

Zimmermann, Karl R. Steamboats: The Story of Lakers, Ferries, & Majestic Paddlewheelers. 2007. (Illus.). 48p. (J). (gr. 5-8). 19.95 (978-1-59078-434-1(0)) Boyds Mills Pr.

FERRIES—FICTION

Briggs, Martha Wren. Travels with Virginia, the Little Ferry Vol. 4: The Little Ferry Meets the Colonial Ships. Beale, Ella L., illus. 1999. 18p. (J). (gr. 3-8). pap. 6.95 (978-0-9633240-6-1(3)) Dory Pr.

Fuller, Harvey. Tommy & the Island. Fuller, Harvey, illus. 2007. (J). pap. 18.95 ***978-0-9773725-7-7(X))** Flat Hammock Pr.

Law, Felicia. Rumble Meets Harry Hippo. Pak, Yoon Mi, illus. 2006. (Read-It! Readers Ser.). 32p. (J). (gr. 2-4). 18.60 (978-1-4048-1338-0(1)) Picture Window Bks.

Rockwell, Anne F. Ferryboat Ride! 1999. (Illus.). (J). (978-0-606-18088-7(5)) Tandem Library Bks.

FESTIVALS

see also Fasts and Feasts; Holidays; Pageants

Ada, Alma Flor, et al. Joaquín Arlequín, Celebra el Mardi Gras. Nobati, Eugenia, illus. 2005. (Cuentos para Celebrar Ser.). (ENG & SPA.). (J). (978-1-59820-116-1(6) , Alfaguara) Santillana USA Publishing Co., Inc.

Al-Gailani, Noorah. Islamic Year: Surahs, Stories & Celebrations. 2003. (gr. 3-6). lib. bdg. 38.45 (978-0-613-80442-4(2)) Tandem Library Bks.

Ancona, George. Carnaval. 1999. (Illus.). 48p. (J). (gr. 2-5). 18.00 (978-0-15-201793-4(3)) Harcourt Children's Bks.

—Carnaval. 1999. (978-0-606-17486-2(9)) Tandem Library Bks.

—The Fiestas: Viva Mexico! 2001. (Viva Mexico! Ser.). (Illus.). 48p. (J). (gr. 3-6). lib. bdg. 27.07 (978-0-7614-1327-1(8) , Benchmark Bks.) Cavendish, Marshall Corp.

—Mis Fiestas. 32p. (J). 2006. (SPA.). (gr. 1-3). pap. 8.95 (978-0-516-25497-5(9)); 2005. (ENG & SPA.). 21.00 (978-0-516-25290-2(9)) Scholastic Library Publishing. (Children's Pr.).

Baumbusch, Brigitte. Festivals in Art. 2005. (Illus.). 32p. (J). lib. bdg. 22.00 (978-0-8368-4781-9(4)) Stevens, Gareth Inc.

Berg, Elizabeth. Nigeria. 1998. (Festivals of the World Ser.). (Illus.). 32p. (J). (gr. 3 up). lib. bdg. 24.67 (978-0-8368-2017-1(7)) Stevens, Gareth Inc.

Berger, Samantha & Chanko, Pamela. Festivals. 1999. (J). 2.50 (978-0-439-04561-2(4)) Scholastic, Inc.

—Festivals. 1999. (ps-2). lib. bdg. 10.10 (978-0-613-21533-6(8)) Tandem Library Bks.

Brownlie, Alison. West Africa. 1999. (Food & Festivals Ser.). (Illus.). 32p. (J). (gr. 1-4). lib. bdg. 25.69 (978-0-8172-5552-7(4)) Raintree.

Bujjai. Dussehra. 2000. 16p. (J). mass mkt. 4.00 (978-81-7767-010-3(7)) Devamala Bks. Private, Ltd. IND. *Dist:* Ameya, LLC.

Candle Time, 8 bks., Set. 2002. (J). (ps-1). 148.00 (978-1-58810-472-4(9)) Heinemann Library.

Cann, Helen, illus. A Calendar of Festivals. 2000. 80p. (J). (gr. 3-7). pap. 9.99 (978-1-84148-244-6(7)) Barefoot Bks., Inc.

Carnivals Around the World: Individual Title Six-Pack Pouch - Level H. (Lighthouse Ser.). 16p. (gr. 1 up). 26.00 (978-0-7578-0842-5(5)) Rigby Education.

Chan, Arlene. The Moon Festival: A Chinese Mid-Autumn Celebration. ed. 2004. (J). (gr. k-3). spiral bd. (978-0-616-01615-2(8)) Canadian National Institute for the Blind/Institut National Canadien pour les Aveugles.

Chandler, Clare. Carnival. 1998. (Festivals Ser.). (Illus.). 32p. (gr. 2-4). lib. bdg. 22.90 (978-0-7613-0373-2(1) , Millbrook Pr.) Lerner Publishing Group.

Chrisp, Peter. Celebraciones y Festivales. Sanz, Maria T., tr. Goffe, Toni, illus. 1998. (Coleccion Descubre Tu Mundo). (SPA.). 32p. (J). (gr. 3-5). 11.95 (978-1-58087-012-2(0) , SY8646) Stampley, C.D. Enterprises, Inc.

—Celebrations & Festivals. Goffe, Toni, illus. 1998. (Launch Pad Library). 32p. (J). (gr. k-4). 11.95 (978-1-58087-005-4(8)) Stampley, C.D. Enterprises, Inc.

—Celebrations & Festivals. 2004. (Discovery Guides Ser.). (SPA., Illus.). 32p. (gr. 2-5). (J). pap. 6.95 (978-1-58728-229-4(1)); 11.95 (978-1-58728-235-5(6)) T&N Children's Publishing. (Two Can Publishing).

Civardi, Anne & King, Penny. Festival Decorations. 1998. (Craft Workshop Ser.). (Illus.). 32p. (J). (gr. 3). pap. (978-0-86505-790-6(7)); lib. bdg. (978-0-86505-780-7(X)) Crabtree Publishing Co.

Conrad, Heather. Lights of Winter: Winter Celebrations Around the World. 2001. (Illus.). 26p. (J). 11.95 (978-0-9712425-1-7(8)) Lightport Bks.

Cooper, Walsh. Holiday Celebrations. 2002. (Holidays & Festivals Ser.). 165.14 (978-1-58952-216-9(8)) Rourke Publishing, LLC.

Coppendale, Jean. Family Festivals. 2006. (Illus.). 32p. (YA). (gr. 1 up). lib. bdg. 27.10 (978-1-931983-96-9(8)) Chrysalis Education.

—Party Time. 2006. (Illus.). 32p. (YA). (gr. 1 up). lib. bdg. 27.10 (978-1-931983-97-6(6)) Chrysalis Education.

—Special Holidays. 2006. (Illus.). 32p. (YA). (gr. 1 up). lib. bdg. 27.10 (978-1-931983-98-3(4)) Chrysalis Education.

Dewey, Jennifer Owings. Zozobra: Old Man Gloom. Fleming, Jeanie Puleston, illus. Fleming, Jeanie Puleston, photos by. 2004. (J). (978-0-8263-3278-3(1)) Univ. of New Mexico Pr.

—Zozobra: The Story of Old Man Gloom. Fleming, Jeanie Puleston, illus. Fleming, Jeanie Puleston, photos by. 2004. 32p. (J). (gr. 3 up). pap. 9.95 (978-0-8263-3279-0(X)) Univ. of New Mexico Pr.

Doney, Meryl. Festivals. 1998. (World Crafts Ser.). (Illus.). 32p. (J). (gr. 3-5). pap. 6.95 (978-0-531-15329-1(0) , Watts, Franklin) Scholastic Library Publishing.

—Festivals. 2004. (Crafts from Many Cultures Ser.). (Illus.). 32p. (J). (gr. 3 up). lib. bdg. 23.33 (978-0-8368-4043-8(7)) Stevens, Gareth Inc.

Festival Fun. Date not set. (Illus.). 8p. (J). (gr. k-2). pap. 3.75 (978-1-58323-017-6(3) , Seedling Pubns.) Continental Pr., Inc.

Festival Tales, 4 bks., Set. Incl. Christian Festivals. Pirotta, Saviour & Cann, Helen. lib. bdg. 25.69 (978-0-7398-2732-1(4)); Hindu Festivals. Marchant, Kerena. lib. bdg. 25.69 (978-0-7398-2734-5(0)); Jewish Festivals. Pirotta, Saviour & Kelly, Anne M. lib. bdg. 25.69 (978-0-7398-2733-8(2)); Muslim Festivals. Marchant, Kerena. Barber, Tina, illus. lib. bdg. 25.69 (978-0-7398-2735-2(9)); 32p. (J). (gr. 4-7). 2001. Set lib. bdg. 102.76 (978-0-7398-2736-9(7)) Raintree.

Festivals, 3 bks., Set 2. 2004. (Illus.). 55.68 (978-1-4109-0781-3(3)) Raintree.

Festivals & Feasts: Individual Title Six-Packs. (Rigby Infoquest Ser.). 32p. (gr. 4 up). 37.00 (978-0-7578-5726-3(4)) Rigby Education.

Festivals of the World, 39 bks. Incl. Argentina. Furlong, Arlene. 1999. lib. bdg. 24.67 (978-0-8368-2030-0(4)); Australia. Griffiths, Diana. 1999. lib. bdg. 24.67 (978-0-8368-2021-8(5)); Canada. Barlas, Bob & Tompsett, Norman. 1997. lib. bdg. 24.67 (978-0-8368-1680-8(3)); Chile. Roraff, Susan. 1998. lib. bdg. 24.67 (978-0-8368-2012-6(6)); China. Cheong, Colin. 1997. lib. bdg. 24.67 (978-0-8368-1681-5(1)); Costa Rica. Frerer, Fredrick. 1999. lib. bdg. 24.67 (978-0-8368-2022-5(3)); Czech Republic. Nollen, Tim. 1999. lib. bdg. 24.67 (978-0-8368-2031-7(2)); England. Whyte, Harlinah. 1997. lib. bdg. 24.67 (978-0-8368-1932-8(2)); Ethiopia. Berg, Elizabeth. 1999. lib. bdg. 24.67 (978-0-8368-2032-4(0)); Finland. Tan Chung Lee. 1998. lib. bdg. 24.67 (978-0-8368-2013-3(4)); France. McKay, Susan. 1998. lib. bdg. 23.93 (978-0-8368-2003-4(7)); Germany. Lord, Richard. 1997. lib. bdg. 24.67 (978-0-8368-1682-2(X)); Greece. Sioras, Efstathia. 1998. lib. bdg. 24.67 (978-0-8368-2014-0(2)); Haiti. NgCheong-Lum, Roseline. 1999. lib. bdg. 24.67 (978-0-8368-2015-7(0)); India. Kagaa, Falaq. 1997. lib. bdg. 24.67 (978-0-8368-1683-9(8)); Indonesia. Berg, Elizabeth. 1997. lib. bdg. 24.67 (978-0-8368-1933-5(0)); Ireland. McKay, Patricia. 1998. lib. bdg. 24.67 (978-0-8368-2004-1(5)); Israel. Foy, Don. 1997. lib. bdg. 24.67 (978-0-8368-1684-6(6)); Japan. McKay, Susan. 1997. lib. bdg. 24.67 (978-0-8368-1935-9(7)); Madagascar. Ellis, Royston & Jones, John R. 1999. lib. bdg. 24.67 (978-0-8368-2023-2(1)); Mongolia. Fisher, Frederick. 1999. lib. bdg. 24.67 (978-0-8368-2024-9(X)); Netherlands. Van Fenema, Joyce. 1998. lib. bdg. 24.67 (978-0-8368-2016-4(9)); New Zealand. Griffiths, Jonathan. 1999. lib. bdg. 24.67 (978-0-8368-2033-1(9)); Nigeria. Berg, Elizabeth. 1998. lib. bdg. 24.67 (978-0-8368-2017-1(7)); Peru. Jermyn, Leslie. 1998. lib. bdg. 24.67 (978-0-8368-2006-5(1)); Philippines. Mendoza, Lunita. 1999. lib. bdg. 24.67 (978-0-8368-2025-6(8)); Poland. Zwierzynska-Coldicott, Aldona M. 1998. lib. bdg. 24.67 (978-0-8368-2018-8(5)); Saudi Arabia. O'Shea, Maria. 1999. lib. bdg. 24.67 (978-0-8368-2026-3(6)); Scotland. Griffiths, Jonathan. 1999. lib. bdg. 24.67 (978-0-8368-2034-8(7)); South Africa. Heale, Jay. 1998. lib. bdg. 24.67 (978-0-8368-2007-2(X)); South Korea. Ho Siow Yen & Rabe, Monica. 1998. lib. bdg. 24.67 (978-0-8368-2019-5(3)); Spain. McKay, Susan. 1999. lib. bdg. 24.67 (978-0-8368-2035-5(5)); Sweden. Rabe, Monica. 1998. lib. bdg. 24.67 (978-0-8368-2008-9(8)); Switzerland. McKay, Susan. 1999. lib. bdg. 24.67 (978-0-8368-2027-0(4)); Trinidad. Ellis, Royston. 1999. lib. bdg. 24.67 (978-0-8368-2036-2(3)); Turkey. O'Shea, Maria. 1999. lib. bdg. 24.67 (978-0-8368-2037-9(1)); Ukraine. Bassis, Vladimir. 1998. lib. bdg. 23.93 (978-0-8368-2010-2(X)); USA (Festivals of the World) Berg, Elizabeth. 1999. lib. bdg. 24.67 (978-0-8368-2028-7(2)); Vietnam. McKay, Susan. 1997. lib. bdg. 24.67 (978-0-8368-1937-3(3)); 32p. (J). (gr. 3 up). (Illus.). Set lib. bdg. 789.44 (978-0-8368-2478-0(4)) Stevens, Gareth Inc.

Fisher, Frederick. Mongolia. 1999. (Festivals of the World Ser.). (Illus.). 32p. (J). (gr. 3 up). lib. bdg. 24.67 (978-0-8368-2024-9(X)) Stevens, Gareth Inc.

Flanagan, Alice K. Carnival. Collier-Morales, Roberta, illus. 2003. (Holidays & Festivals Ser.). 32p. (J). (gr. 3 up). lib. bdg. 22.60 (978-0-7565-0478-6(3)) Compass Point Bks.

—Holidays & Festivals, 8 bks. Incl. Carnival. Collier-Morales, Roberta, illus. 2003. lib. bdg. 22.60 (978-0-7565-0478-6(3)); Chinese New Year. Zhurkina, Svetlana, illus. 2003. lib. bdg. 22.60 (978-0-7565-0479-3(1)); Christmas. Woodworth, Viki, illus. 2001. lib. bdg. 22.60 (978-0-7565-0085-6(0)); Cinco de Mayo. Girouard, Patrick, illus. 2003. lib. bdg. 22.60 (978-0-7565-

0480-9(5)); Halloween. Girouard, Patrick, illus. 2001. lib. bdg. 22.60 (978-0-7565-0086-3(9)); Passover. Koffsky, Ann D., illus. 2003. lib. bdg. 22.60 (978-0-7565-0481-6(3)); Thanksgiving. Kelleher, Kathie, illus. 2001. lib. bdg. 22.60 (978-0-7565-0087-0(7)); Valentine's Day. Dieterichs, Shelley, illus. 2001. lib. bdg. 22.60 (978-0-7565-0088-7(5)); 32p. (J). (gr. 3 up). Set lib. bdg. 180.80 (978-0-7565-0497-7(X)) Compass Point Bks.

Food & Festival, 12 bks., Set. 2000. (Illus.). (J). (978-0-7398-4190-7(4)) Raintree.

Food & Festivals, 6 vols. 1999. (Illus.). (J). 154.14 (978-0-7398-1506-9(7)) Raintree.

Foran, Jill. Mardi Gras. 2003. (Celebrating Cultures Ser.). (Illus.). 24p. (J). lib. bdg. 15.95 (978-1-59036-093-4(1)) Weigl Pubs., Inc.

—Oktoberfest. 2003. (Celebrating Cultures Ser.). (Illus.). 24p. (J). lib. bdg. 15.95 (978-1-59036-094-1(X)) Weigl Pubs., Inc.

—Powwow. 2003. (Celebrating Cultures Ser.). (Illus.). 24p. (J). lib. bdg. 15.95 (978-1-59036-095-8(8)) Weigl Pubs., Inc.

Ganeri, Anita. The Divali Story. 2007. (J). (***978-1-84234-433-0(1)***) Cherrytree Pubns., Inc.

—The Divali Story. Gray, Carole, illus. 2003. (Festival Stories Ser.). 24p. (YA). pap. 9.99 (978-0-237-52471-5(6) , Evans Brothers, Limited) Evans Publishing Group GBR. *Dist:* Independent Pubs. Group.

Ganeri, Anita & Saunders, Mary. The First Book of Festivals: A Resource Book. 2005. (Illus.). 80p. (J). 29.95 (978-0-237-53104-1(6) , Evans Brothers, Limited) Evans Publishing Group GBR. *Dist:* Independent Pubs. Group.

Ganeri, Anita, et al. I-Read Year 2 Anthology: Celebrate. 2007. (I-read Ser.). (Illus.). 40p. pap. (***978-0-521-70485-4(5)***) Cambridge Univ. Pr.

Gilchrist, Cherry. A Calendar of Festivals. Mistry, Nilesh, illus. 2005. 80p. (J). pap. 12.99 (978-1-84148-970-4(0)) Barefoot Bks., Inc.

—A Calendar of Festivals. Cann, Helen, illus. 1998. 80p. (J). (gr. 3-7). 18.95 (978-1-901223-68-2(X)) Barefoot Bks., Inc.

—A Calendar of Festivals. Cann, Helen, illus. 2006. 79p. (J). (gr. 4-8). reprint ed. pap. 10.00 (978-1-4223-5551-0(9)) DIANE Publishing Co.

—A Calendar of Festivals. 2000. (J). (978-0-606-19700-7(1)) Tandem Library Bks.

Gillis, Jennifer Blizin. Candle Time 123. 2002. (Candle Time Ser.). (Illus.). 24p. (J). (ps-1). pap. 5.25 (978-1-58810-742-8(6) , 91382); lib. bdg. 18.50 (978-1-58810-533-2(4)) Heinemann Library.

—Candle Time ABC. 2002. (Candle Time Ser.). (Illus.). 24p. (J). (ps-1). lib. bdg. 18.50 (978-1-58810-532-5(6)) Heinemann Library.

Gillis, Jennifer Blizin & Jordan, Denise M. Candle Time ABC. 2002. (Candle Time Ser.). (Illus.). 24p. (J). (ps-1). pap. 5.25 (978-1-58810-741-1(8) , 91383) Heinemann Library.

—Fiestas con Velas 123. 2002. (Fiestas Con Velas (Candle Time) Ser.). (SPA.). 24p. (J). (ps-1). lib. bdg. 18.50 (978-1-58810-787-9(6)); (Illus.). pap. 5.25 (978-1-58810-834-0(1) , 91589) Heinemann Library.

Glupker, Dianne. Great Tastes of Michigan. Delsi, Dawna, illus. 2006. (J). per. 9.95 (978-0-9769846-1-0(X)) Harambee Pr.

Griffin, Robert H. & Shurgin, Ann H. Buddha's Birthday, Carnival, Christmas, Vol. 1. 2000. (Illus.). (J). (978-0-7876-3928-0(1) , UXL) Thomson Gale.

—Easter, Halloween & Festivals of the Dead, Vol. 2. 2000. (Illus.). (J). (978-0-7876-3929-7(X) , UXL) Thomson Gale.

—Hanukkah, Independence Day, Kwanzaa, Vol. 3. 2000. (Illus.). (J). (978-0-7876-3930-3(3) , UXL) Thomson Gale.

Griffiths, Diana. Australia. 1999. (Festivals of the World Ser.). (Illus.). 32p. (J). (gr. 3 up). lib. bdg. 24.67 (978-0-8368-2021-8(5)) Stevens, Gareth Inc.

Grolier Educational Staff, contrib. by. Argentina. 2003. (Illus.). 32p. (J). (978-0-7172-5789-8(4)); (978-0-7172-5788-1(6)) Scholastic Library Publishing. (Grolier).

—Haiti. 2003. (Illus.). 32p. (J). (978-0-7172-5792-8(4) , Grolier) Scholastic Library Publishing.

—Hungary. 2003. (Illus.). 32p. (J). (978-0-7172-5793-5(2) , Grolier) Scholastic Library Publishing.

—Iran. 2003. (Illus.). 32p. (J). (978-0-7172-5794-2(0) , Grolier) Scholastic Library Publishing.

—Kenya. 2003. (Illus.). 32p. (J). (978-0-7172-5795-9(9) , Grolier) Scholastic Library Publishing.

—Mongolia. 2003. (Illus.). 32p. (J). (978-0-7172-5796-6(7) , Grolier) Scholastic Library Publishing.

—Nicaragua. 2003. (Illus.). 32p. (J). (978-0-7172-5797-3(5) , Grolier) Scholastic Library Publishing.

—Norway. 2003. (Illus.). 32p. (J). (978-0-7172-5798-0(3) , Grolier) Scholastic Library Publishing.

—Portugal. 2003. (Illus.). 32p. (J). (978-0-7172-5799-7(1) , Grolier) Scholastic Library Publishing.

—Scotland. 2003. (Illus.). 32p. (J). (978-0-7172-5800-0(9) , Grolier) Scholastic Library Publishing.

—Sri Lanka. 2003. (Illus.). 32p. (J). (978-0-7172-5801-7(7) , Grolier) Scholastic Library Publishing.

—Syria. 2003. (Illus.). 32p. (J). (978-0-7172-5802-4(5) , Grolier) Scholastic Library Publishing.

—Thailand. 2003. (Illus.). 32p. (J). (978-0-7172-5803-1(3) , Grolier) Scholastic Library Publishing.

—Tunisia. 2003. (Illus.). 32p. (J). (978-0-7172-5804-8(1) , Grolier) Scholastic Library Publishing.

Gutierrez, Javiera. El Baul de Mis Fiestas: Un Libro Sobre los Colores. Clocchiatti, Constanza, illus. (Coleccion el Baul Ser.). (SPA.). 10p. (J). (gr. k-1). (978-950-46-1157-8(5)) Santillana USA Publishing Co., Inc.

Hall, Margaret. Festivals. (Around the World Ser.). 32p. pap. 6.95 (978-1-4034-4003-7(4)) Heinemann Library.

Hall, Margaret C. Festivals. 2002. (Around the World Ser.). (Illus.). 32p. (J). (gr. k-2). lib. bdg. 22.79 (978-1-58810-479-3(6)) Heinemann Library.

Harcourt School Publishers Staff. Fun Days Around the World Advanced Level. 3rd ed. 2002. (Trophies Reading Program Ser.). (Illus.). pap. 5.10 (978-0-15-323114-8(9)) Harcourt Schl. Pubs.

—Winter Celebrations. 3rd ed. 2002. (Horizons Ser.). (Illus.). (J). pap. 3.70 (978-0-15-333168-8(2)) Harcourt Schl. Pubs.

Harris, David. Weird & Wacky Festivals. 2005. (X-Zone Ser.). (Illus.). 30p. (gr. 4-8). 23.00 (978-0-7910-8981-1(9)) Facts On File, Inc.

Harris, Zoe & Williams, Suzanne. Pinatas & Smiling Skeletons: Celebrating Mexican Festivals. Woo, Yolanda G., illus. 1998. 48p. (YA). (gr. 2-8). lib. bdg. 19.95 (978-1-881896-19-7(6) , Dragon Bks.) Pacific View Pr.

Heiligman, Deborah. Celebrate Diwali. 2006. (Holidays Around the World Ser.). (Illus.). 32p. (J). (gr. 1-4). pap. 15.95 (978-0-7922-5922-0(X)); lib. bdg. 23.90 (978-0-7922-5923-7(8)) National Geographic Society. (National Geographic Children's Bks.).

Heinrichs, Ann. Mardi Gras. Bryan-Hunt, Jan, illus. 2006. (Holidays, Festivals, & Celebrations Ser.). 32p. (J). (gr. k-4). 22.79 (978-1-59296-578-6(4)) Child's World, Inc.

Ho Siow Yen & Rabe, Monica. South Korea. 1998. (Festivals of the World Ser.). (Illus.). 32p. (J). (gr. 3 up). lib. bdg. 24.67 (978-0-8368-2019-5(3)) Stevens, Gareth Inc.

Holidays & Celebrations, Vol. 2. 2005. (One World, Many Cultures Ser.). (YA). (gr. k-3). 356.40 (978-0-7368-4194-8(6) , Pebble Bks.) Capstone Pr., Inc.

Hughes. Festivals, 5 vols., Set 1. 2003. (Illus.). (J). pap. 24.75 (978-1-4109-0662-5(0)) Raintree.

Hughes, Monica. Festivals, 8 bks., Set 1&2. 2004. (Illus.). (J). pap. 39.60 (978-1-4109-0787-5(2)) Raintree.

Illsley, Linda. Mexico. 1999. (Food & Festivals Ser.). (Illus.). 32p. (J). (gr. 1-4). lib. bdg. 25.69 (978-0-8172-5553-4(2)) Raintree.

Jackson, Ellen B. The Autumn Equinox: Celebrating the Harvest. 2003. (Illus.). 32p. (J). (gr. 3-6). pap. 7.95 (978-0-7613-1984-9(0) , Millbrook Pr.) Lerner Publishing Group.

—The Autumn Equinox: Celebrating the Harvest. Ellis, Jan Davey, illus. 2000. 32p. (gr. 2-4). (978-0-7613-1442-4(3) , Millbrook Pr.) Lerner Publishing Group.

—The Spring Equinox: Celebrating the Greening of the Earth. Ellis, Jan Davey, illus. 2002. (Traditions of the Seasons Ser.). 32p. (gr. 2-4). lib. bdg. 24.90 (978-0-7613-1955-9(7) , Millbrook Pr.) Lerner Publishing Group.

—Spring Equinox: The Greening of the Earth. 2003. (gr. k-3). lib. bdg. 16.40 (978-0-613-90690-6(X)) Tandem Library Bks.

Jarvie, Frances. Festivals in Scotland. Galloway, Fhiona, illus. 1999. (Scottie Bks.). 40p. (J). (gr. 3-7). pap. 6.95 (978-0-11-495271-6(X)) Stationery Office, The GBR. *Dist:* Balogh International, Inc.

Jones, Lynda. Kids Around the World Celebrate! the Best Feasts & Festivals from Many Lands. 2000. (gr. 3-6). lib. bdg. 22.20 (978-0-613-25878-4(9)) Tandem Library Bks.

Kindersley, Barnabas & Kindersley, Anabel, photos by. Celebraciones. 2005. Tr. of Celebrations. (SPA., Illus.). (J). (gr. 1-4). 18.95 (978-0-9628720-5-1(9)) Iaconi, Mariuccia Bk. Imports.

Krishnaswami, Uma. Holi. 2003. (Rookie Read-About Holidays Ser.). (Illus.). 32p. (J). (gr. 1-2). 20.50 (978-0-516-22863-1(3)); pap. 5.95 (978-0-516-27764-6(2)) Scholastic Library Publishing. (Children's Pr.).

—Holi. 2003. (gr. k-3). lib. bdg. 14.10 (978-0-613-59633-6(1)) Tandem Library Bks.

Lakeshore Learning Materials Staff, contrib. by. Festivals Around the World - Complete Set, 4 vols., Set. 2000. (J). pap. 115.00 (978-1-929255-84-9(5)) Lakeshore Learning Materials.

Legge, R. H. Annals of the N.O.R.F. & N.O.R.W. Festivals. 2001. (YA). reprint ed. 150.00 (978-0-7222-5125-6(4)) Library Reprints, Inc.

Luenn, Nancy. Celebrations of Light: A Year of Holidays Around the World. Bender, Mark, illus. 1998. 32p. (J). (gr. 2-5). 16.99 (978-0-689-31986-0(X) , Atheneum) Simon & Schuster Children's Publishing.

MacMillan, Dianne M. Diwali: Hindu Festival of Lights. 2008. (Best Holiday Books Ser.). 48p. (J). (gr. 3-4). lib. bdg. 23.93 (***978-0-7660-3060-2(1)***) Enslow Pubs., Inc.

—Mardi Gras. 2nd ed. 2008. (Best Holiday Books Ser.). 48p. (J). (gr. 3-4). lib. bdg. 23.93 (***978-0-7660-3062-6(8)***) Enslow Pubs., Inc.

Markham, Lois. Harvest. 1998. (World Celebrations & Ceremonies Ser.). (Illus.). 24p. (J). (gr. 3-5). 22.45 (978-1-56711-275-7(7) , Blackbirch Pr., Inc.) Thomson Gale.

McKay, Susan. Switzerland. 1999. (Festivals of the World Ser.). (Illus.). 32p. (J). (gr. 3 up). lib. bdg. 24.67 (978-0-8368-2027-0(4)) Stevens, Gareth Inc.

McNeil, Niki, et al. HOCPP 1108 Harvest Festival. 2006. spiral bd. 14.00 (***978-1-60308-108-5(9)***) In the Hands of a Child.

Milet Limited Publishing Staff & Swain, Gwenyth. Celebrating. 2000. (Small World Ser.). (Illus.). 24p. (J). (BEN & ENG.). pap. 9.95 (978-1-84059-131-6(5)); (CHI & ENG., pap. 9.95 (978-1-84059-132-3(3)); (GUJ & ENG., pap. 9.95 (978-1-84059-133-0(1)); (PAN & ENG., pap. 9.95 (978-1-84059-134-7(X)); (URD & ENG., pap. 9.95 (978-1-84059-136-1(6)) Milet Publishing.

—Celebrating. Wood, Kim Marie, tr. from ENG. 2000. (Small World Ser.). (VIE & ENG., Illus.). 24p. (J). pap. 9.95 (978-1-84059-137-8(4)) Milet Publishing.

—Celebrating. 2nd ed. 2000. (Small World Ser.). (TUR & ENG., Illus.). 24p. (J). pap. 9.95 (978-1-84059-135-4(8)) Milet Publishing.

—Celebrating. Al-Hamdi, Ahmed, tr. from ENG. 2nd ed. 2000. (Small World Ser.). (ARA & ENG., Illus.). 24p. (J). pap. 9.95 (978-1-84059-130-9(7)) Milet Publishing.

Miteff, Deb & Falk, Cathy. The un-Halloween Book: A Complete Fall Festival for Children's Ministry. 2004. (Illus.). 248p. (J). pap. 16.99 (978-1-885358-74-5(1) , Legacy Pr.) Rainbow Pubs. & Legacy Pr.

Moehn, Heather. World Holidays: A Watts Guide for Children. 2000. (Watts Reference Ser.). (Illus.). 124p. (YA). (gr. 4 up). pap. 19.95 (978-0-531-16490-7(X) , Watts, Franklin) Scholastic Library Publishing.

—World Holidays: A Watts Guide for Children. 2000. (gr. 3-6). lib. bdg. 30.35 (978-0-613-72663-4(4)) Tandem Library Bks.

Moyse, Sarah. Chinese New Year. 1998. (Festivals Ser.). (Illus.). 32p. (gr. 2-4). lib. bdg. 22.90 (978-0-7613-0374-9(X) , Millbrook Pr.) Lerner Publishing Group.

My Puptatl Book. 2006. (J). spiral bd. 8.00 (***978-0-9786947-0-8(8)***) Puptattle Pr., Inc.

My Puptatl Youth Book. 2006. (J). spiral bd. 8.00 (***978-0-9786947-1-5(6)***) Puptattle Pr., Inc.

NgCheong-Lum, Roseline. Haiti. 1999. (Festivals of the World Ser.). (Illus.). 32p. (J). (gr. 3 up). lib. bdg. 24.67 (978-0-8368-2015-7(0)) Stevens, Gareth Inc.

Nicholas, St. Our Holidays (Their Meaning & Spirit) 2006. 94.99 (***978-1-4280-0657-7(5)***); pap. 88.99 (***978-1-4280-0678-2(8)***) IndyPublish.com.

Pandya, Meenal. Here Comes Diwali: Festival of Lights. Mehta, Ashish J., illus. 2nd rev. ed. 2000. 32p. (J). (ps-3). 14.95 (978-0-9635539-3-5(3)) MeeRa Pubns.

Pfeffer, Wendy. A New Beginning. Bleck, Linda, illus. 2008. 40p. (J). (gr. 1). 17.99 (***978-0-525-47874-4(4)*** , Dutton Juvenile) Penguin Group (USA) Inc.

Pfeffer, Wendy. The Shortest Day: Celebrating the Winter Solstice. Reisch, Jesse, illus. 2003. 40p. (J). (gr. 1-4). 16.99 (978-0-525-46968-1(0) , Dutton Juvenile) Penguin Group (USA) Inc.

Pickels, Dwayne E. Ancient & Annual Customs. 1999. (Looking Into the Past Ser.). (Illus.). 64p. (YA). (gr. 5 up). 14.00 (978-0-7910-4682-1(6) , Chelsea Hse.) Facts On File, Inc.

Pirotta, Saviour. Divali. 2007. (J). lib. bdg. (978-1-4042-3706-3(2) , PowerKids Pr.) Rosen Publishing Group, Inc., The.

Plum-Ucci, Carol. Celebrate Diwali. 2007. (Celebrate Holidays Ser.). (Illus.). 128p. (J). (gr. 5). lib. bdg. 31.93 (***978-0-7660-2778-7(3)***) Enslow Pubs., Inc.

Powell, Jillian. Divali. 2006. (Illus.). 30p. (J). (978-1-58340-946-6(7) , 1262390) Smart Apple Media.

—Harvest Festival. 2006. (Illus.). 30p. (J). (978-1-58340-950-3(5)) Smart Apple Media.

Preszler, June. Diwali: Hindu Festival of Lights. 2007. (First Facts Ser.). (Illus.). 24p. (J). 21.26 (978-0-7368-6395-7(8)) Capstone Pr., Inc.

Raintree Steck-Vaughn Staff. A World of Holidays, 13 bks., Set. 1998. (World of Holidays Ser.). (Illus.). (J). lib. bdg. 333.97 (978-0-8172-4618-1(5)) Raintree.

Raintree Steck-Vaughn Staff, ed. Food & Festivals, 12 bks., Set. 2000. (Illus.). (J). lib. bdg. 308.28 (978-0-8172-5761-3(6)) Raintree.

Renaud, Anne. A Bloom of Friendship: The Story of the Canadian Tulip Festival. Spires, Ashley, illus. 2005. 24p. pap. (978-1-897073-35-3(6)) Lobster Pr.

Reynolds, Jan. Celebrate! Connections among Cultures. 2006. (Illus.). 32p. (J). (gr. k-3). 16.95 (978-1-58430-253-7(4)) Lee & Low Bks., Inc.

Rock. First Festivals: Harvest. 1999. (Illus.). 48p. (J). 16.99 (978-0-7459-3908-7(2) , Lion) Lion Hudson plc GBR. *Dist:* Trafalgar Square Publishing.

Roraff, Susan. Chile. 1998. (Festivals of the World Ser.). (Illus.). 32p. (J). (gr. 3 up). lib. bdg. 24.67 (978-0-8368-2012-6(6)) Stevens, Gareth Inc.

Russell, Ching Yeung & Boyds Mills Press Staff. Moon Festival. Zhang, Christopher Zhong-Yuan, illus. 2003. 32p. (J). (gr. 2-4). pap. 9.95 (978-1-59078-079-4(5)) Boyds Mills Pr.

Sanna, Ellyn. Folk Festivals. 2002. (North American Folklore Ser.). (Illus.). 112p. (YA). (gr. 7 up). lib. bdg. (978-1-59084-340-6(1)) Mason Crest Pubs.

Simonds, Nina, et al. Moonbeams, Dumplings & Dragon Boats: A Treasury of Chinese Holiday Tales, Activities & Recipes. So, Meilo, illus. 2002. 80p. (J). (gr. 4-7). 21.00 (978-0-15-201983-9(9)) Harcourt Children's Bks.

Sioras, Efstathia. Greece. 1998. (Festivals of the World Ser.). (Illus.). 32p. (J). (gr. 3 up). lib. bdg. 24.67 (978-0-8368-2014-0(2)) Stevens, Gareth Inc.

Stull. Festival Foods Around-the-World. 1999. (Illus.). (J). pap. (978-0-7398-2405-4(8)) Steck-Vaughn.

Swain, Gwenyth. Celebrating. 1999. (Small World Ser.). (Illus.). 24p. (J). (ps-2). lib. bdg. 19.93 (978-1-57505-258-8(X) , Carolrnoda Bks.) Lerner Publishing Group.

Tabor, Nancy Maria Grande. Celebrations/Celebraciones: Holidays of the United States of America & Mexico/Dias Feriados de los Estados Unidos y Mexico. Tabor, Nancy Maria Grande, illus. 2004. (SPA & ENG., Illus.). 32p. (J). pap. 7.95 (978-1-57091-550-5(4)) Charlesbridge Publishing, Inc.

Tan Chung Lee. Finland. 1998. (Festivals of the World Ser.). (Illus.). 32p. (J). (gr. 3 up). lib. bdg. 24.67 (978-0-8368-2013-3(4)) Stevens, Gareth Inc.

Van Fenema, Joyce. Netherlands. 1998. (Festivals of the World Ser.). (Illus.). 32p. (J). (gr. 3 up). lib. bdg. 24.67 (978-0-8368-2016-4(9)) Stevens, Gareth Inc.

The Whole World Loves Festivals, 6 vols. (Book2WebTM Ser.). (gr. 4-8). 36.50 (978-0-322-02990-3(2)) Wright Group, The.

Williams, Colleen Madonna Flood. The Festivals of Mexico. 2002. (Encyclopedia of Mexico Ser.). (Illus.). 64,80p. (YA). (gr. 5 up). lib. bdg. (978-1-59084-078-8(X)) Mason Crest Pubs.

Winne, Joanne. Celebrations, 6 bks., Set. 2004. (Illus.). 24p. (J). (ps-2). 174.00 (978-0-516-22995-9(8) , Children's Pr.) Scholastic Library Publishing.

World Book, Inc. Staff, contrib. by. Harvest Celebrations. 2002. (World Book's Celebrations & Rituals Around the World Ser.). (Illus.). 44p. (J). (978-0-7166-5007-2(X)) World Bk., Inc.

—National Celebrations. 2002. (World Book's Celebrations & Rituals Around the World Ser.). (Illus.). 44p. (J). (978-0-7166-5009-6(6)) World Bk., Inc.

—New Year Celebrations. 2002. (World Book's Celebrations & Rituals Around the World Ser.). (Illus.). 44p. (J). (978-0-7166-5006-5(1)) World Bk., Inc.

—Religious Celebrations. 2003. (World Book's Celebrations & Rituals Around the World Ser.). (Illus.). 46p. (J). (978-0-7166-5015-7(0)) World Bk., Inc.

—Spring Celebrations. 2002. (World Book's Celebrations & Rituals Around the World Ser.). (Illus.). 44p. (J). (978-0-7166-5008-9(8)) World Bk., Inc.

—Winter Celebrations. 2003. (World Book's Celebrations & Rituals Around the World Ser.). (Illus.). 46p. (J). (978-0-7166-5013-3(4)) World Bk., Inc.

Zocchi, Judy. On Halloween Night. Wallis, Rebecca, illus. 2005. (Holiday Happenings Ser.). (ENG.). 32p. (J). lib. bdg. 20.65 (978-1-891997-77-8(7)) Dingles & Co.

Zwierzynska-Coldicott, Aldona M. Poland. 1998. (Festivals of the World Ser.). (Illus.). 32p. (J). (gr. 3 up). lib. bdg. 24.67 (978-0-8368-2018-8(5)) Stevens, Gareth Inc.

FESTIVALS—FICTION

Aikins, Dave, illus. At the Carnival. 2005. (J). (***978-1-4156-0769-5(9)*** , Simon Spotlight/Nickelodeon) Simon & Schuster Children's Publishing.

Alderson, Lisa, illus. The Snow Family: A Winter's Tale. 2005. 12p. (J). 12.95 (978-1-58117-233-1(8) , Intervisual/Piggy Toes) Dalmatian Pr.

Ancona, George. Fiesta Fireworks. 2007. (Illus.). 28p. (YA). (gr. 4-8). reprint ed. 16.00 (***978-1-4223-6257-0(4)***) DIANE Publishing Co.

Big Night in Booville. 2002. (Booville Ser.). (Illus.). 24p. (J). (gr. k-4). 2.99 (978-1-57759-834-3(2)) Dalmatian Pr.

Blumenthal, Deborah. Ice Palace. Rand, Ted, illus. 2003. 32p. (J). (gr. k-3). 16.00 (978-0-618-15960-4(6) , Clarion Bks.) Houghton Mifflin Co. Trade & Reference Div.

Bond, Michael. Paddington Bear & the Busy Bee Carnival. Alley, R. W., illus. 1998. (Paddington Ser.). 40p. (J). (ps-3). 13.95 (978-0-06-027765-9(3)) HarperCollins Pubs.

—Paddington Bear & the Busy Bee Carnival. 2000. (Paddington Ser.). (J). (ps-3). (978-0-606-18710-7(3)) Tandem Library Bks.

Bowdish, Lynea. The Carousel Ride. Girouard, Patrick, illus. 1999. (Rookie Reader Skill Set Ser.). 32p. (J). (gr. k-2). pap. 4.95 (978-0-516-26410-3(9) , Children's Pr.) Scholastic Library Publishing.

Bowman, Crystal. Windmills & Woodenshoes. Tanis, Joel E., illus. 1999. 40p. (J). (gr. 2-6). 15.00 (978-0-9636050-2-3(X)) Cygnet Publishing Co.

Carr, Richard Wallace. Dolly & Ike Cherry Blossom Time. Parrish, Mary, illus. 2006. 32p. (J). (gr. k-3). per. 15.95 (978-0-933165-09-0(9)) Dicmar Publishing Co.

Cook, Jean Thor. Los Amiguitos' Fiesta. Wilson, Lincoln, ed. Shade, Judith Donoho, illus. l.t. ed. 2001. Tr. of Little Friends' Fiesta. (SPA.). 28p. (J). (ps-3). 17.00 (978-0-9708940-0-7(7)) Gently Worded Bks., LLC.

D'Amico, Carmela & D'Amico, Steven. Ella Sets Sail. 2008. (J). (***978-0-439-83156-7(3)***); pap. (***978-0-439-83155-0(5)***) Scholastic, Inc. (Levine, Arthur A. Bks.).

Damschroder, Scott. The Crazy Carnival Clown We Call Croc. 2006. (Illus.). 40p. (J). lib. bdg. 19.95 (***978-0-9754728-1-1(X)*** , Blue Foot Pr.) MidAmerica Publishing Co.

Dole, Mayra L. Drum, Chavi, Drum! / Toca, Chavi, Toca! Tonel, illus. 2003. Tr. of Toca, Chavi, Toca!. (ENG & SPA.). 32p. (J). 16.95 (978-0-89239-186-8(3)) Children's Bk. Pr.

Evans, Clay Bonnyman. The Winter Witch. Bender, Robert, illus. 2005. 32p. (J). (ps-ps). 16.95 (978-0-8234-1615-8(1)) Holiday Hse., Inc.

Frank's 1st Pumpkin. 2002. (Booville Ser.). (Illus.). 24p. (J). (gr. k-4). 2.99 (978-1-57759-833-6(4)) Dalmatian Pr.

Gantos, Jack. Practice Makes Perfect for Rotten Ralph: A Rotten Ralph Rotten Reader. Rubel, Nicole, illus. 2002. (Rotten Ralph Rotten Readers Ser.). 48p. (J). (ps-2). 15.00 (978-0-374-36356-7(0) , Farrar, Straus & Giroux (BYR)) Farrar, Straus & Giroux.

Geisert, Arthur. Pigaroons. 2004. (Illus.). 32p. (J). (gr. k-3). tchr. ed. 16.00 (978-0-618-41058-3(9) , Walter Lorraine) Houghton Mifflin Co. Trade & Reference Div.

Gelsey, James. Scooby-Doo & the Carnival Creeper. 1999. (Scooby-Doo Mysteries Ser.: No. 7). (Illus.). 64p. (J). (ps-3). 3.99 (978-0-439-11346-5(6)) Scholastic, Inc.

Gilmore, Rachna. Mina's Spring of Colors. 2000. 150p. (J). (gr. 4-7). (978-1-55041-549-0(2)); (978-1-55041-534-6(4)) Fitzhenry & Whiteside, Ltd.

—Mina's Spring of Colors. 2000. (gr. 3-6). lib. bdg. 17.60 (978-0-613-43201-6(0)) Tandem Library Bks.

Gorman, Carol. A Midsummer Night's Dork. 224p. (J). 2006. (Illus.). pap. 5.99 (978-0-06-050720-6(9) , Harper Trophy); 2004. 15.99 (978-0-06-050718-3(7)); 2004. lib. bdg. 16.89 (978-0-06-050719-0(5)) HarperCollins Pubs.

Guy, Ginger Foglesong. Fiesta! Moreno, Rene King, illus. 2003. (SPA & ENG.). 34p. (J). (ps-k). bds. 6.99 (978-0-06-009263-4(7)) HarperCollins Pubs.

E F G

Hahn, Mary Downing. Janey & the Famous Author. Bush, Timothy, illus. 2005. 48p. (J). (gr. k-3). 15.00 (978-0-618-35408-5(5) , Clarion Bks.) Houghton Mifflin Co. Trade & Reference Div.

Hall, Francie. The Scottish Highland Games. Oehm, Kent, illus. 2002. 32p. (J). 16.95 (978-1-57072-237-0(4)) Overmountain Pr.

Hall, Kirsten. At the Carnival. Rader, Laura, illus. 2003. 32p. (J). pap. 3.99 (978-0-439-59427-1(8) , Scholastic, Inc.) Scholastic, Inc.

Hats for the Carnival: Individual Title Six-Pack Pouch - Level I. (Lighthouse Ser.). 16p. (gr. 1 up). 26.00 (978-0-7578-0851-7(4)) Rigby Education.

Hennessy, B. G. One Little, Two Little, Three Little Pilgrims. 2001. (gr. k-3). lib. bdg. 15.30 (978-0-613-85724-6(0)) Tandem Library Bks.

Hobden, Helen. Be in the Place. 2006. 198p. (J). pap. 9.99 (*978-1-84270-460-8(5)) Andersen GBR. *Dist:* Independent Pubs. Group.

Ip, Ivy S. Clues at the Carnival. 2001. (ps-2). lib. bdg. 11.80 (978-0-613-54137-4(5)) Tandem Library Bks.

Johnson, Lisa Sferlazza. Winter's Eve: Love & Lights. Johnson, Tucker, illus. 2007. 32p. (J). (ps-k). 15.95 (*978-0-9773096-3-4(0)) Positive Spin Pr.

Kate's Tricky Treat. 2002. (Booville Ser.). (Illus.). 24p. (J). (gr. k-4). 2.99 (978-1-57759-832-9(6)) Dalmatian Pr.

Keene, Carolyn. The Apple Bandit. Jones, Jan Naimo, illus. 2005. 74p. (J). lib. bdg. 15.00 (*978-1-4242-0917-0(X)) Fitzgerald Bks.

—The Apple Bandit. Jones, Jan Naimo, illus. 2005. 74p. (J). (978-1-4156-2882-9(3) , Aladdin) Simon & Schuster Children's Publishing.

Landen, Cynthia & Phillips, Lorrie. The Elson Readers, Primer. 2005. pap. (*978-1-890623-24-1(5)) Lost Classics Bk. Co.

Larsen, Sandy. Ice Festival. Taylor, Wanda, illus. 1999. (Jackpine Point Adventure Ser.: Vol. 2). 126p. (J). (gr. 4-6). pap. 5.99 (978-0-9666677-1-4(9)) Merritt Park Pr.

Lee, Uk-Bae. Sori's Harvest Moon Day: A Story of Korea. Lee, Uk-Bae, illus. 1999. (Make Friends Around the World Ser.). Orig. Title: Sori's Chu-Suk. (Illus.). 32p. (J). (gr. k-3). 15.95 (978-1-56899-687-5(X) , B8001); 5.95 (978-1-56899-688-2(8) , S8001) Soundprints.

Leigh, Tina. Groundhog Day for Essex Ed. Leigh, Tina, illus. 2001. (Illus.). 32p. (J). pap. 14.95 (978-0-9715673-0-6(1)) Leigh, Tina Illustrator.

Martin, W. Lyon. Aidan's First Full Moon Circle. Martin, W. Lyon, illus. 2008. (Illus.). 32p. (J). lib. bdg. 16.95 (*978-0-9796834-4-2(0)) Shades of White.

McAllister, Margaret. The Octave of Angels. 2004. 128p. (J). pap. 8.00 (978-0-8028-5240-3(8)) Eerdmans, William B. Publishing Co.

McConnie Zapater, Beatriz. Fiesta. Ortega, Jose, illus. 2005. (Multicultural Celebrations Ser.). 32p. (J). 4.95 (978-1-59373-009-3(8)) Bunker Hill Publishing, Inc.

Pandya, Meenal. Here Comes Holi: The Festival of Colors. 2003. (Illus.). 32p. (J). lib. bdg. 14.95 (978-0-9635539-4-2(1)) MeeRa Pubns.

Pinkwater, Daniel M. Irving & Muktuk: Two Bad Bears. Pinkwater, Jill & Pinkwater, Daniel M., illus. 2001. 32p. (J). (gr. k-3). tchr. ed. 15.00 (978-0-618-09334-2(6)) Houghton Mifflin Co. Trade & Reference Div.

—Irving & Muktuk: Two Bad Bears. ed. 2004. (Illus.). (J). (gr. k-3). spiral bd. (978-0-616-11136-9(3)); spiral bd. (978-0-616-11137-6(1)) Canadian National Institute for the Blind/Institut National Canadien pour les Aveugles.

Piper, Watty. Little Engine That Could & the Snowy, Blowy Christmas. 1998. (gr. k-3). lib. bdg. 11.25 (978-0-613-72413-5(5)) Tandem Library Bks.

Rice, James. Gaston Goes to Mardi Gras Coloring Book. 2000. (Illus.). 32p. (J). (ps-3). pap. 3.25 (978-1-56554-773-5(X)) Pelican Publishing Co., Inc.

Rochester & Merle: A Day at the Carnival. 2000. 32p. (J). pap. (978-0-9701450-5-5(5)) Long Hill Productions, Inc.

Rodgers, Frank. Little T & the Dragon's Tooth. 2007. (Read-It! Chapter Books). (J). 21.26 (978-1-4048-2727-1(7)) Picture Window Bks.

Rumbley, Rose-Mary. What? No Chili? Rowden, Susan, illus. rev. ed. 2000. 144p. (J). (gr. 6-8). pap. 16.95 (978-0-89015-992-7(0)) Eakin Pr.

Russell, Ching Yeung. Moon Festival. 2003. (gr. k-3). lib. bdg. 17.60 (978-0-613-59335-9(9)) Tandem Library Bks.

Ryder, Joanne. Rainbow Wings. 2000. (Illus.). 40p. (J). (gr. k-5). 15.89 (978-0-688-14129-5(3)) HarperCollins Pubs.

—Rainbow Wings. Lee, Victor, illus. 2000. 40p. (J). (gr. k-3). 15.95 (978-0-688-14128-8(5)) HarperCollins Pubs.

Stephens, Monique. Fantastic Four: Meet the Fantastic Four. 2005. (Festival Reader Ser.). 32p. (J). 14.99 (978-0-06-082244-6(9)) HarperCollins Pubs.

Stevens, Jan Romero. Carlos & the Carnival. Arnold, Jeanne, illus. Tr. of Carlos y la Feria. (ENG & SPA.). 32p. (J). (gr. k-3). 7.95 (978-0-87358-811-9(8) , Rising Moon Bks. for Young Readers) Northland Publishing.

Tapahonso, Luci. Songs of Shiprock Fair. Emerson, Anthony C., illus. 1999. 32p. (J). (ps-3). 15.95 (978-1-885772-11-4(4)) Kiva Publishing, Inc.

Torres, Leyla. El Festival de Cometas. Torres, Leyla, illus. 2004. (SPA., Illus.). 32p. (J). 16.00 (978-0-374-32299-1(6) , Frances Foster Bks.) Farrar, Straus & Giroux.

Valdes, Leslie. At the Carnival. Roper, Robert, illus. 2005. 24p. (J). lib. bdg. 9.00 (*978-1-4242-0982-8(X)) Fitzgerald Bks.

Van Patten, Barbara. Whoo Saves the Symphony. 2007. (J). per. 9.99 (*978-1-60247-150-4(9)) Tate Publishing & Enterprises, L.L.C.

Vanderhoop, Jannette. Cranbery Day: A Wampanoag Harvest Celebration. 2002. 9.95 (978-0-9725679-0-9(9)) Aquinnah Wampanoag Education Department.

Wallace, Ian. Chin Chiang & the Dragon's Dance. 1998. (Illus.). 32p. (J). (ps-2). pap. 5.95 (978-0-88899-167-6(3)) Groundwood Bks. CAN. *Dist:* Perseus Distribution.

Wallace, Ian, illus. Chin Chiang & the Dragon's Dance. 1998. 32p. (J). (ps-2). 19.95 (978-0-88899-020-4(0)) Groundwood Bks. CAN. *Dist:* Perseus Distribution.

Weeks, Sarah. The Cake Lady. (Growing Tree Ser.). 24p. (J). (ps up). 9.99 (978-0-694-01074-5(X) , Geringer, Laura Book) HarperCollins Pubs.

Zucker, Jonny. Lighting a Lamp: A Diwali Story. Cohen, Jan Barger, illus. 2004. (Festival Time! Ser.). 24p. (J). pap. 6.95 (978-0-7641-2670-3(9)) Barron's Educational Series, Inc.

FESTIVALS—JEWS

see Fasts and Feasts—Judaism

FETT, BOBA (FICTITIOUS CHARACTER)—FICTION

Bisson, Terry. Crossfire. 2003. (Star Wars Ser.: Vol. 2). (gr. 7-12). lib. bdg. 13.00 (978-0-613-63273-7(7)) Tandem Library Bks.

Hand, Elizabeth. A New Threat. 2004. (Star Wars Ser.: Vol. 5). 139p. (J). lib. bdg. 20.00 (*978-1-4242-0781-7(9)) Fitzgerald Bks.

FEUDALISM

see also Chivalry; Middle Ages; Peasantry

Anderson, Mercedes Padrino. Feudalism & Village Life in the Middle Ages. 2005. (World Almanac Library of the Middle Ages). (Illus.). 48p. (J). pap. (978-0-8368-5903-4(0) , World Almanac Library) Stevens, Gareth Inc.

Davenport, John. Age of Feudalism. 2007. (World History Ser.). 128p. (gr. 7-10). 28.70 (*978-1-59018-649-7(4) , Lucent Bks.) Thomson Gale.

Eastwood, Kay. Medieval Society. 2003. (Medieval World Ser.). (Illus.). 32p. (J). (gr. 5). (978-0-7787-1345-6(8)) Crabtree Publishing Co.

Padrino, Mercedes. Feudalism & Village Life in the Middle Ages. 2006. (World Almanac' Library of the Middle Ages). (Illus.). 48p. (YA). (gr. 7-10). lib. bdg. 30.00 (978-0-8368-5894-5(8) , World Almanac Library) Stevens, Gareth Inc.

FEVER

Burles, Kenneth T. Fever. 1998. (Learning about Your Health Ser.). (J). lib. bdg. 26.60 (978-0-86625-651-3(2)) Rourke Publishing, LLC.

Burles, Kenneth T. & Hundley, David H. Fever. 1998. (Learning about Your Health Ser.). (Illus.). 32p. (J). (gr. 2-5). lib. bdg. 26.60 (978-1-57103-256-0(8)) Rourke Publishing, LLC.

Calamandrei, Camilla. Fever. 2008. (J). (*978-0-7614-2915-9(8)) Cavendish, Marshall Bks., Ltd.

Emmeluth, Donald. Typhoid Fever. 2003. (Deadly Diseases & Epidemics Ser.). (Illus.). 112p. (gr. 9-13). 31.95 (978-0-7910-7464-0(1) , Chelsea Hse.) Facts On File, Inc.

Walker, David H. Rocky Mountain Spotted Fever. 2007. (Deadly Diseases & Epidemics Ser.). 112p. (J). (gr. 9). 31.95 (*978-0-7910-8678-0(X) , Chelsea Hse.) Facts On File, Inc.

FIAT MONEY

see Paper Money

FIBERS

see also Cotton; Paper; Silk

Alford, Douglas. Cozy Clozy: From Fibers to Fabrics. Hayes, Betsy, illus. 2004. (J). 6.96 net. (978-0-9762208-0-0(6)) Mfg Application Konsulting Engineering.

Fibers from Plants: 6 Each of 1 Student Book, 6 vols. (Sunshinetm Science Ser.). 24p. (gr. 1-2). 41.95 (978-0-7802-1431-6(5)) Wright Group, The.

Fibers from Plants: Big Book. (Sunshinetm Science Ser.). 24p. (gr. 1-2). 37.50 (978-0-7802-1432-3(3)) Wright Group, The.

Fibers Made by People, 6 vols. (Sunshinetm Science Ser.). 24p. (gr. 1-2). 41.95 (978-0-7802-1437-8(4)) Wright Group, The.

Parker, Steve. Textiles. 2002. (Science Files Ser.). (Illus.). 32p. (J). (gr. 3 up). lib. bdg. 24.67 (978-0-8368-3086-6(5)) Stevens, Gareth Inc.

Rainis, Kenneth G. Hair, Clothing, & Tire Track Evidence: Crime-Solving Science Experiments. 2006. (Forensic Science Projects Ser.). (Illus.). 128p. (J). (gr. 5 up). lib. bdg. 31.93 (978-0-7660-2729-9(5)) Enslow Pubs., Inc.

Royston, Angela. Water & Fiber for a Healthy Body. 2003. (Body Needs Ser.). (Illus.). 48p. pap. 7.99 (978-1-4034-3314-5(3)); (J). (gr. 4-6). lib. bdg. 27.07 (978-1-4034-0760-3(6)) Heinemann Library.

—Water & Fiber for a Healthy Body. 2003. (gr. 3-6). lib. bdg. 16.40 (978-0-613-60999-9(9)) Tandem Library Bks.

FICTION—HISTORY AND CRITICISM

Bitetto, Marco A. V. Corrections to Article Inaccuracy. l.t. ed. 2003. (Illus.). 120p. (YA). reprint ed. pap. 2.50 (978-1-58578-487-5(7)) Institute of Cybernetics Research, Inc.

—Theme Stream Vol. 11: Helicopters. l.t. ed. 2003. (Illus.). 120p. (YA). pap. 2.50 (978-1-58578-484-4(2)) Institute of Cybernetics Research, Inc.

—Theme Stream Vol. 13: Helicopters. l.t. ed. 2003. (Illus.). 120p. (YA). pap. 10.00 (978-1-58578-485-1(0)) Institute of Cybernetics Research, Inc.

Bloom, Harold. Bloom's Major Short Story Writers. 2003. (Illus.). (J). 642.60 (978-0-7910-6818-2(8) , Chelsea Hse.) Facts On File, Inc.

Bloom, Harold. Jane Eyre. 2007. (Bloom's Guides). 104p. (YA). (gr. 9 up). 30.00 (*978-0-7910-9362-7(X) , Chelsea Hse.) Facts On File, Inc.

Bloom, Harold & Walsh, Judith E. Novelists & Novels. (Brief History Ser.). 368p. (gr. 9). pap. 19.95 (*978-0-8160-7334-4(1) , Checkmark Bks.) Facts On File, Inc.

Brouwer, Sigmund, et al. Fiction Starter Kit. 1999. (Illus.). (J). (gr. 3-9). 9.97 (978-0-8499-7539-4(5)) Nelson, Thomas Inc.

Cocoro Books Staff, compiled by. The Dragon Ball Z Legend: The Quest Continues. 2004. (Illus.). 192p. (J). 11.95 (978-0-9723124-9-3(8)) DH Publishing, Inc.

Hamilton, John. Time Travel. 2007. (World of Science Fiction Ser.). (Illus.). 32p. (J). 24.21 (978-1-59679-996-7(X)) ABDO Publishing Co.

Hamilton, Sue L. Masters of Horror. 2007. (ENG., Illus.). 32p. (YA). lib. bdg. 24.21 (*978-1-59928-770-6(6) , ABDO & Daughters) ABDO Publishing Co.

Rollyson, Carl, ed. Critical Survey of Long Fiction, 8 vols., 8 vols. 2nd rev. ed. 2000. (Critical Survey Ser.). (Illus.). 4392p. lib. bdg. 499.00 (978-0-89356-882-5(1) , 13) Salem Pr., Inc.

Teitelbaum, Michael. Story of Spider-Man. 2001. (gr. k-3). lib. bdg. 11.80 (978-0-613-43959-6(7)) Tandem Library Bks.

Wade, Mary Dodson. Joan Lowery Nixon: Masterful Mystery Writer. 2004. (Authors Teens Love Ser.). (Illus.). 128p. (J). lib. bdg. 26.60 (978-0-7660-2194-5(7)) Enslow Pubs., Inc.

Waters, Galadriel & Fossa, E. L. Ultimate Unofficial Guide to the Mysteries of Harry Potter. 2007. 280p. pap. 19.95 (*978-0-9723936-6-9(8)) Wizarding World Pr.

FICTITIOUS ANIMALS

see Animals, Mythical

FIEFS

see Feudalism

FIELD ATHLETICS

see Track Athletics

FIELD SPORTS

see Hunting; Sports

FIFTH COLUMN

see Subversive Activities

FIGHTER PLANES

Abramson, Andra Serlin. Fighter Planes up Close. 2008. 28p. (J). 9.95 (*978-1-4027-4796-0(9)) Sterling Publishing Co., Inc.

Batchelor, John. Jet Fighters Coloring Book. 1998. (Illus.). 48p. (J). pap. 3.95 (978-0-486-40357-1(2)) Dover Pubns., Inc.

—World War II Fighter Planes: 24 Cards. 2001. (Illus.). 6p. pap. 5.95 (978-0-486-41338-9(1)) Dover Pubns., Inc.

Beyer, Julie. Jet Fighter: The Harrier AV-8B. 2000. (gr. 7-12). lib. bdg. 15.25 (978-0-613-58702-0(2)) Tandem Library Bks.

Bledsoe, Karen & Bledsoe, Glen. Fighter Planes: Fearless Fliers. 2006. (Mighty Military Machines Ser.). (Illus.). 48p. (J). (gr. 4-10). lib. bdg. 23.93 (978-0-7660-2660-5(4)) Enslow Pubs., Inc.

Braulick, Carrie A. U.S. Air Force Fighters. 2006. (Blazers—Military Vehicles Ser.). (Illus.). 32p. (J). (978-0-7368-5467-2(3)) Capstone Pr., Inc.

Chant, Christopher. Early Fighters. 1999. (World's Greatest Aircraft Ser.). (Illus.). 64p. (YA). (gr. 5 up). 24.15 (978-0-7910-5418-5(7) , Chelsea Hse.) Facts On File, Inc.

—Role of the Fighters & Bombers. 1999. (World's Greatest Aircraft Ser.). (Illus.). 60p. (J). (gr. 5 up). 24.15 (978-0-7910-5419-2(5) , Chelsea Hse.) Facts On File, Inc.

Combat Aircraft. 2003. (Illus.). 32p. (YA). pap. (978-1-904516-32-3(7)) Chrysalis Children's Bks.

Dartford, Mark. Fighter Planes. 2004. (Military Hardware in Action Ser.). (Illus.). 48p. (J). (gr. 4-9). lib. bdg. 25.26 (978-0-8225-4706-8(6)) Lerner Publishing Group.

David, Jack. F-16 Fighting Falcons. 2007. (Illus.). 24p. (J). lib. bdg. 19.95 (978-1-60014-104-1(8)) Bellwether Media.

Discovery Channel & Staff. Fighters. 2004. (Planet's Most Extreme Ser.). (Illus.). 48p. (J). (gr. 4-7). 24.95 (978-1-4103-0383-7(7) , Blackbirch Pr., Inc.) Thomson Gale.

Doeden, Matt. Aviones Caza. 2006. (ENG & SPA.). (J). (978-0-7368-5872-4(5)) Capstone Pr., Inc.

—Fighter Planes. 2005. (Pebble Plus: Mighty Machines Ser.). (Illus.). 24p. (J). 19.93 (978-0-7368-3657-9(8)) Capstone Pr., Inc.

Fighter Planes. (Mighty MacHines Ser.). 24p. (J). 6.95 (978-0-7368-5138-1(0)) Capstone Pr., Inc.

Gardner, Adrian. The F-14 Tomcat. 2005. (U. S. Warplanes Ser.). (Illus.). 48p. (YA). (gr. 5-8). lib. bdg. 26.50 (978-0-8239-3870-4(0)) Rosen Publishing Group, Inc., The.

Graham, Ian. Attack Fighters. 2003. (Designed for Success Ser.). 32p. pap. 7.50 (978-1-4034-3356-5(9)); (Illus.). (J). 24.22 (978-1-4034-0769-6(X)) Heinemann Library.

Green, Michael & Green, Gladys. Carrier-Based Strike Fighters: The F-14 Tomcat. 2003. (War Planes Ser.). (Illus.). 32p. (J). lib. bdg. 22.60 (978-0-7368-2149-0(X) , Capstone High/Low Bks.) Capstone Pr., Inc.

—Close Air Support Fighters: A-10 Thunderbolt II. 2003. (War Planes Ser.). (Illus.). 32p. (J). lib. bdg. 22.60 (978-0-7368-2150-6(3) , Capstone High/Low Bks.) Capstone Pr., Inc.

—Heavy Bombers: The B-52 Stratofortresses. 2003. (War Planes Ser.). (Illus.). 32p. (J). lib. bdg. 22.60 (978-0-7368-2151-3(1) , Capstone High/Low Bks.) Capstone Pr., Inc.

Gunston, Bill. Fighter Planes. 1999. (History Ser.). (Illus.). 32p. (J). (gr. 5-9). pap. 5.95 (978-0-7641-0645-3(7)) Barron's Educational Series, Inc.

Hansen, Ole Steen. The AV-8B Harrier Jumpjet. 2006. (Illus.). 32p. (J). (978-0-7368-5254-8(9) , 1244016) Capstone Pr., Inc.

—The F/A-22 Raptor. 2006. (Illus.). 32p. (J). (978-0-7368-5253-1(0) , 1244015) Capstone Pr., Inc.

Patterson, Don. Spitfire! Parenteau, Mary, ed. Schug, Sonny, illus. 2000. (Tales of the R. A. F. Ser.). 104p. (J). (gr. 3-8). per. 7.95 (978-1-929031-18-4(1)) Hindsight, Ltd.

Rohr, Ian. Fighter Planes. 2006. (Real Deal - Yellow Ser.). (Illus.). 32p. (gr. 4-8). 19.00 (978-0-7910-9061-9(2)) Facts On File, Inc.

Rustad, Martha E. H. U.S. Marine Corps Combat Jets. 2007. (Blazers—Military Vehicles Ser.). (Illus.). 32p. (J). 19.93 (978-0-7368-6457-2(1)) Capstone Pr., Inc.

Schaefer, A. R. Jet Fighter Planes. 2004. (Wild Rides! Ser.). (Illus.). 32p. (J). lib. bdg. 22.60 (978-0-7368-2725-6(0)) Capstone Pr., Inc.

Seidman, David. F/A-18C Hornet. 2005. (U. S. Warplanes Ser.). (Illus.). 48p. (YA). (gr. 5-8). lib. bdg. 26.50 (978-0-8239-3874-2(3)) Rosen Publishing Group, Inc., The.

Trumbauer, Lisa. Fighter Jet. 2007. (J). pap. (*978-1-4109-2869-6(1)); lib. bdg. (*978-1-4109-2852-8(7)) Steck-Vaughn.

White Steve D. Combat Fighter: F-22 Raptor. 2007. (High-Tech Military Weapons Ser.). (Illus.). 48p. (J). pap. (978-0-531-18706-7(3)) Children's Pr., Ltd.

—Combat Fighter: F-22 Raptor. 2006. (High-Tech Military Weapons Ser.). (Illus.). 48p. (J). (978-0-531-12090-3(2) , Children's Pr.) Scholastic Library Publishing.

Zuehlke, Jeffrey. Fighter Planes. 2006. (Pull Ahead Books). (Illus.). 32p. (J). (ps-7). 22.60 (978-0-8225-2667-4(0) , Lerner Pubns.) Lerner Publishing Group.

FIGHTING

see Battles; Boxing; Bullfights; Fencing; Naval Art and Science; Self-Defense; War

FIGURE DRAWING

Court, Rob. How to Draw People. 2007. (Doodle Bks.). 32p. (J). 21.36 (*978-1-59296-809-1(0)) Child's World, Inc.

Foster, Walter & Kaufman Yaun, Debra. Faces & Features. 2006. (How to Draw & Paint/Art Instruction Program Ser.). 32p. (J). pap. 7.95 (978-1-56010-965-5(3)) Foster, Walter Publishing, Inc.

Gray, Peter C. How to Draw Manga Male Action Figures. 2006. (Kid's Guide to Drawing Ser.). (Illus.). 32p. (J). lib. bdg. (978-1-4042-3328-7(8) , PowerKids Pr.) Rosen Publishing Group, Inc., The.

Hosley, Maria. People. 2007. (Illus.). 24p. (J). 21.35 (*978-1-59679-812-0(2)) ABDO Publishing Co.

Levin, Freddie. 1-2-3 Draw People. 2007. (Illus.). 64p. pap. 8.99 (*978-0-939217-63-2(5)) Peel Productions, Inc.

FIGURE SKATING

see Skating

FIJI

NgCheong-Lum, Roseline. Fiji. 2000. (Cultures of the World Ser.). (Illus.). 128p. (gr. 5-12). lib. bdg. 37.07 (978-0-7614-0996-0(3) , Benchmark Bks.) Cavendish, Marshall Corp.

Stevens, Kathryn. Fiji. 2003. (Countries: Faces & Places Ser.). (Illus.). 32p. (J). (gr. 1-5). 25.64 (978-1-56766-907-7(5)) Child's World, Inc.

FILLING STATIONS

see Service Stations

FINANCE

see also Banks and Banking; Bonds; Commerce; Credit; Finance, Personal; Insurance; Investments; Money; Paper Money; Securities; Stock Exchanges

Bailey, Gerry & Law, Felicia. Money, It's Our Job: Money Careers. Phillips, Mike & Brooks, Rosie, illus. 2006. (My Money Ser.). 24p. (J). 27.93 (978-0-7565-1675-8(7)) Compass Point Bks.

Barratt Brown, Michael. Young Person's Guide to the Global Crisis & the Alternative. 1999. (Illus.). 111p. (YA). pap. 26.50 (978-0-85124-620-8(6)) Spokesman Bks. GBR. *Dist:* Coronet Bks.

Bell, N. Wayne. Childrens' Economics: A Book on Money & Finance. l.t. ed. 2004. (Illus.). 32p. (J). per. (978-0-9729753-5-3(7)) Really Big Coloring Bks., Inc.

Berg, Adriane G. Totally Awesome Business Book for Kids. 2001. (J). lib. bdg. 22.20 (978-0-613-45349-3(2)) Tandem Library Bks.

Cassedy, Patrice, tr. Finance. 2003. (Illus.). 112p. (J). 29.95 (978-1-59018-520-9(X) , Lucent Bks.) Thomson Gale.

Catalano, Angela. Community Plans: Economic Decision Making in Communities. 2005. (Communities at Work Ser.). (Illus.). 24p. (J). 19.95 (978-1-4042-2779-8(2) , PowerKids Pr.) Rosen Publishing Group, Inc., The.

Cooper, Terry, ed. Stock Market: Scholastic Technology Activity Folder. 2001. (Instant Internet Activities Folder Ser.). 6p. 3.95 (978-0-439-30952-3(2)) Scholastic, Inc.

Hocking, Justin. Taking Action: How to Get Your City to Build a Public Skatepark. 2004. (World of Skateboard Parks Ser.). (Illus.). 48p. (J). lib. bdg. 26.50 (978-1-4042-0341-9(9)) Rosen Publishing Group, Inc., The.

January, Brendan. Globalize It! The Stories of the IMF, the World Bank, the WTO - And Those Who Protest. 2003. (Single Titles Ser.). (Illus.). 144p. (gr. 7 up). 26.90 (978-0-7613-2417-1(8) , Twenty-First Century Bks.) Lerner Publishing Group.

Maybury, Richard J. Uncle Eric Talks about Personal, Career, & Financial Security. Williams, Jane A. & Daniels, Kathryn, eds. 2nd ed. 2004. ("Uncle Eric" Bk.). (Illus.). 187p. (YA). pap. 14.95 (978-0-942617-38-2(X)) Bluestocking Pr.

McAlpine, Margaret. Working in Banking & Finance. 2005. (My Future Career Ser.). (Illus.). 64p. (J). lib. bdg. 26.00 (978-0-8368-4772-7(5)) Stevens, Gareth Inc.

Reeves, Diane Lindsey & Bryan, Gayle. Career Ideas for Kids Who Like Money. Bond, Nancy, illus. 2001. (Career Ideas for Kids Ser.). (J). (gr. 4-8). 144p. pap. 12.95 (978-0-8160-4320-0(5)); 192p. 23.00 (978-0-8160-4319-4(1)) Facts On File, Inc. (Checkmark Bks.).

Simpson, Carolyn. Choosing a Career in Banking & Finance. rev. ed. 1999. (World of Work Ser.). (Illus.). 64p. (YA). (gr. 7-12). lib. bdg. 25.25 (978-0-8239-3016-6(5) , WW-BAFI) Rosen Publishing Group, Inc., The.

Weiss, Anne. Easy Credit. 2000. (Single Titles Ser.: up). 128p. (gr. 7 up). lib. bdg. (978-0-7613-1503-2(9) , Twenty-First Century Bks.) Lerner Publishing Group.

FINANCE, PERSONAL

see also Insurance; Investments

Andrade, J. Jack. Mom, Dad, Tell Me about Money: A Primer. 2004. 68p. (YA). per. 19.95 (978-0-9759494-0-5(3) , 2004-money01) Thundermist Consulting and Research Co.

Bailey, Gerry & Law, Felicia. Common Cents: The Money in Your Pocket. Phillips, Mike & Brooks, Rosie, illus. 2006. (My Money Ser.). 24p. (J). (gr. 4-6). 27.93 (978-0-7565-1671-0(4)) Compass Point Bks.

—Get Rich Quick? Earning Money. Phillips, Mike & Brooks, Rosie, illus. 2006. (My Money Ser.). 24p. (J). (gr. 4-6). 27.93 (978-0-7565-1674-1(9)) Compass Point Bks.

Bamford, Janet. Street Wise: A Guide for Teen Investors. 2000. (Bloomberg Personal Bookshelf). (Illus.). 240p. (YA). (gr. 7-12). pap. 16.95 (978-1-57660-039-9(4)) Bloomberg Pr.

Bateman, Katherine R. The Young Investor: Projects & Activities for Making Your Money Grow. 2001. (Illus.). 144p. (J). (gr. 6-9). pap. 14.95 (978-1-55652-396-0(3)) Chicago Review Pr., Inc.

Biedenweg, Kaarl. Personal Finance. 1999. (Illus.). 80p. (J). pap. 9.95 (978-1-58037-091-2(8)) Twain, Mark Media, Inc. Pubs.

Bijlefeld, Marjolijn K. & Zoumbaris, Sharon. Teen Guide to Personal Financial Management. 2000. (Illus.). 288p. 56.95 (978-0-313-31107-9(2) , GR1107, Greenwood Pr.) Greenwood Publishing Group, Inc.

Blatt, Jessica. The Teen Girl's Gotta-Have-It Guide to Money: Getting Smart about Making It, Saving It, & Spending It! Frenette, Cynthia, illus. 2007. (Teen Girl's Gotta-Have-It Guides). 96p. (YA). pap. 8.95 (***978-0-8230-1727-0(3)***) Watson-Guptill Pubns., Inc.

Bochner, Arthur & Bochner, Rose. The New Totally Awesome Money Book for Kids. 3rd rev. ed. 2007. (Illus.). 160p. (J). pap. 9.95 (978-1-55704-738-0(3)) Newmarket Pr.

Bochner, Arthur Berg & Berg, Adriane G. The Totally Awesome Money Book for Kids. 2nd ed. 2002. (Childcare/Parenting Guides Ser.). 160p. 12.95 (978-1-55704-493-8(7)) Newmarket Pr.

Bowman-Kruhm, Mary. Money: Save It, Manage It, Spend It. 2000. (Teen Issues Ser.). (Illus.). 64p. (J). (gr. 6-12). lib. bdg. 17.95 (978-0-7660-1363-6(4)) Enslow Pubs., Inc.

Brooks, Yvonne. Financial Planning for Teens. 2002. (Teen Success Ser.: Vol. 1). 156p. (YA). pap. 11.95 (978-0-595-22797-6(X) , Writers Club Pr.) iUniverse, Inc.

Brooks, Yvonne. Kids Finance 101: A Guide to Financial Success for Parents & their Children. 2007. 208p. per. 17.95 (***978-0-595-45962-9(5)***) iUniverse, Inc.

Bumcrot, Curt. Personal Finance Packet. Zyp, Nicole, ed. 2005. 41p. (YA). (gr. 10-12). pap. 15.00 (978-1-888786-46-0(9)) Basic Skills Assessment & Educational Services.

Bundlie, Mike, et al. Make More Than Your Parents: Your Guide to Financial Freedom. 2003. (Illus.). 144p. (YA). pap. 12.95 (978-0-7573-0122-3(3)) Health Communications, Inc.

Burkett, Larry. All about Money. Locke, Gary, illus. 2003. (All about Ser.). 32p. (J). pap., pap. 7.99 (978-0-7814-3786-8(5) , 0781437865) Cook, David C. Publishing Co.

—All about Talent: Discovering Your Gifts & Personality. 2003. (All about Ser.). 32p. (J). pap., pap. 7.99 (978-0-7814-3787-5(3) , 0781437873) Cook, David C. Publishing Co.

—Money Matters for Teens. 2001. (gr. 7-12). lib. bdg. 22.25 (978-0-613-90343-1(9)) Tandem Library Bks.

Burkett, Larry & Temple, Todd. Money Matters Workbook for Teens (11-14) 1998. 120p. (gr. 6-9). pap., wbk. ed. 12.99 (978-0-8024-6345-6(2)) Moody Pubs.

—Money Matters Workbook for Teens (15-18) 1998. 120p. (gr. 10-13). pap., wbk. ed. 13.99 (978-0-8024-6346-3(0)) Moody Pubs.

Burkett, Larry, et al. Money Matters for Kids. 2001. 64p. (gr. 1-7). pap. 10.99 (978-0-8024-4635-0(3)) Moody Pubs.

—Money Matters for Teens. rev. ed. 2001. 160p. (gr. 8-12). pap. 12.99 (978-0-8024-4636-7(1)) Moody Pubs.

Burnard, Patty. Teenage Money Management $kills: A Workbook Guaranteed to Help Make You Money $mart. 2002. 56p. (YA). 12.95 (978-0-9717022-2-6(5)) Onesti Online.

Can I Have Some Money Please? 2006. (J). bds. 14.95 (***978-0-9759527-3-3(0)*** , Prindle House Publishing Co.) Prindle Hse. Publishing Co.

Chambers, Don. The Entitlement Trap. 2003. 14.95 (978-0-9722071-1-9(2)) Healthy Wealth.

—Money Basics: For Young Adults. 2003. 14.95 (978-0-9722071-2-6(0)) Healthy Wealth.

Chariot, F. Home Allowance & Chore Kit. 2004. (Christian Financial Concept Ser.). (gr. 10-7). 17.99 (978-983-45025-8-4(3) , 9834502583) Cook, David C. Publishing Co.

The Chavo Cuentos of Zito & Lilis: The Importance of Savings. 2004. (J). pap. 2.50 (978-0-9770312-0-7(9)) Itiya Publishing, Inc.

A Child's Guide to Money. 2007. (YA). per. (***978-1-59916-190-7(7)***) Printing Systems.

Cooper, Jason. Paying Without Money. 2003. (Rourke Discovery Library). (Illus.). 24p. (gr. 3-6). 14.95 (978-1-58952-213-8(3)) Rourke Publishing, LLC.

Dayton, Howard & Dayton, Beverly. The ABC's of Handling Money God's Way. Davenport, Andy, illus. 2003. 96p. (J). pap., tchr. ed. 9.99 (978-0-8024-3151-6(8)) Moody Pubs.

—The Secret of Handling Money God's Way. 2003. (Leading Young Hearts & Minds to God Ser.). 144p. (J). pap. 13.99 (978-0-8024-3154-7(2)) Moody Pubs.

Dear Mommy & Daddy, When I Grow up I Don't Want to Be Broke! 2001. (Illus.). 160p. (gr. 2-5). per. 11.95 (978-0-9707837-0-7(1)) Williams, John Anthony.

Dollars & Sense: An Interactive Guide to Money Management. (YA). cd-rom 89.95 (978-0-7365-4319-4(8)) Films Media Group.

Donovan, Sandy. Budgeting. 2006. (How Economics Works). (Illus.). 48p. (J). (gr. 3-7). 25.26 (978-0-8225-2665-0(4) , Lerner Pubns.) Lerner Publishing Group.

Drobot, Eve. Money, Money, Money: Where It Comes from, How to Save It, Spend It, & Make It. 2004. (Illus.). 96p. (J). 19.95 (978-1-897066-10-2(4)); pap. 12.95 (978-1-897066-11-9(2)) Maple Tree Pr. CAN. *Dist:* Perseus Distribution.

Edelstein, Judy. Money Matters: How to Become a Smart Consumer. 2005. 48p. 10.95 (978-1-59363-108-6(1)) Prufrock Pr.

Elias, Keith James. The Friendly Dragons & the Secrets of K-star: Kids Learning the Wisdom of Money Management. 2003. (J). per. 12.95 (978-0-9726247-0-1(8)) Elias Pubns., LLC.

Firestone, Mary. Saving Money. 2004. (Learning about Money Ser.). (Illus.). 24p. (J). lib. bdg. 21.26 (978-0-7368-2640-2(8)) Capstone Pr., Inc.

—Spending Money. 2004. (Learning about Money Ser.). (Illus.). 24p. (J). lib. bdg. 21.26 (978-0-7368-2641-9(6)) Capstone Pr., Inc.

Forgue, Raymond, et al. Personal Finance Handbook: A Guide to Securing Your Financial Future. 9th ed. 2003. 107p. (YA). 11.96 (978-0-618-37231-7(8) , 345462) Houghton Mifflin College Div.

Freeman, Cynthia & Wilson, Clifford. Money Does Grow on Trees! Kids Learn How to Earn, Spend, Save & Invest Your Money. Cicetti, Kim, illus. 2000. 165p. (J). (978-0-9673735-0-8(6)) Magic Penny Publishing Co., The.

Gardner, David. Motley Fool Investment Guide for Teen: 8 Steps to Having More Money Than Your Pa. 2002. (gr. 7-12). lib. bdg. 23.45 (978-0-613-56819-7(2)) Tandem Library Bks.

Gardner, David, et al. The Motley Fool Investment Guide for Teens: 8 Steps to Having More Money Than Your Parents Ever Dreamed Of. 2002. (Illus.). 256p. (YA). (gr. 9-12). pap. 14.95 (978-0-7432-2996-8(7) , Fireside) Simon & Schuster.

Giesecke, Ernestine. Dollars & Sense: Managing Your Money. 2003. (Everyday Economics Ser.). (Illus.). 48p. (J). (gr. 2-5). lib. bdg. 27.07 (978-1-58810-492-2(3)) Heinemann Library.

—Everyday Banking: Consumer Banking. 2003. (Everyday Economics Ser.). (Illus.). 48p. (J). (gr. 3-5). lib. bdg. 27.07 (978-1-58810-489-2(3)) Heinemann Library.

—Everyday Banking: Consumer Banking. 2003. (gr. 3-6). lib. bdg. 16.40 (978-0-613-45748-4(X)) Tandem Library Bks.

God's Way of Handling Money: Crown Financial Study for Teens. 2002. 180p. (YA). pap., wbk. ed. 15.99 (978-1-893946-10-1(X) , TS2010) Crown Financial Ministries, Inc.

Green, Meg. Everything You Need to Know about Credit Cards & Fiscal Responsibility. 2001. (Need to Know Library). (Illus.). 64p. (YA). (gr. 4-6). lib. bdg. 25.25 (978-0-8239-3327-3(X)) Rosen Publishing Group, Inc., The.

Greene, Meg. The Young Zillionaire's Guide to Investments & Savings. 2000. (Be a Zillionaire Ser.). (Illus.). 48p. (YA). (gr. 5-8). lib. bdg. 23.95 (978-0-8239-3261-0(3) , ZIINSA, Rosen Central) Rosen Publishing Group, Inc., The.

Guthrie, Donna. Real World Math: Money & Other Numbers in Your Life. Kline, Robyn, illus. 1998. 128p. (gr. 7 up). 26.90 (978-0-7613-0251-3(4) , Millbrook Pr.) Lerner Publishing Group.

Guy, Pauline. Let's Count. 2004. 24p. (J). (ps). 15.99 (978-0-9744205-6-1(5)) Golden Eagle Publishing Hse., Inc.

Hall, Margaret. Credit Cards & Checks. 2nd ed. 2007. (J). (***978-1-4034-9816-8(4)***); pap. (***978-1-4034-9821-2(0)***) Heinemann Library.

—Your Allowance. 2007. (J). (***978-1-4034-9817-5(2)***); pap. (***978-1-4034-9822-9(9)***) Heinemann Library.

Haugen, Janie & Bowers, Jackie. Where Does My Money Go? Software Mac/Win Cd: Level 1 - 2. 1999. (YA). cd-rom 89.95 (978-1-884074-91-2(X) , PCI900) PCI Educational Publishing.

Heckman, Philip. Saving Money. 2006. (How Economics Works). (Illus.). 48p. (J). (gr. 3-7). 25.26 (978-0-8225-2664-3(6) , Lerner Pubns.) Lerner Publishing Group.

Henderson, Susan & White, Emily. Bank on It: Destination Reality. 2002. (YA). pap. 14.99 (978-0-89265-965-4(3)) Randall Hse. Pubns.

Hendricks, Tim. The Mentor: The True Story of an Hourly Factory Employee who Became Financially Independent. 2005. 240p. per. 16.99 (978-1-933215-09-9(7)) Music City Publishing.

Hill, Mary. Money Matters, 6 Bks., Set. 2005. (J). (ps-2). 96.00 (978-0-516-25218-6(6) , Children's Pr.) Scholastic Library Publishing.

—Spending & Saving. 2005. (Welcome Bks.). (Illus.). 24p. (ps-2). (J). pap. 4.95 (978-0-516-25174-5(0)); 18.00 (978-0-516-25059-5(0)) Scholastic Library Publishing. (Children's Pr.).

If You Made a Million. 2004. pap. 18.95 incl. audio compact disk (978-1-55592-178-1(7)); pap. 38.75 incl. audio compact disk (978-1-55592-634-2(7)); pap. 32.75 incl. audio (978-1-55592-365-5(8)); pap. 32.75 incl. audio (978-1-55592-364-8(X)); pap. 14.95 incl. audio (978-1-55592-166-8(3)) Weston Woods Studios, Inc.

Jaffe, Max. My Money, Myself: Lessons on Keeping More of What You Make. 2003. (Illus.). 128p. (YA). pap. 12.95 (978-0-9729732-0-5(6)) Spending Solutions Pr.

Karlitz, Gail & Honig, Debbie. Growing Money: A Complete Investing Guide for Kids. rev. ed. 2001. (Illus.). 128p. (J). pap. 7.99 (978-0-8431-7702-2(0) , Price Stern Sloan) Penguin Group (USA) Inc.

Keller, Ellen. Kids Manage Money. 2002. (Illus.). 32p. (J). pap. (978-0-7922-8694-3(4)) National Geographic Society.

Kiyosaki, Robert T. & Lechter, Sharon L. Rich Dad Poor Dad for Teens: The Secrets about Money—That You Don't Learn in School! 2004. (Rich Dad Ser.). 160p. pap. 14.99 (978-0-446-69321-9(9)) Little Brown & Co.

—Rich Dad's Escape from the Rat Race: How to Become a Rich Kid by Following Rich Dad's Advice. Hoseley, Rantz, illus. 2005. 56p. (J). (gr. 4-7). pap. 9.99 (978-0-316-00047-5(7)) Little, Brown Bks. for Young Readers.

Linde, Barbara M. Managing Your Money: Understanding Math Operations Involving Decimals & Integers. 2006. (Math for the Real World Ser.). (Illus.). 32p. (J). pap. (978-1-4042-6091-7(9)); lib. bdg. (978-1-4042-3369-0(5)) Rosen Publishing Group, Inc., The.

Loewen, Nancy. Save, Spend, or Donate? A Book about Managing Money. Fitzpatrick, Brad, illus. 2004. (Money Matters Ser.). 24p. (J). 22.60 (978-1-4048-0952-9(X)) Picture Window Bks.

Maybury, Richard J. Uncle Eric Talks about Personal, Career, & Financial Security. Williams, Jane A. & Daniels, Kathryn, eds. 2nd ed. 2004. ("Uncle Eric" Bk.). (Illus.). 187p. (YA). pap. 14.95 (978-0-942617-38-2(X)) Bluestocking Pr.

Mayr, Diane. Kids' Everything Money: From Saving to Spending to Investing - Learn All about Money! 2000. (Everything Kids Ser.). 144p. (gr. 4-7). pap. 6.95 (978-1-58062-685-9(8)) Adams Media Corp.

McGillian, Jamie Kyle. The Kids' Money Book. Phillips, Ian, illus. 2006. 96p. (J). (gr. 4-8). reprint ed. 18.00 (978-0-7567-9900-7(7)) DIANE Publishing Co.

Minden, Cecilia. Investing: Making Your Money Work for You. 2008. (J). lib. bdg. 25.26 (***978-1-60279-003-2(5)***) Cherry Lake Publishing.

—Living on a Budget. 2008. (J). lib. bdg. 25.26 (***978-1-60279-004-9(3)***) Cherry Lake Publishing.

—Payday! 2008. (J). lib. bdg. 25.26 (***978-1-60279-000-1(0)***) Cherry Lake Publishing.

—Saving for the Future. 2008. (J). lib. bdg. 25.26 (***978-1-60279-001-8(9)***) Cherry Lake Publishing.

—Using Credit Wisely. 2008. (J). lib. bdg. 25.26 (***978-1-60279-002-5(7)***) Cherry Lake Publishing.

Money Matters: How to Become a Smart Consumer. 2000. (J). per. 10.95 (978-1-883055-36-3(9)) Dandy Lion Pubns.

Morgan, Rowland. How to Make a Million. Morgan, Rowland, illus. 2001. (How to Ser.). (Illus.). 96p. (J). (gr. 5-7). 16.00 (978-0-531-14638-5(3) , Watts, Franklin) Scholastic Library Publishing.

—How to Make a Million. Brown, Judy, illus. 2001. (How to Ser.). 96p. (J). (gr. 5-7). pap. 4.95 (978-0-531-14819-8(X) , Watts, Franklin) Scholastic Library Publishing.

—How to Make a Million. 2001. (gr. 5-8). lib. bdg. 12.95 (978-0-613-54550-1(8)) Tandem Library Bks.

Mototsune, Kat. Money: Pay the Price. Geoffroi, Remie, illus. 2007. (Deal with It Ser.). 32p. (J). (gr. 4-8). pap., pap. 12.95 (***978-1-55028-958-9(6)***) Lorimer, James & Co., Ltd., Pubs. CAN. *Dist:* Casemate Pubs. & Bk. Distributors, LLC.

Murphy, Stuart J. Less Than Zero. Remkiewicz, Frank, illus. 2003. (MathStart Ser.: Vol. 49). 40p. (J). (gr. 2 up). 16.99 (978-0-06-000124-7(0)); pap. 5.99 (978-0-06-000126-1(7)) HarperCollins Pubs.

—Less Than Zero. 2003. (gr. k-3). lib. bdg. 13.00 (978-0-613-68443-9(5)) Tandem Library Bks.

My Money Series, 6 bks. 2006. (Illus.). (J). (gr. 4-6). 167.58 (978-0-7565-1699-4(4)) Compass Point Bks.

Nathan, Amy. The Kids' Allowance Book. Palen, Debbie, illus. 1998. 128p. (J). (gr. 3-7). 15.95 (978-0-8027-8651-7(0)) Walker & Co.

O'Neill, Lucy. Money Smarts. 2002. (Smarts Ser.). (Illus.). 48p. (YA). (gr. 7-12). pap. 23.00 (978-0-516-23929-3(5)); pap. 6.95 (978-0-516-24014-5(5)) Scholastic Library Publishing. (Children's Pr.).

Pasternak, Sam. Minding Your Money - Advice for Tots & Teens. Jacks, Howard, ed. 2000. 16p. (J). 7.00 (978-0-9704613-0-8(5)) Orange Creations, Inc.

Patton, Elizabeth A. & Thomas Nelson Publishing Staff. The Big Bucks: How to Manage Money Now That You're on Your Own. 2003. (gr. 7-12). lib. bdg. 22.25 (978-0-613-74995-4(2)) Tandem Library Bks.

Pellegrini, Mary Ellen. Managing Money: Spending & Saving Wisely. 2007. (J). pap. (***978-1-58760-040-1(4)***) Child Welfare League of America, Inc.

The Penny Project. 2005. (YA). (978-0-88441-693-7(3)) Girl Scouts of the USA.

Prindle, Twyla. Where Is My Money? Jennings, Randy, illus. 2007. (J). bds. 14.95 (***978-0-9759527-8-8(1)*** , 1000, Prindle House Publishing Co.) Prindle Hse. Publishing Co.

Ramsey, Dave. The Super Red Racer: Junior Discovers Work. 2003. (J). 9.99 (978-0-9726323-0-0(1)) Lampo Group Inc., The.

—La Transformacion Total de Su Dinero. 2003. (SPA.). 240p. pap. 11.99 (978-0-88113-772-9(3)) Grupo Nelson.

Rau, Dana Meachen. Saving Money. 2005. (Money & Banks Ser.). (Illus.). 24p. (J). pap. (978-0-8368-4878-6(0)); lib. bdg. 19.33 (978-0-8368-4871-7(3)) Stevens, Gareth Inc.

—Spending Money. 2005. (Money & Banks Ser.). (Illus.). 24p. (J). pap. (978-0-8368-4879-3(9)); lib. bdg. 19.33 (978-0-8368-4872-4(1)) Stevens, Gareth Inc.

Reeves, Diane Lindsey & Bryan, Gayle. Career Ideas for Kids Who Like Money. Bond, Nancy, illus. 2001. (Career Ideas for Kids Ser.). 192p. (J). (gr. 4-9). 23.00 (978-0-8160-4319-4(1) , Checkmark Bks.) Facts On File, Inc.

Roderick, Stacey & Warwick, Ellen. Centsibility: The Planet Girl Guide to Money. Melnychuk, Monika, illus. 2008. 80p. (***978-1-55453-208-7(6)***) Kids Can Pr., Ltd.

Rosen, Maureen Dolan. Kidsca$h: Cash Management for Kids. 2002. (YA). spiral bd. 13.95 (978-0-9746811-0-8(5) , 919-264-5976) Rosen & Assocs., Inc.

Rosinsky, Natalie M. Earning Money. 2003. (Let's See Library). (Illus.). 24p. (J). (gr. 1 up). 19.93 (978-0-7565-0483-0(X)) Compass Point Bks.

—Spending Money. 2003. (Let's See Library). (Illus.). 24p. (J). (gr. 1 up). 19.93 (978-0-7565-0485-4(6)) Compass Point Bks.

sapara, Jim. Money Freedom: Achieve the Millionaire Lifestyle of Your Dreams. 2004. per. 19.95 (978-0-9755681-1-8(6)) Quantum One Publishing.

Savage, Jeff. Millionaire By 40: 100 Secrets to Creating Wealth—Not Taught in School. 2005. 136p. 19.95 (978-0-9743844-1-2(0)) Buckeye Publishing.

Schwartz, Stuart B. Budgeting Your Money. 1998. (Life Skills Ser.). (J). lib. bdg. (978-0-516-21460-3(8) , Children's Pr.) Scholastic Library Publishing.

—Living on Your Own. 1998. (Life Skills Ser.). (J). lib. bdg. (978-0-516-21294-4(X) , Children's Pr.) Scholastic Library Publishing.

Schwartz, Stuart B. & Conley, Craig. Budgeting Your Money. 1998. (Career Books). (Illus.). 32p. (J). (gr. 3-4). lib. bdg. 21.26 (978-0-7368-0044-0(1) , LifeMatters Bks.) Capstone Pr., Inc.

—Opening a Bank Account. 1998. (Career Books). (Illus.). 32p. (J). (gr. 3-4). lib. bdg. 21.26 (978-0-7368-0047-1(6) , LifeMatters Bks.) Capstone Pr., Inc.

Shelly, Susan. Money for Teens. 2001. (Complete Idiot's Guide Ser.). (Illus.). 264p. (gr. 7-12). pap. 12.95 (978-0-02-864006-8(3) , Alpha Bks.) Penguin Group (USA) Inc.

Simon, Les. How To: Have Money & Avoid & Dump Debt. 2004. (SPA.). 110p. (YA). pap. 10.00 (978-0-9761914-0-7(7)) Simon, Les.

The SmartiPantz Money Organizer Child Workbook. 2004. (J). spiral bd. (978-0-9747563-0-1(X)) SmartiPantz Publishing.

Spinks, Tom & Spinks-Burleson, Kimberly. Prepare to Be A Teen Millionaire. 2008. 304p. (YA). pap. 16.95 (***978-0-7573-0723-2(X)***) Health Communications, Inc.

Stahl, Michael. Early to Rise: A Young Adult's Guide to Investing... & Financial Decisions That Can Shape Your Life. 2nd ed. 2005. 240p. 14.95 (978-1-56343-791-5(0)) Silver Lake Publishing.

—Early to Rise: A Young Person's Guide to Investing... & Financial Decisions Tha. 2000. (gr. 7-12). lib. bdg. 30.35 (978-0-613-89929-1(6)) Tandem Library Bks.

Symonds, Doris. How I Saved $10,500 with Only 4 Quarters a Day. 2003. (YA). spiral bd. 14.95 (978-0-9741182-0-8(6) , 2500) TALK.

Thayer, Tanya. Earning Money. 2005. (First Step Nonfiction Ser.). (Illus.). 24p. (gr. k-2). lib. bdg. 17.27 (978-0-8225-1259-2(9)) Lerner Publishing Group.

—Saving Money. 2005. (First Step Nonfiction Ser.). (Illus.). 24p. (gr. k-2). lib. bdg. 17.27 (978-0-8225-1260-8(2)) Lerner Publishing Group.

—Spending Money. 2005. (First Step Nonfiction Ser.). (Illus.). 24p. (gr. k-2). lib. bdg. 17.27 (978-0-8225-1261-5(0)) Lerner Publishing Group.

Thomas, Keltie. The Kids Guide to Money Cent$ MacEachern, Stephen, tr. MacEachern, Stephen, illus. 2004. 56p. (J). (gr. 4-6). (978-1-55337-389-6(8)); (978-1-55337-390-2(1)) Kids Can Pr., Ltd.

Thornton, Jewell. A Kids Journey to Being Rich. 2006. 12p. (J). 15.08 (978-1-4116-8618-2(7)) Lulu.com.

Thouin, Juanita. Get Your Wallet On: The Money Quiz for High School Grads. 2003. 97p. (YA). per. 6.49 (978-0-9740641-0-9(6)) Daisy Publishing.

Weeldreyer, Laura. Cha-Ching! A Girl's Guide to Spending & Saving. 1999. (Girls' Guides). (Illus.). 48p. (YA). (gr. 5-8). lib. bdg. 23.95 (978-0-8239-2988-7(4) , GGCHCH) Rosen Publishing Group, Inc., The.

Williams, Anna Graf, et al. The Family Guide to the American Workplace. Williams, Anna Graf, ed. 2003. (Illus.). 272p. per. 31.00 (978-0-9705790-4-1(7) , 866/332-5905) Learnovation, LLC.

Willson, Sarah. 50 Ways to Make & Save Money. 1999. (Nick Reference Ser.). (Illus.). (J). mass mkt. 5.99 (978-0-689-84558-1(8) , Simon Spotlight/Nickelodeon) Simon & Schuster Children's Publishing.

FINANCE, PERSONAL—FICTION

Berenstain, Stan & Berenstain, Jan. The Berenstain Bears' Dollars & Sense. 2001. (Berenstain Bears First Time Bks.). (J). (gr. k-3). 10.79 (978-0-606-22793-3(8)); (gr. 3-6). lib. bdg. 10.95 (978-0-613-32322-2(X)) Tandem Library Bks.

Brown, Marc & Schulman, Lester. Arthur Breaks the Bank. 2004. (Arthur Ser.). (Illus.). 24p. (J). (gr. k-3). pap. 3.99 (978-0-375-81002-2(1)); lib. bdg. 11.99 (978-0-375-91002-9(6)) Random Hse. Children's Bks. (Random Hse. Bks. for Young Readers).

Durham, Kathryn. Mom Can You Buy Me This? 2000. (Illus.). 70p. (YA). (gr. 4-10). pap. 9.95 (978-0-9703876-0-8(1)) Pen & Paper Publishing.

Dussling, Jennifer. Fair Is Fair! Palmisciano, Diane, illus. 2003. (Math Matters Ser.). 32p. (J). (gr. 1-3). pap. 4.99 (978-1-57565-131-6(9)) Kane Pr., The.

—Fair Is Fair! 2003. (gr. k-3). lib. bdg. 12.95 (978-0-613-79279-0(3)) Tandem Library Bks.

Give, Save, Spend. 2006. 16p. (J). pap. 1.99 (978-0-7847-1691-5(9) , 02993) Standard Publishing.

E
F
G

Harris, Trudy. Jenny Found a Penny. Hovell, John, illus. 2008. (P). lib. bdg. (***978-0-8225-6725-7(3)**, Millbrook Pr.) Lerner Publishing Group.

Johnson, D. B. Henry Builds a Cabin. 2002. (Illus.). 32p. (J). (gr. k-3). 15.00 (978-0-618-13201-0(5)) Houghton Mifflin Co. Trade & Reference Div.

FINANCE, PUBLIC

Ruffin, David C. The Duties & Responsibilities of the Secretary of the Treasury. 2005. (Your Government in Action Ser.). (Illus.). 32p. (J). 21.95 (978-1-4042-2690-6(7), PowerKids Pr.) Rosen Publishing Group, Inc., The.

FINANCE—UNITED STATES

Ruffin, David C. The Duties & Responsibilities of the Secretary of the Treasury. 2005. (Your Government in Action Ser.). (Illus.). 32p. (J). 21.95 (978-1-4042-2690-6(7), PowerKids Pr.) Rosen Publishing Group, Inc., The.

Samuel, Charlie. Money & Finance in Colonial America. 2003. (Primary Sources of Everyday Life in Colonial America Ser.). (Illus.). 24p. (J). lib. bdg. 21.25 (978-0-8239-6602-8(X), PowerKids Pr.) Rosen Publishing Group, Inc., The.

FINANCIERS

see Capitalists and Financiers

FINCAYRA (IMAGINARY PLACE)—FICTION

Barron, T. A. The Fires of Merlin. 1998. (Lost Years of Merlin Ser.: Vol. 3). (Illus.). 272p. (J). (gr. 5-9). 20.99 (978-0-399-23020-2(3), Philomel) Penguin Group (USA) Inc.

—The Fires of Merlin Bk. 3. 2000. (Lost Years of Merlin Ser.: Vol. 3). (Illus.). 304p. (gr. 4-7). reprint ed. mass mkt. 6.99 (978-0-441-00713-4(9), Ace Bks.) Penguin Group (USA) Inc.

—The Lost Years of Merlin, Bk. 1. 1999. (Lost Years of Merlin Ser.). (Illus.). 304p. (gr. 4-7). reprint ed. mass mkt. 6.99 (978-0-441-00668-7(X), Ace Bks.) Penguin Group (USA) Inc.

—Wings of Merlin. 2000. (Lost Years of Merlin Ser.: Vol. 5). (Illus.). 272p. (J). (gr. 6-9). 19.99 (978-0-399-23456-9(X), Philomel) Penguin Group (USA) Inc.

—Wings of Merlin. (gr. 3-6). 2003. lib. bdg. 14.15 (978-0-613-81180-4(1)); 2002. lib. bdg. 15.30 (978-0-613-81178-1(X)) Tandem Library Bks.

FINGER PAINTING

Emberley, Ed. Ed Emberley's Fingerprint Drawing Book. Emberley, Ed, illus. 2005. (Illus.). 48p. (J). (gr. 2-17). pap., pap. 7.99 (978-0-316-78969-1(0)) Little Brown & Co.

Lipsey, Jennifer. I Love to Finger Paint! 2006. (My Very Favorite Art Bks.: Bk. 1). (Illus.). 48p. (J). 9.95 (978-1-57990-771-6(7), 1260505) Lark Bks.

Schecter, Deborah. Fun with Finger Paint. Mullarkey, Julie, illus. 2001. 32p. (J). (978-0-439-33616-1(3)) Scholastic, Inc.

FINGER PLAY

Briggs, Diane. 101 Fingerplays, Stories & Songs to Use with Finger Puppets. 1999. 144p. 25.00 (978-0-8389-0749-8(0), 074902270) American Library Assn.

Brown, Marc. Hand Rhymes. Brown, Marc, illus. 2002. (Illus.). (J). 13.19 (978-0-7587-2677-3(5)) Book Wholesalers, Inc.

Delacre, Lulu, illus. & compiled by. Arrorro Mi Nino: Latino Lullabies & Gentle Games. Delacre, Lulu, compiled by. 2004. (ENG & SPA.). 32p. (J). 16.95 (978-1-58430-159-2(7)) Lee & Low Bks., Inc.

Douglas, Vincent & School Specialty Publishing Staff. Stories & Finger Plays. 2004. (Playful Learning Ser.). (Illus.). 128p. (J). (gr. k-k). pap. 10.95 (978-0-7696-3303-9(X), American Education Publishing) School Specialty Publishing.

Dowell, Ruth I. Move over, Mother Goose! Finger Plays, Action Verses & Funny Rhymes. Charner, Kathleen, ed. Scott, Concetta C., illus. 2004. 126p. (Orig.). (ps-1). pap. 12.95 (978-0-87659-113-0(6), 10006) Gryphon Hse., Inc.

Itsy Bitsy Spider. 2004. (J). per. (978-1-57657-427-0(X)) Paradise Pr., Inc.

Itsy Bitsy Spider. 2002. (Illus.). (J). bds. (978-1-59069-261-5(6), MS1002) Studio Mouse LLC.

Juego de Dedos. 2004. (SPA.). 12p. (J). (978-968-494-161-8(7)) Centro de Informacion y Desarrollo de la Comunicacion y la Literatura MEX. *Dist:* AIMS International Bks., Inc., Lectorum Pubns., Inc., Iaconi, Mariuccia Bk. Imports.

Kozlina, Yvonne. Fingerplays & Action Chants, Vols. 1 & 2. 1999. (Illus.). 128p. (J). reprint ed. pap. 29.95 (978-0-936823-18-8(6)) Pearce-Evetts Publishing.

Lewis, Stephen. Action Rhymes for You & Your Friends. 2000. ([DK Read & Listen] Ser.). (Illus.). 29p. (J). pap. (978-0-7894-4873-6(4)) Dorling Kindersley Publishing, Inc.

MansBach, Sara. Round & Round the Garden, Finger Games in English & Spanish. Arroyave, Heidy, tr. Landau, Donna, illus. 2007. 42p. spiral bd. (***978-0-9785477-2-1(1)**) BladeRunner Publishing.

Orozco, Jose. Diez Deditos & Other Play Rhymes & Action Songs from Latin America. Orozco, Jose, tr. Kleven, Elisa, illus. 2002. (SPA.). 56p. (J). pap. 7.99 (978-0-14-230087-9(X), Puffin) Penguin Group (USA) Inc.

Poulsson, Emilie. Finger Plays for Nursery & Kindergarten. 1998. (Illus.). 88p. (J). (ps-1). reprint ed. 15.00 (978-0-89904-758-4(0)); spiral bd. 10.00 (978-0-89904-759-1(9)) Crumb Elbow Publishing. (Silhouette Imprints).

Przybille, Crystal, illus. Bible Stories with Songs & Fingerplays: Stories Come Alive for Young Children. 1998. (Whole People of God Library). 64p. (J). pap. 9.95 (978-1-55145-297-5(9)) Wood Lake Bks., Inc. CAN. *Dist:* Logos Productions, Inc.

Qualey, Marsha, ed. The Wheels on the Bus. D'Antonio, Sandra, illus. 2004. (Traditional Songs Ser.). 24p. (ps-2). 22.60 (978-1-4048-0154-7(5)) Picture Window Bks.

Reeves, Sue & Smith, Jane, illus. Itsy Bitsy Spider. 2002. (Nursery Rhymes Ser.). 10p. (J). bds. (978-1-59069-281-3(0), MB1004) Studio Mouse LLC.

Roberts, Lynda S. Mitt Magic: Finger Plays for Finger Puppets. Morris, James, illus. 2004. 89p. (Orig.). (ps-1). pap. 14.95 (978-0-87659-111-6(X), 10004) Gryphon Hse., Inc.

Stetson, Emily & Congdon, Vicky. Little Hands Fingerplays & Action Songs: Seasonal Rhymes & Creative Play for 2 to 6 Year-Olds. Day, Betsy, illus. 2001. (Little Hands Bks.). 128p. (J). (ps-3). pap. 12.95 (978-1-885593-53-5(8), Williamson Bks.) Ideals Pubns.

Yolen, Jane, ed. This Little Piggy & Other Rhymes to Sing & Play: Lap Songs, Finger Plays, Clapping Games & Pantomime Rhymes. Hillenbrand, Will, illus. 2006. 80p. (J). (gr. k-ps). 19.99 (978-0-7636-1348-8(7)) Candlewick Pr.

FINGERPRINTS

Ahouse, Jeremy John & Barber, Jacqueline. Fingerprinting. Bevilacqua, Carol & Klofkorn, Lisa, illus. Hoyt, Richard, photos by. 2006. (Great Explorations in Math & Science Ser.). 72p. (J). 10.50 (978-1-931542-06-7(6), GEMS) Univ. of California, Berkeley, Lawrence Hall of Science.

Beres, D. B. Dusted & Busted! The Science of Fingerprinting. 2007. (24/7 - Science Behind the Scenes Ser.). (Illus.). 64p. (J). (gr. 8-12). pap. 7.95 (***978-0-531-15457-1(2)**, Watts, Franklin) Scholastic Library Publishing.

Beres, D. B. & Franklin, Watts. Dusted & Busted! The Science of Fingerprinting. 2006. (24/7 - Science Behind the Scenes Ser.). (Illus.). 64p. (J). (gr. 8-12). 25.00 (978-0-531-11822-1(3), Watts, Franklin) Scholastic Library Publishing.

Emberley, Ed. Ed Emberley's Fingerprint Drawing Book. 2001. (Illus.). (J). 14.50 (978-0-606-21169-7(1)) Tandem Library Bks.

Holzer, David. Prime Suspect: Suspect Identification System. 2004. (Illus.). 48p. (J). pap. (978-0-439-68027-1(1)) Scholastic, Inc.

Libal, Angela. Fingerprints, Bite Marks, Ear Prints: Human Signposts. 2006. (Forensics, the Science of Crime-Solving Ser.). (Illus.). 112p. (J). (gr. 7 up). 22.95 (978-1-4222-0031-5(0), 1248051) Mason Crest Pubs.

Mauro, Paul, et al. Prints & Impressions. Aycock, Daniel et al, illus. 2003. (Detective Academy Ser.). 48p. (J). pap. (978-0-439-57177-7(4)) Scholastic, Inc.

Rainis, Kenneth G. Fingerprints: Crime-Solving Science Experiments. 2006. (Forensic Science Projects Ser.). (Illus.). 128p. (J). (gr. 5 up). lib. bdg. 31.93 (978-0-7660-1960-7(8)) Enslow Pubs., Inc.

Rollins, Barbara B. & Dahl, Michael. Finding a Match: Examining Fingerprints. 2004. (Forensic Crime Solvers Ser.). (Illus.). 32p. (J). 22.60 (978-0-7368-2419-4(7)) Capstone Pr., Inc.

FINK, MIKE, 1770-1823?

Kellogg, Steven. Mike Fink. Kellogg, Steven, illus. 1998. (Illus.). 48p. (J). (ps-ps). pap., pap. 6.99 (978-0-688-13577-5(3), Harper Trophy) HarperCollins Pubs.

Kellogg, Steven, illus. & retold by. Mike Fink. Kellogg, Steven, retold by. 1998. (J). (ps-ps). lib. bdg. 15.30 (978-0-613-08345-4(8)) Tandem Library Bks.

FINLAND

Alatalo, Jakko. In a Nordic Village. 2002. (Child's Day Ser.). (Illus.). 32p. (J). 25.64 (978-0-7614-1411-7(8), Benchmark Bks.) Cavendish, Marshall Corp.

Hutchinson, Linda. Finland. 2004. (Modern Nations of the World Ser.). (Illus.). 112p. (J). 29.95 (978-1-59018-518-6(8), Lucent Bks.) Thomson Gale.

Lemke, Donald B. Finland: A Question & Answer Book. 2006. (Fact Finders Ser.). (Illus.). 32p. (J). (978-0-7368-4355-3(8), Fact Finders) Capstone Pr., Inc.

Meichun, Zhong. Finland. 2001. (Countries of the World Ser.). (Illus.). 96p. (J). (gr. 6 up). lib. bdg. 30.00 (978-0-8368-2331-8(1)) Stevens, Gareth Inc.

Sia, Nicole. Finland. 2006. (European Union Ser.). (Illus.). 88p. (J). (gr. 5 up). lib. bdg. (978-1-4222-0046-9(9), 1247998) Mason Crest Pubs.

Tan Chung Lee. Finland. 1998. (Festivals of the World Ser.). (Illus.). 32p. (J). (gr. 3 up). lib. bdg. 24.67 (978-0-8368-2013-3(4)) Stevens, Gareth Inc.

Tan, Chung Lee. Finland. 2nd ed. 2007. (Cultures of the World Ser.). 144p. (J). lib. bdg. 39.93 (978-0-7614-2073-6(8), Benchmark Bks.) Cavendish, Marshall Corp.

World Book, Inc. Staff. Christmas in Finland. 2002. (Christmas Around the World Ser.). 1760p. (gr. 2-8). 24.95 (978-0-7166-0863-9(4), 20066) World Bk., Inc.

Yip, Dora & Zhong, Meichun. Welcome to Finland. 2002. (Welcome to My Country Ser.). (Illus.). 48p. (J). (gr. 2 up). lib. bdg. 26.00 (978-0-8368-2531-2(4)) Stevens, Gareth Inc.

FINLAND—FICTION

Dick, Lois Hoadley. Mercy at Midnight: How One Courageous Woman Set Prisoners Free. 2002. 224p. (YA). pap. 8.99 (978-0-8024-2647-5(6)) Moody Pubs.

Doyle, Roddy. Wilderness. 2007. (J). (***978-0-439-02357-3(2)**); 224p. (gr. 7 up). pap. 16.99 (***978-0-439-02356-6(4)**) Scholastic, Inc. (Levine, Arthur A. Bks.).

Durbin, William. The Winter War. 2008. (J). (***978-0-385-90889-4(X)**); 240p. (gr. 7). 15.99 (***978-0-385-74652-6(0)**) Dell Publishing. (Delacorte Pr.).

Gerber, Linda. The Finnish Line. 2007. (S. A. S. S. (Students Across the Seven Seas) Ser.). 224p. (YA). (gr. 7). pap. 6.99 (***978-0-14-240916-9(2)**, Puffin) Penguin Group (USA) Inc.

FINN, HUCKLEBERRY (FICTITIOUS CHARACTER)—FICTION

Brook, Henry. Huckleberry Finn. McNee, Ian, illus. 2007. (Usborne Classics Retold Ser.). 150p. (J). pap. 4.99 (978-0-7945-1603-1(3), Usborne) EDC Publishing.

Lauter. The Scarlett Letter Plus Huckleberry Finn. 2005. (YA). pap., pap. 21.56 (978-0-618-68657-5(6), 396801) Houghton Mifflin College Div.

Literature Connections English: The Adventures of Huckleberry Finn. 2004. (gr. 6-12). (978-0-395-77550-9(7), 2-80119) McDougal Littell Inc.

Literature Connections Spanish: Las Aventuras de Huckleberry Finn (the Adventures of Huckleberry Finn) 2004. (gr. 6-12). (978-0-395-81742-1(0), 2-70492) McDougal Littell Inc.

Twain, Mark. Adventures of Huckleberry Finn: Prestwick House Literary Touchstone Edition. 2005. 280p. (YA). per. 4.99 (978-1-58049-583-7(4), PWH5834) Prestwick Hse., Inc.

—The Adventures of Huckleberry Finn. Pablo Marcos Studio Staff, illus. 2002. (Great Illustrated Classics Ser.). 240p. (J). (gr. 3-8). 21.35 (978-1-57765-676-0(8), ABDO & Daughters) ABDO Publishing Co.

—The Adventures of Huckleberry Finn. 2001. (J). pap. 7.95 (978-0-8010-1220-4(1)) Baker Bks.

—The Adventures of Huckleberry Finn. 1999. reprint ed. pap. 28.00 (978-1-4047-1118-1(X)) Classic Textbooks.

—The Adventures of Huckleberry Finn. 2002. (Spot the Classics Ser.). (Illus.). 180p. (J). (gr. k-5). 4.99 (978-1-57759-553-3(X)) Dalmatian Pr.

—The Adventures of Huckleberry Finn. Redondo, Francisco, illus. 2nd ed. 1998. (Illustrated Classic Book Ser.). 61p. (J). (gr. 3 up). reprint ed. pap. 4.95 (978-1-56767-255-8(8)) Educational Insights, Inc.

—The Adventures of Huckleberry Finn. (Coleccion Clasicos de la Juventud). (SPA., Illus.). 192p. (J). 12.95 (978-84-7189-027-6(5), ORT313) Ortells, Alfredo Editorial S.L. ESP. *Dist:* Continental Bk. Co., Inc.

—The Adventures of Huckleberry Finn. 2002. (Classics Ser.). (Illus.). 368p. (gr. 12). pap. 7.00 (978-0-14-243717-9(4), Penguin Classics) Penguin Group (USA) Inc.

—The Adventures of Huckleberry Finn. 2007. (Children's Classics Ser.). (Illus.). 256p. (J). 6.99 (978-0-517-22999-6(4), Gramercy) Random Hse. Value Publishing.

—The Adventures of Huckleberry Finn. unabr. ed. 2002. (YA). pap. incl. audio compact disk (978-1-58472-261-8(4), In Audio) Sound Room Pubs., Inc.

—The Adventures of Huckleberry Finn. McKowen, Scott, illus. 2006. (Unabridged Classics Ser.). 320p. 9.95 (978-1-4027-2600-2(7)) Sterling Publishing Co., Inc.

—The Adventures of Huckleberry Finn. 2003. (gr. 7-12). lib. bdg. 14.15 (978-0-613-64012-1(8)); 1999. 10.64 (978-0-606-17508-1(3)); 1999. (gr. 3-6). lib. bdg. 11.80 (978-0-613-63171-6(4)); 1999. (gr. 7-12). lib. bdg. 15.25 (978-0-613-32245-4(2)) Tandem Library Bks.

—The Adventures of Huckleberry Finn. Fischer, Victor et al, eds. Kemble, E. W. & Harley, John, illus. 2001. (Mark Twain Library). 596p. 55.00 (978-0-520-22806-1(5)); pap. 14.95 (978-0-520-22838-2(3)) Univ. of California Pr.

—The Adventures of Huckleberry Finn: Juvenile Classic. 2005. (Illus.). 192p. (J). 5.99 (978-1-4037-1383-4(9)) Dalmatian Pr.

—Las Aventuras de Huckleberry Finn. 2002. (Classics for Young Readers Ser.). (SPA.). (YA). 14.95 (978-84-392-0925-6(8), EV30617) Gaviota Ediciones ESP. *Dist:* Lectorum Pubns., Inc.

—Las Aventuras de Huckleberry Finn. 2000. (SPA.). 352p. (YA). 15.95 (978-84-207-3396-8(2)) Grupo Anaya, S.A. ESP. *Dist:* AIMS International Bks., Inc.

—Las Aventuras de Huckleberry Finn. 2000. (SPA.). 244p. (YA). 13.95 (978-84-348-2796-7(4)) SM Ediciones ESP. *Dist:* AIMS International Bks., Inc.

—Las Aventuras de Tom Sawyer. 2002. (SPA.). (YA). 7.95 (978-956-13-1069-8(4)) Bello, Andres CHL. *Dist:* AIMS International Bks., Inc.

—Las Aventuras de Tom Sawyer. 2000. (SPA., Illus.). 272p. (J). 7.95 (978-84-406-8397-7(9)) Ediciones B ESP. *Dist:* Distribooks, Inc.

—Las Aventuras de Tom Sawyer. 2003. (Advanced Reading Ser.). (SPA.). 124p. (J). 11.95 (978-84-239-9045-0(1)) Espasa Calpe, S.A. ESP. *Dist:* Planeta Publishing Corp.

—Las Aventuras de Tom Sawyer. 2002. (Classics for Young Readers Ser.). (SPA.). (YA). 13.99 (978-84-392-0908-9(8), EV30591) Gaviota Ediciones ESP. *Dist:* Lectorum Pubns., Inc.

—Las Aventuras de Tom Sawyer. (Coleccion Estrella). (SPA., Illus.). 64p. (YA). 14.95 (978-950-11-0012-9(X), SGM012) Sigmar ARG. *Dist:* Continental Bk. Co., Inc.

—Huckleberry Finn's Abentuer. 2000. Tr. of Adventures of Huckleberry Finn. (GER.). (J). pap. 14.95 (978-3-596-50167-0(9)) Fischer Taschenbuch Verlag DEU. *Dist:* Distribooks, Inc.

Twain, Mark & Olmos. The Adventures of Huckleberry Finn. 2004. (SPA.). 360p. pap. 17.95 (***978-84-263-5252-1(9)**) Vives, Luis Editorial (Edelvives) ESP. *Dist:* Lectorum Pubns., Inc.

FINN MACCUMHAILL, 3RD CENT.

Souhami, Jessica. Mrs. McCool & the Giant Cuhullin: An Irish Tale. rev. ed. 2002. (Illus.). 32p. (J). (ps-3). 16.95 (978-0-8050-6852-8(X), Holt, Henry & Co. Bks. For Young Readers) Holt, Henry & Co.

FIRE

see also Fires; Fuel; Heat; Heating

Barber, Nicky. Fire & Flood. 1999. (Natural Disasters Ser.). (Illus.). 31p. (J). (gr. 5 up). pap. 5.95 (978-0-7641-1058-0(6)) Barron's Educational Series, Inc.

Beil, Karen Magnuson. Fire in Their Eyes: Wildfires & the People Who Fight Them. Beil, Karen Magnuson, photos by. 1999. (Illus.). 64p. (YA). (gr. 5-9). pap. 11.00 (978-0-15-201042-3(4), Harcourt Paperbacks) Harcourt Children's Bks.

—Fire in Their Eyes: Wildfires & the People Who Fight Them. 1999. (gr. 5-8). lib. bdg. 19.95 (978-0-613-15785-8(0)) Tandem Library Bks.

Briscoe, Diana. Smokejumpers: Battling the Forest Flames, 6 vols. (gr. 4 up). 49.95 (978-0-7368-9537-8(X), High Five) Red Brick Learning.

Burton, Jane & Taylor, Kim. The Nature & Science of Fire. 2001. (Exploring the Science of Nature Ser.). (Illus.). 32p. (J). (gr. 3 up). lib. bdg. 24.67 (978-0-8368-2198-7(X)) Stevens, Gareth Inc.

Carroll, Colleen. Elements: Earth, Air, Fire & Water. 1998. (How Artists See Ser.). (Illus.). 48p. (gr. 3 up). 12.95 (978-0-7892-0476-9(2)) Abbeville Pr., Inc.

Connolly, Sean. Fire. 2003. (Illus.). 32p. (J). lib. bdg. (978-1-58340-392-1(2)) Smart Apple Media.

Craats, Rennay. The Science of Fire. 2000. (Living Science Ser.). (Illus.). 32p. (J). (gr. 2 up). lib. bdg. 24.67 (978-0-8368-2680-7(9)) Stevens, Gareth Inc.

Davis, Gary W. From Rock to Fireworks. 1998. (Changes Ser.). (Illus.). 32p. (J). (gr. 2-3). pap. 6.95 (978-0-516-20364-5(9), Children's Pr.) Scholastic Library Publishing.

Deedrick, Tami. Fires. 2000. (Nature on the Rampage Ser.). (Illus.). 32p. (J). (gr. 4-7). lib. bdg. 22.83 (978-0-7398-1798-8(1)) Raintree.

Feuer: Freund Oder Feind?Tr. of Fire: Friend or Enemy?. (GER., Illus.). (YA). 31.95 (978-3-411-09031-0(6), MY9031E) Bibliographisches Institut & F. A. Brockhaus AG DEU. *Dist:* Continental Bk. Co., Inc.

Fire. 2000. (What About...? Ser.). (J). (gr. 1-4). pap. 5.72 (978-0-8114-9658-2(9)) Steck-Vaughn.

Fire. 2001. (Let's Explore Ser.). (Illus.). 32p. (J). (gr. 1 up). lib. bdg. 23.33 (978-0-8368-2961-7(1)) Stevens, Gareth Inc.

Fire! Fire! 6 Each of 1 Anthology, 6 vols. (Wildcats Ser.). 32p. (gr. 2-8). (978-0-322-00581-5(7)) Wright Group, The.

Frisch, Aaron. Fire. 2001. (Elements Ser.). (Illus.). 24p. (J). 21.35 (978-1-58340-075-3(3)) Smart Apple Media.

Godkin, Celia. Fire. 2006. (Illus.). 32p. (J). 17.95 (978-1-55041-889-7(0)) Fitzhenry & Whiteside, Ltd. CAN. *Dist:* F & W Pubns., Inc.

Gunderson, Jessica Sarah. The Triangle Shirtwaist Factory Fire. Miller, Phil & Barnett, Charles, illus. 2006. (Graphic Library). 32p. (J). (978-0-7368-5483-2(5)) Capstone Pr., Inc.

Hook, Jason. Fire. 2002. (Young Library). (Illus.). 32p. (J). lib. bdg. 25.69 (978-0-7398-6314-5(2)) Raintree.

Kyi, Tanya Lloyd. Burn: The Life Story of Fire. 2007. (Illus.). 128p. (J). (gr. 5-7). 19.95 (***978-1-55451-082-5(1)**); pap. 9.95 (***978-1-55451-081-8(3)**) Annick Pr., Ltd. CAN. *Dist:* Firefly Bks., Ltd.

Marzollo, Jean. Soy el Fuego. Moffatt, Judith, illus. 2002. (Coleccion "Hola, Lector" Ser.).Tr. of I Am Fire. (SPA.). 32p. (J). (ps-1). pap. 3.99 (978-0-439-17309-4(4), SO5702, Scholastic en Espanol) Scholastic, Inc.

—Soy el Fuego. 2001. Tr. of I Am Fire. (SPA.). (J). (gr. 3-6). lib. bdg. 11.80 (978-0-613-81409-6(6)) Tandem Library Bks.

Open Court Staff. Fire Fire. (J). pap. (978-0-8126-1012-3(1), 61012) Open Court Publishing Co.

Owen, Ann. Protecting Your Home: A Book about Firefighters. Thomas, Eric, illus. 2004. (Community Workers Ser.). 24p. (C). (gr. k-3). 22.60 (978-1-4048-0088-5(3)) Picture Window Bks.

Peluso, Beth. Charcoal Forest. 64p. (J). pap. 12.00 (***978-0-87842-532-7(2)**) Mountain Pr. Publishing Co., Inc.

Pluckrose, Henry Arthur. Fire. 2007. (Illus.). 32p. (J). (***978-1-59771-034-3(2)**) Sea-To-Sea Pubns.

Porell, John. Fire! 2005. (Real Deal-Red Plus Ser.). (Illus.). 32p. (gr. 4-8). 19.00 (978-0-7910-8895-1(2)) Facts On File, Inc.

Roca, Nuria. Aprendamos sobre los 4 Elementos: The 4 Elements (Spanish Edition) Curto, Rosa M., illus. 2006. (Let's Learn About Ser.). (SPA.). 36p. (J). pap. 6.99 (978-0-7641-3315-2(2)) Barron's Educational Series, Inc.

—Let's Learn about the 4 Elements. Curto, Rosa M., illus. 2006. (Let's Learn About Ser.). 36p. (J). pap. 6.99 (978-0-7641-3314-5(4)) Barron's Educational Series, Inc.

Sloan, Peter. Using Fire. 1999. (gr. k-3). lib. bdg. 11.80 (978-0-613-30831-1(X)) Tandem Library Bks.

Stein, R. Conrad. The Great Chicago Fire. 2005. (Cornerstones of Freedom Ser.). (Illus.). 48p. (J). 26.00 (978-0-516-23640-7(7), Children's Pr.) Scholastic Library Publishing.

Weil, Ann. Fires. 2003. (Illus.). 64p. (YA). per. 3.95 (978-1-56254-656-4(2), SP6562) Saddleback Educational Publishing.

Wright, John D. Fire & Explosives. 2007. (Forensic Evidence Ser.). (Illus.). 96p. (gr. 6 up). 39.95 (***978-0-7656-8117-1(X)**) Sharpe, M.E. Inc.

FIRE—FICTION

Allison, Samuel Buel. An American Robinson Crusoe. 2006. pap. (***978-1-4065-0803-1(9)**) Dodo Pr.

The Arsonist. 2001. (YA). (gr. 6-12). pap. incl. audio (978-0-8224-3297-5(8)) Globe Fearon Educational Publishing.

Barnum, Vance. Joe Strong the Boy Fire-Eater or the Mos. 2006. 95.99 (***978-1-4280-0327-9(4)**); pap. 89.99 (***978-1-4280-0329-3(0)**) IndyPublish.com.

Blackaby, Susan. A Fire Drill with Mr. Dill. Muehlenhardt, Amy Bailey, illus. 2004. (Read-It! Readers Ser.). 32p. (C). (gr. k-3). 18.60 (978-1-4048-0584-2(2)) Picture Window Bks.

Blackaby, Susan. Todd's Fire Drill. Greathouse, Justin, illus. 2007. (J). lib. bdg. (*978-1-4048-2332-7(8))* Picture Window Bks.

Blazin' Hot: Coloring/Activity Book (English) 2005. (Illus.). (J). (978-0-9770455-0-1(1)) Educational Adventures.

Blazin' Hot: Picture Book (English) 8x8. 2006. (J). (978-1-933934-29-7(8)) Educational Adventures.

Blazin' Hot Picture Book (English) 2005. (Illus.). (J). (978-0-9765953-9-7(7)) Educational Adventures.

BlueWolf, James Don. Speaking for Fire. Greenlee, Carolyn Wing, illus. 2003. 44p. (J). (gr. 2-7). 14.95 (978-1-887400-31-2(1)) Earthen Vessel Production, Inc.

Carris, Joan Davenport. Welcome to the Bed & Biscuit. Jones, Noah Z., illus. 2006. 128p. (J). (gr. 1-5). 15.99 (978-0-7636-2151-3(X)) Candlewick Pr.

Claybourne, Anna, retold by. Jane Eyre. 2004. (Paperback Classics Ser.). 144p. (J). lib. bdg. 12.95 (978-1-58086-639-2(5) , Usborne) EDC Publishing.

Daher, Anita. Two Foot Punch. 2007. (Orca Sports Ser.). 176p. pap. (*978-1-55143-876-4(3))* Orca Bk. Pubs.

Del Amo, Montserrat. El Fuego y el Oro. (SPA.). 112p. (YA). (gr. 5-8). (978-84-279-3150-3(6) , NG3976) Noguer y Caralt Editores, S. A. ESP. *Dist:* Lectorum Pubns., Inc.

Denega, Danielle. Meet the Team. Harris, Annmarie, ed. 2006. (Firehouse Tales Ser.). (Illus.). 16p. (J). pap. 4.99 (978-0-439-83723-1(5) , Scholastic) Scholastic, Inc.

Eden, Alexandra. Holy Smoke: A Bones & the Duchess Mystery. 2004. (Illus.). 117p. (J). 16.00 (978-1-888310-46-7(4)) Knoll, Allen A. Pubs.

Educational Adventures, creator. Blazin' Hot: Picture Book (Spanish) 9x9. 2006. (SPA., Illus.). (J). (*978-0-9770455-4-9(4))* Educational Adventures.

Erickson, John R. The Case of the Blazing Sky #51. Holmes, Gerald L., illus. 2008. (Hank the Cowdog Ser.). 144p. (J). (gr. 3). 15.99 (*978-0-670-06260-7(X)* , Viking Juvenile) Penguin Group (USA) Inc.

Fire! Individual Title Six-Packs. (Bookweb Ser.). 32p. (gr. 4 up). 34.00 (978-0-7635-3739-5(X)) Rigby Education.

Fire at Fry's Farm. 2004. (J). lib. bdg. (978-0-9727273-2-7(9)) Leadership Loft, The.

Funke, Cornelia. Ghosthunters & the Gruesome Invincible Lightning Ghost. 2006. (Ghosthunters Ser.). 192p. (J). pap. 4.99 (978-0-439-83309-7(4) , Scholastic Paperbacks); (Illus.). pap. 16.99 (978-0-439-84962-3(4) , Chicken Hse., The) Scholastic, Inc.

Gibbons, Alan. Playing with Fire. 2nd ed. 2003. (Illus.). pap. 9.99 (978-1-85881-385-1(9)) Orion Bks. Ltd. GBR. *Dist:* Trafalgar Square Publishing.

Goodhart, Pippa. Dragon Boy. Ursell, Martin, illus. 2005. (Red Bananas Ser.). 48p. (J). (978-0-7787-1071-4(8)) Crabtree Publishing Co.

—Dragon Boy. 2005. (Red Bananas Ser.). (Illus.). 48p. (J). (ps). pap. (978-0-7787-1087-5(4)) Crabtree Publishing Co.

Goodman, Susan E. Cora Frear. Ettlinger, Doris, illus. ed. 2005. 55p. (J). lib. bdg. 15.00 (978-1-59054-901-8(5)) Fitzgerald Bks.

Guy, Glen. The Adventure Fire: Adventures of Dusty Sourdough. 2005. 9.95 (978-1-59433-006-3(9)) Publication Consultants.

Hale, Shannon. Enna Burning. (J). 2006. 336p. pap. 8.95 (978-1-58234-906-0(1)); 2004. (Illus.). 300p. 17.95 (978-1-58234-889-6(8)) Bloomsbury Publishing. (Bloomsbury Children).

Harcourt School Publishers Staff. Where There's Smoke There's Fire: Take-Home Book. 2001. (Collections Ser.). (Illus.). (J). pap. 1.90 (978-0-15-319503-7(7)); pap. 1.90 (978-0-15-319551-8(7)) Harcourt Schl. Pubs.

Hate Fighters. (Good News Club Ser.). (J). (gr. 4-9). pap. 4.99 (978-1-55976-492-6(9)) CEF Pr.

Hill, David. Running Hot. 2006. 116p. (Orig.). (gr. 5-8). pap. 9.95 (978-1-894965-52-1(3)) Simply Read Bks. CAN. *Dist:* Perseus Distribution.

Hooker, Lou. The Year of the Fire. lt. ed. 2004. (Illus.). 102p. (J). pap. 8.95 (978-0-9755106-0-5(6)) Hooker, Lou.

Hooper, Mary. Petals in the Ashes. 2004. 200p. (J). (gr. 5 up). 16.95 (978-1-58234-936-7(3) , Bloomsbury Children) Bloomsbury Publishing.

Huriet, Genvieve. Beignets Flambes. 2000. Tr. of Flaming Donuts. (FRE.). (J). 19.99 (978-2-84113-135-8(1)) Editions Milan FRA. *Dist:* AIMS International Bks., Inc.

Lorimer, Janet. The Bad Luck Play: Set 3. 2002. 32p. (YA). 2.95 (978-1-56254-425-6(X) , SP 425X) Saddleback Educational Publishing.

Lough, Loree. Fire by Night: The Great Fire Devastates Boston. 1999. (American Adventure Ser.: No. 4). 144p. (J). (gr. 3-7). lib. bdg. 15.95 (978-0-7910-5044-6(0) , Chelsea Hse.) Facts On File, Inc.

Martin, Ann M. The Fire at Mary Anne's House. 1999. (Baby-Sitters Club Ser.: No. 131). (Illus.). 136p. (J). (gr. 3-7). pap. 4.50 (978-0-590-50390-7(1) , Scholastic Paperbacks) Scholastic, Inc.

McFarlane, Brian. Fire in the North. 2007. (Mitchell Brothers Ser.). 220p. pap. 6.99 (*978-1-55168-243-3(5))* Key Porter Bks. CAN. *Dist:* Perseus Distribution.

McKay, Hilary. Echo in the Chimney. (Illus.). 80p. (J). mass mkt. 7.99 (978-0-340-72288-6(6) , Hodder & Stoughton) Hodder General Publishing Division GBR. *Dist:* Trafalgar Square Publishing.

Moore, Nancy Ann. The Safety Scouts: Fire Call. 2000. mass mkt. 8.95 (978-1-931179-42-3(5)) Long Hill Productions, Inc.

Morgan, Allen, et al. Au Feu, Mathieu! 2001. (Drtles d'Histoires Ser.). (FRE., Illus.). 24p. (YA). (ps up). pap. (978-2-89021-418-7(4)) Diffusion du livre Mirabel.

Myers, Anna. Fire in the Hills. 1998. (Puffin Novel Ser.). (978-0-606-13385-2(2)) Tandem Library Bks.

Nez, John A., illus. One Smart Cookie. 2006. 32p. (J). lib. bdg. 15.95 (978-0-8075-6099-0(5)) Whitman, Albert & Co.

Okereke, Laurence. Barry Plays with Fire. 2007. (Illus.). 20p. (J). spiral bd. (*978-0-9795739-1-0(2))* Dion's Pubn.

Park, Linda Sue. The Firekeeper's Son. Downing, Julie, illus. 2004. 40p. (J). (gr. k-3). 16.00 (978-0-618-13337-6(2) , Clarion Bks.) Houghton Mifflin Co. Trade & Reference Div.

Roberts, Bethany. Gramps & the Fire Dragon. Iwai, Melissa, illus. 2000. 32p. (J). (gr. k-3). tchr. ed. 15.00 (978-0-395-69849-5(9) , Clarion Bks.) Houghton Mifflin Co. Trade & Reference Div.

Robinet, Harriette Gillem. Children of the Fire. 2001. (J). 11.64 (978-0-606-20601-3(9)); (gr. 3-6). lib. bdg. 13.00 (978-0-613-33685-7(2)) Tandem Library Bks.

Sandburg, Carl. The Huckabuck Family: And How They Raised Popcorn in Nebraska & Quit & Came Back. Small, David, illus. 2004. 40p. (J). reprint ed. pap. 6.95 (978-0-374-43449-6(2) , Farrar, Straus & Giroux (BYR)) Farrar, Straus & Giroux.

Sargent, Dave & Sargent, Pat. The Fire: A Second Chance, 10 vols., Vol. 10. Lenoir, Jane, illus. 2005. (Colorado Cowboys Ser.: 10). 32p. (J). pap. 9.95 (978-1-59381-105-1(5)) Ozark Publishing.

Thomas, Joyce Carol. Marked by Fire. 1999. 176p. (J). (gr. 7-12). pap. 7.95 (978-0-380-81434-3(X)) HarperCollins Pubs.

—Marked by Fire. 2001. (YA). (gr. 6-12). 21.25 (978-0-8446-7191-8(6)) Smith, Peter Pub., Inc.

Urrea, Lourdes, et al. Si Juegas Con Fuego. 2005. (Ediciones Castillo Castillo Del Terror Ser.).Tr. of If You Play with Fire. (SPA.). (J). (gr. 2-6). pap. 7.95 (978-970-20-0394-6(6)) Castillo, Ediciones, S. A. de C. V. MEX. *Dist:* Iaconi, Mariuccia Bk. Imports.

Wood, Gail. Lizzie & the Prairie Fire: Girl Pioneer in the American Midwest. 2006. (Illus.). (J). pap. 7.95 (978-1-57249-381-0(X) , White Mane Kids) White Mane Publishing Co., Inc.

Wooding, Chris. Kerosene. 2002. (gr. 7-12). lib. bdg. 15.30 (978-0-613-57077-0(4)) Tandem Library Bks.

Zephaniah, Benjamin. Face. 2004. 208p. (J). reprint ed. pap. 6.95 (978-1-58234-921-3(5) , Bloomsbury Children) Bloomsbury Publishing.

FIRE BALLS

see Meteors

FIRE DEPARTMENTS

Adair, Amy. Fire Truck: Lift-a-Flap Fun. Wieland, Don, illus. 2000. (Active Minds Ser.). 12p. (J). bds. 15.98 (978-0-7853-4172-7(2) , 3996300) Publications International, Ltd.

All Around the Fire Station. 32p. 3.99 (978-0-7682-0180-2(2) , FS83146) Schaffer, Frank Pubns.

Behrman, Carol H. Thomas Jefferson. 2006. (Just the Facts Biographies Ser.). (Illus.). 112p. (J). (gr. 3-7). 27.93 (978-0-8225-2645-2(X) , Lerner Pubns.) Lerner Publishing Group.

Blevins, Wiley. Fire Station. 2006. (Let's Find Out Ser.). 24p. (J). pap. 8.99 (978-0-439-72606-1(9) , Cartwheel Bks.) Scholastic, Inc.

Butler, Dori Hillestad & Waites, Joan C. F Is for Firefighting. 2007. (Illus.). 32p. (J). (ps-1). 15.95 (978-1-58980-420-3(1)) Pelican Publishing Co., Inc.

Canizares, Susan & Waugh, Betsey. Firehouse. 2000. (Illus.). (J). pap. 15.94 (978-0-439-15370-6(0)) Scholastic, Inc.

Daly, Mark & Tipeo. Caillou: My First Field Trip. rev. ed. 2004. (Out & About Ser.). (Illus.). 24p. (J). pap. 3.95 (978-2-89450-498-7(5)) Chouette Publishing CAN. *Dist:* Independent Pubs. Group.

Dorling Kindersley Publishing Staff. Firefighter for a Day. 2003. (Illus.). 12p. (J). pap. 12.99 (978-0-7894-9854-0(5)) Dorling Kindersley Publishing, Inc.

Gordon, Sharon. What's Inside a Firehouse? (¿Qué Hay Dentro de un Cuartel de Bomberos?) 2006. (Bookworms Ser.). (ENG & SPA., Illus.). 32p. (J). lib. bdg. 22.79 (978-0-7614-2473-4(3)) Cavendish, Marshall Corp.

Gordon, Sharon, ed. ¿Qué Hay Dentro de un Cuartel de Bomberos? 2006. (Bookworms Ser.). (SPA.). 32p. (J). lib. bdg. 22.79 (978-0-7614-2393-5(1)) Cavendish, Marshall Corp.

Hoena, B. A. A Visit to the Fire Station. 2004. (Pebble Plus, Let's Visit Ser.). (Illus.). 24p. (J). 17.26 (978-0-7368-2392-0(1) , Pebble Bks.) Capstone Pr., Inc.

Johnston, Marianne. Let's Visit the Fire Station. 2000. (Our Community Ser.). (Illus.). 24p. (J). (gr. 3). lib. bdg. 18.75 (978-0-8239-5435-3(8) , PowerKids Pr.) Rosen Publishing Group, Inc., The.

Kids Can Press Staff, Press Can, ed. This Is Daniel Cook at the Fire Station. 2006. (Illus.). 28p. (J). (978-1-55453-076-2(8)); (978-1-55453-075-5(X)) Kids Can Pr., Ltd.

Lewison, Wendy Cheyette. A Trip to the Firehouse. 1998. (J). (978-0-606-13870-3(6)) Tandem Library Bks.

Liebman, Dan. I Want to Be a Firefighter. 1999. (I Want to Be Ser.). (Illus.). 24p. (J). (ps-2). lib. bdg. 14.95 (978-1-55209-448-8(0)) Firefly Bks., Ltd.

Out & about at the Fire Station. (Field Trips Ser.). 24p. (J). 8.95 (978-1-4048-0167-7(7)) Picture Window Bks.

Saunders-Smith, Gail. The Fire Station. 1998. (Field Trips Ser.). 24p. (J). (gr. k-2). pap. 13.25 (978-0-516-21320-0(2) , Children's Pr.) Scholastic Library Publishing.

—The Fire Station. 2005. (Transportation Ser.). 24p. (YA). (gr. k-3). pap. 5.95 (978-1-56065-838-2(X) , Pebble Bks.) Capstone Pr., Inc.

Schaefer, Lola M. Fire Station. 2001. (Who Works Here? Ser.). (Illus.). 32p. (J). (gr. 1-3). lib. bdg. 21.36 (978-1-58810-126-6(6)) Heinemann Library.

School Specialty Publishing. The Fire Station. 2003. (Brighter Child Activity Bks.). 32p. (J). (ps-1). pap. 2.99 (978-0-7696-3213-1(0) , Brighter Child) School Specialty Publishing.

Silver Dolphin en Español Editors. Que? Como? Por que? Los Bomberos: What? How? Why? the Fire Department. 2006. (SPA., Illus.). 16p. (J). 9.95 (978-970-718-344-5(6)) Advantage Pubs. Group.

Sweeney, Alyse. A Very Busy Firehouse. 2007. (Scholastic News Nonfiction Readers Ser.). (Illus.). 24p. (J). (gr. k-2). 19.00 (978-0-531-16840-0(9) , Watts, Franklin) Scholastic Library Publishing.

Torr, James D. Responding to Attack: Firefighters & Police. 2003. (Lucent Library of Homeland Security). (Illus.). 112p. (J). 29.95 (978-1-59018-375-5(4) , Lucent Bks.) Thomson Gale.

A Trip to the Fire Station. (Rosen Real Readers Big Bookstm Ser.). 12p. (J). (gr. 1-2). 31.95 (978-1-4042-6216-4(4)) Rosen Publishing Group, Inc., The.

FIRE DEPARTMENTS—FICTION

Baggette, Susan K. Jonathan Goes to the Fire Station. Moriarty, William J., photos by. 1998. (Jonathan Adventures Ser.). (Illus.). 16p. (J). (ps-k). bds. 5.95 (978-0-9660172-4-3(2)) Brookfield Reader, Inc., The.

Cutlip, Kimbra L. Firefighter's Night Before Christmas. Rice, James, illus. 2002. 32p. (J). (gr. k-3). 15.95 (978-1-58980-054-0(0)) Pelican Publishing Co., Inc.

Denega, Danielle. Firehouse Field Trip: Dick & Jane Picture Readers. 2005. (Dick & Jane Ser.). 32p. (J). (gr. k-1). pap. 3.99 (978-0-448-43980-8(8) , Grosset & Dunlap) Penguin Group (USA) Inc.

DiCamillo, Kate. Mercy Watson to the Rescue. Van Dusen, Chris, illus. 2005. 80p. (J). (gr. 1-3). 12.99 (978-0-7636-2270-1(2)) Candlewick Pr.

Forrester, Emma, et al. Part of the Team. Mawhinney, Art & Nunn, Paul E., illus. 2007. (Firehouse Tales Ser.). 224p. (J). 4.99 (*978-1-4169-3507-0(X)* , Simon Scribbles) Simon & Schuster Children's Publishing.

Freeman, Don & McCue, Lisa. Corduroy Goes to the Fire Station. 2003. (Illus.). 24p. (J). (gr. 1). 11.99 (978-0-670-03600-4(5) , Viking Juvenile) Penguin Group (USA) Inc.

Gershenson, Harold P. The Kindertown Fire Brigade. Mills, Christopher, illus. 2006. (J). (978-1-58987-019-2(0)) Kindermusik International.

Grambling, Lois G. My Mom Is a Firefighter. Manning, Jane, illus. 2007. 32p. (J). (ps-3). 16.99 (*978-0-06-058640-9(0))* HarperCollins Pubs.

Lewison, Wendy Cheyette. A Trip to the Firehouse. 1998. (J). (978-0-606-13870-3(6)) Tandem Library Bks.

Lukasewich, Lori. The Night Fire. 2001. (Illus.). 26p. (J). (ps-3). 15.95 (978-0-7737-3296-4(9)) Stoddart Kids CAN. *Dist:* Fitzhenry & Whiteside, Ltd.

Monica, Carol. Fisher Price Let's Go on a Class Trip Lift the Flap. SI Artists, illus. 2007. 10p. (J). bds. 8.99 (*978-0-7944-1291-3(2))* Reader's Digest Assn., Inc., The.

Rey, H. A. Curious George & Firefighters. Rey, Margret, illus. 2007. 24p. (J). (ps-k). bds. 9.95 (*978-0-618-89194-8(3))* Houghton Mifflin Co. Trade & Reference Div.

Rockwell, Anne F. At the Firehouse. Rockwell, Anne F., illus. 2003. (Illus.). 40p. (J). (ps-1). 16.89 (978-0-06-029816-6(2)) HarperCollins Pubs.

Scarry, Richard. A Day at the Fire Station. 2003. (Richard Scarry's Ser.). (Illus.). 24p. (J). (gr. k-3). pap. 3.25 (978-0-307-10545-5(8) , Golden Bks.) Random Hse. Children's Bks.

Scholastic, Inc. Staff. Let's Go to the Firehouse. 2007. (Barney Ser.). 24p. (J). pap. 2.99 (*978-0-545-01716-9(5))* Scholastic, Inc.

Slater, Jean M. At the Fire Station: An Interactive Book. 2nd ed. 2003. (Illus.). 13p. (J). bds. (978-0-9743149-0-7(0)) Slater Software, Inc.

Vaughan, Christina. There's a Pig in the Firehouse! 2000. 32p. (J). (gr. 1-5). spiral bd. 18.95 (978-0-9641697-8-4(9) , You-Draw-It Bks.) Castlebrook Pubns.

A Visit to the Fire Station. 2003. (J). per. (978-1-57657-900-8(X)) Paradise Pr., Inc.

Woodworth, Viki. Daisy the FireCow. 2003. (Illus.). 32p. (J). (gr. k-2). 15.95 (978-1-56397-934-7(9)) Boyds Mills Pr.

FIRE ENGINES

Abramson, Andra Serlin. Fire Engines up Close. 2008. 28p. (J). 9.95 (*978-1-4027-4798-4(5))* Sterling Publishing Co., Inc.

Adair, Amy. Fire Truck: Lift-a-Flap Fun. Wieland, Don, illus. 2000. (Active Minds Ser.). 12p. (J). bds. 15.98 (978-0-7853-4172-7(2) , 3996300) Publications International, Ltd.

Anderson, Catherine. Fire Truck Factory. 2004. (Field Trip! Ser.). (Illus.). 24p. (J). pap. (978-1-4034-6168-1(6)); lib. bdg. 18.50 (978-1-4034-6162-9(7)) Heinemann Library.

Augarde, Steve. Fire Engine to the Rescue. 1998. (Illus.). 10p. (J). pap. 14.95 (978-0-688-16328-0(9)) HarperCollins Pubs.

Biesty, Stephen. Stephen Biesty's Incredible Pop-up Cross-Sections. Biesty, Stephen, illus. 2004. (Illus.). 6p. (gr. 4-8). reprint ed. 17.00 (978-0-7567-7292-5(3)) DIANE Publishing Co.

Bridges, Sarah. I Drive a Fire Engine. Muehlenhardt, Amy Bailey, illus. 2006. 24p. (J). (ps-2). 22.60 (978-1-4048-1606-0(2)) Picture Window Bks.

Budd, E. S. Fire Engines. 1999. (Machines at Work Ser.). (Illus.). 24p. (J). (ps-3). 21.36 (978-1-56766-656-4(6)) Child's World, Inc.

Coppendale, Jean. Fire Trucks & Rescue Vehicles. 2007. (J). lib. bdg. 16.95 (*978-1-59566-342-9(8))* QEB Publishing Inc.

DK Publishing Staff. Fire Truck. 2003. (Wheelies Ser.). (Illus.). 12p. (J). (ps-3). bds. 6.99 (978-0-7894-9712-3(3)) Dorling Kindersley Publishing, Inc.

—Rescue Vehicles: Fire Truck. 2007. 10p. (J). (ps-1). bds. 9.99 (978-0-7566-2722-5(2)) Dorling Kindersley Publishing, Inc.

Dorling Kindersley Publishing Staff. Drive a Fire Engine. 1999. (Illus.). 12p. (J). (ps-2). pap. 12.99 (978-0-7894-4744-9(4)) Dorling Kindersley Publishing, Inc.

—Fire Engine. (Touch & Feel Ser.). (Illus.). 12p. (J). 2002. bds. 6.99 (978-0-7894-8855-8(8)); 1998. bds. 5.99 (978-0-7894-3711-2(2)) Dorling Kindersley Publishing, Inc.

—Fire Truck. 2003. (Machines at Work Ser.). (Illus.). 32p. (J). 8.99 (978-0-7894-9221-0(0)) Dorling Kindersley Publishing, Inc.

—Fire Truck. 2000. 12.79 (978-0-606-17808-2(2)) Tandem Library Bks.

—Toca y Apprende Camion de Bomberos/Touch & Feel Fire Engine. 2006. (Touch & Feel Ser.). 12p. (J). bds. 6.99 (978-0-7566-2135-3(6)) Dorling Kindersley Publishing, Inc.

Dorling Kindersley Publishing Staff, ed. Camion de Bomberos. 2004. (Things That Go Board Books Ser.).Tr. of Fire Engine. (SPA.). 12p. (J). (ps-3). bds. 3.99 (978-0-7566-0626-8(8)) Dorling Kindersley Publishing, Inc.

Dorling Kindersley Publishing Staff & Bingham, Caroline. Fire Truck. 2000. (Mighty Machines Ser.). (Illus.). 24p. (J). (gr. k-3). pap. 5.99 (978-0-7894-6103-2(X)) Dorling Kindersley Publishing, Inc.

Ethan, Eric. Fire Engines. Ethan, Eric, photos by. 2002. (Emergency Vehicles Ser.). (Illus.). 24p. (YA). (gr. 1 up). lib. bdg. 20.67 (978-0-8368-3045-3(8)) Stevens, Gareth Inc.

Fire Truck. 2000. (ps-2). lib. bdg. 14.15 (978-0-613-28485-1(2)) Tandem Library Bks.

Fire Trucks. (Mighty MacHines Ser.). 24p. (J). 6.95 (978-0-7368-5139-8(9)) Capstone Pr., Inc.

Franks, Pete & S. I. International. Flames! (with fire Hovercraft) 2006. (Matchbox Ser.). (Illus.). 16p. (J). (ps-2). bds. 6.99 (978-1-4169-0500-4(6) , Little Simon) Simon & Schuster Children's Publishing.

Freeman, Marcia S. Fire Engines. 2005. (Transportation Ser.). 24p. (YA). (gr. k-3). pap. (978-0-7368-8103-6(4) , Pebble Bks.) Capstone Pr., Inc.

—Fire Engines. Saunders-Smith, Gail, ed. 1998. (Community Vehicles Ser.). (Illus.). 24p. (J). (gr. k-1). lib. bdg. 15.93 (978-0-7368-0102-7(2) , Pebble Bks.) Capstone Pr., Inc.

—Fire Engines, 6 vols. (gr. k-2). 28.95 (978-0-7368-8127-2(1)) Red Brick Learning.

—Fire Engines. 1998. (Community Vehicles Ser.). (J). lib. bdg. 13.25 (978-0-516-21490-0(X) , Children's Pr.) Scholastic Library Publishing.

Glover, David & Glover, Penny. Fire Trucks. 2005. (Big Machines Ser.). (Illus.). 30p. (J). (gr. 2-5). lib. bdg. 27.10 (978-1-58340-704-2(9)) Smart Apple Media.

Gordon, Sharon. Whats Inside a Fire Truck? (¿Qué Hay Dentro de un Camion de Bomberos?) 2006. (Bookworms Ser.). (ENG & SPA., Illus.). 32p. (J). lib. bdg. 22.79 (978-0-7614-2472-7(5)) Cavendish, Marshall Corp.

Hanson, Anne E. Fire Engines. 2001. (Transportation Library). (Illus.). 24p. (J). (gr. 1-2). lib. bdg. 18.60 (978-0-7368-0842-2(6) , Bridgestone Bks.) Capstone Pr., Inc.

Hickle, Victoria. Fire Trucks in Action. DePew, Bob, illus. 2003. (Tonka Ser.). 4p. (J). (ps-2). bds. 6.99 (978-0-439-43432-4(7)) Scholastic, Inc.

Innovative Kids Staff. My Fire Truck. Brooks, David, illus. 2006. (Soft Shapes Ser.). 8p. (J). (ps-ps). 8.99 (978-1-58476-349-9(3)) Innovative Kids.

Jango-Cohen, Judith. Fire Trucks. 2003. (Pull Ahead Bks.). (Illus.). 32p. (J). (gr. k-2). lib. bdg. 22.60 (978-0-8225-0077-3(9)) Lerner Publishing Group.

—Fire Trucks. 2003. (gr. k-3). lib. bdg. 14.10 (978-0-613-52373-8(3)) Tandem Library Bks.

LaFontaine, Bruce. Shiny Fire Engines. 2006. 2p. (J). 1.50 (978-0-486-44826-8(6)) Dover Pubns., Inc.

Lindeen, Mary. Fire Trucks. 2007. (Illus.). 24p. (J). lib. bdg. 16.95 (978-1-60014-059-4(9)) Bellwether Media.

—Fire Trucks. 2007. (Blastoff! Readers Ser.). 24p. (J). (gr. k-2). 18.50 (*978-0-531-17557-6(X)* , Children's Pr.) Scholastic Library Publishing.

Martinez, Heather, illus. Shiver Me Timbers! 2003. (SpongeBob SquarePants Ser.). 32p. (J). (ps-3). pap. 3.99 (978-0-307-10470-0(2) , 14596695, Golden Bks.) Random Hse. Children's Bks.

Miller, Edward. Fire Trucks. 1998. (Sticker Stories Ser.). (Illus.). 16p. (J). (ps-1). pap. 4.99 (978-0-448-41825-4(8) , Grosset & Dunlap) Penguin Group (USA) Inc.

—Fire Trucks. 1998. (ps-2). lib. bdg. 13.00 (978-0-613-72349-7(X)) Tandem Library Bks.

Miller, Heather. Camiones de Bombero. (Ruedas, Alas y Agua Ser.).Tr. of Fire Trucks. 24p. pap. 5.25 (978-1-4034-3531-6(6)) Heinemann Library.

—Fire Trucks. 2003. (Wheels, Wings, & Water Ser.). (Illus.). 24p. (J). lib. bdg. 18.50 (978-1-4034-0883-9(1)); pap. (978-1-4034-3620-7(7)) Heinemann Library.

Mitton, Tony. Flashing Fire Engines. Parker, Ant, illus. 2000. (Amazing Machines Ser.). 24p. (J). (ps-k). pap. 3.95 (978-0-7534-5307-0(X) , Kingfisher) Houghton Mifflin Co. Trade & Reference Div.

—Flashing Fire Engines. 2000. (ps-2). lib. bdg. 11.80 (978-0-613-90366-0(8)) Tandem Library Bks.

Molzahn, Arlene Bourgeois. Fire Engines. 2001. (Transportation & Communication Ser.). (Illus.). 48p. (J). (gr. 1-4). lib. bdg. 23.93 (978-0-7660-1643-9(9)) Enslow Pubs., Inc.

My Fire Engine. 2002. (Chunky Vehicle Shaped Boards Ser.). (J). bds. 1.98 (978-0-7525-7047-1(1)); bds. 4.98 (978-0-7525-4770-1(4)) Parragon, Inc.

E F G

Oxlade, Chris. Fire Engine. Grey, Mike, illus. 1999. (Take It Apart Ser.). (J). lib. bdg. 22.00 (978-0-382-42069-6(1)) Silver, Burdett & Ginn, Inc.

Page, Josephine. I Am a Fire Truck. Bryan, Beth, ed. 2007. (J). bds. 4.99 (978-0-439-91618-9(6)) Scholastic, Inc.

Pomaska, Anna & Petruccio, Steven James. Fire Engines Stickers. 1998. (Stickers Ser.). (Illus.). 4p. (J). (ps-5). 1.50 (978-0-486-40502-5(8)) Dover Pubns., Inc.

Randolph, Joanne. Fire Trucks. 2008. lib. bdg. (*978-1-4042-4149-7(3)*, PowerKids Pr.) Rosen Publishing Group, Inc., The.

Randolph, Joanne. Let's Draw a Fire Truck with Shapes: Vamos a Dibujar un Camion de Bomberos Usando Figuras. Muschinske, Emily, illus. 2005. (Let's Draw with Shapes/ Vamos a dibujar con Figuras Ser.). (ENG & SPA.). (J). 17.25 (978-1-4042-7556-0(8), PowerKids Pr.) Rosen Publishing Group, Inc., The.

Red Rescue Fire Engine. 2002. (Vehicle Lights Ser.). (J). (ps-k). 6.98 (978-0-7525-8889-6(3)) Parragon, Inc.

Roberts, Cynthia. Fire Trucks. 2007. (Machines at Work Ser.). 24p. (J). 22.79 (978-1-59296-831-2(7)) Child's World, Inc.

Sis, Peter. Fire Truck. Sis, Peter, illus. 2004. (Illus.). 28p. (J). (ps-1). bds. 6.99 (978-0-06-056259-5(5), Harper Festival) HarperCollins Pubs.

Stickland, Paul. Special Engines. 2004. (By Air, Sea, & Land Ser.). (Illus.). 24p. (J). pap. 3.99 (978-0-7696-3376-3(5), Waterbird Bks.) School Specialty Publishing.

Stille, Darlene R. Fire Trucks. 2002. (Illus.). 32p. (J). (gr. 1 up). lib. bdg. 19.93 (978-0-7565-0288-1(8)) Compass Point Bks.

Tieck, Sarah. Fire Trucks. 2005. (Buddy Book Ser.). (Illus.). 24p. (gr. k-4). lib. bdg. 21.35 (978-1-59197-828-2(9)) ABDO Publishing Co.

Trumbauer, Lisa. Fire Trucks. 2005. (Pebble Plus: Mighty Machines Ser.). (Illus.). 24p. (J). 19.93 (978-0-7368-3653-1(5), Pebble Bks.) Capstone Pr., Inc.

E F G

FIRE ENGINES—FICTION

Armstrong, Jennifer. Magnus at the Fire. Smith, Owen, illus. 2005. 32p. (J). 15.95 (978-0-689-83922-1(7), Simon & Schuster Children's Publishing) Simon & Schuster Children's Publishing.

Auerbach, Annie. Three-Alarm Fire! 2003. (gr. k-3). lib. bdg. 11.25 (978-0-613-66548-3(1)) Tandem Library Bks.

Awdry, Wilbert V. Thomas & the Big, Big Bridge. 2003. (Illus.). 24p. (J). (gr. k-k). 2.99 (978-0-307-10335-2(8), Golden Bks.) Random Hse. Children's Bks.

Baggette, Susan K. Jonathan Goes to the Fire Station. Moriarty, William J., photos by. 1998. (Jonathan Adventures Ser.). (Illus.). 16p. (J). (ps-k). bds. 5.95 (978-0-9660172-4-3(2)) Brookfield Reader, Inc., The.

Barthelme, Donald. The Slightly Irregular Fire Engine: Or, The Hithering, Thithering Djinn. 2006. (Illus.). 32p. (J). 19.95 (978-1-58567-828-0(7)) Overlook Pr., The.

Bryant, Megan E. Little Engine That Could & the Fire Rescue: Based on Original Story by Watty Piper. Ong, Cristina & Lustig, Loretta, illus. 2003. (Reading Railroad Bks.). 32p. (J). pap. 3.49 (978-0-448-43279-3(X), Grosset & Dunlap) Penguin Group (USA) Inc.

Conlon, Mara. Firehouse Tales: Super Truck. Harris, Annmarie, ed. 2006. (Scholastic Reader Ser.). (Illus.). 32p. (J). pap. 3.99 (978-0-439-84632-5(3), Scholastic) Scholastic, Inc.

Cousins, Lucy. El Coche de Bomberos de Maisy. 2002. (Illus.). 14p. (J). (SPA.). 7.95 (978-84-8488-044-8(3), RR31039); (CAT., bds. 7.95 (978-84-8488-045-5(1)) Serres, Ediciones, S. L. ESP. *Dist:* Lectorum Pubns., Inc.

—Maisy's Fire Engine. Cousins, Lucy, illus. 2002. (Maisy Bks.). (Illus.). 16p. (J). (gr. k-k). bds. 4.99 (978-0-7636-1780-6(6)) Candlewick Pr.

Estes, Don. Willy: The Little Jeep Who Wanted to Be a Fire Truck. Garrison, Sue, illus. 2003. (J). lib. bdg. 14.95 (978-1-883551-47-6(1), ASP-471, Attic Studio Pr.) Attic Studio Publishing Hse.

—Willy & Friends traveling through the Seasons: The continuing story of Willy the little fire Jeep. Glass, Eric, illus. 2006. (J). (978-1-883551-75-9(7), Maple Corners Press) Attic Studio Publishing Hse.

Gergely, Tibor, illus. The Fire Engine Book. 2001. (Little Golden Bks.). 24p. (J). (gr. k-k). 2.99 (978-0-307-96024-5(2), Golden Bks.) Random Hse. Children's Bks.

Golden Books Staff. The Fire Engine Book. Gergely, Tibor, illus. 2004. (Little Golden Treasures Ser.). 26p. (J). (gr. k-k). bds. 4.99 (978-0-375-82841-6(9), Golden Bks.) Random Hse. Children's Bks.

Golden Books Staff. The Fire Engine Book & Other Stories to Color. Gergely, Tibor, illus. 2007. (Super Coloring Book Ser.). 96p. (J). (ps-2). pap. 2.99 (*978-0-375-83929-0(1)*, Golden Bks.) Random Hse. Children's Bks.

Hickle, Victoria. Firehouse Action. 2007. (Tonka Power Reading Ser.). 32p. (J). pap. 3.99 (*978-0-439-88482-2(9)*) Scholastic, Inc.

Hurley, Jo. Firehouse Tales: New Truck on the Block. Harris, Annmarie, ed. 2006. (Firehouse Tales Ser.). (Illus.). 24p. (J). pap. 3.50 (978-0-439-84296-9(4), Scholastic) Scholastic, Inc.

Jane, Pamela. Milo & the Fire Engine Parade. Johnson, Meredith, ed. Johnson, Meredith, illus. 2002. 32p. (J). pap. 13.95 (978-1-59034-036-3(1)); (gr. 1-4). 13.95 (978-1-59034-192-6(9)) Mondo Publishing.

Lenski, Lois. The Little Fire Engine. Kilgras, Heidi, ed. Lenski, Lois, illus. 2000. (Lois Lenski Bks.). (Illus.). 56p. (J). (gr. k-3). 13.95 (978-0-375-81070-1(6), Random Hse. Bks. for Young Readers) Random Hse. Children's Bks.

Lukasewich, Lori. The Night Fire. 2001. (Illus.). 26p. (J). (ps-3). 15.95 (978-0-7737-3296-4(9)) Stoddart Kids CAN. *Dist:* Fitzhenry & Whiteside, Ltd.

Mayer, Mercer. New Fire Truck. 2001. (gr. k-3). lib. bdg. 11.80 (978-0-613-67652-6(1)) Tandem Library Bks.

—The New Fire Truck, Vol. 2. 2002. (Little Critter First Readers Ser.). (Illus.). 24p. (J). (gr. k-1). pap. 3.95 (978-1-57768-843-3(0)) School Specialty Publishing.

Parker, Marjorie. Hello, Fire Truck! Kolar, Bob, illus. 2004. (Scholastic Reader Ser.). 32p. (J). (ps-3). pap. 3.99 (978-0-439-59890-3(7), Cartwheel Bks.) Scholastic, Inc.

Rex, Michael. My Fire Engine. rev. ed. 1999. (Illus.). 28p. (J). (ps-k). 16.95 (978-0-8050-5391-3(3), Holt, Henry & Co. Bks. For Young Readers) Holt, Henry & Co.

Rockwell, Anne F. At the Firehouse. Rockwell, Anne F., illus. 2003. (Illus.). 40p. (J). (ps-1). 16.89 (978-0-06-029816-6(2)) HarperCollins Pubs.

—Fire Engines. Rockwell, Anne F., illus. 2002. (Illus.). (J). 22.38 (978-0-7587-2494-6(2)) Book Wholesalers, Inc.

Schisgall, Jim. Spritzer Rides Again. Timmins, John, illus. 2000. 32p. (J). pap. 6.95 (978-1-890997-05-2(6)); 15.95 (978-1-890997-04-5(8)) Hardy Hill Enterprises, Inc.

Sis, Peter. Fire Truck. Sis, Peter, illus. 1998. (Illus.). 28p. (J). (ps-1). 16.99 (978-0-688-15878-1(1)) HarperCollins Pubs.

Teitelbaum, Michael. If I Could Drive a Fire Truck! Klavins, Uldis & Walker, Jeff, illus. 2001. (Tonka Ser.). 24p. (J). pap. 3.99 (978-0-439-31815-0(7), Cartwheel Bks.) Scholastic, Inc.

Watanabe, Shigeo. Jeeper the Fire Engine. Yamamoto, Tadayoshi, illus. 2005. 28p. (J). 11.95 (978-4-902216-14-1(0)) R.I.C. Publications Asia Co, Inc. JPN. *Dist:* Continental Enterprises Group, Inc. (CEG).

Wilson-Max, Ken. The Big Red Fire Truck. 2001. (Illus.). 14p. (J). (ps-1). bds. 7.95 (978-0-439-24024-6(7)) Scholastic, Inc.

Wood, Audrey & Wood, Bruce. Alphabet Rescue. 2006. (Illus.). 40p. (J). pap. 15.99 (978-0-439-85316-3(8), Blue Sky Pr., The) Scholastic, Inc.

FIRE EXTINCTION

see also Fire Engines

Adair, Amy. Fire Truck: Lift-a-Flap Fun. Wieland, Don, illus. 2000. (Active Minds Ser.). 12p. (J). bds. 15.98 (978-0-7853-4172-7(2), 3996300) Publications International, Ltd.

Adamson, Heather. A Day in the Life of a Farmer. 2003. (First Facts Ser.). (Illus.). 24p. (J). lib. bdg. 21.26 (978-0-7368-2284-8(4)) Capstone Pr., Inc.

Anderson, Sheila. Fire Station. 2008. (J). pap. (*978-0-8225-8841-2(2)*) Lerner Publishing Group.

Aylmore, Angela. We Work at the Fire Station. 2006. (Where We Work Ser.). (Illus.). 24p. (J). 21.36 (978-1-4109-2243-4(X)) Raintree.

—We Work at the Fire Station. 2006. (Where We Work Ser.). (Illus.). 24p. (J). (978-1-4109-2248-9(0)) Steck-Vaughn.

Battistoni, Ilse. I Fight Fires: Learning the Long I Sound. (PowerPhonics Ser.). (Illus.). (J). 2002. 24p. (gr. 1). lib. bdg. 18.50 (978-0-8239-5928-0(7)); 2001. 23p. pap. 26.40 (978-0-8239-8273-8(4)) Rosen Publishing Group, Inc., The. (PowerKids Pr.).

Behrman, Carol H. Thomas Jefferson. 2006. (Just the Facts Biographies Ser.). (Illus.). 112p. (J). (gr. 3-7). 27.93 (978-0-8225-2645-2(X), Lerner Pubns.) Lerner Publishing Group.

Behrman, Carol H., ed. Thomas Jefferson. 2004. (First Step Nonfiction Ser.). (J). pap. (978-0-8225-5358-8(9), Lerner Pubns.) Lerner Publishing Group.

Biesty, Stephen. Stephen Biesty's Incredible Pop-up Cross-Sections. Biesty, Stephen, illus. 2004. (Illus.). 6p. (gr. 4-8). reprint ed. 17.00 (978-0-7567-7292-5(3)) DIANE Publishing Co.

Bridges, Sarah. I Drive a Fire Engine. Muehlenhardt, Amy Bailey, illus. 2006. 24p. (J). (ps-2). 22.60 (978-1-4048-1606-0(2)) Picture Window Bks.

Brooks, Felicity. Fred the Firefighter. Litchfield, Jo, illus. rev. ed. 2004. 24p. (J). pap. 6.99 (978-0-7945-1496-9(0), Usborne) EDC Publishing.

Camenson, Blythe. Firefighting. 1999. (VGM Career Portraits Ser.). (Illus.). 96p. (gr. 7 up). 13.95 (978-0-8442-4374-0(4), 9780844243740) McGraw-Hill Cos., The.

Catala, Ellen. What Does a Firefighter Do? 2003. (Yellow Umbrella Bks. for Early Readers). (Illus.). 17p. (J). 15.93 (978-0-7368-2911-3(3)); pap. (978-0-7368-2870-3(2)) Yellow Umbrella Pr.

Caviezel, Giovanni. Los Bomberos y Tu: Fireman8217;s Safety Hints, Spanish Edition. 2006. Tr. of Fireman's Safety Hints. (SPA.). 10p. (J). bds. 10.99 (978-0-7641-5909-1(7)) Barrons Educational Series, Inc.

Christy, Lee Louis. I Go to Work as a Firefighter. 2003. (I Go to Work As Ser.). (Illus.). (J). (978-1-58417-039-6(5)) Lake Street Pubs.

Connolly, Sean. Fire. 2003. (Illus.). 32p. (J). lib. bdg. (978-1-58340-392-1(2)) Smart Apple Media.

Cutter, Jack. Phoenix the Fireboat. 2002. (Illus.). 32p. (J). (ps-6). pap. 9.95 (978-0-9719188-0-1(5)) ABC Pr.

Daynes Katie, et al. Firefighters. Fox, Christyan, illus. 2006. (Usborne Beginners Ser.). 32p. (J). (*978-0-439-88992-6(8)*) Scholastic, Inc.

Demarest, Chris L. Firefighters A to Z. Demarest, Chris L., illus. (Illus.). (J). 2003. 32p. 6.99 (978-0-689-85999-1(6), Aladdin); 2000. 40p. 17.99 (978-0-689-83798-2(4), McElderry, Margaret K.) Simon & Schuster Children's Publishing.

Dorling Kindersley Publishing Staff. Fire Truck. 2003. (Machines at Work Ser.). (Illus.). 32p. (J). 8.99 (978-0-7894-9221-0(0)) Dorling Kindersley Publishing, Inc.

—Firefighter for a Day. 2003. (Illus.). 12p. (J). pap. 12.99 (978-0-7894-9854-0(5)) Dorling Kindersley Publishing, Inc.

Dubois, Muriel L. Out & About at the Fire Station. McMullen, Anne, illus. 2004. (Field Trips Ser.). 24p. (C). (gr. k-3). 23.93 (978-1-4048-0039-7(5)) Picture Window Bks.

The Fire Station, 6 vols. (gr. k-2). 28.95 (978-0-7368-8006-0(2)) Red Brick Learning.

Gallimard Jeunesse Publishing Staff & Moignot, Daniel. Fire Fighting. Barish, Wendy, tr. from FRE. Moignot, Daniel, illus. 1999. (First Discovery Book Ser.). (Illus.). 24p. (J). (ps-2). spiral bd. 12.95 (978-0-439-04403-5(0)) Scholastic, Inc.

Ganci, Chris. Chief: The Life of Peter J. Ganci, a New York City Firefighter. 2003. 40p. (J). (gr. 3-7). pap. 16.95 (978-0-439-44386-9(5), Orchard Bks.) Scholastic, Inc.

Goldberg, Jan. Fire Fighter. (Careers Without College Ser.). pap. 6.95 (978-0-7368-8543-0(9)); 1998. (Illus.). 48p. (J). (gr. 3-4). lib. bdg. 21.26 (978-0-7368-0033-4(6)) Capstone Pr., Inc. (LifeMatters Bks.).

Gordon, Sharon. Whats Inside a Fire Truck? (¿Qué Hay Dentro de un Camion de Bomberos?) 2006. (Bookworms Ser.). (ENG & SPA., Illus.). 32p. (J). lib. bdg. 22.79 (978-0-7614-2472-7(5)) Cavendish, Marshall Corp.

Gorman, Jacqueline Laks. Firefighter. Andersen, Gregg, photos by. 2002. (People in My Community Ser.). (Illus.). 24p. (J). (ps up). lib. bdg. 19.33 (978-0-8368-3295-2(7), Weekly Reader Early Learning Library) Stevens, Gareth Inc.

—Firefighter/El Bombero. Acosta, Tatiana & Gutiérrez, Guillermo, trs. 2002. (Weekly Reader Early Learning Library). (SPA & ENG., Illus.). 24p. (J). (ps up). lib. bdg. 19.33 (978-0-8368-3309-6(0), Weekly Reader Early Learning Library) Stevens, Gareth Inc.

Gorman, Jacqueline Laks & Macken, JoAnn Early. Firefighter. Andersen, Gregg, photos by. 2002. (Weekly Reader Early Learning Library). (Illus.). 24p. (J). (ps up). pap. 7.93 (978-0-8368-3302-7(3), Weekly Reader Early Learning Library) Stevens, Gareth Inc.

—Firefighter/El Bombero. Coffey, Colleen & Carrillo, Consuelo, trs. from ENG. Andersen, Gregg, photos by. 2002. (Weekly Reader Early Learning Library). (ENG & SPA., Illus.). 24p. (J). (ps up). pap. 7.93 (978-0-8368-3343-0(0), Weekly Reader Early Learning Library) Stevens, Gareth Inc.

Gorrell, Gena K. Catching Fire: The Story of Firefighting. 1999. (gr. 5-8). lib. bdg. 26.85 (978-0-613-49292-8(7)) Tandem Library Bks.

—Catching Fire: The Story of Firefighting. 1999. (Illus.). 160p. (J). (gr. 5 up). pap. 16.95 (978-0-88776-430-1(4)) Tundra Bks., Inc./Livres Toundra, Inc. CAN. *Dist:* Random Hse., Inc.

Harcourt School Publishers Staff. El Barco de Bomberos On Level. 3rd ed. 2002. (Trofeos Ser.).Tr. of Firemen's Ship. (SPA., Illus.). pap. 6.80 (978-0-15-324181-9(0)) Harcourt Schl. Pubs.

Hayward, Katherine. Fire Extinguisher Training. 2004. (Illus.). 40p. 5.95 (978-0-9740473-1-7(7)) Pivotal Force.

Hayward, Linda & Dorling Kindersley Publishing Staff. Jobs People Do: A Day in the Life of a Firefighter. 2001. (Readers Ser.). (Illus.). 32p. (J). (ps-3). pap. 3.99 (978-0-7894-7365-3(8)) Dorling Kindersley Publishing, Inc.

High Interest Books: Danger Is My Business. 2004. (Illus.). 100.00 (978-0-516-29806-1(2)) Scholastic Library Publishing.

Kalman, Bobbie. Bomberos Al Rescate. 2006. (ENG & SPA., Illus.). 32p. (J). (978-0-7787-8428-9(2)) Crabtree Publishing Co.

—Bomberos al Rescate. 2006. (ENG & SPA., Illus.). 32p. (gr. 1-2). pap. (978-0-7787-8442-5(8)) Crabtree Publishing Co.

—Firefighters to the Rescue! 2004. (My Community & Its Helpers Ser.). (Illus.). 32p. (J). (978-0-7787-2096-6(9)); pap. (978-0-7787-2124-6(8)) Crabtree Publishing Co.

Kalman, Maira. Fireboat: The Heroic Adventure of the John J. Harvey. Kalman, Maira, illus. (Illus.). pap. 16.95 incl. audio (978-1-59112-983-7(4)); pap. incl. audio (978-1-59112-985-1(0)); pap. 18.95 incl. audio compact disk (978-1-59112-987-5(7)); pap. incl. audio compact disk (978-1-59112-989-9(3)) Live Oak Media.

—Fireboat: The Heroic Adventures of the John J. Harvey. Kalman, Maira, illus. (Illus.). 48p. (J). 2002. (gr. 2-6). 16.99 (978-0-399-23953-3(7), Putnam Juvenile); 2005. (ps). reprint ed. pap. 6.99 (978-0-14-240362-4(8), Puffin) Penguin Group (USA) Inc.

Kalz, Jill. A Fire Station. 2003. 24p. (J). lib. bdg. 14.95 (978-1-58340-326-6(4)) Smart Apple Media.

Kelley, Alison Turnbull. First to Arrive: Firefighters at Ground Zero. 2002. (United We Stand Ser.). (Illus.). 64p. (gr. 6-12). 25.00 (978-0-7910-6957-8(5), Chelsea Hse.) Facts On File, Inc.

Kuklin, Susan. Fighting Fires. 1999. (Illus.). (J). 13.79 (978-0-606-16293-7(3)) Tandem Library Bks.

Lewis, Brenda Ralph. Firefighters. 2003. (Rescue & Prevention Ser.). (Illus.). 96p. (J). (gr. 7 up). lib. bdg. (978-1-59084-402-1(5)) Mason Crest Pubs.

Liebeman, Dan. I Want to Be a Firefighter. 1999. (I Want to Be Ser.). (Illus.). 24p. (J). (ps-2). lib. bdg. 14.95 (978-1-55209-448-8(0)) Firefly Bks., Ltd.

Masoff, Joy. Fire! Resnicki, Jack & Smith, Barry D., illus. 1998. (J). pap. 5.99 (978-0-590-97585-8(4)) Scholastic, Inc.

—Fire! 2002. (gr. 3-6). lib. bdg. 15.25 (978-0-613-72000-7(8)) Tandem Library Bks.

Maze, Stephanie. I Want to Be a Firefighter. 2000. (I Want to Be Ser.). (Illus.). 48p. (YA). (gr. 4-9). lib. bdg. 18.98 (978-0-7398-1365-2(X)) Raintree.

Miller, Heather. Firefighter. 2003. (This is What I Want To Be Ser.). (Illus.). 24p. (ps-1). (J). lib. bdg. 18.50 (978-1-4034-0368-1(6)); pap. 5.25 (978-1-4034-0590-6(5)) Heinemann Library.

—Firefighter. 2003. (ps-2). lib. bdg. 13.30 (978-0-613-90954-9(2)) Tandem Library Bks.

Molzahn, Arlene Bourgeois. Fire Engines. 2001. (Transportation & Communication Ser.). (Illus.). 48p. (J). (gr. 1-4). lib. bdg. 23.93 (978-0-7660-1643-9(9)) Enslow Pubs., Inc.

Pohl, Kathleen. What Happens at a Firehouse? Qué Pasa en una Estacion de Bomberos? 2006. (ENG & SPA., Illus.). 24p. (J). pap. 9.95 (978-0-8368-7395-5(5)); lib. bdg. (978-0-8368-7388-7(2)) Stevens, Gareth Inc. (Weekly Reader Early Learning Library).

Rau, Dana Meachen. Firefighter. 2007. (Jobs in Town Ser.). 24p. (J). lib. bdg. 22.79 (*978-0-7614-2617-2(5)*, Benchmark Bks.) Cavendish, Marshall Corp.

Schmidt, Erin. Lo Que Hacen los Bomberos: What Firefighters Do. 2007. (What Does a Community Helper Do? Bilingual Ser.). (ENG & SPA., Illus.). 32p. (J). lib. bdg. 22.60 (978-0-7660-2826-5(7), Enslow Elementary) Enslow Pubs., Inc.

—What Does a Firefighter Do? 2005. (What Does a Community Helper Do? Ser.). (Illus.). 24p. (J). lib. bdg. 21.26 (978-0-7660-2539-4(X), Enslow Elementary) Enslow Pubs., Inc.

Shapiro, Larry. Firefighters. 2003. (Enthusiast Color Ser.). (Illus.). 96p. pap. 14.95 (978-0-7603-1494-4(2)) MBI Publishing Co. LLC.

Simon, Charnan. Firefighter Tom to the Rescue! Snyder, Joel, illus. 2006. (Magic Door to Learning Ser.). 24p. (J). (gr. k-2). 21.36 (978-1-59296-621-9(7)) Child's World, Inc.

Simon, Seymour. Fighting Fires. 2002. (SeeMore Readers Ser.). (Illus.). 32p. (J). pap. 3.95 (978-1-58717-169-7(4), SeaStar Bks.) Chronicle Bks. LLC.

Smoke Jumpers: Individual Title Six-Packs. (On Deck Ser.). 24p. (gr. 4-5). 35.00 (978-0-7578-1029-9(2)) Rigby Education.

Wheeler, Jill C. Firefighters. 2003. (Everyday Heroes (cb) Ser.). (Illus.). 32p. (J). (gr. k-6). lib. bdg. 22.78 (978-1-57765-855-9(8)) ABDO Publishing Co.

Willett, Edward. Fires & Wildfires. 2005. (Library of Emergency Preparedness). (Illus.). 64p. (J). (978-1-4042-0532-1(2)) Rosen Publishing Group, Inc., The.

FIRE EXTINCTION—HISTORY

Lewison, Wendy Cheyette. A Trip to the Firehouse. Hathon, Elizabeth, photos by. 1998. (Grossett & Dunlap All Aboard Books & Cassettes Ser.). (Illus.). 32p. (J). (ps-3). pap. 3.99 (978-0-448-41740-0(5), Grosset & Dunlap) Penguin Group (USA) Inc.

FIRE EXTINCTION—VOCATIONAL GUIDANCE

Abraham, Philip. Firefighter. 2003. (High Interest Bks.). (Illus.). 48p. (YA). (gr. 7-12). pap. 6.95 (978-0-516-27866-7(5), Children's Pr.) Scholastic Library Publishing.

—Firefighter. 2003. (gr. 7-12). lib. bdg. 15.25 (978-0-613-67896-4(6)) Tandem Library Bks.

Adamson, Heather. A Day in the Life of a Firefighter. 2003. (First Facts Ser.). (Illus.). 24p. (J). lib. bdg. 21.26 (978-0-7368-2283-1(6)) Capstone Pr., Inc.

Beyer, Mark. Smokejumpers: Life Fighting Fires. 2005. (Extreme Careers Ser.). (Illus.). 64p. (YA). (gr. 5-8). 26.50 (978-0-8239-3370-9(9)) Rosen Publishing Group, Inc., The.

Demarest, Chris L. Smokejumpers One to Ten. Demarest, Chris L., illus. 2002. (Illus.). 32p. (J). (gr. k-3). 17.00 (978-0-689-84120-0(5), McElderry, Margaret K.) Simon & Schuster Children's Publishing.

Englart, Mindi. Firefighter. 2002. (How Do I Become a... Ser.). (Illus.). 32p. (J). 23.70 (978-1-56711-687-8(6), Blackbirch Pr., Inc.) Thomson Gale.

Fall, Mitchell. Careers in the Fire Department's Search & Rescue Unit. 2005. (Careers in Search & Rescue Operations Ser.). (Illus.). 64p. (YA). (gr. 5-8). lib. bdg. 26.50 (978-0-8239-3833-9(6)) Rosen Publishing Group, Inc., The.

Firefly, Books, ed. I Want to Be a Firefighter. 1999. (gr. k-3). lib. bdg. 11.80 (978-0-613-25643-8(3)) Tandem Library Bks.

Goldberg, Jan. Fire Fighter. 1998. (Careers Without College Ser.). (Illus.). 48p. (J). (gr. 3-4). lib. bdg. 21.26 (978-0-7368-0033-4(6), LifeMatters Bks.) Capstone Pr., Inc.

Hayward, Linda. A Day in the Life of a Firefighter. 2001. (Jobs People Do Ser.). (Illus.). (J). 10.79 (978-0-606-21140-6(3)) Tandem Library Bks.

Hayward, Linda & Dorling Kindersley Publishing Staff. Jobs People Do: A Day in the Life of a Firefighter. 2001. (Readers Ser.). (Illus.). 32p. (J). (ps-3). 14.99 (978-0-7894-7366-0(6)); pap. 3.99 (978-0-7894-7365-3(8)) Dorling Kindersley Publishing, Inc.

Kottke, Jan. A Day with Firefighters. 2000. (Welcome Bks.). (Illus.). 24p. (J). (ps-2). pap. 4.95 (978-0-516-23013-9(1), Children's Pr.) Scholastic Library Publishing.

Landau, Elaine. Smokejumpers. Klaffke, Ben, photos by. 2002. (Illus.). 48p. (gr. 2-6). lib. bdg. 23.90 (978-0-7613-2324-2(4), Millbrook Pr.) Lerner Publishing Group.

Liebman, Dan. I Want to Be a Firefighter. 1999. (I Want to Be Ser.). (Illus.). 24p. (J). (ps-2). pap. 3.99 (978-1-55209-433-4(2)) Firefly Bks., Ltd.

Limmer, Daniel & O'Keefe, Michael. Emergency Care Fire Service Version. 9th ed. 2002. (Illus.). 908p. (C). stu. ed. 86.33 incl. cd-rom (978-0-13-146258-8(X), Prentice Hall) Prentice Hall PTR.

Miller, Heather. Firefighter. 2003. (This is What I Want To Be Ser.). (Illus.). 24p. (ps-1). (J). lib. bdg. 18.50 (978-1-4034-0368-1(6)); pap. 5.25 (978-1-4034-0590-6(5)) Heinemann Library.

—Firefighter. 2003. (ps-2). lib. bdg. 13.30 (978-0-613-90954-9(2)) Tandem Library Bks.

Minden, Cecilia. Firefighters. 2006. (Neighborhood Helpers Ser.). (Illus.). 32p. (J). (gr. k-4). 22.79 (978-1-59296-564-9(4)) Child's World, Inc.

Oleksy, Walter G. Choosing a Career as a Firefighter. 2005. (World of Work Ser.). (Illus.). 64p. (YA). (gr. 7-12). lib. bdg. 25.25 (978-0-8239-3245-0(1) , WWFIRE) Rosen Publishing Group, Inc., The.

Parks, Peggy J. Firefighter. 2004. (Illus.). 48p. (J). 26.20 (978-0-7377-2066-2(2) , Greenhaven Pr., Inc.) Thomson Gale.

Riddle, John. Firefighter. 2002. (Careers with Character Ser.). (Illus.). 96p. (J). (gr. 7 up). (978-1-59084-314-7(2)) Mason Crest Pubs.

FIRE FIGHTERS

Abraham, Philip. Firefighter. 2003. (High Interest Bks.). (Illus.). 48p. (YA). (gr. 7-12). pap. 6.95 (978-0-516-27866-7(5) , Children's Pr.) Scholastic Library Publishing.

—Firefighter. 2003. (gr. 7-12). lib. bdg. 15.25 (978-0-613-67896-4(6)) Tandem Library Bks.

Adamson, Heather. A Day in the Life of a Farmer. 2003. (First Facts Ser.). (Illus.). 24p. (J). lib. bdg. 21.26 (978-0-7368-2284-8(4)) Capstone Pr., Inc.

—A Day in the Life of a Firefighter. 2003. (First Facts Ser.). (Illus.). 24p. (J). lib. bdg. 21.26 (978-0-7368-2283-1(6)) Capstone Pr., Inc.

Aylmore, Angela. We Work at the Fire Station. 2006. (Where We Work Ser.). (Illus.). 24p. (J). 21.36 (978-1-4109-2243-4(X)) Raintree.

—We Work at the Fire Station. 2006. (Where We Work Ser.). (Illus.). 24p. (J). (978-1-4109-2248-9(0)) Steck-Vaughn.

Behnke, Alison & Markle, Sandra. Firefighters. 2005. (Pull Ahead Bks.). (Illus.). 32p. (J). lib. bdg. 22.60 (978-0-8225-0063-6(9)) Lerner Publishing Group.

Behrman, Carol H. Thomas Jefferson. 2006. (Just the Facts Biographies Ser.). (Illus.). 112p. (J). (gr. 3-7). 27.93 (978-0-8225-2645-2(X) , Lerner Pubns.) Lerner Publishing Group.

Behrman, Carol H., ed. Thomas Jefferson. 2004. (First Step Nonfiction Ser.). (J). pap. (978-0-8225-5358-8(9) , Lerner Pubns.) Lerner Publishing Group.

Bourgeois, Paulette. Fire Fighters. LaFave, Kim, illus. (Kids Can Read Ser.). 32p. (J). 2005. (gr. 1-3). (978-1-55337-751-1(6)); 2005. (gr. 1-3). (978-1-55337-750-4(8)); 2003. (gr. k-3). (978-1-55074-783-6(5)) Kids Can Pr., Ltd.

—Fire Fighters. La Fave, Kim, illus. unabr. ed. 2003. (In My Neighborhood Ser.). 32p. (J). (gr. k-3). (978-1-55074-438-5(0)) Kids Can Pr., Ltd.

—Fire Fighters. 2000. (Illus.). (J). 12.75 (978-0-606-18224-9(1)) Tandem Library Bks.

Bowman-Kruhm, Mary & Wirths, Claudine G. Firefighter, a Day in the Life. 2004. (Kids' Career Library). (Illus.). 24p. (J). lib. bdg. 18.75 (978-0-8239-6809-1(X) , PowerKids Pr.) Rosen Publishing Group, Inc., The.

Bridges, Sarah. I Drive a Fire Engine. Muehlenhardt, Amy Bailey, illus. 2006. 24p. (J). (ps-2). 22.60 (978-1-4048-1606-0(2)) Picture Window Bks.

Brigadas aereas Contraincendios: Individual Title Six-Packs. (On Deck en Espanol Ser.).Tr. of Smoke Jumpers. (SPA.). 24p. (gr. 4-5). 35.00 (978-0-7578-6408-7(2)) Rigby Education.

Briscoe, Diana. Smokejumpers: Battling the Forest Flames. 2002. (High Five Reading Ser.). (Illus.). 48p. (J). (gr. 3-4). lib. bdg. 22.60 (978-0-7368-9548-4(5) , Capstone High-Interest Bks.) Capstone Pr., Inc.

—Smokejumpers Battling the Forest Flames. 2002. (High Five Reading Ser.). (Illus.). 48p. (J). pap. (978-0-7368-9526-2(4)) Capstone Pr., Inc.

Brooks, Felicity. Fred the Firefighter. Litchfield, Jo, illus. 2004. (Jobs People Do Ser.). 24p. (J). pap. 6.95 (978-0-7945-0725-1(5)); pap. 6.99 (978-0-7945-1496-9(0)) EDC Publishing. (Usborne).

Brown, Mike. Rescue Services. 2003. (Twentieth-Century Developments in Fashion & Costume Ser.). (Illus.). 64p. (J). (gr. 7 up). lib. bdg. (978-1-59084-428-1(9)) Mason Crest Pubs.

Catala, Ellen. What Does a Firefighter Do? 2003. (Yellow Umbrella Books for Early Readers). (Illus.). 17p. (J). 15.93 (978-0-7368-2911-3(3)); pap. (978-0-7368-2870-3(2)) Yellow Umbrella Pr.

—Who Keeps Us Safe? 2006. (Illus.). 18p. (J). (978-0-7368-5984-4(5)) Capstone Pr., Inc.

—Who Keeps Us Safe? 2006. (Illus.). 8,16p. (J). 6.50 (978-0-7368-1720-2(4)) Red Brick Learning.

—Who Keeps Us Safe. 2006. (ENG & SPA., Illus.). 18p. (J). (978-0-7368-6020-8(7)) Yellow Umbrella Pr.

Caviezel, Giovanni. Fireman's Safety Hints. Mesturini, Cristina, illus. 2004. 10p. (J). bds. 10.99 (978-0-7641-5757-8(4)) Barron's Educational Series, Inc.

Christy, Lee Louis. I Go to Work as a Firefighter. 2003. (I Go to Work As Ser.). (Illus.). (J). (978-1-58417-039-6(5)) Lake Street Pubs.

Clemson, Wendy & Clemson, David. Firefighters to the Rescue. 2006. (Illus.). 32p. (J). pap. (***978-0-8368-8138-7(9)***); lib. bdg. (***978-0-8368-7839-4(6)***) Stevens, Gareth Inc.

Compass Point Books, contrib. by. Fire Fighters. (Community Workers Ser.). 24p. (J). pap. 7.95 (978-0-7565-1190-6(9)) Compass Point Bks.

Daynes, Katie. Firefighters Internet Referenced. Fox, Christyan, illus. 2004. 32p. (J). (gr. 1 up). pap. 4.95 (978-0-7945-0773-2(5) , Usborne) EDC Publishing.

Daynes, Katie. Firefighters (Level 1) - Internet Referenced. 2007. (Beginners Social Studies). 32p. (J). 4.99 (***978-0-7945-1658-1(0)*** , Usborne) EDC Publishing.

Daynes Katie, et al. Firefighters. Fox, Christyan, illus. 2006. (Usborne Beginners Ser.). 32p. (J). (***978-0-439-88992-6(8)***) Scholastic, Inc.

Demarest, Chris L. Firefighters A to Z. Demarest, Chris L., illus. (Illus.). (J). 2003. 32p. 6.99 (978-0-689-85999-1(6) , Aladdin); 2000. 40p. 17.99 (978-0-689-83798-2(4) , McElderry, Margaret K.) Simon & Schuster Children's Publishing.

—Firefighters A to Z. 2003. (gr. k-3). lib. bdg. 15.30 (978-0-613-66404-2(3)) Tandem Library Bks.

Englart, Mindi. Firefighter. 2002. (How Do I Become a... Ser.). (Illus.). 32p. (J). 23.70 (978-1-56711-687-8(6) , Blackbirch Pr., Inc.) Thomson Gale.

Fire Fighters. (Community Helpers Ser.). 24p. (J). 6.95 (978-0-7368-8455-6(6)) Capstone Pr., Inc.

Fire Fighters, 6 vols. (gr. 2-5). 36.95 (978-0-7368-8470-9(X)) Red Brick Learning.

Firefly, Books, ed. I Want to Be a Firefighter. 1999. (gr. k-3). lib. bdg. 11.80 (978-0-613-25643-8(3)) Tandem Library Bks.

Forgotten Heroes of Ground Zero. 2005. (J). per. (978-1-59872-131-7(3)) Instantpublisher.com.

Ganci, Chris. Chief: The Life of Peter J. Ganci, a New York City Firefighter. 2003. 40p. (J). (gr. 3-7). pap. 16.95 (978-0-439-44386-9(5) , Orchard Bks.) Scholastic, Inc.

Gigliotti, Jim. Smoke Jumpers. 2006. (Boys Rock! Ser.). (Illus.). 32p. (J). (gr. 1-5). 24.21 (978-1-59296-735-3(3)) Child's World, Inc.

Goldberg, Jan. Fire Fighter. (Careers Without College Ser.). pap. 6.95 (978-0-7368-8543-0(9) , LifeMatters Bks.) Capstone Pr., Inc.

Gorman, Jacqueline Laks. Firefighter. Andersen, Gregg, photos by. 2002. (People in My Community Ser.). (Illus.). 24p. (J). (ps up). lib. bdg. 19.33 (978-0-8368-3295-2(7) , Weekly Reader Early Learning Library) Stevens, Gareth Inc.

—Firefighter/El Bombero. Acosta, Tatiana & Gutiérrez, Guillermo, trs. 2002. (Weekly Reader Early Learning Library). (SPA & ENG., Illus.). 24p. (J). (ps up). lib. bdg. 19.33 (978-0-8368-3309-6(0) , Weekly Reader Early Learning Library) Stevens, Gareth Inc.

Gorman, Jacqueline Laks & Macken, JoAnn Early. Firefighter. Andersen, Gregg, photos by. 2002. (Weekly Reader Early Learning Library). (Illus.). 24p. (J). (ps up). pap. 7.93 (978-0-8368-3302-7(3) , Weekly Reader Early Learning Library) Stevens, Gareth Inc.

—Firefighter/El Bombero. Coffey, Colleen & Carrillo, Consuelo, trs. from ENG. Andersen, Gregg, photos by. 2002. (Weekly Reader Early Learning Library). (ENG & SPA., Illus.). 24p. (J). (ps up). pap. 7.93 (978-0-8368-3343-0(0) , Weekly Reader Early Learning Library) Stevens, Gareth Inc.

Gorrell, Gena K. Catching Fire: The Story of Firefighting. 1999. (Illus.). 160p. (J). (gr. 5 up). pap. 16.95 (978-0-88776-430-1(4)) Tundra Bks., Inc./Livres Toundra, Inc. CAN. *Dist:* Random Hse., Inc.

Hamilton, Kersten. Firefighters to the Rescue. Davis, Rich, illus. 2005. 32p. (J). (ps-3). 15.99 (978-0-670-03503-8(3) , Viking Juvenile) Penguin Group (USA) Inc.

Harcourt School Publishers Staff. Donde Hay Humo Hay Fuego Below Level. 3rd ed. 2002. (Trofeos Ser.). (SPA., Illus.). pap. 6.80 (978-0-15-324152-9(7)) Harcourt Schl. Pubs.

—Heroes in the Flames: Take-Home Book. 2001. (Collections Ser.). (Illus.). (J). pap. 1.90 (978-0-15-319524-2(X)) Harcourt Schl. Pubs.

—Heroes in the Flames Below Level. 3rd ed. 2002. (Trophies Reading Program Ser.). (Illus.). pap. 5.10 (978-0-15-323322-7(2)) Harcourt Schl. Pubs.

—Vamos de Fiesta: Donde Hay Humo, Hay Fuego Take Home Book. 2001. (SPA., Illus.). (J). pap. 2.80 (978-0-15-321302-1(7)) Harcourt Schl. Pubs.

Harvey, Al. I Want to Be a Firefighter. 1999. (978-0-606-17483-1(4)) Tandem Library Bks.

Hayward, Linda. Day in the Life of a Firefighter. 2001. (gr. k-3). lib. bdg. 11.80 (978-0-613-35098-3(7)) Tandem Library Bks.

High Interest Books: Danger Is My Business. 2004. (Illus.). 100.00 (978-0-516-29806-1(2)) Scholastic Library Publishing.

Holden, Henry M. Fire-Fighting Aircraft & Smoke Jumpers. 2002. (Aircraft Ser.). (Illus.). 48p. (J). (gr. 4-10). lib. bdg. 23.93 (978-0-7660-1720-7(6)) Enslow Pubs., Inc.

Jackson, Abby. Que hace un Bombero? 2005. Tr. of What Does a Firefighter Do?. (SPA., Illus.). 16p. (J). (gr. 1 up). lib. bdg. 15.93 (978-0-7368-4180-1(6)) Capstone Pr., Inc.

Kalman, Bobbie. Bomberos Al Rescate. 2006. (ENG & SPA., Illus.). 32p. (J). (978-0-7787-8428-9(2)) Crabtree Publishing Co.

—Bomberos al Rescate. 2006. (ENG & SPA., Illus.). 32p. (gr. 1-2). pap. (978-0-7787-8442-5(8)) Crabtree Publishing Co.

—Emergency Workers Are on Their Way! 2004. (My Community & Its Helpers Ser.). (Illus.). (J). 158p. (978-0-7787-2094-2(2)); 32p. pap. (978-0-7787-2122-2(1)) Crabtree Publishing Co.

—Firefighters to the Rescue! 2004. (My Community & Its Helpers Ser.). (Illus.). 32p. (J). (978-0-7787-2096-6(9)); pap. (978-0-7787-2124-6(8)) Crabtree Publishing Co.

Kelley, Alison Turnbull. First to Arrive: Firefighters at Ground Zero. 2002. (United We Stand Ser.). (Illus.). 64p. (gr. 6-12). 25.00 (978-0-7910-6957-8(5) , Chelsea Hse.) Facts On File, Inc.

Kleinberg, Naomi. Firefighters! Nelson, Mary Beth, illus. 2005. (Elmo's World Ser.). 12p. (J). (gr. k-ps). bds. 4.99 (978-0-375-83372-4(2) , Random Hse. Bks. for Young Readers) Random Hse. Children's Bks.

Kottke, Jan. A Day with Firefighters. 2000. (Welcome Bks.). (Illus.). 24p. (J). (ps-2). 17.00 (978-0-516-23088-7(3) , Children's Pr.) Scholastic Library Publishing.

—Day with Firefighters. 2000. (gr. k-3). lib. bdg. 12.95 (978-0-613-58766-2(9)) Tandem Library Bks.

Larousse Mexico Staff, ed. Mi Pequena Enciclopedia Larousse Los Bomberos. 2006. (Mi Pequena Enciclopedia Ser.). 38p. (ps-k). pap. 3.95 (978-970-22-1191-4(3)) Larousse, Ediciones, S. A. de C. V. MEX. *Dist:* Houghton Mifflin Co. Trade & Reference Div.

Lewis, Brenda Ralph. Firefighters. 2003. (Rescue & Prevention Ser.). (Illus.). 96p. (J). (gr. 7 up). lib. bdg. (978-1-59084-402-1(5)) Mason Crest Pubs.

Liebman, Dan. Je veux etre Pompier. Lior, Tsipora, tr. from ENG. 2006. (Je veux Etre Ser.).Tr. of I Want to Be A Firefighter. (FRE., Illus.). 24p. (J). (ps-2). pap. 5.95 (978-1-55407-104-3(6)) Firefly Bks., Ltd.

—Quiero ser Bombero. 2003. (Quiero Ser.). (SPA., Illus.). 24p. (J). (ps-2). pap. 5.99 (978-1-55297-743-9(9)) Firefly Bks., Ltd.

—Quiero Ser Bombero. 2003. Tr. of I Want to Be a Firefighter. (SPA.). (gr. k-3). lib. bdg. 14.15 (978-0-613-78626-3(2)) Tandem Library Bks.

Maass, Robert. Fire Fighters. rev. ed. 2002. (Illus.). 32p. (J). pap. 5.99 (978-0-439-41781-5(3)) Scholastic, Inc.

Magnuson-Beil, Karen. Fire in the Eyes: Wildfires & the People Who Fight Them. 1999. (J). 17.80 (978-0-606-16518-1(5)) Tandem Library Bks.

Mann, Rachel. Race to a Fire! 2003. (Compass Point Phonics Readers Ser.). (Illus.). 16p. (J). (gr. 1 up). 13.26 (978-0-7565-0522-6(4)) Compass Point Bks.

Masoff, Joy. Fire! Resnicki, Jack & Smith, Barry D., illus. 1998. (J). pap. 5.99 (978-0-590-97585-8(4)) Scholastic, Inc.

—Fire! 2002. (gr. 3-6). lib. bdg. 15.25 (978-0-613-72000-7(8)) Tandem Library Bks.

Mattern, Joanne. Brigadas Aereas Contraincendios. 2004. (Trabajo en Grupo Ser.). (SPA & ENG., Illus.). 24p. (J). (gr. 3-6). lib. bdg. 17.25 (978-0-8239-6844-2(8) , Buenas Letra) Rosen Publishing Group, Inc., The.

—Smoke Jumpers. 2002. (Reading Power Ser.). (Illus.). 24p. (J). (gr. 1). lib. bdg. 17.25 (978-0-8239-5978-5(3) , PowerKids Pr.) Rosen Publishing Group, Inc., The.

Miller, Heather. Bombero. 2003. (Esto es lo Que Quiero Ser (This Is What I Want to Be) Ser.).Tr. of Firefighter. (SPA.). 24p. (J). (ps-1). lib. bdg. 18.50 (978-1-4034-0378-0(3)) Heinemann Library.

Mullican, Judy & Crowell, Knox. A Firefighter in Class. l.t. ed. 1999. (Little Bks.). (Illus.). 8p. (J). (ps-k). pap. 10.95 (978-1-57332-148-8(6)); pap. 10.95 (978-1-57332-143-3(5)) HighReach Learning, Inc.

Neiman, Tommy & Reynolds, Sue. Sirens for the Cross for the Rookie Rescuer. Reynolds, Sue & Hygh, Angela, eds. 2003. (J). per. 14.95 (978-0-9668878-2-2(4)) Embrace Communications.

Owen, Ann. Protecting Your Home: A Book about Firefighters. Thomas, Eric, illus. 2004. (Community Workers Ser.). 24p. (C). (gr. k-3). 22.60 (978-1-4048-0088-5(3)) Picture Window Bks.

Picture Window Books, contrib. by. Protecting Your Home. (Community Workers Ser.). 24p. (J). pap. 7.95 (978-1-4048-0482-1(X)) Picture Window Bks.

Pohl, Kathleen. What Happens at a Firehouse? Qué Pasa en una Estacion de Bomberos? 2006. (ENG & SPA., Illus.). 24p. (J). pap. (978-0-8368-7395-5(5)); lib. bdg. (978-0-8368-7388-7(2)) Stevens, Gareth Inc. (Weekly Reader Early Learning Library).

Que hace un bombero? Social Studies, 6 vols.Tr. of What Does a Firefighter Do? Social Studies. (SPA.). (gr. k-2). 28.95 (978-0-7368-3024-9(3) , Yellow Umbrella Bks.) Capstone Pr., Inc.

Raatma, Lucia. Fire Fighters. 2000. (Community Workers Ser.). (Illus.). 32p. (J). (gr. 1 up). lib. bdg. 21.26 (978-0-7565-0009-2(5)) Compass Point Bks.

Rau, Dana Meachen. Firefighter. 2007. (Jobs in Town Ser.). 24p. (J). lib. bdg. 22.79 (***978-0-7614-2617-2(5)*** , Benchmark Bks.) Cavendish, Marshall Corp.

Riddle, John. Firefighter. 2002. (Careers with Character Ser.). (Illus.). 96p. (J). (gr. 7 up). (978-1-59084-314-7(2)) Mason Crest Pubs.

Royston, Angela. Bomberos! 2005. (Dk Readers Ser.). (SPA.). 32p. (J). pap. 3.99 (978-0-7566-1195-8(4)) Dorling Kindersley Publishing, Inc.

—Fire Fighter!, Vol. 2. 1998. (Eyewitness Readers). (Illus.). 32p. (J). (gr. 1-3). pap. 3.99 (978-0-7894-2960-5(8)) Dorling Kindersley Publishing, Inc.

Sanna, Ellyn. Firefighters' Folklore. 2002. (North American Folklore Ser.). (Illus.). 112p. (YA). (gr. 7 up). lib. bdg. (978-1-59084-334-5(7)) Mason Crest Pubs.

Scarry, Richard. A Day at the Fire Station. 2003. (gr. k-3). lib. bdg. 10.95 (978-0-613-83879-5(3)) Tandem Library Bks.

Schaefer, Lola M. We Need Fire Fighters. Saunders-Smith, Gail, ed. 2000. (Helpers in Our Community Ser.). (Illus.). 24p. (J). (gr. k-1). lib. bdg. 15.93 (978-0-7368-0391-5(2) , Pebble Bks.) Capstone Pr., Inc.

—We Need Fire Fighters, 6 vols. Saunders-Smith, Gail, ed. (gr. k-2). 28.95 (978-0-7368-8601-7(X)) Red Brick Learning.

—We Need Fire Fighters. 1999. pap. 13.25 (978-0-516-21904-2(9) , Children's Pr.) Scholastic Library Publishing.

Schmidt, Erin. Lo Que Hacen los Bomberos: What Firefighters Do. 2007. (What Does a Community Helper Do? Bilingual Ser.). (ENG & SPA., Illus.). 32p. (J). lib. bdg. 22.60 (978-0-7660-2826-5(7) , Enslow Elementary) Enslow Pubs., Inc.

—What Does a Firefighter Do? 2005. (What Does a Community Helper Do? Ser.). (Illus.). 24p. (J). lib. bdg. 21.26 (978-0-7660-2539-4(X) , Enslow Elementary) Enslow Pubs., Inc.

Shapiro, Larry. Firefighters. 2003. (Enthusiast Color Ser.). (Illus.). 96p. pap. 14.95 (978-0-7603-1494-4(2)) MBI Publishing Co. LLC.

Simon, Charnan. Firefighter Tom to the Rescue! Snyder, Joel, illus. 2006. (Magic Door to Learning Ser.). 24p. (J). (gr. k-2). 21.36 (978-1-59296-621-9(7)) Child's World, Inc.

Wheeler, Jill C. Firefighters. 2003. (Everyday Heroes (cb) Ser.). (Illus.). 32p. (J). (gr. k-6). lib. bdg. 22.78 (978-1-57765-855-9(8)) ABDO Publishing Co.

FIRE FIGHTERS—FICTION

Appleton, Victor. Tom Swift among the Fire Fighters or Bat. 2006. pap. (***978-1-4065-0893-2(4)***) Dodo Pr.

Auerbach, Annie. Three-Alarm Fire! 2003. (gr. k-3). lib. bdg. 11.25 (978-0-613-66548-3(1)) Tandem Library Bks.

Barbaresi, Nina. Firemouse. Barbaresi, Nina, illus. 2004. (Illus.). 40p. (J). (gr. k-3). pap. 6.99 (978-0-553-11177-4(9) , Dragonfly Bks.) Random Hse. Children's Bks.

Blackaby, Susan. A Fire Drill with Mr. Dill. Muehlenhardt, Amy Bailey, illus. 2004. (Read-It! Readers Ser.). 32p. (C). (gr. k-3). 18.60 (978-1-4048-0584-2(2)) Picture Window Bks.

Boelts, Maribeth. The Firefighters' Thanksgiving. Widener, Terry, illus. 32p. (J). (ps). 2006. pap. 6.99 (978-0-14-240631-1(7) , Puffin); 2004. 15.99 (978-0-399-23600-6(7) , Putnam Juvenile) Penguin Group (USA) Inc.

Bond, Felicia. Poinsettia & the Firefighters. Bond, Felicia, illus. 2003. (Illus.). 32p. (J). (ps-2). 14.99 (978-0-06-053509-4(1)); lib. bdg. 15.89 (978-0-06-053510-0(5)) HarperCollins Pubs. (Geringer, Laura Book).

Bourgeois, Paulette. Firefighters. LaFave, Kim, illus. 2005. 32p. (J). lib. bdg. 15.38 (***978-1-4242-1189-0(1)***) Fitzgerald Bks.

Desimini, Lisa. Spot the Fire Dog. Desimini, Lisa, illus. 2001. (Illus.). 40p. (J). (ps up). pap. 16.95 (978-0-439-23322-4(4) , Blue Sky Pr., The) Scholastic, Inc.

Dot the Fire Dog. 2004. (J). 29.95 incl. cd-rom (978-1-55592-623-6(1)); 24.95 incl. audio (978-1-55592-621-2(5)) Weston Woods Studios, Inc.

Durden, Angela K. Heroes Need Practice, Too! Hohn, Tracy, illus. 2006. (J). 11.95 (978-0-9701356-1-2(0)) WRITER for HIRE!.

Edwards, Julie Andrews & Hamilton, Emma Walton. Dumpy & the Firefighters. Walton, Tony, illus. 2003. 32p. (J). (ps-2). 15.99 (978-0-06-052681-8(5) , Julie Andrews Collection) HarperCollins Pubs.

Fireman Bear: New Heroes Backpack Story. 2002. (J). (978-1-931312-58-5(3)) SoftPlay, Inc.

Fox, Diane. Firefighter Piggywiggy. Fox, Christyan, illus. 2001. 24p. (J). (ps-k). 9.95 (978-1-929766-16-1(5)) Handprint Bks.

Gergely, Tibor, illus. The Fire Engine Book. 2001. (Little Golden Bks.). 24p. (J). (gr. k-k). 2.99 (978-0-307-96024-5(2) , Golden Bks.) Random Hse. Children's Bks.

Golden Books Staff. The Fire Engine Book. Gergely, Tibor, illus. 2004. (Little Golden Treasures Ser.). 26p. (J). (gr. k-k). bds. 4.99 (978-0-375-82841-6(9) , Golden Bks.) Random Hse. Children's Bks.

Grambling, Lois G. My Mom Is a Firefighter. Manning, Jane, illus. 2007. 32p. (J). (ps-3). 16.99 (***978-0-06-058640-9(0)***) HarperCollins Pubs.

Greene, Rhonda Gowler. Firebears, the Rescue Team. Andreasen, Dan, illus. rev. ed. 2005. 32p. (J). 15.95 (978-0-8050-7010-1(9) , Holt, Henry & Co. Bks. For Young Readers) Holt, Henry & Co.

Harris, Annmarie, ed. Firehouse Fun. 2006. (Firehouse Tales Ser.). (Illus.). 5p. (J). bds. 9.99 (978-0-439-83722-4(7) , Scholastic) Scholastic, Inc.

—Help's on the Way! 2006. (Firehouse Tales Ser.). (Illus.). 5p. (J). bds. 7.99 (978-0-439-84633-2(1) , Scholastic) Scholastic, Inc.

Hicks, John B. The Ghost of Fire Company 18. 2005. 149p. (J). per. 6.50 (978-0-9742829-2-3(8)) Quiet Man Publishing.

Hoppey, Tim. Tito, the Firefighter/Tito, el Bombero. de la Vega, Eida, tr. Hoffman, Kimberly, illus. 2003. Tr. of Tito, el Bombero. (SPA & ENG.). 32p. (J). (gr. 1-3). 16.95 (978-0-9724973-3-6(1) , 626999) Raven Tree Pr.

—Tito, the Firefighter/Tito, el Bombero. Hoffman, Kimberly, illus. 2005. Tr. of Tito, el Bombero. (SPA & ENG.). 32p. (J). pap. 4.99 (978-0-9741992-6-9(5) , 626999) Raven Tree Pr.

Hubbell, Patricia. Firefighters! Speeding! Spraying! Saving! Garofoli, Viviana, illus. (J). 2007. (***978-1-4287-3584-2(4)*** , Cavendish Children's Bks.); 2006. 14.99 (978-0-7614-5337-6(7)) Cavendish, Marshall Corp.

Hughes, Michael J. Firefightin' Sam. 2002. 122p. pap. 9.95 (978-0-595-24616-8(8) , Writers Club Pr.) iUniverse, Inc.

Lukasewich, Lori. The Night Fire. 2001. (Illus.). 26p. (J). (ps-3). 15.95 (978-0-7737-3296-4(9)) Stoddart Kids CAN. *Dist:* Fitzhenry & Whiteside, Ltd.

Mackinnon, Debbie & Sieveking, Anthea. What Am I? 2004. (Illus.). 24p. (J). pap. 7.95 (978-1-84507-243-8(X)) Lincoln, Frances Ltd. GBR. *Dist:* Perseus Distribution.

Mammano, Julie. Rhinos Who Rescue. 2007. (Illus.). 32p. (J). (ps-2). 13.95 (978-0-8118-5419-1(1)) Chronicle Bks. LLC.

Marsh, Carole. The Adventure Diaries of Felipe, the Fearless Firefighter!, 12 vols. 48p. 2003. (J). (gr. 1-4). pap. 5.95 (978-0-635-01096-4(8)); 2002. (Illus.). lib. bdg. 9.95 (978-0-635-01270-8(7)) Gallopade International.

McMullan, Kate. Fluffy & the Firefighters. Smith, Mavis, illus. 2004. 40p. (J). lib. bdg. 15.00 (978-1-59054-430-3(7)) Fitzgerald Bks.

—Fluffy & the Firefighters, Level 3. Smith, Mavis, illus. 2001. (Hello Reader! Ser.). 40p. (J). (gr. 1-3). pap. 3.99 (978-0-439-12917-6(6) , Cartwheel Bks.) Scholastic, Inc.

—Fluffy & the Firefighters. 1999. (gr. k-3). lib. bdg. 11.80 (978-0-613-35510-0(5)) Tandem Library Bks.

Metaxas, Eric. Mose the Fireman. Peck, Everett, illus. 2005. (Rabbit Ears-A Classic Tale Ser.). 40p. (J). (gr. k-5). 25.65 (978-1-59197-766-7(5)) Spotlight.

Mitter, Matt. Fisher Price Let's Meet Firefighter Cheryl. SI Artists, illus. 2007. 10p. (J). bds. 6.99 (***978-0-7944-1292-0(0)***) Reader's Digest Assn., Inc., The.

Morgan, Allen. Matthew & the Midnight Firefighter. Martchenko, Michael, tr. Martchenko, Michael, illus. 2003. (Wild Midnight Adventure Ser.). (J). 46p. pap. (978-1-55041-877-4(7)); 40p. lib. bdg. (978-1-55041-875-0(0)) Fitzhenry & Whiteside, Ltd.

—Matthew & the Midnight Firefighter. Martchenko, Michael, illus. 2000. (Matthew's Midnight Adventures Ser.). 32p. (J). (ps-3). 6.99 (978-0-7737-6090-5(3)) Stoddart Kids CAN. *Dist:* Fitzhenry & Whiteside, Ltd.

—Matthew & the Midnight Firefighter. 2003. (gr. k-3). lib. bdg. 12.95 (978-0-613-81245-0(X)) Tandem Library Bks.

—Matthew & the Midnight Firefighters. ed. 2004. (Illus.). (J). (gr. k-3). spiral bd. (978-0-616-07242-4(2)) Canadian National Institute for the Blind/Institut National Canadien pour les Aveugles.

O'Donnell, Liam. Duncan, a Brave Rescue. Hynes, Robert, illus. 2005. (Pet Tales Ser.). 32p. (J). (ps-2). 4.95 incl. cd-rom (978-1-59249-291-6(6) , 1B001); 2.95 (978-1-59249-292-3(4) , 1B003) Soundprints.

Osborne, Mary Pope. New York's Bravest. Johnson, Stephen T. et al, illus. 2002. 32p. (J). (gr. k-3). 15.95 (978-0-375-82196-7(1) , Knopf Bks. for Young Readers) Random Hse. Children's Bks.

—New York's Bravest. Johnson, Steve & Fancher, Lou, illus. 2006. 32p. (J). (gr. k-3). pap. 6.99 (978-0-375-83841-5(4) , Dragonfly Bks.) Random Hse. Children's Bks.

Parker, Marjorie. Hello, Fire Truck! Kolar, Bob, illus. 2004. (Scholastic Reader Ser.). 32p. (J). (ps-3). pap. 3.99 (978-0-439-59890-3(7) , Cartwheel Bks.) Scholastic, Inc.

Rabley, Stephen. The Fireboy. Date not set. (Illus.). 16p. pap. 73.13 (978-0-582-06072-2(9)) Addison-Wesley Longman, Ltd. GBR. *Dist:* Trans-Atlantic Pubns., Inc.

Rex, Michael. Firefighter! Rex, Michael, illus. 2003. (Word-by-Word First Reader Ser.). (Illus.). 32p. (J). pap. 3.99 (978-0-439-52785-9(6)) Scholastic, Inc.

—Word by Word First Reader: Firefighter. 2003. (ps-2). lib. bdg. 11.80 (978-0-613-72247-6(7)) Tandem Library Bks.

Rey, H. A. Curious George & Firefighters. Rey, Margret, illus. 2007. 24p. (J). (ps-k). bds. 9.95 (***978-0-618-89194-8(3)***) Houghton Mifflin Co. Trade & Reference Div.

Rey, H. A., et al. Curious George & the Firefighters. 2004. (Illus.). 24p. (J). (gr. k-3). 3.95 (978-0-618-49496-5(0)); 12.00 (978-0-618-49497-2(9)) Houghton Mifflin Co. Trade & Reference Div.

Rockwell, Anne F. At the Firehouse. Rockwell, Anne F., illus. 2003. (Illus.). 40p. (J). (ps-1). 16.89 (978-0-06-029816-6(2)) HarperCollins Pubs.

Rucker, Mike. Terry the Smokejumper. 2001. (Terry the Tractor Ser.: Vol. 9). (Illus.). (J). (ps-5). pap. 3.95 (978-0-9711659-0-8(4)) Univ. Editions.

Salmassian, Jennifer. Sally the Firefighter. 2007. (J). per. 0.01 net. (***978-1-60402-164-6(0)***) Independent Pub.

Santillo, LuAnn. The Fire Fighter. Santillo, LuAnn, ed. 2003. (Half-Pint Kids Readers Ser.). (Illus.). 7p. (J). (ps-1). pap. (978-1-59256-124-7(1)) Half-Pint Kids, Inc.

Searcy, Doc. Jimmy Jack & Jilly Jan, the Fireman. 2005. 33p. (J). 10.73 (978-1-4116-2564-8(1)) Lulu.com.

Slater, Dashka. Firefighters in the Dark. Ceccoli, Nicoletta, illus. 2006. 32p. (J). (gr. k-3). 16.00 (978-0-618-55459-1(9)) Houghton Mifflin Co.

Soda, Masahito. Daigo of Fire Company M. Soda, Masahito, illus. 2005. (Firefighter Ser.: Vol. 10). 208p. (YA). pap. 9.95 (978-1-59116-635-1(7)) Viz Media.

—Firefighter! (Firefighter Daigo of Fire Company M Ser.). (YA). Vol. 13. 2005. (Illus.). 200p. pap. 9.95 (978-1-4215-0130-7(9)); Vol. 14. 2006. 208p. pap. 9.95 (978-1-4215-0318-9(2)); Vol. 15. 2006. 208p. pap. 9.95 (978-1-4215-0451-3(0)) Viz Media.

—Firefighter, Vol. 16. 2006. (Firefighter Daigo of Fire Company M Ser.). 208p. (YA). pap. 9.95 (978-1-4215-0452-0(9)) Viz Media.

Swallow/Nascimbeni, Su/Barbara. Luke's Own Ladder. 2005. (Illus.). 32p. (J). lib. bdg. 9.00 (***978-1-4242-0880-7(7)***) Fitzgerald Bks.

Theiss, Lewis E. The Young Wireless Operator-As a Fire Patrol: The Story of a Young Wireless Amateur Who Made Goo. 2007. 234p. pap. 12.99 (***978-1-4264-6428-7(2));*** 256p. pap. 16.99 (***978-1-4264-6502-4(5)***) BiblioBazaar.

Van Straaten, Harmen. Little trunk Late. 2008. 32p. 12.95 (***978-1-60136-004-5(5)***) Mars Media Pubs.

Weissman, Steven. The Kid Firechief. 2004. (Illus.). 96p. pap. 12.95 (978-1-56097-596-0(2)) Fantagraphics Bks.

Wellington, Monica. Firefighter Frank. Wellington, Monica, illus. 2004. (Illus.). 32p. (J). (ps-k). pap. 5.99 (978-0-14-240188-0(9) , Puffin) Penguin Group (USA) Inc.

—Firefighter Frank. Wellington, Monica, illus. 2004. (Illus.). 32p. (J). (ps-3). lib. bdg. 13.19 (978-0-606-32705-3(3)) Tandem Library Bks.

Yee, Wong Herbert. Fireman Small - Fire down Below! 32p. (J). (gr. k-3). 2004. pap. 5.95 (978-0-618-49492-7(8)); 2001. (Illus.). tchr. ed. 15.00 (978-0-618-00707-3(5)) Houghton Mifflin Co. Trade & Reference Div.

—A Small Christmas. 2004. (Illus.). 32p. (J). (gr. k-3). tchr. ed. 12.95 (978-0-618-32612-9(X)) Houghton Mifflin Co. Trade & Reference Div.

Yee, Wong Herbert. Small Christmas. 2007. (Illus.). 32p. (J). (ps-3). 6.95 (***978-0-618-91534-7(6)***) Houghton Mifflin Co. Trade & Reference Div.

Yoder, Karen L. Fire Kids! The Adventures of Hose Company. 2nd l.t. ed. 2002. 124p. (J). pap. 6.95 (978-0-9700487-3-8(4)) Stoney Creek Pr.

Zimmerman, Andrea Griffing. Fire Engine Man. Clemesha, David, illus. 2007. 32p. (J). (ps-1). 15.95 (978-0-8050-7905-0(X)) Holt, Henry & Co.

Zimmerman, Andrea Griffing & Clemesha, David. Fire! Fire! Hurry! Hurry! Barbour, Karen, illus. 2003. 32p. (J). lib. bdg. 16.89 (978-0-06-029760-2(3)) HarperCollins Pubs.

Zytman, Leah. The Bravest Fireman. Diskind, Leah M., illus. 1998. 32p. (J). (ps-1). 9.95 (978-0-922613-88-5(5)) Hachai Publishing.

FIRE ISLAND (N.Y.)—FICTION

Estes, Eleanor. Pinky Pye. 2000. (J). (978-0-606-20042-4(8)); (978-0-606-20170-4(X)) Tandem Library Bks.

Howe, James. The Watcher. 2001. 192p. (YA). (gr. 8-12). pap. 5.99 (978-0-689-83533-9(7) , Simon Pulse) Simon & Schuster Children's Publishing.

FIRE PREVENTION

see also Fire Extinction

also names of cities with the subdivision Fires and Fire Prevention, e.g. Chicago—Fires and Fire Prevention, etc.

Barraclough, Sue. Fire Safety. 2007. (J). (***978-1-4034-9854-0(7));*** pap. (***978-1-4034-9861-8(X)***) Heinemann Library.

Beatty, Monica Driscoll. Fire Night. Allan-Piper, Christine, illus. 1998. 32p. (J). (gr. 3-7). pap. 8.95 (978-0-929173-31-3(7)) Health Pr. NA, Inc.

Beeping Ben Fire Safety Rules for the Whole. (J). 29.50 (978-1-56230-327-3(9)) Syndistar, Inc.

Carter, K. Cuando Hay Fuego. Palacios, Argentina, tr. 2002. (Seguridad (Safety) Ser.).Tr. of With Fire. (SPA., Illus.). 24p. (J). mass mkt. 5.95 (978-1-58952-262-6(1) , RK31476) Rourke Publishing, LLC.

DeAngelis, Gina. Triangle Shirtwaist Company Fire of 1911. 2000. (Great Disasters, Reforms & Ramifications Ser.). (Illus.). 112p. (J). (gr. 5 up). 30.00 (978-0-7910-5267-9(2) , Chelsea Hse.) Facts On File, Inc.

Ferguson. What Can I Do Now: Safety & Security. 2nd rev. ed. 2007. (What Can I Do Now Ser.). 200p. (gr. 6-12). 29.95 (***978-0-8160-6030-6(4)*** , Ferguson Publishing Co.) Facts On File, Inc.

Fire!Fire! Level K, 6 vols. 128p. (gr. 2-3). 40.50 (978-0-7699-0997-4(3)) Shortland Pubns. (U. S. A.) Inc.

Goldberg, Jan. Fire Fighter. (Careers Without College Ser.). pap. 6.95 (978-0-7368-8543-0(9) , LifeMatters Bks.) Capstone Pr., Inc.

Harcourt School Publishers Staff. To the Rescue. 3rd ed. 2002. (Horizons Ser.). (Illus.). (J). (gr. k). pap. 3.70 (978-0-15-333106-0(2)) Harcourt Schl. Pubs.

I Don't Play with Matches. (J). 29.50 (978-1-56230-054-8(7)) Syndistar, Inc.

Johnson, Sandi. Red Hot Dot: Fire Safety. Johnson, Britt, ed. Vu, Thi, illus. l.t. ed. 2002. 16p. (J). (gr. k-5). spiral bd. 6.50 (978-1-929063-86-4(5) , 279) Moons & Stars Publishing For Children.

Kids Can Press Staff, Press Can, ed. This Is Daniel Cook at the Fire Station. 2006. (Illus.). 28p. (J). (978-1-55453-076-2(8)); (978-1-55453-075-5(X)) Kids Can Pr., Ltd.

Pancella, Peggy. Fire Safety. 2004. (Illus.). 32p. (J). pap. 6.95 (978-1-4034-4940-5(6)); lib. bdg. 22.79 (978-1-4034-4931-3(7)) Heinemann Library.

Pendziwol, Jean. No Dragons for Tea. ed. 2004. (Illus.). (J). (gr. k-3). spiral bd. (978-0-616-01755-5(3)); spiral bd. (978-0-616-01756-2(1)) Canadian National Institute for the Blind/Institut National Canadien pour les Aveugles.

—No dragons for tea: Fire safety for kids (and dragons) Gourbault, Martine, illus. 2001. 32p. (J). (gr. k-3). (978-1-55074-571-9(9)) Kids Can Pr., Ltd.

Pohl, Kathleen. What Happens at a Firehouse? 2006. (Illus.). 24p. (J). pap. (978-0-8368-6894-4(3)); lib. bdg. (978-0-8368-6887-6(0)) Stevens, Gareth Inc.

Raatma, Lucia. Fire Safety. 2003. (Living Well). (Illus.). 32p. (J). (gr. 2-6). 27.07 (978-1-59296-086-6(3)) Child's World, Inc.

—Fire Safety, 4 bks. Incl. Crawl Low Under Smoke. lib. bdg. 18.60 (978-0-7368-0194-2(4)); Home Fire Drills. lib. bdg. 18.60 (978-0-7368-0195-9(2)); Smoke Alarms. lib. bdg. 18.60 (978-0-7368-0196-6(0)); Stop, Drop & Roll. lib. bdg. 18.60 (978-0-7368-0197-3(9)); 24p. (J). (gr. 1-2). 1999. (Illus.). Set lib. bdg. 74.40 (978-0-7368-0297-0(5) , Bridgestone Bks.) Capstone Pr., Inc.

—Smoke Alarms. 1999. (Fire Safety Ser.). (Illus.). 24p. (J). (gr. 1-2). lib. bdg. 18.60 (978-0-7368-0196-6(0) , Bridgestone Bks.) Capstone Pr., Inc.

—Stop, Drop & Roll. 1999. (Fire Safety Ser.). (Illus.). 24p. (J). (gr. 1-2). lib. bdg. 18.60 (978-0-7368-0197-3(9) , Bridgestone Bks.) Capstone Pr., Inc.

Rivera, Sheila, text. Fire Safety. 2006. (First Step Nonfiction Ser.). (J). pap. (978-0-8225-6820-9(9)) Lerner Publishing Group.

Ruiz, John. A, B, C's of Fire Safety. 2000. (Illus.). 24p. (J). (gr. k-6). 3.99 (978-0-9715245-3-8(X)) Teamwork Foundation, Inc.

Scarry, Richard. A Day at the Fire Station. 2003. (gr. k-3). lib. bdg. 10.95 (978-0-613-83879-5(3)) Tandem Library Bks.

FIRE PREVENTION—FICTION

Bentley, Dawn. Fire Engine Freddie to the Rescue! Wind-Up Fire Engine with Pop-Up Playset. Welply, Michael, illus. 1998. (J). (ps-k). 16.95 (978-1-58117-012-2(2) , Intervisual/Piggy Toes) Dalmatian Pr.

Cruz, Sarah, et al. Bernie Burn: A Storybook about Burn Injury Prevention & Safety in the Home. 2004. (Illus.). 38p. (J). 3.50 (978-0-9767230-0-4(X)) Little Boots Publishing.

Cuyler, Margery. Stop Drop & Roll. Howard, Arthur, illus. 25.95 incl. audio (978-1-59112-976-9(1)); 28.95 incl. audio compact disk (978-1-59112-980-6(X)); pap. 16.95 incl. audio (978-1-59112-975-2(3)); pap. incl. audio (978-1-59112-977-6(X)); pap. 18.95 incl. audio compact disk (978-1-59112-979-0(6)); pap. incl. audio compact disk (978-1-59112-981-3(8)) Live Oak Media.

—Stop, Drop, & Roll. Howard, Arthur, illus. 2001. (Jessica Worries Ser.). 32p. (J). (ps-2). 17.99 (978-0-689-84355-6(0)) Simon & Schuster Children's Publishing.

Erickson, John R. The Case of the Blazing Sky, No. 51. Holmes, Gerald L., illus. 2008. (Hank the Cowdog Ser.). 144p. (J). (gr. 3). 5.99 (***978-0-14-241015-8(2)*** , Puffin) Penguin Group (USA) Inc.

Flanagan, Alice K. Ms. Murphy Fights Fires. 1998. (Our Neighborhood Ser.). (Illus.). 32p. (J). (ps-3). pap. 6.95 (978-0-516-26249-9(1) , Children's Pr.) Scholastic Library Publishing.

Hughes, Michael J. Firefightin' Sam. 2002. 122p. pap. 9.95 (978-0-595-24616-8(8) , Writers Club Pr.) iUniverse, Inc.

Leaney, Cindy. Do You Smell Smoke? Safety with Fire. Wilks, Peter, tr. Wilks, Peter, illus. 2003. 32p. (J). 28.50 (978-1-58952-741-6(0)) Rourke Publishing, LLC.

Pockets Learning Staff. Fire Station. 1998. (Illus.). (YA). (ps-1). 35.00 (978-1-888074-95-6(7)) Pockets of Learning.

Wasserman, Shannon & Wasserman, Curt. The Adventures of Ruff-n-Rescue. 2006. 40p. 16.95 (***978-1-931643-87-0(3)***) Seven Locks Pr.

FIREARMS

see also Gun Control; Ordnance; Rifles

Antarctic Press. Weaponsfile Supersized. 2006. 144p. (YA). pap. 24.95 (978-0-9768043-3-8(6)) Antarctic Pr., Inc.

Arms & Fire Power. 1998. (Illus.). 32p. (YA). (gr. 6 up). pap. 4.00 (978-1-890541-13-2(3)) Americana Souvenirs & Gifts.

Atkin, S. Beth. Gunstories: Life-Changing Experiences with Guns. Atkin, S. Beth, illus. 2006. (Illus.). 256p. (YA). 16.99 (978-0-06-052659-7(9) , Tegen, Katherine Bks) HarperCollins Pubs.

Brezina, Corona. Weapons of Mass Destruction: Proliferation & Control. 2004. (Library of Weapons of Mass Destruction). (Illus.). 64p. (J). lib. bdg. 26.50 (978-1-4042-0298-6(6)) Rosen Publishing Group, Inc., The.

Brownell, Frank R., 3rd. Gunsmith's Firearms Repair Log, 1. 2004. (Illus.). 48p. 3.00 (978-0-9767409-8-8(2)) Brownell, F. & Son, Pubs.

Croft, Jennifer. Everything You Need to Know about Guns in Your Home. 2005. (Need to Know Library). (Illus.). 64p. (YA). (gr. 7-12). lib. bdg. 25.25 (978-0-8239-3162-0(5) , NTGUHO) Rosen Publishing Group, Inc., The.

Dailey, D. C. Guns Are Not for Fun. Boudreau, Dawn, photos by. 1999. (Illus.). 34p. (J). (gr. 1-3). pap. 3.75 (978-1-929662-00-5(9)) Brighter Horizons Publishing.

Egan, Tracie. Weapons of Mass Destruction & North Korea. 2004. (Library of Weapons of Mass Destruction). (Illus.). 64p. (J). lib. bdg. 26.50 (978-1-4042-0296-2(X)) Rosen Publishing Group, Inc., The.

Fischer, Rusty. Weapons of the West. 2002. (History of the Old West Ser.). (Illus.). 64p. (J). (gr. 5 up). lib. bdg. (978-1-59084-066-5(6)) Mason Crest Pubs.

Hamilton, John. Weapons of World War I. 2004. (World War I Ser.). (Illus.). 32p. (J). (gr. 4-8). lib. bdg. 24.21 (978-1-57765-917-4(1)) ABDO Publishing Co.

Herbst, Judith. The History of Weapons. 2006. (Major Inventions Through History Ser.). (Illus.). 56p. (J). (gr. 3-7). 26.60 (978-0-8225-3805-9(9) , Twenty-First Century Bks.) Lerner Publishing Group.

Jamieson, G. Scott. Bullard Firearms. 2nd ed. 2002. (Schiffer Military History Ser.). (Illus.). 368p. (gr. 10-13). 100.00 (978-0-7643-1465-0(3)) Schiffer Publishing, Ltd.

Joyce, Jaime. Bullet Proof! The Evidence That Guns Leave Behind. (24/7 - Science Behind the Scenes Ser.). (Illus.). 64p. (YA). (gr. 8-12). 2007. pap. 7.95 (***978-0-531-15455-7(6));*** 2006. 25.00 (978-0-531-11820-7(7)) Scholastic Library Publishing. (Watts, Franklin).

Kim, Henry R. Guns & Violence. 1999. (Current Controversies Ser.). (Illus.). 224p. (YA). (gr. 7-12). pap. 21.20 (978-0-7377-0064-0(5) , Greenhaven Pr., Inc.) Thomson Gale.

Laidacker, John S. Engraved Handguns of . 22 Calibre, 1855-1885. 2002. (Illus.). 168p. (gr. 10-13). 69.95 (978-0-7643-1683-8(4)) Schiffer Publishing, Ltd.

Logan, Michael. Weapons of Mass Destruction. 2006. (Current Controversies Ser.). (Illus.). 244p. (gr. 10-12). 24.95 (978-0-7377-2786-9(1)); pap. 36.20 (978-0-7377-2785-2(3)) Thomson Gale. (Greenhaven Pr., Inc.).

Magoon, Kekla. Gun Control. 2007. (Essential Viewpoints Ser.). (Illus.). 112p. (YA). (gr. 7-9). lib. bdg. 32.79 (***978-1-59928-860-4(5)*** , Essential Library) ABDO Publishing Co.

Mitchell, Barbara. Maker of Machines: A Story about Eli Whitney. Jones, Jan Naimo, tr. Jones, Jan Naimo, illus. 2004. (Creative Minds Biography Ser.). 64p. (J). 22.60 (978-1-57505-603-6(8) , Carolrhoda Bks.) Lerner Publishing Group.

Moe, Barbara A. The Search for Weapons of Mass Destruction in Iraq. 2004. (Library of Weapons of Mass Destruction). (Illus.). 64p. (J). lib. bdg. 26.50 (978-1-4042-0295-5(1)) Rosen Publishing Group, Inc., The.

Parker, Steve. The M109A6 Paladin. 2008. (J). (***978-1-4296-0094-1(2)***) Capstone Pr., Inc.

Schleifer, Jay. Everything You Need to Know about Weapons in School & at Home. rev. ed. 2005. (Need to Know Library). (Illus.). 64p. (YA). (gr. 7-12). lib. bdg. 25.25 (978-0-8239-3315-0(6)) Rosen Publishing Group, Inc., The.

Schulson, Rachel. Guns: What You Should Know. 1999. (Illus.). (J). (978-0-606-18774-9(X)) Tandem Library Bks.

Schwarz, Ted. Kids & Guns: The History, the Present, the Dangers, & the Remedies. 1999. (Single Titles Ser.). (Illus.). 128p. (YA). (gr. 8-12). 24.00 (978-0-531-11723-1(5) , Watts, Franklin) Scholastic Library Publishing.

Valdez, Angela. Gun Control. 2003. (Point/Counterpoint Ser.). (Illus.). 112p. (gr. 9-13). 32.95 (978-0-7910-7371-1(8) , Chelsea Hse.) Facts On File, Inc.

Wright, Susan. Weapons of Mass Destruction: Illicit Trade & Trafficking. 2004. (Library of Weapons of Mass Destruction). (Illus.). 64p. (J). lib. bdg. 26.50 (978-1-4042-0297-9(8)) Rosen Publishing Group, Inc., The.

FIREARMS—HISTORY

Atkin, S. Beth. Gunstories: Life-Changing Experiences with Guns. Atkin, S. Beth, illus. 2007. 256p. (J). pap. 7.99 (***978-0-06-052661-0(0)***) HarperCollins Pubs.

Quinlan. The History of Weapons of War. 2004. (World History Ser.). (Illus.). 112p. (J). 32.45 (978-1-59018-183-6(2) , Lucent Bks.) Thomson Gale.

FIREARMS—LAW AND LEGISLATION

Here are entered works on the legal aspects of gun control. General and non-legal works on the control of guns are entered under Gun Control.

Everything You Need to Know about (Legally) Carrying a Handgun in Missouri. 2nd unabr. ed. 2004. per. 24.95 (978-0-9741480-1-4(6) , 18) Certified Firearms Instructors, LLC.

Fernandez, Justin. Guns, Crime & the 2nd Amendment. 2001. (Crime, Justice & Punishment Ser.). (Illus.). 80p. (J). 30.00 (978-0-7910-5765-0(8) , Chelsea Hse.) Facts On File, Inc.

Gonzales, Doreen. A Look at the Second Amendment: To Keep & Bear Arms. 2007. (Constitution of the United States Ser.). (Illus.). 128p. (J). (gr. 5). lib. bdg. 33.27 (978-1-59845-061-3(1) , MyReportLinks.com Bks.) Enslow Pubs., Inc.

Hanson, Freya Ottem. The Second Amendment: The Right to Own Guns. 1998. (Constitution Ser.). (Illus.). 128p. (YA). (gr. 6-12). lib. bdg. 26.60 (978-0-89490-925-2(8)) Enslow Pubs., Inc.

Lunger, Norman L. Big Bang: The Loud Debate over Gun Control. 2002. (Worlds Beyond Ser.). (Illus.). 160p. (gr. 7 up). lib. bdg. 25.90 (978-0-7613-2260-3(4) , Twenty-First Century Bks.) Lerner Publishing Group.

Schulson, Rachel. Guns: What You Should Know. Jones, Mary, illus. 2004. (Concept Book Ser.). 24p. (J). (gr. k-5). pap. 5.95 (978-0-8075-3094-8(8)) Whitman, Albert & Co.

Smith, Rich. Second & Third Amendments: The Right to Security. 2007. (Bill of Rights Ser.). (ENG., Illus.). 32p. (J). (gr. 4-8). lib. bdg. 25.65 (***978-1-59928-915-1(6)*** , ABDO & Daughters) ABDO Publishing Co.

Sommers, Michael A. The Right to Bear Arms. 2001. (Individual Rights & Civic Responsibility Ser.). (Illus.). 64p. (YA). (gr. 7-12). lib. bdg. 26.50 (978-0-8239-3232-0(X)) Rosen Publishing Group, Inc., The.

Streissguth, Thomas. Gun Control: The Pros & Cons. 2001. (Issues in Focus Ser.). (Illus.). 128p. (J). (gr. 6-12). lib. bdg. 26.60 (978-0-7660-1673-6(0)) Enslow Pubs., Inc.

Valdez, Angela. Gun Control. 2003. (Point/Counterpoint Ser.). (Illus.). 112p. (gr. 9-13). pap. 15.95 (978-0-7910-7507-4(9) , Chelsea Hse.) Facts On File, Inc.

—Gun Control. 2003. (gr. 7-12). lib. bdg. 21.05 (978-0-613-85627-0(9)) Tandem Library Bks.

FIREBOATS

Fire Boats. 2005. (Transportation Ser.). (YA). (gr. k-3). (978-0-7368-8102-9(6) , Pebble Bks.) Capstone Pr., Inc.

Freeman, Marcia S. Fire Boats. Saunders-Smith, Gail, ed. 1999. (Community Vehicles Ser.). (Illus.). 24p. (J). (gr. k-1). lib. bdg. 15.93 (978-0-7368-0101-0(4) , Pebble Bks.) Capstone Pr., Inc.

—Fire Boats. 1998. (Community Vehicles Ser.). (J). lib. bdg. 13.25 (978-0-516-21489-4(6) , Children's Pr.) Scholastic Library Publishing.

Kalman, Maira. Fireboat: The Heroic Adventures of John J. Harvey. 2004. (Illus.). (J). 25.95 incl. audio (978-1-59112-984-4(2)); 28.95 incl. audio compact disk (978-1-59112-988-2(5)) Live Oak Media.

FIREFLIES

Ashley, Susan. Fireflies. 2004. (Weekly Reader Early Learning Library). (Illus.). 24p. (gr. 1 up). (J). pap. 5.95 (978-0-8368-4060-5(7)); (YA). lib. bdg. 19.93 (978-0-8368-4053-7(4)) Stevens, Gareth Inc. (Weekly Reader Early Learning Library).

Bryant, Megan E. Fireflies. Schwartz, Carol, illus. 2008. (All Aboard Science Reader Ser.). 48p. (J). (gr. 1-3). pap. 3.99 (***978-0-448-44834-3(3)*** , Grosset & Dunlap) Penguin Group (USA) Inc.

Collard, Sneed B., III. A Firefly Biologist at Work. 2001. (Wildlife Conservation Society Bks.). (Illus.). 48p. (J). (gr. 4-6). 24.50 (978-0-531-11798-9(7) , Watts, Franklin) Scholastic Library Publishing.

—A Firefly Biologist at Work. 2001. (gr. 3-6). lib. bdg. 15.25 (978-0-613-54218-0(5)) Tandem Library Bks.

Coughlan, Cheryl. Fireflies. 2005. (Bugs, Bugs, Bugs Ser.). 24p. (YA). (gr. k-3). pap. (978-0-7368-8210-1(3) , Pebble Bks.) Capstone Pr., Inc.

Dickmann, Nancy. Fireflies. 2005. (Creepy Creatures Ser.). (Illus.). 24p. (J). (978-1-4109-1770-6(3)); (gr. 4-7). pap. 6.00 (978-1-4109-1775-1(4)) Steck-Vaughn.

Fireflies. (Nature's Friends Ser.). 32p. (J). 7.95 (978-0-7565-1228-6(X)) Compass Point Bks.

Fireflies, 6 vols. (gr. k-2). 28.95 (978-0-7368-8250-7(2)) Red Brick Learning.

Fireflies World of Insects. 2006. (Illus.). 24p. (J). (gr. k-2). 18.50 (***978-0-531-17863-8(3)***) Scholastic Library Publishing.

Green, Emily K. Fireflies. 2006. (Blastoff! Readers Ser.). (Illus.). 24p. (J). lib. bdg. 16.95 (978-1-60014-013-6(0)) Bellwether Media.

Halfmann, Janet. Fireflies. 1998. (Bugs Ser.). (Illus.). 32p. (YA). (gr. 3-12). lib. bdg. 16.95 (978-1-887068-33-8(3)) Smart Apple Media.

E F G

Hall, Margaret. Fireflies. 2006. (Bugs, Bugs, Bugs! Ser.). (Illus.). 24p. (J). (978-0-7368-4253-2(5)) Capstone Pr., Inc.

Heinrichs, Ann. Fireflies. 2004. (Illus.). 32p. (J). (gr. 2 up). lib. bdg. 21.26 (978-0-7565-0588-2(7)) Compass Point Bks.

Helget, Nicole Lea. Fireflies. 2007. (J). (978-1-58341-542-9(4) , Creative Education) Creative Co., The.

Jacobs, Liza. Fireflies. 2003. (Wild Wild World Ser.). (Illus.). 24p. (J). 22.45 (978-1-4103-0048-5(X) , Blackbirch Pr., Inc.) Thomson Gale.

Kuntz, Lynn. Firefly. 2005. (Bugs Ser.). (Illus.). 32p. (J). (ps-8). lib. bdg. 24.95 (978-0-7377-3132-3(X) , Greenhaven Pr., Inc.) Thomson Gale.

Living Lights. (Backyard Bugs Ser.). 24p. (J). 7.95 (978-1-4048-0447-0(1)) Picture Window Bks.

Loewen, Nancy. Living Lights: Fireflies n Your Backyard. Reibeling, Brandon, illus. 2004. (Backyard Bugs Ser.). 24p. (C). (gr. k-3). 22.60 (978-1-4048-0145-5(6)) Picture Window Bks.

McLaughlin, Kari Massie. My Adventure with Flamingos. 2007. 44p. (J). 8.99 (978-1-59092-454-9(1) , Orchard Academy Pr.) Windstorm Creative.

Meister, Cari. Fireflies. 2001. (Insects Ser.). (Illus.). 24p. (J). (gr. k-6). lib. bdg. 21.35 (978-1-57765-462-9(5) , Checkerboard Library) ABDO Publishing Co.

Miller, Connie Colwell. Fireflies. 2005. (Illus.). 24p. (J). 21.26 (978-0-7368-3707-1(8)) Capstone Pr., Inc.

Rau, Dana Meachen. ¡Brilla, Luciérnaga, Brilla! 2007. (¡Vamos Criaturita, Vamos! Ser.). (SPA.). 24p. (J). lib. bdg. 22.79 (*978-0-7614-2792-6(9) , Benchmark Bks.) Cavendish, Marshall Corp.

—Flash, Firefly, Flash! 2007. (Go, Critter, Go! Ser.). (Illus.). 23p. (J). (ps-3). lib. bdg. 22.79 (*978-0-7614-2651-6(5) , Benchmark Bks.) Cavendish, Marshall Corp.

—Flash, Firefly, Flash!/Brilla, Luciérnaga, Brilla! 2007. (Go, Critter, Go!/¡Vamos Criaturita, Vamos! Ser.). (SPA & ENG.). 24p. (J). lib. bdg. 22.79 (*978-0-7614-2816-9(X) , Benchmark Bks.) Cavendish, Marshall Corp.

St. Pierre, Stephanie. Metals. 2001. (Bug Books Ser.). (Illus.). 48p. (YA). (gr. 6-8). lib. bdg. 25.64 (978-1-58810-198-3(3)) Heinemann Library.

Walker, Sally M. Fireflies. (Early Bird Nature Bks.). 48p. (J). 2003. 6.95 (978-0-8225-0025-4(6) , Carolrhoda Bks.); 2001. (Illus.). (gr. 2-4). lib. bdg. 25.26 (978-0-8225-3047-3(3) , Lerner Pubns.) Lerner Publishing Group.

FIREFLIES—FICTION

Bailey, Arthur Scott. The Tale of Freddie Firefly. 2004. reprint ed. pap. 15.95 (978-1-4191-8478-9(4)); pap. 1.99 (978-1-4192-8478-6(9)) Kessinger Publishing, LLC.

Bailey, Arthur Scott. Tuck-Me-in Tales: The Tale of Freddie Fi. 2006. pap. (*978-1-4065-0449-1(1)) Dodo Pr.

Barkan, Joanne. Firefly's First Flight. Cook, Ande, illus. 2005. 12p. (J). 12.99 (978-0-7944-0612-7(2)) Reader's Digest Assn., Inc., The.

Bedford, William. The Glow-Worm Who Lost Her Glow. Joyce, Sophie, illus. 2005. (Blue Go Bananas Ser.). 38p. (J). (978-0-7787-2630-2(4)) Crabtree Publishing Co.

Black, Cassandra. Twinkle: A Chapter Book. 2003. 113p. (J). 7.99 (978-0-9742739-0-7(2)) Lavender Bks.

Brown, Elizabeth. Aristotle: the Firefly's Message. Schuna, Ramona, illus. 2007. 40p. pap. 19.95 (*978-1-59800-557-8(X)) Outskirts Press, Inc.

Carle, Eric. My Own Very Lonely Firefly Coloring Book. Carle, Eric, illus. 2006. 32p. (J). (ps). pap. 5.99 (978-0-399-24646-3(0) , Philomel) Penguin Group (USA) Inc.

—Shine with the Very Lonely Firefly. 2006. (World of Eric Carle Ser.). 16p. (J). (ps-1). pap. 4.99 (978-0-448-44422-2(4) , Grosset & Dunlap) Penguin Group (USA) Inc.

—The Very Lonely Firefly. 1999. (Illus.). 32p. (J). (ps-k). 11.99 (978-0-399-23427-9(6) , Philomel) Penguin Group (USA) Inc.

Catalano, Dominic. Mr. Basset Plays. 2004. (Illus.). 32p. (YA). (gr. k-2). pap. 7.95 (978-1-59078-314-6(X)) Boyds Mills Pr.

Connelly, Wendy. Fiona the Firefly! 2003. (Illus.). (J). 12.95 (978-1-929039-16-6(6)) Ambassador Bks., Inc.

Dean, Carol S. The Live Bale of Hay: A Real Maine Adventure. Dunn, Sandra, illus. 2005. 32p. (ps-ps). 15.95 (978-0-89272-674-5(1)) Down East Bks.

Gerber, Carole. Firefly Night. Husted, Marty, illus. 2000. 32p. (J). (ps-1). 16.95 (978-1-58089-051-9(2)); pap. 6.95 (978-1-58089-066-3(0)) Charlesbridge Publishing, Inc.

—Firefly Night. Husted, Marty, illus. 2000. (J). (ps-3). lib. bdg. 15.25 (978-0-613-35117-1(7)) Tandem Library Bks.

—Firefly Night. 2000. (J). (978-0-606-19687-1(0)) Tandem Library Bks.

Hardy, Lorién Trover. Firefly Summer. Yilmaz, Necdet, illus. 2007. (Read-It! Readers Ser.). (J). 19.93 (978-1-4048-2397-6(2)) Picture Window Bks.

Jennings, Patrick. The Lightning Bugs. Alter, Anna, illus. 2003. 56p. (J). (gr. k-3). tchr. ed. 15.95 (978-0-8234-1673-8(9)) Holiday Hse., Inc.

Klier, Kimberly. Firefly Friend. Garland, Michael, illus. 2004. (Rookie Reader Ser.). 32p. (J). 19.50 (978-0-516-25895-9(8) , Children's Pr.) Scholastic Library Publishing.

Klier, Kimberly Wagner. Firefly Friend. Garland, Michael, illus. 2005. 32p. (J). (gr. 1-2). lib. bdg. 12.15 (978-0-606-33169-2(7)) Tandem Library Bks.

Lewandowski, Lisa & Trost, Shannon. Darcy Daisy & the Firefly Festival: Learning about Bipolar Disorder & Community. Shaw-Peterson, Kimberly, illus. 2005. 32p. (J). pap. 9.95 (978-0-9785075-2-7(5) , Ferne Pr.) Nelson Publishing & Marketing.

London, Jonathan. When the Fireflies Come. Widener, Terry, illus. 2003. 32p. (J). (ps). 15.99 (978-0-525-45404-5(7) , Dutton Juvenile) Penguin Group (USA) Inc.

Lott, Cheryl Lynn. My Firefly Friends. 2003. 32p. (J). pap. 10.00 (978-0-8059-5533-0(X)) Dorrance Publishing Co., Inc.

Martin, Bill, Jr. & Sampson, Michael. The Little Squeegy Bug. Corrigan, Patrick, illus. 2001. 32p. (J). (ps-2). reprint ed. pap. 5.95 (978-0-7614-5243-0(5)) Cavendish, Marshall Corp.

Ochiltree, Dianne. It's a Firefly Night. Snyder, Betsy, illus. 2008. (J). (*978-1-55971-991-9(5) , NorthWord Bks. for Young Readers) T&N Children's Publishing.

Parks, Kathy, illus. Christmas with Night-Light. 2006. 18p. (J). bds. 8.99 (978-0-7847-1522-2(X) , 04413) Standard Publishing.

Pfeffer, Wendy. Firefly at Stony Brook Farm. Mikec, Larry, illus. 2005. (Smithsonian's Backyard Ser.). 32p. (J). (ps-2). 4.99 (978-1-59249-283-1(5) , B5076); 15.95 (978-1-59249-282-4(7) , B5026); pap. 6.95 (978-1-59249-284-8(3) , S5026) Soundprints.

Pinczes, Elinor J. My Full Moon Is Square. Enos, Randall, illus. 2002. 32p. (J). (gr. k-3). tchr. ed. 15.00 (978-0-618-15489-0(2)) Houghton Mifflin Co. Trade & Reference Div.

Plotkin, Victor. The Immortal Firefly. 2004. (J). pap. 7.95 (978-0-533-14801-1(4)) Vantage Pr., Inc.

Porter, Todd. Firefly Fred. 2004. (Illus.). 36p. (J). 19.95 (978-1-932278-00-2(1)) Mayhaven Publishing.

Raye, Donna. Edison the Firefly: And His Buddy Bell. 2007. (J). pap. 7.99 (*978-1-60247-097-2(9)) Tate Publishing & Enterprises, L.L.C.

Rogers, Pamela Sue. Gods Creatures Freddie the Firefly Unexp. 2006. pap. 29.99 (*978-1-4259-6037-7(5)) AuthorHouse.

Sargent, Dave & Sargent, Pat. Lizzy Lightning Bug, 10, 17. Robinson, Laura, illus. 2004. (Learn to Read Ser.: 10). 18p. (J). lib. bdg. 19.95 (978-1-56763-829-5(5)); lib. bdg. 9.95 (978-1-56763-830-1(9)) Ozark Publishing.

—Lizzy Lightning Bug/Lizzy la Luciérnaga, 10. Robinson, Laura, illus. 2004. (Learn to Read Ser.: 10). (ENG & SPA.). 18p. (J). pap. 9.95 (978-1-56763-994-0(1)) Ozark Publishing.

Sudduth, Brent H. Buster. Spengler, Kenneth J., illus. (J). 2003. 32p. 15.95 (978-1-59034-478-1(2)); 2002. pap. (978-1-59034-477-4(4)) Mondo Publishing.

Tarver, Monroe S. Little Light Shine Bright. Tarver, Monroe S., illus. l.t. ed. 2004. (Illus.). 32p. (J). 6.99 (978-0-9743568-4-6(0)) Tarver, Monroe.

Thomas, Patricia. Firefly Mountain. Sylvada, Peter, illus. 2007. 32p. (J). (gr. k-2). 16.95 (*978-1-56145-360-3(9) , Peachtree Junior) Peachtree Pubs., Ltd.

Thong, Roseanne. Ten Friendly Fireflies. 2007. 20p. 11.95 (*978-1-58117-561-5(2)) Dalmatian Pr.

Winnick, Karen B. The Night of the Fireflies. Ito, Yoriko, illus. 2004. 32p. (J). (ps up). 15.95 (978-1-56397-725-1(7)) Boyds Mills Pr.

FIREMEN

see Fire Fighters

FIRES

see also Fire Extinction; Fire Prevention; Forest Fires

Armentrout, David & Armentrout, Patricia. Fires. 2007. (Illus.). 32p. (J). (978-1-60044-231-5(5)) Rourke Publishing, LLC.

Barber, Nicky. Fire & Flood. 1999. (Natural Disasters Ser.). (Illus.). 31p. (J). (gr. 5 up). pap. 5.95 (978-0-7641-1058-0(6)) Barron's Educational Series, Inc.

Bredeson, Carmen. Fire in Oakland, California: Billion-Dollar Blaze. 1999. (American Disasters Ser.). (Illus.). 48p. (YA). (gr. 4-10). lib. bdg. 23.93 (978-0-7660-1220-2(4)) Enslow Pubs., Inc.

Brunelle, Lynn. Earthquake! The 1906 San Francisco Nightmare. 2005. (X-Treme Disasters That Changed America Ser.). (J). lib. bdg. 25.27 (978-1-59716-008-7(3)) Bearport Publishing Co., Inc.

Burgan, Michael. The Great San Francisco Earthquake & Fire. 2008. (J). (*978-1-4296-0155-9(8)) Capstone Pr., Inc.

Chippendale, Lisa. San Francisco Earthquake of 1906. 2000. (Great Disasters Ser.). (Illus.). 112p. (J). (gr. 5-9). 30.00 (978-0-7910-5270-9(2) , Chelsea Hse.) Facts On File, Inc.

Ford, Jean. Explosives & Arson Investigation. 2006. (Forensics, the Science of Crime-Solving Ser.). (Illus.). 112p. (YA). (gr. 7 up). 22.95 (978-1-4222-0034-6(5)) Mason Crest Pubs.

Ganeri, Anita. Forest Furnace 6-Pack. 2004. (Turbulent Planet Ser.). (Illus.). (J). pap. 45.90 (978-1-4109-1031-8(8)) Raintree.

Gentle, Victor & Perry, Janet. Fires. 2001. (Natural Disasters Ser.). (Illus.). 24p. (J). (gr. 2 up). lib. bdg. 22.00 (978-0-8368-2833-7(X)) Stevens, Gareth Inc.

Haas, Jessie. Fire! My Parents' Story. 1998. (Illus.). 72p. (YA). (gr. 3 up). 15.00 (978-0-688-15203-1(1)) HarperCollins Pubs.

Kelley, Alison Turnbull. First to Arrive: Firefighters at Ground Zero. 2002. (United We Stand Ser.). (Illus.). 64p. (gr. 6-12). 25.00 (978-0-7910-6957-8(5) , Chelsea Hse.) Facts On File, Inc.

Kyi, Tanya Lloyd. Fires! 2004. (True Stories from the Edge Ser.). (Illus.). 112p. (J). (gr. 3). 18.95 (978-1-55037-877-1(5)); pap. 8.95 (978-1-55037-876-4(7)) Annick Pr., Ltd. CAN. *Dist:* Firefly Bks., Ltd.

Landau, Elaine. Fires. (Watts Library). (Illus.). 64p. (gr. 5-7). 2000. (J). pap. 8.95 (978-0-531-16423-5(3)); 1999. (YA). 25.50 (978-0-531-20343-9(3)) Scholastic Library Publishing. (Watts, Franklin).

—Fires. 1999. (gr. 3-6). lib. bdg. 17.60 (978-0-613-29427-0(0)) Tandem Library Bks.

Lieurance, Suzanne. The Triangle Shirtwaist Fire & Sweatshop Reform in American History. 2003. (In American History Ser.). (Illus.). 128p. (J). (gr. 5-12). lib. bdg. 26.60 (978-0-7660-1839-6(3)) Enslow Pubs., Inc.

McHugh, Janet. The Great Chicago Fire. 2007. (Code Red Ser.). (Illus.). 32p. (J). lib. bdg. 25.27 (978-1-59716-360-6(0)) Bearport Publishing Co., Inc.

Murphy, Jim. The Great Fire. 2006. 144p. (J). pap. 8.99 (978-0-439-20307-4(4) , Scholastic Paperbacks) Scholastic, Inc.

Nobleman, Marc Tyler. The Great Chicago Fire. 2005. (We the People Ser.). (Illus.). 48p. (J). (gr. 4-6). (978-0-7565-1263-7(8) , 1244096) Compass Point Bks.

Nobleman, Marc Tyler. The San Francisco Earthquake of 1906. 2006. 48p. (J). (*978-0-7565-2460-9(1)) Compass Point Bks.

Olson, Kay Melchisedech. The Great Chicago Fire of 1871. Miller, Phil & Barnett, Charles, illus. 2006. (Graphic Library). 32p. (J). (978-0-7368-5480-1(0)) Capstone Pr., Inc.

Robson, Pam. The Great Fire of London 1666. Marwood, Dez, illus. 2nd ed. 2003. 48p. pap. (978-0-7500-1935-4(2) , Hodder Wayland) Hodder Children's Division.

Schaefer, A. R. The Triangle Shirtwaist Factory Fire. 2003. (Landmark Events in American History Ser.). (Illus.). 48p. (J). (gr. 5 up). pap. 14.95 (978-0-8368-5411-4(X) , World Almanac Library) Stevens, Gareth Inc.

Scher, Linda. The Texas City Disaster. 2007. (Code Red Ser.). (Illus.). 32p. (J). (gr. 3-7). lib. bdg. 25.27 (978-1-59716-363-7(5)) Bearport Publishing Co., Inc.

Simon, Seymour. Wildfires. 2000. (Illus.). (J). (gr. k-3). lib. bdg. 13.79 (978-0-606-22856-5(X)) Tandem Library Bks.

Sipiera, Paul P. & Sipiera, Diane M. Wildfires. 1998. (True Bks.). (Illus.). 48p. (J). (gr. 3-5). 25.00 (978-0-516-20682-0(6) , Children's Pr.) Scholastic Library Publishing.

Stein, R. Conrad. The Great Chicago Fire. 2007. (Cornerstones of Freedomtrade;, Second Ser.). 48p. (J). pap. 5.95 (*978-0-531-18766-1(7) , Children's Pr.) Scholastic Library Publishing.

Tanaka, Shelley. Earthquake! A Day That Changed America. Craig, David, illus. 2006. 48p. (J). (gr. 4-8). reprint ed. 17.00 (978-1-4223-5635-7(3)) DIANE Publishing Co.

VandeCreek, Drew E. The Great Chicago Fire. 2007. (Essential Events Ser.). (ENG., Illus.). 112p. (YA). (gr. 8-12). lib. bdg. 32.79 (*978-1-59928-851-2(6) , Essential Library) ABDO Publishing Co.

Willett, Edward. Fires & Wildfires. 2005. (Library of Emergency Preparedness). (Illus.). 64p. (J). (978-1-4042-0532-1(2)) Rosen Publishing Group, Inc., The.

Woods, Michael & Woods, Mary B. Fires. 2007. (Disasters up Close Ser.). (Illus.). 64p. (J). 27.93 (978-0-8225-4713-6(9) , Lerner Pubns.) Lerner Publishing Group.

FIRES—FICTION

Auerbach, Annie. Three-Alarm Fire! Ewers, Joe & Mitchell, Steve, illus. 2003. (Matchbox Ser.). 24p. (J). pap. 3.50 (978-0-689-85897-0(3) , Little Simon) Simon & Schuster Children's Publishing.

Blazin' Hot: Coloring/Activity Book (English) Incl. Stickers. 2007. (J). (*978-1-933934-51-8(4)) Educational Adventures.

Blazin' Hot: Picture Book (English) NL 9x9 with Snipe. 2007. (J). (*978-1-933934-46-4(8)) Educational Adventures.

Brown, Marc. Arthur's Fire Drill. Brown, Marc, illus. 2000. (Arthur Ser.). (Illus.). 24p. (J). (gr. k-3). pap. 3.99 (978-0-679-88476-7(9) , Random Hse. Bks. for Young Readers) Random Hse. Children's Bks.

—Arthur's Fire Drill. 2000. (Arthur Ser.). (ps-2). lib. bdg. 11.80 (978-0-613-46251-8(3)) Tandem Library Bks.

Cash, Rosanne. Penelope Jane: A Fairy's Tale. Karas, G. Brian, illus. 2006. 32p. (J). pap. 6.99 (978-0-06-084230-7(X) , Harper Trophy) HarperCollins Pubs.

Duey, Kathleen & Bale, Karen A. Fire, Chicago, 1871. 1998. (Survival! Ser.: No. 4). (J). (gr. 4-7). (978-0-606-13828-4(5)) Tandem Library Bks.

Ehlert, Lois. Cuckoo/Cucu: A Mexican Folktale/Un Cuento Folklorico Mexicano. Andujar, Gloria de Aragon, illus. 2000. (SPA & ENG.). 36p. (J). (ps-3). pap. 7.00 (978-0-15-202428-4(X) , Voyager Bks./Libros Viajeros) Harcourt Children's Bks.

Enderle, Dotti. Playing with Fire. Leuthner, Sandy, ed. 2003. (Fortune Tellers Club Ser.: Bk. 2). (Illus.). 160p. pap. 4.99 (978-0-7387-0340-4(0)) Llewellyn Pubns.

—Playing with Fire: Fortune Tellers Club. 2003. (gr. 3-6). lib. bdg. 13.00 (978-0-613-90789-7(2)) Tandem Library Bks.

Ferber, Brenda A. Julia's Kitchen. 2006. (Illus.). 160p. (J). 16.00 (978-0-374-39932-0(8)) Farrar, Straus & Giroux.

Fire Safe! Life Safety Coloring/Activity Book. 2007. (Illus.). (J). (*978-1-933934-23-5(9)) Educational Adventures.

Good, Merle. Reuben & the Fire. Moss, P. Buckley, illus. 2003. (Bestselling Children's Book Ser.). 32p. (J). (ps-3). 14.95 (978-1-56148-091-3(6)) Good Bks.

Griessman, Annette. The Fire. Gore, Leonid, illus. 2005. 32p. (J). (ps-3). 16.99 (978-0-399-24019-5(5) , Putnam Juvenile) Penguin Group (USA) Inc.

Gunnery, Sylvia. Out of Bounds. 2004. (Sports Stories Ser.). 104p. (J). (gr. 3-8). 7.95 (978-1-55028-826-1(1)); (*978-1-55028-827-8(X)) Lorimer, James & Co., Ltd., Pubs. CAN. *Dist:* Casemate Pubs. & Bk. Distributors, LLC.

Harshman, Marc. A Little Excitement. Rand, Ted, illus. 2002. 32p. (J). per. 6.95 (978-1-891852-21-3(3)) Quarrier Pr.

Hopkinson, Deborah. Into the Firestorm: A Novel of San Francisco, 1906. 2006. 208p. (J). (gr. 3-7). 15.95 (978-0-375-83652-7(7)); lib. bdg. 17.99 (978-0-375-93652-4(1)) Random Hse. Children's Bks. (Knopf Bks. for Young Readers).

Hopkinson, Deborah. Into the Firestorm: A Novel of San Francisco 1906. 2008. 208p. (J). (gr. 4-7). 5.99 (*978-0-440-42129-0(2) , Yearling) Random Hse. Children's Bks.

Janeczko, Paul B. Worlds Afire: The Hartford Circus Fire of 1944. 2004. 112p. (J). (gr. 7 up). 15.99 (978-0-7636-2235-0(4)) Candlewick Pr.

Martin, Rafe. The Brave Little Parrot. Gaber, Susan, illus. 1998. 1p. (J). (ps-3). 16.99 (978-0-399-22825-4(X) , Putnam Juvenile) Penguin Group (USA) Inc.

Moore, Nancy Ann. The Safety Scouts: Fire Call. 2000. mass mkt. 4.50 (978-1-931179-41-6(7)) Long Hill Productions, Inc.

Peterson, Elizabeth J. Christina & the Little Red Bird. Mcknight, C. D., illus. 1999. 23p. (J). (ps-5). reprint ed. spiral bd. 5.95 (978-0-938911-02-9(3)) Individualized Education Systems/Poppy Lane Publishing.

Reynolds, Marilynn. The Prairie Fire. Kilby, Don, illus. 2001. 32p. (J). (ps-2). 6.95 (978-1-55143-175-8(0)) Orca Bk. Pubs. USA.

Robinet, Harriette Gillem. Children of the Fire. 2001. (Illus.). 144p. (J). (gr. 3-7). pap. 5.99 (978-0-689-83968-9(5) , Aladdin) Simon & Schuster Children's Publishing.

Rucker, Mike. Terry & the Wild Well Blowout. 2002. (Terry the Tractor Ser.: Vol. 10). (Illus.). 72p. (J). (gr. k-4). pap. 3.95 (978-0-9711659-1-5(2)) Univ. Editions.

Schultz, Jan Neubert. Firestorm. 2003. (Adventures in Time Ser.). 204p. (YA). (gr. 4-7). 15.95 (978-0-87614-276-9(5) , Carolrhoda Bks.) Lerner Publishing Group.

Shaw, Janet Beeler. Changes for Kaya. 2002. (gr. 3-6). lib. bdg. 14.10 (978-0-613-46214-3(9)) Tandem Library Bks.

—Changes for Kaya Bk. 6: A Winter Story. Farnsworth, Bill & McAliley, Susan, illus. 2002. (American Girls Collection: Bk. 6). 80p. (gr. 2-7). (J). 12.95 (978-1-58485-434-0(0)); 6.95 (978-1-58485-433-3(2)) American Girl Publishing, Inc.

Spinelli, Eileen. Hero Cat. McAllister Stammen, Jo Ellen, illus. 2006. 32p. (J). 16.95 (978-0-7614-5223-2(0)) Cavendish, Marshall Corp.

Sula, Sondra. The Expanders: Quest for the Flubulator. 2000. mass mkt. 8.95 (978-1-931179-11-9(5)) Long Hill Productions, Inc.

—The Expanders: Quest for the Flubulator. Johnson, Terri L., illus. 2000. 32p. (J). (gr. 1-3). pap. (978-0-9701450-2-4(0)) Long Hill Productions, Inc.

Welling, Peter J. Darlene Halloween & the Great Chicago Fire. Welling, Peter J., illus. 2007. 32p. (J). (gr. k-3). 15.95 (*978-1-58980-479-1(1)) Pelican Publishing Co., Inc.

Welsh, T. K. The Unresolved. 2006. 160p. (YA). (gr. 9). 16.99 (978-0-525-47731-0(4) , Dutton Juvenile) Penguin Group (USA) Inc.

FIREWORKS

Cobb, Vicki. Fireworks. 2006. (Where's the Science Here? Ser.). (Illus.). 48p. (J). (gr. 3-5). 23.93 (978-0-7613-2771-4(1) , Millbrook Pr.) Lerner Publishing Group.

Firestone, Mary. Pyrotechnician. 2005. (Weird Careers in Science Ser.). (Illus.). 69p. (J). (gr. 4-8). lib. bdg. 25.00 (978-0-7910-8703-9(4) , Chelsea Hse.) Facts On File, Inc.

Mingo, Jack. Firecrackers: The Art & History. 2000. (gr. 7-12). lib. bdg. 30.35 (978-0-613-45140-6(6)) Tandem Library Bks.

Rocker, Megan. How It Happens at the Fireworks Factory. Wolfe, Bob & Wolfe, Diane, photos by. 2004. (How It Happens Ser.). (Illus.). 32p. (J). (gr. 2-5). lib. bdg. 19.95 (978-1-881508-97-7(8)) Oliver Pr., Inc.

Thomas, Isabel. Fireworks! 2006. (Illus.). 32p. (J). (978-1-4109-2589-3(7)) Steck-Vaughn.

FIREWORKS—FICTION

Clark, Karen. Flash, Bang, Wheee! White, Ian, illus. 2004. (CZE, VIE, SPA, GUJ & PER.). 24p. (J). (978-1-85269-280-3(4)); (978-1-85269-350-3(9)); (978-1-85269-351-0(7)); (978-1-85269-352-7(5)); (978-1-85269-353-4(3)); (978-1-85269-355-8(X)); (978-1-85269-356-5(8)); (978-1-85269-374-9(6)); (978-1-85269-430-2(0)); (978-1-85269-431-9(9)); (978-1-85269-432-6(7)); (978-1-85269-433-3(5)); (978-1-85269-434-0(3)); (978-1-85269-435-7(1)); (978-1-85269-437-1(8)); (978-1-85269-438-8(6)) Mantra Publishing, Ltd.

—Flash Bang Wheee! White, Ian, illus. 2004. (J). (CHI & ENG.). (978-1-85269-678-8(8)); (ENG & VIE.). (978-1-85269-808-9(X)) Mantra Publishing, Ltd.

Clark, Karen & White, Ian, illus. Flash, Bang, Wheee! Bing, Bang, Boum! 2004. (CZE, VIE, SPA, GUJ & PER.). 24p. (J). (978-1-85269-354-1(1)) Mantra Publishing, Ltd.

—Flash, Bang, Wheee! Shkreptime, Gjemim Dhe Vershellime! 2004. (CZE, VIE, SPA, GUJ & PER.). 24p. (J). (978-1-85269-349-7(5)) Mantra Publishing, Ltd.

Damitz, Charlie. The Shot Not Heard Around the World. 1999. 86p. (YA). (gr. 5 up). 9.99 (978-0-88092-440-5(3) , 4403) Royal Fireworks Publishing Co.

Dowling, Paul. The Night Journey. 2003. 12p. (J). 7.95 (978-1-57717-290-1(6)) New Line Bks.

Jane, Hale. Boomland. 2003. (Land Ser.: 4). 240p. (J). per. 12.95 (978-0-934426-20-6(1)) NAPSAC Reproductions.

Pullman, Philip. The Firework-Maker's Daughter. 1999. 120p. (J). 16.95 (978-0-7540-6055-0(1) , Galaxy Children's Large Print) BBC Audiobooks America.

—The Firework-Maker's Daughter. Gallagher, Susan Saelig, illus. 1999. (J). pap. (978-0-590-12943-5(0) , Levine, Arthur A. Bks.) Scholastic, Inc.

Wilde, Oscar. El Famoso Cohete. Zwerger, Lisbeth, illus. (SPA.). 72p. (J). (978-84-392-8693-6(7)) Gaviota Ediciones ESP. *Dist:* Lectorum Pubns., Inc.

E
F
G

FIRST AID

American Academy of Pediatrics Staff, contrib. by. Babysitter Lessons & Safety Training. 2nd rev. ed. 2006. (Illus.). 75p. pap. 5.95 (978-0-7637-3516-6(7)) Jones & Bartlett Pubs., Inc.

Berry, Joy Wilt. Let's Talk about Getting Hurt. Smith, Maggie, tr. Smith, Maggie, illus. 2002. (J). (978-0-439-34165-3(5)) Scholastic, Inc.

Boelts, Maribeth & Boelts, Darwin. Kids to the Rescue! First Aid Techniques for Kids. Megale, Marina, illus. rev. ed. 2003. 72p. (J). 18.95 (978-1-884734-79-3(0)); pap. 8.95 (978-1-884734-78-6(2)) Parenting Pr., Inc.

Burles, Kenneth T. & Hundley, David H. Bruises. 1998. (Learning about Your Health Ser.). (Illus.). 32p. (J). (gr. 2-5). lib. bdg. 26.60 (978-1-57103-254-6(1)) Rourke Publishing, LLC.

Canizares, Susan & Chanko, Pamela. First Aid. 1999. (Learning Center Emergent Readers Ser.). (J). pap. 2.50 (978-0-439-04590-2(8)) Scholastic, Inc.

Emergency Medical Technicians: Individual Title Six-Packs. (On Deck Ser.). 24p. (gr. 4-5). 35.00 (978-0-7578-1026-8(8)) Rigby Education.

Farrow, Peter. Soccer. 2003. (Sports Injuries Ser.). (Illus.). 64p. (J). lib. bdg. (978-1-59084-637-7(0)) Mason Crest Pubs.

First Aid & Home Safety. (YA). (gr. 6-12). pap. 10.95 (978-0-8224-4366-7(X)) Globe Fearon Educational Publishing.

Fryer, Jane Eayre. The Mary Frances' First Aid Book. 2000. (Illus.). 144p. (J). 28.00 (978-1-891656-29-3(5), LE93) Lacis Pubns.

Furgang, Kathy. Frequently Asked Questions about Sports Injuries. 2007. (J). (***978-1-4042-1933-5(1)***) Rosen Publishing Group, Inc., The.

Gale, Karen Buhler. The Kids' Guide to First Aid: All about Bruises, Burns, Stings, Sprains, & Other Ouches. Kline, Michael P., illus. 2002. (Kids Can Bks.). 128p. (J). (gr. 4 up). pap. 12.95 (978-1-885593-58-0(9), Williamson Bks.) Ideals Pubns.

Gordon, Melanie Apel. Let's Talk about Scratches, Scrapes & Bug Bites. 2000. (Let's Talk Library). (Illus.). 24p. (J). (gr. 3). lib. bdg. 18.75 (978-0-8239-5416-2(1), PowerKids Pr.) Rosen Publishing Group, Inc., The.

Gordon, Melanie Apel, et al, contrib. by. Let's Talk about Poison Ivy. 2000. (Let's Talk Library). (Illus.). 24p. (J). (gr. 3). lib. bdg. 18.75 (978-0-8239-5415-5(3), PowerKids Pr.) Rosen Publishing Group, Inc., The.

Gordon, Sharon. Bruises. 2002. (Rookie Read-About Health Ser.). (Illus.). 32p. (J). (gr. k-2). pap. 5.95 (978-0-516-26872-9(4), Children's Pr.) Scholastic Library Publishing.

—Bruises. 2002. (gr. k-3). lib. bdg. 14.10 (978-0-613-50670-0(7)) Tandem Library Bks.

—Cuts & Scrapes. 2002. (Rookie Read-About Health Ser.). (Illus.). 32p. (J). (gr. k-2). pap. 5.95 (978-0-516-26870-5(8)); 20.50 (978-0-516-22566-1(9)) Scholastic Library Publishing. (Children's Pr.).

—Cuts & Scrapes. 2002. (gr. k-3). lib. bdg. 14.10 (978-0-613-50677-9(4)) Tandem Library Bks.

Green, M. I. Primeros Auxilios para Ninos (First Aid for Children) (SPA., Illus.). 192p. (J). pap. 10.50 (978-968-416-411-6(4), FN4114) Fernandez USA Publishing.

Hewitt, Sally. Happy Doctor. Cameron, Craig, illus. 2003. 14p. (J). pap. 10.95 (978-1-57145-734-9(8), Silver Dolphin Bks.) Advantage Pubs. Group.

Lennard-Brown, Sarah. Sports Injuries. 2004. (Health Issues Ser.). (Illus.). 64p. (J). 28.56 (978-0-7398-6892-8(6)) Harcourt Schl. Pubs.

Llewellyn, Claire. The Kid's Survival Guide. 2002. (Illus.). 96p. (J). pap. 9.95 (978-0-439-35325-0(4)) Scholastic, Inc.

Longnecker, Steve. Steve Longenecker's Wilderness Emergency Medical Aid Book for Kids & Their Adults. Lee, Frank, illus. 2005. 176p. (YA). (gr. 5 up). pap. 16.95 (978-1-889596-18-1(3)) Milestone Pr., Inc.

MacNab, Chris. Weight Training. 2003. (Sports Injuries Ser.). (Illus.). 64p. (J). lib. bdg. (978-1-59084-641-4(9)) Mason Crest Pubs.

McCoy, Lisa. Cheerleading. 2003. (Sports Injuries Ser.). (Illus.). 64p. (J). lib. bdg. (978-1-59084-628-5(1)) Mason Crest Pubs.

—Lacrosse. 2003. (Sports Injuries Ser.). (Illus.). 64p. (J). lib. bdg. (978-1-59084-636-0(2)) Mason Crest Pubs.

McEwen, Rebecca. First Aid for You. 2004. (Spyglass Books). (Illus.). 24p. (J). (gr. 1 up). lib. bdg. 18.60 (978-0-7565-0623-0(9)) Compass Point Bks.

McNab, Chris. Gymnastics. 2003. (Sports Injuries Ser.). (Illus.). 64p. (J). lib. bdg. (978-1-59084-633-9(8)) Mason Crest Pubs.

—Track. 2003. (Sports Injuries Ser.). (Illus.). 64p. (J). lib. bdg. (978-1-59084-638-4(9)) Mason Crest Pubs.

Olson, Karen. Cooper Gets a CT Scan. Pritchett and Hull Associates, Inc., illus. 2002. (J). 4.50 (978-0-939838-87-5(7)) Pritchett & Hull Assocs., Inc.

Royston, Angela. Bumps & Bruises. 2004. (Illus.). 32p. (J). lib. bdg. (978-1-4034-4823-1(X)) Heinemann Library.

—Stings & Bites. 2004. (Illus.). 32p. (J). lib. bdg. (978-1-4034-4826-2(4)) Heinemann Library.

Schnapp, Eric Cesar, et al. First Aid Clueless: An Emergency Guide for Young People. 2003. (YA). per. 8.95 (978-0-9719337-3-6(1)) Elma Colletes & Sons.

Shannon, Joyce Brennfleck, ed. Sports Injuries Information for Teens: Health Tips about Sports Injuries & Injury Prevention. 2003. (Teen Health Ser.). (Illus.). 405p. (gr. 7 up). (978-0-7808-0447-0(3)) Omnigraphics, Inc.

Silverstein, Alvin. Burns & Blisters. 2002. (gr. 3-6). lib. bdg. 15.25 (978-0-613-53974-6(5)) Tandem Library Bks.

Silverstein, Alvin, et al. Burns & Blisters. 2002. (My Health Ser.). (Illus.). 48p. (J). (gr. 3-5). 25.50 (978-0-531-11871-9(1), Watts, Franklin) Scholastic Library Publishing.

—Cuts, Scrapes, Scabs, & Scars. (My Health Ser.). (Illus.). 48p. (J). (gr. 3-5). 2000. pap. 6.95 (978-0-531-16411-2(X)); 1999. 25.50 (978-0-531-11582-4(8)) Scholastic Library Publishing. (Watts, Franklin).

Sliverstein, Alvin. Cuts, Scrapes, Scabs, & Scars. 1999. (gr. 3-6). lib. bdg. 15.25 (978-0-613-31102-1(7)) Tandem Library Bks.

Streeter, Michael. Ice Skating. 2003. (Sports Injuries Ser.). (Illus.). 64p. (J). lib. bdg. (978-1-59084-635-3(4)) Mason Crest Pubs.

Wright, John. Baseball. 2003. (Sports Injuries Ser.). (Illus.). 64p. (J). lib. bdg. (978-1-59084-626-1(5)) Mason Crest Pubs.

—Basketball. 2003. (Sports Injuries Ser.). (Illus.). 64p. (J). lib. bdg. (978-1-59084-627-8(3)) Mason Crest Pubs.

—Equestrian Sport. 2003. (Sports Injuries Ser.). (Illus.). 64p. (J). lib. bdg. (978-1-59084-629-2(X)) Mason Crest Pubs.

—Hockey. 2003. (Sports Injuries Ser.). (Illus.). 64p. (J). lib. bdg. (978-1-59084-634-6(6)) Mason Crest Pubs.

FIRST AID—FICTION

Chipponeri, Kelli. Ouch! Bye Bye, Boo-Boos. Gott, Barry, illus. 2002. 14p. (J). pap. 5.99 (978-0-689-84931-2(1), Little Simon) Simon & Schuster Children's Publishing.

Marsh, Carole. The Adventure Diaries of Li, the Excellent EMT!, 7 vols. 2004. 48p. (J). (gr. 1-4). pap. 5.95 (978-0-635-01145-9(X)) Gallopade International.

Teitelbaum, Michael. If I Could Drive an Ambulance! Mones, Marc & Mones, Isidre, illus. 2003. (Tonka Ser.). 24p. (J). (ps-2). pap. 3.50 (978-0-439-43433-1(5)) Scholastic, Inc.

—If I Could Drive an Ambulance! 2003. (gr. k-3). lib. bdg. 11.25 (978-0-613-67095-1(7)) Tandem Library Bks.

FIRST DAY OF SCHOOL

Busic, Valerie. Jason's First Day. OI Foundation, ed. Meyers, Jeff, illus. l.t. ed. 2004. 48p. per. 8.50 (978-0-9642189-4-9(1)) Osteogenesis Imperfecta Foundation.

Civardi, Anne. Going to School. Cartwright, Stephen, illus. 2005. 16p. (J). pap. 4.95 (978-0-7945-1008-4(6), Usborne) EDC Publishing.

The First Day of School: Kindergarten Big Books. (On Our Way to English Ser.). (gr. k up). 29.95 (978-0-7578-1614-7(2)) Rigby Education.

The First Day of School: Small Versions of Big Books. (On Our Way to English Ser.). (gr. k up). 29.00 (978-0-7578-7221-1(2)) Rigby Education.

Hughes, Monica. First Day at School. 2003. (Raintree Sprouts Ser.). (Illus.). 24p. (J). pap. 5.50 (978-1-4109-0669-4(8)) Raintree.

—First Day at School. 2003. (ps-2). lib. bdg. 13.55 (978-0-613-78205-0(4)) Tandem Library Bks.

—My First Day at School. 2003. (Raintree Sprouts Ser.). (Illus.). 24p. (J). lib. bdg. 18.56 (978-1-4109-0643-4(4)) Raintree.

Jackson, Ellen B. It's Back to School We Go! First Day Stories Fro Around the World. Ellis, Jan Davey, illus. 2003. 32p. lib. bdg. 23.90 (978-0-7613-2562-8(X), Millbrook Pr.) Lerner Publishing Group.

—It's Back to School We Go! First Day Stories from Around the World. Ellis, Jan Davey, illus. 2003. 32p. (J). 15.95 (978-0-7613-1948-1(4), Millbrook Pr.) Lerner Publishing Group.

Radabaugh, Melinda Beth. Going to School. 2003. (First Time Ser.). (Illus.). 24p. (ps-1). (J). lib. bdg. 18.50 (978-1-4034-0227-1(2)); pap. 5.25 (978-1-4034-0466-4(6)) Heinemann Library.

Steck-Vaughn Staff. Feelings. 2000. pap. (978-0-7398-4475-5(X)) Steck-Vaughn.

—First Day of School. 2000. pap. (978-0-7398-4490-8(3)) Steck-Vaughn.

Usborne Books. Going to School Kid Kit. 2005. 16p. (J). pap. 9.99 (978-1-58086-846-4(0), Usborne) EDC Publishing.

FIRST DAY OF SCHOOL—FICTION

Adler, David A. Cam Jansen & the First Day of School Mystery, Vol. 22. Natti, Susanna, illus. 2002. (Cam Jansen Ser.: No. 22). 80p. (J). 13.99 (978-0-670-03575-5(0), Viking Juvenile) Penguin Group (USA) Inc.

Alexandria, Shalayne. Nyville High No. 1: Welcome to Nyville. 2007. 124p. (YA). per. 4.99 (***978-0-9786180-1-8(7)***) 5 Muses Publishing.

Allyson, Libby. Scottie Rides the Bus. 2004. 27p. pap. 14.95 (978-1-4137-3298-6(4)) PublishAmerica, Inc.

Anholt, Laurence. Billy & the Big New School. 1999. (gr. k-3). lib. bdg. 16.40 (978-0-613-62597-5(8)) Tandem Library Bks.

—Billy & the Big New School. Anholt, Catherine, illus. 2004. (Concept Book Ser.). 32p. (J). (ps-1). pap. 7.95 (978-0-8075-0744-5(X)) Whitman, Albert & Co.

Armstrong-Ellis, Carey. Seymour Slug Starts School. 2005. (Illus.). 32p. (J). (ps-3). 14.95 (978-0-8109-5779-4(5), Abrams Bks. for Young Readers) Abrams, Harry N., Inc.

Asher Penny. My First Day of School. 2006. 32p. 12.95 (978-0-9755902-2-5(7)) Change Is Strange, Inc.

Bader, Bonnie & West, Tracey. First Day Fright. Molnar, Albert, illus. 2000. (Spooky School Ser.). 28p. (J). (978-0-439-21553-4(6)) Scholastic, Inc.

Bienvenido a nuestra escuela - el primer día de escuela de Katy (Teacher Guide) Fiction-to-Fact Big Book Pairs. 2004. (SPA.). instr.'s gde. ed. 12.95 (978-1-4108-2370-0(9)) Benchmark Education Co.

Blomberg, Dianne L. Sam & Gram & the First Day of School. Ulrich, George, illus. 1999. 32p. (J). (ps-1). (978-1-55798-562-0(6), 441-5626, Magination Pr.) American Psychological Assn.

Bloom, Suzanne. The Bus for Us. 2003. (Illus.). 32p. (J). (gr. k-2). 13.95 (978-1-56397-932-3(2)) Boyds Mills Pr.

Borden, Louise. Off to First Grade. Schindler, S. D., illus. 2007. 40p. (J). (***978-0-689-87395-9(6)***, McElderry, Margaret K.) Simon & Schuster Children's Publishing.

Bourgeois, Paulette. Franklin Va a la Escuela. Lopez Varela, Alejandra, tr. from ENG. Clark, Brenda, illus. 1998. (Franklin Ser.). (SPA.). 32p. (J). (ps-3). pap. 5.95 (978-1-880507-41-4(2), LC7792) Lectorum Pubns., Inc.

Bourgeois, Paulette & Moore, Eva. Franklin's First Day of School. Clark, Brenda, illus. 2000. (Franklin Ser.). 12p. (J). (ps-3). bds. 5.99 (978-0-439-20298-5(1)) Scholastic, Inc.

Brillhart, Julie. Molly Rides the School Bus. 2002. (Illus.). 32p. (J). (ps-2). 15.95 (978-0-8075-5210-0(0)) Whitman, Albert & Co.

Brown, Marc. Arthur's Back-to-School Surprise. 2002. (Arthur Ser.). (Illus.). 24p. (J). (gr. k-3). pap. 3.99 (978-0-375-81000-8(5)); lib. bdg. 11.99 (978-0-375-91000-5(X)) Random Hse. Children's Bks. (Random Hse. Bks. for Young Readers).

Carlson, Nancy. Look Out Kindergarten, Here I Come! (Preparante, Kindergarten, Alla Voy!) 1999. (Illus.). 32p. (J). (ps up). 15.99 (978-0-670-88378-3(6), Viking Juvenile) Penguin Group (USA) Inc.

Carlson, Nancy L. First Grade, Here I Come! Carlson, Nancy L., illus. 2006. (Illus.). 32p. (J). (ps-1). 15.99 (978-0-670-06127-3(1), Viking Adult) Penguin Group (USA) Inc.

—First Grade, Here I Come! 2006. (Illus.). (J). (***978-1-4156-8114-5(7)***, Viking Adult) Penguin Group (USA) Inc.

Carson, Jana. We Both Read-Stop Teasing Taylor! Treatner, Meryl, illus. 2005. (We Both Read Ser.). 44p. (J). (gr. 1-2). 7.99 (978-1-891327-61-2(5)); pap. 3.99 (978-1-891327-62-9(3)) Treasure Bay, Inc.

Child, Lauren. I Am Too Absolutely Small for School. Child, Lauren, illus. (Illus.). 32p. (J). (ps-1). 2004. 16.99 (978-0-7636-2403-3(9)); 2005. reprint ed. pap. 6.99 (978-0-7636-2887-1(5)) Candlewick Pr.

Chips, Nathan. Winston's First Day of School. 2006. 24p. pap. 9.95 (978-1-929661-23-7(1), 379-007) Transpersonal Publishing.

Chlebowy, Tane. Billy's First Day of School. 2005. 17.00 (978-0-8059-9789-7(X)) Dorrance Publishing Co., Inc.

Cocca-Leffler, Maryann. Jack's Talent. 2007. (Illus.). 32p. (J). (ps-3). 16.00 (***978-0-374-33681-3(4)***) Farrar, Straus & Giroux.

Collicott, Sharleen. Mildred & Sam & Their Babies. Collicott, Sharleen, illus. (I Can Read Bks.). 48p. (J). 2007. pap. 3.99 (***978-0-06-058113-8(1)***, Harper Trophy); 2005. (Illus.). 15.99 (978-0-06-058111-4(5), Geringer, Laura Book); 2005. (Illus.). lib. bdg. 16.89 (978-0-06-058112-1(3), Geringer, Laura Book) HarperCollins Pubs.

Corey, Shana. Horus's Horrible Day. Teague, Mark, illus. 2001. (First Graders from Mars Ser.: No. 1). 32p. (J). (gr. k-2). pap. 14.95 (978-0-439-26220-0(8)); pap. 4.99 (978-0-439-31955-3(2)) Scholastic, Inc. (Levine, Arthur A. Bks.).

Cork, Barbara. Sam Starts School. Smee, Nicola, illus. 2002. (First Experiences Ser.). 32p. (J). (gr. k-2). 15.00 (978-1-57768-989-8(5), Waterbird Bks.) School Specialty Publishing.

Danneberg, Julie. First Day Jitters. Love, Judith DuFour, illus. 2000. 32p. (J). (gr. k-4). 16.95 (978-1-58089-054-0(7)) Charlesbridge Publishing, Inc.

—First Day Jitters. Love, Judy, illus. 2000. 32p. (J). (gr. k-4). pap. 6.95 (978-1-58089-061-8(X)) Charlesbridge Publishing, Inc.

—First Day Jitters. 2000. (gr. k-3). lib. bdg. 15.25 (978-0-613-34040-3(X)); (Illus.). (J). 13.75 (978-0-606-18748-0(0)) Tandem Library Bks.

Danziger, Paula. Get Ready for Second Grade, Amber Brown. Ross, Tony, illus. (Easy-to-Read Ser.). 48p. (J). (gr. k-2). 2003. pap. 3.99 (978-0-14-250081-1(X), Puffin); 2002. 13.99 (978-0-399-23607-5(4), Putnam Juvenile) Penguin Group (USA) Inc.

Danzinger, Paula. Get Ready for Second Grade, Amber Brown. Ross, Tony, illus. 2003. 28.95 incl. audio compact disk (978-1-59112-563-1(4)); pap. 31.95 incl. audio compact disk (978-1-59112-562-4(6)); (J). 25.95 incl. audio (978-1-59112-234-0(1)); (J). pap. 16.95 incl. audio (978-1-59112-233-3(3)); (J). pap. 29.95 incl. audio (978-1-59112-235-7(X)) Live Oak Media.

Davis, Katie. Kindergarten Rocks! 2005. (Illus.). 32p. (J). 15.00 (978-0-15-204932-4(0)) Harcourt Trade Pubs.

de Paola, Tomie. Meet the Barkers. 2003. (Barker Twins Ser.). (Illus.). 32p. (J). (gr. k-1). pap. 5.99 (978-0-14-250083-5(6), Puffin) Penguin Group (USA) Inc.

—Meet the Barkers: Morgan & Moffat Go to School. de Paola, Tomie, illus. 2001. (Illus.). 1p. (J). (ps-1). 13.99 (978-0-399-23708-9(9), Putnam Juvenile) Penguin Group (USA) Inc.

—Meet the Barkers: Morgan & Moffat Go to School. 2005. (J). (gr. k-3). pap. 17.95 incl. audio (978-0-8045-6934-7(7), SAC6934); pap. 19.95 incl. audio compact disk (978-0-8045-4129-9(9), SACD4129) Spoken Arts, Inc.

—Morgan & Moffat Go to School. 2003. (gr. k-3). lib. bdg. 14.15 (978-0-613-66367-0(5)) Tandem Library Bks.

The Deer Report. 2005. (J). (978-1-58453-311-5(0)) Pioneer Valley Educational Pr., Inc.

deGroat, Diane. Brand-New Pencils, Brand-New Books. deGroat, Diane, illus. 32p. (J). (ps-3). 2007. pap. 6.99 (***978-0-06-072616-4(4)***, Harper Trophy); 2005. (Illus.). 15.99 (978-0-06-072613-3(X)); 2005. (Illus.). lib. bdg. 16.89 (978-0-06-072615-7(6)) HarperCollins Pubs.

Derby, Kenneth. The Top Ten Ways to Ruin the First Day of School. 2006. 176p. (J). pap. 4.99 (978-0-439-82322-7(6), Scholastic Paperbacks) Scholastic, Inc.

Dyer, Olive. Nia's First Day. 2001. (Illus.). 36p. pap. 29.95 (978-1-85902-939-8(6)) Beekman Bks., Inc.

Edwards, Becky. My First Day at Nursery School. 2004. (Illus.). 32p. (J). (ps-1). pap. 6.95 (978-1-58234-909-1(6), Bloomsbury Children) Bloomsbury Publishing.

—My First Day at Nursery School. Flintoft, Anthony, illus. 2002. 32p. (J). 15.95 (978-1-58234-761-5(1), Bloomsbury Children) Bloomsbury Publishing.

Edwards, Julie Andrews & Hamilton, Emma Walton. Dumpy at School. Walton, Tony, illus. 2000. (Dumpy Ser.). 32p. (ps-2). 15.99 (978-0-7868-0610-2(9)) Hyperion Bks. for Children.

Edwards, Pamela. Ms. Bitsy Bat's Kindergarten. Cole, Henry, illus. 2005. 32p. (ps-2). 15.99 (978-0-7868-0669-0(9)) Hyperion Bks. for Children.

Edwards, Pamela Duncan. Ms. Bitsy Bat's Kindergarten. Cole, Henry, illus. 2005. (J). (***978-1-4156-2782-2(7)***) Hyperion Bks. for Children.

Erickson, Mary Ellen. First Day of School. 2004. pap. 5.00 (978-0-9765453-0-9(6)) Dr. Mary's Bks.

Falwell, Cathryn. David's Drawings. 2001. (Illus.). 32p. (J). (ps-3). 16.00 (978-1-58430-031-1(0)) Lee & Low Bks., Inc.

Fitzgerald, Joanne. Yum! Yum! Delicious Nursery Rhymes. 2007. (Illus.). 32p. (J). (ps-1). (***978-1-55041-888-0(2)***) Fitzhenry & Whiteside, Ltd.

Fontes, Justine. My First Day of Preschool. Novak, Matt, illus. 2006. 12p. (J). 6.99 (978-0-689-86477-3(9), Little Simon) Simon & Schuster Children's Publishing.

Forward, Toby. What Did You Do Today? The First Day of School. Thompson, Carol, illus. 2004. 32p. (J). (ps-k). 15.00 (978-0-618-49586-3(X), Clarion Bks.) Houghton Mifflin Co. Trade & Reference Div.

Friedman, Laurie B. Back to School, Mallory. Schmitz, Tamara, illus. (J). 2005. 175p. (ps-7). pap. 5.95 (978-1-57505-865-8(0)); 2004. 160p. (gr. 2-5). 15.95 (978-1-57505-658-6(5)) Lerner Publishing Group.

Gantos, Jack. Back to School for Rotten Ralph. Rubel, Nicole, illus. (Rotten Ralph Ser.). 40p. (J). (ps-3). 2000. pap. 6.99 (978-0-06-443705-9(1), Harper Trophy); Bk. 1. 1998. 14.89 (978-0-06-027532-7(4)) HarperCollins Pubs.

—Back to School for Rotten Ralph. 2000. 12.75 (978-0-606-22184-9(0)); (gr. 3-6). lib. bdg. 14.10 (978-0-613-30974-5(X)) Tandem Library Bks.

Gorbachev, Valeri. Chicken Chickens Go to School. Gorbachev, Valeri, illus. 2003. (Illus.). (J). (ps-1). 28p. 15.95 (978-0-7358-1600-8(X)); 32p. 16.50 (978-0-7358-1767-8(7)) North-South Bks., Inc.

Greene, Kathi. Betty Gets Ready for School. 2006. (ENG.). 36p. per. 15.49 (***978-1-4259-5888-6(5)***) AuthorHouse.

Greene, Marjorie. Cassie's Big Day. 2003. (Illus.). (J). 16.95 (978-0-9741764-0-6(0)) Greene, Marjorie A.

Greenfield, Eloise. Me & Neesie. Gilchrist, Jan Spivey, illus. 2005. (Amistad Ser.). 32p. (J). (ps-3). lib. bdg. 16.89 (978-0-06-000702-7(8)); 15.99 (978-0-06-000701-0(X), Amistad) HarperCollins Pubs.

Gutman, Anne. Penelope at School. Hallensleben, Georg, illus. 2004. 12p. (J). (ps up). pap. 12.95 (978-0-439-67357-0(7), Cartwheel Bks.) Scholastic, Inc.

Hale, Nathan. Yellowbelly & Plum Go to School. Hale, Nathan, illus. 2007. (Illus.). 32p. (J). (ps-1). 16.99 (978-0-399-24624-1(X), Putnam Juvenile) Penguin Group (USA) Inc.

Hall, Kirsten. First Day of School: All about Shapes & Sizes. Luedecke, Bev, illus. 2003. (Beastieville Ser.). 32p. (J). (ps-1). 19.50 (978-0-516-22893-8(5), Children's Pr.) Scholastic Library Publishing.

Hapka, Cathy & Titlebaum, Ellen. How Not to Start Third Grade. Palen, Debbie, illus. 2007. (Step into Reading Ser.). 48p. (J). (gr. 2-4). 3.99 (***978-0-375-83904-7(6)***); lib. bdg. 11.99 (***978-0-375-93904-4(0)***) Random Hse. Children's Bks. (Random Hse. Bks. for Young Readers).

Harper, Jamie. Miss Mingo & the First Day of School. Harper, Jamie, illus. 2006. (Illus.). 32p. (J). (ps-2). 15.99 (978-0-7636-2410-1(1)) Candlewick Pr.

—Miss Mingo & the First Day of School. 2006. (Illus.). 26p. (J). (***978-1-4156-9174-8(6)***) Candlewick Pr.

Harris, Annmarie. The Countdown to the First Day of School. Motoyama, Keiko, illus. 2003. 24p. (J). (ps-4). pap. 3.99 (978-0-8431-0463-9(5), Price Stern Sloan) Penguin Group (USA) Inc.

Harris, Elsie. Lizzie's First Day at School. 2006. pap. 7.95 (978-0-533-15344-2(1)) Vantage Pr., Inc.

Harris, Robie H. I Am Not Going to School Today! Ormerod, Jan, illus. 2003. 32p. (J). (ps-3). 16.95 (978-0-689-83913-9(8), McElderry, Margaret K.) Simon & Schuster Children's Publishing.

Hays, Anna Jane. Kindergarten Countdown. Davick, Linda, illus. 2007. 24p. (J). (ps-1). lib. bdg. 11.99 (978-0-375-94252-5(1)); 8.99 (978-0-375-84252-8(7)) Random Hse. Children's Bks. (Knopf Bks. for Young Readers).

Henkes, Kevin. Wemberly Worried. Henkes, Kevin, illus. 2000. (Illus.). 32p. (J). (ps-3). 16.99 (978-0-688-17027-1(7)); lib. bdg. 17.89 (978-0-688-17028-8(5)) HarperCollins Pubs.

—Wemberly Worried. Henkes, Kevin, illus. (Illus.). pap. 16.95 incl. audio (978-0-87499-806-1(9)); pap. incl. audio (978-0-87499-808-5(5)); pap. 18.95 incl. audio compact disk (978-1-59112-359-0(3)); pap. incl. audio compact disk (978-1-59112-561-7(8)) Live Oak Media.

—Wemberly Worried. unabr. ed. 2001. (Illus.). (J). (ps-2). 25.95 incl. audio (978-0-87499-807-8(7)) Live Oak Media.

Hennessy, B. G. Mr. Ouchy's First Day. Meisel, Paul, illus. 2006. 32p. (J). (ps-3). 15.99 (978-0-399-24248-9(1), Putnam Juvenile) Penguin Group (USA) Inc.

—Mr. Ouchy's First Day. Meisel, Paul, illus. 2007. 27.95 incl. audio (***978-0-8045-6946-0(0)***); 29.95 incl. audio compact disk (***978-0-8045-4160-2(4)***) Spoken Arts, Inc.

Hest, Amy. Off to School, Baby Duck! Barton, Jill, illus. 2002. (J). 26.15 (978-0-7587-3294-1(5)) Book Wholesalers, Inc.

Hest, Amy. Off to School, Baby Duck! Barton, Jill, illus. 2007. 32p. (J). (ps-1). pap. 6.99 (*978-0-7636-3438-4(7)) Candlewick Pr.

Hill, Eric. Spot Goes to School. Hill, Eric, illus. 2004. (Illus.). (J). (ps-1). (SPA.). 12p. bds. 7.99 (978-0-399-24246-5(5) , Putnam Juvenile); 24p. pap. 6.99 (978-0-14-240167-5(6) , Puffin) Penguin Group (USA) Inc.

Himle, Lisa. Hands As Warm As Toast. Langton, Bruce, illus. 2006. 32p. (J). 17.95 (978-1-58726-298-2(3) , Mitten Pr.) Ann Arbor Media Group, LLC.

Horse, Harry, illus. Little Rabbit Goes to School. 2004. 32p. (J). 15.95 (978-1-56145-320-7(X)) Peachtree Pubs., Ltd.

Jeffs, Stephanie. Christopher Bear Makes Friends. Thomas, Jacqui, illus. 2004. (Christopher Bear Ser.). 32p. 5.99 (978-0-8066-4401-1(X) , Augsburg Bks.) Augsburg Fortress, Pubs.

Jinkins, Jim. Pinky Dinky Doo: Back to School Is Cool! 2005. (Step into Reading Ser.). (Illus.). 48p. (J). (gr. 1-3). pap. 3.99 (978-0-375-83237-6(8) , Random Hse. Bks. for Young Readers) Random Hse. Children's Bks.

—Pinky Dinky Doo: Back to School Is Cool! 2005. (Step into Reading Ser.). (Illus.). 48p. (J). (gr. 1-3). lib. bdg. 11.99 (978-0-375-93237-3(2) , Random Hse. Bks. for Young Readers) Random Hse. Children's Bks.

Johnston, Tony. Off to Kindergarten. Sweet, Melissa, illus. 2007. 32p. (J). (ps-3). 7.99 (*978-0-439-73090-7(2) , Cartwheel Bks.) Scholastic, Inc.

Jones, Christianne C. Joey's First Day. Trover, Zachary, illus. 2005. (Read-It! Readers Ser.). 32p. (J). (gr. k-3). 18.60 (978-1-4048-1174-4(5)) Picture Window Bks.

—El Primer Dia. Demski, James, Jr., illus. 2006. (Read-It! Readers en Espanol Ser.).Tr. of Joey's First Day. (SPA.). 32p. (J). (ps-3). 19.95 (978-1-4048-1627-5(5)) Picture Window Bks.

Jones, Tammy & Smith, Carrie. Katy's First Day of School. ed. 2004. (Shared Connections Ser.). (J). pap. 27.00 (978-1-4108-1625-2(7)); pap., instr.'s gde. ed. 27.00 (978-1-4108-1601-6(X)) Benchmark Education Co.

Kaufmann, Nancy. Bye, Bye! Spetter, Jung-Hee, illus. 2004. 32p. (J). (ps-1). 14.95 (978-1-886910-95-9(2) , Lemniscaat) Boyds Mills Pr.

Kirk, David. Little Miss Spider at Sunny Patch School. Kirk, David, illus. 2000. (Miss Spider Ser.:). (Illus.). 32p. (J). (ps-2). pap. 12.95 (978-0-439-08727-8(9)) Scholastic, Inc.

Kleven, Elisa. The Apple Doll. 2007. (Illus.). 40p. (J). (ps-3). 16.00 (978-0-374-30380-8(0)) Farrar, Straus & Giroux.

Klingel, Cynthia Fitterer & Noyed, Robert B. Sabina at School & the Letter S. 2003. (Alphaphonics Ser.). (Illus.). 24p. (J). (ps-2). 21.36 (978-1-59296-109-2(6)) Child's World, Inc.

Krulik, Nancy E. Drat! You Copycat, No. 7. 2003. (Katie Kazoo, Switcheroo Ser.: No. 7). (gr. 3-6). lib. bdg. 11.80 (978-0-613-62943-0(4)) Tandem Library Bks.

—Drat! You Copycat!, No. 7. 2003. (Katie Kazoo, Switcheroo Ser.: No. 7). (Illus.). 80p. (J). (gr. 2-4). pap. 3.99 (978-0-448-43171-0(8) , Grosset & Dunlap) Penguin Group (USA) Inc.

Leonard, Marie. Tibili: The Little Boy Who Didn't Want to Go to School. Prigent, Andree, illus. 2002. 36p. (J). (ps-2). 15.95 (978-1-929132-20-1(4)) Kane/Miller Bk. Pubs., Inc.

Lillian's First Day. 2003. (J). 12.00 (978-0-9724442-3-1(8)) LightHouse Pr.

Lindgren, Astrid. Pippi Goes to School. 1999. (Pippi Longstocking Storybooks). (Illus.). 64p. (J). (gr. k-2). pap. 5.99 (978-0-14-130236-2(4) , Puffin) Penguin Group (USA) Inc.

—Pippi Goes to School. 1999. (J). (gr. k-3). lib. bdg. 14.15 (978-0-613-22923-4(1)) Tandem Library Bks.

MacDowell, Maureen. Tomorrow Is the First Day of School. Hergenrother, Max, illus. 2007. 32p. (J). 15.95 (*978-0-9791463-0-5(5)) Wading River Bks., LLC.

MacKall, Dandi Daley. First Day. Beeke, Tiphanie, illus. 2003. 32p. (J). 16.00 (978-0-15-216577-2(0) , Silver Whistle) Harcourt Trade Pubs.

Mayfield, Julie. The Magical First Day. Reis, Michael, illus. 1998. (J). pap. 5.95 (978-1-56763-337-5(4)); lib. bdg. 17.25 (978-1-56763-336-8(6)) Ozark Publishing.

McDonald, Megan. Judy Moody. Reynolds, Peter H., illus. (Judy Moody Ser.: No. 1). (J). (gr. 1-5). 2002. 160p. pap. 5.99 (978-0-7636-1231-3(6)); 2000. 196p. 15.99 (978-0-7636-0685-5(5)) Candlewick Pr.

—Judy Moody. Reynolds, Peter H., illus. 2002. (Judy Moody Ser.: No. 1). 160p. (J). (ps-7). per. 14.15 (978-0-613-56467-0(7)) Tandem Library Bks.

McGhee, Alison. Countdown to Kindergarten. Bliss, Harry, illus. 2006. 32p. (J). reprint ed. pap. 6.00 (978-0-15-205586-8(X) , Voyager Bks./Libros Viajeros) Harcourt Children's Bks.

—Countdown to Kindergarten. Bliss, Harry, illus. 2002. 32p. (J). (ps-2). 16.00 (978-0-15-202516-8(2) , Silver Whistle) Harcourt Trade Pubs.

—Countdown to Kindergarten. Bliss, Harry, illus. pap. 16.95 incl. audio (978-1-59112-467-2(0)); pap. incl. audio compact disk (978-1-59112-469-6(7)); pap. 18.95 incl. audio compact disk (978-1-59112-927-1(3)); pap. incl. audio (978-1-59112-929-5(X)) Live Oak Media.

—Mrs. Watson Wants Your Teeth. Bliss, Harry, illus. 2007. 32p. (J). reprint ed. 16.00 (*978-1-4223-6777-3(0)) DIANE Publishing Co.

—Mrs. Watson Wants Your Teeth. Bliss, Harry, illus. 2004. 36p. (J). 16.00 (978-0-15-204931-7(2)) Harcourt Children's Bks.

McGinty, Alice B. Eliza's Kindergarten Surprise. Speir, Nancy, illus. 2007. (J). (ps-k). 14.99 (978-0-7614-5351-2(2)) Cavendish, Marshall Corp.

McMullan, Kate. A Fine Start Bk. 3: Meg's Prairie Diary. 2003. (My America Ser.: No. 3). 112p. (J). pap. 12.95 (978-0-439-37061-5(2)) Scholastic, Inc.

—The New Kid at School. 2006. (Dragon Slayers' Academy Ser.: No. 1). (J). (gr. 1-6). 24.21 (978-1-59961-126-6(0)) Spotlight.

McNamara, Margaret. The First Day of School. Gordon, Mike, illus. 2005. (Ready-To-Read Ser.). 32p. (J). (ps-1). pap. 3.99 (978-0-689-86914-3(2)); lib. bdg. 11.89 (978-0-689-86915-0(0)) Simon & Schuster Children's Publishing. (Aladdin).

Millman, Isaac. Moses Goes to School. Millman, Isaac, illus. 2000. (Moses Goes To Ser.). (Illus.). 32p. (J). (gr. k-3). 16.00 (978-0-374-35069-7(8) , Farrar, Straus & Giroux (BYR)) Farrar, Straus & Giroux.

Mills, David. Sam's First Day. Finlay, Lizzie, illus. 2004. 24p. (J). (TAM, CZE, VIE, SPA & GUJ.). (978-1-85269-630-6(3)); (TAM, CZE, VIE, SPA & GUJ.). (978-1-85269-632-0(X)); (TAM, CZE, VIE, SPA & GUJ.). (978-1-85269-633-7(8)); (TAM, CZE, VIE, SPA & GUJ.). (978-1-85269-634-4(6)); (TAM, CZE, VIE, SPA & GUJ.). (978-1-85269-635-1(4)); (TAM, CZE, VIE, SPA & GUJ.). (978-1-85269-636-8(2)); (TAM, CZE, VIE, SPA & GUJ.). (978-1-85269-637-5(0)); (TAM, CZE, VIE, SPA & GUJ.). (978-1-85269-639-9(7)); (TAM, CZE, VIE, SPA & GUJ.). (978-1-85269-640-5(0)); (TAM, CZE, VIE, SPA & GUJ.). (978-1-85269-642-9(7)); (CZE, TAM, VIE, SPA & GUJ.). (978-1-85269-643-6(5)); (TAM, CZE, VIE, SPA & GUJ.). (978-1-85269-645-0(1)); (TAM, CZE, SPA, VIE & GUJ.). (978-1-85269-646-7(X)); (TAM, CZE, VIE, SPA & GUJ.). (978-1-85269-702-0(4)); (POR, TAM, CZE, VIE & SPA.). (978-1-85269-644-3(3)); (ENG & SHO.). (978-1-84444-166-2(0)) Mantra Publishing, Ltd.

Mills, David & Finlay, Lizzie. Sam's First Day. 2004. (TAM, CZE, VIE, SPA & GUJ., Illus.). 24p. (J). (978-1-85269-641-2(9)) Mantra Publishing, Ltd.

Milord, Susan. Happy School Year! DePalma, Mary Newell, illus. 2008. (J). pap. (*978-0-439-88280-4(X) , Scholastic Pr.) Scholastic, Inc.

Moncure, Jane Belk. Word Bird's New Friend. 2002. (New Word Bird Library). (Illus.). 32p. (J). (ps-3). 22.79 (978-1-56766-844-5(5)) Child's World, Inc.

Montanari, Eva. A Very Full Morning. 2006. (Illus.). 32p. (J). (gr. k-3). 16.00 (978-0-618-56318-0(0)) Houghton Mifflin Co. Trade & Reference Div.

Munsch, Robert. We Share Everything. Martchenko, Michael, illus. 1999. 32p. (J). (ps-1). 11.95 (978-0-590-89600-9(8) , Cartwheel Bks.) Scholastic, Inc.

Myracle, Lauren. The Fashion Disaster That Changed My Life. 2008. 160p. (J). (gr. 5). 6.99 (978-0-14-240717-2(8) , Puffin); 2005. 144p. (YA). (gr. 4-6). 15.99 (978-0-525-47222-3(3) , Dutton Juvenile) Penguin Group (USA) Inc.

Neubecker, Robert. Wow! School! 2007. 32p. (ps-1). 16.99 (978-0-7868-3896-7(5)) Hyperion Bks. for Children.

O'Brien, Gerry. Bubba Begonia, You'll Be Sorry. 2006. (Illus.). 64p. 6.95 (*978-1-894838-23-8(8)) Acorn Pr., The CAN. *Dist:* Univ. of Toronto Pr.

Oh, Jiwon. Mr. Monkey's Classroom. Oh, Jiwon, illus. 2005. (Illus.). 32p. (J). (ps-2). lib. bdg. 15.89 (978-0-06-055722-5(2)) HarperCollins Pubs.

Ormerod, Jan. When an Elephant Comes to School. Ormerod, Jan, illus. 2005. (Illus.). 32p. (J). pap. 16.95 (978-0-439-73967-2(5) , Orchard Bks.) Scholastic, Inc.

Pak, Soyung. Sumi's First Day of School Ever. Kim, Joung Un, illus. 2003. 32p. (J). (ps-3). 15.99 (978-0-670-03522-9(X) , Viking Juvenile) Penguin Group (USA) Inc.

Parish, Herman. Amelia Bedelia's First Day of School. 2007. 32p. (J). pap. 6.99 (*978-0-06-154457-6(4) , Harper Trophy) HarperCollins Pubs.

Park, Barbara. Junie B. Jones & the Stupid Smelly Bus. unabr. ed. 2004. (Junie B. Jones Ser.: Vol. 1). 69p. (J). (gr. k-3). pap. 17.00 incl. audio (978-0-8072-0778-9(0) , LFTR 237 SP, Listening Library) Random Hse. Audio Publishing Group.

Parr, Todd. Otto Goes to School. Parr, Todd, illus. 2005. (Illus.). 24p. (J). (ps-1). 9.99 (978-0-316-83533-6(1)) Little Brown & Co.

Pennypacker, Sara. Stuart Goes to School. Matje, Martin, illus. 64p. (J). 2003. pap. 15.95 (978-0-439-30182-4(3) , Orchard Bks.); 2005. reprint ed. pap. 4.99 (978-0-439-30183-1(1) , Scholastic Paperbacks) Scholastic, Inc.

Perez, L. King. First Day in Grapes. Casilla, Robert, illus. 2002. 32p. (J). (gr. 1-3). 16.95 (978-1-58430-045-8(0)) Lee & Low Bks., Inc.

Perrine, David L. Birdie School Days: The First Day of School. Perry, Margie, illus. 2005. (J). pap. 15.00 (978-0-8059-6699-2(4)) Dorrance Publishing Co., Inc.

Petty, Kate. Gus Goes to School. 2007. (J). lib. bdg. 16.95 (*978-1-59566-337-5(1)) QEB Publishing Inc.

Poydar, Nancy. First Day, Hooray! Poydar, Nancy, illus. 1999. (Illus.). 32p. (J). (gr. k-3). 6.95 (978-0-8234-1630-1(5)); tchr. ed. 16.95 (978-0-8234-1437-6(X)) Holiday Hse., Inc.

Puttock, Simon. You're Too Big. 2003. (Illus.). 32p. (J). 19.99 (978-0-385-60432-1(7) , Doubleday) Transworld Publishers Ltd. GBR. *Dist:* Trafalgar Square Publishing.

—You're Too Big! 2004. (Illus.). 39p. pap. 9.99 (978-0-552-54828-1(6) , Corgi) Transworld Publishers Ltd. GBR. *Dist:* Independent Pubs. Group.

Recorvits, Helen. My Name Is Yoon. Swiatkowska, Gabi, illus. 2003. 32p. (J). (gr. k-3). 16.00 (978-0-374-35114-4(7) , Farrar, Straus & Giroux (BYR)) Farrar, Straus & Giroux.

Robbins, Beth. Tom's First Day at School. Stuart, Jon, illus. 2001. (It's OK! Ser.). 24p. (J). (ps-k). pap. 3.95 (978-0-7894-7422-3(0) , D K Ink) Dorling Kindersley Publishing, Inc.

Rodman, Mary Ann. First Grade Stinks! Spiegel, Beth, illus. 2006. 32p. (J). (ps-3). 15.95 (978-1-56145-377-1(3) , Peachtree Junior) Peachtree Pubs., Ltd.

Rosenberry, Vera. Vera's First Day of School. rev. ed. (Illus.). 32p. (J). (ps-2). 2003. pap. 7.95 (978-0-8050-7269-3(1)); 1999. 16.95 (978-0-8050-5936-6(9)) Holt, Henry & Co. (Holt, Henry & Co. Bks. For Young Readers).

—Vera's First Day of School. Rosenberry, Vera, illus. unabr. ed. 2006. (Picture Book Readalong Ser.). (Illus.). (J). (ps-2). 25.95 incl. audio (978-1-59519-662-0(5)); 28.95 incl. audio compact disk (978-1-59519-663-7(3)); pap. 16.95 incl. audio (978-1-59519-658-3(7)); pap. 18.95 incl. audio compact disk (978-1-59519-659-0(5)); pap. 39.95 incl. audio compact disk (978-1-59519-661-3(7)); Set. pap. 37.95 incl. audio (978-1-59519-660-6(9)) Live Oak Media.

—Vera's First Day of School. 2003. (ps-2). lib. bdg. 15.25 (978-0-613-75619-8(3)) Tandem Library Bks.

Rubel, Nicole. Ham & Pickles: First Day of School. 2006. (Illus.). 32p. (J). 16.00 (978-0-15-205039-9(6)) Harcourt Trade Pubs.

Rusackas, Francesca. I Love You All Day Long. Burris, Priscilla, illus. 2004. 32p. (J). (ps-k). reprint ed. pap. 6.99 (978-0-06-050278-2(9) , Harper Trophy) HarperCollins Pubs.

Schlepp, Tammy J. Going to School. 2001. 11.79 (978-0-606-22431-4(9)); lib. bdg. 13.00 (978-0-613-45184-0(8)) Tandem Library Bks.

Scott, C. Anne. Lizard Meets Ivana the Terrible. 2001. (gr. 3-6). lib. bdg. 11.80 (978-0-613-81946-6(2)) Tandem Library Bks.

Scott, C. Anne & Roth, Stephanie. Lizard Meets Ivana the Terrible. 2001. 128p. (J). pap. 3.99 (978-0-439-21999-0(X) , Scholastic Paperbacks) Scholastic, Inc.

Scott, Cynthia A. Lizard Meets Ivana the Terrible. 2001. (978-0-606-22173-3(5)) Tandem Library Bks.

Scurlock, Val & Dyer, Olive. Nia's First Day. Evans, Fran, illus. 2001. 32p. pap. 12.95 (978-1-85902-938-1(8)) Beekman Bks., Inc.

Siebold, Jan. My Nights at the Improv. 2005. 98p. (YA). (gr. 6-9). lib. bdg. 14.95 (978-0-8075-5630-6(0)) Whitman, Albert & Co.

Silverman, Erica. Cowgirl Kate & Cocoa: School Days. Lewin, Betsy, illus. 2007. (Cowgirl Kate & Cocoa Ser.). 48p. (J). 15.00 (978-0-15-205378-9(6)) Harcourt Trade Pubs.

Silverman, Erica. Cowgirl Kate & Cocoa: School Days. Lewin, Betsy, illus. 2008. (Cowgirl Kate & Cocoa Ser.). 48p. (J). pap. 5.95 (*978-0-15-206130-2(4) , Harcourt Paperbacks) Harcourt Children's Bks.

Skarmeas, Nancy J. My First Day of School. Johnson, Meredith, illus. 2001. 32p. (J). (ps-3). 9.95 (978-0-8249-4198-7(5)) Ideals Pubns.

Slate, Joseph. Miss Bindergarten Gets Ready for Kindergarten. Wolff, Ashley, illus. 2001. 40p. (J). pap. 6.99 (978-0-14-056273-6(7) , Puffin) Penguin Group (USA) Inc.

Stiles, Norman. On My Very First Day of School I Met... 2005. 32p. 9.95 (978-1-59687-182-3(2) , Milk & Cookies) ibooks, Inc.

—On My Very First School Day I Met... Mayer, Bill, illus. 2005. 32p. (J). (ps). 9.95 (978-0-689-03924-9(7) , Milk & Cookies) ibooks, Inc.

Stuve-Bodeen, Stephanie. Elizabeti's School. Hale, Christy, illus. 2002. 32p. (J). (gr. k-3). 16.95 (978-1-58430-043-4(4)) Lee & Low Bks., Inc.

—Elizabeti¿s School. Christy, Hale, illus. ed. 2007. 32p. (J). pap. 7.95 (*978-1-60060-234-4(7)) Lee & Low Bks., Inc.

—La escuela de Elizabeti. Christy, Hale, illus. 2007. (SPA.). (J). pap. 7.95 (*978-1-60060-235-1(5)) Lee & Low Bks., Inc.

Swain, Cynthia. Bill's First Day. 2006. (Early Explorers Ser.). (J). 30.00 (*978-1-4108-6033-0(7)) Benchmark Education Co.

Swimpson, Alayne. Murphy & Scootie. 2006. pap. 17.99 (*978-1-4259-7251-6(9)) AuthorHouse.

Symes, Ruth Louise. Mondays at Monster School. Reeve, Rosie, illus. 2007. 32p. (J). (ps). 19.99 (978-1-84255-126-4(4)); pap. 11.99 (978-1-84255-536-1(7)) Orion Children's Bks. GBR. *Dist:* Independent Pubs. Group, Trafalgar Square Publishing.

Taulbert, Clifton L. Little Cliff's First Day of School. Taulbert, Clifton L. & Lewis, Earl, illus. 2003. 32p. (J). (gr. k-3). pap. 6.99 (978-0-14-250082-8(8) , Puffin) Penguin Group (USA) Inc.

—Little Cliff's First Day of School. Lewis, Earl, illus. 2001. 32p. (J). (ps-3). 15.99 (978-0-8037-2557-7(4) , Dial) Penguin Group (USA) Inc.

—Little Cliff's First Day of School. 2003. (gr. k-3). lib. bdg. 15.30 (978-0-613-67561-1(4)) Tandem Library Bks.

Thaler, Mike. Teacher from Black Lagoon Read along Library. 2006. (J). 18.95 (978-0-439-87596-7(X)) Scholastic, Inc.

Thompson, Lauren, et al. Mouse's First Day of School. 2003. (Illus.). 32p. (J). (ps-1). 12.95 (978-0-689-84727-1(0)) Simon & Schuster Children's Publishing.

Torrisi, Cathy. Not Now, Mr. N! Yeagle, Barbara, illus. 2002. (Read-to-Me Ser.). 24p. (J). (978-0-7665-1214-6(2)) Letter People, The.

Tuitel, Johnnie. Searching the Noonday Trail. 2000. (Gun Lake Adventure Ser.: Bk. 4). 112p. (J). (gr. 4-7). pap. 5.99 (978-0-9658075-3-1(3)) Cedar Tree Publishing.

Tuminelly, Nancy. Horse Shoes. Nobens, C. A., illus. 2006. (Fact & Fiction Ser.). 24p. (J). pap. (978-1-59679-944-8(7)) ABDO Publishing Co.

Umansky, Kaye & Currey, Anna, illus. Sophie & Abigail. 2004. 30p. (J). 3.95 (978-1-56148-444-7(X)); 9.95 (978-1-56148-434-8(2)) Good Bks.

Van Kersen, Elizabeth. Whos' Riley? Stevens, Debra, illus. l.t. ed. 2006. 23p. (J). 15.99 (978-1-59879-173-0(7)) Lifevest Publishing, Inc.

Van Leeuwen, Jean. Amanda Pig, School Girl. 1999. (ps-2). lib. bdg. 11.80 (978-0-613-19333-7(4)) Tandem Library Bks.

Vulliamy, Clara. Tom & Small: A Big Moment in a Little Boy's Life. 2004. (Illus.). 32p. pap. 8.99 (978-0-00-713788-6(5)) HarperCollins Pubs. Ltd. GBR. *Dist:* Trafalgar Square Publishing.

Webb, Leonard. Corinthia: My Name Is Corinthia. 2005. 72p. pap. 11.95 (978-1-59113-693-4(8)) Booklocker-.com, Inc.

Weiss, Ellen. I Don't Want to Go to School! A Fold-Out Surprise Book. Bennett, Andy, illus. 2006. (PBS Kids(R) Ser.). 18p. (J). 6.95 (*978-1-57791-313-9(2)) Brighter Minds Children's Publishing.

Wells, Rosemary. Emily's First 100 Days of School. 2000. (Illus.). 64p. (J). (ps-1). 16.99 (978-0-7868-0507-5(2)) Hyperion Bks. for Children.

—Emily's First 100 Days of School. 2000. (Illus.). 64p. (ps-1). pap. 5.99 (978-0-7868-1354-4(7)) Hyperion Paperbacks for Children.

—Emily's First 100 Days of School. 2006. (Illus.). (J). (ps-4). 29.95 incl. audio compact disk (978-0-439-84900-5(4) , WHCD654); 24.95 incl. audio (978-0-439-84898-5(9) , WHRA654); pap. 14.95 incl. audio (978-0-439-84902-9(0) , WPRA654); pap. 18.95 incl. audio compact disk (978-0-439-84903-6(9) , WPCD654) Weston Woods Studios, Inc.

—Timothy Goes to School. 2000. (Illus.). 32p. (J). (ps-3). pap. 5.99 (978-0-14-056742-7(9) , Puffin) Penguin Group (USA) Inc.

—Timothy Goes to School. 2000. (978-0-606-18457-1(0)); lib. bdg. 14.15 (978-0-8085-3410-5(6)) Tandem Library Bks.

Whybrow, Ian. Harry & the Dinosaurs Go to School. Reynolds, Adrian, illus. 2007. 32p. (J). (ps-2). 15.99 (978-0-375-84180-4(6) , Random Hse. Bks. for Young Readers) Random Hse. Children's Bks.

Williams, Jacklyn. Welcome to Third Grade, Gus! Cushman, Doug, illus. 2006. (Read-It! Readers Ser.). (J). 19.93 (978-1-4048-2714-1(5)) Picture Window Bks.

Willis, Jeanne. Be Gentle, Python! Birchall, Mark, illus. 2005. (Picture Bks.). 28p. (J). (gr. k-2). 7.95 (978-1-57505-508-4(2)) Lerner Publishing Group.

—Be Quiet, Parrot! Birchall, Mark, illus. 2005. (Picture Bks.). 32p. (J). (gr. k-2). 7.25 (978-1-57505-492-6(2)) Lerner Publishing Group.

—Take Turns, Penguin! Birchall, Mark, illus. 2003. (Picture Bks.). 32p. (J). (ps-3). 7.95 (978-1-57505-493-3(0) , Carolrhoda Bks.) Lerner Publishing Group.

Wing, Natasha. The Night Before First Grade. Zemke, Deborah, illus. 2005. 32p. (J). (ps-4). 3.99 (978-0-448-43747-7(3) , Grosset & Dunlap) Penguin Group (USA) Inc.

Winget, Susan. Tucker's Four-Carrot School Day. Winget, Susan, illus. 2005. (Illus.). 40p. (J). (ps-k). 12.99 (978-0-06-054642-7(5)); lib. bdg. 13.89 (978-0-06-054643-4(3)) HarperCollins Pubs.

Zalben, Jane Breskin. Don't Go! Zalben, Jane Breskin, illus. 2001. (Illus.). 32p. (J). (gr. k-ps). tchr. ed. 15.00 (978-0-618-07250-7(0) , Clarion Bks.) Houghton Mifflin Co. Trade & Reference Div.

FISH

see Fishes

FISH-CULTURE

Aquaculture Interactive Version 1: A Digital Aquaculture Textbook. 2000. (Aquaculture Interactive). (C). cd-rom 49.95 (978-0-9659686-5-2(0)) Harbor Branch Oceanographic Institution, Inc.

Stone, Lynn M. Fish Farms. 1999. (Funky Farms Ser.). (Illus.). 24p. (J). (gr. 1-4). lib. bdg. 19.27 (978-0-86593-543-3(2)) Rourke Publishing, LLC.

FISHERIES

Here are entered works on the fishing industry.

see also Fishes

Harcourt School Publishers Staff. The Fish Market Advanced Level. 3rd ed. 2002. (Trophies Reading Program Ser.). (Illus.). (J). pap. 3.70 (978-0-15-323018-9(5)) Harcourt Schl. Pubs.

Moore, Willamarie. StarFestival Grades 3-6 Fishing Industry Team: Exploring Cultural Heritage. Miyagawa, Shigeru, ed. 2000. (Illus.). 50p. (J). (gr. 3-6). pap., stu. ed., wbk. ed. 10.00 (978-1-929724-06-2(3)) StarFestival, Inc.

Seven Foolish Fishermen, 6 Packs. 32p. (gr. 2 up). 37.00 (978-0-7635-9399-5(0)) Rigby Education.

Winters, Adam. Choosing a Career in the Fishing Industry. 2005. (World of Work Ser.). (Illus.). 64p. (YA). (gr. 7-12). lib. bdg. 25.25 (978-0-8239-3330-3(X)) Rosen Publishing Group, Inc., The.

FISHERIES—FICTION

Boyd, Roland. The Fisherman & His Wife. Wright, Carol, ed. Zarvatski, Derek, illus. rev. ed. 20p. (J). (gr. 1-2). pap. 6.95 (978-0-9701573-0-0(4)) Chameleon Designs.

Buklis, Lawrence S. Mysteries from the Yukon: Three Fisheries Adventures for Students. 2003. 217p. (J). pap. 21.00 (978-1-888569-52-0(2)) American Fisheries Society.

Kreisler, Ken. Billy the Oysterman. O'Connor, John P., ed. Kolb, Joe, illus. 1999. 32p. (J). (gr. k-2). spiral bd. 9.95 (978-1-892216-12-0(4)) Bristol Fashion Publishing Co.

FISHES

see also Aquariums; Fish-Culture; Fisheries; Fishing; Tropical Fish

also names of fishes, e.g. Salmon, etc.

Aaseng, Nathan. Piranhas. 2005. (Animals Attack Ser.). (Illus.). 48p. (J). (ps-8). lib. bdg. 26.20 (978-0-7377-3130-9(3) , Greenhaven Pr., Inc.) Thomson Gale.

Amdahl, Paul. The Barefoot Fisherman: A Fishing Book for Kids. 2001. (Illus.). 124p. (YA). (gr. 4-7). pap. 7.95 (978-0-9627815-0-6(9)) Clearwater Publishing Co., Inc.

Arnold, Caroline. Shockers of the Sea & Other Electric Animals. 1999. (gr. k-3). lib. bdg. 15.25 (978-0-613-35227-7(0)) Tandem Library Bks.

Baquedano, Elizabeth & Parker, Steve. Pesces. 2004. (Dk Eyewitness Books Ser.).Tr. of Fish. (SPA.). 64p. (J). 15.99 (978-0-7566-0418-9(4)) Dorling Kindersley Publishing, Inc.

Barnard, Edward S. Fishes. 2007. (J). (*978-1-59939-136-6(8) , Reader's Digest Young Families, Inc.) Reader's Digest Children's Publishing, Inc.

Barrett, Katherine & Sneider, Cary I. Mapping Fish Habitats. Bergman, Lincoln & Fairwell, Kay, eds. Bevilacqua, Carol, illus. Hoyt, Richard & Neumann, Bob, photos by. rev. ed. 1999. (Great Explorations in Math & Science Ser.). 60p. (YA). (gr. 6-10). pap. 10.50 (978-0-924886-25-6(0) , GEMS) Univ. of California, Berkeley, Lawrence Hall of Science.

Baumbusch, Brigitte. Fish in Art. 2005. (Illus.). 32p. (J). lib. bdg. 22.00 (978-0-8368-4446-7(7)) Stevens, Gareth Inc.

Bedry, Christa. Fish. 2004. (Prehistoric Life Ser.). (J). pap. 7.95 (978-1-59036-172-6(5)); (Illus.). 32p. lib. bdg. 15.95 (978-1-59036-112-2(1)) Weigl Pubs., Inc.

Berendes, Mary. Piranhas. 2007. (New Naturebooks Ser.). 32p. (J). (gr. 1-5). 27.07 (*978-1-59296-851-0(1)) Child's World, Inc.

Berger, Melvin & Berger, Gilda. Fish Live in Water. 2003. (Illus.). (J). pap. (978-0-439-47180-0(X)) Scholastic, Inc.

Bertolucci, Cristiano, et al. Animals above & below Water. Bartolozzi, Alle, illus. 2004. (Contrasts Ser.). 32p. (J). (gr. 1-4). 14.95 (978-1-57768-524-1(5) , Waterbird Bks.) School Specialty Publishing.

Binns, Tristan Boyer. Freshwater Fish. 2006. (Keeping Pets Ser.). (Illus.). 48p. (J). (978-1-4034-7700-2(0)) Heinemann Library.

Birds & Fish. 2001. 63p. (YA). 8.65 (978-0-7525-4877-7(8)) Parragon, Inc.

Blackaby, Susan. Fish for You: Caring for Your Fish. DeLage, Charlene, illus. 2004. (Pet Care Ser.). 24p. (C). (gr. k-3). 22.60 (978-1-4048-0116-5(2)) Picture Window Bks.

Bowman, Crystal. Mommy, May I Hug the Fishes? 2004. (Illus.). 16p. (J). pap. 4.99 (978-0-310-70814-8(1)) Zonderkidz.

Bozzo, Linda. My First Fish. 2007. (My First Pet Library from the American Humane Association Ser.). (Illus.). 32p. (J). (gr. 1-2). lib. bdg. 22.60 (978-0-7660-2751-0(1) , Enslow Elementary) Enslow Pubs., Inc.

Brian Wildsmith's Fishes. 2004. (J). 24.95 incl. audio (978-1-56008-167-8(8)); pap. 14.95 incl. audio (978-1-56008-166-1(X)) Weston Woods Studios, Inc.

Buckmaster, Marjorie L. Freshwater Fishes. 2007. (Great Pets Ser.). 48p. (J). lib. bdg. 28.50 (*978-0-7614-2712-4(0) , Benchmark Bks.) Cavendish, Marshall Corp.

Chelsea House Publishing Staff. Fish Set: Keeping & Breeding Them in Captivity, 9 vols. 1998. 161.55 (978-0-7910-5086-6(6) , Chelsea Hse.) Facts On File, Inc.

—Marine Aquarium. 1999. (Fish). (Illus.). 64p. (YA). (gr. 4-7). lib. bdg. 19.75 (978-0-7910-5092-7(0) , Chelsea Hse.) Facts On File, Inc.

Chessen, Betsey & Chanko, Pamela. A Dolphin Is Not a Fish. 1998. (Science Emergent Readers Ser.). (J). pap. 3.25 (978-0-05-906388-1(2)) Scholastic, Inc.

Clish, Marian L. Fish Don't Swim in a Tree. Clish, Lori, illus. (J). (gr. k-3). pap. 7.95 (978-1-928632-12-2(2)); 1999. pap. 10.95 incl. audio (978-1-928632-13-9(0)); 1999. pap. 14.95 incl. audio compact disk (978-1-928632-14-6(9)) Writers Marketplace:Consulting, Critiquing & Publishing.

Clown Fish. (Under the Sea Ser.). 24p. (J). 6.95 (978-0-7368-5110-7(0)) Capstone Pr., Inc.

Coldiron, Deborah. Anglerfish. 2007. (Underwater World Ser.). (Illus.). 32p. (J). (gr. k-4). lib. bdg. 24.21 (*978-1-59928-819-2(2) , Buddy Bks.) ABDO Publishing Co.

—Eels. 2007. (Underwater World Ser.). (ENG., Illus.). 32p. (J). (gr. k-4). lib. bdg. 24.21 (*978-1-59928-818-5(4) , Buddy Bks.) ABDO Publishing Co.

—Stingrays. 2007. (Underwater World Ser.). (ENG., Illus.). 32p. (J). (gr. k-4). lib. bdg. 24.21 (*978-1-59928-817-8(6) , Buddy Bks.) ABDO Publishing Co.

—Swordfish. 2007. (Underwater World Ser.). (Illus.). 32p. (J). (gr. k-4). lib. bdg. 24.21 (*978-1-59928-820-8(6) , Buddy Bks.) ABDO Publishing Co.

Crawford, Tracey. Fish. 2006. (Illus.). 24p. (J). (978-1-4034-8457-4(0)); pap. (978-1-4034-8464-2(3)) Heinemann Library.

Dalgleish, Sharon. Sharks & Rays. 1999. (Explorers Ser.). (Illus.). 32p. (J). (978-0-7699-0467-2(X)) Shortland Pubns. (U. S. A.) Inc.

—Underwater Animals. 1999. (Explorers Ser.). (Illus.). 32p. (J). (978-0-7699-0468-9(8)) Shortland Pubns. (U. S. A.) Inc.

Dalmatian Press Staff. Rainbow Fish: 400 Pages of Coloring Fun. 2004. (Illus.). 400p. (J). pap. 5.99 (978-1-4037-0810-6(X)) Dalmatian Pr.

Dawes, John, et al. Fish. 2006. (Facts at Your Fingertips Ser.). (Illus.). 64p. (J). (*978-1-933834-01-6(3)) Brown Bear Books.

Delafosse, Claude, et al. Fish. Miller, Heather, tr. from ENG. 1998. (First Discovery Book Ser.). (Illus.). 24p. (J). (ps-2). 12.95 (978-0-590-38155-0(5)) Scholastic, Inc.

Dollar, Sam. Piranhas. 2000. (Animals of the Rain Forest Ser.). (Illus.). 32p. (J). (gr. 4-7). lib. bdg. 22.83 (978-0-7398-3101-4(1)) Raintree.

Dorling Kindersley Publishing Staff. Fish. 2005. (J). 8p. 5.99 (978-0-7566-1711-0(1)); 72p. 15.99 (978-0-7566-1073-9(7)); (Illus.). 72p. lib. bdg. 19.99 (978-0-7566-1074-6(5)) Dorling Kindersley Publishing, Inc.

Earle, Sylvia A. Hello, Fish! Visiting the Coral Reef. Henry, Wolcott, illus. 32p. (J). (ps-3). 2001. pap. 6.95 (978-0-7922-6697-6(8)); 1999. 15.95 (978-0-7922-7103-1(3)) National Geographic Society. (National Geographic Children's Bks.).

Einhorn, Kama. Sesame Subjects: My First Book about Fish. Moroney, Christopher, illus. 2006. (Sesame Street Ser.). 24p. (J). (gr. k). 7.99 (978-0-375-83513-1(X) , Random Hse. Bks. for Young Readers) Random Hse. Children's Bks.

Electric Eels. 2002. (J). pap. (978-0-7398-5812-7(2)) Steck-Vaughn.

Elson, Gary & Lucanus, Oliver. Catfish: Everything about Natural History, Purchase, Health, Care, Breeding, & Species Identification. 2003. (Complete Pet Owner's Manual Ser.). (Illus.). 96p. pap. 7.99 (978-0-7641-2397-9(1)) Barron's Educational Series, Inc.

Evans, Mark. Fish. 2001. (ASPCA Pet Care Guides for Kids). (Illus.). (J). (978-0-606-21189-5(6)) Tandem Library Bks.

Fabulous Fish: Individual Title, 6 pack. (Rigby Focus Ser.). 16p. (gr. 1 up). 30.00 (978-0-7578-5560-3(1)) Rigby Education.

Fabulous Fish: Individual Title Six-Packs. (Rigby Focus Ser.). 16p. (gr. 1 up). 28.00 (978-0-7578-5328-9(5)) Rigby Education.

Farrington, S. Kip, Jr. Bill, the Broadbill Swordfish. Date not set. lib. bdg. 16.95 (978-0-8488-1855-5(5)) Amereon LTD.

Felix, the Very Hungry Fish. 2005. (Emergent Library: Vol. 2). (YA). (ps-1). 23.94 (978-0-8215-8920-5(2)) Sadlier, William H. Inc.

Fish. 2007. (Illus.). (J). cd-rom 9.99 (*978-0-9795190-4-8(7)) Color & Learn.

Fish. 2001. pap. (978-1-930871-41-0(4) , Family Christian Pr.) Family Christian Stores, Inc.

Fish. 2004. (J). per. (978-1-57657-355-6(9)) Paradise Pr., Inc.

Fish, 6 vols. (gr. k-2). 28.95 (978-0-7368-9237-7(0)) Red Brick Learning.

Fish: Know It Alls. 2001. (Illus.). 24p. (J). pap. 2.79 (978-0-7681-0231-4(6) , 57091) Learning Horizons, Inc.

Fish: Level E, 6 vols. (Wonder Worldtm Ser.). 16p. 29.95 (978-0-7802-1994-6(5)); 26.50 (978-0-7802-7004-6(5)) Wright Group, The.

Fish Facts. 2002. (Illus.). (J). pap. 3.74 (978-0-7398-5837-0(8)) Steck-Vaughn.

Fish for You. (Pet Care Ser.). 24p. (J). 7.95 (978-1-4048-0393-0(9)) Picture Window Bks.

Fish Sets: 1 Each of 3 Big Books. (Sunshinetm Science Ser.). (gr. 1-2). 111.50 (978-0-7802-1447-7(1)) Wright Group, The.

Foley, Cate. Find the Fish. 2000. (Welcome Bks.). (Illus.). 24p. (J). (ps-2). 17.00 (978-0-516-23095-5(6) , Children's Pr.) Scholastic Library Publishing.

—Find the Fish. 2000. (gr. k-3). lib. bdg. 12.95 (978-0-613-52044-7(0)) Tandem Library Bks.

Foster, Walter, ed. Finding Nemo. 2003. (Disney's How to Draw Classic Character Ser.). (Illus.). 32p. (J). pap. 5.95 (978-1-56010-689-0(1)) Foster, Walter Publishing, Inc.

Frost, Helen. Fish. 2000. (All about Pets Ser.). (Illus.). 24p. (J). (gr. k-1). lib. bdg. 15.93 (978-0-7368-0657-2(1) , Pebble Bks.) Capstone Pr., Inc.

Gareth Stevens Publishing Staff, contrib. by. Fish & Amphibians. 2002. (Discovery Channel School Science Ser.). (Illus.). 32p. (J). (gr. 5 up). lib. bdg. 24.67 (978-0-8368-3212-9(4)) Stevens, Gareth Inc.

Geis, Richard. Catfish. 1999. (Fish). (Illus.). 64p. (J). (gr. 4-7). lib. bdg. 19.75 (978-0-7910-5089-7(0) , Chelsea Hse.) Facts On File, Inc.

Goldish, Meish. Salmon & Other Bony Fish, Vol. 6. 2002. (World Book's Animals of the World Ser.: Set 3). (Illus.). 64p. (J). (978-0-7166-1229-2(1)) World Bk., Inc.

Grolier Educational Staff. Rays. 2001. (Nature's Children Ser.). (Illus.). 48p. (J). (978-0-7172-5546-7(8) , Grolier) Scholastic Library Publishing.

Grolier Educational Staff, contrib. by. Parrotfish. 2001. (Nature's Children Ser.). (Illus.). 48p. (J). (978-0-7172-5541-2(7) , Grolier) Scholastic Library Publishing.

Gross, Miriam J. The Jellyfish. 2006. (Illus.). 24p. (J). lib. bdg. (978-1-4042-3192-4(7) , PowerKids Pr.) Rosen Publishing Group, Inc., The.

Hamilton, Lynn. Caring for Your Fish. 2002. (Caring for Your Pet Ser.). (Illus.). 32p. (J). lib. bdg. 16.95 (978-1-59036-035-4(4)) Weigl Pubs., Inc.

Hamilton, Lynn A. Caring for Your Fish. Kissock, Heather & Marshall, Diana, eds. 2003. (Caring for Your Pet Ser.). (Illus.). 32p. (J). pap. 7.95 (978-1-59036-065-1(6)) Weigl Pubs., Inc.

Harvey, Bev. Fish. (Eyes on Nature Ser.). (J). (gr. 1). 32p. pap. (978-1-882210-53-4(0)); 36p. pap. (978-1-882210-06-0(9)) Action Publishing, Inc.

—Fish. 2002. (Chelsea Clubhouse Science Exploration Ser.). (Illus.). 32p. (gr. k-2). 23.00 (978-0-7910-6982-0(6) , Chelsea Hse.) Facts On File, Inc.

Hayashi, Leslie Ann. A Fishy Alphabet in Hawaii. Bishop, Kathleen Wong, illus. 2007. (J). (*978-1-56647-830-4(8)) Mutual Publishing LLC.

Heinrichs, Ann. Fish. 2003. (Nature's Friends Ser.). (Illus.). 32p. (J). (gr. 2 up). lib. bdg. 21.26 (978-0-7565-0435-9(X)) Compass Point Bks.

Heller, D. M. Let's Make a Fish with Everyday Materials. 2006. (Illus.). 24p. (J). lib. bdg. (978-1-4042-3062-0(9)) Rosen Publishing Group, Inc., The.

Hibbert, Clare. Fish. 2004. (Illus.). 32p. (J). lib. bdg. (978-1-58340-435-5(X)) Smart Apple Media.

Hirschmann, Kris. Flying Fish. 2004. (Illus.). 48p. (J). (gr. 4-7). 26.20 (978-0-7377-2341-0(6) , Greenhaven Pr., Inc.) Thomson Gale.

—Rays. 2002. (Creatures of the Sea Ser.). (Illus.). 48p. (J). (gr. 3-5). 23.70 (978-0-7377-0988-9(X) , Kidhaven) Thomson Gale.

Hodgson, Mona Gansberg. I Wonder How Fish Sleep. 1999. (I Wonder Ser.). (Illus.). 32p. (J). (ps-2). 6.99 (978-0-570-05066-7(9)) Concordia Publishing Hse.

Holt, Rinehart and Winston Staff. Holt Science & Technology Chapter 16: Life Science: Fishes, Amphibians, & Reptiles. 5th ed. 2004. (Illus.). pap. 12.86 (978-0-03-030221-3(8)) Holt, Rinehart & Winston.

—Holt Science & Technology Chptr. 9: Fishes & Amphibians: Chapter Resources - Tennessee Edition. 3rd ed. 2003. (YA). pap. 11.40 (978-0-03-069139-3(7)) Holt, Rinehart & Winston.

How do Fish Live? 6 Each of 1 Student Book, 6 vols. (Sunshinetm Science Ser.). 24p. (gr. 1-2). 41.95 (978-0-7802-1425-5(0)) Wright Group, The.

How do Fish Live? Big Book. (Sunshinetm Science Ser.). 24p. (gr. 1-2). 37.50 (978-0-7802-1426-2(9)) Wright Group, The.

Hudak, Heather C. Fish. 2004. (Animal Facts Ser.). (Illus.). 24p. (J). lib. bdg. 24.45 (978-1-59036-202-0(0)) Weigl Pubs., Inc.

Jango-Cohen, Judith. Freshwater Fishes. 2002. (Perfect Pets Ser.). (Illus.). 32p. (J). 25.64 (978-0-7614-1398-1(7) , Benchmark Bks.) Cavendish, Marshall Corp.

Jay, Michael. Sea Monsters. 2003. (Illus.). 32p. (J). lib. bdg. 25.70 (978-1-4109-0010-4(X)) Raintree.

Jeffrey, Laura S. Fish: How to Choose & Care for a Fish. 2004. (American Humane Pet Care Library). (Illus.). 48p. (J). lib. bdg. 23.93 (978-0-7660-2517-2(9)) Enslow Pubs., Inc.

Kalman, Bobbie. What Is a Fish? 1999. (Science of Living Things Ser.). (Illus.). 32p. (J). (gr. 2-3). (978-0-86505-882-8(2)); pap. (978-0-86505-894-1(6)) Crabtree Publishing Co.

Kalman, Bobbie & Larin, Allison. What Is a Fish? 1998. (Illus.). 32p. (J). (ps-ps). lib. bdg. 14.10 (978-0-613-12261-0(5)) Tandem Library Bks.

Kalman, Bobbie & Sjonger, Rebecca. The Life Cycle of a Crayfish. 2006. (Life Cycle Ser.). (Illus.). 32p. (J). (gr. 2-3). pap. (978-0-7787-0703-5(2)) Crabtree Publishing Co.

Kids: Fish & Fishing. 2003. (J). 1.00 (978-1-888631-30-2(9)) Watercourse, The.

Konings, Ad. The Cichlids of Lake Malawi. 2001. cd-rom 49.50 (978-0-9668255-4-1(3)) Cichlid Pr.

Kramer, Sydelle. Freaky Fishes. Barnard, Bryn, illus. 2006. (Step into Reading Ser.). (J). pap. (978-0-375-83014-3(6)); lib. bdg. (978-0-375-93014-0(0)) Random Hse., Inc.

Kuhn, Dwight & Pascoe, Elaine. Freshwater Fish. 2004. (Illus.). 48p. (J). (gr. 2-4). 24.95 (978-1-4103-0308-0(X) , Blackbirch Pr., Inc.) Thomson Gale.

Lakeshore Learning Materials Staff, contrib. by. Sorting Fish Kit. 2000. (J). pap. 29.95 (978-1-929255-57-3(8)) Lakeshore Learning Materials.

Landau, Elaine. Electric Fish. 1999. (True Bks.). (Illus.). 48p. (J). (gr. 3-5). pap. 6.95 (978-0-516-26491-2(5) , Children's Pr.) Scholastic Library Publishing.

—Electric Fish. 1999. (gr. 3-6). lib. bdg. 15.25 (978-0-613-37335-7(9)) Tandem Library Bks.

—Piranhas. 1999. (gr. 3-6). lib. bdg. 15.25 (978-0-613-37505-4(X)) Tandem Library Bks.

—Siamese Fighting Fish. 1999. (True Bks.). (Illus.). 48p. (J). (gr. 3-5). pap. 6.95 (978-0-516-26504-9(0) , Children's Pr.) Scholastic Library Publishing.

Lee, Justin. How to Draw Fish. 2002. (Kid's Guide to Drawing Ser.). (Illus.). 24p. (J). lib. bdg. 21.25 (978-0-8239-5792-7(6) , PowerKids Pr.) Rosen Publishing Group, Inc., The.

Lindeen, Carol. Pez Payaso/Por Carol K. Lindeen: Clown Fish. 2007. (SPA & ENG.). 24p. (J). (*978-0-7368-7646-9(4)) Capstone Pr., Inc.

Lindeen, Carol K. Clown Fish. 2004. (Under the Sea Ser.). (Illus.). 24p. (J). lib. bdg. 19.93 (978-0-7368-2598-6(3) , Pebble Bks.) Capstone Pr., Inc.

Listen to your Fish. 2007. 24p. pap. 3.50 (*978-1-4037-3610-9(3)) Dalmatian Pr.

Look Out, Fish! Individual Title Six-Pack Pouch - Level C. (Lighthouse Ser.). 12p. (gr. k-1). 24.00 (978-0-7578-0819-7(0)) Rigby Education.

Loves, June. Fish. 2003. (Pets Ser.). (Illus.). 32p. (gr. 2-4). 23.00 (978-0-7910-7550-0(8) , Chelsea Hse.) Facts On File, Inc.

Lundblad, Kristina & Kalman, Bobbie. Animales Llamados Peces. 2005. (SPA., Illus.). 32p. (J). (978-0-7787-8833-1(4)) Crabtree Publishing Co.

—Animales Llamados Peces: Animals Called Fish. 2006. (SPA., Illus.). 32p. pap. (978-0-7787-8869-0(5)) Crabtree Publishing Co.

—Animals Called Fish. 2005. (What Kind of Animal Is It? Ser.). (Illus.). 32p. (J). (978-0-7787-2161-1(2)); pap. (978-0-7787-2219-9(8)) Crabtree Publishing Co.

MacCallum, Jess. Swimming with the Fishes. 2nd ed. 2004. per. 4.95 (978-0-9749673-0-1(0)) In Ardua Tendit Pr.

Makowski, Robin. Fish Drawing Made Fun. 2005. 32p. pap. 6.45 (978-1-59515-785-0(9)) Rourke Publishing, LLC.

Marston, Hope Irvin. Wings in the Water: The Story of a Manta Ray. Petruccio, Steven James, illus. 1998. (Smithsonian Oceanic Collection: Vol. 16). 32p. (J). (ps-2). 15.95 (978-1-56899-577-9(6) , B4016); 19.95 incl. audio (978-1-56899-579-3(2) , BC4016); Incl. toy. 29.95 (978-1-56899-581-6(4)); Incl. toy. 34.95 incl. audio (978-1-56899-583-0(0)) Soundprints.

—Wings in the Water: The Story of a Manta Ray - Micro Book. Petruccio, Steven James, illus. 1998. (Smithsonian Oceanic Collection: Vol. 16). 32p. (J). (ps-2). 4.95 (978-1-56899-578-6(4) , B4066); Incl. micro toy. 9.95 incl. audio (978-1-56899-584-7(9)) Soundprints.

—Wings in the Water: The Story of a Manta Ray - Micro Edition. Petruccio, Steven James, illus. 1998. (Smithsonian Oceanic Collection: Vol. 16). 32p. (J). (ps-2). incl. audio (978-1-56899-580-9(6)) Soundprints.

Martineau, Susan. Healthy Eating. 2006. (Illus.). 32p. (J). (978-1-58340-893-3(2) , 1262657) Smart Apple Media.

Maydak, Michael S., illus. Wild Stickers - Sharks & Rays. 2003. 4p. (J). 2.50 (978-0-941042-34-5(0)) Dog-Eared Pubns.

Mayer, Cassie. Scales. 2006. (Illus.). 24p. (J). (978-1-4034-8374-4(4)); pap. (978-1-4034-8380-5(9)) Heinemann Library.

McCall, Gerrie. Weird & Wonderful Fish. 2006. (Nature's Monsters Ser.). (Illus.). 32p. (J). lib. bdg. 23.33 (978-0-8368-6179-2(5)) Stevens, Gareth Inc.

Miles, Elizabeth. Skin, Scales, & Shells. 2003. (Animal Parts Ser.). (Illus.). 32p. (J). (gr. k-2). lib. bdg. 21.36 (978-1-4034-0021-5(0)); pap. 6.95 (978-1-4034-0430-5(5)) Heinemann Library.

Miller, Sara Swan. Funny Fishes. 2001. (Animals Ser.). (Illus.). 63p. (J). (gr. 5-7). 25.50 (978-0-531-11797-2(9) , Watts, Franklin) Scholastic Library Publishing.

Mills, Dick. Aquarium Fish. 2004. (101 Essential Tips Ser.). (Illus.). 72p. pap. 5.00 (978-0-7566-0611-4(X)) Dorling Kindersley Publishing, Inc.

Morgan, Sally. Fish. 2004. (Illus.). 64p. (J). (978-1-4109-1048-6(2)); pap. 9.50 (978-1-4109-1345-6(7)) Harcourt Schl. Pubs.

—Fish. 2007. (QEB Down on the Farm Ser.). (J). lib. bdg. 15.95 (*978-1-59566-388-7(6)) QEB Publishing Inc.

Morley, Christine & Orbell, Carole. Mon Paisson Rouge. 2000. (Me & My Pet Ser.). (FRE., Illus.). 32p. (J). (gr. 2-5). pap. 4.95 (978-1-58728-199-0(6) , Two Can Publishing) T&N Children's Publishing.

Mozart, Homer. Guppies. 1999. (Fish). (Illus.). 64p. (YA). (gr. 4-7). lib. bdg. 19.75 (978-0-7910-5091-0(2) , Chelsea Hse.) Facts On File, Inc.

Murray, Peter. Fish. 2004. (Science Around Us Ser.). 32p. (J). (gr. 2-6). 27.07 (978-1-59296-214-3(9)) Child's World, Inc.

Nelson, Robin. Pet Fish. (First Step Nonfiction). (J). (gr. k-2). 2003. (Illus.). 24p. lib. bdg. 18.60 (978-0-8225-1267-7(X)); 2002. pap. 3.95 (978-0-8225-1298-1(X)) Lerner Publishing Group.

Nuzzolo, Deborah. Barracudas. 2008. (J). (*978-1-4296-0032-3(2) , Pebble Bks.) Capstone Pr., Inc.

O'Hare, Ted. Fish. 2006. (What Is an Animal Ser.). (Illus.). 24p. (J). (gr. 1-4). 14.95 (978-1-59515-417-0(5)) Rourke Publishing, LLC.

Ohare, Ted. Fish. 2005. 24p. pap. 5.45 (978-1-59515-731-7(X)) Rourke Publishing, LLC.

—Peces. 2005. (Que Es un Animal? Biblioteca del Descubrimiento Ser.). (SPA.). 24p. pap. 5.45 (978-1-59515-687-7(9)) Rourke Publishing, LLC.

Orbell, Carole. Fish. Morley, Christine, illus. rev. ed. 2004. (Me & My Pet Ser.). 32p. (J). (ps-1). pap. 4.95 (978-1-58728-202-7(X) , Two Can Publishing) T&N Children's Publishing.

Orr, Tamra. Piranhas. 2003. (Animal Attacks Ser.). (Illus.). 48p. (J). 23.70 (978-0-7377-1888-1(9) , Greenhaven Pr., Inc.) Thomson Gale.

Parker, Steve. Angelfish, Megamouth Sharks & Other Fish. 2005. (Animal Kingdom Classification Ser.). (Illus.). 48p. (J). (gr. 4-6). (978-0-7565-1252-1(2)) Compass Point Bks.

—Pesces. 2004. (DK Guides Ser.). 64p. (J). lib. bdg. 19.99 (978-0-7566-0419-6(2)) Dorling Kindersley Publishing, Inc.

Parrotfish. 2006. (Under the Sea Ser.). 24p. (J). 6.95 (978-0-7368-6133-5(5)) Capstone Pr., Inc.

Peterson, Roger T. & Filisky, Michael. Peterson First Guide to Fishes of North America. Landry, Sarah B., illus. 2nd ed. 1998. (First Guides). 128p. pap. 5.95 (978-0-395-91179-2(6)) Houghton Mifflin Co. Trade & Reference Div.

Pfeffer, Wendy. What's It Like to Be a Fish? 2001. 24.75 (978-0-06-000307-4(3)) HarperCollins Pubs.

Pfister, Marcus. Scaredy-Cat Fish with Sticker. 2002. (ps-2). lib. bdg. 11.80 (978-0-613-84701-8(6)) Tandem Library Bks.

Piehl, Janet. Crayfish. 2007. (Pull Ahead Books-Animals Ser.). (J). 22.60 (*978-0-8225-5931-3(5) , Lerner Pubns.) Lerner Publishing Group.

Piehl Janet. Pinching Crayfish. 2007. (Pull Ahead Books-Animals Ser.). (J). pap. 6.95 (*978-0-8225-6706-6(7) , First Avenue Editions) Lerner Publishing Group.

Pinkguni, Manolito. Piranhas. 1999. (Fish). (Illus.). 64p. (YA). (gr. 4-7). lib. bdg. 19.75 (978-0-7910-5093-4(9) , Chelsea Hse.) Facts On File, Inc.

Powell, R. This Little Fish. Curry, Peter, illus. 2004. (Mini Movers Ser.). 14p. (J). bds. 3.50 (978-0-7641-5738-7(8)) Barron's Educational Series, Inc.

Pratt-Serafini, Kristin Joy. A Swim Through the Sea. Pratt-Serafini, Kristin Joy, illus. 2006. (Illus.). 26p. (J). bds. 7.95 (978-1-58469-080-1(1)) Dawn Pubns.

Pronek, Neal. Tropical Fish. 1999. (Fish). (Illus.). 64p. (YA). (gr. 4-7). 32.00 (978-0-7910-5094-1(7) , Chelsea Hse.) Facts On File, Inc.

Pyers, Greg. Why Am I a Fish? 2005. (Raintree Perspectives Ser.). (Illus.). 32p. (J). (978-1-4109-2015-7(1)); (gr. 5-8). pap. 7.85 (978-1-4109-2022-5(4)) Steck-Vaughn.

Raintree Steck-Vaughn Staff. Encyclopedia of Fishes. 2nd ed. 1999. (Encyclopedias of Animals Ser.). (Illus.). 240p. (J). (gr. 4-7). lib. bdg. 47.95 (978-0-7398-0683-8(1)) Raintree.

Rake, Jody Sullivan. Eels. 2007. (Illus.). 24p. (J). 19.93 (978-0-7368-6362-9(1)) Capstone Pr., Inc.

—Puffer Fish. 2006. (Under the Sea Ser.). (Illus.). 24p. (J). (gr. k-2). lib. bdg. 19.93 (978-0-7368-6364-3(8) , Pebble Bks.) Capstone Pr., Inc.

—Rays. 2006. (Illus.). 24p. (J). (978-0-7368-6365-0(6) , Pebble Bks.) Capstone Pr., Inc.

Randolph, Joanne. Fish. 2007. (Classroom Pets Ser.). (Illus.). 24p. (J). (gr. k-5). lib. bdg. 21.25 (***978-1-4042-3681-3(3)*** , 1266091, PowerKids Pr.) Rosen Publishing Group, Inc., The.

Rays, 6 vols. (gr. k-2). 28.95 (978-0-7368-9102-8(1)) Red Brick Learning.

Richardson, Adele. Caring for Your Fish. 2007. (First Facts Ser.). (Illus.). 24p. (J). (gr. k-3). lib. bdg. 21.26 (978-0-7368-6386-5(9)) Capstone Pr., Inc.

Richardson, Adele D. Fish. 2004. (First Facts Ser.). (Illus.). 24p. (J). lib. bdg. 21.26 (978-0-7368-2622-8(X)) Capstone Pr., Inc.

Richardson, Joy. Fish. 2005. (Illus.). 32p. (J). lib. bdg. 23.33 (978-0-8368-4503-7(X)) Stevens, Gareth Inc.

Ring, Susan. Cuantos Peces? 2005. Tr. of How Many Fish?. (SPA., Illus.). 16p. (J). (gr. k-1). lib. bdg. 15.93 (978-0-7368-4130-6(X)) Capstone Pr., Inc.

Ripley's Big, Weird & Dangerous Fish, 6 vols., Vol. 3. 2nd ed. 2000. 64p. (YA). 14.95 (978-1-893951-02-0(2)) Ripley Entertainment, Inc.

Robinson, Fay. Faucet Fish. Robinson, Fay, illus. 2005. 32p. (J). (ps). 15.99 (978-0-525-47166-0(9) , Dutton Juvenile) Penguin Group (USA) Inc.

Rothaus, Don P. Moray Eels. 2006. (New Naturebooks). (Illus.). 32p. (J). (gr. 1-5). 27.07 (978-1-59296-644-8(6)) Child's World, Inc.

Royston, Angela. Fish. (Illus.). 32p. (YA). (gr. 2 up). lib. bdg. 27.10 (978-1-932333-35-0(5)) Chrysalis Education.

Rubin, Alan. How Many Fish? 2003. (Yellow Umbrella Books). (Illus.). 16p. (J). (gr. 1). lib. bdg. 14.60 (978-0-7368-2013-4(2) , Pebble Bks.) Capstone Pr., Inc.

—How Many Fish? 2003. (Math Ser.). (J). (978-0-7368-1699-1(2)) Yellow Umbrella Pr.

Rustad, Martha E. Rays. 2005. (Ocean Life Ser.). 24p. (YA). (gr. k-3). pap. (978-0-7368-9081-6(5) , Pebble Bks.) Capstone Pr., Inc.

Rustad, Martha E. H. Parrotfish. 2007. (Illus.). 24p. (J). lib. bdg. 19.95 (978-1-60014-079-2(3)) Bellwether Media.

—Rays. Saunders-Smith, Gail, ed. 2001. (Ocean Life Ser.). (Illus.). 24p. (J). (gr. k-1). lib. bdg. 15.93 (978-0-7368-0858-3(2) , Pebble Bks.) Capstone Pr., Inc.

Sadorus, Lauri. Pacific Halibut Flat or Fiction?, 1. Soderlund, Birgit, illus. 2005. 24p. (J). per. (978-0-9776931-0-8(4)) International Pacific Halibut Commission.

Salzmann, Mary Elizabeth. Flashy Fish. Nobens, C. A., illus. 2007. (Perfect Pets Ser.). 24p. (J). (gr. k-3). lib. bdg. 19.93 (***978-1-59928-747-8(1)*** , SandCastle) ABDO Publishing Co.

—What Has Scales? 2007. (Creature Features Ser.). (ENG., Illus.). 24p. (J). (ps-3). lib. bdg. 24.21 (***978-1-59928-870-3(2)*** , Super SandCastle) ABDO Publishing Co.

Samson, Suzanne. Sea Dragons & Rainbow Runners: Exploring Fish with Children. Neel, Preston, illus. 2000. 32p. (ps-3). pap. 10.95 (978-1-57098-052-7(7)) Rinehart, Roberts Pubs.

Sanger, Amy Wilson. First Book of Sushi. 2004. (Illus.). 20p. (J). (ps). bds. 6.95 (978-1-58246-050-5(7) , Tricycle Pr.) Ten Speed Pr.

Savage, Stephen. Fish. 1999. (What's the Difference? Ser.). (Illus.). 32p. (J). (gr. 2-4). lib. bdg. 25.69 (978-0-7398-1357-7(9)) Raintree.

—Fish. 2000. (What's the Difference? Ser.). (Illus.). 32p. (J). (ps-3). pap. 9.95 (978-0-7398-1821-3(X)) Steck-Vaughn.

Sayre, April Pulley. Trout, Trout, Trout! 2004. (Illus.). 32p. (J). (gr. k-3). ring bd. 15.95 (978-1-55971-889-9(7) , NorthWord Bks. for Young Readers) T&N Children's Publishing.

Schaefer, Lola M. Parrotfish. Saunders-Smith, Gail, ed. 1999. (Ocean Life Ser.). (Illus.). 24p. (J). (gr. k-1). lib. bdg. 15.93 (978-0-7368-0247-5(9) , Pebble Bks.) Capstone Pr., Inc.

—Parrotfish, 6 vols. Saunders-Smith, Gail, ed. (gr. k-2). 28.95 (978-0-7368-8258-3(8)) Red Brick Learning.

—Parrotfish. 2005. (Ocean Life Ser.). 24p. (YA). (gr. k-3). pap. (978-0-7368-8218-7(9) , Pebble Bks.) Capstone Pr., Inc.

—What Is a Fish? 2005. (Animals, Animals, Animals Ser.). 24p. (YA). (gr. k-3). pap. (978-0-7368-9094-6(7) , Pebble Bks.) Capstone Pr., Inc.

—What Is a Fish? Saunders-Smith, Gail, ed. 2001. (Animal Kingdom Ser.). (Illus.). 24p. (J). (gr. k-1). lib. bdg. 14.60 (978-0-7368-0865-1(5) , Pebble Bks.) Capstone Pr., Inc.

Scheff, Duncan. Electric Eels. 2002. (Animals of the Rain Forest Ser.). (Illus.). 32p. (YA). lib. bdg. 22.83 (978-0-7398-5527-0(1)) Raintree.

School Specialty Publishing. Fish. 2004. (On-File Ser.). 4p. (J). (gr. 3-5). ring bd. 4.99 (978-0-7424-2889-8(3) , Instructional Fair) Schaffer, Frank Pubns.

—Go Fish. 2006. (Brighter Child Flash Cards Ser.). 54p. (J). 2.99 (978-0-7696-4839-2(8) , Brighter Child) School Specialty Publishing.

Schulte, Mary. Piranhas & Other Fish. 2005. (Scholastic News Nonfiction Readers Ser.). (Illus.). 24p. (J). pap. (978-0-516-24791-5(3)) Children's Pr., Ltd.

Schulte, Mary Knudson. Piranhas & Other Fish. 2005. (Scholastic News Nonfiction Readers Ser.). (Illus.). 24p. (J). (gr. 1-2). 19.00 (978-0-516-24932-2(0) , Children's Pr.) Scholastic Library Publishing.

Schwartz, David M. El Combatiente. Kuhn, Dwight, photos by. 2001. (Springboards into Science Ser.). (SPA., Illus.). 24p. (J). (gr. 1 up). lib. bdg. 20.67 (978-0-8368-2993-8(X) , GHS31412) Stevens, Gareth Inc.

—Fighting Fish. Kuhn, Dwight, photos by. 2001. (Springboards into Science Ser.). (Illus.). 24p. (J). (gr. 1 up). lib. bdg. 20.67 (978-0-8368-2972-3(7)) Stevens, Gareth Inc.

Sexton, Colleen. Clown Fish. 2007. (Illus.). 24p. (J). lib. bdg. 16.95 (978-1-60014-054-9(8)) Bellwether Media.

—Clown Fish. 2007. (Blastoff! Readers Ser.). 24p. (J). (gr. k-2). 18.50 (***978-0-531-17562-0(6)*** , Children's Pr.) Scholastic Library Publishing.

Sheather, Allan. One Less Fish. Toft, Kim Michelle, illus. 1998. 32p. (J). (ps-3). 15.95 (978-0-88106-322-6(3)); pap. 6.95 (978-0-88106-323-3(1)) Charlesbridge Publishing, Inc.

Shoemaker, Hurst H. & Zim, Herbert S. Fishes. 2001. (J). mass mkt. 6.95 net. (978-0-307-64059-8(0)) St. Martin's Pr.

Sill, Cathryn. About Fish: A Guide for Children. Sill, John, illus. 2005. 40p. (J). pap. 7.95 (978-1-56145-335-1(8)) Peachtree Pubs., Ltd.

Sill, Cathryn P. & Sill, John. About Fish: A Guide for Children. Sill, Cathryn P. & Sill, John, illus. 2002. (Illus.). 40p. (J). (ps-2). 15.95 (978-1-56145-256-9(4)) Peachtree Pubs., Ltd.

Silverstein, Alvin, et al. Fabulous Fish. 2003. (What a Pet! Ser.). (Illus.). 48p. (gr. 5-8). lib. bdg. 23.90 (978-0-7613-2514-7(X) , Millbrook Pr.) Lerner Publishing Group.

Sjonger, Rebecca & Kalman, Bobbie. Skates & Rays. 2005. (Living Ocean Ser.). (Illus.). 32p. (J). (978-0-7787-1303-6(2)); pap. (978-0-7787-1325-8(3)) Crabtree Publishing Co.

Slater, Patrick. Australian Marine Fish. 2002. (Nature Kids Ser.). (Illus.). 52p. (J). (gr. 3 up). lib. bdg. (978-1-59084-215-7(4)) Mason Crest Pubs.

Smith, C. Lavett & National Audubon Society Staff. Fishes. 2000. (National Audubon Society First Field Guides). (Illus.). (J). (gr. 3-7). 160p. pap. 8.95 (978-0-590-64198-2(0)); 159p. pap. 17.95 (978-0-590-64130-2(1)) Scholastic, Inc. (Scholastic Reference).

Snedden, Robert. Fish. 2007. (J). (***978-1-59920-077-4(5)***) Smart Apple Media.

Solway, Andrew. Killer Fish. 2004. (J). 29.93 (978-1-4034-5768-4(9)); pap. 8.50 (978-1-4034-5774-5(3)) Heinemann Library.

—Sharks & Other Fish. 2006. (Illus.). 48p. (J). (978-1-4034-8221-1(7)); pap. (978-1-4034-8228-0(4)) Heinemann Library.

Souza, Dorothy M. Sea Creatures with Many Arms. 1998. (Creatures All Around Us Ser.). (Illus.). 40p. (J). (gr. 2-4). lib. bdg. (978-1-57505-262-5(8) , Carolrhoda Bks.) Lerner Publishing Group.

Spicer, Magee & Thompson, Richard. Fishes in the Ocean, Level 1. Hartmann, Barbara, illus. 1998. (First Flight Ser.). 32p. (J). (ps-k). pap. (978-1-55041-387-8(2)); lib. bdg. (978-1-55041-395-3(3)) Fitzhenry & Whiteside, Ltd.

Spicer, Maggee & Thompson, Richard. Fishes in the Ocean. Hartmann, Barbara, illus. 2001. (First Flight Ser.). 32p. (J). (ps-2). (978-1-55041-660-2(X)) Fitzhenry & Whiteside, Ltd.

Spilsbury, Louise & Spilsbury, Richard. Classifying Fish. 2003. (Classifying Living Things Ser.). (Illus.). 32p. (J). (gr. 3-5). lib. bdg. 24.22 (978-1-4034-0846-4(7)); pap. (978-1-4034-3345-9(3)) Heinemann Library.

—Classifying Fish. 2003. (Illus.). 32p. (J). (gr. 4-7). lib. bdg. 15.25 (978-0-613-60871-8(2)) Tandem Library Bks.

—The Life Cycle of Fish. 2003. (From Egg to Adult Ser.). (J). lib. bdg. 24.22 (978-1-4034-0783-2(5)); 32p. pap. 7.50 (978-1-4034-3405-0(0)) Heinemann Library.

Steck-Vaughn Staff. All Kinds of Fish. 1998. (Illus.). (J). pap. (978-0-8172-8690-3(X)) Steck-Vaughn.

Stefoff, Rebecca. The Fish Classes. 2007. (Family Trees Ser.). 96p. (J). lib. bdg. 32.79 (***978-0-7614-2695-0(7)*** , Benchmark Bks.) Cavendish, Marshall Corp.

Stewart, Melissa. Fishes. 2001. (True Bks.). (Illus.). 48p. (J). (gr. 3-5). pap. 6.95 (978-0-516-25955-0(5)); 25.00 (978-0-516-22038-3(1)) Scholastic Library Publishing. (Children's Pr.).

—Fishes. 2001. (Illus.). 47p. (J). (gr. 3-7). lib. bdg. 15.25 (978-0-613-54219-7(3)) Tandem Library Bks.

Stille, Darlene. I Am a Fish: The Life of a Clown Fish. Ouren, Todd, illus. 2004. (I Live in the Ocean Ser.). 24p. (J) (gr. k-2). lib. bdg. 22.60 (978-1-4048-0595-8(8)) Picture Window Bks.

Stone, Lynn M. Eels. 2006. (Rourke Discovery Library). (Illus.). 24p. (gr. 1-4). 14.95 (978-1-59515-438-5(8)) Rourke Publishing, LLC.

—Rays. 2006. (Rourke Discovery Library). (Illus.). 24p. (gr. 1-4). 14.95 (978-1-59515-441-5(8)) Rourke Publishing, LLC.

Sullivan, Jody. Parrotfish. 2006. (Illus.). 24p. (J). (978-0-7368-4270-9(5)) Capstone Pr., Inc.

The Survival of Fish, 6 vols. (Sunshinetm Science Ser.). 24p. (gr. 1-2). 37.50 (978-0-7802-1423-1(4)); 41.95 (978-0-7802-1422-4(6)) Wright Group, The.

Tate, Suzanne. Jenny Jelly Fish: A Tale of Wiggly Jellies. Melvin, James, illus. 2001. (Suzanne Tate's Nature Ser.: Vol. 23). 28p. (J). (ps-5). pap. 4.95 (978-1-878405-30-2(6)) Nags Head Art, Inc.

Taylor, L. R. Anemone Fish. 2007. (Early Bird Nature Books). (J). 25.26 (978-0-8225-6467-6(X) , Lerner Pubns.) Lerner Publishing Group.

Theodorou, Rod. Fish. (Illus.). 32p. (J). 2007. (***978-1-4034-9250-0(6)); 2007. (978-1-4034-9243-2(3));*** 2000. (gr. 1-4). pap. 6.95 (978-1-57572-542-0(8) , 90484) Heinemann Library.

—Fish. 2000. (Animal Babies Ser.). (Illus.). (J). (978-0-606-21994-5(3)) Tandem Library Bks.

Torckler, Gillian & Torckler, Darryl. Life-Size Guide to New Zealand Fish. 2003. (Illus.). 33p. (J). pap. (978-1-86941-586-0(8)) Random Hse. New Zealand.

Townsend. Incredible Fish, 6 Pack. 2004. (Illus.). (J). pap. 51.30 (978-1-4109-0862-9(3)) Harcourt Schl. Pubs.

Townsend, John. Incredible Fish. 2004. (J). 31.36 (978-1-4109-0529-1(2)); pap. (978-1-4109-0853-7(4)) Harcourt Schl. Pubs.

—Incredible Fish. 2005. (J). 56p. (978-1-4109-1723-2(1)); (978-1-4109-1714-0(2)) Steck-Vaughn.

University Of Portsmouth, prod. The Dogfish: A Functional Anatomy-on CD-ROM. (Multimedia Dissection Library). (YA). cd-rom 149.95 (978-0-7365-3851-0(8)) Films Media Group.

Van Dyck, Sara. Electric Eels. 2008. (Early Bird Nature Books Ser.). (J). lib. bdg. 26.60 (***978-0-8225-7886-4(7)*** , Lerner Pubns.) Lerner Publishing Group.

Visca, Curt. How to Draw Cartoon Fish. 2003. (Kids Guide to Drawing Ser.). (Illus.). 24p. (J). lib. bdg. 21.25 (978-0-8239-6159-7(1) , PowerKids Pr.) Rosen Publishing Group, Inc., The.

Walker, Jane. Tiburones. 2001. (SPA., Illus.). 32p. (J). (ps-3). 10.95 (978-84-263-3453-4(9)) Lectorum Pubns., Inc.

Walker, Pam. My Goldfish. 2001. (My Pets Ser.). (Illus.). 24p. (J). (ps-2). 17.00 (978-0-516-23185-3(5) , Children's Pr.) Scholastic Library Publishing.

Walker, Sally M. Mystery Fish. Gould, Shawn, illus. 2006. (On My Own Science Ser.). 47p. (J). pap. 5.95 (978-1-57505-850-4(2) , First Avenue Editions) Lerner Publishing Group.

—Mystery Fish: Secrets of the Coelacanth. 2006. (On My Own Science Ser.). (Illus.). 48p. (J). (gr. 2-4). lib. bdg. 25.26 (978-1-57505-638-8(0)) Lerner Publishing Group.

—Rays. 2002. (Nature Watch Ser.). (Illus.). 48p. (J). lib. bdg. 25.26 (978-1-57505-172-7(9) , Carolrhoda Bks.) Lerner Publishing Group.

Wallace, Karen. Think of an Eel. Bostock, Mike, illus. 2004. (Big Books! Ser.). 32p. (J). (ps up). pap. 19.99 (978-0-7636-2470-5(5)) Candlewick Pr.

—Think of an Eel. Bostock, Mike & Jenkins, Martin, illus. 2001. (Read & Wonder Ser.). 32p. (J). (ps up). pap. 6.99 (978-0-7636-1522-2(6)) Candlewick Pr.

—Think of an Eel. 2001. (Read & Wonder Ser.). (Illus.). (J). (978-0-606-20940-3(9)) Tandem Library Bks.

Waters, Jo. Fish. 2004. (Raintree Perspectives Ser.). (Illus.). 32p. (J). (gr. 6-8). lib. bdg. 25.70 (978-1-4109-1020-2(2)) Harcourt Schl. Pubs.

—The Wild Side of Pet Fish. 2004. (Raintree Perspectives Ser.). (Illus.). 32p. (J). pap. 7.50 (978-1-4109-1160-5(8)) Harcourt Schl. Pubs.

Weber, Valerie. Coelacanth: The Living Fossil. 2005. (Weird Wonders of the Deep Ser.). (Illus.). 24p. (J). lib. bdg. 22.00 (978-0-8368-4561-7(7)) Stevens, Gareth Inc.

Weber, Valerie J. Anglerfish. 2005. (Weird Wonders of the Deep Ser.). (Illus.). 24p. (J). lib. bdg. 22.00 (978-0-8368-4560-0(9)) Stevens, Gareth Inc.

Weingartz, Jill. Aquariums. 2001. (Created Environments Ser.). (Illus.). 24p. (J). 21.35 (978-1-58340-104-0(0)) Smart Apple Media.

What Is a Fish?, 6 vols. (gr. k-2). 28.95 (978-0-7368-9115-8(3)) Red Brick Learning.

Wickham, Mike. What Your Fish Needs. 2000. (gr. 7-12). lib. bdg. 12.95 (978-0-613-33229-3(6)) Tandem Library Bks.

Wilkes, Sarah. Fish. 2006. (J). pap. (978-0-8368-6229-4(5)); (Illus.). 48p. lib. bdg. 30.00 (978-0-8368-6210-2(4)) Stevens, Gareth Inc. (World Almanac Library).

Windsor, Jo. Animal Lights: Early Level Satellite Individual Title Six-Packs. (Sails Literacy Ser.). 16p. (gr. 1-2). 27.00 (978-0-7578-2938-3(4)) Rigby Education.

—Eating Fish: Emergent Level Satellite Individual Title Six-Packs. (Sails Literacy Ser.). (gr. k-1). 27.00 (978-0-7578-7924-1(1)) Rigby Education.

Winkelman, Barbara Gaines. Puffer's Surprise. 2005. (Illus.). (J). (ps-2). 30p. 4.95 (978-1-59249-033-2(6) , B4074); 32p. 9.95 (978-1-59249-038-7(7) , PB4074); 32p. 19.95 incl. audio (978-1-59249-035-6(2) , BC4024) Soundprints.

—Puffer's Surprise. Petruccio, Steven James, illus. 2005. (Smithsonian Oceanic Collection). 32p. (J). (ps-2). 15.95 (978-1-59249-032-5(8) , B4024); pap. 6.95 (978-1-59249-034-9(4) , S4024) Soundprints.

Wolfsheimer, Gene. Siamese Fighting Fish. 1999. (Fish). (Illus.). 64p. (YA). (gr. 4-7). lib. bdg. 19.75 (978-0-7910-5088-0(2) , Chelsea Hse.) Facts On File, Inc.

Wood, Selina. Fish. 2006. (Owning a Pet Ser.). (J). (978-1-59771-057-2(1)) Sea-To-Sea Pubns.

Yin, Robert, illus. & photos by. Octopuses, Squid & Cuttlefish. Yin, Robert, photos by. 1999. 24p. (J). 6.50 (978-0-7685-0351-7(5)) Dominie Pr., Inc.

—Sharks & Rays. Yin, Robert, photos by. 1999. 24p. (J). (978-0-7685-0357-9(4)) Dominie Pr., Inc.

Zappler, Georg. Learn about... Texas Freshwater Fishes. Ivy, Elena T., illus. 2001. (Learn about Texas Ser.). 96p. (J). pap. 9.95 (978-1-885696-36-6(1)) Texas Parks & Wildlife Pr.

Zoller, Arthur David. Fish Colors. 2004. 14p. (J). (ps-k). bds. 6.95 (978-0-88106-073-7(9)) Charlesbridge Publishing, Inc.

—Fish Counting. 2004. (Illus.). 14p. (J). (ps-k). bds. 6.95 (978-0-88106-074-4(7)) Charlesbridge Publishing, Inc.

FISHES—FICTION

Aardvark, D. The Congraduation Fish. Aardvark, D., illus. l.t. ed. 2005. (Illus.). 48p. (J). per. 12.95 (978-0-9755567-1-9(1)) Aardvark's Weedpatch Pr.

Aloha Potter! Evaluation Guide: Evaluation Guide. 2006. (J). (978-1-55942-397-7(8)) Marsh Media.

Amon, Ras Ran. Gerald, Fish of the Spirit! A Caribbean Tale of Fortune & Greed. Betiku, Olatukunbo, illus. ed. 2006. Orig. Title: Gerald, Fish of the Spirit! A Caribbean Tale of Fortune & Greed. (ENG.). (J). 7.99 (***978-0-9776603-0-8(3)***) One Love Assn. Books.

—Gerald Fish of the Spirit! Activity Book. 2006. (J). act. bk. ed. 3.99 (***978-0-9776603-2-2(X)***) One Love Assn. Books.

Amon, Ras Ran, adapted by. Gerald, Fish of the Spirit! A Caribbean Tale of Fortune & Greed. 2005. Orig. Title: Gerald, Fish of the Spirit! A Caribbean Tale of Fortune & Greed. (J). cd-rom 5.99 (978-0-9776603-1-5(1)) One Love Assn. Books.

Andrew, Tommy. Neqsulartukut. Swope, Dean, illus. 1998. Tr. of We Fish. (ESK.). 8p. (J). (gr. k-3). pap. 6.00 (978-1-58084-032-3(9)) Lower Kuskokwim Schl. District.

Arena, Felice & Kettle, Phil. Crawfish Hunt. Vane, Mitch, illus. 2004. (J). pap. (978-1-59336-358-1(3)) Mondo Publishing.

Arends, Donald L. Grandpa Grouper, the Fish with Glasses. 2006. (J). (978-0-9768880-0-0(9)) Mission Manuscripts, Inc.

Arenson, Roberta, illus. Manu & the Talking Fish. 2000. 32p. (J). (ps-3). 15.95 (978-1-84148-032-9(0)) Barefoot Bks., Inc.

Avi. What Do Fish Have to Do with Anything? And Other Stories. 2004. 208p. (J). (gr. 5-9). reprint ed. pap. 6.99 (978-0-7636-2319-7(9)) Candlewick Pr.

Azordegan, Kambiz. Precarious Pond. Sajem, Johnny, illus. 1998. (Tootee's Magical Stories Ser.: Vol. 1). 40p. (J). 9.95 (978-1-890571-25-2(3)) Positive Children's Programming Corp.

Bailey, Beth. Raining Fish. 2006. (Illus.). 32p. (J). per. 14.95 (978-1-933148-34-2(9)) Tate Publishing & Enterprises, L.L.C.

Barner, Bob. Fish Wish. Barner, Bob, illus. 2005. (Illus.). 32p. (J). (gr. k-3). 6.95 (978-0-8234-1663-9(1)) Holiday Hse., Inc.

Batson, Susann. Gilly the Seasick Fish. l.t. ed. 2006. (Illus.). (J). 28p. 15.99 (978-1-933090-22-1(7)); 32p. E-Book 5.00 incl. cd-rom (978-1-933090-37-5(5)) Guardian Angel Publishing, Inc.

Beckenstein, Cara. The True Story of Federico Fish & Ana Alligator. Tanchak, Diane, illus. 2003. 32p. 11.95 (978-0-9726699-0-0(6)) Laughing Gull Pr.

Bennett, Kelly. Not Norman: A Goldfish Story. Jones, Noah, illus. 2005. 32p. (J). (ps-3). 15.99 (978-0-7636-2384-5(9)) Candlewick Pr.

Benson, Laura. A Fish Named Fred. Adams Marks, Elizabeth, illus. 2002. (Two Can Read Ser.). 16p. (J). 2.99 (978-1-56472-666-7(5)) Edupress, Inc.

Berkes, Marianne. Over in the Ocean: In a Coral Reef. Canyon, Jeanette, illus. 2004. (J). (ps-2). 32p. 16.95 (978-1-58469-063-4(1)); 36p. pap. 8.95 (978-1-58469-062-7(3)) Dawn Pubns.

The Big Fish. 2001. (978-1-58453-163-0(0)) Pioneer Valley Educational Pr., Inc.

Blade, Adam. Sepron the Sea Serpent. 2007. (Beast Quest Ser.: No. 2). 80p. (J). pap. 4.99 (978-0-439-90654-8(7) , Scholastic Paperbacks) Scholastic, Inc.

Blair, Eric. El Pescador y su Mujer: Version del Cuento de los Hermanos Grimm. Ouren, Todd, illus. 2006. (Read-It! Readers en Espanol Ser.).Tr. of Fisherman & His Wife: A Retelling of the Grimm's Fairy Tale. (SPA.). 32p. (J). (ps-3). 19.95 (978-1-4048-1630-5(5)) Picture Window Bks.

Boniface, William. The Adventures of Max the Minnow. Sullivan, Don, illus. 2000. 28p. (J). bds. 9.99 (978-1-57939-075-4(7)) Accord Publishing, Ltd.

Bonnell, Kris. A Friend for Jellyfish. 2006. (J). 3.95 (***978-1-933727-28-8(4)***) Reading Reading Bks., LLC.

—Looking at Fish. 2005. (J). 3.75 (978-1-933727-08-0(X)) Reading Reading Bks., LLC.

Bonnell, Kris. The Mudskipper. 2006. (J). 3.75 (***978-1-933727-24-0(1)***) Reading Reading Bks., LLC.

Bowman, Crystal. Mommy, May I Hug the Fishes? 2000. 24p. (J). 6.99 (978-0-310-23209-4(0)) Zondervan.

Boyle, Alison. 1, 2, 3, 4, 5 Once I Caught a Fish Alive! Pichon, Liz, illus. 2000. (Finger Puppet Bks.). 16p. (J). (ps-k). 10.95 (978-1-86233-116-7(2)) Sterling Publishing Co., Inc.

Brooke, Susan Rich, adapted by. Finding Nemo. 2003. (Interactive Play-A-Sound Ser.). (Illus.). (J). (978-0-7853-8916-3(4)); 24p. 15.98 (978-0-7853-8420-5(0) , 7184400) Publications International, Ltd.

Brothers Grimm Staff. The Fisherman & His Wife/ el pescador y su Esposa. 2004. (Illus.). (J). (978-1-933530-20-8(0)) Bingo Bks., Inc.

Brovelli, Tito Alberto. Mary, la Ostra Timida: Cuentos Bilingues. Anderson, Kirk, tr. Munoz, Rafael Sanchez, illus. 2000. Tr. of Mary, the Shy Oyster: Bilingual Stories. (ENG & SPA.). 24p. (J). (gr. k up). 14.00 (978-0-9673032-1-5(4)) Sweet Dreams Bilingual Pubs.

Brumett, Jonas O. A Real Fishing Experience: Froginhood & Friends. Johnson, Sandra L., illus. l.t. ed. 2002. 64p. (J). (ps-3). 16.95 (978-1-892812-00-1(2)) Froginhood & Friends, Inc.

Buckeridge, Anthony. Jennings & Darbishire. 2002. 196p. pap. (978-0-7551-0153-5(7)) House of Stratus, Inc.

Buckingham, Matt. Bright Stanley. Buckingham, Matt, illus. 2006. (Illus.). 32p. (J). (ps-2). 15.95 (978-1-58925-059-8(1) , tiger tales) ME Media LLC.

Bunting, Eve. Gleam & Glow. Sylvada, Peter, illus. 32p. (J). 2001. (gr. 1-4). 17.00 (978-0-15-202596-0(0)); 2005. (ps-ps). reprint ed. pap., pap. 7.00 (978-0-15-205380-2(8) , Voyager Bks./Libros Viajeros) Harcourt Children's Bks.

—Gleam & Glow. Sylvada, Peter, illus. 2005. 32p. (J). (gr. 1-4). lib. bdg. 14.20 (978-0-606-33528-7(5)) Tandem Library Bks.

Carle, Eric. Mister Seahorse. Carle, Eric, illus. 2004. (Illus.). 32p. (J). (ps-2). 17.99 (978-0-399-24269-4(4) , Philomel) Penguin Group (USA) Inc.

Cheng, Andrea. Goldfish & Chrysanthemums. Chang, Michelle, illus. 2003. 32p. (J). 16.95 (978-1-58430-057-1(4)) Lee & Low Bks., Inc.

E F G

Christie, Jean. Stella Starfish. Canals, Sonia, illus. 2002. 8p. (J). 6.95 (978-0-8069-8229-8(2)) Sterling Publishing Co., Inc.

Clements, Andrew. Big Al & Shrimpy. Kogo, Yoshi, illus. 40p. (J). (gr. k-3). 2002. 16.95 (978-0-689-84247-4(3)); 2005. reprint ed. pap. 6.99 (978-1-4169-0366-6(6) , Aladdin) Simon & Schuster Children's Publishing.

—Big Al & Shrimpy. Kogo, Yoshi, illus. 2005. 30p. (J). (ps-3). lib. bdg. 14.19 (978-0-606-33907-0(8)) Tandem Library Bks.

Clish, Marian L. I Wonder... What Would a Fish Wish For? Clish, Lori, illus. unabr. ed. 1999. (J). (gr. k-3). pap. 14.95 incl. audio compact disk (978-1-928632-06-1(8)); 56p. pap. 7.95 (978-1-928632-04-7(1)) Writers Marketplace:Consulting, Critiquing & Publishing.

—I Wonder...What Would a Fish Wish For? Clish, Lori, illus. unabr. ed. 1999. (J). (gr. k-3). pap. 10.95 incl. audio (978-1-928632-05-4(X)) Writers Marketplace:Consulting, Critiquing & Publishing.

Cocca-Leffler, Maryann. Clams All Year. 1998. (J). (978-0-606-13277-0(5)) Tandem Library Bks.

Codell, Esmé Raji. Sing a Song of Tuna Fish: Hard-to-Swallow Stories from Fifth Grade. Pham, LeUyen, illus. 2006. 304p. (gr. 3-7). reprint ed. pap. 5.99 (978-0-7868-3652-9(0)) Hyperion Pr.

Cohen, Barbara. The Carp in the Bathtub. 48p. (J). (gr. 2-4). pap. 5.95 (978-0-8072-1332-2(2) , Listening Library) Random Hse. Audio Publishing Group.

Cohen, Caron Lee. How Many Fish? Schindler, S. D., illus. (My First I Can Read Bks.). 32p. (J). (ps up). 2000. pap. 3.99 (978-0-06-444273-2(X)); 1998. 14.89 (978-0-06-027714-7(9)); 1998. pap. 12.95 (978-0-06-027713-0(0)) HarperCollins Pubs.

—How Many Fish? 2000. (gr. k-3). lib. bdg. 11.80 (978-0-613-22995-1(9)); (Illus.). (J). 10.79 (978-0-606-18695-7(6)) Tandem Library Bks.

Collier, Kevin Scott. Journeys of Hope, a Star Shall Lead Them. 2005. (Illus.). 32p. (J). E-Book 6.00 incl. cd-rom (978-1-933090-28-3(6)) Guardian Angel Publishing, Inc.

Collins, Terry. SpongeBob Naturepants. 2001. (gr. 3-6). lib. bdg. 11.80 (978-0-613-43972-5(4)) Tandem Library Bks.

—Spongebob NaturePants, Vol. 7. 2004. 64p. (J). (gr. 2-5). pap. 17.00 incl. audio (978-1-4000-8630-6(2) , Listening Library) Random Hse. Audio Publishing Group.

Concepcion, Julio Antonio. Carlitos y Pescaito. Pontet, Daniel, illus. Diamond, Bobi, photos by. l.t. ed. 1998. Tr. of Carlitos & the Little Fish. (SPA.). 120p. pap. 10.00 (978-0-9659592-1-6(X)) Nadir Pubn.

Conejito Azul: Salva a los Peces.Tr. of Bunny Rabbit Saves the Fish. (SPA.). (J). 2.98 (978-970-22-0021-5(0)) Larousse, Ediciones, S. A. de C. V. MEX. *Dist:* Continental Bk. Co., Inc.

Cook, Bernadine. The Little Fish That Got Away. Johnson, Crockett, illus. 2005. 64p. (J). (ps-3). lib. bdg. 15.89 (978-0-06-055714-0(1)); reprint ed. 14.99 (978-0-06-055713-3(3)) HarperCollins Pubs.

Cooper, Louise. Creatures: Once I Caught a Fish Alive. unabr. ed. 2000. (Read-Along Ser.). 152p. (J). pap. incl. audio (978-0-7540-6225-7(2) , RA026, Chivers Children's Audio Bks.) BBC Audiobooks America.

Copeland, Cynthia L. & Lewis, Alexandra P. Splashy Fins, Flashy Skins: Deep-Sea Rhymes to Make You Grin. 2003. (Silly Millies Ser.: 4). (Illus.). 32p. lib. bdg. 17.90 (978-0-7613-2906-0(4) , Millbrook Pr.) Lerner Publishing Group.

Cousins, Lucy. Hooray for Fish! Cousins, Lucy, illus. 2005. (Illus.). 40p. (J). (gr. k-k). 14.99 (978-0-7636-2741-6(0)) Candlewick Pr.

Dakin, Glenn. Finding Nemo: The Essential Guide. 2003. (Illus.). 48p. (J). (gr. k-3). 12.99 (978-0-7894-9244-9(X)) Dorling Kindersley Publishing, Inc.

Davis, Guy. Freddi Fish & the Pirate's Treasure. Winslow, Becky, illus. 2001. (Humongous Ser.). 12p. (J). bds. 9.99 incl. cd-rom (978-1-58668-066-4(8)) Lyrick Studios.

De Matos, Isabel Freire. El Pececito Magico. Torres, Walter, illus. 2004. (SPA.). 22p. (J). pap. 6.95 (978-1-57581-578-7(8)) Santillana USA Publishing Co., Inc.

De Vries, Maggie. Tale of a Great White Fish: A Sturgeon Story. Benoit, Renné, illus. 2006. 48p. 15.95 (978-1-55365-125-3(1) , Greystone Bks.) Douglas & McIntyre, Ltd. CAN. *Dist:* Transition Vendor.

Denton, Terry. Gasp! The Breathtaking Adventures of a Fish Left Home Alone. 2004. (Illus.). 32p. pap. 6.99 (978-0-14-055700-8(8) , Penguin Global) Penguin Group (USA) Inc.

—Squish! An Eat-Your-Own Adventure for Mad Fish! Denton, Terry, illus. 2005. (Illus.). 32p. (J). pap. 10.00 (978-0-14-350111-4(9) , Penguin Global) Penguin Group (USA) Inc.

DePrisco, Dorothea. Little School of Fish. 2006. 12p. 10.95 (978-1-58117-485-4(3) , Intervisual/Piggy Toes) Dalmatian Pr.

Diesen, Deborah. The Pout-Pout Fish. Hanna, Dan, illus. 2008. 32p. (J). 16.00 (***978-0-374-36096-2(0)***) Farrar, Straus & Giroux.

Disney Press Staff. Finding Nemo. 2006. (Disney Junior Graphic Novel Ser.: Vol. 1). (Illus.). 48p. (gr. 1-4). pap. 3.99 (978-1-4231-0140-6(5)) Disney Pr.

Donaldson, Julia. The Fish Who Cried Wolf. Scheffler, Axel, illus. 2008. (J). pap. (***978-0-545-03454-8(X));*** 40p. 15.99 (***978-0-439-92825-0(7)***) Scholastic, Inc. (Levine, Arthur A. Bks.).

Donovan, Gail. Lost at Sea. 2001. (gr. k-3). lib. bdg. 11.80 (978-0-613-62525-8(0)) Tandem Library Bks.

—100th Day Fun. Clar, David Austin, illus. 2003. (Rainbow Fish & Friends Ser.). 24p. (J). lib. bdg. 9.95 (978-1-59014-141-0(5)); mass mkt. 3.99 (978-1-59014-140-3(7)) Night Sky Bks.

Dorling Kindersley Publishing Staff. Finding Nemo Sticker Book. 2003. (Ultimate Sticker Bks.). (Illus.). 16p. (J). pap. 6.99 (978-0-7894-9245-6(8)) Dorling Kindersley Publishing, Inc.

Doudna, Kelly. Jellyfish Role. Chawla, Neena, illus. (Fact & Fiction Ser.). 24p. (J). 2007. 21.35 (978-1-59928-446-0(4)); 2006. (978-1-59928-447-7(2)) ABDO Publishing Co.

Douglas, Babette. Squirt: The Magic Cuddlefish. 2005. (Illus.). (J). 9.99 (978-1-890343-47-7(1)) Kiss A Me Productions, Inc.

Douglis, Carole. Tessa & the Fishy Mystery. Kennaway, Adrienne, tr. 2005. (Tunza Environmental Series for Children). (Illus.). 30p. (J). pap. 8.00 (978-92-807-2462-2(2) , E.04.III.D.29) United Nations Environment Programme KEN. *Dist:* United Nations Pubns.

Dubovoy, Silvia. Turquesita. (SPA.). (J). pap. (978-968-6465-18-1(9)) Casa de Estudios de Literatura y Talleres Artisticos Amaquemecan A.C. MEX. *Dist:* Lectorum Pubns., Inc.

Ehlert, Lois. Fish Eyes: A Book You Can Count On. Ehlert, Lois, illus. 2001. (Illus.). 40p. (J). bds. 6.95 (978-0-15-216281-8(X) , Red Wagon Bks.) Harcourt Children's Bks.

Ettwein, George. Edgar the Fish. Jansen, Kristen, illus. 2002. 38p. (J). pap. 12.95 (978-1-889276-02-1(2)) Animal Sounds.

Eure, Wesley. A Fish Out of Water. Meredith College Art Department Staff, illus. 2000. 32p. (J). (ps-3). 15.95 (978-1-56554-850-3(7)) Pelican Publishing Co., Inc.

Farley, Jeanene. I Can Swim. Strasshofer, Craig, ed. Iniquez, Alex & Cortez, Steve, illus. 2000. (Mighty Minnows Adventure Ser.). 16p. (J). (ps-2). pap. 10.99 (978-0-9700101-0-0(9)) LittleJeanie Publishing Co.

Feierabend, John M. The Crabfish. Nguyen, Vincent, illus. 2004. (First Steps in Music Ser.). 24p. (J). 24.95 (978-1-57999-383-2(4)) GIA Pubns., Inc.

Ferrier, Charlotte. A Home for Little Fish. Hirashima, Jean, illus. 2005. (J). (978-1-890647-16-2(0)) RC2 Corp.

Finn, D., adapted by. Workin' at the Whale Wash. 2004. (Shark Tale Ser.). (Illus.). 24p. (J). (ps-3). pap. 3.99 (978-0-439-64153-1(5)) Scholastic, Inc.

The Fish That Made A Wish. 2005. (J). 15.95 (978-0-9762835-0-8(6)) Shooting Star Publishing.

Floyd, Cheri & Kotabe, Yago. Mauswara Fish. McGrath, Jeff, illus. 2000. 15p. (J). (gr. 1-3). pap. 5.99 (978-0-89827-209-3(2)) Wesleyan Publishing Hse.

Follow the Fish. 2005. (J). bds. 6.66 (978-0-9753127-4-2(X)) Family Bks. at Home.

Follow the Fish: A Touch & Say ABC Book. 2002. (DK Ladybird Ser.). 12p. (J). bds. 6.95 (978-0-7894-8470-3(6)) Dorling Kindersley Publishing, Inc.

Fontenot, Mary Alice. Clovis Crawfish & Echo Gecko. Buckner, Julie Dupre, illus. 2003. 32p. (J). 15.95 (978-1-56554-708-7(X)) Pelican Publishing Co., Inc.

—Clovis Crawfish & Raoul Raccoon. Landry, Cat, illus. 1999. (Clovis Crawfish Ser.). 32p. (J). (gr. k-3). 15.95 (978-1-56554-369-0(6)) Pelican Publishing Co., Inc.

—Clovis Ecrevisse et Charles Chatoui. Landry, Julie Fontenot, tr. Landry, Cat, illus. 2001. (FRE.). 32p. (J). (gr. k-3). 16.95 (978-1-56554-699-8(7)) Pelican Publishing Co., Inc.

Ford, Carole S. Timothy Turtle & Sammy Scallop. Edwin, Kimberly, illus. 30p. (J). (ps-k). pap. 4.95 (978-1-891533-02-0(9)) Calvin Partnership, LLC.

Frazier, Craig. Stanley Goes Fishing. 2006. (Illus.). 40p. (J). 15.95 (978-0-8118-5244-9(X)) Chronicle Bks. LLC.

A Friend in Need. 2007. (J). 9.95 (***978-0-9787995-6-4(9)***) High-Pitched Hum Inc.

Friends, Paz. Dos Amigos. 2001. Tr. of Two Friends. (SPA.). (J). (gr. 2-4). 16.76 (978-84-88342-17-1(9)) S.A. Kokinos ESP. *Dist:* Lectorum Pubns., Inc.

Galbraith, Ben. The Three Fishing Brothers Gruff. 2007. (Illus.). 32p. (J). (***978-0-340-89341-8(9)***) Hodder General Publishing Division.

Galjanic, Lisa. When Fish Are Mean. Hope, Michelle, illus. 2007. (J). 9.95 (978-1-933532-01-1(7)) LSG Pubns.

Galjanic, Lisa. When Series 6 Volume Set, 6, 6. 2007. (Illus.). 100p. (J). 34.95 (***978-1-933532-06-6(8)***) LSG Pubns.

Gall, Chris. Dear Fish. 2006. (Illus.). 36p. (J). (ps-1). 16.99 (978-0-316-05847-6(5)) Little Brown & Co.

Galloway, Ruth. Fidgety Fish. Galloway, Ruth, illus. (Illus.). (J). 2006. 16p. bds. 6.95 (978-1-58925-772-6(3)); 2003. 32p. pap. 6.95 (978-1-58925-377-3(9)) ME Media LLC. (tiger tales).

Gay, Marie-Louise. Estela, la Estrella del Mar. (Buenas Noches Coleccion). (SPA.). (J). 8.95 (978-958-04-5628-5(3)) Norma S.A. COL. *Dist:* Distribuidora Norma, Inc., Lectorum Pubns., Inc.

Geist, Ken & Grace, Will. The Three Little Fish & the Big Bad Shark. Gorton, Julia, illus. 2007. 32p. (J). (ps-1). pap. 6.99 (***978-0-439-71962-9(3)***) Scholastic, Inc.

Gliori, Debi. Little Bear & the Wish Fish. (Illus.). 32p. (J). (ps-2). pap. 9.99 (978-0-7112-0986-2(3)) Lincoln, Frances Ltd. GBR. *Dist:* Transition Vendor.

Goldfinger, Jennifer P. A Fish Named Spot. 2001. (Illus.). 32p. (J). (ps-3). pap. 14.95 (978-0-316-32047-4(1)) Little Brown & Co.

Goldfish. 2004. (J). per. (978-1-57657-399-0(0)) Paradise Pr., Inc.

Gorski, Grzegorz. Bajka o rybaku i prawie zA¿otej Rybce. 2005. 28p. 11.99 (978-1-4116-2826-7(8)) Lulu.com.

Graham, Wendy. Robbie Robinson & the Last Crayfish. Novak, Jiri Tibor, illus. 2004. 32p. (Orig.). pap. 13.50 (978-1-920694-34-0(X)) Univ. of Western Australia Pr. AUS. *Dist:* International Specialized Bk. Services.

Grant, Joan. Cat & Fish. Curtis, Neil, illus. 2005. 32p. (J). 16.95 (978-1-894965-14-9(0)) Simply Read Bks. CAN. *Dist:* Perseus Distribution.

Grant, Joan & Curtis, Neil. Cat & Fish Go to See. 2006. (Illus.). 32p. (J). 16.95 (978-1-894965-39-2(6)) Simply Read Bks. CAN. *Dist:* Perseus Distribution.

Green, Bessie. Paniqtuliutiq Kilitanik (How to Make Fish Strips) Nevak, Caroline, illus. l.t. ed. 1999. (ESK.). 12p. (J). (gr. k-3). pap. 17.00 (978-1-58084-120-7(1)) Lower Kuskokwim Schl. District.

Greenwood, Dwayne. The Tales of Wally the Whale & Sammy the Salmon. 2006. 17.00 (978-0-8059-9074-4(7)) Dorrance Publishing Co., Inc.

Gritton, Steve. Plain Fish. 2007. (J). 17.95 (***978-0-9795361-2-0(X)***) Bad Frog Art/SMG Bks.

Gummelt, Donna & Melchiorre, Dondino. Do Fish Kiss? Wall, Randy Hugh, ed. Varela, Juan D., illus. l.t. ed. 2006. Tr. of Los peces Besan. (SPA.). 32p. (J). 14.95 (978-0-9764798-0-2(X)) Story Store Collection Publishing.

Guzman, Stephanie. Oliver the Clownfish: Acting Cool. 2008. (Illus.). 32p. (J). (***978-1-59664-002-3(2));*** pap. (***978-1-59664-003-0(0)***) R J Communications, LLC.

Hans, Marie-Pierre. Mister William. 2007. (J). bds. 13.50 (***978-1-59692-237-2(0)***) MacAdam/Cage Publishing, Inc.

Hanson, Anders. Lone Shark. Haberstroh, Anne, illus. (Fact & Fiction Ser.). 24p. (J). 2007. 21.35 (978-1-59928-452-1(9)); 2006. (978-1-59928-453-8(7)) ABDO Publishing Co.

Hapka, Catherine. Mucha Lucha! A Little Fishy. 2004. (gr. k-3). lib. bdg. 11.25 (978-0-613-71488-4(1)) Tandem Library Bks.

Harcourt School Publishers Staff. Fish Friends: Take-Home Book. 1999. (Signatures Ser.). (Illus.). (J). pap. 1.90 (978-0-15-313907-9(2)) Harcourt Schl. Pubs.

—The Fish Market, 6 Nos., Pack. 3rd ed. 2002. (Trophies Reading Program Ser.). (Illus.). (gr. 1). pap. 20.10 (978-0-15-326868-7(9)) Harcourt Schl. Pubs.

—The Fish's Wish: Take-Home Book. rev. ed. 2001. (Collections Ser.: Bk. 11). (Illus.). (J). pap. 1.90 (978-0-15-319069-8(8)) Harcourt Schl. Pubs.

—Flip, the Funny Fish: Below Level. 3rd ed. 2002. (Trophies Reading Program Ser.). (Illus.). (J). pap. 3.20 (978-0-15-322950-3(0)) Harcourt Schl. Pubs.

—Renacuajo Curioso: Take-Home Book. 1999. (Vamos Ser.). (SPA., Illus.). (J). pap. 2.50 (978-0-15-318847-3(2)) Harcourt Schl. Pubs.

—So Many Fish: Take-Home Book. rev. ed. 2001. (Collections Ser.: Bk. 9). (Illus.). (J). pap. 1.90 (978-0-15-319067-4(1)) Harcourt Schl. Pubs.

—Swimmy: Library Book. 1999. (Collections Ser.). (Illus.). pap. 14.90 (978-0-15-313418-0(6)) Harcourt Schl. Pubs.

—Trofeos Below Level: Pinto/Divertido. 3rd ed. 2002. (SPA., Illus.). (J). pap. 3.50 (978-0-15-323861-1(5)) Harcourt Schl. Pubs.

—Yes You Can, Kerry On Level. 3rd ed. 2002. (Trophies Reading Program Ser.). (Illus.). pap. 5.10 (978-0-15-323075-2(4)) Harcourt Schl. Pubs.

Harris, Geraldine. David & the Whirly Fish. 2000. (Illus.). 192p. (J). (gr. 4-7). pap. 11.95 (978-0-595-14262-0(1)) iUniverse, Inc.

Hassanein, Amany F. Little Puffer Fish. Becker, Neesa, illus. 2000. (Books for Young Learners). 12p. (J). pap. 5.00 (978-1-57274-281-9(X)) Owen, Richard C. Pubs., Inc.

Hayward, Allan J. The Lost Little Fish. 2003. pap. 9.00 (978-0-8059-6284-0(0)) Dorrance Publishing Co., Inc.

Heck, Ed. Big Fish Little Fish. 2007. 20p. (J). (ps). pap. 9.99 (***978-0-8431-2681-5(7)*** , Price Stern Sloan) Penguin Group (USA) Inc.

Hill, James. Larry the Lunker. 2004. 35p. pap. 17.95 (978-1-4137-2972-6(X)) PublishAmerica, Inc.

Hofmeister, Alan, et al. The Fun Fish. (Reading for All Learners Ser.). (Illus.). (J). pap. (978-1-56861-121-1(8)) Swift Learning Resources.

Holding, James Malcolm, 3rd, et al. The Mullet Masters. 2007. pap. 8.00 (***978-0-8059-7147-7(5)***) Dorrance Publishing Co., Inc.

Hoobler, David. Zonk & the Secret Lagoon: The Further Adventures of Zonk the Dreaming Tortoise. l.t. ed. 2005. (Illus.). 32p. (J). lib. bdg. 16.95 (978-0-9706537-1-0(9)) Zonk Galleries.

Humu, the Little Fish Who Wished. 2000. (J). 8.99 (978-0-89610-347-4(1)) Island Heritage Publishing.

Humu the Little Fish Who Wished Away His Colors. 2003. (J). 10.99 (978-0-89610-548-5(2)) Island Heritage Publishing.

Hurd, Edith Thacher. Starfish. Brickman, Robin, illus. 2000. 40p. (J). (ps-1). (Let's-Read-and-Find-Out Science Ser.: Vol. 1). pap. 5.99 (978-0-06-445198-7(4) , Harper Trophy); (Let's-Read-&-Find-Out Science Bks.). 15.95 (978-0-06-028356-8(4)) HarperCollins Pubs.

—Starfish. Brickman, Robin, illus. 2000. (Let's-Read-and-Find-Out Ser.). 33p. lib. bdg. 11.79 (978-0-606-18720-6(0)) Tandem Library Bks.

Hutchens, Paul. Thousand Dollar Fish. rev. ed. 1998. (Sugar Creek Gang Ser.: Vol. 15). 112p. (J). (gr. 4-7). 4.99 (978-0-8024-7019-5(X)) Moody Pubs.

If I Were a Fish. (J). 26.20 (978-0-8136-8443-7(9)); 59.50 (978-0-8136-8008-8(5)) Modern Curriculum Pr.

Isadora, Rachel. The Fisherman & His Wife. Isadora, Rachel, illus. 2008. 32p. (J). (ps). 16.99 (***978-0-399-24771-2(8)*** , Putnam Juvenile) Penguin Group (USA) Inc.

James, Brian. The Fishy Field Trip. Woodman, Ned, illus. 2007. (Catkid Ser.: Bk. 2). 96p. (J). pap. 3.99 (***978-0-439-88855-4(7)***) Scholastic, Inc.

James, Brian. The Shark Who Was Afraid of Everything. 2006. (Illus.). 32p. (J). pap. 5.99 (978-0-439-78672-0(X) , Cartwheel Bks.) Scholastic, Inc.

—The Shark Who Was Afraid of Everything. McNally, Bruce J., illus. 2002. (J). (978-0-439-36865-0(0)) Scholastic, Inc.

James, Charlie. Billy the Fish. Jolliffe, Ned, illus. 2006. 176p. (J). 14.95 (978-1-58234-732-5(8)); pap. 5.95 (978-1-58234-733-2(6)) Bloomsbury Publishing. (Bloomsbury Children).

Jennings, Richard W. Stink City. 2006. 192p. (YA). (gr. 4-6). 16.00 (978-0-618-55248-1(0) , Walter Lorraine) Houghton Mifflin Co. Trade & Reference Div.

Johnson, Bailey. The Three Lady Fish. 2006. 37p. (J). pap. 10.95 (978-0-9777290-5-0(2) , 349-024) High-Pitched Hum Inc.

Jones, Christianne C. Finny Learns to Swim. Schultz, Sara, illus. 2006. (Read-It! Readers Ser.). 24p. (J). (ps-3). 18.60 (978-1-4048-1582-7(1)) Picture Window Bks.

—Goldies New Home. Muehlenhardt, Amy Bailey, illus. 2005. (Read-It! Readers Ser.). 24p. (J). (ps). lib. bdg. 18.60 (978-1-4048-1171-3(0)) Picture Window Bks.

Kalan, Robert. Blue Sea. 2002. (Illus.). (J). 14.43 (978-0-7587-2127-3(7)) Book Wholesalers, Inc.

Kalar, Bonnie. Josh & the Fish. Spreen, Kathe, illus. Date not set. 8p. (J). (ps-2). pap. (978-1-891619-14-4(4)) Corona Pr.

Kessler, Liz. The Tail of Emily Windsnap. Gibb, Sarah, illus. 2004. (Emily Windsnap Ser.). 224p. (J). (gr. 3-7). 15.99 (978-0-7636-2483-5(7)) Candlewick Pr.

Kinefield, David. Little Angel. Lawson, Peter, illus. 2004. 12p. (J). bds. 5.99 (978-0-689-86734-7(4) , Little Simon) Simon & Schuster Children's Publishing.

Kitamura, Satoshi. El Pececito Juega a las Escondidas. (Buenas Noches Coleccion). (SPA.). (J). pap. 7.95 (978-958-04-5089-4(7)) Norma S.A. COL. *Dist:* Distribuidora Norma, Inc., Lectorum Pubns., Inc.

Klett, David. The Adventures of Willy & Billy Bk. 1: The Lake Lure Chronicles - Book 1. Lang, Carole, illus. l.t. ed. 2006. 32p. (J). lib. bdg. 17.95 (978-0-9779325-0-4(8)) Five Oaks Pr.

Knudsen, Michelle. Fish & Frog. Petrone, Valeria, illus. 2005. 8p. (J). (ps-2). pap. 5.99 (978-0-7636-2457-6(8)) Candlewick Pr.

Komaiko, Leah. Just My Dad & Me. Greene, Jeffrey, illus. 1999. (Trophy Picture Bk.). 32p. (J). (ps-2). pap. 5.95 (978-0-06-443562-8(8) , Harper Trophy) HarperCollins Pubs.

—Just My Dad & Me. 1999. (J). (978-0-606-16691-1(2)); lib. bdg. 14.10 (978-0-613-18259-1(6)) Tandem Library Bks.

Korba, Joanna. Yeh-shen: A Cinderella Tale from China. 2006. 42.00 (***978-1-4108-6162-7(7)***) Benchmark Education Co.

Korman, Susan. Swordfish Returns. Stegos, Daniel, illus. 2005. 32p. (J). (ps-2). 4.95 (978-1-59249-126-1(X) , B4075); 9.95 (978-1-59249-132-2(4) , PB4075); 19.95 incl. audio (978-1-59249-128-5(6) , BC4025) Soundprints.

—Swordfish Returns. Stegos, Daniel, tr. Stegos, Daniel, illus. 2005. 32p. (J). (ps-2). 15.95 (978-1-59249-125-4(1) , B4025); pap. 6.95 (978-1-59249-127-8(8) , S4025) Soundprints.

—Swordfish Returns. Stegos, Daniel, illus. 2003. 32p. (J). (ps-2). 8.95 incl. audio (978-1-59249-129-2(4) , SC4025) Soundprints.

Kreloff, Elliot. Harry Bear & Friends Count Fish. 2007. (Illus.). 16p. (ps-k). bds. 7.95 (***978-1-59354-619-9(X)***) Handprint Bks.

Kreloff, Elliot, illus. Fish Wish. 2005. (J). (ps-k). lib. bdg. 11.15 (978-0-606-33866-0(7)) Tandem Library Bks.

Kristina Learns about Fishing. 2007. (J). (***978-0-9792728-0-6(7)***) Tracepaper Bks. Inc.

Krulik, Nancy E. Something's Fishy, No. 26. John and Wendy Staff, illus. 2007. (Katie Kazoo, Switcheroo Ser.: No. 26). 80p. (J). (gr. 2-5). pap. 3.99 (***978-0-448-44442-0(9)*** , Grosset & Dunlap) Penguin Group (USA) Inc.

Kurlansky, Mark. The Cod's Tale. Schindler, S. D., illus. 2001. 48p. (J). (gr. 2-5). 16.99 (978-0-399-23476-7(4) , Putnam Juvenile) Penguin Group (USA) Inc.

Lagonegro, Melissa. Just Keep Swimming. Harchy, Atelier Philippe, illus. 2005. (Step into Reading Ser.). 32p. (J). (ps-2). pap. 3.99 (978-0-7364-2319-9(2) , RH/Disney) Random Hse. Children's Bks.

Lairla, Sergio. La Carta de la Senora Gonzalez. Lartitegui, Ana G., illus. 2001. Tr. of Mrs. Gonzalez's Letter. (SPA.). 35p. (ps-ps). per. 14.00 (978-968-16-6233-2(4)) Fondo de Cultura Economica USA.

Landes, David. The Three Little Fish. 2007. (Illus.). 22p. (J). per. 8.99 (***978-1-60247-117-7(7)***) Tate Publishing & Enterprises, L.L.C.

LaReau, Kara. Ugly Fish. Magoon, Scott, illus. 2006. 40p. (J). (ps-2). 16.00 (978-0-15-205082-5(5)) Harcourt Trade Pubs.

Larsen, Dean. Fish Dreams. 2006. 32p. (J). 14.25 (978-1-4116-7783-8(8)) Lulu.com.

Le, Guo, illus. The Dragon's Tears. 2004. 24p. (J). (TAM, CZE, VIE, SPA & GUJ.). pap. (978-1-85269-686-3(9)); (TAM, CZE, VIE, SPA & GUJ.). pap. (978-1-85269-687-0(7)); (TAM, CZE, VIE, SPA & GUJ.). pap. (978-1-85269-688-7(5)); (TAM, CZE, VIE, SPA & GUJ.). pap. (978-1-85269-691-7(5)); (TAM, CZE, VIE, SPA & GUJ.). pap. (978-1-85269-692-4(3)); (TAM, CZE, VIE, SPA & GUJ.). pap. (978-1-85269-693-1(1)); (TAM, CZE, VIE, SPA & GUJ.). pap. (978-1-85269-694-8(X)); (TAM, CZE, VIE, SPA & GUJ.). pap. (978-1-85269-695-5(8)); (CZE, TAM, VIE, SPA & GUJ.). pap. (978-1-85269-696-2(6)); (TAM, CZE, VIE, SPA & GUJ.). pap. (978-1-85269-697-9(4)); (TAM, CZE, VIE, SPA & GUJ.). pap. (978-1-85269-698-6(2)); (TAM, CZE, VIE, SPA & GUJ.). pap. (978-1-85269-699-3(0)); (TAM, CZE, SPA, VIE & GUJ.). pap. (978-1-85269-700-6(8)); (TAM, CZE, VIE, SPA & GUJ.). pap. (978-1-85269-787-7(3)); (TAM, CZE, VIE, SPA & GUJ.). pap. (978-1-85269-805-8(5)); (TAM, CZE, VIE, SPA & GUJ.). pap. (978-1-85269-810-2(1)) Mantra Publishing, Ltd.

Leaney, Cindy. Fish Can Fly. Whitehouse, Patty, ed. King, Sue & Wilks, Peter, illus. 2004. (Friendly Phonics Ser.). 24p. (J). lib. bdg. 14.95 (978-1-59054-106-7(5)) Fitzgerald Bks.

—Rachel the Shy Jellyfish. Whitehouse, Patty, ed. King, Sue & Wilks, Peter, illus. 2004. (Friendly Phonics Ser.). 24p. (J). lib. bdg. 14.95 (978-1-59054-274-3(6)) Fitzgerald Bks.

Learning Colors. 1999. (Illus.). (J). (978-1-56156-835-2(X)) Kidsbooks, Inc.

Leon, Georgina Lazaro. The Girl & the Starfish. Perez-Moliere, Marnie, illus. 2004. (Yellow Ser.). (SPA.). 31p. (J). (gr. k-3). pap. 5.95 (978-1-57581-436-0(6)) Santillana USA Publishing Co., Inc.

Lim, Charlotte. Attack of the Swordfish & Other Singapore Tales: Text by Charlotte Lim: Illustrations by Alicia Tan Yen Ping: Creative Directing by Ruby Lim-Yang. 2005. (Illus.). 48p. (978-981-05-3215-4(6)) National Heritage Board.

Linn, Margot. Fish Wish. Kreloff, Elliot, illus. 2005. (I'm Going to Read Ser.: Level 1). 28p. (J). 11.95 (978-1-4027-2085-7(8)) Sterling Publishing Co., Inc.

Lionni, Leo. Fish Is Fish. Lionni, Leo, illus. 2002. (Illus.). (J). 13.83 (978-0-7587-2509-7(4)) Book Wholesalers, Inc.

—Nadarin. 2002. (SPA.). 32p. (J). (978-1-4000-0134-7(X)) Plaza & Janes Editories, S.A.

—Nadarin. Mlawer, Teresa, tr. from SPA. 2005. (SPA., Illus.). 24p. (J). (ps-3). pap. 6.99 (978-1-930332-80-5(7)) Lectorum Pubns., Inc.

Little Fish Christmas Merchandiser. (J). 128.16 (978-0-8307-2909-8(7) , Gospel Light) Gospel Light Pubns.

Little Fish Easter Merchandiser. (J). 128.16 (978-0-8307-2908-1(9) , Gospel Light) Gospel Light Pubns.

Little Fish Jesus Merchandiser. (J). 128.16 (978-0-8307-2907-4(0) , Gospel Light) Gospel Light Pubns.

Little Is Big. 2006. (Illus.). (J). (978-1-882601-58-5(0)) See-More's Workshop.

Loo, Sanne te. Little Fish. Loo, Sanne te, illus. 2004. (Illus.). 32p. (J). 15.95 (978-1-929132-59-1(X)) Kane/Miller Bk. Pubs., Inc.

Luenn, Nancy. Nessa's Fish. Waldman, Neil, illus. unabr. ed. 2001. (J). (gr. k-3). pap. 16.95 incl. audio (978-0-8045-6844-9(8) , 6844) Spoken Arts, Inc.

Luke, Deanna. Marky & the Fish. Chambers, Lynne, illus. 2001. (Marky Ser.: Vol. No. 4). 48p. (J). (gr. 2-4). 8.95 (978-1-928777-09-0(0) , BOW Bks.) Blessing Our World, Inc.

—Marky & the Fish: Story Book. 2001. (Marky Ser.: Vol. 4). (J). cd-rom 5.95 (978-1-928777-31-1(7) , BOW Bks.) Blessing Our World, Inc.

Lumry, Amanda & Hurwitz, Laura. Survival of Salmon. 2006. (Illus.). 36p. 15.95 (978-0-9748411-3-7(7)) Eaglemont Pr.

Lynne Enden, Rebecca. Ryan's Dinosaur & the Neon Fish: Two Stories from Rebecca's. 2006. (ENG.). 44p. per. 16.99 ***(*978-1-4208-5670-5(7))*** AuthorHouse.

MacLean, Christine. Mary Margaret & the Perfect Pet Plan. 2004. (Illus.). 128p. (J). (gr. 3-7). 15.99 (978-0-525-47183-7(9) , Dutton Juvenile) Penguin Group (USA) Inc.

Marsh, Carole. The Mystery at the Georgia Aquarium. 2006. 128p. (gr. 7-14). 14.95 ***(*978-0-635-06227-7(5))*** Gallopade International.

Marston, Hope Irvin. Wings in the Water: The Story of a Manta Ray. Petruccio, Steven James, illus. 1998. (Smithsonian Oceanic Collection: Vol. 16). 32p. (J). (ps-2). 15.95 (978-1-56899-577-9(6) , B4016) Soundprints.

—Wings in the Water: The Story of a Manta Ray - Micro Book. Petruccio, Steven James, illus. 1998. (Smithsonian Oceanic Collection: Vol. 16). 32p. (J). (ps-2). 4.95 (978-1-56899-578-6(4) , B4066) Soundprints.

Martin, Cynthia. A Jellyfish Named Jane Who Wanted to Meet Other Fish in the Sea. 2006. 17.95 (978-0-533-15014-4(0)) Vantage Pr., Inc.

Matthews, L. S. Fish. 2006. 192p. (gr. 5). reprint ed. 5.99 (978-0-440-42021-7(0) , Yearling) Random Hse. Children's Bks.

McGrath, Barbara Barbieri. The Pepperidge Farm Goldfish Fun Book. Bolster, Rob & Mazzola, Frank, Jr., illus. 1999. 16p. (J). (ps up). 5.99 (978-0-694-01450-7(8) , Harper Festival) HarperCollins Pubs.

McOmber, Rachel B., ed. McOmber Phonics Storybooks. rev. ed. (Illus.). (J). (978-0-944991-72-5(6)) Swift Learning Resources.

Metaxas, Eric. Princess Scargo & the Birthday Pumpkin. Barbour, Karen, illus. 2005. (Rabbit Ears-A Classic Tale Ser.). 40p. (J). (gr. k-5). 25.65 (978-1-59197-769-8(X)) Spotlight.

Miller, Nicole M. Curiosity Shop: Amazing Fish. 1998. 17p. 39.95 (978-1-878631-43-5(8)) Kovalik, Susan & Assocs.

Milliman, Linda & Soles, Gail. Briny the Starfish. 2002. (Illus.). 26p. (J). (ps-4). pap. 15.00 (978-0-9717603-0-1(6)) Isaiah's Promise Publishing Co.

Mitchell, Mary Esther. The Adventures of Timmy Gills. 2005. (J). pap. 20.00 (978-0-8059-9660-9(5) , RoseDog Bks.) Dorrance Publishing Co., Inc.

Miyahira, Linda. Fish for Salmon. 2005. 37p. pap. 7.95 (978-0-533-15097-7(3)) Vantage Pr., Inc.

Moriarty, Sinéad. From Here to Maternity. 2006. 304p. pap. ***(*978-1-84488-068-3(0))*** Penguin Ireland.

My Fish. (Early Intervention Levels Ser.). 21.30 (978-0-7362-0359-3(1)) Hampton-Brown Bks.

My Fish Are Fine with Me, 6 vols., Pack. (ps-2). 27.00 (978-0-7635-9465-7(2)) Rigby Education.

Myers, Tim & Arakaki, Daryl. Let's Call Him Lau-Wiliwili-Humuhumu-Nukunuku-Nukunuku-Apua'a-'Oi'Oi. 2005. (Illus.). 24p. (J). 16.95 incl. cd-rom (978-1-57306-252-7(9)) Bess Pr., Inc.

Napp, Daniel. Professor Bumble & the Monster of the Deep. 2008. 32p. (J). 15.95 ***(*978-0-8109-9484-3(4)*** , Abrams Bks. for Young Readers) Abrams, Harry N. , Inc.

Nesin, Aziz, et al. The Dance of the Eagle & the Fish. Christie, Ruth, tr. from TUR. 2001. (Illus.). 24p. (J). pap. 7.95 (978-1-84059-316-7(4)) Milet Publishing.

Nickel, Scott. Freddi Fish a Whale of a Tale! Johnson, Jay B., illus. 2001. (Humongous Ser.). 24p. (J). (ps-3). pap. 4.99 (978-1-58668-061-9(7)) Lyrick Studios.

Nicola, Robbin. Fighter Joe: The Fish of Which Dreams Are Made. Wolf, Claudia, illus. 2006. 24p. (J). per. 2.99 (978-1-59958-001-2(2)) Journey Stone Creations, LLC.

O'Connor, Ilett. Misaiah's Pet Fish - Gerard. Kahn, Alisha, illus. Wells, Wadell, photos by. 2002. 20p. pap. 10.00 (978-0-9717003-2-1(X)) O'Connor, Ilett K.

O'Donnell, Jim. Topa, the Bold Fish: Novel. Pacey, Janet, illus. 2000. 65p. (J). (ps-3). (978-1-894303-27-9(X)) Raven Rock Publishing.

Oliver the Clownfish: The Invitation Slip-up. 2006. (J). 5.95 (978-1-59664-000-9(6)); 14.95 (978-1-59664-001-6(4)) Not So Plain Jane Publishing.

O'Neill, Michael Patrick. Fishy Friends: A Journey Through the Coral Kingdom. O'Neill, Michael Patrick, photos by. 2003. (Illus.). 64p. (J). 19.95 (978-0-9728653-0-2(6)) Batfish Bks.

Ostow, Micol. Mumble's Journey: The Junior Novelization-Happy Feet. 2006. 96p. (J). (gr. 1-3). pap. 4.99 (978-0-8431-2104-9(1) , Price Stern Sloan) Penguin Group (USA) Inc.

Page, Nick & Claire. Loaves & Fishes. 2006. (Read with Me (Make Believe Ideas) Ser.). (Illus.). 30p. (J). (gr. k-2). 3.95 (978-1-84610-175-5(1)) Make Believe Ideas GBR. *Dist:* Ingram Pub. Services.

Parent, Nancy. Freddi Fish What's Different? Rillo, Cary, illus. 2001. (Humongous Ser.). 32p. (J). (ps-3). pap. 3.99 (978-1-58668-063-3(3)) Lyrick Studios.

Parish, Steve, illus. Clown Fish Finds a Friend. 2005. 24p. (J). lib. bdg. 20.67 (978-0-8368-5969-0(3)) Stevens, Gareth Inc.

Park, Barbara. Junie B. Jones Smells Something Fishy. unabr. ed. 2004. (Junie B. Jones Ser.: No. 12). 66p. (J). (gr. k-3). pap. 17.00 incl. audio (978-0-8072-0533-4(8) , Listening Library) Random Hse. Audio Publishing Group.

—Junie B. Jones Smells Something Fishy. Brunkus, Denise & Silverpin Studio Staff, illus. 1998. (Junie B. Jones Ser.: No. 12). 80p. (J). (gr. k-3). lib. bdg. 11.99 (978-0-679-99130-4(1) , Random Hse. Bks. for Young Readers) Random Hse. Children's Bks.

—Junie B. Jones Smells Something Fishy. Brunkus, Denise, illus. 1998. (Junie B. Jones Ser.: No. 12). 80p. (J). (gr. 1-4). pap. 3.99 (978-0-679-89130-7(7) , Random Hse. Bks. for Young Readers) Random Hse. Children's Bks.

Paul Ahrens-Gray & Ericka Grogan. Fish. 2005. (Illus.). 60p. (J). pap., act. bk. ed. 4.95 (978-1-59867-001-1(8)) Global Learning, Inc.

Pfister, Marcus. The Copycat Fish. 2001. (Rainbow Fish & Friends Ser.). (Illus.). 24p. (J). (ps-3). pap. 3.99 (978-1-59014-000-0(1)) North-South Bks., Inc.

—Lost at Sea. Pfister, Marcus & Clar, David Austin, illus. 2001. (Rainbow Fish & Friends Ser.). 24p. (J). (ps-3). pap. 3.99 (978-1-59014-002-4(8)) North-South Bks., Inc.

—Pececitos Miedosos. 2002. Tr. of Scaredy-Cat Fish. (SPA.). (gr. k-3). lib. bdg. 11.80 (978-0-613-87418-2(8)) Tandem Library Bks.

—El Pez Arco Iris al Rescate! Pfister, Marcus, illus. 1998. (Rainbow Fish Ser.). Orig. Title: Regenbogenfisch, Komm Hilf Mir!. (SPA., Illus.). 12p. (J). (ps-3). bds. 9.95 (978-1-55858-885-1(X)) North-South Bks., Inc.

—Pez Arco Iris y la Balena Azul, el Big Book: Rainbow Fish. Pfister, Marcus, illus. 1999. (Rainbow Fish Ser.). Orig. Title: Regenbogenfisch und Grosser Blauer Wal. (SPA., Illus.). 32p. (J). (ps-3). pap. 25.00 (978-0-7358-1215-4(2)) North-South Bks., Inc.

—Pez Arco Iris y la Ballena Azul. Pfister, Marcus, illus. 1998. (Rainbow Fish Ser.). Orig. Title: Regenbogenfisch und Grosser Blauer Wal. (SPA., Illus.). 32p. (J). (ps-3). 18.95 (978-0-7358-1002-0(8) , NSB028) North-South Bks., Inc.

—El Pez Arco Iris y la Cueva de los Monstruos. Gambolini, Gerardo, tr. from GER. 2001. (Rainbow Fish Ser.). (SPA., Illus.). 32p. (J). (ps-3). 18.95 (978-0-7358-1549-0(6)) North-South Bks., Inc.

—The Rainbow Fish. Pfister, Marcus, illus. ed. 2000. (Rainbow Fish Ser.). (Illus.). 32p. (J). (ps-3). 8.95 (978-0-7358-1232-1(2)) North-South Bks., Inc.

—Rainbow Fish: Dangerous Deep. 2002. (ps-2). lib. bdg. 11.80 (978-0-613-50438-6(0)) Tandem Library Bks.

—Rainbow Fish: Finders Keepers. (Illus.). 128p. (J). (978-0-06-059708-5(9)) HarperCollins Pubs.

—Rainbow Fish: Tattle Tale. 2002. (ps-2). lib. bdg. 11.80 (978-0-613-52730-9(5)) Tandem Library Bks.

—Rainbow Fish A, B, C. Pfister, Marcus, illus. 2002. (Rainbow Fish Ser.). (Illus.). 20p. (J). (ps). 9.95 (978-0-7358-1714-2(6)) North-South Bks., Inc.

—Rainbow Fish & the Big, Blue Whale. James, J. Alison, tr. from GER. Pfister, Marcus, illus. 1998. (Rainbow Fish Ser.). Orig. Title: Regenbogenfisch und Grosser Blauer Wal. (Illus.). 32p. (J). (ps-3). 18.88 (978-0-7358-1010-5(9)) North-South Bks., Inc.

—Rainbow Fish & the Big Blue Whale. 2001. (Rainbow Fish Ser.). Orig. Title: Regenbogenfisch und Grosser Blauer Wal. (Illus.). 14p. (J). (ps-3). bds. 9.95 (978-0-7358-1430-1(9)) North-South Bks., Inc.

—Rainbow Fish & the Big Blue Whale. James, J. Alison, tr. from GER. Pfister, Marcus, illus. 1998. (Rainbow Fish Ser.). Orig. Title: Regenbogenfisch und Grosser Blauer Wal. (Illus.). 32p. (J). (ps-3). 18.95 (978-0-7358-1009-9(5)) North-South Bks., Inc.

—Rainbow Fish & the Big Blue Whale. Pfister, Marcus, illus. 1999. (Rainbow Fish Ser.). Orig. Title: Regenbogenfisch und Grosser Blauer Wal. (Illus.). 32p. (J). (ps-3). reprint ed. pap. 25.00 (978-0-7358-1214-7(4)) North-South Bks., Inc.

—Rainbow Fish & the Sea Monsters' Cave. James, J. Alison, tr. from GER. 2001. (Rainbow Fish Ser.). (Illus.). 32p. (J). (ps-3). 18.88 (978-0-7358-1537-7(2)) North-South Bks., Inc.

—Rainbow Fish & the Seamonsters' Cave. James, J. Alison, tr. from GER. 2001. (Rainbow Fish Ser.). (Illus.). 32p. (J). (ps-3). 18.95 (978-0-7358-1536-0(4)) North-South Bks., Inc.

—Rainbow Fish Finds His Way. James, J. Alison, tr. from GER. 2006. (Illus.). 32p. (J). 18.95 (978-0-7358-2084-5(8)) North-South Bks., Inc.

—Rainbow Fish Finds His Way. 2006. (Illus.). 32p. (J). 18.88 (978-0-7358-2085-2(6)) North-South Bks., Inc.

—Rainbow Fish Hide & Seek Clothbook. 2006. (J). 12.95 (978-0-7358-2034-0(1)) North-South Bks., Inc.

—Rainbow Fish Opposites/Opuestos: A Bilingual Book. 2006. (ENG & SPA.). 24p. (J). (ps). bds. 4.99 (978-0-7358-2039-5(2)) North-South Bks., Inc.

—The Rainbow Fish Sticker Storybook. 2001. (Rainbow Fish Ser.). (Illus.). 12p. (J). (ps-3). pap. 6.95 (978-0-7358-1454-7(6)) North-South Bks., Inc.

—Rainbow Fish to the Rescue! ed. 2001. (Rainbow Fish Ser.).Tr. of Regenbogenfisch, Komm Hilf Mir!. (Illus.). 32p. (J). (ps-3). 8.95 (978-0-7358-1481-3(3)) North-South Bks., Inc.

—Rainbow Fish to the Rescue! Minibook & Audio Package. James, J. Alison, tr. from GER. Pfister, Marcus, illus. 1998. (Rainbow Fish Ser.).Tr. of Regenbogenfisch, Komm Hilf Mir!. (ENG & SPA., Illus.). 12p. (J). (ps-3). bds. 9.95 (978-1-55858-880-6(9)) North-South Bks., Inc.

—Rainbow Fish Undersea Fun Sticker Storybook. 2003. (Illus.). (J). pap. 6.95 (978-1-59014-147-2(4)) North-South Bks., Inc.

Piterski, Brahm & Piterski, Paul. Like a Fish on a Bike! l.t. ed. 1999. (Illus.). 32p. (J). (gr. 2-5). 14.95 (978-0-9658435-0-8(5)) Verdant Publishing, Inc.

Puffy. 2006. (J). ***(*978-0-9779521-0-6(X))*** City on a Hill, Inc.

Pursh, Eric. I Sette Pesci: The Seven Fishes. Lucot, Erica, illus. 2005. (J). per. (978-0-9727319-3-5(8) , Blacktypewriter Pr.) Pittsburgh Literary Arts Network LLC.

Rain Fish & Big Blue Whale Readers Guide. 2005. (J). pap. (978-0-7358-1174-4(1)) North-South Bks., Inc.

Rainbow Fish Readers Guide. 2005. (J). pap. (978-0-7358-1172-0(5)) North-South Bks., Inc.

Rainbow Fish to Rescue Reader Guide. 2005. (J). pap. (978-0-7358-1173-7(3)) North-South Bks., Inc.

Raintree Steck-Vaughn Staff. El Pez Maravilloso. 1999. (SPA.). (J). pap., stu. ed. 31.05 (978-0-7398-0753-8(6)) Steck-Vaughn.

—Video Quest. 2000. (Adventure Ser.). (Illus.). (J). pap. 3.41 (978-0-8114-9315-4(6)) Steck-Vaughn.

Random House Disney Staff. Best Dad in the Sea. 2003. (gr. k-3). lib. bdg. 11.80 (978-0-613-73685-5(0)) Tandem Library Bks.

—Finding Nemo. 2004. (Disney Read-Aloud Board Books). (Illus.). 24p. (J). (gr. k-k). bds. 4.99 (978-0-7364-2249-9(8) , RH/Disney) Random Hse. Children's Bks.

—Fish in a Box. 2003. (Illus.). 10p. (J). (ps-3). bds. 9.99 (978-0-7364-2154-6(8) , RH/Disney) Random Hse. Children's Bks.

Raschka, Chris. Arlene Sardine. 1998. (Illus.). 40p. (J). (ps-3). 16.99 (978-0-531-33111-8(3) , Orchard Bks.) Scholastic, Inc.

Ready Reader Staff. I Got a Goldfish: Hard & Soft G, 6 bks., set, Level B. 2003. (J). (ps-3). 24.50 (978-0-8136-2040-4(6)) Modern Curriculum Pr.

Reedy, Mokena Potae. Timo & the Kingfish. Gregory, Elton, illus. 2000. 32p. (J). pap. 12.95 (978-1-877266-26-3(4)) Huia Pubs. NZL. *Dist:* Pacific Island Bks.

Rectz, Kurt. Catfish Lewy: All Aboard. 2000. mass mkt. 4.50 (978-1-931179-26-3(3)); mass mkt. 8.95 (978-1-931179-37-9(9)) Long Hill Productions, Inc.

Richards, Kitty. SpongeBob AirPants: The Lost Episode, Vol. 8. 2004. 64p. (J). (gr. 2-5). pap. 17.00 incl. audio (978-1-4000-8631-3(0) , Listening Library) Random Hse. Audio Publishing Group.

Richards, Lucy & Finn, Rebecca, illus. Silly Sea (W/Hang Tag) 2004. (Cuddly Cuffs Ser.: No. 8). 10p. (J). tchr. ed. 5.95 (978-1-58925-728-3(6) , tiger tales) ME Media LLC.

—Silly Sea (W/Header Card) 2004. (Cuddly Cuffs Ser.: 8). 10p. (J). tchr. ed. 5.95 (978-1-58925-732-0(4) , tiger tales) ME Media LLC.

Ridinger, Gayle. A Star at the Bottom of the Sea. Parpajola, Andreina, illus. 2002. 32p. (J). (ps up). lib. bdg. 24.67 (978-0-8368-3175-7(6)) Stevens, Gareth Inc.

Rinaldo, Luana, illus. Clackers: FISH. 2008. (Clackers Ser.). 14p. (J). (gr. k-ps). bds. 4.99 ***(*978-0-375-84230-6(6)*** , Robin Corey Bks.) Random Hse. Children's Bks.

Robertson, Elysia Hill. Do Fish Cry ? Robertson, Elysia Hill, illus. 2005. (Illus.). 116p. (J). per. 12.95 (978-0-9764444-1-1(0) , EJWV-002) E. J. Publishing.

Robinson, Fay. Fish Wish. 2005. (Illus.). 32p. (J). ***(*978-1-84011-605-2(6))*** Templar Publishing, Dorking.

Robles, Anthony D. Lakas & the Manilatown Fish / Si Lakas at Ang Isdang Manilatown. de Jesus, Eloisa D. & de Guzman, Magdalena, trs. Angel, Carl, illus. 2003. Tr. of Si Lakas at Ang Isdang Manilatown. (ENG & TAG.). 32p. (J). 16.95 (978-0-89239-182-0(0)) Children's Bk. Pr.

Rohmann, Eric. Clara & Asha. Rohmann, Eric, illus. 2005. (Illus.). 40p. (J). (ps-ps). 16.95 (978-1-59643-031-0(1)) Roaring Brook Pr.

Rosario, Joann. Joey & His Famous Fish! Rosario, Joann, illus. 2004. (Illus.). 20p. (J). (ps-5). pap. 10.00 (978-0-9758746-2-2(4) , 1246169) J.G.R. Enterprises.

Roy, James. The Legend of Big Red. Dale, Rae, illus. 2005. (UQP Children's Fiction Ser.). 96p. (J). pap. 16.95 (978-0-7022-3528-3(8)) Univ. of Queensland Pr. AUS. *Dist:* International Specialized Bk. Services.

Rylant, Cynthia. Mr. Putter & Tabby Feed the Fish. Howard, Arthur, illus. (Mr. Putter & Tabby Ser.). 44p. (J). (gr. 1-4). 2002. pap. 5.95 (978-0-15-216366-2(2) , Harcourt Paperbacks); 2001. 15.00 (978-0-15-202408-6(5)) Harcourt Children's Bks.

—Mr. Putter & Tabby Feed the Fish. 2001. (Mr. Putter & Tabby Ser.). (gr. k-3). lib. bdg. 14.10 (978-0-613-44315-9(2)) Tandem Library Bks.

Salzmann, Mary Elizabeth. Goldfish Bowl. Chawla, Neena, illus. 2006. (Fact & Fiction Ser.). 24p. (J). 21.35 (978-1-59679-939-4(0) , SandCastle); pap. (978-1-59679-940-0(4)) ABDO Publishing Co.

Sander, Sonia. Tattle Tale. 2002. (Rainbow Fish Ser.). 32p. (J). (ps-2). pap. 3.99 (978-0-694-52587-4(1) , Harper Festival) HarperCollins Pubs.

Savage, Derek. Trolly Finds a Gun. Bustamante, Denny, illus. 2001. (Trolly the Trout Ser.: Vol. 2). 32p. (J). pap. 9.95 (978-0-9673000-1-6(0)) Savage Bks.

—Trolly Makes Friends. Bustamante, Denny, illus. 2001. (Trolly the Trout Ser.: Vol. 1). 32p. (J). pap. 9.95 (978-0-9673000-0-9(2)) Savage Bks.

Scallan, Dee. Moby Pincher's Wonderful Christmas Present/ Dee Scallan. 2004. (J). pap. 9.95 (978-1-59453-542-0(6)) Airleaf Publishing & Bookselling.

Scroggs, Kirk Brandon. Monster Fish Frenzy. 3rd ed. 2006. (Wiley & Grampa's Creature Features Ser.: No. 3). (Illus.). 112p. (J). (gr. 3-7). 12.99 (978-0-316-05944-2(7)); pap. 3.99 (978-0-316-05945-9(5)) Little Brown & Co.

Seay, LaNell. The Great Parting. Seay, LaNell, illus. 1998. (Illus.). 32p. (J). (gr. k-4). pap. (978-1-891797-11-8(5)) Silver Fox Marketing.

Seuling, Barbara. How Does a Fish Take a Bath? 2008. (Illus.). 32p. 16.00 ***(*978-0-15-216654-0(8))*** Harcourt Children's Bks.

Seuss, Dr. One Fish, Two Fish, Red Fish, Blue Fish. 2005. (Illus.). 64p. (J). (ps-2). audio compact disk 9.95 (978-0-375-83497-4(4) , Random Hse. Bks. for Young Readers) Random Hse. Children's Bks.

—One Fish, Two Fish, Three, Four, Five Fish. 2005. (Dr. Seuss Nursery Collection). (Illus.). 10p. (J). (gr. k-ps). bds. 7.99 (978-0-375-83387-8(0) , Random Hse. Bks. for Young Readers) Random Hse. Children's Bks.

Shaw, Cynthia. Grouper Moon. 1999. (Illus.). ix, 151p. (J). pap. 9.95 (978-0-9670595-2-5(6)) Aurelia Pr.

Siegel, Author R. V. The Seagull & the Starfish. 2005. 48p. pap. 16.73 (978-1-4116-3505-0(1)) Lulu.com.

Siegel, R. V. The Seagull & the Starfish. 2005. 38p. 11.23 (978-1-4116-3283-7(4)) Lulu.com.

Silva, Judith. Frobb the Big Fish: Can Do Attitude! Silva, Judith, illus. 2001. (J). 14.95 (978-0-9715753-0-1(4)) Sunshine Pubs.

Simmons, Steven J. Jasper: The Fish Who Saved a Marriage. Bartkus, Ray, illus. 1998. 32p. (J). (ps-3). 15.95 (978-0-88106-989-1(2)) Charlesbridge Publishing, Inc.

Sims, Lesley. Wish Fish. 2007. (First Reading Level 1 Ser.). 32p. (J). 8.99 ***(*978-0-7945-1697-0(1)*** , Usborne) EDC Publishing.

Smith, Iain. Angel Fish: A Pull & Lift Book. Smith, Iain, illus. 2005. (Stories to Share Ser.). (Illus.). 12p. (J). 10.95 (978-1-58117-084-9(X) , Intervisual/Piggy Toes) Dalmatian Pr.

Smith, Laura A. Frank the Fish Gets His Wish. Neel, Preston, illus. 1998. (J). (ps-3). 17.95 (978-0-9658246-1-3(6) , Books To Remember) Flyleaf Publishing.

Smith, Norma J. A Fish Named Willie Blue. Tuzzolo, Thomas, illus. 2002. 36p. (J). (gr. k-5). pap. 15.99 (978-0-9672763-1-1(4)) Bookmark Pr.

Smith, R. Cadwallade. Within the Deep. 2004. reprint ed. pap. 15.95 (978-1-4191-9456-6(9)) Kessinger Publishing, LLC.

Smith, R. Cadwallader. Within the Deep. 2004. reprint ed. pap. 1.99 (978-1-4192-9456-3(3)) Kessinger Publishing, LLC.

Spalding, Andrea. The Keeper & the Crows. 1999. (Young Reader Ser.). (Illus.). 128p. (J). (gr. 3-6). pap. 5.95 (978-1-55143-141-3(6)) Orca Bk. Pubs. USA.

—The Keeper & the Crows. 2000. (gr. 3-6). lib. bdg. 12.40 (978-0-613-83717-0(7)) Tandem Library Bks.

Stanley, Jan. If I Could Breathe Like Fishes Do, 11 vols. Wennekes, Ron, illus. 2006. 25p. (J). bds. 12.99 (978-0-9776893-0-9(1)) Midwest Graphics, Inc.

Stender, Joshua. Na Makana a Na I'a: The Fish & Their Gifts. 2004. (Illus.). 52p. (J). 15.95 (978-0-87336-081-4(8)) Kamehameha Schools Pr.

Stephens, Ann Marie. Surprise for Ray. 2005. (Illus.). 44p. (J). pap. 16.99 ***(*978-1-59092-115-9(1)*** , Little Blue Works) Windstorm Creative.

Stowell. Cuentos de Peces - Fish Tale, 6 titles. (SPA.). (J). (978-1-56063-777-6(3)) Editorial Unilit.

Sweeney, Jacqueline. Pond Monster. 2001. (We Can Read! Ser.). (Illus.). 32p. (J). (gr. 1-2). lib. bdg. 21.36 (978-0-7614-1123-9(2) , Benchmark Bks.) Cavendish, Marshall Corp.

Swift, Austin Christopher. A Mako Meets a Puffer: A Reel Fish Story. Breeden, Don, illus. 2004. (J). per. 10.95 (978-0-9764208-0-4(5)) Austin Christopher Swift.

Swish Swish Hawaiian Fish. 2002. per. 6.99 (978-0-89610-145-6(2)) Island Heritage Publishing.

Talley, Linda. Aloha Potter! - hardcover Book. Chase, Andra, illus. 2004. 30p. (J). (978-1-55942-200-0(9)) Marsh Media.

Tate, Suzanne. Rosie Ray: A Tale of Watery Wings. Melvin, James, illus. 2003. (Suzanne Tate's Nature Ser.). 28p. (J). (ps-3). pap. 4.95 (978-1-878405-40-1(3)) Nags Head Art, Inc.

Taylor. Pudge Ate a Prophet. 2004. 10.99 (978-0-8254-3868-4(3)) Kregel Pubns.

Thiele, Colin. Speedy. (Illus.). 160p. pap. (978-0-7344-0404-6(2) , Lothian Bks.) Hachette Livre Australia.

Toki, Wilfred. Grandpa, What's a Humuhumu? Toki, Wilfred, illus. Hoover, John, photos by. 2004. (Illus.). 64p. (J). pap. 8.95 (978-0-9729905-9-2(3)) Beachhouse Publishing, LLC.

ToyBox Innovations, creator. Disney's Finding Nemo. 2006. (Disney's Read Along Ser.). (Illus.). 24p. (J). pap. 7.99 incl. audio compact disk (978-0-7634-2172-4(3)) Walt Disney Records.

—Disney's Princess Little Mermaid. abr. ed. 2006. (Disney's Read along Collection). (J). (ps-3). pap. 14.99 incl. audio compact disk (978-0-7634-2184-7(7)) Walt Disney Records.

Triti. Changes: A True Story about Oscar Turtle & Amazon Red. 2000. (Illus.). (J). (978-0-915180-36-3(7)) Harrowood Bks.

Turcotte, Elise & Franson, Leanne. Guillaume Rioux, le Poisson Orphelin. 2001. (FRE., Illus.). 24p. (J). pap. (978-2-89021-502-3(4)) Diffusion du livre Mirabel.

Tyler, Amy J. Best Dad in the Sea. 2003. (Step into Reading Ser.). (Illus.). 32p. (J). (ps-1). pap. 3.99 (978-0-7364-2131-7(9) , RH/Disney) Random Hse. Children's Bks.

Tyler, Craig, illus. A Fine Kettle of Fish. adapted ed. 2005. 42p. (J). lib. bdg. 16.95 (978-0-9761953-0-6(5)) Stairway Publishing.

VanHook, Natalie. The Little Fish Who Prayed. 2002. (Illus.). 36p. (J). per. 5.95 (978-1-930648-36-4(7)) Goose River Pr.

Vasconsellos, Daniel. Max Makes Millions: The Adventures of Max Continued... 2005. (Illus.). 32p. (J). 15.99 (978-1-57939-198-0(2)) Accord Publishing, Ltd.

Waechter, Friedrich Karl. Der Kleine im Glaspott. 1999. (GER.). 48p. (J). pap. (978-3-257-00858-6(9)) Diogenes Verlag AG CHE. *Dist:* International Bk. Import Service, Inc.

Walker, Sally M. Seahorse Reef: A Story of the South Pacific. Petruccio, Steven James, illus. 2005. (Smithsonian Oceanic Collection: No. 20). 32p. (J). (ps-2). 15.95 (978-1-56899-869-5(4) , B4020) Soundprints.

—Seahorse Reef: A Story of the South Pacific, Micro Edition. Petruccio, Steven James, illus. 2005. (Smithsonian Oceanic Collection: No. 20). 30p. (J). (ps-2). 4.95 (978-1-56899-870-1(8) , B4070) Soundprints.

E F G

Walt Disney Company Staff & Pixar Animation Studios Staff, contrib. by. Finding Nemo: Fish in a Box. 2003. (Illus.). (978-0-7364-2155-3(6)); (978-0-7364-2156-0(4)); (978-0-7364-2157-7(2)); (978-0-7364-2158-4(0)) Random Hse., Inc.

Warnes, Tim & Galloway, Ruth. Fidgety Fish. 2001. (Illus.). 32p. (J). (ps-3). tchr. ed. 14.95 (978-1-58925-012-3(5) , tiger tales) ME Media LLC.

Waterton, Betty. Salmon for Simon. 2003. (ps-2). lib. bdg. 12.95 (978-0-613-88592-8(9)) Tandem Library Bks.

—A Salmon for Simon. rev. ed. 1998. (Illus.). 32p. (J). (ps-1). pap. 6.95 (978-0-88899-276-5(9)) Groundwood Bks. CAN. *Dist:* Perseus Distribution.

Weber, Lou, ed. Spongebob Jellyfish Jam. 2005. 14p. (J). bds. 15.98 (978-1-4127-3293-2(X) , 7243700) Publications International, Ltd.

Weeks, Sarah. Splish, Splash! Wolff, Ashley, illus. 1999. (My First I Can Read Bks.). 32p. (J). (ps up). 12.89 (978-0-06-027893-9(5)) HarperCollins Pubs.

Wells, Ronnie. The Legend of Catfish & Little Bream: Paintings & story by Ronnie Wells. 2000. (Illus.). 40p. (J). (ps-3). 19.95 (978-0-925417-26-8(2)) Acadian Hse. Publishing.

Weston, Martha. Cats Are Like That. Weston, Martha, illus. (Holiday House Reader Ser.). (Illus.). 32p. (J). (gr. k-3). tchr. ed. 15.95 (978-0-8234-1419-2(1)) Holiday Hse., Inc.

Wiebe, Trina. Goldfish Don't Take Bubble Baths. Pavanel, Jane, ed. Sarrazin, Marisol, illus. 2004. (Abby & Tess Pet-Sitters Ser.: Vol. 1). 96p. (J). (gr. 2-4). pap. 5.95 (978-1-894222-10-5(5)) Lobster Pr. CAN. *Dist:* Univ. of Toronto Pr.

—Goldfish Don't Take Bubble Baths. 2000. (gr. 3-6). lib. bdg. 15.25 (978-0-613-62555-5(2)) Tandem Library Bks.

Williamson, Stafford. Puppyfish. 2005. 48p. (J). pap. 18.49 (978-1-4116-3836-5(0)) Lulu.com.

Winkelman, Barbara Gaines. Sockeye's Journey Home. Popeo, Joanie, illus. 2000. (J). incl. audio (978-1-56899-837-4(6)) Soundprints.

Wise, William. Ten Sly Piranhas: A Counting Story in Reverse (A Tale of Wickedness - And Worse!) 2004. (Illus.). 32p. (J). pap. 5.99 (978-0-14-240074-6(2) , Puffin) Penguin Group (USA) Inc.

The Wish Fish: Individual Title Six-Packs. (Action Packs Ser.). 104p. (gr. 3-5). 44.00 (978-0-7635-8411-5(8)) Rigby Education.

Wlodarski, Loran. If A Dolphin Were A Fish. Klein, Laurie Allen, illus. 2006. 32p. (J). 15.95 (978-0-9768823-2-9(9)) Sylvan Dell Pubng.

Wood, Audrey. Ten Little Fish. Wood, Bruce, illus. 2004. 40p. (J). (ps up). pap. 15.95 (978-0-439-63569-1(1) , Blue Sky Pr., The) Scholastic, Inc.

Wood, Ellen. Hundreds of Fish. Felix, Monique, illus. 2000. (Notebooks Ser.). 40p. (gr. 4 up). 17.95 (978-1-56846-162-5(3) , Creative Editions) Creative Co., The.

Yaccarino, Dan. The Birthday Fish. rev. ed. 2005. (Illus.). 40p. (J). 16.95 (978-0-8050-7493-2(7) , Holt, Henry & Co. Bks. For Young Readers) Holt, Henry & Co.

Yep, Laurence. Angelfish. 2001. 1p. (J). (gr. 5 up). 16.99 (978-0-399-23041-7(6) , Putnam Juvenile) Penguin Group (USA) Inc.

Yoo, Tae-Eun. The Little Red Fish. 2007. (Illus.). (J). (***978-1-4287-3601-6(8)*** , Dial) Penguin Group (USA) Inc.

Yoo, Tae-Eun, illus. The Little Red Fish. 2007. 40p. (J). (ps). 15.99 (978-0-8037-3145-5(0) , Dial) Penguin Group (USA) Inc.

Yoshida, Akimi. Banana Fish. 2006. (Banana Fish Ser.). 208p. (YA). Vol. 14. pap. 9.99 (978-1-4215-0524-4(X)); Vol. 15. pap. 9.99 (978-1-4215-0525-1(8)) Viz Media.

Zardinejad, Nooshin. Ladyfish: The Golden Voice of "Ladyfish" Brophy, Drew, illus. l.t. ed. 2001. 28p. (J). (ps-5). 15.95 (978-0-9709750-0-3(7)) Bloomstreet Bks.

Zimelman, Nathan. A Fishy Story. O'Malley, Kathleen, illus. 2003. (Books for Young Learners). 16p. (J). pap. 5.00 net. (978-1-57274-538-4(X) , 2453) Owen, Richard C. Pubs., Inc.

Zondervan. Fish's Big Catch & Jonah's Big Journey. Pulley, Kelly, illus. 2006. (Beginner's Bible' Ser.). 20p. (J). 6.99 (978-0-310-71339-5(0)) Zonderkidz.

FISHING

Amdahl, Paul. Barefoot Fisherman: A Fishing Book for Kids. 2000. (gr. 3-6). lib. bdg. 24.55 (978-0-613-77747-6(6)) Tandem Library Bks.

Arnosky, Jim. Hook, Line & Seeker: A Beginner's Guide to Fishing, Boating & Watching Water Wildlife. Arnosky, Jim, illus. 2005. (Hook, Line & Seeker Ser.). (Illus.). 192p. (J). pap. 12.95 (978-0-439-45584-8(7) , Scholastic Reference) Scholastic, Inc.

Befus, Tyler. A Kid's Guide to Flyfishing: It's More Than Catching Fish. 2006. (Illus.). 128p. (J). pap. 16.00 (978-1-55566-394-0(X)) Johnson Bks.

Bell, David M. The Bass' Tale: A Conversational Life History. 1998. (Illus.). 70p. (YA). (gr. 8-12). pap. 9.95 (978-1-893120-02-0(3) , TL-01) Glamorgan Bks.

Bowman, Turner & Bowman, Foster. Fishing with Foster: The Legend Begins. Brooks, Larry, illus. 2001. 80p. (YA). (gr. k up). 21.95 (978-0-9677118-0-5(0)) Always Kids Publishing.

Complete Guide to Fishing, 7 vols., Set. (Illus.). 64,144p. (YA). (gr. 7 up). lib. bdg. (978-1-59084-492-2(0)) Mason Crest Pubs.

Dad Goes Fishing: Individual Title Six-Packs. (Sails Literacy Ser.). (gr. 1-2). 36.00 (978-0-7578-4002-9(7)) Rigby Education.

Davis, James (Jim) W. Out-takes of 55 Years of Camping, 2004. (Illus.). 168p. (YA). per. 5.95 (978-0-9760960-0-9(5)) Davis, James (Jim).

Destination Disaster: Individual Title Six-Packs. (Action Packs Ser.). 104p. (gr. 3-5). 44.00 (978-0-7635-3300-7(9)) Rigby Education.

Un dia de Pesca, 6 packs. (Literatura 2000 Ser.). (SPA.). (gr. 2-3). 33.00 (978-0-7635-1260-6(5)) Rigby Education.

DK Publishing. Fishing. 2008. 352p. pap. 25.00 (***978-0-7566-3347-9(8)***) Dorling Kindersley Publishing, Inc.

Dorman, Clive & Dorman, Helen. Okomi Goes Fishing, Vol. 7. Hutchings, Tony, illus. 2004. (Okomi Stories Ser.). 24p. (J). pap. 4.95 (978-1-58469-057-3(7)) Dawn Pubns.

Drinkard, Lawson. Fishing in a Brook: Angling Activities for Kids. Lee, Fran, illus. 2000. 64p. (YA). (gr. 1 up). pap. 9.95 (978-0-87905-940-8(0)) Gibbs Smith, Publisher.

Dyer, Hadley & Kalman, Bobbie. Fishing in Action. 2005. (Sports in Action Ser.). (Illus.). 32p. (J). (978-0-7787-0343-3(6)); pap. (978-0-7787-0363-1(0)) Crabtree Publishing Co.

Eagle, Kin. Rub a Dub Dub. Gilbert, Rob, illus. 2000. (Extended Nursery Rhymes Ser.). 32p. (J). (ps up). lib. bdg. 23.33 (978-0-8368-2669-2(8)) Stevens, Gareth Inc.

Early Bird Books Staff. Going Fishing: Step 2, Level C. Date not set. (J). (gr. 2). 1.95 (978-0-394-86705-2(X) , Random Hse. Bks. for Young Readers) Random Hse. Children's Bks.

Eckart, Edana. I Can Go Fishing. 2003. (Welcome Bks.). (Illus.). 24p. (J). (ps-2). pap. 4.95 (978-0-516-24371-9(3) , Children's Pr.) Scholastic Library Publishing.

Fishing: Level F, 6 vols. (Wonder Worldtm Ser.). 16p. 29.95 (978-0-7802-1996-0(1)) Wright Group, The.

Fitzgerald, Ron. Essential Fishing for Teens. 2000. (High Interest Bks.). (Illus.). 48p. (gr. 7-12). (J). 24.00 (978-0-516-23355-0(6)); (YA). pap. 6.95 (978-0-516-23555-4(9)) Scholastic Library Publishing. (Children's Pr.).

Fly Fishing the Flat Tops. 2nd l.t. ed. 2000. 62p. 14.00 (978-0-9715563-0-0(X)) Hidden Lakes Pr.

Freshwater, F. Trout Fishing Tactics. 2006. 96p. 19.99 (978-1-86513-080-4(X)) Australian Fishing Network AUS. *Dist:* Cardinal Pubs. Group.

Gibbons, Gail. Surrounded by Sea: Life on a New England Fishing Island. Gibbons, Gail, illus. (Illus.). 32p. (J). (ps-3). 2006. 6.95 (978-0-8234-2021-6(3)); 2005. 17.95 (978-0-8234-1941-8(X)) Holiday Hse., Inc.

Gleason, Michael & Gannon, Robert. Fishing in the Alphabet: The A. B. C.'s of Freshwater. Packard, Justin, illus. 1999. 52p. (J). (gr. k-5). 15.95 (978-0-9669961-0-4(0)) Bobber Down Bks., LLC.

Grandad's Fishin Notes: A Tackle Box Book for Every Angler. 2001. 60p. spiral bd. 7.00 (978-0-9708925-9-1(4)) Base Of The Bays.

Greenlaw, Linda. The Hungry Ocean. 2000. 265p. (gr. 7-12). per. 23.15 (978-0-613-25611-7(5)) Tandem Library Bks.

Hansen, Jens Ploug. Spinning & Baitcasting. 2003. (Illus.). 128p. (YA). (gr. 7 up). lib. bdg. (978-1-59084-493-9(9)) Mason Crest Pubs.

Harcourt School Publishers Staff. Fishing: Take-Home Book. 1999. (Signatures Ser.). (Illus.). (J). pap. 1.90 (978-0-15-313942-0(0)) Harcourt Schl. Pubs.

Hopkins, Ellen. Fly Fishing. (J). 2008. (***978-1-4296-0819-0(6)***); 2001. (Illus.). 48p. (gr. 3-4). lib. bdg. 21.26 (978-0-7368-0914-6(7) , Capstone High-Interest Bks.) Capstone Pr., Inc.

—Freshwater Fishing. (J). 2008. (***978-1-4296-0820-6(X)***); 2001. (Illus.). 48p. (gr. 3-4). lib. bdg. 21.26 (978-0-7368-0915-3(5) , Capstone High-Interest Bks.) Capstone Pr., Inc.

Hunt, Chris. Stream Dreams: A Fly Fisher's Guide to Eastern Idaho's Small Water, 2004. (Illus.). 120p. per. 17.95 net. (978-0-9749865-0-0(X)) Idaho State Journal.

Indiana - Fishing Map Guide - Northeastern Region Vol. 1: Lake Maps & Fishing Information for over 200 Lakes in Northeastern Indiana. 2002. (Illus.). 184p. (YA). spiral bd. 21.95 (978-1-885010-48-3(6)) Sportsman's Connection.

Indiana - Fishing Map Guide - Outside of the NE Region Vol. 2: Lake Maps & Fishing Information for Inland Aleks & Reservoirs Outside of the NE Region Plus Lake Michigan & Ohio River Coverage. 2002. (Illus.). 192p. (YA). spiral bd. 21.95 (978-1-885010-49-0(4)) Sportsman's Connection.

Jacobs, Robert P. & O'Connell, Eileen B. Fisheries Guide to Lakes & Ponds of Connecticut: Including the Connecticut River & Its Coves. 2002. (DEP Bulletin Ser.: 35). 368p. lib. bdg. 29.95 (978-0-942085-12-9(4)); (Illus.). pap. 19.95 (978-0-942085-11-2(6)) Connecticut Dept. of Environmental Protection, Environmental & Geographic Information Ctr.

Kentucky - Fishing Map Guide: Lake Maps & Fishing Information for Kentucky Lakes Plus Ohio River Coverage. 2002. (Illus.). 224p. (YA). spiral bd. 21.95 (978-1-885010-60-5(5)) Sportsman's Connection.

Kids: Fish & Fishing. 2003. (J). 1.00 (978-1-888631-30-2(9)) Watercourse, The.

Kihm, Steve. The Lost Candy Bar. 2004. (J). mass mkt. 6.95 (978-0-9786794-0-8(7)) Lost Candy Bar Pr., LLC.

Klobuchar, Lisa. Fishing. 2004. (Get Going! Hobbies Ser.). (Illus.). 32p. (J). 24.22 (978-1-4034-6117-9(1)); pap. (978-1-4034-6124-7(4)) Heinemann Library.

Labignan, Italo. Hook, Line & Sinker: Everything Kids Want to Know about Fishing! MacRae, Jock, illus. rev. ed. 2007. 64p. (J). (gr. 3-7). pap. 14.95 (***978-1-55263-549-0(X)***) Key Porter Bks. CAN. *Dist:* Perseus Distribution.

Let's Go Fishing, 6 bks., Set. (Illus.). (J). (gr. 2-5). lib. bdg. 153.86 (978-0-86593-461-0(4)) Rourke Publishing, LLC.

Love, Ann. Fishing. ed. 2004. (Illus.). (J). (gr. k-3). spiral bd. (978-0-616-00141-7(X)) Canadian National Institute for the Blind/Institut National Canadien pour les Aveugles.

—Fishing. 2002. (America at Work Ser.). (Illus.). 32p. (J). (gr. k-3). (978-1-55074-457-6(7)) Kids Can Pr., Ltd.

—Fishing. 2002. (gr. 3-6). lib. bdg. 14.10 (978-0-613-87150-1(2)) Tandem Library Bks.

Love, Ann & Drake, Jane. Canada at Work: Fishing. Cupples, Pat, illus. 2001. (Canada at Work Ser.). 32p. (J). (gr. 2-5). (978-1-55074-919-9(6)) Kids Can Pr., Ltd.

—Fishing. Cupples, Pat, illus. 2002. (America at Work Ser.). 32p. (J). (gr. k-3). (978-1-55337-422-0(3)) Kids Can Pr., Ltd.

Lucas, Kimberly H. Fly-Fishing with Trout-Tail: A Child's Journey. Lucas, Kimberly H., illus. 2002. (Illus.). 40p. 19.95 (978-0-9722506-0-3(3)) Trout-Tail, LLC.

Lyon, Harold C., Jr. Angling in the Smile of the Great Spirit: Six Centuries of Wisdom from the Master Anglers of Lake Winnipesaukee, 2004. (Illus.). 304p. per. 24.95 (978-0-9748171-1-8(2)) Deep Waters Pr.

Maas, Dave & Creative Publishing international Editors. Kids Gone Fishin' The Young Angler's Guide to Catching More & Bigger Fish. 2001. (Illus.). 96p. (gr. 3-7). pap. 12.95 (978-0-86573-129-5(2) , Creative Publishing International) Quayside.

Mason, Paul. Fishing. 2007. (J). (***978-1-59920-131-3(3)***) Smart Apple Media.

McMillan, Bruce. Going Fishing. 2005. (Illus.). 32p. (J). (gr. k-3). 16.00 (978-0-618-47201-7(0) , Walter Lorraine) Houghton Mifflin Co. Trade & Reference Div.

Michigan - Eastern Upper Penninsula Fishing Map Guide: Lake Maps & Fishing Information for over 250 Lakes Plus Great Lake Coverage Including the Following Counties: Alger, Chippewa, Delta, Luce, Mackinac, Marquette & Schoolcraft. 2002. (Illus.). 208p. (YA). spiral bd. 21.95 (978-1-885010-56-8(7)) Sportsman's Connection.

Michigan - Northwestern Fishing Map Guide: Lake Maps & Fishing Information for over 130 Lakes Plus Lake Huron & Lake Michigan Covering the Counties of Antrim, Benzie, Charlevoix, Cheboygan, Emmet, Grand Traverse, Kalkaska, Leelanau & Otesgo. 2002. (Illus.). 184p. (YA). spiral bd. 21.95 (978-1-885010-54-4(0)) Sportsman's Connection.

Michigan - Southeastern Fishing Map Guide: Lake Maps & Fishing Information for about 200 Lakes Plus Lake Erie, Detroit & St. Claire Rivers Covering the Counties of Clinton, Genesee Hillsdale, Ingham, Jackson, Lapeer, Lenawee, Livingston, Macomb, Oakland, St. Clair, Washtenaw & Wayne. 2002. (Illus.). 200p. (YA). spiral bd. 21.95 (978-1-885010-51-3(6)) Sportsman's Connection.

Michigan - Southwestern Fishing Map Guide: Lake Maps & Fishing Information for over 180 Lake Plus Lake Michigan Covering the Counties of Ionia, Kent, Manistee, Mason, Mecosta, Missaukee, Muskegon, Newaygo, Oceana, Osceola & Wexford. 2002. (Illus.). 192p. (YA). spiral bd. 21.95 (978-1-885010-50-6(8)) Sportsman's Connection.

Michigan - West Central Fishing Map Guide. 2002. (Illus.). 192p. (YA). spiral bd. 21.95 (978-1-885010-52-0(4)) Sportsman's Connection.

Michigan - Western Upper Penninsula Fishing Map Guide. 2002. (Illus.). (YA). spiral bd. 21.95 (978-1-885010-55-1(9)) Sportsman's Connection.

Murray, Eric. Fishing for Fun! 2006. (For Fun! Ser.). (Illus.). 48p. (J). (gr. 3-5). 22.60 (978-0-7565-1684-0(6)) Compass Point Bks.

Mysling, Donald & Murphy, Brian. Small Ponds in Connecticut: A Guide for Fish Management. 2nd ed. 2000. (DEP Bulletin Ser.: Vol. 30). 78p. pap. 9.95 (978-0-942085-07-5(8)) Connecticut Dept. of Environmental Protection, Environmental & Geographic Information Ctr.

Nkard, G. Fishing in a Brook: Angling Activities for Kids. 1999. (gr. 3-6). lib. bdg. 18.75 (978-0-613-52560-2(4)) Tandem Library Bks.

Nordin, Hans. Ice Fishing. 2004. (Illus.). 96p. (YA). (gr. 7 up). lib. bdg. (978-1-59084-497-7(1)) Mason Crest Pubs.

Ohio - Northern Fishing Map Guide: Lake Maps & Fishing Information for over 130 Inland Lakes in Northern Ohio Plus Lake Erie. 2001. (Illus.). 192p. (YA). spiral bd. 21.95 (978-1-885010-46-9(X)) Sportsman's Connection.

Ohio - Southern Fishing Map Guide: Lake Maps & Fishing Information for over 80 Inland Lakes in Southern Ohio Plus the Ohio River. 2001. (Illus.). 192p. (YA). spiral bd. 21.95 (978-1-885010-47-6(8)) Sportsman's Connection.

Orsi, Leo N., Jr. Striper Chronicles: East Coast Surf Fishing Legends & Adventures, 1. 2004. (Illus.). 180p. 24.95 (978-0-9745952-9-0(2) , 888-792-1414) AKMO Pubs.

The Outdoor Youth Adventures Bass Fishing Coloring Book. 2003. (J). pap. (978-0-9745863-4-2(X)) Cypress Knees Publishing.

The Outdoor Youth Adventures Freshwater Fishing Coloring & Activity Book. 2004. (J). pap. (978-0-9745863-7-3(4)) Cypress Knees Publishing.

The Outdoor Youth Adventures Saltwater Fishing Activity & Coloring Book. 2003. (J). pap. (978-0-9745863-2-8(3)) Cypress Knees Publishing.

The Outdoor Youth Adventures Trout Fishing Activity & Coloring Book. 2003. (J). pap. (978-0-9745863-5-9(8)) Cypress Knees Publishing.

Pastel, JoAnne, et al. Bur Bur's Fishing Adventure: Learn Fun Things about Fishing & What to Bring! 2007. (J). (***978-0-9777121-3-7(3)***) Interface Publishing.

Patchett, Fiona. Starting Fishing: Internet-Linked. 2004. (First Skills Ser.). 32p. (J). lthr. 12.95 (978-1-58086-643-9(3) , Usborne) EDC Publishing.

—Starting Fishing - Internet Linked. Venus, Joanna, illus. rev. ed. 2004. (First Skills Ser.). 32p. (J). pap. 4.95 (978-0-7945-0672-8(0) , Usborne) EDC Publishing.

Patchett, Fiona, ed. Starting Fishing. 1999. (Usborne First Skills Ser.). (Illus.). 32p. (J). (gr. k-3). pap. 4.95 (978-0-7460-3119-3(X)) EDC Publishing.

Salas, Laura Purdie. Ice Fishing. 2008. (***978-1-4296-0822-0(6)***); 2002. (Illus.). 48p. (J). (gr. 3-4). lib. bdg. 21.26 (978-0-7368-1056-2(0) , Capstone High-Interest Bks.) Capstone Pr., Inc.

—Saltwater Fishing. (J). 2008. (***978-1-4296-0824-4(2)***); 2004. (Illus.). 48p. 16.95 (978-0-7368-2412-5(X)) Capstone Pr., Inc.

The Saltwater Game Fish Coloring Book. 2005. (J). mass mkt. (978-0-9763757-1-5(0)) Cypress Knees Publishing.

Seeberg, Timothy J. Fly-Fishing. 2004. (Complete Guides Ser.). (Illus.). 32p. (J). (gr. 1-5). 25.64 (978-1-59296-034-7(0)) Child's World, Inc.

—Freshwater Fishing. 2004. (Complete Guides Ser.). (Illus.). 32p. (J). (gr. 1-5). 25.64 (978-1-59296-035-4(9)) Child's World, Inc.

Slade, Suzanne. Let's Go Fishing. 2007. (Adventures Outdoors Ser.). (Illus.). 32p. (J). (gr. 4-6). lib. bdg. 23.95 (978-1-4042-3647-9(3) , PowerKids Pr.) Rosen Publishing Group, Inc., The.

Solomon, Dane. Fishing: Have Fun, Be Smart. 2005. (Explore the Outdoors Ser.). (Illus.). 64p. (YA). (gr. 7-12). lib. bdg. 26.50 (978-0-8239-3168-2(4) , EOFISH) Rosen Publishing Group, Inc., The.

Spatenka, Cheryl & Spatenka, Brian. Bass Fishing Is Awesome. 2000. (Illus.). 40p. (J). pap. 9.95 (978-0-9702117-0-5(8)) One-More-Cast for KIDS.

Vander Hook, Sue. Deep-Sea Fishing. 2000. (World of Sports Ser.). (Illus.). 32p. (J). (gr. 4 up). lib. bdg. 16.95 (978-1-887068-54-3(6)) Smart Apple Media.

Walters, Keith. Chesapeake Outdoors: Tales of Fishing & Hunting on Maryland's Eastern Shore & Beyond. 2003. (Illus.). 288p. pap. 19.95 (978-0-9627039-4-2(X)) Aerie Hse.

FISHING—EQUIPMENT AND SUPPLIES

Wessman, Bo. Building Your Own Rod. 2004. (Illus.). 72p. (YA). (gr. 7 up). lib. bdg. (978-1-59084-550-9(1)) Mason Crest Pubs.

FISHING—FICTION

Akinje, Wale. The Adventures of Imhotep. Young, Craig, illus. 2006. (J). (978-0-9768485-0-9(3)) Nile Publishing.

Anderson, Max Elliot. North Woods Poachers, 2004. 144p. pap. 10.95 (978-0-9729256-8-6(6) , Tweener Pr.) Baker Trittin Pr.

Arena, Felice & Kettle, Phil. Crawfish Hunt. Vane, Mitch, illus. 2004. (J). pap. (978-1-59336-358-1(3)) Mondo Publishing.

—Gone Fishing. Boyer, Susy, illus. 2004. (J). pap. (978-1-59336-359-8(1)) Mondo Publishing.

Aruego, Jose. Splash! 2001. (gr. k-3). lib. bdg. 11.80 (978-0-613-66386-1(1)) Tandem Library Bks.

Aruego, Jose & Dewey, Ariane. Splash! 2003. (Green Light Readers Level 2 Ser.). (Illus.). 32p. (J). 11.95 (978-0-15-204872-3(3)); pap. 3.95 (978-0-15-204832-7(4)) Harcourt Children's Bks. (Green Light Readers).

Awdry, Wilbert V. Thomas Goes Fishing. Courtney, Richard, illus. 2005. (Step into Reading Bks.). 32p. (J). (ps-1). pap. 3.99 (978-0-375-83118-8(5) , Random Hse. Bks. for Young Readers) Random Hse. Children's Bks.

—Thomas Goes Fishing. Courtney, Richard, illus. 2005. 32p. (J). (ps-1). lib. bdg. 11.99 (978-0-375-93118-5(X) , Random Hse. Bks. for Young Readers) Random Hse. Children's Bks.

Baker, Keith. More Mr. & Mrs. Green. (Mr. & Mrs. Green Ser.). (Illus.). 68p. (J). 2005. pap. 5.95 (978-0-15-205246-1(1) , Harcourt Paperbacks); 2004. 16.00 (978-0-15-216494-2(4)) Harcourt Children's Bks.

—More Mr. & Mrs. Green. 2007. (Mr. & Mrs. Green Ser.). 72p. (J). (gr. 2-4). 27.07 (*978-1-59961-302-4(6)) Spotlight.

Bania, Michael. Kumak's Fish: A Tall Tale from the Far North. 2005. (Illus.). 32p. 15.95 (978-0-88240-583-4(7)); pap. 8.95 (978-0-88240-584-1(5)) Graphic Arts Ctr. Publishing Co.

Barrett, Dean. The Boat Girl & the Magic Fish. 2nd ed. 2002. 32p. 6.95 (978-0-9661899-5-7(7)) Village East Bks.

Bauer, Marion Dane. An Early Winter. 1999. (Illus.). 128p. (J). (gr. 5-9). tchr. ed. 15.00 (978-0-395-90372-8(6) , Clarion Bks.) Houghton Mifflin Co. Trade & Reference Div.

—An Early Winter. 2000. (YA). pap. 42.00 incl. audio (978-0-7887-4328-3(7) , 41123) Recorded Bks., LLC.

Baumhofer, J. A. Where the Boats Are. 2002. (Illus.). 96p. (J). pap. 12.95 (978-0-9703086-2-7(0)) Simpson, J.R. & Assocs., Inc.

Bedford, William. The Stowaway. Fletcher, Claire, illus. 2001. 89p. (J). pap. 7.50 (978-0-7497-4273-7(9)) Egmont Bks., Ltd. GBR. *Dist:* Independent Pubs. Group.

Bell, Lili. The Sea Maidens of Japan. Brammer, Erin McGonigle, illus. 2004. 28p. (J). (gr. k-4). reprint ed. (978-0-7567-7881-1(6)) DIANE Publishing Co.

—The Sea Maidens of Japan. Brammer, Erin McGonigle, illus. 2001. 32p. (J). (ps-3). 14.95 (978-0-8249-5426-0(2) , Ideals Children's Bks.) Ideals Pubns.

Benedetti, Marie. Fishing with Grandpapa: The Most Important Rules. 2007. (J). per. 8.99 (*978-1-59886-975-0(2)) Tate Publishing & Enterprises, L.L.C.

Bennett, Dean. Finding a Friend in the Forest: A True Story. 2005. (Illus.). 15.95 (978-0-89272-662-2(8)) Down East Bks.

—The Late Loon. 2006. (Illus.). 32p. 15.95 (978-0-89272-730-8(6)) Down East Bks.

Bick, Janice. Belinda Lee. 2006. 17.00 (*978-0-8059-8850-5(5)) Dorrance Publishing Co., Inc.

The Big Catch: Individual Title Six-Packs. (Literatura 2000 Ser.). (gr. 2-3). 33.00 (978-0-7635-0253-9(7)) Rigby Education.

Blackaby, Susan. De Pesca. Haugen, Ryan, illus. 2006. (Read-It! Readers en Espanol Ser.).Tr. of Fishing Trip. (SPA.). 32p. (J). (ps-3). 19.95 (978-1-4048-1684-8(4)) Picture Window Bks.

—Fishing Trip. Haugen, Ryan, illus. 2005. (Read-It! Readers Ser.). 32p. (J). (gr. k-3). 18.60 (978-1-4048-1004-4(8)) Picture Window Bks.

Blackwood, Gary L. Moonshine. 1999. (Accelerated Reader Bks.). 160p. (J). (gr. 3-7). 14.95 (978-0-7614-5056-6(4) , Cavendish Children's Bks.) Cavendish, Marshall Corp.

Bonehill, Ralph. Young Hunters of the Lake. rev. ed. 2006. 212p. 27.95 (978-1-4218-1805-4(1)); pap. 12.95 (978-1-4218-1905-1(8)) 1st World Publishing, Inc. (1st World Library - Literary Society).

Bonehill, Ralph. Young Hunters of the Lake or Out with Ro. 2006. 78.99 (*978-1-4280-0115-2(8)); pap. 71.99 (*978-1-4280-0100-8(X)) IndyPublish.com.

Bootman, Colin. Fish for the Grand Lady. Bootman, Colin, illus. 2006. (Illus.). 32p. (J). 16.95 (978-0-8234-1898-5(7)) Holiday Hse., Inc.

Bowman, Crystal. Jake Goes Fishing. Maizel, Karen, illus. 2007. (I Can Read!). 32p. (J). pap. 3.99 (*978-0-310-71454-5(0)) Zonderkidz.

Brooks, Bertha. The Big Fishing Trip. 2004. (Illus.). 32p. (J). 12.00 (978-1-58374-086-6(4)) Chicago Spectrum Pr.

Carlson, Nancy. Loudmouth George & the Fishing Trip. 2nd rev. ed. 2005. (Illus.). 32p. (J). (gr. k-3). pap. 6.95 (978-1-57505-733-0(6) , First Avenue Editions) Lerner Publishing Group.

Carney, Margaret. The Biggest Fish in the Lake. Wilson, Janet, illus. 2003. 32p. (J). (gr. k-3). (978-1-55337-528-9(9)) Kids Can Pr., Ltd.

—Biggest Fish in the Lake. 2003. (Illus.). (gr. k-3). lib. bdg. 14.10 (978-0-613-86544-9(8)) Tandem Library Bks.

—The Biggest Fish in the Lake. Wilson, Janet, illus. unabr. ed. 2003. 32p. (J). (gr. k-3). (978-1-55074-720-1(7)) Kids Can Pr., Ltd.

Castle, Caroline. The Big Fuzzy. 2007. (J). lib. bdg. 16.95 (*978-1-59566-368-9(1)) QEB Publishing Inc.

Chronicle Books LLC Staff. Stanley Goes Fishing Hc (French) 2006. (J). 15.95 (*978-92-0-195244-8(9)) Chronicle Bks. LLC.

Cole, James. The Lost Island. 2005. 180p. pap. 19.95 (978-1-4137-7572-3(1)) PublishAmerica, Inc.

Couch, Joann. Catching Old Catfish Joe. 2003. (Illus.). 27p. pap. 6.95 (978-0-533-14100-5(1)) Vantage Pr., Inc.

Creech, Sharon. Fishing in the Air. Raschka, Chris, illus. 32p. (J). (ps-3). 2003. pap. 6.99 (978-0-06-051606-2(2) , Harper Trophy); 2000. 15.89 (978-0-06-028112-0(X) , Cotler, Joanna Books) HarperCollins Pubs.

—Fishing in the Air. 2003. (Live Oak Readalong Ser.). (Illus.). (J). pap. 16.95 incl. audio (978-1-59112-224-1(4)); pap. 18.95 incl. audio compact disk (978-1-59112-512-9(X)) Live Oak Media.

—Fishing in the Air. Raschka, Chris, illus. 2003. pap. 9.95 incl. audio (978-1-59112-223-4(6)); (J). 25.95 incl. audio (978-1-59112-225-8(2)); (J). pap. 37.95 incl. audio (978-1-59112-226-5(0)); (J). pap. 39.95 incl. audio compact disk (978-1-59112-521-1(9)) Live Oak Media.

—Fishing in the Air. Rashka, Chris, illus. 2000. 29p. (J). (ps-3). 28.95 (978-1-59112-513-6(8)) Live Oak Media.

—Fishing in the Air. 2000. (gr. k-3). lib. bdg. 15.30 (978-0-613-66967-2(3)) Tandem Library Bks.

Cronin, Doreen. Click, Clack, Splish, Splash. 2006. (J). (ps-3). 22.78 (978-1-59961-090-0(6)) Spotlight.

—Click, Clack, Splish, Splash: A Counting Adventure. Lewin, Betsy, illus. 2006. 24p. (J). (ps-k). 12.95 (978-0-689-87716-2(1) , Atheneum) Simon & Schuster Children's Publishing.

Croteau-Fleury, Marie-Danielle & St. Aubin, Bruno. Ma Nuit Dans les Glaces. 2001. (FRE., Illus.). 64p. (J). pap. (978-2-89021-506-1(7)) Diffusion du livre Mirabel.

Croteau, Marie-Danielle. Fred on the Ice Floes. Cummins, Sarah, tr. from FRE. St. Aubin, Bruno, illus. 2001. (First Novels Ser.: Vol. 38). 64p. (gr. 1-5). (J). (978-0-88780-547-9(7)); 4.95 (978-0-88780-546-2(9)) Formac Publishing Co., Ltd. CAN. *Dist:* Casemate Pubs. & Bk. Distributors, LLC.

Damitz, Charlie. Diving for el Corazon. Diefendorf, Cathy, illus. 2007. 100p. (J). pap. 7.95 (978-0-9744446-3-5(4)) All About Kids Publishing.

DeFelice, Cynthia. The Missing Manatee. 2008. 192p. (J). pap. 6.95 (*978-0-374-40020-0(2) , Farrar, Straus & Giroux (BYR)) Farrar, Straus & Giroux.

DeFelice, Cynthia C. Death at Devil's Bridge. 2000. 192p. (J). (gr. 3-7). 16.00 (978-0-374-31723-2(2) , Farrar, Straus & Giroux (BYR)) Farrar, Straus & Giroux.

—Death at Devil's Bridge. 2002. 192p. (J). (gr. 3-7). pap. 5.99 (978-0-06-441037-3(4) , Harper Trophy) HarperCollins Pubs.

—Death at Devil's Bridge. 2002. (gr. 3-6). lib. bdg. 14.10 (978-0-613-82528-3(4)) Tandem Library Bks.

—The Missing Manatee. 2005. 192p. (J). 16.00 (978-0-374-31257-2(5) , Farrar, Straus & Giroux (BYR)) Farrar, Straus & Giroux.

—The Missing Manatee. l.t. ed. 2005. 183p. (J). 20.95 (978-0-7862-8178-7(2)) Thorndike Pr.

DeGrazia, John. The Three Little Tigers Go Fishing. Spirin, Ilya, illus. 1999. (Three Little Tigers Ser.: Vol. 2). 15p. (J). (gr. 1-8). pap. 5.00 (978-0-9670522-1-2(1)) Big Cats Publishing.

Un dia de Pesca, 6 packs. (Literatura 2000 Ser.). (SPA.). (gr. 2-3). 33.00 (978-0-7635-1260-6(5)) Rigby Education.

DiLorenzo, Michael A. Adventures with Jonny: Let's Go Fishing! Julich, Jenniffer, illus. 2006. 68p. (J). 17.95 (978-0-9777210-0-9(0)) Running Moose Publications.

DiLorenzo, Michael A. Ice Fishing: The Coolest Sport on Earth. Julich, Jennifer, illus. 2007. (Adventures with Jonny Ser.). 80p. 17.95 (*978-0-9777210-1-6(9)) Running Moose Publications.

Dingles, Molly. Little Lee Lee Goes Fishing. Bingler, Aimee, illus. 2000. (Little Lee Lee Ser.). 32p. (J). (ps-1). 9.99 (978-1-891997-13-6(0)) Dingles & Co.

Dion. Fishing with Balloons. 2004. (Illus.). 68p. (J). (978-1-881929-34-5(5)) Oxton Hse., Pubs.

The Dolphin Caller: Chapter Book, 6 Packs. Vol. 30. 32p. (gr. 5 up). 44.00 (978-0-7578-0983-5(9)) Rigby Education.

Dougherty, Terri. The Flying Fish. Visser, Kristy, illus. 2006. (Read-It! Readers Ser.). (J). 19.93 (978-1-4048-2410-2(3)) Picture Window Bks.

Eagle, Kin. Rub a Dub Dub. Gilbert, Rob, illus. 1998. (Kids at Our House Book Ser.). 32p. (J). (ps-3). 15.95 (978-1-58089-008-3(3)) Charlesbridge Publishing, Inc.

Farish, Terry. The Cat Who Liked Potato Soup. Root, Barry, illus. 40p. (J). (gr. 1). 2007. pap. 6.99 (978-0-7636-3297-7(X)); 2003. 16.99 (978-0-7636-0834-7(3)) Candlewick Pr.

Fishing: KinderReaders Individual Title Six-Packs. (Kinderstarters Ser.). 8p. (ps-1). 21.00 (978-0-7635-8665-2(X)) Rigby Education.

Fitka, Alice N. Kuvyallrem Aperyarai. Fitka, Alice N. & Shantz, Joy, illus. 1998. Tr. of Fishing Words. (ESK.). 16p. (J). (gr. k-3). pap. 6.00 (978-1-58084-035-4(3)) Lower Kuskokwim Schl. District.

Fox, Mary Virginia. A Fishing Adventure. McMahon, Kelly, illus. 2002. (Two Can Read Ser.). 16p. 2.99 (978-1-56472-661-2(4)) Edupress, Inc.

Frank, John. How to Catch a Fish. Sylvada, Peter, illus. 2007. (Neal Porter Bks.). 32p. (J). (ps-3). 17.95 (*978-1-59643-163-8(6)) Roaring Brook Pr.

Franklin, Kristine L. The Gift. Lavallee, Barbara, illus. 1999. 40p. (J). (ps-3). 14.95 (978-0-8118-0447-9(X)) Chronicle Bks. LLC.

Frazier, Craig. Stanley Goes Fishing. 2006. (Illus.). 40p. (J). 15.95 (978-0-8118-5244-9(X)) Chronicle Bks. LLC.

Galvin, Jill. My Lucky Fishing Spot. Piro, Maryanne, illus. 2001. 24p. (J). (ps-3). 14.95 (978-0-9708938-0-2(9)) Fox Den Bks.

Goldberg, Myla. Catching the Moon. Sheban, Chris, illus. 2007. 40p. (J). (ps-3). pap. 16.99 (978-0-439-57686-4(5) , Levine, Arthur A. Bks.) Scholastic, Inc.

Graf, Virginia L., ed. Gone Fishing No. 4: Stories for Children by Children. Yourell, Pamela, illus. 1998. 140p. (J). (gr. 2-8). pap. 9.95 (978-1-882788-15-6(X)) Vangar Pubs./Baltimore.

Greban, Quentin. Nestor. 2001. (Illus.). 27p. (J). pap. 15.95 (978-1-59034-012-7(4)) Mondo Publishing.

—Nestor. Greban, Quentin, illus. 2001. (Illus.). 27p. (J). (ps-4). 15.95 (978-1-58653-855-2(1)) Mondo Publishing.

—Nestor. (Buenas Noches Coleccion). (SPA., Illus.). (J). (gr. k-3). 8.95 (978-958-04-6032-9(9)) Norma S.A. COL. *Dist:* Distribuidora Norma, Inc., Lectorum Pubns., Inc.

Hancock, H. Irving. The High School Boys' Fishing Trip. rev. ed. 2006. 216p. 27.95 (978-1-4218-1749-1(7)); pap. 12.95 (978-1-4218-1849-8(3)) 1st World Publishing, Inc. (1st World Library - Literary Society).

Hancock, Irving H. The High School Boys Fishing Trip or Dic. 2006. 78.99 (*978-1-4219-9912-8(9)); pap. 72.99 (*978-1-4219-9915-9(3)) IndyPublish.com.

Harcourt School Publishers Staff. The Fishing Trip: Take-Home Book. 1999. (Illus.). (J). pap. 1.90 (978-0-15-313869-0(6)) Harcourt Schl. Pubs.

—Rainy Day Pals: Below Level. 3rd ed. 2002. (Trophies Reading Program Ser.). (Illus.). (J). pap. 4.10 (978-0-15-322966-4(7)) Harcourt Schl. Pubs.

—Rainy Day Pals 5-Pack, Below Level. 3rd ed. 2002. (Trophies Reading Program Ser.). (Illus.). (gr. 1). pap. 20.10 (978-0-15-326816-8(6)) Harcourt Schl. Pubs.

—Trish Had a Wish: On Level. 3rd ed. 2002. (Trophies Reading Program Ser.). (Illus.). (J). pap. 4.10 (978-0-15-322984-8(5)) Harcourt Schl. Pubs.

—Trish Had a Wish 5-Pack, On Level. 3rd ed. 2002. (Trophies Reading Program Ser.). (Illus.). (gr. 1). pap. 20.10 (978-0-15-326834-2(4)) Harcourt Schl. Pubs.

—Trofeos On Level: A Pescar! 3rd ed. 2002. (SPA., Illus.). pap. 5.50 (978-0-15-323895-6(X)) Harcourt Schl. Pubs.

Hill, Elizabeth Starr. Bird Boy. 2003. (gr. 3-6). lib. bdg. 14.10 (978-0-613-71735-9(X)) Tandem Library Bks.

Hite, Sid. The King of Slippery Falls. 2004. 224p. (J). pap. 16.95 (978-0-439-34257-5(0)) Scholastic, Inc.

Holland, Diane. Sally Butterfield Goes Fishing! 2005. 49p. pap. 12.95 (978-1-4137-9767-1(9)) PublishAmerica, Inc.

Holubitsky, Katherine. The Big Snapper. 2006. (Illus.). 144p. (J). pap. 5.95 (978-1-55143-563-3(2)) Orca Bk. Pubs. USA.

Howell, Gill. Selkie Child. Keen, Sophie, illus. 2005. 24p. (J). lib. bdg. 22.65 (*978-1-59646-750-7(9)) Dingles & Co.

Hurcomb, Fran. One Lucky Fish. Schlagintweit, Kris, illus. l.t. ed. 1999. 32p. (J). (gr. k-5). pap. (978-1-894303-15-6(6)) Raven Rock Publishing.

Hyde, Dayton O. The Major, the Poacher: And the Wonderful One-Trout River. 2003. (Illus.). 160p. (YA). (gr. 4-6). pap. 12.95 (978-1-56397-691-9(9)) Boyds Mills Pr.

Ilutsik, Paul. Neqsurtek. Slim, Zacharias & Horesh, David, illus. l.t. ed. 1999. Tr. of Two Subsistence Fishermen. (ESK.). 16p. (J). (gr. 3-5). pap. 6.00 (978-1-58084-173-3(2)) Lower Kuskokwim Schl. District.

Just One Fish Would Do: Individual Title Six-Packs. (gr. k-1). 23.00 (978-0-7635-8847-2(4)) Rigby Education.

Kalz, Jill. Bears on Ice. Olin, Troy, illus. 2006. (Read-It! Readers Ser.). 32p. (J). (ps-3). 18.60 (978-1-4048-1577-3(5)) Picture Window Bks.

Kilaka, John. Fresh Fish: A Tale from Tanzania. 2005. (Illus.). 32p. (J). 16.95 (978-0-88899-656-5(X)) Groundwood Bks. CAN. *Dist:* Perseus Distribution.

Kipling, Rudyard. Captains Courageous. Landgraf, Ken, illus. 2002. (Great Illustrated Classics Ser.).Tr. of 200. 240p. (J). (gr. 3-8). 21.35 (978-1-57765-683-8(0) , ABDO & Daughters) ABDO Publishing Co.

—Captains Courageous. 1999. (Dover Juvenile Classics Ser.).Tr. of 200. (J). (Illus.). 176p. (gr. 4-7). pap. 2.50 (978-0-486-40786-9(1)); (978-0-04-864078-9(6)) Dover Pubns., Inc.

—Captains Courageous. 1999. Tr. of 200. (gr. 3-6). lib. bdg. 10.10 (978-0-613-90755-2(8)) Tandem Library Bks.

Knipe, Floyd P. Forest & Grandpa Go Fishing. Jackson, James K., illus. 2000. (Forest the Huggable Dog Ser.: Vol. 2). 23p. (J). (ps-3). pap. 4.95 (978-1-930130-06-7(6)) Nature's Nest Bks.

—Forest & Grandpa Go Fishing Coloring Book. Jackson, James K., illus. 2000. (Forest the Huggable Dog Ser.: Vol. 2). 23p. (J). (ps-3). pap. 2.00 (978-1-930130-07-4(4)) Nature's Nest Bks.

Kristina Learns about Fishing. 2007. (J). (*978-0-9792728-0-6(7)) Tracepaper Bks. Inc.

Kulling, Monica. Edgar Badger's Fishing Day. Twinem, Nancy, illus. 1999. 48p. (J). (gr. 1-5). pap. 4.50 (978-1-57255-603-4(X)) Mondo Publishing.

—Edgar Badger's Fishing Day. 1999. (gr. 3-6). lib. bdg. 12.40 (978-0-613-17198-4(5)) Tandem Library Bks.

LaMarche, Jim. Up. 2006. (Illus.). 32p. (J). 16.95 (978-0-8118-4445-1(5)) Chronicle Bks. LLC.

Lane, Deborah. Fishing with Mom. 2003. pap. 9.00 (978-0-8059-6321-2(9)) Dorrance Publishing Co., Inc.

LeBox, Annette. Salmon Creek. Reczuch, Karen, illus. 2005. 32p. (J). pap. 12.95 (978-0-88899-644-2(6)) Groundwood Bks. CAN. *Dist:* Perseus Distribution.

The Little Fishing Fufu's. l.t. ed. 2001. 65p. (J). 14.95 (978-0-9709119-3-3(9)) Limpid Butterfly Productions, The.

Live Bait. 2001. 32p. (YA). (gr. 6-12). pap. (978 0 8224-3770-3(8)) Globe Fearon Educational Publishing.

Louthain, J. A. Tagger: Alone along the Mystic River. 2002. (Illus.). 215p. (YA). per. 14.95 (978-0-9679416-0-8(1) , 0-1) Alexie Bks.

Lovett, Darrell F. Darrell's Lake Franklin. 2007. 13.00 (*978-0-8059-8807-9(6)) Dorrance Publishing Co., Inc.

Loving, W. The Flibbertigibbet - A Mess-O-Fish. Loving, W., illus. 2000. (Illus.). 47p. (J). (ps-6). pap. 12.95 (978-0-9708193-0-7(7)) Loving, William M.

Lowrie, Paul & Nicholaus, Bret. Hooray for Minnesota Winters! For Minnesotans (and Those Who Wish They Were) of All Ages. Lindholm, Joe, ed. Awes, Jennifer, illus. 2005. 53p. (J). (ps-16). 16.95 (978-0-9755801-7-2(5)) Questmarc Publishing.

Maddox, Tony & Wen, Dref. Ffred ar y Dwr. 2005. (WEL., Illus.). 28p. (978-1-85596-666-6(2)) Dref Wen.

Manivong, Laura. One Smart Fish. Beaky, Suzanne, illus. 2006. (Rookie Reader Skill Set Ser.). 32p. (J). (gr. k-2). 19.50 (978-0-516-24982-7(7) , Children's Pr.) Scholastic Library Publishing.

Manivong, Laura & Beaky, Suzanne. One Smart Fish. 2006. (Rookie Reader Ser.). (Illus.). 32p. (J). pap. 4.95 (978-0-516-24996-4(7) , Children's Pr.) Scholastic Library Publishing.

Martin, Ann M. Karen's Fishing Trip. 1998. (Baby-Sitters Little Sister Ser.: No. 98). (Illus.). (J). (gr. 3-7). pap. 3.99 (978-0-590-06596-2(3) , Scholastic Paperbacks) Scholastic, Inc.

—Karen's Fishing Trip. 1998. (Baby-Sitters Little Sister Ser.: No. 98). (J). (gr. 3-7). (978-0-606-13174-2(4)) Tandem Library Bks.

Martin, David. Piggy & Dad Go Fishing. Remkiewicz, Frank, illus. 2005. (Brand New Readers Ser.). 32p. (J). (ps-1). 14.99 (978-0-7636-2506-1(X)) Candlewick Pr.

Massey, Ed. Jedlo, Defender of the Deep. 2005. (J). 17.95 (978-0-9766799-0-5(6)) Moombaya Bks.

McCloskey, Robert. Burt Dow: Deep-Water Man. 2001. (J). (gr. 1-4). 12.00 (978-0-7887-5510-1(2)) Recorded Bks., LLC.

McDonald, Rae. A Fishing Surprise. Kemly, Kathleen Hadam, illus. 2007. 32p. (J). (*978-1-55971-977-3(X) , NorthWord Bks. for Young Readers) T&N Children's Publishing.

Miller, Jennifer. Run, Rasputin, Run! Trials & Friendships (Book 2) 2006. (ENG., Illus.). 172p. per. (*978-1-4120-8494-9(6)) Trafford Publishing.

Mills, Claudia. Gus & Grandpa Go Fishing. Stock, Catherine, illus. 2003. (Gus & Grandpa Ser.). 48p. (J). 15.00 (978-0-374-32815-3(3) , Farrar, Straus & Giroux (BYR)) Farrar, Straus & Giroux.

Muluka, B. Kandu & the Lake. 2004. (Illus.). 40p. 13.95 (978-9966-25-165-7(0)) Heinemann Kenya, Limited (East African Educational Publishers Ltd E.A.E.P.) KEN. *Dist:* Michigan State Univ. Pr.

Nicolai, Margaret. Kitaq Goes Ice Fishing. Rubin, David, illus. 32p. (gr. k up). 2002. pap. 8.95 (978-0-88240-569-8(1)); 1998. 15.95 (978-0-88240-504-9(7)) Graphic Arts Ctr. Publishing Co.

Olsen, Sylvia. Catching Spring. 2004. (Orca Young Readers Ser.). (Illus.). 144p. (J). (gr. 3-6). pap. 4.99 (978-1-55143-298-4(6) , 1234542) Orca Bk. Pubs. USA.

Oppel, Kenneth. Peg & the Whale. ed. 2004. (Illus.). (J). (gr. k-3). spiral bd. (978-0-616-07245-5(7)) Canadian National Institute for the Blind/Institut National Canadien pour les Aveugles.

Osborne, Susan Titus. Flip-Flop Fishing. Durrell, Julie, illus. 2001. (Parables in Action Ser.: Vol. 7). 48p. (J). (ps-2). 4.99 (978-0-570-07139-6(9)) Concordia Publishing Hse.

Partridge, Elizabeth. Oranges on Golden Mountain. Sogabe, Aki, illus. 2003. 36p. (J). pap. 6.99 (978-0-14-250033-0(X) , Puffin) Penguin Group (USA) Inc.

—Oranges on Golden Mountain. 2003. (gr. k-3). lib. bdg. 15.30 (978-0-613-61651-5(0)) Tandem Library Bks.

Pennington, Tony. Fishing with Granddaddy B. 2004. (Illus.). 24p. pap. 8.00 (978-0-687-02570-1(2)) Abingdon Pr.

Percy, Carrie. Ridley Bluefox & the Flying Fish of Fortune Falls. 2007. 96p. (J). (gr. 2-5). pap. (978-1-897073-59-9(3)) Lobster Pr.

Phelps, Elizabeth Stuart. Jack the Fisherman. Reed, C. W., illus. 2005. reprint ed. pap. 15.95 (978-1-4179-3778-3(5)) Kessinger Publishing, LLC.

Philbrick, Rodman. The Young Man & the Sea. 2004. 192p. (J). pap. 16.95 (978-0-439-36829-2(4) , Blue Sky Pr., The) Scholastic, Inc.

—The Young Man & the Sea. 2005. 192p. (J). (ps-7). per. 12.64 (978-0-606-33810-3(1)) Tandem Library Bks.

Pickering, H. G. The Pickering Collection: Neighbors Have My Ducks, Merry Xmas, Mr. Williams Dog Days on Trout Waters & Angling of the Test. Timmins, Harry L. & Gardner, Donald, illus. 1999. (Fifty Greatest Bks.: Bk. 47). 288p. (gr. 10 up). reprint ed. 50.00 (978-1-56416-047-8(5)) Derrydale Pr., The.

Pinkney, Andrea Davis. Fishing Day. Evans, Shane W., illus. 2003. 32p. (gr. k-4). 15.99 (978-0-7868-0766-6(0)); 16.49 (978-0-7868-2614-8(2) , Jump at the Sun) Hyperion Bks. for Children.

Potter, Beatrix. Mr. Jeremy Fisher. 2007. (Potter Shaped Board Book Ser.). 12p. (J). bds. 3.99 (978-0-7232-5858-2(9) , Warne) Penguin Group (USA) Inc.

—The Tale of Mr. Jeremy Fisher. Potter, Beatrix, illus. 2002. (Illus.). (J). 15.23 (978-0-7587-6802-5(8)) Book Wholesalers, Inc.

—The Tale of Mr. Jeremy Fisher. 2002. (Illus.). 64p. (J). 6.99 (978-0-7232-4776-0(5) , Warne) Penguin Group (USA) Inc.

—The Tale of Mr. Jeremy Fisher. (Beatrix Potter Bookmark Board Book Ser.). (Illus.). 6p. (J). bds. 3.95 (978-1-58989-202-6(X)) Thurman Hse., LLC.

Prosek, James. The Day My Mother Left. Prosek, James, illus. 2007. (Illus.). 304p. (J). 15.99 (978-1-4169-0770-1(X)) Simon & Schuster Children's Publishing.

—A Good Day's Fishing. Prosek, James, illus. 2004. (Illus.). 40p. (J). 15.95 (978-0-689-85327-2(0)) Simon & Schuster Children's Publishing.

Quigley, Mary. Granddad's Fishing Buddy. Jorisch, Stephane, illus. 2007. 32p. (J). (ps-3). 16.99 (978-0-8037-2942-1(1) , Dial) Penguin Group (USA) Inc.

Rey, Margret & Rey, H. A., creators. Curious George Goes Fishing. 2001. (Curious George Ser.). (Illus.). 24p. (J). (gr. k-ps). bds. 5.95 (978-0-618-12071-0(8)) Houghton Mifflin Co. Trade & Reference Div.

Rhyne, Nancy. The Crab Boys. 2007. (J). pap. (*978-0-87844-183-9(2)) Sandlapper Publishing Co., Inc.

Richter, Jutta. The Summer of the Pike. Brailovsky, Anna, tr. from GER. Buchholz, Quint, illus. 2006. 132p. (J). pap. 6.95 (978-1-57131-672-1(8)); 16.95 (978-1-57131-671-4(X)) Milkweed Editions.

Rigby Education Staff. Fish for Dinner. (Sails Literacy Ser.). (Illus.). 16p. (gr. 1-2). 27.00 (978-0-7635-9896-9(8) , 698968C99) Rigby Education.

Robbins, Neal. The Crimson Fish. Eisenfeld, Candice, illus. 58p. (Orig.). (J). (gr. 1 up). pap. 4.00 (978-1-884993-02-2(8)) Koldarana Pubns.

Root, Phyllis. Mouse Goes Out. Croft, James, illus. 2002. (Brand New Readers Ser.). (J). (ps-2). 48p. 12.99 (978-0-7636-1351-8(7)); 32p. pap. 5.99 (978-0-7636-1352-5(5)) Candlewick Pr.

Roth, Roger. Fishing for Methuselah. 1998. (Illus.). 32p. (J). (ps-3). 14.95 (978-0-06-027592-1(8)) HarperCollins Pubs.

Salisbury, Graham. Lord of the Deep. braille ed. 2003. (J). (gr. 2). spiral bd. (978-0-616-15872-2(6)) Canadian National Institute for the Blind/Institut National Canadien pour les Aveugles.

E F G

—Lord of the Deep. 2003. 192p. (J). (gr. 5). pap. 5.99 (978-0-440-22911-7(1) , Laurel Leaf) Random Hse. Children's Bks.

—Lord of the Deep. 2003. (gr. 5-8). lib. bdg. 13.55 (978-0-613-61296-8(5)) Tandem Library Bks.

Salisbury, Graham. Lord of the Deep: A Novel. 2006. 182p. (J). (gr. 6-10). reprint ed. 16.00 (***978-1-4223-5841-2(0)***) DIANE Publishing Co.

Santillo, LuAnn. Fishing. Santillo, LuAnn, ed. 2003. (Half-Pint Kids Readers Ser.). (Illus.). 7p. (J). (ps-1). pap. (978-1-59256-093-6(8)) Half-Pint Kids, Inc.

Sargent, Dave & Sargent, Pat. Young Roy: I Love Adventure!, vol. 1. Woodward, Elaine, illus. 2003. (Young Animal Pride Ser.: 1). 24p. (J). pap. 6.95 (978-1-56763-864-6(3)); lib. bdg. 19.95 (978-1-56763-863-9(5)) Ozark Publishing.

Sinke, Janet Mary. Grandpa's Fishin' Friend. Pennington, Craig, illus. 2nd ed. 2006. (J). 16.95 (978-0-9742732-7-3(9)) My Grandma & Me Pubs.

Smiley, Lucy Ireland. Bass-Fishing Bears. 2006. (J). pap. 8.00 (978-0-8059-7017-3(7)) Dorrance Publishing Co., Inc.

Stanley, Andy. Go Fish Study Guide: Because of What's on the Line. 2005. 96p. pap. 9.99 (978-1-59052-548-7(5) , Multnomah) WaterBrook Pr.

Stone, Charlene. The Greatest Fishing Adventure of a Lifetime: American Kids Greatest Adventures. 2004. 47p. pap. 19.95 (978-1-4137-2862-0(6)) PublishAmerica, Inc.

Tremblay, Carole. The Old Man & the C. 2006. (Illus.). 27p. (J). 15.95 (978-1-56164-354-7(8)) Pineapple Pr., Inc.

Van Scoyoc, Pam. I Could Catch a Whale/ Yo Podria Pescar una Ballena. Santillan-Cruz, Sylvia R., tr. Lewis, R. J., illus. l.t. ed. 2005. (ENG & SPA.). 32p. (J). (gr. k-2). lib. bdg. 16.98 (978-0-9663629-5-4(0)) By Grace Enterprises.

Varner, Carla. Theodore Goes Fishing. 2003. (J). 11.95 (978-0-9745787-2-9(X)) I Can Do All Things Productions.

Villanueva, Leonard. Kaipo & the Mighty Ahi. Villanueva, Leonard, illus. 2004. (Illus.). (J). 14.95 (978-0-9729905-6-1(9)) Beachhouse Publishing, LLC.

Wackwitz, Winnie. The Creature of Lost Bayou. 2004. (YA). pap. 12.95 (978-1-58752-107-2(5)) Timberwolf Pr., Inc.

Wells, Eva. Wishing I Was Fishing. 2006. 32p. lib. bdg. 16.95 (***978-1-59298-168-7(2)***) Beaver's Pond Pr., Inc.

White, James C. David Goes Fishing. Chapin, Patrick, illus. 2003. 32p. (J). 6.95 (978-0-9747752-0-3(7)) White, James C.

Williams, Jacklyn. Let's Go Fishing, Gus! Cushman, Doug, illus. 2006. (Read-It! Readers Ser.). (J). 19.93 (978-1-4048-2713-4(7)) Picture Window Bks.

Williams, Laura E. Torch Fishing with the Sun. Broeck, Fabricio Vanden, illus. 2003. 32p. (J). (gr. 4-6). 15.95 (978-1-56397-685-8(4)) Boyds Mills Pr.

Wilson, Barbara Ker. Maui & the Big Fish. Lessac, Frane, illus. 2004. 32p. (J). (978-0-7112-2066-9(2)); pap. 7.95 (978-1-84507-159-2(X)) Lincoln, Frances Ltd. GBR. *Dist:* Transition Vendor, Perseus Distribution.

Wolo, Elaine Armour. Nippeh's Fishing Surprise. 2nd rev. ed. 2001. 32p. 4.00 (978-0-9708998-2-8(3)) Wolo, Armour Foundation.

Wunderle, Steve L. & Wunderle, Sharon. Bucky Bear & the Surprise Fishing Trip. Wunderle, Steve L., photos by. l.t. ed. 1999. (Illus.). 28p. (J). (gr. k-4). pap. 5.95 (978-0-9611162-4-8(2)) Wunderle Outdoor Bks.

Yukish, Joe. The Fishing Contest. Palmer, Kate Salley, illus. 2002. 24p. (J). (gr. k-2). pap. 5.25 (978-1-57874-031-4(2)) Kaeden Corp.

FISHING INDUSTRY

see Fisheries

FISHING TACKLE

see Fishing—Equipment and Supplies

FITZGERALD, F. SCOTT (FRANCIS SCOTT), 1896-1940

Bankston, John. F. Scott Fitzgerald. 2004. (Classic Storytellers Ser.). (Illus.). 48p. (J). (gr. 4-8). lib. bdg. 20.95 (978-1-58415-249-1(4)) Mitchell Lane Pubs., Inc.

Becnel, Kim. Bloom's How to Write about F. Scott Fitzgerald. 2007. (Bloom's How to Write about Literature Ser.). 256p. (YA). (gr. 9 up). 45.00 (***978-0-7910-9482-2(0)*** , Chelsea Hse.) Facts On File, Inc.

Brackett, Virginia R. F. Scott Fitzgerald: Writer of the Jazz Age. 2004. (World Writers Ser.). (Illus.). 128p. (YA). (gr. 6-12). 23.95 (978-1-883846-90-9(0) , First Biographies) Reynolds, Morgan Inc.

Hensley, Laura. The Story Behind F. Scott Fitzgerald's the Great Gatsby. 2006. (History in Literature Ser.). (Illus.). 56p. (J). lib. bdg. (978-1-4034-8205-1(5)) Heinemann Library.

Lazo, Caroline Evensen. F. Scott Fitzgerald: Voice of the Jazz Age. 2002. (Lerner Long Biographies Ser.). (Illus.). 128p. (J). lib. bdg. 27.93 (978-0-8225-0074-2(4) , Lerner Pubns.) Lerner Publishing Group.

Stewart, Gail B., et al. F. Scott Fitzgerald. 1999. (Importance of Ser.). (Illus.). 112p. (YA). (gr. 7-10). 27.45 (978-1-56006-541-8(9) , Lucent Bks.) Thomson Gale.

Stielau, Allison. F. Scott Fitzgerald. 2nd rev. ed. 2006. (Bloom's Modern Critical Views Ser.). viii, 261p. 45.00 (978-0-7910-8570-7(8) , Chelsea Hse.) Facts On File, Inc.

Weisbrod, Eva. A Student's Guide to F. Scott Fitzgerald. 2004. (Understanding Literature Ser.). (Illus.). 160p. (J). lib. bdg. 27.93 (978-0-7660-2202-7(1)) Enslow Pubs., Inc.

Welsch, Gabriel. The Great Gatsby. 2006. (Bloom's Guides Ser.). 144p. 30.00 (978-0-7910-8580-6(5) , Chelsea Hse.) Facts On File, Inc.

FLAG DAY

Ansary, Mir Tamim. Flag Day. (Heinemann First Library). (Illus.). (J). (gr. k-2). 2001. 32p. lib. bdg. 21.36 (978-1-58810-222-5(X)); 2nd ed. 2006. 31p. (***978-1-4034-8886-2(X)***) Heinemann Library.

—Flag Day. 2001. (Holiday Histories Ser.). 13.75 (978-0-606-22382-9(7)) Tandem Library Bks.

Ansary, Tamim. Flag Day. 2002. (Holiday Histories Ser.). (Illus.). 32p. (J). (gr. k-2). pap. 6.95 (978-1-58810-572-1(5) , 91687) Heinemann Library.

Bennett, Kelly. Flag Day. 2003. (Rookie Read-About Holidays Ser.). (Illus.). 32p. (J). (gr. 1-2). 20.50 (978-0-516-22862-4(5)); pap. 5.95 (978-0-516-27755-4(3)) Scholastic Library Publishing. (Children's Pr.).

—Flag Day. 2003. (Illus.). 31p. (J). (ps-3). lib. bdg. 14.10 (978-0-613-59618-3(8)) Tandem Library Bks.

Cooper, Jason. Flag Day. 2002. 24p. (J). lib. bdg. 20.64 (978-1-58952-219-0(2)) Rourke Publishing, LLC.

Dean, Sheri. Flag Day/dia De La Bandera. 2006. (Illus.). 24p. (J). (ENG & SPA.). 19.33 (978-0-8368-6518-9(9)); pap. (978-0-8368-6511-0(1)); (ENG & SPA., pap. 5.95 (978-0-8368-6525-7(1)); lib. bdg. 19.33 (978-0-8368-6504-2(9)) Stevens, Gareth Inc.

Kaplan, Leslie C. Flag Day. 2004. (Library of Holidays). (Illus.). 24p. (J). lib. bdg. 18.75 (978-0-8239-6659-2(3) , PowerKids Pr.) Rosen Publishing Group, Inc., The.

Schuh, Mari C. Flag Day. 2003. (National Holidays Ser.). (Illus.). 24p. (J). (gr. k-1). lib. bdg. 15.93 (978-0-7368-1652-6(6) , Pebble Bks.) Capstone Pr., Inc.

FLAGS

see also Signals and Signaling

Ansary, Mir Tamim. Flag Day. 2nd ed. 2006. (Illus.). 31p. (J). (***978-1-4034-8886-2(X)***) Heinemann Library.

—Flag Day. 2001. (Holiday Histories Ser.). 13.75 (978-0-606-22382-9(7)) Tandem Library Bks.

Baker, Karle Wilson. Texas Flag Primer. 2005. reprint ed. pap. 20.95 (978-0-7661-9572-1(4)) Kessinger Publishing, LLC.

Banting, Erinn. Flags & Seals. 2004. (American Symbols Ser.). (J). pap. 6.95 (978-1-59036-176-4(8)); (Illus.). 24p. lib. bdg. 15.95 (978-1-59036-130-6(X)) Weigl Pubs., Inc.

Bartoletti, Susan Campbell. The Flag Maker. Nivola, Claire A., illus. 2007. 32p. (J). (gr. 3-5). 6.95 (***978-0-618-80911-0(2)***) Houghton Mifflin Co. Trade & Reference Div.

Benton, Celia. Our Flag. 2003. (Compass Point Phonics Readers Ser.). (Illus.). 16p. (J). (gr. 1 up). 13.26 (978-0-7565-0517-2(8)) Compass Point Bks.

Binns, Tristan Boyer. The American Flag. (Symbols of Freedom Ser.). (Illus.). 32p. (J). (gr. k-2). 2002. pap. 6.95 (978-1-58810-401-4(X) , 91143); 2001. lib. bdg. 21.36 (978-1-58810-117-4(7)) Heinemann Library.

—The American Flag. 2001. 13.75 (978-0-606-22577-9(3)); (gr. 3-6). lib. bdg. 14.75 (978-0-613-43293-1(2)) Tandem Library Bks.

—La Bandera. 2003. (Simbolos de Libertad Ser.).Tr. of American Flag. (SPA & ENG., 32p. (J). Illus.). lib. bdg. 22.79 (978-1-4034-3001-4(2)); pap. 6.95 (978-1-4034-3024-3(1)) Heinemann Library.

—La Bandera. 2003. Tr. of American Flag. (SPA.). (gr. k-3). lib. bdg. 14.75 (978-0-613-88572-0(4)) Tandem Library Bks.

—El Juramento de Lealtad. 2003. (Simbolos de Libertad Ser.).Tr. of Pledge of Allegiance. (SPA., Illus.). 32p. (J). lib. bdg. 22.79 (978-1-4034-2997-1(9)) Heinemann Library.

—El Juramento de Lealtad. 2003. Tr. of Pledge of Allegiance. (SPA.). (gr. k-3). lib. bdg. 14.75 (978-0-613-89945-1(8)) Tandem Library Bks.

Bloss, Janet Adele. State Flags. 2000. (Illus.). 80p. (J). (gr. 5-7). reprint ed. pap. 15.00 (978-0-7881-6933-5(5)) DIANE Publishing Co.

Bowdish, Lynea. Francis Scott Key & "The Star Spangled Banner" 2002. (Illus.). 32p. (J). 15.95 (978-1-59034-195-7(3)) Mondo Publishing.

Britton, Tamara L. The American Flag. 2005. (Symbols, Landmarks & Monuments Ser.). (Illus.). 32p. (J). (gr. k-6). lib. bdg. 22.78 (978-1-57765-852-8(3)) ABDO Publishing Co.

Cohan, George M. & Kimble, Warren. You're a Grand Old Flag. Kimble, Warren, illus. 2007. (Illus.). 32p. (J). (ps-1). 17.85 (***978-0-8027-9576-2(5)***); 16.95 (***978-0-8027-9575-5(7)***) Walker & Co.

Congress (U.S.), Joint Committee on Printing, compiled by. Our Flag. 2007. (Illus.). 60p. pap. 4.50 (***978-0-16-076598-8(6)*** , Joint Committee on Printing) United States Government Printing Office.

Cooper, Jason. Banderas/Flags. 2003. (La Guia De Rourke Para Los Simbolos De Los Estados). (ENG & SPA.). (gr. 3-8). 20.95 (978-1-58952-397-5(0)) Rourke Publishing, LLC.

Cox, Vicki. Betsy Ross: Flag for a New Nation. 2005. (Leaders of the American Revolution Ser.). (Illus.). 148p. (J). (gr. 4-8). lib. bdg. 30.00 (978-0-7910-8618-6(6) , Chelsea Hse.) Facts On File, Inc.

Crampton, W. Flags of the World. 2004. (Spotter's Guides). 64p. (J). pap. 5.95 (978-0-7945-0450-2(7)); lib. bdg. 13.95 (978-1-58086-530-2(5)) EDC Publishing.

Crampton, William G. Flag. 2000. (Eyewitness Bks.). (Illus.). 64p. (J). (gr. 4-7). 15.99 (978-0-7894-5824-7(1)) Dorling Kindersley Publishing, Inc.

Crampton, William G. & Dorling Kindersley Publishing Staff. Flag. 2000. (Eyewitness Bks.). (Illus.). 64p. (J). (gr. 4-7). lib. bdg. 19.99 (978-0-7894-6565-8(5)) Dorling Kindersley Publishing, Inc.

Crewe, Sabrina & Ingram, Scott. The Writing of "The Star-Spangled Banner" 2004. (Events That Shaped America Ser.). (Illus.). 32p. lib. bdg. 24.67 (978-0-8368-3409-3(7)) Stevens, Gareth Inc.

Dell, Pamela. The National Anthem. 2004. (Let's See Library). (Illus.). 24p. (J). (gr. 1 up). lib. bdg. 19.93 (978-0-7565-0619-3(0)) Compass Point Bks.

—The Pledge of Allegiance. 2004. (Let's See Library). (Illus.). 24p. (J). (gr. 1 up). lib. bdg. 19.93 (978-0-7565-0620-9(4)) Compass Point Bks.

Denega, Danielle. Let's Read About— Betsy Ross. Graeff, Renee, illus. 2004. (Scholastic First Biographies Ser.). (J). pap. (978-0-439-56635-3(5)) Scholastic, Inc.

Douglas, Lloyd G. The American Flag. 2003. (Welcome Book Ser.). (Illus.). 24p. (J). 18.00 (978-0-516-25850-8(8)); pap. 4.95 (978-0-516-27873-5(8)) Scholastic Library Publishing. (Children's Pr.).

—American Flag. 2003. (gr. k-3). lib. bdg. 12.95 (978-0-613-67685-4(8)) Tandem Library Bks.

—The Pledge of Allegiance. 2003. (Welcome Book Ser.). (Illus.). 24p. (J). 18.00 (978-0-516-25853-9(2)); pap. 4.95 (978-0-516-27876-6(2)) Scholastic Library Publishing. (Children's Pr.).

Duden, Jane. Betsy Ross. 2000. (Let Freedom Ring Ser.). (Illus.). 48p. (J). (gr. 3-4). lib. bdg. 22.60 (978-0-7368-1036-4(6) , Bridgestone Bks.) Capstone Pr., Inc.

Fata, Heather. The Pledge of Allegiance. 2003. (Primary Source Library of American Citizenship). (Illus.). 32p. (J). pap. (978-1-4042-5090-1(5)) Rosen Publishing Group, Inc., The.

Firestone, Mary. Our American Flag. Skeens, Matthew, illus. 2006. (J). 23.93 (978-1-4048-2212-2(7)) Picture Window Bks.

—Our National Anthem. Skeens, Matthew, illus. 2006. (J). 23.93 (978-1-4048-2215-3(1)) Picture Window Bks.

Flags. (Kid Kits Ser.). (Illus.). 32p. (J). 9.95 (978-1-58086-413-8(9)) EDC Publishing.

Flags: Individual Title Six-Packs. (Action Packs Ser.). 104p. (gr. 3-5). 44.00 (978-0-7635-8413-9(4)) Rigby Education.

Flags of the World Action Sticker Book. 2002. 12p. (J). pap. 3.98 (978-0-7525-8036-4(1)) Parragon, Inc.

Flags over Corydon Coloring Book. 2005. (J). 4.95 (978-0-9769829-1-3(9)) Dorcas Pubns., LLC.

Frost, Helen. Betsy Ross. Saunders-Smith, Gail, ed. 2003. (Famous Americans Ser.). (Illus.). 24p. (J). (gr. k-1). lib. bdg. 15.93 (978-0-7368-1641-0(0) , Pebble Bks.) Capstone Pr., Inc.

Gray, Susan Heinrichs. The American Flag. 2001. (Let's See Library). (Illus.). 24p. (J). (gr. 1 up). lib. bdg. 19.93 (978-0-7565-0140-2(7)) Compass Point Bks.

Hancock, Maryann. The U.S. Flag. 2006. (Illus.). 32p. (J). (978-1-4034-7002-7(2)); pap. (978-1-4034-7009-6(X)) Heinemann Library.

Harris, Nancy. The American Flag. 2007. (J). (***978-1-4034-9379-8(0)***); pap. (***978-1-4034-9386-6(3)***) Heinemann Library.

Healy, Nick. The American Flag. 2003. (J). pap. (978-1-58417-116-4(2)); lib. bdg. (978-1-58417-053-2(0)) Lake Street Pubs.

—The Star-Spangled Banner. 2003. (J). (978-1-58417-055-6(7)); pap. (978-1-58417-118-8(9)) Lake Street Pubs.

Herman, John. Red, White & Blue: The Story of the American Flag. Roraback, Robin, illus. 1998. (All Aboard Reading Ser.). 48p. (J). (ps-3). pap. 3.99 (978-0-448-41270-2(5) , Grosset & Dunlap) Penguin Group (USA) Inc.

Hicks, Terry Allan. The Pledge of Allegiance. 2006. (Symbols of America Ser.). (Illus.). 40p. (J). lib. bdg. 28.50 (978-0-7614-2136-8(X) , Benchmark Bks.) Cavendish, Marshall Corp.

Hicks, Terry Allan. Symbols of America Group 2, 6 bks., Set. Incl. Bald Eagle. lib. bdg. 28.50 (978-0-7614-2133-7(5)); Capitol. lib. bdg. 28.50 (978-0-7614-2132-0(7)); Declaration of Independence. lib. bdg. 28.50 (978-0-7614-2135-1(1)); Ellis Island. lib. bdg. 28.50 (978-0-7614-2134-4(3)); Pledge of Allegiance. lib. bdg. 28.50 (978-0-7614-2136-8(X)); Uncle Sam. lib. bdg. 28.50 (978-0-7614-2137-5(8)); (Illus.). 40p. (J). 2006. 2007. Set lib. bdg. 171.00 (***978-0-7614-2130-6(0)*** , Benchmark Bks.) Cavendish, Marshall Corp.

Howard, Rebecca. Flagtastic Flags. 2006. (Illus.). 32p. (J). 14.95 (978-0-7145-3305-6(X)) Boyars, Marion Pubs., Inc.

I Pledge Allegiance. . . 2003. (J). bds. 6.95 (978-0-9726762-2-9(8)) Star Spangled Baby, Ltd.

Ingram, Scott. The Writing of "The Star-Spangled Banner" 2004. (Landmark Events in American History Ser.). (Illus.). 48p. (J). (gr. 5 up). pap. 11.95 (978-0-8368-5418-3(7)); lib. bdg. 30.00 (978-0-8368-5390-2(3)) Stevens, Gareth Inc. (World Almanac Library).

Israel, Fred L., intro. National Flags. 1999. (Looking Into the Past Ser.). (Illus.). 64p. (YA). (gr. 5 up). lib. bdg. 19.75 (978-0-7910-4686-9(9) , Chelsea Hse.) Facts On File, Inc.

Jacobson, Ryan. The Story of the Star-Spangled Banner. Martin, Cynthia, illus. 2006. (Graphic Library). 32p. (J). (978-0-7368-5493-1(2)) Capstone Pr., Inc.

Jango-Cohen, Judith. The American Flag. (Pull Ahead Bks.). 32p. (J). (gr. k-3). 2004. (Illus.). lib. bdg. 22.60 (978-0-8225-3804-2(0)); 2003. pap. 5.95 (978-0-8225-3753-3(2)) Lerner Publishing Group.

Jordan, Shirley. The American Flag: Moments in History. 2003. (Cover-To-Cover Books). (Illus.). 72p. (J). pap. (978-0-7891-5917-5(1)); (gr. 4-7). lib. bdg. 17.95 (978-0-7569-1185-0(0)) Perfection Learning Corp.

Katcher, Philip R. N. Confederate Flags of the Civil War. 2003. (Battle Ready Ser.). (Illus.). 48p. (J). 28.56 (978-1-4109-0122-4(X)) Raintree.

—Union Flags of the Civil War. 2003. (Battle Ready Ser.). (Illus.). 48p. (J). 28.56 (978-1-4109-0123-1(8)) Raintree.

Landau, Elaine. The American Flag. (True Booktrade;: American History Ser.). 48p. (J). 2008. pap. 6.95 (***978-0-531-14775-7(4)***); 2007. (Illus.). (gr. 3-5). lib. bdg. 26.00 (***978-0-531-12625-7(0)***) Scholastic Library Publishing. (Children's Pr.).

Larson, Wanda Z. Our Flag: Born Through Valor. 1999. (Illus.). 75p. (J). (gr. 4-12). pap. 12.00 (978-0-9628584-1-3(2)) Blue Unicorn Pr., Inc.

Lewison, Wendy Cheyette. F Is for Flag. Duke, Barbara, illus. 2002. (Reading Railroad Bks.). 32p. (J). pap. 3.49 (978-0-448-42838-3(5) , Grosset & Dunlap) Penguin Group (USA) Inc.

—F Is for Flag. 2002. (ps-2). lib. bdg. 11.25 (978-0-613-45263-2(1)) Tandem Library Bks.

Lilly, Melinda. The Star Spangled Banner. 2003. (Rourke Discovery Library). (Illus.). 24p. (gr. 1-4). 14.95 (978-1-58952-365-4(2)) Rourke Publishing, LLC.

Mader, Jan. Betsy Ross. 2007. (J). (978-0-7368-6702-3(3) , Pebble Bks.) Capstone Pr., Inc.

Mara, Wil. Betsy Ross. (J). 2006. 32p. (gr. 1-2). pap. 4.95 (978-0-516-25369-5(7)); 2005. (Illus.). 31p. (ps-ps). 20.50 (978-0-516-25268-1(2)) Scholastic Library Publishing. (Children's Pr.).

Marcovitz, Hal. The Confederate Flag. 2002. (American Symbols & Their Meanings Ser.). (Illus.). 48p. (YA). (gr. 4 up). lib. bdg. (978-1-59084-035-1(6)) Mason Crest Pubs.

Marcovitz, Hal & Ferry, Joseph. The American Flag. 2002. (American Symbols & Their Meanings Ser.). (Illus.). 48p. (YA). (gr. 4 up). lib. bdg. (978-1-59084-026-9(7)) Mason Crest Pubs.

Marsh, Carole. The New Georgia Flag. 2001. (Illus.). (J). pap., tchr. ed. 7.95 (978-0-635-00506-9(9)) Gallopade International.

Martin, Bill, Jr. & Sampson, Michael. I Pledge Allegiance. Raschka, Chris, illus. 2004. (J). (ps-ps). lib. bdg. 13.64 (978-0-606-30994-3(2)) Tandem Library Bks.

Martin, Bill, Jr. & Sampson, Michael R. I Pledge Allegiance. Raschka, Chris, illus. 2002. 40p. (J). (gr. 1-4). 15.99 (978-0-7636-1648-9(6)) Candlewick Pr.

Miles, L. Flags Sticker Book. 2004. (Spotter's Guides Sticker Bks.). (SPA., Illus.). 32p. (J). (gr. 2 up). pap. 7.95 (978-0-7945-0184-6(2) , Usborne) EDC Publishing.

Miles, Lisa. Libro de Pegatinas Banderas Todos los Paises del Mundo. 2004. (Spotter's Guides Sticker Bks.). (SPA., Illus.). 23p. (J). (gr. 2 up). pap. 7.95 (978-0-7460-3644-0(2) , EDC6442) EDC Publishing.

Miles, Lisa, ed. Flags Sticker Book. 1998. (Spotter's Guides Sticker Bks.). (Illus.). 23p. (YA). (gr. 2 up). pap. 7.95 (978-0-7460-3151-3(3) , EDC1513) EDC Publishing.

Miller, Susan Martins. Betsy Ross: American Patriot. 2000. (Revolutionary War Leaders Ser.). (J). 15.75 (978-0-606-19340-5(5)) Tandem Library Bks.

My Red, White & Blue. (Illus.). (J). bds. 5.00 net. (978-1-56021-388-8(4)) W.J. Fantasy, Inc.

Nobleman, Marc Tyler. The Pledge of Allegiance. 2003. (American Symbols Ser.). (Illus.). 24p. (J). (gr. 1-2). lib. bdg. 18.60 (978-0-7368-1631-1(3) , Bridgestone Bks.) Capstone Pr., Inc.

O Say Can You See. . . 2003. bds. 6.99 (978-0-9726762-0-5(1)) Star Spangled Baby, Ltd.

Olson, Kay Melchisedech. Betsy Ross & the American Flag. Cool, Anna-Maria et al, illus. 2005. (Graphic Library). 32p. (J). (gr. 3-7). lib. bdg. 25.26 (978-0-7368-4962-3(9)) Capstone Pr., Inc.

Our Flag: First Grade Guided Reading Level C. (On Our Way to English Ser.). (gr. 1 up). 27.75 (978-0-7578-7038-5(4)) Rigby Education.

Ouren, Todd, illus. You're a Grand Old Flag. 2004. (Patriotic Songs Ser.). 24p. (J). (ps-4). 22.60 (978-1-4048-0173-8(1)) Picture Window Bks.

Owens, Ann-Maureen, et al. Canada's Maple Leaf: The Story of Our Flag. 1999. (Illus.). 112p. (J). (gr. 3-7). (978-1-55074-516-0(6)) Kids Can Pr., Ltd.

Los Paises Tienen Banderas. 2003. (Enciclopedia Me Pregunto Por Que). (SPA., Illus.). (J). (gr. 3-5). (978-84-241-1969-0(X) , EV2042) Everest de Ediciones y Distribucion, S.L. ESP. *Dist:* Lectorum Pubns., Inc.

Pearl, Norman. The Pledge of Allegiance. Skeens, Matthew, illus. 2006. 24p. (J). lib. bdg. (***978-1-4048-2644-1(0)***) Picture Window Bks.

Pledge of Allegiance. 2000. (gr. k-3). lib. bdg. 11.25 (978-0-613-42429-5(8)) Tandem Library Bks.

Poolos, Christine. The American Flag. 2003. (Primary Source Library of American Citizenship). (Illus.). 32p. (J). pap. (978-1-4042-5086-4(7)) Rosen Publishing Group, Inc., The.

Prince, April Jones. Meet Our Flag, Old Glory. Paley, Joan, illus. 2006. 30p. (J). (gr. k-4). reprint ed. 16.00 (978-0-7567-9822-2(1)) DIANE Publishing Co.

Purcell, John. American City Flags Vols. 9&10: 146 Flags from Akron to Yonkers. l.t. ed. 2004. (Illus.). 400p. per. (978-0-9747728-0-6(1) , 48) North American Vexillological Assoc. (NAVA).

Randolph, Ryan P. Betsy Ross: The American Flag & Life in Young America. 2005. (Library of American Lives & Times). (Illus.). 112p. (J). (gr. 4-8). lib. bdg. 31.95 (978-0-8239-5730-9(6)) Rosen Publishing Group, Inc., The.

Roop, Peter & Roop, Connie. Sew What, Betsy Ross? 2002. (Before I Made History Ser.). (Illus.). 57p. (J). (978-0-439-43925-1(6)) Scholastic, Inc.

Rothman, Cynthia. Our Flag. Baran, Esther, illus. 2002. 16p. (J). (978-0-439-35097-6(2)) Scholastic, Inc.

Rubin, Susan Goldman. The Flag with Fifty-Six Stars: A Gift from the Survivors of Mauthausen. Farnsworth, Bill, illus. 2005. 40p. (J). (gr. 1-5). 16.95 (978-0-8234-1653-0(4)) Holiday Hse., Inc.

Ryan, Pam Muñoz. La Bandera Que Amamos. 2002. (SPA.). (gr. k-3). lib. bdg. 16.40 (978-0-613-88751-9(4)) Tandem Library Bks.

—The Flag We Love. Masiello, Ralph, illus. 2004. 32p. (J). (ps-3). pap. 7.95 (978-0-88106-844-3(6)) Charlesbridge Publishing, Inc.

—The Flag We Love. 2000. (J). 14.75 (978-0-606-19327-6(8)) Tandem Library Bks.

Ryan, Pam Muñoz & Masiello, Ralph. La Bandera Que Amamos. 2004. (SPA., Illus.). 32p. (J). pap. 7.95 (978-1-57091-519-2(9)) Charlesbridge Publishing, Inc.

—The Flag We Love. 10th ed. 2006. (Illus.). 32p. (J). 17.95 (978-1-57091-707-3(8)) Charlesbridge Publishing, Inc.

Schaefer, Lola M. El Juramento de Lealtad. 2003. (Símbolos de Libertad Ser.). (SPA.). 32p. pap. 6.95 (978-1-4034-3020-5(9)) Heinemann Library.

—The Pledge of Allegiance. (Symbols of Freedom Ser.). (Illus.). 32p. (J). (gr. k-2). 2002. pap. 6.95 (978-1-58810-398-7(6) , 91193); 2001. lib. bdg. (978-1-58810-177-8(0)) Heinemann Library.

Scholastic, Inc. Staff. Pledge of Allegiance: Commemorative Edition. 2001. (Illus.). 32p. (J). pap. 3.99 (978-0-439-39962-3(9) , Scholastic Paperbacks) Scholastic, Inc.

Silate, Jennifer. The American Flag. 2004. (Illus.). 24p. (J). lib. bdg. (978-1-4042-2686-9(9)) Rosen Publishing Group, Inc., The.

—Betsy Ross. 2003. (Famous People in American History Ser.). (Illus.). 32p. (J). pap. (978-0-8239-4176-6(0)) Rosen Publishing Group, Inc., The.

Smith, Whitney. Flag Lore of All Nations. (Illus.). 112p. (J). (gr. 3-6). 2003. pap. 12.95 (978-0-7613-1899-6(2)); 2001. lib. bdg. 29.90 (978-0-7613-1753-1(8)) Lerner Publishing Group. (Millbrook Pr.).

Sonneborn, Liz. The Pledge of Allegiance: The Story Behind Our Patriotic Promise. 2003. (America in Words & Song Ser.). (Illus.). 32p. (gr. 3-5). 23.00 (978-0-7910-7336-0(X) , Chelsea Hse.) Facts On File, Inc.

—The Star-Spangled Banner: The Story Behind Our National Anthem. 2003. (America in Words & Song Ser.). (Illus.). 32p. (gr. 3-5). 23.00 (978-0-7910-7337-7(8) , Chelsea Hse.) Facts On File, Inc.

Sorensen, Lynda. La Bandera Americana. Palacios, Argentina, tr. 2002. (Simbolos Americanos Ser.). (SPA., Illus.). 24p. mass mkt. 5.95 (978-1-58952-269-5(9) , RK31482) Rourke Publishing, LLC.

Swanson, June. I Pledge Allegiance. 2nd rev. ed. 2003. (On My Own History Ser.). (Illus.). 48p. (J). (gr. 1-3). pap. 5.95 (978-0-87614-912-6(3) , Carolrhoda Bks.) Lerner Publishing Group.

—I Pledge Allegiance. 2002. (gr. 3-6). lib. bdg. 14.10 (978-0-613-46141-2(X)) Tandem Library Bks.

Thomson, Sarah L. American Flag QandA. 2008. 48p. (J). 16.99 (***978-0-06-089959-2(X)***); pap. 6.99 (***978-0-06-089958-5(1)***) HarperCollins Pubs. (Collins).

—My Flag Book. 2007. 16p. (J). 5.99 (***978-0-06-089957-8(3)***) HarperCollins Pubs.

Thomson, Sarah L. Stars & Stripes: The Story of the American Flag. Dacey, Bob & Bandelin, Debra, illus. 2003. 32p. (J). (ps-3). 16.99 (978-0-06-050416-8(1)) HarperCollins Pubs.

TNT Stone and Associates Staff & Petertil Design Partners Staff, illus. Our Fifty States & Their Flags. 1998. (Powertools for Kids Ser.: No. 15). 4p. (J). (gr. 2-5). pap., wbk. ed. 4.95 (978-1-58220-014-9(9) , 32505, PowerTools for Kids) Navigator Systems, Inc.

Top That Publishing Staff, ed. Flags. 2004. (Stickertastic Ser.). (Illus.). 24p. (J). pap. (978-1-84510-118-3(9)) Top That! Publishing PLC.

The United States & Its Flag, 6 bks., Set. (Illus.). (J). (gr. 3-12). lib. bdg. 109.70 (978-1-56674-913-8(1)) Forest Hse. Publishing Co., Inc.

Warren, Jean. Flags. Cubley, Kathleen, ed. 1998. (Sticker Book Ser.). (Illus.). 32p. (J). (ps). pap. 3.95 (978-1-57029-218-7(3) , WPH 3708, Totline Pubns.) Schaffer, Frank Pubns.

Webster, Christine. The Pledge of Allegiance. 2007. (Cornerstones of Freedomtrade;, Second Ser.). 48p. (J). (gr. 4-6). pap. 5.95 (***978-0-531-18768-5(3)*** , Children's Pr.) Scholastic Library Publishing.

Welch, Catherine A. The Star-Spangled Banner. Warwick, Carrie, illus. 2005. (On My Own History Ser.). 48p. (J). 25.26 (978-1-57505-590-9(2)) Lerner Publishing Group.

World of Flags Wallchart. 2004. (Wall Charts Ser.). (J). 4.99 (978-1-85997-277-9(2)) Byeway Bks.

Yanuck, Debbie L. The American Flag. 2003. (American Symbols Ser.). (Illus.). 24p. (J). (gr. 1-2). lib. bdg. 18.60 (978-0-7368-1628-1(3) , Bridgestone Bks.) Capstone Pr., Inc.

Yoon, Salina. Stars & Stripes. 2007. (Salina Yoon Bks.). 10p. (J). (ps-k). bds. 5.99 (978-0-8431-2176-6(9) , Price Stern Sloan) Penguin Group (USA) Inc.

FLATS

see Apartment Houses

FLEAS

Hartley, Karen, et al, contrib. by. Flea. 2000. (Bug Books Ser.). (Illus.). 32p. (J). lib. bdg. 21.36 (978-1-57572-547-5(9)) Heinemann Library.

Silverman, Buffy. Fleas. 2004. (Parasites Ser.). 32p. (J). (gr. 4-7). 22.45 (978-0-7377-2632-9(6) , Greenhaven Pr., Inc.) Thomson Gale.

Stevens, Kathryn. Fleas. 2000. (Naturebooks: Creepy Crawlers Ser.). (Illus.). 32p. (J). (gr. 1-5). 25.64 (978-1-56766-632-8(9)) Child's World, Inc.

Twist, Clint. Fleas. 2006. (Illus.). 32p. (J). lib. bdg. 23.33 (978-0-8368-6375-8(5)) Stevens, Gareth Inc.

FLEAS—FICTION

Downey, Lynn. The Flea's Sneeze. Firehammer, Karla, illus. 32p. (J). 2005. reprint ed. pap. 6.95 (978-0-8050-7756-8(1)); 2000. 17.95 (978-0-8050-6103-1(7)) Holt, Henry & Co. (Holt, Henry & Co. Bks. For Young Readers).

Hanson, Mary Elizabeth. The Old Man & the Flea. Merrell, David W., illus. 2001. 32p. (gr. k-3). 15.95 (978-0-87358-776-1(6) , Rising Moon Bks. for Young Readers) Northland Publishing.

Levy, Elizabeth. A Hare-Raising Tale: A Fletcher Mystery. Gorstein, Mordicai, illus. unabr. ed. 2006. (First Chapter Bks.). (J). (gr. 2-4). pap. 17.95 incl. audio (***978-1-59519-704-7(4)***); pap. 20.95 incl. audio compact disk (***978-1-59519-705-4(2)***) Live Oak Media.

—The Mixed-Up Mask Mystery: A Fletcher Mystery. Gorstein, Mordicai, illus. unabr. ed. 2006. (First Chapter Bks.). (J). (gr. 2-4). pap. 20.95 incl. audio compact disk (***978-1-59519-711-5(7)***); pap. 17.95 incl. audio (***978-1-59519-710-8(9)***) Live Oak Media.

McNulty, Faith. The Silly Story of a Flea & His Dog. Smith, Mavis, illus. 1999. (Hello Reader! Ser.). (J). (978-0-590-22860-2(9)) Scholastic, Inc.

Peutrell, Ann. No More Fleas. 1999. 28p. (J). (ps-2). 7.95 (978-0-7641-5213-9(0)) Barron's Educational Series, Inc.

Radford, Tom. Healing Rex. 2007. (Illus.). pap. (***978-1-84426-417-9(3)***) Upfront Publishing Ltd.

Raintree Steck-Vaughn Staff, contrib. by. The Napping House. 1999. (J). (ps-3). 16.00 (978-0-8172-9783-1(9)); pap. 22.00 (978-0-8172-9789-3(8)) Steck-Vaughn.

Rodgers, Paul. Tiny. Paul, Korky, illus. 2002. 32p. (J). (gr. k-3). pap. 7.95 (978-1-929132-26-3(3)) Kane/Miller Bk. Pubs., Inc.

Roldan, Gustavo. Las Pulgas No Vuelan. (la Orilla Del Viento Ser.). (SPA., Illus.). 40p. (J). 6.99 (978-968-16-6316-2(0) , 142) Fondo de Cultura Economica USA.

Shreeve, Elizabeth. Hector Springs Loose. Levy, Pamela R., illus. 2004. (Ready-for-Chapters Ser.). 80p. (J). pap. 3.99 (978-0-689-86414-8(0) , Aladdin) Simon & Schuster Children's Publishing.

Spearman, Andy. Barry Boyhound. 2007. 240p. (J). (gr. 3-7). 5.50 (***978-0-440-42058-3(X)*** , Yearling) Random Hse. Children's Bks.

Ware, Cheryl. Flea Circus Summer. 1998. (J). (978-0-606-13391-3(7)); (gr. 3-6). lib. bdg. 11.80 (978-0-613-89786-0(2)) Tandem Library Bks.

Weninger, Brigitte. Elf's Hat. 2002. (gr. k-3). lib. bdg. 15.25 (978-0-613-84073-6(9)) Tandem Library Bks.

Witschen, Kay. Clinkers Flea. Luckemeyer, Norma, illus. 1998. 16p. (J). (ps-2). pap. 4.95 (978-0-9652044-7-7(2)) Park Pr.

Wood, Audrey. The Napping House. Wood, Audrey, illus. 2002. (Illus.). (J). 21.70 (978-0-7587-3238-5(4)) Book Wholesalers, Inc.

—The Napping House. Wood, Don, illus. 2000. 16p. (J). (ps-k). bds. 6.95 (978-0-15-202632-5(0) , Red Wagon Bks.) Harcourt Children's Bks.

FLEMING, ALEXANDER, SIR, 1881-1955

Bankston, John. Alexander Fleming & the Story of Penicillin. l.t. ed. 2002. (Unlocking the Secrets of Science Ser.). (Illus.). 56p. (gr. 4-10). lib. bdg. 25.70 (978-1-58415-106-7(4)) Mitchell Lane Pubs., Inc.

Birch, Beverley & Fleming, Alexander. Alexander Fleming: Pioneer with Antibiotics. 2002. (Giants of Science Ser.). (Illus.). 64p. (J). 26.20 (978-1-56711-656-4(6) , Blackbirch Pr., Inc.) Thomson Gale.

Hantula, Richard. Alexander Fleming. 2003. (Trailblazers of the Modern World Ser.). (Illus.). 48p. (J). (gr. 5 up). pap. 14.95 (978-0-8368-5243-1(5)); lib. bdg. 30.00 (978-0-8368-5083-3(1)) Stevens, Gareth Inc. (World Almanac Library).

Parker, Steve. Alexander Fleming. (Groundbreakers Ser.). 48p. pap. 8.50 (978-1-4034-4060-0(3)); 2001. (Illus.). (J). (gr. 5-7). lib. bdg. 25.64 (978-1-58810-050-4(2)) Heinemann Library.

Tocci, Salvatore. Alexander Fleming: The Man Who Discovered Penicillin. 2002. (Great Minds of Science Ser.). (Illus.). 128p. (J). (gr. 4-10). lib. bdg. 26.60 (978-0-7660-1998-0(5)) Enslow Pubs., Inc.

Trailblazers of the Modern World: Winston Churchill; Alexander Fleming; Pablo Picasso; Elvis Presley; Venus & Serena Williams; Oprah Winfrey, 6 bks. 2002. (Illus.). (J). (gr. 5 up). pap. 89.70 (978-0-8368-5241-7(9) , World Almanac Library) Stevens, Gareth Inc.

FLIES

Brimner, Larry Dane. Flies. (True Bks.). (Illus.). 48p. (J). (gr. 3-5). 2000. pap. 6.95 (978-0-516-26761-6(2)); 1999. 25.00 (978-0-516-21161-9(7)) Scholastic Library Publishing. (Children's Pr.).

—Flies. 1999. (gr. 3-6). lib. bdg. 15.25 (978-0-613-37344-9(8)) Tandem Library Bks.

Coughlan, Cheryl. Flies. 2005. (Bugs, Bugs, Bugs Ser.). 24p. (YA). (gr. k-3). pap. (978-0-7368-8211-8(1) , Pebble Bks.) Capstone Pr., Inc.

Eggs, Larvae, & Flies: Big Book. (Sunshinetm Science Ser.). 24p. (gr. 1-2). 37.50 (978-0-7802-1389-0(0)) Wright Group, The.

Eggs, Larve, & Flies: 6 Each of 1 Student Book, 6 vols. (Sunshinetm Science Ser.). 24p. (gr. 1-2). 41.95 (978-0-7802-1388-3(2)) Wright Group, The.

Flies, 6 vols. (gr. k-2). 28.95 (978-0-7368-8251-4(0)) Red Brick Learning.

Flies Sets: 1 Each of 3 Big Books. (Sunshinetm Science Ser.). (gr. 1-2). 111.50 (978-0-7802-1448-4(X)) Wright Group, The.

Flies Sets: 1 Each of 3 Student Books. (Sunshinetm Science Ser.). (gr. 1-2). 20.95 (978-0-7802-1750-8(0)) Wright Group, The.

Hall, Margaret. Flies. 2006. (Pebble Plus Ser.). (Illus.). 24p. (J). (978-0-7368-5350-7(2)) Capstone Pr., Inc.

Hartley, Karen, et al, contrib. by. Fly. 2000. (Bug Books Ser.). (Illus.). 32p. (J). (gr. k-2). lib. bdg. 21.36 (978-1-57572-548-2(7)) Heinemann Library.

Hartley, Karen, et al. Fly. (Bug Bks.). 32p. pap. 6.95 (978-1-4034-3325-1(9)) Heinemann Library.

How Flies Live. (Sunshinetm Science Ser.). 24p. (gr. 1-2). 37.50 (978-0-7802-1386-9(6)) Wright Group, The.

How Flies Live: 6 Each of 1 Student Book, 6 vols. (Sunshinetm Science Ser.). 24p. (gr. 1-2). 41.95 (978-0-7802-1385-2(8)) Wright Group, The.

I Can Fly: Big Book: Level A. Group 1. (Sunshinetm Ser.). 8p. 20.95 (978-0-7802-5709-2(X)) Wright Group, The.

Lockwood, Sophie. Flies. 2007. (World of Insects Ser.). 40p. (J). (gr. 2-6). 29.93 (***978-1-59296-822-0(8)***) Child's World, Inc.

McEvey, Shane F. Flies. 2001. (Insects & Spiders Ser.). (Illus.). 32p. (J). (gr. 4 up). 28.00 (978-0-7910-6596-9(0) , 010554, Chelsea Hse.) Facts On File, Inc.

Merrick, Patrick. Biting Flies. 2000. (Naturebooks: Creepy Crawlers Ser.). (Illus.). 32p. (J). (gr. 1-5). 25.64 (978-1-56766-631-1(0)) Child's World, Inc.

Miller, Sara Swan. Flies: From Flower Flies to Mosquitoes. (Animals in Order Ser.). (Illus.). 48p. (J). (gr. 4-6). 1999. pap. 6.95 (978-0-531-15919-4(1)); 1998. 26.50 (978-0-531-11486-5(4)) Scholastic Library Publishing. (Watts, Franklin).

Morgan, Sally. Flies & Mosquitoes. 2001. (Illus.). 32p. (J). lib. bdg. 24.25 (978-1-930643-12-3(8)) Chrysalis Education.

Pascoe, Elaine. Flies. Kuhn, Dwight, photos by. 2001. (Nature Close-Up Ser.). (Illus.). 48p. (J). (gr. 4-8). 27.44 (978-1-56711-149-1(1) , Blackbirch Pr., Inc.) Thomson Gale.

Trapani, Iza. Shoo Fly! 2004. (Illus.). 26p. (J). bds. 6.95 (978-1-58089-080-9(6)) Charlesbridge Publishing, Inc.

—Shoo Fly! Trapani, Iza, illus. 2000. (Extended Nursery Rhymes Ser.). (Illus.). 32p. (J). (ps up). lib. bdg. 23.33 (978-0-8368-2670-8(1)) Stevens, Gareth Inc.

Trapani, Iza, illus. & as told by. Shoo Fly! Trapani, Iza, as told by. 2007. (J). pap. 6.95 (***978-1-58089-076-2(8)***) Charlesbridge Publishing, Inc.

What Is a Fly?, 6 vols. (Sunshinetm Science Ser.). 24p. (gr. 1-2). 37.50 (978-0-7802-1383-8(1)); 41.95 (978-0-7802-1382-1(3)) Wright Group, The.

Woodward, John. Flies. 2003. (Secret World Of... Ser.). (Illus.). 48p. (J). lib. bdg. 27.14 (978-0-7398-7021-1(1)) Raintree.

FLIGHT

see also Aeronautics

Alcraft, Rob. Flight. 2004. (Twenty4Sevens Ser.). (Illus.). 48p. (J). pap. (978-0-439-68103-2(0)) Scholastic, Inc.

Andersen, Ashley C. First Book of Flight: A Child's History of Aviation & Flight Log. 2000. (Illus.). 48p. (J). (ps-3). pap. 7.95 (978-1-882663-48-4(9)) Plymouth Toy & Book.

Baum, Brian. Super Jumbo Jets: Por Dentro y por Fuera. 2002. (Tecnología Ser.). (SPA.). 48p. (YA). lib. bdg. 26.50 (978-0-8239-6154-2(0) , Buenas Letra) Rosen Publishing Group, Inc., The.

Billings, Henry & Billings, Melissa. Stunt Flying: Livewire Investigates. 1999. (Livewires Ser.). (Illus.). 32p. pap. (978-0-340-74780-3(3) , Hodder Arnold) Hodder Education.

Bledsoe, Karen E. Daredevils of the Air: Thrilling Tales of Pioneer Aviators. 2003. (Avisson Young Adult Ser.). (Illus.). 155p. (J). pap. 19.95 (978-1-888105-58-2(5)) Avisson Pr., Inc.

Burton, Jane & Taylor, Kim. The Nature & Science of Wings. Burton, Jane, photos by. 1998. (Exploring the Science of Nature Ser.). (Illus.). 32p. (J). (gr. 3 up). lib. bdg. 23.93 (978-0-8368-2108-6(4)) Stevens, Gareth Inc.

Coupe, Robert. High Flying. 2002. (Junior Adventure Ser.). (Illus.). 32p. (J). (gr. 3 up). lib. bdg. (978-1-59084-191-4(3)) Mason Crest Pubs.

Crowther, Robert. Flight: A Pop-Up Book of Aircraft. Crowther, Robert, illus. 2007. (Illus.). 10p. (J). (gr. 1). 17.99 (***978-0-7636-3459-9(X)***) Candlewick Pr.

Denton, Terry. It's True! Pigs Do Fly. Denton, Terry, illus. 2006. (It's True! Ser.). (Illus.). 88p. (J). (gr. 5-8). 19.95 (978-1-55037-949-5(6)); pap. 5.95 (978-1-55037-948-8(8)) Annick Pr., Ltd. CAN. *Dist:* Firefly Bks., Ltd.

Dibben, Colin. Flight. 2007. (J). (***978-1-60044-259-9(5)***) Rourke Publishing, LLC.

Dibben, Colin. Know How, Know Why Flight. Thomas, Mike, illus. 2005. (Know How Know Why Ser.). 48p. (J). (ps-7). pap. (978-1-84510-029-2(8)) Top That! Publishing PLC.

DiSpezio, Michael Anthony. Flying Things: Simple Experiments in the Science of Flight. 2000. (Illus.). 77p. (J). (gr. k-12). 12.95 (978-1-57232-864-8(9)) Seymour, Dale Pubns.

Dorling Kindersley Publishing Staff. Flight. 2006. (Experience Ser.). (Illus.). 64p. (J). 15.99 (978-0-7566-1411-9(2)) Dorling Kindersley Publishing, Inc.

Edwards, Pamela Duncan. The Wright Brothers. Cole, Henry, illus. 2003. 40p. (gr. k-4). 16.49 (978-0-7868-2682-7(7)) Hyperion Bks. for Children.

Englehart, Steve. Countdown to Flight! 1999. (gr. 7-12). lib. bdg. 17.60 (978-0-613-85422-1(5)) Tandem Library Bks.

—Countdown to Flight! rev. ed. 2000. (Illus.). 112p. (gr. 8-12). pap. 8.95 (978-1-58348-403-6(5)) iUniverse, Inc.

Evans, David & Williams, Claudette. Air & Flying. (Let's Explore Science Ser.). (Illus.). (J). 12.95 (978-0-590-74943-5(9)) Scholastic, Inc.

Farndon, John. Flight. 2001. (Science Experiments Ser.). (Illus.). 32p. (J). (gr. 3-5). lib. bdg. 25.64 (978-0-7614-1342-4(1) , Benchmark Bks.) Cavendish, Marshall Corp.

Feathers & Flight: 6 Each of 1 Student Book, 6 vols. (Sunshinetm Science Ser.). 24p. (gr. 1-2). 41.95 (978-0-7802-1395-1(5)) Wright Group, The.

Feathers & Flight: Big Book. (Sunshinetm Science Ser.). 24p. (gr. 1-2). 37.50 (978-0-7802-1396-8(3)) Wright Group, The.

A Fifty Year Affair: Living with Light Planes. l.t. ed. 2004. (Illus.). 208p. (YA). pap. 18.95 (978-0-9746564-0-3(2)) Julson, D. K.

Fight Deck: Level D, 6 vols. (Wonder Worldtm Ser.). 16p. 24.95 (978-0-7802-1203-9(7)) Wright Group, The.

Flight. (Make It Work Ser.). 42p. (J). (gr. 4-8). pap. (978-1-882210-47-3(6)) Action Publishing, Inc.

Flight. (J). 41.95 (978-0-382-40669-0(9)) Cobblestone Publishing Co.

Flight. 2002. (gr. 7-12). lib. bdg. 14.15 (978-0-613-50608-3(1)) Tandem Library Bks.

Flight Sets: 1 Each of 3 Big Books. (Sunshinetm Science Ser.). (gr. 1-2). 111.50 (978-0-7802-2816-0(2)) Wright Group, The.

Flight Sets: 1 Each of 3 Student Books. (Sunshinetm Science Ser.). (gr. 1-2). 20.95 (978-0-7802-2817-7(0)) Wright Group, The.

Flying Without an Engine: 6 Each of 1 Student Book, 6 vols. (Sunshinetm Science Ser.). 24p. (gr. 1-2). 41.95 (978-0-7802-2712-5(3)) Wright Group, The.

Flying Without an Engine: Big Book. (Sunshinetm Science Ser.). 24p. (gr. 1-2). 37.50 (978-0-7802-2790-3(5)) Wright Group, The.

Flying Without Wings: 6 Each of 1 Student Book, 6 vols. (Sunshinetm Science Ser.). 24p. (gr. 1-2). 41.95 (978-0-7802-2714-9(X)) Wright Group, The.

Flying Without Wings: Big Book. (Sunshinetm Science Ser.). 24p. (gr. 1-2). 37.50 (978-0-7802-2791-0(3)) Wright Group, The.

Graham, Ian. The World of Flight. 2006. (World Of Ser.). 64p. (J). (gr. 4-6). pap. 8.95 (978-0-7534-6008-5(4) , Kingfisher) Houghton Mifflin Co. Trade & Reference Div.

Grist, Julie. Flying: Just Plane Fun. 2006. (Illus.). 24p. (J). pap. 8.95 (978-0-9725750-2-7(2)) Spoonbender Bks.

—Flying: Just Plane Fun. Grist, Julie, illus. 2003. (Illus.). 24p. (J). (gr. 1-7). 17.95 (978-0-9725750-0-3(6)) Spoonbender Bks.

Hansen, Ole Steen. Amazing Flights: The Golden Age. 2003. (Story of Flight Ser.). (Illus.). 32p. (J). (gr. 4). pap. (978-0-7787-1218-3(4)); lib. bdg. (978-0-7787-1202-2(8)) Crabtree Publishing Co.

—The Story of Flight. 2003. (Illus.). 190p. (J). (978-0-7787-1212-1(5)) Crabtree Publishing Co.

—The Story of Flight, 12 bks. Incl. Air Combat. (gr. 4). lib. bdg. (978-0-7787-1206-0(0)); Amazing Flights : The Golden Age. (gr. 4). lib. bdg. (978-0-7787-1202-2(8)); Commercial Aviation. (gr. 4). lib. bdg. (978-0-7787-1205-3(2)); Flying for Fun. (gr. 4). lib. bdg. (978-0-7787-1211-4(7)); Helicopters. (gr. 4). lib. bdg. (978-0-7787-1208-4(7)); Military Aircraft of WWI. (gr. 4). lib. bdg. (978-0-7787-1201-5(X)); Military Aircraft of WWII. (gr. 4). lib. bdg. (978-0-7787-1203-9(6)); Modern Military Aircraft. (gr. 4). lib. bdg. (978-0-7787-1204-6(4)); Seaplanes & Naval Aviation. (gr. 4). lib. bdg. (978-0-7787-1209-1(5)); Space Flight. (gr. 2-9). lib. bdg. (978-0-7787-1207-7(9)); Weird & Wonderful Aircraft. (gr. 4). lib. bdg. (978-0-7787-1210-7(9)); Wright Brothers & Other Pioneers of Flight. (gr. 4). lib. bdg. (978-0-7787-1200-8(1)); 32p. (J). 2003. (Illus.). 2003. (978-0-7787-1198-8(6)); Set pap. (978-0-7787-1214-5(1)) Crabtree Publishing Co.

—The Wright Brothers & Other Pioneers of Flight. 2003. (Story of Flight Ser.). (Illus.). 32p. (J). (gr. 4). pap. (978-0-7787-1216-9(8)); lib. bdg. (978-0-7787-1200-8(1)) Crabtree Publishing Co.

Harcourt School Publishers Staff. Floating Around the World. 3rd ed. 2002. (Trophies English Language Learners Ser.). (Illus.). pap. 5.10 (978-0-15-327881-5(1)) Harcourt Schl. Pubs.

Haslam, Andrew, et al. Flight. (Make It Work! Ser.). (Illus.). 48p. (J). pap. 7.99 (978-0-590-24687-3(9)) Scholastic, Inc.

Hay DeSimone, Corkey. Air & Space Activity & Coloring Book: An Early Introduction to the History of Flight. Hay DeSimone, Corkey, illus. 2006. (J). 7.95 (978-0-9747921-4-9(4)) Gentle Giraffe Pr.

—Air & Space Board Book: An Early Introduction to the History of Flight. Hay DeSimone, Corkey, illus. 2005. (J). bds. 7.99 (978-0-9747921-3-2(6)) Gentle Giraffe Pr.

Hewitt, Sally. Air & Flight. 2000. (It's Science! Ser.). (Illus.). 32p. (J). (gr. k-3). 23.50 (978-0-516-21652-2(X) , Children's Pr.) Scholastic Library Publishing.

Hinkler Books. Flight: Let's Take Off! 2006. (Illus.). 32p. (J). (gr. 3-7). 7.95 (978-1-74157-579-8(6)) Hinkler Bks. Pty, Ltd. AUS. *Dist:* Penton Overseas, Inc.

Hodgkins, Fran. How People Learned to Fly. 2006. lib. bdg. (978-0-06-029599-8(6)) HarperCollins Canada, Ltd.

—How People Learned to Fly. Kelley, True, illus. 2007. (Let's-Read-and-Find-Out Science Ser.). 40p. (J). (gr. k-4). pap. 5.99 (978-0-06-445221-2(2)); 15.99 (978-0-06-029558-5(9)) HarperCollins Pubs.

Howatson, Ian & Quigley, Sebastian, illus. The World of Flight. 2001. (Inside Look Ser.). 48p. (J). (gr. 4 up). lib. bdg. 26.00 (978-0-8368-2903-7(4)) Stevens, Gareth Inc.

Jacobs, Marian B. Why Can Airplanes Fly? 1999. (Library of Why). (Illus.). 24p. (J). (gr. k-4). lib. bdg. 18.75 (978-0-8239-5274-8(6) , PowerKids Pr.) Rosen Publishing Group, Inc., The.

Jay Jay the Jet Plane: High-Flying Adventures. (Illus.). (J). spiral bd. (978-1-58605-820-3(7)) LeapFrog Enterprises, Inc.

Jeffrey, Gary. The History of Flight. 2007. (Graphic Discoveries Ser.). (J). (Illus.). 48p. (gr. 3-7). lib. bdg. (***978-1-4042-1087-5(3)***); (***978-1-4042-9590-2(9)***); pap. (***978-1-4042-9589-6(5)***) Rosen Publishing Group, Inc., The.

Kids Can Press Staff, Press Can, ed. This Is Daniel Cook on a Plane. 2006. (Illus.). 24p. (J). (978-1-55453-081-6(4)) Kids Can Pr., Ltd.

—This Is Daniel Cook on A Plane. 2006. (Illus.). 24p. (J). (978-1-55453-082-3(2)) Kids Can Pr., Ltd.

E
F
G

Lindgren, Astrid. Karlsson Vom Dach. 2003. Tr. of Karlsson Fl. (GER.). 384p. pap. 19.00 (978-1-4000-3991-3(6) , New Media German Language) Random House Foreign Language Publishing.

Loeschnig, Louis V. No-Sweat Science: Space & Flight Experiments. Gallagher, Jack, illus. 2006. (No Sweat Science Ser.). 128p. (J). pap. 5.95 (978-1-4027-2334-6(2) , 1262283) Sterling Publishing Co., Inc.

Lou Weber Staff, ed. Creative Minds Flying Fun Kit. 2005. 32p. 12.98 (978-1-4127-0610-0(6) , 5501700) Publications International, Ltd.

Loves, June. Helicopters. 2001. (Flight Ser.). (Illus.). 32p. (J). (gr. 5 up). 22.95 (978-0-7910-6562-4(6) , 010304, Chelsea Hse.) Facts On File, Inc.

—Military Aircraft. 2001. (Flight Ser.). (Illus.). 32p. (J). (gr. 5 up). 22.95 (978-0-7910-6559-4(6) , 010305, Chelsea Hse.) Facts On File, Inc.

Mellet, Peter, et al, trs. All about Aircraft & Flight. 2004. (All About...Ser.). (Illus.). 64p. pap. 7.99 (978-1-84215-892-0(9) , Southwater) Anness Publishing GBR. *Dist:* National Bk. Network.

Mellet, Peter & Rostron, John. Aircraft & Flight. 2000. (Investigations Ser.). (Illus.). 64p. (gr. 4-7). 15.00 (978-0-7548-0586-1(7) , Lorenz Bks.) Anness Publishing, Inc.

Mellett, Peter. Flight. 2000. (Fantastic Facts Ser.). (Illus.). 64p. (gr. 2-7). pap. 6.95 (978-1-84215-322-2(6) , Southwater) Anness Publishing GBR. *Dist:* National Bk. Network.

—Flight. Bowyer, Dave, illus. 1998. (Young Scientist Concepts & Projects Ser.). 68p. (J). (gr. 4 up). lib. bdg. 27.33 (978-0-8368-2162-8(9)) Stevens, Gareth Inc.

Millican, Judy. The Helicopter Ride. Gray, Stacy A., illus. 2003. 8p. (J). (ps-1). bds. 10.95 (978-1-57332-252-2(0)) HighReach Learning, Inc.

Mullican, Judy. The Helicopter Ride: Big Book. Gray, Stacy A., illus. 2003. 8p. (J). (ps-1). bds. 10.95 (978-1-57332-245-4(8)) HighReach Learning, Inc.

O'Brien, Patrick. Fantastic Flights: One Hundred Years of Flying on the Edge. O'Brien, Patrick, illus. 2003. (Illus.). 40p. (J). 17.95 (978-0-8027-8880-1(7)) Walker & Co.

—Fantastic Flights: One Hundred Years of Flying on the Edge. 2003. (Illus.). 40p. (J). 18.85 (978-0-8027-8881-8(5)) Walker & Co.

Page, Robin & Jenkins, Steve. Animals in Flight. Jenkins, Steve, illus. (Illus.). 32p. (J). (gr. k-3). 2005. pap. 5.95 (978-0-618-54882-8(3)); 2001. tchr. ed. 16.00 (978-0-618-12351-3(2)) Houghton Mifflin Co. Trade & Reference Div.

Las Plumas y el Vuelo, 6 vols. (Explorers. Exploradores Nonfiction Sets Ser.). (SPA.). 32p. (gr. 3-6). 44.95 (978-0-7699-0633-1(8)) Shortland Pubns. (U. S. A.) Inc.

Raintree Steck-Vaughn Staff. Century in Flight. 2002. pap. 254.32 (978-1-4109-0189-7(0)) Raintree.

Rau, Dana Meachen, ed. ¡A Volar! 2006. (En Movimiento Ser.). (SPA & ENG., Illus.). 24p. (J). lib. bdg. 22.79 (978-0-7614-2425-3(3) , Benchmark Bks.) Cavendish, Marshall Corp.

—Flying. 2006. (On the Move Ser.). (Illus.). 24p. (J). (ps-1). lib. bdg. 22.79 (978-0-7614-2319-5(2) , Benchmark Bks.) Cavendish, Marshall Corp.

Rees, Peter. How Does It Fly? The Science of Flight. 2007. (Shockwave: Technology & Manufacturing Ser.). (Illus.). 36p. (J). (gr. 4-6). lib. bdg. 25.00 (*978-0-531-17587-3(1)* , Children's Pr.) Scholastic Library Publishing.

Richards, Jon. Air & Flight. 2008. (J). lib. bdg. (*978-1-4042-3907-4(3)*) Rosen Publishing Group, Inc., The.

Sarver, Amy. Science at the Airport. 2004. (Illus.). 24p. (J). pap. (978-0-7922-4568-1(7)) National Geographic Society.

School Specialty Publishing. Flight. 2005. (Science Search Lab Ser.). (J). (gr. 3-5). pap. 24.95 (978-0-7682-2844-1(1) , Ideal School Supply) Schaffer, Frank Pubns.

Seymour, Tres. Our Neighbor Is a Strange, Strange Man. Krudop, Walter Lyon, illus. 1999. 32p. (J). (gr. k-4). 16.99 (978-0-531-33107-1(5)); pap. 15.95 (978-0-531-30107-4(9)) Scholastic, Inc. (Orchard Bks.).

Sian revision flight!gliders to Jets. 2004. (Science in A Nutshell(R) Ser.). (J). (978-1-59242-028-5(1)) Delta Education, LLC.

Sobey, Edwin J. C. Fantastic Flying Fun with Science: 69 Projects You Can Fly, Spin, Launch, & Ri. 2000. (gr. 5-8). lib. bdg. 21.05 (978-0-613-71530-0(6)) Tandem Library Bks.

Sundance, ed. What Can Fly. 2000. (ps-2). lib. bdg. 11.65 (978-0-613-37635-8(8)) Tandem Library Bks.

Taylor, Kim. Flight. (Illus.). 32p. (YA). (gr. 3 up). lib. bdg. 27.10 (978-1-931983-74-7(7)) Chrysalis Education.

Top That Publishing Staff, ed. Flight. 2005. (Illus.). 24p. pap. (978-1-84510-158-9(8)) Top That! Publishing PLC.

Der Traum Von Fliegen.Tr. of Dream of Flying. (GER.). (YA). 31.95 (978-3-411-09091-4(X)) Bibliographisches Institut & F. A. Brockhaus AG DEU. *Dist:* Continental Bk. Co., Inc.

Tucker, Mary. History Hands on! Lindbergh's Flight Across the Atlantic. Mitchell, Judy, ed. Hierstein, Judith, illus. 2004. 32p. (J). pap. 6.95 (978-1-57310-426-5(4)) Teaching & Learning Co.

—Wright Brothers. Mitchell, Judy, ed. Hierstein, Judith, illus. 2002. (History - Hands On! Ser.). 32p. (J). (gr. 1-4). pap. 6.95 (978-1-57310-353-4(5)) Teaching & Learning Co.

Upgrade kit dsm-3 Flight&rocketry. (J). 2004. (978-1-59242-530-3(5)); 2003. (978-1-59242-413-9(9)) Delta Education, LLC.

Vuelo en Las Alturas, 6 vols., Vol. 2. (Explorers. Exploradores Nonfiction Sets Ser.). (SPA.). 32p. (gr. 3-6). 44.95 (978-0-7699-0643-0(5)) Shortland Pubns. (U. S. A.) Inc.

Wallace, Lane E. Wild Blue Wonders: Exploring the Magic of Flight. 2001. (Illus.). 164p. (J). per. 19.95 (978-1-58932-002-4(6)) EAA (Experimental Aircraft Assn.).

Whitehouse, Patricia. What Can Fly? 2003. (Illus.). 24p. (J). (ps-ps). lib. bdg. 18.50 (978-1-4034-4365-6(3)); pap. (978-1-4034-4372-4(6)) Heinemann Library.

—What Can Fly? 2003. (ps-2). lib. bdg. 28.65 (978-0-613-89937-6(7)) Tandem Library Bks.

Willis, Shirley. Dime por Que Tienen Alas los Aviones. (Los Estupendos Whiz Kids, Spanish Edition Ser.). (SPA., Illus.). 32p. (J). 2000. (gr. 1-3). pap. 5.95 (978-0-531-15998-9(1) , OD30032); 1999. (gr. 2-4). 20.00 (978-0-531-11848-1(7) , OD30033) Scholastic Library Publishing. (Watts, Franklin).

—Dime por Que Tienen Alas los Aviones. 2000. (Estupendos Ser.). (J). 12.75 (978-0-606-20151-3(3)) Tandem Library Bks.

FLIGHT—FICTION

Alborough, Jez. Some Dogs Do. Alborough, Jez, illus. 2003. (Illus.). 40p. (J). (ps-2). 15.99 (978-0-7636-2201-5(X)) Candlewick Pr.

Anholt, Laurence. Leonardo & the Flying Boy. 2007. (Anholt's Artists Books for Children Ser.). 32p. (J). (ps-3). pap. 7.99 (*978-0-7641-3851-5(0)*) Barron's Educational Series, Inc.

—Leonardo & the Flying Boy: A Story about Leonardo da Vinci. 2000. (Illus.). 32p. (J). (ps-2). 15.99 (978-0-7641-5225-2(4)) Barron's Educational Series, Inc.

—Leonardo y el Aprendiz Volador: Un Cuento Sobre Leonardo Da Vinci. 2000. Tr. of Leonardo & the Flying Boy. (CAT., Illus.). 30p. (J). (gr. 3-5). 14.95 (978-84-95040-79-4(4)) Serres, Ediciones, S. L. ESP. *Dist:* Lectorum Pubns., Inc.

Barkan, Joanne. Firefly's First Flight. Cook, Ande, illus. 2005. 12p. (J). 12.99 (978-0-7944-0612-7(2)) Reader's Digest Assn., Inc., The.

Beck, Katie. The Moas. Thatch, Nancy R., ed. 1999. (Books for Students by Students). (Illus.). 29p. (J). (gr. 4-7). lib. bdg. 15.95 (978-0-933849-73-0(7)) Landmark Editions, Inc.

Berkeley, Jon. Chopsticks. 2005. (Illus.). 32p. (J). (ps-3). 16.95 (978-0-375-83309-0(9) , Random Hse. Bks. for Young Readers) Random Hse. Children's Bks.

Bigosinski, Jeremi. Harry Hippo's Flight: Adventures in Hippoville. Bigosinski, Jeremi, illus. l.t. ed. 2002. (Illus.). 24p. (J). 9.95 (978-0-9722265-0-9(8)) Hippoville Publishing, LLC.

Bogacki, Tomek. The Story of a Blue Bird. Bogacki, Tomek, illus. 1998. (Illus.). 32p. (J). (ps-k). 16.00 (978-0-374-37197-5(0) , Farrar, Straus & Giroux (BYR)) Farrar, Straus & Giroux.

Boonen, Stefan. When Pigs Fly! Loufane, illus. 2004. 32p. (J). 6.95 (978-1-58925-384-1(1) , tiger tales) ME Media LLC.

Brooks, Walter R. Freddy & the Pilot. Wiese, Kurt, illus. 1999. 288p. (J). (gr. 3-7). 23.95 (978-0-87951-941-4(X)) Overlook Pr., The.

—Freddy the Pilot. 2000. (YA). pap. 67.95 incl. audio (978-0-7887-4167-8(5) , 41111) Recorded Bks., LLC.

—Freddy the Pilot. 2001. (978-0-606-22516-8(1)) Tandem Library Bks.

Brother to the Wind. 2004. (J). 24.95 incl. audio (978-1-56008-169-2(4)) Weston Woods Studios, Inc.

Cain, Sheridan. Crunching Munching Caterpillar. Tickle, Jack, illus. 2003. 32p. (J). tchr. ed. 15.95 (978-1-58925-025-3(7) , tiger tales) ME Media LLC.

Clarke, Covington. For Valor & Desert Wings. 2005. reprint ed. pap. 42.95 (978-0-7661-9827-2(8)) Kessinger Publishing, LLC.

Cockcroft, Jason & Nicholls, Judith. Billywise. Cockcroft, Jason, illus. 2004. (Illus.). 32p. (J). (ps-2). pap. 6.95 (978-1-58234-893-3(6) , Bloomsbury Children) Bloomsbury Publishing.

Conover, Chris. The Lion's Share. Conover, Chris, illus. 2003. (Illus.). 40p. (J). pap. 6.95 (978-0-374-44481-5(1) , Sunburst) Farrar, Straus & Giroux.

Cosby, Bill. Friends of a Feather: One of Life's Little Fables. Cosby, Erika, illus. 2003. 64p. (gr. k-3). 16.95 (978-0-06-009147-7(9) , Harper Entertainment) HarperCollins Pubs.

Coulman, Valerie. Rafi et les Cochons Volants. Duchesne, Christiane, tr. from ENG. Girard, Roge, illus. (FRE.). 32p. (J). pap. 6.95 (*978-2-922435-02-3(4)*) Editions Homard CAN. *Dist:* Univ. of Toronto Pr.

Cunliffe, John. Post Pat 11: Takes Flight. 1999. (Illus.). 32p. (J). pap. 12.99 incl. audio (978-1-84032-006-0(0) , Hodder & Stoughton) Hodder General Publishing Division GBR. *Dist:* Trafalgar Square Publishing.

de Beer, Hans. Leonardo's Dream. Miller, Marisa, tr. from GER. de Beer, Hans, illus. 2007. (Illus.). 32p. (J). (ps-3). pap. 6.95 (*978-0-7358-2168-2(2)*) North-South Bks., Inc.

de Beer, Hans. Little Polar Bear & the Big Balloon. Lanning, Rosemary, tr. from GER. de Beer, Hans, illus. 2002. (Illus.). 32p. (J). (gr. k-3). 16.50 (978-0-7358-1533-9(X)) North-South Bks., Inc.

De Beer, Hans. Little Polar Bear & the Big Balloon. Lanning, Rosemary, tr. from GER. De Beer, Hans, illus. 2006. (Illus.). 22p. (J). (gr. k-4). reprint ed. 16.00 (978-0-7567-9875-8(2)) DIANE Publishing Co.

de Beers, Hans. Little Polar Bear & Big Balloo. 2006. (Illus.). 32p. (J). 6.95 (978-0-7358-2077-7(5)) North-South Bks., Inc.

—Osito Polar y el Gran Globo. 2006. (SPA., Illus.). 32p. (J). pap. 6.95 (978-0-7358-1739-5(1)) North-South Bks., Inc.

Dorros, Arthur. Abuela. Kleven, Elisa, illus. 2002. (J). 14.04 (978-0-7587-1901-0(9)) Book Wholesalers, Inc.

Doudna, Kelly. Goose Down. Haberstroh, Anne, illus. 2006. (Fact & Fiction Ser.). 24p. (J). 21.35 (978-1-59679-941-7(2) , SandCastle); pap. (978-1-59679-942-4(0)) ABDO Publishing Co.

Draper, Rochelle, illus. The Stone Wall Dragon. 2007. 32p. 15.95 (*978-0-89272-690-5(3)*) Down East Bks.

Drawson, Blair. Flying Dimitri. (Illus.). (J). 16.95 (978-0-88899-284-0(X)) Groundwood Bks. CAN. *Dist:* Transition Vendor.

Duble, Kathleen Benner. Bravo Zulu, Samantha! 2007. 144p. (J). (gr. 4-7). 14.95 (*978-1-56145-401-3(X)* , Peachtree Junior) Peachtree Pubs., Ltd.

Dychtwald, Ken, et al. Gideon's Dream: A Tale of New Beginnings. Zaboski, Dave & Zaboski, Grace, illus. 2008. 40p. (J). lib. bdg. 17.89 (*978-0-06-143498-3(1)*) HarperCollins Pubs.

Fanelli, Sara. First Flight. 2002. (Illus.). 40p. (J). (gr. k-4). 18.00 (978-0-224-06457-6(6) , Jonathan Cape) Random Hse. Children's Bks. GBR. *Dist:* Trafalgar Square Publishing.

French, Vivian. Pig in Love, Level 3. Archbold, Tim, illus. 2005. (Lightning Readers Ser.). 32p. (J). (gr. 1-2). pap., pap. 3.95 (978-0-7696-4221-5(7) , Gingham Dog Pr.) School Specialty Publishing.

French/Archbold, Vivian/Tim. Pig in Love. 2005. (Illus.). 32p. (J). lib. bdg. 9.00 (*978-1-4242-0889-0(0)*) Fitzgerald Bks.

Furlong, Marguerite, text. Alexander's First Plane Ride. 2002. (Alexander, the Elephant Who Couldn't Eat Peanuts Ser.). (J). pap. 5.00 (978-1-882541-33-1(2)) Food Allergy & Anaphylaxis Network.

Garber, Linda. Will This Tale Fly? Garber, Linda, illus. 2nd l.t. ed. 1999. (Illus.). 23p. (J). (gr. 1-4). spiral bd. 9.95 (978-1-892218-03-2(8)) Murlin Pubns.

Gardner, Sally. The Boy Who Could Fly. Gardner, Sally, illus. l.t. ed. 2005. (Illus.). 86p. (J). pap. (978-0-7540-7815-9(9) , CLP 405) BBC Audio.

Garis, Howard Roger. Uncle Wiggily's Airship. Date not set. 192p. (J). 20.95 (978-0-8488-2277-4(3)) Amereon LTD.

Glass, Andrew. The Wondrous Whirligig: The Wright Brothers¿ First Flying Machine. Glass, Andrew, illus. 2007. (Illus.). 30p. (J). reprint ed. 17.00 (*978-1-4223-6765-0(7)*) DIANE Publishing Co.

Goldfrap, John Henry. The Boy Aviators' Polar Dash: Or Facing Death in the Antarctic. 2006. 180p. pap. 11.99 (*978-1-4264-5072-3(9)*); 200p. pap. 15.99 (*978-1-4264-5373-1(6)*) BiblioBazaar.

Gonzalez, Julie. Wings. 208p. (gr. 7). 2006. (YA). mass mkt. 5.99 (978-0-440-23904-8(4) , Laurel Leaf); 2005. (J). 15.95 (978-0-385-73227-7(9) , Delacorte Bks. for Young Readers) Random Hse. Children's Bks.

Graham, Bob. Max. 2002. (gr. k-3). lib. bdg. 14.15 (978-0-613-56517-2(7)) Tandem Library Bks.

Grey, Mini. Egg Drop. 2002. (Illus.). 32p. (J). (978-0-224-06458-3(4) , Jonathan Cape) Random Hse. Children's Bks.

Gutman, Dan. Race for the Sky. 2003. (Illus.). 192p. (J). (gr. 3-6). 16.99 (978-0-689-84554-3(5)) Simon & Schuster Children's Publishing.

—Race for the Sky: The Kitty Hawk Diaries of Johnny Moore. l.t. ed. 2004. 299p. 22.95 (978-0-7862-6466-7(7)) Thorndike Pr.

Hansen, Ole Steen. Amazing Flights: The Golden Age. 2003. (gr. 3-6). lib. bdg. 17.60 (978-0-613-59038-9(4)) Tandem Library Bks.

Harcourt School Publishers Staff. Fly, Dilly! Fly! Take-Home Book. 1999. (Signatures Ser.). (Illus.). (J). pap. 1.70 (978-0-15-313845-4(9)) Harcourt Schl. Pubs.

—Ladybugs Can Fly: Take-Home Book. 1999. (Collections Ser.). (Illus.). (J). pap. 1.90 (978-0-15-317225-0(8)) Harcourt Schl. Pubs.

—Trofeos Below Level: Vuela Muy Alto. 3rd ed. 2002. (SPA., Illus.). pap. 5.50 (978-0-15-323876-5(3)) Harcourt Schl. Pubs.

—Unrefueled Flight Level D: Library Edition. 2001. (Collections Ser.). (Illus.). (J). 6.90 (978-0-15-314411-0(4)) Harcourt Schl. Pubs.

Harley, Bill. The Amazing Flight of Darius Frobisher. 2006. (Illus.). 160p. (J). 14.95 (978-1-56145-381-8(1) , Peachtree Junior) Peachtree Pubs., Ltd.

Harper, Piers. Little Owl. Harper, Piers, illus. 2004. (Illus.). 32p. (J). 15.95 (978-0-439-59703-6(X) , Cartwheel Bks.) Scholastic, Inc.

Henry, Heather French. Flying Away. Henry, Heather French, illus. 2004. (Claire's Everyday Adventures Ser.). (Illus.). 32p. (gr. k-4). (J). pap. 8.95 (978-0-9706341-8-4(8) , 1231610); 15.95 (978-0-9706341-4-6(5) , 1231610) Cubbie Blue Publishing.

Henry, Panya A. Francis' Fear of Flying. 2006. (ENG.). 40p. per. 24.95 (*978-1-4259-3162-9(6)*) AuthorHouse.

Homan, Lynn M. & Reilly, Thomas. Girls Fly! Shepherd, Rosalie M., tr. Shepherd, Rosalie M., illus. 2003. 32p. (J). pap. 14.95 (978-1-58980-154-7(7)) Pelican Publishing Co., Inc.

Hooray for Boys & Girls! ed. 2006. (J). 15.95 (978-0-9776837-0-3(2)) West Woods Pr.

Hughes, Shirley. Up & Up. 2007. (Illus.). 32p. (J). pap. 8.95 (*978-0-09-992250-6(9)* , Red Fox) Random Hse. Children's Bks. GBR. *Dist:* Independent Pubs. Group.

Johnson, Paul Brett. The Cow Who Wouldn't Come Down. Johnson, Paul Brett, illus. 2002. (Illus.). (J). 13.83 (978-1-4046-2066-7(4)) Book Wholesalers, Inc.

Kalz, Jill. Flying with Oliver. Mahan, Ben, illus. 2006. (Read-It! Readers Ser.). 24p. (J). (ps-3). 18.60 (978-1-4048-1583-4(X)) Picture Window Bks.

Kartarik, Joey. Flight Dreams. Maval Publishing Inc. Staff, illus. 2001. 32p. (J). (ps-3). pap. 7.50 (978-1-884083-72-3(2)) Maval Publishing, Inc.

Kibuishi, Kazu, ed. Flight Explorer: Vol. 1. 2008. 112p. pap. 9.95 (*978-0-345-50313-8(9)* , Villard Bks.) Random House Publishing Group.

Kinerk, Robert. Clorinda Takes Flight. Kellogg, Steven, illus. 2007. 40p. (J). (ps-3). 16.99 (978-0-689-86864-1(2) , Simon & Schuster/Paula Wiseman Bks.) Simon & Schuster Children's Publishing.

Langen, Annette. Felix & the Flying Suitcase Adventure. Droop, Constanza, illus. 2003. 47p. (J). 14.99 (978-1-59384-035-8(7)) Parklane Publishing.

Lawton, Wilbur Capta. The Boy Aviators in Africa or an Aerial. 2006. 25.99 (*978-1-4219-7625-9(0)*); pap. 19.99 (*978-1-4219-7629-7(3)*) IndyPublish.com.

Lewis, H. B. Winnie Mae. 2001. (Illus.). 40p. (J). (gr. 3). pap. 8.95 (978-0-89812-013-4(6) , Creative Paperbacks) Creative Co., The.

Lottridge, Celia Barker & Gerber, Mary Jane. Wings to Fly. 1999. (Illus.). 216p. (J). (gr. 3-7). pap. 5.95 (978-0-88899-346-5(3) , Libros Tigrillo) Groundwood Bks. CAN. *Dist:* Perseus Distribution.

Loux, Lynn Crosbie. The Day I Could Fly. Porfirio, Guy, illus. 2003. 32p. (gr. k-3). 15.95 (978-1-55971-866-0(8) , NorthWord Bks. for Young Readers) T&N Children's Publishing.

Marcus, John V. Birdy Bird & the Plane. 2007. 9.00 (*978-0-8059-7312-9(5)*) Dorrance Publishing Co., Inc.

McCarty, Peter. Moon Plane. 2006. (Illus.). 40p. (J). 16.95 (978-0-8050-7943-2(2)) Holt, Henry & Co.

McKee, David. Elmer Takes Off. McKee, David, illus. 2004. (Elmer Bks.). 32p. (J). 9.99 (978-0-06-075241-5(6)) HarperCollins Pubs.

Minshull, Evelyn. Eaglet's World. Gabriel, Andrea, illus. 2002. 32p. (J). (ps-3). 16.95 (978-0-8075-8929-8(2)) Whitman, Albert & Co.

Morison, Toby. Little Louie Takes Off. Morison, Toby, illus. 2007. (Illus.). 32p. (J). (ps-2). 16.95 (*978-0-8027-9645-5(1)*) Walker & Co.

Morris, Kimberly. Beck Beyond the Sea. Clarke, Judith, illus. 2007. 128p. (J). (gr. 1-5). 5.99 (*978-0-7364-2456-1(3)* , RH/Disney) Random Hse. Children's Bks.

Myers, Christopher A. Wings. Myers, Christopher A., illus. 2000. (Illus.). 40p. (J). (gr. 1-3). pap. 16.95 (978-0-590-03377-0(8)) Scholastic, Inc.

Nettrour, Nelani. Dragonfly Flight. Lesnick, Tina, illus. l.t. ed. 2003. 62p. (J). pap. 11.94 (978-1-932657-02-9(9)) Third Millennium Pubns.

O'Donnell, Jim. Topa, the Bold Fish: Novel. Pacey, Janet, illus. 2000. 65p. (J). (ps-3). (978-1-894303-27-9(X)) Raven Rock Publishing.

Okorafor-Mbachu, Nnedi. Zahrah the Windseeker. Cooper, Stephanie & Hall, Amanda, illus. 2005. 320p. (YA). (gr. 5-7). 16.00 (978-0-618-34090-3(4)) Houghton Mifflin Co. Trade & Reference Div.

O'Malley, Kevin. Little Buggy. 2002. (Gulliver Books). (Illus.). 32p. (J). (gr. k-2). 16.00 (978-0-15-216339-6(5) , Gulliver Bks.) Harcourt Children's Bks.

O'Neal, Kerry. I Wish I Could Fly/I Can Fly! The Lonely Caterpillar BOOK I & the Lonely Butterfly BOOK II. O'Neal, Kerry, illus. l.t. ed. 2006. (Illus.). 60p. (J). 29.99 (*978-1-59879-197-6(4)*); per. 17.99 (*978-1-59879-196-9(6)*) Lifevest Publishing, Inc.

Pacovska, Kveta. Flying. Pacovska, Kveta, illus. 2005. Tr. of Turme. (Illus.). 39p. (J). reprint ed. 20.00 (978-0-7567-8532-1(4)) DIANE Publishing Co.

Papineau, Lucie. No Bananas for This Giraffe. Sarrazin, Marisol, illus. 2005. (Gilda the Giraffe Ser.). 32p. (J). 22.60 (978-1-4048-1292-5(X)) Picture Window Bks.

Petrie, Kathye Fetsko. Flying Jack. Mahoney, Paula J., illus. 2003. 32p. (YA). (gr. k-2). 15.95 (978-1-56397-971-2(3)) Boyds Mills Pr.

Pinkney, Brian. Adventures of Sparrow Boy. 2000. (J). 13.79 (978-0-606-19246-0(8)) Tandem Library Bks.

—The Adventures of Sparrowboy. Pinkney, Brian, illus. 2002. (Illus.). (J). 14.47 (978-0-7587-1906-5(X)) Book Wholesalers, Inc.

—The Adventures of Sparrowboy. Pinkney, Brian, illus. 2000. (Illus.). 40p. (J). (ps-3). 7.99 (978-0-689-83534-6(5) , Aladdin) Simon & Schuster Children's Publishing.

—Adventures of Sparrowboy. 2000. (gr. k-3). lib. bdg. 14.15 (978-0-613-28396-0(1)) Tandem Library Bks.

Plourde, Paulette. I Can Fly. l.t. ed. 2005. (Illus.). 40p. (J). per. 9.95 (978-1-59879-012-2(9)) Lifevest Publishing, Inc.

Reece, Robert. Freeman A. Freelander. Gallina, Todd, illus. 2002. 40p. (J). 11.95 (978-0-9702308-1-2(8)) Dark Horse Pr.

Renov, Ruki D. Don't Burst My Bubble. Renov, Ruki D., illus. 2001. (Illus.). 32p. (J). (gr. k-4). 15.95 (978-0-9667483-2-1(8)) Priority Multimedia Group, Inc.

Richardson, Nigel. The Wrong Hands. 272p. (YA). (gr. 7). 2008. mass mkt. 6.50 (*978-0-553-49500-3(3)* , Laurel Leaf); 2006. 15.95 (978-0-375-83459-2(1) , Knopf Bks. for Young Readers); 2006. lib. bdg. 17.99 (978-0-375-93459-9(6) , Knopf Bks. for Young Readers) Random Hse. Children's Bks.

Rigsby, Annelle & Raffa, Edwina. Race to Kitty Hawk. 2003. (Adventures in America Ser.). (Illus.). 84p. (J). 14.95 (978-1-893110-33-5(8)) Silver Moon Pr.

Ringgold, Faith. Tar Beach. Ringgold, Faith, illus. 2002. (Illus.). (J). 14.79 (978-0-7587-5352-6(7)) Book Wholesalers, Inc.

Rix, Jamie. Mr. Mumble's Fabulous Flybrows. 2003. (Illus.). 64p. (J). pap. 8.99 (978-0-552-54747-5(6) , Corgi) Transworld Publishers Ltd. GBR. *Dist:* Trafalgar Square Publishing.

Rockwell, Anne F. I Fly. 1998. (978-0-606-13502-3(2)) Tandem Library Bks.

Ruby, Laura. The Wall & the Wing. 2007. 352p. (J). (gr. 5 up). pap. 6.99 (*978-0-06-075257-6(2)* , Eos) HarperCollins Pubs.

Ryan, Pam Muñoz. Amelia & Eleanor Go for a Ride. Selznick, Brian, illus. 1999. 40p. (J). (gr. k-4). pap. 16.95 (978-0-590-96075-5(X)) Scholastic, Inc.

Sabench, Esteve. Queria Volar. 2001. (SPA., Illus.). 32p. (J). (gr. k-2). (978-84-261-2525-5(5) , JV4522) Juventud, Editorial ESP. *Dist:* Lectorum Pubns., Inc.

Sepulveda, Luis. The Story of a Seagull & the Cat Who Taught Her to Fly. Peden, Margaret Sayers, tr. from SPA. Sheban, Chris, illus. Tr. of Historia de una Gaviota y del Gato Que le Enseano a Volar. 128p. (J). 2003. (gr. 3-6). pap. 15.95 (978-0-439-40186-9(0)); 2006. reprint ed. pap. 5.99 (978-0-439-40187-6(9)) Scholastic, Inc. (Levine, Arthur A. Bks.).

Solo Flyer, 6 Packs. 16p. (gr. 2 up). 35.00 (978-0-7635-9375-9(3)) Rigby Education.

Stamper, Judith Bauer. Up, up, & Away! Ramsey, Marcy Dunn, illus. 2000. (Scholastic At-Home Phonics Reading Program Ser.: Vol. 55). 24p. (J). (978-0-590-68857-4(X)) Scholastic, Inc.

Stephas, Kristi. Flying Solo, Smith, Rachael, illus. 2005. 40p. (J). 16.95 (978-0-9764983-2-2(4)) Toy Truck Publishing.

Stine, R. L. Goosebumps: How I Learned to Fly. 2006. 144p. (J). pap. 4.99 (978-0-439-79620-0(2)) Scholastic, Inc.

Tanaka, Shinsuke, illus. Wings. 2006. 80p. (J). 14.95 (978-1-933327-19-8(7)) Purple Bear Bks., Inc.

Taylor, Theodore. The Boy Who Could Fly Without a Motor. (Illus.). 2004. 168p. (J). pap. 5.95 (978-0-15-204767-2(0) , Harcourt Paperbacks); 2002. 144p. (YA). (gr. 3-6). 15.00 (978-0-15-216529-1(0)) Harcourt Children's Bks.

Terri, Branson. Brother Dragon. l.t. ed. 2007. (Illus.). 24p. (J). 9.99 ***(978-0-9787421-9-5(2))*** Dragonfly Publishing, Inc.

Thompson, Colin. Falling Angels. 2001. (Illus.). 32p. (J). (gr. k-3). 18.00 (978-0-09-176817-1(9)) Random Hse. GBR. *Dist:* Trafalgar Square Publishing.

Thompson, D. R. My New Town: A Flying Naptime Adventure. Thompson, D. R. & Thompson, Dave, illus. 2003. (Naptime Adventure Ser.: Vol. 1). 32p. 14.95 (978-0-9723252-0-2(4)) This New World Publishing, LLC.

Townsend, Tom. Nadia of the Night Witches. Kemnitz, Myrna, ed. 1998. 158p. (YA). (gr. 8 up). 9.99 (978-0-88092-273-9(7) , 2737) Royal Fireworks Publishing Co.

Uhlberg, Myron. Flying over Brooklyn. 2003. (Illus.). 32p. (J). (gr. k-3). pap. 6.95 (978-1-56145-294-1(7)) Peachtree Pubs., Ltd.

—Flying over Brooklyn. Fitzgerald, Gerald, illus. 1999. 32p. (J). (ps-3). 15.95 (978-1-56145-194-4(0)) Peachtree Pubs., Ltd.

Wallace, Carol. Flying Flea, Callie & Me. 1999. (gr. 3-6). lib. bdg. 13.00 (978-0-613-84533-5(1)) Tandem Library Bks.

Wells, Helen. Cherry Ames, Flight Nurse. 2006. ix, 211p. (J). (978-0-8261-0397-0(9)) Springer.

Wilson, Anna. The Foolish Turtle. Gordon, Mike, illus. 2005. 32p. (J). (gr. k-1). lib. bdg. 11.15 (978-0-606-33597-3(8)) Tandem Library Bks.

Wishinsky, Frieda. Flying High! Griffiths, Dean, illus. 2007. (Canadian Flyer Adventures Ser.: No. 5). 96p. (J). (gr. 1-4). 16.95 ***(*978-1-897066-98-0(8));*** pap. 6.95 ***(*978-1-897066-99-7(6))*** Maple Tree Pr. CAN. *Dist:* Perseus Distribution.

FLIGHT ATTENDANTS

Wallner, Rosemary. Flight Attendant. 2000. (Career Exploration Ser.). (Illus.). 48p. (J). (gr. 3-4). lib. bdg. 21.26 (978-0-7368-0489-9(7) , LifeMatters Bks.) Capstone Pr., Inc.

FLIGHT TO THE MOON

see Space Flight to the Moon

FLIGHT TRAINING

see Airplanes—Piloting

FLIGHTS AROUND THE WORLD

see Aeronautics—Flights

FLOATS (PARADES)

see Parades

FLOODS

see also Rivers

Allaby, Michael. Floods. 2nd rev. ed. 2003. (Facts on File Science Library). (Illus.). 208p. (J). (gr. 6-12). 35.00 (978-0-8160-4794-9(4)) Facts On File, Inc.

Allan, Tony. Wild Water: Floods. 2004. (Turbulent Planet Ser.). (Illus.). 48p. (J). 28.56 (978-1-4109-1102-5(0)); pap. 8.50 (978-1-4109-1207-7(8)) Harcourt Schl. Pubs.

—Wild Water: Floods. 2005. (Turbulent Planet Ser.). (Illus.). 48p. (J). pap. (978-1-4109-1748-5(7)); lib. bdg. (978-1-4109-1738-6(X)) Steck-Vaughn.

Allen, Jean. Floods. 2001. (Natural Disasters Ser.). (Illus.). 48p. (J). (gr. 3-4). lib. bdg. 21.26 (978-0-7368-0900-9(7) , Capstone High-Interest Bks.) Capstone Pr., Inc.

Barber, Nicky. Fire & Flood. 1999. (Natural Disasters Ser.). (Illus.). 31p. (J). (gr. 5 up). pap. 5.95 (978-0-7641-1058-0(6)) Barron's Educational Series, Inc.

Barber, Nicola. Inside Fires & Floods. 2006. (Inside Nature's Disasters Ser.). (Illus.). 36p. (J). lib. bdg. (978-0-8368-7248-4(7)) Stevens, Gareth Inc.

Bennett, Paul. Flood. 1999. (World Reacts Ser.). (Illus.). 32p. (J). (gr. 2-5). lib. bdg. 16.95 (978-1-887068-89-5(9)) Smart Apple Media.

Bredeson, Carmen. The Mighty Midwest Flood: Raging Rivers. 1999. (American Disasters Ser.). (Illus.). 48p. (YA). (gr. 4-10). lib. bdg. 23.93 (978-0-7660-1221-9(2)) Enslow Pubs., Inc.

Brennan, Kristine. The Galveston Hurricane. 2002. (Great Disasters, Reforms & Ramifications Ser.). (Illus.). 112p. (J). 30.00 (978-0-7910-6740-6(8) , Chelsea Hse.) Facts On File, Inc.

Ceban, Bonnie J. Floods & Mudslides: Disaster & Survival. 2005. (Deadly Disasters Ser.). (Illus.). 48p. (J). (ps-10). lib. bdg. 23.93 (978-0-7660-2389-5(3)) Enslow Pubs., Inc.

Chambers, Catherine. Flood. (Illus.). 32p. (J). 2007. ***(*978-1-4034-9577-8(7));*** 2002. lib. bdg. 21.36 (978-1-58810-655-1(1)) Heinemann Library.

Chambers, Catherine. Floods. 2000. (Disasters in Nature Ser.). (Illus.). 48p. (J). (gr. 4-6). lib. bdg. 22.79 (978-1-57572-428-7(6)) Heinemann Library.

Connolly, Sean. Floods. 2003. (Illus.). 32p. (J). lib. bdg. (978-1-58340-390-7(6)) Smart Apple Media.

Dahl, Michael. Rising Waters: A Book about Floods. Shea, Denise, illus. 2005. (Amazing Science Ser.). 24p. (C). (gr. k-3). 22.60 (978-1-4048-0926-0(0)) Picture Window Bks.

Deedrick, Tami. Floods. 2000. (Nature on the Rampage Ser.). (Illus.). 32p. (J). (gr. 4-7). lib. bdg. 22.83 (978-0-7398-1797-1(3)) Raintree.

Donnelly, Karen J. Floods of the Past & Future. 2003. (Earths Changing Weather & Climate Ser.). (Illus.). 24p. (J). lib. bdg. 18.75 (978-0-8239-6218-1(0)) Rosen Publishing Group, Inc., The.

Drohan, Michele Ingber. Floods. 1999. (Natural Disasters Ser.). (Illus.). 24p. (J). (gr. k-4). lib. bdg. 19.95 (978-0-8239-5288-5(6) , PowerKids Pr.) Rosen Publishing Group, Inc., The.

Duden, Jane. Floods! Rising, Raging Waters. Ewald, Kay, illus. 1999. (Cover-to-Cover Bks.). 56p. (J). pap. 8.95 (978-0-7891-2935-2(3)); (gr. 4-7). lib. bdg. 17.95 (978-0-7807-8960-9(1)) Perfection Learning Corp.

Durham, Emma. Floods. 1999. (Restless Planet Ser.). (Illus.). 48p. (J). (gr. 4-6). lib. bdg. 27.12 (978-0-7398-1329-4(3)) Raintree.

Eagen, Rachael. Flood & Monsoon Alert! 2004. (Disaster Alert! Ser.). (Illus.). 32p. (J). (978-0-7787-1577-1(9)) Crabtree Publishing Co.

Eagen, Rachel. Flood & Monsoon Alert! 2004. (Disaster Alert! Ser.). (Illus.). 32p. (J). pap. (978-0-7787-1609-9(0)) Crabtree Publishing Co.

Egan, Lorraine Hopping. Wild Weather: Floods! 2000. (Hello Reader! Ser.). (978-0-606-18893-7(2)) Tandem Library Bks.

Fine, Jil. Floods. 2007. (Illus.). 48p. (J). pap. (978-0-531-18721-0(7)) Children's Pr., Ltd.

—Floods. 2006. (Natural Disasters Ser.). (Illus.). 48p. (J). (978-0-531-12435-2(5) , Children's Pr.) Scholastic Library Publishing.

Gallagher, Jim. Johnstown Flood. 1999. (Great Disasters Ser.). (Illus.). 112p. (YA). (gr. 5 up). 30.00 (978-0-7910-5266-2(4) , Chelsea Hse.) Facts On File, Inc.

Ganeri, Anita. Flood! 2007. (Illus.). 32p. (J). (978-1-84193-566-9(2)) Arcturus Pubs., Inc.

—Rain. 2004. (Illus.). 24p. (J). pap. (978-0-8368-4304-0(5)); lib. bdg. 19.33 (978-0-8368-4299-9(5)) Stevens, Gareth Inc.

Gifford, Clive. Flooding & Drought. 2005. (Looking at Landscapes Ser.). (Illus.). 47p. (J). (gr. 6-9). lib. bdg. 29.95 (978-1-58340-732-5(4)) Smart Apple Media.

Gow, Mary. Johnstown Flood: The Day the Dam Burst. 2003. (American Disasters Ser.). (Illus.). 48p. (J). (gr. 4-10). lib. bdg. 23.93 (978-0-7660-2109-9(2)) Enslow Pubs., Inc.

Green, Jen. 1993 Mississippi River Floods. 2005. (Illus.). 32p. (J). lib. bdg. 24.67 (978-0-8368-4495-5(5)) Stevens, Gareth Inc.

La Inundacion: Individual Title Six-Packs. (Coleccion Pm Ser.).Tr. of Flood. (SPA.). 16p. (gr. 1 up). 26.00 (978-0-7578-3039-6(0)) Rigby Education.

Jennings, Terry. Floods & Tidal Waves. 1999. (Natural Disasters Ser.). (Illus.). (J). lib. bdg. 16.95 (978-1-929298-46-4(3)) Chrysalis Education.

Keller, Ellen. Floods! 1999. (J). (978-0-606-16972-1(5)) Tandem Library Bks.

Kent, Deborah. The Great Mississippi Flood of 1927. 2006. (Cornerstones of Freedom Ser.). (Illus.). 48p. (J). (978-0-516-23628-5(8)) Children's Pr., Ltd.

Kleinhenz. Facing the Flood. 1999. pap. 5.65 (978-0-7398-0874-0(5)) Steck-Vaughn.

Kline, Lisa Williams. Floods. 2004. (J). 27.45 (978-1-59018-132-4(8) , Lucent Bks.) Thomson Gale.

Knox, Barbara. Flood! The 1993 Midwest Downpours. 2006. (X-Treme Disasters That Changed America Ser.). (Illus.). 32p. (J). lib. bdg. 25.27 (978-1-59716-172-5(1)) Bearport Publishing Co., Inc.

Larson, Erik. Isaac's Storm: A Man, a Time, & the Deadliest Hurricane in History. 2000. 323p. (gr. 7-12). per. 22.25 (978-0-613-29271-9(5)) Tandem Library Bks.

Meister, Cari. Floods. 1999. (Nature's Fury Ser.). (Illus.). 32p. (J). (gr. 3-8). lib. bdg. 24.21 (978-1-57765-082-9(4) , ABDO & Daughters) ABDO Publishing Co.

Menon, Sujatha. Wild Nature: Fire & Flood. 2008. (J). lib. bdg. ***(*978-1-4042-3899-2(9)*** , PowerKids Pr.) Rosen Publishing Group, Inc., The.

Nobleman, Marc Tyler. The Johnstown Flood. 2005. (We the People Ser.). (Illus.). 48p. (J). (gr. 4-6). (978-0-7565-1267-5(0)) Compass Point Bks.

Pingry, Patricia A. The Story of Noah & the Rainbow. Venturi-Pickett, Stacy, illus. 2001. (J). (ps-3). pap. 3.95 (978-0-8249-5414-7(9) , Ideals Children's Bks.) Ideals Pubns.

Richards, Julie. Furious Floods. 2001. (Natural Disasters Ser.). (Illus.). 32p. (J). (gr. 5 up). 28.00 (978-0-7910-6580-8(4) , 010456, Chelsea Hse.) Facts On File, Inc.

Spilsbury, Louise & Spilsbury, Richard. Raging Floods. 2003. (Heinemann Infosearch Ser.). (Illus.). 32p. (J). pap. (978-1-4034-4232-1(0)); lib. bdg. 24.22 (978-1-4034-3724-2(6)) Heinemann Library.

Stein, Paul. Floods of the Future. 2001. (Library of Future Weather & Climate). (Illus.). 64p. (YA). (gr. 4-6). lib. bdg. 26.50 (978-0-8239-3412-6(8)) Rosen Publishing Group, Inc., The.

Thomas, Jerry D. Secret of Noah's Flood. 2003. (Detective Zack Ser.). 132p. (J). pap., pap. 6.99 (978-0-7814-3730-1(X) , 078143730X) Cook, David C. Publishing Co.

Thompson, Luke. Floods. 2000. (High Interest Bks.). (Illus.). 48p. (J). (gr. 7-12). 23.00 (978-0-516-23369-7(6)); pap. 6.95 (978-0-516-23569-1(9)) Scholastic Library Publishing. (Children's Pr.).

—Floods. 2000. (gr. 7-12). lib. bdg. 15.25 (978-0-613-52051-5(3)) Tandem Library Bks.

Trumbauer, Lisa. Floods. 2005. (Watts Library). (Illus.). 64p. (J). 25.50 (978-0-531-12283-9(2) , Watts, Franklin) Scholastic Library Publishing.

Walker, Jane & Saunders, Mike. Tidal Waves & Flooding. 2004. (Natural Disasters Ser.). (J). lib. bdg. 27.10 (978-1-932799-62-0(1)) Stargazer Bks.

Weather Wise: Frightful Floods! 2001. (J). pap. 5.95 (978-1-56911-728-6(4)) Learning Resources, Inc.

Weingartz, Jill. Floods. 2001. (Natural Disasters Ser.). (Illus.). 24p. (J). 21.35 (978-1-58340-125-5(3)) Smart Apple Media.

Wetterer, Margaret K. Kate Shelley & the Midnight Express. 2005. (On My Own History Ser.). (Illus.). (J). pap. 18.95 incl. audio compact disk (978-1-59112-663-8(0)) Live Oak Media.

Woods, Michael & Woods, Mary B. Floods. 2007. (Disasters up Close Ser.). (J). 27.93 ***(*978-0-8225-4712-9(0)*** , Lerner Pubns.) Lerner Publishing Group.

World Book, Inc Staff, contrib. by. Floods. 2007. (J). ***(*978-0-7166-9805-0(6))*** World Bk., Inc.

FLOODS—FICTION

Alston, Emerson. Moccasins. 2000. 128p. (gr. 7-12). 11.95 (978-1-56315-220-7(7)) SterlingHouse Pubs., Inc.

—Moccasins. 2000. (gr. 7-12). lib. bdg. 16.40 (978-0-613-88171-5(0)) Tandem Library Bks.

Artful Doodlers, illus. Ice Age 2: Join the Pack. 2006. 32p. (J). lib. bdg. 13.85 ***(*978-1-4242-0692-6(8))*** Fitzgerald Bks.

Croteau-Fleury, Marie-Danielle & St. Aubin, Bruno. Trois Punaises Contre Deux Geants. 2001. (FRE., Illus.). 64p. (J). pap. (978-2-89021-504-7(0)) Diffusion du livre Mirabel.

Duey, Kathleen & Bale, Karen A. Flood: Mississippi 1927. 1998. (Survival! Ser.: No. 5). 176p. (J). (gr. 4-7). pap. 4.99 (978-0-689-82116-5(6) , Aladdin) Simon & Schuster Children's Publishing.

—Flood, Mississippi, 1927. 1998. (Survival! Ser.: No. 5). (J). (gr. 4-7). 10.64 (978-0-606-13829-1(3)) Tandem Library Bks.

Flaherty, Mildred. The Great Saint Patrick's Day Flood. 2004. (Illus.). 104p. (J). pap. (978-0-9711835-8-2(9)) Local History Co., The.

Hanson, Bonnie Compton. A Stormy Spring. 2004. (Ponytail Girls Ser.). (Illus.). 192p. (J). pap. 7.99 (978-1-58411-032-3(5) , Legacy Pr.) Rainbow Pubs. & Legacy Pr.

Harcourt School Publishers Staff, Cuando Vinron... Below Level. 3rd ed. 2002. (Trofeos Ser.). (SPA., Illus.). pap. 6.80 (978-0-15-324062-1(8)) Harcourt Schl. Pubs.

—Floodplain: Take-Home Book. 2001. (Collections Ser.). (Illus.). (J). pap. 1.90 (978-0-15-319552-5(5)) Harcourt Schl. Pubs.

—Floodplain Below Level. 3rd ed. 2002. (Trophies Reading Program Ser.). (Illus.). pap. 5.10 (978-0-15-323410-1(5)) Harcourt Schl. Pubs.

—When the Rain Comes: Take-Home Book. 1999. (Collections Ser.). (Illus.). (J). pap. 1.90 (978-0-15-317309-7(2)) Harcourt Schl. Pubs.

Heneghan, James. Flood. 2002. (YA). (gr. 5 up). pap. (978-0-88899-466-0(4)) Groundwood Bks. CAN. *Dist:* Transition Vendor.

Jolly, Jane. Limpopo Lullaby. Huxley, Dee, illus. 2006. 32p. 16.95 (978-1-894965-58-3(2)) Simply Read Bks. CAN. *Dist:* Perseus Distribution.

Kehret, Peg. Flood Disaster. 1999. (978-0-606-17854-9(6)) Tandem Library Bks.

Kurtz, Jane. River Friendly, River Wild. Brennan, Neil, illus. 2007. 40p. (J). 7.99 (978-1-4169-3487-5(1) , Aladdin) Simon & Schuster Children's Publishing.

Manos, John. Big Ben Helps the Town. 2006. (Early Explorers Ser.). (J). 34.00 ***(*978-1-4108-6119-1(8))*** Benchmark Education Co.

Morgan, Allen. Matthew & the Midnight Flood. Martchenko, Michael, illus. 1998. (Matthew's Midnight Adventures Ser.). 32p. (J). (ps-3). 6.99 (978-0-7737-5941-1(7)) Stoddart Kids CAN. *Dist:* Fitzhenry & Whiteside, Ltd.

O'Ryan, Ellie, adapted by. Ice Age 2: The Meltdown: Join the Pack! 2006. (I Can Read Bks.). (Illus.). 31p. (J). ***(*978-1-4156-5155-1(8))*** HarperCollins Pubs.

Petersen, P. J. Rising Water. 2003. (Illus.). 128p. (J). pap. 4.99 (978-0-689-86356-1(X) , Aladdin) Simon & Schuster Children's Publishing.

Raintree Steck-Vaughn Staff. Facing the Flood. 1999. (Illus.). (J). pap. 35.60 (978-0-7398-0905-1(9)) Steck-Vaughn.

Rivard, Ken. Mom, the School Flooded. Weissmann, Joe, illus. rev. ed. 2007. 24p. (J). (gr. k-2). pap. 6.95 ***(*978-1-55451-095-5(3));*** lib. bdg. 19.95 ***(*978-1-55451-096-2(1))*** Annick Pr., Ltd. CAN. *Dist:* Firefly Bks., Ltd.

Schneider, Josh. You'll Be Sorry. Schneider, Josh, illus. 2007. (Illus.). 32p. (J). (ps-1). 15.00 ***(*978-0-618-81932-4(0)*** , Clarion Bks.) Houghton Mifflin Co. Trade & Reference Div.

Somerville, Kirra. The Lizard Gang. Fielding, Grace, illus. 2006. 28p. (J). pap. 17.95 (978-1-875641-89-5(0)) Magabala Bks. AUS. *Dist:* International Specialized Bk. Services.

Stewart, Dianne. The Dove. Daly, Jude, illus. 2005. 32p. (J). (ps-3). pap. 7.95 (978-1-84507-022-9(4)) Lincoln, Frances Ltd. GBR. *Dist:* Perseus Distribution.

Storm, Jill. The Mabbul. 1999. 220p. (YA). pap. 10.95 (978-1-929078-18-9(8) , MABOO) God's Kids Publishing.

Tomos, Angharad. Strempan. 2005. (WEL., Illus.). 48p. pap. (978-0-86243-127-3(1)) Y Lolfa.

Weatherford, Carole Boston. Princeville: The 500 Year Flood. Alvord, Douglas, illus. 2001. 32p. 14.95 (978-1-928556-32-9(9)) Coastal Carolina Pr.

Westen, Betty. A Boat Ride for Two Raccoons. Thompson, Lisa Ann, illus. 2001. 93p. 14.95 (978-0-9718177-0-8(7) , W7770001) Westen Integrity Bk. Pubs.

Woelfle, Gretchen. Katje, the Windmill Cat. Bayley, Nicola, illus. 2006. 32p. (J). (ps). pap. 6.99 (978-0-7636-2089-9(0)) Candlewick Pr.

FLORA

see Botany; Plants

FLORAL DECORATION

see Flower Arrangement

FLORAL DESIGN

see Design, Decorative

FLORENCE (ITALY)

Barter, James E. Renaissance Florence. 2002. (Traveler's Guide to Ser.). (Illus.). 112p. (YA). (gr. 5). 29.95 (978-1-59018-145-4(X) , Lucent Bks.) Thomson Gale.

Kids Go Europe: Treasure Hunt Florence. 2006. (J). spiral bd. 9.95 (978-0-9772699-1-4(4)) Kids Go Europe, Inc.

Wagner, Heather Lehr. Machiavelli: Renaissance Political Analyst & Author. 2005. (Makers of the Middle Ages & Renaissance Ser.). (Illus.). 138p. (J). (gr. 4-8). lib. bdg. 30.00 (978-0-7910-8629-2(1) , Chelsea Hse.) Facts On File, Inc.

—The Medicis: A Ruling Dynasty. 2005. (Makers of the Middle Ages & Renaissance Ser.). (Illus.). 156p. (J). (gr. 4-8). lib. bdg. 30.00 (978-0-7910-8630-8(5) , Chelsea Hse.) Facts On File, Inc.

Zelasco, Marco & Zelasco, Pierangelo. Florence in the 1440s. Ripamonti, Aldo, illus. 2001. (Journey to the Past Ser.). 56p. (J). (gr. 6-8). lib. bdg. 27.12 (978-0-7398-1957-9(7)) Raintree.

FLORENCE (ITALY)—FICTION

Fern, Tracey E. Pippo the Fool. Estrada, Pau, illus. 2008. (J). ***(*978-1-57091-655-7(1))*** Charlesbridge Publishing, Inc.

Osborne, Mary Pope. Monday with a Mad Genius. Murdocca, Sal, illus. 2007. (Stepping Stone Bks.). 128p. (J). (gr. 2-6). 11.99 ***(*978-0-375-83729-6(9));*** lib. bdg. 14.99 ***(*978-0-375-93729-3(3))*** Random Hse. Children's Bks. (Random Hse. Bks. for Young Readers).

—Monday with a Mad Genius. Murdocca, Sal, illus. 2007. (J). pap. ***(*978-0-375-83730-2(2))*** Random Hse., Inc.

Sabuda, Robert. Uh-Oh Leonardo! 2003. (Illus.). 48p. (J). 16.95 (978-0-689-81160-9(8) , Atheneum) Simon & Schuster Children's Publishing.

Willard, Nancy. The Flying Bed. Thompson, John, illus. 2007. 48p. (J). (ps-3). pap. 16.99 (978-0-590-25610-0(6) , Blue Sky Pr., The) Scholastic, Inc.

FLORICULTURE

see Flower Gardening

FLORIDA

Aronson, Virginia. Konnichiwa Florida Moon: The Story of George Morikami, Pineapple Pioneer. 2002. (Illus.). 64p. (J). (gr. 3-7). 10.95 (978-1-56164-263-2(0)) Pineapple Pr., Inc.

Avery, Sherrie. Miami Metrozoo. 2003. (Great Zoos of the United States Ser.). (Illus.). 24p. (J). lib. bdg. 18.75 (978-0-8239-6316-4(0) , PowerKids Pr.) Rosen Publishing Group, Inc., The.

Bredeson, Carmen. Florida. 2005. (Rookie Espanol: Geografia Ser.). (SPA., Illus.). 32p. (J). (gr. k-2). pap. 5.95 (978-0-516-25514-9(2) , Children's Pr.) Scholastic Library Publishing.

—Florida. Risco, Eida del, tr. Ancona, George, photos by. 2004. (Rookie Readers - Spanish Ser.). (SPA., Illus.). 32p. (J). 19.50 (978-0-516-25108-0(2) , Watts, Franklin) Scholastic Library Publishing.

—Florida. 2003. (Rookie Read-About Geography Ser.). (Illus.). 32p. (J). (gr. 1-2). pap. 5.95 (978-0-516-27498-0(8) , Children's Pr.) Scholastic Library Publishing.

—Florida. 2002. (gr. k-3). lib. bdg. 14.10 (978-0-613-59480-6(0)) Tandem Library Bks.

Brown, Robin C. The Crafts of Florida's First People. 2003. (Illus.). 64p. (J). pap. 9.95 (978-1-56164-282-3(7)) Pineapple Pr., Inc.

Bruun, Erik. Florida. Peterson, Rick, illus. 2006. 48p. (J). (gr. 3-7). 9.95 (978-1-57912-231-7(0)) Black Dog & Leventhal Pubs., Inc.

Capstone Press Staff, contrib. by. Florida. rev. ed. 2002. (One Nation Ser.). (Illus.). 48p. (J). (gr. 3-4). lib. bdg. 22.60 (978-0-7368-1233-7(4) , Bridgestone Bks.) Capstone Pr., Inc.

Chang, Perry. Florida. 1998. (Celebrate the States Ser.). (Illus.). 144p. (gr. 4-8). lib. bdg. 37.07 (978-0-7614-0420-0(1) , Benchmark Bks.) Cavendish, Marshall Corp.

Christian, Sandra J. Florida. 2003. (Land of Liberty Ser.). (Illus.). 64p. (J). (gr. 3-4). lib. bdg. 23.93 (978-0-7368-1577-2(5) , Bridgestone Bks.) Capstone Pr., Inc.

Chui, Patricia. Florida. Porras, Carlos & D'Andrea, Patricia, trs. 2003. (World Almanac Biblioteca de los Estados). (SPA., Illus.). 48p. (J). (gr. 5 up). lib. bdg. 30.00 (978-0-8368-5543-2(4) , World Almanac Library) Stevens, Gareth Inc.

—Florida: The Sunshine State. 2002. (World Almanac Library of the States). (Illus.). 48p. (J). (gr. 5 up). pap. 14.95 (978-0-8368-5283-7(4)); lib. bdg. 30.00 (978-0-8368-5114-4(5)) Stevens, Gareth Inc. (World Almanac Library).

—Florida: The Sunshine State. 2002. (gr. 5-8). lib. bdg. 24.15 (978-0-613-52374-5(1)) Tandem Library Bks.

Costello, Emily. Realm of the Panther: A Story of South Florida's Forests. 2005. (Habitat Ser.). (Illus.). 32p. (J). (gr. 1-4). 19.95 incl. audio (978-1-56899-849-7(X)) Soundprints.

—Realm of the Panther: A Story of South Florida's Forests. Siegrist, Wes, illus. (Habitat Ser.). (J). (gr. 1-4). 2005. 32p. 15.95 (978-1-56899-847-3(3)); 2005. 32p. pap. 6.95 (978-1-56899-848-0(1)); 2000. 36p. 26.95 (978-1-56899-851-0(1)) Soundprints.

Crane, Carol. S Is for Sunshine: A Florida Alphabet. Monroe, Michael Glenn, illus. 2000. 40p. (J). (ps-3). 16.95 (978-1-58536-012-3(0)) Sleeping Bear Pr.

Duling, Jean Saunders. Marco Island A-Z: A Coloring Book for You. Duling, Jean Saunders, ed. 2003. (Illus.). 36p. (J). (ps-6). pap. 5.95 (978-0-9743445-0-8(8)) Duling Designs.

Eagen, Rachel. Ponce de Léon: Exploring Florida & Puerto Rico. 2005. (In the Footsteps of Explorers Ser.). (Illus.). 32p. (J). (gr. 3-9). (978-0-7787-2412-4(3)) Crabtree Publishing Co.

Evans, Eileen M. The Sidewalk Tour Vol. 2: Discovery Key West-the Seaport, 4 vols. 1998. (Illus.). 24p. (J). (gr. 3-7). pap. (978-0-9704695-1-9(9)) Moffatt Business Research.

—The Sidewalk Tours: Discovering Key West, 4 vols. 1998. (Illus.). 24p. (J). (gr. 3-7). pap. (978-0-9704695-0-2(0)) Moffatt Business Research.

Feinstein, Stephen. Florida: A MyReportLinks.com Book. 2003. (States Ser.). (Illus.). 48p. (J). (gr. 4-10). lib. bdg. 25.26 (978-0-7660-5027-3(0) , MyReportLinks.com Bks.) Enslow Pubs., Inc.

Florida. 2003. (World Almanac Biblioteca de los Estados). (SPA., Illus.). 48p. (J). (gr. 5 up). pap. 11.95 (978-0-8368-5550-0(7) , World Almanac Library) Stevens, Gareth Inc.

Florida. (One Nation Ser.). 48p. (YA). 6.95 (978-0-7368-8334-4(7)) Capstone Pr., Inc.

Florida's Colorful Critters. 2002. (Illus.). (J). pap. 2.95 (978-0-8200-1102-8(9)) Great Outdoors Publishing Co.

Gamble, Adam. Good Night Florida. Hansen, Red, illus. 2006. (Good Night Our World Ser.). 22p. (J). bds. 9.95 (978-0-9777979-7-4(X)) Our World of Books.

Hart, Joyce & Chang, Perry. Florida. 2nd ed. 2007. (Celebrate the States Ser.). (J). lib. bdg. 39.93 (978-0-7614-2348-5(6) , Benchmark Bks.) Cavendish, Marshall Corp.

Heinrichs, Ann. Florida. 2005. (Welcome to the USA Ser.). (Illus.). 40p. (J). (gr. 1-5). 27.07 (978-1-59296-284-6(X)) Child's World, Inc.

—Florida. 2002. (This Land Is Your Land Ser.). (Illus.). 48p. (J). (gr. 3 up). lib. bdg. 22.60 (978-0-7565-0309-3(4)) Compass Point Bks.

Hess, Debra. Florida. 2003. (It's My State! Ser.). (Illus.). 80p. (J). 27.07 (978-0-7614-1527-5(0) , Benchmark Bks.) Cavendish, Marshall Corp.

Imagineers Staff. The Imagineering Field Guide to Epcot at Walt Disney World. Wright, Alex, illus. 2006. 128p. (ps-17). pap. 9.95 (978-0-7868-4886-7(3) , Disney Editions) Disney Pr.

Johnson, Russ & Johnson, Annie. My Florida Alphabet. 2007. (Illus.). 63p. (J). 14.95 ***(*978-1-56164-392-9(0))*** Pineapple Pr., Inc.

Knight, Bertram T. Working at a Zoo. 1998. (Working Here Ser.). (Illus.). 32p. (J). (gr. 2-4). 23.50 (978-0-516-20751-3(2) , Children's Pr.) Scholastic Library Publishing.

Knotts, Bob. All Around Florida: Regions & Resources. (Heinemann State Studies). (Illus.). 48p. (J). 2003. (gr. 3-5). lib. bdg. (978-1-4034-0346-9(5)); 2002. pap. 8.50 (978-1-4034-0562-3(X)) Heinemann Library.

—All Around Florida: Regions & Resources. 2003. (gr. 3-6). lib. bdg. 17.05 (978-0-613-60845-9(3)) Tandem Library Bks.

—People of Florida. 2002. (State Studies). (Illus.). 48p. (J). pap. 8.50 (978-1-4034-0565-4(4)) Heinemann Library.

—Uniquely Florida. 2002. (State Studies). (Illus.). 48p. (J). pap. 8.50 (978-1-4034-0567-8(0)); lib. bdg. (978-1-4034-0351-3(1)) Heinemann Library.

—Uniquely Florida. 2003. (gr. 3-6). lib. bdg. 17.05 (978-0-613-60944-9(1)) Tandem Library Bks.

Knowles, Elizabeth & Smith, Martha. Discovering Florida Through Literature. 2003. 112p. pap. 14.95 (978-0-929895-54-3(1)) Maupin Hse. Publishing.

Lantz, Peggy S. & Hale, Wendy A. The Florida Water Story: From Raindrops to the Sea. Barnes, Jean, illus. 1998. 132p. (J). (gr. 5-7). 19.95 (978-1-56164-099-7(9)) Pineapple Pr., Inc.

Marsh, Carole. The Fabulous Florida Coloring Book. 2000. (Florida Experience! Ser.). (Illus.). 32p. (J). (gr. k-2). pap. 3.95 (978-0-7933-9468-5(6)) Gallopade International.

—Florida Classic Christmas Trivia. 2002. (Carole Marsh Florida Bks.). (Illus.). 32p. pap. 6.95 (978-0-635-01385-9(1) , 13851, Marsh, Carole Bks.); lib. bdg. 21.95 (978-0-635-01386-6(X) , 1386X) Gallopade International.

—Florida Current Events Projects: 30 Cool, Activities, Crafts, Experiments & More for Kids to Do to Learn about Your State! 2003. (Florida Experience Ser.). 32p. (gr. k-5). pap. 5.95 (978-0-635-02028-4(9) , Marsh, Carole Bks.) Gallopade International.

—The Florida Experience Pocket Guide. 2004. (Florida Experience! Ser.). (Illus.). 96p. (J). (gr. 3-8). pap. 6.95 (978-0-7933-9448-7(1)) Gallopade International.

—Florida Geography Projects: 30 Cool, Activities, Crafts, Experiments & More for Kids to Do to Learn about Your State! 2003. (Florida Experience Ser.). 32p. (gr. k-5). pap. 5.95 (978-0-635-01828-1(4) , Marsh, Carole Bks.) Gallopade International.

—Florida Government Projects: 30 Cool, Activities, Crafts, Experiments & More for Kids to Do to Learn about Your State! 2003. (Florida Experience Ser.). 32p. (gr. k-5). pap. 5.95 (978-0-635-01928-8(0) , Marsh, Carole Bks.) Gallopade International.

—Florida Jeopardy! Answers & Questions about Our State! 2000. (Florida Experience! Ser.). (Illus.). 32p. (J). (gr. 3-8). pap. 7.95 (978-0-7933-9507-1(0)) Gallopade International.

—Florida "Jography" A Fun Run Thru Our State! 2000. (Florida Experience! Ser.). (Illus.). 32p. (J). (gr. 3-8). pap. 7.95 (978-0-7933-9508-8(9)) Gallopade International.

—Florida Millionaire: Game Book. 2001. (Carole Marsh Florida Bks.). (Illus.). 32p. (J). (gr. 3-8). pap., act. bk. ed. 9.95 (978-0-635-00034-7(2)) Gallopade International.

—Florida People Projects: 30 Cool, Activities, Crafts, Experiments & More for Kids to Do to Learn about Your State! 2003. (Florida Experience Ser.). 32p. (gr. k-5). pap. 5.95 (978-0-635-01978-3(7) , Marsh, Carole Bks.) Gallopade International.

—Florida Survivor: Game Book. 2001. (Carole Marsh Florida Bks.). (Illus.). 32p. (J). (gr. 3-8). pap., act. bk. ed. 9.95 (978-0-635-00530-4(1) , Marsh, Carole Bks.) Gallopade International.

—Florida Symbols & Facts Projects: 30 Cool, Activities, Crafts, Experiments & More for Kids to Do to Learn about Your State! 2003. (Florida Experience Ser.). 32p. (gr. k-5). pap. 5.95 (978-0-635-01878-6(0) , Marsh, Carole Bks.) Gallopade International.

—Florida's Big Activity Book. 2004. (Florida Experience! Ser.). (Illus.). 96p. (J). (gr. 2-6). pap. 9.95 (978-0-7933-9458-6(9)) Gallopade International.

—My First Book about Florida. 2000. (Florida Experience! Ser.). (Illus.). 32p. (J). (gr. k-4). pap. 7.95 (978-0-7933-9506-4(2)) Gallopade International.

McAuliffe, Emily. Florida: Facts & Symbols. 1998. (States & Their Symbols Ser.). 24p. (J). lib. bdg. 13.75 (978-0-531-11550-3(X) , Watts, Franklin) Scholastic Library Publishing.

—Florida Facts & Symbols. rev. ed. 2003. (States & Their Symbols Ser.). 24p. (J). lib. bdg. 19.93 (978-0-7368-2239-8(9)) Capstone Pr., Inc.

McNamara, Connie. My First Florida State Words. 2004. (J). bds. 11.95 (978-0-9743244-7-0(7)) Shamrock Publishing, Inc.

—My First University of Florida Words. 2004. (J). bds. 11.95 (978-0-9743244-4-9(2)) Shamrock Publishing, Inc.

McNeil, Niki, et al. HOCPP 1075 Florida. 2006. spiral bd. 24.00 ***(*978-1-60308-075-0(9))*** In the Hands of a Child.

Meister, Cari. Disney World. 2000. (Going Places Ser.). (Illus.). 24p. (J). (gr. k-6). lib. bdg. 21.35 (978-1-57765-025-6(5) , Checkerboard Library) ABDO Publishing Co.

Michelin Travel Publications Staff. Florida. 2000. (Switched on Schoolhouse Ser.). (Illus.). (YA). (gr. 7-12). pap. 24.95 incl. cd-rom (978-0-7403-0261-9(2) , SOSFL) Alpha Omega Pubns., Inc.

Murray, Julie. Florida. 2006. (Buddy Book Ser.). (Illus.). 32p. (J). (gr. k-4). lib. bdg. 22.78 (978-1-59197-668-4(5) , Buddy Bks.) ABDO Publishing Co.

Nemcek, Mark. Iggs' Florida Adventure. Nemcek, Kathy, ed. Nemcek, Kathy, illus. 1999. 18p. (Orig.). (J). (ps-6). pap. (978-0-9669289-0-7(3)) Publish To Go Pubns., LLC.

Nudelman, Edward, ed. Cruising Guide to Eastern Florida. 5th ed. 2004. (Illus.). 12p. ring bd. 32.00 (978-1-58980-255-1(1)) Pelican Publishing Co., Inc.

Obregon, Jose M. Florida. 2005. (Bilingual Library of the United States of America: Set 1). (ENG & SPA., Illus.). 32p. (J). (ps-k). lib. bdg. 22.50 (978-1-4042-3074-3(2) , Buenas Letra) Rosen Publishing Group, Inc., The.

Obregon, José María & Brusca, María Cristina. Florida. 2006. (Bilingual Library of the United States of America). (ENG & SPA.). (J). lib. bdg. (978-1-4042-3141-2(2) , PowerKids Pr.) Rosen Publishing Group, Inc., The.

Ocala National Forest Staff, prod. Exploring Ocala National Forest & Central Florida's Parks. 2007. (Illus.). 52p. 5.95 (978-1-888213-67-6(1)) Eastern National.

Orr, Tamra. Florida. 2007. (America the Beautiful, Third Ser.). (Illus.). 144p. (YA). (gr. 5-8). lib. bdg. 38.00 ***(*978-0-531-18558-2(3)*** , Children's Pr.) Scholastic Library Publishing.

Quasha, Jennifer. Florida's Sights & Symbols. 2004. 48p. pap. 8.95 (978-1-4042-8501-9(6)) Rosen Publishing Group, Inc., The.

Rudy, Carol-Ann. Coral Gables, Gateway to the Sun. George, Paul S., ed. Date not set. (Hometown Heritage Ser.). (Illus.). 32p. (Orig.). (J). (gr. 2-4). pap. 3.50 (978-1-889300-03-0(9)) Dormouse Productions, Inc.

—Crossing to Freedom. George, Paul S., ed. Rudy, Carol-Ann, illus. Date not set. (Hometown Heritage Ser.). (Illus.). 48p. (Orig.). (J). (gr. 2-4). pap. 4.95 (978-1-889300-02-3(0)) Dormouse Productions, Inc.

Ryan, Susan Jane. Florida A to Z. Tornatore, Carol, illus. 2003. 64p. (J). 19.95 (978-1-56164-249-6(5)) Pineapple Pr., Inc.

Safro, Jill & Birnbaum, Stephen, contrib. by. Birnbaum's Walt Disney World for Kids, by Kids: Real Kids Give Honest Advice for the Most Awesome Vacation in the World. rev. ed. 2000. (Birnbaum's Walt Disney World for Kids, by Kids Ser.). (Illus.). 160p. (J). (gr. 4-7). pap. 10.95 (978-0-7868-5315-1(8) , Disney Editions) Disney Pr.

Sirvaitis, Karen. Florida. 2nd rev. exp. ed. (Hello U. S. A. Ser.). (Illus.). 84p. (J). (gr. 3-6). 2003. pap. 6.95 (978-0-8225-4144-8(0)); 2002. lib. bdg. 25.26 (978-0-8225-4066-3(5)) Lerner Publishing Group.

Somervill, Barbara A. Florida. 80p. (J). 2008. (From Sea to Shining Sea, Second Ser.). pap. 7.95 ***(*978-0-531-18802-6(7));*** 2001. (From Sea to Shining Sea Ser.: 2). (Illus.). (gr. 3-5). 30.50 (978-0-516-22308-7(9)) Scholastic Library Publishing. (Children's Pr.).

Sullivan, Ann. A Guide to Florida. 2000. (American States Ser.). (Illus.). 32p. (J). (gr. 3-7). lib. bdg. 16.95 (978-1-930954-30-4(1)) Weigl Pubs., Inc.

Thorpe, Sandy. Sand in Their Shoes. 2004. (Illus.). 192p. per. (978-0-9764147-0-4(8)) Thorpe, Sandy.

Warner, David T. Vanishing Florida: A Personal Guide to Sights Rarely Seen. 2001. (gr. 7-12). lib. bdg. 30.35 (978-0-613-64775-5(0)) Tandem Library Bks.

Wimmer, Teresa. Florida. 2008. (J). ***(*978-1-58341-634-1(X)*** , Creative Education) Creative Co., The.

Wright, Author O. The Adventures of Orlando: Our Family Trail of Fun. 2002. per. 9.95 (978-0-9679676-3-9(5)) Wright, Dr. Author O.

FLORIDA—FICTION

The Airs of Tillie. 2004. 150p. pap. 12.95 (978-1-932162-24-0(0)) Benoy Publishing.

Alexander, Goldie. Body & Soul. 2003. 236p. pap. 17.50 (978-0-9578735-9-9(X)) Indra Publishing AUS. *Dist:* International Specialized Bk. Services.

Allen, Quinc. The Outdoor Chums on the Gulf. 2006. pap. ***(*978-1-4065-0781-2(4))*** Dodo Pr.

Allen, Quincy. The Outdoor Chums on the Gulf or Rescuin. 2006. 77.99 ***(*978-1-4280-1998-0(7))*** IndyPublish.com.

Anderson, Laurie Halse. Manatee Blues, No. 4. 2008. (Vet Volunteers Ser.). 144p. (J). (gr. 3). 6.99 ***(*978-0-14-241084-4(5)*** , Puffin) Penguin Group (USA) Inc.

—Manatee Blues. 2003. (Wild at Heart Ser.). (Illus.). 114p. (J). (gr. 4 up). lib. bdg. 23.33 (978-0-8368-3258-7(2)) Stevens, Gareth Inc.

—Manatee Blues. 2000. (American Girl Wild at Heart Ser.: Bk. 4). (Illus.). (YA). (978-0-606-20455-2(5)) Tandem Library Bks.

Arnosky, Jim. A Manatee Morning. 2001. (J). (978-0-606-21615-9(4)) Tandem Library Bks.

Aryal, Aimee. Let's Go 'Noles! Higgins, Krystal, illus. 2004. (J). 19.95 (978-1-932888-20-1(9)) Mascot Bks., Inc.

Ashkenas, Bruce. Auntie's Ghost. 2007. 108p. 34.50 ***(*978-1-4303-1929-0(1))*** Lulu.com.

August, Elaine Schiller. Southern Mischief. 2005. 78p. pap. 14.95 (978-1-4137-7893-9(3)) PublishAmerica, Inc.

Barkley, Brad & Hepler, Heather. Dream Factory. 2007. 224p. (YA). (gr. 8 up). 16.99 (978-0-525-47802-7(7) , Dutton Juvenile) Penguin Group (USA) Inc.

Barnes, Peter W. & Barnes, Cheryl Shaw. Mizner Mouse: The Toast of Palm Beach. Kramer, Anthony, illus. 2002. 32p. (J). 16.95 (978-1-893622-12-8(6)) Vacation Spot Publishing.

Bell, Rebecca. Message from Miami - the Adventures of Sharp-Eye - Book2. Bell, Rebecca, illus. 2005. (Adventures of Sharp-Eye). 30p. (J). per. 9.95 ***(*978-1-934138-09-0(6))*** Bouncing Ball Bks., Inc.

Bloor, Edward. Tangerine. 2006. (Illus.). 324p. (YA). pap. 6.95 (978-0-15-205780-0(3) , Harcourt Paperbacks) Harcourt Children's Bks.

—Tangerine. 1998. (Apple Signature Edition Ser.). 304p. (YA). (gr. 6 up). pap. 4.99 (978-0-590-43277-1(X) , Scholastic Paperbacks) Scholastic, Inc.

Bonner, Anne. Intrigue at Pine Haven: Civil War in Florida. Akridge, Bill, illus. 2006. 220p. (YA). 12.95 net. (978-1-878398-76-5(8) , Blue Note Bks.) Blue Note Pubns.

Brooks, Walter R. Freddy Goes to Florida. Wiese, Kurt, illus. 2001. 208p. (J). (gr. 4-7). pap. 7.99 (978-0-14-131233-0(5) , Puffin) Penguin Group (USA) Inc.

—Freddy Goes to Florida. Wiese, Kurt, illus. 2001. 196p. (J). (gr. 4-7). per. 15.30 (978-0-613-36062-3(1)) Tandem Library Bks.

Brouwer, Sigmund. Hurricane Power. 2007. (Orca Sports Ser.). 176p. (YA). (gr. 5 up). pap. ***(*978-1-55143-865-8(8))*** Orca Bk. Pubs.

Brown, Marc. Buster Catches a Wave. 2005. (Postcards from Buster Ser.). (Illus.). 32p. (J). (gr. 1-4). pap. 14.99 (978-0-316-15903-6(4)); 7th ed. pap. 3.99 (978-0-316-00122-9(8)) Little Brown & Co.

Campbell, Joanna. Perfect Challenge. 2002. (gr. 3-6). lib. bdg. 13.00 (978-0-613-67217-7(8)) Tandem Library Bks.

Carter, Dorothy. Grandma's General Store - The Ark. Allen, Thomas B., illus. 2005. 144p. (J). 16.00 (978-0-374-32766-8(1) , Farrar, Straus & Giroux (BYR)) Farrar, Straus & Giroux.

Chappell, Crissa-Jean. Total Constant Order. 2007. 288p. (YA). (gr. 7 up). 16.99 ***(*978-0-06-088605-9(6));*** lib. bdg. 17.89 ***(*978-0-06-088606-6(4))*** HarperCollins Pubs. (HarperTeen).

Christelow, Eileen. The Great Pig Search. Christelow, Eileen, illus. 2001. (Illus.). 40p. (J). (gr. k-3). tchr. ed. 15.00 (978-0-618-04910-3(X) , Clarion Bks.) Houghton Mifflin Co. Trade & Reference Div.

Clague, Mary H. Fort Brooke Drummer Boy: A Story of Old Florida. 1998. 93p. (J). pap. 6.99 (978-1-57502-747-0(X) , PO2075) Morris Publishing.

Clairday, Robynn. Confessions of a Boyfriend Stealer. 2005. 240p. (YA). (gr. 7-12). pap. 7.95 (978-0-385-73242-0(2) , Delacorte Bks. for Young Readers) Random Hse. Children's Bks.

Cola, Arthur. Papa & the Gingerbread Man. 2006. 14.95 ***(*978-0-9789423-0-4(2))*** Cola, Arthur.

Colebank, Susan. Black Tuesday. 2007. 208p. (YA). 16.99 (978-0-525-47766-2(7) , Dutton Juvenile) Penguin Group (USA) Inc.

Corbett, Sue. Free Baseball. 160p. (J). (gr. 3). 2008. 5.99 ***(*978-0-14-241080-6(2)*** , Puffin); 2006. 15.99 (978-0-525-47120-2(0) , Dutton Juvenile) Penguin Group (USA) Inc.

Crane, Carol. Sunny Numbers: A Florida Counting Book. Donovan, Jane Monroe, illus. 2001. 40p. (J). 16.95 (978-1-58536-050-5(3)) Sleeping Bear Pr.

Crist-Evans, Craig. Amaryllis. (YA). (gr. 9). 2006. 192p. pap. 7.99 (978-0-7636-2990-8(1)); 2003. 208p. 15.99 (978-0-7636-1863-6(2)) Candlewick Pr.

Crocker, Carter & Snyder, Carrie A. The Tale of the Swamp Rat. 2005. 176p. (J). (gr. 4). reprint ed. pap. 6.99 (978-0-14-240314-3(8) , Puffin) Penguin Group (USA) Inc.

Day, Jan. Kissimmee Pete, Cracker Cow Hunter: A Tall Tale. Mason, Janeen I., illus. 2005. 32p. (J). (gr. 2-4). 15.95 (978-1-58980-325-1(6)) Pelican Publishing Co., Inc.

Day, Robert O. & Day, Linda S. There's a Frog on a Log in the Bog. Day, Linda S., illus. 2002. (Florida Tales Ser.: Vol. 1). (Illus.). 112p. (J). (gr. 4-6). pap. 8.95 (978-1-890905-20-0(8)) Day to Day Enterprises.

De Palma, Toni. Under the Banyan Tree. 2007. 192p. (YA). (gr. 7 up). 16.95 (978-0-8234-1965-4(7)) Holiday Hse., Inc.

DeFelice, Cynthia. The Missing Manatee. 2008. 192p. (J). pap. 6.95 ***(*978-0-374-40020-0(2)*** , Farrar, Straus & Giroux (BYR)) Farrar, Straus & Giroux.

DeFelice, Cynthia C. The Missing Manatee. 2005. 192p. (J). 16.00 (978-0-374-31257-2(5) , Farrar, Straus & Giroux (BYR)) Farrar, Straus & Giroux.

—The Missing Manatee. l.t. ed. 2005. 183p. (J). 20.95 (978-0-7862-8178-7(2)) Thorndike Pr.

DiCamillo, Kate. Because of Winn-Dixie. (Because of Winn-Dixie Ser.). (J). 2001. 192p. (gr. 3 up). pap. 5.99 (978-0-7636-1605-2(2)); 2000. 184p. (gr. 4-7). 15.99 (978-0-7636-0776-0(2)); 2004. 184p. 19.99 (978-0-7636-2557-3(4)); 2004. (Illus.). 192p. (gr. 3). mass mkt. 5.99 (978-0-7636-2558-0(2)) Candlewick Pr.

—Because of Winn-Dixie. pap. 17.95 (978-3-423-70771-8(2)) Deutscher Taschenbuch Verlag GmbH & Co KG DEU. *Dist:* Distribooks, Inc.

—Because of Winn-Dixie. 2001. (gr. 3-6). lib. bdg. 14.15 (978-0-613-39503-8(4)) Tandem Library Bks.

—Because of Winn-Dixie. l.t. ed. 2002. 125p. (J). 23.95 (978-0-7862-3665-7(5)) Thomson Gale.

—Gracias a Winn-Dixie. 2005. (SPA.). pap. 4.99 (978-84-279-3254-8(5)) Noguer y Caralt Editores, S. A. ESP. *Dist:* Lectorum Pubns., Inc.

—The Tiger Rising. Sheban, Chris, illus. 2006. 144p. (J). (gr. 5). pap. 5.99 (978-0-7636-2916-8(2)) Candlewick Pr.

—The Tiger Rising. 128p. (gr. 5-12). 2002. (YA). pap. 5.99 (978-0-7636-1898-8(5)); 2001. (Illus.). (J). 15.99 (978-0-7636-0911-5(0)) Candlewick Pr.

—The Tiger Rising. unabr. ed. 2004. (Middle Grade Cassette Librariestm Ser.). 128p. (J). (gr. 5-9). pap. 29.00 incl. audio (978-0-8072-0998-1(8) , S YA 285 SP, Listening Library) Random Hse. Audio Publishing Group.

—The Tiger Rising. 2002. (gr. 5-8). lib. bdg. 14.15 (978-0-613-66924-5(X)) Tandem Library Bks.

Doerr, Bonnie J. Kenzie's Key. Aberle, Xylena Apotheloz, illus. 2003. 211p. (J). 16.95 (978-0-9619155-6-8(0)) Laurel & Herbert, Inc.

Dole, Mayra L. Drum, Chavi, Drum ! / Toca, Chavi, Toca! Tonel, illus. 2003. Tr. of Toca, Chavi, Toca!. (ENG & SPA.). 32p. (J). 16.95 (978-0-89239-186-8(3)) Children's Bk. Pr.

Douglas, Marjory Stoneman. Alligator Crossing. Nicholson, Trudy, illus. 2003. 192p. (J). (gr. 3-8). pap. 6.95 (978-1-57131-644-8(2)) Milkweed Editions.

—Alligator Crossing. 2003. (gr. 3-6). lib. bdg. 15.25 (978-0-613-79196-0(7)) Tandem Library Bks.

Draper, Sharon M. Copper Sun. (YA). 2008. 336p. pap. 8.99 ***(*978-1-4169-5348-7(5)*** , Simon Pulse); 2006. 320p. (gr. 8 up). 16.95 (978-0-689-82181-3(6) , Atheneum) Simon & Schuster Children's Publishing.

—Copper Sun. l.t. ed. 2006. 358p. (YA). (gr. 8 up). 22.95 (978-0-7862-8948-6(1)) Thorndike Pr.

Edwards, Kris. Santa Paws on Christmas Island. 2007. (Santa Paws Ser.). 144p. (J). pap. 4.99 ***(*978-0-439-88812-7(3)*** , Scholastic Paperbacks) Scholastic, Inc.

Enriquez, Jose. Saving the Mango Farm. 2006. 23p. (J). 10.98 (978-1-4116-5917-9(1)) Lulu.com.

Faris, Debi. Kaya & Nannas First Excellent Adventur. 2006. pap. 18.99 ***(*978-1-4259-7780-1(4))*** AuthorHouse.

Farley, Steven. Wild Spirit. 1999. (Young Black Stallion Ser.: No. 4). (J). (gr. 4-6). (978-0-606-16963-9(6)) Tandem Library Bks.

—The Yearling. Schwartz, Joanie, illus. 1999. (Young Black Stallion Ser.: No. 5). 144p. (J). (gr. 4-6). lib. bdg. 11.99 (978-0-375-90091-4(8) , Random Hse. Bks. for Young Readers) Random Hse. Children's Bks.

—The Yearling. 1999. (Young Black Stallion Ser.: No. 5). (J). (gr. 4-6). (978-0-606-16964-6(4)) Tandem Library Bks.

Feathers at Las Flores - Evaluation Guide: Evaluation Guide. 2006. (J). (978-1-55942-405-9(2)) Marsh Media.

Feathers at Las Flores - Teaching Guide. 2000. 17.95 (978-1-55942-172-0(X)) Marsh Media.

Flinn, Alex. Nothing to Lose. 2004. 288p. (J). 16.99 (978-0-06-051750-2(6)); lib. bdg. 17.89 (978-0-06-051751-9(4)) HarperCollins Pubs. (HarperTeen).

Fogelin, Adrian. Anna Casey's Place in the World. 2003. 224p. (J). (gr. 3-6). pap. 6.95 (978-1-56145-295-8(5) , Q32694) Peachtree Pubs., Ltd.

—Anna Casey's Place in the World. Schultz, Suzy, illus. 2001. 224p. (J). (gr. 3-7). 14.95 (978-1-56145-249-1(1) , Q32694) Peachtree Pubs., Ltd.

—Anna Casey's Place in the World. 2003. 207p. (J). (gr. 4-7). lib. bdg. 15.25 (978-0-613-53133-7(7)) Tandem Library Bks.

—The Big Nothing. 2004. 224p. (J). 14.95 (978-1-56145-326-9(9)) Peachtree Pubs., Ltd.

—Big Nothing. 2006. 224p. (YA). pap. 6.95 (978-1-56145-388-7(9)) Peachtree Pubs., Ltd.

—My Brother's Hero. (Peachtree Junior Publication Ser.). 224p. (J). 2002. (gr. 3-7). 14.95 (978-1-56145-274-3(2)); 2005. reprint ed. pap. 6.95 (978-1-56145-352-8(8)) Peachtree Pubs., Ltd.

—The Real Question. 2006. 240p. (YA). 15.95 (978-1-56145-383-2(8) , Peachtree Junior) Peachtree Pubs., Ltd.

Fogelin, Adrian. The Sorta Sisters. 2007. 240p. (J). (gr. 3-7). 14.95 ***978-1-56145-424-2(9)** , Peachtree Junior) Peachtree Pubs., Ltd.

Forney, Melissa. Oonawassee Summer: Something is Lurking Beneath the Surface... Scott, Gregg, illus. 2000. 126p. (J). (gr. 4-8). pap. 14.95 (978-1-928961-04-8(5)) Barker Creek Publishing, Inc.

Gantos, Jack. Jack on the Tracks: Four Seasons of Fifth Grade. 1999. (Jack Henry Ser.). (Illus.). 192p. (J). (gr. 5-9). 16.00 (978-0-374-33665-3(2) , Farrar, Straus & Giroux (BYR)) Farrar, Straus & Giroux.

—Jack on the Tracks: Four Seasons of Fifth Grade. 2001. (gr. 5-8). lib. bdg. 14.10 (978-0-613-85137-4(4)) Tandem Library Bks.

—Jack on the Tracks: Four Seasons of Fifth Grade. l.t. ed. 2002. 210p. (J). 22.95 (978-0-7862-4394-5(5)) Thorndike Pr.

Gonzalez, Gabriela & Triana, Gaby. Backstage Pass. 2004. (Illus.). 224p. (J). (gr. 7 up). 15.99 (978-0-06-056017-1(7)); lib. bdg. 16.89 (978-0-06-056018-8(5)) HarperCollins Pubs.

Grover, Lorie Ann. Hold Me Tight. 2005. 352p. (J). 16.95 (978-0-689-85248-0(7) , McElderry, Margaret K.) Simon & Schuster Children's Publishing.

Haddix, Margaret Peterson. The House on the Gulf. (Illus.). 208p. (J). 2006. pap. 5.99 (978-1-4169-1406-8(4) , Aladdin); 2004. 15.95 (978-0-689-85422-4(6)) Simon & Schuster Children's Publishing.

Hanson, Ed. Danger at 20 Fathoms. 2003. (Barclay Family Adventure Ser.: Bk. 2). 64p. (J). (gr. k-6). pap. 3.95 (978-1-56254-551-2(5) , SP 5515) Saddleback Educational Publishing.

Harcourt School Publishers Staff. Are We Having Fun Yet? 3rd ed. 2002. (Trophies English Language Learners Ser.). (Illus.). (gr. 5). pap. 5.10 (978-0-15-327812-9(9)) Harcourt Schl. Pubs.

Harlow, Joan Hiatt. Blown Away! 2007. 272p. (J). (gr. 4-7). 15.99 (978-1-4169-0781-7(5) , McElderry, Margaret K.) Simon & Schuster Children's Publishing.

Harris, Loretta. Hard Life. 2006. (YA). (***978-0-9786681-2-9(X)**) Children's Heart Publishing Co.

Heck, C. S. Memory-Kisses. 2007. 104p. per. 9.95 (***978-0-595-41514-4(8)**) iUniverse, Inc.

Hiaasen, Carl. Flush. 272p. (J). (gr. 5). 2007. pap. 8.99 (***978-0-375-84185-9(7)**); 2005. 16.95 (978-0-375-82182-0(1)) Random Hse. Children's Bks. (Knopf Bks. for Young Readers).

—Flush. l.t. ed. 2005. 335p. (YA). 23.95 (978-0-7862-7908-1(7)) Thorndike Pr.

—Hoot. 304p. (gr. 5). 2005. 6.50 (978-0-440-41939-6(5) , Yearling); 2002. (Illus.). (J). 15.95 (978-0-375-82181-3(3) , Knopf Bks. for Young Readers); 2002. (Illus.). (J). lib. bdg. 17.99 (978-0-375-92181-0(8) , Knopf Bks. for Young Readers); 2006. (J). 6.50 (978-0-440-42170-2(5) , Yearling); 2004. (YA). reprint ed. pap. 8.95 (978-0-375-82916-1(4) , Knopf Bks. for Young Readers) Random Hse. Children's Bks.

—Hoot. 2003. 25.95 (978-0-7862-5014-1(3)) Thorndike Pr.

Hill, Elizabeth Starr. Wildfire! Shepperson, Rob, illus. 2004. 80p. (J). 16.00 (978-0-374-31712-6(7) , Farrar, Straus & Giroux (BYR)) Farrar, Straus & Giroux.

Hobbs, Valerie. Letting Go of Bobby James: Or How I Found My Self of Steam. 2004. 144p. (YA). 16.00 (978-0-374-34384-2(5) , Frances Foster Bks.) Farrar, Straus & Giroux.

Holt, Kimberly Willis. Piper Reed, Navy Brat. Davenier, Christine, illus. 2007. 160p. (J). (gr. 3-6). 14.95 (***978-0-8050-8197-8(6)** , Holt, Henry & Co. Bks. For Young Readers) Holt, Henry & Co.

—Piper Reed, Navy Brat. Davenier, Christine, illus. 2008. 176p. (J). pap. 6.99 (***978-0-312-38020-5(8)**) Square Fish.

Hope, Laura Lee. Outdoor Girls in Florida or Wintering in. 2007. 95.99 (***978-1-4280-5353-3(0)**); pap. 88.99 (***978-1-4280-5357-1(3)**) IndyPublish.com.

Jackson, Alison. Rainmaker. 2004. (Illus.). 200p. (J). 16.95 (978-1-59078-309-2(3)) Boyds Mills Pr.

Jacobson, Ryan. Santa Claus: Super Spy: The Case of the Florida Freeze. Belkholm, Erica, illus. l.t. ed. 2005. 80p. (J). per. 4.99 (978-0-9774122-0-4(2)) Lake 7 Creative.

Jasper, Mark. Good Night Florida Keys. Rosen, Anne, illus. 2008. (Good Night Our World Ser.). 20p. (J). bds. 9.95 (***978-1-60219-020-7(8)**) Our World of Books.

Jordan, Rosa. The Goatnappers. 2007. 224p. (J). (gr. 5-7). 14.95 (***978-1-56145-400-6(1)** , Peachtree Junior) Peachtree Pubs., Ltd.

Kaminski, Tom. Miss Olivia, the Little Red Poodle: Her First Big Adventure. Fallon, Lisa, illus. 2006. (J). pap. 16.00 (***978-0-8059-7253-5(6)**) Dorrance Publishing Co., Inc.

Katschke, Judy. Shore Thing. 2001. (gr. 3-6). lib. bdg. 13.00 (978-0-613-43957-2(0)) Tandem Library Bks.

Klima, Charlene Hudgins. Give Me Five. 2000. 106p. (YA). (gr. 4-9). pap. 12.00 (978-1-883911-36-2(2)) Brandylane Pubs., Inc.

Konigsburg, E. L. T-Backs, T-Shirts, Coat, & Suit. 2003. (Illus.). 176p. (J). pap. 4.99 (978-0-689-85682-2(2) , Aladdin) Simon & Schuster Children's Publishing.

—T-Backs, T-Shirts, Coat, & Suit. 2003. (gr. k-3). lib. bdg. 13.00 (978-0-613-61661-4(8)) Tandem Library Bks.

Kropp, Joseph. Bowlegs' Bounty. 2005. 192p. (J). pap. 9.95 (978-1-890905-24-8(0)) Day to Day Enterprises.

Kwon, Jean. Because of Winn Dixie Movie Scrapbook. Tenner, Suzanne, photos by. 2004. (Because of Winn-Dixie Ser.). (Illus.). 48p. (J). pap. 6.99 (978-0-7636-2817-8(4)) Candlewick Pr.

Lantz, Francess L. Heart Breakers. 2004. (gr. 5-8). lib. bdg. 13.00 (978-0-613-71465-5(2)) Tandem Library Bks.

—Lights, Camera, Love! 2000. (gr. 3-6). lib. bdg. 11.80 (978-0-613-21906-8(6)) Tandem Library Bks.

Leppard, Lois Gladys. Mandie & the Seaside Rendezvous, Vol. 32. 2000. (Mandie Bks.: No. 32). 176p. (J). (gr. 4-7). mass mkt. 5.99 (978-1-55661-673-0(2)) Bethany Hse. Pubs.

—Mandie & the Seaside Rendezvous. 2000. (Mandie Bks.: No. 32). (J). (gr. 4-7). (978-0-606-18919-4(X)); 1999. (gr. 3-6). lib. bdg. 13.00 (978-0-613-27969-7(7)) Tandem Library Bks.

Llewellyn, Sam. Bad Bad Darlings. 2005. 240p. (J). (***978-0-14-131701-4(9)** , Puffin) Penguin Group (USA) Inc.

Lopez, David Mark. Walk Like an Egyptian. 2006. (J). (gr. 3-7). (***978-0-9744097-0-2(7)**) Lopez, David.

Manatee Moon. 2006. (J). per. 9.95 (978-0-9766620-3-7(5)) Avery Goode-Reid Pubs.

Mass, Wendy. Leap Day. 2006. 224p. (J). (gr. 5-8). pap. 7.99 (978-0-316-05828-5(9)) Little Brown & Co.

Matheson, Shirlee Smith. Fastback Beach. 2006. (Orca Soundings Ser.). 112p. (YA). lib. bdg. 14.95 (978-1-55143-580-0(2)) Orca Bk. Pubs. USA.

Matson, Laurie. Jaz-O & 'G' in Key West. Matson, Laurie, illus. l.t. ed. 2003. (Illus.). (J). 4.95 (978-0-9673704-5-3(0)) Seastory Pr.

McDaniel, Lurlene. The Girl Death Left Behind. 1999. 192p. (YA). (gr. 7-12). pap. 5.50 (978-0-553-57091-5(9) , Laurel Leaf) Random Hse. Children's Bks.

—The Girl Death Left Behind. 1999. (J). 11.64 (978-0-606-16371-2(9)) Tandem Library Bks.

—Holly's Story. 2005. (Angels in Pink Ser.). 224p. (gr. 7). (YA). 10.95 (978-0-385-73158-4(2)); (J). lib. bdg. 12.99 (978-0-385-90195-6(X)) Random Hse. Children's Bks. (Delacorte Bks. for Young Readers).

—Raina's Story. (Angels in Pink Ser.). 208p. (gr. 7). 2006. (YA). pap. 6.50 (978-0-440-23866-9(8) , Laurel Leaf); 2005. (J). lib. bdg. 12.99 (978-0-385-90194-9(1) , Delacorte Bks. for Young Readers) Random Hse. Children's Bks.

McDonald, Joyce. Devil on My Heels. 272p. (YA). (gr. 7 up). 2005. pap. 6.50 (978-0-440-23829-4(3) , Laurel Leaf); 2004. 15.95 (978-0-385-73107-2(8) , Delacorte Bks. for Young Readers) Random Hse. Children's Bks.

McDonald, Megan. Beezy & Funnybone. Poydar, Nancy, illus. 2000. 48p. (J). (gr. 1-4). 15.99 (978-0-531-33211-5(X)); pap. 14.95 (978-0-531-30211-8(3)) Scholastic, Inc. (Orchard Bks.).

—Beezy & Funnybone. 2000. (J). (978-0-606-19481-5(9)) Tandem Library Bks.

—Beezy at Bat. Poydar, Nancy, illus. 48p. (J). (gr. 1-4). 2000. pap. 4.95 (978-0-531-07164-9(2)); 1998. pap. 13.95 (978-0-531-30085-5(4)) Scholastic, Inc. (Orchard Bks.).

—Beezy at Bat. 2000. (J). (978-0-606-20453-8(9)) Tandem Library Bks.

McDonald, Megan & Poydar, Nancy. Beezy at Bat. 1998. (Illus.). 48p. (J). (gr. 1-4). 14.99 (978-0-531-33085-2(0) , Orchard Bks.) Scholastic, Inc.

Mullican, Judy. Fun in Florida. Gillen, Lisa P., illus. 2005. (J). pap. (978-1-57332-369-7(1)) HighReach Learning, Inc.

Munroe, Kirk. Flamingo Feather. 2006. pap. 27.95 (***978-1-4304-4189-2(5)**) Kessinger Publishing, LLC.

My First Seminoles Book. 2004. (J). bds. 8.95 (978-0-9754317-1-9(4)) JEM Bks., Inc.

Myers, Anna. Flying Blind. 2003. 192p. (YA). 16.95 (978-0-8027-8879-5(3)) Walker & Co.

Nixon-Weaver, Elizabeth. Rooster. 2001. (Illus.). 320p. (J). (gr. 7 up). 16.95 (978-1-58837-001-3(1)) Winslow Pr.

Nolan, Peggy. The Spy Who Came in from the Sea. 144p. (J). 2001. pap. 8.95 (978-1-56164-245-8(2)); 2000. (gr. 5 9). 14.95 (978-1-56164-186-4(3)) Pineapple Pr., Inc.

—Spy Who Came in from the Sea. 1999. (gr. 5-8). lib. bdg. 17.60 (978-0-613-37048-6(1)) Tandem Library Bks.

Pallas-Luke, Barbara. Cryptic Society. ed. 2005. (YA). 5.00 (978-0-9765637-0-9(3)) Iris Pallas-Luke E-Writings/E-Literature.

Patterson, James. School's Out - Forever. 2006. (Maximum Ride Ser.: No. 2). 414p. (YA). 16.99 (978-0-316-01449-6(4)) Little Brown & Co.

Peck, Robert Newton. Bro. 2004. 160p. (J). (gr. 7 up). 16.99 (978-0-06-052974-1(1)); lib. bdg. 17.89 (978-0-06-052975-8(X)) HarperCollins Pubs.

—Cowboy Ghost. 1999. 208p. (YA). (gr. 7 up). 15.95 (978-0-06-028168-7(5) , Harper Trophy) HarperCollins Pubs.

—Cowboy Ghost. 1999. (YA). pap., stu. ed. 52.95 incl. audio (978-0-7887-3189-1(0) , 40924) Recorded Bks., LLC.

—Cowboy Ghost. 2000. (Illus.). (J). 11.60 (978-0-606-18684-1(0)) Tandem Library Bks.

—Horse Thief: A Novel. 2003. (gr. 7-12). lib. bdg. 14.15 (978-0-613-65695-5(4)) Tandem Library Bks.

Princesa Stephanie. 2005. (SPA.). (YA). per. 9.95 (978-0-9764982-8-5(6)) Legacy Publishing Services, Inc.

Pyle, Jack R. The Gold Bug of Farrow Point. 2003. 130p. (J). (978-1-887905-78-7(2)) Parkway Pubs., Inc.

Quindlen, Anna. Black & Blue: A Novel. 1999. (gr. 7-12). lib. bdg. 15.90 (978-0-613-12312-9(3)) Tandem Library Bks.

Rawlings, Marjorie Kinnan. The Yearling. 1999. (Illus.). 444p. (J). 17.90 (978-0-03-054778-2(4)) Holt, Rinehart & Winston.

—The Yearling. 2002. 480p. pap. 15.00 (978-0-7432-2525-0(2) , Scribner) Simon & Schuster.

—The Yearling. 2001. (Aladdin Classics Ser.). 528p. mass mkt. 5.99 (978-0-689-84623-6(1) , Aladdin) Simon & Schuster Children's Publishing.

—Yearling. 2001. (gr. 3-6). lib. bdg. 14.15 (978-0-613-90195-6(9)) Tandem Library Bks.

—The Yearling, Level 3. 2001. 64p. (C). pap. 9.00 (978-0-582-34439-6(5)) Pearson ESL.

Rogers, Kirby. Operation Dewey. 2002. (Illus.). ix, 100p. (J). pap. (978-1-877633-65-2(8)) Luthers.

Roy, Ron. The Goose's Gold. Gurney, John Steven, illus. (A to Z Mysteries Ser.: No. 7). 96p. (gr. k-3). 1999. lib. bdg. 11.99 (978-0-679-99078-9(X)); 1998. (J). mass mkt. 3.99 (978-0-679-89078-2(5)) Random Hse. Children's Bks. (Random Hse. Bks. for Young Readers).

—The Goose's Gold. Gurney, John Steven, illus. 1999. (A to Z Mysteries Ser.: No. 7). (J). (gr. k-3). 10.79 (978-0-606-15977-7(0)); lib. bdg. 11.80 (978-0-613-11591-9(0)) Tandem Library Bks.

Rubel, Nicole. It's Hot & Cold in Miami. 2006. (Illus.). 208p. (J). 17.00 (978-0-374-33611-0(3)) Farrar, Straus & Giroux.

Rust, Ann O'Connell. Nonie of the Everglades. Rust, Allen F., ed. 1998. 72p. (J). (gr. 4-7). pap. 7.95 (978-1-883203-04-7(X)) Amaro Bks.

—Walking with Irma. 1999. 248p. pap. 14.95 (978-1-883203-05-4(8)) Amaro Bks.

Sabina, C. Frosted August. 2007. 128p. (YA). per. 10.95 (***978-0-595-44636-0(1)**) iUniverse, Inc.

Samantha's Florida Adventure. 1998. (Illus.). 2p. (J). (ps-1). 15.00 (978-1-888074-86-4(8)) Pockets of Learning.

Schraff, Anne. The Terrible Orchid Sky. 2001. (PageTurner Adventure Ser.). 80p. (YA). per. 3.95 (978-1-56254-185-9(4) , SP 1854) Saddleback Educational Publishing.

—Terrible Orchid Sky. 2001. (gr. 7-12). lib. bdg. 11.80 (978-0-613-33129-6(X)) Tandem Library Bks.

Schrecengost, Maity. Tasso of Tarpon Springs. Stock, Rose, illus. 1998. 118p. (J). (gr. 3-6). pap. 5.95 (978-0-929895-24-6(X) , Hoot Owl Bks.) Maupin Hse. Publishing.

Scott, James W. The Thumbtwiddlers of Twiddlewickham. Scott, James W., illus. 2002. (Illus.). 32p. (J). 6.99 (978-0-9719868-0-0(0)) Scott, J & N Pubs.

Scott, Kieran. Brunettes Strike Back. (YA). 2007. 272p. (gr. 7). pap. 7.99 (978-0-14-240778-3(X) , Puffin); 2006. 256p. (gr. 5). 16.99 (978-0-399-24493-3(X) , Putnam Juvenile) Penguin Group (USA) Inc.

Scott, Kieran. I Was a Non-Blonde Cheerleader. 2007. 272p. (YA). (gr. 7). 7.99 (***978-0-14-240910-7(3)** , Puffin) Penguin Group (USA) Inc.

Sdoia-Satz, Phyllis & Satz, Barry. The Husky Gang Tales. 2002. 21.95 incl. audio compact disk (978-0-7579-9918-5(2) , Warner Bros. Pubns.) Alfred Publishing Co., Inc.

Secrets at Pine Haven: Civil War Comes to Florida. 2006. (Illus.). 180p. (J). per. 12.95 (978-1-878398-75-8(X) , Blue Note Bks.) Blue Note Pubns.

Settle, Sally. In the Shadow of the Lone Cypress: One Man's Florida. 2003. 360p. (YA). per. 14.95 (978-0-9707267-3-5(2)) Bluefish Bay Publishing.

Shaw, Marilyn Bishop. Solomon. 2006. 203p. (J). 14.95 (978-1-56164-349-3(1)) Pineapple Pr., Inc.

Shearin, Effie Mae. Pedro Menendez: The Adelantado of Florida. 2005. (Illus.). pap. 7.95 (978-0-9773506-0-5(6)) Dolly Dimple Ink Children's Bks.

Shepperson, Jacqueline. Martins of the Everglades. 2007. (ENG.). 152p. per. 19.95 (***978-1-4241-5446-3(4)**) PublishAmerica, Inc.

Siegelson, Kim L. Escape South. Jackson, Shelley, illus. 2004. (Road to Reading Ser.). 80p. (J). (gr. k-3). pap. 3.99 (978-0-307-26504-3(8) , Random Hse. Bks. for Young Readers) Random Hse. Children's Bks.

—Escape South. 2000. (J). 10.79 (978-0-606-18931-6(9)) Tandem Library Bks.

Skelton, Vonda Skinner. Bitsy & the Mystery at Amelia Island. 2005. (Bitsy Burroughs Mysteries Ser.). 183p. (J). 15.95 (978-1-57072-306-3(0) , Silver Dagger Mysteries) Overmountain Pr.

Smith, Patrick. Land Remembered. 2001. (gr. 5-8). lib. bdg. 16.40 (978-0-613-55622-4(4)) Tandem Library Bks.

Smith, Patrick D. A Land Remembered, 2 vols. 2001. (Illus.). Vol. 1. 240p. (J). (gr. 5-12). pap., stu. ed. 7.95 (978-1-56164-223-6(1)); Vol. 1. 240p. (gr. 5-12). stu. ed. 14.95 (978-1-56164-230-4(4)); Vol. 2. 200p. (J). pap., stu. ed. 7.95 (978-1-56164-224-3(X)); Vol. 2. 200p. (J). (gr. 5-12). stu. ed. 14.95 (978-1-56164-231-1(2)) Pineapple Pr., Inc.

Snadowsky, Daria. Anatomy of a Boyfriend. 2007. 272p. (YA). (gr. 9). 16.99 (978-0-385-73320-5(8)); 16.99 (978-0-385-90339-4(1)) Random Hse. Children's Bks. (Delacorte Bks. for Young Readers).

Sullivan, R. J. Tales of a Florida Boyhood. Voldseth, Beverly & Sullivan, Myra L., eds. rev. ed. Orig. Title: Tales of Boyhood RJL 1892-1907. (Illus.). 122p. (YA). (gr. 5 up). pap. 12.00 (978-1-887649-20-9(4)) Black Hat Pr.

Sweeney, Joyce. Head Lock. 2002. 200p. (J). (gr. 7 up). 16.95 (978-1-58837-010-5(0)) Winslow Pr.

—Spirit Window. 1999. (978-0-606-16717-8(X)) Tandem Library Bks.

—Waiting for June. 2006. 160p. 5.99 (978-0-7614-5329-1(6)) Cavendish, Marshall Corp.

Thomas, Timothy. Buddy Manatee. 2nd l.t. ed. 2001. (Buddy Manatee). (Illus.). 48p. (J). per. 12.99 (978-0-9713573-0-3(7)) Thomas Expressions, Inc.

Tomblin, Marian Strong. The Mystery at Hotel Ormond, 2004. (Illus.). 142p. (J). per. 9.95 (978-0-9766620-0-6(0)) Avery Goode-Reid Pubs.

—Where's Capone's Cash? 2005. (Illus.). 232p. (J). per. 9.95 (978-0-9766620-1-3(9)) Avery Goode-Reid Pubs.

Triana, Gaby. Cubanita. 2006. 208p. (J). pap. 7.99 (978-0-06-056022-5(3)) HarperCollins Pubs.

Tylander, Robert. Mystery at Manatee Creek. 2000. 182p. (J). pap. 11.95 (978-1-56315-204-7(5)) SterlingHouse Pubs., Inc.

Veciana-Suarez, Ana. Flight to Freedom. 2002. (First Person Fiction Ser.). 224p. (J). (gr. 6-9). pap. 16.95 (978-0-439-38199-4(1) , Orchard Bks.) Scholastic, Inc.

—Flight to Freedom. 2004. 215p. (YA). (gr. 8-12). lib. bdg. 13.64 (978-0-606-30967-7(5)) Tandem Library Bks.

Warner, Gertrude Chandler, creator. The Boxcar Children Summer Special. 2007. (Boxcar Children Mysteries Ser.). 376p. (J). pap. 7.95 (***978-0-8075-0885-5(3)**) Whitman, Albert & Co.

Waters, Zack C. Blood Moon Rider. 2006. 126p. (J). 13.95 (978-1-56164-350-9(5)) Pineapple Pr., Inc.

Weaver, Elizabeth Nixon. Rooster. 2005. 208p. (J). reprint ed. pap. 5.95 (978-0-7614-5218-8(4)) Cavendish, Marshall Corp.

Weltman, June. Mystery of the Missing Candlestick. 2004. 216p. (J). 23.95 (978-1-878044-98-3(2)) Mayhaven Publishing.

West, Tracey & Noll, Katherine. Mayhem in Miami #2. 2008. 144p. (J). (gr. 4-6). 5.99 (***978-0-448-44843-5(2)** , Grosset & Dunlap) Penguin Group (USA) Inc.

Weyn, Suzanne & Gonzalez, Diana. South Beach Sizzle. 2005. 249p. (YA). (978-1-4155-7724-0(2) , Simon Pulse) Simon & Schuster Children's Publishing.

Weyn, Suzanne & Gonzalez, Diana. South Beach Sizzle. 2005. 249p. (YA). (gr. 9-12). per. 14.45 (978-1-4176-6059-9(7)) Tandem Library Bks.

Wilsdon, Christina. An Alligator Adventure in Florida. Mayo, Frank, illus. 2006. 26p. (J). 7.99 (978-1-59939-010-9(8) , Reader's Digest Young Families, Inc.) Reader's Digest Children's Publishing, Inc.

Woods, Brenda. My Name Is Sally Little Song. 192p. (J). 2007. (gr. 2). 5.99 (***978-0-14-240943-5(X)** , Puffin); 2006. (gr. 3-6). 15.99 (978-0-399-24312-7(7) , Putnam Juvenile) Penguin Group (USA) Inc.

Yorinks, Arthur. The Miami Giant. Sendak, Maurice, illus. 1999. 36p. (J). (gr. 5-8). 16.00 (978-0-7881-6464-4(3)) DIANE Publishing Co.

FLORIDA—HISTORY

Addario, Yvonne. Treasure Diving with Captain Dom: Special Archival Section. 2007. (Illus.). 56p. (YA). per. 15.99 (***978-0-9743414-1-5(X)**) Adventure in Discovery.

Allen, Dale & Capone, Rick. Deerfield Beach, Florida. 2000. (Images of America Ser.). 128p. (J). pap. 18.99 (978-0-7385-0646-3(X)) Arcadia Publishing.

Ancona, George. Mi Familia: My Family. 2004. (Somos Latino (We Are Latinos) Ser.). 20.00 (978-0-516-23687-2(3) , Watts, Franklin) Scholastic Library Publishing.

Bentley, Altermese S. Black America: Seminole County, Florida. 2000. (Black America Ser.). 128p. (J). pap. 18.99 (978-0-7385-0634-0(6)) Arcadia Publishing.

Bial, Raymond. Missions & Presidios. 2004. (American Community Ser.). (Illus.). 48p. (J). (gr. 2-5). 29.00 (978-0-516-23708-4(X) , Children's Pr.) Scholastic Library Publishing.

Binns, Tristan Boyer. St. Augustine. (Visiting the Past Ser.). (Illus.). 32p. (J). (gr. 5-7). 2002. pap. 6.95 (978-1-58810-411-3(7) , 91184); 2001. lib. bdg. 24.22 (978-1-58810-273-7(4)) Heinemann Library.

Brown, Jonatha A. Florida. 2005. (Portraits of the States Ser.). (Illus.). 32p. (J). pap. 8.95 (978-0-8368-4641-6(9)); lib. bdg. 23.33 (978-0-8368-4622-5(2)) Stevens, Gareth Inc.

Brown, Rachel K. Daily Life in a Southern Colonial Town: St. Augustine. 2003. (J). (978-1-58417-014-3(X)); pap. (978-1-58417-077-8(8)) Lake Street Pubs.

Cannavale, Matthew C. Florida 1513-1821. 2006. (Voices from Colonial America Ser.). (Illus.). 112p. (J). (gr. 5-9). 21.95 (978-0-7922-6409-5(6)); 32.90 (978-0-7922-6866-6(0)) National Geographic Society. (National Geographic Children's Bks.).

Cerulean, Susan, et al, eds. Between Two Rivers: Stories from the Red Hills to the Gulf. Meyer, Nancy, illus. 2004. 352p. (YA). per. 21.95 (978-0-9759339-0-9(6)) Red Hills Writers Project.

Coetzee, Mark M., et al. Where Art Is Happening - Artcenter/South Florida. 2003. (Illus.). 120p. (YA). (gr. 7-12). 200.00 (978-0-9719492-1-8(2)); pap. 30.00 (978-0-9719492-0-1(4)); lthr. 500.00 (978-0-9719492-2-5(0)) South Florida Art Ctr., Inc.

Cooper, Jason. Historic St. Augustine. 2000. (Historic Landmarks Ser.). (Illus.). 24p. (J). (gr. 1-4). lib. bdg. 20.64 (978-1-55916-328-6(3)) Rourke Publishing, LLC.

Crewe, Sabrina & Riehecky, Janet. The Settling of St. Augustine. 2003. (Events That Shaped America Ser.). (Illus.). 32p. (J). (gr. 3 up). lib. bdg. 24.67 (978-0-8368-3395-9(3)) Stevens, Gareth Inc.

DeGraaf, Rob L. Fat Tire Favorites: South Florida off-Road Bicycling. DeGraaf, Rob L. & DeGraaf, Rebecca L., eds. DeGraaf, Rebecca L., photos by. 2003. Orig. Title: Guide to South Florida off-Road Bicycling. (Illus.). 111p. per. 12.95 (978-0-9678385-2-6(5)) DeGraaf Publishing.

Downs, Sandra. Florida in the Civil War: A State in Turmoil. 2001. (Single Titles Ser.). (Illus.). 80p. (J). (gr. 8 up). lib. bdg. 25.90 (978-0-7613-1973-3(5) , Millbrook Pr.) Lerner Publishing Group.

Fairbanks, George R. George Rainsford. History of Florida from Its Discovery by Ponce de Leon, in 1512, to the Close of the Florida War, In 1842, 5 vols. 2006. (Illus.). (YA). cd-rom (978-1-892824-22-6(1)) AFCHRON.

Florida Activity & Coloring Book. 2001. (978-0-9715160-0-7(6)) Coloring Bks. 'N Stuff.

Florida's Women's Heritage Trail. (Heritage Trail Ser.). (J). (ps-7). pap. 2.40 (978-1-889030-19-7(8)) Florida Div. of Historical Resources.

Friend, Sandra. Florida. Filippucci, Laura, illus. 2004. 32p. (J). 16.95 (978-1-57091-444-7(3)) Charlesbridge Publishing, Inc.

—Florida. Filipucci, Laura, tr. Filipucci, Laura, illus. 2004. 32p. (J). pap. 6.95 (978-1-57091-445-4(1)) Charlesbridge Publishing, Inc.

Gallagher, Jim. Hernando de Soto & the Exploration of Florida. 1999. (Explorers of the New World Ser.). (Illus.). 63p. (J). (gr. 4 up). 31.00 (978-0-7910-5512-0(4), Chelsea Hse.) Facts On File, Inc.

Harcourt School Publishers Staff. Historic St. Augustine. 3rd ed. 2002. (Horizons Ser.). (Illus.). (J). pap. 3.70 (978-0-15-333216-6(6)) Harcourt Schl. Pubs.

Hemmel, David Lee & Knutson, Janette C. Alexis' Island: Growing up in the Tropical Paradise of Key West. 2006. (J). per. 14.95 (978-0-9745637-2-5(2)) Duval Publishing.

Isaacs, Sally Senzell. Life in St. Augustine. (Picture the Past Ser.). (Illus.). 32p. (J). 2003. lib. bdg. (978-1-58810-694-0(2)); 2002. (gr. 1-3). pap. 7.50 (978-1-4034-0526-5(3)) Heinemann Library.

—Life in St. Augustine. 2003. (J). (gr. k-3). lib. bdg. 15.25 (978-0-613-67337-2(9)) Tandem Library Bks.

Jenkins, Lizzie L. P. R. The Real Rosewood. 2003. per. 24.95 (978-0-9724926-3-8(1), 0-9724926-3-1) Book-ends Pr.

Kennedy, Patricia. Miami Beach in Vintage Postcards, Florida. 2000. (Postcard History Ser.). (Illus.). 128p. (J). pap. 18.99 (978-0-7385-0644-9(3)) Arcadia Publishing.

—Miami in Vintage Postcards, Florida. 2000. (Postcard History Ser.). 128p. pap. 18.99 (978-0-7385-0643-2(5)) Arcadia Publishing.

Knotts, Bob. All Around Floirda. 2002. (State Studies). (Illus.). 48p. (J). pap. 8.50 (978-1-4034-0563-0(8)) Heinemann Library.

—Florida, 6 bks., Set. 2003. (Heinemann State Studies). (J). (gr. 3-5). lib. bdg. 162.42 (978-1-58810-553-0(9)) Heinemann Library.

—Florida History. 2002. (State Studies). (Illus.). 48p. (J). lib. bdg. (978-1-4034-0347-6(3)) Heinemann Library.

—Florida History. 2003. (gr. 3-6). lib. bdg. 17.05 (978-0-613-60872-5(0)) Tandem Library Bks.

—Florida Native Peoples. 2002. (State Studies). (Illus.). 48p. (J). pap. 8.50 (978-1-4034-0564-7(6)); (gr. 3-5). lib. bdg. (978-1-4034-0348-3(1)) Heinemann Library.

—People of Florida. 2002. (Heinemann State Studies). (Illus.). 48p. (J). (gr. 3-5). lib. bdg. (978-1-4034-0349-0(X)) Heinemann Library.

Kurtti, Jeff. Walt Disney's Legends of Imagineering & the Genesis of the Disney Theme Park. Gordon, Bruce, illus. 2008. 160p. 35.00 (978-0-7868-5559-9(2), Disney Editions) Disney Pr.

Lilly, Melinda. St. Augustine. 2003. (Rourke Discovery Library). (Illus.). 24p. (gr. 1-4). 14.95 (978-1-58952-368-5(7)) Rourke Publishing, LLC.

Marsh, Carole. Florida History Projects: 30 Cool, Activities, Crafts, Experiments & More for Kids to Do to Learn about Your State! 2003. (Florida Experience Ser.). 32p. (gr. k-5). pap. 5.95 (978-0-635-01778-9(4), Marsh, Carole Bks.) Gallopade International.

—My First Pocket Guide Florida. 2000. (Florida Experience! Ser.). (Illus.). 96p. (J). (gr. 3-8). 12.95 (978-0-635-01299-9(5), 12995) Gallopade International.

Marx, Trish. Everglades Forever. Karp, Cindy, illus. Karp, Cindy, photos by. 2004. 40p. (J). 17.95 (978-1-58430-164-6(3)) Lee & Low Bks., Inc.

Maynard, Charles W. Castillo de San Marcos. 2002. (Famous Forts Throughout American History Ser.). (Illus.). 24p. (J). (gr. 3). lib. bdg. 18.75 (978-0-8239-5841-2(8), PowerKids Pr.) Rosen Publishing Group, Inc., The.

McCarthy, Kevin M. Native Americans in Florida. 1999. (Illus.). 216p. (J). (gr. 3-7). 25.95 (978-1-56164-181-9(2)); pap. 18.95 (978-1-56164-182-6(0)) Pineapple Pr., Inc.

Mountjoy, Shane. St. Augustine. 2007. (Colonial Settlements in America Ser.). 104p. (J). (gr. 5-8). 30.00 (***978-0-7910-9337-5(9)***, Chelsea Hse.) Facts On File, Inc.

Quasha, Jennifer. How to Draw Floridas Sights & Symbols. 2002. (Kids Guide to Drawing America Ser.). 32p. (J). lib. bdg. 25.25 (978-0-8239-6064-4(1), PowerKids Pr.) Rosen Publishing Group, Inc., The.

Riehecky, Janet. The Settling of St. Augustine. 2003. (Landmark Events in American History Ser.). (Illus.). 48p. (J). (gr. 5 up). pap. 14.95 (978-0-8368-5404-6(7)); lib. bdg. 30.00 (978-0-8368-5376-6(8)) Stevens, Gareth Inc. (World Almanac Library).

Ruffin, Frances E. St. Augustine. 2006. (Illus.). 24p. (J). pap. 5.95 (978-0-8368-6419-9(0)); lib. bdg. 19.33 (978-0-8368-6412-0(3)) Stevens, Gareth Inc.

Sutcliffe, Jane. Juan Ponce de Leon. 2006. (History Maker Bios Ser.). (Illus.). 48p. (J). (gr. 3-7). 26.60 (978-0-8225-2944-6(0), Lerner Pubns.) Lerner Publishing Group.

Thompson, William & Thompson, Dorcas. The Spanish Exploration of Florida. 2002. (Exploration & Discovery Ser.). (Illus.). 64p. (YA). (gr. 5 up). lib. bdg. (978-1-59084-053-5(4)) Mason Crest Pubs.

—St. Augustine. 2004. (American Forts & Their Strategic Importance Ser.). (J). (978-1-59084-715-2(6)) Mason Crest Pubs.

Vollstadt, Elizabeth Weiss. Florida. 2001. (Seeds of a Nation Ser.). (Illus.). 48p. (J). (gr. 3-5). 23.70 (978-0-7377-0947-6(2), LML00902-178533, Kidhaven) Thomson Gale.

War Comes to Florida's Northern Gulf Coast. 2002. (Illus.). 208p. lib. bdg. 40.00 (978-0-9724101-0-6(4)) New Hope Pr.

Weitzel, Kelley G. The Timucua Indians: A Native American Detective Story. 2000. (UPF Young Readers Library). (Illus.). 176p. (gr. 4-7). pap. 12.95 (978-0-8130-1738-9(6)) Univ. Pr. of Florida.

FLORISTS DESIGNS

see Flower Arrangement

FLOWER ARRANGEMENT

Sato, Shozo & Sato, Alice Ogura. Ikebana. 2004. (Asian Arts & Crafts for Creative Kids Ser.). (Illus.). 64p. 12.95 (978-0-8048-3502-2(0)) Tuttle Publishing.

Tarbox, Charlene. Beautiful Flower Arrangements. 2004. (Illus.). 32p. (J). pap. 3.95 (978-0-486-43697-5(7)) Dover Pubns., Inc.

FLOWER GARDENING

Here are entered works on the cultivation of flowering plants for either commercial or private purposes.

see also Flowers; House Plants; Plant Propagation

The Flower Garden: Individual Title Two-Packs. (Chiquilibros Ser.). (ps-1). 12.00 (978-0-7635-8530-3(0)) Rigby Education.

El Jardin de Flores: Individual Title, 2 Packs. (Chiquilibros Ser.). (SPA.). (ps-1). 12.00 (978-0-7635-8550-1(5)) Rigby Education.

Maurer, Tracy. Growing Flowers. 2000. (Green Thumb Guides Ser.). (Illus.). 24p. (J). (gr. 2-6). lib. bdg. 23.93 (978-1-55916-251-7(1)) Rourke Publishing, LLC.

O'Brien, Joan. Flower Garden Sticker Activity Book. 2000. (Dover Little Activity Bks.). 4p. (J). pap. 1.50 (978-0-486-40983-2(X)) Dover Pubns., Inc.

Otten, Jack. Watch Me Plant a Garden. (Welcome Bks.). (Illus.). 24p. (J). (ps-2). 2002. pap. 4.95 (978-0-516-23593-6(1)); 2001. 18.00 (978-0-516-23945-3(7)) Scholastic Library Publishing. (Children's Pr.).

—Watch Me Plant a Garden. 2002. (gr. k-3). lib. bdg. 12.95 (978-0-613-58814-0(2)) Tandem Library Bks.

Pupeza, Lori K. Flower Gardens. 2002. (Gardening Ser.). (Illus.). 32p. (J). (gr. k-6). lib. bdg. 22.78 (978-1-57765-031-7(X), Checkerboard Library) ABDO Publishing Co.

Roman, Bobbi. Walking in Grandma's Garden. Kirsch, Lorelei, illus. 1999. 32p. (Orig.). (J). (ps-6). pap. 16.95 (978-0-9668846-0-9(4)) Stargazer.

Saunders, Gail. Leaves. 1998. (Growing Flowers Ser.). 24p. (J). pap. 13.25 (978-0-516-21323-1(7), Children's Pr.) Scholastic Library Publishing.

—Seeds. 1998. (Growing Flowers Ser.). (Illus.). 24p. (J). (ps-3). pap. 13.25 (978-0-516-21324-8(5), Children's Pr.) Scholastic Library Publishing.

—Stems. 1998. (Growing Flowers Ser.). 24p. (J). (gr. k-2). pap. 13.25 (978-0-516-21325-5(3), Children's Pr.) Scholastic Library Publishing.

Saunders-Smith, Gail. Growing Flowers, 4 bks., Set. 1998. (J). 56.00 (978-0-516-29739-2(2), Children's Pr.) Scholastic Library Publishing.

Stone, Lynn M. Flowers. 2002. (Harvest to Home Ser.). (Illus.). 24p. (J). (gr. 2-5). 14.95 (978-1-58952-127-8(7)) Rourke Publishing, LLC.

FLOWER PAINTING AND ILLUSTRATION

Baumbusch, Brigitte. Flowers in Art. 2005. (Illus.). 32p. (J). 22.00 (978-0-8368-4447-4(5)) Stevens, Gareth Inc.

Muehlenhardt, Amy Bailey. Drawing & Learning about Fish: Using Shapes & Lines. Muehlenhardt, Amy Bailey, illus. 2005. (Sketch It! Ser.). (Illus.). 24p. (J). (ps-k). lib. bdg. 22.60 (978-1-4048-1192-8(3), 1243856) Picture Window Bks.

Noble, Marty. Color Your Own Great Flower Paintings. 2004. (Dover Coloring Bks.). (Illus.). 32p. pap. 3.95 (978-0-486-43335-6(8)) Dover Pubns., Inc.

Samuel, Anna. Flower Paintings: 16 Art Stickers. Grafton, Carol Belanger, ed. 2004. (Illus.). 4p. pap. 1.50 (978-0-486-43070-6(7)) Dover Pubns., Inc.

Tarbox, Charlene. Color Your Own Great Flower Prints. 2001. (Dover Coloring Bks.). (Illus.). 32p. (J). pap. 3.95 (978-0-486-41553-6(8)) Dover Pubns., Inc.

Tarbox, Charlene. Floral Beauty Coloring Book. 2006. 96p. (J). pap. 7.95 (***978-0-486-45922-6(5)***) Dover Pubns., Inc.

FLOWERS

see also Flower Arrangement; Flower Gardening; Flower Painting and Illustration; Plants; State Flowers; Wild Flowers

Aloian, Molly & Kalman, Bobbie. El Ciclo de vida de la Flor. 2006. (SPA., Illus.). 32p. (gr. 2-3). pap. (978-0-7787-8717-4(6)) Crabtree Publishing Co.

—The Life Cycle of a Flower. 2004. (Life Cycle Ser.). (Illus.). 32p. (J). (978-0-7787-0667-0(2)); pap. (978-0-7787-0697-7(4)) Crabtree Publishing Co.

Ayers, Patricia. A Kids Guide to How Flowers Grow. 2000. (Digging in the Dirt Ser.). 24p. (J). (gr. 2-4). lib. bdg. 18.75 (978-0-8239-5462-9(5), PowerKids Pr.) Rosen Publishing Group, Inc., The.

Barker, Cicely Mary. Flower Fairies Sticker Book. 1998. (Flower Fairies Collection). (Illus.). 24p. (J). pap. 7.99 (978-0-7232-4377-9(8), Warne) Penguin Group (USA) Inc.

Blackaby, Susan. Buds & Blossoms: A Book about Flowers. DeLage, Charlene, illus. 2004. (Growing Things Ser.). 24p. (C). (gr. k-2). 22.60 (978-1-4048-0112-7(X)) Picture Window Bks.

Bodach, Vijaya. Flowers. 2007. (Illus.). 24p. (J). 19.93 (978-0-7368-6342-1(7), Pebble Bks.) Capstone Pr., Inc.

Boyston, Angela. Flowers, Fruits & Seeds. 1999. (Plants Ser.). (Illus.). 32p. (J). (gr. k-3). lib. bdg. 21.36 (978-1-57572-822-3(2)) Heinemann Library.

Branigan, Carrie & Dunne, Richard. Flowers & Seeds. 2005. (World of Plants Ser.). (Illus.). 31p. (J). (gr. 2-5). lib. bdg. 27.10 (978-1-58340-612-0(3)) Smart Apple Media.

Burton, Jane & Taylor, Kim. The Nature & Science of Flowers. Burton, Jane & Taylor, Kim, photos by. 1998. (Exploring the Science of Nature Ser.). (Illus.). 32p. (J). (gr. 3 up). lib. bdg. 23.93 (978-0-8368-2106-2(8)) Stevens, Gareth Inc.

¿Como Crecen las Flores? (Coleccion Primeros Pasos en la Ciencia). (SPA.). (J). (gr. 1-3). 3.16 (978-950-724-014-0(4), LMA8216) Lumen ARG. *Dist:* Lectorum Pubns., Inc.

Corwin, Judith Hoffman. Bright Yellow Flower. 2003. (Illus.). (J). (978-0-439-44162-9(5)) Scholastic, Inc.

Court, Rob. How to Draw Things in Nature. 2007. (Doodle Bks.). 32p. (J). 21.36 (***978-1-59296-807-7(4)***) Child's World, Inc.

Dickens, Paulette. My Little Handbook of Flowers. Dickens, Paulette, illus. 2001. (Illus.). 14p. (J). pap. 9.95 (978-0-9711564-4-9(1)) Pendleton Publishing, Inc.

Dorling Kindersley Publishing Staff. Garden Flowers. 2006. (Ultimate Sticker Bks.). 16p. (J). pap. 6.99 (978-0-7566-2099-8(6)) Dorling Kindersley Publishing, Inc.

Dover. Flowers. 2007. (Dover Pictura Ser.). (Illus.). 128p. pap. 39.95 (***978-0-486-99887-9(8)***) Dover Pubns., Inc.

Dwyer, Jacqueline. Flowers. 2001. (PowerKids Readers Ser.). (Illus.). 24p. (J). (gr. 1). lib. bdg. 16.00 (978-0-8239-5677-7(6), PKFLOW, PowerKids Pr.) Rosen Publishing Group, Inc., The.

Edwards, Nicola. Flowers. 2007. (J). lib. bdg. (978-1-4042-3699-8(6)) Rosen Publishing Group, Inc., The.

Farndon, John. Flowering Plants. 2004. (Illus.). 32p. (J). 23.70 (978-1-4103-0121-5(4), Blackbirch Pr., Inc.) Thomson Gale.

—Flowers. 2005. 24p. (J). (gr. 2-4). (Illus.). 23.70 (978-1-4103-0423-0(X)); pap. 22.45 (978-1-4103-0517-6(1)) Thomson Gale. (Blackbirch Pr., Inc.).

La Flor. 2003. 23.95 (978-0-673-77772-0(3)) Celebration Pr.

Flowers: 6 Each of 1 Student Book, 6 vols. (Sunshinetm Science Ser.). 24p. (gr. 1-2). 41.95 (978-0-7802-2684-5(4)) Wright Group, The.

Flowers: Big Book. (Sunshinetm Science Ser.). 24p. (gr. 1-2). 37.50 (978-0-7802-2776-7(X)) Wright Group, The.

Flowers & Fruit Sets: 1 Each of 3 Big Books. (Sunshinetm Science Ser.). (gr. 1-2). 111.50 (978-0-7802-2818-4(9)) Wright Group, The.

Flowers & Fruit Sets: 1 Each of 3 Student Books. (Sunshinetm Science Ser.). (gr. 1-2). 20.95 (978-0-7802-2819-1(7)) Wright Group, The.

Flowers, Pam. Douggie's Story. Rubin, David, illus. 2007. (J). pap. (***978-0-88240-655-8(8)***, Alaska Northwest Bks.) Graphic Arts Ctr. Publishing Co.

Flowers Set F, 6 vols. (Phonics Readers Ser.). (gr. k-2). 28.95 (978-0-7368-4077-4(X)) Red Brick Learning.

Fowler, Allan. It Could Still Be a Flower. 2001. (Rookie Read-About Science Ser.). (Illus.). 32p. (J). (gr. 1-2). pap. 4.95 (978-0-516-27308-2(6)); 19.50 (978-0-516-21681-2(3)) Scholastic Library Publishing. (Children's Pr.).

—It Could Still Be a Flower. 2001. (gr. k-3). lib. bdg. 12.95 (978-0-613-54583-9(4)) Tandem Library Bks.

Gamman, Tonya M. The Flowers Secret. Williams, Jennifer & Gamman, Paul, eds. Devine, Rachella, illus. 2002. (Seven Little Secrets: Vol. 1). 22p. (J). (gr. k-3). pap. 7.95 (978-0-9667511-0-9(8), 101) New-Swan Bks.

Gierecke, Ernestine. Flowers. 1999. (Outside My Window Ser.). (Illus.). 24p. (J). (gr. 1-3). lib. bdg. 21.36 (978-1-57572-683-0(1)) Heinemann Library.

Green, John. The Language of Flowers Coloring Book. 2004. (Dover Coloring Bks.). (Illus.). 32p. (J). pap. 3.95 (978-0-486-43035-5(9)) Dover Pubns., Inc.

Greenfield Educational Center Staff. A Flower. 2000. (I Can Read Ser.: Bk. 9). (CHI & ENG., Illus.). 8p. (J). pap. 2.99 (978-962-563-111-0(9)); pap. 24.99 (978-962-563-289-6(1)) Greenfield Enterprises, Ltd. HKG. *Dist:* Cheng & Tsui Co.

Grieveson, Margaret. Flowers & Seeds. 2005. (Illus.). 32p. (J). (gr. 3-7). lib. bdg. 27.10 (978-1-59604-039-7(4)) Stargazer Bks.

Growing Flowers Set. (gr. k-2). 114.95 (978-0-7368-9051-9(3)) Red Brick Learning.

Helbrough, Emma. How Flowers Grow. 2004. (Beginners Ser.). 32p. (J). (gr. 1 up). pap. 4.95 (978-0-7945-0382-6(9)); lib. bdg. 12.95 (978-1-58086-508-1(9)) EDC Publishing.

Helbrough, Emma. How Flowers Grow (Level 1) - Internet Referenced. 2007. (Beginners Nature Ser.). 32p. (J). 4.99 (***978-0-7945-1340-5(9)***, Usborne) EDC Publishing.

Heller, Ruth. Motivo de una Flor (Reason for a Flower) (SPA.). (J). 8.95 (978-968-419-959-0(7)) Grijalbo, Editorial MEX. *Dist:* AIMS International Bks., Inc.

—The Reason for a Flower. 1999. (Ruth Heller's World of Nature Ser.). (Illus.). 48p. (J). (ps-3). pap. 6.99 (978-0-698-11559-0(7), Putnam Juvenile) Penguin Group (USA) Inc.

—The Reason for a Flower. (FRE.). (J). 6.99 (978-0-590-71999-5(8)) Scholastic, Inc.

Hewitt, Sally. Plants & Flowers. 1999. (Illus.). 30p. (J). (gr. k-3). lib. bdg. 15.25 (978-0-613-37507-8(6)) Tandem Library Bks.

Hirschmann, Kris. Sea Anemones. 2005. (Creatures of the Sea Ser.). (Illus.). 48p. (J). (ps-8). lib. bdg. 26.20 (978-0-7377-3009-8(9), Greenhaven Pr., Inc.) Thomson Gale.

Holmes, Anita. Flowers & Friends. 2000. (We Can Read about Nature! Ser.). (Illus.). 32p. (J). (gr. 1-2). lib. bdg. 21.36 (978-0-7614-1113-0(5), Benchmark Bks.) Cavendish, Marshall Corp.

Honey Bees & Flowers, 6 vols. (gr. k-2). 28.95 (978-0-7368-8243-9(X)) Red Brick Learning.

Howell, Laura. Little book of flowers - internet Linked. 2005. 64p. (J). 7.95 (978-0-7945-1086-2(8), Usborne) EDC Publishing.

Huggins-Cooper, Lynn. Plants & Flowers. McNicholas, Shelagh & Burroughs, Dave, trs. McNicholas, Shelagh & Burroughs, Dave, illus. 2004. 30p. (J). lib. bdg. (978-1-58340-447-8(3)) Smart Apple Media.

Ichikawa, Satomi. Rosy's Garden. (Illus.). (J). (978-0-399-22388-4(6), Philomel) Penguin Group (USA) Inc.

Jensen, Karl. Flowers for Grandma. 2002. (Windows on Literacy Ser.). (Illus.). 12p. (J). (978-0-7922-8457-4(7)) National Geographic Society.

Kababik, Dana. From Bulb to Flower. 2003. (Grow up! Ser.). (J). (978-1-58417-175-1(8)) Lake Street Pubs.

—From Seed to Flower. 2003. (Grow up! Ser.). (J). (978-1-58417-170-6(7)); pap. (978-1-58417-176-8(6)) Lake Street Pubs.

Keyes, Daniel. Flores para Algernon (Flowers for Algernon) (SPA.). 98p. (J). 11.95 (978-84-348-5274-7(8)) SM Ediciones ESP. *Dist:* AIMS International Bks., Inc.

Klutz Press Staff, contrib. by. Squashing Flowers, Squeezing Leaves: A Nature Press & Book. 2001. (Illus.). 48p. (J). (gr. 4-7). spiral bd. 19.95 (978-1-57054-591-7(X)) Klutz.

Knudsen, Natalie S. A Child's Garden of Flowers. Graham, Margaret Ann Baker, ed. Case, Teena Martin, illus. 2001. 64p. (J). lib. bdg. 9.95 (978-0-9710093-0-1(9)) Reiman Gardens.

Lloyd, Sue & Wernham, Sara. Jolly Phonics Tricky Word Wall Flowers (Precursive Letters) Stephen, Lib, illus. 2002. (Jolly Phonics Ser.). (J). 16.50 (978-1-903619-11-7(4), JL114) Jolly Learning, Ltd. GBR. *Dist:* American International Distribution Corp.

Loves, June. Flowers. 2004. (Plants Ser.). (Illus.). 32p. (J). (gr. 2-4). 23.00 (978-0-7910-8265-2(2), Chelsea Hse.) Facts On File, Inc.

Mattern, Joanne. How Tulips Grow. 2006. (ENG & SPA., Illus.). 24p. (J). 19.33 (978-0-8368-6465-6(4)) Stevens, Gareth Inc.

—How Tulips Grow: Como Crecen Los Tulipanes. 2006. (ENG & SPA., Illus.). 24p. (J). pap. (978-0-8368-6472-4(7), Weekly Reader Early Learning Library) Stevens, Gareth Inc.

McEvoy, Paul. Flowers. 2003. (Plant Facts Ser.). (Illus.). 24p. (J). (gr. 2-4). 23.00 (978-0-7910-7290-5(8), Chelsea Hse.) Facts On File, Inc.

Mettler, Ren'e. La Flor. (Coleccion Mundo Maravilloso). (SPA., Illus.). 40p. (J). (978-84-348-3537-5(1), FL9916) SM Ediciones ESP. *Dist:* Lectorum Pubns., Inc.

Miles, L. Flowers Sticker Book. 2004. (Spotter's Guides Sticker Bks.). (Illus.). 32p. (J). (gr. 2 up). pap. 7.95 (978-0-7945-0189-1(3), Usborne) EDC Publishing.

Miles, Lisa, ed. Flowers Sticker Book. 1998. (Spotter's Guides Sticker Bks.). (Illus.). 24p. (YA). (gr. 2 up). pap. 7.95 (978-0-7460-2997-8(7)) EDC Publishing.

Mitchell, Melanie S. Flowers. 2003. (First Step Nonfiction Ser.). (Illus.). 8p. (J). pap. 3.95 (978-0-8225-3917-9(9), Lerner Pubns.) Lerner Publishing Group.

—Tulips. (First Step Nonfiction Ser.). (Illus.). (gr. k-2). 2005. 24p. lib. bdg. 17.27 (978-0-8225-4614-6(0)); 2003. 23p. (J). pap. 5.95 (978-0-8225-4615-3(9), Lerner Pubns.) Lerner Publishing Group.

Morgan, Sally. Flowers, Fruits & Seeds. (Looking at Plants Ser.). (Illus.). 32p. (J). lib. bdg. 24.25 (978-1-931983-10-5(0)) Chrysalis Education.

Mullican, Judy. The Flowers. Meier, Kerry L., illus. l.t. ed. 2003. (HRL Big Book Ser.). 8p. (Orig.). (J). (ps-k). pap. 10.95 (978-1-57332-255-3(5)); pap. 10.95 (978-1-57332-256-0(3)) HighReach Learning, Inc.

Paine, Penelope C. Gift of Flowers. Maeno, Itoko, illus. 2006. 24p. per. 5.95 (978-0-9707944-5-1(2)) Paper Posie.

Pascoe, Elaine. Flowers. 2003. (Illus.). 48p. (J). 24.95 (978-1-56711-432-4(6), Blackbirch Pr., Inc.) Thomson Gale.

Picture Window Books, contrib. by. Bud & Blossoms. (Growing Things Ser.). 24p. (J). pap. 7.95 (978-1-4048-0388-6(2)) Picture Window Bks.

Piluso, Piero, illus. Friendly Flowers. 2003. (Dora the Explorer Ser.). 16p. (J). (ps-2). pap. 3.99 (978-0-307-10288-1(2), Golden Bks.) Random Hse. Children's Bks.

Plants & Flowers of Desert. (Butterfly Bks.). (ARA., Illus.). 32p. (J). (gr. 3-5). 8.95 (978-0-86685-402-3(9), LDL252) International Bk. Ctr., Inc.

Renaud, Anne. A Bloom of Friendship: The Story of the Canadian Tulip Festival. Spires, Ashley, illus. 2005. 24p. pap. (978-1-897073-35-3(6)) Lobster Pr.

Richardson, Joy. Flowers. 2005. (Illus.). 32p. (J). lib. bdg. 23.33 (978-0-8368-4504-4(8)) Stevens, Gareth Inc.

Rohrer, Martha. Flowers, Flowers, Flowers. 2004. (Illus.). 32p. (ps-5). 1.70 (978-0-7399-2350-4(1), 2952) Rod & Staff Pubs., Inc.

Royston, Angela. Flowers. (Illus.). 32p. (YA). (gr. 2 up). lib. bdg. 27.10 (978-1-932333-39-8(8)) Chrysalis Education.

Saunders, Gail. Flowers. 1998. 24p. (J). (gr. k-2). pap. 13.25 (978-0-516-21322-4(9), Children's Pr.) Scholastic Library Publishing.

Schaefer, Lola M. Pick, Pull, Snap! Where Once a Flower Bloomed. George, Lindsay B., illus. 2003. 32p. (J). 15.99 (978-0-688-17834-5(0)) HarperCollins Pubs.

—This Is the Sunflower. Crews, Donald, illus. 2000. 24p. (J). (ps up). 15.99 (978-0-688-16413-3(7)) HarperCollins Pubs.

Schaub, Michelle. Honeybees Help Flowers. 2006. (Early Explorers Ser.). (J). 36.00 (***978-1-4108-6122-1(8)***) Benchmark Education Co.

School Specialty Publishing. Flowers. 2004. (On-File Ser.). 4p. (J). (gr. 1-2). ring bd. 4.99 (978-0-7424-2896-6(6), Instructional Fair) Schaffer, Frank Pubns.

Schwartz, David M. Among the Flowers. Kuhn, Dwight, photos by. 1999. (Springboards into Science Ser.). (Illus.). 24p. (J). (gr. 1 up). lib. bdg. 19.93 (978-0-8368-2241-0(2)) Stevens, Gareth Inc.

Sian Flowering Plants. 2004. (J). (978-1-59242-030-8(3)) Delta Education, LLC.

Snedden, Robert. Flowers. 2007. (J). (***978-1-59920-078-1(3)***) Smart Apple Media.

Soffer, Ruth. Butterflies & Flowers to Paint or Color. 2005. 48p. (J). (gr. 3). pap. 4.95 (978-0-486-44496-3(1)) Dover Pubns., Inc.

—The Flower Garden Coloring Book. 2005. (Illus.). 32p. (J). (gr. 3-3). pap. 3.95 (978-0-486-44497-0(X)) Dover Pubns., Inc.

Souza, D.M. Freaky Flowers. 2002. (Illus.). 63p. (J). (gr. 4-7). lib. bdg. 17.60 (978-0-613-53812-1(9)) Tandem Library Bks.

Souza, Dorothy M. Freaky Flowers. 2002. (Watts Library). (Illus.). (J). (gr. 5-7). 63p. pap. 8.95 (978-0-531-16221-7(4)); 64p. 25.50 (978-0-531-11981-5(5)) Scholastic Library Publishing. (Watts, Franklin).

Spilsbury, Louise & Spilsbury, Richard. Why Do Plants Have Flowers? 2005. (World of Plants Ser.). (Illus.). 32p. (J). (978-1-4034-7363-9(3)); pap. (978-1-4034-7368-4(4)) Heinemann.

Sterling Publishing Co., Inc. & Arena Verlag. Kids' Flower Mandalas. 2005. (Illus.). 64p. pap. 4.95 (978-1-4027-1803-8(9)) Sterling Publishing Co., Inc.

Stone, Lynn M. Flowers. 2008. (J). ***(978-1-60044-551-4(9));*** 2002. (Illus.). 24p. (gr. 2-5). 14.95 (978-1-58952-127-8(7)) Rourke Publishing, LLC.

Stoutland, Allison. Take a Deep Breath: Little Lessons from Flowers for a Happier World. Hofher, Cathy, illus. l.t. ed. 2003. 32p. 14.95 (978-0-9670941-2-0(7)) Inch By Inch Pubns., LLC.

Tenenbaum, Frances. Wildflowers. Savage, Virginia, illus. 2003. (Peterson Field Guide Coloring Bks.). 64p. pap. 7.95 (978-0-618-30735-7(4)) Houghton Mifflin Co. Trade & Reference Div.

Time-Life Staff. Flowers & Trees. 1999. (Illus.). 88p. (J). (gr. 1-4). 14.95 (978-0-8094-4857-9(2)) Time-Life, Inc.

Turner. All Kinds of Flowers. 1999. (Illus.). (J). bds. (978-0-7398-2450-4(3)); pap. 4.93 (978-0-7398-2413-9(9)) Steck-Vaughn.

—Every Flower is Beautiful. 1999. (Illus.). (J). pap. 4.93 (978-0-7398-2412-2(0)) Steck-Vaughn.

—Every Flower Is Beautiful. 1999. (J). bds. (978-0-7398-2449-8(X)) Steck-Vaughn.

Tuxworth, Nicola & Lorenz Editors. Flowers. 2002. (Let's Look at Board Bks.). (Illus.). 20p. (ps-3). 5.95 (978-0-7548-1030-8(5) , Lorenz Bks.) Anness Publishing GBR. *Dist:* National Bk. Network.

Walker, Jane. Las Flores. 2001. (SPA., Illus.). 32p. (J). (ps-3). 10.95 (978-84-263-3169-4(6)) Lectorum Pubns., Inc.

Warren, Jean. Flowers. Cubley, Kathleen, ed. 1998. (Sticker Book Ser.). (Illus.). 32p. (J). (ps). pap. 3.95 (978-1-57029-219-4(1) , WPH 3709, Totline Pubns.) Schaffer, Frank Pubns.

Whitehouse, Patricia. Las Flores. 2002. (Plantas (Plants) Ser.). (SPA., Illus.). 24p. (J). (ps-1). pap. 5.25 (978-1-58810-823-4(6) , 91646) Heinemann Library.

—Flowers. 2002. (Plants Ser.). (Illus.). 24p. (J). (ps-1). pap. 5.25 (978-1-58810-729-9(9) , 91403); lib. bdg. 17.08 (978-1-58810-520-2(2)) Heinemann Library.

—Flowers. 2002. (ps-2). lib. bdg. 13.30 (978-0-613-89419-7(7)) Tandem Library Bks.

Worth, Bonnie. Oh Say Can You Seed? All about Flowering Plants. Ruiz, Aristides, illus. 2001. (Cat in the Hat's Learning Library). 48p. (J). (gr. k-3). 8.99 (978-0-375-81095-4(1) , Random Hse. Bks. for Young Readers) Random Hse. Children's Bks.

FLOWERS—ARRANGEMENT

see Flower Arrangement

FLOWERS, ARTIFICIAL

see Artificial Flowers

FLOWERS—FICTION

Adler, David A. One Yellow Daffodil: A Hanukkah Story. Bloom, Lloyd, illus. 1999. 32p. (J). (gr. 1-5). pap. 7.00 (978-0-15-202094-1(2) , Harcourt Paperbacks) Harcourt Children's Bks.

Akley, Jason. Sweet Pea & the Bumblebee. 2007. (ENG.). 36p. (J). per. 16.95 ***(978-1-4327-0341-7(2))*** Outskirts Press, Inc.

Alcott, Louisa May. Flower Fables. 2005. (Illus.). 210p. (J). (gr. 4-7). 15.95 (978-1-55709-954-9(5)) Applewood Bks.

Apperley, Dawn. Princess Rosebud: Perfectly Perfect Princess. 2007. 32p. (J). (gr. k-1). 14.99 (978-0-7641-6033-2(8)) Barron's Educational Series, Inc.

Arroyo, Andrea, illus. The Legend of the Lady Slipper. 2004. 32p. (J). (gr. k-3). reprint ed. pap. 5.95 (978-0-618-43231-8(0)) Houghton Mifflin Co. Trade & Reference Div.

Barker, Cicely Mary. Buttercup Goes to the Ball: Book, Bag & Necklace. 2005. (Flower Fairies Ser.). 24p. (J). (ps). pap. 5.99 (978-0-7232-5375-4(7) , Warne) Penguin Group (USA) Inc.

—Flower Fairies Masks & Wings Book. 2006. 24p. (J). pap. 5.99 (978-0-7232-5731-8(0) , Warne) Penguin Group (USA) Inc.

—How to Be a Flower Fairy. ed. 2005. (Flower Fairies Ser.). 32p. (J). (ps). pap. 9.99 (978-0-7232-4993-1(8) , Warne) Penguin Group (USA) Inc.

—Lavender's Midsummer Mix-up. 2006. 80p. (J). (gr. 2). 3.99 (978-0-7232-5773-8(6) , Warne) Penguin Group (USA) Inc.

—Lily's Seaside Adventure: A Flower Fairies Friends Chapter Book. 2008. (Flower Fairies Ser.). 80p. (J). (gr. 2). pap. 3.99 ***(978-0-7232-6286-2(1)*** , Warne) Penguin Group (USA) Inc.

—My Garden of Flower Fairies. 2004. (Flower Fairies Ser.). (Illus.). 48p. (J). (gr. k-3). 12.99 (978-0-7232-4926-9(1) , Warne) Penguin Group (USA) Inc.

Barker, Cicely Mary. Tansy's New Petals: A Flower Fairies Friends Chapter Book. 2008. (Flower Fairies Ser.). 80p. (J). (gr. 2). pap. 3.99 ***(978-0-7232-6285-5(3)*** , Warne) Penguin Group (USA) Inc.

Baxter, David. The Tournesol Twins. 2006. 68p. pap. ***(978-1-84401-901-4(2))*** Athena Pr.

Beamer, Winona Desha & Beamer-Trapp, Kaliko. Pua Polu: The Pretty Blue Hawaiian Flower. Loebel-Fried, Caren Keala, illus. 2005. (HAW & ENG.). 36p. (J). audio compact disk 14.95 (978-1-58178-041-3(9)) Bishop Museum Pr.

Bickel, Karla. Lilac Rose: A Flower's Lifetime. Bickel, Karla, illus. l.t. ed. 2004. (Illus.). 16p. (J). (ps-6). pap. 5.00 (978-1-891452-10-9(X) , 8) Heart Arbor Bks.

Bonnell, Kris. A Flower for a Bee. 2006. (J). 3.95 ***(978-1-933727-23-3(3))*** Reading Reading Bks., LLC.

—The Little Sprout. 2007. (J). 3.95 ***(978-1-933727-54-7(3))*** Reading Reading Bks., LLC.

—Yellow Flowers. 2006. (J). 3.95 ***(978-1-933727-36-3(5))*** Reading Reading Bks., LLC.

Boynton, Cara. Sam's Secret World. 2006. (ENG.). 48p. per. 12.95 ***(978-1-4241-4529-4(5))*** PublishAmerica, Inc.

Brimner, Larry Dane. The Birthday Flowers. 2002. (gr. k-3). lib. bdg. 14.10 (978-0-613-50185-9(3)) Tandem Library Bks.

Brouillet, Chrystine. No Orchids for Andrea! Gaboriau, Linda, tr. Gagnon, Nathalie, illus. 1998. (FRE.). 116p. (J). (gr. 3-7). pap. 6.95 (978-0-921556-62-6(4)) Ragweed Pr. CAN. *Dist:* Univ. of Toronto Pr.

—Pas d'Orchidees pour Miss Andrea! 2002. (Roman Jeunesse Ser.). (FRE.). 96p. (YA). (gr. 4-7). pap. (978-2-89021-207-7(6)) Diffusion du livre Mirabel.

Bunting, Eve. Sunflower House. Hewitt, Kathryn, illus. 1999. 32p. (J). (ps-3). pap. 6.00 (978-0-15-201952-5(9) , Harcourt Paperbacks) Harcourt Children's Bks.

—Sunflower House. 1999. (978-0-606-16517-4(7)); lib. bdg. 14.15 (978-0-613-18048-1(8)) Tandem Library Bks.

Burrowes, Adjoa J. Grandma's Purple Flowers. ed. 2004. (J). (gr. k-3). spiral bd. (978-0-616-07252-3(X)); spiral bd. (978-0-616-08496-0(X)) Canadian National Institute for the Blind/Institut National Canadien pour les Aveugles.

Byars, Betsy. Wanted... Mud Blossom. 2002. (J). (gr. 3-4). tchr. ed. (978-1-56137-724-4(4)) Novel Units, Inc.

—Wanted... Mud Blossom. (Blossom Ser.). 148p. (J). (gr. 4-6). pap. 4.99 (978-0-8072-1470-1(1) , Listening Library) Random Hse. Audio Publishing Group.

Carle, Eric. The Tiny Seed. Carle, Eric, illus. 2005. (Classic Board Bks.). (Illus.). 34p. (J). bds. 7.99 (978-0-689-87149-8(X) , Little Simon) Simon & Schuster Children's Publishing.

Cheng, Andrea. Goldfish & Chrysanthemums. Chang, Michelle, illus. 2003. 32p. (J). 16.95 (978-1-58430-057-1(4)) Lee & Low Bks., Inc.

Coates, Theresa. Imaginary Time of Life. 2007. 102p. pap. 10.95 ***(978-0-7414-4067-9(9))*** Infinity Publishing.

Crawford, K. Michael, illus. The Munched-Up Flower Garden. 2006. 32p. (J). pap. 10.95 (978-1-933176-06-2(7) , Red Pebble Bks.); (978-1-933176-04-8(0)) Red Rock Pr., Inc.

Davies, C. & Ladybird Books Staff. Shiny Flower. 1999. (Touch & Feel Ser.). (Illus.). 10p. (J). 5.99 (978-0-7214-2969-4(6) , Dutton Juvenile) Penguin Group (USA) Inc.

Diederich, Ellen Jean. Where's Petunia? 2003. (Illus.). 32p. (J). per. 18.99 (978-0-9728654-0-1(3)) Givinity Pr.

Don't Eat the Bluebonnets. 2006. (J). lib. bdg. 17.95 (978-0-9645493-3-3(6)) Bluebonnets, Boots & Bks.

Dubarle-Bossy, Philippe. Hello, Flower! Moon, Jo, illus. 2006. 8p. (J). 9.95 (978-1-4027-3236-2(8)) Sterling Publishing Co., Inc.

Ehlert, Lois. Planting a Rainbow. Ehlert, Lois, illus. 2003. (Illus.). 32p. (J). bds. 6.95 (978-0-15-204633-0(X) , Red Wagon Bks.) Harcourt Children's Bks.

Ehlert, Lois. Planting a Rainbow: Lap-Sized Board Book. 2008. (Illus.). 32p. (J). bds. 10.95 ***(978-0-15-206304-7(8)*** , Red Wagon Bks.) Harcourt Children's Bks.

Elizondo, Gabriela Riveros. El Encargo de Fernanda. Castillo, Jesus, illus. rev. ed. 2006. (Castillo de la Lectura Blanca Ser.). (SPA.). 64p. (J). (gr. 1-3). pap. 6.95 (978-970-20-0126-3(9)) Castillo, Ediciones, S. A. de C. V. MEX. *Dist:* Macmillan.

Ellison, Penny. Daisy the Dancing Flower. 2006. (J). 15.95 (978-0-9771121-2-8(8)) Ellison, Penny.

Ennis, Scott. Ah Sunflower. 2004. 27p. (J). per. 7.99 (978-1-4116-0571-8(3)) Lulu.com.

Fairy-Tale Flowers: Individual Title, 6 pack. (Story Steps Ser.). (gr. k-2). 23.00 (978-0-7635-9842-6(9)) Rigby Education.

Foreman, Michael. Mia's Story: A Sketchbook of Hopes & Dreams. Foreman, Michael, illus. 2006. (Illus.). 32p. (J). (gr. k-3). 15.99 (978-0-7636-3063-8(2)) Candlewick Pr.

Gaines, Isabel. Pooh's Surprise Basket. 1999. (Winnie the Pooh First Readers Ser.: No. 13). (Illus.). 37p. (J). (gr. k-3). pap. 3.99 (978-0-7868-4332-9(2)) Disney Pr.

Galjanic, Lisa. When Flowers Dance. Hope, Michelle, illus. 2007. (J). 9.95 (978-1-933532-05-9(X)) LSG Pubns.

Galjanic, Lisa. When Series 6 Volume Set, 6, 6. 2007. (Illus.). 100p. (J). 34.95 ***(978-1-933532-06-6(8))*** LSG Pubns.

Gallacher, Marcie. Amaryllis Lilies. 148p. (YA). pap. 7.95 (978-1-56236-451-9(0)) Aspen Bks.

Gruetzke, Mary, ed. Bunny Book & Purse. McDonald, Jill, illus. 2006. 8p. (J). bds. 5.99 (978-0-439-73022-8(8) , Cartwheel Bks.) Scholastic, Inc.

Gunn, Barbara & Dunn, Richard. Flowers: Read Well Level K Unit 9 Storybook. Nolte, Larry, illus. 2004. (Read Well Level K Ser.). 20p. (J). (978-1-57035-680-3(7)) Sopris West Educational Services.

Gutierrez, Debbi Miller. Cactus Factory. 2007. (J). 6.00 ***(978-0-9740173-4-1(5))*** Prints By Mail.

Harper, Wilhelmina. The Gunniwolf. Upton, Barbara, illus. 2003. 32p. (J). (ps). 15.99 (978-0-525-46785-4(8) , Dutton Juvenile) Penguin Group (USA) Inc.

Hearn, Diane Dawson. Anna in the Garden. 2006. (Illus.). 29p. (J). (gr. k-4). reprint ed. 15.00 (978-1-4223-5087-4(8)) DIANE Publishing Co.

Hearson, Ruth. Daisy's Fairy Flowers. Hearson, Ruth, illus. abr. ed. 2006. (Flips & Flaps Book Ser.). (Illus.). 14p. (J). 5.99 (978-1-4169-1221-7(5) , Little Simon) Simon & Schuster Children's Publishing.

Henkes, Kevin. A Box Full of Lilly. Henkes, Kevin, illus. 2006. (J). 24.99 (978-0-06-112852-3(X)) HarperCollins Pubs.

—So Happy! Lobel, Anita, illus. 2005. 32p. (J). 15.99 (978-0-06-056483-4(0)); lib. bdg. 16.89 (978-0-06-056484-1(9)) HarperCollins Pubs.

Hill, Susanna Leonard. No Sword Fighting in the House. Kelley, True, illus. (Holiday House Reader Ser.: Level 2). 32p. (J). (gr. k-3). 14.95 (978-0-8234-1916-6(9)) Holiday Hse., Inc.

Karon, Jan. The Trellis & the Seed: A Book of Encouragement for All Ages. Steele, Robert Gantt, illus. 32p. (J). 2005. pap. 5.99 (978-0-14-240317-4(2) , Puffin); 2003. 15.95 (978-0-670-89289-1(0) , Viking Juvenile) Penguin Group (USA) Inc.

Kline, Trish & Donev, Mary. Where Can Lost Bee Be? KA Reader 6. 2007. (Illus.). 32p. (J). per. 20.00 ***(978-0-9717234-9-8(4))*** Ghost Hunter Productions.

Korty, Carol. Baba Yaga & the Black Sunflower. 2000. (J). pap. 7.00 (978-0-87602-374-7(X)) Anchorage Pr.

Landreth, Christina. Tommy Picks Flowers. 2004. 27p. pap. 14.95 (978-1-4137-3943-5(1)) PublishAmerica, Inc.

Laube, Sigrid. The Flower Ball. Boehm, Philip, tr. from GER. Leffler, Silke, illus. 2006. Orig. Title: Der Blumenball. 30p. (J). 15.95 (978-0-9646010-2-4(8)) Pumpkin Hse., Ltd.

Laurie, Peter. Mauby's Quest for the Magic Flower. Dodson, H. Ann, illus. rev. ed. 2002. 48p. (J). 12.95 (978-0-333-95313-6(4)) Macmillan Caribbean GBR. *Dist:* Interlink Publishing Group, Inc.

Law, Felicia. The Flower's Busy Day. Evans, Nicola, illus. 2005. (Bamboo & Friends Ser.). 24p. (J). (ps-3). lib. bdg. 22.60 (978-1-4048-1281-9(4)) Picture Window Bks.

Lewis, Bisa, as told by. How Flowers Get Their Colors. 2005. (J). (978-0-9745469-9-5(2)) Ashley & Taylor Publishing, Co.

Lewison, Wendy Cheyette. Princess Buttercup: A Flower Princess Story. Smath, Jerry, illus. 2001. (All Aboard Reading Ser.). 32p. (J). (ps-3). pap. 3.99 (978-0-448-42472-9(X) , Grosset & Dunlap) Penguin Group (USA) Inc.

Light, John. Flower. 2005. (Illus.). 26p. (978-1-897968-17-8(5)) Photon Pr.

Lisa, Bruce. Fran's Flower. 1999. 32p. (J). (ps-2). pap. 4.95 (978-0-06-443610-6(1)) HarperCollins Pubs.

Lisle, Janet Taylor. The Lost Flower Children. Ichikawa, Satomi, illus. 2001. 112p. (J). (ps-7). pap. 5.99 (978-0-698-11880-5(4) , Putnam Juvenile) Penguin Group (USA) Inc.

—Lost Flower Children. 2001. (gr. 3-6). lib. bdg. 14.15 (978-0-613-35975-7(5)) Tandem Library Bks.

—The Lost Flower Children. l.t. ed. 2000. (Illus.). 188p. (J). 21.95 (978-0-7862-2890-4(3)) Thorndike Pr.

Louie, Therese On. Raymond's Perfect Present. Wang, Suling, illus. 2002. (J). (gr. 2-4). 16.95 (978-1-58430-055-7(8)) Lee & Low Bks., Inc.

Major, Roberta Olsen. Royal Pains Bk. 4: The Bottle of DJINN. 2006. (YA). pap. 9.95 (978-1-59705-824-7(6)) Wings ePress, Inc.

Marsoli, Lisa Ann. Leaping Lily: A Ballet Story. Leijten, Aileen, illus. 2005. (J). bds. 14.99 (978-0-9767325-3-2(X)) Toy Quest.

Martin, Mary. Miss Lilly & the Hollyhock Garden. 2001. (Illus.). 48p. (J). 24.95 (978-1-58597-107-7(3)) Leathers Publishing.

Matsuura, Richard & Matsuura, Ruth. Fruit, the Tree & the Flower. (J). 8.95 (978-1-887916-02-8(4)) Orchid Isle Publishing Co.

McAndrew, Laura. Little Flower: A Story for Children. Conrad, Nancy, illus. 1999. (ps-3). 6.95 (978-0-87868-714-5(9) , 7149) Child Welfare League of America, Inc.

Noyes, Deborah. Hana in the Time of the Tulips. Ibatoulline, Bagram, illus. 2004. 40p. (J). (gr. 1-6). 16.99 (978-0-7636-1875-9(6)) Candlewick Pr.

O'Connor, Jane & Heller, Ruth. More Flowers. 1999. (Designs for Coloring Ser.). (Illus.). 64p. (J). (gr. 4-7). pap. 5.99 (978-0-448-41993-0(9) , Grosset & Dunlap) Penguin Group (USA) Inc.

O'Shannon, Dan. Fan & the Flowers. 2001. 96p. (J). 15.99 (978-0-7868-0604-1(4)) Hachette Bk. Group.

Park, Linda Sue. What Does Bunny See? A Book of Colors & Flowers. Smith, Maggie, illus. 2005. 32p. (J). (ps-k). 15.00 (978-0-618-23485-1(3) , Clarion Bks.) Houghton Mifflin Co. Trade & Reference Div.

Philips, Dana. Blacksmith's Tale, or Once Upon a Flower. 2000. (J). (gr. 4-6). 24.95 (978-1-889274-07-2(0)) Posterity Pr., Inc.

Pin, Isabel. Bumblebee Blues. James, J. Alison, tr. from GER. 2003. (Illus.). 32p. (J). (gr. k-3). 15.95 (978-0-7358-1813-2(4)); lib. bdg. 16.50 (978-0-7358-1814-9(2)) North-South Bks., Inc. (Michael Neugebauer Bks.).

Quinones, Laura-Ann. Rainbow Flowers. 2006. 16p. (J). 10.68 (978-1-4116-6873-7(1)) Lulu.com.

Raintree Steck-Vaughn Staff, contrib. by. Planting a Rainbow. 1999. (J). (ps-3). pap. 22.00 (978-0-8172-9787-9(1)) Steck-Vaughn.

Ray, Miasyn Summer. One Lucky Petal. 2005. (Illus.). 36p. (J). per. 16.99 (978-0-9761844-3-0(5)) South Hadley Publishing.

Reed, Jennifer. The Falling Flowers. Cole, Dick, illus. 2005. (J). 16.95 (978-1-885008-28-2(7)) Shen's Bks.

Ridley, Sharon, illus. My Wildflower Friends. Phillips, Marilyn, photos by. 2006. (J). (978-0-9786168-0-9(4)) Rio Wildflower Pubns.

Roche, Hannah. Have You Ever Picked a Dandelion? 1998. (Lifecycle Stories Ser.). 16p. (J). (ps-1). spiral bd. (978-1-84089-005-1(3) , 868223Q, Zero to Ten, Limited) Evans Publishing Group.

Rockwell, Anne F. Bumblebee, Bumblebee, Do You Know Me. Rockwell, Anne F., illus. 1999. (Illus.). 24p. (J). (ps-2). 15.89 (978-0-06-028212-7(6)) HarperCollins Pubs.

Rodda, Emily. The Peskie Spell. Vitale, Raoul, illus. 2006. (Fairy Realm Ser.). 128p. (J). 8.99 (978-0-06-077764-7(8)); lib. bdg. 14.89 (978-0-06-077766-1(4)) HarperCollins Pubs.

—The Rainbow Wand. Vitale, Raoul, illus. 2006. (Fairy Realm Ser.: No. 10). 128p. (J). lib. bdg. 14.89 (978-0-06-077769-2(9)); 8.99 (978-0-06-077768-5(0)) HarperCollins Pubs.

—The Rainbow Wand. Vitale, Raoul, illus. 2007. (Fairy Realm Ser.). 128p. (J). (gr. 3-6). 25.65 (978-1-59961-332-1(8)) Spotlight.

The Rose. 2001. (Teddy Fairies Ser.). (Illus.). 8p. (J). (ps-k). bds. 4.95 (978-0-439-20851-2(3)) Scholastic, Inc.

Scheunemann, Pam. Spelling Bee. Nobens, C. A., illus. 2007. (Fact & Fiction Ser.). 24p. (J). pap. (978-1-59928-473-6(1)); 21.35 (978-1-59928-472-9(3)) ABDO Publishing Co.

Schwartz, Roslyn. Mole Sisters & the Busy Bees. 2000. (ps-2). lib. bdg. 12.95 (978-0-613-78377-4(8)) Tandem Library Bks.

Schwartz, Suzanne & Schwartz, Robert. The Christmas Palm Tree: A Storybook to Color. Schwartz, Suzanne & Schwartz, Robert, illus. l.t. ed. 2005. (Illus.). 22p. (J). spiral bd. 3.99 (978-0-9764152-3-7(2)) Seascay Productions.

Shaw, M. Beatryce. Mr. Browne's Roses: A Story of Early Childhood Color Awareness. 2000. 40p. (J). (gr. k-4). pap. 8.95 (978-1-929234-00-4(7)) Schooner Pubns.

Shay, Ruth Ann. The Littlest Susan. Mertes, Charles, illus. 2000. 32p. (J). (ps-4). lib. bdg. 20.00 (978-0-9701167-0-3(5)) Guided Pen Pr.

Siegel, Rv. A Bee Called Kangaroo. 2005. 81p. pap. 9.16 (978-1-4116-2890-8(X)) Lulu.com.

Sloniker, Phyllis. The Quest for the Golden Flower. 2005. 11.00 (978-0-8059-9399-8(1)) Dorrance Publishing Co., Inc.

Spalding, Andrea. Me & Mr. Mah. Wilson, Janet, illus. 32p. (J). (ps-2). 2001. 7.95 (978-1-55143-177-2(7)); 2000. 14.95 (978-1-55143-168-0(8)) Orca Bk. Pubs. USA.

Steadman, Ralph. Flowers for the Moon. 2004. (Illus.). 42p. 100.00 (978-0-9760742-0-5(6)) Sylph Pubns.

Stein-Aubert, Danielle. The Blossoms' Ball. Peyre, Virginie, illus. 2004. 34p. (J). 12.95 (978-1-58246-096-3(5) , Tricycle Pr.) Ten Speed Pr.

Surber, Shawn-Michelle. Hope, 1. Surber, Shawn-Michelle, illus. collector's ed. 2007. (Illus.). 35p. (J). 19.99 (978-0-9763534-0-9(7) , Mornin'Light Media) Mornin' Light Media.

Tagg, Christine. Cinderlily: A Floral Fairy Tale. Ellwand, David, ed. Ellwand, David, photos by. 2006. (Illus.). 26p. (J). (gr. k-4). reprint ed. 17.00 (978-1-4223-5558-9(6)) DIANE Publishing Co.

Taylor-Butler, Christine. Step-by-Step. Miller, Susan, illus. 2005. (My First Reader Ser.). 32p. (J). 18.50 (978-0-516-24875-2(8) , Children's Pr.) Scholastic Library Publishing.

—Step by Step. Miller, Susan, illus. 2006. 32p. (J). (gr. k-1). pap. 3.95 (978-0-516-24974-2(6) , Children's Pr.) Scholastic Library Publishing.

Thatcher, Fran, illus. Teddy Fairies: A Story about Buttercup. 2001. (Teddy Fairies Ser.). 8p. (J). (ps-k). bds. 4.95 (978-0-439-20852-9(1) , Cartwheel Bks.) Scholastic, Inc.

Thatcher, Frances, tr. & illus. Violet. Thatcher, Frances, illus. 2001. (Teddy Fairies Ser.). 8p. (J). (ps-k). bds. 4.95 (978-0-439-20853-6(X) , Cartwheel Bks.) Scholastic, Inc.

Trotman, Althea. How the East Pond Got Its Flowers. Sasso, illus. Date not set. 88p. (J). (gr. 3-7). pap. (978-0-920813-85-0(2)) Sister Vision Pr.

Ure, Jean. The Flower Power Collection: Passion Flower, Shrinking Violet & Pumpkin Pie. 2006. (Illus.). 544p. (J). pap. 16.99 (978-0-00-720155-6(9) , HarperCollins Children's Bks.) HarperCollins Pubs. Ltd. GBR. *Dist:* Independent Pubs. Group.

Waddell, Martin. Something So Big. Canty, Charlotte, illus. 2004. 24p. (J). lib. bdg. 22.65 ***(978-1-59646-706-4(1))*** Dingles & Co.

Watts, Irene N. Flower. 2005. 192p. (J). (gr. 4). pap. 8.95 (978-0-88776-710-4(9)) Tundra Bks., Inc./Livres Toundra, Inc. CAN. *Dist:* Random Hse., Inc.

Wheeler, Leslie. Dolly's Day in the Garden. 2006. 18p. (J). per. 10.99 ***(978-1-59886-708-4(3))*** Tate Publishing & Enterprises, L.L.C.

Williams, Jill Ann. Listen to the Flowers: Ten Flower Stories for Children. 2006. pap. 8.00 ***(978-0-8059-7198-9(X))*** Dorrance Publishing Co., Inc.

Willis, Wren. The Flower I Met in My Garden. 2004. 116p. per. 6.85 (978-1-4116-1783-4(5)) Lulu.com.

Wojtowicz, Jen. The Boy Who Grew Flowers. Adams, Steve, illus. 2005. 32p. (J). (ps-3). 16.99 (978-1-84148-686-4(8)) Barefoot Bks., Inc.

FLOWERS, STATE

see State Flowers

FLOWERS, WILD

see Wild Flowers

FLOWERS IN ART

see Design, Decorative; Flower Painting and Illustration

FLY

see Flies

FLYING
see Flight

FLYING BOMBS
see Guided Missiles

FLYING SAUCERS
see Unidentified Flying Objects

FODDER
see Feeding and Feeds

FOG
Dunn, Andrew. Fog, Mist & Smog. 1998. (Living with the Weather Ser.). (Illus.). 48p. (J). (gr. 4-7). 18.98 (978-0-8172-5053-9(0)) Raintree.

Frost, Helen. Fog. Saunders-Smith, Gail, ed. 2004. (Weather Ser.). (Illus.). 24p. (J). (gr. k-1). lib. bdg. 15.93 (978-0-7368-2093-6(0) , Pebble Bks.) Capstone Pr., Inc.

Miles, Elizabeth. Fog & Mist. 2005. (J). pap. (978-1-4034-6562-7(2)); (Illus.). 32p. pap. (978-1-4034-6557-3(6)); (Illus.). 32p. lib. bdg. (978-1-4034-6552-8(5)) Heinemann Library.

FOG—FICTION
Harcourt School Publishers Staff. A Visit to San Francisco Below Level. 3rd ed. 2002. (Trophies Reading Program Ser.). (Illus.). (gr. 3). pap. 5.10 (978-0-15-323133-9(5)) Harcourt Schl. Pubs.

Herbert, James. The Fog. 2003. (Illus.). vi, 345p. (J). pap. 13.99 (978-0-330-37615-0(2) , Pan) Pan Macmillan GBR. *Dist:* Trafalgar Square Publishing.

McDonnell, Patrick. Just Like Heaven: A Mutts Children's Book. 2006. (Illus.). 44p. (J). (ps-1). 14.99 (978-0-316-11493-6(6)) Little Brown & Co.

Trotter, Deborah W. How Do You Know? Downing, Julie, illus. 2006. 32p. (J). (ps-k). 16.00 (978-0-618-46343-5(7) , Clarion Bks.) Houghton Mifflin Co. Trade & Reference Div.

FOG SIGNALS
see Signals and Signaling

FOLIAGE
see Leaves

FOLK ART
Here are entered general and historical works on peasant and popular art in the fields of decorative arts, music, dancing, theater, etc.

see also Art, Primitive; Art Industries and Trade

Ancona, George. The Folk Arts: Viva Mexico! 2001. (Viva Mexico! Ser.). (Illus.). 48p. (J). (gr. 3-6). lib. bdg. 27.07 (978-0-7614-1326-4(X) , Benchmark Bks.) Cavendish, Marshall Corp.

Bonnice, Sherry. Folk Arts & Crafts. 2002. (North American Folklore Ser.). (Illus.). 112p. (J). (gr. 7 up). lib. bdg. (978-1-59084-335-2(5)) Mason Crest Pubs.

Caravan to America: Living Arts of the Silk Road. 2002. (gr. 3-6). lib. bdg. 25.70 (978-0-613-76180-2(4)) Tandem Library Bks.

Colonial Williamsburg Foundation Staff & Watson, Amy Z. The Folk Art Counting Book: From the Abby Aldrich Rockefeller Folk Art Center. 1999. (Illus.). 40p. (J). (ps). 9.95 (978-0-87935-084-0(9)) Colonial Williamsburg Foundation.

Jabbour, Alan, ed. Folk Speech, 21 vols., Set. 2003. (North American Folklore Ser.). (Illus.). 112p. (J). (gr. 7 up). lib. bdg. (978-1-59084-328-4(2)) Mason Crest Pubs.

Kafka, Tina. Folk Art. 2007. (Eye on Art Ser.). 128p. (J). (gr. 7-10). 31.20 (***978-1-59018-960-3(4)*** , Lucent Bks.) Thomson Gale.

Major, John & Belanus, Betty J. Caravan to America: Living Arts of the Silk Road. 2002. (Illus.). 144p. (J). (gr. 3-6). pap. 15.95 (978-0-8126-2677-3(X)); (gr. 4-6). 24.95 (978-0-8126-2666-7(4)) Cricket Bks.

Panchyk, Richard & Ketchum, William C., Jr. American Folk Art for Kids: With 21 Activities. 2004. (For Kids Ser.). (Illus.). 128p. (J). pap. 16.95 (978-1-55652-499-8(4)) Chicago Review Pr., Inc.

Raintree Steck-Vaughn Staff, ed. Artisans Around the World, 6 bks., Set. 1999. (Illus.). (J). lib. bdg. 162.72 (978-0-7398-0123-9(6)) Raintree.

Rich, Susan, et al. Africa South of the Sahara: Understanding Geography & History Through Art. 1999. (Artisans Around the World Ser.). (Illus.). 48p. (J). (gr. 4-8). lib. bdg. 27.12 (978-0-7398-0118-5(X)) Raintree.

Terzian, Alexandra M. The Kids' Multicultural Art Book. 1999. (Williamson Kids Can! Ser.). (Illus.). 160p. (J). (gr. 3 up). lib. bdg. 25.26 (978-0-8368-2233-5(1)) Stevens, Gareth Inc.

Terzian, Alexandria M. The Kids Multicultural Art Book. Terzian, Alexandria M., illus. 2007. 160p. (gr. 1-2). pap. 12.99 (***978-0-8249-6808-3(5)*** **);** (Illus.). 16.99 (***978-0-8249-6807-6(7)***) Ideals Pubns. (Williamson Bks.).

Weill, Cynthia & Basseches, K. B. ABeCedarios: Mexican Folk Art ABCs in Spanish & English. Jiménez, Moisés & Jiménez, Armando, illus. 2007. (SPA & ENG.). 32p. (J). (ps up). 14.95 (***978-1-933693-13-2(4)***) Cinco Puntos Pr.

FOLK DANCING
Ancona, George. Let's Dance! 1998. (Illus.). 40p. (J). (ps-3). 15.89 (978-0-688-16212-2(6)) HarperCollins Pubs.

—Mis Bailes: My Dances. 2004. (Somos Latino (We Are Latinos) Ser.). (ENG & SPA., Illus.). 32p. (J). 21.00 (978-0-516-23691-9(1) , Children's Pr.) Scholastic Library Publishing.

Bonnice, Sherry. Folk Dance. 2002. (North American Folklore Ser.). (Illus.). 112p. (YA). (gr. 7 up). lib. bdg. (978-1-59084-337-6(1)) Mason Crest Pubs.

Miller, Randy & Perron, Jack. New England Fiddler's Repertoire: A Source Book of Established Contra Dance Music, Bley-Vroman, Robert, ed. 2nd rev. ed. 2003. (Illus.). 96p. spiral bd. 20.00 (978-0-9770530-0-1(8)) Miller, Randy.

Rinaldi, Robin. European Dance: Ireland, Poland & Spain. 2003. (World of Dance Ser.). (Illus.). 120p. (gr. 9-13). 30.00 (978-0-7910-7643-9(1) , Chelsea Hse.) Facts On File, Inc.

Stanford, Candice & Wroth, William. The Man Who Set the Town Dancing. Dougherty, Flo Hosa, illus. 2002. (ENG & SPA.). 40p. (J). (gr. 2-4). 16.95 (978-1-57416-050-5(8)) Clear Light Pubs.

Storey, Rita. Irish Dancing. 2006. (Get Dancing Ser.). (Illus.). 32p. (J). (978-1-59771-050-3(4)) Sea-To-Sea Pubns.

FOLK LORE
see Folklore

FOLK MUSIC
see Folk Songs

FOLK SONGS
see also Ballads; Carols; Folklore; National Songs

Adams, Pam. There Was an Old Lady Who Swallowed a Fly. Adams, Pam, illus. 2001. (Live Oak Readalong Ser.). (Illus.). (J). 28.95 incl. audio compact disk (978-1-59112-409-2(3)) Live Oak Media.

Armentrout, David & Armentrout, Patricia. Folk. 1999. (Sounds of Music Ser.). (Illus.). 24p. (J). (gr. 1-4). lib. bdg. 19.27 (978-0-86593-532-7(7)) Rourke Publishing, LLC.

Bladey, Conrad, ed. A Beuk of the Sangs of Tommy Armstrong the Pitman's Poet. 2003. (Illus.). 90p. (978-0-9702386-8-9(1)) Hutman Productions.

Cauthen, Joyce, prod. Bullfrog Jumped: Children's Folksongs from the Byron Arnold Collection. 2006. (J). 17.00 incl. audio compact disk (978-0-9672672-9-6(3)) Alabama Folklife Assn.

Clementine. (Traditional Songs Ser.). 24p. (J). 7.95 (978-1-4048-0423-4(4)) Picture Window Bks.

Drummer Hoff. 2004. 29.95 incl. cd-rom (978-1-55592-407-2(7)); 29.95 incl. cd-rom (978-1-55592-408-9(5)); 24.95 incl. audio (978-1-56008-191-3(0)) Weston Woods Studios, Inc.

Farmer in the Dell. (Traditional Songs Ser.). 24p. (J). 7.95 (978-1-4048-0424-1(2)) Picture Window Bks.

Feierabend, John M. The Book of Call & Response. Caton, Tim, illus. 2003. (First Steps in Music Ser.). 88p. (J). pap. 11.95 (978-1-57999-215-6(3)) GIA Pubns., Inc.

—The Book of Children's Song Tales. Caton, Tim, illus. 2003. (First Steps in Music Ser.). 104p. (J). pap. 11.95 (978-1-57999-213-2(7)) GIA Pubns., Inc.

—The Book of Echo Songs. Caton, Tim, illus. 2003. (First Steps in Music Ser.). 88p. (J). pap. 11.95 (978-1-57999-214-9(5)) GIA Pubns., Inc.

Frazee, Maria. Hush, Little Baby: A Folk Song with Pictures. 2003. (gr. k-3). lib. bdg. 14.15 (978-0-613-70498-4(3)) Tandem Library Bks.

Handyside, Chris. A History of Folk. 2006. (Illus.). 48p. (J). 31.43 (978-1-4034-8150-4(4)) Heinemann Library.

—A History of Folk. 2006. (J). (978-1-4109-1813-0(0)) Steck-Vaughn.

Hush Little Baby. 2004. pap. 14.95 incl. audio (978-0-7882-0622-1(2)) Weston Woods Studios, Inc.

I Know an Old Lady. (Traditional Songs Ser.). 24p. (J). 7.95 (978-1-4048-0430-2(7)) Picture Window Bks.

I've Been Working on the Railroad. (Traditional Songs Ser.). 24p. (J). 7.95 (978-1-4048-0431-9(5)) Picture Window Bks.

Julian, Alison, illus. The 12 Days of Christmas. 2005. (J). (***978-1-74157-281-0(9)***) Hinkler Bks. Pty, Ltd.

Kellogg, Steven. Give the Dog a Bone. (Illus.). (J). (gr. k-3). 2000. 33p. 16.50 (978-1-58717-002-7(7) , SeaStar Bks.); 2004. 40p. reprint ed. pap. 6.95 (978-0-8118-4609-7(1)) Chronicle Bks. LLC.

—Give the Dog a Bone. 2000. (gr. k-3). lib. bdg. 26.35 (978-0-613-83676-0(6)) Tandem Library Bks.

Kirgiss, Crystal. Folk Music. 2001. (World of Music Ser.). (Illus.). 32p. (J). (gr. 2-7). lib. bdg. 22.60 (978-1-58340-044-9(3)) Smart Apple Media.

Long, Sylvia. Hush Little Baby. 2002. (Illus.). 26p. (J). bds. 6.95 (978-0-8118-2290-9(7)) Chronicle Bks. LLC.

MacDonald, Margaret Read. Three-Minute Tales: Stories from Around the World to Tell or Read When Time Is Short. 2004. 160p. 24.95 (978-0-87483-728-5(6)); pap. 17.95 (978-0-87483-729-2(4)) August Hse. Pubs., Inc.

Neimark, Anne E. There Ain't Nobody That Can Sing Like Me. 2002. (Illus.). 128p. (J). (gr. 5-9). 17.95 (978-0-689-83369-4(5) , Atheneum) Simon & Schuster Children's Publishing.

Ochs, Bill. The Clarke Tin Whistle. 2000. 80p. pap. 12.95 incl. audio compact disk (978-0-9623456-3-0(6)) Pennywhistler's Pr.

Old MacDonald Had a Farm. (Traditional Songs Ser.). 24p. (J). 7.95 (978-1-4048-0432-6(3)) Picture Window Bks.

O'Neal, Debbie Trafton. O Christmas Tree. Cook, Ande, illus. 2004. 32p. 8.99 (978-0-8066-4560-5(1) , Augsburg Bks.) Augsburg Fortress, Pubs.

Orozco, Jose-Luis. De Colores & Other Latin-American Folk Songs for Children. 1999. (SPA.). (gr. k-3). lib. bdg. 16.45 (978-0-613-19510-2(8)) Tandem Library Bks.

Orozco, Jose-Luis, ed. De Colores & Other Latin-American Folk Songs for Children. Kleven, Elisa, illus. 2004. 56p. (J). (gr. k-4). reprint ed. 17.00 (978-0-7567-7700-5(3)) DIANE Publishing Co.

Partridge, Elizabeth. This Land Was Made for You & Me: The Life & Songs of Woody Guthrie. 2002. (Illus.). 224p. (J). (gr. 6-12). 21.99 (978-0-670-03535-9(1) , Viking Juvenile) Penguin Group (USA) Inc.

Pinkney, Brian. Hush, Little Baby. Pinkney, Brian, illus. 2006. (Illus.). 32p. (J). 15.99 (978-0-06-055993-9(4)); lib. bdg. 17.89 (978-0-06-055994-6(2)) HarperCollins Pubs.

Qualey, Marsha, ed. The Ants Go Marching. D'Antonio, Sandra, illus. 2004. (Traditional Songs Ser.). 24p. (J). (gr. k-2). 22.60 (978-1-4048-0148-6(0)) Picture Window Bks.

Raffi. This Little Light of Mine. Schuett, Stacey, illus. 2006. 32p. (J). (gr. k-k). bds. 6.99 (978-0-375-82887-4(7) , Knopf Bks. for Young Readers) Random Hse. Children's Bks.

Riggs, Kate. Folk Music. 2008. (J). (***978-1-58341-566-5(1)*** , Creative Education) Creative Co., The.

Seeger, Laura Vaccaro & Seeger, Pete. I Had a Rooster: A Traditional Folk Song. 2000. (Illus.). (J). (978-0-7894-2669-7(2)) Dorling Kindersley Publishing, Inc.

Sharma, Elizabeth. Music Worldwide. 1998. (Cambridge Assignments in Music Ser.). (Illus.). 72p. (gr. 9-11). pap. 19.00 (978-0-521-37622-8(X)) Cambridge Univ. Pr.

She'll Be Coming around the Mountain. (Traditional Songs Ser.). 24p. (J). 7.95 (978-1-4048-0433-3(1)) Picture Window Bks.

Tyler, Gillian. Froggy Went A-Courtin' Tyler, Gillian, illus. 2004. (Illus.). 32p. (J). (ps-2). 15.99 (978-0-7636-2306-7(7)) Candlewick Pr.

Vilsaint, Fequiere. Children Songs from Haiti: Chante Timoun Ayiti. Date not set. 28p. (J). (gr. 1-5). wbk. ed. 25.00 (978-1-881839-55-2(9)) Educa Vision.

Woog, Adam. The History of American Folk Music. 2006. 112p. (J). (gr. 7-10). 32.45 (978-1-59018-734-0(2) , Lucent Bks.) Thomson Gale.

Young, Marianne, illus. If You're Happy & You Know It. 16p. (J). (gr. k-3). pap. 4.95 (978-0-88272-448-5(7)) Santillana USA Publishing Co., Inc.

Zanes, Dan. Hello Hello. Saaf, Donald, illus. 2004. 32p. (J). (ps-3). 16.99 (978-0-316-16808-3(4)) Little, Brown Bks. for Young Readers.

—Jump Up! Saaf, Donald, illus. 2005. 28p. (J). (ps-3). 16.99 (978-0-316-16796-3(7)) Little Brown & Co.

Ziefert, Harriet & Brand, Oscar. When I First Came to This Land. Taback, Simms, illus. 2007. 32p. (J). (gr. k). 16.99 (***978-0-399-24793-4(9)*** , Putnam Juvenile) Penguin Group (USA) Inc.

FOLK SONGS, AMERICAN
see Folk Songs—United States

FOLK SONGS, CANADIAN
Barbeau, Marius. Folk Songs of French Canada. 2001. 216p. (YA). reprint ed. 98.00 (978-0-7222-5075-4(4)) Library Reprints, Inc.

FOLK SONGS, ENGLISH
Adams, Pam. There Was an Old Lady Who Swallowed a Fly. Adams, Pam, illus. 2002. (Illus.). (J). 22.72 (978-0-7587-0154-1(3)) Book Wholesalers, Inc.

—There Was an Old Lady Who Swallowed a Fly. Adams, Pam, illus. (Illus.). pap. 16.95 incl. audio (978-0-87499-778-1(X)); pap. incl. audio (978-0-87499-780-4(1)); pap. 18.95 incl. audio compact disk (978-1-59112-408-5(5)); pap. incl. audio compact disk (978-1-59112-607-2(X)) Live Oak Media.

—There Was an Old Lady Who Swallowed a Fly. unabr. ed. 2001. (Live Oak Readalong Ser.). (Illus.). (J). (ps-2). 25.95 incl. audio (978-0-87499-779-8(8)) Live Oak Media.

—This Old Man. 2000. (Books with Holes Ser.). (Illus.). 16p. (J). (ps-3). 19.99 (978-0-85953-636-3(X)) Child's Play-International.

Adams, Pam, illus. This Old Man. 2000. 16p. (J). (ps-k). bds. 5.99 (978-0-85953-661-5(0)) Child's Play-International.

Child's Play Staff. There Was an Old Lady Who Swallowed a Fly. Adams, Pam, illus. 1999. (Books with Holes Ser.). 16p. (J). (ps-3). 19.99 (978-0-85953-635-6(1)) Child's Play-International.

Chwast, Seymour, illus. Had Gadya: A Passover Song. rev. ed. 2007. 32p. (J). pap. 7.95 (***978-1-59643-298-7(5)***) Roaring Brook Pr.

Colandro, Lucille. There Was an Old Lady Who Swallowed a Bat! Lee, Jared D., illus. 2005. 28p. (J). (ps-3). lib. bdg. 13.19 (978-0-606-33828-8(4)) Tandem Library Bks.

Colandro, Lucille. There Was an Old Lady Who Swallowed a Shell! Lee, Jared D., illus. 2006. (J). (***978-0-439-81536-9(3)***) Scholastic, Inc.

Cooper, Floyd. Cumbayah. 1998. (Illus.). 32p. (J). (ps-3). lab manual ed. 16.89 (978-0-688-13544-7(7)) HarperCollins Pubs.

Cooper, Floyd, illus. Cumbayah. 1998. 32p. (J). (ps-3). 16.99 (978-0-688-13543-0(9)) HarperCollins Pubs.

de Paola, Tomie. The Friendly Beasts: An Old English Christmas Carol. 1998. (Illus.). 40p. (J). (ps-3). pap. 6.99 (978-0-698-11661-0(5) , Putnam Juvenile) Penguin Group (USA) Inc.

Frog Went a Courtin. 2004. (J). pap. 14.95 incl. audio (978-0-7882-0506-4(4)) Weston Woods Studios, Inc.

Frog Went A-Courtin' 2004. pap. 14.95 incl. audio (978-1-56008-053-4(1)); (J). 24.95 incl. audio (978-0-89719-874-5(3)); (J). pap. 32.75 incl. audio (978-1-55592-225-2(2)); (J). pap. 32.75 incl. audio (978-1-55592-226-9(0)) Weston Woods Studios, Inc.

Greene, Ellin & Levi, Paul Alan. Mother's Song: An English Lullaby. Sayles, Elizabeth & McCully, Emily Arnold, illus. 2008. 34p. (J). 17.00 (978-0-395-71527-7(X) , Clarion Bks.) Houghton Mifflin Co. Trade & Reference Div.

Guthrie, Woody. This Land Is Your Land. Jakobsen, Kathy, illus. 1998. 32p. (J). (ps-17). 16.99 (978-0-316-39215-0(4)) Little Brown & Co.

Kellogg, Steven. Give the Dog a Bone. 2000. (Illus.). 33p. (J). (gr. k-3). 16.50 (978-1-58717-002-7(7) , SeaStar Bks.) Chronicle Bks. LLC.

Plume, Ilse. The Farmer in the Dell: Pictures by Ilse Plume. 2004. (Illus.). 64p. (J). 17.95 (978-1-56792-270-7(8)) Godine, David R. Pub.

Qualey, Marsha, ed. Clementine. D'Antonio, Sandra, illus. 2004. (Traditional Songs Ser.). 24p. (C). (gr. k-2). 22.60 (978-1-4048-0155-4(3)) Picture Window Bks.

—The Farmer in the Dell. D'Antonio, Sandra, illus. 2004. (Traditional Songs Ser.). 24p. (ps-2). 22.60 (978-1-4048-0149-3(9)) Picture Window Bks.

—I Know an Old Lady Who Swallowed a Fly. D'Antonio, Sandra, illus. 2004. (Traditional Songs Ser.). 24p. (ps-2). 22.60 (978-1-4048-0150-9(2)) Picture Window Bks.

—I've Been Working on the Railroad. D'Antonio, Sandra, illus. 2004. (Traditional Songs Ser.). 24p. (ps-2). 22.60 (978-1-4048-0151-6(0)) Picture Window Bks.

Schanzer, Rosalyn. The Old Chisholm Trail: A Cowboy Song. 2001. (Illus.). 32p. (J). (ps-3). 16.95 (978-0-7922-7559-6(4) , National Geographic Children's Bks.) National Geographic Society.

Seeger, Pete. One Grain of Sand: A Lullaby. Wingerter, Linda, illus. 2005. 30p. (J). (ps-4). reprint ed. 16.00 (978-0-7567-8586-4(3)) DIANE Publishing Co.

—One Grain of Sand: A Lullaby. Wingerter, Linda, illus. 2003. 32p. (J). (ps-1). 15.95 (978-0-316-78140-4(1) , Tingley, Megan Bks.) Little, Brown Bks. for Young Readers.

Spier, Peter. Fox Went Out on a Chilly Night. Spier, Peter, illus. 2002. (Illus.). (J). 14.79 (978-0-7587-0108-4(X)) Book Wholesalers, Inc.

Sweet, Melissa. On Christmas Day in the Morning: A Traditional Carol. 2001. (978-0-606-22503-8(X)) Tandem Library Bks.

Sweet, Melissa & Langstaff, John M. On Christmas Day in the Morning: A Traditional Carol. 1999. (J). (978-0-7636-0634-3(0)) Candlewick Pr.

Trapani, Iza. Froggie Went A-Courtin' Trapani, Iza, illus. 2004. (Illus.). 32p. (J). 15.95 (978-1-58089-028-1(8)) Charlesbridge Publishing, Inc.

Trapani, Iza, illus. Froggie Went A-Courtin' 2006. (J). pap. 6.95 (978-1-58089-029-8(6)) Charlesbridge Publishing, Inc.

Tyrell, Frances. Woodland Christmas: Twelve Days of Christmas in the North Woods. 2000. (J). (978-0-606-19624-6(2)) Tandem Library Bks.

Vagin, Vladimir Vasil'evich, illus. The Twelve Days of Christmas. 1999. 32p. (J). (ps-3). 15.95 (978-0-06-027652-5(5)); 15.89 (978-0-06-028399-5(8)) HarperCollins Pubs.

Vojtech, Anna, illus. The Friendly Beasts. 2003. (J). 15.95 (978-0-7358-1764-7(2)); lib. bdg. 16.50 (978-0-7358-1765-4(0)) North-South Bks., Inc.

Westcott, Nadine Bernard. I Know an Old Lady Who Swallowed a Fly. Westcott, Nadine Bernard, illus. 2002. (Illus.). (J). 13.79 (978-0-7587-6681-6(5)) Book Wholesalers, Inc.

—I Know an Old Lady Who Swallowed a Fly, 3 vols. Westcott, Nadine Bernard, illus. 2003. (Sing-Along Stories Ser.). (Illus.). 11p. (J). (ps-ps). bds. 6.99 (978-0-316-93084-0(9) , Tingley, Megan Bks.) Little, Brown Bks. for Young Readers.

FOLK SONGS, FRENCH
O'Neal, Debbie Trafton. Are You Sleeping? Huang, Benrei, illus. 2004. (Sing-It! Ser.). 32p. (J). 8.99 (978-0-8066-4351-9(X) , Augsburg Bks.) Augsburg Fortress, Pubs.

FOLK SONGS, JEWISH
Chwast, Seymour, illus. Had Gadya: A Passover Song. rev. ed. 2005. 32p. (J). 16.95 (978-1-59643-033-4(8)) Roaring Brook Pr.

FOLK SONGS, SPANISH
Hague, Eleanor. Spanish-American Folk-Songs. 2001. 115p. (YA). reprint ed. 88.00 (978-0-7222-5076-1(2)) Library Reprints, Inc.

Orozco, Jose-Luis. De Colores & Otras Canciones Folclor-icas Latino-Americanas Para Ninos. 1999. Tr. of De Colores & Other Latin-American Folk Songs for Children. (J). 14.79 (978-0-606-16784-0(6)) Tandem Library Bks.

FOLK SONGS—UNITED STATES
Bissex, Rachel. Dancing With My Mother. Passman, Emily, illus. 2003. 14p. (J). spiral bd. 10.00 (978-0-9742516-0-8(7)) Salmon Hole Poetry Pr.

Candlewick Books Staff, Books. Old MacDonald Had a Farm. 2003. (gr. k-3). lib. bdg. 11.80 (978-0-613-74739-4(9)) Tandem Library Bks.

Guthrie, Woody. This Land Is Your Land. Jakobsen, Kathy, illus. 1998. 32p. (J). (ps-17). 16.99 (978-0-316-39215-0(4)) Little Brown & Co.

Lomax, John A. & Lomax, Alan, eds. Our Singing Country: Folk Songs & Ballads. 2000. 464p. pap. 16.95 (978-0-486-41089-0(7)) Dover Pubns., Inc.

Priceman, Marjorie. Froggie Went A-Courting. 2001. (J). (gr. k-3). 26.90 incl. audio (978-0-8045-6879-1(0) , 6879) Spoken Arts, Inc.

Qualey, Marsha, ed. She'll Be Coming 'Round the Mountain. D'Antonio, Sandra, illus. 2004. (Traditional Songs Ser.). 24p. (ps-2). 22.60 (978-1-4048-0153-0(7)) Picture Window Bks.

Seeger, Ruth Crawford. American Folksongs for Children. 2004. 190p. 19.95 (978-0-8256-0346-4(3)) Music Sales Corp.

Seeger, Ruth Crawford, ed. Animal Folk Songs for Children: Traditional American Songs. Cooney, Barbara, illus. 2004. 80p. (J). (gr. k-4). reprint ed. pap. 17.00 (978-0-7567-7968-9(5)) DIANE Publishing Co.

Sieling, Peter. Folk Music. 2002. (North American Folklore Ser.). (Illus.). 112p. (YA). (gr. 7 up). lib. bdg. (978-1-59084-342-0(8)) Mason Crest Pubs.

—Folk Songs. 2002. (North American Folklore Ser.). (Illus.). 112p. (YA). (gr. 7 up). lib. bdg. (978-1-59084-344-4(4)) Mason Crest Pubs.

FOLK TALES
see Folklore

FOLKLORE

see also Fairies; Grail; Monsters; Mythology; Superstition

Aardema, Verna. Why Mosquitoes Buzz in People's Ears. 2004. 24.95 incl. audio (978-0-89719-695-6(3)); pap. 14.95 incl. audio (978-1-55592-675-5(4)); (J). pap. 32.75 incl. audio (978-1-55592-335-8(6)); (J). pap. 32.75 incl. audio (978-1-55592-336-5(4)); (J). pap. 14.95 incl. audio (978-1-56008-081-7(7)) Weston Woods Studios, Inc.

Ada, Alma Flor. The Lizard & the Sun - La Lagartija y el Sol: A Folktale in English & Spanish. 1999. (SPA.). (gr. k-3). lib. bdg. 15.30 (978-0-613-85708-6(9)) Tandem Library Bks.

—With Love, Little Red Hen. Tryon, Leslie, illus. 2004. 40p. (J). pap. 7.99 (978-0-689-87061-3(2) , Aladdin) Simon & Schuster Children's Publishing.

Ada, Alma Flor & Tryon, Leslie. With Love, Little Red Hen. 2001. (Illus.). 40p. (J). (gr. k-3). 16.95 (978-0-689-82581-1(1) , Atheneum) Simon & Schuster Children's Publishing.

Aesop. Aesop's Fox. Sogabe, Aki, illus. 1999. 32p. (J). (gr. k-3). 16.00 (978-0-15-201671-5(6)) Harcourt Children's Bks.

—Belling the Cat: A Retelling of Aesop's Fable. Silverman, Diane, illus. 2004. (Read-It! Readers Ser.). 24p. (C). (gr. k-3). 18.60 (978-1-4048-0321-3(1)) Picture Window Bks.

—The Boy Who Cried Wolf: A Retelling of Aesop's Fable. Silverman, Diane, illus. 2004. (Read-It! Readers Ser.). 24p. (C). (gr. k-3). 18.60 (978-1-4048-0319-0(X)) Picture Window Bks.

—The Boy Who Cried Wolf: Sincerity. Goodell, Jon, illus. 2005. (J). ***978-1-4127-3760-9(5))** Publications International, Ltd.

—The Country Mouse & the City Mouse: A Retelling of Aesop's Fable. Silverman, Diane, illus. 2004. (Read-It! Readers Ser.). 24p. (C). (gr. k-3). 18.60 (978-1-4048-0318-3(1)) Picture Window Bks.

—The Crow & the Pitcher: A Retelling of Aesop's Fable. Silverman, Diane, illus. 2004. (Read-It! Readers Ser.). 24p. (C). (gr. k-3). 18.60 (978-1-4048-0322-0(X)) Picture Window Bks.

—The Dog & the Wolf: A Retelling of Aesop's Fable. Silverman, Diane, illus. 2004. (Read-It! Readers Ser.). 24p. (C). (gr. k-3). 18.60 (978-1-4048-0323-7(8)) Picture Window Bks.

—The Donkey in the Lion's Skin: A Retelling of Aesop's Fable. Silverman, Diane, illus. 2004. (Read-It! Readers Ser.). 24p. (C). (gr. k-3). 18.60 (978-1-4048-0320-6(3)) Picture Window Bks.

—Unwitting Wisdom. Ward, Helen, illus. 2004. 64p. (J). 18.95 (978-0-8118-4450-5(1)) Chronicle Bks. LLC.

Allen, Debbie. Brothers of the Knight. Nelson, Kadir, illus. 2001. 40p. (J). (gr. k-4). pap. 6.99 (978-0-14-230016-9(0) , Puffin) Penguin Group (USA) Inc.

—Brothers of the Knight. Nelson, Kadir, illus. 2001. (J). (ps-3). lib. bdg. 15.30 (978-0-613-44379-1(9)) Tandem Library Bks.

Amery, Heather. Stories from Around the World. Edwards, Linda, illus. 2004. (Stories for Young Children Ser.). (SPA.). 128p. (J). (ps-3). 16.95 (978-0-7460-4207-6(8)); lib. bdg. 24.95 (978-1-58086-330-8(2)) EDC Publishing.

Andrews, Jan. Out of the Everywhere: New Tales for Canada. Ng, Simon, illus. 2001. (J). (gr. 2 up). (978-0-88899-402-8(8)) Groundwood Bks.

Andruetto, Maria Teresa. El Anillo Encantado. 2002. (SPA.). 64p. (J). pap. 6.95 (978-1-4000-0009-8(2)) Random Hse., Inc.

Animal Tales. (3-Minute Treasury Ser.). 160p. (J). (978-0-7853-6999-8(6) , 7168100) Publications International, Ltd.

Appleby, Sue. Umoyana the Little Wind. Torgah, F. K. Atakpa Kple Edoh, tr. 2000. (EWE., Illus.). pap. 3.00 (978-0-521-79579-1(6)) Cambridge Univ. Pr.

—Umoyana the Little Wind: Amharic Version. Duguma, Melaku Wakuma, tr. 1999. (Cambridge Reading Routes Ser.). (AMH., Illus.). 16p. pap. 3.70 (978-0-521-66833-0(6)) Cambridge Univ. Pr.

—Umoyana the Little Wind: Dagbani Version. Abdulai, Fuseini-Bila, tr. 2000. (Illus.). pap. 3.00 (978-0-521-79598-2(2)) Cambridge Univ. Pr.

—Umoyana the Little Wind: Fante Version. Aggrey, Safohen J. E. K., tr. 2000. (Illus.). pap. 3.00 (978-0-521-79569-2(9)) Cambridge Univ. Pr.

—Umoyana the Little Wind: Tigre Version. Kebebew, Amare Hagos, tr. 1999. (Cambridge Reading Routes Ser.). (TIG., Illus.). 16p. pap. 3.70 (978-0-521-66823-1(9)) Cambridge Univ. Pr.

Arrow to the Sun. 2004. 29.95 incl. cd-rom (978-1-55592-372-3(0)); pap. 32.75 incl. audio (978-1-55592-189-7(2)); (J). 24.95 incl. audio (978-0-89719-859-2(X)); (J). pap. 18.95 incl. audio compact disk (978-1-55592-371-6(2)); (J). pap. 38.75 incl. audio compact disk (978-1-55592-373-0(9)) Weston Woods Studios, Inc.

Artell, Mike. Petite Rouge: A Cajun Red Riding Hood. 2001. lib. bdg. 15.30 (978-0-613-67470-6(7)) Tandem Library Bks.

Aspengren, Michael A., illus. Tales of Silliness: Retold Timeless Classics. 1999. (Cover-to-Cover Timeless Classics Ser.). 63p. (J). pap. (978-0-7891-2328-2(2)); (gr. 1-4). lib. bdg. 13.95 (978-0-7807-7749-1(2)) Perfection Learning Corp.

Atwater-Rhodes, Amelia. Hawksong. 2004. 256p. (YA). (gr. 7). reprint ed. mass mkt. 5.99 (978-0-440-23803-4(X) , Laurel Leaf) Random Hse. Children's Bks.

—Hawksong Vol. 1: The Kiesha'ra. 2003. 256p. (YA). (gr. 7-10). 9.95 (978-0-385-73071-6(3) , Delacorte Bks. for Young Readers) Random Hse. Children's Bks.

Aylesworth, Jim. Full Belly Bowl. Halperin, Wendy Anderson, illus. 1999. 40p. (J). (ps-3). 17.99 (978-0-689-81033-6(4) , Atheneum) Simon & Schuster Children's Publishing.

—The Gingerbread Man. 2002. (Illus.). (J). 25.06 (978-0-7587-2597-4(3)) Book Wholesalers, Inc.

—The Gingerbread Man. McClintock, Barbara, illus. 1998. 32p. (J). (ps-1). pap. 16.95 (978-0-590-97219-2(7)) Scholastic, Inc.

Babbitt, Ellen C. More Jataka Tales. Young, Ellsworth, illus. 2006. pap. ***978-1-4065-0347-0(9))** Dodo Pr.

—More Jataka Tales. 2004. reprint ed. pap. 1.99 (978-1-4192-3522-1(2)) Kessinger Publishing, LLC.

Bailey, Sian, illus. Grandfather Mountain: Stories of Gods & Heroes from Many Cultures. 2004. 80p. (J). (gr. 3-6). 19.99 (978-1-84148-789-2(9)) Barefoot Bks., Inc.

Bania, Michael. Kumak's House: A Tale of the Far North. 2005. (Illus.). 32p. (gr. k-3). pap. 8.95 (978-0-88240-541-4(1)); 15.95 (978-0-88240-540-7(3)) Graphic Arts Ctr. Publishing Co.

—Kumak's House: A Tale of the Far North. 2002. (gr. k-3). lib. bdg. 17.60 (978-0-613-61914-1(5)) Tandem Library Bks.

Barclay, Aegea & Barclay, Katrina. The Hand of Zeus. 2004. 48p. 16.95 (978-0-9758803-6-4(5)) Aegean Design.

Barker, Cicely Mary. Home Sweet Home. 2005. (Flower Fairies Friends Ser.). (Illus.). 32p. (J). 5.99 (978-0-7232-5381-5(1) , Warne) Penguin Group (USA) Inc.

Batt, Tanya Robyn. The Faerie's Gift. Ceccoli, Nicoletta, illus. 2003. 32p. (J). (ps-3). 16.99 (978-1-84148-998-8(0)) Barefoot Bks., Inc.

Bauer, John, illus. Swedish Folk Tales. 2004. 240p. (J). 28.00 (978-0-86315-457-7(3)) Floris Bks. GBR. *Dist:* SteinerBooks, Inc.

Baum, F. E. & Baum, L. Frank. Mother Goose in Prose. Parrish, Maxfield, illus. unabr. ed. 2002. 288p. (J). (gr. 4-7). reprint ed. pap. 9.95 (978-0-486-42086-8(8)) Dover Pubns., Inc.

Baum, L. Frank. Magic of Oz. 2003. pap. 14.95 (978-1-58726-043-8(3) , Mundus) Ann Arbor Media Group, LLC.

Beake, Lesley. One Dark Night: Akwapim Twi Version. Asante, Comfort, tr. 2000. (TWI., Illus.). pap. 3.00 (978-0-521-79618-7(0)) Cambridge Univ. Pr.

—One Dark Night: Dagbani Version. Abdulai, Fuseini-Bila, tr. 2000. (Illus.). pap. 3.00 (978-0-521-79597-5(4)) Cambridge Univ. Pr.

Beeler, Selby B. Throw Your Tooth on the Roof: Tooth Traditions from Around the World. Karas, G. Brian, illus. 1998. 32p. (J). (gr. k-3). tchr. ed. 16.00 (978-0-395-89108-7(6)) Houghton Mifflin Co. Trade & Reference Div.

Benedek, Elek. Palko the Piper. 1999. (J). pap. 21.00 (978-963-13-4781-4(8)) Corvina Books HUN. *Dist:* State Mutual Bk. & Periodical Service, Ltd.

Besant, Annie W. Legends & Tales Lotus Leaves for the Y. 2006. pap. 19.95 ***978-1-4286-2494-8(5))** Kessinger Publishing, LLC.

Beschi, Viramamooni. The Adventure of the Gooroo Noodle. 2001. 112p. reprint ed. (978-81-206-1592-2(1)) Laurier Bks., Ltd.

Between the Lions - Early Literacy Kit - Oh, Yes, It Can!, 1 cass., 1 bk. 2005. (Between the Lions Ser.). 36p. (J). VHS 29.95 (978-1-59375-286-6(5) , WG38643) WGBH Boston Video.

Bevan, Finn. Sacred Skies. 1998. (Landscapes of Legend Ser.). (Illus.). 32p. (J). (gr. 4-8). pap. 6.95 (978-0-516-26300-7(5) , Children's Pr.) Scholastic Library Publishing.

Bischel, Mark, illus. Tales of Honor. 1999. (Cover-to-Cover Timeless Classics Ser.). 55p. (J). pap. (978-0-7891-2861-4(6)); (gr. 1-4). lib. bdg. 13.95 (978-0-7807-7855-9(3)) Perfection Learning Corp.

Bishop, Dorothy S., et al. Perez y Martina. 2001. (SPA & ENG., Illus.). 64p. (J). 6.95 (978-0-8442-7167-5(5) , NT169) McGraw-Hill/Contemporary.

Blair, Eric. The Gingerbread Man: A Retelling of the Classic Traditional Tale. Peterson, Ben, illus. 2005. (Read-It! Readers Ser.). 32p. (J). (gr. k-3). 18.60 (978-1-4048-0969-7(4)) Picture Window Bks.

—Pecos Bill Tames the Wild West: A Retelling of the Classic Traditional Tale. Chambers-Goldbert, Micah, illus. 2005. (Read-It! Readers Ser.). 32p. (C). (gr. k-3). 18.60 (978-1-4048-0977-2(5)) Picture Window Bks.

—The Pied Piper: A Retelling of the Classic Traditional Tale. Peterson, Ben, illus. 2005. (Read-It! Readers Ser.). 32p. (C). (gr. k-3). 18.60 (978-1-4048-0979-6(1)) Picture Window Bks.

—Tom Thumb: A Retelling of the Classic Fairy Tale. Ouren, Todd, illus. 2004. (Read-It! Readers Ser.). 32p. (J). (gr. k-3). 18.60 (978-1-4048-0593-4(1)) Picture Window Bks.

Bloch, Marie H., ed. Ukrainian Folk Tales. Hnizdovsky, Jacques, illus. 1999. (Hippocrene Folk Tale Ser.). 76p. (gr. 2-5). 12.50 (978-0-7818-0744-9(1)) Hippocrene Bks., Inc.

Boada, Francesc & Perrault, Charles. Puss in Boots: A Bilingual Book. Merino, Jose Luis, tr. from CAT. Merino, Jose Luis, illus. 2004. Tr. of El Gato con Botas. (ENG & SPA.). 32p. (J). pap. 6.95 (978-0-8118-3924-2(9)) Chronicle Bks. LLC.

Boada, Francesc, et al. Puss in Boots: A Bilingual Book. 2004. Tr. of El Gato con Botas. (ENG & SPA., Illus.). 32p. (J). (gr. k-3). 14.95 (978-0-8118-3923-5(0)) Chronicle Bks. LLC.

Bofill, Francesc. Juan y los Frijoles Magicos. Alejando, Alis, tr. from SPA. Ballester, Arnal, illus. 1998. Tr. of Jack & the Beanstalk. (SPA.). 32p. (J). (ps-3). 14.95 (978-0-8118-2062-2(9)) Chronicle Bks. LLC.

Bonnice, Sherry. Christmas & Santa Claus Folklore. 2003. (North American Folklore Ser.). (Illus.). 112p. (YA). (gr. 7 up). lib. bdg. (978-1-59084-330-7(4)) Mason Crest Pubs.

—Folk Fashion. 2002. (North American Folklore Ser.). (Illus.). 112p. (J). (gr. 7 up). lib. bdg. (978-1-59084-338-3(X)) Mason Crest Pubs.

Bosom, Monica, ed. The Ugly Duckling. Peris, Carme, illus. 1999. 32p. (J). (ps-3). 8.95 (978-0-7641-5149-1(5)) Barron's Educational Series, Inc.

Brabourne, Edward Hugessen Knatchbull-Hugessen. River Legends of the Thames & Rhine. Doré, Gustave, illus. 2005. (J). pap. (978-0-486-44372-0(8)) Dover Pubns., Inc.

Brill, Marlene Targ. Tooth Tales from Around the World. Krenina, Katya, illus. 1998. 32p. (J). (ps-3). 15.95 (978-0-88106-398-1(3)); pap. 6.95 (978-0-88106-399-8(1)) Charlesbridge Publishing, Inc.

Brinkerhoff, Shirley. Family Folklore. 2003. (North American Folklore Ser.). (Illus.). 112p. (YA). (gr. 7 up). lib. bdg. (978-1-59084-333-8(9)) Mason Crest Pubs.

Brown, Stephanie Gwyn. Professor Aesop's the Crow & the Pitcher. 2004. (Illus.). 30p. (J). tchr. ed. 15.95 (978-1-58246-087-1(6) , Tricycle Pr.) Ten Speed Pr.

Brun, Samuel J. Tales of Laguedoc: From the South of France. 1999. (Library of Folklore). (Illus.). 240p. (gr. 7-12). 14.95 (978-0-7818-0715-9(8)) Hippocrene Bks., Inc.

Bukiet, Suzanne. Scripts of the World. 2nd ed. (Illus.). 91p. (YA). reprint ed. 19.95 (978-0-9656274-1-2(1)) Another Language Pr.

Bulloch, Ivan. I Wish I Were a Fairy. 1999. (ps-2). lib. bdg. 15.25 (978-0-613-43331-0(9)) Tandem Library Bks.

Burkett, Beverley. Baby Monkey's Bananas. Torgah, F. K. Atakpa Kple Edoh, tr. 2000. (EWE., Illus.). pap. 3.00 (978-0-521-79584-5(2)) Cambridge Univ. Pr.

—Baby Monkey's Bananas: Akwapim Twi Version. Asante, Comfort, tr. 2000. (TWI., Illus.). pap. 3.00 (978-0-521-79623-1(7)) Cambridge Univ. Pr.

—Baby Monkey's Bananas: Asant Twi Version. Asenso, Okofo, tr. 2000. (TWI., Illus.). pap. 3.00 (978-0-521-79613-2(X)) Cambridge Univ. Pr.

—Baby Monkey's Bananas: Dagbani Version. Abdulai, Fuseini-Bila, tr. 2000. (Illus.). pap. 3.00 (978-0-521-79603-3(2)) Cambridge Univ. Pr.

—Baby Monkey's Bananas: Fante Version. Aggrey, Safohen J. E. K., tr. 2000. (Illus.). pap. 3.00 (978-0-521-79574-6(5)) Cambridge Univ. Pr.

—Baby Monkey's Bananas Hausa Version. Bello, Gidado, tr. 1998. (Cambridge African Language Library). (HAU., Illus.). 16p. pap. 6.60 (978-0-521-64794-6(0)) Cambridge Univ. Pr.

Busquets, Jordi. Leo y Veo, las Hadas.Tr. of I Read & See, the Fairies. (SPA.). 24p. (J). 3.48 (978-84-305-9408-5(6)) Susaeta Ediciones, S.A. ESP. *Dist:* AIMS International Bks., Inc.

Cha, Dia & Livo, Norma. Teaching with Folk Stories of the Hmong: An Activity Book. 2000. (Learning Through Folklore Ser.). (Illus.). 109p. (J). (gr. k-12). pap., act. bk. ed. 28.00 (978-1-56308-668-7(9) , LU6689) Libraries Unlimited, Inc.

Chang, Monica. Story of the Chinese Zodiac. 2000. (VIE & ENG.). (J). 18.95 (978-957-32-2144-9(6)) Yuan-liou Publishing Co., Ltd. TWN. *Dist:* AIMS International Bks., Inc.

Chapman, Jane. Sing a Song of Sixpence: A Pocketful of Nursery Rhymes & Tales. Chapman, Jane, illus. 2004. (Illus.). 64p. (J). (ps-1). 15.99 (978-0-7636-2545-0(0)) Candlewick Pr.

Chung, Chi, illus. Captain Stormalong. 2004. (Imagination Ser.). 32p. (C). (gr. 3-5). 22.60 (978-0-7565-0601-8(8)) Compass Point Bks.

Clayton, Sally. Tales Told in Tents. Herxheimer, Sophie, illus. 2004. 64p. (J). 16.95 (978-1-84507-066-3(6)) Lincoln, Frances Ltd. GBR. *Dist:* Perseus Distribution.

Climo, Shirley. Irish Cinderlad. 2000. 12.79 (978-0-606-17881-5(3)); lib. bdg. 14.15 (978-0-613-28540-7(9)) Tandem Library Bks.

—Monkey Business: Stories from Around the World. Brooks, Erik, illus. rev. ed. 2005. 128p. (J). 18.95 (978-0-8050-6392-9(7) , Holt, Henry & Co. Bks. For Young Readers) Holt, Henry & Co.

—Persian Cinderella. 2002. (978-0-606-22280-8(4)); 2001. lib. bdg. 14.10 (978-0-613-44245-9(8)) Tandem Library Bks.

—Pride of Princesses: Princess Tales from Around the World. 1999. (978-0-606-16696-6(3)) Tandem Library Bks.

—A Serenade of Mermaids: Mermaid Tales from Around the World. Falkenstern, Lisa, illus. 1999. (Trophy Chapter Bks.). 112p. (J). (gr. 2-5). pap. 4.25 (978-0-06-442103-4(1) , Harper Trophy) HarperCollins Pubs.

—Serenade of Mermaids: Mermaid Tales from Around the World. 1999. (978-0-606-16697-3(1)) Tandem Library Bks.

Cohen, Caron Lee. Digger Pig & the Turnip. 2000. (gr. k-3). lib. bdg. 11.80 (978-0-613-89283-4(6)); lib. bdg. 11.80 (978-0-613-63276-8(1)); (Illus.). (J). (978-0-606-18171-6(7)) Tandem Library Bks.

Coleman, Melvin. B. C. & Phoenicia: A Traditional Folktale. 2004. (Illus.). 201p. 25.00 (978-0-9764065-0-1(0)) Gestalt Pubns.

Collins, Sheila Hebert. Les Trois Cochons. Soper, Patrick, illus. 1999. Tr. of Three Little Pigs. (FRE.). 32p. (J). (gr. k-3). 15.95 (978-1-56554-325-6(4)) Pelican Publishing Co., Inc.

Corneilse, Janine. The Terrible Graakwa. Ablorh, Samuel Adjei & Bahemuka, Gaetano, trs. 2000. (GAA., Illus.). pap. 3.00 (978-0-521-79595-1(8)) Cambridge Univ. Pr.

—The Terrible Graakwa: Akwapim Twi Version. Asante, Comfort & Bahemuka, Gaetano, trs. 2000. (TWI., Illus.). pap. 3.00 (978-0-521-79626-2(1)) Cambridge Univ. Pr.

—The Terrible Graakwa: Amharic Version. Wako, Tegegn Nuresu, tr. 1999. (Cambridge Reading Routes Ser.). (AMH., Illus.). 16p. pap. 3.70 (978-0-521-66832-3(8)) Cambridge Univ. Pr.

—The Terrible Graakwa: Asante Twi Version. Asenso, Okofo & Bahemuka, Gaetano, trs. 2000. (TWI., Illus.). pap. 3.00 (978-0-521-79615-6(6)) Cambridge Univ. Pr.

—The Terrible Graakwa: Dagbani Version. Abdulai, Fuseini-Bila & Bahemuka, Gaetano, trs. 2000. (Illus.). pap. 3.00 (978-0-521-79605-7(9)) Cambridge Univ. Pr.

—The Terrible Graakwa: Fante Version. Bahemuka, Gaetano & Aggrey, Safohen J. E. K., trs. 2001. (Illus.). pap. 3.00 (978-0-521-79576-0(1)) Cambridge Univ. Pr.

—The Terrible Graakwa: Luganda Version. Lubega, Bonnie, tr. 1998. (Cambridge African Language Library). (LUG., Illus.). 16p. pap. 3.65 (978-0-521-63797-8(X)) Cambridge Univ. Pr.

—The Terrible Graakwa: Tigre Version. Kebebew, Amare Hagos, tr. 1999. (Cambridge Reading Routes Ser.). (TIG., Illus.). 16p. pap. 3.70 (978-0-521-66822-4(0)) Cambridge Univ. Pr.

Cornelison, Sue F., illus. Tales of Beauty. 1999. (Cover-to-Cover Timeless Classics Ser.). 63p. (J). pap. (978-0-7891-2326-8(6)); (gr. 1-4). lib. bdg. 13.95 (978-0-7807-7747-7(6)) Perfection Learning Corp.

Councell, Ruth T., illus. Once upon a Bedtime Story: Classic Tales. 2003. 96p. (J). (ps-1). 17.95 (978-1-56397-484-7(3)) Boyds Mills Pr.

Cousins, Coleen, et al. Ntsiki's Surprise. Torgah, F. K. Atakpa Kple Edoh, tr. 2001. (EWE., Illus.). 16p. pap. 1.40 (978-0-521-79580-7(X)) Cambridge Univ. Pr.

—Ntsiki's Surprise. Ablorh, Samuel Adjei, tr. 2000. (GAA., Illus.). pap. 3.00 (978-0-521-79590-6(7)) Cambridge Univ. Pr.

—Ntsiki's Surprise: Akwapim Twi Version. Asante, Comfort, tr. 2000. (TWI., Illus.). pap. 3.00 (978-0-521-79620-0(2)) Cambridge Univ. Pr.

—Ntsiki's Surprise: Asante Twi Version. Asenso, Okofo, tr. 2000. (TWI., Illus.). pap. 3.00 (978-0-521-79609-5(1)) Cambridge Univ. Pr.

—Ntsiki's Surprise: Dagbani Version. Abdulai, Fuseini-Bila, tr. 2000. (Illus.). pap. 3.00 (978-0-521-79599-9(0)) Cambridge Univ. Pr.

Craft, Kinuko. Cinderella. 2000. (Illus.). 32p. (J). (ps-3). 16.95 (978-1-58717-004-1(3) , SeaStar Bks.) Chronicle Bks. LLC.

Craft, Kinuko Y., illus. Cinderella. 2000. 32p. (J). (ps-4). 16.50 (978-1-58717-005-8(1) , SeaStar Bks.) Chronicle Bks. LLC.

Crossley-Holland, Kevin. Tales from the Old World. 2nd ed. 2000. (J). pap. 9.95 ***978-1-85881-794-1(3))** Orion Publishing Group, Ltd. GBR. *Dist:* Independent Pubs. Group.

Daily, Don, illus. The Classic Treasury of Aesop's Fables. 1999. 56p. (J). (ps-3). 9.98 (978-0-7624-0413-1(2) , Courage Bks.) Running Pr. Bk. Pubs.

Daning, Tom. The Four Dragons: A Chinese Myth. 2007. (Graphic Myths (New York, N.Y.) Ser.). (Illus.). 24p. (J). (978-1-4042-2343-1(6)); pap. (978-1-4042-2153-6(0)); (gr. 2-6). lib. bdg. 21.25 (978-1-4042-3400-0(4)) Rosen Publishing Group, Inc., The. (PowerKids Pr.).

Davila, Andrew. Prophecies of the Ancient. 2003. 110p. (YA). pap. 9.95 (978-0-595-26851-1(X)) iUniverse, Inc.

Davol, Marguerite W. The Snake's Tales. Heo, Yumi, illus. 2002. 32p. (J). (gr. k-4). 15.95 (978-0-439-35241-3(X) , Orchard Bks.) Scholastic, Inc.

DeSpain, Pleasant. Sweet Land of Story: Thirty-Six American Tales to Tell. Bell, Donald-, illus. 2000. 176p. (J). (gr. 3-7). lib. bdg. 22.20 (978-0-613-35886-6(4)) Tandem Library Bks.

—Tales of Cats, Vol. 9. Bell, Don, tr. Bell, Don, illus. 2003. 80p. 14.95 (978-0-87483-713-1(8)) August Hse. Pubs., Inc.

—Tales of Enchantment, Vol. 7. Bell, Don, tr. Bell, Don, illus. 2003. 80p. 14.95 (978-0-87483-711-7(1)) August Hse. Pubs., Inc.

—Tales of Heroes, Vol. 4. Bell, Don, illus. 2002. (Books of Nine Lives: Vol. 4). 80p. (ps-3). 14.95 (978-0-87483-666-0(2)) August Hse. Pubs., Inc.

—Tales of Holidays, Vol. 5. Bell, Don, illus. 2002. (Books of Nine Lives: Vol. 5). 80p. (gr. 4-7). 14.95 (978-0-87483-667-7(0)) August Hse. Pubs., Inc.

—Tales of Insects, Vol. 6. Bell, Don, illus. 2002. (Books of Nine Lives: Vol. 6). 80p. (gr. 4-7). 14.95 (978-0-87483-668-4(9)) August Hse. Pubs., Inc.

—Tales of Nonsense & Tomfoolery. Bell, Don, illus. 2001. 80p. (gr. 2-8). pap. 3.99 (978-0-87483-645-5(X)); Vol. 2. (Books of Nine Lives: Vol. 2). (ps-3). 14.95 (978-0-87483-670-7(0)) August Hse. Pubs., Inc.

—Tales of Tricksters. Bell, Don, illus. 2001. (Books of Nine Lives: Vol. 1). 80p. (ps-3). 14.95 (978-0-87483-669-1(7)) August Hse. Pubs., Inc.

—Tales of Tricksters: Books of Nine Lives, Vol. 1. Bell, Don, illus. 2001. 80p. (gr. 2-4). pap. 3.99 (978-0-87483-644-8(1)) August Hse. Pubs., Inc.

—Tales of Wisdom & Justice, Vol. 3. Bell, Don, illus. 2001. (Books of Nine Lives: Vol. 3). 80p. (ps-3). 14.95 (978-0-87483-671-4(9)) August Hse. Pubs., Inc.

—Tales of Wisdom & Justice: Books of Nine Lives. Bell, Don, illus. 2001. (Books of Nine Lives: Vol. 3). 80p. (ps-3). pap. 3.99 (978-0-87483-646-2(8)) August Hse. Pubs., Inc.

—Tales to Frighten & Delight, Vol. 8. Bell, Don, tr. Bell, Don, illus. 2003. 80p. 14.95 (978-0-87483-712-4(X)) August Hse. Pubs., Inc.

Diakite, Baba Wague. The Magic Gourd. 2003. (BAM & ENG., Illus.). 32p. (J). (gr. k-3). pap. 16.95 (978-0-439-43960-2(4) , Blue Sky Pr., The) Scholastic, Inc.

Dijkstra, Lida. Little Mouse. Grobler, Piet, illus. 2004. 32p. (J). 15.95 (978-1-932425-06-2(3) , Lemniscaat) Boyds Mills Pr.

Diouf, Sylviane A. Bintou's Braids. 2004. (Illus.). 40p. (J). pap. 6.95 (978-0-8118-4629-5(6)) Chronicle Bks. LLC.

Disney Staff, creator. Chicken Little, Vol. 1. 2005. (Illus.). 96p. pap. 7.99 (978-1-59532-724-6(X) , Tokyopop Kids) TOKYOPOP, Inc.

Djurklou, Baron G. Swedish Folk Tales. Braekstad, H. L., tr. from SWE. 1998. (Library of Folklore). (Illus.). 178p. (gr. 4-7). 12.50 (978-0-7818-0717-3(4)) Hippocrene Bks., Inc.

Downie, Mary Alice & Zola, Mequido. How the Devil Got His Cat & Other Multicultural Folktales for Children. Gilliland, Jillian Hulme, illus. 144p. (J). pap. 16.95 (978-1-55082-100-0(8)) Quarry Pr. CAN. *Dist:* LPC/ InBook.

Dracott, Alice E. Folk Tales from Simla (Himalayan Region of India) Stories from the Himalayas. 2nd ed. 1998. (Library of Folklore). (Illus.). 225p. (gr. 7-12). 14.95 (978-0-7818-0704-3(2)) Hippocrene Bks., Inc.

Drummer Hoff. 2004. (J). pap. 38.75 incl. audio compact disk (978-1-55592-406-5(9)); pap. 32.75 incl. audio (978-1-55592-223-8(6)); pap. 14.95 incl. audio (978-1-56008-192-0(9)) Weston Woods Studios, Inc.

East, Helen & Maddern, Eric. Spirit of the Forest: Tree Tales from Around the World. Marks, Alan, illus. 2003. 48p. (J). pap. 10.95 (978-0-7112-1879-6(X)) Lincoln, Frances Ltd. GBR. *Dist:* Transition Vendor.

Edens, Cooper, compiled by. Princess Stories: A Classic Illustrated Edition. 2004. (Illus.). 136p. (J). (gr. 1-5). 19.95 (978-0-8118-4032-3(8)) Chronicle Bks. LLC.

Egelberg, Arlene & Clark, Raymond C. How & Why Folktales: From Around the World. 2004. 106p. pap. 14.00 (978-0-86647-180-0(4)) Pro Lingua Assocs., Inc.

Escott, John. The Little Red Hen. West, Annie, illus. 2003. 32p. (J). (ps-3). 15.95 (978-1-57768-492-3(3) , Gingham Dog Pr.) School Specialty Publishing.

Evetts-Secker, Josephine. The Barefoot Book of Father & Son Tales. Cann, Helen, illus. 2000. 80p. (J). (gr. 4-7). 19.95 (978-1-902283-32-6(5)) Barefoot Bks., Inc.

—The Barefoot Book of Mother & Son Tales. Cann, Helen, illus. 2000. 80p. (YA). (gr. 4-7). 19.95 (978-1-902283-05-0(8)) Barefoot Bks., Inc.

Fabulous Tales (English) 2000. (J). (978-1-58805-034-2(3)) DS-Max USA, Inc.

Fatus, Sophie, illus. The Story Tree: Tales to Read Aloud. 2005. 64p. (J). (ps-2). pap. 14.99 incl. audio compact disk (978-1-905236-13-8(1)) Barefoot Bks., Inc.

Ferrin, Wendy Wakefield. Grandmother's Alligator: Burukenge Wa Nyanya. Mwangi, Simmon, tr. Broyles, Beverly Ashley, illus. 2003. (SWA & ENG.). 56p. (J). (gr. 1 up). 17.95 (978-0-9703632-3-7(0)) Wakefield Connection, The.

Fillmore, Parker H. Czech Moravian & Slovak Fairy Tales. 1998. (Library of Folklore). (Illus.). 243p. (gr. 7-12). 14.95 (978-0-7818-0714-2(X)) Hippocrene Bks., Inc.

Finch, Mary. The Little Red Hen & the Ear of Wheat. Bell, Elisabeth, illus. 32p. (J). (ps-1). 2001. pap. 5.99 (978-1-84148-234-7(X)); 1999. 15.95 (978-1-902283-47-0(3)) Barefoot Bks., Inc.

Fish, Becky Durost & Fish, Bruce. Fables & Their Morals Vol. 2: The Fighting Roosters & the Eagle to the Lion in Love. 1999. (Illus.). 64p. (J). 19.24 (978-0-7910-5212-9(5) , Chelsea Hse.) Facts On File, Inc.

Fish, Bruce & Fish, Becky Durost. Fables & Their Morals Vol. 1: Androcles & the Lion to The Field of Treasure. 1999. (Illus.). 64p. (J). 19.23 (978-0-7910-5211-2(7) , Chelsea Hse.) Facts On File, Inc.

Fleischman, Paul. Glass Slipper, Gold Sandal: A Worldwide Cinderella. Paschkis, Julie, illus. 2007. 32p. (J). (gr. k up). 16.95 ***(978-0-8050-7953-1(X))** Holt, Henry & Co.

Floyd, Lucy. Rabbit & Turtle Go to School. Denise, Christopher, illus. 2003. (Green Light Readers Level 1 Ser.). 24p. (J). 11.95 (978-0-15-204811-2(1)); pap. 3.95 (978-0-15-204851-8(0)) Harcourt Children's Bks. (Green Light Readers).

—Rabbit & Turtle Go to School. 2000. (Green Light Readers Ser.). (J). (978-0-606-20034-9(7)); lib. bdg. 11.80 (978-0-613-63339-0(3)) Tandem Library Bks.

Folktales from Ecosystems Around the World. 2002. (Illus.). (J). pap. 6.25 (978-0-7398-6171-4(9)) Steck-Vaughn.

Fontes, Justine & Fontes, Ron. How the Leopard Got Its Spots. Motoyama, Keiko, illus. 2002. (Tales from Around the World Ser.). 24p. (J). (gr. k-k). 2.99 (978-0-307-99501-8(1) , Golden Bks.) Random Hse. Children's Bks.

—How the Turtle Got Its Shell. Motoyama, Keiko, illus. 2000. (Tales from Around the World Ser.). 24p. (J). (gr. k-k). 2.99 (978-0-307-96007-8(2) , Golden Bks.) Random Hse. Children's Bks.

The Fool of the World & the Flying Ship. 2004. 24.95 incl. audio (978-0-7882-0557-6(9)) Weston Woods Studios, Inc.

Fowler, Sharon H. Fairies of Spencer's Meadow: Fairy Tales. Gooch, ed. Fowler, Sharon H. & Hargis, illus. 1999. 75p. (J). (gr. k-7). 19.95 (978-0-9651588-3-1(7)) Stringer, Alicia.

French, Fiona. Jamil's Clever Cat: A Folk Tale from Bengal. French, Fiona, illus. 1999. (Illus.). 32p. (J). (ps-3). 13.95 (978-1-887734-72-1(4)) Star Bright Bks., Inc.

The Funny Little Woman. 2001. pap., tchr. ed., wbk. ed. (978-1-56137-472-4(5)) Novel Units, Inc.

The Funny Little Woman. 2004. 24.95 incl. audio (978-0-89719-875-2(1)); pap. 18.95 incl. audio compact disk (978-1-55592-415-7(8)); pap. 38.75 incl. audio compact disk (978-1-55592-416-4(6)); pap. 32.75 incl. audio (978-1-55592-227-6(9)); pap. 14.95 incl. audio (978-1-56008-054-1(X)) Weston Woods Studios, Inc.

Gag, Wanda. Gone Is Gone or the Story of a Man Who Wanted to Do Housework. 2003. (Illus.). 64p. 14.95 (978-0-8166-4243-4(5)) Univ. of Minnesota Pr.

Garrity, Linda K. The Tale Spinner: Folktales, Themes, & Activities. Markovich, Emilia, illus. 1999. 192p. (J). (gr. 3-6). pap. 18.95 (978-1-55591-970-2(7)) Fulcrum Publishing.

Geringer, Laura. Stubborn Pumpkin. 1999. (Hello Reader! Ser.). (978-0-606-17269-1(6)) Tandem Library Bks.

Ghose, Sudhindra Nath. The Flame of the Forest. 2003. 288p. pap. 29.00 (978-0-7581-9376-6(9)) Textbook Pubs.

Gibbons, Gail. Behold... the Dragons! Gibbons, Gail, illus. 1999. (Illus.). 32p. (J). (ps-3). 16.99 (978-0-688-15526-1(X)); lib. bdg. 17.89 (978-0-688-15527-8(8)) HarperCollins Pubs.

Glaser, Jason. Achilles. 2004. (World Mythology Ser.). (Illus.). 24p. (J). lib. bdg. 21.26 (978-0-7368-2660-0(2) , Bridgestone Bks.) Capstone Pr., Inc.

Goble, Paul. The Love Flute. 1998. (J). pap. 5.99 (978-0-87628-517-6(5)) Ctr. for Applied Research in Education, The.

Gonzalez, Lucia. Bossy Gallito. 1999. Tr. of El Gallo De Bodas. (SPA.). (gr. k-3). lib. bdg. 14.15 (978-0-613-16611-9(6)) Tandem Library Bks.

Gorbachev, Valeri. Goldilocks & the Three Bears. Gorbachev, Valeri, illus. 2003. (Illus.). 40p. (J). (ps). pap. 6.95 (978-0-7358-1782-1(0)) North-South Bks., Inc.

—Goldilocks & the Three Bears. 2001. (Illus.). 40p. (J). (ps). 15.95 (978-0-7358-1438-7(4)) North-South Bks., Inc.

—Ricitos de Oro y los Tres Osos. 2003. Tr. of Goldilocks & the Three Bears. (SPA.). (gr. 7-12). lib. bdg. 15.25 (978-0-613-81368-6(5)) Tandem Library Bks.

Gorbachev, Valeri & Antresyan, Augustin. Ricitos de Oro y los Tres Osos. 2003. Tr. of Goldilocks & the Three Bears. (SPA & ENG., Illus.). 40p. (J). (ps). pap. 6.95 (978-0-7358-1777-7(4)) North-South Bks., Inc.

Gossage, Peter. In the Beginning. Gossage, Peter, illus. 2001. (Illus.). 30p. (J). (978-1-86943-464-9(1)) Scholastic, Inc.

Gould, F. J. The Childrenus Plutarch: Tales of the Romans. 2002. 194p. pap. 25.00 (978-1-59244-081-8(9) , Resource Pubns.) Wipf & Stock Pubs.

Greene, Ellin. The Little Golden Lamb. Litzinger, Rosanne, illus. 2000. 32p. (J). (gr. k-3). tchr. ed. 15.00 (978-0-395-71526-0(1) , Clarion Bks.) Houghton Mifflin Co. Trade & Reference Div.

Grimm, Jacob W. & Grimm, Wilhelm K. Snow White. Santore, Charles, illus. 2004. 48p. (J). (gr. k-3). 19.95 (978-0-375-83001-3(4) , Random Hse. Bks. for Young Readers) Random Hse. Children's Bks.

Gross, Ila Lane. Folk Tales Around the World. 2001. (Global Understanding - Cultural Literacy Ser.). (Illus.). 104p. (J). (gr. 3-6). pap. 4.95 (978-0-9713649-2-9(3)) L.E.A.P. (Learning through an Expanded Arts Program, Inc).

Hale, Nathan. The Devil You Know. Hale, Nathan, illus. 2005. (Illus.). 32p. (J). (ps-3). 17.85 (978-0-8027-8983-9(8)) Walker & Co.

Hall, Amanda. The Stolen Sun. Hall, Amanda, illus. 2004. (Illus.). 32p. (J). (gr. 10 up). 17.00 (978-0-8028-5225-0(4)) Eerdmans, William B. Publishing Co.

Hall, Amanda, illus. The Barefoot Book of Animal Tales: From Around the World. 2002. 80p. (J). (gr. 2-4). 19.99 (978-1-84148-941-4(7)) Barefoot Bks., Inc.

Hamilton, John. Fantasy & Folklore Set II. 2006. (J). (gr. 4-8). 145.26 (978-1-59679-334-7(1) , ABDO & Daughters) ABDO Publishing Co.

—Magic Rings & Other Magical Things. 2005. (Illus.). 32p. (J). (gr. 4-8). lib. bdg. 24.21 (978-1-59679-337-8(6) , ABDO & Daughters) ABDO Publishing Co.

—Weapons of Fantasy & Folkore. 2005. (Illus.). 32p. (J). (gr. 4-8). lib. bdg. 24.21 (978-1-59679-340-8(6) , ABDO & Daughters) ABDO Publishing Co.

Hamilton, Martha & Weiss, Mitch. Noodlehead Stories: World Tales Kids Can Read & Tell. Elsammak, Ariane, illus. 2000. 96p. (J). (gr. 3 up). 24.95 (978-0-87483-584-7(4)) August Hse. Pubs., Inc.

Hamilton, Martha, et al. Noodlehead Stories: World Tales Kids Can Read & Tell. 2000. (Illus.). 96p. (J). (gr. 3-7). pap. 14.95 (978-0-87483-585-4(2)) August Hse. Pubs., Inc.

Harcourt School Publishers Staff. Cat in Boots: On Level. 3rd ed. 2002. (Trophies Reading Program Ser.). (Illus.). (J). pap. 4.10 (978-0-15-322991-6(8)) Harcourt Schl. Pubs.

—Colorful Characters Below Level. 3rd ed. 2002. (Trophies Reading Program Ser.). (Illus.). pap. 5.10 (978-0-15-323317-3(6)) Harcourt Schl. Pubs.

—Thrice Told Tales Advanced Level. 3rd ed. 2002. (Trophies Reading Program Ser.). (Illus.). pap. 5.10 (978-0-15-323299-2(4)) Harcourt Schl. Pubs.

Harris, Jim. Three Little Dinosaurs. Harris, Jim, illus. 1999. (Illus.). 32p. (J). (gr. k-3). 15.95 (978-1-56554-371-3(8)) Pelican Publishing Co., Inc.

Harris, Joel Chandler, et al. The Tar-Baby & Other Rhymes of Uncle Remus. 2005. (Illus.). 208p. (J). (ps). per. 15.95 (978-1-55709-489-6(6)) Applewood Bks.

Harrison, Michael & Stuart-Clark, Christopher. The Oxford Treasury of World Stories. 2000. (Illus.). 144p. (YA). 17.95 (978-0-19-278181-9(2)) Oxford Univ. Pr., Inc.

Hartman, Bob. Crocodile Brother. 2004. (Illus.). 64p. (J). pap. 6.99 (978-0-7459-4823-2(5) , Lion) Lion Hudson plc GBR. *Dist:* Independent Pubs. Group.

—The Generous Rabbit: And Other Animal Stories. Hudson, Brett, illus. 2004. 64p. (J). pap. 8.99 (978-0-7459-4697-9(6) , Lion) Lion Hudson plc GBR. *Dist:* Independent Pubs. Group.

—Polly & the Frog. 2004. (Illus.). 64p. (J). pap. 7.50 (978-0-7459-4698-6(4) , Lion) Lion Hudson plc GBR. *Dist:* Independent Pubs. Group.

—Why Dogs Chase Cats. Hudson, Brett, illus. 2004. 64p. (J). pap. 8.99 (978-0-7459-4696-2(8) , Lion) Lion Hudson plc GBR. *Dist:* Independent Pubs. Group.

Hassett, John & Hassett, Ann. The Three Silly Girls Grubb. Hassett, John & Hassett, Ann, illus. 2002. (Illus.). 32p. (J). (gr. k-3). tchr. ed. 15.00 (978-0-618-14183-8(9) , Walter Lorraine) Houghton Mifflin Co. Trade & Reference Div.

—Three Silly Girls Grubb. 2006. (Illus.). 32p. (J). (gr. k-3). reprint ed. pap. 6.95 (978-0-618-69334-4(3)) Houghton Mifflin Co.

Hayes, Joe. Pajaro Verde. Castro, Antonio, illus. 2002. (SPA & ENG.). 40p. (J). (gr. 1-3). 16.95 (978-0-938317-65-4(2)) Cinco Puntos Pr.

Hayward, Linda. Pepe & Papa. 2001. (Road to Reading Ser.). (Illus.). (J). (978-0-606-20852-9(6)) Tandem Library Bks.

—Pepe & Papa. Huliska-Beith, Laura, illus. 2001. (J). (ps-3). lib. bdg. 11.80 (978-0-613-50227-6(2)) Tandem Library Bks.

Hepker, Sue. A Long Way to Baba. Ablorh, Samuel Adjei, tr. 2000. (GAA., Illus.). pap. 3.00 (978-0-521-79587-6(7)) Cambridge Univ. Pr.

—A Long Way to Baba: Akwapim Twi Version. Asante, Comfort, tr. 2000. (TWI., Illus.). pap. 3.00 (978-0-521-79617-0(2)) Cambridge Univ. Pr.

—A Long Way to Baba: Dagbani Version. Abdulai, Fuseini-Bila, tr. 2000. (Illus.). pap. 3.00 (978-0-521-79596-8(6)) Cambridge Univ. Pr.

Highlights for Children Editorial Staff. Day of the Great Wave: And Other Folktales. 2000. (Illus.). (J). (ps up). pap. 3.95 (978-0-87534-618-2(9)) Highlights for Children.

Hillert, Margaret. Not I, Not I: The Little Red Hen Retold. Magnuson, Diana, illus. rev. exp. ed. 2007. (Beginning to Read Ser.). 32p. (J). lib. bdg. (978-1-59953-052-9(X)) Norwood Hse. Pr.

—The Three Little Pigs. Wilde, Irma, illus. rev. exp. ed. 2007. (Beginning to Read Ser.). 30p. (J). lib. bdg. (978-1-59953-050-5(3)) Norwood Hse. Pr.

Hobson, Sally. Chicken Little. 2000. (Illus.). (J). 12.79 (978-0-606-17917-1(8)) Tandem Library Bks.

Hodson, Christopher. Lizo's Song: Akwapim Twi Version. Asante, Comfort, tr. 2000. (TWI., Illus.). pap. 3.00 (978-0-521-79621-7(0)) Cambridge Univ. Pr.

—Lizo's Song: Dagbani Version. Abdulai, Fuseini-Bila, tr. 2000. (Illus.). pap. 3.00 (978-0-521-79600-2(8)) Cambridge Univ. Pr.

Hoffman, Mary. The Barefoot Book of Brother & Sister Tales. Shaw-Smith, Emma, illus. 2000. 64p. (J). (gr. 3-7). 19.99 (978-1-84148-029-9(0)) Barefoot Bks., Inc.

Holleman, Monika. Chameleon's Clever Trick: Akwapim Twi Version. Asante, Comfort, tr. 2000. (TWI., Illus.). pap. 3.00 (978-0-521-79622-4(9)) Cambridge Univ. Pr.

—Chameleon's Clever Trick: Asante Twi Version. Asenso, Okofo, tr. 2000. (TWI., Illus.). pap. 3.00 (978-0-521-79612-5(1)) Cambridge Univ. Pr.

—Chameleon's Clever Trick: Dagbani Version. Abdulai, Fuseini-Bila, tr. 2000. (Illus.). pap. 3.00 (978-0-521-79602-6(4)) Cambridge Univ. Pr.

Holub, Joan. Jack & the Jellybeanstalk. 2002. (gr. k-3). lib. bdg. 11.25 (978-0-613-72447-0(X)) Tandem Library Bks.

Horn, Sandra A. Babushka. Ratto, Cinzia, illus. 2002. 32p. (J). (gr. k-2). 16.99 (978-1-84148-353-5(2)) Barefoot Bks., Inc.

Horowitz, Anthony. Myths & Legends. 2003. (gr. 5-8). lib. bdg. 15.25 (978-0-613-90168-0(1)) Tandem Library Bks.

Hughes, Brenda. Folk Tales from Chile. 1999. (Library of Folklore). (Illus.). 121p. (gr. 2-5). 12.50 (978-0-7818-0712-8(3)) Hippocrene Bks., Inc.

Hughes, Mary. Popular Superstitions. 1999. (Costume, Tradition & Culture). (Illus.). 64p. (YA). (gr. 5 up). 28.00 (978-0-7910-5172-6(2) , Chelsea Hse.) Facts On File, Inc.

Hurston, Zora Neale. The Three Witches. Tankersley, Ann & Ringgold, Faith, illus. 2006. 32p. (J). (gr. 1-5). 15.99 (978-0-06-000649-5(8)) HarperCollins Pubs.

Hyman, Tina Schart. Snow White. 2000. (J). (978-0-606-19845-5(8)) Tandem Library Bks.

Hyman, Trina Schart, illus. The Kitchen Knight: A Tale of King Arthur. 32p. (J). (gr. k-3). tchr. ed. 17.95 (978-0-8234-0787-3(X)) Holiday Hse., Inc.

Ingham, Donna. Tales with a Texas Twist: Original Stories & Enduring Folklore from the Lone Star State. Hoffman, Paul G., illus. 2005. 160p. (ps-7). pap. 12.95 (978-0-7627-3899-1(5)) Globe Pequot Pr., The.

Ivanova, Olga V. The Tall Book of Nursery Tales. Ivanov, Aleksey, illus. 2006. 80p. (J). 6.99 (978-0-06-054372-3(8) , Harper Festival) HarperCollins Pubs.

Jackson, Ellen B. January. DeWitt, Pat & DeWitt, Robin, illus. 2004. (It Happens in the Month of... Ser.). 32p. (YA). (gr. k-3). 8.95 (978-0-88106-995-2(7)) Charlesbridge Publishing, Inc.

—July. DeWitt, Pat & DeWitt, Robin, illus. 2004. (It Happens in the Month of... Ser.). 32p. (YA). 8.95 (978-0-88106-920-4(5)) Charlesbridge Publishing, Inc.

—June. Life, Kay, illus. 2004. (It Happens in the Month of... Ser.). 32p. (YA). 8.95 (978-0-88106-919-8(1)) Charlesbridge Publishing, Inc.

—March. Life, Kay, illus. 2004. (It Happens in the Month of... Ser.). 32p. (YA). 8.95 (978-0-88106-905-1(1)) Charlesbridge Publishing, Inc.

—May. Life, Kay, illus. 2004. (It Happens in the Month of... Ser.). 32p. (YA). 8.95 (978-0-88106-918-1(3)) Charlesbridge Publishing, Inc.

—November. DeWitt, Pat & DeWitt, Robin, illus. 2004. (It Happens in the Month of... Ser.). 32p. (YA). 8.95 (978-0-88106-927-3(2)) Charlesbridge Publishing, Inc.

—October. DeWitt, Robin & DeWitt, Pat, illus. 2004. (It Happens in the Month of... Ser.). 32p. (YA). (gr. 2-3). 8.95 (978-0-88106-923-5(X)) Charlesbridge Publishing, Inc.

—September. DeWitt, Robin & DeWitt, Pat, illus. 2004. (It Happens in the Month of... Ser.). 32p. (YA). 8.95 (978-0-88106-922-8(1)) Charlesbridge Publishing, Inc.

Jaffe, Nina. Patakin: World Tales of Drums & Drummers. 2001. (Illus.). 160p. (J). (gr. 4-8). pap. 15.95 incl. cd-rom (978-0-8126-4877-5(3)) Cricket Bks.

—Tales for the Seventh Day: A Collection of Sabbath Stories. Sutherland, Kelly Stribling, illus. 2000. 73p. (J). (gr. 3-7). pap. 15.95 (978-0-590-12054-8(9)) Scholastic, Inc.

Johnson, Richard, illus. The Giant Turnip. 2004. 24p. (J). (TAM, CZE, VIE, SPA & URD.). (978-1-85269-733-4(4)); (TAM, CZE, VIE, SPA & URD.). (978-1-85269-734-1(2)); (TAM, CZE, VIE, SPA & URD.). (978-1-85269-735-8(0)); (TAM, CZE, VIE, SPA & URD.). (978-1-85269-736-5(9)); (TAM, CZE, VIE, SPA & PER.). (978-1-85269-737-2(7)); (TAM, CZE, VIE, SPA & URD.). (978-1-85269-739-6(3)); (TAM, CZE, VIE, SPA & GUJ.). (978-1-85269-740-2(7)); (TAM, CZE, VIE, SPA & URD.). (978-1-85269-741-9(5)); (TAM, CZE, VIE, SPA & URD.). (978-1-85269-742-6(3)); (TAM, CZE, VIE, SPA & URD.). (978-1-85269-743-3(1)); (TAM, CZE, VIE, SPA & URD.). (978-1-85269-744-0(X)); (TAM, CZE, VIE, SPA & SER.). (978-1-85269-745-7(8)); (TAM, CZE, VIE, SPA & URD.). (978-1-85269-746-4(6)); (TAM, CZE, VIE, SPA & URD.). (978-1-85269-747-1(4)); (CZE, TAM, VIE, SPA & URD.). (978-1-85269-748-8(2)); (TAM, CZE, VIE, SPA & URD.). (978-1-85269-749-5(0)); (TAM, CZE, VIE, SPA & POL.). (978-1-85269-750-1(4)); (TAM, CZE, VIE, SPA & URD.). (978-1-85269-788-4(1)); (TAM, CZE, SPA, VIE & URD.). (978-1-85269-789-1(X)) Mantra Publishing, Ltd.

Jones, Carol. The Gingerbread Man. 2002. (J). 15.00 (978-0-618-18823-9(1)); (Illus.). 32p. 16.00 (978-0-618-18822-2(3)) Houghton Mifflin Co. Trade & Reference Div. (Walter Lorraine).

Jones, Christianne. Chicken Little: A Retelling of the Classic Traditional Tale. Hermanson, Kyle, illus. 2005. (Read-It! Readers Ser.). 32p. (J). (gr. k-3). 18.60 (978-1-4048-0972-7(4)) Picture Window Bks.

—How Many Spots Does a Leopard Have? A Retelling of the Classic Traditional Tale. Zhurkina, Svetlana, illus. 2005. (Read-It! Readers Ser.). 32p. (J). (gr. k-3). 18.60 (978-1-4048-0973-4(2)) Picture Window Bks.

—The Little Red Hen: A Retelling of the Classic Traditional Tale. Magnuson, Natalie, illus. 2005. (Read-It! Readers Ser.). 32p. (J). (gr. k-3). 18.60 (978-1-4048-0975-8(9)) Picture Window Bks.

—Stone Soup. Chambers-Goldberg, Micah, illus. 2005. (Read-It! Readers Ser.). 32p. (J). (ps). lib. bdg. 18.60 (978-1-4048-0978-9(3)) Picture Window Bks.

Jorgensen, David, illus. The Three Little Pigs. 2005. (J). (gr. k-5). 25.65 (978-1-59197-755-1(X)) Spotlight.

Joseph Had a Little Overcoat. 2004. 29.95 incl. cd-rom (978-1-55592-109-5(4)); 24.95 incl. audio (978-1-55592-083-8(7)); pap. 18.95 incl. audio compact disk (978-0-7882-0325-1(8)); pap. 32.75 incl. audio (978-0-7882-0326-8(6)); pap. 14.95 incl. audio (978-0-7882-0324-4(X)) Weston Woods Studios, Inc.

Kann, Alice G. Tales from Time & Beyond the Stars, Vol. 1. Date not set. (Illus.). 50p. (J). (ps-6). 16.95 (978-0-9654522-1-2(2)) Metapublishing.

Karlin, Barbara. Cinderella. 2001. 13.79 (978-0-606-22509-0(9)) Tandem Library Bks.

—James Marshall's Cinderella. Marshall, James, illus. 2001. 32p. (J). pap. 6.99 (978-0-14-230048-0(9) , Puffin) Penguin Group (USA) Inc.

Kearney, Milo. A Childs History of Brownsville: Stories Brownsville Told Its Children. 2001. (J). (gr. 4-7). pap. 7.95 (978-1-57168-599-5(5)) Eakin Pr.

Keens-Douglas, Richardo. The Trial of the Stone: A Folk Tale. 2000. (gr. k-3). lib. bdg. 15.25 (978-0-613-50384-6(8)) Tandem Library Bks.

Kellogg, Steven. Sally Ann Thunder Ann Whirlwind Crockett: A Tall Tale. 1999. (978-0-606-17396-4(X)) Tandem Library Bks.

Kennard, Edward A. Field Mouse Goes to War. Kabotie, Fred, illus. 2000. 48p. (J). (gr. k-5). 6.95 (978-1-885772-19-0(X)) Kiva Publishing, Inc.

Kilgras, Heidi. Cinderella's Countdown to the Ball. Harchy, Atelier Philippe, illus. 2002. 32p. (J). (ps-1). pap. 3.99 (978-0-7364-1225-4(5) , RH/Disney) Random Hse. Children's Bks.

—Cinderella's Countdown to the Ball. 2002. (gr. k-3). lib. bdg. 11.80 (978-0-613-73603-9(6)) Tandem Library Bks.

Kimmel, Eric A. Grizz! Glass, Andrew, illus. 2000. 32p. (J). (gr. k-3). tchr. ed. 16.95 (978-0-8234-1469-7(8)) Holiday Hse., Inc.

—The Runaway Tortilla. Cecil, Randy, illus. 40p. (J). (ps-2). 2002. pap. 6.95 (978-1-58837-022-8(4)); 2000. 16.95 (978-1-890817-18-3(X)) Winslow Pr.

Kirk, Diana & Devine, Debra. Rachel Serves a Stew/Maggie Boo: Twin Spins #8. Devine, Debra & Batson, Susann, illus. 2002. (Twin Spins Ser.: 8). 112p. (YA). pap. 10.95 (978-0-7599-1007-2(3)) Hard Shell Word Factory.

Kite, L. Patricia. Insect Facts & Folklore. 2001. (Illus.). 80p. (gr. 3-6). lib. bdg. 29.90 (978-0-7613-1822-4(4) , Millbrook Pr.) Lerner Publishing Group.

Korty, Carol. Silly Soup. Landes, William-Alan, ed. Colombo, David, illus. Helms, Tina, photos by. 2003. (Plays & Play Collections). 128p. (Orig.). (J). (gr. k-6). pap. 17.00 (978-0-88734-679-8(0)) Players Pr., Inc.

Kremer, Isaias Leo. Milomga de la Independencia (Milongue Fun Frai) 2000. (J). 23.25 (978-987-9333-08-2(X)) Acervo Cultural ARG. *Dist:* Latin American Bk. Source, Inc.

E F G

Lang, Andrew. The Green Fairy Book. 2004. reprint ed. pap. 28.95 (978-1-4191-6492-7(9)) ; pap. 1.99 (978-1-4192-6492-4(3)) Kessinger Publishing, LLC.

Lang, Andrew, ed. Crimson Fairy Book. (Twelve-Point Ser.). 2003. lib. bdg. 25.00 (978-1-58287-205-6(8)); 2004. 455p. 26.00 (978-1-58287-689-4(4)) North Bks.

Laverde, Arlene. Alaska's Three Pigs. Dwyer, Mindy, illus. 32p. (J). (gr. k-3). 2002. pap. 9.95 (978-1-57061-229-9(3)); 2000. pap. 9.95 (978-1-57061-239-8(0)) Sasquatch Bks.

—Alaska's Three Pigs. 2000. (gr. k-3). lib. bdg. 17.60 (978-0-613-79146-5(0)) Tandem Library Bks.

Layne, Steven L. & Layne, Deborah Dover. P Is for Princess: A Royal Alphabet. Papp, Robert & Papp, Lisa, illus. rev. ed. 2007. 40p. (J). 17.95 ***(978-1-58536-306-3(5))*** Sleeping Bear Pr.

Leavy, Una. Irish Fairy Tales & Legends. 1999. (J). 9.95 (978-1-57098-292-7(9)) Rinehart, Roberts Pubs.

Lectorum Publications Staff. Lo Que Cuentan los Inuit. 2000. Tr. of Tales of the Inuit. (SPA.). (gr. 3-6). lib. bdg. 16.40 (978-0-613-82034-9(7)) Tandem Library Bks.

Levine, Shar. Cinderella & the Glass Hill. 1999. 112p. (J). (gr. 2-7). pap. 4.95 (978-0-06-442104-1(X)) HarperCollins Pubs.

Lewis, Hara. Cinderella. 2004. (gr. k-3). lib. bdg. 11.80 (978-0-613-71998-8(0)) Tandem Library Bks.

Lewis, Hara, et al. Cinderella. 2004. (Scholastic Readers Ser.). (Illus.). 32p. (J). pap. 3.99 (978-0-439-47153-4(2)) Scholastic, Inc.

Lish, Ted. The Three Little Puppies & the Big Bad Flea. Jordan, Charles, illus. 2001. 32p. (J). (gr. k-3). 15.95 (978-0-7940-0000-4(2)) ; lib. bdg. 16.95 (978-0-7940-0001-1(0)) Munchweiler Pr.

The Little Red Hen. 2004. 29.95 incl. cd-rom (978-1-55592-823-0(4)) ; 24.95 incl. audio (978-0-89719-889-9(1)) ; pap. 18.95 incl. audio compact disk (978-1-55592-807-0(2)) ; pap. 38.75 incl. audio compact disk (978-1-55592-757-8(2)) ; pap. 32.75 incl. audio (978-1-55592-259-7(7)) ; pap. 14.95 incl. audio (978-1-56008-062-6(0)) Weston Woods Studios, Inc.

Littlewort, Elizabeth. The Terrible Graakwe. Bahemuka, Gaetano & Torgah, F. K. Atakpa Kple Edoh, trs. 2000. (EWE., Illus.). pap. 3.00 (978-0-521-79586-9(9)) Cambridge Univ. Pr.

—Thuli's Mattress. Bahemuka, Gaetano & Torgah, F. K. Atakpa Kple Edoh, trs. 2000. (EWE., Illus.). pap. 3.00 (978-0-521-79585-2(0)) Cambridge Univ. Pr.

—Thuli's Mattress. Ablorh, Samuel Adjei & Bahemuka, Gaetano, trs. 2000. (GAA., Illus.). pap. 3.00 (978-0-521-79594-4(X)) Cambridge Univ. Pr.

—Thuli's Mattress. Tadjo, Veronique, tr. from ENG. 1998. (Cambridge African Language Library Ser.). (FRE., Illus.). 16p. pap. 3.75 (978-0-521-64784-7(3)) Cambridge Univ. Pr.

—Thuli's Mattress: Akwapim Twi Version. Asante, Comfort & Bahemuka, Gaetano, trs. 2000. (TWI., Illus.). pap. 3.00 (978-0-521-79624-8(5)) Cambridge Univ. Pr.

—Thuli's Mattress: Amharic Version. Duguma, Melaku Wakuma, tr. 1999. (Cambridge Reading Routes Ser.). (AMH., Illus.). 16p. pap. 3.70 (978-0-521-66829-3(8)) Cambridge Univ. Pr.

—Thuli's Mattress: Asante Twi Version. Asenso, Okofo & Bahemuka, Gaetano, trs. 2000. (TWI., Illus.). pap. 3.00 (978-0-521-79614-9(8)) Cambridge Univ. Pr.

—Thuli's Mattress: Dagbani Version. Abdulai, Fuseini-Bila & Bahemuka, Gaetano, trs. 2000. (Illus.). pap. 3.00 (978-0-521-79604-0(0)) Cambridge Univ. Pr.

—Thuli's Mattress: Fante Version. Aggrey, Safohen J. E. K. & Bahemuka, Gaetano, trs. 2000. (Illus.). pap. 3.00 (978-0-521-79575-3(3)) Cambridge Univ. Pr.

—Thuli's Mattress: Luganda Version. Lubega, Bonnie, tr. 1998. (Cambridge African Language Library Ser.). (LUG., Illus.). 16p. pap. 3.65 (978-0-521-63796-1(1)) Cambridge Univ. Pr.

—Thuli's Mattress: Tigre Version. Hagos, Amare & Kebebew, Amare Hagos, trs. 1999. (Cambridge Reading Routes Ser.). (TIG., Illus.). 16p. pap. 3.70 (978-0-521-66819-4(0)) Cambridge Univ. Pr.

Lively, Joe. Notes of a Time Traveler: Our Forgotten Folk Heritage. 2nd ed. (Illus.). 260p. (YA). (gr. 6 up). reprint ed. 28.95 (978-0-9656688-2-8(7)) ABM Enterprises, Inc.

Livo, Norma J., ed. Moon Cakes to Maize: Delicious World Folk Tales. 1999. (Illus.). 192p. (gr. 3-4). pap. 16.95 (978-1-55591-973-3(1)) Fulcrum Publishing.

Loebel-Fried, Caren. Hawaiian Legends of Dreams. 2005. (Illus.). 130p. (J). 19.95 (978-0-8248-2961-2(1)) Univ. of Hawaii Pr.

Loo, Sanne te. Ping-Li's Kite. 1998. (Illus.). 30p. (J). (ps-1). 15.95 (978-1-886910-75-1(8) , Lemniscaat) Boyds Mills Pr.

Lottridge, Celia Barker & Chan, Harvey. Music for the Tsar of the Sea. 2006. (Illus.). 30p. (J). (gr. k-4). reprint ed. 17.00 (978-0-7567-9931-1(7)) DIANE Publishing Co.

Lowell, Susan. Dusty Locks & the Three Bears. Cecil, Randy, illus. rev. ed. 2004. 32p. (J). (ps-3). pap. 6.95 (978-0-8050-7534-2(8) , Holt, Henry & Co. Bks. For Young Readers) Holt, Henry & Co.

Lunge-Larsen, Lise. The Hidden Folk: Stories of Fairies, Dwarves, Selkies, & Other Secret Beings. Krommes, Beth, illus. 2004. 80p. (J). (gr. k-3). tchr. ed. 18.00 (978-0-618-17495-9(8)) Houghton Mifflin Co. Trade & Reference Div.

Lupton, Hugh. The Story Tree: Tales to Read Aloud. Fatus, Sophie, illus. 2001. 64p. (J). (ps-2). 18.99 (978-1-84148-312-2(5)) Barefoot Bks., Inc.

—Tales of Wisdom & Wonder. Sharkey, Niamh, illus. 1998. 64p. (J). (ps-7). 18.95 (978-1-901223-09-5(4)) Barefoot Bks., Inc.

Lutz, A. Fowler. Stories of the Child Jesus from Many Lands. 2003. (Illus.). viii, 175p. (J). pap. 10.95 (978-1-928832-96-6(2)) Sophia Institute Pr.

Lyon, Carol, illus. Through the Grapevine: World Tales Kids Can Read & Tell. 2001. 128p. (gr. 2-7). 24.95 (978-0-87483-625-7(5)) ; pap. 14.95 (978-0-87483-624-0(7)) August Hse. Pubs., Inc.

MacDonald, Margaret Read. Earth Care: World Folktales to Talk About. 1999. (Illus.). (YA). (ps up). xii, 163p. pap. 17.50 (978-0-208-02426-8(3)) ; xii,163p. lib. bdg. 26.50 (978-0-208-02416-9(6)) Shoe String Pr., Inc. (Linnet Bks.).

—Tuck-Me-In Tales: Bedtime Stories from Around the World. 2001. (Illus.). 64p. (ps-2). pap. 9.95 (978-0-87483-622-6(0)) August Hse. Pubs., Inc.

Mackall, Dandi Daley. The Legend of Ohio. LaFever, Greg, illus. 2005. (Legend Ser.). 40p. (J). (gr. k-5). 17.95 (978-1-58536-244-8(1)) Sleeping Bear Pr.

MacKenzie, Donald. Folk Tales from Russia. 1999. (Library of Folklore). (Illus.). 192p. (J). (gr. 4-7). 12.50 (978-0-7818-0696-1(8)) Hippocrene Bks., Inc.

MacLaren, Dorothy H. Esopus Hodie, Aesop Today, Vol. 1. (ENG & LAT.). 64p. (YA). (gr. 9-12). 9.75 (978-0-939507-06-1(4) , B20) American Classical League, The.

Maddern, Eric & East, Helen. Spirit of the Forest: Tree Tales from Around the World. Marks, Alan, illus. 2004. 48p. (J). pap. 10.95 (978-1-84507-268-1(5)) Lincoln, Frances Ltd. GBR. *Dist:* Perseus Distribution.

Madsen, Jim, illus. The Adventures of Thor the Thunder God. 2007. 80p. (gr. 4-6). 19.95 (978-0-618-47301-4(7)) Houghton Mifflin Co.

Maggi, Maria Elena. The Great Canoe: A Karina Legend. ed. 2004. (Illus.). (J). (ps up). spiral bd. (978-0-616-14620-0(5)) ; spiral bd. (978-0-616-14621-7(3)) Canadian National Institute for the Blind/Institut National Canadien pour les Aveugles.

—The Great Canoe: A Karina Legend. Amado, Elisa, tr. from SPA. Calderon, Gloria, illus. 2001. 32p. (J). (ps-k). 15.95 (978-0-88899-444-8(3)) Groundwood Bks. CAN. *Dist:* Perseus Distribution.

Malnic, Jutta. Gilabwala & His Sister: A Trobriand Legend Told by Chief Nalubutau. Bibby, Peter, ed. Turner, Carina, illus. 2002. 32p. pap. 12.00 (978-0-9581267-1-7(2)) Cowrie Bks. AUS. *Dist:* Univ. of Hawaii Pr.

Mama, Raouf. The Barefoot Book of Tropical Tales. Hyde, Deidre, illus. 2000. 64p. (J). (gr. 3-7). 19.95 (978-1-902283-21-0(X)) Barefoot Bks., Inc.

Mama, Raouf & Romney, Mary. Pearls of Wisdom: African & Caribbean Folktales. Webber-Feeney, Siri, illus. 2005. pap. 27.00 incl. audio compact disk (978-0-86647-218-0(5)) Pro Lingua Assocs., Inc.

—Pearls of Wisdom Text/Workbook/2 CD's Package: African & Caribbean Folktales. 2005. pap. 39.00 incl. audio compact disk (978-0-86647-201-2(0)) Pro Lingua Assocs., Inc.

Mardon, John & Krystanovich, Vesna, illus. Ancient Tales for Modern Kids: Stories from Far-Away Places. 2000. 270p. (J). 29.95 (978-1-55263-151-5(6)) Key Porter Bks. CAN. *Dist:* Firefly Bks., Ltd.

Marshall, Bonnie. Tales from the Heart of the Balkans. Mihailovich, Vasa D., ed. 2001. (World Folklore Ser.). (Illus.). 166p. (J). (gr. k-12). 40.00 (978-1-56308-870-4(3) , LU8703) Libraries Unlimited, Inc.

Martin, Sharene. Lilah Birdsong's Original Little Perrytales. 2004. 49p. pap. 12.95 (978-1-4137-1367-1(X)) PublishAmerica, Inc.

Mason, Victor & Beal, Gillian. Balinese Children's Favorite Stories. Bohan-Tyrie, Trina, illus. 2001. 96p. (gr. 1-5). 16.95 (978-962-593-440-2(5)) Periplus Editions (HK), Ltd. HKG. *Dist:* Tuttle Publishing.

Matthews, Caitlin. While the Bear Sleeps: Winter Tales & Traditions. Mills, Judith Christine, photos by. 1999. (Illus.). 80p. (gr. 4-7). 19.95 (978-1-902283-81-4(3)) Barefoot Bks., Inc.

Matthews, John. The Barefoot Book of Giants, Ghosts & Goblins: Traditional Tales from Around the World. Manna, Giovanni, illus. 2000. 80p. (J). (gr. 1-5). 19.95 (978-1-902283-27-2(9)) Barefoot Bks., Inc.

Matthews, John & Matthews, Caitlin. The Wizard King: And Other Spellbinding Tales. Press, Jenny, illus. 2000. 80p. (J). (ps-3). 18.95 (978-1-901223-84-2(1)) Barefoot Bks., Inc.

Mayhew, James, illus. Shakespeare's Storybook: Folk Tales That Inspired the Bard. 2001. 80p. (J). (gr. 3 up). 19.99 (978-1-84148-307-8(9)) Barefoot Bks., Inc.

McCaughrean, Geraldine & Marks, Alan. King Arthur. 2007. (Illus.). (J). pap. ***(978-0-340-89437-8(7)*** , Hodder Children's Books) Hodder Children's Division.

McDermott, Gerald. Zomo el Conejo: Un Cuento de Africa Occidental. Ada, Alma Flor & Campoy, F. Isabel, trs. 2002. Tr. of Zomo the Rabbit. (SPA., Illus.). 32p. (J). (gr. k-3). pap. 7.00 (978-0-15-216777-6(3) , Voyager Bks./Libros Viajeros) Harcourt Children's Bks.

—Zomo el Conejo: Un Cuento de Africa Occidental. 2002. Tr. of Zomo the Rabbit. (SPA.). (gr. k-3). lib. bdg. 15.30 (978-0-613-82221-3(8)) Tandem Library Bks.

McGrath, Barbara Barbieri. The Little Green Witch. Alexander, Martha, illus. 2005. 32p. (J). (ps-ps). per. 14.95 (978-1-58089-042-7(3)) Charlesbridge Publishing, Inc.

McIntosh, Gavin. Hausaland Tales: An Anthology of Folktales from Northern Nigeria. 2002. (Illus.). 128p. (J). (gr. 3-9). pap. 22.50 (978-0-208-02523-4(5)) Shoe String Pr., Inc.

McNaughton, Janet. An Earthly Knight. 2005. 352p. (YA). (gr. 7 up). pap. 6.99 (978-0-06-008994-8(6) , Harper Trophy) HarperCollins Pubs.

McQueen, Lucinda. The Little Red Hen. (FRE., Illus.). (J). 6.99 (978-0-590-71720-5(0)) ; 13.99 (978-0-590-73915-3(8)) Scholastic, Inc.

Messer, Randy, illus. Tales of Animals: Retold Timeless Classics. 1999. (Cover-to-Cover Timeless Classics Ser.). 54p. (J). pap. (978-0-7891-2858-4(6)) ; (gr. 1-4). lib. bdg. 13.95 (978-0-7807-7852-8(9)) Perfection Learning Corp.

Miller, Raymond H. Vampires. 2004. (Illus.). 48p. (J). (gr. 4-7). 26.20 (978-0-7377-2619-0(9) , Greenhaven Pr., Inc.) Thomson Gale.

Milord, Susan. Tales Alive! Donato, Michael A., illus. 2007. 128p. pap. 16.99 ***(978-0-8249-6804-5(2)*** , Williamson Bks.) Ideals Pubns.

Milord, Susan. Tales Alive! Ten Multicultural Folktales with Activities. 2003. (gr. k-3). lib. bdg. 22.20 (978-0-613-87696-4(2)) Tandem Library Bks.

Moore, Maggie. The Three Little Pigs. Hefferan, Rob, illus. 2004. (Read-It! Readers Ser.). 32p. (C). (gr. k-3). 18.60 (978-1-4048-0071-7(9)) Picture Window Bks.

Mora, Pat. La Noche Que Se Caybo la Luna. Domi, illus. 2000. (SPA.). 32p. (J). (ps-1). 18.95 (978-0-88899-399-1(4) , GRO8516) Groundwood Bks. CAN. *Dist:* Lectorum Pubns., Inc., Perseus Distribution.

Moreno, Juan. El Cuento de las Mentiras. 2002. (SPA.). 64p. (J). pap. 6.95 (978-1-4000-0048-7(3)) Random Hse., Inc.

Mott, A. S. Fireside Ghost Stories, Vol. 1. rev. ed. 2003. (Ghost Stories Ser.). 216p. (J). (gr. 4). pap. (978-1-894877-40-4(3)) Lone Pine Publishing.

Muldrow, Diane, ed. The Little Red Hen. Miller, J. P., illus. 2001. (Little Golden Bks.). 24p. (J). (gr. k-k). 2.99 (978-0-307-96030-6(7) , Golden Bks.) Random Hse. Children's Bks.

Musa da Calice, Romeo. La Luna Sul Salice (The Moon on the Willowtree); Racconto di Nonna Zibetta (The Tale of Nonna Zibetta) Williams, Adelia V., ed. Williams, Adelia V., tr. from ITA. 2000. (Crossings Ser.). (Illus.). 82p. (J). 10.00 (978-1-884419-39-3(9)) Bordighera Incorporated.

Myths & Legends. pap. (978-1-84458-374-4(0)) Chrysalis Children's Bks.

Neilan, Eujin Kim, illus. The Rabbit & the Dragon King: Based on a Korean Folk Tale. 2003. 32p. (J). (gr. 2-4). 17.95 (978-1-56397-880-7(6)) Boyds Mills Pr.

Nestorowich, Sherri, illus. Wisdom of the Golden Goose. 2003. (Jataka Tales Ser.). 32p. (J). (ps-4). pap. 7.95 (978-0-89800-320-8(2)) Dharma Publishing.

Newman, Paul. Ambrose the Whale: A Novel for Children & Adults. 2003. 108p. pap. 9.95 (978-0-595-27091-0(3)) iUniverse, Inc.

Nikola-Lisa, W., et al. The Dancin' Fox. Sewall, Marcia, illus. 2000. (J). (978-0-689-82621-4(4) , Atheneum) Simon & Schuster Children's Publishing.

Norfolk, Bobby & Norfolk, Sherry. The Moral of the Story: Folktales for Character Development. 1999. 176p. 24.95 (978-0-87483-542-7(9)) August Hse. Pubs., Inc.

Norman, Howard. Between Heaven & Earth: Bird Tales from Around the World. Dillon, Leo & Dillon, Diane, illus. 2004. 88p. (YA). 22.00 (978-0-15-201982-2(0)) Harcourt Children's Bks.

Olson, Arielle North & Schwartz, Howard. Ask the Bones: Scary Stories from Around the World. Linn, David, illus. 160p. (J). 2002. pap. 5.99 (978-0-14-230140-1(X) , Puffin); 1999. (gr. 3-7). 16.99 (978-0-670-87581-8(3) , Viking Juvenile) Penguin Group (USA) Inc.

Orme, David. El Burro Que Fue Muy Rapido, Level 3: Basado en un Cuento Folclorico Filipino. Rivers, Ruth, illus. 2005. (Lightning Readers Ser.). 32p. (J). (gr. 1-2). pap., pap. 3.95 (978-0-7696-4231-4(4) , Gingham Dog Pr.) School Specialty Publishing.

—The Donkey That Went Too Fast, Level 3 Level 3: A Philippine Folktale. Rivers, Ruth, illus. 2005. (Lightning Readers Ser.). 32p. (J). (gr. 1-2). pap., pap. 3.95 (978-0-7696-4211-6(X) , Gingham Dog Pr.) School Specialty Publishing.

Ormerod, Jan. Story of Chicken Licken: Level 4, Green, 7 vols. Ormerod, Jan, illus. 2nd ed. 1999. (Reading Together Ser.). (Illus.). 32p. (J). pap. (978-0-7636-0871-2(8)) Candlewick Pr.

Osborne, Mary Pope. Mermaid Tales from Around the World. Howell, Troy, illus. 1999. 96p. (J). (gr. 2-6). pap. 7.99 (978-0-439-04781-4(1)) Scholastic, Inc.

—Mermaid Tales from Around the World. 1999. (J). (978-0-606-16602-7(5)) Tandem Library Bks.

Palermo, Miguel Angel. Lo Que Cuentan los Guaranies. (Cuentamerica Ser.). (SPA.). (YA). (gr. 4 up). pap. (978-950-07-1337-5(3) , SA30062) Editorial Sudamericana S.A. ARG. *Dist:* Lectorum Pubns., Inc.

Panzarella, Genna, illus. Piecing Earth & Sky Together: A Creation Story from the Mien Tribe of Laos. 2001. (J). 17.95 (978-1-885008-19-0(8)) Shen's Bks.

Parker, Vic. Traditional Tales from Around the World, 4 vols., Set. Incl. Traditional Tales from Ancient Egypt. lib. bdg. 16.95 (978-1-929298-70-9(6)) ; Traditional Tales from Ancient Greece. lib. bdg. 16.95 (978-1-929298-72-3(2)) ; Traditional Tales from Celtic Lands. lib. bdg. 16.95 (978-1-929298-71-6(4)) ; Traditional Tales from Norse Lands. lib. bdg. 16.95 (978-1-929298-73-0(0)) ; 48p. (J). (gr. 2-6). (Illus.). 2000. Set lib. bdg. 67.80 (978-1-929298-74-7(9)) Chrysalis Education.

Parry, Alan. Little Fairy Books: Fairy Chants. 2005. (Illus.). 14p. bds. 7.99 (978-1-903816-83-7(1)) O Bks. GBR. *Dist:* National Bk. Network.

—Little Fairy Books: Fairy Lullabies. 2005. (Illus.). 14p. bds. 7.99 (978-1-903816-76-9(9)) O Bks. GBR. *Dist:* National Bk. Network.

—Little Fairy Books: Fairy Magic. 2005. (Illus.). 14p. bds. 7.99 (978-1-903816-84-4(X)) O Bks. GBR. *Dist:* National Bk. Network.

—Little Fairy Books: Fairy Spells. 2005. (Illus.). 14p. bds. 7.99 (978-1-903816-82-0(3)) O Bks. GBR. *Dist:* National Bk. Network.

Paterson, Judy. The Fisherman's Son. Collins, Sally J., illus. 1999. 32p. (J). (gr. k-4). pap. (978-1-871512-61-8(1)) Glowworm Bks., Ltd.

—Thomas the Rhymer. Collins, Sally J., illus. 1999. 32p. (J). (gr. k-4). pap. (978-1-871512-60-1(3)) Glowworm Bks., Ltd.

Paterson, Katherine. Parzival: The Quest of the Grail Knight. 2000. 128p. (J). (gr. 5-9). pap. 5.99 (978-0-14-130573-8(8) , Puffin) Penguin Group (USA) Inc.

—Parzival: The Quest of the Grail Knight. 2000. (978-0-606-18443-4(0)) Tandem Library Bks.

Paul Bunyan: 6 Small Books. (gr. k-2). 23.00 (978-0-7635-8508-2(4)) Rigby Education.

Paul, John. Porcupine. (Illus.). (J). pap. 3.00 (978-1-55500-072-1(X)) Alaska Native Language Ctr.

Pawagi, Manjusha. Pianomania. Franson, Leanne, illus. 2005. 24p. (J). 11.95 (978-1-896764-63-4(0)) Second Story Pr. CAN. *Dist:* Orca Bk. Pubs. USA.

Pearson, Maggie. The Headless Horseman & Other Ghoulish Tales. Rowe, Gavin, illus. 2000. 96p. (J). (gr. k-6). 18.95 (978-1-56656-377-2(1) , Crocodile Bks.) Interlink Publishing Group, Inc.

Percy, Graham, illus. Little Red Riding Hood. l.t. ed. 2001. (SPA.). 28p. (ps-3). incl. audio compact disk (978-84-8214-086-5(8) , 1622) Peralt Montagut.

—Little Red Riding Hood. l.t. ed. 2001. 28p. (J). (ps-3). 8.49 incl. audio (978-84-86154-90-5(1)) Peralt Montagut ESP. *Dist:* imaJen, Inc.

—The Wolf & the Seven Little Kids. l.t. ed. 2001. (SPA.). 28p. (ps-3). incl. audio compact disk (978-84-8214-070-4(1) , 1622) Peralt Montagut.

—The Wolf & the Seven Little Kids. l.t. ed. 2001. 28p. (J). (ps-3). 8.99 incl. audio (978-84-86154-37-0(5)) Peralt Montagut ESP. *Dist:* imaJen, Inc.

Peris, Carme. Goldilocks & the Three Bears. 1998. (Fairy Tale Theater Ser.). (Illus.). 32p. (J). (gr. k-3). pap. 8.95 (978-0-7641-5116-3(9)) Barron's Educational Series, Inc.

—Ricitos de Oro y Los Tres Osos. 1998. (Fairy Tale Theater Ser.).Tr. of Goldilocks & the Three Bears. (SPA., Illus.). 32p. (J). (gr. k-3). pap. 8.95 (978-0-7641-5148-4(7)) Barron's Educational Series, Inc.

Peris, Carme, illus. Puss 'n Boots. 1999. 32p. (J). (ps-3). 8.95 (978-0-7641-5156-9(8)) Barron's Educational Series, Inc.

Peris, Carmie, illus. Snow White & the Seven Dwarfs. 1999. 32p. (J). (gr. k-3). 8.95 (978-0-7641-5151-4(7)) Barron's Educational Series, Inc.

Peters, Amy. The Everything Fairy Tales Book: A Magical Collection of All-Time Favorites to Delight the Whole Family. 2001. (Illus.). 304p. 14.95 (978-1-58062-546-3(0)) Adams Media Corp.

Pirotta, Saviour. Joy to the World: Christmas Stories from Around the Globe. Moxley, Sheila, illus. 1998. 48p. (J). (ps-3). 15.95 (978-0-06-027902-8(8)) HarperCollins Pubs.

Pirotta, Saviour & Cann, Helen. Christian Festivals. 2001. (Festival Tales Ser.). (Illus.). 32p. (J). (gr. 4-7). lib. bdg. 25.69 (978-0-7398-2732-1(4)) Raintree.

Polacco, Patricia. Luba & the Wren. Polacco, Patricia, illus. 2002. 40p. (J). pap. 6.99 (978-0-698-11922-2(3) , Putnam Juvenile) Penguin Group (USA) Inc.

—Luba & the Wren. 2002. (gr. k-3). lib. bdg. 15.30 (978-0-613-50465-2(8)) Tandem Library Bks.

Powell, Patricia Hruby. Zinnia: How the Corn Was Saved. Ruffenach, Jessie, ed. Thomas, Peter, tr. Benally, Kendrick, illus. 2004. (ENG & NAV.). 32p. 17.95 (978-1-893354-38-8(5)) Salina Bookshelf.

Prince, Sarah. Three Little Pigs. 1999. (ps-2). lib. bdg. 11.80 (978-0-613-19472-3(1)) Tandem Library Bks.

Prose, Francine. You Never Know: A Legend of the Lamed-Vavniks. Podwal, Mark H., illus. 1998. 24p. (J). (gr. k-3). 14.89 (978-0-688-15807-1(2)) HarperCollins Pubs.

Puerto, Carlos. La Luna en Sus Manos. 2003. (Disney Collection). (SPA.). 96p. (J). 6.95 (978-84-670-0304-8(9)) Espasa Calpe, S.A. ESP. *Dist:* Planeta Publishing Corp.

QEB Start Reading & Writing National Book Stores Edition: Little Red Riding Hood. 2006. (J). per. (978-1-59566-267-5(7)) QEB Publishing Inc.

Raczek, Linda Theresa. Stories from Native North America. Hook, Richard, illus. 1999. (Multicultural Stories Ser.). 48p. (J). (ps-3). lib. bdg. 27.12 (978-0-7398-1336-2(6)) Raintree.

Ramirez, Michael Rose. Legend of the Hummingbird: A Tale from Puerto Rico. 1998. (gr. k-3). lib. bdg. 12.95 (978-0-613-87443-4(9)) Tandem Library Bks.

Rapunzel. 2004. 29.95 incl. cd-rom (978-1-55592-738-7(6)) ; pap. 18.95 incl. audio compact disk (978-1-55592-744-8(0)) ; pap. 38.75 incl. audio compact disk (978-1-55592-752-3(1)) ; pap. 32.75 incl. audio (978-0-7882-0246-9(4)) ; pap. 14.95 incl. audio (978-0-7882-0398-5(3)) Weston Woods Studios, Inc.

Reichstein, Alexander, illus. The Eagle & the Wren. 2002. 40p. (J). (gr. k-3). pap. 6.95 (978-0-7358-1706-7(5)) North-South Bks., Inc.

Repchuk, Caroline & Aesop. The Race. Jay, Alison, illus. 2002. 32p. (J). (gr. k-1). 15.95 (978-0-8118-3500-8(6)) Chronicle Bks. LLC.

Retana, Maria L. Tall Tails from a Mountain Slope. Retana, Guillermo, tr. Weaver, Marian, illus. 1999. Tr. of Rabos Altos de la Ladera. (SPA.). 32p. (Orig.). (J). (gr. k-3). pap. 6.95 (978-0-9652920-0-9(2)) High Desert Productions.

Retana, Maria Luisa. Tanili: An Afrocuban Folktale. 2004. 36p. 17.95 (978-0-9652920-1-6(0)) High Desert Productions.

Riordan, James, ed. Stories from the Sea. Hall, Amanda, illus. 2002. 79p. (J). (gr. 4-6). 20.00 (978-0-7567-5638-3(3)) DIANE Publishing Co.

Rius, R. Los Tres Cerditos. 1998. (Fairy Tale Theater Ser.).Tr. of Three Little Pigs. (SPA., Illus.). 32p. (J). (gr. k-3). pap. 8.95 (978-0-7641-5147-7(9)) Barron's Educational Series, Inc.

Rius, Roser. The Three Little Pigs. 1998. (Fairy Tale Theater Ser.). (Illus.). 32p. (J). (gr. k-3). pap. 8.95 (978-0-7641-5115-6(0)) Barron's Educational Series, Inc.

Roberts, Tom. Goldilocks. Kubinyi, Laszlo, illus. 2006. (J). (gr. 2-6). 25.65 (978-1-59197-748-3(7)) Spotlight.

Rogers, Fred. The Giving Box. 2000. (Illus.). 96p. (J). pap. 12.95 (978-0-7624-0825-2(1) , Running Pr. Kids) Running Pr. Bk. Pubs.

Rose, Gerald. The Raven & the Fox ELT Edition. 2001. (Cambridge Storybooks Ser.). (Illus.). 16p. pap. 5.00 (978-0-521-00721-4(6)) Cambridge Univ. Pr.

Running Press Staff, et al. The Classic Treasury of Bulfinch's Mythology. 2003. (Illus.). 56p. (J). 9.98 (978-0-7624-1497-0(9) , Courage Bks.) Running Pr. Bk. Pubs.

Salley, Coleen. Epossumondas. Stevens, Janet, illus. 2002. 40p. (J). (ps-2). 16.00 (978-0-15-216748-6(X)) Harcourt Children's Bks.

—Why Epossumondas Has No Hair on His Tail. Stevens, Janet, illus. 2004. 40p. (J). 16.00 (978-0-15-204935-5(5) , Harcourt Children's Bks) Harcourt Children's Bks.

San Souci, Robert D. Nicholas Pipe. 2000. (978-0-606-18436-6(8)) Tandem Library Bks.

—Short & Shivery: Thirty Chilling Tales. Coville, Katherine, illus. 2001. 192p. (J). (gr. 5). pap. 5.50 (978-0-440-41804-7(6) , Yearling) Random Hse. Children's Bks.

—Short & Shivery: Thirty Chilling Tales. 2001. (gr. 5-8). lib. bdg. 13.00 (978-0-613-85704-8(6)) Tandem Library Bks.

—A Terrifying Taste of Short & Shivery: Thirty Creepy Tales. Coville, Katherine, illus. 2004. 176p. (gr. 3-7). 5.99 (978-0-440-41878-8(X) , Yearling) Random Hse. Children's Bks.

Sand, George. The Castle of Pictures & Other Stories, Vol. 1. Hirko, Holly E., ed. Warshaw, Mary, illus. 2004. 175p. (gr. 7 up). pap. 12.95 (978-1-55861-092-7(8)) Feminist Pr. at The City Univ. of New York.

Sanderson, Ruth. Cinderella. Sanderson, Ruth, illus. 2002. (Illus.). 32p. (J). (gr. 1-3). 15.95 (978-0-316-77965-4(2)) Little, Brown Bks. for Young Readers.

Sanna, Ellyn. Firefighters' Folklore. 2002. (North American Folklore Ser.). (Illus.). 112p. (YA). (gr. 7 up). lib. bdg. (978-1-59084-334-5(7)) Mason Crest Pubs.

Sarn, John. Inside the Magic Mountain. 2000. 224p. pap. 10.95 (978-1-881636-18-2(6)) Windsor Hse. Publishing Group, The.

Sastrias, Martha. El Uso del folklore Para Motivar a los Ninos a Leer y Escribir. 2005. (SPA., Illus.). 238p. pap., pap. 18.00 incl. audio compact disk (978-968-860-532-5(8)) Editorial Pax MEX. *Dist:* Independent Pubs. Group.

Sax, Boria. Serpent & the Swan: The Animal Bride in Folklore & Literature. 1998. (Illus.). 268p. pap. 18.95 (978-0-939923-68-7(8)) McDonald & Woodward Publishing Co., The.

Sayler, Machelle, illus. Folkeminnevitskap II. 2004. 144p. (978-0-9744422-1-1(6)) Erickson, Rakel L.

Scarry, Richard. Richard Scarry's Animal Nursery Tales. 2006. (Illus.). 72p. (J). (ps-3). 14.95 (978-0-375-83791-3(4) , Golden Bks.) Random Hse. Children's Bks.

Scholey, Arthur. Baboushka: A Christmas Folktale from Russia. Cann, Helen, illus. 2005. 28p. (J). (gr. 4-8). reprint ed. 16.00 (978-0-7567-9646-4(6)) DIANE Publishing Co.

Schuh, Mari C. & Sautter, Aaron. Zombies. 2007. (Blazers Ser.). 32p. (J). 19.93 (978-0-7368-6446-6(6)) Capstone Pr., Inc.

Seeger, Pete & Jacobs, Paul DuBois. Some Friends to Feed: The Story of Stone Soup. Hays, Michael, illus. 2005. 40p. (J). (ps-3). 16.99 incl. audio compact disk (978-0-399-24017-1(9) , Putnam Juvenile) Penguin Group (USA) Inc.

Semelet, Camille, illus. The Little Red Hen. 1999. (Little Pebbles Ser.). 32p. (ps-1). 6.95 (978-0-7892-0514-8(9)) Abbeville Pr., Inc.

Sendak, Maurice. Marchen der Bruder Grimm. (GER.). pap. 29.95 (978-3-257-00866-1(X)) Diogenes Verlag AG CHE. *Dist:* Distribooks, Inc.

Shah, Idries. The Farmer's Wife. Santiago, Rose Mary, illus. (Sounds of Afghanistan Ser.). (J). 2005. (ps-3). 28.95 incl. audio compact disk (978-1-883536-67-1(7) , FAWCB1); 1998. 32p. (gr. 4-7). 17.00 (978-1-883536-07-7(3) , FAWI1) ISHK. (Hoopoe Bks.).

—The Farmer's Wife/la Esposa Del Granjero. Santiago, Rose Mary, illus. 2003. (SPA & ENG.). (J). 18.00 (978-1-883536-33-6(2) , FAWI2, Hoopoe Bks.) ISHK.

—The Lion Who Saw Himself in the Water. Rodriguez, Ingrid, illus. 2005. (Sounds of Afghanistan Ser.). (J). (ps-3). 28.95 incl. audio compact disk (978-1-883536-71-8(5) , LIWCB1, Hoopoe Bks.) ISHK.

—The Lion Who Saw Himself in the Water. Santiago, Rose Mary, illus. 2001. 32p. (J). 18.00 (978-1-883536-25-1(1) , LIWS2, Hoopoe Bks.) ISHK.

—The Lion Who Saw Himself in the Water. Rodriguez, Ingrid, illus. 1998. 32p. (J). (gr. 4-7). 17.00 (978-1-883536-12-1(X) , LIWS1, Hoopoe Bks.) ISHK.

—The Lion Who Saw Himself in the Water/el Leon Que Se Vio en el Aqua. Rodriguez, Ingrid, illus. 2003. (SPA & ENG.). (J). 18.00 (978-1-883536-31-2(6) , LIWS3); 6.95 (978-1-883536-32-9(4) , LIWS4) ISHK. (Hoopoe Bks.).

—The Man & the Fox. 2006. (Illus.). 32p. (J). 18.00 (978-1-883536-43-5(X)); pap. 7.99 (***978-1-883536-60-2(X)***) ISHK. (Hoopoe Bks.).

—Neem the Half-boy. Revels, Robert & Mori, Midori, illus. 1998. 32p. (J). (gr. 4-7). 17.00 (978-1-883536-10-7(3) , NEHB1, Hoopoe Bks.) ISHK.

—The Silly Chicken. Jackson, Jeff, illus. 2000. 32p. (J). (ps-3). 17.00 (978-1-883536-19-0(7) , SICH1, Hoopoe Bks.) ISHK.

Shah, Idries & Caron, Mona. The Boy Without a Name. 2000. (Illus.). 32p. (J). (ps-3). 17.00 (978-1-883536-20-6(0) , BOWN1, Hoopoe Bks.) ISHK.

Shah, Idries & Santiago, Rose Mary. The Clever Boy & the Terrible, Dangerous Animal. 2000. (Illus.). 32p. (J). (gr. 1-4). 17.00 (978-1-883536-18-3(9) , CLBT1, Hoopoe Bks.) ISHK.

Shakespeare, William, et al. Tales from Shakespeare. Green Elliott, Elizabeth Shippen, illus. 1999. (Children's Classics Ser.). 384p. (J). 6.99 (978-0-517-20574-7(2) , Children's Classics) Random Hse. Value Publishing.

Shannon, George. More Stories to Solve: Fifteen Folktales from Around the World. 2001. (Illus.). (J). (978-0-606-20811-6(9)); 2000. (gr. 3-6). lib. bdg. 12.95 (978-0-613-34861-4(3)) Tandem Library Bks.

—Stories to Solve. Katcher, R. A., ed. Sis, Peter, illus. 2000. 56p. (J). (gr. 2 up). pap. 4.99 (978-0-380-73260-9(2) , Harper Trophy) HarperCollins Pubs.

—Stories to Solve: Folktales from Around the World. 2000. (gr. 5-8). lib. bdg. 12.95 (978-0-613-52997-6(9)) Tandem Library Bks.

Sharkey, Niamh, illus. Juan y los Frijoles Magicos (Jack & the Beanstalk) 2002. (SPA.). 40p. (J). (gr. k-3). 6.99 (978-1-84148-894-3(1) , BFP31244) Barefoot Bks., Inc.

Shepard, Aaron. The Sea King's Daughter: A Russian Legend. 2001. (978-0-606-20899-4(2)) Tandem Library Bks.

Sherman, Josepha. Magic Hoofbeats: Horse Tales from Many Lands. Wingerter, Linda, illus. 2004. 80p. (J). 19.99 (978-1-84148-091-6(6)) Barefoot Bks., Inc.

Shulevitz, Uri. The Treasure. 2001. (Illus.). (J). pap. 18.95 incl. audio compact disk (978-1-59112-332-3(1)) Live Oak Media.

Siddiqui, Ashraf & Lerch, Marilyn. Pakistani Folk Tales: Toontoony Pie & Other Stories. Fairservis, Jan, illus. 2nd ed. 1998. (Library of Folklore). 158p. (gr. 2-5). 12.50 (978-0-7818-0703-6(4)) Hippocrene Bks., Inc.

Sieling, Peter. Folk Medicine. 2002. (North American Folklore Ser.). (Illus.). 112p. (YA). (gr. 7 up). lib. bdg. (978-1-59084-341-3(X)) Mason Crest Pubs.

Sierra, Judy. Can You Guess My Name? Traditional Tales Around the World. Vitale, Stefano, illus. 2002. 128p. (J). (gr. k-3). tchr. ed. 20.00 (978-0-618-13328-4(3) , Clarion Bks.) Houghton Mifflin Co. Trade & Reference Div.

—Silly & Sillier: Read Aloud Tales from Around the World. Gorbachev, Valeri, illus. 2002. 96p. (J). (gr. k-3). lib. bdg. 21.99 (978-0-375-90609-1(6) , Knopf Bks. for Young Readers) Random Hse. Children's Bks.

—Silly & Sillier: Read-Aloud Tales from Around the World. Gorbachev, Valeri, illus. 2002. 96p. (J). (gr. k-3). 19.95 (978-0-375-80609-4(1) , Knopf Bks. for Young Readers) Random Hse. Children's Bks.

—Tasty Baby Belly Buttons. 2001. (Illus.). (J). (978-0-606-21481-0(X)) Tandem Library Bks.

Singh, Rina. A Forest of Stories: Magical Tree Tales from Around the World. Cann, Helen, illus. 2003. 64p. (J). 19.99 (978-1-84148-963-6(8)) Barefoot Bks., Inc.

—Moon Tales. Lush, Debbie, illus. 2001. 80p. (J). pap. 16.99 (978-0-7475-4795-2(5)) Bloomsbury Publishing Plc GBR. *Dist:* Trafalgar Square Publishing.

Smith, Victor. Pokes Folks, Tales & Trails. 2001. (Illus.). 224p. pap. 12.95 (978-1-889668-22-2(2)) Smith & Daniel.

Sneed, Brad & Aesop. Aesop's Fables. Sneed, Brad, illus. 2003. (Illus.). 40p. (J). (gr. k-3). 16.99 (978-0-8037-2751-9(8) , Dial) Penguin Group (USA) Inc.

Sommer, Carl. Three Little Pigs. 2003. (Another Sommer-Time Story Ser.). (Illus.). 48p. (J). (gr. 1-4). 16.95 incl. audio compact disk (978-1-57537-511-3(7)); 16.95 incl. audio (978-1-57537-560-1(5)) Advance Publishing, Inc.

—Three Little Pigs. Budwine, Greg, illus. 2000. (Another Sommer-Time Story Ser.). 48p. (J). (gr. k-3). lib. bdg. 16.95 (978-1-57537-063-7(8)); 9.95 (978-1-57537-011-8(5)) Advance Publishing, Inc.

Souhami, Jessica. Rama & the Demon King: A Tale of Ancient India. Souhami, Jessica, illus. 2005. (Illus.). 36p. (J). pap. 7.95 (978-1-84507-361-9(4)) Lincoln, Frances Ltd. GBR. *Dist:* Perseus Distribution.

The Spanish Fairy Book (Folk Lore) 2000. 346p. (YA). per. (978-1-59085-198-2(6)) World of Wonders, Inc.

Spiegelman, Art. Folklore & Fairy Tale Funnies. Mouly, Francoise, ed. Spiegelman, Art, illus. 2000. (Little Lit Ser.: Vol. 1). (Illus.). 64p. (J). (ps up). 19.95 (978-0-06-028624-8(5) , Cotler, Joanna Books) HarperCollins Pubs.

Spirin, Gennady. The Tale of the Firebird. Popova, Tatiana, tr. Spirin, Gennady, illus. 2002. (Illus.). 32p. (J). (ps-3). 16.99 (978-0-399-23584-9(1) , Philomel) Penguin Group (USA) Inc.

Stampler, Ann Redisch. Something for Nothing. Cohen, Jacqueline M., illus. 2003. 32p. (J). (gr. 3-5). tchr. ed. 15.00 (978-0-618-15982-6(7) , Clarion Bks.) Houghton Mifflin Co. Trade & Reference Div.

Steck-Vaughn Staff. Goldilocks & the Three Bears Level 1-2: Orange Level 1-2. 2000. (gr. 3-6). lib. bdg. 14.35 (978-0-613-75926-7(5)) Tandem Library Bks.

—Point of View, 30 bks., Set. 1998. (C). pap. incl. audio (978-0-8172-6874-9(X)) Steck-Vaughn.

—Three Billy Goats Gruff: Green Level 1-2. 2000. (gr. 3-6). lib. bdg. 14.35 (978-0-613-75882-6(X)) Tandem Library Bks.

Stern, Anita. Tales from Many Lands: An Anthology of Multicultural Folk Literature. 2001. (Illus.). 199p. (gr. 7-9). pap. 29.69 (978-0-8442-0855-8(8) , 9780844208558) McGraw-Hill Higher Education.

Stevens, Janet. The Tortoise & the Hare. Stevens, Janet, illus. 2002. (Illus.). (J). 15.49 (978-0-7587-3847-9(1)) Book Wholesalers, Inc.

Stevens, Molly, tr. from FRE. The Gingerbread Man: A Classic Fairy Tale. Thibault, Dominique, illus. 2001. (Little Pebbles Ser.). 32p. 6.95 (978-0-7892-0733-3(8)) Abbeville Pr., Inc.

Stewig, John Warren & Wittmann, Patricia, illus. Clever Gretchen. 2000. 32p. (J). (gr. k-3). 15.95 (978-0-7614-5066-5(1) , Cavendish Children's Bks.) Cavendish, Marshall Corp.

Storrie, Paul D. Robin Hood: Outlaw of Sherwood Forest. Yeates, Thomas, illus. 2007. (Graphic Myths & Legends Ser.). 48p. (J). (gr. 4-8). 26.60 (978-0-8225-5964-1(1)) Lerner Publishing Group.

STORYBOOK. Disney's Princess Treasury. 2001. (Illus.). 576p. (J). (ps-17). 19.99 (978-0-7868-3348-1(3)) Disney Pr.

Sturges, Philemon. The Little Red Hen Makes a Pizza. Walrod, Amy, illus. 2002. (J). 14.04 (978-1-4046-1782-7(5)) Book Wholesalers, Inc.

Swinson, Cyril, ed. Twenty Scottish Tales & Legends. Stewart, Allan, illus. 1998. (Library of Folklore). 215p. (J). (gr. 4-7). 14.95 (978-0-7818-0701-2(8)) Hippocrene Bks., Inc.

Tales from Around the World. 1999. pap. 152.87 (978-0-8172-3906-0(5)) Raintree.

Tan, Amy. Sagwa, the Chinese Siamese Cat. 2001. (gr. k-3). lib. bdg. 15.30 (978-0-613-50496-6(8)) Tandem Library Bks.

Taylor, Sybil. What the Pumpkins Learned. 2004. (Illus.). 32p. pap. 12.95 (978-0-89346-942-9(4)) Heian International Publishing, Inc.

Tchana, Katrin. The Serpent Slayer: And Other Stories of Strong Women. Hyman, Trina Schart, illus. 2000. 128p. (J). (ps-17). 22.99 (978-0-316-38701-9(0)) Little Brown & Co.

Tezel, Mark. The Legend of Rosa's Window. Tezel, Mark, illus. 1999. (Illus.). 36p. (J). (gr. k-7). pap. 6.95 (978-0-9667687-1-8(X)) Assaca Pr.

Thompson, Susan, et al. Mayan Folktales: Cuentos Folkloricos Mayas. 2007. (World Folklore Ser.). (SPA & ENG.). 236p. 35.00 (***978-1-59158-138-3(9)*** , LU1389) Libraries Unlimited, Inc.

Three Folk Tales. Date not set. (Nelson Readers Ser.). (J). pap. (978-0-17-557041-6(8)) Addison-Wesley Longman, Inc.

Tolstoy, Alexei. Gigantic Turnip. 2000. (gr. k-3). lib. bdg. 15.30 (978-0-613-23639-3(4)) Tandem Library Bks.

Townsend. Mysterious Urban Myths. 2004. (Out There Ser.). (Illus.). pap. 8.95 (978-1-4109-0968-8(9)) Raintree.

—Out There 6-Pack (48 Books), Set. 2004. (Illus.). pap. 386.65 (978-1-4109-1270-1(1)) Raintree.

Townsend, John. Mysterious Urban Myths. 2004. (Illus.). 56p. (J). lib. bdg. 28.56 (978-1-4109-0567-3(5)) Raintree.

Troughton, Joanna. Folk Tales of the World How Night Came. (Illus.). 32p. (J). pap. 13.95 (978-0-14-056379-5(2)) Penguin Bks., Ltd. GBR. *Dist:* Trafalgar Square Publishing.

Tsihnahjinnie, Andrew, illus. Coyote Tales. 2000. 32p. (J). (gr. k-5). 6.95 (978-1-885772-18-3(1)) Kiva Publishing, Inc.

Uberoi, Meera. The Puffin Book of Classic Indian Tales for Children. 2003. (Illus.). 208p. 10.99 (978-0-14-333540-5(5) , Puffin Global) Penguin Group (USA) Inc.

Ungar, Richard. Rachel's Gift. 2003. (Illus.). 32p. (J). (gr. 2-5). 16.95 (978-0-88776-616-9(1)) Tundra Bks., Inc./Livres Toundra, Inc. CAN. *Dist:* Random Hse., Inc.

—Rachel's Library. 2004. 32p. (J). (gr. 2-5). 15.95 (978-0-88776-678-7(1)) Tundra Bks., Inc./Livres Toundra, Inc. CAN. *Dist:* Random Hse., Inc.

van Kampen, Vlasta, illus. Monkey Tales. 1998. 40p. (J). (gr. k-3). pap. 6.95 (978-1-55037-530-5(X)); lib. bdg. 18.95 (978-1-55037-531-2(8)) Annick Pr., Ltd. CAN. *Dist:* Firefly Bks., Ltd.

Van Laan, Nancy. With a Whoop & a Holler: A Bushel of Lore from Way down South. 2001. (J). (978-0-606-21532-9(8)) Tandem Library Bks.

Varnai, Gyorgy & Kyle, Kathryn. Pride. Mark, Steve, illus. 2002. (Wonder Books Level 3: Values Ser.). 32p. (J). (ps-3). 22.79 (978-1-56766-091-3(6)) Child's World, Inc.

Wade, Barrie. Goldilocks & the Three Bears. Stephenson, Kristina, illus. 2004. (Read-It! Readers Ser.). 32p. (C). (gr. k-3). 18.60 (978-1-4048-0057-1(3)) Picture Window Bks.

Walker, Richard. Barefoot Book of Pirates. Whelan, Owen, illus. 2002. 63p. (J). (ps-6). pap. 9.99 (978-1-84148-886-8(0)) Barefoot Bks., Inc.

—The Barefoot Book of Trickster Tales. Munoz, Claudio, illus. 1998. 80p. (J). (gr. 4-7). 18.95 (978-1-902283-08-1(2)) Barefoot Bks., Inc.

Wallace, Ian. The Man Who Walked the Earth. Wallace, Ian, illus. 2003. (Illus.). 32p. (J). 16.95 (978-0-88899-545-2(8)) Groundwood Bks. CAN. *Dist:* Perseus Distribution.

Wang, Eva, illus. Auntie Tigress & Other Favorite Chinese Folk-Tales. 2006. 48p. (J). 16.50 (978-1-933327-29-7(4)); 15.95 (978-1-933327-28-0(6)) Purple Bear Bks., Inc.

Ward, John, illus. The Freedom Riddle. 2002. 32p. (J). 14.95 (978-1-57768-441-1(9)) School Specialty Publishing.

Wasserman, Robin. A Cinderella Story. novel movie tie-in ed. 2004. (Cinderella Ser.). (Illus.). 152p. (J). (gr. 3-6). mass mkt. 4.99 (978-0-439-65341-1(5)) Scholastic, Inc.

Weiner, Andy J. & Whipple, Rick. The Legacy of John Cyclone. 2000. (Publish-a-Book Ser.). (Illus.). 24p. (J). (ps-3). 7.95 (978-0-7398-2370-5(1)) Steck-Vaughn.

Wenig, Adolf. Folk Tales from Bohemia. 1998. (Library of Folklore). (Illus.). 89p. (gr. 4-7). 14.95 (978-0-7818-0718-0(2)) Hippocrene Bks., Inc.

White, Mark. The Ant & the Grasshopper: A Retelling of Aesop's Fable. Rojo, Sara, illus. 2004. (Read-It! Readers Ser.). 24p. (C). (gr. k-3). 18.60 (978-1-4048-0217-9(7)) Picture Window Bks.

—The Fox & the Grapes: A Retelling of Aesop's Fable. Rojo, Sara, illus. 2004. (Read-It! Readers Ser.). 24p. (C). (gr. k-3). 18.60 (978-1-4048-0218-6(5)) Picture Window Bks.

—The Goose That Laid the Golden Egg: A Retelling of Aesop's Fable. Rojo, Sara, illus. 2004. (Read-It! Readers Ser.). 24p. (C). (gr. k-3). 18.60 (978-1-4048-0219-3(3)) Picture Window Bks.

—The Lion & the Mouse: A Retelling of Aesop's Fable. Rojo, Sara, illus. 2004. (Read-It! Readers Ser.). 24p. (C). (gr. k-3). 18.60 (978-1-4048-0216-2(9)) Picture Window Bks.

—The Wolf in Sheep's Clothing: A Retelling of Aesop's Fable. Rojo, Sara, illus. 2004. (Read-It! Readers Ser.). 24p. (C). (gr. k-3). 18.60 (978-1-4048-0220-9(7)) Picture Window Bks.

Who's in Rabbit's House? 2004. pap. 38.75 incl. audio compact disk (978-1-55592-489-8(1)); (J). 24.95 incl. audio (978-0-7882-0581-1(1)); (J). pap. 18.95 incl. audio compact disk (978-1-55592-488-1(3)); (J). pap. 32.75 incl. audio (978-1-55592-334-1(8)); (J). pap. 14.95 incl. audio (978-0-7882-0642-9(7)) Weston Woods Studios, Inc.

Wilhelm, Hans. All for the Best! The Secret to Happiness. 2003. (Illus.). 32p. (J). (ps-3). 16.95 (978-1-57174-344-2(8)) Hampton Roads Publishing Co., Inc.

Willard, Nancy. Cinderella's Dress. Dyer, Jane, illus. 2003. 32p. (J). pap. 16.95 (978-0-590-56927-9(9) , Blue Sky Pr., The) Scholastic, Inc.

Wilson, Barbara Ker & So, Meilo. Wishbones: A Folk Tale from China. (Illus.). 32p. (J). (ps-2). pap. 9.99 (978-0-7112-1415-6(8)) Lincoln, Frances Ltd. GBR. *Dist:* Transition Vendor.

Wingerter, Linda S., illus. Bird Tales from Near & Far. 1999. (Tales Alive Bks.: Vol. 3). 96p. (J). (ps up). pap. 12.95 (978-1-885593-18-4(X) , Williamson Bks.) Ideals Pubns.

Wolfson, Margaret & Clavero, Juan Caneba, illus. The Patient Stone: A Persian Love Story. 2001. 32p. (J). (gr. 3 up). 16.99 (978-1-84148-085-5(1)) Barefoot Bks., Inc.

Yolen, Jane. Firebird. 1999. 32p. (J). (ps-1). pap. 5.95 (978-0-06-443600-7(4)) HarperCollins Pubs.

—The Firebird. Vagin, Vladimir, illus. 2002. 32p. (J). (ps-1). lib. bdg. 17.89 (978-0-06-028539-5(7)); 15.95 (978-0-06-028538-8(9)) HarperCollins Pubs.

—Fish Prince & Other Stories: Mermen Folk Tales. 2001. (gr. 5-8). lib. bdg. 24.60 (978-0-613-78986-8(5)) Tandem Library Bks.

—Mightier Than the Sword: World Folktales for Strong Boys. Colon, Raul, illus. 2003. 128p. (YA). 19.00 (978-0-15-216391-4(3) , Silver Whistle) Harcourt Trade Pubs.

—Not One Damsel in Distress: World Folktales for Strong Girls. Guevara, Susan, illus. 2000. 128p. (YA). (gr. 3-7). 21.00 (978-0-15-202047-7(0) , Silver Whistle) Harcourt Trade Pubs.

Young, Ed. Lon Po Po. unabr. ed. 2006. (J). (gr. k-4). pap. 18.95 incl. audio compact disk (978-0-439-87366-6(5) , WPCD690); (Illus.). 29.95 incl. audio compact disk (978-0-439-87367-3(3) , WHCD690); (Illus.). 24.95 incl. audio (978-0-439-87365-9(7) , WHRA690); (Illus.). pap. 14.95 incl. audio (978-0-439-87364-2(9) , WPRA690) Weston Woods Studios, Inc.

Zelinsky, Paul O. Rapunzel. 2002. (Illus.). (J). (ps-ps). lib. bdg. 16.45 (978-0-613-60832-9(1)) Tandem Library Bks.

Zeman, Ludmila. La Derniere Quete de Gilgamesh. 2000. (Gilgamesh Trilogy Ser.). (FRE & SPA.). 24p. (J). (gr. 3). pap. 9.95 (978-0-88776-528-5(9) , Livres Toundra) Tundra Bks., Inc./Livres Toundra, Inc. CAN. *Dist:* Random Hse., Inc.

Zeman, Ludmila, illus. & retold by. The Revenge of Ishtar. Zeman, Ludmila, retold by. 1998. (J). (ps-7). lib. bdg. 17.60 (978-0-613-09466-5(2)) Tandem Library Bks.

Zeman, Ludmila & Boileau, Michele. La Revanche D'Ishtar. 2000. (Gilgamesh Trilogy Ser.). (FRE & SPA., Illus.). 24p. (J). (gr. 3). pap. 9.95 (978-0-88776-527-8(0) , Livres Toundra) Tundra Bks., Inc./Livres Toundra, Inc. CAN. *Dist:* Random Hse., Inc.

3 Little Wolves & the Big Bad Pig. 1998. (J). pap. 3.95 (978-0-439-04446-2(4)) Scholastic, Inc.

FOLKLORE—AFRICA

Aardema, Verna. Koi & the Kola Nuts: A Tale from Liberia. Cepeda, Joe, illus. rev. ed. 2003. 32p. (J). (gr. k-3). 6.99 (978-0-689-85677-8(6) , Aladdin) Simon & Schuster Children's Publishing.

African Tales & Myths, 6 bks., Set. (Illus.). (J). (gr. 2-5). lib. bdg. 159.60 (978-1-57103-242-3(8)) Rourke Publishing, LLC.

Appleby, Sue. Umoyana the Little Wind. Ablorh, Samuel Adjei, tr. 2000. (GAA., Illus.). pap. 3.00 (978-0-521-79589-0(3)) Cambridge Univ. Pr.

—Umoyana the Little Wind: Asante Twi Version. Asenso, Okofo, tr. 2000. (Illus.). pap. 3.00 (978-0-521-79608-8(3)) Cambridge Univ. Pr.

Balaguac, Lin & Long, Robert. La Dama y el Leaon. 2000. (Cuentos y Leyendas Bilingues Ser.).Tr. of Princess & the Lion. (ENG & SPA.). (J). 22.48 (978-0-658-01013-2(1)) National Textbook Co.

Balague, Lin & Long, Robert. La Dama y el Leon. 2000. (Cuentos y Leyendas Bilingues Ser.).Tr. of Princess & the Lion. (ENG & SPA., Illus.). (J). pap. (978-0-658-01015-6(8)) McGraw-Hill/Contemporary.

Beake, Lesley. One Dark Night: Asante Twi Version. Asenso, Okofo, tr. 2000. (Illus.). pap. 3.00 (978-0-521-79607-1(5)) Cambridge Univ. Pr.

—One Dark Night: Fante Version. Aggrey, Safohen J. E. K., tr. 2000. (Illus.). pap. 3.00 (978-0-521-79568-5(0)) Cambridge Univ. Pr.

Bryan, Ashley. Beautiful Blackbird. Bryan, Ashley, illus. 2003. (Illus.). 40p. (J). (ps-2). 17.99 (978-0-689-84731-8(9) , Atheneum) Simon & Schuster Children's Publishing.

Bryant, Laura J., illus. Tales of Africa: Retold Timeless Classics. 1999. (Cover-to-Cover Timeless Classics Ser.). 56p. (J). pap. (978-0-7891-2857-7(8)); (gr. 1-4). lib. bdg. 13.95 (978-0-7807-7851-1(0)) Perfection Learning Corp.

Burkett, Beverley. Baby Monkey's Bananas. Ablorh, Samuel Adjei, tr. 2000. (GAA., Illus.). pap. 3.00 (978-0-521-79593-7(1)) Cambridge Univ. Pr.

Cabral, Len. La Cinturita de Anansi, Level 3. Ada, Alma Flor, tr. Diaz, David, illus. 3rd ed. 2003. (Dejame Leer Ser.). (SPA.). 16p. (J). (ps-3). 6.50 (978-0-673-36294-0(9) , Good Year Bks.) Celebration Pr.

Chocolate, Deborah M. Newton & Boies, Alex. Imani in the Belly. 2002. 32p. (J). (gr. k-3). 15.00 (978-0-9718310-0-1(9)) WaterShed Bks.

Eisner, Will. Sundiata: A Legend of Africa. 2003. (Illus.). 32p. 7.95 (978-1-56163-340-1(2)) NBM Publishing Co.

Eisner, Will, illus. & retold by. Sundiata: A Legend of Africa. Eisner, Will, retold by. 2003. 32p. (gr. k-3). 15.95 (978-1-56163-332-6(1)) NBM Publishing Co.

Fowler, Rosamund, illus. Tales from West Africa. 2001. (Oxford Myths & Legends Ser.). 112p. (Orig.). (YA). suppl. ed. 11.95 (978-0-19-275076-1(3)) Oxford Univ. Pr., Inc.

Gershator, Phillis. Only One Cowry: A Dahomean Tale. Soman, David, illus. 2000. 32p. (J). (ps-2). pap. 16.95 (978-0-531-30288-0(1) , Orchard Bks.) Scholastic, Inc.

Gregorowski, Christopher. Fly, Eagle, Fly! An African Tale. Daly, Niki, illus. 2000. 32p. (J). (gr. k-4). 18.95 (978-0-689-82398-5(3) , McElderry, Margaret K.) Simon & Schuster Children's Publishing.

Hepker, Sue. A Long Way to Baba. Torgah, F. K. Atakpa Kple Edoh, tr. 2000. (EWE., Illus.). pap. 3.00 (978-0-521-79577-7(X)) Cambridge Univ. Pr.

—A Long Way to Baba: Amharic Version. Duguma, Melaku Wakuma, tr. 1999. (Cambridge Reading Routes Ser.). (AMH., Illus.). 16p. pap. 3.70 (978-0-521-66830-9(1)) Cambridge Univ. Pr.

—A Long Way to Baba: Asante Twi Version. Asenso, Okofo, tr. 2000. (TWI., Illus.). pap. 3.00 (978-0-521-79606-4(7)) Cambridge Univ. Pr.

—A Long Way to Baba: Fante Version. Aggrey, Safohen J. E. K., tr. 2000. (Illus.). pap. 3.00 (978-0-521-79567-8(2)) Cambridge Univ. Pr.

—A Long Way to Baba: Ndebele Version. Dube, Grace, tr. 1999. (Cambridge African Language Library Ser.). (NBL & NDE., Illus.). 16p. pap. 3.70 (978-0-521-65812-6(8)) Cambridge Univ. Pr.

—A Long Way to Baba: Shona Version. Chateuka, Keresia, tr. 1999. (Cambridge African Language Library Ser.). (SHO., Illus.). 16p. pap. 3.70 (978-0-521-65827-0(6)) Cambridge Univ. Pr.

—A Long Way to Baba: Tigre Version. Kebebew, Amare Hagos, tr. 2000. (Cambridge Reading Routes Ser.). (TIG., Illus.). 16p. pap. 3.70 (978-0-521-66820-0(4)) Cambridge Univ. Pr.

Hodson, Christopher. Lizo's Song: Amharic Version. Duguma, Melaku Wakuma, tr. 1999. (Cambridge Reading Routes Ser.). (AMH., Illus.). 16p. pap. 3.70 (978-0-521-66828-6(X)) Cambridge Univ. Pr.

—Lizo's Song: Asante Twi Version. Asenso, Okofo, tr. 2000. (TWI., Illus.). pap. 3.00 (978-0-521-79610-1(5)) Cambridge Univ. Pr.

—Lizo's Song: Fante Version. Aggrey, Safohen J. E. K., tr. 2000. (Illus.). pap. 3.00 (978-0-521-79571-5(0)) Cambridge Univ. Pr.

—Lizo's Song: Hausa Version. Gusau, Saidu Mohammed, tr. 1998. (Cambridge African Language Library Ser.). (HAU., Illus.). 16p. pap. 6.60 (978-0-521-64798-4(3)) Cambridge Univ. Pr.

—Lizo's Song: Luganda Version. Lubega, Bonnie, tr. 1998. (Cambridge African Language Library Ser.). (LUG., Illus.). 16p. pap. 3.65 (978-0-521-63791-6(0)) Cambridge Univ. Pr.

—Lizo's Song: Tigre Version. Kebebew, Amare Hagos, tr. 1999. (Cambridge Reading Routes Ser.). (TIG., Illus.). 16p. pap. 3.70 (978-0-521-66818-7(2)) Cambridge Univ. Pr.

—Lizo's Song French Version. Ablorh, Samuel Adjei, tr. 2001. (GAA., Illus.). 16p. pap. 0.90 (978-0-521-79591-3(5)) Cambridge Univ. Pr.

—Lizo's Song French Version. Torgah, F. K. Atakpa Kple Edoh, tr. 2000. (EWE., Illus.). pap. 3.00 (978-0-521-79581-4(8)) Cambridge Univ. Pr.

—Lizo's Song French Version. Tadjo, Veronique, tr. from ENG. 1998. (Cambridge African Language Library Ser.). (FRE., Illus.). 16p. pap. 3.75 (978-0-521-64786-1(X)) Cambridge Univ. Pr.

Holleman, Monika. Chameleon's Clever Trick: Fante Version. Aggrey, Safohen J. E. K., tr. 2000. (Illus.). pap. 3.00 (978-0-521-79573-9(7)) Cambridge Univ. Pr.

Hollemann, Monika. Chameleon's Clever Trick: Amharic Version. Torgah, F. K. Atakpa Kple Edoh, tr. 2000. (EWE., Illus.). pap. 3.00 (978-0-521-79583-8(4)) Cambridge Univ. Pr.

—Chameleon's Clever Trick: Amharic Version. Ablorh, Samuel A., tr. 2000. (GAA., Illus.). pap. 3.00 (978-0-521-79616-3(4)) Cambridge Univ. Pr.

—Chameleon's Clever Trick: Amharic Version. Wako, Tegegn Nuresu, tr. 2000. (Cambridge Reading Routes Ser.). (AMH., Illus.). 16p. pap. 3.70 (978-0-521-66826-2(3)) Cambridge Univ. Pr.

—Chameleon's Clever Trick: Amharic Version. Dube, Grace, tr. 1999. (Cambridge African Language Library Ser.). (NBL & NDE., Illus.). 16p. pap. 3.70 (978-0-521-65811-9(X)) Cambridge Univ. Pr.

—Chameleon's Clever Trick: Amharic Version. Gusau, Saidu Mohammed, tr. 1998. (Cambridge African Language Library Ser.). (HAU., Illus.). 16p. pap. 6.60 (978-0-521-64799-1(1)) Cambridge Univ. Pr.

—Chameleon's Clever Trick: Amharic Version. Tadjo, Veronique, tr. from ENG. 1998. (Cambridge African Language Library Ser.). (FRE., Illus.). 16p. pap. 3.75 (978-0-521-64785-4(1)) Cambridge Univ. Pr.

—Chameleon's Clever Trick: Luganda Version. Lubega, Bonnie, tr. 1998. (Cambridge African Language Library Ser.). (LUG., Illus.). 16p. pap. 3.65 (978-0-521-63799-2(6)) Cambridge Univ. Pr.

—Chameleon's Clever Trick: Shona Version. Chateuka, Keresia, tr. 1999. (Cambridge African Language Library Ser.). (SHO., Illus.). 16p. pap. 3.70 (978-0-521-65826-3(8)) Cambridge Univ. Pr.

—Chameleon's Clever Trick: Tigre Version. Kebebew, Amare Hagos, tr. 1999. (Cambridge Reading Routes Ser.). (TIG., Illus.). 16p. pap. 3.70 (978-0-521-66816-3(6)) Cambridge Univ. Pr.

Kerven, Rosalind. Kintu's Mistake. 1998. (Myths & Legends Ser.). (Illus.). 24p. (J). 14.60 (978-1-57572-015-9(9)) Heinemann Library.

Lilly, Melinda. Tamba & the Chief: A Temne Tale. Reasoner, Charles, illus. 1998. (African Tales & Myths Ser.). (J). lib. bdg. 26.60 (978-0-86625-634-6(2)) Rourke Publishing, LLC.

—Zimani's Drum: A Malawian Legend. Reasoner, Charles, illus. 1998. (African Tales & Myths Ser.). (J). lib. bdg. (978-0-86625-633-9(4)) Rourke Publishing, LLC.

Mandela, Nelson, ed. Favorite African Folktales. 2004. (Illus.). 192p. pap. 13.95 (978-0-393-32624-6(1)) Norton, W. W. & Co., Inc.

—Nelson Mandela's Favorite African Folktales. 2002. (Illus.). 144p. (gr. 7 up). 24.95 (978-0-393-05212-1(5)) Norton, W. W. & Co., Inc.

Mankell, Henning. Secrets in the Fire. Stuksrud, Anne Connie, tr. from SWE. 2003. 176p. (J). (gr. 6-10). 17.95 (978-1-55037-801-6(5)); pap. 7.95 (978-1-55037-800-9(7)) Annick Pr., Ltd. CAN. *Dist:* Firefly Bks., Ltd.

Mbanze, Dinah M. & Daly, Niki. The Berry Basket: Three African Tales. 2002. (Illus.). 48p. 11.95 (978-0-7957-0100-9(4)) Kwela Bks. ZAF. *Dist:* Independent Pubs. Group.

McDermott, Gerald. Anansi the Spider: A Tale from the Ashanti. 2004. (J). (ps-4). pap. 14.95 incl. audio (978-1-56008-046-6(9) , PRA151) Weston Woods Studios, Inc.

Mead, Katherine. How Spiders Got Eight Legs. O'Malia, Carol, illus. 1998. (Easy to Read Folktales Ser.). 24p. (ps-3). pap. 4.95 (978-0-8172-7979-0(2)) Steck-Vaughn.

Medlicott, Mary. Tales from Africa. 2000. (J). (978-0-606-19437-2(1)) Tandem Library Bks.

Mhlophe, Gcina. Stories of Africa. (Illus.). 2003. 64p. (YA). pap. 19.95 (978-1-86914-035-9(4)); 2nd ed. 2004. 53p. reprint ed. 19.95 (978-1-86914-061-8(3)) Univ. of Natal Pr. ZAF. *Dist:* International Specialized Bk. Services.

Mollel, Tololwa M. Rhinos for Lunch & Elephants for Supper! 2000. (ps-2). lib. bdg. 15.25 (978-0-613-30110-7(2)) Tandem Library Bks.

The Old Hermit & the Boy Who Couldn't Stop Laughing: An African Fable - Revised & Expanded Edition. 2001. 19.95 (978-1-893811-01-0(8)) United African Educational Foundation.

Oseki, Iku, illus. How the Turtle Got Its Shell. 2001. (See-More's Stories Ser.). 32p. (J). pap. 11.95 incl. audio (978-1-882601-35-6(1)); pap. 16.95 incl. audio compact disk (978-1-882601-40-0(8)); pap. 6.95 (978-1-882601-34-9(3)) See-More's Workshop.

Parker, Vic. Africa. 2001. (Illus.). 48p. (J). lib. bdg. 24.25 (978-1-930643-35-2(7)) Chrysalis Education.

Toussaint, Kimani C. The Old Hermit & the Boy Who Couldn't Stop Laughing: An African Fable. Toussaint, Alice I. & Toussaint, Princess E., eds. Lassiter, Alphonso, illus. 1999. (African Fables for Children Ser.). vi, 32p. (J). (gr. 6-12). 10.00 (978-1-893811-00-3(X)) United African Educational Foundation.

Vernon-Jackson, Hugh O., ed. African Folk Tales. Green, Yuko, illus. 1999. (Dover Children's Thrift Classics Ser.). 64p. (J). (gr. 3-6). pap. 1.50 (978-0-486-40553-7(2)) Dover Pubns., Inc.

Vulliez, Hyacinthe. The Secrets of Kaidara. Marsh, Gwen, tr. from FRE. Souppart, Etienne, illus. 1998. (Tales of Heaven & Earth Ser.).Tr. of Secrets de Kaidara. 32p. (YA). (gr. 3-7). pap. 19.95 (978-0-88682-823-3(6) , Creative Education) Creative Co., The.

Warnes, Tim, illus. Counting Leopard's Spots: And Other Animal Stories. 1998. 104p. (J). (gr. k-4). 16.95 (978-1-888444-31-5(2) , 21029) Little Tiger Pr.

Washington, Donna L. A Pride of African Tales. Ransome, James E., illus. 2004. 80p. (J). (gr. 3-7). 16.99 (978-0-06-024929-8(3)) HarperCollins Pubs.

Watson, Jane Werner. The Lion's Paw. Tenggren, Gustaf, illus. 2000. (Little Golden Bks.). 24p. (J). (gr. k-k). 2.99 (978-0-307-96008-5(0) , Golden Bks.) Random Hse. Children's Bks.

FOLKLORE—AFRICA, CENTRAL

Grifalconi, Ann. The Village of Round & Square Houses. 2004. (J). (gr. k-5). 24.95 incl. audio (978-0-89719-796-0(8) , HRA326) Weston Woods Studios, Inc.

FOLKLORE—AFRICA, EAST

Arrington, H. J. Heart of a Friendship & Friends Again. 9.95 (978-1-56554-888-6(4)) Pelican Publishing Co., Inc.

Mollel, Tololwa M. Rhinos for Lunch & Elephants for Supper! Spurll, Barbara, illus. 2000. 32p. (J). (gr. k-ps). pap. 6.95 (978-0-618-05156-4(2) , Clarion Bks.) Houghton Mifflin Co. Trade & Reference Div.

—Subira Subira. Saport, Linda, illus. 2000. 32p. (J). (gr. k-3). tchr. ed. 15.00 (978-0-395-91809-8(X) , Clarion Bks.) Houghton Mifflin Co. Trade & Reference Div.

FOLKLORE—AFRICA, SOUTHERN

Scholtz, Pieter. Tokoloshe: An African Zulu Folktale. 1998. (J). pap. 6.00 (978-0-87602-364-8(2)) Anchorage Pr.

Seeger, Pete. Abiyoyo. 1998. (J). pap. 5.95 (978-0-87628-380-6(6)) Ctr. for Applied Research in Education, The.

—Abiyoyo. Hays, Michael, illus. 48p. (J). 2001. 19.95 (978-0-689-84693-9(2)); 2nd ed. 2005. 4.99 (978-0-689-87825-1(7) , Aladdin) Simon & Schuster Children's Publishing.

Seeger, Pete & Jacobs, Paul DuBois. Abiyoyo Returns. Hays, Michael, illus. 2004. 40p. (J). pap. 6.99 (978-0-689-87054-5(X) , Aladdin) Simon & Schuster Children's Publishing.

Seeger, Pete, et al. Abiyoyo Returns. 2001. (Illus.). 40p. (J). (ps-3). 17.99 (978-0-689-83271-0(0)) Simon & Schuster Children's Publishing.

Turkington, Nola. The Dancer. Daly, Niki, illus. 1999. 36p. (J). (978-0-7112-1427-9(1)) Lincoln, Frances Ltd.

—The Dancer. Daly, Niki, illus. 2001. 36p. (J). (gr. 1 up). pap. 8.99 (978-0-7112-1541-2(3)) Lincoln, Frances Ltd. GBR. *Dist:* Transition Vendor.

Wolfson, Margaret Olivia. Marriage of the Rain Goddess: A South African Myth. Parms, Clifford Alexander, illus. 2000. 32p. (J). (gr. 1-5). pap. 6.99 (978-1-84148-233-0(1)) Barefoot Bks., Inc.

FOLKLORE—AFRICA, WEST

Aardema, Verna. Anansi Does the Impossible. Desimini, Lisa, illus. 2000. (Aladdin Picture Bks.). 32p. (J). (ps-3). 7.99 (978-0-689-83933-7(2) , Aladdin) Simon & Schuster Children's Publishing.

—Anansi Does the Impossible. 2000. (J). 13.79 (978-0-606-20096-7(7)); lib. bdg. 15.30 (978-0-613-30942-4(1)) Tandem Library Bks.

—Why Mosquitoes Buzz in People's Ears. 2002. (Illus.). (J). 14.04 (978-0-7587-0081-0(4)) Book Wholesalers, Inc.

Arroyo, Imna, illus. Why Goats Smell Bad: And Other Stories from Benin. 1998. xvii, 138p. (J). (ps up). 21.50 (978-0-208-02469-5(7) , Linnet Bks.) Shoe String Pr., Inc.

Bryan, Ashley. Story of Lightning & Thunder. 1999. (978-0-606-16282-1(8)) Tandem Library Bks.

Cleveland, Rob. The Clever Monkey Rides Again. 2007. (Story Cove Ser.). 32p. (J). pap. 3.95 (***978-0-87483-828-2(2)***) August Hse. Pubs., Inc.

Diakite, Baba Wague. The Hatseller & the Monkeys. Diakite, Baba Wague, illus. 1999. (Illus.). 32p. (J). (ps-2). pap. 16.95 (978-0-590-96069-4(5)) Scholastic, Inc.

Giles, Bridget. Myths of West Africa. 2002. (Mythic World Ser.). (Illus.). 48p. (J). (gr. 7-10). lib. bdg. 27.12 (978-0-7398-4976-7(X)) Raintree.

Hull, Robert. Stories from West Africa. 2000. (Multicultural Stories Ser.). (Illus.). 48p. (J). (ps-3). pap. 9.95 (978-0-7398-1819-0(8)) Steck-Vaughn.

Hull, Robert & Clarey, Tim, illus. Stories from West Africa. 1999. (Multicultural Stories Ser.). 48p. (J). (ps-3). lib. bdg. 27.12 (978-0-7398-1333-1(1)) Raintree.

Kimmel, Eric A. Anansi & the Magic Stick. Stevens, Janet, illus. 2005. 32p. (J). (gr. k-3). 6.95 (978-0-8234-1763-6(8)) Holiday Hse., Inc.

Offodile, Buchi, compiled by & retold by. The Orphan Girl & Other Stories: West African Folk Tales. Offodile, Buchi, retold by. 2004. (International Folk Tales Ser.). (Illus.). 272p. 15.00 (978-1-56656-375-8(5)) Interlink Publishing Group, Inc.

Paye, Won-Ldy & Lippert, Margaret H. Mrs. Chicken & the Hungry Crocodile. Paschkis, Julie, illus. rev. ed. 2003. 32p. (J). (ps-2). 16.95 (978-0-8050-7047-7(8) , Holt, Henry & Co. Bks. For Young Readers) Holt, Henry & Co.

Souhami, Jessica. The Leopard's Drum: An Asante Tale from West Africa. 2006. (Illus.). 32p. (J). pap. 7.95 (978-1-84507-506-4(4)) Lincoln, Frances Ltd. GBR. *Dist:* Perseus Distribution.

Vernon-Jackson, Hugh. West African Folk Tales. Wright, Patricia, illus. 2003. (Dover African-American Bks.). 144p. pap. 7.95 (978-0-486-42764-5(1)) Dover Pubns., Inc.

FOLKLORE, AFRICAN AMERICAN

see African Americans—Folklore

FOLKLORE—ALASKA

Williams, Maria. How Raven Stole the Sun. Vigil, Felix, illus. 2001. (Tales of the People Ser.). 32p. (J). (ps-3). 14.95 (978-0-7892-0163-8(1)) Abbeville Pr., Inc.

FOLKLORE—ARAB COUNTRIES

Ali Baba & the Forty Thieves. 2004. (J). (ARA & ENG.). (978-1-84444-527-1(5)); (BEN & ENG.). (978-1-84444-528-8(3)); (CHI & ENG.). (978-1-84444-529-5(1)); (CHI & ENG.). (978-1-84444-530-1(5)); (ENG & GUJ.). (978-1-84444-646-9(8)); (ENG & ITA.). (978-1-84444-535-6(6)); (ENG & PAN.). (978-1-84444-537-0(2)); (ENG & POL.). (978-1-84444-538-7(0)); (ENG & RUS.). (978-1-84444-540-0(2)); (ENG & SOM.). (978-1-84444-541-7(0)); (ENG & SPA.). (978-1-84444-542-4(9)); (ENG & TAM.). (978-1-84444-544-8(5)); (ENG & TUR.). (978-1-84444-545-5(3)); (ENG & URD.). (978-1-84444-546-2(1)); (ENG & VIE.). (978-1-84444-547-9(X)) Mantra Publishing, Ltd.

Ali BabaForty Thieves. 2004. (J). cd-rom (978-1-84444-452-6(X)) Mantra Publishing, Ltd.

Anonymous. The Arabian Nights. Goodenow, Earle, illus. deluxe ed. 2002. (Illustrated Junior Library Ser.). 352p. (J). (gr. 4-7). reprint ed. 17.99 (978-0-448-06006-4(X) , Grosset & Dunlap) Penguin Group (USA) Inc.

Attard, Enebor. Ali Baba & the Forty Thieves. Holland, Richard, illus. 2005. (GRE & ENG.). 32p. (J). pap. 12.95 (978-1-84444-526-4(7)) Mantra Lingua GBR. *Dist:* Mantra Publishing, Ltd.

Auerbach, Annie. Sinbad: Legend of the Seven Seas Pop-up. McMahon, Brad, illus. 2003. (Media Favorites!! Ser.). 10p. (J). 9.95 (978-1-58117-171-6(4) , Intervisual/Piggy Toes) Dalmatian Pr.

Balaguae, Lin & Long, Robert, contrib. by. Alai Babaa y los 40 Ladrones: Ali Baba & the 40 Thieves. 2000. (Cuentos y Leyendas Bilingues Ser.). (ENG & SPA.). (J). 21.20 (978-0-658-01023-1(9) , National Textbook Co.) McGraw-Hill/Contemporary.

Balague, Lin & Long, Robert. Ali Baba y los 40 Ladrones (Ali Baba & the 40 Thieves) 2000. (Cuentos y Leyendas Bilingues Ser.). (SPA & ENG., Illus.). (J). 17.68 (978-0-658-01024-8(7)) McGraw-Hill/Contemporary.

Barkow, Henriette. Ali Baba & the Forty Thieves. Brazell, Derek, illus. 2004. (ENG, POR & SWE.). (J). (978-1-84444-539-4(9)) Mantra Publishing, Ltd.

Clynes, Kate & Anstey, David. Ali Baba & the Forty Thieves. 2005. (Illus.). 32p. (J). (ALB & ENG.). pap. 12.95 (978-1-84444-400-7(7)); (ARA & ENG., pap. 12.95 (978-1-84444-401-4(5)); (BEN & ENG., pap. 12.95 (978-1-84444-402-1(3)); (BUL & ENG., pap. 12.95 (978-1-84444-403-8(1)); (CHI & ENG., pap. 12.95 (978-1-84444-404-5(X)); (CHI & ENG., pap. 12.95 (978-1-84444-405-2(8)); (CRO, SER & ENG., pap. 12.95 (978-1-84444-406-9(6)); (ENG, PER & FAR., pap. 12.95 (978-1-84444-407-6(4)); (ENG & FRE., pap. 12.95 (978-1-84444-408-3(2)); (ENG & GER., pap. 12.95 (978-1-84444-409-0(0)); (ENG & GUJ., pap. 12.95 (978-1-84444-410-6(4)); (ENG & HIN., pap. 12.95 (978-1-84444-411-3(2)); (ENG & ITA., pap. 12.95 (978-1-84444-412-0(0)); (ENG & KUR., pap. 12.95 (978-1-84444-413-7(9)); (ENG & PAN., pap. 12.95 (978-1-84444-414-4(7)); (ENG & POL., pap. 12.95 (978-1-84444-415-1(5)); (ENG & POR., pap. 12.95 (978-1-84444-416-8(3)); (ENG & RUS., pap. 12.95 (978-1-84444-417-5(1)); (ENG & SHO., pap. 12.95 (978-1-84444-418-2(X)); (ENG & SOM., pap. 12.95 (978-1-84444-419-9(8)); (ENG & SPA., pap. 12.95 (978-1-84444-420-5(1)); (ENG & TAM., pap. 12.95 (978-1-84444-421-2(X)); (ENG & TUR., pap. 12.95 (978-1-84444-422-9(8)); (ENG & URD., pap. 12.95 (978-1-84444-424-3(4)); (ENG & VIE., pap. 12.95 (978-1-84444-425-0(2)); (ENG, RUM & ROM., pap. 12.95 (978-1-84444-427-4(9)) Mantra Lingua GBR. *Dist:* Mantra Publishing, Ltd.

Comelles, Salvador. Cuentame un Cuento, Vol. 5. Decis, Anne, illus. 2003. (SPA.). 96p. (978-84-480-1674-6(2) , TM30559) Timun Mas, Editorial S.A. ESP. *Dist:* Lectorum Pubns., Inc.

Jago, illus. Ali Baba & the Forty Thieves. 2004. (ENG, TAG, KUR & ITA.). 31p. (J). (978-1-84444-543-1(7)) Mantra Publishing, Ltd.

Kubler, Annie. The Wheels on the Bus. Kubler, Annie, illus. (ENG, PER & IRA., Illus.). 16p. (J). 2005. bds. (978-1-84444-532-5(1)); 2005. bds. (978-1-84444-533-2(X)); 2004. bds. (978-1-84444-534-9(8)) Mantra Publishing, Ltd.

Larousse Mexico Staff, ed. Ali Baba y los cuarenta Ladrones. 2004. (Encuentro con la Lectura Ser.).Tr. of Ali Baba & the Forty Thieves. (SPA.). 48p. pap. 6.50 (978-970-22-0727-6(4)) Larousse, Ediciones, S. A. de C. V. MEX. *Dist:* Houghton Mifflin Co. Trade & Reference Div.

Lodge, Jo. Ali Baba & the Forty Thieves. 2004. (COR, ENG & SWA., Illus.). 10p. (J). (978-1-84444-531-8(3)) Mantra Publishing, Ltd.

Muhawi, Ibrahim & Kananah, Sharif. Tunjur! Tunjur! Tunjur! A Palestinian Folktale. Arzoumanian, Alik, illus. 2006. 32p. (J). (ps-3). 16.95 (978-0-7614-5225-6(7)) Cavendish, Marshall Corp.

Pullman, Philip & Parker, Kim. Aladdin & the Enchanted Lamp. Williams, Sophy, illus. 2005. 64p. (J). pap. 16.95 (978-0-439-69255-7(5) , Levine, Arthur A. Bks.) Scholastic, Inc.

Vera, Luisa, illus. Ali Baba & the Forty Thieves. 2004. (ENG & KUR.). (J). (978-1-84444-536-3(4)) Mantra Publishing, Ltd.

Williams, Sophy, illus. Aladdin & the Enchanted Lamp. 2007. 70p. (J). (978-0-439-69257-1(1) , Levine, Arthur A. Bks.) Scholastic, Inc.

Yeoman, John. The Seven Voyages of Sinbad the Sailor. Blake, Quentin, illus. 2003. (Chrysalis Children's Classics Ser.). (YA). pap. (978-1-84365-040-9(1)) Chrysalis Children's Bks.

FOLKLORE—ARMENIA

Hogrogian, Nonny, illus. The Golden Bracelet. 1998. 32p. (J). (gr. 4-7). tchr. ed. 16.95 (978-0-8234-1362-1(4)) Holiday Hse., Inc.

San Souci, Robert D. A Weave of Words. Colon, Raul, illus. 1998. 32p. (J). (gr. k-4). 17.99 (978-0-531-33053-1(2)); pap. 16.95 (978-0-531-30053-4(6)) Scholastic, Inc. (Orchard Bks.).

FOLKLORE—ASIA

Baker, Barrie. The Village of a Hundred Smiles. Jorisch, Stephane, illus. 1998. 48p. (J). (gr. k-3). lib. bdg. 18.95 (978-1-55037-522-0(9)) Firefly Bks., Ltd.

Bowler, Ann Martin & Sukanada, I. Gusti Made. Gecko's Complaint: A Balinese Folktale. 2003. (Illus.). 32p. 12.95 (978-0-7946-0165-2(0)) Tuttle Publishing.

Chodzin, Sherab & Kohn, Alexandra. The Wisdom of the Crows & Other Buddhist Tales. Cameron, Marie, illus. 2004. 80p. (J). (gr. 2 up). pap. 17.95 (978-1-883672-68-3(6) , Tricycle Pr.) Ten Speed Pr.

Dutta-Yean, Tutu & Maire, Lucy Bedoya. Twelve Treasures of the East: Legends & Folk Tales from Asia. Dutta-Yean, Tutu, ed. Konatich, James, illus. ed. 2005. (J). per. (978-0-9768436-0-3(9) , 20) Maire, Lucy Bedoya.

Leeson, Robert. My Sister Shahrazad: Tales from the Arabian Nights. Balit, Christina, illus. 2004. 88p. (J). 16.95 (978-1-84507-265-0(0)) Lincoln, Frances Ltd. GBR. *Dist:* Perseus Distribution.

Leeson, Robert & Balit, Christina. My Sister Shahrazad: Tales from the Arabian Nights. (Illus.). 84p. (978-0-7112-1707-2(6)) Lincoln, Frances Ltd. GBR. *Dist:* Transition Vendor.

Shah, Idries. The Man with Bad Manners. Santiago, Rose Mary, illus. 2005. (Sounds of Afghanistan Ser.). (J). (ps-3). 28.95 incl. audio compact disk (978-1-883536-75-6(8) , Hoopoe Bks.) ISHK.

—The Man with Bad Manners. Santiago, Rose Mary, tr. Santiago, Rose Mary, illus. 2003. 32p. (J). 18.00 (978-1-883536-30-5(8) , MABM1, Hoopoe Bks.) ISHK.

—The Old Woman & the Eagle. Delmar, Natasha, illus. (Sounds of Afghanistan Ser.). (J). (ps-3). 2005. 28.95 incl. audio compact disk (978-1-883536-77-0(4)); 2005. 32p. pap. 6.99 (978-1-883536-28-2(6)); 2003. 32p. 18.00 (978-1-883536-27-5(8) , OLWE1) ISHK. (Hoopoe Bks.).

Verniero, Joan C. & Cloutier, John Kashiwazaki. 101 Read-Aloud Asian Myths & Legends: Ten Minute Readings from the World's Best-Loved Asian Literature. 2001. (Illus.). 368p. (J). (ps-3). tchr. ed. 12.95 (978-1-57912-164-8(0) , 81164) Black Dog & Leventhal Pubs., Inc.

FOLKLORE—AUSTRALIA

Flood, Bo, et al. Pacific Island Legends: Tales from Micronesia, Melanesia, Polynesia & Australia. Adams, Connie J., illus. 1999. 280p. (gr. 4-8). pap. 14.95 (978-1-57306-078-3(X)); 22.95 (978-1-57306-084-4(4)); tchr. ed. 19.93 (978-1-57306-103-2(4)) Bess Pr., Inc.

The Giant Devil-Dingo. 2004. 24.95 incl. audio (978-1-56008-202-6(X)) Weston Woods Studios, Inc.

Morin, Paul. Animal Dreaming. 1998. (Illus.). 32p. (J). 16.00 (978-0-15-200054-7(2)) Harcourt Trade Pubs.

Wolkstein, Diane. Sun Mother Wakes the World: An Australian Creation Story. Bancroft, Bronwyn, illus. 2004. 32p. (J). (ps-2). 17.99 (978-0-688-13915-5(9)) Harper-Collins Pubs.

FOLKLORE, BLACK

see African Americans—Folklore

FOLKLORE—CANADA

A. Ghostwriter. The Adventures of Grey-Dawn. Aubichon, Carla, illus. unabr. ed. 2001. 80p. (J). pap. (978-0-920576-93-9(1)) Caitlin Pr., Inc.

Craigan, Charles J., illus. Mayuk the Grizzly Bear: A Legend of the Sechelt People. braille ed. 2004. (J). (gr. k-3). spiral bd. (978-0-616-07562-3(6)) Canadian National Institute for the Blind/Institut National Canadien pour les Aveugles.

Finnigan, Joan. Witches, Ghosts & Loups-Garous. (Illus.). 96p. (J). pap. 10.95 (978-1-55082-086-7(9)) Quarry Pr. CAN. *Dist:* LPC/InBook.

Jorisch, Stephane, illus. & adapted by. As for the Princess? A Folktale from Quebec. Jorisch, Stephane, adapted by. 2001. 32p. (J). (ps-1). pap. 7.95 (978-1-55037-694-4(2)); lib. bdg. 19.95 (978-1-55037-695-1(0)) Annick Pr., Ltd. CAN. *Dist:* Firefly Bks., Ltd.

Sechelt Nation Staff. How the Robin Got Its Red Breast: A Legend of the Sechelt People. Craigan, Charles J., illus. unabr. ed. 40p. (J). (978-0-88971-158-7(5)) Harbour Publishing Co., Ltd.

—Mayuk the Grizzly Bear: A Legend of the Sechelt People. Craigan, Charles J., illus. unabr. ed. 40p. (J). (978-0-88971-156-3(9)) Harbour Publishing Co., Ltd.

Vitale, Ann E. Regional Folklore. 2002. (North American Folklore Ser.). (Illus.). 112p. (YA). (gr. 7 up). lib. bdg. (978-1-59084-349-9(5)) Mason Crest Pubs.

Wood, Douglas. The Rabbit & the Moon. Baker, Leslie A., illus. 2001. 40p. (J). (ps-3). 12.99 (978-0-689-84304-4(6) , Aladdin) Simon & Schuster Children's Publishing.

FOLKLORE—CARIBBEAN AREA

Breinburg, Petronella. Stories from the Caribbean. Arnold, Syrah & Barber, Tina, illus. 1999. (Multicultural Stories Ser.). 48p. (J). (ps-3). lib. bdg. 27.12 (978-0-7398-1334-8(X)) Raintree.

—Stories from the Caribbean. 2000. (Multicultural Stories Ser.). (Illus.). 48p. (J). (ps-3). 9.95 (978-0-7398-2032-2(X)) Steck-Vaughn.

Clementson, John, illus. Sing Me a Story: Song & Dance Stories from the Carribean. 2002. 48p. (ps-3). 19.95 (978-0-87483-672-1(7)) August Hse. Pubs., Inc.

Hurst, Margaret M., illus. Grannie & the Jumbie: A Caribbean Tale. 2001. 32p. (J). (ps-2). 15.89 (978-0-06-623633-9(9)); 15.95 (978-0-06-623632-2(0)) Harper-Collins Pubs. (Geringer, Laura Book).

Keens-Douglas, Richardo. Mama God, Papa God: A Caribbean Tale. Czernecki, Stefan, illus. 1999. 32p. (J). (ps-3). 15.95 (978-1-56656-307-9(0) , Crocodile Bks.) Interlink Publishing Group, Inc.

Moreton, Daniel. La Cucaracha Martina. 1999. Tr. of Caribbean Folktale. (J). 14.75 (978-0-606-17407-7(9)) Tandem Library Bks.

—La Cucaracha Martina: A Caribbean Folktale. Moreton, Daniel, illus. 1999. (Illus.). 40p. (J). (ps-3). 8.95 (978-1-890515-17-1(5)) Turtle Bks.

—La Cucaracha Martina: Un Cuento Folklorico del Caribe. Arisa, Miguel, tr. Moreton, Daniel, illus. 1999. (SPA., Illus.). 40p. (J). (ps-3). pap. 7.95 (978-1-890515-18-8(3)) Turtle Bks.

Parker, Vic. The Caribbean. 2001. (Illus.). 48p. (J). lib. bdg. 24.25 (978-1-930643-36-9(5)) Chrysalis Education.

San Souci, Robert D. The Twins & the Bird of Darkness: A Hero Tale from the Caribbean. Widener, Terry, illus. ed. 2004. (J). (gr. k-3). spiral bd. (978-0-616-14625-5(6)) Canadian National Institute for the Blind/Institut National Canadien pour les Aveugles.

FOLKLORE, CELTIC

see Celts—Folklore

FOLKLORE—CHINA

Berger, Barbara Helen. All the Way to Lhasa: A Tale from Tibet. Berger, Barbara Helen, illus. 2002. (Illus.). 32p. (J). (gr. k-3). 16.99 (978-0-399-23387-6(3) , Philomel) Penguin Group (USA) Inc.

Carpenter, Frances. Tales of a Chinese Grandmother. 293p. (J). (gr. 5-6). reprint ed. lib. bdg. 24.95 (978-0-89190-481-6(6) , Rivercity Pr.) Amereon LTD.

—Tales of a Chinese Grandmother. 2002. (gr. k-3). lib. bdg. 21.05 (978-0-613-75256-5(2)) Tandem Library Bks.

Casanova, Mary. The Hunter: A Chinese Folktale. Young, Ed, illus. 2000. 32p. (J). (ps-3). 17.99 (978-0-689-82906-2(X) , Atheneum) Simon & Schuster Children's Publishing.

Chan, Arlene. The Moon Festival: A Chinese Mid-Autumn Celebration. ed. 2004. (J). (gr. k-3). spiral bd. (978-0-616-01615-2(8)) Canadian National Institute for the Blind/Institut National Canadien pour les Aveugles.

Chen, Kerstin. Lord of the Cranes: A Chinese Tale. James, J. Alison, tr. Chen, Jian Jiang, illus. 2004. 28p. (J). (gr. k-4). reprint ed. 16.00 (978-0-7567-8040-1(3)) DIANE Publishing Co.

Compestine, Ying Chang. The Real Story of Stone Soup. Jorisch, Stéphane, illus. 2007. 32p. (J). (gr. k-3). 16.99 (978-0-525-47493-7(5) , Dutton Adult) Penguin Group (USA) Inc.

Crawford, Gregory. Animals in the Stars: Chinese Astrology for Children. Crawford, Gregory, illus. 2002. (Illus.). 32p. (gr. 3-7). 15.95 (978-1-59143-000-1(3)) Bear & Co.

Demi, illus. The Empty Pot. 2002. (Demi Ser.). (J). 15.49 (978-0-7587-2458-8(6)) Book Wholesalers, Inc.

Demi, Hitz. The Greatest Treasure. Demi, Hitz, illus. 1998. (Illus.). 32p. (J). (gr. k-3). pap. 16.95 (978-0-590-31339-1(8)) Scholastic, Inc.

DeSpain, Pleasant. The Magic Pot. 2007. (Story Cove Ser.). 32p. (J). pap. 3.95 ***(978-0-87483-827-5(4))*** August Hse. Pubs., Inc.

Downe, Lawrence. The Empty Pot: Lub Taig Qhuav/Lub Tais Qhuav. 2000. (Illus.). 32p. (J). (ps-3). pap. 6.95 (978-0-9629298-5-4(9) , MHC-5-9) Minnesota Humanities Commission.

—Liang & the Magic Paintbrush: Liang Hab Tug Cwj Mem Pleev Kws Muaj Siv/Liang Thiab Tus Cwj Mem Pleev Uas Muaj Yees Siv. Vang, Bo & Vang, Mao J., trs. 2000. (Illus.). 32p. (J). (ps-3). pap. 6.95 (978-0-9629298-4-7(0) , MHC-4-0) Minnesota Humanities Commission.

Fowler, Rosamund, illus. Tales from China. 2000. (Oxford Myths & Legends Ser.). 208p. (Orig.). (YA). 11.95 (978-0-19-275078-5(X)) Oxford Univ. Pr., Inc.

Fu, Shelley. Ho Yi the Archer & Other Classic Chinese Tales. 2001. (Illus.). vii, 575p. (YA). (gr. 3 up). 22.50 (978-0-208-02479-4(4) , Linnet Bks.) Shoe String Pr., Inc.

—Ho Yi the Archer & Other Classic Chinese Tales. Abboreno, Joseph, illus. 2001. xvi, 144p. (J). (gr. 3 up). 22.50 (978-0-208-02487-9(5) , Linnet Bks.) Shoe String Pr., Inc.

Granfield, Linda. The Legend of the Panda. braille ed. 2004. (Illus.). (J). (gr. k-3). spiral bd. (978-0-616-01343-4(4)) Canadian National Institute for the Blind/Institut National Canadien pour les Aveugles.

Hildebrandt, Ziporah. Sea Girl & the Dragon King: A Chinese Folktale. Cooper, Floyd, illus. 1999. (J). 16.00 (978-0-689-80540-0(3) , Atheneum) Simon & Schuster Children's Publishing.

James, J. Alison, tr. Lord of the Cranes: A Chinese Tale. Chen, Jian Jiang, illus. 2002. (J). (ps-ps). lib. bdg. 15.25 (978-0-613-53830-5(7)) Tandem Library Bks.

Jiang, Ji-Li. The Magical Monkey King: Mischief in Heaven. Su-Kennedy, Hui Hui, illus. 2002. 128p. (J). (gr. 2-6). lib. bdg. 14.89 (978-0-06-029544-8(9)) HarperCollins Pubs.

—The Magical Monkey King: Mischief in Heaven. Tang, You-shan, illus. 2004. 124p. (J). 14.95 (978-1-885008-24-4(4)); pap. 8.95 (978-1-885008-25-1(2)) Shen's Bks.

Kerven, Rosalind. In the Court of the Jade Emperor: Stories from Old China. 2nd rev. ed. 1999. (Cambridge Reading Ser.). (Illus.). 92p. pap. 12.00 (978-0-521-63524-0(1)) Cambridge Univ. Pr.

Krasno, Rena & Chiang, Yeng-Fong. Cloud Weavers: Ancient Chinese Legends. 2003. (Illus.). 96p. 22.95 (978-1-881896-26-5(9) , CLWE) Pacific View Pr.

Li, Yao-Wen & Kendall, Carol. Sweet & Sour: Tales from China. Felts, Shirley, illus. 2007. 112p. (J). (gr. 4-6). pap. 6.95 (978-0-618-75245-4(5) , Clarion Bks.) Houghton Mifflin Co. Trade & Reference Div.

Lobb, Fred H., ed. & tr. from CHI. The Wonderful Treasure Horse: Manchu, Mongolian & Turkic Folktales from China. Lobb, Fred H., tr. 1998. (Illus.). xii, 180p. (J). (gr. 4-8). pap. 21.95 (978-0-9662833-0-3(9)) Cal-Asia Publishing.

Martens, Frederick H. Chinese Fairy Tales. 1998. (Dover Children's Thrift Classics Ser.). 80p. (J). (gr. 3-6). pap. 1.50 (978-0-486-40140-9(5)) Dover Pubns., Inc.

Mosel, Arlene. Tikki Tikki Tembo. Lent, Blair, illus. 1998. (SPA.). (J). (gr. k-3). pap. 6.99 (978-1-880507-80-3(3) , LC0238) Lectorum Pubns., Inc.

Parker, Vic. China. 2001. (Illus.). 48p. (J). lib. bdg. 24.25 (978-1-930643-37-6(3)) Chrysalis Education.

Pfeffer, Wendy. Mysterious Spinners. Kim, Julie J., illus. 2005. 48p. (J). (978-1-59336-315-4(X)); pap. (978-1-59336-316-1(8)) Mondo Publishing.

Pirotta, Saviour. Stories from China. 1999. (Multicultural Stories Ser.). (Illus.). 48p. (J). (ps-3). lib. bdg. 27.12 (978-0-7398-1337-9(4)) Raintree.

—Stories from China. Clarey, Tim, illus. 2000. (Multicultural Stories Ser.). 48p. (J). (978-0-7398-2034-6(6)) Steck-Vaughn.

Poole, Amy Lowry, retold by. How the Rooster Got His Crown: A Chinese Folktale. 1999. (Illus.). 36p. (J). (gr. k-3). tchr. ed. 15.95 (978-0-8234-1389-8(6)) Holiday Hse., Inc.

Reinhard, B. J. Sanji's Seed. 2000. (Backyard Ser.). (Illus.). 32p. (J). 13.99 (978-0-7642-2210-8(4)) Bethany Hse. Pubs.

Rose, Naomi. Tibetan Tales for Little Buddhas. 2003. (Illus.). 64p. (J). pap. 16.95 (978-1-57416-081-9(8)) Clear Light Pubs.

Rose, Naomi C. Tibetan Tales from the Top of the World. 2006. (ENG & TIB.). (J). (gr. 1-7). 16.95 (978-1-57416-089-5(3)) Clear Light Pubs.

San Souci, Robert D. Fa Mulan: The Story of a Woman Warrior. 2000. (Illus.). (J). (978-0-606-18257-7(8)) Tandem Library Bks.

—FA Mulan: The Story of a Woman Warrior. Tseng, Jean & Tseng, Mou-Sien, illus. 2000. 32p. (gr. k-4). pap. 6.99 (978-0-7868-1421-3(7)) Disney Pr.

Shepard, Aaron. Lady White Snake: A Tale from Chinese Opera. Zhang, Song Nan, illus. 2001. 32p. (J). (gr. 2-5). 16.95 (978-1-57227-072-5(1)) Pan Asia Pubns. (USA), Inc.

—Lady White Snake: A Tale from Chinese Opera. de la Vega, Eida, tr. Zhang, Song Nan, illus. 2001. (ENG & SPA.). 32p. (J). 16.95 (978-1-57227-073-2(X)) Pan Asia Pubns. (USA), Inc.

—Lady White Snake: A Tale from Chinese Opera. Chen, Isabella, tr. Zhang, Song Nan, illus. 2001. (ENG & CHI.). 32p. (J). 16.95 (978-1-57227-074-9(8)) Pan Asia Pubns. (USA), Inc.

—Lady White Snake: A Tale from Chinese Opera. Vu, Khanh Yen, tr. Zhang, Song Nan, illus. 2001. (ENG & VIE.). 32p. (J). 16.95 (978-1-57227-075-6(6)) Pan Asia Pubns. (USA), Inc.

Storrie, Paul D. Yu Conquers the Flood: The Empire of China. Aw, Aldrin, illus. 2007. (Graphic Myths & Legends Ser.). 48p. (J). (gr. 4-8). 26.60 (978-0-8225-3088-6(0)) Lerner Publishing Group.

Thompson, Lauren. One Riddle, One Answer. Wingerter, Linda S., illus. 2001. 32p. (J). (gr. k-2). pap. 16.95 (978-0-590-31335-3(5)) Scholastic, Inc.

Tikki Tikki Tembo. 2004. 29.95 incl. cd-rom (978-1-55592-854-4(4)); 24.95 incl. audio (978-0-89719-691-8(0)); pap. 18.95 incl. audio compact disk (978-1-55592-812-4(9)); pap. 18.95 incl. audio compact disk (978-1-55592-778-3(5)); pap. 38.75 incl. audio compact disk (978-1-55592-762-2(9)); pap. 38.75 incl. audio compact disk (978-1-55592-725-7(4)); pap. 32.75 incl. audio (978-1-55592-325-9(9)); pap. 32.75 incl. audio (978-1-55592-326-6(7)); pap. 14.95 incl. audio (978-1-56008-077-0(9)); pap. 14.95 incl. audio (978-1-55592-672-4(X)) Weston Woods Studios, Inc.

Wang, Ping. The Dragon Emperor. Tang, Ge, illus. 2007. (On My Own Folklore Ser.). (J). 48p. (gr. 2-5). lib. bdg. 25.26 ***(978-0-8225-6740-0(7));*** lib. bdg. ***(978-0-8225-6744-8(X))*** Lerner Publishing Group. (Millbrook Pr.).

Wilson, Barbara Ker & So, Meilo. Wishbones: A Folk Tale from China. (Illus.). 32p. (J). (ps-2). pap. 9.99 (978-0-7112-1415-6(8)) Lincoln, Frances Ltd. GBR. *Dist:* Transition Vendor.

Xuan, Yong-Sheng, illus. The Rooster's Antlers: A Story of the Chinese Zodiac. 1999. 32p. (J). (gr. k-3). tchr. ed. 16.95 (978-0-8234-1385-0(3)) Holiday Hse., Inc.

Yep, Laurence. The Dragon Prince: A Chinese Beauty & the Beast Tale. Mak, Kam, illus. 1999. 32p. (J). (gr. k-3). reprint ed. pap. 6.99 (978-0-06-443518-5(0) , Harper Trophy) HarperCollins Pubs.

—The Dragon Prince: A Chinese Beauty & the Beast Tale. 1999. (J). 13.79 (978-0-606-15845-9(6)) Tandem Library Bks.

Young, Ed. Cat & Rat: The Legend of the Chinese Zodiac. Young, Ed, illus. rev. ed. 1998. (Illus.). 32p. (J). (ps-ps). pap., pap. 7.95 (978-0-8050-6049-2(9) , Holt, Henry & Co. Bks. For Young Readers) Holt, Henry & Co.

—The Sons of the Dragon King: A Chinese Legend. Young, Ed, illus. 2004. (Illus.). 32p. (J). 16.95 (978-0-689-85184-1(7) , Atheneum) Simon & Schuster Children's Publishing.

Zoehfeld, Kathleen Weidner. Mulan: Illustration Classic. 1998. (Illustrated Classics Ser.). (Illus.). 48p. (J). lib. bdg. 11.49 (978-0-7868-5064-8(7)) Disney Pr.

FOLKLORE—CZECH REPUBLIC

Krykora, Ian & Vladyana. Silver Moon. 2004. (Illus.). 72p. (978-1-55041-684-8(7)) Fitzhenry & Whiteside, Ltd.

FOLKLORE—CZECHOSLOVAKIA

Cooper, David, ed. & tr. from SLO. Traditional Slovak Folktales. Cooper, David, tr. 2001. (Folklore & Folk Cultures of Eastern Europe Ser.). (Illus.). 328p. 78.95 (978-0-7656-0718-8(2) , Sharpe Reference) Sharpe, M.E. Inc.

FOLKLORE—DENMARK

Andersen, Hans Christian. The Little Match Girl. Pinkney, Jerry, illus. 2002. 32p. (J). pap. 6.99 (978-0-14-230188-3(4) , Puffin) Penguin Group (USA) Inc.

—The Little Match Girl. Isadora, Rachel, illus. 2001. 32p. (J). (ps-3). pap. 6.99 (978-0-698-11417-3(5) , Putnam Juvenile) Penguin Group (USA) Inc.

—The Little Match Girl. unabr. ed. (World of Words Ser.). (J). (gr. k-3). pap. 10.00 incl. audio Spoken Arts, Inc.

Andersen, Hans Christian & San Jose, Christine. The Little Match Girl. Kasparavicius, Kestutis, illus. 2002. 32p. (J). (gr. 2-4). pap. 15.95 (978-1-59078-000-8(0)) Boyds Mills Pr.

MacDonald, Margaret Read. Fat Cat: A Danish Folktale. Paschkis, Julie, illus. 2001. 32p. pap. 7.95 (978-0-87483-765-0(0)); (J). 15.95 (978-0-87483-616-5(6)) August Hse. Pubs., Inc.

Malak, Annabel, illus. The Little Match Girl. 2000. (Classic Stories Ser.). 42p. (J). (ps-2). audio, audio compact disk (978-2-921997-88-1(6)) Coffragants.

Werner, Niels. The Meeting of the Mountebanks. 1999. (Niels Werner Collector Ser.: No. 2). 64p. (J). (gr. k-8). pap. 9.95 (978-0-9663019-2-2(7)) Pocket of Sanity.

FOLKLORE—EGYPT

Parker, Vic. Traditional Tales from Ancient Egypt. 2000. (Traditional Tales from Around the World Ser.). (Illus.). 48p. (J). (gr. 2-6). lib. bdg. 16.95 (978-1-929298-70-9(6)) Chrysalis Education.

FOLKLORE—ENGLAND

Bull, Angela. Robin Hood. 2000. (gr. k-3). lib. bdg. 11.80 (978-0-613-26766-3(4)) Tandem Library Bks.

Bull, Angela & Dorling Kindersley Publishing Staff. Robin Hood, Vol. 4. 2000. (Classic Readers Ser.). (Illus.). 48p. (J). (gr. 2-4). pap. 3.99 (978-0-7894-5391-4(6)) Dorling Kindersley Publishing, Inc.

Cohen, Barbara. Robin Hood & Little John. 1998. (978-0-606-13744-7(0)) Tandem Library Bks.

Colum, Padraic. The Story of King Arthur & Other Celtic Heroes. Jones, Wilfred, illus. 2005. 208p. pap. 9.95 (978-0-486-44061-3(3)) Dover Pubns., Inc.

Creswick, Paul & Wyeth, N. C. Robin Hood. 2003. (Scribner Storybook Classic Ser.: Vol. 4). (Illus.). 64p. (J). 18.95 (978-0-689-85467-5(6) , Atheneum) Simon & Schuster Children's Publishing.

Deutsch, Andre. Adventures of Robin Hood. 1999. (Andre Deutsch Classics). (Illus.). 192p. (J). 9.99 (978-0-233-99252-5(9)) Andre Deutsch GBR. *Dist:* Independent Pubs. Group.

Dorling Kindersley Publishing Staff. Robin Hood. 2000. (Classic Readers Ser.). (Illus.). 32p. (J). (gr. 2-4). 14.99 (978-0-7894-5701-1(6)) Dorling Kindersley Publishing, Inc.

Folklore. Jack & the Robbers. (J). pap. 2.99 (978-0-8136-2417-4(7)) Modern Curriculum Pr.

Gelders-Sterne, Emma. King Arthur & the Knights of the Round Table Treasury. 2002. (Illus.). x, 144p. (J). lib. bdg. 21.99 (978-0-375-92296-1(2) , Random Hse. Bks. for Young Readers) Random Hse. Children's Bks.

Gelders-Sterne, Emma & Lindsay, Barbara. King Arthur & the Knights of the Round Table Treasury. Tenggren, Gustaf, illus. 2002. x, 144p. (J). 19.95 (978-0-375-82296-4(8) , Random Hse. Bks. for Young Readers) Random Hse. Children's Bks.

Halverson, Lydia, illus. We Both Read-Jack & the Beanstalk. 2nd ed. 1999. (We Both Read Ser.). 44p. (J). (gr. 1-2). pap. 3.99 (978-1-891327-15-5(1)) Treasure Bay, Inc.

Hartland, Edwin Sidney, ed. English Fairy & Folk Tales. 2000. 320p. pap. 8.95 (978-0-486-41135-4(4)) Dover Pubns., Inc.

Harvey, Amanda, illus. Up the Chimney. 1998. 32p. (J). (ps-3). tchr. ed. 15.95 (978-0-8234-1354-6(3)) Holiday Hse., Inc.

Heyer, Carol, illus. & retold by. Robin Hood. Heyer, Carol, retold by. 2002. 32p. (J). (gr. k-5). 9.95 (978-1-59093-027-4(4) , Eager Minds Pr.) Warehousing & Fulfillment Specialists, LLC (WFS, LLC).

Johnson, Richard, tr. & illus. Jack & the Beanstalk. Johnson, Richard, illus. 2004. 31p. (J). (978-1-84444-108-2(3)) Mantra Publishing, Ltd.

Ketcham, Sallie. The Christmas Bird. 2004. (Illus.). 32p. (J). (ps-3). 16.99 (978-0-8066-3871-3(0) , Augsburg Bks.) Augsburg Fortress, Pubs.

Kimmel, Eric A. The Hero Beowulf. Fisher, Leonard Everett, illus. 2005. 32p. (J). 16.00 (978-0-374-30671-7(0) , Farrar, Straus & Giroux (BYR)) Farrar, Straus & Giroux.

Lang, Andrew. King Arthur: Tales from the Round Table. unabr. ed. 2002. (Dover Juvenile Classics Ser.). (Illus.). 192p. (J). (gr. 4-7). pap. 3.00 (978-0-486-42180-3(5)) Dover Pubns., Inc.

Malory, Thomas & Lanier, Sidney. The Boy's King Arthur. Wyeth, N. C., illus. 2006. 352p. pap. 14.95 (978-0-486-44800-8(2)) Dover Pubns., Inc.

McGovern, Ann. Robin Hood of Sherwood Forest. 2001. (Scholastic Junior Ser.). (Illus.). (J). (978-0-606-21401-8(1)) Tandem Library Bks.

McKay, Sindy. We Both Read-Jack & the Beanstalk. 1998. (We Both Read Ser.). (Illus.). 44p. (J). (gr. 1-2). 7.99 (978-1-891327-00-1(3)) Treasure Bay, Inc.

McKinley, Robin. Outlaws of Sherwood. 2002. (gr. 5-8). lib. bdg. 15.30 (978-0-613-64445-7(X)) Tandem Library Bks.

McSpadden, J. Walker. Robin Hood. 2004. reprint ed. pap. 22.95 (978-1-4191-4516-2(9)); pap. 1.99 (978-1-4192-4516-9(3)) Kessinger Publishing, LLC.

McSpadden, Joseph Walker. Robin Hood. 2000. (Dover Evergreen Classics Ser.). 208p. (J). (gr. 4-7). pap. 3.50 (978-0-486-41021-0(8)) Dover Pubns., Inc.

Moore, Maggie. Jack & the Beanstalk. Cox, Steve, illus. 2004. (Read-It! Readers Ser.). 32p. (C). (gr. k-3). 18.60 (978-1-4048-0059-5(X)) Picture Window Bks.

Muldrow, Diane. Jacky & the Giant. Andriani, Vincent, illus. 1999. (Scholastic At-Home Phonics Reading Program Ser.: Vol. 42). 24p. (J). (978-0-590-68810-9(3)) Scholastic, Inc.

Osborne, Mary Pope. Kate & the Beanstalk. Potter, Giselle, illus. 2005. 40p. (J). reprint ed. 7.99 (978-1-4169-0818-0(8) , Aladdin) Simon & Schuster Children's Publishing.

Paterson, Katherine. Parzival: The Quest of the Grail Knight. 2000. (gr. 5-8). lib. bdg. 13.00 (978-0-613-28601-5(4)) Tandem Library Bks.

Potter, Mélisande, illus. Dick Whittington & His Cat. 2006. 32p. (J). (ps-3). 16.95 (978-0-8234-1987-6(8)) Holiday Hse., Inc.

Pyle, Howard. The Adventures of Robin Hood. Corvino, Lucy, illus. 2005. (Classic Starts Ser.). 160p. 4.95 (978-1-4027-1257-9(X)) Sterling Publishing Co., Inc.

—The Merry Adventures of Robin Hood. 2002. (Great Illustrated Classics Ser.). (Illus.). 240p. (J). (gr. 3-8). 21.35 (978-1-57765-694-4(6) , ABDO & Daughters) ABDO Publishing Co.

—The Merry Adventures of Robin Hood. (Young Collector's Illustrated Classics Ser.). (Illus.). 192p. (J). (gr. 3-7). 9.95 (978-1-56156-454-5(0)) Kidsbooks, Inc.

—The Merry Adventures of Robin Hood. (Twelve-Point Ser.). 2002. 321p. lib. bdg. 25.00 (978-1-58287-200-1(7)); 2004. 518p. 26.00 (978-1-58287-684-9(3)) North Bks.

—The Story of King Arthur & His Knights. 2002. (Great Illustrated Classics Ser.). (Illus.). 240p. (J). (gr. 3-8). 21.35 (978-1-57765-691-3(1) , ABDO & Daughters) ABDO Publishing Co.

—The Story of Sir Lancelot & His Companions. 2004. reprint ed. pap. 27.95 (978-1-4179-5609-8(7)) Kessinger Publishing, LLC.

Red Riding Hood. 2004. 24.95 incl. audio (978-1-56008-209-5(7)); pap. 14.95 incl. audio (978-0-7882-0649-8(4)); pap. 32.75 incl. audio (978-1-55592-301-3(1)); pap. 32.75 incl. audio (978-1-55592-302-0(X)); pap. 14.95 incl. audio (978-1-56008-087-9(6)); pap. 14.95 incl. audio (978-0-7882-0399-2(1)) Weston Woods Studios, Inc.

Ross, Tony. Lazy Jack. 2002. (Illus.). 32p. (J). pap. 8.99 (978-1-84270-166-9(5)) Andersen GBR. *Dist:* Independent Pubs. Group.

—Lazy Jack. 2003. (ps-2). lib. bdg. 15.90 (978-0-613-84694-3(X)) Tandem Library Bks.

Rumford, James. Beowulf: A Hero's Tale Retold. 2007. (Illus.). 48p. (J). (gr. 5-8). 17.00 (***978-0-618-75637-7(X)***) Houghton Mifflin Co.

Shulevitz, Uri. Tesoro. 1999. Tr. of Treasure. (978-0-606-18135-8(0)) Tandem Library Bks.

Spinner, Stephanie. King Arthur's Courage. Sokolova, Valerie, illus. 2006. (Stepping Stones Ser.). 48p. (J). (gr. 1-4). pap. 3.99 (978-0-307-26410-7(6) , Random Hse. Bks. for Young Readers) Random Hse. Children's Bks.

Venti, Anthony Bacon, illus. Magic & Mischief: Tales from Cornwall. 1999. 144p. (J). (gr. 4-6). tchr. ed. 17.00 (978-0-395-86968-0(4) , Clarion Bks.) Houghton Mifflin Co. Trade & Reference Div.

Wahl, Jan. Little Johnny Buttermilk: After an Old English Folktale. Mazzucco, Jennifer, illus. 1999. 32p. (ps-1). 15.95 (978-0-87483-559-5(3)) August Hse. Pubs., Inc.

Wiesner, David, illus. & retold by. The Loathsome Dragon. Wiesner, David, retold by. 2005. 32p. (J). (gr. k-3). 16.00 (978-0-618-54359-5(7) , Clarion Bks.) Houghton Mifflin Co. Trade & Reference Div.

FOLKLORE, ESKIMO

see Eskimos—Folklore

FOLKLORE—ETHIOPIA

Janisch, Heinz. The Fire: A Folktale from Ethiopia. Vanden Broeck, Fabricio, illus. 2002. 32p. (J). 15.95 (978-0-88899-450-9(8)) Groundwood Bks. CAN. *Dist:* Perseus Distribution.

Yohannes, Gebregeorgis & Belachew, Bogale. Silly Mammo: An Ethiopian Tale. 2002. (AMH & ENG., Illus.). 32p. (J). (ps-4). pap. 10.00 (978-1-883701-04-8(X)) African Sun Publishing.

FOLKLORE—EUROPE

Andersen, Hans Christian. El Patito Feo: Farm Animals, The Farm, Seasons, The Weather. 1999. (Mi Primeros Cuentos Ser.). (SPA & ENG., Illus.). (J). (ps-3). pap. 7.95 (978-88-8148-251-1(7)) European Language Institute ITA. *Dist:* Distribooks, Inc., Midwest European Pubns.

—The Princess & the Pea: A Fairy Tale. Semelet, Camille, illus. 1999. (Little Pebbles Ser.). 32p. (J). (ps-1). 6.95 (978-0-7892-0515-5(7) , Abbeville Kids) Abbeville Pr., Inc.

Barber, Antonia. Hidden Tales from Eastern Europe. Guild, Shena, ed. Hess, Paul, illus. 2004. 48p. (J). pap. 9.95 (978-1-84507-147-9(6)) Lincoln, Frances Ltd. GBR. *Dist:* Perseus Distribution.

Bedard, Michael, adapted by. The Painted Wall & Other Strange Tales. 2003. (Illus.). 120p. (J). (gr. 5 up). 16.95 (978-0-88776-652-7(8)) Tundra Bks., Inc./Livres Toundra, Inc. CAN. *Dist:* Random Hse., Inc.

Beneduce, Ann K. Jack & the Beanstalk. Spirin, Gennady, illus. 2002. (J). 23.64 (978-0-7587-4185-1(5)) Book Wholesalers, Inc.

Beneduce, Ann K. & Spirin, Gennady. Jack & the Beanstalk. 1999. (Illus.). 1p. (J). (ps-3). 17.99 (978-0-399-23118-6(8) , Philomel) Penguin Group (USA) Inc.

Currier, Alvin Alexsi. How the Monastery Came to Be on the Top of the Mountain: A Romanian Oral Tradition. 2000. 24p. (J). (ps-3). pap. 8.95 (978-1-888212-16-7(0)) Conciliar Pr.

Finch, Mary. La Gallinita Roja y la Espiga de Triga (The Little Red Hen & the Ear of Wheat) Sarfatti, Esther, tr. Bell, Elisabeth, illus. 2001. (SPA.). 32p. (J). (ps-2). pap. 6.99 (978-1-84148-087-9(8) , BFP31242) Barefoot Bks., Inc.

Guild, Shena. Hidden Tales from Eastern Europe. Hess, Paul, illus. 2004. 48p. (J). (978-0-7112-1949-6(4)) Lincoln, Frances Ltd. GBR. *Dist:* Transition Vendor.

Henny Penny. 2002. (Puppy Tales Ser.). (Illus.). 24p. (J). (gr. k-3). 1.49 (978-1-57759-220-4(4)) Dalmatian Pr.

Hillert, Margaret. Tom Thumb. 2002. (Illus.). (J). 15.00 (978-0-7587-5743-2(3)) Book Wholesalers, Inc.

Keding, Dan. Stories of Hope & Spirit: Folktales from Eastern Europe. 2004. (Illus.). 112p. 18.95 (978-0-87483-727-8(8)) August Hse. Pubs., Inc.

Martin, Rafe. The Language of Birds. Gaber, Susan, illus. 2000. 1p. (J). (ps-3). 15.99 (978-0-399-22925-1(6) , Putnam Juvenile) Penguin Group (USA) Inc.

Percy, Graham, illus. The Sleeping Beauty. l.t. ed. 2001. (SPA.). 28p. (ps-3). incl. audio compact disk (978-84-8214-071-1(X) , 1622) Peralt Montagut.

—The Sleeping Beauty. l.t. ed. 2001. 28p. (J). (ps-3). 8.99 incl. audio (978-84-87650-26-0(0)) Peralt Montagut ESP. *Dist:* imaJen, Inc.

Rogasky, Barbara & Fisher, Leonard Everett. Dybbuk: A Version. 2005. (Illus.). 64p. (J). (gr. 5 up). 16.95 (978-0-8234-1616-5(X)) Holiday Hse., Inc.

Taback, Simms. Joseph Had a Little Overcoat. Taback, Simms, illus. 2001. (Live Oak Readalong Ser.). (Illus.). (J). 28.95 incl. audio compact disk (978-1-59112-412-2(3)) Live Oak Media.

—Kibitzers & Fools: Tales My Zayda Told Me. 2005. (Illus.). 48p. (J). (gr. 1-6). 16.99 (978-0-670-05955-3(2) , Viking Juvenile) Penguin Group (USA) Inc.

Tolstoy, Alexei. Nabo Gigante. 2000. (SPA.). (gr. k-3). lib. bdg. 14.15 (978-0-613-31520-3(0)) Tandem Library Bks.

Trembinski, Donna. Medieval Myths, Legends, & Songs. 2005. (Medieval World Ser.). (Illus.). 32p. (J). (gr. 4-9). (978-0-7787-1359-3(8)) Crabtree Publishing Co.

Umansky, Kaye. The Emperor's New Clothes. 2003. (Curtain up! Ser.: Vol. 6). (Illus.). 48p. (J). (gr. 1-4). pap. 16.95 (978-0-7136-4624-5(1)) A & C Black GBR. *Dist:* Lubrecht & Cramer, Ltd.

FOLKLORE—FINLAND

Shepard, Aaron & Gore, Leonid. The Princess Mouse: A Tale of Finland. 2003. (Illus.). 32p. (J). (gr. k-3). 16.95 (978-0-689-82912-3(4) , Atheneum) Simon & Schuster Children's Publishing.

FOLKLORE—FRANCE

Beauty & the Beast. unabr. ed. (Read-Along Ser.). (J). 7.99 incl. audio (978-1-55723-252-6(0)) Walt Disney Records.

Crane, Walter. Beauty & the Beast, & Other Tales. [47] p. :p. (978-0-87099-303-9(8)) Bow Historical Bks.

De Beaumont, Leprince, et al. Beauty & the Beast & Other Fairy Tales. 2001. (Dover Juvenile Classics Ser.). (Illus.). 96p. (J). (gr. 4-7). pap. 2.00 (978-0-486-41716-5(6)) Dover Pubns., Inc.

Disney Staff. Beauty & the Beast. ed. 2004. (J). (ps-2). spiral bd. (978-0-616-01630-5(1)) Canadian National Institute for the Blind/Institut National Canadien pour les Aveugles.

—Beauty & the Beast. (FRE.). 96p. (J). (gr. k-5). pap. 9.95 (978-0-7859-8844-1(0)) French & European Pubns., Inc.

Ehrlich, Amy. Cinderella. Battcock, Gregory, ed. Jeffers, Susan, illus. 2004. 32p. (J). (ps). 16.99 (978-0-525-47345-9(9) , Dutton Juvenile) Penguin Group (USA) Inc.

Ellwand, David, des. Cinderlily: A Floral Fairy Tale. 2003. (Illus.). 32p. (J). 16.99 (978-0-7636-2328-9(8)) Candlewick Pr.

Huling, Jan. Puss in Cowboy Boots. Huling, Phil, illus. 2002. 40p. (J). (gr. 1-4). 16.95 (978-0-689-83119-5(6)) Simon & Schuster Children's Publishing.

Jones, Christianne C. La Bella y la Bestia. Muehlenhardt, Amy Bailey, illus. 2006. (Read-It! Readers en Espanol Ser.).Tr. of Beauty & the Beast. (SPA.). 32p. (J). (ps-3). 19.95 (978-1-4048-1626-8(7)) Picture Window Bks.

Knight, Hilary. Hilary Knight's Cinderella. 2001. (Illus.). 40p. (J). (ps-1). 14.95 (978-0-375-81422-8(1) , Random Hse. Bks. for Young Readers) Random Hse. Children's Bks.

Levine, Gail Carson. Cinderellis & the Glass Hill. Elliott, Mark, illus. 2000. (Princess Tales Ser.). 112p. (J). (gr. 2-7). 14.89 (978-0-06-028337-7(8)); 9.99 (978-0-06-028336-0(X)) HarperCollins Pubs.

Light, Steve. Puss in Boots. 2002. (Illus.). 32p. (J). (ps-1). 14.95 (978-0-8109-4368-1(9)) Abrams, Harry N. , Inc.

Lowell, Susan. Cindy Ellen: A Wild Western Cinderella. Manning, Jane, illus. 2000. (Joanna Cotler Bks.). 40p. (J). (ps-3). 16.99 (978-0-06-027446-7(8)); lib. bdg. 17.89 (978-0-06-027447-4(6)) HarperCollins Pubs. (Cotler, Joanna Books).

Mayer, Marianna. Beauty & the Beast. Mayer, Mercer, illus. 2002. 48p. (J). pap. 5.95 (978-1-58717-148-2(1) , SeaStar Bks.) Chronicle Bks. LLC.

—Beauty & the Beast. 2002. (ps-2). lib. bdg. 14.10 (978-0-613-56213-3(5)) Tandem Library Bks.

Mouse Works Staff. Beauty & the Beast. 1999. (SPA.). 64p. (978-0-7364-0127-2(X)) Mouse Works.

Muth, Jon J., illus. Stone Soup. 2003. 32p. (J). (gr. 1 up). pap. 16.95 (978-0-439-33909-4(X) , Scholastic Pr.) Scholastic, Inc.

O'Neil, Sharron, illus. Stone Soup: Cooperation. 2005. (J). (***978-1-4127-3757-9(5)***) Publications International, Ltd.

Perrault, Charles. Cinderella: A Fairy Tale. Baudrand, Edith, illus. 1999. (Little Pebbles Ser.). 32p. (ps-1). 6.95 (978-0-7892-0512-4(2)) Abbeville Pr., Inc.

—Puss in Boots. Bell, Anthea, tr. Lunelli, Giuliano, illus. 2003. 24p. (J). (gr. 3-5). reprint ed. 18.00 (978-0-7567-6600-9(1)) DIANE Publishing Co.

—Puss in Boots. Arthur, Malcolm, tr. Marcellino, Fred, illus. 1998. 32p. (J). (ps up). pap. 8.95 (978-0-374-46034-1(5) , Sunburst) Farrar, Straus & Giroux.

Perrault, Charles & Moon, Sarah. Little Red Riding Hood. 2002. (Illus.). 40p. (J). (gr. 9 up). 17.95 (978-1-56846-143-4(7) , Creative Editions) Creative Co., The.

Le Petit Chaperon Rouge.Tr. of Little Red Riding Hood. (FRE.). 48p. (J). pap. 12.95 incl. audio compact disk (978-2-89558-051-5(0)) Coffragants CAN. *Dist:* Penton Overseas, Inc.

Le Petit Chaperon Rouge. (Musicontes Ser.).Tr. of Little Red Riding Hood. (FRE.). (J). 24.95 incl. audio (978-2-09-230468-6(2)); 2000. (Illus.). 32p. 13.95 (978-2-09-202104-0(4)) Nathan, Fernand FRA. *Dist:* Distribooks, Inc.

Random House Disney Staff. Cinderella. Random House Disney Staff, tr. (FRE.). 96p. (J). (gr. k-5). pap. 9.95 (978-0-7859-8855-7(6)) French & European Pubns., Inc.

—Cinderella. 2005. (Illus.). 16p. (J). (ps). pap. 6.99 (978-0-7364-2355-7(9) , RH/Disney) Random Hse. Children's Bks.

—Cinderella. Random House Disney Staff, tr. 2002. (Illus.). (J). lib. bdg. 14.99 (978-0-7364-8020-8(X) , RH/Disney) Random Hse. Children's Bks.

San Souci, Daniel, illus. The Flying Canoe: La Chasse-Gallerie: A Christmas Story. 2003. (J). (978-0-8234-1730-8(1)) Holiday Hse., Inc.

San Souci, Robert D. & Perrault, Charles. Little Pierre: A Cajun Story from Louisiana. Catrow, David, illus. 2003. 32p. (J). (gr. k-3). 16.00 (978-0-15-202482-6(4)) Harcourt Children's Bks.

Schroeder, Alan. Smoky Mountain Rose: An Appalachian Cinderella. Sneed, Brad, illus. 2000. (Picture Puffin Ser.). 32p. (J). (gr. k-4). pap. 6.99 (978-0-14-056673-4(2) , Puffin) Penguin Group (USA) Inc.

—Smoky Mountain Rose: An Appalachian Cinderella. 2000. (978-0-606-18451-9(1)); lib. bdg. 15.30 (978-0-613-28647-3(2)) Tandem Library Bks.

FOLKLORE—GERMANY

Allen, Debbie. Brothers of the Knight. 2001. 13.79 (978-0-606-22528-1(5)) Tandem Library Bks.

Balaguae, Lin & Long, Robert, contrib. by. Hansel y Gretel: Hansel & Gretel. 2000. (Cuentos y Leyendas Bilingues Ser.). (ENG & SPA.). (J). 21.20 (978-0-658-01037-8(9) , National Textbook Co.) McGraw-Hill/Contemporary.

Balague, Lin & Long, Robert. Hansel y Gretel (Hansel & Gretel) 2000. (Cuentos y Leyendas Bilingues Ser.). (SPA & ENG., Illus.). (J). 19.88 (978-0-658-01038-5(7)) McGraw-Hill/Contemporary.

La Belle au Bois Dormant. (FRE.). 48p. pap. 12.95 incl. audio compact disk (978-2-89558-067-6(7)) Coffragants CAN. *Dist:* Penton Overseas, Inc.

Blair, Eric. The Bremen Town Musicians. 2004. (Illus.). (J). pap. 13.95 (978-1-4048-0536-1(2)) Picture Window Bks.

—Hansel y Gretel: Version del Cuento de los Hermanos Grimm. Wolf, Claudia, illus. 2006. (Read-It! Readers en Espanol Ser.).Tr. of Hansel & Gretel: A Retelling of the Grimm's Fairy Tale. (SPA.). 32p. (J). (ps-3). 19.95 (978-1-4048-1632-9(1)) Picture Window Bks.

Boddy, Joe, illus. The Elves & the Shoemaker. 2002. 26p. 6.95 (978-0-8249-4230-4(2)) Ideals Pubns.

Brothers Grimm Staff. Hansel y Gretel. Martinez, Miriam, tr. Browne, Anthony, illus. 2004. (SPA.). (J). 9.95 (978-968-16-7062-7(0)) Fondo de Cultura Economica MEX. *Dist:* Lectorum Pubns., Inc.

Buskers of Bremen. 2004. (J). E-Book incl. cd-rom (978-1-84444-455-7(4)) Mantra Publishing, Ltd.

Buskers of Bremen: Big Book English Only. 2004. (J). (978-1-84444-301-7(9)) Mantra Publishing, Ltd.

Butterfield, Moira. Hansel & Gretel. 1998. (Playtales Ser.). 24p. (J). (ps-3). lib. bdg. 19.92 (978-1-57572-648-9(3)) Heinemann Library.

Ceccoli, Nicoletta, illus. Little Red Riding Hood. 2004. 32p. (J). 16.99 (978-1-84148-621-5(3)) Barefoot Bks., Inc.

Collins, Sheila Hebert. Blanchette et les Sept Petits Cajuns: A Cajun Snow White. Soper, Patrick, illus. 2002. 32p. (J). 15.95 (978-1-56554-912-8(0)) Pelican Publishing Co., Inc.

Collins, Sheila Hebert, et al. 'T Pousette et 't Poulette: A Cajun Hansel & Gretel. Hebert, Barbara H., ed. Soper, Patrick, illus. 2001. 32p. (J). (gr. 1-3). 15.95 (978-1-56554-764-3(0)) Pelican Publishing Co., Inc.

Craft, Mahlon & Craft, Mahlon F. Le Sleeping Beauty. Craft, K. Y., illus. 2002. 32p. (J). (gr. k-3). 16.50 (978-1-58717-121-5(X) , SeaStar Bks.) Chronicle Bks. LLC.

Craft, Mahlon F. & Craft, K. Y., illus. Sleeping Beauty. 2002. 32p. (J). (gr. k-3). 15.95 (978-1-58717-120-8(1) , SeaStar Bks.) Chronicle Bks. LLC.

Davidson, Susanna. Twelve Dancing Princesses. 2007. 24p. (J). 9.99 (978-0-7945-1604-8(1) , Usborne) EDC Publishing.

Delessert, Etienne. The Seven Dwarfs. 2001. (Illus.). 32p. (J). (ps-3). 17.95 (978-1-56846-139-7(9) , Creative Editions) Creative Co., The.

—Snow White & the Seven Dwarfs. 2001. (Illus.). (J). (978-1-56846-152-6(6)) Creative Co., The.

Disney Staff. Snow White & the Seven Dwarfs. ed. 2004. (J). (ps-2). spiral bd. (978-0-616-01632-9(8)); spiral bd. (978-0-616-01633-6(6)) Canadian National Institute for the Blind/Institut National Canadien pour les Aveugles.

—Snow White & the Seven Dwarfs. (FRE.). 96p. (J). (gr. k-5). pap. 9.95 (978-0-7859-8853-3(X)) French & European Pubns., Inc.

Dockray, Tracy Arah, illus. Grimm's Grimmest. 2005. 144p. 22.95 (978-0-8118-5046-9(3)) Chronicle Bks. LLC.

Downes, Belinda. Snow White & the Seven Dwarfs. 2002. (Illus.). 48p. (J). 15.99 (978-0-7894-8799-5(3)) Dorling Kindersley Publishing, Inc.

Favorite Tales from Grimm. 2002. (Illus.). 96p. (J). (gr. k-7). 9.99 (978-1-57759-421-5(5)) Dalmatian Pr.

Gay, Marie-Louise. Rumpelstiltskin. ed. 2004. (J). (ps-2). spiral bd. (978-0-616-01348-9(5)); spiral bd. (978-0-616-01646-6(8)) Canadian National Institute for the Blind/Institut National Canadien pour les Aveugles.

Grimm, Jacob W. The Bremen Town Musicians. 1998. 13.79 (978-0-606-13226-8(0)) Tandem Library Bks.

—The Golden Goose. 1998. (J). (978-0-606-13434-7(4)) Tandem Library Bks.

Grimm, Jacob W. & Grimm, Wilhelm K. The Brave Little Tailor. 2005. 12p. pap. (978-958-30-1783-4(3)) Panamericana Editorial.

—Favorite Fairy Tales. 2001. (gr. 3-6). lib. bdg. 9.50 (978-0-613-88890-5(1)) Tandem Library Bks.

—Favorite Fairy Tales of the Brothers Grimm. unabr. ed. 2001. (Dover Juvenile Classics Ser.). 96p. (J). (gr. 4-7). pap. 2.50 (978-0-486-41979-4(7)) Dover Pubns., Inc.

—The Frog Prince. Gilbert, Anne Yvonne, illus. 2007. 32p. (J). 18.95 (978-1-58726-279-1(7) , Mitten Pr.) Ann Arbor Media Group, LLC.

—Grandpa Mouse & Little Mouse: A Tale about Respect for Elders. Lonaytis, Olga, illus. 2006. (J). (978-1-59939-088-8(4) , Reader's Digest Young Families, Inc.) Reader's Digest Children's Publishing, Inc.

—Hansel & Gretel. Felix, Monique, illus. 2001. 32p. (gr. 5 up). 17.95 (978-1-56846-137-3(2) , Creative Editions) Creative Co., The.

—Sleeping Beauty. Stevens, Molly, tr. from FRE. Novi, Nathalie, illus. 2001. (Little Pebbles Ser.). 32p. 6.95 (978-0-7892-0734-0(6)) Abbeville Pr., Inc.

—Sleeping Beauty. 2005. 12p. pap. (978-958-30-1781-0(7)) Panamericana Editorial.

—Snow White. 2005. 12p. pap. (978-958-30-1777-3(9)) Panamericana Editorial.

Grimm, Jacob W., et al. The Fisherman & His Wife. 2001. (Illus.). 32p. (gr. 6). 17.95 (978-1-56846-140-3(2)) Creative Co., The.

—Little Red Riding Hood/Caperucita Roja: A Bilingual Book. Surges, James, tr. from CAT. Estrada, Pau, illus. 1999. (ENG & SPA.). 32p. (J). (ps-3). pap. 6.95 (978-0-8118-2562-7(0)) Chronicle Bks. LLC.

—Rumpelstiltskin. 2007. 48p. (J). 8.99 (978-0-7945-1446-4(4) , Usborne) EDC Publishing.

Grimm, Wilhelm K. & Grimm, Jacob W. Grimm's Fairy Tales. Rackham, Arthur, illus. 2001. (Peter Glassman Bk.). 160p. (J). 19.95 (978-1-58717-092-8(2) , SeaStar Bks.) Chronicle Bks. LLC.

—Hansel & Gretel. Wolf, Claudia, tr. Wolf, Claudia, illus. 2003. (J). pap. (978-1-4048-0542-2(7)) Picture Window Bks.

—Snow White & the Seven Dwarfs. Deru, Myriam, illus. 2001. (Little Pebbles Ser.). 32p. (ps-3). 6.95 (978-0-7892-0693-0(5)) Abbeville Pr., Inc.

Grimm, Wilhelm K., et al. The Rabbit's Bride. Meade, Holly, illus. 2001. 32p. (J). (ps-3). 15.95 (978-0-7614-5081-8(5) , Cavendish Children's Bks.) Cavendish, Marshall Corp.

Gross, Ruth B. Hansel y Gretel. 2001. Tr. of Hansel & Gretel. (978-0-606-22654-7(0)) Tandem Library Bks.

Hamilton, Virginia. The Girl Who Spun Gold. Dillon, Leo & Dillon, Diane, illus. 2000. 40p. (J). (ps up). pap. 17.95 (978-0-590-47378-1(6) , Blue Sky Pr., The) Scholastic, Inc.

Hansel & Gretel. 2002. (Puppy Tales Ser.). (Illus.). 24p. (J). (gr. k-3). 1.49 (978-1-57759-277-8(8)) Dalmatian Pr.

Hansel & Gretel. Date not set. (J). 4.99 (978-0-7214-5406-1(2)) Nickel Pr.

Hansel et Gretel.Tr. of Hansel & Gretel. (FRE.). 48p. pap. 12.95 incl. audio compact disk (978-2-89558-055-3(3)) Coffragants CAN. *Dist:* Penton Overseas, Inc.

Hansel y Gretel. 2nd ed. 2002. (Troquelados Clasicos Ser.). (SPA & ENG., Illus.). 16p. pap. 2.95 (978-84-7864-377-6(X)) Combel Editorial, S.A. ESP. *Dist:* Independent Pubs. Group.

Holden, Robert. The Pied Piper of Hamelin. Zak, Drahos, illus. 2004. 28p. (J). (gr. k-4). reprint ed. 15.00 (978-0-7567-7686-2(4)) DIANE Publishing Co.

Hyman. Sleeping Beauty. 2000. (J). (978-0-606-19844-8(X)) Tandem Library Bks.

Jacob & Grimm, Wilhelm K. Rapunzel PB. 2007. (Illus.). 32p. (J). pap. 7.95 (978-0-7358-2113-2(5)) North-South Bks., Inc.

Knighton, Kate. Sleeping Beauty. Costa, Jana, illus. 2007. 48p. (J). 8.99 (978-0-7945-1458-7(8) , Usborne) EDC Publishing.

LaMarche, Jim. Elves & the Shoemaker. 2003. (Illus.). 32p. (J). 16.95 (978-0-8118-3477-3(8)) Chronicle Bks. LLC.

Levine, Gail Carson. The Fairy's Return. Elliott, Mark, illus. 2002. (Princess Tales Ser.). 112p. (J). (gr. 2-6). 9.99 (978-0-06-623800-5(5)) HarperCollins Pubs.

Ljungkvist, Laura. Snow White & the Seven Dwarfs. Ljungkvist, Laura, illus. 2003. (Illus.). 32p. (J). (ps-3). 14.95 (978-0-8109-4241-7(0)) Abrams, Harry N. , Inc.

Marshall, James. Red Riding Hood. Marshall, James, illus. 2002. (Illus.). (J). 14.04 (978-0-7587-3507-2(3)) Book Wholesalers, Inc.

Mayer, Marianna. Iron John. 1999. (Illus.). 40p. (J). (gr. k-3). 15.89 (978-0-688-11555-5(1)) HarperCollins Pubs.

Moore, Maggie. Little Red Riding Hood. Knight, Paula, illus. 2004. (Read-It! Readers Ser.). 32p. (C). (gr. k-3). 18.60 (978-1-4048-0064-9(6)) Picture Window Bks.

Moses, Will. Hansel & Gretel. Moses, Will, illus. 2006. (Illus.). 40p. (J). (ps). 16.99 (978-0-399-24234-2(1) , Philomel) Penguin Group (USA) Inc.

Page, Nick & Claire. Elves & the Shoemaker. 2006. (Read with Me (Make Believe Ideas) Ser.). (Illus.). 32p. (J). (gr. k-2). 3.95 (978-1-84610-161-8(1)) Make Believe Ideas GBR. *Dist:* Ingram Pub. Services.

Percy, Graham, illus. Snow White & the Seven Dwarfs. l.t. ed. 2001. (SPA.). 28p. (ps-3). incl. audio compact disk (978-84-8214-069-8(8) , 1622) Peralt Montagut.

—The Three Little Pigs. l.t. ed. 2001. (SPA.). 28p. (ps-3). incl. audio compact disk (978-84-8214-068-1(X) , 1622) Peralt Montagut.

—The Three Little Pigs. l.t. ed. 2001. 28p. (J). (ps-3). 8.49 incl. audio (978-84-87650-03-1(1)) Peralt Montagut ESP. *Dist:* imaJen, Inc.

Peris, Carme. La Caperucita Roja. 1998. (Fairy Tale Theater Ser.).Tr. of Little Red Riding Hood. (SPA., Illus.). 32p. (J). (gr. k-3). pap. 8.95 (978-0-7641-5146-0(0)) Barron's Educational Series, Inc.

—Little Red Riding Hood. 1998. (Fairy Tale Theater Ser.). (Illus.). 32p. (J). (gr. k-3). pap. 8.95 (978-0-7641-5114-9(2)) Barron's Educational Series, Inc.

Perrault, Charles. Tom Thumb. Roederer, Charlotte, illus. 2001. (Little Pebbles Ser.). 32p. (J). (ps-3). 6.95 (978-0-7892-0694-7(3)) Abbeville Pr., Inc.

Pied Piper. 2004. (J). (978-1-84444-299-7(3)); E-Book incl. cd-rom (978-1-84444-466-3(X)) Mantra Publishing, Ltd.

Price, Kathy. The Bourbon Street Musicians. Glass, Andrew, illus. 2002. 40p. (J). (gr. k-3). 16.00 (978-0-618-04076-6(5) , Clarion Bks.) Houghton Mifflin Co. Trade & Reference Div.

Random House Disney Staff. Snow White & the Seven Dwarfs. 2003. (Little Golden Book Ser.). (Illus.). 24p. (J). (gr. k-k). 2.99 (978-0-7364-2186-7(6) , Golden/Disney) Random Hse. Children's Bks.

Redbank, Tennant. Barbie in the Twelve Dancing Princesses. 2006. (Step into Reading Ser.). (Illus.). 32p. (J). (ps-2). lib. bdg. 11.99 (978-0-375-93780-4(3) , Random Hse. Bks. for Young Readers) Random Hse. Children's Bks.

Rius, Roser. Hansel & Gretel. 1998. (Fairy Tale Theater Ser.). (Illus.). 32p. (J). (gr. k-3). pap. 8.95 (978-0-7641-5113-2(4)) Barron's Educational Series, Inc.

—Hansel y Gretel. 1998. (Fairy Tale Theater Ser.). (SPA., Illus.). 32p. (J). (gr. k-3). 8.95 (978-0-7641-5145-3(2)) Barron's Educational Series, Inc.

Ros, Roser. The Musicians of Bremen/Los Musicos de Bremen. Montserrat, Pep, illus. 2005. (ENG & SPA.). 32p. (J). (ps-ps). 14.95 (978-0-8118-4795-7(0)); pap. 6.95 (978-0-8118-4796-4(9)) Chronicle Bks. LLC.

Tarcov, Edith. Frog Prince. 1999. (Illus.). (J). (gr. k-3). lib. bdg. 11.80 (978-0-7857-1145-2(7)) Tandem Library Bks.

Von Drogas, Johann. Snow White, the Whole Story. 2000. 24p. (J). (gr. 5-12). pap. 8.50 (978-0-9620016-3-5(5)) Great Lakes Publishing Co.

Wells, Rosemary. The Fisherman & His Wife. Hubbard, Eleanor, illus. 1998. 32p. (J). (ps-3). 16.99 (978-0-8037-1850-0(0) , Dial) Penguin Group (USA) Inc.

Wilhelm, Hans. Los Musicos de Bremen. 2001. (978-0-606-22655-4(9)) Tandem Library Bks.

Wilhelm, Hans, retold by. Los Musicos de Bremen. (SPA.). (J). pap. 4.80 net. (978-0-439-17707-8(3) , SO30111) Scholastic, Inc.

Ziefert, Harriet. Little Red Riding Hood. 2000. (ps-2). lib. bdg. 11.80 (978-0-613-26034-3(1)); (Illus.). (J). (978-0-606-18421-2(X)) Tandem Library Bks.

FOLKLOVE—GHANA

Mollel, Tololwa M. Ananse's Feast: An Ashanti Tale. Glass, Andrew, illus. 2002. 32p. (J). (gr. k-3). 6.95 (978-0-618-19598-5(X) , Clarion Bks.) Houghton Mifflin Co. Trade & Reference Div.

FOLKLORE—GREAT BRITAIN

Flynn, Benedict. King Arthur & the Knights of the Round Table. 2008. (Hear It Read It Ser.). 160p. (J). (gr. 2 up). 9.95 (***978-1-4022-1243-7(7)** , Sourcebooks Jabberwocky) Sourcebooks, Inc.

Hicks, Ray. Jack Tales. Smith, Owen, illus. 2000. 40p. (J). (gr. 4-7). 24.95 (978-0-935112-58-0(8)) Simon & Schuster.

Hodges, Margaret & Malory, Thomas. Merlin & the Making of the King. Hyman, Trina Schart, tr. Hyman, Trina Schart, illus. 2004. 40p. (J). (gr. 4-6). tchr. ed. 16.95 (978-0-8234-1647-9(X)) Holiday Hse., Inc.

Kerven, Rosalind. King Arthur. Humphries, Tudor, illus. 1998. (Eyewitness Classics Ser.). 64p. (J). (gr. 3-6). 14.99 (978-0-7894-2887-5(3)) Dorling Kindersley Publishing, Inc.

MacDonald, Margaret Read. The Old Woman Who Lived in a Vinegar Bottle. 2003. (Illus.). 32p. pap. 6.95 (978-0-87483-723-0(5)) August Hse. Pubs., Inc.

Riggio, Anita, retold by. Beware the Brindlebeast. 2003. (Illus.). 32p. (J). (ps-1). pap. 8.95 (978-1-56397-684-1(6)) Boyds Mills Pr.

FOLKLORE—GREECE

Morpurgo, Michael & Aesop. The McElderry Book of Aesop's Fables. Clark, Emma Chichester, illus. 2005. 96p. (J). 21.99 (978-1-4169-0290-4(2) , McElderry, Margaret K.) Simon & Schuster Children's Publishing.

Raintree Steck-Vaughn Staff. Aesop's Fox. 2000. 32p. (J). (gr. 4-7). lib. bdg. 25.69 (978-0-7398-1364-5(1)) Raintree.

FOLKLORE—HAITI

Di Benedetto, Angelo, illus. How the Donkeys Came to Haiti & Other Folk Tales. 124p. (J). (gr. 4-9). 12.95 (978-0-8159-5706-5(8)) Devin-Adair Pubs., Inc.

MacDonald, Amy. Please, Malese! A Trickster Tale from Haiti. Lisker, Emily, illus. 2001. (J). (978-0-7894-2647-5(1)) Dorling Kindersley Publishing, Inc.

—Please, Malese! A Trickster Tale from Haiti. Lisker, Emily, illus. 2002. 32p. (J). (gr. k-3). 16.00 (978-0-374-36000-9(6) , Farrar, Straus & Giroux (BYR)) Farrar, Straus & Giroux.

FOLKLORE—HAWAII

Ehlers, Sabine. Hawaiian Stories for Boys & Girls. (J). pap. 4.95 (978-0-681-26583-7(3)) Booklines Hawaii, Ltd.

Loebel-Fried, Caren. Hawaiian Legends of the Guardian Spirits. 2002. (Illus.). 128p. 19.95 (978-0-8248-2537-9(3)) Univ. of Hawaii Pr.

Lum, Leimomi o. Kamahae Kuamoo Mookini. The Legend of Kuamo'o Mo'okini & Hamumu the Great Whale. Kam, Kathleen, illus. 2004. 24p. (J). 12.95 (978-1-58178-036-9(2)) Bishop Museum Pr.

Nordenstrom, Michael, illus. & adapted by. Hina & the Sea of Stars. Nordenstrom, Michael, adapted by. 2003. 32p. 10.95 (978-1-57306-167-4(0)) Bess Pr., Inc.

—Pele & the Rivers of Fire. Nordenstrom, Michael, adapted by. 2002. 32p. (J). 10.95 (978-1-57306-079-0(8)) Bess Pr., Inc.

Two Tales of Hawaii. 2003. (J). 10.99 (978-0-89610-923-0(2)) Island Heritage Publishing.

Varez, Dietrich. The Legend of La'ieikawai. 2004. (Latitude 20 Book Ser.). (Illus.). 88p. 12.95 (978-0-8248-2839-4(9)) Univ. of Hawaii Pr.

FOLKLORE—HUNGARY

Ginsburg, Mirra. Two Greedy Bears: Adapted from a Hungarian Folktale. Aruego, Jose, illus. 1999. pap. 18.95 incl. audio compact disk (978-1-59112-743-7(2)); pap. 35.95 incl. audio compact disk (978-1-59112-864-9(1)) Live Oak Media.

Molnar, Irma. One-Time Dog Market at Buda & Other Hungarian Folktales. Enesel, Georgeta Elena, illus. 2001. 130p. (J). (gr. 3 up). 25.00 (978-0-208-02505-0(7) , Linnet Bks.) Shoe String Pr., Inc.

Tarbescu, Edith. The Boy Who Stuck Out His Tongue: A Yiddish Folk Tale. Mills, Judith Christine, illus. 2000. 32p. (J). (ps-3). 15.99 (978-1-84148-067-1(3)) Barefoot Bks., Inc.

FOLKLORE—ICELAND

Wyatt, Isabel. Thorkill of Iceland: Viking Hero-Tales. 1998. (Illus.). 160p. (J). (gr. 4-7). pap. 14.95 (978-0-86315-256-6(2)) Floris Bks. GBR. *Dist:* Gryphon Hse., Inc., SteinerBooks, Inc.

FOLKLORE—INDIA

Adhikary, Qiron. Feminist Folktales from India. 2003. (Illus.). 97p. (YA). per. 9.95 (978-0-9714127-3-6(1)) Masalai Pr.

Backstein, Karen. The Blind Men & the Elephant. Mitra, Annie, illus. 2004. 48p. (J). lib. bdg. 15.00 (978-1-59054-401-3(3)) Fitzgerald Bks.

Bash, Barbara. In the Heart of the Village: The World of the Indian Banyan Tree. Bash, Barbara, illus. 2004. (Illus.). 27p. (J). (gr. k-4). reprint ed. 17.00 (978-0-7567-9082-0(4)) DIANE Publishing Co.

—In the Heart of the Village: The World of the Indian Banyan Tree. Bash, Barbara, illus. 2nd ed. 2002. (Illus.). 32p. (J). reprint ed. pap. 6.95 (978-1-57805-080-2(4)) Gibbs Smith, Publisher.

—In the Heart of the Village: The World of the Indian Banyan Tree. Bash, Barbara, illus. 2002. (Illus.). (J). (gr. 4-7). lib. bdg. 15.25 (978-0-613-79298-1(X)) Tandem Library Bks.

Brucker, Meredith Babeaux, ed. Anklet for a Princess: A Cinderella Story from India. Tang, You-shan, illus. 2002. 32p. (YA). 16.95 (978-1-885008-20-6(1)) Shen's Bks.

Buri & the Marrow. 2004. (J). (ENG & HIN.). (978-1-84444-668-1(9)); cd-rom (978-1-84444-454-0(6)) Mantra Publishing, Ltd.

Candappa, Beulah. The Bharunda Bird. 1998. (Myths & Legends Ser.). (Illus.). 24p. (J). 14.60 (978-1-57572-013-5(2)) Heinemann Library.

Cleveland, Robert. Drum. Wrenn, Tom, illus. 2006. 32p. (J). pap. 3.95 (978-0-87483-802-2(9)) August Hse. Pubs., Inc.

Gleeson, Brian. The Tiger & the Brahmin. Vargo, Kurt, illus. 2004. 32p. (J). (gr. k-4). reprint ed. 20.00 (978-0-7567-8205-4(8)) DIANE Publishing Co.

Greene, Josh. Hanuman. 2004. (Illus.). 40p. (J). 7.95 (978-1-58246-125-0(2) , Tricycle Pr.) Ten Speed Pr.

Johari, Harish & Sperling, Vatsala. How Ganesh Got His Elephant Head. Weltevrede, Pieter, illus. 2003. 32p. (J). 15.95 (978-1-59143-021-6(6)) Bear & Co.

Khalsa, Shakta Kaur. The Five Fingered Family. Khalsa, Siri-Kartar K., illus. 2000. 32p. (J). (ps-4). 16.95 (978-0-9660172-9-8(3)) Brookfield Reader, Inc., The.

Naidu, Vayu. Stories from India. 1999. (Multicultural Stories Ser.). (Illus.). 48p. (J). (ps-3). lib. bdg. 27.12 (978-0-7398-1335-5(8)) Raintree.

—Stories from India. 2000. (Multicultural Stories Ser.). (Illus.). 48p. (J). (978-0-7398-2035-3(4)) Steck-Vaughn.

Okada, Amina. The Prince Who Became a Beggar. Marsh, Gwen, tr. from FRE. Thibault, Dominique, illus. 1998. (Tales of Heaven & Earth Ser.).Tr. of Prince Qui Se Fit Mendiant. 32p. (YA). (gr. 3-7). pap. 19.95 (978-0-88682-828-8(7) , Creative Education) Creative Co., The.

Parker, Vic. India. 2001. (Illus.). 48p. (J). lib. bdg. 24.25 (978-1-930643-38-3(1)) Chrysalis Education.

Peters, Andrew. Monkey's Clever Tale. Montgomery-Higham, Amanda, tr. Montgomery-Higham, Amanda, illus. 2003. 32p. (J). 7.99 (978-0-85953-051-4(5)) Child's Play-International.

Rao, Sandhya & Krishnaswamy, Uma. And Land Was Born. 1999. (Illus.). 24p. (J). (gr. 2-7). (978-81-86895-13-9(2)) Tulika Pubs.

Rose, Deborah Lee. People Who Hugged the Trees. 2001. (gr. 3-6). lib. bdg. 16.40 (978-0-613-86356-8(9)) Tandem Library Bks.

Singh, Vijay. The River Goddess. De Hugo, Pierre, illus. 1998. (Tales of Heaven & Earth Ser.).Tr. of Deesse Qui Devint Fleuve. 32p. (YA). (gr. 3-7). pap. 19.95 (978-0-88682-825-7(2) , Creative Education) Creative Co., The.

So, Meilo. Gobble, Gobble, Slip, Slop: A Tale of a Very Greedy Cat. So, Meilo, illus. 2004. (Illus.). 30p. (J). (ps-3). 15.95 (978-0-375-82504-0(5)); lib. bdg. 17.99 (978-0-375-92504-7(X)) Random Hse. Children's Bks. (Knopf Bks. for Young Readers).

Souhami, Jessica. Rama & the de Mon King: An Ancient Tale from India. 2006. (Illus.). 30p. (J). (gr. k-4). reprint ed. 15.00 (978-0-7567-9813-0(2)) DIANE Publishing Co.

Weitzman, David L. Rama & Sita: A Tale of Ancient Java. Weitzman, David L., illus. 2002. (Illus.). 32p. 19.95 (978-1-56792-151-9(5)) Godine, David R. Pub.

Young, Ed. Seven Blind Mice. Young, Ed, illus. 2002. (Illus.). 14.04 (978-1-4046-0752-1(8)) Book Wholesalers, Inc.

FOLKLORE, INDIAN

see Indians of North America—Folklore

FOLKLORE—INDONESIA

Davis, Grania & Gellek, Nazli. The Monkey King. Johnson, Sheila, illus. 1998. (Jataka Tales Ser.). 32p. (J). (gr. k-6). reprint ed. pap. 7.95 (978-0-89800-292-8(3)) Dharma Publishing.

Martowiredjo, Salim & Suyenaga, Joan. Indonesian Children's Favorite Stories. 2005. (Illus.). 64p. 16.95 (978-0-7946-0171-3(5)) Tuttle Publishing.

Sierra, Judy. The Dancing Pig. Sweetwater, Jesse, illus. 1999. (J). 16.00 (978-0-15-201521-3(3)) Harcourt Trade Pubs.

—The Gift of the Crocodile: A Cinderella Story. Ruffins, Reynold, illus. 2000. 40p. (J). (ps-3). 17.95 (978-0-689-82188-2(3)) Simon & Schuster Children's Publishing.

Sugiura, Kuniko. Indonesian Fables of Feats & Fortunes. Galgani, Matthew, tr. from JPN. Honda, Koji, illus. 2007. (Asian Folktales Retold Ser.). 32p. (J). (gr. k-6). 16.95 (***978-0-89346-950-4(5)***) Stone Bridge Pr.

—Indonesian Tales of Treasures & Brides. Galgani, Matthew, tr. from JPN. Honda, Koji, illus. 2007. (Asian Folktales Retold Ser.). 32p. (J). (gr. k-6). 16.95 (***978-0-89346-951-1(3)***) Stone Bridge Pr.

Valerio, Geraldo, illus. Go to Sleep, Gecko! A Balinese Folktale. 2006. 32p. (gr. 4-7). 16.95 (978-0-87483-780-3(4)) August Hse. Pubs., Inc.

FOLKLORE, JEWISH

see Jews—Folklore

FOLKLORE—IRAQ

Foster, Karen Polinger. The City of Rainbows: A Tale from Ancient Sumer. 1999. 28p. (J). pap. 6.95 (978-0-924171-70-3(7)) Univ. Museum Pubns.

Henderson, Kathy. Lugalbanda: The Boy Who Got Caught up in a War. Ray, Jane, illus. 2006. 80p. (J). (gr. 3-5). 16.99 (978-0-7636-2782-9(8)) Candlewick Pr.

McCaughrean, Geraldine. Gilgamesh the Hero. Parkins, David, illus. 2004. 96p. (J). (gr. 6-9). 20.00 (978-0-8028-5262-5(9)) Eerdmans, William B. Publishing Co.

FOLKLORE—IRELAND

Brown, Barbara. Irish Folk & Fairy Tales. Jarvie, Gordon, ed. 2003. (Illus.). 254p. pap. 11.95 (978-0-85640-731-4(3)) Blackstaff Pr., The IRL. *Dist:* Dufour Editions, Inc.

Carroll, Yvonne. Leprechaun Tales. East, Jacqueline, illus. 2001. 64p. (J). (gr. k-5). 14.95 (978-0-7171-2698-9(6)) Gill & MacMillan, Ltd. IRL. *Dist:* Pelican Publishing Co., Inc.

—Leprechaun Tales. 2001. (Illus.). 64p. (J). (ps-3). 16.95 (978-1-56554-921-0(X)) Pelican Publishing Co., Inc.

Children of Lir. 2004. (J). cd-rom (978-1-84444-456-4(2)) Mantra Publishing, Ltd.

Climo, Shirley. The Irish Cinderlad. Krupinski, Loretta, illus. 2000. (Trophy Picture Bk.). 32p. (J). (gr. k-4). pap. 6.99 (978-0-06-443577-2(6) , Harper Trophy) HarperCollins Pubs.

Crosbie, Duncan. A Claddagh Ring for Nuala. 2002. (Illus.). 12p. (J). 7.95 (978-0-7171-3393-2(1)) Gill & MacMillan, Ltd. IRL. *Dist:* Irish Bks. & Media, Inc.

—A Claddagh Ring for Nuala. Rutherford, Peter, illus. gif. ed. 2004. 16p. (J). pap. 7.95 (978-1-58980-175-2(X)) Pelican Publishing Co., Inc.

Daly, Jude. Fair, Brown & Trembling: An Irish Cinderella Story. 2005. (Illus.). 32p. (J). reprint ed. pap. 6.95 (978-0-374-42257-8(5) , Sunburst) Farrar, Straus & Giroux.

de Paola, Tomie. Jamie O'Rourke & the Big Potato: An Irish Folktale. de Paola, Tomie, illus. 2002. (Illus.). (J). 14.04 (978-0-7587-2895-1(6)) Book Wholesalers, Inc.

Doyle, Malachy. Tales from Old Ireland. 2006. (Illus.). 96p. (J). 16.99 (978-1-905236-32-9(8)) Barefoot Bks., Inc.

—Tales from Old Ireland. Sharkey, Niamh, illus. 2000. 96p. (J). (gr. 5-9). 19.99 (978-1-902283-97-5(X)) Barefoot Bks., Inc.

Gleeson, Brian. Finn McCoul. De Sève, Peter, illus. 2005. (Rabbit Ears Ser.). 40p. (J). (gr. k-5). 25.65 (978-1-59679-223-4(X)) Spotlight.

Heaney, Marie. Irish Tales & Myths. Lynch, Patrick J., illus. 1999. 95p. (J). pap. (978-0-590-68060-8(9) , Levine, Arthur A. Bks.) Scholastic, Inc.

Lawrie, Robin, illus. Great Irish Legends for Children. 1999. 64p. (J). 15.95 (978-0-7171-2467-1(3)) Gill & MacMillan, Ltd. IRL. *Dist:* Irish Bks. & Media, Inc.

MacGill-Callahan, Sheila. The Last Snake in Ireland: A Story about St. Patrick. Hillenbrand, Will, illus. 1999. 36p. (J). (gr. k-3). tchr. ed. 16.95 (978-0-8234-1425-3(6)) Holiday Hse., Inc.

McDermott, Gerald. Daniel O'Rourke: An Irish Tale. McDermott, Gerald, illus. 2002. (Illus.). (J). 13.19 (978-0-7587-9300-3(6)) Book Wholesalers, Inc.

Milligan, Bryce. Brigid's Cloak: An Ancient Irish Story. Cann, Helen, illus. 32p. (J). (gr. k-17). 2005. pap. 8.00 (978-0-8028-5297-7(1) , Eerdmans Bks For Young Readers); 2004. 16.00 (978-0-8028-5224-3(6)) Eerdmans, William B. Publishing Co.

Mortensen, Lori. Leprechauns. 2007. (Mysterious Encounters Ser.). (Illus.). 48p. (J). (gr. 4-8). 26.20 (***978-0-7377-3663-2(1)*** , Kidhaven) Thomson Gale.

Newsham, Ian, illus. The Kingfisher Treasury of Irish Stories. 2004. (Kingfisher Treasury of Stories Ser.). 160p. (J). (gr. k-3). pap. 5.95 (978-0-7534-5672-9(9) , Kingfisher) Houghton Mifflin Co. Trade & Reference Div.

Parker, Vic. Traditional Tales from Celtic Lands. 2000. (Traditional Tales from Around the World Ser.). (Illus.). 48p. (J). (gr. 2-6). lib. bdg. 16.95 (978-1-929298-71-6(4)) Chrysalis Education.

San Souci, Robert D. Brave Margaret: An Irish Adventure. Comport, Sally Wern, illus. 1999. 40p. (J). (gr. k-5). 17.95 (978-0-689-81072-5(5)) Simon & Schuster Children's Publishing.

—Brave Margaret: An Irish Adventure. 2002. (gr. 3-6). lib. bdg. 15.30 (978-0-613-45016-4(7)) Tandem Library Bks.

San Souci, Robert D. & Comport, Sally. Brave Margaret: An Irish Adventure. 2002. (Illus.). 40p. (J). pap. 7.99 (978-0-689-84850-6(1) , Aladdin) Simon & Schuster Children's Publishing.

Schmidt, Gary D. The Wonders of Donal O'Donnell: A Folktale of Ireland. Long, Loren, illus. rev. ed. 2002. 40p. (J). (gr. 3-6). 17.95 (978-0-8050-6516-9(4) , Holt, Henry & Co. Bks. For Young Readers) Holt, Henry & Co.

The Selkie Girl. 2004. 24.95 incl. audio (978-0-7882-0590-3(0)); pap. 14.95 incl. audio (978-0-7882-0664-1(8)) Weston Woods Studios, Inc.

Souhami, Jessica. Mrs. McCool & the Giant Cuhullin: An Irish Tale. rev. ed. 2002. (Illus.). 32p. (J). (ps-3). 16.95 (978-0-8050-6852-8(X) , Holt, Henry & Co. Bks. For Young Readers) Holt, Henry & Co.

FOLKLORE—ISLANDS OF THE PACIFIC

Flood, Bo, et al. Pacific Island Legends: Tales from Micronesia, Melanesia, Polynesia & Australia. Adams, Connie J., illus. 1999. 280p. (gr. 4-8). pap. 14.95 (978-1-57306-078-3(X)); 22.95 (978-1-57306-084-4(4)); tchr. ed. 19.93 (978-1-57306-103-2(4)) Bess Pr., Inc.

FOLKLORE—ITALY

Caduto, Michael J. The Crimson Elf: Italian Tales of Wisdom. Sarmo, Tom, illus. 1999. 64p. (gr. 3 up). pap. 12.95 (978-1-55591-995-5(2)) Fulcrum Publishing.

—Crimson Elf: Italian Tales of Wisdom. 1999. (gr. 3-6). lib. bdg. 22.20 (978-0-613-89936-9(9)) Tandem Library Bks.

Collodi, Carlo. Pinocchio. Ingpen, Robert R., illus. 2005. 136p. (J). (gr. 2-7). 19.95 (978-1-933327-00-6(6)) Purple Bear Bks., Inc.

de Paola, Tomie. The Clown of God. 2004. (J). (gr. k-5). pap. 14.95 incl. audio (978-0-89719-767-0(4) , PRA260) Weston Woods Studios, Inc.

—Strega Nona. 2002. (Illus.). (J). 15.49 (978-0-7587-0151-0(9)) Book Wholesalers, Inc.

Egielski, Richard. Saint Francis & the Wolf. Egielski, Richard, illus. 2005. (Illus.). 40p. (J). (gr. 1-3). 15.99 (978-0-06-623870-8(6) , Geringer, Laura Book) HarperCollins Pubs.

—Saint Francis & the Wolf of Gubbio. Egielski, Richard, illus. 2005. (Illus.). 40p. (J). (gr. 1-3). lib. bdg. 16.89 (978-0-06-623871-5(4) , Geringer, Laura Book) HarperCollins Pubs.

Kunhardt, Dorothy, ed. Pinocchio. (FRE.). 96p. (J). (gr. k-5). pap. 9.95 (978-0-7859-8845-8(9)) French & European Pubns., Inc.

Sanderson, Ruth. Papa Gatto: An Italian Fairy. 1999. (978-0-606-17849-5(X)) Tandem Library Bks.

FOLKLORE—JAMAICA

Hausman, Gerald. Duppy Talk: West Indian Tales of Mystery & Magic. Hausman, Mariah, illus. rev. ed. 1999. 102p. (YA). (gr. 5 up). pap. 10.00 (978-0-9709112-0-9(3)) Irie Bks.

Temple, Frances. Tiger Soup: An Anansi Story from Jamaica. 1998. (J). (978-0-606-13850-5(1)) Tandem Library Bks.

FOLKLORE—JAPAN

Armstrong, Jennifer. Kenji & Little Mouse Boy. 1998. (J). pap. 3.99 (978-0-679-88279-4(0)); lib. bdg. 11.99 (978-0-679-98279-1(5)) Random Hse. Children's Bks. (Random Hse. Bks. for Young Readers).

Bodkin, Odds. The Crane Wife. Spirin, Gennady, illus. 2002. 32p. (J). pap. 6.00 (978-0-15-216350-1(6) , Voyager Bks./Libros Viajeros) Harcourt Children's Bks.

—The Crane Wife. 1998. (Easy to Read Folktales Ser.). (Illus.). 32p. (J). (ps-3). lib. bdg. 24.26 (978-0-8172-5767-5(5)) Raintree.

French, Fiona. Little Inchkin. (Illus.). 32p. (J). 2004. pap. 19.95 (978-1-84507-009-0(7)); 2000. pap. 7.99 (978-0-7112-0917-6(0)) Lincoln, Frances Ltd. GBR. *Dist:* Transition Vendor.

Hearn, Lafcadio, et al. The Boy Who Drew Cats & Other Japanese Fairy Tales. Green, Yuko, illus. 1998. (Dover Children's Thrift Classics Ser.). 64p. (J). (gr. 3-6). pap. 2.00 (978-0-486-40348-9(3)) Dover Pubns., Inc.

Metaxas, Eric. Peachboy. Smith, Jeffrey, illus. 2005. (Rabbit Ears Ser.). 40p. (J). (gr. k-6). 25.65 (978-1-59679-227-2(2)) Spotlight.

Myers, Tim. Tanuki's Gift: A Japanese Tale. Roth, Robert, illus. 2003. 32p. (J). 16.95 (978-0-7614-5101-3(3)) Cavendish, Marshall Corp.

Nishimoto, Keiske. Japanese Fairy Tales, Vol. 1. Imoto, Yoko, illus. 2004. (Japanese Fairy Tale Ser.: Vol. 1). 32p. (gr. k-4). reprint ed. 14.95 (978-0-89346-845-3(2)) Heian International Publishing, Inc.

Okada, Amina. The Prince Who Became a Beggar. Marsh, Gwen, tr. from FRE. Thibault, Dominique, illus. 1998. (Tales of Heaven & Earth Ser.).Tr. of Prince Qui Se Fit Mendiant. 32p. (YA). (gr. 3-7). pap. 19.95 (978-0-88682-828-8(7) , Creative Education) Creative Co., The.

Paterson, Katherine. The Tale of the Mandarin Ducks. Dillon, Leo & Dillon, Diane, illus. 2004. 32p. (J). (gr. k-4). reprint ed. 15.00 (978-0-7567-7698-5(8)) DIANE Publishing Co.

Sakade, Florence. Japanese Children's Favorite Stories. Yoshi, Kurosake, illus. 2005. Bk. 1. 112p. 21.95 incl. audio compact disk (978-0-8048-3717-0(1)); Vol. 2. 96p. 21.95 incl. audio compact disk (978-0-8048-3718-7(X)) Tuttle Publishing.

Sakade, Florence & Kurosaki, Yoshisuke. Japanese Children's Favorite Stories, Vol. 2. 2004. (Illus.). 96p. 19.95 (978-0-8048-3381-3(8)) Tuttle Publishing.

Sansouci, Robert D. The Silver Charm: A Folktale from Japan. Ito, Yoriko, illus. 2005. 29p. (J). (gr. k-4). reprint ed. 17.00 (978-0-7567-8544-4(8)) DIANE Publishing Co.

Schroeder, Alan. The Tale of Willie Monroe. Glass, Andrew, illus. 1999. 32p. (J). (gr. k-3). tchr. ed. 15.00 (978-0-395-69852-5(9) , Clarion Bks.) Houghton Mifflin Co. Trade & Reference Div.

Sierra, Judy. Tasty Baby Belly Buttons. So, Meilo, illus. 1999. 40p. (J). (gr. k-ps). 17.00 (978-0-679-89369-1(5) , Knopf Bks. for Young Readers) Random Hse. Children's Bks.

The Tale of the Mandarin Ducks. 2004. 29.95 incl. cd-rom (978-1-55592-736-3(X)); pap. 18.95 incl. audio compact disk (978-1-55592-742-4(4)); pap. 18.95 incl. audio compact disk (978-1-55592-743-1(2)); pap. 38.75 incl. audio compact disk (978-1-55592-750-9(5)); pap. 38.75 incl. audio compact disk (978-1-55592-751-6(3)); pap. 32.75 incl. audio (978-1-55592-320-4(8)); pap. 32.75 incl. audio (978-1-55592-321-1(6)); pap. 14.95 incl. audio (978-1-55592-049-4(7)) Weston Woods Studios, Inc.

Urashima Taro. 2003. (J). 10.99 (978-0-89610-639-0(X)) Island Heritage Publishing.

FOLKLORE—KOREA

Han, Suzanne Crowder. The Rabbit's Tail: A Story from Korea. Wehrman, Richard, illus. rev. ed. 1999. 32p. (J). (gr. k-3). 16.95 (978-0-8050-4580-2(5) , Holt, Henry & Co. Bks. For Young Readers) Holt, Henry & Co.

Kim, Yon-Kyong, illus. The Ogres' Magic Clubs - the Tiger & the Dried Persimmons. 2000. (Korean Folk Tales for Children Ser.: Vol. 5). 46p. (J). (gr. 2-5). lib. bdg. (978-0-930878-88-7(4)) Hollym International Corp.

Kim, Yong-Kol. Brave Hong Kil-Dong/the Man Who Bought the Shade of a Tree. Kang, Mi-Sun & Kim, Yon-Kyong, illus. 1998. (Korean Folk Tales for Children Ser.: Vol. 8). 46p. (J). (gr. 2-5). lib. bdg. (978-0-930878-91-7(4)) Hollym International Corp.

Park, Janie Jaehyun. The Tiger & the Dried Persimmon. 2002. (Illus.). 32p. (J). 15.95 (978-0-88899-485-1(0)) Groundwood Bks. CAN. *Dist:* Perseus Distribution.

—The Tiger & the Persimmon. ed. 2004. (Illus.). (J). (ps up). spiral bd. (978-0-616-14622-4(1)); spiral bd. (978-0-616-14623-1(X)) Canadian National Institute for the Blind/Institut National Canadien pour les Aveugles.

Park, Janie Jaehyun, retold by. The Love of Two Stars: A Korean Legend. 2005. (Illus.). 32p. (J). (ps-7). 16.95 (978-0-88899-672-5(1)) Groundwood Bks. CAN. *Dist:* Perseus Distribution.

San Souci, Daniel. In the Moonlight Mist: A Korean Tale. Neilan, Eujin Kim, illus. 2003. 32p. (J). (gr. 2-4). 16.95 (978-1-56397-754-1(0)) Boyds Mills Pr.

So-un, Kim. Korean Children's Favorite Stories. 2004. (Illus.). 96p. (YA). 16.95 (978-0-7946-0170-6(7) , PeriplusEdition) Tuttle Publishing.

So-Un, Kim & Kyoung-Sim, Jeong. Korean Children's Favorite Stories. 2004. (Illus.). 96p. 16.95 (978-0-8048-3591-6(8)) Tuttle Publishing.

Vorhees, Duance & Mueller, Mark. The Faithful Daughter Shim Ch'Ong/the Little Frog Who Never Listened. Kang, Mi-Sun & Kim, Yon-Kyong, illus. 1998. (Korean Folk Tales for Children Ser.: Vol. 9). 46p. (J). (gr. 2-5). lib. bdg. (978-0-930878-92-4(2)) Hollym International Corp.

—The Greedy Princess/the Rabbit & the Tiger. Pak, Mi-Son & Kim, Yon-Kyong, illus. 1998. (Korean Folk Tales for Children Ser.: Vol. 7). 46p. (J). (gr. 2-5). lib. bdg. (978-0-930878-90-0(6)) Hollym International Corp.

—The Snail Lady/The Magic Vase. Kang, Mi-Sun, illus. 1998. (Korean Folk Tales for Children Ser.: Vol. 6). 46p. (J). (gr. 2-5). lib. bdg. (978-0-930878-89-4(2)) Hollym International Corp.

—The Son of the Cinnamon Tree/the Donkey's Egg. Kim, Yon-Kyong & Kang, Mi-Sun, illus. 2000. (Korean Folk Tales for Children Ser.: Vol. 10). (KOR.). 46p. (J). (gr. 2-5). lib. bdg. (978-0-930878-93-1(0)) Hollym International Corp.

FOLKLORE—LATIN AMERICA

Ada, Alma Flor & Campoy, F. Isabel. Tales Our Abuelitas Told: A Hispanic Folktale Collection. Davalos, Felipe et al, illus. 2000. 128p. (J). (gr. k-5). 19.95 (978-0-689-82583-5(8) , Atheneum) Simon & Schuster Children's Publishing.

Dearden, Carmen D. The Little Book of Latin American Folktales. Dearden, Carmen Diana, ed. Wald, Susana & Zeller, Beatriz, trs. from SPA. Oliver, Maria Fernanda et al, illus. 2003. 132p. (J). (gr. 1-4). 8.95 (978-0-88899-543-8(1)) Groundwood Bks. CAN. *Dist:* Perseus Distribution.

DeSpain, Pleasant. Emerald Lizard: Fifteen Latin American Tales to Tell in English & Spanish. 1999. (SPA.). (gr. 3-6). lib. bdg. 21.05 (978-0-613-25016-0(8)) Tandem Library Bks.

Gonzalez, Lucia. Senor Cat's Romance. 2001. lib. bdg. 14.15 (978-0-613-35749-4(3)); (Illus.). (J). (978-0-606-21425-4(9)) Tandem Library Bks.

Gonzalez, Lucia M. Senor Cat's Romance: And Other Favorite Stories from Latin America. Delacre, Lulu, illus. 2001. 48p. (J). (ps-2). pap. 5.99 (978-0-439-27863-8(5)) Scholastic, Inc.

Hayes, Joe. A Spoon for Every Bite/Una Cuchara para Cada Bocado. Leer, Rebecca, illus. 1999. 32p. (J). (ps-2). pap. 5.95 (978-0-531-07143-4(X) , Orchard Bks.) Scholastic, Inc.

—A Spoon for Every Bite/Una Cuchara para Cada Bocado. 1999. (J). (978-0-606-18936-1(X)) Tandem Library Bks.

Lilly, Melinda. The Snake's Toothache: A Q'Eqchi Maya Myth. Reasoner, Charles, illus. 1999. (Latin American Tales & Myths Ser.). 32p. (J). (gr. 2-5). lib. bdg. 26.60 (978-1-57103-266-9(5)) Rourke Publishing, LLC.

MacDonald, Margaret Read. Conejito: A Folktale from Panama. Valerio, Geraldo, illus. 2006. 32p. 16.95 (978-0-87483-779-7(0)) August Hse. Pubs., Inc.

Ouriou, Susan, tr. from SPA. Little Book of Nursery Tales. Salvador, Carmen, illus. 2005. (Little Book Ser.). 104p. (J). (ps-7). 8.95 (978-0-88899-673-2(X)) Groundwood Bks. CAN. *Dist:* Perseus Distribution.

Walsh, Maria Elena. Versos Tradicionales para Cebollitas. Garofoli, Viviana, illus. 2001. (SPA.). 164p. (J). (gr. 3-5). pap. 11.95 (978-950-511-632-4(2)) Santillana USA Publishing Co., Inc.

FOLKLORE—LIBERIA

Paye, Won-Ldy. Why Leopard Has Spots: Dan Stories from Liberia. 1999. (gr. 3-6). lib. bdg. 22.20 (978-0-613-58141-7(5)) Tandem Library Bks.

Paye, Won-Ldy & Lippert, Margaret. Why Leopard Has Spots: Dan Stories from Liberia. Bryan, Asley, illus. 1998. 64p. (gr. 3-4). 12.95 (978-1-55591-991-7(X)) Fulcrum Publishing.

Paye, Won-Ldy & Lippert, Margaret H. Head, Body, Legs: A Story from Liberia. Paschkis, Julie, illus. 32p. (J). 2005. pap. 6.95 (978-0-8050-7890-9(8)); 2002. 16.95 (978-0-8050-6570-1(9)) Holt, Henry & Co. (Holt, Henry & Co. Bks. For Young Readers).

FOLKLORE, MAORI

Reed, A. W. Maori Myths & Legendary Tales. Turner, Dennis, illus. 1999. 254p. (J). pap. (978-1-877246-10-4(7)) New Holland Pubs. (NZ) Ltd.

FOLKLORE—MEXICO

Aardema, Verna. Borreguita & the Coyote. 2002. (Illus.). (J). 14.79 (978-0-7587-2137-2(4)) Book Wholesalers, Inc.

Ada, Alma Flor. La Lagartija el Sol. 1999. Tr. of Lizard & the Sun. (J). (978-0-606-16441-2(3)) Tandem Library Bks.

—The Lizard & the Sun. Davalos, Felipe, illus. 1999. 48p. (gr. k-3). pap. 6.99 (978-0-440-41531-2(4) , Dragonfly Bks.) Random Hse. Children's Bks.

Czernecki, Stefan & Rhodes, Timothy. Pancho's Pinata. 1999. (SPA.). (J). pap. 15.49 (978-0-7868-2189-1(2)) Hyperion Bks. for Children.

de Paola, Tomie. Adelita: A Mexican Cinderella Story. 2002. (SPA., Illus.). 32p. (J). 16.99 (978-0-399-23866-6(2) , Putnam Juvenile) Penguin Group (USA) Inc.

—The Legend of the Poinsettia. de Paola, Tomie, illus. 2002. (Illus.). (J). 13.19 (978-0-7587-2965-1(0)) Book Wholesalers, Inc.

Eckhardt, Jason C., illus. The Legend of the China Poblana. 2003. (J). 10.95 (978-1-57168-731-9(9) , Eakin Pr.) Eakin Pr.

Ehlert, Lois. Cuckoo. 2000. Tr. of Cucu. (SPA.). (gr. k-3). lib. bdg. 15.30 (978-0-613-29917-6(5)) Tandem Library Bks.

Fisher, Leonard Everett, illus. The Two Mountains: An Aztec Legend. 2000. 32p. (J). (gr. k-3). tchr. ed. 16.95 (978-0-8234-1504-5(X)) Holiday Hse., Inc.

Gerson, Mary-Joan. Fiesta Femenina: Celebrating Women in Mexican Folktale. Gonzalez, Maya Christina, illus. 64p. (J). 2003. (SPA.). pap. 19.99 (978-1-84148-964-3(6)); 2001. (gr. 3 up). 19.99 (978-1-84148-365-8(6)) Barefoot Bks., Inc.

—Fiesta Femenina: Celebrating Women in Mexican Folktale. Gonzalez, Maya Christina, illus. 2004. 64p. (J). (gr. k-4). reprint ed. 20.00 (978-0-7567-7829-3(8)) DIANE Publishing Co.

Gollub, Matthew. Uncle Snake. Martinez, Leovigildo, illus. 2004. (J). (978-1-889910-31-4(7)); pap. (978-1-889910-32-1(5)) Tortuga Pr.

Harper, Jo. The Legend of Mexicatl. 2000. (gr. k-3). lib. bdg. 16.40 (978-0-613-32759-6(4)) Tandem Library Bks.

—The Legend of Mexicatl. Casilla, Robert, illus. 2000. 40p. (J). (ps-3). pap. 7.95 (978-1-890515-21-8(3)) Turtle Bks.

—La Leyenda de Mexicatl. Lans, Tatiana, tr. Casilla, Robert, illus. 2000. (SPA.). 40p. (J). (ps-3). pap. 7.95 (978-1-890515-22-5(1)) Turtle Bks.

Harris, Zoe & Williams, Suzanne. Pinatas & Smiling Skeletons: Celebrating Mexican Festivals. Woo, Yolanda G., illus. 1998. 48p. (YA). (gr. 2-8). lib. bdg. 19.95 (978-1-881896-19-7(6) , Dragon Bks.) Pacific View Pr.

Hayes, Joe. El Cucuy: A Bogeyman Cuento in English & Spanish. Robledo, Honorio, illus. 2003. (Working Classics Ser.). (SPA.). 40p. pap. 7.95 (978-0-938317-78-4(4)) Cinco Puntos Pr.

—El Cucuy: A Bogeyman Cuento in English & Spanish. 2003. (SPA.). (gr. k-3). lib. bdg. 16.40 (978-0-613-77771-1(9)) Tandem Library Bks.

—La Llorona, the Weeping Woman: An Hispanic Legend Told in Spanish & English. Trego-Hill, Vicki & Pennypacker, Mona, illus. 3rd ed. 2004. (ENG & SPA.). 32p. (J). (gr. 4 up). 16.95 (978-0-938317-86-9(5)) Cinco Puntos Pr.

Johnston, Tony. The Tale of Rabbit & Coyote. DePaola, Tomie, illus. 1998. 32p. (J). (ps-ps). pap. 6.99 (978-0-698-11630-6(5) , Putnam Juvenile) Penguin Group (USA) Inc.

—The Tale of Rabbit & Coyote. de Paola, Tomie, illus. 1998. (978-0-606-13834-5(X)) Tandem Library Bks.

Johnston, Tony & Johnston, Tony. The Tale of Rabbit & Coyote. DePaola, Tomie, illus. 1998. (J). (ps-ps). lib. bdg. 15.30 (978-0-613-08864-0(6)) Tandem Library Bks.

Kimmel, Eric A. Cactus Soup. Huling, Phil, tr. Huling, Phil, illus. 2004. 32p. (J). 16.95 (978-0-7614-5155-6(2)) Cavendish, Marshall Corp.

Larson, Bonnie. When Animals Were People: A Huichol Indian Tale. Rivera Lemos, Modesto, illus. 2002. Tr. of Cuando los Animales Fueron Gente. (ENG & SPA.). 32p. (J). (gr. 1-3). pap. 16.95 (978-1-57416-051-2(6)) Clear Light Pubs.

Mair, Jacqueline, illus. Horse Hooves & Chicken Feet: Mexican Folktales. 2003. 92p. (J). (gr. k-3). tchr. ed. 19.00 (978-0-618-19463-6(0) , Clarion Bks.) Houghton Mifflin Co. Trade & Reference Div.

Marcos, Subcomandante. The Story of Colors (La Historia de los Colores) A Bilingual Folktale from the Jungles of Chiapas. 2003. (ENG & SPA., Illus.). 40p. (J). pap. 8.95 (978-0-938317-71-5(7)) Cinco Puntos Pr.

McDermott, Gerald. Musicians of the Sun. McDermott, Gerald, illus. 2002. (Illus.). (J). 26.17 (978-0-7587-3202-6(3)) Book Wholesalers, Inc.

McLennan, Connie, illus. Domitila: A Cinderella Tale from the Mexican Tradition. 2004. 32p. (gr. 3-7). (SPA.). 16.95 (978-1-885008-18-3(X)); 16.95 (978-1-885008-13-8(9)) Shen's Bks.

Morales, Yuyi. Just a Minute: A Trickster Tale & Counting Book. 2003. (SPA & ENG., Illus.). 36p. (J). 15.95 (978-0-8118-3758-3(0)) Chronicle Bks. LLC.

Petersen, Patricia. Magali/Magali: An Aztec Legend about Good Fortune (Una Ieyenja Azteca Sobre La Buena Fortuna) Petersen, Sheli, illus. 1998. (Cuentos en Dos Idiomas Ser.). 32p. (J). (gr. 3-6). 16.95 (978-1-56492-250-2(2)) Laredo Publishing Co., Inc.

Robledo, Honorio, illus. El Cucuy: A Bogeyman Cuento in English & Spanish. 2001. (SPA & ENG.). 32p. (J). (gr. 4-7). 15.95 (978-0-938317-54-8(7)) Cinco Puntos Pr.

Sastrias, Martha. La Melodia de la Naturaleza: Leyendas Mexicanas. 1999. (SPA., Illus.). 92p. (J). (gr. 3 up). 12.95 (978-84-241-7969-4(2) , EV3908) Lectorum Pubns., Inc.

Villaseñor, Victor. Frog & His Friends Save Humanity/la Rana y Sus Amigos Salvan ALA Humanidad. Ochoa, Edna, tr. Ramirez, Jose, illus. (ENG & SPA.). 32p. (J). (ps). 15.95 (978-1-55885-429-1(0) , Piñata Books) Arte Publico Pr.

—Mother Fox & Mr. Coyote / Mama Zorra y Don Coyote. Turcios, Guadalupe Vanessa, tr. Ugalde Alcantara, Felipe, illus. (ENG & SPA.). 32p. (gr. 2-4). 15.95 (978-1-55885-428-4(2) , Piñata Books) Arte Publico Pr.

FOLKLORE—MIDDLE EAST

Gold, Sharlya & Caspi, Mishael. The Answered Prayer: And Other Yemenite Folktales. Wunsch, Marjory, illus. 2004. 80p. (J). pap. 9.95 (978-0-8276-0772-9(5)) Jewish Pubn. Society.

Johnson-Davies, Denys. Goha the Wise Fool. Hamdy, Hag et al, illus. 2005. 44p. (J). (ps-7). 16.99 (978-0-399-24222-9(8) , Philomel) Penguin Group (USA) Inc.

Shah, Idries. The Magic Horse. Freeman, Julie, illus. 1998. 32p. (J). (gr. 4-7). 17.00 (978-1-883536-11-4(1) , MAHO1, Hoopoe Bks.) ISHK.

Soman, David, illus. Only One Cowry. 2000. 32p. (J). (ps-2). 17.99 (978-0-531-33288-7(8) , Orchard Bks.) Scholastic, Inc.

Young, Ed. What about Me? Young, Ed, illus. 2002. (Illus.). 40p. (J). (ps-3). 16.99 (978-0-399-23624-2(4) , Philomel) Penguin Group (USA) Inc.

Zeghidour, Slimane. I Want to Talk to God. Matthews, Sarah, tr. from FRE. Thibault, Dominique, illus. 1998. (Tales of Heaven & Earth Ser.).Tr. of Homme Qui Voulait Rencontrer Dieu. 32p. (YA). (gr. 3-7). pap. 19.95 (978-0-88682-824-0(4) , Creative Education) Creative Co., The.

FOLKLORE—MOROCCO

Fowles, Shelley. The Bachelor & the Bean. 2007. (Illus.). 32p. (J). pap. 7.95 ***(978-1-84507-020-5(8))*** Lincoln, Frances Ltd. GBR. *Dist:* Perseus Distribution.

FOLKLORE—NEAR EAST

see Folklore—Asia; Folklore—Middle East

FOLKLORE, NEGRO

see African Americans—Folklore

FOLKLORE—NETHERLANDS

Shepard, Aaron. The Baker's Dozen: A Saint Nicholas Tale. 1999. (J). (978-0-606-17192-2(4)) Tandem Library Bks.

FOLKLORE—NEW ENGLAND

Aylesworth, Jim. The Tale of the Tricky Fox: A New England Trickster Tale. McClintock, Barbara, illus. 2001. 32p. (J). (ps-1). pap. 16.95 (978-0-439-09543-3(3) , Scholastic Pr.) Scholastic, Inc.

Drake, Samuel Adams. New England Legends & Folk Lore. 2001. 498p. (YA). reprint ed. (978-1-58218-443-2(7)) Digital Scanning, Inc.

FOLKLORE—NIGERIA

Baumann, Margaret. Ajapa the Tortoise: A Book of Nigerian Folk Tales. unabr. ed. 2003. (Dover Evergreen Classics Ser.). (Illus.). 112p. (J). (gr. 4-7). pap. 5.95 (978-0-486-42361-6(1)) Dover Pubns., Inc.

Echewa, T. Obinkaram. The Magic Tree: A Folktale from Nigeria. Lewis, Earl, illus. 1999. 32p. (ps-3). (J). 15.89 (978-0-688-16232-0(0)); (YA). 16.00 (978-0-688-16231-3(2)) HarperCollins Pubs.

Olaleye, Isaac. In the Rainfield: Who Is the Greatest? Grifalconi, Ann, illus. 2000. 32p. (J). (ps-4). pap. 16.95 (978-0-590-48363-6(3) , Blue Sky Pr., The) Scholastic, Inc.

Shepard, Aaron. Master Man: A Tale of Nigeria. Wisniewski, David, illus. 2001. 32p. (J). (gr. k-3). 15.95 (978-0-688-13783-0(0)) HarperCollins Pubs.

FOLKLORE—NORTH AMERICA

Bonnice, Sherry. Children's Folklore. 2003. (North American Folklore Ser.). (Illus.). 112p. (YA). (gr. 7 up). lib. bdg. (978-1-59084-329-1(0)) Mason Crest Pubs.

Brinkerhoff, Shirley. Contemporary Folklore. 2002. (North American Folklore Ser.). (Illus.). 112p. (YA). (gr. 7 up). lib. bdg. (978-1-59084-331-4(2)) Mason Crest Pubs.

Bruchac, Joseph. Earth under Sky Bear's Feet: Native American Poems of the Land. 1998. (gr. k-3). lib. bdg. 15.30 (978-0-613-88299-6(7)) Tandem Library Bks.

Grey, Herman. American Indian Love Stories: Traditional Stories of Love & Romance from Tribes Across America. 2002. 160p. (YA). pap. 14.95 (978-1-57416-063-5(X)) Clear Light Pubs.

Hurston, Zora Neale & Thomas, Joyce Carol. Lies & Other Tall Tales. Myers, Christopher, illus. 2005. 40p. (J). 15.99 (978-0-06-000655-6(2)) HarperCollins Pubs.

Rayner, Olivia, illus. North American Myths & Legends. 2001. (World Book Myths & Legends Ser.). 64p. (J). (978-0-7166-2611-4(X)) World Bk., Inc.

Sanna, Ellyn. Ethnic Folklore. 2003. (North American Folklore Ser.). (Illus.). 112p. (YA). (gr. 7 up). lib. bdg. (978-1-59084-332-1(0)) Mason Crest Pubs.

—Folk Customs. 2002. (North American Folklore Ser.). (Illus.). 112p. (YA). (gr. 7 up). lib. bdg. (978-1-59084-336-9(3)) Mason Crest Pubs.

—Folk Religion. 2002. (North American Folklore Ser.). (Illus.). 112p. (J). (gr. 7 up). lib. bdg. (978-1-59084-348-2(7)) Mason Crest Pubs.

—Folk Tales & Legends. 2002. (North American Folklore Ser.). (Illus.). 112p. (YA). (gr. 7 up). lib. bdg. (978-1-59084-346-8(0)) Mason Crest Pubs.

—Food Folklore. 2002. (North American Folklore Ser.). (Illus.). 112p. (YA). (gr. 7 up). lib. bdg. (978-1-59084-347-5(9)) Mason Crest Pubs.

FOLKLORE—NORWAY

Appleby, Ellen. The Three Billy Goats Gruff. (FRE.). (J). 6.99 (978-0-590-71770-0(7)) Scholastic, Inc.

—Les Trois Barbichu, Big Bk. l.t. ed. (FRE.). (J). bds. 29.99 (978-0-590-71769-4(3)) Scholastic, Inc.

Asbjornsen, Peter Christen. The Three Billy Goats Gruff. Carpenter, Stephen, illus. 1998. (Growing Tree Ser.). 24p. (J). (ps up). 9.99 (978-0-694-01033-2(2)) HarperCollins Pubs.

Asbjornsen, Peter Christen, et al. East O' the Sun & West O' the Moon & Other Norwegian Fairy Tales. 2001. (Dover Juvenile Classics Ser.). (Illus.). 128p. (J). (gr. 4-7). pap. 2.00 (978-0-486-41724-0(7)) Dover Pubns., Inc.

Batt, Tanya Robyn. The Princess & the White Bear King. Ceccoli, Nicoletta, illus. 2004. 40p. (J). 16.99 (978-1-84148-339-9(7)) Barefoot Bks., Inc.

Biro, Val, illus. & retold by. The Three Billy Goats Gruff. Biro, Val, retold by. 1998. 32p. (J). (gr. k-3). pap. 4.99 (978-1-887734-46-2(5)) Star Bright Bks., Inc.

D'Aulaire, Ingri & D'Aulaire, Edgar Parin. D'aulaires' Book of Trolls. 2006. (New York Review Children's Collection Ser.). (Illus.). 72p. (J). (ps-3). 19.95 (978-1-59017-217-9(5) , NYR Children's Collection) New York Review of Bks., Inc., The.

Finch, Mary & Arenson, Roberta. The Three Billy Goats Gruff. Asbjornsen, Peter Christen, illus. 2001. 32p. (J). pap. 6.99 (978-1-84148-351-1(6)) Barefoot Bks., Inc.

Finch, Mary & Asbjornsen, Peter Christen. The Three Billy Goats Gruff. Arenson, Roberta, illus. 2001. 32p. (J). (gr. 1-3). 15.99 (978-1-84148-349-8(4)) Barefoot Bks., Inc.

Hopkins, Jackie & Asbjornsen, Peter Christen. The Three Armadillies Tuff. Brooks, S. G., illus. 2002. (J). 15.95 (978-1-56145-258-3(0) , Q34266) Peachtree Pubs., Ltd.

Lunge-Larsen, Lise. The Race of the Birkebeiners. Azarian, Mary, illus. 2001. 32p. (J). (gr. k-3). tchr. ed. 16.00 (978-0-618-10313-3(9)) Houghton Mifflin Co. Trade & Reference Div.

—The Troll with No Heart in His Body. Bowen, Betsy, illus. 2003. 96p. (J). (gr. 4-6). pap. 7.95 (978-0-618-35403-0(4)) Houghton Mifflin Co. Trade & Reference Div.

Parker, Vic. Traditional Tales from Norse Lands. 2000. (Traditional Tales from Around the World Ser.). (Illus.). 48p. (J). (gr. 2-6). lib. bdg. 16.95 (978-1-929298-73-0(0)) Chrysalis Education.

Salley, Coleen. Who's That Trippin' over My Bridge? Dixon, Amy Jackson, illus. 2002. 32p. (J). (gr. k-3). 14.95 (978-1-56554-890-9(6)) Pelican Publishing Co., Inc.

Wade, Barrie. The Three Billy Goats Gruff. 2004. (Read-It! Readers Ser.). (Illus.). 32p. (C). (gr. k-3). 18.60 (978-1-4048-0070-0(0)) Picture Window Bks.

FOLKLORE, ORIENTAL

see Folklore—Asia

FOLKLORE—PERSIA

Climo, Shirley. The Persian Cinderella. Florczak, Robert, illus. 1999. 32p. (J). (ps-3). 16.99 (978-0-06-026763-6(1)) HarperCollins Pubs.

FOLKLORE—PHILIPPINES

Climo, Shirley. Tuko & the Birds: A Tale from the Philippines. Mora, Francisco X., illus. 2002. 40p. (J). 16.95 (978-0-8050-6559-6(8) , Holt, Henry & Co. Bks. For Young Readers) Holt, Henry & Co.

FOLKLORE—POLAND

Kroll, Virginia. Marta & the Manger Straw: A Christmas Tradition from Poland. Belton, Robyn, illus. 2005. (Traditions of Faith from Around the World Ser.). 40p. (J). (ps-3). 15.99 (978-0-310-70994-7(6)) Zonderkidz.

FOLKLORE—POLYNESIA

Sperry, Armstrong. Call It Courage. Sperry, Armstrong, illus. 2002. Tr. of Newbery Summer. (Illus.). (YA). 13.40 (978-0-7587-0175-6(6)) Book Wholesalers, Inc.

—Call It Courage. Sperry, Armstrong, illus. l.t. ed. 2000. (LRS Large Print Cornerstone Ser.).Tr. of Newbery Summer. (Illus.). 114p. (YA). (gr. 5-12). lib. bdg. 24.95 (978-1-58118-063-3(2) , 23477) LRS.

—Call It Courage. unabr. ed. 2004. Tr. of Newbery Summer. 95p. (J). (gr. 5-9). pap. 29.00 incl. audio (978-0-8072-8685-2(0) , YA235SP, Listening Library) Random Hse. Audio Publishing Group.

FOLKLORE—PUERTO RICO

Delacre, Lulu, illus. Shake It, Morena! And Other Folklore from Puerto Rico. 2002. (Around the World Ser.). (ENG & SPA.). 48p. (gr. k-3). lib. bdg. 24.90 (978-0-7613-1910-8(7) , Millbrook Pr.) Lerner Publishing Group.

Mohr, Nicholasa. The Song of el Coqui & Other Tales of Puerto Rico. Martorell, Antonio, illus. 2004. 39p. (J). (gr. k-4). reprint ed. 16.00 (978-0-7567-7697-8(X)) DIANE Publishing Co.

Ramirez, Michael Rose. The Legend of the Hummingbird: A Tale from Puerto Rico. Sanfilippo, Margaret, illus. 1998. (Mondo Folktales Ser.). 32p. (J). (gr. k-4). pap. 4.95 (978-1-57255-232-6(8)) Mondo Publishing.

Sanchez, Enrique O., illus. The Golden Flower: A Taino Myth from Puerto Rico. 32p. (J). (ps). 15.95 (978-1-55885-452-9(5) , Piñata Books) Arte Publico Pr.

Shake It, Morena! And Other Folklore from Puerto Rico. 2007. (J). pap. 6.95 (***978-0-8225-7026-4(2)** , First Avenue Editions) Lerner Publishing Group.

FOLKLORE—ROMANIA

Rascol, Sabina. The Impudent Rooster: A Romanian Folktale. Berry, Holly, illus. 2004. 32p. (J). (ps). 16.99 (978-0-525-47179-0(0) , Dutton Juvenile) Penguin Group (USA) Inc.

FOLKLORE—SCOTLAND

Heo, Yumi, illus. Pirican Pic & Pirican Mor. 2003. 40p. (J). (gr. 1-3). 16.99 (978-1-84148-070-1(3)) Barefoot Bks., Inc.

Huck, Charlotte S. Black Bull of Norway: A Scottish Tale. 2001. (978-0-606-22802-2(0)) Tandem Library Bks.

The Selkie Girl. 2004. 24.95 incl. audio (978-0-7882-0590-3(0)); pap. 14.95 incl. audio (978-0-7882-0664-1(8)) Weston Woods Studios, Inc.

Van Laan, Nancy. Tiny, Tiny Boy & the Big, Big Cow. 2000. (978-0-606-18092-4(3)) Tandem Library Bks.

FOLKLORE—SLAVIC COUNTRIES

Bateson-Hill, Margaret. Masha & the Firebird. Wilson, Anne, illus. 2005. (Folk Tales Ser.). (RUS & ENG.). 32p. (J). pap. 7.99 (978-1-84089-201-7(3) , Zero to Ten, Limited) Evans Publishing Group GBR. *Dist:* Independent Pubs. Group.

FOLKLORE—SOUTH AMERICA

Arnold, Syrah, illus. South American Myths & Legends. 2001. (World Book Myths & Legends Ser.). 64p. (J). (978-0-7166-2612-1(8)) World Bk., Inc.

Ehlert, Lois. Moon Rope/Un Lazo a la Luna. Prince, Amy, tr. 2003. (ENG & SPA., Illus.). 40p. (J). pap. 7.00 (978-0-15-201702-6(X) , Voyager Bks./Libros Viajeros) Harcourt Children's Bks.

Fatus, Sophie, illus. A Hen, a Chick & a String Guitar. 2005. 32p. (J). 17.99 incl. audio compact disk (978-1-84148-796-0(1)) Barefoot Bks., Inc.

Knutson, Barbara. Love & Roast Chicken: A Trickster Tale from the Andes Mountains. 2004. (Carolrhoda Picture Books Ser.). (Illus.). 40p. (J). (ps-3). 16.95 (978-1-57505-657-9(7)) Lerner Publishing Group.

Pirotta, Saviour. Stories from the Amazon. 2000. (Multicultural Stories Ser.). (Illus.). 48p. (J). (ps-3). pap. 9.95 (978-0-7398-1818-3(X)) Steck-Vaughn.

Pirotta, Saviour & Gryspeerdt, Becky, illus. Stories from the Amazon. 1999. (Multicultural Stories Ser.). 48p. (J). (ps-3). lib. bdg. 27.12 (978-0-7398-1332-4(3)) Raintree.

Pitcher, Caroline. Mariana & the Merchild. Morris, Jackie, illus. 2004. 32p. (J). (ps-7). 17.00 (978-0-8028-5204-5(1)) Eerdmans, William B. Publishing Co.

Rudel, Christian. Children of the Moon. Sideri, Simona, tr. from FRE. Souppart, Etienne, illus. 1998. (Tales of Heaven & Earth Ser.).Tr. of Enfants de la Lune. 32p. (YA). (gr. 3-7). pap. 19.95 (978-0-88682-829-5(5) , Creative Education) Creative Co., The.

FOLKLORE—SOUTHEAST ASIA

Coburn, Jewell R. Angkat: The Cambodian Cinderella. Flotte, Edmund, illus. 1998. 32p. (gr. 1-3). 16.95 (978-1-885008-09-1(0)) Shen's Bks.

Krishnaswami, Uma. Shower of Gold: Girls & Women in the Stories of India. Selven, Maniam, illus. 1999. vii, 125p. (J). (ps up). 21.50 (978-0-208-02484-8(0) , Linnet Bks.) Shoe String Pr., Inc.

Souhami, Jessica. No Dinner! The Story of the Old Woman & the Pumpkin. 2000. (Accelerated Reader Bks.). (Illus.). 32p. (J). (gr. k-3). 15.95 (978-0-7614-5059-7(9) , Cavendish Children's Bks.) Cavendish, Marshall Corp.

FOLKLORE—SOVIET UNION

Arnold, Katya R., illus. & retold by. That Apple Is Mine! Arnold, Katya R., retold by. 2000. 32p. (J). (gr. k-3). tchr. ed. 15.95 (978-0-8234-1629-5(1)) Holiday Hse., Inc.

Dole, Nathan Haskell, tr. The Russian Fairy Book. 2000. 128p. (J). (gr. 4-7). pap. 5.95 (978-0-486-41019-7(6)) Dover Pubns., Inc.

Evanishen, Danny. Yalynka & Other Ukrainian Folk Tales Retold in English. Zurowsky, J., tr. from UKR. Critchlow, Ralph, illus. 2002. 136p. per. (978-0-9681596-7-5(2)) Ethnic Enterprises.

Giant Turnip. 2004. (J). E-Book incl. cd-rom (978-1-84444-459-5(7)) Mantra Publishing, Ltd.

Koopmans, Loek. The Woodcutter's Mitten: An Old Ukrainian Tale. 2000. (Illus.). 32p. (J). (ps-2). pap. 6.95 (978-1-56656-176-1(0) , Crocodile Bks.) Interlink Publishing Group, Inc.

Mayhew, James. The Kingfisher Book of Tales from Russia. Mayhew, James, illus. 2000. (Story Collections). (Illus.). 80p. (J). (gr. 3-5). pap. 12.95 (978-0-7534-5293-6(6) , Kingfisher) Houghton Mifflin Co. Trade & Reference Div.

McCaughrean, Geraldine. Grandma Chickenlegs. Kemp, Moira, illus. 2003. (Picture Bks.). 32p. (J). (ps-3). 15.95 (978-1-57505-415-5(9)); pap. 6.95 (978-0-87614-908-9(5) , Carolrhoda Bks.) Lerner Publishing Group.

Peck, Jan. The Giant Carrot. Root, Barry, illus. 1998. 32p. (J). (ps-3). 16.99 (978-0-8037-1823-4(3) , Dial) Penguin Group (USA) Inc.

Pogorelsky, Antony. The Little Black Hen. Spirin, Gennady, illus. 2003. 32p. (gr. 1-6). 16.95 (978-1-894965-03-3(5)) Simply Read Bks. CAN. *Dist:* Perseus Distribution.

Polacco, Patricia. Luba & the Wren. 1999. (Illus.). 32p. (J). (ps-3). 16.99 (978-0-399-23168-1(4) , Philomel) Penguin Group (USA) Inc.

Scholey, Arthur & Holder, Mig. Baboushka & Papa Panov's Special Day. Burrows, Ray et al, illus. 2000. 64p. 6.99 (978-0-7459-4559-0(7) , Lion) Lion Hudson plc GBR. *Dist:* Independent Pubs. Group.

Shepard, Aaron. The Sea King's Daughter: A Russian Legend. 1999. (Illus.). 28p. (J). (gr. k-3). per. 17.00 (978-0-689-82743-3(1) , Simon & Schuster Children's Publishing) Simon & Schuster Children's Publishing.

Singh, Pushpinder. Baba Ditta's Turnip. Singh, Pushpinder, illus. 1999. (Illus.). 38p. (J). (ps-3). pap. 4.95 (978-0-9700363-1-5(0)) Sikh Foundation.

Stihler, Cherie. The Giant Cabbage: An Alaska Folktale. Trammell, Jeremiah, illus. 2003. (PAWS IV Ser.). 32p. (J). (ps-3). pap. 9.95 (978-1-57061-357-9(5)) Sasquatch Bks.

Yolen, Jane. Baba Yaga. Date not set. 32p. (J). (ps-1). pap. 5.99 (978-0-06-443599-4(7)) HarperCollins Pubs.

—The Flying Witch. Vagin, Vladimir, illus. 2003. 40p. (J). (ps-1). 15.99 (978-0-06-028536-4(2)) HarperCollins Pubs.

Yolen, Jane & Oppenheim, Shulamith Levey. The Sea King. Czernecki, Stefan, illus. 2002. 32p. (J). (gr. k-4). 15.95 (978-1-56656-459-5(X) , Crocodile Bks.) Interlink Publishing Group, Inc.

Ziefert, Harriet. The Snow Child. 2000. (Easy-to-Read Ser.). (J). (978-0-606-20254-1(4)) Tandem Library Bks.

FOLKLORE—SPAIN

Chess, Victoria, illus. The Beautiful Butterfly: A Folktale from Spain. 2000. 32p. (J). (gr. k-3). tchr. ed. 15.00 (978-0-395-90015-4(8) , Clarion Bks.) Houghton Mifflin Co. Trade & Reference Div.

Eisner, Will. Last Knight. 2003. (gr. k-3). lib. bdg. 16.40 (978-0-613-82318-0(4)) Tandem Library Bks.

Walsh, Maria Elena. Versos Tradicionales para Cebollitas. Garofoli, Viviana, illus. 2001. (SPA.). 164p. (J). (gr. 3-5). pap. 11.95 (978-950-511-632-4(2)) Santillana USA Publishing Co., Inc.

FOLKLORE—TIBET

Rose, Naomi C. Tibetan Tales from the Top of the World. 2006. (ENG & TIB.). (J). (gr. 1-7). 16.95 (978-1-57416-089-5(3)) Clear Light Pubs.

FOLKLORE—TURKEY

Demi. The Hungry Coat: A Tale from Turkey. Demi, illus. 2004. (Illus.). 40p. (J). 19.95 (978-0-689-84680-9(0) , McElderry, Margaret K.) Simon & Schuster Children's Publishing.

FOLKLORE—UKRAINE

Kimmel, Eric A. The Castle of Cats: A Story from Ukraine. Krenina, Katya, illus. 2004. 32p. (J). (gr. k-3). tchr. ed. 16.95 (978-0-8234-1565-6(1)) Holiday Hse., Inc.

Krenina, Katya, illus. The Birds' Gift: A Ukrainian Easter Story. 32p. (J). (gr. k-3). tchr. ed. 16.95 (978-0-8234-1384-3(5)) Holiday Hse., Inc.

—The Spider's Gift: A Ukrainian Christmas Story. 2005. (J). (978-0-8234-1743-8(3)) Holiday Hse., Inc.

Skrypuch, Marsha. Enough. 2004. (Illus.). 32p. (J). (gr. 2-4). (978-1-55041-884-2(X)) Fitzhenry & Whiteside, Ltd.

FOLKLORE—UNITED STATES

Arroyo, Andrea, illus. The Legend of the Lady Slipper. 1999. 32p. (J). (gr. k-3). tchr. ed. 15.00 (978-0-395-90512-8(5)) Houghton Mifflin Co. Trade & Reference Div.

Balcziak, Bill. John Henry. 2003. (Tall Tales Ser.). (Illus.). 32p. (J). (gr. 3 up). 22.60 (978-0-7565-0457-1(0)) Compass Point Bks.

—Johnny Appleseed. 2003. (Tall Tales Ser.). (Illus.). 32p. (C). (gr. 3-5). 22.60 (978-0-7565-0458-8(9)) Compass Point Bks.

—Paul Bunyan. 2003. (Tall Tales Ser.). (Illus.). 32p. (J). (gr. 3 up). 22.60 (978-0-7565-0459-5(7)) Compass Point Bks.

—Pecos Bill. 2003. (Tall Tales Ser.). (Illus.). 32p. (J). (gr. 3 up). 22.60 (978-0-7565-0460-1(0)) Compass Point Bks.

Bang, Molly Garrett. Wiley & the Hairy Man. Bang, Molly Garrett, illus. 2000. (Illus.). pap. 18.95 incl. audio compact disk (978-1-59112-398-9(4)); pap. 31.95 incl. audio compact disk (978-1-59112-598-3(7)) Live Oak Media.

—Wiley & the Hairy Man: Adapted from an American Folk Tale. 2000. (J). pap. 19.97 incl. audio (978-0-7366-9221-2(5)) Books on Tape, Inc.

—Wiley & the Hairy Man: Adapted from an American Folk Tale. 1998. pap. 3.99 (978-0-87628-337-0(7)) Ctr. for Applied Research in Education, The.

—Wiley & the Hairy Man: Adapted from an American Folk Tale. adapted ed. 2000. (Illus.). (J). (gr. k-3). 24.95 incl. audio (978-0-87499-618-0(X)) Live Oak Media.

—Wiley & the Hairy Man, Grades K-3, 2 Bks. 2000. (Illus.). (J). pap., tchr. ed. 29.95 incl. audio (978-0-87499-619-7(8)) Live Oak Media.

Beaverhead, Peter, et al. Mary Quequesah's Love Story: A Pend d'Oreille Indian Tale. 2000. (Illus.). 32p. pap. 5.95 (978-0-917298-71-4(3)) Montana Historical Society Pr.

Becker, Sandra. Paul Bunyan. 2003. (Folk Heroes Ser.). (Illus.). 24p. (J). lib. bdg. 15.95 (978-1-59036-076-7(1)) Weigl Pubs., Inc.

Birenbaum, Barbara. Groundhog Phil's Message: Groundhog Legends & Lore. 2003. (Story Within a Story Ser.). (Illus.). 45p. (J). 21.00 (978-0-935343-69-4(5)) Peartree.

Bruchac, Joseph & Bruchac, James. Turtle's Race with Beaver: A Traditional Seneca Story. Aruego, Jose & Dewey, Ariane, illus. 2003. 32p. (J). (gr. k-3). 15.99 (978-0-8037-2852-3(2) , Dial) Penguin Group (USA) Inc.

Chase, Richard. Grandfather Tales: American-English Folk Tales. 2003. (Illus.). 240p. (J). (gr. 5 up). tchr. ed. 17.00 (978-0-618-34691-2(0)); pap. 7.95 (978-0-618-34690-5(2)) Houghton Mifflin Co. Trade & Reference Div.

—The Jack Tales. 2003. 240p. (J). (gr. 5 up). tchr. ed. 17.00 (978-0-618-34693-6(7)) Houghton Mifflin Co. Trade & Reference Div.

—The Jack Tales: Folk Tales from the Southern Appalachians. 2003. (Illus.). 240p. (J). (gr. 5 up). pap. 7.95 (978-0-618-34692-9(9)) Houghton Mifflin Co. Trade & Reference Div.

Daise, Ronald H. Little Muddy Waters: A Gullah Folk Tale. Tuynman, Carol E., ed. McArtor, Barbara A., illus. 1998. 32p. (J). (gr. 2-6). 14.95 (978-1-891503-01-6(4) , CP101) G.O.G. Enterprises.

Daniel, Alan & Daniel, Lea, illus. Sody Salleratus. unabr. ed. 1998. 32p. (J). (gr. k-3). (978-1-55074-281-7(7)) Kids Can Pr., Ltd.

Davis, Donald. The Pig Who Went Home on Sunday: An Appalachian Folktale. Mazzucco, Jennifer, illus. 2004. 40p. (J). 16.95 (978-0-87483-571-7(2)) August Hse. Pubs., Inc.

DeSpain, Pleasant. Sweet Land of Story: Thirty-Six American Tales to Tell. 2001. (Illus.). 176p. (J). (gr. 3-7). 19.95 (978-0-87483-569-4(0)); pap. 12.95 (978-0-87483-600-4(X)) August Hse. Pubs., Inc.

Donohoe, Kitty & Warstler, Pasqua Cekola. Bunyan & Banjoes: Michigan Songs & Stories. Warstler, Pasqua Cekola, illus. 2004. (Illus.). 48p. (J). pap. 19.95 incl. audio compact disk (978-1-882376-58-2(7)) Thunder Bay Pr.

Doucet, Sharon Arms. Lapin Plays Possum: Trickster Tales from the Louisiana Bayou. Cook, Scott, illus. 2002. 64p. (J). (gr. k-5). 18.00 (978-0-374-34328-6(4) , Farrar, Straus & Giroux (BYR)) Farrar, Straus & Giroux.

Duvall, Deborah L., text. How Rabbit Lost His Tail: A Traditional Cherokee Legend. 2004. (Grandmother Stories Ser.: Vol. 3). (Illus.). 32p. (J). 14.95 (978-0-8263-3010-9(X)) Univ. of New Mexico Pr.

Farmer, Nancy. Casey Jones's Fireman: The Story of Sim Webb. Fogelman, Phyllis, ed. Bernardin, James, illus. 1999. 40p. (J). (ps-3). 16.99 (978-0-8037-1929-3(9) , Dial) Penguin Group (USA) Inc.

Flood, Nancy Bo. The Navajo Year: Walk Through Many Seasons. Whitethorne, Billy, illus. 2006. 32p. 17.95 (978-1-893354-06-7(7)) Salina Bookshelf.

Glass, Andrew, illus. The Legend of Strap Buckner: A Texas Tale. 2001. 32p. (J). (gr. k-3). tchr. ed. 16.95 (978-0-8234-1536-6(8)) Holiday Hse., Inc.

Gleeson, Brian. Paul Bunyan. Meyerowitz, Rick, illus. 2005. (Rabbit Ears-A Classic Tale Ser.). 40p. (J). (gr. k-5). 25.65 (978-1-59197-767-4(3)) Spotlight.

Haley, Gail E., illus. & as told by. Mountain Jack Tales. Haley, Gail E., as told by. 2001. 142p. (J). 19.95 (978-1-887905-51-0(0)) Parkway Pubs., Inc.

Hamilton, Virginia. Bruh Rabbit & the Tar Baby Girl. Ransome, James E., illus. 2003. 40p. (J). (gr. k-4). pap. 16.95 (978-0-590-47376-7(X) , Blue Sky Pr., The) Scholastic, Inc.

—The People Could Fly: American Black Folktales. Schulman, Janet, ed. Dillon, Leo & Dillon, Diane, illus. 2000. 192p. (YA). (gr. 3 up). 24.95 (978-0-375-80471-7(4) , Knopf Bks. for Young Readers) Random Hse. Children's Bks.

Hamilton, Virginia. The People Could Fly: The Picture Book. Dillon, Leo & Dillon, Diane, illus. 32p. (J). 2007. audio compact disk 20.99 (***978-0-375-94553-3(9)***); 2004. 16.95 (978-0-375-82405-0(7)) Random Hse. Children's Bks. (Knopf Bks. for Young Readers).

Harris, Joel Chandler. The Story of Brer Rabbit & the Wonderful Tar Baby. Drescher, Henrik, illus. 2005. (Rabbit Ears-A Classic Tale Ser.). 40p. (J). (gr. k-5). 25.65 (978-1-59197-761-2(4)) Spotlight.

Haskins, James. Moaning Bones: African-American Ghost Stories. Marshall, Felicia, illus. 1998. 64p. (YA). (gr. 2 up). 14.00 (978-0-688-16021-0(2)) HarperCollins Pubs.

Hayes, Joe. The Day It Snowed Tortillas: A Classic from the American Southwest. Castro Lopez, Antonio, illus. 2003. Tr. of El Dia Que Nevo Tortillas. (ENG & SPA.). 160p. (J). pap. 12.95 (978-0-938317-76-0(8)) Cinco Puntos Pr.

—Juan Verdades: The Man Who Couldn't Tell a Lie. Fiedler, Joseph Daniel, illus. 2001. (Juan Verdades Ser.). 32p. (J). (gr. 2-5). pap. 16.95 (978-0-439-29311-2(1) , Orchard Bks.) Scholastic, Inc.

—La Llorona (The Weeping Woman) Trego-Hill, Vicki, illus. 2004. (SPA & ENG.). 32p. (gr. 5-7). pap. 5.95 (978-0-938317-02-9(4) , CPP204X) Cinco Puntos Pr.

Hurst, Hawk. The Story of the First Flute: Based on an Ancient Cherokee Legend. Sharp, Lindley, illus. 2001. 16p. (J). 9.95 (978-1-887905-53-4(7)) Parkway Pubs., Inc.

Ippisch, Hanneke. Spotted Bear: A Rocky Mountain Folktale. Ort, Kathleen, ed. Rappe-Flowers, Hedvig, illus. rev. ed. 49p. (J). (gr. 3-4). 15.00 (978-0-87842-387-3(7) , 326) Mountain Pr. Publishing Co., Inc.

Jenson, Edgar M., illus. Sanpete Tales: Humorous Folklore from Central Utah. 1999. 150p. pap. 15.95 (978-1-56085-127-1(9)) Signature Bks., LLC.

Johnson, Paul Brett. Old Dry Frye: A Deliciously Funny Tall Tale. 2001. (Illus.). (J). (ps-ps). lib. bdg. 12.79 (978-0-606-22764-3(4)) Tandem Library Bks.

Johnson, Paul Brett, illus. & adapted by. Jack Outwits the Giants. Johnson, Paul Brett, adapted by. 2002. 32p. (J). (gr. k-3). 16.95 (978-0-689-83902-3(2) , McElderry, Margaret K.) Simon & Schuster Children's Publishing.

Journey Cake, Ho! 2004. pap. 14.95 incl. audio (978-0-7882-0613-9(3)) Weston Woods Studios, Inc.

Kellogg, Steven. Paul Bunyan. Kellogg, Steven, illus. 2006. (SPA.). 48p. (J). pap. 6.99 (978-0-06-088705-6(2)) HarperCollins Pubs.

Kessler, Brad. John Henry. Jackson, Barry, illus. 2005. (Rabbit Ears-A Classic Tale Ser.). 40p. (J). (gr. k-5). 25.65 (978-1-59197-764-3(9)) Spotlight.

Kessler, Brad & Harris, Joel Chandler. Brer Rabbit & Boss Lion. Mayer, Bill, illus. 2005. (Rabbit Ears-A Classic Tale Ser.). 40p. (J). (gr. k-5). 25.65 (978-1-59197-760-5(6)) Spotlight.

Krensky, Stephen, adapted by. John Henry. 2007. (On My Own Folklore Ser.). (Illus.). 48p. (J). (gr. 2-5). lib. bdg. 25.26 (978-1-57505-887-0(1) , Millbrook Pr.) Lerner Publishing Group.

Lester, Julius. John Henry. Pinkney, Jerry, illus. 2002. (J). 14.04 (978-0-7587-0123-7(3)) Book Wholesalers, Inc.

—John Henry. Pinkney, Jerry, illus. 1999. 40p. (J). (ps-17). pap. 7.99 (978-0-14-056622-2(8) , Puffin) Penguin Group (USA) Inc.

—John Henry. unabr. ed. 1998. (Illus.). (J). (ps-4). 24.95 incl. audio (978-0-7882-0682-5(6) , HRA377) Weston Woods Studios, Inc.

—Tales of Uncle Remus: The Adventures of Brer Rabbit. Pinkney, Jerry, illus. 2006. (Puffin Modern Classics Ser.). 160p. (J). (gr. 3). pap. 5.99 (978-0-14-240720-2(8) , Puffin) Penguin Group (USA) Inc.

Mathews, Judith. Nathaniel Willy, Scared Silly. 1999. (J). (978-0-606-18951-4(3)) Tandem Library Bks.

McGill, Alice. Way up & over Everything. 2005. (J). (978-0-618-38796-0(X)) Houghton Mifflin Co.

Metaxas, Eric. Stormalong. Vanderbeek, Don, illus. 2005. (Rabbit Ears-A Classic Tale Ser.). 40p. (J). (gr. k-5). 25.65 (978-1-59197-772-8(X)) Spotlight.

Moreno-Hinojosa, Hernan. The Ghostly Rider & Other Chilling Tales. 96p. (J). pap. 9.95 (978-1-55885-400-0(2) , Piñata Books) Arte Publico Pr.

Parker, Vic. North America. 2001. (Illus.). 48p. (J). lib. bdg. 24.25 (978-1-930643-39-0(X)) Chrysalis Education.

Philip, Neil. American Fairy Tales: From Rip Van Winkle to the Rootabaga Stories. 1998. (J). (978-0-606-13122-3(1)) Tandem Library Bks.

Raglin, Tim, illus. Pecos Bill. 2005. (Rabbit Ears-A Classic Tale Ser.). 40p. (J). (gr. k-5). 25.65 (978-1-59197-768-1(1)) Spotlight.

Rigby Education Staff. Paul Bunyan: Jumbled Tumble. (gr. k-2). 21.00 (978-0-7635-2425-8(5)) Rigby Education.

Robbins, Sandra. Big Annie: An American Tall Tale. Oseki, Iku, illus. 1998. (See-More's Stories Ser.). 32p. (J). (ps-4). pap. 11.95 incl. audio (978-1-882601-27-1(0)) See-More's Workshop.

Rosales, Melodye. Leola & the Honeybears. Rosales, Melodye, illus. 1999. (Illus.). 40p. (J). (ps-3). pap. 15.95 (978-0-590-38358-5(2) , Cartwheel Bks.) Scholastic, Inc.

Salish Culture Committee & Montana Historical Society Staff. Coyote Stories of the Montana Salish Indians. 1999. (Illus.). 64p. (ps up). pap. 9.95 (978-0-917298-61-5(6)) Montana Historical Society Pr.

San Souci, Robert D. Cut from the Same Cloth: American Women of Myth, Legend & Tall Tale. 2000. (gr. 3-6). lib. bdg. 15.30 (978-0-613-28458-5(5)) Tandem Library Bks.

—The Secret of the Stones: A Folktale. 2000. (Illus.). 40p. (J). (ps-3). 16.99 (978-0-8037-1640-7(0) , Dial) Penguin Group (USA) Inc.

—Six Foolish Fishermen. Kennedy, Doug, illus. 2000. 32p. (gr. k-3). 15.49 (978-0-7868-2335-2(6)) Hyperion Bks. for Children.

Shepard, Aaron. The Baker's Dozen: A Saint Nicholas Tale. 1999. (J). (978-0-606-17192-2(4)) Tandem Library Bks.

Stevens, Janet. Tops & Bottoms. Stevens, Janet, illus. 2002. (Illus.). (J). 23.40 (978-0-7587-0158-9(6)) Book Wholesalers, Inc.

—Tops & Bottoms. unabr. ed. 2001. (J). 26.95 incl. audio (978-0-8045-6837-1(5) , 6837) Spoken Arts, Inc.

Tate, Don, illus. The Hidden Feast: A Folktale from the American South. 2006. 32p. (J). 16.95 (978-0-87483-758-2(8)) August Hse. Pubs., Inc.

Vitale, Ann E. Regional Folklore. 2002. (North American Folklore Ser.). (Illus.). 112p. (YA). (gr. 7 up). lib. bdg. (978-1-59084-349-9(5)) Mason Crest Pubs.

Vogel, Carole Garbuny. Weather Legends: Native American Lore & the Science of Weather. 2001. (Illus.). 80p. (gr. 4-6). lib. bdg. 29.90 (978-0-7613-1900-9(X) , Millbrook Pr.) Lerner Publishing Group.

Willey, Margaret. Clever Beatrice. Solomon, Heather M., illus. 2004. 40p. (J). reprint ed. 6.99 (978-0-689-87068-2(X) , Aladdin) Simon & Schuster Children's Publishing.

—Clever Beatrice & the Best Little Pony. Solomon, Heather M., illus. 2004. 40p. (J). (ps-3). 16.95 (978-0-689-85339-5(4) , Atheneum) Simon & Schuster Children's Publishing.

FOLKLORE—VIETNAM

Garland, Sherry. Children of the Dragon: Selected Tales from Vietnam. Hyman, Trina Schart, illus. 2001. 64p. (YA). (gr. 3-7). 18.00 (978-0-15-224200-8(7)) Harcourt Children's Bks.

FOLKLORE—WALES

Jones, Gwyn E., ed. Welsh Legends & Folk Tales. 288p. (J). 3.99 (978-0-14-036770-6(5) , Puffin) Penguin Group (USA) Inc.

Jones, Jac, et al. Dianc. 2005. (WEL., Illus.). 39p. 5.99 (978-1-84323-372-5(X)) Gomer Pr. GBR. *Dist:* Gomer Pr.

Lewis, Sian. Cities in the Sea. Morris, Jackie, illus. 1998. 32p. (J). (gr. 2-6). 22.95 (978-0-8464-4637-8(5)) Beekman Bks., Inc.

Thomas, W. Jenkyn. The Welsh Fairy Book. 2001. (Illus.). 256p. (J). pap. 7.95 (978-0-486-41711-0(5)) Dover Pubns., Inc.

—The Welsh Fairy Book. 2001. (Illus.). 310p. (C). reprint ed. pap. 16.95 (978-0-7083-1257-5(8)) Univ. of Wales Pr. GBR. *Dist:* Chicago Distribution Ctr.

E
F
G

FOLKLORE—WEST INDIES

Gonzalez Egido, Luciano. The Bossy Gallito. 1999. Tr. of Bossy Little Rooster. (J). 12.79 (978-0-606-16651-5(3)) Tandem Library Bks.

Hamilton, Martha. Rooster's Night Out. 2007. (Story Cove Ser.). 32p. (J). pap. 3.95 (***978-0-87483-826-8(6)*** August Hse. Pubs., Inc.

San Souci, Robert D. The Faithful Friend. Pinkney, Brian, illus. 2002. (J). 15.53 (978-0-7587-0107-7(1)) Book Wholesalers, Inc.

—The Faithful Friend. Pinkney, Brian, illus. 1999. 40p. (J). (ps-ps). 6.99 (978-0-689-82458-6(0) , Aladdin) Simon & Schuster Children's Publishing.

FOLKWAYS

see Manners and Customs

FOOD

see also Beverages; Cookery; Diet; Farm Produce; Fruit; Markets; Nutrition; Nuts; Poultry; Vegetables; Vegetarianism; Vitamins

also names of foods, e.g. Bread, etc.

Aboff, Marcie. The Pizza Palace. Doerrfeld, Cori, illus. 2007. (J). lib. bdg. (***978-1-4048-3665-5(9))*** Picture Window Bks.

Abrams, Pam. Now I Eat My ABCs. Wolf, Bruce, illus. 2004. 14p. (J). (ps up). bds. 7.99 (978-0-439-64942-1(0) , Cartwheel Bks.) Scholastic, Inc.

Adams-Crymes, Phyllis. My First Meal, Vol. 2. Redel, Nicole, illus. 2000. (Children's Diary Ser.). (J). (gr. k-3). pap. (978-1-930659-02-5(4)) Adams-Crymes, Phyllis.

Alexander's Enrichment Activties. 2006. (J). pap. 5.95 (***978-0-9742806-6-0(6))*** Heart to Heart Publishing.

Allen, Julia & Iggulden, Margaret. Food & the World. 2005. (Your Environment Ser.). (Illus.). 32p. (J). (978-1-59604-065-6(3)) Stargazer Bks.

Allen, Nancy Kelly. Whose Food Is This: A Look at What Animals Eat - Seeds, Bugs, & Nuts. Alderman, Derrick & Shea, Denise, illus. 2004. (Whose Is It? Ser.). 24p. (C). (gr. k-2). 22.60 (978-1-4048-0607-8(5)) Picture Window Bks.

Allsop, Marcus. We Like to Help Cook. Iverson, Diane, illus. 2007. 32p. (J). pap. 9.95 (***978-1-890772-70-3(4))*** Hohm Pr.

Ashworth, Sue. Snacks. 2004. (World of Recipes Ser.). (Illus.). 48p. (J). lib. bdg. (978-1-4034-4700-5(4)) Heinemann Library.

Ball, Jacqueline A. Food Creations: From Hot Dogs to Ice Cream Cones. 2006. (Which Came First? Ser.). (Illus.). 32p. (J). lib. bdg. 25.27 (978-1-59716-130-5(6)) Bearport Publishing Co., Inc.

Ballard, Carol. Special Diets & Food Allergies. 2006. (Making Healthy Food Choices Ser.). (Illus.). 56p. (J). (978-1-4034-8572-4(0)) Heinemann Library.

Basel, Roberta. From Corn to Cereal. 2005. (First Facts Ser.). (Illus.). 24p. (J). (ps-7). lib. bdg. 21.26 (978-0-7368-4284-6(5)) Capstone Pr., Inc.

—From Milk to Cheese. 2005. (First Facts Ser.). (Illus.). 24p. (J). (ps-7). lib. bdg. 21.26 (978-0-7368-4285-3(3)) Capstone Pr., Inc.

Bellamy, Rufus. Food for All. 2005. (Action for the Environment Ser.). (Illus.). 32p. (J). (gr. 4-7). lib. bdg. 27.10 (978-1-58340-598-7(4) , 1247276) Smart Apple Media.

Benduhn, Tea. Meat & Beans. 2007. (J). pap. (***978-0-8368-8259-9(8));*** 24p. lib. bdg. 19.93 (***978-0-8368-8252-0(0))*** Stevens, Gareth Inc. (Weekly Reader Early Learning Library).

—Meat & Beans: Carne y Legumbres. 2007. (SPA & ENG.). (J). pap. (***978-0-8368-8463-0(9)*** , Weekly Reader Early Learning Library) Stevens, Gareth Inc.

—Meat & Beans/Carne y Legumbres. 2007. (Find Out about Food/Conoce la Comida Ser.). (SPA & ENG.). 24p. (J). (gr. k-2). lib. bdg. 19.93 (***978-0-8368-8456-2(6)*** , Weekly Reader Early Learning Library) Stevens, Gareth Inc.

—Oils: Aceites. 2007. (SPA & ENG.). (J). pap. (***978-0-8368-8465-4(5)*** , Weekly Reader Early Learning Library) Stevens, Gareth Inc.

—Oils/Aceites. 2007. (Find Out about Food/Conoce la Comida Ser.). (SPA & ENG.). 24p. (J). (gr. k-2). lib. bdg. 19.93 (***978-0-8368-8458-6(2)*** , Weekly Reader Early Learning Library) Stevens, Gareth Inc.

Bentley, Joyce. Beans. 2005. (Illus.). 32p. (J). (gr. 2 up). lib. bdg. 27.10 (978-1-59389-217-3(9)) Chrysalis Education.

—Pasta. 2005. (Illus.). 32p. (J). (gr. 2 up). lib. bdg. 27.10 (978-1-59389-221-0(7)) Chrysalis Education.

Berendes, Mary. Food/la Comida. 2007. (WordBooks/Libros de Palabras Ser.). (SPA & ENG.). 24p. (J). 19.93 (***978-1-59296-798-8(1))*** Child's World, Inc.

Bickerstaff, Linda. Nutrition Sense: Counting Calories, Figuring Out Fats, & Eating Balanced Meals. 2004. (Library of Nutrition). (Illus.). 48p. (J). lib. bdg. 25.25 (978-1-4042-0299-3(4)) Rosen Publishing Group, Inc., The.

Blackbirch Press Staff, creator. Eaters. 2005. (Planet's Most Extreme Ser.). (Illus.). 48p. (J). (ps-7). lib. bdg. 24.95 (978-1-4103-0401-8(9) , Blackbirch Pr., Inc.) Thomson Gale.

Blevins, Wiley. Food. Pillo, Cary, illus. 1999. (Scholastic At-Home Phonics Reading Program Ser.: Vol. 27). 16p. (J). (978-0-590-68759-1(X)) Scholastic, Inc.

Bolchazy, Marie Carducci. Quis Me Amat?/Who Loves Me? 2003. (I Am Reading Latin Ser.). (ENG & LAT., Illus.). 64p. (J). (gr. k-3). 12.00 (978-0-86516-541-0(6)) Bolchazy-Carducci Pubs.

—What Will I Eat? Quid Edam? Fraczak, Michelle Kathryn, illus. 2002. (I Am Reading Latin Ser.). (LAT & ENG.). 64p. (J). 12.00 (978-0-86516-542-7(4)) Bolchazy-Carducci Pubs.

Boothroyd, Jennifer. Foods. 2006. (First Step Nonfiction Ser.). (Illus.). 8p. (J). pap. (978-0-8225-5727-2(4) , Lerner Pubns.) Lerner Publishing Group.

Brown, Susan. Comidas/Food. 2005. 80p. (J). per. 9.99 (978-1-59441-399-5(1) , FI-704002) Carson-Dellosa Publishing Co., Inc.

Bullard, Lisa. Brown Food Fun. 2006. (A+ Books). (Illus.). 32p. (J). (978-0-7368-5380-4(4)) Capstone Pr., Inc.

—Green Food Fun. 2006. (A+ Books). (Illus.). 32p. (J). (978-0-7368-5381-1(2)) Capstone Pr., Inc.

—Orange Food Fun. 2006. (A+ Books). (Illus.). 32p. (J). (978-0-7368-5382-8(0)) Capstone Pr., Inc.

—Red Food Fun. 2006. (A+ Books). (Illus.). 32p. (J). (978-0-7368-5383-5(9)) Capstone Pr., Inc.

—White Food Fun. 2006. (A+ Books). (Illus.). 32p. (J). (978-0-7368-5384-2(7)) Capstone Pr., Inc.

—Yellow Food Fun. 2006. (A+ Books). (Illus.). 32p. (J). (978-0-7368-5385-9(5)) Capstone Pr., Inc.

Bulloch, Ivan & James, Diane. Tomate, Lechuga, Cuchara y Tenedor. 2004. (Me Toca a Mi Ser.). (SPA., Illus.). 12p. (J). (ps-k). bds. 6.95 (978-1-58728-492-2(8) , Two Can Publishing) T&N Children's Publishing.

Burckhardt, Ann L. Alimentos (Foods), 2 bks. Incl. Calabazas. lib. bdg. 18.60 (978-1-56065-786-6(3) , CAP1291); Manzanas. lib. bdg. 18.60 (978-1-56065-785-9(5) , CAP1388); 24p. (J). (gr. k-3). 1998. (SPA., Illus.). Set lib. bdg. 37.20 (978-0-7368-0144-7(8) , Bridgestone Bks.) Capstone Pr., Inc.

—Foods, 4 bks. Incl. Apples. lib. bdg. 18.60 (978-1-56065-448-3(1)); Corn. lib. bdg. 18.60 (978-1-56065-450-6(3)); Potatoes. lib. bdg. 18.60 (978-1-56065-451-3(1)); Pumpkins. lib. bdg. 18.60 (978-1-56065-449-0(X)); 24p. (J). (gr. 1-2). 1996. (Illus.). Set lib. bdg. 74.40 (978-1-56065-633-3(6) , Bridgestone Bks.) Capstone Pr., Inc.

Burton, Margie, et al. Food Around the World. Adams, Alison, ed. 1999. (Early Connections Ser.). 16p. (J). (gr. k-2). pap. 4.50 (978-1-58344-061-2(5)) Benchmark Education Co.

Butler, Daphne. What Happens When Food Cooks? 2004. (Illus.). 31p. (J). (gr. k-4). reprint ed. 10.00 (978-0-7567-7561-2(2)) DIANE Publishing Co.

Carle, Eric. My Very First Book of Food. Carle, Eric, illus. 2007. 10p. (J). (ps). bds. 5.99 (978-0-399-24747-7(5) , Philomel) Penguin Group (USA) Inc.

—Today Is Monday. Carle, Eric, illus. 2002. (Illus.). (J). 14.04 (978-0-7587-3823-3(4)) Book Wholesalers, Inc.

—Today Is Monday. Carle, Eric, illus. 2001. (Illus.). 1p. (J). (ps-k). bds. 6.99 (978-0-399-23605-1(8) , Philomel) Penguin Group (USA) Inc.

Cesa, Irene, ed. Chemistry of Food, 28 vols. 2003. (ChemTopic Labs Ser.: 23). (Illus.). 96p. (YA). pap. 11.95 (978-1-877991-91-2(0)) Flinn Scientific, Inc.

Cipriano, Jeri S. Harvest Time. (Social Studies). (Illus.). (J). 2004. 16p. lib. bdg. 15.93 (978-0-7368-2926-7(1) , Yellow Umbrella Bks.); 2003. 17p. pap. (978-0-7368-2885-7(0)) Capstone Pr., Inc.

Clark, Joan & Taylor, Dorothy J. Food - 2. 2004. (Topic Bks.). (Illus.). 36p. bds. 5.00 (978-0-7188-1787-9(7)) Lutherworth Pr., The GBR. *Dist:* Parkwest Pubns., Inc.

Cobb, Vicki. Junk Food. 2006. (Where's the Science Here? Ser.). (Illus.). 48p. (J). (gr. 3-5). 23.93 (978-0-7613-2773-8(8) , Millbrook Pr.) Lerner Publishing Group.

Collins, S. H. Food Signs: Early Sign Language. 2002. (Beginning Sign Language Ser.). (Illus.). 26p. (J). bds. 6.95 (978-1-930820-09-8(7) , GP-109) Garlic Pr.

Counting Is Fun with Food. 1998. (Illus.). 7p. (J). 8.99 (978-1-929174-11-9(X)) Oshkosh B'Gosh, Inc.

A Day at the Playground. 2004. (J). pap. 12.95 (***978-1-59526-606-4(2))*** Media Creations, Inc.

Dingles, Molly. Crescent Kitchen. Brodie, Neale, illus. 2006. (Community of Shapes Ser.). (J). (***978-1-59646-049-2(0))*** Dingles & Co.

Dinner: KinderWords Individual Title, 6 packs. (Kinderstarters Ser.). 8p. (ps-1). 21.00 (978-0-7635-8702-4(8)) Rigby Education.

DK Publishing Staff. My Food Pyramid. 2007. 32p. (J). (gr. k-3). 5.99 (978-0-7566-2992-2(6)); 15.99 (978-0-7566-2993-9(4)) Dorling Kindersley Publishing, Inc.

Doering, Amanda. Food ABC: An Alphabet Book. 2004. 17p. (J). 22.60 (978-0-7368-2610-5(6) , Aplus Bks.) Capstone Pr., Inc.

Dorling Kindersley Publishing Staff. French Cheese. 2005. (Eyewitness Companions Ser.). (Illus.). 288p. pap. 20.00 (978-0-7566-1402-7(3)) Dorling Kindersley Publishing, Inc.

Dorling Kindersley Publishing Staff & Millard, Anne. Mealtime. 2002. (Touch & Feel Ser.). (Illus.). 12p. (J). (ps-k). bds. 6.95 (978-0-7894-8537-3(0)) Dorling Kindersley Publishing, Inc.

Eat Right. (Your Health Ser.). 24p. (J). 6.95 (978-0-7368-4451-2(1)) Capstone Pr., Inc.

Eat Well. 2002. (YA). 21.95 (978-1-58810-135-8(5)) Heinemann Library.

Eating Food, 6 Pks. (Sails Literacy Ser.). (gr. 1-2). 36.00 (978-0-7578-4023-4(X)) Rigby Education.

Eck, Kristin. Hide-and-Seek Food. 2004. (Hide-And-Seek Books). (Illus.). 16p. (J). lib. bdg. 7.95 (978-1-4042-2703-3(2) , PowerKids Pr.) Rosen Publishing Group, Inc., The.

Egendorf, Laura K. Food Safety. 2000. (At Issue Ser.). (Illus.). 126p. (gr. 9-12). (J). lib. bdg. 26.20 (978-0-7377-0151-7(X)); (YA). pap. 17.45 (978-0-7377-0150-0(1)) Thomson Gale. (Greenhaven Pr., Inc.).

Ehrlich, Fred. Does a Camel Cook? Early Experiences. Bolam, Emily, illus. 2007. 32p. (J). 13.50 (978-1-59354-588-6(6)) Handprint Bks.

—Does a Camel Cook? Early Experiences. Bolam, Emily, illus. 2007. 28p. pap. 5.95 (978-1-59354-595-6(9)) Blue Apple Bks.

Evening Meals around the World. (Meals Around the World Ser.). 24p. (J). 7.95 (978-1-4048-1132-4(X)) Picture Window Bks.

Faiella, Graham. The Food Pyramid & Basic Nutrition: Assembling the Building Blocks of a Healthy Diet. 2004. (Library of Nutrition). (Illus.). 48p. (J). lib. bdg. 25.25 (978-1-4042-0304-4(4)) Rosen Publishing Group, Inc., The.

Fandel, Jennifer. Louis Pasteur & Pasteurization. Wilson, Keith et al, illus. 2007. 32p. (***978-0-7368-6844-0(5))*** Capstone Pr., Inc.

Farndon, John. From DNA to GM Wheat: Discovering Genetically Modified Food. 2006. (Chain Reactions Ser.). (Illus.). 64p. (J). (978-1-4034-8841-1(X)) Heinemann Library.

Fiedler, Julie. Learning about Food Chains & Food Webs with Graphic Organizers. 2007. (Graphic Organizers in Science Ser.). (Illus.). 24p. (J). (978-1-4042-2397-4(5)); pap. (978-1-4042-2207-6(3)) Rosen Publishing Group, Inc., The. (PowerKids Pr.).

Fischer, Jean. God Gives Us Food. Brooks, Nan & Ring, Laura, eds. 1999. (Handle Board Bks.). (Illus.). 10p. (ps up). 2.99 (978-0-7847-0906-1(8) , 04271, Bean Sprouts) Standard Publishing.

Fisher, Enid Broderick. Food & Health. 1998. (Good Health Guides). (Illus.). 32p. (J). (gr. 4 up). lib. bdg. 22.60 (978-0-8368-2178-9(5)) Stevens, Gareth Inc.

Fleisher, Paul. Forest Food Webs. 2007. (Early Bird Food Webs Ser.). 48p. (J). (gr. 2-5). 26.60 (***978-0-8225-6729-5(6)*** , Lerner Pubns.) Lerner Publishing Group.

Fontes, Justine & Fontes, Ron. Proteins. 2006. 32p. (J). (gr. k-2). pap. 5.95 (978-0-516-24650-5(X) , Children's Pr.) Scholastic Library Publishing.

Fontes, Ron. Proteins. 2005. (Rookie Read-About Health Ser.). (Illus.). 31p. (J). (ps-ps). 20.50 (978-0-516-23647-6(4) , Children's Pr.) Scholastic Library Publishing.

Food, Set 2. 2003. (Illus.). (J). lib. bdg. 128.16 (978-1-58810-621-6(7)) Heinemann Library.

Food - Set1: Outside-Inside-Name. 2004. (J). spiral bd. 23.40 (978-0-9770248-1-0(4)) Sidedoor Publishing LLC.

Food & Festival, 12 bks., Set. 2000. (Illus.). (J). (978-0-7398-4190-7(4)) Raintree.

Food & Festivals, 6 vols. 1999. (Illus.). (J). 154.14 (978-0-7398-1506-9(7)) Raintree.

Food Fit for a King: 3-in-1 Package. (Sails Literacy Ser.). 24p. (gr. 2 up). 57.00 (978-0-7578-3215-4(6)) Rigby Education.

Food Fit for a King: 6 Small Books. (Sails Literacy Ser.). 24p. (gr. 2 up). 25.00 (978-0-7578-3191-1(5)) Rigby Education.

Food Fit for a King: Big Book Only. (Sails Literacy Ser.). 24p. (gr. 2 up). 27.00 (978-0-7635-6997-6(6)) Rigby Education.

Food for Healthy Teeth, 6 vols. (gr. k-2). 28.95 (978-0-7368-8138-8(7)) Red Brick Learning.

Food from the Water: Individual Title Six-Packs. (Sails Literacy Ser.). (gr. 1-2). 36.00 (978-0-7578-4025-8(6)) Rigby Education.

Food Groups. 2004. (Illus.). lib. bdg. 7.95 (978-0-8225-4787-7(2)) Lerner Publishing Group.

The Food Guide Pyramid Set. (gr. k-2). 230.95 (978-0-7368-9037-3(8)) Red Brick Learning.

The Food Journey: Individual Title Six-Packs. (gr. k-1). 23.00 (978-0-7635-9045-1(2)) Rigby Education.

Food Signs: Flip Charts. (J). spiral bd. 15.95 (978-1-930820-36-4(4)) Garlic Pr.

Foods of the World, 6 vols. (Book2WebTM Ser.). (gr. 4-8). 36.50 (978-0-322-02985-9(6)) Wright Group, The.

Fowler, Allan. The Wheat We Eat. 2000. (Rookie Read-About Science Ser.). (Illus.). 32p. (J). (gr. 1-2). pap. 4.95 (978-0-516-26569-8(5) , Children's Pr.) Scholastic Library Publishing.

Francis, Suzanne. How to Make an Egg Swim, Grow Mold, Eat "Ants," & Other Ways to Play with Your Food. 2004. (How to Survive Anything Club Ser.). (Illus.). 80p. (J). (978-0-439 57009-4(0)) Scholastic, Inc.

Freedman, Jeri. Everything You Need to Know about Genetically Modified Foods. 2005. (Need to Know Library). (Illus.). 64p. (YA). (gr. 4-6). lib. bdg. 25.25 (978-0-8239-3612-0(0)) Rosen Publishing Group, Inc., The.

Frost, Helen. Eating Right. Saunders-Smith, Gail, ed. 2000. (Food Guide Pyramid Ser.). (Illus.). 24p. (J). (gr. k-1). lib. bdg. 15.93 (978-0-7368-0535-3(4) , Pebble Bks.) Capstone Pr., Inc.

—The Food Guide Pyramid, 8 bks. Saunders-Smith, Gail, ed. Incl. Dairy Group. lib. bdg. 15.93 (978-0-7368-0540-7(0)); Drinking Water. lib. bdg. 15.93 (978-0-7368-0534-6(6)); Eating Right. lib. bdg. 15.93 (978-0-7368-0535-3(4)); Fats, Oils & Sweets. lib. bdg. 15.93 (978-0-7368-0536-0(2)); Fruit Group. lib. bdg. 15.93 (978-0-7368-0537-7(0)); Grain Group. lib. bdg. 15.93 (978-0-7368-0538-4(9)); Meat & Protein Group. lib. bdg. 15.93 (978-0-7368-0539-1(7)); Vegetable Group. lib. bdg. 15.93 (978-0-7368-0541-4(9)); 24p. (J). (gr. k-1). (Illus.). 2000. Set lib. bdg. 127.44 (978-0-7368-0561-2(3) , Pebble Bks.) Capstone Pr., Inc.

—The Meat & Protein Group. Saunders-Smith, Gail, ed. 2000. (Food Guide Pyramid Ser.). (Illus.). 24p. (J). (gr. k-1). lib. bdg. 15.93 (978-0-7368-0539-1(7) , Pebble Bks.) Capstone Pr., Inc.

Fun with Food Discover & Do. 2006. (J). pap. (***978-1-57332-394-9(2))*** HighReach Learning, Inc.

Ganeri, Anita. Religious Food. 1999. (What's Sacred to Me Ser.). (Illus.). 32p. (J). (ps-3). lib. bdg. 25.69 (978-0-7398-2762-8(6)) Raintree.

—Religious Food. 2001. (What's Sacred to Me Ser.). (Illus.). 32p. (J). (ps-3). pap. 10.34 (978-0-7398-3124-3(0)) Steck-Vaughn.

—Religious Food. 2000. (gr. k-3). lib. bdg. 17.60 (978-0-613-74050-0(5)) Tandem Library Bks.

Gifford, Clive. Food Technology. 2004. (World Issues Ser.). (J). lib. bdg. 28.50 (978-1-59389-152-7(0)) Chrysalis Education.

Gillis, Jennifer Blizin. Unusual Farms. 2004. (Let's See Ser.). (Illus.). 24p. (J). (gr. 1 up). lib. bdg. 19.93 (978-0-7565-0668-1(9)) Compass Point Bks.

Good Food. 2005. (Emergent (Prek-2) Health Package Ser.). 12p. (YA). (ps-2). 25.20 (978-0-8215-7847-6(2)) Sadlier, William H. Inc.

Good to Eat: Individual Title Six-Packs. (Rigby Focus Ser.). 16p. (gr. 1 up). 28.00 (978-0-7578-5314-2(5)); 30.00 (978-0-7578-5546-7(6)) Rigby Education.

Gordon, Sharon. Food Safety. 2002. (Rookie Read-About Health Ser.). (Illus.). 32p. (J). (gr. k-2). pap. 5.95 (978-0-516-25988-8(1) , Children's Pr.) Scholastic Library Publishing.

—Food Safety. 2001. (gr. k-3). lib. bdg. 14.10 (978-0-613-50692-2(8)) Tandem Library Bks.

Gordon, Sherri Mabry. Peanut Butter, Milk, & Other Deadly Threats: What You Should Know about Food Allergies. 2006. (Issues in Focus Today). (Illus.). 104p. (J). lib. bdg. 31.93 (978-0-7660-2529-5(2)) Enslow Pubs., Inc.

Green, Jen. Genetically Modified Food. 2005. (Your Environment Ser.). (Illus.). 32p. (J). (gr. 4-17). lib. bdg. 27.10 (978-1-59604-058-8(0)) Stargazer Bks.

Greenaway, Theresa. Food Chains. 2000. (Cycles in Nature Ser.). (Illus.). 32p. (J). (gr. 2-4). lib. bdg. 25.69 (978-0-7398-2730-7(8)) Raintree.

Group/McGraw-Hill, Wright. Set 1: Los Alimentos, 6 vols. (First Explorers. Primeros Exploradores Nonfiction Sets Ser.). (SPA.). (gr. 1-2). 29.95 (978-0-7699-1469-5(1)) Shortland Pubns. (U. S. A.) Inc.

Hall, Margaret. Food. (Around the World Ser.). 32p. pap. 6.95 (978-1-4034-4004-4(2)) Heinemann Library.

Hall, Margaret C. Food. 2001. (Around the World Ser.). (Illus.). 32p. (J). (gr. k-2). lib. bdg. 21.36 (978-1-58810-102-0(9)) Heinemann Library.

Harcourt School Publishers Staff. The Food on Your Plate. 3rd ed. 2002. (Trophies English Language Learners Ser.). (Illus.). pap. 5.10 (978-0-15-327778-8(5)) Harcourt Schl. Pubs.

—Harcourt Science: What Is a Food Chain Reader. 1999. pap. 3.10 (978-0-15-314865-1(9)) Harcourt Schl. Pubs.

—A Peanut, an Apple & Toast: Library Book. 1999. (Collections Ser.). (Illus.). pap. 14.90 (978-0-15-313399-2(6)) Harcourt Schl. Pubs.

—Time for Breakfast. 3rd ed. 2002. (Trophies English Language Learners Ser.). (Illus.). pap. 5.10 (978-0-15-327631-6(2)) Harcourt Schl. Pubs.

Harmon, Daniel E. The Food & Drug Administration. 2002. (Your Government Ser.). 64p. (J). (gr. 4-7). 25.00 (978-0-7910-6791-8(2) , Chelsea Hse.) Facts On File, Inc.

Hawes, Alison. My Breakfast: Individual Title Six-Pack Pouch - Level D. (Lighthouse Ser.). 12p. (gr. k-1). 24.00 (978-0-7578-0827-2(1)) Rigby Education.

Hayhurst, Chris. Everything You Need to Know about Food Additives. 2005. (Need to Know Library). (Illus.). 64p. (YA). (gr. 4-6). lib. bdg. 25.25 (978-0-8239-3548-2(5)) Rosen Publishing Group, Inc., The.

Hazan, Maurice, creator. Resto Presto. 2000. (SPA.). (J). 120.00 (978-1-932770-42-1(9) , SG3) Symtalk, Inc.

Holt, Rinehart and Winston Staff. Environmental Science Chptr. 15: Food & Agriculture. 4th ed. Date not set. pap. 11.20 (978-0-03-068076-2(X)) Holt, Rinehart & Winston.

Hosack, Karen. Food. 2004. (J). lib. bdg. 24.22 (978-1-4034-4852-1(3)) Heinemann Library.

Hughes, Meredith Sayles. Flavor Foods: Spices & Herbs. 2005. (Plants We Eat Ser.). (Illus.). 104p. (gr. 6-9). 26.60 (978-0-8225-2835-7(5)) Lerner Publishing Group.

Hunt, Angela Elwell. Pretzels by the Dozen: A Story with a Twist. 2002. (Illus.). 32p. (J). 14.99 (978-0-310-70173-6(2)) Zonderkidz.

Immell, Myra H., ed. Eating Disorders. 1998. (Contemporary Issues Companion Ser.). 191p. (YA). (gr. 9-12). lib. bdg. 32.45 (978-1-56510-895-0(7) , Greenhaven Pr., Inc.) Thomson Gale.

James, Diane. Tasty Treats. 2004. (Jigsaw Rhymes Ser.). (Illus.). 12p. (J). (ps-k). bds. 9.95 (978-1-58728-023-8(X) , Two Can Publishing) T&N Children's Publishing.

—Tomato, Lettuce & Wriggly Worms! Bulloch, Ivan, illus. 2004. (My Turn Ser.). 12p. (J). (ps-k). bds. 6.95 (978-1-58728-339-0(5) , Two Can Publishing) T&N Children's Publishing.

—What We Eat: A First Look at Food. Lynn, Sara, illus. rev. ed. 2000. (Play & Discover Ser.). (J). (ps). 32p. pap. 4.95 (978-1-58728-045-0(0)); 9.95 (978-1-58728-041-2(8)) T&N Children's Publishing. (Two Can Publishing).

Jones, Charlotte Foltz. Eat Your Words! A Fascinating Look at the Language of Food. 2000. (Illus.). (J). (978-0-606-17996-6(8)) Tandem Library Bks.

Judy/Instructo. Food Groups Roundup. 2001. (Science Card Games Ser.). (J). (gr. 1-2). 3.99 (978-0-7682-1976-0(0) , J53004) School Specialty Publishing.

Julius, Jennifer. I Like Cereal. 2001. (Welcome Bks.). (Illus.). 24p. (J). (ps-2). pap. 4.95 (978-0-516-23055-9(7) , Children's Pr.) Scholastic Library Publishing.

—I Like Cereal. 2001. (gr. k-3). lib. bdg. 12.95 (978-0-613-52083-6(1)) Tandem Library Bks.

Julius, Jennifer & Pickering, Robin. Good Food, 12 bks., Set. 2004. (Illus.). 24p. (J). (ps-2). 174.00 (978-0-516-23226-3(6) , Children's Pr.) Scholastic Library Publishing.

Kalman, Bobbie. Food Chains & You. 2004. (Food Chains Ser.). (Illus.). 32p. (J). (978-0-7787-1942-7(1)) Crabtree Publishing Co.

—Forest Food Chains. 2004. (Food Chains Ser.). (Illus.). 32p. (J). (978-0-7787-1943-4(X)) Crabtree Publishing Co.

E F G

—Multicultural Meals. 2003. (gr. 3-6). lib. bdg. 17.60 (978-0-613-87232-4(0)) Tandem Library Bks.

—Multicultural Meals: Step-by-Step Healthy Recipes for Kids. 2003. (Kid Power Ser.). (Illus.). 32p. (J). (gr. 3). (978-0-7787-1255-8(9)); pap. (978-0-7787-1277-0(X)) Crabtree Publishing Co.

—Super Snacks: Step-by-Step Recipes. 2003. (Kid Power Ser.). (Illus.). 32p. (J). (gr. 3). (978-0-7787-1252-7(4)); pap. (978-0-7787-1274-9(5)) Crabtree Publishing Co.

Kalman, Bobbie & MacAulay, Kelley. Desert Food Chains. 2004. (Food Chains Ser.). (Illus.). 32p. (J). (978-0-7787-1944-1(8)); pap. (978-0-7787-1990-8(1)) Crabtree Publishing Co.

—Meadow Food Chains. 2004. (Food Chains Ser.). (Illus.). 32p. (J). (978-0-7787-1945-8(6)) Crabtree Publishing Co.

Keller, Kristin Thoennes. Peanuts to Peanut Butter. 2004. (First Facts Ser.). 24p. (J). lib. bdg. 21.26 (978-0-7368-2637-2(8)) Capstone Pr., Inc.

Keoke, Emory Dean & Porterfield, Kay Marie. Food, Farming, & Hunting. 2005. (American Indian Contributions to the World Ser.). (Illus.). 160p. (J). (gr. 4-9). 35.00 (978-0-8160-5393-3(6)) Facts On File, Inc.

King, Hazel & Shepard, Tristram. Food Technology for Key Stage 3. 2000. (Design & Make It Ser.). (Illus.). 144p. (J). (gr. 6-9). pap., stu. ed. 22.50 (978-0-7487-4427-5(4)) Nelson Thornes Ltd. GBR. *Dist:* Trans-Atlantic Pubns., Inc.

Klingel, Cynthia Fitterer & Noyed, Robert B. Bread & Cereal. Andersen, Gregg, photos by. 2002. (Weekly Reader Early Learning Library). (Illus.). 24p. (J). (ps up). pap. 5.95 (978-0-8368-3144-3(6) , Weekly Reader Early Learning Library) Stevens, Gareth Inc.

—Fats & Sweets. Andersen, Gregg, photos by. 2002. (Weekly Reader Early Learning Library). (Illus.). 24p. (J). (ps up). pap. 7.93 (978-0-8368-3145-0(4)); lib. bdg. 19.33 (978-0-8368-3056-9(3)) Stevens, Gareth Inc. (Weekly Reader Early Learning Library).

—Fruit. Andersen, Gregg, photos by. 2002. (Weekly Reader Early Learning Library). (Illus.). 24p. (J). (ps up). pap. 5.95 (978-0-8368-3146-7(2)); lib. bdg. 19.33 (978-0-8368-3057-6(1)) Stevens, Gareth Inc. (Weekly Reader Early Learning Library).

—Let's Read about Food, 6 bks. Andersen, Gregg, photos by. Incl. Bread & Cereal. pap. 5.95 (978-0-8368-3144-3(6)); Fats & Sweets. pap. 7.93 (978-0-8368-3145-0(4)); Fruit. pap. 5.95 (978-0-8368-3146-7(2)); Meat. pap. 5.95 (978-0-8368-3147-4(0)); Milk & Cheese. pap. 5.95 (978-0-8368-3148-1(9)); Vegetables. pap. 7.93 (978-0-8368-3149-8(7)); (J). (ps up). (Illus.). 24p. 2002. pap. (978-0-8368-3143-6(8)); Set lib. bdg. 115.98 (978-0-8368-3054-5(7)) Stevens, Gareth Inc. (Weekly Reader Early Learning Library).

—Meat. Andersen, Gregg, photos by. 2002. (Weekly Reader Early Learning Library). (Illus.). 24p. (J). (ps up). pap. 5.95 (978-0-8368-3147-4(0)); lib. bdg. 19.33 (978-0-8368-3058-3(X)) Stevens, Gareth Inc. (Weekly Reader Early Learning Library).

—Milk & Cheese. Andersen, Gregg, photos by. 2002. (Weekly Reader Early Learning Library). (Illus.). 24p. (J). (ps up). pap. 5.95 (978-0-8368-3148-1(9)); lib. bdg. 19.33 (978-0-8368-3059-0(8)) Stevens, Gareth Inc. (Weekly Reader Early Learning Library).

—Vegetables. Andersen, Gregg, photos by. 2002. (Weekly Reader Early Learning Library). (Illus.). 24p. (J). (ps up). pap. 7.93 (978-0-8368-3149-8(7)); lib. bdg. 19.33 (978-0-8368-3060-6(1)) Stevens, Gareth Inc. (Weekly Reader Early Learning Library).

Kompelien, Tracy. Ahi to Ziti: Food from A to Z. 2007. (Let's See A to Z Ser.). (ENG., Illus.). 32p. (J). (ps-3). lib. bdg. 25.65 (***978-1-59928-880-2(X)*** , Super SandCastle) ABDO Publishing Co.

Kramer, Barbara. The Founders of Famous Food Companies. 2002. (Collective Biographies Ser.). (Illus.). 112p. (YA). (gr. 6-12). lib. bdg. 26.60 (978-0-7660-1537-1(8)) Enslow Pubs., Inc.

Kroll, Mary. Cycling Back to Nature: Food Production & Pesticides. Clapp, Katie & Hoff, Mary, eds. 1998. (Illus.). 94p. (J). (gr. k-12). pap. 30.00 (978-0-7881-4297-0(6)) DIANE Publishing Co.

Kuntz, Lynn & Fleming, Jan. American Grub: Eats for Kids from All Fifty States. Hicks, Mark A., illus. 2003. 80p. (YA). pap. 7.95 (978-1-58685-260-3(4)) Gibbs Smith, Publisher.

Lakin, Patricia. Food: Around the World. 1999. (We All Share Ser.). (Illus.). 32p. (J). (gr. 3-6). 22.45 (978-1-56711-147-7(5) , Blackbirch Pr., Inc.) Thomson Gale.

Lambert, Angela. Food. 2006. (All Change! Ser.). (Illus.). 10p. (YA). (ps). 6.99 (978-1-904550-18-1(5)) Child's Play-International.

Landau, Elaine. A Healthy Diet. 2003. (Watts Library). (Illus.). 64p. (J). 25.50 (978-0-531-12027-9(9) , Watts, Franklin) Scholastic Library Publishing.

Lappi, Megan. Decomposers. 2004. (Nature's Food Chain Ser.). (Illus.). 24p. (J). lib. bdg. (978-1-59036-239-6(X)) Weigl Pubs., Inc.

Leap Frog Frogalicious Foods Wipe off Mat. 2006. (J). 3.95 (***978-1-59545-091-3(2)***) Learning Horizons, Inc.

LeapFrog Staff, compiled by. Food: (Blue Book) 2002. (J). (ps-2). 19.95 (978-1-58605-700-8(6)) LeapFrog Enterprises, Inc.

—Food: (Green Book) 2002. (J). (ps-2). 19.95 (978-1-58605-698-8(0)) LeapFrog Enterprises, Inc.

—Food: (Orange Book) 2002. (J). (ps-2). 19.95 (978-1-58605-699-5(9)) LeapFrog Enterprises, Inc.

—Food: (Purple Book) 2002. (J). (ps-2). 19.95 (978-1-58605-697-1(2)) LeapFrog Enterprises, Inc.

Leonard, Marcia. Food Is Fun! Handelman, Dorothy, photos by. 2000. (Hanna Bks.). (Illus.). 24p. (J). (ps up). 7.95 (978-0-694-01366-1(8)) HarperCollins Pubs.

The Letter Cc: Food, 6 vols. (gr. k-2). 17.50 (978-0-7368-4102-3(4)) Red Brick Learning.

The Letter Pp: Healthy Foods, 6 vols. (gr. k-2). 17.50 (978-0-7368-4115-3(6)) Red Brick Learning.

Litchfield, J. My Food. 2004. (Rattle Books). 16p. (J). 4.95 (978-0-7945-0053-5(6) , Usborne) EDC Publishing.

Llewellyn, Claire. Eating. 2004. (J). pap. 27.10 (978-1-58340-436-2(8)) Smart Apple Media.

Llewellyn, Claire. Your Food. 2007. (J). (***978-1-59771-098-5(9)***) Sea-To-Sea Pubns.

Lobb, Janice. Munch! Crunch! What's for Lunch? Experiments in the Kitchen. Savage, Ann & Utton, Peter, illus. 2002. (At Home with Science Ser.). 32p. (J). pap. 5.95 (978-0-7534-5460-2(2) , Kingfisher) Houghton Mifflin Co. Trade & Reference Div.

Lochmann, Christina, et al. Pop'n Kimchi. 1998. (Illus.). (J). 13.95 (978-1-879965-17-1(8)) Polychrome Publishing Corp.

MacDonald, Fiona. Food. (Discovering World Cultures Ser.). (Illus.). 40p. (J). (gr. 4). 2001. lib. bdg. (978-0-7787-0238-2(3)); 2000. pap. (978-0-7787-0248-1(0)) Crabtree Publishing Co.

—Food. 2001. (gr. 3-6). lib. bdg. 17.60 (978-0-613-32575-2(3)); 2000. (J). (978-0-606-20108-7(4)) Tandem Library Bks.

Macleod, E. Everything but the Kitchen Sink: Weird Stuff You. 2008. (Everything but the Kitchen Sink Ser.). 128p. (J). pap. 7.99 (***978-0-545-00398-8(9)*** , Scholastic Reference) Scholastic, Inc.

The Magic School Bus Gets Eaten: A Book about Food Chains. 2002. (Magic School Bus Ser.). (Illus.). (J). 11.45 (978-0-7587-6376-1(X)) Book Wholesalers, Inc.

Mann, Holly, illus. Food. 2005. 8p. pap. (978-0-7624-2361-3(7)) Running Pr. Bk. Pubs.

Martineau, Susan. Healthy Eating. 2006. (Illus.). 32p. (J). (978-1-58340-893-3(2) , 1262657) Smart Apple Media.

Mattern, Joanne. Eating Lunch at School. 2006. 24p. (J). pap. (978-0-8368-6791-6(2)); lib. bdg. (978-0-8368-6784-8(X)) Stevens, Gareth Inc.

Mayo, Gretchen Will. Cereal. 2004. (Weekly Reader Early Learning Library). (Illus.). 24p. (gr. 2 up). (J). pap. 5.95 (978-0-8368-4072-8(0)); (YA). lib. bdg. 19.33 (978-0-8368-4065-0(8)) Stevens, Gareth Inc. (Weekly Reader Early Learning Library).

—Pasta. 2004. (Weekly Reader Early Learning Library). (Illus.). 24p. (gr. 2 up). (J). pap. 5.95 (978-0-8368-4076-6(3)); (YA). lib. bdg. 19.33 (978-0-8368-4069-8(0)) Stevens, Gareth Inc. (Weekly Reader Early Learning Library).

—Where Does Our Food Come From?, 6 bks. Incl. Applesauce. pap. 5.95 (978-0-8368-4071-1(2)); Cereal. pap. 5.95 (978-0-8368-4072-8(0)); Frozen Vegetables. pap. 5.95 (978-0-8368-4073-5(9)); Milk. pap. 5.95 (978-0-8368-4074-2(7)); Orange Juice. pap. 5.95 (978-0-8368-4075-9(5)); Pasta. pap. 5.95 (978-0-8368-4076-6(3)); 24p. (J). (gr. 2 up). (Illus.). 2004. pap. (978-0-8368-4070-4(4)); Set lib. bdg. 115.98 (978-0-8368-4063-6(1)) Stevens, Gareth Inc. (Weekly Reader Early Learning Library).

McCarthy, Rose. Food Labels: Using Nutritional Information to Create a Healthy Diet. 2004. (Library of Nutrition). (Illus.). 48p. (J). lib. bdg. 25.25 (978-1-4042-0300-6(1)) Rosen Publishing Group, Inc., The.

Mehas, Kay Yockey, et al. Food Science: The Biochemistry of Food & Nutrition, 2 vols. 4th ed. 2002. 496p. (gr. 9-12). stu. ed. 58.00 (978-0-07-822603-8(1) , 9780078226038) Glencoe/McGraw-Hill.

Meltzer, Milton. Food: How We Hunt & Gather It, How We Grow & Eat It, How We Buy & Sell It, How We Preserve & Waste It, & How Some Have Too Much & Others Have Too Little of It. Holm, Sharon Lane, illus. 1998. (Single Titles Ser.: up). 96p. (gr. 5 up). lib. bdg. 24.90 (978-0-7613-0354-1(5) , Twenty-First Century Bks.) Lerner Publishing Group.

Miller, Connie Colwell. Disgusting Foods. 2007. (Illus.). 32p. (J). (978-0-7368-6799-3(6)) Capstone Pr., Inc.

Miller, Debra A. Organic Foods. 2007. (Hot Topics Ser.). (Illus.). 128p. (gr. 7-10). 31.20 (***978-1-59018-994-8(9)*** , Lucent Bks.) Thomson Gale.

Minden, Cecilia. Breakfast by the Numbers. 2008. (J). lib. bdg. 25.26 (***978-1-60279-011-7(6)***) Cherry Lake Publishing.

—Restaurants by the Numbers. 2008. (J). lib. bdg. 25.26 (***978-1-60279-009-4(4)***) Cherry Lake Publishing.

Mommy, Is it safe to Eat? 2006. (YA). per. (978-1-59872-386-1(3)) Instantpublisher.com.

Moore, Hugh. Food Jokes. 2005. (More Jokes! Ser.). (Illus.). 24p. (gr. k-4). lib. bdg. 21.35 (978-1-59197-871-8(8)) ABDO Publishing Co.

Moore, Willamarie. StarFestival Grades 7-9 Food & Clothing Team: Exploring Cultural Heritage. Miyagawa, Shigeru, ed. 2000. (Illus.). 47p. (YA). (gr. 7-11). pap., stu. ed., wbk. ed. 10.00 (978-1-929724-08-6(X)) Star-Festival, Inc.

Morgan, Sally. Superfoods: Genetic Modification of Foods. (Science at the Edge Ser.). 64p. 8.95 (978-1-4034-4123-2(5)) Heinemann Library.

Morris, Neil. Do You Know What's in Your Food? 2006. (Making Healthy Food Choices Ser.). (Illus.). 56p. (J). pap. (978-1-4034-8580-9(1)); (YA). (gr. 6-10). lib. bdg. 32.86 (978-1-4034-8574-8(7)) Heinemann Library.

Murphy, Frank. Thomas Jefferson's Feast. Walz, Richard, illus. 2003. 48p. (J). (gr. 2-4). pap. 3.99 (978-0-375-82289-6(5) , Random Hse. Bks. for Young Readers) Random Hse. Children's Bks.

—Thomas Jefferson's Feast. 2003. (gr. k-3). lib. bdg. 11.80 (978-0-613-86238-7(4)) Tandem Library Bks.

Nathan, Emma. El Alimento. 2002. (Abre los Ojos y Aprende Serie).Tr. of Eyeopeners: Food. (SPA.). 24p. (J). (-3). 22.45 (978-1-4103-0022-5(6) , Blackbirch Pr., Inc.) Thomson Gale.

—Food. 2002. (Eyeopeners Ser.). (Illus.). 24p. (J). 22.45 (978-1-56711-599-4(3) , Blackbirch Pr., Inc.) Thomson Gale.

Nelson, Angela, creator. Lang-O-Learn: Food Cards. 2002. (SPA, FRE, GER, ITA & RUS.). (J). 19.95 (978-0-9668008-2-1(6)) Stages Learning Materials.

Nelson, Robin. Las Carnes y las Proteinas. 2003. (First Step Nonfiction Ser.). (SPA., Illus.). 24p. (J). (gr. k-2). lib. bdg. 18.60 (978-0-8225-5064-8(4)) Lerner Publishing Group.

—Las Grasas, los Aceites, y los Dulces. 2003. (First Step Nonfiction Ser.). (SPA., Illus.). 24p. (J). (gr. k-2). lib. bdg. 18.60 (978-0-8225-5061-7(X)) Lerner Publishing Group.

The New Food Guide Pyramid, 8 vols., Set. 2006. (Blastoff! Readers Ser.). (Illus.). (J). (gr. k-2). 148.00 (***978-0-531-16875-2(1)***) Scholastic Library Publishing.

Nsrc. Science & Technology for Books, Food Chemistry. 2004. (Illus.). 64p. (J). (978-1-933008-06-6(7)) National Science Resources Ctr.

Olson, Nathan. Food Patterns. 2007. 32p. (J). (978-0-7368-6729-0(5)) Capstone Pr., Inc.

Parker, Victoria. Food. 2006. (Heinemann Read & Learn Ser.). (Illus.). 24p. (J). pap. (978-1-4034-7890-0(2)); lib. bdg. (978-1-4034-7884-9(8)) Steck-Vaughn.

Party Food: Individual Title Six-Packs. (Rigby Focus Ser.). 16p. (gr. k up). 26.00 (978-0-7578-5284-8(X)); 28.00 (978-0-7578-5518-4(0)) Rigby Education.

Peanut Butter & Jelly. 2002. (Illus.). (J). pap. 5.43 (978-0-7398-5927-8(7)) Steck-Vaughn.

Perkins, Wendy. Animals Building Homes. 2004. (First Facts Ser.). (Illus.). 24p. (J). 15.95 (978-0-7368-2508-5(8)) Capstone Pr., Inc.

Peters, Celeste A., contrib. by. Peppers, Popcorn & Pizza: The Science of Food. 1998. (Science @ Work Ser.). (Illus.). 48p. (J). (gr. 4-6). lib. bdg. 27.12 (978-0-7398-0136-9(8)) Raintree.

Peterson, Tiffany. Clarence Birdseye. 2003. (Illus.). 32p. (J). lib. bdg. 22.79 (978-1-4034-3247-6(3)) Heinemann Library.

—Clarence Birdseye. 2003. (gr. k-3). lib. bdg. 14.75 (978-0-613-86558-6(8)) Tandem Library Bks.

Pichette, Marise. Show & Tell Food. Rousseau, Serge, illus. 2000. 12p. (J). bds. (978-2-922148-83-1(1)) Presses aventure/Adventure Pr.

Pizza: KinderFacts Individual Title Six-Packs. (Kinderstarters Ser.). 8p. (ps-1). 21.00 (978-0-7635-8748-2(6)) Rigby Education.

Platt, Richard. They Ate What ?! The Weird History of Food. 2006. (Illus.). 48p. (J). 9.95 (978-1-58728-578-3(9) , Two Can Publishing) T&N Children's Publishing.

—They Ate What ?! Weird History of Food. 2006. (Illus.). 48p. 16.95 (978-1-58728-577-6(0) , Two Can Publishing) T&N Children's Publishing.

Plews, Sue, et al. Dylunio a Thechnoleg, Cwrs Sylfaen Bwyd. 2005. (WEL., Illus.). 96p. (978-1-85644-603-7(4)) Univ. of Wales, Aberystwyth, Centre for Educational Studies.

Pocket Chart Science: Food Chains. 2001. (J). pap. 9.95 (978-1-56911-715-6(2)) Learning Resources, Inc.

Podwal, Mark H. A Sweet Year: A Taste of the Jewish Holidays. Podwal, Mark H., illus. 2003. (Illus.). 32p. (J). (ps-3). lib. bdg. 14.99 (978-0-385-90869-6(5) , Doubleday Bks. for Young Readers) Random Hse. Children's Bks.

Popular Science Editors. Try It with Food. 2007. (Experiment with Science Ser.). 32p. (J). pap. 7.95 (***978-0-531-18761-6(6));*** (Illus.). (gr. 3-6). lib. bdg. 25.00 (***978-0-531-18544-5(3)***) Scholastic Library Publishing. (Children's Pr.).

¿Por Que Come la Gente? (Coleccion Primeros Pasos en la Ciencia). (SPA., Illus.). (J). (gr. 1-3). pap. (978-950-724-487-2(5) , LMA8228) Lumen ARG. *Dist:* Lectorum Pubns., Inc.

Powell, Jillian. Food Matters. (Life Files Ser.). (Illus.). 1999. 62p. pap. 15.99 (978-0-237-51812-7(0)); 1998. 64p. 24.99 (978-0-237-51811-0(2)) Evans Publishing Group GBR. (Evans Brothers, Limited). *Dist:* Independent Pubs. Group.

Priddy, Roger. Natural Baby Eat. 2008. (J). bds. 6.95 (***978-0-312-50199-0(4)*** , Priddy Bks.) St. Martin's Pr.

Primm & Petelinsek. Food/Comida. 2004. (Talking Hands, Listening Eyes Ser.). (ENG & SPA., Illus.). 24p. (J). (ps-3). 21.36 (978-1-59296-020-0(0)) Child's World, Inc.

Processed Food: Level G, 6 vols. (Wonder Worldtm Ser.). 16p. 29.95 (978-0-7802-2022-5(6)) Wright Group, The.

Raintree Steck-Vaughn Staff, ed. Food & Festivals, 12 bks., Set. 2000. (Illus.). (J). lib. bdg. 308.28 (978-0-8172-5761-3(6)) Raintree.

Randall, Ronne. Do French Fries Come from France? 2003. (What? Where? Why? Ser.). (Illus.). 24p. (J). (gr. 1 up). lib. bdg. 20.67 (978-0-8368-3787-2(8)) Stevens, Gareth Inc.

Rau, Dana Meachen. Food & Cooking in American History. 2006. (Illus.). 24p. (J). pap. (978-0-8368-7213-2(4)); lib. bdg. (978-0-8368-7206-4(1)) Stevens, Gareth Inc.

Rau, Dana Meachen. Pizza. 2008. (J). (***978-0-7614-2891-6(7)***) Cavendish, Marshall Bks., Ltd.

Ribke, Simone T. The Shapes We Eat. (Rookie Read-About Math Ser.). (J). 2005. (Illus.). 32p. (gr. 1-2). pap. 5.95 (978-0-516-25848-5(6)); 2004. 20.50 (978-0-516-24431-0(0)) Scholastic Library Publishing. (Children's Pr.).

Riley, Peter D. Food. 1998. (Cycles in Science Ser.). (Illus.). 32p. (J). (gr. 4-7). lib. bdg. (978-1-57572-618-2(1)) Heinemann Library.

—Food Chains. 1999. (Illus.). (J). (978-0-606-18148-8(2)) Tandem Library Bks.

Robinson, Jill, et al. Food Technology. 2nd rev. ed. 2001. (Design & Make It Ser.). (Illus.). 168p. pap. 27.50 (978-0-7487-6084-8(9)) Nelson Thornes Ltd. GBR. *Dist:* Trans-Atlantic Pubns., Inc.

Rockwell, Lizzy. Good Enough to Eat: A Kid's Guide to Food & Nutrition. Date not set. 40p. (J). (gr. k-4). pap. 5.99 (978-0-06-445174-1(7)) HarperCollins Pubs.

—Good Enough to Eat: A Kid's Guide to Food & Nutrition. Rockwell, Lizzy, illus. 1999. (Illus.). 40p. (J). (gr. k-4). 16.99 (978-0-06-027434-4(4)); lib. bdg. 17.89 (978-0-06-027435-1(2)) HarperCollins Pubs.

Rose, Elizabeth. Food & Nutrition. 2006. (Life Science Library). (Illus.). 24p. (J). 21.25 (978-1-4042-2821-4(7) , PowerKids Pr.) Rosen Publishing Group, Inc., The.

Rotner, Shelley & Goss, Gary. Where Does Food Come From? 2006. (Illus.). 32p. (J). 22.60 (978-0-7613-2935-0(8) , Millbrook Pr.) Lerner Publishing Group.

Running Press Staff & Mann, Holly. Food. 2005. (Illus.). 8p. (J). pap. 4.95 (978-0-7624-2344-6(7) , Running Pr. Kids) Running Pr. Bk. Pubs.

Salzmann, Mary Elizabeth. Eating Right. 2004. (Healthy Habits Ser.). (Illus.). 23p. (J). (ps-3). lib. bdg. 19.93 (978-1-59197-551-9(4)) ABDO Publishing Co.

Sanger, Amy Wilson. First Book of Sushi. 2004. (Illus.). 20p. (J). (ps). bds. 6.95 (978-1-58246-050-5(7) , Tricycle Pr.) Ten Speed Pr.

Saunders-Smith, Gail, ed. From Farm to Table. 2005. (First Facts Ser.). (Illus.). (J). (gr. 1-2). lib. bdg. 212.60 (978-0-7368-4411-6(2)) Capstone Pr., Inc.

Schaefer, A. R. Food Around the World. 2007. (ENG & SPA.). (J). (978-1-59515-959-5(2)) Rourke Publishing, LLC.

Schaefer, Lola M. Meat & Protein. 2007. (J). (***978-1-4329-0146-2(X));*** pap. (***978-1-4329-0153-0(2)***) Heinemann Library.

—Vegetables. 2007. (J). (***978-1-4329-0142-4(7));*** pap. (***978-1-4329-0149-3(4)***) Heinemann Library.

Schlepp, Tammy J. I Love Food. 2001. 11.79 (978-0-606-22437-6(8)) Tandem Library Bks.

Schuh, Mari C. Healthy Snacks. 2006. (Illus.). 24p. (J). 19.93 (978-0-7368-5369-9(3) , Pebble Bks.) Capstone Pr., Inc.

Science & Technology for Children Books, Food Chemistry Set, 8 vols. 2004. (Illus.). 64p. (J). (978-1-933008-18-9(0)) National Science Resources Ctr.

Scott, Janine. The Food Pyramid. 2003. (Spyglass Books). (Illus.). 24p. (J). (gr. 1 up). lib. bdg. 18.60 (978-0-7565-0447-2(3)) Compass Point Bks.

—Let's Eat: Foods of Our World. 2002. (Spyglass Books). (Illus.). 24p. (J). (gr. 1 up). lib. bdg. 18.60 (978-0-7565-0365-9(5)) Compass Point Bks.

Scratch N Sniff Staff. Scratch N Sniff Food. 2005. 12p. 6.95 (978-0-9762524-6-7(5)) Gimme Gimme Toys & Games Inc.

Seaborn, Ron. The Children's Health Food Book. rev. ed. 2006. 40p. 16.95 (***978-0-9647089-2-1(2)***) Life Line, Inc.

Sheen, Barbara. Foods of Germany. 2006. 64p. (J). (gr. 3-6). 27.45 (978-0-7377-3554-3(6) , Kidhaven) Thomson Gale.

Shepard, Tristram, et al. Design & Make It! Food & Textiles. 1998. (Illus.). 128p. pap. 115.00 (978-0-7487-3512-9(7)) Nelson Thornes Ltd. GBR. *Dist:* Trans-Atlantic Pubns., Inc.

Sherrow, Victoria. Food Safety. 2007. (Point/Counterpoint Ser.). 136p. (gr. 9). 32.95 (***978-0-7910-9289-7(5)*** , Chelsea Hse.) Facts On File, Inc.

Shofner, Shawndra. How It Happens at the Pizza Company. Wolfe, Bob & Wolfe, Diane, photos by. 2006. (How It Happens Ser.). (Illus.). 32p. (J). (gr. 2-5). lib. bdg. 19.95 (978-1-881508-98-4(6)) Oliver Pr., Inc.

Shryer, Donna. Body Fuel: A Guide to Good Nutrition. 2007. (Food & Fitness Ser.). 144p. (J). lib. bdg. 37.07 (***978-0-7614-2552-6(7)*** , Benchmark Bks.) Cavendish, Marshall Corp.

Shuter, Jane. Food & Farming. 1999. (Ancient Egypt Ser.). 32p. (J). (gr. 3-5). lib. bdg. 22.79 (978-1-57572-730-1(7)) Heinemann Library.

Siddiqui, Rifat & Foster, John. I-Read Year 1 Anthology: Rumbling Tums. 2007. (I-read Ser.). (Illus.). 40p. pap. (***978-0-521-70477-9(4)***) Cambridge Univ. Pr.

Silverman, Buffy. Follow That Food. 2006. (Illus.). 32p. (J). pap. (978-1-4109-2624-1(9)) Raintree.

Smallwood, Sally. Cool as a Cucumber. 2005. (Things I Eat Ser.). (Illus.). 24p. (J). 11.95 (978-1-84089-418-9(0) , Zero to Ten, Limited) Evans Publishing Group GBR. *Dist:* Independent Pubs. Group.

—Sweet as a Strawberry. 2005. (Things I Eat Ser.). (Illus.). 24p. (J). 11.95 (978-1-84089-419-6(9) , Zero to Ten, Limited) Evans Publishing Group GBR. *Dist:* Independent Pubs. Group.

Smart Kids Publishing Staff. Its Meal Time. 2000. (Time to... Board Books Ser.). 16p. (J). bds. 6.95 (978-1-56015-247-7(8)) Penton Overseas, Inc.

Smith, Alastair, ed. What Happens to Your Food? 1999. (Big Bks.). (Illus.). 16p. (J). (ps-3). pap. 19.95 (978-0-7460-3490-3(3)) EDC Publishing.

Smith, Andrea Claire Harte. Food Safety & Farming. 2003. (In the News Ser.). (J). lib. bdg. 24.25 (978-1-58340-394-5(9)) Smart Apple Media.

Snack-It Cafe. 2004. 9.99 (978-0-7644-1643-9(X)); 2004. 9.99 (978-0-7644-1714-6(2)); 2003. 9.99 (978-0-7644-1625-5(1)) Group Publishing, Inc. (Flagship Church Resources).

Sohn, Emily. Food & Nutrition. 2006. (Science News for Kids Ser.). (Illus.). 64p. (J). 30.00 (978-0-7910-9121-0(X) , Chelsea Clubhouse) Facts On File, Inc.

Solheim, James. Its Disgusting & We Ate It: True Food Facts from Around the World & Throughout History. 2001. (Illus.). (J). 13.79 (978-0-606-21255-7(8)) Tandem Library Bks.

Solway, Andrew. What's Living in Your Kitchen? 2004. (Hidden Life Ser.). (Illus.). 32p. (J). pap. 7.50 (978-1-4034-5483-6(3)); lib. bdg. 25.64 (978-1-4034-4844-6(2)) Heinemann Library.

Spilsbury, Louise & Spilsbury, Richard. Desert Food Chains. 2004. (Food Webs Ser.). (Illus.). 32p. (J). 24.22 (978-1-4034-5855-1(3)); pap. (978-1-4034-5862-9(6)) Heinemann Library.

—Food Chains & Webs: From Producers to Decomposers. 2004. (Science Answers Ser.). (Illus.). 32p. (J). pap. 7.50 (978-1-4034-5510-9(4)) Heinemann Library.

Stephens, William R. Finding Food in the Wild. 2003. (Extreme Animals Ser.). (J). pap. (978-1-58417-247-5(9)); lib. bdg. (978-1-58417-246-8(0)) Lake Street Pubs.

Stone, Lynn M. Maple Syrup. 2002. (Harvest to Home Ser.). (Illus.). 24p. (gr. 2-5). 14.95 (978-1-58952-128-5(5)) Rourke Publishing, LLC.

Stull. Theme Pack: Food. 2002. (Pair-It Bks.). (Illus.). (J). pap. (978-0-7398-6376-3(2)) Steck-Vaughn.

Swanson, Diane. Animals Eat the Weirdest Things. Smith, Terry, illus. 1998. 64p. (J). (gr. 3-2). pap. 12.95 (978-1-55110-809-4(7)) Whitecap Bks., Ltd. CAN. *Dist:* Firefly Bks., Ltd.

Taste Bud Travels: Individual Title Six-Packs. (Bookweb Ser.). 32p. (gr. 4 up). 34.00 (978-0-7635-3742-5(X)) Rigby Education.

Tasty Treats, 6 bks., Set. (J). (gr. 1-4). lib. bdg. 143.58 (978-1-57103-334-5(3)) Rourke Publishing, LLC.

Taylor, Dorothy J. & Clark, Joan. Food - 1. 2004. (Topic Bks.). (Illus.). 36p. bds. 5.00 (978-0-7188-1786-2(9)) Lutherworth Pr., The GBR. *Dist:* Parkwest Pubns., Inc.

Thomas, Ann. Food: Grains. 2002. (Food Ser.). (Illus.). 32p. (gr. k-2). 23.00 (978-0-7910-6975-2(3) , Chelsea Hse.) Facts On File, Inc.

—Food Series, 6 vols., Set. 2005. (Illus.). 32p. (gr. 2-4). pap. 138.00 (978-0-7910-7052-9(2) , Chelsea Hse.) Facts On File, Inc.

Thomas, Isabel. Black Foods. (Colors We Eat Ser.). (Illus.). 24p. (J). (ps-1). 2005. lib. bdg. 20.64 (978-1-4034-6315-9(8)); 2004. pap. 5.75 (978-1-4034-6322-7(0)) Heinemann Library.

—Blue & Purple Foods. (Colors We Eat Ser.). (Illus.). 24p. (J). (ps-1). 2005. lib. bdg. 21.36 (978-1-4034-6316-6(6)); 2004. pap. 5.75 (978-1-4034-6323-4(9)) Heinemann Library.

—Pink Foods. (Colors We Eat Ser.). (J). (ps-1). 2005. (Illus.). 24p. lib. bdg. 20.64 (978-1-4034-6314-2(X)); 2004. pap. 5.75 (978-1-4034-6321-0(2)) Heinemann Library.

Tocci, Salvatore. Experiments with Foods. 2004. (True Bks.). (J). (gr. 3-5). pap. 6.95 (978-0-516-27806-3(1) , Children's Pr.) Scholastic Library Publishing.

Trumbauer, Lisa. Food for Thought. 2000. (Yellow Umbrella Books). (Illus.). 16p. (J). (gr. 1). lib. bdg. 14.60 (978-0-7368-0729-6(2) , Pebble Bks.) Capstone Pr., Inc.

Turck, Mary. Food & Emotions. 2000. (Nutrition & Fitness Ser.). (Illus.). 64p. (J). (gr. 4-6). lib. bdg. 23.93 (978-0-7368-0711-1(X) , LifeMatters Bks.) Capstone Pr., Inc.

Turnbull, Stephanie. Why Do We Eat? (Level 2) - Internet Referenced. 2006. (Illus.). 32p. (J). 4.99 (978-0-7945-1333-7(6) , Usborne) EDC Publishing.

Tuxworth, Nicola. Food: A Very First Picture Book. 1999. (Pictures & Words Ser.). (Illus.). 24p. (J). (ps up). lib. bdg. 22.00 (978-0-8368-2430-8(X)) Stevens, Gareth Inc.

Twist, Clint. The Search for Food Breakthroughs. 2005. (Science Quest Ser.). (Illus.). 32p. (J). lib. bdg. 24.67 (978-0-8368-4555-6(2)) Stevens, Gareth Inc.

VanCleave, Janice Pratt. Janice VanCleave's Food & Nutrition for Every Kid: Easy Activities That Make Learning Science Fun. 1999. (Science for Every Kid Ser.: Vol. 117). (Illus.). 240p. (gr. 3-7). pap. 12.95 (978-0-471-17665-7(6) , Wiley) Wiley, John & Sons, Inc.

Vander Klipp, Michael A. God Made Food. 1999. (God Made Bks.). (Illus.). 12p. (J). (ps). 2.99 (978-0-310-97857-2(2)) Zonderkidz.

A Visit to the Farmers' Market. 2006. (J). (978-0-9771010-0-9(2)) Brain Child Bks.

Wallace, Paula S. The World of Food. 2003. (Life Around the World Ser.). (Illus.). 48p. (J). (gr. 2 up). lib. bdg. 24.67 (978-0-8368-3660-8(X)) Stevens, Gareth Inc.

Ward, Brian R. Microscopic Life in Your Food. 2004. (Illus.). 32p. (J). lib. bdg. (978-1-58340-471-3(6)) Smart Apple Media.

Waters, Jennifer. Harvest Time. 2002. (Spyglass Books). (Illus.). 24p. (J). (gr. 1 up). 18.60 (978-0-7565-0239-3(X)) Compass Point Bks.

Watt, F. Vamos a Comer! 2004. Tr. of Baby's Mealtime. (SPA., Illus.). 16p. (J). (ps). pap. 4.95 (978-0-7460-4540-4(9)) EDC Publishing.

Weber, Rebecca. Foods from the Farm. 2004. (Spyglass Books). (Illus.). 24p. (J). (gr. k-1). lib. bdg. 18.60 (978-0-7565-0624-7(7)) Compass Point Bks.

Weekly Reader Early Learning Library (Firm) Staff, contrib. by. Things I Eat. 2006. (Things in My World Ser.). (Illus.). 16p. (J). pap. (978-0-8368-6817-3(X)); lib. bdg. (978-0-8368-6810-4(2)) Stevens, Gareth Inc.

—Things I Eat: Las Cosas Que Como. 2006. (ENG & SPA.). 16p. (J). pap. (978-0-8368-7229-3(0)); lib. bdg. (978-0-8368-7222-4(3)) Stevens, Gareth Inc. (Weekly Reader Early Learning Library).

What Do You Eat? 1999. 16p. pap. 4.99 (978-0-310-97862-6(9)) Zondervan.

What Is Delicious?, 6, Pack. (gr. 1-2). 22.00 (978-0-7635-9091-8(6)) Rigby Education.

Whitehouse, Patricia. Agrupemos Alimentos. 2002. (Colores Para Comer (The Colors We Eat) Ser.).Tr. of Sorting Foods. 24p. (J). (ps-1). pap. 5.25 (978-1-58810-840-1(6) , 91577); (SPA.). lib. bdg. 18.50 (978-1-58810-793-0(0)) Heinemann Library.

—Alimantos Blancos. 2002. (Colores Para Comer (The Colors We Eat) Ser.). (SPA.). 24p. (J). (ps-1). lib. bdg. 18.50 (978-1-58810-792-3(2)) Heinemann Library.

—Alimentos Amarillos. 2002. (SPA.). 24p. (J). (ps-1). pap. 5.25 (978-1-58810-838-8(4) , 91573); lib. bdg. 18.50 (978-1-58810-791-6(4)) Heinemann Library.

—Alimentos Anaranjados. 2003. (Colores Para Comer (The Colors We Eat) Ser.). (SPA.). 24p. pap. 5.25 (978-1-4034-3846-1(3)) Heinemann Library.

—Alimentos Color Cafe. 2003. (Colores Para Comer (The Colors We Eat) Ser.). 24p. pap. 5.25 (978-1-4034-3845-4(5)) Heinemann Library.

—Alimentos Marron. 2003. Tr. of Brown Foods. (SPA.). (ps-2). lib. bdg. 13.30 (978-0-613-82825-3(9)) Tandem Library Bks.

—Alimentos Rojos. 2002. (Colores Para Comer (The Colors We Eat) Ser.).Tr. of Red Foods. (SPA.). 24p. (J). (ps-1). pap. 5.25 (978-1-58810-837-1(6) , 91575); lib. bdg. 18.50 (978-1-58810-790-9(6)) Heinemann Library.

—Alimentos Verdes. 2002. (Colores Para Comer (The Colors We Eat) Ser.). (SPA.). 24p. (J). (ps-1). pap. 5.25 (978-1-58810-836-4(8) , 91576); lib. bdg. 18.50 (978-1-58810-789-3(2)) Heinemann Library.

—Brown Foods. 2003. (Colors We Eat Ser.). (Illus.). 24p. (J). pap. (978-1-4034-3840-9(4)); lib. bdg. 18.50 (978-1-4034-3850-8(1)) Heinemann Library.

—Food ABC. 2002. 24p. (J). (ps-1). pap. 5.25 (978-1-58810-748-0(5) , 91416); (Illus.). lib. bdg. 18.50 (978-1-58810-540-0(7)) Heinemann Library.

—Green Foods. 2002. 24p. (J). (ps-1). pap. 5.25 (978-1-58810-743-5(4) , 91417); (Illus.). lib. bdg. 18.50 (978-1-58810-535-6(0)) Heinemann Library.

—Orange Foods. 2003. (Colors We Eat Ser.). (Illus.). 24p. (J). pap. (978-1-4034-3841-6(2)); lib. bdg. 18.50 (978-1-4034-3851-5(X)) Heinemann Library.

—Red Foods. 2002. 24p. (J). (ps-1). pap. 5.25 (978-1-58810-744-2(2) , 91418); (Illus.). lib. bdg. 18.50 (978-1-58810-536-3(9)) Heinemann Library.

—Sorting Foods. 2002. (Heinemann Read & Learn Ser.). (Illus.). 24p. (J). (ps-1). pap. 5.25 (978-1-58810-747-3(7) , 91415); lib. bdg. 18.50 (978-1-58810-539-4(3)) Heinemann Library.

—White Foods. 2002. (Colors We Eat Ser.). (Illus.). 24p. (J). (ps-1). lib. bdg. 18.50 (978-1-58810-538-7(5)) Heinemann Library.

—Yellow Foods. 2002. (Heinemann Read & Learn Ser.). (Illus.). 24p. (J). (ps-1). pap. 5.25 (978-1-58810-745-9(0) , 91420); lib. bdg. 18.50 (978-1-58810-537-0(7)) Heinemann Library.

Whitman, Sylvia. What's Cooking? The History of American Food. 2005. (People's History Ser.). (Illus.). 96p. (gr. 6-12). lib. bdg. 26.60 (978-0-8225-1732-0(9)) Lerner Publishing Group.

Wilkinson, Doris J. Food. Wilkinson, Doris J., ed. Chipping, Oliver, illus. 2000. (Jacob's Magic Box Discovery Ser.). 20p. (J). (ps). pap. 4.95 (978-0-9700386-9-2(0)) Magic Box Pubns.

Williams, Brenda. Food. 1999. (Environment Starts Here Ser.). (Illus.). 32p. (J). (gr. 1-4). lib. bdg. 25.69 (978-0-8172-5351-6(3)) Raintree.

Williams, Kara. Frequently Asked Questions about My Pyramid: Eating Right. 2006. (FAQ Ser.). (Illus.). 64p. (J). (gr. 7-12). lib. bdg. 27.95 (***978-1-4042-1974-8(9)***) Rosen Publishing Group, Inc., The.

Zeifert, Harriet. Yum: Baby Flipaface. SAMi, illus. 2006. 24p. bds. 8.95 (978-1-59354-139-2(2)) Blue Apple Bks.

Ziegler, Mark. Lunchbox Laughs: A Book of Food Jokes. Haberstroh, Anne, illus. 2005. (Read-It! Readers Ser.). 24p. (C). (gr. 1-3). 18.60 (978-1-4048-0963-5(5)) Picture Window Bks.

Zoehfeld, Kathleen Weidner. Food Chains. 1999. (J). lib. bdg. 17.99 (978-0-517-70991-7(0)) Crown Publishing Group.

—Food Chains. 1999. (J). 15.95 (978-0-517-70990-0(2) , Random Hse. Bks. for Young Readers) Random Hse. Children's Bks.

Zurakowski, Michele. Snack Time Around the World. Yesh, Jeff, illus. 2004. (Meals Around the World Ser.). 24p. (J). (gr. k-4). 22.60 (978-1-4048-0283-4(5) , 1229528) Picture Window Bks.

FOOD, CANNED

see Canning and Preserving

FOOD—FICTION

Abela, Deborah. Mission: Spy Force Revealed. O'Connor, George, illus. (Spy Force Ser.). 288p. (J). 2006. pap. 5.99 (978-1-4169-4024-1(3) , Aladdin); 2005. (gr. 4-7). 9.95 (978-0-689-87358-4(1) , Simon & Schuster Children's Publishing) Simon & Schuster Children's Publishing.

Accorsi, William. Apple, Apple, Alligator: A Picture-Puzzle Book. 2000. (Illus.). 20p. (J). (ps). bds. 14.95 (978-0-7611-1787-2(3)) Workman Publishing Co., Inc.

Ada, Alma Flor. The Three Golden Oranges. Cartwright, Reg, illus. 1999. 32p. (J). (gr. k-3). 16.99 (978-0-689-80775-6(9) , Atheneum) Simon & Schuster Children's Publishing.

Adler, David A. Bones & the Cupcake Mystery. Newman, Barbara, illus. 2008. (Jeffrey Bones Mystery Ser.: No. 3). 32p. (J). (gr. 1-3). pap. 3.99 (***978-0-14-241147-6(7)*** , Puffin) Penguin Group (USA) Inc.

Adler, Karen A. Maybe Donna Wants a Cheeseburger! 2004. (Illus.). 32p. (J). 16.95 (978-0-9679772-2-5(3)) Adler, Karen.

The Adventures of Molly. 2004. pap. 13.95 (***978-1-59526-180-9(X)***) Media Creations, Inc.

Ahlberg, Allan. The Runaway Dinner. Ingman, Bruce, illus. 2006. 40p. (J). (ps-3). 15.99 (978-0-7636-3142-0(6)) Candlewick Pr.

Aiken, Joan. Moon Cake. (Illus.). 244p. (J). pap. 8.99 (978-0-340-70926-9(X) , Hodder & Stoughton) Hodder General Publishing Division GBR. *Dist:* Trafalgar Square Publishing.

Albee, Sarah, retold by. Stone Soup. 2006. (J). per. 6.99 (978-1-59939-037-6(X) , Reader's Digest Young Families, Inc.) Reader's Digest Children's Publishing, Inc.

Albrecht, Jeff. Barney Says. Albrecht, Jeff, illus. 2006. (Barney Ser.). 5p. (J). bds. 9.99 (978-0-439-74410-2(5)) Scholastic, Inc.

Alexander Enjoys His Fruits & Vegetables. 2006. (J). 14.99 (***978-0-9742806-4-6(X)***) Heart to Heart Publishing.

Alexander's First Babysitter. 2004. (J). 5.00 (978-1-882541-38-6(3)) Food Allergy & Anaphylaxis Network.

Anderson, Derek, illus. Gladys Goes Out to Lunch. 2005. 40p. (J). 15.95 (978-0-689-85688-4(1) , Simon & Schuster Children's Publishing) Simon & Schuster Children's Publishing.

Anderson, Scoular. Stan the Dog & the Sneaky Snacks. 2006. (Read-It! Chapter Books). (J). 21.26 (978-1-4048-2742-4(0)) Picture Window Bks.

Angeles, Maria. Una Tortilla para Emilia. 2001. (SPA.). (J). (978-0-7608-2265-4(4)) Sundance/Newbridge Educational Publishing.

Anna's Sandwich 6 Packs: Individual Title. (gr. 1-2). 22.00 (978-0-7635-9176-2(9)) Rigby Education.

Arengo, Sue. The Enormous Turnip. 1998. (Illus.). 24p. (J). 5.50 (978-0-19-422002-6(8)) Oxford Univ. Pr., Inc.

Arma, Tom. Fruity Cutie Colors. 2004. (Illus.). 10p. (J). (ps-ps). bds. 5.95 (978-0-8109-5022-1(7)) Abrams, Harry N. , Inc.

Armenteros, Sarah. Emma & the Mashed Potato Monster. 2007. 44p. (J). 16.99 (978-1-59092-384-9(7) , Little Blue Works) Windstorm Creative.

Armour, Peter. Stop That Pickle! Shachat, Andrew, illus. 2005. 32p. (J). (gr. k-3). 5.95 (978-0-618-54889-7(0)) Houghton Mifflin Co. Trade & Reference Div.

Arnold, Tedd. Huggly's Pizza. 2000. (Monster under the Bed Ser.). (Illus.). 32p. (J). (ps-3). pap. 3.25 (978-0-439-13498-9(6) , Cartwheel Bks.) Scholastic, Inc.

Aronson, Emme. What Are You Hungry For? Feed Your Tummy & Your Heart. Brooks, Erik, illus. 2007. 32p. (J). lib. bdg. 16.89 (978-0-06-054308-2(6)) HarperCollins Pubs.

Aronson, Emme & Aronson, Phillip. What Are You Hungry For? Feed Your Tummy & Your Heart. Brooks, Erik, illus. 2007. 32p. (J). 15.99 (978-0-06-054307-5(8)) HarperCollins Pubs.

Aston, Dianna Hutts. An Orange in January. Maren, Julie, illus. 2007. 32p. (J). (ps). 16.99 (978-0-8037-3146-2(9) , Dial) Penguin Group (USA) Inc.

Athey, Victoria. No Peas, Please! Delaney, Molly, illus. 2005. (J). pap. 4.95 (978-1-57874-087-1(8)) Kaeden Corp.

Baby Strawberry Loves to Count. 2007. (Strawberry Shortcake Baby Ser.). 10p. (J). bds. 6.99 (***978-0-448-44717-9(7)*** , Grosset & Dunlap) Penguin Group (USA) Inc.

Baby Strawberry's First Christmas. 2007. (Strawberry Shortcake Baby Ser.). 10p. (J). (ps). bds. 4.99 (***978-0-448-44669-1(3)*** , Grosset & Dunlap) Penguin Group (USA) Inc.

Baca, Ana. Benito's Sopaipillas: Las Sopaipillas de Benito. Villarroel, Carolina, tr. Accardo, Anthony, illus. (ENG & SPA.). 32p. (J). (gr. 2-4). 15.95 (978-1-55885-370-6(7) , Piñata Books) Arte Publico Pr.

Backx, Patsy. Josie & Mr. Fernandez. Backx, Patsy, illus. 2002. (Illus.). 32p. (J). (ps up). lib. bdg. 24.67 (978-0-8368-3079-8(2)) Stevens, Gareth Inc.

Badoe, Adwoa A. Crabs for Dinner. ed. 2004. (J). (gr. k-3). spiral bd. (978-0-616-01533-9(X)); spiral bd. (978-0-616-01534-6(8)) Canadian National Institute for the Blind/Institut National Canadien pour les Aveugles.

Baker, Keith. On the Go with Mr. & Mrs. Green. 2007. (Mr. & Mrs. Green Ser.). (Illus.). 72p. (J). pap. 5.95 (978-0-15-205867-8(2) , Harcourt Paperbacks) Harcourt Children's Bks.

—On the Go with Mr. & Mrs. Green. 2007. (Mr. & Mrs. Green Ser.). 72p. (J). (gr. 2-4). 27.07 (***978-1-59961-303-1(4)***) Spotlight.

Balmer, Fred. Festus & the Missing Bag of Feed. Newcomb, Kristene, illus. 2004. 26p. (J). per. 7.00 (***978-0-9760790-0-2(3)***) Folsom Fallies Pr.

Barrett, Judi. Cloudy with a Chance of Meatballs. Barrett, Ron, illus. 2002. (J). 14.47 (978-0-7587-2256-0(7)) Book Wholesalers, Inc.

—Cloudy with a Chance of Meatballs. Barrett, Ron, illus. 2000. (J). pap. 19.97 incl. audio (978-0-7366-9210-6(X)) Books on Tape, Inc.

—Cloudy with a Chance of Meatballs. Barrett, Ron, illus. 2005. (J). pap. 18.95 incl. audio compact disk (978-1-59112-701-7(7)) Live Oak Media.

—Cloudy with a Chance of Meatballs. Barrett, Judi, illus. 2002. 32p. (J). mass mkt. 1.00 (978-0-689-85523-8(0) , Aladdin) Simon & Schuster Children's Publishing.

—Pickles to Pittsburgh: The Sequel to Cloudy with A Chance of Meatballs. (Illus.). (J). 2005. pap. 16.95 incl. audio (978-0-87499-537-4(X)); 2005. pap. 18.95 incl. audio compact disk (978-1-59112-749-9(1)); 1999. (gr. 1-6). 25.95 incl. audio (978-0-87499-538-1(8)) Live Oak Media.

—Pickles to Pittsburgh: The Sequel to Cloudy with A Chance of Meatballs. Barrett, Ron, illus. 1999. 28.95 incl. audio compact disk (978-1-59112-750-5(5)); pap. 37.95 incl. audio (978-0-87499-539-8(6)); pap. 39.95 incl. audio compact disk (978-1-59112-751-2(3)) Live Oak Media.

—Pickles to Pittsburgh: The Sequel to Cloudy with A Chance of Meatballs. Barrett, Ron, illus. 2000. 32p. (J). (ps-3). pap. 6.99 (978-0-689-83929-0(4) , Aladdin) Simon & Schuster Children's Publishing.

—Pickles to Pittsburgh: The Sequel to Cloudy with A Chance of Meatballs. 2000. (J). (978-0-606-20089-9(4)); lib. bdg. 15.30 (978-0-613-30090-2(4)) Tandem Library Bks.

—Pickles to Pittsburgh & Cloudy with a Change of Meaballs. Barrett, Ron, illus. 1999. pap. 30.95 incl. audio (978-0-87499-819-1(0)); pap. 34.95 incl. audio compact disk (978-1-59112-842-7(0)) Live Oak Media.

Barron, Rex. Showdown at the Food Pyramid. Barron, Rex, illus. 2004. (Illus.). 32p. (J). (ps-3). 16.99 (978-0-399-23715-7(1) , Putnam Juvenile) Penguin Group (USA) Inc.

Bass, Jules. Herb, the Vegetarian Dragon. Harter, Debbie, illus. 1999. 32p. (J). (gr. 1-5). 15.95 (978-1-902283-36-4(8)) Barefoot Bks., Inc.

Beckerman, Menucha. The Candy Kids. 2004. (My Smiling World Ser.: No. 3). (Illus.). 32p. (J). 11.95 (978-1-931681-54-4(6)) Israel Bk. Shop.

Beeke, Joel & Kleyn, Diana. How God Sent a Dog to Save a Family. Anderson, Jeff, illus. (Building on the Rock Ser.). 176p. (J). pap. (978-1-85792-819-8(9) , Christian Focus) Christian Focus Pubns. GBR. *Dist:* Riverside.

Bell, Cece. Food Friends: Fun Foods That Go Together. Bell, Cece, illus. 2006. (Illus.). 20p. (J). (gr. k-ps). bds. 5.99 (978-0-7636-2777-5(1)) Candlewick Pr.

Bell, Julia. Massive. 2005. (Illus.). 272p. (YA). (gr. 7 up). pap. 6.99 (978-1-4169-0207-2(4) , Simon Pulse) Simon & Schuster Children's Publishing.

Berenstain, Stan & Berenstain, Jan. The Berenstain Bears & Too Much Junk Food. 1999. (Berenstain Bears First Time Bks.). (Illus.). (J). (ps-2). lib. bdg. 10.95 (978-0-8085-3551-5(X)) Tandem Library Bks.

Berofsky, Adrienne. The Disney Bakery: 30 Magical Recipes. 2001. 64p. (J). 14.99 (978-0-7868-5322-9(0)) Disney Pr.

Biers-Ariel, Matt. The Seven Species. Goodman, Tama, illus. 2003. 48p. 19.95 (978-0-8074-0852-0(2) , 161902) URJ Pr.

Blackaby, Susan. The Word of the Day. Muehlenhardt, Amy Bailey, illus. 2004. (Read-It! Readers Ser.). 32p. (C). (gr. k-3). 18.60 (978-1-4048-0588-0(5)) Picture Window Bks.

Blackwell-Burke, Melissa & Kunkel, Kristen. Pizza Pie Pizzazz. 2003. (J). spiral bd. 14.95 (978-1-58605-957-6(2) , LeapFrog Schl. Hse.) LeapFrog Enterprises, Inc.

Blake-Brekke, Carri. Panuk, Princess & Prince. Melton, Jodi, illus. 2002. (J). pap. (978-0-9720549-1-1(X)) Mom's Pride Enterprises.

Blake, Jan. Give Me My Yam. Melnyczuk, Peter, illus. 1999. (Reading Together Ser.). 32p. (J). (ps). pap. 3.99 (978-0-7636-0873-6(4)) Candlewick Pr.

Blumenthal, Deborah. Don't Let the Peas Touch: And Other Stories. Ering, Timothy B., illus. 2004. 48p. (J). (ps-3). pap. 15.95 (978-0-439-29732-5(X) , Levine, Arthur A. Bks.) Scholastic, Inc.

Bodden, Michelle, adapted by. Obara & the Merchants. 2004. (Illus.). 32p. (J). 14.95 (978-0-9753089-0-5(4)) Water Daughter Publishing.

Boniface, William. Christmastime Is Cookie Time. Rooney, Ronnie, illus. 2001. (Top This! Ser.). 12p. (J). bds. 9.99 (978-0-8431-7678-0(4) , Price Stern Sloan) Penguin Group (USA) Inc.

—What Do You Want on Your Pizza? Palen, Debbie, illus. 2000. 12p. (J). (ps-3). bds. 9.99 (978-0-8431-7473-1(0) , Price Stern Sloan) Penguin Group (USA) Inc.

Bonnell, Kris. The Big Hungry Cat. 2006. (J). 3.95 (***978-1-933727-33-2(0)***) Reading Reading Bks., LLC.

—Dad's Hamburger. 2005. (J). 3.75 (978-1-933727-04-2(7)) Reading Reading Bks., LLC.

—Eating Mud. 2005. (J). 3.75 (978-1-933727-05-9(5)) Reading Reading Bks., LLC.

—Lemonade. 2006. (J). 3.95 (***978-1-933727-31-8(4)***) Reading Reading Bks., LLC.

—Mmm, Apples. 2006. (J). 3.95 (***978-1-933727-22-6(5)***) Reading Reading Bks., LLC.

—Pickles are Great. 2005. (J). 3.75 (978-1-933727-12-7(8)) Reading Reading Bks., LLC.

—Pizza for Carl. 2006. (J). 3.95 (***978-1-933727-27-1(6)***) Reading Reading Bks., LLC.

—Red Apples for Me. 2007. (J). 3.95 (***978-1-933727-52-3(7)***) Reading Reading Bks., LLC.

—Soda Pop. 2005. (J). 3.75 (978-1-933727-16-5(0)) Reading Reading Bks., LLC.

—Vegetable Soup. 2005. (J). 3.75 (978-1-933727-18-9(7)) Reading Reading Bks., LLC.

Bossley, Michele Martin. Swiped. 2006. 112p. (J). lib. bdg. 14.95 (978-1-55143-652-4(3)) Orca Bk. Pubs. USA.

Bowman, Eddie. Gravy on a Bucket Lid. Prater, Howard, illus. 1998. (Silly Songs Ser.). (J). pap. 6.95 (978-1-56763-430-3(3)); lib. bdg. 19.95 (978-1-56763-429-7(X)) Ozark Publishing.

Boza, Eduardo Robles. Mi Amiga No Quiere Comer.Tr. of My Friend Doesn't Want to Eat. (SPA.). (J). 4.95 (978-968-419-873-9(6)) Grijalbo, Editorial MEX. *Dist:* AIMS International Bks., Inc.

Bradley, Alex. Hot Lunch. 2007. 272p. (YA). (gr. 7 up). 16.99 (***978-0-525-47830-0(2)*** , Dutton Juvenile) Penguin Group (USA) Inc.

Brave M.A., Kathryn A. & Lavin, Paul J. A Fit ting Fairy Tale. 2006. 60p. pap. 12.95 (978-1-4241-2992-8(3)) PublishAmerica, Inc.

Brown, Marcia. Sopa de Piedras. Mlawer, Teresa, tr. 2001. (SPA., Illus.). (J). (gr. k-3). 7.96 net. (978-1-56137-559-2(4) , NU5657) Novel Units, Inc.

—Stone Soup. Brown, Marcia, illus. 2005. (Stories to Go! Ser.). (Illus.). 48p. (J). pap. 4.99 (978-0-689-87836-7(2) , Aladdin) Simon & Schuster Children's Publishing.

Brown, Rick, illus. Halloween Party. 2007. (I'm Going to Read Ser.). 32p. (J). (gr. 1-2). pap. 3.95 (***978-1-4027-4298-9(3)***) Sterling Publishing Co., Inc.

Bruel, Nick. Bad Kitty. Bruel, Nick, illus. 2005. (Illus.). 40p. (J). (ps-3). 15.95 (978-1-59643-069-3(9)) Roaring Brook Pr.

The Bubble Gum Contest. 2007. (J). per. (***978-1-932570-62-5(4)***) Literacy Footprints Inc.

Buckley, Charlie. Show Jo How to Make a Sandwich. 2007. (Show Jo Language Development Ser.). (Illus.). 16p. (J). (ps-1). per., bds. 14.95 (***978-1-933669-08-3(X)***) Literary Architects, LLC.

Buehner, Caralyn & Buehner, Mark. A Job for Wittilda. Buehner, Caralyn & Buehner, Mark, illus. 2004. (Illus.). 32p. (J). (gr. k-3). pap. 5.99 (978-0-14-240137-8(4) , Puffin) Penguin Group (USA) Inc.

Burningham, John. Where's Julius? 2001. (Illus.). 32p. (J). pap. 8.99 (978-0-09-941429-2(5)) Random Hse. GBR. *Dist:* Trafalgar Square Publishing.

The Cake: Individual Title Six-Packs. (Story Steps Ser.). (gr. k-2). 29.00 (978-0-7635-9601-9(9)) Rigby Education.

Capone, Deborah. Dumplings Are Delicious. 2005. 24p. (J). 14.95 (978-0-9728666-4-4(7)) As Simple As That Publishing.

Capucilli, Alyssa Satin. Biscuit's Picnic. Schories, Pat, illus. 1998. (Biscuit Ser.). 24p. (J). (ps-1). 12.95 (978-0-06-028072-7(7)) HarperCollins Pubs.

Carle, Eric. Pancakes, Pancakes! Carle, Eric, illus. 1998. (Illus.). 32p. (J). (ps-3). pap. 7.99 (978-0-689-82246-9(4) , Aladdin) Simon & Schuster Children's Publishing.

—What's for Lunch? Carle, Eric, illus. 1998. (Play-and-Read Book Ser.). (Illus.). 12p. (J). (ps). bds. 6.95 (978-0-590-32842-5(5)) Scholastic, Inc.

Carpenter, Suzanne, illus. So Hungry. 2004. 32p. pap. 29.95 (978-1-84323-455-5(6)) Beekman Bks., Inc.

Carry-out Food: 6 Small Books. (gr. k-3). 24.00 (978-0-7635-6234-2(3)) Rigby Education.

Catalanotto, Peter & Schembri, Pamela. The Secret Lunch Special. 2006. (Illus.). (J). 56p. (***978-1-4156-9204-2(1)***); Bk. 1. 64p. 15.95 (978-0-8050-7838-1(X) , Holt, Henry & Co. Bks. For Young Readers) Holt, Henry & Co.

Catling, Patrick Skene. The Chocolate Touch. 87p. (J). (gr. 3-5). pap. 4.99 (978-0-8072-1454-1(X) , Listening Library) Random Hse. Audio Publishing Group.

Chanda, J-P. Healthy Snacks with Blue! Kanemoto, Dan, illus. 2007. (Blue's Clues Ser.). 24p. (J). pap. 3.99 (978-1-4169-2778-5(6) , Simon Spotlight/Nickelodeon) Simon & Schuster Children's Publishing.

Chapman, Jane, illus. Bear Wants More. unabr. ed. 2006. (J). (ps-2). 24.95 incl. audio (***978-0-439-90572-5(9)***); 29.95 incl. audio compact disk (***978-0-439-90578-7(8)***) Weston Woods Studios, Inc.

Chapman, Jean. Flying Damper. Spoor, Mike, illus. 96p. pap. 10.95 (978-0-7022-2588-8(6)) Univ. of Queensland Pr. AUS. *Dist:* International Specialized Bk. Services.

Child, Lauren. I Will Never Not Ever Eat a Tomato. 2003. (Illus.). 32p. (J). (ps-3). reprint ed. pap. 6.99 (978-0-7636-2180-3(3)) Candlewick Pr.

Child, Lauren, et al. Fydda i Byth Bythoedd yn Bwyta Tomato. 2005. (WEL., Illus.). 32p. pap. (978-1-85596-668-0(9)) Dref Wen.

Chipponeri, Kelli. The Timmy Touch. Moore, Harry, illus. 2005. (Ready-to-Read Ser. Level 1). 24p. (J). lib. bdg. 15.00 (978-1-59054-966-7(X)) Fitzgerald Bks.

The Chocolate Moose. 2007. (Illus.). 48p. (J). per. 13.00 (***978-0-9767189-5-6(2)***) Better Day Publishing Co.

Church, Caroline Jayne. Woof's Snacktime: Woof Touch-and-Feel. Church, Caroline Jayne, illus. 2007. (Illus.). 10p. (J). (ps). 5.95 (***978-0-8027-9622-6(2)***) Walker & Co.

Clement, Maryceleste. Mr. Tootles & Those Oodles of Noodles. 2002. (Tootle Tales Ser.: Vol. 1). (Illus.). 32p. (J). (ps-3). 14.95 (978-0-9721706-0-4(X)) Tootle Time Publishing Co.

Cochran, Jean M. Your Tummy's Talking. Gullens, Lee, illus. 2007. 32p. (J). 16.95 (***978-0-9792035-3-4(8)***) Pleasant St. Pr.

Cohen, Caron Lee. Digger Pig & the Turnip/Marranita Poco Rabo y el Nabo. Campoy, F. Isabel, tr. Denise, Christopher, illus. 2008. (Green Light Readers Level 2 Ser.). 28p. (J). pap. 3.95 (***978-0-15-206255-2(6)*** , Green Light Readers) Harcourt Children's Bks.

Cohen, Milly. La Dulceria de Don Tono. Velazquez, Jose Luis Reyes, illus. rev. ed. 2006. (Castillo de la Lectura Verde Ser.). (SPA.). 112p. (J). pap. 7.95 (978-970-20-0198-0(6)) Castillo, Ediciones, S. A. de C. V. MEX. *Dist:* Macmillan.

Conlon, Mara. One Hungry Bunny. Wittwer, Hala, illus. 2003. (Reading Railroad Bks.). 14p. (J). (ps-1). bds. 5.99 (978-0-448-43121-5(1) , Grosset & Dunlap) Penguin Group (USA) Inc.

Cookies for Santa. 2006. (J). (***978-1-932570-75-5(6)***) Literacy Footprints Inc.

Cooper, Helen, et al. Pinsiaid o Bupur. 2005. (WEL., Illus.). 28p. (978-1-84512-022-1(1)) Cymdeithas Lyfrau Ceredigion.

Coplans, Peta. Spaghetti for Suzy. 2003. (Illus.). 32p. (J). pap. 6.95 (978-1-84270-100-3(2)) Andersen GBR. *Dist:* Trafalgar Square Publishing.

Cormier, Robert. Beyond the Chocolate War. 2000. (YA). 22.25 (978-0-8446-7140-6(1)) Smith, Peter Pub., Inc.

—Guerra Dei Cioccolatini. pap. 19.95 (978-88-451-2161-6(5)) Fabbri - RCS Libri ITA. *Dist:* Distribooks, Inc.

—La Guerra del Chocolate. 2003. (SPA.). 258p. (J). (gr. 5-8). 11.95 (978-1-56014-666-7(4)) Santillana USA Publishing Co., Inc.

Cousins, Lucy. Snacktime, Maisy! Cousins, Lucy, illus. 2001. (Maisy Bks.). (Illus.). 6p. (J). (gr. k-ps). pap. 6.99 (978-0-7636-1603-8(6)) Candlewick Pr.

Cox, Rhonda. Watermelon. Cox, Rhonda, photos by. 1999. (Books for Young Learners). (Illus.). 12p. (J). (gr. k-2). pap. 5.00 (978-1-57274-236-9(4) , A2540) Owen, Richard C. Pubs., Inc.

Cullimore, Stan. Alien Swap. Schon, Nick, illus. 2005. 24p. (J). lib. bdg. 22.65 (***978-1-59646-744-6(4)***) Dingles & Co.

Dad's Turkey Sandwich. 2003. (J). (978-1-58453-255-2(6)) Pioneer Valley Educational Pr., Inc.

Dague, Paige A. ScribbleMonster & the Crunchy, Crunchy Carrots. Dague, James, illus. 2001. (J). (ps). pap. 5.50 (978-0-9706406-0-4(9)) ScribbleBooks Co., The.

Dahl, Roald. Charlie & the Chocolate Factory. Blake, Quentin, illus. 40th anniv. movie tie-in ed. 2004. 160p. (J). (gr. k). 22.95 (978-0-375-83197-3(5) , Knopf Bks. for Young Readers) Random Hse. Children's Bks.

Daisy, April. The Crazy 8 Diner. 2004. (Illus.). 28p. (J). per. 7.95 (978-1-59466-023-8(9) , Little Ones) Port Town Publishing.

Dalmatian Press Staff. Let's Eat. 2007. 24p. pap. 3.50 (***978-1-4037-3428-0(3)***) Dalmatian Pr.

Davies, Jacqueline. The Lemonade War. 2007. 192p. (J). (gr. 3-5). 16.00 (***978-0-618-75043-6(6)***) Houghton Mifflin Co.

Davis, Aubrey. Bagels from Benny. Petricic, Dusan, illus. 2005. 32p. (J). (gr. 3). (978-1-55337-749-8(4)) Kids Can Pr., Ltd.

—Bagels from Benny. Petriecic, Duesan, illus. 2004. 32p. (J). (gr. k-3). (978-1-55337-417-6(7)) Kids Can Pr., Ltd.

—The Enormous potato. Petricic, Dusan, illus. 2001. 32p. (J). (gr. k-3). (978-1-55074-669-3(3)) Kids Can Pr., Ltd.

Davis, Tanita S. A la Carte. 2008. 288p. (J). (gr. 7). 15.99 (***978-0-375-84815-5(0)*** , Knopf Bks. for Young Readers) Random Hse. Children's Bks.

De Regniers, Beatrice Schenk. What Did You Put in Your Pocket? Date not set. 32p. (J). (ps-1). pap. 5.95 (978-0-06-443700-4(0)) HarperCollins Pubs.

—What Did You Put in Your Pocket? Grejniec, Michael, illus. 2003. 40p. (J). (ps-1). 16.99 (978-0-06-029028-3(5)) HarperCollins Pubs.

Derrickson, Jim. Bomo & the Beef Snacks. 2001. (Illus.). 29p. (J). pap. 19.99 (978-0-439-98775-2(X)) Scholastic, Inc.

Dhami, Narinder. Samosa Thief. Blundell, Tony, illus. 2005. 24p. (J). lib. bdg. 22.65 (***978-1-59646-708-8(8)***) Dingles & Co.

Dickinson, Rebecca. Monster Cake. Dickinson, Rebecca, illus. 2000. (Illus.). 32p. (J). (ps-2). pap. 4.99 (978-0-439-06752-2(9)) Scholastic, Inc.

—Monster Cake. 2000. (J). (978-0-606-19579-9(3)) Tandem Library Bks.

Dinner: Individual Title Six-Packs. (Sails Literacy Ser.). 16p. (gr. k up). 27.00 (978-0-7635-4445-4(0)) Rigby Education.

Dinnertime. 2003. (J). per. (978-1-57657-965-7(4)) Paradise Pr., Inc.

Dixon, Ann. The Blueberry Shoe. Zerbetz, Evon, illus. 1999. 32p. (J). (ps-3). 22.95 (978-0-88240-518-6(7) , Alaska Northwest Bks.) Graphic Arts Ctr. Publishing Co.

Donohue, Dorothy. Veggie Soup. 40p. (J). (ps-1). 2002. pap. 6.95 (978-1-58837-020-4(8)); 2000. (Illus.). 16.95 (978-1-890817-21-3(X)) Winslow Pr.

The Doorbell Rang. 2004. (Illus.). 24p. (J). (ps-2). 28.95 (978-1-59112-713-0(0)) Live Oak Media.

Dorling Kindersley Publishing Staff, contrib. by. Are These Peas? 2004. (Dk See-throughs Ser.). (Illus.). 21p. (J). 6.99 (978-0-7566-0208-6(4)) Dorling Kindersley Publishing, Inc.

Dougherty, Terri. The Best Lunch. Kouse, Patrick, illus. 2006. (Read-It! Readers Ser.). 32p. (J). (ps-3). 18.60 (978-1-4048-1578-0(3)) Picture Window Bks.

Dowling, Paul. Beans on Toast: Level Three, Blue. Dowling, Paul, illus. 1999. (Reading Together Ser.). (Illus.). (J). pap. (978-0-7636-0875-0(0)) Candlewick Pr.

Doyle, Malachy. Jody's Beans. Allibone, Judith, illus. 2002. (Read & Wonder Bks.). 32p. (J). (ps-1). pap. 6.99 (978-0-7636-1713-4(X)) Candlewick Pr.

—Jody's Beans. 2002. (gr. k-3). lib. bdg. 14.15 (978-0-613-74776-9(3)) Tandem Library Bks.

Drew, Rosa. Lemonade, Vol. 4472. Kupperstein, Joel, ed. 1998. (Learn to Read Math Ser.). (Illus.). 16p. (J). pap. 2.75 (978-1-57471-379-4(5) , 4472) Creative Teaching Pr., Inc.

Dubowski, Mark, illus. Stone Soup. 1998. (Domino Readers Ser.). 24p. (J). (ps-1). 5.95 (978-1-887734-22-6(8)) Star Bright Bks., Inc.

Dumas, Bianca. Tia Luisa, the Magical Cook: A Tale in English & Spanish. Dumas, Bianca, illus. 2000. (SPA & ENG., Illus.). 32p. (J). (gr. k-4). per. 7.95 (978-0-9669645-4-7(3) , AlterLingo Bks.) O'Hollow Publishing.

Dunbar, Joyce. Eggday. Cabrera, Jane, illus. 1999. 32p. (J). (ps-3). 15.95 (978-0-8234-1510-6(4)) Holiday Hse., Inc.

Dunrea, Olivier. BooBoo. 2004. (Illus.). 32p. (J). (gr. k-ps). tchr. ed. 9.95 (978-0-618-35654-6(1)) Houghton Mifflin Co. Trade & Reference Div.

Durant, Alan. Burger Boy. 2006. (Illus.). 32p. (J). (ps-4). pap. (978-1-84270-537-7(7)) Andersen.

Eat! 2002. (Baby Faces Ser.). (Illus.). (J). bds. (978-0-439-33945-2(6)) Scholastic, Inc.

Edwards, Julie Andres & Hamilton, Emma Walton. Dumpy's Apple Shop. Walton, Tony, illus. 2004. 24p. (J). lib. bdg. 13.85 (***978-1-4242-0708-4(8)***) Fitzgerald Bks.

Edwards, Pat. A Visit to Cousin Boris. Selway, Martina, illus. 1999. 24p. (J). (978-0-7608-3196-0(3)) Sundance/Newbridge Educational Publishing.

Eggleton, Jill. Rupert's Rainbow Ice Cream: Early Level Satellite Individual Title Six-Packs. (Sails Literacy Ser.). 16p. (gr. 1-2). 27.00 (978-0-7578-2935-2(X)) Rigby Education.

Ehlert, Lois. Feathers for Lunch. Ehlert, Lois, illus. 2002. (Illus.). (J). 14.04 (978-0-7587-2487-8(X)) Book Wholesalers, Inc.

Ehlert, Lois. Growing Vegetable Soup. 2007. (Illus.). 32p. (J). (ps). bds. 10.95 (***978-0-15-206176-0(2)*** , Red Wagon Bks.) Harcourt Children's Bks.

Elgar, Rebecca. Munch! What Are You Eating? 1999. (Illus.). 10p. (J). (ps-k). bds. 6.95 (978-1-899607-57-0(9)) Sterling Publishing Co., Inc.

—Where's My Dinner? With Flaps & a Pop-Up! 2003. (Illus.). 12p. (J). bds. 9.99 (978-1-4052-0451-4(6)) Egmont Bks., Ltd. GBR. *Dist:* Trafalgar Square Publishing.

Emberley, Rebecca. My Food/Mi Comida. Emberley, Rebecca, illus. 2002. (SPA & ENG., Illus.). 10p. (J). (ps-ps). bds. 6.99 (978-0-316-17718-4(0)) Little, Brown Bks. for Young Readers.

Emmett, Jonathan. A Mouse in the Marmalade. Church, Caroline, illus. 2002. (J). tchr. ed. 14.95 (978-1-58925-687-3(5) , tiger tales) ME Media LLC.

English, Karen. Just Right Stew. Rich, Anna, illus. 32p. (J). (gr. k-2). pap. 8.95 (978-1-59078-168-5(6)) Boyds Mills Pr.

—Just Right Stew. 2003. (Illus.). 32p. (J). (gr. k-4). 15.95 (978-1-56397-487-8(8)) Boyds Mills Pr.

Ericsson, Jennifer A. No Milk! Eitan, Ora, illus. 1998. 32p. (J). (ps-3). pap. 4.95 (978-0-688-15848-4(X)) HarperCollins Pubs.

—No Milk! 1998. (978-0-606-13666-2(5)) Tandem Library Bks.

Everett, F. The Burglar's Breakfast. (Young Reading Ser.: Vol. 1). 48p. (J). (gr. 2 up). lib. bdg. 13.95 (978-1-58086-786-3(3)) ; 2004. (Illus.). pap. 5.95 (978-0-7945-0221-8(0)) EDC Publishing. (Usborne).

Everitt, Betsy. Mean Soup. Everitt, Betsy, illus. 2002. (Illus.). (J). 15.23 (978-0-7587-3119-7(1)) Book Wholesalers, Inc.

Farish, Terry. The Cat Who Liked Potato Soup. Root, Barry, illus. 2007. 40p. (J). (gr. 1). pap. 6.99 (978-0-7636-3297-7(X)) Candlewick Pr.

Fast Food Felicity: Individual Title Six-Packs. (Bookweb Ser.). 32p. (gr. 3 up). 34.00 (978-0-7635-3933-7(3)) Rigby Education.

Fearnley, Jan. Mr Wolf's Pancakes. 2001. (gr. k-3). lib. bdg. 14.10 (978-0-613-53842-8(0)) Tandem Library Bks.

Fields, Terri. Burro's Tortillas. Rogers, Sherry, illus. 2007. 32p. (J). (ps-2). 15.95 (978-0-9768823-9-8(6)) Sylvan Dell Pubng.

Fleming, Candace. Big Cheese for the White House: The True Tale of a Tremendous Cheddar. Schindler, S. D., illus. 2004. 32p. (J). (ps-ps). lib. bdg. 14.15 (978-0-606-30286-9(7)) Tandem Library Bks.

—A Big Cheese for the White House: The True Tale of a Tremendous Cheddar. Schindler, S. D., illus. 2004. 32p. (J). reprint ed. pap. 6.95 (978-0-374-40627-1(8) , Sunburst) Farrar, Straus & Giroux.

Foreman, Michael. War & Peas. 2002. (Illus.). 32p. (J). (gr. k-3). pap. 9.99 (978-1-84270-083-9(9)) Andersen GBR. *Dist:* Independent Pubs. Group.

Forest, Heather. Stone Soup. 2000. (gr. 3-6). lib. bdg. 15.25 (978-0-613-54363-7(7)) Tandem Library Bks.

Franco, Betsy. Sally, la Divertida. Lamb, Stacey, illus. rev. ed. 2002. (Rookie Readers - Spanish Ser.).Tr. of Silly Sally. (SPA.). 24p. (J). (gr. k-2). 19.50 (978-0-516-22686-6(X) , Children's Pr.) Scholastic Library Publishing.

Freed, Shirley Ann & Moon, Louise. A Big Big Lunch. Morelan, Bill, ed. Butler, Steven, illus. l.t. ed. 2002. 16p. (J). (gr. 1-2). pap. 3.99 (978-1-58938-030-1(4)) Concerned Communications.

Freeman, Michelle. The Ravioli Kid. Abbott, Jason, illus. 2005. 32p. (J). 15.95 (978-1-58685-438-6(0)) Gibbs Smith, Publisher.

French, Jackie. Too Many Pear (Japanese/English Bilingual) Whatley, Bruce, illus. 2007. (JPN.). 32p. (J). pap. 5.95 (***978-1-59572-112-9(6)***) Star Bright Bks., Inc.

French, Vivien. Oliver's Fruit Salad. Bartlett, Alison, illus. 1998. 32p. (J). (ps-1). pap. 14.95 (978-0-531-30087-9(0) , Orchard Bks.) Scholastic, Inc.

Friesen, Ray. Lookit! Vol. 2: Yarg! & Other Stories. 2007. 96p. (J). (gr. 3-6). pap. 11.95 (978-0-9728177-9-0(4)) Don't Eat Any Bugs Prodns.

Fry, Sonali. A Day with Mom. Workman, Lisa, illus. 2007. (Holly Hobbie & Friends Ser.). 24p. (J). 8.99 (978-1-4169-3579-7(7) , Little Simon) Simon & Schuster Children's Publishing.

Gabriel, Nat. Bubble Trouble. Nez, John, illus. 2004. 32p. (J). lib. bdg. 20.00 (***978-1-4242-1085-5(2)***) Fitzgerald Bks.

Garfield, Valerie. Who Stole the Cookies from the Cookie Jar? Manning, Jane, illus. 2001. (Playtime Rhymes Ser.). 24p. (J). (ps up). 7.99 (978-0-694-01515-3(6) , Harper Festival) HarperCollins Pubs.

Gautier, Gary. Spaghetti & Peas. Guevara, Linda L., ed. Bailey, Sheila, illus. 2002. 40p. (J). (ps-5). 16.95 (978-0-9700863-6-5(9)) All About Kids Publishing.

Gerritsen, Paula. Nuts. 2006. 32p. (J). 15.95 (978-1-932425-66-6(7) , Lemniscaat) Boyds Mills Pr.

Gershator, David & Gershator, Phillis. Kallaloo: A Caribbean Tale. Greenseid, Diane, illus. 2005. 32p. (J). 16.95 (978-0-7614-5110-5(2)) Cavendish, Marshall Corp.

Giff, Patricia Reilly. All the Way Home. 2003. (Illus.). 176p. (J). (gr. 3-7). pap. 5.99 (978-0-440-41182-6(3) , Yearling) Random Hse. Children's Bks.

—Decid "Patata" 2000. (SPA.). (YA). (gr. 1 up). 3.95 (978-0-922852-45-1(6)) AIMS International Bks., Inc.

Glazer, Tom. On Top of Spaghetti. 32p. (J). pap. 4.95 (978-0-06-443547-5(4)) HarperCollins Pubs.

Golden Books Staff. Mission: Marketropolis. 2007. (Illus.). 24p. (J). (ps-2). pap. 3.99 (978-0-375-83767-8(1) , Golden Bks.) Random Hse. Children's Bks.

—The Secret's Inside! 2007. (Illus.). 16p. (J). (ps-3). pap. 6.99 (978-0-375-83792-0(2) , Golden Bks.) Random Hse. Children's Bks.

—Snack Time. 2001. (Illus.). 48p. (J). (ps-3). pap. 3.99 (978-0-307-28042-8(X) , Golden Bks.) Random Hse. Children's Bks.

—Top Dog. 2007. (Deluxe Coloring Book Ser.). (Illus.). 64p. (J). (ps-3). pap. 3.99 (978-0-375-83708-1(6) , Golden Bks.) Random Hse. Children's Bks.

—When Good Food Goes Bad. 2007. (Paint Box Book Ser.). (Illus.). 32p. (J). (ps-3). pap. 3.99 (978-0-375-83707-4(8) , Golden Bks.) Random Hse. Children's Bks.

Goldstone, Bruce. The Beastly Feast. Lent, Blair, illus. 2001. 32p. (J). (ps-1). pap. 7.95 (978-0-8050-6709-5(4) , Holt, Henry & Co. Bks. For Young Readers) Holt, Henry & Co.

—The Beastly Feast. 2001. 13.75 (978-0-606-22584-7(6)) Tandem Library Bks.

—Beastly Feast. 2001. (ps-2). lib. bdg. 15.25 (978-0-613-75496-5(4)) Tandem Library Bks.

Goodin, Carolyn M. Candy Land. Goodin, Carolyn M., illus. 2007. (Illus.). 38p. (J). per. 14.99 (***978-0-9797879-1-1(2)***) Family Legacy Ministries.

Graham, Elspeth. Sandwich that Jack Made. Mould, Chris, illus. 2004. 24p. (J). lib. bdg. (***978-1-59646-698-2(7)***) Dingles & Co.

Greenburg, Dan. The Day Everything Tasted Like Broccoli. 2001. (Maximum Boy Ser.: No. 2). (Illus.). 96p. (gr. 2-4). mass mkt. 3.99 (978-0-439-21945-7(0)) Scholastic, Inc.

—The Day Everything Tasted Like Broccoli. 2001. (Maximum Boy Ser.). (Illus.). (J). 10.79 (978-0-606-21320-2(1)) Tandem Library Bks.

—The Misfortune Cookie. Davis, Jack E., illus. 1998. (Zack Files Ser.: No. 13). 64p. (J). (gr. 2-5). pap. 4.99 (978-0-448-41748-6(0) , Grosset & Dunlap) Penguin Group (USA) Inc.

Greenwald, Marni. What Kind of Bagel Am I? 2005. (Illus.). 34p. per. 8.99 (978-1-932338-46-1(2)) Lifevest Publishing, Inc.

Gretz, Susanna. Rabbit Food. Gretz, Susanna, illus. 2001. (Illus.). 32p. (J). (ps-2). pap. 6.99 (978-0-7636-1293-1(6)) Candlewick Pr.

—Rabbit Food. 2001. (ps-2). lib. bdg. 14.15 (978-0-613-51406-4(8)) ; (Illus.). (J). (978-0-606-21393-6(7)) Tandem Library Bks.

Grey, Mini. Ginger Bear. 2007. 32p. (J). (gr. k-3). 15.99 (978-0-375-84253-5(5)) ; lib. bdg. 18.99 (978-0-375-94253-2(X)) Random Hse. Children's Bks. (Knopf Bks. for Young Readers).

Grimm, Jacob W. & Grimm, Wilhelm K. Doctor All-Knowing: A Folk Tale from Grimm. Boiger, Alexandra, illus. 2008. (J). (978-1-4169-1246-0(0)) Simon & Schuster Children's Publishing.

Groves. Tea Break. Date not set. (Illus.). 16p. pap. 129.15 (978-0-582-18297-4(2)) Addison-Wesley Longman, Ltd. GBR. *Dist:* Trans-Atlantic Pubns., Inc.

Gudule. Nouille Vivante. pap. 15.95 (978-2-09-250239-6(5)) Nathan, Fernand FRA. *Dist:* Distribooks, Inc.

Gustafson, Scott. Alphabet Soup: A Feast of Letters. Gustafson, Scott, illus. 2003. (Illus.). 48p. (J). (ps-3). tchr. ed. 15.95 (978-0-86713-025-6(3) , 88071) Greenwich Workshop Pr.

Gym Shoe Salad. 2007. (J). pap. 15.00 (***978-0-9779207-7-8(1)***) Text 4m Publishing.

Haas, Jessie. Runaway Radish. Apple, Margot, illus. 2001. 56p. (J). (gr. 2 up). lib. bdg. 16.89 (978-0-06-029159-4(1)) HarperCollins Pubs.

Hale, Natalie. Spaghetti! Date not set. (Illus.). 32p. (J). (ps-3). pap. 14.95 (978-0-9702698-0-5(3)) Special Reads for Special Needs.

Hall, Mary. Porcupines & Pancakes. Hall, Mary, illus. 1998. (Illus.). 16p. (J). (gr. k-2). pap. 12.95 (978-0-9668006-0-9(5)) Scoty 1 Publishing.

Hammelef, Danielle S. The MYST of the Missing Cookies. 2006. (Early Explorers Ser.). (J). 36.00 (***978-1-4108-6131-3(7)***) Benchmark Education Co.

Harcourt School Publishers Staff. The Best Food: On Level. 3rd ed. 2002. (Trophies Reading Program Ser.). (Illus.). (J). pap. 4.10 (978-0-15-322990-9(X)) Harcourt Schl. Pubs.

—The Fish Market, 6 Nos., Pack. 3rd ed. 2002. (Trophies Reading Program Ser.). (Illus.). (gr. 1). pap. 20.10 (978-0-15-326868-7(9)) Harcourt Schl. Pubs.

—Let's Make a Pie On Level. 3rd ed. 2002. (Trophies Reading Program Ser.). (Illus.). pap. 5.10 (978-0-15-323077-6(0)) Harcourt Schl. Pubs.

—The Potluck Picnic. 3rd ed. 2002. (Trophies English Language Learners Ser.). (Illus.). pap. 5.10 (978-0-15-327832-7(3)) Harcourt Schl. Pubs.

—Silly Sandwich: A Reader. 1999. (Collections Ser.). (Illus.). (J). pap. 2.10 (978-0-15-313443-2(7)) Harcourt Schl. Pubs.

—Spaghetti & Meatballs. 3rd ed. 2002. (Trophies English Language Learners Ser.). (Illus.). pap. 5.10 (978-0-15-327713-9(0)) Harcourt Schl. Pubs.

—Trofeos On Level: La Mejor Comida. 3rd ed. 2002. (SPA., Illus.). pap. 5.50 (978-0-15-323901-4(8)) Harcourt Schl. Pubs.

Harrison, Paul. El misterio del Queso. Rivers, Ruth, illus. 2005. (Lightning Readers Ser.). 32p. (J). (gr. 1-2). pap. 3.95 (978-0-7696-4081-5(8) , Gingham Dog Pr.) School Specialty Publishing.

—The Mystery of the Cheese. Rivers, Ruth, illus. 2005. (Lightning Readers Ser.). 32p. (J). (gr. 1-2). pap. 3.95 (978-0-7696-4041-9(9) , Gingham Dog Pr.) School Specialty Publishing.

Hartman, Bob. The Wolf Who Cried Boy. Raglin, Tim, illus. 2004. 32p. (J). (gr. k up). pap. 6.99 (978-0-14-240159-0(5) , Puffin) Penguin Group (USA) Inc.

Hauck, Phillip E. Ciruela Lleno de Ciruelas Pasas, Vol. 1500. Arena, Audrey R., illus. l.t. ed. 1999. Tr. of Plum Full of Prunes. (SPA.). 32p. (J). (gr. 3-5). 12.95 (978-0-9662228-6-9(5)) Dab Publishing Co.

—Plum Full of Prunes. Wilhem, Casper & Folchi, Robert A., eds. Arena, Audrey R., illus. l.t. ed. 1999. 26p. (J). (gr. 3-4). 12.95 (978-0-9662228-5-2(7)) Dab Publishing Co.

Head, Judith. Mud Soup. 2003. (gr. k-3). lib. bdg. 11.80 (978-0-613-87310-9(6)) Tandem Library Bks.

Heiligman, Deborah. Mike Swan, Sink or Swim. 1998. (978-0-606-13610-5(X)) Tandem Library Bks.

E F G

Henkes, Kevin. A Box of Treats: Five Little Picture Books about Lilly & Her Friends. Henkes, Kevin, illus. 2004. (Illus.). (J). 14.99 (978-0-06-073211-0(3) , Harper Festival) HarperCollins Pubs.

Herman, Debbie. Carla's Sandwich. Bailey, Sheila, illus. 2004. 32p. (J). 15.95 (978-0-9729225-2-4(0)) Flashlight Pr.

Herman, R. A. Pat-A-Cake. Ivanov, Olga & Ivanov, Aleksey, illus. 2005. 6p. (J). (ps-k). bds. 7.95 (978-1-59354-039-5(6)) Handprint Bks.

Hernandez, Richard J. Smelly Cheese. 2001. (J). (ps-3). pap. (978-0-9708489-1-8(9)) Storitime Publishing.

Heurtelou, Maude. Konpe Kabrit ak Konpe Kodenn. Louissaint, Louis, illus. 1999. Tr. of Turkey & Goat. (CRP.). 26p. (J). (gr. 3-5). pap. 19.00 incl. audio (978-1-881839-94-1(X)) Educa Vision.

Hillert, Margaret. The Little Cookie. Charles, Donald, illus. rev. ed. 2006. (Beginning to Read Ser.). 32p. (J). lib. bdg. 18.60 (978-1-59953-024-6(4)) Norwood Hse. Pr.

Hills, Ian. Toxic Toadburger Conspiracy. 2007. 368p. pap. 8.95 (***978-1-84046-564-8(6)***) Totem Bks. GBR. *Dist:* National Bk. Network.

Hiss, Jill. Peppeto's Magic Jelly Bean. 2005. 19.00 (978-0-8059-9893-1(4)) Dorrance Publishing Co., Inc.

Hobbs, Valerie. Get It While It's Hot, or Not. 1998. (YA). (gr. 7-12). pap. 3.99 (978-0-380-73101-5(0)) HarperCollins Pubs.

Hogg, Gary. Scrambled Eggs & Spider Legs. 1999. (Illus.). 80p. (gr. 2-5). pap. 3.50 (978-0-590-20589-4(7)) Scholastic, Inc.

Holub, Joan. Gingerbread Kid Goes to School. 2002. (gr. k-3). lib. bdg. 11.80 (978-0-613-52263-2(X)) Tandem Library Bks.

—Pizza That We Made. 2001. (gr. k-3). lib. bdg. 11.80 (978-0-613-64422-8(0)) Tandem Library Bks.

Horvath, Polly. Everything on a Waffle. braille ed. 2001. (gr. 2). spiral bd. (978-0-616-08846-3(9)) Canadian National Institute for the Blind/Institut National Canadien pour les Aveugles.

—Everything on a Waffle. 2004. 160p. (J). reprint ed. pap. 5.95 (978-0-374-42208-0(7) , Sunburst) Farrar, Straus & Giroux.

Howe, James. Bunnicula & Friends: Hot Fudge. Mack, Jeff, illus. 2004. 42p. (J). lib. bdg. 15.00 (***978-1-4242-1149-4(2)***) Fitzgerald Bks.

Howe, James. Hot Fudge. 1999. (Bunnicula & Friends Ser.). (J). (gr. k-3). (978-0-606-17394-0(3)) Tandem Library Bks.

Hubbard, Sharron/Y. Link & Rosie Pick Berries. Schleihs, Krostin, illus. 2007. (J). bds. 7.95 (***978-0-9762434-2-7(3)***) Link & Rosie Pr.

Hull, Larry A. & Plummer, Sherry K. All Twelve of Them. Winters, Kas, ed. Winters, Kas, illus. 1998. 24p. (J). (gr. k-6). pap. 7.50 (978-1-892225-12-2(3) , ATT-1) Winmark Communications.

Hulme, Joy N. Mary Clare Likes to Share: A Math Reader. Rockwell, Lizzy, illus. 2006. (Step into Reading Ser.). 32p. (J). (ps-2). lib. bdg. 11.99 (978-0-375-93421-6(9)); 3.99 (978-0-375-83421-9(4)) Random Hse. Children's Bks. (Random Hse. Bks. for Young Readers).

The Hungry Giant's Lunch: Level H. Group 1. (Story Box(R) Ser.). 16p. 31.50 (978-0-7802-9371-7(1)) Wright Group, The.

Hungry, Hungry Jack 6 Packs. Pack Pouch - Level J. (Lighthouse Ser.). 16p. (gr. 2 up). 28.00 (978-0-7578-0862-3(X)) Rigby Education.

Hunt, Darleen L. Farm Pizza. Hoskin, Tom, ed. Komarck, Michael, illus. l.t. ed. 1999. (Readers Ser.). 8p. (J). (ps-2). pap. 15.00 (978-1-929591-51-0(9)) Reading Rock, Inc.

—Farm Pizza: Little Book. Hoskin, Tom, ed. Komarck, Michael, illus. l.t. ed. 1999. (Readers Ser.). 8p. (J). (ps-2). pap. 4.00 (978-1-929591-50-3(0)) Reading Rock, Inc.

Hurwitz, Johanna. Ethan Out & About. Floca, Brian, illus. 2002. (Brand New Readers Ser.). 32p. (J). (ps-2). pap. 5.99 (978-0-7636-1099-9(2)) Candlewick Pr.

Hutchins, Pat. The Doorbell Rang. Hutchins, Pat, illus. (Illus.). 2005. (J). pap. 18.95 incl. audio compact disk (978-1-59112-712-3(2)); 2001. pap. 33.95 incl. audio (978-0-87499-803-0(4)); 2001. pap. 35.95 incl. audio compact disk (978-1-59112-714-7(9)) Live Oak Media.

—Ten Red Apples. Hutchins, Pat, illus. 2000. (Illus.). 32p. (J). (ps up). 16.99 (978-0-688-16797-4(7)); lib. bdg. 17.89 (978-0-688-16798-1(5)) HarperCollins Pubs.

Ice Cream for Breakfast. 2006. (J). 10.00 (978-0-9785002-0-7(2)) Johnson, Colleen.

The ice cream Truck. 2004. (J). per. 15.95 (978-0-9778937-4-4(X)) Priceless Ink Publishing Co., Inc.

Irbinskas, Heather. Pauly the Adventurous Pallid Bat. Anthis, Brian, illus. Tuttle, Merlin D., photos by. 2003. 32p. (J). pap. 7.95 (978-1-58369-032-1(8)) Western National Parks Assn.

It's Time for Dinner. 2002. 12p. (J). bds. 7.95 (978-1-84250-495-6(9) , Bright Sparks) Parragon, Inc.

Jackson, Alison. I Know an Old Lady Who Swallowed a Pie. Schachner, Judith B., illus. 2002. 32p. (J). (ps-3). pap. 6.99 (978-0-14-056595-9(7) , Puffin) Penguin Group (USA) Inc.

—I Know an Old Lady Who Swallowed a Pie. Schachner, Judith Byron, illus. 2002. (J). (ps-ps). lib. bdg. 15.30 (978-0-613-55215-8(6)) Tandem Library Bks.

Jarrell, Pamela R. A Nice Cool Drink. Teeple, Jackie, illus. l.t. ed. 2005. (J). (ps-k). pap. 10.95 (978-1-57332-340-6(3)); pap. 10.95 (978-1-57332-341-3(1)) HighReach Learning, Inc.

Jennings, Sharon. Franklin & the Cookies. Gagnon, Celeste et al, illus. 2005. 32p. (J). lib. bdg. 15.38 (***978-1-4242-1167-8(0)***) Fitzgerald Bks.

Jinkins, Jim. Pinky Dinky Doo: Where Are My Shoes? 2004. (Illus.). 48p. (J). (gr. 1-3). pap. 3.99 (978-0-375-82712-9(9) , Random Hse. Bks. for Young Readers) Random Hse. Children's Bks.

Joe's Pizza Parlor: Individual Title, 6 Packs. (ps-2). 27.00 (978-0-7635-9455-8(5)) Rigby Education.

Johns, Linda. Crazy Fruit Salad. ed. 2004. (Shared Connections Ser.). (J). pap. 27.00 (978-1-4108-1648-1(6)) Benchmark Education Co.

—Crazy Fruit Salad (Big Book) ed. 2004. (Shared Connections Ser.). (J). pap., instr.'s gde. ed. 27.00 (978-1-4108-1624-5(9)) Benchmark Education Co.

Johnston, Tony. Big Red Apple, Level 1. Corwin, Judith Hoffman, illus. 2000. (Hello Reader! Ser.: Level 1). 32p. (J). (ps-1). pap. 3.99 (978-0-439-09860-1(2)) Scholastic, Inc.

—Big Red Apple. 1999. (gr. k-3). lib. bdg. 11.80 (978-0-613-24361-2(7)) Tandem Library Bks.

Johnston, Tony & Johnston, Tony. Big Red Apple. Corwin, Judith Hoffman, illus. 2000. (Hello Reader! Ser.). 24p. lib. bdg. 10.79 (978-0-606-18519-6(4)) Tandem Library Bks.

Jones, Robert. The Odd Cookie. 1999. (Illus.). 28p. (YA). (gr. 5-13). pap. 9.00 (978-1-881524-53-1(1)) Milligan Bks., Inc.

Judge for a Day. (Greetings Ser.: Vol. 1). 32p. (gr. 3-5). 31.00 (978-0-7635-3173-7(1)) Rigby Education.

Judge for a Day: 6 Small Books. (Greetings Ser.: Vol. 1). 32p. (gr. 3-5). 31.00 (978-0-7635-1795-3(X)) Rigby Education.

Jukes, Mavis. Blackberries in the Dark. 2002. (J). (gr. 2-6). 20.00 (978-0-8446-7220-5(3)) Smith, Peter Pub., Inc.

The Junk-Food Files. 2003. (Illus.). pap. 5.60 (978-0-7398-7513-1(2)) Steck-Vaughn.

Junk Food June. 2006. (J). 7.95 (***978-0-9788536-3-1(6)***) G Publishing LLC.

Kadono, Eiko. Grandpa's Soup. Ichikawa, Satomi, illus. 2004. 32p. (J). (ps-3). 16.00 (978-0-8028-5195-6(9)) Eerdmans, William B. Publishing Co.

Kamau, G. How Porcupine Got His Spines. 2004. (Illus.). 22p. 13.95 (978-9966-25-168-8(5)) Heinemann Kenya, Limited (East African Educational Publishers Ltd E.A.E.P.) KEN. *Dist:* Michigan State Univ. Pr.

Kasza, Keiko. The Wolf's Chicken Stew. Kasza, Keiko, illus. 2002. (Illus.). (J). 13.19 (978-0-7587-4045-8(X)) Book Wholesalers, Inc.

Keenan, Penny. Cooking with Ginger: Ginger Gets Lost Book I. Murray, Carol, illus. 2005. (J). per. 19.95 (***978-1-932604-23-8(5)***) Tennessee Valley Publishing.

Keene, Carolyn. The Apple Bandit. Jones, Jan Naimo, illus. 2005. 74p. (J). lib. bdg. 15.00 (***978-1-4242-0917-0(X)***) Fitzgerald Bks.

Kehret, Peg. Wally Amos Presents Chip & Cookie - The First Adventure: No More Chocolate Chips. 2002. (Illus.). 40p. (J). (ps-3). 14.95 (978-1-58497-018-7(9)) Addax Publishing Group, Inc.

Kelley, True. School Lunch. Kelley, True, illus. 2005. (Illus.). 32p. (J). (ps-ps). 16.95 (978-0-8234-1894-7(4)) Holiday Hse., Inc.

Kendall, Jack. The Magic Apple Tree. Bostrom, Sally, illus. l.t. ed. 2006. (ENG.). 48p. (J). per. 9.95 (978-0-9787740-4-2(3)) Peppertree Pr., The.

Kimmel, Eric. Sopa de Cactus. Huling, Phil, illus. 2007. 32p. (J). 16.99 (***978-0-7614-5344-4(X)***) Cavendish, Marshall Corp.

Kittinger, Jo S. Un Almuerzo Con Ponche. 2004. (Rookie Reader Espanol Ser.). (J). (gr. k-2). pap. 4.95 (978-0-516-24619-2(4) , Children's Pr.) Scholastic Library Publishing.

—A Lunch with Punch. 2004. (Rookie Reader Espanol Ser.). (Illus.). 31p. (J). (gr. k-2). pap. 4.95 (978-0-516-27785-1(5) , Children's Pr.) Scholastic Library Publishing.

—A Lunch with Punch. Medoff, Jack, illus. 2003. (Rookie Reader - Level B Ser.). 32p. (J). 19.50 (978-0-516-22879-2(X) , Children's Pr.) Scholastic Library Publishing.

Klein, Adria F. Max Goes to the Grocery Store. Gallagher-Cole, Mernie, illus. 2007. (J). lib. bdg. (***978-1-4048-3682-2(9)***) Picture Window Bks.

Kline, Suzy. Horrible Harry Takes the Cake. Remkiewicz, Frank, illus. 2007. (Horrible Harry Ser.). 64p. (J). (gr. 2). 3.99 (***978-0-14-240939-8(1)*** , Puffin) Penguin Group (USA) Inc.

Knudsen, Michelle. Autumn Is for Apples. Denise, Fernando, illus. 2001. 24p. (J). (ps-1). pap. 3.25 (978-0-375-81090-9(0) , Random Hse. Bks. for Young Readers) Random Hse. Children's Bks.

Krensky, Stephen. Arthur & the Crunch Cereal Contest. 1998. (Arthur Chapter Bks.: Bk. 4). (J). (gr. 3-6). 11.05 (978-0-606-13150-6(7)) Tandem Library Bks.

Krulik, Nancy E. Any Way You Slice It, No. 9. John and Wendy Staff, illus. 2003. (Katie Kazoo, Switcheroo Ser.: No. 9). 80p. (J). (gr. 2-6). pap. 3.99 (978-0-448-43204-5(8) , Grosset & Dunlap) Penguin Group (USA) Inc.

—Any Way You Slice It, No. 9. 2003. (Katie Kazoo, Switcheroo Ser.: No. 9). (gr. 3-6). lib. bdg. 11.80 (978-0-613-72520-0(4)) Tandem Library Bks.

Kurzweil, Allen. Leon & the Champion Chip. Bertholf, Bret, illus. 2007. 352p. (J). pap. 6.99 (***978-0-06-053935-1(6)*** , Harper Trophy) HarperCollins Pubs.

Labatt, Mary. Pizza for Sam. Sarrazin, Marisol, illus. 2004. (Kids Can Read! Ser.). 32p. (J). (gr. k-3). (978-1-55337-331-5(6)); (978-1-55337-329-2(4)) Kids Can Pr., Ltd.

—Pizza for Sam. 2003. (gr. k-3). lib. bdg. 11.80 (978-0-613-84966-1(3)) Tandem Library Bks.

Landy, Sarah. Blue's Snack Party. Cardinali, Kevin, illus. 2000. (Blue's Clues Ser.). 16p. (J). (ps-k). 5.99 (978-0-689-83432-5(2) , Simon Spotlight/Nickelodeon) Simon & Schuster Children's Publishing.

LeapFrog Staff, compiled by. Leap's Snack. 2001. (J). (ps-2). spiral bd. 11.95 (978-1-58605-025-2(7)) LeapFrog Enterprises, Inc.

—Pooh Gets Stuck. 2001. (SPA.). (J). (ps-2). spiral bd. 14.99 (978-1-58605-133-4(4)) LeapFrog Enterprises, Inc.

LeBlanc, Ellen Lieb. Tea & Cookie. Pape, Wendy Fehrle, illus. 2005. (J). bds. (978-0-9773010-0-3(1)) Talmage Publishing.

Lenam, Salva. Kiko No Quiere Comer. Roman, Santi, illus. 2005. (Kiko Ser.). (SPA.). 10p. (J). 3.95 (978-84-95761-77-4(7)) Ediciones Norte, Inc.

Lenny Learns about Food Labels. 2004. (J). 5.00 (978-1-882541-39-3(1)) Food Allergy & Anaphylaxis Network.

LeSieg, Theo., et al. Ten Apples up on Top. 1998. (Bright & Early Board Bks.). (Illus.). 24p. (J). (gr. k-ps). bds. 4.99 (978-0-679-89247-2(8) , Random Hse. Bks. for Young Readers) Random Hse. Children's Bks.

Levert, Mireille. An Island in the Soup. 2002. (Illus.). 24p. (J). (ps-k). pap. 5.95 (978-0-88899-505-6(9)) Groundwood Bks. CAN. *Dist:* Perseus Distribution.

Levine, Anna. Running on Eggs. 1999. 128p. (J). (gr. 5-9). 15.95 (978-0-8126-2875-3(6)) Cricket Bks.

Liebig, Nelda J. Carrie & the Apple Pie. 1999. 122p. (J). (gr. 3-7). pap. (978-1-883953-30-0(8)) Midwest Traditions, Inc.

Ling, Bettina. Lemonade for Sale. Handelman, Dorothy, photos by. 1998. (Real Kids Readers Ser.). (Illus.). 48p. (gr. 1-3). lib. bdg. 18.90 (978-0-7613-2010-4(5)); 32p. (J). (gr. 2-4). pap. 4.99 (978-0-7613-2035-7(0)) Lerner Publishing Group. (Millbrook Pr.).

Lipe, Riki. Sooty. Spears-Stewart, Reta, ed. 1998. (Illus.). 34p. (J). (ps-6). 10.00 (978-0-9659381-3-6(1)) Hoot N' Cackle Pr.

Little, Robert. Grandma's Biscuits. Richmond, Jamea, illus. 2004. 32p. (J). (ps-7). 15.95 (978-0-9701863-5-5(5)) Relde Publishing.

Loehr, Patrick, illus. Mucumber McGee & the Lunch Lady's Liver. 2008. (J). (***978-0-06-082330-6(5)***); lib. bdg. (***978-0-06-082331-3(3)***) HarperCollins Pubs.

Lovelace, Kelley. Ready Set Go Organic. 2006. 7.99 (***978-0-9791029-0-5(1)***) KelleyGreenworks Publishing.

Lukas, Catherine & Cosby, Bill. Super Detective Little Bill: A Dial-the-Answer Book. Mastrocinque, Andy, illus. 2002. (Little Bill Ser.). 14p. (J). 8.99 (978-0-689-84200-9(7) , Simon Spotlight/Nickelodeon) Simon & Schuster Children's Publishing.

Lutz, Nancie Anne. Patsy & Freckles Make Christmas Cookies. Lutz, Nancie Anne, illus. 2005. (Illus.). 25p. (J). (978-0-9760064-1-1(3)) Dollworks.

Macaroni & Baloney. 2001. 32p. (J). spiral bd. 14.95 (978-0-9702698-1-2(1)) Special Reads for Special Needs.

Macaroni & Baloney: Wordless Edition. 2001. 22p. (J). spiral bd. 14.95 (978-0-9702698-2-9(X)) Special Reads for Special Needs.

Maccarone, Grace. El Almuerzo Sorpresa. Lewin, Betsy, illus. 2000. (Coleccion "Hola, Lector" Ser.). (SPA.). (J). (ps-1). pap. 3.20 net. (978-0-439-08696-7(5) , SO5844) Scholastic, Inc.

MacKinnon, Debbie. Find My Cake! Sieveking, Anthea, photos by. 1999. (Illus.). 10p. (J). (978-0-7112-0920-6(0)) Lincoln, Frances Ltd. GBR. *Dist:* Antique Collectors' Club.

Mackinnon, Mairi. Fox & the Crow. 2007. (First Reading Level 1 Ser.). 32p. (J). 8.99 (***978-0-7945-1813-4(3)*** , Usborne) EDC Publishing.

Magoo, Biz. Pajama Sam Out to Lunch! DiCicco, Sue, illus. 2001. (Humongous Ser.). 14p. (J). (ps-k). bds. 5.99 incl. cd-rom (978-1-58668-065-7(X)) Lyrick Studios.

Mahy, Margaret. Rattlebang Picnic. 1998. (Picture Puffin Ser.). (J). (978-0-606-13728-7(9)) Tandem Library Bks.

—Simply Delicious! Allen, Jonathan, illus. 1999. 32p. (J). (gr. k-4). pap. 15.95 (978-0-531-30181-4(8) , Orchard Bks.) Scholastic, Inc.

Manning, Mick. Snap! Granstrom, Brita, illus. 2006. 24p. 14.95 (978-1-84507 408 1(4)) Lincoln, Frances Ltd. GBR. *Dist:* Perseus Distribution.

Marshall, Janet. A Honey of a Day. 2000. (Illus.). 24p. (J). (ps up). 15.95 (978-0-688-16917-6(1)) HarperCollins Pubs.

Mason, Cherie. Everybody's Somebody's Lunch. Moore, Gustav, illus. 2005. 40p. (J). (gr. 3-6). 7.95 (978-0-88448-200-0(6)) Tilbury Hse. Pubs.

Mayer, Mercer. Little Critter: Snowball Soup. Mayer, Mercer, illus. 2007. (My First I Can Read Bks.). 32p. (J). (ps-k). 16.99 (***978-0-06-083544-6(3)***); pap. 3.99 (***978-0-06-083543-9(5)*** , Harper Trophy) HarperCollins Pubs.

Mayer, Mercer. A Yummy Lunch. 2002. (Little Critter Ser.). (Illus.). 24p. (J). (ps-2). 10.95 (978-1-57768-627-9(6)); Vol. 2. pap. 3.95 (978-1-57768-809-9(0)) School Specialty Publishing.

Mayfield, Marilee Joy. Chef Etouffee & the Great Gumbo Day. 2005. 64p. (J). lib. bdg. 19.95 (978-0-9659222-6-5(X)) Leaping Antelope Productions.

Mazer, Anne. That's the Way the Cookie Crumbles. 2005. (Amazing Days of Abby Hayes Ser.: No. 16). 119p. (J). lib. bdg. 16.92 (***978-1-4242-0748-0(7)***) Fitzgerald Bks.

McAllister, Margaret. The Magic Porridge Pot. Utton, Peter, illus. 2006. 32p. (J). (***978-1-4048-3122-3(3)***) Picture Window Bks.

McCafferty, Catherine. The Gingerbread Man. Bowles, Doug, illus. 2002. (Brighter Child Keepsake Stories Ser.). 32p. (J). (ps-3). pap. 3.99 (978-1-57768-368-1(4) , Brighter Child) School Specialty Publishing.

McCurry, Miya. The Foods Return. 2005. (J). per. 8.99 (978-0-9764690-3-2(0)) Milligan Bks., Inc.

McCurry, Miya Lynn. The Foods. McCurry, Miya Lynn, illus. 1999. (Illus.). 34p. (J). (ps-3). pap. 7.99 (978-1-881524-66-3(3)) Milligan Bks., Inc.

McDonald, Megan. Beetle McGrady Eats Bugs! Manning, Jane K., illus. 2005. 32p. (J). 15.99 (978-0-06-001354-7(0)); lib. bdg. 17.89 (978-0-06-001355-4(9)) HarperCollins Pubs.

McDonald, Rae. A Fishing Surprise. Kemly, Kathleen Hadam, illus. 2007. 32p. (J). (***978-1-55971-977-3(X)*** , NorthWord Bks. for Young Readers) T&N Children's Publishing.

McFarland, Lyn Rossiter. Mouse Went Out to Get a Snack. McFarland, Jim, illus. 2005. 32p. (J). 16.00 (978-0-374-37672-7(7) , Farrar, Straus & Giroux (BYR)) Farrar, Straus & Giroux.

McGrath, Meggan. My Grapes. McGrath, Meggan, illus. 2001. (Illus.). 48p. (J). (ps-1). pap. 16.95 (978-0-439-09259-3(0)) Scholastic, Inc.

McKee, Violet. Macaroni. McKee, David, illus. 1998. 32p. (J). (ps-3). 19.99 (978-0-86264-806-0(8)) Andersen GBR. *Dist:* Independent Pubs. Group.

McMullan, Kate. Fluffy Goes Apple Picking. Smith, Mavis, illus. 2002. (Hello Reader! Ser.). 40p. (J). 3.99 (978-0-439-31420-6(8)) Scholastic, Inc.

Meddaugh, Susan. Martha Blah Blah. Meddaugh, Susan, illus. 2002. (Martha Ser.). (Illus.). (J). 13.79 (978-0-7587-3094-7(2)) Book Wholesalers, Inc.

—Martha Blah Blah. Meddaugh, Susan, illus. 1998. (Illus.). 32p. (J). (gr. k-3). pap. 6.95 (978-0-395-90118-2(9) , Walter Lorraine) Houghton Mifflin Co. Trade & Reference Div.

Melton, Lisa Lete. The Giant Bean Burrito: A Funny Fart Fable. Dillard, Travis, illus. 2002. 20p. (J). (gr. k-4). pap. 7.95 (978-0-9721426-0-1(6)) Paragon Publishing.

Miller, Dennis. Jelly Beans. Baird, Mary Lynn, illus. 2002. 36p. (J). lib. bdg. (978-0-9722259-0-8(0)) Twin Peaks Publishing, Inc.

Mills, David. Lima's Red Hot Chilli. Brazell, Derek, illus. 2004. 24p. (J). (TAM, VIE, GUJ, PER & JPN.). (978-1-85269-420-3(3)); (TAM, VIE, GUJ, PER & JPN.). (978-1-85269-421-0(1)); (TAM, VIE, GUJ, PER & JPN.). (978-1-85269-422-7(X)); (TAM, VIE, GUJ, PER & JPN.). (978-1-85269-423-4(8)); (TAM, VIE, GUJ, PER & JPN.). (978-1-85269-424-1(6)); (TAM, VIE, GUJ, PER & JPN.). (978-1-85269-425-8(4)); (TAM, VIE, GUJ, PER & JPN.). (978-1-85269-426-5(2)); (TAM, VIE, GUJ, PER & JPN.). (978-1-85269-427-2(0)); (TAM, VIE, GUJ, PER & JPN.). (978-1-85269-467-8(X)); (TAM, VIE, GUJ, PER & JPN.). (978-1-85269-466-1(1)); (TAM, VIE, GUJ, PER & JPN.). (978-1-85269-468-5(8)); (TAM, VIE, GUJ, PER & JPN.). (978-1-85269-469-2(6)); (TAM, VIE, GUJ, PER & JPN.). (978-1-85269-506-4(4)); (TAM, VIE, GUJ, PER & JPN.). (978-1-85269-533-0(1)); (TAM, VIE, GUJ, PER & JPN.). (978-1-85269-543-9(9)); (978-1-85269-429-6(7)); (ENG, URD & BEN.). (978-1-85269-504-0(8)); (ENG, URD & BEN.). (978-1-85269-505-7(6)); (CAM & ENG.). (978-1-85269-542-2(0)) Mantra Publishing, Ltd.

—Lima's Red Hot Chilli. Brazell, Derek, illus. 2004. (TAM, VIE, GUJ, PER & JPN.). 24p. (J). 13.50 (978-1-85269-465-4(3)); 14.95 (978-1-85269-534-7(X)) Mantra Publishing, Ltd. GBR. *Dist:* AIMS International Bks., Inc.

Mills, David & Tang, My. Lima's Red Hot Chilli. Brazell, Derek, illus. 2004. (TAM, VIE, GUJ, PER & JPN.). 24p. (J). 13.50 (978-1-85269-428-9(9)) Mantra Publishing, Ltd. GBR. *Dist:* AIMS International Bks., Inc.

Miranda, Anne. Food Court. Cleyet-Merle, Laurence, illus. 2002. 16p. (J). (978-0-439-35090-7(5)) Scholastic, Inc.

Mitchell, Susan K. Stone Pizza. Hayes, McNevin, illus. 2007. (J). (***978-1-891795-26-8(0)***) RGU Group, The.

Mitton, Tony & Rider, Cynthia. The Magic Porridge Pot. Shaw-Smith, Emma, illus. 2001. (Cambridge Reading Ser.). 16p. pap., stu. ed. 8.00 (978-0-521-01429-8(8)) Cambridge Univ. Pr.

Mitzo Thompson, Kim. My Grandma Likes to Cook / A mi abuela le gusta Cocinar. 2006. (Dual Language Readers Ser.). 32p. (J). pap. 4.99 (978-0-7696-4624-4(7)) School Specialty Publishing.

Monk, Isabell. Family. Porter, Janice Lee, illus. 32p. (J). (ps-ps). 2005. pap. 6.95 (978-1-57505-917-4(7)); 2003. 15.95 (978-1-57505-485-8(X) , Carolrhoda Bks.) Lerner Publishing Group.

Moody-Luther, Jacqueline. Bear & the pizza tree - word World. 2007. 12p. (J). 12.95 (***978-1-59764-297-2(5)***) New Line Bks.

Moran, Alex. Popcorn. Everitt, Betsy, illus. 2003. (Green Light Readers Level 1 Ser.). 24p. (J). 11.95 (978-0-15-204821-1(9)); pap. 3.95 (978-0-15-204861-7(8)) Harcourt Children's Bks. (Green Light Readers).

—Popcorn. 1999. (Green Light Readers Ser.). (978-0-606-16508-2(8)); lib. bdg. 11.80 (978-0-613-66372-4(1)) Tandem Library Bks.

Morgan, Ruth. Batter Splatter! Mikhail, Jess, illus. 2005. 24p. (J). lib. bdg. 22.65 (***978-1-59646-704-0(5)***) Dingles & Co.

Mullican, Judy. Time to Eat! Board Book & Felt Puppet Set. Coates, Jennifer, illus. 2005. (J). bds. (978-1-57332-359-8(4)) HighReach Learning, Inc.

—Wishing for Vegetables. 2006. (J). pap. (978-1-57332-411-3(6)) HighReach Learning, Inc.

Munoz-Furlong, Anne. Alexander & His Pals Visit the Main Street School. 1999. (J). (gr. k-6). pap. (978-1-882541-07-2(3)) Food Allergy & Anaphylaxis Network.

—Alexander Goes to a Birthday Party. Furlong, Mariel Christine, illus. 1999. 24p. (J). (gr. k-6). pap. 5.00 (978-1-882541-11-9(1)) Food Allergy & Anaphylaxis Network.

—Alexander Goes Trick-or-Treating. Furlong, Mariel Christine, illus. 1999. 24p. (J). (gr. k-6). pap. 5.00 (978-1-882541-13-3(8)) Food Allergy & Anaphylaxis Network.

—How Lenny Found Out about His Food Allergy. Furlong, Mariel Christine, illus. 2001. (Alexander, the Elephant Who Couldn't Eat Peanuts Ser.: Vol. 7). 24p. (J). (ps-5). 5.00 (978-1-882541-22-5(7)) Food Allergy & Anaphylaxis Network.

Munsch, Robert. Algo Bueno. 2001. (SPA.). (gr. k-3). lib. bdg. 14.10 (978-0-613-78388-0(3)) Tandem Library Bks.

—Mmm, Cookies! Martchenko, Michael, illus. 2000. 28p. (J). (ps-3). pap. 11.95 (978-0-590-89603-0(2) , Cartwheel Bks.) Scholastic, Inc.

—More Pies. Martchenko, Michael, illus. ed. 2004. (J). (gr. k-3). spiral bd. (978-0-616-14590-6(X)) Canadian National Institute for the Blind/Institut National Canadien pour les Aveugles.

—Une Tonne de Tartes! ed. 2004. (FRE., Illus.). (J). (gr. k-3). spiral bd. (978-0-616-14602-6(7)) Canadian National Institute for the Blind/Institut National Canadien pour les Aveugles.

Munson, Derek. Enemy Pie. King, Tara Calahan, illus. 2000. 40p. (J). (gr. k-3). 15.95 (978-0-8118-2778-2(X)) Chronicle Bks. LLC.

Murphy, Stuart J. Seaweed Soup. 2001. (ps-2). lib. bdg. 12.95 (978-0-613-50243-6(4)) Tandem Library Bks.

My Lunch: Kindergarten Newcomer Books. (On Our Way to English Ser.). (gr. k up). 23.50 (978-0-7578-7189-4(5)) Rigby Education.

Myers, Bernice. The Super-Duper Sandwich. Ziegler, Judy, illus. 2000. (Books for Young Learners). 16p. (J). pap. 5.00 (978-1-57274-283-3(6)) Owen, Richard C. Pubs., Inc.

Nanji, Shenaaz. Treasure for Lunch. Cathcart, Yvonne, illus. 2005. 24p. (J). (gr. k-3). 13.95 (978-1-896764-32-0(0)) Second Story Pr. CAN. *Dist:* Orca Bk. Pubs. USA.

Napoli, Donna Jo & Furrow, Robert. Sly the Sleuth & the Food Mysteries. Maione, Heather Harms, illus. 2007. 144p. (J). (gr. 2-4). 16.99 (978-0-8037-3119-6(1) , Dial) Penguin Group (USA) Inc.

Nassau, Elizabeth Sussman. The Peanut Butter Jam. Ott, Margot J., illus. 2001. 32p. (J). (ps-3). 14.95 (978-0-929173-35-1(X)) Health Pr. NA, Inc.

Nechaer, Michelle W. Apron Annie's Pies, Vol. 4467. Kupperstein, Joel, ed. Allen, Joy, illus. 1998. (Learn to Read Math Ser.). 16p. (J). pap. 2.99 (978-1-57471-374-9(4) , 4467) Creative Teaching Pr., Inc.

—Our Favorites, Vol. 4473. Kupperstein, Joel, ed. Jarrett, Michael, photos by. 1998. (Learn to Read Math Ser.). (Illus.). 16p. (J). pap. 2.75 (978-1-57471-380-0(9) , 4473) Creative Teaching Pr., Inc.

Newth, Rebecca. Tinkum's Dog. Primm, Thomas, illus. 2005. 32p. (J). 15.00 (***978-0-9630310-7-5(4)***) Will Hall Bks.

Nickerson, Margaret. Gathering Food. Nevak, Caroline, illus. l.t. ed. 1999. 8p. (J). (gr. k-3). pap. 14.50 (978-1-58084-060-6(4)) Lower Kuskokwim Schl. District.

—Katitchirugut Niqinik. Nevak, Caroline, illus. l.t. ed. 1999. Tr. of Gathering Food. (ESK.). 8p. (J). (gr. k-3). pap. 14.50 (978-1-58084-136-8(8)) Lower Kuskokwim Schl. District.

—Katitchiyuanni Niqinik. Nevak, Caroline, illus. l.t. ed. 1999. Tr. of Gathering Food. (ESK.). 8p. (J). (gr. k-3). pap. 14.50 (978-1-58084-126-9(0)) Lower Kuskokwim Schl. District.

—Neqengnaqler. Nevak, Caroline, illus. l.t. ed. 1999. Tr. of Gathering Food. (ESK.). 8p. (J). (gr. k-3). pap. 14.50 (978-1-58084-105-4(8)) Lower Kuskokwim Schl. District.

—Niginik Katittigaangapta. Nevak, Caroline, illus. l.t. ed. 1999. Tr. of Gathering Food. (ESK.). 8p. (J). (gr. k-3). pap. 14.50 (978-1-58084-133-7(3)) Lower Kuskokwim Schl. District.

—Quyurciyaraq Neqnek. Nevak, Caroline, illus. l.t. ed. 1999. Tr. of Gathering Food. (ESK.). 8p. (J). (gr. k-3). pap. 14.50 (978-1-58084-061-3(2)) Lower Kuskokwim Schl. District.

Nolen, Jerdine. Lauren Mcgill's Pickle Museum. Tilley, Debbie, illus. 2006. 29p. (J). (gr. k-4). reprint ed. 16.00 (978-1-4223-5191-8(2)) DIANE Publishing Co.

Norfolk, Bobby. Anansi Goes to Lunch. 2007. 32p. (J). pap. 3.95 (***978-0-87483-852-7(5)***) August Hse. Pubs., Inc.

North, Merry. All Gone. Woolf, Julia, illus. 2005. (J). (***978-1-57151-753-1(7)***) Playhouse Publishing.

November, Deborah. Sesame Street Big Block Party! Story Cookbook & Recipe Cards. 2006. (Sesame Street Ser.). 32p. (J). pap. 10.99 (978-0-7944-1104-6(5)) Reader's Digest Assn., Inc., The.

Numeroff, Laura Joffe. If You Give a Mouse a Cookie. ed. 2004. (Illus.). (J). (gr. k-3). spiral bd. (978-0-616-01751-7(0)); spiral bd. (978-0-616-01752-4(9)) Canadian National Institute for the Blind/Institut National Canadien pour les Aveugles.

—If You Give a Mouse a Cookie. Bond, Felicia, illus. Date not set. 32p. (J). (ps-2). 4.95 (978-0-06-443166-8(5)) HarperCollins Pubs.

—If You Give a Pig a Pancake. braille ed. 2004. (Illus.). (J). (gr. k-3). spiral bd. (978-0-616-07243-1(0)); spiral bd. (978-0-616-07244-8(9)) Canadian National Institute for the Blind/Institut National Canadien pour les Aveugles.

Numeroff, Laura Joffe & Bond, Felicia. If You Give a Pig a Pancake. 2000. (J). 11.98 incl. audio Random Hse. Audio Publishing Group.

Nutrition Adventures with the Nutri Gang, Race Day, Issue #1: The Nutri Gang. 2007. (J). 2.99 (***978-0-9792383-0-7(7)***) KJ Pubns.

O'Keefe, Susan Heyboer. More Hungry Monsters. 2004. (Illus.). 32p. (J). 15.95 (978-0-316-61061-2(5)) Little Brown & Co.

Pace, Dianne. Odel's Diner. 2007. (J). per. 12.95 (***978-0-89315-419-6(9)***) Lambert Bk. Hse., Inc.

Page, Nick & Page, Claire. Read with Me Gingerbread Fred: Sticker Activity Book. 2006. (Read with Me (Make Believe Ideas) Ser.). (Illus.). 12p. (J). (gr. k-2). pap. 4.95 (978-1-84610-178-6(6)) Make Believe Ideas GBR. *Dist:* Ingram Pub. Services.

Palatini, Margie. Zak's Lunch. Fine, Howard, illus. 1998. 32p. (J). (gr. k-3). tchr. ed. 16.00 (978-0-395-81674-5(2) , Clarion Bks.) Houghton Mifflin Co. Trade & Reference Div.

—Zak's Lunch. Fine, Howard, illus. 2004. 32p. (J). (gr. k-3). reprint ed. pap. 6.95 (978-0-618-48603-8(8) , Clarion Bks.) Houghton Mifflin Co. Trade & Reference Div.

—Zak's Lunch. unabr. ed. 1999. (J). pap., stu. ed. 32.00 incl. audio (978-0-7887-2983-6(7) , 40865) Recorded Bks., LLC.

Palmer, Catherine. Fatal Harvest. l.t. ed. 2004. (Matthew 25 Ser.). 496p. (YA). 28.95 (978-0-7862-6259-5(1)) Thorndike Pr.

Pantuso, Mike & Henson, Jim. Food! 2001. (Illus.). (J). lib. bdg. (978-0-375-91391-4(2) , Random Hse. Bks. for Young Readers) Random Hse. Children's Bks.

Park, Barbara. Junie B. Jones & the Yucky Blucky Fruitcake. unabr. ed. 2004. (Junie B. Jones Ser.: No. 5). 71p. (J). (gr. k-3). pap. 17.00 incl. audio (978-0-8072-0641-6(5) , Listening Library) Random Hse. Audio Publishing Group.

Patterson, Irania. Chipi Chipis, Small Shells of the Sea. McElvane, Catherine, illus. 2005. Tr. of Chipi Chipis, Caracolitos del Mar. (SPA.). 44p. (J). per. 12.99 (978-1-59494-006-4(1)) CPCC Pr.

Paulsen, Gary. The Tortilla Factory. 1998. (J). (978-0-606-13857-4(9)) Tandem Library Bks.

Pearson, Mary E. Pickles in My Soup. Payne, Tom, illus. 2000. (Rookie Reader Skill Set Ser.). 32p. (J). (gr. k-2). pap. 4.95 (978-0-516-26550-6(4) , Children's Pr.) Scholastic Library Publishing.

Peck, Jan. The Giant Carrot. Root, Barry, illus. 1998. 32p. (J). (ps-3). 16.99 (978-0-8037-1823-4(3) , Dial) Penguin Group (USA) Inc.

Pedersen, Janet. Pino & the Signora's Pasta. Pedersen, Janet, illus. 2005. (Illus.). 32p. (J). (ps-3). 16.99 (978-0-7636-2396-8(2)) Candlewick Pr.

Perez-Mercado, Mary Margaret. Zas! Torrey, Richard L., illus. 2000. (Rookie Espanol Ser.). (SPA.). 24p. (J). (gr. k-2). 19.50 (978-0-516-21692-8(9) , Children's Pr.) Scholastic Library Publishing.

Perret, Gene, text. Harvey Green, the Eating Machine. 2002. (Illus.). 32p. (J). 12.95 (978-1-893860-78-0(7)) Arizona Highways.

Peterson, Cris. Extra Cheese, Please! Mozzarella's Journey from Cow to Pizza. 2004. (Illus.). 32p. (J). (gr. k-2). pap. 9.95 (978-1-59078-246-0(1)) Boyds Mills Pr.

Pete's a Pizza. 2004. (Illus.). 32p. (J). (ps-2). 28.95 (978-1-59112-740-6(8)) Live Oak Media.

Pete's a Pizza. 2004. 24.95 incl. audio (978-1-55592-068-5(3)) Weston Woods Studios, Inc.

Petricic, Dusan, illus. The Enormous potato. 1998. 32p. (J). (gr. k-3). (978-1-55074-386-9(4)) Kids Can Pr., Ltd.

Pienkowski, Jan. Pizza! A Yummy Pop-Up. Pienkowski, Jan, illus. 2004. (Illus.). 12p. (J). (gr. k-4). reprint ed. 13.00 (978-0-7567-7815-6(8)) DIANE Publishing Co.

Pinkwater, Daniel M. Rainy Morning. Pinkwater, Jill, illus. 1999. (Pinkwater Ser.: Vol. 1). 32p. (J). (gr. k-3). 16.00 (978-0-689-81143-2(8) , Atheneum) Simon & Schuster Children's Publishing.

Polacco, Patricia. Thunder Cake. Polacco, Patricia, illus. 2002. (Illus.). (J). 14.04 (978-0-7587-3808-0(0)) Book Wholesalers, Inc.

The Power of Chocolate. 2005. (YA). (978-0-9771020-0-6(9)) Savas, Bachtsoglou.

Preller, James. The Case of the Food Fight. 2005. (Jigsaw Jones Ser.: No. 28). (Illus.). 80p. (J). pap. 3.99 (978-0-439-67807-0(2) , Scholastic Paperbacks) Scholastic, Inc.

—The Case of the Food Fight. Smith, Jamie C., illus. 2005. (Little Apple Ser.). 75p. (J). (978-1-4156-2391-6(0)) Scholastic, Inc.

Pugliano-Martin, Carol. The Day I Followed the Pickle: Reader's Theater Levels I-K (15-20) Beckes, Shirley, illus. ed. 2004. (Reader's Theater Ser.). 16p. (J). pap. 22.00 (978-1-4108-2297-0(4) , A22974) Benchmark Education Co.

Purmell, Ann. The Apple Cider Making Days. Friar, Joanne, illus. 2002. 32p. (J). (gr. k-2). 14.95 (978-0-7613-2364-8(3) , Millbrook Pr.) Lerner Publishing Group.

Quadrillion Media Staff. Show Me the Apple! 1999. bds. 3.95 (978-1-58185-214-1(2)) Quadrillion Media LLC.

The Queen of Hearts: 6 Small Books. (gr. k-2). 23.00 (978-0-7635-8494-8(0)) Rigby Education.

Quest, Stacy. Sad Sam & the Magic Cookies. 2006. (Illus.). (J). lib. bdg. 16.95 (978-1-932367-01-0(2)) BookBound Publishing.

Rade, Erin P. Who Wants Some Pizza? Smith, Len, illus. 2007. (Meet the Robinsons Ser.). 20p. (J). pap. 6.99 (978-0-06-112480-8(X)) HarperCollins Pubs.

Rader, Josh. Detective Stephy Wephy Holmes: In the Missing Cake. Meyers, Sarah, illus. 2007. (J). per. 14.99 (***978-1-59879-399-4(3)***) Lifevest Publishing, Inc.

Raintree Steck-Vaughn Staff. Sandwiches, Sandwiches. 2000. (Illus.). (J). pap. 19.24 (978-0-8172-6455-0(8)) Steck-Vaughn.

Random House Staff & Monster, Cookie. Food! by Cookie Monster. Pantuso, Mike, illus. 2006. 32p. (J). (gr. k-ps). bds. 6.99 (978-0-375-83509-4(1) , Random Hse. Bks. for Young Readers) Random Hse. Children's Bks.

Rattigan, Jama Kim. Dumpling Soup. 1998. (J). 13.50 (978-0-606-13349-4(6)) Tandem Library Bks.

Rau, Dana Meachen. My Favorite Foods, Level C. Lin, Grace, illus. 2001. (Early Reader Ser.). 32p. (J). (gr. k up). lib. bdg. 18.60 (978-0-7565-0076-4(1)) Compass Point Bks.

Reberg, Evelyne. Roi des de la Tambouille. pap. 21.95 (978-2-227-73104-2(4)) Bayard Editions FRA. *Dist:* Distribooks, Inc.

Redhead, Janet S. & Dale, Christine. The Big Block of Chocolate. (Illus.). (J). pap. (978-0-908643-75-2(6)) Scholastic New Zealand Ltd.

Reetz, Kurt. Sir Noodlefish: The Cake Wars. 2000. mass mkt. 8.95 (978-1-931179-16-4(6)) Long Hill Productions, Inc.

Reid, Suzan. The Meat Eaters Arrive. Hendry, Linda, illus. 2003. 32p. (J). (ps-3). pap. 4.95 (978-1-55209-004-6(3)) Firefly Bks., Ltd.

Rentschler, Nancy, des. Food Friend Puppet Set. 2006. (J). per. (978-1-57332-403-8(5)) HighReach Learning, Inc.

Rex, Michael. The Pie Is Cherry. 2001. (J). 15.95 (978-0-8050-6308-0(0) , Holt, Henry & Co. Bks. For Young Readers) Holt, Henry & Co.

Rey. Panique a la Chocolaterie. 16.95 (978-2-09-250165-8(8)) Nathan, Fernand FRA. *Dist:* Distribooks, Inc.

Rey, Margret. Curious George & the Pizza. Rey, Margret, illus. 2002. (Curious George TV Bks.). (Illus.). (J). 11.87 (978-0-7587-2312-3(1)) Book Wholesalers, Inc.

Reynolds, Aaron. Buffalo Wings. Bogan, Paulette, illus. 2007. 32p. (J). 17.85 (***978-1-59990-139-8(0));*** 16.95 (***978-1-59990-062-9(9)***) Bloomsbury Publishing.

Rigby Education Staff. Fish for Dinner. (Sails Literacy Ser.). (Illus.). 16p. (gr. 1-2). 27.00 (978-0-7635-9896-9(8) , 698968C99) Rigby Education.

—Honey, Honey. (Sails Literacy Ser.). (Illus.). 16p. (gr. k-1). 27.00 (978-0-7635-9872-3(0)) Rigby Education.

—Rupert's Ice Cream Shop. (Sails Literacy Ser.). (Illus.). 16p. (gr. 1-2). 27.00 (978-0-7635-9902-7(6) , 699026C99) Rigby Education.

Riley, Linnea A. Mouse Mess. Riley, Linnea A., illus. 2002. (Illus.). (J). 25.06 (978-0-7587-3179-1(5)) Book Wholesalers, Inc.

Rivers, Freya A. Maat & the Cookie Jar. Brooks, Julian A. & Rivers, Shariba W., eds. Moore, La Mailede, illus. Rivers, Freya A. & Moore, La Mailede, photos by. 2001. 57p. (J). (ps-2). pap. 20.00 (978-0-9667215-4-6(3)) Sankofa Publishing Co.

Roberts, Daniel. There's a Cookie Stuck to My Nose! 2006. (ENG., Illus.). 36p. per. 16.99 (***978-1-4259-7093-2(1)***) AuthorHouse.

Robey, Stephanie. My Favorite Food. Loeffelholz, Sarah, illus. 2006. (J). 14.95 (978-0-9786850-0-3(8)) Overdue Bks.

Rockwell, Anne F. Apples & Pumpkins. Rockwell, Anne F., illus. 2002. (Illus.). (J). 14.47 (978-0-7587-1964-5(7)) Book Wholesalers, Inc.

Rockwell, Anne F. & Rockwell, Lizzy, illus. Apples & Pumpkins. 2nd ed. 2005. (Stories to Go! Ser.). (J). (***978-1-4156-2884-3(X)*** , Aladdin) Simon & Schuster Children's Publishing.

Rodriguez Vidal, Andrea. Who Is Devouring Me? 2006. (Little Books for Big Kids Ser.). (Illus.). 32p. (J). pap. 9.95 (978-9974-7896-4-7(8)) Hardenville SA URY. *Dist:* Independent Pubs. Group.

Ron, Kare. The Adventures of Sir Noodlefish: The Cake Wars. McCracken, Ken, illus. 2000. 32p. (J). (gr. 1-3). pap. (978-1-931179-00-3(X)) Long Hill Productions, Inc.

Root, Phyllis. Mouse Has Fun. Croft, James, illus. 2002. (Brand New Readers Ser.). 32p. (J). (ps-2). pap. 5.99 (978-0-7636-1358-7(4)) Candlewick Pr.

Rosa-Casanova, Sylvia. Mama Provi & the Pot of Rice. ed. 2004. (Illus.). (J). (gr. k-3). spiral bd. (978-0-616-07257-8(0)) Canadian National Institute for the Blind/Institut National Canadien pour les Aveugles.

—Mama Provi & the Pot of Rice. 2001. (Illus.). (J). (978-0-606-20782-9(1)) Tandem Library Bks.

Rosenwald, Laurie. And to Name but Just a Few: Red, Yellow, Green, Blue. 2007. (Illus.). 40p. (ps-3). 16.95 (978-1-59354-596-3(7)) Blue Apple Bks.

Ross, Andrea. Nutmeg & the Mutu. 2000. (Illus.). 60p. (J). (gr. 3-5). lib. bdg. 9.95 (978-1-887683-29-6(1)) Storybook Pr. & Productions.

Rothenberg, Joan. Matzah Ball Soup. Rothenberg, Joan, illus. 2005. (Illus.). 29p. (J). (ps-2). reprint ed. 15.00 (978-0-7567-8930-5(3)) DIANE Publishing Co.

Ruelle, Karen Gray. Easy As Apple Pie: A Harry & Emily Adventure. (Holiday House Readers Ser.). (Illus.). 32p. (J). (gr. k-3). 4.95 (978-0-8234-1800-8(6)) Holiday Hse., Inc.

Rylant, Cynthia. Henry & Mudge & the Funny Lunch. Bracken, Carolyn, illus. 2005. (Henry & Mudge Ser.). 40p. (J). (gr. k-2). lib. bdg. 12.10 (978-1-4176-7107-6(6)) Tandem Library Bks.

—Puppy Mudge Has a Snack. Mones, Isidre, illus. 2003. (Puppy Mudge Ser.). 32p. (J). (ps-k). 14.95 (978-0-689-83981-8(2)) Simon & Schuster Children's Publishing.

Rylant, Cynthia & Bracken, Carolyn. Henry & Mudge & the Funny Lunch. 2004. (Henry & Mudge Ser.). (Illus.). 40p. (J). (gr. k-3). 14.95 (978-0-689-81178-4(0)) Simon & Schuster Children's Publishing.

Saintil, Claire J. Mariel & the Cookie. 1999. (J). (gr. k-3). pap. 6.95 (978-0-533-12743-6(2)) Vantage Pr., Inc.

Saintil-van Goodman, Claire J. Mariel & the Cookie. 2003. (J). pap. 10.00 (978-0-8059-9230-4(8) , RoseDog Bks.) Dorrance Publishing Co., Inc.

Salvatore, Antonietta. Chocolates or Lollipops? 2003. (J). pap. 7.95 (978-0-533-10750-6(4)) Vantage Pr., Inc.

Sam, 6 Packs. (Kinderstarters Ser.). 8p. (ps-1). 21.00 (978-0-7635-8657-7(9)) Rigby Education.

Sams, Carl R., II & Stoick, Jean. Stranger in the Woods: A Photographic Fantasy. 2002. (gr. 2-5). 12.95 (978-0-9671748-2-1(1)) Sams, II, Carl R. Photography, Inc.

—Stranger in the Woods: A Photographic Fantasy. Sams, Carl R., II & Stoick, Jean, photos by. 1999. (Illus.). 48p. (J). (gr. 2-4). pap. 19.95 (978-0-9671748-0-8(5)) Sams, II, Carl R. Photography, Inc.

Samton, Sheila W. Hurray for Rosa! 2001. (Brand New Readers Ser.). (Illus.). 1p. (J). (ps-2). pap. 5.99 (978-0-7636-1127-9(1)) Candlewick Pr.

SanAngelo, Ryan. Spaghetti Eddie. Urbanovic, Jackie, illus. 2003. 32p. (J). (gr. k-2). 15.95 (978-1-56397-974-3(8)) Boyds Mills Pr.

Sanger, Rick. No Eat Not Food: The Search for Intelligent Food on Planet Earth. Russell, Carol, illus. l.t. ed. 2006. 48p. (J). 19.95 (978-0-9653149-2-3(8)) Mountain Path Pr.

Santillo, LuAnn. Good Food. Santillo, LuAnn, ed. 2003. (Half-Pint Kids Readers Ser.). (Illus.). 7p. (J). (ps-1). pap. (978-1-59256-118-6(7)) Half-Pint Kids, Inc.

Sayre, April Pulley. Noodle Man: The Pasta Superhero. Costanza, Stephen, illus. 2002. 40p. (J). (ps-2). 16.95 (978-0-439-29307-5(3) , Orchard Bks.) Scholastic, Inc.

Scelsa, Greg. Muffin Man. Faulkner, Stacey, ed. Allen, Joy, illus. 2006. (J). pap. 2.99 (***978-1-59198-321-7(5)***) Creative Teaching Pr., Inc.

Schachner, Judith B. Mr. Emerson's Cook. 2002. (J). per. 17.95 (978-1-930654-27-3(8)) Reading Matters, Inc.

Schoenecker, Pamela L. Kerbie the Kernel. Schoenecker, Sheri L., illus. ltd. ed. 1998. 16p. (J). (gr. k-1). pap. 3.50 (978-0-9664852-0-2(3)) KerbieKo.

Scholastic, Inc. Staff. We Love Our Fans! 2008. (Doodlebops Ser.). 32p. (J). pap. 3.99 (***978-0-545-03426-5(4)***) Scholastic, Inc.

Scholastic, Inc. Staff & Kraft, Erik P. Chocolatina. 2008. (I Love You Ser.). 32p. (J). pap. 5.99 (***978-0-545-03765-5(4)*** , Cartwheel Bks.) Scholastic, Inc.

Schulz. Tutti qui Biscotti. pap. 19.95 (978-88-451-2810-3(5)) Fabbri - RCS Libri ITA. *Dist:* Distribooks, Inc.

Schwartz, Ellen. Mr. Belinsky's Bagels. Czernecki, Stefan, illus. 1999. 32p. (J). 14.95 (978-1-896580-14-2(9)) Tradewind Bks. CAN. *Dist:* Orca Bk. Pubs. USA.

Scott-Cameron, Nancy. Santa Claus Is on a Diet. Conlan, Craig, illus. 2007. 32p. (J). (ps-k). 19.95 (***978-0-9546576-9-7(1)***) Mogzilla GBR. *Dist:* Independent Pubs. Group.

Scraper, Katherine. Garden Lunch. 2006. (Early Explorers Ser.). (J). 30.00 (***978-1-4108-6027-9(2)***) Benchmark Education Co.

Scroggs, Kirk. Night of the Living Eggnog. 7th rev. ed. 2007. (Wiley & Grampa Ser.). 112p. (J). (gr. 1). pap. 3.99 (***978-0-316-00685-9(8)***) Little, Brown Bks. for Young Readers.

Sendak, Maurice. La Cocina de Noche. Sendak, Maurice, illus. 2003. (Picture Books Collection). (SPA., Illus.). 40p. (J). (gr. k-3). 10.95 (978-84-204-4570-0(3)) Alfaguara, Ediciones, S.A.- Grupo Santillana ESP. *Dist:* Santillana USA Publishing Co., Inc.

Seuss, Dr. Green Eggs & Ham. 2001. (Nifty Lift-and-Look Bks.). (Illus.). 12p. (J). (gr. k-ps). bds. 7.99 (978-0-375-81088-6(9) , Random Hse. Bks. for Young Readers) Random Hse. Children's Bks.

Sharmat, Mitchell. Gregory, the Terrible Eater. Aruego, Jose, illus. 2002. (J). 12.87 (978-0-7587-2663-6(5)) Book Wholesalers, Inc.

Shaw, Dana Alton, III. My Friend Zundel. 2006. per. (***978-0-9791091-0-2(8)***) Shaw, Dana.

Sherman, Deborah. Triple Chocolate Brownie Genius. 2007. 120p. (J). (gr. 4-6). pap. (***978-1-55455-035-7(1)***) Fitzhenry & Whiteside, Ltd.

Shields, Carol Diggory. Food Fight! Gay-Kassel, Doreen, illus. 2002. 32p. (J). (ps-2). 15.95 (978-1-929766-29-1(7)) Handprint Bks.

Shivers, Juliette. Brenda Doesn't Like Broccoli. 2006. Tr. of Brenda no le Gusta Broculi. (SPA.). (J). 6.50 (978-0-9769379-1-3(3)) Ingram's Nutrition Consultations.

Shulman, Lisa. The Moon Might Be Milk. Hillenbrand, Will, illus. 2007. (J). (***978-1-4287-3291-9(8)*** , Dutton Juvenile) Penguin Group (USA) Inc.

Sicherer, Scott H. Andrew & Maya Learn about Food Allergies. Munoz-Furlong, Anne, ed. Taylor, Alyssa C. & Furlong, Mariel Christine, illus. 2000. 36p. (J). (gr. 2-8). pap. 8.00 (978-1-882541-16-4(2)) Food Allergy & Anaphylaxis Network.

Silvano, Wendi J. Pancakes for Breakfast. Hartung, Susan Kathleen, illus. 1999. (Books for Young Learners). 12p. (J). (gr. k-2). pap. 5.00 (978-1-57274-277-2(1) , A2493) Owen, Richard C. Pubs., Inc.

Sinclair, Nicholas, et al. The Cookie Story. Wall, Randy Hugh, ed. Varela, Juan D., tr. Varela, Juan D., illus. l.t. ed. 2005. Tr. of Cuent de Galletas. (SPA.). 33p. (J). 14.95 (978-0-9764798-1-9(8)) Story Store Collection Publishing.

Slater, David Michael. Missy Swiss. Reibeling, Brandon, illus. 2007. (Missy Swiss & More Ser.). 32p. (J). (ps-4). lib. bdg. 27.07 (***978-1-60270-010-9(9)*** , Looking Glass Library) Magic Wagon.

Slepian, Jan. Hungry Thing. 2001. (Illus.). (J). 12.79 (978-0-606-21242-7(6)) Tandem Library Bks.

Slippery, Sloppery Spaghetti: Individual Title Six-Packs. (gr. k-1). 23.00 (978-0-7635-9025-3(8)) Rigby Education.

Sloat, Teri, illus. & retold by. The Eye of the Needle. Sloat, Teri, retold by. 2005. 32p. (J). (ps-3). pap. 8.95 (978-0-88240-535-3(7)) Graphic Arts Ctr. Publishing Co.

Sloat, Teri & Huffmon, Betty. Berry Magic. 2005. (Illus.). 32p. 15.95 (978-0-88240-575-9(6)); pap. 8.95 (978-0-88240-576-6(4)) Graphic Arts Ctr. Publishing Co.

Slonim, David. Oh, Ducky: A Chocolate Calamity. Slonim, David, illus. 2006. (Illus.). 36p. (J). pap. 6.95 (978-0-8118-5227-2(X)) Chronicle Bks. LLC.

—Oh, Ducky! A Chocolate Calamity. Slonim, David, illus. 2006. (Illus.). 28p. (J). (gr. k-4). 16.00 (978-1-4223-5259-5(5)) DIANE Publishing Co.

Smith, Alexander McCall. The Perfect Hamburger & Other Delicious Stories. Rankin, Laura, illus. 2007. 288p. (J). (gr. 2-4). 15.95 (***978-1-59990-134-3(X));*** pap. 7.95 (***978-1-59990-157-2(9)***) Bloomsbury Publishing. (Bloomsbury Children).

E F G

Smith, Nicole. Chad the Allergic Chipmunk: A Children's Story of Nut Allergies. 2006. (Illus.). (J). per. 11.95 (978-1-58628-054-3(6)) Allergic Child Publishing Group.

Smith, Robert Kimmel. Chocolate Fever. 2002. (Illus.). (J). 12.87 (978-0-7587-6963-3(6)) Book Wholesalers, Inc.

—Chocolate Fever. Fiammenghi, Gioia, illus. 2006. 93p. (J). (***978-1-4156-7192-4(3)***, Puffin) Penguin Group (USA) Inc.

—Chocolate Fever. 2004. 96p. (J). (gr. 3). 14.99 (978-0-399-24355-4(0), Putnam Juvenile) Penguin Group (USA) Inc.

—Chocolate Fever. 93p. (J). (gr. 2-4). pap. 3.99 (978-0-8072-1405-3(1)); pap. 4.50 (978-0-8072-1500-5(7)) Random Hse. Audio Publishing Group. (Listening Library).

—Chocolate Fever. 2006. (Illus.). 96p. (J). (gr. 2). 4.99 (978-0-14-240595-6(7), Puffin) Penguin Group (USA) Inc.

Smith, Robert Kimmel, ed. Chocolate Fever. unabr. ed. 2004. (Middle Grade Cassette Librariestm Ser.). 93p. (J). (gr. 2-4). pap. 29.00 incl. audio (978-0-8072-7785-0(1), S YA 917 SP, Listening Library) Random Hse. Audio Publishing Group.

Smith, Stu & Wolff, Julian. The Bubble Gum Kid. 2006. (Illus.). 32p. 15.95 (978-0-7624-2046-9(4)) Running Pr. Bk. Pubs.

A Snack for Gilbert. 2002. (J). (978-1-58453-177-7(0)) Pioneer Valley Educational Pr., Inc.

Sokol, Edward. Meet Stinky Magee. Sokol, Edward, illus. 2000. (Illus.). 32p. (J). (ps-3). 14.95 (978-0-688-17416-3(7)) HarperCollins Pubs.

—Meet Stinky Magee. 2000. (Illus.). 32p. (J). (ps-3). 14.89 (978-0-688-17417-0(5)) HarperCollins Pubs.

Solheim, James. Its Disgusting & We Ate It: True Food Facts from Around the World & Throughout History. Brace, Eric, illus. 2001. 48p. (J). 7.99 (978-0-689-84393-8(3), Aladdin) Simon & Schuster Children's Publishing.

Soto, Gary. Too Many Tamales. 2002. (Illus.). (J). 14.04 (978-0-7587-3837-0(4)) Book Wholesalers, Inc.

Sperring, Mark. The Fairytale Cake. Langley, Jonathan, illus. 2005. 32p. (J). (ps-ps). pap. 15.95 (978-0-439-68329-6(7), Chicken Hse., The) Scholastic, Inc.

Stanley, George Edward. Secret of the Green Skin. 2003. (gr. 3-6). lib. bdg. 11.80 (978-0-613-66539-1(2)) Tandem Library Bks.

Starks, R. The Fish Gut Experiment. Jellett, Tom, illus. 2008. (J). lib. bdg. (***978-1-59889-862-0(0)***); 80p. pap. (***978-1-59889-918-4(X)***) Stone Arch Bks.

Steck-Vaughn Staff. Ice Cream Dream Level B: Early Reader. 2003. (Illus.). pap. (978-0-7398-8220-7(1)) Steck-Vaughn.

Steig, William. Pete's a Pizza. Steig, William, illus. 1998. (Illus.). 32p. (J). (ps up). lib. bdg. 16.89 (978-0-06-205158-5(X)); 62nd ed. 16.99 (978-0-06-205157-8(1)) HarperCollins Pubs.

—Pete's a Pizza. Steig, William, illus. (Illus.). pap. 18.95 incl. audio compact disk (978-1-59112-739-0(4)); pap. incl. audio compact disk (978-1-59112-741-3(6)) Live Oak Media.

Stephens, Ann Marie. Stella Eats Out. Bolan, Michael, illus. 2004. 32p. (J). per. 12.95 (978-0-9729285-2-6(9), 2-9) Kinkachoo Pr., The.

Sterling, Christina. What Makes a Sandwich... 2006. 15.50 (978-0-8059-9954-9(X)) Dorrance Publishing Co., Inc.

Stevenson, James. Cornflakes: Poems. Stevenson, James, illus. 2000. (Illus.). 56p. (J). (gr. 3 up). 16.99 (978-0-688-16718-9(7)) HarperCollins Pubs.

Stine, R. L. The Big Blueberry Barf-Off! Park, Trip, illus. 2005. (Rotten School Ser.: Vol. 1). 128p. (J). lib. bdg. 14.89 (978-0-06-078587-1(X)) HarperCollins Pubs.

Stine, R.L. Night of the Creepy Things. Park, Trip, illus. 2007. (Rotten School Ser.: No. 14). 128p. (J). lib. bdg. 14.89 (***978-0-06-123273-2(4)***); (gr. 3-7). 6.99 (***978-0-06-123272-5(6)***) HarperCollins Pubs.

String Food: Individual Title Six-Packs. (gr. k-1). 23.00 (978-0-7635-9023-9(1)) Rigby Education.

Stuchner, Joan Betty. A Peanut Butter Waltz. Durrand, Diana, illus. 2003. (Annikins Ser.: Series 10). 15p. (Orig.). (J). (ps-2). pap. 0.99 (978-1-55037-126-0(6)) Annick Pr., Ltd. CAN. *Dist:* Firefly Bks., Ltd.

Susie's Sister Has Food Allergy. 2004. (J). 5.00 (978-1-882541-36-2(7)) Food Allergy & Anaphylaxis Network.

Sweetwater, Jesse. illus. Lunching & Munching. 2001. (J). 14.00 (978-0-689-81564-5(6), Simon & Schuster Children's Publishing) Simon & Schuster Children's Publishing.

Tabby, Abigail. Cookie Kisses. Goldberg, Barry, illus. 2004. (Sesame Beginnings Ser.). 14p. (J). (gr. k). bds. 6.99 (978-0-375-82694-8(7), Random Hse. Bks. for Young Readers) Random Hse. Children's Bks.

Tango Hampton, Doreen. I Like Gum. 2007. 32p. (J). 15.95 (***978-0-9726614-2-3(5)***) Shenanigan Bks.

Taulbert, Clifton L. Little Cliff & the Porch People. Kane, Cindy, ed. Lewis, Earl, illus. 1999. 32p. (J). (ps-3). 16.99 (978-0-8037-2174-6(9), Dial) Penguin Group (USA) Inc.

Taylor, Dan & Taylor, Damon J. Lenny Loses His Lunch: A Lion's Tale. Taylor, Damon J., illus. 2005. (Illus.). 32p. (J). (ps-ps). 10.99 (978-0-8254-3871-4(3)) Kregel Pubns.

Taylor, Gaylia. George Crum & the Saratoga Chip. Morrison, Frank, illus. 2006. 32p. (J). (gr. 1-5). 16.95 (978-1-58430-255-1(0)) Lee & Low Bks., Inc.

A Teeny Tiny Taste: Individual Title Six-Packs. (ps-2). 27.00 (978-0-7635-9478-7(4)) Rigby Education.

Tennsiwood, Mark. Thank You God for Onions. Motz, Mike, illus. 2006. (J). 14.95 (978-1-60131-003-3(X)) Big Tent Bks.

Theriault, Francis Patrick. The Candy Coated Castle's Catastrophe: A Christmas Crisis. 2006. (ENG.). 48p. per. 10.95 (978-1-59800-555-4(3)) Outskirts Press, Inc.

Thompson, Lauren. The Apple Pie That Papa Baked. Bean, Jonathan, illus. 2007. 32p. (J). (gr. k up). 15.99 (***978-1-4169-1240-8(1)***) Simon & Schuster Children's Publishing.

Thonney, Patricia F. A Pyramid of Snacks. 1998. 76p. (J). (gr. 4-7). pap. 7.75 (978-1-57753-287-3(2), 399LM19) Resource Centre, The.

Titus, Eve. Anatole. Galdone, Paul, illus. 2006. 40p. (J). (gr. k-4). 16.99 (978-0-375-93901-3(6), Knopf Bks. for Young Readers) Random Hse. Children's Bks.

Tolstoy, Alexei. The Enormous Turnip. Goto, Scott, illus. 2003. (Green Light Readers Level 2 Ser.). 24p. (J). 11.95 (978-0-15-204883-9(9)); pap. 3.95 (978-0-15-204843-3(X)) Harcourt Children's Bks. (Green Light Readers).

Trimble, Irene. Foodfight! Jr Novel. 2007. (Junior Novel Ser.). (Illus.). 128p. (J). (gr. 4-7). mass mkt. 4.99 (978-0-375-83794-4(9), Golden Bks.) Random Hse. Children's Bks.

Vagnozzi, Barbara. Hungry Baby. 2002. (Baby's Day Ser.). (Illus.). 16p. (J). (ps up). 3.95 (978-1-84089-238-3(2), Zero to Ten, Limited) Evans Publishing Group GBR. *Dist:* Independent Pubs. Group.

Vere, Ed. Everyone's Hungry. 2003. (Illus.). 12p. (J). 6.95 (978-0-333-78041-1(8)) Macmillan Publishers Ltd. GBR. *Dist:* Trafalgar Square Publishing.

—Everyones Hungry. Vere, Ed, illus. 2000. (Illus.). 12p. (J). (ps). bds. 6.95 (978-0-531-30299-6(7), Orchard Bks.) Scholastic, Inc.

Voorheis, Tracy. Nibbles... a strawberry Tale. Voorheis, Tracy, illus. 2007. (Illus.). 60p. (J). per. 19.00 (***978-0-9787113-0-6(0)***, Ithaca Pr.) Authors & Artists Publishers of New York, Inc.

Vote for Us! Individual Title Six-Packs. (Bookweb Ser.). 32p. (gr. 6 up). 34.00 (978-0-7578-0907-1(3)) Rigby Education.

Waber, Bernard. Fast Food! Gulp! Gulp! 2001. (Illus.). 32p. (J). (gr. k-3). tchr. ed. 16.00 (978-0-618-14189-0(8), Walter Lorraine) Houghton Mifflin Co. Trade & Reference Div.

Walburg, Lori. The Legend of the Candy Cane. Bernardin, James, illus. gif. ed. 2002. (J). (gr. k-3). 19.99 (978-0-310-70328-0(X)) Zondervan.

Walde, Christine. The Candy Darlings. 2006. 320p. (YA). (gr. 10). pap. 8.99 (978-0-618-58969-2(4), Graphia) Houghton Mifflin Co. Trade & Reference Div.

Wallace, Karen. Albert's Raccoon. Percy, Graham, illus. 2004. 48p. (J). (ps-ps). lib. bdg. 10.75 (978-0-606-32861-6(0)) Tandem Library Bks.

Wallace, Nancy Elizabeth. A Taste of Honey. Wallace, Nancy Elizabeth, illus. 2004. 32p. (J). pap. 5.95 (978-0-7614-5181-5(1)) Cavendish, Marshall Corp.

—A Taste of Honey. 2001. (Illus.). 40p. (J). (ps-3). 15.95 (978-1-890817-51-0(1)) Winslow Pr.

—A Taste of Honey. Wallace, Nancy Elizabeth, illus. 2000. (Illus.). 40p. (J). (ps-3). 15.95 (978-1-890817-19-0(8)) Winslow Pr.

Wallace, Nancy Elizabeth, illus. A Taste of Honey. 2005. 32p. (J). pap. 5.95 (978-0-7614-5215-7(X)) Cavendish, Marshall Corp.

Wang, Margaret. Who Stole the Cookie Form the Cookie Jar? Schneider, Christine, illus. 2005. 12p. (J). (ps-ps). 4.95 (978-1-58117-429-8(2), Intervisual/Piggy Toes) Dalmatian Pr.

—Who Stole the Cookie from the Cookie Jar? Schneider, Christine, illus. 2005. 22p. (J). 10.95 (978-1-58117-383-3(0), Intervisual/Piggy Toes) Dalmatian Pr.

Ward Appleton's Pancakes a Special Way. 2005. 10.95 (***978-0-9754779-6-0(X)***) Chosen Word Publishing.

Warner, Cheryl Ware. Chunkerella. 2006. (J). pap. 8.00 (***978-0-8059-7060-9(6)***) Dorrance Publishing Co., Inc.

Watt, Fiona. Baby's Mealtime. 2004. (Baby's World Bathbooks Ser.). (Illus.). 10p. (YA). (ps-k). 7.95 (978-0-7460-4176-5(4)) EDC Publishing.

Weiss, Ellen. Fruit Salad: A Touch & Learn Book. Jourdan, Jason, illus. 2006. (PBS Kids(R) Ser.). 14p. (J). 6.95 (***978-1-57791-314-6(0)***) Brighter Minds Children's Publishing.

Wellington, Monica. Crepes by Suzette. Wellington, Monica, illus. 2004. (Illus.). 32p. (J). (ps). 15.99 (978-0-525-46934-6(6), Dutton Juvenile) Penguin Group (USA) Inc.

—Mr. Cookie Baker. Wellington, Monica, illus. 2006. (Illus.). 32p. (J). (ps). 15.99 (978-0-525-47763-1(2), Dutton Juvenile) Penguin Group (USA) Inc.

Weston, Tamson. Hey, Pancakes! Gammell, Stephen, illus. 2003. 32p. (J). 17.00 (978-0-15-216502-4(9)) Harcourt Trade Pubs.

Whaley, Barbara P. Rutabagas for Dinner. Acey-Hendrick, Betty, illus. 1998. 32p. (Orig.). (J). (gr. 3-5). pap. 7.95 (978-1-884242-87-8(1)) Multicultural Pubns.

Wherry, Alwyn. The Hungry Little Mouse. 2006. 17p. (J). 12.08 (978-1-4116-8056-2(1)) Lulu.com.

Whitehouse, Elizabeth. Sushi for Lunch. 2005. (J). pap. 5.95 (978-1-933031-82-8(4)) Whitehouse Publishing.

Whytock, Cherry. My Saucy Stuffed Ravioli: The Life of Angelica Cookson Potts. Whytock, Cherry, illus. 2005. (Illus.). 176p. (YA). 14.95 (978-0-689-86550-3(3)) Simon & Schuster Children's Publishing.

Wieder, Joy Nelkin. The Great Potato Plan. Rosenfeld, Dina, ed. Wieder, Joy Nelkin, illus. 1999. (Fun to Read Bks.). (Illus.). 112p. (J). (gr. 2-5). pap. 6.95 (978-0-922613-89-2(3)) Hachai Publishing.

Williams, Arlene & Williams, A. Susan. The Tiny Tortilla. Karas, G. Brian, illus. 2005. 32p. (J). (ps). 15.99 (978-0-525-47382-4(3), Dutton Juvenile) Penguin Group (USA) Inc.

Willson, Sarah. Perfect Formula. 1999. (gr. 3-6). lib. bdg. 11.80 (978-0-613-15939-5(X)) Tandem Library Bks.

Wilson, Karma. Bear Wants More. Chapman, Jane, illus. (Classic Board Bks.). (J). 2008. 34p. 7.99 (***978-1-4169-4922-0(4)***, Little Simon); 2003. 40p. 16.95 (978-0-689-84509-3(X), McElderry, Margaret K.) Simon & Schuster Children's Publishing.

Wilson, Mary. Mark & the Mega Buffet. 2005. 37p. (J). pap. 15.58 (978-1-4116-4172-3(8)) Lulu.com.

Wishinsky, Frieda. Each One Special. 2000. (J). 14.75 (978-0-606-20203-9(X)) Tandem Library Bks.

Wojtowycz, David. Eat up Dudley! Counting. 2002. (Dudley! Ser.). (Illus.). (J). 3.95 (978-1-58925-669-9(7), tiger tales) ME Media LLC.

Wolff, Virginia Euwer. Make Lemonade. unabr. ed. 2004. (Young Adult Cassette Librariestm Ser.). 200p. (J). (gr. 7 up). pap. 36.00 incl. audio (978-0-8072-0793-2(4), S YA 348 SP, Listening Library) Random Hse. Audio Publishing Group.

Wood, A. & Hawkins, Emily A. Amazing Baby Yum-Yum, Baby! Jolley, Mike, illus. 2007. (Amazing Baby Ser.). 16p. (J). bds. 5.95 (***978-1-59223-803-3(3)***, Silver Dolphin Bks.) Advantage Pubs. Group.

Wynne-Jones, Tim. Lord of the Fries. (Illus.). pap. 6.95 (978-0-88899-384-7(6)) Groundwood Bks. CAN. *Dist:* Transition Vendor.

Yaldezian, Lisa M. 500 Presents for Penelope Potts. Motz, Mike, illus. 2006. (J). 16.95 (978-1-60131-005-7(6)) Big Tent Bks.

Yarbrough, Elizabeth. Where Do Pizzas Grow? Ragsdale, Cathy, illus. 2001. (J). (gr. k-5). lib. bdg. 14.95 (978-1-931650-02-1(0)) Coastal Publishing Carolina, Inc.

Yee, Wong Herbert. Hamburger Heaven. Yee, Wong Herbert, illus. 1999. (Illus.). 32p. (J). (gr. k-3). tchr. ed. 16.00 (978-0-395-87548-3(X)) Houghton Mifflin Co. Trade & Reference Div.

—Hamburger Heaven. 2005. (Illus.). 32p. (J). (gr. k-3). reprint ed. 5.95 (978-0-618-54885-9(8)) Houghton Mifflin Co. Trade & Reference Div.

Young, Eugene Randolph, illus. & des. The Food Convention. Young, Eugene Randolph, des. l.t. ed. 2006. 32p. (J). 16.95 (***978-0-9792000-0-7(8)***) Les Lurn Pubs.

Young, Shelley. Doc Broc's Cave Adventure. Young, Shelley, illus. 2005. (Illus.). 44p. 19.95 (978-1-58054-406-1(1)) Woodland Publishing, Inc.

Yoyo Books Staff. Food: Mini Baby's First Library. 2005. 42p. bds. 4.95 (978-90-5843-829-4(5)) YoYo Bks. BEL. *Dist:* National Bk. Network.

Yurcheshen, Richard P. My Gum Is Gone. Flanagan, Kate, illus. 2000. 32p. (J). (ps-3). pap. (978-1-55798-662-7(2), 441-6622, Magination Pr.) American Psychological Assn.

Zafra, Jose. Historias de Sergio. (SPA.). 160p. (J). (978-84-216-2870-6(4), BU6937) Bruño, Editorial ESP. *Dist:* Lectorum Pubns., Inc.

Zambon, Wendy. Spaghetti for Breakfast. Wise, Noreen, ed. Bowman, Sharon, illus. 2000. (Book-a-Day Collection). 32p. (YA). (ps up). pap. 5.95 (978-1-58584-436-4(5)) Huckleberry Pr.

Zevy, Aaron. No Nuts for Me! 1998. (J). pap. 5.95 (978-0-9680678-0-2(8)) Tumbleweed Pr.

Zigler, Violet Vaughn. Mr. chocolate Bar. 2007. 16.95 (***978-0-533-15741-9(2)***) Vantage Pr., Inc.

Zvonar, Louise. The Great Cookie Humble. l.t. ed. 1998. (Illus.). 48p. (J). (gr. k-6). (978-0-9668358-0-9(8)) Siloam Publishing.

FOOD—PRESERVATION

see also Canning and Preserving

Checkout! Individual Title Six-Packs. (Bookweb Ser.). 32p. (gr. 4 up). 34.00 (978-0-7635-3741-8(1)) Rigby Education.

Jango-Cohen, Judith. The History of Food. 2006. (Major Inventions Through History Ser.). (Illus.). 56p. (J). (ps-7). 26.60 (978-0-8225-2484-7(8), Twenty-First Century Bks.) Lerner Publishing Group.

Mecozzi, Maureen. The Uncanny Can. 2007. (Shockwave: Science in Practice Ser.). (Illus.). 36p. (J). (gr. 4-6). lib. bdg. 25.00 (***978-0-531-17584-2(7)***, Children's Pr.) Scholastic Library Publishing.

Sarver, Amy. Science at the Grocery. 2004. (National Geographic Reading Expeditions Ser.). (Illus.). 24p. (J). pap. (978-0-7922-4567-4(9)) National Geographic Society.

FOOD CONTROL

see Food Supply

FOOD FOR INVALIDS

see Cookery for the Sick

FOOD HABITS

Ackroyd, Dorothea. Eating & Drinking Bird Book. 1999. 3.95 (978-1-58185-200-4(2)) Quadrillion Media LLC.

Ancona, George. Let's Eat. 2003. (J). (978-0-7636-1805-6(5)) Candlewick Pr.

Colores para Comer, 5 bks., Set. 2002. (SPA.). (J). (ps-1). lib. bdg. 92.50 (978-1-58810-794-7(9)) Heinemann Library.

Dawson, Imogen. Food & Feasts with the Aztecs. 2004. (Illus.). 32p. (J). (gr. 4-8). reprint ed. 14.00 (978-0-7567-7143-0(9)) DIANE Publishing Co.

Dosier, Susan. Colonial Cooking. 2000. (Blue Earth Books). (Illus.). 32p. (J). (gr. 3-4). lib. bdg. 22.60 (978-0-7368-0352-6(1), Bridgestone Bks.) Capstone Pr., Inc.

—Colonial Cooking. 1999. (Exploring History Through Simple Recipes Ser.). (Illus.). 32p. (J). (gr. 2-7). pap. 14.60 (978-0-516-21863-2(8), Children's Pr.) Scholastic Library Publishing.

Fischer, Maureen M. Nineteenth-Century Lumber Camp Cooking. 2000. (Blue Earth Books). (Illus.). 32p. (J). (gr. 3-4). lib. bdg. 22.60 (978-0-7368-0604-6(0), Bridgestone Bks.) Capstone Pr., Inc.

Fun Food: Individual Title Six-Packs. (ps-2). 23.00 (978-0-7635-8995-0(0)) Rigby Education.

Gilpin, Daniel. Food & Clothing. 2004. (History of Invention Ser.). (Illus.). 96p. (YA). (gr. 6-12). 35.00 (978-0-8160-5441-1(X)) Facts On File, Inc.

Goodwin, Bob. Taste of Spain. 2000. (Food Around the World Ser.). (J). (gr. 4-7). 7.14 (978-0-8172-4857-4(9)) Raintree.

Gray, Shirley W. Eating for Good Health. 2003. (Living Well). (Illus.). 32p. (J). (gr. 2-6). 27.07 (978-1-59296-079-8(0)) Child's World, Inc., The.

Gregoire, Maryellen. Morning Meals Around the World. Yesh, Jeff, illus. 2004. (Meals Around the World Ser.). 24p. (J). (gr. k-4). 22.60 (978-1-4048-0280-3(0), 1229527) Picture Window Bks.

Gunderson, Mary. Cooking on the Lewis & Clark Expedition. 2000. (Blue Earth Books). (Illus.). 32p. (J). (gr. 3-4). lib. bdg. 22.60 (978-0-7368-0354-0(8), Bridgestone Bks.) Capstone Pr., Inc.

—Cooking on the Lewis & Clark Expedition. 1999. (Exploring History Through Simple Recipes Ser.). (Illus.). 32p. (J). (gr. 2-7). pap. 14.60 (978-0-516-21865-6(4), Children's Pr.) Scholastic Library Publishing.

Hollyer, Beatrice. Let's Eat: What Children Eat Around the World. rev. ed. 2004. (Illus.). 48p. (J). 16.95 (978-0-8050-7322-5(1), Holt, Henry & Co. Bks. For Young Readers) Holt, Henry & Co.

Jones, Susan Smith & Warren, Dianne. Vegetable Soup - The Fruit Bowl. Lindman, Amy Sorvaag, illus. rev. ed. 2006. 64p. (J). (ps-3). per. 14.95 (978-0-9652736-0-2(1)) Oasis Pubns.

Kalbacken, Joan. Food Safety. De Capua, Sarah E., ed. 1998. (Illus.). 48p. (J). (ps-ps). lib. bdg. 13.75 (978-0-606-22896-1(9)) Tandem Library Bks.

Kalman, Bobbie. Lunch Munch: Step-by-Step Recipes. 2003. (Kid Power Ser.). (Illus.). 32p. (J). (gr. 3). (978-0-7787-1251-0(6)); pap. (978-0-7787-1273-2(7)) Crabtree Publishing Co.

—Pioneer Recipes. 2001. (gr. 3-6). lib. bdg. 16.40 (978-0-613-32950-7(3)); 2000. (J). (978-0-606-20111-7(4)) Tandem Library Bks.

—Super Snacks. 2003. (gr. 3-6). lib. bdg. 17.60 (978-0-613-59139-3(9)) Tandem Library Bks.

Kalman, Bobbie, et al. Pioneer Recipes. 2000. (Historic Communities Ser.). (Illus.). 32p. (J). (gr. 3). pap. (978-0-86505-468-4(1)); lib. bdg. (978-0-86505-438-7(X)) Crabtree Publishing Co.

Kudlinski, Kathleen V. Food for Life. 2003. (Science Links Ser.). (Illus.). 32p. (J). (gr. 3-5). 23.00 (978-0-7910-7421-3(8), Chelsea Hse.) Facts On File, Inc.

Lakin, Patricia. Food: Around the World. 1999. (We All Share Ser.). (Illus.). 32p. (J). (gr. 3-6). 22.45 (978-1-56711-147-7(5), Blackbirch Pr., Inc.) Thomson Gale.

Lauber, Patricia. What You Never Knew about Fingers, Forks, & Chopsticks. Manders, John, illus. 2002. 30p. (J). reprint ed. 17.00 (978-0-7567-5681-9(2)) DIANE Publishing Co.

—What You Never Knew about Fingers, Forks, & Chopsticks. Manders, John, illus. 1999. (Around-the-House History Ser.). 40p. (J). (gr. 1-4). 17.95 (978-0-689-80479-3(2)) Simon & Schuster Children's Publishing.

Lewis, Carole. First Place Food Exchange Pocket Guide. 2004. 72p. mass mkt. 5.99 (978-0-8307-3232-6(2), Gospel Light) Gospel Light Pubns.

Locricchio, Matthew. The Cooking of India. 2003. (Superchef Ser.). (Illus.). 80p. (J). 29.93 (978-0-7614-1730-9(3), Benchmark Bks.) Cavendish, Marshall Corp.

—The Cooking of Italy. 2002. (Superchef Ser.). (Illus.). 72p. (J). 29.93 (978-0-7614-1215-1(8), Benchmark Bks.) Cavendish, Marshall Corp.

—The Cooking of Mexico. 2002. (Superchef Ser.). (J). 29.93 (978-0-7614-1217-5(4), Benchmark Bks.) Cavendish, Marshall Corp.

—The Cooking of Thailand. 2004. (Superchef Ser.). (Illus.). 80p. (J). 29.93 (978-0-7614-1731-6(1), Benchmark Bks.) Cavendish, Marshall Corp.

Midday Meals around the World. (Meals Around the World Ser.). 24p. (J). 7.95 (978-1-4048-1131-7(1)) Picture Window Bks.

Milet Limited Publishing Staff & Swain, Gwenyth. Eating. (Illus.). 24p. 2005. (PAN & ENG.). pap. 9.95 (978-1-84059-142-2(0)); 2000. (BEN & ENG., (J). pap. 9.95 (978-1-84059-139-2(0)); 2000. (CHI & ENG., (J). pap. 9.95 (978-1-84059-140-8(4)); 2000. (GUJ & ENG., (J). pap. 9.95 (978-1-84059-141-5(2)); 2000. (TUR & ENG., (J). pap. 9.95 (978-1-84059-143-9(9)); 2000. (VIE & ENG., (J). pap. 9.95 (978-1-84059-145-3(5)); 2000. (ARA & ENG., (J). pap. 9.95 (978-1-84059-138-5(2)) Milet Publishing.

—Eating. Iqbal, Gulshan, tr. from ENG. 2000. (Small World Ser.). (URD & ENG., Illus.). 24p. (J). pap. 9.95 (978-1-84059-144-6(7)) Milet Publishing.

Miller, Margaret. Baby Food. Miller, Margaret, illus. 2000. (Look Baby Bks.). (Illus.). 14p. (J). (ps-k). bds. 6.99 (978-0-689-83190-4(0), Little Simon) Simon & Schuster Children's Publishing.

Morning Meals around the World. (Meals Around the World Ser.). 24p. (J). 7.95 (978-1-4048-1130-0(3)); 7.95 (978-1-4048-1133-1(8)) Picture Window Bks.

Naik, Anita. Eating. 2nd ed. 2005. (Illus.). 144p. (YA). pap. 12.00 (978-0-340-88393-8(6), Hodder & Stoughton) Hodder General Publishing Division GBR. *Dist:* Trafalgar Square Publishing.

Nelson, Robin. Food. 2003. (First Step Nonfiction Ser.). (Illus.). 8p. (J). pap. 3.95 (978-0-8225-3928-5(4), Lerner Pubns.) Lerner Publishing Group.

Olson, Karen W. Eat, Run & Live Healthy. Hamelin, Marie-Micheline, illus. 2006. 20p. (J). pap. 10.95 (978-1-894778-32-9(4)) Theytus Bks., Ltd. CAN. *Dist:* Orca Bk. Pubs. USA.

E F G

Petrie, Kristin. The Food Pyramid. (Illus.). (J). 2007. (ENG.). lib. bdg. 22.78 (978-1-59928-692-1(0) , Checkerboard Library); 2004. 32p. lib. bdg. 22.78 (978-1-59197-403-1(8)) ABDO Publishing Co.

Platt, Richard. They Ate What ?! The Weird History of Food. 2006. (Illus.). 48p. (J). 9.95 (978-1-58728-578-3(9) , Two Can Publishing) T&N Children's Publishing.

—They Ate What ?! Weird History of Food. 2006. (Illus.). 48p. 16.95 (978-1-58728-577-6(0) , Two Can Publishing) T&N Children's Publishing.

Powell, Jillian. Food Matters. 1999. (Life Files Ser.). (Illus.). 62p. pap. 15.99 (978-0-237-51812-7(0) , Evans Brothers, Limited) Evans Publishing Group GBR. *Dist:* Independent Pubs. Group.

Ring, Susan. Places We Live. (J). (gr. k-2). 2006. (Illus.). 16p. 15.93 (978-0-7368-5850-2(4) , Yellow Umbrella Bks.); 2005. (978-0-7368-5316-3(2)); 2005. (Illus.). 16p. (978-0-7368-5280-7(8)) Capstone Pr., Inc.

Rose, Elizabeth. Food & Nutrition. 2006. (Life Science Library). (Illus.). 24p. (J). 21.25 (978-1-4042-2821-4(7) , PowerKids Pr.) Rosen Publishing Group, Inc., The.

Royston. Eating 6-Pack. 2004. (My Amazing Body Ser.). (Illus.). pap. 40.50 (978-1-4109-0956-5(5)) Raintree.

Sanna, Ellyn. America's Unhealthy Lifestyle: Supersize It! 2004. (Obesity Ser.). (Illus.). 104p. (J). (ps-7). (978-1-59084-942-2(6)) Mason Crest Pubs.

Schlosser, Eric & Wilson, Charles. Chew on This: Everything You Don't Want to Know about Fast Food. 2006. (Illus.). 304p. (YA). (gr. 7). 16.00 (978-0-618-71031-7(0)) Houghton Mifflin Co.

—Chew on This: Everything You Don't Want to Know about Fast Food. 2007. (Illus.). 320p. (YA). (gr. 7). pap. 8.95 (***978-0-618-59394-1(2)*** , Graphia) Houghton Mifflin Co. Trade & Reference Div.

Scott, Janine. Let's Eat: Foods of Our World. 2002. (Spyglass Books). (Illus.). 24p. (J). (gr. 1 up). lib. bdg. 18.60 (978-0-7565-0365-9(5)) Compass Point Bks.

Spilsbury, Louise. Why Should I Eat This Carrot? And Other Questions about Healthy Eating. 2003. (Body Matters Ser.). (Illus.). 32p. (J). lib. bdg. (978-1-4034-4680-0(6)) Heinemann Library.

Swain, Gwenyth. Eating. (Small World Ser.). (Illus.). 24p. (J). (ps-2). 2003. pap. 6.95 (978-1-57505-369-1(1)); 1999. lib. bdg. 19.93 (978-1-57505-257-1(1) , Carolrhoda Bks.) Lerner Publishing Group.

—Eating. 1999. (gr. k-3). lib. bdg. 15.25 (978-0-613-42497-4(2)) Tandem Library Bks.

Time for Dinner: Individual Title Six-Packs. (Chiquilibros Ser.). (gr. k-1). 23.00 (978-0-7635-0414-4(9)) Rigby Education.

Townsend, Sue & Young, Caroline. Egypt. 2003. (Illus.). 48p. (J). lib. bdg. (978-1-4034-0979-9(X)) Heinemann Library.

—Indonesia. 2003. (World of Recipes Ser.). (Illus.). 48p. (J). lib. bdg. (978-1-4034-0976-8(5)) Heinemann Library.

—Russia. 2003. 48p. (J). 7.95 (978-1-4034-3651-1(7)); (Illus.). lib. bdg. 27.07 (978-1-4034-0981-2(1)) Heinemann Library.

—Spain. 2003. (World of Recipes Ser.). (Illus.). 48p. (J). lib. bdg. 27.07 (978-1-4034-0978-2(1)) Heinemann Library.

—Vietnam. 2003. 48p. (J). pap. 7.95 (978-1-4034-3654-2(1)); (Illus.). lib. bdg. 27.07 (978-1-4034-0980-5(3)) Heinemann.

Walton, Adrienne. Food. 2004. (Activities for 3-5 Year Olds Ser.). (Illus.). 32p. pap. 11.00 (978-1-897675-57-1(7)) Brilliant Pubns. GBR. *Dist:* Parkwest Pubns., Inc.

Yesh, Jeff, illus. Meals Around the World. 4 bks. Incl. Evening Meals Around the World. Zurakowski, Michele. 22.60 (978-1-4048-0282-7(7)); Midday Meals Around the World. Zurakowski, Michele. 22.60 (978-1-4048-0281-0(9) , 1229526); Morning Meals Around the World. Gregoire, Maryellen. 22.60 (978-1-4048-0280-3(0) , 1229527); Snack Time Around the World. Zurakowski, Michele. 22.60 (978-1-4048-0283-4(5) , 1229528); 24p. (J). (gr. k-4). 2004. (Illus.). 2004. 85.04 (978-1-4048-0279-7(7)) Picture Window Bks.

Zurakowski, Michele. Evening Meals Around the World. Yesh, Jeff, illus. 2004. (Meals Around the World Ser.). 24p. (J). (gr. k-4). 22.60 (978-1-4048-0282-7(7)) Picture Window Bks.

—Midday Meals Around the World. Yesh, Jeff, illus. 2004. (Meals Around the World Ser.). 24p. (J). (gr. k-4). 22.60 (978-1-4048-0281-0(9) , 1229526) Picture Window Bks.

—Snack Time Around the World. Yesh, Jeff, illus. 2004. (Meals Around the World Ser.). 24p. (J). (gr. k-4). 22.60 (978-1-4048-0283-4(5) , 1229528) Picture Window Bks.

FOOD HABITS—FICTION

Adams, Jean Ekman. Clarence & the Purple Horse Bounce into Town. Adams, Jean Ekman, illus. 2003. (Illus.). 32p. (ps-3). 15.95 (978-0-87358-826-3(6) , Rising Moon Bks. for Young Readers) Northland Publishing.

Beets, Beans & Turnip Greens. l.t. ed. 2001. 19p. (978-1-893595-20-0(X)) Four Seasons Bks., Inc.

Brouwer, Sigmund. Mommy Ant, Eat Your Vegetables. 2004. (Bug's-Eye View Bks.). (Illus.). 18p. (J). bds. 4.99 (978-0-8499-7756-5(8)) Nelson, Thomas Inc.

Brown, Marc. D. W. la Quisquillosa. Sarfatti, Esther, tr. from ENG. 2003. (SPA.). (J). (gr. k-2). pap. 6.95 (978-1-930332-42-3(4)) Lectorum Pubns., Inc.

—D. W. la Quisquillosa. 2003. (SPA.). (gr. k-3). lib. bdg. 15.25 (978-0-613-64480-8(8)) Tandem Library Bks.

Butler, M. Christina. Who's Been Eating My Porridge? Howarth, Daniel, illus. 2004. 32p. (J). (ps). tchr. ed. 15.95 (978-1-58925-040-6(0) , tiger tales) ME Media LLC.

Child, Lauren. I Will Never Not Ever Eat a Tomato. Child, Lauren, illus. 2000. (Illus.). 32p. (J). (ps-3). 16.99 (978-0-7636-1188-0(3)) Candlewick Pr.

Child, Lauren. I Will Never Not Ever Eat a Tomato Pop-up. Child, Lauren, illus. 2007. (Charlie & Lola Ser.). (Illus.). 16p. (J). (ps). 18.99 (***978-0-7636-3708-8(4)***) Candlewick Pr.

Collins, Ross. Alvie Eats Soup. 2002. (Illus.). (J). (978-0-439-27265-0(3) , Levine, Arthur A. Bks.) Scholastic, Inc.

Deem, Saitofi Anne. Myrtle Learns to Eat Well. 1998. (Teachable Moments Ser.). (Illus.). 12p. (J). (ps-3). pap. 7.95 (978-1-930694-05-7(9)) Myrtle Learns.

Demar, Regier. Good Food. Clar, David Austin, illus. 2005. (My First Reader Ser.). 31p. (J). (ps-ps). 18.50 (978-0-516-24879-0(0) , Children's Pr.) Scholastic Library Publishing.

Dining with Prunella. 1998. (Books to Go). (J). pap. (978-0-8136-7877-1(3)) Modern Curriculum Pr.

Donnio, Sylviane. I'd Really Like to Eat a Child. De Monfreid, Dorothée, illus. 2007. (Picture Book Ser.). 32p. (J). (ps-1). lib. bdg. 17.99 (978-0-375-93761-3(7) , Random Hse. Bks. for Young Readers) Random Hse. Children's Bks.

—I'd Really Like to Eat a Child. Martin, Leslie, tr. from FRE. De Monfreid, Dorothée, illus. 2007. (Picture Book Ser.). 32p. (J). (ps-1). 14.99 (978-0-375-83761-6(2) , Random Hse. Bks. for Young Readers) Random Hse. Children's Bks.

Downing, Johnette. Today Is Monday in Louisiana. Kadair, Deborah Ousley, illus. 2006. 32p. (J). 15.95 (978-1-58980-406-7(6)) Pelican Publishing Co., Inc.

Drescher, Henrik. Hubert the Pudge: A Vegetarian Tale. Drescher, Henrik, illus. 2006. (Illus.). 40p. (J). (ps-3). 16.99 (978-0-7636-1992-3(2)) Candlewick Pr.

Durant, Alan. Burger Boy. Matsuoka, Mei, illus. 2006. 32p. (J). (gr. k-3). 16.00 (978-0-618-71466-7(9) , Clarion Bks.) Houghton Mifflin Co. Trade & Reference Div.

Dussling, Jennifer. Picky Peggy. Adams, Lynn, illus. 2004. 32p. (J). lib. bdg. 20.00 (***978-1-4242-1099-2(2)***) Fitzgerald Bks.

—Picky Peggy. Adams, Lynn, tr. Adams, Lynn, illus. 2004. (Science Solves It! Ser.). 32p. (J). 4.99 (978-1-57565-138-5(6)) Kane Pr., The.

Erickson, Gina Clegg & Foster, Kelli C. The Pancake Day. Gifford, Kerri, illus. 2004. 30p. (J). (ps-ps). lib. bdg. 11.30 (978-0-606-30082-7(1)) Tandem Library Bks.

Flaherty, Alice. The Luck of the Loch Ness Monster: A Tale of Picky Eating. Magoon, Scott, illus. 2007. 40p. (J). (gr. 3-5). 16.00 (***978-0-618-55644-1(3)***) Houghton Mifflin Co.

French, Vivian. Oliver's Milk Shake. Bartlett, Alison, illus. 2001. 32p. (J). (ps-1). 15.95 (978-0-531-30304-7(7) , Orchard Bks.) Scholastic, Inc.

—Oliver's Vegetables. 1998. (Illus.). 32p. (J). (ps-1). pap. 6.95 (978-0-531-07104-5(9) , Orchard Bks.) Scholastic, Inc.

Gantos, Jack. Rotten Ralph Feels Rotten: A Rotten Ralph Rotten Reader. Rubel, Nicole, tr. Rubel, Nicole, illus. 2004. (Rotten Ralph Rotten Readers Ser.). 48p. (J). 15.00 (978-0-374-36357-4(9) , Farrar, Straus & Giroux (BYR)) Farrar, Straus & Giroux.

Gray, Kes. Eat Your Peas: A Daisy Book. Sharratt, Nick, illus. 2006. 32p. (J). (ps-1). 10.95 (978-0-8109-5974-3(7)) Abrams, Harry N., Inc.

Greene, Renea Russ. Thunder in the Coffee Pot. Greene, Laura Hampton, illus. 2002. 36p. (J). pap. 8.95 (978-0-9723719-0-2(7)) FUN 4 5 Pubns.

Halverson, Deborah. Big Mouth. 2008. 144p. (J). (gr. 5). 15.99 (***978-0-385-73394-6(1)***); lib. bdg. 18.99 (***978-0-385-90408-7(8)***) Random Hse. Children's Bks. (Delacorte Bks. for Young Readers).

Harrison, Paul. Hmm, que rica mosca, Level P. Worsley, Belinda, illus. 2006. (Lightning Readers Ser.). 32p. (J). pap. 3.95 (978-0-7696-4228-4(4) , Gingham Dog Pr.) School Specialty Publishing.

—Yummy, Yummy Fly. Worsley, Belinda, illus. 2006. (Lightning Readers Ser.). 32p. (J). (ps-k). pap. 3.95 (978-0-7696-4198-0(9) , Gingham Dog Pr.) School Specialty Publishing.

Helmer, Diana Star. The Cat Who Came for Tacos. Escriva, Vivi, illus. 2003. 32p. (J). (gr. 1-3). 15.95 (978-0-8075-5106-6(6)) Whitman, Albert & Co.

Hoberman, Mary Ann. The Seven Silly Eaters. Frazee, Marla, illus. 2000. 40p. (J). (ps-3). pap. 7.00 (978-0-15-202440-6(9) , Voyager Bks./Libros Viajeros) Harcourt Children's Bks.

—Seven Silly Eaters. 2000. (ps-2). lib. bdg. 14.15 (978-0-613-30122-0(6)) Tandem Library Bks.

—The Seven Silly Eaters. Frazee, Marla, illus. ed. 2004. (J). (gr. k-3). spiral bd. (978-0-616-14576-0(4)) Canadian National Institute for the Blind/Institut National Canadien pour les Aveugles.

Ide, Laurie Shimizu. Okazu at the Zoo. Kanekuni, Daniel, illus. 2006. (J). (978-1-56647-776-5(X)) Mutual Publishing LLC.

Jeffers, Oliver. The Incredible Book Eating Boy. Jeffers, Oliver, illus. 2007. 32p. (J). (ps-3). 16.99 (978-0-399-24749-1(1) , Philomel) Penguin Group (USA) Inc.

Jones, Christianne C. Just Try It. Trover, Zachary, illus. 2005. (Read-It! Readers Ser.). 32p. (J). (gr. k-3). 18.60 (978-1-4048-1175-1(3)) Picture Window Bks.

—Pruebalo. Yi, Hye Won, illus. 2006. (Read-It! Readers en Espanol Ser.).Tr. of Just Try it. (SPA.). 32p. (J). (ps-3). 19.95 (978-1-4048-1692-3(5)) Picture Window Bks.

Jones, Nathan Smith. The Boy Who Ate America. Nelson, Carey, illus. 2007. 32p. (J). (ps-3). 16.95 (***978-1-59038-814-3(3)*** , Shadow Mountain) Deseret Bk. Co.

Kann, Elizabeth & Kann, Victoria. Pinkalicious. Kann, Victoria, illus. 2006. (Illus.). 40p. (J). 16.99 (978-0-06-077639-8(0)); lib. bdg. 16.89 (978-0-06-077640-4(4)) HarperCollins Pubs.

King, Daren. Mouse Noses on Toast. Roberts, David, illus. 2008. 128p. (J). (gr. 3). 15.99 (***978-0-399-25037-8(9)*** , Putnam Juvenile) Penguin Group (USA) Inc.

Kompelien, Tracy. Fly Paper. Haberstroh, Anne, illus. (Fact & Fiction Ser.). 24p. (J). 2007. 21.35 (978-1-59928-438-5(3)); 2006. (978-1-59928-439-2(1)) ABDO Publishing Co.

Krulik, Nancy E. Free the Worms!, No. 28. John and Wendy Staff, illus. 2008. (Katie Kazoo, Switcheroo Ser.: No. 28). 80p. (J). (gr. 2-5). pap. 3.99 (***978-0-448-44675-2(8)*** , Grosset & Dunlap) Penguin Group (USA) Inc.

Landry, Leo. Eat Your Peas, Ivy Louise. 2005. (J). (ps-k). 12.00 (978-0-618-58112-2(X)); (Illus.). 32p. 12.00 (978-0-618-44886-9(1)) Houghton Mifflin Co. Trade & Reference Div.

Manning, Mick & Granstrom, Brita. Chomp, Chomp! 2003. (Mick Manning & Brita Granstrom Ser.). (SPA., Illus.). (J). (978-970-690-586-4(3)) Planeta Mexicana Editorial S. A. de C. V.

McClements, George. Night of the Veggie Monster. 2008. (Illus.). 32p. (J). 15.85 (***978-1-59990-234-0(6)***) Bloomsbury Publishing.

—Night of the Veggie Monster. McClements, George, illus. 2008. (Illus.). 32p. (J). 14.95 (***978-1-59990-061-2(0)***) Bloomsbury Publishing.

Miller, Deborah U. & Ostrove, Karen. Fins & Scales: A Kosher Tale. Ostrove, Karen, illus. 2004. (Israel Ser.). (Illus.). 32p. (J). (gr. 1-3). pap. 4.95 (978-0-929371-25-2(9)) Kar-Ben Publishing.

Mitton, Tony. Planet Ocky: Ham & Jam. Chatterton, Ann & Chatterton, Martin, illus. 1999. (Cambridge Reading Ser.). 14p. pap. 5.00 (978-0-521-64704-5(5)); pap., pap. 16.95 (978-0-521-66701-2(1)) Cambridge Univ. Pr.

—Planet Ocky: Jump & Bump. Chatterton, Ann & Chatterton, Martin, illus. 1999. (Cambridge Reading Ser.). 14p. pap., pap. 16.95 (978-0-521-66700-5(3)) Cambridge Univ. Pr.

Namm, Diane. Little Bear. McCue, Lisa, illus. 2003. (My First Reader Ser.). 32p. (J). 18.50 (978-0-516-22931-7(1) , Children's Pr.) Scholastic Library Publishing.

Palatini, Margie & Davis, Jack E. Sweet Tooth. 2004. (Illus.). 40p. (J). 16.95 (978-0-689-85159-9(6)) Simon & Schuster Children's Publishing.

Pantuso, Mike & Henson, Jim. Food! 2001. (Illus.). (J). lib. bdg. (978-0-375-91391-4(2) , Random Hse. Bks. for Young Readers) Random Hse. Children's Bks.

Reggier, DeMar & Jensen, Patricia. Good Food. Clar, David Austin, illus. 2006. 32p. (J). (gr. k-1). pap. 3.95 (978-0-516-24969-8(X) , Children's Pr.) Scholastic Library Publishing.

Rosenthal, Amy Krouse. Little Pea. Corace, Jen, illus. 2005. 36p. (J). 12.95 (978-0-8118-4658-5(X)) Chronicle Bks. LLC.

Rubel, Nicole. No More Vegetables! Rubel, Nicole, illus. 2002. (Illus.). 32p. (J). (gr. k-2). 16.00 (978-0-374-36362-8(5) , Farrar, Straus & Giroux (BYR)) Farrar, Straus & Giroux.

Salerno, Steven. Harry Hungry. 2008. (J). (***978-0-15-206257-6(2)***) Harcourt Trade Pubs.

Schechter, Lynn R. Jenna's Big Fat Secret: A Story about Food & Feelings. 2007. 96p. per. 9.95 (***978-0-595-44001-6(0)***) iUniverse, Inc.

Schneider, David. Dillan Mcmillan, Please Eat Your Peas. Shelly, Jeff, Sr., illus. 2007. 36p. (J). pap. 14.95 (***978-0-9744446-4-2(2)***) All About Kids Publishing.

Schnitzlein, Danny. The Monster Who Ate My Peas. Faulkner, Matt, illus. 2001. 32p. (J). (gr. k-3). 15.95 (978-1-56145-216-3(5) , Q32689) Peachtree Pubs., Ltd.

Stonesifer, Gertrude. The Peanut Butter Kid. Rogers, Denny, illus. 2003. 32p. (J). (gr. 1-4). pap. 9.95 (978-1-878044-44-0(3) , Wild Rose) Mayhaven Publishing.

Sula, Sondra. The Expanders: Quest for the Flubulator. 2000. mass mkt. 8.95 (978-1-931179-11-9(5)) Long Hill Productions, Inc.

—The Expanders: Quest for the Flubulator. Johnson, Terri L., illus. 2000. 32p. (J). (gr. 1-3). pap. (978-0-9701450-2-4(0)) Long Hill Productions, Inc.

Van Fleet, Matthew. Monday the Bullfrog. 2006. (J). (978-978-141-691-0(2) , Simon & Schuster Children's Publishing) Simon & Schuster Children's Publishing.

—Monday the Bullfrog. Van Fleet, Matthew, illus. 2006. (Illus.). 20p. (J). 17.99 (978-1-4169-1231-6(2)) Simon & Schuster Children's Publishing.

Van Laan, Nancy. Tickle Tum! Pons, Bernadette, illus. 2005. (Stories to Go! Ser.). 32p. (J). 4.99 (978-1-4169-0836-4(6) , Aladdin) Simon & Schuster Children's Publishing.

Walton, Rick. Bullfrog Pops. McAllister, Chris, illus. 2005. 32p. pap. 6.95 (978-1-58685-840-7(8)) Gibbs Smith, Publisher.

Whitehead, Pete, illus. Hungry Dinosaur. 2006. (I'm Going to Read Ser.). 32p. (J). pap. 3.95 (978-1-4027-3418-2(2)) Sterling Publishing Co., Inc.

Yaccarino, Dan. The Lima Bean Monster. McCauley, Adam, illus. 32p. (J). (ps-2). 2002. 16.85 (978-0-8027-8777-4(0)); 2001. 15.95 (978-0-8027-8776-7(2)) Walker & Co.

Yee, Wong Herbert. Hamburger Heaven. Yee, Wong Herbert, illus. 1999. (Illus.). 32p. (J). (gr. k-3). tchr. ed. 16.00 (978-0-395-87548-3(X)) Houghton Mifflin Co. Trade & Reference Div.

—Hamburger Heaven. 2005. (Illus.). 32p. (J). (gr. k-3). reprint ed. 5.95 (978-0-618-54885-9(8)) Houghton Mifflin Co. Trade & Reference Div.

FOOD INDUSTRY AND TRADE—VOCATIONAL GUIDANCE

Aaseng, Nathan. Business Builders in Sweets & Treats. 2005. (Business Builders Ser.: Vol. 9). (Illus.). 160p. (J). (gr. 5 up). lib. bdg. 24.95 (978-1-881508-84-7(6)) Oliver Pr., Inc.

Center for Mathematics, Science, and Technology, Illinois State University Staff, contrib. by. Integrated Mathematics, Science & Technology: Food Production. 1999. (Illus.). (YA). (gr. 6-12). stu. ed. 14.99 (978-0-02-647840-3(4)) Glencoe/McGraw-Hill.

Ferguson. Careers in Focus: Food. 3rd rev. ed. 2007. (Careers in Focus Ser.). 192p. (J). (gr. 6-12). 29.95 (***978-0-8160-6591-2(8)*** , Ferguson Publishing Co.) Facts On File, Inc.

Hall, Margaret. H. J. Heinz. 2003. (Illus.). 32p. (J). lib. bdg. 22.79 (978-1-4034-3248-3(1)) Heinemann Library.

Hughes, Sarah. My Aunt Works in a Cheese Shop. 2001. (Welcome Bks.). (Illus.). 24p. (J). (ps-2). pap. 4.95 (978-0-516-29573-2(X) , Children's Pr.) Scholastic Library Publishing.

—My Aunt Works in a Cheese Shop. 2001. (gr. k-3). lib. bdg. 12.95 (978-0-613-58856-0(8)) Tandem Library Bks.

McAlpine, Margaret. Working in the Food Industry. 2005. (My Future Career Ser.). (Illus.). 64p. (J). lib. bdg. 26.00 (978-0-8368-4776-5(8)) Stevens, Gareth Inc.

FOOD PLANTS

see Plants, Edible

FOOD POISONING

Hirschmann, Kris. Salmonella. 2003. (Parasites Ser.). (Illus.). 32p. (J). 24.95 (978-0-7377-1785-3(8) , Greenhaven Pr., Inc.) Thomson Gale.

Isle, Mick. Everything You Need to Know about Food Poisoning. 2001. (Need to Know Library). (Illus.). 64p. (YA). (gr. 4-6). lib. bdg. 25.25 (978-0-8239-3396-9(2)) Rosen Publishing Group, Inc., The.

Latta, Sara L. Food Poisoning & Foodborne Diseases. 1999. (Diseases & People Ser.). (Illus.). 128p. (YA). (gr. 6-12). lib. bdg. 26.60 (978-0-7660-1183-0(6)) Enslow Pubs., Inc.

Pascoe, Elaine, ed. Spreading Menace: Salmonella Attack & the Hunger Craving. 2003. (Body Story Ser.). (Illus.). 48p. (J). 24.95 (978-1-4103-0064-5(1)); 11.20 (978-1-4103-0185-7(0)) Thomson Gale. (Blackbirch Pr., Inc.).

Sheen, Barbara. Food Poisoning. 2004. (Illus.). 112p. (J). 32.45 (978-1-59018-409-7(2) , Lucent Bks.) Thomson Gale.

Silverstein, Alvin, et al. The Food Poisoning Update. 2007. (Disease Update Ser.). (Illus.). 128p. (J). (gr. 5 up). lib. bdg. 31.93 (***978-0-7660-2748-0(1)***) Enslow Pubs., Inc.

Taylor-Butler, Christine. Food Safety. 2007. (True Booktrade;: Health & the Human Body Ser.). 48p. (J). spiral bd. 26.00 (***978-0-531-16860-8(3)*** , Children's Pr.) Scholastic Library Publishing.

FOOD PRESERVATION

see Food—Preservation

FOOD SERVICE—VOCATIONAL GUIDANCE

Beal, Eileen J. Choosing a Career in the Restaurant Industry. rev. ed. 1999. (World of Work Ser.). (Illus.). 64p. (YA). (gr. 7-12). lib. bdg. 25.25 (978-0-8239-3002-9(5) , WWREST) Rosen Publishing Group, Inc., The.

Ferguson. Careers in Focus: Food. 3rd rev. ed. 2007. (Careers in Focus Ser.). 192p. (J). (gr. 6-12). 29.95 (***978-0-8160-6591-2(8)*** , Ferguson Publishing Co.) Facts On File, Inc.

Heibel, Jane & Strom, Sharon. Wisconsin's Skill Standards for Food Service. 2001. 110p. (YA). ring bd. 36.00 (978-1-57337-095-0(9)) Wisconsin Dept. of Public Instruction.

Pasternak, Ceel & Thornburg, Linda. Cool Careers for Girls in Food. 1999. (Illus.). 118p. (J). (gr. 5 up). 19.95 (978-1-57023-127-8(3)) Impact Pubns.

Quinlan, Kathryn A. Food Service Manager. 1998. (Careers Without College Ser.). (Illus.). 48p. (J). (gr. 3-4). lib. bdg. 21.26 (978-0-7368-0034-1(4) , LifeMatters Bks.) Capstone Pr., Inc.

Rue, Nancy N. Choosing a Career in Hotels, Motels & Resorts. rev. ed. 1999. (World of Work Ser.). (Illus.). 64p. (YA). (gr. 7-12). lib. bdg. 25.25 (978-0-8239-2999-3(X) , WWHOMO) Rosen Publishing Group, Inc., The.

Yanuck, Debbie L. Food Service Workers. 2002. (Community Helpers Ser.). (Illus.). 24p. (J). (gr. 1-2). lib. bdg. 18.60 (978-0-7368-1128-6(1) , Bridgestone Bks.) Capstone Pr., Inc.

FOOD SUPPLY

see also Food—Preservation; Meat Industry and Trade

Allen, Julia & Iggulden, Margaret. Food & the World. 2005. (Your Environment Ser.). (Illus.). 32p. (J). (978-1-59604-065-6(3)) Stargazer Bks.

Baines, John. Food for Life. 2006. (Sustainable Futures Ser.). (Illus.). 48p. (J). (978-1-58340-978-7(5) , 1262622) Smart Apple Media.

Bellamy, Rufus. Food for All. 2005. (Action for the Environment Ser.). (Illus.). 32p. (J). (gr. 4-7). lib. bdg. 27.10 (978-1-58340-598-7(4) , 1247276) Smart Apple Media.

Bowden, Rob. Food Supply: Our Impact on the Planet. 2002. (Twenty-First Century Debates Ser.). (Illus.). 64p. (YA). (gr. 6-8). lib. bdg. 27.12 (978-0-7398-4871-5(2)) Raintree.

Fix, Alexandra. Food. 2007. (J). (***978-1-4034-9713-0(3)***); pap. (***978-1-4034-9721-5(4)***) Heinemann Library.

Food & Nutrition. 2004. (Atlases of the Earth & Its Resources Ser.). (Illus.). 80p. (J). (gr. 5 up). lib. bdg. 34.00 (978-0-8368-5617-0(1) , World Almanac Library) Stevens, Gareth Inc.

Fridell, Ron. The War on Hunger: Dealing with Dictators, Deserts, & Debt. 2003. (In a Perfect World Ser.). (Illus.). 80p. (gr. 5-8). lib. bdg. 26.90 (978-0-7613-2650-2(2) , Twenty-First Century Bks.) Lerner Publishing Group.

Hunnicut, Susan C. World Hunger. 2006. (Illus.). 128p. (J). (gr. 10-12). 21.20 (978-0-7377-2762-3(4)); pap. 29.95 (978-0-7377-2761-6(6)) Thomson Gale. (Greenhaven Pr., Inc.).

Maddocks, Steven. World Hunger. 2004. (21st Century Issues Ser.). (J). 11.95 (978-0-8368-5663-7(5)); lib. bdg. 30.00 (978-0-8368-5646-0(5)) Stevens, Gareth Inc. (World Almanac Library).

Stradling, Jan. Food for All: Level I, 6 vols. (First Explorers Ser.). 24p. (gr. 1-2). 29.95 (978-0-7699-1445-9(4)) Shortland Pubns. (U. S. A.) Inc.

Walpole, Brenda. Feeding the World. 2007. (Illus.). 32p. (J). (***978-1-59771-064-0(4))*** Sea-To-Sea Pubns.

Where Food Comes From. 2003. 48p. (J). pap. 12.99 (978-0-7894-9256-2(3)) Dorling Kindersley Publishing, Inc.

FOOD TRADE

see Farm Produce—Marketing

FOOLS AND JESTERS—FICTION

Brouwer, Sigmund. The Angel & the Sword: A Supernatural Adventure. 2005. (Guardian Angel Ser.). 172p. (J). (ps-7). pap. 7.99 (978-0-7369-0293-9(7)) Harvest Hse. Pubs.

Caveney, Philip. Sebastian Darke: Prince of Fools. 2008. 272p. (YA). (gr. 7). lib. bdg. 18.99 (***978-0-385-90465-0(7)*** , Delacorte Pr.) Dell Publishing.

Howard, Arthur. Serious Trouble. (Illus.). 32p. (J). 2007. pap. 6.00 (978-0-15-205853-1(2) , Voyager Bks./Libros Viajeros); 2003. 16.00 (978-0-15-202664-6(9)) Harcourt Children's Bks.

Olofsson, Helena-Adapt. The Little Jester. Board, Helena, tr. from SWE. Olofsson, Helena-Adapt, illus. 2002. (Illus.). 28p. (J). (gr. k-3). 16.00 (978-91-29-65499-8(8)) R & S Bks. SWE. *Dist:* Macmillan.

Santillo, LuAnn. Stop Hopping. Santillo, LuAnn, ed. 2003. (Half-Pint Kids Readers Ser.). (Illus.). 7p. (J). (ps-1). pap. (978-1-59256-054-7(7)) Half-Pint Kids, Inc.

Yolen, Jane. Queen's Own Fool: A Novel of Mary Queen of Scots. 2001. (gr. 7-12). lib. bdg. 16.45 (978-0-613-44410-1(8)) Tandem Library Bks.

FOOT

Aliki. My Feet. Aliki, illus. 2001. (Let's-Read-and-Find-Out Science Ser.). (Illus.). 32p. (J). (ps-1). 15.89 (978-0-690-04815-5(7)) HarperCollins Pubs.

Bedford, David. Toes. Worthington, Leonie, illus. 2007. 16p. (J). (ps-k). 9.95 (***978-1-921049-64-4(2))*** Little Hare Bks. AUS. *Dist:* Independent Pubs. Group.

Bozzo, Linda. Amazing Animal Feet. 2008. (J). lib. bdg. (***978-1-4042-4167-1(1)*** , PowerKids Pr.) Rosen Publishing Group, Inc., The.

Brown, Jonatha A. Animal Feet & Legs. 2006. (Illus.). 24p. (J). pap. (978-0-8368-6865-4(X)); lib. bdg. (978-0-8368-6860-9(9)) Stevens, Gareth Inc.

Butler, John. Whose Nose & Toes? 2004. (Illus.). 20p. (J). (ps-ps). 10.99 (978-0-670-05904-1(8) , Viking Juvenile) Penguin Group (USA) Inc.

Degezelle, Terri. Taking Care of My Hands & Feet. 2005. (Pebble Plus Ser.). (Illus.). 24p. (J). (ps-7). lib. bdg. 19.93 (978-0-7368-4262-4(4)) Capstone Pr., Inc.

Douglas, Lloyd G. My Legs & Feet. 2004. (Wel-My Body Ser.). (J). 18.00 (978-0-516-24064-0(1)); 24p. pap. 4.95 (978-0-516-22130-4(2)) Scholastic Library Publishing. (Children's Pr.).

Hall, Peg. Whose Feet Are These? A Look at Hooves, Paws, & Claws. Landmark, Ken, illus. 2004. (Whose Is It? Ser.). 24p. (C). (gr. k-2). 22.60 (978-1-4048-0006-9(9)) Picture Window Bks.

Hansen, Rosanna. Bones! All Kinds of Hands, All Kinds of Feet. 2001. (Hello Reader! Science Ser.). (Illus.). (J). (978-0-439-31707-8(X)) Scholastic, Inc.

Harcourt School Publishers Staff. Hello Toes! Hello.. Library Book. 1999. (Collections Ser.). (Illus.). pap. 14.90 (978-0-15-313395-4(3)) Harcourt Schl. Pubs.

Hess, Nina. Whose Feet? Kanzler, John, tr. Kanzler, John, illus. 2004. (Step into Reading Ser.). 32p. (J). (ps-2). pap. 3.99 (978-0-375-82623-8(8) , Random Hse. Bks. for Young Readers) Random Hse. Children's Bks.

—Whose Feet? 2004. (ps-2). lib. bdg. 11.80 (978-0-613-86693-4(2)) Tandem Library Bks.

Hunt, Connie. Hooray for Feet! Melmon, Deborah, illus. 2008. (J). (***978-1-58728-699-5(8)*** , Two Can Publishing) T&N Children's Publishing.

Klingel, Cynthia Fitterer & Noyed, Robert B. Feet. Andersen, Gregg, photos by. 2002. (Weekly Reader Early Learning Library). (Illus.). 24p. (J). (ps up). pap. 5.95 (978-0-8368-3153-5(5)); lib. bdg. 19.33 (978-0-8368-3064-4(4)) Stevens, Gareth Inc. (Weekly Reader Early Learning Library).

—Feet/Pies. Acosta, Tatiana & Gutiérrez, Guillermo, trs. Andersen, Gregg, photos by. 2002. (Weekly Reader Early Learning Library). (Illus.). 24p. (J). (ps up). (SPA & ENG.). pap. (978-0-8368-3322-5(8)); (ENG & SPA., lib. bdg. 19.33 (978-0-8368-3073-6(3)) Stevens, Gareth Inc. (Weekly Reader Early Learning Library).

Leake, Diyan. Feet. 2007. (J). (***978-1-4329-0000-7(5));*** pap. (***978-1-4329-0005-2(6))*** Heinemann Library.

Miles, Elizabeth. Paws & Claws. 2003. (Animal Parts Ser.). (Illus.). 32p. pap. 6.95 (978-1-4034-0429-9(1)) Heinemann Library.

Miller, Sara Swan. All Kinds of Feet. 2007. (All Kinds Of Ser.). (Illus.). 48p. (J). (ps-3). lib. bdg. 28.50 (978-0-7614-2520-5(9)) Cavendish, Marshall Corp.

Mitchell, Melanie S. Feet. 2003. (First Step Nonfiction Ser.). (Illus.). 8p. (J). pap. (978-0-8225-3912-4(8) , Lerner Pubns.) Lerner Publishing Group.

Perkins, Wendy. Animal Feet. 2007. (Pebble Plus Ser.). (Illus.). 24p. (J). 19.93 (978-0-7368-6352-0(4) , Pebble Bks.) Capstone Pr., Inc.

Prostova, Elena & Shaw, Cathleen. Toe-rrific: A Simple Guide to Creating Healthy & Beautiful Feet. 2005. (Illus.). 72p. pap. 24.95 (978-0-9745627-0-4(X) , 1234067) Happy Women Publishing Co.

Salzmann, Mary Elizabeth. What Has Paws? 2007. (Creature Features Ser.). (ENG., Illus.). 24p. (J). (ps-3). lib. bdg. 24.21 (***978-1-59928-869-7(9)*** , Super SandCastle) ABDO Publishing Co.

—What Has Webbed Feet? 2007. (Creature Features Ser.). (ENG., Illus.). 24p. (J). (ps-3). lib. bdg. 24.21 (***978-1-59928-875-8(3)*** , Super SandCastle) ABDO Publishing Co.

Sayre, April Pulley & Sayre, Jeff. One Is a Snail, Ten Is a Crab: A Counting by Feet Book. Cecil, Randy, illus. 2003. 40p. (J). (gr. k-3). 15.99 (978-0-7636-1406-5(8)) Candlewick Pr.

Schaefer, Lola M. Legs, Knees, Feet, & Toes. 2003. (It's My Body Ser.). (Illus.). 24p. (J). (ps-1). lib. bdg. 18.50 (978-1-4034-0890-7(4)); pap. 5.25 (978-1-4034-3482-1(4)) Heinemann Library.

Sideri, Simona. Feet. Noble, Sheilagh, tr. Noble, Sheilagh, illus. 2004. (J). lib. bdg. (978-1-58340-492-8(9)) Smart Apple Media.

—Let's Look at Feet. Noble, Sheilagh, illus. 2002. 24p. (YA). (ps up). (978-1-84089-144-7(0) , Zero to Ten, Limited) Evans Publishing Group.

—Let's Look at Hands. Noble, Sheilagh, illus. 2002. 24p. (YA). (ps up). (978-1-84089-145-4(9) , Zero to Ten, Limited) Evans Publishing Group.

Silverstein, Alvin & Silverstein, Virginia B. The Story of Your Foot. Wenzel, Greg, illus. 1999. 80p. (YA). (gr. 6-12). reprint ed. 12.00 (978-0-7881-6234-3(9)) DIANE Publishing Co.

Souza, D.M. Look What Feet Can Do. 2007. (Look What Animals Can Do Ser.). (Illus.). 48p. (J). 22.60 (978-0-7613-9460-0(5) , Lerner Pubns.) Lerner Publishing Group.

Verdick, Elizabeth. Feet Are Not for Kicking. Heinlen, Marieka, illus. 2004. (Best Behavior Ser.). 24p. (J). 7.95 (978-1-57542-158-2(5)) Free Spirit Publishing, Inc.

Whittaker, Nicola. Feet. 2002. (Creature Features Ser.). (Illus.). 32p. (J). (ps up). lib. bdg. 23.33 (978-0-8368-3163-4(2)) Stevens, Gareth Inc.

FOOTBALL

see also Rugby Football; Soccer

The ABC's of Oklahoma Sooner Football. 2003. (Illus.). 32p. (J). (978-0-9747689-0-8(1)) Little Scribblers Bks., LLC.

Adelson, Bruce. Touchdown Trivia. 1998. (Sports Trivia Ser.). (Illus.). 64p. (YA). (gr. 5-9). pap. (978-0-8225-9805-3(1) , Lerner Pubns.) Lerner Publishing Group.

—Touchdown Trivia. Pulver, Harry, illus. 1998. (Sports Trivia Ser.). 64p. (J). (gr. 5-9). lib. bdg. (978-0-8225-3312-2(X) , Lerner Pubns.) Lerner Publishing Group.

At the Game, 6, Packs. (ps-2). 27.00 (978-0-7635-9436-7(9)) Rigby Education.

Bass, Tom. Between the Lines. 2007. (NFL Reader Ser.). 32p. (J). pap. 3.99 (***978-0-439-92455-9(3))*** Scholastic, Inc.

Bernards, Neal. Garnet & Gold: The Florida State Seminoles Story. 1999. (College Football Today Ser.). (Illus.). 32p. (J). (gr. 4-7). pap. 21.30 (978-0-88682-977-3(1) , Creative Education) Creative Co., The.

—Go Big Blue: The Michigan Wolverines Story. 1999. (College Sports Today Ser.). (Illus.). 32p. (YA). (gr. 4-7). pap. 21.30 (978-0-88682-979-7(8) , Creative Education) Creative Co., The.

Bianchi, Mike & Novak, Marisol. Swampmeet: A Gator Counting Book. Marlette, Andy, illus. 2004. 32p. (J). (ps-k). 6.95 (978-1-58261-780-0(5)) Sports Publishing, LLC.

Booth, Tanis. For the Love of Football. Craats, Rennay, ed. 2001. (For the Love of Sports Ser.). (Illus.). 24p. (J). (gr. k-3). lib. bdg. 15.95 (978-1-930954-25-0(5)) Weigl Pubs., Inc.

Bradley, Michael. Donovan McNabb. 2004. (Illus.). 48p. (J). 27.07 (978-0-7614-1756-9(7) , Benchmark Bks.) Cavendish, Marshall Corp.

—Football All-Stars. Gramling, Scott, ed. 1999. (Illus.). 94p. (J). (gr. 2-8). pap. 3.99 (978-1-886749-64-1(7)) Sports Illustrated For Kids.

Brandon's Story. 2nd l.t. ed. 2001. 110p. (YA). spiral bd. 7.99 (978-0-9716330-0-1(2)) Deacon Denny Bks.

Bratton, Deboral B. & Bratton, Ashley A. Record-a-Sport Football Sport Organizer. Bratton, Deboral B. & Bratton, Ashley A., eds. Bratton, Ashley A., illus. 2003. (Illus.). (gr. 1 up). 18.95 (978-1-931746-05-2(2)) Sport Your Stuff Corp.

Braun, Eric. Fight On: The USC Trojans Story. 1999. (College Sports Today Ser.). (Illus.). 32p. (YA). (gr. 4-7). pap. 21.30 (978-0-88682-985-8(2) , Creative Education) Creative Co., The.

Brenner, Richard J. Superstars Album 1998: Football. 1998. (Illus.). 48p. (J). (gr. 4-7). pap. 4.50 (978-0-688-16229-0(0) , Harper Trophy) HarperCollins Pubs.

Brown, Jonatha A. Football. 2004. (J). pap. (978-0-8368-4346-0(0)); lib. bdg. 19.33 (978-0-8368-4339-2(8)) Stevens, Gareth Inc.

Buckley, James, Jr. AFC North. 2005. (Inside the NFL Ser.). (Illus.). 48p. (J). (gr. 1-5). 28.50 (978-1-59296-509-0(1)) Child's World, Inc.

—NFL Rules! Bloopers, Pranks, Upsets, & Touchdowns. 1999. (Monday Night Football Club Ser.). 96p. 3.95 (978-0-7868-1412-1(8)) Disney Pr.

Buckley Jr., James. Afc South. 2005. (Inside the NFL Ser.). 48p. (J). (gr. 1-5). 28.50 (978-1-59296-510-6(5)) Child's World, Inc.

Carroll, Bob & Horrigan, Joe. Football Legends of All Times. 1999. (Sports Legends Ser.). (Illus.). 216p. (J). (gr. k up). lib. bdg. 24.95 (978-1-56674-284-9(6)) Forest Hse. Publishing Co., Inc.

Charpentier, Cliff. Charpentier's 1998 Fantasy Football. 1998. 120p. (J). pap. 12.95 (978-0-8225-9947-0(3)) Lerner Publishing Group.

Crosby, Jim. Devotions for the Armchair Quarterback. 2004. 109p. per. 12.95 (978-1-932338-33-1(0)) Lifevest Publishing, Inc.

Crossingham, John. Football in Action. 2000. (Sports in Action Ser.). (Illus.). 32p. (J). (gr. 3-4). (978-0-7787-0166-8(2)); pap. (978-0-7787-0178-1(6)) Crabtree Publishing Co.

—Football in Action. 2000. (Illus.). 32p. (J). (gr. 1-4). lib. bdg. 14.10 (978-0-613-32576-9(1)) Tandem Library Bks.

—Futbol Americano. 2005. (FRE & SPA., Illus.). 32p. (J). (978-0-7787-8573-6(4)) Crabtree Publishing Co.

Crossingham, John & Kalman, Bobbie. Futbol Americano. 2005. (Deportes en Accion Ser.). (SPA., Illus.). 32p. (J). (gr. 6-9). pap. (978-0-7787-8619-1(6)) Crabtree Publishing Co.

Crumley, Daniel Wade. 4 -0n- 4 Flag Football Training Manual: Flag Football. 2005. spiral bd. 19.99 (978-0-9772203-0-4(3)) Go Flag Football.

Davis, Terry. Roll Tide! The Alabama Crimson Tide Story. 1999. (College Sports Today Ser.). (Illus.). 32p. (YA). (gr. 4-7). pap. 21.30 (978-0-88682-975-9(5) , Creative Education) Creative Co., The.

Deitsch, Richard. (Quarter)Backs-to-(Running)Backs: The NFL's Finest Passers & Rushers. Wolf, Cathrine, ed. 1998. 32p. (J). (gr. 4-6). pap. 3.95 (978-1-886749-45-0(0)) Sports Illustrated For Kids.

Deutsch, Richard. Passers & Receivers: The NFL's Top Touchdown Duos. Gramling, Scott & Northrop, Michael, eds. 1999. 32p. (J). (gr. 2-8). pap. 3.99 (978-1-886749-67-2(1)) Sports Illustrated For Kids.

Dorling Kindersley Publishing Staff. NFL Reader: Super Bowl! 2003. (gr. k-3). lib. bdg. 11.80 (978-0-613-75250-3(3)) Tandem Library Bks.

Epstein, Brad M. University of Notre Dame Fighting Irish 123: My first counting Book. l.t. ed. 2006. (Illus.). 22p. (J). bds. 15.95 (***978-1-932530-52-0(5)*** , 123 Bk.) Michaelson Entertainment.

Fauchald, Nick. Touchdown! You Can Play Football. Dickson, Bill, illus. 2004. (Game Day Ser.). 24p. (J). (gr. k-3). 22.60 (978-1-4048-0260-5(6) , 1229518) Picture Window Bks.

Football for Fun! (For Fun Ser.). 48p. (YA). 8.95 (978-0-7565-1154-8(2)) Compass Point Bks.

Football Hall of Famers, 6 bks. Incl. Deacon Jones. Donnelly, Karen. lib. bdg. 29.25 (978-0-8239-3606-9(6)); Fran Tarkenton. Hulm, David. lib. bdg. 29.25 (978-0-8239-3608-3(2)); Joe Montana. Ramen, Fred. lib. bdg. 29.25 (978-0-8239-3607-6(4)); Terry Bradshaw. Roza, Greg. lib. bdg. 29.25 (978-0-8239-3609-0(0)); Vince Lombardi. Roensch, Greg. lib. bdg. 29.25 (978-0-8239-3610-6(4)); Walter Payton. Gallagher, Aileen. lib. bdg. 29.25 (978-0-8239-3611-3(2)); 112p. (YA). (gr. 5-8). 2003. (Illus.). 2002. Set lib. bdg. 175.50 (978-0-8239-3885-8(9) , Rosen Central) Rosen Publishing Group, Inc., The.

Gibbons, Gail. My Football Book. Gibbons, Gail, illus. 2000. (Illus.). 24p. (J). (ps-2). 5.99 (978-0-688-17139-1(7)) HarperCollins Pubs.

—My Football Book. 2000. (J). lib. bdg. 5.89 (978-0-06-029221-8(0)) HarperCollins Pubs.

Goin, Kenn. Football for Fun. 2003. (Sports for Fun Ser.). (Illus.). 48p. (J). (gr. 3 up). lib. bdg. 21.26 (978-0-7565-0430-4(9)) Compass Point Bks.

Green, Tim. Road to the NFL. 2003. (gr. 3-6). lib. bdg. 11.80 (978-0-613-87590-5(7)) Tandem Library Bks.

Griffin, Gwen. Irish Legends: The Notre Dame Fighting Irish Story. 1999. (College Sports Today Ser.). (Illus.). 32p. (YA). (gr. 4-7). lib. bdg. 21.30 (978-0-88682-982-7(8) , Creative Education) Creative Co., The.

Hackler, Tracy. Super Players, Super Teams, Super Bowl! 2000. (Illus.). 32p. (J). (gr. 3-9). pap. 4.99 (978-1-930623-00-2(3)) Sports Illustrated For Kids.

Helmer, Diana Star. The History of Football. 2000. (Sports Throughout History Ser.). 24p. (J). (gr. k-4). lib. bdg. 18.75 (978-0-8239-5471-1(4) , PowerKids Pr.) Rosen Publishing Group, Inc., The.

Herzog, Brad. A Football Alphabet. 2007. 40p. pap. 7.95 (***978-1-58536-337-7(5))*** Sleeping Bear Pr.

Herzog, Brad. T Is for Touchdown: A Football Alphabet. Stacy, Alan, illus. 2004. 40p. (J). 16.95 (978-1-58536-233-2(6)) Sleeping Bear Pr.

Hill, Bert. How to Get in Football Shape: Strength Training. 2003. (Illus.). 144p. per. 19.99 (978-1-59186-005-1(9)) Cool Springs Pr.

Hill, Bert & Watterson, Steve. Conditioning: How to Get in Football Shape. 2007. (Illus.). 136p. (YA). pap. 20.00 (***978-1-4223-6674-5(X))*** DIANE Publishing Co.

Hill, Bert & Watterson, Steve. How to Get in Football Shape: Conditioning. 2003. (Illus.). 144p. pap. 19.99 (978-1-59186-004-4(0)) Cool Springs Pr.

Holden, Stephen. Football: Passing. 2000. (High Interest Bks.). (Illus.). 48p. (YA). (gr. 7-12). 23.00 (978-0-516-23364-2(5)); pap. 6.95 (978-0-516-23564-6(8)) Scholastic Library Publishing. (Children's Pr.).

—Football: Rushing & Tackling. 2000. (High Interest Bks.). (Illus.). 48p. (YA). (gr. 7-12). 23.00 (978-0-516-23365-9(3) , Children's Pr.) Scholastic Library Publishing.

Ingram, Scott. A Football All-Pro. 2004. (Making of a Champion Ser.). (J). 29.93 (978-1-4034-5364-8(0)); pap. 8.50 (978-1-4034-5548-2(1)) Heinemann Library.

Kalman, Bobbie & Crossingham, John. Huddle up Football. 2007. (Illus.). 32p. (J). (gr. 1-5). (***978-0-7787-3137-5(5));*** pap. (***978-0-7787-3169-6(3))*** Crabtree Publishing Co.

Kennedy, Mike. Football. 2003. (Watts Library). (Illus.). 64p. (J). 25.50 (978-0-531-12272-3(7) , Watts, Franklin) Scholastic Library Publishing.

Knapp, Ron. Top 10 NFL Super Bowl Most Valuable Players. 2000. (Sports Top 10 Ser.). (Illus.). 48p. (YA). (gr. 4-10). lib. bdg. 23.93 (978-0-7660-1273-8(5)) Enslow Pubs., Inc.

Kristof-Mohn, Beti. The First Football ABC Pretzel Book. 2004. (J). spiral bd. 9.95 net. (978-0-9717148-0-9(0)) Hardway Pr.

Layden, Joe. NFL: Super Bowl - Behind the Scenes. 2004. (Illus.). 32p. (J). pap. 5.99 (978-0-439-69178-9(8)) Scholastic, Inc.

Layden, Joe & Preller, James. Super Bowl: Super Quarterbacks. 2005. (Nfl Ser.). (Illus.). 32p. (J). (ps-k). pap. 5.99 (978-0-439-78433-7(6)) Scholastic, Inc.

—Team Tracker. 2005. (Nfl Ser.). (Illus.). 40p. (J). (ps-k). pap. 7.99 (978-0-439-78434-4(4)) Scholastic, Inc.

Legette, Esther & Legette, C. F. My Little Black Book of Football: The language of American Football. Legette, C. F., illus. 2002. (Illus.). 144p. (J). per. 14.95 (978-0-9722212-0-7(4)) CALs Ltd.

Lerner, Adam & Charpentier, Cliff. Fantasy Football: Playing to Win. Day, Bruce, illus. 1998. 112p. (YA). (gr. 8-12). pap. 5.95 (978-0-8225-9968-5(6)) Lerner Publishing Group.

Logan, Jim. Nfc South. 2005. (Inside the NFL Ser.). (Illus.). 48p. (J). (gr. 1-5). 28.50 (978-1-59296-514-4(8)) Child's World, Inc.

Mader, Jan. Let's Play Football! 2007. (Sports & Activities Ser.). (Illus.). 24p. (J). (ps-1). lib. bdg. 19.93 (978-0-7368-6361-2(3)) Capstone Pr., Inc.

Mattern, Joanne. At the Football Game. 2006. (Rosen Publishing Group's Reading Room Collection). (Illus.). 16p. (J). lib. bdg. (978-1-4042-3339-3(3) , PowerKids Pr.) Rosen Publishing Group, Inc., The.

Milito, John. Football Puzzles. 2001. (Champion Sport Word Game Ser.). 120p. (J). pap. (978-1-894622-04-2(9)) Warwick Publishing.

Newman, Elizabeth. Instant Replay. Goehner, Amy Lennard, ed. (Illus.). 32p. (J). (gr. 2-8). pap. 3.99 (978-1-886749-79-5(5)) Sports Illustrated For Kids.

NFL Staff. NFL 1999 Championship. 2000. 96p. (J). pap. 15.00 (978-0-06-107593-3(0)) HarperCollins Pubs.

Nichols, John. Baltimore Ravens. 3rd rev. ed. 2000. (Pro Football Today Ser.). (Illus.). 32p. (J). (gr. 3 up). lib. bdg. 22.60 (978-1-58341-036-3(8) , Creative Education) Creative Co., The.

—Big Red: The Nebraska Cornhuskers Story. 1999. (College Sports Today Ser.). (Illus.). 32p. (YA). (gr. 4-7). pap. 21.30 (978-0-88682-980-3(1) , Creative Education) Creative Co., The.

Patey, R. L. The Illustrated Rules of Football. McRae, Patrick T., illus. 2001. 32p. (J). (ps-3). pap. 5.95 (978-0-8249-5419-2(X) , Ideals Children's Bks.) Ideals Pubns.

Pellowski, Michael J. A Little Giant Book: Football Facts. 2007. (Illus.). 360p. (J). pap. 6.95 (***978-1-4027-4976-6(7))*** Sterling Publishing Co., Inc.

Picture Window Books, contrib. by. Touchdown! (Game Day Ser.). 24p. (J). pap. 7.95 (978-1-4048-0511-8(7)) Picture Window Bks.

Polzer, Tim. Super Bowl Stories. 2007. (NFL Ser.). 32p. (J). pap. 5.99 (***978-0-439-92456-6(1))*** Scholastic, Inc.

Rekela, George R. Brett Favre: Star Quarterback. 2000. (Sports Reports). (Illus.). 104p. (YA). (gr. 4-10). lib. bdg. 26.60 (978-0-7660-1332-2(4)) Enslow Pubs., Inc.

Rhome, Jerry. How to Grow a Winning Quarterback. 2003. (Illus.). 144p. pap. 19.99 (978-1-930604-97-1(1)) Cool Springs Pr.

Royston, Angela. How Is a Football Made? 2005. (How Are Things Made? Ser.). (Illus.). 32p. (J). (978-1-4034-6642-6(4)); pap. (978-1-4034-6649-5(1)) Heinemann Library.

Sampler, Robert. Mind Mastery for Football. 2000. 115p. (YA). (gr. 11 up). pap. 29.95 (978-0-9653920-7-5(4) , 121191) Aries International (U.B.T.O.).

Savage, Jeff. Michael Vick. 2005. (Illus.). 32p. (J). (ps-7). pap. 5.95 (978-0-8225-2955-2(6)) Lerner Publishing Group.

—Tom Brady. 2005. (Illus.). 32p. (J). (gr. 4-7). pap. 5.95 (978-0-8225-2956-9(4)) Lerner Publishing Group.

—Top 10 Professional Football Coaches. 1998. (Sports Top 10 Ser.). (Illus.). 48p. (YA). (gr. 4-10). lib. bdg. 23.93 (978-0-7660-1006-2(6)) Enslow Pubs., Inc.

Savage, Jeff, photos by. Play-by-Play Football. 2005. (Play-by-Play Ser.). (Illus.). 80p. (gr. 4-8). lib. bdg. 23.93 (978-0-8225-3935-3(7)) Lerner Publishing Group.

Scholastic, Inc. Staff. Superstars 2007. 2007. (NFL Ser.). 32p. (J). pap. 5.99 (***978-0-439-92454-2(5))*** Scholastic, Inc.

Simpson, Fiona, ed. Playmakers. 2006. (Nfl Ser.). (Illus.). 32p. (J). pap. 3.99 (978-0-439-84838-1(5) , Scholastic) Scholastic, Inc.

Smith, Stewart & Johnson, Chris. Get Fit Now for High School Football. Peck, Peter Field, photos by. 2001. (Illus.). 144p. (YA). (gr. 7-13). 14.95 (978-1-57826-065-2(5) , Hatherleigh Pr.) Hatherleigh Co., Ltd., The.

Stone, Lynn M. Quarterbacks. 2008. (J). (***978-1-60044-596-5(9))*** Rourke Publishing, LLC.

Suen, Anastasia. La Historia Del Futbol Americano. 2004. (Historia de los Deportes Ser.). (SPA & ENG., Illus.). 24p. (J). (gr. 3-6). lib. bdg. 17.25 (978-0-8239-6869-5(3) , Buenas Letra) Rosen Publishing Group, Inc., The.

Sullivan, George E. Power Football: The Greatest Running Backs. 2001. (Illus.). 64p. (J). (gr. 4 up). 18.00 (978-0-689-82432-6(7) , Atheneum) Simon & Schuster Children's Publishing.

Sweeny, Sheila. Wacky Football Facts to Kick Around. Safro, Jill, ed. Haggerty, Tim, illus. Date not set. 32p. (Orig.). (J). (gr. k-3). pap. (978-1-886749-17-7(5)) Sports Illustrated For Kids.

Torres, John Albert. Fitness Stars of Pro Football. 2000. (Legends of Health & Fitness Ser.). (Illus.). 96p. (gr. 6-10). lib. bdg. 25.70 (978-1-58415-014-5(9)) Mitchell Lane Pubs., Inc.

EFG

Tuttle, Dennis R. Football. 1999. (Composite Guide Ser.). (Illus.). 64p. (YA). (gr. 4-7). lib. bdg. 28.00 (978-0-7910-4725-5(3) , Chelsea Hse.) Facts On File, Inc.

Velazquez, Mauricio, tr. Cobi Jones, Estrella del Futbol Soccer. 2002. (Power Kids Coleccion). (SPA.). 24p. (J). (gr. 2-3). lib. bdg. 17.25 (978-0-8239-6117-7(6) , RN30774, Buenas Letra) Rosen Publishing Group, Inc., The.

Walters, John. AFC West: The Denver Broncos, the Kansas City Chiefs, the Oakland Raiders, & the San Diego Chargers. 2005. (Inside the NFL Ser.). 48p. (J). (gr. 1-5). 28.50 (978-1-59296-511-3(3)) Child's World, Inc.

—NFC West. 2005. (Inside the NFL Ser.). (Illus.). 48p. (J). (gr. 1-5). 28.50 (978-1-59296-515-1(6)) Child's World, Inc.

Welsh, Nick. NFC East. 2005. (Inside the NFL Ser.). (Illus.). 48p. (J). (gr. 1-5). 28.50 (978-1-59296-512-0(1)) Child's World, Inc.

Wilson, Danny. Lots & Lots of Orange: A Trip to Neyland Stadium. Wilson, Danny, illus. 2003. (Illus.). 24p. (J). 8.95 (978-0-9743968-0-4(X)) Satellite Studio.

Wingate, Brian. Football: Rules, Tips, Strategy, & Safety. 2006. (Sports from Coast to Coast Ser.). (Illus.). 48p. (YA). (gr. 5-8). lib. bdg. 26.50 (978-1-4042-0993-0(X)) Rosen Publishing Group, Inc., The.

Woods, Bob. AFC East. 2005. (Inside the NFL Ser.). 48p. (J). (gr. 1-5). 28.50 (978-1-59296-508-3(3)) Child's World, Inc.

—NFC North. 2005. (Inside the NFL Ser.). (Illus.). 48p. (J). (gr. 1-5). 28.50 (978-1-59296-513-7(X)) Child's World, Inc.

Wright, John D. Football. 2003. (Sports Injuries Ser.). (Illus.). 64p. (J). lib. bdg. (978-1-59084-632-2(X)) Mason Crest Pubs.

FOOTBALL—BIOGRAPHY

Aretha, David A. Tiki Barber. 2008. (Football Superstars Ser.). (gr. 6-12). 30.00 (***978-0-7910-9836-3(2)*** , Chelsea Hse.) Facts On File, Inc.

Balzer, Howard. Kurt Warner: The Quarterback. 2000. (Sport Snaps Ser.). (Illus.). 56p. (J). pap. 12.95 (978-1-892920-34-8(4)) GHB Publishers, LLC.

Barber, Tiki & Barber, Ronde. By My Brother's Side. Root, Barry, illus. 2004. 32p. (J). (gr. 1-5). 16.95 (978-0-689-86559-6(7) , Simon & Schuster/Paula Wiseman Bks.) Simon & Schuster Children's Publishing.

—Game Day. Root, Barry, illus. 2005. 32p. (J). 16.95 (978-1-4169-0093-1(4) , Simon & Schuster Children's Publishing) Simon & Schuster Children's Publishing.

—Teammates. Root, Barry, illus. 2006. 32p. (J). (gr. 1-5). 16.95 (978-1-4169-2489-0(2) , Simon & Schuster Children's Publishing) Simon & Schuster Children's Publishing.

Barnidge, Tom & Dorling Kindersley Publishing Staff. Whiz Kid Quarterbacks. 2003. (NFL Readers Ser.). (Illus.). 48p. (J). 12.99 (978-0-7894-9863-2(4)); pap. 3.99 (978-0-7894-9862-5(6)) Dorling Kindersley Publishing, Inc.

Bernstein, Ross. Randy Moss: Star Wide Receiver. 2002. (Sports Reports). (Illus.). 104p. (J). (gr. 4-10). lib. bdg. 26.60 (978-0-7660-1503-6(3)) Enslow Pubs., Inc.

—Sports Great Daunte Culpepper. 2003. (Sports Great Books). (Illus.). 64p. (J). lib. bdg. 22.60 (978-0-7660-2037-5(1)) Enslow Pubs., Inc.

Bradley, Michael. Football All-Stars: The NFL's Best. 2005. (Sports Illustrated for Kids Bks.). (Illus.). 176p. (YA). (gr. 7-12). lib. bdg. 27.95 (978-0-8239-3690-8(2)) Rosen Publishing Group, Inc., The.

Brenner, Richard J. Superstars Album 1998: Football. 1998. (Illus.). 48p. (J). (gr. 4-7). pap. 4.50 (978-0-688-16229-0(0) , Harper Trophy) HarperCollins Pubs.

Buckley, James, Jr. Super Bowl Heroes. 2000. (Eyewitness Readers Ser.). (J). (978-0-606-20128-5(9)) Tandem Library Bks.

Buckman, Virginia. Football Stars. 2007. (Sports Stars Ser.). (Illus.). 48p. (J). pap. (978-0-531-18703-6(9)) Children's Pr., Ltd.

—Football Stars. 2006. (Sports Stars Ser.). (Illus.). 48p. (J). (978-0-531-12586-1(6) , Children's Pr.) Scholastic Library Publishing.

Christopher, Matt. In the Huddle with... John Elway. 1999. (J). (978-0-606-16726-0(9)) Tandem Library Bks.

—John Elway. 1999. (J). pap. (978-0-316-14283-0(2)) Little Brown & Co.

Collie, Ashley. Football Super 8: Today's Hottest NFL Stars. 2000. (Illus.). 64p. (J). pap. 3.99 (978-1-930623-02-6(X)) Sports Illustrated For Kids.

Collie, Ashley Jude. Gridiron Greats: 8 of Today's Hottest NFL Stars. 2005. (Sports Illustrated for Kids Bks.). (Illus.). 176p. (YA). (gr. 7-12). lib. bdg. 25.25 (978-0-8239-3691-5(0)) Rosen Publishing Group, Inc., The.

De Capua, Sarah. J. C. Watts, JR: Character Counts. 1999. (Illus.). 42p. (J). (gr. 3-7). lib. bdg. 15.25 (978-0-613-51077-6(1)) Tandem Library Bks.

DeMarco, Tony. Ed McCaffrey: Catching a Star. 2003. (SuperStar Ser.: Vol. 1). 96p. (gr. 4-7). 4.95 (978-1-58261-170-9(X)) Sports Publishing, LLC.

Dietsch, Richard & Schwarz, Alan. Rising Stars: The 10 Best Young Players in the NFL. 2005. (Sports Illustrated for Kids Bks.). (Illus.). 176p. (YA). (gr. 7-12). lib. bdg. 32.00 (978-0-8239-3573-4(6)) Rosen Publishing Group, Inc., The.

Doeden, Matt. Doug Flutie. 2007. (J). lib. bdg. (***978-0-8225-7162-9(5)***) Twenty First Century Bks.

Donnelly, Karen. Deacon Jones. 2003. (Football Hall of Famers Ser.). (Illus.). 112p. (YA). (gr. 5-8). lib. bdg. 29.25 (978-0-8239-3606-9(6) , Rosen Central) Rosen Publishing Group, Inc., The.

Dorling Kindersley Publishing Staff. Super Bowl. 2003. (NFL Readers Ser.). (Illus.). 48p. (J). pap. 3.99 (978-0-7894-9865-6(0)) Dorling Kindersley Publishing, Inc.

—Whiz Kid Quarterbacks. 2003. (gr. k-3). lib. bdg. 11.80 (978-0-613-75182-7(5)) Tandem Library Bks.

Dougherty, Denis. John Elway. 1999. (Jam Session Ser.). (Illus.). 32p. (J). (gr. 4). lib. bdg. 24.21 (978-1-57765-040-9(9) , ABDO & Daughters) ABDO Publishing Co.

—Michael Vick. 2003. (Awesome Athletes Ser.). (J). 22.78 (978-1-59197-487-1(9)) ABDO Publishing Co.

Dougherty, Terri. Barry Sanders. 1999. (Jam Session Ser.). (Illus.). 32p. (J). (gr. 3-8). lib. bdg. 24.21 (978-1-57765-037-9(9) , ABDO & Daughters) ABDO Publishing Co.

—Brett Favre. 1999. (Jam Session Ser.). (Illus.). 32p. (J). (gr. 3-8). lib. bdg. 24.21 (978-1-57765-036-2(0) , ABDO & Daughters) ABDO Publishing Co.

—Kurt Warner. 2000. (Jam Session Ser.). (Illus.). 32p. (J). (gr. 3-8). lib. bdg. 24.21 (978-1-57765-426-1(9) , ABDO & Daughters) ABDO Publishing Co.

Ellenport, Craig. LaDainian Tomlinson: All-Pro on & off the Field. 2006. (Sports Stars with Heart Ser.). (Illus.). 128p. (J). lib. bdg. 31.93 (978-0-7660-2820-3(8)) Enslow Pubs., Inc.

Flutie, Doug. Never Say Never. 2000. (Positively for Kids Ser.). (Illus.). 40p. 14.95 (978-0-87833-165-9(4)) Taylor Trade Publishing.

Gallagher, Aileen. Walter Payton. 2003. (Football Hall of Famers Ser.). (Illus.). 112p. (YA). (gr. 5-8). lib. bdg. 29.25 (978-0-8239-3611-3(2) , Rosen Central) Rosen Publishing Group, Inc., The.

Gatto, Kimberly. Tom Brady: Never-Quit Quarterback. 2005. (Sports Leaders Ser.). (Illus.). 104p. (J). (gr. k-9). lib. bdg. 26.60 (978-0-7660-2475-5(X)) Enslow Pubs., Inc.

Gigliotti, Jim. Football Superstars. 2006. (Boys Rock! Ser.). (Illus.). 32p. (J). (gr. 1-5). 24.21 (978-1-59296-730-8(2)) Child's World, Inc.

—Peyton Manning. 2006. (World's Greatest Athletes Ser.). (Illus.). 32p. (J). (gr. 1-5). 27.07 (978-1-59296-758-2(2)) Child's World, Inc.

—Tom Brady. 2007. (World's Greatest Athletes Ser.). 32p. (J). (gr. 1-5). 27.07 (978-1-59296-794-0(9)) Child's World, Inc.

Grabowski, John F. Legendary Football Quarterbacks. 2003. (History Makers Ser.). (Illus.). 112p. (J). 29.95 (978-1-59018-230-7(8) , Lucent Bks.) Thomson Gale.

—Sports Great Emmitt Smith. 1998. (Sports Great Bks.). (Illus.). 64p. (YA). (gr. 4-10). lib. bdg. 17.95 (978-0-7660-1002-4(3)) Enslow Pubs., Inc.

Griffin, Gwen. Barry Sanders. 1999. (Ovations Ser.). (Illus.). 32p. (YA). (gr. 4-7). pap. (978-0-88682-938-4(0) , Creative Education) Creative Co., The.

Gutman, Bill. Brett, Favre: Leader of the Pack. 1998. (Millbrook Sports World Ser.). (Illus.). 48p. (J). (gr. 3-6). lib. bdg. 22.90 (978-0-7613-0310-7(3) , Millbrook Pr.) Lerner Publishing Group.

Hoffman, Mary Ann. Peyton Manning: Football Star. 2006. (Illus.). 24p. (J). lib. bdg. (978-1-4042-3531-1(0) , PowerKids Pr.) Rosen Publishing Group, Inc., The.

—Shaun Alexander: Football Star. 2006. (Sports Superstars Ser.). (Illus.). 24p. (J). lib. bdg. (978-1-4042-3532-8(9) , PowerKids Pr.) Rosen Publishing Group, Inc., The.

Horn, Geoffrey M. Peyton Manning. 2006. (Today's Superstars). (Illus.). 32p. (YA). (gr. 5 up). lib. bdg. 23.93 (978-0-8368-6183-9(3)) Stevens, Gareth Inc.

Hulm, David. Fran Tarkenton. 2003. (Football Hall of Famers Ser.). (Illus.). 112p. (YA). (gr. 5-8). lib. bdg. 29.25 (978-0-8239-3608-3(2) , Rosen Central) Rosen Publishing Group, Inc., The.

Hunt, Donald. Top 10 Football Legends. 2001. (Sports Top 10 Ser.). (Illus.). 48p. (J). (gr. 4-10). lib. bdg. 23.93 (978-0-7660-1499-2(1)) Enslow Pubs., Inc.

Jacksonville Jaguars Staff. Jacksonville Jaguars. CWC Sports Inc., ed. 1998. (NFL Team Yearbooks Ser.). (J). (gr. 1-12). pap. 9.99 (978-1-891613-11-1(1)) Everett Sports Publishing & Marketing.

Jones, Steven L. Football's Fallen Hero: The Jack Trice Story. 2000. (Cover-to-Cover Bks.). (Illus.). 64p. (J). (gr. 4-7). lib. bdg. 17.95 (978-0-7807-9043-8(X)) Perfection Learning Corp.

Keith, Ted. Shaun Alexander. 2008. (World's Greatest Athletes Ser.). 32p. (J). (gr. 1-5). 27.07 (***978-1-59296-880-0(5)***) Child's World, Inc.

Kennedy, Nick. Dan Marino: Star Quarterback. 1998. (Sports Reports). (Illus.). 112p. (YA). (gr. 4-10). lib. bdg. 26.60 (978-0-89490-933-7(9)) Enslow Pubs., Inc.

Kirkpatrick, Rob. Doug Flutie, Estrella Internacional de Futbol Americano. 2002. (Deportistas de Poder Ser.). (SPA & ENG., Illus.). 24p. (J). lib. bdg. 17.25 (978-0-8239-6127-6(3) , Buenas Letra); lib. bdg. 17.25 (978-0-8239-6145-0(1) , RN31314, PowerKids Pr.) Rosen Publishing Group, Inc., The.

—Terrell Davis, Corredor de Super Bowl. 2002. (Coleccion Power Kids). (SPA & ENG., Illus.). 24p. (J). (gr. k-2). lib. bdg. 17.25 (978-0-8239-6144-3(3) , RN31313, Buenas Letra) Rosen Publishing Group, Inc., The.

Knapp, Ron. Sports Great Barry Sanders. rev. ed. 1999. (Sports Great Bks.). (Illus.). 64p. (YA). (gr. 4-10). lib. bdg. 22.60 (978-0-7660-1067-3(8)) Enslow Pubs., Inc.

—Top 10 College Football Coaches. 1999. (Sports Top 10 Ser.). (Illus.). 48p. (YA). (gr. 4-10). lib. bdg. 23.93 (978-0-7660-1073-4(2)) Enslow Pubs., Inc.

Layden, Joe & Preller, James. NFL Rising Stars. 2005. (NFL Reader Ser.). (Illus.). 32p. (J). (ps-k). pap. 5.99 (978-0-439-78432-0(8)) Scholastic, Inc.

Layden, Joseph. Rising Stars, NFL. 2005. (Illus.). 32p. (J). pap. (***978-0-439-80247-5(4)***) Scholastic, Inc.

Lowenstein, Felicia. Super Sports Star Terrell Davis. 2003. (Super Sports Star Ser.). (Illus.). 48p. (J). lib. bdg. 18.95 (978-0-7660-2052-8(5)) Enslow Pubs., Inc.

Macnow, Glen. Sports Great Deion Sanders. 1999. (Sports Great Bks.). (Illus.). 64p. (YA). (gr. 4-10). lib. bdg. 22.60 (978-0-7660-1068-0(6)) Enslow Pubs., Inc.

Mattern, Joanne. Donovan Mcnabb. 2004. (Robbie Reader Ser.). (Illus.). 32p. (J). (gr. 1-4). lib. bdg. 25.70 (978-1-58415-294-1(X)) Mitchell Lane Pubs., Inc.

—Peyton Manning. 2006. (Blue Banner Biography Ser.). (Illus.). 32p. (J). (gr. 4-8). lib. bdg. 25.70 (978-1-58415-506-5(X)) Mitchell Lane Pubs., Inc.

—Tiki Barber. 2006. (Robbie Reader Ser.). (Illus.). 32p. (J). (gr. 1-4). lib. bdg. (978-1-58415-522-5(1)) Mitchell Lane Pubs., Inc.

Molzahn, Arlene Bourgeois. Randy Moss. 2002. (Sports Heroes Ser.). (Illus.). 48p. (J). (gr. 3-4). lib. bdg. 21.26 (978-0-7368-1053-1(6) , Capstone High-Interest Bks.) Capstone Pr., Inc.

Murcia, Rebecca Thatcher. Landon Donovan. 2005. (No Hands Allowed Ser.). (Illus.). 32p. (J). (gr. 1-4). lib. bdg. 25.70 (978-1-58415-386-3(5)) Mitchell Lane Pubs., Inc.

Needham, Tom. Tiki Barber: All-Pro on & off the Field. 2007. (Sports Stars with Heart Ser.). (Illus.). 128p. (J). (gr. 5). lib. bdg. 31.93 (***978-0-7660-2865-4(8)***) Enslow Pubs., Inc.

Nelson, Sharlene P. & Nelson, Ted. Brett Favre. 2000. (Sports Heroes Ser.). (Illus.). 48p. (J). (gr. 3-4). lib. bdg. 21.26 (978-0-7368-0576-6(1) , Capstone High-Interest Bks.) Capstone Pr., Inc.

Pace, Gene. A True Blood. 2005. 290p. pap. 24.95 (978-1-4137-5163-5(6)) PublishAmerica, Inc.

Polzer, Tim. Peyton Manning: Leader on & off the Field. 2006. (Sports Stars with Heart Ser.). (Illus.). 128p. (J). lib. bdg. 31.93 (978-0-7660-2822-7(4)) Enslow Pubs., Inc.

—Super Bowl. 2003. (NFL Readers Ser.). (Illus.). 48p. (J). 12.99 (978-0-7894-9864-9(2)) Dorling Kindersley Publishing, Inc.

Preller, James. Megastars, 2006. 2006. (Nfl Ser.). (Illus.). 32p. (J). pap. 5.99 (978-0-439-82816-1(3) , Scholastic) Scholastic, Inc.

—Touchdown Heroes. 2006. (Nfl Ser.). (Illus.). 32p. (J). pap. 5.99 (978-0-439-82815-4(5) , Scholastic) Scholastic, Inc.

Prisco, Pete. Mark Brunnell: Super Southpaw. 2003. (SuperStar Ser.: Vol. 5). (Illus.). 96p. (gr. 4-7). 4.95 (978-1-58261-166-2(1)) Sports Publishing, LLC.

Rains, Rob. Marshall Faulk: Rushing to Glory. 2003. (SuperStar Ser.: Vol. 8). (Illus.). 96p. (J). pap. 4.95 (978-1-58261-191-4(2)) Sports Publishing, LLC.

Ramen, Fred. Joe Montana. 2003. (Football Hall of Famers Ser.). (Illus.). 112p. (YA). (gr. 5-8). lib. bdg. 29.25 (978-0-8239-3607-6(4) , Rosen Central) Rosen Publishing Group, Inc., The.

Rappoport, Ken. Super Sports Star Jerome Bettis. 2003. (Super Sports Star Ser.). (Illus.). 48p. (J). (gr. 1-4). lib. bdg. 23.93 (978-0-7660-2053-5(3)) Enslow Pubs., Inc.

—Super Sports Star Peyton Manning. 2003. (Super Sports Star Ser.). (Illus.). 48p. (J). lib. bdg. 23.93 (978-0-7660-2079-5(7)) Enslow Pubs., Inc.

Rekela, George R. Sports Great Kurt Warner. 2003. (Sports Great Books). (Illus.). 64p. (J). (gr. 4-10). lib. bdg. 22.60 (978-0-7660-2034-4(7)) Enslow Pubs., Inc.

Robinson, Tom. Donovan Mcnabb: Leader on & off the Field. 2007. (Sports Stars with Heart Ser.). (Illus.). 128p. (J). (gr. 5). lib. bdg. 31.93 (***978-0-7660-2864-7(X)***) Enslow Pubs., Inc.

Roensch, Greg. Vince Lombardi. 2003. (Football Hall of Famers Ser.). (Illus.). 112p. (YA). (gr. 5-8). lib. bdg. 29.25 (978-0-8239-3610-6(4) , Rosen Central) Rosen Publishing Group, Inc., The.

Roza, Greg. Terry Bradshaw. 2003. (Football Hall of Famers Ser.). (Illus.). 112p. (YA). (gr. 5-8). lib. bdg. 29.25 (978-0-8239-3609-0(0) , Rosen Central) Rosen Publishing Group, Inc., The.

Sandler, Michael. Dexter Jackson & the Tampa Bay Buccaneers: Super Bowl XXXVII. 2008. (Super Bowl Superstars Ser.). (Illus.). 24p. (J). (gr. k-5). lib. bdg. 22.61 (***978-1-59716-537-2(9)***) Bearport Publishing Co., Inc.

—Hines Ward & the Pittsburgh Steelers: Super Bowl XL. 2008. (Super Bowl Superstars Ser.). (Illus.). 24p. (J). (gr. k-10). lib. bdg. 22.61 (***978-1-59716-538-9(7)***) Bearport Publishing Co., Inc.

—John Elway & the Denver Broncos: Super Bowl XXXIII. 2008. (Super Bowl Superstars Ser.). (Illus.). 24p. (J). (gr. k-5). lib. bdg. 22.61 (***978-1-59716-536-5(0)***) Bearport Publishing Co., Inc.

—Kurt Warner & the St. Louis Rams: Super Bowl XXXIV. 2008. (Super Bowl Superstars Ser.). (Illus.). 24p. (J). (gr. k-5). lib. bdg. 22.61 (***978-1-59716-539-6(5)***) Bearport Publishing Co., Inc.

—Peyton Manning & the Indianapolis Colts: Super Bowl XLI. 2008. (Super Bowl Superstars Ser.). (Illus.). 24p. (J). (gr. k-5). lib. bdg. 22.61 (***978-1-59716-540-2(9)***) Bearport Publishing Co., Inc.

—Tom Brady & the New England Patriots: Super Bowl XXXVIII. 2008. (Super Bowl Superstars Ser.). (Illus.). 24p. (J). (gr. k-5). lib. bdg. 22.61 (***978-1-59716-535-8(2)***) Bearport Publishing Co., Inc.

Savage, Jeff. Michael Vick. 2006. (Amazing Athletes Ser.). (Illus.). 32p. (J). (ps-7). 23.93 (978-0-8225-2430-4(9) , Lerner Pubns.) Lerner Publishing Group.

—Peyton Manning. (J). 2007. lib. bdg. (***978-0-8225-6445-4(9)*** , Lerner Pubns.); 2005. (Illus.). 32p. (gr. 3-4). lib. bdg. 23.93 (978-0-8225-4034-2(7)) Lerner Publishing Group.

—Peyton Manning: Precision Passer. (Sports Achievers Biographies Ser.). (Illus.). 2005. 80p. (gr. 7-12). lib. bdg. 22.60 (978-0-8225-3683-3(8)); 2003. 64p. (YA). (gr. 4-9). pap. 5.95 (978-0-8225-9865-7(5) , LernerSports) Lerner Publishing Group.

—Terrell Davis: TD! 1999. (Sports Achievers Biographies Ser.). (Illus.). 80p. (YA). (gr. 4-9). pap. (978-0-8225-9847-3(7) , LernerSports) Lerner Publishing Group.

—Terrell Davis: Td. 2000. (gr. 3-6). lib. bdg. 14.10 (978-0-613-58101-1(6)) Tandem Library Bks.

—Tom Brady. 2006. (Amazing Athletes Ser.). (Illus.). 32p. (J). (gr. 3-7). 23.93 (978-0-8225-2948-4(3) , Lerner Pubns.) Lerner Publishing Group.

—Top 10 Heisman Trophy Winners. 1999. (Sports Top 10 Ser.). (Illus.). 48p. (YA). (gr. 4-10). lib. bdg. 23.93 (978-0-7660-1072-7(4)) Enslow Pubs., Inc.

—Top 10 Professional Football Coaches. 1998. (Sports Top 10 Ser.). (Illus.). 48p. (YA). (gr. 4-10). lib. bdg. 23.93 (978-0-7660-1006-2(6)) Enslow Pubs., Inc.

Schaefer, A. R. Kurt Warner. 2002. (Sports Heroes Ser.). (Illus.). 48p. (J). (gr. 3-4). lib. bdg. 21.26 (978-0-7368-1295-5(4) , Capstone High-Interest Bks.) Capstone Pr., Inc.

Schoendfeld, Steve. Jake Plummer: The Comeback Cardinal. 2003. (SuperStar Ser.: Vol. 4). 96p. (gr. 4-7). 4.95 (978-1-58261-165-5(3)) Sports Publishing, LLC.

Shalin, Mike. Drew Bledsoe: Patriot Rifle. 2003. (SuperStar Ser.: Vol. 6). 96p. (gr. 4-7). 4.95 (978-1-58261-168-6(8)) Sports Publishing, LLC.

Sherman, Josepha. Terrell Davis. 2001. (Sports Files Ser.). (Illus.). 32p. (J). (gr. 1-3). lib. bdg. (978-1-58810-115-0(0)) Heinemann Library.

Smithwicks, John. Meet Peyton Manning: Football's Top Quarterback. 2007. (All-Star Players Ser.). (Illus.). 32p. (J). (gr. 4-6). lib. bdg. 23.95 (978-1-4042-3634-9(1) , PowerKids Pr.) Rosen Publishing Group, Inc., The.

—Meet Shaun Alexander: Football's Top Running Back. 2007. (All-Star Players Ser.). (Illus.). 32p. (J). (gr. 4-6). lib. bdg. 23.95 (978-1-4042-3635-6(X) , PowerKids Pr.) Rosen Publishing Group, Inc., The.

Steenkamer, Paul. Mark Brunell: Star Quarterback. 2002. (Sports Reports). (Illus.). 104p. (J). (gr. 4-10). lib. bdg. 26.60 (978-0-7660-1830-3(X)) Enslow Pubs., Inc.

—Sports Great Donovan Mcnabb. 2003. (Sports Great Books). (Illus.). 64p. (J). lib. bdg. 22.60 (978-0-7660-2114-3(9)) Enslow Pubs., Inc.

Stewart, Mark. Daunte Culpepper: Command & Control. 2002. (New Wave Ser.). (Illus.). 48p. (gr. 4 up). lib. bdg. 22.90 (978-0-7613-2613-7(8) , Millbrook Pr.) Lerner Publishing Group.

—Jevon Kearse: Force of One. 2001. (New Wave Ser.). (Illus.). 48p. (gr. 4 up). lib. bdg. 22.90 (978-0-7613-2269-6(8) , Millbrook Pr.) Lerner Publishing Group.

—Kurt Warner: Can't Keep Him Down. 2001. (New Wave Ser.). (Illus.). 48p. (gr. 4 up). lib. bdg. 22.90 (978-0-7613-1953-5(0) , Millbrook Pr.) Lerner Publishing Group.

—Peyton Manning: Rising Son. 2000. (New Wave Ser.). (Illus.). 48p. (gr. 4 up). lib. bdg. 22.90 (978-0-7613-1517-9(9) , Millbrook Pr.) Lerner Publishing Group.

—Peyton Manning: Rising Son. 2000. (J). (978-0-606-19169-2(0)); (gr. 3-6). lib. bdg. 15.25 (978-0-613-26582-9(3)) Tandem Library Bks.

—Randy Moss: First in Flight. 2000. (New Wave Ser.). (Illus.). 48p. (gr. 4 up). lib. bdg. 22.90 (978-0-7613-1518-6(7) , Millbrook Pr.) Lerner Publishing Group.

—Terrell Davis: Toughing It Out. 1999. (New Wave Ser.). (Illus.). 48p. (gr. 4 up). lib. bdg. 22.90 (978-0-7613-1514-8(4) , Millbrook Pr.) Lerner Publishing Group.

—Tom Brady: Heart of the Huddle. 2003. (gr. 5-8). lib. bdg. 16.40 (978-0-613-59026-6(0)) Tandem Library Bks.

Stewart, Mark Alan. Drew Bledsoe: Stand & Deliver. 2000. (Sports Stars Ser.). (Illus.). 48p. (J). (gr. 3-4). pap. 5.95 (978-0-516-27072-2(9) , Children's Pr.) Scholastic Library Publishing.

—Kordell Stewart: Steelers Sensation. 1999. (Sports Stars Ser.). (Illus.). 48p. (J). (gr. 3-4). 22.00 (978-0-516-21553-2(1) , Children's Pr.) Scholastic Library Publishing.

—Randy Moss: First in Flight. 2000. (J). (978-0-606-19170-8(4)) Tandem Library Bks.

—Tom Brady: Heart of the Huddle. 2003. (Football's New Wave Ser.: up). (Illus.). 48p. (gr. 4 up). lib. bdg. 22.90 (978-0-7613-2907-7(2) , Millbrook Pr.) Lerner Publishing Group.

Stotts, Stuart. Curly Lambeau: Building the Green Bay Packers. 2007. (Badger Biographies Ser.). 128p. (J). pap. 12.95 (***978-0-87020-389-3(4)***) Wisconsin Historical Society.

Thornley, Stew. Super Sports Star Brett Favre. 2003. (Super Sports Star Ser.). (Illus.). 48p. (J). (gr. 1-4). lib. bdg. 23.93 (978-0-7660-2048-1(7)) Enslow Pubs., Inc.

—Super Sports Star Daunte Culpepper. 2003. (Super Sports Star Ser.). (Illus.). 48p. (J). (gr. 1-4). lib. bdg. 23.93 (978-0-7660-2051-1(7)) Enslow Pubs., Inc.

—Super Sports Star Eddie George. 2003. (Super Sports Star Ser.). (Illus.). 48p. (J). (gr. 1-4). lib. bdg. 23.93 (978-0-7660-2050-4(9)) Enslow Pubs., Inc.

—Super Sports Star Randy Moss. 2003. (Super Sports Star Ser.). (Illus.). 48p. (J). (gr. 1-4). lib. bdg. 23.93 (978-0-7660-2049-8(5)) Enslow Pubs., Inc.

Towle, Mike. Walter Payton: Football's Sweetest Superstar. 2005. (Great American Sports Legends Ser.). (Illus.). 225p. (ps-7). pap. 12.95 (978-1-58182-476-6(9) , 1249190) Cumberland Hse. Publishing.

Trotter, Jim. Junior Seau: Overcoming the Odds. 2003. (SuperStar Ser.: Vol. 7). 96p. (gr. 4-7). 4.95 (978-1-58261-169-3(6)) Sports Publishing, LLC.

Wargin, Kathy Jo. Win One for the Gipper: America's Football Hero. Langton, Bruce, illus. 2004. 40p. (J). (gr. 2-4). 16.95 (978-1-58536-221-9(2)) Sleeping Bear Pr.

Warner, Kurt. Keep Your Head Up. 2000. (Illus.). 40p. (gr. 4-7). 14.95 (978-0-87833-251-9(0)) Taylor Trade Publishing.

Weber, Terri. Ricky Williams. 2004. (J). pap. (978-1-932724-33-2(8)); lib. bdg. (978-1-932724-32-5(X)) Panda Publishing, L.L.C. (Bios for Kids).

Wheeler, Jill C. Michael Vick. 2007. (Awesome Athletes Ser.). (Illus.). 32p. (J). 22.78 (978-1-59928-308-1(5)) ABDO Publishing Co.

—Tom Brady. 2007. (Awesome Athletes Ser.). (Illus.). 32p. (J). 22.78 (978-1-59928-305-0(0)) ABDO Publishing Co.

Williams, Sylvia B. Paul Bryant: Football Legend. 2002. (Alabama Roots Biography Ser.). (Illus.). 104p. (J). per. 7.95 (978-1-878561-92-3(8)) Seacoast Publishing, Inc.

Wilner, Barry. Sports Great Peyton Manning. 2003. (Sports Great Books). (Illus.). 64p. (J). (gr. 4-10). lib. bdg. 22.60 (978-0-7660-2033-7(9)) Enslow Pubs., Inc.

Worthington, Joe. The Mannings: Football's Famous Family. 2005. (High Five Reading Ser.). (J). (Illus.). 64p. (gr. 4-5). lib. bdg. incl. audio (978-0-7368-5751-2(6)); (978-0-7368-5731-4(1)); (978-0-7368-5741-3(9)) Capstone Pr., Inc.

Yaeger, Don. Never Die Easy: The Autobiography of Walter Payton. 2000. (978-0-606-22352-2(5)) Tandem Library Bks.

Zuehlke Jeffrey. Ben Roethlisberger. 2007. (Amazing Athletes Ser.). (J). pap. 6.95 (***978-0-8225-7665-5(1)** , First Avenue Editions) Lerner Publishing Group.

FOOTBALL—DICTIONARIES

Buckley Jr., James. Aikman, Troy to Guard, Vol. 1. 2007. (Child's World' Encyclopedia of the NFL Ser.). 112p. (J). (gr. 2-6). 67.50 (***978-1-59296-922-7(4)**) Child's World, Inc.

—Hail Mary Pass to Numbers, Uniform, Vol. 2. 2007. (Child's World' Encyclopedia of the NFL Ser.). 112p. (J). (gr. 2-6). 67.50 (***978-1-59296-923-4(2)**) Child's World, Inc.

—Oakland Raiders to Super Bowl XII, Vol. 3. 2007. (Child's World' Encyclopedia of the NFL Ser.). 112p. (J). (gr. 2-6). 67.50 (***978-1-59296-924-1(0)**) Child's World, Inc.

—Super Bowl XIII to Zone Blitz, Vol. 4. 2007. (Child's World' Encyclopedia of the NFL Ser.). 112p. (J). (gr. 2-6). 67.50 (***978-1-59296-925-8(9)**) Child's World, Inc.

FOOTBALL—FICTION

Altman, Adam. Liliana's Fan. 2001. 116p. (gr. 4-7). pap. 9.95 (978-0-595-15873-7(0)) iUniverse, Inc.

Aryal, Aimee. Go, Pack, Go! de Angel, Miguel, illus. 2007. (J). 14.95 (***978-1-932888-94-2(2)**) Mascot Bks., Inc.

—How 'Bout Them Cowboys! Coloring Book. 2007. (YA). pap. 4.95 (***978-1-932888-77-5(2)**) Mascot Bks., Inc.

—Let's Go Blue! Perez, Gerry, illus. 2004. (J). (978-1-932888-19-5(5)) Mascot Bks., Inc.

—Let's Go, Chiefs! de Angel, Miguel, illus. 2007. (J). 14.95 (***978-1-932888-93-5(4)**) Mascot Bks., Inc.

—Let's Go, Colts! 2007. (YA). 14.95 (***978-1-932888-86-7(1)**) Mascot Bks., Inc.

—Let's Go Illini! Shrestha, Anuj, illus. 2004. (J). 19.95 (978-1-932888-21-8(7)) Mascot Bks., Inc.

—Let's Go 'Noles! Higgins, Krystal, illus. 2004. (J). 19.95 (978-1-932888-20-1(9)) Mascot Bks., Inc.

—Let's Go, Panthers! De Angel, Miguel, illus. 2007. 24p. (J). (ps-3). 14.95 (***978-1-932888-97-3(7)**) Mascot Bks., Inc.

—Let's Go, Patriots! Aryal, Aimee, illus. 2007. (J). 14.95 (***978-1-932888-98-0(5)**) Mascot Bks., Inc.

—Let's Go, Seahawks! de Angel, Miguel, illus. 2007. (J). 14.95 (***978-1-932888-95-9(0)**) Mascot Bks., Inc.

—Let's Go Sooners! Shrestha, Anuj, illus. 2004. (J). 19.95 (978-1-932888-29-4(2)) Mascot Bks., Inc.

—Let's Go Steelers! 2007. (YA). 14.95 (***978-1-932888-78-2(0)**) Mascot Bks., Inc.

—Let's Go, Vikings! 2007. (YA). 14.95 (***978-1-932888-99-7(3)**) Mascot Bks., Inc.

Ashley, Bernard. Justin & the Demon Drop Kick. (Illus.). 96p. (J). 7.95 (978-0-14-038015-6(9)) Penguin Bks., Ltd. GBR. *Dist:* Trafalgar Square Publishing.

Attanas, John. Eddie & the Jets. 2005. 142p. (J). (gr. 4-6). 15.95 (978-1-58196-026-6(3)) Darby Creek Publishing.

Barber, Tiki & Barber, Ronde. Kickoff! 2007. 160p. (J). (gr. 3-7). 15.99 (***978-1-4169-3618-3(1)** , Simon & Schuster/Paula Wiseman Bks.) Simon & Schuster Children's Publishing.

Barbour, Ralph Henry. Behind the Line: A Story of College Life & Football. 2006. (Illus.). pap. (***978-1-4065-0775-1(X)**) Dodo Pr.

—The Half-Back. 2006. (Illus.). pap. (***978-1-4065-0776-8(8)**) Dodo Pr.

Bee, Clair. Fiery Fullback, Vol. 24. 2002. (Chip Hilton Sports Ser.: No. 24). (Illus.). 198p. (J). (gr. 4-7). pap. 5.99 (978-0-8054-2395-2(8)); 17.99 (978-0-8054-2418-8(0)) B&H Publishing Grp.

—Freshman Quarterback, Vol. 9. 1999. (Chip Hilton Sports Ser.). 208p. (J). reprint ed. pap. 5.99 (978-0-8054-1991-7(8)) B&H Publishing Grp.

—A Pass & a Prayer, Vol. 5. 1999. (Chip Hilton Sports Ser.: Vol. 5). ix, 212p. (J). reprint ed. 5.99 (978-0-8054-1987-0(X)) B&H Publishing Grp.

—Ten Seconds to Play!, Vol. 12. 1999. (Chip Hilton Sports Ser.). x, 191p. (J). reprint ed. pap. 5.99 (978-0-8054-1994-8(2)) B&H Publishing Grp.

—Ten Seconds to Play! 1999. (gr. 7-12). lib. bdg. 14.15 (978-0-613-90142-0(8)) Tandem Library Bks.

—Touchdown Pass. Farley, Cynthia B. & Farley, Randall, eds. rev. ed. 1998. (Chip Hilton Ser.: Vol. 1). 198p. (J). 5.99 (978-0-8054-1686-2(2)) B&H Publishing Grp.

—Triple-Threat Trouble, Vol. 18. 2001. (Chip Hilton Sports Ser.: No. 18). (Illus.). viii, 183p. (J). (gr. 3-8). pap. 5.99 (978-0-8054-2097-5(5)) B&H Publishing Grp.

Berrill, Jack. Under the Friday Night Lights! A Gil Thorp Football Collection. 2004. (Illus.). 328p. per. 32.95 (978-0-930099-14-5(1)) Take Five Pubs.

Bietz, Barbara. Like a Maccabee. White, Anita, illus. l.t. ed. 2006. 136p. (J). (978-1-59287-136-0(4) , 59287-1364) Yaldah Publishing.

Bildner, Phil. Turkey Bowl. Payne, C. F., illus. 2006. (J). 16.99 (978-0-689-87896-1(6) , Simon & Schuster Children's Publishing) Simon & Schuster Children's Publishing.

Bogart, Mike. The Henderson Twins in Muckleball! 2006. 107p. pap. 14.95 (978-1-4241-3050-4(6)) PublishAmerica, Inc.

Born to be a Tiger. 2004. (J). per. 18.50 net. (978-0-615-12596-1(4)) Little Band Man Co., LLC, The.

Boushell, Mike. Freshman Flash. Dodge, Chris, illus. 2002. 120p. (YA). (gr. 5-8). 9.99 (978-0-88092-600-3(7) , 600-7) Royal Fireworks Publishing Co.

Bradman, Tony. Game Over! 2003. 169p. pap. (978-0-552-54762-8(X) , Corgi) Transworld Publishers Ltd.

Brighter Minds, creator. Backyard Football Multimedia Kit. gif. ed. 2005. (Illus.). 32p. (J). pap. 9.99 incl. cd-rom (978-1-57791-189-0(X)) Brighter Minds Children's Publishing.

Brooks, Walter R. Freddy Plays Football. Wiese, Kurt, illus. 2001. 265p. (J). (gr. 4-7). 23.95 (978-1-58567-133-5(9)) Overlook Pr., The.

—Freddy Plays Football. Wiese, Kurt, illus. 2002. 272p. (J). pap. 7.99 (978-0-14-230207-1(4) , Puffin) Penguin Group (USA) Inc.

—Freddy Plays Football. 2002. (gr. 3-6). lib. bdg. 16.45 (978-0-613-54415-3(3)) Tandem Library Bks.

Brouwer, Sigmund. Cobra Threat: Football. 2007. (Orca Sports Ser.). 176p. (YA). (gr. 5 up). pap. (***978-1-55143-725-5(2)**) Orca Bk. Pubs.

Carlson, Nancy. Louanne Pig in Making the Team. 2005. (Illus.). 32p. (J). (ps-ps). lib. bdg. 15.95 (978-1-57505-914-3(2)) Lerner Publishing Group.

Childs. Big Kick. 2000. (Illus.). 79p. (J). pap. 7.95 (978-0-552-52663-0(0)) Transworld Publishers Ltd. GBR. *Dist:* Trafalgar Square Publishing.

Childs, Rob. Big Match. 2000. (Illus.). 95p. (J). pap. 7.95 (978-0-552-52451-3(4)) Transworld Publishers Ltd. GBR. *Dist:* Trafalgar Square Publishing.

—Football Daft. 2000. (Yearling Soccer Ser.: No. 2). (Illus.). 144p. (J). pap. 8.99 (978-0-440-86353-3(8)) Transworld Publishers Ltd. GBR. *Dist:* Trafalgar Square Publishing.

Christopher, Matt. Catch That Pass. 2007. 110p. (J). lib. bdg. (***978-1-59953-105-2(4)**) Norwood Hse. Pr.

—Catch That Pass! ed. 2005. (Sports Classics III Ser.). 110p. (J). lib. bdg. 15.00 (978-1-59054-748-9(9)) Fitzgerald Bks.

—Center Court Sting. ed. 2005. (Sports Classics II Ser.). 140p. (J). lib. bdg. 15.00 (978-1-59054-749-6(7)) Fitzgerald Bks.

—Center Court Sting. 2007. 140p. (J). lib. bdg. (***978-1-59953-106-9(2)**) Norwood Hse. Pr.

—Football Nightmare. 2001. 128p. (J). (gr. 3-7). 15.95 (978-0-316-14370-7(7)); pap. 4.99 (978-0-316-14307-3(3)) Little, Brown Bks. for Young Readers.

—Football Nightmare. 2001. (gr. 3-6). lib. bdg. 12.40 (978-0-613-44166-7(4)) Tandem Library Bks.

—Football Nightmare: Football Nightmare: the #1 Sports Series for Kids. ed. 2005. (Sports Classics II Ser.). 123p. (J). lib. bdg. 15.00 (978-1-59054-757-1(8)) Fitzgerald Bks.

—Halfback Attack. Meyer, Karen, illus. ed. 2005. (Sports Classics II Ser.). 104p. (J). lib. bdg. 15.00 (978-1-59054-752-6(7)) Fitzgerald Bks.

—Long Arm Quarterback. 1999. (Illus.). 144p. (J). (gr. 3-7). 15.95 (978-0-316-10571-2(6)) Little Brown & Co.

—Long Arm Quarterback. 1999. (978-0-606-17504-3(0)); (gr. 3-6). lib. bdg. 12.40 (978-0-613-21924-2(4)) Tandem Library Bks.

—Long-Arm Quarterback. 2007. (J). lib. bdg. (***978-1-59953-114-4(3)**) Norwood Hse. Pr.

—Long Arm Quarterback. ed. 2005. (Sports Classics II Ser.). 117p. (J). lib. bdg. 15.00 (978-1-59054-761-8(6)) Fitzgerald Bks.

—Long Arm Quarterback: A New Football Team Sparks an Old Rivalry. 1999. 144p. (J). (gr. 3-7). pap. 4.99 (978-0-316-10562-0(7)) Little Brown & Co.

Chronicle Books LLC Staff. Football Heroes. 2008. (J). 14.95 (978-0-8118-5661-4(5)) Chronicle Bks. LLC.

Cochran, Thomas. Roughnecks. 1999. 256p. (YA). (gr. 7-12). pap. 6.95 (978-0-15-202200-6(7) , Harcourt Paperbacks) Harcourt Children's Bks.

—Roughnecks. 1999. pap. 6.00 (978-0-15-201432-2(2)) Harcourt Trade Pubs.

—Roughnecks. 1999. (978-0-606-16531-0(2)); (gr. 7-12). lib. bdg. 14.15 (978-0-613-18274-4(X)) Tandem Library Bks.

Collar, Bill. It;s More Than A Game! Vervoort, Sarah, illus. 2007. (J). per. 6.95 (***978-1-933556-81-9(1)**) Publishers' Graphics, L.L.C.

Coy, John. Crackback. (J). 2007. 224p. pap. 6.99 (***978-0-439-69734-7(4)** , Scholastic Paperbacks); 2005. 208p. (gr. 7 up). pap. 16.99 (978-0-439-69733-0(6) , Scholastic Pr.) Scholastic, Inc.

Davie, Jan. Apollo Cafe. 2005. 76p. pap. (***978-1-84401-565-8(3)**) Athena Pr.

Deuker, Carl. Gym Candy. 2007. 320p. (J). (gr. 7 up). 16.00 (***978-0-618-77713-6(X)**) Houghton Mifflin Co. Trade & Reference Div.

Devard, Nancy, et al, illus. I Told You I Can Play. 2006. (ENM.). 32p. (J). 16.95 (***978-1-933491-06-6(X)**) Just Us Bks., Inc.

Dixon, Franklin W. Kickoff to Danger. ed. 2005. (Hardy Boys I Ser.: No. 170). 149p. (J). lib. bdg. 15.00 (978-1-59054-843-1(4)) Fitzgerald Bks.

Dooley, Vince. How 'Bout Them 'Dawgs! 2006. (J). 17.95 (978-1-932888-46-1(2)) Mascot Bks., Inc.

Durant, Alan. Leggs United: The Phantom Footballer. Smedley, Chris, illus. l.t. ed. 1999. 112p. (J). pap. (978-0-7540-6084-0(5) , CLP 282) BBC Audio.

Dye, Pat. War Eagle! 2006. (J). 17.95 (978-1-932888-47-8(0)) Mascot Bks., Inc.

Dygard, Thomas J. Second Stringer. 1998. 192p. (J). (gr. 7-12). 15.99 (978-0-688-15981-8(8)) HarperCollins Pubs.

Ellis, Deborah & Walters, Eric. Bifocal. 2007. 240p. (YA). (gr. 7 up). (***978-1-55455-036-4(X)**) Fitzhenry & Whiteside, Ltd.

Escott, John & Escott, Colin. Lucky Break, EasyStarts. 2003. (Illus.). 16p. (C). pap. 9.00 (978-0-582-50497-4(X)) Pearson ESL.

Florie, Christine. Cori Plays Football. Tripp, Christine, illus. (Rookie Reader Ser.). (J). (gr. k-2). 2006. 32p. pap. 4.95 (978-0-516-25023-6(X)); 2005. 31p. 19.50 (978-0-516-24864-6(2)) Scholastic Library Publishing. (Children's Pr.).

Frazer, Rebecca. Barbie Loves Cheerleading. Wolcott, Karen, illus. 2007. 24p. (J). (ps-2). 3.99 (978-0-375-87485-7(2) , Golden Bks.) Random Hse. Children's Bks.

Ganzer, Diane. Patrick the Wayward Setter: A Christmas Miracle. 2005. 60p. pap. 12.95 (978-1-4137-8351-3(1)) PublishAmerica, Inc.

Grambling, Lois G. Nicky Jones & the Roaring Rhinos. Geer, William J., illus. 2004. 32p. (J). 6.95 (978-1-877810-14-5(2)) Rayve Productions, Inc.

Green, Tim. Football Genius. 2007. 256p. (J). (gr. 5-8). 16.99 (***978-0-06-112270-5(X)**); lib. bdg. 17.89 (***978-0-06-112272-9(6)**) HarperCollins Pubs.

Greene, Janice. The Ritual: Set 1. 2002. 32p. (YA). 2.95 (978-1-56254-412-6(8) , SP 4128) Saddleback Educational Publishing.

Grindele, Jenny. Josh, the Jock of High School. 2005. 48p. pap. 12.95 (978-1-4137-6950-0(0)) PublishAmerica, Inc.

Gruska, Denise Eliana. The Only Boy in Ballet Class. Wummer, Amy, illus. 2007. 32p. (J). (ps-3). 15.95 (***978-1-4236-0220-0(X)**) Gibbs Smith, Publisher.

Hafer, Todd. Cody's Varsity Rush. 2005. (Spirit of the Game, Sports Fiction Ser.). (Illus.). 144p. (J). (gr. k-17). pap. 4.99 (978-0-310-70794-3(3)) Zonderkidz.

Hale, Bruce. This Gum for Hire: A Chet Gecko Mystery. (Chet Gecko Mystery Ser.: No. 6). (Illus.). (J). (gr. 3-7). 2003. 144p. pap. 4.95 (978-0-15-202497-0(2) , Harcourt Paperbacks); 2002. 136p. 15.00 (978-0-15-202491-8(3)) Harcourt Children's Bks.

—This Gum for Hire: A Chet Gecko Mystery. 2003. (Chet Gecko Mystery Ser.: No. 6). (J). (gr. 3-6). lib. bdg. 12.95 (978-0-613-59895-8(4)) Tandem Library Bks.

Hancock, H. Irving. The High School Captain of the Team. rev. ed. 2006. 212p. 27.95 (978-1-4218-1740-8(3)); pap. 12.95 (978-1-4218-1840-5(X)) 1st World Publishing, Inc. (1st World Library - Literary Society).

—The High School Left End. rev. ed. 2006. 212p. 27.95 (978-1-4218-1742-2(X)); pap. 12.95 (978-1-4218-1842-9(6)) 1st World Publishing, Inc. (1st World Library - Literary Society).

Hancock, H. Irving. The High School Left End: Dick & Co. Grilling on the Football Gridiron. 2007. 156p. pap. 11.99 (***978-1-4264-6385-3(5)**); 174p. pap. 14.99 (***978-1-4264-6459-1(2)**) BiblioBazaar.

Hancock, Irving H. The High School Captain of the Team or D. 2006. 78.99 (***978-1-4219-9894-7(7)**); pap. 71.99 (***978-1-4219-9905-0(6)**) IndyPublish.com.

—The High School Left End or Dick & Co. G. 2006. 78.99 (***978-1-4219-9906-7(4)**); pap. 72.99 (***978-1-4219-9911-1(0)**) IndyPublish.com.

Hand, Jimmie. The Long Way Around. 2003. (Dream Series Ser.). 160p. 9.95 (978-0-9708992-7-9(0)) Scobre Pr. Corp.

Hanson, Ed. The Pass. 2003. (Barclay Family Adventure Ser.: Bk. 9). 64p. (J). (gr. k-6). per. 3.95 (978-1-56254-557-4(4) , SP 5574) Saddleback Educational Publishing.

Hautman, Pete. Rash. (YA). 2007. 272p. pap. 8.99 (***978-0-689-86904-4(5)** , Simon Pulse); 2006. 256p. (gr. 7 up). 16.99 (978-0-689-86801-6(4) , Simon & Schuster Children's Publishing) Simon & Schuster Children's Publishing.

—Rash. l.t. rev. ed. 2007. 307p. (YA). 22.95 (***978-0-7862-9312-4(8)**) Thorndike Pr.

Herman, Gail. Scooby Doo! & the Football Fright. 2002. (gr. k-3). lib. bdg. 11.80 (978-0-613-58152-3(0)) Tandem Library Bks.

Herman, Gail & del Sur, Duendes. Football Fright. 2002. (Scooby-Doo! Reader Ser.: No. 14). (Illus.). 32p. (J). (gr. k-3). pap. 3.99 (978-0-439-34116-5(7)) Scholastic, Inc.

Higuchi, Daisuke. Whistle!, Vol. 7. Higuchi, Daisuke, illus. 2005. (Whistle! Ser.). 200p. (YA). pap. 7.99 (978-1-59116-973-4(9)) Viz Media.

How 'Bout Them Cowboys! 2007. (J). 17.95 (***978-1-932888-90-4(X)**) Mascot Bks., Inc.

Hughes, Mair Wynn & Davidson, Nadine. Colli Pêl. 2005. (WEL., Illus.). 15p. pap. (978-0-86243-454-0(8)) Y Lolfa.

Hurwitz, Johanna. Starting School. Dugan, Karen M., illus. 1998. 144p. (J). (gr. 2 up). 15.00 (978-0-688-15685-5(1)) HarperCollins Pubs.

Inagaki, Riichiro. Eyeshield 21. 2006. (Eyeshield 21 Ser.). 208p. (YA). Vol. 8. pap. 7.99 (978-1-4215-0637-1(8)); Vol. 9. (Illus.). pap. 7.99 (978-1-4215-0638-8(6)) Viz Media.

Jenkins, A. M. Damage. 2003. (Illus.). 192p. (J). (gr. 7 up). pap. 7.99 (978-0-06-447255-5(8)) HarperCollins Pubs.

Jenkins, Wendy. Big Game. 1999. 184p. (J). pap. 12.95 (978-1-86368-183-4(3)) Fremantle Pr. AUS. *Dist:* International Specialized Bk. Services.

—Gunna Burn. 2000. 192p. (J). pap. 13.95 (978-1-86368-283-1(X)) Fremantle Pr. AUS. *Dist:* International Specialized Bk. Services.

Jordan & the Northside Reps: Individual Title Six-Packs. (gr. 3 up). 35.00 (978-0-7635-9669-9(8)) Rigby Education.

Kearney, Thomas John. Little Husky's Big Game. 2004. (J). bds. (978-0-9745454-0-0(6)) Timberwood Pr.

Kearney, Tom. Spartans Big Game. 2005. (J). bds. 8.95 (978-0-9745454-6-2(5)) Timberwood Pr.

Kearney, Tom John. Cougars Big Game. 2004. (Illus.). 11p. (J). bds. 7.95 (978-0-9745454-1-7(4)) Timberwood Pr.

Kessler, Leonard. Kick, Pass, & Run. Kessler, Leonard, illus. 2002. (Illus.). (J). 12.34 (978-0-7587-6173-6(2)) Book Wholesalers, Inc.

Kilby, Jan. Friday Knights: Football Challenges. 1999. (Harbor Lights Ser.). 124p. (J). (gr. 7-12). pap. 7.95 (978-1-880292-62-4(9)) LangMarc Publishing.

Korman, Gordon. No More Dead Dogs. Orig. Title: Touchdown Stage Left. 192p. (gr. 5-9). 2002. (J). pap. 5.99 (978-0-7868-1601-9(5)); 2000. (Illus.). 15.99 (978-0-7868-0531-0(5)) Hyperion Bks. for Children.

—No More Dead Dogs. 2002. Orig. Title: Touchdown Stage Left. (gr. 5-8). lib. bdg. 14.15 (978-0-613-61850-2(5)) Tandem Library Bks.

Krulik, Nancy E. Cordelia Collection. 2002. (gr. 7-12). lib. bdg. 14.15 (978-0-613-63270-6(2)) Tandem Library Bks.

Lee, Marie G. Necessary Roughness. 1998. 240p. (J). (gr. 7 up). pap. 6.50 (978-0-06-447169-5(1) , Harper Trophy) HarperCollins Pubs.

—Necessary Roughness. 1998. (J). (978-0-606-13000-4(4)) Tandem Library Bks.

Levy, Elizabeth. Tackling Dad. 2005. 144p. (J). 16.89 (978-0-06-000050-9(3)); 15.99 (978-0-06-000051-6(1)) HarperCollins Pubs.

Lipsyte, Robert. Raiders Night. 2007. 256p. (J). (gr. 9 up). pap. 6.99 (***978-0-06-059948-5(0)**); 2006. 240p. (YA). 15.99 (978-0-06-059946-1(4)); 2006. 240p. (YA). lib. bdg. 16.89 (978-0-06-059947-8(2)) HarperCollins Pubs. (HarperTeen).

Literature Connections English: Maniac Magee. 2004. (gr. 6-12). (978-0-395-77524-0(8) , 2-80093) McDougal Littell Inc.

Lupica, Mike. Two-Minute Drill. 2007. (Mike Lupica's Comeback Kids Ser.). 180p. (J). (gr. 4-7). 9.99 (***978-0-399-24715-6(7)** , Philomel) Penguin Group (USA) Inc.

Lynch, Chris. Inexcusable. 176p. (YA). 2007. (gr. 9 up). pap. 6.99 (978-1-4169-3972-6(5) , Simon Pulse); 2005. (Illus.). (gr. 7 up). 16.95 (978-0-689-84789-9(0) , Atheneum) Simon & Schuster Children's Publishing.

Maddox, Jake. On the Line. Tiffany, Sean, illus. 2007. (Jake Maddox Sports Story Ser.). 65p. (J). (gr. 4-8). lib. bdg. 21.26 (978-1-59889-062-4(X)) Stone Arch Bks.

Marsh, Carole. The Football Phantom. 2006. 64p. (gr. 2-4). 14.95 (***978-0-635-06223-9(2)**); pap. 3.99 (***978-0-635-06217-8(8)**) Gallopade International.

Marshall, James, illus. Miss Nelson Has a Field Day. 2002. (Miss Nelson Ser.). (J). 13.79 (978-0-7587-3145-6(0)) Book Wholesalers, Inc.

Martin, Bill, Jr. & Sampson, Michael. Little Granny Quarterback. Chesworth, Michael, illus. 2003. 32p. (J). (gr. k-2). 15.95 (978-1-56397-930-9(6)) Boyds Mills Pr.

McEwan, Jamie. Rufus the Scrub Does Not Wear a Tutu! Margeson, John, illus. 2007. 64p. (J). (gr. 2-3). 14.95 (***978-1-58196-060-0(3)**) Darby Creek Publishing.

McKee, David. Mr. Benn, Gladiator. 2002. (Illus.). 32p. (J). (ps-3). 17.99 (978-1-84270-024-2(3)) Andersen GBR. *Dist:* Trafalgar Square Publishing.

Mitchell, Carolyn. The Tale of the Pumpkin Seed Squad. 2006. (ENG.). 40p. per. 16.99 (***978-1-4259-7004-8(4)**) AuthorHouse.

Morpurgo, Michael. Billy the Kid. Foreman, Michael, illus. 2006. 72p. (J). pap. 13.95 (***978-1-84458-366-9(X)**) Anova Bks. GBR. *Dist:* Independent Pubs. Group.

Muller, Neil K. Touchdowns. 1998. (Drew Neilson Ser.). 116p. (YA). pap. 12.95 (978-1-57502-905-4(7) , PO 2583) Morris Publishing.

Murdock, Catherine Gilbert. Dairy Queen: A Novel. 2006. 288p. (YA). (gr. 7-10). 16.00 (978-0-618-68307-9(0)) Houghton Mifflin Co.

—Dairy Queen: A Novel. 2007. 288p. (YA). (gr. 7 up). pap. 8.99 (***978-0-618-86335-8(4)** , Graphia) Houghton Mifflin Co. Trade & Reference Div.

—The Off Season. 2007. 288p. (YA). (gr. 7-10). 16.00 (***978-0-618-68695-7(9)**) Houghton Mifflin Co. Trade & Reference Div.

Myrddin ap Dafydd. Brwydr y Brodyr. 2005. (WEL.). 66p. (978-0-86381-906-3(0)) Gwasg Carreg Gwalch.

Owens, Terrell & Parker, Courtney. Little T Learns to Share. Harris, Todd, illus. 2006. 24p. (J). 14.95 (978-1-933771-20-5(8)) BenBella Bks.

Parker, Laurie. Mad for Maroon. 2005. (Illus.). (J). 17.95 (978-0-9772096-1-3(X)) Wild Hare Publishing.

Paul, Ann W. Hello Toes! Hello Feet! Wescott, Nadine Bernard, illus. 2000. (J). (978-0-606-19770-0(2)) Tandem Library Bks.

Pee-Wee Football. 2003. (J). per. (978-1-57657-940-4(9)) Paradise Pr., Inc.

Peterson, Dan A. Fergus: The Soccer-Playing Colt. Weber, Ryan S., illus. 2005. 180p. (J). per. 9.00 (978-0-9714161-7-8(6)) Raven Publishing Inc. of Montana.

Powell, Randy. Three Clams & an Oyster. 224p. (YA). 2006. pap. 6.95 (978-0-374-40007-1(5)); 2002. (gr. 7-10). 16.00 (978-0-374-37526-3(7)) Farrar, Straus & Giroux. (Farrar, Straus & Giroux (BYR)).

Regan, Peter. Shannon Harps. Myler, Terry, illus. 2003. 128p. (YA). (gr. 3 up). pap. 9.95 (978-1-901737-41-7(1)) Anvil Bks., Ltd. IRL. *Dist:* Dufour Editions, Inc.

Rennie, C. Goal Behind the Curtain. Date not set. 176p. (YA). mass mkt. 4.99 (978-1-871676-47-1(9) , Christian Focus) Christian Focus Pubns. GBR. *Dist:* Riverside, Spring Arbor Distributors, Inc.

Robins, Eleanor. Back-up Quarterback. 2003. (Illus.). 48p. (YA). per. 3.95 (978-1-56254-675-5(9) , SP6759) Saddleback Educational Publishing.

Rud, Jeff. First & Ten. 2007. No. 3. 176p. (J). (gr. 3-7). pap. (***978-1-55143-690-6(6)**) Orca Bk. Pubs.

Rylant, Cynthia. The Case of the Troublesome Turtle. Karas, G. Brian, illus. 2003. (High-Rise Private Eyes Ser.: No. 4). (J). (gr. k-3). 25.95 incl. audio (978-1-59112-202-9(3)) Live Oak Media.

Schulz, Charles M. Kick the Football, Charlie Brown! 2001. (gr. k-3). lib. bdg. 11.80 (978-0-613-61786-4(X)) Tandem Library Bks.

E
F
G

Schulz, Charles M., illus. Kick the Football, Charlie Brown! 2001. (Ready-to-Read Ser.). 32p. (J). pap. 3.99 (978-0-689-84594-9(4) , Little Simon) Simon & Schuster Children's Publishing.

Sinclair, Jay. It's Magic. 2000. (Jersey Ser.: 1). 128p. (gr. 3-7). pap. 4.99 (978-0-7868-4261-2(X)) Disney Pr.

—The Jersey. 2000. (Jersey Ser.). (Illus.). (J). 11.64 (978-0-606-20736-2(8)) Tandem Library Bks.

Skead, Robert. Elves Can't Tackle. 2004. (J). pap. 7.99 (978-1-929478-64-4(X)) Cross Training Publishing.

Stabler, Ken. Roll Tide! de Angel, Miguel, illus. 2006. (J). 17.95 ***(978-1-932888-48-5(9))*** Mascot Bks., Inc.

Stadler, John. Snail Saves the Day. Stadler, John, illus. 2006. (Illus.). 32p. (J). reprint ed. pap. 5.95 (978-1-59572-045-0(6)) Star Bright Bks., Inc.

Stahler, David, Jr. Doppelganger. 2006. 272p. (J). 16.99 (978-0-06-087232-8(2)); lib. bdg. 17.89 (978-0-06-087233-5(0)) HarperCollins Pubs.

Steel, Richard. Touchdown. Taylor, Marjorie, illus. rev. ed. 1999. (Take Ten Ser.). 48p. (YA). (gr. 4 up). pap. 3.95 (978-1-58659-003-1(0)) Artesian Pr.

Stein, Joshua. Chasing the King. 2003. (Dream Series Ser.). 160p. 9.95 (978-0-9708992-4-8(6)) Scobre Pr. Corp.

Stephen, Smith. Fourth & Long. 2006. 128p. (J). pap. 5.99 (978-0-7847-1471-3(1) , 42142) Standard Publishing.

Tharp, Tim. Knights of the Hill Country. 2006. 240p. (YA). (gr. 7). 16.95 (978-0-375-83653-4(5)); lib. bdg. 18.99 (978-0-375-93653-1(X)) Random Hse. Children's Bks. (Knopf Bks. for Young Readers).

Wallace, Rich. Emergency Quarterback. 2006. (Winning Season Ser.: No. 5). 128p. (J). (gr. 2). pap. 4.99 (978-0-14-240615-1(5) , Puffin) Penguin Group (USA) Inc.

—Emergency Quarterback: Winning Season. 2005. 128p. (J). (gr. 4-7). 14.99 (978-0-670-06045-0(3) , Viking Adult) Penguin Group (USA) Inc.

—The Roar of the Crowd. 2005. (Winning Season Ser.: Bk. 1). 112p. (YA). (gr. 3-7). pap. 4.99 (978-0-14-240443-0(8) , Puffin) Penguin Group (USA) Inc.

Wallace, Rich. Roar of the Crowd. 2004. 101p. (J). lib. bdg. 15.38 ***(978-1-4242-2165-3(X))*** Fitzgerald Bks.

Walter, Dan. Hello, Willie! 2007. (J). 14.95 ***(978-1-932888-52-2(7))*** Mascot Bks., Inc.

Walters, Eric. Juice. 112p. 2006. (YA). lib. bdg. 14.95 (978-1-55143-588-6(8)); 2005. (J). (gr. 7-12). pap. 7.95 (978-1-55143-351-6(0)) Orca Bk. Pubs. USA.

—Juice. 2005. 101p. (YA). (gr. 7-11). per. 15.90 (978-0-606-33183-8(2)) Tandem Library Bks.

White, Tim. A Single Heart. 2006. 193p. pap. 19.95 (978-1-4137-9418-2(1)) PublishAmerica, Inc.

Wojciechowska, Maia. Dreams of the Super Bowl. Karsky, A. K., illus. (Dreams of...Ser.). 80p. (J). 14.50 (978-1-883740-20-7(7)) Pebble Beach Pr., Ltd.

Wolkoff, Stephen D. The Athletic Adventures of Hart Coleman Vol. 1: Story I - Football Championship. Donnelly, Celestine, illus. 2000. 70p. (J). (gr. 3-9). pap. 11.95 (978-0-9702421-0-5(7)) S & A Assocs., Inc.

FOOTBALL—HISTORY

Aretha, David. The Michigan Wolverines Football Team. 1999. (Great Sports Teams Ser.). (Illus.). 48p. (YA). (gr. 4-10). lib. bdg. 23.93 (978-0-7660-1101-4(1)) Enslow Pubs., Inc.

Bailer, Darice. Touchdown! Great Quarterbacks in Football History. 1999. (J). (978-0-606-19521-8(1)) Tandem Library Bks.

Bell, Lonnie. The History of the New England Patriots. 2004. (NFL Today Ser.). (Illus.). 32p. 18.95 (978-1-58341-304-3(9) , Creative Education) Creative Co., The.

—The History of the New Orleans Saints. 2004. (NFL Today Ser.). (Illus.). 32p. 18.95 (978-1-58341-305-0(7) , Creative Education) Creative Co., The.

—The History of the San Francisco 49ers. 2004. (NFL Today Ser.). (Illus.). 32p. 18.95 (978-1-58341-313-5(8) , Creative Education) Creative Co., The.

—The History of the St. Louis Rams. 2004. (NFL Today Ser.). (Illus.). 32p. 18.95 (978-1-58341-311-1(1) , Creative Education) Creative Co., The.

Brar, Aneel. Super Bowl. 2007. (J). ***(978-1-59036-689-9(1)); (978-1-59036-690-5(5))*** Weigl Pubs., Inc.

Buckley, James, Jr. Great Moments in Football. 2002. (Great Moments in Sports Ser.). (Illus.). 48p. (J). (gr. 5 up). pap. 14.60 (978-0-8368-5360-5(1)); lib. bdg. 30.00 (978-0-8368-5346-9(6)) Stevens, Gareth Inc. (World Almanac Library).

—NFL's Greatest Upsets. 2000. (Eyewitness Readers Ser.). (J). (978-0-606-20124-7(6)) Tandem Library Bks.

—Super Bowl Heroes. 2000. (Eyewitness Readers Ser.). (J). (978-0-606-20128-5(9)) Tandem Library Bks.

Christopher, Matt. The Superbowl: 40 Years of Amazing Games. 2006. (Legendary Sports Events Ser.). (Illus.). 128p. (J). (gr. 3-7). pap. 4.99 (978-0-316-01116-7(9)) Little Brown & Co.

Cox, Gene. Go Big Red! A History of Leon High School Football 1916-2001. 2003. (Illus.). 400p. (YA). (gr. 7-12). 46.50 (978-0-9669672-1-0(6)) Cox, Gene.

Day, Chuck. Jacksonville Football History. 2004. (YA). lib. bdg. 29.95 (978-0-9760906-0-1(0)) Spectrum Films Inc.

Deitsch, Richard. (Quarter)Backs-to-(Running)Backs: The NFL's Finest Passers & Rushers. Wolf, Cathrine, ed. 1998. 32p. (J). (gr. 4-6). pap. 3.95 (978-1-886749-45-0(0)) Sports Illustrated For Kids.

—Super Bowl Heroes: Read about the Super Bowl's Biggest Stars. Sieck, Margaret, ed. 1999. 32p. (J). (gr. 2-7). pap. 3.99 (978-1-886749-53-5(1)) Sports Illustrated For Kids.

Frederick, Sara. The History of the Cincinnati Bengals. 2004. (NFL Today Ser.). (Illus.). 32p. 18.95 (978-1-58341-292-3(1) , Creative Education) Creative Co., The.

Frisch, Aaron. Chicago Bears, the History. 2004. (NFL Today Ser.). (Illus.). 32p. 18.95 (978-1-58341-291-6(3) , Creative Education) Creative Co., The.

—The History of the Detroit Lions. 2004. (NFL Today Ser.). (Illus.). 32p. 18.95 (978-1-58341-296-1(4) , Creative Education) Creative Co., The.

—The History of the Minnesota Vikings. 2004. (NFL Today Ser.). (Illus.). 32p. 18.95 (978-1-58341-303-6(0) , Creative Education) Creative Co., The.

—The History of the Oakland Raiders. 2003. (NFL Today Ser.). (Illus.). 32p. 18.95 (978-1-58341-308-1(1) , Creative Education) Creative Co., The.

—The History of the Tennessee Titans. 2004. (NFL Today Ser.). (Illus.). 32p. 18.95 (978-1-58341-316-6(2) , Creative Education) Creative Co., The.

Gilbert, Sara. The History of the Arizona Cardinals. 2004. (NFL Today Ser.). (Illus.). 32p. 18.95 (978-1-58341-286-2(7) , Creative Education) Creative Co., The.

—The History of the Cleveland Browns. 2004. (NFL Today Ser.). (Illus.). 32p. 18.95 (978-1-58341-293-0(X) , Creative Education) Creative Co., The.

—The History of the Seattle Seahawks. 2004. (NFL Today Ser.). (Illus.). 32p. 18.95 (978-1-58341-314-2(6) , Creative Education) Creative Co., The.

Goodman, Michael E. The History of the Atlanta Falcons. 2004. (NFL Today Ser.). (Illus.). 32p. 18.95 (978-1-58341-287-9(5) , Creative Education) Creative Co., The.

—The History of the Carolina Panthers. 2004. (NFL Today Ser.). (Illus.). 32p. 18.95 (978-1-58341-290-9(5) , Creative Education) Creative Co., The.

—The History of the New York Giants. 2004. (NFL Today Ser.). (Illus.). 32p. (J). 18.95 (978-1-58341-306-7(5) , Creative Education) Creative Co., The.

—The History of the New York Jets. 2004. (NFL Today Ser.). (Illus.). 32p. 18.95 (978-1-58341-307-4(3) , Creative Education) Creative Co., The.

—The History of the Tampa Bay Buccaneers. 2004. (NFL Today Ser.). (Illus.). 32p. 18.95 (978-1-58341-315-9(4) , Creative Education) Creative Co., The.

—The History of the Washington Redskins. 2004. (NFL Today Ser.). (Illus.). 32p. 18.95 (978-1-58341-317-3(0) , Creative Education) Creative Co., The.

Grabowski, John F. Football. 2000. (History of Sports Ser.). (Illus.). 96p. (YA). (gr. 6-9). 27.45 (978-1-56006-743-6(8) , Lucent Bks.) Thomson Gale.

—The Minnesota Vikings. 2002. (Great Sports Teams in History Ser.). (Illus.). 112p. (J). 29.95 (978-1-56006-943-0(0) , Lucent Bks.) Thomson Gale.

Hawkes, Brian. The History of the Dallas Cowboys. 2004. (NFL Today Ser.). (Illus.). 32p. 18.95 (978-1-58341-294-7(8) , Creative Education) Creative Co., The.

—The History of the Indianapolis Colts. 2004. (NFL Today Ser.). (Illus.). 32p. 18.95 (978-1-58341-299-2(9) , Creative Education) Creative Co., The.

—The History of the Jacksonville Jaguars. 2004. (NFL Today Ser.). (Illus.). 32p. 18.95 (978-1-58341-300-5(6) , Creative Education) Creative Co., The.

—The History of the Kansas City Chiefs. 2004. (NFL Today Ser.). (Illus.). 32p. 18.95 (978-1-58341-301-2(4) , Creative Education) Creative Co., The.

La Historia del Futbol: Individual Title Six-Packs. (On Deck en Espanol Ser.).Tr. of Story of Soccer. (SPA.). 24p. (gr. 4-5). 35.00 (978-0-7578-6396-7(5)) Rigby Education.

La Historia del Futbol Americano, 6 Packs. (On Deck en Espanol Ser.).Tr. of Story of Football. (SPA.). 24p. (gr. 4-5). 35.00 (978-0-7578-6394-3(9)) Rigby Education.

Jacksonvllle Jaguars: Auditing Cases. 1999. (J). 4.00 (978-0-13-016925-9(0)) Prentice Hall PTR.

Jones, Rob Lloyd. Story of Football. 2007. 64p. 8.99 (978-0-7945-1553-9(3) , Usborne) EDC Publishing.

Kirkpatrick, Rob. Doug Flutie: International Football Star. 2003. (Reading Power Ser.). (Illus.). 24p. (J). (gr. 1). lib. bdg. 17.25 (978-0-8239-5537-4(0) , PowerKids Pr.) Rosen Publishing Group, Inc., The.

—Terrell Davis: Super Bowl Running Back. (Deportistas de Poder Ser.). 24p. (J). 2002. (SPA.). lib. bdg. 17.25 (978-0-8239-6126-9(5) , Buenas Letras); 2000. (Illus.). (gr. 1). lib. bdg. 17.25 (978-0-8239-5536-7(2) , PowerKids Pr.) Rosen Publishing Group, Inc., The.

Lace, William W. The Pittsburgh Steelers Football Team. 1999. (Great Sports Teams Ser.). (Illus.). 48p. (YA). (gr. 4-10). lib. bdg. 23.93 (978-0-7660-1099-4(6)) Enslow Pubs., Inc.

Macnow, Glen. The Denver Broncos Football Team. 2001. (Great Sports Teams Ser.). (Illus.). 48p. (J). (gr. 4-10). lib. bdg. 23.93 (978-0-7660-1489-3(4)) Enslow Pubs., Inc.

Madden, John. John Madden's Heroes of Football: The Story of America's Games. 2006. (Illus.). 80p. (J). (gr. 5-6). 18.99 (978-0-525-47698-6(9) , Dutton Juvenile) Penguin Group (USA) Inc.

Molzahn, Arlene Bourgeois. The San Francisco 49ers Football Team. 2000. (Great Sports Teams Ser.). (Illus.). 48p. (YA). (gr. 4-10). lib. bdg. 23.93 (978-0-7660-1280-6(8)) Enslow Pubs., Inc.

Morgan, Brendan. Sports Illustrated for Kids Game Time! An Inside Look at Football. Holder, Sherie, ed. 1999. 32p. (J). (gr. 2-8). pap. 3.99 (978-1-886749-65-8(5)) Sports Illustrated For Kids.

Nelson, Julie. Jacksonville Jaguars. 3rd rev. ed. 2000. (Pro Football Today Ser.). (Illus.). 32p. (J). (gr. 3 up). lib. bdg. 22.60 (978-1-58341-046-2(5) , Creative Education) Creative Co., The.

—Minnesota Vikings. 3rd rev. ed. 2000. (Pro Football Today Ser.). (Illus.). 32p. (J). (gr. 3). lib. bdg. 22.60 (978-1-58341-049-3(X) , Creative Education) Creative Co., The.

—New Orleans Saints. 3rd rev. ed. 2000. (NFL Today Ser.). (Illus.). 32p. (J). (gr. 3 up). lib. bdg. 22.60 (978-1-58341-051-6(1) , Creative Education) Creative Co., The.

—San Francisco 49ers. 3rd rev. ed. 2000. (Pro Football Today Ser.). (Illus.). 32p. (J). (gr. 3 up). lib. bdg. 22.60 (978-1-58341-059-2(7) , Creative Education) Creative Co., The.

—St. Louis Rams. 3rd rev. ed. 2000. (Pro Football Today Ser.). (Illus.). 32p. (J). (gr. 3 up). lib. bdg. 22.60 (978-1-58341-057-8(0) , Creative Education) Creative Co., The.

—Tampa Bay Buccaneers. 3rd rev. ed. 2000. (Pro Football Today Ser.). (Illus.). 32p. (J). (gr. 3 up). lib. bdg. 22.60 (978-1-58341-061-5(9) , Creative Education) Creative Co., The.

—Tennessee Titans. 3rd rev. ed. 2000. (Pro Football Today Ser.). (Illus.). 32p. (J). (gr. 3 up). lib. bdg. 22.60 (978-1-58341-062-2(7) , Creative Education) Creative Co., The.

Nichols, John. Arizona Cardinals. 3rd rev. ed. 2000. (Pro Football Today Ser.). (Illus.). 32p. (J). (gr. 3 up). lib. bdg. 22.60 (978-1-58341-034-9(1) , Creative Education) Creative Co., The.

—Atlanta Falcons. 3rd rev. ed. 2000. (NFL Today Ser.). (Illus.). 32p. (J). (gr. 3-7). lib. bdg. 22.60 (978-1-58341-035-6(X) , Creative Education) Creative Co., The.

—Buffalo Bills. 3rd rev. ed. 2000. (Pro Football Today Ser.). (Illus.). 32p. (J). (gr. 3 up). lib. bdg. 22.60 (978-1-58341-037-0(6) , Creative Education) Creative Co., The.

—Chicago Bears. 3rd rev. ed. 2000. (Pro Football Today Ser.). (Illus.). 32p. (J). (gr. 3 up). lib. bdg. 22.60 (978-1-58341-039-4(2) , Creative Education) Creative Co., The.

—Cincinnati Bengals. 3rd rev. ed. 2000. (Pro Football Today Ser.). (Illus.). 32p. (J). (gr. 3 up). lib. bdg. 22.60 (978-1-58341-040-0(6) , Creative Education) Creative Co., The.

—Cleveland Browns. 2000. (Pro Football Today Ser.). (Illus.). 32p. (J). (gr. 3-7). lib. bdg. 22.60 (978-1-58341-080-6(5) , Creative Education) Creative Co., The.

—Denver Broncos. 3rd rev. ed. 2000. (Pro Football Today Ser.). (Illus.). 32p. (J). (gr. 3 up). lib. bdg. 22.60 (978-1-58341-042-4(2) , Creative Education) Creative Co., The.

—Detroit Lions. 3rd rev. ed. 2000. (Pro Football Today Ser.). (Illus.). 32p. (J). (gr. 3 up). lib. bdg. 22.60 (978-1-58341-043-1(0) , Creative Education) Creative Co., The.

—The History of the Baltimore Ravens. 2004. (NFL Today Ser.). (Illus.). 32p. 18.95 (978-1-58341-288-6(3) , Creative Education) Creative Co., The.

—The History of the Buffalo Bills. 2004. (NFL Today Ser.). (Illus.). 32p. 18.95 (978-1-58341-289-3(1) , Creative Education) Creative Co., The.

—The History of the Houston Texans. 2004. (NFL Today Ser.). (Illus.). 32p. 18.95 (978-1-58341-298-5(0) , Creative Education) Creative Co., The.

Potts, Steve. Dallas Cowboys. 2001. (Championship Teams Ser.). (Illus.). (J). (978-1-58340-086-9(9)) Smart Apple Media.

—Green Bay Packers. 2001. (Championship Teams Ser.). (Illus.). (J). (978-1-58340-090-6(7)) Smart Apple Media.

Schmalzbauer, Adam. The History of the Denver Broncos. 2004. (NFL Today Ser.). (Illus.). 32p. 18.95 (978-1-58341-295-4(6) , Creative Education) Creative Co., The.

—The History of the Miami Dolphins. 2004. (NFL Today Ser.). (Illus.). 32p. 18.95 (978-1-58341-302-9(2) , Creative Education) Creative Co., The.

—The History of the Philadelphia Eagles. 2004. (NFL Today Ser.). (Illus.). 32p. 18.95 (978-1-58341-309-8(X) , Creative Education) Creative Co., The.

—The History of the Pittsburgh Steelers. 2004. (NFL Today Ser.). (Illus.). 32p. 18.95 (978-1-58341-310-4(3) , Creative Education) Creative Co., The.

—The History of the San Diego Chargers. 2004. (NFL Today Ser.). (Illus.). 32p. 18.95 (978-1-58341-312-8(X) , Creative Education) Creative Co., The.

Stewart, Mark. The Philadelphia Eagles. 2006. (Team Spirit Ser.). (Illus.). 48p. (J). lib. bdg. 25.27 (978-1-59953-007-9(4)) Norwood Hse. Pr.

—Pittsburgh Steelers. 2006. (Team Spirit Ser.). (Illus.). 48p. (J). lib. bdg. 25.27 (978-1-59953-063-5(5)) Norwood Hse. Pr.

Stewart, Mark & Aikens, Jason. The San Francisco 49ers. 2008. (J). ***(978-1-59953-134-2(8))*** Norwood Hse. Pr.

—The Washington Redskins. 2008. (J). ***(978-1-59953-135-9(6))*** Norwood Hse. Pr.

Stewart, Mark Alan. Football: A History of the Gridiron Game. 1998. (History of Sports Ser.). (Illus.). 144p. (YA). (gr. 5-8). 34.50 (978-0-531-11493-3(7) , Watts, Franklin) Scholastic Library Publishing.

The Story of Football, 6 Pack. (On Deck Ser.). 24p. (gr. 4-5). 35.00 (978-0-7578-1011-4(X)) Rigby Education.

Suen, Anastasia. The Story of Football. 2002. (Reading Power Ser.). (Illus.). 24p. (J). (gr. 2). lib. bdg. 17.25 (978-0-8239-5996-9(1) , PowerKids Pr.) Rosen Publishing Group, Inc., The.

FOOTBALL—YEARBOOKS

Atlanta Falcons. Atlanta Falcons. CWC Sports Inc., ed. 1998. (NFL Team Yearbooks Ser.). 32p. (J). pap. 9.99 (978-1-891613-02-9(2)) Everett Sports Publishing & Marketing.

FOOTBALL TEAMS

Aretha, David. The Michigan Wolverines Football Team. 1999. (Great Sports Teams Ser.). (Illus.). 48p. (YA). (gr. 4-10). lib. bdg. 23.93 (978-0-7660-1101-4(1)) Enslow Pubs., Inc.

—The Notre Dame Fighting Irish Football Team. 2001. (Great Sports Teams Ser.). (Illus.). 48p. (YA). (gr. 4-10). lib. bdg. 23.93 (978-0-7660-1486-2(X)) Enslow Pubs., Inc.

—Steel Tough¿the Pittsburgh Steelers. 2007. (Sensational Sports Teams Ser.). (Illus.). 128p. (J). (gr. 5). lib. bdg. 33.27 (978-1-59845-047-7(6) , MyReportLinks.com Bks.) Enslow Pubs., Inc.

Atlanta Falcons. Atlanta Falcons. CWC Sports Inc., ed. 1998. (NFL Team Yearbooks Ser.). 32p. (J). pap. 9.99 (978-1-891613-02-9(2)) Everett Sports Publishing & Marketing.

Balzer, Howard. Kurt Warner: The Quarterback. 2000. (Sport Snaps Ser.). (Illus.). 56p. (J). pap. 12.95 (978-1-892920-34-8(4)) GHB Publishers, LLC.

Bell, Lonnie. The History of the New Orleans Saints. 2004. (NFL Today Ser.). (Illus.). 32p. 18.95 (978-1-58341-305-0(7) , Creative Education) Creative Co., The.

—The History of the San Francisco 49ers. 2004. (NFL Today Ser.). (Illus.). 32p. 18.95 (978-1-58341-313-5(8) , Creative Education) Creative Co., The.

—The History of the St. Louis Rams. 2004. (NFL Today Ser.). (Illus.). 32p. 18.95 (978-1-58341-311-1(1) , Creative Education) Creative Co., The.

Buffalo Bills Staff. Buffalo Bills: NFL Today. CWC Sports Inc., ed. 1998. (NFL Team Yearbooks Ser.). 32p. (J). (gr. 1-12). pap. 9.99 (978-1-891613-12-8(X)) Everett Sports Publishing & Marketing.

Chicago Bears Staff. Chicago Bears: NFL Today. CWC Sports Inc., ed. 1998. (NFL Team Yearbooks Ser.). 32p. (J). (gr. 1-12). pap. 9.99 (978-1-891613-03-6(0)) Everett Sports Publishing & Marketing.

Dallas Cowboys Staff. Dallas Cowboys. CWC Sports Inc, ed. 1998. (NFL Team Yearbooks Ser.). (J). (gr. 1-12). pap. 9.99 (978-1-891613-06-7(5)) Everett Sports Publishing & Marketing.

Denver Broncos Organization Staff. Denver Broncos. CWC Sports Inc., ed. 1998. (NFL Team Yearbooks Ser.). (J). (gr. 1-12). pap. 9.99 (978-1-891613-07-4(3)) Everett Sports Publishing & Marketing.

Detroit Lions Staff. Detroit Lions. CWC Sports Inc., ed. 1998. (NFL Team Yearbooks Ser.). (J). (gr. 1-12). pap. 9.99 (978-1-891613-08-1(1)) Everett Sports Publishing & Marketing.

Dickinson, Clive. Dickinson. McGregor, John, illus. 1999. 24p. (J). pap. 6.99 (978-0-233-99584-7(6)) Andre Deutsch GBR. *Dist:* Independent Pubs. Group.

Fried, Mark. Great Teams in College Football. 2005. (Great Teams Ser.). (Illus.). 48p. (J). 27.79 (978-1-4109-1487-3(9)); pap. 8.50 (978-1-4109-1494-1(1)) Raintree.

—Great Teams in College Football 6-Pack. 2005. pap. 51.00 (978-1-4109-1501-6(8)) Raintree.

—Great Teams in Football. 2005. (Great Teams Ser.). (Illus.). 48p. (J). 27.95 (978-1-4109-1483-5(6)); pap. 8.50 (978-1-4109-1490-3(9)) Raintree.

—Great Teams in Football 6-Pack. 2005. pap. 51.00 (978-1-4109-1497-2(6)) Raintree.

Frisch, Aaron. The History of the Tennessee Titans. 2004. (NFL Today Ser.). (Illus.). 32p. 18.95 (978-1-58341-316-6(2) , Creative Education) Creative Co., The.

Gilbert, Sara. The History of the Arizona Cardinals. 2004. (NFL Today Ser.). (Illus.). 32p. 18.95 (978-1-58341-286-2(7) , Creative Education) Creative Co., The.

Goodman, Michael E. The History of the Atlanta Falcons. 2004. (NFL Today Ser.). (Illus.). 32p. 18.95 (978-1-58341-287-9(5) , Creative Education) Creative Co., The.

—The History of the Carolina Panthers. 2004. (NFL Today Ser.). (Illus.). 32p. 18.95 (978-1-58341-290-9(5) , Creative Education) Creative Co., The.

—The History of the Tampa Bay Buccaneers. 2004. (NFL Today Ser.). (Illus.). 32p. 18.95 (978-1-58341-315-9(4) , Creative Education) Creative Co., The.

Hawkes, Brian. The History of the Indianapolis Colts. 2004. (NFL Today Ser.). (Illus.). 32p. 18.95 (978-1-58341-299-2(9) , Creative Education) Creative Co., The.

—The History of the Jacksonville Jaguars. 2004. (NFL Today Ser.). (Illus.). 32p. 18.95 (978-1-58341-300-5(6) , Creative Education) Creative Co., The.

Indianapolis Colts Staff. Indianapolis Colts. CWC Sports Inc., ed. 1998. (NFL Team Yearbooks Ser.). (J). (gr. 1-12). pap. 9.99 (978-1-891613-10-4(3)) Everett Sports Publishing & Marketing.

Jacksonville Jaguars Staff. Jacksonville Jaguars. CWC Sports Inc., ed. 1998. (NFL Team Yearbooks Ser.). (J). (gr. 1-12). pap. 9.99 (978-1-891613-11-1(1)) Everett Sports Publishing & Marketing.

Leboutillier, Nate. San Francisco 49ers. 2005. (Super Bowl Champions Ser.). (Illus.). 24p. (gr. 1-4). 16.95 (978-1-58341-391-3(X) , Creative Education) Creative Co., The.

—St. Louis Rams. 2005. (Super Bowl Champions Ser.). (Illus.). 24p. (J). (gr. 1-4). 16.95 (978-1-58341-390-6(1) , Creative Education) Creative Co., The.

Miami Dolphins. Miami Dolphins. CWC Sports Inc., ed. 1998. (NFL Team Yearbooks Ser.). (J). (gr. 1-12). pap. 9.99 (978-1-891613-13-5(8)) Everett Sports Publishing & Marketing.

Minnesota Vikings Staff. Minnesota Vikings. CWC Sports Inc., ed. 1998. (NFL Team Yearbooks Ser.). (Illus.). (J). (gr. 1-12). pap. 9.99 (978-1-891613-14-2(6)) Everett Sports Publishing & Marketing.

Nelson, Julie. Indianapolis Colts. 3rd rev. ed. 2000. (Pro Football Today Ser.). (Illus.). 32p. (J). (gr. 3 up). lib. bdg. 22.60 (978-1-58341-045-5(7) , Creative Education) Creative Co., The.

—Jacksonville Jaguars. 3rd rev. ed. 2000. (Pro Football Today Ser.). (Illus.). 32p. (J). (gr. 3 up). lib. bdg. 22.60 (978-1-58341-046-2(5) , Creative Education) Creative Co., The.

—Kansas City Chiefs. 3rd rev. ed. 2000. (Pro Football Today Ser.). (Illus.). 32p. (J). (gr. 3 up). lib. bdg. 22.60 (978-1-58341-047-9(3) , Creative Education) Creative Co., The.

—Miami Dolphins. 3rd rev. ed. 2000. (Pro Football Today Ser.). (Illus.). 32p. (YA). (gr. 3). lib. bdg. 22.60 (978-1-58341-048-6(1) , Creative Education) Creative Co., The.

—New York Giants. 3rd rev. ed. 2000. (Pro Football Today Ser.). (Illus.). 32p. (J). (gr. 3 up). lib. bdg. 22.60 (978-1-58341-052-3(X) , Creative Education) Creative Co., The.

—Philadelphia Eagles. 3rd rev. ed. 2000. (Pro Football Today Ser.). (Illus.). 32p. (J). (gr. 3-12). lib. bdg. 22.60 (978-1-58341-055-4(4) , Creative Education) Creative Co., The.

—Pittsburgh Steelers. 3rd rev. ed. 2000. (Pro Football Today Ser.). (Illus.). 32p. (J). (gr. 3 up). lib. bdg. 22.60 (978-1-58341-056-1(2) , Creative Education) Creative Co., The.

—San Diego Chargers. 3rd rev. ed. 2000. (Pro Football Today Ser.). (Illus.). 32p. (J). (gr. 3 up). lib. bdg. 22.60 (978-1-58341-058-5(9) , Creative Education) Creative Co., The.

—San Francisco 49ers. 3rd rev. ed. 2000. (Pro Football Today Ser.). (Illus.). 32p. (J). (gr. 3 up). lib. bdg. 22.60 (978-1-58341-059-2(7) , Creative Education) Creative Co., The.

—Seattle Seahawks. 3rd rev. ed. 2000. (Pro Football Today Ser.). (Illus.). 32p. (J). (gr. 3 up). lib. bdg. 22.60 (978-1-58341-060-8(0) , Creative Education) Creative Co., The.

—St. Louis Rams. 3rd rev. ed. 2000. (Pro Football Today Ser.). (Illus.). 32p. (J). (gr. 3 up). lib. bdg. 22.60 (978-1-58341-057-8(0) , Creative Education) Creative Co., The.

—Washington Redskins. 3rd rev. ed. 2000. (Pro Football Today Ser.). (Illus.). 32p. (J). (gr. 3 up). lib. bdg. 22.60 (978-1-58341-063-9(5) , Creative Education) Creative Co., The.

New York Giants. New York Giants. CWC Sports Inc., ed. 1998. (NFL Team Yearbooks Ser.). (J). (gr. 1-12). pap. 9.99 (978-1-891613-09-8(X)) Everett Sports Publishing & Marketing.

New York Jets. New York Jets. CWC Sports Inc., ed. 1998. (NFL Team Yearbooks Ser.). (J). (gr. 1-12). pap. 9.99 (978-1-891613-17-3(0)) Everett Sports Publishing & Marketing.

Nichols, John. Buffalo Bills. 3rd rev. ed. 2000. (Pro Football Today Ser.). (Illus.). 32p. (J). (gr. 3 up). lib. bdg. 22.60 (978-1-58341-037-0(6) , Creative Education) Creative Co., The.

—Carolina Panthers. 3rd rev. ed. 2000. (Pro Football Today Ser.). (Illus.). 32p. (J). (gr. 3 up). lib. bdg. 22.60 (978-1-58341-038-7(4) , Creative Education) Creative Co., The.

—Green Bay Packers. 3rd rev. ed. 2000. (Pro Football Today Ser.). (Illus.). 32p. (J). (gr. 3 up). lib. bdg. 22.60 (978-1-58341-044-8(9) , Creative Education) Creative Co., The.

—The History of the Baltimore Ravens. 2004. (NFL Today Ser.). (Illus.). 32p. 18.95 (978-1-58341-288-6(3) , Creative Education) Creative Co., The.

—The History of the Buffalo Bills. 2004. (NFL Today Ser.). (Illus.). 32p. 18.95 (978-1-58341-289-3(1) , Creative Education) Creative Co., The.

—The History of the Houston Texans. 2004. (NFL Today Ser.). (Illus.). 32p. 18.95 (978-1-58341-298-5(0) , Creative Education) Creative Co., The.

O'Shei, Tim. The Chicago Bears Football Team. 2001. (Great Sports Teams Ser.). (Illus.). 48p. (J). (gr. 4-10). lib. bdg. 23.93 (978-0-7660-1285-1(9)) Enslow Pubs., Inc.

Patrick, James. Football Madness: The Road to Super Bowl XXXVII. 2003. (Illus.). 24p. (J). (978-0-439-48650-7(5)) Scholastic, Inc.

Ross, Dalton. The Top Teams Ever: Football, Baseball, Basketball & Hockey Winners. 2005. (Sports Illustrated for Kids Bks.). (Illus.). 176p. (YA). (gr. 7-12). lib. bdg. 27.95 (978-0-8239-3693-9(7)) Rosen Publishing Group, Inc., The.

San Diego Chargers Staff. San Diego Chargers. CWC Sports Inc., ed. 1998. (NFL Team Yearbooks Ser.). (J). (gr. 1-12). pap. 9.99 (978-1-891613-05-0(7)) Everett Sports Publishing & Marketing.

Sandler, Michael. Dexter Jackson & the Tampa Bay Buccaneers: Super Bowl XXXVII. 2008. (Super Bowl Superstars Ser.). (Illus.). 24p. (J). (gr. k-5). lib. bdg. 22.61 (***978-1-59716-537-2(9)***) Bearport Publishing Co., Inc.

Schmalzbauer, Adam. The History of the Philadelphia Eagles. 2004. (NFL Today Ser.). (Illus.). 32p. 18.95 (978-1-58341-309-8(X) , Creative Education) Creative Co., The.

—The History of the Pittsburgh Steelers. 2004. (NFL Today Ser.). (Illus.). 32p. 18.95 (978-1-58341-310-4(3) , Creative Education) Creative Co., The.

Seattle Seahawks Staff. Seattle Seahawks. CWC Sports Inc, ed. 1998. (NFL Team Yearbooks Ser.). (J). (gr. 1-12). pap. 9.99 (978-1-891613-16-6(2)) Everett Sports Publishing & Marketing.

Stewart, Mark. Pittsburgh Steelers. 2006. (Team Spirit Ser.). (Illus.). 48p. (J). lib. bdg. 25.27 (978-1-59953-063-5(5)) Norwood Hse. Pr.

Stewart, Mark & Aikens, Jason. The Buffalo Bills. 2008. (J). lib. bdg. (***978-1-59953-132-8(1)***); lib. bdg. (***978-1-59953-128-1(3)***) Norwood Hse. Pr.

—The Carolina Panthers. 2008. (J). (***978-1-59953-130-4(5)***) Norwood Hse. Pr.

—The San Francisco 49ers. 2008. (J). (***978-1-59953-134-2(8)***) Norwood Hse. Pr.

—The Washington Redskins. 2008. (J). (***978-1-59953-135-9(6)***) Norwood Hse. Pr.

Tampa Bay Buccaneers Staff. Tampa Bay Buccaneers. CWC Sports Inc., ed. 1998. (NFL Team Yearbooks Ser.). (J). (gr. 1-12). pap. 9.99 (978-1-891613-15-9(4)) Everett Sports Publishing & Marketing.

Washington Redskins Staff. Washington Redskins. CWC Sports Inc., ed. 1998. (NFL Team Yearbooks Ser.). (J). (gr. 1-12). pap. 9.99 (978-1-891613-04-3(9)) Everett Sports Publishing & Marketing.

FORCE AND ENERGY

see also Dynamics; Mechanics; Motion

Ardley. The Science Book of Energy. 1998. (Illus.). (978-0-8172-9799-2(5)) Steck-Vaughn.

Barraclough, Sue. Pushing & Pulling. 2006. (Illus.). 24p. (J). (978-1-4109-2263-2(4)); (978-1-4109-2258-8(8)) Steck-Vaughn.

—Straight & Curving. 2006. (Illus.). 24p. (J). (978-1-4109-2260-1(X)); pap. (978-1-4109-2270-0(7)) Steck-Vaughn.

Benchmark Education Staff, compiled by. Forces & Energy. 2006. spiral bd. 125.00 (***978-1-4108-7061-2(8)***) Benchmark Education Co.

—Forces & Motion. 2006. spiral bd. 330.00 (***978-1-4108-7014-8(6)); 2006. spiral bd. 165.00 (***978-1-4108-7030-8(8)); 2006. spiral bd. 169.00 (***978-1-4108-7146-6(0)); 2005. (J). spiral bd. 265.00 (***978-1-4108-5760-6(3)***) Benchmark Education Co.

—Science Theme: Forces & Motion. 2005. spiral bd. 115.00 (***978-1-4108-5312-7(8)***) Benchmark Education Co.

Binns, Tristan Boyer. A Bright Idea: Conserving Energy. 2005. (You Can Save the Planet Ser.). (Illus.). 32p. (J). (ps-7). lib. bdg. 28.21 (978-1-4034-6844-4(3)); pap. (978-1-4034-6850-5(8)) Heinemann Library.

Blevins, Wiley. Push or Pull? 2003. (Compass Point Phonics Readers Ser.). (Illus.). 16p. (J). (gr. 1 up). 13.26 (978-0-7565-0521-9(6)) Compass Point Bks.

Bradley, Kimberly Brubaker. Energy Makes Things Happen. Meisel, Paul, illus. 2003. (Let's-Read-and-Find-Out Science Ser.). 40p. (J). (gr. k-4). 15.99 (978-0-06-028908-9(2)); pap. 5.99 (978-0-06-445213-7(1) , Harper Trophy); lib. bdg. 16.89 (978-0-06-028909-6(0)) HarperCollins Pubs.

—Energy Makes Things Happen. 2003. (gr. k-3). lib. bdg. 13.00 (978-0-613-59379-3(0)) Tandem Library Bks.

—Forces Make Things Move. Meisel, Paul, illus. 2005. (Let's-Read-and-Find-Out Science Ser.). 40p. (J). (gr. k-4). pap. 5.99 (978-0-06-445214-4(X)); 15.99 (978-0-06-028906-5(6)); lib. bdg. 16.89 (978-0-06-028907-2(4)) HarperCollins Pubs.

Brudnak, Karen, ed. Investigating Science - Energy, Light, & Sound. 2000. 48p. 9.95 (978-1-56234-429-0(3) , Mailbox Bks., The) Education Ctr., Inc.

Bryant-Mole, Karen & Ansary, Mir Tamim. Forces. 2002. (Science All Around Me Ser.). (Illus.). 24p. (J). (gr. 1-3). pap. 6.50 (978-1-4034-0050-5(4) , 91494) Heinemann Library.

Bug, Amy L. Forces & Motion. 2007. (Physics in Action Ser.). 128p. (gr. 9). 30.00 (***978-0-7910-8931-6(2)*** , Chelsea Hse.) Facts On File, Inc.

Bundey, Nikki. In the Gym. Gray, Virginia, illus. 1999. (First Sports Science Ser.). 32p. (J). (gr. 2-4). lib. bdg. 21.27 (978-1-57505-358-5(6) , Carolrhoda Bks.) Lerner Publishing Group.

—On the Field. Gray, Virginia, illus. 1999. (First Sports Science Ser.). 32p. (J). (gr. 2-4). lib. bdg. 21.27 (978-1-57505-357-8(8) , Carolrhoda Bks.) Lerner Publishing Group.

Burton, Jane & Taylor, Kim. The Nature & Science of Energy. Bingxin, Wang et al, trs. 2000. (Nature & Science Ser.). (CHI & ENG., Illus.). 32p. (J). 8.95 (978-7-5600-1749-5(5)) Foreign Languages Teaching & Research Pr. CHN. *Dist:* Cheng & Tsui Co.

Burton, Margie & French, Tammy, Cathy - Jones. ¿Qué empuja? ¿Qué jala? & What Pushes? What Pulls? 2005. spiral bd. 66.00 (***978-1-4108-5641-8(0)***) Benchmark Education Co.

Cherry Lake Publishing, compiled by. Power Up. 2008. lib. bdg. (***978-1-60279-107-7(4)***) Cherry Lake Publishing.

Cheshire, Gerard. Forces & Motion. 2006. (Fundamental Physics Ser.). (Illus.). 48p. (J). (978-1-58340-995-4(5)) Smart Apple Media.

Cipriano, Jeri. Empujar y Halar. 2005. Tr. of Push & Pull. (SPA., Illus.). 16p. (J). (gr. 1 up). lib. bdg. 15.93 (978-0-7368-4164-1(4)) Capstone Pr., Inc.

Clemmet, Mike & Oxlade, Chris. Forces & Energy. 1998. (Fact Finders Ser.). (Illus.). 144p. (J). (gr. 3-7). (978-0-563-37621-7(X)) BBC Worldwide.

Clifford, Tim. Energy. 2008. (J). (***978-1-60044-622-1(1)***) Rourke Publishing, LLC.

Cobb, Allan B. Super Science Projects about Energy & Motion. 2005. (Psyched for Science Ser.). (Illus.). 48p. (YA). (gr. 5-8). lib. bdg. 23.95 (978-0-8239-3116-3(1) , SCENMO) Rosen Publishing Group, Inc., The.

Cole, Joanna. El Autobus Magico Juega a la Pelota: Un Libro Sobre Fuerzas. 1998. (Magic School Bus Ser.). (SPA., Illus.). 32p. (J). (gr. 1-4). pap. 3.50 (978-0-590-76128-4(5) , Blue Sky Pr., The) Scholastic, Inc.

—The Magic School Bus Plays Ball: A Book about Forces. Degan, Bruce & Ruiz, Art, illus. 1998. (Magic School Bus Ser.). 32p. (J). (gr. 1-4). pap. 3.50 (978-0-590-92240-1(8)) Scholastic, Inc.

—The Magic School Bus Plays Ball: A Book about Forces. 1998. (Magic School Bus Ser.). (Illus.). (J). (gr. 1-4). (978-0-606-13591-7(X)) Tandem Library Bks.

Crawford, Leslie & Holm, Amy E. Environmental Action. 26p. (YA). (gr. 6-12). pap. 8.50 (978-0-201-49549-2(X)) Globe Fearon Educational Publishing.

Creighton, Jayne, contrib. by. Boomerangs, Blades & Basketballs: The Science of Sports. 1999. (Science @ Work Ser.). (Illus.). 48p. (J). (gr. 4-6). lib. bdg. 27.12 (978-0-7398-0132-1(5)) Raintree.

Curry, Don L. How Things Move. 2000. (Yellow Umbrella Books). (Illus.). 16p. (J). (gr. 1). lib. bdg. 14.60 (978-0-7368-0724-1(1) , Pebble Bks.) Capstone Pr., Inc.

Dalton, Cindy Devine. Force & Motion. 2001. (How Can I Experiment With? Ser.). (Illus.). 32p. (J). (gr. 1-4). lib. bdg. 28.50 (978-1-58952-012-7(2)) Rourke Publishing, LLC.

DiSpezio, Michael A. Awesome Experiments in Force & Motion. 2006. (Illus.). 160p. pap. 6.95 (978-1-4027-2371-1(7)) Sterling Publishing Co., Inc.

Dixon, Malcolm & Smith, Karen. Forces & Movement. 1998. (Young Scientists Ser.). (Illus.). 32p. (J). (ps-3). lib. bdg. 16.95 (978-1-887068-68-0(6)) Smart Apple Media.

Dorling Kindersley Publishing Staff & Hammond, Richard. Can You Feel the Force? 2006. (Illus.). 96p. (J). (gr. 5-8). 15.99 (978-0-7566-2033-2(3)) Dorling Kindersley Publishing, Inc.

Dreier, David Louis. Forces & Motion. 2007. (J). (***978-1-4034-9923-3(3)***); pap. (***978-1-4034-9931-8(4)***) Heinemann Library.

Endres, Hollie J. Push & Pull. 2003. (Yellow Umbrella Books for Early Readers). (Illus.). 17p. (J). 15.93 (978-0-7368-2921-2(0)); pap. (978-0-7368-2880-2(X)) Yellow Umbrella Pr.

Everyday Forces: Individual Title Six-Packs. (Discovery World Ser.). 24p. (gr. 1-2). 33.00 (978-0-7635-8480-1(0)) Rigby Education.

Farndon, John. Energy. 2002. (Science Experiments Ser.). (J). 25.64 (978-0-7614-1469-8(X) , Benchmark Bks.) Cavendish, Marshall Corp.

Foland, Andrew Dean. Energy. 2007. (Physics in Action Ser.). 128p. (gr. 9). 30.00 (***978-0-7910-8930-9(4)*** , Chelsea Hse.) Facts On File, Inc.

Freeman, Marcia S. The Work Book. 2005. (Everything Science Ser.). (Illus.). 24p. (gr. 1-4). 14.95 (978-1-59515-125-4(7)) Rourke Publishing, LLC.

Frisch, Joy. Motion & Movement. 2002. (Illus.). 32p. (J). lib. bdg. 24.25 (978-1-58340-160-6(1)) Smart Apple Media.

Fullick, Ann. Turning up the Heat: Energy. (Illus.). 56p. (J). 2005. pap. (978-1-4034-6423-1(5)); 2004. lib. bdg. (978-1-4034-4817-0(5)) Heinemann Library.

—Under Pressure: Forces. (Illus.). 56p. (J). 2005. pap. (978-1-4034-6424-8(3)); 2004. (gr. 6-8). lib. bdg. 32.86 (978-1-4034-4818-7(3)) Heinemann Library.

Galko, Francine. Earth Friends at School. 2004. (Heinemann First Library). (Illus.). 32p. (J). pap. 6.95 (978-1-4034-4902-3(3)) Heinemann Library.

Gardner, Robert. Bicycle Science Projects: Physics on Wheels. 2004. (Science Fair Success Ser.). (Illus.). 112p. (J). lib. bdg. 26.60 (978-0-7660-1630-9(7)) Enslow Pubs., Inc.

—Sizzling Science Projects with Heat & Energy. 2006. (Fantastic Physical Science Experiments Ser.). (Illus.). 48p. (J). lib. bdg. 23.93 (978-0-7660-2586-8(1) , Enslow Elementary) Enslow Pubs., Inc.

Glover, David. Forces & Movements. 2001. (Experiments in Science Ser.). (Illus.). (J). (978-0-7894-7463-6(8)) Dorling Kindersley Publishing, Inc.

Gold-Dworkin, Heidi. Learning about the Way Things Move. 2001. (gr. 3-6). lib. bdg. 22.20 (978-0-613-27931-4(X)) Tandem Library Bks.

Goodstein, Madeline. Science Fair Success Using Newton's Laws of Motion. 2002. (Science Fair Success Ser.). (Illus.). 128p. (YA). (gr. 6-12). lib. bdg. 26.60 (978-0-7660-1628-6(5)) Enslow Pubs., Inc.

—Sports Science Projects: The Physics of Balls in Motion. 1999. (Science Fair Success Ser.). (Illus.). 128p. (YA). (gr. 6-12). lib. bdg. 26.60 (978-0-7660-1174-8(7)) Enslow Pubs., Inc.

Graham, John. Forces & Motion: Over 40 Fantastic Experiments. 2001. (Hands-On Science Ser.). (Illus.). (J). 13.75 (978-0-606-21194-9(2)) Tandem Library Bks.

Graham, John & Angliss, Sarah. Forces & Motion: Over 40 Fantastic Experiments. 2001. (Hands-On Science Ser.). (Illus.). 40p. (J). (gr. 3-5). pap. 6.95 (978-0-7534-5348-3(7) , Kingfisher) Houghton Mifflin Co. Trade & Reference Div.

Green, Jen. Saving Energy. 2005. (Improving Our Environment Ser.). (Illus.). 32p. (J). lib. bdg. 24.67 (978-0-8368-4430-6(0)) Stevens, Gareth Inc.

—Why Should I Save Energy? Gordon, Mike, illus. 2005. (Why Should I? Bks.). 32p. (J). pap. 6.99 (978-0-7641-3156-1(7)) Barron's Educational Series, Inc.

Greenberger, Robert. How Do We Know the Nature of Energy. 2005. (Great Scientific Questions & the Scientists Who Answered Them Ser.). (Illus.). 112p. (J). (gr. 7-12). lib. bdg. 26.50 (978-1-4042-0076-0(2)) Rosen Publishing Group, Inc., The.

Grimshaw, Caroline. Energy. 2000. (Invisible Journeys Ser.). (Illus.). 32p. (J). (gr. 3-6). 10.95 (978-1-58728-331-4(X)); pap. 5.95 (978-1-58728-327-7(1)) T&N Children's Publishing. (Two Can Publishing).

Grossman, Marvin C., et al. ARIES Exploring Energy: Waterwheels, Windmills & Sunlight. 2000. (Aries Ser.). (Illus.). (J). tchr. ed., ring bd. 95.00 (978-1-57091-260-3(2)) Charlesbridge Publishing, Inc.

Haber-Schaim, Uri, et al. Force, Motion, & Energy Assessment Package. 2003. pap. (978-1-882057-15-3(5) , SCI-777-3393) Science Curriculum, Inc.

Halls, Kelly Milner. Forces & Motion. 2006. (Science Fair Projects Ser.). (Illus.). 48p. (YA). (gr. 6-9). lib. bdg. 30.00 (978-1-4034-7910-5(0)) Heinemann Library.

Hands on Science: Forces & Motion. 1999. (J). 58.43 (978-0-7398-1710-0(8)) Raintree.

Hewitt, Sally. Amazing Forces & Movement. 2007. 32p. pap. (***978-0-7787-3625-7(3)***) Crabtree Publishing Co.

—Energy. (Illus.). 32p. (YA). (gr. 1 up). lib. bdg. 27.10 (978-1-931983-93-8(3)) Chrysalis Education.

—Forces: Tractors. 2005. (Illus.). 32p. (J). (gr. 1-4). lib. bdg. 27.10 (978-1-59604-008-3(4)) Stargazer Bks.

—Forces & Motion. (Illus.). 32p. (YA). (gr. 2 up). lib. bdg. 27.10 (978-1-932333-32-9(0)) Chrysalis Education.

—Full of Energy. 1998. (It's Science! Ser.). (Illus.). 32p. (J). (gr. k-3). 23.50 (978-0-516-20792-6(X) , Children's Pr.) Scholastic Library Publishing.

—Jump to the Moon: (Energy) 2002. (Why Can't I Ser.). (Illus.). 32p. (J). lib. bdg. 24.95 (978-1-930643-67-3(5)) Chrysalis Education.

Hillman, Ben. How Strong Is It? A Mighty Book About Strength. 2008. 48p. (J). pap. 14.99 (***978-0-439-91866-4(9)*** , Scholastic Reference) Scholastic, Inc.

Hodge, Deborah. Simple Machines. unabr. ed. 2000. (Starting with Science Ser.). (Illus.). 32p. (J). (gr. k-3). (978-1-55074-399-9(6)) Kids Can Pr., Ltd.

Holt, Rinehart and Winston Staff. Holt Science & Technology Chapter 9: Physical Science: Energy & Energy Resources. 5th ed. 2004. (Illus.). pap. 12.86 (978-0-03-030396-8(6)) Holt, Rinehart & Winston.

—Holt Science & Technology Chptr. 9: Energy & Reserves: Chapter Resources - Tennessee Edition. 3rd ed. 2003. (YA). pap. 11.40 (978-0-03-069168-3(0)) Holt, Rinehart & Winston.

—Holt Science & Technology Chptr. 12: Energy & Reserves: Chapter Resources - Tennessee Edition. 3rd ed. 2003. (J). pap. 11.40 (978-0-03-069119-5(2)) Holt, Rinehart & Winston.

—Holt Science & Technology Chptr. 15: Energy & Waves: Chapter Resources - Tennessee Edition. 3rd ed. 2003. (J). pap. 11.40 (978-0-03-069123-2(0)) Holt, Rinehart & Winston.

—Holt Science & Technology Chptr. 17: Forces & Motion: Chapter Resources - Tennessee Edition. 3rd ed. 2003. (YA). pap. 11.40 (978-0-03-069178-2(8)) Holt, Rinehart & Winston.

—Holt Science & Technology M: Forces, Motion & Energy. 3rd ed. 2003. (SPA.). 18.60 (978-0-03-069323-6(3)) Holt, Rinehart & Winston.

—Holt Science & Technology Pt. M: Forces, Motion & Energy - Spanish Annotated Teacher's Edition. 3rd ed. 2002. 46.66 (978-0-03-069379-3(9)) Holt, Rinehart & Winston.

—Holt Science & Technology 2002 Pt. M: Forces & Energy. 2nd ed. 2002. 18.60 (978-0-03-064802-1(5)); 46.66 (978-0-03-064803-8(3)) Holt, Rinehart & Winston.

Hunter, Rebecca. The Facts about Forces & Motion. 2004. (Science the Facts Ser.). (Illus.). 32p. (J). lib. bdg. (978-1-58340-451-5(1)) Smart Apple Media.

Hunter, Rebecca M. Energy. 2000. (Discovering Science Ser.). (Illus.). 32p. (J). (gr. 3-5). lib. bdg. 25.69 (978-0-7398-2971-4(8)) Raintree.

Issues, Evidence & You - Energy Mega Module Complete Materials Package. 2003. (Illus.). (YA). tchr. ed., stu. ed., per. (978-1-887725-62-0(8)) Lab-Aids, Inc.

Juettner, Bonnie. Motion. 2004. (KidHaven Science Library). (Illus.). 48p. (J). (gr. 4-7). 26.20 (978-0-7377-1536-1(7) , Greenhaven Pr., Inc.) Thomson Gale.

Kids Publishing Science Staff. Transforming Energy: All about Heat, Work & Energy. 1999. (J). pap. 6.95 (978-1-891418-17-4(3)) Science Kids.

Lafferty, Peter. Force & Motion. 1999. (Eyewitness Bks.). (Illus.). 64p. (J). (gr. 3-7). 15.99 (978-0-7894-4882-8(3)) Dorling Kindersley Publishing, Inc.

Lancaster, Juliana. PBIS- Building Big Things. 2005. pap., stu. ed. 8.00 (978-1-58591-565-1(3)) It's About Time, Herff Jones Education Diiv.

Lilly, Melinda. Energy. 2005. (Rourke Discovery Library). (Illus.). 24p. (J). (978-1-59515-401-9(9) , 1244272) Rourke Publishing, LLC.

Llewellyn, Claire. And Everyone Shouted, "Pull!" A First Look at Forces & Motion. Abel, Simone, illus. 2004. (First Look Science Ser.). 32p. (C). (gr. k-3). 22.60 (978-1-4048-0656-6(3)) Picture Window Bks.

Madgwick, Wendy. On the Move. 1999. (Science Starters Ser.). (Illus.). 32p. (J). (gr. k-4). 25.70 (978-0-8172-5333-2(5)) Raintree.

—On the Move. 1999. (Science Starters Ser.). (Illus.). 32 p. (gr. k-4). 7.95 (978-0-8172-5884-9(1)) Steck-Vaughn.

Manolis, Kay. Energy. 2007. (Illus.). 24p. (J). lib. bdg. 19.95 (978-1-60014-096-9(3)) Bellwether Media.

Margulies, Phillip. The Department of Energy. 2005. (This Is Your Government Ser.). (Illus.). 64p. (J). (gr. k-3). pap. 13.25 (978-1-4042-0661-8(2)) Rosen Publishing Group, Inc., The.

Mason, Adrienne. Move It! Motion, Forces & You. Davila, Claudia, illus. 2005. (Primary Physical Science Ser.). 32p. (J). (ps-ps). (978-1-55337-758-0(3)) Kids Can Pr., Ltd.

—Move It! Movement, Forces & You. Davila, Claudia, illus. 2005. (Primary Physical Science Ser.). 32p. (J). (gr. k-2). (978-1-55337-759-7(1)) Kids Can Pr., Ltd.

Mason, Paul. The Extreme Zone: Forces & Motion. 2005. (Illus.). 32p. (J). (978-1-4109-1950-2(1)); lib. bdg. (978-1-4109-1919-9(6)) Steck-Vaughn.

—Roller Coaster! 2006. (Illus.). 32p. (J). pap. (978-1-4109-2616-6(8)); lib. bdg. (978-1-4109-2587-9(0)) Steck-Vaughn.

—Wackiest Machines Ever: Forms of Energy. 2005. (Illus.). 32p. (J). (978-1-4109-1946-5(3)) Steck-Vaughn.

—Wackiest Machines Ever! Forms of Energy. 2005. (Illus.). 32p. (J). (gr. 3-5). lib. bdg. 28.21 (978-1-4109-1915-1(3)) Steck-Vaughn.

McGraw-Hill Staff. Glencoe Science: Motion, Forces, & Energy. 2001. stu. ed. 20.64 (978-0-07-825607-3(0) , 9780078256073) Glencoe/McGraw-Hill.

—Glencoe Science: Motion, Forces, & Energy, Spanish Student Edition. 2001. (SPA.). (C). 20.64 (978-0-07-825907-4(X) , 9780078259074) Glencoe/McGraw-Hill.

Mondello, Cindy, ed. Investigating Science - Energy, Magnetism, & Machines. 2000. 48p. 9.95 (978-1-56234-446-7(3) , Mailbox Bks., The) Education Ctr., Inc.

Morgan, Sally. Energy. 2007. (***978-1-4034-9924-0(1)***); pap. (***978-1-4034-9932-5(2)***) Heinemann Library.

Morgan, Sally. Future Energy. 2005. (Your Environment Ser.). (Illus.). 32p. (J). (gr. 3-7). lib. bdg. 27.10 (978-1-59604-061-8(0)) Stargazer Bks.

Morris, Neil. Biomass Power. 2006. (Illus.). 32p. (J). (978-1-58340-816-2(9)) Smart Apple Media.

Motion & Force: Integrated Physics & Chemistry / Algebra I Instructional Unit. 2003. (Region IV ESC Resources for Mathematics & Science Ser.). stu. ed., per. (978-1-932524-69-7(X)) Region IV Education Service Ctr.

Murphy, Brian. Movement. 2004. (Experiment with Ser.). (SPA., Illus.). 32p. (J). (gr. 2-5). 9.95 (978-1-58728-248-5(8)); pap. 5.95 (978-1-58728-116-7(3)) T&N Children's Publishing. (Two Can Publishing).

Murphy, Patricia. Push & Pull. 2002. (gr. k-3). lib. bdg. 12.95 (978-0-613-54310-1(6)) Tandem Library Bks.

Murphy, Patricia J. Push & Pull. 2002. (Rookie Read-About Science Ser.). (Illus.). 32p. (J). (gr. 1-2). 20.50 (978-0-516-22551-7(0) , Children's Pr.) Scholastic Library Publishing.

Murray, Julie & Abdo Publishing Staff. Hot & Cold. 2007. (Illus.). 24p. (J). 21.35 (978-1-59679-825-0(4)) ABDO Publishing Co.

Muschal, Frank. Biofuels. 2008. (J). pap. 7.95 ***978-1-60279-094-0(9))** Cherry Lake Publishing.

Nankivell-Aston, Sally. Science Experiments with Forces. 2000. (J). (978-0-606-19791-5(5)) Tandem Library Bks.

Nardo, Don. Kinetic Energy: The Energy of Motion. Schultz, Ashlee & Hossain, Farhana, illus. 2007. (J). lib. bdg. (***978-0-7565-3378-6(3))** Compass Point Bks.

Nelson, Robin. Como Se Mueven las Cosas (Ways Things Move) 2007. (Mi Primer Paso al Mundo Real - Fuerzas y Movimiento (First Step Nonfiction - Forces & Motion) Ser.). (SPA.). 24p. (J). (gr. k-2). lib. bdg. 18.60 (***978-0-8225-7811-6(5)** , Ediciones Lerner) Lerner Publishing Group.

—Empujar y Jalar (Push & Pull) 2007. (Mi Primer Paso al Mundo Real - Fuerzas y Movimiento (First Step Nonfiction - Forces & Motion) Ser.). (SPA.). 24p. (J). (gr. k-2). lib. bdg. 18.60 (***978-0-8225-7810-9(7)** , Ediciones Lerner) Lerner Publishing Group.

—Push & Pull. 2004. (First Step Nonfiction Ser.). (Illus.). 24p. (J). (gr. k-2). lib. bdg. 18.60 (978-0-8225-5134-8(9)) Lerner Publishing Group.

—Ways Things Move. (Forces & Motion Ser.). (Illus.). (J). 2005. 22p. pap. (978-0-8225-5300-7(7)); 2004. 24p. lib. bdg. 18.60 (978-0-8225-5136-2(5)) Lerner Publishing Group.

O'Daley, Anne. Motion. 2003. (Illus.). 24p. (J). 22.45 (978-1-4103-0082-9(X) , Blackbirch Pr., Inc.) Thomson Gale.

Oxlade, Chris. Endless Energy. 2004. (Energy Forever? Ser.). (Illus.). (J). 28.56 (978-1-4109-0493-5(8)); pap. 7.95 (978-1-4109-0499-7(7)) Raintree.

—Energy. 2003. (Science Topics Ser.). (Illus.). 32p. (YA). (gr. 6-8). lib. bdg. 24.22 (978-1-57572-766-0(8)) Heinemann Library.

—Energy Essentials, 4 vols., Set 1. 2004. pap. 30.60 (978-1-4109-0504-8(7)) Harcourt Schl. Pubs.

—Energy Transformation 6-Pack. 2004. (Energy Forever? Ser.). lib. bdg. 42.90 (978-1-4109-0806-3(2)) Raintree.

—Friction & Resistance. 2006. (Fantastic Forces Ser.). (Illus.). 32p. (J). pap. (978-1-4034-8176-4(8)); lib. bdg. (978-1-4034-8171-9(7)) Heinemann Library.

—Gravity. 2006. (Fantastic Forces Ser.). (Illus.). 32p. (J). pap. (978-1-4034-8177-1(6)); lib. bdg. (978-1-4034-8172-6(5)) Heinemann Library.

Parker, Steve. Forces & Movement. 2004. (Science View Ser.). (Illus.). 32p. (gr. 4-8). 28.00 (978-0-7910-8211-9(3) , Chelsea Hse.) Facts On File, Inc.

—The Science of Forces: Projects with Experiments on Forces & Machines. 2005. (Illus.). 32p. (J). pap. 11.09 (978-1-4034-7292-2(0)); lib. bdg. (978-1-4034-7285-4(8)) Heinemann Library.

Peters, Celeste, ed. The Energy Dilemma. 2002. (Understanding Global Issues). (Illus.). 56p. (YA). (gr. 10-12). 19.95 (978-1-58340-169-9(5)) Weigl Pubs., Inc.

Peterson, Virginia, et al, eds. The Environment: Protecting Our Home. 3rd rev. ed. 1998. (Information Plus Compact Ser.). (Illus.). 88p. (YA). (gr. 6-9). pap. 22.00 (978-1-57302-080-0(X)) Thomson Gale.

Phelan, Glen. Forces & Motion in Sports. 2005. (Navigators Ser.). (J). pap. 44.00 (***978-1-4108-5088-1(9))** Benchmark Education Co.

—Forces & Motion on Earth. 2005. (Navigators Ser.). (J). pap. 44.00 (***978-1-4108-5087-4(0))** Benchmark Education Co.

—Introduction to Energy. 2004. (Illus.). 32p. (J). pap. (978-0-7922-4580-3(6)) National Geographic Society.

—Newton's Laws. 2004. (National Geographic Reading Expeditions Ser.). (Illus.). 32p. (J). pap. (978-0-7922-4584-1(9)) National Geographic Society.

Pinna, Simon de. Transfer of Energy. 2006. pap. (***978-0-8368-8100-4(1));** lib. bdg. (***978-0-8368-8091-5(9))** Stevens, Gareth Inc.

Riley, Peter D. Energy. 1998. (Cycles in Science Ser.). (Illus.). 32p. (J). (gr. 4-7). lib. bdg. 21.36 (978-1-57572-617-5(3)) Heinemann Library.

—Forces & Friction. 2007. (J). (***978-1-59920-026-2(0))** Smart Apple Media.

—Forces & Motion. 1999. (Science Topics Ser.). 32p. (YA). (gr. 6-8). lib. bdg. 24.22 (978-1-57572-772-1(2)) Heinemann Library.

—Forces & Movement. 2005. (Illus.). 32p. (J). (gr. 4-7). lib. bdg. 27.10 (978-1-58340-712-7(X)) Smart Apple Media.

—Pushing & Pulling. Moller, Ray, photos by. 2002. (Everyday Science Ser.). (Illus.). 32p. (J). (gr. 1 up). lib. bdg. 23.33 (978-0-8368-3252-5(3)) Stevens, Gareth Inc.

Riley, Peter D. & Snedden, Robert. Forces & Motion. 1999. (Smart Science Ser.). (Illus.). 32p. (J). (gr. 3-5). lib. bdg. 22.79 (978-1-57572-869-8(9)) Heinemann Library.

Royston, Angela. Forces & Motion. (My World of Science Ser.). (Illus.). 32p. (J). (gr. k-2). 2002. pap. 6.95 (978-1-4034-0039-0(3) , 91483); 2001. lib. bdg. 21.36 (978-1-58810-240-9(8)) Heinemann Library.

—Fuerzas y Movimiento. 2006. (ENG & SPA., Illus.). 32p. (J). pap. (978-1-4034-9115-2(1)); lib. bdg. 25.36 (978-1-4034-9108-4(9)) Heinemann Library.

Royston, Angela. Looking at Forces & Motion: How Do Things Move? 2008. (Looking at Science: How Things Change Ser.). 32p. (J). (gr. 1-3). lib. bdg. 22.60 (***978-0-7660-3089-3(X))** Enslow Pubs., Inc.

Sadler, Wendy. Forces: The Ups & Downs! 2005. (Raintree Perspectives Ser.). (Illus.). 32p. (J). pap. (978-1-4109-1558-0(1)); lib. bdg. (978-1-4109-1550-4(6)) Steck-Vaughn.

Saunders, N. & Chapman, Steven. Renewable Energy. 2005. (J). (978-1-4109-1696-9(0)) Steck-Vaughn.

Saunders, Nigel & Chapman, Steven. Renewable Energy. 2005. 48p. (J). (978-1-4109-1701-0(0)) Steck-Vaughn.

School Specialty Publishing. Energy. 2004. (On-File Ser.). 4p. (J). (gr. 5-7). ring bd. 4.99 (978-0-7424-2920-8(2) , Instructional Fair) Schaffer, Frank Pubns.

—Force & Motion. 2005. (Science Search Lab Ser.). (J). (gr. 3-5). pap. 24.95 (978-0-7682-2833-5(6) , Ideal School Supply) Schaffer, Frank Pubns.

Searle, Bobbi. Heat & Energy. 2001. (978-0-606-22380-5(0)) Tandem Library Bks.

Simon, Seymour. Let's Try It Out with Seesaws & Swings. 2001. (J). lib. bdg. 15.00 (978-0-689-82921-5(3) , Simon & Schuster Children's Publishing) Simon & Schuster Children's Publishing.

Smith, A. Energy, Forces & Motion. 2004. (Internet-Linked Library of Science). 64p. (J). pap. 9.95 (978-0-7945-0084-9(6) , Usborne); lib. bdg. 17.95 (978-1-58086-374-2(4)) EDC Publishing.

Snedden, Robert. Energy Alternatives. 2001. (Essential Energy Ser.). (Illus.). 48p. (J). (gr. 5-7). lib. bdg. 24.22 (978-1-57572-441-6(3)) Heinemann Library.

—Energy Transfer. (Illus.). 48p. (J). 2006. (978-1-4034-8733-9(2)); 2001. (gr. 5-7). lib. bdg. 24.22 (978-1-57572-443-0(X)); 2nd ed. 2006. pap. (978-1-4034-8738-4(3)) Heinemann Library.

—Essential Energy: Power up Their Knowledge!, 4 bks., Set. 2001. (Illus.). 48p. (J). (gr. 5-7). lib. bdg. 96.88 (978-1-57572-445-4(6)) Heinemann Library.

Sohn, Emily. A Crash Course in Forces & Motion with Max Axiom, Super Scientist. Erwin, Steve & Barnett, Charles, illus. 2007. (Graphic Library). 32p. (J). (***978-0-7368-6837-2(2)** , 1264931) Capstone Pr., Inc.

Solway, Andrew. Forces & Motion. 2007. (J). lib. bdg. (***978-1-4042-3747-6(X)** , Rosen Central) Rosen Publishing Group, Inc., The.

Spilsbury, Richard. Speed & Acceleration. 2006. (Fantastic Forces Ser.). (Illus.). 32p. (J). pap. (978-1-4034-8178-8(4)); lib. bdg. (978-1-4034-8173-3(3)) Heinemann Library.

Spilsbury, Richard & Spilsbury, Louise. What Are Forces & Motion? Exploring Science with Hands-On Activities. 2008. (In Touch with Basic Science Ser.). 32p. (J). (gr. 3-4). lib. bdg. 22.60 (***978-0-7660-3095-4(4))** Enslow Pubs., Inc.

—What Is Energy? Exploring Science with Hands-On Activities. 2008. (In Touch with Basic Science Ser.). 32p. (J). (gr. 3-4). lib. bdg. 22.60 (***978-0-7660-3099-2(7))** Enslow Pubs., Inc.

Stewart, Melissa. Energy in Motion. 2006. (Rookie Read-About Science Ser.). (Illus.). 32p. (J). (gr. 1-2). 20.50 (978-0-516-24956-8(8) , Children's Pr.) Scholastic Library Publishing.

Stille, Darlene R. Energy: Heat, Light, & Food. Boyd, Sheree, illus. 2004. (Amazing Science Ser.). 24p. (C). (gr. k-4). 22.60 (978-1-4048-0249-0(5)) Picture Window Bks.

—Motion: Push & Pull, Fast & Slow. Boyd, Sheree, tr. Boyd, Sheree, illus. 2004. (Amazing Science Ser.). 24p. (J). (gr. k-4). 22.60 (978-1-4048-0250-6(9)) Picture Window Bks.

Stringer, John. The Science of a Spring. 1999. (Science World Ser.). (Illus.). 32p. (J). (gr. 2-4). lib. bdg. 25.69 (978-0-7398-1322-5(6)) Raintree.

Sussman, Art. Dr. Art's Guide to Science: Connecting Atoms, Galaxies & Everything in Between. 2006. (Illus.). 256p. 22.95 (978-0-7879-8326-0(8) , Jossey-Bass) Wiley, John & Sons, Inc.

Thomas, Isabel. Search & Rescue. 2007. (J). pap. (***978-1-4109-2867-2(5));** lib. bdg. (***978-1-4109-2850-4(0))** Steck-Vaughn.

Tocci, Salvatore. Experiments with Motion. 2003. (True Book Ser.). (Illus.). 48p. (J). 25.00 (978-0-516-22603-3(7) , Children's Pr.) Scholastic Library Publishing.

Two-Can Publishing Ltd. Staff. Experiment with Movement. 2001. (gr. 3-6). lib. bdg. 14.10 (978-0-613-84873-2(X)) Tandem Library Bks.

VanCleave, Janice Pratt. Energy for Every Kid: Easy Activities That Make Learning Science Fun. 2005. (Science for Every Kid Ser.). (Illus.). 240p. (gr. 3-7). pap. 12.95 (978-0-471-33099-8(X) , Wiley) Wiley, John & Sons, Inc.

Viegas, Jennifer. Kinetic & Potential Energy: Understanding Changes Within Physical Systems. 2004. (Library of Physics). (Illus.). 48p. (J). (gr. 7 up). lib. bdg. 25.25 (978-1-4042-0333-4(8)) Rosen Publishing Group, Inc., The.

Wadsworth, Pamela. Defnyddio Egni. 2005. (WEL., Illus.). 24p. pap. (978-1-85596-243-9(8)) Dref Wen.

—Golwg Gyntaf Ar Egni. 2005. (WEL., Illus.). 24p. pap. (978-1-85596-257-6(8)) Dref Wen.

—Grymoedd a Symud. 2005. (WEL., Illus.). 24p. pap. (978-1-85596-227-9(6)) Dref Wen.

—Rhagor Am Ddefnyddio Egni. 2005. (WEL., Illus.). 24p. pap. (978-1-85596-244-6(6)) Dref Wen.

—Rhagor Am Rymoedd a Symud. 2005. (WEL., Illus.). 24p. pap. (978-1-85596-228-6(4)) Dref Wen.

Walker, Niki. Biomass: Fuelling Change. 2006. (Energy Revolution Ser.). (Illus.). 32p. (J). (gr. 3-9). lib. bdg. (978-0-7787-2914-3(1) , 1259460) Crabtree Publishing Co.

Waters, Jennifer. Move It! McEwen, Rebecca & Auch, Alison, eds. 2002. (Spyglass Books). (Illus.). 24p. (J). (gr. 1 up). lib. bdg. 18.60 (978-0-7565-0238-6(1)) Compass Point Bks.

Welch, Catherine A. Forces & Motion: A Question & Answer Book. 2006. (Fact Finders Ser.). (Illus.). 32p. (978-0-7368-5445-0(2)) Capstone Pr., Inc.

Wheeler, Jill C. The Forces with Us: A Book about Energy. 1998. (Kid Physics Ser.). (J). lib. bdg. 13.98 (978-1-56239-628-2(5)) ABDO Publishing Co.

Whitehouse, Patricia. Matter & Energy. 2007. (J). (***978-1-4034-7917-4(8))** Heinemann Library.

—Pulling. 2003. (Illus.). 24p. (J). pap. (978-1-4034-3468-5(9)); lib. bdg. 18.50 (978-1-4034-0909-6(9)) Heinemann Library.

—Pushes & Pulls. 2007. (J). 6.00 (978-1-60044-193-6(9)) Rourke Publishing, LLC.

—Pushing. 2003. (Illus.). 24p. (J). pap. (978-1-4034-3469-2(7)); lib. bdg. 18.50 (978-1-4034-0908-9(0)) Heinemann Library.

Whyman, Kathryn. Energy & Heat. 2004. (J). lib. bdg. (978-1-932799-22-4(2)) Stargazer Bks.

—Forces in Action. 2004. (J). lib. bdg. (978-1-932799-20-0(6)) Stargazer Bks.

Wilson, A. Science Museum Book: Energy. (Illus.). 119p. pap. (978-0-340-71477-5(8) , Hodder & Stoughton) Hodder General Publishing Division.

Woodford, Chris. Energy. 2007. (See for Yourself Ser.). (Illus.). 64p. (YA). (gr. 5 up). 14.99 (978-0-7566-2561-0(0)) Dorling Kindersley Publishing, Inc.

Young, June. Energy Is Everywhere. 2006. 32p. (gr. 1-2). (YA). pap. 4.95 (978-0-516-28003-5(1)); (Illus.). (J). 20.50 (978-0-516-25902-4(4)) Scholastic Library Publishing. (Children's Pr.).

FORD, GERALD R., 1913-2006

Joseph, Paul. Gerald Ford. 2000. (United States Presidents Ser.). (Illus.). 32p. (J). (gr. k-6). lib. bdg. 22.78 (978-1-57765-245-8(2) , Checkerboard Library) ABDO Publishing Co.

Margaret, Amy. Gerald R. Ford Library & Museum. 2004. (Presidential Libraries Ser.). (Illus.). 24p. (J). lib. bdg. 18.75 (978-0-8239-6270-9(9) , PowerKids Pr.) Rosen Publishing Group, Inc., The.

O'Shei, Tim. Gerald R. Ford: A MyReportLinks.com Book. 2003. (Presidents Ser.). (Illus.). 48p. (J). (gr. 5-10). lib. bdg. 25.26 (978-0-7660-5050-1(5) , MyReportLinks.com Bks.) Enslow Pubs., Inc.

Plaut, Michael F. How to Draw the Life & Times of Gerald R. Ford. 2007. (Kid's Guide to Drawing the Presidents of the United States of America Ser.). (Illus.). 32p. (J). 25.25 (978-1-4042-3014-9(9) , PowerKids Pr.) Rosen Publishing Group, Inc., The.

Santella, Andrew. Gerald R. Ford. 2003. (Profiles of the Presidents Ser.). (Illus.). 64p. (J). (gr. 4 up). lib. bdg. 23.93 (978-0-7565-0282-9(9)) Compass Point Bks.

Stein, R. Conrad. Gerald R. Ford. 2005. (Encyc of Presidents, 2ND Ser.). (Illus.). 112p. (J). (gr. 6-8). 34.00 (978-0-516-22973-7(7) , Watts, Franklin) Scholastic Library Publishing.

Venezia, Mike. Gerald R. Ford. 2008. (Getting to Know the U. S. Presidents Ser.). 32p. (J). pap. 7.95 (***978-0-516-25597-2(5)** , Children's Pr.) Scholastic Library Publishing.

Venezia, Mike, illus. Gerald R. Ford. 2007. 32p. (J). 28.00 (***978-0-516-22642-2(8)** , Children's Pr.) Scholastic Library Publishing.

Winget, Mary. Gerald R. Ford. 2007. (Presidential Leaders Ser.). 112p. (J). (gr. 6-12). 29.27 (978-0-8225-1509-8(1) , Twenty-First Century Bks.) Lerner Publishing Group.

FORD, HENRY, 1863-1947

Arrathoon, Leigh A. Men Who Changed the World Vol. I: The Henry Ford Story. Davio, John, ed. Hajdyla, Ken, illus. 56p. (J). (gr. 5-6). pap. 5.95 (978-0-9648564-5-5(X)) Paint Creek Pr., Ltd.

Brown, Jonatha A. Henry Ford. 19.33 (978-0-8368-4582-2(X)); 2005. (Illus.). 24p. (J). pap. (978-0-8368-4473-3(4)); 2005. (Illus.). 24p. (YA). lib. bdg. 19.33 (978-0-8368-4466-5(1) , Weekly Reader Early Learning Library) Stevens, Gareth Inc.

Burgan, Michael. Henry Ford. 2002. (Trailblazers of the Modern World Ser.). (Illus.). 48p. (J). (gr. 5 up). pap. 14.95 (978-0-8368-5230-1(3)); lib. bdg. 30.00 (978-0-8368-5070-3(X)) Stevens, Gareth Inc. (World Almanac Library).

—Henry Ford. 2002. (gr. 3-6). lib. bdg. 16.40 (978-0-613-76803-0(5)) Tandem Library Bks.

—Henry Ford: Industrialist. 2001. (Career Biographies Ser.). (Illus.). 128p. (J). (gr. 6-12). 25.00 (978-0-89434-369-8(6) , F412, Ferguson Publishing Co.) Facts On File, Inc.

Ford, Carin T. Henry Ford: The Car Man. 2003. (Famous Inventors Ser.). (Illus.). 32p. (J). (gr. 1-4). lib. bdg. 22.60 (978-0-7660-2179-2(3)) Enslow Pubs., Inc.

Gaines, Ann Graham. Henry Ford. Sarfatti, Esther & de la Vega, Eida, trs. 2002. (Inventores Famosos Ser.). (SPA., Illus.). 24p. mass mkt. 5.95 (978-1-58952-235-0(4) , RK31452); (J). (gr. 1-4). lib. bdg. 19.27 (978-1-58952-175-9(7) , RK5956) Rourke Publishing, LLC.

—Henry Ford. 2001. (Illus.). 24p. (J). (gr. 1-4). lib. bdg. 20.64 (978-1-58952-120-9(X)) Rourke Publishing, LLC.

—Henry Ford. 2002. (SPA.). (gr. k-3). lib. bdg. 14.10 (978-0-613-79410-7(9)) Tandem Library Bks.

Henry Ford. (Photo Illustrated Biographies Ser.). 24p. (J). 6.95 (978-0-7368-3439-1(7)) Capstone Pr., Inc.

Henry Ford, 6 vols. (gr. k-2). 28.95 (978-0-7368-8754-0(7)) Red Brick Learning.

Henry Ford. 2006. (People We Should Know Ser.). (SPA.). (J). (gr. 3-4). 4.76 (978-0-8368-4589-1(7) , GHS33821) Stevens, Gareth Inc.

Kent, Zachary. The Story of Henry Ford & the Automobile: Cornerstones of Freedom. 2004. (Illus.). 31p. (J). (gr. k-4). reprint ed. 17.00 (978-0-7567-7648-0(1)) DIANE Publishing Co.

Kulling, Monica. Eat My Dust! Henry Ford's First Race. Walz, Richard, illus. 2004. (Step into Reading Ser.). 48p. (gr. 1-3). (J). pap. 3.99 (978-0-375-81510-2(4)); (YA). lib. bdg. 11.99 (978-0-375-91510-9(9)) Random Hse. Children's Bks. (Random Hse. Bks. for Young Readers).

Malam, John. Henry Ford. 2001. (Profiles Ser.). (Illus.). 56p. (J). (gr. 4-6). lib. bdg. 24.22 (978-1-58810-058-0(8)) Heinemann Library.

Mara, Wil. Henry Ford. (Rookie Biographies Ser.). (Illus.). (J). 2004. 31p. (gr. 1-2). pap. 4.95 (978-0-516-27917-6(3)); 2003. 32p. 20.50 (978-0-516-25863-8(X)) Scholastic Library Publishing. (Children's Pr.).

McCarthy, Pat. Henry Ford: Building Cars for Everyone. 2002. (Historical American Biographies Ser.). (Illus.). 128p. (YA). (gr. 6-12). lib. bdg. 26.60 (978-0-7660-1620-0(X)) Enslow Pubs., Inc.

O'Hearn, Michael. Henry Ford & the Model T. 2007. (Graphic Library). (Illus.). 32p. (J). (978-0-7368-6480-0(6)) Capstone Publishing.

Parker, Lewis K. Henry Ford & the Automobile Industry. 2003. (Reading Power Ser.). (Illus.). 24p. (J). lib. bdg. 17.25 (978-0-8239-6451-2(5) , PowerKids Pr.) Rosen Publishing Group, Inc., The.

—Henry Ford & the Automobile Industry: Individual Title Six-Packs. (On Deck Ser.: Vol. 2). 24p. (gr. 4-5). 35.00 (978-0-7578-5849-9(X)) Rigby Education.

Rausch, Monica. Henry Ford & the Model T Car. 2006. (Illus.). 24p. (J). pap. (***978-0-8368-7731-1(4));** lib. bdg. (***978-0-8368-7500-3(1))** Stevens, Gareth Inc. (Weekly Reader Early Learning Library).

—Henry Ford y el Modelo T. 2006. (ENG & SPA.). (J). pap. (***978-0-8368-8000-7(5));** lib. bdg. (***978-0-8368-7995-7(3))** Stevens, Gareth Inc. (Weekly Reader Early Learning Library).

Schaefer, Lola M. Henry Ford. 2005. (Transportation Ser.). 24p. (YA). (gr. k-3). pap. (978-0-7368-8730-4(X) , Pebble Bks.) Capstone Pr., Inc.

Shores, Erika L. Henry Ford: A Photo-Illustrated Biography. 2003. (Photo-Illustrated Biographies Ser.). (Illus.). 24p. (J). lib. bdg. 19.93 (978-0-7368-2223-7(2) , Bridgestone Bks.) Capstone Pr., Inc.

Shuter, Jane. Henry Ford. 2000. (Lives & Times Ser.). (Illus.). 24p. (J). lib. bdg. 19.92 (978-1-57572-229-0(1)) Heinemann Library.

Slade, Suzanne. My Adventure with Henry Ford. 2007. 44p. (J). 8.99 (978-1-59092-455-6(X) , Orchard Academy Pr.) Windstorm Creative.

Temple, Bob. Henry Ford: Automobile Manufacturer & Innovator. 2003. (Spirit of America: Our People Ser.). (Illus.). 32p. (J). (gr. 2-6). 27.07 (978-1-56766-447-8(4)) Child's World, Inc., The.

Wyborny, Sheila. Henry Ford. 2002. (Inventors & Creators Ser.). (Illus.). 48p. (J). (gr. 3-5). 23.70 (978-0-7377-1286-5(4) , LML00902-181325, Kidhaven) Thomson Gale.

Young, Jeff C. Henry Ford: Genius Behind the Affordable Car. 2007. (Inventors Who Changed the World Ser.). (Illus.). 128p. (J). (gr. 5). lib. bdg. 33.27 (***978-1-59845-053-8(0)** , MyReportLinks.com Bks.) Enslow Pubs., Inc.

Zuehlke, Jeffrey. Henry Ford. 2007. (History Maker Bios Ser.). (J). 26.60 (978-0-8225-6583-3(8) , Lerner Pubns.) Lerner Publishing Group.

FORD AUTOMOBILE

Bullard, Lisa. Ford Mustang. 2008. (J). (***978-1-4296-0100-9(0))** Capstone Publishing.

Kent, Zachary. The Story of Henry Ford & the Automobile: Cornerstones of Freedom. 2004. (Illus.). 31p. (J). (gr. k-4). reprint ed. 17.00 (978-0-7567-7648-0(1)) DIANE Publishing Co.

Maurer, Tracy. Ford GT. 2008. (J). (***978-1-60044-571-2(3))** Rourke Publishing, LLC.

—Ford Thunderbird. 2008. (J). (***978-1-60044-572-9(1))** Rourke Publishing, LLC.

Rausch, Monica. Henry Ford & the Model T Car. 2006. (Illus.). 24p. (J). pap. (***978-0-8368-7731-1(4));** lib. bdg. (***978-0-8368-7500-3(1))** Stevens, Gareth Inc. (Weekly Reader Early Learning Library).

—Henry Ford y el Modelo T. 2006. (ENG & SPA.). (J). pap. (***978-0-8368-8000-7(5));** lib. bdg. (***978-0-8368-7995-7(3))** Stevens, Gareth Inc. (Weekly Reader Early Learning Library).

FORD MOTOR COMPANY

Kent, Zachary. The Story of Henry Ford & the Automobile: Cornerstones of Freedom. 2004. (Illus.). 31p. (J). (gr. k-4). reprint ed. 17.00 (978-0-7567-7648-0(1)) DIANE Publishing Co.

Musolf, Nell. The Story of Ford. 2008. (J). (***978-1-58341-604-4(8)** , Creative Education) Creative Co., The.

O'Hearn, Michael. Henry Ford & the Model T. 2007. (Graphic Library). (Illus.). 32p. (J). (978-0-7368-6480-0(6)) Capstone Publishing.

Parker, Lewis K. Henry Ford & the Automobile Industry. 2003. (Reading Power Ser.). (Illus.). 24p. (J). lib. bdg. 17.25 (978-0-8239-6451-2(5) , PowerKids Pr.) Rosen Publishing Group, Inc., The.

FORECASTING, WEATHER

see Weather Forecasting

FOREIGN AID PROGRAM

see Economic Assistance

FOREIGN ECONOMIC RELATIONS

see International Economic Relations

FOREIGN MISSIONS

see Missions

FOREIGN POPULATION

see Emigration and Immigration

FOREIGN RELATIONS

see International Relations
see names of countries with subdivision Foreign Relations

FOREIGNERS

see Citizenship

FOREST ANIMALS

Art, Henry W. & Robbins, Michael W. Woodswalk: Peepers, Pikas, & Exploding Puff Balls! 2003. (Illus.). 128p. (J). (gr. 3-7). tchr. ed. 21.95 (978-1-58017-477-0(9) , 67477, Storey Kids) Storey Publishing, LLC.

—WoodsWalk: Peepers, Porcupines, & Exploding Puff Balls! 2003. (Illus.). 128p. (J). (gr. 3-7). pap. 14.95 (978-1-58017-452-7(3) , 67452, Storey Kids) Storey Publishing, LLC.

Bateman, Helen & Denshire, Jayne. Of the Forests & Woodlands. 2005. (Illus.). 32p. (J). (gr. 4-7). lib. bdg. 27.10 (978-1-58340-766-0(9)) Smart Apple Media.

—Of the Tropical Rainforests. 2005. (Illus.). 32p. (J). (gr. 4-7). lib. bdg. 27.10 (978-1-58340-769-1(3)) Smart Apple Media.

Behrens, Janice. Let's Find Rain Forest Animals: Up, down, Around. 2007. (Let's Find Out Early Learning Bks.). (Illus.). 24p. (J). (ps-k). 18.00 (***978-0-531-14874-7(2)*** , Children's Pr.) Scholastic Library Publishing.

Berkes, Marianne. Over in the Jungle: A Rainforest Rhyme. Canyon, Jeanette, illus. 2007. 32p. (J). (ps-2). 16.95 (***978-1-58469-091-7(7)***); pap. 8.95 (***978-1-58469-092-4(5)***) Dawn Pubns.

Bishop, Nic. A Life-Sized Field Guide. 2004. (Forest Explorer Ser.). (Illus.). 48p. (J). (gr. k up). pap. 17.95 (978-0-439-17480-0(5)) Scholastic, Inc.

Butterfield, Moira. Animals in Trees. 1999. (Looking at-...Ser.). (Illus.). 32p. (J). (gr. 1-4). lib. bdg. 24.26 (978-0-7398-0110-9(4)) Raintree.

—Animals in Trees. 1999. (Looking at...Ser.). (Illus.). 32p. (J). (gr. k-3). pap. 5.95 (978-0-7398-0716-3(1)) Steck-Vaughn.

Butz, Christopher. Forest Animals. 2002. (Animals of the Biomes Ser.). (Illus.). 48p. (J). lib. bdg. 25.70 (978-0-7398-5687-1(1)) Raintree.

—Forest Animals. 2002. (Animals of the Biomes Ser.). (Illus.). 48p. (J). pap. 7.20 (978-0-7398-6407-4(6)) Steck-Vaughn.

Carole Telford and Rod Theodorou. Up a Rainforest Tree. 2nd ed. 2006. (Illus.). 32p. (J). pap. (***978-1-4034-8800-8(2)***) Heinemann Library.

Creative Publishing international Editors. Forest Animals. 2004. (Our Wild World Ser.). (Illus.). 192p. (J). (gr. 2-5). ring bd. 16.95 (978-1-55971-708-3(4) , NorthWord Bks. for Young Readers) T&N Children's Publishing.

de Lambilly-Bresson, Elisabeth. Animals in the Forest. 2007. (Animal Show & Tell Ser.). 16p. (J). (ps-2). lib. bdg. 17.27 (***978-0-8368-8205-6(9)***) Stevens, Gareth Inc.

Dixon, Dougal. Triceratops & Other Forest Dinosaurs. Field, James & Weston, Steve, illus. 2004. (Dinosaur Find Ser.). 24p. (J). (gr. k-3). 22.60 (978-1-4048-0671-9(7)) Picture Window Bks.

Doering, Amanda. Rain Forest ABC: An Alphabet Book. 2004. (A+ Alphabet Books). (Illus.). 32p. (J). 22.60 (978-0-7368-2611-2(4) , Aplus Bks.) Capstone Pr., Inc.

Dover. Animals of the Forest, Wetlands & Desert. 2006. 144p. (J). pap. 8.95 (***978-0-486-45939-4(X)***) Dover Pubns., Inc.

Feely, Jenny. The Forest. 2004. (Illus.). 12p. (J). pap. (978-0-7608-7866-8(8)) Sundance/Newbridge Educational Publishing.

Galko, Francine. Forest Animals. 2003. (Animals in Their Habitats Ser.). (Illus.). 32p. (J). (gr. k-2). lib. bdg. 21.36 (978-1-4034-0179-3(9)); pap. 6.95 (978-1-4034-0436-7(4)) Heinemann Library.

—Forest Animals. 2003. (gr. k-3). lib. bdg. 14.75 (978-0-613-45756-9(0)) Tandem Library Bks.

Graham-Barber, Lynda. Spy Hops & Belly Flops: Curious Behaviors of Woodland Animals. Lies, Brian, tr. Lies, Brian, illus. 2004. 32p. (J). (gr. k-3). tchr. ed. 15.00 (978-0-618-22291-9(X)) Houghton Mifflin Co. Trade & Reference Div.

Green, Jen. Dead Log. 1999. (gr. 3-6). lib. bdg. 17.60 (978-0-613-19511-9(6)) Tandem Library Bks.

Hodge, Deborah. Rain Forest Animals. Stephens, Pat, illus. 2008. 24p. pap. (***978-1-55453-042-7(3)***) Kids Can Pr., Ltd.

Jeunesse, Gallimard. In the Forest. De Hugo, Pierre, illus. 2003. (First Discovery Look-and-Learn Bks.). 24p. (J). bds. 6.95 (978-0-439-33636-9(8) , Cartwheel Bks.) Scholastic, Inc.

Klingel, Cynthia Fitterer & Noyed, Robert B. Forests. 2001. (Wonder Books Level 2: Habitats Ser.). (Illus.). 24p. (J). (ps-3). 22.79 (978-1-56766-973-2(5)) Child's World, Inc.

Leroux-Hugon, Helene. I Can Draw Forest Animals. Leroux-Hugon, Helene, illus. 2001. (I Can Draw Animals! Ser.). (Illus.). 40p. (J). (gr. 1 up). lib. bdg. 24.67 (978-0-8368-2839-9(9)) Stevens, Gareth Inc.

Lindeen, Carol. Life in a Forest. 2003. (Pebble Plus: Living in a Biome Ser.). (Illus.). 24p. (J). lib. bdg. 17.26 (978-0-7368-2098-1(1) , Pebble Bks.) Capstone Pr., Inc.

Lindeen, Carol K. Life in a Forest, Vol. 3. 2005. (Earth & Outer Space Ser.). 24p. (YA). (gr. k-3). pap. (978-0-7368-3400-1(1) , Pebble Bks.) Capstone Pr., Inc.

Longnecker, Theresa. Who Grows Up in the Forest? A Book about Forest Animals & Their Offspring. Carpenter, Melissa, illus. 2004. (Who Grows Up Here? Ser.). 24p. (C). (gr. k-4). 21.26 (978-1-4048-0025-0(5)) Picture Window Bks.

Mattern, Joanne. What Forest Animals Eat: Qué Comen Los Animales Del Bosque? 2006. (ENG & SPA., Illus.). 24p. (J). pap. (978-0-8368-7379-5(3)); lib. bdg. (978-0-8368-7372-6(6)) Stevens, Gareth Inc. (Weekly Reader Early Learning Library).

—What Forest Animals Eat/By Joanne Mattern. 2006. (Illus.). 24p. (J). pap. (978-0-8368-6878-4(1)); lib. bdg. (978-0-8368-6871-5(4)) Stevens, Gareth Inc.

McGehee, Claudia. A Woodland Counting Book. 2006. (Bur Oak Book Ser.). (Illus.). 32p. (J). 17.95 (978-0-87745-989-7(4)) Univ. of Iowa Pr.

McKissack, Fredrick, Jr. & McKissack, Lisa Beringer. Counting in the Rain Forest. 2008. (J). (***978-0-7660-2992-7(1)***) Enslow Pubs., Inc.

—Counting in the Temperate Forest. 2008. (J). (***978-0-7660-2990-3(5)***) Enslow Pubs., Inc.

Meyers. Quien Vive en el Bosque. 1999. (SPA.). (J). pap. 5.18 (978-0-7398-0723-1(4)) Steck-Vaughn.

Miller, Debbie S. Are Trees Alive? Schuett, Stacey, illus. (J). (ps-2). 2003. 32p. 16.95 (978-0-8027-8801-6(7)); 2002. 17.85 (978-0-8027-8802-3(5)) Walker & Co.

Morgan, Sally. Under a Leaf in Forests & Jungles. 2006. (Hidden Habitats Ser.). (J). (978-1-59389-284-5(5)) Chrysalis Education.

Parker, Edward, photos by. Birds. 2002. (Rain Forest Pilot Ser.). (Illus.). 48p. (J). lib. bdg. 27.12 (978-0-7398-5239-2(6)) Raintree.

Patent, Dorothy Hinshaw. Fabulous Fluttering Tropical Butterflies. Jubb, Kendahl Jan, illus. 2003. 32p. (J). (gr. 1-5). 17.85 (978-0-8027-8839-9(4)); 16.95 (978-0-8027-8838-2(6)) Walker & Co.

Peluso, Beth. Charcoal Forest. 64p. (J). pap. 12.00 (***978-0-87842-532-7(2)***) Mountain Pr. Publishing Co., Inc.

Phillips, Dee. Find It in a Rain Forest. 2006. (Can You Find It? Ser.). (Illus.). 24p. (J). lib. bdg. 22.00 (978-0-8368-6299-7(6)) Stevens, Gareth Inc.

Radley, Gail. Forests & Jungles. Sherlock, Jean, illus. (Vanishing from Ser.). 2005. 32p. (gr. 6-12). lib. bdg. 22.60 (978-1-57505-405-6(1)); 2003. 32p. (J). (gr. 3-5). 6.95 (978-1-57505-567-1(8)); 1998. (J). lib. bdg. (978-0-8225-1937-9(2)) Lerner Publishing Group.

—Forests & Jungles. Sherlock, Jean, illus. 2001. 32p. (J). (ps-7). lib. bdg. 15.25 (978-0-613-64497-6(2)) Tandem Library Bks.

Raintree Steck-Vaughn Staff. Forest Community. 1999. (J). pap. 35.60 (978-0-7398-0890-0(7)) Steck-Vaughn.

—¿Quién Vive en el Bosque? 1999. (SPA.). (J). pap., stu. ed. 31.05 (978-0-7398-0758-3(7)) Steck-Vaughn.

Riley, Peter D. & Gerstein, Sherry. Nightwatch: Nightlife in the Tropical Rain Forest. Croucher, Barry & Edwards, Brin, illus. Coleman, Bruce & Natural History Photographs Agency Staff, photos by. 1999. (Windows on Science Ser.). 16p. (YA). (gr. 3-7). 12.99 (978-1-57584-251-6(3) , Reader's Digest Children's Bks.) Reader's Digest Children's Publishing, Inc.

Ring, Elizabeth. Forestlands. 2004. (Illus.). 48p. (J). (gr. 2-4). 24.95 (978-1-4103-0319-6(5) , Blackbirch Pr., Inc.) Thomson Gale.

Ring, Susan. One Green Frog. 2003. (Illus.). 17p. (J). 15.93 (978-0-7368-2917-5(2)); pap. (978-0-7368-2876-5(1)) Yellow Umbrella Pr.

Rivera, Sheila. Forest. 2005. (First Step Nonfiction Ser.). (Illus.). 23p. (J). (ps-7). lib. bdg. 17.27 (978-0-8225-2596-7(8) , Lerner Pubns.) Lerner Publishing Group.

Ryan, Marla. Into Wild Amazonia. 2004. (Jeff Corwin Experience Ser.). (Illus.). 48p. (J). 11.20 (978-1-4103-0252-6(0) , Blackbirch Pr., Inc.) Thomson Gale.

Sackett, Hannah Kate. Animal Faces in the Forest. Camm, Martin, illus. 2003. (Animal Faces Ser.). 32p. (J). (gr. k-3). 16.95 (978-1-57768-428-2(1) , Waterbird Bks.) School Specialty Publishing.

Salas, Laura Purdie. Temperate Deciduous Forests: Lands of Falling Leaves. Yesh, Jeff, illus. 2006. (Amazing Science Ser.). 24p. (J). (978-1-4048-3099-8(5)) Picture Window Bks.

Schofield, Jennifer. Animal Babies in Rain Forests. 2004. (Animal Babies Ser.). (Illus.). 32p. (J). (ps-k). 7.95 (978-0-7534-5788-7(1) , Kingfisher) Houghton Mifflin Co. Trade & Reference Div.

Schwartz, David M. In the Forest. Kuhn, Dwight, photos by. 1998. (Springboards into Science Ser.). (Illus.). 24p. (J). (gr. 1 up). lib. bdg. 20.67 (978-0-8368-2222-9(6)) Stevens, Gareth Inc.

Serafini, Frank. Looking Closely Through the Forest. 2008. (Illus.). 40p. (***978-1-55453-212-4(4)***) Kids Can Pr., Ltd.

Sharp, Zoe. In the Tree. 2002. (Windows on Literacy Ser.). (Illus.). 12p. (J). (978-0-7922-8461-1(5)) National Geographic Society.

Steele, Christy. Ants. 2000. (Animals of the Rain Forest Ser.). (Illus.). 32p. (J), (gr. 4-7). lib. bdg. 22.83 (978-0-7398 3098-7(8)) Raintree.

Stewart, David. Rain Forest Animals! (World of Wonder Ser.). 32p. (J). 2008. pap. 9.95 (***978-0-531-20543-3(6)***); 2007. spiral bd. 29.00 (***978-0-531-20452-8(9)***) Scholastic Library Publishing. (Children's Pr.).

Swinburne, Stephen R. The Woods Scientist. Morse, Susan C., photos by. 2003. (Scientists in the Field Ser.). (Illus.). 48p. (J). (gr. 4-6). tchr. ed. 16.00 (978-0-618-04602-7(X)) Houghton Mifflin Co. Trade & Reference Div.

Telford, Carole & Theodorou, Rod. Up a Rainforest Tree. 2006. (Illus.). 32p. (J). (***978-1-4034-8793-3(6)***) Heinemann Library.

Townsend, Emily Rose. Woodland Animals, 4 bks. Saunders-Smith, Gail, ed. Incl. Deer. lib. bdg. 15.93 (978-0-7368-2067-7(1)); Owls. lib. bdg. 15.93 (978-0-7368-2068-4(X)); Squirrels. lib. bdg. 15.93 (978-0-7368-2069-1(8)); Woodpeckers. lib. bdg. 15.93 (978-0-7368-2070-7(1)); 24p. (J). (gr. k-1). 2004. (Illus.). 2004. Set lib. bdg. 63.72 (978-0-7368-2318-0(2) , Pebble Bks.) Capstone Pr., Inc.

Trumbauer, Lisa. Double the Animals. 2006. 16p. (J). (gr. k-2). 15.93 (978-0-7368-5854-0(7) , Yellow Umbrella Bks.) Capstone Pr., Inc.

Walsh, Patricia & Westerfield, David. Woodlands Animals. 2000. (Draw It! Ser.). (Illus.). 32p. (J). (gr. 3-5). lib. bdg. 22.79 (978-1-57572-352-5(2)) Heinemann Library.

Whitehouse, Patricia. Hiding in a Forest. 2003. (Illus.). 32p. pap. 6.50 (978-1-4034-3187-5(6)); (J). lib. bdg. 22.79 (978-1-4034-0797-9(5)) Heinemann Library.

Who Grows up in the Forest? (Who Grows up Here? Ser.). 24p. (J). 7.95 (978-1-4048-0207-0(X)) Picture Window Bks.

Who Grows up in the Rain Forest? (Who Grows up Here? Ser.). 24p. (J). 7.95 (978-1-4048-0209-4(6)) Picture Window Bks.

Wickings, Ruth. On the Forest Floor. 2007. (World at Your Feet Ser.). (Illus.). 10p. (J). 9.95 (978-1-84560-027-3(4)) Mercury Bks. Ltd. GBR. *Dist:* International Publishers Marketing.

Woods, Mae. Animals of the Rain Forest. 1999. (Rain Forest Ser.). (Illus.). 24p. (J). (gr. k-6). lib. bdg. 21.35 (978-1-57765-019-5(0) , Checkerboard Library) ABDO Publishing Co.

Woodward, John. Into Wild Guyana. 2004. (Jeff Corwin Experience Ser.). (Illus.). 48p. (J). 11.20 (978-1-4103-0232-8(6)); (gr. 4-7). 24.95 (978-1-4103-0231-1(8)) Thomson Gale. (Blackbirch Pr., Inc.).

FOREST CONSERVATION

see Forests and Forestry

FOREST ECOLOGY

see also Rain Forest Ecology

Baldwin, Carol. Living in a Temperate Deciduous Forest. 2003. (Living Habitats Ser.). (Illus.). 32p. (J). lib. bdg. 24.22 (978-1-4034-0839-6(4)) Heinemann Library.

Blomgren, Jennifer. Where Would I Be in an Evergreen Tree? Gabriel, Andrea, illus. 2004. 32p. (J). 15.95 (978-1-57061-414-9(8)) Sasquatch Bks.

Bradley, Catherine. Mountains. 2004. (Life In... Ser.). (SPA., Illus.). (gr. 3-6). 32p. (J). pap. 6.95 (978-1-58728-569-1(X)); 31p. 12.95 (978-1-58728-554-7(1)) T&N Children's Publishing. (Two Can Publishing).

Brenner, Barbara. One Small Place in a Tree. Leonard, Tom, illus. 2004. 32p. (J). (gr. k-3). 16.99 (978-0-688-17180-3(X)); lib. bdg. 16.89 (978-0-688-17181-0(8)) HarperCollins Pubs.

Carlisi, Alison & Foxx, Teralene S. The Forest & the Fire. 2005. (Illus.). (J). (978-0-941232-31-9(X)) Los Alamos Historical Society.

Cefrey, Holly. Coniferous Forests. 2003. (Reading Power Ser.). (Illus.). 24p. (J). lib. bdg. 17.25 (978-0-8239-6455-0(8) , PowerKids Pr.) Rosen Publishing Group, Inc., The.

—Deciduous Forests. 2003. (Reading Power Ser.). (Illus.). 24p. (J). lib. bdg. 17.25 (978-0-8239-6454-3(X) , PowerKids Pr.) Rosen Publishing Group, Inc., The.

Champion, Neil. Temperate Woodlands. 2005. (Caring for the Planet Ser.). (Illus.). 48p. (J). (978-1-58340-509-3(7)) Smart Apple Media.

Cole, Melissa S. Forest. 2003. (Wild America Habitats Ser.). (Illus.). 24p. (J). 21.20 (978-1-56711-802-5(X) , Blackbirch Pr., Inc.) Thomson Gale.

Collard, Sneed B., III. The Forest in the Clouds. Rothman, Michael, illus. 2000. (J). (ps-3). lib. bdg. 16.45 (978-0-613-35121-8(5)) Tandem Library Bks.

Dorling Kindersley Publishing Staff. Forest: Open Your Eyes to a World of Discovery. 2003. (Eye Wonder Ser.). (Illus.). 48p. (J). 9.99 (978-0-7894-9759-8(X)) Dorling Kindersley Publishing, Inc.

Fielding, Eileen. The Eastern Forest. 1999. (Ecosystems of North America Ser.). (Illus.). 64p. (YA). (gr. 6 up). lib. bdg. 28.50 (978-0-7614-0895-6(9) , Benchmark Bks.) Cavendish, Marshall Corp.

Fleisher, Paul. Forest Food Webs. 2007. (Early Bird Food Webs Ser.). 48p. (J). (gr. 2-5). 26.60 (***978-0-8225-6729-5(6)*** , Lerner Pubns.) Lerner Publishing Group.

Fowler, Allan. Our Living Forests. 1999. (Rookie Read-About Science Ser.). (Illus.). 32p. (gr. 1-2). pap. 4.95 (978-0-516-26481-3(8) , Children's Pr.) Scholastic Library Publishing.

Gaff, Jackie. Pine Trees Have Needles: And Other Questions about Forests. 2005. (I Wonder Why Ser.). (Illus.). 32p. (J). (gr. k-3). 11.95 (978-0-7534-5861-7(6) , Kingfisher) Houghton Mifflin Co. Trade & Reference Div.

Gaff, Jackie. Pine Trees Have Needles & Other Questions about Forests. 2007. (I Wonder Why Ser.). (Illus.). 32p. (J). pap. 6.95 (***978-0-7534-6096-2(3)*** , Kingfisher) Houghton Mifflin Co. Trade & Reference Div.

Ganeri, Anita. Forests. 2003. (Science Files Ser.). (Illus.). 32p. (J). (gr. 3 up). lib. bdg. 24.67 (978-0-8368-3567-0(0)) Stevens, Gareth Inc.

Godkin, Celia. Fire. 2006. (Illus.). 32p. (J). 17.95 (978-1-55041-889-7(0)) Fitzhenry & Whiteside, Ltd. CAN. *Dist:* F & W Pubns., Inc.

Green, Jen. A Dead Log. 1999. (Small Worlds Ser.). (Illus.). 32p. (J). (gr. 3-4). pap. (978-0-7787-0150-7(6)); lib. bdg. (978-0-7787-0136-1(0)) Crabtree Publishing Co.

—Dead Log. 1999. (gr. 3-6). lib. bdg. 17.60 (978-0-613-19511-9(6)) Tandem Library Bks.

Group/McGraw-Hill, Wright. La Vida en la Selva Tropical, 6 vols., Vol. 2. (First Explorers. Primeros Exploradores Nonfiction Sets Ser.). (SPA.). (gr. 1-2). 29.95 (978-0-7699-1487-9(X)) Shortland Pubns. (U. S. A.) Inc.

Haugen, Hayley Mitchell. Life in a Forest. 2005. (Ecosystems Ser.). (Illus.). 48p. (J). (ps-7). lib. bdg. 26.20 (978-0-7377-3080-7(3) , Greenhaven Pr., Inc.) Thomson Gale.

Hazen, Barbara Shook. Secret Life of Trees. 1999. (Eyewitness Readers Ser.). (J). (978-0-606-19387-0(1)) Tandem Library Bks.

Hazen, Barbara Shook & Dorling Kindersley Publishing Staff. The Secret Life of Trees. 1999. (Eyewitness Readers). (Illus.). 32p. (J). (ps-3). 14.99 (978-0-7894-4761-6(4)) Dorling Kindersley Publishing, Inc.

Hazen, Barbara Shook, et al. The Secret Life of Trees. 1999. (Eyewitness Readers). (Illus.). 32p. (J). (ps-3). pap. 3.99 (978-0-7894-4760-9(6)) Dorling Kindersley Publishing, Inc.

Hooper, Roseanne. Life in the Woodlands. 2000. (gr. 3-6). lib. bdg. 12.95 (978-0-613-23323-1(9)) Tandem Library Bks.

—Life in the Woodlands. 2001. (World Book Ecology Ser.). (Illus.). 32p. (J). (978-0-7166-5225-0(0)) World Bk., Inc.

—Life in the Woodlands: Animals, People, Plants. 2000. (gr. 3-6). lib. bdg. 15.25 (978-0-613-43348-8(3)) Tandem Library Bks.

Hughes, Monica. What Is a Forest? 2004. (Heinemann Read & Learn Ser.). (Illus.). 24p. (J). pap. (978-1-4034-6281-7(X)); lib. bdg. (978-1-4034-6275-6(5)) Steck-Vaughn.

Hurtig, Jennifer. Deciduous Forests. 2006. (J). (978-1-59036-441-3(4)); (Illus.). 32p. (gr. 4-6). lib. bdg. 26.00 (978-1-59036-440-6(6)) Weigl Pubs., Inc.

Jackson. Tropical Forests. 2003. (Biomes Atlas Ser.). (Illus.). 64p. pap. 9.50 (978-1-4109-0018-0(5)); pap. 48.30 (978-1-4109-0253-5(6)) Raintree.

Kalman, Bobbie. Cadenas Alimentarias del Bosque. (Cadenas Alimentarias Ser.). (SPA., Illus.). 32p. (J). (978-0-7787-8529-3(7)); 2006. pap. (978-0-7787-8545-3(9)) Crabtree Publishing Co.

—Forest Food Chains. 2004. (Food Chains Ser.). (Illus.). 32p. (J). (978-0-7787-1943-4(X)); pap. (978-0-7787-1989-2(8)) Crabtree Publishing Co.

—A Forest Habitat. 2006. (Illus.). 32p. (J). (978-0-7787-2951-8(6)); (gr. 2). pap. (978-0-7787-2979-2(6)) Crabtree Publishing Co.

—Un Habitat de Bosque. 2007. (SPA.). 32p. (J). (gr. 1-2). (***978-0-7787-8327-5(8)***); pap. (***978-0-7787-8351-0(0)***) Crabtree Publishing Co.

Kalman, Bobbie. What Is a Forest? 2003. (gr. 3-6). lib. bdg. 14.10 (978-0-613-52932-7(4)) Tandem Library Bks.

Kalman, Bobbie & Smithyman, Kathryn. La Foret. 2004. (FRE., Illus.). 32p. (J). pap. (978-2-89579-012-9(4)) Crabtree Publishing Co.

—What Is a Forest? 2002. (Science of Living Things Ser.). (Illus.). 32p. (J). (gr. 2-3). (978-0-86505-992-4(6)); pap. (978-0-86505-969-6(1)) Crabtree Publishing Co.

Kavanagh, James. African Wildlife Nature Activity Book. 2004. (Pocket Naturalist Ser.). (Illus.). 32p. pap. 6.95 (978-1-58355-259-9(6)) Waterford Pr., Ltd.

—Arctic Wildlife Nature. 2004. (Pocket Naturalist Ser.). (Illus.). 32p. pap. 6.95 (978-1-58355-261-2(8)) Waterford Pr., Ltd.

—Great Lakes Wildlife Nature Activity Book. 2004. (Pocket Naturalist Ser.). (Illus.). 32p. pap. 6.95 (978-1-58355-263-6(4)) Waterford Pr., Ltd.

Loughran, Donna. Living in the Forest. 2004. (Rookie Read-About Geography Ser.). (Illus.). 31p. (J). (gr. 1-2). pap. 5.95 (978-0-516-27330-3(2) , Children's Pr.) Scholastic Library Publishing.

MacMillan, Dianne M. Life in a Deciduous Forest. 2003. (Ecosystems in Action Ser.). (Illus.). 71p. (J). (gr. 6-12). 26.60 (978-0-8225-4684-9(1)) Lerner Publishing Group.

Martin, Patricia. Woods & Forests. 2000. (gr. 7-12). lib. bdg. 15.25 (978-0-613-54787-1(X)) Tandem Library Bks.

Martin, Patricia A. Fink. Woods & Forests. 2000. (Exploring Ecosystems Ser.). (Illus.). 144p. (YA). (gr. 8-12). pap. 6.95 (978-0-531-16459-4(4) , Watts, Franklin) Scholastic Library Publishing.

—Woods & Forests. 2000. (J). (978-0-606-19799-1(0)) Tandem Library Bks.

McKissack, Fredrick, Jr. & McKissack, Lisa Beringer. Counting in the Temperate Forest. 2008. (J). (***978-0-7660-2990-3(5)***) Enslow Pubs., Inc.

McNeil, Niki, et al. HOCPP 1099 Forest Habitats. 2006. spiral bd. 22.50 (***978-1-60308-099-6(6)***) In the Hands of a Child.

Miller. Forest Scientists. 2001. (Scientists of the Biomes Ser.). (Illus.). (J). pap. (978-0-7398-4936-1(0)) Steck-Vaughn.

Miller, Chuck. Forest Scientists. 2001. (Scientists of the Biomes Ser.). (Illus.). 48p. (J). lib. bdg. 24.26 (978-0-7398-4751-0(1)) Raintree.

Miller, Debbie S. Are Trees Alive? Schuett, Stacey, illus. (J). (ps-2). 2003. 32p. 16.95 (978-0-8027-8801-6(7)); 2002. 17.85 (978-0-8027-8802-3(5)) Walker & Co.

Miller-Schroeder, Patricia. Boreal Forests. 2005. (Illus.). 32p. (J). (ps-6). lib. bdg. 24.45 (978-1-59036-345-4(0)); pap. 7.95 (978-1-59036-351-5(5)) Weigl Pubs., Inc.

Moore & Peter, D. Tropical Forests. 2007. (Ecosystem Ser.). 224p. (J). (gr. 9). 70.00 (***978-0-8160-5934-8(9)***) Facts On File, Inc.

Morgan, Sally. A Clearing in the Forest. 2000. (Life in... Ser.). (Illus.). 32p. (J). (gr. 2-6). lib. bdg. 16.95 (978-1-929298-84-6(6)) Chrysalis Education.

—Under a Leaf in Forests & Jungles. 2006. (Hidden Habitats Ser.). (J). (978-1-59389-284-5(5)) Chrysalis Education.

Morris, Neil. Forests. 1998. (Wonders of Our World Ser.). (Illus.). 32p. (J). (gr. 3-4). pap. (978-0-86505-845-3(8)); lib. bdg. (978-0-86505-833-0(4)) Crabtree Publishing Co.

Morrison, Gordon. Oak Tree. 2005. (Illus.). 32p. (J). (gr. k-3). 6.95 (978-0-618-60918-5(0) , Walter Lorraine) Houghton Mifflin Co. Trade & Reference Div.

Nadeau, Issac. Food Chains in a Forest Habitat. Kuhn, Dwight, photos by. 2002. (Library of Food Chains & Food Webs). (Illus.). 24p. (J). (gr. 2-4). lib. bdg. 18.75 (978-0-8239-5758-3(6) , PowerKids Pr.) Rosen Publishing Group, Inc., The.

Nelson. The Tundra. 2000. (Biomes Ser.). (Illus.). (J). pap. (978-0-7398-4162-4(9)) Steck-Vaughn.

Nelson, Julie. Forests. Sloan, Frank, ed. 2001. (Biomes Ser.). (Illus.). 32p. (J). (gr. 4-7). lib. bdg. 22.83 (978-0-7398-3561-6(0)) Raintree.

Oliver, Clare. Life in a Tree: Clare Oliver. 2002. (Microhabitats Ser.). (Illus.). 32p. (J). 25.69 (978-0-7398-4334-5(0)) Raintree.

Parker, Janice, ed. The Disappearing Forests. 2002. (Understanding Global Issues). (Illus.). 56p. (YA). (gr. 10-12). lib. bdg. 19.95 (978-1-58340-168-2(7)) Weigl Pubs., Inc.

E F G

Pascoe, Elaine. Forest Floor. Kuhn, Dwight, illus. Kuhn, Dwight, photos by. 2004. 24p. (J). (gr. 2-4). 22.45 (978-1-4103-0314-1(4) , Blackbirch Pr., Inc.) Thomson Gale.

Peluso, Beth. Charcoal Forest. 64p. (J). pap. 12.00 (***978-0-87842-532-7(2)***) Mountain Pr. Publishing Co., Inc.

Penny, Malcolm. Life in a Rotten Log. 2003. (Microhabitats Ser.). (Illus.). 32p. (J). pap. 7.50 (978-1-4109-0349-5(4)); lib. bdg. 24.28 (978-0-7398-6804-1(7)) Raintree.

—Life in a Rotten Log. 2003. (gr. k-3). lib. bdg. 15.90 (978-0-613-78244-9(5)) Tandem Library Bks.

Pfeffer, Wendy. A Log's Life. Brickman, Robin, illus. 2007. 32p. (J). 6.99 (978-1-4169-3483-7(9) , Aladdin) Simon & Schuster Children's Publishing.

Pyers. Forest Explorer. 2004. (Habitat Explorer Ser.). (Illus.). pap. 7.50 (978-1-4109-0907-7(7)) Raintree.

—Forest Explorer 6-Pack. 2004. (Habitat Explorer Ser.). (Illus.). pap. 40.50 (978-1-4109-0912-1(3)) Raintree.

Pyers, Greg. Forest Explorer. 2004. (Habitat Explorer Ser.). (Illus.). 32p. (J). lib. bdg. 25.70 (978-1-4109-0508-6(X)) Raintree.

Quinlan, Susan E. The Case of the Monkeys That Fell from the Trees: And Other Mysteries in Tropical Nature. Quinlan, Susan E., illus. 2003. (Illus.). 172p. (YA). (gr. 4-6). pap. 15.95 (978-1-56397-902-6(0)) Boyds Mills Pr.

Raintree Steck-Vaughn Staff. Forest Community. 1999. (J). pap. 35.60 (978-0-7398-0890-0(7)) Steck-Vaughn.

—¿Quién Vive en el Bosque? 1999. (SPA.). (J). pap., stu. ed. 31.05 (978-0-7398-0758-3(7)) Steck-Vaughn.

Rapp, Valerie. Life in an Old Growth Forest. Staub, Frank, illus. 2003. (Ecosystems in Action Ser.). 72p. (J). (gr. 6-12). 26.60 (978-0-8225-2135-8(0)) Lerner Publishing Group.

Raven, Catherine. Forestry. 2006. (Green World Ser.). (Illus.). 136p. (J). (gr. 6-12). 37.50 (978-0-7910-8752-7(2) , Chelsea Hse.) Facts On File, Inc.

Reid, Greg. Temperate Forests. 2004. (Ecosystems Ser.). (Illus.). 32p. (J). (gr. 3-5). 23.00 (978-0-7910-7942-3(2) , Chelsea Hse.) Facts On File, Inc.

Richards, Julie. Ferocious Fires. 2001. (Natural Disasters Ser.). (Illus.). 32p. (J). (gr. 5 up). 28.00 (978-0-7910-6583-9(9) , 010451, Chelsea Hse.) Facts On File, Inc.

Scraper, Katherine. What Is in a Forest? 2006. (Early Explorers Ser.). (J). 30.00 (***978-1-4108-6022-4(1)***) Benchmark Education Co.

Sharp, Zoe. In the Tree. 2002. (Windows on Literacy Ser.). (Illus.). 12p. (J). (978-0-7922-8461-1(5)) National Geographic Society.

Shook-Hazen, Barbara. Secret Life of Trees. 1999. (gr. k-3). lib. bdg. 11.80 (978-0-613-22356-0(X)) Tandem Library Bks.

Slater, Pat. Discover & Learn about Australian Forests & Woodlands. Parish, Steve, photos by. 2001. (Habitats & Ecosystems Ser.). (Illus.). 48p. (J). pap. (978-1-74021-088-1(3)) Parish, Steve Publishing.

Snedden, Robert. Northern Forests. 2003. (Illus.). 32p. (J). lib. bdg. (978-1-58340-385-3(X)) Smart Apple Media.

Somervill, Barbara A. Our Living World: Earth's Biomes, 7 vols., Set. 2005. (Illus.). (J). (gr. 4-8). 350.00 (978-1-59187-052-4(6)) Tradition Publishing Co.

Staub, Frank. America's Forests. 1998. (Earth Watch Ser.). (Illus.). 56p. (gr. 4-6). lib. bdg. 21.27 (978-1-57505-265-6(2)) Lerner Publishing Group.

Staub, Frank J., photos by. America's Forests & Woodlands. 2006. (Illus.). 48p. (J). pap. (978-1-59034-806-2(0)) Mondo Publishing.

Stone, Lynn M. Forests. 2003. (Rourke Discovery Library). (Illus.). 24p. (J). 20.64 (978-1-58952-684-6(8)) Rourke Publishing, LLC.

Tagliaferro, Linda. Explore the Deciduous Forest. 2006. (Fact Finders Ser.). (Illus.). 32p. (J). 22.60 (978-0-7368-6403-9(2) , Fact Finders) Capstone Pr., Inc.

Temperate Forests. (Ecosystems Ser.). 24p. (J). 6.95 (978-0-7368-9166-0(8)) Capstone Pr., Inc.

Tocci, Salvatore. Life in the Temperate Forests. 2005. (Watts Library). (Illus.). 63p. (J). (gr. k-7). 25.50 (978-0-531-12363-8(4) , Watts, Franklin) Scholastic Library Publishing.

—Life in the Tropical Forests. 2005. (Illus.). 63p. (J). (gr. k-7). 25.50 (978-0-531-12364-5(2) , Watts, Franklin) Scholastic Library Publishing.

Warhol, Tom. Forest. 2006. (Earth's Biomes Ser.). (Illus.). 80p. (J). lib. bdg. 32.79 (978-0-7614-2189-4(0) , Benchmark Bks.) Cavendish, Marshall Corp.

Weird Wildlife 6-Pack (30 Books), Set. 2004. (Illus.). pap. 214.65 (978-1-4109-1277-0(9)) Raintree.

Wickings, Ruth. On the Forest Floor. 2007. (World at Your Feet Ser.). (Illus.). 10p. (J). 9.95 (978-1-84560-027-3(4)) Mercury Bks. Ltd. GBR. *Dist:* International Publishers Marketing.

Woodward. Temperate Forests. 2003. (Biomes Atlas Ser.). (Illus.). 64p. pap. 9.50 (978-1-4109-0022-7(3)); pap. 48.30 (978-1-4109-0257-3(9)) Raintree.

Woodward, John. Temperate Forests. 2002. (Biomes Atlases Ser.). (Illus.). 64p. (J). lib. bdg. 31.40 (978-0-7398-5248-4(5)) Raintree.

FOREST FIRES

Alcraft, Rob & Spilsbury, Louise. Fire Disasters. 1999. (World's Worst Ser.). 32p. (J). (gr. 4-6). lib. bdg. 22.79 (978-1-57572-988-6(1)) Heinemann Library.

Allman, Toney. From Jewel Beetles to Fire Sensors. 2006. (Imitating Nature Ser.). (Illus.). 32p. (gr. 3-6). 24.95 (978-0-7377-3626-7(7) , 1256743, Kidhaven) Thomson Gale.

Arlbach, Arlene. Forest Fires. 2001. (Illus.). 51p. (J). (gr. 2-4). reprint ed. 17.00 (978-0-7881-9735-2(5)) DIANE Publishing Co.

Ball, Jacqueline A. Wildfire! The 1871 Peshtigo Firestorm. 2005. (X-Treme Disasters That Changed America Ser.). 32p. (J). lib. bdg. 25.27 (978-1-59716-011-7(3)) Bearport Publishing Co., Inc.

Barber, Nicola. Inside Fires & Floods. 2006. (Inside Nature's Disasters Ser.). (Illus.). 36p. (J). lib. bdg. (978-0-8368-7248-4(7)) Stevens, Gareth Inc.

Bell, Karen Magnuson. Fire in Their Eyes: Wildfires & the People Who Fight Them. 1999. (Illus.). 64p. (gr. 4-8). 18.98 (978-0-8172-3774-5(7)) Raintree.

Briscoe, Diana. Smokejumpers: Battling the Forest Flames. 2002. (High Five Reading Ser.). (Illus.). 48p. (J). (gr. 3-4). lib. bdg. 22.60 (978-0-7368-9548-4(5) , Capstone High-Interest Bks.) Capstone Pr., Inc.

—Smokejumpers Battling the Forest Flames. 2002. (High Five Reading Ser.). (Illus.). 48p. (J). pap. (978-0-7368-9526-2(4)) Capstone Pr., Inc.

Bryan, Nichol. Los Alamos: Wildfires. 2003. (Environmental Disasters Ser.). (Illus.). 48p. (gr. 5 up). (YA). lib. bdg. 30.00 (978-0-8368-5507-4(8)); (J). pap. 11.95 (978-0-8368-5514-2(0)) Stevens, Gareth Inc. (World Almanac Library).

Carlisi, Alison & Foxx, Teralene S. The Forest & the Fire. 2005. (Illus.). (J). (978-0-941232-31-9(X)) Los Alamos Historical Society.

Colson, Mary. Forest Furnace Wildfires. 2005. (Turbulent Planet Ser.). (Illus.). 48p. (J). (978-1-4109-1742-3(8)); pap. (978-1-4109-1752-2(5)) Steck-Vaughn.

Costain, Meredith. Science Chapters: Devouring Flames: The Story of Forest Fires. 2006. (National Geographic Science Chapters Ser.). (Illus.). 48p. (J). (gr. 1-4). 17.90 (978-0-7922-5944-2(0) , National Geographic Children's Bks.) National Geographic Society.

Drohan, Michele Ingber. Forest Fires. 1999. (Natural Disasters Ser.). (Illus.). 24p. (J). (gr. k-4). lib. bdg. 19.95 (978-0-8239-5287-8(8) , PowerKids Pr.) Rosen Publishing Group, Inc., The.

Fires in the Wild: MainSails Individual Title Six-Packs. (Sails Literacy Ser.). (gr. 5 up). 37.00 (978-0-7578-8045-2(2)) Rigby Education.

Fraser, Mary Ann. Forest Fire! 1999. (J). (978-0-606-16873-1(7)) Tandem Library Bks.

Ganeri, Anita. Forest Fire! 2007. (Illus.). 32p. (J). (978-1-84193-563-8(8)) Arcturus Pubs., Inc.

—Forest Furnace. 2004. (Turbulent Planet Ser.). (Illus.). (J). 48p. 28.56 (978-1-4109-0588-8(8)); pap. 8.50 (978-1-4109-1026-4(1)) Raintree.

—Forest Furnace 6-Pack. 2004. (Turbulent Planet Ser.). (Illus.). (J). pap. 45.90 (978-1-4109-1031-8(8)) Raintree.

Gentle, Victor & Perry, Janet. Fires. 2001. (Natural Disasters Ser.). (Illus.). 24p. (J). (gr. 2 up). lib. bdg. 22.00 (978-0-8368-2833-7(X)) Stevens, Gareth Inc.

Godkin, Celia. Fire. 2006. (Illus.). 32p. (J). 17.95 (978-1-55041-889-7(0)) Fitzhenry & Whiteside, Ltd. CAN. *Dist:* F & W Pubns., Inc.

Magnuson-Beil, Karen. Fire in the Eyes: Wildfires & the People Who Fight Them. 1999. (J). 17.80 (978-0-606-16518-1(5)) Tandem Library Bks.

Martinucci, Suzanne. Where There Was Smoke. 2002. (Illus.). 16p. (J). (978-0-439-35115-7(4)) Scholastic, Inc.

Morrison, Taylor. Wildfire. 2006. (Illus.). 48p. (J). 17.00 (978-0-618-50900-3(3)) Houghton Mifflin Co.

Nobisso, Josephine. Forest Fires: Run for You Life! 2000. (gr. 3-6). lib. bdg. 15.25 (978-0-613-27830-0(5)) Tandem Library Bks.

—Forest Fires: Run for Your Life! 2000. (Illus.). 42p. (J). (gr. 2-5). pap. 6.95 (978-1-57255-793-2(1)); 6.95 (978-1-57255-802-1(4)) Mondo Publishing.

Peppas, Lynn. Wildfire Alert! 2004. (Disaster Alert! Ser.). (Illus.). 32p. (J). pap. (978-0-7787-1606-8(6)); (978-0-7787-1574-0(4)) Crabtree Publishing Co.

Piehl, Janet. Forest Fires. 2008. (Pull Ahead Books-Forces of Nature Ser.). (J). lib. bdg. 22.60 (***978-0-8225-7907-6(3)*** , Lerner Pubns.) Lerner Publishing Group.

Platts, Linda E. Forest Fires. 2004. (Illus.). 96p. (J). lib. bdg. 33.70 (978-0-7377-2300-7(9) , Greenhaven Pr., Inc.) Thomson Gale.

Richards, Julie. Ferocious Fires. 2001. (Natural Disasters Ser.). (Illus.). 32p. (J). (gr. 5 up). 28.00 (978-0-7910-6583-9(9) , 010451, Chelsea Hse.) Facts On File, Inc.

Ring, Susan. Wildfires. 2003. (Science Links Ser.). (Illus.). 32p. (gr. 3-5). 23.00 (978-0-7910-7432-9(3) , Chelsea Hse.) Facts On File, Inc.

Salas, Laura Purdie. Forest Fires. 2001. (Natural Disasters Ser.). (Illus.). 48p. (J). (gr. 3-4). lib. bdg. 21.26 (978-0-7368-0901-6(5) , Capstone High-Interest Bks.) Capstone Pr., Inc.

Simon, Seymour. Wildfires. 2000. (Illus.). 32p. (J). (gr. k-3). pap. 6.99 (978-0-688-17530-6(9) , Harper Trophy) HarperCollins Pubs.

—Wildfires. 2000. (Illus.). (J). (ps-ps). lib. bdg. 15.30 (978-0-613-27586-6(1)) Tandem Library Bks.

Sipiera, Paul P. & Sipiera, Diane M. Wildfires. 1998. (True Bks.). (Illus.). 48p. (J). (gr. 3-5). 25.00 (978-0-516-20682-0(6) , Children's Pr.) Scholastic Library Publishing.

Spilsbury, Louise & Spilsbury, Richard. Blazing Bush & Forest Fires. 2003. (Heinemann Infosearch Ser.). (Illus.). 32p. (J). pap. (978-1-4034-4229-1(0)); lib. bdg. 24.22 (978-1-4034-3722-8(X)) Heinemann Library.

Thompson, Luke. Forest Fires. 2000. (High Interest Bks.). (Illus.). 48p. (YA). (gr. 7-12). pap. 6.95 (978-0-516-23570-7(2) , Children's Pr.) Scholastic Library Publishing.

—Forest Fires. 2000. (gr. 7-12). lib. bdg. 15.25 (978-0-613-52055-3(6)) Tandem Library Bks.

Trumbauer, Lisa. Forest Fires. 2005. (Watts Library). (Illus.). 64p. (J). 25.50 (978-0-531-12284-6(0) , Watts, Franklin) Scholastic Library Publishing.

Woodcock, Sandra. Forest Fire. 2001. (Livewire Ser.). (Illus.). 32p. pap. (978-0-340-80065-2(8) , Hodder Arnold) Hodder Education.

World Book, Inc Staff, contrib. by. Wildfires. 2007. (J). (***978-0-7166-9816-6(1)***) World Bk., Inc.

FOREST FIRES—FICTION

Braun, Lilian Jackson. The Cat Who Smelled a Rat. 2002. (gr. 5-8). lib. bdg. 15.30 (978-0-613-51533-7(1)) Tandem Library Bks.

Daher, Anita. Flight from Big Tangle. 2003. (Orca Young Readers Ser.). (Illus.). 144p. (J). (gr. 3-6). pap. 4.99 (978-1-55143-234-2(X)) Orca Bk. Pubs. USA.

—Flight from Big Tangle. 2003. (gr. 3-6). lib. bdg. 13.00 (978-0-613-90073-7(1)) Tandem Library Bks.

Donahue, Michael. The Fire That Saved the Forest. Grove, Diane O., illus. 2002. 32p. (ps-3). 24.95 (978-1-57098-420-4(4)); pap. 9.95 (978-1-57098-421-1(2)) Rinehart, Roberts Pubs.

Duey, Kathleen & Bale, Karen A. Forest Fire, Hinckley, Minnesota, 1894. 1999. (Survival! Ser.: No. 10). (J). (gr. 4-7). (978-0-606-16301-9(8)) Tandem Library Bks.

Fleck, Earl. Chasing Fire: Danger in Canoe Country. 2002. (Illus.). 160p. pap. 12.95 (978-0-930100-53-7(0)) Holy Cow! Pr.

George, Jean Craighead. Fire Storm. Minor, Wendell, illus. 2003. (Outdoor Adventures Ser.). 32p. (J). 15.99 (978-0-06-000263-3(8)); lib. bdg. 16.89 (978-0-06-000264-0(6)) HarperCollins Pubs. (Tegen, Katherine Bks).

Hanson, Ed. Forest Fire. 2003. (Barclay Family Adventure Ser.: Bk. 4). 64p. (J). (gr. k-6). per. 3.95 (978-1-56254-553-6(1) , SP 5531) Saddleback Educational Publishing.

Harcourt School Publishers Staff. Hazanas para Gigantes Below Level. 3rd ed. 2002. (Trofeos Ser.). (SPA., Illus.). pap. 6.80 (978-0-15-324159-8(4)) Harcourt Schl. Pubs.

—Tall Tales, Big Numbers: Take-Home Book. 2001. (Collections Ser.). (Illus.). (J). pap. 1.90 (978-0-15-319509-9(6)) Harcourt Schl. Pubs.

Hill, Elizabeth Starr. Wildfire! Shepperson, Rob, illus. 2004. 80p. (J). 16.00 (978-0-374-31712-6(7) , Farrar, Straus & Giroux (BYR)) Farrar, Straus & Giroux.

Ingold, Jeanette. The Big Burn. 2003. (Illus.). 320p. (YA). pap. 6.95 (978-0-15-204924-9(X) , Harcourt Paperbacks) Harcourt Children's Bks.

—The Big Burn. 2003. (gr. 5-8). lib. bdg. 15.25 (978-0-613-55148-9(6)) Tandem Library Bks.

Lewis, Carolyn & DeVince, James. Hairy Beary Book Three: The Blue Ribbon Hero, 3 bks., Vol. 3. DeVince, James, ed. Porcheron, Tammy, illus. 2003. (Hairy Beary Ser.: 3). 46p. (J). pap. 9.95 (978-0-9712641-2-0(0)) J M D's Business Services.

Liebig, Nelda J. Carrie & the Apple Pie. 1999. 122p. (J). (gr. 3-7). pap. (978-1-883953-30-0(8)) Midwest Traditions, Inc.

Livingston, Timothy J. & Livingston, Mary A. FireStorm in the Forest: When A forest Burns. Livingston, Timothy J., illus. 2006. (Illus.). 32p. (J). 20.95 (***978-0-9635757-1-5(6)***) Red Tail Publishing.

—Working with Nature Set, 2 bks. Livingston, Timothy J., illus. 2006th ed. 2006. (Illus.). (J). 32.95 (***978-0-9635757-3-9(2)***) Red Tail Publishing.

McCracken, Mary. Grandpappy Ump. 2001. 120p. pap. 10.95 (978-0-595-20648-3(4) , Writers Club Pr.) iUniverse, Inc.

Rucker, Mike. Terry the Smokejumper. 2001. (Terry the Tractor Ser.: Vol. 9). (Illus.). (J). (ps-5). pap. 3.95 (978-0-9711659-0-8(4)) Univ. Editions.

Schaaf, Ron. BearClaw: Finding Courage Within. 2007. (J). (***978-0-9787555-1-5(0)***) Hickory Tales Publishing.

Shands, Linda I. Wild Fire. 2001. (Wakara of Eagle Lodge Ser.: Vol. 1). (Illus.). 176p. (J). (gr. 7-9). pap. 5.99 (978-0-8007-5746-5(7)) Revell.

Sims, Matt. Bass Lake. 1999. (gr. 3-6). lib. bdg. 10.85 (978-0-613-30258-6(3)) Tandem Library Bks.

Smith, Debra. Hattie Marshall & the Dangerous Fire. 2007. 144p. (J). pap. 7.95 (***978-1-58980-492-0(9)***) Pelican Publishing Co., Inc.

Southall, Ivan. Ash Road. 2004. (Illus.). 192p. (J). pap. 7.95 (978-1-932425-11-6(X) , Lemniscaat) Boyds Mills Pr.

Wagner, Jerri. Jako's Vacation. 2001. 58p. pap. 9.95 (978-0-7414-0704-7(3)) Infinity Publishing.

FOREST PLANTS

Art, Henry W. & Robbins, Michael W. WoodsWalk: Peepers, Porcupines, & Exploding Puff Balls! 2003. (Illus.). 128p. (J). (gr. 3-7). pap. 14.95 (978-1-58017-452-7(3) , 67452, Storey Kids) Storey Publishing, LLC.

Giesecke, Ernestine. Forest Plants. 1999. (Plants Ser.). (Illus.). 32p. (J). (gr. k-2). lib. bdg. 21.36 (978-1-57572-823-0(0)) Heinemann Library.

Klingel, Cynthia Fitterer & Noyed, Robert B. Forests. 2001. (Wonder Books Level 2: Habitats Ser.). (Illus.). 24p. (J). (ps-3). 22.79 (978-1-56766-973-2(5)) Child's World, Inc.

Lindeen, Carol. Life in a Forest. 2003. (Pebble Plus: Living in a Biome Ser.). (Illus.). 24p. (J). lib. bdg. 17.26 (978-0-7368-2098-1(1) , Pebble Bks.) Capstone Pr., Inc.

Lindeen, Carol K. Life in a Forest, Vol. 3. 2005. (Earth & Outer Space Ser.). 24p. (YA). (gr. k-3). pap. (978-0-7368-3400-1(1) , Pebble Bks.) Capstone Pr., Inc.

McGehee, Claudia. A Woodland Counting Book. 2006. (Bur Oak Book Ser.). (Illus.). 32p. (J). 17.95 (978-0-87745-989-7(4)) Univ. of Iowa Pr.

Parker, Edward, photos by. Trees & Plants. 2002. (Rain Forest Pilot Ser.). (Illus.). 48p. (J). lib. bdg. 27.12 (978-0-7398-5244-6(2)) Raintree.

Peluso, Beth. Charcoal Forest. 64p. (J). pap. 12.00 (***978-0-87842-532-7(2)***) Mountain Pr. Publishing Co., Inc.

Ring, Elizabeth. Forestlands. 2004. (Illus.). 48p. (J). (gr. 2-4). 24.95 (978-1-4103-0319-6(5) , Blackbirch Pr., Inc.) Thomson Gale.

Ring, Susan. One Green Frog. 2003. (Illus.). 17p. (J). 15.93 (978-0-7368-2917-5(2)); pap. (978-0-7368-2876-5(1)) Yellow Umbrella Pr.

Rivera, Sheila. Forest. 2005. (First Step Nonfiction Ser.). (Illus.). 23p. (J). (ps-7). lib. bdg. 17.27 (978-0-8225-2596-7(8) , Lerner Pubns.) Lerner Publishing Group.

Salas, Laura Purdie. Temperate Deciduous Forests: Lands of Falling Leaves. Yesh, Jeff, illus. 2006. (Amazing Science Ser.). 24p. (J). (978-1-4048-3099-8(5)) Picture Window Bks.

Schwartz, David M. In the Forest. Kuhn, Dwight, photos by. 1998. (Springboards into Science Ser.). (Illus.). 24p. (J). (gr. 1 up). lib. bdg. 20.67 (978-0-8368-2222-9(6)) Stevens, Gareth Inc.

Serafini, Frank. Looking Closely Through the Forest. 2008. (Illus.). 40p. (***978-1-55453-212-4(4)***) Kids Can Pr., Ltd.

Wickings, Ruth. On the Forest Floor. 2007. (World at Your Feet Ser.). (Illus.). 10p. (J). 9.95 (978-1-84560-027-3(4)) Mercury Bks. Ltd. GBR. *Dist:* International Publishers Marketing.

FOREST PRODUCTS

see also Lumber and Lumbering; Rubber; Wood

Parker, Edward, photos by. Trees & Plants. 2002. (Rain Forest Pilot Ser.). (Illus.). 48p. (J). lib. bdg. 27.12 (978-0-7398-5244-6(2)) Raintree.

Pirotta, Saviour. Trees & Plants in the Rain Forest. 1999. (Deep in the Rain Forest Ser.). (Illus.). 32p. (J). (978-0-7502-2198-6(4)) Steck-Vaughn.

FORESTRY

see Forests and Forestry

FORESTS AND FORESTRY

see also Forest Plants; Lumber and Lumbering; Rain Forests; Tree Planting; Trees; Wood

Armentrout, David & Armentrout, Patricia. Fires. 2007. (Illus.). 32p. (J). (978-1-60044-231-5(5)) Rourke Publishing, LLC.

Baker, Nick. Forests & Woods. 2007. (Collins Nature Explorers Ser.). (Illus.). 72p. pap. 9.95 (978-0-06-089078-0(9) , HarperCollins) HarperCollins Pubs.

Baldwin, Carol. Living in a Temperate Deciduous Forest. 2003. (Living Habitats Ser.). (Illus.). 32p. (J). lib. bdg. 24.22 (978-1-4034-0839-6(4)) Heinemann Library.

—Living in a Temperate Forest. 2003. (Living Habitats Ser.). (Illus.). 32p. pap. 6.95 (978-1-4034-3227-8(9)) Heinemann Library.

Balloon Books Staff, ed. Scout in the Woods: 85 Removable Stickers. 2003. (Sticker Story Bks.). (Illus.). 18p. (J). (ps-1). pap. 4.95 (978-1-4027-0101-6(2) , Balloon Bks.) Sterling Publishing Co., Inc.

Bash, Barbara. Ancient Ones: The World of the Old-Growth Douglas Fir. Bash, Barbara, illus. 2nd ed. 2002. (Illus.). 32p. (J). (ps-6). reprint ed. pap., pap. 6.95 (978-1-57805-081-9(2)) Gibbs Smith, Publisher.

—Ancient Ones: The World of the Old-Growth Douglas Fir. 2002. (gr. 3-6). lib. bdg. 15.25 (978-0-613-79299-8(8)) Tandem Library Bks.

Beilenson, Suzanne. Rain Forest Scratch & Sketch: An Art Activity Book for Adventurous Artists & Explorers of All Ages. 2007. (Illus.). 64p. (YA). 12.99 (***978-1-59359-862-4(9)***) Peter Pauper Pr. Inc.

Bellamy, David & Dow, Jill. The Forest. 1999. (Our Changing World Ser.). (Illus.). 32p. (J). (gr. 1-5). pap. 7.99 (978-0-7112-1385-2(2)) Lincoln, Frances Ltd. GBR. *Dist:* Transition Vendor.

—Our Changing World: The Forest. 2004. (Our Changing World Ser.). (Illus.). 32p. (J). pap. 7.95 (978-1-84507-217-9(0)) Lincoln, Frances Ltd. GBR. *Dist:* Perseus Distribution.

Benchmark Education Staff. Forests. 2005. 2.00 (***978-1-4108-4664-8(4)***) Benchmark Education Co.

BHB International Staff. Forest. 1998. (Here We Go Round Ser.). (J). (978-2-215-06182-3(0)) Editions Fleurus.

Brannon, Barbara. Discover Forests. 2005. 39.00 (***978-1-4108-5138-3(9)***) Benchmark Education Co.

Burton. Introduction to Forestry Science. 2nd rev. ed. 2007. 512p. (C). 100.95 (***978-1-4180-3087-2(2)***) Thomson Delmar Learning.

Butterfield, Moira. Protecting Temperate Forests. 2005. (Protecting Habitats Ser.). (J). lib. bdg. 24.67 (978-0-8368-4995-0(7)) Stevens, Gareth Inc.

Carlisi, Alison & Foxx, Teralene S. The Forest & the Fire. 2005. (Illus.). (J). (978-0-941232-31-9(X)) Los Alamos Historical Society.

Casper, Julie Kerr. Forests: More Than Just Trees. 2007. (Natural Resources Ser.). 208p. (J). (gr. 6-12). 39.50 (***978-0-8160-6355-0(9)*** , Chelsea Hse.) Facts On File, Inc.

Champion, Neil. Temperate Woodlands. 2005. (Caring for the Planet Ser.). (Illus.). 48p. (J). (978-1-58340-509-3(7)) Smart Apple Media.

Cherry, Alan J. & McKenzie, Rita. The Talking Tree. Kutzko, Elizabeth & Jester, Beth, eds. 1998. (Illus.). 27p. (J). (gr. 2-6). pap. 8.95 (978-1-881956-22-8(9)) International Society of Arboriculture.

Chinery, Michael. Los Bosques.Tr. of Forests. (SPA.). 40p. (J). (gr. 3-5). 12.76 (978-84-241-2057-3(4)) Everest de Ediciones y Distribucion, S.L. ESP. *Dist:* Lectorum Pubns., Inc.

Chunko, Shelby E. & Madsen, Jane M. Hablemonos de la Tala Forestal: Un Libro de Silvicultura para Jovenes. De Banegas, Marianne N., tr. Smith, Heidi L., illus. l.t. unabr. ed. 1998. (SPA.). v, 32p. (J). (gr. 4-9). pap. 7.50 (978-0-9661896-2-9(0)) Pennsylvania Forestry Assn., The (PFA).

Cole, Melissa S. Forest. 2003. (Wild America Habitats Ser.). (Illus.). 24p. (J). 21.20 (978-1-56711-802-5(X) , Blackbirch Pr., Inc.) Thomson Gale.

Collard, Sneed B., III. Forest in the Clouds. Rothman, Michael, illus. 2000. 32p. (J). (ps-3). 16.95 (978-0-88106-985-3(X)); pap. 6.95 (978-0-88106-986-0(8)) Charlesbridge Publishing, Inc.

Coniferous Forests: Individual Title Six-Packs. (On Deck Ser.: Vol. 2). 24p. (gr. 4-5). 35.00 (978-0-7578-5823-9(6)) Rigby Education.

Cowan, Mary Morton. Timberrr! A History of Logging in New England. 2003. (Women at War Ser.). (Illus.). 128p. (gr. 5 up). lib. bdg. 25.90 (978-0-7613-1866-8(6) , Twenty-First Century Bks.) Lerner Publishing Group.

Dalgleish, Sharon. Protecting Forests. 2002. (Our World Ser.). (Illus.). 32p. (gr. 4-8). 28.00 (978-0-7910-7017-8(4) , Chelsea Hse.) Facts On File, Inc.

Daniels, Frank J. Petrified Wood: The World of Fossilized Wood, Cones, Ferns, & Cycads. 1998. (Illus.). vi, 170p. (YA). (gr. 9-12). 75.00 (978-0-9662938-0-7(0)) Western Colorado Publishing Co.

Deciduous Forests: Individual Title Six-Packs. (On Deck Ser.: Vol. 2). 24p. (gr. 4-5). 35.00 (978-0-7578-5824-6(4)) Rigby Education.

Dennard, Deborah. Koala Country: A Story of an Australian Eucalyptus Forest. McKinnon, James, illus. 2005. (Wild Habitats Ser.: Vol. 17). 32p. (J). (gr. 1-4). 15.95 (978-1-56899-887-9(2) , B7018); pap. 6.95 (978-1-56899-888-6(0) , S7018) Soundprints.

—Koala Country: A Story of an Australian Eucalyptus Forest. 2000. (gr. 3-6). lib. bdg. 15.25 (978-0-613-56800-5(1)) Tandem Library Bks.

—Koala Country: A Story of an Australian Eucalyptus Forest Including 8" Toy. McKinnon, James, illus. 2000. (Wild Habitats Ser.: Vol. 17). 36p. (J). (gr. 1-4). 26.95 (978-1-56899-891-6(0) , PB7018) Soundprints.

Dorling Kindersley Publishing Staff. Jungle. 2005. (Ultimate sticker Bks.). 16p. (J). pap. 6.99 (978-0-7566-0976-4(3)) Dorling Kindersley Publishing, Inc.

Drake, Jane. Forestry. Cupples, Pat, illus. 2002. 31p. (J). (gr. 4-7). lib. bdg. 14.10 (978-0-613-87151-8(0)) Tandem Library Bks.

Dunmire, Marjorie S. Faces of the Forests. Dunmire, Marjorie S., illus. 1998. (Illus.). 64p. (Orig.). (J). (gr. 3 up). pap. 5.95 (978-0-942559-08-8(8)) Pegasus Graphics.

Field, Nancy, ed. Wild Stickers - Forests. Turvik, Sharon, illus. 1998. (Wild Stickers Ser.: Vol. 2). 8p. (J). (gr. k-6). pap. 2.50 (978-0-941042-22-2(7)) Dog-Eared Pubns.

—Wild Stickers - Wetlands. Maydak, Michael S., illus. 1998. (Wild Stickers Ser.: Vol. 1). 8p. (J). (gr. k-6). pap. 2.50 (978-0-941042-21-5(9)) Dog-Eared Pubns.

Forest. 2003. (J). per. (978-1-57657-887-2(9)) Paradise Pr., Inc.

Forest. 32p. 1.99 (978-0-7682-0246-5(9) , FS144008) Schaffer, Frank Pubns.

The Forest: Kindergarten Guided Reading Level A. (On Our Way to English Ser.). (gr. k up). 27.75 (978-0-7578-7005-7(8)) Rigby Education.

Forest Giants: Individual Title Six-Packs. (Rigby Infoquest Ser.). 24p. (gr. 3 up). 34.00 (978-0-7578-5766-9(3)) Rigby Education.

Forests Learning about the Earth. 2006. (Illus.). 24p. (J). (gr. k-2). 18.50 (***978-0-531-17888-1(9)***) Scholastic Library Publishing.

Gilkerson, Patricia. My Adventure in an Enchanted Forest. 2006. 44p. (J). 8.99 (978-1-59092-277-4(8) , Orchard Academy Pr.) Windstorm Creative.

Greeley, August. Fading Forests: The Destruction of Our Rainforests. 2003. (Reading Power Ser.). (Illus.). 24p. (J). lib. bdg. 17.25 (978-0-8239-6486-4(8) , PowerKids Pr.) Rosen Publishing Group, Inc., The.

Green, Emily K. Forests. 2006. (Blastoff! Readers Ser.). (Illus.). 24p. (J). lib. bdg. 16.95 (978-1-60014-036-5(X)) Bellwether Media.

Green, Jen. Rain Forests. 1999. (Young Scientist Concepts & Projects Ser.). (Illus.). 68p. (J). (gr. 4 up). lib. bdg. 27.33 (978-0-8368-2268-7(4)) Stevens, Gareth Inc.

Halfmann, Janet. Life in a Tree. 2000. (Lifeviews Ser.). (Illus.). 32p. (J). lib. bdg. (978-1-58341-077-6(5) , Creative Education) Creative Co., The.

Hamilton, John. Wildfires. 2006. (Illus.). 32p. (J). (gr. 3-8). lib. bdg. 24.21 (978-1-59679-330-9(9) , ABDO & Daughters) ABDO Publishing Co.

Haugen, Hayley Mitchell. Life in a Forest. 2005. (Ecosystems Ser.). (Illus.). 48p. (J). (ps-7). lib. bdg. 26.20 (978-0-7377-3080-7(3) , Greenhaven Pr., Inc.) Thomson Gale.

Hines, Gary. Midnight Forests: A Story of Gifford Pinchot & Our National Forests. Casilla, Robert, illus. 2005. 32p. (J). (ps-17). 16.95 (978-1-56397-148-8(8)) Boyds Mills Pr.

Holmes, Bonnie. Quaking Aspen. Jansen, Paula, photos by. 1999. (Nature Watch Ser.). (Illus.). 48p. (J). (gr. 3-6). lib. bdg. 25.26 (978-1-57505-351-6(9) , Carolrhoda Bks.) Lerner Publishing Group.

Hooper, Roseanne. Life in the Woodlands. 2001. (World Book Ecology Ser.). (Illus.). 32p. (J). (978-0-7166-5225-0(0)) World Bk., Inc.

—Woodlands. 2004. (Life In... Ser.). (SPA., Illus.). 32p. (J). (gr. 3-6). pap. 6.95 (978-1-58728-574-5(6) , Two Can Publishing) T&N Children's Publishing.

Howard, Fran. Forests. 2007. (Habitats Ser.). (Illus.). 32p. (J). (gr. k-4). lib. bdg. 22.78 (978-1-59679-777-2(0)) ABDO Publishing Co.

Hughes, Monica. What Is a Forest? 2004. (Heinemann Read & Learn Ser.). (Illus.). 24p. (J). pap. (978-1-4034-6281-7(X)); lib. bdg. (978-1-4034-6275-6(5)) Steck-Vaughn.

Jeunesse, Gallimard. In the Forest. De Hugo, Pierre, illus. 2003. (First Discovery Look-and-Learn Bks.). 24p. (J). bds. 6.95 (978-0-439-33636-9(8) , Cartwheel Bks.) Scholastic, Inc.

Johansson, Philip. The Temperate Forest: A Web of Life. 2004. (World of Biomes Ser.). (Illus.). 48p. (J). lib. bdg. 23.93 (978-0-7660-2198-3(X)) Enslow Pubs., Inc.

Johnson, Rebecca J. A Walk in the Boreal Forest. Saroff, Phyllis V., illus. Braasch, Gary, photos by. 2005. (Biomes of North America Ser.). 48p. (gr. 3-6). lib. bdg. 23.93 (978-1-57505-156-7(7)) Lerner Publishing Group.

Johnson, Rebecca L. A Walk in the Deciduous Forest. Saroff, Phyllis V., illus. Braasch, Gary, photos by. 2005. (Biomes of North America Ser.). 48p. (gr. 3-6). lib. bdg. 23.93 (978-1-57505-155-0(9)) Lerner Publishing Group.

Kalman, Bobbie & Smithyman, Kathryn. La Foret. 2004. (FRE., Illus.). 32p. (J). pap. (978-2-89579-012-9(4)) Crabtree Publishing Co.

Karecki, Jason, illus. The Adventures of Drake Montana Vol. 3: North American Forests. 1998. 24p. (J). (gr. k-5). (978-1-890716-10-3(3)) K&M International.

Kite, Lorien. A Rain Forest Tree. 1999. (Small Worlds Ser.). (Illus.). 32p. (J). (gr. 3-4). lib. bdg. (978-0-7787-0132-3(8)); pap. (978-0-7787-0146-0(8)) Crabtree Publishing Co.

Klingel, Cynthia Fitterer & Noyed, Robert B. Forests. 2001. (Wonder Books Level 2: Habitats Ser.). (Illus.). 24p. (J). (ps-3). 22.79 (978-1-56766-973-2(5)) Child's World, Inc.

Langeland, Deirdre. Kangaroo Island: A Story of An Australian Mallee Forest. Ordaz, Frank, illus. 1998. (Nature Conservancy Habitat Ser.). (J). (gr. 1-4). 32p. 15.95 (978-1-56899-543-4(1) , B7007); 32p. pap. 6.95 (978-1-56899-544-1(X)); Incl. toy. 36p. 26.95 (978-1-56899-547-2(4)); Incl. toy. 36p. 31.95 incl. audio (978-1-56899-549-6(0)) Soundprints.

Lim, Cheng Puay. Vanishing Forests. 2004. (Green Alert Ser.). (Illus.). 48p. (J). lib. bdg. 28.56 (978-0-7398-7012-9(2)) Raintree.

Linde, Barbara M. Deforestation & Desertification. 2005. (Navigators Ser.). (J). pap. 44.00 (***978-1-4108-5090-4(0)***) Benchmark Education Co.

Lopatka, Michael. Southern Forests. 2002. (YA). (gr. 9-12). cd-rom 24.95 (978-0-9703694-7-5(6)) Awesome Guides, Inc.

Loughran, Donna. Living in the Forest. 2004. (Rookie Read-About Geography Ser.). (Illus.). 31p. (J). (gr. 1-2). pap. 5.95 (978-0-516-27330-3(2) , Children's Pr.) Scholastic Library Publishing.

Love, Ann & Drake, Jane. Forestry. Cupples, Pat, illus. 2002. (America at Work Ser.). 32p. (J). (gr. k-3). (978-1-55337-423-7(1)) Kids Can Pr., Ltd.

Lynetter, Rachel. Julia Butterfly Hill. 2007. (Young Heros Ser.). 64p. (J). (gr. 4-8). 27.45 (***978-0-7377-3628-1(3)*** , Kidhaven) Thomson Gale.

Lyon, George Ella & Dorling Kindersley Publishing Staff. Counting on the Woods. Olson, Ann W., illus. 1998. 32p. (J). (ps-3). 15.99 (978-0-7894-2480-8(0)) Dorling Kindersley Publishing, Inc.

MacDonald, Fiona, et al. Rain Forest. 2000. (Topic Bks.). (Illus.). 32p. (J). (gr. 2-5). 23.50 (978-0-531-14541-8(7) , Watts, Franklin) Scholastic Library Publishing.

MacMillan, Dianne M. Life in a Deciduous Forest. 2003. (Ecosystems in Action Ser.). (Illus.). 71p. (J). (gr. 6-12). 26.60 (978-0-8225-4684-9(1)) Lerner Publishing Group.

Massie, Elizabeth. A Forest Community. (Pair-It Books). (Illus.). 32p. (J). 2000. 6.20 (978-0-7398-0859-7(1)); 1999. (gr. 2-4). pap. 5.95 (978-0-7398-1480-2(X)) Steck-Vaughn.

Mays, Sheryl Kingery. Explore Poplar Forest, Thomas Jefferson's Retreat. 2000. (Illus.). 32p. (J). 4.95 (978-0-9667169-2-4(2)) Thomas Jefferson's Poplar Forest.

McKay, Sindy. We Both Read-about the Rain Forest. 2000. (We Both Read Ser.). (Illus.). 44p. (J). (gr. 1-2). 7.99 (978-1-891327-23-0(2)) Treasure Bay, Inc.

McKissack, Fredrick, Jr. & McKissack, Lisa Beringer. Counting in the Temperate Forest. 2008. (J). (***978-0-7660-2990-3(5)***) Enslow Pubs., Inc.

Menetrez, Marc Yves, et al. Encyclopedia of Environmental Studies. 3rd rev. ed. 2008. (Science Encyclopedia Ser.). 800p. (gr. 9). 150.00 (***978-0-8160-6511-0(X)***) Facts On File, Inc.

Miller. Forest Scientists. 2001. (Scientists of the Biomes Ser.). (Illus.). (J). pap. (978-0-7398-4936-1(0)) Steck-Vaughn.

Miller, Chuck. Forest Scientists. 2001. (Scientists of the Biomes Ser.). (Illus.). 48p. (J). lib. bdg. 24.26 (978-0-7398-4751-0(1)) Raintree.

Moore & Peter, D. Tropical Forests. 2007. (Ecosystem Ser.). 224p. (J). (gr. 9). 70.00 (***978-0-8160-5934-8(9)***) Facts On File, Inc.

Morris, Neil. Forests. 1998. (Wonders of Our World Ser.). (Illus.). 32p. (J). (gr. 3-4). pap. (978-0-86505-845-3(8)); lib. bdg. (978-0-86505-833-0(4)) Crabtree Publishing Co.

Nelson. Forests. 2000. (Biomes Ser.). (Illus.). (J). pap. (978-0-7398-4158-7(0)) Steck-Vaughn.

Nelson, Julie. Forests. Sloan, Frank, ed. 2001. (Biomes Ser.). (Illus.). 32p. (J). (gr. 4-7). lib. bdg. 22.83 (978-0-7398-3561-6(0)) Raintree.

Owen, Andy, et al. Forests. 2002. (Geography Starts Ser.). (Illus.). 32p. (J). (gr. k-2). pap. 6.95 (978-1-58810-971-2(2) , 91454) Heinemann Library.

Parker, Janice, ed. The Disappearing Forests. 2002. (Understanding Global Issues). (Illus.). 56p. (YA). (gr. 10-12). lib. bdg. 19.95 (978-1-58340-168-2(7)) Weigl Pubs., Inc.

Parsons, Michelle Hyde. Forests. 2005. 39.00 (***978-1-4108-4616-7(4)***) Benchmark Education Co.

Penny, Malcolm. Life in a Rotten Log. 2003. (Microhabitats Ser.). (Illus.). 32p. (J). pap. 7.50 (978-1-4109-0349-5(4)); lib. bdg. 24.28 (978-0-7398-6804-1(7)) Raintree.

—Life in a Rotten Log. 2003. (gr. k-3). lib. bdg. 15.90 (978-0-613-78244-9(5)) Tandem Library Bks.

Petersen, Christine. Land Preservation. 2004. (True Book Ser.). (Illus.). 48p. (J). 25.00 (978-0-516-22806-8(4) , Children's Pr.) Scholastic Library Publishing.

La Proteccion del Basque. (Coleccion Biblioteca Juvenil de Ecología). (SPA., Illus.). (YA). (gr. 5-8). pap. (978-958-04-2407-9(1) , 80424079) Norma S.A. COL. *Dist:* Lectorum Pubns., Inc.

Raven, Catherine. Forestry. 2006. (Green World Ser.). (Illus.). 136p. (J). (gr. 6-12). 37.50 (978-0-7910-8752-7(2) , Chelsea Hse.) Facts On File, Inc.

Reid, Greg. Temperate Forests. 2004. (Ecosystems Ser.). (Illus.). 32p. (J). (gr. 3-5). 23.00 (978-0-7910-7942-3(2) , Chelsea Hse.) Facts On File, Inc.

Royston, Angela. Forests. 2004. (Heinemann First Library). (Illus.). 32p. (J). 22.79 (978-1-4034-5589-5(9)) Heinemann Library.

Salzmann, Mary Elizabeth. In a Forest. l.t. ed. 2001. (What Do You See? Ser.). (Illus.). 24p. (J). (ps-3). lib. bdg. 19.93 (978-1-57765-565-7(6) , SandCastle) ABDO Publishing Co.

Saunders-Smith, Gail, ed. Earth Features, 8 bks. Incl. What Are Caves? Schuh, Mari C. 2002. lib. bdg. 15.93 (978-0-7368-1169-9(9)); What Are Deserts? Trumbauer, Lisa. 2001. lib. bdg. 15.93 (978-0-7368-0987-0(2)); What Are Forests? Trumbauer, Lisa. 2001. lib. bdg. 15.93 (978-0-7368-0988-7(0)); What Are Lakes? Schuh, Mari C. 2002. lib. bdg. 15.93 (978-0-7368-1170-5(2)); What Are Mountains? Trumbauer, Lisa. 2001. lib. bdg. 15.93 (978-0-7368-0989-4(9)); What Are Oceans? Trumbauer, Lisa. 2001. lib. bdg. 15.93 (978-0-7368-0990-0(2)); What Are Rivers? Schuh, Mari C. 2002. lib. bdg. 15.93 (978-0-7368-1171-2(0)); What Are Volcanoes? Schuh, Mari C. 2002. lib. bdg. 15.93 (978-0-7368-1172-9(9)); 24p. (J). (gr. k-1). (Illus.). 2001. Set lib. bdg. 127.44 (978-0-7368-1198-9(2) , Pebble Bks.) Capstone Pr., Inc.

School Specialty Publishing. Learn about the Forest. 2005. (Learn about Coloring Bks.). 32p. (J). pap. 1.99 (978-0-7696-4159-1(8) , Brighter Child) School Specialty Publishing.

Schwartz, David M. In the Forest. Kuhn, Dwight, photos by. 1998. (Springboards into Science Ser.). (Illus.). 24p. (J). (gr. 1 up). lib. bdg. 20.67 (978-0-8368-2222-9(6)) Stevens, Gareth Inc.

Selvas. (Coleccion Planeta Vivo).Tr. of Forests. (SPA.). (J). (gr. 5-8). 12.00 (978-84-342-1976-2(X)) Parramon Ediciones S.A. ESP. *Dist:* Distribuidora Norma, Inc., Lectorum Pubns., Inc.

Staub, Frank. America's Forests. 1998. (Earth Watch Ser.). (Illus.). 56p. (gr. 4-6). lib. bdg. 21.27 (978-1-57505-265-6(2)) Lerner Publishing Group.

Staub, Frank J., photos by. America's Forests & Woodlands. 2006. (Illus.). 48p. (J). pap. (978-1-59034-806-2(0)) Mondo Publishing.

Steck-Vaughn Staff. Science Level H-J: In the Forest. 2003. (Illus.). (J). bds. (978-0-7398-7640-4(6)) Steck-Vaughn.

Stone, Lynn M. Forests. 2003. (Rourke Discovery Library). (Illus.). 24p. (J). 20.64 (978-1-58952-684-6(8)) Rourke Publishing, LLC.

Taylor, Barbara. Temperate Forest Habitats. 2006. (Exploring Habitats Ser.). (Illus.). 36p. (J). lib. bdg. (978-0-8368-7257-6(6)) Stevens, Gareth Inc.

Temperate Forest. 2001. (Rough Cuts Ser.). (J). cd-rom 69.95 (978-1-56791-300-2(8)) Environmental Media Corp.

Temperate Forests, 6 vols. (gr. 2-5). 36.95 (978-0-7368-9263-6(X)) Red Brick Learning.

Toupin, Laurie Peach. The Taiga: Life in the Boreal Forest. 2005. (Watts Library). (Illus.). 63p. (J). (gr. k-7). 25.50 (978-0-531-12387-4(1) , Watts, Franklin) Scholastic Library Publishing.

Trumbauer, Lisa. What Are Forests? Saunders-Smith, Gail, ed. 2001. (Earth Features Ser.). (Illus.). 24p. (J). (gr. k-1). lib. bdg. 15.93 (978-0-7368-0988-7(0) , Pebble Bks.) Capstone Pr., Inc.

Tundra: Individual Title Six-Packs. (On Deck Ser.: Vol. 2). 24p. (gr. 4-5). 35.00 (978-0-7578-5828-4(7)) Rigby Education.

Warhol, Tom. Forest. 2006. (Earth's Biomes Ser.). (Illus.). 80p. (J). lib. bdg. 32.79 (978-0-7614-2189-4(0) , Benchmark Bks.) Cavendish, Marshall Corp.

Weinhold, Angela. Que? Como? Por que?: el Bosque: What? How? Why?: the Forest, Spanish-Language Edition. 2007. 16p. (J). 9.95 (***978-970-718-493-0(0)*** , Silver Dolphin en Español) Advanced Marketing, S. de R. L. de C. V. MEX. *Dist:* Perseus Distribution.

What Are Forests?, 6 vols., Vol. 2. 2005. (Earth & Outer Space Ser.). (gr. k-2). 28.95 (978-0-7368-3275-5(0)) Red Brick Learning.

Whitehouse, Patricia. Living in a Forest. 2007. (Illus.). 24p. (J). (978-1-60044-184-4(X)) Rourke Publishing, LLC.

Wickman, Allen, ed. Forest Management Digest. 9th ed. 2004. 460p. (YA). reprint ed. pap. 45.00 (978-0-913163-36-8(8) , KAP22004) Hobar Pubns.

Wilkins, Sally. Temperate Forests. 2001. (Bridgestone Science Library). (Illus.). 24p. (J). (gr. 2-3). lib. bdg. 18.60 (978-0-7368-0836-1(1) , Bridgestone Bks.) Capstone Pr., Inc.

Williams, Heather L. Deep in the Forest. Middleton, Mikell, illus. l.t. ed. 2003. (HRL Board Book Ser.). 10p. (J). (ps-k). bds. 10.95 (978-1-57332-264-5(4)) HighReach Learning, Inc.

Zak, Monica. Salven Mi Selva. 2002. (SPA.). (J). 19.95 (978-968-6048-24-7(3)) Larousse, Ediciones, S. A. de C. V. MEX. *Dist:* AIMS International Bks., Inc.

FORESTS AND FORESTRY—FICTION

Abernathy, Mary. Tales of the Black Jack Forest. 2002. per. (978-1-930493-61-2(4)) Athena Pr.

Addy, Sharon. In Grandpa's Woods. Akins, Tamlyn, illus. 2004. (J). (***978-1-931599-42-9(4)*** , Trails Bks.) Big Earth Publishing.

Adventures in the Purple Forest. 2003. (J). (978-1-932570-06-9(3)) Literacy Footprints Inc.

The Adventures of Chip Green the Forestry Kid. l.t. ed. 2005. (Illus.). 34p. (J). per. (978-0-9729753-8-4(1)) Really Big Coloring Bks., Inc.

Anholt, Laurence. The Forgotten Forest. 1999. (Illus.). 32p. (J). (ps-3). pap. (978-0-7112-1141-4(8)) Lincoln, Frances Ltd. GBR. *Dist:* Antique Collectors' Club.

Arias, Carlos Ballesteros. The Magic Forest. 2006. (J). pap. 8.00 (***978-0-8059-7022-7(3)***) Dorrance Publishing Co., Inc.

Austin, Margot & McPhail, David M. A Friend for Growl Bear Board Book. 1999. (Illus.). 32p. (J). (ps-k). 6.95 (978-0-694-01257-2(2) , Harper Festival) HarperCollins Pubs.

Avi. Tales from Dimwood Forest Box Set. Floca, Brian, illus. 2001. (Tales from Dimwood Forest Ser.). (J). pap. 23.96 (978-0-06-441017-5(X) , Harper Trophy) HarperCollins Pubs.

Ballman, Swanee. The Chocolate Kingdom Caper. Brunson, Stephanie, illus. 2003. 32p. (J), per. 6.95 (978-1-59094-025-9(3) , 1590940253) Jawbone Publishing Corp.

Barlow, Steve L. Goodknyght No. 1: Tales of the Dark Forest. 2001. (Tales of the Dark Forest Ser.). (Illus.). 192p. (J). pap. 9.99 (978-0-00-710863-3(X)) HarperCollins Pubs. Ltd. GBR. *Dist:* Independent Pubs. Group.

Baum, Roger S. The Oz Odyssey. Seitzinger, Victoria, illus. 2006. 176p. (J). 19.95 (978-1-57072-299-8(4)) Overmountain Pr.

Baumbach, Rudolph. Summer Legends. 2004. reprint ed. pap. 21.95 (978-1-4191-4993-1(8)); pap. 1.99 (978-1-4192-4993-8(2)) Kessinger Publishing, LLC.

Brooks, John. The Sundarbans Tiger. 2006. 115p. (J). pap. 13.58 (978-0-9661789-4-4(7)) Lulu.com.

Brooks, Walter R. & Slayton-Mitchell, Joyce. Knuckleboom Loaders Load Logs: A Trip to the Sawmill. Wiese, Kurt, illus. 2003. 40p. (J). 15.95 (978-1-58567-368-1(4)) Overlook Pr., The.

Brown, Ruth. The Old Tree: An Environmental Fable. Brown, Ruth, illus. 2007. (Illus.). 32p. (J). (ps-3). 16.99 (***978-0-7636-3461-2(1)***) Candlewick Pr.

Burgess, Thornton W. The Adventures of Happy Jack. 2004. (Dover Children's Thrift Classics Ser.). (Illus.). 128p. (J). (gr. 3-6). pap. 2.00 (978-0-486-43321-9(8)) Dover Pubns., Inc.

—Whitefoot the Wood Mouse. 2006. (Dover Children's Thrift Classics Ser.). 112p. (J). pap. 2.00 (978-0-486-44944-9(0)) Dover Pubns., Inc.

Burgess, W. Thornton. Whitefoot the Wood Mouse. 2006. 24.99 (***978-1-4280-4184-4(2)***); pap. 18.99 (***978-1-4280-4180-6(X)***) IndyPublish.com.

The Busy Forest. (J). 26.20 (978-0-8136-8413-0(7)); 26.20 (978-0-8136-8414-7(5)); 59.50 (978-0-8136-7948-8(6)); 1998. pap. (978-0-8136-8297-6(5)) Modern Curriculum Pr.

Campbell, Jean M. Wally Walnuts Journey to the Forest. Olson, Ralph C., illus. unabr. ed. 2001. 23p. (J). (gr. k-6). pap. (978-0-9651833-1-4(9)) Campbell, Jean.

Capaul, Roxanne. Snakey Jake to the Rescue! Whiting, Anne, illus. 2002. 40p. (J). (ps-6). 17.00 (978-0-9719222-0-4(9)) Rotire, Inc.

Carman, Patrick. The Dark Hills Divide. (Land of Elyon Ser.: Bk. 1). (J). 2006. 288p. pap. 6.99 (978-0-439-79175-5(8)); 2005. (Illus.). 272p. pap. 11.95 (978-0-439-70093-1(0) , Orchard Bks.); 2005. (Illus.). 253p. (978-0-439-75843-7(2) , Orchard Bks.) Scholastic, Inc.

—The Dark Hills Divide. l.t. ed. 2005. (Land of Elyon Ser.: Bk. 1). 356p. 23.95 (978-0-7862-7752-0(1) , Large Print Pr.) Thorndike Pr.

Chambers, Melinda. We Are Whoooo We Are. Spiker, Sue Ann, illus. 2006. 32p. (J). 16.95 (978-0-929915-46-3(1)) Headline Bks., Inc.

Cherry, Lynne & Plotkin, Mark J. The Shaman's Apprentice: A Tale of the Amazon Rain Forest. Cherry, Lynne, illus. 1998. (Illus.). 40p. (J). 16.00 (978-0-15-201281-6(8)) Harcourt Children's Bks.

Collier, Kevin Scott. Tales from Kensington Forest. l.t. ed. 2006. (Illus.). 26p. (J). E-Book 5.00 incl. cd-rom (978-1-933090-26-9(X)) Guardian Angel Publishing, Inc.

Colshorn, Carl & Colshorn, Theodore. The Porridge Pot. Carls, Claudia, illus. 2007. 32p. (J). (ps). 16.99 (***978-0-698-40073-3(9)*** , Minedition) Penguin Group (USA) Inc.

Cote, Denis. La Foret aux Cent Perils. Poulin, Stephane, tr. 2003. (Roman Jeunesse Ser.). (FRE., Illus.). 96p. (J). (gr. 4-7). pap. (978-2-89021-647-1(0)) Diffusion du livre Mirabel.

Coté, Denis. La Forêt aux Mille et un Périls, Tome 2. Poulin, Stephane, illus. 2004. (Roman Jeunesse Ser.). (FRE.). 96p. (J). (gr. 4-7). pap. (978-2-89021-696-9(9)) Diffusion du livre Mirabel.

Cotten, Cynthia S. At the Edge of the Woods: A Counting Book. Cartwright, Reg, illus. rev. ed. 2002. 32p. (J). (ps-1). 16.95 (978-0-8050-6354-7(4) , Holt, Henry & Co. Bks. For Young Readers) Holt, Henry & Co.

Crum, Shutta. The Bravest of the Brave. Bowers, Tim, illus. 2005. 40p. (J). (ps-3). 15.95 (978-0-375-82637-5(8) , Knopf Bks. for Young Readers) Random Hse. Children's Bks.

de Brunhoff, Laurent. Babar et ses Amis en Foret. (Babar Ser.). (FRE., Illus.). 48p. (J). (ps-3). 19.95 (978-0-7859-8811-3(4)) French & European Pubns., Inc.

Derrick, Patricia. Montgomery the Moose. 2007. 32p. 18.95 (978-1-933818-18-4(2)) Animalations.

Drake, Jane & Love, Ann. Forestry. Cupples, Pat, illus. (America at Work Ser.). (J). 2002. 32p. (gr. k-3). (978-1-55074-462-0(3)); 2000. 118p. (gr. 2-5). (978-1-55074-819-2(X)) Kids Can Pr., Ltd.

Du Chaillu, Paul. The World of the Great Forest: How Animals, Birds, Reptiles & Insects Talk, Think, Work & Live. Knight, C. R., illus. 2004. reprint ed. pap. 31.95 (978-1-4179-0914-8(5)) Kessinger Publishing, LLC.

Dube, Jasmine & Barrette, Doris. Grattelle au Bois Mordant. 1998. (Etait une Fois Ser.). (Illus.). 24p. (J). pap. (978-2-89021-332-6(3)) Diffusion du livre Mirabel.

Ebeltoft, Christine. Koo & Jay in the Rainforest. 2004. 34p. pap. 17.95 (978-1-4137-3698-4(X)) PublishAmerica, Inc.

Edwards, Carol. Jacy Meets Betsy: Jacy's Search for Jesus Book II. Frey, Daniel, illus. 2006. 32p. (J). 15.95 (978-0-9755314-1-9(7)) Majestic Publishing, LLC.

Eiselen, Claire. The Imagination Chronicles Pt. 1: The Wizard's Legacy. 2000. 116p. pap. 9.95 (978-0-595-13996-5(5), Writers Club Pr.) iUniverse, Inc.

Equipo Staff. No Hay Miel en el Bosque! 2000. (Adventures of Winnie the Pooh! Ser.). (SPA., Illus.). 118p. (J). 12.95 (978-84-488-0734-4(0)) Beascoa, Ediciones S.A. ESP. *Dist:* Distribooks, Inc.

Erickson, John R. Lost in the Dark Unchanted Forest. Holmes, Gerald L., illus. 1998. (Hank the Cowdog Ser.: No. 11). 144p. (J). (gr. 2-5). 14.99 (978-0-670-88418-6(9), Viking Juvenile) Penguin Group (USA) Inc.

—Lost in the Dark Unchanted Forest. Holmes, Gerald L., illus. 1999. (Hank the Cowdog Ser.: No. 11). (J). (gr. 3-6). lib. bdg. 13.00 (978-0-8335-6824-3(8)) Tandem Library Bks.

Fisscher, Tiny. RUBY & the LION. 2008. 48p. 11.95 (***978-1-60136-014-4(2)***) Mars Media Pubs.

Fontes, Justine & Tagel, Peggy. Who Lives in the Forest? 2000. (Wiggly Tab Bks.). (Illus.). 6p. (J). (ps-k). bds. 5.99 (978-1-57584-352-0(8)) Reader's Digest Children's Publishing, Inc.

The Forest of the Frendibles. 2006. (J). mass mkt. (***978-0-9791982-0-5(8)***) Donnellan, Martha.

Francis-Harris, Annabel. The Other Side of the Forest. 2006. pap. 19.95 (***978-1-59526-458-9(2)***) Media Creations, Inc.

Gallego Garcia, Laura. Retorno a la Isla Blanca. 2004. 143p. pap. 14.00 (978-84-931888-6-3(7)) Editorial Brief ESP. *Dist:* Independent Pubs. Group.

George, Jean Craighead. Frightful's Daughter Meets the Baron Weasel. San Souci, Daniel, illus. 2007. 48p. (J). (ps). 16.99 (***978-0-525-47202-5(9)***, Dutton Juvenile) Penguin Group (USA) Inc.

George, Lindsay B. In the Woods: Who's Been Here? George, Lindsay B., illus. 1998. (Mulberry Bks.). (Illus.). 48p. (J). (ps-3). pap. 7.99 (978-0-688-16163-7(4), Harper Trophy) HarperCollins Pubs.

A Giant in the Forest, Level 18. 1999. (J). (gr. k-3). 3.95 (978-0-673-61481-0(6)) Addison-Wesley Longman, Inc.

Goldilocks & the Three Bears. 2004. (My First Fairy Tales Ser.). (Illus.). 24p. (J). pap. 3.99 (978-1-85854-686-5(9)) Brimax Books Ltd. GBR. *Dist:* Byeway Bks.

Goldilocks & the Three Bears. 2002. (Puppy Tales Ser.). (Illus.). 24p. (J). (gr. k-3). 1.49 (978-1-57759-219-8(0)); pap. 2.99 (978-1-57759-479-6(7)) Dalmatian Pr.

Goldilocks & the Three Bears. (Ladybird Bks.). (ARA., Illus.). 52p. (J). 12.95 incl. audio (978-0-86685-254-8(9), LDL109C) International Bk. Ctr., Inc.

Grahame, Kenneth. The Wind in the Willows Vol. 3: The Wild Wood. Iosa, Ann, illus. 2007. (Easy Reader Classics Ser.). 32p. (J). pap. 3.95 (978-1-4027-3295-9(3)) Sterling Publishing Co., Inc.

—The Wind in the Willows Vol. 4: Home Sweet Home. Iosa, Ann, illus. 2007. (Easy Reader Classics Ser.). 32p. (J). pap. 3.95 (978-1-4027-3296-6(1)) Sterling Publishing Co., Inc.

Greathouse, Rebecca. Katie & Riley's Magical Adventures: Journey to the Amazon. 2006. 48p. pap. 12.95 (***978-1-4241-5341-1(7)***) PublishAmerica, Inc.

Green, John. Terdellaline: A Free-Spirited, Energeti. 2005. 48p. pap. 12.95 (978-1-4137-9528-8(5)) PublishAmerica, Inc.

Grimm, Jacob W. Little Red Riding Hood. 1999. (gr. k-3). lib. bdg. 15.25 (978-0-613-89995-6(4)) Tandem Library Bks.

Grimm, Jacob W. & Grimm, Wilhelm K. Little Red Riding Hood: Caperucita Roja. Surges, James, tr. Estrada, Pau, illus. 2006. 22p. (J). (gr. k-4). reprint ed. 15.00 (978-0-7567-9994-6(5)) DIANE Publishing Co.

Grimm, Jacob W., et al. Little Red Riding Hood/Caperucita Roja: A Bilingual Book. Surges, James, tr. from CAT. Estrada, Pau, illus. 1999. (ENG & SPA.). 32p. (J). (ps-3). 12.95 (978-0-8118-2561-0(2)) Chronicle Bks. LLC.

Gummelt, Donna & Melchiorre, Dondino. Michelina the Magical Musical Good Witch of the Forest. Wall, Randy Hugh, ed. Varela, Juan D., tr. Varela, Juan D., illus. 2006. (SPA.). 34p. (J). 14.95 (978-0-9764798-6-4(9)) Story Store Collection Publishing.

Habia una vez un Bosque 17: Leveled Books. 2001. (McGraw-Hill. Lectura Ser.). (ENG & SPA.). (gr. 2 up). (978-0-02-188042-3(5)) Macmillan/McGraw-Hill Schl. Div.

Hamilton, Elizabeth L. Charley Chimp's Jungle Fairness. l.t. ed. 2005. (Character Critters Ser.: No. 10). (Illus.). 32p. (J). per. 5.95 (978-0-9754629-7-3(0), Character-in-Action) Quiet Impact, Inc.

Hapka, Catherine. Wildfire Track Record, No. 2. 2nd rev. ed. 2007. 256p. (gr. 7-17). pap. 5.99 (978-1-4231-0189-5(8)) Disney Pr.

Henley, Karyn. A Noise in the Woods. 2000. (Tails Ser.). (Illus.). 28p. (J). (ps-5). 9.99 (978-0-8054-2197-2(1)) B&H Publishing Grp.

Hobbs, Valerie. Stefan's Story. 2003. 176p. (J). 16.00 (978-0-374-37240-8(3), Farrar, Straus & Giroux (BYR)) Farrar, Straus & Giroux.

Hood, Karen Jean Matsko. A Walk in the Woods. 2003. (J). 24.95 (978-1-930948-26-6(3)); pap. 15.95 (978-1-930948-27-3(1)) Whispering Pine Pr., Inc.

Hope, Laura Lee. The Mystery of the Dinosaur in the Forest. Ruppert, Larry, illus. 2005. (Bobbsey Twins Ser.). 24p. (J). pap. 3.99 (978-1-4169-0705-3(X), Little Simon) Simon & Schuster Children's Publishing.

Howard-Parlnam, Pam. If You Go into the Forest. Meier, Kerry L., illus. l.t. ed. 2005. (Hrl Board Book Ser.). (J). (ps-k). pap. 10.95 (978-1-57332-324-6(1)) HighReach Learning, Inc.

Hunter, Erin. Warriors Set: Into the Wild; Fire & Ice; Forest of Secrets; Rising Storm; A Dangerous Path; The Darkest Hour. 2007. (Warriors Ser.: Bks. 1-6). (J). pap. 36.99 (***978-0-06-147793-5(1)***, Harper Trophy) HarperCollins Pubs.

Hunter, Tammy. Tede's Search for his Mom. 2004. 27p. pap. 14.95 (978-1-4137-2854-5(5)) PublishAmerica, Inc.

Ichikawa, Satomi. En Busca de Tesoros. (SPA., Illus.). 40p. (J). (gr. k-2). (978-84-95150-33-2(6), COR0428) Corimbo, Editorial S.L. ESP. *Dist:* Lectorum Pubns., Inc.

Interiano, Jeffrey. Critters of Forest City. 2006. pap. 10.00 (***978-1-4257-1721-6(7)***) Xlibris Corp.

Jacques, Brian. The Bellmaker. Curless, Allan, illus. 2004. (Redwall Ser.). 352p. (YA). reprint ed. 8.99 (978-0-14-240030-2(0), Puffin) Penguin Group (USA) Inc.

Jessop, Sherry. The Great BooDinie Bird: Faith, 5 vols., Vol. 1. Staples, Deb, ed. Sketchit, Elly, illus. 2000. cd-rom 6.50 (978-1-931540-25-4(X)) SynergEbks.

Jones, E. Payson, 3rd. The Penny Tree Stories: Bumble Bunny & the Enchanted Forest. 2002. ring bd. 20.00 (978-0-9729194-0-1(6)) Jones, E. Payson.

Jordan, Polly, illus. In the Forest. (What's Missing? Ser.). 24p. (J). (ps-2). pap. 2.95 (978-1-56293-453-8(8), McClanahan Bk.) Learning Horizons, Inc.

Kasey & the Dream Forest: The First Dream (Interactive Cd-rom) 2000. cd-rom 9.95 (978-1-931179-61-4(1)) Long Hill Productions, Inc.

Khan, Joe. The Forest Eggimals. 2006. pap. 26.49 (***978-1-4208-9589-6(3)***) AuthorHouse.

Kipling, Rudyard. El Libro de la Selva. Alfonso Lopez, Javier, tr. 2005. (Clasicos de la literatura Ser.). (SPA., Illus.). 376p. pap. 5.95 (978-84-9764-492-1(1)) Edimat Libros, S. A. ESP. *Dist:* Independent Pubs. Group.

—El Libro de la Selva. 2000. (SPA.). lib. bdg. 10.55 (978-0-613-83762-0(2)) Tandem Library Bks.

Kline, Trish & Donev, Mary. A Scary Day in the Forest: KA Reader 5. 2007. (Illus.). 32p. (J). per. 20.00 (***978-0-9717234-8-1(6)***) Ghost Hunter Productions.

Klingel, Cynthia Fitterer & Noyed, Robert B. Walter in the Woods & the Letter W. 2003. (Alphaphonics Ser.). (Illus.). 24p. (J). (ps-2). 21.36 (978-1-59296-113-9(4)) Child's World, Inc.

Kposowa, Tibbie S. The Forests Are No Longer Green. 1999. 320p. (Orig.). (gr. 7 up). pap. 14.00 (978-1-887935-25-8(8)) Tabay Pubns.

Kraatz, David. La Cancion del Geco. Luengas, Mauricio, illus. (SPA.). 16p. (J). (gr. 3-5). pap. 11.95 (978-1-56014-579-0(X)) Santillana USA Publishing Co., Inc.

Kramer, Alan & Kramer, Candice. Brer Rabbit Hears a Big Noise in the Woods: An African /American Folktale. 2006. spiral bd. 42.00 (***978-1-4108-7163-3(0)***) Benchmark Education Co.

Lancett, Peter. Dark Words. 2007. (Dark Man Ser.). 36p. pap. 6.95 (***978-1-84167-602-9(0)***) Ransom Publishing Ltd. GBR. *Dist:* International Publishers Marketing.

Landstrom, Olof. Boo & Baa in the Woods. 2000. (978-0-606-22354-6(1)) Tandem Library Bks.

Larson, Verna. Bernie's Forest Adventure: A Case for Secular Humanism. Jones, Sharon, ed. Tagnetti, Nikki, illus. 2nd rev. ed. 1999. (Bearables of Bernie Bear Ser.: No. 1). 24p. (J). (ps-k). 8.95 (978-1-56550-085-3(7)) Vision Bks. International.

Lasky, Kathryn. Sugaring Time. 2003. (Illus.). 21.25 (978-0-8446-7248-9(3)) Smith, Peter Pub., Inc.

Lawrence, Ann. Between the Forest & the Hills. 1999. (Adventure Library). (Illus.). 264p. (J). (gr. 9-12). reprint ed. pap. 12.95 (978-1-883937-39-3(6), 39-6) Bethlehem Bks.

Lechner, John. Sticky Burr: Adventures in Burrwood Forest. Lechner, John, illus. 2007. (Illus.). 56p. (J). (gr. 1-5). 15.99 (978-0-7636-3054-6(3)) Candlewick Pr.

LeMonde, Stephanie. Misty Forest. Fryba, Borivoj, illus. 2007. (YA). per. 14.95 (***978-1-934138-13-7(4)***) Bouncing Ball Bks., Inc.

Leone, Jason, illus. the Enchantress of Caratunk. Manna, Elizabeth, photos by. 2003. 30p. (J). (gr. 1-5). pap. 9.95 (978-0-9729807-0-8(9)) Murray, David M.

Livingston, Timothy J. & Livingston, Mary A. Working with Nature Set, 2 bks. Livingston, Timothy J., illus. 2006th ed. 2006. (Illus.). (J). 32.95 (***978-0-9635757-3-9(2)***) Red Tail Publishing.

Lopez, Minia. Friends in the Forest. Jimenez, Resu, illus. 2006. (J). 8.00 (978-0-9773531-4-9(1)) Charming Pubns.

Lowry, Lois. Messenger. 2006. 176p. (YA). pap. 6.50 (978-0-440-23912-3(5), Laurel Leaf) Random Hse. Children's Bks.

Lunsford, Susie. The Magical Wishing Well Forest Series. 2006. pap. 25.32 (***978-1-4134-9491-4(9)***) Xlibris Corp.

MacHale, D. J. Black Water. 2004. (Pendragon Ser.: Bk. 5). 448p. (gr. 3-6). pap. 7.99 (978-0-689-86911-2(8), Aladdin) Simon & Schuster Children's Publishing.

Marie, E. The Porcupine Connection: The Story of a Young Girl's Journey from Tragedy to Healing, with the Help of Her Forest Friends. 2004. 48p. pap. 19.95 (978-1-4137-3480-5(4)) PublishAmerica, Inc.

Markowitz, Susan Meredith. The el gran bosque verde & Great Green Forest. 2005. spiral bd. 66.00 (***978-1-4108-5653-1(4)***) Benchmark Education Co.

Marryat, Frederick & Hedge, Tricia. The Children of the New Forest, Level 2. 2nd rev. ed. 2000. (Bookworms Ser.). (Illus.). 6.50 (978-0-19-422967-8(X)) Oxford Univ. Pr., Inc.

Marshall, James. Goldilocks & the Three Bears. Marshall, James, illus. 2002. (Illus.). (J). 14.04 (978-0-7587-2613-1(9)) Book Wholesalers, Inc.

—Goldilocks & the Three Bears. 1998. (J). 13.79 (978-0-606-12946-6(4)) Tandem Library Bks.

Martin, JoElle. Moonlight in the Forest. 2009. 280p. (YA). pap. 14.99 (978-1-59092-563-8(7), Blue Works) Windstorm Creative.

Martin, Rafe. The Brave Little Parrot. Gaber, Susan, illus. 1998. 1p. (J). (ps-3). 16.99 (978-0-399-22825-4(X), Putnam Juvenile) Penguin Group (USA) Inc.

McPhail, David M. Edward in the Jungle. McPhail, David M., illus. 2002. (Illus.). 32p. (J). (ps-3). 16.99 (978-0-316-56391-8(9)) Little, Brown Bks. for Young Readers.

Melling, David. The Tale of Jack Frost. 2003. (Illus.). 32p. (J). 14.95 (978-0-7641-5675-5(6)) Barron's Educational Series, Inc.

Meredith-Markowitz, Susan. The Great Green Forest. ed. 2003. (Early Connections Ser.). (J). pap. 33.00 (978-1-4108-1373-2(8)) Benchmark Education Co.

Mishkin, Dan. The Forest King: Woodlark's Shadow. Mandrake, Tom, illus. 2006. 101p. (J). (gr. 5-8). 12.95 (978-0-9742803-5-6(6)) Komikwerks, LLC.

Mitchell, Adrian. Maudie & the Green Children. Hamann, Sigune, illus. 2000. 32p. (J). (gr. k-4). pap. (978-1-896580-06-7(8)) Tradewind Bks.

Moncomble, Gérard. The Nine Lives of the Cat. Arinouchkine, Andreï, illus. 2005. 32p. 16.95 (978-1-59687-189-2(X), Milk & Cookies) ibooks, Inc.

Mullican, Judy. In the Forest. Cress, Michelle H., illus. l.t. ed. 1998. (Cuddle Bks.). 7p. (J). (ps-k). pap. 10.95 (978-1-57332-129-7(X)) HighReach Learning, Inc.

Musick, David. Jeremy Daniels with the Bambles: The Adventure in the Mountains. 2003. 172p. pap. 12.95 (978-0-595-27944-9(9)) iUniverse, Inc.

Mykowski, Michelle. Explore God's Forest. Ring, Laura, ed. Mykowski, Michelle, illus. 1999. (Shaped Paperback Bks.). (Illus.). 24p. (J). (ps-1). pap. 3.99 (978-0-7847-0900-9(9), 03790, Bean Sprouts) Standard Publishing.

The Night Crossing: Individual Title, 6 packs. (Bookweb Ser.). 32p. (gr. 4 up). 34.00 (978-0-7635-3729-6(2)) Rigby Education.

Nivola, Claire A. El Bosque. 2002. (SPA.). 32p. (J). (978-84-261-3255-0(3)) Juventud, Editorial.

Nunn, Paul E., illus. Forest Adventure. 2008. 16p. (J). (ps-2). pap. 5.99 (***978-0-448-44779-7(7)***, Grosset & Dunlap) Penguin Group (USA) Inc.

Page, Terry. The Fathers of the Friendly Forest. Page, Terry, illus. (Illus.). 24p. (J). (gr. 2-6). pap. 4.00 (978-1-887864-69-5(5)); lib. bdg. 7.00 (978-1-887864-38-1(5)) Boo Bks., Inc.

Paquette-Pelc, Linda L. The Adventure of Little Opal: Lost in the Forest. 2002. (YA). cd-rom 14.99 (978-0-9713132-0-0(2)) Natures Trail.

Pearce, Philippa. The Squirrel Wife. Anderson, Wayne, illus. 2007. 32p. (J). (gr. k-3). 16.99 (***978-0-7636-3551-0(0)***) Candlewick Pr.

Perkins, T. J. The Secret in Phantom Forest: A Kim & Kelly Mystery. 2004. (Illus.). 130p. (YA). 10.99 (978-0-9777538-1-9(6)) GumShoe Press.

Perry, Holly Lynn. Spinner's Mystic Travels: Lost in the Black Forest. 2003. pap. 9.00 (978-0-8059-6291-8(3)) Dorrance Publishing Co., Inc.

Pferdehirt, Julia. Wisconsin Forest Tales. 2004. (Illus.). vii, 152p. (J). (978-1-931599-47-4(5), Trails Bks.) Big Earth Publishing.

Pintozzi, Nick. Bentley & the Cactus Rustlers. Pintozzi, Nick & Pintozzi, Connie, illus. 2006. per. 11.00 (***978-0-9749465-4-2(0)***) BentDaiSha, LLC.

Plotkin, Mark. Shaman's Apprentice. 2001. (gr. k-3). lib. bdg. 14.15 (978-0-613-35566-7(0)) Tandem Library Bks.

Random House Disney Staff. Bambi. unabr. ed. (Read-Along Ser.). (J). 7.99 incl. audio (978-1-55723-008-9(0)) Walt Disney Records.

Rau, Dana Meachen. Walk in the Woods. 2001. (Illus.). 24p. (J). (gr. k-2). lib. bdg. 19.27 (978-1-57103-322-2(X)) Rourke Publishing, LLC.

Reetz, Kurt & Schure, Kimberley. Kasey & the Dream Forest: The First Dream. Voelker, Marty, illus. 2000. 24p. (J). (gr. 1-3). pap. (978-0-9701450-0-0(4)) Long Hill Productions, Inc.

Reetz, Kurt & Schure, Kimberly. Kasey & the Dream Forest: The First Dream. 2000. mass mkt. 8.95 incl. audio compact disk (978-1-931179-05-8(0)) Long Hill Productions, Inc.

Reid, Roger. Longleaf. 2006. 136p. (J). 19.95 (978-1-58838-194-1(3), Junebug Bks.) NewSouth, Inc.

Robertson, M. P. Big Foot. 2004. (Illus.). 32p. (J). pap. 7.95 (978-1-84507-153-0(0)) Lincoln, Frances Ltd. GBR. *Dist:* Perseus Distribution.

Rueda, Claudia. Let's Play in the Forest While the Wolf Is Not Around. 2006. (Illus.). 32p. (J). pap. 16.99 (978-0-439-82323-4(4), Scholastic Pr.) Scholastic, Inc.

Sanderson, Ruth. The Enchanted Wood. Sanderson, Ruth, illus. 1999. (Illus.). 32p. (J). (gr. k-6). reprint ed. 14.95 (978-0-9672902-0-1(1)) Golden Wood Studio.

Savary, Fabien. Caillou - Who Lives in the Forest? Johanson, Sarah Margaret, tr. from FRE. Brignaud, Pierre, illus. rev. ed. 2005. (Butterfly Ser.).Tr. of Caillou Découvre les Animaux. 20p. (J). (ps-1). pap. 5.95 (978-2-89450-541-0(8)) Chouette Publishing CAN. *Dist:* Independent Pubs. Group.

Schaefer, Carole Lexa. Down in the Woods at Sleepytime. Cabban, Vanessa, illus. 2000. 32p. (J). (gr. k-k). 15.99 (978-0-7636-0843-9(2)) Candlewick Pr.

Schmidt, Werner. The Forests of Adventure. 2005. 137p. pap. 12.50 (978-1-4116-4721-3(1)) Lulu.com.

Sculthorp, Jeffrey A. A Surprise for Rascal. Wingate, Lynae & Kober, John R., eds. Walter, Lorin, illus. 2000. (Wickleville Woods Ser.). 28p. (J). (ps-2). pap. 4.99 (978-1-889319-76-6(7), Wickleville Woods) Trend Enterprises, Inc.

—The Wickleville Woods Pond. Wingate, Lynae & Kober, John R., eds. Walter, Lorin, illus. 2000. (Wickleville Woods Ser.). 28p. (J). (ps-2). pap. 4.99 (978-1-889319-70-4(8), Wickleville Woods) Trend Enterprises, Inc.

Shetterly, Susan Hand. Shelterwood. 1999. (gr. 3-6). lib. bdg. 16.40 (978-0-613-63530-1(2)) Tandem Library Bks.

—Shelterwood. McCall, Rebecca H., illus. 40p. (J). 2005. (gr. 3-6). 7.95 (978-0-88448-256-7(1)); 1999. (gr. k-3). 16.95 (978-0-88448-210-9(3)) Tilbury Hse. Pubs.

Shulman, Mark. Magic Fairy Forest. Wilburn, Kathy, illus. 2005. (Storytime Stickers Ser.). 16p. (J). pap. 4.95 (978-1-4027-1806-9(3)) Sterling Publishing Co., Inc.

Smith, Beth Esh. Phyllis the Forest Ranger. Crowell, Knox, illus. l.t. ed. 2000. (LB Ser.). 8p. (J). (ps-1). pap. 10.95 (978-1-57332-164-8(8)); pap. 10.95 (978-1-57332-163-1(X)) HighReach Learning, Inc.

Smith, Timothy R. The Owls Don't Give a Hoot. 2007. (Buck Wilder's Adventure Ser.: 4). (Illus.). 96p. (J). pap. 5.95 (***978-1-934133-11-8(6)***) Mackinac Island Pr., Inc.

Steck-Vaughn Staff. The Great Kapok Tree. 2000. (Illus.). (J). pap. (978-0-7398-3367-4(7)) Steck-Vaughn.

Sterling Publishing Co., Inc. & Fernleigh Books Staff. Snow White: A Magic 3-Dimensional Fairy-Tale World. 2006. (Step Inside Ser.). (Illus.). 12p. (J). 9.95 (978-1-4027-3656-8(8)) Sterling Publishing Co., Inc.

Stewart, Paul & Riddell, Chris. Beyond the Deepwoods. 2004. (Edge Chronicles Ser.: Bk. 1). (Illus.). 288p. (J). (gr. 5-7). 12.95 (978-0-385-75068-4(4), Fickling, David Bks.) Random Hse. Children's Bks.

Stewart, Paul & Riddell, Chris. Edge Chronicles 1: Beyond the Deepwoods. 2008. (Edge Chronicles Ser.). 288p. (J). (gr. 5-7). 6.99 (***978-0-440-42087-3(3)***, Yearling) Random Hse. Children's Bks.

Stratton-Porter, Gene. Freckles. (J). reprint ed. lib. bdg. 24.95 (978-0-89190-949-1(4), Rivercity Pr.) Amereon LTD.

Stratton-Porter, Gene & Matthews, Andrew. Freckles. 2000. (Illus.). 32p. (C). pap. 9.00 (978-0-582-42655-9(3)) Pearson ESL.

Theiss, Lewis E. The Young Wireless Operator -As a Fire. 2006. pap. (***978-1-4068-1180-3(7)***) Echo Library.

Tibo, Gilles & Vaillancourt, Francois. El Senor Patapum. (Barril Sin Fondo Ser.). (SPA.). (J). (gr. 3-5). pap. (978-968-6465-58-7(8)) Casa de Estudios de Literatura y Talleres Artisticos Amaquemecan A.C. MEX. *Dist:* Lectorum Pubns., Inc.

Toma, Al. Rainbow on the Tree of Life. 2005. (J). pap. 15.00 (978-0-8059-6607-7(2)) Dorrance Publishing Co., Inc.

Tomlinson, Theresa. Child of the May. 1998. (Illus.). 128p. (YA). (gr. 5-9). pap. 15.95 (978-0-531-30118-0(4), Orchard Bks.) Scholastic, Inc.

Townsend, John. Hunter's Moon. Dietrich, Sean, illus. 2007. (J). 80p. (***978-1-59889-352-6(1)***); 71p. pap. (***978-1-59889-447-9(1)***) Stone Arch Bks.

Tumbrello, Shannon. Freedom Forest. 2007. 17.00 (***978-0-8059-8880-2(7)***) Dorrance Publishing Co., Inc.

Tunison, Dick. Tale of Marley & His Forest Friends. 2001. (Illus.). (J). (ps-5). pap. 9.95 (978-0-9707015-1-0(9)) Emmaus Pr.

Tyrrell, Melissa. Hansel & Gretel. McMullen, Nigel, illus. 2005. (Fairytale Friends Ser.). 12p. (J). bds. 5.95 (978-1-58117-152-5(8), Intervisual/Piggy Toes) Dalmatian Pr.

Vermeulen, Marleen. Forest Tales from Far & Wide. Moran, Rosslyn, illus. 1998. 48p. (J). (ps-2). 15.95 (978-1-901223-33-0(7)) Barefoot Bks., Inc.

Vincent, Annie. Adventures at Honeybee Hive: Trouble in the New Forest. 2004. 69p. pap. 14.95 (978-1-4137-4676-1(4)) PublishAmerica, Inc.

Wargin, Kathy-Jo. Legend of the Lady's Slipper. 2003. (gr. k-3). lib. bdg. 16.40 (978-0-613-79712-2(4)) Tandem Library Bks.

Whybrow, Ian. Little Wolf, Forest Detective. Ross, Tony, illus. 2005. 112p. (J). (gr. 3-6). pap. 6.95 (978-1-57505-829-0(4)) Lerner Publishing Group.

Wilder, Laura Ingalls. Little House in the Big Woods. Williams, Garth, illus. 2001. (Little House Ser.). 256p. (J). (gr. k-4). 19.95 (978-0-06-029647-6(X)) HarperCollins Pubs.

Wilhelm, Hans. Hello, Sun! Wilhelm, Hans, illus. 2005. (Illus.). 32p. (gr. k-2). 15.25 (978-1-57505-348-6(9)) Lerner Publishing Group.

Wilson, Karma. Bear's New Friend. Chapman, Jane, illus. 2006. 40p. (J). (ps-2). 16.95 (978-0-689-85984-7(8), McElderry, Margaret K.) Simon & Schuster Children's Publishing.

Winfield, Arthur M. The Rover Boys in the Jungle. 2004. reprint ed. pap. 21.95 (978-1-4191-8118-4(1)); pap. 1.99 (978-1-4192-8118-1(6)) Kessinger Publishing, LLC.

Zabel, Alanna. The Seven Doors. 2006. 59p. pap. 18.50 (978-1-4116-4369-7(0)) Lulu.com.

Zalonis, C. B. Strangers in the Forest. 2006. (J). pap. 8.00 (978-0-8059-6820-0(2)) Dorrance Publishing Co., Inc.

Zarley, Jacqualynn. Adventures with Lucy the Llama: Book One: Justice for the Great Forest. 2004. 56p. pap. 12.95 (978-1-4137-4906-9(2)) PublishAmerica, Inc.

Ziefert, Harriet. Noisy Forest! 2004. (Illus.). 7p. bds. 8.95 (978-1-59354-058-6(2)) Blue Apple Bks.

FORGERY OF WORKS OF ART

Nilsen, Anna. Art Fraud Detective: Spot the Difference, Solve the Crime! Parker, Andy, illus. 2000. 48p. (J). (gr. 3-5). tchr. ed. 17.95 (978-0-7534-5308-7(8), Kingfisher) Houghton Mifflin Co. Trade & Reference Div.

Wright, Russell G. Fraud! Investigations in Art Forgery Detection. 2000. (Event-Based Science Ser.). (Illus.). (J). pap., stu. ed. 25.95 (978-0-7690-0030-5(4)) Seymour, Dale Pubns.

FORM, MUSICAL
see Musical Form

FORMER SOVIET REPUBLICS
Here are entered works discussing collectively the independent countries that emerged from the dissolution of the former Soviet Union in 1991.

Adams, Simon. Russian Republics. 2005. (Illus.). 44p. (J). (gr. 6-9). lib. bdg. 29.95 (978-1-58340-606-9(9)) Smart Apple Media.

Cheng, Pang Guek. Kazakhstan. 2001. (Cultures of the World Ser.). (Illus.). 128p. (J). (gr. 5-12). lib. bdg. 37.07 (978-0-7614-1193-2(3) , Benchmark Bks.) Cavendish, Marshall Corp.

Docalavich, Heather. Slovakia. 2006. (European Union Ser.). (Illus.). 88p. (YA). (gr. 5 up). lib. bdg. (978-1-4222-0060-5(4)) Mason Crest Pubs.

Giragosian, Richard & Streissguth, Thomas. The Transcaucasus. 2002. (Former Soviet Republics Ser.). (Illus.). 112p. (J). (gr. 6-9). 29.95 (978-1-56006-736-8(5) , Lucent Bks.) Thomson Gale.

FORMOSA
see Taiwan

FORT, CHARLES, 1874-1932

Innes, Brian. The Cosmic Joker. 1999. (Unsolved Mysteries Ser.). 48p. (YA). (gr. 3 up). lib. bdg. 25.69 (978-0-8172-5487-2(0)) Raintree.

FORT TICONDEROGA (N.Y.)

Haugen, Brenda & Santella, Andrew. Ethan Allen: Green Mountain Rebel. 2004. (Signature Lives Ser.). (Illus.). 112p. (J). 30.60 (978-0-7565-0824-1(X) , 1240131) Compass Point Bks.

Maynard, Charles W. Fort Ticonderoga. 2002. (Famous Forts Throughout American History Ser.). (Illus.). 24p. (J). (gr. 3). lib. bdg. 18.75 (978-0-8239-5836-8(1) , PowerKids Pr.) Rosen Publishing Group, Inc., The.

Price Hossell, Karen. Ethan Allen. 2004. (American War Biographies Ser.). (J). lib. bdg. 29.93 (978-1-4034-5077-7(3)); (Illus.). pap. 8.50 (978-1-4034-5084-5(6)) Heinemann Library.

Stein, R. Conrad. Ethan Allen & the Green Mountain Boys. 2003. (Cornerstones of Freedom). (Illus.). 48p. (J). (gr. 4-6). 26.00 (978-0-516-24206-4(7) , Children's Pr.) Scholastic Library Publishing.

Strum, Richard M. Fort Ticonderoga. 2004. (American Forts & Their Strategic Importance Ser.). (J). (978-1-59084-707-7(5)) Mason Crest Pubs.

FORTEN, JAMES, 1766-1842

Figley, Marty Rhodes. Prisoner for Liberty. Orback, Craig, illus. 2008. (On My Own History Ser.). (J). lib. bdg. 25.26 (*978-0-8225-7280-0(X) , Millbrook Pr.) Lerner Publishing Group.

Krebs, Laurie. A Day in the Life of a Colonial Sailmaker. 2004. (Library of Living & Working in Colonial Times). (Illus.). 24p. (J). lib. bdg. 18.75 (978-0-8239-6231-0(8) , PowerKids Pr.) Rosen Publishing Group, Inc., The.

FORTIFICATION

Adams, Simon. Castles & Forts. 2007. (Kingfisher Knowledge Ser.). (Illus.). 64p. (J). (gr. 4-6). pap. 8.95 (*978-0-7534-6119-8(6) , Kingfisher) Houghton Mifflin Co. Trade & Reference Div.

Bial, Raymond. The Forts: Building America. 2001. (Building America Ser.). (Illus.). 56p. (J). (gr. 4 up). lib. bdg. 27.07 (978-0-7614-1334-9(0) , Benchmark Bks.) Cavendish, Marshall Corp.

—Missions & Presidios. 2004. (American Community Ser.). (Illus.). 48p. (J). (gr. 2-5). 29.00 (978-0-516-23708-4(X) , Children's Pr.) Scholastic Library Publishing.

Chrisp, Peter. Warfare. 2004. (Medieval Realms Ser.). (J). (gr. 7-10). 29.95 (978-1-59018-537-7(4) , Lucent Bks.) Thomson Gale.

Copeland, Peter F. Historic North American Forts. 2000. 48p. (J). pap. 3.95 (978-0-486-41036-4(6)) Dover Pubns., Inc.

Davis, Susan Burdick. Old Forts & Real Folks. 2006. pap. 31.95 (*978-1-4286-5582-9(4)) Kessinger Publishing, LLC.

Gravett, Christopher. Castle. 2008. (DK Eyewitness Bks.). 72p. (J). (gr. 3-8). 15.99 (*978-0-7566-3769-9(4)) Dorling Kindersley Publishing, Inc.

Hamilton, John. Castles & Dungeons. 2005. (Illus.). 32p. (J). (gr. 4-8). lib. bdg. 24.21 (978-1-59679-335-4(X) , ABDO & Daughters) ABDO Publishing Co.

Hicks, Peter. How Castles Were Built. 1999. (Age of Castles Ser.). (Illus.). 48p. (J). (gr. 4-8). (978-0-7502-2144-3(5)) Steck-Vaughn.

Higgins, Christopher. Alcatraz Island. 2004. (American Forts & Their Strategic Importance Ser.). (J). (978-1-59084-710-7(5)) Mason Crest Pubs.

MacDonald, Fiona. Warfare in the Middle Ages. 2003. (Battle Zones Ser.). (Illus.). 48p. (J). 18.95 (978-1-57768-596-8(2) , Bedrick, Peter Bks.) School Specialty Publishing.

Marcovitz, Hal. Fort Clatsop. 2004. (American Forts & Their Strategic Importance Ser.). (J). (978-1-59084-706-0(7)) Mason Crest Pubs.

Maynard, Charles W. Fort Clatsop. 2002. (Famous Forts Throughout American History Ser.). (Illus.). 24p. (J). (gr. 3). lib. bdg. 18.75 (978-0-8239-5837-5(X) , PowerKids Pr.) Rosen Publishing Group, Inc., The.

Morley, Jacqueline, et al. A Roman Fort. 1999. (Magnifications Ser.). (Illus.). 48p. (J). (gr. 3-8). 18.95 (978-0-87226-650-6(8) , Bedrick, Peter Bks.) School Specialty Publishing.

Mulvihill, Margaret. Roman Forts. Wood, Gerlad, illus. 2006. (Hallmarks of History Ser.). 32p. (J). (gr. 4-6). lib. bdg. 27.10 (978-1-59604-121-9(8)) Stargazer Bks.

Patrick, Bethanne Kelly. Forts of the West. 2002. (History of the Old West Ser.). (Illus.). 64p. (YA). (gr. 5 up). lib. bdg. (978-1-59084-071-9(2)) Mason Crest Pubs.

Pickett, Margaret F. Jamestown. 2004. (American Forts & Their Strategic Importance Ser.). (J). (978-1-59084-716-9(4)) Mason Crest Pubs.

Shapiro, Stephen. Battle Stations! Fortifications Through the Ages. Tsao, Mei H. & Nice, Ken, illus. 2005. 32p. (J). (gr. 4-12). pap. 7.95 (978-1-55037-888-7(0)); lib. bdg. 19.95 (978-1-55037-889-4(9)) Annick Pr., Ltd. CAN. *Dist:* Firefly Bks., Ltd.

Shuter, Jane. Life in a Roman Fort. 2004. (Picture the Past Ser.). (Illus.). 32p. (J). 24.22 (978-1-4034-5829-2(4)); pap. (978-1-4034-5837-7(5)) Heinemann Library.

Taylor, Barbara. World of Castles. 2000. (gr. 3-6). lib. bdg. 16.40 (978-0-613-89411-1(1)) Tandem Library Bks.

Williams, Jack S. The California Presidios. 2004. (American Forts & Their Strategic Importance Ser.). (J). (978-1-59084-711-4(3)) Mason Crest Pubs.

FORTS
see Fortification

FORTUNE
see Probabilities; Success

FORTUNE-TELLING
see also Astrology; Cards; Dreams

Blackwood, Gary L. Fateful Forebodings. 1998. (Secrets of the Unexplained Ser.). (Illus.). 64p. (J). (gr. 5-9). lib. bdg. 28.50 (978-0-7614-0467-5(8) , Benchmark Bks.) Cavendish, Marshall Corp.

Burns, Jane & Gottlieb, Dale. Wise Gal Tarot: Amazing Ways to Read Your Fortune! Slattery, Joan, ed. 2000. (Illus.). 64p. (J). (gr. 3-7). lib. bdg. 15.99 (978-0-375-90644-2(4) , Random Hse. Bks. for Young Readers) Random Hse. Children's Bks.

Dickson, Louise. The Kids Guide to Fortune Telling. Cupples, Pat, illus. 1998. 40p. (J). (gr. 4-6). (978-1-55074-479-8(8)) Kids Can Pr., Ltd.

Filipak, Christine & Vargo, Joseph, illus. Madame Endora's Fortune Cards. 2003. mass mkt. 17.99 (978-0-9675756-3-6(X)) Monolith Graphics.

Johnson, Julie Tallard. I Ching for Teens: Take Charge of Your Destiny with the Ancient Chinese Oracle. 2001. (Illus.). 232p. 14.95 (978-0-89281-860-0(3) , Bindu Bks.) Inner Traditions International, Ltd.

Joly, Kimberly. Unfold Your Future. Middlewick, Paul, illus. 2004. 28p. (J). pap. 4.95 (978-0-7641-2778-6(0)) Barron's Educational Series, Inc.

Kanto, Erik & Kanto, Ilona. Your Face Tells All: Learn the Wisdom of the Chinese Art of Face Reading. 2004. (Illus.). 176p. pap. 16.95 (978-1-929956-13-5(4)) Kanto Productions, LLC.

Mahabal, Vernon. The Secret Code on Your Hands: An Illustrated Guide to Palmistry. Dolphin-Kingsley, Kamala, illus. 2002. 62p. 19.95 (978-1-886069-31-2(X) , BK4011HB) Mandala Publishing.

Moorey, Teresa. Fortune Telling: What Does the Future Hold for You? 2005. (Illus.). 128p. (J). pap. 7.99 (978-0-340-88431-7(2) , Hodder & Stoughton) Hodder General Publishing Division GBR. *Dist:* Trafalgar Square Publishing.

Moss, Marissa. Madame Amelia Tells All. Moss, Marissa, illus. 2007. (Amelia's Notebooks). 64p. (J). 9.99 (978-1-4169-0918-7(4) , Simon & Schuster/Paula Wiseman Bks.) Simon & Schuster Children's Publishing.

O'Neill, Terry. Fortune Telling. 2006. (Illus.). 168p. (gr. 10-12). 32.45 (978-0-7377-3508-6(2) , Greenhaven Pr., Inc.) Thomson Gale.

Zaruni, Isabella. The Magic Fortune-Teller: A Window into Your Future on Every Page. Triplett, Gina, illus. 2007. 16p. (J). (gr. 2-7). 12.95 (978-0-8118-5922-6(3)) Chronicle Bks. LLC.

FOSSIL MAMMALS
see Mammals, Fossil

FOSSIL PLANTS
see Plants, Fossil

FOSSILS
see also Extinct Animals; Mammals, Fossil; Plants, Fossil; Reptiles, Fossil

Acorn, John. Deep Alberta: Fossil Facts & Dinosaur Digs. 2007. (Illus.). 200 p. (YA). (gr. 7 up). pap. 26.95 (*978-0-88864-481-7(7)) Univ. of Alberta Pr. CAN. *Dist:* Michigan State Univ. Pr.

Agenbroad, Larry D. & Nelson, Lisa W. Mammoths: Ice-Age Giants. 2003. (Illus.). 120p. (J). (gr. 7-12). pap. 7.95 (978-0-8225-0470-2(7)) Lerner Publishing Group.

Aliki. Digging up Dinosaurs. 33p. (J). (gr. 1-3). pap. 4.95 (978-0-8072-1339-1(X) , Listening Library) Random Hse. Audio Publishing Group.

Anholt, Laurence. Stone Girl, Bone Girl: The Story of Mary Anning. Moxley, Sheila, illus. 1999. 32p. (J). (gr. k-4). pap. 15.95 (978-0-531-30148-7(6) , Orchard Bks.) Scholastic, Inc.

Arato, Rona. Fossils. 2004. (Rocks, Minerals, & Resources Ser.). (Illus.). 32p. (J). (978-0-7787-1419-4(5)); pap. (978-0-7787-1451-4(9)) Crabtree Publishing Co.

Arnold, Caroline. Dinosaurs with Feathers: The Ancestors of Modern Birds. Caple, Laurie A., illus. 2001. 32p. (J). (gr. 4-6). tchr. ed. 15.00 (978-0-618-00398-3(3) , Clarion Bks.) Houghton Mifflin Co. Trade & Reference Div.

—Giant Shark: Megalodon, the Super Prehistoric Predator. Caple, Laurie A., illus. 2000. 32p. (J). (gr. 4-6). tchr. ed. 16.00 (978-0-395-91419-9(1) , Clarion Bks.) Houghton Mifflin Co. Trade & Reference Div.

—Pterosaurs: Rulers of the Skies in the Dinosaur Age. Caple, Laurie A., illus. 2004. 40p. (J). (gr. 4-6). tchr. ed. 16.00 (978-0-618-31354-9(0) , Clarion Bks.) Houghton Mifflin Co. Trade & Reference Div.

—When Mammoths Walked the Earth. Caple, Laurie A., illus. 2002. 40p. (J). (gr. k-3). tchr. ed. 16.00 (978-0-618-09633-6(7) , Clarion Bks.) Houghton Mifflin Co. Trade & Reference Div.

Atkins, Jeannine. Mary Anning & the Sea Dragon. Dooling, Michael, illus. 1999. 32p. (J). (gr. k-3). 16.00 (978-0-374-34840-3(5) , Farrar, Straus & Giroux (BYR)) Farrar, Straus & Giroux.

Bailey, Jacqui. Monster Bones: The Story of a Dinosaur Fossil. Lilly, Matthew, illus. 2004. (Science Works Ser.). 32p. (J). (gr. 3-6). 23.93 (978-1-4048-0565-1(6)) Picture Window Bks.

Bakker, Robert T. Prehistoric Monsters! 2008. (J). pap. (*978-0-375-83945-0(3)); lib. bdg. (*978-0-375-93945-7(8)) Random Hse., Inc.

Barker, Charles Ferguson. Under Ohio: The Story of Ohio's Rocks & Fossils. 2007. (Illus.). 56p. (J). 17.95 (*978-0-8214-1755-3(X)) Ohio Univ. Pr.

Barner, Bob. Dinosaur Bones. 2001. (Illus.). 36p. (J). (ps-3). 15.95 (978-0-8118-3158-1(2)) Chronicle Bks. LLC.

—Dinosaur Bones. Barner, Bob, illus. unabr. ed. 2006. (J). (ps-2). 24.95 incl. audio (*978-0-439-90574-9(5)); 29.95 incl. audio compact disk (*978-0-439-90580-0(X)) Weston Woods Studios, Inc.

Batten, Mary. Extinct! Creatures of the Past. 2000. (J). 10.79 (978-0-606-18926-2(2)) Tandem Library Bks.

Bedry, Christa. Fish. 2004. (Prehistoric Life Ser.). (J). pap. 7.95 (978-1-59036-172-6(5)); (Illus.). 32p. lib. bdg. 15.95 (978-1-59036-112-2(1)) Weigl Pubs., Inc.

—Insects. 2004. (Prehistoric Life Ser.). (J). pap. 7.95 (978-1-59036-173-3(3)); (Illus.). 32p. lib. bdg. 15.95 (978-1-59036-113-9(X)) Weigl Pubs., Inc.

Benanti, Carol. Real Fossils. Frank, Michael, ed. Dickens, Earl, illus. (Real Collections). 32p. (Orig.). (J). (gr. 3-8). pap. 6.95 (978-1-880592-06-9(1)) Pace Products, Inc.

Benchmark Education Staff. Plant & Animal Fossils. 2005. 2.00 (*978-1-4108-4669-3(5)) Benchmark Education Co.

Bennett, Leonie. Dinosaur Fossils. 2008. (J). lib. bdg. (*978-1-59716-555-6(7)) Bearport Publishing Co., Inc.

—Dinosaur Hunting. 2008. (I Love Reading Ser.). (J). lib. bdg. 19.96 (*978-1-59716-554-9(9)) Bearport Publishing Co., Inc.

—Dinosaurs that Ate Meat. 2006. (I Love Reading Ser.). (Illus.). 24p. (J). lib. bdg. 19.96 (978-1-59716-151-0(9)) Bearport Publishing Co., Inc.

—Dinosaurs that Ate Plants. 2006. (I Love Reading Ser.). (Illus.). 24p. (J). lib. bdg. 19.96 (978-1-59716-152-7(7)) Bearport Publishing Co., Inc.

Beres, Samantha, et al. 101 Things Every Kid Should Know about Dinosaurs. 2000. (Illus.). 128p. (J). (gr. 3-7). 14.95 (978-0-7373-0518-0(5)) Lowell Hse. Juvenile.

Berger, Melvin. Did Dinosaurs Live in Your Backyard? 1999. (Question & Answer Ser.). (J). 12.75 (978-0-606-20053-0(3)) Tandem Library Bks.

Berger, Melvin & Berger, Gilda. Did Dinosaurs Live in Your Backyard? Male, Alan, illus. 1999. (Scholastic Question & Answer Ser.). 48p. (J). (gr. 2-4). pap. 12.95 (978-0-590-13078-3(1) , Scholastic Reference) Scholastic, Inc.

—Did Dinosaurs Live in Your Backyard? Questions & Answers about Dinosaurs. Male, Alan, illus. 1999. (Scholastic Question & Answer Ser.). 48p. (J). (gr. 2-4). 5.95 (978-0-439-08568-7(3) , Scholastic Reference) Scholastic, Inc.

Birch, Robin. Relatives of Dinosaurs. 2002. (Chelsea Clubhouse Science Exploration Ser.). (Illus.). 32p. (gr. k-2). 23.00 (978-0-7910-6991-2(5) , Chelsea Hse.) Facts On File, Inc.

Bishop, Nic. Digging for Bird Dinosaurs: An Expedition to Madagascar. 2000. (Scientists in the Field Ser.). (Illus.). 48p. (J). (gr. 4-6). tchr. ed. 16.00 (978-0-395-96056-1(8)) Houghton Mifflin Co. Trade & Reference Div.

Blashfield, Jean F. & Jacobs, Richard P. When Life Took Root on Land. 2005. (Illus.). 80p. (J). (978-1-4034-7659-3(4)) Heinemann Library.

—When Life Took Root on Land. 2004. (J). 35.64 (978-1-4109-1290-9(6)) Raintree.

Bonner, Hannah. When Bugs Were Big, Plants Were Strange, & Tetrapods Stalked the Earth: Prehistoric Life in a World Before Dinosaurs. 2004. (Illus.). 48p. (J). (gr. 3-7). 16.95 (978-0-7922-6326-5(X) , National Geographic Children's Bks.) National Geographic Society.

Bonner, Hannah, illus. When Fish Got Feet, Sharks Got Teeth, & Bugs Began to Swarm: A Cartoon Prehistory of Life Long Before Dinosaurs. 2007. 48p. (YA). (gr. 5 up). 16.95 (978-1-4263-0078-3(6)); lib. bdg. 25.90 (978-1-4263-0079-0(4)) National Geographic Society. (National Geographic Children's Bks.).

Bramwell, M. Rocks & Fossils. rev. ed. 2007. (Hobby Guides). 32p. (J). pap. 6.99 (*978-0-7945-1526-3(6) , Usborne) EDC Publishing.

Brannon, Barbara. Discover Fossils. 2005. 39.00 (*978-1-4108-5121-5(4)) Benchmark Education Co.

Burnie, David. The Concise Dinosaur Encyclopedia. 2004. (Concise Ser.). (Illus.). 224p. (J). (gr. 4-8). 12.95 (978-0-7534-5754-2(7) , Kingfisher) Houghton Mifflin Co. Trade & Reference Div.

Burns, Jasper. Virginia Fossils: An Educational Activity Book. Burns, Jasper, illus. 1998. (Illus.). 40p. (Orig.). (J). (gr. 4-7). pap. 4.95 (978-1-884549-03-8(9)) Virginia Museum of Natural History.

Burton, Jane & Taylor, Kim. The Nature & Science of Fossils. Burton, Jane & Taylor, Kim, photos by. 1999. (Exploring the Science of Nature Ser.). (Illus.). 32p. (J). (gr. 3 up). lib. bdg. 23.93 (978-0-8368-2183-3(1)) Stevens, Gareth Inc.

Butz, Steve. The Bone Race: A Quest for Dinosaur Fossils. 2007. 248p. (YA). pap. 16.95 (*978-1-933255-30-9(7)) DNA Pr.

Carr, Karen & Diffily, Deborah. Jurassic Shark. Carr, Karen, illus. 2004. (Illus.). 32p. (J). (ps-3). 17.99 (978-0-06-008249-9(6)); lib. bdg. 18.89 (978-0-06-008250-5(X)) HarperCollins Pubs.

Cefrey, Holly. Fossils. 2003. (Reading Power Ser.). (Illus.). 24p. (J). lib. bdg. 17.25 (978-0-8239-6469-7(8) , PowerKids Pr.) Rosen Publishing Group, Inc., The.

Chandler, Fiona, et al. The Usborne Internet-Linked Prehistoric World. Firenze, Inklink, illus. 2005. 96p. (J). pap. (*978-0-439-78504-4(9)) Scholastic, Inc.

Chapman, Todd & Judge, Lita. D Is for Dinosaur: A Prehistoric Alphabet. Judge, Lita, illus. 2007. (General Alphabet Ser.). 48p. (J). 17.95 (*978-1-58536-242-4(5)) Sleeping Bear Pr.

Chrisp, Peter. Dinosaur Detectives. 2001. (Illus.). (J). (ps-3). 48p. lib. bdg. 11.80 (978-0-613-35101-0(0)); 10.79 (978-0-606-21146-8(2)) Tandem Library Bks.

Christian, Spencer & Felix, Antonia. Is There a Dinosaur in Your Backyard: The World's Most Fascinating Fossils, Rocks, & Minerals. 1998. (Spencer Christians World of Wonders: Vol. 12). (Illus.). 120p. (gr. 4-7). pap. 12.95 (978-0-471-19616-7(9) , Wiley) Wiley, John & Sons, Inc.

Clemson, Wendy & Clemson, David. Digging for Dinosaurs. 2006. (J). pap. (*978-0-8368-8137-0(0)); lib. bdg. (*978-0-8368-7838-7(8)) Stevens, Gareth Inc.

Cohen, Daniel. Pteranodon. 2000. (Bridgestone Science Library). (Illus.). 108p. (J). (gr. 1-2). 18.60 (978-0-7368-0617-6(2) , Bridgestone Bks.) Capstone Pr., Inc.

—Sarcosuchus Imperator. 2004. (Illus.). 24p. (J). 14.95 (978-0-7368-2525-2(8) , Bridgestone Bks.) Capstone Pr., Inc.

Cryute, Clay. Tales of a Prehistoric Sponge: The Rock Cycle. 2005. (Illus.). 32p. (J). (gr. 3-5). 7.85 (978-1-4109-1953-3(6)) Steck-Vaughn.

Cutchins, Judy. Ice Age Giants of the South. 2000. (Southern Fossil Discoveries Ser.: Vol. 1). (Illus.). 48p. (J). (gr. 3-7). 14.95 (978-1-56164-195-6(2)) Pineapple Pr., Inc.

Cutchins, Judy & Johnston, Ginny. Giant Predators of the Ancient Seas. Cutchins, Judy, illus. 2001. (Southern Fossil Discoveries Ser.). (Illus.). 48p. (J). (gr. 3-7). 14.95 (978-1-56164-237-3(1)) Pineapple Pr., Inc.

Daniel. Fossils: Pictures from the Past. 1999. (Illus.). (J). pap. 5.65 (978-0-7398-0865-8(6)) Steck-Vaughn.

—Fossils Alive! 1999. (Illus.). (J). pap. 5.65 (978-0-7398-0864-1(8)) Steck-Vaughn.

Dayton, Connor. Fossils. 2007. (Rocks & Minerals Ser.). (Illus.). 24p. (J). (gr. 2-7). lib. bdg. 21.25 (*978-1-4042-3689-9(9) , PowerKids Pr.) Rosen Publishing Group, Inc., The.

Dixon, Dougal. Carnivores. 2001. (Dinosaurs Ser.). (Illus.). 36p. (J). (gr. 4 up). lib. bdg. 24.67 (978-0-8368-2915-0(8)) Stevens, Gareth Inc.

—Ceratosaurus & Other Fierce Dinosaurs. Weston, Steve & Field, James, illus. 2006. 24p. (J). (gr. k-3). 22.60 (978-1-4048-1327-4(6)) Picture Window Bks.

—Cretaceous Life. 2006. (Prehistoric World Bks.). 32p. (J). pap. 4.99 (978-0-7641-3483-8(3)) Barron's Educational Series, Inc.

—Dinosaurs in the Sea: Dinosaurs in the Sky. 2003. (J). pap. (978-0-8368-3329-4(5)) Stevens, Gareth Inc.

—The Discovery of T. Rex. 2006. (Stories from History Ser.). 48p. (J). 14.95 (*978-0-7696-4712-8(X)); pap. 6.95 (*978-0-7696-4693-0(X)) School Specialty Publishing.

—Early Life. 2006. (Prehistoric World Bks.). 32p. (J). pap. 4.99 (978-0-7641-3482-1(5)) Barron's Educational Series, Inc.

—Herbivores. 2001. (Dinosaurs Ser.). (Illus.). 36p. (J). (gr. 4 up). lib. bdg. 24.67 (978-0-8368-2916-7(6)) Stevens, Gareth Inc.

—In the Sea. 2001. (Dinosaurs Ser.). (Illus.). 36p. (J). (gr. 4 up). lib. bdg. 24.67 (978-0-8368-2917-4(4)) Stevens, Gareth Inc.

—In the Sky. 2001. (Dinosaurs Ser.). (Illus.). 36p. (J). (gr. 4 up). lib. bdg. 24.67 (978-0-8368-2918-1(2)) Stevens, Gareth Inc.

—Jurassic Life. 2006. (Prehistoric World Bks.). 32p. (J). pap. 4.99 (978-0-7641-3478-4(7)) Barron's Educational Series, Inc.

—Prehistoric World: The Age of Mammals. 2006. (Prehistoric World Bks.). 32p. (J). pap. 4.99 (978-0-7641-3480-7(9)) Barron's Educational Series, Inc.

DK Publishing. Prehistoric Life. 2008. (DK Eyewitness Bks.). 48p. (J). (gr. 2-8). pap. 9.99 (*978-0-7566-3784-2(8)) Dorling Kindersley Publishing, Inc.

Dorling Kindersley Publishing Staff, ed. Fossil. 2004. (Dk Eyewitness Books Ser.). (Illus.). 72p. (J). 15.99 (978-0-7566-0682-4(9)) Dorling Kindersley Publishing, Inc.

Dunn, Mary. My Adventure on a Dinosaur Dig. 2006. 44p. (J). 8.99 (978-1-59092-281-1(6) , Orchard Academy Pr.) Windstorm Creative.

Eid, Alain. 1000 Photos of Minerals & Fossils. Viard, Michel, illus. 2003. (One Thousand Photos Ser.). 128p. (YA). (gr. 5 up). pap. 24.95 (978-0-7641-5218-4(1)) Barron's Educational Series, Inc.

Eldredge, Niles, et al. The Fossil Factory: A Kid's Guide to Digging up Dinosaurs, Exploring Evolution & Finding Fossils. Kelley, True & Lindblom, Steve, illus. rev. ed. 2002. 112p. pap. 12.95 (978-1-57098-417-4(4)) Rinehart, Roberts Pubs.

An Encyclopedia of Fossils: Third Grade Guided Reading Level M. (On Our Way to English Ser.). (gr. 3 up). 34.50 (978-0-7578-7133-7(X)) Rigby Education.

Erickson, Jon. Lost Creatures of the Earth: Mass Extinction in the History of Life. 2001. (Living Earth Ser.). (Illus.). 272p. (YA). (gr. 6-12). 55.00 (978-0-8160-4337-8(X)) Facts On File, Inc.

Evert, Laura. Rocks, Fossils, & Arrowheads. 2002. (gr. 3-6). lib. bdg. 16.40 (978-0-613-55890-7(1)) Tandem Library Bks.

—Rocks, Fossils & Arrowheads. 2002. (Take-Along Guide Ser.). (Illus.). 48p. (gr. 2-5). 10.95 (978-1-55971-805-9(6) , NorthWord Bks. for Young Readers) T&N Children's Publishing.

Exciting World: Includes: Fossil & Bones; The Hidden Past; The Search for Riches; Volcano, Earthquake & Hurricane, 4 bks., Set. (Remarkable World Ser.). (Illus.). (J). (gr. 4-7). lib. bdg. 75.92 (978-0-8172-5155-0(3)) Raintree.

Facchini, Fiorenzo. A Day with Homo Sapiens: Life 15,000 Years Ago. 2003. (Early Humans Ser.). (Illus.). 48p. (gr. 6 up). lib. bdg. 23.90 (978-0-7613-2768-4(1) , Twenty-First Century Bks.) Lerner Publishing Group.

Faulkner, Rebecca. Fossils. 2007. (J). (***978-1-4109-2752-1(0)***) Steck-Vaughn.

—Soil. 2007. (J). pap. (***978-1-4109-2760-6(1)***) Steck-Vaughn.

Fortey, Richard. Trilobite: Eyewitness to Evolution. 2001. (Illus.). 320p. pap. 14.00 (978-0-375 70621-9(6) , Vintage) Knopf Publishing Group.

Fossil Fuels: Individual Title Six-Packs. (Rigby Focus Ser.). 24p. (gr. 2 up). 28.00 (978-0-7578-5359-3(5)); 30.00 (978-0-7578-5589-4(X)) Rigby Education.

Fossil Hunting, 6 Packs. (Rigby Focus Ser.). 24p. (gr. 2 up). 30.00 (978-0-7578-5565-8(2)) Rigby Education.

Fossil Hunting: Individual Title Six-Packs. (Rigby Focus Ser.). 24p. (gr. 2 up). 28.00 (978-0-7578-5335-7(8)) Rigby Education.

Fossils, 6 Pks. (On Deck Ser.: Vol. 2). 24p. (gr. 4-5). 35.00 (978-0-7578-5817-8(1)) Rigby Education.

Fossils Set F, 6 vols. (Phonics Readers Ser.). (gr. k-2). 28.95 (978-0-7368-4081-1(8)) Red Brick Learning.

Francis, Suzanne. Ancient Animals. 2006. (Illus.). 32p. (J). pap. (***978-0-439-83876-4(2)***) Scholastic, Inc.

—Prehistoric Hunters. 2006. (Illus.). 32p. (J). (***978-0-439-83863-4(0)***) Scholastic, Inc.

Frank, Marjorie Slavick, et al. Science Instant Readers Bk. 6: The Fossil Hunters. 1999. (Harcourt Science Ser.). (gr. 2 up). pap. 15.50 (978-0-15-316216-9(3)) Harcourt Schl. Pubs.

Furgang, Kathy. Biling - en busca de fosiles/Finding Fossils. 2005. spiral bd. 66.00 (***978-1-4108-5654-8(2)***) Benchmark Education Co.

Furgang, Kathy. Finding Fossils. 2003. (Early Connections Ser.). (J). pap. 33.00 (978-1-4108-1086-1(0)) Benchmark Education Co.

Gaines, Richard. Coelophysis. 2001. (Dinosaurs Ser.). (Illus.). 32p. (J). (gr. k-4). lib. bdg. 22.78 (978-1-57765-488-9(9) , Buddy Bks.) ABDO Publishing Co.

Gallant, Roy A. Early Humans. 1999. (Story of Science Ser.). (Illus.). 80p. (J). (gr. 5 up). lib. bdg. 29.93 (978-0-7614-0960-1(2) , Benchmark Bks.) Cavendish, Marshall Corp.

—Fossils. 2000. (Kaleidoscope Ser.). (Illus.). 48p. (J). (gr. 3 up). lib. bdg. 25.64 (978-0-7614-1041-6(4) , Benchmark Bks.) Cavendish, Marshall Corp.

—The Tales Fossils Tell. 2001. (Story of Science Ser.). (Illus.). 80p. (J). (gr. 5 up). lib. bdg. 29.93 (978-0-7614-1153-6(4) , Benchmark Bks.) Cavendish, Marshall Corp.

Gish, Melissa & Shaw, Nancy J. Fossils. (Illus.). 32p. pap. 8.95 (978-0-89812-319-7(4)) Creative Co., The.

Goecke, Michael P. American Mastodon. 2004. (Prehistoric Animals Set II Ser.). (Illus.). 24p. (J). (gr. k-4). lib. bdg. 21.35 (978-1-57765-973-0(2)) ABDO Publishing Co.

—Dire Wolf. 2003. (Prehistoric Animals Ser.). (Illus.). 24p. (J). (gr. k-4). lib. bdg. 21.35 (978-1-57765-966-2(X)) ABDO Publishing Co.

—Giant Ape. 2003. (Prehistoric Animals Ser.). (Illus.). 24p. (J). (gr. k-4). lib. bdg. 21.35 (978-1-57765-967-9(8)) ABDO Publishing Co.

—Giant Armadillo. 2004. (Prehistoric Animals Set II Ser.). (Illus.). 24p. (J). (gr. k-4). lib. bdg. 21.35 (978-1-57765-974-7(0)) ABDO Publishing Co.

—Giant Ground Sloth. 2003. (Prehistoric Animals Ser.). (Illus.). 24p. (J). (gr. k-4). lib. bdg. 21.35 (978-1-57765-968-6(6)) ABDO Publishing Co.

—Giant Rhino. 2003. (Prehistoric Animals Ser.). (Illus.). 24p. (J). (gr. k-4). lib. bdg. 21.35 (978-1-57765-969-3(4)) ABDO Publishing Co.

—Irish Elk. 2004. (Prehistoric Animals Set II Ser.). (Illus.). 24p. (J). (gr. k-4). lib. bdg. 21.35 (978-1-57765-975-4(9)) ABDO Publishing Co.

—Prehistoric Animals. 2003. (J). (gr. k-4). lib. bdg. 128.10 (978-1-57765-965-5(1) , Buddy Bks.) ABDO Publishing Co.

—Prehistoric Animals Set II. 2004. (J). (gr. k-4). lib. bdg. 128.10 (978-1-57765-972-3(4) , Buddy Bks.) ABDO Publishing Co.

—Scimitar Cat. 2004. (Prehistoric Animals Set II Ser.). (Illus.). 24p. (J). (gr. k-4). lib. bdg. 21.35 (978-1-57765-977-8(5)) ABDO Publishing Co.

—Short-Faced Bear. 2004. (Prehistoric Animals Set II Ser.). (Illus.). 23p. (J). (gr. k-4). lib. bdg. 21.35 (978-1-57765-976-1(7)) ABDO Publishing Co.

—Woolly Rhinoceros. 2004. (Prehistoric Animals Set II Ser.). (Illus.). 24p. (J). (gr. k-4). lib. bdg. 21.35 (978-1-57765-978-5(3)) ABDO Publishing Co.

Goldish, Meish. The Fossil Feud: Marsh & Cope's Bone Wars. 2007. (Fossil Hunters Ser.). 32p. (J). (gr. 3-7). lib. bdg. 25.27 (978-1-59716-256-2(6)) Bearport Publishing Co., Inc.

—Fossil Tales. 2003. (On the Job Ser.). (Illus.). 32p. (gr. 3-5). 23.00 (978-0-7910-7411-4(0) , Chelsea Hse.) Facts On File, Inc.

Goldsmith, Andrew. Prehistoric Beasts. 2005. (Top Tens Ser.). (Illus.). 32p. (J). lib. bdg. 25.27 (978-1-59716-063-6(6)) Bearport Publishing Co., Inc.

Gomi, Taro. Escapes. (Los Especiales de A la Orilla Del Viento Ser.). (SPA.). 18p. (J). 6.99 (978-968-16-5413-9(7)) Fondo de Cultura Economica USA.

Graham, Ian. Fossil Fuels. 1999. (Energy Forever? Ser.). 48p. (J). (gr. 3-7). lib. bdg. 27.12 (978-0-8172-5365-3(3)) Raintree.

—Fossil Fuels: A Resource Our World Depends On. 2004. (J). pap. 7.50 (978-1-4034-5623-6(2)); lib. bdg. 24.22 (978-1-4034-5615-1(1)) Heinemann Library.

Grambo, Rebecca L. Digging Canadian Dinosaurs. Bonder, Dianna, illus. 2004. 64p. (J). (gr. 2-6). pap. 12.95 (978-1-55285-395-5(0)) Whitecap Bks., Ltd. CAN. *Dist:* Firefly Bks., Ltd.

Gray, Susan H. Archaeopteryx. 2005. (Exploring Dinosaurs & Prehistoric Creatures Ser.). 32p. (J). (gr. 2-6). 27.07 (978-1-59296-364-5(1)) Child's World, Inc.

—Crinoids & Blastoids. 2005. (Exploring Dinosaurs & Prehistoric Creatures Ser.). 32p. (J). (gr. 2-6). 27.07 (978-1-59296-365-2(X)) Child's World, Inc.

—Dinosaur Dig! 2007. (Scholastic News Nonfiction Readers: Prehistoric World Ser.). 24p. (J). pap. 6.95 (***978-0-531-18776-0(4)*** , Children's Pr.) Scholastic Library Publishing.

—Dinosaur Eggs. 2007. (Scholastic News Nonfiction Readers: Prehistoric World Ser.). 24p. (J). pap. 6.95 (***978-0-531-18777-7(2)*** , Children's Pr.) Scholastic Library Publishing.

Gray, Susan H. Glyptodonts. 2005. (Exploring Dinosaurs & Prehistoric Creatures Ser.). (Illus.). 32p. (J). (gr. 2-6). 27.07 (978-1-59296-408-6(7)) Child's World, Inc.

Gray, Susan Heinrichs. Dinosaur Dig! 2007. (Scholastic News Nonfiction Readers Ser.). (Illus.). 24p. (J). (gr. 1-2). 19.00 (***978-0-531-17482-1(4)*** , Children's Pr.) Scholastic Library Publishing.

—Dinosaur Eggs. 2007. (Scholastic News Nonfiction Readers Ser.). (Illus.). 24p. (J). (gr. 1-2). 19.00 (***978-0-531-17483-8(2)*** , Children's Pr.) Scholastic Library Publishing.

—Dinosaur Tracks. 2007. (Scholastic News Nonfiction Readers Ser.). (Illus.). 24p. (J). (gr. 1-2). 19.00 (***978-0-531-17485-2(9)*** , Children's Pr.) Scholastic Library Publishing.

Group/McGraw-Hill, Wright. Fossils Reveal Clues about Ancient Life, 6 vols. (Book2WebTM Ser.). (gr. 4-8). 36.50 (978-0-322-04431-9(6)) Wright Group, The.

Halls, Kelly Milner. Dinosaur Mummies: Beyond Bare-Bone Fossils. 2007. (J). pap. 8.95 (***978-1-58196-034-1(4)***) Darby Creek Publishing.

—Dinosaur Mummies: Beyond Bare-Bone Fossils. Spears, Rick, illus. 2003. (Junior Library Guild Selection Ser.). 48p. (J). (gr. 4 up). 17.95 (978-1-58196-000-6(X)) Darby Creek Publishing.

Hantula, Richard. Rocks & Fossils. 2006. (J). pap. (***978-0-8368-7876-9(0)***) Stevens, Gareth Inc.

Harcourt School Publishers Staff. Fossil Hunters: Science Reader. 1999. (SPA., Illus.). (J). pap. 3.70 (978-0-15-316121-6(3)) Harcourt Schl. Pubs.

—Titansoaur Treasure Advanced Level. 3rd ed. 2002. (Trophies Reading Program Ser.). (Illus.). pap. 5.10 (978-0-15-323306-7(0)) Harcourt Schl. Pubs.

Hartzog, Brooke. The Dinosaur Footprints & Roland T. Bird. 1999. (Dinosaurs & Their Discoverers Ser.). (Illus.). 24p. (J). (gr. k-4). lib. bdg. 18.75 (978-0-8239-5330-1(0) , PowerKids Pr.) Rosen Publishing Group, Inc., The.

—Tyrannosaurus Rex & Barnum Brown. 1999. (Dinosaurs & Their Discoverers Ser.). (Illus.). 24p. (J). (gr. k-4). lib. bdg. 18.75 (978-0-8239-5328-8(9) , PowerKids Pr.) Rosen Publishing Group, Inc., The.

Helm, Charles. Daniel's Dinosaurs: A True Story of Discovery. Zimmer, Joan, illus. 2004. 32p. (J). (gr. k-3). 16.95 (978-1-897066-06-5(6)); pap. 6.95 (978-1-897066-07-2(4)) Maple Tree Pr. CAN. *Dist:* Perseus Distribution.

High-Low Reading: Prehistoric Creatures Then & Now, 6 bks., Set. Incl. Ichthyosaurus. Rodriguez, K. S. 2000. lib. bdg. 22.83 (978-0-7398-0099-7(X)); Iguanodon. Rodriguez, K. S. 2000. lib. bdg. 22.83 (978-0-7398-0100-0(7)); Pteranodon. Rodriguez, K. S. 2000. lib. bdg. 22.83 (978-0-7398-0101-7(5)); Stegosaurus. Rodriguez, K. S. 2000. lib. bdg. 22.83 (978-0-7398-0102-4(3)); Triceratops. Bergen, Lara Rice. 2000. lib. bdg. 22.83 (978-0-7398-0103-1(1)); Tyrannosaurus Rex. Rodriguez, K. S. 1998. lib. bdg. 22.83 (978-0-7398-0104-8(X)); (Illus.). 32p. (J). (ps-3). 1998. Set lib. bdg. 136.98 (978-0-7398-0105-5(8)) Raintree.

Hodge, Judith. Las riquezas de la tierra & Riches from Earth. 2005. spiral bd. 84.00 (***978-1-4108-5716-3(6)***) Benchmark Education Co.

Holmes, Thom & Holmes, Laurie. Baby Dinosaurs: Eggs, Nests, & Recent Discoveries. Skrepnick, Michael William, illus. 2003. (Dinosaur Library). 104p. (J). (gr. 6-12). lib. bdg. 26.60 (978-0-7660-2074-0(6)) Enslow Pubs., Inc.

—Great Dinosaur Expeditions & Discoveries: Adventures with the Fossil Hunters. Skrepnick, Michael William, illus. 2003. (Dinosaur Library). 112p. (J). lib. bdg. 26.60 (978-0-7660-2078-8(9)) Enslow Pubs., Inc.

—Prehistoric Flying Reptiles: The Pterosaurs. Skrepnick, Michael William, illus. 2003. (Dinosaur Library). 104p. (J). (gr. 6-12). lib. bdg. 26.60 (978-0-7660-2072-6(X)) Enslow Pubs., Inc.

Holt, Rinehart and Winston Staff. Holt Science & Technology Chptr. 5: Rocks & Fossils: Chapter Resources - Tennessee Edition. 3rd ed. 2003. (J). pap. 11.40 (978-0-03-069111-9(7)) Holt, Rinehart & Winston.

—Holt Science & Technology Chptr. 10: Rocks & Fossils: Chapter Resources - Tennessee Edition. 3rd ed. 2003. (YA). pap. 11.40 (978-0-03-069169-0(9)) Holt, Rinehart & Winston.

Holtz, Thomas & Benton, Michael J., contrib. by. Dinosaurs of the World, 11 vols., Set. 1999. (Illus.). 700p. (gr. 4 up). 471.36 (978-0-7614-7072-4(7) , Cavendish, Marshall Reference Bks.) Cavendish, Marshall Corp.

Horner, John R. Digging up Dinosaurs with Jack Horner. 2007. 48p. (J). (gr. 3-7). 12.95 (978-1-56037-396-4(2)) Farcountry Pr.

Hunter, Rebecca M. Rocks, Minerals & Fossils. 2001. (Discovering Science Ser.). (Illus.). 32p. (J). (gr. 4-7). lib. bdg. 25.69 (978-0-7398-3250-9(6)) Raintree.

Hynes, Margaret. Rocks & Fossils. 2006. (Kingfisher Knowledge Ser.). (Illus.). 64p. (J). (gr. 5-9). 12.95 (978-0-7534-5974-4(4) , Kingfisher) Houghton Mifflin Co. Trade & Reference Div.

Investigating Earth Systems Fossils. 2002. stu. ed., per. (978-1-58591-083-0(X)); stu. ed., bds. (978-1-58591-107-3(0)) It's About Time, Herff Jones Education Diiv.

Jay. The Young Library: The Prehistoric World, 5 vols., Set 1. 2003. (Illus.). 128.50 (978-1-4109-0011-1(8)) Raintree.

Jay, Michael. Sea Monsters. 2003. (Illus.). 32p. (J). lib. bdg. 25.70 (978-1-4109-0010-4(X)) Raintree.

Johnson, Rebecca L. & Sereno, Paul C. Paul Sereno: Digging for Dinosaurs. 2003. (National Geographic Reading Expeditions Ser.). (Illus.). 32p. (J). pap. (978-0-7922-8887-9(4)) National Geographic Society.

Johnston, Marianne. Horses Past & Present. 2000. (Prehistoric Animals & Their Modern-Day Relatives Ser.). 24p. (J). (gr. k-4). lib. bdg. 18.75 (978-0-8239-5207-6(X) , PowerKids Pr.) Rosen Publishing Group, Inc., The.

—Prehistoric Sharks & Modern-Day Sharks. 2000. (Prehistoric Animals & Their Modern-Day Relatives Ser.). 24p. (J). (gr. k-4). lib. bdg. 18.75 (978-0-8239-5206-9(1) , PowerKids Pr.) Rosen Publishing Group, Inc., The.

Katz Cooper, Sharon. Learning from Fossils. 2007. (Illus.). 24p. (J). (***978-1-4034-9325-5(1)***); lib. bdg. (***978-1-4034-9317-0(0)***) Heinemann.

Kelley, K. C. Deadly Dinos. 2006. (Boys Rock! Ser.). (Illus.). 32p. (J). (gr. 1-5). 24.21 (978-1-59296-728-5(0)) Child's World, Inc.

Kelly, Diane. Fossils. 2005. (KidHaven Science Library). (Illus.). 48p. (J). (ps-8). lib. bdg. 26.20 (978-0-7377-2636-7(9) , Greenhaven Pr., Inc.) Thomson Gale.

Kelsey, Elin. Canadian Dinosaurs. rev. ed. 2007. (Wow Canada! Collection). (Illus.). 96p. (J). (gr. 3-7). 29.95 (***978-1-897349-08-3(4)***); pap. 19.95 (***978-1-897066-85-0(6)***) Maple Tree Pr. CAN. *Dist:* Perseus Distribution.

Kim, F. S. Dig Deep! Looking for Dinosaurs. 2006. (Illus.). 32p. (J). pap. (***978-0-439-83877-1(0)***) Scholastic, Inc.

Kurtz, Jane. Mister Bones: Dinosaur Hunter. Haverfield, Mary, illus. 2004. (Ready-to-Read Ser.). 32p. (J). pap. 3.99 (978-0-689-85960-1(0) , Aladdin) Simon & Schuster Children's Publishing.

Lambert, David. The Giant Dinosaur Book. 2001. (Illus.). 96p. (J). (gr. 4-6). tchr. ed. 14.95 (978-0-7534-5421-3(1) , Kingfisher) Houghton Mifflin Co. Trade & Reference Div.

Lambert, David & Diagram Visual Staff. Super Little Giant Book of Prehistoric Creatures. 2006. (Illus.). 288p. (J). pap. 6.95 (978-1-4027-2593-7(0)) Sterling Publishing Co., Inc.

Lappi, Megan. Birds. 2004. (Prehistoric Life Ser.). (J). pap. 7.95 (978-1-59036-170-2(9)); (Illus.). 32p. lib. bdg. 15.95 (978-1-59036-111-5(3)) Weigl Pubs., Inc.

—Fossils. 2004. (Science Matters Ser.). (Illus.). 24p. (J). lib. bdg. 24.45 (978-1-59036-213-6(6)) Weigl Pubs., Inc.

Larson, Peter L. & Donnan, Kristin. Bones Rock! Everything You Need to Know to Be a Paleontologist. 2004. (Illus.). 160p. (J). pap. 19.95 (978-1-931229-35-7(X)) Invisible Cities Pr.

Lessem, Don. Carnivoros Gigantes. Bindon, John, illus. 2005. Tr. of Giant Meat-Eating Dinosaurs. (SPA.). 32p. (J). (gr. 2-4). pap. 6.95 (978-0-8225-2963-7(7)); (ps-7). lib. bdg. 23.93 (978-0-8225-2962-0(9) , Ediciones Lerner) Lerner Publishing Group.

—Giant Plant-Eating Dinosaurs. Bindon, John, illus. 2005. (Meet the Dinosaurs Ser.). 32p. (J). (gr. 2-4). lib. bdg. 23.93 (978-0-8225-1371-1(4)) Lerner Publishing Group.

—Sea Giants of Dinosaur Time. Bindon, John, illus. 2005. 32p. (J). (gr. 2-5). pap. 6.95 (978-0-8225-2623-0(9)); 23.93 (978-0-8225-1425-1(7)) Lerner Publishing Group.

Lessem, Don & Dodson, Peter. Dinosaurs: Facts, Profiles, & Amazing Information. 2007. (Illus.). 32p. (J). (***978-1-4127-1343-6(9)***); (***978-1-4127-1344-3(7)***) Publications International, Ltd.

Let's Investigate Series, 8 vols., Set. Incl. Australia. Richardson, Adele D. pap. 10.60 (978-0-89812-002-8(0)); Bats. Shaw, Nancy J. pap. 10.60 (978-0-89812-003-5(9)); Fossils. Shaw, Nancy J. & Gish, Melissa. pap. 10.60 (978-0-89812-004-2(7)); Japan. Richardson, Adele D. pap. 10.60 (978-0-89812-005-9(5)); Mexico. Richardson, Adele D. pap. 10.60 (978-0-89812-006-6(3)); Russia. Richardson, Adele D. pap. 10.60 (978-0-89812-007-3(1)); Seashells. Richardson, Adele D. pap. 10.60 (978-0-89812-008-0(X)); Snakes. Gish, Melissa. pap. 10.60 (978-0-89812-009-7(8)); 32p. (J). 2000. (Illus.). Set pap. 84.80 (978-0-89812-011-0(X) , Creative Paperbacks) Creative Co., The.

Lewis, Brenda Ralph. Prehistoric Creatures in the Sea & Sky. 2006. (Nature's Monsters Ser.). (Illus.). 32p. (J). lib. bdg. 26.60 (978-0-8368-6845-6(5)) Stevens, Gareth Inc.

Lindeen, Carol. Terror Bird: Phorusrhacos Longissimus. 2008. (J). (***978-1-4296-0116-0(7)***) Capstone Pr., Inc.

Living Earth Set. 2002. (Living Earth Ser.). 272-336p. (gr. 6-12). 550.00 (978-0-8160-5171-7(2)) Facts On File, Inc.

Markle, Sandra. Outside & Inside Dinosaurs. 2003. (Outside Inside Ser.). (Illus.). 40p. (J). 7.99 (978-0-689-85778-2(0) , Aladdin) Simon & Schuster Children's Publishing.

—Outside & Inside Dinosaurs. 2003. (gr. 3-6). lib. bdg. 15.30 (978-0-613-66531-5(7)) Tandem Library Bks.

Mattern, Joanne. Prehistoric Creatures. 24p. 115.98 (978-0-8368-4895-3(0)) Stevens, Gareth Inc.

—Seres prehistoricos (Prehistoric Creatures- Spanish edition), 6 Vols. 115.98 (978-0-8368-6012-2(8)) Stevens, Gareth Inc.

Matthews, Rupert. Cretaceous Dinosaurs. Stalio, Ivan, illus. 2002. (Dinosaurs Undercover Ser.). 40p. (J). 29.94 (978-1-56711-602-1(7) , Blackbirch Pr., Inc.) Thomson Gale.

—Gone Fovever!, 6 bks., Set 3. 2004. (J). (gr. k-2). lib. bdg. 145.29 (978-1-4034-4915-3(5)) Heinemann Library.

—Jurassic Dinosaurs. Stalio, Ivan, illus. 2002. (Dinosaurs Undercover Ser.). 40p. (J). 29.94 (978-1-56711-601-4(9) , Blackbirch Pr., Inc.) Thomson Gale.

—Sabre Tooth. 2003. (Gone Forever Ser.). (Illus.). 32p. pap. 6.50 (978-1-4034-3419-7(0)) Heinemann Library.

—Sabretooth Tiger. 2003. (Gone Forever Ser.). (Illus.). 32p. (J). lib. bdg. 22.79 (978-1-4034-0791-7(6)) Heinemann Library.

McConnell, William. Rocks & Fossils. 2006. (Rosen Publishing Group's Reading Room Collection). (J). lib. bdg. (978-1-4042-3344-7(X) , PowerKids Pr.) Rosen Publishing Group, Inc., The.

McMullan, Kate. Dinosaur Hunters. Jones, John R., illus. 2005. 48p. (J). (gr. 2-4). lib. bdg. 11.19 (978-0-606-33717-5(2)) Tandem Library Bks.

McNamara, Ken. It's True! We Came from Slime. Plant, Andrew, illus. 2006. (It's True! Ser.). 88p. (J). (gr. 5-8). 19.95 (978-1-55037-953-2(4)); pap. 5.95 (978-1-55037-952-5(6)) Annick Pr., Ltd. CAN. *Dist:* Firefly Bks., Ltd.

Mead, Brian. Monsters of the Ice Age Coloring Book. 2003. 32p. (J). (ps-3). pap. 3.99 (978-0-9717509-2-0(0)) Mead, Brian Publishing.

Monster Bones. (Science Works). 32p. (YA). 8.95 (978-1-4048-1126-3(5)) Picture Window Bks.

Monstruos Gigantes. 2005. (Jeff Corwin Experience Ser.). (ENG & SPA., Illus.). 48p. (J). (ps-7). lib. bdg. 24.95 (978-1-4103-0675-3(5) , Blackbirch Pr., Inc.) Thomson Gale.

Morris, Neil. Everyday Life in Prehistory. 2005. (Uncovering History Ser.). (Illus.). 46p. (J). (gr. 6-9). lib. bdg. 29.95 (978-1-58340-709-7(X)) Smart Apple Media.

Morris, Ting & Morris, Neil. Dinosaurs. Levy, Ruth & Cowne, Joanne, illus. 2007. 32p. (J). (***978-1-59771-029-9(6)***) Sea-To-Sea Pubns.

Munro, Margaret. The Story of Life on Earth. Reczuch, Karen, illus. 2000. 64p. (J). (ps-3). pap. (978-0-88899-401-1(X)) Groundwood Bks.

Murray, Peter. Apatosaurus. 2001. (J). (978-1-58340-078-4(8)) Smart Apple Media.

—Pterodactyls. 2001. (J). (978-1-58340-079-1(6)) Smart Apple Media.

—Stegosaurus. 2001. (J). (978-1-58340-080-7(X)) Smart Apple Media.

—Triceratops. 2001. (J). (978-1-58340-081-4(8)) Smart Apple Media.

—Velociraptor. 2001. (J). (978-1-58340-083-8(4)) Smart Apple Media.

Nelson, Lisa W. & Agenbroad, Larry D. Mammoths: Ice-Age Giants. Jansen, Paula, illus. Jansen, Paula, photos by. 2005. (Discovery! Ser.). 120p. (gr. 5-12). lib. bdg. 27.93 (978-0-8225-2862-3(2)) Lerner Publishing Group.

O'Brien, Patrick. Mammoth. rev. ed. 2002. (Illus.). 40p. (J). 16.95 (978-0-8050-6596-1(2) , Holt, Henry & Co. Bks. For Young Readers) Holt, Henry & Co.

Olien, Rebecca. Fossils. 2001. (Bridgestone Science Library). (Illus.). 24p. (J). (gr. 2-3). lib. bdg. 18.60 (978-0-7368-0951-1(1) , Bridgestone Bks.) Capstone Pr., Inc.

Padma, T. V. The Albertosaurus Mystery: Philip Currie's Hunt in the Badlands. 2007. (Fossil Hunters Ser.). (Illus.). 32p. (J). (gr. 3-7). lib. bdg. 25.27 (978-1-59716-254-8(X)) Bearport Publishing Co., Inc.

Palmer, Douglas & Dorling Kindersley Publishing Staff. Fossils. 2nd ed. 2004. (Pocket Guides Ser.). (Illus.). 160p. (J). pap. 6.99 (978-0-7566-0206-2(8)) Dorling Kindersley Publishing, Inc.

Parker, Gary. The Fossil Book. 2005. (Wonders of Creation Ser.). (Illus.). 80p. (J). 5.99 (978-0-89051-438-2(0) , 303-212) Master Bks.

Patent, Dorothy Hinshaw. In Search of the Maiasaurs. 1998. (Frozen in Time Ser.). (Illus.). (J). (gr. 5-9). lib. bdg. 28.50 (978-0-7614-0787-4(1) , Benchmark Bks.) Cavendish, Marshall Corp.

Pearcey, Alice, ed. Dinosaur Jigsaw Atlas. Bird, Glen, illus. 2004. 20p. (J). 14.95 (978-0-7945-0913-2(4) , Usborne) EDC Publishing.

Pellant, Chris. The Best Book of Fossils, Rocks & Minerals. 2007. (Best Book of... Ser.). 32p. (J). (gr. k-3). pap. 6.95 (978-0-7534-6081-8(5) , Kingfisher) Houghton Mifflin Co. Trade & Reference Div.

—Fossils of the World, 11 vols. Charman, Andrew, ed. Galsworthy, Gay, illus. 1998. (Science Nature Guides). 16p. (J). (gr. 4-7). 12.95 (978-1-85028-262-4(5) , Thunder Bay Pr.) Advantage Pubs. Group.

—Fossils of the World. 2004. (World Book's Science & Nature Guides Ser.). (Illus.). 80p. (J). (978-0-7166-4212-1(3)) World Bk., Inc.

Pellant, Chris. Rocks & Fossils. (Science Kids Ser.). (Illus.). 48p. (J). (gr. k-3). 2007. pap. 6.95 (***978-0-7534-6126-6(9)***); 2003. tchr. ed. 9.95 (978-0-7534-5619-4(2)) Houghton Mifflin Co. Trade & Reference Div. (Kingfisher).

Pellant, Chris & Perrault, Chris. The Best Book of Fossils, Rocks & Minerals. Grinaway, Ray & Forsey, Chris, illus. 2000. (Best Book of... Ser.). 32p. (J). (gr. k-3). tchr. ed. 12.95 (978-0-7534-5274-5(X) , Kingfisher) Houghton Mifflin Co. Trade & Reference Div.

Petruccio, Steven James. Learning about Prehistoric Animals. 2002. (Learning about Ser.). (Illus.). 16p. (J). pap. 1.50 (978-0-486-42151-3(1)) Dover Pubns., Inc.

Phelan, Glen. Uncovering Earth's History. 2003. (National Geographic Reading Expeditions Ser.). (Illus.). 32p. (YA). pap. (978-0-7922-8878-7(5)) National Geographic Society.

Plesiosaurs. 2004. pap. 7.50 (978-1-4109-1228-2(0)); Pack. pap. 40.50 (978-1-4109-1235-0(3)) Raintree.

Potts, Aidan. Uneversaurus. 2007. 48p. (J). (gr. k-3). lib. bdg. 19.99 (978-0-385-75120-9(6)); (Illus.). 16.99 (978-0-385-75119-3(2)) Random Hse. Children's Bks. (Fickling, David Bks.).

Prehistoric Animals. (First Facts about Ser.). 24p. (J). (gr. 3-7). pap. (978-1-882210-19-0(0)) Action Publishing, Inc.

Prehistoric Creatures Collection. 2001. (Illus.). (J). pap. (978-0-7398-4556-1(X)) Steck-Vaughn.

Quigley, Mary. Dinosaur Digs. 2005. (Excavating the Past Ser.). (J). (978-1-4034-5996-1(7)) Heinemann Library.

Raintree Steck-Vaughn Staff. Fossils: Pictures from the Past. 1999. (Illus.). (J). pap. 35.60 (978-0-7398-0896-2(6)) Steck-Vaughn.

Reed, W. Maxwell. The Earth for Sam the Story of Mountains. 2005. reprint ed. pap. 34.95 (978-0-7661-9449-6(3)) Kessinger Publishing, LLC.

Relf, Patricia. A Dinosaur Named Sue: The World's Most Complete T. Rex. 2000. (Hello Reader Ser.). (Illus.). 64p. (J). (gr. 1-5). pap. 15.95 (978-0-439-09985-1(4)) Scholastic, Inc.

Richards, Julie. Fossil Fuels. 2003. 32p. (J). lib. bdg. 24.25 (978-1-58340-334-1(5)) Smart Apple Media.

Richardson, Hazel. Dinosaurs & Other Prehistoric Life. 2003. (Smithsonian Handbooks Ser.). (Illus.). 224p. pap. 20.00 (978-0-7894-9361-3(6)) Dorling Kindersley Publishing, Inc.

Riehecky, Janet. Pteranodon. 2006. (Pebble Plus Ser.). (Illus.). 24p. (J). (978-0-7368-5355-2(3)) Capstone Pr., Inc.

Riehecky, Janet. Sabertooth Cat: Smilodon Fatalis. 2008. (J). (***978-1-4296-0117-7(5)***) Capstone Pr., Inc.

Ring, Susan. Animals of Long Ago. Nelson, Will, illus. 2002. 16p. (J). (978-0-439-35123-2(5)) Scholastic, Inc.

Ripley, Esther. The Big Dinosaur Dig, Vol. 3. 2003. (DK Readers Ser.). (Illus.). 48p. (J). pap. 3.99 (978-0-7894-9290-6(3)) Dorling Kindersley Publishing, Inc.

—The Big Dinosaur Dig. 2003. (Illus.). 48p. (J). (ps-3). lib. bdg. 11.80 (978-0-613-62432-9(7)) Tandem Library Bks.

Ripley, Esther & Dorling Kindersley Publishing Staff. The Big Dinosaur Dig. 2003. (Readers Ser.). (Illus.). 48p. (J). 12.99 (978-0-7894-9540-2(6)) Dorling Kindersley Publishing, Inc.

Robb, Jackie & Stringle, Berny. The Story of Plankton. Duncan, Karen & Stringle, Sam, illus. 2004. (Bang on the Door Ser.). 32p. (YA). pap. (978-1-85602-336-8(2)) Chrysalis Children's Bks.

Robinson, Fay. A Dinosaur Named Sue: The Find of the Century. Sloan, Portia, illus. 1999. (Hello Reader! Ser.). 48p. (J). (gr. 1-4). pap. 3.99 (978-0-439-09983-7(8)) Scholastic, Inc.

—A Dinosaur Named Sue: The Find of the Century. Sloan, Portia, illus. 1999. 48p. (J). (ps-ps). lib. bdg. 11.80 (978-0-613-21435-3(8)) Tandem Library Bks.

—A Dinosaur Named Sue: The Find of the Century. 1999. 10.79 (978-0-606-17539-5(3)) Tandem Library Bks.

Rocks & Fossils. (Rosen Real Readers Big Bookstm Ser.). 16p. (J). (gr. 2-3). 38.75 (978-1-4042-6221-8(0)) Rosen Publishing Group, Inc., The.

Rocks & Fossils Kid Kit. 32p. (J). 14.99 (978-1-58086-758-0(8) , Usborne) EDC Publishing.

Rodriguez, K. S. Ichthyosaurus. 2000. (Prehistoric Creatures Then & Now Ser.). (Illus.). 32p. (J). (ps-3). lib. bdg. 22.83 (978-0-7398-0099-7(X)) Raintree.

Romero, Libby. Plant & Animal Fossils. 2005. 39.00 (***978-1-4108-4621-1(0)***) Benchmark Education Co.

Saunders, N. & Chapman, Steven. Fossil Fuel. 2005. (Freestyle Express Ser.). (Illus.). 48p. (J). lib. bdg. (978-1-4109-1693-8(6)) Steck-Vaughn.

Saunders, Nigel & Chapman, Steven. Fossil Fuel. 2005. (Freestyle Express Ser.). (Illus.). 48p. (J). (978-1-4109-1698-3(7)) Steck-Vaughn.

Saunders-Smith, Gail, ed. Dinosaurs & Prehistoric Animals. 2005. (Pebble Plus Ser.). (Illus.). (J). (gr. k-1). lib. bdg. 199.30 (978-0-7368-4405-5(8)) Capstone Pr., Inc.

Schatz, Dennis. T. Rex. 2005. (Fossil Detective Ser.). (Illus.). 40p. 16.95 (978-1-59223-373-1(2) , Silver Dolphin Bks.) Advantage Pubs. Group.

Shaw, Nancy J. & Gish, Melissa. Fossils. (Let's Investigate Ser.). (Illus.). 32p. (J). 2000. pap. 10.60 (978-0-89812-004-2(7) , Creative Paperbacks); 1998. lib. bdg. (978-0-88682-987-2(9) , Creative Education) Creative Co., The.

Sherman, Josepha. Fossil Fuel Power. 2004. (Fact Finders Ser.). (Illus.). 32p. (J). 16.95 (978-0-7368-2470-5(7)) Capstone Pr., Inc.

Showers, Paul. A Drop of Blood. pap. 4.50 (978-0-06-445004-1(X)) HarperCollins Pubs.

Sian Revision Fossil Formations. 2004. (Science in A Nutshell(R) Ser.). (J). (978-1-59242-032-2(X)) Delta Education, LLC.

Slade, Suzanne. What Do You Know about Fossils? 2008. (J). lib. bdg. (***978-1-4042-4197-8(3)*** , PowerKids Pr.) Rosen Publishing Group, Inc., The.

Sloan, Christopher. Feathered Dinosaurs. 2000. (Illus.). 64p. (J). (gr. 3-7). 17.95 (978-0-7922-7219-9(6) , National Geographic Children's Bks.) National Geographic Society.

So You Want to Dig Dinosaurs: A Field Manual on the Practice, Principles & Politics of Vertebrate Paleontology. l.t. ed. 2001. 280p. (YA). 59.99 (978-0-9716206-0-5(1)) Dragons Claw Pr.

Sovak, Jan. Invisible Prehistoric Animals Magic Picture Book. 2004. (Illus.). 32p. (J). pap. 1.50 (978-0-486-43719-4(1)) Dover Pubns., Inc.

Spilsbury, Louise & Spilsbury, Richard. Journal of a Fossil Hunter: Fossils. 2005. (Illus.). 32p. (J). (978-1-4109-1954-0(4)); lib. bdg. (978-1-4109-1923-6(4)) Steck-Vaughn.

Squire, Ann O. Fossils. 2002. (True Bks.). (Illus.). 48p. (J). (gr. 3-5). pap. 6.95 (978-0-516-26982-5(8) , Children's Pr.) Scholastic Library Publishing.

—Fossils. 2002. (gr. 3-6). lib. bdg. 15.25 (978-0-613-54222-7(3)) Tandem Library Bks.

Steck-Vaughn Staff. Fossils: Pictures from the Past/Follils Alive! 1999. (Take Me Home Ser.). (Illus.). (J). pap. 11.30 (978-0-7398-0943-3(1)) Steck-Vaughn.

—Prehistoric Creatures: Then & Now. 1999. pap., tchr. ed. (978-0-7398-2206-7(3)) Steck-Vaughn.

Stewart, Melissa. Fossils. 2003. (Simply Science Ser.). (Illus.). 32p. (J). (gr. 3 up). lib. bdg. 19.93 (978-0-7565-0442-7(2)) Compass Point Bks.

—Fossils. 2002. (Rocks & Minerals Ser.). (Illus.). 32p. (J). (gr. 4-6). lib. bdg. 24.22 (978-1-58810-255-3(6)); pap. 7.50 (978-1-4034-0091-8(1) , 91658) Heinemann Library.

Storad, Conrad J. Fossil Fuels. 2007. (Early Bird Earth Science Ser.). (J). 26.60 (***978-0-8225-6736-3(9)*** , Lerner Pubns.) Lerner Publishing Group.

Tanaka, Shelley. Graveyards of the Dinosaurs: What It Is Like to Discover Prehistoric Creatures. 2001. (I Was There Bk.). (Illus.). (J). 14.79 (978-0-606-20684-6(1)) Tandem Library Bks.

Taplin, Sam. Mi Primera Enciclopedia de Dinosaurios y el Mundo Prehistorico Internet Linked. 2005. (SPA.). 64p. (J). pap. 9.99 (978-0-7460-6639-3(2) , Usborne) EDC Publishing.

Taylor, Paul D. & Dorling Kindersley Publishing Staff. Fossil. Keates, Colin, illus. 2004. (Eyewitness Books). 72p. (J). lib. bdg. 19.99 (978-0-7566-0681-7(0)) Dorling Kindersley Publishing, Inc.

Trueit, Trudi Strain. Fossils. 2003. (Watts Library). 64p. (gr. 5-7). pap. 8.95 (978-0-531-16242-2(7) , Watts, Franklin) Scholastic Library Publishing.

—Fossils. 2003. (gr. 5-8). lib. bdg. 17.60 (978-0-613-67617-5(3)) Tandem Library Bks.

Upgrade kit dsm-3 Dinos&fossils. (J). 2004. (978-1-59242-528-0(3)); 2003. (978-1-59242-411-5(2)) Delta Education, LLC.

Walker, Sally M. Fossils. 2007. (Early Bird Earth Science Ser.). (Illus.). 48p. (J). (gr. 2-4). 25.26 (978-0-8225-5945-0(5) , Lerner Pubns.) Lerner Publishing Group.

—Mary Anning: Fossil Hunter. Saroff, Phyllis V., illus. 2000. (On My Own Biographies Ser.). 64p. (J). (gr. 1-3). lib. bdg. 23.93 (978-1-57505-425-4(6) , Carolrhoda Bks.) Lerner Publishing Group.

—The Search for Antarctic Dinosaurs. Bindon, John, illus. 2007. (On My Own Science Ser.). 48p. (J). (gr. 2-4). lib. bdg. 25.26 (***978-0-8225-6749-3(0)*** , Millbrook Pr.) Lerner Publishing Group.

Walker, Sally M. Supercroc Found. Hood, Philip, illus. 2006. (On My Own Science Ser.). (J). pap. 5.95 (978-1-57505-852-8(9) , First Avenue Editions); 48p. (gr. 2-4). lib. bdg. 25.26 (978-1-57505-760-6(3)) Lerner Publishing Group.

Washington, Curtis. The Story of Sue. 2005. (Illus.). 12p. (J). pap. (***978-0-328-14253-8(0)*** , Scott Foresman) Addison-Wesley Educational Pubs., Inc.

Weinberger, Kimberly. A Dinosaur Named Sue. 2001. (Jurassic Park Ser.). (Illus.). 24p. (J). (ps-2). pap. 5.99 (978-0-439-28367-0(1)) Scholastic, Inc.

Wenzell, Gregory. Feathered Dinosaurs of China. 2004. (Illus.). 32p. (J). 16.95 (978-1-57091-561-1(X)) Charlesbridge Publishing, Inc.

—Giant Dinosaurs of the Jurassic. Wenzell, Gregory, illus. 2004. (Illus.). 32p. (J). 16.95 (978-1-57091-563-5(6)); pap. 6.95 (978-1-57091-564-2(4)) Charlesbridge Publishing, Inc.

Wenzell, Gregory, illus. The Feathered Dinosaurs of China. 2004. 32p. (J). pap. 6.95 (978-1-57091-562-8(8)) Charlesbridge Publishing, Inc.

West, Krista. Hands-On Projects about Rocks, Minerals & Fossils. 2002. (Great Earth Science Projects Ser.). (Illus.). 24p. (J). lib. bdg. 19.95 (978-0-8239-5842-9(6) , PowerKids Pr.) Rosen Publishing Group, Inc., The.

Wheeler, Jill C. Fossil Fuels. 2007. (Eye on Energy Ser.). (Illus.). 32p. (J). (gr. k-6). lib. bdg. 24.21 (***978-1-59928-805-5(2)*** , Checkerboard Library) ABDO Publishing Co.

Whitfield, Philip. Scholastic's Children's Guide to Dinosaurs. (Illus.). 96p. (J). pap. 21.95 (978-0-590-24329-2(2)) Scholastic, Inc.

Williams, Judith. Discovering Dinosaurs with a Fossil Hunter. Skrepnick, Michael William, illus. 2004. (I Like Science! Ser.). 24p. (J). lib. bdg. 21.26 (978-0-7660-2267-6(6)) Enslow Pubs., Inc.

—The Discovery & Mystery of a Dinosaur Named Jane. 2007. (Prime Ser.). (Illus.). 48p. (J). (gr. 3-7). pap. 13.26 (***978-0-7660-2709-1(0)***); lib. bdg. 23.93 (978-0-7660-2730-5(9)) Enslow Pubs., Inc.

Wood, Robert Muir. Discovering Prehistory. 2001. (Inside Look Ser.). (Illus.). 48p. (J). (gr. 4 up). lib. bdg. 26.00 (978-0-8368-2900-6(X)) Stevens, Gareth Inc.

Woolly Mammoth. (Dinosaurs & Prehistoric Animals Ser.). 24p. (J). 6.95 (978-0-7368-5109-1(7)) Capstone Pr., Inc.

World Book, Inc Staff, contrib. by. Resources & Cumulative Index. 2005. (World Book's Science & Nature Guides Ser.). 80p. (J). (978-0-7166-4216-9(6)) World Bk., Inc.

Zoehfeld, Kathleen Weidner. Dinosaur Parents, Dinosaur Young: Uncovering the Mystery of Dinosaur Families. 2007. (Illus.). 64p. (J). (gr. 4-6). pap. 6.95 (978-0-618-75244-7(7) , Clarion Bks.) Houghton Mifflin Co. Trade & Reference Div.

—Dinosaur Parents, Dinosaur Young: Uncovering the Mystery of Dinosaur Families. Carrick, Paul & Shillinglaw, Bruce, illus. 2001. 64p. (J). (gr. 4-6). tchr. ed. 17.00 (978-0-395-91338-3(1) , Clarion Bks.) Houghton Mifflin Co. Trade & Reference Div.

—Terrible Tyrannosaurs. Washburn, Lucia, illus. 2001. (Let's-Read-&-Find-Out Science Bks.). 40p. (J). (gr. k-4). 15.95 (978-0-06-027933-2(8)) HarperCollins Pubs.

—Terrible Tyrannosaurs. Washburn, Lucas, illus. 2001. (Let's-Read-and-Find-Out Science Ser.). 40p. (J). (gr. k-4). 15.89 (978-0-06-027934-9(6)) HarperCollins Pubs.

—Terrible Tyrannosaurs. Washburn, Lucia, illus. 2001. (Let's-Read-and-Find-Out Science Ser.). 40p. (J). (gr. k-4). pap. 5.99 (978-0-06-445181-9(X) , Harper Trophy) HarperCollins Pubs.

FOSTER, STEPHEN COLLINS, 1826-1864

Pancella, Peggy. Stephen Foster. 2005. (J). pap. (978-1-4034-6756-0(0)); (Illus.). 32p. 24.21 (978-1-4034-6748-5(X)) Heinemann Library.

FOSTER HOME CARE

see also Adoption

Braley and Thompson, Inc. Staff. Treatment Team Foster Care. (Illus.). 100p. (J). 4th ed. pap. 6.00 (978-1-883239-00-8(1)); 5th ed. pap. 6.00 (978-1-883239-01-5(X)) Braley & Thompson, Inc.

Do You Have What It Takes. 2007. (YA). per. 35.00 (***978-0-9661256-9-6(X)***) Youth Communication - New York Center.

Hardaway, Francine. Foster Mom: A Journey of Self-Discovery. 2004. 152p. (YA). pap. 14.95 (978-0-595-31431-7(7)) iUniverse, Inc.

Levy, Janice. Finding the Right Spot: When Kids Can't Live with Their Parents. Martin, Whitney, illus. 2004. 48p. (J). 14.95 (978-1-59147-073-1(0)); pap. 8.95 (978-1-59147-074-8(9)) American Psychological Assn. (Magination Pr.).

Libal, Joyce. A House Between Homes: Youth in the Foster Care System. 2004. (Youth with Special Needs Ser.). (Illus.). 128p. (J). lib. bdg. (978-1-59084-740-4(7)) Mason Crest Pubs.

Nelson, Julie. Kids Are Important: A Book for Young Children in Foster Care. 2003. (Illus.). (J). (978-0-9743826-1-6(2)) Lifetrack Resources.

—Kids Need to Be Safe: A Book for Young Children in Foster Care. 2005. (Kids Are Important Ser.). (Illus.). 32p. (J). (ps-5). pap. 9.95 (978-1-57542-192-6(5)) Free Spirit Publishing, Inc.

Wagner, Heather Lehr. The Blending of Foster & Adopted Children into the Family. 2002. (Focus on Family Matters Ser.). (Illus.). 64p. (J). 25.00 (978-0-7910-6694-2(0) , Chelsea Hse.) Facts On File, Inc.

Wilgocki, Jennifer & Wright, Marcia Kahn. Maybe Days: A Book for Children in Foster Care. Geis, Alissa Imre, illus. 2002. 32p. (J). (ps-5). 14.95 (978-1-55798-803-4(X)); pap. 8.95 (978-1-55798-802-7(1)) American Psychological Assn. (Magination Pr.).

FOSTER HOME CARE—FICTION

Ashley, Bernard. Little Soldier: A Novel. 2002. (Illus.). 240p. (J). (gr. 9 up). pap. 16.95 (978-0-439-22424-6(1) , Scholastic Pr.) Scholastic, Inc.

At Aunt Hattie's House. 2005. (YA). 12.00 net. (978-0-9763793-1-7(7)) Mitchell, Karan.

Benedict, Helen. Opposite of Love. 2007. 256p. (J). (gr. 6 up). 16.99 (***978-0-670-06135-8(2)*** , Viking Juvenile) Penguin Group (USA) Inc.

Busic, Valerie. Billy's New Home: For Foster Children Everywhere. Meyers, Jeff, illus. 1998. 40p. (J). (gr. 2-6). pap. 9.95 (978-1-882021-15-4(0)) Summerland Pr.

Caldwell, V. M. The Ocean Within. Magnus, Erica, illus. 1999. (Milkweed Prize for Children's Literature Ser.). 236p. (J). (gr. 3-8). pap. 6.95 (978-1-57131-624-0(8)) Milkweed Editions.

—The Ocean Within. 1999. (J). (gr. 3-9). (978-0-606-19035-0(X)) Tandem Library Bks.

Cooney, Caroline B. What Child Is This? A Christmas Story. 1999. 160p. (YA). (gr. 7-12). mass mkt. 5.50 (978-0-440-22684-0(8) , Laurel Leaf) Random Hse. Children's Bks.

—What Child Is This? A Christmas Story. 1999. (978-0-606-17218-9(1)) Tandem Library Bks.

De Guzman, Michael. Finding Stinko. 2007. 144p. (J). (gr. 5 up). 16.00 (978-0-374-32305-9(4)) Farrar, Straus & Giroux.

de La Pena, Matt. Ball Don't Lie. 2005. 288p. (YA). (gr. 8-12). lib. bdg. 18.99 (978-0-385-90258-8(1)); (gr. 9-12). 16.95 (978-0-385-73232-1(5)) Random Hse. Children's Bks. (Delacorte Bks. for Young Readers).

de la Pena, Matt. Ball Don't Lie. 2007. 288p. (YA). (gr. 9). pap. 7.99 (978-0-385-73425-7(5) , Delacorte Bks. for Young Readers) Random Hse. Children's Bks.

Dowell, Frances O'Roark. Where I'd Like to Be. 240p. (J). 2003. (Illus.). (gr. 5-9). 15.95 (978-0-689-84420-1(4) , Atheneum); 2004. reprint ed. pap. 5.99 (978-0-689-87067-5(1) , Aladdin) Simon & Schuster Children's Publishing.

—Where I'd Like to Be. 2004. 232p. (J). (gr. k-9). lib. bdg. 11.64 (978-0-606-32673-5(1)) Tandem Library Bks.

—Where I'd Like to Be. l.t. ed. 2003. 162p. (J). 22.95 (978-0-7862-5741-6(5)) Thorndike Pr.

Eige, Lillian. Dangling. 2003. (gr. 3-6). lib. bdg. 13.00 (978-0-613-90716-3(7)) Tandem Library Bks.

Fleischman, Paul. Breakout. 2003. 160p. 15.95 (978-0-8126-2696-4(6)) Cricket Bks.

—Breakout. 2005. 144p. (YA). reprint ed. pap. 6.99 (978-0-689-87189-4(9) , Simon Pulse) Simon & Schuster Children's Publishing.

Fogelin, Adrian. Anna Casey's Place in the World. 2003. 224p. (J). (gr. 3-6). pap. 6.95 (978-1-56145-295-8(5) , Q32694) Peachtree Pubs., Ltd.

—Anna Casey's Place in the World. Schultz, Suzy, illus. 2001. 224p. (J). (gr. 3-7). 14.95 (978-1-56145-249-1(1) , Q32694) Peachtree Pubs., Ltd.

—Anna Casey's Place in the World. 2003. 207p. (J). (gr. 4-7). lib. bdg. 15.25 (978-0-613-53133-7(7)) Tandem Library Bks.

Fogelin, Adrian. The Sorta Sisters. 2007. 240p. (J). (gr. 3-7). 14.95 (***978-1-56145-424-2(9)*** , Peachtree Junior) Peachtree Pubs., Ltd.

Giff, Patricia Reilly. Pictures of Hollis Woods. 176p. (gr. 3-8). 2004. (J). pap. 6.50 (978-0-440-41578-7(0) , Yearling); 2002. lib. bdg. 17.99 (978-0-385-90070-6(8) , Lamb, Wendy) Random Hse. Children's Bks.

—Pictures of Hollis Woods. Giff, Patricia Reilly, illus. 2002. (Illus.). 176p. (gr. 3-8). 15.95 (978-0-385-32655-1(6) , Lamb, Wendy) Random Hse. Children's Bks.

—Pictures of Hollis Woods. l.t. ed. 2003. 158p. (J). 23.95 (978-0-7862-5094-3(1)) Thorndike Pr.

Gray, Dianne. Holding up the Earth. 2006. 224p. (J). (gr. 5-9). pap. 6.95 (978-0-618-73747-5(2)) Houghton Mifflin Co. Trade & Reference Div.

Gray, Dianne E. Holding up the Earth. 2000. 224p. (J). (gr. 5-9). tchr. ed. 15.00 (978-0-618-00703-5(2)) Houghton Mifflin Co. Trade & Reference Div.

—Holding up the Earth. l.t. ed. 2002. 198p. (J). 22.95 (978-0-7862-3889-7(5)) Thomson Gale.

Gregory, Nan. I'll Sing You One-O. 2006. 224p. (J). (gr. 4-6). 16.00 (978-0-618-60708-2(0) , Clarion Bks.) Houghton Mifflin Co. Trade & Reference Div.

Grimes, Nikki. The Road to Paris. 2008. 160p. (J). (gr. 3). 6.99 (***978-0-14-241082-0(9)*** , Puffin) Penguin Group (USA) Inc.

Hansen, Joyce. One True Friend. 2005. 160p. (J). (gr. 5-9). pap. 6.95 (978-0-618-60991-8(1) , Clarion Bks.) Houghton Mifflin Co. Trade & Reference Div.

Harrison, Mette Ivie. The Monster in Me. 2003. 160p. (J). (gr. 7 up). tchr. ed. 16.95 (978-0-8234-1713-1(1)) Holiday Hse., Inc.

Hartinger, Brent. The Last Chance Texaco. 2004. 240p. (J). 15.99 (978-0-06-050912-5(0) , HarperTeen) HarperCollins Pubs.

Hayden, Torey L. The Very Worst Thing. 2003. 176p. (J). (gr. 5 up). 15.99 (978-0-06-029792-3(1)) HarperCollins Pubs.

Heneghan, James. The Grave. 2000. (Illus.). (J). (gr. 7-10). pap. 7.95 (978-0-88899-414-1(1)) Groundwood Bks. CAN. *Dist:* Transition Vendor.

Hernandez, Jo Ann Yolanda. The Throw-Away Piece. 246p. (Orig.). (YA). pap. 9.95 (978-1-55885-353-9(7) , Piñata Books) Arte Publico Pr.

Hobbs, Will. The Maze. 1999. 248p. (J). (gr. k-9). lib. bdg. 14.15 (978-0-613-19524-9(8)) Tandem Library Bks.

Hobbs, William. The Maze. (J). (gr. 5 up). 1999. (Illus.). 256p. pap. 5.99 (978-0-380-72913-5(X) , Harper Trophy); 1998. 208p. 17.99 (978-0-688-15092-1(6)) HarperCollins Pubs.

—The Maze. unabr. ed. 1999. (YA). pap., stu. ed. 59.00 incl. audio (978-0-7887-3990-3(5) , 41062X4) Recorded Bks., LLC.

—The Maze. 1999. (J). (978-0-606-16369-9(7)) Tandem Library Bks.

Horowitz, Anthony. Ravens Gate. (Power of Five Ser.: Vol. 1). 2006. 272p. (J). pap. 6.99 (978-0-439-68009-7(3) , Scholastic Paperbacks); 2005. 256p. (YA). pap. 17.95 (978-0-439-67995-4(8)) Scholastic, Inc.

—Ravens Gate. l.t. ed. 2006. (Power of Five Ser.: Vol. 1). (YA). 23.95 (978-0-7862-8584-6(2)) Thorndike Pr.

Horvath, Polly. Everything on a Waffle. 2001. 160p. (J). (gr. 5 up). 16.00 (978-0-374-32236-6(8) , Farrar, Straus & Giroux (BYR)) Farrar, Straus & Giroux.

—Everything on a Waffle. 2008. 176p. (J). pap. 6.99 (***978-0-312-38004-5(6)***) Square Fish.

Hubler, Marsha. Skye's Final Test, Vol. 6. 2005. (Keystone Stables Ser.). (Illus.). 112p. (J). pap. 4.99 (978-0-310-70799-8(4)) Zonderkidz.

—The Trouble with Skye. 2004. (Keystone Stables Ser.: No. 1). 144p. (J). pap. 4.99 (978-0-310-70572-7(X)) Zonderkidz.

—A True Test for Skye. 2004. (Keystone Stables Ser.). (Illus.). 144p. (J). pap. 4.99 (978-0-310-70573-4(8)) Zonderkidz.

—The Winning Summer. 2005. (Keystone Stables Ser.: Bk. 5). (Illus.). 144p. (J). pap. 4.99 (978-0-310-70798-1(6)) Zonderkidz.

Huser, Glen. Skinnybones & the Wrinkle Queen. 192p. 2008. (J). pap. 8.95 (***978-0-88899-733-3(7)***); 2006. (gr. 7 up). 16.95 (978-0-88899-732-6(9)) Groundwood Bks. CAN. *Dist:* Perseus Distribution.

Johnston, Julie. Adam & Eve & Pinch-Me. 2003. 232p. (J). (gr. 6). pap. 9.95 (978-0-88776-648-0(X)) Tundra Bks., Inc./Livres Toundra, Inc. CAN. *Dist:* Random Hse., Inc.

Koertge, Ron. Strays. 2006. 176p. (YA). (gr. 9 up). 16.99 (978-0-7636-2705-8(4)) Candlewick Pr.

Lauber, Patricia. The True-or-False Book of Cats. Lauber, Patricia, illus. 2001. (Illus.). 32p. (J). (gr. 3-7). pap. 6.95 (978-0-7922-6694-5(3) , National Geographic Children's Bks.) National Geographic Society.

Lewis, Richard. The Demon Queen. 2008. 252p. (J). (***978-1-4169-3589-6(4)*** , Simon & Schuster Children's Publishing) Simon & Schuster Children's Publishing.

Lowell, Pamela. Returnable Girl. 2006. 240p. (YA). 16.99 (978-0-7614-5317-8(2)) Cavendish, Marshall Corp.

Lowry, Lois. Gossamer. 2006. 144p. (J). (gr. 5). 16.00 (978-0-618-68550-9(2)) Houghton Mifflin Co.

—Gossamer. 2008. 160p. (J). (gr. 4-7). pap. 6.99 (***978-0-385-73416-5(6)*** , Delacorte Bks. for Young Readers) Random Hse. Children's Bks.

—Gossamer. l.t. ed. 2006. 151p. (YA). 23.95 (978-0-7862-8947-9(3)) Thorndike Pr.

E F G

McNeal, Laura & McNeal, Tom. The Decoding of Lana Morris. 2007. 304p. (J). (gr. 7). lib. bdg. 18.99 (978-0-375-93106-2(6)); 15.99 (978-0-375-83106-5(1)) Random Hse. Children's Bks. (Knopf Bks. for Young Readers).

Monninger, Joseph. Baby. 2007. 204p. (YA). (gr. 8 up). 16.95 ***978-1-59078-502-7(9)*** , Front Street) Boyds Mills Pr.

Montgomery, L. M. & Devereux, Cecily Margaret. Anne of Green Gables. 2004. (Broadview Editions Ser.). (Illus.). 400p. pap. (978-1-55111-362-3(7)) Broadview Pr.

Mussi, Sarah. The Door of No Return. 2008. (YA). ***(978-1-4169-1550-8(8)*** , McElderry, Margaret K.) Simon & Schuster Children's Publishing.

Myers, Walter Dean. Won't Know Till I Get There. 2000. (J). (gr. 4-8). 20.25 (978-0-8446-7149-9(5)) Smith, Peter Pub., Inc.

Olmstead, Kathleen A. Thirsty Moves to a Foster Home. Giudice, Nancy, illus. 2001. 15p. (J). (gr. k-7). pap. 6.60 (978-0-9711419-0-2(8)) Tassie.

Paterson, Katherine. La Gran Gilly Hopkins.Tr. of THE GREAT GILLY HOPKINS. (SPA.). 160p. (J). (gr. 1-6). 8.95 (978-84-204-3222-9(9)) Santillana USA Publishing Co., Inc.

—Great Gilly Hopkins. 2004. 178p. (J). lib. bdg. 20.00 ***(978-1-4242-0840-1(8))*** Fitzgerald Bks.

Paterson, Katherine. The Great Gilly Hopkins. l.t. ed. 1999. (LRS Large Print Cornerstone Ser.). 300p. (YA). (gr. 5-12). lib. bdg. 29.95 (978-1-58118-052-7(7) , 22770) LRS.

Pixley, Marcella. Freak. 2007. 144p. (YA). (gr. 7 up). 16.00 ***(978-0-374-32453-7(0))*** Farrar, Straus & Giroux.

Polacco, Patricia. Welcome Comfort. Polacco, Patricia, illus. 2002. 40p. (J). pap. 6.99 (978-0-698-11965-9(7) , Putnam Juvenile) Penguin Group (USA) Inc.

—Welcome Comfort. 1999. (Illus.). 40p. (J). (ps-3). 16.99 (978-0-399-23169-8(2) , Philomel) Penguin Group (USA) Inc.

—Welcome Comfort. 2002. (gr. k-3). lib. bdg. 15.30 (978-0-613-50524-6(7)) Tandem Library Bks.

Quattlebaum, Mary. Grover G. Graham & Me. 2003. 192p. (J). (gr. 3-7). pap. 5.99 (978-0-440-41918-1(2) , Yearling) Random Hse. Children's Bks.

Salisbury, Linda G. The Mysterious Jamestown Suitcase: A Bailey Fish Adventure. Grotke, Christopher, illus. 2007. 192p. (J). per. 8.95 (978-1-881539-43-8(1)) Tabby Hse. Bks.

Samuels, Gertrude. Yours, Brett. 2000. 180p. (YA). (gr. 4-7). pap. 13.95 (978-0-595-00806-3(2)) iUniverse, Inc.

Shaw, Susan. The Boy from the Basement. 208p. (gr. 7). 2006. (YA). pap. 6.99 (978-0-14-240546-8(9) , Puffin); 2004. (J). 16.99 (978-0-525-47223-0(1) , Dutton Juvenile) Penguin Group (USA) Inc.

Skurzynski, Gloria. Out of the Deep. 2002. (gr. 3-6). lib. bdg. 14.10 (978-0-613-62818-1(7)) Tandem Library Bks.

—Over the Edge. 2002. (gr. 3-6). lib. bdg. 14.10 (978-0-613-62819-8(5)) Tandem Library Bks.

—Valley of Death. 2002. (gr. 3-6). lib. bdg. 14.10 (978-0-613-62873-0(X)) Tandem Library Bks.

Skurzynski, Gloria & Ferguson, Alane. Cliff-Hanger. 1998. (National Parks Mysteries Ser.: No. 3). (Illus.). 160p. (J). (gr. 3-7). 15.95 (978-0-7922-7036-2(3) , National Geographic Children's Bks.) National Geographic Society.

—Ghost Horses. 2000. (National Parks Mysteries Ser.: Vol. 6). (Illus.). 160p. (J). (gr. 3-7). 15.95 (978-0-7922-7055-3(X) , National Geographic Children's Bks.) National Geographic Society.

—Out of the Deep. 2002. (Mysteries in Our National Parks Ser.: Vol. 10). 160p. (J). (gr. 3-7). 15.95 (978-0-7922-8230-3(2)); pap. 5.95 (978-0-7922-8231-0(0)) National Geographic Society. (National Geographic Children's Bks.).

—Over the Edge. 2002. (Mysteries in Our National Parks Ser.: Vol. 7). 160p. (J). (gr. 3-7). pap. 5.95 (978-0-7922-6686-0(2)); Vol. 7. 15.95 (978-0-7922-6677-8(3)) National Geographic Society. (National Geographic Children's Bks.).

—Valley of Death. 2002. (Mysteries in Our National Parks Ser.: Vol. 8). 160p. (J). (gr. 3-7). pap. 5.95 (978-0-7922-6699-0(4)); Vol. 8. 15.95 (978-0-7922-6698-3(6)) National Geographic Society. (National Geographic Children's Bks.).

Stephenson, Lynda. Dancing with Elvis. 2006. 331p. (YA). pap. 8.00 (978-0-8028-5300-4(5) , Eerdmans Bks For Young Readers) Eerdmans, William B. Publishing Co.

Sullivan, Therese M. & Bitner, Pamela. A Gift from Valentine. 2007. 24p. (J). per. 12.95 ***(978-1-58939-981-5(1))*** Virtualbookworm.com Publishing, Inc.

Thill, Mary Kay. Wablenica: The Tale of a Lakotah Orphan. 2004. 240p. (J). per. (978-0-9743908-0-2(1) , 1232791) Balance Bks., Inc.

Watkins, Dawn L. Jenny Wren. 2000. (J). (gr. 3-7). pap. 14.98 incl. audio (978-0-89084-909-5(9) , 100065) Jones, Bob Univ. Pr.

Wilson, Jacqueline. The Story of Tracy Beaker. Sharratt, Nick, illus. l.t. ed. 1998. 200p. (J). pap. 16.95 (978-0-7540-6021-5(7) , Galaxy Children's Large Print) BBC Audiobooks America.

—The Story of Tracy Beaker. 2002. (gr. 3-6). lib. bdg. 13.00 (978-0-613-58804-1(5)) Tandem Library Bks.

Wolfson, Jill. Home, & Other Big, Fat Lies. 2006. (Illus.). 224p. (J). 16.95 (978-0-8050-7670-7(0) , Holt, Henry & Co. Bks. For Young Readers) Holt, Henry & Co.

Wolfson, Jill. What I Call Life. rev. ed. 2005. (Illus.). 272p. (J). (ps-7). 16.95 (978-0-8050-7669-1(7)) Holt, Henry & Co.

—What I Call Life. 2008. 288p. (J). pap. 6.99 ***(978-0-312-37752-6(5))*** Square Fish.

Woodruff, Elvira. Orphan of Ellis Island. 2000. (gr. 5-8). lib. bdg. 12.40 (978-0-613-30079-7(3)) Tandem Library Bks.

—The Orphan of Ellis Island: A Time Travel Adventure. 2000. 192p. (J). pap. 4.99 (978-0-590-48246-2(7)) Scholastic, Inc.

Zephaniah, Benjamin. Refugee Boy. 2004. 296p. (J). (gr. 5-12). reprint ed. pap. 7.95 (978-1-58234-908-4(8) , Bloomsbury Children) Bloomsbury Publishing.

FOUR-H CLUBS

Wolfman, Judy. Life on a Pig Farm. Winston, David L., illus. 1998. (Carolrhoda Photo Bks.). 48p. (J). (gr. k-4). lib. bdg. 23.93 (978-1-57505-237-3(7) , Carolrhoda Bks.) Lerner Publishing Group.

—Life on a Pig Farm. Winston, David Lorenz, photos by. 2nd ed. 2005. (Life on a Farm Ser.). (Illus.). 48p. (gr. 2-5). lib. bdg. 23.93 (978-1-57505-236-6(9)) Lerner Publishing Group.

FOURTH OF JULY

Amato, Carol A. & Koffsky, Ann D. The Fourth of July: An Independence Day Feast of Fun, Facts, & Activities. Lane, Nancy, illus. 2007. (Let's Celebrate Ser.). 48p. (J). (gr. 1-5). pap. 8.99 (978-0-7641-3567-5(8)) Barron's Educational Series, Inc.

Ansary, Mir Tamim. Independence Day. (Illus.). 32p. (J). 2006. ***(978-1-4034-8887-9(8));*** 2001. lib. bdg. 21.36 (978-1-58810-223-2(8)) Heinemann Library.

—Independence Day. 2001. 13.75 (978-0-606-22385-0(1)) Tandem Library Bks.

Ansary, Tamim. Independence Day. 2002. (Holiday Histories Ser.). (Illus.). 32p. (J). (gr. k-2). pap. 6.95 (978-1-58810-573-8(3) , 91688) Heinemann Library.

Court, Rob. How to Draw Independence Day Things. 2008. (Doodle Bks.). 32p. (J). 21.36 ***(978-1-59296-954-8(2))*** Child's World, Inc.

Dean, Sheri. Fourth of July. 2006. (Illus.). 24p. (J). pap. 5.95 (978-0-8368-6512-7(X)); (ENG & SPA., pap. 5.95 (978-0-8368-6526-4(X)); lib. bdg. 19.33 (978-0-8368-6505-9(7)) Stevens, Gareth Inc.

—The Fourth of July (Cuatro de Julio) 2006. (ENG & SPA., Illus.). 24p. (J). lib. bdg. 19.33 (978-0-8368-6519-6(7)) Stevens, Gareth Inc.

Foran, Jill. Independence Day. 2004. (American Holidays Ser.). (Illus.). 24p. (J). pap. 6.95 (978-1-59036-165-8(2)); lib. bdg. 15.95 (978-1-59036-109-2(1)) Weigl Pubs., Inc.

The Fourth of July. (Rosen Real Readers Big Bookstm Ser.). 12p. (J). (gr. 1-2). 31.95 (978-1-4042-6217-1(2)) Rosen Publishing Group, Inc., The.

Frost, Helen. Independence Day. (National Holidays Ser.). 24p. (J). pap. 5.95 (978-0-7368-8726-7(1)) Capstone Pr., Inc.

Giblin, James Cross. Fireworks, Picnics, & Flags: The Story of the Fourth of July Symbols. Arndt, Ursula, illus. 2001. 96p. (YA). (gr. 4-6). tchr. ed. 16.00 (978-0-618-09652-7(3)); pap. 7.95 (978-0-618-09654-1(X)) Houghton Mifflin Co. Trade & Reference Div. (Clarion Bks.).

—Fireworks, Picnics, & Flags: The Story of the Fourth of July Symbols. 1999. (Illus.). (J). (978-0-606-16423-8(5)) Tandem Library Bks.

Harcourt School Publishers Staff. Timefor Kids, 5 Pack., Bk. 12. 3rd ed. 2003. (Horizontes (Social Studies) Ser.). (SPA.). (gr. 1 up). pap. 24.00 (978-0-15-333731-4(1)) Harcourt Schl. Pubs.

Heinrichs, Ann. Independence Day. Squiers, Robert, illus. 2006. (Holidays, Festivals, & Celebrations Ser.). 32p. (J). (gr. k-4). 22.79 (978-1-59296-577-9(6)) Child's World, Inc.

Kaplan, Leslie C. Independence Day. 2004. (Library of Holidays). (Illus.). 24p. (J). lib. bdg. 18.75 (978-0-8239-6663-9(1) , PowerKids Pr.) Rosen Publishing Group, Inc., The.

Klingel, Cynthia Fitterer & Noyed, Robert B. The Fourth of July. 2002. (Wonder Books Level 2: Holidays Ser.). (Illus.). 24p. (J). (ps-3). 22.79 (978-1-56766-954-1(9)) Child's World, Inc.

Landau, Elaine. Independence Day: Birthday of the United States. 2001. (Finding Out about Holidays Ser.). (Illus.). 48p. (J). (gr. 1-4). lib. bdg. 23.93 (978-0-7660-1571-5(8)) Enslow Pubs., Inc.

Lilly, Melinda. Independence Day. 2002. (Rourke Discovery Library). (Illus.). 24p. (J). lib. bdg. 20.64 (978-1-58952-359-3(8)) Rourke Publishing, LLC.

Marx, David F. Independence Day. 2001. (Rookie Read-About Holidays Ser.). (Illus.). 32p. (J). (gr. 1-2). pap. 5.95 (978-0-516-27176-7(8) , Children's Pr.) Scholastic Library Publishing.

—Independence Day: Holidays. 2001. (Rookie Read-About Holidays Ser.). (Illus.). 32p. (J). (gr. 1-2). 19.50 (978-0-516-22232-5(5) , Children's Pr.) Scholastic Library Publishing.

Mir Tamim Ansary. Independence Day. 2nd ed. 2006. (Illus.). 32p. (J). pap. ***(978-1-4034-8900-5(9))*** Heinemann Library.

Murray, Julie. Independence Day. 2005. (Buddy Book Ser.). (Illus.). 24p. (J). (gr. k-4). lib. bdg. 21.35 (978-1-59197-588-5(3)) ABDO Publishing Co.

Nelson, Robin. Independence Day. 2003. (First Step Nonfiction Ser.). (Illus.). 24p. (J). (gr. k-2). lib. bdg. 18.60 (978-0-8225-1274-5(2)) Lerner Publishing Group.

—Independence Day. 2003. (gr. k-3). lib. bdg. 11.80 (978-0-613-52404-9(7)) Tandem Library Bks.

Nobleman, Marc Tyler. Independence Day. 2004. (Let's See Ser.). (Illus.). 24p. (J). (gr. 1 up). lib. bdg. 19.93 (978-0-7565-0769-5(3)) Compass Point Bks.

Ross, Kathy. Star-Spangled Crafts. 2003. (gr. k-3). lib. bdg. 16.40 (978-0-613-59022-8(8)) Tandem Library Bks.

Sanders, Nancy I. Independence Day. 2003. (True Book Ser.). (Illus.). 48p. (J). 25.00 (978-0-516-22764-1(5) , Children's Pr.) Scholastic Library Publishing.

—Independence Day. 2003. (Illus.). 47p. (J). (gr. 3-5). lib. bdg. 15.25 (978-0-613-89015-1(9)) Tandem Library Bks.

Schauffler, Robert Haven, ed. Independence Day: Its Celebration, Spirit, & Significance As Related in Prose & Verse. 1999. (Our American Holidays Ser.). 318p. (J). (gr. 3-6). reprint ed. lib. bdg. 42.00 (978-0-7808-0394-7(9)) Omnigraphics, Inc.

The Story of America's Birthday. 1999. (Illus.). 24p. (J). (ps-k). 6.95 (978-0-8249-4170-3(5)) Ideals Pubns.

Trueit, Trudi Strain. Independence Day. 2006. (Rookie Read-About Holidays Ser.). (Illus.). 31p. (J). (978-0-531-12457-4(6)) Children's Pr., Ltd.

—Independence Day. rev. ed. 2006. 32p. (YA). (gr. 1-2). pap. 5.95 (978-0-531-11838-2(X) , Children's Pr.) Scholastic Library Publishing.

Williams, Colleen Madonna Flood. My Adventure on the Fourth of July. 2007. 44p. (J). 8.99 (978-1-59092-560-7(2) , Orchard Academy Pr.) Windstorm Creative.

Zocchi, Judy. On Independence Day. Wallis, Rebecca, illus. 2005. (Holiday Happenings Ser.). 32p. (J). pap. 9.95 (978-1-59646-208-3(6)); lib. bdg. 20.65 (978-1-891997-43-3(2)) Dingles & Co.

—On Independence Day/el día de la Independencia. Wallis, Rebecca, illus. 2005. (Holiday Happenings Ser.).Tr. of día de la Independencia. (ENG & SPA.). 32p. (J). pap. 9.95 (978-1-59646-210-6(8)); lib. bdg. 20.65 (978-1-891997-44-0(0)) Dingles & Co.

FOURTH OF JULY—FICTION

Bertrand, Diane Gonzales. Uncle Chente's Picnic/el picnic de Tío Chente. Castilla, Julia Mercedes, tr. Howard, Pauline Rodriguez, illus. Tr. of Picnic de Tío Chente. (ENG & SPA.). 32p. (J). (ps-3). 15.95 (978-1-55885-337-9(5) , Piñata Books) Arte Publico Pr.

Brown, Rick, illus. I'm Going to Read (Level 2): Hooray for the 4th of July. 2007. (I'm Going to Read Ser.). 28p. (J). pap. 3.95 (978-1-4027-4241-5(X)) Sterling Publishing Co., Inc.

Caraballo, Samuel. Estrellita se despide de su isla/Estrellita Says Good-bye to Her Island. Caraballo, Samuel, tr. Torrecilla, Pablo, illus. Tr. of Estrellita Says Good-Bye to Her Island. (ENG & SPA.). 32p. (J). stu. ed. 15.95 (978-1-55885-338-6(3) , Piñata Books) Arte Publico Pr.

Chall, Marsha Wilson. Happy Birthday, America! Porfirio, Guy, illus. 2000. 32p. (J). (ps-3). 17.99 (978-0-688-13051-0(8)) HarperCollins Pubs.

Clark, Katie. Grandma Drove the Garbage Truck. Huntington, Amy, illus. 2006. 32p. 15.95 (978-0-89272-698-1(9)) Down East Bks.

Dower, Laura. Just Visiting. rev. ed. 2002. (From the Files of Madison Finn Ser.). 176p. (J). (gr. 3-7). pap. 4.99 (978-0-7868-1683-5(X) , Volo) Hyperion Bks. for Children.

—Just Visiting. 2002. (gr. 3-6). lib. bdg. 13.00 (978-0-613-90688-3(8)) Tandem Library Bks.

Grosgebauer, Clare Ham. Snickerdoodle's Star-Spangled Fourth of July! Rissing, Karen, illus. 4th ed. 2005. 36p. 12.99 (978-0-9741888-6-7(7)) Small Wonders Enterprises.

Henry, Henther French. Life, Liberty & the Pursuit of Jellybeans: A Fourth of July Story. Henry, Henther French, illus. 2004. (Claire's Holiday Adventures Ser.). (Illus.). 32p. (gr. k-4). 15.95 (978-0-9706341-6-0(1)) Cubbie Blue Publishing.

—Life, Liberty & the Pursuit of Jellybeans: An Independence Day Story. Henry, Henther French, illus. 2004. (Claire's Holiday Adventures Ser.). (Illus.). 32p. (gr. k-4). 16.95 (978-0-9706341-5-3(3)) Cubbie Blue Publishing.

Hill, Elizabeth Starr. Wildfire! Shepperson, Rob, illus. 2004. 80p. (J). 16.00 (978-0-374-31712-6(7) , Farrar, Straus & Giroux (BYR)) Farrar, Straus & Giroux.

Keep, Linda Lowery. Red, White, & Blue Jeans: By Linda Lowery: Illustrated by Ann Field. Field, Ann, illus. 2005. 144p. (J). 9.95 (978-0-375-82540-8(1) , Golden Bks.) Random Hse. Children's Bks.

Ketteman, Helen. The Great Cake Bake. Collins, Matt, illus. 2005. 32p. (J). 16.95 (978-0-8027-8950-1(1)) Walker & Co.

Kimmelman, Leslie. Happy 4th of July, Jenny Sweeney! Cote, Nancy, illus. 2003. 32p. (J). (ps-1). 16.95 (978-0-8075-3152-5(9)) Whitman, Albert & Co.

Maguire, Gregory. One Final Firecracker. 2007. (Hamlet Chronicles Ser.). 320p. (J). pap. 6.99 ***(978-0-06-085284-9(4)*** , Harper Trophy) HarperCollins Pubs.

McCue, Lisa, illus. Corduroy's Fourth of July. 2007. 16p. (J). bds. 5.99 (978-0-670-06159-4(X) , Viking Juvenile) Penguin Group (USA) Inc.

McGrath, Barbara Barbieri. The M & M's' Brand All-American Parade Book. Tagel, Peggy, illus. 2004. 12p. (J). (ps-k). bds. 6.95 (978-1-57091-430-0(3)) Charlesbridge Publishing, Inc.

Osborne, Mary Pope. Happy Birthday, America. Catalanotto, Peter, illus. 2008. 32p. (J). pap. 6.99 ***(978-0-312-38050-2(X))*** Square Fish.

—Happy Birthday, America. Catalanotto, Peter, illus. 2005. 32p. (J). (gr. k-4). lib. bdg. 13.15 (978-0-606-33702-1(4)) Tandem Library Bks.

Roberts, Bethany. Fourth of July Mice! Cushman, Doug, illus. 2004. (Holiday Mice Ser.). 32p. (J). (gr. k-ps). 13.00 (978-0-618-31366-2(4) , Clarion Bks.) Houghton Mifflin Co. Trade & Reference Div.

Roy, Ron. The Talking T. Rex. Gurney, John Steven, illus. 2003. (A to Z Mysteries Ser.: No. 20). 96p. (J). (gr. 2-5). pap. 3.99 (978-0-375-81369-6(1)); lib. bdg. 11.99 (978-0-375-91369-3(6)) Random Hse. Children's Bks. (Random Hse. Bks. for Young Readers).

Schories, Pat, illus. Biscuit's Fourth of July. 2005. (J). ***(978-1-4156-0311-6(1)*** , Harper Festival) HarperCollins Pubs.

Watson, Wendy. Hurray for the Fourth of July. 2000. (Illus.). 32p. (J). (gr. k-ps). pap. 5.95 (978-0-618-04036-0(6) , Clarion Bks.) Houghton Mifflin Co. Trade & Reference Div.

—Hurray for the Fourth of July. 2000. (Illus.). (J). (978-0-606-18043-6(5)) Tandem Library Bks.

Whitehead, Kathy. Looking for Uncle Louie on the Fourth of July. Torrecilla, Pablo, illus. 2004. 32p. (J). 15.95 (978-1-59078-061-9(2)) Boyds Mills Pr.

Wong, Janet S. Apple Pie Fourth of July. Chodos-Irvine, Margaret, illus. 40p. (J). 2006. pap. 7.00 (978-0-15-205708-4(0) , Voyager Bks./Libros Viajeros); 2002. 17.00 (978-0-15-202543-4(X)) Harcourt Children's Bks.

Zawadsky, Pat. The Boy Who Stole the Fourth of July: A Musical Comedy. 1998. (Illus.). 29p. (YA). (gr. 5-12). pap. 4.00 (978-0-88680-450-3(7) , C4507) Clark, I. E. Pubns.

Ziefert, Harriet. Hats off for the Fourth of July! Miller, Gustaf, illus. 2002. 32p. (J). (ps-ps). pap. 6.99 (978-0-14-056709-0(7) , Puffin) Penguin Group (USA) Inc.

FOXES

Barnard, Edward S. Foxes. 2007. (J). ***(978-1-59939-120-5(1)*** , Reader's Digest Young Families, Inc.) Reader's Digest Children's Publishing, Inc.

Barret & Allen. El Zorro. 2002. (Perros Salvajes Serie).Tr. of Wild Dogs: The Fox. (SPA.). 24p. (J). (gr. 3-5). 22.45 (978-1-4103-0015-7(3) , Blackbirch Pr., Inc.) Thomson Gale.

Berger, Melvin & Berger, Gilda. Foxes. 2002. (Scholastic Readers Ser.). (Illus.). (J). (978-0-439-44534-4(5)) Scholastic, Inc.

Chottin, Ariane. Little Foxes. 2005. (Born to Be Wild Ser.). (Illus.), 23p. (J). lib. bdg. 22.00 (978-0-8368-4435-1(1)) Stevens, Gareth Inc.

DK Publishing. Fox: See How They Grow. 2008. (See How They Grow Ser.). 1p. (J). (ps-k). pap. 3.99 ***(978-0-7566-3763-7(5))*** Dorling Kindersley Publishing, Inc.

Donovan, Sandy. A Fox in Its Den. 2003. (Where Do Animals Live? Ser.). (J). pap. (978-1-58417-191-1(X)) Lake Street Pubs.

Foxes: Individual Title Six-Packs. 16p. (gr. 2 up). 36.00 (978-0-7635-9391-9(5)) Rigby Education.

Foxes & Their Dens. (Animal Homes Ser.). 24p. (J). 6.95 (978-0-7368-5127-5(5)) Capstone Pr., Inc.

Gentle, Victor & Perry, Janet. Red Foxes. 2002. (Imagination Library). (Illus.). 24p. (J). (gr. 2 up). lib. bdg. 22.00 (978-0-8368-3098-9(9)) Stevens, Gareth Inc.

George, Jean Craighead. Summer Moon. 2002. (Seasons of the Moon Ser.). (Illus.). 112p. (J). pap. 5.95 (978-0-06-440995-7(3) , Harper Trophy) HarperCollins Pubs.

—Summer Moon. 2003. (J). (gr. 3-7). 20.75 (978-0-8446-7243-4(2)) Smith, Peter Pub., Inc.

—Summer Moon. 2002. (gr. 3-6). lib. bdg. 14.10 (978-0-613-50513-0(1)) Tandem Library Bks.

Gibson, Deborah C. Foxes & Their Homes. 1999. (Animal Habitats Ser.). (Illus.). 24p. (J). (gr. k-4). lib. bdg. 18.75 (978-0-8239-5309-7(2) , PowerKids Pr.) Rosen Publishing Group, Inc., The.

Greenaway, Theresa. Wolves, Wild Dogs & Foxes. 2001. (Secret World Of... Ser.). (Illus.). 48p. (J). (gr. 4-7). lib. bdg. 27.12 (978-0-7398-3507-4(6)) Raintree.

Hodge, Deborah. Wild dogs: Wolves, coyotes & foxes. Stephens, Pat, illus. unabr. ed. 2004. (Kids Can Press Wildlife Ser.). 32p. (J). (gr. k-3). (978-1-55074-420-0(8)) Kids Can Pr., Ltd.

Johnson, Jinny. Fox. Ch'en-Ling, illus. 2001. (Busy Baby Animals Ser.). (Illus.). 16p. (J). (ps up). lib. bdg. 19.33 (978-0-8368-2924-2(7)) Stevens, Gareth Inc.

Lang, Aubrey. Baby Fox. Lynch, Wayne, photos by. 2002. (Nature Babies Ser.). (Illus.). 36p. (J). (gr. k-3). (978-1-55041-688-6(X)) Fitzhenry & Whiteside, Ltd.

Lantier-Sampon, Patricia & Schuler, Judy. The Wonder of Foxes. McGee, John F., illus. 2001. (Animal Wonders Ser.). 48p. (J). (gr. 1 up). lib. bdg. 26.00 (978-0-8368-2765-1(1)) Stevens, Gareth Inc.

Levine, Michelle. Red Foxes. 2004. (Pull Ahead Bks.). (Illus.). 32p. (J). (gr. k-2). pap. 5.95 (978-0-8225-9887-9(6)); 22.60 (978-0-8225-3774-8(5) , Carolrhoda Bks.) Lerner Publishing Group.

Lockwood, Sophie. Foxes. 2008. (World of Mammals Ser.). 40p. (J). (gr. 2-6). 29.93 ***(978-1-59296-932-6(1))*** Child's World, Inc.

Lynch, Wayne, illus. Baby Fox. (Nature Babies Ser.). 32p. (J). (gr. k-3). pap. (978-1-55041-724-1(X)) Fitzhenry & Whiteside, Ltd.

Mason, Cherie. Wild Fox. unabr. ed. 1998. (YA). (gr. k up). audio 10.95 (978-1-883332-35-8(4) , 396094) Audio Bookshelf.

—Wild Fox: A True Story. Stammen, JoEllen McAllister, illus. 2004. 33p. pap. 9.95 (978-0-89272-659-2(8)) Down East Bks.

McClanahan. Fox. 1999. (Wild Baby Animals Ser.). (Illus.). 16p. (J). (ps-k). 4.99 (978-0-7681-0189-8(1) , McClanahan Bk.) Learning Horizons, Inc.

McDonald, Mary Ann. Foxes. 2007. (New Naturebooks Ser.). 32p. (J). (gr. 1-5). 27.07 ***(978-1-59296-845-9(7))*** Child's World, Inc.

Mitchell, Pratima & Askew, Gordon. I-Read Year 1 Anthology: Follow the Fox. 2007. (I-read Ser.). (Illus.). 40p. pap. ***(978-0-521-70479-3(0))*** Cambridge Univ. Pr.

Murphy, Patricia J. Red Foxes. Saunders-Smith, Gail, ed. 2004. (Grassland Animals Ser.). (Illus.). 24p. (J). (gr. k-1). lib. bdg. 15.93 (978-0-7368-2074-5(4) , Pebble Bks.) Capstone Pr., Inc.

Nobleman, Marc Tyler. Foxes. 2006. (Animals Animals Ser.). (Illus.). 48p. (J). lib. bdg. 28.50 (978-0-7614-2237-2(4) , Benchmark Bks.) Cavendish, Marshall Corp.

Olien, Becky. Foxes: Clever Hunters. 2002. (Wild World of Animals Ser.). (Illus.). 24p. (J). (gr. 1-2). lib. bdg. 18.60 (978-0-7368-1137-8(0) , Bridgestone Bks.) Capstone Pr., Inc.

Perry, Phyllis J. Crafty Canines: Coyotes, Foxes & Wolves. 1999. (Watts Library). (Illus.). 64p. (J). (gr. 5-7). 25.50 (978-0-531-11680-7(8) , Watts, Franklin) Scholastic Library Publishing.

—Crafty Canines: Coyotes, Foxes, & Wolves. 1999. (gr. 3-6). lib. bdg. 17.60 (978-0-613-29416-4(5)) Tandem Library Bks.

Renard. 1999. (Pocket Pals Ser.). (FRE.). (J). (ps-1). pap. 1.99 (978-0-85953-738-4(2)) Child's Play-International.

Richardson, Adele. Foxes. 2006. (Illus.). 24p. (J). (978-0-7368-5416-0(9) , Bridgestone Bks.) Capstone Pr., Inc.

Rigby Education Staff. The Fox: Jumbled Tumble. (gr. k-2). 21.00 (978-0-7635-2422-7(0)) Rigby Education.

Rustad, Martha E. H. Foxes & Their Dens. 2004. (Animal Homes Ser.). (Illus.). 24p. (J). lib. bdg. 19.93 (978-0-7368-2583-2(5) , Pebble Bks.) Capstone Pr., Inc.

Schuler, Judy. Fox Magic for Kids. McGee, John F., illus. 1999. (Animal Magic for Kids Ser.). 48p. (J). (gr. 3 up). lib. bdg. 26.00 (978-0-8368-2633-3(7)) Stevens, Gareth Inc.

Smith van Frankenhuyzen, Robbyn. Saving Samantha: A True Story. van Frankenhuyzen, Gijsbert, illus. 2004. 48p. (J). 17.95 (978-1-58536-220-2(4)) Sleeping Bear Pr.

Swanson, Diane. Foxes. 2003. (Welcome to the World of Animals Ser.). (Illus.). 32p. (J). (gr. 3 up). lib. bdg. 23.33 (978-0-8368-3562-5(X)) Stevens, Gareth Inc.

Townsend, Emily Rose. Arctic Foxes. 2004. (Polar Animals Ser.). (Illus.). 24p. (J). (gr. k-1). lib. bdg. 15.93 (978-0-7368-2356-2(5) , Pebble Bks.) Capstone Pr., Inc.

Windsor, Jo. Foxes: Early Level Satellite Individual Title Six-Packs. (Sails Literacy Ser.). 16p. (gr. 1-2). 27.00 (978-0-7578-2941-3(4)) Rigby Education.

FOXES—FICTION

Aggs, Patrice. Ooh la Booga Bomp. Aggs, Patrice, illus. 2002. (Panda Ser.). (Illus.). 64p. (YA). (gr. k up). pap. 4.95 (978-0-86278-753-0(X)) O'Brien Pr., Ltd., The IRL. *Dist:* Independent Pubs. Group.

Ahlberg, Allan. Fast Fox Goes Crazy. (Illus.). 32p. (J). pap. 9.95 (978-0-14-056400-6(4)) Penguin Bks., Ltd. GBR. *Dist:* Trafalgar Square Publishing.

—Slow Dog's Nose, Bk. 5. 2000. (Illus.). 32p. (J). pap. 9.95 (978-0-14-056401-3(2)) Penguin Group (USA) Inc.

Allen, Jan. Now I Know the Story of Samson. l.t. ed. 2006. (Illus.). 40p. (J). (978-0-9765514-1-6(1)) Light Bugs Publishing.

Augustyn, Heather. Chi-Town Coyote. 2005. 215p. pap. 12.59 (978-1-4116-3365-0(2)) Lulu.com.

Aylesworth, Jim. Old Fox's Sack. McClintock, Barbara, illus. 2001. (J). pap. (978-0-439-09544-0(1)) Scholastic, Inc.

—The Tale of Tricky Fox. 2001. (J). (gr. k-3). 26.90 incl. audio (978-0-8045-6885-2(5)) Spoken Arts, Inc.

Azordegan, Kambiz. The Brave Donkey & the Cowardly Lion: Donkey, Lion & Fox. Sajem, Johnny, illus. abr. l.t. ed. 1998. (Tootee's Magical Stories Ser.: Vol. 6). 40p. (J). 9.95 (978-1-890571-30-6(X)) Positive Children's Programming Corp.

Baglio, Ben M. Fox in the Frost. McNicholas, Shelagh & Gregory, J., illus. 2000. (Animal Ark Ser.: No. 18). 160p. (J). (gr. 3-5). pap. 3.99 (978-0-439-23017-9(9)) Scholastic, Inc.

Bailey, Arthur Scott. Sleepy-Time Tales: The Tale of Tommy Fox. 2006. pap. (***978-1-4065-0453-8(X)***) Dodo Pr.

Bailey, Arthur Scott. The Tale of Tommy Fox. 2004. reprint ed. pap. 15.95 (978-1-4191-8481-9(4)); pap. 1.99 (978-1-4192-8481-6(9)) Kessinger Publishing, LLC.

Baker, Harriet Lila. Boyduck Goose: His Life & Times, Bk. II. 2005. (J). pap. 9.00 (978-0-8059-6694-7(3)) Dorrance Publishing Co., Inc.

Baker, Liza. I Love You Because You're You. 2008. (Scooby-Doo Ser.). 24p. (J). bds. 8.99 (***978-0-545-02931-5(7)*** , Cartwheel Bks.) Scholastic, Inc.

—I Love You Because You're You. McPhail, David M., illus. 2001. 32p. (J). (ps-k). pap. 9.95 (978-0-439-20638-9(3) , Cartwheel Bks.) Scholastic, Inc.

—I Love You Because You're You Read Along. 2006. (J). 9.95 (978-0-439-89558-3(8)) Scholastic, Inc.

Barkaw, Henriette. Don't Cry Sly: Big Book English Only. Johnson, Richard, illus. 2004. (J). pap. (978-1-85269-999-4(X)) Mantra Publishing, Ltd.

Barkow, Henriette & Finlay, Lizzie, illus. Buri & the Marroow: An Indian Folk Tale: Un Conte Traditionnel Indien = Buri et la Courge. 2004. (TAM, VIE, SPA, GUJ & PER.). 24p. (J). pap. (978-1-85269-583-5(8)) Mantra Publishing, Ltd.

Bingham, Janet. Mommy's Little Star. 2008. (Barbie Fairytopia Ser.). 32p. (J). pap. 9.99 (***978-0-545-03408-1(6)*** , Cartwheel Bks.) Scholastic, Inc.

Bodnar, Judit Z. Tale of a Tail. Sandford, John B., illus. 1998. 40p. (J). (ps-3). 15.95 (978-0-688-12174-7(8)); 15.89 (978-0-688-12175-4(6)) HarperCollins Pubs.

Bonning, Tony. Another Fine Mess. Hobson, Sally, illus. 1998. 32p. (J). (ps-2). 14.95 (978-1-888444-43-8(6)) Little Tiger Pr.

Bonning, Tony & Hobson, Sally. Another Fine Mess. 2001. (Illus.). 32p. (J). 5.95 (978-1-58925-356-8(6) , tiger tales) ME Media LLC.

Book Buddy: Fox with Story Book. Orig. Title: Child's Play. (Illus.). 10p. (J). (ps-3). reprint ed. (978-1-881469-46-9(8)) Safari, Ltd.

Boujon, Claude. Bon Appetit Monsieur Renard. pap. 14.95 (978-2-211-04878-1(1)) Archimede Editions FRA. *Dist:* Distribooks, Inc.

Brookes, Diane & Dahl, Roald. A Novel Study for Grades One & Two Based on Fantastic Mr. Fox. Blake, Quentin, illus. 1998. (J). pap., tchr. ed. (978-0-9683449-5-8(X)) Raven Rock Publishing.

Browne, N. M. Hunted. 2004. 336p. (J). (gr. 5 up). reprint ed. pap. 7.95 (978-1-58234-903-9(7) , Bloomsbury Children) Bloomsbury Publishing.

Burgess, Thornton W. The Adventures of Reddy Fox. 2005. 26.95 (978-1-4218-0995-3(8)); 84p. pap. 10.95 (978-1-59540-695-8(6)) 1st World Publishing, Inc. (1st World Library - Literary Society).

—The Adventures of Reddy Fox. (J). 18.95 (978-0-8488-0380-3(9)) Amereon LTD.

—The Adventures of Reddy Fox. 2000. mass mkt. 3.99 (978-1-55902-938-4(2) , Aerie) Doherty, Tom Assocs., LLC.

—The Adventures of Reddy Fox. 2004. reprint ed. pap. 15.95 (978-1-4191-5161-3(4)); pap. 1.99 (978-1-4192-5161-0(9)) Kessinger Publishing, LLC.

—The Adventures of Reddy Fox. 2006. 144p. per. 13.45 (***978-1-59462-395-0(3)*** , 431, Book Jungle) Standard Pubns., Inc.

Burgess, Thornton W. Old Granny Fox. (J). 18.95 (978-0-8488-0392-6(2)) Amereon LTD.

—Old Granny Fox. 2001. (Dover Children's Thrift Classics Ser.). (Illus.). 96p. (J). (gr. 3-6). pap. 1.50 (978-0-486-41659-5(3)) Dover Pubns., Inc.

Burgess, W. Thornton. Old Granny Fox. 2006. pap. 55.99 (***978-1-4280-3691-8(1)***) IndyPublish.com.

Burningham, John. Harquin: Fox Who Went Down. 2000. (Illus.). 32p. (J). pap. 8.99 (978-0-09-982510-4(4) , Red Fox) Random Hse. Children's Bks. GBR. *Dist:* Trafalgar Square Publishing.

Byars, Betsy. The Midnight Fox. 1999. (J). 9.95 (978-1-56137-667-4(1)) Novel Units, Inc.

—La Zorra Negra. (SPA.). 102p. (YA). (gr. 5-8). 6.80 (978-84-279-3247-0(2) , NG2893) Noguer y Caralt Editores, S. A. ESP. *Dist:* Lectorum Pubns., Inc.

Campoy, F. Isabel. Rosa Raposa. Aruego, Jose & Dewey, Ariane, illus. 2002. 32p. (J). (gr. k-2). 16.00 (978-0-15-202161-0(2) , Gulliver Bks.) Harcourt Children's Bks.

Cantillon, Eli A. A New Home for Fab the Fox. Pons, Bernadette, illus. 1998. 14p. (J). (ps-1). 14.98 (978-1-58048-043-7(8)) Sandvik Publishing.

Chanticleer & the Fox. 2004. (J). 24.95 incl. audio (978-1-56008-178-4(3)); pap. 14.95 incl. audio (978-1-56008-179-1(1)) Weston Woods Studios, Inc.

Church, Caroline Jane. One Smart Goose. 2005. (Illus.), 32p. (J). 16.95 (978-0-439-68765-2(9) , Orchard Bks.) Scholastic, Inc.

Cook, Sherry & Johnson, Terri. X. E. Ecology, 26. Kuhn, Jesse, illus. l.t. ed. 2006. (Quirkles—Exploring Phonics through Science Ser.: 24). 32p. (J). 7.99 (978-1-933815-23-7(X) , Quirkles, The) Creative 3, LLC.

Cowley, Joy. Chicken Feathers. Elliott, David W., illus. 2008. 160p. (J). (gr. 3-6). 15.99 (***978-0-399-24791-0(2)*** , Philomel) Penguin Group (USA) Inc.

Coxe, Molly. Fox Trot. 1999. (Road to Reading Ser.). (J). lib. bdg. (978-0-03-074629-1(9) , Saunders) Elsevier - Health Sciences Division.

Cruickshank, Margrit. Down by the Pond: A Surprise Farmyard Book. Saunders, Dave, illus. 1999. 32p. (J). (ps-k). pap. 7.99 (978-0-7112-0978-7(2)) Lincoln, Frances Ltd. GBR. *Dist:* Transition Vendor.

Dahl, Roald. Fantastic Mr. Fox. Blake, Quentin, illus. 2002. (J). 13.19 (978-0-7587-5599-5(6)) Book Wholesalers, Inc.

—Fantastic Mr. Fox. Blake, Quentin, illus. 2002. 96p. (J). (gr. 3-7). 15.95 (978-0-375-82207-0(0)); lib. bdg. 17.99 (978-0-375-92207-7(5)) Random Hse. Children's Bks. (Knopf Bks. for Young Readers).

—El Superzorro. Elena, Horacio, illus. 2003. (SPA.). 96p. (J). (gr. 3-5). pap. 11.95 (978-968-19-0719-8(1)) Santillana USA Publishing Co., Inc.

—El Superzorro. 2000. (SPA.). (gr. 3-6). lib. bdg. 25.75 (978-0-613-57280-4(7)) Tandem Library Bks.

Dalmatian Press Staff. Fox & hound/ Aristocats. 2007. 64p. pap. 4.99 (***978-1-4037-3592-8(1)***) Dalmatian Pr.

Daniels, Lucy. Cub in the Cupboard. 1999. (Animal Ark Ser.: No. 8). (J). (gr. 3-5). 10.64 (978-0-606-19087-9(2)) Tandem Library Bks.

Defosse, Rosana Curiel. Santiago & the Fox of Hatsune. Barradas, Leticia, illus. (SPA.). 32p. (J). (gr. 3-5). pap. 7.95 (978-970-29-0134-1(0)) Santillana USA Publishing Co., Inc.

Donaldson, Julia & Richards, Lucy. The Quick Brown Fox Club. 2006. (Red Bananas Ser.). (Illus.). 48p. (J). (978-0-7787-1080-6(7)) Crabtree Publishing Co.

Don't Cry Sly. 2004. (J). E-Book incl. cd-rom (978-1-84444-457-1(0)) Mantra Publishing, Ltd.

Dubowski, Cathy East. Fortune Cookie Fox. 1999. (gr. 3-6). lib. bdg. 12.40 (978-0-613-21556-5(7)) Tandem Library Bks.

Dunmore, Helen. Go Fox. 2000. (Illus.). 63p. (J). pap. 5.95 (978-0-552-52963-1(X)) Transworld Publishers Ltd. GBR. *Dist:* Trafalgar Square Publishing.

Duran Armengol, Teresa. El Zorro. 2002. Tr. of Fox. (SPA., Illus.). 24p. (J). 6.50 (978-84-246-1722-6(3)) La Galera, S.A. Editorial ESP. *Dist:* AIMS International Bks., Inc.

Eggleton, Jill. The Robber Fox. (Sails Literacy Ser.). 24p. (gr. 1 up). 27.00 (978-0-7578-6204-5(7)) Rigby Education.

—The Robber Fox: 3-in-1 Package. (Sails Literacy Ser.). 24p. (gr. 1 up). 57.00 (978-0-7578-8621-8(3)) Rigby Education.

—The Robber Fox: 6 Small Books. (Sails Literacy Ser.). 24p. (gr. 1 up). 25.00 (978-0-7578-7732-2(X)) Rigby Education.

—The Rock Boss: Early Level Satellite Individual Title Six-Packs. (Sails Literacy Ser.). 16p. (gr. 1-2). 27.00 (978-0-7578-2934-5(1)) Rigby Education.

Egielski, Richard. Gingerbread Boy. 2000. (gr. k-3). lib. bdg. 14.15 (978-0-613-29964-0(7)) Tandem Library Bks.

Erickson, John R. The Case of the Fiddle-Playing Fox. Holmes, Gerald L., illus. 1998. (Hank the Cowdog Ser.: No. 12). 144p. (J). (gr. 2-5). 14.99 (978-0-670-88419-3(7) , Viking Juvenile) Penguin Group (USA) Inc.

—The Case of the Fiddle-Playing Fox. Holmes, Gerald L., illus. 1999. (Hank the Cowdog Ser.: No. 12). 131p. (J). (gr. 3-6). lib. bdg. 13.00 (978-0-8335-6825-0(6)) Tandem Library Bks.

Ernst, Lisa Campbell. The Gingerbread Girl. Ernst, Lisa Campbell, illus. 2006. (Illus.). 36p. (J). (ps). 16.99 (978-0-525-47667-2(9) , Dutton Juvenile) Penguin Group (USA) Inc.

Finley, Mary Pearce. Little Fox's Secret: The Mystery of Bent's Fort. Spurlock, Martha J., illus. 2000. 60p. (J). (gr. 3-5). pap. 5.95 (978-0-86541-050-3(X)) Filter Pr., LLC.

The Fix It Fox. (Little Book Practice Reader Ser.). (J). (978-0-8136-0690-3(X)) Modern Curriculum Pr.

Flossie & the Fox. 2004. (J). pap. 18.95 incl. audio compact disk (978-1-55592-772-1(6)); pap. 38.75 incl. audio compact disk (978-1-55592-787-5(4)); pap. 32.75 incl. audio (978-1-55592-224-5(4)); pap. 14.95 incl. audio (978-1-55592-051-7(9)) Weston Woods Studios, Inc.

Ford, Carole S. Freddie the Fox & Peter the Cheetah. Edwin, Kimberly, illus. 30p. (J). (ps). pap. 4.95 (978-1-891533-03-7(7)) Calvin Partnership, LLC.

Foreman, Michael. Fox Tale. 2007. (Illus.). (J). (gr. k-2). 28p. 16.95 (***978-1-84270-542-1(3)***); 32p. pap. 16.95 (***978-1-84270-610-7(1)***) Andersen GBR. *Dist:* Independent Pubs. Group.

The Fox & the Grapes: 6 Small Books. (gr. k-2). 23.00 (978-0-7635-8504-4(1)) Rigby Education.

Fox & the Hound. (Read-Along Ser.). (J). 7.99 incl. audio (978-1-55723-019-5(6)) Walt Disney Records.

The Fox & the Stork, Vol. 2. l.t. ed. 1999. (Illus.). 43p. (J). (gr. k-6). reprint ed. pap. 2.50 (978-1-893688-06-3(2)) Carroll Schl., The.

The Fox & the Thrush. l.t. ed. 1999. (Illus.). 15p. (J). (gr. k-6). reprint ed. pap. 2.50 (978-1-893688-03-2(8)) Carroll Schl., The.

Fox, L. B. The Adventures of Marky, Slash & Levy. 2006. (ENG.). 184p. per. 19.95 (***978-1-4241-4992-6(4)***) PublishAmerica, Inc.

Fox, Mem. Hattie & the Fox. 2002. (Illus.). (J). 15.53 (978-0-7587-2704-6(6)) Book Wholesalers, Inc.

—Hattie & the Fox. 3rd ed. 2002. (Trophies Reading Program Ser.). (Illus.). (J). pap. 10.20 (978-0-15-329360-3(8)) Harcourt Schl. Pubs.

—Hattie & the Fox. Mullins, Patricia, illus. 2005. (Stories to Go! Ser.). 32p. (J). 4.99 (978-1-4169-0308-6(9) , Aladdin) Simon & Schuster Children's Publishing.

Fox on the Run. (J). (978-0-02-583113-1(5) , Scribner) Simon & Schuster.

Fox's Socks. (Acorn Wood Lift-the-Flap Bks.). (Illus.). (YA). bds. 3.50 net. (978-1-56021-379-6(5)) W.J. Fantasy, Inc.

Galdone, Paul. The Gingerbread Boy Big Book. 2006. 40p. (J). (ps-k). 25.00 (978-0-618-83686-4(1)) Houghton Mifflin Co. Trade & Reference Div.

Galera Staff. Cuervo y la Raposa (Raven & the Fox) (SPA.). 24p. (J). 9.95 (978-84-246-1601-4(4)) La Galera, S.A. Editorial ESP. *Dist:* AIMS International Bks., Inc.

El Gallo, la Zorra, y el Perro. (Coleccion Fabulas y Cuentos Populares). (SPA.). (J). (gr. 2-4). (978-84-246-1559-8(X) , GL0414) La Galera, S.A. Editorial ESP. *Dist:* Lectorum Pubns., Inc.

Gardiner, John Reynolds. Stone Fox. 48p. (J). pap. 4.50 (978-0-8072-1267-7(9) , Listening Library) Random Hse. Audio Publishing Group.

Garis, Howard Roger. Buddy & Brighteyes Pigg. 2004. reprint ed. pap. 15.95 (978-1-4191-1107-5(8)); pap. 1.99 (978-1-4192-1107-2(2)) Kessinger Publishing, LLC.

Garside, Alice H. The Man, the Fox & the Skunk, Set 1. l.t. ed. 1999. (Illus.). 19p. (Orig.). (J). (gr. k-6). reprint ed. pap. 2.50 (978-1-893688-01-8(1)) Carroll Schl., The.

Gave, Marc. Fox & the Hound: Read Aloud Storybook. 2000. (Illus.). 64p. (J). (ps-3). 6.99 (978-0-7364-0194-4(6)) Mouse Works.

Gerstein, Mordicai. Fox Eyes. 2001. (gr. k-3). lib. bdg. 11.80 (978-0-613-43036-4(0)) Tandem Library Bks.

—The Old Country. 144p. 2006. (J). pap. 7.95 (978-1-59643-192-8(X)); 2005. (YA). 14.95 (978-1-59643-047-1(8)) Roaring Brook Pr.

Giffard, Hannah. Red Fox. (Illus.). 36p. pap. (978-0-7112-2158-1(8)) Lincoln, Frances Ltd. GBR. *Dist:* Transition Vendor.

—Red Fox on the Move. (Illus.). 36p. pap. (978-0-7112-2159-8(6)) Lincoln, Frances Ltd. GBR. *Dist:* Transition Vendor.

Gifford, Hannah. Red Fox. 2004. (Illus.). 36p. (J). pap. 7.95 (978-1-84507-223-0(5)) Lincoln, Frances Ltd. GBR. *Dist:* Perseus Distribution.

—Red Fox on the Move. 2004. (Illus.). 36p. (J). pap. 7.95 (978-1-84507-224-7(3)) Lincoln, Frances Ltd. GBR. *Dist:* Perseus Distribution.

Gill, Janice. Can a Fox Wear Polka Dotted Socks. 1998. (ps-3). lib. bdg. 10.95 (978-0-89868-302-8(5)) ARO Publishing Co.

The Gingerbread Boy. 2005. (J). (978-1-58453-306-1(4)) Pioneer Valley Educational Pr., Inc.

Gliori, Debi. No Matter What. (Illus.). (J). 2008. 24p. bds. 6.95 (***978-0-15-206343-6(9)*** , Red Wagon Bks.); 1999. 32p. 16.00 (978-0-15-202061-3(6)) Harcourt Children's Bks.

Grindley, Sally. Will You Forgive Me? Dann, Penny, illus. 2001. 32p. (J). (ps-k). tchr. ed. 15.95 (978-0-7534-5295-0(2) , Kingfisher) Houghton Mifflin Co. Trade & Reference Div.

Hagen, Oddmund. Campo Abierto (Open Field) Santos, Nuria G., tr. from NOR. Dezakin, Akin, illus. 2003. (Rosa y Manzana Ser.). (SPA.). 32p. 16.95 (978-84-89804-42-5(7)) Loguez Ediciones ESP. *Dist:* Baker & Taylor Bks., Lectorum Pubns., Inc.

Hamilton, Martha & Weiss, Mitch. How Fox Became Red. O'Malley, Kathy, illus. 2005. 12p. (J). pap. 5.00 (978-1-57274-717-3(X) , 2749, Bks. for Young Learners) Owen, Richard C. Pubs., Inc.

—Two Fables of Aesop. MacDonald, Bruce, illus. 2005. 16p. (J). pap. 5.00 (978-1-57274-718-0(8) , 2788, Bks. for Young Learners) Owen, Richard C. Pubs., Inc.

Harcourt School Publishers Staff. The Best Food: On Level. 3rd ed. 2002. (Trophies Reading Program Ser.). (Illus.). (J). pap. 4.10 (978-0-15-322990-9(X)) Harcourt Schl. Pubs.

—Can You Find the Fox: Take-Home Book. 1999. (Collections Ser.). (Illus.). (J). pap. 1.90 (978-0-15-317195-6(2)) Harcourt Schl. Pubs.

—Fuego de Hielo: Take-Home Book. 2001. (Vamos Ser.). (SPA., Illus.). (J). pap. 2.80 (978-0-15-319946-2(6)) Harcourt Schl. Pubs.

—The Surprise Box: On Level. 3rd ed. 2002. (Trophies Reading Program Ser.). (Illus.). (J). pap. 3.20 (978-0-15-322977-0(2)) Harcourt Schl. Pubs.

Hartzell, Andy. Fox Bunny Funny. 2007. 104p. pap. 10.00 (***978-1-891830-97-6(X)***) Top Shelf Productions.

Harvey, Damian. Mr. Fox's Socks. Rescek, Sanja, illus. 2004. 16p. (J). lib. bdg. 22.65 (***978-1-59646-678-4(2)***) Dingles & Co.

Heinz, Brian J. Red Fox at McCloskey's Farm. Sheban, Chris, illus. 2006. 32p. (J). 17.95 (978-1-56846-195-3(X) , Creative Editions) Creative Co., The.

Hindley, Judy. Do Like a Duck Does! Bates, Ivan, illus. 40p. (J). (ps-k). 2007. pap. 4.99 (978-0-7636-3284-7(8)); 2002. 14.99 (978-0-7636-1668-7(0)) Candlewick Pr.

Hinkle, Clark Thomas. Doctor Rabbit & Brushtail the Fox. 2006. pap. 33.99 (***978-1-4280-4109-7(5)***) IndyPublish.com.

Hogrogian, Nonny. One Fine Day. Hogrogian, Nonny, illus. 2002. (Illus.). (J). 15.53 (978-0-7587-0063-6(6)) Book Wholesalers, Inc.

—One Fine Day. Hogrogian, Nonny, illus. 2nd ed. 2005. (Stories to Go! Ser.). (Illus.). 32p. (J). 4.99 (978-1-4169-0312-3(7) , Aladdin) Simon & Schuster Children's Publishing.

Holland, Janice R. Reynard Fox & the Great Fox Hunt. 1999. (Illus.). 33p. (J). (ps-6). 8.00 (978-0-9672199-0-5(6)) Bloomin' Tulip Studios.

Hollenbeck, Kathleen M. Red Fox at Hickory Lane. Smith, Wendy, illus. 2005. (Smithsonian's Backyard Ser.). (J). (ps-2). 30p. 4.95 (978-1-59249-114-8(6) , B5075); 32p. 8.95 incl. audio (978-1-59249-117-9(0) , SC5025); 32p. 19.95 incl. audio (978-1-59249-116-2(2) , BC5025) Soundprints.

—Red Fox at Hickory Lane. Smith, Wendy, tr. Smith, Wendy, illus. 2005. (Smithsonian's Backyard Ser.). 32p. (J). (ps-2). 15.95 (978-1-59249-113-1(8) , B5025); pap. 6.95 (978-1-59249-115-5(4) , S5025) Soundprints.

Houser, Marlin L. The Adventures of Little Fox, Book Four, Escape. 2008. (Adventures of Little Fox Ser.). (J). 16.95 (***978-0-9752703-8-7(9)***); pap. 7.95 (***978-0-9752703-9-4(7)***) Marhouse, Inc.

—The Adventures of Little Fox, Book Three, Unfamiliar Territory. 2007. (Adventures of Little Fox Ser.). (J). 16.95 (***978-0-9752703-6-3(2)***); pap. 7.95 (***978-0-9752703-7-0(0)***) Marhouse, Inc.

—The Adventures of Little Fox, Book Two, the Secret of Squirrel Meadow. 2006. (Illus.). 194p. 16.95 (978-0-9752703-4-9(6)); pap. 7.95 (978-0-9752703-5-6(4)) Marhouse, Inc.

—The Adventures of Little Fox, Generations, Bk. 1. 2006. (Illus.). 208p. pap. 7.95 (978-0-9752703-1-8(1)); (Adventures of Little Fox Ser.: Bk. 1). 16.95 (978-0-9752703-0-1(3)) Marhouse, Inc.

—The Adventures of Little Fox, Generations, Teachers Guide & Reproducibles Bk. 1: Generations. 2005. (Illus.). 112p. (J). tchr. ed., per. 11.95 (978-0-9752703-2-5(X)) Marhouse, Inc.

How the Chick Tricked the Fox. (Little Book Practice Reader Ser.). (J). (978-0-8136-0821-1(X)) Modern Curriculum Pr.

Hutchins, Pat. Rosie's Walk. Hutchins, Pat, illus. 2002. 32p. (J). mass mkt. 1.00 (978-0-689-85548-1(6) , Aladdin) Simon & Schuster Children's Publishing.

—Rosie's Walk. 2nd ed. 2005. (Stories to Go! Ser.). (Illus.). (J). (***978-1-4156-3112-6(3)*** , Aladdin) Simon & Schuster Children's Publishing.

Jacobs, Joseph. Most Delectable History of Reynard the F. 2006. (Illus.). pap. 28.95 (***978-1-4286-1384-3(6)***) Kessinger Publishing, LLC.

Jacobson, Jennifer Richard. Moon Sandwich Mom. Huang, Benrei, illus. 2004. 24p. (J). (ps-1). pap. 6.95 (978-0-8075-4072-5(2)) Whitman, Albert & Co.

Jacques, Brian. Eulalia! 2007. (Redwall Ser.). 400p. (J). (gr. 5). 23.99 (***978-0-399-24209-0(0)*** , Philomel) Penguin Group (USA) Inc.

Jacques, Brian. Marlfox. 2000. (Redwall Ser.). (Illus.). 365p. (YA). (gr. 7-12). per. 13.64 (978-0-606-17602-6(0)) Tandem Library Bks.

Jobling, Brenda. A Foxcub Named Freedom. Anderson, Fred, illus. 1998. (Animal Tales Ser.). 131p. (J). (gr. 3-7). pap. 3.95 (978-0-7641-0600-2(7)) Barron's Educational Series, Inc.

—A Foxcub Named Freedom. 1998. (Animal Tales Ser.). (978-0-606-13399-9(2)) Tandem Library Bks.

Jongbloed, Marijcke. Sophie the Sand Fox. 2000. (J). 5.95 (978-0-9534689-2-8(5) , TAX-SOPHIE) Serpent's Tale Natural History Bk. Distributors, Inc.

Kasza, Keiko. My Lucky Day. Kasza, Keiko, illus. 2005. 30p. (J). pap. 5.99 (978-0-14-240456-0(X) , Puffin) Penguin Group (USA) Inc.

—My Lucky Day. 2003. (Illus.). 32p. (J). (ps-3). 15.99 (978-0-399-23874-1(3) , Putnam Juvenile) Penguin Group (USA) Inc.

E
F
G

—My Lucky Day. 2006. (J). (gr. k-3). incl. audio (978-0-8045-6937-8(1) , SAC6937); 29.95 incl. audio compact disk (978-0-8045-4136-7(1) , SACD4136) Spoken Arts, Inc.

Keller, John G. The Rubber-Legged Duck. Cole, Henry, illus. 2008. (J). (***978-0-15-205289-8(5)***) Harcourt Trade Pubs.

Korba, Joanna. The Fox & the Cheese Queen. 2006. spiral bd. 42.00 (***978-1-4108-7174-9(6)***) Benchmark Education Co.

Korschunow, Irina. El Zorrito Abandonado. (Torre de Papel Ser.).Tr. of Abandoned Fox. (SPA., Illus.). (J). (gr. 2). 7.95 (978-958-04-1380-6(0)) Norma S.A. COL. *Dist:* Distribuidora Norma, Inc.

Kratzer, Mary. The Adventure Club Catches the Poachers. 2006. 76p. pap. 14.95 (978-1-4137-7376-7(1)) PublishAmerica, Inc.

Kroll, Virginia L. & Jones, Dawn L. Flurry's Frozen Tundra. Maydak, Michael S., illus. 2001. (J). (978-0-9712840-4-3(0)) Boyds Collection Ltd., The.

Kvasnosky, Laura McGee. Zelda & Ivy. Kvasnosky, Laura McGee, illus. 2007. (Candlewick Sparks Ser.). (Illus.). 40p. (J). (ps-3). pap. 4.99 (978-0-7636-3261-8(9)) Candlewick Pr.

—Zelda & Ivy. 2001. (J). (gr. k-4). 26.95 incl. audio (978-0-8045-6868-5(5) , 6868) Spoken Arts, Inc.

—Zelda & Ivy: One Christmas. Kvasnosky, Laura McGee, illus. 2004. (Illus.). 39p. (J). (gr. k-4). reprint ed. pap. 7.00 (978-0-7567-7997-9(9)) DIANE Publishing Co.

—Zelda & Ivy: The Runaways. Kvasnosky, Laura McGee, illus. (Candlewick Sparks Ser.). (Illus.). 48p. (J). 2007. (ps-3). pap. 4.99 (978-0-7636-3061-4(6)); 2006. (gr. 1-4). 14.99 (978-0-7636-2689-1(9)) Candlewick Pr.

—Zelda & Ivy & the Boy Next Door: Three Stories about the Fabulous Fox Sisters. Kvasnosky, Laura McGee, illus. 2003. (Illus.). 48p. (J). (gr. k-4). pap. 6.99 (978-0-7636-1053-1(4)) Candlewick Pr.

—Zelda & Ivy One Christmas. 2001. (J). (gr. k-3). incl. audio Spoken Arts, Inc.

—Zelda & Ivy: One Christmas. Kvasnosky, Laura McGee, illus. 2006. 40p. (J). (gr. 1-4). pap. 4.99 (978-0-7636-3047-8(0)) Candlewick Pr.

Lobel, Gillian & Braun, Sebastien. Too Small for Honey Cake. 2006. (Illus.). 32p. (J). 16.00 (978-0-15-206097-8(9)) Harcourt Trade Pubs.

Mackinnon, Mairi. Fox & the Crow. 2007. (First Reading Level 1 Ser.). 32p. (J). 8.99 (***978-0-7945-1813-4(3)*** , Usborne) EDC Publishing.

—Fox & the Stork. 2007. (First Reading Level 1 Ser.). 32p. (J). 8.99 (***978-0-7945-1812-7(5)*** , Usborne) EDC Publishing.

Malone, Geoffrey. Torn Ear. (Illus.). 157p. pap. (978-0-340-68295-1(7) , Hodder & Stoughton) Hodder General Publishing Division.

—Torn Ear. 2nd ed. 2002. 160p. (J). pap. 9.99 (978-0-340-86057-1(X) , Hodder & Stoughton) Hodder General Publishing Division GBR. *Dist:* Trafalgar Square Publishing.

Marshall, Edward. Fox All Week. Marshall, James, illus. 2002. (J). 11.49 (978-0-7587-1183-0(2)) Book Wholesalers, Inc.

—Fox & His Friends. Marshall, James, illus. 2002. (J). 11.49 (978-0-7587-1184-7(0)) Book Wholesalers, Inc.

—Fox at School. Marshall, James, illus. 2002. (J). 11.49 (978-0-7587-1186-1(7)) Book Wholesalers, Inc.

—Fox Be Nimble. Marshall, James, illus. 2002. (J). 11.49 (978-0-7587-1187-8(5)) Book Wholesalers, Inc.

—Fox in Love. Marshall, James, illus. 2002. (J). 11.49 (978-0-7587-1188-5(3)) Book Wholesalers, Inc.

—Fox on Stage. Marshall, James, illus. 2002. (J). 11.49 (978-0-7587-1189-2(1)) Book Wholesalers, Inc.

—Fox on the Job. Marshall, James, illus. 2002. (J). 11.49 (978-0-7587-1190-8(5)) Book Wholesalers, Inc.

—Fox on Wheels. Marshall, James, illus. 2002. (J). 11.49 (978-0-7587-1191-5(3)) Book Wholesalers, Inc.

—Fox Outfoxed. Marshall, James, illus. 2002. (J). 11.49 (978-0-7587-1192-2(1)) Book Wholesalers, Inc.

Marshall, Edward & Marshall, James. Fox & His Friends. (Fox Ser.). 56p. (J). (gr. k-2). pap. 3.99 (978-0-8072-1350-6(0) , Listening Library) Random Hse. Audio Publishing Group.

—Fox at School. (Fox Ser.). 48p. (J). (gr. k-2). pap. 3.99 (978-0-8072-1349-0(7) , Listening Library) Random Hse. Audio Publishing Group.

—Fox in Love. (Fox Ser.). 48p. (J). (gr. k-2). pap. 3.99 (978-0-8072-1352-0(7) , Listening Library) Random Hse. Audio Publishing Group.

—Fox on Wheels. (Fox Ser.). 48p. (J). (gr. k-2). pap. 3.99 (978-0-8072-1353-7(5) , Listening Library) Random Hse. Audio Publishing Group.

Matteren, Joanne. The Old Lion & the Fox. 2005. 22.00 (***978-1-4108-4206-0(1)***) Benchmark Education Co.

McBratney, Sam. I'll Always Be Your Friend. ed. 2004. (Illus.). (J). (gr. k-3). spiral bd. (978-0-616-14587-6(X)); spiral bd. (978-0-616-14588-3(8)) Canadian National Institute for the Blind/Institut National Canadien pour les Aveugles.

—I'll Always Be Your Friend. Lewis, Kim, illus. 32p. (J). (ps-3). 2004. pap. 6.99 (978-0-06-055548-1(3) , Harper Trophy); 2001. 16.99 (978-0-06-029485-4(X)) HarperCollins Pubs.

McCaughren, Tom. Run with the Wind. 2002. (Illus.). 144p. pap. 7.95 (978-0-86327-568-5(0)) Interlink Publishing Group, Inc.

McDermott, Gerald. The Fox & the Stork. 2003. (Green Light Readers Level 2 Ser.). (Illus.). 24p. (J). 11.95 (978-0-15-204877-8(4)); pap. 3.95 (978-0-15-204837-2(5)) Harcourt Children's Bks. (Green Light Readers).

—The Fox & the Stork. 1999. (Illus.). (J). (978-0-606-18173-0(3)) Tandem Library Bks.

—Fox & the Stork. 1999. (gr. k-3). lib. bdg. 11.80 (978-0-613-63154-9(4)) Tandem Library Bks.

McKissack, Patricia C. Flossie & the Fox. 2002. (Illus.). (J). 24.43 (978-0-7587-2518-9(3)) Book Wholesalers, Inc.

McPhail, David M. The Blue Door. O'Connor, John, illus. 2004. 32p. (978-1-55041-917-7(X)) Fitzhenry & Whiteside, Ltd.

—The Sled & other Fox & Rabbit Stories. O'Connor, John, illus. 1999. (First Flight Ser.). 32p. (J). lib. bdg. (978-1-55041-515-5(8)) Fitzhenry & Whiteside, Ltd.

McPhail, David M. & O'Connor, John. The Blue Door. 2001. (Illus.). 32p. (J). (ps-k). (978-1-55041-647-3(2)) Fitzhenry & Whiteside, Ltd.

Metzler, Rosemary. The Dangerous Ride: A Snooty the Fox Adventure. Lankenau, Gaynel, illus. 2002. (J). (gr. 3-5). pap. 10.95 (978-0-88100-128-0(7)) National Writers Pr., The.

Metzler, Rosemary M. Snooty the Fox & the Mysterious Black Box. Lahknau, Gaynel, illus. l.t. ed. 1998. 84p. (YA). (gr. 3 up). pap. 10.95 (978-0-88100-106-8(6)) National Writers Pr., The.

Meyer, Ronald. Freddy Fox. 2005. (ENG., Illus.). 32p. (J). 19.95 (978-0-9754701-0-7(8)) Natures Beauty Publishing.

Mini Cuentos: Atletas se Entrenan, Zorro y la Ciguena.Tr. of Mini Fairy Tales: Fox & the Swan. (SPA.). (J). (gr. k-4). 4.98 (978-970-607-621-2(2)) Larousse, Ediciones, S. A. de C. V. MEX. *Dist:* Continental Bk. Co., Inc.

Moore, Stephen. Skin & Bone. mass mkt. 8.99 (978-0-340-70455-4(1) , Hodder & Stoughton) Hodder General Publishing Division GBR. *Dist:* Trafalgar Square Publishing.

Moran, Alex. Six Silly Foxes. 2000. (Green Light Readers Ser.). (978-0-606-18190-7(3)); lib. bdg. 11.80 (978-0-613-64595-9(2)) Tandem Library Bks.

—Six Silly Foxes. Baker, Keith, illus. 2003. (Green Light Readers Level 1 Ser.). 24p. (J). 11.95 (978-0-15-204823-5(5)); pap. 3.95 (978-0-15-204863-1(4)) Harcourt Children's Bks. (Green Light Readers).

Mox's Shop. 2004. (Illus.). (J). (978-1-59577-004-2(6)) Starfall Education.

Myers, Tim. Basho & Fox. Han, Oki S., illus. 2005. 32p. (J). pap. 5.95 (978-0-7614-5190-7(0)) Cavendish, Marshall Corp.

—Basho & the Fox. Han, Oki S., illus. 2000. 32p. (J). (gr. k-3). 15.95 (978-0-7614-5068-9(8) , Cavendish Children's Bks.) Cavendish, Marshall Corp.

—Basho & the River Stones. Han, Oki S., illus. 2004. 32p. (J). 16.95 (978-0-7614-5165-5(X)) Cavendish, Marshall Corp.

—The Furry-Legged Teapot: A Unique Retelling. McGuire, Robert, illus. 2007. (J). 16.99 (978-0-7614-5295-9(8)) Cavendish, Marshall Corp.

Myers, Tim. The Outfoxed Fox. Pang, Ariel Ya-Wen, illus. 2007. 32p. (J). (gr. k-3). 16.99 (***978-0-7614-5356-7(3)***) Cavendish, Marshall Corp.

Neal, Michael. Rex's Secret: A Courageous CrittersTM Book. 2004. 56p. (J). pap. 8.95 (978-0-595-30773-9(6)) iUniverse, Inc.

Nikola-Lisa, W. Setting the Turkeys Free. Wilson-Max, Ken, illus. 2004. 32p. (ps-1). 15.99 (978-0-7868-1952-2(9) , Jump at the Sun) Hyperion Bks. for Children.

Nolte, Nancy. The Gingerbread Man. Scarry, Richard, illus. 2004. 32p. (J). (gr. k-k). 8.99 (978-0-375-82589-7(4)); lib. bdg. 10.99 (978-0-375-92589-4(9)) Random Hse. Children's Bks. (Golden Bks.).

Oates, Joyce Carol. Where Is Little Reynard? Graham, Mark, illus. 2003. 32p. (J). 16.89 (978-0-06-029583-7(X)) HarperCollins Pubs.

Oldfield, Jenny. Tell Me the Truth, Tom! Layton, Neal, illus. (J). mass mkt. 7.99 (978-0-340-85102-9(3) , Hodder & Stoughton) Hodder General Publishing Division GBR. *Dist:* Trafalgar Square Publishing.

Olick, Hilda. Kaviam Iqvaryallra. Olick, Hilda & Nevak, Caroline, illus. l.t. ed. 1999. (ESK.). 8p. (J). (gr. k-3). pap. 14.50 (978-1-58084-057-6(4)) Lower Kuskokwim Schl. District.

—Kayuqturuuq Ahiariarnirman. Nevak, Caroline, illus. l.t. ed. 1999. (ESK.). 8p. (J). (gr. k-3). pap. 14.50 (978-1-58084-142-9(2)) Lower Kuskokwim Schl. District.

—Pisukti Asianik Pukugiarami. Olick, Hilda & Nevak, Caroline, illus. l.t. ed. 1999. Tr. of When the Fox Went Berry Picking. (ESK.). 8p. (J). (gr. k-3). pap. 14.50 (978-1-58084-128-3(7)) Lower Kuskokwim Schl. District.

—Tiriganniaq Kablatariahuni Ahiariaqtuqhani. Olick, Hilda & Nevak, Caroline, illus. l.t. ed. 1999. Tr. of When the Fox Went Berry Picking. (ESK.). 8p. (J). (gr. k-3). pap. 14.50 (978-1-58084-135-1(X)) Lower Kuskokwim Schl. District.

—When the Fox Went Berry Picking. Olick, Hilda & Nevak, Caroline, illus. l.t. ed. 1999. 8p. (J). (gr. k-3). pap. 14.50 (978-1-58084-056-9(6)) Lower Kuskokwim Schl. District.

Once upon a Time Spanish Version-the Gingerbread Man. 2005. (J). (978-1-57022-556-7(7)) ECS Learning Systems, Inc.

O'Neil, Sarah. Fox & the Crow. 1999. (gr. k-3). lib. bdg. 11.80 (978-0-613-19354-2(7)) Tandem Library Bks.

Palatini, Margie. Three French Hens. Egielski, Richard, illus. 2005. 40p. (ps-3). 15.99 (978-0-7868-5167-6(8)) Hyperion Pr.

—Zoom Broom. Fine, Howard, illus. 2000. 32p. (ps-4). pap. 5.99 (978-0-7868-1467-1(5)) Disney Pr.

Papish, Ramiel. The Little Fox. 2006. (J). (978-1-889963-87-7(9)) Univ. of Alaska Pr.

PC Treasures, prod. The Gingerbread Man. 2007. (J). (***978-1-60072-015-4(3)***) PC Treasures, Inc.

Potter, Beatrix. Jemima Puddle-Duck. 2007. 12p. (J). bds. 3.99 (978-0-7232-5856-8(2) , Warne) Penguin Group (USA) Inc.

Potter, Beatrix, text. Jemima Puddle-Duck. 2003. (Play-A-Sound Ser.). (Illus.). (J). (978-0-7853-7970-6(3)); (978-0-7853-7969-0(X)) Publications International, Ltd.

Puttock, Simon. Miss Fox. Swain, Holly, illus. 2006. 32p. (J). (gr. k-4). 15.95 (***978-1-84507-475-3(0)***) Lincoln, Frances Ltd. GBR. *Dist:* Perseus Distribution.

Rawlinson, Julia. Fletcher & the Falling Leaves. Beeke, Tiphanie, illus. 2006. 32p. (J). 16.99 (978-0-06-113401-2(5)) HarperCollins Pubs.

Relf, Adam. Fox Makes Friends. 2005. (Illus.). 32p. (J). (ps). 14.95 (978-1-4027-2756-6(9)) Sterling Publishing Co., Inc.

Remolina, Tere. Un Cambio de Piel. Martinez, Enrique, illus. (Barril Sin Fondo Ser.). (SPA.). (J). (gr. 3-5). pap. (978-968-6465-20-4(0)) Casa de Estudios de Literatura y Talleres Artisticos Amaquemecan A.C. MEX. *Dist:* Lectorum Pubns., Inc.

Riordan, James. Little Bunny Bobkin. Warnes, Tim, illus. 1999. 32p. (J). (ps-2). 14.95 (978-1-888444-38-4(X)) Little Tiger Pr.

Rogan, Sally Jones. The Daring Adventures of Penhaligon Brush. Slade, Christian, illus. 2007. 230p. (J). (gr. 3-7). 15.99 (***978-0-375-84344-0(2)***); lib. bdg. 18.99 (***978-0-375-94344-7(7)***) Random Hse. Children's Bks. (Knopf Bks. for Young Readers).

Roldan, Gustavo. Cuentos del Zorro. (Cuentamerica Ser.). (SPA.). 64p. (J). (gr. 4-6). (978-950-07-1557-7(0) , SA30061) Editorial Sudamericana S.A. ARG. *Dist:* Lectorum Pubns., Inc.

Ross, Dev. We Both Read-Fox's Best Trick Ever. Reinhart, Larry, illus. 2006. (We Both Read Ser.). 48p. (J). 7.99 (978-1-891327-69-8(0)) Treasure Bay, Inc.

Rylant, Cynthia. The Case of the Fidgety Fox. Karas, G. Brian, illus. 2003. (High-Rise Private Eyes Ser.: No. 6). 56p. (J). (gr. 1 up). lib. bdg. 16.89 (978-0-06-009102-6(9)) HarperCollins Pubs.

Sargent, Dave & Sargent, David M. Buzz Buzzard: Obey the Rules, 19, 5. Lenoir, Jane, illus. 2003. (Feather Tales Ser.: 5). 42p. (J). pap. 6.95 (978-1-56763-728-1(0)); 2nd ed. lib. bdg. 19.95 (978-1-56763-727-4(2)) Ozark Publishing.

Sargent, Dave & Sargent, Pat. Redi Fox: Friendship, 15 vols., 3. Huff, Jeane, illus. 2nd rev. ed. 2003. (Animal Pride Ser.: 3). 42p. (J). pap. (978-1-56763-764-9(7)); lib. bdg. 19.95 (978-1-56763-763-2(9)) Ozark Publishing.

—Young Redi: Friendship!, 3. Woodward, Elaine, illus. 2003. (Young Animal Pride Ser.: 3). 24p. (J). pap. 6.95 (978-1-56763-868-4(6)); lib. bdg. 19.95 (978-1-56763-867-7(8)) Ozark Publishing.

Scholastic, Inc. Staff. Cars & Trucks. 2008. (Littlest Pet Shop Ser.). (SPA.). 24p. (J). pap. 3.99 (***978-0-545-02728-1(4)*** , Scholastic en Espanol) Scholastic, Inc.

Scraper, Katherine. Fox in the Forest. 2006. (Early Explorers Ser.). (J). 30.00 (***978-1-4108-6023-1(X)***) Benchmark Education Co.

Seuss, Dr. Fox in Socks. 2005. (Illus.). 64p. (J). (ps-2). audio compact disk 9.95 (978-0-375-83494-3(X) , Random Hse. Bks. for Young Readers) Random Hse. Children's Bks.

Shah, Idries. The Man & the Fox. 2006. (Illus.). 32p. (J). 18.00 (978-1-883536-43-5(X)); pap. 7.99 (***978-1-883536-60-2(X)***) ISHK. (Hoopoe Bks.).

Sidjanski, Brigitte & Burg, Sarah. Little Chicken & Little Fox. 2006. 32p. (J). (ps-3). 16.99 (978-0-698-40044-3(5) , Minedition) Penguin Group (USA) Inc.

Sly Fox & Little Red Hen: Individual Title Six-Packs. 32p. (gr. 2 up). 37.00 (978-0-7635-9221-9(8)) Rigby Education.

Sly Fox & the Little Red Hen. 2005. (J). bds. 3.99 (978-1-933200-11-8(1)) Family Bks. at Home.

Small, David. Eulalie & the Hopping Head. Small, David, illus. 2003. (Illus.). pap. 35.95 incl. audio compact disk (978-1-59112-520-4(0)) Live Oak Media.

Sommer, Carl. The Sly Fox & the Chicks. 2003. (Another Sommer-Time Story Ser.). (Illus.). 48p. (J). 16.95 incl. audio compact disk (978-1-57537-504-5(4)); (gr. 1-4). 16.95 incl. audio (978-1-57537-553-3(2)) Advance Publishing, Inc.

—The Sly Fox & the Chicks. James, Kennon, illus. 2000. (Another Sommer-Time Story Ser.). 48p. (J). (gr. k-3). lib. bdg. 16.95 (978-1-57537-062-0(X)); 9.95 (978-1-57537-004-0(2)) Advance Publishing, Inc.

—The Sly Fox & the Chicks Read-along. 2003. (Another Sommer-Time Story Ser.). 48p. (J). lib. bdg. 23.95 incl. audio compact disk (978-1-57537-704-9(7)); lib. bdg. 23.95 incl. audio (978-1-57537-754-4(3)) Advance Publishing, Inc.

Souhami, Jessica. King Pom & the Fox. 2007. (Illus.). 36p. (J). (gr. k-3). 16.95 (***978-1-84507-478-4(5)***) Lincoln, Frances Ltd. GBR. *Dist:* Perseus Distribution.

Spier, Peter, illus. The Fox Went Out on a Chilly Night. unabr. ed. 2006. (J). (ps-3). pap. 16.95 incl. audio (***978-1-59112-440-5(9)***); pap. 18.95 incl. audio compact disk (***978-1-59112-441-2(7)***); Set. pap. 39.95 incl. audio compact disk (***978-1-59112-443-6(3)***) Live Oak Media.

Steig, William. Doctor De Soto. 2003. (Picture Books Collection). (SPA.). 32p. (J). (gr. k-3). 16.95 (978-84-372-6616-9(5)) Altea, Ediciones, S.A. - Grupo Santillana ESP. *Dist:* Santillana USA Publishing Co., Inc.

—Doctor De Soto. Steig, William, illus. 2002. (Illus.). (J). 14.43 (978-0-7587-0256-2(6)) Book Wholesalers, Inc.

—Doctor De Soto. ed. 2004. (J). (gr. k-3). spiral bd. (978-0-616-01784-5(7)); spiral bd. (978-0-616-01785-2(5)) Canadian National Institute for the Blind/Institut National Canadien pour les Aveugles.

—Doctor De Soto. Puncel, María, tr. 1998. (SPA., Illus.). pap., tchr. ed. 37.95 incl. audio (978-0-87499-459-9(4)); (J). pap. 16.95 incl. audio (978-0-87499-458-2(6)) Live Oak Media.

—Doctor De Soto. 2004. (J). (gr. k-5). pap. 14.95 incl. audio (978-0-89719-771-7(2) , PRA284) Weston Woods Studios, Inc.

Stone, Forrest. The Fox & Grapes at Belleville Elementary. 2006. spiral bd. 42.00 (***978-1-4108-7172-5(X)***) Benchmark Education Co.

Sweeney, Matthew. Fox. 2002. (Illus.). 176p. (J). pap. 12.95 (978-0-7475-6040-1(4)) Bloomsbury Publishing Plc GBR. *Dist:* Independent Pubs. Group.

Tessa on Her Own: Evaluation Guide. 2006. (J). (978-1-55942-422-6(2)) Marsh Media.

Thompson, Margaret. Fox Winter. Akin, Galan, tr. 2005. (Illus.). 60p. (J). (gr. 3-5). 8.95 (978-0-9730831-5-6(8)) Hodgepog Bks. CAN. *Dist:* Coteau Bks., Fitzhenry & Whiteside, Ltd.

Trottier, Maxine. There Have Always Been Foxes. Ricci, Regolo, illus. 2001. 20p. (ps-4). 15.95 (978-0-7737-3278-0(0)) Stoddart Kids CAN. *Dist:* Fitzhenry & Whiteside, Ltd.

Ure, Jean. Foxglove. 1999. (We Love Animals Bks.). (Illus.). 160p. (J). (gr. 4-7). pap. 3.95 (978-0-7641-0971-3(5)) Barron's Educational Series, Inc.

Walton, Rick. Around the House, the Fox Chased the Mouse: A Prepositional Tale. Bradshaw, Jim, illus. 2006. 32p. (J). 15.95 (978-1-4236-0006-0(1)) Gibbs Smith, Publisher.

Ward, Helen, illus. & retold by. The Rooster & the Fox. Ward, Helen, retold by. 2003. 40p. (J). (gr. k-3). 16.95 (978-0-7613-1846-0(1) , First Avenue Editions) Lerner Publishing Group.

Ward, Helen & Ward, Helen. The Rooster & the Fox. 2003. (Single Titles Ser.: Vol. 3). 40p. (gr. k-4). lib. bdg. 24.90 (978-0-7613-2920-6(X) , Millbrook Pr.) Lerner Publishing Group.

Waring, Richard. Hungry Hen. Church, Caroline Jayne, illus. 2002. 24.00 (978-1-4046-0466-7(9)) Book Wholesalers, Inc.

—Hungry Hen. Church, Caroline Jayne, illus. 2001. 32p. (J). (ps-1). 16.99 (978-0-06-623880-7(3)) HarperCollins Pubs.

—Hungry Hen. 1998. (J). (978-0-385-32608-7(4) , Dell Books for Young Readers) Random Hse. Children's Bks.

Wattenberg, Jane, illus. & retold by. Henny-Penny. Wattenberg, Jane, retold by. 2001. (J). (gr. k-3). 26.90 incl. audio (978-0-8045-6877-7(4)) Spoken Arts, Inc.

Weston, Carrie. If a Chicken Stayed for Supper. Fatus, Sophie, illus. 2007. 32p. (J). (ps-3). 16.95 (978-0-8234-2067-4(1)) Holiday Hse., Inc.

White, Mark. La Zorra y las Uvas: Version de la Fabula de Esopo. Rojo, Sara, illus. 2006. (Read-It! Readers en Espanol Ser.).Tr. of Fox & the Grapes: A Retelling of Aesop's Fable. (SPA.). 32p. (J). (ps-3). 19.95 (978-1-4048-1621-3(6)) Picture Window Bks.

Whybrow, Ian. Little Wolf's Diary of Daring Deeds. Ross, Tony, illus. (Middle Grade Fiction Ser.). 132p. (gr. 3-6). 2005. 14.95 (978-1-57505-411-7(6)); 2003. (J). pap. 6.95 (978-0-87614-536-4(5) , Carolrhoda Bks.) Lerner Publishing Group.

—Little Wolf's Diary of Daring Deeds. 2000. (gr. 3-6). lib. bdg. 15.25 (978-0-613-68105-6(3)) Tandem Library Bks.

Wiberg, Harald, illus. The Tomten & the Fox. 2nd rev. ed. 2001. 32p. (J). 17.95 (978-0-86315-154-5(X)) Floris Bks. GBR. *Dist:* SteinerBooks, Inc.

Wild, Margaret. Fox. Brooks, Ron, illus. 2000. 40p. (J). (978-1-86448-465-6(9)); mass mkt. (978-1-86448-933-0(2)) Allen & Unwin.

—Fox. Brooks, Ron, illus. 2006. 32p. (J). pap. 7.95 (978-1-933605-15-9(4)) Kane/Miller Bk. Pubs., Inc.

William Morrow Publishers Staff. Chicken Little. 1999. (J). (ps-3). pap. (978-0-673-80925-4(0) , Good Year Bks.) Celebration Pr.

Woods, Shirley E. & Godkin, Celia. Amber: The Story of a Red Fox. 2004. (Illus.). 96p. (J). (gr. 3-5). (978-1-55041-811-8(4)) Fitzhenry & Whiteside, Ltd.

Zuckerman, Linda. A taste for Rabbit. 2007. 320p. (J). (gr. 7 up). pap. 16.99 (***978-0-439-86977-5(3)*** , Levine, Arthur A. Bks.) Scholastic, Inc.

—A Taste for Rabbit. 2007. (J). (***978-0-439-86978-2(1)*** , Levine, Arthur A. Bks.) Scholastic, Inc.

FOXES—SONGS AND MUSIC

Spier, Peter. Fox Went Out on a Chilly Night. Spier, Peter, illus. 2002. (Illus.). (J). 14.79 (978-0-7587-0108-4(X)) Book Wholesalers, Inc.

FOYT, A. J., 1935-

Prentzas, G. S. A. J. Foyt. rev. ed. 2007. (Race Car Legends Ser.). 72p. (J). (gr. 5-8). 25.00 (978-0-7910-8759-6(X) , Chelsea Hse.) Facts On File, Inc.

FRACTIONS

Adler, David A. Working with Fractions. Miller, Edward, illus. 2007. 32p. (J). (gr. 1-5). 16.95 (***978-0-8234-2010-0(8)***) Holiday Hse., Inc.

Aihara, Masaaki & Sarris, Eno, eds. Grade 4 Decimals & Fractions: Kumon Math Workbooks. 2008. (J). per. 6.95 (***978-1-933241-58-6(6)***) Kumon Publishing North America, Inc.

—Grade 5 Decimals & Fractions: Kumon Math Workbooks. 2008. (J). per. 6.95 (***978-1-933241-59-3(4)***) Kumon Publishing North America, Inc.

—Grade 6 Fractions: Kumon Math Workbooks. 2008. (J). per. 6.95 (***978-1-933241-60-9(8)***) Kumon Publishing North America, Inc.

Alexander, Ruth Bell. Fraction Jugglers: A Math Gamebook for Kids & Their Parents. 2001. (Illus.). 128p. (J). (ps-3). pap. 12.95 (978-0-7611-2104-6(8) , 12104) Workman Publishing Co., Inc.

American Education Publishing Staff & School Specialty Publishing Staff. Fractions. 2001. (Brighter Child Fact Card Ser.). (Illus.). 54p. (J). (gr. 3-5). 2.99 (978-1-56189-692-9(6) , 31388, American Education Publishing) School Specialty Publishing.

Beginning Fractions. 2002. (J). pap. 8.95 (978-1-56911-044-7(1)) Learning Resources, Inc.

Beginning Fractions. (Math Minders Ser.). 32p. (gr. 1-2). 5.99 (978-0-7682-0029-4(6) , FS12013) Schaffer, Frank Pubns.

Beginning Fractions. 2003. (Illus.). (gr. k up). 9.99 (978-0-7682-1900-5(0) , J41010) School Specialty Publishing.

Caron, Lucille & St. Jacques, Philip M. Fractions & Decimals. 2000. (Math Success Ser.). (Illus.). 64p. (YA). (gr. 4-10). lib. bdg. 22.60 (978-0-7660-1430-5(4)) Enslow Pubs., Inc.

Cefrey, Holly. Let's Take a Hike! Converting Fractions to Decimals. 2004. (PowerMath Ser.). (Illus.). 24p. (J). lib. bdg. (978-0-8239-8928-7(3)); lib. bdg. 21.25 (978-0-8239-8979-9(8)) Rosen Publishing Group, Inc., The. (PowerKids Pr.).

Collins, Kathleen. Music Math: Exploring Different Interpretations of Fractions. 2004. (Powermath Ser.). (Illus.). 32p. (J). lib. bdg. (978-0-8239-8877-8(5)); lib. bdg. 22.50 (978-0-8239-8984-3(4)) Rosen Publishing Group, Inc., The. (PowerKids Pr.).

Dalmatian Press Staff. Money, Time & Fractions: Chalkboard Book. 2003. (Home Learning Tools Ser.). 10p. (J). (gr. 2 up). pap. 3.99 (978-1-4037-0331-6(0)) Dalmatian Pr.

Decimals & Fractions. 2003. 16.95 (978-0-7690-0837-0(2)) Seymour, Dale Pubns.

Dobson, Christina. The Pizza Counting Book. Holmes, Matthew, illus. 2004. 32p. (J). 16.95 (978-0-88106-338-7(X)); pap. 6.95 (978-0-88106-339-4(8)) Charlesbridge Publishing, Inc.

Dodds, Dayle Ann. Full House: An Invitation to Fractions. Carter, Abby, illus. 2007. 32p. (J). (gr. 1-4). 16.99 (***978-0-7636-2468-2(3)***) Candlewick Pr.

Douglas, Vincent & School Specialty Publishing Staff. Simple Fractions. 2003. (Modified Basic Skills Ser.). (Illus.). 48p. (J). (gr. k-4). pap. 6.99 (978-0-7424-1935-3(5) , LL90008) Schaffer, Frank Pubns.

Ekblad, Linda. Fractions. 2000. (Metro Math Readers Yellow Level Ser.). (J). (gr. 1-2). 46.95 (978-1-58830-104-8(4)) Metropolitan Teaching & Learning Co.

—Una Mitad es lo Justo: Metro Math Readers Yellow Level. 2000. (Metro Math Readers Yellow Level Ser.). (J). (gr. 1-2). 3.75 (978-1-58120-486-5(8)) Metropolitan Teaching & Learning Co.

Encyclopaedia Britannica Publishers, Inc. Staff. Math in Context: Fraction Times. 6th ed. 2005. pap. 10.60 (978-0-03-039619-9(0)) Harcourt Schl. Pubs.

Everything's Coming up Fractions with Cuisenaire Rods. 2000. (J). pap. 10.95 (978-1-56911-022-5(0)) Learning Resources, Inc.

Fract Burger Foam New in Center. 2004. (J). (978-1-59242-142-8(3)) Delta Education, LLC.

Fraction Basics (Gr. 2-3) 2003. (J). (978-1-58232-089-2(6)) Bryan Hse. Pubs., Inc.

Fraction Basics Spanish Version. 2007. (J). per. (***978-1-58232-158-5(2)***) Bryan Hse. Pubs., Inc.

Fraction Burger Magnetic. 2004. (J). (978-1-59242-145-9(8)) Delta Education, LLC.

Fraction Towers Activity Cards. 2000. (J). 7.95 (978-1-56911-750-7(0)) Learning Resources, Inc.

Fractions Cards Staff. Learning Wrap Ups Palette. 2004. 7.99 (978-1-59204-020-9(9)) Learning Wrap-Ups.

Gangel, Kathryn. Fractions. 1998. (Basic Skills Ser.). (Illus.). 32p. (gr. 3-5). pap. 4.99 (978-0-88724-464-3(5) , CD-2132) Carson-Dellosa Publishing Co., Inc.

George, Lynn. Civil War Recipes: Adding & Subtracting Simple Fractions. 2004. (PowerMath Ser.). (Illus.). 24p. (J). lib. bdg. (978-0-8239-8896-9(1)); lib. bdg. 21.25 (978-0-8239-8973-7(9)) Rosen Publishing Group, Inc., The. (PowerKids Pr.).

Gifford, Scott. Piece = Part = Portion: Fractions = Decimals = Percents. Thaler, Shmuel, photos by. 2004. (Illus.). 32p. (J). (gr. 3-5). 14.95 (978-1-58246-102-1(3) , Tricycle Pr.) Ten Speed Pr.

Gifford, Scott. Piece=Part=Portion/Pedazo=Parte=Porcion: Fractions=Decimals=Percents/ Fracciones=Decimales=Porcentajes. Thaler, Shmuel, photos by. 2007. (ENG & SPA., Illus.). 32p. (J). 14.95 (***978-1-58246-225-7(9)***); pap. 7.95 (***978-1-58246-226-4(7)***) Ten Speed Pr. (Tricycle Pr.).

Goodnow, Judy & Hoogeboom, Shirley. Operations & Beginning Place Value. 2001. (Funtastic Frogstm Ser.). 32p. (J). (gr. k-2). pap. 4.99 (978-1-56451-365-6(3) , ID43024) School Specialty Publishing.

Greenes, Carol, et al. Fractions & Decimals. 2003. (Illus.). 60p. (J). (gr. 4-7). 16.95 (978-0-7690-0002-2(9)) Seymour, Dale Pubns.

Harcourt School Publishers Staff. Math Program Development, Grades 3-6: Fraction Concepts Binder Package. 3rd ed. 2003. ring bd. 360.00 (978-0-15-340578-5(3)) Harcourt Schl. Pubs.

Harris, Nancy. Is an Inchworm an Inch? Measuring with Fractions. 2008. (J). (***978-1-60044-645-0(0)***) Rourke Publishing, LLC.

Hillen, Judith A. Fabulous Fractions. Cordel, Betty, ed. Mason, Renee, illus. 2000. 119p. (J). (gr. 3-6). 18.95 (978-1-881431-82-4(7)) AIMS Education Foundation.

HSP. Fractions, Bk. C. 2nd ed. 2002. (First-Place Math Ser.). (gr. 4 up). pap. 12.60 (978-0-15-334629-3(9)) Harcourt Schl. Pubs.

—Fractions & Decimals, Bk. D. 2nd ed. 2002. (First-Place Math Ser.). (gr. 3 up). pap. 12.60 (978-0-15-334624-8(8)) Harcourt Schl. Pubs.

—Measurement, Geometry, & Fractions, Bk. F. 2nd ed. 2002. (First-Place Math Ser.). (gr. 1 up). pap. 12.60 (978-0-15-334614-9(0)); (gr. 2 up). pap. 12.60 (978-0-15-334620-0(5)) Harcourt Schl. Pubs.

Hunt, Darleen L. Baby's Fraction Lunch. Komarck, Michael, illus. 2003. (Sherman's Math Corner Ser.). (J). (ps-3). (978-1-929591-07-7(1)) Reading Rock, Inc.

Jaffe, Elizabeth Dana. Can You Eat a Fraction? 2002. (Yellow Umbrella Books). (Illus.). 16p. (J). (gr. 1). lib. bdg. 14.60 (978-0-7368-1279-5(2) , Pebble Bks.) Capstone Pr., Inc.

Jones, Colleen. Vamos a Compartir Yellow Level: Metro Math Reader. 2000. (Metro Math Readers Yellow Level Ser.). (SPA., Illus.). (J). (gr. 1-2). 3.75 (978-1-58120-479-7(5)) Metropolitan Teaching & Learning Co.

Kiernan, Denise. Math Games to Master Basic Skills: Fractions & Decimals: Familiar & Flexible Games with Dozens of Variations That Help Struggling Learners Practice & Really Master Basic Fraction & Decimal Skills & Concepts. 2007. 48p. pap. 10.99 (978-0-439-51772-0(9) , Teaching Resources) Scholastic, Inc.

Kompelien, Tracy. I Know Fractions by Their Actions! (Math Made Fun Ser.). (Illus.). 24p. (J). 2007. 19.93 (978-1-59928-529-0(0)); 2006. (978-1-59928-530-6(4)) ABDO Publishing Co.

Koomen, Michele. Fractions: Making Fair Shares. 2001. (Exploring Math Ser.). (Illus.). 24p. (J). (gr. 1-2). lib. bdg. 18.60 (978-0-7368-0817-0(5) , Bridgestone Bks.) Capstone Pr., Inc.

Learning Wrap-Ups Fractions. 2004. 7.99 (978-0-943343-36-5(4)) Learning Wrap-Ups.

Levy, Janey. Recipes for a Medieval Feast: Working Flexibly with Fractions. 2006. (Math for the Real World Ser.). (Illus.). 32p. (J). pap. (978-1-4042-6061-0(7)); lib. bdg. (978-1-4042-3354-6(7)) Rosen Publishing Group, Inc., The.

Linde, Barbara M. Managing Your Money: Understanding Math Operations Involving Decimals & Integers. 2006. (Math for the Real World Ser.). (Illus.). 32p. (J). pap. (978-1-4042-6091-7(9)); lib. bdg. (978-1-4042-3369-0(5)) Rosen Publishing Group, Inc., The.

Math Discoveries about Fractions. (Math Discoveries about Fractions & Decimals Ser.). 64p. (gr. 3-4). 7.99 (978-1-56451-189-8(8) , ID7684) School Specialty Publishing.

Math Discoveries about Fractions & Decimals. (Math Discoveries about Fractions & Decimals Ser.). 64p. (gr. 5-6). 7.99 (978-1-56451-190-4(1) , ID7685); (gr. 7-8). 7.99 (978-1-56451-191-1(X) , ID7686) School Specialty Publishing.

McNabb, Jeffrey G. Rule of Thumb Measuring System: Both English & Metric. Zimmerman, Pam & Kelley, Jim, illus. l.t. ed. 1999. (J). (gr. 4-8). pap. 5.00 (978-0-9669794-0-4(0)) Rule of Thumb Publishing.

Miles Moran, Andrea. Fractions, Decimals, Percents. 1999. (Homework Booklets Ser.). (Illus.). 80p. (J). (gr. 5-5). pap. 2.99 (978-1-56822-068-0(5) , IF0281); (J). (gr. 6-6). pap. 2.99 (978-1-56822-069-7(3) , IF0282); (YA). (gr. 7-8). pap. 2.99 (978-1-56822-070-3(7) , IF0283) Schaffer, Frank Pubns. (Instructional Fair).

Mitchell, Cindi. Math Skills Made Fun: Great Graph Art Decimals & Fractions. 2000. (Illus.). 64p. (J). pap. 10.95 (978-0-590-64375-7(4)) Scholastic, Inc.

Murphy, Stuart J. Jump, Kangaroo, Jump! O'Malley, Kevin, illus. 1999. (MathStart Ser.). 40p. (gr. 2 up). (J). pap. 5.99 (978-0-06-446721-6(X) , Harper Trophy); (YA). 15.89 (978-0-06-027615-7(0)); (J). 15.95 (978-0-06-027614-0(2)) HarperCollins Pubs.

—Jump, Kangaroo, Jump! 1999. (Math Start Ser.). (J). 11.79 (978-0-606-16681-2(5)); lib. bdg. 13.00 (978-0-613-11724-1(7)) Tandem Library Bks.

Nagda, Ann Whitehead & Bickel, Cindy. Polar Bear Math: Learning about Fractions from Klondike & Snow. 2007. (Illus.). 32p. (J). pap. 7.99 (***978-0-312-37749-6(5)***) Square Fish.

Packard, Edward. Little Numbers: And Pictures That Just Show Just How Little They Are. Murdocca, Sal, illus. 2001. (Fun Early Math Concepts Ser.). 32p. (gr. k-3). lib. bdg. 22.90 (978-0-7613-1904-7(2) , Millbrook Pr.) Lerner Publishing Group.

Pallotta, Jerry. Apple Fractions. Bolster, Rob, illus. 2003. 32p. (J). pap. 5.99 (978-0-439-38901-3(1)) Scholastic, Inc.

—Apple Fractions. 2002. (gr. k-3). lib. bdg. 14.10 (978-0-613-67054-8(X)) Tandem Library Bks.

Pistoia, Sara. Fractions. 2006. (MathBooks Ser.). (Illus.). 24p. (J). 24.21 (978-1-59296-686-8(1)) Child's World, Inc.

Practice Power Flip & Learn Fractions. 2000. (Illus.). 16p. (J). (gr. 3-5). spiral bd. (978-1-930355-24-8(6)) Greenbrier/Scentex.

Ratios, Percents, & Decimals. 2003. (Illus.). (gr. 3 up). 9.99 (978-0-7682-1990-6(6) , J53018) School Specialty Publishing.

Realtime Associates and Mazer Corporation Staff, et al, compiled by. Relate Fractions & Decimals. 2002. (J). (978-1-58605-510-3(0) , LeapFrog Schl. Hse.) LeapFrog Enterprises, Inc.

Realtime Associates and Mazer Corporation Staff & LeapFrog Staff, compiled by. Add Fractions with Like Denominators. 2002. (J). (gr. 4). 66.75 (978-1-58605-455-7(4) , LeapFrog Schl. Hse.) LeapFrog Enterprises, Inc.

—Add Fractions with Unlike Denominators. 2002. (J). (gr. 5). 66.75 (978-1-58605-512-7(7) , LeapFrog Schl. Hse.) LeapFrog Enterprises, Inc.

—Multiply Fractions. 2002. (J). (gr. 5). 66.75 (978-1-58605-514-1(3) , LeapFrog Schl. Hse.) LeapFrog Enterprises, Inc.

—Relate Fractions & Decimals. 2002. (J). (gr. 4). 66.75 (978-1-58605-453-3(8) , LeapFrog Schl. Hse.) LeapFrog Enterprises, Inc.

Reed, Janet. Parts of a Whole. 2003. (J). 15.93 (978-0-7368-2935-9(0)); pap. (978-0-7368-2894-9(X)) Yellow Umbrella Pr.

Robinson, C. L. MATH1on1 Fractions & Decimals. 2006. (YA). per. 9.99 (978-0-9786767-1-1(8)) Robinson, Consuelo.

—MATH1on1 Multiply & Divide Fractions. 2006. (YA). per. 9.99 (978-0-9786767-3-5(4)) Robinson, Consuelo.

Roy, Jennifer Rozines & Roy, Gregory. Holiday Fractions. 2005. (Math All Around Ser.). (Illus.). 31p. (J). (978-0-7614-2001-9(0) , Benchmark Bks.) Cavendish, Marshall Corp.

Roza, Greg. Olympic Math: Working with Percents & Decimals. 2006. (Math for the Real World Ser.). (Illus.). 32p. (J). pap. (978-1-4042-6057-3(9)); lib. bdg. (978-1-4042-3352-2(0)) Rosen Publishing Group, Inc., The.

Safro, Jill. Fractions & Decimals. 2003. (5-Minute Daily Practice Ser.). (Illus.). 64p. pap., tchr. ed. 11.95 (978-0-439-40917-9(9) , Teaching Resources) Scholastic, Inc.

School Specialty Publishing. Complete Fractions Skills, Grades 1-2. 2006. 80p. (J). (gr. 1-2). pap. 10.99 (978-0-7682-3391-9(7)) Schaffer, Frank Pubns.

—Complete Fractions Skills, Grades 3-4. 2006. 80p. (C). pap. 10.99 (***978-0-7682-3393-3(3)*** , Schaffer, Frank) Schaffer, Frank Pubns.

—Complete Fractions Skills, Grades 5-6. 2006. 80p. (J). (gr. 5-6). pap. 10.99 (978-0-7682-3395-7(X) , Schaffer, Frank) Schaffer, Frank Pubns.

—Fractions. 1999. 160p. (J). (gr. 3 up). pap. 7.99 (978-1-56451-350-2(5) , ID7874, Ideal School Supply) Schaffer, Frank Pubns.

—Fractions. 2004. (On-File Ser.). 4p. (J). (gr. 1-3). ring bd. 4.99 (978-0-7424-2910-9(5) , Instructional Fair) Schaffer, Frank Pubns.

—Fractions. 2006. (Brighter Child Flash Cards Ser.). 54p. (J). 2.99 (978-0-7696-7733-0(9) , Brighter Child) School Specialty Publishing.

—Fractions Decimals & % Gr 3. 2005. (Math 2 Master Ser.). 32p. (J). pap. 3.99 (978-0-7696-3933-8(X) , Brighter Child) School Specialty Publishing.

—Fractions, Decimals, & Percents, Grade 6. 2005. (Math 2 Master Ser.). 32p. (J). pap. 3.99 (978-0-7696-3936-9(4) , Brighter Child) School Specialty Publishing.

—Mathematics: A Step-by-Step Approach. 1999. (Homework Booklets Ser.). 86p. (J). (gr. 6-6). pap. 2.99 (978-0-88012-481-2(4) , IF0160); (YA). (gr. 7-7). pap. 2.99 (978-0-88012-484-3(9) , IF0170) Schaffer, Frank Pubns. (Instructional Fair).

—Step-by-Step Homework Booklets: Fractions. 2003. (Homework Booklets Ser.). 80p. (C). pap. 2.99 (978-0-7682-2636-2(8) , IFG99146) School Specialty Publishing.

School Zone Interactive Staff. Time, Money & Fractions. rev. ed. 2003. (On-Track Software Ser.). 64p. (J). (gr. k-2). pap. 15.99 incl. cd-rom (978-1-58947-832-9(0)) School Zone Publishing Co.

School Zone Publishing Interactive Staff. Time, Money & Fractions. 2001. (On-Track Software Ser.). (Illus.). 32p. (J). pap. 13.99 incl. cd-rom (978-0-88743-954-4(3) , 08830) School Zone Publishing Co.

School Zone Staff, ed. Time, Money & Fractions. 2003. (J). (gr. 1-2). cd-rom 19.99 (978-1-58947-930-2(0)) School Zone Publishing Co.

Schulz, Charles M. I'm Halfway to Failing Fractions. 2000. 16p. (J). (ps up). pap. 3.25 (978-0-694-01045-5(6)) HarperCollins Pubs.

Shea. Fractions Core Skills. 2001. pap. (978-0-7398-4897-5(6)) Steck-Vaughn.

Sherard, Wade H., III. Logic Decimal Problems. 1999. 64p. (gr. 4-11). pap. 10.95 (978-0-7690-0082-4(7)) Seymour, Dale Pubns.

Smart, Margaret & Tuel, Patricia. Focus on Fractions, 3 bks., Set. Incl. Bk. 1. 1986. 7.95 (978-0-918932-14-3(9) , A-1394); Bk. 2. 1989. 7.95 (978-0-918932-15-0(7) , A-1395); Bk. 3. 1987. 7.95 (978-0-918932-16-7(5) , A-1396); (Illus.). 48p. (J). (gr. 5-9). Set pap. 23.85 (978-0-918932-69-3(6)) Activity Resources Co., Inc.

Stckvagn. AC Ems Fractions. 2004. pap. (978-0-7398-9856-7(6)) Harcourt Schl. Pubs.

Steck-Vaughn Staff. At-Home Workbooks: Fractions. 2004. (Illus.). pap., wbk. ed. (978-0-7398-8530-7(8)) Steck-Vaughn.

—Early Math: Fractions I, 10 Pack. 2005. pap. 29.95 (978-1-4190-0354-7(2)) Steck-Vaughn.

—Early Math: Fractions II, 10 Pack. 2005. pap. 29.95 (978-1-4190-0364-6(X)) Steck-Vaughn.

—Focus on Math Level C 10-pack: Fractions. 2005. pap. 29.95 (978-1-4190-0291-5(0)) Harcourt Schl. Pubs.

—Focus on Math Level D: Fractions. 2005. pap. 2.99 (978-1-4190-0267-0(8)); pap. 2.99 (978-1-4190-0273-1(2)) Harcourt Schl. Pubs.

—Focus on Math Level D 10-pack: Fractions. 2005. pap. 29.95 (978-1-4190-0297-7(X)) Harcourt Schl. Pubs.

—Focus on Math Level E: Fractions. 2005. pap. 2.99 (978-1-4190-0280-9(5)) Harcourt Schl. Pubs.

—Focus on Math Level E 10-pack: Fractions. 2005. pap. 29.95 (978-1-4190-0304-2(6)) Harcourt Schl. Pubs.

—Focus on Math Level F: Fractions. 2005. pap. 2.99 (978-1-4190-0285-4(6)) Harcourt Schl. Pubs.

—Focus on Math Level F 10-pack: Fractions. 2005. pap. 29.95 (978-1-4190-0309-7(7)) Harcourt Schl. Pubs.

—Fractions: Concepts & Problem Solving. 2000. (Illus.). (J). (gr. 3). pap. (978-0-7398-3406-0(1)); (gr. 4). pap. (978-0-7398-3407-7(X)); (gr. 5). pap. (978-0-7398-3408-4(8)) Steck-Vaughn.

—Math Remediation 10-Pack: Fractions. 2005. pap. 54.95 (978-1-4190-0389-9(5)) Harcourt Schl. Pubs.

—Middle School Fractions. 1999. (Illus.). (J). pap. (978-0-7398-1300-3(5)) Steck-Vaughn.

—Top Line Math: Fractions. 2005. pap. 5.49 (978-1-4190-0368-4(2)) Harcourt Schl. Pubs.

Sterling, Kristin. Fractions. 2008. (J). pap. (***978-0-8225-8847-4(1)***) Lerner Publishing Group.

Taylor, Loretta & Taylor, Harold. Understanding Fractions, Bk. 2. 2000. (Basic Computation Ser.: Bk. 2). 110p. (YA). (gr. 6-12). pap. 18.95 (978-0-7690-0115-9(7)) Seymour, Dale Pubns.

—Working with Fractions. 2000. (Basic Computation Ser.: Bk. 3). 116p. (YA). (gr. 6-12). pap. 18.95 (978-0-7690-0116-6(5)) Seymour, Dale Pubns.

Townsend, Donna. Apple Fractions. (Rookie Read-About Math Ser.). (Illus.). (J). 2005. 32p. (gr. 1-2). pap. 5.95 (978-0-516-24670-3(4)); 2004. 31p. 20.50 (978-0-516-24419-8(1)) Scholastic Library Publishing. (Children's Pr.).

Trumbauer, Lisa. Partes de un Entero. 2005. Tr. of Parts of a Whole. (SPA., Illus.). 16p. (J). (gr. k-1). lib. bdg. 15.93 (978-0-7368-4158-0(X)) Capstone Pr., Inc.

Using Cuisenaire Rods: Fractions & Decimals. 2001. (J). pap. 7.95 (978-1-56911-738-5(1)) Learning Resources, Inc.

Vorderman, Carol. Learn Your Fractions & Decimlas Kit. 2007. 48p. (J). (gr. 3-6). 15.99 (978-0-7566-2943-4(8)) Dorling Kindersley Publishing, Inc.

Watt, Fiona & Wells, Rachel. Fractions. 2004. (Sticker Math Ser.). (Illus.). 28p. (J). (gr. 1-2). pap., act. bk. ed. 6.95 (978-0-7945-0038-2(2) , Usborne) EDC Publishing.

Wingard-Nelson, Rebecca. Decimals & Fractions. 2008. (Math Busters Ser.). (Illus.). 64p. (J). (gr. 5 up). lib. bdg. 27.93 (***978-0-7660-2877-7(1)***) Enslow Pubs., Inc.

Work with Fractions, Decimals & Percents. 2004. (Math "How To" Ser.). (Illus.). 48p. 7.99 (978-1-57690-956-0(5)); (J). (gr. 4). 7.99 (978-1-57690-955-3(7)) Teacher Created Materials, Inc.

Zuravicky, Orli. The Stock Market: Understanding & Applying Ratios, Decimals, Fractions, & Percentages. 2005. (PowerMath Ser.). (Illus.). 32p. (J). 22.50 (978-1-4042-2929-7(9) , PowerKids Pr.); (978-1-4042-5122-9(7) , PowerKids Pr.); pap. (978-1-4042-5121-2(9)) Rosen Publishing Group, Inc., The.

FRACTURES

Burles, Kenneth T. Broken Bones. 1998. (Learning about Your Health Ser.). (J). lib. bdg. 26.60 (978-0-86625-652-0(0)) Rourke Publishing, LLC.

Glaser, Jason. Broken Bones. 2007. (First Facts Ser.). (Illus.). 24p. (J). 21.26 (978-0-7368-6330-8(3)) Capstone Pr., Inc.

Landau, Elaine. Broken Bones. 2008. (J). (***978-0-7614-2847-3(X)***) Cavendish, Marshall Bks., Ltd.

Royston, Angela. Broken Bones. 2004. (Illus.). 32p. (J). lib. bdg. (978-1-4034-4822-4(1)) Heinemann Library.

Silverstein, Alvin, et al. Broken Bones. 2001. (My Health Ser.). (Illus.). 48p. (J). (gr. 3-5). pap. 6.95 (978-0-531-13968-4(9)); 25.50 (978-0-531-11781-1(2)) Scholastic Library Publishing. (Watts, Franklin).

FRACTURES—FICTION

Harcourt School Publishers Staff. Emergency! 3rd ed. 2002. (Trophies English Language Learners Ser.). (Illus.). pap. 5.10 (978-0-15-327886-0(2)) Harcourt Schl. Pubs.

Perkins, Lynne Rae. The Broken Cat. Perkins, Lynne Rae, illus. 2002. (Illus.). 32p. (J). (ps-1). 16.99 (978-0-06-029263-8(6)) HarperCollins Pubs.

—The Broken Cat. 2002. (Illus.). 32p. (J). (ps-1). 16.89 (978-0-06-029264-5(4)) HarperCollins Pubs.

FRAMING OF PICTURES

see Picture Frames and Framing

FRANCE

Alcraft, Rob. France. 1999. (Illus.). 32p. (J). lib. bdg. 21.36 (978-1-57572-851-3(6)) Heinemann Library.

Axworthy, Anni. Anni's Diary of France. Axworthy, Anni, illus. 2000. (Illus.). 32p. (J). (gr. 2-5). pap. 6.95 (978-1-58089-024-3(5)) Charlesbridge Publishing, Inc.

—Anni's Diary of France. 2000. (gr. 3-6). lib. bdg. 15.25 (978-0-613-35063-1(4)); (Illus.). (J). (978-0-606-18746-6(1)) Tandem Library Bks.

Boast, Clare. France. 1998. (Next Stop! Ser.). 32p. (J). (gr. 2-4). lib. bdg. 19.92 (978-1-57572-565-9(7)) Heinemann Library.

Burnham, Brad. Cave of Lascaux: The Cave of Prehistoric Wall Paintings. 2003. (Famous Caves of the World Ser.). (Illus.). 24p. (J). lib. bdg. 18.75 (978-0-8239-6257-0(1) , PowerKids Pr.) Rosen Publishing Group, Inc., The.

Byers, Helen. Colors of France. Byers, Helen, illus. (Colors of the World Ser.). (Illus.). 24p. 2005. (gr. 3-6). 5.95 (978-1-57505-565-7(1)); 2001. (J). (gr. 1-4). lib. bdg. (978-1-57505-514-5(7) , Carolrhoda Bks.) Lerner Publishing Group.

—Colors of France. 2001. (gr. k-3). lib. bdg. 14.10 (978-0-613-79240-0(8)) Tandem Library Bks.

Chandler, Virginia. France. 2002. (Changing Face Of... Ser.). (Illus.). 48p. (J). lib. bdg. 27.12 (978-0-7398-5215-6(9)) Raintree.

Conboy, Fiona & NgCheong-Lum, Roseline. Welcome to France. 1999. (Welcome to My Country Ser.). (Illus.). 48p. (J). (gr. 2 up). lib. bdg. 26.00 (978-0-8368-2495-7(4)) Stevens, Gareth Inc.

Cooper, Sharon Katz. France ABCs: A Book about the People & Places of France. Previn, Stacey, illus. 2006. (Country ABCs Ser.). 32p. (J). (gr. k-5). 23.93 (978-1-4048-1568-1(6)) Picture Window Bks.

Corona, Laurel. France. 2002. (Modern Nations of the World Ser.). (Illus.). 120p. (YA). (gr. 7-10). 29.95 (978-1-56006-760-3(8) , Lucent Bks.) Thomson Gale.

Costain, Meredith & Collins, Paul. Welcome to France. 2001. (Countries of the World Ser.). (Illus.). 32p. (J). (gr. 4 up). 28.00 (978-0-7910-6551-8(0) , 010203, Chelsea Hse.) Facts On File, Inc.

Discovering Major Cities of France. 2007. (YA). 13.95 (***978-1-931463-22-5(0)***) French Workshop, The.

E F G

Discovering the Regions of France. 2001. ii, 72p. (YA). spiral bd. 15.95 (978-1-931463-12-6(3)) French Workshop, The.

Feinstein, Stephen. Louis Pasteur: The Father of Microbiology. 2008. (Inventors Who Changed the World Ser.). 128p. (J). (gr. 6 up). lib. bdg. 33.27 (***978-1-59845-078-1(6)*** , MyReportLinks.com Bks.) Enslow Pubs., Inc.

Fisher, Teresa. France. Johnstone, Andy, photos by. 2005. (Letters from Around the World Ser.). (Illus.). 32p. (J). (gr. 3-7). lib. bdg. (978-1-84234-250-3(9) , Cherrytree Books) Evans Publishing Group.

—France. 1999. (We Come from Ser.). (Illus.). 32p. (J). (gr. 1-4). lib. bdg. 25.69 (978-0-8172-5212-0(6)) Raintree.

Fontes, Justine & Fontes, Ron. France. (to Z Ser.). (J). 2004. (gr. 2-4). pap. 6.95 (978-0-516-26808-8(2)); 2003. (ENG & FRE.). 40p. 24.50 (978-0-516-24557-7(0)) Scholastic Library Publishing. (Children's Pr.).

Frost, Helen. A Look at France. Saunders-Smith, Gail, ed. 2002. (Our World Ser.). (Illus.). 24p. (J). (gr. k-1). lib. bdg. 15.93 (978-0-7368-1167-5(2) , Pebble Bks.) Capstone Pr., Inc.

—A Look at Japan. 2005. (One World, Many Cultures Ser.). 24p. (YA). (gr. k-3). pap. (978-0-7368-9366-4(0) , Pebble Bks.) Capstone Pr., Inc.

Ganeri, Anita. France & the French. 2004. (Focus on Europe Ser.). (J). lib. bdg. 28.50 (978-1-932799-18-7(4)) Stargazer Bks.

Glavich, Mary Kathleen. Saint Therese of Lisieux: The Way of Love. Esquinaldo, Virginia, tr. Esquinaldo, Virginia, illus. 2003. (Encounter the Saints Ser.). 132p. (J). pap. 5.95 (978-0-8198-7074-2(9) , 332-370) Pauline Bks. & Media.

Harvey, Miles. Look What Came from France. 1999. (Look What Came from Ser.). (Illus.). 32p. (gr. 2-4). pap. 6.95 (978-0-531-15964-4(7) , Watts, Franklin) Scholastic Library Publishing.

—Look What Came from France. 1999. (Illus.). (J). (978-0-606-18153-2(9)) Tandem Library Bks.

Hesse, Joseph M. Les Régions de France. 2nd ed. 2004. (Geography Capsules Ser.). (FRE.). 144p. (YA). (gr. 7-12). 88.00 (978-1-885888-32-7(5)) Global Awareness Publishing Co.

Ingham, Richard. France. 2000. (Nations of the World Ser.). (Illus.). 128p. (YA). (gr. 6-8). lib. bdg. 34.26 (978-0-8172-5782-8(9)) Raintree.

Italia, Bob. France. 2001. (Countries Ser.). (Illus.). 40p. (J). (gr. k-6). lib. bdg. 22.78 (978-1-57765-494-0(3) , Checkerboard Library) ABDO Publishing Co.

Jett, Stephen C. & Roberts, Lisa. France. 2003. (Modern World Nations Ser.). (Illus.). 150p. (gr. 6-12). 30.00 (978-0-7910-7607-1(5) , Chelsea Hse.) Facts On File, Inc.

Klingel, Cynthia Fitterer & Noyed, Robert B. France. 2002. (First Reports). (Illus.). 48p. (J). (gr. 3 up). lib. bdg. 22.60 (978-0-7565-0184-6(9)) Compass Point Bks.

Knoell, Donna L. France. 2002. (Countries & Cultures Ser.). (Illus.). 64p. (J). (gr. 3-4). lib. bdg. 23.93 (978-0-7368-1077-7(3) , Bridgestone Bks.) Capstone Pr., Inc.

Landau, Elaine. France. 2000. (Illus.). 47p. (J). (gr. 3-7). lib. bdg. 15.25 (978-0-613-54491-7(9)) Tandem Library Bks.

A Look at France. 2005. (One World, Many Cultures Ser.). (YA). (gr. k-3). (978-0-7368-9364-0(4) , Pebble Bks.) Capstone Pr., Inc.

A Look at France, 6 vols. (gr. k-2). 28.95 (978-0-7368-9365-7(2)) Red Brick Learning.

Malone, Margaret Gay. France. 2002. (Discovering Cultures Ser.). (Illus.). 48p. (J). 25.64 (978-0-7614-1178-9(X) , Benchmark Bks.) Cavendish, Marshall Corp.

March, Michael. Guide to France. 1998. (World Guides Ser.). (Illus.). 32p. (J). (gr. 2-6). lib. bdg. 21.27 (978-1-884756-43-6(3)) Davidson Titles, Inc.

Mason, Paul. France. 2005. (Destination Detectives Ser.). (Illus.). 48p. (J). lib. bdg. 31.43 (978-1-4109-1862-8(9)) Raintree.

—France. 2006. (Illus.). 48p. (J). lib. bdg. (***978-1-4109-2459-9(9)***) Steck-Vaughn.

Mathur-Kamat, Ambika. Miss Panda in France. Crawford, K. Michael, illus. 2001. (Miss Panda Ser.). 40p. (J). pap. 11.99 (978-1-59092-026-8(0) , Little Blue Works) Windstorm Creative.

Mitten, Christopher. France. 2002. (Steadwell Books World Tour). (Illus.). 48p. (J). lib. bdg. 24.26 (978-0-7398-5753-3(3)) Raintree.

Moritz, Patricia M. France. 2000. (Dropping in on Ser.). (Illus.). 32p. (J). (gr. 2-5). lib. bdg. 28.50 (978-1-55916-280-7(5)) Rourke Publishing, LLC.

Nardo, Don. France. 2007. 144p. (J). 37.00 (***978-0-516-25948-2(2)*** , Children's Pr.) Scholastic Library Publishing.

NgCheong-Lum, Roseline. France. 1999. (Countries of the World Ser.). (Illus.). 96p. (J). (gr. 6 up). lib. bdg. 30.00 (978-0-8368-2260-1(9)) Stevens, Gareth Inc.

Nickles, Greg. France: The Culture. 2000. (Lands, Peoples, & Cultures Ser.). (Illus.). (J). (978-0-606-18054-2(0)) Tandem Library Bks.

—France - the People. 2000. (gr. 3-6). lib. bdg. 16.40 (978-0-613-27837-9(2)) Tandem Library Bks.

—France the Land. 2000. (gr. 3-6). lib. bdg. 16.40 (978-0-613-27836-2(4)) Tandem Library Bks.

Park, Ted. Taking Your Camera To... Includes: Australia, Brazil, Canada, Egypt, France, Israel, Italy, Japan, Mexico, Panama, Russia, Spain, 12 bks., Set. 2000. (Taking Your Camera to Ser.). (Illus.). (J). (gr. 4-7). 273.96 (978-0-7398-3096-3(1)) Raintree.

—Taking Your Camera to France. 1999. (Illus.). pap. (978-0-7398-2153-4(9)) Steck-Vaughn.

Patent, Dorothy Hinshaw. Mystery of the Lascaux Cave. 1998. (Frozen in Time Ser.). (Illus.). 64p. (J). (gr. 5-9). lib. bdg. 28.50 (978-0-7614-0784-3(7)) Cavendish, Marshall Corp.

Paul Mason. France. 2006. (Illus.). 48p. (J). pap. (***978-1-4109-2466-7(1)***) Steck-Vaughn.

Pickwell, Linda. France. 2004. (QEB Travel Through Ser.). (Illus.). 32p. (J). lib. bdg. 18.95 (978-1-59566-062-6(3)) QEB Publishing Inc.

Pluckrose, Henry Arthur. France. 1999. (Picture a Country Ser.). (Illus.). 32p. (J). (gr. k-2). pap. 6.95 (978-0-531-15378-9(9) , Watts, Franklin) Scholastic Library Publishing.

Popper, Garry. Paul in France. Johnson, Andi, illus. 2004. 36p. (ps-7). 4.00 (978-1-84161-056-6(9)) Ravette Publishing, Ltd. GBR. *Dist:* Parkwest Pubns., Inc.

Poussin, Nichol. Still Spins the Spider of Rennes-le-Chateau. l.t. ed. 2004. Tr. of arraignee tisse sa toile a Rennes-le-Chateaua. (Illus.). 347p. pap. (978-0-9541527-1-0(9) , http//www.keysofantiquity.com) DEK Publishing.

Powell, Jillian. Descubramos Francia. 2006. (ENG & SPA.). (J). pap. (***978-0-8368-7960-5(0)***); lib. bdg. (***978-0-8368-7953-7(8)***) Stevens, Gareth Inc.

—Looking at France. 2006. (Illus.). 32p. (J). pap. (***978-0-8368-7675-8(X)***); lib. bdg. (***978-0-8368-7668-0(7)***) Stevens, Gareth Inc.

Prosser, Robert. France. 2003. (Countries of the World Ser.). (Illus.). 64p. (gr. 6-12). (J). 30.00 (978-0-8160-5381-0(2)); 30.00 (978-0-8160-5380-3(4)) Facts On File, Inc.

Raabe, Emily. France, a Primary Source Guide. 2005. (Countries of the World, a Primary Source Journey Ser.). (Illus.). 24p. (J). 19.95 (978-1-4042-2752-1(0) , PowerKids Pr.) Rosen Publishing Group, Inc., The.

Ruth, Angie. My Adventure in France. 2007. 44p. (J). 8.99 (978-1-59092-428-0(2) , Orchard Academy Pr.) Windstorm Creative.

Sandak, Cass R. France. 1999. (Taking Your Camera to Ser.). (Illus.). 32p. (J). (gr. 4-7). lib. bdg. 22.83 (978-0-7398-1800-8(7)) Raintree.

Sanna, Jeanine. France. 2006. (European Union Ser.). (Illus.). 88p. (J). (gr. 5 up). lib. bdg. (978-1-4222-0047-6(7) , 1247999) Mason Crest Pubs.

Sommers, Michael A. France: A Primary Source Cultural Guide. 2005. (Primary Sources of World Cultures Ser.). (Illus.). 128p. (J). (gr. 4-8). lib. bdg. 34.60 (978-1-4042-2909-9(4)) Rosen Publishing Group, Inc., The.

Sookram, Brian. France. 1999. (Major World Nations Ser.). (Illus.). 144p. (YA). (gr. 4-7). 29.95 (978-0-7910-4738-5(5) , Chelsea Hse.) Facts On File, Inc.

Spengler, Kremena. France: A Question & Answer Book. 2004. (Fact Finders Ser.). 32p. (J). lib. bdg. 22.60 (978-0-7368-2689-1(0)) Capstone Pr., Inc.

Stevens, Kathryn. France. 2000. (Countries: Faces & Places Ser.). (Illus.). 32p. (J). (gr. 1-5). 25.64 (978-1-56766-714-1(7)) Child's World, Inc.

Stevens, Kathryn. Welcome to France. 2008. (Welcome to the World Ser.). 32p. (J). (gr. 1-5). 27.07 (***978-1-59296-971-5(2)***) Child's World, Inc.

Thomson, Ruth. France. Hampton, David, photos by. 2007. (Living In- Ser.). (Illus.). 32p. (J). (***978-1-59771-042-8(3)*** , 1268838) Sea-To-Sea Pubns.

Tidmarsh, Celia. Focus on France. 2006. (Illus.). 64p. (J). pap. 11.95 (978-0-8368-6236-2(8)); lib. bdg. 32.67 (978-0-8368-6217-1(1)) Stevens, Gareth Inc. (World Almanac Library).

—France. 2000. (Country Studies). (Illus.). 64p. (J). (gr. 6-8). lib. bdg. 27.07 (978-1-57572-421-8(9)) Heinemann Library.

—France. 2002. (Country File Ser.). (Illus.). 32p. (J). lib. bdg. 24.25 (978-1-58340-202-3(0)) Smart Apple Media.

Walsh, Kieran. France. 2005. (Countries in the News Ser.). (Illus.). 24p. (gr. 1-4). 17.95 (978-1-59515-172-8(9)) Rourke Publishing, LLC.

Welby, Rebecca, illus. Bonjour France! rev. ed. 2006. (Young Traveler's Club Ser.). (ENG.). 60p. pap. 16.95 (978-0-9549476-0-6(6)) Beautiful Bks. GBR. *Dist:* International Publishers Marketing.

FRANCE—COURT AND COURTIERS

Barter, James E. The Palace of Versailles. 1998. (Building History Ser.). (Illus.). 112p. (YA). (gr. 6-9). 27.45 (978-1-56006-433-6(1) , Lucent Bks.) Thomson Gale.

FRANCE—FICTION

Anderson, Rachel. Red Moon. 2007. 336p. pap. 10.95 (***978-0-340-79940-6(4)***) Hodder Children's Division GBR. *Dist:* Independent Pubs. Group.

Angeletti, Roberta. The Cave Painter of Lascaux. 2004. (Illus.). 32p. (J). (978-1-56290-323-7(3)) Crystal Productions.

Anholt, Laurence. The Magical Garden of Claude Monet. 2003. (Illus.). 32p. (J). 14.95 (978-0-7641-5574-1(1)) Barron's Educational Series, Inc.

—Matisse: The King of Color. 2007. (Anholt's Artists Books for Children Ser.). 32p. (J). (ps-3). 14.99 (***978-0-7641-6047-9(8)***) Barron's Educational Series, Inc.

—Van Gogh & the Sunflowers. 2007. (Anholt's Artists Books for Children Ser.). 32p. (J). (ps-3). pap. 7.99 (***978-0-7641-3854-6(5)***) Barron's Educational Series, Inc.

Banks, Kate. The Cat Who Walked Across France. Hallensleben, Georg, illus. 2004. 40p. (J). 16.00 (978-0-374-39968-9(9) , Farrar, Straus & Giroux (BYR)) Farrar, Straus & Giroux.

Bea's Own Good: Evaluation Guide. 2006. (J). (978-1-55942-401-1(X)) Marsh Media.

Bemelmans, Ludwig. Madeline: Edicion en Espanol. Anasal, Arshes, ed. 2005. (SPA., Illus.). 44p. (J). (gr. k-4). reprint ed. 16.00 (978-0-7567-8842-1(0)) DIANE Publishing Co.

—Madeline & the Bad Hat. Bemelmans, Ludwig, illus. 2002. (Madeline Ser.). (Illus.). (J). 14.04 (978-0-7587-4084-7(0)) Book Wholesalers, Inc.

—Madeline & the Bad Hat. Bemelmans, Ludwig, illus. 2000. (Madeline Ser.). (Illus.). 64p. (J). (ps-3). pap. 7.99 (978-0-14-056648-2(1) , Viking Juvenile) Penguin Group (USA) Inc.

—Madeline & the Gypsies. Bemelmans, Ludwig, illus. 2000. (Madeline Ser.). (Illus.). 64p. (J). (ps-3). pap. 7.99 (978-0-14-056647-5(3) , Viking Juvenile) Penguin Group (USA) Inc.

—Madeline & the Gypsies. 2000. (gr. k-3). lib. bdg. 15.30 (978-0-8085-2352-9(X)) Tandem Library Bks.

—Madeline & the Gypsies. Bemelmans, Ludwig, illus. 2000. (Madeline Ser.). (Illus.). (J). (ps-3). (978-0-606-18428-1(7)) Tandem Library Bks.

—Madeline in America & Other Holiday Tales. Bemelmans, Ludwig, illus. 2002. (Madeline Ser.). (Illus.). (J). 18.68 (978-0-7587-4186-8(3)) Book Wholesalers, Inc.

—Madeline in America & Other Holiday Tales. Marciano, John Bemelmans, illus. 1999. (Madeline Ser.). (J). (ps-3). 112p. pap. 19.95 (978-0-590-03910-9(5) , Levine, Arthur A. Bks.); pap. 125.00 (978-0-439-09633-1(2)) Scholastic, Inc.

—Madeline's Rescue. ed. 2004. (J). (ps-2). spiral bd. (978-0-616-11864-1(3)) Canadian National Institute for the Blind/Institut National Canadien pour les Aveugles.

—Madeline's Rescue. Bemelmans, Ludwig, illus. 2000. (Madeline Ser.). (Illus.). 64p. (J). (ps-3). pap. 7.99 (978-0-14-056651-2(1) , Viking Juvenile) Penguin Group (USA) Inc.

Bemelmans, Ludwig & Wheeler, Jody. Madeline's Birthday. 1999. (Madeline Ser.). (Illus.). 16p. (J). (ps-3). act. bk. ed. 7.99 (978-0-670-88767-5(6) , Viking Juvenile) Penguin Group (USA) Inc.

Blain, Christophe. Los Hielos, Vol. 2. 2005. (SPA., Illus.). 48p. (gr. 8-17). 19.95 (978-1-59497-114-3(5)) Public Square Bks.

Bott, Elizabeth. Vinnie in France. Frosini, Guido & Cecchetti, Alessandra, illus. 2001. (Vinnie Ser.: Vol. 2). 54p. (YA). (gr. 5 up). 15.95 (978-0-9704678-1-2(8)) Pageturner Bks.

Bresnan, Lynn. Vincent: The Magnificent Cat. 2005. 213p. pap. 19.95 (978-1-4137-7459-7(8)) PublishAmerica, Inc.

Broome, Errol. Gracie & the Emperor. 2005. 160p. (J). (gr. 5-9). pap. 7.95 (978-1-55037-890-0(2)) Annick Pr., Ltd. CAN. *Dist:* Firefly Bks., Ltd.

Burn, Michael. Childhood at Oriol. 2005. 360p. pap. 16.95 (978-1-885586-32-2(9)) Turtle Point Pr.

Cadic, Olivier & Gheysens, Francois. Queen Margot: The Age of Innocence. Spear, Luke, tr. from FRE. Derenne, Juliette, illus. 2007. 48p. pap. 13.95 (***978-1-905460-10-6(4)***) CineBook GBR. *Dist:* Biblio Distribution.

Capodanno, Sophie & Neff, Lisi, illus. The Misadventures of Sophie. 2002. 163p. (J). (gr. 2 up). per. 9.95 (978-0-9719396-0-8(8)) Neff, Lisi A.

Christopher, John. The White Mountains: The Tripods Trilogy. l.t. ed. 2000. 168p. (J). 25.95 (978-0-7838-9170-5(9)) Thorndike Pr.

Cillero Goiriastuena, Javi. The Girl Who Swam to Euskadi: Euskadiraino Igerian Joan Zen Neska. Kurlansky, Mark, illus. 2005. (ENG & BAQ.). 32p. (J). pap. 18.95 (978-1-877802-54-6(9)) Univ. of Nevada, Reno-Center for Basque Studies.

Clements, Bruce. A Chapel of Thieves. 2002. 224p. (J). (gr. 6-9). 16.00 (978-0-374-37701-4(4) , Farrar, Straus & Giroux (BYR)) Farrar, Straus & Giroux.

The Count of Monte Cristo. 2000. (Illus.). (YA). 80p. per. 6.95 (978-1-56254-283-2(4) , SP2834); 48p. per. 17.95 (978-1-56254-284-9(2) , SP2842) Saddleback Educational Publishing.

Craig, Joe. Jimmy Coates: Target. 2007. 272p. (J). 15.99 (978-0-06-077266-6(2)); lib. bdg. 16.89 (978-0-06-077267-3(0)) HarperCollins Pubs.

DeRegnier, Elaine. The Leather Pouch, 4 vols. abr. ed. 2003. 159p. (YA). 9.95 (978-1-59453-021-0(1) , 1603) Airleaf Publishing & Bookselling.

Dumas, Alexandre. The Man in the Iron Mask. 1998. (978-0-606-13594-8(4)) Tandem Library Bks.

—The Three Musketeers. Nino, Alex, illus. 2nd ed. 1998. (Illustrated Classic Book Ser.). 61p. (J). (gr. 3 up). reprint ed. pap. 4.95 (978-1-56767-251-0(5)) Educational Insights, Inc.

—The Three Musketeers. Bair, Lowell, tr. Kidd, Thomas, illus. 1998. (Books of Wonder). 656p. (J). (gr. 4-7). 25.00 (978-0-688-14583-5(3)) HarperCollins Pubs.

—The Three Musketeers. (Classics Ser.). (Illus.). 56p. (J). 3.50 (978-0-7214-1753-0(1) , Dutton Juvenile) Penguin Group (USA) Inc.

—The Three Musketeers. Le Clercq, Jacques, tr. from ENG. 1999. (Modern Library Ser.). 624p. (J). (gr. 4-11). 24.95 (978-0-679-60332-0(8) , Modern Library) Random House Publishing Group.

—The Three Musketeers. 2001. (Saddleback Classics). (Illus.). (J). (978-0-606-21573-2(5)) Tandem Library Bks.

—Los Tres Mosqueteros. (SPA.). (J). 2.49 (978-968-890-125-0(3)) Edivision Compania Editorial, S.A. de C.V. MEX. *Dist:* Continental Bk. Co., Inc., Giron Bks.

Dumas, Alexandre & Mantell, Paul. The Man in the Iron Mask. abr. ed. 1998. (Stepping Stone Book Classic Ser.). (Illus.). 128p. (J). (gr. 2-4). pap. 3.99 (978-0-679-89433-9(0) , Random Hse. Bks. for Young Readers) Random Hse. Children's Bks.

Edwards, Julie Andrews. Little Bo in France. Cole, Henry, illus. 2002. 128p. (gr. 2-17). 19.49 (978-0-7868-2540-0(5)) Hyperion Pr.

—Little Bo in France: The Further Adventures of Bonnie Boadicea. Cole, Henry, illus. 2004. 117p. (J). (gr. k-4). reprint ed. 19.00 (978-0-7567-8163-7(9)) DIANE Publishing Co.

Eilenberg, Max. Beauty & the Beast. Barrett, Angela, illus. 2006. 64p. (J). (gr. 1-5). 17.99 (978-0-7636-3160-4(4)) Candlewick Pr.

Elliott, Laura Malone. Under a War-Torn Sky. 2001. 288p. (gr. 5-9). 16.49 (978-0-7868-2485-4(9)) Hyperion Bks. for Children.

Escaich, Bertrand & Roque, Caroline. The Rugger Boys: Why Are We Here Again? Spear, Luke, tr. from FRE. 2007. (Illus.). 52p. pap. 9.99 (***978-1-905460-33-5(3)***) CineBook GBR. *Dist:* Biblio Distribution.

Gascoyne, Val. Brittany Lifeline. 2005. (Illus.). 308p. (ps-7). pap. 17.95 (978-1-901130-34-8(7)) Survival Bks. GBR. *Dist:* National Bk. Network.

Giono, Jean. The Man Who Planted Trees. 2000. (Helen & Scott Nearing Titles Ser.). 8.95 (978-0-930031-78-7(4)) Chelsea Green Publishing.

—The Man Who Planted Trees. 2000. 74p. pap. 6.00 (978-1-57062-538-1(7)) Shambhala Pubns., Inc.

Gomez Ojea, Carmen. A Punta de Navaja. 2002. (Joven Coleccion Ser.). (SPA., Illus.). 140p. (978-84-89804-59-3(1)) Loguez Ediciones ESP. *Dist:* Lectorum Pubns., Inc.

Goscinny, René. Nicholas. Bell, Anthea, tr. from FRE. Sempé, Jean-Jacques, illus. 2005. 160p. 19.95 (978-0-7148-4482-4(9)) Phaidon Pr. GBR. *Dist:* Hachette Bk. Group.

Goscinny, René. Nicholas & the Gang. 2007. (Illus.). 120p. (J). 19.95 (***978-0-7148-4788-7(7)***) Phaidon Pr., Inc.

Hapka, Cathy. Pardon My French. 2005. (S. A. S. S. (Students Across the Seven Seas) Ser.). (Illus.). 224p. (YA). (gr. 7). pap. 6.99 (978-0-14-240459-1(4) , Puffin) Penguin Group (USA) Inc.

Hatton, Caroline K. Vero & Philippe. McDaniels, Preston, illus. 2001. 144p. (J). (gr. 3-7). 14.95 (978-0-8126-2940-8(X)) Cricket Bks.

Hayes, Clair W. The Boy Allies at Verdun. 2005. 28.95 (978-1-4218-0324-1(0)); 264p. pap. 13.95 (978-1-4218-0424-8(7)) 1st World Publishing, Inc. (1st World Library - Literary Society).

Hayes, W. Clair. The Boy Allies at Verdun or Saving France. 2006. 78.99 (***978-1-4280-0009-4(7)***); pap. 72.99 (***978-1-4280-0002-5(X)***) IndyPublish.com.

Henty, G. A. In the Reign of Terror: The Adventures of a Westminster Boy. 2004. reprint ed. pap. 26.95 (978-1-4191-2606-2(7)); pap. 1.99 (978-1-4192-2606-9(1)) Kessinger Publishing, LLC.

Hergé. Les Bijoux de la Castafiore. 1999. (Tintin Ser.).Tr. of Castafiore Emerald. (FRE.). (J). (gr. 4-7). 21.95 (978-2-203-00120-6(8)) Casterman, Editions FRA. *Dist:* Distribooks, Inc.

—The Castafiore Emerald. (Illus.). 62p. (J). 19.95 (978-0-8288-5016-2(X)) French & European Pubns., Inc.

Hite, Sid. The King of Slippery Falls. 2004. 224p. (J). pap. 16.95 (978-0-439-34257-5(0)) Scholastic, Inc.

Horowitz, Anthony. Eagle Strike. (Alex Rider Ser.: Bk. 4). 2006. 352p. (J). (gr. 7). pap. 7.99 (978-0-14-240613-7(9) , Puffin); 2004. (Illus.). 272p. (YA). (gr. 4). 17.99 (978-0-399-23979-3(0) , Philomel) Penguin Group (USA) Inc.

—Eagle Strike. 2003. 352p. (YA). pap. (978-0-7445-9057-9(4)) Walker & Co.

Hugo, Victor. Les Miserables. adapted ed. 2001. (Stepping Stone Bks.). (Illus.). (J). (978-0-606-21560-2(3)) Tandem Library Bks.

Hutchinson, Emily. Man in the Iron Mask. 2003. (gr. 7-12). lib. bdg. 15.25 (978-0-613-65745-7(4)) Tandem Library Bks.

Isom, Joan Shaddox. The First Starry Night. Isom, Joan Shaddox, illus. 2001. (Illus.). 32p. (J). (gr. k-7). pap. 6.95 (978-1-58089-027-4(X)) Charlesbridge Publishing, Inc.

—The First Starry Night. 2001. (978-0-606-20660-0(4)); lib. bdg. 15.25 (978-0-613-35118-8(5)) Tandem Library Bks.

Jinks, Catherine. Pagan in Exile. 2005. (Pagan Chronicles Ser.: Bk. 2). (Illus.). 336p. (J). (gr. 7 up). reprint ed. pap. 6.99 (978-0-7636-2691-4(0)) Candlewick Pr.

Knight, Joan MacPhail. Charlotte in Giverny. Rock, Victoria, ed. Sweet, Melissa, illus. 2000. 64p. (J). (gr. 4-7). 16.95 (978-0-8118-2383-8(0)) Chronicle Bks. LLC.

Kochka. The Boy Who Ate Stars. Adams, Sarah, tr. from FRE. 2006. 112p. (J). 12.95 (978-1-4169-0038-2(1)) Simon & Schuster Children's Publishing.

Lamensdorf, Len. The Crouching Dragon. 1999. (Will to Conquer Ser.: Bk. 1). (Illus.). 278p. (YA). (gr. 7-12). 19.95 (978-0-9669741-5-7(8)) SeaScape Pr., Ltd.

Lawrence, Iain. Lord of the Nutcracker Men. (gr. 5). 2003. (Illus.). 240p. (J). pap. 5.99 (978-0-440-41812-2(7) , Laurel Leaf); 2001. 224p. lib. bdg. 17.99 (978-0-385-90024-9(4) , Delacorte Bks. for Young Readers) Random Hse. Children's Bks.

—Lord of the Nutcracker Men. l.t. ed. 2002. 280p. (J). 24.95 (978-0-7862-4155-2(1)) Thomson Gale.

Leroux, Gaston. The Phantom of the Opera. l.t. ed. 1999. (Large Print Heritage Ser.). 420p. (J). (gr. 7-12). lib. bdg. 35.95 (978-1-58118-043-5(8) , 22512) LRS.

Maddox, Joseph & Maddox, Diana. See You in Hell. 2004. 215p. (YA). pap. 14.95 (978-0-7414-1872-2(X)) Infinity Publishing.

Mantell, Paul. The Man in the Iron Mask. 1998. (Bullseye Step into Classics Ser.). (J). (978-0-606-13965-6(6)) Tandem Library Bks.

Marcellino, Fred. I, Crocodile. Marcellino, Fred, illus. (Illus.). (J). (ps-3). 2002. 32p. pap. 7.99 (978-0-06-008859-0(1) , Harper Trophy); 1999. 40p. 19.99 (978-0-06-205168-4(7)) HarperCollins Pubs.

McLaren, Chesley. Zat Cat! A Haute Couture Tail. McLaren, Chesley, illus. 2002. (Illus.). 40p. (J). (ps-3). pap. 16.95 (978-0-439-27316-9(1) , Scholastic Pr.) Scholastic, Inc.

Metaxas, Eric. Puss in Boots. Le-Tan, Pierre, illus. 2007. (J). 25.65 (978-1-59961-311-6(5)) ABDO Publishing Co.

Morgenstern, Susie. Secret Letters from 0 To 10. 2000. (gr. 3-6). lib. bdg. 13.00 (978-0-613-28635-0(9)) Tandem Library Bks.

Morris, Gilbert. Amazon Quest. 2001. (gr. 5-8). lib. bdg. 21.10 (978-0-613-55559-3(7)) Tandem Library Bks.

Mosher, Richard. Zazoo. (YA). (gr. 7 up). 2001. 256p. tchr. ed. 16.00 (978-0-618-13534-9(0) , Clarion Bks.); 2004. 272p. reprint ed. pap. 6.99 (978-0-618-43904-1(8) , Graphia) Houghton Mifflin Co. Trade & Reference Div.

Mourlevat, Jean-Claude. The Pull of the Ocean. Maudet, Y., tr. from FRE. 2006. 208p. (gr. 7). (J). 13.95 (978-0-385-73348-9(8)); (YA). lib. bdg. 15.99 (978-0-385-90364-6(2)) Random Hse. Children's Bks. (Delacorte Bks. for Young Readers).

Nascimbene, Yan. Day in September. 2002. (J). (978-0-89812-328-9(3) , Creative Paperbacks) Creative Co., The.

Pirotta, Saviour & Marks, Alan. The Enchanted Gazelle. 2007. (J). (***978-1-59771-081-7(4)***) Sea-To-Sea Pubns.

—The Golden Slipper. 2007. (J). (***978-1-59771-077-0(6)***) Sea-To-Sea Pubns.

Polacco, Patricia. The Butterfly. Polacco, Patricia, illus. 2000. (Illus.). 48p. (J). (ps-3). 16.99 (978-0-399-23170-4(6) , Philomel) Penguin Group (USA) Inc.

Richardson, Kara. Simon & Barklee in France. 2000. (Another Country Calling Ser.: No. 1). (Illus.). 48p. (J). (gr. 2-5). per. 15.00 (978-0-9704661-0-5(2) , Explorer Media) Simon & Barklee, Inc./ExplorerMedia.

Sand, George. The Wings of Courage. Bloom, Margaret, tr. from FRE. Frasconi, Antonio, illus. 1998. 70p. (gr. 4-7). 12.95 (978-0-8076-1434-1(3)) Braziller, George Inc.

Scherer, Catherine W. Simon & Barklee in France - Fun-Book. 2001. (Another Country Calling Ser.). (Illus.). 32p. (J). (gr. 2-6). 7.50 (978-0-9704661-3-6(7) , Explorer Media) Simon & Barklee, Inc./ExplorerMedia.

Scimone, Diana. Adventures with Pawpaw: France. Wiedemer, Leah, illus. 2003. (Adventures with PawPaw Ser.). 32p. (J). 8.85 (978-0-9729507-1-8(0)) Peapod Publishing, Inc.

Sempé, Jean-Jacques & Goscinny, René. Nicholas. Bell, Anthea, tr. from FRE. rev. ed. 2005. (Illus.). 136p. (ps-7). 19.95 (978-0-7148-4529-6(9)) Phaidon Pr. GBR. *Dist:* Hachette Bk. Group.

Smith, Annie Laura. Will Paris Burn? Casteel, Kay, illus. 2004. (ENG.). (YA). mass mkt. 6.99 (978-0-9753367-4-8(6)) Onstage Publishing, LLC.

Spillebeen, Geert. Kipling's Choice. Edelstein, Terese, tr. 2007. 160p. (YA). (gr. 7 up). pap. 7.99 (***978-0-618-80035-3(2)*** , Graphia) Houghton Mifflin Co. Trade & Reference Div.

Spirn, Michele Sobel. The Bridges in Paris. 2000. (Going to Ser.). (Illus.). 121p. (J). (gr. 4-8). pap. 6.95 (978-1-893577-04-6(X)) Four Corners Publishing Co., Inc.

Sweeney, Joan. Suzette & the Puppy: A Story about Mary Cassatt. Wharton, Jennifer Heyd, illus. 2000. 28p. (J). (ps-3). 14.99 (978-0-7641-5294-8(7)) Barron's Educational Series, Inc.

Thompson, Kay & Knight, Hilary. Eloise in Paris. 1999. (Eloise Ser.). (Illus.). 72p. (J). (ps-3). 18.00 (978-0-689-82704-4(0)) Simon & Schuster Children's Publishing.

Tomlinson, Jill. Cat Wanted to Go Home - Picture Boo. Howard, Paul, illus. 2004. 32p. (J). (ps). pap. 9.99 (978-1-4052-1873-3(8)) Egmont Bks., Ltd. GBR. *Dist:* Independent Pubs. Group.

Waldron, Ann. The French Detection. 2000. 140p. (YA). (gr. 4-7). pap. 10.95 (978-0-595-00066-1(5)) iUniverse, Inc.

Wallace, Ian & De Brebeuf, Jean. The Huron Carol. Middleton, Jesse Edgar, tr. from FRE. 2006. (Illus.). 32p. 16.95 (978-0-88899-711-1(6)) Groundwood Bks. CAN. *Dist:* Perseus Distribution.

Watson, Sally. Lark. 2002. (J). pap. 12.95 (978-1-930009-65-3(8) , 800-691-7779) Image Cascade Publishing.

Wells, Rosemary. The Miraculous Tale of the Two Maries. Mathers, Petra, illus. 2006. 32p. (J). (gr. 1). 16.99 (978-0-670-05960-7(9) , Viking Juvenile) Penguin Group (USA) Inc.

Wyre, Yvonne. The Further Adventures of Cuthbert the Coal Lorry & all His Friends. 2007. (Illus.). 204p. pap. (***978-1-84401-801-7(6)***) Athena Pr.

Yorinks, Arthur. Harry & Lulu. braille ed. 2004. (Illus.). (J). (gr. k-3). spiral bd. (978-0-616-07249-3(X)); spiral bd. (978-0-616-07250-9(3)) Canadian National Institute for the Blind/Institut National Canadien pour les Aveugles.

—Harry & Lulu. Matje, Martin, illus. 2020. 32p. (J). pap. 4.99 (978-0-7868-1221-9(4)) Hyperion Paperbacks for Children.

Zellers, Michelle. Maya's Magic Carpet. 2006. (J). per. 11.95 (978-1-889743-48-6(8)) Robbie Dean Pr.

FRANCE—HISTORY

Bhote, Themina. Charlemagne: Life & Times of an Early Medieval Emperor. 2004. (Medieval Leaders Ser.). (Illus.). 112p. (J). lib. bdg. 31.95 (978-1-4042-0161-3(0)) Rosen Publishing Group, Inc., The.

Burleigh, Robert. Napoleon: The Story of the Little Corporal. 2007. (Illus.). 48p. (J). (gr. 4-7). 18.95 (978-0-8109-1378-3(X) , Abrams Bks. for Young Readers) Abrams, Harry N. , Inc.

Forest, James H. Silent As a Stone: Mother Maria of Paris & the Trash Can Rescue. Pancheshnaya, Dasha, illus. 2007. (J). 18.00 (***978-0-88141-314-4(3)***) St. Vladimir's Seminary Pr.

Greenblatt, Miriam. Charlemagne & the Early Middle Ages. 2002. (Rulers & Their Times Ser.). (Illus.). 80p. (J). (gr. 8-12). 29.93 (978-0-7614-1487-2(8) , Benchmark Bks.) Cavendish, Marshall Corp.

—Napoleon Bonaparte & Imperial France. 2005. (Rulers & Their Times Ser.). (Illus.). 96p. (J). (gr. 3-7). lib. bdg. (978-0-7614-1837-5(7) , Benchmark Bks.) Cavendish, Marshall Corp.

Hilliam, David. Joan of Arc: Heroine of France. 2004. (Medieval Leaders in Ancient History Ser.). (Illus.). 112p. (J). lib. bdg. 31.95 (978-1-4042-0164-4(5)) Rosen Publishing Group, Inc., The.

Hilliam, Paul. William the Conqueror: First Norman King of England. 2004. (Leaders of the Middle Ages Ser.). (Illus.). 112p. (J). lib. bdg. 31.95 (978-1-4042-0166-8(1)) Rosen Publishing Group, Inc., The.

Holmes, Burton. Paris. Schlesinger, Arthur M., Jr. & Isreal, Fred L., eds. 1999. (World 100 Years Ago Ser.). (Illus.). 144p. (YA). (gr. 4-7). lib. bdg. 29.95 (978-0-7910-4662-3(1) , Chelsea Hse.) Facts On File, Inc.

Horton, Casey. The French: From New France to Louisiana. 2006. (Illus.). 32p. (J). (gr. 4-8). reprint ed. 19.00 (978-0-7567-9910-6(4)) DIANE Publishing Co.

Israel, Fred L. & Schlesinger, Arthur M., Jr., eds. Paris. 1999. (World 100 Years Ago Ser.). (Illus.). 144p. (YA). (gr. 4-7). pap. 19.95 (978-0-7910-4663-0(X) , Chelsea Hse.) Facts On File, Inc.

Kacer, Kathy. Hiding Edith. 2006. (Illus.). 120p. (J). pap. 10.95 (978-1-897187-06-7(8)) Second Story Pr. CAN. *Dist:* Orca Bk. Pubs. USA.

Lace, William W. Joan of Arc & the Hundred Years' War in World History. 2003. (In World History Ser.). (Illus.). 128p. (J). (gr. 5-12). lib. bdg. 26.60 (978-0-7660-1938-6(1)) Enslow Pubs., Inc.

Mason, Anthony. Versailles. 2005. (Places in History Ser.). (Illus.). 48p. (J). pap. (978-0-8368-5822-8(0)); lib. bdg. 30.00 (978-0-8368-5815-0(8)) Stevens, Gareth Inc. (World Almanac Library).

Matthews, Elizabeth. Different Like Coco. 2007. (Illus.). (J). (***978-1-4287-3582-8(8)***) Candlewick Pr.

McGowen, Tom. D-Day. 2004. (Cornerstones of Freedom Ser.). (J). 26.00 (978-0-516-24245-3(8) , Children's Pr.) Scholastic Library Publishing.

Nickles, Greg. France the Culture. 2000. (gr. 3-6). lib. bdg. 16.40 (978-0-613-27835-5(6)) Tandem Library Bks.

Olson, Tod. In the Line of Fire: A Story about D-Day. 2002. (Read 180 Ser.). (Illus.). 56p. (J). (978-0-439-12352-5(6)) Scholastic, Inc.

Parker, Lewis K. French Colonies in the Americas. 2003. (Reading Power Ser.). (Illus.). 24p. (J). lib. bdg. 17.25 (978-0-8239-6473-4(6) , PowerKids Pr.) Rosen Publishing Group, Inc., The.

Plain, Nancy. Eleanor of Aquitaine & the High Middle Ages. 2005. (Rulers & Their Times Ser.). (Illus.). 96p. (J). (gr. 3-7). lib. bdg. 29.93 (978-0-7614-1834-4(2) , Benchmark Bks.) Cavendish, Marshall Corp.

Polisar, Patti. Inside France's DGSE: General Directorate for External Security. 2005. (Inside the World's Most Famous Intelligence Agencies Ser.). (Illus.). 64p. (YA). (gr. 7-12). lib. bdg. 26.50 (978-0-8239-3814-8(X)) Rosen Publishing Group, Inc., The.

Rawlins, Carol B. The Seine River. 2001. (World of Water Ser.). (Illus.). 64p. (J). (gr. 5-7). 25.50 (978-0-531-11853-5(3) , Watts, Franklin) Scholastic Library Publishing.

Ross, Nancy Wilson. Joan of Arc. 2003. vii, 182p. pap. 29.00 (978-0-7581-5017-2(2)) Textbook Pubs.

Rossi, Renzo. Paris. 2003. (Great Cities Through the Ages Ser.). (Illus.). 44p. (J). 18.95 (978-1-59270-004-2(7)) Enchanted Lion Bks., LLC.

Ruelle, Karen Gray & DeSaix, Deborah Durland. Hidden on the Mountain: Stories of Children Sheltered from the Nazis in Le Chambon. 2006. (Illus.). 272p. (J). (gr. 5 up). 24.95 (978-0-8234-1928-9(2)) Holiday Hse., Inc.

Sapet, Kerrily. Eleanor of Aquitaine: Medieval Queen. 2006. (European Queens Ser.). (Illus.). 176p. (J). (gr. 6-12). 26.95 (978-1-931798-90-7(7)) Reynolds, Morgan Inc.

Schlesinger, Arthur M., Jr., intro. Ancient World Leaders. (Illus.). (gr. 6-12). lib. bdg. (978-0-7910-8056-6(0) , Chelsea Hse.) Facts On File, Inc.

Schoyer-Brooks, Polly. Beyond the Myth: The Story of Joan of Arc. 1999. (J). 15.60 (978-0-606-17364-3(1)) Tandem Library Bks.

Sidinger, Jim. Eternal Companions: Faces of the Pere Lachaise, Paris. 2003. (Illus.). 48p. pap. 24.95 (978-0-9729414-0-2(1) , SIDJAM-0305) Catslip Arts, LLC.

Somervill, Barbara A. Catherine de Medici: The Power Behind the French Throne. 2006. (Signature Lives Ser.). (Illus.). 112p. (J) (gr 5-7). 30.60 (978 0 7565-1581-2(5)) Compass Point Bks.

Stanley, Diane. Joan of Arc. 2002. (gr. 3-6). lib. bdg. 15.25 (978-0-613-44855-0(3)) Tandem Library Bks.

Tagliaferro, Linda. Palace of Versailles: France's Royal Jewel. 2005. (Castles, Palaces, & Tombs Ser.). (J). lib. bdg. 25.27 (978-1-59716-003-2(2)) Bearport Publishing Co., Inc.

Thompson, Paul B. Joan of Arc: Warrior Saint of France. 2007. (Rulers of the Middle Ages Ser.). (Illus.). 160p. (YA). (gr. 7-9). lib. bdg. 34.60 (***978-0-7660-2716-9(3)***) Enslow Pubs., Inc.

Whiting, Jim. The Life & Times of Charlemagne. 2005. (Biography from Ancient Civilizations Ser.). (Illus.). 48p. (J). (gr. 4-8). lib. bdg. 29.95 (978-1-58415-346-7(6)) Mitchell Lane Pubs., Inc.

—The Life & Times of Joan of Arc. 2005. (Biography from Ancient Civilizations Ser.). (Illus.). 48p. (J). (gr. 4-8). lib. bdg. 29.95 (978-1-58415-345-0(8)) Mitchell Lane Pubs., Inc.

Wilkinson, Philip. Joan of Arc: The Teenager Who Saved Her Nation. 2007. (World History Biographies Ser.). (Illus.). 64p. (J). (gr. 3-7). 17.95 (978-1-4263-0116-2(2)); lib. bdg. 27.90 (978-1-4263-0117-9(0)) National Geographic Society. (National Geographic Children's Bks.).

FRANCE—HISTORY—BIOGRAPHY

Allport, Alan. Jacques Chirac. 2007. (Modern World Leaders Ser.). 112p. (J). (gr. 6-12). 30.00 (***978-0-7910-9265-1(8)*** , Chelsea Hse.) Facts On File, Inc.

Brewster, Hugh. The Other Mozart: The Life of the Famous Chevalier de Saint-George. Velasquez, Eric, illus. 2006. 48p. (J). (gr. k-5). 18.95 (978-0-8109-5720-6(5) , Abrams Bks. for Young Readers) Abrams, Harry N. , Inc.

Hilliam, David. Eleanor of Aquitaine: The Richest Queen in Medieval Europe. 2004. (Leaders of the Middle Ages Ser.). (Illus.). 112p. (J). lib. bdg. 31.95 (978-1-4042-0162-0(9)) Rosen Publishing Group, Inc., The.

Kathleen, Kudlinski. Dk Biography Joan of Arc Hc. 2008. 128p. 14.99 (***978-0-7566-3527-5(6)***) Dorling Kindersley Publishing, Inc.

Koestler-Grack, Rachel A. Eleanor of Aquitaine: Heroine of the Middle Ages. 2005. (Makers of the Middle Ages & Renaissance Ser.). (Illus.). 158p. (J). (gr. 4-8). lib. bdg. 30.00 (978-0-7910-8633-9(X) , Chelsea Hse.) Facts On File, Inc.

Kudlinski, Kathleen. Dk Biography Joan of Arc Pb. 2008. 128p. pap. 4.99 (***978-0-7566-3526-8(8)***) Dorling Kindersley Publishing, Inc.

Landau, Elaine. Napoleon Bonaparte. 2006. (Illus.). 112p. (J). 27.93 (978-0-8225-3420-4(7) , Twenty-First Century Bks.) Lerner Publishing Group.

Roberts, Russell. The Life & Times of Nostradamus. 2007. (Biography from Ancient Civilizations Ser.). 48p. (J). lib. bdg. 29.95 (***978-1-58415-544-7(2)***) Mitchell Lane Pubs., Inc.

Ungerer, Tomi. Tomi: A Childhood under the Nazis. 1998. (Illus.). 175p. (YA). (gr. 6 up). 29.95 (978-1-57098-163-0(9) , Rinehart, Roberts International) Rinehart, Roberts Pubs.

Wilkinson, Philip. Joan of Arc: The Teenager Who Saved Her Nation. 2007. (World History Biographies Ser.). (Illus.). 64p. (J). (gr. 3-7). 17.95 (978-1-4263-0116-2(2)); lib. bdg. 27.90 (978-1-4263-0117-9(0)) National Geographic Society. (National Geographic Children's Bks.).

Williams, Jay. Joan of Arc: Warrior Saint. 2007. (Sterling Point Bks.). 144p. (YA). (gr. 7 up). pap. 6.95 (***978-1-4027-5120-2(6)***) Sterling Publishing Co., Inc.

FRANCE—HISTORY—FICTION

Alcock, Deborah. Done & Dared in Old France. 2002. (Huguenot Inheritance Ser.: Vol. 7). (Illus.). 286p. (J). (978-1-894666-03-9(8)) Inheritance Pubns.

Bennett, Cherie & Gottesfeld, Jeff. Anne Frank & Me. 2002. 291p. (YA). pap. 6.99 (978-0-698-11973-4(8) , Putnam Juvenile) Penguin Group (USA) Inc.

Cadic, Oliver. Queen Margot. 2007. (Illus.). 52p. pap. 13.95 (***978-1-905460-19-9(8)***) CineBook GBR. *Dist:* Biblio Distribution.

Casanova, Mary. Curse of a Winter Moon. 2000. (gr. 5-8). lib. bdg. 14.15 (978-0-613-68226-8(2)) Tandem Library Bks.

—Curse of the Winter Moon. 2000. 144p. (gr. 3-7). 16.49 (978-0-7868-2475-5(1)) Hyperion Bks. for Children.

—Curse of the Winter Moon. 2002. (Illus.). 144p. (gr. 5-9). pap. 5.99 (978-0-7868-1602-6(3)) Hyperion Paperbacks for Children.

Chandler, Pauline. Warrior Girl: A Novel of Joan of Arc. 2006. 368p. (J). 16.99 (978-0-06-084102-7(8)); lib. bdg. 17.89 (978-0-06-084103-4(6)) HarperCollins Pubs.

Crichton, Michael. Timeline. 2000. xii, 496p. (gr. 7-12). lib. bdg. 16.45 (978-0-613-33633-8(X)) Tandem Library Bks.

Distribooks Inc. Staff. Asterix Bind-Ups: Asterix & Friends. 1998. (Asterix Ser.). (Illus.). 240p. (J). (978-0-340-72755-3(1) , Hodder & Stoughton) Hodder General Publishing Division.

Dumas, Alexandre. Classic Starts: the Three Musketeers. Akib, Jamel, illus. 2007. (Classic Starts Ser.). 160p. (J). 4.95 (978-1-4027-3695-7(9)) Sterling Publishing Co., Inc.

—The Count of Monte Cristo. abr. ed. 2001. (gr. 7-12). lib. bdg. 15.25 (978-0-613-43810-0(8)) Tandem Library Bks.

—Man in the Iron Mask. Lynch, Brendan, illus. 2005. (Great Illustrated Classics Ser.). 238p. (J). (gr. 3-8). 21.35 (978-1-59679-247-0(7) , ABDO & Daughters) ABDO Publishing Co.

—The Man in the Iron Mask. Ho, Oliver & Howell, Troy, illus. 2008. (Classic Starts Ser.). 160p. (J). 5.95 (***978-1-4027-4579-9(6)***) Sterling Publishing Co., Inc.

The Man in the Iron Mask. 2006. (Illus.). 61p. (J). lib. bdg. 30.77 (***978-1-4242-1332-0(0)***) Fitzgerald Bks.

—The Man in the Iron Mask. abr. ed. 1998. 118p. (J). (ps-7). per. 11.80 (978-0-613-11836-1(7)) Tandem Library Bks.

—The Three Musketeers. 2002. (Great Illustrated Classics Ser.). (Illus.). 240p. (J). (gr. 3-8). 21.35 (978-1-57765-803-0(5) , ABDO & Daughters) ABDO Publishing Co.

—The Three Musketeers. 2004. reprint ed. pap. 1.99 (978-1-4192-8527-1(0)) Kessinger Publishing, LLC.

—The Three Musketeers. 2006. 656p. (gr. 12). pap. 6.95 (978-0-451-53003-5(9) , Signet Classics) Penguin Group (USA) Inc.

—The Three Musketeers. abr. ed. 2001. (gr. 7-12). lib. bdg. 15.25 (978-0-613-43901-5(5)) Tandem Library Bks.

Dumas, Alexandre & Pipe, Jim. The Man in the Iron Mask. Gelev, Penko, illus. 2007. (Graphic Classics Ser.). 48p. (J). (gr. 3 up). 15.99 (***978-0-7641-6055-4(9)***); pap. 8.99 (***978-0-7641-3779-2(4)***) Barron's Educational Series, Inc.

Edwards, Julie Andrews & Hamilton, Emma Walton. Dragon: Hound of Honor. 2004. 192p. (J). (gr. 4 up). 16.99 (978-0-06-057119-1(5)); lib. bdg. 17.89 (978-0-06-057120-7(9)) HarperCollins Pubs. (Julie Andrews Collection).

Everett-Green, Evelyn. A Heroine of France. 2007. 188p. pap. 14.99 (***978-1-4264-7060-8(6)***); 206p. pap. 15.99 (***978-1-4264-7136-0(X)***) BiblioBazaar.

Farenhorst, Christine. Wings like a Dove: The Courage of Queen Jeanne D'Albret. 2006. (Chosen Daughters Ser.). 208p. (J). per. 11.99 (978-0-87552-642-3(X)) P & R Publishing.

Fernandez Ardavín, Luis, et al. The Three Musketeers. 2006. (J). lib. bdg. (***978-0-8368-7664-2(4)***) Stevens, Gareth Inc.

Floyer, Edith S. The Young Huguenots. 1998. (Huguenots Inheritance Ser.). (J). (978-0-921100-65-2(5)) Inheritance Pubns.

Friedman, Michael Jan. Hunchdog of Notre Dame. l.t. ed. 1999. (Adventures of Wishbone Ser.: No. 5). (Illus.). 139p. (J). (gr. 4 up). lib. bdg. 22.60 (978-0-8368-2301-1(X)) Stevens, Gareth Inc.

Goscinny, René. Absolutely Asterix. 1998. (Illus.). 204p. (J). 24.95 (978-0-340-72756-0(X) , Hodder & Stoughton) Hodder General Publishing Division GBR. *Dist:* Trafalgar Square Publishing.

—Asterix & Caesar's Gift. Uderzo, Albert, illus. 2005. 48p. 12.95 (978-0-7528-6645-1(1)) Orion Bks. Ltd. GBR. *Dist:* Sterling Publishing Co., Inc.

—Asterix & Cleopatra. Uderzo, Albert, illus. 2004. 48p. 12.95 (978-0-7528-6606-2(0)) Orion Bks. Ltd. GBR. *Dist:* Sterling Publishing Co., Inc.

—Asterix & the Banquet. Uderzo, Albert, illus. 2004. 48p. 12.95 (978-0-7528-6608-6(7)) Orion Bks. Ltd. GBR. *Dist:* Sterling Publishing Co., Inc.

—Asterix & the Big Fight. Uderzo, Albert, illus. 2004. 48p. 12.95 (978-0-7528-6616-1(8)) Orion Bks. Ltd. GBR. *Dist:* Sterling Publishing Co., Inc.

—Asterix & the Cauldron. Uderzo, Albert, illus. 2004. 48p. 12.95 (978-0-7528-6628-4(1)) Orion Bks. Ltd. GBR. *Dist:* Sterling Publishing Co., Inc.

—Asterix & the Great Crossing. Uderzo, Albert, illus. 2005. 48p. 12.95 (978-0-7528-6647-5(8)) Orion Bks. Ltd. GBR. *Dist:* Sterling Publishing Co., Inc.

—Asterix & the Normans. (Illus.). (J). pap. 9.95 (978-0-02-497290-3(8)) International Language Centre.

—Asterix & the Normans. Uderzo, Albert, illus. 2004. 48p. 12.95 (978-0-7528-6622-2(2)) Orion Bks. Ltd. GBR. *Dist:* Sterling Publishing Co., Inc.

—Asterix at the Olympic Games. Uderzo, Albert, illus. 2004. 48p. 12.95 (978-0-7528-6626-0(5)) Orion Bks. Ltd. GBR. *Dist:* Sterling Publishing Co., Inc.

—Asterix aux Jeux Olympiques. (FRE.). (J). pap. 21.95 (***978-2-01-210144-9(5)***) Hachette Groupe Livre FRA. *Dist:* Distribooks, Inc.

—Asterix et Cleopatre. (FRE.). (J). pap. 21.95 (***978-2-01-210138-8(0)***); (Illus.). 21.95 (978-2-01-210111-1(9)) Hachette Groupe Livre FRA. *Dist:* Distribooks, Inc.

—Asterix in Britain. Uderzo, Albert, illus. 2004. 48p. 12.95 (978-0-7528-6618-5(4)) Orion Bks. Ltd. GBR. *Dist:* Sterling Publishing Co., Inc.

—Asterix in Spain. Uderzo, Albert, illus. 2004. 48p. 12.95 (978-0-7528-6630-7(3)) Orion Bks. Ltd. GBR. *Dist:* Sterling Publishing Co., Inc.

—Asterix in Switzerland. Uderzo, Albert, illus. 2004. 48p. 12.95 (978-0-7528-6634-5(6)) Orion Bks. Ltd. GBR. *Dist:* Sterling Publishing Co., Inc.

—Asterix the Gaul. Uderzo, Albert, illus. 2004. 48p. 12.95 (978-0-7528-6604-8(4)) Orion Bks. Ltd. GBR. *Dist:* Sterling Publishing Co., Inc.

—Asterix the Gladiator. Uderzo, Albert, illus. 2004. 48p. 12.95 (978-0-7528-6610-9(9)) Orion Bks. Ltd. GBR. *Dist:* Sterling Publishing Co., Inc.

Goscinny, René & Uderzo, Albert. Asterix & Cleopatra. Uderzo, Albert, illus. 2004. (Illus.). 48p. pap. 9.95 (978-0-7528-6607-9(9)) Orion Bks. Ltd. GBR. *Dist:* Sterling Publishing Co., Inc.

—Asterix & the Big Fight. Uderzo, Albert, illus. 2004. (Illus.). 48p. pap. 9.95 (978-0-7528-6617-8(6)) Orion Bks. Ltd. GBR. *Dist:* Sterling Publishing Co., Inc.

—Asterix & the Golden Sickle. 2004. (Illus.). 48p. 12.95 (978-0-7528-6612-3(5)) Orion Bks. Ltd. GBR. *Dist:* Sterling Publishing Co., Inc.

—Asterix & the Laurel Wreath. Uderzo, Albert, illus. 2005. (Illus.). 48p. 12.95 (978-0-7528-6636-9(2)) Orion Bks. Ltd. GBR. *Dist:* Sterling Publishing Co., Inc.

—Asterix & the Soothsayer. Uderzo, Albert, illus. 2005. (Illus.). 48p. 12.95 (978-0-7528-6641-3(9)) Orion Bks. Ltd. GBR. *Dist:* Sterling Publishing Co., Inc.

—Asterix in Britain. Uderzo, Albert, illus. 2004. (Illus.). 48p. pap. 9.95 (978-0-7528-6619-2(2)) Orion Bks. Ltd. GBR. *Dist:* Sterling Publishing Co., Inc.

Goscinny, René & Uderzo, M. Asterix el Galo. (SPA., Illus.). (J). (gr. 7-10). 24.95 (978-0-8288-4933-3(1)) French & European Pubns., Inc.

—Streit um Asterix. (GER., Illus.). (J). 24.95 (978-0-8288-4906-7(4)) French & European Pubns., Inc.

Gregory, Kristiana. Eleanor: Crown Jewel of Aquitaine: France 1136. 2002. (Royal Diaries Ser.). (Illus.). 192p. (gr. 4-9). pap. 10.95 (978-0-439-16484-9(2) , Scholastic Pr.) Scholastic, Inc.

Hartnett, Sonya. The Silver Donkey. Powers, Don, illus. 272p. (J). (gr. 5). 2007. pap. 7.99 (***978-0-7636-3681-4(9)***); 2006. 15.99 (978-0-7636-2937-3(5)) Candlewick Pr.

—The Silver Donkey. Spudvilas, Anne, illus. 2004. viii, 193p. (J). (978-0-670-04240-1(4) , Viking Adult) Penguin Group (USA) Inc.

Hendry, Frances. Quest for a Queen: The Lark. 2006. pap. (***978-1-905665-04-4(0)***) Pollinger In Print.

Ho, Oliver & Dumas, Alexandre. The Three Musketeers. Akib, Jamel, illus. 2007. (Classic Starts Ser.). 151p. (J). (***978-1-4287-4206-2(9)***) Sterling Publishing Co., Inc.

Hugo, Victor. The Hunchback of Notre- Dame. Famig, Jon L., illus. 1998. (Illustrated Classic Book Ser.). 61p. (J). (gr. 3 up). pap. 4.95 (978-1-56767-247-3(7)) Educational Insights, Inc.

—The Hunchback of Notre- Dame. unabr. ed. 1998. (Wordsworth Classics Ser.). (YA). (gr. 6-12). 5.27 (978-0-89061-068-8(1) , R0681WW) Jamestown.

—The Hunchback of Notre- Dame. (Young Collector's Illustrated Classics Ser.). (Illus.). 192p. (J). (gr. 3-7). 9.95 (978-1-56156-458-3(3)) Kidsbooks, Inc.

E
F
G

—Hunchback of Notre Dame. 2002. (Great Illustrated Classics Ser.). (Illus.). 240p. (J). (gr. 3-8). 21.35 (978-1-57765-813-9(2) , ABDO & Daughters) ABDO Publishing Co.

—The Hunchback of Notre Dame: Level 2. Solimene, Laura, ed. 1999. (Illus.). 72p. (YA). (gr. 4 up). act. bk. ed. 9.95 (978-1-55576-324-4(3) , EDCTR-208B) AV Concepts Corp.

—The Hunchback of Notre Dame: With a Discussion of Compassion. Butterfield, Ned, tr. Butterfield, Ned, illus. 2003. (Values in Action Illustrated Classics Ser.). (J). (978-1-59203-049-1(1)) Learning Challenge, Inc.

The Hunchback of Notre Dame. (Read-Along Ser.). (J). 7.99 incl. audio (978-1-55723-992-1(4)) Walt Disney Records.

Jennings, Patrick. The Wolving Time. 2003. 208p. (J). pap. 15.95 (978-0-439-39555-7(0)) Scholastic, Inc.

Jinks, Catherine. Pagan's Scribe. 2006. (Pagan Chronicles Ser.: Bk. 4). 368p. (YA). (gr. 7). pap. 6.99 (978-0-7636-2973-1(1)) Candlewick Pr.

—Pagan's Scribe. De Seve, Peter, illus. 2005. (Pagan Chronicles Ser.: Bk. 4). 368p. (J). (gr. 7 up). 16.99 (978-0-7636-2022-6(X)) Candlewick Pr.

—Pagan's Vows. 2005. (Pagan Chronicles Ser.: Bk. 3). 336p. (YA). (gr. 7 up). pap. 6.99 (978-0-7636-2754-6(2)) Candlewick Pr.

—Pagan's Vows. De Seve, Peter, illus. 2004. (Pagan Chronicles Ser.: Bk. 3). 336p. (J). (gr. 7 up). 16.99 (978-0-7636-2021-9(1)) Candlewick Pr.

Lasky, Kathryn. Marie Antoinette: Princess of Versailles, Austria-France, 1769. 2000. (Royal Diaries Ser.). (Illus.). 240p. (J). (gr. 4-8). pap. 10.95 (978-0-439-07666-1(8)) Scholastic, Inc.

—Mary, Queen of Scots: Queen Without a Country, France 1553. 2002. (Royal Diaries Ser.). (Illus.). 112p. (J). (gr. 4-8). pap. 10.95 (978-0-439-19404-4(0) , Scholastic Pr.) Scholastic, Inc.

Litowinsky, Olga. The Pawloined Paper. l.t. ed. 1999. (Adventures of Wishbone Ser.: No. 11). (Illus.). (J). (gr. 4 up). lib. bdg. 22.60 (978-0-8368-2589-3(6)) Stevens, Gareth Inc.

Malot, Hector & Crewe-Jones, Florence. Nobody's Boy: Companion Story to Nobody's Girl. Gooch, Thelma & Gruelle, Johnny, illus. 2006. 237p. (J). pap. (978-1-894666-75-6(5)) Inheritance Pubns.

—Nobody's Girl: Companion Story to Nobody's Boy. Gooch, Thelma, illus. 2006. 220p. (J). pap. (978-1-894666-76-3(3)) Inheritance Pubns.

The Man in the Iron Mask. 2002. (Illus.). 80p. (YA). per. 6.95 (978-1-56254-527-7(2) , SP5272) Saddleback Educational Publishing.

The Man in the Iron Mask Study Guide. 2002. (Illus.). 48p. (YA). per. 17.95 (978-1-56254-528-4(0) , SP5280) Saddleback Educational Publishing.

McCaughrean, Geraldine. Cyrano. 2006. (Illus.). 128p. (J). (gr. 7 up). 16.00 (978-0-15-205805-0(2)) Harcourt Children's Bks.

Rostand, Edmond, as told by. Cyrano de Bergerac. Rostand, Edmond, . 8.97 (978-0-673-58340-6(6)) Addison-Wesley Longman, Inc.

—Cyrano de Bergerac. Rostand, Edmond, . 1999. (J). 11.95 (978-1-56137-622-3(1)) Novel Units, Inc.

Sauerwein, Leigh. Song for Eloise. 2004. 136p. (YA). 15.95 (978-1-886910-90-4(1) , Lemniscaat) Boyds Mills Pr.

Selznick, Brian. The Invention of Hugo Cabret. Selznick, Brian, illus. 2007. (Illus.). 544p. (J). (gr. 4-7). pap. 22.99 (978-0-439-81378-5(6) , Scholastic Pr.) Scholastic, Inc.

Skurzynski, Gloria. The Minstrel in the Tower. Heller, Julek, illus. 2004. (Stepping Stone Bks.). 64p. (J). (gr. 4-7). pap. 3.99 (978-0-394-89598-7(3) , Random Hse. Bks. for Young Readers) Random Hse. Children's Bks.

Stead, Richard. With Marlborough to Malplaquet. 2006. pap. ***978-1-4068-3012-5(7))** Echo Library.

Strang, Herbert. With Marlborough to Malplaquet. 2006. pap. (***978-1-4068-3126-9(3))** Echo Library.

The Three Musketeers Study Guide. 2000. (Illus.). 48p. (YA). per. 17.95 (978-1-56254-298-6(2) , SP2982) Saddleback Educational Publishing.

Tucker, Charlotte Maria. Driven into Exile: A Story of the Huguenots. 2003. (Huguenot Inheritance Ser.: Vol. 5). (Illus.). 141p. (J). (978-0-921100-66-9(3)) Inheritance Pubns.

Van der Jagt, A. The Secret Mission, No. 2. 2001. (Huguenots Inheritance Ser.: Vol. 2). (Illus.). 187p. (J). (978-0-921100-18-8(3)) Inheritance Pubns.

Vogiel, Eva. Facing the Music. 2003. 284p. 19.95 (978-1-880582-94-7(5)) Judaica Pr., Inc., The.

Watson, Pat. The Scarlet Pimpernel. Robbins, Dawn Michelle, ed. 2000. (YA). 9.95 (978-1-58130-638-5(5)); 11.95 (978-1-58130-639-2(3)) Novel Units, Inc.

Weil, Sylvie. My Guardian Angel. 2004. 208p. (J). (gr. 4-7). pap. 16.95 (978-0-439-57681-9(4) , Levine, Arthur A. Bks.) Scholastic, Inc.

FRANCE—HISTORY—TO 1328—FICTION

Weil, Sylvie. My Guardian Angel. 2007. 208p. (J). pap. 5.99 (***978-0-439-57682-6(2)** , Scholastic Paperbacks) Scholastic, Inc.

FRANCE—HISTORY—HOUSE OF VALOIS, 1328-1589

see also Hundred Years' War, 1339-1453

Hodges, Margaret. Joan of Arc: The Lily Maid. Rayevsky, Robert, illus. 1999. 32p. (J). (gr. 4-6). tchr. ed. 16.95 (978-0-8234-1424-6(8)) Holiday Hse., Inc.

Stanley, Diane. Joan of Arc. Stanley, Diane, illus. 1998. (Illus.). 48p. (J). (gr. 3 up). 16.89 (978-0-688-14330-5(X)) HarperCollins Pubs.

FRANCE—HISTORY—HOUSE OF VALOIS, 1328-1589—FICTION

Brouwer, Sigmund. The Angel & the Sword: A Supernatural Adventure. 2005. (Guardian Angel Ser.). 172p. (J). (ps-7). pap. 7.99 (978-0-7369-0293-9(7)) Harvest Hse. Pubs.

FRANCE—HISTORY—BOURBONS, 1589-1789

Barter, James E. The Palace of Versailles. 1998. (Building History Ser.). (Illus.). 112p. (YA). (gr. 6-9). 27.45 (978-1-56006-433-6(1) , Lucent Bks.) Thomson Gale.

Plain, Nancy. Louis XVI, Marie Antoinette & the French Revolution. 2001. (Rulers & Their Times Ser.). (Illus.). 80p. (J). (gr. 6 up). lib. bdg. 29.93 (978-0-7614-1029-4(5) , Benchmark Bks.) Cavendish, Marshall Corp.

FRANCE—HISTORY—REVOLUTION, 1789-1799

Barber, Nicola. The French Revolution. 2004. (Questioning History Ser.). (J). lib. bdg. 28.50 (978-1-58340-440-9(6)) Smart Apple Media.

Clare, John D. The French Revolution, 1789-94. 2002. (Illus.). 48p. pap. 23.50 (***978-0-340-78951-3(4)** , Hodder Murray) Hodder Education GBR. *Dist:* Trans-Atlantic Pubns., Inc.

Connolly, Sean. The French Revolution. 2003. (Illus.). 56p. (J). pap. (978-1-4034-3637-5(1)); (gr. 6-8). lib. bdg. 27.07 (978-1-4034-0973-7(0)) Heinemann Library.

Daynes, Katie. Marie Antoinette. Mistry, Nilesh, illus. 2005. 64p. (J). 8.95 (978-0-7945-1049-7(3) , Usborne) EDC Publishing.

Dunn, John M. The French Revolution: The Fall of the Monarchy. 2002. (History's Great Defeats Ser.). (Illus.). 112p. (J). (gr. 6-9). 29.95 (978-1-59018-064-8(X) , Lucent Bks.) Thomson Gale.

French Revolution: Dba. 2003. spiral bd. 16.95 (978-1-56004-110-8(2)) Social Studies Schl. Service.

Gilbert, Adrian. The French Revolution. (Illus.). 32p. (YA). (gr. 4 up). lib. bdg. 27.10 (978-1-932889-27-7(2)) Sea-To-Sea Pubns.

Henderson, Harry. The Age of Napoleon. 1998. (Illus.). 112p. (YA). (gr. 4-12). 27.45 (978-1-56006-319-3(X) , LML00902-177711, Lucent Bks.) Thomson Gale.

Jones, Peter. The French Revolution: 1787-1804. 2003. (Seminar Studies in History Ser.). (Illus.). 176p. (C). pap. 20.00 (978-0-582-77289-2(3)) Longman Publishing.

MacDonald, Fiona. Marie Antoinette. 2000. (World in the Time of... Ser.). (Illus.). 48p. (J). (gr. 4-7). 22.95 (978-0-7910-6034-6(9) , Chelsea Hse.) Facts On File, Inc.

McGowen, Tom. Robespierre & the French Revolution in World History. 2000. (In World History Ser.). (Illus.). 128p. (YA). (gr. 5-12). lib. bdg. 26.60 (978-0-7660-1397-1(9)) Enslow Pubs., Inc.

McNeil, Niki, et al. HOCPP 1060 the French Revolution. 2006. spiral bd. 20.00 (***978-1-60308-060-6(0))** In the Hands of a Child.

Otfinoski, Steven. Triumph & Terror: The French Revolution. 1999. (Illus.). 128p. (YA). (gr. 6-9). lib. bdg. 24.95 (978-0-7351-0213-2(9)) Replica Bks.

Pipe, Jim. You Wouldn't Want to Be an Aristocrat in the French Revolution! A Horrible Time in Paris You'd Rather Avoid. Antram, David, illus. 2007. (You Wouldn't Want to... : History of the World Ser.). 32p. (J). 29.00 (***978-0-531-18745-6(4));** (gr. 2-5). pap. 9.95 (***978-0-531-13927-1(1))** Scholastic Library Publishing. (Watts, Franklin).

Ross, Stewart. The Fall of the Bastille: Revolution in France. 2001. (Illus.). 32p. (J). (gr. 5-7). lib. bdg. 24.22 (978-1-58810-076-4(6)) Heinemann Library.

—The French Revolution. 2002. (Events & Outcomes Ser.). (Illus.). 80p. (J). lib. bdg. 31.42 (978-0-7398-5798-4(3)) Raintree.

Stewart, Gail B. The French Revolution. 2005. (People at the Center of Ser.). (Illus.). 48p. (J). (gr. 7-10). lib. bdg. 24.95 (978-1-56711-919-0(0) , Blackbirch Pr., Inc.) Thomson Gale.

Whittock, Martyn J. The French Revolution, 1789-94. 2002. (Illus.). 48p. pap. 23.50 (***978-0-340-78950-6(6)** , Hodder Murray) Hodder Education GBR. *Dist:* Trans-Atlantic Pubns., Inc.

FRANCE—HISTORY—REVOLUTION, 1789-1799—BIOGRAPHY

DiConsiglio, John. Robespierre: Master of the Guillotine. 2007. (Wicked Historytrade; Ser.). 128p. (J). spiral bd. 30.00 (***978-0-531-18554-4(0)** , Children's Pr.) Scholastic Library Publishing.

FRANCE—HISTORY—REVOLUTION, 1789-1799—FICTION

Barkan, Joanne. A Tale of Two Sitters. l.t. ed. 1999. (Adventures of Wishbone Ser.: No. 9). (Illus.). 144p. (J). (gr. 4 up). lib. bdg. 22.60 (978-0-8368-2305-9(2)) Stevens, Gareth Inc.

Bradley, Kimberly Brubaker. The Lacemaker & the Princess. 2007. 208p. (J). (gr. 3-7). 16.99 (978-1-4169-1920-9(1) , McElderry, Margaret K.) Simon & Schuster Children's Publishing.

Coatsworth, Elizabeth Jane. The Fair American. Sewell, Helen, illus. 2005. 137p. (J). (***978-1-883937-85-0(X))** Bethlehem Bks.

Dickens, Charles. A Tale of Two Cities. Lynch, Brendan, illus. 2002. (Great Illustrated Classics Ser.). 240p. (J). (gr. 3-8). 21.35 (978-1-57765-802-3(7) , ABDO & Daughters) ABDO Publishing Co.

A Tale of Two Cities: Abridged. (ARA., Illus.). 48p. (J). 12.00 (978-0-86685-627-0(7)) International Bk. Ctr., Inc.

Watson, Pat. The Scarlet Pimpernel. Robbins, Dawn Michelle, ed. 2000. (YA). 9.95 (978-1-58130-638-5(5)); 11.95 (978-1-58130-639-2(3)) Novel Units, Inc.

Williams, Maiya. The Golden Hour. 2006. 288p. (J). (gr. 5-10). pap. 5.95 (978-0-8109-9216-0(7)) Abrams, Harry N., Inc.

FRANCE—HISTORY—1799-1914—FICTION

Dumas, Alexandre. The Count of Monte Cristo. 2002. (Great Illustrated Classics Ser.). (Illus.). 240p. (J). (gr. 3-8). 21.35 (978-1-57765-684-5(9) , ABDO & Daughters) ABDO Publishing Co.

FRANCE—HISTORY—CONSULATE AND FIRST EMPIRE, 1799-1815

Westwell, Ian. Revolutionary & Napoleonic Wars. 1999. (History of Warfare Ser.). (Illus.). 80p. (YA). (gr. 7-12). lib. bdg. 29.97 (978-0-8172-5446-9(3)) Raintree.

FRANCE—HISTORY—GERMAN OCCUPATION, 1940-1945

Draper, Allison Stark. Pastor André Trocme: Spiritual Leader of the French Village, Le Chambon. 2005. (Holocaust Biographies Ser.). (Illus.). 112p. (YA). (gr. 7-12). lib. bdg. 26.50 (978-0-8239-3378-5(4)) Rosen Publishing Group, Inc., The.

FRANCE—HISTORY—GERMAN OCCUPATION, 1940-1945—FICTION

Barry, Rick. Gunner's Run. 2007. (YA). (***978-1-59166-761-2(5))** Jones, Bob Univ. Pr.

Bradley, Kimberly Brubaker. For Freedom: The Story of a French Spy. 2005. 192p. (J). (gr. 5-9). pap. 5.50 (978-0-440-41831-3(3) , Laurel Leaf) Random Hse. Children's Bks.

Burnford, Sheila. Bel Ria: Dog of War. 2006. 256p. (J). (gr. 5). 17.95 (978-1-59017-211-7(6) , NYR Children's Collection) New York Review of Bks., Inc., The.

Elliott, Laura Malone. Under a War-Torn Sky. 2001. (gr. 7-12). lib. bdg. 14.15 (978-0-613-69092-8(3)) Tandem Library Bks.

Graber, Janet. Resistance. 2005. 144p. (YA). 15.95 (978-0-7614-5214-0(1)) Cavendish, Marshall Corp.

Maguire, Gregory. The Good Liar. 1999. 144p. (J). (gr. 5-9). tchr. ed. 15.00 (978-0-395-90697-2(0) , Clarion Bks.) Houghton Mifflin Co. Trade & Reference Div.

—Good Liar. 2002. (gr. 3-6). lib. bdg. 14.10 (978-0-613-46219-8(X)) Tandem Library Bks.

Matas, Carol & Matas, Carol. Greater Than Angels. 1999. 177p. lib. bdg. 11.64 (978-0-606-17196-0(7)) Tandem Library Bks.

Polacco, Patricia. The Butterfly. Polacco, Patricia, illus. 2000. (Illus.). 48p. (J). (ps-3). 16.99 (978-0-399-23170-4(6) , Philomel) Penguin Group (USA) Inc.

Sachs, Marilyn. Lost in America. rev. ed. 2005. 160p. (J). 16.95 (978-1-59643-040-2(0)) Roaring Brook Pr.

FRANCE—SOCIAL LIFE AND CUSTOMS

Fisher, Teresa. A Flavor of France. 1999. (Food & Festivals Ser.). (Illus.). 32p. (J). (gr. 1-4). lib. bdg. 25.69 (978-0-8172-5550-3(8)) Raintree.

—France. Johnstone, Andy, photos by. 2005. (Letters from Around the World Ser.). (Illus.). 32p. (J). (gr. 3-7). lib. bdg. (978-1-84234-250-3(9) , Cherrytree Books) Evans Publishing Group.

Ganeri, Anita & Wright, Rachel. France. 2005. (Illus.). 32p. (J). (978-1-932889-91-8(4)) Sea-To-Sea Pubns.

Gofen, Ethel C. & Reymann, Blandine Pengili. France. 2nd ed. 2003. (Illus.). 144p. (gr. 5 up). lib. bdg. 37.07 (978-0-7614-1498-8(3) , Cavendish, Marshall Reference Bks.) Cavendish, Marshall Corp.

Kranz, Nickie & Compass Point Books Staff. Teens in France. 2006. (Global Connections Ser.). (Illus.). 96p. (J). (gr. 5-7). 31.93 (978-0-7565-2062-5(2)) Compass Point Bks.

Mitchell, Alycen. France. 2002. (Cultures & Costumes Ser.). (Illus.). 64p. (J). (gr. 7 up). lib. bdg. (978-1-59084-442-7(4) , 1247999) Mason Crest Pubs.

Nickles, Greg. France - The Culture. 2000. (Lands, Peoples & Cultures Ser.). (Illus.). 32p. (J). (gr. 4-5). (978-0-86505-243-7(3)); pap. (978-0-86505-323-6(5)) Crabtree Publishing Co.

—France - The Land. 2000. (Lands, Peoples & Cultures Ser.). (Illus.). 32p. (J). (gr. 4-5). (978-0-86505-241-3(7)); pap. (978-0-86505-321-2(9)) Crabtree Publishing Co.

—France - The People. 2000. (Lands, Peoples & Cultures Ser.). (Illus.). 32p. (J). (gr. 4-5). (978-0-86505-242-0(5)); pap. (978-0-86505-322-9(7)) Crabtree Publishing Co.

—France - the People. 2000. (gr. 3-6). lib. bdg. 16.40 (978-0-613-27837-9(2)) Tandem Library Bks.

Parks, Peggy J. Foods of France. 2005. (Taste of Culture Ser.). (Illus.). 64p. (J). (gr. 4-8). lib. bdg. 27.45 (978-0-7377-3032-6(3) , Greenhaven Pr., Inc.) Thomson Gale.

Plante, Charles. A French Alphabet Book Of 1814: For Alfred Bourdier de Beauregard, Created by his uncle Arnaud at the Chateau Debeaumoont de Beauregard. 2007. (Illus.). 114p. 24.95 (***978-0-8478-3010-7(1))** Rizzoli International Pubns., Inc.

Scarry, Huck. Life on a Farm: A Sketchbook. (J). 16.95 (978-0-945912-32-3(3)) Pippin Pr.

Tartaglino, Anna Cazzini & Torcellan, Nanda. Medieval Paris. 2001. (Journey to the Past Ser.). (Illus.). 56p. (J). (gr. 6-8). lib. bdg. 27.12 (978-0-7398-1956-2(9)) Raintree.

Thoennes, Kristin. Christmas in France. 1998. (Christmas Around the World Ser.). (Illus.). 24p. (J). (gr. 2-3). 18.60 (978-0-7368-0088-4(3) , Bridgestone Bks.) Capstone Pr., Inc.

Thomson, Ruth. France. Hampton, David, photos by. 2007. (Living In- Ser.). (Illus.). 32p. (J). (***978-1-59771-042-8(3)** , 1268838) Sea-To-Sea Pubns.

Waldee, Lynne Marie. Cooking the French Way. 2nd rev. exp. ed. 2002. (Easy Menu Ethnic Cookbooks). (Illus.). 72p. (J). (gr. 5-12). 25.26 (978-0-8225-4106-6(8)) Lerner Publishing Group.

FRANCIS, OF ASSISI, SAINT, 1182-1226

Billington, Rachel. The Life of Saint Francis. (Illus.). 48p. pap. 11.99 (978-0-340-71427-0(1) , Hodder & Stoughton) Hodder General Publishing Division GBR. *Dist:* Trafalgar Square Publishing.

De Roma, Giuseppino. Francis of Assisi. (Illus.). 31p. 7.95 (978-1-875570-64-5(0)) St Pauls Pubns. AUS. *Dist:* Alba Hse.

Egielski, Richard. Saint Francis & the Wolf. Egielski, Richard, illus. 2005. (Illus.). 40p. (J). (gr. 1-3). 15.99 (978-0-06-623870-8(6) , Geringer, Laura Book) HarperCollins Pubs.

—Saint Francis & the Wolf of Gubbio. Egielski, Richard, illus. 2005. (Illus.). 40p. (J). (gr. 1-3). lib. bdg. 16.89 (978-0-06-623871-5(4) , Geringer, Laura Book) HarperCollins Pubs.

Francis of Assisi: Activities & Coloring Fun for Children. 2001. (Illus.). 72p. (J). (gr. 4-7). pap. 9.95 (978-0-86716-458-9(1)) St. Anthony Messenger Pr. & Franciscan Communications.

Frazier, Jo F. Saints for Today's Youth. Ueyeda, Brad, Jr., illus. 1998. (Saints Alive Ser.: Vol. 2). 64p. (Orig.). (J). (gr. 3-6). pap. 4.00 (978-0-9650704-1-6(7)) Saints Alive Pr.

Gray, Tricia. The Wondrous Adventures of St. Francis of Assisi. rev. ed. 2003. (Illus.). 164p. (J). pap. 14.95 (978-0-86716-480-0(8)) St. Anthony Messenger Pr. & Franciscan Communications.

Kennedy, Robert F., Jr. Saint Francis of Assisi: A Life of Joy. Nolan, Dennis, illus. 2005. 32p. (J). (gr. k-17). 18.99 (978-0-7868-1875-4(1)) Hyperion Bks. for Children.

Le Tord, Bijou, illus. Saint Francis Sings to Brother Sun: A Celebration of His Kinship with Nature. gif. ed. 2005. 64p. (J). (gr. 3 up). 18.99 (978-0-7636-1563-5(3)) Candlewick Pr.

Vintrou, Francoise. Saint Francis of Assisi: God's Gentle Knight. Morson, Caroline, tr. from FRE. Curelli, Augusta, illus. 1998. (Along the Paths of the Gospel Ser.). 72p. (J). (gr. 2-5). 6.95 (978-0-8198-7006-3(4) , 332-334) Pauline Bks. & Media.

Visconti, Guido. Clare & Francis. Landmann, Bimba, illus. 2004. 40p. 20.00 (978-0-8028-5269-4(6)) Eerdmans, William B. Publishing Co.

Walsh, Mary C. Saint Francis Celebrates Christmas. Caswell, Helen Rayburn, illus. 1998. 32p. (ps-3). 15.95 (978-0-8294-1112-6(7)) Loyola Pr.

FRANCIS, OF ASSISI, SAINT, 1182-1226—FICTION

Gibfried, Diane Friemoth. Brother Juniper. So, Meilo, illus. 2006. 32p. (J). (ps-k). 16.00 (978-0-618-54361-8(9) , Clarion Bks.) Houghton Mifflin Co. Trade & Reference Div.

Langton, Jane. Saint Francis & the Wolf. Plume, Ilse, illus. 2007. 32p. (J). 16.95 (***978-1-56792-320-9(8))** Godine, David R. Pub.

Mora, Pat. The Song of Francis & the Animals. Frampton, David, illus. 2005. 32p. (J). (ps-2). 16.00 (978-0-8028-5253-3(X)) Eerdmans, William B. Publishing Co.

O'Dell, Scott. The Road to Damietta. 2004. 320p. (YA). (gr. 7). pap. 6.99 (978-0-618-49493-4(6) , Graphia) Houghton Mifflin Co. Trade & Reference Div.

Strasser, Myrna. Story of the Nativity. 2005. (J). (978-0-310-70890-2(7)) Zonderkidz.

Wintz, Jack. St. Francis in San Francisco. Baron, Kathy, illus. 2001. 32p. (J). (gr. k-3). 12.95 (978-0-8091-6684-8(4) , 6684-4) Paulist Pr.

FRANCISCANS

Anderson, Dale. The California Missions. 2002. (Landmark Events in American History Ser.). (Illus.). 48p. (J). (gr. 5 up). lib. bdg. 30.00 (978-0-8368-5339-1(3)); pap. 14.60 (978-0-8368-5353-7(9)) Stevens, Gareth Inc. (World Almanac Library).

Binns, Tristan Boyer. Mission San Juan Capistrano. 2002. (Visiting the Past Ser.). (Illus.). 32p. (J). (gr. 5-7). pap. 6.95 (978-1-58810-410-6(9) , 91183) Heinemann Library.

—San Juan Capistrano. 2001. (Visiting the Past Ser.). (Illus.). 32p. (J). (gr. 5-7). lib. bdg. 24.22 (978-1-58810-272-0(6)) Heinemann Library.

Ditchfield, Christin. Spanish Missions. 2006. 48p. (gr. 3-5). (YA). pap. 6.95 (978-0-516-21746-8(1)); (Illus.). (J). 25.00 (978-0-516-22834-1(X)) Scholastic Library Publishing. (Children's Pr.).

Heinrichs, Ann. The California Missions. 2002. (We the People Ser.). (Illus.). 48p. (J). (gr. 4 up). lib. bdg. 22.60 (978-0-7565-0208-9(X)) Compass Point Bks.

Herrera, Matthew D. History Guide to Old Mission San Luis Obispo de Tolosa. 2003. (Illus.). 77p. 9.95 (978-0-9723720-1-5(6)) Tixlini Scriptorium, Inc.

Keremitsis, Eileen. Life in a California Mission. 2002. (Way People Live Ser.). (Illus.). 112p. (J). (gr. 7-10). 29.95 (978-1-59018-159-1(X) , Lucent Bks.) Thomson Gale.

Scarbrough, Mary Hertz. A California Mission. 2005. (Daily Life Ser.). (J). (978-0-7377-3090-6(0) , Greenhaven Pr., Inc.) Thomson Gale.

Williams, Jack S. & Davis, Thomas L. Padres of the California Mission Frontier. 2004. (People of the California Missions Ser.). (Illus.). 64p. (J). lib. bdg. 25.50 (978-0-8239-6283-9(0) , PowerKids Pr.) Rosen Publishing Group, Inc., The.

FRANK, ANNE, 1929-1945

Abramson, Ann. Who Was Anne Frank? Harrison, Nancy, illus. 2007. (Who Was... ? Ser.). 112p. (J). pap. 4.99 (978-0-448-44482-6(8) , Grosset & Dunlap) Penguin Group (USA) Inc.

Alagna, Magdalena. Anne Frank: Young Voice of the Holocaust. 2005. (Holocaust Biographies Ser.). (Illus.). 112p. (YA). (gr. 7-12). lib. bdg. 26.50 (978-0-8239-3373-0(3)) Rosen Publishing Group, Inc., The.

Ashby, Ruth. Anne Frank: Young Diarist. 2005. 186p. (J). lib. bdg. 18.46 (***978-1-4242-2208-7(7)***) Fitzgerald Bks.

—Anne Frank: Young Diarist. 2005. (Childhood of World Figures Ser.). 192p. (J). pap. 5.99 (978-0-689-87468-0(5) , Aladdin) Simon & Schuster Children's Publishing.

Brown, Jonatha A. Anne Frank. 2004. (People to Know Ser.). (J). pap. (978-0-8368-4316-3(9)); (Illus.). 24p. (J). pap. (978-0-8368-4358-3(4)); (Illus.). 24p. (YA). lib. bdg. 19.33 (978-0-8368-4309-5(6)) Stevens, Gareth Inc.

—Anne Frank. Acosta, Tatiana & Gutierrez, Guillermo, trs. 2004. (Gente Que Hay Que Conocer Ser.). (SPA., Illus.). 24p. (J). lib. bdg. 19.33 (978-0-8368-4351-4(7)) Stevens, Gareth Inc.

—Anne Frank. 2003. (Trailblazers of the Modern World Ser.). (Illus.). 48p. (J). (gr. 5 up). lib. bdg. 30.00 (978-0-8368-5090-1(4)); pap. 10.95 (978-0-8368-5250-9(8)) Stevens, Gareth Inc. (World Almanac Library).

Davidson, Susanna. Anne Frank - Internet Referenced. Goransky, Natacha, illus. 2006. 64p. (J). 8.99 (978-0-7945-1259-0(3) , Usborne) EDC Publishing.

Denenberg, Barry. Portrait of Anne Frank & Her Family. 2005. (Shadow Life Ser.). (Illus.). 240p. (J). pap. 16.95 (978-0-439-41678-8(7)) Scholastic, Inc.

Dunn, Joeming W. & Dunn, Ben. Anne Frank. Dunn, Joeming W. & Dunn, Ben, illus. 2007. (Bio-Graphics Ser.). (Illus.). 32p. (J). (gr. 3-6). lib. bdg. 27.07 (***978-1-60270-065-9(6)*** , Graphic Planet) Magic Wagon.

Frank, Anne. Anne Frank: The Diary of a Young Girl. adapted ed. pap., tchr. ed. 4.95 (978-0-8359-0138-3(6)) Globe Fearon Educational Publishing.

Goff, Elizabeth Hudson & Brown, Jonatha A. Anne Frank. 2006. (Graphic Biographies (World Almanac Library (Firm))). (Illus.). (J). pap. (978-0-8368-6248-5(1)); 32p. lib. bdg. 26.00 (978-0-8368-6196-9(5)) Stevens, Gareth Inc. (World Almanac Library).

Heims, Neil. Reading the Diary of Anne Frank. 2005. (Engaged Reader Ser.). (Illus.). 81p. (J). (gr. 4-8). lib. bdg. 25.00 (978-0-7910-8829-6(4) , Chelsea Hse.) Facts On File, Inc.

Hermann, Spring. Anne Frank: Hope in the Shadows of the Holocaust. 2005. (Holocaust Heroes & Nazi Criminals Ser.). (Illus.). 160p. (J). (gr. 6-12). lib. bdg. 27.93 (978-0-7660-2531-8(4)) Enslow Pubs., Inc.

Johnson, Emma. Anne Frank. 2003. (Twentieth Century History Makers Ser.). (Illus.). 112p. (J). lib. bdg. 32.85 (978-0-7398-5261-3(2)) Raintree.

Koestler-Grack, Rachel A. The Story of Anne Frank. 2003. (Breakthrough Biographies Ser.). (Illus.). 32p. (gr. 3-5). 23.00 (978-0-7910-7311-7(4) , Chelsea Hse.) Facts On File, Inc.

Kramer, Ann. Anne Frank: The Young Writer Who Told the World Her Story. 2007. (World History Biographies Ser.). (Illus.). 64p. (J). (gr. 3-7). 17.95 (978-1-4263-0004-2(2)); lib. bdg. 27.90 (978-1-4263-0005-9(0)) National Geographic Society. (National Geographic Children's Bks.).

Lee, Carol Ann. Anne Frank & the Children of the Holocaust. 256p. (gr. 4). 2008. (J). 6.99 (***978-0-14-241069-1(1)*** , Puffin); 2006. (YA). 16.99 (978-0-670-06107-5(7) , Viking Juvenile) Penguin Group (USA) Inc.

Lewis, Brenda Ralph. Anne Frank Biography, Vol. 3. 2001. (Readers Ser.: Vol. 3). (Illus.). 48p. (J). (ps-3). pap. 3.99 (978-0-7894-7379-0(8)) Dorling Kindersley Publishing, Inc.

—Anne Frank Biography. 2001. (Eyewitness Readers Ser.). (Illus.). (J). (978-0-606-21469-8(0)) Tandem Library Bks.

—Story of Anne Frank. 2001. (gr. k-3). lib. bdg. 11.80 (978-0-613-35242-0(4)) Tandem Library Bks.

Lewis, Brenda Ralph & Dorling Kindersley Publishing Staff. Anne Frank Biography. 2001. (Readers Ser.: Vol. 3). (Illus.). 48p. (J). (ps-3). 14.99 (978-0-7894-7380-6(1)) Dorling Kindersley Publishing, Inc.

Maarsen, Jacqueline Van. A Friend Called Anne: One Girl's Story of War, Peace & a Unique Friendship with Anne Frank. 2005. (Illus.). 176p. (J). (gr. 3). 15.99 (978-0-670-05958-4(7) , Viking Juvenile) Penguin Group (USA) Inc.

Mara, Wil. Anne Frank. 2006. (Illus.). 31p. (978-0-516-29841-2(0)) Children's Pr., Ltd.

Metzger, Lois. Yours, Anne: The Life of Anne Frank. 2004. (Illus.). 97p. (J). (978-0-439-59099-0(X)) Scholastic, Inc.

Poole, Josephine. Anne Frank. Barrett, Angela, illus. 2005. 40p. (J). (gr. 5). lib. bdg. 19.99 (978-0-375-93242-7(9)); 17.95 (978-0-375-83242-0(4)) Random Hse. Children's Bks. (Knopf Bks. for Young Readers).

Pressler, Mirjam. Anne Frank: A Hidden Life. 2001. (Illus.). 192p. (gr. 7 up). pap. 7.99 (978-0-14-131226-2(2) , Puffin) Penguin Group (USA) Inc.

—Anne Frank: A Hidden Life. Bell, Anthea, tr. 2001. (Illus.). 176p. (J). (ps-7). lib. bdg. 16.45 (978-0-613-44185-8(0)) Tandem Library Bks.

—Anne Frank: A Hidden Life. 2001. (Illus.). (J). 14.64 (978-0-606-21038-6(5)) Tandem Library Bks.

Ross, Stewart. The Story of Anne Frank. 2001. (Illus.). 48p. (J). lib. bdg. 24.25 (978-1-930643-20-8(9)) Chrysalis Education.

Saunders, Nicholas. The Life of Anne Frank. 2006. (Stories from History Ser.). 48p. (J). 14.95 (978-0-7696-4714-2(6)); pap. 6.95 (978-0-7696-4695-4(6)) School Specialty Publishing.

Senker, Cath. Anne Frank: Voice of Hope. 2001. (Famous Lives Ser.). (Illus.). 48p. (J). (gr. 3-7). lib. bdg. 27.12 (978-0-8172-5719-4(5)) Raintree.

Trailblazers of the Modern World: Louis Armstrong; Anne Frank; Martin Luther King, Jr.; Theodore Roosevelt; Gloria Steinem; The Wright Brothers, 6 bks. 2003. (Illus.). (J). (gr. 5 up). lib. bdg. 175.60 (978-0-8368-5088-8(2) , World Almanac Library) Stevens, Gareth Inc.

van Maarsen, Jacqueline & Lee, Carol Ann. A Friend Called Anne. 2007. 176p. (J). (gr. 3). pap. 6.99 (978-0-14-240719-6(4) , Puffin) Penguin Group (USA) Inc.

Venable, Alan. The Story of Anne Frank. Ham, Jeff, illus. 2001. (J). (gr. 5-6). 65.00 incl. audio, cd-rom (978-1-58702-398-9(9)) Johnston, Don Inc.

—The Story of Anne Frank. Stemach, Jerry, ed. Ham, Jeff, illus. l.t. ed. 2001. (J). (gr. 5-6). 50.00 (978-1-58702-520-4(5)) Johnston, Don Inc.

Whiting, Jim. Anne Frank. 2007. (What's So Great About...? Ser.). (J). lib. bdg. 25.70 (***978-1-58415-581-2(7)***) Mitchell Lane Pubs., Inc.

Woog, Adam. Anne Frank. 2004. (Heroes & Villains Ser.). (Illus.). 112p. (J). 29.95 (978-1-59018-349-6(5) , Lucent Bks.) Thomson Gale.

Woronoff, Kristen. Anne Frank: Voice of Hope. 2002. (Famous Women Juniors Ser.). (Illus.). 32p. (J). (gr. 3-5). 23.70 (978-1-56711-586-4(1) , Blackbirch Pr., Inc.) Thomson Gale.

FRANKENSTEIN (FICTITIOUS CHARACTER)—FICTION

Dadey, Debbie & Jones, Marcia Thornton. Frankenstein Doesn't Start Food Fights. Gurney, John Steven, illus. 2003. (Adventures of the Bailey School Kids Ser.: No. 47). 80p. (J). 3.99 (978-0-439-55999-7(5) , Scholastic Paperbacks) Scholastic, Inc.

—Frankenstein Doesn't Start Food Fights. 2003. (gr. 3-6). lib. bdg. 11.80 (978-0-613-82754-6(6)) Tandem Library Bks.

Dalmatian Press Staff, adapted by. Frankenstein. 2003. (Spot the Classics Ser.). 178p. (J). 4.99 (978-1-4037-0051-3(6)) Dalmatian Pr.

Frankenstein: Picture Book. 2002. 32p. (J). 16.99 (978-0-7868-0798-7(9)) Disney Pr.

Shelley, Mary Wollstonecraft. Frankenstein. Pablo Marcos Studio Staff, illus. 2002. (Great Illustrated Classics Ser.). 240p. (J). (gr. 3-8). 21.35 (978-1-57765-686-9(5) , ABDO & Daughters) ABDO Publishing Co.

—Frankenstein. Stevens, David, ed. 1998. (Illus.). 286p. pap. 13.00 (978-0-521-58702-0(6)) Cambridge Univ. Pr.

—Frankenstein. Jones, Barry, illus. 2004. (Paperback Classics Ser.). 144p. (J). pap. 4.95 (978-0-7945-0090-0(0) , Usborne) EDC Publishing.

—Frankenstein. 2001. (Fast Track Classics Ser.). (Illus.). 46p. pap. 9.99 (978-0-237-52280-3(2) , Evans Brothers, Limited) Evans Publishing Group GBR. *Dist:* Independent Pubs. Group.

—Frankenstein. (J). 9.95 (978-1-56156-309-8(9)) Kidsbooks, Inc.

—Frankenstein. Barr, Ken, illus. 2005. (Stepping Stone Bks.). 96p. (J). (gr. 3-5). pap. 3.99 (978-0-394-84827-3(6) , Random Hse. Bks. for Young Readers) Random Hse. Children's Bks.

—Frankenstein. 2000. (gr. 3-6). lib. bdg. 11.80 (978-0-613-89266-7(6)); 2000. xxviii, 212p. (gr. 7-12). lib. bdg. 11.80 (978-0-8085-1955-3(7)); 1999. (Illus.). (J). 13.75 (978-0-606-21551-0(4)) Tandem Library Bks.

—Frankenstein. Munteanu, Anca, ed. 2001. (Illus.). 240p. pap., stu. ed. 9.99 (978-0-7645-8726-9(9) , Cliff Notes) Wiley, John & Sons, Inc.

—Frankenstein. Hegarty, Carol, ed. 1998. (Classics Ser.: Set I). (Illus.). 80p. (YA). (gr. 5-12). 6.95 (978-1-56254-264-1(8) , SP2648) Saddleback Educational Publishing.

—Frankenstein. abr. ed. 1999. (gr. 7-12). lib. bdg. 15.25 (978-0-613-32586-8(9)) Tandem Library Bks.

—Frankenstein: Or the Modern Prometheus. Joseph, M. K., ed. 1998. (Oxford World's Classics Ser.). 260p. (gr. 7 up). 7.95 (978-0-19-283487-4(8)) Oxford Univ. Pr., Inc.

Shelley, Mary Wollstonecraft. Frankenstein. Munch, Philippe, tr. 2002. (SPA., Illus.). 284p. (J). 29.95 (978-84-348-5617-2(4)) SM Ediciones ESP. *Dist:* AIMS International Bks., Inc.

Weinberg, Larry. Frankenstein. 2000. (Golden Star Reader Ser.). (Illus.). (J). 10.79 (978-0-606-18854-8(1)) Tandem Library Bks.

FRANKLIN (FICTITIOUS CHARACTER : BOURGEOIS)—FICTION

Bourgeois, Paulette. Adventures with Franklin. 2000. (Franklin Color & Activity Bks.). (Illus.). 32p. (J). (ps-3). pap. (978-0-7666-0492-6(6)) Modern Publishing.

—Benjamin et Sa Petite Soeur. ed. 2004. Tr. of Franklin's Baby Sister. (FRE., Illus.). (J). (gr. k-3). spiral bd. (978-0-616-14597-5(7)) Canadian National Institute for the Blind/Institut National Canadien pour les Aveugles.

—El Club Secreto de Franklin. Clark, Brenda, illus. 2001. (Franklin Ser.). (SPA.). (J). (ps-3). 10.95 (978-1-930332-14-0(9) , LC6913) Lectorum Pubns., Inc.

—El Club Secreto de Franklin. Varela, Alejandra Lopez, tr. from ENG. Clark, Brenda, illus. 1998. (Franklin Ser.). (SPA.). 32p. (J). (ps-3). pap. 5.95 (978-1-880507-50-6(1) , LC8146) Lectorum Pubns., Inc.

—El Diente de Franklin. Vareta, Alejandra Lopez, tr. Clark, Brenda, illus. 2001. (Franklin Ser.). (SPA.). (J). (ps-3). pap. 5.95 (978-1-880507-88-9(9) , LC1651); ring bd. 10.95 (978-1-880507-89-6(7) , LC1736) Lectorum Pubns., Inc.

—El Diente de Franklin. 2001. (Franklin Ser.). (SPA., Illus.). (J). 12.75 (978-0-606-21171-0(3)) Tandem Library Bks.

—Finders Keepers for Franklin. Clark, Brenda, illus. 1998. (Franklin the Turtle Ser.). 32p. (J). (gr. k-3). (978-1-55074-368-5(6)) Kids Can Pr., Ltd.

—Franklin & Friends. 2000. (Franklin Color & Activity Bks.). (Illus.). 96p. (J). (ps-3). pap. (978-0-7666-0495-7(0)) Modern Publishing.

—Franklin & Harriet. Clark, Brenda, illus. unabr. ed. 2004. (Franklin the Turtle Ser.). 32p. (J). (gr. k-3). (978-1-55074-874-1(2)) Kids Can Pr., Ltd.

—Franklin & Harriet. Clark, Brenda, illus. 2001. (Franklin Ser.). 32p. (J). (ps-3). pap. 4.50 (978-0-439-20381-4(3)) Scholastic, Inc.

—Franklin & the Hero. Clark, Brenda, illus. 2004. (Franklin TV StoryBks.). 32p. (J). (gr. k-3). (978-1-55074-827-7(0)) Kids Can Pr., Ltd.

—Franklin & the Hero. Clark, Brenda, illus. 2000. (Franklin TV-Tie In Ser.). 32p. (J). (ps-3). pap. 4.50 (978-0-439-20380-7(5)) Scholastic, Inc.

—Franklin & the Hero. 2000. (Franklin TV Storybook Ser.). (J). (ps-3). 11.30 (978-0-606-20057-8(6)) Tandem Library Bks.

—Franklin & the Thunderstorm. Clark, Brenda, illus. 1998. (Franklin the Turtle Ser.). 32p. (J). (gr. k-3). (978-1-55074-403-3(8)) Kids Can Pr., Ltd.

—Franklin & the Thunderstorm. Clark, Brenda, illus. 1998. (Franklin Ser.). 32p. (J). (ps-3). pap. 4.99 (978-0-590-02635-2(6) , Cartwheel Bks.) Scholastic, Inc.

—Franklin & the Thunderstorm. Clark, Brenda, illus. 1998. (Franklin Ser.). (J). (ps-3). 11.30 (978-0-606-13403-3(4)); lib. bdg. 12.40 (978-0-613-07814-6(4)) Tandem Library Bks.

—Franklin & the Tooth Fairy. 1999. (Franklin Ser.). (Illus.). 180p. (J). (ps-3). (978-1-55074-793-5(2)) Kids Can Pr., Ltd.

—Franklin en el Museo. Varela, Alejandra Lopez, tr. Clark, Brenda, illus. (SPA.). (J). (gr. k-2). ring bd. 10.95 (978-1-930332-12-6(2) , LC30199) Lectorum Pubns., Inc.

—Franklin en el Museo. Clark, Brenda, illus. 1999. (Franklin Ser.). (SPA.). (J). (ps-3). pap. 5.95 (978-1-880507-57-5(9) , LC2801) Lectorum Pubns., Inc.

—Franklin en el Museo. 1999. (Franklin Ser.). (SPA.). (J). (ps-3). 12.75 (978-0-606-17007-9(3)) Tandem Library Bks.

—Franklin en la Oscuridad. Varela, Alejandra Lopez, tr. Clark, Brenda, illus. 2001. (SPA.). (J). ring bd. 10.95 (978-1-880507-87-2(0) , LC3565) Lectorum Pubns., Inc.

—Franklin Es un Mandon. Varela, Alejandra Lopez, tr. Clark, Brenda, illus. (SPA.). ring bd. 10.95 (978-1-930332-16-4(5) , LC6564) Lectorum Pubns., Inc.

—Franklin Es un Mandon. Lopez Varela, Alejandra, tr. from ENG. Clark, Brenda, illus. 1998. (Franklin Ser.). (SPA.). 32p. (J). (ps-3). pap. 5.95 (978-1-880507-42-1(0) , LC7795) Lectorum Pubns., Inc.

—Franklin Forgets. 2000. (Franklin TV Storybook Ser.). (J). (ps-3). 11.30 (978-0-606-20058-5(4)) Tandem Library Bks.

—Franklin Goes to Day Camp: A Story & Activity Book. Clark, Brenda, illus. (Franklin Ser.). 74p. (J). (ps-3). (978-1-55074-372-2(4)) Kids Can Pr., Ltd.

—Franklin Goes to Day Camp: A Story & Activity Book. Clark, Brenda, illus. 1998. (Franklin Ser.). (J). (ps-3). pap. 4.50 (978-0-590-06828-4(8) , Cartwheel Bks.) Scholastic, Inc.

—Franklin Goes to the Hospital. ed. 2004. (Illus.). (J). (ps-2). spiral bd. (978-0-616-03024-0(X)); spiral bd. (978-0-616-04547-3(6)) Canadian National Institute for the Blind/Institut National Canadien pour les Aveugles.

—Franklin Goes to the Hospital. Clark, Brenda, illus. 2000. (Franklin Ser.). (J). (ps-3). 30p. (978-1-55074-734-8(7)); 32p. (978-1-55074-732-4(0)) Kids Can Pr., Ltd.

—Franklin Goes to the Hospital. Clark, Brenda, illus. 2000. (Franklin Ser.). 32p. (J). (ps-3). pap. 4.99 (978-0-439-08370-6(2)) Scholastic, Inc.

—Franklin Goes to the Hospital. Clark, Brenda, illus. 2000. (J). (ps-ps). lib. bdg. 12.40 (978-0-613-25254-6(3)) Tandem Library Bks.

—Franklin Goes to the Hospital. 2000. (Franklin Ser.). (Illus.). (J). (ps-3). 11.30 (978-0-606-18547-9(X)) Tandem Library Bks.

—Franklin Helps Out. Clark, Brenda, illus. 2004. (Franklin TV StoryBks.). 32p. (J). (gr. k-3). (978-1-55074-823-9(8)) Kids Can Pr., Ltd.

—Franklin Helps Out. 2000. (Franklin TV Storybook Ser.). (J). (ps-3). 11.30 (978-0-606-20059-2(2)) Tandem Library Bks.

—Franklin in the Dark. ed. 2004. (Illus.). (J). (ps-2). spiral bd. (978-0-616-01574-2(7)); spiral bd. (978-0-616-01575-9(5)) Canadian National Institute for the Blind/Institut National Canadien pour les Aveugles.

—Franklin Is Bossy. Clark, Brenda, illus. 1998. (Franklin Ser.). 30p. (J). (ps-3). 19.95 (978-0-590-25764-0(1)) Scholastic, Inc.

—Franklin Juega al Futbol. Varela, Alejandra Lopez, tr. Clark, Brenda, illus. (SPA.). (J). (gr. k-2). ring bd. 10.95 (978-1-930332-17-1(3) , LC6563) Lectorum Pubns., Inc.

—Franklin Juega al Futbol. Lopez Varela, Alejandra, tr. from ENG. Clark, Brenda, illus. 1998. (Franklin Ser.). (SPA.). 32p. (J). (ps-3). pap. 5.95 (978-1-880507-44-5(7) , LC7851) Lectorum Pubns., Inc.

—Franklin Miente. Clark, Brenda, illus. 2000. (Franklin Ser.). (SPA.). (J). (ps-3). pap. 5.95 (978-1-880507-69-8(2) , LC4551) Lectorum Pubns., Inc.

—Franklin Miente. 2000. (Franklin Ser.). (SPA., Illus.). (J). (ps-3). 12.75 (978-0-606-18243-0(8)) Tandem Library Bks.

—Franklin Plants a Tree. 2001. (Franklin Ser.). (Illus.). (J). 11.30 (978-0-606-21196-3(9)) Tandem Library Bks.

—Franklin Quiere una Mascota. Varela, Alejandra Lopez, tr. from ENG. Clark, Brenda, illus. 1998. (Franklin Ser.). (SPA.). 32p. (J). (ps-3). pap. 5.95 (978-1-880507-49-0(8) , LC8143) Lectorum Pubns., Inc.

—Franklin Rides A Bike. Clark, Brenda & Southern, Shelley, illus. ed. 2005. (Franklin Picture Books II). 30p. (J). lib. bdg. 15.00 (978-1-59054-712-0(8)) Fitzgerald Bks.

—Franklin Says I Love You. ed. 2004. (Illus.). (J). (gr. k-3). spiral bd. (978-0-616-14561-6(6)); spiral bd. (978-0-616-14562-3(4)) Canadian National Institute for the Blind/Institut National Canadien pour les Aveugles.

—Franklin Says I Love You. Clark, Brenda & Southern, Shelley, illus. ed. 2005. (Franklin Picture Books II). 30p. (J). lib. bdg. 15.00 (978-1-59054-700-7(4)) Fitzgerald Bks.

—Franklin Says I Love You. Clark, Brenda, illus. 2004. (Franklin the Turtle Ser.). 32p. (J). (gr. k-3). (978-1-55337-035-2(X)) Kids Can Pr., Ltd.

—Franklin Says Sorry. 2000. (Franklin TV Storybook Ser.). (J). (ps-3). 11.30 (978-0-606-20060-8(6)) Tandem Library Bks.

—Franklin Se Pierde. Clark, Brenda, illus. 2000. (Franklin Ser.). (SPA.). (J). (ps-3). pap. 5.95 (978-1-880507-70-4(6) , LC6163) Lectorum Pubns., Inc.

—Franklin Se Pierde. 2000. (SPA.). (gr. k-3). lib. bdg. 14.10 (978-0-613-28393-9(7)); (Illus.). (J). 12.75 (978-0-606-18244-7(6)) Tandem Library Bks.

—Franklin Tiene un Mal Dia. Varela, Alejandra Lopez, tr. Clark, Brenda, illus. (Franklin Ser.). (SPA.). (J). (ps-3). 2001. ring bd. 10.95 (978-1-880507-86-5(2) , LC4083); 1999. pap. 5.95 (978-1-880507-52-0(8) , LC8141) Lectorum Pubns., Inc.

—Franklin Tiene un Mal Dia. 1999. (Franklin Ser.). (SPA.). (J). (ps-3). 12.75 (978-0-606-17011-6(1)) Tandem Library Bks.

—Franklin Treasury. 2000. (Franklin Ser.). (Illus.). (J). (ps-3). (978-1-55337-018-5(X)) Kids Can Pr., Ltd.

—Franklin Va a la Escuela. Lopez Varela, Alejandra, tr. Clark, Brenda, illus. (Franklin Ser.). (SPA.). (J). (ps-3). 2001. ring bd. 10.95 (978-1-880507-85-8(4) , LC4919); 1998. 32p. pap. 5.95 (978-1-880507-41-4(2) , LC7792) Lectorum Pubns., Inc.

—Franklin Va al Hospital. Varela, Alejandra Lopez, tr. Clark, Brenda, illus. (SPA.). (J). (gr. k-2). pap. 5.95 (978-1-930332-26-3(2) , LC1130); ring bd. 10.95 (978-1-930332-27-0(0) , LC1301) Lectorum Pubns., Inc.

—Franklin Wants a Badge. Clark, Brenda, illus. 2004. (Franklin TV StoryBks.). 32p. (J). (gr. k-3). (978-1-55337-467-1(3)) Kids Can Pr., Ltd.

—Franklin Wants a Badge. Clark, Brenda, illus. 2003. (Franklin TV-Tie In Ser.: No. 7). 32p. (J). (gr. k-3). pap. 4.50 (978-0-439-43122-4(0) , Scholastic Pr.) Scholastic, Inc.

—Franklin Wants a Badge. 2003. (ps-2). lib. bdg. 12.40 (978-0-613-89577-4(0)) Tandem Library Bks.

—Franklin Wants a Pet. 2000. (Franklin Ser.). (Illus.). 180p. (J). (ps-3). (978-1-55074-795-9(9)) Kids Can Pr., Ltd.

—Franklin y el Dia de Accion de Gracias. Varela, Alejandra Lopez, tr. Clark, Brenda, illus. (SPA.). pap. 5.95 (978-1-930332-06-5(8) , LC30183); ring bd. 10.95 (978-1-930332-07-2(6) , LC30184) Lectorum Pubns., Inc.

—Franklin y el Dia de Accion de Gracias. 2001. (978-0-606-22645-5(1)) Tandem Library Bks.

—Franklin y el Regalo de Navidad. Clark, Brenda, illus. 1999. (Franklin Ser.). (SPA.). (J). (ps-3). pap. 5.95 (978-1-880507-56-8(0) , LC2911) Lectorum Pubns., Inc.

—Franklin y el Regalo de Navidad. Varela, Alejandra Lopez, tr. from ENG. Clark, Brenda, illus. 1999. (Franklin Ser.). (SPA.). (J). (ps-3). ring bd. 10.95 (978-1-880507-67-4(6) , LC6006) Lectorum Pubns., Inc.

—Franklin y Harriet. 2001. (SPA., Illus.). (J). pap. 5.95 (978-1-880507-96-4(X) , LC8512); ring bd. 10.95 (978-1-880507-97-1(8) , LC0630) Lectorum Pubns., Inc.

—Franklin y Harriet. 2001. (SPA.). (gr. k-3). lib. bdg. 14.10 (978-0-613-36038-8(9)); (Illus.). (J). 12.75 (978-0-606-21197-0(7)) Tandem Library Bks.

—Franklin's Baby Sister. ed. 2004. (Illus.). (J). (gr. k-3). spiral bd. (978-0-616-07218-9(X)) Canadian National Institute for the Blind/Institut National Canadien pour les Aveugles.

—Franklin's Baby Sister. Clark, Brenda, illus. (Franklin Ser.). (J). (ps-3). 96p. (978-1-55074-858-1(0)); 2000. 32p. (978-1-55074-794-2(0)) Kids Can Pr., Ltd.

—Franklin's Baby Sister. Clark, Brenda, illus. 2000. (Franklin Ser.). (J). (ps-3). 11.30 (978-0-606-19919-3(5)) Tandem Library Bks.

—Franklin's Bad Day. Clark, Brenda & Wood, Murial Hughes, illus. ed. 2005. (Franklin Picture Books II). 30p. (J). lib. bdg. 15.00 (978-1-59054-711-3(X)) Fitzgerald Bks.

—Franklin's Bicycle Helmet. 2000. (Franklin TV Storybook Ser.). (J). (ps-3). 11.30 (978-0-606-20061-5(4)) Tandem Library Bks.

—Franklin's Birthday Party. 2001. (Franklin TV Storybook Ser.). (Illus.). (J). 11.30 (978-0-606-21198-7(5)) Tandem Library Bks.

—Franklin's Blanket. 2000. (Franklin Ser.). (Illus.). 180p. (J). (ps-3). (978-1-55074-686-0(3)) Kids Can Pr., Ltd.

—Franklin's Christmas: A Sticker Activity Book. Clark, Brenda, illus. 2004. (Franklin Sticker & Activity Bks.). 16p. (J). (gr. k-3). (978-1-55337-506-7(8)) Kids Can Pr., Ltd.

—Franklin's Christmas Gift. Clark, Brenda, illus. 1998. (Franklin the Turtle Ser.). (J). (gr. k-3). 32p. (978-1-55074-466-8(6)); 96p. (978-1-55074-468-2(2)) Kids Can Pr., Ltd.

—Franklin's Christmas Gift. Clark, Brenda, illus. 1998. (Franklin Ser.). (J). (ps-3). pap. 54.00 (978-0-590-95169-2(6) , Cartwheel Bks.) Scholastic, Inc.

—Franklin's Class Trip. Clark, Brenda, illus. (Franklin Ser.). (J). (ps-3). 1999. 30p. (978-1-55074-472-9(0)); 2004. 32p. (978-1-55074-470-5(4)) Kids Can Pr., Ltd.

—Franklin's Class Trip. Clark, Brenda, illus. 1999. (Franklin Ser.). 32p. (J). (ps-3). pap. 4.50 (978-0-590-13002-8(1)) Scholastic, Inc.

—Franklin's Class Trip. 1999. (Franklin Ser.). (Illus.). (J). (ps-3). 11.30 (978-0-606-18548-6(8)) Tandem Library Bks.

—Franklin's Classic Treasury. Clark, Brenda, illus. (Franklin Treasuries Ser.). 128p. (J). (gr. k-3). 1999. (978-1-55074-742-3(8)); Vol. 2. 2000. (978-1-55074-813-0(0)) Kids Can Pr., Ltd.

E F G

—Franklin's Friendship Treasury. Clark, Brenda, illus. 2000. (Franklin Treasuries Ser.). 128p. (J). (gr. k-3). (978-1-55074-872-7(6)) Kids Can Pr., Ltd.
—Franklin's Fun Book. 2000. (Franklin Color & Activity Bks.). (Illus.). 96p. (J). (ps-3). pap. (978-0-7666-0494-0(2)) Modern Publishing.
—Franklin's Holiday Treasury. Clark, Brenda, illus. 2002. (Franklin Treasuries Ser.). 128p. (J). (gr. k-3). (978-1-55337-045-1(7)) Kids Can Pr., Ltd.
—Franklin's Neighborhood. ed. 2004. (Illus.). (J). (gr. k-3). spiral bd. (978-0-616-01588-9(7)); spiral bd. (978-0-616-01589-6(5)) Canadian National Institute for the Blind/Institut National Canadien pour les Aveugles.
—Franklin's Neighborhood. Clark, Brenda, illus. 1999. (Franklin Ser.). (J). (ps-3). 32p. (978-1-55074-704-1(5)); 270p. (978-1-55074-702-7(9)) Kids Can Pr., Ltd.
—Franklin's Neighborhood. Clark, Brenda, illus. 1999. (Franklin Ser.). 32p. (J). (ps-3). pap. 4.50 (978-0-439-08369-0(9)) Scholastic, Inc.
—Franklin's Neighborhood. 1999. (Franklin Ser.). (J). (ps-3). 11.30 (978-0-606-17271-4(8)) Tandem Library Bks.
—Franklin's New Friend. ed. 2004. (Illus.). (J). (gr. k-3). spiral bd. (978-0-616-01590-2(9)); spiral bd. (978-0-616-01591-9(7)) Canadian National Institute for the Blind/Institut National Canadien pour les Aveugles.
—Franklin's New Friend. Clark, Brenda, illus. (Franklin Ser.). 96p. (J). (ps-3). (978-1-55074-363-0(5)) Kids Can Pr., Ltd.
—Franklin's School Treasury. Clark, Brenda, illus. unabr. ed. 2001. (Franklin Treasuries Ser.). 128p. (J). (gr. k-3). (978-1-55074-877-2(7)) Kids Can Pr., Ltd.
—Franklin's Secret Club. ed. 2004. (Illus.). (J). (gr. k-3). spiral bd. (978-0-616-01593-3(3)); spiral bd. (978-0-616-01594-0(1)) Canadian National Institute for the Blind/Institut National Canadien pour les Aveugles.
—Franklin's Secret Club. Clark, Brenda, illus. ed. 2005. (Franklin Picture Books II). 30p. (J). lib. bdg. 15.00 (978-1-59054-710-6(1)) Fitzgerald Bks.
—Franklin's Secret Club. Clark, Brenda, illus. 1998. (Franklin the Turtle Ser.). (J). (gr. k-3). 32p. (978-1-55074-474-3(7)); 96p. (978-1-55074-476-7(3)) Kids Can Pr., Ltd.
—Franklin's Secret Club. Clark, Brenda, illus. 1998. (Franklin Ser.). 32p. (J). (ps-3). pap. 4.99 (978-0-590-13000-4(5) , Scholastic Paperbacks) Scholastic, Inc.
—Franklin's Secret Club. Clark, Brenda, illus. 1998. (Franklin Ser.). (J). (ps-3). 11.30 (978-0-606-13406-4(9)) Tandem Library Bks.
—Franklin's Thanksgiving. 2001. (Franklin Ser.). (Illus.). (J). 11.30 (978-0-606-22045-3(3)) Tandem Library Bks.
—Franklin's Valentine Cards. Clark, Brenda, illus. 1998. (Franklin Sticker & Activity Bks.). 32p. (J). (gr. k-3). (978-1-55074-625-9(1)) Kids Can Pr., Ltd.
—Franklin's Valentines. Clark, Brenda, illus. 2002. (Franklin Ser.). (J). 12.40 (978-0-7587-2534-9(5)) Book Wholesalers, Inc.
—Franklin's Valentines. Clark, Brenda, illus. 1998. (Franklin the Turtle Ser.). (J). (gr. k-3). 32p. (978-1-55074-480-4(1)); 96p. (978-1-55074-482-8(8)) Kids Can Pr., Ltd.
—Franklin's Valentines. Clark, Brenda, illus. 1999. (Franklin Ser.). (J). (ps-3). pap. 54.00 (978-0-439-04355-7(7)) Scholastic, Inc.
—Franklin's Valentines. 1999. (gr. k-3). lib. bdg. 12.40 (978-0-613-11557-5(0)) Tandem Library Bks.
—Franklin's Valentines. Clark, Brenda, illus. 1999. (Franklin Ser.). (J). (ps-3). 11.30 (978-0-606-15536-6(8)) Tandem Library Bks.
—Fun & Games with Franklin. 2000. (Franklin Color & Activity Bks.). (Illus.). 32p. (J). (ps-3). pap. (978-0-7666-0493-3(4)) Modern Publishing.
—Fun with Franklin: A Learning to Read Book. Clark, Brenda, illus. (Franklin Ser.). (J). (ps-3). (978-1-55074-646-4(4)) Kids Can Pr., Ltd.
—Fun with Franklin: Math Activity Book. Clark, Brenda, illus. 1998. (Franklin Ser.). 72p. (J). (ps-3). (978-1-55074-452-1(6)) Kids Can Pr., Ltd.
—El Hallazgo de Franklin. Varela, Alejandra Lopez, tr. Clark, Brenda, illus. (SPA.). (J). (gr. k-2). ring bd. 10.95 (978-1-930332-10-2(6) , LC1928); 1999. pap. 5.95 (978-1-880507-51-3(X) , LC8142) Lectorum Pubns., Inc.
—Hallazgo de Franklin. 1999. (SPA.). (gr. k-3). lib. bdg. 12.95 (978-0-613-18115-0(8)) Tandem Library Bks.
—La Hermanita de Franklin. Clark, Brenda, illus. 2000. (Franklin Ser.). (SPA.). (J). (ps-3). pap. 5.95 (978-1-880507-83-4(8) , LC7611); ring bd. 10.95 (978-1-880507-84-1(6) , LC3577) Lectorum Pubns., Inc.
—La Hermanita de Franklin. 2000. (Franklin Ser.). (SPA.). (J). (ps-3). 12.75 (978-0-606-20188-9(2)) Tandem Library Bks.
—Un Nouvel Ami pour Benjamin. ed. 2004. Tr. of Franklin's New Friend. (FRE., Illus.). (J). (ps-2). spiral bd. (978-0-616-01828-6(2)) Canadian National Institute for the Blind/Institut National Canadien pour les Aveugles.
—Time to Play with Franklin. 2000. (Franklin Color & Activity Bks.). (Illus.). 32p. (J). (ps-3). pap. (978-0-7666-0491-9(8)) Modern Publishing.
—Welcome to Franklin's World. 2000. (Franklin Color & Activity Bks.). (Illus.). 32p. (J). (ps-3). pap. (978-0-7666-0490-2(X)) Modern Publishing.
Bourgeois, Paulette & Clark, Brenda. Franklin Celebrates. 2005. (Franklin TV Storybook Ser.). (Illus.). 32p. (J). (ps-ps). (978-1-55337-501-2(7)) Kids Can Pr., Ltd.
—Franklin Fibs. 1999. (Franklin Ser.). (Illus.). 162p. (J). (ps-3). (978-1-55074-668-6(5)) Kids Can Pr., Ltd.
—Franklin Forgets. (Franklin TV StoryBks.). (Illus.). 32p. (J). (ps-3). 2005. (978-1-55074-722-5(3)); 2000. (978-1-55074-726-3(6)) Kids Can Pr., Ltd.
—Franklin Has a Sleepover. 1999. (Franklin Ser.). (Illus.). 168p. (J). (ps-3). (978-1-55074-664-8(2)) Kids Can Pr., Ltd.
—Franklin Is Lost. 1999. (Franklin Ser.). (Illus.). 162p. (J). (ps-3). (978-1-55074-670-9(7)) Kids Can Pr., Ltd.
—Franklin Is Messy. 1999. (Franklin Ser.). (Illus.). 180p. (J). (ps-3). (978-1-55074-678-5(2)) Kids Can Pr., Ltd.
—Franklin Says Sorry. (Franklin TV StoryBks.). (Illus.). 32p. (J). (gr. k-3). 2004. (978-1-55074-712-6(6)); 1999. (978-1-55074-714-0(2)) Kids Can Pr., Ltd.
—Franklin's Bicycle Helmet. 2000. (Franklin TV StoryBks.). (Illus.). 32p. (J). (gr. k-3). (978-1-55074-730-0(4)); (978-1-55074-728-7(2)) Kids Can Pr., Ltd.
—Franklin's Family Treasury. 2003. (Franklin Treasuries Ser.). (Illus.). 128p. (J). (gr. k-3). (978-1-55337-479-4(7)) Kids Can Pr., Ltd.
—Franklin's Neighborhood. 1999. (Franklin Ser.). (Illus.). 194p. (J). (ps-3). (978-1-55074-752-2(5)) Kids Can Pr., Ltd.
—Franklin's New Friend. 1999. (Franklin Ser.). (Illus.). 180p. (J). (ps-3). (978-1-55074-797-3(5)) Kids Can Pr., Ltd.
—Franklin's Secret Club. 1999. (Franklin Ser.). (Illus.). 194p. (J). (ps-3). (978-1-55074-672-3(3)) Kids Can Pr., Ltd.
Bourgeois, Paulette & Clark, Brenda, creators. Franklin & the Baby. 1999. (Illus.). (J). (978-0-439-12065-4(9)) Scholastic, Inc.
—Hurry up, Franklin. 2000. (Franklin Ser.). (Illus.). 180p. (J). (ps-3). (978-1-55074-682-2(0)) Kids Can Pr., Ltd.
Bourgeois, Paulette & Jennings, Sharon. Franklin Plants a Tree. Jeffrey, Sean et al, illus. 2003. (Franklin TV StoryBks.). 32p. (J). (gr. k-3). (978-1-55074-878-9(5)) Kids Can Pr., Ltd.
—Franklin's Thanksgiving. Clark, Brenda, illus. 2004. (Franklin the Turtle Ser.). 32p. (J). (gr. k-3). (978-1-55074-798-0(3)) Kids Can Pr., Ltd.
—Franklin's Valentines. Clark, Brenda, illus. 1999. (Franklin Ser.). 32p. (J). (ps-3). pap. 4.50 (978-0-590-13001-1(3) , Cartwheel Bks.) Scholastic, Inc.
Bourgeois, Paulette & Moore, Eva. Franklin's First Day of School. Clark, Brenda, illus. 2000. (Franklin Ser.). 12p. (J). (ps-3). bds. 5.99 (978-0-439-20298-5(1)) Scholastic, Inc.
Bourgeois, Paulette, et al. Franklin en la Oscuridad. Lopez Varela, Alejandra, tr. from ENG. Clark, Brenda, illus. 1998. (Franklin Ser.). (SPA.). 32p. (J). (ps-3). pap. 5.95 (978-1-880507-43-8(9) , LC7861) Lectorum Pubns., Inc.
—Franklin's Neighborhood. Clark, Brenda, illus. 1999. (Franklin the Turtle Ser.). 32p. (J). (gr. k-3). (978-1-55074-729-4(0)) Kids Can Pr., Ltd.
Franklin's Birthday Party. 2004. (Franklin Tv Storybooks Ser.). (Illus.). 32p. (J). (ps-ps). (978-1-55074-882-6(3)) Kids Can Pr., Ltd.
Jenkins, Susan. Franklin & the Magic Show. 2004. (Kids Can Read Ser.). (Illus.). 32p. (J). (gr. k-3). (978-1-55074-992-2(7)); (978-1-55074-990-8(0)) Kids Can Pr., Ltd.
—The Franklin Annual. 2002. (Franklin Annual Ser.). (Illus.). 96p. (J). (gr. k-3). (978-1-55337-481-7(9)) Kids Can Pr., Ltd.
Jennings, Sharon. Franklin & Otter's Visit. Koren, Mark et al, illus. 2003. (Franklin TV StoryBks.). 32p. (J). (gr. k-3). (978-1-55337-021-5(X)) Kids Can Pr., Ltd.
—Franklin & the Contest. Jeffrey, Sean et al, illus. 2004. 32p. (J). lib. bdg. 15.38 ***(*978-1-4242-1166-1(2))*** Fitzgerald Bks.
—Franklin & the Cookies. Gagnon, Celeste et al, illus. 2005. 32p. (J). lib. bdg. 15.38 ***(*978-1-4242-1167-8(0))*** Fitzgerald Bks.
—Franklin & the Scooter. Gagnon, Celeste et al, illus. 2004. 32p. (J). lib. bdg. 15.38 ***(*978-1-4242-1169-2(7))*** Fitzgerald Bks.
—Franklin & the Tin Flute. Gagnon, Celeste et al, illus. 2005. 32p. (J). lib. bdg. 15.38 ***(*978-1-4242-1180-7(8))*** Fitzgerald Bks.
—Franklin Goes to the Hospital. Clark, Brenda & Southern, Shelley, illus. ed. 2005. (Franklin Picture Books I). 30p. (J). lib. bdg. 15.00 (978-1-59054-688-8(1)) Fitzgerald Bks.
—Franklin Has the Hiccups. Gagnon, Celeste et al, illus. 2006. 32p. (J). lib. bdg. 15.38 ***(*978-1-4242-1178-4(6))*** Fitzgerald Bks.
—Franklin Plays Hockey. Koren, Mark et al, illus. ed. 2005. (Franklin Picture Books I). 30p. (J). lib. bdg. 15.00 (978-1-59054-709-0(8)) Fitzgerald Bks.
—Franklin Stays Up. Jeffrey, Sean et al, illus. 2003. 32p. (J). pap. (978-0-439-41815-7(1)) Scholastic, Inc.
—Franklin the Detective. Gagnon, Celeste et al, illus. 2004. 32p. (J). lib. bdg. 15.38 ***(*978-1-4242-1171-5(9))*** Fitzgerald Bks.
—Franklin the Detective. 2004. (Illus.). 32p. (J). (ps-ps). lib. bdg. 10.75 (978-0-606-32910-1(2)) Tandem Library Bks.
—Franklin's Library Books. Gagnon, Celeste et al, illus. 2005. 32p. (J). lib. bdg. 15.38 ***(*978-1-4242-1172-2(7))*** Fitzgerald Bks.
—Franklin's Picnic. Jeffrey, Sean et al, illus. 2006. 32p. (J). lib. bdg. 15.38 ***(*978-1-4242-1179-1(4))*** Fitzgerald Bks.
—Franklin's Pond Phantom. McIntyre, Sasha et al, illus. 2005. 32p. (J). lib. bdg. 15.38 ***(*978-1-4242-1181-4(6))*** Fitzgerald Bks.
—Franklin's Pumkin. McIntyre, Sasha et al, illus. 2004. 32p. (J). lib. bdg. 15.38 ***(*978-1-4242-1174-6(3))*** Fitzgerald Bks.
Jennings, Sharon, et al. Franklin & the Baby-Sitter. Southern, Shelley et al, illus. 2001. (Franklin TV Storybook Ser.). 32p. (J). (ps-3). (978-1-55074-916-8(1)) Kids Can Pr., Ltd.
—Franklin & the Big Kid. Southern, Shelley et al, illus. 2002. (Franklin TV Storybook Ser.). 27p. (J). (ps-3). (978-1-55337-054-3(6)) Kids Can Pr., Ltd.
—Franklin & the Computer. Southern, Shelley et al, illus. 2003. (Franklin TV Storybook Ser.). 32p. (J). (ps-3). (978-1-55337-362-9(6)) Kids Can Pr., Ltd.
—Franklin & the Cookies. Gagnon, Celeste, illus. 2005. (Kids Can Read Ser.). 32p. (J). (gr. 1-2). (978-1-55337-716-0(8)) Kids Can Pr., Ltd.
—Franklin & the New Teacher. Gagnon, Celeste, illus. 2005. 32p. (J). (gr. k-3). (978-1-55337-500-5(9)); (978-1-55337-499-2(1)) Kids Can Pr., Ltd.
—Franklin Has the Hiccups. Lei, John, illus. 32p. (978-1-55337-802-0(4)) Kids Can Pr., Ltd.
—Franklin Has the Hiccups. Lei, John, illus. 2006. 32p. 3.95 (978-1-55337-803-7(2)) Kids Can Pr., Ltd. CAN. *Dist:* Wybel Marketing Group.
—Franklin Plays Hockey. Koren, Mark & Lei, John, illus. 2002. (Franklin TV Storybook Ser.). 32p. (J). (ps-3). (978-1-55337-056-7(2)) Kids Can Pr., Ltd.
—Franklin Runs Away. Jeffrey, Sean, illus. 2001. (Franklin TV Storybook Ser.). 32p. (J). (ps-3). (978-1-55074-912-0(9)) Kids Can Pr., Ltd.
—Franklin Stays Up. Southern, Shelley et al, illus. 2004. (Kids Can Read Ser.). 32p. (J). (gr. k-3). (978-1-55337-372-8(3)); (978-1-55337-371-1(5)) Kids Can Pr., Ltd.
—Franklin the Detective. Gagnon, Celeste, illus. 2005. (Kids Can Read Ser.). 32p. (J). (gr. 1-2). (978-1-55337-498-5(3)); (978-1-55337-497-8(5)) Kids Can Pr., Ltd.
—Franklin's Canoe Trip. Jeffrey, Sean et al, illus. 2003. (Franklin TV Storybook Ser.). 32p. (J). (gr. k-3). (978-1-55337-019-2(8)) Kids Can Pr., Ltd.
—Franklin's Music Lessons. Southern, Shelley et al, illus. 2004. (Kids Can Read Ser.). 32p. (J). (gr. k-3). (978-1-55337-171-7(2)); (978-1-55337-172-4(0)) Kids Can Pr., Ltd.
—Franklin's Picnic. Southern, Shelley et al, illus. 32p. (978-1-55337-714-6(1)) Kids Can Pr., Ltd.
—Franklin's Pumpkin. Southern, Shelley et al, illus. 2005. (Kids Can Read Ser.). 32p. (J). (gr. 1-2). (978-1-55337-496-1(7)); (978-1-55337-495-4(9)) Kids Can Pr., Ltd.
—Franklin's Surprise. Jeffrey, Sean, illus. 2004. (Kids Can Read Ser.). 32p. (J). (gr. k-3). (978-1-55337-466-4(5)); (978-1-55337-465-7(7)) Kids Can Pr., Ltd.
Moore, Eva. Franklin & the Baby. 2004. (Franklin TV StoryBks.). (Illus.). 32p. (J). (gr. k-3). (978-1-55074-706-5(1)) Kids Can Pr., Ltd.
—Franklin & the Baby. 1999. (Franklin TV-Tie In Ser.). (Illus.). 32p. (J). (ps-3). pap. 4.50 (978-0-439-08365-2(6)) Scholastic, Inc.
—Franklin & the Baby. 1999. (Franklin TV Storybook Ser.). (J). (ps-3). 11.30 (978-0-606-20056-1(8)) Tandem Library Bks.
Moore, Eva & Nelvana Staff. Franklin & the Baby. 2000. (Franklin TV Storybook Ser.). (Illus.). 96p. (J). (ps-3). (978-1-55074-708-9(8)) Kids Can Pr., Ltd.

FRANKLIN, BENJAMIN, 1706-1790

Abraham, Philip. Benjamin Franklin. 2002. (Wel-Real People Ser.). (Illus.). 24p. (J). (ps-2). 18.00 (978-0-516-23954-5(6)); pap. 4.95 (978-0-516-23601-8(6)) Scholastic Library Publishing. (Children's Pr.).
—Benjamin Franklin. 2002. (gr. k-3). lib. bdg. 12.95 (978-0-613-58824-9(X)) Tandem Library Bks.
Adams, Colleen. Benjamin Franklin: American Inventor. 2002. (Reading Room Collection). (Illus.). 24p. (J). lib. bdg. 18.75 (978-0-8239-3745-5(3)) Rosen Publishing Group, Inc., The.
Adler, David A. B. Franklin, Printer. 2001. (Illus.). 136p. (J). (gr. 4-6). tchr. ed. 19.95 (978-0-8234-1675-2(5)) Holiday Hse., Inc.
Ashby, Ruth. The Amazing Mr. Franklin: Or the Boy Who Read Everything. Montgomery, Michael, illus. 2004. 144p. (J). (gr. 3-4). 12.95 (978-1-56145-306-1(4)) Peachtree Pubs., Ltd.
Baldwin, James. Four Great Americans. 2006. pap. ***(*978-1-4065-0509-2(9))*** Dodo Pr.
Baldwin, James. Four Great Americans: Washington, Franklin, Webster, Lincoln: A Book for Young Americans. 2000. (Illus.). (J). (978-0-89526-203-5(7)) Regnery Publishing, Inc., An Eagle Publishing Co.
Barretta, Gene. Now & Ben: The Modern Inventions of Benjamin Franklin. 2006. (Illus.). 40p. (J). 16.95 (978-0-8050-7917-3(3)) Holt, Henry & Co.
Beardsley, Laura E. Benjamin Franklin. 2007. (Essential Lives Ser.). (ENG., Illus.). 112p. (YA). (gr. 8-12). lib. bdg. 32.79 ***(*978-1-59928-840-6(0)*** , Essential Library) ABDO Publishing Co.
Ben Franklin. 2000. (McGraw-Hill Ciencias Ser.). (ENG & SPA.). (gr. 3 up). (978-0-02-279642-6(8)) Macmillan/McGraw-Hill Schl. Div.
Ben Franklin: Libros Aventuras (Adventure Books) 2000. (MacMillan/McGraw-Hill. Estudios Sociales Ser.). (ENG & SPA.). (gr. 3 up). (978-0-02-148692-1(1)) Macmillan/McGraw-Hill Schl. Div.
Ben Franklin y sus Cuadernos 19: Leveled Books. 2001. (McGraw-Hill. Lectura Ser.). (ENG & SPA.). (gr. 3 up). (978-0-02-188116-1(2)) Macmillan/McGraw-Hill Schl. Div.
Ben Franklin's Big Shock. 2007. (J). pap. 5.95 ***(*978-0-8225-6450-8(5)*** , First Avenue Editions) Lerner Publishing Group.
Benge, Janet & Benge, Geoff. Benjamin Franklin: A Useful Life. 2005. (Illus.). 197p. (J). (978-1-932096-14-9(0)) Emerald Bks.
Benjamin Franklin. (Photo Illustrated Biographies Ser.). 24p. (J). 6.95 (978-0-7368-4463-5(5)); 48p. (YA). 7.95 (978-0-7368-4496-3(1)); Vol. 2. 2005. (YA). (978-0-7368-9442-5(X) , Pebble Bks.) Capstone Pr., Inc.
Benjamin Franklin. (Compass Point Early Biographies Ser.). 32p. (J). 7.95 (978-0-7565-1165-4(8)) Compass Point Bks.
Benjamin Franklin. (Biographies Ser.). 24p. (J). 7.95 (978-1-4048-0459-3(5)) Picture Window Bks.
Benjamin Franklin, 6 vols. (gr. k-2). 28.95 (978-0-7368-9443-2(8)); (gr. 2-5). 39.95 (978-0-7368-4582-3(8)) Red Brick Learning.
Benjamin Franklin: Printer, Scientist, Statesman. 2005. (Discovery Readers Ser.). (Illus.). 32p. (J). (gr. 1-2). 3.95 (978-0-8249-5509-0(9)) Ideals Pubns.
Boekhoff, P. M. & Kallen, Stuart A. Benjamin Franklin. 2006. (Illus.). 48p. (J). (gr. 4-8). 17.00 (978-1-4223-5322-6(2)) DIANE Publishing Co.
Burke, Rick. Benjamin Franklin. 2003. (American Lives Ser.). (Illus.). 32p. (J). lib. bdg. 24.22 (978-1-4034-0726-9(6)); pap. 6.95 (978-1-4034-3101-1(9)) Heinemann Library.
Clark, Brenda, illus. Franklin & His Friend. 2002. (Franklin Ser.). 12.40 (978-1-4046-2101-5(6)) Book Wholesalers, Inc.
Collard, Sneed B., III. Benjamin Franklin: The Man Who Could Do Just about Anything. 2006. (American Heroes Ser.). (Illus.). 48p. (J). (gr. 3-5). lib. bdg. 28.50 ***(*978-0-7614-2161-0(0)*** , Benchmark Bks.) Cavendish, Marshall Corp.
Collier, James Lincoln. The Benjamin Franklin You Never Knew. 2004. (You Never Knew Ser.). (Illus.). 80p. (J). 25.50 (978-0-516-24427-3(2) , Children's Pr.) Scholastic Library Publishing.
Copeland, Peter F. Benjamin Franklin Coloring Book. 2005. 32p. (J). pap. 3.95 (978-0-486-43988-4(7)) Dover Pubns., Inc.
Cousins, Margaret. Ben Franklin of Old Philadelphia. 2004. (Landmark Bks.: No. 10). (Illus.). 160p. (gr. 4-7). reprint ed. pap. 5.99 (978-0-394-84928-7(0) , Random Hse. Bks. for Young Readers) Random Hse. Children's Bks.
Dash, Joan. A Dangerous Engine: Benjamin Franklin, from Scientist to Diplomat. Petricic, Dusan, illus. 2005. 256p. (J). 17.00 (978-0-374-30669-4(9) , Frances Foster Bks.) Farrar, Straus & Giroux.
Daugherty, James. Poor Richard. 2001. (Illus.). (J). pap. 16.95 (978-1-893103-03-0(X)) Beautiful Feet Bks.
D'Aulaire, Ingri. Benjamin Franklin. D'Aulaire, Edgar Parin, illus. 1998. 48p. (J). (gr. k-6). pap. 12.95 (978-0-9643803-9-4(0)) Beautiful Feet Bks.
Donlan, Leni. A Life Well Lived: Ben Franklin. 2007. (J). ***(*978-1-4109-2698-2(2));*** pap. ***(*978-1-4109-2709-5(1))*** Steck-Vaughn.
Espinosa, Rod. Benjamin Franklin. 2007. (Bio-Graphics Ser.). (Illus.). 32p. (J). (gr. 3-6). lib. bdg. 27.07 ***(*978-1-60270-066-6(4)*** , Graphic Planet) Magic Wagon.
Feinstein, Stephen. Read about Benjamin Franklin. 2006. (I Like Biographies! Ser.). (Illus.). 24p. (J). lib. bdg. 21.26 (978-0-7660-2596-7(9) , Enslow Elementary) Enslow Pubs., Inc.
Fish, Bruce. Benjamin Franklin: American Statesman, Scientist & Writer. 1999. (Colonial Leaders Ser.). (Illus.). 80p. (gr. 3 up). (J). pap. 8.95 (978-0-7910-5690-5(2)); (YA). 27.50 (978-0-7910-5347-8(4)) Facts On File, Inc. (Chelsea Hse.).
Fleming, Candace. Ben Franklin's Almanac. 2003. (Illus.). 128p. (J). (gr. 5-9). 19.95 (978-0-689-83549-0(3) , Atheneum/Anne Schwartz Bks.) Simon & Schuster Children's Publishing.
Fleming, Thomas. Sterling Point Books: Ben Franklin: Inventing America. 2007. (Sterling Point Bks.). (Illus.). 192p. (J). 12.95 (978-1-4027-4523-2(0)); pap. 6.95 (978-1-4027-4143-2(X)) Sterling Publishing Co., Inc.
Fleming, Thomas J. Benjamin Franklin: Inventing America. 2007. (Sterling Point Bks.). (Illus.). viii, 177p. (J). ***(*978-1-4287-2411-2(7))*** Sterling Publishing Co., Inc.
Ford, Carin T. Benjamin Franklin: Inventor & Patriot. 2003. (Meeting Famous People Ser.). (Illus.). 32p. (J). (gr. 1-4). lib. bdg. 22.60 (978-0-7660-1859-4(8)) Enslow Pubs., Inc.
Fradin, Dennis Brindell. Who Was Ben Franklin? 2002. (gr. 3-6). lib. bdg. 13.00 (978-0-613-43654-0(7)) Tandem Library Bks.
—Who Was Benjamin Franklin? O'Brien, John & Harrison, Nancy, illus. 2002. (Who Was...? Ser.). 112p. (J). (gr. 3-5). pap. 4.99 (978-0-448-42495-8(9) , Grosset & Dunlap) Penguin Group (USA) Inc.
Furgang, Kathy. The Declaration of Independence & Benjamin Franklin of Pennsylvania. 2002. (Framers of the Declaration of Independence Ser.). (Illus.). 24p. (J). (gr. 3). lib. bdg. 18.75 (978-0-8239-5591-6(5) , PowerKids Pr.) Rosen Publishing Group, Inc., The.
Gaustad, Edwin S. Benjamin Franklin: Inventing America. 2006. 143p. (J). (gr. 4-8). reprint ed. 22.00 (978-1-4223-5227-4(7)) DIANE Publishing Co.
Giblin, James Cross. The Amazing Life of Benjamin Franklin. Dooling, Michael, illus. 2006. 48p. (J). pap. 5.99 (978-0-439-81065-4(5) , Scholastic Paperbacks) Scholastic, Inc.
Gillis, Jennifer Blizin. Benjamin Franklin. 2004. (Illus.). 32p. (J). pap. 6.50 (978-1-4034-5332-7(2)); lib. bdg. 22.79 (978-1-4034-5324-2(1)) Heinemann Library.
Glass, Maya. Benjamin Franklin: Early American Genius. 2003. (Primary Sources of Famous People in American History Ser.). (Illus.). 32p. (YA). pap. (978-0-8239-4175-9(2)) Rosen Publishing Group, Inc., The.
Gosda, Randy T. Ben Franklin. 2002. (First Biographies Ser.). (Illus.). 32p. (J). (gr. k-4). lib. bdg. 22.78 (978-1-57765-733-0(0) , Buddy Bks.) ABDO Publishing Co.
Gregson, Susan R. Benjamin Franklin. 2000. (Let Freedom Ring Ser.). (Illus.). 48p. (J). (gr. 3-4). lib. bdg. 22.60 (978-0-7368-1031-9(5) , Bridgestone Bks.) Capstone Pr., Inc.
Harcourt School Publishers Staff. Lights Out! 3rd ed. 2002. (Trophies English Language Learners Ser.). (Illus.). pap. 5.10 (978-0-15-327837-2(4)) Harcourt Schl. Pubs.
—Wise Ben: Take-Home Book. 2001. (Collections Ser.). (Illus.). (J). pap. 1.90 (978-0-15-319539-6(8)) Harcourt Schl. Pubs.

—Wise Ben Below Level. 3rd ed. 2002. (Trophies Reading Program Ser.). (Illus.). pap. 5.10 (978-0-15-323338-8(9)) Harcourt Schl. Pubs.

Harness, Cheryl. The Remarkable Benjamin Franklin. 2005. (Illus.). 48p. (J). (gr. 2 up). 17.95 (978-0-7922-7882-5(8)); 27.90 (978-0-7922-7884-9(4)) National Geographic Society. (National Geographic Children's Bks.).

Haugen, Brenda & Santella, Andrew. Benjamin Franklin: Scientist & Statesman. 2004. (Signature Lives Ser.). (Illus.). 112p. (J). 30.60 (978-0-7565-0826-5(6) , 1240128) Compass Point Bks.

Heiligman, Deborah. Mysterious Ocean Highway. 1999. (Illus.). (J). pap. (978-0-7398-0013-3(2)) Steck-Vaughn.

—The Mysterious Ocean Highway: Benjamin Franklin & the Gulf Stream. 1999. (Turnstone Ocean Pilot Bks.). (Illus.). 48p. (J). (gr. 3-7). pap. 7.95 (978-0-7398-1227-3(0)) Steck-Vaughn.

Heinrichs, Ann. Benjamin Franklin. 2004. (Our People Ser.). (Illus.). 32p. (J). (gr. 2-6). 27.07 (978-1-59296-173-3(8)) Child's World, Inc.

Higgins, Maria Mihalik. Sterling Biographies: Benjamin Franklin: Revolutionary Inventor. 2007. (Sterling Biographies Ser.). (Illus.). 128p. (J). 12.95 ***(978-1-4027-4952-0(X));*** pap. 5.95 ***(978-1-4027-3283-6(X))*** Sterling Publishing Co., Inc.

HSP. First-Place Reading for Title I: A Picture Book of Benjamin Franklin. 2nd ed. 2002. (Harcourt Title I Reading Programs Ser.). (gr. 4 up). pap. 69.60 (978-0-15-338155-3(8)) Harcourt Schl. Pubs.

Jango-Cohen, Judith. Ben Franklin's Big Shock. Lepp, Kevin, illus. 2006. (On My Own Science Ser.). 48p. (J). (gr. 2-4). 25.26 (978-1-57505-873-3(1) , Millbrook Pr.) Lerner Publishing Group.

Kallen, Stuart A. Benjamin Franklin. 2001. (Founding Fathers Ser.). (Illus.). 64p. (J). (gr. 3-8). lib. bdg. 25.65 (978-1-57765-009-6(3) , ABDO & Daughters) ABDO Publishing Co.

Kelly, Jack. Benjamin Franklin. Tafalla, Ortiz, illus. 2005. (Heroes of America Ser.). 240p. (J). (gr. 3-8). lib. bdg. 21.35 (978-1-59679-257-9(4)) ABDO Publishing Co.

Krensky, Stephen. Ben Franklin & His First Kite. Dodson, Bert, illus. 2002. (Childhood of Famous Americans Ser.). 32p. (J). (gr. 1-3). pap. 3.99 (978-0-689-84984-8(2) , Aladdin) Simon & Schuster Children's Publishing.

—Ben Franklin & His First Kite. 2002. (gr. k-3). lib. bdg. 11.80 (978-0-613-45010-2(8)) Tandem Library Bks.

Landau, Elaine. Meet Ben Franklin with Elaine Landau. 2006. (Explore Colonial America with Elaine Landau Ser.). (Illus.). 48p. (J). lib. bdg. 23.93 (978-0-7660-2555-4(1) , Enslow Elementary) Enslow Pubs., Inc.

Lawson, Robert. Ben & Me: An Astonishing Life of Benjamin Franklin by His Good Mouse Amos. 1999. (J). (978-0-316-52533-6(2)); pap. (978-0-316-52520-6(0)) Little Brown & Co.

Lemisch, Jesse. Benjamin Franklin: The Autobiography & Other Writings. 2001. (gr. 7-12). lib. bdg. 12.95 (978-0-613-45644-9(0)) Tandem Library Bks.

Mara, Wil. Benjamin Franklin. rev. ed. 2006. (Rookie Biography Ser.). (Illus.). 31p. (J). (978-0-531-12450-5(9)) Children's Pr., Ltd.

—Benjamin Franklin. 2002. (Rookie Biographies Ser.). (Illus.). 32p. (J). (gr. 1-2). 19.50 (978-0-516-22516-6(2) , Children's Pr.) Scholastic Library Publishing.

—Benjamin Franklin. 2002. (gr. k-3). lib. bdg. 12.95 (978-0-613-59451-6(7)) Tandem Library Bks.

Marcovitz, Hal. Benjamin Franklin: Scientist, Inventor, Printer, & Statesman. 2006. (Leaders of the American Revolution Ser.). (Illus.). 176p. (J). (gr. 5-8). 30.00 (978-0-7910-9219-4(4) , Chelsea Hse.) Facts On File, Inc.

Marsh, Carole. Benjamin Franklin. 2002. (One Thousand Readers Ser.). (Illus.). 12p. (J). (gr. k-4). 2.95 (978-0-635-01475-7(0) , 14750) Gallopade International.

—The Virginia Reader: Benjamin Franklin. 2001. (Virginia Experience! Ser.). (Illus.). 12p. (J). (gr. k-4). pap. 2.95 (978-0-635-00377-5(5)) Gallopade International.

Mayer, Cassie. Benjamin Franklin. 2007. (J). ***(978-1-4034-9970-7(5));*** pap. ***(978-1-4034-9979-0(9))*** Heinemann Library.

McCurdy, Michael. So Said Ben. 2007. (Illus.). 32p. (YA). (gr. 4 up). 17.95 ***(978-1-56846-147-2(X)*** , Creative Editions) Creative Co., The.

McDonough, Yona Zeldis. The Life of Benjamin Franklin: An American Original. Zeldis, Malcah, illus. 2006. 48p. (J). 17.95 (978-0-8050-7856-5(8)) Holt, Henry & Co.

McLeese, Don. Benjamin Franklin. 2005. (Heroes of the American Revolution Ser.). (Illus.). 32p. (gr. 2-5). 19.95 (978-1-59515-216-9(4)) Rourke Publishing, LLC.

McNeil, Niki, et al. HOCPP 1058 Benjamin Franklin. 2006. spiral bd. 18.50 ***(978-1-60308-058-3(9))*** In the Hands of a Child.

Miller, Chuck. Benjamin Franklin. 2003. (America's Founders Ser.). (J). pap. (978-1-58417-084-6(0)); lib. bdg. (978-1-58417-021-1(2)) Lake Street Pubs.

Murphy, Frank. Ben Franklin & the Magic Squares. 2001. (gr. k-3). lib. bdg. 11.80 (978-0-613-33790-8(5)); (Illus.). (J). 10.79 (978-0-606-20568-9(3)) Tandem Library Bks.

Nettleton, Pamela Hill. Benjamin Franklin. Yesh, Jeff, illus. 2004. (Biographies Ser.). 24p. (C). (gr. k-3). 22.60 (978-1-4048-0186-8(3)) Picture Window Bks.

Olson, Kay Melchisedech. Benjamin Franklin: An American Genius. Purcell, Gordon & Schulz, Barbara, illus. 2005. (Graphic Library). 32p. (J). (gr. 3-7). lib. bdg. 25.26 (978-0-7368-4629-5(8)) Capstone Pr., Inc.

Parks, Peggy J. Benjamin Franklin: Genius Inventor & Electricity Pioneer. 2002. (Giants of Science Ser.). (Illus.). 64p. (J). 26.20 (978-1-56711-658-8(2) , Blackbirch Pr., Inc.) Thomson Gale.

Pingry, Patricia A. Meet Benjamin Franklin. Britt, Stephanie M., illus. 2001. (Meet Ser.). 32p. (J). 9.95 (978-0-8249-4133-8(0)) Ideals Pubns.

Raatma, Lucia. Benjamin Franklin. 2001. (Compass Point Early Biographies Ser.). (Illus.). 32p. (J). (gr. 2 up). lib. bdg. 21.26 (978-0-7565-0067-2(2)) Compass Point Bks.

Randolph, Ryan P. Benjamin Franklin: Inventor, Writer & Patriot. 2005. (Library of American Lives & Times). (Illus.). 112p. (YA). (gr. 4-8). lib. bdg. 31.95 (978-0-8239-5751-4(9)) Rosen Publishing Group, Inc., The.

Rausch, Monica. Benjamin Franklin. 2006. (J). (ENG & SPA.). pap. ***(978-0-8368-7988-9(0));*** (ENG & SPA.). lib. bdg. ***(978-0-8368-7981-0(3));*** (Illus.). 24p. pap. ***(978-0-8368-7689-5(X));*** (Illus.). 24p. lib. bdg. ***(978-0-8368-7682-6(2))*** Stevens, Gareth Inc. (Weekly Reader Early Learning Library).

Riehecky, Janet. Benjamin Franklin. 2002. (Raintree Biographies Ser.). (Illus.). 32p. (J). lib. bdg. 25.69 (978-0-7398-5675-8(8)) Raintree.

Riley, Gail Blasser. Benjamin Franklin & Electricity. 2004. (Cornerstones of Freedom Ser.). (Illus.). 48p. (J). 26.00 (978-0-516-24240-8(7) , Children's Pr.) Scholastic Library Publishing.

Riley, John B. Benjamin Franklin: A Photo Biography. l.t. ed. 2004. (First Biographies Ser.). (Illus.). 24p. (YA). (gr. 5 up). 16.95 (978-1-883846-64-0(1) , First Biographies) Reynolds, Morgan Inc.

Rushby, Pamela. Benjamin Franklin: Printer, Author, Inventor, Politician. 2007. (History Chapters Ser.). 48p. (J). (gr. 1-4). lib. bdg. 17.90 ***(978-1-4263-0191-9(X)*** , National Geographic Children's Bks.) National Geographic Society.

Rustad, Martha E. H. Benjamin Franklin. Saunders-Smith, Gail, ed. 2001. (First Biographies Ser.). (Illus.). 24p. (J). (gr. k-1). lib. bdg. 15.93 (978-0-7368-0995-5(3) , Pebble Bks.) Capstone Pr., Inc.

Satterfield, Kathryn Hoffman. Benjamin Franklin A Man of Many Talents. 2005. 44p. (J). lib. bdg. 15.00 ***(978-1-4242-0846-3(7))*** Fitzgerald Bks.

Schiffer, Michael B., et al. Draw the Lightning Down - Benjamin Franklin & Electrical Technology in the Age of Enlightenment. 2003. (Illus.). 380p. 50.00 (978-0-520-23802-2(8)) Univ. of California Pr.

Shah, Ruchir, ed. Benjamin Franklin. 2007. (YA). 6.95 ***(978-0-9795887-2-3(3))*** EZ Comics.

Sherrow, Victoria. Benjamin Franklin. 2002. (History Maker Bios Ser.). (Illus.). (J). 47p. pap. 6.95 (978-0-8225-0383-5(2) , Lerner Pubns.); 48p. (gr. 3-5). lib. bdg. 26.60 (978-0-8225-0198-5(8)) Lerner Publishing Group.

Stephen, Krensky. Dk Bio: Benjamin Franklin Hc. 2007. 128p. 14.99 ***(978-0-7566-3529-9(2))*** Dorling Kindersley Publishing, Inc.

—Dk Bio: Benjamin Franklin Pb. 2007. 128p. pap. 4.99 ***(978-0-7566-3528-2(4))*** Dorling Kindersley Publishing, Inc.

The Story of Benjamin Franklin. 2002. (Illus.). 24p. (J). (ps-k). 6.95 (978-0-8249-4227-4(2)) Ideals Pubns.

Streissguth, Thomas & Streissguth, Tom. Benjamin Franklin. 2005. (Biography Ser.). (Illus.). 112p. (gr. 6-12). 27.93 (978-0-8225-4997-0(2)) Lerner Publishing Group.

Streissguth, Tom. Benjamin Franklin. 2005. (Bios for Challenged Readers Ser.). (Illus.). 112p. (J). (gr. 6-12). lib. bdg. 27.93 (978-0-8225-2210-2(1)) Lerner Publishing Group.

Thayer, William M. From Boyhood to Manhood - the Life of Be. 2006. pap. ***(978-1-4068-0906-0(3))*** Echo Library.

Time for Kids Editors. Benjamin Franklin: A Man of Many Talents. 2005. (Time for Kids Ser.). (Illus.). 48p. (J). 14.99 (978-0-06-057610-3(3)); pap. 3.99 (978-0-06-057609-7(X)) HarperCollins Pubs.

Uglow, Loyd. Benjamin Franklin - You Know What to Say. Budwine, Greg, illus. 2000. (Another Great Achiever Ser.). 48p. (J). (gr. 3-6). 9.95 (978-1-57537-108-5(1)); lib. bdg. 16.95 (978-1-57537-106-1(5)) Advance Publishing, Inc.

—Benjamin Franklin You Know What to Say Read-Along. Budwine, Greg, illus. 2003. (J). lib. bdg. 23.95 incl. audio (978-1-57537-791-9(8)); lib. bdg. 23.95 incl. audio compact disk (978-1-57537-741-4(1)) Advance Publishing, Inc.

Usel, T. M. Benjamin Franklin, 6 vols. (gr. 2-5). 36.95 (978-0-7368-4555-7(0)) Red Brick Learning.

Van Vleet, Carmella. Amazing Ben Franklin Inventions You Can Build Yourself. 2007. (Build It Yourself Ser.). 128p. (J). (gr. 4-7). pap. 14.95 ***(978-0-9771294-7-8(0))*** Nomad Pr.

Warrick, Karen Clemens. Benjamin Franklin: Creating a Nation. 2004. (America's Founding Fathers Ser.). (Illus.). 128p. (J). lib. bdg. 26.60 (978-0-7660-2195-2(5)) Enslow Pubs., Inc.

Whiting, Jim. Benjamin Franklin. 2006. (Profiles in American History Ser.). (Illus.). 48p. (J). (gr. 4-8). lib. bdg. 20.95 (978-1-58415-435-8(7)) Mitchell Lane Pubs., Inc.

FRANKLIN, BENJAMIN, 1706-1790—FICTION

Ain, Beth Levine. The Portrait. 2008. (J). ***(978-0-7636-3396-7(8))*** Candlewick Pr.

D'Lacey, Chris. Franklin's Bear. Taylor, Thomas, illus. 2005. (Red Go Bananas Ser.). 42p. (J). lib. bdg. (978-0-7787-2674-6(6)) Crabtree Publishing Co.

Fleming, Candace. The Hatmaker's Sign: A Story by Benjamin Franklin. Parker, Robert A., illus. 1998. 40p. (J). (gr. k-4). pap. 15.95 (978-0-531-30075-6(7) , Orchard Bks.) Scholastic, Inc.

—The Hatmaker's Sign: A Story by Benjamin Franklin. Parker, Robert, illus. 2000. (J). (978-0-606-19857-8(1)) Tandem Library Bks.

Gutman, Dan. Qwerty Stevens Stuck in Time with Benjamin Franklin. 192p. (J). 2005. pap. 4.99 (978-0-689-87884-8(2) , Aladdin); 2002. (Illus.). (gr. 5-8). 17.95 (978-0-689-84553-6(7)) Simon & Schuster Children's Publishing.

Harcourt School Publishers Staff. The Great Franklin Debate On Level. 3rd ed. 2002. (Trophies Reading Program Ser.). (Illus.). pap. 5.10 (978-0-15-323368-5(0)) Harcourt Schl. Pubs.

Hedstrom-Page, Deborah. From Settlement to City with Benjamin Franklin. Martinez, Sergio, illus. 2007. 80p. (J). (gr. 3-9). 9.99 (978-0-8054-3267-1(1)) B&H Publishing Grp.

Hi-stories Presents Bengalmin Franklin. 2005. (J). per. (978-0-9763233-1-0(1)) Little Germ That Could...Creations, Inc., The.

Hume, Stephen Eaton. Ben Franklin's War. 2006. 120p. (J). pap. 10.99 ***(978-1-55002-638-2(0)*** , Sandcastle Bks.) Dundurn Group, The CAN. *Dist:* Univ. of Toronto Pr.

Kramer, Candice. De visita con Benjamin Franklin & Ben Franklin's Visit A When Machine Play. 2005. spiral bd. 76.00 ***(978-1-4108-5787-3(5))*** Benchmark Education Co.

Lawson, Robert. Ben & Me: An Astonishing Life of Benjamin Franklin by His Good Mouse Amos. (J). (ps-5). 2005. pap. 6.99 (978-0-316-01636-0(5)); 1999. (978-0-316-52533-6(2)); 1999. pap. (978-0-316-52520-6(0)) Little Brown & Co.

Murphy, Frank. Ben Franklin & the Magic Squares. Walz, Richard, illus. 2001. (Step into Reading Ser.). 48p. (J). (gr. k-3). pap. 3.99 (978-0-375-80621-6(0)); lib. bdg. 11.99 (978-0-375-90621-3(5)) Random Hse. Children's Bks. (Random Hse. Bks. for Young Readers).

Sargent, Dave & Sargent, Pat. Sugar: (Cream) Curiosity Is Good, 25, 57. Lenoir, Jane, illus. 2001. (Saddle Up Ser.: 57). 36p. (J). pap. 6.95 (978-1-56763-668-0(3)); lib. bdg. 22.60 (978-1-56763-667-3(5)) Ozark Publishing.

The Spirited Philadelphia Adventure. 2000. (Illus.). 32p. (J). (gr. k-2). (978-0-9626959-1-9(2)) Junior League of Philadelphia, Inc.

Uglow, Loyd. Benjamin Franklin - You Know What to Say. Budwine, Greg, illus. 2000. (Another Great Achiever Ser.). 48p. (J). (gr. 3-6). lib. bdg. 16.95 (978-1-57537-106-1(5)) Advance Publishing, Inc.

FRANKLIN D. ROOSEVELT LIBRARY, HYDE PARK, NEW YORK

Margaret, Amy. Franklin D. Roosevelt Library & Museum. 2004. (Presidential Libraries Ser.). (Illus.). 24p. (J). lib. bdg. 18.75 (978-0-8239-6268-6(7) , PowerKids Pr.) Rosen Publishing Group, Inc., The.

FRANZ FERDINAND, ARCHDUKE OF AUSTRIA, 1863-1914—ASSASSINATION

Ross, Stewart. Assassination in Sarajevo: The Trigger for World War I. 2006. (Point of Impact Ser.). (Illus.). 32p. (J). ***(978-1-4034-9138-1(0))*** Heinemann Library.

Stewart Ross. Assassination in Sarajevo. 2nd ed. 2006. (Point of Impact Ser.). (Illus.). 32p. (J). pap. ***(978-1-4034-9147-3(X))*** Heinemann Library.

Woolf, Alex. Assassination in Sarajevo. 2003. (Days That Shook the World Ser.). (Illus.). 47p. (J). lib. bdg. 28.56 (978-0-7398-6048-9(8)) Raintree.

FRAUD

see also Impostors and Imposture

Berry, Joy Wilt. A Book about Cheating. 2005. (Illus.). (J). (978-0-7172-8583-9(9)) Scholastic, Inc.

Marvis, B. & DeAngelis, Gina. White-Collar Crime. Sarat, Austin, ed. 1999. (Crime, Justice & Punishment Ser.). (Illus.). 80p. (YA). (gr. 7-12). 30.00 (978-0-7910-4279-3(0) , Chelsea Hse.) Facts On File, Inc.

Mauro, Paul & Melton, H. Keith. Forgery & Frauds. 2004. (Detective Academy Ser.). (Illus.). 48p. (J). (978-0-439-57181-4(2)) Scholastic, Inc.

Schroeder, Andreas. Scams! 2004. (True Stories from the Edge Ser.). (Illus.). 160p. (J). (gr. 4). 18.95 (978-1-55037-853-5(8)); pap. 7.95 (978-1-55037-852-8(X)) Annick Pr., Ltd. CAN. *Dist:* Firefly Bks., Ltd.

Stewart, Gail B. Forgery. 2006. (Crime Scene Investigations Ser.). (Illus.). 112p. (J). (gr. 7-10). 32.45 (978-1-59018-949-8(3) , 1256792, Lucent Bks.) Thomson Gale.

Thompson, Lisa. Hoaxes, Fibs & Fakes. 2005. (Real Deal Ser.). (Illus.). 32p. (J). 18.50 (978-0-7910-8428-1(0) , Chelsea Hse.) Facts On File, Inc.

Townsend, John. Fakes & Forgeries. 48p. (J). 2006. pap. 8.90 (978-1-4109-1430-9(5)); 2005. lib. bdg. 31.43 (978-1-4109-1424-8(0)) Raintree.

Weil, Ann. Fakes. 2007. (J). pap. ***(978-1-4109-2988-4(4));*** lib. bdg. ***(978-1-4109-2967-9(1))*** Steck-Vaughn.

Woolf, Alex. Fakes & Hoaxes. 2004. (Forensic Files Ser.). (Illus.). 48p. (J). lib. bdg. 27.07 (978-1-4034-4829-3(9)) Heinemann Library.

—Investigating Fakes & Hoaxes. 2004. (Forensic Files Ser.). (Illus.). 48p. (J). pap. 8.50 (978-1-4034-5469-0(8)) Heinemann Library.

FRAUD—FICTION

Alger, Horatio. Hector's Inheritance: Or, The Boys of Smith Institute. 2006. pap. ***(978-1-4065-0708-9(3))*** Dodo Pr.

—Hector's Inheritance: Or, The Boys of Smith Institute. unabr. ed. 2002. (Polyglot Press Alger Ser.). (Illus.). (J). pap. 17.95 (978-1-4115-0004-4(0)) Polyglot Pr., Inc.

Alger Jr. Horatio Staff. Hector's Inheritance. rev. ed. 2006. 276p. 28.95 (978-1-4218-1758-3(6)); pap. 13.95 (978-1-4218-1858-0(2)) 1st World Publishing, Inc. (1st World Library - Literary Society).

Amos, Janine. Cheat. 2007. (Good & Bad Ser.). (Illus.). 32p. (J). (ps-2). pap. 9.95 ***(978-1-84234-396-8(3)*** , Evans Brothers, Limited) Evans Publishing Group GBR. *Dist:* Independent Pubs. Group.

Curtis, Christopher Paul. Bucking the Sarge. 2006. 288p. (YA). (gr. 7). reprint ed. mass mkt. 6.50 (978-0-440-41331-8(1) , Laurel Leaf) Random Hse. Children's Bks.

Singleton, Linda Joy. Oh No! UFO! Karre, Andrew, ed. 2004. (Strange Encounters Ser.). 192p. (gr. 8-12). pap. 4.99 (978-0-7387-0579-8(9)) Llewellyn Pubns.

Thomas, Paul R., reader. The Reeve's Tale. 2006. pap. 10.00 ***(978-0-8425-2667-8(6))*** Brigham Young Univ.

FREAKS

see Monsters

FREDDI FISH (FICTITIOUS CHARACTER)—FICTION

Nickel, Scott. Freddi Fish a Whale of a Tale! Johnson, Jay B., illus. 2001. (Humongous Ser.). 24p. (J). (ps-3). pap. 4.99 (978-1-58668-061-9(7)) Lyrick Studios.

FREDDY THE DETECTIVE (FICTITIOUS CHARACTER)—FICTION

Brooks, Walter R. Freddy & Mr. Camphor. Wiese, Kurt, illus. 2000. 234p. (J). (gr. 3-7). 23.95 (978-1-58567-027-7(8)) Overlook Pr., The.

—Freddy & the Baseball Team from Mars. Wiese, Kurt, illus. 1999. 256p. (J). (gr. 3-7). 23.95 (978-0-87951-942-1(8)) Overlook Pr., The.

—Freddy & the Baseball Team from Mars. 2000. (J). pap. 67.95 incl. audio (978-0-7887-4461-7(5) , 41150) Recorded Bks., LLC.

—Freddy & the Bean Home News. Wiese, Kurt, illus. 2000. (Freddy Ser.). 230p. (J). (gr. 3-7). 23.95 (978-1-58567-081-9(2)) Overlook Pr., The.

—Freddy & the Dragon. Wiese, Kurt, illus. 2000. 239p. (J). (gr. 3 up). 23.95 (978-1-58567-026-0(X)) Overlook Pr., The.

—Freddy & the Flying Saucer Plans. Wiese, Kurt, illus. 1998. (Freddy Ser.). 243p. (J). (gr. 3-7). 23.95 (978-0-87951-883-7(9)) Overlook Pr., The.

—Freddy & the Flying Saucer Plans. unabr. ed. 2000. (J). pap. 66.95 incl. audio (978-0-7887-3639-1(6) , 41004X4) Recorded Bks., LLC.

—Freddy & the IgnormOus. Wiese, Kurt, illus. 2001. 288p. (J). pap. 6.99 (978-0-14-230043-5(8) , Puffin) Penguin Group (USA) Inc.

—Freddy & the Ignormus. Wiese, Kurt, illus. 1998. (Freddy Ser.). 288p. (J). (gr. 3-7). 23.95 (978-0-87951-882-0(0)) Overlook Pr., The.

—Freddy & the Ignormus. 1999. (J). pap. 66.95 incl. audio (978-0-7887-2996-6(9) , 40878) Recorded Bks., LLC.

—Freddy & the Pilot. Wiese, Kurt, illus. 1999. 288p. (J). (gr. 3-7). 23.95 (978-0-87951-941-4(X)) Overlook Pr., The.

FREE SPEECH

see Freedom of Speech

FREEBOOTERS

see Pirates

FREEDOM

see Liberty

FREEDOM MARCHES (CIVIL RIGHTS)

see Civil Rights Demonstrations

FREEDOM OF ASSEMBLY

see Assembly, Right of

FREEDOM OF RELIGION

see also Church and State

Connolly, Sean. Religious Freedom. 2005. (Campaigns for Change Ser.). (Illus.). 48p. (J). (gr. 6-9). lib. bdg. 29.95 (978-1-58340-514-7(3) , 1247337) Smart Apple Media.

Conway, John Richard. A Look at the First Amendment: Freedom of Speech & Religion. 2008. (J). ***(978-1-59845-069-9(7)*** , MyReportLinks.com Bks.) Enslow Pubs., Inc.

Currie, Stephen. Religious Oppression. 2003. (Great Escapes Ser.). (Illus.). 112p. (J). 29.95 (978-1-59018-280-2(4) , Lucent Bks.) Thomson Gale.

Gaustad, Edwin S. Roger Williams: Prophet of Liberty. 2001. (Oxford Portraits Ser.). (Illus.). 144p. (YA). (gr. 9 up). 28.00 (978-0-19-513000-3(6)) Oxford Univ. Pr., Inc.

Head, Tom. Freedom of Religion. 2005. (American Rights Ser.). (Illus.). 160p. (J). (gr. 4-9). 35.00 (978-0-8160-5664-4(1)) Facts On File, Inc.

Hirst, Mike. Freedom of Belief. 2005. (What Do We Mean by Human Rights? Ser.). (Illus.). 46p. (J). (gr. 5-9). lib. bdg. 29.95 (978-1-932889-66-6(3)) Sea-To-Sea Pubns.

Nelson, Sheila. The Northern Colonies. 2005. (How America Became America Ser.). (Illus.). 96p. (J). lib. bdg. (978-1-59084-901-9(9)) Mason Crest Pubs.

Raum, Elizabeth. Roger Williams. 2004. (Illus.). 32p. (J). pap. 7.50 (978-1-4034-5969-5(X)); lib. bdg. 25.64 (978-1-4034-5961-9(4)) Heinemann Library.

Smith, Rich. First Amendment: The Right of Expression. 2007. (Bill of Rights Ser.). (ENG., Illus.). 32p. (J). (gr. 4-8). lib. bdg. 25.65 ***(978-1-59928-914-4(8)*** , ABDO & Daughters) ABDO Publishing Co.

FREEDOM OF SPEECH

see also Assembly, Right of

Allport, Alan. Freedom of Speech. 2003. (Point/Counterpoint Ser.). (Illus.). 112p. (gr. 9-13). 32.95 (978-0-7910-7370-4(X) , Chelsea Hse.) Facts On File, Inc.

Axelrod-Contrada, Joan. Reno v. ACLU: Internet Censorship. 2006. (Supreme Court Milestones Ser.). (Illus.). 144p. (J). lib. bdg. 39.93 (978-0-7614-2144-3(0) , Benchmark Bks.) Cavendish, Marshall Corp.

Barbour, Scott. Free Speech. 2000. (Current Controversies Ser.). (Illus.). 206p. (YA). (gr. 9-12). lib. bdg. 32.45 (978-0-7377-0143-2(9)); 2nd ed. (gr. 7-12). pap. 21.20 (978-0-7377-0142-5(0)) Thomson Gale. (Greenhaven Pr., Inc.).

Burns, Kate. Fighters Against Censorship. 2003. (History Makers Ser.). (Illus.). 112p. (J). 29.95 (978-1-59018-340-3(1) , Lucent Bks.) Thomson Gale.

Ditchfield, Christin. Freedom of Speech. 2004. (True Bks.). (Illus.). 48p. (J). (gr. 3-5). pap. 6.95 (978-0-516-27909-1(2) , Children's Pr.) Scholastic Library Publishing.

Edwards, Nicola. Voice. 2004. (Children's Rights Ser.). (J). lib. bdg. 27.10 (978-1-58340-423-2(6)) Smart Apple Media.

Egendorf, Laura K. Free Speech. 2007. (J). lib. bdg. ***978-1-60152-018-0(2))** ReferencePoint Pr., Inc.

Fontanetta, Karen & Isler, Claudia. The Right to Free Speech. 2001. (Individual Rights & Civic Responsibility Ser.). (Illus.). 64p. (YA). (gr. 7-12). lib. bdg. 26.50 (978-0-8239-3234-4(6)) Rosen Publishing Group, Inc., The.

Freedom of Speech DBA. 2003. spiral bd. 16.95 (978-1-56004-150-4(1)) Social Studies Schl. Service.

Friedman, Ian C. Freedom of Speech & the Press. 2005. (American Rights Ser.). (Illus.). 128p. (J). (gr. 4-9). per. 35.00 (978-0-8160-5662-0(5)) Facts On File, Inc.

Gold, Susan Dudley. Tinker v. Des Moines: Free Speech for Students. 2006. (Supreme Court Milestones Ser.). (Illus.). 143p. (J). lib. bdg. 39.93 (978-0-7614-2142-9(4) , Benchmark Bks.) Cavendish, Marshall Corp.

Icenoggle, Jodi. Schenck V. United States & the Freedom of Speech Debate: Debating Supreme Court Decisions. 2005. (Debating Supreme Court Decisions Ser.). (Illus.). 128p. (YA). (gr. 7-13). lib. bdg. 26.60 (978-0-7660-2392-5(3)) Enslow Pubs., Inc.

Smith, Rich. First Amendment: The Right of Expression. 2007. (Bill of Rights Ser.). (ENG., Illus.). 32p. (J). (gr. 4-8). lib. bdg. 25.65 (***978-1-59928-914-4(8)** , ABDO & Daughters) ABDO Publishing Co.

Steele, Philip. Freedom of Speech. 2005. (What Do We Mean by Human Rights? Ser.). (Illus.). 46p. (J). (gr. 5-9). lib. bdg. 29.95 (978-1-932889-67-3(1)) Sea-To-Sea Pubns.

Steffens, Bradley. Censorship. rev. ed. 2004. (Overview Ser.). (Illus.). 112p. (gr. 7-10). 29.95 (978-1-59018-187-4(5) , Lucent Bks.) Thomson Gale.

Steffens, Bradley. Free Speech. 2007. (J). (***978-1-60217-015-5(0))** Erickson Pr.

FREEDOM OF THE PRESS

Burns, Kate. Fighters Against Censorship. 2003. (History Makers Ser.). (Illus.). 112p. (J). 29.95 (978-1-59018-340-3(1) , Lucent Bks.) Thomson Gale.

Egendorf, Laura K. Censorship. 2003. (Examining Issues Through Political Cartoons Ser.). (Illus.). 80p. (YA). pap. 29.95 (978-0-7377-1250-6(3) , Greenhaven Pr., Inc.) Thomson Gale.

Freedom of the Press DBA. 2003. spiral bd. 16.95 (978-1-56004-149-8(8)) Social Studies Schl. Service.

Friedman, Ian C. Freedom of Speech & the Press. 2005. (American Rights Ser.). (Illus.). 128p. (J). (gr. 4-9). per. 35.00 (978-0-8160-5662-0(5)) Facts On File, Inc.

Gold, Susan Dudley. The Pentagon Papers: National Security or the Right to Know. 2004. (Supreme Court Milestones Ser.). (Illus.). 144p. (J). 37.07 (978-0-7614-1843-6(1) , Benchmark Bks.) Cavendish, Marshall Corp.

Smith, Rich. First Amendment: The Right of Expression. 2007. (Bill of Rights Ser.). (ENG., Illus.). 32p. (J). (gr. 4-8). lib. bdg. 25.65 (***978-1-59928-914-4(8)** , ABDO & Daughters) ABDO Publishing Co.

Westermann, Karen T. John Peter Zenger: Free Press Advocate. 2000. (Colonial Leaders Ser.). (Illus.). 80p. (J). (gr. 8-12). 27.50 (978-0-7910-5966-1(9) , Chelsea Hse.) Facts On File, Inc.

—John Peter Zenger: Free Press Advocate. 2000. (Illus.). 80p. (J). (gr. 4-7). lib. bdg. 17.60 (978-0-613-32727-5(6)) Tandem Library Bks.

FREEDOM OF WORSHIP

see Freedom of Religion

FREEMASONS

Crook, Carol. The Masonic Lodge: Where Will It Take You? 1998. 32p. (YA). (gr. 10 up). pap. 5.75 (978-0-939399-23-9(7)) Books of Truth.

Vang, Richard. My Dad Is a Freemason. 2006. (Illus.). 32p. (J). per. (978-0-9789066-0-3(8)) Square Circle Pr. LLC.

FREEZING

see Ice; Refrigeration and Refrigerating Machinery

FREIGHT AND FREIGHTAGE

see also Aeronautics, Commercial

Chelsea House Publishing Staff. Freight by Rail. 2000. (World's Railroads Ser.). (Illus.). 64p. (YA). (gr. 5 up). 27.50 (978-0-7910-5562-5(0) , Chelsea Hse.) Facts On File, Inc.

DeRouin, Edward M. North Shore Line - Interurban Freight. 2005. (Midwestern Rail Ser.: #2). (Illus.). 96p. per. 34.95 (978-0-9728743-1-1(3)) Pixels Publishing.

Hill, Lee Sullivan. Get Around with Cargo. 1999. (Get Around Bks.). (Illus.). 32p. (J). (gr. k-3). lib. bdg. 14.60 (978-1-57505-311-0(X) , Carolrhoda Bks.) Lerner Publishing Group.

Richardson, Adele D. Freight Trains. 2000. (Transportation Library). (Illus.). 24p. (J). (gr. 1-2). lib. bdg. 18.60 (978-0-7368-0607-7(5) , Bridgestone Bks.) Capstone Pr., Inc.

FREMONT, JOHN CHARLES, 1813-1890

Faber, Harold. John Charles Fremont: Pathfinder to the West. 2002. (Great Explorations Ser.). (Illus.). 79p. (J). 29.93 (978-0-7614-1481-0(9) , Benchmark Bks.) Cavendish, Marshall Corp.

Marcovitz, Hal. John C. Fremont: Pathfinder of the West. 2001. (Explorers of New Worlds Ser.). (Illus.). (J). 63p. pap. 25.00 (978-0-7910-6431-3(X)); 64p. 25.00 (978-0-7910-6430-6(1)) Facts On File, Inc. (Chelsea Hse.).

—John C. Fremont: Pathfinder of the West. 2002. (gr. 3-6). lib. bdg. 17.60 (978-0-613-65429-6(3)) Tandem Library Bks.

Maynard, Charles W. John Charles Fremont: The Pathfinder. 2003. (Famous Explorers of the American West Ser.). (Illus.). 24p. (J). lib. bdg. 18.75 (978-0-8239-6289-1(X) , PowerKids Pr.) Rosen Publishing Group, Inc., The.

Petrie, Kristin. John C. Fremont. 2004. (Explorers Ser.). (Illus.). 32p. (J). (gr. k-6). lib. bdg. 22.78 (978-1-59197-602-8(2) , Checkerboard Library) ABDO Publishing Co.

Price Hossell, Karen. John C. Fremont. (Groundbreakers Ser.). (Illus.). 48p. (J). 2003. (gr. 5-7). lib. bdg. 27.07 (978-1-4034-0244-8(2)); 2002. pap. 8.50 (978-1-4034-0480-0(1)) Heinemann Library.

Souza, Dorothy M. John C. Fremont. 2004. (Watts Library). (Illus.). 64p. (J). (gr. 5-7). pap. 8.95 (978-0-531-16652-9(X)); 25.50 (978-0-531-12288-4(3)) Scholastic Library Publishing. (Watts, Franklin).

Witteman, Barbara. John Charles Fremont: Western Pathfinder. 2002. (Let Freedom Ring Ser.). (Illus.). 48p. (J). (gr. 3-4). lib. bdg. 22.60 (978-0-7368-1348-8(9) , Bridgestone Bks.) Capstone Pr., Inc.

FRENCH—AMERICA

Deiters, Erika & Deiters, Jim. The French Community in America. 2003. (J). (978-1-58417-031-0(X)); pap. (978-1-58417-094-5(8)) Lake Street Pubs.

Horton, Casey. The French. 2000. (J). 15.75 (978-0-606-22833-6(0)) Tandem Library Bks.

—French. 2000. (gr. 3-6). lib. bdg. 17.60 (978-0-613-27841-6(0)) Tandem Library Bks.

FRENCH AND INDIAN WAR, 1755-1763

see United States—History—French and Indian War, 1755-1763

FRENCH-CANADIANS

Pelletier, Fran. Little Pine to King Spruce: A Franco-American Childhood. 2003. (Illus.). 192p. pap. 15.00 (978-0-88448-254-3(5)) Tilbury Hse. Pubs.

FRENCH-CANADIANS—FICTION

Downie, Mary Alice & Rawlyk, George. A Song for Acadia. 2004. (Illus.). 60p. pap. (978-1-55109-474-8(6)) Nimbus Publishing, Ltd.

FRENCH LANGUAGE

ABC. 2002. (First Steps Reading Ser.). 24p. (J). pap. 3.95 (978-0-7894-8487-1(0)) Dorling Kindersley Publishing, Inc.

Amery, H. First Hundred Words French Sticker Book. rev. ed. 2004. (Picture Puzzles Ser.). (FRE.). 40p. (J). pap. 8.95 (978-0-7945-0191-4(5) , Usborne) EDC Publishing.

—First Thousand Words. rev. ed. 2004. (First Learning Ser.). (FRE.). 64p. (J). 12.99 (978-0-7945-0283-6(0)) EDC Publishing.

Amery, Heather. First Thousand Words in French Sticker Book. Cartwright, Stephen, illus. rev. ed. 2004. (First Thousand Words Sticker Bks.). (FRE & ENG.). 70p. (J). (ps-6). pap. 9.95 (978-0-7945-0425-0(6) , Usborne) EDC Publishing.

Amery, Heather & Cartwright, Stephen. First French Word Book. 2004. (Farmyard Tales First Words Ser.). (ENG & FRE., Illus.). 48p. (J). 10.95 (978-0-7945-0295-9(4) , Usborne) EDC Publishing.

Ariew, Robert & Nerenz, Anne. Par Ici: Text with free student Cassette. 484p. (YA). pap. 55.96 (978-0-669-35187-3(3) , 035187) Houghton Mifflin College Div.

Avp, prod. Perspectives Francaises. (YA). cd-rom 79.95 (978-0-7365-1744-7(8)) Films Media Group.

Beaton, Clare. Toys: English-French. 2003. (ps-2). lib. bdg. 12.95 (978-0-613-81896-4(2)) Tandem Library Bks.

Berlitz Publishing Staff. French. rev. ed. 2003. (Berlitz Kids Language Pack Ser.). (FRE & ENG., Illus.). 26.95 (978-981-246-366-1(6) , 463666) Berlitz Publishing.

Berlitz Publishing Staff, ed. French. 2007. (FRE & ENG., Illus.). 12p. bds. 7.95 (***978-981-268-037-2(3))** APA Publications Services SGP. *Dist:* Langenscheidt Pubs Inc.

—French. 2nd rev. ed. 2005. (Berlitz 1,000 Words Ser.). (FRE & ENG., Illus.). 64p. pap. 9.95 (978-981-246-525-2(1) , 465251) Berlitz Publishing.

Blair, Robert. Power-Glide French Junior Additional Learner Package, 2 bks. l.t. ed. 2002. (Illus.). 346p. (J). pap. 39.95 (978-1-58204-220-6(9)) Power-Glide Foreign Language Courses.

—Power-Glide French Lower Elementary, 4 vols. l.t. ed. 2002. (Illus.). 512p. pap. 99.95 incl. cd-rom, audio compact disk (978-1-58204-207-7(1)) Power-Glide Foreign Language Courses.

Blair, Robert, told to. Power-Glide French Children's Course Upgrade, 2 bks. l.t. ed. 2001. (Illus.). 197p. (J). pap. 59.95 incl. audio compact disk (978-1-58204-211-4(X)) Power-Glide Foreign Language Courses.

Bruzzone, Catherine. French for Children. Beaton, Clare, illus. 2nd rev. ed. 2003. (Language for Children Ser.). (FRE.). 80p. pap. 29.95 incl. cd-rom (978-0-07-140767-0(7) , 9780071407670) McGraw-Hill Cos., The.

—French for Children. 2003. (FRE & ENG., Illus.). 80p. (J). (gr. 1-6). 29.95 (978-0-8442-9179-6(X)) McGraw-Hill Trade.

Carole Marsh. False Paw! French for Kids. 2004. (Little Linguist Ser.). (J). (gr. 2-6). pap. 5.95 (978-0-635-02430-5(6)) Gallopade International.

Clark, Augusta, et al. C'est a Toil!, Level 3. 1998. (FRE.). (YA). (gr. 10-12). pap., wbk. ed. 11.95 (978-0-8219-1751-0(X) , 40672) EMC/Paradigm Publishing.

Davis, Carla Norman. French Made Fun. 1999. (J). Vol. 1, Bk. 1. (gr. 1-3). wbk. ed. 15.00 (978-1-930272-04-0(9)); Vol. 1, Bk. 2. 22.00 (978-1-930272-07-1(3)); Vol. 1, Bk. 2. (gr. 4-5). wbk. ed. 15.00 (978-1-930272-05-7(7)) Queen Enterprises, Inc.

Daynes, Katie. Easy French. 2002. (gr. 3-6). lib. bdg. 22.20 (978-0-613-90009-6(X)) Tandem Library Bks.

Daynes, Katie & Irving, N. Easy French. 2004. (Easy Languages Ser.). (FRE., Illus.). 128p. (J). (gr. 6 up). lib. bdg. 20.95 (978-1-58086-429-5(5)) EDC Publishing.

de Brunhoff, Laurent. Babar et sa Fille Isabelle. 2000. (Babar Ser.).Tr. of Babar & His Sister Isabelle. (FRE.). (J). 13.95 (978-2-01-223682-0(0)) Istra FRA. *Dist:* Distribooks, Inc.

DeCesare, Ruth. Songs for the French Class. 2001. (J). pap. 9.95 (978-0-8442-1421-4(3) , National Textbook Co.) McGraw-Hill/Contemporary.

Demado. Allez Viens! Level 3. 3rd ed. 2001. 74.20 (978-0-03-056596-0(0)) Holt, Rinehart & Winston.

—Se Allez, Viens! En Route!, Level 1B. 6th ed. 2006. (FRE.). 58.60 (978-0-03-036972-8(X)) Holt, Rinehart & Winston.

Discovering French Blanc, Euro Edition. 2003. (YA). (-12). stu. ed. (978-0-618-03505-2(2)); (FRE.). act. bk. ed. (978-0-618-04709-3(3)) McDougal Littell Inc.

Discovering French Bleu, Euro Edition. 2003. (FRE.). (YA). (-12). act. bk. ed. (978-0-618-04708-6(5)); (FRE.). (gr. 9-12). tchr. ed. (978-0-618-03509-0(5)); (FRE.). (gr. 9-12). (978-0-618-09504-9(7)); (YA). (gr. 9-12). stu. ed. (978-0-618-03504-5(4)) McDougal Littell Inc.

Discovering French Rouge, Euro Edition. 2003. (YA). (-12). stu. ed. (978-0-618-03506-9(0)); (FRE.). act. bk. ed. (978-0-618-04710-9(7)) McDougal Littell Inc.

Dunn, Opal. Leo le Chat Comes to Play: A First French Story. Gale, Cathy, illus. (ENG & FRE.). 24p. (978-0-7112-1930-4(3)) Lincoln, Frances Ltd. GBR. *Dist:* Transition Vendor.

—Leo le Chat Comes to Play! A First French Story. Gale, Cathy, illus. 2004. 24p. (J). 7.95 (978-1-84507-308-4(8)) Lincoln, Frances Ltd. GBR. *Dist:* Perseus Distribution.

—Un, Deux, Trois. Aggs, Patrice, illus. 2006. (FRE.). 24p. (J). pap. 9.95 (978-1-84507-623-8(0)) Lincoln, Frances Ltd. GBR. *Dist:* Perseus Distribution.

Furstenberg, Gilberte & Levet, Sabine. Dans un Quartier de Paris. 1999. (Yale Language Ser.). (FRE.). 96p. stu. ed., wbk. ed. 20.00 (978-0-300-07850-3(1)) Yale Univ. Pr.

Hallsworth, Gill & Bell, Jacqueline. French. Trotter, Stuart, illus. 4th rev. unabr. ed. 2003. (ENG & FRE.). 32p. (J). 8.99 (978-0-330-32068-9(8) , Pan) Pan Macmillan GBR. *Dist:* Trafalgar Square Publishing.

Haughom, Lisa, illus. Jeux de Vocabulaire. 1999. 76p. pap. 21.95 (978-0-9723849-7-1(9)) Languages For Kids.

Haughom, Lisa, illus. & text. Jeux Pour la Classe de Francais. Haughom, Lisa, text. 1999. 55p. pap. 21.95 (978-0-9723849-4-0(4)) Languages For Kids.

Hazan, Maurice, creator. Allons en Ville: Directions in the City. 2000. (FRE.). (YA). 199.00 (978-1-932770-70-4(4) , FG15) Symtalk, Inc.

—Le Chemin: Practicing Everyday Vocabulary for French. 2000. (FRE.). (J). 90.00 (978-1-932770-60-5(7) , FC5) Symtalk, Inc.

—Clothes & Colors Game in French. 2000. (FRE.). (J). 99.00 (978-1-932770-68-1(2) , FG13) Symtalk, Inc.

—The Conversation Game for French. 2000. (FRE.). (YA). 90.00 (978-1-932770-63-6(1) , FG8) Symtalk, Inc.

—Dis moi qui c Est: French Dialogues Level 2. 2000. (FRE.). (J). 99.00 (978-1-932770-61-2(5) , FG6) Symtalk, Inc.

—Dis moi qui c Est: French Dialogues Level 3. 2000. (FRE.). (YA). 199.00 (978-1-932770-71-1(2) , FG16) Symtalk, Inc.

—Escrivons: Introduction to Writing in French. 2000. (FRE.). (J). 175.00 (978-1-932770-66-7(6) , FG11) Symtalk, Inc.

—French Conjugating Cards. 2004. (FRE.). 195.00 (978-1-932770-87-2(9) , FCC) Symtalk, Inc.

—The French Question Game. 2000. (FRE.). (YA). 99.00 (978-1-932770-64-3(X) , FG9) Symtalk, Inc.

—Objects, Colors & Numbers Bingo for French. 2000. (FRE.). (J). 90.00 (978-1-932770-57-5(7) , FG2) Symtalk, Inc.

—Phrases et Photos: Long sentence Bingo. 2000. (FRE.). (YA). 90.00 (978-1-932770-62-9(3) , FG7) Symtalk, Inc.

—The Prom Game in French. 2000. (FRE.). (YA). 99.00 (978-1-932770-67-4(4) , FG12) Symtalk, Inc.

—Resto Presto French. 2000. (FRE.). (J). 120.00 (978-1-932770-58-2(5) , FC3) Symtalk, Inc.

—Savoir, devoir, vouloir, Pouvoir: Symtalk Verb + Verb Infinitive Game for French. 2000. (FRE.). (YA). 99.00 (978-1-932770-65-0(8) , FG10) Symtalk, Inc.

—Unusual Suspects: The Past Tense in French. 2000. (FRE.). (YA). 99.00 (978-1-932770-69-8(0) , FG14) Symtalk, Inc.

—Les Verbes: Symtalk Verb Bingo. 2000. (FRE.). (J). 90.00 (978-1-932770-56-8(9) , FG1) Symtalk, Inc.

Hazan, Maurice, illus. French, Bk. 1. 2004. (FRE.). (J). 140.00 (978-1-932770-30-8(5) , FC-FB1) Symtalk, Inc.

Hazan, Maurice, illus. & creator. French. Hazan, Maurice, creator. 2004. (FRE.). Bk. 2. (J). 175.00 (978-1-932770-32-2(1) , FC-FB2); Bk. 3. 199.00 (978-1-932770-34-6(8) , FC-FB3) Symtalk, Inc.

Hendry, Linda & Farris, Katherine. Mon Plus Bel Album de Mots Illustres. (FRE., Illus.). (J). pap. 11.99 (978-0-590-73945-0(X)) Scholastic, Inc.

Holt, Rinehart and Winston Staff. Allez Viens! Grammar Tutor. 3rd ed. 2001. pap. 21.66 (978-0-03-065668-2(0)) Holt, Rinehart & Winston.

—Allez Viens! Level 1. 3rd annot. ed. 2001. tchr. ed. 88.40 (978-0-03-057328-6(9)) Holt, Rinehart & Winston.

—Allez Viens! Level 1: 1-Stop Planner. 3rd ed. 2002. 110.26 (978-0-03-065671-2(0)) Holt, Rinehart & Winston.

—Allez Viens! Level 1: Standard Assessment Tutorial. 3rd ed. 2001. pap. 13.53 (978-0-03-066002-3(5)) Holt, Rinehart & Winston.

—Allez Viens! Level 1: Standard Make-up Tests & Quizzes. 3rd ed. 2001. pap. 21.66 (978-0-03-065673-6(7)) Holt, Rinehart & Winston.

—Allez Viens! Level 1: Videodisc Guide. 1998. pap. 36.80 (978-0-03-052648-0(5)) Holt, Rinehart & Winston.

—Allez Viens! Level 2. 3rd annot. ed. 2001. tchr. ed. 90.26 (978-0-03-057329-3(7)) Holt, Rinehart & Winston.

—Allez Viens! Level 2: Activities for Communication. 1999. pap. 21.86 (978-0-03-052758-6(9)); 3rd ed. 2001. pap. 21.66 (978-0-03-065563-0(3)) Holt, Rinehart & Winston.

—Allez Viens! Level 2: Alternative Assessment Guide. 3rd ed. 2001. pap. 18.20 (978-0-03-065564-7(1)) Holt, Rinehart & Winston.

—Allez Viens! Level 2: Cahier d'Act. 3rd ed. 2001. pap. 18.60 (978-0-03-065001-7(1)); pap., tchr. ed. 22.93 (978-0-03-065002-4(X)) Holt, Rinehart & Winston.

—Allez Viens! Level 2: Indiana Edition. 3rd annot. ed. 2002. tchr. ed. 90.26 (978-0-03-067139-5(6)) Holt, Rinehart & Winston.

—Allez Viens! Level 2: Listening Activities. 3rd ed. 2001. pap. 37.86 (978-0-03-065562-3(5)) Holt, Rinehart & Winston.

—Allez Viens! Level 2: Reading Strategies Guide. 3rd ed. 2001. 22.06 (978-0-03-065633-0(8)) Holt, Rinehart & Winston.

—Allez Viens! Level 2: Standard Assessment: Indiana Edition. 3rd ed. 2002. pap. 13.53 (978-0-03-067143-2(4)) Holt, Rinehart & Winston.

—Allez Viens! Level 2: Standard Assessment Tutorial. 3rd ed. 2001. pap. 13.53 (978-0-03-066003-0(3)) Holt, Rinehart & Winston.

—Allez Viens! Level 2: Standard Make-Up Tests & Quizzes. 3rd ed. 2001. pap. 21.66 (978-0-03-065681-1(8)) Holt, Rinehart & Winston.

—Allez Viens! Level 2: Storytelling Book. 3rd ed. 2001. (FRE.). pap. 14.60 (978-0-03-065478-7(5)) Holt, Rinehart & Winston.

—Allez Viens! Level 2: Testing Program. 3rd ed. 2001. pap. 43.26 (978-0-03-065566-1(8)) Holt, Rinehart & Winston.

—Allez Viens! Level 2: Video Guide. 1999. pap. 21.46 (978-0-03-052892-7(5)); 3rd ed. 2001. pap. 21.06 (978-0-03-065683-5(4)) Holt, Rinehart & Winston.

—Allez Viens! Level 2: Videodisc Guide. 1999. pap. 36.33 (978-0-03-052894-1(1)) Holt, Rinehart & Winston.

—Allez Viens! Level 3: Activities for Communication. 1999. pap. 21.86 (978-0-03-054442-2(4)); 3rd ed. 2002. pap. 21.66 (978-0-03-065568-5(4)) Holt, Rinehart & Winston.

—Allez Viens! Level 3: Alternate Assessment Guide. 3rd ed. 2002. pap. 20.60 (978-0-03-065569-2(2)) Holt, Rinehart & Winston.

—Allez Viens! Level 3: Alternative Assessment Guide. 1999. pap. 20.80 (978-0-03-054443-9(2)) Holt, Rinehart & Winston.

—Allez Viens! Level 3: Cahier d'Activities. 3rd ed. 2002. pap. 17.20 (978-0-03-065003-1(8)); pap., tchr. ed. 25.33 (978-0-03-065004-8(6)) Holt, Rinehart & Winston.

—Allez Viens! Level 3: Listening Activities. 1999. 43.73 (978-0-03-054444-6(0)); 3rd ed. 2002. (FRE.). pap. 37.86 (978-0-03-065567-8(6)) Holt, Rinehart & Winston.

—Allez Viens! Level 3: Practice & Activities. 1999. pap., tchr. ed. 28.13 (978-0-03-054447-7(5)) Holt, Rinehart & Winston.

—Allez Viens! Level 3: Reading Strategies Guide. 3rd ed. 2002. 22.06 (978-0-03-065636-1(2)) Holt, Rinehart & Winston.

—Allez Viens! Level 3: Standard Assessment Tutorial. 3rd ed. 2002. pap. 13.53 (978-0-03-066004-7(1)) Holt, Rinehart & Winston.

—Allez Viens! Level 3: Standard Make-Up Tests & Quizzes. 3rd ed. 2002. pap. 21.66 (978-0-03-065687-3(7)) Holt, Rinehart & Winston.

—Allez Viens! Level 3: Testing Program. 1999. pap. 53.33 (978-0-03-054451-4(3)); 3rd ed. 2002. pap. 43.26 (978-0-03-065571-5(4)) Holt, Rinehart & Winston.

—Allez Viens! Level 3: Video Guide. 3rd ed. 2002. pap. 21.06 incl. VHS (978-0-03-065689-7(3)) Holt, Rinehart & Winston.

—En Avant/En Route. 4th annot. ed. 2003. (J). tchr. ed. 70.00 (978-0-03-070184-9(8)) Holt, Rinehart & Winston.

HOP, LLC. Hooked on French. 2006. 99.99 (978-1-933863-87-0(0)) HOP, LLC.

Kenny, Chantal Lacourciere. The Kids Can Press French & English Phrase Book. 1999. (ENG & FRE., Illus.). 40p. (J). (gr. 4-6). (978-1-55074-477-4(1)) Kids Can Pr., Ltd.

Lafiche, Tammy. Beginning French: Les Saisons/Seasons Resource Book. 2003. (Songs That Teach French Ser.). 64p. (J). pap. (978-1-894262-82-8(4)) Crabtree Publishing Co.

Leigh, Susannah. L' Ile Fantastique: Fantastic Island. Gemmell, Kathy & Irving, Nicole, eds. Haw, Brenda, illus. (FRE.). 25p. (J). (gr. 2-3). reprint ed. 17.00 (978-0-7881-9300-2(7)) DIANE Publishing Co.

Levesque, Suzanne, tr. from ENG. Le Secret de Sindbad. 2003. (FRE & SPA., Illus.). 32p. (J). (gr. 1). 17.95 (978-0-88776-623-7(4) , Livres Toundra) Tundra Bks., Inc./Livres Toundra, Inc. CAN. *Dist:* Random Hse., Inc.

Litchfield, Jo. Everyday Words in French. 48p. 2006. (J). pap. 9.99 (978-0-7945-0882-1(0) , Usborne); 1999. (FRE.). (YA). lib. bdg. 20.95 (978-1-58086-276-9(4)) EDC Publishing.

Mahoney, Judy. Joyeux Noel: Learning Songs & Traditions in French. Bjornson, Barb, illus. 2006. (FRE.). (J). (gr. k-4). lib. bdg. 19.95 incl. audio compact disk (978-1-59972-061-6(2) , Teach Me...) Teach Me Tapes, Inc.

Marcie, Marie-France. French for Kids Beginning Lessons. 2006. 64p. (J). pap. (978-1-55386-055-6(1)) Crabtree Publishing Co.

—French for Kids Thematic Lessons. 2006. 64p. (J). pap. (978-1-55386-056-3(X)) Crabtree Publishing Co.

McDougal-Littell Staff, et al. Discovering French: Nouveau! Rouge, 2 vols. 3rd l.t. ed. 2004. 534p. (YA). (gr. 9-12). 267.00 (978-0-395-87486-8(6)) McDougal Littell Inc.

McGraw-Hill Staff. Bon Voyage, Level 1. 2005. pap., stu. ed. 106.00 (978-0-07-868657-3(1) , 9780078686573) Glencoe/McGraw-Hill.

—Bon Voyage!, Level 1. 3rd ed. 2001. (FRE.). pap., act. bk. ed. 7.96 (978-0-07-824275-5(4) , 9780078242755) Glencoe/McGraw-Hill.

—Bon Voyage! Level 1A, Audio Activities Booklet. 3rd ed. 2001. (C). pap. 7.00 (978-0-07-824277-9(0) , 9780078242779) Glencoe/McGraw-Hill.

—Bon Voyage! Level 1A Writing. 3rd ed. 2001. (FRE.). pap., wbk. ed., act. bk. ed. 10.64 (978-0-07-824271-7(1) , 9780078242717) Glencoe/McGraw-Hill.

—Bon Voyage! Level 1B Audio Activities Booklet. 3rd ed. 2001. (C). pap. 7.00 (978-0-07-824278-6(9) , 9780078242786) Glencoe/McGraw-Hill.

—Bon Voyage! Level 1B Writing Activities. 3rd ed. 2001. (FRE.). (C). pap., wbk. ed. 10.64 (978-0-07-824272-4(X) , 9780078242724) Glencoe/McGraw-Hill.

—Bon Voyage! Writing Activities. 3rd ed. 2001. (FRE.). Level 1. (C). pap., wbk. ed. 14.64 (978-0-07-824269-4(X) , 9780078242694); Level. 2. pap., wbk. ed. 14.64 (978-0-07-824344-8(0) , 9780078243448) Glencoe/McGraw-Hill.

McGraw-Hill Staff & Zaun, Kathy. French: Middle/High School, Level 3. 1999. (Homework Booklets Ser.). (FRE & GER., Illus.). 80p. (J). (gr. k-12). pap. 2.99 (978-0-88012-994-7(8) , IF0219) School Specialty Publishing.

Melling, David, illus. My First French Words. 1999. (My First Words to See & Learn Ser.). (FRE.). 48p. (ps-3). 11.95 (978-0-8442-2406-0(5) , 24065, Passport Bks.) McGraw-Hill Trade.

Morton, Lone & Bougard, Marie-Therese. Georges, le Poisson Rouge: English-French Edition. Noyes, Leighton, illus. 2005. (I Can Read French Ser.). (FRE & ENG.). 28p. (J). (ps). 7.99 (978-0-7641-5874-2(0)) Barron's Educational Series, Inc.

Ninos Aprenden Ingles Corp. Children Learning French. 2004. (Illus.). 119p. (J). pap. 19.95 (***978-1-934665-08-4(8)***) Ninos Aprenden Ingles Corp.

Penfornis. Business French with Intext Audio Cd. 2005. (YA). pap. 84.36 incl. cd-rom (978-0-618-70901-4(0) , 345125) Houghton Mifflin College Div.

Plante, Charles. A French Alphabet Book Of 1814: For Alfred Bourdier de Beauregard, Created by his uncle Arnaud at the Chateau Debeaumoont de Beauregard. 2007. (Illus.). 114p. 24.95 (***978-0-8478-3010-7(1)***) Rizzoli International Pubns., Inc.

Random House Staff. Random House Easy Learning French Dictionary. 1999. (FRE.). pap. (978-0-375-70596-0(1)) Random Hse. Information Group.

Rice, Anne-Christine. French Wide Web: 1,000 Internet Sites on France, the French Language, & the Francophone World. 2001. (FRE.). 110p. (YA). pap. 12.95 net. (978-1-58510-044-6(7)) Focus Publishing/R. Pullins Co., Inc.

Rojo, Andrea Szekasy. Arc-en-Ciel: French for Elementary Students. Porter, Susana, illus. Date not set. (FRE.). (J). (gr. k-6). pap. (978-0-9671053-2-1(3) , 0210) Language Adventure Pubns.

The Rosetta Stone Language Library: French Level 2. 1999. (J). (gr. 1 up). cd-rom 239.00 (978-1-883972-57-8(4)) Fairfield Language Technologies.

Stanley, Mandy, illus. My First French Book: A bilingual introduction to words, numbers, shapes, & Colours. 2007. 48p. (J). pap. (***978-0-7534-5998-0(1)*** , Kingfisher) Houghton Mifflin Co. Trade & Reference Div.

Thibaut, Francois. Unassigned. 2004. (FRE.). (J). 0.01 (978-0-9755659-7-1(4)) Language Workshop for Children, The.

Traynor, Tracy. French with Abby & Zak. Hambleton, Laura, illus. 2007. (Abby & Zak Ser.). 48p. (J). pap. 16.95 (978-1-84059-490-4(X)) Milet Publishing.

Valette, Jean-Paul & Valette, Rebecca M. Discovering French: Nouveau! 1B, Bleu, Deuxieme Partie. l.t. ed. 2004. (YA). (gr. 6-8). 56.52 (978-0-395-88143-9(9)) McDougal Littell Inc.

—Discovering French, Nouveau! Premiere Partie, Level 1A Middle School. 2004. (YA). (gr. 6-8). stu. ed. (978-0-618-03215-0(0)) McDougal Littell Inc.

Walz, Joel & Piriou, Jean-Pierre. Rapports: An Introduction to French Language & Francophone Culture. 5th ed. 2003. (ENG & FRE.). 540p. (YA). 117.16 incl. cd-rom (978-0-618-26705-7(0) , 313971) Houghton Mifflin College Div.

Welling, Peter J. Michael le Souffle & the April Fool. Welling, Peter J., illus. 2003. (Illus.). 32p. (J). 15.95 (978-1-58980-105-9(9)) Pelican Publishing Co., Inc.

Woods, Caroline. Quick Revision KS3 French. 2007. 46p. pap. 9.95 (***978-0-340-94311-3(4)*** , Hodder Murray) Hodder Education GBR. *Dist:* Trans-Atlantic Pubns., Inc.

FRENCH LANGUAGE—CONVERSATION AND PHRASE BOOKS

Bennett, Veronique. Chez Moi. 2003. (First French Ser.). (ENG & FRE., Illus.). 64p. 12.95 (978-0-7548-1056-8(9) , Lorenz Bks.) Anness Publishing GBR. *Dist:* National Bk. Network.

Berwick, Gwen & Thorne, Sydney. Voila! 1, Bk. 1. 2004. (Illus.). 144p. (J). pap., stu. ed. 29.50 (978-0-7487-7847-8(0)) Nelson Thornes Ltd. GBR. *Dist:* Trans-Atlantic Pubns., Inc.

Bruzzone, Catherine. French Fun. 2004. (Illus.). 20p. 12.95 (978-0-07-142825-5(9) , 9780071428255) McGraw-Hill Cos., The.

Bruzzone, Catherine & Beaton, Clare. Action French! A Lively Activity Starter Pack for Adults & Children. 2000. (Illus.). 20p. (J). (ps-5). pap., suppl. ed. 14.95 incl. audio (978-0-658-00448-3(4) , 004484) McGraw-Hill/Contemporary.

Crosbie, Duncan. Find Out about France: Learn French Words & Phrases & about Life in France. Hutchinson, Tim, illus. 2006. (Find Out about Bks.). 64p. (J). (gr. 3 up). spiral bd. 12.99 (978-0-7641-5953-4(4)) Barron's Educational Series, Inc.

Finnie, Sue & Bourdais, Daniele. Harry Learns French. Tempest, Annabel, illus. 2003. (Language Learners Ser.). (ENG & FRE.). 32p. (J). (gr. 2-5). 11.95 (978-0-7641-7630-2(7)) Barron's Educational Series, Inc.

Hooked on Phonics Staff. Hooked on French: Premium Edition. abr. ed. 2007. 64.99 (***978-1-60143-380-0(8)***) HOP, LLC.

Jordan, Sara. Francais pour Debutants. Obando, Hector, illus. 2001. (FRE.). 48p. (J). pap. 14.95 incl. audio (978-1-895523-44-7(3) , JMP F05K) Jordan Music Productions, Inc.

Morton, Lone & Risk, Mary. Bon Anniversaire. 1998. (I Can Read Bks.).Tr. of Happ Birthday. (ENG & FRE.). (J). (ps up). 9.95 incl. audio (978-0-7641-7187-1(9)) Barron's Educational Series, Inc.

—I'm Too Big. 1998. (I Can Read Bks.).Tr. of Je Suis Mucho Grande. (ENG & FRE., Illus.). 28p. (J). (ps up). pap. 9.95 incl. audio (978-0-7641-7189-5(5)) Barron's Educational Series, Inc.

Poulin, Stephane. As-Tu Vu Josephine? 2003. (FRE & SPA., Illus.). 24p. (J). (gr. k-3). pap. 6.95 (978-0-88776-645-9(5) , Livres Toundra) Tundra Bks., Inc./Livres Toundra, Inc. CAN. *Dist:* Random Hse., Inc.

Rivera, Donald S. LinguaFun! French. 2004. (Travel Ser.). (ENG & FRE.). 12.95 (978-1-56015-603-1(1)) Penton Overseas, Inc.

Tulip, Jenny, illus. My First French Word Book. 2004. (ENG & FRE.). 48p. (J). 5.99 (978-1-85854-237-9(5)) Brimax Books Ltd. GBR. *Dist:* Byeway Bks.

Watson, Carol. Let's Learn French. 2003. (gr. 3-6). lib. bdg. 18.75 (978-0-613-74876-6(X)) Tandem Library Bks.

Watson, Carol & Moyle, Philippa. Let's Learn French. Foster, Teresa, illus. 2003. (Let's Learn Ser.). 32p. pap. 9.95 (978-0-7818-1014-2(0)) Hippocrene Bks., Inc.

Wightwick, Jane. Way-Cool French Phrase Book. 2001. (gr. 5-8). lib. bdg. 15.25 (978-0-613-73008-2(9)) Tandem Library Bks.

—Way-Cool French Phrase Book: The French That Kids Really Speak. 2001. (Way-Cool Ser.). (ENG & FRE., Illus.). 96p. (gr. 3-9). pap. 6.95 (978-0-658-01690-5(3) , 9780658016905) McGraw-Hill Cos., The.

—Way Cool French Phrasebook. 2005. (ENG & FRE., Illus.). 96p. audio compact disk 12.95 (978-0-07-144839-0(X) , 9780071448390) McGraw-Hill Cos., The.

FRENCH LANGUAGE—DICTIONARIES

A la Fete. 2000. (Collection des Mots pour Lire). (FRE.). 28p. (J). 15.95 (978-2-03-653002-7(8)) Librairie Larousse FRA. *Dist:* Distribooks, Inc.

Brooks, Felicity & Mackinnon, Mairi. Picture Dictionary in French. 2004. (Picture Dictionaries Ser.). (FRE., Illus.). 112p. (J). 16.95 (978-0-7945-0306-2(3) , Usborne) EDC Publishing.

Davies, H. & Holmes, F. French Dictionary for Beginners. 2004. (Beginner's Dictionaries Ser.). (FRE.). 128p. (J). pap. 12.95 (978-0-7945-0287-4(3)); lib. bdg. 20.95 (978-1-58086-475-6(9)) EDC Publishing.

Davies, Helen. Beginner's French Dictionary. 2003. (gr. 3-6). lib. bdg. 22.20 (978-0-613-70994-1(2)) Tandem Library Bks.

Greisman, Joan & Wittels, Harriet. French Thesaurus for Children. Touzet-Rall, Yvonne, tr. 1999. (ENG & FRE., Illus.). 128p. (J). (gr. 3-7). pap. 7.99 (978-0-7641-0896-9(4)) Barron's Educational Series, Inc.

Harrap. French Student's Dictionary. (ENG & FRE., Illus.). 800p. (978-0-245-60676-2(9)) Harrap, Larousse Pubs.

Hippocrene Books Staff. Hippocrene Children's Illustrated French Dictionary: English-French. 2001. Tr. of French-Engli. (ENG & FRE.). (gr. 3-6). lib. bdg. 21.05 (978-0-613-74943-5(X)) Tandem Library Bks.

Hippocrene Books Staff, ed. Children's Illustrated French Dictionary: French-English/English-French. 1998. (Children's Illustrated Foreign Language Dictionaries Ser.). (ENG & FRE., Illus.). 122p. (J). (gr. k-5). 14.95 (978-0-7818-0710-4(7)) Hippocrene Bks., Inc.

Larousse Staff. Mon premier Larousse du Monde. (FRE.). pap. 39.95 (978-2-03-553015-8(6)) Librairie Larousse FRA. *Dist:* Distribooks, Inc.

Larousse Staff, ed. Larousse Student Dictionary: French-English / English-French. l.t. ed. 2003. (FRE & ENG., Illus.). 732p. (gr. 5). pap. 10.95 (978-2-03-542055-8(5)) Larousse, Editions FRA. *Dist:* Houghton Mifflin Co. Trade & Reference Div.

Lipton, Gladys C. French Bilingual Dictionary: A Beginner's Guide in Words & Pictures. 3rd rev. ed. 1998. (Barron's Bilingual Dictionaries Ser.). (ENG & FRE., Illus.). 180p. (gr. 3 up). pap. 8.99 (978-0-7641-0279-0(6)) Barron's Educational Series, Inc.

Mabileau, Christine, et al. My First French Picture Dictionary. 2001. (ENG & FRE., Illus.). 48p. (J). 14.95 (978-0-7641-5436-2(2)) Barron's Educational Series, Inc.

Mahoney, Marie-Paule, et al. En Francais: Rapid Success in French for Beginners. 2003. (Language Immersion Institute Ser.). (ENG & FRE., Illus.). 192p. pap. 32.95 incl. cd-rom (978-0-07-140648-2(4) , 9780071406482) McGraw-Hill Cos., The.

McGraw-Hill Staff. Bon Voyage!, Level 1B. 2nd ed. 2004. (FRE.). (C). pap., stu. ed., wbk. ed. 16.64 (978-0-07-865629-3(X) , 9780078656293) Glencoe/McGraw-Hill.

Spot Decouvre les Formes. 2000. (FRE., Illus.). 16p. (J). bds. 11.95 (978-2-09-270190-4(8)) Nathan, Fernand FRA. *Dist:* Distribooks, Inc.

FRENCH LANGUAGE—DICTIONARIES—ENGLISH

American Education Publishing, et al. French-English Picture Dictionary. 2005. (Illus.). 48p. (J). (ps-k). 9.95 (978-0-7696-4149-2(0) , American Education Publishing) School Specialty Publishing.

Demarest, Chris L., illus. French. 2nd ed. 2004. (Berlitz Kids Ser.). (ENG & FRE.). 128p. pap. 12.95 (978-981-246-387-6(9) , 463879) Berlitz Publishing.

Diaz, Natacha. Larousse Picture Dictionary: English-French/French-English. Brophy, Peter, illus. 2002. (ENG & FRE.). 48p. (J). (gr. k-3). tchr. ed. 13.95 (978-2-03-542095-4(4)) Larousse, Editions FRA. *Dist:* Houghton Mifflin Co. Trade & Reference Div.

Diaz, Natacha & Brophy, Peter. Larousse Picture Dictionary: English-French, Francais-Anglais. 2002. (ENG & FRE., Illus.). 48p. (J). (978-2-03-540175-5(5)) Houghton Mifflin Co.

Hippocrene Books Firm Staff, contrib. by. Hippocrene Children's Illustrated French Dictionary: English-French, French-English. 2001. (Hippocrene Children's Illustrated Foreign Language Dictionaries Ser.). (FRE & ENG., Illus.). 94p. (gr. k-5). pap. 11.95 (978-0-7818-0847-7(2)) Hippocrene Bks., Inc.

Lipton, Gladys C. French Bilingual Dictionary: A Beginner's Guide in Words & Pictures. 3rd rev. ed. 1998. (Barron's Bilingual Dictionaries Ser.). (ENG & FRE., Illus.). 180p. (gr. 3 up). pap. 8.99 (978-0-7641-0279-0(6)) Barron's Educational Series, Inc.

McGraw-Hill Staff. McGraw-Hill's French Picture Dictionary. 2004. (ENG & FRE.). 96p. 10.95 (978-0-07-142813-2(5) , 9780071428132) McGraw-Hill Cos., The.

Oates. Entre Amis with Cassette Plus Cd One Point 0 Plus Larousse French English Pocket Dictionary. 4th ed. 2004. (YA). 122.36 incl. cd-rom (978-0-618-59520-4(1) , 395671) Houghton Mifflin College Div.

FRENCH LANGUAGE—GRAMMAR

Demaray, Carolyn F. & Smith, Josette J. Triangle: Manuel de l'Etudiant: Applications Pratiques de la Langue Francaise. Wilson, Ken, illus. 3rd ed. 1998. (FRE.). 197p. (YA). (gr. 11-12). pap. 10.94 (978-1-877653-54-4(3)) Wayside Publishing.

Fawbush, Karla Winther, et al. C'est a Toi! French Grammar & Vocabulary Exercises, Level 1. rev. ed. (FRE.). (YA). (gr. 9-12). pap. 15.95 (978-0-8219-1980-4(6) , 40674) EMC/Paradigm Publishing.

Foundations of French Grammar-Negatives, Question Words, Articles. 2004. (YA). 9.95 (***978-1-931463-21-8(2)***) French Workshop, The.

Foundations of French Grammar-Object Pronouns & Prepositions. 2004. (YA). 9.95 (***978-1-931463-20-1(4)***) French Workshop, The.

Haughom, Lisa, illus. & text. Jeux de Grammaire. Haughom, Lisa, text. l.t. ed. 2001. pap. 21.95 (978-0-9723849-8-8(7)); Vol. 2. 79p. pap. 21.95 (978-0-9723849-9-5(5)) Languages For Kids.

Hazan, Maurice, illus. & creator. Les Animaux et les verbes flash card Set. Hazan, Maurice, creator. 2003. (FRE.). (J). 95.00 (978-1-932770-38-4(0) , FC-FWLB1) Symtalk, Inc.

—Chiffres, couleurs, verbes et phrases flash card Set. Hazan, Maurice, creator. 2003. (FRE.). (J). 115.00 (978-1-932770-39-1(9) , FC-FWLB2) Symtalk, Inc.

Holt, Rinehart and Winston Staff. Allez Viens! Level 1: Cahier d'Act. 3rd ed. 2003. (FRE.). pap., tchr. ed. 22.66 (978-0-03-064997-4(8)) Holt, Rinehart & Winston.

—Allez Viens! Level 2: Travaux/Grammar. 3rd ed. 2001. pap. 15.00 (978-0-03-064998-1(6)); pap., tchr. ed. 21.66 (978-0-03-064999-8(4)) Holt, Rinehart & Winston.

—Allez Viens! Level 3: Travaux/Grammar. 3rd ed. 2002. pap. 14.60 (978-0-03-065006-2(2)); pap., tchr. ed. 21.46 (978-0-03-065007-9(0)) Holt, Rinehart & Winston.

Pattis, Anne-Francoise. Let's Learn French Coloring Book. 2003. (ENG & FRE., Illus.). 64p. pap. 4.95 (978-0-07-142141-6(6) , 9780071421416) McGraw-Hill Cos., The.

Spot Decouvre les Contraires. 2000. (FRE., Illus.). 16p. (J). bds. 11.95 (978-2-09-270194-2(0)) Nathan, Fernand FRA. *Dist:* Distribooks, Inc.

Spot Decouvre les Couleurs. 2000. (FRE., Illus.). 16p. (J). bds. 11.95 (978-2-09-270195-9(9)) Nathan, Fernand FRA. *Dist:* Distribooks, Inc.

Travis, Joelle & Figueras, Ligaya, eds. Les Animaux et les Verbes. Hazan, Maurice, illus. 2003. (FRE.). (J). per. 20.00 (978-1-932770-18-6(6) , FWLB1) Symtalk, Inc.

—Chiffres, Couleurs, Verbes et Phrases. Hazan, Maurice, illus. 2003. (FRE.). 114p. (J). per. 20.00 (978-1-932770-19-3(4) , FWLB2) Symtalk, Inc.

Tullet, Herve. Night & Day. 2005. (Illus.). 140p. (J). 16.95 (978-1-84059-111-8(0)) Milet Publishing.

FRENCH LANGUAGE—READERS

A Apicella, M & Challier, H. Gaston - Level 10, Level 1. 2000. (FRE & ENG.). (J). pap., act. bk. ed. 7.95 (978-88-8148-347-1(5)) European Language Institute ITA. *Dist:* Distribooks, Inc., Midwest European Pubns.

Andersen, Hans Christian. Les Habits Neufs de l'Empereur. 1999. Tr. of Emperor's New Clothes. (FRE.). 32p. (J). (ps-3). 13.95 (978-2-09-202112-5(5)) Nathan, Fernand FRA. *Dist:* Distribooks, Inc.

Apicella, A. Gaston: Level 2. 2000. (FRE & ENG., Illus.). (J). pap., act. bk. ed. 7.95 (978-88-8148-348-8(3)) European Language Institute ITA. *Dist:* Distribooks, Inc., Midwest European Pubns.

Bemelsman, Ludwig. La Noel de Madeleine. 2000. (Adventures of Madeleine Ser.).Tr. of Madeleine's Christmas. (FRE.). (J). pap. 14.95 (978-2-211-05079-1(4)) Archimede Editions FRA. *Dist:* Distribooks, Inc.

Berwick, Gwen & Thorne, Sydney. Voila! 2. Green, Julie, ed. 2005. (Illus.). (YA). 144p. pap. 29.50 (978-0-7487-9090-6(X)); 160p. pap., stu. ed. 29.50 (978-0-7487-9094-4(2)) Nelson Thornes Ltd. GBR. *Dist:* Trans-Atlantic Pubns., Inc.

Berwick, Gwen Thorne & Thorne, Sydney. Voila! 3: Students' Book Higher. 2005. (Illus.). 160p. (YA). pap. 29.50 (978-0-7487-9147-7(7)) Nelson Thornes Ltd. GBR. *Dist:* Trans-Atlantic Pubns., Inc.

—Voila! 3: Students' Book Lower. 2005. (Illus.). 144p. (YA). pap. 29.50 (978-0-7487-9148-4(5)) Nelson Thornes Ltd. GBR. *Dist:* Trans-Atlantic Pubns., Inc.

Blair, Robert W., creator. Power-Glide French Ultimate Adventure Course, 2 vols. 2002. (Illus.). (YA). pap. 149.95 incl. cd-rom, audio compact disk (978-1-58204-201-5(2)) Power-Glide Foreign Language Courses.

Blanche-Neige. 2000. Tr. of Snow White. (FRE., Illus.). 32p. (J). 13.95 (978-2-09-202109-5(5)) Nathan, Fernand FRA. *Dist:* Distribooks, Inc.

Bruzzone, Catherine. First French with Superchat. 2007. (Teach Yourself Language Ser.). 13.95 (978-0-07-148101-4(X) , 9780071481014) McGraw-Hill Cos., The.

Bulloch, Ivan & James, Diane. Debout! C'est L'Heure! 2000. (My Turn Ser.). (Illus.). 12p. (J). (ps-k). bds. 6.95 (978-1-58728-170-9(8) , Two Can Publishing) T&N Children's Publishing.

—Et Hop! Je Saute! 2000. (My Turn Ser.). (FRE., Illus.). 12p. (J). (ps-k). bds. 6.95 (978-1-58728-171-6(6) , Two Can Publishing) T&N Children's Publishing.

—Le Tamps Qu'il Fait. 2000. (My Turn Ser.). (Illus.). 12p. (J). (ps-k). bds. 6.95 (978-1-58728-172-3(4) , Two Can Publishing) T&N Children's Publishing.

Burke, David, adapted by. Goldilocks (English to French - Level 2) Learn FRENCH Through Fairy Tales. 2007. (Learn French Through Fairy Tales Ser.). (ENG & FRE., Illus.). (J). per. 14.95 incl. audio compact disk (***978-1-891888-81-6(1)***) Slangman Publishing.

Burnett, Frances Hodgson. La Petit Princesse.Tr. of Little Princess. (FRE.). (J). pap. 12.95 (978-2-07-056710-2(9)) Gallimard, Editions FRA. *Dist:* Distribooks, Inc.

Chansons Autour du Monde pour les Grandes. 2000. (Prelude Ser.).Tr. of Songs from Around the World. (FRE., Illus.). (J). pap. 19.95 incl. audio compact disk (978-2-7005-0218-3(3)) Assimil France FRA. *Dist:* Distribooks, Inc.

Chansons de Tous le Jours pour les Petits. 2000. (Prelude Ser.).Tr. of Nursery Songs for Little Ones. (FRE.). (J). (ps-1). pap. 19.95 incl. audio compact disk (978-2-7005-0216-9(7)) Assimil France FRA. *Dist:* Distribooks, Inc.

Crossley, David, illus. ABC. 2004. (Baby's First Learning Ser.). 12p. (J). bds. 4.99 (978-1-85854-890-6(X)) Brimax Books Ltd. GBR. *Dist:* Byeway Bks.

Dahl, Roald. James et la Grosse Peche.Tr. of James & the Giant Peach. (FRE.). (J). pap. 17.95 (978-2-07-051374-1(2)) Gallimard, Editions FRA. *Dist:* Distribooks, Inc.

de Brunhoff, Laurent. Babar a la Fete de Celesteville. 2000. (Babar Ser.). (FRE., Illus.). (J). 13.95 (978-2-01-002631-7(4)) Istra FRA. *Dist:* Distribooks, Inc.

—Babar et ce Coquin d'Arthur. 2000. (Babar Ser.). (FRE., Illus.). (J). (ps-3). 13.95 (978-2-01-002548-8(2)) Istra FRA. *Dist:* Distribooks, Inc.

—Babar et le Fantome. 2000. (Babar Ser.). (FRE., Illus.). (J). 13.95 (978-2-01-008444-7(6)) Istra FRA. *Dist:* Distribooks, Inc.

—Babar et les Quatre Voleurs. 2000. (Babar Ser.). (FRE., Illus.). (J). 13.95 (978-2-01-005889-5(9)) Istra FRA. *Dist:* Distribooks, Inc.

Deluc, Yves & Ruck. Prisunic. (FRE.). 48p. (YA). (gr. 9-12). pap. 4.95 (978-0-88436-905-9(6) , 40287) EMC/Paradigm Publishing.

Demado. En Route: Enhanced Online Edition. 4th ed. 2003. cd-rom 54.80 (978-0-03-031976-1(5)) Holt, Rinehart & Winston.

Fralin, Alfred G. & Szeps-Fralin, Christiane. Le Francais Vivant 1. (YA). (gr. 6-8). pap. 9.95 (978-0-8219-0517-3(1) , 40662) EMC/Paradigm Publishing.

—Le Francais Vivant 2. (J). stu. ed. 45.95 (978-0-8219-0604-0(6) , 40455); (YA). pap., wbk. ed. 10.50 (978-0-8219-0606-4(2) , 40663) EMC/Paradigm Publishing.

Fralin, Alfred G., et al. Le Francais Vivant 3. (YA). (gr. 9-12). stu. ed. 46.95 (978-0-8219-0892-1(8) , 40456); pap., wbk. ed. 10.95 (978-0-8219-0893-8(6) , 40664) EMC/Paradigm Publishing.

Frere Jacques. 2000. (Musicontes Ser.). (FRE.). (J). 24.95 incl. audio (978-2-09-230365-8(1)) Nathan, Fernand FRA. *Dist:* Distribooks, Inc.

Goscinny, R. French Asterix: Et Latraviata. 2001. (FRE.). 48p. 14.95 (978-2-86497-143-6(7)) Albert Rene, Editions FRA. *Dist:* Last Gasp of San Francisco.

Le Grand Jeu des Verbes. 2000. (FRE., Illus.). (J). (gr. k-8). tchr. ed., suppl. ed. 26.95 (978-88-8148-311-2(4)) European Language Institute ITA. *Dist:* Distribooks, Inc., Midwest European Pubns.

Hébert, Marie-Francine & Germain, Philippe. Une Tempete dans un Verre d'Eau. 2001. (FRE., Illus.). 64p. (J). pap. (978-2-89021-477-4(X)) Diffusion du livre Mirabel.

Hemingway, Ernest. Le Vieil Homme et la Mer. 2000. (FRE.). (J). pap. 16.95 (978-2-07-051388-8(2)) Gallimard, Editions FRA. *Dist:* Distribooks, Inc.

Holt, Rinehart and Winston Staff. Allez Viens! Level 1: Storytelling Book. 3rd ed. 2003. (FRE.). pap. 14.60 (978-0-03-065477-0(7)) Holt, Rinehart & Winston.

—En Route: Online Edition. 4th ed. 2003. 43.86 (978-0-03-031817-7(3)) Holt, Rinehart & Winston.

Le Jardin. 2000. (Collection des Mots pour Lire). (FRE.). 28p. (J). 15.95 (978-2-03-553020-2(2)) Librairie Larousse FRA. *Dist:* Distribooks, Inc.

Lomba, Ana. Easy French Storybook: Little Red Riding Hood. 2005. (ENG & FRE., Illus.). 41p. 14.95 incl. cd-rom (978-0-07-146167-2(1) , 9780071461672) McGraw-Hill Cos., The.

—EasyFrench Storybook: Goldilocks & the Three Bears. 2005. (ENG & FRE., Illus.). 41p. 14.95 incl. cd-rom (978-0-07-146173-3(6) , 9780071461733) McGraw-Hill Cos., The.

Look & Learn ABC Book. (Illus.). 18p. (J). bds. (978-1-86515-520-3(9)) Hinkler Bks. Pty. Ltd.

Minarik, Else Holmelund & Sendak, Maurice. Baiser pour Petit Ours. 2000. Tr. of Kiss for Little Bear. (FRE.). (J). pap. 17.95 (978-2-211-01767-1(3)) Archimede Editions FRA. *Dist:* Distribooks, Inc.

Molzan, Janet & Lloyd, Sue. Le Manuel Phonique. 2001. (Jolly Phonics Ser.). (FRE.). 218p. (J). 32.50 (978-1-870946-98-8(7)) Jolly Learning, Ltd. GBR. *Dist:* American International Distribution Corp.

Morton, Lone & Risk, Mary. Bon Anniversaire. 1998. (I Can Read Bks.).Tr. of Happ Birthday. (ENG & FRE.). (J). (ps up). 9.95 incl. audio (978-0-7641-7187-1(9)) Barron's Educational Series, Inc.

—I'm Too Big. 1998. (I Can Read Bks.).Tr. of Je Suis Mucho Grande. (ENG & FRE., Illus.). 28p. (J). (ps up). pap. 9.95 incl. audio (978-0-7641-7189-5(5)) Barron's Educational Series, Inc.

Personagges de Contes en Chanson pour les Petits et les Grandes. 2000. (Prelude Ser.).Tr. of Fairy Tale Characters in Songs for Children of All Ages. (FRE., Illus.). (J). pap. 19.95 incl. audio compact disk (978-2-7005-0217-6(5)) Assimil France FRA. *Dist:* Distribooks, Inc.

Le Petit Poucet. 2000. Tr. of Tom Thumb. (FRE., Illus.). 32p. (J). 13.95 (978-2-09-202108-8(7)) Nathan, Fernand FRA. *Dist:* Distribooks, Inc.

La Petite Sirene: Family, The Weather, Gardens, Underwater Life. 2000. (FRE & ENG., Illus.). 24p. (J). (ps-5). pap., stu. ed. 7.95 (978-88-8148-361-7(0)) European Language Institute ITA. *Dist:* Distribooks, Inc., Midwest European Pubns.

Robinson, Bryan, ed. Bilingual Baby Vol. 1: Introduce Your Child to French. 2000. (FRE.). (J). pap., stu. ed. 16.95 incl. VHS (978-1-892703-09-5(2)) Small Fry Productions.

Le Roi Arthur et Autres Rois. 2000. (Musicontes Ser.).Tr. of King Arthur & Other Kings. (FRE.). (J). 24.95 incl. audio (978-2-09-230490-7(9)) Nathan, Fernand FRA. *Dist:* Distribooks, Inc.

Szeps-Fralin, Christiane. Drole de Mission. (FRE.). (YA). (gr. 9-12). stu. ed. 5.95 (978-0-8219-0024-6(2) , 40292); pap., wbk. ed. 4.95 (978-0-8219-0025-3(0) , 40654); pap., tchr.'s training gde. ed. 5.95 (978-0-8219-0026-0(9) , 40816) EMC/Paradigm Publishing.

—Poursuite Inattendue. (FRE.). (gr. 9-12). (J). stu. ed. 5.95 (978-0-8219-0021-5(8) , 40291); (YA). pap., wbk. ed. 4.95 (978-0-8219-0022-2(6) , 40653); (YA). pap., tchr.'s training gde. ed. 5.95 (978-0-8219-0023-9(4) , 40815) EMC/Paradigm Publishing.

Yong, Tohmoh J., et al. Tune in CM2 Pupil's Workbook. 2007. pap., stu. ed. (***978-0-521-69599-2(6)***) Cambridge Univ. Pr.

FRENCH LANGUAGE—STUDY AND TEACHING

Amery, H. First Hundred Words Words in French. 2004. (First Hundred Words Ser.). (FRE.). 34p. (J). pap. 6.99 (978-0-7945-0013-9(7) , Usborne); (Illus.). lib. bdg. 14.99 (978-1-58086-394-0(9)) EDC Publishing.

Blair, Robert. Power-Glide French Ultimate Academic Guide, 1 bk. 2001. 128p. (YA). pap. 19.95 (978-1-58204-068-4(0)) Power-Glide Foreign Language Courses.

Bruzzone, Catherine & Martineau, Susan. Hide & Speak French. Comfort, Louise, illus. 2003. (Hide & Speak Ser.). (FRE & ENG.). 32p. (J). pap. 7.99 (978-0-7641-2588-1(5)) Barron's Educational Series, Inc.

Croteau-Fleury, Marie-Danielle & St. Aubin, Bruno. Les Corsaires du Capitaine Croquette. 2001. (Roman Jeunesse Ser.). (FRE., Illus.). 96p. (J). (gr. 4-7). pap. (978-2-89021-437-8(0)) Diffusion du livre Mirabel.

Croteau, Marie-Danielle. La Petite Reine au Nez Rouge. St. Aubin, Bruno, illus. 2004. (Premier Roman Ser.). (FRE.). 64p. (J). (gr. 1-4). pap. (978-2-89021-706-5(X)) Diffusion du livre Mirabel.

Daizovi, Lonnie G. Francais Joyeux: Simple Songs That Teach French. 1999. (FRE., Illus.). 32p. (J). pap. 13.95 (978-0-935301-78-6(X)) Vibrante Pr.

de Gregory, Danielle, tr. French. 1999. (100+ Seriestm Ser.). (FRE & GER., Illus.). 128p. (gr. k-12). (J). pap. 12.99 (978-1-56822-666-8(7) , IF8792); (YA). pap. 12.99 (978-1-56822-667-5(5) , IF8793) School Specialty Publishing.

Desrosiers, Sylvie & Franson, Leanne. Le Concert de Thomas. 2001. (Premier Roman Ser.). (FRE., Illus.). 64p. (J). (gr. 1-4). pap. (978-2-89021-443-9(5)) Diffusion du livre Mirabel.

Gilbert-Dumas, Mylène. Mystique. 2004. (Mon Roman Ser.). (FRE.). 256p. (J). (gr. 2). pap. (978-2-89021-652-5(7)) Diffusion du livre Mirabel.

Gingras, Charlotte. La Boite a Bonheur. Jorisch, Stephane, illus. 2004. (Mon Roman Ser.). (FRE.). 64p. (J). (gr. 2). pap. (978-2-89021-668-6(3)) Diffusion du livre Mirabel.

Jackman, Monique. Speaking Better French: Achieving Fluency with Everyday Speech. 2nd ed. 2000. (Studymates Ser.). (ENG & FRE., Illus.). 136p. (C). pap. (978-1-84285-020-6(2) , Financial Times/Prentice Hall) Pearson Education, Ltd.

Laflhche, Tammy & Lafleche, Tammy. Beginning French Vol. 2: Les Fetes / Seasons Resource Book. 2003. (Songs That Teach French Ser.). 64p. (J). pap. (978-1-894262-83-5(2) , JMP B02) Crabtree Publishing Co.

Lemieux, Jean. Le Fil de la Vie. Casson, Sophie, illus. 2004. (Premier Roman Ser.). (FRE.). 64p. (J). (gr. 1-4). pap. (978-2-89021-644-0(6)) Diffusion du livre Mirabel.

McGraw-Hill Staff. Contes et Fables des Isles. 2003. (FRE.). 128p. (gr. 6-12). pap. 23.32 (978-0-07-860042-5(1) , 9780078600425) Glencoe/McGraw-Hill.

Merola, Caroline. Le Tresor du Bibinocolendi. 2001. (Itait une Fois Ser.). (FRE., Illus.). 24p. (YA). (ps up). pap. (978-2-89021-445-3(1)) Diffusion du livre Mirabel.

Meunier, Sylvain & Eudes-Pascal, Elisabeth. Le Seul Ami. 2002. (Roman Jeunesse Ser.). (FRE., Illus.). 96p. (J). (gr. 4-7). pap. (978-2-89021-535-1(0)) Diffusion du livre Mirabel.

My First 100 Words in French/English. 2003. (First Words & Pictures Book Ser.).Tr. of My First 100 Words. (FRE.). 32p. (J). 11.95 (978-0-7525-7768-5(9)) Parragon, Inc.

NTC Publishing Group Staff. Drive-In French for Kids: Songs & Games for On-the-Go Children. 2000. (Drive-In Ser.). (FRE & ENG., Illus.). 32p. (ps-2). pap. 9.95 incl. audio (978-0-658-00868-9(4) , 008684) McGraw-Hill Cos., The.

Valette, Jean-Paul & Valette, Rebecca M. Discovering French: Nouveau! 1, Bleu. l.t. ed. 2004. (YA). (gr. 9-12). 75.08 (978-0-395-87482-0(3)) McDougal Littell Inc.

—Discovery French: Nouveau! 2, Blanc. l.t. ed. 2004. (YA). (gr. 9-12). 76.48 (978-0-395-87489-9(0)) McDougal Littell Inc.

Wightwick, Jane. Way Cool French Phrasebook. 2005. (ENG & FRE., Illus.). 96p. audio compact disk 12.95 (978-0-07-144839-0(X) , 9780071448390) McGraw-Hill Cos., The.

Wildridge, Cynthia S. Bun E. Learns to Count in French: Bun E. Append a Compter: with Accompanying CD. Wildridge, Cynthia S., tr. Wildridge, Alyssa A., illus. 2003. (FRE & ENG.). (J). 25.00 incl. cd-rom (978-0-9744810-0-5(9) , Limestock Pr.) Moonlight on the Wabash Publishing.

Yong, Tohmoh J., et al. Tune in CM2 Teacher's Book. 2007. pap., tchr. ed. (***978-0-521-69600-5(3)***) Cambridge Univ. Pr.

FRENCH LITERATURE

Davoust, Eugene-Pierre. Resistance? Defendu, Mademoiselle! (FRE.). (YA). (gr. 9-12). 4.95 (978-0-8219-1034-4(5) , 40324) EMC/Paradigm Publishing.

Les Miserables. 2000. (YA). 11.95 (978-1-56137-757-2(0)) Novel Units, Inc.

FRENCH LITERATURE—HISTORY AND CRITICISM

Baselis-Bitoun, Lison. La Guerre de Troie: Advanced Placement French Literature. 1999. (FRE.). 63p. (YA). (gr. 9-12). stu. ed., wbk. ed. 6.67 (978-1-877653-69-8(1)) Wayside Publishing.

—Le Mariage de Figaro: Advanced Placement French Literature. 1999. (FRE.). 95p. (YA). (gr. 9-12). stu. ed., wbk. ed. 7.34 (978-1-877653-68-1(3)) Wayside Publishing.

Bloom, Harold, ed. & tr. Emile Zola. Bloom, Harold, tr. 2003. (Bloom's Modern Critical Views Ser.). 150p. 45.00 (978-0-7910-7663-7(6) , Chelsea Hse.) Facts On File, Inc.

Novel Units, Inc. Staff, ed. Cyrano de Bergerac. 1999. (YA). 9.95 (978-1-56137-621-6(3)) Novel Units, Inc.

FRENCH REVOLUTION

see France—History—Revolution, 1789-1799

FRESH-WATER ANIMALS

see also Aquariums; Marine Animals

also names of individual fresh-water animal, e.g. Beavers, etc.

Dollar. Piranhas. 2001. (Animals of the Rain Forest Ser.). (SPA., Illus.). (J). pap. (978-0-7398-3361-2(8)) Steck-Vaughn.

Donovan, Sandy. Animals of Rivers, Lakes & Ponds. 2002. (Animals of the Biomes Ser.). (Illus.). 48p. (J). lib. bdg. 25.70 (978-0-7398-5690-1(1)) Raintree.

—Animals of Rivers, Lakes & Ponds. 2002. (Animals of the Biomes Ser.). (Illus.). 48p. (J). pap. 6.95 (978-0-7398-6411-1(4)) Steck-Vaughn.

Duck Pond Dip. 2006. (Illus.). 32p. (J). (978-1-4156-7634-9(8)) Dorling Kindersley Publishing, Inc.

First Book about Animals in the Water. 2000. (First Book about Animals Ser.). (Illus.). 16p. (J). (ps up). lib. bdg. 19.33 (978-0-8368-2653-1(1)) Stevens, Gareth Inc.

Heinz, Brian. Butternut Hollow Pond. 2006. (Illus.). (J). pap. 6.95 (978-0-8225-5993-1(5) , First Avenue Editions) Lerner Publishing Group.

Marshall Cavendish Corporation Staff. Aquatic Life of the World, 11 vols., Vols. 1-10. 2000. (Illus.). (J). (978-0-7614-7181-3(2)) Cavendish, Marshall Corp.

Marshall Cavendish Corporation Staff, contrib. by. Aquatic Life of the World, 11 vols., Set. 2000. (Illus.). 700p. (gr. 4-6). 471.36 (978-0-7614-7170-7(7) , Cavendish, Marshall Reference Bks.) Cavendish, Marshall Corp.

Marshall Cavendish Corporation Staff, ed. Aquatic Life of the World, 11 vols. 2000. (Illus.). (J). (978-0-7614-7171-4(5)); 700p. 329.95 (978-0-7614-7172-1(3)); (978-0-7614-7173-8(1)); (978-0-7614-7174-5(X)); (978-0-7614-7175-2(8)); (978-0-7614-7176-9(6)); (978-0-7614-7177-6(4)); (978-0-7614-7178-3(2)); (978-0-7614-7179-0(0)); (978-0-7614-7180-6(4)) Cavendish, Marshall Corp.

Perry, Phyllis J. Freshwater Giants: Hippopotamuses, River Dolphins & Manatees. (Watts Library). (Illus.). 64p. (J). (gr. 5-7). 2000. pap. 8.95 (978-0-531-16424-2(1)); 1999. 25.50 (978-0-531-11681-4(6)) Scholastic Library Publishing. (Watts, Franklin).

Radley, Gail. Waterways. 1998. (Vanishing from Ser.). (J). lib. bdg. (978-0-8225-1939-3(9)) Lerner Publishing Group.

Schofield, Jennifer. Animal Babies in Ponds & Rivers. 2004. (Animal Babies Ser.). (Illus.). 32p. (J). (ps-k). 7.95 (978-0-7534-5790-0(3) , Kingfisher) Houghton Mifflin Co. Trade & Reference Div.

World Book, Inc. Staff, contrib. by. Freshwater Life of the United States & Canada. 2004. (World Book's Science & Nature Guides Ser.). (Illus.). 80p. (J). (978-0-7166-4213-8(1)) World Bk., Inc.

FRESH-WATER BIOLOGY

see also Aquariums; Fresh-Water Animals; Fresh-Water Plants; Marine Biology

Ampt, Peter. Fresh Water. 2001. (Water Worlds Ser.). (Illus.). 32p. (J). (gr. 4 up). 28.00 (978-0-7910-6569-3(3) , 010353, Chelsea Hse.) Facts On File, Inc.

Aspen-Baxter, Linda. Fresh Waters. 2006. (J). (978-1-59036-442-0(2)); (978-1-59036-443-7(0)) Weigl Pubs., Inc.

Beatty, Richard. Rivers, Lakes, Streams, & Ponds. 2002. (Biomes Atlases Ser.). (Illus.). 64p. (J). lib. bdg. 31.42 (978-0-7398-5513-3(1)) Raintree.

—Rivers, Lakes, Streams, & Ponds. 2003. (gr. 5-8). lib. bdg. 18.20 (978-0-613-78187-9(2)) Tandem Library Bks.

Bernhard, Annika. Freshwater Pond Coloring Book. 2000. (Illus.). 48p. (J). pap. 3.95 (978-0-486-41035-7(8)) Dover Pubns., Inc.

Cooper, Ann C. Around the Pond: The Wild Wonders Series. Emerling, Dorothy, illus. 1998. (Wild Wonders Ser.). 48p. (gr. k-4). pap. 9.95 (978-1-57098-223-1(6)) Rinehart, Roberts Pubs.

DeStrulle, Arlene & Johnson, Tora. Guide to Freshwater Animals Without Backbones. Sayre, Tamara, illus. Date not set. (Orig.). (J). (gr. 4-6). pap. 10.95 (978-0-9616712-6-6(2)) Catskill Ctr. for Conservation & Development, Inc.

Disney Staff. Pooh's Playful Pond. Disney Staff, illus. 1999. (Pooh's Learn & Grow Ser.: Vol. 6). (Illus.). 12p. (J). 3.49 (978-1-57973-040-6(X)) Advance Pubs. LLC.

Dorling Kindersley Publishing Staff. Pond & River. 2005. (Eyewitness Books). 72p. (J). 15.99 (978-0-7566-1085-2(0)); lib. bdg. 19.99 (978-0-7566-1086-9(9)) Dorling Kindersley Publishing, Inc.

Duck Pond Dip. 2006. (Illus.). 32p. (J). (978-1-4156-7634-9(8)) Dorling Kindersley Publishing, Inc.

Edelstein, Karen. Pond & Stream Safari: A Guide to the Ecology of Aquatic Invertebrates. Sayre, Tamara, illus. 2nd rev. ed. 1999. (Experience 4-H Natural Resources Ser.). 56p. (J). (gr. 5-7). 15.75 (978-1-57753-254-5(6) , 147L24) Resource Centre, The.

Fleisher, Paul. Lake & Pond Food Webs. 2007. (Early Bird Food Webs Ser.). 48p. (J). (gr. 2-5). 26.60 (***978-0-8225-6731-8(8)*** , Lerner Pubns.) Lerner Publishing Group.

Fleisher, Paul. Pond. 1998. (Webs of Life Ser.). (Illus.). 40p. (J). (gr. 2-5). lib. bdg. 22.79 (978-0-7614-0835-2(5) , Benchmark Bks.) Cavendish, Marshall Corp.

Galko, Francine. Pond Animals. 2003. (Animals in Their Habitats Ser.). (Illus.). 32p. (J). (gr. k-2). lib. bdg. 21.36 (978-1-4034-0181-6(0)); pap. 6.95 (978-1-4034-0438-1(0)) Heinemann Library.

Halfmann, Janet. Life in a Pond. 2001. (Lifeviews Ser.). (Illus.). 32p. (J). (978-1-58341-073-8(2) , Creative Education) Creative Co., The.

Hammersmith, Craig. Kerplunk! 2002. (Spyglass Books). (Illus.). 24p. (J). (gr. 1 up). lib. bdg. 18.60 (978-0-7565-0236-2(5)) Compass Point Bks.

Heinz, Brian. Butternut Hollow Pond. 2006. (Illus.). (J). pap. 6.95 (978-0-8225-5993-1(5) , First Avenue Editions) Lerner Publishing Group.

Hibbert, Adam. A Freshwater Pond. 1999. (Small Worlds Ser.). (Illus.). 32p. (J). (gr. 3-4). pap. (978-0-7787-0147-7(6)); lib. bdg. (978-0-7787-0133-0(6)) Crabtree Publishing Co.

Holt, Rinehart and Winston Staff. Holt Science & Technology Chapter 11: Earth Science: The Flow of Fresh Water. 5th ed. 2004. (Illus.). pap. 12.86 (978-0-03-030316-6(8)) Holt, Rinehart & Winston.

Hunter, Anne. What's in the Pond? Hunter, Anne, illus. 1999. (Illus.). 32p. (J). (gr. k-3). tchr. ed. 5.95 (978-0-395-91224-9(5)) Houghton Mifflin Co. Trade & Reference Div.

Kuhn, Dwight, illus. & photos by. Pond. Kuhn, Dwight, photos by. 2004. 24p. (J). (gr. 2-4). 22.45 (978-1-4103-0312-7(8) , Blackbirch Pr., Inc.) Thomson Gale.

Lantz, Peggy S. & Hale, Wendy A. The Florida Water Story: From Raindrops to the Sea. Barnes, Jean, illus. 1998. 132p. (J). (gr. 5-7). 19.95 (978-1-56164-099-7(9)) Pineapple Pr., Inc.

Lindeen, Carol. Life in a Pond. 2003. (Pebble Plus: Living in a Biome Ser.). (Illus.). 24p. (J). lib. bdg. 17.26 (978-0-7368-2101-8(5) , Pebble Bks.) Capstone Pr., Inc.

Lindeen, Carol K. Life in a Pond, Vol. 3. 2005. (Earth & Outer Space Ser.). 24p. (YA). (gr. k-3). pap. (978-0-7368-3402-5(8) , Pebble Bks.) Capstone Pr., Inc.

—Life in a Stream, Vol. 3. 2005. (Earth & Outer Space Ser.). 24p. (YA). (gr. k-3). pap. (978-0-7368-3404-9(4) , Pebble Bks.) Capstone Pr., Inc.

Morgan, Sally. A Pond in the Meadow. 2000. (Life in... Ser.). (Illus.). 32p. (J). (gr. 2-6). lib. bdg. 16.95 (978-1-929298-86-0(2)) Chrysalis Education.

Nadeau, Isaac. Food Chains in a Pond Habitat. Kuhn, Dwight, photos by. 2002. (Library of Food Chains & Food Webs). (Illus.). 24p. (J). (gr. 2-4). lib. bdg. 18.75 (978-0-8239-5763-7(2) , PowerKids Pr.) Rosen Publishing Group, Inc., The.

Oliver, Clare. Life in a Pond. 2002. (Microhabitats Ser.). (Illus.). 32p. (J). lib. bdg. 25.69 (978-0-7398-4331-4(1)) Raintree.

Reid, George K. Pond Life: A Golden Guide from St. Martin's Press. Zim, Herbert S., ed. Dolan, Tom & Kaicher, Sally D., illus. rev. ed. 2001. (Golden Guides Ser.). 160p. pap. 6.95 (978-1-58238-130-5(5) , Golden Guides from Saint Martin's Pr.) St. Martin's Pr.

Ross, Michael Elsohn. Pond Watching with Ann Morgan. Smith, Wendy, illus. 2005. (Naturalist's Apprentice Biographies Ser.). 48p. (gr. 3-6). lib. bdg. 19.93 (978-1-57505-385-1(3)) Lerner Publishing Group.

Schwartz, David M. At the Pond. Kuhn, Dwight, photos by. 1999. (Springboards into Science Ser.). (Illus.). 24p. (J). (gr. 1 up). lib. bdg. 19.93 (978-0-8368-2244-1(7)) Stevens, Gareth Inc.

Silverstein, Alvin. World in a Drop of Water: Exploring with a Microscope. 1998. (gr. 3-6). lib. bdg. 12.40 (978-0-613-90637-1(3)) Tandem Library Bks.

Silverstein, Alvin & Silverstein, Virginia B. A World in a Drop of Water: Exploring with a Microscope. 1998. (Illus.). 64p. (J). (gr. 5-8). pap. 4.95 (978-0-486-40381-6(5) , 40381-5) Dover Pubns., Inc.

Stewart, David. Pond Life. 2002. (gr. k-3). lib. bdg. 15.25 (978-0-613-53073-6(X)) Tandem Library Bks.

Taylor, Barbara. Inland Water Habitats. 2006. (Exploring Habitats Ser.). (Illus.). 36p. (J). lib. bdg. (978-0-8368-7254-5(1)) Stevens, Gareth Inc.

Toupin, Laurie. Freshwater Habitats: Life in Freshwater Ecosystems. 2005. (Watts Library Ser.). (Illus.). 64p. (J). (gr. 5-7). pap. 8.95 (978-0-531-16675-8(9) , Watts, Franklin) Scholastic Library Publishing.

Toupin, Laurie Peach. Freshwater Habitats: Life in Freshwater Ecosystems. 2004. (Watts Library Ser.). (J). 25.50 (978-0-531-12305-8(7) , Watts, Franklin) Scholastic Library Publishing.

Twinem, Neecy. Peek at a Pond. 1999. (Lift-the-Flap Book Ser.). (Illus.). 24p. (J). (ps-1). pap. 6.99 (978-0-448-41953-4(X) , Grosset & Dunlap) Penguin Group (USA) Inc.

Wickings, Ruth. In the Pond. 2007. (World at Your Feet Ser.). (Illus.). 10p. (J). 9.95 (978-1-84560-026-6(6)) Mercury Bks. Ltd. GBR. *Dist:* International Publishers Marketing.

FRESH-WATER PLANTS

see also Aquariums; Marine Plants

Sullivan, Victoria I. Why Water Plants Don't Drown. 1999. (First Bks.). (J). (978-0-531-20366-8(2) , Watts, Franklin) Scholastic Library Publishing.

FREUD, SIGMUND, 1856-1939

Bankston, John. Sigmund Freud: Exploring the Mysteries of the Mind. 2006. (Great Minds of Science Ser.). (Illus.). 128p. (J). lib. bdg. 31.93 (978-0-7660-2336-9(2)) Enslow Pubs., Inc.

Gogerly, Liz. Sigmund Freud. 2003. (20th Century History Makers Ser.). (Illus.). 112p. (J). lib. bdg. 32.85 (978-0-7398-6142-4(5)) Raintree.

Krull, Kathleen. Sigmund Freud. Kulikov, Boris, illus. 2006. (Giants of Science Ser.: No. 3). 128p. (YA). (gr. 5 up). 15.99 (978-0-670-05892-1(0) , Viking Juvenile) Penguin Group (USA) Inc.

Reef, Catherine. Sigmund Freud: Pioneer of the Mind. 2001. (Illus.). 160p. (J). (gr. 5-9). tchr. ed. 19.00 (978-0-618-01762-1(3) , Clarion Bks.) Houghton Mifflin Co. Trade & Reference Div.

FRICTION

Hewitt, Sally. Friction. 2007. (J). (***978-1-59604-139-4(0)***) Stargazer Bks.

Niz, Ellen Sturm. Friction. 2005. (First Facts Ser.). (Illus.). 24p. (J). (978-0-7368-5402-3(9)) Capstone Pr., Inc.

Oxlade, Chris. Friction & Resistance. 2006. (Fantastic Forces Ser.). (Illus.). 32p. (J). pap. (978-1-4034-8176-4(8)); lib. bdg. (978-1-4034-8171-9(7)) Heinemann Library.

Riley, Peter D. Forces & Friction. 2007. (J). (***978-1-59920-026-2(0)***) Smart Apple Media.

Sadler, Wendy. Forces: The Ups & Downs! 2005. (Raintree Perspectives Ser.). (Illus.). 32p. (J). pap. (978-1-4109-1558-0(1)); lib. bdg. (978-1-4109-1550-4(6)) Steck-Vaughn.

Tocci, Salvatore. Experiments with Friction. (True Bks.). (Illus.). 48p. (J). (gr. 3-5). 2003. pap. 6.95 (978-0-516-29363-9(X)); 2002. pap. 25.00 (978-0-516-22512-8(X)) Scholastic Library Publishing. (Children's Pr.).

Trumbauer, Lisa. What Is Friction? 2004. (Rookie Read about Science Ser.). (Illus.). 31p. (J). 20.50 (978-0-516-23447-2(1) , Watts, Franklin) Scholastic Library Publishing.

—What Is Friction. 2004. (Rookie Read-About Science Ser.). 32p. (J). (gr. 1-2). pap. 4.95 (978-0-516-25843-0(5) , Children's Pr.) Scholastic Library Publishing.

Whitehouse, Patricia. Good Friction, Bad Friction. 2007. (J). (978-1-60044-190-5(4)) Rourke Publishing, LLC.

—Sliding. 2003. (Illus.). 24p. (J). pap. (978-1-4034-3471-5(9)); lib. bdg. 18.50 (978-1-4034-0906-5(4)) Heinemann Library.

FRIENDS, SOCIETY OF

see Society of Friends

FRIENDSHIP

see also Love

Aboff, Marcie. Mike's Mystery. Muehlenhardt, Amy Bailey, illus. 2007. (J). lib. bdg. (***978-1-4048-3667-9(5)***) Picture Window Bks.

—The Pizza Palace. Doerrfeld, Cori, illus. 2007. (J). lib. bdg. (***978-1-4048-3665-5(9)***) Picture Window Bks.

Abraham, Ken & Fitzgerald, Annie. Dear God, Thank You for Friends. 2003. (Dear God Kids Ser.). (Illus.). 12p. (J). 4.99 (978-0-8254-2647-6(2)) Kregel Pubns.

Albregts, Lisa & Cape, Elizabeth. Best Friends: Tons of Crazy, Cool Things to Do with Your Girlfriends. 1998. (Illus.). 152p. (J). (gr. 3-7). pap. 12.95 (978-1-55652-326-7(2)) Chicago Review Pr., Inc.

All about Us Interactive Packages: Making Friends. (Pebble Soup Explorations Ser.). (ps up). 52.00 (978-0-7578-5228-2(9)) Rigby Education.

American Girl Editorial Staff. Best Friends Kit: Games & Goodies for Friends to Share. Lukatz, Casey, illus. 2004. (Coconut an American Girls Best Friendtm Ser.). (J). (gr. 2 up). 9.95 (978-1-58485-880-5(X)) American Girl Publishing, Inc.

—Pages & Pockets: Four Mini Books for Secrets & Stuff. Higgins, Anne Keegan, illus. 2004. (Americangirl Library(R) Ser.). 96p. (J). (gr. 3 up). 12.95 (978-1-58485-873-7(7)) American Girl Publishing, Inc.

American Girl Editorial Staff, ed. Licorice Book & Plush Set. Casey, Lukatz, illus. 2005. (American Girl Today Ser.). 80p. (J). 21.95 (978-1-58485-970-3(9) , American Girl) American Girl Publishing, Inc.

Amistad: Juego Entero. (SPA.). 150.00 (978-1-55883-109-4(6) , 602605) C R C World Literature Ministries/Libros Desafio.

Amistad: Manual para Lideres. (SPA.). tchr. ed. 25.00 (978-1-55883-108-7(8) , 602604) C R C World Literature Ministries/Libros Desafio.

Amistad: Recursos para Adultos. (SPA.). 11.75 (978-1-55883-107-0(X) , 602603) C R C World Literature Ministries/Libros Desafio.

Amistad: Recursos para Jovenes. (SPA.). (YA). (gr. 5 up). stu. ed. 11.75 (978-1-55883-106-3(1) , 602602) C R C World Literature Ministries/Libros Desafio.

Amos, Janine. Making Friends. Spenceley, Annabel, illus. 2002. (Courteous Kids Ser.). 32p. (J). (ps up). lib. bdg. 23.33 (978-0-8368-3171-9(3)) Stevens, Gareth Inc.

Amos, Janine, et al. Why Be Unfriendly? 2007. (Problem Solvers Ser.). (Illus.). 32p. (J). pap. 12.95 (***978-1-84234-192-6(8)*** , Evans Brothers, Limited) Evans Publishing Group GBR. *Dist:* Independent Pubs. Group.

Ancona, George. Mis Amigos: My Friends. (Somos Latinos (We Are Latinos) Ser.). 2005. (SPA., Illus.). 32p. (J). (gr. 1-3). pap. 8.95 (978-0-516-25068-7(X) , Children's Pr.); 2004. 20.00 (978-0-516-23690-2(3) , Watts, Franklin) Scholastic Library Publishing.

Anderson, Judith. Me & My Friends. 2007. (J). (***978-1-59771-089-3(X)***) Sea-To-Sea Pubns.

Andrews, Kate. Cool It, Carrie. 1999. (Making Friends Ser.: No. 2). (Illus.). 128p. (J). (gr. 3-7). mass mkt. 3.99 (978-0-380-80931-8(1)) HarperCollins Pubs.

—Wise up, Alex. 1999. (Making Friends Ser.: No. 1). (Illus.). 128p. (J). (gr. 3-7). mass mkt. 3.99 (978-0-380-80930-1(3)) HarperCollins Pubs.

Andrews McMeel Publishing Staff & Engelbreit, Mary. Treasury of Friendship: Take Four!, 4 bks. 2000. (Little Book Libraries). (Illus.). (YA). mass mkt. 19.95 (978-0-7407-1179-4(2)) Andrews McMeel Publishing.

Anza, Ana Luisa. Amigos del Otro Lado. Gomez, Eddie Martinez, illus. rev. ed. 2004. (Castillo de la Lectura Naranja Ser.). (SPA.). 136p. (J). pap. 7.95 (978-970-20-0130-0(7)) Castillo, Ediciones, S. A. de C. V. MEX. *Dist:* Lectorum Pubns., Inc., Macmillan.

Bailey, Debbie. Mis Amigos. Huszar, Susan, photos by. 2003. (Hablemos Ser.).Tr. of My Friends. (SPA., Illus.). 14p. (J). (gr. k-ps). bds. 5.95 (978-1-55037-827-6(9)) Annick Pr., Ltd. CAN. *Dist:* Firefly Bks., Ltd.

—My Friends. Huszar, Susan, photos by. 2003. (Talk-about-Bks.). (Illus.). 14p. (J). (gr. k-ps). bds. 5.95 (978-1-55037-817-7(1)) Annick Pr., Ltd. CAN. *Dist:* Firefly Bks., Ltd.

Basic Friendship Curriculum: Year 2. stu. ed. 13.25 (978-1-56212-732-9(2) , 300210); instr.'s gde. ed. 22.25 (978-1-56212-730-5(6) , 300200) CRC Pubns. (Faith Alive Christian Resources).

Basic Friendship Curriculum: Year 3. (YA). (gr. 5 up). stu. ed. 13.25 (978-1-56212-737-4(3) , 300320, Faith Alive Christian Resources) CRC Pubns.

Be a Friend. 2006. 16p. (J). pap. 1.99 (978-0-7847-1451-5(7) , 22130) Standard Publishing.

Benchmark Education Staff, compiled by. Families & Friends. 2006. spiral bd. 249.00 (***978-1-4108-7069-8(3)***) Benchmark Education Co.

Bishop, Vincent. You, Your Friends & Your Family. 2005. (Family Matters Ser.). (Illus.). 48p. (J). (gr. 5-8). lib. bdg. 23.95 (978-0-8239-3351-8(2)) Rosen Publishing Group, Inc., The.

Bloom, Poppy. Best Friends: A Special Book of True Friendship! 1999. (Illus.). 96p. (YA). (gr. 4-7). pap. 4.95 (978-1-902618-47-0(5)) Element Children's Bks.

Braithwaite, Althea. Being Friends. Jude, Conny, illus. Best, Charlie, photos by. 1998. (Exploring Emotions Ser.). 32p. (J). (gr. 3 up). lib. bdg. 19.93 (978-0-8368-2115-4(7)) Stevens, Gareth Inc.

Brian, Sarah Jane. Friendship Bracelets Girls Club Handbook. Barbas, Kerren & Gershman, Jo, illus. 2005. (Activity Journals Ser.). 128p. 12.99 (978-0-88088-365-8(0)) Peter Pauper Pr. Inc.

Brown, Laurie Krasny. How to Be a Friend. Brown, Marc, illus. 1998. 32p. (J). (ps-3). 16.99 (978-0-316-10913-0(4)) Little Brown & Co.

—How to Be a Friend: A Guide to Making Friends & Keeping Them. Brown, Marc, illus. 2001. 32p. (J). (ps-3). pap. 6.99 (978-0-316-11153-9(8)) Little, Brown Bks. for Young Readers.

—How to Be a Friend: A Guide to Making Friends & Keeping Them. 2001. 13.54 (978-0-606-22566-3(8)) Tandem Library Bks.

Bruna, Dick & Running Press Staff. Miffy's Book of Friendship. 2003. (Irresistible Miniature Editionstm Ser.). (Illus.). 56p. 4.95 (978-0-7624-1648-6(3) , Running Pr. Minature Editions) Running Pr. Bk. Pubs.

Burch, Regina G. Be a Friend: Learning about Friendship & Fairness. Hamaguchi, Carla, ed. Edwards, Karl, illus. 2002. (Character Education Readers). 16p. (J). (gr. k-3). pap. 2.99 (978-1-57471-827-0(4) , CTP 3126) Creative Teaching Pr., Inc.

Burkholder, Kelly. Pen Pals. 2000. (Artistic Adventures Ser.). (Illus.). 24p. (J). (gr. 2-6). lib. bdg. 23.93 (978-1-57103-353-6(X)) Rourke Publishing, LLC.

Burks, Catherine. Different Friends, 5 bks., Set. Lee, Rudolph, illus. Incl. Vol. 1. Hi! Let's Meet Billy. pap. 6.95 (978-1-892750-00-6(7)); Vol. 2. Hi! Let's Meet Pete. pap. 6.95 (978-1-892750-01-3(5)); Vol. 3. Hi! Let's Meet Sam. pap. 6.95 (978-1-892750-02-0(3)); Vol. 4. Hi! Let's Meet Bertha. pap. 6.95 (978-1-892750-03-7(1)); Vol. 5. Hi! Let's Meet Doris. pap. 6.95 (978-1-892750-05-1(8)); (Illus.). (J). (gr. 1-5). 1998. 34.75 (978-1-892750-04-4(X)) Different Friends.

Burns, Peggy. Make Friends, Break Friends. 2004. (Kids' Guides Ser.). (Illus.). 32p. (J). (gr. 1-4). lib. bdg. 25.64 (978-1-4109-0571-0(3)) Raintree.

Burton, Margie & French, Tammy, Cathy - Jones. Sola y acompañada & Alone & Together. 2005. spiral bd. 66.00 (***978-1-4108-5629-6(1)***) Benchmark Education Co.

Burton, Margie, et al. Friends. Adams, Alison, ed. 1999. (Early Connections Ser.). 16p. (J). (gr. k-2). pap. 4.50 (978-1-58344-062-9(3)) Benchmark Education Co.

Butcher, Sam, illus. My Friend Forever. 2000. (Precious Moments Seasons of Faith Ser.). 32p. (J). (ps-3). 5.99 (978-0-7852-5552-9(4)) Nelson, Thomas Inc.

Chobanian, Elizabeth, ed. Friendship File: Facts on Friends from A to Z. Lukatz, Casey, illus. 2003. (Coconut Ser.). 120p. (J). 7.95 (978-1-58485-797-6(8)) American Girl Publishing, Inc.

Christopher, Matt. How to Be a Friend. 2001. (J). pap. 5.95 (978-0-316-13584-9(4)) Little Brown & Co.

Clough, Sandy Lynam. Come to My Tea Party: Fun & Friendship for Young Ladies. gif. ed. 2002. (Illus.). 32p. 13.99 (978-0-7369-0670-8(3)) Harvest Hse. Pubs.

Criswell, Patti. Friends: Making Them & Keeping Them. Watkins, Michelle, ed. 2006. 80p. (J). pap. (978-1-59369-154-7(8)) American Girl Publishing, Inc.

Criswell, Patti Kelley. Smart Girl's Guide to Friendship Troubles: Dealing with Fights, Being Left Ou. 2003. (gr. 3-6). lib. bdg. 18.75 (978-0-613-85866-3(2)) Tandem Library Bks.

—A Smart Girl's Guide to Friendship Troubles: Dealing with Fights, Being Left Out & the Whole Popularity Thing. Martini, Angela, illus. 2003. (American Girl Library). 88p. pap. 9.95 (978-1-58485-711-2(0)) American Girl Publishing, Inc.

Custom Curricul Staff. Can I Really Relate? 2004. (Custom Curriculum Ser.). 256p. pap., pap. 19.99 (978-0-7814-4088-2(2) , 0781440882) Cook, David C. Publishing Co.

Dalmatian Press Staff. Belle & Friends: Coloring & Activity Book with Stickers. 2004. (Disney Princess Ser.). (Illus.). 64p. (J). pap. 1.69 (978-1-4037-0863-2(0)) Dalmatian Pr.

—God's Girls: Friends Forever, Sticker Book in Full Color. 2003. (Sticker Book in Full Color Ser.). (Illus.). 16p. (J). pap. 2.99 (978-1-57759-888-6(1)) Dalmatian Pr.

Davi. Chichonazo! 2004. Tr. of Bump on the Head!. (SPA.). (J). pap. 7.99 (978-84-236-6323-1(X)) Edebé ESP. *Dist:* Lectorum Pubns., Inc.

Dee, Catherine. The Girls' Book of Friendship: Cool Quotes, True Stories, Secrets & More. 2001. (Illus.). (J). 12.95 (978-0-316-34884-3(8) , Tingley, Megan Bks.) Little, Brown Bks. for Young Readers.

Dellasega, Cheryl. The Girl's Friendship Journal: A Guide to Relationshps. 2005. 128p. (J). (gr. 4-7). pap. 16.00 (978-1-932783-59-9(8)) Champion Pr., Ltd.

Design 23. School Checks. 2003. 72p. (J). (gr. 4-7). pap. 6.95 (978-1-903840-99-3(6)) O'Mara, Michael Bks., Ltd. GBR. *Dist:* Independent Pubs. Group.

Dietrich, Julie. David & His Friend, Jonathan. Ramsey, Marcy, illus. 2005. (Arch Books). (ENG.). 16p. (J). 1.99 (978-0-7586-0723-2(7)) Concordia Publishing Hse.

Dowell, Andrea C. & Rokke, Kathi R. Miguel & Sarah: Close Friends & Cystic Fibrosis. Madden, Randi, illus. l.t. ed. 1999. 22p. (J). (gr. k-4). pap. 8.00 (978-0-9644972-1-4(2)) Children's Hospitals & Clinics.

Drake, Jane & Love, Ann. My Best Friend & Me: A Memory Scrapbook for Kids. Ritchie, Scot, illus. 2001. (Memory Scrapbks. for Kids). 32p. (J). (gr. k-3). (978-1-55074-875-8(0)) Kids Can Pr., Ltd.

Dumont, Ninda, ed. My Heart 2 Heart Girlfriends' Book. Franklin, Linda C., illus. 1999. 64p. (J). 11.95 (978-1-892951-02-1(9)) Fine Print Publishing Co.

Duran, Magdelena, illus. The Jewel of Friendship: A Jataka Tale. 2001. (Jataka Tales Ser.). (J). pap. 7.95 (978-0-89800-319-2(9)) Dharma Publishing.

Espeland, Pamela & Verdick, Elizabeth. Making Choices & Making Friends. 2006. (Illus.). 80p. (J). (gr. 3-7). pap. 9.95 (978-1-57542-201-5(8)) Free Spirit Publishing, Inc.

Feldman, Heather. My Best Friend: A Book about Friendship. 2000. (PowerKids Readers Ser.). (Illus.). 24p. (J). (gr. 1). lib. bdg. 16.00 (978-0-8239-5526-8(5) , PK-MYFR, PowerKids Pr.) Rosen Publishing Group, Inc., The.

Feltes, Kim & Chen, Grace. Yo, Yolanda! Advice from an Expert. 2002. (Read 180 Ser.). (Illus.). 70p. (J). (978-0-439-12333-4(X)) Scholastic, Inc.

Friendliness. (Everyday Character Education Ser.). 24p. (J). 6.95 (978-0-7368-5148-0(8)); 6.95 (978-0-7368-9152-3(8)) Capstone Pr., Inc.

Friends Rule! 2002. (Far Out Girls Ser.). (Illus.). 16p. (J). (ps). pap. 2.99 (978-1-57759-442-0(8)) Dalmatian Pr.

Friendship & Hair Braiding. 2003. 32p. 12.98 (978-1-4054-1639-9(4)) Parragon, Inc.

Friendship Bracelets. 2004. (Whizz Kits Ser.). (Illus.). 48p. (J). (978-1-84229-938-8(7)) Top That! Publishing PLC.

Friendship, Rites of Passage for Males & Females: Strange Stuff in the Bible. 2000. (Connect Ser.: Vol. 8). (YA). 20.00 (978-0-687-72149-8(0)) Abingdon Pr.

Fry, Erin. The Power of Friendship. 2005. (Illus.). 16p. (J). pap. (978-0-7367-2920-8(8)) Zaner-Bloser, Inc.

Gamblin, Rose Tooley. The Birthday Party. 2007. (J). (***978-0-8127-0464-8(9)***) Autumn Hse. Publishing Co.

Garris, Norma. Friendship Fun! 1999. (Illus.). 48p. (J). (ps-2). pap. 2.49 (978-0-7847-0886-6(X) , Bean Sprouts) Standard Publishing.

George, Jean Craighead. Nutik & Amaroq Play Ball. 2001. (Book of Friends Ser.). (Illus.). 40p. (J). (gr. k-3). 15.89 (978-0-06-028167-0(7)) HarperCollins Pubs.

Goldsack, Gaby. The Ultimate Sleepover Pack. Reeves, Sue, illus. 24p. (J). 79.60 (978-0-7641-7662-3(5)) Barron's Educational Series, Inc.

Golosi, Rosanne. Best Friends Forever! Martini, Angela, illus. 2005. 64p. (J). (***978-0-439-80072-3(2)***) Scholastic, Inc.

Good Friends. 2002. (Illus.). (J). pap. 3.74 (978-0-7398-5847-9(5)) Steck-Vaughn.

The Good, the Bad, & Everything Else: Individual Title Six-Packs. (Action Packs Ser.). 104p. (gr. 3-5). 44.00 (978-0-7635-2994-9(X)) Rigby Education.

Harcourt School Publishers Staff. All Kinds of Friends Bk. 2: Standard Anthology. 95th ed. 1998. (Treasury of Literature Ser.). (Illus.). (gr. 2). 53.70 (978-0-15-301252-5(8)) Harcourt Schl. Pubs.

—Han & Juan Are Friends. 3rd ed. 2002. (Trophies English Language Learners Ser.). (Illus.). pap. 5.10 (978-0-15-327633-0(9)) Harcourt Schl. Pubs.

—Making Friends: Library Edition. 1999. (Collections Ser.). (Illus.). (J). 5.30 (978-0-15-314322-9(3)) Harcourt Schl. Pubs.

Hatkoff, Craig, et al. Owen & Mzee: The Language of Friendship. Greste, Peter, photos by. 2007. (Illus.). 40p. (J). (ps-3). pap. 16.99 (978-0-439-89959-8(1) , Scholastic Pr.) Scholastic, Inc.

—Owen & Mzee: The True Story of a Remarkable Friendship. Greste, Peter, illus. 2006. 40p. (J). (ps-3). pap. 16.99 (978-0-439-82973-1(9) , Scholastic Pr.) Scholastic, Inc.

Holyoke, Nancy. A Smart Girl's Guide to Boys: Surviving Crushes, Staying True to Yourself & Other Stuff! 2001. (gr. 3-6). lib. bdg. 18.75 (978-0-613-50064-7(4)) Tandem Library Bks.

Hopkins, Amy. Girlfriends Make the Best Friends. 2005. 96p. pap. 9.95 (978-1-84601-011-8(X)) M Q Pubns. GBR. *Dist:* Ingram Pub. Services, Koen-Levy Bk. Wholesalers LLC.

Howard Publishing Staff. Friends for Life. 2007. (Hugs Expression Ser.). 96p. 11.99 (978-1-4165-3583-6(7) , Howard Bks.) Simon & Schuster.

Hunt, Rameck, et al. We Beat the Street: How a Friendship Pact Led to Success. 2006. (Illus.). 208p. (J). (gr. 5). pap. 6.99 (978-0-14-240627-4(9) , Puffin) Penguin Group (USA) Inc.

I Love You Because You're. 2004. (J). pap. 6.99 (978-0-439-57711-3(X)) Scholastic, Inc.

Jesus Company: Friendship. 32p. (J). (gr. 4). 10.99 (978-0-570-00675-6(9) , 22-2778); (gr. 5). 10.99 (978-0-570-00681-7(3) , 22-2784); (gr. 6). 10.99 (978-0-570-00687-9(2) , 22-2790) Concordia Publishing Hse.

Johanson, Sarah Margaret. Caillou: My Imaginary Friend. 2003. (Clubhouse Ser.). (Illus.). 24p. (J). pap. 2.50 (978-2-89450-478-9(0)) Chouette Publishing CAN. *Dist:* Independent Pubs. Group.

Johnson, Kevin W. Stick Tight: Glue Yourself to Godly Friends. 2001. (Early Teen Discipleship Ser.). 128p. (J). pap. 7.99 (978-0-7642-2434-8(4)) Bethany Hse. Pubs.

Johnston, Kurt & Oestreicher, Mark. My Friends. 2007. 144p. (J). pap. 9.99 (***978-0-310-27881-8(3)***) Zondervan.

Jordan, Denise. We Can Be Friends. 2003. (Heinemann Read & Learn Ser.). (Illus.). 24p. (J). pap. 5.25 (978-1-4034-4413-4(7)); lib. bdg. 18.50 (978-1-4034-4407-3(2)) Heinemann Library.

Karres, Erika V. Shearin. Crushes, Flirts, & Friends: A Real Girl's Guide to Boy Smarts. 2005. 160p. (YA). (gr. 8-12). pap. 8.95 (978-1-59337-363-4(5)) Adams Media Corp.

Keating-Velasco, Joanna. A Is for Autism F Is for Friend: A Kid's Book for Making Friends with a Child Who Has Autism. 2007. (J). pap. 12.95 (***978-1-931282-43-7(9)***) Autism Asperger Publishing Co.

Kemp, Kristen. What to Do When Your Best Friend Hates You. 2002. (Genny in a Bottle Ser.: No. 2). (Illus.). 144p. (J). (gr. 3-7). pap. 4.50 (978-0-439-21179-6(4) , Scholastic Paperbacks) Scholastic, Inc.

Kent, Susan. Let's Talk about Being a Good Friend. 2000. (Let's Talk Library). (Illus.). 24p. (J). (gr. 3). lib. bdg. 18.75 (978-0-8239-5419-3(6) , PowerKids Pr.) Rosen Publishing Group, Inc., The.

Kermani, Faiz. My Alien Penfriend. 2005. (ENG., Illus.). 89p. pap. 11.49 (***978-1-4208-5860-0(2)***) AuthorHouse.

Kirberger, Kimberly. Teen Love: On Friendship. 2000. (gr. 7-12). lib. bdg. 22.20 (978-0-613-30774-1(7)) Tandem Library Bks.

Kirberger, Kimberly & Mortensen, Colin. On Friendship. 2000. (Teen Love Ser.). (Illus.). 400p. (YA). (gr. 7-12). pap. 12.95 (978-1-55874-815-6(6)) Health Communications, Inc.

Klingel, Cynthia Fitterer. Friendliness. 2007. (Learn about Values Ser.). 24p. (J). 21.36 (978-1-59296-669-1(1)) Child's World, Inc.

Klutz Editors & Dzwonik, Cristian. Amigas para Siempre. Esteve, Laura, tr. 2005. (SPA., Illus.). 33p. (J). spiral bd. 18.95 (978-987-1078-29-5(3)) Klutz Latino MEX. *Dist:* Independent Pubs. Group.

Klutz Press Staff, ed. Me & My Friends: The Book of Us. 2004. (Illus.). 56p. (YA). 14.95 (978-1-57054-813-0(7)) Klutz.

Krulik, Nancy E. A Best Friend & 999 Other Things to Make You Happy. 2001. (Illus.). 78p. (J). pap. (978-0-439-21313-4(4)) Scholastic, Inc.

Langrish, Bob. Horses & Friends Poster Book. 2004. (Illus.). 64p. (J). pap. 9.95 (978-1-58017-580-7(5) , 67580, Storey Kids) Storey Publishing, LLC.

Levete, Sarah. Making Friends. 2007. (J). (***978-1-59604-152-3(8)***) Stargazer Bks.

Liberts, Jennifer. Beauty & the Beast: Friends Are Sweet. Baker, Darrell, illus. 2001. (Pictureback(R) Ser.). 24p. (J). (gr. k-k). pap. 3.25 (978-0-7364-1178-3(X) , RH/Disney) Random Hse. Children's Bks.

Lorbiecki, Marybeth. Friendship Book Set: That's Life! Literature Series, 4 vols. Gallop, Jim, photos by. 2004. (Illus.). 18p. (YA). 45.00 (978-0-9666667-3-1(9)) AbleNet, Inc.

Marshall, Paula, ed. Best Friends Forever: Deluxe Sound Storybook. 2006. 22p. (J). 15.95 (978-0-696-22917-6(X)) Meredith Bks.

Matlock, Mark. Have a Friend - Be a Friend: Wisdom on Friendship. 1998. (Wise Guides Ser.). 48p. (YA). pap. 5.95 (978-1-888237-21-4(X)) Baxter Pr.

Mattern, Joanne. Do You Help Others? 2007. (Are You a Good Friend? Ser.). 24p. (J). (gr. k-2). pap. 5.95 (***978-0-8368-8278-0(4)***); lib. bdg. 19.93 (***978-0-8368-8273-5(3)***) Stevens, Gareth Inc. (Weekly Reader Early Learning Library).

—Do You Help Others?/¿Ayudas a los Demas? 2007. (Are You a Good Friend?/Buenos Amigos Ser.). (SPA & ENG.). 24p. (J). (gr. k-2). pap. 5.95 (***978-0-8368-8288-9(1)***); lib. bdg. 19.93 (***978-0-8368-8283-4(0)***) Stevens, Gareth Inc. (Weekly Reader Early Learning Library).

—Do You Listen? 2007. (Are You a Good Friend? Ser.). 24p. (J). (gr. k-2). pap. 5.95 (***978-0-8368-8279-7(2)***); lib. bdg. 19.93 (***978-0-8368-8274-2(1)***) Stevens, Gareth Inc. (Weekly Reader Early Learning Library).

—Do You Share? 2007. (Are You a Good Friend? Ser.). 24p. (J). (gr. k-2). pap. 5.95 (***978-0-8368-8280-3(6)***); lib. bdg. 19.93 (***978-0-8368-8275-9(X)***) Stevens, Gareth Inc. (Weekly Reader Early Learning Library).

—Do You Take Turns? 2007. (Are You a Good Friend? Ser.). 24p. (J). (gr. k-2). pap. 5.95 (***978-0-8368-8281-0(4)***); lib. bdg. 19.93 (***978-0-8368-8276-6(8)***) Stevens, Gareth Inc. (Weekly Reader Early Learning Library).

Maurer, Tracy. A to Z of Friends & Family. 2002. (A to Z Ser.). (Illus.). 48p. (gr. k-2). 20.95 (978-1-58952-060-8(2)) Rourke Publishing, LLC.

Mayer, Cassie. Making Friends. 2007. (J). (***978-1-4034-9488-7(6)***); pap. (***978-1-4034-9496-2(7)***) Heinemann Library.

McCauley, John. Harley Teaches. McCauley, John, illus. 1998. (Illus.). 34p. (J). (gr. k-6). 12.95 (978-0-9664005-7-1(7)) American Health Pr.

McCoy, Sharon, et al. The Ultimate Best Friends Book. 1999. (Illus.). 80p. (J). (gr. 3-7). pap. 6.95 (978-0-7373-0225-7(9) , 02259W) McGraw-Hill/Contemporary.

MCP Staff. Eight Friends in All, Level 4, Bk. 44. 2003. (J). (ps-3). 24.50 (978-0-8136-0772-6(8)) Modern Curriculum Pr.

Mefford, David. How to Make A Friend in Three Days or Less. 2004. (YA). (978-0-9762143-0-4(X)) Mefford, David.

Michelson, Richard. As Good as Anybody. 2008. 40p. (J). (gr. 1-5). lib. bdg. 19.99 (***978-0-375-93335-6(2)*** , Knopf Bks. for Young Readers) Random Hse. Children's Bks.

Modern Staff. Best Friends: Short e; Consonants f, y; Blends fr, fl, Level A. 2003. ("Plaid" Phonics & Stories Libraries). (gr. 1-2). 38.50 (978-0-8136-9142-8(7)) Modern Curriculum Pr.

Moehn, Heather. Everything You Need to Know about Cliques. 2005. (Need to Know Library). (Illus.). 64p. (J). (gr. 7-12). 25.25 (978-0-8239-3326-6(1)) Rosen Publishing Group, Inc., The.

Molesworth. The Rectory Children. 2006. 130p. pap. 10.99 (***978-1-4264-5149-2(0)***) BiblioBazaar.

—The Rectory Children. 2006. 92p. pap. (978-1-84702-690-3(7)) Echo Library.

—The Rectory Children. 2006. pap. 12.95 (***978-1-55742-913-1(8)***) Wildside Pr.

—Rectory Children. 2006. 41.99 (***978-1-4280-2640-7(1)***); pap. 34.99 (***978-1-4280-2634-6(7)***) IndyPublish.com.

—The Rectory Children. l.t. ed. 2006. 146p. pap. 13.99 (***978-1-4264-5450-9(3)***) BiblioBazaar.

Mullican, Judy. Picnic Pals. Middleton, Mikell, illus. 2003. 8p. (J). (ps-1). bds. 10.95 (978-1-57332-251-5(2)) High-Reach Learning, Inc.

—Picnic Pals: Big Book. Middleton, Mikell, illus. 2003. 8p. (J). (ps-1). bds. 10.95 (978-1-57332-244-7(X)) High-Reach Learning, Inc.

Nettleton, Pamela Hill. Want to Play? Kids Talk about Friendliness. Muehlenhardt, Amy Bailey, illus. 2004. (Kids Talk Ser.). 32p. (C). (gr. 2-5). 23.93 (978-1-4048-0623-8(7)) Picture Window Bks.

Norwich, Grace & West, Betsy. Together Forever. 2007. 512p. (J). (gr. 3). 15.99 (***978-0-8431-2692-1(2)*** , Price Stern Sloan) Penguin Group (USA) Inc.

Orloff, Erica & Milo, Alexa. The Best Friends' Handbook: The Totally Cool One-of-a-Kind Book about You & Your Best Friend. Fisher, Carolyn, illus. 2002. (J). 10.95 (978-0-8027-8820-7(3)) Walker & Co.

Otto, Connie & Bader, Marilyn. Friendship Builders. 16p. stu. ed. 3.45 (978-0-570-00600-8(7) , 22-2730) Concordia Publishing Hse.

Ouriou, Katie. Love Ya Like a Sister: A Story of Friendship. Johnston, Julie, ed. 1999. (Illus.). 208p. (J). (gr. 5-9). pap. 7.95 (978-0-88776-454-7(1)) Tundra Bks., Inc./Livres Toundra, Inc. CAN. *Dist:* Random Hse., Inc.

Painter, Carol. Friends Helping Friends: A Handbook for Helpers. 2nd ed. 2003. (Illus.). 224p. (J). pap. 10.95 (978-1-930572-21-8(2)) Educational Media Corp.

—Leading a Friends Helping Friends Peer Program. Sorenson, Don L., ed. 1998. 210p. (YA). (gr. 9-12). pap. 9.95 (978-0-932796-29-5(X)) Educational Media Corp.

E F G

—Leading a Friends Helping Friends Peer Program. 2nd ed. 2003. 116p. (J). spiral bd. 9.95 (978-1-930572-22-5(0)) Educational Media Corp.

Patrick, Denise Lewis. A Lesson for Martin Luther King, Jr. Pate, Rodney S., illus. 2003. (Ready-to-Read Ser.). 32p. (J). pap. 3.99 (978-0-689-85397-5(1) , Aladdin) Simon & Schuster Children's Publishing.

—Lesson for Martin Luther King Jr. 2003. (gr. k-3). lib. bdg. 11.80 (978-0-613-73360-1(6)) Tandem Library Bks.

Pen Pals: Second Grade Guided Reading Level J. (On Our Way to English Ser.). (gr. 2 up). 34.50 (978-0-7578-7090-3(2)) Rigby Education.

Penchina, Sharon. Dogs & Bugs Go Together, Really They Do! 2007. 28p. 12.95 (978-0-9740684-8-0(9)) 2 Imagine.

Phidal Publishing Staff, ed. Girls World: My Best Friends. (Illus.). 64p. (J). pap. (978-2-7643-0145-6(6)) Phidal Publishing, Inc./Editions Phidal, Inc.

Play with Me Sesame I am a Friend. 2007. (J). pap. 2.95 (****978-1-59545-142-2(0)***) Learning Horizons, Inc.

PowerXpress Living God's Word Friendship. 2005. 115.00 (978-0-687-06301-7(9)) Abingdon Pr.

Priddy Books Staff. Frosty Friends: These Cool Animals Can't Waint to Meet You. rev. ed. 2004. (Priddy Books Big Ideas for Little People). (Illus.). 14p. (J). bds. 8.95 (978-0-312-49375-2(4) , Priddy Bks.) St. Martin's Pr.

Ray, Nan. Friends, Friends, Friends. 2004. (J). per. 24.95 (978-0-9760280-1-7(8)) You're On!, Inc.

Reader, Jenny. Girl 2 Girl: The Swap Book You Share with Your Friends. Martin, Caroline & Davies, Nic, illus. 2003. 96p. (J). pap. (978-0-439-56743-5(2)) Scholastic, Inc.

Rice, Ashley. Friends Rule: A Very Special Book of Friendship Especially for Girls. 2003. (Illus.). 64p. (J). pap. (978-0-88396-772-0(3) , Blue Mountain Pr.) Blue Mountain Arts Inc.

Richmond, Marianne R. Thank You for Your Friendship. 2004. (Illus.). 40p. (YA). 7.95 (978-0-9741465-4-6(4)) Marianne Richmond Studios, Inc.

Rigby Education Staff. Friends Together. (Illus.). 8p. (J). bds. 3.95 (978-0-7635-6435-3(4) , 764354C99) Rigby Education.

Roca, Nuria. Friendship: From Your Old Friends to Your New Friends. 2001. (From ... to Ser.). (Illus.). 36p. (J). (ps-1). pap. 6.95 (978-0-7641-1838-8(2)) Barron's Educational Series, Inc.

—Tus Amigos: de Antes a los Amigos de Ahora: Friendship: from Your Old Friends to Your New Friends Spanish Edition. 2001. (Dehellip;A(fromhellip;to Series) Ser.). (SPA.). 36p. (J). (ps-1). pap. 7.95 (978-0-7641-1839-5(0)) Barron's Educational Series, Inc.

Roca, Nuria. Tus Amigos, de los Amigos de Antes a los Amigos de Ahora. 2001. Tr. of Your Friends, Past & Present. (J). (978-0-606-22728-5(8)) Tandem Library Bks.

Romain, Trevor. Cliques, Phonies, & Other Baloney. Romain, Trevor, illus. 1998. (Laugh & Learn Ser.). (Illus.). 136p. (YA). (gr. 3-8). pap. 8.95 (978-1-57542-045-5(7)) Free Spirit Publishing, Inc.

—Cliques, Phonies, & Other Baloney. 1998. (gr. 5-8). lib. bdg. 18.75 (978-0-613-87131-0(6)) Tandem Library Bks.

Rosen, Jeff. Best Friends. 2005. (Illus.). 12p. (J). 5.95 (978-1-897073-17-9(8)) Lobster Pr. CAN. *Dist:* Univ. of Toronto Pr.

Rosenberg, Carol & Rosenberg, Gary. Jonand Jayne's Guide to Making Friendsand "'Getting"' the Guy (or Girl) 2008. 128p. (YA). pap. 9.95 (****978-0-7573-0659-4(4)***) Health Communications, Inc.

Ross, Dave. A Book of Friends. Rader, Laura, illus. 1999. 40p. (J). (ps-3). 12.89 (978-0-06-028362-9(9)) HarperCollins Pubs.

Rue, Nancy N. The Buddy Book: It's a God Thing. 2001. (Ywof Library Ser.). (Illus.). 128p. (J). (gr. 3-7). pap. 7.99 (978-0-310-70064-7(7)) Zonderkidz.

Running Press Staff. Bear Hugs for Friends. 2003. (Inspirio/Zondervan Miniature Editionstm Ser.). (Illus.). 128p. 4.95 (978-0-7624-1672-1(6) , Running Pr. Minature Editions) Running Pr. Bk. Pubs.

Sage, Angie. Give a Little Love: Stories of Love & Friendship. 2000. (Illus.). 63p. (YA). (ps up). 18.95 (978-1-902618-60-9(2)) Element Children's Bks.

Santos, Dina. Friends: Learning the FR Sound. (PowerPhonics Ser.). (Illus.). (J). 2002. 24p. (gr. 1). lib. bdg. 18.50 (978-0-8239-5944-0(9)); 2001. 23p. pap. 26.40 (978-0-8239-8289-9(0)) Rosen Publishing Group, Inc., The. (PowerKids Pr.).

Schick-Jacobowitz, Jeannie & Schick-Pierce, Susan. You're My Friend Beclaus. gif. ed. 2006. (Illus.). 48p. 7.95 (978-1-4022-0737-2(9)) Sourcebooks, Inc.

Schuette, Sarah L. I Am Friendly. 2007. (Character Values Ser.). 24p. (J). 15.93 (978-0-7368-6336-0(2)) Capstone Pr., Inc.

Seder, Isaac. Friendship. 2003. (Illus.). 32p. (J). pap. 7.50 (978-1-4109-0324-2(9)); lib. bdg. 24.28 (978-0-7398-7005-1(X)) Raintree.

Sha'Ban, Mervet A., et al. If You Could Be My Friend: Letters of Mervet Akram Sha'Ban & Galit Fink. Ellbaz, Ariane & Khadige, Beatrice, trs. from FRE. 1998. (Illus.). 118p. (YA). (gr. 5-9). 16.99 (978-0-531-33113-2(X) , Orchard Bks.) Scholastic, Inc.

—If You Could Be My Friend: Letters of Mervet Akram Sha'Ban & Galit Fink. Elbaz, Ariane & Khadige, Beatrice, trs. from FRE. 1998. (Illus.). 118p. (YA). (gr. 5-9). pap. 15.95 (978-0-531-30113-5(3) , Orchard Bks.) Scholastic, Inc.

Shaw, Victoria. Best Buds: A Girl's Guide to Friendship. 1999. (Girls' Guides). (Illus.). 48p. (YA). (gr. 5-8). lib. bdg. 23.95 (978-0-8239-2987-0(6) , GGBEBU) Rosen Publishing Group, Inc., The.

Sheridan, Susan M. Why Don't They Like Me? Helping Your Child Make & Keep Friends. Gebhordt, Suzanne, illus. 1998. 150p. (J). (gr. k-6). pap. 18.50 (978-1-57035-124-2(4) , 25LIKEME) Sopris West Educational Services.

Sim, David. Girlz Cos You're My Friend. 2001. (Illus.). 32p. (J). pap. 6.99 (978-0-7459-4541-5(4) , Lion) Lion Hudson plc GBR. *Dist:* Independent Pubs. Group.

Simm, Joanna & Ladybird Books Staff. Friends 4-Ever! 2004. (Lil' Bratz Ser.). (Illus.). 32p. pap. 5.43 (978-1-84422-520-0(8) , Grosset & Dunlap) Penguin Group (USA) Inc.

Solomon, Iris L. & Solomon, Ron. Friendz Pakz: Friends. 2003. (YA). (gr. 3 up). 4.99 (978-1-930680-04-3(X) , SSP-08FR) Swingset Pr., LLC.

Sommers, Michael A. Chillin' A Guy's Guide to Friendship. 2005. (Guys' Guides Ser.). (Illus.). 48p. (YA). (gr. 5-8). lib. bdg. 23.95 (978-0-8239-3160-6(9) , GUCHIL) Rosen Publishing Group, Inc., The.

Soto, Gary. Cebollas Enterradas. 2002. (SPA.). 150p. 8.50 (978-968-16-6669-9(0)) Fondo de Cultura Economica USA.

Sportelli-Rehak, Angela. Moving Again Mom! Hinlicky, Gregg, illus. (J). (ps-7). 2004. (Uncle Sam's Kids Ser.: Bk. 2). 40p. pap. 7.95 (978-0-9714515-0-6(8)); 2003. pap. (978-0-9714515-3-7(2)) Abidenme Bks.

—Uncle Sam's Kids: Moving Again Mom. Hinlicky, Gregg, illus. 2004. (Uncle Sam's Kids Ser.: Bk. 2). 40p. (gr. k-6). 16.95 (978-0-9714515-2-0(4)) Abidenme Bks.

Steck-Vaughn Staff. Friends. 2000. (J). pap. (978-0-7398-4483-0(0)) Steck-Vaughn.

—Friends: Best Friends/hello Fr: Best Friends/Hello Friends. 1998. (Illus.). (J). pap. (978-0-8172-8630-9(6)) Steck-Vaughn.

Stephens, Andrea. Girlfriend, You Are A B. A. B. E. ! Beautiful, Accepted, Blessed, Eternally Significant. 2005. (B. A. B. E. Book Ser.). 224p. (J). (gr. 8-12). pap. 12.99 (978-0-8007-5951-3(6)) Revell.

Suben, Eric. Friendship. Lanza, Barbara, illus. 1999. (Doing the Right Thing Ser.). 32p. (J). (gr. k-3). lib. bdg. 26.60 (978-1-55916-231-9(7)) Rourke Publishing, LLC.

Taylor, Julie. The Girls' Guide to Friends: Straight Talk for Teens on Making Close Pals, Creating Lasting Ties, & Being an All-Around Great Friend. 2002. 224p. pap. 12.00 (978-0-609-80857-3(5) , Three Rivers Pr.) Crown Publishing Group.

Thebo, Patricia J. Uncle Looker & the Hurricane. 2003. (Illus.). 50p. (J). (gr. k-9). 16.50 (978-0-9725706-0-2(8)) Seaforth Publishing.

Thoennes Keller, Kristin. Friendliness. 2005. (Illus.). 24p. (J). 21.26 (978-0-7368-3680-7(2)) Capstone Pr., Inc.

True Friends. 2004. (Fun Kits Ser.). (Illus.). 48p. (J). (978-1-84229-862-6(3)) Top That! Publishing PLC.

Trumbauer, Lisa. Who Is a Friend? 2000. (Yellow Umbrella Books). (Illus.). 16p. (J). (gr. 1). lib. bdg. 14.60 (978-0-7368-0738-8(1) , Pebble Bks.) Capstone Pr., Inc.

Vescia, Monique & Sachar, Louis. A Reading Guide to Holes by Louis Sachar. 2003. (Bookfiles Ser.). 64p. (J). pap. 4.99 (978-0-439-46336-2(X) , Scholastic Reference) Scholastic, Inc.

Villet, Olivia. Chester's Big Surprise. 2001. (Illus.). 32p. (J). 17.99 (978-0-7475-5247-5(9)) Bloomsbury Publishing Plc GBR. *Dist:* Trafalgar Square Publishing.

Warburton, Olivia, compiled by. Friends: A Gift for a Great Friend. 2002. (Illus.). 25p. (J). pap. 7.99 (978-0-7459-4798-3(0) , Lion) Lion Hudson plc GBR. *Dist:* Independent Pubs. Group.

Warner, Carly. Best Friends Forever: A Friendship Journal. Dietrich, Amy, illus. 2000. (Journal Ser.). 128p. (J). 11.99 (978-0-88088-227-9(1)) Peter Pauper Pr. Inc.

Waters, Jennifer. Be a Good Friend! 2002. (Spyglass Books). (Illus.). 24p. (J). (gr. 1 up). lib. bdg. 18.60 (978-0-7565-0376-5(0)) Compass Point Bks.

Webber, Diane. Your Space: Dealing with friends & Peers. 2008. (Scholastic Choices Ser.). 112p. (J). pap. 8.95 (****978-0-531-14774-0(6)*** , Watts, Franklin) Scholastic Library Publishing.

Weedn, Lisa. Just Hangin' Out: Chick Chat Between Best Friends. Weedn, Flavia M., illus. 2001. 60p. (gr. 7-12). pap. 14.95 (978-0-7683-2238-5(3)) CEDCO Publishing.

Weinberger, Kimberly. Have a Heart Book of Friendship. 2002. (Necco Sweethearts Ser.). (Illus.). 48p. (J). (gr. 2-4). pap. 4.99 (978-0-439-36539-0(2) , Cartwheel Bks.) Scholastic, Inc.

Who Can Be a Friend? (J). 26.20 (978-0-8136-8401-7(3)); 26.20 (978-0-8136-8402-4(1)); 1998. pap. (978-0-8136-8293-8(2)) Modern Curriculum Pr.

Widenhouse, Kathy. The Christian Girl's Guide to Friendship. 2004. (Illus.). 192p. (J). pap. 9.99 (978-1-58411-043-9(0) , Legacy Pr.) Rainbow Pubs. & Legacy Pr.

Wilkinson, Doris J. Friends. Wilkinson, Doris J., ed. Chipping, Oliver, illus. 2000. (Jacob's Magic Box Discovery Ser.). 20p. (Orig.). (J). (ps). pap. 4.95 (978-0-9700386-8-5(2)) Magic Box Pubns.

Williams, Dave. Windgalore Farm. 2005. (Illus.). 182p. pap. 21.95 (978-0-937921-56-2(4)) Acorn Publishing.

Williams-Kinsey, Rose & Williams, Carolyn. Be a Dreamer Team & Company with Friends: No Color: The Character Within. Williams-Kinsey, Rose et al, illus. Nelson, Melvin L. et al, illus. 1998. (Orig.). (J). (ps up). pap. (978-0-9628539-2-0(5)) Be A Dreamer Pubs.

Zielin, Lara. Make Things Happen: The Key to Networking for Teens. 2003. (gr. 7-12). lib. bdg. 18.75 (978-0-613-68912-0(7)) Tandem Library Bks.

FRIENDSHIP—FICTION

A. A Friend with No Name. 2006. (ENG., Illus.). 28p. per. 11.95 (978-1-59800-476-2(X)) Outskirts Press, Inc.

Abbott, Hailey. Getting Lost with Boys. 2006. 240p. (J). pap. 8.99 (978-0-06-082432-7(8)) HarperCollins Pubs.

—The Perfect Boy. 2007. 272p. (YA). (gr. 9 up). pap. 8.99 (****978-0-06-082434-1(4)*** , HarperTeen) HarperCollins Pubs.

Abbott, Hailey. The Secrets of Boys. 2006. 272p. (J). pap. 8.99 (978-0-06-082433-4(6)) HarperCollins Pubs.

Abbott, Tony. Firegirl. 2006. 160p. (J). (gr. 3-7). 15.99 (978-0-316-01171-6(1)) Little Brown & Co.

—Queen of Shadowthorn. 2007. (Secrets of Droon Ser.). 128p. (J). pap. 4.99 (****978-0-439-90252-6(5)*** , Scholastic Paperbacks) Scholastic, Inc.

—Race to Doobesh. 2005. (Illus.). 127p. (J). lib. bdg. 15.38 (****978-1-4242-0311-6(2)***) Fitzgerald Bks.

—Secrets Droon Spec Ed #5 Moon Magic. 2008. 176p. pap. 5.99 (****978-0-439-90255-7(X)*** , Scholastic Paperbacks) Scholastic, Inc.

—The Secrets of Droon: The Riddle of Zorfendorf Castle. Merrell, David, illus. 25th ed. 2005. (Secrets of Droon Ser.). 128p. (J). 3.99 (978-0-439-67173-6(6) , Scholastic Paperbacks) Scholastic, Inc.

—Sorcerer. ed. 2006. (Secrets of Droon Ser.: No. 4). 176p. (J). pap. 5.99 (978-0-439-67178-1(7) , Scholastic Paperbacks) Scholastic, Inc.

Abdo Publishing Staff, contrib. by. Flower Girl Friends. 2000. (Faithful Friends Ser.). (Illus.). 64p. (J). (gr. 4). lib. bdg. 21.35 (978-1-57765-229-8(0) , ABDO & Daughters) ABDO Publishing Co.

Abela, Deborah. Mission: Hollywood. O'Connor, George, illus. 2006. (Spy Force Ser.). 240p. (J). 9.95 (978-0-689-87360-7(3)) Simon & Schuster Children's Publishing.

—Mission: Spy Force Revealed. O'Connor, George, illus. (Spy Force Ser.). 288p. (J). 2006. pap. 5.99 (978-1-4169-4024-1(3) , Aladdin); 2005. (gr. 4-7). 9.95 (978-0-689-87358-4(1) , Simon & Schuster Children's Publishing) Simon & Schuster Children's Publishing.

Abela, Deborah. Mission: Hollywood. O'Connor, George, illus. 2007. (Spy Force Ser.). 240p. (J). pap. 5.99 (****978-1-4169-3969-6(5)*** , Aladdin) Simon & Schuster Children's Publishing.

Aboff, Marcie. Alex & Marty Run Wild. 2005. (Madagascar Ser.). 32p. (J). pap. 3.99 (978-0-439-69631-9(3)) Scholastic, Inc.

—Foster's Home for Imaginary Friends. 2006. 96p. (J). pap. 2.99 (978-0-439-75019-6(9) , Scholastic) Scholastic, Inc.

—When I Grow Up. Style Guide Staff & YOE! Studio Staff, illus. 2007. (Baby Looney Tunes Ser.). 32p. (J). 3.99 (978-1-4169-3509-4(6) , Simon Scribbles) Simon & Schuster Children's Publishing.

Ackerman, Tova. Group Soup. Gorbachev, Valeri, illus. (Orig.). pap. 6.95 (978-0-9720183-0-2(1)) Puppetry in Practice.

Ada, Alma Flor. Pio Peep! 2000. pap. 8.95 (978-0-06-443868-1(6)) HarperCollins Pubs.

Adair Scott, Paul. Benito Boton e Isabel Hilo. Adair, Pam, tr. 2004. Orig. Title: Blue Button & Red Thread. (SPA., Illus.). 25p. (J). pap. 5.95 (978-0-9740419-2-6(0)) words4u.

Adamchuk, Rachelle G. Disappearance: The First Part of Trickery & Honest Deception. 2006. 169p. pap. (****978-1-4120-8991-3(3)***) Trafford Publishing.

Adams, Jean Ekman. Clarence & the Purple Horse Bounce into Town. Adams, Jean Ekman, illus. 2003. (Illus.). 32p. (ps-3). 15.95 (978-0-87358-826-3(6) , Rising Moon Bks. for Young Readers) Northland Publishing.

Adams, Jeanette. Within the Circle, one. 2003. (Camelot Rabbitry Ser.: Two). 108p. (YA). per. 9.95 (978-0-9672375-2-7(1)) Camelot Tales.

Adams, Jeff. Philemon: Real Friendships in an Unreal World. Date not set. (J). 14.95 (978-0-9643021-9-8(5)) Reality Living Publishing, Inc.

Adams, John. The Dragonfly Door. Gibson, Barbara Leonard, illus. rev. ed. 2007. 40p. (J). (gr. k-5). 17.95 (****978-1-934066-12-6(5)***) Feather Rock Bks., Inc.

Adams, Kylie. Beautiful Disaster. 2006. (Fast Girls, Hot Boys Ser.: No. 3). 240p. pap. 9.95 (978-1-4165-2042-9(2) , MTV) Simon & Schuster.

—Bling Addiction. 2006. (Fast Girls, Hot Boys Ser.: No. 2). 240p. pap. 9.95 (978-1-4165-2041-2(4) , MTV) Simon & Schuster.

Adams, Michael. The Little King & the Honeybee. 2005. (J). per. 9.95 (978-1-58597-327-9(0)) Leathers Publishing.

Adams, Sherred Willc. Five Little Friends. 2006. pap. (****978-1-4065-0483-5(1)***) Dodo Pr.

Adams, Sherred Willco. Five Little Friends. 2006. pap. 15.95 (****978-1-4304-4149-6(6)***) Kessinger Publishing, LLC.

Adams, Sherred Willcox. Five Little Friends. 2004. reprint ed. pap. 15.95 (978-1-4191-1988-0(5)); pap. 1.99 (978-1-4192-1988-7(X)) Kessinger Publishing, LLC.

Addie's Bad Day. 2003. 22.95 (978-0-673-75904-7(0)) Celebration Pr.

Adler, C. S. The Magic of the Glits. 2000. 112p. (gr. 4-7). pap. 9.95 (978-0-595-09233-8(0) , Backinprint.com) iUniverse, Inc.

—One Unhappy Horse. 2001. (Illus.). 160p. (J). (gr. 4-6). tchr. ed. 16.00 (978-0-618-04912-7(6) , Clarion Bks.) Houghton Mifflin Co. Trade & Reference Div.

Adler, Carole S. Magic of the Glits. 2000. (gr. 3-6). lib. bdg. 18.75 (978-0-613-81397-6(9)) Tandem Library Bks.

Adler, David A. Andy & Tamika. 1999. (Illus.). (J). 11.60 (978-0-606-18166-2(0)) Tandem Library Bks.

—Don't Talk to Me about the War. 2008. (YA). (gr. 5). 15.99 (****978-0-670-06307-9(X)*** , Viking Adult) Penguin Group (USA) Inc.

Adler, David A. The Many Troubles of Andy Russell. Hillenbrand, Will, illus. 2005. (Andy Russell Ser.). 144p. (J). pap. 5.95 (978-0-15-205440-3(5) , Gulliver Bks.) Harcourt Children's Bks.

Adoff, Jaime. Names Will Never Hurt Me. 2005. 192p. (YA). (gr. 7). pap. 5.99 (978-0-14-240457-7(8) , Puffin) Penguin Group (USA) Inc.

Advantage Publishers Group & Saidens, Amy. Glamour Girl Sticker Book. 2007. (Illus.). 24p. (J). 14.95 (****978-1-59223-631-2(6)*** , Silver Dolphin Bks.) Advantage Pubs. Group.

The Adventures of Rowdy Raccoon. 2006. (J). per. 16.95 incl. audio compact disk (****978-0-9766823-8-7(9)***) Sable Creek Pr. LLC.

The Adventures of Sammy the Snowflake: The Facts of Life, Flying & Finding Weather. 2007. (J). 19.95 (****978-0-9795260-0-8(0)***) Courtyard Publishing, LLC.

The Adventures of the Original Pumpkin Patch Pals. l.t. ed. 2005. (Illus.). 32p. (J). 15.00 (978-0-9770960-1-5(7)) 3 Pals Media, LLC.

The Adventures of Tom Sawyer. 2004. (Classic Retelling Ser.). (gr. 6-12). (978-0-618-12053-6(X) , 2-00218) McDougal Littell Inc.

The Adventures of Tom Sawyer. 1998. 44p. (YA). stu. ed. 11.95 (978-1-56137-528-8(4) , NU5284SP) Novel Units, Inc.

The Adventures of Tom Sawyer. 2004. (Literature Units Ser.). (Illus.). 48p. 7.99 (978-1-57690-637-8(X)) Teacher Created Materials, Inc.

Agard, John & Paul, Korky. Brer Rabbit & the Great Tug-O-War. 1998. (Illus.). 32p. (J). (ps-2). 13.95 (978-0-7641-5077-7(4)) Barron's Educational Series, Inc.

Agell, Charlotte. Welcome Home or Someplace Like It. rev. ed. 2003. (Illus.). 240p. (J). 16.95 (978-0-8050-7083-5(4) , Holt, Henry & Co. Bks. For Young Readers) Holt, Henry & Co.

Aiken, Joan. Bridle the Wind. 2007. (Illus.). 352p. (YA). pap. 6.95 (978-0-15-206058-9(8)) Harcourt Trade Pubs.

Aimard, Gustave. The Indian Scout: a Story of the Aster City. 2006. (ENG.). 464p. per. 37.95 (****978-1-4286-1776-6(0)***) Kessinger Publishing, LLC.

Albee, Sarah. Sesame Street Fun with Friends. 2005. (CarryAlong Book Ser.). 24p. (J). bds. 14.99 (978-0-7944-0685-1(8)) Reader's Digest Assn., Inc., The.

Alberto, Daisy. Pete for President! Sims, Blanche, illus. 2004. 32p. (J). lib. bdg. 20.00 (****978-1-4242-1115-9(8)***) Fitzgerald Bks.

—Pete for President! Sims, Blanche, illus. 2004. (Social Studies Connects). 32p. (J). (gr. 1-3). pap. 4.99 (978-1-57565-142-2(4)) Kane Pr., The.

Alcott, Louisa May. Jack & Jill. Date not set. 352p. (YA). 25.95 (978-0-8488-2671-0(X)) Amereon LTD.

—Jack & Jill. l.t. ed. 2005. 496p. pap. (978-1-84637-054-0(X)) Echo Library.

—Under the Lilacs. Exams Unlimited, Inc. Staff, ed. 2001. 256p. (C). reprint ed. cd-rom 5.45 (978-1-59132-028-9(3)) Exams Unlimited, Inc.

Alderink, Georgia. Who's Been Soaking in My Hot Tub? 2005. 50p. pap. 12.95 (978-1-4137-6077-4(5)) PublishAmerica, Inc.

Aldridge, Janet. Meadow Brook Girls Afloat. l.t. ed. 2006. 156p. pap. 14.99 (978-1-4264-0859-5(5)) BiblioBazaar.

—Meadow Brook Girls Afloat: Or the Stormy Cruise of the Red Rover. 2006. 160p. pap. 11.99 (978-1-4264-0878-6(1)) BiblioBazaar.

Aldridge, Janet. The Meadow-Brook Girls under Canvas (Ill. 2006. pap. (****978-1-4065-0695-2(8)***) Dodo Pr.

Alegria, Malin. Estrella's Quinceañera. 2007. 288p. (YA). (gr. 7 up). pap. 8.99 (978-0-689-87810-7(9) , Simon Pulse) Simon & Schuster Children's Publishing.

—Estrellas Quinceanera. 2006. (Illus.). 272p. (YA). 15.99 (978-0-689-87809-1(5)) Simon & Schuster Children's Publishing.

Aleixandre, Marilar. La Branda Sin Futuro. 2003. (SPA.). 156p. (978-84-348-7193-9(9) , SM30543) SM Ediciones ESP. *Dist:* Lectorum Pubns., Inc.

Alexander, Lloyd. The Castle of Llyr. 3rd rev. ed. 2006. (Chronicles of Prydain Ser.: Bk. 3). 208p. (J). (gr. 5 up). pap. 5.99 (978-0-8050-8050-6(3) , Holt, Henry & Co. Bks. For Young Readers) Holt, Henry & Co.

Alexandria, Shalayne. Nyville High No. 1: Welcome to Nyville. 2007. 124p. (YA). per. 4.99 (****978-0-9786180-1-8(7)***) 5 Muses Publishing.

Alfonsi, Alice. A Weakened Heart. rev. ed. 2006. (W. I. T. C. H. Ser.: Bk. 21). 144p. (gr. 3-7). pap. 4.99 (978-0-7868-5595-7(9)) Hyperion Pr.

Alger, Horatio. Cast upon the Breakers. unabr. ed. 2002. (Polyglot Press Alger Ser.). (Illus.). (J). pap. 17.95 (978-1-931927-81-9(2)) Polyglot Pr., Inc.

—Do & Dare. 2006. pap. (****978-1-4250-1766-8(5));*** pap. (****978-1-4250-2027-9(5));*** pap. (****978-1-4250-2300-3(2));*** pap. (****978-1-4250-2118-4(2)***) Assistedreadingbooks.com Inc.

—Do & Dare: Or, A Brave Boy's Fight for Fortune. 2006. 182p. pap. 11.99 (978-1-4264-0880-9(3)); 170p. pap. 14.99 (978-1-4264-0861-8(7)) BiblioBazaar.

—Do & Dare: Or, A Brave Boy's Fight for Fortune. 2006. pap. (****978-1-4065-0701-0(6)***) Dodo Pr.

—Do & Dare: Or, A Brave Boy's Fight for Fortune. unabr. ed. 2002. (Illus.). (J). pap. 17.95 (978-1-931927-90-1(1)) Polyglot Pr., Inc.

All Aboard! Softi's Adventures. 2003. (J). mass mkt. (978-1-932233-36-0(9)) Aurora Libris Corp.

Allan-Meyer, Kathleen. Little Bear's Crunch-a-Roo Cookies. Garvin, Elaine, illus. 2000. (Little Bear Adventure Ser.: Vol. 5). 27p. (J). (ps-1). pap. 6.49 (978-1-57924-438-5(6)) Jones, Bob Univ. Pr.

Allan, Nicholas. You're All Animals. 2001. (Illus.). 32p. (J). pap. 11.99 (978-0-09-941125-3(3)) Random Hse. GBR. *Dist:* Independent Pubs. Group.

Allen, C. William. The African Interior Mission. Lee, Xiongpao, illus. 2006. 232p. (J). pap. 20.00 (978-0-9653308-5-5(0)) Africana Homestead Legacy Pubs.

Allen, J. J. Hello Kitty's Fun Friend Day! 2003. (Illus.). 32p. (J). pap. (978-0-439-44917-5(0)) Scholastic, Inc.

Alley, R. W., illus. A Know-Nothing Halloween. 2002. (Know-Nothings Ser.). (J). 12.30 (978-0-7587-6905-3(9)) Book Wholesalers, Inc.

—The Know-Nothings Talk Turkey. 2002. (Know-Nothings Ser.). (J). 12.30 (978-0-7587-6906-0(7)) Book Wholesalers, Inc.

Allie, Debora. The Meanest Girl. rev. ed. 2005. 128p. (J). 15.95 (978-1-59643-014-3(1)) Roaring Brook Pr.

Alonso, Fernando. La Historia de un Hombrecillo de Papel. (Leer Es Vivir Serie Teatro). (SPA.). 96p. (J). (gr. 3-5). 6.36 (978-84-241-7711-9(8)) Everest de Ediciones y Distribucion, S.L. ESP. *Dist:* Lectorum Pubns., Inc.

Alpert, Sandra F. Horrible Howard: The Bully & Coward. Date not set. (Bully Busting Trilogy Ser.: Bk. 1). (Illus.). (Orig.). (J). (gr. k-5). pap. (978-1-884931-02-4(2)) Global Commitment Publishing.

Altein, Chani. The Gift of Friendship. 2006. 144p. (J). (gr. 3-5). 14.95 (978-1-932443-47-9(9) , GOFH) Judaica Pr., Inc., The.

Amado, Elisa. Tricycle. Ruano, Alfonso, illus. 2007. 32p. (J). (gr. 1-4). 17.95 (***978-0-88899-614-5(4)***); (SPA.). (gr. 2-5). 17.95 (***978-0-88899-613-8(6)***) Groundwood Bks. CAN. *Dist:* Perseus Distribution.

Amano, Shiro. Kingdom Hearts: Chain of Memories, Vol. 2. 2nd rev. ed. 2007. 232p. (gr. 4-7). pap. 9.99 (978-1-59816-638-5(7) , Tokyopop Kids) TOKYOPOP, Inc.

Ameen, Judith. Harold & the Magic Books. 2005. 40p. pap. 8.95 (978-1-933265-42-1(6)) Wasteland Pr.

Andersen, Hans Christian. La Reina de las Nieves. (SPA., Illus.). 48p. (J). (gr. 3-5). (978-84-241-5526-1(2) , EV1028) Everest de Ediciones y Distribucion, S.L. ESP. *Dist:* Lectorum Pubns., Inc.

—La Reina de las Nieves. Bravo-Villasante, Carmen, tr. Catagan, Tino, illus. (SPA.). (J). (gr. 2-4). 6.50 (978-84-355-0695-3(9)) Minon, S.A. ESP. *Dist:* Lectorum Pubns., Inc.

Andersen, Rachel. Los mejores Amigos. McNicholas, Shelagh, illus. (SPA.). 62p. (J). (gr. 3-5). pap. 8.95 (978-968-19-1010-5(9)) Santillana USA Publishing Co., Inc.

Anderson, Derek. Blue Burt & Wiggles. Anderson, Derek, illus. 2006. (Illus.). 32p. (J). (ps-3). 14.95 (978-1-4169-0593-6(6) , Simon & Schuster Children's Publishing) Simon & Schuster Children's Publishing.

Anderson, Derek. Romeo & Lou Blast Off. Anderson, Derek, illus. 2007. 32p. (J). (ps-3). 15.99 (***978-1-4169-3784-5(6)*** , Simon & Schuster Children's Publishing) Simon & Schuster Children's Publishing.

Anderson, Doug. Too Big to Dance. Anderson, Sara, illus. 2004. 32p. (J). 15.95 (978-1-59354-046-3(9)) Handprint Bks.

Anderson, Dwayne. Partially Human. 2006. (YA). per. 12.00 (***978-0-9788612-0-9(5)***) Capri Publishing.

Anderson, Ho Che. The No-Boys Club. 1998. 160p. (J). (gr. 4-7). 14.95 (978-0-88899-322-9(6)) Groundwood Bks. CAN. *Dist:* Perseus Distribution.

Anderson, Jessica Lee. Trudy. 2005. (Milkweed Prize for Children's Literature Ser.). 192p. (J). (gr. 3-7). 16.95 (978-1-57131-660-8(4)); (gr. 4-7). pap. 6.95 (978-1-57131-659-2(0)) Milkweed Editions.

Anderson, Jodi Lynn. The Secrets of Peaches. 2006. 304p. (gr. 9 up). (J). lib. bdg. 17.89 (978-0-06-073309-4(8)); (YA). 16.99 (978-0-06-073308-7(X)) HarperCollins Pubs. (HarperTeen).

Anderson, Joseph P. The Kickball Game. 2007. (Illus.). 24p. (J). (***978-1-4048-2443-0(X)***) Picture Window Bks.

—The Kickball Game. Greathouse, Justin, illus. 2006. 24p. (J). (***978-1-4048-2413-3(8)***) Picture Window Bks.

Anderson, Lena. Hedgehog, Pig, & the Sweet Little Friend. Sandin, Joan, tr. from SWE. 2007. (Illus.). 32p. (J). (ps-1). 16.00 (***978-91-29-66742-4(9)***) R & S Bks. SWE. *Dist:* Macmillan.

Anderson, Marilyn D. Bring Back Barkley. 1998. (Illus.). 112p. (J). (gr. 3-5). pap. 3.99 (978-0-87406-890-0(8) , Willowisp Pr.) Darby Creek Publishing.

Anderson, Max Elliot. Newspaper Caper. 2003. 136p. 16.95 (978-0-9729256-5-5(1)); pap. 9.95 (978-0-9729256-4-8(3)) Baker Trittin Pr. (Tweener Pr.).

Anderson, Rachael. Los Mejores Amigos. McNicholas, Shelagh, illus. 2003. (SPA.). 120p. (J). (gr. 3-5). 9.95 (978-84-204-4377-5(8)) Alfaguara, Ediciones, S.A.-Grupo Santillana ESP. *Dist:* Santillana USA Publishing Co., Inc.

Andracki, Zenon. Dear Ashley: A Middle Grade Novel. 2006. (ENG.). 84p. per. 14.95 (***978-1-4241-6168-3(1)***) PublishAmerica, Inc.

Andrade, Brigitte. The Adventures of Bibi & Friends: Summer Season in Miami Beach, 1 vol., 7 bks. 7th ed. 2004. Orig. Title: The Adventures of Bibi 7 Friends. (Illus.). 65p. per. 7.95 (978-0-9754329-0-7(7)) BB International Productions, Inc.

Andreae, Giles. The Lion Who Wanted to Love. Wojtowycz, David, illus. 1998. 32p. (J). (ps-2). 14.95 (978-1-888444-25-4(8) , 21023) Little Tiger Pr.

Andrews, Kate. Cool It, Carrie. 1999. (Making Friends Ser.: No. 2). (Illus.). 128p. (J). (gr. 3-7). mass mkt. 3.99 (978-0-380-80931-8(1)) HarperCollins Pubs.

—Wise up, Alex. 1999. (Making Friends Ser.: No. 1). (Illus.). 128p. (J). (gr. 3-7). mass mkt. 3.99 (978-0-380-80930-1(3)) HarperCollins Pubs.

Andy & the Lion. 2004. (J). 24.95 incl. audio (978-0-89719-698-7(8)) Weston Woods Studios, Inc.

Anfousse, Ginette & Sarrazin, Marisol. Le Grand Roman d'Amour de Rosalie. 2001. (Roman Jeunesse Ser.). (FRE., Illus.). 96p. (J). pap. (978-2-89021-499-6(0)) Diffusion du livre Mirabel.

Angelin. Date not set. (978-0-517-80137-6(X)) Random Hse. Value Publishing.

Angelo, Alyssa. Sherlock the Circus Dog. 2007. 108p. pap. 11.95 (***978-1-60145-137-8(7)***); pap. 21.95 (***978-1-60145-133-0(4)***) Booklocker.com, Inc.

Anglund, Joan Walsh. Cowboy & His Friend. 2002. (Illus.). 40p. 6.95 (978-0-7407-2211-0(5)) Andrews McMeel Publishing.

Anholt, Laurence. I Like Me, I Like You. 2001. (Illus.). (J). (978-0-606-21295-3(7)) Tandem Library Bks.

Anholt, Laurence. Van Gogh & the Sunflowers. 2007. (Anholt's Artists Books for Children Ser.). 32p. (J). (ps-3). pap. 7.99 (***978-0-7641-3854-6(5)***) Barron's Educational Series, Inc.

Animal Friends Squeaky. 2005. (J). bds. (978-1-4194-0094-0(0)) Paradise Pr., Inc.

Animal Friends Squeaky - Cat. 2005. (J). bds. (978-1-4194-0092-6(4)) Paradise Pr., Inc.

Anonymous. Arthur Hamilton & His Dog. 2004. reprint ed. pap. 15.95 (978-1-4191-0774-0(7)); pap. 1.99 (978-1-4192-0774-7(1)) Kessinger Publishing, LLC.

Ansley, Frank & Wheeler, Lisa. Invasion of the Pig Sisters. Ansley, Frank, illus. 2006. (Fitch & Chip Ser.). (Illus.). 48p. (J). 14.95 (978-0-689-84953-4(2) , Atheneum) Simon & Schuster Children's Publishing.

The Ant & the Grasshopper: Individual Title Six-Packs. (Story Steps Ser.). (gr. k-2). 32.00 (978-0-7635-9846-4(1)) Rigby Education.

The Ant & the Grasshopper: Small Book. (Pebble Soup Explorations Ser.). 16p. (ps up). 5.00 (978-0-7635-7049-1(4)) Rigby Education.

Anthony, David & David, Charles. Trek Through Tangleroot: Knightscares #5. 2004. (Illus.). 200p. (J). per. 5.99 (978-0-9728461-4-1(X)) Sigil Publishing.

Anthony, E. A Friend Indeed. 1999. 48p. (J). pap. 8.50 (978-1-890622-71-8(0)) Leathers Publishing.

Apostolina, M. Hazing Meri Sugarman. 2005. 272p. (YA). pap. 8.99 (978-1-4169-0610-0(X) , Simon Pulse) Simon & Schuster Children's Publishing.

Appelt, Kathi. The Alley Cat's Meow. Goodell, Jon, illus. 2002. 32p. (J). (gr. k-2). 16.00 (978-0-15-201980-8(4)) Harcourt Children's Bks.

—Bubba & Beau, Best Friends. Howard, Arthur, illus. 2006. (Bubba & Beau Ser.). 32p. (J). pap. 6.00 (978-0-15-205580-6(0) , Voyager Bks./Libros Viajeros) Harcourt Children's Bks.

Applegate, Cathy. Red Sand, Blue Sky. 2002. (Girls First! Ser.). 144p. (gr. 4-7). pap. 13.50 (978-1-55861-278-5(5)) Feminist Pr. at The City Univ. of New York.

Applegate, Katherine. Second Chance. 2001. (True Love Ser.: No. 7). 208p. (YA). pap. 4.99 (978-1-931497-40-4(0)) 17th Street Productions, An Alloy Online Inc. Co.

Arena, Jacqueline. Basketball Showdown. Foye, Lloyd, illus. 2005. (Girlz Rock! Ser.). (J). pap. (978-1-59336-704-6(X)) Mondo Publishing.

—Horsing Around. Maddock, Monika, illus. 2005. (Girlz Rock! Ser.). (J). pap. (978-1-59336-703-9(1)) Mondo Publishing.

Armistead, John. The Return of Gabriel. Gregory, Fran, illus. 2002. 240p. (J). (gr. 3-8). 17.95 (978-1-57131-637-0(X)); pap. 6.95 (978-1-57131-638-7(8)) Milkweed Editions.

—The Return of Gabriel. 2002. (gr. 5-8). lib. bdg. 15.25 (978-0-613-79202-8(5)) Tandem Library Bks.

—The $66 Summer. 2000. (978-0-606-21752-1(5)) Tandem Library Bks.

—The $66 Summer: A Novel of the Segregated South. 2nd ed. 2006. (Milkweed Prize for Children's Literature Ser.). 240p. (J). reprint ed. pap. 6.95 (978-1-57131-663-9(9)) Milkweed Editions.

Armstrong, Cindy. Boudreaux & His Buddies. 2006. 98p. pap. 14.95 (978-1-4241-3906-4(6)) PublishAmerica, Inc.

Armstrong, Robb. Got Game? Smith, Bruce, illus. 1998. (Patrick's Pals Ser.: No. 3). 96p. (J). (gr. 2-7). mass mkt. 3.99 (978-0-06-107069-3(6) , Harper Entertainment) HarperCollins Pubs.

—Large & in Charge. Smith, Bruce, illus. 1999. (Patrick's Pals Ser.: No. 7). 96p. (J). (gr. 2-7). pap. 3.99 (978-0-06-107073-0(4)) HarperCollins Pubs.

—Runnin' with the Big Dawgs. Smith, Bruce, illus. 1998. (Patrick's Pals Ser.: No. 1). 96p. (J). (gr. 2-7). mass mkt. 3.99 (978-0-06-107067-9(X) , Harper Entertainment) HarperCollins Pubs.

—Schoolin' Smith, Bruce, illus. 1999. (Patrick's Pals Ser.: No. 5). 96p. (J). (gr. 2-7). mass mkt. 3.99 (978-0-06-107071-6(8) , Harper Entertainment) HarperCollins Pubs.

—Trashmaster. Smith, Bruce, illus. 1999. (Patrick's Pals Ser.: No. 6). 96p. (J). (gr. 2-7). pap. 3.99 (978-0-06-107072-3(6) , Harper Entertainment) HarperCollins Pubs.

Arnold, Caroline. Wiggle & Waggle. Peterson, Mary, illus. 2007. 48p. (J). (gr. k-3). 12.95 (***978-1-58089-306-0(6)***) Charlesbridge Publishing, Inc.

Arnold, Louise. Golden & Grey: An Unremarkable Boy & a Rather Remarkable Ghost. 2005. 272p. (J). 15.95 (978-0-689-87473-4(1) , McElderry, Margaret K.) Simon & Schuster Children's Publishing.

—Golden & Grey: (an Unremarkable Boy & a Rather Remarkable Ghost) l.t. ed. 2006. 317p. 22.95 (978-0-7862-8290-6(8)) Thorndike Pr.

—Golden & Grey: The Nightmares That Ghosts Have. 2006. 304p. (J). (gr. 3-7). 16.99 (978-0-689-87586-1(X) , McElderry, Margaret K.) Simon & Schuster Children's Publishing.

—Golden & Grey (an Unremarkable Boy & a Rather Remarkable Ghost) 2006. (Illus.). 272p. (J). reprint ed. pap. 5.99 (978-0-689-87585-4(1) , Aladdin) Simon & Schuster Children's Publishing.

Arnold, Louise. Golden & Grey: the Nightmares That Ghosts Have. 2007. 304p. (J). pap. 5.99 (***978-0-689-87587-8(8)*** , Aladdin) Simon & Schuster Children's Publishing.

Arnold, Tedd. Huggly & the Toy Monster. 1999. (Huggly Ser.). (Illus.). 32p. (J). (ps-3). pap. 3.25 (978-0-439-10270-4(7)) Scholastic, Inc.

Arnosky, Jim. Wild & Swampy. 2000. (Illus.). 32p. (J). (gr. 1-5). 15.95 (978-0-688-17119-3(2)) HarperCollins Pubs.

Arrigan, Mary & Myler, Terry. Seascape with Barber's Harp. 1998. 160p. pap. 9.95 (978-1-901737-02-8(0)) Anvil Bks., Ltd. IRL. *Dist:* Dufour Editions, Inc.

Arrington, H. J. Friends Again? Kitchel, JoAnn E., illus. 2001. 32p. (J). 15.95 (978-1-56554-834-3(5)) Pelican Publishing Co., Inc.

Arthur. 2001. (Illus.). (J). 7.98 (978-0-7853-4852-8(2)) Publications International, Ltd.

Arvella, Wendy. Pray for a Rainbow. Takazono, Wayne, illus. 2002. pap. 5.99 (978-0-89610-201-9(7)) Island Heritage Publishing.

Aryal, Aimee. Hello Albert! McArdle Pflueger, Maura, illus. 2004. (J). 19.95 (978-1-932888-12-6(8)) Mascot Bks., Inc.

—Hello Aubie! Moore, Danny, illus. 2004. (J). 19.95 (978-0-9743442-8-7(1)) Mascot Bks., Inc.

—Hello Baldwin! Goh, Tai Hwa, illus. 2004. (J). 19.95 (978-1-932888-13-3(6)) Mascot Bks., Inc.

—Hello Bully! Moore, Danny, illus. 2004. (J). 19.95 (978-0-9743442-6-3(5)) Mascot Bks., Inc.

—Hello CavMan! Perez, Gerry, illus. 2004. (J). 19.95 (978-0-9743442-3-2(0)) Mascot Bks., Inc.

—Hello Goldy! Sable, Katherine, illus. 2004. (J). 19.95 (978-0-9743442-4-9(9)) Mascot Bks., Inc.

—Hello Mountaineer! Ramondelli, Livio, illus. 2004. (J). 19.95 (978-0-9743442-7-0(3)) Mascot Bks., Inc.

—Hello Nittany Lion! Ramondelli, Livio, illus. 2004. (J). 19.95 (978-0-9743442-9-4(X)) Mascot Bks., Inc.

—Hello Otto! Shrestha, Anuj, illus. 2004. 22p. (J). 19.95 (978-0-9743442-2-5(2)) Mascot Bks., Inc.

Asai, Carrie. Book of the Shadow. 2003. (gr. 7-12). lib. bdg. 15.30 (978-0-613-65534-7(6)) Tandem Library Bks.

Asare, Meshack. Cat in Search of a Friend. 1999. Tr. of Die Katze Sucht Sich Einen Freund. pap. (978-9988-550-18-9(9)) Sub-Saharan Pubs. & Traders.

Asch, Frank. The Earth & I. 2008. (Illus.). 32p. (J). pap. 7.00 (***978-0-15-206395-5(1)*** , Voyager Bks./Libros Viajeros) Harcourt Children's Bks.

Asch, Frank. Moonbear's Pet. Asch, Frank, illus. 2002. (Moonbear Ser.). (Illus.). (J). 14.47 (978-1-4046-0167-3(8)) Book Wholesalers, Inc.

Ashby, Lenore. The Magic of the Bear. 2003. (Illus.). 162p. (YA). per. 7.95 (978-0-9728535-0-7(2) , 853502) Grandma Chubby's Bks.

Ashford, Ann. If I Found a Wistful Unicorn: A Gift of Love. Drath, Bill, illus. anniv. gif. ed. 2002. 32p. 8.95 (978-1-56145-271-2(8)) Peachtree Pubs., Ltd.

Ashley, Elana. Splunkunio Splunkey Detective & Peacemaker Detective y Pacificador: Case One: The Missing Friendship Bracelet Caso Primero: El Brazalete de la Amistad Desaparecido. Nikolov, Stefan V., tr. Ashley, Elana, photos by. 2005. (SPA & ENG., Illus.). 32p. (J). (gr. k-3). 17.95 (978-0-9744812-1-0(1)) Dream Image Pr., LLC.

Ashworth, Sherry. Paralysed. 2007. 304p. (J). pap. 12.00 (***978-1-4169-0094-8(2)***) Simon & Schuster, Ltd. GBR. *Dist:* Independent Pubs. Group.

Atwood, Margaret. Bashful Bob & Doleful Dorinda. Petricic, Dusan, illus. 2006. 32p. (J). 17.95 (978-1-59990-004-9(1) , Bloomsbury Children) Bloomsbury Publishing.

Auerbach, Annie. Welcome to Horseland. 2007. (Horseland Ser.: Vol. 1). 96p. (J). (gr. 2-5). pap. 3.99 (***978-0-06-134167-0(3)*** , Harper Entertainment) HarperCollins Pubs.

Avi. Encounter at Easton. 2000. 144p. (J). (gr. 3-7). pap. 6.99 (978-0-380-73241-8(6) , Harper Trophy) HarperCollins Pubs.

—Ragweed. Floca, Brian, illus. 1999. (Avon Camelot Bks.). 192p. (J). (gr. 3-7). 16.99 (978-0-380-97690-4(0)) HarperCollins Pubs.

Awdry, W. Thomas & Friends: Lift-the-Flap Freight. Courtney, Richard, illus. 2008. (Thomas & Friends Ser.). 10p. (J). (gr. k-k). bds. 6.99 (***978-0-375-84301-3(9)*** , Random Hse. Bks. for Young Readers) Random Hse. Children's Bks.

—Thomas & Friends: Thomas' Read along Storybook. Stubbs, Tommy, illus. 2007. 112p. (J). (ps-2). 15.99 (***978-0-375-84182-8(2)*** , Random Hse. Bks. for Young Readers) Random Hse. Children's Bks.

Awdry, Wilbert V. Calling All Engines. Courtney, Richard, illus. 2005. (Thomas & Friends Ser.). 24p. (J). (ps-1). pap. 3.99 (978-0-375-83119-5(3) , Random Hse. Bks. for Young Readers) Random Hse. Children's Bks.

—Thomas & Friends: On the Track. . . There & Back. Red Giraffe, illus. 2004. 16p. (J). (gr. k-ps). bds. 4.99 (978-0-375-82774-7(9) , Random Hse. Bks. for Young Readers) Random Hse. Children's Bks.

—Thomas & Friends Movie Theater Storybook & Movie Projector. 2007. (RD Innovative Book & Player Format Ser.). 48p. (J). 24.99 (***978-0-7944-1362-0(5)***) Reader's Digest Assn., Inc., The.

Awdry, Wilbert V. Track Stars! Three Thomas & Friends Stories. Courtney, Richard, photos by. 2006. (Thomas & Friends Ser.). (Illus.). 24p. (J). (ps-1). pap. 3.99 (978-0-375-83462-2(1) , Random Hse. Bks. for Young Readers) Random Hse. Children's Bks.

Aylesworth, Jim. McGraw's Emporium. 1998. (ps-2). lib. bdg. 16.40 (978-0-613-90149-9(5)) Tandem Library Bks.

Azr, Teferu. The Ronin Poetz: Hip-Hop's First Novel in Rhyme. 2002. (Illus.). 184p. (YA). per. 15.95 (978-0-9762627-1-8(1)) DaChosen Publishing.

Baby Lauren & Theodore, Paperback. 2007. (J). pap. 9.95 (***978-0-9779643-0-7(2)***) Healing Tree Arts.

Baby Strawberry Loves to Count. 2007. (Strawberry Shortcake Baby Ser.). 10p. (J). bds. 6.99 (***978-0-448-44717-9(7)*** , Grosset & Dunlap) Penguin Group (USA) Inc.

Baglio, Ben M. Frog Friends. 2001. (Animal Ark Pets Ser.: Vol. 16). (Illus.). 128p. (J). (ps-3). pap. 3.99 (978-0-439-23025-4(X)) Scholastic, Inc.

—Labrador on the Lawn. Gregory, Jenny, illus. 2005. (Animal Ark Hauntings Ser.: No. 38). 144p. (J). (gr. 2-5). pap. 3.99 (978-0-439-68488-0(9)) Scholastic, Inc.

Baguley, Elizabeth. The Little Lost Robin. Macnaughton, Tina, illus. 2007. 28p. (J). (ps-2). 16.95 (***978-1-56148-590-1(X)***) Good Bks.

Baiker, Karen. Barnyard Friends. (Felt Read-and-Play Ser.). (Illus.). 14p. (J). 17.95 (978-1-59354-052-4(3)) Handprint Bks.

Bailie, Helen. The Azura Stones. 2007. 212p. (YA). per. 18.00 (***978-1-58982-374-7(5)*** , Bedside Bks.) American Bk. Publishing Group.

Bain, Michelle. The Adventures of Thumbs up Johnnie: Johnnie's Missing Boot! Lizana, Lorenzo, illus. 2007. (J). 14.95 (***978-0-9761421-8-8(X)***) Pixie Stuff LLC.

Baker, Barbara. Digby & Kate 1-2-3. Winborn, Marsha, illus. 2004. (Dutton Easy Reader Ser.). 48p. (J). (gr. 1-4). 14.99 (978-0-525-46854-7(4) , Dutton Juvenile) Penguin Group (USA) Inc.

BAKER, E. D. Story of kitten Cuckoo. 2007. 32p. 15.95 (***978-1-933572-04-8(3)***) Centro Bks., LLC.

Baker, Jennifer. Eternally Yours. 1999. (Enchanted Hearts Ser.: No. 2). 176p. (YA). (gr. 7-12). pap. 4.50 (978-0-380-80073-5(X)) HarperCollins Pubs.

Balaam, Steven & Balaam, Lisa. Abbey the Cavi: And Friends. 2007. (Illus.). 102p. (J). per. 9.95 (978-0-9785585-0-5(2)) Balaam Books LLC.

Baldwin, Jean S. More George. 2001. (Illus.). 34p. (J). (gr. 3-6). pap. 44.95 (978-1-879418-58-5(4)) Biddle Publishing Co.

Balfour, Melissa. The Magic Footprints. Julian, Russell, illus. 2005. (Green Bananas Ser.). 48p. (J). (978-0-7787-1023-3(8)) Crabtree Publishing Co.

—The Magic Footprints. 2005. (Green Bananas Ser.). (Illus.). 48p. (J). (ps). pap. (978-0-7787-1039-4(4)) Crabtree Publishing Co.

Balfour, Melissa, et al. Yr Olion Traed Hud. 2005. (WEL., Illus.). 47p. (978-1-85596-677-2(8)) Dref Wen.

Balkovec, Lisa. Setting It Straight. 2006. (YA). per. 13.95 (978-1-932172-24-9(6)) McKenna Publishing Group.

Ballantyne, Michael. Blown to Bits or the Lonely Man of Rakat. 2006. 36.99 (***978-1-4280-4221-6(0)***); pap. 30.99 (***978-1-4280-4226-1(1)***) IndyPublish.com.

Ballantyne, R. M. Blown to Bits; or, the Lonely Man of Rak. 2006. pap. (***978-1-4065-0515-3(3)***) Dodo Pr.

Ballard, Carol L. & Ballard, Bryan L. Nikki's Adventures. 1999. (Illus.). 40p. (J). (gr. k-6). pap. 18.00 (978-0-8059-4675-8(6)) Dorrance Publishing Co., Inc.

Balloon Books Staff & Ward, Adam. Me & My Friends. 2003. (Illus.). 64p. 5.95 (978-1-4027-0419-2(4)) Sterling Publishing Co., Inc.

Balmer, Fred. Festus & His New Job. Newcomb, Kristene, illus. 2004. 26p. (J). per. 7.00 (***978-0-9760790-1-9(1)***) Folsom Fallies Pr.

—Festus & the Hole in the Fence Gang. Newcomb, Kristene, illus. 2005. 33p. (J). per. 7.00 (***978-0-9760790-3-3(8)***) Folsom Fallies Pr.

—Festus & the Missing Bag of Feed. Newcomb, Kristene, illus. 2004. 26p. (J). per. 7.00 (***978-0-9760790-0-2(3)***) Folsom Fallies Pr.

—Festus & the Stranger. Miller, Callie, ed. Newcomb, Kristene, illus. 2007. 30p. (J). per. 7.00 (***978-0-9760790-4-0(6)***) Folsom Fallies Pr.

Bamboo & Friends. (C). 180.80 (978-1-4048-1528-5(7)) Picture Window Bks.

Bamboo Zoo Set: Meet Lester Panda & his Friends. 2006. (J). 17.95 (978-0-9774493-1-6(9)) Bamboo Zoo, LLC.

Banks, Kate. Friends of the Heart: Amici Del Cuore. 2005. 144p. (J). 16.00 (978-0-374-32455-1(7)) Farrar, Straus & Giroux.

Banks, Kate. Lenny's Space. 2007. 160p. (J). (gr. 3-7). 16.00 (***978-0-374-34575-4(9)*** , Farrar, Straus & Giroux (BYR)) Farrar, Straus & Giroux.

Banks, Steven. Battle of the Band. Goldberg, Barry, illus. ed. 2005. (Adventures of Jimmy Neutron Ser.: 1). 24p. (J). lib. bdg. 15.00 (978-1-59054-779-3(9)) Fitzgerald Bks.

—The Big Halloween Scare. Martinez, Heather, illus. 2005. (Ready-to-Read Ser. Level 2: 1). 32p. (J). lib. bdg. 15.00 (978-1-59054-987-2(2)) Fitzgerald Bks.

Bannister, Bram. Rupert, the Alien & the Bank Robbery. 2007. 56p. per. 8.95 (***978-0-595-44839-5(9)***) iUniverse, Inc.

Banscherus, Jurgen. Detective's Duel. Baron, Daniel C., tr. from GER. Butschkow, Ralf, illus. 2007. 65p. (J). (gr. 3-6). lib. bdg. 22.60 (***978-1-59889-339-7(4)***) Stone Arch Bks.

—The Great Snake Swindle. Baron, Daniel C., tr. from GER. Butschkow, Ralf, illus. 2007. 67p. (J). (gr. 3-6). lib. bdg. 22.60 (***978-1-59889-340-3(8)***) Stone Arch Bks.

Banscherus, Jurgen & Baron, Daniel C. Detective's Duel. Butschkow, Ralf, illus. 2007. 65p. (J). pap. (***978-1-59889-434-9(X)***) Stone Arch Bks.

—The Great Snake Swindle. Butschkow, Ralf, illus. 2007. 67p. (J). pap. (***978-1-59889-435-6(8)***) Stone Arch Bks.

Barad, Alexis. Eyes, Ears, Toes! Discovering Me! 2008. (Fisher-Price Ser.). 16p. (J). 4.99 (***978-0-06-144769-3(2)*** , Harper Festival) HarperCollins Pubs.

Barasch, Lynne. The Reluctant Flower Girl. Barasch, Lynne, illus. 2001. (Illus.). 40p. (J). (gr. k-3). 14.95 (978-0-06-028809-9(4)) HarperCollins Pubs.

Barber, Antonia. Dancing Shoes Friends & Rivals. (Illus.). 96p. (J). 5.95 (978-0-14-038684-4(X)) Penguin Group (USA) Inc.

Barbie Kindergarten Educational Box Set. 2004. (J). (978-0-7666-1354-6(2) , 64066) Modern Publishing.

Barbour, Ralph Henry. The Half-Back. 2006. (Illus.). pap. (***978-1-4065-0776-8(8)***) Dodo Pr.

E F G

Bardhan-Quallen, Sudipta. Meet Rainbow Sherbet. Yee, Josie, illus. 2005. (Strawberry Shortcake Ser.). 32p. (J). (ps-2). 3.99 (978-0-448-43826-9(7) , Grosset & Dunlap) Penguin Group (USA) Inc.

Bardhan-Quallen, Sudipta. The Mine-O-Saur. Clark, David, illus. 2007. 32p. (J). (ps). 16.99 (*978-0-399-24642-5(8) , Putnam Juvenile) Penguin Group (USA) Inc.

Barkan, Joanne. A Tale of Two Sitters. l.t. ed. 1999. (Adventures of Wishbone Ser.: No. 9). (Illus.). 144p. (J). (gr. 4 up). lib. bdg. 22.60 (978-0-8368-2305-9(2)) Stevens, Gareth Inc.

Barker, Cicely Mary. Candytuft's Enchanting Treats. 2007. 80p. (J). pap. 3.99 (978-0-7232-5904-6(6) , Warne) Penguin Group (USA) Inc.

—Flower Fairies Best Friends. Barker, Cicely Mary, illus. 2005. 24p. (J). 9.99 (978-0-7232-5714-1(0) , Warne) Penguin Group (USA) Inc.

—Lily's Seaside Adventure: A Flower Fairies Friends Chapter Book. 2008. (Flower Fairies Ser.). 80p. (J). (gr. 2). pap. 3.99 (*978-0-7232-6286-2(1) , Warne) Penguin Group (USA) Inc.

—Merry Fairy Holidays: Three Enchanted Christmas Stories. 2007. 244p. (J). (gr. 2). 8.99 (*978-0-7232-5972-5(0) , Warne) Penguin Group (USA) Inc.

—Strawberry's New Friend. 2007. 80p. (J). 3.99 (978-0-7232-5905-3(4) , Warne) Penguin Group (USA) Inc.

—Sweet Pea's Precious Promise: A Flower Fairies Friends Chapter Book. 2007. (Flower Fairies Ser.). 80p. (J). (gr. 2). 3.99 (*978-0-7232-5921-3(6) , Warne) Penguin Group (USA) Inc.

—Tansy's New Petals: A Flower Fairies Friends Chapter Book. 2008. (Flower Fairies Ser.). 80p. (J). (gr. 2). pap. 3.99 (*978-0-7232-6285-5(3) , Warne) Penguin Group (USA) Inc.

Barkley, Roger C. Johnny Grasshopper. 2006. 52p. pap. 12.95 (978-1-4241-0221-1(9)) PublishAmerica, Inc.

Barnes, Dawn. Night on the Mountain of Fear. Chang, Bernard, illus. 2006. (Black Belt Club Ser.: No. 2). 176p. (J). pap. 4.99 (978-0-439-63939-2(5)); (gr. 2-5). 16.99 (978-0-439-63937-8(9)) Scholastic, Inc. (Blue Sky Pr., The).

Barnes, Jennifer Lynn. Tattoo. 2007. 272p. (YA). (gr. 7 up). pap. 7.99 (978-0-385-73347-2(X)); lib. bdg. 12.99 (978-0-385-90363-9(4)) Random Hse. Children's Bks. (Delacorte Bks. for Young Readers).

Barnes, Laura T. Teeny Tiny Ernest. Camburn, Carol A., illus. 2002. (Ernest Ser.: Vol. 2). 32p. (J). (ps-3). 15.95 (978-0-9674681-1-2(6)) Barnesyard Bks.

Barnholdt, Lauren. Reality Chick. 2006. 288p. (YA). pap. 8.99 (978-1-4169-1317-7(3) , Simon Pulse) Simon & Schuster Children's Publishing.

Barnholdt, Lauren. The Secret Identity of Devon Delaney. 2007. 272p. (J). (gr. 4-8). pap. 5.99 (*978-1-4169-3503-2(7) , Aladdin) Simon & Schuster Children's Publishing.

Barra, Nancy. Carlos y Sus Amigos. Zuman, John, ed. Rooney, Veronica, illus. 2002. (Sunflower/Girasol Ser.). (SPA.). 20p. tchr. ed., spiral bd. 5.95 (978-1-58332-059-4(8)) Intercultural Center for Research in Education (I N C R E).

—Carlos y Sus Amigos. Rooney, Veronica, illus. 2002. (Sunflower/Girasol Ser.). (SPA.). 38p. (J). 5.95 (978-1-58332-058-7(X)) Intercultural Center for Research in Education (I N C R E).

Barrett. Lethal Delivery, Postage Prepaid. (Thumbprint Mysteries Ser.). 32.86 (978-0-8092-0425-0(8)) McGraw-Hill/Contemporary.

Barrett, Anna Pearl. Neecie & the Swarming Germs. Carmical, Phillip, ed. 1998. (Illus.). 50p. (J). (gr. 2-4). pap. 9.95 (978-0-9661330-0-4(5)) Over the Rainbow Productions.

Barrie, J. M. Tommy & Grizel, Vol. 6. (J). reprint ed. 57.50 (978-0-404-08786-9(8)) AMS Pr., Inc.

—Tommy & Grizel. reprint ed. (J). lib. bdg. 98.00 (978-0-7426-2515-0(X)); 2001. pap. 28.00 (978-0-7426-7515-5(7)) Classic Bks.

Barringer, William. Gregory & Alexander. LaFave, Kim, illus. 2003. 32p. (J). (ps-2). 15.95 (978-1-55143-252-6(8)) Orca Bk. Pubs. USA.

Barron, David. The Adventures of Bob & Red. Thatch, Nancy R., ed. 1999. (Books for Students by Students). (Illus.). 29p. (J). (ps-3). lib. bdg. 15.95 (978-0-933849-71-6(0)) Landmark Editions, Inc.

Barron, Kirk W. Johnny Tractor & Friends: A New Kind of Job. Torgerson, Dell & Reyner, Mark, eds. Barron, Kirk W., illus. 1999. (John Deere Storybook for Little Folks Ser.). (Illus.). 14p. (J). (gr. 3 up). 6.95 (978-1-887327-26-8(6)) Ertl Co., Inc.

—Johnny Tractor & Friends: Afraid of Nothing. Torgerson, Dell & Reyner, Mark, eds. Barron, Kirk W., illus. 1999. (John Deere Storybook for Little Folks Ser.). (Illus.). 14p. (J). (gr. 3 up). 6.95 (978-1-887372-25-1(3)) Ertl Co., Inc.

Barrows, Ann F. Ivy & Bean & the Ghost That Had to Go. Blackall, Sophie, illus. 2006. (Ivy + Bean Ser.: Bk. 2). 136p. (J). (gr. 1-5). 14.95 (978-0-8118-4910-4(4)) Chronicle Bks. LLC.

Barrows, Annie. Ivy & Bean, Bk. 1. Blackall, Sophie, illus. 2006. 120p. (J). (gr. 1-5). 14.95 (978-0-8118-4903-6(1)) Chronicle Bks. LLC.

—Ivy & Bean Break the Fossil Record, Bk. 3. Blackall, Sophie, illus. 2007. (Ivy & Bean Ser.). 132p. (J). (gr. 1-3). 14.95 (978-0-8118-5683-6(6)) Chronicle Bks. LLC.

Barry, Dave & Pearson, Ridley. Peter & the Starcatchers. Call, Greg, illus. 2006. 480p. (gr. 5-17). reprint ed. pap. 7.99 (978-0-7868-4907-9(X) , Disney Editions) Disney Pr.

—Peter & the Starcatchers. 2004. 464p. (gr. 5-17). 17.99 (978-0-7868-5445-5(6)) Hyperion Bks. for Children.

Barry, Frances. Duckie's Splash. Barry, Frances, illus. 2006. (Illus.). 14p. (J). (gr. k-ps). bds. 5.99 (978-0-7636-2897-0(2)) Candlewick Pr.

Bartels, Korin. A Secret in My Shoes. l.t. ed. 2005. (Illus.). 20p. (J). per. 10.00 (978-1-59879-031-3(5)) Lifevest Publishing, Inc.

Baskin, Nora Raleigh. What Every Girl. 2002. (gr. 5-8). lib. bdg. 13.00 (978-0-613-89779-2(X)) Tandem Library Bks.

Bass, Ruth. Sarah's Daughter. 2007. pap. 14.95 (*978-0-9774053-4-3(6)) North River Pr. Publishing Corp., The.

Bassede, Francine. A Day with the Bellyflops. Bassede, Francine, illus. 2000. (Illus.). 32p. (J). (ps-2). pap. 14.95 (978-0-531-30242-2(3) , Orchard Bks.) Scholastic, Inc.

Bastet - Evaluation Guide: Evaluation Guide. 2006. (J). (978-1-55942-400-4(1)) Marsh Media.

Bastet - Teaching Guide. 2000. (J). 17.95 (978-1-55942-175-1(4)) Marsh Media.

Bates, Ivan. All by Myself. Bates, Ivan, illus. 2000. (Illus.). 32p. (J). (ps-2). 14.95 (978-0-06-028585-2(0)) HarperCollins Pubs.

Bateson, Catherine. Being Bee. 2007. 136p. (J). (gr. 3-7). 16.95 (*978-0-8234-2104-6(X)) Holiday Hse., Inc.

Battleson, Mariella. Her Name Was Emaline. 2005. 60p. (J). pap. 25.99 (978-1-4141-0364-8(6)) Pleasant Word.

Bauer, Joan. Sticks. 192p. (YA). 2005. (Illus.). (gr. 5-7). pap. 7.99 (978-0-14-240428-7(4) , Puffin); 2002. 18.99 (978-0-399-23752-2(6) , Putnam Juvenile) Penguin Group (USA) Inc.

Bauer, Marion Dane. The Double-Digit Club. 2004. 126p. (J). (gr. 4-6). tchr. ed. 15.95 (978-0-8234-1805-3(7)) Holiday Hse., Inc.

—A Frog's Best Friend: A Holiday House Reader. Hearn, Diane Dawson, illus. 2002. (Reader Level 2 Ser.). 32p. (J). (gr. k-3). tchr. ed. 14.95 (978-0-8234-1501-4(5)) Holiday Hse., Inc.

—Killing Miss Kitty & Other Sins. 2007. 176p. (YA). (gr. 7). 16.00 (*978-0-618-69000-8(X) , Clarion Bks.) Houghton Mifflin Co. Trade & Reference Div.

—One Brown Bunny. Bates, Ivan, illus. 2008. (J). (*978-0-439-68010-3(7) , Orchard Bks.) Scholastic, Inc.

Baumgart, Klaus. Laura's Star. 2002. (Illus.). 32p. (J). pap. 7.95 (978-1-58925-374-2(4) , tiger tales) ME Media LLC.

—Laura's Star. 2002. (gr. k-3). lib. bdg. 16.40 (978-0-613-62788-7(1)) Tandem Library Bks.

—Lenny & Tweek. 2002. (Illus.). (J). 31p. pap. (978-1-59034-387-6(5)); 32p. 15.95 (978-1-59034-197-1(X)) Mondo Publishing.

Bayer, Dorothy. Special Friends. 2005. 17.00 (978-0-8059-9711-8(3)) Dorrance Publishing Co., Inc.

Be Kind, Be Friendly, Be Thankful: The Adventures of Brisky Bear & Trooper Dog. 2007. Orig. Title: Friends for Always. (J). pap. 7.95 incl. audio compact disk (*978-0-9795127-0-4(0)) Glory Be Collectibles.

Be Nice to Your Friends: Super Paint with Water. 1999. (Disney Ser.). (Illus.). 64p. (J). (ps-4). pap. 2.99 (978-0-307-08362-3(4) , 08362, Golden Bks.) Random Hse. Children's Bks.

Beacon Street Girls Staff. Meet the Beacon Street Girls. 2004. (Illus.). 36p. (J). 3.99 (978-0-9746587-5-9(8) , Beacon Street Girls) B*tween Productions, Inc.

Beamish, Diane. Brucie Learns a Lesson. 2006. 25p. (J). 10.25 (978-1-4116-6631-3(3)) Lulu.com.

—Gentle Jack. 2006. 25p. (J). 10.25 (978-1-4116-5553-9(2)) Lulu.com.

Beard, Darleen Bailey. The Flimflam Man. Christelow, Eileen, illus. 96p. (J). 2003. pap. 5.95 (978-0-374-42345-2(8) , Sunburst); 1998. (gr. 2-6). 15.00 (978-0-374-32346-2(1) , Farrar, Straus & Giroux (BYR)) Farrar, Straus & Giroux.

Beaumont, Karen. Being Friends. 2002. (Illus.). 32p. (J). 15.99 (978-0-8037-2529-4(9) , Dial) Penguin Group (USA) Inc.

Beck, Ana. Elliot's Shipwreck. 2000. (gr. 3-6). lib. bdg. 14.10 (978-0-613-36328-0(0)) Tandem Library Bks.

Becker, Bonny. A Visitor for Bear. Denton, Kady MacDonald, illus. 2008. (J). (*978-0-7636-2807-9(7)) Candlewick Pr.

Becker, Joseph C., 3rd. Twilight: The Waning Days of Youth. 2002. 176p. (YA). pap. 12.95 (978-0-595-22731-0(7) , Writers Club Pr.) iUniverse, Inc.

Becker, Suzy. Bud & Scooter. Date not set. 48p. (J). (gr. k-3). pap. 3.99 (978-0-06-444286-2(1)) HarperCollins Pubs.

—Bud & Scooter. Becker, Suzy, illus. Date not set. (Illus.). 48p. (J). (gr. k-3). 16.89 (978-0-06-028971-3(6)); 15.99 (978-0-06-028970-6(8)) HarperCollins Pubs.

Beckerman, Menucha. Friends on the Farm. 2004. (My Smiling World Ser.: No. 1). (Illus.). 32p. (J). 11.95 (978-1-931681-53-7(8)) Israel Bk. Shop.

—Michael & the Secret of Making Friends. 2003. (My Middos World Ser.: Vol. 9). (Illus.). 24p. (J). (gr. k-5). 11.95 (978-1-931681-15-5(5)) Israel Bk. Shop.

Bedard, Michael. Stained Glass. 2001. (gr. 7-12). lib. bdg. 17.60 (978-0-613-57923-0(2)) Tandem Library Bks.

—Stained Glass. 2002. 312p. (J). (gr. 6). pap. 8.95 (978-0-88776-602-2(1)) Tundra Bks., Inc./Livres Toundra, Inc. CAN. *Dist:* Random Hse., Inc.

Bedford, David. Ahora Me Toca a Mi! Field, Elaine, illus. (SPA.). 32p. (J). (978-84-8418-051-7(4)) Corimbo, Editorial S.L. ESP. *Dist:* Lectorum Pubns., Inc.

—The Copy Crocs. Bolam, Emily, tr. Bolam, Emily, illus. 2004. 32p. (J). (gr. k). 15.95 (978-1-56145-304-7(8)) Peachtree Pubs., Ltd.

—It's My Turn! 2000. 12.75 (978-0-606-20731-7(7)) Tandem Library Bks.

Bedford, David & Field, Elaine. It's My Turn! 2001. (Illus.). 30p. (J). (ps-k). 5.95 (978-1-58925-351-3(5) , tiger tales) ME Media LLC.

Bednar, Martin. Sandy's Vision. 2006. (J). lib. bdg. 19.95 (*978-1-933732-15-2(6) , Bear Hug Bks.) MidAmerica Publishing Co.

Beech, Sandy. Worst Class Trip Ever. Holder, Jimmy, illus. 2005. (Castaways Ser.). 176p. pap. 4.99 (978-0-689-87596-0(7) , Aladdin) Simon & Schuster Children's Publishing.

Begin, Mary Jane. Willow Buds #1. 2008. 40p. 14.99 (*978-0-316-01352-9(8)) Little Brown & Co.

Behrens, Andy. All the Way. 2006. 256p. (YA). (gr. 9). 16.99 (978-0-525-47761-7(6) , Dutton Juvenile) Penguin Group (USA) Inc.

Bell, C. A O G Bk. 1: Army of God. 2005. 108p. pap. 16.95 (978-1-4137-8130-4(6)) PublishAmerica, Inc.

Bell, Cece. Busy Buddies: Silly Stuff That Goes Together. Bell, Cece, illus. 2006. (Board Books). (Illus.). 20p. (J). (gr. k-ps). bds. 5.99 (978-0-7636-2776-8(3)) Candlewick Pr.

—Food Friends: Fun Foods That Go Together. Bell, Cece, illus. 2006. (Illus.). 20p. (J). (gr. k-ps). bds. 5.99 (978-0-7636-2777-5(1)) Candlewick Pr.

Bell, Hilari. The Wizard Test. 176p. (J). 2006. pap. 5.99 (978-0-06-059942-3(1)); 2005. (gr. 5 up). 15.99 (978-0-06-059940-9(5)); 2005. (gr. 5 up). lib. bdg. 16.89 (978-0-06-059941-6(3)) HarperCollins Pubs.

Bell, Linda Simmons. Best Friends. 2006. (ENG.). 28p. per. 13.99 (*978-1-4259-7559-3(3)) AuthorHouse.

Bell, Rebecca. Capitano Ricco. Bell, Rebecca, illus. 2005. 36p. (J). per. 9.95 (*978-1-934138-06-9(1)) Bouncing Ball Bks., Inc.

Bell, William. Death Wind. 2002. (Soundings Ser.). 96p. (J). (gr. 7-12). pap. 7.95 (978-1-55143-215-1(3)) Orca Bk. Pubs. USA.

—Death Wind. 2002. (gr. 7-12). lib. bdg. 16.40 (978-0-613-62940-9(X)) Tandem Library Bks.

Beller, Jasmine. Bring It On. 2006. (Hip-Hop Kidz Ser.: Vol. 1). 160p. (J). (gr. 4-7). pap. 4.99 (978-0-448-44362-1(7) , Grosset & Dunlap) Penguin Group (USA) Inc.

Bellingham, Brenda. Lilly Makes a Friend. MacDonald, Clarke, illus. 2004. (First Novel Ser.). 64p. (J). (gr. 1-5). 4.95 (978-0-88780-624-7(4)); (*978-0-88780-625-4(2)) Formac Publishing Co., Ltd. CAN. *Dist:* Casemate Pubs. & Bk. Distributors, LLC.

—Lilly's Special Gift. MacDonald, Clarke, illus. 2005. (First Novel Ser.). 64p. (gr. 2-5). (*978-0-88780-665-0(1)); 4.95 (978-0-88780-664-3(3)) Formac Publishing Co., Ltd. CAN. *Dist:* Casemate Pubs. & Bk. Distributors, LLC.

Benge, Judy. My Name Is Sandy. 2004. 152p. pap. 19.95 (978-1-4137-1947-5(3)) PublishAmerica, Inc.

Benjamin, Ruth. Belle of the Ball. Edwards, Ken, illus. 2004. (Festival Reader Ser.). 24p. (J). (ps-1). pap. 3.99 (978-0-06-073267-7(9) , Harper Festival) HarperCollins Pubs.

Bennett, Cherie. Zink: The Myth, the Legend, the Zebra. 2001. (Illus.). (J). (978-0-606-21543-5(3)) Tandem Library Bks.

Bennett, Elizabeth. The New Bug. Scherer, Jeffrey, illus. 2003. 32p. (J). (978-0-439-46641-7(5)) Scholastic, Inc.

Bennett, Holly. The Bonemender. 2005. (Illus.). 208p. (YA). (gr. 7-12). pap. 7.95 (978-1-55143-336-3(2)) Orca Bk. Pubs. USA.

Bennett, James W. Blue Star Rapture. 2001. (J). (978-0-606-20574-0(8)) Tandem Library Bks.

Bennett, Jill. Teeny Tiny. de Paola, Tomie, illus. 1998. (978-0-606-13050-9(0)) Tandem Library Bks.

Bennett, Kelly. Not Norman: A Goldfish Story. Jones, Noah, illus. 2005. 32p. (J). (ps-3). 15.99 (978-0-7636-2384-5(9)) Candlewick Pr.

Bensimon, Gladys. Paha Sapa: Black Hills. 2005. 81p. pap. 14.95 (978-1-4137-6972-2(1)) PublishAmerica, Inc.

Bentley, Dawn. Velociraptor. Carr, Karen, illus. 2005. (Smithsonian's Prehistoric Pals Ser.). 36p. (J). (ps-2). 9.95 (978-1-59249-168-1(5) , PS2453) Soundprints.

Benton, Jim. The Fran with Four Brains. Benton, Jim, illus. 2007. (Franny K. Stein, Mad Scientist Ser.: Bk. 6). 112p. (J). (gr. 2-5). pap. 4.99 (*978-1-4169-0232-4(5) , Aladdin) Simon & Schuster Children's Publishing.

—Frantastic Voyage. Benton, Jim, illus. 2005. (Franny K. Stein, Mad Scientist Ser.: Bk. 5). (Illus.). 112p. (J). 14.95 (978-1-4169-0229-4(5)) Simon & Schuster Children's Publishing.

—The Invisible Fran. Benton, Jim, illus. 2004. (Franny K. Stein, Mad Scientist Ser.: Bk. 3). (Illus.). 112p. (J). (gr. 2-5). 14.95 (978-0-689-86293-9(8)) Simon & Schuster Children's Publishing.

—Let's Pretend This Never Happened. Benton, Jim, illus. 2004. (Dear Dumb Diary Ser.: Bk. 1). (Illus.). 80p. (J). 4.99 (978-0-439-62904-1(7) , Scholastic Paperbacks) Scholastic, Inc.

Bentz, Lindsay. Really Good Friends. 2007. (ENG.). 184p. per. 12.95 (*978-1-59526-720-7(4) , Llumina Pr.) Media Creations, Inc.

Berenstain, Michael, et al. The Berenstain Bears & the Golden Rule. 2008. (J). pap. (*978-0-310-71247-3(5)) Zonderkidz.

Berenstain, Stan & Berenstain, Jan. The Berenstain Bears Lose a Friend. Berenstain, Stan & Berenstain, Jan, illus. 2007. (Berenstain Bears Ser.). 32p. (J). (ps-2). pap. 3.99 (*978-0-06-057389-8(9) , Harper Festival) HarperCollins Pubs.

Berenzy, Alix. Sammy: The Classroom Guinea Pig. rev. ed. 1999. (Illus.). 32p. (J). (ps-ps). 16.95 (978-0-8050-4024-1(2) , Holt, Henry & Co. Bks. For Young Readers) Holt, Henry & Co.

Berg, Brook. What Marion Taught Willis. Alberg, Nathan, illus. 2005. (J). 16.95 (978-1-932146-31-8(8) , 1242215) Highsmith Inc.

Bergen, Lara. Candy Apple #8 I've Got A Secret. 2008. (Candy Apple Ser.). 176p. (J). pap. 4.99 (*978-0-545-03427-2(2)) Scholastic, Inc.

—Drama Queen. 2007. (Candy Apple Ser.: No. 5). 176p. (J). pap. 4.99 (*978-0-439-92953-0(9) , Scholastic Paperbacks) Scholastic, Inc.

Berger, Kathy L. The Hailey & Max Stories. Wise, Noreen, ed. Crawford, K. Michael, illus. 2000. (Book-a-Day Collection). 48p. (YA). (ps up). pap. 6.95 (978-1-58584-415-9(2)) Huckleberry Pr.

Berk, Sheryl. Barney's Little Lessons: Be My Friend! Valentine-Ruppe, June, illus. 2002. (Barney Ser.). 8p. (J). (ps-1). bds. 5.99 (978-1-58668-293-4(8)) Scholastic, Inc.

Bernardo, Anilu. Loves Me, Loves Me Not. 1998. 169p. (YA). (gr. 6-12). 16.95 (978-1-55885-258-7(1) , Piñata Books) Arte Publico Pr.

—Loves Me, Loves Me Not. 1999. (gr. 7-12). lib. bdg. 18.75 (978-0-613-23737-6(4)) Tandem Library Bks.

Bernier-Grand, Carmen T. In the Shade of the Nispero Tree. 1999. 192p. (J). (gr. 4-7). 16.99 (978-0-531-33154-5(7)); pap. 15.95 (978-0-531-30154-8(0)) Scholastic, Inc. (Orchard Bks.).

—In the Shade of the Nispero Tree. 2001. (978-0-606-20722-5(8)) Tandem Library Bks.

Berry, Eileen M. Haiku on Your Shoes. Regan, Dana, illus. 2005. 56p. (J). (ps-ps). pap. 7.49 (978-1-59166-374-4(1)) Jones, Bob Univ. Pr.

Bertrand, Diane Gonzales. My Pal, Victor/Mi amigo, Víctor. Raven Tree Press Staff, ed. de la Vega, Eida, tr. Sweetland, Robert, illus. 2004. Tr. of Mi amigo, Víctor. (SPA & ENG.). 32p. (J). 16.95 (978-0-9720192-9-3(4) , 626999) Raven Tree Pr.

Betancourt, Jeanne. Close-Up. 2004. (Three Girls in the City Ser.: No. 4). 160p. (J). pap. 4.99 (978-0-439-49842-5(2) , Scholastic Paperbacks) Scholastic, Inc.

—Exposed. 2003. (Three Girls in the City Ser.: No. 2). (Illus.). 160p. (J). pap. 4.99 (978-0-439-49840-1(6) , Scholastic Paperbacks) Scholastic, Inc.

—Moving Pony. Bachem, Paul, illus. 1999. (Pony Pals Ser.: Vol. 19). 112p. (J). (gr. 2-5). pap. 3.99 (978-0-590-63397-0(X)) Scholastic, Inc.

—Moving Pony. 1999. (Pony Pals Ser.: Vol. 19). (J). (gr. 2-5). (978-0-606-19597-3(1)) Tandem Library Bks.

—The Pony & the Lost Swan. 2002. (Pony Pals Ser.: No. 34). (Illus.). 96p. (J). pap. 3.99 (978-0-439-30644-7(2) , Scholastic Paperbacks) Scholastic, Inc.

Beveridge, Donna. Henry. Nicol, Brock, illus. 1999. (Books for Young Learners).Tr. of Henry. 12p. (J). (gr. k-2). pap. 5.00 (978-1-57274-263-5(1)) Owen, Richard C. Pubs., Inc.

Bial, Raymond. A Handful of Dirt. Bial, Raymond, photos by. (Illus.). 32p. (J). (gr. 3-7). 2001. 16.95 (978-0-8027-8698-2(7)); 2000. lib. bdg. 17.85 (978-0-8027-8699-9(5)) Walker & Co.

—Shadow Island: A Tale of Lake Superior. 2006. 176p. (J). (gr. 3-7). 18.95 (978-1-883953-37-9(5)); (gr. 4-7). pap. 12.95 (978-1-883953-36-2(7)) Midwest Traditions, Inc. (Blue Horse Bks.).

Bidoli, Katie. Karate Adventures of Kisho, Hana, & Nobu: Karate Is for Everyone! 2006. (Illus.). 16p. (J). 10.00 (*978-1-60243-029-7(2)) Keen's Martial Arts Academy.

Bidwell, Dafne. Danger Unlimited: Action, Mystery & Adventure. 2007. 181p. pap. 15.50 (*978-1-921064-89-0(7)) Fremantle Pr. AUS. *Dist:* International Specialized Bk. Services.

The Big Balloon Festival: Individual Title Six-Packs. 16p. (gr. 2 up). 35.00 (978-0-7635-9381-0(8)) Rigby Education.

Big Bird's Best Friends. 2001. (J). (978-1-931312-02-8(8)) SoftPlay, Inc.

The Big Race: Individual Title Six-Packs. (gr. k-1). 23.00 (978-0-7635-9061-1(4)) Rigby Education.

The Big Toe Robbery: Individual Chapter Book Title Six-Packs. Vol. 28. 32p. (gr. 4 up). 44.00 (978-0-7578-0602-5(3)) Rigby Education.

Biggs, Pauline. A Wild Ride. Mayne, Michael, illus. 2004. 20p. (J). per. 12.95 (978-0-9760129-0-0(1)) Avant Garde Publishing.

Billingsley, ReShonda Tate. With Friends Like These. 2007. 256p. pap. 9.95 (978-1-4165-2562-2(9) , Pocket) Simon & Schuster.

Binaohan, Simon & Tacang, Brian. The Misadventures of Millicent Madding No. 1: Bully-Be-Gone. 2006. (Illus.). 224p. (J). lib. bdg. 17.89 (978-0-06-073912-6(6)) HarperCollins Pubs.

—The Misadventures of Millicent Madding Vol. 1: Bully-Be-Gone. 2006. (Illus.). 224p. (J). 16.99 (978-0-06-073911-9(8)) HarperCollins Pubs.

Bird Song: The Little Stories of Manoosh & Baloosh. 2003. (J). mass mkt. (978-1-932233-02-5(4)) Aurora Libris Corp.

Birney, Betty G. Friendship According to Humphrey. (J). (gr. 2-4). 2006. 176p. pap. 5.99 (978-0-14-240633-5(3) , Puffin); 2005. 160p. 14.99 (978-0-399-24264-9(3) , Putnam Juvenile) Penguin Group (USA) Inc.

Biro, Val. Gumdrop Forever. (Illus.). 26p. (J). (978-0-340-71448-5(4) , Hodder & Stoughton) Hodder General Publishing Division.

Bishop, Beverly. My Friend with Autism. Bishop, Craig, illus. 2002. 30p. (J). (ps-3). pap. 9.95 (978-1-885477-89-7(9)) Future Horizons, Inc.

Bishop, Jennie. The Garden Wall. 2006. (J). 12.99 (*978-1-59317-168-1(4)) Warner Pr. Pubs.

Bistricean, Karen. The Adventures of Fergus & Lady: Home Sweet Home. Bistricean, Claudius, illus. 2006. (J). (978-0-9786975-1-8(0)) Fergus & Lady Publishing.

—The Adventures of Fergus & Lady: The Beginning. Bistricean, Claudius, illus. 2006. (J). (978-0-9786975-0-1(2)) Fergus & Lady Publishing.

Black, Jessica L. Teamwork. l.t. ed. 2003. (HRL Big Book Ser.). (Illus.). 8p. (Orig.). (J). (ps-k). pap. 10.95 (978-1-57332-261-4(X)) HighReach Learning, Inc.

—Teamwork. Crowell, Knox, illus. l.t. ed. 2003. (HRL Little Book Ser.). 8p. (Orig.). (J). (ps-k). pap. 10.95 (978-1-57332-262-1(8)) HighReach Learning, Inc.

Blackall, Barrows. Ivy & Bean Take Care of the Babysitter. 2008. 124p. (J). 14.99 (978-0-8118-5685-0(2)) Chronicle Bks. LLC.

Blackman, Malorie. Cloud Busting. 2004. (Illus.). 149p. (J). (978-0-385-60796-4(2)) Hudson Hills Pr. LLC.

Blake, Emily. No Accident. (Little Secrets Ser.: No. 2). (J). 2008. 208p. pap. 4.99 (***978-0-545-02825-7(6)***); 2006. 160p. pap. 6.99 (978-0-439-82913-7(5)) Scholastic, Inc. (Scholastic Paperbacks).

—Nothing but the Truth. 2006. (Little Secrets Ser.). 160p. (J). pap. 6.99 (978-0-439-86721-4(5) , Scholastic Paperbacks) Scholastic, Inc.

—Playing with Fire. 2006. (Little Secrets Ser.: No. 1). 160p. (J). pap. 6.99 (978-0-439-81053-1(1) , Scholastic Paperbacks) Scholastic, Inc.

Blakeslee, Ann R. Different Kind of Hero. 2003. (gr. 5-8). lib. bdg. 14.10 (978-0-613-82435-4(0)) Tandem Library Bks.

Blance, Ellen & Cook. Monster Looks for Friend. Date not set. (Illus.). 16p. pap. 129.15 (978-0-582-18591-3(2)) Addison-Wesley Longman, Ltd. GBR. *Dist:* Trans-Atlantic Pubns., Inc.

Blaylock, Kathy. Adventures of Buddy Fairy & Friends. 2007. 48p. 12.95 (***978-1-4137-9195-2(6)***) PublishAmerica, Inc.

Blegvad, Lenore. Kitty & Mr. Kipling: Neighbors in Vermont. Blegvad, Erik, illus. 2005. 144p. (J). (gr. 3-5). 16.95 (978-0-689-87363-8(8) , McElderry, Margaret K.) Simon & Schuster Children's Publishing.

Blenkhorn, Les. The Adventures of Tracker. 2006. 26.99 (***978-1-4259-6605-8(5)***); pap. 16.99 (***978-1-4259-6604-1(7)***) AuthorHouse.

Bley, Anette. And What Comes after a Thousand? Bley, Anette, illus. 2007. (Illus.). 32p. (J). (gr. 1-5). 15.95 (978-1-933605-27-2(8) , 05272) Kane/Miller Bk. Pubs., Inc.

Block, Francesca Lia. Violet & Claire. (Illus.). 176p. 2000. (J). (gr. 8-12). pap. 6.99 (978-0-06-447253-1(1) , Harper Trophy); 1999. (YA). (gr. 7-12). 14.89 (978-0-06-027750-5(5)) HarperCollins Pubs.

—Violet & Claire. 2000. (J). (978-0-606-20003-5(7)); (gr. 7-12). lib. bdg. 15.30 (978-0-613-30177-0(3)) Tandem Library Bks.

—Weetzie Bat. (Weetzie Bat Ser.). 128p. 2004. (J). pap. 7.99 (978-0-06-073625-5(9) , Harper Trophy); 10th anniv. ed. 1999. (J). (gr. 5 up). pap. 7.99 (978-0-06-440818-9(3) , Harper Trophy); 10th anniv. ed. 1999. (YA). (gr. 7-k). 14.95 (978-0-06-020534-8(2)) HarperCollins Pubs.

Bloom, Janice Stitziel. Wonderfully Made under My Bed. Woodcock, Marcy, illus. 2007. 36p. (J). per. 15.99 (***978-1-934643-00-6(9)***) Villager Bk. Publishing.

Bloom, Suzanne. Splendid Friend Indeed Big BK. 2007. (Illus.). 32p. pap. 24.95 (***978-1-59078-532-4(0)***) Boyds Mills Pr.

—Treasure. 2007. (Illus.). 32p. (J). (ps-1). 15.95 (***978-1-59078-457-0(X)***) Boyds Mills Pr.

Bloom, Suzanne, illus. A Splendid Friend, Indeed. 2007. 32p. (J). 15.95 (978-1-59078-286-6(0)) Boyds Mills Pr.

Blume, Judy. Are You There God? It's Me, Margaret. 2002. (J). 13.94 (978-0-7587-9131-3(3)) Book Wholesalers, Inc.

—Are You There God? It's Me, Margaret. l.t. ed. 2002. (LRS Large Print Cornerstone Ser.). (J). lib. bdg. 28.95 (978-1-58118-088-6(8) , 24873) LRS.

—Best of Judy Blume Set: Are You There God? It's Me, Margaret; Blubber; Iggie's House; Starring Sally J. Freedman as Herself, 4 vols. 2004. (gr. 3-7). pap. 23.47 (978-0-440-42022-4(9) , Yearling) Random Hse. Children's Bks.

—BFF: Two novels by Judy Blume—Just As Long As We're Together/Here's to You, Rachel Robinson (Best Friends Forever), 2 vols. 2007. (Illus.). 512p. (J). (gr. 4-7). lib. bdg. 22.99 (978-0-385-90416-2(9) , Delacorte Bks. for Young Readers) Random Hse. Children's Bks.

—BFF 2: Two Novels by Judy Blume—Just As Long As We're Together/Here's to You, Rachel Robinson (Best Friends Forever) 2007. (Illus.). 512p. (J). (gr. 4-7). 18.99 (978-0-385-73407-3(7) , Delacorte Bks. for Young Readers) Random Hse. Children's Bks.

—Blubber. 153p. (J). (gr. 4-6). pap. 3.99 (978-0-8072-1404-6(3) , Listening Library) Random Hse. Audio Publishing Group.

—Otherwise Known As Sheila the Great. (Fudge Ser.). (J). 2007. 144p. 5.99 (978-0-14-240879-7(4) , Puffin); 2002. (Illus.). 128p. 15.99 (978-0-525-46928-5(1) , Dutton Juvenile) Penguin Group (USA) Inc.

—Superfudge. 2002. (Fudge Ser.). (Illus.). (J). 13.40 (978-0-7587-6668-7(8)) Book Wholesalers, Inc.

—Superfudge. l.t. ed. 2000. (Fudge Ser.). 216p. (YA). (gr. 5-10). lib. bdg. 28.95 (978-1-58118-061-9(6) , 23475) LRS.

—Superfudge. 1999. (Fudge Ser.). (J). 9.95 (978-1-56137-175-4(0)) Novel Units, Inc.

—Superfudge. 2002. (Fudge Ser.). (Illus.). 176p. (J). 15.99 (978-0-525-46930-8(3) , Dutton Juvenile) Penguin Group (USA) Inc.

—Superfudge. (Fudge Ser.). 166p. (J). (gr. 2-4). pap. 4.99 (978-0-8072-1457-2(4) , Listening Library) Random Hse. Audio Publishing Group.

—Superfudge. (Fudge Ser.). (SPA.). 159p. (J). (gr. 5-8). pap. 9.95 (978-1-56014-665-0(6)) Santillana USA Publishing Co., Inc.

—Tales of a Fourth Grade Nothing. 2002. (Fudge Ser.). (Illus.). (J). 13.40 (978-0-7587-6609-0(2)) Book Wholesalers, Inc.

—Tales of a Fourth Grade Nothing. 1999. (Fudge Ser.). (J). 11.95 (978-1-56137-709-1(0)) Novel Units, Inc.

—Tales of a Fourth Grade Nothing. 2004. (Fudge Ser.). 144p. (gr. 12). mass mkt. 5.99 (978-0-425-19379-2(9) , Berkley) Penguin Group (USA) Inc.

Blume, Lesley. Cornelia & the Audacious Escapades of the Somerset Sisters. 2006. 272p. (J). (gr. 3-7). 15.95 (978-0-375-83523-0(7) , Knopf Bks. for Young Readers) Random Hse. Children's Bks.

Blume, Lesley M. M. Cornelia & the Audacious Escapades of the Somerset Sisters. 2006. 272p. (J). (gr. 3-7). lib. bdg. 17.99 (978-0-375-93523-7(1) , Knopf Bks. for Young Readers) Random Hse. Children's Bks.

Blumenstock, Jacqueline & Pool, David. Making New Friends. 2nd ed. 2005. (Illus.). 32p. (J). per. 5.95 (978-0-9764647-0-9(5)) Big Brown Box, Inc., The.

—Making New Friends. Madden, Colleen, illus. 2nd ed. 2005. 32p. (J). lib. bdg. 14.95 (978-0-9764647-1-6(3)) Big Brown Box, Inc., The.

Blumenthal, Deborah. Fat Camp. 2006. 240p. (gr. 12). pap. 9.99 (978-0-451-21865-0(5) , N A L) Penguin Group (USA) Inc.

Bluthenthal, Diana Cain. I'm Not Invited. Bluthenthal, Diana Cain, illus. 2003. (Illus.). 32p. (J). (gr. k-2). 18.99 (978-0-689-84141-5(8) , Atheneum/Richard Jackson Bks.) Simon & Schuster Children's Publishing.

Blyton, Enid. Mr Pink-Whistle Has Some Fun. 2000. (Enid Blyton's Happy Days Ser.). (Illus.). 93p. (J). (gr. 1-4). pap. 7.99 (978-0-7475-4345-9(3)) Bloomsbury Publishing Plc GBR. *Dist:* Trafalgar Square Publishing.

—A Shock for the Secret Seven. l.t. ed. 2005. 160p. (J). pap. (978-0-7540-6152-6(3) , CLP 344) BBC Audio.

Bo, Ben. Edge. 2002. (gr. 5-8). lib. bdg. 15.25 (978-0-613-76628-9(8)) Tandem Library Bks.

Boczkowski, Tricia. Hello, Patrick! 2005. (Spongebob Squarepants Ser.). 12p. (J). bds. 5.99 (978-1-4169-1001-5(8) , Simon Spotlight/Nickelodeon) Simon & Schuster Children's Publishing.

—Hello, SpongeBob! 2005. (Spongebob Squarepants Ser.). 12p. (J). bds. 5.99 (978-1-4169-1000-8(X) , Simon Spotlight/Nickelodeon) Simon & Schuster Children's Publishing.

—Meet Blue! 2005. (Blue's Clues Ser.). 12p. (J). bds. 5.99 (978-1-4169-0997-2(4) , Simon Spotlight/Nickelodeon) Simon & Schuster Children's Publishing.

—Meet My Friends. 2002. (SpongeBob SquarePants Ser.). (Illus.). 12p. (J). bds. 7.99 (978-0-689-85182-7(0) , Simon Spotlight/Nickelodeon) Simon & Schuster Children's Publishing.

Bodi, Sari. The Ghost in Allie's Pool. 2007. 192p. (YA). (gr. 5 up). pap. 8.95 (***978-0-9768126-6-1(5)***) Brown Barn Bks.

Boegehold, Betty D. The Fight. Oz, Robin, illus. 1999. (Bank Street Reader Collection). (J). (gr. 1-3). lib. bdg. 22.60 (978-0-8368-2420-9(2)) Stevens, Gareth Inc.

Bogaerts, Jorge. El Dia Que Hizo Mucho Viento. (SPA.). 112p. (J). (978-84-207-3535-1(3)) Grupo Anaya, S.A.

Bogart, Jo Ellen. The Big Tree Gang. Griffiths, Dean, illus. 2005. (Orca Echoes Ser.). 64p. (J). (gr. 2-3). pap. 4.99 (978-1-55143-345-5(1)) Orca Bk. Pubs. USA.

Bojunga, Lygia. Los Amigos. (SPA.). (J). 8.95 (978-958-04-6262-0(3)) Norma S.A. COL. *Dist:* Distribuidora Norma, Inc.

Boldizsar, Anneliese. How to Make Friends. Boldizsar, Anneliese, illus. 2000. (Illus.). 59p. pap. (978-0-7541-0916-7(X)) Minerva Pr. GBR. *Dist:* Unity Distribution.

Boldt, Mark. CC & the Cool Rule! l.t. ed. 2000. (U-Do Book Ser.). (Illus.). 32p. (J). (gr. k-8). (978-0-9662556-5-2(8) , U-Do, 06) Boldt.Entertainment.

Bollinger/Papp, illus. King Kong: Meet Kong & Ann. 2005. 32p. (J). lib. bdg. 13.85 (***978-1-4242-0615-5(4)***) Fitzgerald Bks.

Bonin, Liane. Celebrity Skin: Fame Unlimited. 2007. 288p. (YA). pap. 9.99 (978-0-451-22032-5(3) , N A L Trade) Penguin Group (USA) Inc.

—Idol Talk: Fame Unlimited. 2007. 288p. (YA). (gr. 6 up). pap. 9.99 (***978-0-451-22143-8(5)*** , N A L Trade) Penguin Group (USA) Inc.

—Pretty on the Outside: Fame Unlimited. 2007. 288p. (YA). pap. 9.99 (***978-0-451-22122-3(2)*** , N A L Trade) Penguin Group (USA) Inc.

Bonnell, Kris. Can We Be Friends? 2007. (J). 3.95 (***978-1-933727-59-2(4)***) Reading Reading Bks., LLC.

—The Happy Moon. 2006. (J). 3.95 (***978-1-933727-30-1(6)***) Reading Reading Bks., LLC.

—The Little Boat. 2006. (J). 3.95 (***978-1-933727-34-9(9)***) Reading Reading Bks., LLC.

—Mmm, Apples. 2006. (J). 3.95 (***978-1-933727-22-6(5)***) Reading Reading Bks., LLC.

Bonners, Susan. Silver Balloon. 1999. (978-0-606-17355-1(2)); (gr. 3-6). lib. bdg. 12.95 (978-0-613-22775-9(1)) Tandem Library Bks.

Boock, Paula. Dare Truth or Promise. 1999. 176p. (YA). (gr. 7-12). tchr. ed. 15.00 (978-0-395-97117-8(9)) Houghton Mifflin Co. Trade & Reference Div.

Boonstra, Jean Elizabeth. Secrets & Friends. 2004. 95p. (J). (978-0-8163-2021-9(7)) Pacific Pr. Publishing Assn.

Boonstra, Juan S. El Evangelio en Nuestro Mundo. 2004. (SPA.). 348p. 11.99 (978-0-85151-808-4(7)) Banner of Truth, The.

Borden, Louise. Albie the Lifeguard. 1999. (Illus.). 32p. (J). (ps-3). pap. 5.99 (978-0-590-44586-3(3)) Scholastic, Inc.

Bornemann, Elsa. Cuadernos de un Delfin. 2003. (SPA., Illus.). 125p. (J). (gr. 5-8). pap. 11.95 (978-950-511-724-6(8)) Santillana USA Publishing Co., Inc.

Bornstein, Ruth. Little Gorilla. 2000. (Illus.). 32p. (J). (gr. k-ps). bds. 4.95 (978-0-618-05158-8(9) , Clarion Bks.) Houghton Mifflin Co. Trade & Reference Div.

Bornstein, Ruth Lercher. Butterflies & Lizards, Beryl & Me. 2002. (Illus.). 160p. (J). (gr. 3-7). 14.95 (978-0-7614-5118-1(8) , Cavendish Children's Bks.) Cavendish, Marshall Corp.

Bosley, Katherine. Uben Schoomer. 2004. 29p. pap. 14.95 (978-1-4137-0345-0(3)) PublishAmerica, Inc.

Bossley, Michele Martin. Kicker. 2007. (Orca Sports Ser.). 160p. (YA). (gr. 5 up). pap. (***978-1-55143-706-4(6)***) Orca Bk. Pubs.

Botelho, R. J. G. A. R. T. H. (Genetically Altered Radically Transformed Human) Book III: Downeast Maine: A New Beginning. 2006. 90p. pap. 14.95 (978-1-4241-2305-6(4)) PublishAmerica, Inc.

Bottner, Barbara. Raymond & Nelda. Hayashi, Nancy, illus. 2007. 32p. (J). (ps-1). 15.95 (978-1-56145-394-8(3) , Peachtree Junior) Peachtree Pubs., Ltd.

—Rosa's Room. Spiegel, Beth, tr. Spiegel, Beth, illus. 2004. 32p. (J). (gr. 1-2). 15.95 (978-1-56145-302-3(1)) Peachtree Pubs., Ltd.

—Two Messy Friends. 1999. (Hello Reader! Ser.). (Illus.). 32p. (gr. k-2). pap. 3.99 (978-0-590-63285-0(X)) Scholastic, Inc.

Bottner, Barbara & Kruglik, Gerald. Pish & Posh Wish for Fairy Wings. Bottner, Barbara, illus. 2006. (I Can Read Bks.). (Illus.). 48p. (J). 15.99 (978-0-06-051419-8(1) , HarperCollins) HarperCollins Pubs.

—Wallace's Lists. Landstrom, Olof, illus. 2004. 40p. (J). (ps-2). lib. bdg. 16.89 (978-0-06-000225-1(5)) HarperCollins Pubs.

—Wallace's Lists. Landstrom, Olof, tr. Landstrom, Olof, illus. 2004. 40p. (J). (ps-2). 16.99 (978-0-06-000224-4(7) , Tegen, Katherine Bks) HarperCollins Pubs.

Bouchard, John L. A Taste of Soda. 2006. 92p. pap. 14.95 (978-1-4241-2482-4(4)) PublishAmerica, Inc.

Boulden, James. Buddy Gets Angry Video Kit. 2003. (J). pap. 39.95 incl. VHS (978-1-892421-86-9(0) , 739) Boulden Publishing.

Bourgeois, Paulette. Franklin's New Friend. ed. 2004. (Illus.). (J). (gr. k-3). spiral bd. (978-0-616-01590-2(9)); spiral bd. (978-0-616-01591-9(7)) Canadian National Institute for the Blind/Institut National Canadien pour les Aveugles.

—Franklin's New Friend. Clark, Brenda, illus. (Franklin Ser.). 96p. (J). (ps-3). (978-1-55074-363-0(5)) Kids Can Pr., Ltd.

—Franklin's Valentines. Clark, Brenda, illus. 1998. (Franklin the Turtle Ser.). 32p. (J). (gr. k-3). (978-1-55074-480-4(1)) Kids Can Pr., Ltd.

Bourgeois, Paulette & Clark, Brenda. Franklin's New Friend. 1999. (Franklin Ser.). (Illus.). 180p. (J). (ps-3). (978-1-55074-797-3(5)) Kids Can Pr., Ltd.

Bourgeois, Paulette, et al. Franklin en la Oscuridad. Lopez Varela, Alejandra, tr. from ENG. Clark, Brenda, illus. 1998. (Franklin Ser.). (SPA.). 32p. (J). (ps-3). pap. 5.95 (978-1-880507-43-8(9) , LC7861) Lectorum Pubns., Inc.

Bowdish, Lynea. A Friend for Caitlin. 1998. (Illus.). 48p. (J). (gr. 3-5). pap. 3.50 (978-0-87406-894-8(0) , Willowisp Pr.) Darby Creek Publishing.

Bowe, Julie. My Last Best Friend. 2007. (Illus.). 160p. (YA). (gr. 2-5). 16.00 (978-0-15-205777-0(3)) Harcourt Trade Pubs.

Bowen, Debralee. The Little Yellow Clubhouse Diary. 2004. 38p. pap. 17.95 (978-1-4137-1073-1(5)) PublishAmerica, Inc.

Bowen, Fred. Final Cut. 1999. (gr. 3-6). lib. bdg. 12.95 (978-0-613-23227-2(5)) Tandem Library Bks.

Bowers, Tim. A New Home. 2003. (Green Light Readers Level 1 Ser.). (Illus.). 24p. (J). 11.95 (978-0-15-204808-2(1)); pap. 3.95 (978-0-15-204848-8(0)) Harcourt Children's Bks. (Green Light Readers).

—New Home. 2002. (gr. k-3). lib. bdg. 11.80 (978-0-613-63169-3(2)) Tandem Library Bks.

Boyce, Katie. Hector the Hermit Crab. Boyce, Katie, illus. 2003. (Illus.). 32p. (J). (ps-1). 15.95 (978-1-58234-800-1(6) , Bloomsbury Children) Bloomsbury Publishing.

Boyd, David. Pearl Harbor. Ng, Drew, illus. 2007. 48p. (J). lib. bdg. 23.08 (***978-1-4242-1640-6(0)***) Fitzgerald Bks.

Boyd, Kate & Brixton, Iris. The Quercus Quest. 2006. 159p. pap. 12.72 (978-1-4116-8843-8(0)) Lulu.com.

Boykin, Edwina. To the Boy I Shared with the Crabapple Tree. Tinsley, Arnold, ed. Blevins, Shannon, illus. 1999. 105p. (YA). pap. (978-0-9669230-0-1(6)) Ebo Ink.

Boyle, Amanda N. The Dream. 2007. 59p. per. 8.95 (***978-1-59824-506-6(6)***) E-BookTime LLC.

Boyne, John. The Boy in the Striped Pajamas. (YA). (gr. 7). 2007. 240p. pap. 8.99 (***978-0-385-75153-7(2)***); 2006. 224p. 15.95 (978-0-385-75106-3(0)); 2006. 224p. lib. bdg. 17.99 (978-0-385-75107-0(9)) Random Hse. Children's Bks. (Fickling, David Bks.).

—The Boy in the Striped Pyjamas. l.t. ed. 2007. (Isis Softcover Ser.). 208p. 27.99 (***978-0-7531-7651-1(3)***) ISIS Large Print Bks. GBR. *Dist:* Ulverscroft Large Print Bks., Ltd.

—The Boy in the Striped Pyjamas. 2006. 224p. (J). (***978-0-385-60940-1(X)*** , David Fickling Books) Random Hse. Children's Bks.

Boynton, Sandra. Your Personal Penguin. 2006. (Illus.). 24p. (J). bds. 6.95 (978-0-7611-4372-7(6)) Workman Publishing Co., Inc.

Boza, Eduardo Robles. Mi Amiga se Parta Mal. 2000. Tr. of My Friend Misbehaves. (SPA.). (J). 4.95 (978-968-419-980-4(5)) Grijalbo, Editorial MEX. *Dist:* AIMS International Bks., Inc.

Bradbury, Martha Todd. My Friend Christopher Is Dead. 2005. 48p. pap. 12.95 (978-1-4137-6908-1(X)) PublishAmerica, Inc.

Bradby, Marie. Some Friend. 2007. 240p. (J). pap. 5.99 (978-1-4169-3452-3(9) , Aladdin) Simon & Schuster Children's Publishing.

—Some Friend. Frederick, Brooks, illus. 2004. 240p. (J). 15.95 (978-0-689-85615-0(6) , Atheneum/Richard Jackson Bks.) Simon & Schuster Children's Publishing.

Braddock, Paige. Jane's World, Vol. 4. 2006. (Illus.). 160p. pap. 15.00 (978-0-9766707-3-5(9)) Girl Twirl Comics.

Bradley, Alex. 24 Girls in 7 Days (Splashproof Ed) 2007. 1p. (YA). (gr. 7). pap. 5.99 (978-0-14-240834-6(4) , Puffin) Penguin Group (USA) Inc.

Bradley, Kimberly Brubaker. The Lacemaker & the Princess. 2007. 208p. (J). (gr. 3-7). 16.99 (978-1-4169-1920-9(1) , McElderry, Margaret K.) Simon & Schuster Children's Publishing.

Brager, Allison. Off-Colored Rainbows. 2005. 64p. pap. 12.95 (978-1-4241-0267-9(7)) PublishAmerica, Inc.

Bramwell, Wendie & Normand, Bridgid. Rhymitis. Kim, Julie J., tr. Kim, Julie J., illus. 2003. 32p. (J). pap. (978-0-9741388-8-6(6)) Committee for Children.

Bramwell, Wendie, et al. The Friendship Alphabet. Ziegler, Michael, illus. Ziegler, Michael, photos by. 2003. 32p. (J). pap. (978-0-9741388-3-1(5)) Committee for Children.

Brandon, Barbara. Homer the H Shaped Tree. 2005. (J). 8.00 (978-0-9776480-5-4(2) , MSP) Main St Publishing, Inc.

Brashares, Ann. Forever in Blue: The Fourth Summer of the Sisterhood. (Sisterhood of Traveling Pants Ser.). (YA). (gr. 7). 2008. 416p. pap. 9.99 (***978-0-385-73401-1(8)***); 2007. 400p. 18.99 (978-0-385-72936-9(7)); 2007. 400p. lib. bdg. 21.99 (978-0-385-90413-1(4)) Random Hse. Children's Bks. (Delacorte Bks. for Young Readers).

—Girls in Pants. 2006. (Sisterhood of Traveling Pants Ser.: Bk. 3). 368p. (YA). (gr. 7 up). reprint ed. pap. 8.95 (978-0-553-37593-0(8) , Delacorte Bks. for Young Readers) Random Hse. Children's Bks.

—Girls in Pants: The Third Summer of the Sisterhood. (Sisterhood of Traveling Pants Ser.: Bk. 3). (YA). (gr. 7 up). 2007. 416p. mass mkt. 6.99 (***978-0-553-49504-1(6)*** , Dell Books for Young Readers); 2005. 352p. 16.95 (978-0-385-72935-2(9) , Delacorte Bks. for Young Readers); 2005. 352p. lib. bdg. 18.99 (978-0-385-90919-8(5) , Delacorte Bks. for Young Readers) Random Hse. Children's Bks.

—Girls in Pants: The Third Summer of the Sisterhood. l.t. ed. 2005. (Sisterhood of Traveling Pants Ser. : Bk. 3). 405p. (YA). 23.95 (978-0-7862-7264-8(3) , Large Print Pr.) Thorndike Pr.

—The Second Summer of the Sisterhood. 2003. (Sisterhood of Traveling Pants Ser.: Bk. 2). 400p. (YA). (gr. 7 up). 15.95 (978-0-385-72934-5(0) , Delacorte Bks. for Young Readers) Random Hse. Children's Bks.

—Second Summer of the Sisterhood. 2003. (Sisterhood of Traveling Pants Ser.: Bk. 2). 384p. (YA). (gr. 7 up). lib. bdg. 17.99 (978-0-385-90852-8(0) , Delacorte Bks. for Young Readers) Random Hse. Children's Bks.

—The Sisterhood of the Traveling Pants. (Sisterhood of Traveling Pants Ser.: Bk. 1). (YA). (gr. 7 up). 2004. 352p. mass mkt. 6.99 (978-0-440-22970-4(7) , Dell Books for Young Readers); 2001. 320p. 15.95 (978-0-385-72933-8(2) , Delacorte Bks. for Young Readers) Random Hse. Children's Bks.

—The Sisterhood of the Traveling Pants. 2003. (Sisterhood of Traveling Pants Ser. : Bk. 1). (YA). (gr. 7 up). lib. bdg. 17.60 (978-0-613-60397-3(4)) Tandem Library Bks.

—Sisterhood of the Traveling Pants. 2003. (Sisterhood of Traveling Pants Ser.: Bk. 1). 336p. (YA). (gr. 7 up). pap. 8.95 (978-0-385-73058-7(6) , Delacorte Bks. for Young Readers) Random Hse. Children's Bks.

—The Sisterhood of the Traveling Pants. 2003. (Sisterhood of Traveling Pants Ser. : Bk. 1). 294p. (YA). (gr. 7 up). reprint ed. 15.00 (978-0-7567-6771-6(7)) DIANE Publishing Co.

—The Sisterhood of the Traveling Pants. movie tie-in ed. 2005. (Sisterhood of Traveling Pants Ser.: Bk. 1). (Illus.). 352p. (YA). (gr. 7 up). mass mkt. 6.99 (978-0-553-49479-2(1) , Dell Books for Young Readers) Random Hse. Children's Bks.

—The Sisterhood of the Traveling Pants. l.t. ed. 2002. (Sisterhood of Traveling Pants Ser. : Bk. 1). 344p. (YA). 24.95 (978-0-7862-3966-5(2)) Thomson Gale.

Brashares, Ann & Random House Staff. Keep in Touch: Letters, Notes, & More from the Sisterhood of the Traveling Pants. movie tie-in ed. 2005. (Illus.). 144p. (YA). (gr. 7). pap. 7.95 (978-0-553-37608-1(X) , Delacorte Bks. for Young Readers) Random Hse. Children's Bks.

Brashear Hopper, Celia. The Merry Adventures of Blade & Friends. 2007. (YA). lib. bdg. 26.95 (***978-0-9795460-1-3(X)***) Creative Bk. Pubs.

Bray, Jeannine D. Rabbie. Kenyatta, Imani, ed. Mitchell, Denise B., illus. 1998. 56p. (J). (gr. k-6). 14.95 (978-1-886580-68-8(5)) Pinnacle-Syatt Pubns.

Bray, Libba. A Great & Terrible Beauty. 2005. 403p. (YA). (gr. 8-12). per. 15.60 (978-0-606-33978-0(7)) Tandem Library Bks.

Braybrooks, Ann. Just Be Nice... & Help a Friend! 2000. (Disney Ser.). (Illus.). 24p. (J). (ps-k). pap. 3.29 (978-0-307-13312-0(5) , 13312, Golden Bks.) Random Hse. Children's Bks.

Breckenridge, Trula & Breckenridge, Scott. Squiggly the Roach. Breckenridge, Trula & Breckenridge, Scott, illus. 2004. (J). per. (978-0-9749480-6-5(3) , MSPpress) Mama Specific Productions.

Brennan, Herbie. The Purple Emperor. 2006. (Faerie Wars Chronicles Ser.). 432p. (J). pap. 8.95 (978-1-58234-746-2(8) , Bloomsbury Children) Bloomsbury Publishing.

Brenner, Barbara & Hooks, William H. Lion & Lamb Step Out. Degen, Bruce, illus. 1998. (Bank Street Reader Collection). 48p. (J). (gr. 2-4). lib. bdg. 22.60 (978-0-8368-1772-0(9)) Stevens, Gareth Inc.

—Ups & Downs with Lion & Lamb. Degen, Bruce, illus. 1999. (Bank Street Reader Collection). 48p. (J). (gr. 2-4). lib. bdg. 22.60 (978-0-8368-1783-6(4)) Stevens, Gareth Inc.

Brewer, Dottie A. Saul the Pelican. Naenix, Robin, illus. 2004. 30p. (J). 4.95 (978-0-9707945-9-8(2)) Billion $ Baby Pubns.

E F G

Brian, James. Catkid Book #4 Three's A Crowd. 2008. 96p. pap. 3.99 (****978-0-439-88857-8(3)*** , Scholastic Paperbacks) Scholastic, Inc.

Brian, Kate. Fake Boyfriend. 2007. 272p. (YA). (gr. 9 up). 16.99 (****978-1-4169-1367-2(X))*** Simon & Schuster Children's Publishing.

—Inner Circle. 2007. (Private Ser.). 224p. (YA). (gr. 9 up). pap. 9.99 (****978-1-4169-5041-7(9)*** , Simon Pulse) Simon & Schuster Children's Publishing.

—Invitation Only. 2006. (Private Ser.). 272p. (YA). (gr. 9 up). pap. 8.99 (978-1-4169-1874-5(4) , Simon Pulse) Simon & Schuster Children's Publishing.

—Lucky T. 2007. 304p. (YA). (gr. 9 up). pap. 8.99 (978-1-4169-3545-2(2) , Simon Pulse) Simon & Schuster Children's Publishing.

—Private. 2006. (Private Ser.). 240p. (YA). pap. 8.99 (978-1-4169-1873-8(6) , Simon Pulse) Simon & Schuster Children's Publishing.

—The V Club: Wanna Join? 2004. 288p. (YA). 14.95 (978-0-689-86764-4(6)) Simon & Schuster Children's Publishing.

Bridgers, Sue E. Keeping Christina. 1998. 290p. reprint ed. lib. bdg. 29.95 (978-0-7351-0042-8(X)) Replica Bks.

Bridwell, Norman. The Big Red Reader: The Egg Hunt. Bridwell, Norman, illus. 2002. (Big Red Readers Ser.). (Illus.). (J). 11.91 (978-0-7587-9315-7(4)) Book Wholesalers, Inc.

—Clifford & His Friends. 2007. 48p. (J). pap. 4.99 (****978-0-545-00064-2(5)*** , Cartwheel Bks.) Scholastic, Inc.

—Clifford Makes a Friend. Bridwell, Norman, illus. 2002. (Clifford, the Big Red Dog Ser.). (Illus.). (J). 11.91 (978-0-7587-5017-4(X)) Book Wholesalers, Inc.

—Clifford Makes a Friend. 2004. 32p. (J). lib. bdg. 15.00 (978-1-59054-547-8(8)) Fitzgerald Bks.

—Clifford Makes a Friend. Bridwell, Norman, illus. 1998. (Clifford, the Big Red Dog Ser.). (Illus.). 32p. (J). (gr. k-2). pap. 3.99 (978-0-590-37930-4(5)) Scholastic, Inc.

—Clifford Makes a Friend. 1998. (Illus.). (J). (ps-ps). lib. bdg. 11.80 (978-0-613-11422-6(1)) Tandem Library Bks.

Bridwell, Norman. Cliffords Pals Audio. 2008. pap. 9.95 (****978-0-545-05247-4(5)*** , Scholastic) Scholastic, Inc.

Bridwell, Norman & Fry, Sonali. Take Me to School with You! Thompson Brothers Staff, illus. 2002. (Clifford, the Big Red Dog Ser.). 16p. (J). pap. 3.99 (978-0-439-39454-3(6)) Scholastic, Inc.

Bright, J. E. Follow Your Heart: Your Best Friend's Boyfriend. 2006. 240p. (J). pap. 4.99 (978-0-439-79140-3(5) , Scholastic Paperbacks) Scholastic, Inc.

Brightwood, Laura, illus. Red Hat / Blue Hat. Brightwood, Laura, . 2006. (J). (978-0-9779290-5-4(1)) 3-C Institute for Social Development.

Brill, Sarah. Glory. 2002. 140p. pap. 10.95 (978-1-876756-25-3(X)) Spinifex Pr. AUS. *Dist:* Independent Pubs. Group.

—Glory. 2002. (gr. 7-12). lib. bdg. 19.90 (978-0-613-85840-3(9)) Tandem Library Bks.

Brimner, Larry Dane. Aggie & Will. Thornburgh, Rebecca McKillip, illus. (Rookie Reader Skill Set Ser.). 32p. (J). 1999. (gr. k-2). pap. 4.95 (978-0-516-26409-7(5)); 1998. (gr. 1-2). 19.50 (978-0-516-20754-4(7)) Scholastic Library Publishing. (Children's Pr.).

—Aggie & Will. Thornburgh, Rebecca McKillip, illus. 1999. 29p. (J). (gr. k-3). lib. bdg. 12.95 (978-0-613-37258-9(1)) Tandem Library Bks.

—Here Comes Trouble. Torrecilla, Pablo, illus. 2002. (Rookie Reader Skill Set Ser.). 32p. (J). (gr. k-2). pap. 4.95 (978-0-516-25968-0(7) , Children's Pr.) Scholastic Library Publishing.

—Here Comes Trouble. 2001. (gr. k-3). lib. bdg. 12.95 (978-0-613-54535-8(4)) Tandem Library Bks.

—Here Comes Trouble Level B. Torrecilla, Pablo, illus. 2001. (Rookie Readers Ser.). 32p. (J). (gr. 1-2). 19.50 (978-0-516-22220-2(1) , Children's Pr.) Scholastic Library Publishing.

—The New Kid. Tripp, Christine, illus. 2003. (Rookie Choices Ser.). (gr. 1-2). pap. 5.95 (978-0-516-27835-3(5)); 32p. (J). 20.50 (978-0-516-22546-3(4)) Scholastic Library Publishing. (Children's Pr.).

—New Kid. 2003. (gr. k-3). lib. bdg. 14.10 (978-0-613-67653-3(X)) Tandem Library Bks.

Brinkerhoff, Shirley. Balancing Act. 1998. (Nikki Sheridan Ser.: Vol. 4). 208p. (J). (gr. 9-12). pap. 5.99 (978-1-56179-559-8(3)) Bethany Hse. Pubs.

Brinkley, Inez. Rainbows & Promises. 2006. 43p. (J). 15.98 (978-1-4116-9579-5(8)) Lulu.com.

Broach, Elise. Shakespeare's Secret. rev. ed. 2005. (Illus.). 256p. (J). 16.95 (978-0-8050-7387-4(6) , Holt, Henry & Co. Bks. For Young Readers) Holt, Henry & Co.

Brockmann, Carolee. Going for Great. 2000. (Illus.). (J). (978-0-606-18355-0(8)); 1999. (gr. 5-8). lib. bdg. 14.10 (978-0-613-25345-1(0)) Tandem Library Bks.

Brokaw, Nancy Steele. Leaving Emma. 1999. 144p. (J). (gr. 4-6). tchr. ed. 15.00 (978-0-395-90699-6(7) , Clarion Bks.) Houghton Mifflin Co. Trade & Reference Div.

Brooke, Lauren. Chestnut Hill. 2006. 208p. (J). pap. 4.99 (978-0-439-73857-6(1) , Scholastic Paperbacks) Scholastic, Inc.

Brooke, Samantha. A Pony Tale. 2008. 32p. (J). (ps-k). pap. 3.99 (****978-0-448-44719-3(3)*** , Grosset & Dunlap) Penguin Group (USA) Inc.

Brooks, Amy. Princess Polly's Playmates. 2004. reprint ed. pap. 19.95 (978-1-4191-4300-7(X)); pap. 1.99 (978-1-4192-4300-4(4)) Kessinger Publishing, LLC.

Brooks, Amy. Randy & Her Friends. 2006. 32.99 (****978-1-4280-3379-5(3));*** pap. 26.99 (****978-1-4280-3383-2(1))*** IndyPublish.com.

Brooks, Bertha. Somewhere on the Rainbow. 2001. 32p. (J). (gr. 3-5). (978-1-58374-032-3(5)) Chicago Spectrum Pr.

Brooks, Bruce. All That Remains. 2002. 176p. (YA). (gr. 7 up). pap. 6.99 (978-0-689-83442-4(X) , Simon Pulse) Simon & Schuster Children's Publishing.

—The Moves Make the Man. 3rd ed. (J). pap. 3.95 (978-0-13-800079-0(4)) Prentice Hall (Schl. Div.).

Brooks, Hindi. Computer Pals: A Short Comedy. 1998. (Illus.). 8p. pap. 3.50 (978-0-88680-452-7(3) , C4523) Clark, I. E. Pubns.

Brooks, Jillian. The Makeover. 2003. 157p. (J). (978-0-439-35494-3(3)) Scholastic, Inc.

Brooks, Kevin. Martyn Pig. 240p. (J). 2003. pap. 6.99 (978-0-439-50752-3(9)); 2002. (gr. 5 up). pap. 16.95 (978-0-439-29595-6(5) , Chicken Hse., The) Scholastic, Inc.

—Martyn Pig. 2003. (gr. 7-12). lib. bdg. 15.30 (978-0-613-64813-4(7)) Tandem Library Bks.

Brooks, Martha. Being with Henry. 1999. (J). (978-0-88899-377-9(3)) Douglas & McIntyre, Ltd.

—Being with Henry. pap. 8.95 (978-0-88899-502-5(4)) Groundwood Bks. CAN. *Dist:* Transition Vendor.

Brooks, Ron. Oscar y la Gata de Medianoche. 2nd ed. 2002. (Rosa y Manzana Ser.). (SPA.). 32p. (J). (978-84-89804-05-0(2)) Loguez Ediciones ESP. *Dist:* Lectorum Pubns., Inc.

Brooks, Walter R. Freddy & the Popinjay. Wiese, Kurt, illus. 2001. 244p. (J). (gr. 4-7). 23.95 (978-1-58567-134-2(7)) Overlook Pr., The.

Broome, Errol. Missing Mem. 2003. (gr. 3-6). lib. bdg. 13.00 (978-0-613-61801-4(7)) Tandem Library Bks.

Brothers Grimm Staff. Hansel & Gretel/Hansel y Gretel. 2004. (Illus.). (J). (978-1-933530-14-7(6)) Bingo Bks., Inc.

Brouillet, Chrystine. Mon Amie Clémentine. 2003. (Premier Roman Ser.). (FRE.). 64p. (J). (gr. 2-5). pap. (978-2-89021-313-5(7)) Diffusion du livre Mirabel.

Brouillet, Chrystine & Gagnon, Nathalie. La Disparution de Baffuto. 2000. (Roman Jeunesse Ser.). 96p. (J). (gr. 4-7). pap. (978-2-89021-392-0(7)) Diffusion du livre Mirabel.

Brouwer, Sigmund. The Volcano of Doom. 2002. (Accidental Detectives). 144p. (J). pap. 5.99 (978-0-7642-2564-2(2)) Bethany Hse. Pubs.

—Volcano of Doom. 2002. (gr. 3-6). lib. bdg. 14.15 (978-0-613-87242-3(8)) Tandem Library Bks.

Brown, Ann. The Portal & the Key. 2001. 128p. (gr. 4-7). pap. 9.95 (978-0-595-15850-8(1) , Writer's Showcase Pr.) iUniverse, Inc.

Brown, Farwell Abbie. John of the Woods. 2006. 32.99 (****978-1-4280-1771-9(2))*** IndyPublish.com.

Brown, Gladys M. Home Away from Home. 2005. 36p. pap. 6.95 (978-1-4116-3026-0(2)) Lulu.com.

Brown, J. A. Busy Bee. Knight, Paula, illus. 2003. (Funny Faces Ser.). 10p. (J). bds. 3.95 (978-1-58925-715-3(4) , tiger tales) ME Media LLC.

Brown, Marc. Arthur & the Double Dare. 2002. (Arthur Chapter Bks.: Bk. 25). (Illus.). (J). 11.70 (978-0-7587-9423-9(1)) Book Wholesalers, Inc.

—Arthur & the Double Dare. Brown, Marc, illus. 2002. (Arthur Chapter Bks. : Bk. 25). (Illus.). 64p. (J). (gr. 2-4). 13.95 (978-0-316-12264-1(5)); pap. 4.25 (978-0-316-12087-6(1)) Little, Brown Bks. for Young Readers.

—Arthur & the Double Dare. 2002. (Arthur Chapter Bks.: Bk. 25). (gr. k-3). lib. bdg. 12.10 (978-0-613-50586-4(7)) Tandem Library Bks.

—Arthur & the Perfect Brother. ed. 2000. (Arthur Chapter Bks. : Bk. 21). (J). pap. 3.95 (978-0-316-12108-8(8)) Little, Brown Bks. for Young Readers.

—Arthur & the Perfect Brother. Brown, Marc, illus. 21st ed. 2000. (Arthur Chapter Bks. : Bk. 21). (Illus.). 64p. (J). (gr. 2-4). pap. 4.25 (978-0-316-12226-9(2)) Little, Brown Bks. for Young Readers.

—Arthur & the Perfect Brother. 2000. (Illus.). (J). 54p. (ps-ps). lib. bdg. 11.80 (978-0-613-24245-5(9)); (Arthur Chapter Bks.: Bk. 21). (gr. 3-6). 10.75 (978-0-606-18252-2(7)) Tandem Library Bks.

—Arthur Jumps into Fall. 2006. (Illus.). 24p. (J). (ps-1). mass mkt. 3.99 (978-0-316-05775-2(4)) Little Brown & Co.

—Arthur Loses a Friend. 2006. (Illus.). 24p. (J). (gr. 1-3). pap. 3.99 (978-0-375-82974-1(1)); lib. bdg. 11.99 (978-0-375-92974-8(6)) Random Hse. Children's Bks. (Random Hse. Bks. for Young Readers).

—Arthur Rocks with Binky. 11th ed. 1998. (Arthur Chapter Bks. : Bk. 11). (Illus.). 64p. (J). (gr. 2-4). pap. 4.25 (978-0-316-11543-8(6)) Little, Brown Bks. for Young Readers.

—Arthur's Friendship Treasury: Three Arthur Adventures in One Volume. Brown, Marc, illus. 2002. (Arthur Adventure Ser.). (Illus.). 112p. (J). (ps-3). 18.95 (978-0-316-12588-8(1)) Little, Brown Bks. for Young Readers.

—Arthur's Homework. 2004. (Arthur's 8 x 8 Bks.). (Illus.). 24p. (J). (ps-3). pap. 3.99 (978-0-316-73387-8(3)) Little, Brown Bks. for Young Readers.

—Arthur's Mystery Babysitter. Brown, Marc, illus. 2004. (Arthur's 8 x 8 Bks.). (Illus.). 24p. (J). (ps-3). pap. 3.99 (978-0-316-73394-6(6) , Tingley, Megan Bks.) Little, Brown Bks. for Young Readers.

—Binky Rules. 2000. (Arthur Chapter Bks.: Bk. 24). (J). pap. 3.95 (978-0-316-12244-3(0)) Little Brown & Co.

—Cumpleanos de Arturo. 2000. (SPA.). (gr. k-3). lib. bdg. 15.25 (978-0-613-28287-1(6)) Tandem Library Bks.

—El Cumpleaños de Arturo. Sarfatti, Esther, tr. from ENG. 2000. (Arthur Adventure Ser.). (SPA., Illus.). (J). (ps-3). pap. 6.95 (978-1-880507-78-0(1) , LC7609) Lectorum Pubns., Inc.

—Francine, Believe It or Not! unabr. ed. 2004. (Arthur Chapter Bks.: Bk. 14). 58p. (J). (gr. 2-4). pap. 17.00 incl. audio (978-0-8072-0345-3(9) , Listening Library) Random Hse. Audio Publishing Group.

—Francine, Believe It or Not! 1999. (Arthur Chapter Bks.: Bk. 14). (J). (gr. 3-6). 11.05 (978-0-606-17021-5(9)) Tandem Library Bks.

—The World of Arthur & Friends. 2004. (Illus.). 208p. (J). (ps-1). 10.99 (978-0-316-01045-0(6)) Little Brown & Co.

Brown, Mick, et al. Bantam. Gelsthorpe, Loraine & Rex, Sue, eds. 2002. 144p. (J). pap. 14.95 (978-1-86368-373-9(9)) Fremantle Pr. AUS. *Dist:* International Specialized Bk. Services.

Brown, Sally. Alexandra's Travel Adventure: Making Friends in Mexico. Lyons, Deborah, illus. 2005. 32p. (J). pap. 9.95 (978-1-57860-232-2(7)) Emmis Bks.

Brown, Tena L. Tena, Joshua & Friends, 22 vols., Set. Brown, Tena L., illus. Incl. Always, Forever & Five Days Are 5 Big Words. spiral bd. 5.00 (978-1-890925-13-0(6)); Be Careful What You Do : Your Friends Are Always Watching You. spiral bd. 5.00 (978-1-890925-07-9(1)); Clean Your Room. spiral bd. 5.00 (978-1-890925-19-2(5)); Eat Your Veggies. spiral bd. 5.00 (978-1-890925-20-8(9)); Family Comes 1st Is What We Say : Family Comes 1st Each & Everyday. spiral bd. 5.00 (978-1-890925-04-8(7)); Follow Your Dreams to the Stars. spiral bd. 5.00 (978-1-890925-14-7(4)); I Am Me. spiral bd. 5.00 (978-1-890925-15-4(2)); It Is Okay to Be #1. spiral bd. 5.00 (978-1-890925-18-5(7)); It Is Okay to Like You & Everything That You Do : No One Is a Misfit. spiral bd. 5.00 (978-1-890925-11-6(X)); Just Say No & Turn & Walk Away. spiral bd. 5.00 (978-1-890925-17-8(9)); Learn Reading, Writing & Arithmetic : You Cannot Get over If You Think That You Are Slick. spiral bd. 5.00 (978-1-890925-12-3(8)); My 1-2-3's Say Be Kind to You & Me. spiral bd. 5.00 (978-1-890925-08-6(X)); My A-B-Cs Say Be Kind to You & Me. spiral bd. 5.00 (978-1-890925-09-3(8)); No One Is Perfect : Just Be the Best That You Can Be. spiral bd. 5.00 (978-1-890925-06-2(3)); Take Care of Your Body. spiral bd. 5.00 (978-1-890925-10-9(1)); Tena & Joshua Friends 'til the End. spiral bd. 5.00 (978-1-890925-02-4(0)); Tena Gets Help from Her Friend Joshua. per. 5.00 (978-1-890925-01-7(2)); Traffic Light Name Game. spiral bd. 5.00 (978-1-890925-21-5(7)); Trust, Honor & Loyalty - That Is What Friends Are Made Of. spiral bd. 5.00 (978-1-890925-03-1(9)); Use Your Brain for Your Present, Future & Past. spiral bd. 5.00 (978-1-890925-16-1(0)); We Are Growing up Too Fast. spiral bd. 5.00 (978-1-890925-05-5(5)); When Will I Be 1 Year Old. spiral bd. 5.00 (978-1-890925-22-2(5)); (Illus.). 24p. (J). (ps-4). 1997. 125.00 (978-1-890925-00-0(4)) Stori Tyme Huggggs, Inc.

Brown, Terry, creator. Stranger Online. 2005. (Todays-Girls.com Ser.: Vol. 1). 144p. (J). pap. 5.99 (978-1-4003-0755-5(4)) Nelson, Thomas Inc.

Browne, Susan Chalker. Goodness Gracious, Gulliver Mulligan. Nugent, Cynthia, illus. 2004. 32p. (J). pap. 6.95 (978-1-55192-679-7(2)) Raincoast Bk. Distribution CAN. *Dist:* Perseus Distribution.

Brownlee, Browne. Bad Breath. 2007. 108p. 16.95 (****978-1-4241-5487-6(1))*** PublishAmerica, Inc.

Brownlow, Brooke. The Magic of Old Oak Hill. 2005. 48p. pap. 12.95 (978-1-4241-0223-5(5)) PublishAmerica, Inc.

Brownlow, Mike. Mickey Moonbeam. Brownlow, Mike, illus. 2006. (Illus.). 32p. (J). 16.95 (978-1-58234-704-2(2) , Bloomsbury Children) Bloomsbury Publishing.

Brownrigg, Sheri. All Tutus Should Be Pink. Johnson, Meredith, illus. 2004. 32p. (J). lib. bdg. 15.00 (978-1-59054-371-9(8)) Fitzgerald Bks.

—Best Friends Wear Pink Tutus. Johnson, Meredith, illus. 2004. 32p. (J). lib. bdg. 15.00 (978-1-59054-377-1(7)) Fitzgerald Bks.

Bruce, Lisa. Fran's Friend. Beardshaw, Rosalind, illus. 2003. 32p. (J). (ps-1). 15.95 (978-1-58234-777-6(8) , Bloomsbury Children) Bloomsbury Publishing.

Bruce, Robert D. Petey Putt-Putt & His Friends. Bruce, Britta, ed. 1999. (Illus.). 20p. (J). 5.95 (978-0-9664248-9-8(1)) Sloane Pubns.

Bruce, Sheilah. Everybody Wins! Billin-Frye, Paige, illus. 2001. (Math Matters Ser.). 32p. (J). (gr. 1-3). pap. 4.95 (978-1-57565-101-9(7)) Kane Pr., The.

—Everybody Wins! 2001. (gr. k-3). lib. bdg. 12.95 (978-0-613-39315-7(5)) Tandem Library Bks.

Bruchac, Joseph. Hidden Roots. 2006. 160p. (J). pap. 5.99 (978-0-439-35359-5(9) , Scholastic Paperbacks) Scholastic, Inc.

Bruel, Robert O. Bob & Otto. Bruel, Nick, illus. 2007. 32p. (J). (ps-1). 15.95 (978-1-59643-203-1(9)) Roaring Brook Pr.

Brugman, Alyssa. Being Bindy. 2006. 208p. (YA). (gr. 7). 15.95 (978-0-385-73294-9(5)); lib. bdg. 17.99 (978-0-385-90315-8(4)) Random Hse. Children's Bks. (Delacorte Bks. for Young Readers).

—Walking Naked. 2004. 192p. (YA). (gr. 7). 15.95 (978-0-385-73115-7(9) , Delacorte Bks. for Young Readers) Random Hse. Children's Bks.

Bruna, Dick. Miffy & Melanie Storybook. 2000. (Miffy Ser.). (Illus.). 28p. (J). (ps-k). 4.95 (978-1-56836-305-9(2)) Kodansha America, Inc.

—Miffy's Happy New Year. 2004. (Illus.). 24p. (J). pap. 3.99 (978-1-59226-233-5(3)) Big Tent Entertainment, Inc.

Bruzzone, Catherine. A Friendship in French & English. Morton, Lone, illus. 1998. (Pen Pals Ser.). (FRE.). 28p. (J). (gr. 4-7). 14.95 (978-0-8442-1375-0(6) , 13756, Passport Bks.) McGraw-Hill Trade.

—A Spanish & English Friendship. Morton, Lone, illus. 1998. (Pen Pals Ser.). 28p. (J). (gr. 4-7). 14.95 (978-0-8442-7501-7(8) , 75018) McGraw-Hill/Contemporary.

Bryant, Annie. Bad News/Good News. 2004. (Beacon Street Girls Ser.). 236p. (J). 7.99 (978-0-9746587-0-4(7) , Beacon Street Girls) B*tween Productions, Inc.

—Fashion Frenzy. (Beacon Street Girls Ser.: Bk. 9). 232p. (YA). pap. 7.99 (978-1-933566-02-3(7) , Beacon Street Girls) B*tween Productions, Inc.

—Ghost Town. 2007. (Beacon Street Girls Ser.: Bk. 11). 250p. (J). (gr. 4-8). pap. 7.10 (****978-1-933566-09-2(4))*** B*tween Productions, Inc.

—Just Kidding. 2007. (Beacon Street Girls Ser.: Bk. 10). 270p. (YA). pap. 7.99 (****978-1-933566-07-8(8))*** B*tween Productions, Inc.

—Maeve on the Red Carpet. 2007. 240p. pap. 7.10 (****978-1-933566-08-5(6))*** B*tween Productions, Inc.

Bryant, Annie. Worst Enemies/Best Friends. 2004. (Beacon Street Girls Ser.). 232p. (J). 7.99 (978-0-9746587-6-6(6) , Beacon Street Girls) B*tween Productions, Inc.

Bryant, Bonnie. Carole: The Inside Story. 1999. (J). (978-0-606-19288-0(3)) Tandem Library Bks.

—Conformation Faults. 1999. (Pine Hollow Ser.: No. 5). (YA). (gr. 7 up). (978-0-606-18958-3(0)) Tandem Library Bks.

—Course of Action. 1999. (Pine Hollow Ser.: No. 8). (YA). (gr. 7 up). (978-0-606-18959-0(9)) Tandem Library Bks.

—Horse Crazy. 2007. (Saddle Club Ser.: No. 1). 144p. (J). (gr. 4-7). lib. bdg. 11.99 (978-0-385-90417-9(7) , Yearling) Random Hse. Children's Bks.

—Horse Play. 2007. (Saddle Club Ser.: No. 7). 144p. (J). (gr. 4-6). lib. bdg. 11.99 (****978-0-385-90423-0(1)*** , Yearling) Random Hse. Children's Bks.

—Horse Power. 2007. (Saddle Club Ser.: No. 4). 144p. (J). (gr. 4-6). lib. bdg. 11.99 (978-0-385-90420-9(7) , Yearling) Random Hse. Children's Bks.

—Horse Sense. 2007. (Saddle Club Ser.: No. 3). 144p. (J). (gr. 4-7). lib. bdg. 11.99 (978-0-385-90419-3(3) , Yearling) Random Hse. Children's Bks.

—Horse Show. 2007. (Saddle Club Ser.: No. 8). 160p. (J). (gr. 4-6). lib. bdg. 11.99 (****978-0-385-90424-7(X)*** , Yearling) Random Hse. Children's Bks.

—Horse Shy. 2007. (Saddle Club Ser.: No. 2). 144p. (J). (gr. 4-6). lib. bdg. 11.99 (978-0-385-90418-6(5) , Yearling) Random Hse. Children's Bks.

—Penalty Points. 1999. (Pine Hollow Ser.: No. 7). (YA). (gr. 7 up). (978-0-606-18964-4(5)) Tandem Library Bks.

—Riding to Win. 1999. (Pine Hollow Ser.: No. 9). (YA). (gr. 7 up). (978-0-606-19287-3(5)) Tandem Library Bks.

—Rodeo Rider. 2008. (Saddle Club(R) Ser.). 144p. (J). (gr. 4-7). lib. bdg. 11.99 (****978-0-385-90550-3(5)*** , Yearling) Random Hse. Children's Bks.

—Shying at Trouble. 1999. (Pine Hollow Ser.: No. 6). (YA). (gr. 7 up). (978-0-606-18967-5(X)) Tandem Library Bks.

—Stevie: The Inside Story. 1999. (978-0-606-17154-0(1)) Tandem Library Bks.

—Trail Mates. 2007. (Saddle Club Ser.: No. 5). 144p. (J). (gr. 4-6). lib. bdg. 11.99 (978-0-385-90421-6(5) , Yearling) Random Hse. Children's Bks.

Bryant, Megan E. Be My Valentine! 2004. (Strawberry Shortcake Ser.). (Illus.). 32p. (J). (ps-2). pap. 3.99 (978-0-448-43641-8(8) , Grosset & Dunlap) Penguin Group (USA) Inc.

—Berry Big Storm. 2003. (gr. k-3). lib. bdg. 11.80 (978-0-613-64021-3(7)) Tandem Library Bks.

—The Friendship Trip No. 3: Friendship Club. Thomas, Laura, illus. 2007. (Strawberry Shortcake Ser.). 64p. (J). (gr. 1-3). pap. 3.99 (978-0-448-44557-1(3) , Grosset & Dunlap) Penguin Group (USA) Inc.

—Halloween Hideout. Thomas, Laura, illus. 2007. (Strawberry Shortcake Ser.: No. 4). 64p. (J). (gr. 1-3). pap. 3.99 (978-0-448-44558-8(1) , Grosset & Dunlap) Penguin Group (USA) Inc.

—Join the Club! No. 1: Friendship Club. Thomas, Laura, illus. 2007. 64p. (J). pap. 3.99 (978-0-448-44490-1(9) , Grosset & Dunlap) Penguin Group (USA) Inc.

—Paas: The Friendship Egg. 2006. 24p. (J). (ps-1). pap. 3.99 (978-0-448-44137-5(3) , Grosset & Dunlap) Penguin Group (USA) Inc.

—Strawberry Shortcake at the Beach. 2003. (Strawberry Shortcake Ser.). (Illus.). 32p. (J). (ps-2). mass mkt. 3.99 (978-0-448-43187-1(4) , Grosset & Dunlap) Penguin Group (USA) Inc.

—Strawberry Shortcake's World of Friends: 4 Scratch & Sniff Postcards & over 25 Stickers! Workman, Lisa, illus. 2006. (Strawberry Shortcake Ser.). 32p. (J). (ps-2). pap. 4.99 (978-0-448-44101-6(2) , Grosset & Dunlap) Penguin Group (USA) Inc.

Bryant, Megan E. & Thomas, Laura. Secrets & Surprises No. 2: Friendship Club. 2007. (Illus.). 64p. (J). pap. 3.99 (978-0-448-44491-8(7) , Grosset & Dunlap) Penguin Group (USA) Inc.

Bryant, Megan E., et al. Strawberry Shortcake Storybook Treasury. Durk, Jim et al, illus. 2005. (Strawberry Shortcake Ser.). 192p. (J). (ps-2). 10.99 (978-0-448-44303-4(1) , Grosset & Dunlap) Penguin Group (USA) Inc.

Buchanan, Jane. Goodbye, Charley. 2004. (Illus.). 176p. (J). 16.00 (978-0-374-35020-8(5) , Farrar, Straus & Giroux (BYR)) Farrar, Straus & Giroux.

Buchanan, Paul. Friend or Foe. 2000. (gr. 3-6). lib. bdg. 14.15 (978-0-613-72828-7(9)) Tandem Library Bks.

—House Divided. 2001. (gr. 3-6). lib. bdg. 14.15 (978-0-613-72848-5(3)) Tandem Library Bks.

Buchanan, Paul & Randall, Rod. A House Divided, Vol. 20. 2001. (Misadventures of Willie Plummett Ser.: Vol. 20). (Illus.). 128p. (J). (gr. 3-7). 5.99 (978-0-570-07131-0(3)) Concordia Publishing Hse.

Buchanan, Paul & Randall, Rod, contrib. by. Friend or Foe, Vol. 16. 2000. (Misadventures of Willie Plummett Ser.: Vol. 16). 128p. (J). (gr. 3-7). 5.99 (978-0-570-07005-4(8)) Concordia Publishing Hse.

Buchanan, Paul W. Snapshots. 2007. 216p. (J). (gr. 4-7). pap. 8.95 (****978-0-7387-1073-0(3))*** Llewellyn Pubns.

Buchanan, William J. Diablo: The Devil Steer. 2004. 151p. (J). (gr. 6-10). 9.95 (978-0-8263-3139-7(4)) Univ. of New Mexico Pr.

Buckeridge, Anthony. Jennings' Little Hut. l.t. ed. 2005. (Dales Ser.). (Illus.). 272p. (J). 23.99 (978-1-84262-370-1(2)) Magna Large Print Bks. GBR. *Dist:* Ulverscroft Large Print Bks., Ltd.

Buckman, Carole Duncan. Neighbors & Traitors. 2000. (StarMaker Bks.). 81p. (J). (gr. 6-9). pap. 5.50 (978-0-88489-548-0(3)) St. Mary's Pr.

Bullard, Lisa. My Day: Morning, Noon & Night. Wesley, Omarr, illus. 2004. (All about Me Ser.). 24p. (C). (gr. k-1). 21.26 (978-1-4048-0045-8(X)) Picture Window Bks.

Bumble's Sweet Surprise. 2003. (Daisy Board Books Ser.). 10p. (J). bds. 9.95 (978-0-7525-8297-9(6)) Parragon, Inc.

Bunge, Daniela. Cherry Time. Bishop, Kathryn, tr. from GER. Bunge, Daniela, illus. 2007. (Illus.). 40p. (J). (gr. k-2). 16.99 (***978-0-698-40057-3(7)*** , Minedition) Penguin Group (USA) Inc.

Bunting, Eve. The Blue & the Gray. Bittinger, Ned, illus. 2001. 32p. (J). (gr. k-2). pap. 5.99 (978-0-590-60200-6(4)) Scholastic, Inc.

—I Like the Way You Are. O'Brien, John, illus. 2000. 48p. (J). (gr. k-3). tchr. ed. 16.00 (978-0-395-89066-0(7) , Clarion Bks.) Houghton Mifflin Co. Trade & Reference Div.

—My Robot. Fehlau, Dagmar, illus. 2006. (Green Light Readers Level 2 Ser.). 24p. (J). 12.95 (978-0-15-205593-6(2) , Green Light Readers) Harcourt Children's Bks.

—My Robot. Fehlau, Dagmar, illus. 2006. (Green Light Reader Ser.). 24p. (J). pap. 3.95 (978-0-15-205617-9(3)) Harcourt Trade Pubs.

—Snowboarding on Monster Mountain. 2003. (Illus.). 64p. (J). 15.95 (978-0-8126-2704-6(0)) Cricket Bks.

Burchett, Loni R. Bear & Katie in a Day with Friends, Vol. 3. l.t. ed. 2005. (Illus.). 68p. (J). per. 11.95 (978-0-9742815-2-0(2) , bk003) Black Lab Publishing LLC.

Burger, Sharon. Five Amigos: The Mystery of Taboo Island. 2005. 48p. pap. 12.95 (978-1-4137-6300-3(6)) PublishAmerica, Inc.

Burgess, Melvin. The Copper Treasure. Williams, Richard, illus. rev. ed. 2000. 112p. (YA). (gr. 4-7). 15.95 (978-0-8050-6381-3(1) , Holt, Henry & Co. Bks. For Young Readers) Holt, Henry & Co.

—El Fantasma tras la Pared. (SPA.). (J). 8.95 (978-958-04-6483-9(9)) Norma S.A. COL. *Dist:* Distribuidora Norma, Inc.

Burgess, Thornton W. Old Mother West Wind's Animal Friends. 2000. (J). lib. bdg. 21.95 (978-0-88411-779-7(0) , Aeonian Pr.) Amereon LTD.

Burningham, John. Aldo. 2000. (Illus.). 32p. (J). pap. 8.99 (978-0-09-918501-7(6) , Red Fox) Random Hse. Children's Bks. GBR. *Dist:* Trafalgar Square Publishing.

Burton, Margie, et al. Friends. Adams, Alison, ed. 1999. (Early Connections Ser.). 16p. (J). (gr. k-2). pap. 4.50 (978-1-58344-062-9(3)) Benchmark Education Co.

Burton, Martin Nelson. Dear Mr. Leprechaun: Letters from My First Friendship. Hansen, Clint, illus. Tanner, Dean, photos by. 2003. 32p. 17.00 (978-0-9666490-0-0(1)) London Town Pr.

Burton, Rebecca. Leaving Jetty Road. (YA). (gr. 7). 2008. 272p. mass mkt. 6.50 (***978-0-553-49505-8(4)*** , Laurel Leaf); 2006. 256p. 15.95 (978-0-375-83488-2(5) , Knopf Bks. for Young Readers); 2006. 256p. lib. bdg. 17.99 (978-0-375-93488-9(X) , Knopf Bks. for Young Readers) Random Hse. Children's Bks.

Burton, Virginia Lee. La Casita. (SPA., Illus.). (J). (gr. 1-2). pap. 9.95 (978-970-629-050-2(8) , SI6411) Sistemas Tecnicos de Edicion, S.A. de C.V. MEX. *Dist:* AIMS International Bks., Inc., Lectorum Pubns., Inc.

Butcher, Kristin. Cairo Kelly & the Mann. 2002. 176p. (J). (gr. 3-7). pap. 6.95 (978-1-55143-211-3(0)) Orca Bk. Pubs. USA.

Butineau, W. Turning Thirteen. 2005. 165p. pap. 19.95 (978-1-4137-5817-7(7)) PublishAmerica, Inc.

Butler, Berwyn. Dinky the Doorknob: The Adventures of Sir Dinkum Wilhelm, the Third Earl of Surridge. 2005. (J). per. 11.99 (***978-1-933732-02-2(4)*** , Round Rock Chapter Bks.) MidAmerica Publishing Co.

Butler, Berwyn & McClean, Shorty. Dinky the Doorknob. 2006. (J). lib. bdg. 21.95 (***978-1-933732-04-6(0)*** , Round Rock Chapter Bks.) MidAmerica Publishing Co.

Butler, Darren J. The Secret of Crybaby Hollow. 2004. (YA). mass mkt. 6.99 (***978-0-9753367-5-5(4)***) Onstage Publishing, LLC.

Butler, Dori Hillestad. Trading Places with Tank Talbott. 2003. 136p. (J). (gr. 3-6). 15.95 (978-0-8075-1708-6(9)) Whitman, Albert & Co.

Butler, M. Christina. Snow Friends. Macnaughton, Tina, illus. 2005. 28p. (J). (ps-2). 16.00 (978-1-56148-485-0(7)) Good Bks.

Butler, Stephen. The Mouse & the Apple. 2000. (Illus.). 32p. (J). (ps-k). pap. 7.99 (978-0-7112-0856-8(5)) Lincoln, Frances Ltd. GBR. *Dist:* Transition Vendor.

Butterworth, Nick. One Snowy Night, Set. Butterworth, Nick, illus. gif. ed. 2007. (Percy the Park Keeper Ser.). (Illus.). 32p. (J). 22.99 (***978-0-00-720068-9(4)***) HarperCollins Pubs. Ltd. GBR. *Dist:* Independent Pubs. Group.

Butts, Christina. Horse & the Dog A Grand Fairy Tale A. 2006. pap. 15.38 (***978-1-4116-1235-8(3)***) Lulu.com.

Byalick, Marcia. Quit It. 2004. 176p. (J). (gr. 3-7). pap. 5.99 (978-0-440-41865-8(8) , Yearling) Random Hse. Children's Bks.

Byars, Betsy. The Cybil War. l.t. ed. 2003. (LRS Large Print Heritage Ser.). 122p. (J). lib. bdg. 27.95 (978-1-58118-111-1(6)) LRS.

—King of Murder. 2007. (Herculeah Jones Mystery Ser.). 144p. (J). pap. 5.99 (978-0-14-240759-2(3) , Puffin) Penguin Group (USA) Inc.

—The Pinballs. (J). (gr. 4-6). 137p. pap. 4.95 (978-0-8072-1383-4(7)); 137p. pap. 4.95 (978-0-8072-1356-8(X)); 1999. pap. 15.98 incl. audio (978-0-8072-1800-6(6) , JJRH100SP) Random Hse. Audio Publishing Group. (Listening Library).

Byers, Carla Rae. Lucky Little Duck Lessons! The Adventures of Snowflake & Astar. l.t. ed. 2000. Vol. 8. 18p. (gr. 1 up). 7.95 (978-1-930910-05-8(3)) Heyokah Publishing Co.

Byng, Georgia. Molly Moon, Micky Minus, & the Mind Machine. 2007. 416p. (J). (gr. 3-7). 16.99 (***978-0-06-075036-7(7));*** lib. bdg. 17.89 (***978-0-06-075037-4(5)***) HarperCollins Pubs.

Byng, Georgia. Molly Moon's Incredible Book of Hypnotism. 2003. (Illus.). 384p. (J). (gr. 3-7). 16.99 (978-0-06-051406-8(X)); 2003. 135.92 (978-0-06-057217-4(5)); 2004. (Illus.). 400p. (J). reprint ed. pap. 7.99 (978-0-06-051409-9(4) , Harper Trophy) HarperCollins Pubs.

—Molly Moon's Incredible Book of Hypnotism. 2002. (Molly Moon Ser.: Bk. 1). 330p. (J). (gr. 3-7). (978-0-333-98489-5(7) , Macmillan Children's Bks.) Pan Macmillan.

Bynum, Janie. Otis. 2003. (Illus.). 40p. (J). pap. 7.00 (978-0-15-204604-0(6) , Voyager Bks./Libros Viajeros) Harcourt Children's Bks.

—Otis. 2003. (gr. k-3). lib. bdg. 14.15 (978-0-613-70501-1(7)) Tandem Library Bks.

Byrd, Cheryl. Aaron Glen & His Animal Friends. Long, Cristina, illus. 2001. 17p. per. (978-0-9718538-0-5(0)) Rainbow Star Publishing.

Byrd, Jeff, illus. A Tale of Two Tails, el Perro con Dos Colas: A children's story in English & Spanish. 2004. Tr. of Perro con Dos Colas. (SPA.). (J). (ps-3). per. 14.95 (978-0-9746024-0-0(X)) One Arm Publishing.

Byrd, Lee. Treasure on Gold Street / el T. 2007. (SPA.). 40p. (J). pap. 8.95 (***978-1-933693-11-8(8)***) Cinco Puntos Pr.

Byrd, Lee Merrill. Treasure on Gold Street: A Neighborhood Story in Spanish & English. Castro, Antonio, tr. Castro, Antonio, illus. 2003. Tr. of Tesoro de la Calle Oro. (ENG & SPA.). 40p. (J). 16.95 (978-0-938317-75-3(X)) Cinco Puntos Pr.

Byrd, Sandra. Change of Heart. 2002. (gr. 3-6). lib. bdg. 13.00 (978-0-613-84506-9(4)) Tandem Library Bks.

—Cross My Heart. 2001. (Hidden Diary Ser.). 112p. (J). (gr. 3-7). reprint ed. pap. 5.99 (978-0-7642-2480-5(8)) Bethany Hse. Pubs.

—Cross My Heart. 2001. (gr. 3-6). lib. bdg. 13.00 (978-0-613-84512-0(9)) Tandem Library Bks.

—Daisy Chains. 2006. (Friends for a Season Ser.). 240p. pap. 10.99 (978-0-7642-0023-6(2)) Bethany Hse. Pubs.

—Island Girl. 2005. (Friends for A Season Ser.). 240p. (J). reprint ed. pap. 10.99 (978-0-7642-0020-5(8)) Bethany Hse. Pubs.

—Just Between Friends. 2001. (Hidden Diary Ser.). 112p. (J). (gr. 3-7). pap. 4.99 (978-0-7642-2482-9(4)) Bethany Hse. Pubs.

—Pass It On. 2002. (Hidden Diary Ser.: Bk. 5). 112p. (J). pap. 4.99 (978-0-7642-2484-3(0)) Bethany Hse. Pubs.

—Pass It On. 2002. (gr. 3-6). lib. bdg. 13.00 (978-0-613-84505-2(6)) Tandem Library Bks.

Cabal, Graciela Beatriz. Miedo. 2002. (SPA.). 32p. (J). pap. 8.95 (978-1-4000-0014-2(9)) Random Hse., Inc.

Cabrera, Jane. Pram Race. 2004. (Popcorn & Banana Bob Ser.). 32p. 15.99 (***978-0-689-86058-4(7)***) Simon & Schuster, Ltd. GBR. *Dist:* Independent Pubs. Group.

Caffrey-Kira, Albina. The Bear Who Loves Apples. 2006. 25.00 (978-0-8059-9128-4(X)) Dorrance Publishing Co., Inc.

Caho, Cheryl. Jumbo's Tiny Tales - Volume 2: Furry Friends. 2007. (Illus.). 82p. per. 15.97 (***978-0-9779960-3-2(4)***) Thornton Publishing.

Calaci, Iris. Matthew Mouse. Karper, Deborah, ed. Gonzalez, David, Jr., illus. 2002. 40p. (J). pap. (978-1-928681-07-6(7) , MM077) Gladstone Publishing.

Calamari, Barbara. Friends & Foes. Goldberg, Barry, illus. 2001. (Angela Anaconda Ser.: Vol. 4). 64p. (J). pap. 3.99 (978-0-689-84040-1(3) , Simon Spotlight) Simon & Schuster Children's Publishing.

—Friends & Foes. 2001. (gr. 3-6). lib. bdg. 11.80 (978-0-613-87771-8(3)) Tandem Library Bks.

Caldwell, Walter, text. The Tree in the Field of Mathingamy Thame. ltd. ed. 2002. (Stories of Mathingamy Thame Ser.). 30p. 18.95 (978-1-930729-02-5(2)) What's Inside Pr.

Call Me Nikki. 2000. (YA). per. 8.00 (978-1-57861-106-5(7)) Attainment Co., Inc.

Calmenson, Stephanie. May I Pet Your Dog? The How-to Guide for Kids Meeting Dogs (And Dogs Meeting Kids) Ormerod, Jan, illus. 2007. 32p. (J). (gr. k-3). 9.95 (978-0-618-51034-4(6) , Clarion Bks.) Houghton Mifflin Co. Trade & Reference Div.

Calmenson, Stephanie. May I Pet Your Dog? The How-To Guide for Kids Meeting Dogs (and Dogs Meeting Kids) Ormerod, Jan, illus. 2007. 32p. (J). (***978-1-4287-3952-9(1)*** , Clarion Bks.) Houghton Mifflin Co. Trade & Reference Div.

Calmenson, Stephanie & Cole, Joanna. Rockin' Reptiles. Munsinger, Lynn, illus. 1998. 80p. (J). pap. 5.95 (978-0-688-15633-6(9)) HarperCollins Pubs.

Cameron, Ann. Gloria's Way. 2002. (Illus.). 12.34 (978-1-4046-0952-5(0)) Book Wholesalers, Inc.

—Gloria's Way. Toft, Lis, illus. 2000. 112p. (J). (ps-3). 15.00 (978-0-374-32670-8(3) , Farrar, Straus & Giroux (BYR)) Farrar, Straus & Giroux.

—Gloria's Way. 2001. 11.64 (978-0-606-22055-2(0)) Tandem Library Bks.

—The Stories Julian Tells. 1999. (J). 9.95 (978-1-56137-671-1(X)) Novel Units, Inc.

Cameron, Ann & Toft, Lis. Gloria's Way. 2001. (Chapters Ser.). (Illus.). 112p. (J). pap. 4.99 (978-0-14-230023-7(3) , Puffin) Penguin Group (USA) Inc.

Campbell, Joanna. The Prize. 2002. (Ashleigh Ser.: No. 13). 176p. (gr. 3-7). mass mkt. 4.99 (978-0-06-009144-6(4) , Harper Entertainment) HarperCollins Pubs.

Campbell, Julie. The Secret of the Mansion: Trixie Belden. 2004. 236p. (J). (gr. 3-7). pap. 29.00 incl. audio (978-1-4000-9000-6(8) , Listening Library) Random Hse. Audio Publishing Group.

Campbell, Philip. Zion's Special Invitation. 2004. 29p. pap. 14.95 (978-1-4137-1483-8(8)) PublishAmerica, Inc.

Campbell, Tara. The Boy Who Called Heaven. 2006. pap. 32.49 (***978-1-4208-5456-5(9)***) AuthorHouse.

Camus, William. Azules Contra Grises. (Barco de Vapor). (SPA.). 200p. (YA). (gr. 5-8). 7.95 (978-84-348-1455-4(2)) SM Ediciones ESP. *Dist:* AIMS International Bks., Inc.

Canady, Pat. Boots the World's Best Kid-Sitter: Springtime Adventures. Bartley, Michael, illus. 2000. 6p. (J). (ps-4). pap. 10.00 (978-1-929889-02-0(X)) Canady SW Publishing.

Cane, Rochelle & Mada Design Staff. My Little Pony: The Princess Promenade Storybook & Playset. 2006. 10p. (J). 15.99 (978-0-7944-1107-7(X)) Reader's Digest Assn., Inc., The.

Capalija, Ann Marie. Butterfly Hunt. LoRaso, Carlo, illus. 2005. (My Little Pony Ser.). 24p. (J). (ps-1). pap. 3.99 (978-0-06-074442-7(1) , Harper Festival) HarperCollins Pubs.

—Fashion Fun. Edwards, Ken, illus. 2005. (My Little Pony Ser.). 24p. (J). (ps-1). pap. 3.50 (978-0-06-074443-4(X) , Harper Festival) HarperCollins Pubs.

—Five Friends. Rodriguez, Angel & Antonio, Jose, illus. 2004. (My Little Pony Ser.). 20p. (J). (ps-1). pap. 8.99 (978-0-06-055406-4(1) , Harper Festival) HarperCollins Pubs.

—Wishes Do Come True! Fletcher, Lyn, illus. 2004. (My Little Pony Ser.). 24p. (J). (ps-2). pap. 3.99 (978-0-06-073426-8(4) , Harper Festival) HarperCollins Pubs.

Caple, Kathy. The Friendship Tree. Caple, Kathy, illus. (House Readers Ser.). (Illus.). 32p. (J). (gr. k-3). tchr. ed. 15.95 (978-0-8234-1376-8(4)) Holiday Hse., Inc.

Capote, Truman. A Christmas Memory. Peck, Beth, illus. 2006. 48p. (J). (gr. 7). 17.95 incl. audio compact disk (978-0-375-83789-0(2) , Knopf Bks. for Young Readers) Random Hse. Children's Bks.

Caproni, Deidre. Hallowell's Friends. Jones, J'aime L. & Wolkoff, Adam J., illus. 2000. 88p. (J). (gr. k-7). pap. 10.95 (978-0-9678923-1-3(7)) AmityWorks.

Capucilli, Alyssa Satin. Biscuit Finds a Friend. Schories, Pat, illus. 1998. (My First I Can Read Bks.). 32p. (J). (ps up). pap. 3.99 (978-0-06-444243-5(8) , Harper Trophy) HarperCollins Pubs.

—Biscuit Finds a Friend. Schories, Pat, illus. 1998. (My First I Can Read Bks.). (J). (ps-k). 10.79 (978-0-606-13203-9(1)) Tandem Library Bks.

—Biscuit's Big Friend. Schories, Pat, illus. (My First I Can Read Bks.). 32p. (J). (ps up). 2004. pap. 3.99 (978-0-06-444288-6(8) , Harper Trophy); 2003. 16.99 (978-0-06-029167-9(2)); 2003. lib. bdg. 17.89 (978-0-06-029168-6(0)) HarperCollins Pubs.

Cara's Letters: Individual Chapter Book Title Six-Pack. Vol. 29. 32p. (gr. 5 up). 44.00 (978-0-7578-0975-0(8)) Rigby Education.

Carbone, Elisa. Sarah & the Naked Truth. 2005. (J). per. 10.95 (978-0-9769404-8-7(5) , 0-9769404-8-5) Cloonfad Pr.

—Starting School with an Enemy. 1999. (978-0-606-16568-6(1)) Tandem Library Bks.

Carle, Eric. A House for a Hermit Crab. Carle, Eric, illus. 2005. (Stories to Go! Ser.). (Illus.). 32p. (J). 4.99 (978-1-4169-0309-3(7) , Aladdin) Simon & Schuster Children's Publishing.

—A House for a Hermit Crab. 2002. (gr. k-3). lib. bdg. 15.30 (978-0-613-90187-1(8)) Tandem Library Bks.

—Ours Brun, Dis-Moi... 2000. Tr. of Brown Bear, Brown Bear What Do You See?. (FRE., Illus.). (J). pap. 12.95 (978-2-87142-189-4(7)) Mijade Editons BEL. *Dist:* Distribooks, Inc.

Carle, Eric & Iwamura, Kazuo. Where Are You Going? To See My Friend! Carle, Eric, illus. 2003. (JPN & ENG., Illus.). 40p. (J). pap. 19.95 (978-0-439-41659-7(0) , Orchard Bks.) Scholastic, Inc.

Carlson, Margaret. The Canning Season. Smith, Kimanne, illus. 1999. (First Person Ser.). 32p. (J). (gr. 2-4). pap. 7.95 (978-1-57505-283-0(0) , Carolrhoda Bks.) Lerner Publishing Group.

Carlson, Melody. Bitsy's Harvest Party. Reagan, Susan Joy, illus. 2005. 32p. (J). (ps-4). 12.99 (978-0-8054-2684-7(1)) B&H Publishing Grp.

—Bright Purple. 2006. 224p. (YA). pap. 12.99 (978-1-57683-950-8(8) , Th1nk Bks.) NavPress Publishing Group.

—Dark Blue: Color Me Lonely. 2004. 196p. (J). pap. 12.99 (978-1-57683-529-6(4)) NavPress Publishing Group.

—Diary of a Teenage Girl - It's My Life: Diary Number 2. 2002. (gr. 7-12). lib. bdg. 22.25 (978-0-613-88463-1(9)) Tandem Library Bks.

—Project, Girl Power. 2007. (Faithgirlz!#8482; / Girls of 622 Harbor View Ser.). 144p. (J). pap. 6.99 (978-0-310-71186-5(X)) Zonderkidz.

—Project, Rescue Chelsea. 2007. (Faithgirlz!#8482; / Girls of 622 Harbor View Ser.). 144p. (J). pap. 6.99 (978-0-310-71188-9(6)) Zonderkidz.

—Project, Take Charge. 2007. (Faithgirlz!#8482; / Girls of 622 Harbor View Ser.). 144p. (J). pap. 6.99 (978-0-310-71189-6(4)) Zonderkidz.

Carlson, Nancy. Harriet & Walt. Carlson, Nancy, illus. unabr. ed. (Illus.). (J). (gr. k-3). 24.95 incl. audio (978-0-941078-59-7(0)); pap. 15.95 incl. audio (978-0-941078-57-3(4)); pap., tchr. ed. 31.95 incl. audio (978-0-941078-58-0(2)) Live Oak Media.

—Louanne Pig in Witch Lady. 2006. (Illus.). 32p. (J). 15.95 (978-0-8225-6196-5(4) , Carolrhoda Bks.); pap. 6.95 (978-0-8225-6197-2(2) , First Avenue Editions) Lerner Publishing Group.

—My Best Friend Moved Away. Carlson, Nancy, illus. 2003. (Illus.). 32p. (J). (gr. k-2). pap. 5.99 (978-0-14-250067-5(4) , Puffin) Penguin Group (USA) Inc.

—My Best Friend Moved Away. 2003. (gr. k-3). lib. bdg. 14.15 (978-0-613-67291-7(7)) Tandem Library Bks.

Carlson, Nathan, et al. The Great Train Set Robbery. 2001. (Little Dogs on the Prairie Ser.). (Illus.). 64p. (J). (gr. 1-4). 4.99 (978-0-8499-7649-0(9)) Nelson, Thomas Inc.

Carlson, Ron. The Speed of Light. 2003. (Illus.). 288p. (J). 15.99 (978-0-380-97837-3(7)); 16.89 (978-0-06-029825-8(1)) HarperCollins Pubs. (HarperTeen).

Carlstrom, Nancy White. The Way to Wyatt's House. Morgan, Mary, illus. 2000. 32p. (J). (ps-3). 15.95 (978-0-8027-8740-8(1)) Walker & Co.

Carman, Debby. Kittywimpuss, Got Game. 2006. (J). (978-0-9777340-4-7(8)) Faux Paw Media Group.

—Purrlonia's Lullaby. 2006. (J). (978-0-9777340-1-6(3)) Faux Paw Media Group.

Carman, Patrick. Atherton: The House of Power. 2007. (Illus.). (J). 352p. (gr. 3-7). 16.99 (***978-0-316-16670-6(7));*** 330p. (***978-1-4287-4140-9(2)***) Little Brown & Co.

Carman, Patrick. Beyond the Valley of Thorns (Mas Alla Del Valle de Espinos) 2006. (Tierra de Elyon Ser.: Bk. 2). 224p. (J). pap. 6.99 (978-0-439-87480-9(7) , Scholastic en Espanol) Scholastic, Inc.

Carmi, Daniella. Samir y Jonatan en el Planeta Marte. 2002. (Joven Coleccion Ser.). (SPA.). 144p. (YA). (gr. 5-8). (978-84-85334-95-7(7) , LG7474) Loguez Ediciones ESP. *Dist:* Lectorum Pubns., Inc.

Carpenter Czerw, Nancy. Itty & Bitty: Friends on the Farm. Berlin, Rose Mary & Bauer, Dana, illus. 2006. (Itty & Bitty Ser.). 32p. (J). 15.95 (978-0-9755618-3-6(9)) McWitty Pr., Inc.

Carpino, Nancy. The Leprechaun & His Bag of Gold. Carpino, Nancy & McNeilis, Jessica, illus. 2000. 50p. (J). (gr. k-4). 8.95 (978-1-928675-03-7(4)) Carpino Bks.

Carr, David. Trebb the Troll. 2005. 86p. (YA). pap. 8.36 (978-1-4116-3865-5(4)) Lulu.com.

Carr, Dennis & Carr, Elise. Welcome to Wahoo. 2006. 250p. (YA). 16.95 (978-1-58234-696-0(8) , Bloomsbury Children) Bloomsbury Publishing.

Carr, Elise & Carr, Dennis. Welcome to Wahoo. 2007. 240p. (YA). pap. 6.95 (***978-1-59990-096-4(3)*** , Bloomsbury Children) Bloomsbury Publishing.

Carr, Jan. Frozen Noses. Donohue, Dorothy, illus. 1999. 32p. (J). (gr. k-3). tchr. ed. 16.95 (978-0-8234-1462-8(0)) Holiday Hse., Inc.

Carson, Earlene Andreu. Squirrelene & Friends. 2005. pap. 7.95 (978-0-533-15026-7(4)) Vantage Pr., Inc.

Carson, Jana. We Both Read-Stop Teasing Taylor! Treatner, Meryl, illus. 2005. (J). (***978-1-4156-3784-5(9)***) Book Wholesalers, Inc.

Carta, Karla K. Fairy Jane. 2005. 25p. 13.28 (978-1-4116-2296-8(0)) Lulu.com.

Carter, D. J. The Singing Lesson. 2007. (J). per. 6.99 (***978-1-59886-914-9(0)***) Tate Publishing & Enterprises, L.L.C.

Carter, David A. Whoo? Whoo? Carter, David A., illus. 2007. (Illus.). 32p. (J). (ps-1). 12.99 (***978-1-4169-3816-3(8)*** , Little Simon) Simon & Schuster Children's Publishing.

Carville, James & McKissack, Patricia C. Lu & the Swamp Ghost. Catrow, David, tr. Catrow, David, illus. 2004. 40p. (J). 17.95 (978-0-689-86560-2(0) , Atheneum) Simon & Schuster Children's Publishing.

Casagrande, Donata Dal Molin. Amigos en Primavera. Brignole, Giancarla, tr. rev. ed. 2002. (Fabulas De Familia Ser.). (SPA.). 32p. (J). pap. 6.95 (978-970-20-0266-6(4)) Castillo, Ediciones, S. A. de C. V. MEX. *Dist:* Macmillan.

Casanova, Mary. Danger at Snow Hill. Rayyan, Omar, illus. 2006. (Dog Watch Ser.: No. 3). 128p. (J). pap. 4.99 (978-0-689-86812-2(X) , Aladdin) Simon & Schuster Children's Publishing.

—Dog-Napped! Rayyan, Omar, illus. 2006. (Dog Watch Ser.: No. 2). 144p. (J). pap. 4.99 (978-0-689-86811-5(1) , Aladdin) Simon & Schuster Children's Publishing.

—Wolf Shadows. 1999. (978-0-606-16667-6(X)) Tandem Library Bks.

Cassidy, Anne. Jasper & Jess. Hall, Francois, illus. 2004. (Read-It! Readers Ser.). 32p. (C). (gr. k-3). 18.60 (978-1-4048-0061-8(1)) Picture Window Bks.

Cassidy, Cathy. Indigo Blue. 2006. 240p. (J). (gr. 5). pap. 5.99 (978-0-14-240703-5(8) , Puffin) Penguin Group (USA) Inc.

Castellucci, Cecil. The Queen of Cool. 2007. (Illus.). 176p. (YA). (gr. 9 up). pap. 7.99 (***978-0-7636-3413-1(1)***) Candlewick Pr.

Castilla, Julia Mercedes. Emilio. 1999. 160p. (YA). (gr. 4-7). pap. 9.95 (978-1-55885-271-6(9) , Piñata Books) Arte Publico Pr.

—Emilio. (SPA.). (YA). (gr. 5-8). 8.95 (978-958-04-4149-6(9) , NR3970) Norma S.A. COL. *Dist:* Distribuidora Norma, Inc., Lectorum Pubns., Inc.

Catalanotto, Peter & Schembri, Pamela. The Secret Lunch Special. 2006. (Illus.). (J). 56p. (***978-1-4156-9204-2(1));*** Bk. 1. 64p. 15.95 (978-0-8050-7838-1(X) , Holt, Henry & Co. Bks. For Young Readers) Holt, Henry & Co.

Cate, Annette LeBlanc. The Magic Rabbit. Cate, Annette LeBlanc, illus. 2007. (Illus.). 32p. (J). (ps-3). 15.99 (***978-0-7636-2672-3(4)***) Candlewick Pr.

Cates, Karin, et al. The Secret Remedy Book: A Story of Comfort & Love. Halperin, Wendy Anderson, illus. 2003. (My Great-Great-Grandmother's Secret Remedy Book Ser.). 40p. (J). pap. 16.95 (978-0-439-35226-0(6) , Orchard Bks.) Scholastic, Inc.

EFG

Cattanach, Ann. Malpas the Dragon. Renouf, Michael, illus. 2007. 24p. (***978-1-84310-572-5(1)***) Kingsley, Jessica Ltd.

Cave, Kathryn. Something Else. Riddell, Chris, illus. 1998. 32p. (J). (gr. 1-5). pap. 5.95 (978-1-57255-563-1(7)) Mondo Publishing.

Cave, Kathryn & Maland. Brave Little Grork. (Illus.). 30p. (J). (978-0-340-74677-6(7) , Hodder Children's Books) Hodder Children's Division.

Cavender-Jenkin, Barbara. A Is for Abe. 2005. 77p. pap. 14.95 (978-1-4137-6763-6(X)) PublishAmerica, Inc.

Cazet, Denys. Minnie & Moo: Minnie & Moo Go to the Moon. Cazet, Denys, illus. (Live Oak Readalong Ser.). (Illus.). (J). 18.95 incl. audio compact disk (978-1-59112-392-7(5)) Live Oak Media.

—Minnie & Moo Go Dancing. 1999. (Illus.). 48p. (J). pap. 15.95 (978-0-7737-3105-9(9)) Dorling Kindersley Publishing, Inc.

—Minnie & Moo Go to the Moon. Cazet, Denys, illus. 2001. (Illus.). 25.95 incl. audio (978-0-87499-718-7(6)); pap. 29.95 incl. audio (978-0-87499-719-4(4)); pap. 31.95 incl. audio compact disk (978-1-59112-592-1(8)); pap. 18.95 incl. audio compact disk (978-1-59112-593-8(6)) Live Oak Media.

—Never Poke a Squid. Cazet, Denys, illus. 2000. (Illus.). 32p. (J). (ps-2). 17.99 (978-0-531-33279-5(9) , Watts, Franklin) Scholastic Library Publishing.

—Never Poke a Squid. Cazet, Denys, illus. 2000. (Illus.). 32p. (J). (ps-2). pap. 16.95 (978-0-531-30279-8(2) , Orchard Bks.) Scholastic, Inc.

Cazet, Denys & Dorling Kindersley Publishing Staff. Minnie & Moo Go to the Moon. 1998. (Minnie & Moo Ser.: Vol. 1). (Illus.). 48p. (J). (gr. 1-3). 12.99 (978-0-7894-2516-4(5)) Dorling Kindersley Publishing, Inc.

Cecil, Charles. Little Boy Bob's Animal Friends. 2007. 27p. pap. 7.95 (978-0-533-15489-0(8)) Vantage Pr., Inc.

Celenza, Anna Harwell. The Heroic Symphony. Kitchel, JoAnn E., illus. 2004. 32p. (J). 19.95 incl. audio compact disk (978-1-57091-509-3(1)) Charlesbridge Publishing, Inc.

Celestin, Marie. The Unaccepted Child. 2003. (Illus.). 16p. (J). pap. 5.99 (978-1-890035-35-8(1) , 119) New Century Pr.

Center for Learning Network Staff. All the Pretty Horses: Curriculum Unit —Novel Series — Grades 9-12. 2001. (Novel Ser.). 60p. (YA). tchr. ed., spiral bd. 19.95 (978-1-56077-667-3(6)) Ctr. for Learning, The.

Chaconas, Dori. Cork & Fuzz: Good Sports. McCue, Lisa, illus. 2007. (Viking Easy-To-Read Ser.). 32p. (J). (gr. k-2). 13.99 (978-0-670-06145-7(X) , Viking Adult) Penguin Group (USA) Inc.

—Cork & Fuzz: Short & Tall. McCue, Lisa, illus. 2006. (Viking Easy-To-Read Ser.). 32p. (J). (gr. k-3). 13.99 (978-0-670-05985-0(4) , Viking Adult) Penguin Group (USA) Inc.

Chaconas, Dori. Cork & Fuzz: The Collectors. McCue, Lisa, illus. 2008. 32p. (J). (ps-1). 13.99 (***978-0-670-06286-7(3)*** , Viking Adult) Penguin Group (USA) Inc.

Chaconas, Doris J. Cork & Fuzz. McCue, Lisa, illus. 2005. (Viking Easy-To-Read Ser.). 32p. (J). (ps-3). 13.99 (978-0-670-03602-8(1) , Viking Juvenile) Penguin Group (USA) Inc.

Chaikin, Miriam. Getting Even. 2001. 136p. (YA). pap. 11.95 (978-0-595-19868-9(6) , Backinprint.com) iUniverse, Inc.

—Lower! Higher! You're a Liar! Egielski, Richard, illus. 2001. 148p. (YA). pap. 12.95 (978-0-595-19877-1(5) , Backinprint.com) iUniverse, Inc.

Chambers, Barbara Giles. The Disappearance of Livvy. 2003. 77p. pap. 11.95 (978-1-4137-0707-6(6)) PublishAmerica, Inc.

Chambers, Nancy. Patches of Time. 2001. 253p. pap. 21.95 (978-1-58851-171-3(5)) PublishAmerica, Inc.

Chambers, Veronica. Marisol & Magdalena. 2001. 176p. (gr. 3-7). pap. 5.99 (978-0-7868-1304-9(0)) Hyperion Bks. for Children.

—Marisol & Magdalena: The Sound of Our Sisterhood. 2001. (gr. 5-8). lib. bdg. 14.15 (978-0-613-60642-4(6)) Tandem Library Bks.

—Quinceanera Means Sweet Fifteen. 2001. 192p. (Illus.). (J). (gr. 5-8). lib. bdg. 16.49 (978-0-7868-2426-7(3)); (gr. 3-7). 15.99 (978-0-7868-0497-9(1)) Hyperion Bks. for Children.

Champion, Joyce. Emily & Alice, Best Friends. Stevenson, Sucie, illus. 2001. (Emily & Alice Ser.: Bk. 1). 32p. (J). (gr. 1-4). pap. 5.95 (978-0-15-202198-6(1) , Gulliver Bks.) Harcourt Children's Bks.

—Emily & Alice, Best Friends. 2001. (gr. k-3). lib. bdg. 14.10 (978-0-613-35454-7(0)) Tandem Library Bks.

—Emily & Alice Best Friends. 2001. (Illus.). (J). 12.75 (978-0-606-21177-2(2)) Tandem Library Bks.

—Emily & Alice Stick Together. Stevenson, Sucie, illus. 2001. (Emily & Alice Ser.: Bk. 2). 32p. (J). (gr. 1-4). pap. 5.95 (978-0-15-202189-4(2) , Gulliver Bks.) Harcourt Children's Bks.

—Emily & Alice Stick Together. 2001. (gr. k-3). lib. bdg. 14.10 (978-0-613-35455-4(9)); (Illus.). (J). 12.75 (978-0-606-21178-9(0)) Tandem Library Bks.

Chan, Gillian. A Foreign Field. 2004. (Illus.). 192p. (YA). (gr. 13 up). (978-1-55337-350-6(2)) Kids Can Pr., Ltd.

Chanda, J-P. Ah-Choo! Piluso, Piero, illus. 2003. (Oswald Pre-School Ready-to-Read Ser.: Vol. 2). 24p. (J). pap. 3.99 (978-0-689-85853-6(1) , Simon Spotlight/ Nickelodeon) Simon & Schuster Children's Publishing.

Chardiet, Bernice & Maccarone, Grace. The Snowball War. Karas, G. Brian, illus. 1999. (J). (978-0-439-10803-4(0)) Scholastic, Inc.

Charles, Norma M. Sophie's Friend in Need. 2005. 136p. (YA). pap. (978-0-88878-449-0(X) , Sandcastle Bks.) Dundurn Group, The.

Charlip, Remy & Rettenmund, Tamara, illus. Little Old Big Beard & Big Young Little Beard: A Short & Tall Tale. 2002. (J). (978-1-58837-000-6(3)) Winslow Pr.

Charlotte's Web. 1998. 40p. (J). 11.95 (978-1-56137-630-8(2) , NU6302SP) Novel Units, Inc.

Chase, Diana. Daisy Street. Bradley, Vanessa, illus. 2005. 128p. (Orig.). (J). pap. 13.50 (978-1-920731-11-3(3)) Fremantle Pr. AUS. *Dist:* International Specialized Bk. Services.

—Surf's Up. 1999. 200p. (J). pap. 12.95 (978-1-86368-250-3(3)) Fremantle Pr. AUS. *Dist:* International Specialized Bk. Services.

Chass, Vikentia. The Visiting Angels. 1999. 16p. (J). (gr. k-6). pap. 8.00 (978-0-8059-4713-7(2)) Dorrance Publishing Co., Inc.

Chbosky, Stephen. The Perks of Being a Wallflower. 1999. 213p. (gr. 7-12). pap. 14.00 (978-0-671-02734-6(4) , MTV) Simon & Schuster.

—The Perks of Being a Wallflower. 1999. (978-0-606-18378-9(7)) Tandem Library Bks.

Cheaney, J. B. My Friend the Enemy. 2005. 272p. (J). (gr. 5-9). 15.95 (978-0-375-81432-7(9) , Knopf Bks. for Young Readers) Random Hse. Children's Bks.

Chen, Zhiyuan, illus. Artie & Julie. 2007. (J). (***978-0-9787550-3-4(0)***) Heryin Publishing Corp.

Cheng, Andrea. Honeysuckle House. 2004. 136p. (YA). 16.95 (978-1-886910-99-7(5) , Lemniscaat) Boyds Mills Pr.

—The Lace Dowry. 2005. 120p. (J). 16.95 (978-1-932425-20-8(9) , Lemniscaat) Boyds Mills Pr.

Cheng, Andrea. Where the Steps Were. 2008. (J). (***978-1-932425-88-8(8)*** , Front Street) Boyds Mills Pr.

Cheng, Cynthia. Aspirations. 2007. 150p. pap. 9.95 (***978-0-9739097-9-1(X)***) Burman Books, Inc. CAN. *Dist:* Independent Pubs. Group.

Chesterfield, Sadie. Meet the Characters. 2006. (Ice Age 2 Ser.). 18p. (J). pap. 6.99 (978-0-06-083976-5(7)) HarperCollins Pubs.

Chetdav, Rain S. Acidrain. 2003. 108p. (YA). pap. 9.95 (978-0-595-26560-2(X) , Writers Club Pr.) iUniverse, Inc.

Chic, Suzy & Touvay, Monique. Watching. 2007. 48p. (J). 12.00 (***978-1-905341-07-8(5)***) WingedChariot Pr. GBR. *Dist:* Independent Pubs. Group.

Chick, Bryan. The Secret Zoo. 2007. 252p. pap. 5.99 (***978-0-9791887-3-2(3)***) Second Wish Pr.

Child, Lauren. Charlie & Lola: Snow Is My Favorite & My Best. 2006. (Illus.). 32p. (J). (ps). 16.99 (978-0-8037-3174-5(4) , Dial) Penguin Group (USA) Inc.

—Clarice Bean Spells Trouble. Child, Lauren, illus. (Clarice Bean Ser.). 192p. (J). (gr. 3-6). 2006. pap. 5.99 (978-0-7636-2903-8(0)); 2005. (Illus.). bds. 15.99 (978-0-7636-2813-0(1)) Candlewick Pr.

—Clarice Bean, That's Me. Child, Lauren, illus. 1999. (Clarice Bean Ser.). (Illus.). 32p. (J). (gr. 1-5). 16.99 (978-0-7636-0961-0(7)) Candlewick Pr.

Child, Lauren. I Can Do Anything That's Everything All on My Own. 2008. (Charlie & Lola Ser.). 24p. (J). (ps-1). 3.99 (***978-0-448-44792-6(4)*** , Grosset & Dunlap) Penguin Group (USA) Inc.

Childress, H. Lee. The Cane. 2007. pap. 9.00 (***978-0-8059-8453-8(4)***) Dorrance Publishing Co., Inc.

Chiu, Harry. Enve Lopt Unfolded. 2007. 268p. per. 17.95 (***978-0-595-44707-7(4)***) iUniverse, Inc.

Chodos-Irvine, Margaret. Best Best Friends. 2006. (Illus.). 40p. (J). 16.00 (978-0-15-205694-0(7)) Harcourt Trade Pubs.

Choldenko, Gennifer. How to Make Friends with a Giant. Walrod, Amy, illus. 2006. 32p. (J). (ps-3). 16.99 (978-0-399-23779-9(8)) Penguin Group (USA) Inc.

Choldenko, Gennifer. Louder, Lili. Schindler, S. D., illus. 2007. 32p. (J). (ps). 16.99 (***978-0-399-24252-6(X)*** , Putnam Juvenile) Penguin Group (USA) Inc.

Chon, Kye Young. Audition: Volume 1, 10 vols. 2006. (Audition Ser.). (Illus.). 176p. pap. 11.99 (978-1-933809-43-4(4)) DramaQueen, L.L.C.

Chotjewitz, David. Daniel Half Human. Orgel, Doris, tr. 2006. 336p. (YA). reprint ed. mass mkt. 5.99 (978-0-689-85748-5(9) , Simon Pulse) Simon & Schuster Children's Publishing.

—Daniel, Half Human: And the Good Nazi. Orgel, Doris, tr. from GER. 2004. (Illus.). 304p. (YA). 17.95 (978-0-689-85747-8(0) , Atheneum) Simon & Schuster Children's Publishing.

Chotjewitz, David & Orgel, Doris. Daniel, Half Human: And the Good Nazi. 2004. 298p. (J). (978-3-551-58045-0(6)) Carlsen Verlag DEU. *Dist:* Distribooks, Inc.

Choyce, Lesley. Carrie's Crowd. Thurman, Mark, illus. 1998. (First Novels Ser.: Vol. 8). 64p. (J). (gr. 1-5). (978-0-88780-465-6(9)) Formac Publishing Co., Ltd.

—Carrie's Crowd. Thurman, Mark, illus. 1998. (First Novels Ser.: Vol. 8). 64p. (gr. 1-5). 4.95 (978-0-88780-464-9(0)) Formac Publishing Co., Ltd. CAN. *Dist:* Casemate Pubs. & Bk. Distributors, LLC.

—Carrie's Crowd. 1999. (gr. k-3). lib. bdg. 11.80 (978-0-613-88932-2(0)) Tandem Library Bks.

Christian, Cheryl. Matty & Patty. Sampson, Pamela, illus. 1998. (Domino Readers Ser.). 24p. (J). (ps-1). pap. 5.95 (978-1-887734-30-1(9)) Star Bright Bks., Inc.

Christian, Diana. The Lucky Seven. 2005. 71p. pap. 14.95 (978-1-4137-5471-1(6)) PublishAmerica, Inc.

Christopher, Matt. Day of the Dragon. 2nd ed. 2004. (Extreme Team Ser.: Vol. 2). (Illus.). 64p. (J). (gr. 2-4). pap. 4.99 (978-0-316-73753-1(4)) Little, Brown Bks. for Young Readers.

—Inline Skater. 2001. (J). 11.15 (978-0-606-21247-2(7)) Tandem Library Bks.

—Into the Danger Zone. Koelsch, Michael, illus. 6th ed. 2004. (Extreme Team Ser.: Vol. 6). 64p. (J). (gr. 2-4). pap. 4.99 (978-0-316-76267-0(9) , Tingley, Megan Bks.) Little, Brown Bks. for Young Readers.

—On Thin Ice. Koelsch, Michael, illus. 4th ed. 2004. (Extreme Team Ser.: Vol. 4). 64p. (J). (gr. 2-4). pap. 4.99 (978-0-316-73739-5(9)) Little Brown & Co.

—One Smooth Move. Koelsch, Michael, illus. 2004. (Extreme Team Ser.: Vol. 1). 64p. (J). (gr. 2-4). pap. 4.99 (978-0-316-73749-4(6)) Little Brown & Co.

—Slam Dunk. 2004. (Illus.). 128p. (J). (gr. 4-7). pap. 4.99 (978-0-316-60762-9(2)) Little Brown & Co.

—Stranger in Right Field. 2000. (978-0-606-18266-9(7)) Tandem Library Bks.

—Stranger in Right Field: A Peach Street Mudders Story. Dodson, Bert, illus. 2000. (Peach Street Mudders Story Ser.). 64p. (J). (gr. 2-4). pap. 4.50 (978-0-316-10677-1(1)) Little Brown & Co.

Christopher, Matt & #1 Sports Writer for Kids Staff. Mountain Bike Mania. 1998. 160p. (J). (gr. 3-7). pap. 4.99 (978-0-316-14292-2(1)) Little Brown & Co.

—Mountain Bike Mania: Is Will Pedaling Out of Control? 1998. 160p. (J). (gr. 3-7). 15.95 (978-0-316-14355-4(3)) Little Brown & Co.

Chronicle Books. Friendship Stories You Can Share. 2001. (Reading Rainbow Ser.). (Illus.). 64p. (J). (ps-3). pap. 3.99 (978-1-58717-084-3(1) , SeaStar Bks.) Chronicle Bks. LLC.

Chung, Helena. Jennifer, the Special One. 2004. (J). pap. 8.00 (978-0-8059-6395-3(2)) Dorrance Publishing Co., Inc.

Ciminera, Siobhan. Friends Forever: Happy Feet. 2006. (Illus.). 32p. (J). (ps-1). pap. 3.99 (978-0-8431-2129-2(7) , Price Stern Sloan) Penguin Group (USA) Inc.

—Strawberry Shortcake Sleeps Over. 2004. (Strawberry Shortcake Ser.). (Illus.). 24p. (J). (ps-2). pap. 4.99 (978-0-448-43516-9(0) , Grosset & Dunlap) Penguin Group (USA) Inc.

Ciminera, Siobhan & Faulkner, Keith. Time to Play. 2006. (Puppy Scooby-Doo Ser.). (Illus.). 24p. (J). (ps-ps). pap. 3.99 (978-0-448-44407-9(0) , Grosset & Dunlap) Penguin Group (USA) Inc.

Clairmont, Patsy. Stinky. Oeltjenbruns, Joni, illus. 2006. (Tails from the Pantry Ser.). 32p. (J). 9.99 (978-1-4003-0803-3(8)) Nelson, Thomas Inc.

Clairmont, Patsy. 5 Cheesy Stories: About Friendship, Bravery, Bullying, & More. 2007. (Tails from the Pantry Ser.). 144p. (J). 14.99 (***978-1-4003-1042-5(3)***) Nelson, Thomas Inc.

Clamp. Cardcaptor Sakura, Vol. 6. rev. ed. 2005. (Illus.). pap. 9.99 (978-1-59182-883-9(X) , Tokyopop Kids) TOKYOPOP, Inc.

Clark, Brenda, illus. Franklin Is Bossy. 2002. (Franklin Ser.). 12.40 (978-1-4046-0316-5(6)) Book Wholesalers, Inc.

—Franklin's Bad Day. 2002. (Franklin Ser.). 12.40 (978-1-4046-0321-9(2)) Book Wholesalers, Inc.

—Franklin's New Friend. 2002. (Franklin Ser.). 12.40 (978-1-4046-0327-1(1)) Book Wholesalers, Inc.

—Franklin's Secret Club. 2002. (Franklin Ser.). (J). 12.40 (978-0-7587-2533-2(7)) Book Wholesalers, Inc.

Clark, Catherine. The Alison Rules. 2005. 272p. (YA). reprint ed. pap. 6.99 (978-0-06-055982-3(9) , HarperTeen) HarperCollins Pubs.

Clark, Emma Chicester. Will & Squill. 2006. (Illus.). 32p. (J). 15.95 (978-1-57505-936-5(3) , Carolrhoda Bks.) Lerner Publishing Group.

Clark, Emma Chichester. Melrose & Croc: A Christmas to Remember. Clark, Emma Chichester, illus. 2006. (Illus.). 32p. (J). 16.95 (978-0-8027-9597-7(8)) Walker & Co.

—What Shall We Do, Blue Kangaroo? Clark, Emma Chichester, illus. 2003. (Illus.). 32p. (J). (gr. k-k). 15.95 (978-0-385-74635-9(0) , Doubleday Bks. for Young Readers) Random Hse. Children's Bks.

Clark, Joan. Ann Drew Jackson. 2007. (J). pap. 17.95 (***978-1-931282-45-1(5)***) Autism Asperger Publishing Co.

Clark, Joan. Jackson Whole Wyoming. 2005. 16.00 (978-1-931282-72-7(2) , 9945) Autism Asperger Publishing Co.

Clark, Kimberly. Three Is the Perfect Number. Hummel, Victoria, illus. 1998. 16p. (J). (ps-k). pap. 5.95 (978-1-891846-01-4(9)) Business Word, The.

Clark, Maxine. Build-a-Bear Workshop Furry Friends Hall of Fame: The Official Collector's Guide. 2005. (Illus.). 160p. (J). (gr. 4-7). (978-1-59258-142-9(0)) Hylas Publishing.

Clark, Sherryl. Knock It Off! 2000. (gr. 7-12). lib. bdg. 12.25 (978-0-613-28919-1(6)) Tandem Library Bks.

Clarke, Gus. Max & the Rainbow Hat. 2002. (Illus.). 32p. (J). 17.99 (978-1-84270-078-5(2)) Andersen GBR. *Dist:* Independent Pubs. Group.

—Suerte. Clarke, Gus, illus. 2006. (SPA., Illus.). 32p. (J). pap. 4.95 (978-1-933605-08-1(1)) Kane/Miller Bk. Pubs., Inc.

Clarke, Jane. Dippy's Sleepover: A Reassuring Story for Kids Who Have a Bedwetting Problem. McQuillan, Mary, illus. 2006. 32p. (J). pap. 6.99 (978-0-7641-3425-8(6)) Barron's Educational Series, Inc.

—G. E. M. 2008. (Illus.). 32p. (J). pap. 9.95 (***978-0-09-948012-9(3)***) Transworld Publishers Ltd. GBR. *Dist:* Independent Pubs. Group.

Clarke, Jane. Gilbert the Great. Fuge, Charles, illus. 2005. 32p. (J). 12.95 (978-1-4027-2169-4(2)) Sterling Publishing Co., Inc.

Clarke, Lyndia A. Tidy up Tommy. Clarke, Lyndia A., illus. 2006. (Illus.). 28p. (J). per. 19.95 (978-1-59453-971-8(5) , 3513, Airleaf Publishing) Airleaf Publishing & Bookselling.

Cleary, Beverly. Otis Spofford. 2000. (J). pap., stu. ed. 34.24 incl. audio (978-0-7887-4181-4(0) , 47089) Recorded Bks., LLC.

—Ramona's World. Tiegreen, Alan & Dockray, Tracy, illus. 2001. (Ramona Quimby Ser.). 240p. (J). (gr. 3-5). 16.99 (978-0-688-16816-2(7)) HarperCollins Pubs.

Cleary, Christopher. Writing on the Wall. 2007. 198p. (YA). per. 9.99 (***978-0-9795753-5-8(4)***) Immortality Pr.

Clements, Andrew. Big Al & Shrimpy. Kogo, Yoshi, illus. 2002. 40p. (J). (gr. k-3). 16.95 (978-0-689-84247-4(3)) Simon & Schuster Children's Publishing.

—Big Al & Shrimpy. Kogo, Yoshi, illus. 2005. 30p. (J). (ps-3). lib. bdg. 14.19 (978-0-606-33907-0(8)) Tandem Library Bks.

—Jake Drake, Know-It-All. 2001. (gr. 3-6). lib. bdg. 11.80 (978-0-613-35670-1(5)) Tandem Library Bks.

—Jake Drake, Know-It-All. l.t. ed. 2002. (Juvenile Ser.). (Illus.). 76p. (J). 21.95 (978-0-7862-4139-2(X)) Thomson Gale.

—Know-It-All. Pedersen, Janet, illus. 2007. (Jake Drake Ser.: No. 2). 112p. (J). pap. 3.99 (***978-1-4169-3931-3(8)*** , Aladdin) Simon & Schuster Children's Publishing.

—The Last Holiday Concert. Selznick, Brian, illus. 2004. 176p. (J). 15.95 (978-0-689-84516-1(2)) Simon & Schuster Children's Publishing.

—Raggedy Ann & Andy. 1998. (Illus.). 12p. (J). 4.99 (978-0-689-82366-4(5) , Little Simon) Simon & Schuster Children's Publishing.

—The Report Card. (Illus.). (J). 2004. 176p. (gr. 3-7). 15.95 (978-0-689-84515-4(4)); 2005. 192p. reprint ed. pap. 5.99 (978-0-689-84524-6(3) , Aladdin) Simon & Schuster Children's Publishing.

—The Report Card, Vol. 5. l.t. ed. 2004. 148p. 20.95 (978-0-7862-6767-5(4) , Large Print Pr.) Thorndike Pr.

—Room One: A Mystery or Two. Blair, Chris, illus. 2006. 176p. (J). (gr. 3-7). 15.95 (978-0-689-86686-9(0)) Simon & Schuster Children's Publishing.

Clifton, Dorinda. Take the Cake. 2006. (J). 6.95 (978-0-9771973-3-0(6)) Bedbug Pr., Inc.

Clinton, Cathryn. The Eyes of Van Gogh. 2007. (Illus.). 224p. (YA). (gr. 9 up). 16.99 (***978-0-7636-2245-9(1)***) Candlewick Pr.

Clish, Marian L. Brice & Breezy: The Mall Adventure. Robinson, Lori Clish, illus. unabr. ed. 2000. (J). (gr. k-3). pap. 10.95 incl. audio (978-1-928632-47-4(5)); pap. 14.95 incl. audio compact disk (978-1-928632-48-1(3)) Writers Marketplace:Consulting, Critiquing & Publishing.

—Brice & Breezy: The Mall Adventure. Clish-Robinson, Lori, illus. unabr. l.t. ed. 2000. 41p. (J). (gr. k-3). pap. 7.95 (978-1-928632-46-7(7)) Writers Marketplace:Consulting, Critiquing & Publishing.

—Brice & Breezy Set: The Mall Adventure. Robinson, Lori Clish, illus. 2000. (Brice & Breezy Ser.). 41p. (J). (gr. k-3). pap. 7.95 (978-1-928632-45-0(9)) Writers Marketplace:Consulting, Critiquing & Publishing.

Clulow, Helen. The Frog Prince of Barker's Bay. 2003. 162p. pap. 13.50 (978-0-7022-3335-7(8)) Univ. of Queensland Pr. AUS. *Dist:* International Specialized Bk. Services.

Cneut, Carll. The Amazing Love Story of Mr. Morf: An Astonishing Circus Romance. Cneut, Carll, illus. 2003. (Illus.). 32p. (J). (gr. k-3). tchr. ed. 15.00 (978-0-618-33170-3(0) , Clarion Bks.) Houghton Mifflin Co. Trade & Reference Div.

Coady, Mary-Francis. Lucy Maud & Me. 2005. 128p. (YA). pap., tchr. ed. (978-0-88878-398-1(1) , Sandcastle Bks.) Dundurn Group, The.

Coakley, Lena. Mrs. Goodhearth & the Gargoyle. Bailey, Wendy, illus. 2005. 32p. (J). (ps-2). 17.95 (978-1-55143-328-8(1)) Orca Bk. Pubs. USA.

Coatsworth, Elizabeth Jane. The Fair American. Sewell, Helen, illus. 2005. 137p. (J). (***978-1-883937-85-0(X)***) Bethlehem Bks.

Cockburn, Gerrie L. Why Turtles Have Shells. Cockburn, Ian, ed. Cockburn, Gerrie L., illus. (Friendship Ser.). (Illus.). 31p. (Orig.). (J). (gr. k-4). pap. 5.95 (978-1-887461-00-9(0)) Cockburn Publishing.

Cocks, Nancy. Fergie Tries to Fly. Marton, Jirina, illus. 2003. 16p. pap. (978-2-89507-275-1(2)) Novalis Publishing.

—Where, Oh Where, Is Fergie? Marton, Jirina, illus. 2003. 16p. pap. (978-2-89507-273-7(6)) Novalis Publishing.

—You Can Count on Fergie. Marton, Jirina, illus. 2003. 16p. pap. (978-2-89507-272-0(8)) Novalis Publishing.

Cocks, Nancy & Marton, Jirina. Nobody Loves Fergie. 2003. (Illus.). 16p. pap. (978-2-89507-274-4(4)) Novalis Publishing.

Cocos, Deborah. Tale One of the Wignuts: The Golden Sprigget of Fritzwitz. 2007. (J). 19.99 (***978-1-60247-034-7(0)***) Tate Publishing & Enterprises, L.L.C.

Cody's New Friends. 2006. 16p. (J). pap. 1.99 (978-0-7847-1700-4(1) , 04161) Standard Publishing.

Coffey, Maria. A Seal in the Family. Fernandes, Eugenie, illus. 1999. 32p. (J). (ps-2). lib. bdg. 17.95 (978-1-55037-581-7(4)) Annick Pr., Ltd. CAN. *Dist:* Firefly Bks., Ltd.

Cohen, Barbara S. Forever Friends. Hall, Dorothy Louise, illus. 2004. 32p. (J). reprint ed. 9.95 (978-1-931290-54-8(7)) Tallfellow Pr.

Cohen, Miriam. Two Little Mittens. Cohen, Miriam, illus. 2006. (Illus.). 24p. (J). bds. 6.95 (978-1-59572-044-3(8)) Star Bright Bks., Inc.

—Will I Have a Friend? Hoban, Lillian, illus. 2002. (J). 13.40 (978-0-7587-4028-1(X)) Book Wholesalers, Inc.

Coia, Kristina. Lymeria. 2007. 120p. (YA). 20.95 (***978-0-595-69347-4(4)***); per. 10.95 (***978-0-595-45268-2(X)***) iUniverse, Inc.

Colbert, Norman. Norman Okay, Not Today. 2001. 109p. pap. 10.95 (978-0-7414-0674-3(8)) Infinity Publishing.

Cole, Barbara H. Wash Day. Himler, Ronald, illus. 2004. 40p. (J). 15.95 (978-1-932065-36-7(9) , 7187849112) Star Bright Bks., Inc.

Cole, Brock. Celine. 2003. 224p. (YA). (gr. 7-12). pap. 6.95 (978-0-374-41082-7(8) , Sunburst) Farrar, Straus & Giroux.

—The Goats. 2003. 20.75 (978-0-8446-7238-0(6)) Smith, Peter Pub., Inc.

Cole, Joanna. Anna Banana: 101 Jump-Rope Rhymes. 2002. (J). pap. (978-0-590-44846-8(3)) Scholastic, Inc.

—Get Well, Gators! 2000. (gr. 1-4). pap. 4.95 (978-0-688-17641-9(0)) HarperCollins Pubs.

Cole, Kathryn. Pawluk. 2004. 48p. pap. 12.95 (978-1-4137-5477-3(5)) PublishAmerica, Inc.

Cole, Kenneth. Friends & Neighbors: We Love to Learn. Ruebartsch, John, photos by. 2005. (J). pap. 9.95 (978-0-9770816-1-5(3)) SHARP Literacy, Inc.

—Friends & Neighbors: We Love to Learn. Ruebartsch, John, photos by. ed. 2005. (J). 16.95 (978-0-9770816-0-8(5)) SHARP Literacy, Inc.

Cole, Michelle. Lilla Belle the First Stages. 2002. 118p. 21.99 (978-0-9722173-2-3(0)); per. 10.99 (978-0-9722173-0-9(4)) Write World, Inc.

Coleman, Gail S. Kevin & Ben. Williams-Andriani, Renee, illus. 1998. 16p. (J). (ps-k). pap. 5.95 (978-0-9655442-8-3(1)) Business Word, The.

Coleman, Michael. Weirdo's War. 1998. (Illus.). 192p. (J). (gr. 4-8). pap. 16.95 (978-0-531-30103-6(6) , Orchard Bks.) Scholastic, Inc.

Coleman, Ryan. Folli: Children's Book of Characters. 2004. 20p. (J). pap. 14.95 (978-1-4137-4098-1(7)) PublishAmerica, Inc.

Coles, William E., Jr. Another Kind of Monday. 1999. 246p. per. 14.64 (978-0-606-16357-6(3)) Tandem Library Bks.

Colfer, Eoin. Benny & Babe. 2007. 288p. (gr. 5-17). 18.95 (***978-1-4231-0283-0(5)***); pap. 7.95 (***978-1-4231-0284-7(3)***) Miramax Bks.

—Benny & Babe. 2003. 240p. (YA). pap. 7.95 (978-0-86278-603-8(7)) O'Brien Pr., Ltd., The IRL. *Dist:* Independent Pubs. Group.

—The Supernaturalist. 2004. (Illus.). 272p. (gr. 5-17). 16.95 (978-0-7868-5148-5(1)) Hyperion Bks. for Children.

—The Supernaturalist. l.t. ed. 2004. 312p. 23.95 (978-0-7862-6766-8(6) , Large Print Pr.) Thorndike Pr.

Coll, Ivar Da. Garabato. 2001. (SPA.). 32p. (J). (gr. k-2). (978-958-30-0521-3(5)) Panamericana Editorial COL. *Dist:* Lectorum Pubns., Inc.

Collier, Kristi. Jericho Walls. 2007. 224p. (YA). pap. 7.95 (***978-0-8050-8184-8(4)*** , Holt, Henry & Co. Bks. For Young Readers) Holt, Henry & Co.

Collins-Ludwick, Anne. Nancy Drew: Ghost Dogs of Moon Lake. 2002. (YA). cd-rom 19.99 (978-0-9672618-7-4(2)) Her Interactive, Inc.

Collins, P. J. Sarah. Sam & Nate. Jin, Katherine, illus. 2005. 60p. (J). lib. bdg. 20.00 (***978-1-4242-1261-3(8)***) Fitzgerald Bks.

—Sam & Nate. Jin, Katherine, illus. 2005. (Orca Echoes Ser.). 64p. (J). (gr. 2-3). pap. 4.99 (978-1-55143-334-9(6)) Orca Bk. Pubs. USA.

Collins, Paul. Knockout. 2000. (gr. 7-12). lib. bdg. 12.25 (978-0-613-28920-7(X)) Tandem Library Bks.

Collins, Suzanne. Gregor & the Prophecy of Bane. 2004. (Underland Chronicles: Bk. 2). 320p. (J). (gr. 3-6). 16.95 (978-0-439-65075-5(5) , Scholastic Pr.) Scholastic, Inc.

—Gregor & the Prophecy of Bane. l.t. ed. 2006. 297p. 23.95 (978-0-7862-8084-1(0)) Thorndike Pr.

Comfort, Louise. Daisy's Necklace. 2003. (Fairy Phones Ser.). (Illus.). 10p. (J). bds. 4.95 (978-0-7641-5691-5(8)) Barron's Educational Series, Inc.

—Poppy's Party. 2003. (Fairy Phones Ser.). (Illus.). 10p. (J). bds. 4.95 (978-0-7641-5694-6(2)) Barron's Educational Series, Inc.

—Rosie's Surprise. 2003. (Fairy Phones Ser.). (Illus.). 10p. (J). bds. 4.95 (978-0-7641-5693-9(4)) Barron's Educational Series, Inc.

Compestine, Ying Chang. The Runaway Rice Cake. Chau, Tungwai, illus. 2001. 40p. (J). (gr. k-4). 17.95 (978-0-689-82972-7(8)) Simon & Schuster Children's Publishing.

Condie, Allyson B. Yearbook. 2006. 208p. (YA). pap. 14.95 (978-1-59038-690-3(6)) Deseret Bk. Co.

Conley, Deane W. Angelino & Friends. 2007. (J). lib. bdg. 19.95 (***978-1-933732-25-1(3)*** , Bear Hug Bks.) MidAmerica Publishing Co.

Connor, Leslie. Waiting for Normal. 2008. 304p. (J). 16.99 (***978-0-06-089088-9(6)***); lib. bdg. 17.89 (***978-0-06-089089-6(4)***) HarperCollins Pubs.

Constantine. Kiquoti & the Coati. 2001. 40p. (J). (gr. k-3). 15.95 (978-0-06-028309-4(2)) HarperCollins Pubs.

Conte, Alexander. Snow Storm. 2003. (J). per. 14.95 (978-1-932303-56-8(1) , Llumina Pr.) Media Creations, Inc.

Cook, Julia. A Bad Case of Tattle Tongue. DuFalla, Anita, illus. 2006. 32p. (J). pap. (978-0-9747789-8-3(2)) CTC Publishing.

Cook, Lyn. The Hiding Place. 148p. (J). pap. 6.95 (978-0-7737-5838-4(0)) Stoddart Kids CAN. *Dist:* Fitzhenry & Whiteside, Ltd.

Cook, Sherry & Johnson, Martin. Underwater Utley, 26. Kuhn, Jesse, illus. l.t. ed. 2006. (Quirkles—Exploring Phonics through Science Ser.: 21). 32p. (J). 7.99 (978-1-933815-20-6(5) , Quirkles, The) Creative 3, LLC.

Cook, Sherry & Johnson, Terri. Gilbert Gas, 26 vols. Kuhn, Jesse, illus. l.t. ed. 2006. (Quirkles—Exploring Phonics through Science Ser.: 7). 32p. (J). 7.99 (978-1-933815-06-0(X) , Quirkles, The) Creative 3, LLC.

—Hallie Heat, 26 vols. Kuhn, Jesse, illus. l.t. ed. 2006. (Quirkles—Exploring Phonics through Science Ser.: 8). 32p. (J). 7.99 (978-1-933815-07-7(8) , Quirkles, The) Creative 3, LLC.

—Jazzy Jet, 26 vols. Kuhn, Jesse, illus. l.t. ed. 2006. (Quirkles—Exploring Phonics through Science Ser.: 10). 32p. (J). 7.99 (978-1-933815-09-1(4) , Quirkles, The) Creative 3, LLC.

—Kitchen Chemistry Kal, 26 vols. Kuhn, Jesse, illus. l.t. ed. 2006. (Quirkles—Exploring Phonics through Science Ser.: 11). 32p. (J). 7.99 (978-1-933815-10-7(8) , Quirkles, The) Creative 3, LLC.

—Mary Motion, 26 vols. Kuhn, Jesse, illus. l.t. ed. 2006. (Quirkles—Exploring Phonics through Science Ser.: 13). 32p. (J). 7.99 (978-1-933815-12-1(4) , Quirkles, The) Creative 3, LLC.

—Nosey Nina, 26 vols. Kuhn, Jesse, illus. l.t. ed. 2006. (Quirkles—Exploring Phonics through Science Ser.: 14). 32p. (J). 7.99 (978-1-933815-13-8(2) , Quirkles, The) Creative 3, LLC.

—Ollie Oxygen, 26 vols. Kuhn, Jesse, illus. l.t. ed. 2006. (Quirkles—Exploring Phonics through Science Ser.: 15). 32p. (J). 7.99 (978-1-933815-14-5(0) , Quirkles, The) Creative 3, LLC.

—Pressure Pete, 26 vols. Kuhn, Jesse, illus. l.t. ed. 2006. (Quirkles—Exploring Phonics through Science Ser.: 16). 32p. (J). 7.99 (978-1-933815-15-2(9) , Quirkles, The) Creative 3, LLC.

—Ronnie Rock, 26. Kuhn, Jesse, illus. l.t. ed. 2006. (Quirkles—Exploring Phonics through Science Ser.: 18). 32p. (J). 7.99 (978-1-933815-17-6(5) , Quirkles, The) Creative 3, LLC.

—Susie Sound, 26. Kuhn, Jesse, illus. l.t. ed. 2006. 32p. (J). 7.99 (978-1-933815-18-3(3) , Quirkles, The) Creative 3, LLC.

—Timothy Tornado, 26. Kuhn, Jesse, illus. l.t. ed. 2006. (Quirkles—Exploring Phonics through Science Ser.: 20). 32p. 7.99 (978-1-933815-19-0(1) , Quirkles, The) Creative 3, LLC.

—Vinnie Volcano, 26. Kuhn, Jesse, illus. l.t. ed. 2006. (Quirkles—Exploring Phonics through Science Ser.: 22). 32p. (J). 7.99 (978-1-933815-21-3(3) , Quirkles, The) Creative 3, LLC.

—Watery William, 26. Kuhn, Jesse, illus. l.t. ed. 2006. (Quirkles—Exploring Phonics through Science Ser.: 23). 32p. (J). 7.99 (978-1-933815-22-0(1) , Quirkles, The) Creative 3, LLC.

—X. E. Ecology, 26. Kuhn, Jesse, illus. l.t. ed. 2006. (Quirkles—Exploring Phonics through Science Ser.: 24). 32p. (J). 7.99 (978-1-933815-23-7(X) , Quirkles, The) Creative 3, LLC.

—Zany Science Zeke, 26. Kuhn, Jesse, illus. l.t. ed. 2006. (Quirkles—Exploring Phonics through Science Ser.: 26). 32p. (J). 7.99 (978-1-933815-25-1(6) , Quirkles, The) Creative 3, LLC.

Cool Moves: Individual Chapter Book Title Six-Pack. Vol. 29. 32p. (gr. 5 up). 44.00 (978-0-7578-0976-7(6)) Rigby Education.

Cooney, Caroline B. Fatality. 2001. 208p. (J). pap. 6.99 (978-0-439-13524-5(9)) Scholastic, Inc.

—Fatality. 2001. 198p. (YA). (gr. 7-12). per. 13.00 (978-0-613-35776-0(0)) Tandem Library Bks.

—Hit the Road. 2006. 192p. (gr. 7). (J). lib. bdg. 17.99 (978-0-385-90174-1(7)); (YA). 15.95 (978-0-385-72944-4(8)) Random Hse. Children's Bks. (Delacorte Bks. for Young Readers).

Cooney, Doug. I Know Who Likes You. Bernardin, James, illus. 2005. 224p. (J). pap. 4.99 (978-1-4169-0261-4(9) , Aladdin) Simon & Schuster Children's Publishing.

Cooper, Helen. El Nino Que No Queria Ir a Dormir. (SPA., Illus.). 120p. (J). (gr. k-2). 19.99 (978-84-261-3125-6(5) , JV1974) Juventud, Editorial ESP. *Dist:* Distribooks, Inc., Lectorum Pubns., Inc.

—Pumpkin Soup. 2005. (Illus.). 32p. (J). (ps-ps). pap. 6.95 (978-0-374-46031-0(0) , Farrar, Straus & Giroux (BYR)) Farrar, Straus & Giroux.

Cooper, Ilene. The Worst Noel: A Novel. 2006. 143p. (J). (gr. 4-8). reprint ed. pap. 4.00 (978-1-4223-5411-7(3)) DIANE Publishing Co.

Cooper, John. In the Groove Vol. 2: Heroes Start As Kids! l.t. ed. 2003. (Dewey Does Ser.: 2). (Illus.). 95p. (J). (ps-3). pap. 5.95 (978-0-9711474-7-8(7)) A B C-123 Publishing.

Cooper, Mimi. Me Versus Bedtime. 2006. 17p. 9.99 (978-1-4116-8255-9(6)) Lulu.com.

Cooper, Patrick. Tell Me Lies. 2007. (YA). (gr. 9). 304p. 15.99 (978-0-385-73270-3(8)); 288p. lib. bdg. 18.99 (978-0-385-90287-8(5)) Random Hse. Children's Bks. (Delacorte Bks. for Young Readers).

Copeland, Eric, illus. Brer Rabbit & Friends. 2006. 64p. (J). (gr. 8). pap. 6.99 (978-0-7566-1813-1(4)) Dorling Kindersley Publishing, Inc.

Copp, Raymond. Old Number Nine. 2003. 21 p. pap. 14.95 (978-1-4137-0682-6(7)) PublishAmerica, Inc.

Corbett, Kat. Future Perfect. 2000. (gr. 7-12). lib. bdg. 22.20 (978-0-613-83510-7(7)) Tandem Library Bks.

—Future Perfect. 2000. 228p. (YA). (gr. 7-12). pap. 12.95 (978-0-595-12886-0(6)) iUniverse, Inc.

Coren, Alan. Klondike Arthur. 2004. (Illus.). 64p. (978-0-903895-93-4(5) , Robson Bks. Ltd.) Anova Bks.

Cosgrove, Stephen. Bee Double Bopp: Respecting Others. Arroyo, Fian, illus. 2004. (J). (978-1-58804-350-4(9)) PCI Educational Publishing.

—Big Bubba Bigg, Jr: Dealing with Bullies. Arroyo, Fian, illus. 2004. (J). (978-1-58804-352-8(5)) PCI Educational Publishing.

—Catundra. James, Robin, illus. ed. 2001. (Serendipity Bks.). 32p. (J). pap. 4.99 (978-0-8431-7684-1(9) , Price Stern Sloan) Penguin Group (USA) Inc.

—Catundra. 2001. (gr. k-3). lib. bdg. 13.00 (978-0-613-88240-8(7)) Tandem Library Bks.

—Crickle-Crack. James, Robin, illus. rev. ed. 2001. (Serendipity Bks.). 32p. (J). (gr. k-4). pap. 4.99 (978-0-8431-7648-3(2) , Price Stern Sloan) Penguin Group (USA) Inc.

—Morgan & Yew. James, Robin, illus. 2001. (Serendipity Bks.). 32p. (J). pap. 4.99 (978-0-8431-7651-3(2) , Price Stern Sloan) Penguin Group (USA) Inc.

—Morgan & Yew. 2001. (gr. k-3). lib. bdg. 13.00 (978-0-613-58082-3(6)) Tandem Library Bks.

—Morgan Mine. James, Robin, illus. 2002. (J). pap. (978-0-86592-334-8(5)); 32p. reprint ed. pap. 4.99 (978-0-8431-4873-2(X)) Penguin Group (USA) Inc. (Price Stern Sloan).

—Morgan Mine. 2002. (gr. k-3). lib. bdg. 13.00 (978-0-613-64548-5(0)) Tandem Library Bks.

Cosmic Debris Staff. Emily's I Want You to Leave Me Alone. 2001. (Illus.). 128p. (gr. 8 up). 9.95 (978-0-8118-3104-8(3)) Chronicle Bks. LLC.

Costales, A. Lupe Vargas & Her Super Best Friend: Lupe Vargas y su super mejor Amiga. 2006. (ENG & SPA., Illus.). 32p. (J). 15.95 (978-0-87358-888-1(6) , Luna Rising) Northland Publishing.

Costanza, Stephen. Mozart Finds a Melody. rev. ed. 2004. (Illus.). 40p. (J). 17.95 (978-0-8050-6627-2(6) , Holt, Henry & Co. Bks. For Young Readers) Holt, Henry & Co.

Cottringer, Anne. Bruna. McClure, Gillian, illus. 2003. 32p. (J). 16.95 (978-1-58234-836-0(7) , Bloomsbury Children) Bloomsbury Publishing.

—Hot Dog. Walker, Katherine, illus. 2005. 24p. (J). lib. bdg. 22.65 (***978-1-59646-738-5(X)***) Dingles & Co.

—Mary Is Scary. Gale, Cathy, illus. 2007. 32p. (J). pap. 9.99 (***978-0-7475-7927-4(X)***) Bloomsbury Publishing Plc GBR. *Dist:* Independent Pubs. Group.

Coulton, Mia. Danny & Abby Are Friends. Coulton, Mia, photos by. 2001. 16p. (J). 4.95 (978-0-9713518-1-3(3)) Maryruth Bks., Inc.

Couric, Katie. The Brand New Kid. ed. 2004. (Illus.). (J). (ps-3). spiral bd. (978-0-616-07225-7(2)); spiral bd. (978-0-616-07226-4(0)) Canadian National Institute for the Blind/Institut National Canadien pour les Aveugles.

Cousins, Lucy. How Will This Get You There Maisy? Cousins, Lucy, illus. 2004. (Illus.). 16p. (J). (gr. k-k). 7.99 (978-0-7636-2509-2(4)) Candlewick Pr.

—Is This Maisy's House? Cousins, Lucy, illus. 2004. (Maisy Ser.). (Illus.). 16p. (J). (gr. k-k). 7.99 (978-0-7636-2510-8(8)) Candlewick Pr.

—Los Mejores Amigos de Maisy. 2004. (SPA., Illus.). 10p. (J). bds. 11.99 (978-84-8488-123-0(7)) Serres, Ediciones, S. L. ESP. *Dist:* Lectorum Pubns., Inc.

—Maisy Cleans Up. 2002. (Maisy Ser.). (Illus.). 24p. (J). (ps-k). pap. 3.99 (978-0-7636-1712-7(1)) Candlewick Pr.

—Maisy Cleans Up. 2002. (ps-2). lib. bdg. 11.00 (978-0-613-51315-9(0)) Tandem Library Bks.

—Maisy Te Quiere. 2004. (SPA., Illus.). 12p. (J). bds. 9.99 (978-84-8488-077-6(X)) Serres, Ediciones, S. L. ESP. *Dist:* Lectorum Pubns., Inc.

—Smile, Maisy! Cousins, Lucy, illus. 2004. (Maisy Ser.). (Illus.). 16p. (J). (gr. k-k). bds. 7.99 (978-0-7636-2368-5(7)) Candlewick Pr.

Cousins, Lucy. With Love from Maisy: Mini Edition. Cousins, Lucy, illus. 2007. (Maisy Ser.). (Illus.). 16p. (J). (ps). 4.99 (***978-0-7636-3539-8(1)***) Candlewick Pr.

Coville, Bruce. Jeremy Thatcher, Dragon Hatcher: A Magic Shop Book. Lippincott, Gary A., illus. 2007. (Magic Shop Book Ser.). 168p. (J). (gr. 3-7). pap. 5.95 (***978-0-15-206252-1(1)*** , Magic Carpet Bks.) Harcourt Children's Bks.

—My Teacher Flunked the Planet. Pierard, John, illus. 2005. 162p. (J). (gr. 3-7). lib. bdg. 12.04 (978-0-606-33892-9(6)) Tandem Library Bks.

—The Skull of Truth: A Magic Shop Book. Lippincott, Gary A., illus. 2007. (Magic Shop Book Ser.). 208p. (J). pap. 5.95 (978-0-15-206084-8(7) , Magic Carpet Bks.) Harcourt Children's Bks.

Cowan, Catherine. My Life with the Wave. ed. 2004. (Illus.). (J). (gr. k-3). spiral bd. (978-0-616-01621-3(2)) Canadian National Institute for the Blind/Institut National Canadien pour les Aveugles.

—My Life with the Wave. Buehner, Mark, illus. 2004. 32p. (J). (ps-3). reprint ed. pap. 6.99 (978-0-06-056200-7(5) , Harper Trophy) HarperCollins Pubs.

—My Life with the Wave. 2004. (gr. k-3). lib. bdg. 15.30 (978-0-613-83570-1(0)) Tandem Library Bks.

Cox, Judy. Butterfly Buddies. Sims, Blanche, illus. 2001. 96p. (J). (gr. 4-6). tchr. ed. 15.95 (978-0-8234-1654-7(2)) Holiday Hse., Inc.

—That Crazy Eddie & the Science Project of Doom. Simms, Blanche, illus. 2005. 96p. (J). 15.95 (978-0-8234-1931-9(2)) Holiday Hse., Inc.

Cox, Rhonda. Best Friends. Cox, Rhonda, photos by. 2003. (Illus.). 16p. (J). pap. 20.00 net. (978-1-57274-699-2(8) , BB2126) Owen, Richard C. Pubs., Inc.

—Best Friends. 1999. (Books for Young Learners). (Illus.). 16p. (J). (gr. k-2). pap. 5.00 (978-1-57274-237-6(2)) Owen, Richard C. Pubs., Inc.

Cox, Tory. A Silent Cry in the Night. 2005. 148p. pap. 19.95 (978-1-4137-8255-4(8)) PublishAmerica, Inc.

Coxe, Molly. Bookworm. 2000. (J). (978-0-606-18920-0(3)) Tandem Library Bks.

Crabtree, Dianne. On the Road to Royalty. 2005. 222p. (YA). pap. 14.95 (978-1-932898-32-3(8) , 98328) Spring Creek Bk. Co.

Craft, Elizabeth & Fain, Sarah. Bass Ackwards & Belly Up. 2006. 240p. (J). (gr. 7-17). 16.99 (978-0-316-05793-6(2)) Little Brown & Co.

—Bass Ackwards & Belly Up. 2007. 404p. (J). (gr. 10 up). pap. 8.99 (***978-0-316-05794-3(0)*** , Poppy) Little, Brown Bks. for Young Readers.

Crane, E. M. Skin Deep. 2008. (YA). (***978-0-385-73479-0(4)*** , Delacorte Pr.) Dell Publishing.

Craven, Tracy Leininger. Kathleen's Unforgettable Winter. 2006. (Life of Faith': Kathleen Mckenzie Ser.). 160p. (YA). pap. 6.99 (978-1-928749-26-4(7)) Zonderkidz.

Cravens, Dave. Crusaders of a Dying Breed. 2000. 200p. (YA). pap. 9.95 (978-1-893652-91-0(2) , Writers Club Pr.) iUniverse, Inc.

Creech, Sharon. Entre Dos Lunas. 2003. (SPA., Illus.). 191p. (YA). (gr. 5-8). (978-84-279-3221-0(9) , NG7785) Noguer y Caralt Editores, S. A. ESP. *Dist:* Lectorum Pubns., Inc.

—Heartbeat. (J). 2005. 208p. pap. 5.99 (978-0-06-054024-1(9)); 2004. 192p. 15.99 (978-0-06-054022-7(2)); 2004. 192p. lib. bdg. 16.89 (978-0-06-054023-4(0)) HarperCollins Pubs.

—Heartbeat. l.t. ed. 2004. 160p. 23.95 (978-0-7862-6902-0(2) , Large Print Pr.) Thorndike Pr.

—Walk Two Moons. 2002. (Illus.). (J). 15.00 (978-0-7587-0223-4(X)) Book Wholesalers, Inc.

—Walk Two Moons. 2004. 304p. (J). (gr. 7 up). pap. 6.99 (978-0-06-056013-3(4) , Harper Trophy) HarperCollins Pubs.

—Walk Two Moons. 1999. (J). 9.95 (978-1-56137-770-1(8)); 11.95 (978-1-56137-771-8(6)) Novel Units, Inc.

—Walk Two Moons. 1998. (Assessment Packs Ser.). 15p. (J). pap., tchr.'s training gde. ed. 15.95 (978-1-58303-067-7(0)) Pathways Publishing.

—Walk Two Moons. 280p. (J). (gr. 4-6). pap. 4.95 (978-0-8072-1509-8(0) , Listening Library) Random Hse. Audio Publishing Group.

—Walk Two Moons. 2004. (gr. 7-12). lib. bdg. 14.75 (978-0-613-81971-8(3)) Tandem Library Bks.

—Walk Two Moons. l.t. ed. 287p. 2003. pap. 10.95 (978-0-7862-6185-7(4)); 2000. (Illus.). (J). 21.95 (978-0-7862-2773-0(7)) Thorndike Pr.

Crew, Gary. The End of the Line. Rogers, Gregory, illus. 2008. 80p. (J). pap. (***978-1-59889-915-3(5)***); (YA). (gr. 5-9). lib. bdg. 16.95 (***978-1-59889-859-0(0)***) Stone Arch Bks.

Crew, Gary. The Watertower. 2000. 32p. (J). (gr. 2-9). pap. 7.95 (978-1-56656-331-4(3) , Crocodile Bks.) Interlink Publishing Group, Inc.

Crimi, Carolyn. Boris & Bella. Grimly, Gris, illus. 32p. (J). 2004. 15.00 (978-0-15-202528-1(6)); 2006. reprint ed. pap. 6.00 (978-0-15-205900-2(8) , Voyager Bks./Libros Viajeros) Harcourt Children's Bks.

—Don't Need Friends. Munsinger, Lynn, illus. 2001. 32p. (J). (ps-3). reprint ed. pap. 6.99 (978-0-440-41532-9(2) , Dragonfly Bks.) Random Hse. Children's Bks.

—Don't Need Friends. 2001. (gr. k-3). lib. bdg. 15.30 (978-0-613-33752-6(2)) ; (Illus.). (J). 13.79 (978-0-606-21156-7(X)) Tandem Library Bks.

—No Necesito Amigos. 2004. (SPA.). 32p. (978-84-7720-798-6(4)) Obelisco, Ediciones S.A.

Crist, Darlene T. Losing Eubie. Sassano, Deidre, illus. 1998. 40p. (J). (gr. 3-5). pap. 9.95 (978-0-9665072-0-1(7)) Red Bird Publishing.

Criswell, Millie. The Trials of Angela. 2002. 336p. mass mkt. 6.99 (978-0-8041-1993-1(7) , Ivy Bks.) Random House Publishing Group.

—The Trials of Angela. l.t. ed. 2002. (Wheeler Softcover Ser.). 366p. pap. 23.95 (978-1-58724-276-2(1) , Wheeler Publishing, Inc.) Thomson Gale.

Crocker, Nancy. Billie Standish Was Here. 2007. 288p. (YA). (gr. 9 up). 16.99 (978-1-4169-2423-4(X)) Simon & Schuster Children's Publishing.

Crompton, Paul. Remarkable for Short. 2005. 113p. pap. 16.95 (978-1-4241-0287-7(1)) PublishAmerica, Inc.

Cromwell, Patricia L. Marguerita & Sarabella's Glad Day. D. B. and Associates Design Group Staff & Butler, Dwayne, illus. l.t. ed. 2001. 16p. (J). (ps-6). pap. 6.95 (978-0-9664794-0-9(8) , 041998) Patty Cake Bks.

Cronin, Susan L. Gidget Goes Away. 2006. 54p. pap. 12.95 (978-1-4137-9878-4(0)) PublishAmerica, Inc.

Croteau-Fleury, Marie-Danielle. Des Citrouilles pour Cendrillon. 2003. (Premier Roman Ser.). (FRE., Illus.). 64p. (J). (gr. 2-5). pap. (978-2-89021-359-3(5)) Diffusion du livre Mirabel.

Croteau, Marie-Danielle & Beauregard, Christiane. La Petite Fille Qui Voulait Etre Roi. 2001. (FRE., Illus.). 24p. (J). pap. (978-2-89021-541-2(5)) Diffusion du livre Mirabel.

Croteau, Marie-Danielle & Cote, Genevieve. Et Si Quelqu'un Venait un Jour. 2002. (Roman + Ser.). (FRE.). 160p. (YA). (gr. 8). pap. (978-2-89021-560-3(1)) Diffusion du livre Mirabel.

Crouch, Cheryl Lynne. Chosen Girls/Backstage Pass. 2007. (Chosen Girls' Ser.). 144p. (J). pap. 3.99 (978-0-310-71267-1(X)) Zonderkidz.

Crouse, Donna J. The Ruby Ring: The Whispering Cove Kids Club. 2005. 114p. pap. 12.99 (978-0-9765339-0-0(1)) Crouse, Donna J.

Crow, Gary & Crow, Marissa. The Friend Factory. 2002. (Illus.). 71p. (J). pap. 9.95 (978-0-9718758-2-1(0)) Koenisha Pubns.

Crowther, Kitty. Jack & Jim: Picture Book. Date not set. (Illus.). 32p. (J). pap. 5.99 (978-0-7868-1439-8(X)); 15.99 (978-0-7868-0614-0(1)); 16.49 (978-0-7868-2527-1(8)) Hyperion Bks. for Children.

Cruise, Robin. Fiona's Private Pages. 2002. (gr. 3-6). lib. bdg. 14.15 (978-0-613-46254-9(8)) Tandem Library Bks.

Cruise, Robin & Cruise, Roberta Ann. Fiona's Private Pages. 2002. 200p. (YA). (gr. 3-7). pap. 6.95 (978-0-15-216572-7(X) , Harcourt Paperbacks) Harcourt Children's Bks.

Crum, Shutta. Spitting Image. 2003. 224p. (J). tchr. ed. 15.00 (978-0-618-23477-6(2) , Clarion Bks.) Houghton Mifflin Co. Trade & Reference Div.

Crummel, Susan Stevens. Shoe Town. 1999. (gr. k-3). lib. bdg. 11.80 (978-0-613-66029-7(3)) Tandem Library Bks.

Crummel, Susan Stevens & Donohue, Dorothy. City Dog & Country Dog. Donohue, Dorothy, illus. unabr. ed. 2006. (Illus.). (J). (gr. k-3). 27.95 incl. audio (978-0-8045-6942-2(8) , SAC6942); 29.95 incl. audio compact disk (978-0-8045-4156-5(6)) Spoken Arts, Inc.

—City Dog, Country Dog. Donohue, Dorothy, illus. 2004. (Illus.). 32p. (J). 16.95 (978-0-7614-5156-3(0)) Cavendish, Marshall Corp.

Crummel, Susan Stevens & Stevens, Janet. Shoe Town. 2003. (Green Light Readers Level 2 Ser.). (Illus.). 32p. (J). 11.95 (978-0-15-204882-2(0)); pap. 3.95 (978-0-15-204842-6(1) , Green Light Readers) Harcourt Children's Bks.

Cumbie, Patricia. Where People Like Us Live. 2008. 224p. (J). 16.99 (***978-0-06-137597-2(7)***); lib. bdg. 17.89 (***978-0-06-137598-9(5)***) HarperCollins Pubs. (Geringer, Laura Book).

Cumings, Jean. Luna. Cumings, Jean, illus. 2001. (Illus.). 32p. (J). (ps-3). pap. 7.50 (978-1-884083-24-2(2)) Maval Publishing, Inc.

Cumming, Peter. Out on the Ice in the Middle of the Bay. Priestley, Alice, illus. 10th rev. anniv. ed. 2004. 32p. (J). (gr. k-3). pap. 7.95 (978-1-55037-870-2(8)) Annick Pr., Ltd. CAN. *Dist:* Firefly Bks., Ltd.

Cummings, Priscilla. Red Kayak. (gr. 5). 2006. 224p. (YA). pap. 6.99 (978-0-14-240573-4(6) , Puffin); 2004. 192p. (J). 15.99 (978-0-525-47317-6(3) , Dutton Juvenile) Penguin Group (USA) Inc.

Cumyn, Alan. After Sylvia. 2005. 200p. (J). (gr. 4-7). pap. 6.95 (978-0-88899-646-6(2) , Libros Tigrillo) Groundwood Bks. CAN. *Dist:* Perseus Distribution.

Cunningham, Mary. Cynthia's Attic: The Missing Locket. 2005. (J). pap. 9.99 (978-1-59080-441-4(4)) Echelon Press Publishing.

Curry, Kenneth. Star & Peanut. 2007. (Illus.). 22p. (J). 10.95 (***978-0-9798364-9-7(2)***) Curry Brothers Publishing.

Curtis, Alice Turner. A Yankee Girl at Fort Sumter. 2005. 180p. pap. 11.95 (978-1-4218-0401-9(8) , 1st World Library - Literary Society) 1st World Publishing, Inc.

Curtis, Christopher Paul. Bud, Not Buddy. unabr. ed. 2004. 256p. (J). (gr. 4-7). pap. 36.00 incl. audio (978-0-8072-8210-6(3) , LYA 140 S(, Listening Library) Random Hse. Audio Publishing Group.

—Bud, Not Buddy. 2002. (Illus.). 256p. (J). (gr. 5-7). pap. 6.99 (978-0-440-41328-8(1) , Yearling) Random Hse. Children's Bks.

Cushman, Karen. The Loud Silence of Francine Green. 2006. 240p. (J). (gr. 5-9). 16.00 (978-0-618-50455-8(9) , Clarion Bks.) Houghton Mifflin Co. Trade & Reference Div.

Cuthbert, Bob. Friends & More. Beltran, Alex, illus. 1999. 36p. (J). (gr. k-3). 14.95 (978-0-9670394-0-4(1)) Billy B Enterprises.

Cutler, Jane. Rose & Riley. Yezerski, Thomas F., illus. 2005. (Rose & Riley Ser.). 48p. (J). 15.00 (978-0-374-36340-6(4) , Farrar, Straus & Giroux (BYR)) Farrar, Straus & Giroux.

—Rose & Riley Come & Go. Yezerski, Thomas F., illus. 2005. (Rose & Riley Ser.). 48p. (J). 15.00 (978-0-374-36341-3(2) , Farrar, Straus & Giroux (BYR)) Farrar, Straus & Giroux.

Cyr, Joe. Magical Trees & Crayons: Great Stories. 2006. (Illus.). pap. 9.95 (***978-0-9778525-6-7(3)***) Peppertree Pr., The.

D C Thomson Staff, ed. People's Friend Annual 2004. 2004. (Illus.). 176p. 9.95 (978-0-85116-832-6(9)) Thomson, D.C. & Co., Ltd. GBR. *Dist:* APG Sales and Fulfillment.

Dadey, Debbie. The Worst Name in Third Grade. 2007. 80p. (J). pap. 3.99 (***978-0-439-72000-7(1)***) Scholastic, Inc.

Dadey, Debbie & Jones, Marcia Thornton. Class Trip to the Haunted House. 2005. (Ghostville Elementary Ser.: No. 10). (Illus.). 96p. (J). pap. 3.99 (978-0-439-67809-4(9) , Scholastic Paperbacks) Scholastic, Inc.

Daggett, Wade. Coco's New Friend. 2004. 35p. pap. 17.95 (978-1-4137-2001-3(3)) PublishAmerica, Inc.

Dahl, Lesley. The Problem with Paradise. 2006. 224p. (J). (gr. 3-7). 15.95 (978-0-385-73335-9(6)); lib. bdg. 17.99 (978-0-385-90352-3(9)) Random Hse. Children's Bks. (Delacorte Bks. for Young Readers).

D'Allessandro, Alan. Growing Out of Fear. 2005. 62p. pap. 12.95 (978-1-4137-8547-0(6)) PublishAmerica, Inc.

Dalmatian Press Staff. Anne of Green Gables. (Great Classics for Children Ser.). (Illus.). 192p. (J). 5.99 (978-1-4037-0591-4(7)) Dalmatian Pr.

—Disney Best Friends: Valentines Day. 2005. 16p. bds. 5.99 (978-1-4037-1905-8(5)) Dalmatian Pr.

—Disney Mickey Mouse & All His Friends: 400 Pages of Coloring Fun. 2006. 400p. pap. 5.99 (978-1-4037-1967-6(5)) Dalmatian Pr.

—Rosie in the Way. 2002. (Illus.). 24p. (J). (gr. k-5). pap. 2.99 (978-1-57759-367-6(7)) Dalmatian Pr.

Dalmatian Press Staff, adapted by. Anne of Green Gables. 2002. (Spot the Classics Ser.). (Illus.). 176p. (J). (gr. k-5). 4.99 (978-1-57759-543-4(2)) Dalmatian Pr.

Daly, Catherine. Best Friends. 2000. (gr. k-3). lib. bdg. 11.25 (978-0-613-30993-6(6)) Tandem Library Bks.

Daly, Niki. Once upon a Time. Daly, Niki, illus. 2003. (Illus.). 32p. (J). (gr. k-3). 16.00 (978-0-374-35633-0(5) , Farrar, Straus & Giroux (BYR)) Farrar, Straus & Giroux.

Daly-Weir, Catherine. Love Is All You Need. 2000. (gr. k-3). lib. bdg. 14.15 (978-0-613-21934-1(1)) Tandem Library Bks.

D'Amico, Carmela & D'Amico, Steven. Ella Sets the Stage. 2006. (Illus.). 48p. (J). pap. 16.99 (978-0-439-83152-9(0) , Levine, Arthur A. Bks.) Scholastic, Inc.

Daniels, Lucy. Into the Blue. 2002. (J). pap. 29.95 incl. audio (978-0-7540-6245-5(7)) BBC Audiobooks America.

Daniels, Lucy. Oscar's Best Friends. 2005. 57p. (***978-0-439-68199-5(5)***) Scholastic, Inc.

Daniels, Teri. The Feet in the Gym. Foster, Travis, illus. 1999. 40p. (J). (ps-3). 15.95 (978-1-890817-12-1(0)) Winslow Pr.

Danziger, Paula. Amber Brown Goes Fourth. Ross, Tony, illus. 2002. (Amber Brown Ser.: No. 3). (J). (gr. 3-6). 12.17 (978-0-7587-0417-7(8)) Book Wholesalers, Inc.

—Amber Brown Goes Fourth. 2007. (Amber Brown Ser.: No. 3). 112p. (J). (gr. 2-6). 4.99 (***978-0-14-240901-5(4)*** , Puffin) Penguin Group (USA) Inc.

—Amber Brown Goes Fourth. (Amber Brown Ser.: No. 3). 112p. (J). (gr. 3-6). pap. 3.99 (978-0-8072-1291-2(1) , Listening Library) Random Hse. Audio Publishing Group.

—Amber Brown Is Not a Crayon. Ross, Tony, illus. 2006. (Amber Brown Ser.: No. 1). 80p. (J). (gr. 2-6). pap. 4.99 (978-0-14-240619-9(8) , Puffin) Penguin Group (USA) Inc.

—Amber Brown Is Not a Crayon. (Amber Brown Ser.: No. 1). 80p. (J). (gr. 3-6). pap. 3.50 (978-0-8072-1289-9(X) , Listening Library) Random Hse. Audio Publishing Group.

—It's a Fair Day, Amber Brown. Ross, Tony, illus. 2003. 28.95 incl. audio compact disk (978-1-59112-565-5(0)); pap. 31.95 incl. audio compact disk (978-1-59112-564-8(2)) Live Oak Media.

—It's a Fair Day, Amber Brown. Ross, Tony, illus. 2003. 48p. (J). (gr. k-2). pap. 3.99 (978-0-698-11982-6(7) , Puffin) Penguin Group (USA) Inc.

—It's a Fair Day, Amber Brown. 2003. (gr. k-3). lib. bdg. 11.80 (978-0-613-61635-5(9)) Tandem Library Bks.

—It's an Aardvark-Eat-Turtle World. 2000. (Illus.). (J). 11.64 (978-0-606-18469-4(4)) Tandem Library Bks.

—It's Justin Time, Amber Brown. Ross, Tony, illus. 9.95 (978-1-59112-294-4(5)) Live Oak Media.

—It's Justin Time, Amber Brown. 2002. (Illus.). (J). pap., tchr.'s planning gde. ed. 29.95 incl. audio (978-0-87499-908-2(1)) Live Oak Media.

—It's Justin Time, Amber Brown. Ross, Tony, illus. 2002. 28.95 incl. audio compact disk (978-1-59112-567-9(7)); pap. 31.95 incl. audio compact disk (978-1-59112-566-2(9)) Live Oak Media.

—It's Justin Time, Amber Brown. abr. ed. 2002. (Illus.). (J). (ps-2). 25.95 incl. audio (978-0-87499-907-5(3)); pap. 16.95 incl. audio (978-0-87499-906-8(5)) Live Oak Media.

—It's Justin Time, Amber Brown. Ross, Tony, illus. 2001. (Amber Brown Ser.: No. 10). 1p. (J). (gr. 3-6). 13.99 (978-0-399-23470-5(5) , Putnam Juvenile) Penguin Group (USA) Inc.

—It's Justin Time, Amber Brown. 2001. 10.79 (978-0-606-22522-9(6)) Tandem Library Bks.

—Not for a Billion Gazillion Dollars. 1998. (Matthew Martin Ser.: No. 4). (Illus.). 126p. (J). (gr. 3-7). pap. 4.99 (978-0-698-11693-1(3) , Putnam Juvenile) Penguin Group (USA) Inc.

—Orange You Glad It's Halloween, Amber Brown? Ross, Tony, illus. 2005. 48p. (J). (gr. 2-5). 13.99 (978-0-399-23471-2(3) , Putnam Juvenile) Penguin Group (USA) Inc.

—P. S. Longer Letter Later: A Novel in Letters. 1999. (gr. 5-8). lib. bdg. 13.00 (978-0-613-18271-3(5)) Tandem Library Bks.

—Remember Me to Harold Square. 1999. (Illus.). 160p. (J). (gr. 5-9). pap. 5.99 (978-0-698-11694-8(1) , Putnam Juvenile) Penguin Group (USA) Inc.

—Remember Me to Harold Square. 139p. (YA). (gr. 6 up). pap. 3.99 (978-0-8072-1472-5(8) , Listening Library) Random Hse. Audio Publishing Group.

—Remember Me to Harold Square. 1999. (gr. k-9). (Illus.). 139p. (J). per. 13.00 (978-0-8335-1660-2(4)); (978-0-606-16795-6(1)) Tandem Library Bks.

—Seguiremos Siendo Amigos.Tr. of Amber Brown Is Not a Crayon. (J). (gr. 4-5). 8.95 (978-970-29-0185-3(5) , AF33034) Santillana, S.A. de C.V., Editorial MEX. *Dist:* Santillana USA Publishing Co., Inc.

—¿Seguiremos Siendo Amigos? 97th ed. 2003. (SPA., Illus.). 106p. (gr. 3-5). 24.60 (978-84-204-4857-2(5) , SAN8575) Harcourt Schl. Pubs.

—Snail Mail No More. 2001. (Illus.). (J). (978-0-606-21436-0(4)); 2000. (gr. 3-6). lib. bdg. 13.00 (978-0-613-35753-1(1)) Tandem Library Bks.

—United Tates of America. 2006. 144p. (J). pap. 5.99 (978-0-439-83883-2(5) , Scholastic Paperbacks) Scholastic, Inc.

—United Tates of America. Danziger, Paula, illus. 2002. (Illus.). 144p. (J). (gr. 3-7). pap. 17.95 (978-0-590-69221-2(6) , Scholastic Pr.) Scholastic, Inc.

—United Tates of America: The Story & the Scrapbook. 2002. (gr. 3-6). lib. bdg. 14.15 (978-0-613-67042-5(6)) Tandem Library Bks.

—What a Trip, Amber Brown. 2002. (Illus.). (J). pap. 16.95 incl. audio (978-0-87499-910-5(3)); pap. 18.95 incl. audio compact disk (978-1-59112-368-2(2)); pap., tchr.'s planning gde. ed. 29.95 incl. audio (978-0-87499-912-9(X)); 25.95 incl. audio (978-0-87499-911-2(1)) Live Oak Media.

—What a Trip, Amber Brown. Ross, Tony, illus. 2001. (J). 48p. pap. 3.99 (978-0-698-11908-6(8)); (Amber Brown Ser.: No. 9). 1p. (gr. 3-6). 13.99 (978-0-399-23469-9(1)) Penguin Group (USA) Inc. (Putnam Juvenile).

—What a Trip, Amber Brown. 2001. (978-0-606-22523-6(4)); lib. bdg. 11.80 (978-0-613-44429-3(9)) Tandem Library Bks.

Danziger, Paula & Martin, Ann M. P. S. Longer Letter Later: A Novel in Letters. 240p. (J). (gr. 3-5). pap. 4.99 (978-0-8072-1537-1(6) , Listening Library) Random Hse. Audio Publishing Group.

—P. S. Longer Letter Later: A Novel in Letters. 240p. 2006. (J). pap. 5.99 (978-0-439-83884-9(3) , Scholastic Paperbacks); 1999. (gr. 3-7). 6.99 (978-0-590-21311-0(3)); 1998. (J). (gr. 5-8). pap. 16.95 (978-0-590-21310-3(5)) Scholastic, Inc.

—Snail Mail No More. unabr. ed. 2004. 307p. (J). (gr. 3-7). pap. 36.00 incl. audio (978-0-8072-8413-1(0) , Listening Library) Random Hse. Audio Publishing Group.

—Snail Mail No More. 2001. (Illus.). 320p. (J). (gr. 3-7). pap. 5.99 (978-0-439-06336-4(1) , Scholastic Paperbacks) Scholastic, Inc.

Darden, Hunter D. The Reel Thing: A Story of Faith, Hope & Friendship. Arnold, Nicole, illus. 2001. 44p. (J). (gr. k-5). 19.95 (978-0-9653729-3-0(6)) Sunfleur Pubns., Inc.

Davidson, Betsy. Twyla Tulip & Her Talking Toes: A Friendship Story. Norcross, Harry, illus. 2000. 16p. (J). (gr. 1-3). pap. 6.95 (978-1-57543-080-5(0)) MAR*CO Products, Inc.

Davie, Jan. Stairway to the Stars. 2005. 76p. pap. (***978-1-84401-569-6(6)***) Athena Pr.

Davies, Sally J. K. When William Went Away. Davies, Sally J. K., illus. 1998. (Picture Bks.). (Illus.). 32p. (J). (ps-3). lib. bdg. 15.95 (978-1-57505-303-5(9) , Carolrhoda Bks.) Lerner Publishing Group.

Davis, Anne. Bud & Gabby. Davis, Anne, illus. 2006. (Illus.). 32p. (J). 15.99 (978-0-06-075350-4(1)); lib. bdg. 16.89 (978-0-06-075351-1(X)) HarperCollins Pubs.

Davis, Caroline, illus. My Friends. 2007. 12p. (J). (ps). bds. 6.95 (***978-1-58925-823-5(1)*** , tiger tales) ME Media LLC.

Davis, Gwendolyn Michelle. Where I Belong. 2004. 114p. pap. 16.95 (978-1-4137-3757-8(9)) PublishAmerica, Inc.

Davis, Heather J. The Friendship Hole. 2006. (ENG.). 28p. per. 13.99 (***978-1-4259-7184-7(9)***) AuthorHouse.

Davis, Jenny. Good-Bye & Keep Cold. 2005. 224p. (J). pap. 5.99 (978-0-439-70682-7(3) , Scholastic Paperbacks) Scholastic, Inc.

Davis, Mike. Land of the Lost Mammoths: A Science Adventure. 2003. (Illus.). 174p. (J). 15.95 (978-0-9747078-0-8(5)) Perceval Pr.

Davis, Stephie. Smart Boys & Fast Girls. 2005. (YA). mass mkt. 5.99 (978-0-8439-5398-5(5) , SMOOCH) Dorchester Publishing Co., Inc.

Davoll, Barbara. Christopher & His Friends. Hockerman, Dennis, illus. 2003. (Christopher Churchmouse Ser.). 128p. (J). 14.99 (978-0-8423-5734-0(3)) Tyndale Hse. Pubs.

—Saved by the Bell. Hockerman, Dennis, illus. 1999. (Christopher Churchmouse Classics Ser.). 24p. (J). (ps-3). 7.99 (978-0-8024-4934-4(4)) Moody Pubs.

Dawson, JoAnn. Lady's Big Surprise. 2007. (Lucky Foot Stable Ser.). 272p. (J). (gr. 3 up). pap. 6.99 (***978-1-4022-0996-3(7)*** , Sourcebooks Jabberwocky) Sourcebooks, Inc.

—Star of Wonder. 2007. (Lucky Foot Stable Ser.). 192p. (J). (gr. 3 up). pap. 6.99 (***978-1-4022-0997-0(5)*** , Sourcebooks Jabberwocky) Sourcebooks, Inc.

Dawson, JoAnn. Willie to the Rescue. 2006. 264p. 15.95 (978-0-9746561-0-6(0)); pap. 8.95 (978-0-9746561-2-0(7)) FT Richards Publishing.

Dawson, Phoebe. Joshua Finds a Friend. Trader, Julie, illus. 1998. (Child of Destiny Ser.). 24p. (J). (gr. k-5). 9.95 (978-1-889018-47-8(3)) Micah Publishing.

Dawson, Stephanie Mara. The best recess Ever. 2nd ed. 2004. (J). per. 15.95 (978-0-9748990-0-8(3)) Bk. Nook Productions.

Day, Karen. No Cream Puffs. 2008. 160p. (J). (gr. 5). 15.99 (***978-0-375-83775-3(2)***); lib. bdg. 18.99 (***978-0-375-93775-0(7)***) Random Hse. Children's Bks. (Lamb, Wendy).

Day, Lauren. Can You Keep a Secret? 2000. (Rockett's World Ser.: No. 4). (Illus.). 128p. (J). (gr. 4-7). pap. 3.99 (978-0-439-08210-5(2) , Scholastic Paperbacks) Scholastic, Inc.

—Can You Keep a Secret? 2000. (Rockett's World Ser.: No. 4). (J). (gr. 4-7). (978-0-606-18594-3(1)) Tandem Library Bks.

—What Kind of Friend Are You? 1999. (Rockett's World Ser.: No. 2). (Illus.). 128p. (J). (gr. 4-7). pap. 3.99 (978-0-439-06312-8(4)) Scholastic, Inc.

—What Kind of Friend Are You? 1999. (Rockett's World Ser.: No. 2). (J). (gr. 4-7). (978-0-606-17050-5(2)) Tandem Library Bks.

—Who's Running This Show? 6th ed. 2000. (Rockett's World Ser.: No. 6). (Illus.). 128p. (J). (gr. 4-7). pap. 3.99 (978-0-439-08695-0(7)) Scholastic, Inc.

—Who's Running This Show? 2000. (Rockett's World Ser.: No. 6). (J). (gr. 4-7). (978-0-606-18888-3(6)) Tandem Library Bks.

de Beer, Hans. Lars & His Friends: Board Book & Doll. 2004. (Little Polar Bear Story Ser.). (Illus.). 22p. 9.95 (978-1-4027-1341-5(X)) Sterling Publishing Co., Inc.

—Little Polar Bear & the Reindeer. 2005. (Illus.). 28p. (J). (ps up). 15.95 (978-0-7358-2029-6(5)) North-South Bks., Inc.

—Llevame a Casa, Osito Polar! Gambolini, Gerardo, tr. from GER. 2001. (SPA & ENG., Illus.). 32p. (J). (gr. k-3). pap. 6.95 (978-0-7358-1500-1(3) , NS30711) North-South Bks., Inc.

—Llevame a Casa, Osito Polar! 2001. (gr. k-3). (SPA.). lib. bdg. 15.25 (978-0-613-73576-6(5)); (978-0-606-22735-3(0)) Tandem Library Bks.

—El Osito Polar y el Conejito Valiente. 2000. (SPA.). (gr. k-3). lib. bdg. 15.25 (978-0-613-32923-1(6)) Tandem Library Bks.

de Brunhoff, Laurent. Babar y Sus Amigos: Letras y Numeros. l.t. ed. 2000. (Babar Ser.).Tr. of Babar & His Friends: Letters & Numbers. (SPA., Illus.). 48p. (J). 15.95 (978-84-7546-912-6(4)) Beascoa, Ediciones S.A. ESP. *Dist:* Distribooks, Inc.

—Babar y Sus Amigos de Vacaciones. l.t. ed. 2000. (Babar Ser.).Tr. of Babar & His Friends on Vacation. (SPA., Illus.). 48p. (J). 15.95 (978-84-7546-535-7(8)) Beascoa, Ediciones S.A. ESP. *Dist:* Distribooks, Inc.

—Babar's Little Girl Makes a Friend. 2002. (Babar Ser.). (Illus.). 30p. (J). (ps-3). 9.95 (978-0-8109-0556-6(6)) Abrams, Harry N. , Inc.

De Campi, Alex. Kat & Mouse Volume 3. 2007. (Illus.). 96p. pap. 5.99 (***978-1-59816-550-0(X)*** , Tokyopop Kids) TOKYOPOP, Inc.

De Graaf, Anne. Peter. Montero, Jose Perez, illus. 2001. 38p. (J). (ps-1). 5.99 (978-0-8054-2189-7(0)) B&H Publishing Grp.

de la Cruz, Melissa. Angels on Sunset Boulevard, No. 1. Torre, Sigmund, illus. 2007. (Angels on Sunset Boulevard Ser.). 240p. (YA). (gr. 9 up). 15.99 (978-1-4169-2767-9(0)) Simon & Schuster.

—The Au Pairs. 2005. (Au Pairs Ser.: No. 1). 320p. (YA). reprint ed. pap. 8.99 (978-0-689-87319-5(0) , Simon Pulse) Simon & Schuster Children's Publishing.

—The Au Pairs. l.t. ed. 2006. (Au Pairs Ser.: No. 1). 417p. 21.95 (978-0-7862-8291-3(6)) Thorndike Pr.

—Crazy Hot. 2007. (Au Pairs Ser.: No. 4). 288p. (YA). 16.99 (978-1-4169-3961-0(X)) Simon & Schuster Children's Publishing.

—Skinny-dipping. 2006. (Au Pairs Ser.: No. 2). 304p. (YA). (gr. 9 up). reprint ed. pap. 8.99 (978-1-4169-0383-3(6) , Simon & Schuster Children's Publishing) Simon & Schuster Children's Publishing.

—Sun-Kissed. 2007. (Au Pairs Ser.: No. 3). 320p. (YA). pap. 8.99 (978-1-4169-1747-2(0) , Simon Pulse) Simon & Schuster Children's Publishing.

De Lint, Charles. Dingo. 2008. 192p. (YA). (gr. 7). 11.99 (***978-0-14-240816-2(6)*** , Puffin) Penguin Group (USA) Inc.

de Paola, Tomie. Big Anthony: His Story. de Paola, Tomie, illus. 1998. (Illus.). 32p. (J). (ps-3). 16.99 (978-0-399-23189-6(7) , Putnam Juvenile) Penguin Group (USA) Inc.

—Four Friends at Christmas. de Paola, Tomie, illus. 32p. (J). 2005. pap. 6.99 (978-1-4169-0697-1(5) , Aladdin); 2002. (Illus.). 14.95 (978-0-689-85282-4(7)) Simon & Schuster Children's Publishing.

—Four Friends in Autumn. 2004. (Illus.). 32p. (J). 14.95 (978-0-689-85980-9(5)) Simon & Schuster Children's Publishing.

—Four Friends in Summer. de Paola, Tomie, illus. 2003. (Illus.). 32p. (J). reprint ed. 14.95 (978-0-689-85693-8(8)) Simon & Schuster Children's Publishing.

—T-Rex Is Missing! 2002. (gr. k-3). lib. bdg. 11.80 (978-0-613-50544-4(1)) Tandem Library Bks.

—T-Rex Is Missing! A Barkers Book. 2002. (All Aboard Reading Ser.). (Illus.). 32p. (J). pap. 3.99 (978-0-448-42870-3(9) , Grosset & Dunlap) Penguin Group (USA) Inc.

De Regniers, Beatrice Schenk. May I Bring A Friend? 1999. (J). pap. 13.40 (978-0-88103-362-5(6)) Tandem Library Bks.

de Varennes, Monique. The Jewel Box Ballerinas. Juan, Ana, illus. 2007. 40p. (J). (ps-3). lib. bdg. 19.99 (***978-0-375-93605-0(X)*** , Schwartz & Wade Bks.) Random Hse. Children's Bks.

de Witt, Peter. Toaster Pond. 2006. 248p. (YA). pap. 14.95 (978-1-933255-21-7(8)) DNA Pr.

Dean, Carol S. The Live Bale of Hay: A Real Maine Adventure. Dunn, Sandra, illus. 2005. 32p. (ps-ps). 15.95 (978-0-89272-674-5(1)) Down East Bks.

Dean, Zoey. Girls on Film. 2004. (A-List Ser.: Bk. 2). 256p. (YA). (gr. 9-17). pap. 9.99 (978-0-316-73475-2(6) , Poppy) Little, Brown Bks. for Young Readers.

Deaver, Julie Reece. Night I Disappeared. 2002. 242p. (J). (ps-7). per. 14.15 (978-0-613-60586-1(1)) Tandem Library Bks.

DeBear, Kirsten. Be Quiet Marina! Dwight, Laura, photos by. 2001. (Illus.). 40p. (J). (ps-3). 16.95 (978-1-887734-79-0(1)) Star Bright Bks., Inc.

Decary, Marie. Le Combats des Chocolats. Brignaud, Pierre, illus. 2003. (Roman Jeunesse Ser.). (FRE.). 96p. (J). (gr. 4-7). pap. (978-2-89021-611-2(X)) Diffusion du livre Mirabel.

—Une Semaine de Reve. 2000. (Premier Roman Ser.). (FRE.). 64p. (J). (gr. 2-5). pap. (978-2-89021-408-8(7)) Diffusion du livre Mirabel.

Decary, Marie & Beshwaty, Steve. Un Amour de Caramela. 2001. (Premier Roman Ser.). (FRE., Illus.). 64p. (J). pap. (978-2-89021-457-6(5)) Diffusion du livre Mirabel.

Decker, Wendy. The Bedazzling Bowl. 2006. pap. 13.99 (***978-1-60034-468-8(2)***) Xulon Pr., Inc.

Deckers, Amber. Ella Mental: And the Good Sense Guide. 2006. (Illus.). 240p. (YA). mass mkt. 6.99 (978-1-4169-1322-1(X) , Simon Pulse) Simon & Schuster Children's Publishing.

—Ella Mental: Life, Love & More Good Sense. 2006. 256p. (YA). mass mkt. 5.99 (978-1-4169-1323-8(8) , Simon Pulse) Simon & Schuster Children's Publishing.

DeClements, Barthe. Liar, Liar. 1998. (Accelerated Reader Bks.). 144p. (J). (gr. 3-7). lib. bdg. 14.95 (978-0-7614-5021-4(1) , Cavendish Children's Bks.) Cavendish, Marshall Corp.

Decter, Ed. Expedition to Blue Cave. Yuen, Sammy, Jr., illus. 2007. (Outriders Ser.). 208p. (J). (gr. 3-7). pap. 4.99 (978-1-4169-1305-4(X) , Aladdin) Simon & Schuster Children's Publishing.

—Expedition to Pine Hollow. Yuen, Sammy, Jr., illus. 2007. (Outriders Ser.). 240p. (J). pap. 4.99 (978-1-4169-1307-8(6) , Aladdin) Simon & Schuster Children's Publishing.

—Expedition to Willow Key, Vol. 2. Yuen, Sammy, Jr., illus. 2007. (Outriders Ser.). 224p. (J). (gr. 3-7). pap. 4.99 (978-1-4169-1306-1(8) , Aladdin) Simon & Schuster Children's Publishing.

Deem, James M. 3 NBs of Julian Drew. 2004. 208p. (YA). (gr. 7 up). pap. 6.99 (978-0-618-43907-2(2) , Graphia) Houghton Mifflin Co. Trade & Reference Div.

Deem, Saitofi Anne. Myrtle Learns to Make Friends. 1998. (Teachable Moments Ser.). (Illus.). 8p. (J). (ps-3). pap. 7.95 (978-1-930694-07-1(5)) Myrtle Learns.

—Myrtle's Friend Is Very Sick. 1998. (Teachable Moments Ser.). (Illus.). 8p. (J). (ps-3). pap. 7.95 (978-1-930694-15-6(6)) Myrtle Learns.

deGroat, Diane. Happy Birthday to You, You Belong in a Zoo. deGroat, Diane, illus. 2007. 32p. (J). pap. 6.99 (978-0-06-001029-4(0) , Harper Trophy) HarperCollins Pubs.

—Happy Birthday to You, You Belong in a Zoo. 1999. (Illus.). 32p. (J). (ps-3). 15.00 (978-0-688-16544-4(3)) HarperCollins Pubs.

—Happy Birthday to You, You Belong in a Zoo. deGroat, Diane, illus. 1999. (Illus.). 32p. (J). (ps-3). lib. bdg. 16.89 (978-0-688-16545-1(1)) HarperCollins Pubs.

—No More Pencils, No More Books, No More Teacher's Dirty Looks! deGroat, Diane, illus. 2006. (Illus.). 32p. (J). 15.99 (978-0-06-079114-8(4)); lib. bdg. 16.89 (978-0-06-079115-5(2)) HarperCollins Pubs.

DeJong, Meindert. Y Entonces Llego un Perro. (SPA.). 144p. (YA). (gr. 5-9). (978-84-279-3220-3(0) , NG3490) Noguer y Caralt Editores, S. A. ESP. *Dist:* Lectorum Pubns., Inc.

Delaney, Mark. The Vanishing Chip. 1998. (Misfits, Inc. Ser.: No. 1). 240p. (J). (gr. 7-11). pap. 5.95 (978-1-56145-176-0(2) , Q21568) Peachtree Pubs., Ltd.

Delaney, Michael. Birdbrain Amos: Mr. Fun. 2006. (Illus.). 160p. (J). (gr. 3). 15.99 (978-0-399-24278-6(3) , Philomel) Penguin Group (USA) Inc.

Delgado, Linda D. Hijab-Ez Friends, 2006. (YA). per. (978-0-9767861-6-0(8)) Muslim Writers Publishing.

Dell, Pamela. Blood in the Water: A Story of Friendship During the Mexican War. 2003. (Scrapbooks of America Ser.). (Illus.). 48p. (J). (gr. 2-6). 28.50 (978-1-59187-042-5(9)) Child's World, Inc.

Della-Sera, Robert. The Giant Behind the House. 2001. 116p. (J). pap. 9.95 (978-0-595-20582-0(8) , Authors Choice Pr.) iUniverse, Inc.

Delton, Judy. Angel Bites the Bullet. 2000. (Illus.). 144p. (J). (gr. 4-6). tchr. ed. 15.00 (978-0-618-04085-8(4)) Houghton Mifflin Co. Trade & Reference Div.

—Wild, Wild West. 1999. (Pee Wee Scouts Ser.: No. 37). (J). (gr. 2-5). (978-0-606-16585-3(1)) Tandem Library Bks.

Denega, Danielle. Love & Friendship. 2007. (Littlest Pet Shop Ser.). 56p. (J). pap. 6.99 (978-0-439-89751-8(3)) Scholastic, Inc.

Denman, K. L. Mirror Image. 2007. (Orca Currents Ser.). 112p. (YA). (gr. 5 up). pap. (***978-1-55143-665-4(5));** lib. bdg. (***978-1-55143-667-8(1))** Orca Bk. Pubs.

Dent, Grace. Friends Forever. 2006. 272p. (YA). (gr. 4). 16.99 (978-0-399-24189-5(2) , Putnam Juvenile) Penguin Group (USA) Inc.

—LBD: It's a Girl Thing. 2004. 288p. (J). (gr. 7 up). reprint ed. pap. 6.99 (978-0-14-240182-8(X) , Puffin) Penguin Group (USA) Inc.

—LBD: Live & Fabulous! 2006. 288p. (YA). (gr. 5). pap. 6.99 (978-0-14-240662-5(7) , Puffin) Penguin Group (USA) Inc.

—LBD: Friends Forever! Friends Forever! 2007. 272p. (YA). pap. 6.99 (978-0-14-240831-5(X) , Puffin) Penguin Group (USA) Inc.

Dent, Jenny. The Story of Hoppy's Friend Pickle. (Illus.). 28p. (J). (gr. k-3). 2.25 (978-0-85487-074-5(1)) White Eagle Publishing Trust GBR. *Dist:* DeVorss & Co.

Denton, P. J. The Trouble with Brothers. Denos, Julia, illus. 2007. (Sleepover Squad Ser.). 96p. (J). (gr. 1-4). pap. 3.99 (***978-1-4169-2800-3(6)*** , Aladdin) Simon & Schuster Children's Publishing.

DePrisco, Dorothea. Meet Gator: A Picture Clues Touch & Feel Book. Croft, James Lee, illus. 2005. (Learn to Read Ser.). 10p. (J). (ps up). 10.95 (978-1-58117-123-5(4) , Intervisual/Piggy Toes) Dalmatian Pr.

Derbez, Eugenio. Lonjito Moco y Sus Amigos.Tr. of Lonjito Moco & His Friends. (SPA.). 4.98 (978-968-890-497-8(X)) Edivision Compania Editorial, S.A. de C.V. MEX. *Dist:* Continental Bk. Co., Inc., Giron Bks.

Deriso, Christine Hurley. Dreams to Grow On. Archambault, Matthew, illus. 2002. 32p. 15.95 (978-0-9701907-2-7(7)) Illumination Arts Publishing Co., Inc.

Deriso, Christine Hurley. The Right-Under Club. 2007. 208p. (J). (gr. 4-7). lib. bdg. 18.99 (***978-0-385-90351-6(0)*** , Delacorte Bks. for Young Readers) Random Hse. Children's Bks.

DeRosier, Cher. The Plight of the Jelly Bean. Contreras, Gilbert, illus. 2005. (J). (978-1-891685-50-7(3)) Dearborn Publishing.

deRubertis, Barbara. Perky Otter. Cockrille, Eva V., illus. 1998. (Let's Read Together Ser.). 32p. (J). (ps-3). pap. 4.95 (978-1-57565-045-6(2)) Kane Pr., The.

—Rooney 'Roo. Cockrille, Eva V., illus. 1998. (Let's Read Together Ser.). 32p. (J). (ps-3). pap. 4.95 (978-1-57565-044-9(4)); pap. 8.95 incl. audio (978-1-57565-049-4(5)) Kane Pr., The.

Desimini, Lisa. The Sun & Moon: A Giant Love Story. 1999. (Illus.). 40p. (YA). (ps-3). pap. 16.95 (978-0-590-18720-6(1) , Blue Sky Pr., The) Scholastic, Inc.

DeSmet, Sara. Scared Silly. DeSmet, Sara, illus. 2006. (Illus.). 32p. (J). 15.95 (978-1-60108-009-7(3)) Red Cygnet Pr.

Despain, Kellene. A Certain Kind of Treasure. 2000. (Illus.). 215p. (J). (gr. 5-9). per. 7.95 (978-0-9679046-0-3(9)) Gray Hse. Bks.

Desrosiers, Sylvie & Franson, Leanne. Au Revoir, Camille! 2000. (Premier Roman Ser.). 64p. (J). (gr. 2-5). pap. (978-2-89021-399-9(4)) Diffusion du livre Mirabel.

Dessen, Sarah. Someone Like You. 1998. 272p. (J). (gr. 7-12). 17.99 (978-0-670-87778-2(6) , Viking Juvenile) Penguin Group (USA) Inc.

—Someone Like You. 2000. (978-0-606-18847-0(9)) Tandem Library Bks.

Deubreau, Sharon. Heather & Avery & the Magic Kite. Pileggi, Steve, illus. l.t. ed. 2006. 23p. (J). per. 11.99 (978-1-59879-143-3(5)) Lifevest Publishing, Inc.

Deuker, Carl. Heart of a Champion. 2007. 208p. (YA). (gr. 7-17). pap. 7.99 (***978-0-316-06726-3(1))*** Little, Brown Bks. for Young Readers.

Deuker, Carl. Night Hoops. 2001. 256p. (gr. 7 up). pap. 6.99 (978-0-06-447275-3(2) , Harper Trophy) HarperCollins Pubs.

—Night Hoops. 2000. (Illus.). 224p. (J). (gr. 7-12). tchr. ed. 15.00 (978-0-395-97936-5(6)) Houghton Mifflin Co. Trade & Reference Div.

—Night Hoops. 2001. (978-0-606-22927-2(2)); 250p. (gr. 7-12). lib. bdg. 14.15 (978-0-613-61919-6(6)) Tandem Library Bks.

Devine, Arlene P., et al. Among Friends. 1999. (Illus.). 136p. (J). pap. 12.95 (978-1-928970-05-7(2)) GWR Pr.

Devoto, Pat Cunningham. My Last Days As Roy Rogers. 2000. (gr. 7-12). lib. bdg. 23.40 (978-0-613-27988-8(3)) Tandem Library Bks.

Devries, Douglas. Matt Bugs Me. 2005. 132p. pap. 13.99 (978-1-4141-0451-5(0)) Pleasant Word.

Dexter & His Mystery Friend. 2004. (J). per. 15.99 (978-0-9753533-5-6(7)) Golden Eagle Publishing Hse., Inc.

Dexter, Anthony. The Adventures of Manny the Manatee. 2004. 45p. pap. 19.95 (978-1-4137-2751-7(4)) PublishAmerica, Inc.

Diaz, Enrique Perez. El Nino Que Conversaba Con la Mar. 2000. Tr. of Boy Who Talked to the Sea. (SPA., Illus.). 128p. (J). (gr. 5 up). (978-84-236-5075-0(8) , ED4246) Edebé ESP. *Dist:* Lectorum Pubns., Inc.

—El Nino Que Conversaba Con la Mar. 2000. Tr. of Boy Who Talked to the Sea. (SPA.). (gr. 5-8). lib. bdg. 18.75 (978-0-613-85811-3(5)) Tandem Library Bks.

DiCamillo, Kate. The Tiger Rising. Sheban, Chris, illus. 2006. 144p. (J). (gr. 5). pap. 5.99 (978-0-7636-2916-8(2)) Candlewick Pr.

—The Tiger Rising. 128p. (gr. 5-12). 2002. (YA). pap. 5.99 (978-0-7636-1898-8(5)); 2001. (Illus.). (J). 15.99 (978-0-7636-0911-5(0)) Candlewick Pr.

—The Tiger Rising. 2002. (gr. 5-8). lib. bdg. 14.15 (978-0-613-66924-5(X)) Tandem Library Bks.

Dickens, Charles. A Tale of Two Cities. Lynch, Brendan, illus. 2002. (Great Illustrated Classics Ser.). 240p. (J). (gr. 3-8). 21.35 (978-1-57765-802-3(7) , ABDO & Daughters) ABDO Publishing Co.

Diesen, Deborah. The Pout-Pout Fish. Hanna, Dan, illus. 2008. 32p. (J). 16.00 (***978-0-374-36096-2(0))*** Farrar, Straus & Giroux.

Dietl, Erhard. Andres y Su Nuevo Amigo. (Torre de Papel Ser.). (SPA.). (J). 7.95 (978-958-04-4111-3(1)) Norma S.A. COL. *Dist:* Distribuidora Norma, Inc.

Dillingham, Mike. Rivers Book Two: Through the Eyes of a Blind Sled Dog. 2003. 13.95 (978-1-59433-004-9(2)) Publication Consultants.

Dingles, Molly. Little Lee Lee's Birthday Bang. Bingler, Aimee, illus. 2001. 26p. (J). lib. bdg. 19.00 (978-1-891997-18-1(1)) Dingles & Co.

Disney Press Staff. Head over Heels. 2001. (gr. 3-6). lib. bdg. 13.00 (978-0-613-74997-8(9)) Tandem Library Bks.

Disney Press Staff, creator. The Cheetah Girls Quiz Book. 2005. 80p. (gr. 3-7). pap. 3.99 (978-0-7868-4718-1(2) , Jump at the Sun) Hyperion Bks. for Children.

Disney Press Staff, et al. Raven Rocks. 19th rev. ed. 2007. 128p. (gr. 3-7). pap. 4.99 (***978-0-7868-3839-4(6))*** Disney Pr.

Disney Staff. Beauty & the Beast. ed. 2004. (J). (ps-2). spiral bd. (978-0-616-01631-2(X)) Canadian National Institute for the Blind/Institut National Canadien pour les Aveugles.

—Crushes & Camping. 2007. (Hannah Montana Cine-manga Ser.: Vol. 2). 96p. pap. 7.99 (***978-1-4278-0282-8(3)*** , Tokyopop Kids) TOKYOPOP, Inc.

—Friendship Day. 2000. (Lessons from the Hundred-Acre Woods: Vol. 11). (Illus.). 32p. (J). (ps-4). 3.49 (978-1-57973-087-1(6)) Advance Pubs. LLC.

—Lilo's Backpack. 2002. (Illus.). 14p. (J). bds. 7.99 (978-0-7364-1340-4(5) , RH/Disney) Random Hse. Children's Bks.

—The Princess Collection Friendship Box: Cinderella; The Little Mermaid; Sleeping Beauty; Snow White & the Seven Dwarfs. 2001. (Illus.). 48p. (J). (ps-3). bds. 9.99 (978-0-7364-1138-7(0) , RH/Disney) Random Hse. Children's Bks.

Disney Staff. Secrets & Super Sneaks, Vol. 1. 2007. (Hannah Montana Cine-manga Ser.: Vol. 1). pap. 7.99 (***978-1-4278-0281-1(5)*** , Tokyopop Kids) TOKYOPOP, Inc.

Disney Storybook Artists Staff, et al, illus. Cars. 2006. (Little Golden Book Ser.). 24p. (J). (gr. k-k). 2.99 (978-0-7364-2347-2(8) , Golden/Disney) Random Hse. Children's Bks.

Disney Storybook Artists Staff, illus. Finding Nemo. 2003. (Read-Aloud Storybook Ser.). 72p. (J). (ps-3). 8.99 (978-0-7364-2126-3(2) , RH/Disney) Random Hse. Children's Bks.

Disney/Pixar: Finding Nemo CD Read-Along. 2007. 48p. (ps-2). 12.99 (978-1-4231-0270-0(3)) Disney Pr.

DiTerlizzi, Tony. Ted. ed. 2004. (J). (gr. k-3). spiral bd. (978-0-616-07230-1(9)) Canadian National Institute for the Blind/Institut National Canadien pour les Aveugles.

—Ted. DiTerlizzi, Tony, illus. 2004. (Illus.). 40p. (J). reprint ed. pap. 6.99 (978-0-689-86374-5(8) , Aladdin) Simon & Schuster Children's Publishing.

Dixon, Annabelle. Joe's Car: A Book about.Friendship. Archbold, Tim, illus. 2004. (Making Good Choices Ser.). 24p. (J). (gr. k-3). 22.60 (978-1-4048-0662-7(8)) Picture Window Bks.

Dizard, John & Morgan, Melissa J. Best (Boy)Friend Forever. 2006. (Camp Confidential Ser.: No. 9). 160p. (J). (gr. 4-7). pap. 4.99 (978-0-448-44325-6(2) , Grosset & Dunlap) Penguin Group (USA) Inc.

DK Publishing Staff. Backyardigans: The Essential Guide. 2007. (Illus.). 48p. (J). 8.99 (978-0-7566-2703-4(6)) Dorling Kindersley Publishing, Inc.

DK Publishing Staff. Don't Worry Spike about the Something. 2007. 10p. (J). (ps-2). pap. 3.99 (***978-0-7566-3097-3(5))*** Dorling Kindersley Publishing, Inc.

Dockray, Tracy. My Life Story. Dockray, Tracy, illus. 2003. (Illus.). 40p. (J). lib. bdg. 15.95 (978-1-58717-218-2(6) , SeaStar Bks.) Chronicle Bks. LLC.

Doll, Danielle. A Lesson in Friendship. Riley, Kellee, illus. 2007. (Holly Hobbie & Friends Ser.). 24p. (J). 8.99 (***978-1-4169-3831-6(1)*** , Little Simon) Simon & Schuster Children's Publishing.

—Secret Pals. Workman, Lisa, illus. 2007. (Holly Hobbie & Friends Ser.). 18p. (J). (ps-2). 9.99 (***978-1-4169-3924-5(5)*** , Little Simon) Simon & Schuster Children's Publishing.

Dolphin Halloween & Elsie's Scrapbook. l.t. ed. 2004. (Illus.). 32p. (J). mass mkt. 4.99 (978-0-9760868-0-2(8)) Pluegl Bks.

Domínguez, José A. Mamerto: A Children's Story. 2006. (J). mass mkt. 12.50 (978-1-59835-022-7(6)) Cambridge BrickHouse, Inc.

Donaldson, Julia. Follow the Swallow. Ursell, Martin, illus. 2001. (Blue Bananas Ser.). 48p. (J). (gr. 1-2). (978-0-7787-0842-1(X)); pap. (978-0-7787-0888-9(8)) Crabtree Publishing Co.

—Follow the Swallow. 2002. (gr. k-3). lib. bdg. 12.95 (978-0-613-52844-3(1)) Tandem Library Bks.

—Night Monkey, Day Monkey. (Illus.). 32p. (J). pap. 9.99 (978-0-7497-4893-7(1)) Egmont Bks., Ltd. GBR. *Dist:* Trafalgar Square Publishing.

—The Spiffiest Giant in Town. Scheffler, Axel, illus. 2005. 32p. (J). reprint ed. pap. 5.99 (978-0-14-240275-7(3) , Puffin) Penguin Group (USA) Inc.

Donaldson, Julia & Richards, Lucy. The Quick Brown Fox Club. 2006. (Red Bananas Ser.). (Illus.). 48p. (J). pap. (978-0-7787-1096-7(3)) Crabtree Publishing Co.

Donofrio, Beverly. Mary & the Mouse, the Mouse & Mary. McClintock, Barbara, illus. 2007. 32p. (J). (ps-2). 16.99 (***978-0-375-83609-1(8));*** lib. bdg. 19.99 (***978-0-375-93609-8(2))*** Random Hse. Children's Bks. (Schwartz & Wade Bks.).

—Thank You, Lucky Stars. 2008. 240p. (J). 16.99 (***978-0-375-83964-1(X)*** , Schwartz & Wade Bks.) Random Hse. Children's Bks.

Donovan, Kevin. Billy & His Friends Witness a Miracle. 2003. (Illus.). 32p. 10.95 (978-0-9641338-2-2(2)) Billy the Bear & His Friends, Inc.

Dooley, Sarah. Wilfred & Harold's Dinner Party Disaster. 2004. 35p. pap. 17.95 (978-1-4137-1585-9(0)) PublishAmerica, Inc.

Dorion, Betty F. Whose Side Are You On? 2005. (Illus.). 216p. (J). (gr. 6 up). pap. 7.95 (978-1-55050-179-7(8)) Coteau Bks. CAN. *Dist:* Fitzhenry & Whiteside, Ltd.

Dorling Kindersley Publishing Staff. Flushed Away. 2006. (Ultimate Sticker Bks.). 16p. (J). pap. 6.99 (978-0-7566-2240-4(9)) Dorling Kindersley Publishing, Inc.

—Flushed Away Essential Guide. 2006. (Illus.). 48p. (J). 12.99 (978-0-7566-2243-5(3)) Dorling Kindersley Publishing, Inc.

Dorpinghaus, Penny. Fear Balls & Button Wads. 2006. 52p. pap. 12.95 (978-1-4241-2281-3(3)) PublishAmerica, Inc.

Doty, Kathryn Adams. Wild Orphan. 2006. 144p. pap. 14.95 (978-1-889020-20-4(6)) Edinborough Pr.

Douglas, Ann. Freddy & Flossy Flutterby. Douglas, Ann, illus. 2002. (Illus.). 40p. (J). 16.95 (978-0-9723184-0-2(2)) Betta Place, Inc.

Douthwaite, Wendy. The Orange Pony. 2003. (Illus.). 86p. (J). (gr. 2-7). mass mkt. 6.99 (978-0-330-33631-4(2) , Pan) Pan Macmillan GBR. *Dist:* Trafalgar Square Publishing.

Dowell, Frances O'Roark. Chicken Boy. Krause, George, photos by. 2007. 208p. (J). (gr. 5 up). pap. 5.99 (978-1-4169-3482-0(0) , Aladdin) Simon & Schuster Children's Publishing.

—Chicken Boy. 2005. (Illus.). 208p. (J). 15.95 (978-0-689-85816-1(7) , Atheneum) Simon & Schuster Children's Publishing.

—Chicken Boy. l.t. ed. 2006. 169p. (YA). 22.95 (978-0-7862-8280-7(0)) Thorndike Pr.

—Phineas L. MacGuire ... Erupts! The First Experiment. McDaniels, Preston, illus. 2006. (From the Highly Scientific Notebooks of Phineas L. MacGuire Ser.). 176p. (J). (gr. 3-7). 15.95 (978-1-4169-0195-2(7)) Simon & Schuster Children's Publishing.

—Phineas L. MacGuire ... Erupts! The First Experiment. McDaniels, Preston, illus. 2007. (From the Highly Scientific Notebooks of Phineas L. MacGuire Ser.). 176p. (J). pap. 4.99 (***978-1-4169-4734-9(5)*** , Aladdin) Simon & Schuster Children's Publishing.

—Phineas L. MacGuire... Gets Slimed! The Second Experiment. McDaniels, Preston L., illus. 2007. (From the Highly Scientific Notebooks of Phineas L. MacGuire Ser.). 208p. (J). (gr. 3-7). 16.99 (978-1-4169-0196-9(5)) Simon & Schuster Children's Publishing.

—The Secret Language of Girls. (Illus.). 256p. (J). (gr. 3-7). 2005. pap. 5.99 (978-1-4169-0717-6(3) , Aladdin); 2004. 16.95 (978-0-689-84421-8(2) , Atheneum) Simon & Schuster Children's Publishing.

Dower, Laura. The Boy Next Door. 2007. (Candy Apple Ser.: No. 2). 176p. (J). pap. 4.99 (978-0-439-92929-5(6)) Scholastic, Inc.

—Boy, Oh Boy!, Bk. 2. Powers, Stephanie, illus. rev. ed. 2001. (From the Files of Madison Finn Ser.: Bk. 2). 176p. (J). (gr. 3-7). pap. 4.99 (978-0-7868-1554-8(X) , Volo) Hyperion Bks. for Children.

—From the Files of Madison Finn, Bks. 4-6. 2006. 528p. (gr. 3-7). pap. 9.99 (978-1-4231-0287-8(8)) Hyperion Pr.

—From the Files of Madison Finn Bk. 19: Keep It Real. rev. ed. 2005. (From the Files of Madison Finn Ser.: Bk. 19). 176p. (J). (gr. 3-7). pap. 4.99 (978-0-7868-5687-9(4) , Volo) Hyperion Bks. for Children.

—From the Files of Madison Finn No.8: Picture-Perfect. 2002. (gr. 3-6). lib. bdg. 13.00 (978-0-613-75025-7(X)) Tandem Library Bks.

—From the Files of Madison Finn Bind Up, Bks. 1-3. 2006. 528p. (gr. 3-7). pap. 9.99 (978-1-4231-0040-9(9)) Hyperion Pr.

—Give Me a Break. 18th rev. ed. 2005. (From the Files of Madison Finn Ser.: Bk. 18). 176p. (gr. 3-7). pap. 4.99 (978-0-7868-0988-2(4) , Volo) Hyperion Bks. for Children.

—Keep It Real. 2005. 171p. (J). (978-1-4156-1057-2(6) , Volo) Hyperion Bks. for Children.

—Only the Lonely, Bk. 1. Powers, Stephanie, illus. 2001. (From the Files of Madison Finn Ser.). 176p. (J). (gr. 3-7). pap. 4.99 (978-0-7868-1553-1(1) , Volo) Hyperion Bks. for Children.

—Red to the Rescue. 2007. (Firehouse Tales Ser.). (J). bds. 5.99 (978-0-439-89462-3(X)) Scholastic, Inc.

Dowley, Ruth. Hard Rock. 2006. 160p. (J). pap. 9.99 (***978-1-84270-467-7(2))*** Andersen GBR. *Dist:* Independent Pubs. Group.

Dowling, Joni. Friends Forever. 2007. (J). per. 8.99 net. (***978-1-60402-244-5(2))*** Independent Pub.

Downey, Joni J. Will You Be My Friend? —We Really Are No Different. Brudos, Susan E., illus. 2004. (J). pap. (978-0-932991-34-8(3)) Place In The Woods, The.

Doyle, Brian. Pure Spring. 2007. 174p. (J). (gr. 6-9). 16.95 (***978-0-88899-774-6(4))*** Groundwood Bks. CAN. *Dist:* Perseus Distribution.

Doyle, Brian. You Can Pick Me up at Peggy's Cove. 2006. 104p. (J). pap. 6.95 (978-0-88899-709-8(4)) Groundwood Bks. CAN. *Dist:* Perseus Distribution.

Doyle, Malachy. Albert & Sarah Jane. 2007. (J). lib. bdg. 16.95 (***978-1-59566-336-8(3))*** QEB Publishing Inc.

—Hero, Toffer & Wallaby. Nesbitt, Jan, illus. 2000. 46p. pap. 11.95 (978-1-85902-845-2(4)) Beekman Bks., Inc.

Doyle, Malachy. Rory's Lost His Voice. Semple, David, illus. 2005. 24p. (J). lib. bdg. 22.65 (***978-1-59646-714-9(2))*** Dingles & Co.

Doyle, Malachy & Walker, Sholto. Long Gray Norris. 2006. (Yellow Bananas Ser.). (Illus.). 46p. (J). (978-0-7787-0956-5(6)) Crabtree Publishing Co.

Doyle, V. L. & Rohm, Robert. Four Friends Find Fun. Zulewski, Timothy, illus. 2005. 32p. (J). 18.95 (978-0-9651672-4-6(0)) Eklektika Pr.

Drake, David. Search for Rainbow's End. 2002. (Cricket of Dew Drop Dell Ser.). (Illus.). 32p. (J). 3.49 (978-1-885631-65-7(0) , Family Of Man Pr., The) Hutchison, G.F. Pr.

Draper, Sharon M. Copper Sun. 2006. 320p. (YA). (gr. 8 up). 16.95 (978-0-689-82181-3(6) , Atheneum) Simon & Schuster Children's Publishing.

—Double Dutch. 2003. 192p. (J). pap. 5.99 (978-0-689-84231-3(7) , Aladdin) Simon & Schuster Children's Publishing.

—Double Dutch. Gabbidon, O'Lanso, illus. 2002. 192p. (J). (gr. 7 up). 16.99 (978-0-689-84230-6(9) , Atheneum) Simon & Schuster Children's Publishing.

Drechsler, Debbie. The Summer of Love. 2003. (Illus.). 144p. pap. 16.95 (978-1-896597-65-2(3)) Drawn & Quarterly Pubns. CAN. *Dist:* Macmillan.

Driggs, Scout. Glitter Castle. Edwards, Ken, illus. 2005. (My Little Pony Ser.). 10p. (J). (ps-1). 6.99 (978-0-06-074444-1(8) , Harper Festival) HarperCollins Pubs.

Driscoll, Laura. Diego's Animal Friends. Maher, Alex, illus. 2006. (Go, Diego, Go! Ser.). 12p. (J). bds. 6.99 (978-1-4169-1791-5(8) , Simon Spotlight/Nickelodeon) Simon & Schuster Children's Publishing.

Eggs for Everyone! A & J Studio, illus. ed. 2005. 22p. (J). lib. bdg. 15.00 (978-1-59054-973-5(2)) Fitzgerald Bks.

—Stuart Little Bk. 2: Think Big, Vote Little! 2003. (gr. k-3). lib. bdg. 11.80 (978-0-613-69199-4(7)) Tandem Library Bks.

Driscoll, Laura. Thumper Finds a Friend. Disney Storybook Artists Staff & Tyminski, Lori, illus. 2008. 32p. (J). (ps-1). 9.99 (***978-1-4231-0437-7(4))*** Disney Pr.

Driving Mom Crazy 6 Packs: Individual Title. (ps-2). 27.00 (978-0-7635-9446-6(6)) Rigby Education.

Druitt, Tobias. Corydon & the Island of Monsters. 2006. 304p. (J). (gr. 3-7). 15.95 (978-0-375-83382-3(X) , Knopf Bks. for Young Readers) Random Hse. Children's Bks.

Drvenkar, Zoran. Tell Me What You See. 2005. 304p. (J). pap. 16.99 (978-0-439-72452-4(X) , Chicken Hse., The) Scholastic, Inc.

Drvenkar, Zoran. Tell Me What You See. 2008. 304p. (J). pap. 6.99 (***978-0-439-72453-1(8)*** , Scholastic Paperbacks) Scholastic, Inc.

Duchesne, Christiane. Edmond et Amandine. ed. 2004. (FRE., Illus.). (J). (ps-3). spiral bd. (978-0-616-11143-7(6)) Canadian National Institute for the Blind/Institut National Canadien pour les Aveugles.

—Edmund & Amanda. Beshwaty, Steve, illus. 1999. 29p. (J). pap. (978-1-894363-17-4(5)) Dominique & Friends.

—Nox & Archimusse in the Monsters' Feast. Perkes, Carolyn, tr. Jorisch, Stephane, illus. 2000. (J). (ps-3). pap. (978-1-894363-20-4(5)) Dominique & Friends.

—Peter's Secret. Pratt, Mylene, illus. 2005. (Read-It! Readers Ser.). 32p. (J). (ps). lib. bdg. 18.60 (978-1-4048-1351-9(9)) Picture Window Bks.

Duey, Kathleen. Arthur. Epstein, Eugene, illus. Gould, Robert, photos by. 2004. (Time Soldiers Ser.: Bk. 4). 48p. (J). 15.95 (978-1-929945-05-4(1)) Big Guy Bks., Inc.

E
F
G

—Patch. Epstein, Eugene, illus. Gould, Robert, photos by. 2003. (Time Soldiers Ser.: Vol. 3). 48p. (J). (ps-5). pap. 8.95 (978-1-929945-28-3(0)); 15.95 (978-1-929945-02-3(7)) Big Guy Bks., Inc.

Duey, Kathleen & Bale, Karen. Three of Hearts. 1998. (J). (gr. 3-7). pap. 3.99 (978-0-380-78720-3(2)) HarperCollins Pubs.

Duffy, Daniel M., illus. Benny's New Friend, Vol. 3. 1998. (Adventures of Benny & Watch: Vol. No. 3). 32p. (J). (ps-2). pap. 3.95 (978-0-8075-0649-3(4)) Whitman, Albert & Co.

Duffy, Daniel Mark, illus. Benny's New Friend. 1998. (J). (ps-ps). lib. bdg. 11.80 (978-0-613-07332-5(0)) Tandem Library Bks.

DuJardin, Rosamond. One of the Crowd. 2003. (YA). pap. 12.95 (978-1-930009-73-8(9) , 800-691-7779) Image Cascade Publishing.

—The Real Thing. 2003. (YA). pap. 12.95 (978-1-930009-71-4(2) , 800-691-7779) Image Cascade Publishing.

Dukes, LeRoy. The Chill Street Gang. 2005. (Illus.). 40p. (J). 6.99 (978-0-9664506-1-3(2)) Dukes World, Inc.

Dunagan, Ted. A Yellow Watermelon. 2007. 256p. (J). 23.95 (***978-1-58838-197-2(8)*** , Junebug Bks.) NewSouth, Inc.

Dunbar, Joyce. The Secret Friend. Craig, Helen, illus. 1998. (Panda & Gander Stories Ser.). (J). pap. (978-0-7636-0719-7(3)) Candlewick Pr.

Duncan, Lois. The Third Eye. 2002. (Illus.). (J). 13.40 (978-0-7587-4792-1(6)) Book Wholesalers, Inc.

Dunmore, Helen. Great-Grandma's Dancing Dress. 1998. (Cambridge Reading Ser.). (Illus.). 32p. (gr. 2-6). pap. 9.00 (978-0-521-63744-2(9)) Cambridge Univ. Pr.

—Zillah & Me. 2001. 160p. (gr. 3-7). pap. 4.50 (978-0-439-20669-3(3)) Scholastic, Inc.

Dunrea, Olivier. Essie & Myles. 2005. (J). (978-0-374-39991-7(3) , Farrar, Straus & Giroux (BYR)) Farrar, Straus & Giroux.

—Gossie & Gertie. 2007. (Illus.). 16p. (J). (ps-k). bds. 6.95 (978-0-618-74793-1(1)) Houghton Mifflin Co. Trade & Reference Div.

—Gossie & Gertie. Dunrea, Olivier, illus. 2002. (Illus.). 32p. (J). (gr. k-ps). tchr. ed. 9.95 (978-0-618-17676-2(4)) Houghton Mifflin Co. Trade & Reference Div.

—Gossie's Busy Day. 2007. (Illus.). 10p. (J). (ps-k). 11.99 (***978-0-618-82148-8(1)***) Houghton Mifflin Co. Trade & Reference Div.

Dunrea, Olivier. It's Snowing! Dunrea, Olivier, illus. 2002. (Illus.). 32p. (J). (ps-1). 16.00 (978-0-374-39992-4(1) , Farrar, Straus & Giroux (BYR)) Farrar, Straus & Giroux.

—It's Snowing! 2002. 32p. (J). 16.00 (978-0-374-39993-1(X)) Farrar, Straus & Giroux.

Dupont, Matthew. As I Look in Your Eyes. Gutierez, Francisco & Renteria, Justin, illus. 2003. 20p. (YA). pap. 5.99 (978-0-9728134-0-2(3)) A & E Children's Pr.

Durrant, Sabine. Bon Voyage, Connie Pickles. 2008. 240p. (J). 16.99 (***978-0-06-085482-9(0));*** lib. bdg. 17.89 (***978-0-06-085483-6(9)***) HarperCollins Pubs. (HarperTeen).

Dussling, Jennifer. Gotcha! Nez, John, illus. 2003. (Science Solves It! Ser.). 32p. (J). 4.99 (978-1-57565-124-8(6)) Kane Pr., The.

—Gotcha! 2003. (gr. k-3). lib. bdg. 13.00 (978-0-613-79272-1(6)) Tandem Library Bks.

—L. M. Montgomery's Anne of Green Gables. 2001. (gr. k-3). lib. bdg. 11.80 (978-0-613-35608-4(X)) Tandem Library Bks.

Dussling, Jennifer & Montgomery, L. M. Anne of Green Gables. Halverson, Lydia, illus. 2001. (All Aboard Reading Ser.). 48p. (J). (gr. 4-7). pap. 3.99 (978-0-448-42459-0(2) , Grosset & Dunlap) Penguin Group (USA) Inc.

Dutka, Pamela. Madame Cecil's Swamp. 2005. 48p. pap. 12.95 (978-1-4137-9701-5(6)) PublishAmerica, Inc.

Dyahnne. Sweetie's Place: All about Aisha. 2004. 24p. pap. 7.95 (978-1-4116-0794-1(5)) Lulu.com.

Dyer, Heather. The Fish in Room 11. 2005. 160p. (J). reprint ed. pap. 3.99 (978-0-439-57976-6(7) , Scholastic Paperbacks) Scholastic, Inc.

Eager, Edward. Magic or Not? Bodecker, N. M., illus. 1999. (Odyssey Classics). 208p. (J). (gr. 3-7). pap. 7.00 (978-0-15-202080-4(2) , Odyssey Classics) Harcourt Children's Bks.

—Magic or Not? 1999. (J). (978-0-606-19001-5(5)) Tandem Library Bks.

Earhart, Kristin. Happy's Holiday. 2007. (Big Apple Barn Ser.). 96p. (J). pap. 3.99 (***978-0-545-01774-9(2)*** , Scholastic Paperbacks) Scholastic, Inc.

Earhart, Kristin. Patch. 2008. (Stablemates Ser.). 48p. (J). pap. 3.99 (***978-0-439-72240-7(3)*** , Cartwheel Bks.) Scholastic, Inc.

—Patch. Papp, Lisa, illus. 2006. (Breyer Stablemates Ser.). 48p. (J). pap. 4.99 (978-0-439-72236-0(5) , Cartwheel Bks.) Scholastic, Inc.

Eason, Alethea. Hungry. 2007. 208p. (J). (gr. 5 up). 15.99 (***978-0-06-082554-6(5));*** lib. bdg. 16.89 (***978-0-06-082555-3(3)***) HarperCollins Pubs. (Eos).

Eastman, P. D. Big Dog ... Little Dog. 2006. (Bright & Early Board Bks.). (Illus.). 24p. (J). (gr. k-ps). bds. 4.99 (978-0-375-87539-7(5) , Random Hse. Bks. for Young Readers) Random Hse. Children's Bks.

—Big Dog... Little Dog. 2003. (I Can Read It All by Myself Ser.). (Illus.). 48p. (J). (gr. k-3). 8.99 (978-0-375-82297-1(6) , Random Hse. Bks. for Young Readers) Random Hse. Children's Bks.

—Big Dog... Little Dog. Eastman, P. D. & Eastman, Tony, illus. 2003. (I Can Read It All by Myself Ser.). 48p. (J). (gr. k-3). lib. bdg. 13.99 (978-0-375-92297-8(0) , Random Hse. Bks. for Young Readers) Random Hse. Children's Bks.

Easton, Kelly. White Magic: Spells to Hold You, A Novel. 2007. 208p. (YA). (gr. 7-11). 15.99 (***978-0-375-83769-2(8));*** lib. bdg. 18.99 (***978-0-375-93769-9(2)***) Random Hse. Children's Bks. (Lamb, Wendy).

Easton, Richard. A Real American. 2002. 160p. (J). (gr. 4-6). 15.00 (978-0-618-13339-0(9) , Clarion Bks.) Houghton Mifflin Co. Trade & Reference Div.

Eastwood, J. G. Dragon: Enter the Realm. 2007. (YA). per. (***978-0-9792030-7-7(4)***) Light Sword Publishing LLC.

Eaton, Maxwell. Adventures of Max & Pinky: Best Buds. 2006. (Adventures of Max & Pinky Ser.). (Illus.). 32p. (J). (gr. k-3). 12.99 (978-0-375-83803-3(1) , Knopf Bks. for Young Readers) Random Hse. Children's Bks.

—Best Buds. 2006. (Adventures of Max & Pinky Ser.). (Illus.). 32p. (J). (gr. k-3). lib. bdg. 14.99 (978-0-375-93803-0(6) , Knopf Bks. for Young Readers) Random Hse. Children's Bks.

Eaton, Maxwell. Superheroes. 2007. (Adventures of Max & Pinky Ser.). 32p. (J). (gr. k-3). lib. bdg. 15.99 (***978-0-375-93805-4(2)*** , Knopf Bks. for Young Readers) Random Hse. Children's Bks.

Ebeltoft, Christine. Koo & Jay in the Rainforest. 2004. 34p. pap. 17.95 (978-1-4137-3698-4(X)) PublishAmerica, Inc.

Ebert, Tom. My Name Is Blackie. 2000. (J). pap. 6.95 (978-0-533-13601-8(6)) Vantage Pr., Inc.

Echerique, Alfredo Bryce & Duenas, Ana Maria. Goig. Roederer, Charlotte, illus. (Literary Encounters Ser.). (SPA.). (J). (gr. 3-5). pap. (978-968-494-065-9(3) , CI7706) Centro de Informacion y Desarrollo de la Comunicacion y la Literatura MEX. *Dist:* Lectorum Pubns., Inc.

Edelfeldt, Inger. Jim En El Espejo. 2nd ed. 2002. (SPA.). 186p. (978-84-85334-41-4(8)) Loguez Ediciones ESP. *Dist:* Lectorum Pubns., Inc.

Edgemon, Darcie. Seamore, the Very Forgetful Porpoise. Seibold, J. Otto, illus. 2008. 48p. (J). 16.99 (***978-0-06-085075-3(2));*** lib. bdg. 17.89 (***978-0-06-085076-0(0)***) HarperCollins Pubs.

Edgeworth, Maria. The Bracelets or Amiability & Industry Rewarded. 2004. reprint ed. pap. 15.95 (978-1-4191-5513-0(X)); pap. 1.99 (978-1-4192-5513-7(4)) Kessinger Publishing, LLC.

Eding, June. Easter Showers. Chauhan, Manhar, illus. 2007. (Puppy Scooby-Doo Ser.). 32p. (J). pap. 3.99 (978-0-448-44485-7(2) , Grosset & Dunlap) Penguin Group (USA) Inc.

Ed's Terrestrials. 2006. (J). per. 19.99 net. (978-0-9789168-1-7(6)) Blue Dream Studios.

Edwards, Andreanna. Taking Autism to School. Dineen, Tom, illus. 2001. (Special Kids in School Ser.: Vol. 10). 32p. (J). pap. 11.95 (978-1-891383-13-7(2)) JayJo Bks., LLC.

Edwards, Byron. The Mystery of Melissa's First Date: Book One. 2001. 108p. pap. 9.95 (978-0-595-18836-9(2) , Writers Club Pr.) iUniverse, Inc.

Edwards, Helen L. Clara's Imagination. Doggett, Al, illus. 2005. 19.95 (978-0-9765414-0-0(8)) Bad Publishing.

Edwards, Michelle. Pa Lia's First Day. 2005. (Jackson Friends Ser.). (Illus.). 64p. (J). (ps-ps). pap., pap. 5.95 (978-0-15-205748-0(X) , Harcourt Paperbacks) Harcourt Children's Bks.

—Pa Lia's First Day. 2001. (Jackson Friends Book Ser.). (Illus.). (J). (978-0-606-21377-6(5)) Tandem Library Bks.

—The Talent Show. 2005. (Jackson Friends Ser.). (Illus.). 64p. (J). (ps-ps). pap., pap. 5.95 (978-0-15-205760-2(9) , Harcourt Paperbacks) Harcourt Children's Bks.

—Zero Grandparents. 2005. (Jackson Friends Ser.). (Illus.). 64p. (J). (ps-ps). pap., pap. 5.95 (978-0-15-205754-1(4) , Harcourt Paperbacks) Harcourt Children's Bks.

Edwards, Pamela Duncan. Gigi & Lulu's Gigantic Fight. Cole, Henry, tr. Cole, Henry, illus. 2004. 40p. (J). (ps-2). 14.99 (978-0-06-050752-7(7)); lib. bdg. 15.89 (978-0-06-050753-4(5)) HarperCollins Pubs.

Edwards, Pamela Duncan. The Old House. Cole, Henry, illus. 2007. 32p. (J). (ps). 16.99 (***978-0-525-47796-9(9)*** , Dutton Juvenile) Penguin Group (USA) Inc.

Egan, Kate, adapted by. World's Apart. 2005. (W. I. T. C. H. Ser.: Bk. 14). 134p. (J). lib. bdg. 16.92 (***978-1-4242-0788-6(6)***) Fitzgerald Bks.

Egan, Tim. Roasted Peanuts. 2006. (Illus.). 32p. (J). (gr. k-3). 16.00 (978-0-618-33718-7(0)) Houghton Mifflin Co.

Egielski, Richard. Slim & Jim. Date not set. 32p. (J). (ps-2). pap. 5.99 (978-0-06-443564-2(4)) HarperCollins Pubs.

Ehlert, Lois. Nuts to You! 2004. (Illus.). 40p. (J). reprint ed. pap. 7.00 (978-0-15-205064-1(7) , Voyager Bks./Libros Viajeros) Harcourt Children's Bks.

Ehlin, Gina. Emma & Friends: Emma's Airport Adventure. Ayzenberg, Nina, illus. l.t. ed. 2005. 32p. (J). lib. bdg. 15.99 (978-1-59879-015-3(3)); per. 10.99 (978-1-59879-014-6(5)) Lifevest Publishing, Inc.

—Emma & Friends; Emma Rescues Cali. Ayzenberg, Nina, illus. l.t. ed. 2006. 24p. (J). per. 10.99 (978-1-59879-112-9(5)) Lifevest Publishing, Inc.

Ehrenberg, Pamela. Ethan, Suspended. 2007. 336 Pagesp. 16.00 (***978-0-8028-5317-2(X));*** vi, 266p. (J). (gr. 6 up). 16.00 (***978-0-8028-5324-0(2)*** , Eerdmans Bks For Young Readers) Eerdmans, William B. Publishing Co.

Ehrenhaft, Daniel. 10 Things to Do Before I Die. 2006. 224p. (YA). (gr. 7). pap. 7.95 (978-0-385-73406-6(9) , Delacorte Bks. for Young Readers) Random Hse. Children's Bks.

Eickhoff, Kim, et al. Bamboo Zoo: Meet Lester Panda & his Friends! 2005. (Bamboo Zoo Ser.: Bk. 1). (Illus.). (J). per. 9.95 (978-0-9774493-0-9(0)) Bamboo Zoo, LLC.

Eige, Lillian. Dangling. 2003. (gr. 3-6). lib. bdg. 13.00 (978-0-613-90716-3(7)) Tandem Library Bks.

Elder, Elizabeth. When I'm with You. Mansmann, Leslie, illus. 2003. (J). per. 15.95 (978-0-9671662-8-5(4)) Islandport Pr., Inc.

Elkeles, Simone. Leaving Paradise. 2007. 312p. (J). (gr. 9 up). pap. 8.95 (978-0-7387-1018-1(0) , 1265837) Llewellyn Pubns.

Elkins, Stephen. Ebony & Ivory: Discovering 10 Keys to Racial Harmony. Reisch, Jessie, illus. 2003. 32p. (J). (gr. k up). 14.99 incl. audio compact disk (978-0-8054-2674-8(4)) B&H Publishing Grp.

Elliot, David. The Cool Crazy Crickets to the Rescue! 2001. (Illus.). (J). (978-0-606-21642-5(1)) Tandem Library Bks.

Elliott, Ann. GypsyBridge Friends: The Vine. 2003. 40p. pap. 12.95 (978-0-9721825-0-8(0)) Open Vision Entertainment Corp.

Elliott, Laura. Hunter & Stripe & the Soccer Showdown. Munsinger, Lynn, illus. 2005. 32p. (J). (ps-2). lib. bdg. 16.89 (978-0-06-052760-0(9)) HarperCollins Pubs.

—Hunter's Best Friend at School: A Hunter & Stripe Story. Munsinger, Lynn, illus. 2005. 32p. (J). (ps-2). reprint ed. pap. 6.99 (978-0-06-075319-1(6) , Harper Trophy) HarperCollins Pubs.

Elliott, Laura Malone. Hunter & Stripe & the Soccer Showdown. Munsinger, Lynn, illus. 2005. 32p. (J). (ps-2). 15.99 (978-0-06-052759-4(5)) HarperCollins Pubs.

—Hunter's Best Friend at School. Munsinger, Lynn, illus. 2002. 32p. (J). (ps-2). 16.99 (978-0-06-000230-5(1)); 17.89 (978-0-06-000231-2(X)) HarperCollins Pubs.

Ellis, Deborah. A Company of Fools. 192p. (gr. 5 up). 2004. (J). pap. (978-1-55041-721-0(5)); 2002. (YA). (978-1-55041-719-7(3)) Fitzhenry & Whiteside, Ltd.

Ellison, James W. Finding Forrester. 2005. 192p. (YA). pap. 9.95 (978-1-55704-479-2(1)) Newmarket Pr.

Elschner, G. & Devos, X. Friends for All Seasons. 2006. (Illus.). 32p. (J). 15.95 (978-0-7358-2003-6(1)) North-South Bks., Inc.

Emberley, Rebecca. Three Cool Kids. 1998. (J). (978-0-606-13847-5(1)) Tandem Library Bks.

Emerson, Charlotte. Meg's Dearest Wish. 1999. (Little Women Journals). (J). (978-0-606-16350-7(6)) Tandem Library Bks.

Emerson, Charlotte & Alcott, Louisa May. Meg's Dearest Wish. Wasden, Kevin, illus. 1999. (Little Women Journals). 128p. (J). (gr. 3-7). pap. 3.99 (978-0-380-79705-9(4)) HarperCollins Pubs.

Emery, Anne. Dinny Gordon, Freshman. 2004. (J). per. 9.95 (978-1-930009-97-4(6)) Image Cascade Publishing.

—Dinny Gordon Sophomore. 2004. (J). per. 9.95 (978-1-930009-98-1(4)) Image Cascade Publishing.

Emesse, Tea. Nova Rocks. 2005. (Star Sisterz Ser.: Bk. 1). (Illus.). 192p. (J). pap. 5.99 (978-0-7869-3625-0(8)) Wizards of the Coast.

Emigh, Ullie. Nika Watters in the Case of the Misplaced Fossil. 2004. 59p. pap. 12.95 (978-1-4137-2438-7(8)) PublishAmerica, Inc.

Emmett, Jonathan. What Friends Do Best. Reed, Nathan, illus. 2005. 32p. (J). (ps-3). 15.99 (978-0-00-714120-3(3) , Collins) HarperCollins Pubs. Ltd. GBR. *Dist:* Independent Pubs. Group.

—What Friends Do Best. 2004. (Illus.). 32p. (J). pap. 9.99 (978-0-00-714121-0(1)) HarperCollins Pubs. Ltd. GBR. *Dist:* Independent Pubs. Group.

Enderle, Dotti. Secrets of Lost Arrow. Nightingale, Kimberly, ed. 2004. (Fortune Tellers Club Ser.: Bk. 4). (Illus.). 144p. pap. 4.99 (978-0-7387-0389-3(3)) Llewellyn Pubns.

Enderle, Judith R. What's the Matter, Kelly Beans? 1998. (J). (978-0-606-13906-9(0)) Tandem Library Bks.

English, Karen. Francie. 2002. (Illus.). (J). 25.45 (978-0-7587-0355-2(4)) Book Wholesalers, Inc.

—Francie. 2002. 208p. (J). pap. 5.95 (978-0-374-42459-6(4) , Sunburst) Farrar, Straus & Giroux.

—Francie. 2007. 224p. (J). pap. 6.99 (***978-0-312-37383-2(X)***) Square Fish.

—Francie. 2002. (gr. 5-8). lib. bdg. 14.10 (978-0-613-54223-4(1)) Tandem Library Bks.

—Francie. l.t. ed. 2002. 220p. (J). 21.95 (978-0-7862-3717-3(1)) Thomson Gale.

—Hot Day on Abbott Avenue. Steptoe, Javaka, illus. 2004. 32p. (J). (gr. k-3). 16.00 (978-0-395-98527-4(7) , Clarion Bks.) Houghton Mifflin Co. Trade & Reference Div.

—Neeny Coming, Neeny Going. 1998. (978-0-606-13656-3(8)) Tandem Library Bks.

English, Karen. Nikki & Deja. Freeman-Hines, Laura, illus. 2007. 80p. (J). (gr. 1-5). 15.00 (***978-0-618-75238-6(2)*** , Clarion Bks.) Houghton Mifflin Co. Trade & Reference Div.

Enright, Elizabeth. Thimble Summer. unabr. ed. 2004. 136p. (J). (gr. 3-7). pap. 36.00 incl. audio (978-0-8072-0671-3(7) , Listening Library) Random Hse. Audio Publishing Group.

Entara Ltd., illus. Piggley Makes a Friend. 2007. (Jakers! Ser.). 24p. (J). pap. 3.99 (***978-1-4169-3581-0(9)*** , Simon Spotlight) Simon & Schuster Children's Publishing.

Entara Ltd. Staff, photos by. Piggley's Pals. 2006. (Jakers! Ser.). (Illus.). 14p. (J). 7.99 (978-0-689-87617-2(3) , Simon Spotlight) Simon & Schuster Children's Publishing.

Erickson, Betty. Big Bad Rex. Hickman, Estella L., illus. 1998. 12p. (J). (gr. k-2). pap. 3.75 (978-1-880612-77-4(1) , Seedling Pubns.) Continental Pr., Inc.

Ernst, Lisa Campbell. Bubba & Trixie. 2000. (J). (978-0-606-20085-1(1)) Tandem Library Bks.

Esbaum, Jill. To the Big Top. Gordon, David, illus. 2008. 32p. (J). 16.95 (***978-0-374-39934-4(4)***) Farrar, Straus & Giroux.

Estes, Eleanor. The Alley. Ardizzone, Edward, illus. 2003. 288p. pap. 5.95 (978-0-15-204918-8(5) , Odyssey Classics) Harcourt Children's Bks.

—The Alley. (gr. 3-6). lib. bdg. 14.10 (978-0-613-70525-7(4)) Tandem Library Bks.

—The Hundred Dresses. Slobodkin, Louis, illus. 2002. (J). 13.19 (978-0-7587-0272-2(8)) Book Wholesalers, Inc.

—The Hundred Dresses. Slobodkin, Louis, illus. anniv. ed. 2004. 96p. (J). pap. 7.00 (978-0-15-205260-7(7) , Harcourt Paperbacks) Harcourt Children's Bks.

—The Tunnel of Hugsy Goode. Ardizzone, Edward, illus. 2003. 256p. (J). 17.00 (978-0-15-204914-0(2) , Harcourt Young Classics); pap. 6.95 (978-0-15-204916-4(9) , Odyssey Classics) Harcourt Children's Bks.

Estes, Eleanor & Slobodkin, Louis. The Hundred Dresses. anniv. ed. 2004. (Illus.). 96p. (J). 16.00 (978-0-15-205170-9(8) , Harcourt Children's Bks) Harcourt Children's Bks.

Estes-Hill, Katrina. My Imagination. Kwong, Alvina, illus. 2007. 32p. (J). (ps-2). 15.95 (***978-0-9745715-6-0(3)***) KRBY Creations, LLC.

Evangelista, Beth. Gifted. 192p. (J). 2007. pap. 6.95 (***978-0-8027-9644-8(3));*** 2005. (gr. 5-9). 16.95 (978-0-8027-8994-5(3)) Walker & Co.

Evans, Len. Yr Enillwyr. 2005. (WEL.). 64p. pap. (978-1-85596-218-7(7)) Dref Wen.

Evans, Mari. Dear Corinne, Tell Somebody! Love, Annie. 2004. (J). pap. 6.95 (978-0-940975-90-3(4) , Sankofa Bks.) Just Us Bks., Inc.

—Dear Corinne, Tell Somebody! Love, Annie: A Book about Secrets. 2004. (Illus.). 64p. (J). (gr. 3-7). 12.95 (978-0-940975-81-1(5) , Sankofa Bks.) Just Us Bks., Inc.

Evans, Pamela. Tina Queen of the Dragons. 2006. 101p. pap. 14.95 (978-1-4241-3356-7(4)) PublishAmerica, Inc.

Every Day but Sunday, 6 Packs. (ps-2). 23.00 (978-0-7635-9004-8(5)) Rigby Education.

Ewart, Franzeska G. Sita Snake Queen of Speed. 2008. (Illus.). 96p. (J). 15.95 (***978-1-84507-779-2(2));*** pap. 7.95 (***978-1-84507-748-8(2)***) Lincoln, Frances Ltd. GBR. *Dist:* Perseus Distribution.

Fabra, Jordi Sierra. Las Chicas de Alambre. 2003. (SPA., Illus.). 224p. (J). (gr. 8-12). pap. 8.95 (978-84-204-4915-9(6)) Santillana USA Publishing Co., Inc.

Fairbairn, John. Highgate Hill Mob. 96p. pap. 10.95 (978-0-7022-2590-1(8)) Univ. of Queensland Pr. AUS. *Dist:* International Specialized Bk. Services.

Faithful Friends, Set. Incl. Best Friends under the Sun. Whalen, Sharla Scannell. 2000. lib. bdg. 21.35 (978-1-57765-228-1(2)); Flower Girl Friends. Abdo Publishing Staff, contrib. by. 2000. lib. bdg. 21.35 (978-1-57765-229-8(0)); Friends on Ice. Whalen, Sharla Scannell. 1998. lib. bdg. 21.35 (978-1-57765-227-4(4)); Meet the Friends. Whalen, Sharla Scannell. 2000. lib. bdg. 21.35 (978-1-57765-226-7(6)); 64p. (J). (gr. 4). , ABDO & Daughters (Illus.). 1998. Set lib. bdg. 91.12 (978-1-57765-254-0(1)) ABDO Publishing Co.

Falk, Elizabeth Sullivan. Lettie's North Star. Wolf, Elizabeth, illus. 2006. (J). (978-1-59336-694-0(9)) Mondo Publishing.

Falkner, John Meade. Moonfleet. (Twelve-Point Ser.). 2002. (YA). lib. bdg. 25.00 (978-1-58287-175-2(2)); 2004. 370p. 26.00 (978-1-58287-658-0(4)) North Bks.

Falwell, Cathryn. David's Drawings. 2001. (Illus.). 32p. (J). (ps-3). 16.00 (978-1-58430-031-1(0)) Lee & Low Bks., Inc.

—Los Dibujos de David. de la Vega, Eida, tr. Falwell, Cathryn, illus. 2005. (Illus.). 32p. (J). (ps-k). pap. 7.95 (978-1-58430-258-2(5)) Lee & Low Bks., Inc.

Falwell, Cathryn, illus. & text. David's Drawings. Falwell, Cathryn, text. 2005. 32p. (J). (ps-ps). pap. 7.95 (978-1-58430-261-2(5)) Lee & Low Bks., Inc.

Farish, Terry. The Cat Who Liked Potato Soup. Root, Barry, illus. 40p. (J). (gr. 1). 2007. pap. 6.99 (978-0-7636-3297-7(X)); 2003. 16.99 (978-0-7636-0834-7(3)) Candlewick Pr.

Farley, Terri. Phantom Stallion No.9: Gift Horse. 2003. (gr. 5-8). lib. bdg. 13.00 (978-0-613-81135-4(6)) Tandem Library Bks.

Farmer, Gayle. Showtime! 2004. (YA). per. 12.95 (978-0-9748728-0-3(6)) Jeff & Gayle Farmer.

Farnell, Chris. Mark II. 2006. (Illus.). 164p. (YA). (gr. 8-10). pap. 14.95 (978-0-9547913-9-1(8)) Tindal Street Pr. GBR. *Dist:* Dufour Editions, Inc.

Farrell, Mame. And Sometimes Why. 2001. 176p. (J). (gr. 4-7). 16.00 (978-0-374-32289-2(9) , Farrar, Straus & Giroux (BYR)) Farrar, Straus & Giroux.

—Marrying Malcolm Murgatroyd. 1998. 128p. (J). (gr. 4-7). pap. 6.95 (978-0-374-44744-1(6) , Sunburst) Farrar, Straus & Giroux.

—Marrying Malcolm Murgatroyd. 1998. 122p. (J). (ps-7). per. 12.95 (978-0-613-10517-0(6)) Tandem Library Bks.

Faulkner, Keith. Sharing & Caring. James, Rhian Nest, illus. 1998. 4p. (J). bds. 7.99 (978-1-58048-036-9(5)) Sandvik Publishing.

The Fearful Fairy. ed. 2007. (Illus.). 40p. (J). 16.95 (***978-0-9793823-0-7(0)***) StonesThrow Publishing LLC.

Feddersen, Jill. The Very Best Friend There Ever Could Be. Sabanski, Helen, illus. 2004. 8p. pap. 5.73 (978-1-4116-0898-6(4)) Lulu.com.

Feely, Jenny. Last One Picked. 2000. (gr. k-3). lib. bdg. 11.80 (978-0-613-29802-5(0)) Tandem Library Bks.

Feiffer, Jules. A Barrel of Laughs, a Vale of Tears. Feiffer, Jules, illus. 1998. (Illus.). 192p. (gr. 4-7). pap. 11.99 (978-0-06-205926-0(2)) HarperCollins Pubs.

Feld, Ellen F. Shadow: The Curious Morgan Horse. 2006. (Illus.). 32p. (J). 15.95 (978-0-9709002-6-5(0)) Willow Bend Publishing.

Feldman, Thea. Fun Around the Town. 2006. 3p. 5.99 (978-1-932915-34-1(6)) Sandvik Publishing.

Ferguson, Dwayne. Mess at Loch Ness. 2004. (Kid Caramel). 72p. (J). pap. 4.50 (978-0-940975-74-3(2) , Sankofa Bks.) Just Us Bks., Inc.

Ferguson, Sarah. Little Red's Christmas Story. Williams, Sam, illus. 2004. 40p. (J). 15.95 (978-0-689-85561-0(3)) Simon & Schuster Children's Publishing.

Ferguson, Sarah The Duchess of York. Little Red's Christmas Story. Williams, Sam, illus. 2007. 40p. (J). 6.99 (***978-1-4169-5002-8(8)*** , Aladdin) Simon & Schuster Children's Publishing.

Fernandes, Kim & Fernandes, Eugenie. Little Toby & the Big Hair. 1998. (Illus.). 32p. (J). pap. (978-0-385-25678-0(7) , Doubleday Can) Doubleday Canada, Ltd. CAN. *Dist:* Random Hse., Inc.

Fernandez Paz, Agustín & Martínez, Maribel G. La Ciudad de los Deseos. Uhía, Manolo & Martínez, Maribel G., trs. Uhía, Manolo, illus. 2002. (Joven Coleccion Ser.). (SPA.). 48p. (978-84-89804-04-3(4)) Loguez Ediciones ESP. *Dist:* Lectorum Pubns., Inc.

Ferreira, Anton. Zulu Dog. 2002. (Illus.). 208p. (J). (gr. 5 up). 16.00 (978-0-374-39223-9(4) , Farrar, Straus & Giroux (BYR)) Farrar, Straus & Giroux.

Ferris, Amy Schor. A Greater Goode. 2002. 192p. (YA). (gr. 5-9). 15.00 (978-0-618-13154-9(X)) Houghton Mifflin Co. Trade & Reference Div.

Ferris, Jean. Of Sound Mind. 224p. (YA). 2001. (gr. 8 up). 16.00 (978-0-374-35580-7(0) , Farrar, Straus & Giroux (BYR)); 2004. reprint ed. pap. 6.95 (978-0-374-45584-2(8) , Sunburst) Farrar, Straus & Giroux.

—Of Sound Mind. l.t. ed. 2004. 225p. 21.95 (978-0-7862-7036-1(5) , Large Print Pr.) Thorndike Pr.

Ficklin, Jonene H. The Garden Gate. 2005. (YA). 14.95 (978-0-9761188-2-4(3)) Victor's Crown Publishing.

Fienberg, Anna & Fienberg, Barbara. The Big Big Big Book of Tashi. Gamble, Kim, illus. 2002. (Tashi Ser.). 448p. (J). (gr. 1-5). pap. 15.95 (978-1-86508-563-0(4)) Allen & Unwin AUS. *Dist:* Independent Pubs. Group.

Fietzek, Petra. Sophie & the Seagull. Ginsbach, Julia, illus. 2002. 32p. (J). (ps up). lib. bdg. 24.67 (978-0-8368-3174-0(8)) Stevens, Gareth Inc.

Filaretos, William. The Potion of Time: A Story of Demetrios. 2006. per. 12.95 (978-0-9724520-0-7(1)) Filaretos, William.

Finally, Lil Rose. Slowpoke the Turtle & Company. Drape, Kaitlin, illus. 2005. (J). pap. 8.00 (978-0-8059-6778-4(8)) Dorrance Publishing Co., Inc.

Finch, Margo. The Lunch Bunch. Handelman, Dorothy, photos by. 1998. (Real Kids Readers Ser.). (Illus.). 32p. (J). (gr. k-2). pap. 4.99 (978-0-7613-2030-2(X) , Millbrook Pr.) Lerner Publishing Group.

Finch, Susan. The Intimacy of Indiana. 2000. (Illus.). 177p. (YA). pap. 5.95 (978-0-936389-79-0(6)) Tudor Pubs., Inc.

Fine, Anne. The Tulip Touch. l.t. ed. 2000. (Illus.). 228p. (J). pap. (978-0-7540-6091-8(8) , CLP 288) BBC Audio.

—The Tulip Touch. unabr. l.t. ed. 2003. (Read-Along Ser.). 200p. (J). pap. 29.95 incl. audio (978-0-7540-6227-1(9) , RA028, Galaxy Children's Large Print) BBC Audiobooks America.

—The Tulip Touch. 1999. (978-0-606-16711-6(0)) Tandem Library Bks.

—Up on Cloud Nine. l.t. ed. 2005. (Illus.). 232p. (J). pap. incl. audio (978-0-7540-7878-4(7) , CLP 455) BBC Audio.

—Up on Cloud Nine. 2003. 160p. (J). (gr. 5-17). 4.99 (978-0-440-41916-7(6) , Yearling) Random Hse. Children's Bks.

Fine, Anne & Glover, Jamie. Up on Cloud Nine. 2004. (J). pap. 29.95 incl. audio (978-0-7540-6276-9(7) , Chivers Children's Audio Bks.) BBC Audiobooks America.

Finley, Martha. Elsie & the Raymonds, Bk. 15. 2001. mass mkt. 5.99 (978-1-931343-24-4(1)) Hibbard Pubns., Inc.

—Elsie's Friends at Woodburn, Bk. 13. 2001. mass mkt. 5.99 (978-1-931343-22-0(5)) Hibbard Pubns., Inc.

Finsterbusch, Monika. Princess Lillifee. 2006. (Illus.). 28p. (J). (ps-3). 12.95 (978-0-8109-5722-0(1) , Abrams Bks. for Young Readers) Abrams, Harry N., Inc.

—Princess Lillifee's Secret. 2006. 28p. (J). (ps-3). 12.95 (978-0-8109-5724-4(8) , Abrams Bks. for Young Readers) Abrams, Harry N., Inc.

Fiorello, Frank. Pumpkinville. Fiorello, Frank, illus. 2001. 40p. (J). pap. 7.95 (978-0-9708400-0-4(4)); lib. bdg. 12.95 (978-0-9708400-1-1(2)) Pumpkin Patch Publishing.

FitzGerald, Dawn. Getting in the Game. 2007. 160p. (J). pap. 6.99 (***978-0-312-37753-3(3)***) Square Fish.

Fitzgerald, Dawn. Getting in the Game. rev. ed. 2005. 144p. (J). 15.95 (978-1-59643-044-0(3)) Roaring Brook Pr.

Fitzhugh, Louise. Harriet the Spy. 2001. (gr. 3-6). lib. bdg. 14.15 (978-0-613-33759-5(X)); (Illus.). (J). 12.64 (978-0-606-21226-7(4)) Tandem Library Bks.

—The Long Secret. 2001. (Illus.). 288p. (J). (gr. 5 up). 15.95 (978-0-385-32784-8(6) , Delacorte Bks. for Young Readers) Random Hse. Children's Bks.

Fitzhugh, Louise & Gold, Maya. Harriet the Spy, Double Agent. 2007. 160p. (J). (gr. 4-7). 6.50 (978-0-440-41691-3(4) , Yearling) Random Hse. Children's Bks.

Fitzpatrick, Marie-Louise. I'm a Tiger, Too! Fitzpatrick, Marie-Louise, illus. 2002. (Illus.). 6.95 (978-0-86327-871-6(X)) Interlink Publishing Group, Inc.

Flake, Sharon G. The Broken Bike Boy & the Queen of 33rd Street. Bootman, Colin, illus. 2007. 144p. (gr. 3-7). 15.99 (***978-1-4231-0032-4(8)*** , Jump at the Sun) Hyperion Bks. for Children.

Flanders, Heather A. Before the Fridge. Dillard, Kristine, illus. 2000. 8p. (J). (gr. k-2). pap. 3.75 (978-1-58323-012-1(2) , Seedling Pubns.) Continental Pr., Inc.

Fleming, Sean & Ewald, Jenny, eds. To Catch a Mall Thief. 2004. 85p. (YA). pap. 9.95 (978-0-7414-2196-8(8)) Infinity Publishing.

Fleming, Sheila G. A Very Berra Holiday. 2002. 108p. pap. 9.95 (978-0-595-25600-6(7) , Weekly Reader Teacher's Pr) iUniverse, Inc.

Fletcher, Ralph J. Flying Solo. 2000. 144p. (J). (gr. 5-9). 5.50 (978-0-440-41601-2(9) , Yearling) Random Hse. Children's Bks.

Flinn, Lisa. Good News Travels Fast: An Easter Story. 2003. (gr. k-3). lib. bdg. 13.00 (978-0-613-73198-0(0)) Tandem Library Bks.

Flood, Pansie Hart. Secret Holes. Marshall, Felicia, illus. 2004. 128p. (J). (gr. 3-6). 15.95 (978-0-87614-923-2(9) , Carolrhoda Bks.) Lerner Publishing Group.

—Tiger's Trouble with Donut Head. Wummer, Amy, illus. 2005. 71p. (J). lib. bdg. 19.93 (978-1-57505-814-6(6) , Carolrhoda Bks.) Lerner Publishing Group.

Floppy's Friends. 2004. (J). (ALB & ENG.). (978-1-84444-647-6(6)); (ARA & ENG.). (978-1-84444-648-3(4)); (BEN & ENG.). (978-1-84444-649-0(2)); (CHI & ENG.). (978-1-84444-650-6(6)); (CHI & ENG.). (978-1-84444-651-3(4)); (CRO & ENG.). (978-1-84444-652-0(2)); (ENG & PER.). (978-1-84444-653-7(0)); (ENG & FRE.). (978-1-84444-654-4(9)); (ENG & GUJ.). (978-1-84444-655-1(7)); (ENG & HIN.). (978-1-84444-656-8(5)); (ENG & LAO.). (978-1-84444-657-5(3)); (ENG & PAN.). (978-1-84444-658-2(1)); (ENG & POL.). (978-1-84444-659-9(X)); (ENG & POR.). (978-1-84444-660-5(3)); (ENG & SOM.). (978-1-84444-661-2(1)); (ENG & SPA.). (978-1-84444-662-9(X)); (ENG & TAM.). (978-1-84444-663-6(8)); (ENG & TUR.). (978-1-84444-664-3(6)); (ENG & URD.). (978-1-84444-665-0(4)); (ENG & VIE.). (978-1-84444-666-7(2)) Mantra Publishing, Ltd.

Florence, Nancy L. Harold the Goat. 2004. 30p. pap. 14.95 (978-1-4137-3941-1(5)) PublishAmerica, Inc.

Flowers, Natasha. Sammy the Snail. 2006. 10.00 (978-0-8059-9158-1(1)) Dorrance Publishing Co., Inc.

Floyd, Madeleine. Cold Paws, Warm Heart. 2005. (Illus.). 32p. (J). (ps-3). 15.99 (978-0-7636-2761-4(5)) Candlewick Pr.

Fogelin, Adrian. The Sorta Sisters. 2007. 240p. (J). (gr. 3-7). 14.95 (***978-1-56145-424-2(9)*** , Peachtree Junior) Peachtree Pubs., Ltd.

Fogg, K. L. Serpent Tide. 2006. 16.95 (978-1-59156-861-2(7)) Covenant Communications, Inc.

Fogle, Llynda & Gonzalez, Althea. A Friendship Place. 2005. (ENG & SPA., Illus.). (J). (978-0-9760282-6-0(3)) RAPC - Sparkle & Shine Project.

Foland, Constance M. Flying High, Pogo! 2002. (gr. 3-6). lib. bdg. 14.10 (978-0-613-89603-0(3)) Tandem Library Bks.

—A Song for Jeffrey. 1999. (978-0-606-18357-4(4)) Tandem Library Bks.

Fontenot, Mary Alice. Clovis Crawfish & Silvie Sulphur. Buckner, Julie Dupre, illus. 2004. (ENG & FRE.). 32p. (J). pap. 15.95 (978-1-56554-864-0(7)) Pelican Publishing Co., Inc.

—Clovis Ecrevisse et Sidonie Souris-De-Champ. Landry, Julie F., tr. Blazek, Scott R., illus. 1998. (FRE.). 32p. (J). (ps-3). 16.95 (978-1-56554-345-4(9)) Pelican Publishing Co., Inc.

Fontes, Justine. Toy Trouble. Hefferan, Rob, illus. 2003. 24p. (J). pap. (978-1-59034-447-7(2)); 14.95 (978-1-59034-446-0(4)) Mondo Publishing.

Foon, Dennis. Skud. 2004. 176p. (YA). pap. 6.95 (978-0-88899-549-0(0)) Groundwood Bks. CAN. *Dist:* Perseus Distribution.

Forbes, Lucie E. The Adventures of Jesse & Teri. 2005. 16.95 (978-0-533-14957-5(6)) Vantage Pr., Inc.

Ford, Bernette. Don't Hit Me! Grier, Gary, illus. 2004. 32p. (J). lib. bdg. 15.00 (***978-1-4242-0218-8(3)***) Fitzgerald Bks.

Ford, Christine. Scout. 2007. 224p. (J). (gr. 4-7). pap. 5.50 (***978-0-440-42041-5(5)*** , Yearling) Random Hse. Children's Bks.

Forever Friends! 2003. (Illus.). 28p. (J). (ps-k). bds. 7.95 (978-0-8249-5454-3(8)) Ideals Pubns.

Forman, Gayle. Sisters in Sanity. 2007. 304p. (J). lib. bdg. 17.89 (***978-0-06-088748-3(6)***); (YA). (gr. 7 up). 16.99 (***978-0-06-088747-6(8)***) HarperCollins Pubs. (HarperTeen).

Fornof, John. Tad's Glad-Sad-Mad, Glad Day. Adnet, Bernard, illus. 2003. 12p. (J). 6.99 (978-0-310-70647-2(5)) Zonderkidz.

Forrestal, Elaine. Graffiti on the Fence. 1999. 144p. (J). pap. (978-0-14-130519-6(3) , Puffin) Penguin Group (USA) Inc.

Forrester, Izola. Kit of Greenacre Farm. 2006. 33.99 (***978-1-4280-3401-3(3)***); pap. 26.99 (***978-1-4280-3376-4(9)***) IndyPublish.com.

Forrester, Izola L. Kit of Greenacre Farm. 2007. 158p. pap. 11.99 (***978-1-4264-8431-5(3)***); 174p. pap. 14.99 (***978-1-4264-8489-6(5)***) BiblioBazaar.

Forsyth, C. A. Hockey Heat Wave. 1999. (gr. 7-12). lib. bdg. 13.55 (978-0-613-18219-5(7)) Tandem Library Bks.

Foster, Alicia. The Book of Anna. 2005. 206p. pap. 19.95 (978-1-4137-5853-5(3)) PublishAmerica, Inc.

Foster, Kinsley. Wild Abandon Vol. 2: Slam. 1999. (YA). pap. 10.95 (978-0-9667634-8-5(3)) What's Inside Pr.

Foster, Thomas. Travel Buddies: Robby & Sammy Visit China. 2006. (J). pap. 12.00 (978-1-890306-93-9(2)) Warwick Hse. Publishing.

Fowler, Susi Gregg. Albertina, the Animals & Me. 2000. (Illus.). 96p. (YA). (gr. 5 up). 14.89 (978-0-06-029160-0(5)) HarperCollins Pubs.

Fox, L. B. The Adventures of Marky, Slash & Levy. 2006. (ENG.). 184p. per. 19.95 (***978-1-4241-4992-6(4)***) PublishAmerica, Inc.

Fox, Mem. Hunwick's Egg. Lofts, Pamela, tr. Lofts, Pamela, illus. 2005. 32p. (J). 16.00 (978-0-15-216318-1(2)) Harcourt Children's Bks.

—Wilfrid Gordon McDonald Partridge. 2002. (Illus.). (J). 16.55 (978-0-7587-4024-3(7)) Book Wholesalers, Inc.

Fox, Michael. The Timmons Incident: Part Ii of the Tom. 2005. 178p. pap. 19.95 (978-1-4137-6912-8(8)) PublishAmerica, Inc.

Foxx, Darla J. Alexis Mcdougal starring in... Secrets Are Confidential Business!!! A sequel to Alexis Mcdougal starring in... the Day I Met My New Special Friend. 2006. (Illus.). 72p. (J). 9.95 (978-0-9768879-1-1(6) , ISBN0976887916) Universal Messengers Pubns.

—Alexis Mcdougal starring in the Day I Met My New Special Friend. 2005. (Illus.). 79p. (J). per. 7.95 (978-0-9768879-0-4(8) , AM-001) Universal Messengers Pubns.

France, Anthony. From Me to You. Beeke, Tiphanie, illus. 2003. 32p. (J). (ps-2). 15.99 (978-0-7636-2255-8(9)) Candlewick Pr.

Francour, Kathleen, illus. Friends Forever. 2003. (Puzzles Ser.). (J). bds. 10.95 (978-1-74047-342-2(6)) Book Co. Publishing Pty, Ltd., The AUS. *Dist:* Penton Overseas, Inc.

Frank, Lucy. Lucky Stars. (J). 2006. 240p. pap. 5.99 (978-0-689-85934-2(1) , Aladdin); 2005. (Illus.). 304p. 16.95 (978-0-689-85933-5(3) , Atheneum) Simon & Schuster Children's Publishing.

—Will You Be My Brussels Sprout? 1998. (J). (978-0-606-13918-2(4)) Tandem Library Bks.

Franklin, Kristine L. Lone Wolf. 224p. (J). (gr. 4-8). 2006. 5.99 (978-0-7636-2996-0(0)); 1998. (Illus.). pap. 6.99 (978-0-7636-0480-6(1)) Candlewick Pr.

—Lone Wolf. 1998. (J). (978-0-606-13578-8(2)) Tandem Library Bks.

—Nerd No More. 1999. (J). (978-0-606-15653-0(4)) Tandem Library Bks.

Frantz, Jennifer. Wilbur Finds a Friend. Ivanov, Aleksey, illus. 2006. (Charlotte's Web Ser.). 32p. (J). 15.99 (978-0-06-088282-2(4)); pap. 3.99 (978-0-06-088281-5(6) , Harper Trophy) HarperCollins Pubs.

Franz, Kevin. The Princess Sisters & the Underwater City. Stigler, Marilyn, illus. 2004. 112p. (J). per. 7.99 (978-0-9747774-1-2(2)) Starbell Bks.

Frazee, Marla. A Couple of Boys Go to Antarctica (Sort Of) 2008. 40p. (J). 16.00 (***978-0-15-206020-6(0)***) Harcourt Trade Pubs.

Frechette, Carole. In the Key of Do. Ouriou, Susan, tr. from FRE. 2004. 96p. (YA). (gr. 8 up). pap. 9.95 (978-0-88995-254-6(X)) Red Deer Pr. CAN. *Dist:* Fitzhenry & Whiteside, Ltd.

—In the Key of Do. 2003. (gr. 7-12). lib. bdg. 16.40 (978-0-613-82355-5(9)) Tandem Library Bks.

Frederick, Heather Vogel. The Black Paw. Comport, Sally Wern, illus. (Spy Mice Ser.). (J). 2006. 256p. pap. 5.99 (978-1-4169-2770-9(0) , Aladdin); 2006. 256p. pap. 2.99 (978-1-4169-2502-6(3) , Aladdin); 2005. 240p. 9.95 (978-0-689-87753-7(6) , Simon & Schuster Children's Publishing) Simon & Schuster Children's Publishing.

Fredericks, Mariah. Crunch Time. 336p. (YA). 2007. (gr. 7 up). pap. 7.99 (***978-1-4169-3973-3(3)*** , Simon Pulse); 2005. (Illus.). 16.99 (978-0-689-86938-9(X) , Atheneum) Simon & Schuster Children's Publishing.

—Love. Watkins, Liselotte, illus. 2006. (In the Cards Ser.). 288p. (J). (gr. 5-9). 15.99 (978-0-689-87654-7(8) , Atheneum/Richard Jackson Bks.) Simon & Schuster Children's Publishing.

—The True Meaning of Cleavage. (YA). 2003. (Illus.). 224p. 15.95 (978-0-689-85092-9(1) , Atheneum/Richard Jackson Bks.); 2004. 240p. reprint ed. pap. 6.99 (978-0-689-86958-7(4) , Simon Pulse) Simon & Schuster Children's Publishing.

Freed, Shirley Ann. Michael Never Gives Up. Morelan, Bill, ed. Harrell, Rob, illus. l.t. ed. 2002. 24p. (J). (gr. 1). pap. 3.99 (978-1-58938-041-7(X)) Concerned Communications.

Freed, Shirley Ann & Moon, Louise. My Forever Friend. Morelan, Bill, ed. Harrell, Rob, illus. l.t. ed. 2002. 16p. (J). (gr. 1-2). pap. 3.99 (978-1-58938-034-9(7)) Concerned Communications.

Freedman, Claire & Shearing, Leonie. Squabble & Squawk. 2006. (Illus.). 32p. (J). (ps). 19.95 (978-0-689-87307-2(7)) Simon & Schuster, Ltd. GBR. *Dist:* Independent Pubs. Group.

Freeman, Don. Corduroy's Sweet Surprise. 2008. 12p. (J). (ps-k). bds. 7.99 (***978-0-448-44821-3(1)*** , Grosset & Dunlap) Penguin Group (USA) Inc.

Freeman, Don. Gregory's Shadow. 2005. (Readalongs for Beginning Readers Ser.). (Illus.). (J). pap. 16.95 incl. audio (978-1-59112-237-1(6)) Live Oak Media.

—Gregory's Shadow. Freeman, Don, illus. 2003. (Readalongs for Beginning Readers Ser.). (Illus.). (J). 25.95 incl. audio (978-1-59112-238-8(4)); pap. 37.95 incl. audio (978-1-59112-239-5(2)) Live Oak Media.

—Gregory's Shadow. 2002. (gr. k-3). lib. bdg. 15.30 (978-0-613-60806-0(2)) Tandem Library Bks.

Freeman, Martha. The Spy Wore Shades. Date not set. 160p. (YA). (gr. 3 up). pap. 4.99 (978-0-06-440957-5(0)) HarperCollins Pubs.

—The Spy Wore Shades. Cigliano, Bill, illus. 2001. 240p. (J). (gr. 3 up). 15.89 (978-0-06-029270-6(9)) HarperCollins Pubs.

—The Year My Parents Ruined My Life. 1999. (978-0-606-16453-5(7)) Tandem Library Bks.

—1,000 Reasons Never to Kiss a Boy. 2007. 240p. (YA). (gr. 7 up). 16.95 (978-0-8234-2044-5(2)) Holiday Hse., Inc.

Freer, Echo. Magenta Orange. l.t. ed. 2005. 256p. (J). pap. (978-0-7540-7915-6(5) , CLP 474) BBC Audio.

French, Renee. The Soap Lady. French, Renee, illus. 2005. (Illus.). 111p. (J). (gr. 4-8). reprint ed. 20.00 (978-0-7567-9419-4(6)) DIANE Publishing Co.

French, Vivian. Detective Dan. Bartlett, Alison, illus. 2006. (Read-It! Chapter Books). 48p. (J). (gr. 2-4). 19.95 (978-1-4048-1659-6(3)) Picture Window Bks.

—Ellie & Elvis. Terry, Michael, illus. 2007. 32p. (J). pap. 9.99 (***978-0-7475-8403-2(6)***) Bloomsbury Publishing Plc GBR. *Dist:* Independent Pubs. Group.

—Princess Emily & the Wishing Star. Gibb, Sarah, illus. 2007. (J). (Tiara Club Ser.: No.12). 80p. pap. 3.99 (***978-0-06-112451-8(6)*** , Harper Trophy); (***978-0-06-112452-5(4)***) HarperCollins Pubs.

Freschet, Gina. Up & at 'Em with Winnie & Ernst. 2005. (Winnie & Ernst Ser.). (Illus.). 48p. (J). 15.00 (978-0-374-38446-3(0) , Farrar, Straus & Giroux (BYR)) Farrar, Straus & Giroux.

—Winnie & Ernst. Freschet, Gina, illus. 2003. (Winnie & Ernst Ser.). (Illus.). 48p. (J). 15.00 (978-0-374-38452-4(5) , Farrar, Straus & Giroux (BYR)) Farrar, Straus & Giroux.

Friedman, Aimee. French Kiss. 2006. 336p. (J). pap. 8.99 (978-0-439-79281-3(9) , Scholastic Paperbacks) Scholastic, Inc.

—South Beach. 2005. 336p. (YA). 8.99 (978-0-439-70678-0(5) , Scholastic Paperbacks) Scholastic, Inc.

Friedman, Aimee. Year My Sister Got Lucky. 2008. 384p. (J). pap. 16.99 (***978-0-439-92227-2(5)***) Scholastic, Inc.

Friedman, Laurie. Heart to Heart with Mallory. Pollak, Barbara, illus. 2007. (Mallory Ser.). 160p. (J). (gr. 2-7). pap. 5.95 (***978-0-8225-7133-9(1)*** , First Avenue Editions) Lerner Publishing Group.

—Mallory Se Muda (Mallory on the Move) Anaya, Josefina, tr. Schmitz, Tamara, illus. 2007. (Mallory en español (Mallory in Spanish) Ser.). (SPA.). (J). (gr. 2-6). pap. 5.95 (***978-0-8225-7493-4(4)*** , Ediciones Lerner) Lerner Publishing Group.

Friedman, Laurie B. Campfire Mallory. Kalis, Jennifer, illus. 2008. (Mallory Ser.). (J). lib. bdg. 15.95 (***978-0-8225-7657-0(0)*** , Carolrhoda Bks.) Lerner Publishing Group.

—Heart to Heart with Mallory. Pollak, Barbara, illus. 2006. 160p. (J). (gr. 2-5). 15.95 (978-1-57505-932-7(0) , Twenty-First Century Bks.) Lerner Publishing Group.

—Mallory on Board. Pollak, Barbara, illus. 2007. 160p. (J). (gr. 2-6). 15.95 (978-0-8225-6194-1(8) , Carolrhoda Bks.) Lerner Publishing Group.

—Mallory on the Move. Schmitz, Tamara, illus. 2005. 160p. (J). pap. 5.95 (978-1-57505-831-3(6)) Lerner Publishing Group.

—Mallory on the Move. Schmitz, Tamara, tr. Schmitz, Tamara, illus. 2004. (Middle Grade Fiction Ser.). 160p. (J). 15.95 (978-1-57505-538-1(4)) Lerner Publishing Group.

Friedrich, Joachim. The Disappearing Bio Teacher. Date not set. (Illus.). 144p. (J). (gr. 3-7). 14.99 (978-0-7868-0700-0(8)) Hyperion Pr.

—4 1/2 Friends & the Secret Cave, Bk. 1. Crawford, Elizabeth D., tr. from GER. 2001. (Illus.). 160p. (gr. 3-7). 14.99 (978-0-7868-0648-5(6)) Hyperion Bks. for Children.

Friel, Maeve. Charlie's Story. 2004. 112p. (YA). (gr. 7-9). pap. 5.95 (978-1-56145-315-3(3)) Peachtree Pubs., Ltd.

A Friend in Need. 2007. (J). 9.95 (***978-0-9787995-6-4(9)***) High-Pitched Hum Inc.

Friend, Natasha. Perfect. 2004. 232p. (J). 16.95 (978-1-57131-652-3(3)); pap. 6.95 (978-1-57131-651-6(5)) Milkweed Editions.

Friends. 2005. (Illus.). 96p. (J). (gr. 3-7). pap. 4.99 (978-0-7868-0976-9(0) , Volo) Hyperion Bks. for Children.

Friends Forever: Adventures. 2003. per. 12.95 net. (978-1-891929-96-0(8)) Four Seasons Pubs.

Friends of Lulu Present: Storytime. 2000. (YA). per. (978-0-9740960-0-1(8)) Friends of Lulu.

Friends, Paz. Dos Amigos. 2001. Tr. of Two Friends. (SPA.). (J). (gr. 2-4). 16.76 (978-84-88342-17-1(0)) S.A. Kokinos ESP. *Dist:* Lectorum Pubns., Inc.

Friendship Force. 1999. (J). pap. 3.99 (978-0-307-25400-9(3) , Golden Bks.) Random Hse. Children's Bks.

Friendship Keeper. 2001. 60p. 9.99 (978-0-9703731-0-6(4)) Barber, Mark D.

Friesen, Gayle. The Isabel Factor. 2005. 252p. (YA). (Illus.). (gr. 7-17). (978-1-55337-738-2(9)); (978-1-55337-737-5(0)) Kids Can Pr., Ltd.

Fripp, Deborah & Fripp, Michael. Naya & Nathan. Fripp, Jean, ed. Barber, Carol, illus. 2003. (Dolphin Watch Ser.). 32p. (J). (gr. k-4). pap. 5.99 (978-0-9701008-4-9(1)) Bicast, Inc.

Fritz, Jean. The Great Little Madison. 1998. (Illus.). 160p. (J). (gr. 5-9). pap. 6.99 (978-0-698-11621-4(6) , Putnam Juvenile) Penguin Group (USA) Inc.

Fry, Sonali. Best Friends Forever. Berry, Bob, illus. 2007. (Holly Hobbie & Friends Ser.). 24p. (J). (ps-3). pap. 3.99 (***978-1-4169-3898-9(2)*** , Little Simon) Simon & Schuster Children's Publishing.

—A Day with Mom. Workman, Lisa, illus. 2007. (Holly Hobbie & Friends Ser.). 24p. (J). 8.99 (978-1-4169-3579-7(7) , Little Simon) Simon & Schuster Children's Publishing.

—Happy Easter, Holly! Berry, Bob, illus. 2008. (Holly Hobbie & Friends Ser.). 24p. (J). pap. 3.99 (***978-1-4169-4926-8(7)*** , Little Simon) Simon & Schuster Children's Publishing.

Fry, Sonali. My Finest Friends. G Studios, illus. 2007. (Land of Milk & Honey Ser.). 14p. (J). 8.99 (978-1-4169-2765-5(4) , Little Simon Inspirations) Simon & Schuster Children's Publishing.

Frye, Mary M. The Pashofa Pole, 5 vols., Vol. 1. Willis, Henry J., tr. Howard, Norma, illus. 2000. Vol. 1. 30p. (J). 20.00 (978-0-9710250-0-4(2)) Choctaw Crafts & Bks.

Fuchs, Menucha. Chatzkel, Mendel & Me: An adventure Story. Daykin, Rachmiel, tr. from HEB. Hechtkopf, H., illus. 2005. Orig. Title: Mah Shekarah Ba'Ayarah. 192p. (J). 15.95 (978-1-932443-39-4(8) , CHMH) Judaica Pr., Inc., The.

—Children's Stories about Friendship. Miri, illus. 2000. (Children's Learning Ser.: Vol. 5). 48p. (J). (gr. 1-4). pap. 4.95 (978-1-880582-51-0(1)) Judaica Pr., Inc., The.

—Donny Duckling Finds a Friend. Rappaport, Aviva, tr. 2002. (HEB., Illus.). 32p. (J). 9.95 (978-1-880582-99-2(6) , DDFH) Judaica Pr., Inc., The.

—The Flying Invitation. 2004. (Illus.). 20p. (J). 6.95 (978-1-932443-07-3(X) , FLIH) Judaica Pr., Inc., The.

—The Most Beautiful Picture in the World. 2004. (Illus.). 20p. (J). 6.95 (978-1-932443-09-7(6)) Judaica Pr., Inc., The.

Fuchs-Rice, Dwayne. Troika. 2007. 248p. per. 16.95 (***978-0-595-45834-9(3)***) iUniverse, Inc.

Fujikawa, Gyo. Are You My Friend Today? 1999. 3.99 (978-0-375-80125-9(1)) Random Hse., Inc.

Fuller, Bob. Meet the Kids of Paddywhack Lane. 2007. (Paddywhack Lane Ser.). 24p. (J). pap. 3.99 (978-0-448-44508-3(5) , Grosset & Dunlap) Penguin Group (USA) Inc.

Fun in the Park. 1999. (Tami & Moishy Ser.: Vol. 3). (J). bds. 6.95 (978-1-58330-378-8(2)) Feldheim Pubs.

Funke, Cornelia. Inkspell. Bell, Anthea, tr. from GER. 2005. (Illus.). 656p. (J). pap. 19.99 (978-0-439-55400-8(4) , Chicken Hse., The) Scholastic, Inc.

Funkhouser, Allison. Zealk & the Humans. 2005. 60p. 16.99 (978-1-58752-111-9(3)) Timberwolf Pr., Inc.

Fuqua, Jonathon Scott. Catie & Josephine. Parke, Steven, illus. 2003. 72p. (J). (gr. 3-5). 16.00 (978-0-618-39403-6(6)) Houghton Mifflin Co. Trade & Reference Div.

Fuqua, Jonathon Scott. Medusas Daughter Novel. 2007. (Narrative, Ink Ser.). 192p. (J). (***978-1-933368-91-7(8)***) Counterpoint.

Gabel, Claudia. In or Out. 2007. 256p. (YA). (gr. 7 up). pap. 8.99 (***978-0-439-91853-4(7)***) Scholastic, Inc.

—Sweet & Vicious. 2008. (In or Out Ser.). 256p. (J). pap. 8.99 (***978-0-439-91856-5(1)*** , Scholastic Paperbacks) Scholastic, Inc.

Gag, Wanda. Snippy & Snappy. 2003. (Illus.). 48p. (gr. k-3). 14.95 (978-0-8166-4245-8(1)) Univ. of Minnesota Pr.

Gago, Jenny & McKay, Sindy. We Both Read-the Perfect Gift. Harden, Laurie, illus. 2001. (We Both Read Ser.). (ENG & SPA.). 44p. (J). (gr. 1-2). 7.99 (978-1-891327-33-9(X)); pap. 3.99 (978-1-891327-34-6(8)) Treasure Bay, Inc.

Gail, Cornelia. Juvey. 2007. 153p. (YA). per. 14.95 net. (***978-0-9674454-4-1(2)***) Girls In Da Game Publishing.

Gaine-Winkelman, Barbara. Without Friends, You're Nothing: Tales of Friendship. 1999. (One Saturday Morning Ser.: Vol. 2). (Illus.). 105p. (J). (gr. 2-5). pap. 3.99 (978-0-7868-4308-4(X)) Hyperion Pr.

Gainer, Cindy. I'm Like You, You're Like Me: A Child's Book about Understanding & Celebrating Each Other. Gainer, Cindy, illus. 1998. (Illus.). 48p. (J). (ps-3). 12.95 (978-1-57542-039-4(2)) Free Spirit Publishing, Inc.

Gaines, Isabel. Eeyore Finds Friends. 1999. (Winnie the Pooh First Readers Ser.: No. 11). (Illus.). 37p. (J). (gr. k-3). pap. 3.99 (978-0-7868-4269-8(5)) Disney Pr.

—Pooh's Best Friend. Jones, Tim, illus. 1998. (Winnie the Pooh First Readers Ser.: No. 7). 40p. (J). (ps-3). pap. 3.95 (978-0-7868-4265-0(2)) Disney Pr.

—Pooh's Christmas Gifts. 2001. (Winnie the Pooh First Readers Ser.). (Illus.). (J). (978-0-606-21653-1(7)) Tandem Library Bks.

—Pooh's Graduation. 22nd ed. 2000. (Winnie the Pooh Ser.). (Illus.). 37p. (J). (gr. k-3). pap. 3.99 (978-0-7868-4369-5(1)) Disney Pr.

—Pooh's Halloween Parade. 2001. (Winnie the Pooh First Readers Ser.). (Illus.). (J). (978-0-606-21656-2(1)) Tandem Library Bks.

—Pooh's Surprise Basket. 1999. (Winnie the Pooh First Readers Ser.: No. 13). (Illus.). 37p. (J). (gr. k-3). pap. 3.99 (978-0-7868-4332-9(2)) Disney Pr.

—Tiggers Hate to Lose. 2001. (Winnie the Pooh First Readers Ser.). (Illus.). (J). (978-0-606-21664-7(2)) Tandem Library Bks.

Galer, Jeffrey & Galer, Christa. The Big Red Barn. Galer, Jeffrey, illus. 2003. (Illus.). 40p. (J). 11.49 (978-0-9706491-0-2(X)) Purple Crayon Studios.

Gallagher, Diana G. Whatever! The Complicated Life of Claudia Cristina Cortez. Garvey, Brann, illus. 2008. (J). pap. (***978-1-59889-880-4(9)***); 81p. (gr. 4-8). lib. bdg. 23.93 (***978-1-59889-839-2(6)***) Stone Arch Bks.

Gallagher, Liz. The Opposite of Invisible. 2008. (YA). (***978-0-375-84152-1(0)***); (***978-0-375-94329-4(3)***) Dell Publishing. (Delacorte Pr.).

Gallagher, Mary. The Legend of Lisnashee. 2006. (Illus.). 100p. pap. 9.95 (978-1-903464-71-7(4)) Collins Pr., The IRL. *Dist:* Dufour Editions, Inc.

Gallagher, Mary Collins. Ginny Morris & Dad's New Girlfriend. Martin, Whitney, illus. 2006. 63p. (J). (gr. 3-5). 14.95 (978-1-59147-386-2(1)); pap. 8.95 (978-1-59147-387-9(X)) American Psychological Assn. (Magination Pr.).

Gallego Garcia, Laura. Retorno a la Isla Blanca. 2004. 143p. pap. 14.00 (978-84-931888-6-3(7)) Editorial Brief ESP. *Dist:* Independent Pubs. Group.

Gallego García, Laura & Peden, Margaret Sayers. The Valley of the Wolves. 2006. 247p. (J). pap. (978-0-439-58554-5(6) , Levine, Arthur A. Bks.) Scholastic, Inc.

Gallemore, M. H. Annie & the Mermaid. 2005. 9.00 (978-0-8059-9787-3(3)) Dorrance Publishing Co., Inc.

Gallo, Lana. Sometimes Stars Fall for a Reason. Smith, David F. & Holt, Delecia, illus. Holt, Delecia & Gray, R. Paul, III, photos by. 2000. 26p. (J). 9.95 (978-0-9677469-5-1(7)) Van Buren California Publishing.

Galloway, Ruth. Clumsy Crab. Galloway, Ruth, illus. 2005. (Illus.). 28p. (J). (ps-ps). 15.95 (978-1-58925-050-5(8) , tiger tales) ME Media LLC.

Galvin, Laura Gates. Best Friends. rev. ed. 2006. (Disney Princess Ser.). 20 x 4p. 14.99 (978-1-59069-477-0(5)) Studio Mouse LLC.

Gamer, Ron. Hidden Chance: Secrets of the Hermit;s Hideaway. 2007. 240p. (YA). per. 8.95 (***978-1-59193-209-3(2)***) Adventure Pubns., Inc.

Garcia, Angela Irene. His Name Is Joe. Davis, Ami, illus. 2002. 12.99 (978-0-9726313-0-3(5)) From The Heart Bks.

Garcia, Laura Gallego. The Valley of the Wolves. 2006. 336p. (J). (gr. 4-7). pap. 16.99 (978-0-439-58553-8(8) , Levine, Arthur A. Bks.) Scholastic, Inc.

Gardam, Jane. Un Poney en la Nieve. Geldart, William, illus. 2002. (SPA.). 64p. (J). (gr. 3-5). pap. 7.95 (978-968-19-0315-2(3)) Aguilar Editorial MEX. *Dist:* Santillana USA Publishing Co., Inc.

Garden, Nancy. Nora & Liz. 2002. (gr. 7-12). lib. bdg. 22.20 (978-0-613-60499-4(7)) Tandem Library Bks.

Garfinkle, Debra. The Band: Trading Guys: Trading Guys. 2007. 256p. (YA). (gr. 12). pap. 9.99 (***978-0-425-21513-5(X)*** , Berkley Trade) Penguin Group (USA) Inc.

Garland, Robin. Tanglewood, the Gift: Bk. 1. 2005. 133p. pap. 11.95 (978-0-7414-2339-9(1)) Infinity Publishing.

Garland, Sarah. Billy & Belle. 2004. (Illus.). 32p. (J). 15.95 (978-1-84507-037-3(2)); pap. 7.95 (978-1-84507-038-0(0)) Lincoln, Frances Ltd. GBR. *Dist:* Transition Vendor, Perseus Distribution.

Garnham, Laura. The Tiniest Mermaid. MacCarthy, Patricia, illus. 2006. 28p. (J). 16.00 (978-1-56148-512-3(8)) Good Bks.

Gauch, Patricia Lee. Tanya & Emily in a Dance for Two. 1998. (978-0-606-13838-3(2)) Tandem Library Bks.

Gauthier, Gilles. A Gift from Mooch. Cummins, Sarah, tr. from FRE. Derome, Pierre-Andre, illus. 2001. (First Novels Ser.: Vol. 39). 64p. (J). (gr. 1-5). (978-0-88780-549-3(3)) Formac Publishing Co., Ltd. CAN. *Dist:* Casemate Pubs. & Bk. Distributors, LLC.

—A Gift from Mooch. Cummins, Sarah, tr. from FRE. Derome, Pierre-André, illus. 2001. (First Novels Ser.: Vol. 39). 64p. (gr. 1-5). 4.95 (978-0-88780-548-6(5)) Formac Publishing Co., Ltd. CAN. *Dist:* Casemate Pubs. & Bk. Distributors, LLC.

Gauthier, Gilles & Derome, Pierre-Andre, Le Grand Antonio a le Coeur Gros. 2002. (Premier Roman Ser.). (FRE., Illus.). 64p. pap. (978-2-89021-562-7(8)) Diffusion du livre Mirabel.

Gave, Marc. Fox & the Hound: Read Aloud Storybook. 2000. (Illus.). 64p. (J). (ps-3). 6.99 (978-0-7364-0194-4(6)) Mouse Works.

Gay, Francis. The Friendship Book. 2005. (Illus.). 180p. 9.95 (978-1-84535-050-5(2)) Thomson, D.C. & Co., Ltd. GBR. *Dist:* APG Sales and Fulfillment.

—Friendship Book 2004. D C Thomson Staff, ed. 2004. (Illus.). 108p. 9.95 (978-0-85116-834-0(5)) Thomson, D.C. & Co., Ltd. GBR. *Dist:* APG Sales and Fulfillment.

Gay, Marie-Louise. Mademoiselle Moon. Gay, Marie-Louise, illus. 2006. (Illus.). 32p. pap. 7.95 (978-1-55005-134-6(2)) Fitzhenry & Whiteside, Ltd. CAN. *Dist:* F & W Pubns., Inc.

Geary, Judith. Getorix: The Eagle & the Bull. 2006. (Illus.). 278p. 24.95 (978-1-932158-74-8(X)) Ingalls Publishing Group, Inc.

Gee, Genese. The Story of Jack, Sprat, & the Backpack. Gee, Genese, illus. (Illus.). 20p. (J). (ps-1). 2002. 14.99 (978-0-9719935-1-8(3)); 2001. pap. 10.49 (978-0-9719935-0-1(5)) Gee, Genese Celeste.

Gehrman, Jody. Confessions of a Triple Shot Betty. 2008. 256p. (J). (gr. 9). 16.99 (***978-0-8037-3247-6(3)*** , Dial) Penguin Group (USA) Inc.

Gelman, Rita Goldman. More Spaghetti, I Say: Quiero Mas Fideos! 2003. (SPA.). 32p. (J). pap. 3.99 (978-0-590-29377-8(X)) Scholastic, Inc.

Genechten, Guido van. The Cuddle Book. Genechten, Guido van, illus. 2004. (Illus.). 32p. (J). (ps-k). 14.99 (978-0-06-075306-1(4)) HarperCollins Pubs.

—Flop Ear. 2001. (Illus.). (J). (978-0-606-21191-8(8)) Tandem Library Bks.

George & His Best Friend. 2003. (Illus.). 32p. (J). 6.99 (978-0-9744520-0-5(9)) Glitter Creek, Inc.

George, Jean Craighead. Charlie's Raven. 2004. (Illus.). 208p. (J). (gr. 4). 15.99 (978-0-525-47219-3(3) , Dutton Juvenile) Penguin Group (USA) Inc.

—Ratas de Rio, S. A.Tr. of River Rats, Inc.. (SPA.). (YA). (gr. 5-8). pap. (978-84-345-8620-8(7)) Salvat Editores, S.A. ESP. *Dist:* Lectorum Pubns., Inc.

Geras, Adele. Pictures of the Night. 2005. (Egerton Hall Novels: Vol. 3). 192p. (YA). (gr. 7-17). pap. 6.95 (978-0-15-205543-1(6) , Harcourt Paperbacks) Harcourt Children's Bks.

Gerowin, Sean. Catte au Lait & the Big Hurricane. 2005. 36p. (J). 8.99 (978-1-4116-5157-9(X)) Lulu.com.

Gershon, Dann & Gershon, Gina. Hollyhive Hunnie. Robinson, David, illus. 2000. (Hangin' with the Hombeez Ser.: Vol. 5). 40p. (J). (gr. k-6). 9.95 (978-0-9656985-7-3(2)) Noware Bks.

Geshell, Carmen. Waltah Melon: Local-Kine Hero. Pagay, Jeff, illus. 2004. 24p. (J). 10.95 (978-1-57306-205-3(7)) Bess Pr., Inc.

Geter, Maurice. My Friend Buddy. Geter, Maurice, illus. 2006. (Illus.). 24p. (J). (978-1-4120-9646-1(4)) Trafford Publishing.

Ghent, Natale. Piper. 2001. (J). (978-0-606-21772-9(X)); (gr. 5-8). lib. bdg. 15.25 (978-0-613-36600-7(X)) Tandem Library Bks.

Gibbons, Alan. Ganging Up. 2nd ed. 2006. (Illus.). 96p. (J). pap. 11.99 (***978-1-85881-194-9(5)***) Orion Publishing Group, Ltd. GBR. *Dist:* Independent Pubs. Group.

Gibbons, Gail. The Quilting Bee. Gibbons, Gail, illus. 2004. (Illus.). 32p. (J). (gr. 1 up). 17.99 (978-0-688-16397-6(1)) HarperCollins Pubs.

Gibbs, Lynne. Ping Won't Share. Mitchell, Melanie, illus. 2003. (Growing Pains Ser.). 32p. (J). pap. 4.95 (978-1-57768-927-0(5)); 12.95 (978-1-57768-480-0(X)) School Specialty Publishing. (Gingham Dog Pr.).

Gibson, Glen. Angel & the Misfits. 2006. 175p. (YA). per. 11.95 (***978-1-59594-114-5(2)*** , Wingspan Pr.) WingSpan Publishing.

Gibson, Kari Smalley. Mooki & the Too-Proud Peacock. 2004. 32p. (J). pap. 6.99 (978-0-310-70922-0(9)) Zonderkidz.

—Mooki the Berry Bandit. 2004. 32p. (J). pap. 6.99 (978-0-310-70921-3(0)) Zonderkidz.

Giddens, Martha Anne. The Unluckiest Kid in the Universe. 2006. 56p. pap. (***978-1-4120-7935-8(7)***) Trafford Publishing.

Gifaldi, David. Listening for Crickets. 2008. 192p. (J). 16.95 (978-0-8050-7385-0(X) , Holt, Henry & Co. Bks. For Young Readers) Holt, Henry & Co.

Giff, Patricia Reilly. All the Way Home. 2003. (Illus.). 176p. (J). (gr. 3-7). pap. 5.99 (978-0-440-41182-6(3) , Yearling) Random Hse. Children's Bks.

—All the Way Home. 2003. (gr. 3-6). lib. bdg. 14.15 (978-0-613-57891-2(0)) Tandem Library Bks.

—B-E-S-T Friends. 73p. (J). (gr. 1-2). pap. 3.99 (978-0-8072-1277-6(6) , Listening Library) Random Hse. Audio Publishing Group.

—Cara de Pez. 2000. (SPA.). (YA). (gr. 1). 3.95 (978-0-922852-46-8(4)) AIMS International Bks., Inc.

—Concurso de Pastelillos. 2001. (Kids of Polk Street School Ser.). (SPA.). (YA). 4.50 (978-0-922852-44-4(8)) AIMS International Bks., Inc.

—Good Luck, Ronald Morgan! unabr. ed. 2000. (YA). pap. 24.24 incl. audio (978-0-7887-3796-1(1) , 41040X4) Recorded Bks., LLC.

—Good Luck, Ronald Morgan! 1999. (J). (978-0-606-16778-9(1)) Tandem Library Bks.

—Lily's Crossing. 2002. (Illus.). (J). 13.94 (978-0-7587-0287-6(6)) Book Wholesalers, Inc.

—Lily's Crossing. 1999. (Yearling Newbery Ser.). 208p. (J). (gr. 5-7). reprint ed. pap. 6.50 (978-0-440-41453-7(9) , Yearling) Random Hse. Children's Bks.

—Lily's Crossing. 1999. (gr. 5-8). lib. bdg. 13.55 (978-0-613-10350-3(5)); (Illus.). (J). (978-0-606-14423-0(4)) Tandem Library Bks.

—Lily's Crossing. l.t. ed. 200p. 2003. pap. 10.95 (978-0-7862-6189-5(7)); 2000. (Illus.). (J). 22.95 (978-0-7862-2771-6(0)) Thorndike Pr.

—Maggie's Door. 2005. 176p. (J). (gr. 3-7). pap. 5.99 (978-0-440-41581-7(0) , Yearling) Random Hse. Children's Bks.

Gildea, Kathy. The Adventures of Baylee Beagle—Annabelle Beagle. Larson, Amanda, illus. 2005. 28p. (J). 7.95 (978-0-9767096-1-9(9)) Maxim Pr.

—The Adventures of Baylee Beagle—Greenville. 2005. (Illus.). 20p. (J). 7.95 (978-0-9767096-0-2(0)) Maxim Pr.

—The Adventures of Baylee Beagle—Hurricane Hound. Larson, Amanda, illus. 2005. 28p. (J). 7.95 (978-0-9767096-2-6(7)) Maxim Pr.

Gill, Janie S. I Wish What I Could Do for You. 2001. (Predictable Readers Ser.). (Illus.). (J). (gr. k-2). lib. bdg. 11.95 (978-0-89868-540-4(0)) ARO Publishing Co.

—Just Like You. Lambson, Elizabeth, illus. Date not set. 5.95 (978-0-89868-430-8(7)) ARO Publishing Co.

Gillen-Connell, Linda. Laura the Loser. 2006. 66p. pap. 12.95 (978-1-4241-0820-6(9)) PublishAmerica, Inc.

Gilmore, Rachna. Lights for Gita. (Illus.). 24p. (J). 2002. (TUR & ENG.). 15.95 (978-1-85269-298-8(7)); 2000. (BEN & ENG., 15.50 (978-1-85269-283-4(9)); 2000. (GUJ & ENG., 15.95 (978-1-85269-288-9(X)) Mantra Publishing, Ltd. GBR. *Dist:* AIMS International Bks., Inc.

—Lights for Gita. Priestley, Alice, illus. 2005. 24p. (J). (gr. 3-6). pap. 7.95 (978-0-88448-151-5(4)) Tilbury Hse. Pubs.

—Lights for Gita. 2000. (CHI & ENG., Illus.). 24p. (J). 15.50 (978-1-85269-284-1(7)) Yuan-liou Publishing Co., Ltd. TWN. *Dist:* AIMS International Bks., Inc.

—Roses for Gita. Priestley, Alice, illus. 2004. 24p. (J). (CHI, ENG, TUR, PAN & GUJ.). (978-1-85269-367-1(3)); (GUJ, CHI, ENG, PAN & TUR.). (978-1-85269-369-5(X)) Mantra Publishing, Ltd.

—Roses for Gita. 2001. (gr. k-3). lib. bdg. 16.40 (978-0-613-53301-0(1)) Tandem Library Bks.

—Roses for Gita. Priestley, Alice, illus. 2005. 24p. (J). (gr. 3-6). pap. 7.95 (978-0-88448-224-6(3)) Tilbury Hse. Pubs.

Gilson, Jamie. It Goes Eeeeeeeeeeeee! 2001. (gr. 3-6). lib. bdg. 12.95 (978-0-613-35528-5(8)) Tandem Library Bks.

Gingold, Janet. Danger, Long Division. 2006. 164p. (YA). pap. 14.99 (978-1-59092-122-7(4) , Blue Works) Windstorm Creative.

Girard, Jeremy. The Key to Slumber: The Tales of Slumber. 2005. 201p. pap. 19.95 (978-1-4137-7243-2(9)) PublishAmerica, Inc.

Gitomer, Helaine D. & Weinstock, Harriett. The Magic Cow: A Gift. Gitomer, Helaine D. & Weinstock, Harriett, illus. 2000. (Illus.). (J). (978-0-9676205-0-3(3)) Orbin Publishing, Ltd.

Give, Save, Spend. 2006. 16p. (J). pap. 1.99 (978-0-7847-1691-5(9) , 02993) Standard Publishing.

Givner, Joan. Ellen Fremedon: Journalist. 2006. 192p. pap. 6.95 (978-0-88899-691-6(8)) Groundwood Bks. CAN. *Dist:* Perseus Distribution.

—Ellen Fremedon, Volunteer. 2007. 192p. (gr. 3-7). 17.95 (978-0-88899-743-2(4)) Groundwood Bks. CAN. *Dist:* Perseus Distribution.

Glass, Sue. Helping Hop. 2nd ed. 2004. Orig. Title: What's Wrong with Hop?. (J). spiral bd. 10.99 (978-0-9763593-0-2(8)) Closer Looks Bks.

Glassman, Jackie. The Berry Best Friends' Picnic: Strawberry Shortcake. S. I. Artists Staff et al, illus. 2003. (All Aboard Reading Station Stop Ser.). 32p. (J). (ps-2). pap. 3.99 (978-0-448-43134-5(3) , Grosset & Dunlap) Penguin Group (USA) Inc.

—La Merienda de Strawberry Shortcake. Molinero, Nuria, tr. Edwards, Ken, illus. 2005. (Strawberry Shortcake Ser.). 32p. (J). (ps-2). pap. 3.99 (978-0-448-43959-4(X) , Grosset & Dunlap) Penguin Group (USA) Inc.

Glassman, Miriam. Box Top Dreams. 1999. (J). 10.64 (978-0-606-15910-4(X)) Tandem Library Bks.

Glasthal, Jacqueline B. Liberty on 23rd Street. Reingold, Alan, illus. 2006. (Adventures in America Ser.). (J). (978-1-893110-45-8(1)) Silver Moon Pr.

Glatshteyn, Yankev. Emil & Karl. Shandler, Jeffrey, tr. from YID. 2006. 208p. (J). 17.95 (978-1-59643-119-5(9)) Roaring Brook Pr.

Gleeson, Libby. Half a World Away. Blackwood, Freya, illus. (J). pap. (978-0-439-88978-0(2)); 2007. 40p. pap. 15.99 (978-0-439-88977-3(4)) Scholastic, Inc. (Levine, Arthur A. Bks.).

Glinski, Donita. Jeremy. Harris, Leslie, illus. 2006. 32p. 14.95 (978-1-57197-464-8(4) , Ivy House Publishing Group) Pentland Pr., Inc.

Godfrey, Rebecca. Torn Skirt. 2002. (gr. 7-12). lib. bdg. 21.05 (978-0-613-60626-4(4)) Tandem Library Bks.

Goethals, Angela. The Sisterhood of the Traveling Pants. 2004. (Sisterhood of Traveling Pants Ser. : Bk. 1). 320p. (YA). (gr. 7 up). pap. 40.00 incl. audio (978-0-8072-2286-7(0) , Listening Library) Random Hse. Audio Publishing Group.

Going, K. L. The Liberation of Gabriel King. 2007. 160p. (J). (gr. 3 up). pap. 6.99 (978-0-14-240766-0(6) , Puffin) Penguin Group (USA) Inc.

Gold, Maya & Fitzhugh, Louise. Harriet the Spy, Double Agent. 2005. 160p. (J). (gr. 5 up). 15.95 (978-0-385-32787-9(0) , Delacorte Bks. for Young Readers) Random Hse. Children's Bks.

Goldblatt, Stacey. Stray. 2007. 288p. (YA). (gr. 7-10). 15.99 (978-0-385-73443-1(3)); lib. bdg. 18.99 (978-0-385-90448-3(7)) Random Hse. Children's Bks. (Delacorte Bks. for Young Readers).

Golden Books Staff. All Aboard! Red Giraffe (Firm) Staff, illus. 2004. (Thomas the Tank Engine Ser.). 32p. (J). (ps-2). pap. 4.99 (978-0-375-82652-8(1) , Golden Bks.) Random Hse. Children's Bks.

—All My Friends! 2007. (Color Plus Puzzles to Color Ser.). (Illus.). 32p. (J). (ps-2). pap. 6.99 (***978-0-375-84189-7(X)*** , Golden Bks.) Random Hse. Children's Bks.

—Always Friends. Williams, Don, illus. 2004. (Super Coloring Book Ser.). 64p. (J). (ps-2). pap. 2.99 (978-0-7364-2234-5(X) , Golden/Disney) Random Hse. Children's Bks.

—Friends Forever? Schigiel, Gregg, illus. 2003. (SpongeBob SquarePants Ser.). 32p. (J). (ps-3). pap. 4.99 (978-0-307-10304-8(8) , Golden Bks.) Random Hse. Children's Bks.

—Hooray for Best Friends! 2006. (Deluxe Coloring Book Ser.). (Illus.). 96p. (J). (ps-2). 3.99 (978-0-375-83981-8(X) , Golden Bks.) Random Hse. Children's Bks.

—Ready, Set, Race! 2008. (Color Plus Ser.). (Illus.). 48p. (J). (ps-3). pap. 4.99 (***978-0-375-84577-2(1)*** , Golden Bks.) Random Hse. Children's Bks.

—Royal & Loyal. Harchy, Atelier Philippe, illus. 2004. (Disney Princess Ser.). 32p. (J). (ps-2). pap. 2.99 (978-0-375-82654-2(8) , Golden/Disney) Random Hse. Children's Bks.

—Scoop's in Charge. Baker, Darrell, illus. 2003. 64p. (J). (ps-2). pap. 2.99 (978-0-307-10118-1(5) , Golden Bks.) Random Hse. Children's Bks.

—Tawny Scrawny Lion. 2001. (Little Golden Bks.). (Illus.). 24p. (J). (gr. k-k). 2.99 (978-0-307-02168-7(8) , 98093, Golden Bks.) Random Hse. Children's Bks.

—Thomas & Friends Book Bag. 2007. (Bookbag Ser.). 32p. (J). (ps-2). pap. 4.99 (978-0-375-84160-6(1) , Golden Bks.) Random Hse. Children's Bks.

—Very Best Friends. 1999. (Disney Ser.). 24p. (J). (ps-3). pap. 3.29 (978-0-307-13142-3(4) , Golden Bks.) Random Hse. Children's Bks.

Golden Books Staff & Newton, Astora. Blue's Friendship Day/What's Blue Building? Levy, David, illus. 2003. 64p. (J). (ps-2). pap. 2.99 (978-0-307-10122-8(3) , Golden Bks.) Random Hse. Children's Bks.

Golding, Julia. Mines of the Minotaur. Wyatt, David, illus. 2008. (J). (***978-0-7614-5302-4(4)***) Cavendish, Marshall Corp.

Golding, Theresa Martin. Kat's Surrender. 2002. (gr. 3-6). lib. bdg. 18.75 (978-0-613-53826-8(9)) Tandem Library Bks.

Golding, Theresa Martin & Easley, Mary Ann. I Am the Ice Worm. 2004. (Illus.). 128p. (YA). (gr. 4-6). pap. 9.95 (978-1-59078-281-1(X)) Boyds Mills Pr.

Goldsmith, Howard. Thomas Jefferson & the Ghostriders. 2008. (Ready-to-read COFA Ser.). 32p. (J). pap. 3.99 (***978-1-4169-2692-4(5)*** , Aladdin) Simon & Schuster Children's Publishing.

—Thomas Jefferson & the Ghostriders. Rose, Drew, illus. 2008. (Ready-to-read COFA Ser.). 32p. (J). lib. bdg. 13.89 (***978-1-4169-2749-5(2)*** , Aladdin) Simon & Schuster Children's Publishing.

Goldstein, Alrica, ed. Polly & the Perfect Pets. 2008. 24p. (J). pap. 3.99 (***978-0-696-23893-2(4)***) Meredith Bks.

—Polly Lodge: Snowed In! 2008. 32p. (J). pap. 3.99 (***978-0-696-23894-9(2)***) Meredith Bks.

—Pollytastic Adventure. 2007. 24p. (J). pap. 3.99 (***978-0-696-23647-1(8)***) Meredith Bks.

Goldstein, Doris. Imagination Collaboration. Shupe, Bobbi, illus. 1998. 16p. (J). (ps-k). pap. 5.95 (978-0-9655442-6-9(5)) Business Word, The.

Gomes, Barbara K. Esau at the Big House. 2006. 76p. pap. 14.95 (978-1-4241-2288-2(0)) PublishAmerica, Inc.

Gomez de Salazar, Carmen & Martilotti, Carla. Pinky's Birthday. 2007. (ENG.). 28p. per. 12.95 (***978-1-59800-732-9(7)***) Outskirts Press, Inc.

Gomi, Taro. My Friends. 2005. (Illus.). 34p. (J). bds. 6.95 (978-0-8118-4786-5(1)) Chronicle Bks. LLC.

Gonzalez, Julie. Imaginary Enemy. 2008. 256p. (J). (gr. 7). 15.99 (***978-0-385-73552-0(9)***, Delacorte Bks. for Young Readers) Random Hse. Children's Bks.

Gonzalez, Julie. Ricochet. 2007. 208p. (YA). (gr. 9). 15.99 (978-0-385-73228-4(7)); lib. bdg. 18.99 (978-0-385-90254-0(9)) Random Hse. Children's Bks. (Delacorte Bks. for Young Readers).

Goodhart, Pippa. Friends Forever. Busby, Ailie, illus. 2003. (Maxine & Minnie Storybook Ser.). 64p. (J). pap. 7.50 (978-1-4052-0408-8(7)) Egmont Bks., Ltd. GBR. *Dist:* Independent Pubs. Group.

—Pest Friends: A Maxine & Minnie Storybook. Busby, Ailie, illus. 2003. 64p. (J). pap. 7.50 (978-1-4052-0409-5(5)) Egmont Bks., Ltd. GBR. *Dist:* Independent Pubs. Group.

Goodspeed, Judy. Perky Turkey Finds a Friend. 2006. (Illus.). 24p. (J). lib. bdg. 24.95 (978-0-9778651-2-3(6)) Dragonfly Publishing, Inc.

—Perky Turkey Finds a Friend. Taylor, Chet, illus. l.t. ed. 2006. 24p. (J). pap. 14.99 (978-0-9765786-6-6(2)) Dragonfly Publishing, Inc.

Goody, C. A. Charlie & the Rodent Queen, Laaker, Terry, illus. l.t. ed. 2003. (Charlie's Great Adventures: No. 3). 88p. per. 5.95 (978-0-9702546-2-7(8), 623-876-1518) GoodyGoody Bks.

Gorbachev, Valeri. Big Little Elephant. 2005. (Illus.). 32p. (J). (ps-ps). 16.00 (978-0-15-205195-2(3), Harcourt Children's Bks) Harcourt Children's Bks.

—The Big Trip. Gorbachev, Valeri, illus. 2004. (Illus.). 32p. (J). 15.99 (978-0-399-23965-6(0), Philomel) Penguin Group (USA) Inc.

—Chicken Chickens Go to School. Gorbachev, Valeri, illus. 2003. (Illus.). (J). (ps-1). 28p. 15.95 (978-0-7358-1600-8(X)); 32p. 16.50 (978-0-7358-1767-8(7)) North-South Bks., Inc.

—Heron & Turtle. Gorbachev, Valeri, illus. 2006. (Illus.). 40p. (J). (gr. k). 15.99 (978-0-399-24321-9(6), Philomel) Penguin Group (USA) Inc.

—That's What Friends Are For. Gorbachev, Valeri, illus. 2005. (Illus.). 32p. (J). (ps-3). 15.99 (978-0-399-23966-3(9), Philomel) Penguin Group (USA) Inc.

Gordon, Amy. The Gorillas of Gill Park. 2003. 256p. (J). (gr. 4-6). tchr. ed. 16.95 (978-0-8234-1751-3(4)) Holiday Hse., Inc.

—Magic by Heart. Gustavson, Adam, illus. 2007. 128p. (J). (gr. 3-7). 16.95 (***978-0-8234-1995-1(9)***) Holiday Hse., Inc.

Gordon, Amy. Return to Gill Park. 2006. (Illus.). 240p. (J). (gr. 3-7). 16.95 (978-0-8234-1998-2(3)) Holiday Hse., Inc.

Gordon, David. Smitten. Gordon, David, illus. 2007. 40p. (J). (ps-3). 15.99 (978-1-4169-2440-1(X)) Simon & Schuster Children's Publishing.

Gorges, Julie A. Just Call Me Goody-Two-Shoes. 2006. 146p. (YA). per. 9.95 (978-0-9763274-1-7(4)) I.Form Ink, Pub.

Gorman, Carol. Dork in Disguise. 2000. (Harper Trophy Bks.). (Illus.). 176p. (J). (gr. 3-7). pap. 5.99 (978-0-06-440891-2(4), Harper Trophy) HarperCollins Pubs.

—Dork in Disguise. 2000. (gr. 3-6). lib. bdg. 14.15 (978-0-613-30359-0(8)) Tandem Library Bks.

Gould, Jason. Jinx. 2004. 215p. (YA). (gr. 9-17). per. 14.04 (978-0-606-30072-8(4)) Tandem Library Bks.

Goulis, Julie. Something Shiny, Something Round. Ferguson, John, illus. 2005. 32p. (J). (gr. 3-7). 14.99 (978-0-9754621-1-9(3)) Bubblegum Bks.

Grace, N. B. Double Trouble, Bk. 2. 2nd rev. ed. 2006. (Suite Life of Zack & Cody Ser.: Vol. 2). (Illus.). 80p. (gr. 2-5). pap. 3.99 (978-0-7868-4936-9(3)) Disney Pr.

Graef, Renee, illus. Laura & Nellie. 1998. (Little House Chapter Bks.: No. 5). (J). (gr. 3-6). (978-0-606-12979-4(0)) Tandem Library Bks.

—Little House Friends. 1998. (Little House Chapter Bks.: No. 9). 80p. (J). (gr. 3-6). 14.89 (978-0-06-027894-6(3)) HarperCollins Pubs.

Graff, Lisa. The Thing about Georgie. 2007. 224p. (J). (gr. 3-6). 15.99 (978-0-06-087589-3(5)); lib. bdg. 16.89 (978-0-06-087590-9(9)) HarperCollins Pubs. (Geringer, Laura Book).

Graham, Ann M. Cody & Kyle: Big Heroes! Roberson, Sam, illus. 1998. 52p. (J). (gr. k-6). pap. 5.99 (978-0-9655719-1-3(2)) KCDI Publishing.

Graham, Steve. Dear Old Donegal. O'Brien, John, illus. 2000. 32p. (J). reprint ed. 16.00 (978-0-7881-6870-3(3)) DIANE Publishing Co.

Graham, Wendy. Robbie Robinson & the Last Crayfish. Novak, Jiri Tibor, illus. 2004. 32p. (Orig.). pap. 13.50 (978-1-920694-34-0(X)) Univ. of Western Australia Pr. AUS. *Dist:* International Specialized Bk. Services.

Grahame, Kenneth. Mr. Toad, Vol. 2. Johnson, Joe, tr. from FRE. 2003. (Wind in the Willows Ser.: Vol. 2). (Illus.). 32p. (gr. 4-7). 15.95 (978-1-56163-218-3(X)) NBM Publishing Co.

—El Viento en los Sauces. (SPA.). 192p. (J). I. 9.50 (978-84-372-1882-3(9)); II. 9.50 (978-84-372-1883-0(7)) Santillana USA Publishing Co., Inc.

—The Wind in the Willows. Tomei, Lorna, illus. 2002. (Great Illustrated Classics Ser.). 240p. (J). (gr. 3-8). 21.35 (978-1-57765-808-5(6), ABDO & Daughters) ABDO Publishing Co.

—The Wind in the Willows. Percy, Graham, illus. 1999. (Abbeville Classics Ser.). 192p. (J). 12.95 (978-0-7892-0559-9(9)); pap. 7.95 (978-0-7892-0549-0(1)) Abbeville Pr., Inc. (Abbeville Kids).

—The Wind in the Willows. Moss, Joanne, illus. 253p. (J). (gr. 5-6). reprint ed. lib. bdg. 22.95 (978-0-88411-877-0(0)) Amereon LTD.

—The Wind in the Willows. Perry, Graham, illus. 2000. 192p. (J). pap. 8.95 (978-1-85793-914-9(X), Pavilion Bks., Ltd.) Anova Bks. GBR. *Dist:* Trafalgar Square Publishing.

—The Wind in the Willows. Moore, Inga, illus. abr. ed. 2000. 180p. (J). 4.50 (978-0-7445-7553-8(2)) Candlewick Pr.

—The Wind in the Willows. 2003. 192p. (J). 4.99 (978-1-57759-567-0(X)) Dalmatian Pr.

—The Wind in the Willows. 1999. (Illus.). 176p. (J). (gr. 4-7). pap. 3.00 (978-0-486-40785-2(3)) Dover Pubns., Inc.

—The Wind in the Willows. Kliros, Thea, illus. abr. ed. 1998. (Dover Children's Thrift Classics Ser.). 96p. (J). pap. 1.00 (978-0-486-28600-6(2)) Dover Pubns., Inc.

—The Wind in the Willows. Hague, Michael, illus. rev. ed. 2003. 224p. (J). (gr. 1 up). 26.95 (978-0-8050-7237-2(3), Holt, Henry & Co. Bks. For Young Readers) Holt, Henry & Co.

—The Wind in the Willows. l.t. ed. 2000. (LRS Large Print Heritage Ser.). 271p. (J). (gr. 3-8). lib. bdg. 29.95 (978-1-58118-066-4(7), 23661) LRS.

—The Wind in the Willows. 1998. (Twelve-Point Ser.). 185p. reprint ed. lib. bdg. 24.00 (978-1-58287-080-9(2)) North Bks.

—The Wind in the Willows. Green, Peter, ed. 1999. (Oxford World's Classics Ser.). 192p. 11.95 (978-0-19-283515-4(7)) Oxford Univ. Pr., Inc.

—The Wind in the Willows. 240p. (gr. 12). 2006. pap. 5.95 (978-0-451-53014-1(4), Signet Classics); 2005. (YA). 12.00 (978-0-14-303909-9(1), Penguin Classics) Penguin Group (USA) Inc.

—The Wind in the Willows. 1999. (Aladdin Classics Ser.). (Illus.). 304p. (J). (gr. 4-7). pap. 4.99 (978-0-689-83140-9(4), Aladdin) Simon & Schuster Children's Publishing.

—The Wind in the Willows. Hanft, Joshua, ed. (Great Illustrated Classics Ser.: Vol. 39). (Illus.). 240p. (J). (gr. 3-6). 9.95 (978-0-86611-990-0(6)) Waldman Publishing Corp.

—The Wind in the Willows. 1998. (Children's Classics). (ENG., Illus.). 192p. (YA). (ps up). pap. (978-1-85326-122-0(X), 122XWW); (J). (gr. 4-7). pap. (978-1-85326-017-9(7), 0177WW) Wordsworth Editions, Ltd.

—The Wind in the Willows: With Charm. 2003. (Charming Classics). (Illus.). 256p. (J). pap. 6.99 (978-0-06-053723-4(X), Harper Festival) HarperCollins Pubs.

—The Wind in the Willows Vol. 3: The Gates of Dawn. Johnson, Joe, tr. Plessix, Michel, illus. 2003. 32p. (gr. 4-7). 15.95 (978-1-56163-245-9(7)) NBM Publishing Co.

Grahame, Kenneth & Basset, Jennifer. The Wind in the Willows, Level 3. 2nd abr. ed. 2000. (Bookworms Ser.). (Illus.). 74p. 6.50 (978-0-19-423022-3(8)) Oxford Univ. Pr., Inc.

Gralley, Jean. Hogula: Dread Pig of Night. rev. ed. 2002. (Illus.). 32p. (J). (ps-3). pap. 6.95 (978-0-8050-7164-1(4), Holt, Henry & Co. Bks. For Young Readers) Holt, Henry & Co.

—Hogula: Dread Pig of Night. 2002. (gr. k-3). lib. bdg. 15.25 (978-0-613-90145-1(2)) Tandem Library Bks.

Grambling, Lois G. Shoo! Scat! Newman, Barbara Johansen, illus. 2004. 32p. (J). 16.95 (978-0-7614-5167-9(6)) Cavendish, Marshall Corp.

Grant, Joan. Cat & Fish. Curtis, Neil, illus. 2005. 32p. (J). 16.95 (978-1-894965-14-9(0)) Simply Read Bks. CAN. *Dist:* Perseus Distribution.

Grant, Karima. Sofie & the City. Montecalvo, Janet, illus. 2006. 32p. (J). 15.95 (978-1-59078-273-6(9)) Boyds Mills Pr.

Grant, Neil. Rhino Chasers. 2003. (Illus.). 240p. (J). pap. 7.95 (978-1-86508-695-8(9)) Allen & Unwin AUS. *Dist:* Independent Pubs. Group.

Grass, Michael. Impolite Village. 2007. (J). per. 6.99 (***978-1-60247-339-3(0)***) Tate Publishing & Enterprises, L.L.C.

Graves, Ann P. Color Me Santa. l.t. ed. 2002. (Illus.). 108p. per. 4.99 (978-0-9721653-0-3(4)) Stylewriter Pubns.

Graves, Bonnie. No Copycats Allowed! 1998. (J). (978-0-606-13664-8(9)) Tandem Library Bks.

Graves, Kassie. Brave Little Sailboat. Graves, Kassie, illus. 2003. (Illus.). 20p. (J). 14.95 (978-0-9728019-0-4(1)) Bright Eyes Pr.

Gravley, Debbie Bybee. Golden Lace & the Magical Mossy Woods. 2005. 25.00 (978-0-9771793-0-5(3)) Gravley, Debbie Bybee.

Gray, Libba Moore. Is There Room on the Feather Bed? ed. 2004. (Illus.). (J). (ps-2). spiral bd. (978-0-616-03037-0(1)); spiral bd. (978-0-616-04555-8(7)) Canadian National Institute for the Blind/Institut National Canadien pour les Aveugles.

—Is There Room on the Feather Bed? Westcott, Nadine Bernard, illus. 1999. 32p. (J). (ps-1). pap. 5.95 (978-0-531-07137-3(5), Orchard Bks.) Scholastic, Inc.

—Is There Room on the Feather Bed? 1999. (Illus.). (J). (978-0-606-18333-8(7)) Tandem Library Bks.

Grealish, Maureen M. Just Plain Worm. 25p. (J). (gr. k-2). (978-0-9667780-0-7(6)) Ballenwyck Publishing Corp.

Greathouse, Rebecca. Katie & Riley's Magical Adventures: Journey to the Amazon. 2006. 48p. pap. 12.95 (***978-1-4241-5341-1(7)***) PublishAmerica, Inc.

Greene, Bette. I've Already Forgotten Your Name, Philip Hall! Jenkins, Leonard, illus. 2004. 176p. (J). (gr. 5 up). 15.99 (978-0-06-051835-6(9)) HarperCollins Pubs.

—Philip Hall Likes Me: I Reckon Maybe. 1999. (978-0-606-16230-2(5)) Tandem Library Bks.

Greene, Richard. Lawrence the Locomotive. 2004. 49p. pap. 12.95 (978-1-4137-5704-0(9)) PublishAmerica, Inc.

Greene, Stephanie. Moose's Big Idea. Matthieu, Joe, illus. 2005. 51p. (J). (gr. 1-3). 14.95 (978-0-7614-5212-6(5)) Cavendish, Marshall Corp.

—Owen Foote, Frontiersman. Weston, Martha, illus. 2002. 96p. (J). (gr. k-3). pap. 4.95 (978-0-618-24620-5(7), Clarion Bks.) Houghton Mifflin Co. Trade & Reference Div.

—Owen Foote, Frontiersman. 2002. (gr. k-3). lib. bdg. 12.95 (978-0-613-72910-9(2)) Tandem Library Bks.

—Owen Foote, Mighty Scientist. Smith, Catharine Bowman, illus. 2004. 96p. (J). (gr. k-3). tchr. ed. 15.00 (978-0-618-43016-1(4), Clarion Bks.) Houghton Mifflin Co. Trade & Reference Div.

—Owen Foote, Soccer Star. Weston, Martha, illus. 1998. 96p. (J). (gr. k-3). tchr. ed. 14.00 (978-0-395-86143-1(8), Clarion Bks.) Houghton Mifflin Co. Trade & Reference Div.

—Owen Foote, Super Spy. Weston, Martha, illus. 2005. 96p. (J). (gr. k-3). pap. 5.95 (978-0-618-55159-0(X), Clarion Bks.) Houghton Mifflin Co. Trade & Reference Div.

—Pig Pickin' Mathieu, Joseph, illus. 2006. (Marshall Cavendish Chapter Book Ser.). 64p. (J). 14.99 (978-0-7614-5324-6(5)) Cavendish, Marshall Corp.

—Queen Sophie Hartley. 2005. 144p. (J). (gr. 3-5). 15.00 (978-0-618-49461-3(8), Clarion Bks.) Houghton Mifflin Co. Trade & Reference Div.

Greene, Stephanie. The Show-Off. Mathieu, Joseph, illus. 2007. (Moose & Hildy Ser.). 64p. (J). (gr. 1-4). 14.99 (***978-0-7614-5374-1(1)***) Cavendish, Marshall Corp.

Greene, Thomas. Whacked Out Wrestling: Memorial - A tale of Headlocks, Hurricanranas, & High School. 2007. 228p. pap. 14.95 (***978-1-60145-175-0(X)***) Booklocker-.com, Inc.

Greenwald, Lisa & Paley, Sasha. Huge. 2007. 272p. (YA). 15.99 (978-1-4169-3517-9(7)) Simon & Schuster Children's Publishing.

Greenwood, Dwayne. The Tales of Wally the Whale & Sammy the Salmon. 2006. 17.00 (978-0-8059-9074-4(7)) Dorrance Publishing Co., Inc.

Gregar, Steve. Buzz the Fly. 2004. 14p. pap. 9.98 (978-1-4116-1147-4(0)) Lulu.com.

Gregory, Deborah. The Cheetah Girls, No. 2, Bks. 5-8. 2003. 624p. (J). (gr. 3-7). pap. 9.99 (978-0-7868-1790-0(9)) Hyperion Bks. for Children.

—Cheetah Girls No.13: OOPS, Doggy Dog! 2002. (gr. 3-6). lib. bdg. 11.80 (978-0-613-91004-0(4)) Tandem Library Bks.

—Cheetah Girls Bind Up No.1, Bks. 1-4: Livin' Large! 2003. lib. bdg. 18.80 (978-0-613-75036-3(5)) Tandem Library Bks.

—Cheetah Girls Bind Up No.2: Supa Dupa Sparkle! Book 5-8. 2003. (gr. 3-6). lib. bdg. 18.80 (978-0-613-74957-2(X)) Tandem Library Bks.

—The Cheetah Girls Livin' Large, No. 1, Bks. 1-4. 2003. 576p. (J). (gr. 3-7). pap. 9.99 (978-0-7868-1789-4(5)) Hyperion Bks. for Children.

—Off the Hook! 2005. 672p. (gr. 3-7). pap. 9.99 (978-0-7868-5654-1(8), Jump at the Sun) Hyperion Bks. for Children.

Gretz, Susanna. Riley & Rose in the Picture. Gretz, Susanna, illus. 2005. (Illus.). 32p. (J). (gr. k-3). 16.99 (978-0-7636-2681-5(3)) Candlewick Pr.

Griebel, Roberta L. Joyful Noise! 2007. (ENG.). 56p. per. 12.95 (***978-1-4241-6037-2(5)***) PublishAmerica, Inc.

Grimes, Nikki. Danitra Brown, Class Clown. Lewis, Earl, illus. 2005. 32p. (J). 16.99 (978-0-688-17290-9(3)); lib. bdg. 16.89 (978-0-688-17291-6(1)) HarperCollins Pubs.

Grindley, Sally. Bravo, Max! Ross, Tony, illus. 2007. 160p. (J). (gr. 1-4). 15.99 (978-1-4169-0393-2(3), McElderry, Margaret K.); pap. 4.99 (978-1-4169-3645-9(9), Aladdin) Simon & Schuster Children's Publishing.

—Dear Max. Ross, Tony, illus. 144p. (J). 2007. pap. 4.99 (978-1-4169-3443-1(X), Aladdin); 2006. (gr. 1-4). 14.95 (978-1-4169-0392-5(5), McElderry, Margaret K.) Simon & Schuster Children's Publishing.

—Friends Forever. Dann, Penny, illus. 2007. (I Am Reading Ser.). 48p. (J). (gr. k-3). pap. 3.95 (***978-0-7534-5976-8(0)***, Kingfisher) Houghton Mifflin Co. Trade & Reference Div.

—What Are Friends For? Dann, Penny, illus. 1998. 32p. (J). (ps-k). tchr. ed. 15.95 (978-0-7534-5108-3(5), Kingfisher) Houghton Mifflin Co. Trade & Reference Div.

—What Are Friends For? Dann, Penny, illus. 1998. 18p. (J). pap. 11.98 (978-1-58048-053-6(5)) Sandvik Publishing.

—What Will I Do Without You? Dann, Penny, illus. 2001. 32p. (J). (ps-k). 6.95 (978-0-7534-5411-4(4), Kingfisher) Houghton Mifflin Co. Trade & Reference Div.

—What Will I Do Without You? Dann, Penny, illus. 2001. (J). (ps-3). lib. bdg. 15.25 (978-0-613-88863-9(4)) Tandem Library Bks.

Griver, Jeanette A. CURIO a Shetland Sheepdog & her Pals: All ages Will enjoy the Tales of Friendship. 2007. (J). per. 8.50 (***978-0-929948-06-5(8)***) Compsych Systems, Inc., Pubns. Div.

Groce, Michelle. Jasper. Duis, Laura, illus. 2005. 178p. 11.95 (978-0-9760963-1-3(5)) Novello Festival Pr.

Grosgebauer, Clare Ham. Snickerdoodle's Star-Spangled Fourth of July! Rissing, Karen, illus. 4th ed. 2005. 36p. 12.99 (978-0-9741888-6-7(7)) Small Wonders Enterprises.

Gross, S. D. Blue Frog. l.t. ed. 2006. (Illus.). 24p. (J). per. 11.99 (978-1-59879-207-2(5)) Lifevest Publishing, Inc.

Grosset & Dunlap. Guess Who. 2003. (ps-2). lib. bdg. 23.30 (978-0-613-72515-6(8)) Tandem Library Bks.

Grosset and Dunlap Staff, ed. Storybook Treasury of Dick & Jane & Friends. 2003. (Dick & Jane Ser.). (Illus.). 200p. (J). (ps-3). 10.99 (978-0-448-43340-0(0), Grosset & Dunlap) Penguin Group (USA) Inc.

Grove, Vicki. Reaching Dustin. 2000. (Illus.). 208p. (J). (gr. 4-9). pap. 6.99 (978-0-698-11839-3(1), Putnam Juvenile) Penguin Group (USA) Inc.

—Reaching Dustin. 2000. (978-0-606-18844-9(4)); (gr. 5-8). lib. bdg. 14.15 (978-0-613-28619-0(7)) Tandem Library Bks.

Grovet, Heather. Good As Gold: Discovering What Is Really Important. 2007. (Illus.). 95p. (J). (***978-0-8163-2166-7(3)***) Pacific Pr. Publishing Assn.

—A Perfect Star. 2007. (Illus.). 95p. (J). (***978-0-8163-2164-3(7)***) Pacific Pr. Publishing Assn.

—Prince Prances Again. 2001. (Julius & Friends Ser.: Bk. 9). (Illus.). 94p. (J). 6.99 (978-0-8163-1807-0(7)) Pacific Pr. Publishing Assn.

Grovet, Heather. Zippitty Do Dah: Trusting God in Troubles Great & Small. 2007. (Illus.). 95p. (J). (***978-0-8163-2165-0(5)***) Pacific Pr. Publishing Assn.

Grovet, Heather Marie. Marvelous Mark & His No-Good Dog. 2003. 128p. (J). pap. 7.99 (978-0-8280-1734-3(4), 132-670) Review & Herald Publishing Assn.

Gruelle, Johnny. Raggedy Ann's Wishing Pebble. Gruelle, Johnny, illus. 2004. reprint ed. pap. 15.95 (978-1-4179-0709-0(6)) Kessinger Publishing, LLC.

Gruenberg, Jeremiah. Ki'i & Li'i: A Story from the Stories. Salisbury, Graham, ed. Gruenberg, Jeremiah, illus. 2001. 44p. (J). (ps-3). 15.95 (978-0-9662945-3-8(X)) Goodale Publishing.

Gruetzke, Mary, ed. Duck Book & Purse. McDonald, Jill, illus. 2006. 8p. (J). bds. 5.99 (978-0-439-73339-7(1), Cartwheel Bks.) Scholastic, Inc.

Guardo, Attilio. A Special Time in Clear Creek. 2004. 184p. pap. 19.95 (978-1-4137-2872-9(3)) PublishAmerica, Inc.

Guest, Elissa Haden. Iris & Walter. Davenier, Christine, illus. (Iris & Walter Ser.). 44p. (J). 2006. pap. 5.95 (978-0-15-205644-5(0), Harcourt Paperbacks); 2000. (gr. 1-3). 14.00 (978-0-15-202122-1(1), Gulliver Bks.) Harcourt Children's Bks.

—Iris & Walter & Baby Rose. Davenier, Christine, illus. 2006. (Iris & Walter Ser.). 44p. (J). pap. 5.95 (978-0-15-205650-6(5), Harcourt Paperbacks) Harcourt Children's Bks.

—Iris & Walter & Cousin Howie. Davenier, Christine, illus. 2006. (Iris & Walter Ser.). 44p. (J). pap. 5.95 (978-0-15-205656-8(4), Harcourt Paperbacks) Harcourt Children's Bks.

—Iris & Walter & the Field Trip. Davenier, Christine, illus. (Iris & Walter Ser.). 44p. (J). 2007. pap. 5.95 (***978-0-15-205370-3(0)***, Harcourt Paperbacks); 2005. 15.00 (978-0-15-205014-6(0)) Harcourt Children's Bks.

—Iris & Walter & the Substitute Teacher. Davenier, Christine, illus. 2006. (Iris & Walter Ser.). 44p. (J). pap. 5.95 (978-0-15-205376-5(X), Harcourt Paperbacks) Harcourt Children's Bks.

—Iris & Walter, True Friends. Davenier, Christine, illus. 2006. (Iris & Walter Ser.). 44p. (J). pap. 5.95 (978-0-15-205680-3(7), Harcourt Paperbacks) Harcourt Children's Bks.

Gunn, Robin Jones. Christy Miller Collection: A Time to Cherish; Sweet Dreams; A Promise Is Forever, Vol. 4. 2006. (Christy Miller Ser.: Bks. 10-12). 496p. 14.99 (978-1-59052-587-6(6), Multnomah Fiction) WaterBrook Pr.

—Christy Miller Collection: Summer Promise; A Whisper & a Wish; Yours Forever, Vol. 1. 2005. (Christy Miller Ser.: Bks. 1-3). 496p. (J). 14.99 (978-1-59052-584-5(1), Multnomah Fiction) WaterBrook Pr.

—Christy Miller Collection: Surprise Endings; Island Dreamer; A Heart Full of Hope, Vol. 2. 2006. (Christy Miller Ser.: Bks. 4-6). 496p. (J). 14.99 (978-1-59052-585-2(X), Multnomah Fiction) WaterBrook Pr.

—Christy Miller Collection: True Friends; Starry Night; Seventeen Wishes, Vol. 3. 2006. (Christy Miller Ser.: Bks 7-9). 480p. (J). 14.99 (978-1-59052-586-9(8), Multnomah Fiction) WaterBrook Pr.

—Island Dreamer. rev. ed. 1999. (Christy Miller Ser.: Bk. 5). 176p. (J). (gr. 7-12). pap. 6.99 (978-1-56179-718-9(9)) Bethany Hse. Pubs.

—Starry Night. rev. ed. 1999. (Christy Miller Ser.: Bk. 8). 160p. (YA). (gr. 7-12). pap. 6.99 (978-1-56179-721-9(9)) Bethany Hse. Pubs.

—Time Will Tell. 1998. (Sierra Jensen Ser.: Bk. 8). 160p. (YA). (gr. 7-11). pap. (978-1-56179-568-0(2)) Focus on the Family Publishing.

—True Friends. rev. ed. 1999. (Christy Miller Ser.: Bk. 7). 160p. (YA). (gr. 7-12). pap. 6.99 (978-1-56179-720-2(0)) Bethany Hse. Pubs.

Gunnery, Sylvia. Personal Best. 2005. (Sports Stories Ser.). 112p. (J). (gr. 3-8). 7.95 (978-1-55028-896-4(2)); (***978-1-55028-897-1(0)***) Lorimer, James & Co., Ltd., Pubs. CAN. *Dist:* Casemate Pubs. & Bk. Distributors, LLC.

Gutman, Anne. Gaspard & Lisa's Rainy Day. Hallensleben, Georg, illus. 2003. (Misadventures of Gaspard & Lisa Ser.). 32p. (J). (ps-3). 9.95 (978-0-375-82252-0(6), Knopf Bks. for Young Readers) Random Hse. Children's Bks.

Gutman, Dan. The Homework Machine. 2007. 176p. (J). pap. 4.99 (***978-0-689-87679-0(3)***, Aladdin) Simon & Schuster Children's Publishing.

—Honus & Me. 1998. (Baseball Card Adventures Ser.). (J). 12.64 (978-0-606-13487-3(5)) Tandem Library Bks.

—The Million Dollar Putt. 2006. 176p. (gr. 3-7). 15.99 (978-0-7868-3641-3(5)) Hyperion Bks. for Children.

—Million Dollar Putt. 2007. 176p. (gr. 3-7). pap. 5.99 (***978-0-7868-3642-0(3)***) Hyperion Pr.

—The Million Dollar Strike. 2006. 224p. (gr. 3-7). pap. 5.99 (978-0-7868-3751-9(9)) Hyperion Pr.

—Million Dollar Strike. 2004. 176p. (J). lib. bdg. 18.46 (*978-1-4242-2107-3(2)) Fitzgerald Bks.

—Mr. Hynde Is Out of His Mind! Paillot, Jim, illus. 2005. (My Weird School Ser.: Bk. 6). 112p. (J). pap. 3.99 (978-0-06-074520-2(7) , Harper Trophy) HarperCollins Pubs.

—Ms. Todd Is Odd! Paillot, Jim, illus. 2006. (My Weird School Ser.: No. 12). (J). 112p. pap. 3.99 (978-0-06-082231-6(7) , Harper Trophy); 112p. lib. bdg. 15.89 (978-0-06-082232-3(5)); 98p. (*978-1-4156-7916-6(9)) HarperCollins Pubs.

—Shoeless Joe & Me. (Baseball Card Adventures Ser.). (Illus.). 176p. (J). 2003. pap. 5.99 (978-0-06-447259-3(0)); 2002. (gr. 4-7). lib. bdg. 17.89 (978-0-06-029254-6(7)) HarperCollins Pubs.

—Shoeless Joe & Me. 2003. (Baseball Card Adventures Ser.). (gr. 3-6). lib. bdg. 14.15 (978-0-613-61816-8(5)) Tandem Library Bks.

—Shoeless Joe & Me: A Baseball Card Adventure. 2002. (Baseball Card Adventures Ser.). (Illus.). 176p. (J). (gr. 4-7). 16.99 (978-0-06-029253-9(9)) HarperCollins Pubs.

Gutsche, Brigitte. Asaley's Secret. Kemnitz, Myrna, ed. 2000. (Holt's Friends Ser.: Vol. 4). 126p. (J). (gr. 4-6). 9.99 (978-0-88092-517-4(5) , 5175) Royal Fireworks Publishing Co.

—The Intruder. 2006. (Holt's Friends Ser.). (J). pap. 9.99 (978-0-88092-519-8(1)) Royal Fireworks Publishing Co.

—To Be a Friend, Vol. 2. Dodge, Chris, illus. 2000. (Holt's Friends Ser.: No. 2). 116p. (J). (gr. 4-6). 9.99 (978-0-88092-515-0(9) , 5159) Royal Fireworks Publishing Co.

H. Irving Hancock. The High School Captain of the Team: Dick & Co. Leading the Athletic Vanguard. 2007. 156p. pap. 11.99 (*978-1-4264-6386-0(3)) BiblioBazaar.

Haas, Irene. Bess & Bella. Haas, Irene, illus. 2005. (Illus.). 32p. (J). 14.95 (978-1-4169-0013-9(6) , McElderry, Margaret K.) Simon & Schuster Children's Publishing.

Haberman, Lia. Friendship Forever. 2000. (All about You Ser.). (Illus.). 80p. (J). (gr. 4-7). pap. 4.50 (978-0-439-15530-4(4)) Scholastic, Inc.

Hachler, Bruno. Hubert & the Apple Tree. 2006. (Illus.). (J). 15.95 (978-0-7358-2044-9(9)) North-South Bks., Inc.

Hadcroft, Will. Anne Droyd & Century Lodge. 2004. 282p. (J). pap. (978-1-84310-282-3(X)) Kingsley, Jessica Ltd.

Haddix, Margaret Peterson. Because of Anya. 2004. 128p. (J). reprint ed. pap. 5.99 (978-0-689-86993-8(2) , Aladdin) Simon & Schuster Children's Publishing.

—Dexter the Tough. Elliott, Mark, illus. 2007. 144p. (J). (gr. 2-5). 15.99 (978-1-4169-1159-3(6)) Simon & Schuster Children's Publishing.

—Don't You Dare Read This, Mrs. Dunphrey. 2004. 128p. (YA). mass mkt. 4.99 (978-0-689-87102-3(3) , Simon Pulse) Simon & Schuster Children's Publishing.

—The Girl with 500 Middle Names. Hamlin, Janet, illus. 2001. 96p. (J). (gr. 2-5). pap. 4.99 (978-0-689-84136-1(1) , Aladdin) Simon & Schuster Children's Publishing.

—The Girl with 500 Middle Names. 2001. (gr. 3-6). lib. bdg. 11.80 (978-0-613-31244-8(9)); (Illus.). (J). 10.79 (978-0-606-20672-3(8)) Tandem Library Bks.

—The Girl with 500 Middle Names. l.t. ed. 2002. 102p. (J). 21.95 (978-0-7862-4412-6(7)) Thomson Gale.

—Leaving Fishers. Kaminesky, Ken, photos by. 2004. 272p. (YA). (gr. 7 up). mass mkt. 5.99 (978-0-689-86793-4(X) , Simon Pulse) Simon & Schuster Children's Publishing.

Hafner, Marylin. The Adventures of Molly & Emmett. (J). 7.95 (978-0-8126-0052-0(5)) Open Court Publishing Co.

Hagemann, Bernhard. Charlie Gallina Ciega. (Torre de Papel Ser.). (SPA., Illus.). (J). 7.95 (978-958-04-5032-0(3)) Norma S.A. COL. *Dist:* Distribuidora Norma, Inc.

Hagerup, Klaus. Markus & Diana. Chace, Tara, tr. from NOR. 2006. 192p. (J). 17.95 (978-1-932425-59-8(4) , Front Street) Boyds Mills Pr.

Hahn, Mary Downing. Anna on the Farm. 2001. lib. bdg. 14.15 (978-0-613-68401-9(X)) Tandem Library Bks.

Hahn, Mary Downing. The Old Willis Place: A Ghost Story. 208p. (gr. 4-7). 2007. (J). pap. 5.95 (*978-0-618-89741-4(0)); 2004. (Illus.). (YA). 16.00 (978-0-618-43018-5(0)) Houghton Mifflin Co. Trade & Reference Div. (Clarion Bks.).

Haigh, Liz. The Dragon's Ring. 2002. (Illus.). 80p. pap. 11.95 (978-1-85902-724-0(5)) Beekman Bks., Inc.

Haislip, Phyllis Hall. Anybody's Hero: The Battle of Old Men & Young Boys. 2004. (Illus.). 220p. (J). pap. 8.95 (978-1-57249-343-8(7) , White Mane Kids) White Mane Publishing Co., Inc.

Hale, Jane. Heartland. 1999. (Illus.). 288p. (J). (gr. 8-12). pap. 12.95 (978-0-934426-91-6(0)) NAPSAC Reproductions.

Hale, Marian. The Truth about Sparrows. rev. ed. 2004. (Illus.). 272p. (J). 16.95 (978-0-8050-7584-7(4) , Holt, Henry & Co. Bks. For Young Readers) Holt, Henry & Co.

—The Truth about Sparrows. 2007. 288p. (J). pap. 6.99 (*978-0-312-37133-3(0)) Square Fish.

Hale, R. A. Best Friends. 2005. (J). 6.00 (978-0-9708959-5-0(X)) Accent Pubns.

Hale, Rachael. Furry Friends. rev. ed. 2007. (Paw Pals Ser.). 20p. (J). (ps-ps). bds. 6.99 (*978-0-316-11319-9(0)) Little, Brown Bks. for Young Readers.

—Love Tails. rev. ed. 2007. (Paw Pals Ser.). 20p. (J). (ps-ps). bds. 6.99 (*978-0-316-11321-2(2)) Little, Brown Bks. for Young Readers.

Hall, August. Song & Juniper. Hall, August, illus. ed. 2005. 32p. (J). 17.95 (978-0-9771990-0-6(2)) Big Kid Bks.

Hall, John. Is He or Isn't He? 2006. 304p. (J). pap. 8.99 (978-0-06-078747-9(3)) HarperCollins Pubs.

Hall, Kirsten. Double Trouble: All about Colors. 2004. (Beastieville Ser.). (J). (gr. k-1). pap. 3.95 (978-0-516-24653-6(4) , Children's Pr.) Scholastic Library Publishing.

—Double Trouble: All about Colors. Luedecke, Bev, illus. 2003. (Beastieville Ser.). 32p. (J). (ps-1). 19.50 (978-0-516-22892-1(7) , Children's Pr.) Scholastic Library Publishing.

—Help! All about Telling Time. Luedecke, Bev, illus. 2003. (Concept Bks.). 32p. (J). 19.50 (978-0-516-22890-7(0) , Children's Pr.) Scholastic Library Publishing.

—Little Lies: All about Math. Luedecke, Bev, illus. 2003. (Beastieville Ser.). 32p. (J). 19.50 (978-0-516-22896-9(X) , Children's Pr.) Scholastic Library Publishing.

Hall, Patricia. Old Friends, New Friends. Winfield, Alison, illus. ed. 2005. (Ready-to-Read Ser. Level 1). 32p. (J). lib. bdg. 15.00 (978-1-59054-930-8(9)) Fitzgerald Bks.

Hall, Patricia & Winfield, Alison. Old Friends, New Friends. 2002. (Raggedy Ann Ser.). 32p. (J). pap. 3.99 (978-0-689-85224-4(X) , Little Simon) Simon & Schuster Children's Publishing.

Hall, Sharon J. Ridgeway Middle School: Choosing to Embrace Diversity 360 Degrees. 2007. 316p. per. 18.95 (*978-0-595-45109-8(8)) iUniverse, Inc.

Hall, Susan T., illus. Presentamos a Diego! 2005. (Dora the Explorer Ser.). Orig. Title: Meet Diego!. (SPA.). 24p. (J). pap. 3.99 (978-0-689-87749-0(8) , Libros Para Niños) Simon & Schuster Children's Publishing.

Hallagin, Janet. The Way of Courage. 2006. 30.99 (*978-1-4257-1249-5(5)); pap. 20.99 (*978-1-4257-1248-8(7)) Xlibris Corp.

Haller, Reese. Fred the Mouse: Making Friends, 2. Galasterer, Lynne, illus. 2nd ed. 2006. 112p. (J). 4.97 (978-0-9772321-0-9(7)) Personal Power Pr.

Hallinan, P. K. My Daddy & I. 2002. (...and I Ser.). (Illus.). 26p. (J). (ps-k). bds. 7.95 (978-0-8249-4217-5(5)) Ideals Pubns.

—A Rainbow of Friends. 2006. 32p. pap. 3.95 (978-0-8249-5519-9(6) , Ideals Children's Bks.); 2002. (Illus.). 24p. (J). 5.95 (978-0-8249-5395-9(9)) Ideals Pubns.

—That's What a Friend Is. 2001. (Illus.). 24p. (J). 7.95 (978-0-8249-5390-4(8)) Ideals Pubns.

Hallinan, P. K., illus. A Rainbow of Friends. 2001. 24p. (J). (ps-3). 7.95 (978-0-8249-5394-2(0) , Ideals) Ideals Pubns.

Halpern, Julie. Toby & the Snowflakes. Cordell, Matthew R., illus. 2004. 32p. (J). (gr. k-3). tchr. ed. 15.00 (978-0-618-42004-9(5)) Houghton Mifflin Co. Trade & Reference Div.

Halpern, Sue. Introducing Sasha Abramowitz. 2005. 288p. (J). (gr. 5-8). 17.00 (978-0-374-38432-6(0) , Frances Foster Bks.) Farrar, Straus & Giroux.

Halsey, Jacqueline. Peggy's Letter. 2005. (Orca Young Readers Ser.). (Illus.). 144p. (J). (gr. 3-6). pap. 5.95 (978-1-55143-363-9(X)) Orca Bk. Pubs. USA.

Halverson, Deborah. Big Mouth. 2008. 144p. (J). (gr. 5). 15.99 (*978-0-385-73394-6(1)); lib. bdg. 18.99 (*978-0-385-90408-7(8)) Random Hse. Children's Bks. (Delacorte Bks. for Young Readers).

Halvorson, Marilyn. Blood Brothers. 2004. 240p. (YA). (978-1-55005-085-1(0)) Fitzhenry & Whiteside, Ltd.

—Let It Go. 2004. 224p. (YA). (gr. 7-9). (978-1-55005-105-6(9)) Fitzhenry & Whiteside, Ltd.

Hambrick, Sharon. Tommy's Race. Manning, Maurie, illus. 2004. (Fig Street Kids Ser.). 95p. (J). (gr. 1-2). 7.49 (978-1-59166-286-0(9)) Jones, Bob Univ. Pr.

—Tommy's Rocket. Manning, Maurie, illus. 2003. (Fig Street Kids Ser.). 83p. (J). (gr. 1-2). 7.49 (978-1-59166-186-3(2)) Jones, Bob Univ. Pr.

Hamer, Irene. Booda's Story: A Cross-Cultural Story for Girls & Boys. Kitchens, Nan, illus. 2001. 100p. (J). (gr. 3-7). 12.95 (978-0-9700306-1-0(4) , Cosmic Aye) Hastings Ende Design Partners.

Hamilton, Doris K. Daniel's Christmas Story. 2006. pap. 7.95 (978-0-533-15495-1(2)) Vantage Pr., Inc.

Hamilton, Harriet E. The Sunbeam & the Wave. Bowen, Connie, illus. 2000. 33p. (J). (gr. 4-7). 17.95 (978-0-87159-250-7(9)) Unity Schl. of Christianity.

Hamilton, K. R. A Freaky Kind of Courage. 2007. (J). (*978-0-7847-1909-1(8)) Standard Publishing.

Hamilton, Tisha. Five Times the Trouble. 2006. (Trollz Ser.). (Illus.). 32p. (J). pap. 3.99 (978-0-439-82825-3(2)) Scholastic, Inc.

Hamilton, Tisha, adapted by. Five Times the Trouble. 2006. (Trollz Ser.). (Illus.). 32p. (J). (*978-1-4156-8962-2(8)) Scholastic, Inc.

Hamilton, Virginia. Bluish. 2002. 128p. (J). (gr. 4-6). pap. 5.99 (978-0-439-36786-8(7) , Scholastic Paperbacks) Scholastic, Inc.

—Bluish. Dillon, Leo & Dillon, Diane, illus. 1999. 128p. (J). (gr. 4-9). pap. 16.95 (978-0-590-28879-8(2) , Blue Sky Pr., The) Scholastic, Inc.

—The Planet of Junior Brown. 1998. (J). pap. 4.50 (978-0-87628-347-9(4)) Ctr. for Applied Research in Education, The.

—The Planet of Junior Brown. 2006. (Illus.). 224p. (J). pap. 5.99 (978-1-4169-1410-5(2) , Aladdin) Simon & Schuster Children's Publishing.

—Second Cousins. 2000. (gr. 5-8). lib. bdg. 13.00 (978-0-613-29054-8(2)) Tandem Library Bks.

—A White Romance. 1998. (Point Signature Ser.). 450p. (YA). (gr. 8-12). pap. 4.50 (978-0-590-13005-9(6)) Scholastic, Inc.

Hammerschlag, Carl A. The Go-Away Doll. Havill, Juanita, ed. Soasey, Beverly E., illus. l.t. ed. 1998. (Dr. H. Bks.). 32p. (J). (ps-12). 16.95 (978-1-889166-22-3(7) , 299-5425, Dr. H Bks.) Turtle Island Pr., Inc.

Han, Jenny. Shug. 256p. 2007. (J). pap. 5.99 (*978-1-4169-0943-9(5) , Aladdin); 2006. (Illus.). (YA). (gr. 5-9). 16.99 (978-1-4169-0942-2(7)) Simon & Schuster Children's Publishing.

Hancasky, Carrie A. Curiosity Kitty. 2002. 24p. 14.95 (978-1-56167-762-7(0)) American Literary Pr.

Hancock, H. Irving. The High School Captain of the Team: Dick & Co. Leading the Athletic Vanguard. l.t. ed. 2007. 172p. pap. 14.99 (*978-1-4264-6460-7(6)) BiblioBazaar.

—The High School Left End: Dick & Co. Grilling on the Football Gridiron. 2007. 156p. pap. 11.99 (*978-1-4264-6385-3(5)); 174p. pap. 14.99 (*978-1-4264-6459-1(2)) BiblioBazaar.

Hancock, Susan G. The Wind & Little Cloud. Simmons, Robert, illus. 2006. (J). per. 10.95 (978-0-9741743-0-3(0)) Perlycross Pubs.

Haneberg, Janet. Mighty Mitt. 2006. 36p. (J). pap. 14.99 (978-1-4116-4168-6(X)) Lulu.com.

Hansen, Joyce. The Gift-Giver. 2005. 128p. (J). (gr. 5-9). pap. 6.95 (978-0-618-61123-2(1) , Clarion Bks.) Houghton Mifflin Co. Trade & Reference Div.

—One True Friend. 2005. 160p. (J). (gr. 5-9). pap. 6.95 (978-0-618-60991-8(1) , Clarion Bks.) Houghton Mifflin Co. Trade & Reference Div.

—Yellow Bird & Me. 2005. 168p. (J). (gr. 5-9). pap. 6.95 (978-0-618-61116-4(9) , Clarion Bks.) Houghton Mifflin Co. Trade & Reference Div.

Hansle, Chauline. Mr Frog & Kitty Robin. 2006. (ENG., Illus.). 28p. per. 15.49 (*978-1-4259-6920-2(8)) AuthorHouse.

Hanson, Anders. Lone Shark. Haberstroh, Anne, illus. (Fact & Fiction Ser.). 24p. (J). 2007. 21.35 (978-1-59928-452-1(9)); 2006. (978-1-59928-453-8(7)) ABDO Publishing Co.

Hanson, Shelley. K9 Crew Beginnings. 2004. 160p. (J). per. 9.99 (978-0-9752887-0-2(9)) Tail Wagging Productions.

Hao, K. T. One Pizza, One Penny. Feldman, Roxanne Hsu, tr. from CHI. Ferri, Giuliano, illus. 2003. 32p. 15.95 (978-0-8126-2702-2(4)) Cricket Bks.

Hapka, Catherine, adapted by. Disney's Lilo & Stitch. 2002. (Read-Aloud Storybook Ser.). (Illus.). 72p. (J). (ps-3). 8.99 (978-0-7364-1321-3(9) , RH/Disney) Random Hse. Children's Bks.

Happel, Kathleen. The Smartest Kid I Ever Met. Behles, Liza, illus. 2005. 57p. (J). per. 12.50 (978-0-9763993-3-9(4) , Ithaca Pr.) Authors & Artists Publishers of New York, Inc.

Harcourt School Publishers Staff. The Acting Champ Advanced Level. 3rd ed. 2002. (Trophies Reading Program Ser.). (Illus.). pap. 5.10 (978-0-15-323464-4(4)) Harcourt Schl. Pubs.

—Alone Time, Time Together Below Level. 3rd ed. 2002. (Trophies Reading Program Ser.). (Illus.). pap. 5.10 (978-0-15-323044-8(2)) Harcourt Schl. Pubs.

—Amigos para Siempre On Level. 3rd ed. 2002. (Trofeos Ser.).Tr. of Always Friends. (SPA., Illus.). pap. 6.80 (978-0-15-324088-1(1)) Harcourt Schl. Pubs.

—Andy & Tamika: Reader's Choice Book. 2001. (Collections Ser.). (Illus.). pap. 12.10 (978-0-15-314359-5(2)) Harcourt Schl. Pubs.

—Around the Campfire Below Level. 3rd ed. 2002. (Trophies Reading Program Ser.). (Illus.). pap. 5.10 (978-0-15-323057-8(6)) Harcourt Schl. Pubs.

—Bess & Tess 5-Pack, On Level. 3rd ed. 2002. (Trophies Reading Program Ser.). (Illus.). (gr. 1). pap. 20.10 (978-0-15-326836-6(0)) Harcourt Schl. Pubs.

—Best Friends. 1999. (Collections Ser.). (Illus.). 6.40 (978-0-15-314984-9(1)) Harcourt Schl. Pubs.

—The Big House: Take-Home Book. rev. ed. 2001. (Collections Ser.: Vol. 1). (Illus.). (J). (gr. 1). pap. 1.90 (978-0-15-317813-9(2)) Harcourt Schl. Pubs.

—Breaking Away: Take-Home Book. 1999. (Collections Ser.). (Illus.). (J). pap. 1.90 (978-0-15-317286-1(X)) Harcourt Schl. Pubs.

—Brincar Cuerda Advanced Level. 3rd ed. 2002. (Trofeos Ser.). (SPA., Illus.). pap. 6.80 (978-0-15-324116-1(0)) Harcourt Schl. Pubs.

—Como Me Veo? Advanced Level. 3rd ed. 2002. (Trofeos Ser.). (SPA., Illus.). (gr. 2). pap. 6.80 (978-0-15-324012-6(1)) Harcourt Schl. Pubs.

—Cyber-Stuffing. 3rd ed. 2002. (Trophies English Language Learners Ser.). (Illus.). pap. 51.00 (978-0-15-327898-3(6)) Harcourt Schl. Pubs.

—Dear Berta. 3rd ed. 2002. (Trophies English Language Learners Ser.). (Illus.). (gr. 4). pap. 5.10 (978-0-15-327750-4(5)) Harcourt Schl. Pubs.

—Dear Friend On Level. 3rd ed. 2002. (Trophies Reading Program Ser.). (Illus.). pap. 5.10 (978-0-15-323092-9(4)) Harcourt Schl. Pubs.

—The Down & Up Fall: Reader's Choice Book. 2001. (Collections Ser.). (Illus.). pap. 13.20 (978-0-15-314366-3(5)) Harcourt Schl. Pubs.

—Faces to the Sun On Level. 3rd ed. 2002. (Trophies Reading Program Ser.). (Illus.). pap. 5.10 (978-0-15-323259-6(5)) Harcourt Schl. Pubs.

—Fish Friends: Take-Home Book. 1999. (Signatures Ser.). (Illus.). (J). pap. 1.90 (978-0-15-313907-9(2)) Harcourt Schl. Pubs.

—Follow Me: Below Level. 3rd ed. 2002. (Trophies Reading Program Ser.). (Illus.). (J). pap. 3.20 (978-0-15-322954-1(3)) Harcourt Schl. Pubs.

—Friends Forever On Level. 3rd ed. 2002. (Trophies Reading Program Ser.). (Illus.). pap. 5.10 (978-0-15-323177-3(7)) Harcourt Schl. Pubs.

—The Hideout Champs On Level. 3rd ed. 2002. (Trophies Reading Program Ser.). (Illus.). pap. 5.10 (978-0-15-323434-7(2)) Harcourt Schl. Pubs.

—Home Sweet Home. 3rd ed. 2002. (Trophies English Language Learners Ser.). (Illus.). pap. 5.10 (978-0-15-327709-2(2)) Harcourt Schl. Pubs.

—I Wish... Below Level. 3rd ed. 2002. (Trophies Reading Program Ser.). (Illus.). pap. 5.10 (978-0-15-323141-4(6)) Harcourt Schl. Pubs.

—Jazzbo & Googy: Library Book. 3rd ed. 2002. (Trophies Reading Program Ser.). (Illus.). pap. 13.50 (978-0-15-329250-7(4)) Harcourt Schl. Pubs.

—Jump! Advanced Level. 3rd ed. 2002. (Trophies Reading Program Ser.). (Illus.). pap. 5.10 (978-0-15-323205-3(6)) Harcourt Schl. Pubs.

—The Junk Band: Take-Home Book. 1999. (Collections Ser.). (Illus.). (J). pap. 1.90 (978-0-15-317243-4(6)) Harcourt Schl. Pubs.

—Left Out. 2001. (Reader's Choice Bks.). (Illus.). (gr. 6). pap. 13.20 (978-0-15-314419-6(X)) Harcourt Schl. Pubs.

—The Little School in the Valley Below Level. 3rd ed. 2002. (Trophies Reading Program Ser.). (Illus.). pap. 5.10 (978-0-15-323244-2(7)) Harcourt Schl. Pubs.

—Lonely No More: Take-Home Book. 2001. (Collections Ser.). (Illus.). (J). (gr. 5). pap. 1.90 (978-0-15-319513-6(4)) Harcourt Schl. Pubs.

—Lonely No More Below Level. 3rd ed. 2002. (Trophies Reading Program Ser.). (Illus.). (gr. 5). pap. 5.10 (978-0-15-323311-1(7)) Harcourt Schl. Pubs.

—Mack & Will Are Friends: Independent Reader. 3rd ed. 2002. (Trophies Reading Program Ser.). (Illus.). (J). pap. 2.90 (978-0-15-325493-2(9)) Harcourt Schl. Pubs.

—Mil Palabras: Take-Home Book. 2001. (Vamos Ser.). (SPA., Illus.). (J). pap. 2.80 (978-0-15-319927-1(X)) Harcourt Schl. Pubs.

—My Friend: Below Level. 3rd ed. 2002. (Trophies Reading Program Ser.). (Illus.). (J). pap. 3.20 (978-0-15-322955-8(1)) Harcourt Schl. Pubs.

—My Friend, Boots Advanced Level. 3rd ed. 2002. (Trophies Reading Program Ser.). (Illus.). (J). pap. 3.70 (978-0-15-323014-1(2)) Harcourt Schl. Pubs.

—My Greatest Wish: Take-Home Book. 2001. (Collections Ser.). (Illus.). (J). pap. 1.90 (978-0-15-319485-6(5)) Harcourt Schl. Pubs.

—My Greatest Wish Below Level. 3rd ed. 2002. (Trophies Reading Program Ser.). (Illus.). pap. 5.10 (978-0-15-323223-7(4)) Harcourt Schl. Pubs.

—My School Year. 3rd ed. 2002. (Trophies English Language Learners Ser.). (Illus.). pap. 5.10 (978-0-15-327715-3(7)) Harcourt Schl. Pubs.

—My Two Friends: Take-Home Book. 1999. (Signatures Ser.). (Illus.). (J). pap. 1.70 (978-0-15-313846-1(7)) Harcourt Schl. Pubs.

—Neighborhood Friends: Independent Reader. 3rd ed. 2002. (Trophies Reading Program Ser.). (Illus.). (J). pap. 2.90 (978-0-15-325497-0(1)) Harcourt Schl. Pubs.

—The New Girl: Take-Home Book. 2001. (Collections Ser.). (Illus.). (J). pap. 1.90 (978-0-15-319534-1(7)) Harcourt Schl. Pubs.

—The New Girl Below Level. 3rd ed. 2002. (Trophies Reading Program Ser.). (Illus.). pap. 5.10 (978-0-15-323332-6(X)) Harcourt Schl. Pubs.

—Nosy Nina Advanced Level. 3rd ed. 2002. (Trophies Reading Program Ser.). (Illus.). pap. 5.10 (978-0-15-323202-2(1)) Harcourt Schl. Pubs.

—Over the Gate: Take-Home Book. 1999. (Collections Ser.). (Illus.). (J). pap. 1.90 (978-0-15-317209-0(6)) Harcourt Schl. Pubs.

—The Path: On Level. 3rd ed. 2002. (Trophies Reading Program Ser.). (Illus.). (J). pap. 4.10 (978-0-15-322980-0(2)) Harcourt Schl. Pubs.

—A Pinch of This & That On Level. 3rd ed. 2002. (Trophies Reading Program Ser.). (Illus.). pap. 5.10 (978-0-15-323079-0(7)) Harcourt Schl. Pubs.

—Rainy Day Pals 5-Pack, Below Level. 3rd ed. 2002. (Trophies Reading Program Ser.). (Illus.). (gr. 1). pap. 20.10 (978-0-15-326816-8(6)) Harcourt Schl. Pubs.

—The Red & Blue Hat On Level. 3rd ed. 2002. (Trophies Reading Program Ser.). (Illus.). pap. 5.10 (978-0-15-323347-0(8)) Harcourt Schl. Pubs.

—Renacuajo Curioso: Take-Home Book. 1999. (Vamos Ser.). (SPA., Illus.). (J). pap. 2.50 (978-0-15-318847-3(2)) Harcourt Schl. Pubs.

—Rosa's New Friend: Take-Home Book. 1999. (Signatures Ser.). (Illus.). (J). pap. 1.70 (978-0-15-313855-3(6)) Harcourt Schl. Pubs.

—Sam's Chase On Level. 3rd ed. 2002. (Trophies Reading Program Ser.). (Illus.). pap. 5.10 (978-0-15-323091-2(6)) Harcourt Schl. Pubs.

—Stacy's Surprise: Take-Home Book. 1999. (Collections Ser.). (Illus.). (J). pap. 1.90 (978-0-15-317298-4(3)) Harcourt Schl. Pubs.

—Summer/Maizon Level D: Library Edition. 2001. (Collections Ser.). (Illus.). pap. 12.10 (978-0-15-314435-6(1)) Harcourt Schl. Pubs.

—Tea with Jam. 3rd ed. 2002. (Trophies English Language Learners Ser.). (Illus.). pap. 5.10 (978-0-15-327755-9(6)) Harcourt Schl. Pubs.

—This & That: Library Book. 1999. (Collections Ser.). (Illus.). pap. 13.60 (978-0-15-313406-7(2)) Harcourt Schl. Pubs.

—Titch & Daisy: Library Book. 1999. (Collections Ser.). (Illus.). pap. 14.90 (978-0-15-313404-3(6)) Harcourt Schl. Pubs.

—The Trading Post On Level. 3rd ed. 2002. (Trophies Reading Program Ser.). (Illus.). pap. 5.10 (978-0-15-323184-1(X)) Harcourt Schl. Pubs.

—The Tree House Below Level. 3rd ed. 2002. (Trophies Reading Program Ser.). (Illus.). pap. 5.10 (978-0-15-323050-9(9)) Harcourt Schl. Pubs.

—Trofeos Advanced Level: Almuerzo en el Parque. 3rd ed. 2002. (SPA., Illus.). pap. 6.80 (978-0-15-323933-5(6)) Harcourt Schl. Pubs.

—Trofeos Below Level: Mi Amigo. 3rd ed. 2002. (SPA., Illus.). (J). pap. 3.50 (978-0-15-323866-6(6)) Harcourt Schl. Pubs.

—Trofeos On Level: Tienda General. 3rd ed. 2002. (SPA., Illus.). pap. 6.80 (978-0-15-324095-9(4)) Harcourt Schl. Pubs.

E F G

—The Truest Treasure: Take-Home Book. 2001. (Collections Ser.). (Illus.). (J). pap. 1.90 (978-0-15-319544-0(4)) Harcourt Schl. Pubs.

—The Virtual Tutor: Take-Home Book. 2001. (Collections Ser.). (Illus.). (J). pap. 1.90 (978-0-15-319670-6(X)) Harcourt Schl. Pubs.

—The Virtual Tutor Below Level. 3rd ed. 2002. (Trophies Reading Program Ser.). (Illus.). pap. 5.10 (978-0-15-323429-3(6)) Harcourt Schl. Pubs.

Harding, Kitchener L. Clarence & Amous Become Famous. l.t. ed. 1999. (Illus.). 10p. (J). (gr. 1-5). spiral bd. 4.95 (978-1-930503-01-4(6)) Office Max.

Hardinge, Frances. Well Witched. 2008. 400p. (J). 16.99 (***978-0-06-088038-5(4)***); lib. bdg. 17.89 (***978-0-06-088039-2(2)***) HarperCollins Pubs.

Hardy, Zoey. Brockway High. 2006. 344p. (YA). per. 12.95 (978-0-9765423-1-5(5)) Eudon Publishing.

Harley, Bill. Nothing Happened. Miya, Ann, illus. 2004. 32p. (gr. 1 up). 14.95 (978-1-883672-09-6(0) , Tricycle Pr.) Ten Speed Pr.

Harlin, Kathy. Maverick. 2004. 79p. pap. 14.95 (978-1-4137-2395-3(0)) PublishAmerica, Inc.

Harlow, Joan Hiatt. Blown Away! 2007. 272p. (J). (gr. 4-7). 15.99 (978-1-4169-0781-7(5) , McElderry, Margaret K.) Simon & Schuster Children's Publishing.

—Shadows on the Sea. (Illus.). 256p. (J). 2005. pap. 4.99 (978-0-689-84927-5(3) , Aladdin); 2003. (gr. 3-6). 17.99 (978-0-689-84926-8(5) , McElderry, Margaret K.) Simon & Schuster Children's Publishing.

—Shadows on the Sea. l.t. ed. 2003. 214p. 20.95 (978-0-7862-6145-1(5) , Large Print Pr.) Thorndike Pr.

Harper, Charise Mericle. Flashcards of My Life. (J). 2007. 224p. (gr. 3-7). pap. 6.99 (978-0-316-16676-8(6)); 2006. (Illus.). 240p. (gr. 4-7). 15.99 (978-0-316-75621-1(0)) Little Brown & Co.

—Still Just Grace. Harper, Charise Mericle, illus. 2007. (Illus.). 152p. (J). (gr. 3-5). 15.00 (***978-0-618-64643-2(4)***) Houghton Mifflin Co. Trade & Reference Div.

—When Randolph Turned Rotten. 2007. 40p. (J). (gr. k-3). 16.99 (***978-0-375-84071-5(0)***); lib. bdg. 19.99 (***978-0-375-94071-2(5)***) Random Hse. Children's Bks. (Knopf Bks. for Young Readers).

Harper, Jo. Whistling Willie. 2005. 32p. (J). (978-0-7868-0113-8(1)); (978-0-7868-2095-5(0)) Hyperion Pr.

HarperCollins Staff, ed. Two's a Crowd. 1999. (gr. 3-6). lib. bdg. 12.10 (978-0-613-22544-1(9)) Tandem Library Bks.

Harrar, George. The Wonder Kid. Winiarski, Anthony, illus. 2006. 256p. (J). (gr. 5). 16.00 (978-0-618-56317-3(2)) Houghton Mifflin Co.

Harrington, Jane. Four Things My Geeky-Jock-of-a-Best Friend Must Do in Europe. 2006. 160p. (YA). (gr. 6-10). 15.95 (978-1-58196-041-9(7)) Darby Creek Publishing.

Harris, Carol Flynn. A Place for Joey. 2003. (Illus.). 96p. (YA). (gr. 4-6). 15.95 (978-1-56397-108-2(9)) Boyds Mills Pr.

Harris, Christine. Fugitive. 2005. (Undercover Girl Ser.: No. 2). (Illus.). 160p. (J). (gr. 3-7). pap. 4.99 (978-0-439-76126-0(3) , Scholastic Paperbacks) Scholastic, Inc.

Harris, Daniel. Billy's Bounce. Maval Publishing Inc. Staff, illus. 2001. 32p. (J). (ps-3). pap. 7.50 (978-1-884083-70-9(6)) Maval Publishing, Inc.

Harris, Mark J. The Amazing Adventure in Tovia. 2001. 168p. pap. 12.95 (978-0-595-19230-4(0) , Writers Club Pr.) iUniverse, Inc.

Harris, Peter & Weir, Doffy. Bottomley at the Cattery. 1998. (Illus.). 32p. (J). pap. 5.95 (978-0-7641-0667-5(8)) Barron's Educational Series, Inc.

Harris, Sue. The Little Seal. Boey, Stephanie, illus. 2007. 28p. (J). (ps). pap. 15.99 (***978-0-525-47839-3(6)*** , Dutton Juvenile) Penguin Group (USA) Inc.

Harrison, Dorothy. A Better Tomorrow? 2003. 128p. pap. 13.95 (978-0-595-28429-0(9) , Backinprint.com) iUniverse, Inc.

Harrison, Emma. The Best Girl. 2007. 288p. (YA). (gr. 9 up). pap. 5.99 (***978-0-06-122824-7(9)*** , HarperTeen) HarperCollins Pubs.

—The Cheetah Girls Supa-Star Scrapbook. 2005. (Illus.). 48p. (J). (gr. 3-7). pap. 6.99 (978-0-7868-4717-4(4)) Disney Pr.

—Tourist Trap. 2006. 384p. (J). pap. 5.99 (978-0-06-084735-7(2)) HarperCollins Pubs.

Harrison, John. Fergal Onions. 2005. (Illus.). 32p. pap. 17.95 (978-0-7022-3481-1(8)) Univ. of Queensland Pr. AUS. *Dist:* International Specialized Bk. Services.

Harrison, Lisi. Best Friends for Never. 2004. (Clique Ser.: Bk. 2). 208p. (J). (gr. 5-8). pap. 9.99 (978-0-316-70131-0(9) , Poppy) Little, Brown Bks. for Young Readers.

—Bratfest at Tiffany's. 2008. (Clique Ser.: No. 9). 300p. (gr. 7-12). pap. 9.99 (***978-0-316-00680-4(7)*** , Poppy) Little, Brown Bks. for Young Readers.

Harrison, Lisi. The Clique. 2004. (Clique Ser.: No. 1). 24p. (J). (gr. 5-8). pap. 9.99 (978-0-316-70129-7(7) , Poppy) Little, Brown Bks. for Young Readers.

Harrison, Marie Joseph. Mosanna & Me. 2003. 160p. pap. 12.95 (978-0-916251-62-8(4)) Sunbelt Pubns., Inc.

—Mosanna & Me. 2003. (gr. 7-12). lib. bdg. 22.20 (978-0-613-89684-9(X)) Tandem Library Bks.

Harrison, Troon. Courage to Fly. Huang, Zhong-Yang, illus. 2004. 32p. (J). (ps-2). 17.95 (978-0-88995-273-7(6)) Red Deer Pr. CAN. *Dist:* Fitzhenry & Whiteside, Ltd.

Harvie, Ronald Anthony. The Adventures of Peter Potato & Friends. 2005. (Illus.). 71p. (J). per. 15.95 (978-0-9771939-0-5(X) , 0002) New World Publishing.

Hash, Bill. Jahmon's Adventure Home. 2007. (J). per. 10.99 (***978-1-59886-790-9(3)***) Tate Publishing & Enterprises, L.L.C.

Hatkoff, Craig & Hatkoff, Isabella. Best Friends. 2007. (Owen & Mzee Ser.). 12p. (J). bds. 6.99 (978-0-439-92872-4(9) , Scholastic Pr.) Scholastic, Inc.

Hautman, Pete. Invisible. Hautman, Pete, illus. 160p. (YA). 2005. (gr. 7 up). 16.99 (978-0-689-86800-9(6) , Simon & Schuster Children's Publishing); 2006. reprint ed. pap. 7.99 (978-0-689-86903-7(7) , Simon Pulse) Simon & Schuster Children's Publishing.

—Invisible. l.t. ed. 2005. 192p. (YA). 20.95 (978-0-7862-7909-8(5) , Large Print Pr.) Thorndike Pr.

—Mr. Was. 1998. (J). (978-0-606-13625-9(8)) Tandem Library Bks.

Hawkins, Colin & Hawkins, Jacqui. Foxy & Friends Go Racing. (Illus.). 32p. (J). 8.95 (978-0-00-664565-8(8) , HarperSport) HarperCollins Pubs. Ltd. GBR. *Dist:* Trafalgar Square Publishing.

Hawthorne, Rachel. The Boyfriend League. 2007. 336p. (J). pap. 5.99 (***978-0-06-113837-9(1)*** , HarperTeen) HarperCollins Pubs.

Hawthorne, Rachel. Thrill Ride. 2006. 320p. (J). pap. 5.99 (978-0-06-083954-3(6)) HarperCollins Pubs.

Haydel, Catherine. Uno the Cat & Hurricane Katrina. 2006. 18.00 (978-0-8059-7341-9(9)) Dorrance Publishing Co., Inc.

Hayden, Torey L. The Very Worst Thing. 2003. 176p. (J). (gr. 5 up). 15.99 (978-0-06-029792-3(1)) HarperCollins Pubs.

Hayes, Daniel. Flyers. 1998. (978-0-606-13392-0(5)) Tandem Library Bks.

Hayes, Sonia. Urban Goddess. 2007. 224p. (YA). per. 9.95 (***978-0-9777573-1-2(5)***) NUA Multimedia.

Hayley, Barbara. Boot Camp. 2006. 128p. mass mkt. (978-1-84550-128-0(4)) Christian Focus Pubns.

Haynes, David. Right by My Side, a Novel. 1998. (978-0-606-13740-9(8)) Tandem Library Bks.

Hays, Anna Jane. Silly Sara: A Phonics Reader. Wickstrom, Sylvie K., illus. 2002. (Step into Reading Early Bks.). 32p. (J). (gr. k-3). pap. 3.99 (978-0-375-81231-6(8) , Random Hse. Bks. for Young Readers) Random Hse. Children's Bks.

Haywood, Carolyn. Betsy & the Boys. 2004. (Illus.). 160p. (J). 16.00 (978-0-15-205106-8(6) , Harcourt Young Classics); pap. 5.95 (978-0-15-205102-0(3) , Odyssey Classics) Harcourt Children's Bks.

—Here's a Penny. 2005. (Illus.). 160p. (J). 16.00 (978-0-15-205227-0(5) , Harcourt Young Classics); pap. 5.95 (978-0-15-205225-6(9) , Odyssey Classics) Harcourt Children's Bks.

—Primrose Day. 2005. (Illus.). 176p. (J). 16.00 (978-0-15-205228-7(3)); pap. 5.95 (978-0-15-205229-4(1)) Harcourt Children's Bks.

Hazen, Barbara Shook. Good-Bye Hello. 1999. (SPA.). (J). pap. 4.95 (978-0-689-31953-2(3) , Atheneum) Simon & Schuster Children's Publishing.

Healy, Nick. Fawn Braun's Big City Blues. Erkocak, Sahin, illus. 2007. (Pfeffernut County Ser.). 32p. (J). (gr. k-2). lib. bdg. 23.93 (***978-1-4048-3696-9(9)***) Picture Window Bks.

Heap, Sue. Four Friends in the Garden. Heap, Sue, illus. 2004. (Illus.). 32p. (J). (gr. k-ps). 15.99 (978-0-7636-2371-5(7)) Candlewick Pr.

Heap, Sue, illus. What Shall We Play ? 2006. 28p. (J). 9.95 (978-1-59764-215-6(0)) New Line Bks.

Hearson, Ruth. Cinnamon's Fairy Sleepover. Hearson, Ruth, illus. 2006. (Illus.). 14p. (J). 5.99 (978-1-4169-1401-3(3) , Little Simon) Simon & Schuster Children's Publishing.

Hearty Heart & Friends - 3rd Grade Curriculum. rev. ed. 2002. per. (978-1-932032-00-0(2)) Flaghouse, Inc.

Hector, Rachel Claus. Six Second Slack. 2002. 134p. pap. 10.95 (978-0-595-21513-3(0) , Writers Club Pr.) iUniverse, Inc.

Hedderwick, Mairi. Katie Morag & the Big Boy Cousins. 1999. (Katie Morag Stories Ser.). (Illus.). 32p. (J). pap. 9.99 (978-0-09-911891-6(2)) Random Hse. GBR. *Dist:* Independent Pubs. Group.

—Katie Morag & the Tiresome Ted. 1999. (Illus.). 32p. (J). (gr. 1-4). pap. 9.99 (978-0-09-911881-7(5)) Random Hse. GBR. *Dist:* Independent Pubs. Group.

Hedrick, Georgia. Share Me a Shadow. l.t. ed. 2002. 48p. (J). cd-rom 12.95 (978-0-9706612-7-2(4)) JetKor.

Hegg, Tom. Peef & His Best Friend. Hanson, Warren, illus. 2001. 48p. (J). (ps up). 15.95 (978-0-931674-49-5(2)) Waldman Hse. Pr., Inc.

Heide, Florence Parry. Thats What Friends Are For. Meade, Holly, illus. 2007. 40p. pap. 6.99 (***978-0-7636-3283-0(X)***) Candlewick Pr.

Heide, Florence Parry & Clief, Sylvia Van. That's What Friends Are For. Meade, Holly, illus. 2007. 40p. (J). (ps-3). pap. 6.99 (978-0-7636-2646-4(5)) Candlewick Pr.

Heide, Florence Parry, et al. That's What Friends Are For. 2003. (Illus.). 40p. (J). (ps-3). 15.99 (978-0-7636-1397-6(5)) Candlewick Pr.

Heiman, Herb. Running on Dreams. 2007. (J). pap. 22.95 (***978-1-931282-28-4(5)***) Autism Asperger Publishing Co.

Heine, Helme. Los Tres Amigos. (SPA.). 72p. 15.95 (978-84-667-1659-8(9)) Suma de Letras, S.L. ESP. *Dist:* Distribooks, Inc.

—Trois Amis.Tr. of Three Friends. (FRE.). (J). pap. 12.95 (978-2-07-050533-3(2)) Gallimard, Editions FRA. *Dist:* Distribooks, Inc.

Heiner, Garth Farr. Unwanted Muddy. Melander, Eric, illus. l.t. unabr. ed. 2001. (Fun-with-the-Law Ser.: No. 5). 32p. (J). (gr. k-7). pap. 5.95 (978-1-929905-05-8(X)) Fun With the Law, Inc.

Heldring, Thatcher. Toby Wheeler: Eighth-Grade Benchwarmer. 2007. 224p. (J). (gr. 4-7). 14.99 (***978-0-385-73390-8(9)***); lib. bdg. 17.99 (***978-0-385-90405-6(3)***) Random Hse. Children's Bks. (Delacorte Bks. for Young Readers).

Helfenbein, DeWayne. The Treasure Hunt. 2006. pap. 9.99 (***978-1-60034-562-3(X)***) Xulon Pr., Inc.

Heling, Kathryn & Hembrook, Deborah. I Wish I Had Freckles Like Abby/Quisiera tener pecas como Abby. de la Vega, Eida, tr. Adamson, Bonnie, illus. 2006. Tr. of Quisiera tener pecas como Abby. (SPA.). (J). 4.99 (978-0-9770906-6-2(3)) Raven Tree Pr.

—I Wish I Had Freckles Like Abby/Quisiera tener pecas como Abby. de la Vega, Eida, tr. Parins, Kris, illus. 2005. Tr. of Quisiera tener pecas como Abby. (SPA & ENG.). 32p. (J). 16.95 (978-0-9724973-8-1(2) , 626999) Raven Tree Pr.

—I Wish I Had Glasses Like Rosa/Quisiera tener lentes como Rosa. de la Vega, Eida, tr. Adamson, Bonnie, illus. Tr. of Quisiera tener lentes como Rosa. (SPA.). (J). 2006. 4.99 (978-0-9770906-5-5(5)); 2005. 32p. 16.95 (978-0-9724973-7-4(4) , 626999) Raven Tree Pr.

Heller, Sarah E. Disney's Princess Storybook Collection: Love & Friendship Stories. 1999. (Disneys Ser.). (Illus.). 304p. (J). (gr. k-5). 15.99 (978-0-7868-3247-7(9) , Disney Editions) Disney Pr.

Helmer, Diana Star. Give Me Liberty. Aspengren, Michael A. & Hatala, Dan, illus. 1999. (Cover-to-Cover Historical Moments Bks.). 56p. (J). (gr. 1-4). lib. bdg. 16.95 (978-0-7807-9042-1(1) , Covercraft); (gr. 3-6). pap. 8.95 (978-0-7891-5078-3(6)) Perfection Learning Corp.

Hemery, Kathleen Maresh. Sunflower Promise. Bordelois, Augusto, illus. 2005. (J). (978-1-56123-188-1(6)) Centering Corp.

Hemphill, Stephanie. Things Left Unsaid: A Novel in Poems. 2005. 272p. (gr. 7-17). 16.99 (978-0-7868-1850-1(6)) Hyperion Bks. for Children.

—Things Left Unsaid: A Novel in Poems. 2007. 272p. (gr. 7-17). pap. 7.99 (***978-0-7868-3745-8(4)***) Hyperion Pr.

Henderson, Malcolm. Katie & Her Friends. Moss, P. Buckley, illus. 1998. 32p. (J). (ps-3). 15.95 (978-0-9665198-0-8(9) , 0998001000) Moss Portfolio, The.

Henighan, Stephen. The Places Where Names Vanish. 2004. 183p. pap. (978-1-895449-77-8(4)) Thistledown Pr., Ltd.

Henkes, Kevin. Chester's Way. (Illus.). 25.95 incl. audio (978-1-59112-968-4(0)); 28.95 incl. audio compact disk (978-1-59112-972-1(9)); pap. 33.95 incl. audio (978-1-59112-969-1(9)); pap. 35.95 incl. audio compact disk (978-1-59112-973-8(7)) Live Oak Media.

—Jessica. Henkes, Kevin, illus. 1998. (Illus.). 24p. (J). (ps-ps). pap. 6.99 (978-0-688-15847-7(1) , Harper Trophy) HarperCollins Pubs.

—Jessica. 1998. 12.79 (978-0-606-13536-8(7)) Tandem Library Bks.

Henkes, Kevin. Words of Stone. 2005. (J). 152p. (***978-1-4156-2647-4(2)***); 160p. reprint ed. pap. 5.99 (978-0-06-078230-6(7)) HarperCollins Pubs. (Harper Trophy).

Henry, Ragene. The Barefoot Boys of Fayette. Stich, Carolyn R., illus. 2005. 184p. (YA). per. 9.95 (978-0-9749412-3-3(9)) EDCO Publishing, Inc.

Henry, Rohan. The Perfect Gift. 2007. (Illus.). 32p. 8.95 (***978-1-58479-658-9(8)***) Abrams, Harry N. , Inc.

Henshon, Suzanna E. Spiders on the Ceiling. 2006. (J). (978-0-88092-614-0(7)) Royal Fireworks Publishing Co.

Hensley, Sarah M. I Can Be a Friend. 2006. (J). pap., tchr. ed. (978-1-57332-436-6(1)); pap. (978-1-57332-437-3(X)) HighReach Learning, Inc.

Henson, Heather. Making the Run. 2002. 240p. (J). (gr. k-4). 15.89 (978-0-06-029797-8(2)); (gr. 10 up). 15.95 (978-0-06-029796-1(4)) HarperCollins Pubs. (HarperTeen).

—Making the Run: A Novel. 2003. (gr. 7-12). lib. bdg. 15.30 (978-0-613-65699-3(7)) Tandem Library Bks.

Herbauts, Anne. Monday. 2006. 36p. (J). (gr. 3-5). 16.95 (978-1-59270-057-8(8)) Enchanted Lion Bks., LLC.

Herman, Gail. Color Day Relay. 2004. (Magic School Bus Ser.: No. 19). 96p. (J). pap. 4.99 (978-0-439-56051-1(9) , Scholastic Paperbacks) Scholastic, Inc.

Herman, Gail. Peppa Pig & Her Best Friend. 2007. (My First I Can Read Bks.). 32p. (J). pap. 3.99 (***978-0-06-117305-9(3)*** , Harper Trophy) HarperCollins Pubs.

Herman, R. A. Pal & Sal. Ogden, Betina, illus. 1998. (All Aboard Reading Ser.). 32p. (J). (ps-3). pap. 3.99 (978-0-448-41716-5(2) , Grosset & Dunlap) Penguin Group (USA) Inc.

Herman, R. A. Pal & Sal's New Friend. 2005. (***978-0-439-68119-3(7)***) Scholastic, Inc.

Hermes, Patricia. Summer Secrets. 2004. (Illus.). 144p. (YA). 15.95 (978-0-7614-5074-0(2)) Cavendish, Marshall Corp.

Hernandez, Avelino. Aquel Nino y Aquel Viejo. Delicado, Federico, illus. 2002. (Libros para Soñar Ser.). (SPA.). (J). (978-84-8464-121-6(X)) Kalandraka Editora, S.L.

Hernandez, Malena & Taggart, Kay. The Enchanted Rainbow. Gonzalez, Cristela, illus. 2002. Tr. of Maravilloso Arco Iris. (SPA.). 30p. pap. 8.00 (978-0-944551-64-6(5)) Book Pubs. of El Paso.

Hernandez, Mary. Wedding on Mudpie Island. Wise, Noreen, ed. Wethington, Liz, illus. 2000. (Book-a-Day Collection). 32p. (YA). (ps up). pap. 5.95 (978-1-58584-440-1(3)) Huckleberry Pr.

Hernandez, Mary L. Como el Viento Paso a Ser Tormenta. Maval Publishing Inc. Staff, illus. Tr. of How the Tornado Got It's Wind. (SPA.). (J). (ps-3). pap. 7.50 (978-1-59134-015-7(2)); 2001. 32p. pap. 7.50 (978-1-884083-96-9(X)) Maval Publishing, Inc.

—How the Tornado Got It's Wind. Hernandez, Mary L., illus. 2001. (Illus.). 32p. (J). (ps-3). pap. 7.50 (978-1-884083-69-3(2)) Maval Publishing, Inc.

Herrick, Steven. Do-Wrong Ron. Magerl, Caroline, illus. 2005. 132p. (J). pap. 6.95 (978-1-86508-661-3(4)) Allen & Unwin AUS. *Dist:* Independent Pubs. Group.

Hershey, Mary. My Big Sister Is So Bossy She Says You Can't Read This Book. 2006. 176p. (gr. 4-7). 5.50 (978-0-553-48797-8(3) , Yearling) Random Hse. Children's Bks.

Hesse, Karen. Sable. 1998. (YA). (gr. 4 up). (978-0-606-13755-3(6)) Tandem Library Bks.

—Sable. Sewall, Marcia, illus. 1998. 81p. (J). (ps-k). lib. bdg. 16.40 (978-0-613-08689-9(9)) Tandem Library Bks.

Hesser, Terry Spencer. Kissing Doorknobs. 1999. (J). (978-0-606-17347-6(1)) Tandem Library Bks.

Hest, Amy. Mr. George Baker. Muth, Jon J., illus. 2004. 32p. (J). (gr. k-3). 16.99 (978-0-7636-1233-7(2)) Candlewick Pr.

—Mr. George Baker. Muth, Jon J., illus. 2007. 32p. (J). (gr. k-3). pap. 6.99 (978-0-7636-3308-0(9)) Candlewick Pr.

Hetherington, Sands. Night Buddies. 1999. (Illus.). 64p. (J). (gr. k-6). pap. 8.00 (978-0-8059-4754-0(X)) Dorrance Publishing Co., Inc.

Heuck, Sidgrid. Poni/Oso/Estrella. 2002. Tr. of Pony/Bear & Star. (SPA., Illus.). 32p. (J). 11.95 (978-84-261-2270-4(1)) Juventud, Editorial ESP. *Dist:* AIMS International Bks., Inc.

Heurtelou, Maude. Istwa Tipoul. Louissaint, Louis, illus. 1999. Tr. of Four Friends. (CRP.). 20p. (J). (gr. 3-5). pap. 19.00 incl. audio (978-1-881839-95-8(8)) Educa Vision.

—Twa Zanmi. Louissaint, Louis, illus. 1999. Tr. of Three Friends. (CRP.). 23p. (J). (gr. 3-5). pap. 19.00 incl. audio (978-1-881839-92-7(3)) Educa Vision.

Heusler, Marianna. Annabelle's Monsters. 2005. 190p. pap. 19.95 (978-1-4137-6451-2(7)) PublishAmerica, Inc.

Hickey, Caroline. Cassie Was Here. 2007. 192p. (J). (gr. 4-7). 16.95 (***978-1-59643-205-5(5)***) Roaring Brook Pr.

Hickey, Tony. Where's Jacko? Myler, Terry, illus. 2006. 64p. pap. 9.95 (978-1-901737-47-9(0)) Anvil Bks., Ltd. IRL. *Dist:* Dufour Editions, Inc.

Hickman, Janet. Susannah. 2001. (J). (978-0-606-20934-2(4)) Tandem Library Bks.

Hicks, Betty. Get Real. 2006. 192p. (J). 16.95 (978-1-59643-089-1(3)) Roaring Brook Pr.

Hicks, Betty. Goof-Off Goalie. McCauley, Adam, illus. 2008. (J). (***978-1-59643-244-4(6)***) Roaring Brook Pr.

Hicks, Clifford B. Alvin Fernald Foreign Trader. Schluenderfritz, Theodore, illus. 2007. (J). pap. 11.95 (***978-1-883937-74-4(4)***) Bethlehem Bks.

Hicks, Esther & Hicks, Jerry. Sara Bk. 2: Solomon's Fine Featherless Friends. 2007. (Illus.). 256p. pap. 14.95 (978-1-4019-1159-1(5)) Hay Hse., Inc.

—Sara, Book 1: The Foreverness of Friends of a Feather. 2007. (Illus.). 192p. pap. 14.95 (978-1-4019-1158-4(7)) Hay Hse., Inc.

Hicks, Robert Z. Tommie Turtle's Secret. Rolseth, Ruthie, illus. 2007. 40p. (J). 16.95 (***978-0-9792031-0-7(4)***) R.Z. Enterprises of Florida.

Hidier, Tanuja Desai. Born Confused. 2003. (gr. 7-12). lib. bdg. 16.45 (978-0-613-72235-3(3)) Tandem Library Bks.

Hidier, Tanuja Desai, et al. Born Confused. Hidier, Tanuja Desai, illus. 2002. 432p. (J). pap. 16.95 (978-0-439-35762-3(4) , Scholastic Pr.) Scholastic, Inc.

Higashi, Sandra & Higashi/Glaser Design Inc. Staff. Hello Kitty's Graduation Day. Hirashima, Jean, illus. 2004. 24p. (J). (ps-3). 12.95 (978-0-8109-4818-1(4)) Abrams, Harry N. , Inc.

Higashi/Glaser Design Inc. Staff. Hello Kitty, Hello Love! Red Heart Secret Drawer Locked Diary. 2005. 128p. 12.95 (978-0-8109-8807-1(0) , Abrams Gifts and Stationery) Abrams, Harry N. , Inc.

Higgins, Richard P. Basketballs & Babysteps. 2001. 192p. (YA). pap. 13.95 (978-0-595-20051-1(6) , Authors Choice Pr.) iUniverse, Inc.

Higginson, Hadley. Keeker & Pony Camp Catastrophe, Bk. 5. Parrett, Lisa, illus. 2007. 56p. (J). 15.50 (978-0-8118-5596-9(1)) Chronicle Bks. LLC.

—Keeker & the Pony Camp Catastrophe. Parrett, Lisa, illus. 2007. (Keeker & the Sneaky Pony Ser.: Bk. 5). 56p. (J). (gr. k-3). pap. 3.95 (978-0-8118-5597-6(X)) Chronicle Bks. LLC.

Higginson, Sheila Sweeny. 5+1 Makes More Fun. rev. ed. 2007. 10p. (J). (ps-1). 12.99 (***978-1-4231-0744-6(6)***) Disney Pr.

High, Linda Oatman. Sister Slam & the Poetic Motormouth Road Trip. 2006. 256p. (YA). reprint ed. pap. 7.95 (978-1-58234-896-4(0) , Bloomsbury Children) Bloomsbury Publishing.

—Sister Slam & the Poetic Motormouth Roadtrip. 2004. 250p. (J). 16.95 (978-1-58234-948-0(7) , Bloomsbury Children) Bloomsbury Publishing.

Higman, Anita. The Living Darkness: Texas Caves. 2nd ed. 2003. (Illus.). xiii, 93p. (J). (978-1-57168-783-8(1) , Eakin Pr.) Eakin Pr.

—Texas Twisters. 1999. (Illus.). 64p. 13.95 (978-1-57168-316-8(X)) Eakin Pr.

Hildick, E. W. The Purloined Corn Popper: A Felicity Snell Mystery. unabr. ed. 2000. (Illus.). (J). (gr. 4-7). 38.95 incl. audio (978-0-87499-558-9(2)) Live Oak Media.

Hileman, Linda L. Dawn's Secret. 2006. (J). per. 9.95 (978-1-59571-117-5(1)) Word Association Pubs.

Hill, Clarissa. God Deserves Your Best. Hill, Stephanie, illus. 2005. (ENG.). 20p. (J). pap. 11.00 (***978-0-9785539-0-6(X)***) Hill, Stephanie & Clarissa.

Hill, David. Running Hot. 2006. 116p. (Orig.). (gr. 5-8). pap. 9.95 (978-1-894965-52-1(3)) Simply Read Bks. CAN. *Dist:* Perseus Distribution.

Hill, Helen. A Friend Named You. 2004. (Illus.). 21p. (J). spiral bd. 14.95 (978-1-932373-59-2(4) , Cedar Hill Pr.) Cedar Hill Publishing.

Hill, Janet Muirhead. Starlight's Courage: Revised Edition. Lehmkuhl, Pat, illus. 2nd ed. 2007. 170p. (J). per. 9.00 (***978-0-9772525-4-1(X)***) Raven Publishing Inc. of Montana.

Hill, Liz. Raven's Blood No.5: Twin Spins. 2002. Tr. of Web of Death: Twin Spins #5. (gr. 7-12). lib. bdg. 22.20 (978-0-613-74641-0(4)) Tandem Library Bks.

E F G

Hill, Sandi. Best Friends, Vol. 4409. Kupperstein, Joel, ed. Jarrett, Michael, photos by. 1998. (Learn to Read Social Studies). (Illus.). 16p. (J). (ps-2). pap. 2.99 (978-1-57471-332-9(9), 4409) Creative Teaching Pr., Inc.

Hill, Susan. Ruby Bakes a Cake. Moore, Margie, illus. (I Can Read Bks.). 32p. (J). (gr. k-3). 2005. pap. 3.99 (978-0-06-008977-1(6), Harper Trophy); 2004. 15.99 (978-0-06-008975-7(X)); 2004. lib. bdg. 16.89 (978-0-06-008976-4(8)) HarperCollins Pubs.

—Ruby Bakes a Cake. Moore, Margie, illus. 2004. 32p. (J). lib. bdg. 13.85 ***978-1-4242-0476-2(3))** Fitzgerald Bks.

—Ruby Paints a Picture. Moore, Margie, illus. 2005. (I Can Read Bks.). 32p. (J). (ps-ps). 15.99 (978-0-06-008978-8(4)) HarperCollins Pubs.

—Ruby's Perfect Day. Moore, Margie, illus. 2006. (I Can Read Bks.). 32p. (J). 15.99 (978-0-06-008982-5(2)); lib. bdg. 16.89 (978-0-06-008983-2(0)) HarperCollins Pubs.

Hill, William. The Vampire Hunters. 286p. (YA). (gr. 7-12). 2004. 19.95 (978-1-890611-05-7(0)); 1999. pap. 12.95 (978-1-890611-02-6(6)) Otter Creek Pr., Inc.

Hillenbrand, Jane. What a Treasure! Hillenbrand, Will, illus. 24p. (J). (ps-1). 16.95 (978-0-8234-1896-1(0)); pap. 6.95 ***978-0-8234-2077-3(9))** Holiday Hse., Inc.

Hillert, Margaret. Four Good Friends: The Bremen Town Musicians Retold. Stasiak, Krystyna, illus. rev. exp. ed. 2007. (Beginning to Read Ser.). 32p. (J). lib. bdg. (978-1-59953-047-5(3)) Norwood Hse. Pr.

—Fun Days. 2002. (Illus.). (J). 15.00 (978-0-7587-9470-3(3)) Book Wholesalers, Inc.

Hills, Tad. Duck, Duck, Goose. 2007. (Illus.). 40p. (J). (ps-2). 15.99 (978-0-375-84068-5(0)); lib. bdg. 18.99 (978-0-375-94068-2(5)) Random Hse. Children's Bks. (Schwartz & Wade Bks.).

Hines, Anna Grossnickle. Pieces: A Year in Poems & Quilts. Hines, Anna Grossnickle, illus. 2003. (Illus.). 32p. (J). pap. 6.99 (978-0-06-055960-1(8)) HarperCollins Pubs.

—Pieces: A Year in Poems & Quilts. 2001. (gr. k-3). lib. bdg. 15.30 (978-0-613-68459-0(1)) Tandem Library Bks.

Hines-Stephens, Sarah & Mason, Jane. Princess School: Let Down Your Hair. 2004. (Princess School Ser.). 144p. (J). (gr. 4 up). 4.99 (978-0-439-62939-3(X), Scholastic Paperbacks) Scholastic, Inc.

Hinman, Bonnie. Earthquake in Cincinnati: Disaster Changes Life Forever, 1999. (American Adventure Ser.: No. 14). 144p. (J). (gr. 3-7). lib. bdg. 15.95 (978-0-7910-5589-2(2), Chelsea Hse.) Facts On File, Inc.

Hirsch, Katy. Making Friends with My Ostomy. Daudy, Steve, illus. 1999. 32p. (J). (gr. k-5). pap. 11.95 (978-0-9674418-0-1(3)) Hirsch & Assocs., Inc.

Hirsch, Odo. Hazel Green. (J). 2005. 190p. (gr. 3-6). pap. 5.95 (978-1-58234-940-4(1)); 2003. (Illus.). 188p. (gr. 2-6). 15.95 (978-1-58234-820-9(0)) Bloomsbury Publishing. (Bloomsbury Children).

—Hazel Green. 2004. 190p. (J). (gr. 3-7). lib. bdg. 13.60 (978-0-606-30296-8(4)) Tandem Library Bks.

Hitchcock, Coleen A. Bubbly Bubble. Yoh, Jason, illus. 2001. 16p. (J). 9.95 (978-1-929774-08-1(7)) Greenleaf Book Group Pr.

Hixson, Nancy E. Distorted Vision. 1999. 90p. (J). pap. 15.95 (978-0-936389-62-2(1)) Tudor Pubs., Inc.

Hoban, Lillian. Arthur's Pen Pal. Hoban, Lillian, illus. 2002. (Arthur the Chimpanzee Ser.). (Illus.). (J). 12.34 (978-0-7587-5989-4(4)) Book Wholesalers, Inc.

Hoban, Russell. A Bargain for Frances. Hoban, Lillian, illus. 1999. (I Can Read Bks.). 64p. (J). (ps-3). 12.95 (978-0-694-01295-4(5), Harper Festival) HarperCollins Pubs.

—El Gran Negocio de Francisca. Hoban, Lillian, illus. 2006. (I Can Read Bks.).Tr. of Bargain for Frances. (SPA.). 64p. (J). pap. 3.99 (978-0-06-088703-2(6)) HarperCollins Pubs.

Hobbie, Holly. Charming Opal. Hobbie, Holly, illus. 2003. (Toot & Puddle Ser.). (Illus.). 32p. (J). (ps-3). 16.99 (978-0-316-36633-5(1)) Little Brown & Co.

—Friendship Grows Like a Garden. 2006. (Holly Hobbie Classics). (Illus.). 40p. (J). 9.99 (978-1-4169-1779-3(9), Little Simon) Simon & Schuster Children's Publishing.

—Happiness Comes from the Heart. 2006. (Holly Hobbie Classic Ser.). (Illus.). 40p. (J). 9.99 (978-1-4169-1780-9(2), Little Simon) Simon & Schuster Children's Publishing.

—I'll Be Home for Christmas. Hobbie, Holly, illus. 2001. (Toot & Puddle Ser.: Bk. 5). (Illus.). 32p. (J). (ps-3). 15.95 (978-0-316-36623-6(4), Tingley, Megan Bks.) Little, Brown Bks. for Young Readers.

—Let It Snow. 2007. (Toot & Puddle (Hardcover) Ser.). (Illus.). 32p. (J). (ps-1). 16.99 ***978-0-316-16686-7(3))** Little, Brown Bks. for Young Readers.

—The New Friend. 2004. (Illus.). 32p. (J). (ps-3). 16.99 (978-0-316-36636-6(6), Tingley, Megan Bks.) Little, Brown Bks. for Young Readers.

—Toot & Puddle. 2006. (978-0-316-15654-7(X)) Little Brown & Co.

—Toot & Puddle. 2007. 32p. (J). (ps-3). 16.99 ***978-0-316-16702-4(9))** Little, Brown Bks. for Young Readers.

—Toot & Puddle, 3 vols., Box Set. Hobbie, Holly, illus. 2003. (Illus.). 32p. (J). (ps-1). 11.99 (978-0-316-14564-0(5)) Little, Brown Bks. for Young Readers.

—Wish You Were Here. 2005. (Toot & Puddle Ser.). (Illus.). 32p. (J). (ps-3). 16.99 (978-0-316-36602-1(1)) Little Brown & Co.

—You Are My Sunshine. Hobbie, Holly, illus. 3rd ed. 1999. (Toot & Puddle Ser.). (Illus.). 32p. (J). (ps-3). 16.99 (978-0-316-36562-8(9)) Little Brown & Co.

Hobbs, Valerie. Stefan's Story. 2003. 176p. (J). 16.00 (978-0-374-37240-8(3), Farrar, Straus & Giroux (BYR)) Farrar, Straus & Giroux.

Hobbs, Will. Crossing the Wire. 224p. (J). 2007. pap. 5.99 (978-0-06-074140-2(6), Harper Trophy); 2006. (Illus.). lib. bdg. 16.89 (978-0-06-074139-6(2)) HarperCollins Pubs.

—Crossing the Wire: Hobbs Mid Grade 1. 2006. (Illus.). 224p. (J). 15.99 (978-0-06-074138-9(4)) HarperCollins Pubs.

Hoberman, Mary Ann. And to Think That We Thought That We'd Never Be Friends. Hawkes, Kevin, illus. 2003. 32p. (J). (ps-3). pap. 6.99 (978-0-440-41776-7(7), Dragonfly Bks.) Random Hse. Children's Bks.

—One of Each. Priceman, Marjorie, illus. 2000. 32p. (J). (ps-3). pap. 7.99 (978-0-316-36644-1(7)) Little, Brown Bks. for Young Readers.

—One of Each. Priceman, Marjorie, illus. 2000. (J). (ps-ps). lib. bdg. 14.10 (978-0-613-30077-3(7)) Tandem Library Bks.

—One of Each. 2000. (978-0-606-22189-4(1)) Tandem Library Bks.

Hodgson, Mona Gansberg. I Wonder Who Hung the Moon in the Sky. 1999. (I Wonder Ser.). (Illus.). 32p. (J). (ps-2). 6.99 (978-0-570-05067-4(7)) Concordia Publishing Hse.

—Smelly Tales. Sharp, Chris, illus. 1998. (Desert Critter Friends Ser.: Vol. 4). 48p. (J). (ps-2). 4.99 (978-0-570-05071-1(5), 56-1895) Concordia Publishing Hse.

—Smelly Tales. 1998. (ps-2). lib. bdg. 13.00 (978-0-613-72807-2(6)) Tandem Library Bks.

Hoeffner, Karol Ann. All You've Got. 2005. 272p. (YA). pap. 5.99 (978-1-4169-1472-3(2), Simon Pulse) Simon & Schuster Children's Publishing.

Hoestlandt, Jo. Star of Fear, Star of Hope. 1998. Tr. of Grande Peur sous les Etoiles. (J). pap. 3.95 (978-0-439-04457-8(X)) Scholastic, Inc.

—Star of Fear, Star of Hope. 2000. Tr. of Grande Peur sous les Etoiles. (J). (978-0-606-20296-1(X)); (gr. 3-6). lib. bdg. 17.60 (978-0-613-29518-5(8)) Tandem Library Bks.

Hoeye, Michael. No Time Like Showtime. 2006. (Illus.). 288p. (YA). (gr. 7). pap. 7.99 (978-0-14-240563-5(9), Puffin) Penguin Group (USA) Inc.

Hoffman, Alice. Aquamarine. 2001. (gr. 5-8). lib. bdg. 13.00 (978-0-613-49420-5(2)) Tandem Library Bks.

—Indigo. 96p. (J). 2003. pap. 5.99 (978-0-439-25636-0(4), Scholastic Paperbacks); 2002. (Illus.). (gr. 5 up). pap. 16.95 (978-0-439-25635-3(6), Scholastic Pr.) Scholastic, Inc.

Hoffman, Mary. City of Stars. 2003. (Stravaganza Ser.: Vol. 2). (Illus.). 300p. (J). 17.95 (978-1-58234-839-1(1), Bloomsbury Children) Bloomsbury Publishing.

—Encore, Grace! Allan, June & Binch, Caroline, illus. 2003. 112p. (J). (gr. 2-6). 14.99 (978-0-8037-2951-3(0), Dial) Penguin Group (USA) Inc.

Hoffmann, Burton R. Millicent the Magnificent. du Houx, Emily C., illus. 2004. 64p. pap. 12.00 (978-1-882190-68-3(8)) Polar Bear & Co.

Hofmeister, Alan, et al. Ann & Nan. (Reading for All Learners Ser.). (Illus.). (J). pap. (978-1-56861-085-6(8)) Swift Learning Resources.

—Mit & the Weed. (Reading for All Learners Ser.). (Illus.). (J). pap. (978-1-56861-113-6(7)) Swift Learning Resources.

—Nell & Ed. (Reading for All Learners Ser.). (Illus.). (J). pap. (978-1-56861-097-9(1)) Swift Learning Resources.

—The Pond. (Reading for All Learners Ser.). (Illus.). (J). pap. (978-1-56861-131-0(5)) Swift Learning Resources.

Hol, Coby. Punch & His Friends. (Illus.). 24p. (J). 14.95 (978-0-86315-206-1(6), 1823) Floris Bks. GBR. *Dist:* Gryphon Hse., Inc., SteinerBooks, Inc.

Holabird, Katharine. Angelina & Alice. 2006. (Angelina Ballerina Ser.). 32p. (J). (ps). 12.99 (978-0-670-06125-9(5), Viking Juvenile) Penguin Group (USA) Inc.

—Angelina Ballerina. Craig, Helen, illus. 2006. (Angelina Ballerina Ser.). 32p. (J). (ps). 13.99 (978-0-670-06026-9(7), Viking Juvenile) Penguin Group (USA) Inc.

—A Very Special Secret: Angelina Young Readers. Craig, Helen, illus. 2006. (Angelina Ballerina Ser.: No. 3). 80p. (J). (gr. 1-3). 3.99 (978-0-448-44332-4(5), Grosset & Dunlap) Penguin Group (USA) Inc.

Holabird, Katharine & Mason, James. Dance of Friendship. Craig, Helen, illus. 2006. (Angelina Ballerina Ser.). 24p. (J). (ps-2). 3.99 (978-0-448-44115-3(2), Grosset & Dunlap) Penguin Group (USA) Inc.

Holder, Greg. Patches' Present: A Story about Friendship. 2000. (Threads Ser.). (Illus.). 32p. (J). (ps-1). bds. 8.99 (978-0-7847-1240-5(9), 04412, Bean Sprouts) Standard Publishing.

Holding, James Malcolm, 3rd, et al. The Mullet Masters. 2007. pap. 8.00 ***978-0-8059-7147-7(5))** Dorrance Publishing Co., Inc.

The Hole in the Hill: Individual Title Six-Packs. (Action Packs Ser.). 104p. (gr. 3-5). 44.00 (978-0-7635-2993-2(1)) Rigby Education.

Holeman, Linda. Mercy's Birds. 1998. (gr. 5-8). lib. bdg. 15.25 (978-0-613-77269-3(5)) Tandem Library Bks.

—Mercy's Birds. 1998. 208p. (J). (gr. 6-9). pap. 6.95 (978-0-88776-463-9(0)) Tundra Bks., Inc./Livres Toundra, Inc. CAN. *Dist:* Random Hse., Inc.

Hollaway, David. Ray Jay & the Grumpy Tree of East Side Park. 2006. (J). per. 17.95 (978-1-933211-03-9(2)) Quackenworth Publishing.

Holm, Jennifer L. & Holm, Matthew. Queen of the World! 2005. (Babymouse Ser.). (Illus.). 96p. (J). (gr. 2-5). pap. 5.95 (978-0-375-83229-1(7)); lib. bdg. 12.99 (978-0-375-93229-8(1)) Random Hse. Children's Bks. (Random Hse. Bks. for Young Readers).

Holmes, Barbara W. Letters to Julia. 1999. (Illus.). 320p. (YA). (gr. 7 up). pap. 5.95 (978-0-06-447215-9(9), Harper Trophy) HarperCollins Pubs.

Holmes, Elizabeth. Pretty Is. 2007. 224p. (J). (gr. 4-6). 16.99 (978-0-525-47813-3(2), Dutton Juvenile) Penguin Group (USA) Inc.

Holsather, Kent /Wilson. Sara's Moon. 2007. (Illus.). 176p. (YA). per. 12.95 ***978-0-9729101-3-2(1))** Lonejack Mountain Pr.

Holt, Kimberly Willis. Mister & Me. Jenkins, Leonard, illus. 2000. (Chapters Ser.). 80p. (J). (gr. 2-5). pap. 4.99 (978-0-698-11869-0(3), Putnam Juvenile) Penguin Group (USA) Inc.

—Mister & Me. 2000. (J). (gr. 2 up). pap., stu. ed. 39.99 incl. audio (978-0-7887-4341-2(4), 41135) Recorded Bks., LLC.

—My Louisiana Sky. rev. ed. 1998. 176p. (J). (gr. 4-7). 17.95 (978-0-8050-5251-0(8), Holt, Henry & Co. Bks. For Young Readers) Holt, Henry & Co.

—My Louisiana Sky. 208p. (YA). (gr. 5 up). 4.99 (978-0-8072-8291-5(X), Listening Library) Random Hse. Audio Publishing Group.

—My Louisiana Sky. 2000. 200p. (J). (gr. k-9). lib. bdg. 13.55 (978-0-613-22802-2(2)) Tandem Library Bks.

—Skinny Brown Dog. Saaf, Donald, illus. 2007. 40p. (J). (ps-2). 16.95 (978-0-8050-7587-8(9), Holt, Henry & Co. Bks. For Young Readers) Holt, Henry & Co.

—When Zachary Beaver Came to Town. rev. ed. 1999. 240p. (YA). (gr. 5-9). 17.95 (978-0-8050-6116-1(9), Holt, Henry & Co. Bks. For Young Readers) Holt, Henry & Co.

—When Zachary Beaver Came to Town. 2000. (J). tchr. ed. 9.95 (978-1-58130-674-3(1)); (YA). stu. ed. 11.95 (978-1-58130-675-0(X)) Novel Units, Inc.

—When Zachary Beaver Came to Town. unabr. ed. 2004. 227p. (J). (gr. 5-9). pap. 36.00 incl. audio (978-0-8072-8394-3(0), Listening Library) Random Hse. Audio Publishing Group.

—When Zachary Beaver Came to Town. (gr. 5 up). 2003. (Illus.). 256p. (YA). mass mkt. 6.50 (978-0-440-23841-6(2), Laurel Leaf); 2001. 240p. (J). pap. 6.50 (978-0-440-22904-9(9), Yearling) Random Hse. Children's Bks.

—When Zachary Beaver Came to Town. 2003. (gr. 5-8). lib. bdg. 14.15 (978-0-613-72251-3(5)); 2000. (J). (978-0-606-20113-1(0)); 2000. (J). (978-0-606-20114-8(9)) Tandem Library Bks.

—When Zachary Beaver Came to Town. l.t. ed. 2000. 224p. (YA). 22.95 (978-0-7862-2515-6(7)) Thorndike Pr.

Holub, Joan. Abby Cadabra, Super Speller. Holub, Joan, illus. 2000. (All Aboard Reading Ser.). (Illus.). 48p. (J). (gr. 1-3). pap. 3.99 (978-0-448-42168-1(2), Grosset & Dunlap) Penguin Group (USA) Inc.

—Abby Cadabra, Super Speller. 2000. (All Aboard Reading Ser.). (978-0-606-18849-4(5)); lib. bdg. 11.80 (978-0-613-24083-3(9)) Tandem Library Bks.

Holy Peace: The Story of Iz & Pal. 2003. 91p. (YA). per. 5.99 (978-0-9704361-3-9(0)) LWS Bks.

Honey, Elizabeth. The Ballad of Cauldron Bay. 2005. (Illus.). 312p. (YA). (gr. 7-17). pap. 7.95 (978-1-74114-255-6(5)) Allen & Unwin AUS. *Dist:* Independent Pubs. Group.

Honsinger, Laura. Mike's New Friends. 2005. 35p. (J). pap. 5.92 (978-1-4116-3070-3(X)) Lulu.com.

Hood, Susan. Lets Jump In! 1999. (ps-2). lib. bdg. 11.80 (978-0-613-25948-4(3)) Tandem Library Bks.

—The New Kid. Handelman, Dorothy, photos by. 1998. (Real Kids Readers Ser.). (Illus.). 32p. (ps-1). lib. bdg. 18.90 (978-0-7613-2014-2(8)); (J). pap. 4.99 (978-0-7613-2039-5(3)) Lerner Publishing Group. (Millbrook Pr.).

—Pup & Hound. Hendry, Linda, illus. 2004. 32p. (J). lib. bdg. 15.38 ***978-1-4242-1164-7(6))** Fitzgerald Bks.

Hood, Susan. Too-Tall Paul, Too-Small Paul. Handelman, Dorothy, photos by. 1998. (Real Kids Readers Ser.). (Illus.). 32p. (gr. k-2). lib. bdg. 18.90 (978-0-7613-2021-0(0)); (J). pap. 4.99 (978-0-7613-2046-3(6)) Lerner Publishing Group. (Millbrook Pr.).

Hoogstad, Alice. BOLDER & BOAT. 2008. 32p. 13.95 ***978-1-60136-015-1(0))** Mars Media Pubs.

Hooks, Gwendolyn. Three's a Crowd. Walker, Sylvia, illus. 2004. 32p. (J). lib. bdg. 15.00 ***978-1-4242-0240-9(X))** Fitzgerald Bks.

Hoover, T. A. The Last Eagle. Kaths, Kathy, illus. 2004. 38p. (J). 16.00 (978-0-9702216-3-6(0)) Sport Story Publishing.

Hope. Punctuation Pals. Anders, Tim, ed. Pinson, Richard, illus. 2000. (Life Lessons Ser.). 38p. (J). (gr. k-4). 16.95 (978-1-885624-56-7(5)) Alpine Publishing.

Hopkins, Cathy. Discount Diva. 2007. (Zodiac Girls Ser.). 184p. (J). (gr. 4-7). pap. 5.95 ***978-0-7534-6131-0(5)**, Kingfisher) Houghton Mifflin Co. Trade & Reference Div.

—Double Dare. 2005. (Truth or Dare Ser.: No. 5). 240p. (YA). (gr. 7 up). mass mkt. 5.99 (978-1-4169-0653-7(3), Simon Pulse) Simon & Schuster Children's Publishing.

—From Geek to Goddess. 2007. (Zodiac Girls Ser.). 200p. (J). (gr. 4-6). pap. 5.95 (978-0-7534-5895-2(0), Kingfisher) Houghton Mifflin Co. Trade & Reference Div.

—Love Lottery. 2006. (Truth or Dare Ser.: No. 7). 240p. (J). (gr. 7 up). mass mkt. 5.99 (978-1-4169-2721-1(2), Simon Pulse) Simon & Schuster Children's Publishing.

—Mates, Dates & Sleepover Secrets. 2003. (Mates, Dates Ser.). 208p. (YA). mass mkt. 5.99 (978-0-689-85991-5(0), Simon Pulse) Simon & Schuster Children's Publishing.

—Mates, Dates & Sleepover Secrets. 2003. (gr. 7-12). lib. bdg. 13.00 (978-0-613-73417-2(3)) Tandem Library Bks.

—Midsummer Meltdown. 2006. (Truth or Dare Ser.: No. 6). (Illus.). 224p. (YA). (gr. 7 up). mass mkt. 5.99 (978-1-4169-0654-4(1), Simon Pulse) Simon & Schuster Children's Publishing.

—Recipe for Rebellion: Big Mouth. 2007. (Zodiac Girls Ser.). 192p. (J). (gr. 4-6). pap. 5.95 (978-0-7534-5896-9(9), Kingfisher) Houghton Mifflin Co. Trade & Reference Div.

—Starstruck. 2005. (Truth or Dare Ser.). 208p. (YA). (gr. 7 up). pap. 5.99 (978-0-689-87130-6(9), Simon Pulse) Simon & Schuster Children's Publishing.

Hopper, Celia. The Merry Adventures of Blade & Friends. 2006. (J). lib. bdg. 26.95 (978-0-9779662-8-8(3)) Creative Bk. Pubs.

Horowitz, Jeanine. Latch Key Kid. 2006. 75p. (YA). lib. bdg. 12.99 ***978-1-934190-10-4(1))** Ocean Front Bk. Publishing, Inc.

Horton, Ed J. Buzzy Ghent Mysteries: The Attic's Hidden Secret. 2005. 124p. (J). pap. 12.99 (978-1-4141-0516-1(9)) Pleasant Word.

Hostetter, Joyce Moyer. Blue. 200p. (J). 16.95 (978-1-59078-389-4(1), Calkins Creek) Boyds Mills Pr.

Houghton Mifflin Company Staff. Curious George Finds a Friend. 2007. (Illus.). 16p. (J). (ps-k). 5.99 ***978-0-618-72398-0(6))** Houghton Mifflin Co. Trade & Reference Div.

Houser, Marlin L. The Adventures of Little Fox, Book Four, Escape. 2008. (Adventures of Little Fox Ser.). (J). 16.95 ***978-0-9752703-8-7(9));** pap. 7.95 ***978-0-9752703-9-4(7))** Marhouse, Inc.

—The Adventures of Little Fox, Book Three, Unfamiliar Territory. 2007. (Adventures of Little Fox Ser.). (J). 16.95 ***978-0-9752703-6-3(2));** pap. 7.95 ***978-0-9752703-7-0(0))** Marhouse, Inc.

Howard, Jo Ann. The Little Boy Who Made a Difference. 2001. 41p. per. 8.95 (978-0-7414-0575-3(X)) Infinity Publishing.

Howard, Reginald. The Big, Big Wall. Aruego, Jose & Dewey, Ariane, illus. 2003. (Green Light Readers Level 1 Ser.). 24p. (J). 11.95 (978-0-15-204813-6(8)); pap. 3.95 (978-0-15-204853-2(7)) Harcourt Children's Bks. (Green Light Readers).

—Big, Big Wall. 2001. (gr. k-3). lib. bdg. 11.80 (978-0-613-66350-2(0)) Tandem Library Bks.

Howe, James. Horace & Morris but Mostly Delores. Walrod, Amy, illus. 2002. (J). 25.11 (978-0-7587-2749-7(6)) Book Wholesalers, Inc.

—Horace & Morris but Mostly Delores. Walrod, Amy, illus. 1999. 32p. (J). (ps-3). 16.00 (978-0-689-31874-0(X), Atheneum) Simon & Schuster Children's Publishing.

—Horace & Morris, but Mostly Dolores. 1999. (gr. k-3). lib. bdg. 15.30 (978-0-613-61776-5(2)) Tandem Library Bks.

—Horace & Morris, but Mostly Dolores. Waldrod, Amy, illus. 2003. 28.95 incl. audio compact disk (978-1-59112-342-2(9)); pap. 39.95 incl. audio compact disk (978-1-59112-538-9(3)); (J). pap. 18.95 incl. audio compact disk (978-1-59112-341-5(0)); 25.95 incl. audio (978-1-59112-242-5(2)); pap. 37.95 incl. audio (978-1-59112-243-2(0)) Live Oak Media.

—Horace & Morris Join the Chorus (but what about Dolores?) Walrod, Amy, illus. 2005. 32p. (J). 6.99 (978-1-4169-0616-2(9), Aladdin) Simon & Schuster Children's Publishing.

—Houndsley & Catina. Gay, Marie-Louise, illus. 2006. 48p. (J). (gr. k-2). 14.99 (978-0-7636-2404-0(7)) Candlewick Pr.

—Houndsley & Catina. Gay, Marie-Louise, illus. 2007. (Candlewick Sparks Ser.). 48p. (J). (gr. k-2). pap. 4.99 (978-0-7636-3293-9(7)) Candlewick Pr.

—Houndsley & Catina & the Birthday Surprise. Gay, Marie-Louise, illus. 2006. 48p. (J). (gr. k-3). 14.99 (978-0-7636-2405-7(5)) Candlewick Pr.

—Houndsley & Catina & the Birthday Surprise. Gay, Marie-Louise, illus. 2007. 48p. (J). (gr. k-3). pap. 4.99 ***978-0-7636-3640-1(1))** Candlewick Pr.

—The Misfits. 2002. lib. bdg. 24.00 incl. audio (978-1-932076-12-7(3), 02010A) Full Cast Audio.

—The Misfits. 2003. 288p. (YA). mass mkt. 5.99 (978-0-689-83956-6(1), Aladdin) Simon & Schuster Children's Publishing.

—The Misfits. Slota, Gerald, illus. 2001. 288p. (gr. 5-9). 16.95 (978-0-689-83955-9(3), Atheneum) Simon & Schuster Children's Publishing.

—The Misfits. l.t. ed. 2004. 193p. 22.95 (978-0-7862-6666-1(X), Large Print Pr.) Thorndike Pr.

—Pinky & Rex. Sweet, Melissa, illus. 1998. (Pinky & Rex Ser.). 48p. (J). (gr. 1-4). pap. 3.99 (978-0-689-82348-0(7), Aladdin) Simon & Schuster Children's Publishing.

—Pinky & Rex & the Bully. 2006. (J). (gr. 1-4). 24.21 (978-1-59961-074-0(4)) Spotlight.

—Pinky & Rex & the New Baby. Sweet, Melissa, illus. 1999. (Pinky & Rex Ser.). (J). (gr. 1-4). (978-0-606-15941-8(X)) Tandem Library Bks.

—Pinky & Rex & the New Baby. 1999. (gr. k-3). lib. bdg. 11.80 (978-0-7857-3870-1(3)) Tandem Library Bks.

—Pinky & Rex & the New Baby. 2006. (J). (gr. 1-4). 24.21 (978-1-59961-076-4(0)) Spotlight.

—Pinky & Rex & the School Play. Sweet, Melissa, illus. 1998. (Pinky & Rex Ser.). 48p. (J). (gr. 1-4). pap. 3.99 (978-0-689-81704-5(5), Aladdin) Simon & Schuster Children's Publishing.

—Pinky & Rex & the School Play. 2006. (J). (gr. 1-4). 24.21 (978-1-59961-078-8(7)) Spotlight.

—Pinky & Rex & the Spelling Bee. 1999. (gr. k-3). lib. bdg. 11.80 (978-0-613-22921-0(5)) Tandem Library Bks.

—Pinky & Rex & the Spelling Bee. 2006. (J). (gr. 1-4). 24.21 (978-1-59961-079-5(5)) Spotlight.

—Pinky & Rex Get Married. 1999. (Pinky & Rex Ser.). (J). (gr. 1-4). (978-0-606-16307-1(7)) Tandem Library Bks.

—Pinky & Rex Go to Camp. 1999. (gr. k-3). lib. bdg. 11.80 (978-0-7857-0627-4(5)); (J). (gr. 1-4). (978-0-606-16306-4(9)) Tandem Library Bks.

E F G

—Totally Joe. 2005. (Illus.). 208p. (J). (gr. 5-9). 16.99 (978-0-689-83957-3(X) , Atheneum) Simon & Schuster Children's Publishing.

—Totally Joe. 2007. 208p. (J). (gr. 4-8). pap. 5.99 (***978-0-689-83958-0(8)***) Kaplan Bks.

Howe, James. The Watcher. 2001. 192p. (YA). (gr. 8-12). pap. 5.99 (978-0-689-83533-9(7) , Simon Pulse) Simon & Schuster Children's Publishing.

Howe, James & Sweet, Melissa. Pinky & Rex & the New Baby. 1999. (Pinky & Rex Ser.). (Illus.). 48p. (J). (gr. 1-4). pap. 3.99 (978-0-689-82548-4(X) , Aladdin) Simon & Schuster Children's Publishing.

—Pinky & Rex Go to Camp. 1999. (Pinky & Rex Ser.). (Illus.). 48p. (J). (gr. 1-4). pap. 3.99 (978-0-689-82588-0(9) , 076714003996, Aladdin) Simon & Schuster Children's Publishing.

Howell, Simmone. Notes from the Teenage Underground. 2007. (Illus.). 250p. (YA). (gr. 9 up). 16.95 (978-1-58234-835-3(9) , Bloomsbury Children) Bloomsbury Publishing.

Howell, Trisha Adelena. The Adventures of Melon & Turnip. Lopez, Paul, illus. 2004. 32p. 15.95 (978-1-931210-04-1(7)) Howell Canyon Pr.

—Talia & the Great Sapphire of Knowledge. Hohn, David, illus. 2005. 128p. (J). pap. 11.95 (978-1-931210-11-9(X)) Howell Canyon Pr.

Hubbard, Cynthia H. D. J. & Me. 2004. 48p. pap. 12.95 (978-1-4137-2539-1(2)) PublishAmerica, Inc.

Huber, Penelope. Three's a Crowd. 1999. 118p. pap. 13.00 (978-1-877135-26-2(7)) Longacre Pr. NZL. *Dist:* Pacific Island Bks.

Hubler, Marsha. Teamwork at Camp Tioga. 2005. (Keystone Stables Ser.). (Illus.). 128p. (J). pap. 4.99 (978-0-310-70575-8(4)) Zonderkidz.

—Trouble Times Two. 2005. (Keystone Stables Ser.). (Illus.). 128p. (J). pap. 4.99 (978-0-310-70574-1(6)) Zondervan.

—A True Test for Skye. 2004. (Keystone Stables Ser.). (Illus.). 144p. (J). pap. 4.99 (978-0-310-70573-4(8)) Zonderkidz.

Hudson, Iris. Ask Mia. Sims, Blanche, illus. 2006. (Math Matters Ser.). 32p. (J). (gr. k-3). pap. 4.95 (978-1-57565-188-0(2)) Kane Pr., The.

Huelin, Jodi. A Pony's Tale. Edwards, Ken, illus. 2003. (My Little Pony Ser.). 24p. (J). (ps-1). pap. 3.99 (978-0-06-054948-0(3)) HarperCollins Pubs.

Hughes, Dean. Team Player. 1999. (Scrappers Ser.: No. 3). (J). (gr. 3-7). (978-0-606-16290-6(9)) Tandem Library Bks.

Hughes, Frieda. Rent a Friend Colour Storybook. Riddell, Chris, illus. 48p. (J). pap. 9.99 (978-0-340-86580-4(6) , Hodder & Stoughton) Hodder General Publishing Division GBR. *Dist:* Trafalgar Square Publishing.

Hughes, Mair Wynn & Ward, Jonathan. Ffrindiau Pennaf. 2005. (WEL., Illus.). 13p. pap. (978-0-86243-456-4(4)) Y Lolfa.

Hughes, Monica. Jan on the Trail. Freire, Carlos, illus. 2000. (New First Novels Ser.). 61p. (gr. 1-5). 4.95 (978-0-88780-502-8(7)); (J). (978-0-88780-503-5(5)) Formac Publishing Co., Ltd. CAN. *Dist:* Casemate Pubs. & Bk. Distributors, LLC.

Hughes, Shirley. Alfie's World. 2007. (Illus.). 48p. (J). 19.95 (***978-0-370-32894-2(9)***) Transworld Publishers Ltd. GBR. *Dist:* Independent Pubs. Group.

—All about Alfie. 1998. (Illus.). 128p. (J). (ps-5). pap. 14.98 (978-1-58048-042-0(X)) Sandvik Publishing.

Hughes, Shirley. Dogger. 2007. (Illus.). 32p. (J). pap. 8.95 (***978-0-09-992790-7(X)*** , Red Fox) Random Hse. Children's Bks. GBR. *Dist:* Independent Pubs. Group.

Hughes, Susan. Earth to Audrey. Poulin, Stephane, illus. 2005. 32p. (J). (gr. k-3). (978-1-55337-843-3(1)) Kids Can Pr., Ltd.

Humphreys, C. C. The Fetch. 2006. (Runestone Saga Ser.: No. 1). (Illus.). 368p. (YA). (gr. 7). 15.95 (978-0-375-83292-5(0)); lib. bdg. 17.99 (978-0-375-93292-2(5)) Random Hse. Children's Bks. (Knopf Bks. for Young Readers).

Hunt, Helen, narrated by. Chicken Little. unabr. ed. 1998. (J). (ps-4). 24.95 incl. audio (978-0-7882-0673-3(7) , HRA372) Weston Woods Studios, Inc.

Hunter, Dawn. Heads Up! 2001. (gr. 5-8). lib. bdg. 13.55 (978-0-613-78315-6(8)) Tandem Library Bks.

Hunter, Dawn & Hunter, Karen. Heads Up! 2001. (Sports Stories Ser.). 85p. (gr. 3-8). (J). (***978-1-55028-719-6(2)***); 7.95 (978-1-55028-718-9(4)) Lorimer, James & Co., Ltd., Pubs. CAN. *Dist:* Casemate Pubs. & Bk. Distributors, LLC.

Hupp, Sarah M. The Gatorboat Goof-Up. Adnet, Bernard, illus. 2003. 24p. (J). 9.99 (978-0-310-70566-6(5)) Zonderkidz.

Hurst, Carol Otis. Torchlight. 2006. 160p. (J). (gr. 4-6). 16.00 (978-0-618-27601-1(7)) Houghton Mifflin Co.

Hurwin, Davida Lewis. The Farther You Run. 2005. 224p. (YA). (gr. 7). pap. 6.99 (978-0-14-240294-8(X) , Puffin) Penguin Group (USA) Inc.

Hurwin, Davida Wills. The Farther You Run. 2005. 217p. (YA). (gr. 9-12). per. 14.04 (978-0-606-33126-5(3)) Tandem Library Bks.

Hurwitz, Johanna. Even Stephen. 1998. (Illus.). 128p. (YA). (gr. 5-9). reprint ed. pap. 4.95 (978-0-688-16362-4(9)) HarperCollins Pubs.

—Russell Rides Again. 1999. (Beech Tree Chapter Bks.). (Illus.). (J). (978-0-606-21760-6(6)) Tandem Library Bks.

—Spring Break. 1999. (Illus.). 144p. (J). (gr. 2-7). mass mkt. 4.95 (978-0-688-16672-4(5)) HarperCollins Pubs.

Hutchins, Hazel. Robyn's Party-in-the-Park. Cathcart, Yvonne, illus. 2005. (First Novel Ser.). 64p. (J). (gr. 2-5). (***978-0-88780-663-6(5)***); 4.95 (978-0-88780-662-9(7)) Formac Publishing Co., Ltd. CAN. *Dist:* Casemate Pubs. & Bk. Distributors, LLC.

Hutchins, Hazel J. Robyn Looks for Bears. Cathcart, Yvonne, illus. 2000. (New First Novels Ser.: Vol. 16). 58p. (gr. 1-5). (J). (978-0-88780-497-7(7)); 4.95 (978-0-88780-496-0(9)) Formac Publishing Co., Ltd. CAN. *Dist:* Casemate Pubs. & Bk. Distributors, LLC.

Hutchison, Gary. The Ambassador & the Touchperson. 2nd ed. 2005. (Little People of the Ozark Mountains Ser.: 3). pap. 10.99 (***978-1-885631-95-4(2)***) Hutchison, G.F. Pr.

—Man of the Clan. 2nd ed. 2005. (Little People of the Ozark Mountains Ser.: 3). pap. 10.99 (***978-1-885631-97-8(9)***) Hutchison, G.F. Pr.

—Ring of the Farjumpers. 2nd ed. 2005. (Little People of the Ozark Mountains Ser.: 1). pap. 10.99 (***978-1-885631-94-7(4)***) Hutchison, G.F. Pr.

—Twiggs & Cinnamon. 2nd ed. 2005. (Little People of the Ozark Mountains Ser.: 2). pap. 10.95 (***978-1-885631-96-1(0)***) Hutchison, G.F. Pr.

Hyde, Dayton O. Mr. Beans. 2003. (Illus.). 160p. (YA). (gr. 4-6). 14.95 (978-1-56397-866-1(0)) Boyds Mills Pr.

Hyperion, ed. An Unexpected Return - #8: W. I. T. C. H. Graphic Novel. 8th rev. ed. 2007. 128p. (gr. 3-7). pap. 4.99 (***978-1-4231-0903-7(1)***) Hyperion Pr.

Hyperion Staff. The Other Truth. 19th rev. ed. 2006. (W. I. T. C. H. Ser.: Bk. 19). 144p. (gr. 3-7). pap. 4.99 (978-0-7868-5280-2(1)) Hyperion Pr.

Hyppolite, Joanne. Seth & Samona. 2001. lib. bdg. 21.10 (978-0-613-82989-2(1)) Tandem Library Bks.

Ibarra, Maria Teresa Ornelas. Penny & Me. 2006. (J). (***978-0-9774306-6-6(9)***) Acacia Publishing, Inc.

Ibbotson, Eva. Not Just a Witch. Hawkes, Kevin, illus. 2004. 192p. (gr. 3). pap. 5.99 (978-0-14-240232-0(X) , Puffin) Penguin Group (USA) Inc.

Ichikawa, Satomi. En Busca de Tesoros. (SPA., Illus.). 40p. (J). (gr. k-2). (978-84-95150-33-2(6) , COR0428) Corimbo, Editorial S.L. ESP. *Dist:* Lectorum Pubns., Inc.

If I Play the Tubalatrumlute, Will You Still Be My Friend? 2008. (J). 16.99 (***978-1-60336-482-9(X)***) Mainstream Connections, Inc.

Inches, Alison. Hooray for Polka Dots! Chernichaw, Ian, illus. ed. 2005. 22p. (J). lib. bdg. 15.00 (978-1-59054-972-8(4)) Fitzgerald Bks.

—My Visit with Periwinkle. Levy, David B., illus. 2003. (Ready-to-Read Ser.). 24p. (J). pap. 3.99 (978-0-689-85230-5(4) , Simon Spotlight/Nickelodeon) Simon & Schuster Children's Publishing.

—My Visit with Periwinkle. 2003. (gr. k-3). lib. bdg. 11.80 (978-0-613-58161-5(X)) Tandem Library Bks.

—A Surprise for Wendy. Dubreuil, Diane, illus. 2002. (Bob the Builder Ready-to-Read Ser.: Vol. 4). 24p. (J). pap. 3.99 (978-0-689-84754-7(8) , Simon Spotlight) Simon & Schuster Children's Publishing.

—Wendy Helps Out. 2001. (978-0-606-22131-3(X)); lib. bdg. 11.80 (978-0-613-51329-6(0)) Tandem Library Bks.

Ingram-Jackson, Mandi. My Name Is Guenavere, & I Talk Through My Eyes. 2007. 28p. (J). per. 12.99 (***978-1-59886-749-7(0)***) Tate Publishing & Enterprises, L.L.C.

Innes, Grant. The Flight of the Whirligigs. Innes, Grant, illus. 1999. (Illus.). 24p. (J). (ps-k). lib. bdg. 17.95 (978-1-55037-587-9(3)) Annick Pr., Ltd. CAN. *Dist:* Firefly Bks., Ltd.

Inui, Sekihiko, illus. & creator. Comic Party, Vol. 5. Inui, Sekihiko, creator. 5th rev. ed. 2006. 248p. pap. 9.99 (978-1-59816-272-1(1) , Tokyopop Adult) TOKYOPOP, Inc.

Ioannides, Mara W. Cohen. A Shout in the Sunshine. 2007. 120p. (J). pap. 12.95 (***978-0-8276-0838-2(1)***) Jewish Pubn. Society.

Ira Sleeps Over. 2005. (J). (978-1-59564-973-7(5)) Steps To Literacy, LLC.

Irwin, Esther. Jesse & His New Friends. Puett, Gayle, ed. Vroman, Dave, illus. 2006. (J). spiral bd. 10.00 (***978-0-9778462-1-4(0)***) Irwin, Esther L.

Irwin, Inez Haynes. Maida's Little House. 2004. reprint ed. pap. 27.95 (978-1-4179-4236-7(3)) Kessinger Publishing, LLC.

Isbrecht, Lucky. Rooster's Rescue. 2004. (Illus.). 23p. (J). (ps-7). per. 4.95 (978-1-59453-262-7(1) , 2690) Airleaf Publishing & Bookselling.

Ismail, Suzy. The BFF Sisters: Jennah's New Friends. 2001. 64p. (J). (978-1-59008-005-4(X)) amana pubns.

Istvan. Federica Aburrida. 2004. (SPA.). 32p. (J). 6.50 (978-84-348-7817-4(8)) SM Ediciones ESP. *Dist:* Lectorum Pubns., Inc.

Iversen, Jeremy. 21. 2005. 272p. (YA). pap. 6.99 (978-0-689-87623-3(8) , Simon Pulse) Simon & Schuster Children's Publishing.

Jackson, Barry. Danny Diamondback. 2008. 40p. (J). 17.89 (***978-0-06-113185-1(7)***); 16.99 (***978-0-06-113184-4(9)***) HarperCollins Pubs.

Jackson, Bobby L. Roberto, Berto y el Huerto. Garcia, Jose & Garcia, Diana, trs. Schmidt, Gabriela, illus. l.t. ed. 2001. Orig. Title: Pops, Chops & Crops. (ENG & SPA.). 32p. (YA). (gr. k up). pap. 10.95 (978-1-884242-71-7(5)) Multicultural Pubns.

—Roberto, Berto y el Huerto: First Translated Edition. Garcia, Jose & Garcia, Diana, trs. Schmidt, Gabriela, illus. l.t. ed. 2001. Orig. Title: Pops, Chops & Crops. (ENG & SPA.). 32p. (YA). (gr. k up). lib. bdg. 19.95 (978-1-884242-75-5(8)) Multicultural Pubns.

Jackson, Christine. Amico. 2003. 120p. pap. 14.95 (978-1-59286-794-3(4)) PublishAmerica, Inc.

Jackson, Kamichi. You're Too Much, Reggie Brown. Goldberg, Jeff A., illus. l.t. ed. 2000. 110p. (J). (gr. 2-5). pap. 5.95 (978-0-615-11287-9(0)) Pen Poised Pr.

Jackson, Linda. The Lie That Binds: How Far Would You Go to Protect a Friend? 2002. 144p. (YA). (gr. 5 up). pap. 6.99 (978-0-9716442-0-5(9)) Jackson Publishing.

Jackson, William. The First Step. Spruill, Shawn, ed. Volcan, Trinidad, illus. 1999. 190p. (YA). (gr. 9 up). pap. 10.00 (978-0-9652528-7-4(6)) Neshui Publishing, Inc.

Jacobson, Jack. No Ordinary Boy. 2003. 188p. (YA). pap. 13.95 (978-1-58736-165-4(5) , Starbound Bks.) Wheatmark.

Jacobson, Jennifer. Winnie (Dancing) on Her Own. Geis, Alissa Imre, illus. 2003. 112p. (J). (gr. 3-5). pap. 5.95 (978-0-618-36921-8(X)) Houghton Mifflin Co. Trade & Reference Div.

Jacobson, Jennifer Richard. Truly Winnie. Geis, Alissa Imre, illus. 2006. 112p. (J). (gr. 3-5). pap. 5.95 (978-0-618-68954-5(0)) Houghton Mifflin Co.

—Truly Winnie. Geis, Alissa Imre, illus. 2003. 112p. (J). (gr. 3-5). tchr. ed. 15.00 (978-0-618-28008-7(1)) Houghton Mifflin Co. Trade & Reference Div.

—Winnie at Her Best. Geis, Alissa Imre, illus. 2006. 96p. (J). (gr. 3-5). 15.00 (978-0-618-47277-2(0)) Houghton Mifflin Co.

—Winnie Dancing on Her Own. 2003. (gr. 3-6). lib. bdg. 14.10 (978-0-613-90720-0(5)) Tandem Library Bks.

Jacques, Taryn Elise. What's Wrong with the New Girl? Reilly, Meghan M., illus. 2004. 33p. pap. 17.95 (978-1-4137-1999-4(6)) PublishAmerica, Inc.

Jaffrey, Saeed. The Four Friends - The Musical Donkey. 1998. (Karadi Tales Ser.). (Illus.). 24p. (YA). (gr. 1 up). 15.99 incl. audio (978-81-86838-08-2(2)) APG Sales and Fulfillment.

Jaggi, Harleen. Mystery at the Book Store. 2007. (J). per. (***978-0-9790896-0-2(3)***) Booksmart Pubns.

Jahn-Clough, Lisa. Alicia's Best Friends. 2003. (Illus.). 32p. (J). (gr. k-3). tchr. ed. 15.00 (978-0-618-23951-1(0) , Walter Lorraine) Houghton Mifflin Co. Trade & Reference Div.

—Missing Molly. 2005. (Illus.). 32p. (J). (gr. k-3). reprint ed. pap. 5.95 (978-0-618-55562-8(5) , Walter Lorraine) Houghton Mifflin Co. Trade & Reference Div.

—My Friend & I. 2003. (Illus.). 32p. (J). (gr. k-3). 5.95 (978-0-618-39108-0(8) , Walter Lorraine) Houghton Mifflin Co. Trade & Reference Div.

—My Friend & I. Jahn-Clough, Lisa, illus. 1999. (Illus.). 32p. (J). (gr. k-3). tchr. ed. 15.00 (978-0-395-93545-3(8) , Walter Lorraine) Houghton Mifflin Co. Trade & Reference Div.

—Simon & Molly Plus Hester. 2001. (Illus.). 32p. (J). (gr. k-3). tchr. ed. 15.00 (978-0-618-08220-9(4) , Walter Lorraine) Houghton Mifflin Co. Trade & Reference Div.

Jam, Teddy. Ttum. Chan, Harvey, illus. 1999. (Charlotte Stories). (J). (gr. 2-4). 14.95 (978-0-88899-373-1(0) , Libros Tigrillo) Groundwood Bks. CAN. *Dist:* Transition Vendor.

James, Andrea. Adventures at Ja-Mar Farms: Pup-Pup, Padluck & PIG Take a Walk in the Wet Woods. 2005. 47p. pap. 19.95 (978-1-4137-3437-9(5)) PublishAmerica, Inc.

James, Brian. Everybody Hates Best Friends. 2007. (Everybody Hates Chris Ser.). 96p. (J). (gr. 2-5). pap. 5.99 (***978-1-4169-3796-8(X)*** , Simon Spotlight) Simon & Schuster Children's Publishing.

—The Fishy Field Trip. Woodman, Ned, illus. 2007. (Catkid Ser.: Bk. 2). 96p. (J). pap. 3.99 (***978-0-439-88855-4(7)***) Scholastic, Inc.

—Pure Sunshine. 2002. (Push Ser.). (Illus.). 176p. (J). (gr. 8 up). pap. 6.99 (978-0-439-27989-5(5) , PUSH) Scholastic, Inc.

—Pure Sunshine. 2002. lib. bdg. 15.30 (978-0-613-66729-6(8)) Tandem Library Bks.

—The Shark Who Was Afraid of Everything. 2006. (Illus.). 32p. (J). pap. 5.99 (978-0-439-78672-0(X) , Cartwheel Bks.) Scholastic, Inc.

—The Shark Who Was Afraid of Everything. McNally, Bruce J., illus. 2002. (J). (978-0-439-36865-0(0)) Scholastic, Inc.

James, Catherine. Bobby Cottontail's Gift. Collier, Kevin Scott, illus. 2006. 32p. (J). E-Book 9.95 incl. cd-rom (978-1-933090-24-5(3)) Guardian Angel Publishing, Inc.

James, Gill. Nick's Gallery. 2004. 149p. pap. 19.95 (978-1-4137-2186-7(9)) PublishAmerica, Inc.

James, Leah. Just a Summer Thing. 2002. 158p. (YA). pap. 11.95 (978-0-595-21751-9(6) , Writer's Showcase Pr.) iUniverse, Inc.

Jan Baer: And the Mystery of the Silent Circus. 2005. (J). per. 10.00 (978-1-930052-29-1(4)) Cherokee Bks.

Jane, Pamela. Noelle of the Nutcracker. Brett, Jan, illus. 2003. 64p. (J). (gr. 4-6). pap. 5.95 (978-0-618-36922-5(8)) Houghton Mifflin Co. Trade & Reference Div.

Janover, Caroline D. The Worst Speller in Jr. High. 2001. 208p. (YA). (gr. 4-7). pap. 13.95 (978-0-595-15328-2(3) , Backinprint.com) iUniverse, Inc.

Jarman, Julia. Flying Friends. Parker-Rees, Guy, illus. 2002. 48p. (J). (978-0-439-47138-1(9)) Scholastic, Inc.

—Time Travelling Cat, the & the Roman. l.t. ed. 2006. pap. 16.95 (978-1-4056-6069-3(4)) BBC Audio GBR. *Dist:* BBC Audiobooks America.

Jarrell, Pamela R. Caillou's Family & Friends. Meier, Kerry L., illus. l.t. ed. 2005. (Hrl Board Book Ser.). (J). (gr. k up). pap. 10.95 (978-1-57332-327-7(6)) HighReach Learning, Inc.

Jarrett, Clare. Dancing Maddy. (Illus.). 26p. (J). pap. (978-0-00-664670-9(0)) HarperCollins Canada, Ltd.

Jarvis, James. Vortigern¿s Machine & the Great Sage of Wisdom. 2006. (Illus.). 48p. pap. 24.00 (978-3-89955-098-6(6)) Die Gestalten Verlag DEU. *Dist:* Prestel Publishing.

Jason. Jason & Edeia. pap. 6.95 (978-0-394-74096-6(3)) Random Hse., Inc.

Jax, T. L. Fraidy-Frieda's Light Show. Jax, T. L., illus. l.t. ed. 2004. (Illus.). 30p. (J). 9.95 (978-0-9743890-2-8(1)) Flaxenfluff Pr., LLC.

Jeans, Peter D. Bodger. 2002. (Illus.). 279p. (YA). pap. 13.50 (978-1-876268-65-7(4)) Univ. of Western Australia Pr. AUS. *Dist:* International Specialized Bk. Services.

Jeffers, Dawn. Vegetable Dreams/Huerto Soñado. Schneider, Claude, illus. 2006. Tr. of Huerto Soñado. (SPA & ENG.). (J). pap. 4.99 (978-0-9770906-0-0(4) , 626999); 32p. lib. bdg. 16.95 (978-0-9741992-9-0(X) , 626999) Raven Tree Pr.

Jeffers, Oliver. Lost & Found. Jeffers, Oliver, illus. 2005. (Illus.). 32p. (J). (ps-3). 15.99 (978-0-399-24503-9(0) , Philomel) Penguin Group (USA) Inc.

Jeffers, Stewart. The Collapse of the Crew. 2005. 111p. pap. 16.95 (978-1-4137-8714-6(2)) PublishAmerica, Inc.

Jeffs, Stephanie. Christopher Bear Makes Friends. Thomas, Jacqui, illus. 2004. (Christopher Bear Ser.). 32p. 5.99 (978-0-8066-4401-1(X) , Augsburg Bks.) Augsburg Fortress, Pubs.

—Josh: Coming to Terms with the Death of a Friend. Thomas, Jacqui, illus. 2006. 32p. (ps-3). 14.00 (978-0-687-49719-5(1)) Abingdon Pr.

Jenkins, A. M. Breaking Boxes. 2000. (978-0-606-17834-1(1)) Tandem Library Bks.

Jenkins, Emily. Hug, Hug, Hug! A Bea & Haha Book. Bogacki, Tomek, illus. 2006. (Bea & Haha Board Bks.). 14p. (J). 5.95 (978-0-374-30581-9(1)) Farrar, Straus & Giroux.

—Num, Num, Num! A Bea & Haha Book. Bogacki, Tomek, illus. 2006. (Bea & Haha Board Bks.). 14p. (J). 5.95 (978-0-374-30583-3(8)) Farrar, Straus & Giroux.

—Plonk, Plonk, Plonk! A Bea & Haha Book. Bogacki, Tomek, illus. 2006. (Bea & Haha Board Bks.). 14p. (J). 5.95 (978-0-374-30585-7(4) , Farrar, Straus & Giroux (BYR)) Farrar, Straus & Giroux.

—Skunkdog. Pratt, Pierre, illus. 2008. 32p. (J). 16.95 (***978-0-374-37009-1(5)*** , Farrar, Straus & Giroux (BYR)) Farrar, Straus & Giroux.

—Toys Go Out: Being the Adventures of a Knowledgeable Stingray, a Toughy Little Buffalo, & Someone Called Plastic. Zelinsky, Paul O., illus. 2006. 128p. (J). (gr. 1-4). 16.95 (978-0-375-83604-7(7)); lib. bdg. 18.99 (978-0-375-93604-3(1)) Random Hse. Children's Bks. (Schwartz & Wade Bks.).

—Up, Up, Up! Bogacki, Tomek, illus. 2006. (Bea & Haha Board Bks.). 14p. (J). 5.95 (978-0-374-30584-0(6) , Farrar, Straus & Giroux (BYR)) Farrar, Straus & Giroux.

Jenkins, Gloria. Storm: The Peace Maker. 2006. (J). pap. 8.00 (***978-0-8059-7116-3(5)***) Dorrance Publishing Co., Inc.

Jenkins, Jerry B. & LaHaye, Tim. Heat Wave: Surviving the Fourth Bowl Judgment. 2004. (Left Behind Ser.: Bk. 37). 208p. (J). mass mkt. 5.99 (978-0-8423-8347-9(6)) Tyndale Hse. Pubs.

—The Perils of Love: Breaking Through the Darkness. 2004. (Left Behind Ser.: Bk. 38). 208p. (J). mass mkt. 5.99 (978-0-8423-8348-6(4)) Tyndale Hse. Pubs.

Jennings, Linda. Buster. 1998. (Illus.). 40p. (J). (SOM, ENG, URD, VIE & CHI.). (978-1-85430-543-5(3)); (VIE, ENG, URD, CHI & BEN., (978-1-85430-545-9(X)); (ENG & SPA., (978-1-85430-558-9(1)) Magi Pubns.

—Buster. Walters, Catherine, illus. 1998. 40p. (J). (ps-2). (ENG, PAN, URD, VIE & CHI.). (978-1-85430-542-8(5)); (ENG, URD, VIE, CHI & BEN.). (978-1-85430-544-2(1)); (BEN, ENG, URD, VIE & CHI.). (978-1-85430-540-4(9)) Magi Pubns.

Jennings, Richard W. Scribble: A Dog Story, a Ghost Story, a Love Story. 2004. 160p. (YA). (gr. 5-9). tchr. ed. 15.00 (978-0-618-43367-4(8) , Walter Lorraine) Houghton Mifflin Co. Trade & Reference Div.

Jennings, Sharon. Priscilla & Rosy. Hendry, Linda, illus. 2001. 32p. (gr. k-2). (978-1-55041-676-3(6)) Fitzhenry & Whiteside, Ltd.

Jennings, Sharon, et al. Franklin Forgives. Southern, Shelley & Sinkner, Alice, trs. Southern, Shelley & Sinkner, Alice, illus. 2004. (Franklin TV StoryBks.). 32p. (J). (gr. k-3). (978-1-55337-487-9(8)) Kids Can Pr., Ltd.

—Franklin's Nickname. Southern, Shelley et al, trs. Southern, Shelley et al, illus. 2005. (Franklin TV StoryBks.). 32p. (J). (ps-3). (978-1-55337-489-3(4)) Kids Can Pr., Ltd.

Jesse, Mary. Abbey & Friends M Is for Manners. Cherif, Jennifer, illus. 2003. 48p. (J). 15.95 (978-0-9729958-0-1(3)) Hexagon Blue.

Jett Jackson. 96p. (J). Bk. 1. 2000. pap. 4.99 (978-0-7868-4433-3(7)); Bk. 2. 2000. pap. 4.99 (978-0-7868-4434-0(5)); Bk. 4. 2001. pap. 4.99 (978-0-7868-4436-4(1)) Disney Pr.

Jeyaveeran, Ruth. The Spectacular Adventures of Sophie & Sebastian. Jeyaveeran, Ruth, illus. 2005. (Illus.). 32p. (J). (gr. k-3). 16.00 (978-0-618-50756-6(6)) Houghton Mifflin Co. Trade & Reference Div.

Jiménez, Juan Ramon. Platero & I. 2000. (Illus.). 196p. (YA). pap. 12.95 (978-0-595-00345-7(1)) iUniverse, Inc.

Jimenez, Juan Ramon. Platero & I/Platero y Yo: A Dual Language Book. Appelbaum, Stanley, ed. Appelbaum, Stanley, tr. from SPA. 2004. (Dual-Language Bks.). (ENG & SPA.). 192p. pap. 9.95 (978-0-486-43565-7(2)) Dover Pubns., Inc.

Jiménez, Juan Ramon. Platero y Yo. (SPA.). 192p. (J). 13.95 (978-84-206-1851-7(9) , AZ1851); (Illus.). 159p. 15.95 (978-84-206-3408-1(5)) Alianza Editorial, S. A. ESP. *Dist:* Continental Bk. Co., Inc., Distribooks, Inc., Distribooks, Inc.

—Platero y Yo. (SPA.). (J). pap. 9.95 (978-968-432-357-5(3) , PM223) Editorial Porrua MEX. *Dist:* Continental Bk. Co., Inc.

—Platero y Yo. annot. ed. (SPA., Illus.). 232p. (J). 15.95 (978-84-207-2636-6(2) , ANY010) Grupo Anaya, S.A. ESP. *Dist:* Continental Bk. Co., Inc.

E F G

—Platero y Yo. (SPA.). 240p. (YA). (gr. 5-8). (978-958-30-0744-6(7) , PV0560) Panamericana Editorial COL. *Dist:* Lectorum Pubns., Inc.

—Platero y Yo (Platero & I) (SPA.). (J). pap. 9.95 (978-968-416-022-4(4) , AOR01) Fernandez USA Publishing.

—Platero y Yo/Platero & I. Frasconi, Antonio, illus. 2003. 64p. (J). (gr. 4-6). pap. 5.95 (978-0-618-37838-8(3) , Clarion Bks.) Houghton Mifflin Co. Trade & Reference Div.

Job. Yakari & the Beavers. 2007. 48p. pap. 9.99 (***978-1-905460-09-0(0)***) CineBook GBR. *Dist:* Biblio Distribution.

Johansen, Hanna & Barrett, John S. The Duck & the Owl. Bhend, Kathi, illus. 2005. 80p. (J). 17.95 (978-1-56792-285-1(6)) Godine, David R. Pub.

Johanson, Sarah Margaret. Caillou a Special Friend. 2004. (ps-2). lib. bdg. 10.10 (978-0-613-85210-4(9)) Tandem Library Bks.

Johns, Linda. Carmen Dives In. 2005. (Star Sisterz Ser.: Bk. 2). (Illus.). 192p. (J). pap. 5.99 (978-0-7869-3714-1(9)) Wizards of the Coast.

—Carmen's Crystal Ball. 2006. (Star Sisterz Ser.: Bk. 7). 144p. (YA). pap. 4.99 (978-0-7869-4029-5(8) , Mirrorstone) Wizards of the Coast.

Johns, Michael-Anne. Hangin' with Aaron Carter. 2001. (Hangin' With Ser.). (Illus.). 48p. (J). (gr. 3-7). pap. 5.99 (978-0-439-32693-3(1)) Scholastic, Inc.

Johns, Rebecca. Julie Forgets Annie. l.t. ed. 2003. (Illus.). 8p. (J). (978-0-9740833-1-5(3)) Port Town Publishing.

Johnson, Angela. Maniac Monkeys on Magnolia Street. Ward, John, illus. 2000. 97p. (J). (ps-7). 12.04 (978-0-606-19829-5(6)) Tandem Library Bks.

Johnson, Bob. The Squatland Chronicles: Book 5 - the Dreaded Swamp of the Bubble Dragon. 2005. (Illus.). 56p. (J). per. 11.00 (978-1-59453-853-7(0) , Airleaf Publishing) Airleaf Publishing & Bookselling.

Johnson, Bob. The Squatland Chronicles: The Lost Mine of the Mechanical Spider. 2006. (Illus.). 56p. (J). per. 11.00 (***978-1-60002-185-5(9)*** , 3977, Airleaf Publishing) Airleaf Publishing & Bookselling.

Johnson, Carl & Johnson, Gwen. Dreamland Friends. Johnson, Gwen, illus. 2007. Tr. of Amigos del Tierra del Sue#324;os. (ENG & SPA., Illus.). 18p. (J). 5.95 (***978-0-9795860-7-1(0)***) Fish Tales Publishing.

Johnson, Catherine. Face Value. 2006. 256p. (YA). 16.95 (978-0-8027-8920-4(X)) Walker & Co.

Johnson-Choong, Shelly. A Light to Come Home By. 2nd unabr. ed. 2004. 212p. (C). reprint ed. pap. 12.95 (978-1-932280-52-4(9) , 80529) Granite Publishing & Distribution.

Johnson, Gillian. Gracie's Baby Chub Chop. 2004. 32p. (J). (ps-k). 14.95 (978-0-88776-693-0(5)) Tundra Bks., Inc./ Livres Toundra, Inc. CAN. *Dist:* Random Hse., Inc.

—Thora: A Half-Mermaid Tale. Johnson, Gillian, illus. 2005. (Illus.). 256p. (J). 15.99 (978-0-06-074378-9(6)); lib. bdg. 15.89 (978-0-06-074379-6(4)) HarperCollins Pubs.

Johnson, Judith C. Poppel's Place. Moriarity, Aaron Joel, illus. 2002. 32p. (J). (ps-4). 16.95 (978-0-9724193-1-4(4)) Poppel Pr.

Johnson, Kimberly P. Tag-Along Fred. 2002. (Illus.). 32p. (ps-3). 14.95 (978-1-57197-290-3(0)) Pentland Pr., Inc.

Johnson, Lissa Halls. Stuck in the Sky. 2005. (Brio Girls Ser.). 192p. (YA). (gr. 7-11). pap. 7.99 (978-1-56179-951-0(3)) Focus on the Family Publishing.

Johnson, Lois Walfrid. Invisible Friend, Vol. 3. 2004. (Raiders of the Sea Ser.). 224p. (J). pap. 7.99 (978-0-8024-3114-1(3)) Moody Pubs.

Johnson, Maureen. The Bermudez Triangle. 384p. (YA). (gr. 9-12). 2007. 7.99 (978-1-59514-155-2(3)); 2005. reprint ed. pap. 7.99 (978-1-59514-033-3(6)) Penguin Group (USA) Inc. (Razorbill).

—Devilish. (YA). (gr. 7 up). 2007. 272p. pap. 8.99 (***978-1-59514-132-3(4)***); 2006. 288p. 16.99 (978-1-59514-060-9(3)) Penguin Group (USA) Inc. (Razorbill).

Johnson, Maureen G. The Key to the Golden Firebird. 2004. 304p. (J). (gr. 7 up). 15.99 (978-0-06-054138-5(5)) HarperCollins Pubs.

Johnson, Nora. The World of Henry Orient. 2002. 224p. reprint ed. 12.95 (978-0-9714612-0-8(1) , 01-GMP-001) Green Mansion Pr. LLC.

—The World of Henry Orient. 1998. lib. bdg. 18.95 (978-1-56723-068-0(7)) Yestermorrow, Inc.

Johnson, Paul Brett. Bearhide & Crow. Johnson, Paul Brett, illus. 2000. (Illus.). 32p. (J). (gr. k-3). tchr. ed. 16.95 (978-0-8234-1470-3(1)) Holiday Hse., Inc.

Johnson, Sandi. Lost Island. Johnson, Britt, ed. Sturgeon, Bobbi, illus. l.t. ed. 2001. 22p. (J). (gr. k-5). spiral bd. 5.99 (978-1-929063-69-7(5) , 168) Moons & Stars Publishing For Children.

Johnson-Simpson, Gwendolyn. Difference. 1998. (Illus.). 32p. (J). pap. 8.00 (978-0-8059-4409-9(5)) Dorrance Publishing Co., Inc.

Johnston, Annie Fell. The Story of Dago (Illustrated Edition) 2006. (Illus.). pap. (***978-1-4065-1127-7(7)***) Dodo Pr.

—Two Little Knights of Kentucky (Illustra. 2006. pap. (***978-1-4065-1133-8(1)***) Dodo Pr.

Johnston-Brown, A. M. The Chronicles of Pleasant Grove. 2006. (J). pap. 12.95 (978-0-9760718-5-3(1)) Retriever Pr.

Johnston, Tony. Alien & Possum: Friends No Matter What. 2002. (gr. 3-6). lib. bdg. 11.80 (978-0-613-57565-2(2)) Tandem Library Bks.

—Alien & Possum: Hanging Out. DiTerlizzi, Tony, illus. (Ready-to-Reads Ser.). 48p. (J). 2003. pap. 3.99 (978-0-689-85771-3(3) , Aladdin); 2002. (gr. 1-3). 15.00 (978-0-689-83836-1(0)) Simon & Schuster Children's Publishing.

—Alien & Possum: Hanging Out. 2003. (gr. k-3). lib. bdg. 11.80 (978-0-613-66391-5(8)) Tandem Library Bks.

—Alien & Possum No. 1: Friends No Matter What. DiTerlizzi, Tony, illus. 2002. (Ready-to-Read Ser.). 48p. (J). pap. 3.99 (978-0-689-85326-5(2) , Aladdin) Simon & Schuster Children's Publishing.

—Bone by Bone by Bone. 2007. 192p. (YA). (gr. 7 up). 17.95 (***978-1-59643-113-3(X)***) Roaring Brook Pr.

Johnston, Tony. Sparky & Eddie: Trouble with Rats. Ryan, Susannah, illus. 32p. (J). 1999. pap. 4.95 (978-0-590-47981-3(4)); 1998. 13.95 (978-0-590-47980-6(6)) Scholastic, Inc.

Jolin, Dominique. Deecee Loves Sounds. Perkes, Carolyn, tr. from FRE. Jolin, Dominique, illus. 2001. (Deecee Ser.). (Illus.). 14p. (J). bds. (978-1-894363-65-5(5)) Dominique & Friends.

—A Friend for Washington. Jolin, Dominique, illus. 1999. (Tickle Ser.). (Illus.). 16p. (J). (ps). bds. (978-1-894363-14-3(0)) Dominique & Friends.

—Merry Christmas, Washington! Perkes, Carolyn, tr. from FRE. 2000. (Illus.). 16p. (J). (ps-k). bds. (978-1-894363-63-1(9)) Dominique & Friends.

—Peek-a-Boo, Deecee! Perkes, Carolyn, tr. from FRE. Jolin, Dominique, illus. 2001. (Deecee Ser.). (Illus.). 14p. (J). bds. (978-1-894363-53-2(1)) Dominique & Friends.

—Toupie Aime Toupie. braille ed. 2001. (J). (gr. 1). bds. (978-0-616-07269-1(4)) Canadian National Institute for the Blind/Institut National Canadien pour les Aveugles.

—Washington Dresses Up. Jolin, Dominique, illus. 1999. (Tickle Ser.). (Illus.). 16p. (J). (ps). bds. (978-1-894363-12-9(4)) Dominique & Friends.

—Washington Goes for a Walk. Jolin, Dominique, illus. 2000. (Illus.). 16p. (J). (ps-k). bds. (978-1-894363-28-0(0)) Dominique & Friends.

—Washington Loves Washington. Perkes, Carolyn, tr. from FRE. 2000. (Illus.). 16p. (J). (ps). bds. (978-1-894363-62-4(0)) Dominique & Friends.

—Washington Plays Hide-and-Seek. Jolin, Dominique, illus. 1999. (Tickle Ser.). (Illus.). 16p. (J). (ps). bds. (978-1-894363-13-6(2)) Dominique & Friends.

—Washington Tells a Story. Jolin, Dominique, illus. 2000. (Illus.). 16p. (J). (ps-k). bds. (978-1-894363-27-3(2)) Dominique & Friends.

Jones, D. S. Doubletake. 2004. 183p. pap. 19.95 (978-1-4137-4268-8(8)) PublishAmerica, Inc.

Jones, Deirdre J. White. Something about That Smile. 2002. (Illus.). (J). 18.00 (978-0-9709718-5-2(0)) Plainsong Publishing.

Jones, Jasmine. The Cheetah Girls Movie: Junior Novel. 2004. (Illus.). 128p. (gr. 3-7). pap. 4.99 (978-0-7868-4713-6(1)) Disney Pr.

Jones, Jasmine, adapted by. The Importance of Being Gordo. 2005. (Illus.). 138p. (J). (***978-1-4155-7362-4(X)***) Disney Pr.

—Importance of Being Gordo. 2005. 138p. (J). lib. bdg. 16.92 (***978-1-4242-0688-9(X)***) Fitzgerald Bks.

Jones, Jennifer B. Dear Mrs. Ryan, You're Ruining My Life. 2004. 144p. (J). pap. 5.95 (978-0-8027-7653-2(1)) Walker & Co.

Jones, Lara. Me Gustan Los Besos y Abrazos. (SPA.). 10p. 17.95 (978-84-272-7866-0(7)) Molino, Editorial ESP. *Dist:* Distribooks, Inc.

Jones, Marcia Thornton & Dadey, Debbie. Tattle Tails. 2001. (gr. 3-6). lib. bdg. 11.80 (978-0-613-57448-8(6)) Tandem Library Bks.

Jones, Nancy. The Grandpaws. 2005. 57p. pap. 12.95 (978-1-4137-4778-2(7)) PublishAmerica, Inc.

Jones, Shelley. Lonely Troll. 2000. (gr. k-3). lib. bdg. 11.80 (978-0-613-33388-7(8)) Tandem Library Bks.

Jones, Shelley V. & Sprick, Marilyn. Turtle in the Tuba: Read Well Level K Unit 8 Storybook. McDonnell, Kevin, illus. 2004. (Read Well Level K Ser.). 20p. (978-1-57035-672-8(6)) Sopris West Educational Services.

Jongman, Mariken & Boeke, Wanda. Rits. 2008. (J). (***978-1-59078-545-4(2)*** , Front Street) Boyds Mills Pr.

Jonsberg, Barry. The Crimes & Punishments of Miss Payne. 2006. 288p. (YA). (gr. 7). pap. 8.95 (978-0-375-84022-7(2) , Knopf Bks. for Young Readers) Random Hse. Children's Bks.

Joosse, Barbara M. Alien Brain Fryout. Truesdell, Sue, illus. 2000. (Wild Willie Mystery Ser.). 108p. (J). (gr. 4-6). tchr. ed. 15.00 (978-0-395-68964-6(3) , Clarion Bks.) Houghton Mifflin Co. Trade & Reference Div.

—Dead Guys Talk: A Wild Willie Mystery. Truesdell, Sue & Carter, Abby, illus. 2006. 112p. (J). (gr. 3-5). 15.00 (978-0-618-30666-4(8) , Clarion Bks.) Houghton Mifflin Co. Trade & Reference Div.

—Ghost Trap. Truesdell, Sue, illus. 1998. (Wild Willie Mystery Ser.). 80p. (J). (gr. 4-6). tchr. ed. 15.00 (978-0-395-66587-9(6) , Clarion Bks.) Houghton Mifflin Co. Trade & Reference Div.

—Three Little Girls. Date not set. 32p. (J). (978-0-8050-6671-5(3) , Holt, Henry & Co. Bks. For Young Readers) Holt, Henry & Co.

Jopling, John Perry & Jopling, Hazel Joan. John, the Airport Kid: A Magical Adventure. 2007. (YA). per. (***978-0-9778070-4-8(5)***) SilverBear.

Jordan, Apple & Random House Disney Staff. Driving Buddies. Disney Storybook Artists Staff, illus. 2006. (Step into Reading Ser.). 32p. (J). (ps-2). pap. 3.99 (978-0-7364-2339-7(7)); lib. bdg. 11.99 (978-0-7364-8043-7(9)) Random Hse. Children's Bks. (RH/Disney).

—Just Like Me! 2005. (Step into Reading Ser.). (Illus.). 32p. (J). (ps-1). lib. bdg. 11.99 (978-0-7364-8039-0(0) , RH/ Disney) Random Hse. Children's Bks.

—Just Like Me. 2005. (Step into Reading Ser.). (Illus.). 32p. (J). (ps-1). pap. 3.99 (978-0-7364-2288-8(9) , RH/ Disney) Random Hse. Children's Bks.

Jordano, Kimberly. By Myself or with My Friends, Vol. 4411. Kupperstein, Joel, ed. Snider, Jackie, illus. 1998. (Learn to Read Social Studies). 16p. (J). (ps-2). pap. 2.99 (978-1-57471-334-3(5) , 4411) Creative Teaching Pr., Inc.

Jorgensen, Norman & Harrison-Lever, Brian. The Call of the Osprey. 2004. (Illus.). 36p. (J). 22.50 (978-1-920731-85-4(7)) Fremantle Pr. AUS. *Dist:* International Specialized Bk. Services.

Journey to see the King. 2006. (J). (***978-0-9791168-0-3(5)***) Lighthouse Bk. Publishing.

Joyce, William. Rolie Polie Olie. 2001. (Rolie Polie Olie Ser.). (Illus.). (J). (ps). 5p. 3.99 (978-0-7364-0163-0(6)); Vol. 2. 10p. bds. 3.99 (978-0-7364-0164-7(4)) Mouse Works.

—Rolie Polie Olie & Friends. 2002. (Illus.). 10p. (J). (978-0-7868-3391-7(2)); (978-0-7868-3392-4(0)); (978-0-7868-3393-1(9)); (978-0-7868-3394-8(7)) Disney Pr.

Joyce, William, illus. Buddy. 1999. 48p. (J). (gr. 2-7). pap. 6.95 (978-0-06-440710-6(1)) HarperCollins Pubs.

Juckes, Deborah Sioux. Meesha, Guardian of Grand Mountain: Book One of the Guardian Series. McCleary, Twila, illus. 2005. (Guardian Ser.: Bk. 1). (YA). pap. 12.95 (978-0-9767748-0-8(1)) Red Earth Publishing.

—Meesha, Guardian of Grand Mountain: Book One of the Guardian Series. McCleary, Twila, illus. 2005. (YA). 18.95 (978-0-9767748-1-5(X)) Red Earth Publishing.

Jude, Tracey. Mr. Topaz Takes a Walk. 2005. 43p. (J). spiral bd. 16.99 (978-1-4116-5691-8(1)) Lulu.com.

Jukes, Mavis. Planning the Impossible. 2000. (J). (978-0-606-20022-6(3)) Tandem Library Bks.

Jules, Jacqueline. No English. Huntington, Amy, illus. 2007. 32p. (J). 17.95 (***978-1-58726-474-0(9)*** , Mitten Pr.) Ann Arbor Media Group, LLC.

Julian, B. T. Mirror Me This. 2006. 172p. per. 12.95 (978-1-59886-056-6(9)) Tate Publishing & Enterprises, L.L.C.

Jung, Reinhardt. Bambert's Book of Missing Stories. 2006. 128p. (J). (gr. 4-7). pap. 5.50 (978-0-440-42045-3(8) , Yearling) Random Hse. Children's Bks.

Jungle Limbo. l.t. ed. 2003. (Illus.). 31p. (J). spiral bd. 7.95 (978-0-9741074-0-0(9)) Catterfly Pr.

Jungman, Ann. Resistance. Marks, Alan, illus. 2006. 83p. (J). (gr. 2-3). lib. bdg. (978-1-59889-001-3(8)) Stone Arch Bks.

Justus, Adalu. The Storyteller House. Justus, Adalu, illus. 1999. 180p. (YA). (gr. 5-12). per. (978-0-937109-11-3(8)) Ike, J. Bks.

Kaaberbol, Lene. Heartbreak Island, Vol. 2. rev. ed. 2005. (W. I. T. C. H. Adventures Ser. : Bk. 3). (Illus.). 112p. (J). (gr. 3-7). pap. 4.99 (978-0-7868-0981-3(7) , Volo) Hyperion Bks. for Children.

Kaczman, James. A Bird & His Worm. Kaczman, James, illus. 2002. (Illus.). 32p. (J). (gr. k-3). tchr. ed. 15.00 (978-0-618-09460-8(1)) Houghton Mifflin Co. Trade & Reference Div.

Kadohata, Cynthia. Kira-Kira. 2004. (Illus.). 256p. 16.95 (978-0-689-85639-6(3) , Atheneum); 2006. 272p. (J). reprint ed. pap. 6.99 (978-0-689-85640-2(7) , Aladdin) Simon & Schuster Children's Publishing.

—Kira-Kira. l.t. ed. 2005. 201p. 23.95 (978-0-7862-7616-5(9) , Large Print Pr.) Thorndike Pr.

Kain, P. G. The Social Experiments of Dorie Dilts: Dumped by Popular Demand. 2007. (Social Experiments of Dorie Dilts Ser.). 254p. (J). (gr. 4-8). per. 5.99 (***978-1-4169-3519-3(3)*** , Aladdin) Simon & Schuster Children's Publishing.

Kai's Cake. 2004. (Illus.). 23p. (J). pap. (978-0-9749469-0-0(7)) Crunchpeep Media.

Kako, Satoshi. Little Daruma & Little Tengu. Howlett, Peter & McNamara, Richard B., trs. 2002. (Illus.). 32p. (ps-3). 10.95 (978-0-8048-3347-9(8)) Tuttle Publishing.

Kale, Ann Stephanian. Artie - The Ugly Frog. Kale, Ann Stephanian, illus. 2004. (Illus.). 20p. (J). pap. 10.00 (978-0-9704131-6-1(5)) Abril BookStore & Publishing.

Kallok, Emma. The Diary of Chickabiddy Baby. 2004. (Illus.). 128p. (J). (gr. 4-7). 15.95 (978-1-883672-87-4(2) , Tricycle Pr.) Ten Speed Pr.

—Diary of Chickabiddy Baby. 1999. (gr. 3-6). lib. bdg. 12.95 (978-0-613-18577-6(3)) Tandem Library Bks.

Kantor, Melissa. Confessions of a Not it Girl. 2004. 256p. (gr. 7-17). 15.99 (978-0-7868-1837-2(9)) Hyperion Bks. for Children.

Kapper, Jon. Super Duper Lucy. Ottinger, Jon, illus. 2001. (Little Lucy & Friends Ser.). 24p. (J). (gr. k-3). 9.99 (978-1-57151-703-6(0)) Playhouse Publishing.

Karasyov, Carrie & Kargman, Jill. Bittersweet Sixteen. 2007. 240p. (J). pap. 7.99 (***978-0-06-077846-0(6)*** , Harper-Teen) HarperCollins Pubs.

Kargman, Jill & Karasyov, Carrie. Bittersweet Sixteen. 2006. 240p. (J). 15.99 (978-0-06-077844-6(X)); lib. bdg. 16.89 (978-0-06-077845-3(8)) HarperCollins Pubs.

Karlin, Nurit. I See, You Saw. Karlin, Nurit, illus. 1999. (My First I Can Read Bks.). (Illus.). 32p. (J). (ps up). pap. 3.99 (978-0-06-444249-7(7) , Harper Trophy) HarperCollins Pubs.

—I See, You Saw. 1999. (I Can Read Bks.). (J). 10.79 (978-0-606-16674-4(2)); lib. bdg. 11.80 (978-0-613-14203-8(9)) Tandem Library Bks.

Karoub, Ginny. Oliver & Arthur. 2005. (Illus.). 40p. (J). per. 19.95 (978-1-59453-803-2(4) , Airleaf Publishing) Airleaf Publishing & Bookselling.

Karr, Kathleen. Worlds Apart. 2005. 208p. (J). 15.95 (978-0-7614-5195-2(1)) Cavendish, Marshall Corp.

Kasischke, Laura. Feathered. 2008. 272p. (J). 16.99 (***978-0-06-081317-8(2)***); lib. bdg. 17.89 (***978-0-06-081318-5(0)***) HarperCollins Pubs. (HarperTeen).

Kasza, Keiko. Dorotea y Miguel. Aparicio, Cristina, tr. 2001. (SPA.). (J). (ps-2). 8.95 (978-958-04-6033-6(7)) Norma S.A. COL. *Dist:* Distribuidora Norma, Inc., Lectorum Pubns., Inc.

Kathan, Christine. Ashford's Prayer. Maval Publishing Inc. Staff, illus. 2001. 32p. (J). (ps-3). pap. 7.50 (978-1-884083-68-6(4)) Maval Publishing, Inc.

—La Oracion de Ashford. Maval Publishing Inc. Staff, illus. 2001. Tr. of Ashford's Prayer. (SPA.). 32p. (J). (gr. k-3). pap. 7.50 (978-1-59134-013-3(6)); pap. 7.50 (978-1-884083-65-5(X)) Maval Publishing, Inc.

Katschke, Judy. Shore Thing. 2001. (gr. 3-6). lib. bdg. 13.00 (978-0-613-43957-2(0)) Tandem Library Bks.

Katsura, Masakazu. Is, Vol. 8. 2006. (I's Ser.). 208p. (YA). pap. 7.99 (978-1-4215-0649-4(1)) Viz Media.

—I's, Vol. 9. 2006. (I's Ser.). 208p. (YA). 7.99 (978-1-4215-0650-0(5)) Viz Media.

Kay, Catherine. When I'm by Myself. Morgan, Ron, illus. 1998. (Sis & Beezie Ser.: Vol. 1). 32p. (J). (ps-6). 17.95 (978-0-9663651-0-8(0)) Portos Publishing Co.

Kay, Elizabeth. The Jinx on the Divide. 2005. 384p. (J). pap. 16.99 (978-0-439-72455-5(4) , Chicken Hse., The) Scholastic, Inc.

Keats, Ezra Jack. Apt. 3. Keats, Ezra Jack, illus. 2002. (Illus.). (J). 22.72 (978-0-7587-1965-2(5)) Book Wholesalers, Inc.

—Apt. 3. Keats, Ezra Jack, illus. 1999. (Illus.). 32p. (J). (ps-3). pap. 6.99 (978-0-14-056507-2(8) , Puffin) Penguin Group (USA) Inc.

—Over in the Meadow. Keats, Ezra Jack, illus. 1999. (Illus.). 32p. (J). (ps-3). 16.99 (978-0-670-88344-8(1) , Viking Juvenile) Penguin Group (USA) Inc.

—The Trip. 2007. 40p. (J). (gr. k up). 15.99 (978-0-670-06195-2(6) , Viking Juvenile) Penguin Group (USA) Inc.

Keehn, Sally M. I Am Regina. 2001. (Novels Ser.). 240p. (J). (gr. 5-7). pap. 6.99 (978-0-698-11920-8(7) , Putnam Juvenile) Penguin Group (USA) Inc.

—I Am Regina. 2002. (gr. 3-6). lib. bdg. 14.15 (978-0-613-45282-3(8)) Tandem Library Bks.

Kehret, Peg. The Ghost's Grave. 224p. 2007. pap. 5.99 (***978-0-14-280819-1(9)*** , Puffin); 2007. (YA). (gr. 5). 5.99 (978-0-14-240819-3(0) , Puffin); 2005. (J). (gr. 5). 16.99 (978-0-525-46162-3(0) , Dutton Juvenile) Penguin Group (USA) Inc.

Kehret, Peg. The Stranger Next Door. (J). 2003. (Illus.). 176p. (gr. 3-7). pap. 5.99 (978-0-14-250178-8(6) , Puffin); 2002. 160p. (gr. 4-8). 15.99 (978-0-525-46829-5(3) , Dutton Juvenile) Penguin Group (USA) Inc.

—The Stranger Next Door. 2003. (gr. 5-8). lib. bdg. 14.15 (978-0-613-82994-6(8)) Tandem Library Bks.

Keiser, Frances R. Annie the River Otter: The Adventures of Pelican Pete. Keiser, Hugh M., illus. l.t. ed. 2006. 32p. (J). 17.00 (978-0-9668845-4-8(X)) Sagaponack Bks.

Keister, Douglas. Fernando's Gift/el Regalo de Fernando. Keister, Douglas, photos by. 2001. (SPA., Illus.). 32p. (J). (ps-3). pap. 7.95 (978-0-87156-927-1(2)) Sierra Club Bks. for Children.

—El Regalo de Fernando. 1998. (Sierra Club Bks.).Tr. of Fernando's Gift. (J). 13.75 (978-0-606-13382-1(8)) Tandem Library Bks.

Keizer, Garret. God of Beer. 256p. (J). 2003. pap. 6.99 (978-0-06-447276-0(0)); 2002. (gr. 8 up). 15.95 (978-0-06-029456-4(6)) HarperCollins Pubs.

—God of Beer. 2003. (gr. 7-12). lib. bdg. 15.30 (978-0-613-71500-3(4)) Tandem Library Bks.

Keller, Holly. Farfallina & Marcel. Keller, Holly, illus. (Illus.). 32p. (J). 2002. 16.99 (978-0-06-623932-3(X)); 2005. reprint ed. pap. 6.99 (978-0-06-443872-8(4) , Harper Trophy) HarperCollins Pubs.

—Farfallina & Marcel. 2004. (Illus.). 26p. (J). (ps-ps). lib. bdg. 12.79 (978-0-606-32617-9(0)) Tandem Library Bks.

—Help! A Story of Friendship. Keller, Holly, illus. 2007. (Illus.). 32p. (J). (ps-3). 16.99 (***978-0-06-123913-7(5)***); lib. bdg. 17.89 (***978-0-06-123914-4(3)***) HarperCollins Pubs. (Greenwillow Bks.).

—Nosy Rosie. Keller, Holly, illus. 2006. (Illus.). 32p. (J). (gr. k-2). 16.99 (978-0-06-078758-5(9)); lib. bdg. 17.89 (978-0-06-078759-2(7)) HarperCollins Pubs.

—Sophie's Window. Keller, Holly, illus. 2005. (Illus.). 32p. (J). 15.99 (978-0-06-056282-3(X)); 16.89 (978-0-06-056283-0(8)) HarperCollins Pubs.

Keller, Laurie. Arnie the Doughnut. Keller, Laurie, illus. 2005. (J). (gr. k-4). 24.95 incl. audio (978-0-439-76639-5(7) , WHRA649); 29.95 incl. audio compact disk (978-0-439-76641-8(9) , WHCD649) Weston Woods Studios, Inc.

Kellogg, Steven. Pinkerton & Friends: A Steven Kellogg Treasury. 2004. (Illus.). 336p. (J). (ps). 30.00 (978-0-8037-2979-7(0) , Dial) Penguin Group (USA) Inc.

Kellogg, Steven, illus. & narrated by. Chicken Little. Kellogg, Steven, narrated by. unabr. ed. 1998. (J). (ps-4). pap. 14.95 incl. audio (978-0-7882-0678-8(8) , PRA372) Weston Woods Studios, Inc.

Kelly, Theresa. Dream a Little Dream, Vol. 7. 2000. (Aloha Cove Ser.: Vol. 7). (Illus.). 272p. (J). (gr. 7-11). 5.99 (978-0-570-07072-6(4)) Concordia Publishing Hse.

—Dream a Little Dream. 2000. (gr. 7-12). lib. bdg. 14.15 (978-0-613-72787-7(8)) Tandem Library Bks.

—Tony the Pony: Bugs Are Not Bad. Sampson, Jody, illus. 2005. (J). per. 7.95 (978-1-59466-030-6(1)) Port Town Publishing.

Kelman, Marcy. Leo's Baton. Mastrocinque, Andy, illus. 2007. 24p. (J). (ps-k). pap. 3.99 (***978-1-4231-0215-1(0)***) Disney Pr.

Kemp, Kristen. What a Friend! Friendship Tips from 2 Grrrls. 2000. (Two Grrrls Ser.: Vol. 2). (Illus.). 64p. (J). (gr. 4-7). pap. 3.99 (978-0-439-20893-2(9)) Scholastic, Inc.

Kempf, Molly. Happy Birthday. Huxtable, Tonja & Huxtable, John, illus. 2008. (Strawberry Shortcake Ser.). 24p. (J). (ps-2). 4.99 (***978-0-448-44714-8(2)*** , Grosset & Dunlap) Penguin Group (USA) Inc.

—Let's Go Apple Picking! 2007. (Strawberry Shortcake Ser.). 24p. (J). (ps-1). pap. 3.99 (***978-0-448-44668-4(5)*** , Grosset & Dunlap) Penguin Group (USA) Inc.

EFG

Kempf, Molly. The Sweet Treats Carnival. MJ Illustration Staff, illus. 2007. 16p. (J). pap. 4.99 (978-0-448-44456-7(9) , Grosset & Dunlap) Penguin Group (USA) Inc.

Kempter, C. & Weldin, F. Dear Little Lamb. 2006. (Illus.). 32p. (J). 16.95 (978-0-7358-2086-9(4)) North-South Bks., Inc.

Kenner, Julie. The Good Ghouls' Guide to Getting Even. 2007. 256p. (YA). pap. 9.99 (978-0-425-21391-9(9) , Berkley Trade) Penguin Group (USA) Inc.

Kenrick, Angela Mastrodonato, creator. Flannery Fiddlesticks Seeks Spectacles. 2002. 30p. (J). per. 12.99 (978-0-9707914-5-0(3)) Litterateur Pubns., Inc.

Kent, Renee Holmes. Adventures in Misty Falls, Vol. 8. 2004. (Adventures in Misty Falls Ser.: Vol. 8). (Illus.). 100p. (gr. 4-7). pap. 4.99 (978-1-56309-456-9(8) , N017104) Woman's Missionary Union.

—Best Friends Forever?, Vol. 2. 2004. (Adventures in Misty Falls Ser.: Bk. 2). (Illus.). 100p. (gr. 4-7). pap. 4.99 (978-1-56309-734-8(6) , N007117) New Hope Pubs.

—Girl Talk, Vol. 7. 2004. (Adventures in Misty Falls Ser.: Vol. 7). (Illus.). 100p. (J). (gr. 4-7). pap. 4.99 (978-1-56309-455-2(X) , N017103) New Hope Pubs.

Kerl, Mary. The Secret: A Christian Novel for Middle Readers. 2002. 137p. pap. 19.95 (978-1-59129-907-3(1)) PublishAmerica, Inc.

Kerr, Judith. Mog & Me. 2002. (Illus.). 18p. (J). bds. 5.99 (978-0-00-138416-3(3)) HarperCollins Pubs. Ltd. GBR. *Dist:* Trafalgar Square Publishing.

Kerr, M. E. I Stay near You: One Story in Three. 2006. (Illus.). 216p. (YA). pap. 6.95 (978-0-15-205589-9(4) , Harcourt Paperbacks) Harcourt Children's Bks.

Kerr, M. E. Your Eyes in Stars. 240p. 2007. (J). (gr. 7 up). pap. 6.99 (*978-0-06-075684-0(5)* , HarperTeen); 2006. (J). lib. bdg. 16.89 (978-0-06-075683-3(7)); 2006. (YA). 15.99 (978-0-06-075682-6(9)) HarperCollins Pubs.

Kerrin, Jessica Scott. Out of Orbit! Kelly, Joseph, illus. 2007. (Martin Bridge Ser.). 112p. (J). (gr. 2-5). pap. (*978-1-55453-149-3(7)*) Kids Can Pr., Ltd.

Keselman, Gabriela. El Mejor Amigo. 2003. (SPA.). 48p. (J). 6.95 (978-84-670-0302-4(2)) Espasa Calpe, S.A. ESP. *Dist:* Planeta Publishing Corp.

Kessler, Leonard. Last One in Is a Rotten Egg. Kessler, Leonard, illus. 2002. (Illus.). (J). 11.91 (978-0-7587-6178-1(3)) Book Wholesalers, Inc.

—Last One in Is a Rotten Egg. 1999. (gr. k-3). lib. bdg. 11.80 (978-0-8335-4944-0(8)) Tandem Library Bks.

Kettle, Shey. Surf Girls. Thomas, Meredith, illus. 2005. (Girlz Rock! Ser.). (J). pap. (978-1-59336-708-4(2)) Mondo Publishing.

Khan, Rukhsana. Dahling, If You Luv Me, Would You Please, Please Smile. l.t. ed. 1999. 196p. (YA). (gr. 7-9). pap. 8.95 (978-0-7737-6016-5(4)) Stoddart Kids CAN. *Dist:* Fitzhenry & Whiteside, Ltd.

Kidwell, Leigh-Anne. The Year i Lost My Popularity! 2005. 115p. pap. 16.95 (978-1-4137-8376-6(7)) PublishAmerica, Inc.

Kierstead, Vera. Jamie's Journey: An Early American Adventure. 2003. pap. 8.95 (978-0-533-14424-2(8)) Vantage Pr., Inc.

Kijinski, Paul. Camp Limestone. 2006. (Illus.). 104p. (YA). per. 7.99 (978-1-59958-016-6(0)) Journey Stone Creations, LLC.

Kilborne, Sarah S. Peach & Blue. 1998. (978-0-606-13697-6(5)) Tandem Library Bks.

Kilborne, Sarah S. & Johnson, Steve, illus. Peach & Blue. 1998. (Dragonfly Books Ser.). 32p. (J). (gr. k-3). pap. 6.99 (978-0-679-89095-9(5) , Dragonfly Bks.) Random Hse. Children's Bks.

Kilgras, Heidi. Me Too, Woody! Toy Story 2. Harchy, Atelier Philippe, illus. 2002. (Step into Reading Ser.). 32p. (J). (ps-1). pap. 3.99 (978-0-7364-1266-7(2) , RH/Disney) Random Hse. Children's Bks.

Killian, Beth. Everything She Wants. 2006. (310 Ser.). 240p. pap. 9.95 (978-1-4165-2168-6(2) , MTV) Simon & Schuster.

Kimmel, Elizabeth Cody. Lily B. on the Brink of Cool. 256p. (J). 2005. (gr. 5 up). pap. 6.99 (978-0-06-000588-7(2) , Harper Trophy), 2003. (gr. 3-7). 15.99 (978-0-06-000586-3(6)) HarperCollins Pubs.

—Spin the Bottle. 2008. 240p. (J). (gr. 5). 16.99 (*978-0-8037-3191-2(4)* , Dial) Penguin Group (USA) Inc.

Kimmel, Elizabeth Cody. Visiting Miss Caples. 2001. (978-0-606-22533-5(1)) Tandem Library Bks.

Kimpel, Linda S. Charlie Chose a Champion; Shawn's Tiny Ship; Soldiers, Jeeps & Jelly Beans. Hunt, Courtney M., illus. l.t. ed. 1998. (Speech Creature Ser.). 24p. (J). (ps-3). pap. 24.95 (978-1-893240-00-1(2)) Chestleigh's Bks. Publishing Co.

Kimpton, Diana. A Surprise for Princess Ellie. Finlay, Lizzie, illus. 6th rev. ed. 2007. 96p. (gr. 1-4). pap. 3.99 (978-0-7868-4875-1(8)) Hyperion Pr.

Kimura & North, Lucy. One Stormy Night. Abe, Hiroshi, illus. 2005. 48p. (J). (gr. 1-3). 16.00 (978-4-7700-2970-6(5)) Kodansha International JPN. *Dist:* Cheng & Tsui Co.

—One Sunny Day, 2 vols., Vol. 2. Abe, Hiroshi, illus. 2005. 48p. (J). 16.00 (978-4-7700-2971-3(3)) Kodansha International JPN. *Dist:* Cheng & Tsui Co.

Kindersley, Dorling. Go Diego Go Essential Gd. 2008. 48p. 8.99 (*978-0-7566-3501-5(2)*) Dorling Kindersley Publishing, Inc.

Kindig, Tess Eileen. March Mania, Vol. 6. 2000. (Slam Dunk Ser.: Vol. 6). 96p. (J). (gr. 1-4). 4.99 (978-0-570-07092-4(9)) Concordia Publishing Hse.

—March Mania. 2000. (gr. k-3). lib. bdg. 13.00 (978-0-613-72796-9(7)) Tandem Library Bks.

—Muggsy Makes an Assist. 2000. (Slam Dunk Ser.: Vol. 3). 96p. (J). (gr. 1-4). Vol. 3. (Illus.). 4.99 (978-0-570-07018-4(X)); Vol. 4. 4.99 (978-0-570-07019-1(8)) Concordia Publishing Hse.

—Muggsy Makes an Assist. 2000. (gr. k-3). lib. bdg. 13.00 (978-0-613-72906-2(4)) Tandem Library Bks.

Kinerk, Robert. Clorinda Takes Flight. Kellogg, Steven, illus. 2007. 40p. (J). (ps-3). 16.99 (978-0-689-86864-1(2) , Simon & Schuster/Paula Wiseman Bks.) Simon & Schuster Children's Publishing.

King, M. C. Jump In! The Junior Novel. 2007. 128p. (ps-17). pap. 4.99 (978-1-4231-0683-8(0)) Disney Pr.

King, Steve. The Stone Dragon. 2005. 80p. pap. 14.95 (978-1-4137-9628-5(1)) PublishAmerica, Inc.

Kingfisher Editors, ed. You're the Best! 2006. 224p. (J). (gr. 5-9). pap. 7.95 (978-0-7534-5997-3(3) , Kingfisher) Houghton Mifflin Co. Trade & Reference Div.

Kingston, George. Goldilocks Makes Friends. Hale, Sue, illus. Reime, Cyndee, photos by. 1999. 52p. (J). 7.95 (978-0-9669852-0-7(6)) G Sharp Productions.

Kinney, Jeff. Diary of a Wimpy Kid. 2007. (Illus.). 224p. (J). (gr. 2-8). 12.95 (*978-0-8109-9313-6(9)* , Abrams Bks. for Young Readers) Abrams, Harry N. , Inc.

Kirby. Ida Lou's Story. 2000. (American Quilts Ser.: Vol. 4). (J). 11.64 (978-0-606-20082-0(7)) Tandem Library Bks.

Kirk, David. Basketberry Blues. 2006. (Miss Spider Ser.). (Illus.). 32p. (J). 6.99 (978-0-448-44118-4(7) , Grosset & Dunlap) Penguin Group (USA) Inc.

—A Cloudy Day in Sunny Patch. 2005. (Miss Spider Ser.). (Illus.). 32p. (J). (gr. k-1). 6.99 (978-0-448-43897-9(6)) Callaway Editions, Inc.

—Flower Power. 2007. (Miss Spider Ser.). 32p. (J). 6.99 (978-0-448-44504-5(2)) Callaway Editions, Inc.

—Giddy up Bugs! 2007. (Miss Spider Ser.). 32p. (J). 6.99 (978-0-448-44505-2(0)) Callaway Editions, Inc.

—I'll Fly Away. 2005. (Miss Spider Ser.). (Illus.). 32p. (J). (gr. k-1). 6.99 (978-0-448-43896-2(8)) Callaway Editions, Inc.

—Miss Spider's Family Album. 2005. (Miss Spider's Sunny Patch Friends Ser.). (Illus.). 16p. (J). (ps-1). bds. 7.99 (978-0-448-43829-0(1) , Grosset & Dunlap) Penguin Group (USA) Inc.

—The Most Perfect Parent: Miss Spiders Sunny Patch Friends. 2007. 32p. (J). (ps-2). 6.99 (*978-0-448-44692-9(8)*) Callaway Editions, Inc.

—The Prince, the Princess, & the Bee. 2008. 32p. (J). (ps-2). 17.99 (*978-0-448-44690-5(1)*) Penguin Group (USA) Inc.

Kirk, David. Sing It, Sister! 2005. (Miss Spider's Sunny Patch Friends Ser.). (Illus.). 32p. (J). (ps-1). pap. 3.99 (978-0-448-43974-7(3) , Grosset & Dunlap) Penguin Group (USA) Inc.

Kiss, Kathrin. Que Hace un Cocodrilo por la Noche? Urberuaga, Emilio, illus. 2001. (SPA.). (J). (gr. k-3). (978-84-88342-18-8(7) , KK8906) S.A. Kokinos ESP. *Dist:* Lectorum Pubns., Inc.

Kitamura, Satoshi. Gato Busca un Amigo. 2000. Tr. of Cat Finds a Friend. (SPA., Illus.). 114p. (J). 9.95 (978-84-207-8948-4(8)) Grupo Anaya, S.A. ESP. *Dist:* Distribooks, Inc., Lectorum Pubns., Inc.

Kitten's New Friend. 2002. 10p. (J). bds. 2.50 (978-1-56021-397-0(3)) W.J. Fantasy, Inc.

Kittinger, Jo S. Un Almuerzo con Ponche. Medoff, Jack, illus. 2003. (Rookie Reader Espanol Ser.). (SPA.). (J). 19.50 (978-0-516-25892-8(3) , Children's Pr.) Scholastic Library Publishing.

Klam, Cheryl. Learning to Swim. 2007. 224p. (YA). (gr. 7). pap. 8.99 (978-0-385-73372-4(0)); lib. bdg. 13.99 (978-0-385-90387-5(1)) Random Hse. Children's Bks. (Delacorte Bks. for Young Readers).

Klar, Elizabeth. Lily's Crossing. Robbins, Dawn Michelle, ed. 2000. (J). 9.95 (978-1-58130-644-6(X)); 11.95 (978-1-58130-645-3(8)) Novel Units, Inc.

Klass, Sheila S. The Uncivil War. 1999. (978-0-606-17477-0(X)) Tandem Library Bks.

Klein, Abby. King of Show-and-Tell. McKinley, John, illus. 2004. (Ready, Freddy! Ser.). 96p. (J). pap. 3.99 (978-0-439-55598-2(1) , Blue Sky Pr., The) Scholastic, Inc.

—Super-secret Valentine. 2007. (Ready, Freddy! Ser.: No. 10) 96p. (J). pap. 3.99 (978-0-439-78459-7(X) , Blue Sky Pr., The) Scholastic, Inc.

Klein, Adria F. Max & the Adoption Day Party. 2007. (Read-It! Readers Ser.). (Illus.). 24p. (J). (*978-1-4048-3283-1(1)* , 1265792) Picture Window Bks.

—Max & the Adoption Day Party. Gallagher-Cole, Mernie, illus. 2006. (Read-It! Readers Ser.). 24p. (J). (gr. k-2). lib. bdg. 19.93 (*978-1-4048-3145-2(2)* , 1265792) Picture Window Bks.

—Max Celebrates Chinese New Year. 2007. (Read-It! Readers Ser.). (Illus.). 24p. (J). (*978-1-4048-3287-9(4)* , 1265794) Picture Window Bks.

—Max Celebrates Chinese New Year. Gallagher-Cole, Mernie, illus. 2006. (Read-It! Readers Ser.). 24p. (J). (gr. k-2). lib. bdg. 19.93 (*978-1-4048-3147-6(9)* , 1265794) Picture Window Bks.

—Max Goes to a Cookout. 2007. (Read-It! Readers Ser.). (Illus.). 24p. (J). (*978-1-4048-3290-9(4)* , 1265793) Picture Window Bks.

—Max Goes to a Cookout. Gallagher-Cole, Mernie, illus. 2006. (Read-It! Readers Ser.). 24p. (J). (*978-1-4048-3146-9(0)* , 1265793) Picture Window Bks.

—Max Goes to the Farm. Gallagher-Cole, Mernie, illus. 2007. (J). lib. bdg. (*978-1-4048-3678-5(0)*) Picture Window Bks.

—Max Goes to the Grocery Store. Gallagher-Cole, Mernie, illus. 2007. (J). lib. bdg. (*978-1-4048-3682-2(9)*) Picture Window Bks.

—Max Goes to the Playground. Gallagher-Cole, Mernie, illus. 2007. (J). lib. bdg. (*978-1-4048-3681-5(0)*) Picture Window Bks.

—Max Goes to the Zoo. Gallagher-Cole, Mernie, illus. 2007. (J). lib. bdg. (*978-1-4048-3677-8(2)*) Picture Window Bks.

—Max Stays Overnight. 2007. (Read-It! Readers Ser.). (Illus.). 24p. (J). (*978-1-4048-3547-4(4)* , 1265796) Picture Window Bks.

—Max Stays Overnight. Gallagher-Cole, Mernie, illus. 2006. (Read-It! Readers Ser.). 24p. (J). (*978-1-4048-3149-0(5)* , 1265796) Picture Window Bks.

—Max's Fun Day. 2007. (Read-It! Readers Ser.). (Illus.). 24p. (J). (*978-1-4048-3549-8(0)* , 1265797) Picture Window Bks.

—Max's Fun Day. Gallagher-Cole, Mernie, illus. 2006. (Read-It! Readers Ser.). 24p. (J). (*978-1-4048-3150-6(9)* , 1265797) Picture Window Bks.

Klein, Arnold. The Lemmies. Klein, Karen, illus. 2005. 40p. (J). (ps). pap. 11.95 (978-1-928623-31-1(X)) Klein, Arnold.

Kleinberg, Naomi. Have Yourself a Furry Little Christmas. Womble, Louis, illus. 2007. 12p. (J). (gr. k-ps). bds. 4.99 (*978-0-375-84133-0(4)* , Random Hse. Bks. for Young Readers) Random Hse. Children's Bks.

Kleman, Jamie. Uncovered. 2005. 39p. pap. 10.95 (978-1-4116-6198-1(2)) Lulu.com.

Klim, Christopher. Firecracker Jones Is on the Case. (Illus.). (J). 2006. 116p. lib. bdg. 19.95 (978-1-933435-11-4(9)); 2005. 111p. per. 9.95 (978-0-9726906-7-6(0)) Hopewell Pubns., LLC.

Kline, Lisa Williams. The Princesses of Atlantis. 2002. (Illus.). 192p. (J). 16.95 (978-0-8126-2855-5(1)) Cricket Bks.

Kline, Suzy. Herbie Jones & Hamburger Head. Williams, Richard, illus. 2002. (Herbie Jones Ser.). 112p. (J). pap. 4.99 (978-0-698-11940-6(1) , Putnam Juvenile) Penguin Group (USA) Inc.

—Herbie Jones & Hamburger Head. 2002. (gr. 3-6). lib. bdg. 13.00 (978-0-613-73470-7(X)) Tandem Library Bks.

—Herbie Jones Moves On. 2003. 80p. (J). (gr. 2-5). 14.99 (978-0-399-23635-8(X) , Putnam Juvenile) Penguin Group (USA) Inc.

—Herbie Jones Sails into Second Grade. Sweeten, Sami, illus. 2006. 64p. (J). (gr. 1-4). 14.99 (978-0-399-22665-6(6) , Putnam Juvenile) Penguin Group (USA) Inc.

—Horrible Harry & the Dragon War. Remkiewicz, Frank, illus. 2002. 64p. (J). (gr. 1-3). 13.99 (978-0-670-03559-5(9) , Viking Juvenile) Penguin Group (USA) Inc.

—Marvin & the Meanest Girl. Sims, Blanche, illus. 2002. (Chapters Ser.). 80p. (J). pap. 4.99 (978-0-698-11967-3(3) , Putnam Juvenile) Penguin Group (USA) Inc.

—Marvin & the Meanest Girl. 2002. (gr. 3-6). lib. bdg. 13.00 (978-0-613-63962-0(6)) Tandem Library Bks.

—Molly's in a Mess. Bluthenthal, Diana Cain, illus. 2002. (Chapters Ser.). 80p. (J). pap. 4.99 (978-0-698-11928-4(2) , Putnam Juvenile) Penguin Group (USA) Inc.

—Molly's in a Mess. 2002. (gr. 3-6). lib. bdg. 13.00 (978-0-613-64418-1(2)) Tandem Library Bks.

—Song Lee in Room 2B. Remkiewicz, Frank, illus. 1999. (Song Lee Ser.). 64p. (J). (gr. 2-5). pap. 3.99 (978-0-14-130408-3(1) , Puffin) Penguin Group (USA) Inc.

Kline, Suzy & Kline, Suzy. Horrible Harry & the Dragon War. Remkiewicz, Frank, illus. 2003. 64p. (J). (ps-k). pap. 3.99 (978-0-14-250166-5(2) , Puffin) Penguin Group (USA) Inc.

Kline, Trish. The Fang Gang: KA Reader 4. 2007. (Illus.). 32p. (J). per. 20.00 (*978-0-9717234-6-7(X)*) Ghost Hunter Productions.

—Super Hero: KA Reader 1. 2007. (Illus.). 32p. (J). per. 20.00 (*978-0-9717234-2-9(7)*) Ghost Hunter Productions.

Kline, Trish & Donev, Mary. Don¿t Frown, Clown! KA Reader 9. 2007. (Illus.). 32p. (J). per. 20.00 (*978-1-934307-02-1(5)*) Ghost Hunter Productions.

—Where Can Lost Bee Be? KA Reader 6. 2007. (Illus.). 32p. (J). per. 20.00 (*978-0-9717234-9-8(4)*) Ghost Hunter Productions.

Klingel, Cynthia Fitterer & Noyed, Robert B. Zlata, Me, & the Letter Z. 2003. (Alphaphonics Ser.). (Illus.). 24p. (J). (ps-2). 21.36 (978-1-59296-116-0(9)) Child's World, Inc.

Knister. A Promise Is a Promise. Tharlet, Eve, illus. 2006. 32p. (J). (ps-3). 16.99 (978-0-698-40040-5(2) , Minedition) Penguin Group (USA) Inc.

Knowles, Jo. Lessons from a Dead Girl. 2007. (Illus.). 1p. (YA). (gr. 9). 16.99 (*978-0-7636-3279-3(1)*) Candlewick Pr.

Knudson, Mike & Wilkinson, Steve. Raymond & Graham Rule the School. 2008. 128p. (J). (gr. 3-5). 14.99 (*978-0-670-01101-8(0)* , Viking Juvenile) Penguin Group (USA) Inc.

Kochka. The Boy Who Ate Stars. Adams, Sarah, tr. from FRE. 2006. 112p. (J). 12.95 (978-1-4169-0038-2(1)) Simon & Schuster Children's Publishing.

Koeppel, Ruth. Forever Friends: Storybook. 2006. (Disney Princess Ser.). 32p. (J). 17.99 (978-0-7944-0696-7(3)) Reader's Digest Assn., Inc., The.

—Goddard, Come Home! 2003. (gr. k-3). lib. bdg. 11.80 (978-0-613-66357-1(8)) Tandem Library Bks.

Koertge, Ron. Boy Girl Boy. 2007. (Illus.). 180p. (YA). (gr. 9 up). pap. 6.95 (978-0-15-205865-4(6) , Harcourt Paperbacks) Harcourt Children's Bks.

Koertge, Ronald. Boy Girl Boy. 2005. 176p. (YA). (gr. 9-17). 16.00 (978-0-15-205325-3(5)) Harcourt Children's Bks.

—The Heart of the City. 1998. 128p. (J). (gr. 3-7). 16.99 (978-0-531-33078-4(8) , Orchard Bks.) Scholastic, Inc.

—Stoner & Spaz. 2004. (gr. 7-12). lib. bdg. 15.30 (978-0-613-74820-9(4)) Tandem Library Bks.

Kohlhepp, Michael. Within the Hearthstone: Book 1: the Trea. 2006. 127p. pap. 17.95 (978-1-4241-3744-2(6)) PublishAmerica, Inc.

Kolar, Bob. Do You Want to Play? A Book about Being Friends. 2001. (Illus.). (J). (978-0-606-21153-6(5)) Tandem Library Bks.

Kollar, J. P. Three Tomato Brand. 2005. 127p. per. 12.95 (978-1-59879-076-4(5)) Lifevest Publishing, Inc.

Kollars, Helmut. The Lonely Wizard. Kollars, Helmut, illus. 1998. Tr. of Es War Einmal Zauberer Ganz Allein. (Illus.). 32p. (J). (ps-3). 23.69 (978-1-56711-804-9(6) , Blackbirch Pr., Inc.) Thomson Gale.

Koller, Jackie French. Mole & Shrew Are Two. Reas, Anne, illus. 2000. (J). (978-0-606-19903-2(9)) Tandem Library Bks.

—Mole & Shrew Have Jobs to Do. 2001. (Stepping Stone Bks.). (Illus.). (J). (978-0-606-21335-6(X)) Tandem Library Bks.

—Someday. 2002. 224p. (J). (gr. 5 up). pap. 16.95 (978-0-439-29317-4(0) , Orchard Bks.) Scholastic, Inc.

Komaiko, Leah. Best Friends to the End. 1998. (Annie Bananie Ser.). (J). (gr. 2-6). (978-0-606-13143-8(4)) Tandem Library Bks.

—Earl's Too Cool for Me. Cornell, Laura, illus. 2004. 48p. (J). (ps-3). lib. bdg. 13.19 (978-0-606-30512-9(2)) Tandem Library Bks.

Komorn, Julie, adapted by. Out of the Dark. 2004. (W. I. T. C. H. Ser.: Bk. 8). (Illus.). 128p. (J). lib. bdg. 16.92 (*978-1-4242-0789-3(4)*) Fitzgerald Bks.

Komorn, Julie & Lenhard, Elizabeth, adapted by. The Light of Meridian. 2004. (W. I. T. C. H. Ser.: Bk. 7). (Illus.). 144p. (J). lib. bdg. 16.92 (*978-1-4242-0794-7(0)*) Fitzgerald Bks.

Kompelien, Tracy. Lion Manes. Nobens, C. A., illus. 2006. (Fact & Fiction Ser.). 24p. (J). 21.35 (978-1-59679-949-3(8) , SandCastle); pap. (978-1-59679-950-9(1)) ABDO Publishing Co.

Konigsburg, E. L. Jennifer, Hecate, Macbeth, William McKinley, & Me, Elizabeth. (J). 117p. (gr. 3-6). pap. 4.99 (978-0-8072-1417-6(5)); 1998. 177p. (gr. 4-7). pap. 29.00 incl. audio (978-0-8072-8001-0(1) , YA963SP) Random Hse. Audio Publishing Group. (Listening Library).

—Jennifer, Hecate, Macbeth, William McKinley, & Me, Elizabeth. 2007. 128p. (J). pap. 2.99 (*978-1-4169-4829-2(5)*); pap. 5.99 (978-1-4169-3396-0(4)) Simon & Schuster Children's Publishing. (Aladdin).

—Jennifer, Hecate, Macbeth, William McKinley, & Me, Elizabeth. l.t. ed. 2005. 122p. (J). 20.95 (978-0-7862-7542-7(1)) Thorndike Pr.

—The Mysterious Edge of the Heroic World. 2007. 244p. (J). (gr. 5-9). 16.99 (*978-1-4169-4972-5(0)* , Ginne Seo Bks) Simon & Schuster Children's Publishing.

—Retrato del Sabado. 2002. (SPA.). (gr. 3-6). lib. bdg. 18.75 (978-0-613-64589-8(8)) Tandem Library Bks.

—Sabato di Gloria. pap. 15.95 (978-88-04-47046-5(1)) Mondadori ITA. *Dist:* Distribooks, Inc.

—Silent to the Bone. unabr. ed. 2004. (Middle Grade Cassette Librariestm Ser.). 272p. (J). (gr. 5-9). pap. 38.00 incl. audio (978-0-8072-8741-5(5) , S YA 253 SP, Listening Library) Random Hse. Audio Publishing Group.

—Silent to the Bone. 272p. 2004. (YA). mass mkt. 5.99 (978-0-689-86715-6(8) , Simon Pulse); 2002. pap. 5.99 (978-0-689-83602-2(3) , Aladdin) Simon & Schuster Children's Publishing.

—Silent to the Bone. Konigsburg, E. L., illus. 2000. (Jean Karl Bks.). (Illus.). 272p. (J). (gr. 5-9). 16.00 (978-0-689-83601-5(5) , Atheneum) Simon & Schuster Children's Publishing.

—Silent to the Bone. 2002. (gr. 5-8). lib. bdg. 14.15 (978-0-613-45102-4(3)) Tandem Library Bks.

—Silent to the Bone. l.t. ed. 2001. 271p. (J). (gr. 4-7). 23.95 (978-0-7862-3169-0(6)) Thorndike Pr.

—Throwing Shadows. 1998. 160p. (J). (gr. 5-9). pap. 5.99 (978-0-689-82120-2(4) , Aladdin) Simon & Schuster Children's Publishing.

—The View from Saturday. Konigsburg, E. L., illus. 2002. (Illus.). (J). 25.11 (978-0-7587-0221-0(3)) Book Wholesalers, Inc.

—The View from Saturday. 2000. (J). 11.95 (978-1-56137-936-1(0)) Novel Units, Inc.

—The View from Saturday. 280p. (YA). (gr. 5 up). pap. 4.95 (978-0-8072-1511-1(2) , Listening Library) Random Hse. Audio Publishing Group.

—The View from Saturday. 1998. (Jean Karl Bks.). 176p. (J). (gr. 3-7). reprint ed. pap. 5.99 (978-0-689-81721-2(5) , Aladdin) Simon & Schuster Children's Publishing.

—The View from Saturday. 1998. (J). (978-0-606-13063-9(2)) Tandem Library Bks.

Konnecke, Ole. Anthony & the Girls. Seitz, Nancy, tr. from GER. 2006. (Illus.). 32p. (J). 15.00 (978-0-374-30376-1(2)) Macmillan.

Kornblatt, Marc. Understanding Buddy. l.t. ed. 2002. 100p. (J). 21.95 (978-0-7862-3712-8(0)) Thomson Gale.

Kornfeld, Joanne. The Chocolate Train. Rast, Barbara Mason, illus. 2002. 24p. (J). (ps-4). 12.95 (978-0-9704629-3-0(X)) Earthkids Publishing.

Kornhauser, Barry. Lincoln's Log. 1999. 96p. (YA). (gr. 5-12). pap. 7.00 (978-0-87602-369-3(3)) Anchorage Pr.

Kornreich, Leron. Ivory Towers. 2001. (YA). 7.99 (978-0-9707509-0-7(0)) Banana Peel Bks.

Koss, Amy Goldman. The Ashwater Experiment. 2001. (J). (978-0-606-21046-1(6)) Tandem Library Bks.

—The Ashwater Experiment. l.t. ed. 2000. 188p. (YA). (gr. 8-12). 20.95 (978-0-7862-2686-3(2)) Thorndike Pr.

—The Cheat. 2004. 176p. (J). (gr. 5 up). pap. 5.99 (978-0-14-240128-6(5) , Puffin) Penguin Group (USA) Inc.

—The Girls. 128p. (J). 2002. pap. 5.99 (978-0-14-230033-6(0) , Puffin); 2000. (Illus.). (gr. 5-9). 16.99 (978-0-8037-2494-5(2) , Dial) Penguin Group (USA) Inc.

—Gossip Times Three. 176p. (J). 2003. (gr. 6). 16.99 (978-0-8037-2849-3(2) , Dial); 2005. (gr. 5). reprint ed. pap. 5.99 (978-0-14-240295-5(8) , Puffin) Penguin Group (USA) Inc.

E
F
G

Kostick, Conor. Epic. 2007. 384p. (YA). (gr. 7 up). 17.99 (978-0-670-06179-2(4) , Viking Juvenile) Penguin Group (USA) Inc.

Kovalski, Maryann. Omar on Board. 32p. 2007. pap. (*978-1-55455-033-3(5)); 2005. (Illus.). (J). (978-1-55041-918-4(8)) Fitzhenry & Whiteside, Ltd.

Kowitt, Holly. Ned's Declassified School Survival Guide. 2006. (Teenick Ser.). (Illus.). 96p. (J). pap. 4.99 (978-0-439-83161-1(X)) Scholastic, Inc.

Krailing, Tessa. Beastly Basil. Phillips, Mike, illus. 2006. 48p. (J). lib. bdg. (*978-1-4048-3113-1(4)) Picture Window Bks.

Krauss, Ruth & Noonan, Julia. You're Just What I Need. 1999. (Growing Tree Ser.). (Illus.). 36p. (J). (ps-k). 7.95 (978-0-694-01304-3(8) , Harper Festival) HarperCollins Pubs.

Kraut, Julie & Lester, Shallon. Hot Mess: Summer in the City. 2008. 256p. (YA). (gr. 9). pap. 8.99 (*978-0-385-73506-3(5)); lib. bdg. 12.99 (*978-0-385-90499-5(1)) Random Hse. Children's Bks. (Delacorte Bks. for Young Readers).

Krensky, Stephen. Eeyore Has a Birthday. 2001. 10.79 (978-0-606-22514-4(5)) Tandem Library Bks.

—Lionel & His Friends. 1999. (Illus.). (J). (978-0-606-18418-2(X)) Tandem Library Bks.

Krisher, Trudy. Fallout. 2006. 272p. (J). 17.95 (978-0-8234-2035-3(3)) Holiday Hse., Inc.

Kroll, Virginia L. Forgiving a Friend. Billin-Frye, Paige, illus. 2005. (Way I ACT Ser.). 24p. (J). (gr. k-3). lib. bdg. 15.95 (978-0-8075-0618-9(4)) Whitman, Albert & Co.

—Jason Takes Responsibility. Cote, Nancy, illus. 2005. (Way I ACT Ser.). 24p. (J). (gr. k-3). lib. bdg. 15.95 (978-0-8075-2537-1(5)) Whitman, Albert & Co.

Kropp, Paul. The Countess & Me. 2003. (Illus.). (YA). pap. (978-1-55041-692-3(8)) Fitzhenry & Whiteside, Ltd.

Krosoczka, Jarrett J. My Buddy, Slug. 2006. (Illus.). 40p. (J). (gr. k-3). 15.95 (978-0-375-83342-7(0)); lib. bdg. 17.99 (978-0-375-93342-4(5)) Random Hse. Children's Bks. (Knopf Bks. for Young Readers).

Krulik, Nancy E. Can You Get an F in Lunch? 2007. (How I Survived Middle School Ser.: No. 1). 112p. (J). (gr. 4-7). pap. 4.99 (*978-0-439-02555-3(9)) Scholastic, Inc.

—Floppy Friends Go to School. Dellorco, Chris, illus. 1999. 32p. (J). (978-0-439-08767-4(8)) Scholastic, Inc.

—Friends for Never, No. 14. John and Wendy Staff, illus. 2004. (Katie Kazoo, Switcheroo Ser.: No. 14). 80p. (J). (gr. 2-5). pap. 3.99 (978-0-448-43606-7(X) , Grosset & Dunlap) Penguin Group (USA) Inc.

—Karate Katie, No. 18. John and Wendy Staff, illus. 2006. (Katie Kazoo, Switcheroo Ser.: No. 18). 80p. (J). (gr. 2-5). pap. 3.99 (978-0-448-43767-5(8) , Grosset & Dunlap) Penguin Group (USA) Inc.

—Love & Sk8. 2005. 320p. (YA). mass mkt. 3.99 (978-1-4169-0525-7(1) , Simon Pulse) Simon & Schuster Children's Publishing.

—Madame President. 2007. (How I Survived Middle School Ser.: No. 2). 112p. (J). pap. 3.99 (*978-0-439-02556-0(7)) Scholastic, Inc.

—New Girl. 2008. (How I Survived Middle School Ser.: No. 4). 112p. (J). pap. 4.99 (*978-0-545-01303-1(8) , Scholastic Paperbacks) Scholastic, Inc.

—Ripped at the Seams. 2005. (Romantic Comedies Ser.). 336p. (YA). mass mkt. 3.99 (978-1-4169-1146-3(4) , Simon Pulse) Simon & Schuster Children's Publishing.

—A Whirlwind Vacation. John and Wendy Staff, illus. 2005. (Katie Kazoo, Switcheroo Ser.). 160p. (gr. 2-5). mass mkt. 4.99 (978-0-448-43748-4(1) , Grosset & Dunlap) Penguin Group (USA) Inc.

Kuhn, Betsy. Not Exactly Nashville. 1999. (978-0-606-16708-6(0)) Tandem Library Bks.

Kuivila, Janet. The Gamma Girls of Chagrin Falls: Lillie, Rose & Irisa. 2004. 146p. pap. 12.95 (978-0-9763441-0-0(6)) Cats Ink.

Kulling, Monica. Edgar Badger's Butterfly Day. Twinem, Nancy, illus. 1999. 48p. (J). (gr. 1-5). pap. 4.50 (978-1-57255-604-1(8)) Mondo Publishing.

—Edgar Badger's Fishing Day. Twinem, Nancy, illus. 1999. 48p. (J). (gr. 1-5). pap. 4.50 (978-1-57255-603-4(X)) Mondo Publishing.

—Edgar Badger's Fishing Day. 1999. (gr. 3-6). lib. bdg. 12.40 (978-0-613-17198-4(5)) Tandem Library Bks.

Kulot-Frisch, Daniela. No Nos Pillaras! (SPA., Illus.). 120p. (J). (gr. k-2). 16.95 (978-84-261-3123-2(9) , JV2027) Juventud, Editorial ESP. *Dist:* Lectorum Pubns., Inc.

Kuns, Judith Irvin. While You Were Out. 2006. 144p. (J). (gr. 3). pap. 5.99 (978-0-14-240628-1(7) , Puffin) Penguin Group (USA) Inc.

Kurtz, Jane. Bicycle Madness. Peck, Beth, illus. rev. ed. 2003. 128p. (J). 15.95 (978-0-8050-6981-5(X) , Holt, Henry & Co. Bks. For Young Readers) Holt, Henry & Co.

—Does a Spider Wear a Seatbelt. 2004. (Illus.). (J). 14.00 (978-0-689-84482-9(4) , Aladdin) Simon & Schuster Children's Publishing.

—I'm Sorry Almira Ann. 2001. (J). pap. 10.95 (978-0-439-20645-7(6)) Scholastic, Inc.

Kurzweil, Allen. Leon & the Champion Chip. Bertholf, Bret, illus. 2005. 352p. (J). lib. bdg. 16.89 (978-0-06-053934-4(8)) HarperCollins Pubs.

Kyi, Tanya Lloyd. Truth. 2003. (Orca Soundings Ser.). 96p. (J). (gr. 7-12). pap. 7.95 (978-1-55143-265-6(X)) Orca Bk. Pubs. USA.

La Borde, Roger & Biddulph, Robert. Hello Kitty, Hello Love! 2003. (Illus.). 24p. (J). (ps-3). 12.95 (978-0-8109-8538-4(1)) Abrams, Harry N. , Inc.

La Fon-Cox, Angelique. A Tale of Kooshla & Saboo: in Heavenly Castles. 2006. (ENG.). 48p. per. 19.99 (*978-1-4259-7997-3(1)) AuthorHouse.

LaBate, Jim. Let's Go, Gaels: A Novella by Jim LaBate. Mosher, Jeff, illus. 1998. 60p. (YA). (gr. 7-12). pap. 5.95 (978-0-9662100-4-0(2)) Mohawk River Pr.

Labatt, Mary. Friend for Sam. 2003. (gr. k-3). lib. bdg. 11.80 (978-0-613-84410-9(6)) Tandem Library Bks.

Labatt, Mary & Sarrazin, Marisol. A Friend for Sam. 2004. (Kids Can Read! Ser.). (Illus.). 32p. (J). (gr. k-3). (978-1-55337-375-9(8)); (978-1-55337-374-2(X)) Kids Can Pr., Ltd.

Lacasse, Michael. George & His Special New Friends. 2005. 48p. pap. 12.95 (978-1-4137-8285-1(X)) PublishAmerica, Inc.

Lachtman, Ofelia Dumas. Tina & the Scarecrow Skins/Tina y las pieles de Espantapajaros. Colin, Jose Juan, tr. DeLange, Alex Pardo, illus. 2002. (ENG & SPA.). 32p. (J). 14.95 (978-1-55885-373-7(1) , Piñata Books) Arte Publico Pr.

Lacombe, Benjamin. Cherry & Olive. 2007. (J). (*978-0-8027-9708-7(3)) Walker & Co.

—Cherry & Olive. Lacombe, Benjamin, illus. 2007. (Illus.). 32p. (J). (ps-2). 16.95 (*978-0-8027-9707-0(5)) Walker & Co.

Lagartos, M. L., et al. Entre Amigos. (SPA & ENG., Illus.). (J). (gr. 4). 88p. wbk. ed. (978-84-7861-045-7(6)); Level 2. 2nd ed. 108p. tchr. ed. (978-84-7861-038-9(3)); Level 3. 74p. tchr. ed. (978-84-7861-047-1(2)); Level 3. 192p. stu. ed. (978-84-7861-044-0(8)) Coloquio, Editorial S.A.

—Entre Amigos. (SPA & ENG.). (J). (gr. 4). Level 1. stu. ed. 25.95 (978-84-7143-427-2(X) , SGS427X); Level 1. 64p. wbk. ed. 15.95 (978-84-7143-428-9(8) , SGS4288); Level 2. 4th ed. (Illus.). 160p. stu. ed. 25.95 (978-84-7143-472-2(5) , SGS725); Level 2. 4th ed. (Illus.). 68p. wbk. ed. 15.95 (978-84-7143-477-7(6) , SGS776) Sociedad General Espanola de Libreria ESP. *Dist:* Continental Bk. Co., Inc.

Lagonegro, Melissa. Friends for a Princess. Harchy, Atelier Philippe, illus. 2004. (Disney Princess Ser.). 32p. (J). (ps-1). pap. 3.99 (978-0-7364-2208-6(0) , RH/Disney) Random Hse. Children's Bks.

—Friends for a Princess. 2004. (Disney Princess Ser.). (ps-2). lib. bdg. 11.80 (978-0-613-73713-5(X)) Tandem Library Bks.

—Just Keep Swimming. Harchy, Atelier Philippe, illus. 2005. (Step into Reading Ser.). 32p. (J). (ps-2). pap. 3.99 (978-0-7364-2319-9(2) , RH/Disney) Random Hse. Children's Bks.

Laird, Elizabeth. Secret Friends. 2002. (Illus.). 96p. (J). pap. (978-0-340-66473-5(8) , Hodder Children's Books) Hodder Children's Division.

Lakin, Patricia. Beach Day! Nash, Scott, illus. 2004. 32p. (J). (ps). 15.99 (978-0-8037-2894-3(8) , Dial) Penguin Group (USA) Inc.

Lambert, Janet. Summer for Seven: A Dria Meredith Story. 2002. (J). per. 9.95 (978-1-930009-54-7(2) , 800-691-7779) Image Cascade Publishing.

—Where the Heart Is: A Christy Drayton Story. 2003. (J). pap. 9.95 (978-1-930009-83-7(6) , 800-691-7779) Image Cascade Publishing.

Lambert, Marilyn. Franny & Roxxy. 1999. (J). (gr. k-3). pap. 6.95 (978-0-533-12820-4(X)) Vantage Pr., Inc.

Lamote, Lisa Edman. Booklet Goes to the Doctor. 2006. (J). 15.99 (978-1-933673-02-8(8) , BookMann Pr.) Mann Publishing Group.

Lamperti, Noelle. Brown Like Me. 2nd l.t. ed. 1999. (Illus.). 32p. (J). (gr. 4-7). 12.95 (978-1-892281-03-6(1)) New Victoria Pubs., Inc.

Lamson, Sharon. Squiggz Rides the Big Storm: A Story about Overcoming Fear. Barry, Bruce, illus. 2006. 32p. (J). 7.99 (978-0-310-71005-9(7)) Zonderkidz.

Landolf, Diane Wright. Hog & Dog. Harris, Jennifer Beck, illus. 2005. (Step into Reading Ser.: Vol. 1). 32p. (J). (ps-1). pap. 3.99 (978-0-375-83165-2(7) , Random Hse. Bks. for Young Readers) Random Hse. Children's Bks.

Landon, Kristen. Life in the Pit. Johnson, Regan, illus. 2007. 192p. (YA). (gr. 8-12). 16.95 (*978-1-933831-08-4(1)) Blooming Tree Pr.

Lane, Ronald. Avina's Song: A Children's Story. 2007. (ENG.). 48p. per. 12.95 (*978-1-4241-6252-9(1)) PublishAmerica, Inc.

Lang, George. Pixy's Holiday Journey. 2006. 33.99 (*978-1-4280-4243-8(1)); pap. 26.99 (*978-1-4280-4261-2(X)) IndyPublish.com.

Langan, Paul. Summer of Secrets. 2008. (Bluford Ser.). 160p. (J). pap. 3.99 (*978-0-439-90491-9(9) , Scholastic Paperbacks) Scholastic, Inc.

Lange, Nikki Bataille. Cheer up! a Care Bears Feeling Book: A Plush Face Book with Flocking. Moore, Saxton, illus. 2009. (Care Bears Ser.). 10p. (J). ring bd. 11.95 (*978-1-57791-301-6(9)) Brighter Minds Children's Publishing.

Langston, Laura. Perfect Blue. 2008. 220p. pap. (*978-1-55455-058-6(0)) Fitzhenry & Whiteside, Ltd.

Lankester-Brisley, Joyce. Milly-Molly-Mandy Storybook. 2001. (Milly-Molly-Mandy Ser.). (Illus.). 224p. (J). (gr. k-3). tchr. ed. 13.95 (978-0-7534-5332-2(0) , Kingfisher) Houghton Mifflin Co. Trade & Reference Div.

Larsen, Alison. Thomas the Turtle's Adventures. 2006. (Illus.). 30p. (J). per. 14.95 (978-1-60002-096-4(8) , 3962, Airleaf Publishing) Airleaf Publishing & Bookselling.

Las amigas de Mari: Individual Title Six-Packs. (Coleccion Pm Ser.).Tr. of Sally's friends. (SPA.). 16p. (gr. 1 up). 26.00 (978-0-7578-3010-5(2)) Rigby Education.

Lasenby, Jack. Taur. (Travellers Ser.: No. 2). (Illus.). 160p. (YA). (gr. 8 up). pap. 13.00 (978-1-877135-18-7(6)) Longacre Pr. NZL. *Dist:* Pacific Island Bks.

The Last Coqui. 2002. (J). 16.00 (978-0-9675413-4-1(4)) Libros, Encouraging Cultural Literacy.

Lattany, Kristin Hunter. Kinfolks. 2000. (gr. 7-12). lib. bdg. 15.30 (978-0-613-21861-0(2)) Tandem Library Bks.

Laurens, Jennifer. Falling for Romeo. 2007. (YA). per. 12.95 (*978-1-933963-94-5(8)) Grove Creek Publishing, LLC.

Law, Felicia. Rumble Meets Penny Panther. 2005. (Read-It! Readers Ser.). (Illus.). 32p. (J). (ps-k). lib. bdg. 18.60 (978-1-4048-1331-1(4)) Picture Window Bks.

Lawler, Rick. Majesty Blake in Queen of the Trillis. 2001. (J). pap. 8.50 (978-1-930322-02-8(X) , 193032202X) MinRef Pr.

Lawrence, Megan & Lawrence, Kevin. Sarah on Ice: A Skater's Story. 2002. 128p. pap. 10.95 (978-0-595-25379-1(2) , Writers Club Pr.) iUniverse, Inc.

Lawrinson, Julia. Obsession. 2001. 264p. pap. 13.95 (978-1-86368-324-1(0)) Fremantle Pr. AUS. *Dist:* International Specialized Bk. Services.

—Skating the Edge. 2002. 360p. pap. 14.95 (978-1-86368-379-1(8)) Fremantle Pr. AUS. *Dist:* International Specialized Bk. Services.

Lawson, Julie. Ghost of Avalanche Mountain. 2000. (gr. 5-8). lib. bdg. 16.40 (978-0-613-34731-0(5)) Tandem Library Bks.

Lawson, Rob, illus. Duke Finds a Home. 2006. (Duke's Tails Ser.). 32p. (J). (978-0-9779308-0-7(7)) Bush Brothers & Co.

Lay, Eddie. Mystery of the Hats. 2006. 61p. pap. 12.95 (978-1-4241-2649-1(5)) PublishAmerica, Inc.

Lay, Kathryn. Crown Me! 2004. 208p. (J). (gr. 4-6). tchr. ed. 16.95 (978-0-8234-1845-9(6)) Holiday Hse., Inc.

Lazo, Jeanne Rae. If Looks Could Kill. 2005. 160p. (J). lib. bdg. 14.95 (978-0-9713756-4-2(X)) Stargazer Publishing Co.

Le Guin, Ursula K. Tom Mouse. ed. 2004. (Illus.). (J). (gr. k-3). spiral bd. (978-0-616-14584-5(5)) Canadian National Institute for the Blind/Institut National Canadien pour les Aveugles.

—Very Far Away from Anywhere Else. 2004. 144p. (YA). pap. 6.95 (978-0-15-205208-9(9) , Harcourt Paperbacks) Harcourt Children's Bks.

Le Jars, David. Mis Amigos, Los Animales. 2004. (Hablemos Ser.). (SPA., Illus.). 24p. (J). (ps-k). pap. 5.95 (978-1-58728-950-7(4) , Two Can Publishing) T&N Children's Publishing.

—Mis Amigos, Los Animales. 2000. (SPA., Illus.). (J). (978-0-606-20801-7(1)) Tandem Library Bks.

Leah's Song Apple. 2003. (J). pap. 2.75 (978-0-590-44567-2(7)) Scholastic, Inc.

LeapFrog Staff, compiled by. The Wizard of Oz. 2001. (J). spiral bd. 14.99 (978-1-58605-044-3(3)) LeapFrog Enterprises, Inc.

Leberer, Sigrid. The Adventures of the Three Best Friends. 2004. (Charming Collection of Five Short Stories Ser.). (Illus.). 22p. (J). bds. 6.99 (978-1-59384-056-3(X)) Parklane Publishing.

LeBlanc, Anne & Sterling Publishing Company Staff. Benjamin Finds a Friend. 1999. (Adventures with Benjamin Bear Ser.). (Illus.). 20p. (J). (ps-k). 4.95 (978-0-8069-1923-2(X)) Sterling Publishing Co., Inc.

Leblanc, Louise. Leo & Julio. Cummins, Sarah, tr. Brochard, Philippe, illus. 1999. (First Novels Ser.: Vol. 32). 64p. (J). (gr. 1-5). (978-0-88780-479-3(9)) Formac Publishing Co., Ltd. CAN. *Dist:* Casemate Pubs. & Bk. Distributors, LLC.

Leblanc, Louise. Leo's Poster Challenge. Prud'homme, Jules & Cummins, Sarah, trs. from FRE. Prud'homme, Jules, illus. 2003. (First Novel Ser.). 64p. (J). (gr. 2-5). 4.95 (978-0-88780-608-7(2)) Formac Publishing Co., Ltd. CAN. *Dist:* Casemate Pubs. & Bk. Distributors, LLC.

—Leo's Poster Challenge. Prud'homme, Jules & Cummins, Sarah, trs. from FRE. Prud'homme, Jules & Jules, Prud'homme, illus. 2003. (First Novel Ser.). 64p. (J). (gr. 2-5). (*978-0-88780-609-4(0)) Formac Publishing Co., Ltd. CAN. *Dist:* Casemate Pubs. & Bk. Distributors, LLC.

Ledbetter, Penny S. Mushroom's Day Away. Garrett, Caroline S., illus. 2005. 32p. (J). 9.95 (978-1-933251-19-6(0)) Parkway Pubs., Inc.

Lee, Huy Voun. In the Leaves. rev. ed. 2005. (Illus.). 32p. (J). (ps-ps). 16.95 (978-0-8050-6764-4(7) , Holt, Henry & Co. Bks. For Young Readers) Holt, Henry & Co.

Lee, Janice G. The Adventures of Chewy & Tonk. 2003. (Illus.). 40p. (J). per. (978-1-55306-599-9(9) , Guardian Bks.) Essence Publishing.

Lee, Marie G. F Is for Fabuloso. 1999. 192p. (J). (gr. 5-9). 15.95 (978-0-380-97648-5(X)) HarperCollins Pubs.

Lee, Nancy. Baby Chipmunks & Backyard Friends. 2005. (J). 9.95 (978-0-9772078-2-4(X)) Journey Pubns., LLC.

—Hoover's Funny Little Kids. 2005. (J). spiral bd. 8.95 (978-0-9748087-8-9(4)) Journey Pubns., LLC.

Lee, Quinlan B. Let's Explore!, Bks. 1-6. 2007. (Dora the Explorer Ser.: Bks. 1-6). 112p. (J). pap. 5.99 (978-0-439-90237-3(1)) Scholastic, Inc.

—Littlest Pet Shop: Best Friends. 2006. (Scholastic Reader Ser.: Vol. 2). (Illus.). 32p. (J). pap. 3.99 (978-0-439-88776-2(3)) Scholastic, Inc.

—On the Go! 2007. (Dora the Explorer Ser.: Bks. 7-12). 112p. (J). pap. 5.99 (978-0-439-90238-0(X)) Scholastic, Inc.

Lee, Tiffany A. Meadow City Presents: A New Friend. 2006. 52p. pap. 12.95 (978-1-4241-4374-0(8)) PublishAmerica, Inc.

Leeds, Constance & Bennett, Constance. The Silver Cup. 2007. 240p. (YA). (gr. 6-9). 16.99 (978-0-670-06157-0(3) , Viking Adult) Penguin Group (USA) Inc.

Leese, Jennifer L. B. Two Spots Bakery. 2004. 41p. pap. 19.95 (978-1-4137-3207-8(0)) PublishAmerica, Inc.

Leeson, Christine. Molly & the Storm. Hansen, Gaby, illus. 2003. 32p. (J). (gr. k-2). tchr. ed. 15.95 (978-1-58925-027-7(3) , tiger tales) ME Media LLC.

Leeson, Robert. Liar. 128p. (J). 9.95 (978-0-14-130143-3(0)) Penguin Bks., Ltd. GBR. *Dist:* Trafalgar Square Publishing.

Leeuwen, Jeanne Van. Oliver & Albert, Friends Forever. 2002. (gr. k-3). lib. bdg. 11.80 (978-0-613-86258-5(9)) Tandem Library Bks.

Legault, Anne & Franson, Leanne. Une Fille Pas Comme les Autres. 2002. (Roman Jeunesse Ser.). (FRE.). 96p. (YA). (gr. 4-7). pap. (978-2-89021-299-2(8)) Diffusion du livre Mirabel.

Lehmkuhl, Pat, illus. Starlight, Star Bright: (the Starlight Books, 3), 6 vols. 2003. (Starlight Bks.: Bk. 3). 192p. (J). (gr. 3-7). per. 9.00 (978-0-9714161-2-3(5)) Raven Publishing Inc. of Montana.

Leland, Debbie. The Jalapeno Man. Rife, Ann Hollis, illus. 2000. 24p. (J). (ps-5). 14.95 (978-0-9667086-1-5(X)) Wildflower Run.

LeMieux, Anne Connelly. Dare to Be, M. E.! 1998. (J). (gr. 3-7). pap. 3.99 (978-0-380-72889-3(3)) HarperCollins Pubs.

Lemieux, Jean. Toby's Best Friend. Casson, Sophie & Cummins, Sarah, trs. from FRE. Casson, Sophie, illus. 2003. (First Novel Ser.). 64p. (J). (gr. 2-5). 4.95 (978-0-88780-610-0(4)); (*978-0-88780-611-7(2)) Formac Publishing Co., Ltd. CAN. *Dist:* Casemate Pubs. & Bk. Distributors, LLC.

Lemieux, Jean & Casson, Sophie. Le Bonheur Est une Tempjte Avec un Chien. 2002. (Premier Roman Ser.). (FRE., Illus.). 64p. pap. (978-2-89021-568-9(7)) Diffusion du livre Mirabel.

Lenam, Salva. Kiko Juega con Sus Amigos. Roman, Santi, illus. 2005. (Kiko Ser.). (SPA.). 10p. (J). 3.95 (978-84-95761-79-8(3)) Ediciones Norte, Inc.

L'Engle, Madeleine. A Wrinkle in Time. 2007. 224p. (J). 6.99 (978-0-312-36755-8(4)); pap. 6.99 (978-0-312-36754-1(6)) Square Fish.

Lenhard, Elizabeth. A Bridge Between Worlds. 2004. (W. I. T. C. H. Ser.: Bk. 10). 158p. (J). lib. bdg. 16.92 (*978-1-4242-0796-1(7)) Fitzgerald Bks.

—Different Path. 2004. (W. I. T. C. H. Ser.: Bk. 13). 158p. (J). lib. bdg. 16.92 (*978-1-4242-0791-6(6)) Fitzgerald Bks.

—The Disappearance. 2004. (W. I. T. C. H. Ser.: Bk. 2). 158p. (J). lib. bdg. 16.92 (*978-1-4242-0799-2(1)) Fitzgerald Bks.

—Finding Meridian. 2004. (W. I. T. C. H. Ser.: Bk. 3). 158p. (J). lib. bdg. 16.92 (*978-1-4242-0801-2(7)) Fitzgerald Bks.

—It's a Purl Thing. (YA). 2006. 288p. (gr. 7). pap. 6.99 (978-0-14-240695-3(3) , Puffin); 2005. (Illus.). 272p. (gr. 6-10). 16.99 (978-0-525-47622-1(9) , Dutton Juvenile) Penguin Group (USA) Inc.

—Knit Two Together. 272p. (gr. 7). 2008. (YA). pap. 7.99 (*978-0-14-241013-4(6) , Puffin); 2006. (J). 16.99 (978-0-525-47764-8(0) , Dutton Juvenile) Penguin Group (USA) Inc.

—Knitwise. 2007. 272p. (YA). (gr. 7). 16.99 (*978-0-525-47838-6(8) , Dutton Juvenile) Penguin Group (USA) Inc.

—Power of Five. 2004. 158p. (J). lib. bdg. 16.92 (*978-1-4242-0795-4(9)) Fitzgerald Bks.

Lenhard, Elizabeth, adapted by. The Fire of Friendship. 4th rev. ed. 2004. (W. I. T. C. H. Ser.: Bk. 4). (Illus.). 144p. (gr. 3-7). pap. 4.99 (978-0-7868-1731-3(3) , Disney Editions) Disney Pr.

Lenhard, Elizabeth, adapted by. The Return of a Queen. 2004. (W. I. T. C. H. Ser.: Bk. 12). 152p. (J). lib. bdg. 16.92 (*978-1-4242-0797-8(5)) Fitzgerald Bks.

Lennon, John. Amor Verdadero: Dibujos para Sean (Real Love: The Drawings for Sean) 2001. (SPA & ENG.). 44p. (J). (gr. k-1). 10.36 (978-84-233-3180-2(6)) Ediciones Destino ESP. *Dist:* Lectorum Pubns., Inc.

Leonard, Elise. Monday Morning Blitz. 2007. (Al's World Ser.). 144p. (J). (gr. 5-9). pap. 5.99 (*978-1-4169-3464-6(2) , Aladdin) Simon & Schuster Children's Publishing.

Leonard, Finley Mary. The Story of the Big Front Door. 2007. (ENG.). 192p. 19.99 (*978-1-4280-7183-4(0)); per. 13.99 (*978-1-4280-7193-3(8)) IndyPublish.com.

Leonard, Marcia. Best Friends. Handelman, Dorothy, photos by. 1999. (Real Kids Readers Ser.). (Illus.). 32p. (gr. k-1). (J). pap. 4.99 (978-0-7613-2089-0(X)); lib. bdg. 18.90 (978-0-7613-2064-7(4)) Lerner Publishing Group. (Millbrook Pr.).

—Best Friends. (J). (978-0-606-19144-9(5)); 1999. lib. bdg. 13.00 (978-0-613-18155-6(7)) Tandem Library Bks.

—Mejores Amigas. Handelman, Dorothy, photos by. 2005. (ENG & SPA., Illus.). 32p. (J). (ps-1). pap. 4.99 (978-0-8225-3291-0(3)) Lerner Publishing Group.

—Mejores Amigas: Nivel 1. Handelman, Dorothy, photos by. 2005. (Lecturas para Niños de Verdad (Real Kids Readers) Ser.). (SPA., Illus.). 32p. (J). (gr. 1-1). pap. 4.99 (978-0-8225-3290-3(5) , Ediciones Lerner) Lerner Publishing Group.

—My Pal Al. Handelman, Dorothy, photos by. 1998. (Real Kids Readers Ser.). (Illus.). 32p. (gr. k-1). (J). pap. 4.99 (978-0-7613-2026-5(1)); lib. bdg. 18.90 (978-0-7613-2001-2(6)) Lerner Publishing Group. (Millbrook Pr.).

Leonard, Mary T. Three Best Friends. Russell, Terry, illus. 2004. 96p. (J). per. 12.00 (978-0-9740683-8-1(1)) Authors & Artists Publishers of New York, Inc.

Lerangis, Peter. Too Hot, No. 3. 2008. (Drama Club Ser.). 224p. (YA). (gr. 7). 7.99 (*978-0-14-241051-6(9) , Puffin) Penguin Group (USA) Inc.

Lerman, Drew. Magic City. 2007. 288p. (YA). (gr. 9 up). pap. 7.99 (978-0-439-89027-4(6) , PUSH) Scholastic, Inc.

Les Becquets, Diane. Love, Cajun Style. 2007. (Illus.). 304p. (YA). pap. 7.95 (978-1-59990-030-8(0) , Bloomsbury Children) Bloomsbury Publishing.

—The Stones of Mourning Creek. 2005. 306p. (YA). (gr. 7). reprint ed. pap. 6.95 (978-0-7614-5238-6(9)) Cavendish, Marshall Corp.

—The Stones of Mourning Creek. 2001. (Illus.). 320p. (J). (gr. 7 up). 16.95 (978-1-58837-004-4(6)) Winslow Pr.

Lescarbeau, Nicole. Ellie's Allies. 2006. 79p. pap. 14.95 (978-1-4241-0446-8(7)) PublishAmerica, Inc.

Lesczynski, Jim. The Walton Street Tycoons. 2007. 269p. (YA). pap. 9.95 (***978-0-9791283-0-1(7)***) East River Pr.

Leslie, Robyn. Rinny & the Trail of Clues. 2003. Orig. Title: Miss President & the Trail of Clues. (Illus.). 192p. (J). pap. 7.95 (978-0-9727388-8-0(6)) Sugar Ducky Bks., Inc.

LeSourd, Nancy. Liberty Letters: The Personal Correspondence of Emma Edmonds & Mollie Turner, Civil War Spies, 1862. 2004. (Liberty Letters Ser.). 224p. (J). 9.99 (978-0-310-70352-5(2)) Zonderkidz.

—The Personal Correspondence of Catherine Clark & Meredith Lyons: Pearl Harbor, 1941. 2004. (Liberty Letters Ser.). (Illus.). 240p. (J). (gr. 5 up). 9.99 (978-0-310-70353-2(0)) Zonderkidz.

Lester, Helen. Listen, Buddy. Munsinger, Lynn, illus. 2002. (J). 14.74 (978-0-7587-2993-4(6)) Book Wholesalers, Inc.

Let's Be Friends. 2005. (Illus.). 26p. (J). (ps-k). bds. 7.95 (978-0-8249-6587-7(6)) Ideals Pubns.

Leverich, Kathleen. Best Enemies. 1998. 11.79 (978-0-606-13195-7(7)) Tandem Library Bks.

—Best Enemies Again. 1999. (Best Enemies Ser.). (Illus.). 96p. (J). (gr. 2-5). pap. 4.95 (978-0-688-16197-2(9) , Harper Trophy) HarperCollins Pubs.

Levering-Duff, Judy. Barnaby Wetzel, Boy Wizard. 2003. 128p. (J). 1450.00 (978-0-9725874-2-6(X)); pap. 7.50 (978-0-9725874-3-3(8)) Outskirts Press, Inc.

Levert, Mireille. Lucy's Secret. 2004. (Illus.). 32p. (J). 15.95 (978-0-88899-566-7(0)) Groundwood Bks. CAN. *Dist:* Perseus Distribution.

Levin, Betty. Creature Crossing. Smith, Joseph A., illus. 1999. 96p. (J). (gr. 3 up). 15.00 (978-0-688-16220-7(7)) HarperCollins Pubs.

—Thorn. 2005. 176p. (J). (gr. 5). 16.95 (978-1-932425-46-8(2) , Lemniscaat) Boyds Mills Pr.

Levine, Gail Carson. Ella Enchanted. movie tie-in ed. 2004. 288p. (J). (gr. 7 up). pap. 6.99 (978-0-06-055886-4(5)) HarperCollins Pubs.

—Ella Enchanted. 2004. (gr. 7-12). lib. bdg. 15.30 (978-0-613-71408-2(3)); 1998. 238p. (J). (ps-7). lib. bdg. 14.75 (978-0-613-07691-3(5)) Tandem Library Bks.

—The Wish. 2005. 256p. (J). (gr. 7 up). pap. 6.50 (978-0-06-075911-7(9) , Harper Trophy) HarperCollins Pubs.

—The Wish. 2001. (gr. 3-6). lib. bdg. 14.15 (978-0-613-44274-9(1)); 2000. (978-0-606-22297-6(9)) Tandem Library Bks.

Levinson, Nancy Smiler. Prairie Friends. Schuett, Stacey, illus. 2003. (I Can Read Bks.). 64p. (J). (gr. k-3). 15.99 (978-0-06-028001-7(8)) HarperCollins Pubs.

Levinson, Robin K. Shoshana & the Native Rose. Kehl, Drusilla, illus. 2006. 103p. (J). (gr. 3-5). per. 12.00 (978-0-9773673-2-0(0)) Gali Girls, Inc.

Levithan, David. Are We There Yet? 2005. 224p. (YA). (gr. 7-12). 15.95 (978-0-375-82846-1(X) , Knopf Bks. for Young Readers) Random Hse. Children's Bks.

—Boy Meets Boy. 2005. 192p. (YA). (gr. 7-12). reprint ed. pap. 8.95 (978-0-375-83299-4(8) , Knopf Bks. for Young Readers) Random Hse. Children's Bks.

Levitin, Sonia. Strange Relations. 2007. 304p. (gr. 7). (J). 15.99 (978-0-375-83751-7(5)); (YA). lib. bdg. 18.99 (978-0-375-93751-4(X)) Random Hse. Children's Bks. (Knopf Bks. for Young Readers).

Levoy, Myron. Three Friends. 2000. 196p. (YA). (gr. 7-12). pap. 12.95 (978-0-595-09352-6(3)) iUniverse, Inc.

Levy, Elizabeth. A Hare-Raising Tail. Gerstein, Mordicai, illus. 2002. (gr. 3-6). lib. bdg. 11.80 (978-0-613-70720-6(6)) Tandem Library Bks.

—Seventh-Grade Tango. 2001. (J). (978-0-606-22571-7(4)) Tandem Library Bks.

—Seventh-Grade Tango. l.t. ed. 2001. (Illus.). 174p. (J). (gr. 3-7). 20.95 (978-0-7862-3105-8(X)) Thorndike Pr.

Levy, Michael. The Inspiring Story of Little Goody Two Shoes. 2007. 139p. (YA). per. 12.95 (***978-0-9668069-9-1(9)***) Point of Life, Inc.

Lewis, Beverly. Best Friend, Worst Enemy. rev. ed. 2001. (Holly's Heart Ser.: Bk. 1). 160p. (YA). (gr. 6-9). pap. 6.99 (978-0-7642-2500-0(6)) Bethany Hse. Pubs.

—Better Than Best. 2000. (Girls Only (Go!) Ser.: Vol. 6). (Illus.). 128p. (J). (gr. 3-8). pap. 6.99 (978-1-55661-641-9(4)) Bethany Hse. Pubs.

—Freshman Frenzy. 2003. (Holly's Heart Ser.: Bk. 11). (Illus.). 160p. (YA). pap. 6.99 (978-0-7642-2618-2(5)) Bethany Hse. Pubs.

—Little White Lies. 2003. (Holly's Heart Ser.: Bk. 10). 160p. (YA). (gr. 5-9). reprint ed. pap. 6.99 (978-0-7642-2617-5(7)) Bethany Hse. Pubs.

—Mystery Letters. 2003. (Holly's Heart Ser.: Bk. 12). (Illus.). 160p. (YA). reprint ed. pap. 6.99 (978-0-7642-2619-9(3)) Bethany Hse. Pubs.

—Second-Best Friend. 2002. (Holly's Heart Ser.: Bk. 6). 160p. (YA). pap. 6.99 (978-0-7642-2505-5(7)) Bethany Hse. Pubs.

—Star Status. 2002. (Girls Only (Go!) Ser.: Vol. 8). 128p. (J). reprint ed. pap. 6.99 (978-1-55661-643-3(0)) Bethany Hse. Pubs.

—Straight-A Teacher. 2002. (Holly's Heart Ser.: Bk. 8). 160p. (YA). pap. 6.99 (978-0-7642-2615-1(0)) Bethany Hse. Pubs.

Lewis, C. S. Los Cuatro Amigos. (Coleccion Pequenos Clasicos). (SPA.). 24p. (gr. k-3). (J). (978-84-246-2532-0(3) , GL7952); 2003. (978-84-246-1923-7(4) , GL30509) La Galera, S.A. Editorial ESP. *Dist:* Lectorum Pubns., Inc.

Lewis, Doreen. The Bubblegum Babes' Guide to Sixth Grade. 2005. (J). per. 9.95 (978-0-9769193-0-8(3)) Helm Publishing.

Lewis, E. B. This Little Light of Mine. 2005. (Illus.). 32p. (J). 16.95 (978-0-689-83179-9(X) , Simon & Schuster Children's Publishing) Simon & Schuster Children's Publishing.

Lewis, James. September Saturdays. 2002. 166p. (YA). pap. 12.95 (978-0-595-21219-4(0) , Writers Club Pr.) iUniverse, Inc.

Lewis, Kim. Good Night Harry. Lewis, Kim, illus. 2004. (Illus.). 32p. (J). (ps-1). 15.99 (978-0-7636-2206-0(0)) Candlewick Pr.

—Here We Go, Harry. Lewis, Kim, illus. 2005. (Illus.). 32p. (J). (ps-1). 15.99 (978-0-7636-2549-8(3)) Candlewick Pr.

Lewis, Rob. Friends. (Illus.). 32p. (J). pap. 8.95 (978-0-09-926612-9(1) , Arrow Bks., Ltd.) Random Hse. GBR. *Dist:* Trafalgar Square Publishing.

Lewison, Wendy Cheyette. Easter Bunny's Amazing Egg Machine. 2002. (ps-2). lib. bdg. 10.95 (978-0-613-83538-1(7)) Tandem Library Bks.

—Princess Buttercup: A Flower Princess Story. 2001. (ps-2). lib. bdg. 11.80 (978-0-613-35619-0(5)) Tandem Library Bks.

Lewman, David. Hands Off. 2007. 24p. (J). 21.35 (***978-1-59961-365-9(4)***) Spotlight.

L'Homme, Erik. The Mystery of Lord Sha. 2006. (Book of the Stars Ser.: Bk. 2). 288p. (J). pap. 5.99 (978-0-439-65073-1(9) , Scholastic Paperbacks) Scholastic, Inc.

Licciardi, Paula. Wasting Calvin's Time. 2006. 9.00 (978-0-8059-8138-4(1)) Dorrance Publishing Co., Inc.

Light's Adventure's with Friends. 2005. (J). spiral bd. 7.00 (978-0-9743223-2-2(6)) Jones, Augustine R.

Likins, Kim. Charlie's Special Friends. 2004. (Illus.). 32p. (J). lib. bdg. 19.95 (978-0-9729987-1-0(3)) Island Friends LLC.

Limb, Sue. Girl, 15, Charming but Insane. 2004. (Girl, 15 Ser.). 214p. (J). (gr. 5). per. 16.00 (978-0-606-33729-8(6)) Tandem Library Bks.

—Girl 15, Charming but Insane. 2007. (Girl, 15 Ser.). 224p. (YA). (gr. 7-11). mass mkt. 5.99 (978-0-440-23896-6(X) , Laurel Leaf) Random Hse. Children's Bks.

—Girl, 15, Charming but Insane. 2005. (Girl, 15 Ser.). 240p. (J). (gr. 5). reprint ed. pap. 8.95 (978-0-385-73215-4(5) , Delacorte Bks. for Young Readers) Random Hse. Children's Bks.

—Girl, Going on 17: Pants on Fire. (Girl, 15 Ser.). (gr. 5 up). 2007. 256p. (YA). pap. 8.99 (***978-0-385-73219-2(8)***); 2006. 240p. (J). 14.95 (978-0-385-73218-5(X)); 2006. 240p. (YA). lib. bdg. 17.99 (978-0-385-90246-5(8)) Random Hse. Children's Bks. (Delacorte Bks. for Young Readers).

Limb, Sue. Girl, (Nearly) 16: Absolute Torture. (Girl, 15 Ser.). 224p. (YA). (gr. 5-11). 2008. mass mkt. 6.50 (***978-0-440-23897-3(8)*** , Laurel Leaf); 2006. pap. 8.95 (978-0-385-73217-8(1) , Delacorte Bks. for Young Readers) Random Hse. Children's Bks.

Lin, Grace. Lissy's Friends. Lin, Grace, illus. 2007. (Illus.). 40p. (J). (gr. k-2). 15.99 (978-0-670-06072-6(0) , Viking Juvenile) Penguin Group (USA) Inc.

Lind, Kathleen. Best Friends. Lind, Kathleen & Simonis, Cheryl, illus. 2005. (J). 4.95 (978-1-58597-305-7(X)) Leathers Publishing.

Lindbergh, Anne M. The Worry Week. Hawkes, Kevin, illus. 2003. 142p. reprint ed. pap. 12.95 (978-1-56792-239-4(2)) Godine, David R. Pub.

Lindquist, N. J. Best of Friends, 4 vols., Vol. 1. 2nd rev. ed. 2000. (Circle of Friends Ser.: Vol. 1). 192p. (gr. 4-12). pap. (978-0-9685495-1-3(9)) That's Life! Communications.

—Friends in Need. 2000. (Circle of Friends Ser.: Vol. 3). 208p. (gr. 7 up). pap. 7.95 (978-0-9685495-4-4(3) , 973-008) That's Life! Communications CAN. *Dist:* STL Distribution North America, Spring Arbor Distributors, Inc.

—Friends Like These. 2000. (Circle of Friends Ser.: Vol. 2). 200p. (gr. 7 up). pap. 7.95 (978-0-9685495-2-0(7)) That's Life! Communications CAN. *Dist:* STL Distribution North America, Spring Arbor Distributors, Inc.

—More Than Friends Vol. 4: Circle of Friends. 2004. (Circle of Friends Ser.: 4). 224p. pap. 9.95 (978-0-9685495-5-1(1)) That's Life! Communications CAN. *Dist:* STL Distribution North America.

Linz, Kathryn. Jim Brandon's Adventures. 2006. (ENG.). 100p. per. 14.95 (***978-1-4241-3160-0(X)***) PublishAmerica, Inc.

Lionni, Leo. An Extraordinary Egg. Lionni, Leo, illus. 1998. (Illus.). 32p. (J). (gr. k-ps). pap. 6.99 (978-0-679-89385-1(7) , Dragonfly Bks.) Random Hse. Children's Bks.

Lipp, Frederick J. Bread Song. Gaillard, Jason, tr. Gaillard, Jason, illus. 2004. (J). 15.95 (978-1-59336-000-9(2)); pap. (978-1-59336-001-6(0)) Mondo Publishing.

Lisle, Janet Taylor. Black Duck. (J). (gr. 5 up). 2007. 256p. 6.99 (***978-0-14-240902-2(2)*** , Puffin); 2006. 240p. 15.99 (978-0-399-23963-2(4) , Philomel) Penguin Group (USA) Inc.

Lisle, Janet Taylor. La Tarde de los Elfos. 2001. (SPA.). (YA). (gr. 5-8). 8.95 (978-958-04-2385-0(7) , NR2410) Norma S.A. COL. *Dist:* Distribuidora Norma, Inc., Lectorum Pubns., Inc.

List, Gloria A. A Heart That Finds His Way: More on the Line. Sturcke, Otto, illus. 2005. 18p. (J). pap. 7.95 (978-0-9709861-0-8(6)) Fingerprint Bks.

Literature Connections English: The Friends. 2004. (gr. 6-12). (978-0-395-77541-7(8) , 2-80110) McDougal Littell Inc.

Litkowski, Mary Pelagia. Two Hearts, One Great Love: Frank Duff & Edel Quinn. Slater, Nancy Sandoual et al, illus. 2000. 80p. (YA). (gr. 7 up). pap. 7.95 (978-0-916927-24-0(5)) Growth Unlimited, Inc.

Litteken, Erin. Stinky Mcpew Is Not Gonna Move! 2005. 48p. pap. 12.95 (978-1-4137-6432-1(0)) PublishAmerica, Inc.

Little Blue Kite & Friends Activity Book. 2005. (YA). per. (978-1-59872-122-5(4)) Instantpublisher.com.

Little Engine- Animal Friends. 2005. (J). (978-1-4194-0023-0(1)) Paradise Pr., Inc.

Little Engine-AV Friends Forever. 2005. (J). (978-1-4194-0010-0(X)) Paradise Pr., Inc.

Little Engine-Circus Friends. 2005. (J). (978-1-4194-0005-6(3)) Paradise Pr., Inc.

Little Is Big. 2006. (Illus.). (J). (978-1-882601-58-5(0)) See-More's Workshop.

Little, Jean. Emma's Magic Winter. Plecas, Jennifer, illus. (I Can Read Bks.). 64p. (J). (ps-3). 2000. pap. 3.99 (978-0-06-443706-6(X) , Harper Trophy); 1998. 15.95 (978-0-06-025389-9(4)); 1998. 15.89 (978-0-06-025390-5(8)) HarperCollins Pubs.

—Emma's Magic Winter. 2000. (gr. k-3). lib. bdg. 11.80 (978-0-613-27805-8(4)) Tandem Library Bks.

Little, Rich. Will's New Backpack. Lenoir, Jane, illus. 2000. (J). cd-rom 9.95 (978-1-58338-246-2(1)) Crossroads-Pub.com.

Livingston, Irene. Finklehopper Frog Cheers. Lies, Brian, illus. 2005. 32p. (J). 14.95 (978-1-58246-138-0(4) , Tricycle Pr.) Ten Speed Pr.

Lizzie McGuire Movie Scrapbook. 2003. (Illus.). 48p. (J). pap. 6.99 (978-0-7868-4583-5(X)) Disney Pr.

Llama on the Lam. 2001. (LLAMA ON THE LAM). 96p. (J). 22.00 (978-0-9649083-4-5(4)) Black River Trading Co.

Lloyd-Jones, Sally. Handbag Friends. Heap, Sue, illus. 2006. 64p. (J). bds. 11.95 (978-0-385-75096-7(X) , Fickling, David Bks.) Random Hse. Children's Bks.

Lobel, Arnold. Dias con Sapo y Sepo. (SPA.). 72p. (J). (gr. 1-6). 8.95 (978-84-204-3743-9(3)) Santillana USA Publishing Co., Inc.

—Friendship Stories You Can Share. 2001. (gr. 3-6). lib. bdg. 11.80 (978-0-613-56381-9(6)) Tandem Library Bks.

—Sapo y Sepo, Inseparables. Lobel, Arnold, illus. (Sapo Y Sepo Ser.). (SPA., Illus.). 66p. (J). (gr. k-3). pap. 8.95 (978-968-19-1025-9(7)) Santillana USA Publishing Co., Inc.

—Sapo y Sepo Son Amigos. Lobel, Arnold, illus. 2003. (SPA.). 66p. (J). (gr. k-3). pap. 12.95 (978-968-19-0714-3(0)) Aguilar, Altea, Taurus, Alfaguara, S.A. de C.V MEX. *Dist:* Santillana USA Publishing Co., Inc.

—Sapo y Sepo un Ano Entero. 2003. (Infantil Alfaguara Ser.). (SPA., Illus.). 66p. (J). (gr. k-3). pap. 8.95 (978-84-204-3052-2(8)) Santillana USA Publishing Co., Inc.

Lockhart, E. The Boy Book: A Study of Habits & Behaviors, Plus Techniques for Taming Them. (YA). (gr. 7). 2008. 224p. pap. 8.99 (***978-0-385-73209-3(0)***); 2006. 208p. 15.95 (978-0-385-73208-6(2)); 2006. 208p. 17.99 (978-0-385-90239-7(5)) Random Hse. Children's Bks. (Delacorte Bks. for Young Readers).

—The Boyfriend List. (gr. 7). 2005. 240p. (J). lib. bdg. 17.99 (978-0-385-90238-0(7)); 2006. 256p. (YA). reprint ed. pap. 8.95 (978-0-385-73207-9(4)) Random Hse. Children's Bks. (Delacorte Bks. for Young Readers).

—The Boyfriend List: (15 Guys, 11 Shrink Appointments, 4 Ceramic Frogs, & Me, Ruby Oliver) 2005. 240p. (YA). (gr. 7). 15.95 (978-0-385-73206-2(6) , Delacorte Bks. for Young Readers) Random Hse. Children's Bks.

—Dramarama. 2007. 320p. (gr. 7 up). 15.99 (978-0-7868-3815-8(9)) Hyperion Bks. for Children.

Lohans, Alison. The Raspberry Room. Newland, Gillian, illus. 2006. 64p. (gr. 2-3). pap. 4.99 (978-1-55143-353-0(2)) Orca Bk. Pubs. USA.

Lombard, Jenny. Drita, My Homegirl. 2006. 176p. (J). (gr. 4). 15.99 (978-0-399-24380-6(1) , Putnam Juvenile) Penguin Group (USA) Inc.

Lonborg, Rosemary. Helpin' Bugs. Houghton, Diane R., illus. 32p. (J). (ps-3). reprint ed. 2006. pap. 7.00 (978-1-4223-5405-6(9)); 2004. 15.00 (978-0-7567-8176-7(0)) DIANE Publishing Co.

London, Jonathan. Shawn & Keeper: Show & Tell. 2000. (Puffin Easy-to-Read Ser.). (978-0-606-18450-2(3)) Tandem Library Bks.

The Lonely One. 2001. 32p. (YA). (gr. 6-12). pap. (978-0-8224-3769-7(4)) Globe Fearon Educational Publishing.

The Long-Lost Friends, 6 vols., Vol. 3. (Woodland Mysteriestm Ser.). 133p. (gr. 3-7). 42.50 (978-0-322-02377-2(7)) Wright Group, The.

Longo, Sharon. My Friend Daniel Doesn't Talk: A Story for Children with Social Anxiety & the Friends Who Care about Them. (Illus.). 28p. pap. (978-0-86388-562-4(4) , 002-5288) Speechmark Publishing Ltd.

Look, Lenore. Ruby Lu, Brave & True. 2004. (Illus.). 104p. (J). lib. bdg. 15.00 (***978-1-4242-0914-9(5)***) Fitzgerald Bks.

—Ruby Lu, Brave & True. Wilsdorf, Anne, illus. 2006. (Ready-for-Chapters Ser.). 112p. (J). pap. 3.99 (978-1-4169-1389-4(0) , Aladdin) Simon & Schuster Children's Publishing.

—Ruby Lu, Empress of Everything. Wilsdorf, Anne, illus. (J). (gr. 1-5). 2007. 164p. per. 4.99 (***978-1-4169-5003-5(6)*** , Aladdin); 2006. 176p. 15.95 (978-0-689-86460-5(4) , Atheneum) Simon & Schuster Children's Publishing.

Look, Lenore & Wilsdorf, Anne. Ruby Lu, Brave & True. 2004. (Illus.). 176p. (J). (gr. 1-2). 15.95 (978-0-689-84907-7(9) , Atheneum/Anne Schwartz Bks.) Simon & Schuster Children's Publishing.

Looper, Grace W. Molasses Making Time. l.t. ed. 2004. 152p. (YA). pap. 8.95 (978-0-9747685-5-7(3)) Bella Rosa Bks.

Lopetegui, Leqnor. I Muy Bien! Very Good! La Casa de Ann Mary Big Book. 2001. (SPA., Illus.). 16p. (J). (gr. 1-3). pap. (978-0-9713381-6-6(7)) Double R Publishing, LLC.

—I Muy Bien! (Very Good!) La Escuela de Maricela Big Book. 2001. (SPA., Illus.). 16p. (J). (gr. 1-3). pap. (978-0-9713381-5-9(9)) Double R Publishing, LLC.

Lopetegui, Leqnor, et al. I Muy Bien! (Very Good!) Las Estaciones. 2001. (SPA., Illus.). 16p. (J). (gr. 1-3). pap. (978-0-9713381-7-3(5)) Double R Publishing, LLC.

Lopez, Jack. In the Break. 2006. (Illus.). 208p. (J). (gr. 7-17). 16.99 (978-0-316-00874-7(5)) Little Brown & Co.

—In the Break. 2007. 208p. (J). (gr. 7-17). pap. 7.99 (***978-0-316-06708-9(3)***) Little, Brown Bks. for Young Readers.

Lorbiecki, Marybeth. Jackie's Bat. Pinkney, Brian, illus. 2006. 40p. (J). (gr. k-3). 15.95 (978-0-689-84102-6(7)) Simon & Schuster Children's Publishing.

Lost & Found in JumpStart Town. 2000. (ps-2). lib. bdg. 11.80 (978-0-613-26061-9(9)) Tandem Library Bks.

Lou Weber Staff, ed. Disney Best Friends First Look & Find. 2004. (First Look & Find Ser.). (Illus.). 18p. (J). bds. 7.98 (978-1-4127-3073-0(2) , 7227100) Publications International, Ltd.

—Dora's Desert Friends Plush Sound Book. 2004. 6p. (J). bds. 12.98 (978-1-4127-3095-2(3) , 7229600) Publications International, Ltd.

—Elmo & Friends First Look & Find. 2004. (Illus.). 16p. (J). bds. 7.98 (978-1-4127-3076-1(7) , 7227300) Publications International, Ltd.

Loughead, Deb. A Pocketful of Fur. Birke, Lisa, tr. 2005. (Illus.). 60p. (J). (gr. 2-4). 6.95 (978-0-9730831-6-3(6)) Hodgepog Bks. CAN. *Dist:* Coteau Bks., Fitzhenry & Whiteside, Ltd.

Loupy, Christophe. Little Polar Bear/Little Reind. 2005. (Illus.). 32p. (J). (ps up). 16.50 (978-0-7358-2030-2(9)) North-South Bks., Inc.

Lovejoy, N. L. The DWEEBZ Bk. 1: JaneLee & Some DWEEBZ. Lovejoy, N. L. & Sims, Scott, illus. 2000. 48p. (J). (ps-3). (978-0-9700943-0-8(2)) Small Secrets Unlimted, Inc.

Lovelace, Maud Hart. Carney's House Party. 2000. (gr. 3-6). lib. bdg. 15.25 (978-0-613-31046-8(2)) Tandem Library Bks.

Lowell, Pamela. Returnable Girl. 2006. 240p. (YA). 16.99 (978-0-7614-5317-8(2)) Cavendish, Marshall Corp.

Lowry, Lois. Anastasia Asusordenes. 2003. Tr. of Anastasia at Your Order. (SPA.). 120p. (J). 9.95 (978-84-239-7073-5(6)) Espasa Calpe, S.A. ESP. *Dist:* Planeta Publishing Corp.

—Anastasia at Your Service. 149p. (J). (gr. 4-6). pap. 3.99 (978-0-8072-1409-1(4) , Listening Library) Random Hse. Audio Publishing Group.

—Anastasia Elige Profesion. 2003. Tr. of Anastasia's Chosen Career. (SPA.). 188p. (J). 9.95 (978-84-239-9066-5(4)) Espasa Calpe, S.A. ESP. *Dist:* Planeta Publishing Corp.

—Compte les Etoiles. pap. 16.95 (978-2-211-03436-4(5)) Archimede Editions FRA. *Dist:* Distribooks, Inc.

—Number the Stars. 2004. 144p. (J). (gr. 5-9). pap. 29.00 incl. audio (978-1-4000-8637-5(X) , Listening Library) Random Hse. Audio Publishing Group.

—Number the Stars. 1998. 144p. (YA). (gr. 5-7). reprint ed. mass mkt. 6.50 (978-0-440-22753-3(4) , Laurel Leaf) Random Hse. Children's Bks.

—Number the Stars. 1998. (J). (978-0-606-13670-9(3)); (gr. 5-8). lib. bdg. 14.15 (978-0-613-72319-0(8)) Tandem Library Bks.

—Number the Stars - Musical. 1998. 33p. (J). pap. 6.95 (978-0-87129-834-8(1) , N03) Dramatic Publishing Co.

—Quien Cuenta las Estrellas. 5th ed. 1998. (SPA., Illus.). 152p. (J). 8.95 (978-84-239-8867-9(8)) Espasa Calpe, S.A. ESP. *Dist:* Continental Bk. Co., Inc.

—See You Around, Sam! 1998. (J). (978-0-606-13084-4(5)) Tandem Library Bks.

—The Silent Boy. 2005. 208p. (YA). (gr. 7). reprint ed. pap. 5.99 (978-0-440-41980-8(8) , Laurel Leaf) Random Hse. Children's Bks.

Luberto, Bradley. Clide & Druce: A Repulsive Tale of Trolls & Tax Money. 2006. (ENG.). 48p. per. 12.95 (***978-1-4241-5012-0(4)***) PublishAmerica, Inc.

Lubner, Susan. A Horse's Tale. Moore, Margie, illus. 2008. 32p. (J). 16.95 (***978-0-8109-9490-4(9)*** , Abrams Bks. for Young Readers) Abrams, Harry N. , Inc.

Lucado, Max. Hermie: A Common Caterpillar. 2002. (Max Lucado's Hermie & Friends Ser.). 16p. (J). bds. 6.99 (978-1-4003-0126-3(2)) Nelson, Thomas Inc.

—Hermie y sus Amigos del Jardín: Hermie & His Garden Friends. 2005. (Max Lucado's Hermie & Friends Ser.). (SPA.). 96p. (J). 14.99 (978-0-88113-853-5(3)) Grupo Nelson.

Lucado, Max, creator. Hermie, A Common Caterpillar. 2006. 38p. (J). bds. 12.99 (978-1-4003-0888-0(7)) Nelson, Thomas Inc.

Lucado, Max & Schmidt, Troy. Flo, the Lyin' Fly. 2005. 32p. (J). pap. 3.99 (978-1-4003-0664-0(7)) Nelson, Thomas Inc.

Lucien, Dan. Sandra & Julie. 1999. 72p. (J). (gr. 4-5). pap. (978-0-9686093-0-9(9) , Herald Pr., Ltd.) Lucien, Dan.

Lucky Charm. 2006. (J). pap. 7.99 (978-0-9758511-9-7(5)) B*tween Productions, Inc.

Lucy's New Friend. 2005. 16p. (J). bds. 4.99 (978-1-59384-079-2(9)) Book Club of America.

Lukic, Dragan. Friend to Friend. Vuchic-Radovich, Sladjana, tr. 2005. (J). (978-0-9714039-6-3(1)) Zora.

Lurie, April. Brothers, Boyfriends & Other Criminal Minds. 2007. 304p. (YA). (gr. 7). 15.99 (978-0-385-73124-9(8)); lib. bdg. 18.99 (978-0-385-90152-9(6)) Random Hse. Children's Bks. (Delacorte Bks. for Young Readers).

Lustig, Loretta, illus. The Little Red Hen: A Tale about Cooperation. 2006. (J). 6.99 (978-1-59939-018-5(3) , Reader's Digest Young Families, Inc.) Reader's Digest Children's Publishing, Inc.

E F G

Luthardt, Kevin. Hats! Luthardt, Kevin, illus. 2004. (Illus.). 32p. (J). (gr. k-3). 16.95 (978-0-8075-3171-6(5)) Whitman, Albert & Co.

Lutz, Norma Jean. Carrie's Courage: Battling the Powers of Bigotry. 2005. (Sisters in Time Ser.). 144p. (J). pap. 4.97 (978-1-59310-656-0(4)) Barbour Publishing, Inc.

Ly, Many. Home Is East. 304p. 2007. (YA). (gr. 7-11). mass mkt. 6.50 (*978-0-440-23900-0(1) , Laurel Leaf); 2005. (J). (gr. 5 up). lib. bdg. 17.99 (978-0-385-73223-9(6) , Delacorte Bks. for Young Readers) Random Hse. Children's Bks.

Lynch, Chris. Gold Dust. 2002. 208p. (J). (gr. 5 up). pap. 7.99 (978-0-06-447201-2(9)) HarperCollins Pubs.

—Gold Dust. 2002. (gr. 5-8). lib. bdg. 14.10 (978-0-613-67089-0(2)) Tandem Library Bks.

—Sins of the Fathers. 2006. 240p. (J). lib. bdg. 17.89 (978-0-06-074038-2(8) , HarperTeen) HarperCollins Pubs.

—Slot Machine. 2003. 21.75 (978-0-8446-7249-6(1)) Smith, Peter Pub., Inc.

Lynn, Tracy. Rx. 2005. 272p. (YA). pap. 7.99 (978-1-4169-1155-5(3) , Simon Pulse) Simon & Schuster Children's Publishing.

Lynne, Rustyna. Janel's Shampoo. Lynne, Rustyna, illus. 2002. (Illus.). 17p. (J). (gr. k-2). spiral bd. 11.95 (978-0-9722829-0-1(4)) Red Carpet Publishing.

Lyon, Steve. The Gift Moves. 2004. 240p. (YA). (gr. 5-9). tchr. ed. 15.00 (978-0-618-39128-8(2)) Houghton Mifflin Co. Trade & Reference Div.

MacBride, Roger Lea. The Adventures of Rose & Swiney. Ettlinger, Doris, illus. 2000. (Little House Chapter Bks.: No. 4). 80p. (J). (gr. 2-5). 14.89 (978-0-06-028553-1(2)) HarperCollins Pubs.

—The Adventures of Rose & Swiney. Ettlinger, Doris, illus. 2000. (Little House Chapter Bks.). (J). (978-0-606-19996-4(9)) Tandem Library Bks.

Maccarone, Grace. El Almuerzo Sorpresa. Lewin, Betsy, illus. 2000. (Coleccion "Hola, Lector" Ser.). (SPA.). (J). (ps-1). pap. 3.20 net. (978-0-439-08696-7(5) , SO5844) Scholastic, Inc.

Maccarone, Grace. Fun with First-grade Friends. 2007. (Scholastic Reader Level 1 Ser.). 64p. (J). pap. 4.99 (*978-0-439-93444-2(3) , Cartwheel Bks.) Scholastic, Inc.

MacCarthy, Patricia. Dewdrop Babies: Violet. 2008. (Illus.). 12p. (J). (gr. k-ps). bds. 5.99 (*978-0-375-84362-4(0) , Random Hse. Bks. for Young Readers) Random Hse. Children's Bks.

MacDonald, George. At the Back of the North Wind. 1998. (Twelve-Point Ser.). 280p. reprint ed. lib. bdg. 25.00 (978-1-58287-015-1(2)) North Bks.

MacDonald, Ross. Another Perfect Day. MacDonald, Ross, illus. 2005. (Illus.). 32p. (J). (ps-ps). reprint ed. pap. 6.95 (978-1-59643-079-2(6)) Roaring Brook Pr.

MacHado, Ana Maria. Camilon, Comilon. (Barco de Vapor). (SPA.). 64p. (J). (gr. 2-3). (978-84-348-2703-5(4)) SM Ediciones.

Machen, Sherry Ann. Hannah & Friends. 2004. 75p. (J). per. (978-1-55306-833-4(5) , Epic Pr.) Essence Publishing.

MacIntyre, R. P. & MacIntyre, Wendy. Apart. 2007. 192p. (J). (gr. 8 up). 16.95 (*978-0-88899-750-0(7)) Groundwood Bks. CAN. *Dist:* Perseus Distribution.

Mack, Tracy. Birdland. 2005. 208p. (J). (gr. 7-17). pap. 5.99 (978-0-439-53591-5(3) , Scholastic Paperbacks) Scholastic, Inc.

MacKall, Dandi Daley. Friendly Foal. 2004. (Winnie the Horse Gentler Ser.: No. 7). 224p. (J). mass mkt. 5.99 (978-0-8423-8723-1(4)) Tyndale Hse. Pubs.

—Kyra's Story. 2003. (gr. 7-12). lib. bdg. 18.80 (978-0-613-76717-0(9)) Tandem Library Bks.

—Made for a Purpose. Dibley, Glin, illus. 2004. 40p. (J). 15.99 (978-0-310-70953-4(9)) Zonderkidz.

Mackel, Kathy. MadCat. 2005. (Illus.). 192p. (J). 15.99 (978-0-06-054869-8(X)); lib. bdg. 16.89 (978-0-06-054870-4(3)) HarperCollins Pubs.

Mackenzie, Catherine. The Dark Blue Bike at No 17: Tammy & Jake learn about Friendship & Bullying. (Illus.). 160p. (J). mass mkt. 5.99 (978-1-85792-732-0(X) , Christian Focus) Christian Focus Pubns. GBR. *Dist:* Riverside.

MacLellan, Erin. Run from the Nun! 2003. 128p. (J). (gr. 4-6). tchr. ed. 16.95 (978-0-8234-1796-4(4)) Holiday Hse., Inc.

MacPhee, Phoebe. Alphabetical Hook-up List A-J. 2002. (gr. 7-12). lib. bdg. 18.75 (978-0-613-60525-0(X)) Tandem Library Bks.

Madison, Ron. Ned's Hat: A Lesson about Safety. Cololo, David, illus. l.t. ed. 2002. (Health & Safety Ser.). 20p. (ps-2). 4.95 (978-1-887206-21-1(3)) Ned's Head Productions.

Madonna. The English Roses, Too Good to be True. 2006. (Illus.). 64p. (J). (ps-6). 19.95 (978-0-670-06147-1(6)) Callaway Editions, Inc.

—Goodbye, Grace? Fulvimari, Jeffrey, illus. 2007. (English Roses Ser.). 124p. (J). (gr. 3-7). 9.99 (*978-0-14-240883-4(2) , Puffin) Penguin Group (USA) Inc.

—Madonna Box Set. 2004. 144p. (ps-6). 39.95 (978-0-670-06014-6(3)) Penguin Group (USA) Inc.

—The New Girl. Fulvimari, Jeffrey, illus. 2007. (English Roses Ser.). 123p. (J). (gr. 2). 9.99 (*978-0-14-240884-1(0) , Puffin) Penguin Group (USA) Inc.

—Las Rosas Inglesas. Fulvimari, Jeffrey, illus. 2003. Tr. of English Roses. (SPA.). 48p. (J). 19.95 (978-0-439-60978-4(X) , Scholastic en Espanol) Scholastic, Inc.

Madonna. A Rose by Any Other Name. Fulvimari, Jeffrey, illus. 2007. (English Roses Ser.). 125p. (J). (gr. 2). 9.99 (*978-0-14-240885-8(9) , Puffin) Penguin Group (USA) Inc.

Madonna & Madonna. Friends for Life!, No. 1. Fulvimari, Jeffrey, illus. 2007. (English Roses Ser.). 83p. (J). (gr. 3-7). 9.99 (*978-0-14-241114-8(0) , Puffin) Penguin Group (USA) Inc.

Madrzak, Carole. In the Shadows of Bington Manor. 2006. (ENG.). 132p. per. 19.95 (*978-1-4241-5168-4(6)) PublishAmerica, Inc.

—Moonlight Dare. 2004. 48p. pap. 12.95 (978-1-4137-5144-4(X)) PublishAmerica, Inc.

—Secrets Inside Bington Manor. 2005. 108p. pap. 16.95 (978-1-4241-0720-9(2)) PublishAmerica, Inc.

Magical Max Makes Friends. 2005. (Adventures of Magical Max, Scarlet Feather & Little Lilly Woo-Woo Ser.). (Illus.). 16p. (J). (gr. k-4). 14.95 (978-0-9762408-0-8(7)) Lead Life Pr., LLC.

Mahan, Sue. Yummy. Wise, Noreen, ed. Wethington, Lang, illus. 2001. (Lemonade Collection). 128p. (YA). (gr. 3 up). pap. 9.95 (978-1-58584-266-7(4)) Huckleberry Pr.

Mahoney, Daniel J. The Perfect Clubhouse. 2004. (Illus.). 32p. (J). (gr. k-3). tchr. ed. 15.00 (978-0-618-34672-1(4) , Clarion Bks.) Houghton Mifflin Co. Trade & Reference Div.

Mahy, Margaret. The Catalogue of the Universe. Hopes, illus. 2002. 192p. (YA). pap. 7.99 (978-0-689-85353-1(X) , Simon Pulse) Simon & Schuster Children's Publishing.

—The Catalogue of the Universe. 2002. (gr. 7-12). lib. bdg. 16.45 (978-0-613-57621-5(7)) Tandem Library Bks.

—24 Hours. 2001. (Illus.). (J). (978-0-606-21609-8(X)) Tandem Library Bks.

Maiden, Cecil. The Molliwumps. Price, Christine, illus. 2004. 160p. 12.95 (978-0-9714612-9-1(5)) Green Mansion Pr. LLC.

Main Street 4 & Martin, Martin. Best Friends. 2008. pap. 25.95 (*978-0-545-02517-1(6) , Scholastic Paperbacks) Scholastic, Inc.

Major, Kevin. Hold Fast. 2004. 204p. (YA). pap. 6.95 (978-0-88899-580-3(6)); 25th anniv. ed. 2003. 192p. (J). 16.95 (978-0-88899-579-7(2)) Groundwood Bks. CAN. *Dist:* Perseus Distribution.

Malcolm, Jahnna N. Stupid Cupids: The Gang Has Gone Boy Crazy. 2001. (Bad News Ballet Ser.: Vol. 33). Tr. of Complot de la Saint-Valentin. 160p. (J). pap. 3.95 (978-0-9700164-2-3(5)) Starcatcher Pr.

Malkin, Nina. Loud, Fast, & Out of Control. 2006. (6x Ser.: No. 2). 368p. (J). pap. 9.99 (978-0-439-72422-7(8) , Scholastic Paperbacks) Scholastic, Inc.

Mallat, Kathy. Just Ducky. Mallat, Kathy, illus. 2004. (Illus.). 32p. (J). (ps-k). 15.95 (978-0-8027-8824-5(6)) Walker & Co.

—Just Ducky. 2004. (Illus.). 24p. (J). (ps-1). 16.85 (978-0-8027-8825-2(4)) Walker & Co.

Man-Kong, Ann Marie & Forrester, Emma. Sunshine & Smiles. Cutting, David A. et al, illus. 2006. (Holly Hobbie & Friends Ser.). 224p. (J). act. bk. ed. 4.99 (978-1-4169-4107-1(X) , Simon Scribbles) Simon & Schuster Children's Publishing.

Manchado & His Friends. 2000. Tr. of Manchado y Sus Amigos. 18.95 (978-0-9711930-1-7(0)) Barbed Wire Publishing.

Manchado & His Friends: Manchado y Sus Amigos. 2002. (J). per. 9.95 (978-0-9711930-2-4(9)) Barbed Wire Publishing.

Mann, Paul Z. I Can Jump Higher! 2000. (gr. k-3). lib. bdg. 11.80 (978-0-613-71007-7(X)) Tandem Library Bks.

Manners I. Care. 2005. (J). pap. 5.99 (*978-0-9771143-4-4(1)) Child LIfe Bks., LLC.

Manners, Tyler. Continental Change of Heart. 2006. 65p. pap. 12.95 (978-1-4137-9483-0(1)) PublishAmerica, Inc.

Manning, Sarra. Pretty Things. 2006. 272p. (YA). (gr. 9). pap. 6.99 (978-0-14-240539-0(6) , Puffin) Penguin Group (USA) Inc.

Manns, Nick. Dead Negative. 2003. mass mkt. (978-0-340-85566-9(5) , Hodder Children's Books) Hodder Children's Division.

—Seed Time. 2003. mass mkt. 11.99 (978-0-340-80570-1(6) , Hodder & Stoughton) Hodder General Publishing Division GBR. *Dist:* Trafalgar Square Publishing.

Mansfield, Creina. Cherokee. 2003. 128p. (YA). (gr. 5 up). pap. 7.95 (978-0-86278-368-6(2)) O'Brien Pr., Ltd., The IRL. *Dist:* Independent Pubs. Group.

Mantell, Paul. Mountain Bike Mania. 2007. 148p. (J). lib. bdg. (*978-1-59953-108-3(9)) Norwood Hse. Pr.

Mantell, Paul. Soccer Dual. ed. 2005. (Sports Classics III Ser.). 153p. (J). lib. bdg. 15.00 (978-1-59054-771-7(3)) Fitzgerald Bks.

Manuli'i & the Colorful Cape. 2001. (J). 8.99 (978-0-89610-423-5(0)) Island Heritage Publishing.

Manzel, Michael, illus. Moby's Tale. 2004. 248p. (YA). pap. 19.95 (*978-0-9746345-0-0(6)) River of Life Publishing.

Marcum, Lance. The Cottonmouth Club. 2005. 336p. (J). 18.00 (978-0-374-31562-7(0) , Farrar, Straus & Giroux (BYR)) Farrar, Straus & Giroux.

Marineau, Michele. Lean Mean Machines. Ouriou, Susan, tr. from FRE. 2004. (Northern Lights Books for Children Ser.). (Illus.). 128p. (YA). (gr. 4-9). pap. 7.95 (978-0-88995-230-0(2)) Red Deer Pr. CAN. *Dist:* Fitzhenry & Whiteside, Ltd.

—Lean Mean Machines. 2001. (gr. 7-12). lib. bdg. 16.40 (978-0-613-82356-2(7)) Tandem Library Bks.

Marino, Peter. Dough Boy. 176p. (YA). (gr. 7-12). 16.95 (978-0-8234-1873-2(1)) Holiday Hse., Inc.

Marion the Magnet's First Mission. l.t. ed. 2001. 32p. 14.95 (978-0-9715345-1-3(9)) Hackleman, Sharon.

Mariposa Publishing Inc. Staff. Me Gusta el Invierno! 2003. Tr. of Winter Ice is Nice!. (SPA.). (ps-2). lib. bdg. 11.80 (978-0-613-85121-3(8)) Tandem Library Bks.

Marks, Nancy Freeman. Just As You Are: The Story of Leon & Sam. Buchheim, Su Jen, illus. 2003. 32p. (J). 15.00 (978-0-9722430-1-8(1)) Wave Publishing.

Marlow, Herb. A Long Way Home. l.t. ed. 2003. (Illus.). 14p. (J). 19.95 (978-1-893595-35-4(8)) Four Seasons Bks., Inc.

Marsden, Carolyn. The Gold-Threaded Dress. 2006. 80p. (J). (gr. 2-4). reprint ed. pap. 5.99 (978-0-7636-2993-9(6)) Candlewick Pr.

—Moon Runner. 112p. (J). (gr. 3-7). 2007. pap. 5.99 (*978-0-7636-3304-2(6)); 2005. 15.99 (978-0-7636-2117-9(X)) Candlewick Pr.

Marsden, Carolyn. The Quail Club. 2006. 144p. (J). (gr. 3-5). 15.99 (978-0-7636-2635-8(X)) Candlewick Pr.

Marsden, Carolyn & Loh, Virginia Shin-Mui. The Jade Dragon. 2006. 176p. (J). (gr. 2-5). 15.99 (978-0-7636-3012-6(8)) Candlewick Pr.

Marsden, Carolyn & Mackler, Carolyn. The Gold-Threaded Dress. 2002. 80p. (J). (gr. 2-4). 14.99 (978-0-7636-1569-7(2)) Candlewick Pr.

Marsden, John. Burning for Revenge. 2006. (Tomorrow Ser.). 272p. (J). pap. 8.99 (978-0-439-85803-8(8) , Scholastic Paperbacks) Scholastic, Inc.

Marsh, Carole. The Case of the Crybaby Cowboy. 2006. 64p. (gr. 1-3). 14.95 (*978-0-635-06199-7(6)) Gallopade International.

—The Case of the Hunchback Hairdresser. 2006. 64p. (gr. 1-3). 14.95 (*978-0-635-06202-4(X)) Gallopade International.

Marshall, James. George & Martha. 2007. (Illus.). 24p. (J). (ps-3). 15.00 (*978-0-618-96331-7(6)) Houghton Mifflin Co. Trade & Reference Div.

—George & Martha Back in Town. Marshall, James, illus. 2002. (George & Martha Ser.). (Illus.). (J). 14.74 (978-0-7587-2569-1(8)) Book Wholesalers, Inc.

—George & Martha: the Best of Friends Early Reader #4. 2008. 24p. (J). (ps-3). 15.00 (*978-0-618-98451-0(8)) Houghton Mifflin Co. Trade & Reference Div.

—The Guest. 2001. (978-0-606-22579-3(X)); lib. bdg. 12.95 (978-0-613-35523-0(7)) Tandem Library Bks.

—Jorge y Marta. 2000. (SPA., Illus.). 48p. (J). (gr. k-3). 16.00 (978-0-618-05075-8(2) , HM4632); pap. 6.95 (978-0-618-05076-5(0) , HM0196) Houghton Mifflin Co. Trade & Reference Div.

—Jorge y Marta. 2000. (SPA.). (ps-2). lib. bdg. 15.25 (978-0-613-27917-8(4)); (Illus.). (J). 13.75 (978-0-606-18210-2(1)) Tandem Library Bks.

—Jorge y Marta en la Ciudad. 2001. (SPA., Illus.). 52p. (J). (ps-3). (978-84-239-2829-3(2) , EC0827) Espasa Calpe, S.A. ESP. *Dist:* Lectorum Pubns., Inc.

—Two Great Friends. 2007. (George & Martha Ser.). (Illus.). 24p. (J). (ps-3). 15.00 (*978-0-618-96178-8(X)) Houghton Mifflin Co. Trade & Reference Div.

—Willis. 2001. (Illus.). 48p. (J). (gr. k-3). tchr. ed. 15.00 (978-0-618-12441-1(1)) Houghton Mifflin Co. Trade & Reference Div.

—Willis. 2001. (J). (978-0-606-21530-5(1)) Tandem Library Bks.

—Wings: A Tale of Two Chickens. 2003. (Illus.). 32p. (J). (gr. k-3). 6.95 (978-0-618-31659-5(0)) Houghton Mifflin Co. Trade & Reference Div.

Marsoli, Lisa Ann. Leap's Friends A-Z. Yakovetic Productions Staff, illus. 24p. (J). (gr. k-2). (978-1-58605-008-5(7)) LeapFrog Enterprises, Inc.

Martin, Ann M. Abby & the Best Kid Ever. 1998. (Baby-Sitters Club Ser.: No. 116). (J). (gr. 3-7). (978-0-606-13160-5(4)) Tandem Library Bks.

—Best Friends. 2008. (Main Street Ser.). 208p. (J). 6.99 (*978-0-439-86882-2(3) , Scholastic Paperbacks) Scholastic, Inc.

—A Corner of the Universe. 2004. 208p. (J). pap. 5.99 (978-0-439-38881-8(3) , Scholastic Paperbacks) Scholastic, Inc.

—Everything Changes. 1999. (Baby-Sitters Club Friends Forever Special Ser.: No. 1). (J). (gr. 3-7). pap. 4.50 (978-0-590-50391-4(X)) Scholastic, Inc.

—Friends: Stories Abt New Friends, Old Friends. Levithan, David, ed. 2005. (Friends Ser.). 192p. (J). (ps-7). pap. 16.95 (978-0-439-72991-8(2) , Scholastic Pr.) Scholastic, Inc.

—Kristy's Great Idea. 2006. (Baby-Sitters Club Ser.: No. 1). (Illus.). 192p. (J). (gr. 3-7). pap. 16.99 (978-0-439-80241-3(5) , Graphix) Scholastic, Inc.

—Mary Anne Saves the Day. 2007. (BSC Graphix Ser.: No. 3). 160p. (J). pap. 8.99 (*978-0-439-88516-4(7) , Graphix) Scholastic, Inc.

—Needle & Thread. 2007. (Main Street Ser.: No. 2). 224p. (J). (gr. 4-6). pap. 6.99 (*978-0-439-86880-8(7)) Scholastic, Inc.

—On Christmas Eve. 160p. (J). 2007. pap. 5.99 (*978-0-439-74589-5(6) , Scholastic Paperbacks); 2006. (Illus.). pap. 15.99 (978-0-439-74588-8(8) , Scholastic) Scholastic, Inc.

Martin, Ann M. Sunny: Diary Two. 1998. (California Diaries: Bk. 6). (YA). (gr. 6-8). pap. 3.99 (978-0-590-29840-7(2)) Scholastic, Inc.

Martin, Anne E. Flip Flops for Paige. 2007. (Illus.). 48p. (J). per. 14.99 (*978-1-59879-243-0(1)) Lifevest Publishing, Inc.

Martin, Juan Munoz. La Nariz de Moritz. 2001. Tr. of Moritz's Nose. (SPA.). 184p. (J). 6.95 (978-84-348-1337-3(8)) SM Ediciones ESP. *Dist:* AIMS International Bks., Inc.

Martín Larrañaga, Ana. Pepo & Lolo Are Friends. 2004. (Super Sturdy Picture Booksm Ser.). (Illus.). 24p. (J). (gr. k-ps). 8.99 (978-0-7636-1982-4(5)) Candlewick Pr.

Martin, Marilyn. Friends Forever. 2000. (Illus.). (YA). (gr. 4-7). pap. 12.95 (978-1-891929-58-8(5)) Four Seasons Pubs.

Martin, Martha M. Chipper, the Heroic Chipmunk. Matzen, Deon C., illus. 2004. 32p. (J). (ps-3). 16.95 (978-0-9758580-0-4(9)) M & B Publishing.

Martin, S. R. Talk to Me. 1999. (Insomniacs Ser.: No. 3). (Illus.). 80p. (YA). (gr. 7-12). pap. 2.99 (978-0-590-69142-0(2)) Scholastic, Inc.

Martin, Trude. Obee & Mungedeech. 1999. 107p. (J). (gr. 3-6). reprint ed. 15.00 (978-0-7881-6639-6(5)) DIANE Publishing Co.

Martinez, Agnes. Poe Park. 2004. 128p. (J). (ps-7). tchr. ed. 16.95 (978-0-8234-1834-3(0)) Holiday Hse., Inc.

Martino, Alfred C. Pinned. (YA). 2005. 320p. 17.00 (978-0-15-205355-0(7)); 2006. (Illus.). 324p. reprint ed. pap. 6.95 (978-0-15-205631-5(9) , Harcourt Paperbacks) Harcourt Children's Bks.

Marzollo, Jean. Companeros en el Futbol. Trivas, Irene, illus. 1999. (Coleccion "Hola, Lector" Ser.). (SPA.). 48p. (J). (gr. 2-4). pap. 3.99 (978-0-439-08056-9(8) , SO8904, Scholastic en Espanol) Scholastic, Inc.

—Companeros en el Futbol. 1999. (SPA.). (gr. 3-6). lib. bdg. 11.80 (978-0-613-16916-5(6)) Tandem Library Bks.

Maselli, Christopher P. N. Dangerous Encounters Bk. 5: Tangled Truths & Twisted Tales—Exposed! 2003. (Illus.). 128p. (J). pap. 4.99 (978-0-310-70664-9(5)) Zonderkidz.

—Power Play: Beware of Broken Promises. 2003. (2:52 Soul Gear Ser.). (Illus.). 128p. (J). pap. 4.99 (978-0-310-70341-9(7)) Zonderkidz.

Mason, Adrienne & Cupples, Pat. Lu & Clancy's Secret Codes. 1999. (Lu & Clancy Ser.). (Illus.). 40p. (J). (gr. k-3). (978-1-55074-553-5(0)) Kids Can Pr., Ltd.

Mason, Jane B. & Stephens, Sarah Hines. Appley Ever After. 2005. (Princess School Ser.: No. 6). (Illus.). 128p. (J). (ps-7). pap. 4.99 (978-0-439-69814-6(6) , Scholastic Paperbacks) Scholastic, Inc.

Mass, Wendy. A Mango-Shaped Space. 2005. 240p. (J). (gr. 5-8). pap. 6.99 (978-0-316-05825-4(4)) Little Brown & Co.

Massey, Carol. Not a Friend. 2005. 79p. pap. 9.95 (978-0-7414-2319-1(7)) Infinity Publishing.

Masterson, Carla Jo. What's on the Other Side of the Rainbow? The Secret of the Golden Mirror. Fochtman, Omra Jo, illus. 2006. 40p. (J). 24.95 (978-1-59975-228-0(X)) Father & Son Publishing.

Matas, Carol. Sparks Fly Upward. 2002. 192p. (YA). (gr. 5-9). 15.00 (978-0-618-15964-2(9) , Clarion Bks.) Houghton Mifflin Co. Trade & Reference Div.

Matchette, Katharine E. Oh, Suzannah. 1998. 158p. (YA). (gr. 6 up). pap. 8.75 (978-0-9645045-2-3(9)) Deka Pr.

Mateos, Pilar. Historias de Ninguno. (Barco de Vapor). (SPA.). 120p. (J). (gr. 4-5). (978-84-348-0907-9(9)) SM Ediciones.

—Lucas y Lucas. (Barco de Vapor). (SPA.). 88p. (YA). (gr. 5-8). (978-84-348-1233-8(9)) SM Ediciones.

—Molinete. (Barco de Vapor). (SPA.). 88p. (J). (gr. 4-5). (978-84-348-1372-4(6)) SM Ediciones.

Mathers, Petra. Lottie's New Friend. Mathers, Petra, illus. (Illus.). 32p. (J). (ps-3). 2002. pap. 5.99 (978-0-689-84896-4(X) , Aladdin); 1999. 15.00 (978-0-689-82014-4(3) , Atheneum/Anne Schwartz Bks.) Simon & Schuster Children's Publishing.

—Lottie's New Friend. 2002. (gr. k-3). lib. bdg. 14.15 (978-0-613-73374-8(6)) Tandem Library Bks.

Mathias, B. J. Jeffrey William & The Little Prince. 2002. 10.00 (978-0-9711320-9-2(7)) Electronic Publishing Services.

Matlin, Marlee. Deaf Child Crossing. (Illus.). 208p. (J). 2004. pap. 4.99 (978-0-689-86696-8(8) , Aladdin); 2002. (gr. 3-6). 15.95 (978-0-689-82208-7(1)) Simon & Schuster Children's Publishing.

—Deaf Child Crossing. 2004. (gr. 3-6). lib. bdg. 13.00 (978-0-613-88068-8(4)) Tandem Library Bks.

Mattern, Joanne. My Best Friends. Style Guide Staff & Riley, Kellee, illus. 2006. (Holly Hobbie & Friends Ser.). 48p. (J). act. bk. ed. 3.99 (978-1-4169-1852-3(3) , Simon Scribbles) Simon & Schuster Children's Publishing.

Matteson, Rosemary. Tommy's Circle of Friends at Meadowview Farm. 2002. (Illus.). (J). (ps-5). 21.95 (978-1-881636-64-9(X)) Windsor Hse. Publishing Group, The.

Matthews, Derek. Once upon a Time: Noisy Pop-up Fun with Fun Fairy-Tale Sounds. 2007. (Snappy Sounds Ser.). (Illus.). 10p. (J). 12.95 (*978-1-59223-716-6(9) , Silver Dolphin Bks.) Advantage Pubs. Group.

Matthews, L. S. A Dog for Life. 2006. 176p. (J). (gr. 5). 16.99 (978-0-385-90381-3(2) , Delacorte Bks. for Young Readers) Random Hse. Children's Bks.

Matthew's Web Unplugged. 2003. (J). per. (978-0-9716567-7-2(0)) Book Web Publishing, Ltd.

Matute, Ana M. El Polizon de Ulises.Tr. of Stonaway of Ulises. (SPA.). 126p. (YA). (gr. 5 up). 10.36 (978-84-264-3022-9(8) , LM0588) Editorial Lumen ESP. *Dist:* Lectorum Pubns., Inc.

Maurer, Donna. Annie, Bea & Chi Chi Dolores. 1998. (J). (978-0-606-13144-5(2)) Tandem Library Bks.

May, Sophie. Jimmy, Lucy, & All. 2006. 32.99 (*978-1-4280-2820-3(X)) IndyPublish.com.

Maycock, Dianne. Lucky's Mountain. 2007. (Orca Young Readers Ser.). 112p. pap. (*978-1-55143-682-1(5)) Orca Bk. Pubs.

Mayer, Melody. All Night Long: A Nannies Novel. 2008. 256p. (YA). lib. bdg. 12.99 (*978-0-385-90506-0(8) , Delacorte Bks. for Young Readers) Random Hse. Children's Bks.

—The Nannies. 2005. 288p. (YA). (gr. 9 up). pap. 8.95 (978-0-385-73283-3(X)); lib. bdg. 10.99 (978-0-385-90300-4(6)) Random Hse. Children's Bks. (Delacorte Bks. for Young Readers).

—The Nannies: Friends with Benefits. 2006. (Nannies Ser.). 288p. (YA). (gr. 9). pap. 8.95 (978-0-385-73284-0(8)); lib. bdg. 10.99 (978-0-385-90301-1(4)) Random Hse. Children's Bks. (Delacorte Bks. for Young Readers).

—The Nannies: Have to Have It. 2006. (Nannies Ser.). 256p. (YA). (gr. 7). 8.95 (978-0-385-73351-9(8) , Delacorte Bks. for Young Readers) Random Hse. Children's Bks.

—The Nannies: Have to Have It. 2006. (Nannies Novel Ser.). 256p. (YA). (gr. 9). lib. bdg. 10.99 (978-0-385-90366-0(9) , Delacorte Bks. for Young Readers) Random Hse. Children's Bks.

Mayer, Mercer. Frog on His Own. Mayer, Mercer, illus. 2003. (Illus.). 32p. (J). (gr. k-1). 5.99 (978-0-8037-2883-7(2) , Dial) Penguin Group (USA) Inc.

—Just My Friend & Me. Mayer, Mercer, illus. 2001. (Little Critter Ser.). (Illus.). 24p. (J). pap. 3.29 (978-0-307-11947-6(5) , 11947, Random Hse. Bks. for Young Readers) Random Hse. Children's Bks.

—New Kid in Town, Vol. 3. 2002. (Little Critter First Readers Ser.). (Illus.). 24p. (J). (gr. 1-2). pap. 3.95 (978-1-57768-829-7(5)) School Specialty Publishing.

—New Kid in Town. 2001. (gr. k-3). lib. bdg. 11.80 (978-0-613-67654-0(8)) Tandem Library Bks.

—No One Can Play. 2002. (Little Critter Ser.). (Illus.). 24p. (J). (ps-k). pap. 3.95 (978-1-57768-804-4(X)) School Specialty Publishing.

—Our Friend Sam. 2002. (Little Critter Ser.). (Illus.). 24p. (J). (ps-2). 10.95 (978-1-57768-458-9(3)) School Specialty Publishing.

—Our Friend Sam. 2002. (gr. k-3). lib. bdg. 11.80 (978-0-613-62430-5(0)) Tandem Library Bks.

Mayer, Mercer & Mayer, Marianna. A Boy, a Dog, a Frog & a Friend. Mayer, Mercer & Mayer, Marianna, illus. 2003. (Illus.). 32p. (J). (ps). 6.99 (978-0-8037-2882-0(4) , Dial) Penguin Group (USA) Inc.

—One Frog Too Many. Mayer, Mercer & Mayer, Marianna, illus. 2003. (Illus.). 32p. (J). (gr. k-1). 6.99 (978-0-8037-2885-1(9) , Dial) Penguin Group (USA) Inc.

Mayfield, Sue. Drowning Anna. 2002. 320p. (gr. 5-9). 15.99 (978-0-7868-0870-0(5)) Disney Pr.

—Drowning Anna. 2004. 256p. (gr. 7-17). reprint ed. pap. 5.99 (978-0-7868-0957-8(4)) Hyperion Bks. for Children.

Mayfield, Sue & Padua, Rochelle. I Can, You Can, Toucan! 2006. (Green Bananas Ser.). (Illus.). 47p. (J). (978-0-7787-1032-5(7)) Crabtree Publishing Co.

Mazer, Anne. Good Things Come in Small Packages. 2003. (Amazing Days of Abby Hayes Ser.: No. 12). (Illus.). 112p. mass mkt. 4.99 (978-0-439-48280-6(1) , Scholastic Paperbacks) Scholastic, Inc.

—Good Things Come in Small Packages. 2003. (Amazing Days of Abby Hayes Ser.: No. 12). (gr. 3-6). lib. bdg. 12.40 (978-0-613-72006-9(7)) Tandem Library Bks.

—Home Is Where the Heart Is. 2006. (Amazing Days of Abby Hayes Ser.: No. 17). 128p. (J). pap. 4.99 (978-0-439-82924-3(0) , Scholastic Paperbacks) Scholastic, Inc.

—It's Music to My Ears. 2004. (Amazing Days of Abby Hayes Ser.: No. 14). (Illus.). 110p. (J). lib. bdg. 16.92 (***978-1-4242-0745-9(2)***) Fitzgerald Bks.

—The Pen Is Mightier Than the Sword. Gesue, Monica, illus. 2001. (Amazing Days of Abby Hayes Ser.: No. 6). 128p. (J). (gr. 4-7). pap. 4.99 (978-0-439-17882-2(7)) Scholastic, Inc.

—The Pen Is Mightier Than the Sword. 2001. (Amazing Days of Abby Hayes Ser.: No. 6). (gr. 3-6). lib. bdg. 12.40 (978-0-613-43865-0(5)) Tandem Library Bks.

—Some Things Never Change. 2004. (Amazing Days of Abby Hayes Ser.: No. 13). 101p. (J). lib. bdg. 16.92 (***978-1-4242-0744-2(4)***) Fitzgerald Bks.

Mazer, Anne. Too Close for Comfort. Gesue, Monica, illus. 2003. (Amazing Days of Abby Hayes Ser.: No. 11). 128p. (J). (gr. 3-6). 4.99 (978-0-439-48273-8(9) , Scholastic Paperbacks) Scholastic, Inc.

—Too Close for Comfort. 2003. (Amazing Days of Abby Hayes Ser.: No. 11). (gr. k-3). lib. bdg. 12.40 (978-0-613-72005-2(9)) Tandem Library Bks.

Mazer, Norma Fox. Babyface. 2007. (Illus.). 176p. (YA). pap. 6.95 (978-0-15-206277-4(7) , Harcourt Paperbacks) Harcourt Children's Bks.

—Crazy Fish. 2007. (Illus.). 160p. (J). pap. 5.95 (***978-0-15-206373-3(0)*** , Harcourt Paperbacks) Harcourt Children's Bks.

—Crazy Fish. (J). 1999. 160p. (gr. 4-7). pap. 4.50 (978-0-380-73189-3(4) , Harper Trophy); 1998. 192p. (gr. 5-9). 15.00 (978-0-688-16281-8(9)) HarperCollins Pubs.

—Crazy Fish. 1999. (J). (978-0-606-16339-2(5)) Tandem Library Bks.

Mazer, Norma Fox. Ten Ways to Make My Sister Disappear. 2007. (J). (***978-0-439-83984-6(X)***); 160p. (gr. 4-7). pap. 16.99 (***978-0-439-83983-9(1)***) Scholastic, Inc. (Levine, Arthur A. Bks.).

Mazetti, Katerina. God & I Broke Up. Lundin, Maria, tr. from SWE. 2004. 160p. (J). 15.95 (978-0-88899-584-1(9)) Groundwood Bks. CAN. *Dist:* Perseus Distribution.

Mazzeo Zocchi, Judy. Paulie & Sasha: Circus or Not. Vannozzi, Don, illus. 2001. (Adventures of Paulie & Sasha Ser.). 32p. (J). (gr. k-4). 15.95 (978-1-891997-00-6(9) , Treehouse Court) Dingles & Co.

McAllister, Angela. Digory the Dragon Slayer. Beck, Ian, illus. 2006. 128p. (J). 14.95 (978-1-58234-722-6(0)); pap. 5.95 (978-1-58234-912-1(6)) Bloomsbury Publishing. (Bloomsbury Children).

—Just Like Sisters. Fatus, Sophie, illus. 2006. 32p. (J). (ps-3). 15.95 (978-1-4169-0643-8(6) , Atheneum/Anne Schwartz Bks.) Simon & Schuster Children's Publishing.

McAllister, Margaret. Tromso the Troll. Cox, Steve, illus. 2006. 24p. (J). lib. bdg. (***978-1-4048-3144-5(4)***) Picture Window Bks.

McArdle, Donald. Santa's Newest Friend. 2007. 25p. (J). 21.50 (***978-0-615-14212-8(5)***) McArdle, Donald.

McBratney, Sam. I'm Sorry. Eachus, Jennifer, illus. 1999. 24p. (J). (978-0-7636-0981-8(1)) Candlewick Pr.

—Stranger from Somewhere in Time. Chatterton, Martin & Chatterton, Ann, illus. (Yellow Bananas Ser.). 48p. (J). (gr. 3-4). 2003. lib. bdg. (978-0-7787-0937-4(X)); 2002. pap. (978-0-7787-0983-1(3)) Crabtree Publishing Co.

—Stranger from Somewhere in Time. 2002. (gr. 3-6). lib. bdg. 12.95 (978-0-613-52917-4(0)) Tandem Library Bks.

McBride, Earvin, Jr. The Joyous Adventures of Sam & Pam. McBride, Earvin, Jr., illus. unabr. ed. 2002. (Earvin MacBride's Fun Fun Lovable Cartoons Ser.). (Illus.). 123p. (J). (gr. 7-12). pap. 3.95 (978-1-892511-03-4(7)) MacBride, E. J. Pubn., Inc.

—Neddy Buddy Basil. McBride, Earvin, Jr., illus. unabr. ed. 2002. (Illus.). 6p. (J). (gr. 7-12). pap. (978-1-892511-13-3(4)) MacBride, E. J. Pubn., Inc.

McBride, Eve. Dandelions Help. 160p. (J). pap. (978-0-9698752-5-3(8)) Shoreline.

McCaffrey, Laura Williams. Alia Waking. 2003. 224p. (J). (gr. 5-9). tchr. ed. 16.00 (978-0-618-19461-2(4) , Clarion Bks.) Houghton Mifflin Co. Trade & Reference Div.

McCarty, Barbara. To Save a Unicorn. 2005. 54p. pap. 12.95 (978-1-4137-5428-5(7)) PublishAmerica, Inc.

McClear, Preston. Frannie & Pickles. Dollak, Nicholas, illus. 2003. 48p. (J). (gr. k-5). 16.95 (978-1-929084-13-5(7)) Malibu Bks. for Children.

McClellan, Mae. Just Friends. 2004. (J). pap. 8.00 (978-0-8059-6468-4(1)) Dorrance Publishing Co., Inc.

McClintock, Norah. Snitch. 2005. (Orca Soundings Ser.). 112p. (J). (gr. 7-12). pap. 7.95 (978-1-55143-484-1(9)) Orca Bk. Pubs. USA.

McCloskey, John J. Warrior Ching. 2006. 179p. pap. 19.95 (978-1-4241-2389-6(5)) PublishAmerica, Inc.

McCluskey, J. E. The Adventures of Peter the Pleasant Platypus & Friends: First Adventure, Tidy Time. 2004. 48p. pap. 19.95 (978-1-4137-2546-9(5)) PublishAmerica, Inc.

McClymer, Kelly. She's a Witch Girl. 2007. 272p. (YA). (gr. 7 up). pap. 8.99 (***978-1-4169-4902-2(X)*** , Simon Pulse) Simon & Schuster Children's Publishing.

McCombie, Karen. Indie Kidd: Are We Having Fun Yet? (Hmmm?) Monks, Lydia, illus. 2008. (J). (***978-0-440-42201-3(9)***); 160p. (gr. 2-5). lib. bdg. 9.99 (***978-0-440-42202-0(7)***) Random Hse. Children's Bks. (Yearling).

McCombie, Karen. Oops, I Lost My Best(est) Friends. Monks, Lydia, illus. 2007. (Indie Kidd Ser.). 160p. (J). (gr. 2-5). 5.99 (978-0-440-42197-9(7)); lib. bdg. 11.99 (978-0-440-42198-6(5)) Random Hse. Children's Bks. (Yearling).

McConnell, G. Robert. Norbert Nipkin. Pilcher, Steve, illus. 3rd ed. 2005. 40p. (J). pap. 14.95 (978-1-894917-29-2(4)) Napoleon Publishing/Rendezvous Pr. CAN. *Dist:* AtlasBooks Distribution.

McConnell, Robert. Perfect Pals. Bradford, June, illus. 2004. (Napples Ser.). 34p. (J). (ps-k). pap. 7.95 (978-0-929141-72-5(5)) Napoleon Publishing/Rendezvous Pr. CAN. *Dist:* AtlasBooks Distribution.

McCormick, Angela Barlag. Pie Morgan & the New Girl. 2004. 56p. pap. 12.95 (978-1-4137-1782-2(9)) PublishAmerica, Inc.

McCourt, Lisa & Young, Mary. The New Kid & the Cookie Thief. 1998. (Illus.). 32p. (J). (ps-3). 14.95 (978-1-55874-588-9(2)) Health Communications, Inc.

Mccue, Mimi. The Accidental Cheerleader. 2007. (Candy Apple Ser.: No. 1). 176p. (J). pap. 4.99 (978-0-439-92928-8(8)) Scholastic, Inc.

McCusker, Paul. Danger Lies Ahead. 2006. (Adventures in Odyssey Ser.: No. 2). 336p. (J). pap. 13.99 (978-1-58997-329-9(1)) Focus on the Family Publishing.

—Point of No Return. 2006. (Adventures in Odyssey Bks.). 336p. (J). pap. 13.99 (978-1-58997-332-9(1)) Focus on the Family Publishing.

—Strange Journey Back. 2006. (Adventures in Odyssey Ser.: No. 1). 304p. (J). pap. 13.99 (978-1-58997-325-1(9)) Focus on the Family Publishing.

McDaniel, Lurlene. Angels Watching over Me. 2002. (Angels Trilogy: No. 1). (J). (gr. 7-12). lib. bdg. 15.30 (978-0-613-90626-5(8)) Tandem Library Bks.

—Dawn Rochelle: Four Novels. 2000. (Dawn Rochelle Ser.). (Illus.). (J). (978-0-606-17994-2(1)) Tandem Library Bks.

—Holly's Story. (Angels in Pink Ser.). 224p. (gr. 7-11). 2007. (YA). mass mkt. 5.99 (978-0-440-23867-6(6) , Laurel Leaf); 2005. (YA). 10.95 (978-0-385-73158-4(2) , Delacorte Bks. for Young Readers); 2005. (J). lib. bdg. 12.99 (978-0-385-90195-6(X) , Delacorte Bks. for Young Readers) Random Hse. Children's Bks.

—One Last Wish: Three Novels: Mother, Help Me Live; Let Him Live; Sixteen & Dying. 1998. (One Last Wish Ser.). (gr. 7-12). lib. bdg. 15.30 (978-0-613-88880-6(4)) Tandem Library Bks.

—Raina's Story. (Angels in Pink Ser.). 208p. (gr. 7). 2006. (YA). pap. 6.50 (978-0-440-23866-9(8) , Laurel Leaf); 2005. (J). lib. bdg. 12.99 (978-0-385-90194-9(1) , Delacorte Bks. for Young Readers) Random Hse. Children's Bks.

—Telling Christina Goodbye. 2002. 240p. (YA). (gr. 7 up). mass mkt. 5.50 (978-0-553-57087-8(0) , Laurel Leaf) Random Hse. Children's Bks.

—Telling Christina Goodbye. 2002. (gr. 7-12). lib. bdg. 13.00 (978-0-613-57148-7(7)) Tandem Library Bks.

McDaniels, Preston. A Perfect Snowman. McDaniels, Preston, illus. 2007. 40p. (J). (ps-3). 15.99 (***978-1-4169-1026-8(3)*** Simon & Schuster Children's Publishing.

McDonald, Janet. Spellbound. 2003. 144p. (YA). pap. 5.99 (978-0-14-250193-1(X) , Puffin) Penguin Group (USA) Inc.

—Spellbound. 2003. (gr. 7-12). lib. bdg. 14.15 (978-0-613-86523-4(5)) Tandem Library Bks.

McDonald, Megan. Beezy. Poydar, Nancy, illus. 2000. 48p. (J). (gr. 1-4). pap. 4.95 (978-0-531-07162-5(6) , Orchard Bks.) Scholastic, Inc.

—Beezy. 2000. (J). (978-0-606-19480-8(0)) Tandem Library Bks.

—Beezy & Funnybone. Poydar, Nancy, illus. 2000. 48p. (J). (gr. 1-4). pap. 4.95 (978-0-531-07161-8(8) , Orchard Bks.) Scholastic, Inc.

—Beezy at Bat. Poydar, Nancy, illus. 48p. (J). (gr. 1-4). 2000. pap. 4.95 (978-0-531-07164-9(2)); 1998. pap. 13.95 (978-0-531-30085-5(4)) Scholastic, Inc. (Orchard Bks.).

—Beezy at Bat. 2000. (J). (978-0-606-20453-8(9)) Tandem Library Bks.

—Beezy Magic. 2000. (Illus.). (J). 11.75 (978-0-606-18331-4(0)) Tandem Library Bks.

—Changes for Julie, Bk. 6. McAliley, Susan, illus. 2007. 104p. (YA). (gr. 3 up). 12.95 (***978-1-59369-355-8(9)***) American Girl Publishing, Inc.

—Changes for Julie, Bk. 6. McAliley, Susan & Hunt, Robert, illus. 2007. 104p. (YA). (gr. 3 up). pap. 6.95 (***978-1-59369-354-1(0)***) American Girl Publishing, Inc.

—Judy Moody Around the World in 8 1/2 Days. Reynolds, Peter H., illus. 2006. (Judy Moody Ser.: No. 7). 176p. (J). (gr. 1-4). 15.99 (978-0-7636-2832-1(8)) Candlewick Pr.

—Lucky Star. 2000. (J). (978-0-606-18924-8(6)) Tandem Library Bks.

McDonald, Megan & Poydar, Nancy. Beezy at Bat. 1998. (Illus.). 48p. (J). (gr. 1-4). 14.99 (978-0-531-33085-2(0) , Orchard Bks.) Scholastic, Inc.

—Beezy Magic. 1998. (Illus.). 48p. (J). (gr. 1-4). 14.99 (978-0-531-33064-7(8) , Orchard Bks.) Scholastic, Inc.

McDonald, Meinir & Evans, Anthony. Bant I Batagonia. 2005. (WEL., Illus.). 16p. (978-1-85644-543-6(7)) Univ. of Wales, Aberystwyth, Centre for Educational Studies.

McDonnell, Patrick. The Gift of Nothing. 2005. (Illus.). 52p. (J). (ps-1). 14.99 (978-0-316-11488-2(X)) Little Brown & Co.

McElligott, Matthew. Absolutely Not. 2006. (Illus.). 32p. (J). pap. 6.95 (978-0-8027-8934-1(X)) Walker & Co.

McElroy, Roland. Jibicle & Cokie: Friends at Last. 2006. (J). pap. (978-0-9673917-1-7(7)) McElroy & Assocs.

McGaw, Victoria. The Memory Box. Wise, Noreen, ed. Favazzao, Keith, illus. 2001. (Lemonade Collection). 64p. (J). (gr. 2-8). pap. 7.50 (978-1-58584-256-8(7)) Huckleberry Pr.

—Old Tree, Old Friend. Wise, Noreen, ed. Favazzao, Keith, illus. 2001. (Lemonade Collection). 64p. (J). (gr. 1-5). pap. 7.50 (978-1-58584-260-5(5)) Huckleberry Pr.

McGhee, Alison. Snap! 2004. 144p. (J). (gr. 4-7). 15.99 (978-0-7636-2002-8(5)) Candlewick Pr.

—Snap. 2006. 144p. (J). (gr. 4-7). reprint ed. pap. 5.99 (978-0-7636-2617-4(1)) Candlewick Pr.

McGinnis, Diane. Bimbo: A Friend for Kindsay Lane. 1999. (Illus.). 28p. (J). 14.99 (978-1-57921-190-5(9)) Wine-Press Publishing.

McGugan, Jim. Josepha: A Prairie Boy's Story. Kimber, Murray, illus. 32p. (J). pap. (978-0-88995-142-6(X)) Red Deer Pr.

—Josepha: A Prairie Boy's Story. 1998. (gr. k-3). lib. bdg. 15.25 (978-0-613-81280-1(8)) Tandem Library Bks.

McGuigan, Mary Ann. Morning in a Different Place. 2008. (J). (***978-1-59078-551-5(7)*** , Front Street) Boyds Mills Pr.

McHugh, Fiona, adapted by. Anne of Green Gables Storybook. 2007. (Illus.). 80p. (J). (gr. 2-7). pap. 9.95 (978-0-920668-42-9(9)) Firefly Bks., Ltd.

McIntosh, Helen B. Eric, Jose, & the Peace Rug. 2nd ed. 2005. (J). per. 14.99 (978-0-9763949-0-7(1)) Peace Rug Company, Inc., The.

McIntyre, Pat Henican. ?Oh Freddie!? Richie, Rebecca, illus. 2002. 48p. (J). (978-1-55306-382-7(1) , Epic Pr.) Essence Publishing.

McJunkin, Jehu David & Wethern, Amelia. A Missouri River Tale. l.t. ed. 2005. (ENG., Illus.). 47p. (J). 12.95 (978-0-9766124-0-7(2)) Ap Amelia Pr.

McKann, Anna. Chavos: The Kids of Distrito Federal. 2006. (Illus.). 261p. (YA). per. (***978-0-9554438-0-0(6)***) Sharon Hse. Publishing, Ltd.

McKay, Amanda. Not Sally Marshall Again! 2000. 200p. (J). pap. 12.95 (978-0-7022-3169-8(X)) Univ. of Queensland Pr. AUS. *Dist:* International Specialized Bk. Services.

McKay, Hilary. The Amber Cat. 1999. (YA). pap., stu. ed. 41.00 incl. audio (978-0-7887-3635-3(3) , 41000) Recorded Bks., LLC.

—The Amber Cat. 1999. 'p. (J). 11.64 (978-0-606-16326-2(3)) Tandem Library Bks.

—Happy & Glorious. Offen, Hilda, illus. l.t. ed. 1999. 144p. (J). pap. (978-0-7540-6061-1(6) , CLP 263) BBC Audio.

—Indigo's Star. 272p. (J). (gr. 3-7). 2004. (Illus.). 16.95 (978-0-689-86563-3(5) , McElderry, Margaret K.); 2006. reprint ed. pap. 5.99 (978-1-4169-1403-7(X) , Aladdin) Simon & Schuster Children's Publishing.

—Permanent Rose. (J). (gr. 3-7). 2005. 240p. 16.99 (978-1-4169-0372-7(0) , McElderry, Margaret K.); 2006. 256p. reprint ed. pap. 5.99 (978-1-4169-2804-1(9) , Aladdin) Simon & Schuster Children's Publishing.

McKay, Sharon E. What Are Friends For? 2001. (Hippo Tub Co. Ser.). (Illus.). 40p. (J). pap. 6.95 (978-1-894454-00-1(6)) Balmur Entertainment, Ltd. CAN. *Dist:* General Distribution Services, Inc.

McKee, David. Elmer, Level 4.9. McKee, David, illus. 3rd ed. 2003. (Picture Books Collection). (SPA., Illus.). 32p. (J). (gr. k-3). 12.95 (978-84-372-2186-1(2)) Altea, Ediciones, S.A. - Grupo Santillana ESP. *Dist:* Santillana USA Publishing Co., Inc.

—Elmer. McKee, David, illus. (Historias Para Dormir Ser.). (SPA., Illus.). 32p. (J). (gr. k-3). pap. 9.95 (978-968-19-1029-7(X)) Santillana USA Publishing Co., Inc.

—Elmer & Friends Sticker Story Book. 2006. 16p. (J). (ps-k). pap., act. bk. ed. 6.99 (978-1-84270-535-3(0)) Andersen GBR. *Dist:* Independent Pubs. Group.

—Elmer First Colouring Activity Book. 2006. 32p. (J). pap., act. bk. ed. 6.99 (978-1-84270-536-0(9)) Andersen GBR. *Dist:* Trafalgar Square Publishing.

—Elmer's Baby Record Book. 2007. (Illus.). 32p. (J). 15.99 (***978-1-84270-534-6(2)***) Andersen GBR. *Dist:* Independent Pubs. Group.

—Elmer's Friends. 2004. (Elmers Ser.).Tr. of Amigos de Elmer. (ENG, URD, TUR, VIE & SPA., Illus.). 16p. (J). bds. 6.95 (978-1-84059-069-2(6)); bds. 6.95 (978-1-84059-071-5(8)) Milet Publishing.

—Elmer's Friends. Erdogan, Faith, tr. 2004. (Elmer Ser.).Tr. of Amigos de Elmer. (ENG, URD, TUR, VIE & SPA., Illus.). 16p. (J). bds. 6.95 (978-1-84059-073-9(4)) Milet Publishing.

—Elmer's Friends. Wood, Kim Marie, tr. 2004. (Elmers Ser.).Tr. of Amigos de Elmer. (VIE, ENG, URD, TUR & SPA., Illus.). 16p. (J). bds. 6.95 (978-1-84059-075-3(0)) Milet Publishing.

—Elmer's Friends. Pullin, Beatriz, tr. 2004. (Elmer Ser.).Tr. of Amigos de Elmer. (SPA, ENG, URD, TUR & VIE., Illus.). 16p. (J). (ps-k). bds. 6.95 (978-1-84059-072-2(6)) Milet Publishing.

—Elmer's Friends Board Book. 2004. (Elmer Ser.).Tr. of Amigos de Elmer. (Illus.). 16p. (J). (ARA & ENG.). bds. 6.95 (978-1-84059-401-0(2)); (ENG & SOM., bds. 6.95 (978-1-84059-403-4(9)) Milet Publishing.

—Elmer's Friends Board Book. Umicini, Roberta, tr. 2004. (Elmer Ser.).Tr. of Amigos de Elmer. (ENG & ITA., Illus.). 16p. (J). bds. 6.95 (978-1-84059-402-7(0)) Milet Publishing.

—Elmer's Friends Board Book. 2004. (Elmer Ser.).Tr. of Amigos de Elmer. (ENG, URD, TUR, VIE & SPA., Illus.). 16p. (J). bds. 6.95 (978-1-84059-070-8(X)) Milet Publishing.

—Elmer's New Friend. 2003. (Illus.). 22p. (J). 8.99 (978-1-84270-034-1(0)) Andersen GBR. *Dist:* Trafalgar Square Publishing.

—Elmer's Weather. French, Li Yen, tr. 2004. (Elmers Ser.). (ENG, URD, TUR, VIE & SPA., Illus.). 16p. (J). bds. 6.95 (978-1-84059-077-7(7)) Milet Publishing.

—Isabel's Noisy Tummy. 2007. (Illus.). 26p. (J). (ps-k). pap. 6.99 (978-1-84270-576-6(8)) Andersen GBR. *Dist:* Independent Pubs. Group.

McKenna, Colleen O'Shaughnessy. Doggone... Third Grade! Roth, Stephanie, illus. 2002. 80p. (J). (gr. 4-6). tchr. ed. 15.95 (978-0-8234-1696-7(8)) Holiday Hse., Inc.

McKenna, K. J. Take Three Girls. 2005. 96p. pap. 10.00 (978-1-4116-6290-2(3)) Lulu.com.

McKeowen, Sean. Cualovier Cosa Menos la Inyeccion. McKeowen, Sean, illus. 2001. (SPA.). 32p. (J). (ps-3). pap. 7.50 (978-1-59134-010-2(1)) Maval Publishing, Inc.

McKissack, Patricia C. A Friendship for Today. 2007. 240p. (J). (gr. 4-7). pap. 16.99 (978-0-439-66098-3(X) , Scholastic Pr.) Scholastic, Inc.

—A Picture of Freedom: The Diary of Clotee, a Slave Girl, Belmont Plantation, Virginia, 1859. 2003. (Dear America Ser.). 128p. (J). 12.95 (978-0-439-55501-2(9)) Scholastic, Inc.

McKnew Jr., Thomas I. The Legend of Seal Beach. 2007. 28p. 14.94 (***978-0-615-15593-7(6)***) VideoPresence-.com, A.

McMahen, Chris. Klutzhood. 2007. 160p. (J). (gr. 4-7). pap. (***978-1-55143-710-1(4)***) Orca Bk. Pubs.

Mcmahon, Karen. Toe Tapping Fun. Albrecht, Jeff, illus. 2005. (Barney Ser.). 32p. (J). pap. 4.99 (978-0-439-74409-6(1)) Scholastic, Inc.

McMillen, Charlotte Palmer. The Little Sea Rock & His Friend Arena. 2005. (Illus.). 32p. (J). per. 14.95 (978-0-9771939-4-3(2) , 003) New World Publishing.

McMullan, Kate. Pearl & Wagner: Two Good Friends. Alley, R. W., illus. 2003. (Easy-to-Read Ser.). 48p. (J). (gr. k-3). 13.99 (978-0-8037-2573-7(6) , Dial) Penguin Group (USA) Inc.

McMullen, Jill. Toby & Friends: Therapy Dogs. 2007. (J). pap. 7.99 (***978-1-60247-241-9(6)***) Tate Publishing & Enterprises, L.L.C.

McNamara, Margaret. Snow Day. Gordon, Mike, illus. 2007. (Robin Hill School Ser.). 32p. (J). lib. bdg. 13.89 (***978-1-4169-3492-9(8)***); pap. 3.99 (***978-1-4169-3493-6(6)***) Simon & Schuster Children's Publishing. (Aladdin).

McOmber, Rachel B., ed. McOmber Phonics Storybooks: Hello Again. rev. ed. (Illus.). (J). (978-0-944991-84-8(X)) Swift Learning Resources.

—McOmber Phonics Storybooks: Jud & Nell. rev. ed. (Illus.). (J). (978-0-944991-33-6(5)) Swift Learning Resources.

—McOmber Phonics Storybooks: The Gal Pals. rev. ed. (Illus.). (J). (978-0-944991-42-8(4)) Swift Learning Resources.

McPhail, David. Big Brown Bear's Birthday Surprise. O'Connor, John, illus. 2007. (Big Brown Bear Ser.). 32p. (J). (ps-2). 16.00 (978-0-15-206098-5(7)) Harcourt Trade Pubs.

—Rick Is Siek. McPhail, David, illus. 2004. (Illus.). 24p. (J). lib. bdg. 10.00 (***978-1-4242-0183-9(7)***) Fitzgerald Bks.

—Sylvie & True. 2007. (Illus.). 32p. (J). (ps). 15.00 (978-0-374-37364-1(7)) Farrar, Straus & Giroux.

—The Teddy Bear. 2005. (Illus.). 32p. (J). reprint ed. pap. 6.95 (978-0-8050-7882-4(7) , Holt, Henry & Co. Bks. For Young Readers) Holt, Henry & Co.

McPhail, David M. Big Brown Bear Goes to Town. O'Connor, John, illus. 2006. 40p. (J). 16.00 (978-0-15-205317-8(4)) Harcourt Trade Pubs.

—Big Pig & Little Pig. McPhail, David M., illus. 2002. (Illus.). (J). 11.45 (978-0-7587-5345-8(4)) Book Wholesalers, Inc.

—Big Pig & Little Pig. 2003. (Green Light Readers Level 1 Ser.). (Illus.). 24p. (J). 11.95 (978-0-15-204818-1(9)); pap. 3.95 (978-0-15-204857-0(X)) Harcourt Children's Bks. (Green Light Readers).

—Big Pig & Little Pig. (gr. k-3). 2003. lib. bdg. 11.80 (978-0-613-63254-6(0)); 2001. (Illus.). (J). (978-0-606-21066-9(0)) Tandem Library Bks.

—A Bug, a Bear & a Boy. 1998. (Hello Reader! Ser.). (Illus.). 32p. (J). (ps-1). pap. 3.99 (978-0-590-14904-4(0)) Scholastic, Inc.

—A Girl, a Goat & a Goose. 2000. (Hello Reader! Ser.). (Illus.). (J). 10.79 (978-0-606-18875-3(4)) Tandem Library Bks.

—A Girl, a Goat, & a Goose, & the Storm. 2002. (SPA., Illus.). (J). (978-0-439-41152-3(1)) Scholastic, Inc.

—Jack & Rick. 2003. (Green Light Readers Level 1 Ser.). (Illus.). 24p. (J). 11.95 (978-0-15-204819-8(7)); pap. 3.95 (978-0-15-204859-4(6)) Harcourt Children's Bks. (Green Light Readers).

—Jack & Rick. 2002. (gr. k-3). lib. bdg. 11.80 (978-0-613-63167-9(6)) Tandem Library Bks.

—Rick Is Sick. 2004. (Green Light Readers Level 1 Ser.). (Illus.). 24p. (J). 12.95 (978-0-15-205091-7(4)); pap. 3.95 (978-0-15-205092-4(2)) Harcourt Children's Bks. (Green Light Readers).

McPherson, Dottie. Kizzi's Special Friends. 2003. (Illus.). (J). 14.95 (978-0-9724979-0-9(0) , Advocate Hse.) A Cappela Publishing.

Meacham, Edie M. Roodey's Junk Food Summer. 2004. 50p. pap. 12.95 (978-1-4137-3286-3(0)) PublishAmerica, Inc.

Mead. Junebug in Trouble. 2003. (gr. 3-6). lib. bdg. 13.00 (978-0-613-89785-3(4)) Tandem Library Bks.

Mead, Alice. Girl of Kosovo. 2001. 128p. (J). (gr. 4-7). 16.00 (978-0-374-32620-3(7) , Farrar, Straus & Giroux (BYR)) Farrar, Straus & Giroux.

—Girl of Kosovo. 2003. (Illus.). 128p. (J). (gr. 5). pap. 5.50 (978-0-440-41853-5(4) , Yearling) Random Hse. Children's Bks.

—Girl of Kosovo. 2003. (gr. 3-6). lib. bdg. 13.00 (978-0-613-62205-9(7)) Tandem Library Bks.

Mead, Alice & Weber James, Alice. Madame Squidley & Beanie. 2004. 144p. (J). 16.00 (978-0-374-34688-1(7) , Farrar, Straus & Giroux (BYR)) Farrar, Straus & Giroux.

Mechling, Lauren & Moser, Laura. All Q, No A: More Tales of a 10th-Grade Social Climber. 2006. 288p. (YA). (gr. 7). pap. 7.99 (978-0-618-66378-1(9) , Graphia) Houghton Mifflin Co. Trade & Reference Div.

Mechling, Lauren & Moser, Laura. Foreign Exposure: The Social Climber Abroad. 2007. 320p. (YA). (gr. 7 up). pap. 8.99 (***978-0-618-66379-8(7)*** , Graphia) Houghton Mifflin Co. Trade & Reference Div.

Mechling, Lauren, et al. The Rise & Fall of a 10th Grade Social Climber. 2005. 304p. (YA). (gr. 7). pap. 7.99 (978-0-618-55519-2(6) , Graphia) Houghton Mifflin Co. Trade & Reference Div.

Medearis, Angela Shelf. Best Friends Forever? Papp, Robert, illus. 2004. 124p. (J). (978-0-439-52330-1(3)) Scholastic, Inc.

—I'd Still Pick You. 2003. 32p. 14.95 (978-1-57768-431-2(1)) School Specialty Publishing.

Medina, Jane. My Name Is Jorge: On Both Sides of the River. Broeck, Fabricio Vanden, illus. 2003. (SPA & ENG.). 48p. (YA). (gr. 2-4). pap. 9.95 (978-1-56397-842-5(3)) Boyds Mills Pr.

—My Name Is Jorge: On Both Sides of the River. 1999. (978-0-606-18014-6(1)) Tandem Library Bks.

Medina, Nico. The Straight Road to Kylie. 2007. 320p. (YA). (gr. 9 up). pap. 8.99 (978-1-4169-3600-8(9) , Simon Pulse) Simon & Schuster Children's Publishing.

Meeko's New Friend Little Play. (J). 6.98 (978-0-7853-1336-6(2)) Publications International, Ltd.

Mello, Alondra. Alanora's Magic Tree: Alanora's Spirit Journey. 2007. 48p. per. 12.97 (***978-1-932344-77-6(2)***) Thornton Publishing.

Melmed, Laura Krauss. A Hug Goes Around. Lewin, Betsy, illus. 2002. 32p. (J). (ps-3). 15.95 (978-0-688-14680-1(5)); lib. bdg. 15.89 (978-0-688-14681-8(3)) HarperCollins Pubs.

Melton, Holly. A Day at Moss Lake. Yakovetic Productions Staff, illus. 24p. (J). (gr. k-2). (978-1-58605-010-8(9)) LeapFrog Enterprises, Inc.

Meomi. The Octonauts & the Only Lonely Monster. 2006. (Illus.). 36p. (J). (ps-3). 15.95 (978-1-59702-005-3(2)) Immedium.

Mercer, Rita C. Earl the Squatchem. 2007. 9.00 (***978-0-8059-8823-9(8)***) Dorrance Publishing Co., Inc.

Meredith Books Staff. Polly Pocket. Goldstein, Alrica, ed. 2007. (I Can Find It Ser.). 24p. (J). pap. 4.99 (***978-0-696-23730-0(X)***) Meredith Bks.

Meredith-Markowitz, Susan. A New Friend. 2003. (Early Connections Ser.). (J). pap. 33.00 (978-1-4108-1096-0(8)) Benchmark Education Co.

Meres, Jonathan. Somewhere Out There. Pyle, Liz, illus. 1998. 32p. (gr. 1-4). 22.99 (978-0-09-176638-2(9)) Random Hse. GBR. *Dist:* Independent Pubs. Group.

Merialdo, Lee K. Kidnapped. 2006. 112p. pap. 10.95 (978-0-7414-3407-4(5)) Infinity Publishing.

Mericle, Suzanne. Trippin with Mabel & Margaret. 1998. per. 14.95 (978-1-889131-28-3(8)) Janson Media Group.

Meridith, Brenda C. She's Funny That Way. Meridith, Brenda C., ed. 2003. (C). 22.00 (978-0-9723570-0-5(9)) Dahomey Publishing Co.

Merritt, Gail. Silver Mantle. 2002. (Illus.). 160p. (YA). pap. (978-0-7344-0177-9(9) , Lothian Bks.) Hachette Livre Australia.

—Silver Mantle. 2001. (gr. 7-12). lib. bdg. 22.20 (978-0-613-90916-7(X)) Tandem Library Bks.

Mervyn, Catherine Antolino. Sammy, Pepe & Mumbo-Jumbo. 2004. pap. 7.95 (978-0-533-14829-5(4)) Vantage Pr., Inc.

Metcalf, Paula, illus. Norma No Friends. 1999. 40p. (J). (ps-3). 15.95 (978-1-902283-87-6(2)) Barefoot Bks., Inc.

Metz, Melinda. Sunny & Matt. 2000. (Sweet Sixteen Ser.: No. 6). 224p. (YA). (gr. 12 up). pap. 5.95 (978-0-06-440815-8(9) , Harper Trophy) HarperCollins Pubs.

Metzenthen, David. Adrian over the Top. 2000. (gr. 7-12). lib. bdg. 12.25 (978-0-613-28721-0(5)) Tandem Library Bks.

—Big Wave Day. 2000. (gr. 7-12). lib. bdg. 12.25 (978-0-613-28757-9(6)) Tandem Library Bks.

Metzger, Lois. Missing Girls. 2001. (J). (978-0-606-21334-9(1)) Tandem Library Bks.

Metzger, Steve. Big Shark's Valentine Surprise. Hohnstadt, Cedric, illus. 2007. (J). pap. (***978-0-439-92251-7(8)***) Scholastic, Inc.

—I'm Having a Bad Day! Wilhelm, Hans, illus. 1998. (Dinofours Ser.: No. 2). 32p. (J). (ps-1). pap. 3.25 (978-0-590-03551-4(7)) Scholastic, Inc.

—It's Snowing. Wilhelm, Hans, illus. 1998. (Dinofours Ser.: No. 14). (J). (ps-1). pap. 3.25 (978-0-590-03550-7(9)) Scholastic, Inc.

Meyer, Brad. A Matchless Age. 2006. 302p. pap. 24.95 (978-1-4241-0523-6(4)) PublishAmerica, Inc.

Meyer, Louis A. Curse of the Blue Tattoo: Being an Account of the Misadventures of Jacky Faber, Midshipman & Fine Lady. 2004. (Bloody Jack Adventures Ser.). (Illus.). 496p. (YA). 17.00 (978-0-15-205115-0(5)) Harcourt Children's Bks.

Meyer, M. D. The Mystery of the Lost Friend. 2003. 65p. pap. 9.95 (978-0-7414-1378-9(7)) Infinity Publishing.

Mi Amigo Es un Flash-Flash. (Raton de Biblioteca Coleccion Ser.). (SPA.). (J). (gr. 3). pap. 7.95 (978-84-88061-82-9(X)) Serres, Ediciones, S. L. ESP. *Dist:* Lectorum Pubns., Inc.

Michaels, Anna. Best Friends. Karas, G. Brian, illus. 2004. 24p. (J). lib. bdg. 10.00 (***978-1-4242-0217-1(5)***) Fitzgerald Bks.

—Best Friends. Karas, G. Brian, illus. 2004. (Green Light Readers Level 1 Ser.). 32p. (J). 12.95 (978-0-15-205136-5(8)); pap. 3.95 (978-0-15-205133-4(3)) Harcourt Children's Bks. (Green Light Readers).

Michaels, Kat. Willow's Bend. 2006. 24p. 15.95 (978-0-9745052-6-8(9)) Tree Of Life Publishing.

Michaelson, Richard. Across the Alley. Lewis, E. B., illus. 2006. 32p. (J). (ps-3). 16.99 (978-0-399-23970-0(7) , Putnam Juvenile) Penguin Group (USA) Inc.

Michelin, Linda. Zuzu's Wishing Cake. Johnson, D. B., illus. 2006. 32p. (J). (gr. k-3). 16.00 (978-0-618-64640-1(X)) Houghton Mifflin Co. Trade & Reference Div.

Michelle. Terrible Tina Toomy. 2005. 48p. pap. 12.95 (978-1-4137-2979-5(7)) PublishAmerica, Inc.

Mickles Sr., Robert T. S. Blood Kin, a Savannah Story. 2007. 108p. per. 9.95 (***978-0-595-45129-6(2)***) iUniverse, Inc.

Mighty Fine, Inc. Staff. Ruby Gloom's Guide to Friendship. 2005. (Illus.). 72p. (J). (gr. 5-9). 12.95 (978-0-8109-5862-3(7)) Abrams, Harry N., Inc.

Miglis, Jenny. And the Winner Is ... Meurer, Caleb, illus. 2004. (SpongeBob SquarePants Ser.). 24p. (J). pap. 3.50 (978-0-689-86327-1(6) , Simon Spotlight/Nickelodeon) Simon & Schuster Children's Publishing.

Miles, Betty. I Would If I Could. 2000. 128p. (gr. 4-7). pap. 9.95 (978-0-595-00490-4(3) , Backinprint.com) iUniverse, Inc.

Milgrim, David. See Pip Point. Milgrim, David, illus. 2004. (Adventures of Otto Ser.). (Illus.). 32p. (J). pap. 3.99 (978-0-689-85140-7(5) , Aladdin) Simon & Schuster Children's Publishing.

Miller, Jennifer. Best Friends for Life. Choi Sung Hwan, Aragon Noel, illus. (Trollz Ser.). 120p. (J). 2006. pap. 4.99 (978-0-439-80311-3(X)); 2005. (gr. 2-5). pap. 4.99 (978-0-439-73387-8(1)) Scholastic, Inc.

Miller, Jennifer. Run, Rasputin, Run! Trials & Friendships (Book 2) 2006. (ENG., Illus.). 172p. per. (***978-1-4120-8494-9(6)***) Trafford Publishing.

Miller, Lynda. Two Friends. Miller, Lynda, illus. 1999. (Illus.). 20p. (J). (gr. k-5). 10.00 (978-0-9636140-3-2(7) , Neon Rose Productions) Smart Alternatives, Inc.

Miller, Mary Beth. Aimee. 2004. (Illus.). 288p. (YA). (gr. 9). pap. 6.99 (978-0-14-240025-8(4) , Puffin) Penguin Group (USA) Inc.

—Aimee. 2004. (gr. 7-12). lib. bdg. 15.30 (978-0-613-89043-4(4)) Tandem Library Bks.

Miller, Sara Swan. Better Than TV. 1998. (First Choice Chapter Book Ser.). (J). (978-0-606-13199-5(X)) Tandem Library Bks.

Miller, Sara Swan. My Pod: Libro de Cuentos y Reproductor Personal de Musica. 2007. (SPA., Illus.). 38p. (J). 24.95 (***978-970-718-495-4(7)*** , Silver Dolphin en Español) Advanced Marketing, S. de R. L. de C. V. MEX. *Dist:* Perseus Distribution.

Miller, Sarah. My Pod Storybook & Personal Music Player. 2006. (RD Innovative Book & Player Format Ser.). (Illus.). 40p. (J). 24.99 (978-0-7944-1130-5(4)) Reader's Digest Assn., Inc., The.

Miller, William. The Piano. Keeter, Susan, illus. 2005. 32p. (gr. 1-4). 7.95 (978-1-58430-242-1(9)) Lee & Low Bks., Inc.

Millman, Calanitte. The Adventures of the Gimmel Gang III: The Cave. 2005. (J). pap. 8.95 (***978-1-931681-84-1(8)***) Israel Bk. Shop.

Millman, Isaac. Moses Sees a Play. Millman, Isaac, illus. 2004. (Moses Goes To Ser.). (Illus.). 32p. (J). 16.00 (978-0-374-35066-6(3) , Farrar, Straus & Giroux (BYR)) Farrar, Straus & Giroux.

Millman, M. C. Always Something Else: The whimsical adventures of Elisheva Raskin. 2005. (Illus.). 160p. (J). 14.95 (978-1-932443-23-3(1) , ASEH) Judaica Pr., Inc., The.

—Always Something Else 2. 2006. (Illus.). 160p. (J). 14.95 (978-1-932443-43-1(6) , ASE2H) Judaica Pr., Inc., The.

Mills, Charles. Wings over Oshkosh. 2005. (Honors Club Story Ser.: Vol. 5). 127p. (J). (978-0-8163-2089-9(6)) Pacific Pr. Publishing Assn.

Mills, Claudia. Being Teddy Roosevelt. Alley, R. W., illus. 2007. 96p. (J). (gr. 2-5). 16.00 (978-0-374-30657-1(5) , Farrar, Straus & Giroux (BYR)) Farrar, Straus & Giroux.

Mills, Susan & Shara, Diana. Frankie & Her Little Pals - Save the Watermelons. 2007. 32p. (J). (***978-0-9790690-3-1(3)***) Lucky Red Pr., LLC.

—Frankie & Her Little Pals - Stir It Up. 2007. (J). 7.95 (***978-0-9790690-0-0(9)***) Lucky Red Pr., LLC.

Minarik, Else Holmelund. The Cricket Who Came to Dinner. Hahner, Chris, illus. 2004. 32p. (ps). lib. bdg. 11.19 (978-0-606-29910-7(6)) Tandem Library Bks.

—Little Bear's Friends - Los Amigos de Osito. (SPA.). 64p. (J). 7.95 (978-84-204-3049-2(8)) Santillana USA Publishing Co., Inc.

Minter, J. Hold on Tight. 2006. (Insiders Novel Ser.: Bk. 5). 256p. (YA). pap. 8.95 (978-1-58234-719-6(0) , Bloomsbury Children) Bloomsbury Publishing.

—Inside Girl: A Novel. 2007. (Insiders Novel Ser.). 240p. (YA). (gr. 7 up). pap. 8.95 (***978-1-59990-086-5(6)***) Bloomsbury Publishing.

—The Insiders. 2004. 200p. (gr. 9 up). pap. 8.95 (978-1-58234-895-7(2) , Bloomsbury Children) Bloomsbury Publishing.

—Pass It On. 2004. (Insiders Ser.). 200p. (YA). pap. 8.95 (978-1-58234-954-1(1) , Bloomsbury Children) Bloomsbury Publishing.

Minter, J. The Sweetest Thing: An Inside Girl Novel. 2007. (Insiders Novel Ser.). 224p. (J). (gr. 7 up). pap. 8.95 (***978-1-59990-087-2(4)*** , Bloomsbury Children) Bloomsbury Publishing.

Miracle Mouse Cranky's Miracle. ed. 2006. (J). lib. bdg. 19.95 (978-1-934017-00-5(0)) Hignites, Tom Miracle Studio.

Miranda, Anne. Food Court. Cleyet-Merle, Laurence, illus. 2002. 16p. (J). (978-0-439-35090-7(5)) Scholastic, Inc.

Miranda, Hialeah. One Fun Summer's Day. 2004. 48p. pap. 12.95 (978-1-4137-1858-4(2)) PublishAmerica, Inc.

Miro. The Watermelon Story. Brown, Nick, illus. 2003. 103p. (J). pap. (978-1-84426-258-8(8)) Upfront Publishing Ltd.

Miss Muffin. 2002. 5.99 (978-0-9722679-0-8(5)) Berry Cove Publishing Co.

Miss O, Harlie, Justine, and Isabella, with Devra Newberger Speregen, Juliette. Caught in the Net. 2006. (Miss O & Friends Ser.). (Illus.). 144p. (J). pap. 5.99 (978-0-8230-2948-8(4)) Watson-Guptill Pubns., Inc.

Miss Spider & Kirk, David. Oh Boy, It's Bounce! Miss Spider's Sunny Patch Friends. 2005. (Miss Spider Ser.). (Illus.). 8p. (J). (ps-2). bds. 7.99 (978-0-448-44010-1(5) , Grosset & Dunlap) Penguin Group (USA) Inc.

Modica, Cathy & Van Eyck, Laura. Niik & Bling: The Friendship Begins. Modica, Cathy, photos by. l.t. ed. 2005. (Illus.). 40p. (J). 19.95 (978-0-9762466-0-2(0)) Wholesome Puppy Tales.

Moen Cabanting, Ruth & Jensen, Natalie Mahina. Happy Honu Makes a Friend. 2006. 7p. 6.95 (978-1-933067-15-5(2)) Beachhouse Publishing, LLC.

Molnar, Cheri Eplin. Dee Diddly Dragon Is Not a Wimp. Gutwein, Gwendolyn, illus. 2004. 32p. (J). per. 17.95 (978-0-9746330-3-9(8)) Anton Berkshire Publishing.

Moncure, Jane Belk. Word Bird's New Friend. 2002. (New Word Bird Library). (Illus.). 32p. (J). (ps-3). 22.79 (978-1-56766-844-5(5)) Child's World, Inc.

Montgomery, Bobbie. Fruit Tramp Kids. 2000. (Pathfinder Junior Book Club Ser.). 143p. (J). (gr. 4-7). pap. 6.99 (978-0-8280-1422-9(1)) Review & Herald Publishing Assn.

Montgomery Gibson, Jane. My Christmas Friend. Montgomery Gibson, Jane, illus. 2005. (YA). bds. 8.99 (978-1-4183-0066-1(7)) Christ Inspired, Inc.

Montgomery, L. M. Anne of Green Gables. 2004. 400p. per. 16.95 (978-1-59540-110-6(5)) 1st World Publishing, Inc.

—Anne of Green Gables. Miralles, Joseph, illus. 2002. (Great Illustrated Classics Ser.). 240p. (J). (gr. 3-8). 21.35 (978-1-57765-816-0(7) , ABDO & Daughters) ABDO Publishing Co.

—Anne of Green Gables. 349p. (978-1-58726-053-7(0)) Ann Arbor Media Group, LLC.

—Anne of Green Gables. 2000. (Avonlea Ser.: No. 1). 280p. (YA). (gr. 5-8). pap. 15.00 (978-0-7881-9155-8(1)) DIANE Publishing Co.

—Anne of Green Gables. 2004. (Great Classics for Children Ser.). 288p. (J). 5.99 (978-1-4037-0980-6(7)) Dalmatian Pr.

—Anne of Green Gables. 2007. per. 6.99 (***978-1-4209-2922-5(4)***) Digireads.com.

—Anne of Green Gables. 2000. (Avonlea Ser.: No. 1). 320p. (J). (gr. 4-7). pap. 3.50 (978-0-486-41025-8(0)) Dover Pubns., Inc.

—Anne of Green Gables. 2000. (Avonlea Ser.: No. 1). (YA). (gr. 5-8). (978-0-06-028227-1(4)); 1999. (Charming Classics). 400p. (J). (ps up). pap. 6.99 (978-0-694-01251-0(3) , Harper Festival) HarperCollins Pubs.

—Anne of Green Gables. (Avonlea Ser.: No. 1). (YA). (gr. 5-8). pap. (978-0-340-71500-0(6) , Hodder & Stoughton) Hodder General Publishing Division.

—Anne of Green Gables. 2003. 276p. pap. 15.99 (***978-1-4043-6066-2(2)***) IndyPublish.com.

—Anne of Green Gables. Stemach, Jerry, ed. Ham, Jeff, illus. 2000. 65.00 incl. audio, cd-rom (978-1-58702-311-8(3)) Johnston, Don Inc.

—Anne of Green Gables. 1998. 352p. (J). pap. (978-1-55109-249-2(2)) Nimbus Publishing, Ltd.

—Anne of Green Gables. Rubio, Mary & Waterson, Elizabeth, eds. 2006. (Norton Critical Edition Ser.). (Illus.). 400p. (C). pap. 9.00 (978-0-393-92695-8(8)) Norton, W. W. & Co., Inc.

—Anne of Green Gables. 2004. (Oxford Bookworms Ser.). 8.50 (978-0-19-423273-9(5)) Oxford Univ. Pr., Inc.

—Anne of Green Gables. 2003. 320p. (gr. 12). 4.95 (978-0-451-52882-7(4) , Signet Classics); 2002. (Illus.). (J). pap. 9.99 (978-0-14-250102-3(6) , Puffin) Penguin Group (USA) Inc.

—Anne of Green Gables. Howell, Troy, illus. 2002. 256p. (J). 12.99 (978-0-517-22111-2(X) , Gramercy) Random Hse. Value Publishing.

—Anne of Green Gables. 1998. (Children's Classics Ser.: No. 1). (Illus.). 256p. (J). (gr. 4-7). 6.99 (978-0-517-18968-9(2) , Children's Classics) Random Hse. Value Publishing.

—Anne of Green Gables. 2006. (Scholastic Classics Ser.). (Illus.). viii, 272p. (J). (gr. 9-12). 25.00 (978-0-531-16980-3(4) , Watts, Franklin) Scholastic Library Publishing.

—Anne of Green Gables. 2001. (Aladdin Classics Ser.). (Illus.). 480p. (J). pap. 5.99 (978-0-689-84622-9(3) , Aladdin) Simon & Schuster Children's Publishing.

—Anne of Green Gables. McKowen, Scott, illus. 2004. (Unabridged Classics Ser.). 304p. 9.95 (978-1-4027-1451-1(3)) Sterling Publishing Co., Inc.

—Anne of Green Gables. 1999. (Avonlea Ser.: No. 1). (YA). (gr. 5-8). 23.95 (978-0-8057-8090-1(4) , Macmillan Reference USA) Thomson Gale.

—Anne of Green Gables. Fernandez, Laura & Jacobson, Rick, illus. 2000. (Avonlea Ser.: No. 1). 328p. (J). (gr. 5-8). 24.95 (978-0-88776-515-5(7)) Tundra Bks., Inc./ Livres Toundra, Inc. CAN. *Dist:* Random Hse., Inc.

—Anne of Green Gables. MQ Publications Staff, ed. 1998. (Little Brown Notebooks Ser.). (Illus.). 256p. (978-1-84072-063-1(8)) Watson-Guptill Pubns., Inc.

—Anne of Green Gables. 2001. (Children's Classics). (ENG.). 288p. (J). pap. (978-1-85326-139-8(4)) Wordsworth Editions, Ltd.

—Anne of Green Gables. Corvino, Lucy, illus. 2005. (Classic Starts Ser.). 160p. 4.95 (978-1-4027-1130-5(1)) Sterling Publishing Co., Inc.

—Anne of Green Gables. l.t. ed. 2006. (ENG.). pap. (***978-1-4068-3174-0(3)***) Echo Library.

—Anne of Green Gables. Stemach, Jerry, ed. Ham, Jeff, illus. l.t. ed. 2000. 50.00 (978-1-58702-502-0(7)) Johnston, Don Inc.

—Anne of Green Gables. 1998. (Avonlea Ser.). 252p. (YA). (gr. 5-8). reprint ed. (978-1-55109-013-9(9)) Nimbus Publishing, Ltd.

—Anne of Green Gables. 1998. 310p. (YA). (gr. 5-8). reprint ed. lib. bdg. 25.00 (978-1-58287-014-4(4)) North Bks.

—Anne of Green Gables. l.t. ed. 2000. (Anne of Green Gables Ser.: Vol. 1). 294p. (gr. 5-8). pap. 17.95 (978-1-57646-302-4(8)) Quiet Vision Publishing.

—Anne of Green Gables, 100th Anniversary Edition. 2008. 19.95 (***978-0-399-15478-2(7)*** , Putnam Adult) Penguin Group (USA) Inc.

—Anne's House of Dreams. l.t. ed. 1999. (Avonlea Ser.: No. 5). 364p. (YA). (gr. 5-8). lib. bdg. 34.95 (978-1-58118-048-0(9) , 22517) LRS.

—Anne's House of Dreams, Vol. 5. 1999. 320p. (J). 3.99 (978-0-14-036799-7(3) , Putnam Juvenile) Penguin Group (USA) Inc.

—Anne's House of Dreams. 2000. (Anne of Green Gables Ser.: Vol. No. 5). (gr. 5-8). 182p. 24.95 (978-1-57646-313-0(3)); 182p. pap. 14.99 (978-1-57646-312-3(5)); 336p. pap. 19.99 (978-1-57646-314-7(1)) Quiet Vision Publishing.

Montgomery, L. M. Mary Engelbreit's Classic Library: Anne of Green Gables. Engelbreit, Mary, illus. 2008. (Mary Engelbreit's Classic Library). 464p. (J). 9.99 (***978-0-06-008138-6(4)*** , Harper Festival) HarperCollins Pubs.

Montgomery, L. M. & Greenwood, Barbara. Anne of Green Gables. Wood, Muriel, illus. rev. ed. 2001. (Avonlea Ser.: No. 1). 94p. (J). (gr. 5-8). pap. 9.95 (978-1-55013-431-5(0)) Key Porter Bks. CAN. *Dist:* Firefly Bks., Ltd.

Montgomery, L. M. & Hedge, Tricia. Anne of Green Gables, Level 2. 2nd abr. ed. 2000. (Bookworms Ser.). (Illus.). 64p. 6.50 (978-0-19-422965-4(3)) Oxford Univ. Pr., Inc.

Montijo, Rhode. Cloud Boy. Montijo, Rhode, illus. 2006. (SPA., Illus.). 32p. (J). (ps-1). 12.95 (978-1-4169-0199-0(X)) Simon & Schuster Children's Publishing.

Montoya, Jerry. Do-It's Proof. Montoya, Jerry, illus. l.t. ed. 2002. (Illus.). 40p. (J). per. 6.95 (978-0-9722935-0-1(7)) Do-it's Proof Bks.

Moody, Gloria. Two Beautiful Butterflies. Doering, Kimber, illus. l.t. ed. 2005. 25p. (YA). per. 8.99 (978-1-59879-002-3(1)) Lifevest Publishing, Inc.

Moon, Nicola & Oliver, Mark. Margarine & Marbles. 2005. (Red Go Bananas Ser.). (Illus.). 48p. (J). lib. bdg. (978-0-7787-2676-0(2)) Crabtree Publishing Co.

Moonbeam: The Little Elephant. 2005. (Illus.). 32p. (J). 16.95 (978-0-9763596-0-9(X)) Dream Pubns., I, Inc.

Moore, David. Dynamic Duos, 3. 1998. (Fast Breaks Ser.). (978-0-606-13376-0(3)) Tandem Library Bks.

Moore, Ishbel. Dolina's Decision. 2001. 132p. (YA). (gr. 9 up). pap. (978-1-896184-74-6(X)) Roussan Pubs., Inc./ Roussan Editeur, Inc.

Moore, Julianne. Freckleface Strawberry. Pham, LeUyen, illus. 2007. 32p. (J). (ps-3). 16.95 (***978-1-59990-107-7(2)***) Bloomsbury Publishing.

Moore, Julianne & Pham, LeUyen. Freckleface Strawberry. 2007. (Illus.). 32p. (J). 17.85 (***978-1-59990-137-4(4)***) Bloomsbury Publishing.

Moore, Martha A. Under the Mermaid Angel. 2001. (Illus.). 176p. (YA). (gr. 7). pap. 12.00 (978-0-375-89507-4(8) , Laurel Leaf) Random Hse. Children's Bks.

Moore, Stephanie Perry. Equally Yoked, Vol. 3. 2003. (Laurel Shadrach Ser.: Vol. 3). 192p. (YA). pap. 6.99 (978-0-8024-4037-2(1)) Moody Pubs.
—Equally Yoked. 2003. (gr. 7-12). lib. bdg. 15.30 (978-0-613-90874-0(0)) Tandem Library Bks.
—True Friends. 2005. (Carmen Browne Ser.). 128p. (YA). pap. 5.99 (978-0-8024-8172-6(8)) Moody Pubs.
Moost, Nele. El Perro en la Luna. Lopez, L. Rodriguez, tr. Becker, Jutta, illus. 2002. (Rosa y Manzana Ser.). (SPA.). 24p. 16.95 (978-0-84-89804-35-7(4) , LG30440) Loguez Ediciones ESP. *Dist:* Baker & Taylor Bks., Lectorum Pubns., Inc.
Moran, Alex. Boots for Beth. Ernst, Lisa Campbell, illus. 2003. (Green Light Readers Level 2 Ser.). 24p. (J). 11.95 (978-0-15-204878-5(2)); pap. 3.95 (978-0-15-204838-9(3)) Harcourt Children's Bks. (Green Light Readers).
—Boots for Beth. 2003. (gr. k-3). lib. bdg. 11.80 (978-0-613-66352-6(7)) Tandem Library Bks.
—Sam & Jack: Three Stories. 2001. (gr. k-3). lib. bdg. 11.80 (978-0-613-64590-4(1)) Tandem Library Bks.
—Sam & Jack: Three Stories. Bowers, Tim, illus. 2003. (Green Light Readers Level 1 Ser.). 24p. (J). 11.95 (978-0-15-204822-8(7)); pap. 3.95 (978-0-15-204862-4(6)) Harcourt Children's Bks. (Green Light Readers).
Moray-Williams, Ursula & Williams, Ursula Moray. The Further Adventures of Gobbolino & the Little Wooden Horse. Howard, Paul, illus. 2002. (Kingfisher Modern Classics Ser.). 240p. (J). (gr. k-3). tchr. ed. 15.95 (978-0-7534-5495-4(5) , Kingfisher) Houghton Mifflin Co. Trade & Reference Div.
Morey, Walt. Gentle Ben. Schoenherr, John, illus. 2006. 192p. (J). (gr. 3). pap. 6.99 (978-0-14-240551-2(5) , Puffin) Penguin Group (USA) Inc.
Morgan, Anna & Turkienicz, Rachel. My Worst/Best Sleepover Party. 2007. (Illus.). 96p. (J). (gr. 2-4). pap. 7.95 (***978-1-897187-20-3(3)***) Second Story Pr. CAN. *Dist:* Orca Bk. Pubs. USA.
Morgan, Harry. The Monteverdi Mystery. 2006. per. (***978-1-84685-409-5(1)*** , Exposure Publishing) Meadow Bks.
Morgan, Melissa J. Alex's Challenge. 2007. 22.78 (978-1-59961-150-1(3)) Spotlight.
—Camp Confidential: TTYL. 2007. 22.78 (978-1-59961-154-9(6)) Spotlight.
—Camp Confidential No. 6: Rsvp. 2005. (Camp Confidential Ser.). (Illus.). 160p. (J). (gr. 4-7). pap. 4.99 (978-0-448-43962-4(X) , Grosset & Dunlap) Penguin Group (USA) Inc.
—Camp Confidential Vol. 4: Alex's Challenge. 2005. (Camp Confidential Ser.). 160p. (gr. 4-7). mass mkt. 4.99 (978-0-448-43876-4(3) , Grosset & Dunlap) Penguin Group (USA) Inc.
—Fair to Remember, Vol. 13. 2007. (Camp Confidential Ser.). 160p. (J). pap. 4.99 (978-0-448-44451-2(8) , Grosset & Dunlap) Penguin Group (USA) Inc.
—Falling in Like. 2006. (Camp Confidential Ser.: No. 11). 160p. (J). (gr. 4-7). pap. 4.99 (978-0-448-44391-1(0) , Grosset & Dunlap) Penguin Group (USA) Inc.
—Golden Girls, No. 16. 2007. (Camp Confidential Ser.). 160p. (J). pap. 4.99 (978-0-448-44541-0(7) , Grosset & Dunlap) Penguin Group (USA) Inc.
—Grace's Twist, Vol. 3. 2005. (Camp Confidential Ser.). 160p. (gr. 4-7). mass mkt. 4.99 (978-0-448-43875-7(5) , Grosset & Dunlap) Penguin Group (USA) Inc.
—Over & Out. 2006. (Camp Confidential Ser.: No. 10). 160p. (J). (gr. 4-7). pap. 4.99 (978-0-448-44326-3(0) , Grosset & Dunlap) Penguin Group (USA) Inc.
—Reality Bites, No. 15. 2007. (Camp Confidential Ser.). 160p. (J). pap. 4.99 (978-0-448-44539-7(5) , Grosset & Dunlap) Penguin Group (USA) Inc.
—Ttyl. 2007. 22.78 (978-1-59961-155-6(4)) Spotlight.
—Wish You Weren't Here. 2006. (Camp Confidential Ser.: No. 8). 160p. (J). (gr. 4-7). pap. 4.99 (978-0-448-44266-2(3) , Grosset & Dunlap) Penguin Group (USA) Inc.
Morgan, Michaela. Band of Friends. Price, Nick, illus. 2005. 24p. (J). lib. bdg. 22.65 (***978-1-59646-734-7(7)***) Dingles & Co.
—Bunny Wishes. 2007. 32p. (J). (ps-k). pap. 16.99 (***978-0-439-91812-1(X)*** , Chicken Hse., The) Scholastic, Inc.
—Shy Shark. Gomez, Elena, illus. 2005. 24p. (J). lib. bdg. 22.65 (***978-1-59646-722-4(3)***) Dingles & Co.
Morgan, Nicola. Chicken Friend. 2005. 160p. (J). (gr. 4-7). 15.99 (978-0-7636-2735-5(6)) Candlewick Pr.
Morgan, Ruth. Sglod & the Sand Dragon. Carpenter, Suzanne, illus. 2000. 32p. pap. 12.95 (978-1-85902-831-5(4)) Beekman Bks., Inc.
Morganstern, Mimi. The House at Hemlock Farms. Morganstern, Mimi, illus. 2000. (Illus.). vi, 54p. (J). (gr. 3-6). pap. 6.95 (978-0-9700522-3-0(5)) Morganstern, Mimi.
—The House at Hemlock Farms-"Read-Along with Mimi" A Cool Chapterbook-Package. Morganstern, Mimi, illus. 2000. (Illus.). vi, 54p. (J). (gr. 3-6). per. 9.99 incl. audio (978-0-9700522-4-7(3)) Morganstern, Mimi.
Morgenstern, Susie. Hallo Sarah! Hier Ist Salah. 2003. (GER.). 128p. pap. 15.00 (978-1-4000-3976-0(2) , New Media German Language) Random House Foreign Language Publishing.
—Secret Letters from 0 to 10. Rosner, Gil, Jr., illus. 2000. 144p. (J). (gr. 3-7). pap. 4.99 (978-0-14-130819-7(2) , Puffin) Penguin Group (USA) Inc.
—Secret Letters from 0 to 10. 2000. (978-0-606-18846-3(0)) Tandem Library Bks.
—Secret Letters from 0 To 10. 2000. (gr. 3-6). lib. bdg. 13.00 (978-0-613-28635-0(9)) Tandem Library Bks.
Moriarty, Jaclyn. The Year of Secret Assignments. (Illus.). 352p. 2004. (J). pap. 16.95 (978-0-439-49881-4(3) , Levine, Arthur A. Bks.); 2005. reprint ed. pap. 7.99 (978-0-439-49882-1(1) , Scholastic Paperbacks) Scholastic, Inc.
Moricz-Goodwin, Jennifer. Keys. 2004. 131p. (YA). per. 9.95 (978-0-9716442-3-6(3)) Jackson Publishing.
Morin, James F. Rothshield Chasing Shadows. 2006. pap. 14.95 (***978-1-59330-422-5(6)***) Aventine Pr.
Morningstar, Jeremy. Penalty Kick. 2005. 56p. pap. 9.00 (978-1-4116-6572-9(4)) Lulu.com.
Morozumi, Atsuko. My Friend Gorilla. Morozumi, Atsuko, illus. 2001. (Illus.). 32p. (J). (ps-1). pap. 5.95 (978-0-374-45428-9(0) , Sunburst) Farrar, Straus & Giroux.
—My Friend Gorilla. 2001. (ps-2). lib. bdg. 14.10 (978-0-613-45450-6(2)) Tandem Library Bks.
Morpurgo, Michael. The Amazing Story of Adolphus Tips. 2006. 208p. (J). (gr. 2-5). 16.99 (978-0-439-79661-3(X) , Scholastic Pr.) Scholastic, Inc.
Morris, Karen. Perils from the Seven Seas, Vol. 2. 2005. 127p. pap. 17.95 (978-1-4137-4663-1(2)) PublishAmerica, Inc.
Morrow, John. Ostrich Egg Omelets. 2006. (Illus.). (J). per. 14.95 (***978-0-9790832-1-1(4)***) Three Ring Circus Publishing Company.
Mortenson, R. K. Landon Snow & the Auctors Kingdom # 5. 2007. (Landon Snow Ser.). 224p. (J). 9.97 (***978-1-59789-297-1(1)***) Barbour Publishing, Inc.
Morty, Ducktor. Can Do & Friends to the Rescue! A Story about Getting along & Working Together. l.t. ed. 2005. Orig. Title: Can Do & the Mall. (Illus.). 34p. (J). pap. (978-0-9768384-2-5(7)) Can Do Duck Publishing.
Moser, Cherry. Backyard Adventures. 2005. 51p. pap. 12.95 (978-1-4137-6202-0(6)) PublishAmerica, Inc.
Moser, Erwin. La Rana Solitaria. Moser, Erwin, illus. 2002. (SPA., Illus.). 96p. (J). (gr. 3-5). pap. 8.95 (978-84-204-3695-1(X)) Santillana USA Publishing Co., Inc.
Mosionier, Beatrice. Unusual Friendships: A Little Black Cat & a White Rat. Belmore, Rebecca, illus. 2002. 1p. (J). pap. 10.95 (978-1-894778-04-6(9)) Theytus Bks., Ltd. CAN. *Dist:* Orca Bk. Pubs. USA.
Moss, Alexandra. Boys or Ballet? 2006. (Royal Ballet School Diaries: No. 8). 144p. (J). (gr. 3-5). mass mkt. 4.99 (978-0-448-44251-8(5) , Grosset & Dunlap) Penguin Group (USA) Inc.
—Ellie's Chance to Dance, No. 1. 2005. (Royal Ballet School Diaries Ser.: Bk. 1). 144p. (J). (gr. 4-8). mass mkt. 4.99 (978-0-448-43535-0(7) , Grosset & Dunlap) Penguin Group (USA) Inc.
—New Girl, No. 7. 2006. (Royal Ballet School Diaries). 144p. (J). (gr. 3-5). pap. 4.99 (978-0-448-44250-1(7) , Grosset & Dunlap) Penguin Group (USA) Inc.
—Sophie's Flight of Fancy, No. 4. 2005. (Royal Ballet School Diaries: No. 4). 144p. (J). (gr. 3-5). mass mkt. 4.99 (978-0-448-43770-5(8) , Grosset & Dunlap) Penguin Group (USA) Inc.
Moss, Marissa. The All-New Amelia. Moss, Marissa, illus. 2007. (Amelia's Notebooks). (Illus.). 40p. (J). (gr. 2-5). 9.99 (978-1-4169-0908-8(7) , Simon & Schuster/Paula Wiseman Bks.) Simon & Schuster Children's Publishing.
—The All-New Amelia. 1999. (Amelia's Notebooks). (J). (gr. 3-5). 12.75 (978-0-606-19866-0(0)) Tandem Library Bks.
Moss, Marissa. Amelia's 7th-Grade Notebook. Moss, Marissa, illus. 2007. (Amelia's Notebooks). 80p. (J). 9.99 (***978-1-4169-3661-9(0)*** , Simon & Schuster/Paula Wiseman Bks.) Simon & Schuster Children's Publishing.
Moss, Miriam. I'll Be Your Friend, Smudge! Chapman, Lynne, illus. 2002. 24p. (J). (ps-2). (978-1-86233-207-2(X) , Gullane Children's Bks.) Pinwheel.
Moss, Peggy & Tardif, Dee Dee. Our Friendship Rules. Geis, Alissa Imre, illus. 2007. 32p. (J). (***978-0-88448-291-8(X)***) Tilbury Hse. Pubs.
Mosso, Tyfanny. The Mud Puddle Gang. 2006. 17.00 (978-0-8059-9067-6(4)) Dorrance Publishing Co., Inc.
Mostoller, Gordon. Randy Walter & Rex. 2006. pap. 12.95 (***978-1-4259-6498-6(2)***) AuthorHouse.
Moulton, Mark Kimball. A Snowgirl Named Just Sue. Good, Karen Hillard, illus. 2005. 36p. (J). (ps-3). 14.95 (978-0-8249-5150-4(6)) Ideals Pubns.
—A Snowman Named Just Bob. Crouch, Karen Hillard, illus. 2003. 36p. (J). 14.95 (978-0-8249-5860-2(8) , 53876801) Ideals Pubns.
—A Snowman Named Just Bob. Crouch, Karen Hillard, illus. 1999. 32p. (J). pap. 18.00 (978-0-7412-0283-3(2)) Lang Graphics, Ltd.
—A Snowman Named Just Bob: Boxed Notecards. Good, Karen Hillard, illus. 2006. 16p. (J). 14.95 (978-0-8249-1707-4(3)) Ideals Pubns.
Mouse Works Staff. Cars, Boats, Planes & Trains. 2001. 48p. (J). 12.99 (978-0-7364-0114-2(8)) Mouse Works.
—Goofy. 1998. (Friendly Tales Ser.). (Illus.). 10p. (J). (ps). 6.99 (978-1-57082-928-4(4)) Mouse Works.
—Mickey Mouse. 1998. (Friendly Tales Ser.). (Illus.). 10p. (J). (ps-k). 6.99 (978-1-57082-929-1(2)) Mouse Works.
—Minnie Mouse. 1998. (Friendly Tales Ser.). (Illus.). 10p. (J). (ps). 6.99 (978-1-57082-930-7(6)) Mouse Works.
—Simba. 1999. (Disney's Friendly Tales Ser.). (Illus.). 10p. (J). (ps-k). 6.99 (978-0-7364-1011-3(2)) Mouse Works.
—Toy Story 2: Slheriff Woody & the Roundup Gant. 1999. (Toy Story 2 Ser.). (Illus.). 10p. (J). (ps up). 9.99 (978-0-7364-0170-8(9)) Mouse Works.
Mr Fizzle, the Man Who Went Boo!, 6 Packs. (gr. k-1). 23.00 (978-0-7635-8858-8(X)) Rigby Education.
Mracek, Ann. Friendship Flies the Sun: The Ancient Egyptian Legend of Scarab Beetle. l.t. ed. 2005. (DAN., Illus.). 32p. (J). per. 15.99 (978-0-9766488-0-2(6)) Mracek, Ann.
Mueller, Doris. Marryin' Sam. 2005. 61p. pap. 12.95 (978-1-4137-7557-0(8)) PublishAmerica, Inc.
Muldrow, Diane. Deep Freeze. Pollack, Barbara, illus. 2007. (Dish Ser.: No. 12). 160p. (J). (gr. 4-7). pap. 4.99 (***978-0-448-44693-6(6)*** , Grosset & Dunlap) Penguin Group (USA) Inc.
—Into the Mix. 2002. (gr. 3-6). lib. bdg. 13.00 (978-0-613-72425-8(9)) Tandem Library Bks.
—Lights! Camera! Cook! Pollak, Barbara, illus. 2007. (Dish Ser.: No. 8). 160p. (J). pap. 4.99 (978-0-448-44533-5(6) , Grosset & Dunlap) Penguin Group (USA) Inc.
—Measure of Thanks. Pollack, Barbara, illus. 2007. (Dish Ser.: Vol. 10). 160p. (J). (gr. 4-7). pap. 4.99 (***978-0-448-44662-2(6)*** , Grosset & Dunlap) Penguin Group (USA) Inc.
—On the Back Burner, No. 6. Pollak, Barbara, illus. 2007. (Dish Ser.). 160p. (J). pap. 4.99 (978-0-448-44531-1(X) , Grosset & Dunlap) Penguin Group (USA) Inc.
—Sweet-and-Sour Summer, No. 9. Pollack, Barbara, illus. 2007. (Dish Ser.). 160p. (J). (gr. 4-7). pap. 4.99 (***978-0-448-44661-5(8)*** , Grosset & Dunlap) Penguin Group (USA) Inc.
—Sweet-and-Sour Summer. 2003. (gr. 3-6). lib. bdg. 13.00 (978-0-613-72478-4(X)) Tandem Library Bks.
—Truth Without the Trimmings. Pollak, Barbara, illus. 2007. (Dish Ser.). 160p. (J). pap. 4.99 (978-0-448-44530-4(1) , Grosset & Dunlap) Penguin Group (USA) Inc.
—Truth Without the Trimmings. 2002. (gr. 3-6). lib. bdg. 13.00 (978-0-613-72484-5(4)) Tandem Library Bks.
—Turning up the Heat. Pollak, Barbara, illus. 2007. (Dish! Ser.: Vol. 3). 160p. (J). (gr. 4-7). pap. 4.99 (978-0-448-44527-4(1) , Grosset & Dunlap) Penguin Group (USA) Inc.
Muldrow, Diane. Winner Takes the Cake. Pollack, Barbara, illus. 2007. (Dish Ser.: No. 11). 160p. (J). (gr. 4-7). pap. 4.99 (***978-0-448-44666-0(9)*** , Grosset & Dunlap) Penguin Group (USA) Inc.
Mulford, Carolyn. The Feedsack Dress. 2007. (YA). per. 7.95 (***978-0-9713497-4-2(6)***) Cave Hollow Pr.
Mull, Brandon. The Candy Shop War. 2007. 358p. (YA). (gr. 4 up). 17.95 (***978-1-59038-783-2(X)*** , Shadow Mountain) Deseret Bk. Co.
Muller, Lisa M. Master smokey & mr. Duck. 2006. 15p. (J). 9.99 (978-1-4276-0027-1(9)) Aardvark Global Publishing.
Mullican, Judy. My Forest Friends. Carroll, Ken, Jr., illus. l.t. ed. 2000. (Little Bks.). 8p. (J). (ps-1). pap. 10.95 (978-1-57332-172-3(9)); pap. 10.95 (978-1-57332-180-8(X)) HighReach Learning, Inc.
Mullins, Julie. School Play Stars. Maddock, Monika, illus. 2005. (Girlz Rock! Ser.). (J). pap. (978-1-59336-706-0(6)) Mondo Publishing.
—The Sleepover. Foye, Lloyd, illus. 2005. (Girlz Rock! Ser.). (J). pap. (978-1-59336-707-7(4)) Mondo Publishing.
Munoz-Furlong, Anne. Alexander & His Pals Visit the Main Street School. 1999. (J). (gr. k-6). pap. (978-1-882541-07-2(3)) Food Allergy & Anaphylaxis Network.
Munsch, Robert. Something Good. Martchenko, Michael, illus. 2003. (Annikin Ser.: Vol. 14). 24p. (J). (ps-2). pap. 1.25 (978-1-55037-390-5(0)) Annick Pr., Ltd. CAN. *Dist:* Firefly Bks., Ltd.
—We Share Everything. ed. 2004. (Illus.). (J). (ps-2). spiral bd. (978-0-616-01749-4(9)); spiral bd. (978-0-616-01750-0(2)) Canadian National Institute for the Blind/Institut National Canadien pour les Aveugles.
—We Share Everything. 2000. (978-0-606-18891-3(6)) Tandem Library Bks.
Munsch, Robert & Martchenko, Michael. We Share Everything. 2002. 32p. (J). 3.99 (978-0-439-38824-5(4)) Scholastic, Inc.
Munson, Derek. Enemy Pie. King, Tara Calahan, illus. 2000. 40p. (J). (gr. k-3). 15.95 (978-0-8118-2778-2(X)) Chronicle Bks. LLC.
Murphy, Jill. All for One. ed. 2004. (Illus.). (J). (ps-2). spiral bd. (978-0-616-14591-3(8)); spiral bd. (978-0-616-14592-0(6)) Canadian National Institute for the Blind/Institut National Canadien pour les Aveugles.
Murphy, Mary. Panda Foo & the New Friend. Murphy, Mary, illus. 2007. (Illus.). 32p. (J). (ps-k). 15.99 (***978-0-7636-3405-6(0)***) Candlewick Pr.
Murphy, Patricia J. I Need You. Bryant, Laura J., illus. 2003. (Rookie Reader Espanol Ser.). (J). (gr. k-2). pap. 4.95 (978-0-516-26966-5(6) , Children's Pr.) Scholastic Library Publishing.
—I Need You. 2003. (gr. k-3). lib. bdg. 12.95 (978-0-613-67635-9(1)) Tandem Library Bks.
—Te Necesito. 2004. (Rookie Reader Espanol Ser.). (J). (gr. k-2). pap. 4.95 (978-0-516-24617-8(8) , Children's Pr.) Scholastic Library Publishing.
—Te Necesito. Bryant, Laura J., illus. 2003. (Rookie Reader Espanol Ser.). (SPA.). (J). 19.50 (978-0-516-25890-4(7) , Children's Pr.) Scholastic Library Publishing.
Murphy, Stuart J. Monster Musical Chairs. Nash, Scott, illus. 2000. (MathStart Ser.). 40p. (J). (gr. 1 up). pap. 5.99 (978-0-06-446730-8(9) , Harper Trophy) HarperCollins Pubs.
Murray, Mary & Vischer, Lisa. Junior & Laura Share the Year Together. 2003. (Big Idea Bks.). 12p. 4.99 (978-0-310-70541-3(X)) Zonderkidz.
Murrell, Diane. Friends Learn about Tobin. Kock, W.K., tr. Murrell, Diane, illus. 2007. (Illus.). 29p. (J). (ps-3). pap. 16.95 (***978-1-932565-41-6(8)***) Future Horizons, Inc.
Murrell, Diane. Tobin Learns to Make Friends. 2001. (Illus.). (J). (ps-3). per. 16.95 (978-1-885477-79-8(1)) Future Horizons, Inc.
Murrieta, Ed & Wakeman, Diana, illus. Minnie's Tea Party. 1999. 18p. (J). (ps-1). reprint ed. 10.00 (978-0-7881-6632-7(8)) DIANE Publishing Co.
My Berry First Friends. 2007. (Strawberry Shortcake Baby Ser.). 10p. (J). bds. 4.99 (978-0-448-44454-3(2) , Grosset & Dunlap) Penguin Group (USA) Inc.
My Best Friends. (Girls' World Ser.). 16p. (J). (978-2-7643-0141-8(3)) Phidal Publishing, Inc./Editions Phidal, Inc.
My Brother & I. 2003. (Illus.). 24p. (J). (ps-k). bds. 7.95 (978-0-8249-5455-0(6)) Ideals Pubns.
My Grandma & I! 2002. (Illus.). 24p. (J). (ps-k). bds. 7.95 (978-0-8249-4220-5(5)) Ideals Pubns.
My Grandpa & I! 2002. (Illus.). 24p. (J). (ps-k). bds. 7.95 (978-0-8249-4219-9(1)) Ideals Pubns.
My Mommy & I! 2002. (Illus.). 24p. (J). (ps-k). bds. 7.95 (978-0-8249-4218-2(3)) Ideals Pubns.
My Monster Friends, 6 Packs. (Literatura 2000 Ser.). (gr. 1-2). 28.00 (978-0-7635-0102-0(6)) Rigby Education.
My Two, Very, Special Friends, 1. 2006. (Illus.). 19p. (J). per. 4.00 (978-0-9788386-1-4(0)) Taylor, Y. H.
My Uncle Has Wheels. 2005. (J). 8.00 (978-0-9767077-1-4(3)) Carson, Tracy.
Myers, Anna. Confessions from the Principal's Chair. 2006. 192p. 16.95 (978-0-8027-9560-1(9)) Walker & Co.
—Stolen by the Sea. 2006. 144p. (J). pap. 6.95 (978-0-8027-8976-1(5)) Walker & Co.
Myers, Walter Dean. Autobiography of My Dead Brother. Myers, Christopher, illus. 2006. 224p. (J). pap. 6.99 (978-0-06-058293-7(6) , Amistad) HarperCollins Pubs.
—Autobiography of My Dead Brother. Myers, Christopher, illus. 2005. 224p. (J). 15.99 (978-0-06-058291-3(X)); lib. bdg. 16.89 (978-0-06-058292-0(8)) HarperCollins Pubs. (Amistad).
—Three Swords for Granada. Speirs, John, illus. 2002. 112p. (J). (gr. 4-6). tchr. ed. 15.95 (978-0-8234-1676-9(3)) Holiday Hse., Inc.
Myracle, Lauren. Eleven. 208p. (J). (gr. 3-7). 2004. 16.99 (978-0-525-47165-3(0) , Dutton Juvenile); 2005. reprint ed. pap. 6.99 (978-0-14-240346-4(6) , Puffin) Penguin Group (USA) Inc.
—The Fashion Disaster That Changed My Life. 2008. 160p. (J). (gr. 5). 6.99 (978-0-14-240717-2(8) , Puffin); 2005. 144p. (YA). (gr. 4-6). 15.99 (978-0-525-47222-3(3) , Dutton Juvenile) Penguin Group (USA) Inc.
—Kissing Kate. 2007. 208p. (YA). (gr. 7). pap. 7.99 (978-0-14-240869-8(7) , Puffin) Penguin Group (USA) Inc.
—L8r, G8r. 2007. (Ttyl Ser.). 288p. (J). (gr. 2-8). 15.95 (***978-0-8109-1266-3(X)*** , Amulet Bks.) Abrams, Harry N. , Inc.
—Thirteen. 2008. 224p. (J). (gr. 5). 15.99 (***978-0-525-47896-6(5)*** , Dutton Juvenile) Penguin Group (USA) Inc.
—TTFN (Ta-Ta for Now) (Internet Girls Ser.). 2007. 256p. (J). (gr. 2-8). pap. 6.95 (***978-0-8109-9279-5(5)***); 2006. 240p. (YA). (gr. 9-17). 15.95 (978-0-8109-5971-2(2)) Abrams, Harry N. , Inc. (Amulet Bks.).
—Ttyl. (Internet Girls Ser.). (YA). (gr. 8-17). 2005. 234p. pap. 6.95 (978-0-8109-8788-3(0)); 2004. 224p. 15.95 (978-0-8109-4821-1(4) , Amulet Bks.) Abrams, Harry N. , Inc.
—Twelve. (YA). (gr. 5-8). 2008. 224p. 6.99 (***978-0-14-241091-2(8)*** , Puffin); 2007. 208p. 15.99 (978-0-525-47784-6(5) , Dutton Juvenile) Penguin Group (USA) Inc.
Nadler, Beth. My Favorite Martian. 1999. (Illus.). 48p. (J). pap. 3.99 (978-0-7868-4249-0(0)) Disney Pr.
Nakagawa, Rieko. Guri & Gura's Magical Friend. Yamawaki, Yuriko, illus. 2003. 32p. 10.95 (978-0-8048-3356-1(7)) Tuttle Publishing.
—Guri & Gura's Surprise Visitor. Yamawaki, Yuriko, illus. 2003. (Guri & Gura Ser.). 32p. 10.95 (978-0-8048-3353-0(2)) Tuttle Publishing.
Nakakuma, Chie. Whazzup, Wolly Ayaka? 2007. 128p. per. 10.95 (***978-0-595-44646-9(9)***) iUniverse, Inc.
Namey, Laura. In the Groove. Wethington, Liz, illus. 2001. (Gold Mixed Collection). 128p. (J). (gr. 1-6). pap. 9.95 (978-1-58584-270-4(2)) Huckleberry Pr.
Namm, Diane. My Best Friend. Gordon, Mike, illus. 2004. (My First Reader Ser.). 32p. (J). (gr. k-1). pap. 3.95 (978-0-516-25504-0(5) , Children's Pr.) Scholastic Library Publishing.
—My Best Friend. Gordon, Mike, tr. Gordon, Mike, illus. 2004. (My First Reader Ser.). 31p. (J). 18.50 (978-0-516-24416-7(7) , Children's Pr.) Scholastic Library Publishing.
Nanette. The Black Alligator. 2004. (Life on Granny's Farm Ser.). (J). 12.95 (978-0-9741269-3-7(4)) St. Bernard Publishing, LLC.
—Little Red. 2004. (Life on Granny's Farm Ser.). (J). 12.95 (978-0-9741269-1-3(8)) St. Bernard Publishing, LLC.
—Pancake the Purple Pony. 2004. (Life on Granny's Farm Ser.). (J). 12.95 (978-0-9741269-8-2(5)) St. Bernard Publishing, LLC.
Napoli, Donna Jo. Friends Everywhere. 1999. (Angelwings Ser.: No. 1). (Illus.). (J). 10.79 (978-0-606-17904-1(6)) Tandem Library Bks.
—Zel. 1998. (Puffin Novel Ser.). 240p. (J). (gr. 5-9). pap. 6.99 (978-0-14-130116-7(3) , Puffin) Penguin Group (USA) Inc.
Napoli, Donna Jo & Ben-Ami, Doron. Friends Everywhere. Klementz-Harte, Lauren, illus. 1999. (Angelwings Ser.: No. 1). 96p. (J). (gr. 2-5). pap. 7.95 (978-0-689-82694-8(X) , Aladdin) Simon & Schuster Children's Publishing.
Napoli, Donna Jo & Furrow, Robert. Sly the Sleuth & the Food Mysteries. Maione, Heather Harms, illus. 2007. 144p. (J). (gr. 2-4). 16.99 (978-0-8037-3119-6(1) , Dial) Penguin Group (USA) Inc.
Nara, Yoshitomo. The Lonesome Puppy. 2008. (J). 17.99 (978-0-8118-5640-9(2)) Chronicle Bks. LLC.
Narahashi, Keiko. Two Girls Can! 2000. Orig. Title: Friends. (Illus.). 32p. (ps-3). 16.00 Simon & Schuster Children's Publishing.
Narvaez, Concha Lopez. El Arbol de los Pajaros Sin Vuelo. (SPA.). 128p. (YA). (gr. 5-8). (978-84-207-2905-3(1)) Grupo Anaya, S.A. ESP. *Dist:* Lectorum Pubns., Inc.
Narvaez, Concha Lopez. La Colina de Edeta. (SPA.). 124p. (YA). (gr. 5-8). (978-84-239-9050-4(8) , EC3401) Espasa Calpe, S.A. ESP. *Dist:* Lectorum Pubns., Inc.
—Las Horas Largas. 2001. (SPA.). (gr. 7-12). lib. bdg. 15.70 (978-0-613-80554-4(2)) Tandem Library Bks.

EFG

Nash, Andy. Tatum & Her Tiger: For Kids Blessed with Passion. 2007. (J). (*978-0-8127-0451-8(7)) Autumn Hse. Publishing Co.

Nash, David. A Pete & Charley Adventure: The Sheri. 2005. 131p. pap. 19.95 (978-1-4137-9449-6(1)) PublishAmerica, Inc.

Nation, Kay. Jamie Learns to Love. 2006. pap. 10.00 (*978-1-4257-0534-3(0)) Xlibris Corp.

Natti, Susanna, illus. Lionel & His Friends. 2002. (Lionel Ser.). (J). 12.17 (978-0-7587-1387-2(8)) Book Wholesalers, Inc.

Navarro, Yvonne. Willow Files. 1999. (gr. 7-12). lib. bdg. 13.00 (978-0-613-22639-4(9)) Tandem Library Bks.

Naylor, Phyllis Reynolds. Alice Alone. (Alice Ser.). 240p. 2002. mass mkt. 5.99 (978-0-689-85189-6(8) , Simon Pulse); 2001. (Illus.). (J). (gr. 5-9). 16.00 (978-0-689-82634-4(6) , Atheneum) Simon & Schuster Children's Publishing.

—Alice Alone. 2002. (Alice Ser.). (gr. 5-8). lib. bdg. 13.00 (978-0-613-73352-6(5)) Tandem Library Bks.

—Alice in Blunderland. 2003. (Alice Ser.). (Illus.). 208p. (J). 15.95 (978-0-689-84397-6(6) , Atheneum) Simon & Schuster Children's Publishing.

—Alice in the Know. (Alice Ser.). (YA). 2007. 320p. pap. 5.99 (*978-0-689-87093-4(0) , Simon Pulse); 2006. 288p. (gr. 7 up). 15.95 (978-0-689-87092-7(2)) Simon & Schuster Children's Publishing.

—The Grooming of Alice. Elliott, Mark, illus. (Alice Ser.). 224p. (J). (gr. 5-9). 2001. pap. 4.99 (978-0-689-84618-2(5) , Aladdin); 2000. 16.99 (978-0-689-82633-7(8) , Atheneum) Simon & Schuster Children's Publishing.

—The Grooming of Alice. 2001. (Alice Ser.). 11.64 (978-0-606-22125-2(5)) Tandem Library Bks.

—Lovingly Alice. (Alice Ser.). (J). 2006. 176p. pap. 5.99 (978-0-689-84400-3(X) , Aladdin); 2006. 166p. (*978-1-4156-5199-5(X) , Aladdin); 2004. (Illus.). 176p. 15.95 (978-0-689-84399-0(2) , Atheneum) Simon & Schuster Children's Publishing.

—Patiently Alice. (Alice Ser.). 256p. (YA). 2004. mass mkt. 5.99 (978-0-689-87073-6(6) , Simon Pulse); 2003. (Illus.). 15.95 (978-0-689-82636-8(2) , Atheneum) Simon & Schuster Children's Publishing.

—Saving Shiloh. unabr. ed. 2004. 137p. (J). (gr. 3-7). pap. 29.00 incl. audio (978-0-8072-0456-6(0) , Listening Library) Random Hse. Audio Publishing Group.

—A Spy among the Girls. 2002. 144p. (gr. 4-7). 5.50 (978-0-440-41390-5(7) , Yearling) Random Hse. Children's Bks.

—A Spy among the Girls. l.t. ed. 2003. (Boys=Girls Battle Ser.). 145p. (J). 23.95 (978-0-7862-5821-5(7)) Thorndike Pr.

—Starting with Alice. (Alice Ser.). 192p. (J). 2004. (Illus.). pap. 4.99 (978-0-689-84396-9(8) , Aladdin); 2002. 15.95 (978-0-689-84395-2(X) , Atheneum) Simon & Schuster Children's Publishing.

—Starting with Alice. 2004. (gr. 3-6). lib. bdg. 13.00 (978-0-613-87056-6(5)) Tandem Library Bks.

Naylor, Phyllis Reynolds & Vaccaro, Nick. Alice in Blunderland. 2005. (Alice Ser.). (Illus.). 208p. (J). reprint ed. pap. 4.99 (978-0-689-84398-3(4) , Aladdin) Simon & Schuster Children's Publishing.

Necochea, Kristi Landry. The First Day of Forever. 2007. (J). (*978-0-9792361-0-5(X)) Inspire U., LLC.

Neebe, Charles A. How Back-Back Got His Name. 2007. (J). 15.95 (978-1-933872-20-9(9)) Lima Bear Pr LLC, The.

Nellis, Joann Marotta. Spensers Pencil. 2006. pap. 13.99 (*978-1-4259-8451-9(7)) AuthorHouse.

Nelson, Blake. They Came from Below. 2007. 304p. (YA). (gr. 8 up). 17.95 (*978-0-7653-1423-9(1) , Tor Teen) Doherty, Tom Assocs., LLC.

Nelson, Bruce M. The Magician's Hat. 2006. 127p. pap. 17.95 (978-1-4241-2301-8(1)) PublishAmerica, Inc.

Nelson, Jim. Crosstown Crush. 2005. 82p. Vol. 1, Bk. 1. (YA). pap. 9.00 (978-1-4116-5266-8(5)); Vol. 1,Bk. 2. pap. 9.00 (978-1-4116-6654-2(2)) Lulu.com.

Nelson, Kelly. Boreal, Dragon of the North. 2005. 68p. (YA). pap. 9.99 (978-1-4141-0292-4(5)) Pleasant Word.

Nelson, Theresa. Empress of Elsewhere. 2000. (Illus.). (J). 12.64 (978-0-606-18836-4(3)) Tandem Library Bks.

Nemeth, Sally. The Heights, the Depths, & Everything in Between. 2006. 272p. (J). (gr. 5). 17.99 (978-0-375-93458-2(8)); 15.95 (978-0-375-83458-5(3)) Random Hse. Children's Bks. (Knopf Bks. for Young Readers).

Nettrour, Nelani. Sun Griffins: Dragonlands, Book 4. 2007. (Illus.). 190p. (J). pap. 16.95 (*978-1-932657-90-6(8)) Third Millennium Pubns.

Netzarel, Orly. Yellow, Yellow-Brown, Yellow-Brown & Black. 2001. 160p. pap. 11.95 (978-0-595-18742-3(0) , Writers Club Pr.) iUniverse, Inc.

Neufeld, John. Lisa, Bright & Dark. 1999. (J). (978-0-606-16776-5(5)) Tandem Library Bks.

Neufeld, John. Lisa, Bright & Dark: A Novel. 2007. 152p. per. 12.95 (*978-0-595-45048-0(2) , Backinprint.com) iUniverse, Inc.

Neuschafer-Carlon, Mercedes. Antonio en el Pais del Silencio. (SPA.). 96p. (J). (gr. 3-5). 6.36 (978-84-241-7896-3(3)) Everest de Ediciones y Distribucion, S.L. ESP. *Dist:* Lectorum Pubns., Inc.

The Nevergreen. 2003. (J). 15.99 (978-0-9744565-9-1(4)) Heart-to-Heart Pubns.

A New Friend at the Beach. 2007. (J). per. (*978-1-932570-87-8(X)) Literacy Footprints Inc.

New Frontiers Group. There's Nobody Like You! The World of Howie & Friends. 2006. (J). 2.99 (978-1-58597-370-5(X)) Leathers Publishing.

Newman, Leslea. Hachiko Waits. Kodaira, Machiyo, illus. rev. ed. 2004. 96p. (J). 16.95 (978-0-8050-7336-2(1) , Holt, Henry & Co. Bks. For Young Readers) Holt, Henry & Co.

Newman, Marjorie & Bowman, Peter. Is That What Friends Do? 2000. (Illus.). 32p. (J). (ps). pap. 11.99 (978-0-09-922162-3(4)) Random Hse. GBR. *Dist:* Independent Pubs. Group.

Newton, Robert. Saturday Morning Mozart & Burnt Toast. 2004. 150p. (Orig.). (J). pap. 16.95 (978-0-7022-3436-1(2)) Univ. of Queensland Pr. AUS. *Dist:* International Specialized Bk. Services.

Nielsen-Fernlund, Susin. Hank & Fergus. Laliberte, Louise-Andree, illus. 2005. 32p. (J). (ps-2). 7.95 (978-1-55143-343-1(5)) Orca Bk. Pubs. USA.

Nikly, Michelle. The Perfume of Memory. Claverie, Jean, illus. 1999. 40p. (J). (ps-3). pap. 16.95 (978-0-439-08206-8(4) , Levine, Arthur A. Bks.) Scholastic, Inc.

Niland, Deborah. Let's Play. Niland, Deborah, illus. 2007. (Illus.). 24p. (Orig.). (J). (ps). pap. 4.99 (*978-1-933605-47-0(2)) Kane/Miller Bk. Pubs., Inc.

Nilsen, Anna. My Best Friends. Dood, Emma, illus. 2003. 24p. (J). (gr. k-1). 15.95 (978-0-7696-3159-2(2) , Gingham Dog Pr.) School Specialty Publishing.

Nitz, Kristin Wolden. Defending Irene. 2004. 224p. (J). (gr. 4-6). 14.95 (978-1-56145-309-2(9)) Peachtree Pubs., Ltd.

Noël, Alyson. Art Geeks & Prom Queens: A Novel. 2005. 240p. (YA). pap. 8.95 (978-0-312-33636-3(5) , St. Martin's Griffin) St. Martin's Pr.

Noël, Alyson. Kiss & Blog: A Novel. 2007. 240p. (YA). (gr. 7-9). pap. 8.95 (*978-0-312-35509-8(2) , St. Martin's Griffin) St. Martin's Pr.

Nolen, Jerdine. Raising Dragons. Primavera, Elise, illus. 2002. (J). 21.70 (978-0-7587-3493-8(X)) Book Wholesalers, Inc.

—Raising Dragons. Primavera, Elise, illus. 40p. (J). 2002. (gr. 1-4). pap. 7.00 (978-0-15-216536-9(3) , Voyager Bks./Libros Viajeros); 1998. (ps-3). 16.00 (978-0-15-201288-5(5)) Harcourt Children's Bks.

—Raising Dragons. 2002. (ps-2). lib. bdg. 14.15 (978-0-613-53857-2(9)) Tandem Library Bks.

Noonan, Julia. Friends Forever: Hare & Rabbit. Noonan, Julia, illus. 2000. (Hello Reader! Ser.: Level 3). (Illus.). 40p. (J). (gr. 1-2). pap. 3.99 (978-0-439-08753-7(8)) Scholastic, Inc.

—Hare & Rabbit: Friends Forever. 2004. 40p. (J). lib. bdg. 15.00 (978-1-59054-493-8(5)) Fitzgerald Bks.

—Hare & Rabbit: Friends Forever. 2000. (gr. k-3). lib. bdg. 11.80 (978-0-613-21678-4(4)); (Illus.). (J). 10.79 (978-0-606-18556-1(9)) Tandem Library Bks.

North, Bill. The Disappearing Airplane. 2001. 108p. pap. 9.95 (978-0-595-18789-8(7) , Writers Club Pr.) iUniverse, Inc.

Nosotros Interactive Packages: Los Amigos. (Pebble Soup Exploraciones Ser.). (ps up). 52.00 (978-0-7578-5252-7(1)) Rigby Education.

Nostlinger, Christine. La Autentica Susi. (SPA.). 176p. (J). 5.20 (978-84-348-2912-1(6)) SM Ediciones ESP. *Dist:* Lectorum Pubns., Inc.

—Simbalabim. (SPA.). 96p. (978-84-348-7321-6(4)) SM Ediciones ESP. *Dist:* Lectorum Pubns., Inc.

Novak, Matt. Little Wolf, Big Wolf. Novak, Matt, illus. 2000. (I Can Read Bks.: 2). (Illus.). 48p. (J). (gr. k-3). 14.95 (978-0-06-027486-3(7)) HarperCollins Pubs.

—Little Wolf, Big Wolf. 2001. (I Can Read Bks.). (Illus.). (J). (978-0-606-20769-0(4)) Tandem Library Bks.

November, Deborah. Sesame Street Big Block Party! Story Cookbook & Recipe Cards. 2006. (Sesame Street Ser.). 32p. (J). pap. 10.99 (978-0-7944-1104-6(5)) Reader's Digest Assn., Inc., The.

Nunes, Lygia Bojunga. La Bolsa Amarilla. (SPA.). (YA). (gr. 5-8). pap. (978-958-04-4148-9(0) , NR5368) Norma S.A. COL. *Dist:* Lectorum Pubns., Inc.

—La Cuerda Floja. (SPA.). 136p. (YA). (gr. 5-8). (978-84-204-3122-2(2) , AF1749) Alfaguara, Ediciones, S.A.-Grupo Santillana ESP. *Dist:* Lectorum Pubns., Inc.

Nunez, Ralph da Costa & Ellison, Jesse Andrews. Voyage to Shelter Cove. Simon, Madeline Gerstein, illus. 2005. (J). pap. 5.00 (978-0-9724425-3-4(7)) Homes for the Homeless, Inc.

Nyikos, Stacy Ann. Shelby. Sisneros, Shawn Nathanial, illus. 2006. (J). pap. 15.95 (978-0-9764199-1-4(2)) Stonehorse Publishing, LLC.

Oates, Joyce Carol. Big Mouth & Ugly Girl. 2003. (gr. 5-8). lib. bdg. 16.45 (978-0-613-62725-2(3)) Tandem Library Bks.

Oblich, Kathleen. Jake & the Scarecrow. 2007. 48p. pap. 12.95 (*978-1-4241-3101-3(4)) PublishAmerica, Inc.

O'Callahan, Jay. Herman & Marguerite: An Earth Story. O'Callahan, Laura, illus. 2003. 36p. (J). pap. 7.95 (978-1-56145-283-5(1)) Peachtree Pubs., Ltd.

—Herman & Marguerite: An Earth Story. 2003. (gr. k-3). lib. bdg. 16.40 (978-0-613-60387-4(7)) Tandem Library Bks.

Ocean Friends Books Set 800936, 2 vols. 2005. (J). (978-1-59794-095-5(X)) Environments, Inc.

O'Connell, Jenny. The Book of Luke. 2007. 304p. pap. 9.95 (978-1-4165-2040-5(6) , MTV) Simon & Schuster.

O'Connell, Rebecca. Penina Levine Is a Hard-Boiled Egg. Sue, Majella Lue, illus. 2007. 176p. (J). (gr. 4-6). 16.95 (978-1-59643-140-9(7)) Roaring Brook Pr.

O'Connell, Tyne. Pulling Princes. 2004. (Illus.). 208p. (J). 16.95 (978-1-58234-957-2(6) , Bloomsbury Children) Bloomsbury Publishing.

O'Connell, Tyne. True Love, the Sphinx, & Other Unsolvable Riddles: A Comedy in Four Voices. 2007. 256p. (YA). (gr. 7 up). 16.95 (*978-1-59990-050-6(5)) Bloomsbury Publishing.

O'Connor, Barbara. Beethoven in Paradise. 1999. (Illus.). 160p. (J). (gr. 5-8). pap. 7.95 (978-0-374-40588-5(3) , Sunburst) Farrar, Straus & Giroux.

—Beethoven in Paradise. 1999. (J). (978-0-606-17351-3(X)); (gr. 3-6). lib. bdg. 12.95 (978-0-613-29559-8(5)) Tandem Library Bks.

—Fame & Glory in Freedom, Georgia. l.t. ed. 2003. 126p. (J). 22.95 (978-0-7862-5994-6(9)) Thorndike Pr.

—Me & Rupert Goody. 2003. 106p. (J). pap. 4.95 (978-0-374-44804-2(3) , Sunburst) Farrar, Straus & Giroux.

—Me & Rupert Goody. 2003. (gr. 5-8). lib. bdg. 12.95 (978-0-613-59682-4(X)) Tandem Library Bks.

O'Connor, George. Sally & the Some-Thing. O'Connor, George, illus. 2006. (Illus.). 32p. (J). 16.95 (978-1-59643-141-6(5)) Roaring Brook Pr.

O'Coyne, James. Gravelle's Land of Horror. Baer, Brian, illus. 2007. (J). per. 9.95 (*978-1-59649-604-0(5)) Whispering Pine Pr., Inc.

An Ode to Hoptoad. 2004. (Illus.). 11p. (J). 10.00 (978-0-9749161-0-1(2)) Ray Greer, Mary Lou.

O'Dell, Kathleen. Agnes Parker... Girl in Progress. Harper, Charise Mericle, illus. 2003. 160p. (J). (gr. 5). 16.99 (978-0-8037-2648-2(1) , Dial) Penguin Group (USA) Inc.

—Agnes Parker... Girl in Progress. 2004. 176p. (J). (gr. 3-6). reprint ed. pap. 5.99 (978-0-14-240228-3(1) , Puffin) Penguin Group (USA) Inc.

—Agnes Parker... Happy Camper? 160p. (J). 2005. (Illus.). (gr. 5-7). 16.99 (978-0-8037-2962-9(6) , Dial); 2006. (gr. 3). reprint ed. pap. 5.99 (978-0-14-240618-2(X) , Puffin) Penguin Group (USA) Inc.

—Ophie Out of Oz. 2005. 192p. (J). (gr. 3). pap. 5.99 (978-0-14-240394-5(6) , Puffin) Penguin Group (USA) Inc.

Odom, Mel. His Legacy Avenged, No. 4. 2006. (Hunter's League Ser.). 256p. (YA). mass mkt. 5.99 (978-0-689-86635-7(6) , Simon Pulse) Simon & Schuster Children's Publishing.

Oh, Jiwon. Mr. Monkey's Classroom. Oh, Jiwon, illus. 2005. (Illus.). 32p. (J). (ps-2). lib. bdg. 15.89 (978-0-06-055722-5(2)) HarperCollins Pubs.

Oheal, Katherine. Family Series Clutter Family. 2008. (J). (978-0-310-70985-5(7)) Zonderkidz.

Ohi, Ruth. Clara & the Bossy. Ohi, Ruth, illus. 2006. (Ruth Ohi Picture Book Ser.). (Illus.). 32p. (J). (ps-1). pap. 5.95 (978-1-55037-942-6(9)); lib. bdg. 19.95 (978-1-55037-943-3(7)) Annick Pr., Ltd. CAN. *Dist:* Firefly Bks., Ltd.

Oke, Janette. Animal Friends, 6. 2001. (J Okes Animal Friends Ser.). (J). Set. 432p. pap. 41.99 (978-0-7642-8796-1(6)); Vol. 7-12,Set. 464p. pap. 41.99 (978-0-7642-8857-9(1)) Bethany Hse. Pubs.

—New Kid in Town. Munger, Nancy, illus. 2001. (J Okes Animal Friends Ser.: Vol. 5). 80p. (Orig.). (J). (ps-3). pap. 6.99 (978-0-7642-2449-2(2)) Bethany Hse. Pubs.

—New Kid in Town. 2001. (Orig.). (gr. k-3). lib. bdg. 14.15 (978-0-613-82429-3(6)) Tandem Library Bks.

O'Kelley, Jeff. Sharing Our Stories. 2006. (Early Explorers Ser.). (J). 36.00 (*978-1-4108-6127-6(9)) Benchmark Education Co.

Okimoto, Jean Davies. Dear Ichiro. Keith, Doug, illus. 2006. 29p. (J). (gr. 4-8). reprint ed. 17.00 (*978-1-4223-5803-0(8)) DIANE Publishing Co.

—Dear Ichiro. Keith, Doug, illus. 2002. 32p. (J). 16.95 (978-1-57061-373-9(7)) Sasquatch Bks.

—Jason's Women. 2000. 220p. (gr. 4-7). pap. 12.95 (978-0-595-00797-4(X) , Backinprint.com) iUniverse, Inc.

Okorafor-Mbachu, Nnedi. Zahrah the Windseeker. Cooper, Stephanie & Hall, Amanda, illus. 2005. 320p. (YA). (gr. 5-7). 16.00 (978-0-618-34090-3(4)) Houghton Mifflin Co. Trade & Reference Div.

Olaondo, Susana. Felipe. 2001. (SPA., Illus.). (J). (gr. 2). pap. 7.95 (978-9974-590-34-2(5)) Santillana S. A. URY. *Dist:* Santillana USA Publishing Co., Inc.

Oldfield, J. Sugar & Spice, Bk. 14. (Illus.). 120p. (J). pap. 7.99 (978-0-340-69986-7(8) , Hodder & Stoughton) Hodder General Publishing Division GBR. *Dist:* Trafalgar Square Publishing.

Oliver, Andrew. If Photos Could Talk. 2005. (Sam & Stephanie Mystery Ser.). 264p. (J). per. 12.95 (978-0-9661009-6-9(4)) Adams-Pomeroy Pr.

Oliver, Jasmine. Armani Angels. 2007. (Project Fashion Ser.). 176p. (J). pap. 8.99 (*978-1-4169-3811-8(7) , Simon Pulse) Simon & Schuster Children's Publishing.

Oliver, Jasmine. Gucci Girls. 2007. (Project Fashion Ser.). 192p. (YA). pap. 8.99 (978-1-4169-3534-6(7) , Simon Pulse) Simon & Schuster Children's Publishing.

Oliver, Lin & Winkler, Henry. Hank Zipzer Collection: The World's Greatest Underachiever. 2005. (Hank Zipzer Ser.). 160p. (J). lthr. 19.96 (978-0-448-43977-8(8) , Grosset & Dunlap) Penguin Group (USA) Inc.

Olker, Constance. The Punctuation Pals Go Snow Skiing. 2005. (Illus.). 44p. (J). per. 18.95 (978-1-933449-14-2(4)) Nightengale Pr.

Olsen, Ashley. Starring You & Me. 2002. (gr. 5-8). lib. bdg. 13.00 (978-0-613-64769-4(6)) Tandem Library Bks.

Olsen, Judith K. I Can Hardly Wait. 2006. 100p. (J). pap. 7.95 (*978-1-59800-999-6(0)) Outskirts Press, Inc.

Olsen, Mary-Kate. Closer Than Ever. 2002. (gr. 3-6). lib. bdg. 13.00 (978-0-613-50437-9(2)) Tandem Library Bks.

—How to Train a Boy. 2002. (gr. 5-8). lib. bdg. 13.00 (978-0-613-64731-1(9)) Tandem Library Bks.

—Love-Set-Match. 2003. (gr. 5-8). lib. bdg. 13.00 (978-0-613-64745-8(9)) Tandem Library Bks.

—Making a Splash. 2003. (gr. 3-6). lib. bdg. 13.00 (978-0-613-66365-6(9)) Tandem Library Bks.

—Two for the Road. 2001. (gr. 3-6). lib. bdg. 13.00 (978-0-613-43966-4(X)) Tandem Library Bks.

Olsen, Mary-Kate & Olsen, Ashley. Heart to Heart. 2004. (Two of a Kind Ser.: No. 33). (Illus.). 112p. mass mkt. 4.99 (978-0-06-009329-7(3) , Harper Entertainment) HarperCollins Pubs.

—Holiday Magic. Innelli, ed. 2004. (Two of a Kind Ser.: No. 38). (Illus.). 112p. 4.99 (978-0-06-059590-6(6) , Harper Entertainment) HarperCollins Pubs.

—MKA Two of a Kind 2003 Boxed Set. 2003. mass mkt. 19.96 (978-0-06-072353-8(X) , Harper Entertainment) HarperCollins Pubs.

—So Little Time No.12: Best Friends Forever. 2003. (gr. 3-6). lib. bdg. 13.00 (978-0-613-71368-9(0)) Tandem Library Bks.

Olson, Kris Elingboe. Inside the Painted Box. Wise, Noreen, ed. Favazzao, Keith, illus. 2001. (Lemonade Collection). 48p. (J). (gr. 1-5). pap. 6.95 (978-1-58584-208-7(7)) Huckleberry Pr.

Olson, Kris Ellingboe. Crabby Abby. Wise, Noreen, ed. Bowman, Sharon, illus. 2002. (Book-a-Day Collection). 32p. (J). (ps up). pap. 6.95 (978-1-58584-375-6(X)) Huckleberry Pr.

O'Malley, Kevin. Bud. O'Malley, Kevin, illus. 2000. (Illus.). 32p. (J). (gr. k-3). 15.95 (978-0-8027-8718-7(5)); lib. bdg. 16.85 (978-0-8027-8719-4(3)) Walker & Co.

Once upon a Time Spanish Version-the Little Red Hen. 2005. (J). (978-1-57022-561-1(3)) ECS Learning Systems, Inc.

One Fine Day. 1999. (J). 9.95 (978-1-56137-249-2(8)) Novel Units, Inc.

O'Neil, Catherine. Fine & Dandy. Wise, Noreen, ed. 2000. (Lemonade Collection). (YA). (gr. 4 up). pap. 6.95 (978-1-58584-250-6(8)) Huckleberry Pr.

Onish, Liane. Alphabet Eurps Meet Bipple. 1999. (Eurps Concept Bks.). (Illus.). (J). 7.95 (978-1-892522-03-0(9)) Eurpsville USA, Inc.

Oram, Hiawyn. Badger's Bad Mood. Varley, Susan, illus. 32p. (J). (ps-3). 2002. pap. 5.99 (978-0-590-21693-7(7)); 1998. pap. 15.95 (978-0-590-18920-0(4)) Scholastic, Inc.

—Mine! Rees, Mary, illus. 2005. 32p. (J). (ps-7). pap. 7.95 (978-1-84507-451-7(3)) Lincoln, Frances Ltd. GBR. *Dist:* Perseus Distribution.

—What's Naughty? Reynolds, Adrian, illus. 32p. (J). pap. 11.99 (978-0-340-75447-4(8) , Hodder & Stoughton) Hodder General Publishing Division GBR. *Dist:* Trafalgar Square Publishing.

Orban, Marianne. To Earn a Star. 2000. 172p. (YA). pap. 14.95 (978-0-595-17080-7(3)) iUniverse, Inc.

Ordal, Stina Langlo. Princess Aasta. 2002. (Illus.). 32p. (J). (ps-3). 16.95 (978-1-58234-783-7(2) , Bloomsbury Children) Bloomsbury Publishing.

Orgel, Doris. Devil in Vienna. 2004. 256p. (YA). (gr. 3-6). pap. 6.99 (978-0-14-240236-8(2) , Puffin) Penguin Group (USA) Inc.

Orme, David & Banks, J. Gateway to Hell. 2004. (Shades Ser.). 62p. (J). pap. 7.99 (978-0-237-52623-8(9) , Evans Brothers, Limited) Evans Publishing Group GBR. *Dist:* Independent Pubs. Group.

Orme, Helen. Boys. 2007. (Siti's Sisters Ser.). (Illus.). 36p. pap. 7.95 (*978-1-84167-600-5(4)) Ransom Publishing Ltd. GBR. *Dist:* International Publishers Marketing.

—Moving. 2008. (Siti's Sisters Ser.). 36p. pap. 7.95 (*978-1-84167-689-0(6)) Ransom Publishing Ltd. GBR. *Dist:* International Publishers Marketing.

—Odd One Out. 2007. (Siti's Sisters Ser.). (Illus.). 36p. pap. 7.95 (*978-1-84167-597-8(0)) Ransom Publishing Ltd. GBR. *Dist:* International Publishers Marketing.

—Stalker. 2007. (Siti's Sisters Ser.). (Illus.). 36p. pap. 7.95 (*978-1-84167-595-4(4)) Ransom Publishing Ltd. GBR. *Dist:* International Publishers Marketing.

—Taken for a Ride. 2007. (Siti's Sisters Ser.). (Illus.). 36p. pap. 7.95 (*978-1-84167-596-1(2)) Ransom Publishing Ltd. GBR. *Dist:* International Publishers Marketing.

—Trouble with Teachers. 2007. (Siti's Sisters Ser.). (Illus.). 36p. pap. 7.95 (*978-1-84167-599-2(7)) Ransom Publishing Ltd. GBR. *Dist:* International Publishers Marketing.

Ormondroyd, Edward. Time at the Top. Ericksen, Barbara, illus. 40th anniv. ed. 2003. 191p. (J). 17.95 (978-1-930900-19-6(8)) Purple Hse. Pr.

Orr, Wendy. Nim at Sea. Millard, Kerry, illus. 2008. 192p. (J). (gr. 3-7). 12.99 (*978-0-440-42232-7(9) , Knopf Bks. for Young Readers) Random Hse. Children's Bks.

Orr, Wendy. Nim's Island. Millard, Kerry, illus. (gr. 3-7). 2008. 144p. 5.50 (*978-0-385-73606-0(1)); 2002. 128p. 5.50 (978-0-440-41868-9(2)) Random Hse. Children's Bks. (Yearling).

—Nim's Island. 2002. (gr. 3-6). lib. bdg. 13.00 (978-0-613-46203-7(3)) Tandem Library Bks.

Ortiz, Carolyn. Cat's Got My Tongue! 2006. (ENG., Illus.). 40p. per. 13.90 (978-1-4208-7851-6(4)) AuthorHouse.

Ortiz, Gilberto Rendon. Tuiiiiii el Murcielago. (Barril Sin Fondo Ser.). (SPA.). (J). (gr. 3-5). pap. (978-968-6465-22-8(7)) Casa de Estudios de Literatura y Talleres Artisticos Amaquemecan A.C. MEX. *Dist:* Lectorum Pubns., Inc.

Oryan, Ellie. What Are Friends For. Santanach, Tino, illus. 2005. (Winx Club Ser.). 80p. (J). (ps-k). pap. 2.99 (978-0-439-74420-1(2)) Scholastic, Inc.

Ostrander, P. Martin. P Martin Ostrander's Dangerous Four Series: Book #1. 2007. 112p. 20.95 (*978-0-595-68250-8(2)); per. 10.95 (*978-0-595-43582-1(3)) iUniverse, Inc.

Ostrom, Bob, illus. Friends till the End! ed. 2005. (Teenage Mutant Ninja Turtles Ser.: No. 3). 24p. (J). lib. bdg. 15.00 (978-1-59054-833-2(7)) Fitzgerald Bks.

Otten, Charlotte. Home in a Wilderness Fort: Copper Harbor 1844. 2006. (J). pap. 14.95 (978-0-9766104-5-8(0)) Arbutus Pr.

Ouriou, Katie. Luv Ya Like a Sister: A Story of Friendship. 1999. (gr. 5-8). lib. bdg. 16.40 (978-0-613-77268-6(7)) Tandem Library Bks.

Owens, Terrell & Parker, Courtney. Little T Learns to Share. Harris, Todd, illus. 2006. 24p. (J). 14.95 (978-1-933771-20-5(8)) BenBella Bks.

Packard, Mary. Surprise! 2004. (My First Reader Ser.). (Illus.). 29p. (J). (gr. k-1). pap. 3.95 (978-0-516-24639-0(9) , Children's Pr.) Scholastic Library Publishing.

E
F
G

Peto, Judith & Talwar, Robert. Jenny & Benny: Friends. 2005. (Illus.). 28p. (J). pap. 16.95 (978-0-9767511-0-6(0)) Lasting Bks. Publishing Co.

Petre, Wanda E. The Watch Chicken: The Legend of Russell the Rooster & His Friend Hortense. 2006. 36p. (J). pap. 9.93 (978-1-4116-9990-8(4)) Lulu.com.

Pettee, Sandra. Imagination. Com. 2005. 48p. pap. 12.95 (978-1-4137-7124-4(6)) PublishAmerica, Inc.

Petterson, Aline. El Papalote y el Nopal. Pacheco, Gabriel, illus. 2003. (SPA.). 34p. (J). (gr. 3-5). 15.95 (978-968-19-0750-1(7)) Santillana USA Publishing Co., Inc.

Petty, Dini. The Queen, the Bear & the Bumblebee. Cowles, Rose, illus. 32p. (J). 19.95 (978-1-55285-151-7(6)) Whitecap Bks., Ltd. CAN. *Dist:* Graphic Arts Ctr. Publishing Co.

Petty, Kate. Summer Heat. 2004. (Summer Ser.). 536p. (J). per. 13.95 (*978-1-84255-162-2(0)) Orion Publishing Group, Ltd. GBR. *Dist:* Independent Pubs. Group.

Peyton, K. M. The Boy Who Wasn't There. 2000. 192p. (J). pap. 5.95 (978-0-552-52717-0(3) , Corgi Bks. Ltd.) Random Hse. Children's Bks. GBR. *Dist:* Trafalgar Square Publishing.

Pfeffer, Susan Beth. Revenge of the Aztecs. 2004. 118p. (J). lib. bdg. 16.92 (*978-1-4242-0763-3(0)) Fitzgerald Bks.

Pfister, Marcus. Fishy Story with Sticker. 2001. (ps-2). lib. bdg. 11.80 (978-0-613-85246-3(X)) Tandem Library Bks.

—El Pez Arco Iris al Rescate! Pfister, Marcus, illus. 1998. (Rainbow Fish Ser.). Orig. Title: Regenbogenfisch, Komm Hilf Mir!. (SPA., Illus.). 12p. (J). (ps-3). bds. 9.95 (978-1-55858-885-1(X)) North-South Bks., Inc.

—Pez Arco Iris y la Balena Azul, el Big Book: Rainbow Fish. Pfister, Marcus, illus. 1999. (Rainbow Fish Ser.). Orig. Title: Regenbogenfisch und Grosser Blauer Wal. (SPA., Illus.). 32p. (J). (ps-3). pap. 25.00 (978-0-7358-1215-4(2)) North-South Bks., Inc.

—Pez Arco Iris y la Ballena Azul. Pfister, Marcus, illus. 1998. (Rainbow Fish Ser.). Orig. Title: Regenbogenfisch und Grosser Blauer Wal. (SPA., Illus.). 32p. (J). (ps-3). 18.95 (978-0-7358-1002-0(8) , NSB028) North-South Bks., Inc.

—Rainbow Fish: Dangerous Deep. 2002. (ps-2). lib. bdg. 11.80 (978-0-613-50438-6(0)) Tandem Library Bks.

—Rainbow Fish: Tattle Tale. 2002. (ps-2). lib. bdg. 11.80 (978-0-613-52730-9(5)) Tandem Library Bks.

—Rainbow Fish to the Rescue! Minibook & Audio Package. James, J. Alison, tr. from GER. Pfister, Marcus, illus. 1998. (Rainbow Fish Ser.).Tr. of Regenbogenfisch, Komm Hilf Mir!. (ENG & SPA., Illus.). 12p. (J). (ps-3). bds. 9.95 (978-1-55858-880-6(9)) North-South Bks., Inc.

Philbrick, Rodman. Max the Mighty. 1998. (J). pap. 47.88 (978-0-590-65859-1(X) , Blue Sky Pr., The) Scholastic, Inc.

Philbrick, Rodman & Philbrick, W. R. Max the Mighty. 1998. 166p. (J). (gr. 7-12). pap. 16.95 (978-0-590-18892-0(5) , Blue Sky Pr., The) Scholastic, Inc.

Phillips, Clifton J. Chupacabra, You Don't Scare Me! 1999. (Illus.). 32p. (J). (gr. 3-6). pap. 7.00 (978-0-8059-4490-7(7)) Dorrance Publishing Co., Inc.

Pickering, Jimmy. It's Fall. 2003. (Illus.). 32p. (J). (ps-3). 16.95 (978-1-931290-15-9(6)) Tallfellow Pr.

—It's Winter. 2003. (Illus.). 32p. (J). (ps-3). 16.95 (978-1-931290-16-6(4)) Tallfellow Pr.

Pielichaty, Helena. Starring Brody ... 2006. (Girls of Avenue Z Ser.). 144p. (J). pap. 4.99 (978-1-4169-0062-7(4) , Aladdin) Simon & Schuster Children's Publishing.

Pierce, Tamora. Daja's Book. 1998. (Circle of Magic Ser.: No. 3). (Illus.). 240p. (J). (gr. 6-12). pap. 15.95 (978-0-590-55358-2(5)) Scholastic, Inc.

—Sandry's Book. 1999. (Circle of Magic Ser.: No. 1). (gr. 5-8). lib. bdg. 13.00 (978-0-613-17935-5(8)) Tandem Library Bks.

—The Will of the Empress. (Circle Reforged Ser.: Bk. 1). 560p. (J). 2006. pap. 8.99 (978-0-439-44172-8(2)); 2005. (Illus.). (gr. 9-12). pap. 17.99 (978-0-439-44171-1(4) , Scholastic Pr.) Scholastic, Inc.

Pierson, Jan. The Haunted Horse of Gold Hill (Gold Hill, Nevada) 2006. (Ghostowners Ser.: Vol. 4). (Illus.). 109p. pap. 9.95 (978-0-9721800-3-0(6)) WildWest Publishing.

Pijet, Andre, illus. Snow White. 2000. (Classic Stories Ser.). 48p. (J). (ps-2). audio, audio compact disk (978-2-921997-87-4(8)) Coffragants.

The Pinballs. 1999. (J). 9.95 (978-1-56137-082-5(7)) Novel Units, Inc.

Pinkwater, Daniel M. Looking for Bobowicz: A Hoboken Chicken Story. Pinkwater, Jill, illus. 2004. 208p. (J). 15.99 (978-0-06-053554-4(7)) HarperCollins Pubs.

Pino, Montana. Tessie & Tillie. 10th ed. 2004. (YA). lib. bdg. (978-0-9754365-1-6(1)) Thomson, J P.

Pintozzi, Nick. Bentley & the Great Fire. Pintozzi, Nick et al, illus. 2004. 16.95 (978-0-9749465-2-8(4)) Bent-DaiSha, LLC.

Piper, Molly. Rosey & Amanda. Piper, Molly, illus. Date not set. (Illus.). (J). (gr. k-6). pap. 7.95 (978-1-891360-01-5(9)) Little Deer Pr.

Piper, Sophie. Little Kitten's Friendship Book. Massey, Jane, illus. 2006. 64p. (J). pap. 6.99 (978-0-7459-4710-5(7) , Lion) Lion Hudson plc GBR. *Dist:* Independent Pubs. Group.

Pitchford, Dean. The Big One-Oh. 2007. 192p. (J). (gr. 3). 15.99 (978-0-399-24547-3(2) , Putnam Juvenile) Penguin Group (USA) Inc.

Pittar, Gill. Las Ciruelas de Isa Bela. Rioja, Alberto Jiménez, tr. Morrell, Cris, illus. 2003. (Milly Molly Ser.). (SPA.). 24p. (J). pap. (978-84-241-8687-6(7)) Everest de Ediciones y Distribucion, S.L. ESP. *Dist:* Lectorum Pubns., Inc.

—Milly, Molly & Beefy (book W/dolls) 2006. 28p. pap. (978-1-86972-090-2(3)) Milly Molly Bks.

—Milly, Molly & Henry. 2004. 28p. (978-1-86972-030-8(X)) Milly Molly Bks.

—Milly, Molly & Henry (book W/dolls) 2006. 28p. pap. (978-1-86972-103-9(9)) Milly Molly Bks.

—Milly, Molly & Jimmy's Seeds (book W/dolls) 2006. 28p. pap. (978-1-86972-091-9(1)) Milly Molly Bks.

—Milly, Molly & Oink. 28p. 2006. pap. (978-1-86972-093-3(8)); 2004. (Illus.). (978-1-86972-002-5(4)) Milly Molly Bks.

—Milly, Molly & Special Friends. 2004. 28p. (978-1-86972-017-9(2)) Milly Molly Bks.

—Milly, Molly & Special Friends (book W/dolls) 2006. 28p. pap. (978-1-86972-104-6(7)) Milly Molly Bks.

—Milly, Molly & the Runaway Bean. Morrell, Cris, illus. 2005. 28p. (ps-ps). pap. (978-1-86972-049-0(0)) Milly Molly Bks.

—Milly, Molly & the Stowaways. 2004. 28p. (978-1-86972-026-1(1)) Milly Molly Bks.

—Milly, Molly & the Tree Hut. 2004. 28p. (978-1-86972-028-5(8)) Milly Molly Bks.

—Milly, Molly & What Was That? 2004. 28p. (978-1-86972-031-5(8)) Milly Molly Bks.

Plaisted, Caroline. 10 Things to Do Before You're 16. 2006. 160p. (YA). mass mkt. 5.99 (978-1-4169-2460-9(4) , Simon Pulse) Simon & Schuster Children's Publishing.

Plante, Raymond. Marilou Cries Wolf. Cummins, Sarah, tr. from FRE. Favreau, Marie-Claude, illus. 2002. (First Novel Ser.). 64p. (J). (*978-0-88780-581-3(7)); (gr. 1-5). 4.95 (978-0-88780-580-6(9)) Formac Publishing Co., Ltd. CAN. *Dist:* Casemate Pubs. & Bk. Distributors, LLC.

Playhouse Disney: My Friends Tigger & Pooh. 2007. 22p. (J). mass mkt. 4.99 (*978-1-4037-3941-4(2)) Dalmatian Pr.

Plaza, José María. Ya Soy Mayor. 2003. (Disney Collection). (SPA.). 48p. (J). 6.95 (978-84-670-0303-1(0)) Espasa Calpe, S.A. ESP. *Dist:* Planeta Publishing Corp.

Pliszka, Jodi. Bella & Gizmo's Adventures: Bella Gets A New Sweater. 2005. (Illus.). 24p. (J). per. 18.95 (978-1-933449-04-3(7)) Nightengale Pr.

—Bella & Gizmo's Adventures: The Hairless Sphynx Cats. 2005. (Illus.). 25p. (J). per. 18.95 (978-1-933449-03-6(9)) Nightengale Pr.

—Bella & Gizmo's Adventures — Bella Gets A New Sweater. 2005. 32p. (J). per. 18.95 (978-1-933449-26-5(8)) Nightengale Pr.

Plouff, Amy. Chicken & His Friends Learn How to Prepare for a Pandemic. 2008. (Chicken & His Friends Ser.). 48p. (J). 9.95 (*978-1-933255-40-8(4)) DNA Pr.

—Chicken & His Friends Learn How You Get & Prevent the Flu. 2008. (Chicken & His Friends Ser.). 48p. (J). bds. 9.95 (*978-1-933255-39-2(0)) DNA Pr.

Plourde, Becky. Rose of Many Colors. 2005. 268p. pap. 21.95 (978-1-4137-6775-9(3)) PublishAmerica, Inc.

Pochocki, Ethel. The Mushroom Man. Moser, Barry, illus. 2006. (J). reprint ed. pap. (978-0-88448-278-9(2)) Tilbury Hse. Pubs.

—A Penny for a Hundred. Owens, Mary Beth, illus. 2005. 32p. (J). pap. 9.95 (978-1-883937-52-2(3)) Bethlehem Bks.

—Rosebud & Red Flannel. Owens, Mary Beth, illus. 1999. 32p. (YA). (gr. 2-4). 14.95 (978-0-89272-474-1(9)) Down East Bks.

Pocket Books Staff. Errata: Final Fantasy. (Illus.). (YA). mass mkt. (978-0-7434-4646-4(1) , Aladdin) Simon & Schuster Children's Publishing.

Polacco, Patricia. The Butterfly. Polacco, Patricia, illus. 2002. (Illus.). (J). 23.64 (978-0-7587-2166-2(8)) Book Wholesalers, Inc.

—The Butterfly. unabr. ed. 2001. (J). (gr. 1-6). 27.95 incl. audio (978-0-8045-6875-3(8) , 6875) Spoken Arts, Inc.

—Emma Kate. Polacco, Patricia, illus. 2005. (Illus.). 40p. (J). (ps-1). 16.99 (978-0-399-24452-0(2) , Philomel) Penguin Group (USA) Inc.

—Mrs. Katz & Tush. Polacco, Patricia, illus. 2002. (Illus.). (J). 14.79 (978-0-7587-3191-3(4)) Book Wholesalers, Inc.

—Pink & Say. Polacco, Patricia, illus. 2002. (Illus.). (J). 23.64 (978-0-7587-3418-1(2)) Book Wholesalers, Inc.

—Pink & Say. (Illus.). (J). (gr. 3-4). pap. 6.36 net. (978-1-930332-54-6(8)) Lectorum Pubns., Inc.

—Pink & Say. 2001. (J). 27.95 incl. audio (978-0-8045-6835-7(9) , 6835) Spoken Arts, Inc.

Polanski, Sylvia. Pink Lemonade Sky: Five Girls Must Die. 2005. 111p. pap. 16.95 (978-1-4137-5563-3(1)) PublishAmerica, Inc.

Pollack, Jenny. Klepto. 288p. (gr. 7). 2008. (YA). pap. 7.99 (*978-0-14-241072-1(1) , Puffin); 2006. (J). 16.99 (978-0-670-06061-0(5) , Viking Juvenile) Penguin Group (USA) Inc.

Pollack, Jenny. Klepto (Splashproof Edition) 2007. 1p. (J). (gr. 7). pap. 7.99 (978-0-14-240835-3(2) , Puffin) Penguin Group (USA) Inc.

Pollack, P. & Belviso, M. Challenge of Super. 2007. (Foster's Home for Imaginary Friends Ser.: No. 2). 24p. (J). pap. 3.99 (978-0-439-89949-9(4)) Scholastic, Inc.

—Friends Are Forever. 2006. (Junior Chapter Bk.). (Illus.). 64p. (J). pap. 3.99 (978-0-439-75057-8(1) , Scholastic Paperbacks) Scholastic, Inc.

Pollack, P., et al. Bloo Done It. 2007. (Foster's Home for Imaginary Friends Ser.: No. 3). 48p. (J). pap. 3.99 (978-0-439-89948-2(6)) Scholastic, Inc.

Pollet, Alison. The Pity Party: 8th Grade in the Life of Me, Cass. (Pity Party Ser.). 160p. (J). 2006. pap. 5.99 (978-0-439-68195-7(2) , Scholastic Paperbacks); 2005. (gr. 5-8). pap. 15.95 (978-0-439-68194-0(4) , Orchard Bks.) Scholastic, Inc.

Polo & Cuddles. (J). 14.64 (978-0-8136-0618-7(7)) Modern Curriculum Pr.

Ponti, Claude. DeZert Isle. Holliday, Mary Martin, tr. from FRE. Ponti, Claude, illus. 2003. (Illus.). 64p. (J). 16.95 (978-1-56792-237-0(6)) Godine, David R. Pub.

Pooh Hello Friend Book & Box. 2002. (Illus.). (J). pap. 9.98 (978-0-7853-5251-8(1)) Publications International, Ltd.

Pope, Gisele & Kern, Carla. Tailfeathers, Vol. 2. 1999. (Illus.). 84p. (J). pap. 10.50 (978-1-56770-451-8(4)) Scheewe, Susan Pubns., Inc.

Porter, Cassyashton. Colin's Eagle. 2003. 134p. pap. 19.95 (978-1-59286-517-8(8)) PublishAmerica, Inc.

Porter, Tom. Jesse & the Baby. Leavitt, Deborah, illus. 2000. 12p. (J). (ps-3). pap. 3.00 (978-0-9650312-2-6(5)) Cosmo Starr Bks.

Portman, Frank. Andromeda Klein. 2008. 256p. (YA). (gr. 9). 16.99 (*978-0-385-73525-4(1)); lib. bdg. 19.99 (*978-0-385-90512-1(2)) Random Hse. Children's Bks. (Delacorte Bks. for Young Readers).

Poryes, Michael & Sherman, Susan. Dueling Divas. 2005. (That's So Raven Ser.: Vol. 8). (Illus.). 137p. (J). (*978-1-4156-0366-6(9)) Disney Pr.

Poth, Karen. The Pirates Who Don't Do Anything & Me! 2004. (Illus.). 32p. 7.99 (978-0-310-70725-7(0)) Zonderkidz.

Poth, Karen & Big Ideas Inc. Staff. Larry Aprende a Escuchar. 2004. (Big Idea Bks.). 12p. (J). 5.99 (978-0-8297-4300-5(6)) Vida Pubs.

Potter, Beatrix. Peter Rabbit & Friends. ed. 2008. (Potter Ser.). (Illus.). 12p. (J). (ps). pap. 4.99 (*978-0-7232-5888-9(0) , Warne) Penguin Group (USA) Inc.

Potter, Beatrix & Barker, Cicely Mary. Flower Fairies Best Friends. 2005. 24p. (J). pap. 9.99 (978-0-7232-5395-2(1) , Warne) Penguin Group (USA) Inc.

—Lavender Finds a Friend: Book, Bag, & Necklace. gif. ed. 2004. (Illus.). 24p. (J). 5.99 (978-0-7232-8484-0(9) , Warne) Penguin Group (USA) Inc.

Potters, Harry. Tory the Little Dust Devil. 2006. pap. 15.30 (*978-1-84728-571-3(6)) Lulu.com.

Povandra, Shirley. My Imaginary Friend. 2007. 17.95 (*978-1-59526-669-9(0)) Media Creations, Inc.

Powell, Opal N. Two Lives for Giant Jack Pumpkin: The Story of a Boy, a Jack O'Latern & a Pie. Durham, Lily, illus. 2001. 24p. (J). (ps-4). pap. (978-0-9710477-1-6(5)) Western Printers, Inc.

Powell, Randy. Three Clams & an Oyster. 224p. (YA). 2006. pap. 6.95 (978-0-374-40007-1(5)); 2002. (gr. 7-10). 16.00 (978-0-374-37526-3(7)) Farrar, Straus & Giroux. (Farrar, Straus & Giroux (BYR)).

The Power of Friendship. 2005. (W. I. T. C. H. Graphic Novels Ser.: Bk. 1). (Illus.). 128p. (gr. 3-7). pap. 4.99 (978-0-7868-3674-1(1) , Volo) Hyperion Bks. for Children.

Prats, Joan de Déu. Un Topo en un Mar de Hierba. Caruncho, Isabel, illus. (SPA.). 31p. (978-84-236-5040-8(5)) Edebé ESP. *Dist:* Lectorum Pubns., Inc.

Pray, Ralph. Jingu: The Hidden Princess. Li, Xiaojun, illus. 2002. 80p. (YA). 14.95 (978-1-885008-21-3(X) , 188500821x) Shen's Bks.

Preble, Laura. The Queen Geek Social Club. 2006. 336p. (YA). (gr. 12). pap. 9.99 (978-0-425-21164-9(9) , Berkley Trade) Penguin Group (USA) Inc.

Preller, James. The Case of the Food Fight. 2005. (Jigsaw Jones Ser.: No. 28). (Illus.). 80p. (J). pap. 3.99 (978-0-439-67807-0(2) , Scholastic Paperbacks) Scholastic, Inc.

Prentiss, Elizabeth. Urbane & His Friends. 1999. (J). (ps up). pap. 7.99 (978-1-881545-68-2(7)) A B Publishing.

Presti, Joan Lo. Flump. Danner, Bob, illus. 2001. 32p. (J). (ps-3). pap. 7.50 (978-1-884083-23-5(4)) Maval Publishing, Inc.

Price, Audrey. My best Friend: Best Friend. 2004. (J). pap. 15.95 (978-0-9778937-0-6(7)) Priceless Ink Publishing Co., Inc.

Price, Joan. Truth Is a Bright Star. 2nd rev. ed. 2004. (Illus.). 156p. (J). (gr. 3-7). 8.95 (978-1-58246-055-0(8) , Tricycle Pr.) Ten Speed Pr.

Price, Mary Ellizabeth. Wallbaby Bumblebees. 2004. (Illus.). 40p. (J). per. 15.75 (978-0-9715402-2-4(5) , 410-707-6686) Barnhardt & Ashe Publishing, Inc.

Priddy Book. In the Yard; Fuzzy Bee & Friends. (Illus.). (J). 17.90 (978-0-312-49377-6(0) , Priddy Bks.) St. Martin's Pr.

Priddy, Roger. Squishy Turtle & Friends. rev. ed. 2003. (Cloth Book Ser.). (Illus.). 14p. (J). 8.95 (978-0-312-49184-0(0) , Priddy Bks.) St. Martin's Pr.

Priestley, Chris. Redwulf's Curse. 2008. (Illus.). 272p. (YA). pap. 9.95 (*978-0-552-55483-1(9)) Transworld Publishers Ltd. GBR. *Dist:* Independent Pubs. Group.

Prinz, Yvonne. Still There, Clare Teacher Guide. 2005. 4p. (J). pap. (978-1-55192-821-0(3)) Raincoast Bk. Distribution CAN. *Dist:* Transition Vendor.

Prior, Natalie. Lily Quench & the Dragon of Ashby. Janine, Dawson, illus. 2004. 160p. (YA). (gr. 3 up). pap. 5.99 (978-0-14-240020-3(3) , Puffin) Penguin Group (USA) Inc.

Prou, Suzanne. Les Amis de Monsieur Paul, Level C. (FRE.). (YA). (gr. 7-12). 8.95 (978-0-8219-1218-8(6) , 40331) EMC/Paradigm Publishing.

Provost, Gary & Stockwell, Gail Provost. David & Max. rev. ed. 2006. 185p. (J). pap. 14.95 (978-0-8276-0837-5(3)) Jewish Pubn. Society.

Prowense, Mary J. Amy Goes Country. 2007. (ENG.). 136p. per. 19.95 (*978-1-4241-5519-4(3)) PublishAmerica, Inc.

Pugliano-Martin, Carol. See You in Spring! 2006. (Early Explorers Ser.). (J). 34.00 (*978-1-4108-6105-4(8)) Benchmark Education Co.

Pullman, Philip. Spring-Heeled Jack. Mostyn, David, illus. 2002. 112p. (J). (gr. 3-7). 9.95 (978-0-375-81601-7(1) , Knopf Bks. for Young Readers) Random Hse. Children's Bks.

—Spring-Heeled Jack: A Story of Bravery & Evil. Mostyn, David, illus. 2002. 112p. (J). (gr. 3-7). lib. bdg. 11.99 (978-0-375-91601-4(6) , Knopf Bks. for Young Readers) Random Hse. Children's Bks.

Puttock, Simon. Goat & Donkey in the Great Outdoors. Julian, Russell, illus. 2007. 28p. (J). (ps-2). 16.00 (*978-1-56148-573-4(X)) Good Bks.

—"Here I Am!" Said Smedley. Chatterton, Martin & Chatterton, Ann, illus. 2001. (Blue Bananas Ser.). 48p. (J). (gr. 1-2). (978-0-7787-0838-4(1)); pap. (978-0-7787-0884-1(5)) Crabtree Publishing Co.

—Here I Am! Said Smedley. 2002. (gr. k-3). lib. bdg. 12.95 (978-0-613-52852-8(2)) Tandem Library Bks.

Puzzle House Staff. Friends. Teviotdale, Stuart, illus. 2001. (File-Online.Com). 128p. (J). (gr. 3-8). pap. 7.95 (978-0-439-22008-8(4)) Scholastic, Inc.

Puzzle Track Staff, ed. Hello Ladybug. 2007. (Puzzle Track Ser.). 20p. (J). bds. 18.95 (*978-0-7696-5629-8(3)) School Specialty Publishing.

—Red Car Ride. 2007. (Puzzle Track Ser.). 20p. (J). bds. 18.95 (*978-0-7696-5579-6(3)) School Specialty Publishing.

Qualey, Marsha. Just Like That. 240p. (YA). (gr. 7). 2007. pap. 6.99 (978-0-14-240830-8(1) , Puffin); 2005. 16.99 (978-0-8037-2840-0(9) , Dial) Penguin Group (USA) Inc.

—Too Big a Storm. 2004. 256p. (J). (gr. 9). 16.99 (978-0-8037-2839-4(5) , Dial) Penguin Group (USA) Inc.

Rabe, Tish. Fine Feathered Friends: All about Birds. 1998. (Cat in the Hat's Learning Library). (Illus.). 48p. (gr. k-3). 8.99 (978-0-679-88362-3(2) , Random Hse. Bks. for Young Readers) Random Hse. Children's Bks.

Rabin, Staton. Betsy & the Emperor. 2006. (Illus.). 304p. (YA). reprint ed. mass mkt. 5.99 (978-1-4169-1336-8(X) , Simon Pulse) Simon & Schuster Children's Publishing.

Raffi. Down by the Bay. Westcott, Nadine Bernard, illus. 1999. (Raffi Board Bks.). 32p. (J). (gr. k-ps). bds. 6.99 (978-0-517-80058-4(6) , Crown Books For Young Readers) Random Hse. Children's Bks.

Raffle, Diana. Moondragon. 2006. 161p. pap. 19.95 (978-1-4241-0626-4(5)) PublishAmerica, Inc.

Ragin, M. K. Mildred Row & Improper Bounds. 2006. 185p. pap. 19.95 (978-1-4137-9724-4(5)) PublishAmerica, Inc.

Rainsbury, Julie. Crab-Boy Cranc. Evans, Fran, illus. 2000. 48p. pap. 11.95 (978-1-85902-835-3(7)) Beekman Bks., Inc.

Raintree Steck-Vaughn Staff. Los Amigos. (SPA.). (J). (ps-3). 2000. pap. 19.24 (978-0-7398-0813-9(3)); 1999. pap., stu. ed. 21.50 (978-0-7398-0839-9(7)) Steck-Vaughn.

Rallison, Janette. Life, Love, & the Pursuit of Free Throws. 2006. 192p. (J). pap. 6.95 (978-0-8027-8898-6(X)); 2004. 176p. (YA). 16.95 (978-0-8027-8927-3(7)) Walker & Co.

Ramblin' Rose: The Wire Forests of Peru. 2007. 200p. (YA). pap. 8.99 (*978-0-9776043-9-5(X)) Aspirations Media, Inc.

Rameaka, T. Where's Dorothy? 2005. 73p. pap. 14.95 (978-1-4137-9117-4(4)) PublishAmerica, Inc.

Ramirez, Irma. Once upon a time Tales. 2005. 7.95 (978-0-533-15096-0(5)) Vantage Pr., Inc.

Rand, Edward A. The Knights of the White Shield: Up-the-Ladder Club Series Round One Play. 2007. 166p. pap. 11.99 (*978-1-4264-8273-1(6)); 184p. pap. 14.99 (*978-1-4264-8310-3(4)) BiblioBazaar.

Rand, Gloria & Rand, Ted. A Pen Pal for Max. rev. ed. 2005. (Illus.). 32p. (J). (gr. 4-7). 16.95 (978-0-8050-7586-1(0) , Holt, Henry & Co. Bks. For Young Readers) Holt, Henry & Co.

Rand, Jonathan. The Magical Wading Pool, Freddie Fernortner Bk 7: Fearless First Grader. 2007. pap. 4.99 (*978-1-893699-91-5(9)) AudioCraft Publishing, Inc.

Randall, Barbara. Baby Nadia Learns To Talk. Herning, Kathy, ed. 2006. (Mimi's Kids Ser.: vol. 1). (Illus.). 32p. (J). pap. 12.95 (978-0-9712383-5-0(9)) Culture Connection, The.

Randall, Bob. Tracker Tjugingji. 2003. 32p. 22.50 incl. audio compact disk (978-1-86465-030-3(2)) IAD Pr. AUS. *Dist:* International Specialized Bk. Services.

Randall, Ronne. A Hose of a Nose! Church, Caroline Jayne, illus. 2002. (Little Friends Ser.). 14p. (J). (ps-1). 12.95 (978-1-57145-773-8(9) , Silver Dolphin Bks.) Advantage Pubs. Group.

—Snuggle up, Little Penguin! Church, Caroline Jayne, illus. 2003. (Little Friends Ser.). 14p. (J). 12.95 (978-1-57145-919-0(7) , Silver Dolphin Bks.) Advantage Pubs. Group.

Randle, Kristen D. Breaking Rank. 1999. (J). lib. bdg. (978-0-688-16244-3(4)) HarperCollins Pubs.

—Slumming. 2003. (Illus.). 240p. (J). 16.99 (978-0-06-001022-5(3) , HarperTeen) HarperCollins Pubs.

Random House Disney Staff. Beauty & the Beast. 2004. (Illus.). 24p. (J). (gr. k-k). bds. 4.99 (978-0-7364-2248-2(X) , RH/Disney) Random Hse. Children's Bks.

—Beauty & the Beast. Disney Storybook Artists Staff, illus. 2002. 24p. (J). (gr. k-3). pap. 3.99 (978-0-7364-2065-5(7) , RH/Disney) Random Hse. Children's Bks.

—Cars. 2006. (Read-Aloud Board Book Ser.). (Illus.). 24p. (J). (gr. k-k). bds. 4.99 (978-0-7364-2293-2(5) , RH/Disney) Random Hse. Children's Bks.

—My Best Friend Is a Princess: A Princess Friendship Treasury. 2007. (Toddler Board Bks.). 30p. (J). (gr. k-k). bds. 11.99 (*978-0-7364-2505-6(5) , RH/Disney) Random Hse. Children's Bks.

—Rogue Robots! 2008. 24p. (J). (ps-2). pap. 3.99 (*978-0-7364-2519-3(5) , RH/Disney) Random Hse. Children's Bks.

—Snow White's Secret. Artful Doodlers Limited Staff, illus. 2005. 32p. (J). (ps-2). 4.99 (978-0-7364-2326-7(5) , RH/Disney) Random Hse. Children's Bks.

Random House Disney Staff. Space Chase. 2008. (Holographic Sticker Book Ser.). 48p. (J). (ps-2). pap. 3.99 ***(978-0-7364-2522-3(5)***, Golden/Disney) Random Hse. Children's Bks.

Random House Disney Staff & Marsoli, Lisa Ann. My Best Friend Is Ariel. 2006. (Illus.). 24p. (J). (ps-2). 4.99 (978-0-7364-2388-5(5), RH/Disney) Random Hse. Children's Bks.

—My Best Friend Is Belle. Disney Storybook Artists Staff, illus. 2006. 32p. (J). (ps-2). 4.99 (978-0-7364-2390-8(7), RH/Disney) Random Hse. Children's Bks.

—My Best Friend Is Cinderella. Disney Storybook Artists Staff, illus. 2006. 32p. (J). (ps-2). 4.99 (978-0-7364-2389-2(3), RH/Disney) Random Hse. Children's Bks.

—My Best Friend Is Jasmine. Disney Storybook Artists Staff, illus. 2006. 32p. (J). (ps-2). 4.99 (978-0-7364-2387-8(7), RH/Disney) Random Hse. Children's Bks.

Random House Staff. The Sisterhood of the Traveling Pants: The Official Scrapbook. movie tie-in ed. 2005. (Illus.). 160p. (YA). (gr. 7). pap. 9.95 (978-0-553-37607-4(1), Delacorte Bks. for Young Readers) Random Hse. Children's Bks.

Random House Staff. Thomas' Milkshake Muddle Book & CD. 2008. (Book & CD Ser.). (Illus.). 24p. (J). (ps-2). 9.99 ***(978-0-375-84227-6(6)***, Random Hse. Bks. for Young Readers) Random Hse. Children's Bks.

Rankin, Laura. Fluffy & Baron. 2006. (Illus.). 32p. (J). (ps). 16.99 (978-0-8037-2953-7(7), Dial) Penguin Group (USA) Inc.

Raphael, Taffy E. The View from Saturday. 2002. (Book Club Novel Guide Ser.). 48p. 17.95 (978-1-931376-10-5(7)) Small Planet Communications, Inc.

Raschka, Chris. Yo ! Yes. 2004. (J). (ps-5). pap. 14.95 incl. audio (978-1-55592-067-8(5), QPRA566) Weston Woods Studios, Inc.

—Yo! Yes? 2007. 32p. (J). pap. 6.99 (978-0-439-92185-5(6)) Scholastic, Inc.

Rathmell, Donna & Rathmell, Doreen. Octavia Octopus & Her Purple Ink Cloud. McLennan, Connie, illus. 2006. 32p. (J). 15.95 (978-0-9764943-5-5(3)) Sylvan Dell Pubng.

Ratnayake, Kumari/Keiko. Monsieur Bagel's War. Ratnayake, Kumari/Keiko, illus. 2007. (Illus.). 25p. (J). spiral bd. 15.00 net. ***(978-0-9797015-1-1(1))*** Augustana College Geology Dept. Pr.

Ratto, Linda Lee. Perfection. 2004. (YA). per. (978-0-9748508-3-2(7)) Power Pr.

Rau, Dana Meachen. Sweet Pea: Escape in the Garden. Hannon, Holly, illus. 2006. (J). ***(978-1-58987-200-4(2))*** Kindermusik International.

Raudenbush, Amy. Lucy More Needs Less. 2006. 48p. (J). pap. 13.99 (978-1-4116-6120-2(6)) Lulu.com.

Ravel, Edeet. The Mysterious Adventures of Pauline Bovary. 2007. 168p. (J). (gr. 5-10). pap. 9.95 ***(978-1-55192-986-6(4))*** Raincoast Bk. Distribution CAN. *Dist:* Perseus Distribution.

—The Thrilling Life of Pauline de Lammermoor. 2007. 168p. pap. 9.95 ***(978-1-55192-988-0(0))*** Raincoast Bk. Distribution CAN. *Dist:* Perseus Distribution.

Ravishankar, Anushka. The Fivetongued, Firefanged, Folkadotted Dragon Snake. Roy, Indrapramit & Ramanathan, Rathna, illus. 1999. 50p. (J). pap. (978-81-86211-26-7(8)) Tara Publishing.

Ray, Alvah & Arvilla. 1998. (J). pap. (978-0-15-201547-3(7)) Harcourt Children's Bks.

Rayburn, Tricia. The Melting of Maggie Bean. 2007. 256p. (J). (gr. 4-8). pap. 5.99 (978-1-4169-3348-9(4), Aladdin) Simon & Schuster Children's Publishing.

Raye, Donna. Edison the Firefly: And His Buddy Bell. 2007. (J). pap. 7.99 ***(978-1-60247-097-2(9))*** Tate Publishing & Enterprises, L.L.C.

Rea, Monique F. The Original Story of Toulouse the Moose & His Friends: Book & CD. 2007. (J). ***(978-0-9788926-2-3(3))*** Trails of Discovery.

Reader's Digest Children's Books, creator. Little Cricket & Friends 3 Volume Boxed Set. 2007. (Illus.). 36p. (J). (ps-k). bds., bds. 16.99 ***(978-0-7944-1359-0(5))*** Reader's Digest Assn., Inc., The.

—Little People Welcome to Our Town: A Look-Inside Book. 2007. (Fisher Price Lift the Flap Ser.). (Illus.). 20p. (J). (ps-k). bds. 9.99 ***(978-0-7944-1360-6(9))*** Reader's Digest Assn., Inc., The.

Reader's Digest Staff. Hola! Hello! Storybook & Talking Word Cards. 2006. (Nick Jr. Dora the Explorer Ser.). (Illus.). 40p. (J). pap. 24.99 (978-0-7944-0918-0(0)) Reader's Digest Assn., Inc., The.

RealBuzz Studios Staff. Come & Play: Goofyfoot Gurl Vol 3. 2007. 96p. (YA). pap. 4.97 ***(978-1-59789-575-0(X))*** Barbour Publishing, Inc.

—Out of the Soup. 2007. (Goofyfoot Gurl Ser.: No. 4). 96p. (YA). pap. 4.97 (978-1-59789-576-7(8)) Barbour Publishing, Inc.

—Saved / Esther Queen of Persia: Life Camera Action Book 3. 2007. 128p. (YA). pap. 4.97 (978-1-59789-579-8(2), Barbour Bks.) Barbour Publishing, Inc.

—Space Cadet vs Drama Queen Terror from the Tarantula Nebula: Life Camera Action Book 1. 2007. 128p. (YA). pap. 4.97 (978-1-59789-577-4(6), Barbour Bks.) Barbour Publishing, Inc.

—Sunday Best / Crawling from the Wreckage Life Camera Action BK 2: Life Camera Action Book 2. 2007. 128p. (YA). pap. 4.97 (978-1-59789-578-1(4), Barbour Bks.) Barbour Publishing, Inc.

—When Dolphins Fly. 2007. (Goofyfoot Gurl Ser.: No. 2). 96p. (YA). pap. 4.97 (978-1-59789-574-3(1), Barbour Bks.) Barbour Publishing, Inc.

Reber, Deborah. Magenta & Me. Bishop, Don, illus. 2000. (Blues Clue's Ready to Read Ser.: No. 2). 24p. (J). (ps-1). pap. 3.99 (978-0-689-83123-2(4), Simon Spotlight/Nickelodeon) Simon & Schuster Children's Publishing.

—Magenta & Me. 2000. (gr. k-3). lib. bdg. 11.80 (978-0-613-26094-7(5)) Tandem Library Bks.

Rechkemmer, Jaime Marie. Caillou's Friends in the Garden. Storch, Ellen N., illus. 2006. (J). pap. (978-1-57332-373-4(X)) HighReach Learning, Inc.

Recorvits, Helen. Where Heroes Hide. 2002. (Illus.). 144p. (J). (gr. 4-6). 16.00 (978-0-374-33057-6(3), Farrar, Straus & Giroux (BYR)) Farrar, Straus & Giroux.

—Yoon & the Jade Bracelet. Swiatkowska, Gabriela, illus. 2008. (J). (978-0-374-38689-4(7)) Farrar, Straus & Giroux.

Rector, Rebecca Kraft. Tria & the Great Star Rescue. 2003. (gr. 3-6). lib. bdg. 13.00 (978-0-613-86232-5(5)) Tandem Library Bks.

Redbank, Tennant. Which Way, Wendy? Thornburgh, Rebecca, illus. 2005. 32p. (J). lib. bdg. 20.00 ***(978-1-4242-1118-0(2))*** Fitzgerald Bks.

Redmond, Patrick. Something Dangerous. l.t. ed. 2000. (J). 26.95 (978-1-56895-832-3(3), Wheeler Publishing, Inc.) Thomson Gale.

Reed, Don C. The Kraken. Hunt, Judith, illus. 2003. 224p. (YA). (gr. 5-9). pap. 7.95 (978-1-56397-693-3(5)) Boyds Mills Pr.

Reed, Tom. Pookus & Buckie: A Children's Book Based on a True Story. Carter, Sandy Lewis, illus. l.t. ed. 2005. 36p. (J). per. 11.95 (978-0-9749725-4-1(1), 10000, Lonestar Abilene Publishing) LoneStar Abilene Publishing, LLC.

Rees, Douglas. Smoking Mirror. 2005. (Art Encounters Ser.). (Illus.). 176p. (YA). 15.95 (978-0-8230-4863-2(2)) Watson-Guptill Pubns., Inc.

Reetz, Kurt. Turtle Scott: A Friend in Need. 2000. mass mkt. 4.50 (978-1-931179-03-4(4)); mass mkt. 8.95 (978-1-931179-19-5(0)) Long Hill Productions, Inc.

Regan, Dana, illus. Messy Bessey & the Birthday Overnight. 2002. (Messy Bessey Ser.). (J). 12.83 (978-0-7587-7185-8(1)) Book Wholesalers, Inc.

Regan, Dian Curtis. Cyberpals According to Kaley. 2006. 128p. (J). (gr. 3-5). 15.95 (978-1-58196-051-8(4)) Darby Creek Publishing.

Rehfuss, Mary E. The Pottsville Chronicles: A New Beginning. 2005. 102p. (YA). per. 9.95 (978-1-933290-49-2(8)) Tate Publishing & Enterprises, L.L.C.

Reich, Alfred A. Stolen Friend: A Luke Larson Adventure. 2003. 180p. pap. 14.99 (978-1-57921-561-3(0)) Pleasant Word.

Reimer, Charlotte. Problems with Pies. 2006. 68p. (YA). pap. 10.00 (978-1-4116-7646-6(7)) Lulu.com.

Reisfeld, Randi. Starlet. 2007. 304p. (gr. 7 up). pap. 8.99 ***(978-1-4231-0501-5(X))*** Hyperion Pr.

Reiss-Weimann, Elayne. I'm Different. Yeagle, Dean, illus. 2002. (Read-To-Me Ser.). 25p. (J). (978-0-7665-1224-5(X)) Abrams, Harry N., Inc.

Reiss-Weimann, Elayne & Friedman, Rita. Real Friends. Yeagle, Barbara, illus. 2002. (Read-To-Me Ser.). 24p. (J). (978-0-7665-1218-4(5)) Abrams, Harry N., Inc.

Reisz, Kristopher. Tripping to Somewhere. 2006. 384p. (YA). pap. 6.99 (978-1-4169-4000-5(6), Simon Pulse) Simon & Schuster Children's Publishing.

Reitz, Ric. The Journey of Sir Douglas Fir: A Reader's Musical. Bell, Suzanne, ed. Brewer, David, illus. 1999. 48p. (J). (gr. 2-6). per. 19.95 (978-0-9670160-0-9(2), Sir Fir Bks. & Music) Sir Fir Enterprises, LLC.

Relf, Adam. Fox Makes Friends. 2005. (Illus.). 32p. (J). (ps). 14.95 (978-1-4027-2756-6(9)) Sterling Publishing Co., Inc.

Remick, M. Grace. Glenloch Girls. 2006. 25.99 ***(978-1-4280-1707-8(0))*** IndyPublish.com.

Remkiewicz, Frank, illus. Horrible Harry & the Green Slime. 2002. (Horrible Harry Ser.). (J). 11.49 (978-0-7587-0591-4(3)) Book Wholesalers, Inc.

—Horrible Harry & the Purple People. 2002. (Horrible Harry Ser.). (J). 11.49 (978-0-7587-0593-8(X)) Book Wholesalers, Inc.

Rempt, Fiona. Snail's Birthday Wish. Smit, Noelle, illus. 2007. 32p. (J). (ps-1). 14.95 ***(978-1-905417-52-0(7))*** Boxer Bks., Ltd. GBR. *Dist:* Sterling Publishing Co., Inc.

Rennison, Louise. Knocked Out by My Nunga-Nungas: Further, Further Confessions of Georgia Nicolson. 3rd ed. 2003. (Confessions of Georgia Nicolson Ser.). 208p. (YA). (gr. 5 up). pap. 7.99 (978-0-06-447362-0(7)) HarperCollins Pubs.

—On the Bright Side, I'm Now the Girlfriend of a Sex God: Further Confessions Of. 2002. (gr. 7-12). lib. bdg. 15.30 (978-0-613-49344-4(3)) Tandem Library Bks.

—On the Bright Side, I'm Now the Girlfriend of a Sex God: Further Confessions of Georgia Nicolson. (Confessions of Georgia Nicolson Ser.). 2003. 256p. (J). pap. 6.99 (978-0-06-052185-1(6)); 2002. 272p. (YA). pap. 7.99 (978-0-06-447226-5(4)); 2001. 256p. (J). (gr. 7 up). 17.99 (978-0-06-028813-6(2)) HarperCollins Pubs.

Rescue! 6 Packs. Pouch - Level L. (Lighthouse Ser.). 16p. (gr. 2 up). 28.00 (978-0-7578-0880-7(8)) Rigby Education.

Resnikoff, Irene & Valas, Claudia. OG in Jerusalem. 2003. (OG the Terrible Ser.: Vol. 3). (HEB., Illus.). 24p. (J). pap. 4.50 (978-0-939144-43-3(3)) EKS Publishing Co.

Reviejo, Carlos. La Jirafa Curiosa. 3rd ed. 2000. (Cuentos de Ahora Ser.).Tr. of Curious Giraffe. (SPA., Illus.). 32p. (J). 12.95 (978-84-348-5162-7(8)) SM Ediciones ESP. *Dist:* Distribooks, Inc.

Rex, Michael. Pals, Level 1. Rex, Michael, illus. 2003. (Word-by-Word First Reader Ser.). (Illus.). 32p. (J). pap. 3.99 (978-0-439-49310-9(2), Cartwheel Bks.) Scholastic, Inc.

Reyes, Raquel, et al. I Muy Bien! Very Good!, Level B. 2001. (SPA., Illus.). 126p. (gr. 1-3). spiral bd., tchr.'s training gde. ed. (978-0-9713381-2-8(4)) Double R Publishing, LLC.

Reynolds, Betty. Tokyo Friends. 2006. (Illus.). 64p. pap. 12.95 (978-0-8048-3808-5(9), PeriplusEdition) Tuttle Publishing.

Reynolds, Cynthia Furlong. Across the Reach. 2007. 144p. (J). 16.95 ***(978-1-58726-518-1(4)***, Mitten Pr.) Ann Arbor Media Group, LLC.

Reynolds, Marilyn. Love Rules. (True-to-Life Series from Hamilton High). 224p. (J). (gr. 8 up). 2003. 18.95 (978-1-885356-75-8(7)); 2001. pap. 9.95 (978-1-885356-76-5(5)) Morning Glory Pr., Inc.

Reynolds, Marilynn. A Present for Mrs. Kazinski. Smith-Ary, Lynn, illus. 2001. 32p. (J). (ps-2). 7.95 (978-1-55143-198-7(X)); 15.95 (978-1-55143-196-3(3)) Orca Bk. Pubs. USA.

Reynolds, Mignon C. Life as Bonkers. 2006. 137p. pap. 12.95 (978-1-4116-7357-1(3)) Lulu.com.

Rhodes, Tamika. Francis & His Barnyard Friends. 2005. (J). pap. 8.00 (978-0-8059-6752-4(4)) Dorrance Publishing Co., Inc.

Rhone, Alexus D. Secret Shame, 2003. 237p. (YA). pap. 12.95 (978-0-9708688-1-7(2)) Unshackled Publishing.

Rice, Cindy & Stolarski, Jerry. Mr. Mahaffy on Wisdom Pond: The Beginning. 2007. (ENG.). 84p. per. 14.95 ***(978-1-4241-3097-9(2))*** PublishAmerica, Inc.

Rice, Sheila. The Night Watchers. 2005. 88p. pap. 14.95 (978-1-4137-7663-8(9)) PublishAmerica, Inc.

Richards, Barbara. Barbie Com: Ballet Buddies. 2000. (gr. 3-6). lib. bdg. 11.80 (978-0-613-27723-5(6)) Tandem Library Bks.

Richards, J. Kirk. I'll Be There with Belzon. 2004. (Illus.). 32p. (J). per. 19.95 (978-0-9752553-0-8(4)) Bright-Brights Media Co., The.

Richardson, Delores. Can You Dig It? 2001. (J). 25.00 (978-0-9619482-0-7(5)) Little Spirit Publishing, Inc.

Richardson, Dorothea M. Moose Girl. 2002. 108p. (YA). pap. 16.95 (978-1-58851-797-5(7)) PublishAmerica, Inc.

Richardson, Kara. Simon & Barklee in France. 2000. (Another Country Calling Ser.: No. 1). (Illus.). 48p. (J). (gr. 2-5). per. 15.00 (978-0-9704661-0-5(2), Explorer Media) Simon & Barklee, Inc./ExplorerMedia.

Richemont, Enid. Jamie & the Whippersnapper. 2000. (Illus.). 64p. (J). pap. 6.99 (978-0-09-940098-1(7)) Random Hse. GBR. *Dist:* Independent Pubs. Group.

Riddle, A. Yogi & Me. 2006. 48p. pap. 12.95 (978-1-4241-0565-6(X)) PublishAmerica, Inc.

Riddleburger, Sam. The Qwikpick Adventure Society. 2007. (Illus.). 128p. (J). (gr. 4-6). 16.99 (978-0-8037-3178-3(7), Dial) Penguin Group (USA) Inc.

Ridings, Jim. Ashpile, No. 1. Ridings, Jim, illus. 1998. (Illus.). 142p. (YA). (gr. 6 up). pap. 7.95 (978-0-9664974-2-7(2), Side Show Comics) Ink & Feathers Comics.

Rigby Education Staff. Flying High. (Illus.). (J). suppl. ed. 20.00 (978-0-7635-6505-3(9), 765059C99) Rigby Education.

—Tom Sawyer: Jumbled Tumble. (gr. k-2). 26.00 (978-0-7635-2424-1(7)) Rigby Education.

Riggs, Jenna & Engleman-Berner, Beth. The Best Friends Keepsake Kit. Haley, Amanda, illus. 2005. 10p. (J). (ps-ps). bds. 9.95 (978-1-58117-416-8(0), Intervisual/Piggy Toes) Dalmatian Pr.

Riise, Torben. Emily & the Arabic Letter. 2001. 164p. (YA). pap. 11.95 (978-0-595-17399-0(3), Writers Club Pr.) iUniverse, Inc.

Rika, Tanaka. Kilala Princess. 20th rev. ed. 2007. (Illus.). pap. 5.99 ***(978-1-59816-768-9(5)***, Tokyopop Kids) TOKYOPOP, Inc.

Rinaldi, Ann. The Color of Fire. 2006. 208p. (gr. 5-17). pap. 5.99 (978-0-7868-1825-9(5), Jump at the Sun) Hyperion Bks. for Children.

—An Unlikely Friendship: A Novel of Mary Todd Lincoln & Elizabeth Keckley. 2007. (Harcourt Great Episodes Ser.). (Illus.). 256p. (YA). (gr. 6-9). 17.00 (978-0-15-205597-4(5)) Harcourt Children's Bks.

Riordan, Rick. The Lightning Thief. 2006. (Percy Jackson & the Olympians Ser.: Bk. 1). 392p. (gr. 5 up). reprint ed. pap. 7.99 (978-0-7868-3865-3(5)) Miramax Bks.

—The Sea of Monsters. 2nd rev. ed. 2007. (Percy Jackson & the Olympians Ser.: Bk. 2). 304p. (gr. 5 up). pap. 7.99 ***(978-1-4231-0334-9(3))*** Miramax Bks.

—The Sea of Monsters. l.t. ed. 2006. (Percy Jackson & the Olympians Ser.: Bk. 2). (YA). (gr. 5 up). 22.95 (978-0-7862-9074-1(9)) Thorndike Pr.

Rip Squeak & His Friends. 2003. Tr. of Rip Squeak y Sus Amigos. (J). 16.95 (978-0-9672422-4-8(X)) Rip Squeak, Inc.

Rip Squeak & His Friends Discover the Treasure. 2003. Tr. of Rip Squeak y Sus Amigos Descubren un Tesoro. per. 16.95 (978-0-9672422-5-5(8)) Rip Squeak, Inc.

Risk, Mary, et al. Puppy Finds a Friend: Cachorrito Encuentra a un Amigo. Bendall-Brunello, John, illus. 2000. (I Can Read Bks.). (SPA, ENG & FRE.). 28p. (J). (gr. k-2). 6.95 (978-0-7641-5283-2(1)) Barron's Educational Series, Inc.

Rispin, Karen. Sabrina the Schemer. 2002. 74p. pap. 6.99 (978-1-58586-793-6(4)) ereads.com.

Rissman, Angelica. Julius & the Lost Letter to Santa. 2003. (J). 7.99 (978-1-59384-019-8(5)) Parklane Publishing.

Ritchey, Kate. The Little Engine That Could & Friends: Coloring Book. Linda, Karl, illus. 2006. (Little Engine That Could Ser.). 32p. (J). (ps-2). act. bk. ed. 3.99 (978-0-448-43918-1(2), Grosset & Dunlap) Penguin Group (USA) Inc.

Ritchie, Alison. What Bear Likes Best! Kolanovic, Dubravka, illus. 2005. 28p. (J). 16.00 (978-1-56148-473-7(3)) Good Bks.

Ritchie, Harry. Last Pink Bits: Travels Through the Remnants of the British Empire. 1999. (Illus.). 231p. (J). pap. 13.99 (978-0-340-66683-8(8), Hodder & Stoughton) Hodder General Publishing Division GBR. *Dist:* Trafalgar Square Publishing.

Ritchie, Madonna, ed. & illus. The English Roses. Ritchie, Madonna, illus. Fulvimari, Jeffrey, illus. 2003. 48p. (J). 19.95 (978-0-670-03678-3(1)) Callaway Editions, Inc.

—The English Roses. Ritchie, Madonna, illus. ed. 2006. 48p. (J). (ps-6). 9.95 (978-0-670-06180-8(8)) Callaway Editions, Inc.

Ritter, John H. Choosing up Sides. 2000. 168p. (J). (gr. 5-9). pap. 5.99 (978-0-698-11840-9(5), Putnam Juvenile) Penguin Group (USA) Inc.

Ritter, Philip. Tales in Rhyme from Three Little Mischief Maker's Country Time: The Escapades of Three Little Mischief Makers. 2005. (J). pap. 10.00 (978-0-8059-6928-3(4)) Dorrance Publishing Co., Inc.

Rivers, Karen. The Healing Time of Hickeys. 2004. 304p. pap. 6.95 (978-1-55192-600-1(8)) Raincoast Bk. Distribution CAN. *Dist:* Perseus Distribution.

—The Quirky Girls' Guide to Rest Stops & Road Trips. 2007. 256p. (J). pap. 7.95 (978-1-55192-907-1(4), Polestar Book Pubs.) Raincoast Bk. Distribution CAN. *Dist:* Perseus Distribution.

Rizzo, Cynthia Marie. Julie & the Unicorn. 2003. 49p. pap. 9.95 (978-1-4137-0785-4(8)) PublishAmerica, Inc.

Roach, Hesta. The Friendship Thief. Dillingham, Charlene, illus. (J). (gr. k-5). pap. 9.99 (978-0-9660583-3-8(X)) Sakura Pr.

Robberecht, Thierry. Sam Tells Stories. Goossens, Philippe, illus. 2007. 32p. (J). (gr. k-3). 12.00 (978-0-618-73280-7(2), Clarion Bks.) Houghton Mifflin Co. Trade & Reference Div.

Robberecht, Thierry. Sam's New Friend. Goossens, Philippe, illus. 2008. 32p. (J). (ps-1). 12.00 ***(978-0-618-91448-7(X)***, Clarion Bks.) Houghton Mifflin Co. Trade & Reference Div.

Robbins, Jacqui. The New Girl ... & Me. Phelan, Matt, illus. 2006. 32p. (J). (ps-2). 16.95 (978-0-689-86468-1(X), Atheneum) Simon & Schuster Children's Publishing.

Robbins, Jacqui. Two of a Kind. Phelan, Matt, illus. 2008. (J). ***(978-1-4169-2437-1(X))*** Simon & Schuster Children's Publishing.

Roberts, Barbara A. Phoebe's Best Best Friend. Sternberg, Kate, illus. 2000. (Phoebe Flower's Adventures Ser.). 70p. (J). pap. 5.95 (978-0-9660366-9-5(7)) National Bk. Network.

Roberts, Brenda C. Jazzy Miz Mozetta. Morrison, Frank, illus. 2004. 32p. (J). 16.50 (978-0-374-33674-5(1)) Farrar, Straus & Giroux.

Roberts, Esyllt Nest & Owen, Carys Eurwen. Elidir A'r Tylwyth Teg. 2005. (WEL., Illus.). 35p. (978-0-86381-530-0(8)) Gwasg Carreg Gwalch.

Roberts, Ken. Thumb on a Diamond. Franson, Leanne, illus. 2006. 128p. (J). 15.95 (978-0-88899-629-9(2)) Groundwood Bks. CAN. *Dist:* Perseus Distribution.

Roberts, Laura Peyton. Ghost of a Chance. 2006. 208p. (YA). (gr. 7). mass mkt. 5.99 (978-0-553-49498-3(8), Laurel Leaf) Random Hse. Children's Bks.

—Ghost of a Chance. 1999. (J). (978-0-606-16448-1(0)) Tandem Library Bks.

—The Queen of Second Place. 336p. (YA). (gr. 7). 2006. pap. 5.99 (978-0-440-23871-3(4), Laurel Leaf); 2005. 15.95 (978-0-385-73162-1(0), Delacorte Bks. for Young Readers) Random Hse. Children's Bks.

Roberts, Rachel. All That Glitters. 2007. (Avalon Ser.: Bk. 2). 175p. (J). (gr. 3-7). 9.99 ***(978-1-933164-65-6(4))*** Seven Seas Entertainment, LLC.

Roberts, Rachel. The Secret of the Unicorn. 2003. (Avalon Ser.: Bk. 4). 187p. (YA). (gr. 3-7). pap. 4.99 (978-1-59315-006-8(7)) Perseus Bks. Group.

—The Secret of the Unicorn. 2002. (Avalon Ser.: Bk. 4). (J). (gr. 3-6). lib. bdg. 13.00 (978-0-613-50572-7(7)) Tandem Library Bks.

Roberts, Scott. Patty Cake & Friends. 2006. 96p. pap. 12.95 (978-1-59362-030-1(6)) Slave Labor Bks.

Roberts, Trina. The Lonley Little Birch. 2005. 9.00 (978-0-8059-8053-0(9)) Dorrance Publishing Co., Inc.

Robertson, Elysia Hill. Toley's Sleep over Learning Party. Robertson, Elysia Hill, illus. 2005. (Illus.). 118p. (J). per. 12.95 (978-0-9764444-4-2(5), EJWV-005) E. J. Publishing.

Robertson, Mark. Big Brave Brian. 2007. (Illus.). 32p. (J). (ps-2). 16.95 ***(978-1-84507-559-0(5))*** Lincoln, Frances Ltd. GBR. *Dist:* Perseus Distribution.

Robey, M. Ye Olde Witch Club in the Order of the C. 2005. 226p. pap. 19.95 (978-1-4137-6627-1(7)) PublishAmerica, Inc.

Robins, Eleanor. The Easy Way. 2003. (Illus.). 48p. (YA). per. (978-1-56254-683-0(X), SP683X) Saddleback Educational Publishing.

Robinson, Sharon. Safe at Home. 160p. (J). 2007. (gr. 4-7). pap. 4.99 ***(978-0-439-67198-9(1)***, Scholastic Paperbacks); 2006. pap. 16.99 (978-0-439-67197-2(3), Scholastic) Scholastic, Inc.

—Slam Dunk! 2007. 160p. (J). (gr. 4-7). pap. 16.99 ***(978-0-439-67199-6(X)***, Scholastic Pr.) Scholastic, Inc.

Rocheleau, Nicole. Ollie Ollie in Come Free! 2006. 76p. pap. 14.95 (978-1-4241-0433-8(5)) PublishAmerica, Inc.

Rochman, Hazel & McCampbell, Darlene Z., eds. Who do you Think you Are? 2005. 176p. (YA). 23.00 (978-0-8446-7269-4(6), 3585) Smith, Peter Pub., Inc.

Rocklin, Joanne. For Your Eyes Only! 2001. (J). 10.64 (978-0-606-20492-7(X)) Tandem Library Bks.

Rocks!, Misako. Rock & Roll Love. Rocks!, Misako, illus. 2007. 112p. (YA). (gr. 6-9). pap. 7.99 ***(978-0-7868-3685-7(7))*** Hyperion Pr.

Rodda, Emily. Dead End. 2006. (Emily Rodda's Raven Hill Mysteries Ser.: Vol. 6). (Illus.). 128p. (J). pap. 4.99 (978-0-439-79572-2(9), Scholastic Paperbacks) Scholastic, Inc.

Roddie, Shen. Best of Friends! Lamb, Sally Ann, illus. 2004. 25p. (J). pap. 7.95 (978-1-84507-172-1(7)) Lincoln, Frances Ltd. GBR. *Dist:* Perseus Distribution.

E
F
G

Roddie, Shen, et al. Best of Friends! Lambert, Sally Anne, illus. 32p. (J). pap. (978-0-7112-1226-8(0)) Lincoln, Frances Ltd. GBR. *Dist:* Transition Vendor.

Rodgers, Frank. Eyetooth. l.t. ed. 2006. pap. 16.95 (978-1-4056-6041-9(4)) BBC Audio GBR. *Dist:* BBC Audiobooks America.

Rodman, Mary Ann. My Best Friend. Lewis, Earl, illus. 2005. 32p. (J). 15.99 (978-0-670-05989-8(7) , Viking Juvenile) Penguin Group (USA) Inc.

—My Best Friend. Lewis, E.B., illus. 2007. 32p. (J). (gr. k). pap. 5.99 (978-0-14-240806-3(9) , Puffin) Penguin Group (USA) Inc.

—Yankee Girl. 2004. (Illus.). 224p. (J). 17.00 (978-0-374-38661-0(7) , Farrar, Straus & Giroux (BYR)) Farrar, Straus & Giroux.

Rogers, Gregory. The Boy, the Bear, the Baron, the Bard. Rogers, Gregory, illus. rev. ed. 2004. (Illus.). 32p. (J). 16.95 (978-1-59643-009-9(5)) Roaring Brook Pr.

Rogers, Karen M. Max & Me. 1998. (Think-Kids Book Collection). (Illus.). 16p. (J). (gr. 1-4). pap. 2.95 (978-1-58237-013-2(3)) Creative Thinkers, Inc.

—Yipes! Stripes! Vasquez, Perry, illus. 1998. (Think-Kids Book Collection). 16p. (J). (gr. 1-4). pap. 2.95 (978-1-58237-002-6(8)) Creative Thinkers, Inc.

Rohmann, Eric. My Friend Rabbit. Rohmann, Eric, illus. rev. ed. 2002. (Illus.). 32p. (J). (ps-3). 16.95 (978-0-7613-1535-3(7)) Roaring Brook Pr.

—My Friend Rabbit. Rohmann, Eric, illus. 2007. (Illus.). 32p. (J). pap. 6.95 (*978-0-312-36752-7(X)) Square Fish.

Romanelli, Serena. Little Bobo. 1999. (gr. k-3). lib. bdg. 15.25 (978-0-613-73589-6(7)); (J). (978-0-606-16194-7(5)) Tandem Library Bks.

Romano, Christy. Grace's Turn. 2006. 272p. (gr. 4-7). 15.99 (978-0-7868-4884-3(7)) Hyperion Pr.

Romanova, Yelena. The Perfect Friend. Kulikov, Boris, illus. 2005. 32p. (J). (ps-1). 15.00 (978-0-374-35821-1(4) , Frances Foster Bks.) Farrar, Straus & Giroux.

Romeu, Emma. Gregorio Vuelve a Mexico. 2003. (SPA., Illus.). 148p. (J). (gr. 5-8). pap. 12.95 (978-968-19-0367-1(6)) Santillana USA Publishing Co., Inc.

—Gregorio Vuelve a Mexico. 2000. (SPA.). (gr. 5-8). lib. bdg. 18.75 (978-0-613-82709-6(0)) Tandem Library Bks.

Romulo, Liana. Filipino Friends. Dandan-Albano, Corazon, illus. 2007. 32p. (J). 15.95 (978-0-8048-3822-1(4)) Tuttle Publishing.

Roop, Peter & Roop, Connie. Keep the Lights Burning, Abbie. 2005. (On My Own History Ser.). (Illus.). (J). pap. 18.95 incl. audio compact disk (978-1-59112-666-9(5)) Live Oak Media.

The Rootfriends. 2004. (J). mass mkt. (978-0-9749170-0-9(1)) Dazsling Inc.

Rose, Fredricka Dudley. Quincy: The Boy Who No One Understands. 2003. pap. 7.95 (978-0-533-14345-0(4)) Vantage Pr., Inc.

Rose, Marie. Princess Silver Tears & One Feather. l.t. ed. 2006. (Illus.). 32p. (J). lib. bdg. (*978-1-934190-07-4(1)) Ocean Front Bk. Publishing, Inc.

Rose, Sherrie. A Girl, A Guy & A Ghost. 2003. (YA). mass mkt. 5.99 (978-0-8439-5276-6(8)) Dorchester Publishing Co., Inc.

Rosen, Michael. Bear's Day Out. Reynolds, Adrian, illus. 2007. 32p. (J). (ps-3). 16.95 (*978-1-59990-007-0(6)) Bloomsbury Publishing.

Rosenberry, Vera. Vera's New School. rev. ed. 2006. (Illus.). 32p. (J). 16.95 (978-0-8050-7613-4(1) , Holt, Henry & Co. Bks. For Young Readers) Holt, Henry & Co.

Rosenbloom, Fiona. We Are So Crashing Your Bar Mitzvah! 2007. 224p. (gr. 5 up). 15.99 (*978-0-7868-3890-5(6)) Hyperion Pr.

—You Are So Not Invited to My Bat Mitzvah! 208p. (gr. 7 up). 2007. pap. 8.99 (*978-0-7868-3891-2(4)); 2005. 15.99 (978-0-7868-5616-9(5)) Hyperion Pr.

Rosenbluth, Roz. Getting to Know Ruben Plotnick. Manning, Maurie J., illus. 2005. 32p. (J). 15.95 (978-0-9729225-5-5(5)) Flashlight Pr.

Rosie & Roger. 2002. (Illus.). 32p. (J). 16.95 (978-1-931290-09-8(1)) Tallfellow Pr.

Rosoff, Meg. Jumpy Jack & Googily. Blackall, Sophie, illus. 2008. 32p. (J). 16.95 (*978-0-8050-8066-7(X)) Holt, Henry & Co.

Ross, Andrea. To Touch the Sun. Davenport, May, ed. l.t. ed. 2000. 195p. (YA). (gr. 9-12). pap. 15.95 (978-0-943864-99-0(2)) Davenport, May Pubs.

Ross, Katharine. Sweetie & Petie. McCue, Lisa, illus. 1999. (Jellybean Bks.). 24p. (J). (ps-k). lib. bdg. 7.99 (978-0-375-90143-0(4) , Random Hse. Bks. for Young Readers) Random Hse. Children's Bks.

Ross, Pat. Meet M & M. unabr. ed. 1999. (J). (gr. 2 up). pap., stu. ed. 22.24 incl. audio (978-0-7887-3178-5(5) , 40913X4) Recorded Bks., LLC.

Rosselson, Leon. Tom the Whistling Wonder. Haslam, John, illus. 2005. 24p. (J). lib. bdg. 22.65 (*978-1-59646-758-3(4)) Dingles & Co.

Rossi, Rich, illus. Pillow Fight. 2005. (I'm Going to Read Ser.). 32p. (J). (gr. k-1). pap. 3.95 (978-1-4027-2719-1(4)) Sterling Publishing Co., Inc.

Roth, Carol. Little Bunny's Sleepless Night. Gorbachev, Valeri, illus. 1999. 32p. (J). (ps-2). 15.95 (978-0-7358-1069-3(9)) North-South Bks., Inc.

Roth, Julie Jersild. Knitting Nell. 2006. (Illus.). 32p. (J). (gr. k-3). 16.00 (978-0-618-54033-4(4)) Houghton Mifflin Co.

Rowe, John A. I Want a Hug. 2007. (Illus.). 32p. (J). (ps-3). 16.99 (*978-0-698-40064-1(X) , Minedition) Penguin Group (USA) Inc.

Rowles, Louis. Ida Claire Decorates with Flair. Brownlee, Sunny, illus. 2004. 24p. (J). pap. (978-0-9708748-1-8(2)) Rowles, Louis.

Rubel, William. The Stone Soup Book of Friendship Stories. 2004. (Illus.). 128p. (gr. 3-8). pap., tchr. ed. 8.95 (978-1-883672-76-8(7) , Tricycle Pr.) Ten Speed Pr.

Rubin, Bruce Joel & Michaels, Julie. Stuart Little 2 Vol. 2: El Libro de la Pelicula. 2003. (SPA., Illus.). 60p. (J). (gr. 3-5). 14.95 (978-84-204-6503-6(8)) Santillana USA Publishing Co., Inc.

Ruckdeschel, Liz & James, Sara. What If ... Everyone Knew Your Name. 2006. 352p. (YA). (gr. 7). pap. 8.95 (978-0-385-73296-3(1)); lib. bdg. 10.99 (978-0-385-90317-2(0)) Random Hse. Children's Bks. (Delacorte Bks. for Young Readers).

Rucker, Mike. Terry & the Earthquake. 2006. (Terry the Tractor Ser.: Vol. 14). 72p. (J). (gr. k-4). pap. 4.95 (978-0-9711659-5-3(5)) Univ. Editions.

Ruckman, Ivy. In Care of Cassie Tucker. 2000. (978-0-606-17893-8(7)) Tandem Library Bks.

Rud, Jeff. High & Inside. 2006. 176p. (gr. 3-7). pap. 7.95 (978-1-55143-532-9(2)) Orca Bk. Pubs. USA.

Rudisill, J. J., et al, illus. LouLou's Lemonade Stand. 1999. (Wimzie's House Bks.). 24p. (J). pap. 3.99 (978-0-88724-541-1(2) , CD-4847) Carson-Dellosa Publishing Co., Inc.

Ruditis, Paul. Ready to Glow. Choi Sung Hwan, Aragon Noel, illus. 2005. (Trollz Ser.). 80p. (J). (gr. 2-5). pap. 5.99 (978-0-439-73386-1(3)) Scholastic, Inc.

Rue, Nancy. Sophie Tracks a Thief, Vol. 8. 2005. (Faithgirlz Ser.). (Illus.). 144p. (J). pap. 6.99 (978-0-310-71023-3(5)) Zonderkidz.

Rue, Nancy N. Sophie & the Scoundrels, Bk. 3. Chen, Grace, illus. 2005. (Faithgirlz Ser.). 128p. (J). pap. 6.99 (978-0-310-70758-5(7)) Zonderkidz.

Rundstrom, T. S. Baribold Jones & Big Big Booger Grabber. 2004. (Illus.). per. (978-1-932062-43-4(2)) Hability Solution Services, Inc.

Runholt, Susan. The Mystery of the Third Lucretia. 2008. (J). (gr. 6). 16.99 (*978-0-670-06252-2(9) , Viking Juvenile) Penguin Group (USA) Inc.

Running Press Staff & Deere, John. JT's New Friend. 2007. (Illus.). 12p. (J). pap. 9.95 (*978-0-7624-3140-3(7) , Running Pr. Kids) Running Pr. Bk. Pubs.

Runton, Andy. Owly Volume 4. 2007. (Illus.). 120p. pap. 10.00 (*978-1-891830-89-1(9)) Top Shelf Productions.

Rushby, Pamela. Footsteps. 2000. (gr. 7-12). lib. bdg. 12.25 (978-0-613-28844-6(0)) Tandem Library Bks.

—Midnight Children. 2000. (gr. 7-12). lib. bdg. 12.25 (978-0-613-28957-3(9)) Tandem Library Bks.

—Shadows in the Garden. 2000. (gr. 7-12). lib. bdg. 12.25 (978-0-613-29063-0(1)) Tandem Library Bks.

Rushford, Betty. Best Buddies: And the Fruit of the Spirit. 2003. 41p. pap. 16.95 (978-1-59286-746-2(4)) PublishAmerica, Inc.

Rushford, Patricia H. Secrets of Ghost Island. 2007. (J). (*978-88-02-46255-4(0)) Moody Pubs.

Rushton, Rosie. Friends, Enemies. 2004. 240p. (gr. 5-17). 15.99 (978-0-7868-5177-5(5)) Hyperion Paperbacks for Children.

—Friends, Enemies. 2006. 240p. (gr. 5-17). pap. 5.99 (978-0-7868-5178-2(3)) Hyperion Pr.

—What a Week to Make a Stand. 128p. (J). 7.95 (978-0-14-130225-6(9)) Penguin Bks., Ltd. GBR. *Dist:* Trafalgar Square Publishing.

Rutledge, Margie. The Busybody Buddha. Cowan, Maxine, illus. 2004. 168p. (J). (gr. 4-7). pap. 8.95 (978-0-929141-91-6(1)) Napoleon Publishing/Rendezvous Pr. CAN. *Dist:* AtlasBooks Distribution.

Ruzzier, Sergio. The Little Giant. 2004. (Illus.). 32p. (J). (ps-2). 16.89 (978-0-06-052952-9(0) , Geringer, Laura Book) HarperCollins Pubs.

Ryan, Darlene. Responsible. 2007. (Orca Soundings Ser.). 112p. (YA). (gr. 7 up). pap. (*978-1-55143-685-2(X)); lib. bdg. (*978-1-55143-687-6(6)) Orca Bk. Pubs.

Ryan, Margaret. Littlest Dragon. 2002. (Roaring Good Reads Ser.). (Illus.). 64p. (J). pap. 7.99 (978-0-00-714163-0(7)) HarperCollins Pubs. Ltd. GBR. *Dist:* Independent Pubs. Group.

Ryan, Pam Muñoz. A Box of Friends. 2003. (Illus.). 32p. (J). 14.95 (978-1-57768-420-6(6) , Gingham Dog Pr.) School Specialty Publishing.

Ryan, Patrick. Saints of Augustine. 2007. 320p. (J). lib. bdg. 17.89 (*978-0-06-085811-7(7)); (gr. 7 up). 16.99 (*978-0-06-085810-0(9)) HarperCollins Pubs. (HarperTeen).

Ryder, Joanne. Won't You Be My Kissaroo? Sweet, Melissa, illus. 2004. 32p. (J). 16.00 (978-0-15-202641-7(X) , Gulliver Bks.) Harcourt Children's Bks.

Rylant, Cynthia. Annie & Snowball & the Prettiest House: The Second Book of Their Adventures. Stevenson, Sucie, illus. 2007. (Annie & Snowball Ser.). 40p. (J). (gr. k-2). 15.99 (*978-1-4169-0939-2(7) , Simon & Schuster Children's Publishing) Simon & Schuster Children's Publishing.

—Boris. 2005. (Illus.). 80p. (YA). 16.00 (978-0-15-205412-0(X)) Harcourt Children's Bks.

—A Fine White Dust. 2006. 112p. (J). pap. 4.99 (978-1-4169-2769-3(7) , Aladdin); 2000. (Illus.). (YA). (gr. 5-9). 25.00 (978-0-689-84087-6(X) , Atheneum/Richard Jackson Bks.) Simon & Schuster Children's Publishing.

—Henry y Mudge: El Primer Libro de Sus Aventuras. Stevenson, Sucie, illus. 1999. (Henry & Mudge Ser.). (SPA.). (J). (gr. k-3). 13.00 (978-0-689-80685-8(X) , Atheneum) Simon & Schuster Children's Publishing.

—The High-Rise Private Eyes Series. Karas, G. Brian, illus. 2003. pap. 61.95 incl. audio (978-1-59112-430-6(1)); pap. 68.95 incl. audio compact disk (978-1-59112-858-8(7)) Live Oak Media.

—Poppleton. Teague, Mark, illus. 2002. (Poppleton Ser.). (J). 11.91 (978-0-7587-1590-6(0)) Book Wholesalers, Inc.

—Poppleton & Friends. Teague, Mark, illus. 1998. (Poppleton Ser.). 56p. (J). (gr. k-3). pap. 3.99 (978-0-590-84788-9(0) , Blue Sky Pr., The) Scholastic, Inc.

—Poppleton & Friends. 1998. (Poppleton Ser.). (J). (gr. k-3). (978-0-606-13716-4(5)) Tandem Library Bks.

—Poppleton Forever. Teague, Mark, illus. 2002. (Poppleton Ser.). (J). 11.91 (978-0-7587-1587-6(0)) Book Wholesalers, Inc.

—Poppleton Forever. Teague, Mark, illus. 1998. (Poppleton Ser.). 56p. (J). (gr. k-3). pap. 14.95 (978-0-590-84843-5(7) , Blue Sky Pr., The); pap. 3.99 (978-0-590-84844-2(5)) Scholastic, Inc.

—Poppleton Forever. 1998. (Poppleton Ser.). (J). (gr. k-3). (978-0-606-13718-8(1)) Tandem Library Bks.

—Poppleton Forever. Teague, Mark, illus. 1998. (Poppleton Ser.). 48p. (J). (ps). lib. bdg. 11.80 (978-0-613-11990-0(8)) Tandem Library Bks.

—Poppleton Has Fun. Teague, Mark, illus. 2002. (Poppleton Ser.). (J). 11.91 (978-0-7587-6242-9(9)) Book Wholesalers, Inc.

—Poppleton Has Fun. Teague, Mark, illus. 2000. (Poppleton Ser.). 56p. (J). (gr. k-3). pap. 15.95 (978-0-590-84839-8(9)) Scholastic, Inc.

—Poppleton in Fall. Teague, Mark, illus. 2002. (Poppleton Ser.). (J). 11.91 (978-0-7587-1588-3(9)) Book Wholesalers, Inc.

—Poppleton in Fall. Teague, Mark, illus. 1999. (Poppleton Ser.). 56p. (J). (gr. k-3). pap. 14.95 (978-0-590-84789-6(9) , Blue Sky Pr., The) Scholastic, Inc.

—Poppleton in Fall. 1999. (Poppleton Ser.). (J). (gr. k-3). (978-0-606-17273-8(4)) Tandem Library Bks.

—Poppleton in Winter. Teague, Mark, illus. 2002. (Poppleton Ser.). (J). 11.91 (978-0-7587-6873-5(7)) Book Wholesalers, Inc.

—Poppleton in Winter. Teague, Mark, illus. 2001. (Poppleton Ser.). 58p. (J). (ps-2). pap. 15.95 (978-0-590-84837-4(2) , Blue Sky Pr., The) Scholastic, Inc.

—Puppy Mudge Finds a Friend. Stevenson, Sucie, illus. 2005. (Puppy Mudge Ser.). (J). (ps-k). 32p. pap. 3.99 (978-1-4169-0369-7(0)); (*978-1-4156-3675-6(3)) Simon & Schuster Children's Publishing. (Aladdin).

—Thimbleberry Stories. Kneen, Maggie, illus. 2006. 64p. (J). reprint ed. pap. 7.00 (978-0-15-205645-2(9) , Harcourt Paperbacks) Harcourt Children's Bks.

Sachar, Louis. Buchi nel Deserto. (ITA.). pap. 16.95 (978-88-384-3651-2(7)) Piemme ITA. *Dist:* Distribooks, Inc.

—Buracos. pap. 29.95 (978-85-336-1280-8(X)) Livraria Martins Editora BRA. *Dist:* Distribooks, Inc.

—Holes. 1998. 240p. (J). (gr. 4-7). 17.00 (978-0-374-33265-5(7) , Farrar, Straus & Giroux (BYR)) Farrar, Straus & Giroux.

—Holes. 240p. (J). (gr. 4-6). pap. 5.99 (978-0-8072-8073-7(9) , Listening Library) Random Hse. Audio Publishing Group.

—Holes. 2000. (Newbery Ser.). (Illus.). 240p. (J). (gr. 5-6). reprint ed. pap. 6.50 (978-0-440-41480-3(6) , Yearling) Random Hse. Children's Bks.

—Holes. l.t. ed. 2003. 288p. pap. 10.95 (978-0-7862-6190-1(0)) Thorndike Pr.

—A Magic Crystal? Loehr, Mallory, ed. Wummer, Amy, illus. 2000. (Marvin Redpost Ser.: No. 8). 96p. (J). (gr. k-3). 3.99 (978-0-679-89002-7(5) , Random Hse. Bks. for Young Readers) Random Hse. Children's Bks.

—A Magic Crystal? 2000. (Marvin Redpost Ser.: Bk. 8). (gr. 3-6). lib. bdg. 11.80 (978-0-613-28343-4(0)) Tandem Library Bks.

—Le Passage. pap. 22.95 (978-2-211-05287-0(8)) Archimede Editions FRA. *Dist:* Distribooks, Inc.

Sachs, Marilyn. Amy Moves In. 2001. 212p. (YA). (gr. 4-7). pap. 14.95 (978-0-595-17589-5(9) , Backinprint.com) iUniverse, Inc.

—Jojo & Winnie: Sister Stories. 2001. (Illus.). (J). (978-0-606-21271-7(X)) Tandem Library Bks.

—Laura's Luck. 2001. 224p. (gr. 4-7). pap. 15.95 (978-0-595-17590-1(2) , Backinprint.com) iUniverse, Inc.

The Sacrament Series. 2005. (J). (978-0-9772007-0-2(1)) Layne Morgan Media, Inc.

Sadler, Marilyn. Honey Bunny's Honey Bear. Bollen, Roger, illus. 2008. (Step into Reading Ser.). (J). (978-0-375-84326-6(4)); lib. bdg. 11.99 (978-0-375-94326-3(9)) Random Hse. Children's Bks.

Sage, Michael. One Good Friend. 2nd ed. 1999. iv, 126p. (YA). (gr. 7-12). reprint ed. pap. 10.00 (978-0-9669813-0-8(8)) Sage, Joan.

Said, S. F. The Outlaw Varjak Paw. McKean, Dave, illus. 2007. 272p. (J). (gr. 3-7). 6.50 (978-0-440-42172-6(1) , Yearling) Random Hse. Children's Bks.

Sakai, Komako. Emily's Balloon. 2006. (Illus.). 44p. (J). 14.95 (978-0-8118-5219-7(9)) Chronicle Bks. LLC.

Salas, Macarena, ed. Baby Donald Makes A Snowfriend/beb Donald Hace un Amigo de Nieve: A Book about Shapes/Un Libro Sobre Las Formas. 2005. (SPA.). 10p. (J). bds. 3.99 (978-0-439-66362-5(8) , Scholastic en Espanol) Scholastic, Inc.

—Baby Mickey Finds a Friend/Bebé Mickey Encuentra un Amigo: A Book about Action Words/Un Libro Sobre Palabras de Accion. 2005. (Disney Bil Ser.). (SPA & ENG., Illus.). 10p. (J). bds. 3.99 (978-0-439-66363-2(6) , Scholastic en Espanol) Scholastic, Inc.

Saldana, Rene. The Whole Sky Full of Stars. 2007. 144p. (gr. 7-11). (J). lib. bdg. 18.99 (978-0-385-90078-2(3)); (YA). 15.99 (978-0-385-73053-2(5)) Random Hse. Children's Bks. (Lamb, Wendy).

Salerno, Tony. Dog Tired: A Learning Adventure in Perseverance, 4 vols. 2005. 56p. (J). 14.99 (978-0-89221-605-5(0)) New Leaf Pr., Inc.

—A Sticky Situation: A Learning Adventure in Honesty. 2005. 56p. (J). 14.99 (978-0-89221-606-2(9)) New Leaf Pr., Inc.

—Wise Quacks: A Learning Adventure in Self-Control, 4 vols. 2005. 56p. (J). 14.99 (978-0-89221-604-8(2)) New Leaf Pr., Inc.

Salisbury, Graham. Shark Bait. 1999. (978-0-606-16449-8(9)) Tandem Library Bks.

Salisbury, Linda G. The Mysterious Jamestown Suitcase: A Bailey Fish Adventure. Grotke, Christopher, illus. 2007. 192p. (J). per. 8.95 (978-1-881539-43-8(1)) Tabby Hse. Bks.

—The Thief at Keswick Inn: A Bailey Fish Adventure. 2005. (Illus.). 192p. (J). per. 8.95 (978-1-881539-41-4(5)) Tabby Hse. Bks.

Salmansohn, Karen. Girl Wonders. 2007. 128p. (J). 6.95 (*978-1-58246-162-5(7) , Tricycle Pr.) Ten Speed Pr.

Salmansohn, Karen. One Puppy, Three Tales Bk. 1: Alexandra Rambles On! 2004. (Alexandra Rambles on! Ser.: Bk. 1). (Illus.). 70p. (J). (gr. 4-6). 12.95 (978-1-58246-044-4(2) , Tricycle Pr.) Ten Speed Pr.

Salmansohn, Karen, et al. Crashed, Smashed, & Mashed: A Trip to Junkyard Heaven. 2004. (Alexandra Rambles on! Ser.). (Illus.). 32p. (J). (gr. 3-6). 14.95 (978-1-58246-034-5(5) , Tricycle Pr.) Ten Speed Pr.

Saltzberg, Barney. Hi, Blueberry! 2007. (Illus.). 14p. (J). bds. 8.95 (978-0-15-205984-2(9) , Red Wagon Bks.) Harcourt Children's Bks.

Salyers, Rita. Wood's New Collar. Stafford, Rosalee, illus. 2006. (J). per. 11.95 (978-0-9760129-3-1(6)) Avant Garde Publishing.

Sam Finds a Friend: Social/Emotional Lap Book. (Pebble Soup Explorations Ser.). (ps up). 16.00 (978-0-7635-7564-9(X)) Rigby Education.

Sam tiene una Amiga: Social/Emotional Lap Book. (Pebble Soup Exploraciones Ser.). (SPA.). (ps up). 16.00 (978-0-7578-1785-4(8)) Rigby Education.

Samarasinghe, Sara. Dalaina. 2006. 24.99 (*978-1-4259-6502-0(4)); pap. 17.99 (*978-1-4259-6501-3(6)) AuthorHouse.

Samarrippas, Gloria. In Search for Lucky's Lost Toys. 2006. 17.00 (*978-0-8059-7329-7(X)) Dorrance Publishing Co., Inc.

Samuels, Vallerie. The Village of Time. 2005. 9.00 (978-0-8059-9709-5(1)) Dorrance Publishing Co., Inc.

San Souci, Robert D. Faithful Friend. 1999. (gr. 3-6). lib. bdg. 15.30 (978-0-613-11526-1(0)) Tandem Library Bks.

San Souci, Robert D. & San Souci, Robert D. The Faithful Friend. Pinkney, Brian, illus. 2005. (Stories to Go! Ser.). 40p. (J). 4.99 (978-1-4169-1234-7(1) , Aladdin) Simon & Schuster Children's Publishing.

Sanchez, Alex. Getting It. 2006. 224p. (YA). 16.95 (978-1-4169-0896-8(X)) Simon & Schuster Children's Publishing.

Sanchez, Alex. The God Box. 2007. 272p. (YA). (gr. 7 up). 16.99 (*978-1-4169-0899-9(4) , Simon & Schuster Children's Publishing) Simon & Schuster Children's Publishing.

Sanchez, Alex & Frost, Michael. Getting It. 2007. 240p. (YA). pap. 8.99 (*978-1-4169-0898-2(6) , Simon Pulse) Simon & Schuster Children's Publishing.

Sanchez, Elaine K. & Hughes, Janee. How Francis Got His Wink. 2000. (Illus.). 40p. (J). 14.95 (978-0-89802-737-2(3)) Beautiful America Publishing Co.

Sanchez, Gloria. Chinto y Tom. (SPA.). 80p. (J). (978-84-348-8101-3(2)) SM Ediciones ESP. *Dist:* Lectorum Pubns., Inc.

Sander, Sonia. Meet Blueberry Muffin. S. I. Artists Staff, illus. 2004. (Strawberry Shortcake Ser.). 32p. (J). (ps-2). pap. 3.99 (978-0-448-43570-1(5) , Grosset & Dunlap) Penguin Group (USA) Inc.

—Strawberry Shortcake's Seaberry Mystery. Yee, Josie & Durk, Jim, illus. 2005. (Strawberry Shortcake Ser.). 32p. (J). (ps-2). mass mkt. 3.99 (978-0-448-43639-5(6) , Grosset & Dunlap) Penguin Group (USA) Inc.

—Tattle Tale. 2002. (Rainbow Fish Ser.). 32p. (J). (ps-2). pap. 3.99 (978-0-694-52587-4(1) , Harper Festival) HarperCollins Pubs.

Sanders, Nancy I. & Osborne, Susan Titus. The Super-Duper Seed Surprise. 2000. (Parables in Action Ser.: Vol. 6). (Illus.). 48p. (J). (ps-2). 4.99 (978-0-570-07113-6(5)) Concordia Publishing Hse.

Sandoval, Lynda. Chicks Ahoy. 2006. 224p. (YA). pap. 7.99 (978-0-689-86441-4(8) , Simon Pulse) Simon & Schuster Children's Publishing.

—Who's Your Daddy? 2004. 320p. (YA). pap. 6.99 (978-0-689-86440-7(X) , Simon Pulse) Simon & Schuster Children's Publishing.

—Who's Your Daddy? 2004. 318p. (YA). (gr. 7). lib. bdg. 15.60 (978-1-4176-4527-5(X)) Tandem Library Bks.

Sanschagrin, Joceline. Le Cercle des Magiciens. Pratt, Pierre, illus. 2002. (Roman Jeunesse Ser.). (FRE.). 96p. (YA). (gr. 4-7). pap. (978-2-89021-334-0(X)) Diffusion du livre Mirabel.

Santiesteban, Eugenia. Maya & Miguel: Big Ideas. 2005. (Maya & Miguel Ser.). (Illus.). 64p. (J). 5.99 (978-0-439-69613-5(5)) Scholastic, Inc.

Santillo, LuAnn. The Dog. Santillo, LuAnn, ed. 2003. (Half-Pint Kids Readers Ser.). (Illus.). 7p. (J). (ps-1). pap. (978-1-59256-065-3(2)) Half-Pint Kids, Inc.

—The Wet Dock. Santillo, LuAnn, ed. 2003. (Half-Pint Kids Readers Ser.). (Illus.). 7p. (J). (ps-1). pap. (978-1-59256-089-9(X)) Half-Pint Kids, Inc.

Santomero, Angela C. Super Chubby 2 Blues Felt Friends. Johnson, Traci Paige, illus. 1998. (Blue's Clues Ser.). 20p. (J). (ps-k). bds. 4.99 (978-0-689-81910-0(2) , Simon Spotlight/Nickelodeon) Simon & Schuster Children's Publishing.

—What to Do, Blue? 1999. (gr. k-3). lib. bdg. 11.25 (978-0-613-16035-3(5)) Tandem Library Bks.

Santomero, Angela C., et al. What to Do, Blue? 1999. (Blue's Clues Ser.). (Illus.). 24p. (J). (gr. k-3). pap. 3.50 (978-0-689-83214-7(1) , Simon Spotlight/Nickelodeon) Simon & Schuster Children's Publishing.

Santucci, Barbara. Abby's Chairs. Santini, Debrah L., illus. 2004. 32p. 16.00 (978-0-8028-5205-2(X)) Eerdmans, William B. Publishing Co.

Sarfati, Sonia. Le Manuscrit Envole. 1999. (Roman Jeunesse Ser.). (Illus.). 96p. (J). (gr. 4-7). pap. (978-2-89021-346-3(3)) Diffusion du livre Mirabel.

Sargent, Dave & Sargent, David, Jr. Sandy Sea Gull: Making Friends, 20, 16. Lenoir, Jane, illus. 2003. (Feather Tales Ser.: 16). 42p. (J). pap. 6.95 (978-1-56763-750-2(7)) Ozark Publishing.

Sargent, Dave & Sargent, Pat. Bobby Bobcat: Be a Friend, 15 vols., Vol. 10. Huff, Jeane, illus. 2nd rev. ed. 2003. (Animal Pride Ser.: No. 10). 42p. (J). pap. 6.95 (978-1-56763-778-6(7)); lib. bdg. 19.95 (978-1-56763-777-9(9)) Ozark Publishing.

—Ginny Giraffe: High Standards, 56 vols., Vol. 46. Lenoir, Jane, illus. 2001. (Animal Pride Ser.: Vol. 46). 36p. (J). lib. bdg. 19.95 (978-1-56763-533-1(4)) Ozark Publishing.

—Pal: (Palomino) Be Friendly, 25, 44. Lenoir, Jane, illus. 2001. (Saddle Up Ser.: 44). 36p. (J). pap. 6.95 (978-1-56763-622-2(5)); lib. bdg. 22.60 (978-1-56763-621-5(7)) Ozark Publishing.

—Young Billy: A New Beginning!, 2. Woodward, Elaine, illus. 2003. (Young Animal Pride Ser.: 2). 24p. (J). pap. 6.95 (978-1-56763-866-0(X)); lib. bdg. 19.95 (978-1-56763-865-3(1)) Ozark Publishing.

—Young Redi: Friendship!, 3. Woodward, Elaine, illus. 2003. (Young Animal Pride Ser.: 3). 24p. (J). pap. 6.95 (978-1-56763-868-4(6)); lib. bdg. 19.95 (978-1-56763-867-7(8)) Ozark Publishing.

Sargent, Dave, et al. Ginny Giraffe: High Standards, 17 bks, Vol. 46. 2000. (Animal Pride Ser.: 46). (Illus.). (J). pap. 6.95 (978-1-56763-534-8(2)) Ozark Publishing.

Sasso, Sandy Eisenberg. For Heaven's Sake. Finney, Kathryn Kunz, illus. 1999. 32p. (J). (ps-3). 16.95 (978-1-58023-054-4(7)) Jewish Lights Publishing.

Saunders, Marshall. Beautiful Joe. 1999. (Illus.). 320p. (J). (gr. 4-7). per. 17.95 (978-1-55709-307-3(5)) Applewood Bks.

Saunders, Susan. All-American Puppies No. 1: New Pup on the Block. 2001. (gr. 3-6). lib. bdg. 11.80 (978-0-613-71454-9(7)) Tandem Library Bks.

Sava, Scott C. Eds Terrestrials. 2005. (Illus.). 80p. 19.99 (978-1-933428-64-2(3)) Alias Enterprises LLC.

Savage, Bridgette Z. Fly Like the Wind. Savage, Bridgette Z., illus. 2005. (Illus.). 112p. (J). per. 16.99 (978-0-9771494-0-7(4)) Buckbeech Studios.

Scallan, Dee. Moby Pincher's Wonderful Christmas Present/ Dee Scallan. 2004. (J). pap. 9.95 (978-1-59453-542-0(6)) Airleaf Publishing & Bookselling.

Scelsa, Greg & Debney, John. Friends Forever. Faulkner, Stacey, ed. Mahan, Benton, illus. 2006. (J). pap. 2.99 (***978-1-59198-322-4(3)***) Creative Teaching Pr., Inc.

Schaefer, Carole Lexa. Beeper's Friends. Lacome, Julie, illus. 2002. (Brand New Readers Ser.). 8p. (J). (ps-2). pap. 5.99 (978-0-7636-1244-3(8)) Candlewick Pr.

Schaefer, Lola M. Where Once a Flower Bloomed. 2001. (J). lib. bdg. 15.89 (978-0-688-17835-2(9)) HarperCollins Pubs.

Schaller, Bob. The Adventures of Jack & Diane: A Christian Children's Story about Sports. 2000. 108p. (gr. 4-7). pap. 9.95 (978-0-595-12756-6(8) , Writer's Showcase Pr.) iUniverse, Inc.

Schembri, Pamela & Catalanotto, Peter. No More Pumpkins. 2007. (Second Grade Friends Ser.). (Illus.). 64p. (J). (gr. 2-5). 15.95 (978-0-8050-7839-8(8)) Holt, Henry & Co.

Scherer, Catherine W. Simon & Barklee in England - Fun-Book. Scherer, Catherine W., ed. 2001. (Another Country Calling Ser.). (Illus.). 32p. (J). (gr. 2-6). 7.50 (978-0-9704661-5-0(3) , Explorer Media) Simon & Barklee, Inc./ExplorerMedia.

—Simon & Barklee in France - FunBook. 2001. (Another Country Calling Ser.). (Illus.). 32p. (J). (gr. 2-6). 7.50 (978-0-9704661-3-6(7) , Explorer Media) Simon & Barklee, Inc./ExplorerMedia.

Schertle, Alice. Little Blue Truck. McElmurry, Jill, illus. 2008. (J). (***978-0-15-205661-2(0)***) Harcourt Trade Pubs.

Schield, Allie Schield. Solomon & Lily. Jerome, Barb, illus. 2003. 34p. (J). per. 11.99 (978-0-9743948-0-0(7)) One Little Miracle.

Schlagel, Kay L. Maxwell Saves the Day. 2005. 53p. pap. 12.95 (978-1-4137-7414-6(8)) PublishAmerica, Inc.

Schlegel, Paige. Que Desorden. Schlegel, Paige, illus. 2001. Tr. of What a Mess. (SPA., Illus.). 32p. (J). (ps-3). pap. 7.50 (978-1-884083-20-4(X)) Maval Publishing, Inc.

Schmid, Robert. War Birds-Justice Friends: What Are We Fighting For? 2004. 95p. pap. 14.95 (978-1-4137-5955-6(6)) PublishAmerica, Inc.

Schmidt, Fran. To Tell or Not to Tell. 2002. (Illus.). (J). (gr. 3-7). pap. (978-1-890276-13-3(8)) Peace Education International.

Schmidt, Gary D. Lizzie Bright & the Buckminster Boy. 2004. 224p. (YA). (gr. 5 up). 15.00 (978-0-618-43929-4(3) , Clarion Bks.) Houghton Mifflin Co. Trade & Reference Div.

Schneider, Robyn. Better Than Yesterday. 2007. 240p. (YA). (gr. 9). 15.99 (978-0-385-73345-8(3)); lib. bdg. 18.99 (978-0-385-90362-2(6)) Random Hse. Children's Bks. (Delacorte Bks. for Young Readers).

Schnur, Steven. Hannah & Cyclops. 2000. 108p. (gr. 4-7). pap. 9.95 (978-0-595-00634-2(5) , Backinprint.com) iUniverse, Inc.

Schnurre, Wolfdietrich. La Princesa Viene a las Cuatro. Berner, Rotraut Susanne, illus. 2002. (Rosa y Manzana Ser.). (SPA.). 32p. (J). (gr. k-2). (978-84-89804-32-6(X) , LG30138) Loguez Ediciones ESP. *Dist:* Lectorum Pubns., Inc.

Schoenherr, Ian. Pip & Squeak. Schoenherr, Ian, illus. 2007. (Illus.). 32p. (J). (ps-1). 16.99 (978-0-06-087253-3(5)); lib. bdg. 17.89 (978-0-06-087254-0(3)) HarperCollins Pubs.

Scholastic, Inc. Staff. Best Friends Tattoo Scrapbook. 2001. (gr. k-3). lib. bdg. 14.15 (978-0-613-81944-2(6)) Tandem Library Bks.

—Cleo Plush. 2001. (Clifford Ser.). (J). 10.99 (978-0-439-30184-8(X) , Sidekicks TM) Scholastic, Inc.

—Hello! Hello! Berg, Michelle, illus. 2004. 4p. (J). 12.95 (978-0-439-62158-8(5) , Cartwheel Bks.) Scholastic, Inc.

—Keroppi & Friends: The Best Friends Book. 1998. (Illus.). (J). (gr. 3-7). pap. 3.50 (978-0-590-55823-5(4)) Scholastic, Inc.

—Murphy & Myrtle Beanbag. 2002. (Sidekicks Ser.). (J). 9.99 (978-0-439-40397-9(9) , Sidekicks TM) Scholastic, Inc.

—Murphy & Myrtle Plush. 2002. (Sidekicks Ser.). (J). 27.99 (978-0-439-30503-7(9) , Sidekicks TM) Scholastic, Inc.

—Show & Tell Surprise. 2007. (Junior Chapter Bk.: No. 5). 48p. (J). 3.99 (***978-0-439-92732-1(3)***) Scholastic, Inc.

—Zoey 101: Chapter Book. 2007. (Teenick Ser.). 112p. (J). pap. 4.99 (***978-0-439-91648-6(8)***) Scholastic, Inc.

Scholastic, Inc. Staff & Ford, Bernette G. Don't Hit Me! Grier, Gary, illus. 2004. (Just for You! Ser.). 32p. (gr. k-1). pap. 3.99 (978-0-439-56860-9(9) , Teaching Resources) Scholastic, Inc.

Scholastic, Inc. Staff & Hooks, Gwendolyn. Three's a Crowd. Walker, Sylvia, illus. 2004. (Just for You! Ser.). 32p. (gr. k-3). pap. 3.99 (978-0-439-56865-4(X) , Teaching Resources) Scholastic, Inc.

Schonzeit, Miriam. The Sweetest Song & other Stories. 2006. 304p. (YA). 16.95 (978-1-932443-42-4(8) , SWSH) Judaica Pr., Inc., The.

Schott, Linda G. Theodore & the Town That Cried. 1999. 62p. (J). (gr. 4-6). pap. 4.99 (978-0-9673859-0-7(3)) Newmark Pr.

Schotter, Roni & Dorling Kindersley Publishing Staff. F Is for Freedom. Mordan, C. B., illus. 2000. 96p. (J). (gr. 2-5). 15.99 (978-0-7894-2641-3(2)) Dorling Kindersley Publishing, Inc.

Schraff, Anne. The Boy from Planet Nowhere. 1999. 125p. (J). pap. (978-0-7891-4927-5(3)); (gr. 5-12). lib. bdg. 13.95 (978-0-7807-8004-0(3)) Perfection Learning Corp.

—Darkness. 2000. 119p. (J). pap. (978-0-7891-5183-4(9)); (gr. 5-12). lib. bdg. 13.95 (978-0-7807-9367-5(6)) Perfection Learning Corp.

—Gingerbread Heart. 1999. 114p. (J). pap. (978-0-7891-4926-8(5)); (gr. 5-12). lib. bdg. 13.95 (978-0-7807-8005-7(1)) Perfection Learning Corp.

—The Hyena Laughs at Night. 1999. 111p. (J). pap. (978-0-7891-4925-1(7)); (gr. 5-12). lib. bdg. 13.95 (978-0-7807-8006-4(X)) Perfection Learning Corp.

—Just Another Name for Lonely. 1999. 107p. (J). pap. (978-0-7891-4923-7(0)); (gr. 5-12). lib. bdg. 13.95 (978-0-7807-8007-1(8)) Perfection Learning Corp.

—Memories Are Forever. 1999. 135p. (J). pap. (978-0-7891-4924-4(9)); (gr. 5-12). lib. bdg. 13.95 (978-0-7807-8008-8(6)) Perfection Learning Corp.

Schrag, Ariel, ed. Stuck in the Middle: Seventeen Comics from an Unpleasant Age. 2007. 224p. (J). (gr. 7 up). pap. 18.99 (978-0-670-06221-8(9) , Viking Juvenile) Penguin Group (USA) Inc.

Schreiber, Anne. Brent's B-Day Party. Fisher, Cynthia, illus. 2000. (Scholastic At-Home Phonics Reading Program Ser.). 24p. (J). (978-0-590-68837-6(5)) Scholastic, Inc.

Schroder, Jack. An American Artist. 2004. (YA). per. 7.95 (978-0-9745665-9-7(4)) Catalpa Pr.

Schubert, Ingrid & Schubert, Dieter. Hammer Soup. 2004. (Illus.). 40p. (J). 15.95 (978-1-932425-02-4(0) , Lemniscaat) Boyds Mills Pr.

Schultz, Jan Neubert. Battle Cry. 2006. (Illus.). 240p. (J). 15.95 (978-1-57505-928-0(2) , Carolrhoda Bks.) Lerner Publishing Group.

Schultz Nicholson, Lorna. Northern Star. 2006. (Sports Stories Ser.). 112p. (J). (gr. 3-8). (***978-1-55028-911-4(X)***); 7.95 (978-1-55028-910-7(1)) Lorimer, James & Co., Ltd., Pubs. CAN. *Dist:* Casemate Pubs. & Bk. Distributors, LLC.

Schulz, Charles M. Friends Forever, Snoopy. 2001. (gr. k-3). lib. bdg. 11.80 (978-0-613-61768-0(1)) Tandem Library Bks.

—I Need All the Friends I Can Get. 2006. (Peanuts Ser.). (Illus.). 72p. 5.95 (978-1-933662-39-8(5)) Cider Mill Pr. Bk. Pubs. LLC.

—Von der Rolle. Herbst, Gabriele & Rolle, Ekkehard, trs. from ENG. (Snoopy & die Peanuts Ser.: Vol. 29). (GER., Illus.). 96p. (J). pap. (978-3-8105-1879-8(4)) Kruger, Wolfgang Verlag, GmbH DEU. *Dist:* International Bk. Import Service, Inc.

Schulz, Charles M., illus. Friends Forever, Snoopy. 2001. (Ready-to-Read Ser.). 32p. (J). pap. 3.99 (978-0-689-84597-0(9) , Little Simon) Simon & Schuster Children's Publishing.

Schumacher, Julie. The Chain Letter. 2006. 208p. (gr. 4-7). reprint ed. 5.99 (978-0-440-42011-8(3) , Yearling) Random Hse. Children's Bks.

—Grass Angel. 2004. 208p. (gr. 5-9). lib. bdg. 17.99 (978-0-385-90163-5(1) , Delacorte Bks. for Young Readers) Random Hse. Children's Bks.

—Grass Angel. 2005. 196p. (J). (gr. k-9). per. 12.55 (978-0-606-33725-0(3)) Tandem Library Bks.

Schurr, Cathleen. The Shy Little Kitten. Tenggren, Gustaf, illus. 1999. (Little Golden Bks.). 24p. (J). (gr. k-k). 2.99 (978-0-307-00145-0(8) , 98103, Golden Bks.) Random Hse. Children's Bks.

Schwartz, Corey Rosen & Klein, Tali. Hop! Plop! Dunrea, Olivier, illus. 2006. 32p. (J). 16.85 (978-0-8027-8057-7(1)); 15.95 (978-0-8027-8056-0(3)) Walker & Co.

Schwartz, Ellen. Abby's Birds. Shefrin, Sima Elizabeth, illus. 2007. 32p. (J). (gr. k-3). 16.95 (***978-1-896580-86-9(6)***) Tradewind Bks. CAN. *Dist:* Orca Bk. Pubs. USA.

Schwartz, Suzanne & Schwartz, Robert. The Christmas Palm Tree: A Storybook to Color. Schwartz, Suzanne & Schwartz, Robert, illus. l.t. ed. 2005. (Illus.). 22p. (J). spiral bd. 3.99 (978-0-9764152-3-7(2)) Seascay Productions.

—My Friend Hibby: A Tropical Adventure. Schwartz, Suzanne & Schwartz, Robert, illus. 2005. (Illus.). 20p. (J). spiral bd. 6.00 (978-0-9764152-0-6(8)) Seascay Productions.

Schwiebert, Pat & DeKlyen, Chuck. Tear Soup: A Recipe for Healing after Loss. Bills, Taylor, illus. 2nd rev. l.t. ed. 2004. 56p. reprint ed. 19.95 (978-0-9615197-6-6(2) , 798) Perinatal Loss.

Scieszka, Jon. Cowboy & Octopus. Smith, Lane, illus. 2007. 40p. (J). (ps-5). 16.99 (***978-0-670-91058-8(9)*** , Viking Juvenile) Penguin Group (USA) Inc.

Scieszka, Jon. Domingo, el Dia del Vikingo. (SPA.). (J). 7.95 (978-958-04-7448-7(6)) Norma S.A. COL. *Dist:* Distribuidora Norma, Inc.

Scorcia, Yvonne. Joey's Big Adventure. 2001. 56p. (J). pap. 9.00 (978-0-8059-5485-2(6)) Dorrance Publishing Co., Inc.

Scott, C. Anne. Lizard Meets Ivana the Terrible. 2001. (gr. 3-6). lib. bdg. 11.80 (978-0-613-81946-6(2)) Tandem Library Bks.

Scott, C. Anne & Roth, Stephanie. Lizard Meets Ivana the Terrible. 2001. 128p. (J). pap. 3.99 (978-0-439-21999-0(X) , Scholastic Paperbacks) Scholastic, Inc.

Scott, Carlton T. Little Big Wolf. Scott, Carlton T., illus. 1999. (Illus.). 32p. (J). (gr. k-5). 9.95 (978-0-9636652-8-7(6)) Ends of the Earth Books.com.

Scott, Cynthia A. Lizard Meets Ivana the Terrible. 2001. (978-0-606-22173-3(5)) Tandem Library Bks.

Scott, Elaine. Poles Apart: Why Penguins & Polar Bears Will Never Be Neighbors. 2004. (Illus.). 64p. (J). (gr. 3-7). 17.99 (978-0-670-05925-6(0) , Viking Juvenile) Penguin Group (USA) Inc.

Scott, Jerry. Zits Vol. 7: Carretera y Manta. 2007. (SPA., Illus.). 128p. reprint ed. pap. 19.95 (***978-1-59497-337-6(7)***) Public Square Bks.

Scott, Rosanna. Peter & Friends at Camp. Fargo, Todd, illus. l.t. ed. 2006. (Turtle Books). 32p. (J). (gr. k-4). pap. 9.95 (978-0-944727-51-5(4)); lib. bdg. 15.95 (978-0-944727-52-2(2)) Jason & Nordic Pubs. (Turtle Bks.).

Scrimger, Richard. From Charlie's Point of View. (gr. 3). 2007. 288p. (YA). pap. 6.99 (978-0-14-240818-6(2) , Puffin); 2005. 224p. (J). 10.99 (978-0-525-47374-9(2) , Dutton Juvenile) Penguin Group (USA) Inc.

Scripture Teachers: Solomon & Friends Learn about Forgiveness. 2003. pap. (***978-0-9712894-1-3(7)***) Lighthouse Christian Products Co.

Scripture Teachers: Solomon & Friends Learn about Prayer. 2003. pap. (***978-0-9712894-0-6(9)***) Lighthouse Christian Products Co.

SeaStar Publishing Staff. Friendship Stories You Can Share. 2001. (Reading Rainbow Readers Ser.). (Illus.). (J). 10.79 (978-0-606-21202-1(7)) Tandem Library Bks.

Sebra, Diane. Making Mountains Out of Moles. 2003. 120p. (YA). pap. 9.95 (978-1-55517-712-6(3) , 77123, Bonneville Bks.) Cedar Fort, Inc./CFI Distribution.

Secret of the Ancient Crowns. 2006. per. 14.95 (***978-1-59352-263-6(0)***) Christian Services Publishing.

Secrets Of Droon #28 Staff & Abbott, Tony. In the Shadow of Goll. 2006. (Secrets of Droon Ser.: No. 28). (Illus.). 112p. (J). pap. 3.99 (978-0-439-67176-7(0) , Scholastic Paperbacks) Scholastic, Inc.

Sedita, Francesco. Miss Popularity. 2007. (Candy Apple Ser.: No. 3). 144p. (J). pap. 4.99 (***978-0-439-88814-1(X)*** , Scholastic Paperbacks) Scholastic, Inc.

Seeger, Laura Vaccaro. Dog & Bear. Seeger, Laura Vaccaro, illus. 2007. (Illus.). 32p. (J). (ps-3). 12.95 (978-1-59643-053-2(2)) Roaring Brook Pr.

Seeger, Laura Vaccaro. Dog & Bear, Too! 2008. 32p. (J). 12.95 (***978-1-59643-273-4(X)***) Roaring Brook Pr.

Segal, John. The Lonely Moose. rev. ed. 2007. 40p. (ps-2). 15.99 (***978-1-4231-0173-4(1)***) Hyperion Pr.

Segal, Zoe. Confessions of a Tenth-Grade Social Climber. 2005. 290p. (YA). (978-0-618-44981-1(7)) Houghton Mifflin Co.

Selfors, Suzanne. To Catch a Mermaid. Chien, Catia, illus. rev. ed. 2007. 254p. (J). (gr. 3-7). 14.99 (***978-0-316-01816-6(3)***) Little, Brown Bks. for Young Readers.

Sell, Jeff. The Quarry Cave. 2006. 51p. pap. 12.95 (978-1-4241-1188-6(9)) PublishAmerica, Inc.

Selway, Martina, illus. Fred's Cold. 1999. (J). (978-0-7608-3192-2(0)) Sundance/Newbridge Educational Publishing.

Senate, Melissa. Theodora Twist. 224p. (YA). (gr. 9). 2007. pap. 7.99 (***978-0-385-73302-1(X)***); 2006. 15.95 (978-0-385-73301-4(1)); 2006. lib. bdg. 17.99 (978-0-385-90322-6(7)) Random Hse. Children's Bks. (Delacorte Bks. for Young Readers).

Sendak, Maurice. Very Far Away. Sendak, Maurice, illus. 2005. (Sendak Reissues Ser.). 56p. 15.95 (978-0-06-029723-7(9)) HarperCollins Pubs.

—We Are All in the Dumps with Jack & Guy. Sendak, Maurice, illus. 1998. (Illus.). 54p. (J). (gr. 4-7). pap. 20.00 (978-0-7881-5645-8(4)) DIANE Publishing Co.

Sendak, Maurice, illus. Little Bear's Friend. 2002. (Little Bear Ser.). (J). 12.34 (978-0-7587-6185-9(6)) Book Wholesalers, Inc.

Seppala, Ray. Willowrun Tales. 2006. (Illus.). 122p. (YA). per. 9.95 (978-1-933324-47-0(3)) Cedar Hill Publishing.

Serafin, Michael. 4 Seasons of Baghdad. 2007. (ENG.). 60p. per. 12.95 (***978-1-4241-2303-2(8)***) PublishAmerica, Inc.

Serros, Michele. Honey Blonde Chica. (YA). (gr. 9 up). 2007. 320p. pap. 8.99 (978-1-4169-1592-8(3)); 2006. 304p. 14.95 (978-1-4169-1591-1(5)) Simon & Schuster Children's Publishing. (Simon Pulse).

—Scandalosa. 2007. 320p. (YA). (gr. 9 up). 15.99 (978-1-4169-1593-5(1) , Simon Pulse) Simon & Schuster Children's Publishing.

Sesame Street Storybook COLL 2. 2007. 10.99 (***978-1-4037-3614-7(6)***) Dalmatian Pr.

Seuling, Barbara. Robert & the Great Escape. Brewer, Paul, illus. 2003. (Robert Bks.). 120p. 15.95 (978-0-8126-2700-8(8)) Cricket Bks.

—Robert & the Practical Jokes. Brewer, Paul, illus. 2006. (Robert Bks.). 150p. (J). 16.95 (978-0-8126-2741-1(5)) Cricket Bks.

Seuling, Barbara. Robert Goes to Camp. Brewer, Paul, illus. 2007. (Robert Bks.). 160p. (J). (gr. 2-4). 16.95 (***978-0-8126-2753-4(9)***) Cricket Bks.

Sewell, Anna. Black Beauty. 2002. (Spot the Classics Ser.). (Illus.). 178p. (J). (gr. k-5). 4.99 (978-1-57759-544-1(0)) Dalmatian Pr.

—Black Beauty, Level 2. 2001. (Illus.). 48p. (C). pap. 9.00 (978-0-582-42121-9(7)) Pearson ESL.

Sewell-Shaw, Eve. Every Day Will Be Saturday When You Find a Friend. 1999. (Illus.). 50p. (J). 9.95 (978-0-7541-0786-6(8)) Minerva Pr. GBR. *Dist:* Unity Distribution.

Seymour, Tres. The Revelation of Saint Bruce. 1998. (Illus.). 128p. (YA). (gr. 7-12). pap. 16.95 (978-0-531-30109-8(5) , Orchard Bks.) Scholastic, Inc.

Seymour's Soaring Red Sox: A Bird's-Eye View of the 2004 World Series. 2005. (J). kivar 19.95 (978-0-9761820-1-6(7)) Cassiopeia Pr.

Sh... Sh... Sh... No Talking! 1999. (Tami & Moishy Ser.: Vol. 6). (J). bds. 6.95 (978-0-87306-967-0(6)) Feldheim Pubs.

Shalant, Phyllis. The Great Cape Rescue. 2007. (Society of Super Secret Heroes Ser.: Bk. 1). 128p. (J). (gr. 2-4). 15.99 (978-0-525-47404-3(8) , Dutton Juvenile) Penguin Group (USA) Inc.

—When Pirates Came to Brooklyn. 2002. 176p. (J). (gr. 4-7). 16.99 (978-0-525-46920-9(6) , Dutton Juvenile) Penguin Group (USA) Inc.

Shan, Darren, pseud. A Living Nightmare. 2001. (Cirque du Freak: Bk. 1). (J). 272p. (gr. k-3). 15.95 (978-0-316-60340-9(6)); (Illus.). viii, 279p. (gr. 3-6). pap. (978-0-316-64852-3(3)) Little, Brown Bks. for Young Readers.

Shanks, Melanie. The Squints. 2007. 116p. per. 10.95 (***978-0-595-44849-4(6)***) iUniverse, Inc.

Shann, Taylor. Strange Day. 2003. (J). 13.00 (978-0-9679552-4-7(6)) Mushroom Cloud Pr. of Orlando.

Shannon, David. A Bad Case of Stripes. 2004. (Scholastic Bookshelf Ser.). 32p. (J). reprint ed. 6.99 (978-0-439-59838-5(9) , Scholastic Paperbacks) Scholastic, Inc.

Shannon, Jacqueline. It's in Your Hands, Daisy P. Duckwitz. 1998. (J). (gr. 4-6). pap. 3.99 (978-0-380-78769-2(5)) HarperCollins Pubs.

—It's in Your Hands, Daisy P. Duckwitz. 1998. (978-0-606-13531-3(6)) Tandem Library Bks.

Shannon, Star Erian. Erian's Friend Jeremiah the Owl. 2003. (J). pap. 9.00 (978-0-8059-6068-6(6)) Dorrance Publishing Co., Inc.

Sharmat, Marjorie Weinman & Sharmat, Mitchell. The Pizza Monster. Brunkus, Denise, illus. 2nd ed. 2005. 80p. (J). (gr. 1-4). reprint ed. pap. 4.50 (978-0-440-42059-0(8) , Yearling) Random Hse. Children's Bks.

Sharmat, Marjorie Weinman, et al. The Green Toenails Gang. Brunkus, Denise, illus. 2005. (Oliver Sharp Ser.: Vol. 4). 80p. (J). (gr. 1-4). pap. 4.50 (978-0-440-42063-7(6) , Yearling) Random Hse. Children's Bks.

Sharpe, Gerald. What Lies Beneath the Bed: Tommy's Tales. 2006. 304p. (YA). pap. 7.00 (978-1-933894-00-3(8)) IJN Publishing, Inc.

Shaw, Fran. What a Team! Together Everyone Achieves More. Sakamoto, Ryuichi, illus. 2007. 14p. (J). 14.99 (***978-0-7944-1351-4(X)***) Reader's Digest Assn., Inc., The.

Shaw, Janet Beeler. Kaya & Lone Dog Bk. 4: A Friendship Story. Farnsworth, Bill & McAliley, Susan, illus. 2002. (American Girls Collection: Bk. 4). 96p. (J). (gr. 2-7). 12.95 (978-1-58485-430-2(8)); 6.95 (978-1-58485-429-6(4)) American Girl Publishing, Inc.

Shaw, Mary. Brady Brady & the B Team, 12 vols. Temple, Chuck, illus. l.t. ed. 2006. 32p. (J). per. (***978-1-897169-09-4(4)***) Brady Brady, Inc.

Shaw, Mary. Pierre & Sophia: A True Tale. Agin, Sue, illus. 2000. (ENG & FRE.). 44p. (J). (ps-4). 18.50 (978-0-9705404-0-9(X)) Criqueville Pr.

Shaw, Mary Lewis & Agin, Sue. Pierre & Sophia: A True Tale. 2000. (ENG & FRE.). (978-0-9705404-1-6(8)) Criqueville Pr.

Shaw, Susan. Safe. 2007. 208p. (J). (gr. 9). 16.99 (***978-0-525-47829-4(9)*** , Dutton Juvenile) Penguin Group (USA) Inc.

Shealy, Dennis R. & Random House Disney Staff. Going Buggy. Alvin and Associates, Inc. Staff, illus. 2002. 24p. (J). (gr. k-k). pap. 3.25 (978-0-7364-1173-8(9) , RH/Disney) Random Hse. Children's Bks.

Shearer, A. Wilmot & Chips. 167p. (J). pap. (978-0-340-72740-9(3) , Hodder & Stoughton) Hodder General Publishing Division.

—Wilmot & Chips. 167p. pap. 7.99 (978-0-340-80557-2(9) , Hodder & Stoughton) Hodder General Publishing Division GBR. *Dist:* Trafalgar Square Publishing.

—Wilmot & the Pops. (Illus.). 184p. (J). pap. (978-0-340-71641-0(X) , Hodder & Stoughton) Hodder General Publishing Division.

Sheath, Irene. Lippy Lime Juice. 2004. 144p. (J). per. (978-1-904502-48-7(2)) MediaWorld/BestBooks.

Sheehan, Jennifer E. Miss Bumples Lands on Earth. 2003. (Illus.). 32p. (J). 15.95 (978-0-9700952-5-1(2)) Bumples.

Sheehy-Culhane, Roisin. WHEN MAMA GOES to WORK: DEVIN'S STORY. 2006. (ENG.). 32p. per. 19.99 (***978-1-4257-0596-1(0)***) Xlibris Corp.

EFG

Shefelman, Janice J. & Shefelman, Tom, illus. Son of Spirit Horse. 2004. 74p. (J). (978-1-57168-833-0(1) , Eakin Pr.) Eakin Pr.

Sheldon, Dyan. Confessions of a Teenage Drama Queen. 2005. 272p. (YA). (gr. 7 up). pap. 7.99 (978-0-7636-2827-7(1)); 2004. (J). 107.82 (978-0-7636-2538-2(8)); 2004. (Illus.). 308p. (YA). (gr. 7 up). pap. 5.99 (978-0-7636-2416-3(0)) Candlewick Pr.

—Confessions of a Teenage Drama Queen. 2002. (gr. 7-12). lib. bdg. 15.30 (978-0-613-74762-2(3)) Tandem Library Bks.

—My Perfect Life. 208p. (YA). (gr. 7). 2004. pap. 5.99 (978-0-7636-2436-1(5)); 2005. reprint ed. pap. 7.99 (978-0-7636-2828-4(X)) Candlewick Pr.

Sheldon, Mary. The Shadow Girl. 2000. 204p. (YA). pap. 13.95 (978-0-595-00117-0(3)) iUniverse, Inc.

Shelton, Rick. Hoggle's Christmas. Gates, Donald, illus. 2007. 80p. (J). pap. 11.95 (*978-1-60306-026-4(X)) NewSouth, Inc.

Shepard, Sara. Flawless. 2008. (Pretty Little Liars Ser.: Bk. 2). 352p. (J). pap. 8.99 (*978-0-06-088735-3(4) , HarperTeen) HarperCollins Pubs.

—Perfect. 2007. (Pretty Little Liars Ser.: Bk. 3). 320p. (YA). (gr. 9 up). 16.99 (*978-0-06-088736-0(2) , HarperTeen) HarperCollins Pubs.

—Pretty Little Liars. (Pretty Little Liars Ser.: Bk. 1). 304p. (J). 2007. pap. 8.99 (*978-0-06-088732-2(X)); 2006. 16.99 (978-0-06-088730-8(3)) HarperCollins Pubs. (HarperTeen).

—Unbelievable. 2008. (Pretty Little Liars Ser.: Bk. 4). 352p. (J). 16.99 (*978-0-06-088739-1(7) , HarperTeen) HarperCollins Pubs.

Shepherd, JaiLeen. Anan: Lea's Special Friend—Part II of the Lea Trilogy. 2006. (J). per. 15.95 (978-1-889743-55-4(0)) Robbie Dean Pr.

Shepherd, Jodie. Farm Friends. Ovresat, Laura, illus. 2006. (Guess Who? Ser.). 12p. (J). pap. 7.99 (978-0-7944-1048-3(0)) Reader's Digest Assn., Inc., The.

Shepperson, Jacqueline. Martins of the Everglades. 2007. (ENG.). 152p. per. 19.95 (*978-1-4241-5446-3(4)) PublishAmerica, Inc.

Sherrard, Valerie. Speechless. 2007. 176p. (YA). pap. 12.99 (*978-1-55002-701-3(8) , Boardwalk Bks.) Dundurn Group, The CAN. *Dist:* Univ. of Toronto Pr.

Sherrell, Deborah. Baby Lauren & Theodore,hardcover. 2007. (J). bds. 17.95 (*978-0-9779643-5-2(3)) Healing Tree Arts.

Sherwood, Barbara B. Jan & Ann & the Pet Rabbit. Campbell, Nancy T., illus. 1998. 16p. (J). (ps). pap. 5.95 (978-1-891846-03-8(5)) Business Word, The.

Shi, Sharon. Girlfriends. Sohn, Catherine Jung, illus. rev. ed. 2000. 15p. (J). (ps-2). pap. 4.99 (978-0-9678636-5-8(1) , B006, Tattootles Bks.) Tattoo Manufacturing.

—Wonderful Things. Schaufelberger, Yoka, illus. rev. ed. 2000. 23p. (J). (ps-2). pap. 4.99 (978-0-9678636-1-0(9) , B002, Tattootles Bks.) Tattoo Manufacturing.

Shinn, Sharon. Dream-maker's Magic. 2006. 272p. (YA). (gr. 7). 16.99 (978-0-670-06070-2(4) , Viking Juvenile) Penguin Group (USA) Inc.

Shinn, Sharon. The Dream-Maker's Magic. 2008. 272p. (YA). (gr. 7). pap. 7.99 (*978-0-14-241096-7(9) , Puffin) Penguin Group (USA) Inc.

Shipley, Jocelyn. Getting a Life. 2003. (gr. 7-12). lib. bdg. 16.40 (978-0-613-81037-1(6)) Tandem Library Bks.

Shire, Poppy. Magic Pony Carousel #4: Jewel the Midnight Pony. Berg, Ron, illus. 2008. (Magic Pony Carousel Ser.). 96p. (J). pap. 3.99 (*978-0-06-083788-4(8) , Harper Trophy) HarperCollins Pubs.

Shiro Amano. Kingdom Hearts, 4 vols., Vol. 4. 4th rev. ed. 2006. (Disney Squaresoft Ser.). (Illus.). pap. 5.99 (978-1-59816-220-2(9) , Tokyopop Kids) TOKYOPOP, Inc.

Short, Mary Ann. Friend Indeed. 1999. (gr. 7-12). lib. bdg. 19.80 (978-0-613-79594-4(6)) Tandem Library Bks.

Shouse, Nancy. Any Pet Will Do. 2005. (Orca Young Readers Ser.). (Illus.). 112p. (J). (gr. 3-6). pap. 5.95 (978-1-55143-354-7(0)) Orca Bk. Pubs. USA.

Showalter, Gena. Black Listed. 2007. 256p. pap. 9.95 (*978-1-4165-3225-5(0) , MTV) Simon & Schuster.

Shreeve, Elizabeth. Hector Finds a Fortune. Levy, Pamela R., illus. 2004. 68p. (J). lib. bdg. 15.00 (*978-1-4242-0903-3(X)) Fitzgerald Bks.

—Hector Finds a Fortune. Levy, Pamela R., illus. 2004. (Ready-for-Chapters Ser.). 64p. (J). pap. 3.99 (978-0-689-86415-5(9) , Aladdin) Simon & Schuster Children's Publishing.

—Hector Finds a Fortune. 2004. (gr. k-3). lib. bdg. 11.80 (978-0-613-86966-9(4)) Tandem Library Bks.

Shreeve, Elizabeth. Hector on Thin Ice. Levy, Pamela R., illus. 2004. 71p. (J). lib. bdg. 15.00 (*978-1-4242-0904-0(8)) Fitzgerald Bks.

Shreve, Susan. Kiss Me Tomorrow. 2006. 224p. (YA). (gr. 5-8). 16.99 (978-0-439-68047-9(6) , Levine, Arthur A. Bks.) Scholastic, Inc.

—Under the Watsons' Porch. 2006. 208p. (J). (gr. 5-8). reprint ed. pap. 4.99 (978-0-440-41969-3(7) , Yearling) Random Hse. Children's Bks.

Shreve, Susan Richards. Kiss Me Tomorrow. 2007. 224p. (YA). (gr. 5-8). pap. 5.99 (978-0-439-68048-6(4)); 2006. 220p. (J). (*978-1-4156-5592-4(8)) Scholastic, Inc. (Levine, Arthur A. Bks.).

Shreve, Susan Richards. Under the Watsons' Porch. (J). 2006. 199p. (*978-1-4156-7020-0(X) , Yearling); 2004. 208p. (gr. 5-8). 15.95 (978-0-375-82630-6(0) , Knopf Bks. for Young Readers) Random Hse. Children's Bks.

Shriver, Maria. What's Wrong with Timmy? Speidel, Sandra, illus. 2001. 48p. (J). (ps-3). 14.95 (978-0-316-23337-8(4)) Little, Brown Bks. for Young Readers.

Shua, Ana Maria. La Puerta para Salir del Mundo. 2002. (SPA.). 64p. (J). pap. 6.95 (978-1-4000-0059-3(9)) Random Hse., Inc.

Shuff, Lana Tanaka. Kira Helps A Friend. l.t. ed. 2007. (ENG., Illus.). 28p. (J). per. 9.95 (*978-1-4327-0810-8(4)) Outskirts Press, Inc.

Shulman, Mark. Louis & the Dodo. Nguyen, Vincent, illus. 2005. 36p. (J). (gr. k-2). 14.95 (978-1-4027-2872-3(7)) Sterling Publishing Co., Inc.

—Storytime Stickers: Easter Bunny. Swanson, Maggie, illus. 2007. (Storytime Stickers Ser.). 16p. (J). pap. 4.95 (978-1-4027-3363-5(1)) Sterling Publishing Co., Inc.

Shusterman, Neal. Downsiders. l.t. ed. 2000. 336p. (YA). (gr. 6-12). lib. bdg. 29.95 (978-1-58118-071-8(3)) LRS.

—Downsiders. 2001. 256p. (YA). (gr. 8-12). mass mkt. 5.99 (978-0-689-83969-6(3) , Simon Pulse) Simon & Schuster Children's Publishing.

—Dread Locks, No. 1. 2006. (Dark Fusion Ser.). 176p. (YA). (gr. 7). pap. 6.99 (978-0-14-240599-4(X) , Puffin) Penguin Group (USA) Inc.

—Dread Locks: Dark Fusion # 1. 2005. 176p. (J). (gr. 6-12). 15.99 (978-0-525-47554-5(0) , Dutton Juvenile) Penguin Group (USA) Inc.

—The Schwa Was Here. 240p. (J). 2004. (gr. 6). 16.99 (978-0-525-47182-0(0) , Dutton Juvenile); 2006. (gr. 3). reprint ed. pap. 5.99 (978-0-14-240577-2(9) , Puffin) Penguin Group (USA) Inc.

Sidell, Yvonne. The Fairy Twins: Land of New Friends. 2006. (ENG.). 48p. per. 23.99 (*978-1-4259-4840-5(5)) AuthorHouse.

Sidney, Margaret. Five Little Peppers & Their Friends. 2006. 65.99 (*978-1-4219-9625-7(1)) IndyPublish.com.

Silent to the Bone. 2004. 261p. (J). (gr. 5-9). lib. bdg. 14.15 (978-0-613-73424-0(6)) Tandem Library Bks.

Silk, Richard. Pops. 2002. 182p. pap. 19.95 (978-1-59129-930-1(6)) PublishAmerica, Inc.

Silver Dolphin en Español Editors. Caritas felices: Simba: Happy Faces: Simba, Spanish-Language Edition. 2007. (Illus.). 8p. (J). bds. 7.95 (*978-970-718-392-6(6) , Silver Dolphin en Español) Advanced Marketing, S. de R. L. de C. V. MEX. *Dist:* Perseus Distribution.

Silver Dolphin en Español Staff. Imanes Magicos: Girlfriends: Magnets on the Move: Girlfriends, Spanish-Language Edition. 2006. (Illus.). 8p. (J). bds. 12.95 (978-970-718-371-1(3) , Silver Dolphin en Español) Advanced Marketing, S. de R. L. de C. V. MEX. *Dist:* Perseus Distribution.

Silver, Rita. Best Friends. 2006. 17.00 (978-0-8059-9932-7(9)) Dorrance Publishing Co., Inc.

Silvera, Elvia. Candida. Peli, Peli, illus. 2005. (SPA.). (J). (gr. 2-3). pap. 7.95 (978-980-257-281-6(0)) Ekare, Ediciones VEN. *Dist:* Iaconi, Mariuccia Bk. Imports.

Silverhardt, Lauryn. Best Friends. Style Guide Staff, illus. 2005. (Dora the Explorer Ser.). 8p. (J). 6.99 (978-0-689-87694-3(7) , Simon Spotlight/Nickelodeon) Simon & Schuster Children's Publishing.

—Boots. Thompson Brothers Staff, illus. 2003. (Dora the Explorer Ser.). (SPA & ENG.). 12p. (J). bds. 7.99 (978-0-689-85485-9(4) , Simon Spotlight/Nickelodeon) Simon & Schuster Children's Publishing.

Silvermetz, Marcia A. Gertrude the Albino Frog & Her Friend Rupert the Turtle. Doyel, Ginger, illus. 2003. 48p. (J). (gr. 2-3). 19.95 (978-0-9718724-0-0(6)) Hiccup Cottage Pubns.

Silverstein, Shel. Who Wants a Cheap Rhinoceros? Silverstein, Shel, illus. 2002. (Illus.). 64p. (J). (ps-3). 17.95 (978-0-689-85113-1(8)) Simon & Schuster Children's Publishing.

Simard, Remy. Monsieur Iletaitunefois. Pratt, Pierre, illus. 1998. (FRE.). 32p. (J). (ps-3). pap. 6.95 (978-1-55037-544-2(X)); lib. bdg. 16.95 (978-1-55037-545-9(8)) Annick Pr., Ltd. CAN. *Dist:* Firefly Bks., Ltd.

—Monsieur Iletaitunefois. ed. 2004. (FRE.). (J). (gr. k-3). spiral bd. (978-0-616-01843-9(6)) Canadian National Institute for the Blind/Institut National Canadien pour les Aveugles.

Simmons, H. J. The Little House on the Corner. 2004. 63p. pap. 12.95 (978-1-4137-2934-4(7)) PublishAmerica, Inc.

Simmons, Jane. Together. 2007. (Illus.). 32p. (J). (ps-3). 15.99 (978-0-375-84339-6(6)); lib. bdg. 18.99 (978-0-375-94339-3(0)) Random Hse. Children's Bks. (Knopf Bks. for Young Readers).

Simon & Barklee in England. 2001. (Another Country Calling Ser.). (Illus.). 64p. (J). (gr. 3-5). per. 15.00 (978-0-9704661-1-2(0) , Explorer Media) Simon & Barklee, Inc./ExplorerMedia.

Simon & Barklee in Germany. 2001. (Another Country Calling Ser.). (Illus.). 64p. (J). (gr. 3-5). per. 15.00 (978-0-9704661-2-9(9) , Explorer Media) Simon & Barklee, Inc./ExplorerMedia.

Simon and Schuster Staff, ed. Cuentos de Dora y sus amigos. 2006. (Dora la Exploradora Ser.).Tr. of Dora's Storytime Collection. (SPA.). 160p. (J). 10.95 (978-1-4169-1564-5(8) , Libros Para Ninos) Simon & Schuster Children's Publishing.

Simon-Kerr, Julia. Best Buddies. 2006. (Open Season Ser.). 24p. (J). pap. 3.99 (978-0-06-084602-2(X)) HarperCollins Pubs.

Simon, Mary Manz. Puppy Makes Friends. Couri, Kathy & Clearwater, Linda, illus. 2006. (First Virtues for Toddlers Ser.). 20p. (J). 5.99 (978-0-7847-1414-0(2) , 04066) Standard Publishing.

—Sientate! Maria y Marta, 1. 1999. (Hear Me Read Bible Stories Ser.). (SPA.). 32p. (J). 2.75 (978-0-570-09929-1(3)) Concordia Publishing Hse.

Simpson, Fiona, ed. Unfabulous: Just Deal. 2006. (Teenick Ser.). 112p. (J). pap. 4.99 (978-0-439-84662-2(5) , Scholastic) Scholastic, Inc.

Singletary, Mabel Elizabeth. Something to Jump About! 2008. 150p. pap. 5.99 (*978-0-8024-2252-1(7)) Moody Pubs.

Singleton, Linda Joy. Sea Switch. 2005. (Illus.). 264p. (ps-7). pap. 5.99 (978-0-7387-0712-9(0)) Llewellyn Pubns.

—Shamrocked! 2005. 216p. pap. 4.99 (978-0-7387-0594-1(2)) Llewellyn Pubns.

—Witch Ball. 2006. (Seer Ser.: Bk. 3). 264p. pap. 6.99 (978-0-7387-0821-8(6)) Llewellyn Pubns.

Sis, Peter. An Ocean World. Sis, Peter, illus. 2002. (Illus.). (YA). 14.43 (978-1-4046-0278-6(X)) Book Wholesalers, Inc.

Sitomer, Alan Lawrence. The Hoopster. 2005. 224p. (gr. 7-17). 16.99 (978-0-7868-5483-7(9) , Jump at the Sun) Hyperion Bks. for Children.

Skinner, Daphne. Palapalooza. Smath, Jerry, illus. 2006. 32p. (J). lib. bdg. 20.00 (*978-1-4242-1113-5(1)) Fitzgerald Bks.

—Palapalooza. Smath, Jerry, illus. 2006. (Social Studies Connects). 32p. (J). pap. 4.99 (978-1-57565-163-7(7)) Kane Pr., The.

Skipper, Cecil. The Deer Lick. 2004. 166p. (YA). pap. 12.95 (978-0-595-30949-8(6)) iUniverse, Inc.

Skogan, Joan. The Good Companion. McCallum, Stephen, illus. 1998. 32p. (J). (ps-3). 15.95 (978-1-55143-134-5(3)) Orca Bk. Pubs. USA.

Skolsky, Mindy Warshaw. Love from Your Friend, Hannah. 256p. (J). (gr. 4-6). pap. 5.95 (978-0-8072-1546-3(5)); 1999. pap. 37.00 incl. audio (978-0-8072-8079-9(8) , YA996SP) Random Hse. Audio Publishing Group. (Listening Library).

Skretteberg, James. A New M/Age Dawns, . 2005. 268p. (YA). per. 16.95 (978-0-9766449-8-9(3)) Global Authors Pubns.

Skurnick, Elizabeth. Shadowed. 2004. (Prequel Ser.). 192p. (YA). (gr. 7). mass mkt. 5.99 (978-0-553-49440-2(6) , Bantam Bks. for Young Readers) Random Hse. Children's Bks.

Skurzynski, Gloria. The Tempering. 2000. (Golden Triangle Bks.). 192p. (J). (gr. 4-7). pap. 9.95 (978-0-8229-5741-6(8)) Univ. of Pittsburgh Pr.

Slade, Arthur. The Invasion of the IQ Snatchers. 2007. (Arthur Slade's Canadian Chills Ser.: No. 3). 120p. (YA). (gr. 4 up). 6.95 (*978-1-55050-361-6(8)) Coteau Bks. CAN. *Dist:* Fitzhenry & Whiteside, Ltd.

Slater, David Michael. Missy Swiss. Reibeling, Brandon, illus. 2007. (Missy Swiss & More Ser.). 32p. (J). (ps-4). lib. bdg. 27.07 (*978-1-60270-010-9(9) , Looking Glass Library) Magic Wagon.

—Seven Ate Nine! Trover, Zachary, illus. 2007. (Missy Swiss & More Ser.). 32p. (J). (ps-4). lib. bdg. 27.07 (*978-1-60270-012-3(5) , Looking Glass Library) Magic Wagon.

Slater, Teddy & Springer, Sally. Trouble for Trudy. 2007. (No Bullies Allowed Ser.). (Illus.). (J). (*978-0-439-89709-9(2)) Scholastic, Inc.

Slaughter, Hope. Buckley & Wilberta, Forever Friends. Torrence, Susan, illus. l.t. ed. 1998. 64p. (J). (gr. 1-3). lib. bdg. 14.95 (978-0-931093-16-6(3)) Red Hen Pr.

Slepian, Jan. The Alfred Summer. 2001. (978-0-606-22507-6(2)) Tandem Library Bks.

Sloan, Brian. Tale of Two Summers. 2006. 256p. (YA). 15.95 (978-0-689-87439-0(1) , Simon & Schuster Children's Publishing) Simon & Schuster Children's Publishing.

Sloniker, Phyllis. The Quest for the Golden Flower. 2005. 11.00 (978-0-8059-9399-8(1)) Dorrance Publishing Co., Inc.

Small, Hattie Thompson. Ms. Butterfly & Old Bumblebee. Slack, Una H., ed. 2002. 192p. (J). pap. 7.95 (978-1-56167-362-9(5)) American Literary Pr.

Smallcomb, Pam. The Last Burp of Mac McGerp. Bromley, Lizzy, illus. 2003. 150p. (J). 15.95 (978-1-58234-856-8(1)); pap. 6.95 (978-1-58234-868-1(5)) Bloomsbury Publishing. (Bloomsbury Children).

Smallman, Steve. The Lamb Who Came for Dinner. Dreidemy, Joelle, illus. 2007. 32p. (J). (ps-2). 15.95 (*978-1-58925-067-3(2) , tiger tales) ME Media LLC.

Smalls-Hector, Irene. Because You're Lucky. Hays, Michael, illus. 2004. 48p. (J). (ps-ps). lib. bdg. 13.19 (978-0-606-30471-9(1)) Tandem Library Bks.

Smalls, Irene. Don't Say Ain't. Bootman, Colin, illus. 32p. (J). (gr. k-3). 2004. pap. 6.95 (978-1-57091-382-2(X)); 2003. 15.95 (978-1-57091-381-5(1)) Charlesbridge Publishing, Inc.

—Don't Say Ain't. 2004. (gr. k-3). lib. bdg. 15.25 (978-0-613-70806-7(7)) Tandem Library Bks.

Smee, Nicola. Clip-Clop! 2006. (Illus.). 32p. (J). 12.95 (978-1-905417-09-4(8)) Boxer Bks., Ltd. GBR. *Dist:* Sterling Publishing Co., Inc.

Smith Annie, Laura. Whispers in the Wind. 2006. 144p. pap. 12.95 (978-1-59113-914-0(7)) Booklocker.com, Inc.

Smith, Cheryl Jean. The Journal. 2006. 154p. pap. 11.95 (*978-0-7414-3491-3(1)) Infinity Publishing.

Smith, Dianne M. Cyanne Rose & Sherbet Are Best Friends. l.t. ed. 2004. 22p. (YA). per. (978-1-59196-678-4(7)) Instantpublisher.com.

Smith Dinbergs, Holly. Diary Disaster. Stewart, Chantal, illus. 2005. (Girlz Rock! Ser.). (J). pap. (978-1-59336-700-8(7)) Mondo Publishing.

—Pool Pals. Maddock, Monika, illus. 2005. (Girlz Rock! Ser.). (J). pap. (978-1-59336-705-3(8)) Mondo Publishing.

Smith, Doris Buchanan. Un Sabor a Moras. Rioja, Alberto Jiménez, tr. Wimmer, Mike, illus. (SPA.). (YA). (gr. 3 up). 14.95 (978-1-930332-25-6(4) , LC31160) Lectorum Pubns., Inc.

Smith, Greg Andrew. The Pledge of Three Bk. 1: The Z. O. Chronicles. 2005. 240p. (J). pap. 8.95 (978-0-9760576-5-9(4) , 0976057654) Lucky Pr., LLC.

Smith, H. C. Solving the Strange Mystery of Frances Francoise: And What Led up to "9-11-2001" Snyder, Catherine & Smith, Jennifer, eds. rev. ed. 2001. (Illus.). 164p. ring bd. 24.95 (978-0-945437-49-9(8)) MacDonald Sward Publishing Co.

Smith, Jane D. Charlie Is a Chicken. 2000. (Illus.). 176p. (J). (gr. 3-7). pap. 4.95 (978-0-06-440824-0(8)) HarperCollins Pubs.

—Charlie Is a Chicken. 2000. (Illus.). (J). (978-0-606-18682-7(4)) Tandem Library Bks.

Smith, Jullie. The Magic Carpet Adventures: Finding the Magic Carpet, Vol. 1. 2005. (ENG., Illus.). 36p. per. 19.25 (978-1-4208-6725-1(3)) AuthorHouse.

Smith, Lauren. Ashley Enright & the Mystery at Miller's Pond. 2006. (ENG.). 60p. per. 12.95 (*978-1-4241-5268-1(2)) PublishAmerica, Inc.

Smith, Lauren E. Ashley Enright Investigations. 2006. 48p. pap. 12.95 (978-1-4241-2963-8(X)) PublishAmerica, Inc.

Smith-Leckie, Nina. The Fall & Rise of Abuse-a-Saurus Rex. Gordon, Danny, illus. 2003. 28p. (YA). (gr. 5 up). pap. 6.95 (978-0-9725382-0-6(8)) Prairie Arts, Inc.

Smith, Linda. Mrs. Biddlebox. Frazee, Marla, illus. Date not set. 32p. (J). (ps-3). pap. 5.99 (978-0-06-443620-5(9)) HarperCollins Pubs.

Smith, Lisa. Not So Very Far Away. 2005. (Illus.). 14.95 (978-1-55278-448-8(7)) McArthur & Co. CAN. *Dist:* National Bk. Network.

Smith, Michael. Magenta's Visit. 1999. (gr. k-3). lib. bdg. 11.25 (978-0-613-15894-7(6)) Tandem Library Bks.

Smith, Sherri L. Sparrow. 192p. (YA). (gr. 7). 2008. mass mkt. 6.50 (*978-0-440-23945-1(1) , Laurel Leaf); 2006. 15.95 (978-0-385-73324-3(0) , Delacorte Bks. for Young Readers); 2006. lib. bdg. 17.99 (978-0-385-90343-1(X) , Delacorte Bks. for Young Readers) Random Hse. Children's Bks.

Smith, Stephen & Caldwell, Lise. Downhill Challenge. 2006. (Game on for Girls Ser.). 128p. (J). pap. 5.99 (978-0-7847-1735-6(4) , 42145) Standard Publishing.

Smith, Todd Aaron. Cow Finds a Friend. 2003. (Cows Adventure Ser.). (Illus.). 32p. (J). (gr. k-2). 7.99 (978-0-8010-4516-5(9)) Baker Publishing Group.

Snider, Cindy Gay. Finding Anna Bee. Chambers, Mary, illus. 2007. (J). pap. (*978-0-8361-9392-3(X)) Herald Pr.

Snihura, Ulana. I Miss Franklin P. Shuckles. Franson, Leanne, illus. 1998. 32p. (J). (gr. k-2). 15.95 (978-1-55037-517-6(2)); pap. 5.95 (978-1-55037-516-9(4)) Annick Pr., Ltd. CAN. *Dist:* Firefly Bks., Ltd.

Snyder, George. Tiffani & Hootie-Hoot. Tackett, Steve, illus. 1999. 44p. (J). (ps-6). pap. 5.95 (978-1-928597-02-5(5)) PaPa Fuzz Pubns.

Snyder, Margaret. The Greatest Treasure of All. 2002. (J). pap. 2.99 (978-0-375-81481-5(7) , Random Hse. Bks. for Young Readers) Random Hse. Children's Bks.

Snyder, Zilpha Keatley. The Magic Nation Thing. (gr. 3-7). 2007. 192p. 6.50 (*978-0-440-41931-0(X) , Yearling); 2005. 176p. (J). 15.95 (978-0-385-73085-3(3) , Delacorte Bks. for Young Readers) Random Hse. Children's Bks.

Snyder, Zilpha Keatley. The Treasures of Weatherby. 2006. 224p. (J). 15.95 (978-1-4169-1398-6(X) , Atheneum) Simon & Schuster Children's Publishing.

Sobel, Gerrie. Jacob & His Magical Flying Bears: A Christmas Story. Torres, Dottie, illus. 2007. 32p. (J). 12.95 (*978-0-9798244-4-9(3)) TRIAD Publishing Group.

Soesbee, Ree. City of Fortune. 2006. (Elidor Trilogy Ser.: Vol. 3). (Illus.). 256p. (YA). pap. 5.99 (978-0-7869-4026-4(3) , Mirrorstone) Wizards of the Coast.

Sollie, Andre. Hello, Sailor. Godon, Ingrid, illus. 2004. 32p. (J). 18.00 (978-0-333-98735-3(7)) Macmillan Publishers Ltd. GBR. *Dist:* Independent Pubs. Group.

Somebody Moved in Next Door: Individual Chapter Book Title Six-Pack. Vol. 29. 32p. (gr. 5 up). 44.00 (978-0-7578-0978-1(2)) Rigby Education.

Sommer-Bodenburg, Angela. The Little Vampire Moves In. 2007. (Little Vampire Ser.). (Illus.). 144p. (J). 9.95 (*978-1-84270-596-4(2)) Andersen GBR. *Dist:* Independent Pubs. Group.

Sommer, Carl. You Move, You Lose. 2003. (Another Sommer-Time Story Ser.). (Illus.). 48p. (J). (gr. 1-4). 16.95 incl. audio compact disk (978-1-57537-505-2(2)); 16.95 incl. audio (978-1-57537-554-0(0)) Advance Publishing, Inc.

—You Move, You Lose. James, Kennon, illus. (Another Sommer-Time Story Ser.). 48p. (J). (gr. k-3). 2000. lib. bdg. 16.95 (978-1-57537-056-9(5)); 1999. 9.95 (978-1-57537-005-7(0)) Advance Publishing, Inc.

Somoskey, Rebecca. Summer of the Buckeye Whistle. 2004. (J). 5.00 (978-0-9768514-0-0(7)) Bearwallow Blessings Ministries.

Sonnenblick, Jordan. Dodger & Me. 2008. 176p. (J). 16.95 (*978-0-312-37793-9(2)) Feiwel & Friends.

Sonnenblick, Jordan. Notes from the Midnight Driver. 2007. 288p. (J). pap. 6.99 (*978-0-439-75781-2(9) , Scholastic Paperbacks); 2006. 272p. (YA). pap. 16.99 (978-0-439-75779-9(7) , Scholastic Pr.) Scholastic, Inc.

Soto, Gary. Mercy on These Teenage Chimps. 2008. (Illus.). 168p. (J). pap. 6.95 (*978-0-15-206215-6(7) , Harcourt Paperbacks) Harcourt Children's Bks.

—Mercy on These Teenage Chimps. 2007. (Illus.). 160p. (J). (gr. 5-8). 16.00 (978-0-15-206022-0(7)) Harcourt Trade Pubs.

—The Old Man & His Door. Cepeda, Joe, illus. 1998. 32p. (J). (ps-3). pap. 6.99 (978-0-698-11654-2(2) , Putnam Juvenile) Penguin Group (USA) Inc.

—Taking Sides. 2003. (Illus.). 144p. (YA). pap. 5.95 (978-0-15-204694-1(1) , Harcourt Paperbacks) Harcourt Children's Bks.

—El Viejo y Su Puerta. Cepeda, Joe, illus. 1998. (SPA.). 32p. (J). (ps-3). pap. 6.99 (978-0-698-11655-9(0) , PU8557, Putnam Juvenile) Penguin Group (USA) Inc.

Spaceboy Finds a Friend. 2003. (J). (978-1-932570-01-4(2)) Literacy Footprints Inc.

Spaceboy Plays Hide & Seek. 2003. (J). (978-1-932570-05-2(5)) Literacy Footprints Inc.

Spafford, Suzy. Witzy & Zoom-Zoom. Spafford, Suzy, illus. 1998. (Illus.). 32p. (J). (ps). 14.95 (978-0-9643588-1-2(6)) Suzy's Zoo.

Spalding, Andrea. Me & Mr. Mah. Wilson, Janet, illus. 32p. (J). (ps-2). 2001. 7.95 (978-1-55143-177-2(7)); 2000. 14.95 (978-1-55143-168-0(8)) Orca Bk. Pubs. USA.

—Me & Mr Mah. 2001. (gr. k-3). lib. bdg. 16.40 (978-0-613-88504-1(X)) Tandem Library Bks.

—Solomon's Tree. Wilson, Janet, illus. 2005. 32p. (J). (ps-2). 7.95 (978-1-55143-380-6(X)) Orca Bk. Pubs. USA.

Sparks, Matthew. All I Need. 2005. 48p. pap. 12.95 (978-1-4137-4004-2(9)) PublishAmerica, Inc.

Spelman, Cornelia Maude. When I Feel Good about Myself. Parkinson, Kathy, illus. 2003. (Way I Feel Bks.). 24p. (J). (ps-1). pap. 6.95 (978-0-8075-8901-4(2)) Whitman, Albert & Co.

Spelvin, Justin. My Best Friends. 2006. (Care Bears Ser.). 32p. (J). pap. 3.99 (978-0-439-86232-5(9) , Scholastic) Scholastic, Inc.

Spelvin, Justin. Scholastic Reader Level: My Best Friends. Albrecht, Jeff, illus. 2005. (Scholastic Reader Ser.). 32p. (J). per. **(*978-0-439-75525-2(5))*** Scholastic, Inc.

Spendlove, Owen. Stanley Brambles & the Pirate's Treasure. 2007. 320p. per. 18.95 **(*978-0-595-43792-4(3))*** iUniverse, Inc.

Sperring, Mark. Wanda's First Day. Pope, Kate & Pope, Liz, illus. 2004. 32p. (J). pap. 15.95 (978-0-439-62773-3(7) , Chicken Hse., The) Scholastic, Inc.

Spinelli, Jerry. The Bathwater Gang. Johnson, Meredith, illus. 2005. 64p. (J). (gr. 4-7). pap. 3.99 (978-0-316-01442-7(7)) Little Brown & Co.

Spinelli, Jerry. Eggs. 2007. 224p. (J). (gr. 3-7). 15.99 **(*978-0-316-16646-1(4))*** Little, Brown Bks. for Young Readers.

Spinelli, Jessica. Mondays with Miss McKenna. Wise, Noreen, ed. Wethington, Liz, illus. 2001. (Gold Mixed Collection). 54p. (J). pap. 7.50 (978-1-58584-423-4(3)) Huckleberry Pr.

Spires, Elizabeth. The Mouse of Amherst. 2001. (Illus.). (J). (978-0-606-20812-3(7)) Tandem Library Bks.

Spirn, Michele. The Know-Nothings Talk Turkey. Alley, R. W., illus. 2001. 48p. (J). (gr. k-3). lib. bdg. 11.80 (978-0-613-62145-8(X)) Tandem Library Bks.

Spirn, Michele Sobel. The Know-Nothings Talk Turkey. Alley, R. W., illus. (I Can Read Bks.). 48p. (J). (ps-3). 2001. pap. 3.99 (978-0-06-444251-0(9) , Harper Trophy); 2000. 14.95 (978-0-06-028183-0(9)); 2000. 14.89 (978-0-06-028184-7(7)) HarperCollins Pubs.

—The Know-Nothings Talk Turkey. Alley, Robert W., illus. 2000. 48p. (J). (gr. k-3). lib. bdg. 11.19 (978-0-606-22291-4(X)) Tandem Library Bks.

Spongberg, Emily. Hannibal & the King. Spongberg, Tim, illus. l.t. ed. 1999. 32p. (J). (gr. k-4). 15.95 (978-1-893659-00-1(3)) Rainbow Hse. Publishing.

SpongeBob SquarePants. 2007. (J). 128.10 **(*978-1-59961-361-1(1))*** Spotlight.

Spotlight (Firm) Staff, contrib. by. Jughead with Archie in Power Play. 2007. (Illus.). 80p. (J). 24.21 **(*978-1-59961-275-1(5))*** Spotlight.

Spradlin, Michael P. Spy Goddess, Book Two: to Hawaii, with Love. 2008. (Spy Goddess Ser.). 288p. (J). pap. 6.99 **(*978-0-06-059412-1(8)*** , HarperTeen) HarperCollins Pubs.

Spradlin, Michael P. To Hawaii, with Love. 2006. (Spy Goddess Ser.). (Illus.). 208p. (J). lib. bdg. 16.89 (978-0-06-059411-4(X)); (YA). 15.99 (978-0-06-059410-7(1)) HarperCollins Pubs.

Springer, Nancy. Wild Boy: A Tale of Rowan Hood. 2004. (Tales of Rowan Hood Ser.: No. 4). 128p. (YA). (gr. 5-7). 16.99 (978-0-399-24015-7(2) , Philomel) Penguin Group (USA) Inc.

Spyri, Johanna. Veronica & Other Friends. 2006. pap. **(*978-1-4068-0697-7(8))*** Echo Library.

Spyropulos, Diana. Cornelius y la Estrella Perro. 2004. (SPA.). 48p. (978-84-7720-790-0(9)) Obelisco, Ediciones S.A.

St-Aubin, Bruno. My Favorite Monster. 2005. (Read-It! Readers Ser.). (Illus.). 32p. (J). (gr. k-3). 18.60 (978-1-4048-1029-7(3)) Picture Window Bks.

Stafford, Liliana. Snow Bear. Davis, Lambert, illus. 32p. (J). pap. (978-0-88899-441-7(9)) Groundwood Bks.

—Snow Bear. Davis, Lambert, illus. 2001. 32p. (J). (gr. 1-3). 15.95 (978-0-439-26977-3(6)) Scholastic, Inc.

Stahl, Hilda. Big Trouble for Roxie. 2003. (Best Friends Ser.: No. 2). 160p. (YA). (gr. 4-7). pap. 4.99 (978-0-89107-658-2(1)) Crossway Bks.

Standiford, Natalie. Dating Game: Can True Love Survive High School?, No. 3. 2005. 224p. (YA). (gr. 8-17). pap. 9.99 (978-0-316-11042-6(6)) Little Brown & Co.

Standish, Burt L. Frank Merriwell's College Chums. Rudman, Jack, ed. 2003. (Frank Merriwell Ser.). 29.95 (978-0-8373-9337-7(X)); pap. 9.95 (978-0-8373-9037-6(0)) Merriwell, Frank Inc.

—Frank Merriwell's False Friend. Rudman, Jack, ed. 2003. (Frank Merriwell Ser.). 29.95 (978-0-8373-9370-4(1)); pap. 9.95 (978-0-8373-9070-3(2)) Merriwell, Frank Inc.

Stanek, Gerald R. Sarah 'n' Dippity. Stanek, Joyce Huntington, illus. 2004. 28p. (J). 14.95 (978-0-9747417-0-3(1)) Shiver Hill Bks.

Stanley, Diane. Goldie & the Three Bears. Stanley, Diane, illus. 40p. (J). 2007. pap. 6.99 (978-0-06-113611-5(5) , Harper Trophy); 2003. (Illus.). 15.99 (978-0-06-000008-0(2)); 2003. (Illus.). lib. bdg. 17.89 (978-0-06-000009-7(0)) HarperCollins Pubs.

Stanley, Mandy. Meet Patrick. Stanley, Mandy, illus. 1999. (Illus.). 8p. (J). 6.99 (978-1-58048-057-4(8)) Sandvik Publishing.

Stanley, Mandy, illus. Amadeus "Best Friends" 1999. 9p. (J). bds. 11.98 (978-1-58048-067-3(5)) Sandvik Publishing.

Staples, Suzanne Fisher. Dangerous Skies. 2006. 240p. (J). pap. 6.95 (978-0-374-41670-6(2) , Farrar, Straus & Giroux (BYR)) Farrar, Straus & Giroux.

Stark, Barbara. Blue Dinosaur's Friends. l.t. ed. 2006. (Illus.). 24p. (J). E-Book 9.95 incl. cd-rom (978-1-933090-20-7(0)) Guardian Angel Publishing, Inc.

Starke, Ruth. Stella by the Sea: Stella's Not Just an Ordinary Girl in an Ordinary World! 2006. (Chomps Ser.). (Illus.). 96p. (J). (gr. 3-7). pap. 3.95 (978-0-7624-2625-6(X) , Running Pr. Kids) Running Pr. Bk. Pubs.

Stauffacher, Sue. Donuthead. 2005. 176p. (J). (gr. 3-7). reprint ed. pap. 5.50 (978-0-440-41934-1(4) , Yearling) Random Hse. Children's Bks.

—Harry Sue. 304p. (J). (gr. 3-7). 2007. pap. 6.50 (978-0-440-42064-4(4) , Yearling); 2005. 15.95 (978-0-375-83274-1(2) , Knopf Bks. for Young Readers); 2005. lib. bdg. 17.99 (978-0-375-93274-8(7) , Knopf Bks. for Young Readers) Random Hse. Children's Bks.

Staunton, Ted. Morgan Makes a Deal. Slavin, Bill, illus. 2005. (First Novel Ser.). 64p. (J). (gr. 2-5). **(*978-0-88780-667-4(8)***); 4.95 (978-0-88780-666-7(X)) Formac Publishing Co., Ltd. CAN. *Dist:* Casemate Pubs. & Bk. Distributors, LLC.

—Morgan Makes a Splash. Slavin, Bill, illus. 2004. (First Novel Ser.). 64p. (J). (gr. 1-5). 4.95 (978-0-88780-622-3(8)); **(*978-0-88780-623-0(6))*** Formac Publishing Co., Ltd. CAN. *Dist:* Casemate Pubs. & Bk. Distributors, LLC.

—Stinky. Gardos, Susan, illus. 2004. (Northern Lights Young Novels Ser.). 64p. (J). (gr. 2-5). pap. 4.95 (978-0-88995-263-8(9)) Red Deer Pr. CAN. *Dist:* Fitzhenry & Whiteside, Ltd.

—Stinky. 2003. (gr. 3-6). lib. bdg. 12.95 (978-0-613-84450-5(5)) Tandem Library Bks.

—Super Move, Morgan! Slavin, Bill, illus. 2006. (First Novels Ser.: Vol. 35). 64p. (J). (gr. 2-5). **(*978-0-88780-704-6(6)***); 4.95 (978-0-88780-702-2(X)) Formac Publishing Co., Ltd. CAN. *Dist:* Casemate Pubs. & Bk. Distributors, LLC.

Staunton, Ted. The Trouble with Girls. Gardos, Susan, illus. 2004. (Northern Lights Young Novels Ser.). 72p. (J). (gr. 2-5). pap. 4.95 (978-0-88995-264-5(7)) Red Deer Pr. CAN. *Dist:* Fitzhenry & Whiteside, Ltd.

Staunton, Ted & Gardos, Susan. Second Banana. 2004. (Monkey Mountain Bks.). (Illus.). 72p. (J). (gr. 2-5). pap. 4.95 (978-0-88995-241-6(8)) Red Deer Pr. CAN. *Dist:* Fitzhenry & Whiteside, Ltd.

Stead, Vince. Rusty the Runaway Golden Retriever. 2007. 73p. 14.95 **(*978-1-4241-5739-6(0))*** PublishAmerica, Inc.

Steck-Vaughn Staff. Imaginary Friends: Wild Wooly. 1998. (Illus.). (J). pap. (978-0-8172-8636-1(5)) Steck-Vaughn.

—Special Friends: Grandma J/Buddy. 1998. (Illus.). (J). pap. (978-0-8172-8649-1(7)) Steck-Vaughn.

—Special Friends: My Dog/Sister. 1998. (Illus.). (J). pap. (978-0-8172-8645-3(4)) Steck-Vaughn.

Steele, D. Kelley. Fire in Her Hair: A Story of Friendship. James, Margaret Ray, illus. l.t. ed. 2002. 40p. (J). (gr. 1-6). 18.95 (978-0-9711534-0-0(X)) Hidden Path Pubn., Inc.

Steers, Billy. Tractor Mac Builds a Barn. 2004. (Illus.). 24p. (J). (ps-ps). pap. 3.29 (978-1-59445-075-4(7)) Dogs in Hats Children's Publishing Co.

Steggall, Vicki. Lunchtime Rules. Oswald, Ash, illus. 2007. (Go Girl! Ser.: Bk. 4). 96p. (Orig.). (J). (gr. 2 up). pap. 3.99 **(*978-0-312-34644-7(1))*** Feiwel & Friends.

Steig, William. Amos & Boris. 1999. (J). 13.75 (978-0-606-16476-4(6)) Tandem Library Bks.

—Amos y Boris. Negroni, María, tr. 1999. (SPA., Illus.). 32p. (J). (ps-3). pap. 6.95 (978-0-374-40361-4(9) , Mirasol/Libros Juveniles) Farrar, Straus & Giroux.

—Potch & Polly. Date not set. (J). 15.89 (978-0-06-205145-5(8)) HarperCollins Pubs.

—Potch & Polly. Agee, Jon, illus. Date not set. (J). 14.99 (978-0-06-205144-8(X)) HarperCollins Pubs.

Steig, William. The Real Thief. 2007. (Illus.). 64p. (J). pap. 5.99 **(*978-0-312-37145-6(4))*** Square Fish.

Stein, David Ezra. Cowboy Ned & Andy. Stein, David Ezra, illus. 2006. (Illus.). 32p. (J). (ps-1). 14.95 (978-1-4169-0041-2(1) , Simon & Schuster Children's Publishing) Simon & Schuster Children's Publishing.

—Ned's New Friend. Stein, David Ezra, illus. 2007. (Cowboy Ned & Andy Ser.). 32p. (J). (ps-1). 14.99 (978-1-4169-2490-6(6) , Simon & Schuster Children's Publishing) Simon & Schuster Children's Publishing.

Stein, Tammar. High Dive. 2008. 240p. (YA). (gr. 7). lib. bdg. 18.99 **(*978-0-375-93024-9(8)*** , Knopf Bks. for Young Readers) Random Hse. Children's Bks.

Steiner, Jorg. The Bear Who Wanted to Be a Bear. Mueller, Jorg, illus. 2nd ed. 2007. 44p. (J). 16.95 (978-0-9762056-0-9(2)) Heryin Publishing Corp.

Stenhouse, Ted. Across the Steel River. Deines, Brian, illus. 2003. 224p. (YA). (gr. 13 up). 978-1-55337-015-4(5)); (978-1-55074-891-8(2)) Kids Can Pr., Ltd.

—Across the Steel River. 2001. 222p. (YA). (gr. 8-12). per. 15.25 (978-0-613-84417-8(3)) Tandem Library Bks.

Stephen, Smith. Fourth & Long. 2006. 128p. (J). pap. 5.99 (978-0-7847-1471-3(1) , 42142) Standard Publishing.

Stephens, Ann Marie. A Surprise for Ray. Bolan, Michael P., illus. 2003. 47p. (J). per. 11.95 (978-0-9729285-1-9(0) , 0-9729285-1-0) Kinkachoo Pr., The.

—Surprise for Ray: Complete Story Experience (TM) Edition. Bolan, Michael, illus. 2nd exp. ed. 2006. 44p. (J). pap. 9.99 (978-1-59092-175-3(5) , Little Blue Works) Windstorm Creative.

Stephens, Helen. Ahoyty-Toyty. 2004. (Illus.). 32p. (J). (ps-3). 14.95 (978-0-385-75039-4(0) , Fickling, David Bks.) Random Hse. Children's Bks.

Stephens, Monique Z. Spring for Strawberry Shortcake. Yee, Josie, tr. Yee, Josie, illus. 2004. (Strawberry Shortcake Ser.). 32p. (J). (ps-2). mass mkt. 3.99 (978-0-448-43373-8(7) , Grosset & Dunlap) Penguin Group (USA) Inc.

—Spring for Strawberry Shortcake. 2004. (gr. k-3). lib. bdg. 11.25 (978-0-613-72570-5(0)) Tandem Library Bks.

—Strawberry Shortcake & the Friendship Party. Bracken, Carolyn, illus. 2003. (Strawberry Shortcake Ser.). 24p. (J). (ps-3). mass mkt. 4.99 (978-0-448-43222-9(6) , Grosset & Dunlap) Penguin Group (USA) Inc.

Stephenson, Nancy Ann. The Ducks' New Friends. Coffin, Marilyn, illus. l.t. ed. 2006. 34p. (J). per. 9.99 (978-1-59879-164-8(8)) Lifevest Publishing, Inc.

Sterling & Ward, Adam. My Best Friends. 1999. (Balloon Ser.). (Illus.). 32p. (gr. 1-4). 5.95 (978-0-8069-1950-8(7)) Sterling Publishing Co., Inc.

Stern, Ricki. Beryl E. Bean. 2nd ed. 2002. (Beryl E. Bean Ser.). (Illus.). 64p. (J). 14.89 (978-0-06-028772-6(1)) HarperCollins Pubs.

—Mission Impossible. Date not set. (Beryl E. Bean Ser.: Vol. 3). (Illus.). (J). lib. bdg. 15.89 (978-0-06-028773-3(X) , Harper Trophy) HarperCollins Pubs.

Stern, Ricki & Worcester, Heidi P. Beryl E. Bean: Mission Impossible Friendship. Bates, Amy June, illus. 2002. (J). pap. 5.99 (978-0-06-442122-5(8) , Harper Trophy) HarperCollins Pubs.

—Beryl E. Bean Book 1: Mighty Adventurer of the Planet. Bates, Amy June, illus. 2002. (Beryl E. Bean Ser.). 64p. (J). (gr. 2-4). pap. 5.95 (978-0-06-442120-1(1)) HarperCollins Pubs.

Stevens, Janet & Stevens Crummel, Susan. My Big Dog. Stevens, Janet, illus. 2005. (Illus.). 40p. (J). (gr. k-k). 12.95 (978-0-375-83297-0(1)); lib. bdg. 14.99 (978-0-375-93297-7(6)) Random Hse. Children's Bks. (Golden Bks.).

Stevens, Terry. The Battle at Longshore Causeway. 2006. 64p. pap. **(*978-1-84401-751-5(6))*** Athena Pr.

Stevenson, Robin H. Out of Order. 2007. 224p. (YA). (gr. 7 up). pap. **(*978-1-55143-693-7(0))*** Orca Bk. Pubs.

Stewart, Jane L. A Campfire Girl's Test of Friendship. 2004. reprint ed. pap. 26.95 (978-1-4179-3874-2(9)) Kessinger Publishing, LLC.

Stewart, Jennifer J. Close Encounters of a Third World Kind. 2004. 128p. (J). (gr. 4-6). tchr. ed. 16.95 (978-0-8234-1850-3(2)) Holiday Hse., Inc.

Stewart, Joel. Dexter Bexley & the Big Blue Beastie. Stewart, Joel, illus. 2007. (Illus.). 32p. (J). (ps-3). 16.95 **(*978-0-8234-2068-1(X))*** Holiday Hse., Inc.

Stewart, Melanie. Stage Fright. 1999. (gr. 3-6). lib. bdg. 11.80 (978-0-613-28086-0(5)) Tandem Library Bks.

Stewart, Paul. A Little Bit of Winter. Riddell, Chris, illus. 1999. 32p. (J). (ps-2). 14.95 (978-0-06-028278-3(9)) HarperCollins Pubs.

—Rabbit's Wish. Riddell, Chris, illus. 2001. 32p. (J). (ps-2). 12.95 (978-0-06-029518-9(X)) HarperCollins Pubs.

Stewart, Paul & Riddell, Chris. What Do You Remember? 2002. (Illus.). 32p. (J). 17.99 (978-1-84270-080-8(4)) Andersen GBR. *Dist:* Independent Pubs. Group.

Stewart, Sarah. The Friend. Small, David, illus. 2004. 48p. (J). 16.00 (978-0-374-32463-6(8) , Farrar, Straus & Giroux (BYR)) Farrar, Straus & Giroux.

—The Friend. Small, David, illus. unabr. ed. 2007. (Picture Book Readalong Ser.). (J). (ps-3). 28.95 incl. audio compact disk **(*978-1-59519-918-8(7)***); 25.95 incl. audio **(*978-1-59519-914-0(4))*** Live Oak Media.

Stewart, Toni D., illus. Jill & the Imp. 1999. 13p. (Orig.). (J). (gr. k-2). pap. 2.50 (978-1-889658-04-9(9)) New Canaan Publishing Co. LLC.

Stimson, Joan. Oscar Needs a Friend. Rutherford, Meg, illus. 1998. 32p. (J). (ps-1). pap. 5.95 (978-0-7641-0746-7(1)) Barron's Educational Series, Inc.

Stine, R. L. The Best Friend. 2006. (Fear Street Ser.). 160p. (YA). pap. 5.99 (978-1-4169-1376-4(9) , Simon Pulse) Simon & Schuster Children's Publishing.

—Monster Blood II. 2004. 121p. (J). (ps-7). lib. bdg. 11.64 (978-0-606-32488-5(7)) Tandem Library Bks.

—The New Girl. 2006. (Fear Street Ser.). 176p. (YA). pap. 5.99 (978-1-4169-1810-3(8) , Simon Pulse) Simon & Schuster Children's Publishing.

—Say Cheese & Die! 2005. (Goosebumps Ser.). 144p. (J). pap. 1.99 (978-0-439-79631-6(8) , Scholastic Paperbacks) Scholastic, Inc.

Stine, R. L., ed. Midnight Games. 2005. 183p. (YA). (978-1-4156-1074-9(6) , Simon Pulse) Simon & Schuster Children's Publishing.

Stine, R.L. The Best Friend. 2006. 147p. (J). lib. bdg. 13.00 **(*978-1-4242-0993-4(5))*** Fitzgerald Bks.

—Midnight Games. 2005. 183p. (YA). lib. bdg. 20.00 **(*978-1-4242-1119-7(0))*** Fitzgerald Bks.

—Rich Girl. 2005. 132p. (J). lib. bdg. 13.00 **(*978-1-4242-0999-6(4))*** Fitzgerald Bks.

Stinson, Kathy. Fish House Secrets. 2004. 128p. mass mkt. (978-1-895449-10-5(3)) Thistledown Pr., Ltd.

—The Great Bike Race. 2005. (Streetlights Ser.). 104p. (J). (gr. 2-5). 7.95 (978-1-55028-890-2(3)) Lorimer, James & Co., Ltd., Pubs. CAN. *Dist:* Casemate Pubs. & Bk. Distributors, LLC.

Stockton, Lucille. God in a Child's World & King Catfish Roonie & His Neighbors. 2003. 48p. (J). per. (978-1-932077-34-6(0)) Athena Pr.

Stockwell, Peter. The Market. 2005. 54p. pap. 12.95 (978-1-4137-6087-3(2)) PublishAmerica, Inc.

Stoddard, Jeffery. Pete & Pillar - The Big Rain: A Story of Friendship Based on John 15:13. 2007. (Illus.). 32p. (J). (ps-2). 12.99 **(*978-1-59317-203-9(6))*** Warner Pr. Pubs.

Stolarz, Laurie Faria. Bleed. 2006. 240p. (gr. 7-17). 15.99 (978-0-7868-3854-7(X)) Hyperion Pr.

Stone, Chuck. Squizzy the Black Squirrel: A Fabulous Fable of Friendship. Jackson, Jeannie, tr. Jackson, Jeannie, illus. 2003. 30p. (J). 16.95 (978-0-940880-71-9(7)) Open Hand Publishing, LLC.

Stone, Forrest. The Ant & Grasshopper Show. 2006. 42.00 **(*978-1-4108-6183-2(X))*** Benchmark Education Co.

Stone, Jeff. Eagle. 2008. (Five Ancestors Ser.). 224p. (J). (gr. 5). 15.99 **(*978-0-375-83083-9(9)***); lib. bdg. 18.99 **(*978-0-375-93083-6(3))*** Random Hse. Children's Bks. (Random Hse. Bks. for Young Readers).

Storace, Patricia. Sugar Cane: A Caribbean Rapunzel. Colon, Raul, illus. 2007. 48p. (gr. 1-5). 16.99 (978-0-7868-0791-8(1)) Disney Pr.

Stormer, Kate. Casey's Unexpected Friend. Lowes, Tom, illus. l.t. ed. 2003. 38p. (J). 16.95 (978-0-9722099-7-7(2) , CUF) Caseys World Bks.

Storybook Friends Book Set 800919, 3 vols. 2005. (J). pap. (978-1-59794-084-9(4)) Environments, Inc.

Stouffer, N. K. Larry Potter & His Best Friend Lilly. Stouffer, N. K., illus. 2001. (Larry Potter Storybks.). (Illus.). 22p. (J). (ps-2). 7.95 (978-1-58989-300-9(X)) Thurman Hse., LLC.

Stower, Adam. The Den. 2005. (Illus.). 32p. (ps-k). pap. 12.99 (978-0-7475-7550-4(9)) Bloomsbury Publishing Plc GBR. *Dist:* Independent Pubs. Group.

Strachan, Linda. Edinburgh Adventure. 2005. (Illus.). 32p. pap. 9.00 (978-0-9546701-7-7(5)) GW Publishing GBR. *Dist:* Wilson & Assocs.

—Ghost of Glamis. 2005. (Illus.). 32p. pap. 9.00 (978-0-9546701-9-1(1)) GW Publishing GBR. *Dist:* Wilson & Assocs.

—Serach for Loch Ness Monster. 2005. (Illus.). 32p. pap. 9.00 (978-0-9546701-5-3(9)) GW Publishing GBR. *Dist:* Wilson & Assocs.

—Skye Surprise. 2005. (Illus.). 32p. pap. 9.00 (978-0-9546701-8-4(3)) GW Publishing GBR. *Dist:* Wilson & Assocs.

Strangway, Melissa. 56 Water Street. 2007. 104p. per. 9.95 **(*978-0-595-42429-0(5))*** iUniverse, Inc.

Strasser, Todd. Con-fidence. 164p. (J). (gr. 4-6). tchr. ed. 16.95 (978-0-8234-1394-2(2)) ; (YA). (gr. 5 up). pap. 6.95 **(*978-0-8234-2061-2(2))*** Holiday Hse., Inc.

Stratten, Lou. Hello, I'm Sir Frettirick! Let's Say Hello to Our New Friends! Bennett, Judy, ed. Stratten, Lou & Denaro, Sal, illus. 2006. (J). 6.95 (978-0-9747173-1-9(2)) Stratten, Lou.

Stratton-Porter. At the Foot of the Rainbow. 2006. 19.99 **(*978-1-4219-7512-2(2))*** IndyPublish.com.

Stratton Porter, Gene. At the Foot of the Rainbow. 2007. 180p. 18.95 **(*978-1-934169-52-0(8)***); pap. 7.95 **(*978-1-934169-53-7(6))*** Norilana Bks.

Stren, Patti. Hug Me. 2001. (Illus.). 32p. (J). 14.95 (978-0-06-029317-8(9)) HarperCollins Pubs.

Strepponi, Blanca. Claudia y Daniel. Muller, Cristina, illus. 2004. (SPA.). 28p. (J). pap. 7.99 (978-980-257-268-7(3)) Ekare, Ediciones VEN. *Dist:* Lectorum Pubns., Inc.

Stretton, Hesba. Cassy. Hymper, W. & Stacey, W. S., illus. 2006. (Golden Inheritance Ser.: Vol. 9). 117p. (J). pap. (978-0-921100-94-2(9)) Inheritance Pubns.

—Jessica's First Prayer. 2004. reprint ed. pap. 15.95 (978-1-4191-2751-9(9)); pap. 1.99 (978-1-4192-2751-6(3)) Kessinger Publishing, LLC.

Strickland, Brad & Fuller, Thomas E. Marsquake! 2005. (Mars Year One Ser.). (Illus.). 192p. (J). pap. 4.99 (978-0-689-86402-5(7) , Aladdin) Simon & Schuster Children's Publishing.

Strom, Maria Diaz. Rainbow Joe & Me. ed. 2004. (J). (gr. k-3). spiral bd. (978-0-616-03097-4(5)) Canadian National Institute for the Blind/Institut National Canadien pour les Aveugles.

—Rainbow Joe & Me. Strom, Maria Diaz, illus. (Illus.). 32p. (J). 2002. 6.95 (978-1-58430-050-2(7)); 1999. 15.95 (978-1-880000-93-9(8)) Lee & Low Bks., Inc.

Strong, Frances Dinkins. A Lucky Pair. Roscoe, Mattie Dinkins, illus. l.t. ed. 2002. 28p. pap. 6.49 (978-0-9720267-0-3(3)) Learning Abilities Bks.

Stuart, Duncan. The Whole of the Moon. 200p. (YA). (gr. 8 up). pap. 13.00 (978-1-877135-05-7(4)) Longacre Pr. NZL. *Dist:* Pacific Island Bks.

Stuart-Russell, C. Playtime with the Animals. 2007. 61p. pap. 12.95 **(*978-1-4241-5473-9(1))*** PublishAmerica, Inc.

Stutzman, D. J. The Promise Ring. 2007. (J). pap. 9.00 **(*978-0-8059-7365-5(6))*** Dorrance Publishing Co., Inc.

Su Chen Fang & Gui Fong Chang. Happy Birthday to You! l.t. ed. 1999. (Children's Stories Published in Other Lands Ser.). (Illus.). 32p. (J). (ps up). lib. bdg. 15.95 (978-1-56674-241-2(2)) Forest Hse. Publishing Co., Inc.

Su, Lucy. Peekaboo Friends. 2004. 16p. (J). pap. 7.95 (978-1-84507-222-3(7)) Lincoln, Frances Ltd. GBR. *Dist:* Perseus Distribution.

Suen, Anastasia. The Clubhouse. Eitzen, Allan, illus. 2003. (Easy-to-Read Ser.). 32p. (J). (gr. k-2). pap. 3.99 (978-0-14-250054-5(2) , Puffin) Penguin Group (USA) Inc.

—Helping Sophia. Ebbeler, Jeffrey, illus. 2007. (Main Street School - Kids with Character Ser.). 32p. (J). (ps-4). lib. bdg. 27.07 **(*978-1-60270-030-7(3)*** , Looking Glass Library) Magic Wagon.

—Times Table Cheat. Ebbeler, Jeffrey, illus. 2007. (Main Street School - Kids with Character Ser.). 32p. (J). (ps-4). lib. bdg. 27.07 **(*978-1-60270-034-5(6)*** , Looking Glass Library) Magic Wagon.

Sula, Sondra. Katie: Katie & the Ogre. Ruiz, Marcus, illus. 2000. 32p. (J). (gr. 1-3). pap. (978-1-931179-01-0(8)) Long Hill Productions, Inc.

Sullivan, Arlene R. The Journey of Hanna Heart: You Never Know Where the Wind Will Blow. Sullivan, Arlene R., illus. 1998. (Illus.). 16p. (J). (gr. k-5). pap. 12.95 (978-0-9665793-0-7(5)) Changing Images Art Foundation, Inc.

Sullivan, Sarah. Root Beer & Banana. Shed, Greg, illus. 2005. 32p. (P). (gr. k-3). 16.99 (978-0-7636-1748-6(2)) Candlewick Pr.

Summerall, Tray & Summerall, Tray. Little T & the Egg. 2008. 44p. (J). 16.99 (978-1-59092-567-6(X) , Little Blue Works) Windstorm Creative.

Sumpolec, Sarah Anne. The Masquerade. 2003. (Becoming Beka Ser.). 224p. (YA). pap. 12.99 (978-0-8024-6451-4(3)) Moody Pubs.

Sunderland, Margot & Hancock, Nicky. Ruby & the Rubbish Bin: A Story for Children with Low Self-Esteem. Armstrong, Nicky, tr. Armstrong, Nicky, illus. 32p. pap. (978-0-86388-462-7(8) , 002-5146) Speechmark Publishing Ltd.

—Teenie Weenie in a Too Big World: A Story for Fearful Children, 2 vols. Armstrong, Nicky, tr. Armstrong, Nicky, illus. 32p. pap. (978-0-86388-460-3(1) , 002-5144) Speechmark Publishing Ltd.

Sunkuli, O. Hero & the Dream. 2004. (Illus.). 24p. 13.95 (978-9966-25-161-9(8)) Heinemann Kenya, Limited (East African Educational Publishers Ltd E.A.E.P.) KEN. *Dist:* Michigan State Univ. Pr.

Supeene, Shelagh Lynne. My Name Is Mitch. 2003. 176p. (J). (gr. 3-7). pap. 6.95 (978-1-55143-255-7(2)) Orca Bk. Pubs. USA.

Supplee, Audra. I Almost Love You, Eddie Clegg. 2004. 192p. (J). (gr. 4-6). 14.95 (978-1-56145-308-5(0)) Peachtree Pubs., Ltd.

Surman, Susan. Max & Friends. Owings, Rae, illus. 150p. (J). (gr. k-3). 9.99 (978-0-88092-452-8(7)); 1999. pap. 9.99 (978-0-88092-388-0(1)) Royal Fireworks Publishing Co.

Susan, Sister. The Sun in My Belly. Nghiem, Sister Tin, illus. 2007. 32p. pap. 11.95 (*978-1-888375-64-0(7) , Plum Blossom Bks.) Parallax Pr.

Sutherland, Tui. Fun with Mo & Ella. 2002. (ps-2). lib. bdg. 11.80 (978-0-613-43625-0(3)) Tandem Library Bks.

—Meet Mo & Ella. 2001. (First Friends, First Readers Ser.). (Illus.). (J). (978-0-606-21323-3(6)) Tandem Library Bks.

Suzie Sheep & her Friends. 2004. (Play Pals Ser.). (Illus.). 12p. (J). bds. (978-1-84229-649-3(3)) Top That! Publishing PLC.

Swan, Bill. Road Rage. 2006. (Sports Stories Ser.). 120p. (J). (gr. 3-8). 7.95 (978-1-55028-916-9(0)) Lorimer, James & Co., Ltd., Pubs. CAN. *Dist:* Casemate Pubs. & Bk. Distributors, LLC.

Sweeney, Jacqueline. Meadow Magic. 2001. (We Can Read! Ser.). (Illus.). 32p. (J). (gr. 1-2). lib. bdg. 21.36 (978-0-7614-1124-6(0) , Benchmark Bks.) Cavendish, Marshall Corp.

Sweeney, Joyce. Takedown. 2004. 208p. (J). 15.95 (978-0-7614-5175-4(7)) Cavendish, Marshall Corp.

—Waiting for June. 2006. 160p. 5.99 (978-0-7614-5329-1(6)); 2003. 144p. (YA). 15.95 (978-0-7614-5138-9(2)) Cavendish, Marshall Corp.

Sweet, J. H. The Fairy Chronicles: Thistle & the Shell of Laughter. 2007. (Illus.). 128p. (J). pap. 6.99 (*978-1-4022-0874-4(X) , Sourcebooks Jabberwocky) Sourcebooks, Inc.

—Marigold & the Feather of Hope, the Journey Begins. Chang, Tara Larsen, illus. 2007. (Fairy Chronicles Ser.). 128p. (J). (gr. 2-4). pap. 6.99 (*978-1-4022-0872-0(3) , Sourcebooks Jabberwocky) Sourcebooks, Inc.

Swift, John. Tea with a Vampire. 2007. pap. 9.00 (*978-0-8059-8963-2(3)) Dorrance Publishing Co., Inc.

Swiger, Lenora. Colt under the Wire. 2004. 73p. per. 8.49 (978-1-4116-0884-9(4)) Lulu.com.

Swimley, Alison. Dizzy & Terry. 2000. (Illus.). 29p. (J). pap. 15.95 (978-0-7541-1080-4(X)) Minerva Pr. GBR. *Dist:* Unity Distribution.

Swimpson, Alayne. Murphy & Scootie. 2006. pap. 17.99 (*978-1-4259-7251-6(9)) AuthorHouse.

Swindells, Robert. Room 13 & Inside the Worm. 2008. 352p. (YA). pap. 9.95 (*978-0-552-55591-3(6)) Transworld Publishers Ltd. GBR. *Dist:* Independent Pubs. Group.

Swope, Sam. The Araboolies of Liberty Street. 2001. 12.75 (978-0-606-21040-9(7)) Tandem Library Bks.

Tabernik, John. Ricky the Picky Koala. Wise, Catlin, illus. 2005. (J). 14.95 (978-0-9773936-0-2(7)) Little Munchkin Bks.

Tada, Joni Eareckson. You've Got a Friend. Meyer, Jeff, illus. 2004. 31p. (ps-3). 14.99 (978-1-58134-060-0(5)) Crossway Bks.

Tafuri, Nancy. Where Did Bunny Go? A Bunny & Bird Story. 2001. (Illus.). (J). pap. (978-0-439-16960-8(7)) Scholastic, Inc.

—Where Did Bunny Go? A Bunny & Bird Story. Tafuri, Nancy, illus. 2001. (Illus.). 32p. (J). (ps-2). pap. 15.95 (978-0-439-16959-2(3) , Levine, Arthur A. Bks.) Scholastic, Inc.

—Will You Be My Friend? A Bunny & Bird Story. 2000. (Illus.). 32p. (J). (ps-3). pap. 16.95 (978-0-590-63782-4(7) , Scholastic Reference) Scholastic, Inc.

Takayama, Sandi. The Musubi Man's New Friend. 2002. (Illus.). 24p. (J). 10.95 (978-1-57306-144-5(1)) Bess Pr., Inc.

Talbert, Marc. The Purple Heart. 2000. 148p. (gr. 4-7). pap. 10.95 (978-0-595-09771-5(5) , Backinprint.com) iUniverse, Inc.

Talbot, Amy. Deer & Friends: A Folktale from India. 2006. 23.00 (*978-1-4108-6173-3(2)) Benchmark Education Co.

Talley, Linda. Bastet. Maeno, Itoko, illus. (Key Concepts in Personal Development Ser.). 2001. 32p. pap., tchr. ed. 89.95 incl. VHS (978-1-55942-176-8(2) , 9390K3); 2000. 30p. (J). 89.95 incl. VHS (978-1-55942-161-4(4)) Marsh Media.

Tanabe, Yellow. Kekkaishi, Vol. 6. 2006. (Kekkaishi Ser.). (Illus.). 208p. (YA). pap. 9.99 (978-1-4215-0487-2(1)) Viz Media.

Tarlow, Ellen. Pinwheel Days. Parker, Gretel, illus. 2007. 56p. (J). pap. 6.95 (978-1-59572-059-7(6)) Star Bright Bks., Inc.

Tassies, Josep, illus. Carabola. 1998. (SPA.). 22p. (J). (ps-ps). 13.99 (978-968-16-5342-2(4) , FC3424) Fondo de Cultura Economica MEX. *Dist:* Continental Bk. Co., Inc.

Tate, Eleanora E. A Blessing in Disguise. 2004. 192p. (J). pap. 6.95 (978-0-940975-66-8(1) , Sankofa Bks.) Just Us Bks., Inc.

Tate, Shonett. Friendship Cake: Do You Really Want a Sl. 2005. 189p. pap. 19.95 (978-1-4137-7292-0(7)) PublishAmerica, Inc.

Taulbert, Clifton L. Little Cliff & the Porch People. Kane, Cindy, ed. Lewis, Earl, illus. 1999. 32p. (J). (ps-3). 16.99 (978-0-8037-2174-6(9) , Dial) Penguin Group (USA) Inc.

Tayback, Simms. Where Is My Friend? 2006. (Illus.). 6p. bds. 7.95 (978-1-59354-132-3(5)) Blue Apple Bks.

Taylor-Butler, Christine. A Mom Like No Other. Devard, Nancy, illus. 2004. 32p. (J). lib. bdg. 15.00 (*978-1-4242-0227-0(2)) Fitzgerald Bks.

Taylor-Butler, Christine. Who Needs Friends? Havice, Susan, illus. 2006. (Rookie Reader Skill Set Ser.). 32p. (J). (gr. k-2). 19.50 (978-0-516-24979-7(7) , Children's Pr.) Scholastic Library Publishing.

Taylor-Butler, Christine & Havice, Susan. Who Needs Friends? 2006. (Rookie Reader Ser.). (Illus.). 32p. (J). pap. 4.95 (978-0-516-24997-1(5) , Children's Pr.) Scholastic Library Publishing.

Taylor, Mildred D. The Friendship. Ginsberg, Max, illus. 1998. 56p. (gr. 2-6). pap. 4.99 (978-0-14-038964-7(4) , Puffin) Penguin Group (USA) Inc.

Taylor, Theodore. The Cay. 2000. 171p. (J). 15.60 (978-0-03-054604-4(4)) Holt, Rinehart & Winston.

—The Cay. 144p. 2003. (J). (gr. 5). mass mkt. 5.99 (978-0-440-22912-4(X) , Laurel Leaf); 2002. (gr. 4-7). 5.99 (978-0-440-41663-0(9) , Yearling) Random Hse. Children's Bks.

—Cay. 2003. (gr. 5-8). lib. bdg. 13.55 (978-0-613-72282-7(5)); 2002. (gr. 3-6). lib. bdg. 13.55 (978-0-613-33748-9(4)) Tandem Library Bks.

Teague, Mark. The Lost & Found. 2001. 32p. (J). (ps-2). pap. 5.99 (978-0-439-27869-0(4)) Scholastic, Inc.

Teaming Up. 2002. (Illus.). (J). pap. (978-0-7398-5136-4(5)) Steck-Vaughn.

Tegen, Katherine. Dracula & Frankenstein Are Friends. Cushman, Doug, illus. 2003. 32p. (J). (ps-3). 15.99 (978-0-06-000115-5(1)) HarperCollins Pubs.

Teitelbaum, Michael. Double Team #2. Zalme, Ron, illus. 2008. 80p. (J). (gr. 1-5). 3.99 (*978-0-448-44712-4(6) , Grosset & Dunlap) Penguin Group (USA) Inc.

Tellem, Sundiata. Chaka Goes to Kenya. 2005. (Illus.). 24p. (J). per. 8.99 (978-1-932338-71-3(3)) Lifevest Publishing, Inc.

Tello, Jorge. Pookie & Tushka Find a Little Piano. Tello, Jorge, illus. 2004. (Illus.). 32p. (J). 15.89 incl. cd-rom (978-1-932179-23-1(2)) Pers Publishing.

Temple-West, Mariga. Louise & Edna. 2001. 128p. per. 12.75 (978-1-931633-05-5(3)) New World Media, Inc.

Tenorio-Coscarelli, Jane. The Tamale Quilt. Coscarelli, Nichole, tr. 1998. (Illus.). 48p. (J). (gr. k-6). pap. 11.95 (978-0-9653422-4-7(7)) Quarter-Inch Publishing.

Tenorio-Coscarelli, Jane & Coscarelli, Nicole. The Tamale Quilt. l.t. ed. 1998. (Illus.). 48p. (J). (gr. k-6). 15.95 (978-0-9653422-3-0(9)) Quarter-Inch Publishing.

That's What a Friend Is. 2001. (Illus.). 24p. (J). pap. 5.95 (978-0-8249-5391-1(6)) Ideals Pubns.

The Book Company. Learn to Count: Bee's School Bus. 2005. (Illus.). 22p. (J). (gr. 2-4). bds. 5.95 (978-1-74047-626-3(3)) Book Co. Publishing Pty, Ltd., The AUS. *Dist:* Penton Overseas, Inc.

Theo. Oscar & Hoo. 2003. (Illus.). 32p. (J). pap. 8.95 (978-0-00-710794-0(3) , HarperSport) HarperCollins Pubs. Ltd. GBR. *Dist:* Trafalgar Square Publishing.

—Oscar & Hoo. Dudok de Wit, Michael, illus. 2003. 32p. (J). (ps-2). 17.99 (978-0-00-710793-3(5)) HarperCollins Pubs. Ltd. GBR. *Dist:* Trafalgar Square Publishing.

—Oscar Hoo Forever. 2005. (Illus.). 32p. (J). 17.95 (978-0-00-714008-4(8)) HarperCollins Pubs. Ltd. GBR. *Dist:* Trafalgar Square Publishing.

Theo. Oscar the Hoo Forever. 2004. (Illus.). 32p. (J). pap. 9.99 (*978-0-00-714009-1(6)) HarperCollins Pubs. Ltd. GBR. *Dist:* Independent Pubs. Group.

Thesman, Jean. Other Ones. 2001. (gr. 5-8). lib. bdg. 14.15 (978-0-613-43861-2(2)) Tandem Library Bks.

Thiel, Annie. Danny Is Moving. 2006. (Playdate Kids Ser.). (Illus.). 32p. 14.95 (978-1-933721-02-6(2)) Playdate Kids Publishing.

Thiele, Colin. Storm Boy. Ingpen, Robert R., illus. 2004. 64p. (J). (gr. 4-6). pap. (978-1-74110-187-4(5)) New Holland Pubs. Pty, Ltd.

—Storm Boy. 40th ed. 2002. 60p. (J). (gr. 4-6). pap. (978-1-86436-804-8(7)) New Holland Pubs. Pty, Ltd.

Thieman, Linda. Katie & Kimble: A Ghost Story. l.t. ed. 2007. (Illus.). 148p. (J). pap. 12.48 (*978-0-9794396-0-5(4)) Pale Silver Rainplop Pr.

Things We Like to Do. 1999. (Tami & Moishy Ser.: Vol. 5). (J). bds. 6.95 (978-0-87306-966-3(8)) Feldheim Pubs.

Thomas, Alisa. Anne of Green Gables. 2001. 72p. (J). stu. ed., ring bd. 12.99 (978-1-58609-179-8(4)) Progeny Pr.

Thomas & Friends Picture Day. 2001. (Illus.). (J). 7.98 (978-0-7853-4782-8(8)) Publications International, Ltd.

Thomas, Charolette. Franklin Finds a Friend. 2006. (ENG.). 40p. per. 16.99 (*978-1-4259-6209-8(2)) AuthorHouse.

Thomas, Jan. A Birthday for Cow! 2008. 40p. (J). 12.95 (*978-0-15-206072-5(3)) Harcourt Trade Pubs.

Thomas, Jerry D. My Friend Fang & Other Great Stories for Kids: Learning How to Be Someone Who Has Good Friends. 2001. (Illus.). 95p. (J). (978-0-8163-1822-3(0)) Pacific Pr. Publishing Assn.

Thomas, Marlo. Free to Be You & Me No. 5: A Different Kind of Book for Children & Adults to Enjoy Together. 2002. (Illus.). 144p. pap. 12.95 (978-0-7624-1306-5(9) , Running Pr.) Running Pr. Bk. Pubs.

Thomas Nelson Publishing Staff. Really Woolly Furry Friends. 2007. 12p. (J). bds. 7.99 (978-1-4003-0988-7(3)) Nelson, Thomas Inc.

Thomasson, Clarissa. Who's a Friend? 2001. (Little Green Monkey Stories Ser.). (Illus.). 14p. (J). (gr. k-3). pap. 6.95 (978-1-929202-16-4(4)) Salt Marsh Pubns.

Thompkins, Janet E. Cameron & Sammie Making Friends. Kriskov, Tatjana, illus. 1999. 28p. (J). (gr. 1-5). pap. 6.95 (978-1-890667-10-8(2) , Hand-In-Hand Bks.) Introspect Bks.

Thompson, Joan. Lucy Russell: Stardom & Stinkwater. 2003. 129p. (YA). pap. 10.95 (978-0-595-26867-2(6) , Authors Choice Pr.) iUniverse, Inc.

Thompson, Lauren. Little Quack's New Friend. Anderson, Derek, illus. (Classic Board Bks.). (J). 2008. 34p. bds. 7.99 (*978-1-4169-4923-7(2) , Little Simon); 2006. 32p. 14.95 (978-0-689-86893-1(6)) Simon & Schuster Children's Publishing.

Thompson, Teresa. The Adventures of Shasta & Nikki: A True Friendship. 2004. 34p. pap. 17.95 (978-1-4137-1967-3(8)) PublishAmerica, Inc.

Thomson, Emma. Felicity Wishes Little Book of Friendship. 2002. 20p. (J). 5.99 (978-0-670-03590-8(4) , Viking Juvenile) Penguin Group (USA) Inc.

Thomson, Pat. Cat Baby. Shulman, Dee, illus. 2006. (Read-It! Chapter Books). 64p. (J). lib. bdg. (*978-1-4048-3123-0(1) , 1265800) Picture Window Bks.

Thong, Roseanne. Ten Friendly Fireflies. 2007. 20p. 11.95 (*978-1-58117-561-5(2)) Dalmatian Pr.

Thorn, David. Dollypogs. 2002. (J). cd-rom (978-0-9724995-8-3(X)) Alcazar AudioWorks.

Thorn, Nikki. A Shadow of My Own. 2002. 115p. (J). pap. 9.95 (978-0-595-21887-5(3) , Writers Club Pr.) iUniverse, Inc.

Thorne, Donna Sloan & Felts, Marilyn Sloan. Buzz & Ollie's High, Low Adventure. Thorne, Donna Sloan & Felts, Marilyn Sloan, illus. 2002. (Illus.). 36p. (J). bds. 16.00 (978-0-9724147-0-8(3)) Sloan Publishing.

Thornton-Jones, Marcia. Champ. 2007. 192p. (J). (gr. 4-7). pap. 4.99 (*978-0-439-79399-5(8)) Scholastic, Inc.

Thorpe, Kiki. Ah-Choo! 2003. (ps-2). lib. bdg. 11.80 (978-0-613-73405-9(X)) Tandem Library Bks.

—Lilo & Stitch: The Junior Novelization. 2002. (ps-2). lib. bdg. 13.00 (978-0-613-50630-4(8)) Tandem Library Bks.

—Tink, North of Never Land. Disney Storybook Artists Staff, illus. 2007. 128p. (J). (gr. 1-5). 5.99 (*978-0-7364-2455-4(5) , RH/Disney) Random Hse. Children's Bks.

Thorpe, Kiki. The Trouble with Tink. Clarke, Judith, illus. 2006. (Stepping Stone Bks.). 128p. (J). (gr. 2-4). 5.99 (978-0-7364-2371-7(0) , RH/Disney) Random Hse. Children's Bks.

Thurston, Dorie. Thank-You for the Thistle. Hawkins, Mecca, illus. 2001. 36p. (J). (ps-3). pap. 9.95 (978-0-9703326-0-8(2)) Dorie Bks.

Tibo, Gilles. Naomi & Mrs Lumbago. 2001. (gr. 3-6). lib. bdg. 15.25 (978-0-613-58380-0(9)) Tandem Library Bks.

—Naomi & the Secret Message. Ouriou, Susan, tr. from FRE. Laliberte, Louise-Andree, illus. 2004. 168p. (J). (gr. 1-4). pap. 7.95 (978-0-88776-668-8(4)) Tundra Bks., Inc./Livres Toundra, Inc. CAN. *Dist:* Random Hse., Inc.

—Simon et les Deguisements. 2001. Tr. of Simon's Disguise. (FRE & SPA.). 24p. (J). (ps-1). pap. 4.95 (978-0-88776-546-9(7) , Livres Toundra) Tundra Bks., Inc./Livres Toundra, Inc. CAN. *Dist:* Random Hse., Inc.

Tibo, Gilles & Perkes, Carolyn. Alex & Sarah. Germain, Philippe, illus. 2001. (Little Wolf Bks.: Level 3). 32p. (J). (gr. 1 up). pap. (978-1-894363-76-1(0)) Dominique & Friends.

Tich, Jan. Pope Meets Pin. 2006. (Adventures in Unusual Places Ser.). (Illus.). 28p. (J). 12.95 (978-9974-7925-7-9(6)) Hardenville SA URY. *Dist:* Independent Pubs. Group.

Tich, Jan & Jantti, Mariana. The Sea Fairy's Hat. 2006. (Magical Stories Ser.). (Illus.). 28p. (J). 16.95 (978-9974-7896-8-5(0)) Hardenville SA URY. *Dist:* Independent Pubs. Group.

Tiemann, Amy. High Water. 2004. (YA). per. 9.99 (978-1-880849-81-1(X)) Chapel Hill Pr.

Tiernan, Cate. Eclipse. 2002. (gr. 7-12). lib. bdg. 13.00 (978-0-613-64038-1(1)) Tandem Library Bks.

Tildes, Phyllis Limbacher. The Garden Wall. Tildes, Phyllis Limbacher, illus. 2006. (Illus.). (J). 16.95 (978-1-57091-467-6(2) , 1258423); pap. 7.95 (978-1-57091-468-3(0) , 1258423) Charlesbridge Publishing, Inc.

Tilley, Scott, illus. Finding Nemo. 2003. (Little Golden Book Ser.). 24p. (J). (gr. k-k). lib. bdg. 2.99 (978-0-7364-2139-3(4) , Golden/Disney) Random Hse. Children's Bks.

Time for Your Mind. l.t. ed. 2006. (Illus.). 35p. (J). (978-0-9785480-1-8(9)) Mielcarek, David.

Timothy, Ering. Frog Belly Rat F & G. 2003. (J). bds. 16.99 (978-0-7636-2248-0(6)) Candlewick Pr.

Tingle, Tim. Crossing Bok Chitto: A Choctaw Tale of Friendship & Freedom. Bridges, Jeanne Rorex, illus. 2006. (SPA & ENG.). 40p. (J). 17.95 (978-0-938317-77-7(6)) Cinco Puntos Pr.

Tish, Aunty. Kiddiwink Kingdom. 2006. 68p. pap. 19.95 (978-1-59800-587-5(1)) Outskirts Press, Inc.

To-Do List. 2007. (J). 15.95 (*978-0-9741319-5-5(4)) 4N Publishing LLC.

To Keep Me SAFE! A Story for Children Affected by Military Deployments. 2003. (J). 12.00 (978-0-9740289-0-3(8)) State of Growth Publishing Co.

Tocher, Timothy. Long Shot. 2001. (J). 137p. (978-0-88166-395-2(6)); 144p. pap. 4.95 (978-0-689-84331-0(3)) Meadowbrook Pr.

Together Is Best, Vol. 1. 1999. (Tami & Moishy Ser.: Vol. 1). (J). bds. 6.95 (978-0-87306-962-5(5)) Feldheim Pubs.

Toki, Wilfred. Moku & the Heoe of Waimea. Toki, Wilfred, illus. 2004. (Illus.). 32p. (J). 12.95 (978-0-9729905-7-8(7)) Beachhouse Publishing, LLC.

Tokio, Marnelle. Room 207. Hendry, Linda, illus. 2006. 120p. (J). (gr. 3-6). pap. 8.95 (978-0-88776-695-4(1)) Tundra Bks., Inc./Livres Toundra, Inc. CAN. *Dist:* Random Hse., Inc.

Tokyopop Staff, creator. Contents under Pressure, Vol. 3. 2005. (Lilo & Stitch Ser.). (Illus.). 89p. (gr. 3-7). pap., pap. 7.99 (978-1-59532-069-8(5) , Tokyopop Kids) TOKYOPOP, Inc.

Tolan, Stephanie S. A Good Courage. 1998. 256p. (YA). (gr. 7 up). reprint ed. pap. 4.95 (978-0-688-16124-8(3) , Harper Trophy) HarperCollins Pubs.

Tolson, Aaron J. Washington Putter. 2005. 248p. (YA). per. 22.00 (978-1-58982-243-6(9) , Bedside Bks.) American Bk. Publishing Group.

Tom Sawyer: 6 Small Books. (gr. k-2). 23.00 (978-0-7635-8507-5(6)) Rigby Education.

Tomberlin-Hightower, Patricia. Play Pals. 2008. (Illus.). 24p. (J). 15.95 (*978-1-60131-020-0(X)) Big Tent Bks.

Tomlinson, Theresa. Child of the May. 2000. (Illus.). (J). (978-0-606-18782-4(0)) Tandem Library Bks.

Tomonari, Itsuko. The Adventures of Meow Meow & Friends. 2003. (Illus.). 82p. per. 15.95 (978-1-59405-012-1(0)) New Age World Publishing.

Toms, Kate. Funny Faces Cloth Book: Jogger Dog. 2006. (Funny Faces (Make Believe Ideas) Ser.). (Illus.). 4p. (ps). 8.95 (978-1-84610-289-6(8)) Make Believe Ideas GBR. *Dist:* Ingram Pub. Services.

—Funny Faces Cloth Books: Digger Pig. 2006. (Funny Faces (Make Believe Ideas) Ser.). (Illus.). 4p. (ps). 8.95 (978-1-84610-288-2(X)) Make Believe Ideas GBR. *Dist:* Ingram Pub. Services.

Top That!, ed. One Little Penguin & his Friends. Gevry, Christine, illus. 2007. 10p. (J). (ps). bds. 12.99 (*978-1-84666-268-3(0) , Tide Mill Pr.) Top That! Publishing PLC GBR. *Dist:* Random Hse., Inc.

Torres, Daniel. Tom Tu Gran Amigo: Juega al Futbol, Vol. 5. 2005. (SPA., Illus.). 32p. 17.95 (978-1-59497-120-4(X)) Public Square Bks.

—Tom Tu Gran Amigo en París, Vol. 4. 2005. (SPA., Illus.). 32p. 19.95 (978-1-59497-119-8(6)) Public Square Bks.

Torres, J. Sidekicks Vol. 1: The Transfer Student. 2nd ed. 2003. (Illus.). 144p. (YA). pap. 11.95 (978-1-929998-76-0(7)) Oni Pr., Inc.

—Teen Titans Chapter Book: Blinded by the Light. Mackenzie, Kevin, illus. 3rd ed. 2005. (Teen Titans Ser.). 64p. (J). 3.99 (978-0-439-69635-7(6)) Scholastic, Inc.

Towle, Barbara. How Timbo & Trevor Got Together. Spellman, Susan, illus. 2007. (J). 19.95 (978-1-933002-21-7(2)) PublishingWorks.

Town, Florida Ann. With a Silent Companion. 2004. 112p. (J). (gr. 9 up). pap. 7.95 (978-0-88995-211-9(6)) Red Deer Pr. CAN. *Dist:* Fitzhenry & Whiteside, Ltd.

Tracey, Diane Eurich. Look Out for Virgil. Kuessner, Pat, ed. Golden, Debra Jean, illus. 2001. 24p. (J). (ps-7). pap. 12.00 (978-0-9701441-4-0(8) , 628548) Bokmal Pr.

Trayer, Edward H. Struggles of Felicity Brady: Articulus Quest. 2005. (YA). per. 14.95 (978-1-59571-091-8(4)) Word Association Pubs.

Trejo, Delia. A Fairy Tale for Artemis. 2002. 238p. pap. 14.95 (978-0-595-23437-0(2) , Writer's Showcase Pr.) iUniverse, Inc.

Trembath, Don. Emville Confidential. 2007. 192p. (J). (gr. 4-8). pap. (*978-1-55143-671-5(X)) Orca Bk. Pubs.

Trembath, Don. Lefty Carmichael Has a Fit. 2004. 176p. (J). (gr. 7-12). pap. 6.95 (978-1-55143-166-6(1)) Orca Bk. Pubs. USA.

—Lefty Carmichael Has a Fit. 2000. (Illus.). (J). (978-0-606-18328-4(0)) Tandem Library Bks.

Tremblay, Alain Ulysse. Jeanne la Terrienne. Malepart, Celine, tr. 2003. (Roman Jeunesse Ser.). (FRE., Illus.). 96p. (J). (gr. 4-7). pap. (978-2-89021-631-0(4)) Diffusion du livre Mirabel.

Tremblay, Marc. Le Petit Frere du Chaperon Rouge. Fil et al, illus. 2004. (était une Fois Ser.). (FRE.). 24p. (J). (ps). pap. (978-2-89021-698-3(5)) Diffusion du livre Mirabel.

Trimble, Marcia. Flower Green: A Flower for All Seasons. Dubin, Jill, illus. 2002. 32p. (J). (ps-2). 15.95 (978-1-891577-67-3(0)) Images Pr.

Tripp, Valerie. Changes for Samantha: A Winter Story. Andreasen, Dan & Roberts, Luann, illus. 2004. (American Girls Collection: Bk. 6). 80p. (J). (gr. 2 up). pap. 6.95 (978-0-937295-47-2(7)) American Girl Publishing, Inc.

—Kit's Surprise: A Christmas Story, Bk. 3. Rane, Walter & McAliley, Susan, illus. 2000. (American Girls Collection: Bk. 3). 80p. (J). (gr. 2 up). 12.95 (978-1-58485-021-2(3)) American Girl Publishing, Inc.

—Kit's Surprise: A Christmas Story, Bk. 3. Rane, Walter, illus. 2000. (American Girls Collection: Bk. 3). 80p. (YA). (gr. 2 up). pap. 6.95 (978-1-58485-020-5(5)) American Girl Publishing, Inc.

—Kit's Surprise: A Christmas Story. 2000. (gr. 3-6). lib. bdg. 14.10 (978-0-613-28918-4(8)); (American Girls Collection: Bk. 3). (YA). (gr. 2 up). (978-0-606-18944-6(0)) Tandem Library Bks.

Tromp, Janyre. That Sinking Feeling: Blue Water Mysteries. 2006. 128p. (J). pap. (978-0-8254-3887-5(X)) Kregel Pubns.

Trudel, Sylvain. Une Saison au Paradis. 2002. (Premier Roman Ser.). (Illus.). 64p. (J). (gr. 2-5). pap. (978-2-89021-353-1(6)) Diffusion du livre Mirabel.

Trudel, Sylvain & Langlois, Suzane. Pourquoi le Monde Est Comme il Est? 2004. (Premier Roman Ser.). (FRE., Illus.). 64p. (J). (gr. 1-4). pap. (978-2-89021-587-0(3)) Diffusion du livre Mirabel.

—Un Secret dans Mon Jardin. 2001. (Premier Roman Ser.). (FRE., Illus.). 64p. (J). pap. (978-2-89021-452-1(4)) Diffusion du livre Mirabel.

—Le Voleur du Poisson D'or. 2001. (Premier Roman Ser.). (FRE., Illus.). 64p. (J). pap. (978-2-89021-542-9(3)) Diffusion du livre Mirabel.

Trueit, Trudi. Julep O' Toole: Miss Independent. 2006. (Illus.). 160p. (J). (gr. 3). 15.99 (978-0-525-47637-5(7) , Dutton Juvenile) Penguin Group (USA) Inc.

—Julep O' Toole: Miss Independent. 2007. 176p. (J). 5.99 (978-0-14-240829-2(8) , Puffin) Penguin Group (USA) Inc.

—Julep O'Toole: What I Really Want to Do Is Direct. 2007. 160p. (J). (gr. 3 up). 16.99 (978-0-525-47781-5(0) , Dutton Juvenile) Penguin Group (USA) Inc.

—Julep O'Toole: Confessions of a Middle Child: Confessions of a Middle Child. 2007. 192p. (J). 5.99 (978-0-14-240798-1(4) , Puffin) Penguin Group (USA) Inc.

Trueman, Terry. 7 Days at the Hot Corner, No. 2. 2007. 160p. (J). (gr. 7 up). 15.99 (978-0-06-057494-9(1)); lib. bdg. 16.89 (978-0-06-057495-6(X)) HarperCollins Pubs. (HarperTeen).

Tucker, Author David J. Stickman World. 2005. 36p. (J). pap. 8.40 (978-1-4116-4275-1(9)) Lulu.com.

Tuey. Doug E Do. Martin, Susan, illus. 2006. 76p. pap. 14.95 (978-1-4241-0295-2(2)) PublishAmerica, Inc.

Tullson, Diane. Blue Highway. 2004. 276p. (J). (978-1-55005-124-7(5)) Fitzhenry & Whiteside, Ltd.

Tullson, Diane. Zero. 2006. 176p. (YA). (gr. 7 up). pap. ***978-1-55041-950-4(1)*** Fitzhenry & Whiteside, Ltd.

Tung, Angela. Trane & Me. 2000. (Roxbury Park Bks.). (Illus.). 160p. (J). (gr. 3-7). pap. 4.95 (978-0-7373-0180-9(5) , 01805W) McGraw-Hill/Contemporary.

Twain, Mark. The Adventures of Huckleberry Finn. 2007. (Children's Classics Ser.). (Illus.). 256p. (J). 6.99 (978-0-517-22999-6(4) , Gramercy) Random Hse. Value Publishing.

—The Adventures of Huckleberry Finn. Andreasen, Dan, illus. 2006. (Classic Starts Ser.). 160p. 4.95 (978-1-4027-2499-2(3)) Sterling Publishing Co., Inc.

—The Adventures of Huckleberry Finn. Redondo, Francisco, illus. 2nd ed. 1998. (Illustrated Classic Book Ser.). 61p. (J). (gr. 3 up). reprint ed. pap. 4.95 (978-1-56767-255-8(8)) Educational Insights, Inc.

—The Adventures of Huckleberry Finn: With a Discussion of Friendship. Lauter, Richard, tr. Lauter, Richard, illus. 2003. (Values in Action Illustrated Classics Ser.). (J). (978-1-59203-042-2(4)) Learning Challenge, Inc.

—The Adventures of Tom Sawyer. (Great Classics for Children Ser.). (Illus.). 192p. (J). 5.99 (978-1-4037-0598-3(4)) Dalmatian Pr.

—The Adventures of Tom Sawyer. 2001. 184p. pap. 9.95 (978-1-57002-169-5(4)) University Publishing Hse., Inc.

Twain, Mark & Olmos. The Adventures of Huckleberry Finn. 2004. (SPA.). 360p. pap. 17.95 (***978-84-263-5252-1(9)***) Vives, Luis Editorial (Edelvives) ESP. *Dist:* Lectorum Pubns., Inc.

Tyminski, Lori, illus. The Jungle Book 2. 2003. (J). 15.98 (978-0-7853-7968-3(1)) Publications International, Ltd.

Uff, Caroline. Lulu's Busy Day. 2000. (Illus.). (J). (978-0-8027-8717-0(7)) Walker & Co.

Uhlig, Susan. Lindsey Hits the Club. Wambach, Jennifer, illus. 2001. 96p. (gr. 3-6). pap. 6.75 (978-1-889658-17-9(0)) New Canaan Publishing Co. LLC.

Ullman, Barb Bentler. The Fairies of Nutfolk Wood. 256p. (J). 2008. pap. 5.99 (***978-0-06-134563-0(6)*** , Harper Trophy); 2006. 15.99 (978-0-06-073614-9(3) , Tegen, Katherine Bks); 2006. lib. bdg. 16.89 (978-0-06-073615-6(1) , Tegen, Katherine Bks) HarperCollins Pubs.

Ullrich, Hortense. La Prueba de Valor de Lorenzo. (SPA.). (J). 7.95 (978-958-04-7069-4(3)) Norma S.A. COL. *Dist:* Distribuidora Norma, Inc.

Ulrich, Ann Carol. The Mystery at Hickory Hill: Annette Vetter Adventure #1. 2006. (Illus.). 196p. (YA). per. 9.95 (978-0-944851-25-8(8)) Earth Star Pubns.

Umansky, Kaye. The Silver Spoon of Solomon Snow. Nash, Scott, illus. 2005. 304p. (J). (gr. 2-7). 14.99 (978-0-7636-2792-8(5)) Candlewick Pr.

—Solomon Snow & the Silver Spoon. Nash, Scott, illus. 2007. 304p. (J). (gr. 2-7). 12.99 (978-0-7636-3218-2(X)) Candlewick Pr.

Umansky, Kaye & Currey, Anna, illus. Sophie & Abigail. 2004. 30p. (J). 3.95 (978-1-56148-444-7(X)); 9.95 (978-1-56148-434-8(2)) Good Bks.

Uncle Henry. The Vileburgers: With Friends Like This Who Needs Halloween? Uncle Henry, illus. 100th ed. 2004. (Illus.). 88p. pap. 6.99 (978-1-932568-01-1(8) , UHB002) Uncle Henry Bks.

Urbach, Jourdan. Leaving Jeremiah. 2003. (Illus.). 108p. (J). 19.95 (978-1-930648-57-9(X) , 207-832-6665); per. 10.95 (978-1-930648-50-0(2) , 207-832-6665) Goose River Pr.

Urbanovic, Jackie. Duck Soup. 2008. 32p. (J). 17.89 (***978-0-06-121442-4(6)***) HarperCollins Pubs.

—Duck Soup. Urbanovic, Jackie, illus. 2008. 32p. (J). 16.99 (***978-0-06-121441-7(8)***) HarperCollins Pubs.

Ure, Jean. The Friends Forever Collection. 2007. (Illus.). 608p. (J). pap. 19.95 (***978-0-00-724820-9(2)***) HarperCollins Pubs. Ltd. GBR. *Dist:* Independent Pubs. Group.

—Sugar & Spice. 2005. (Diary Ser.). (Illus.). 224p. (J). pap. 8.99 (***978-0-00-716137-9(9)***) HarperCollins Pubs. Ltd. GBR. *Dist:* Independent Pubs. Group.

Uria, Fernando. Panico en la Discoteca. 1998. (SPA.). (gr. 7-12). lib. bdg. 14.10 (978-0-613-80702-9(2)) Tandem Library Bks.

Urrea, Lourdes, et al. Te Dije Que No Miraras. rev. ed. 2003. (Ediciones Castillo Castillo Del Terror Ser.).Tr. of I Told You Not to Look. (SPA.). 100p. (J). (gr. 2-6). pap. 6.95 (978-970-20-0308-3(3)) Castillo, Ediciones, S. A. de C. V. MEX. *Dist:* Macmillan.

Ustaris, Steven, illus. Malik & His Pals. 1999. (It's up to You Ser.). 65p. (YA). per. 8.95 (978-0-9726099-1-3(1)) BurnsBooks.

Vail, Rachel. The Horrible Play Date. Bjorkman, Steve, illus. 2002. (Mama Rex & T Ser.). 32p. (J). pap. 14.95 (978-0-439-40627-7(7)); pap. 4.99 (978-0-439-28335-9(3)) Scholastic, Inc. (Orchard Bks.).

—If You Only Knew: Zoe. 1998. (Friendship Ring Ser.: No. 1). 240p. (J). (gr. 4-8). pap. 14.95 (978-0-590-03370-1(0)); pap. 4.99 (978-0-590-37451-4(6)) Scholastic, Inc.

—Not That I Care: Morgan. (Friendship Ring Ser.: No.3). (J). (gr. 4-8). 1999. pap. ; 1998. 59.88 (978-0-590-95214-9(5)); 1998. 240p. pap. 14.95 (978-0-590-03476-0(6)); 1998. 240p. pap. 4.99 (978-0-590-37453-8(2)) Scholastic, Inc.

—Please, Please, Please. 1998. (Friendship Ring Ser.: No. 2). 240p. (J). (gr. 4-8). pap. 4.99 (978-0-590-37452-1(4)) Scholastic, Inc.

—Popularity Contest: Zoe. 2000. (Friendship Ring Ser.: No. 5). (J). (gr. 4-8). (Illus.). 240p. pap. 3.99 (978-0-590-68911-3(8) , Scholastic Paperbacks); Vol. 5. pap. 47.88 (978-0-439-16067-4(7)) Scholastic, Inc.

—Righty & Lefty. Cordell, Matthew, illus. 2007. 32p. (J). (ps-k). pap. 16.99 (***978-0-439-63629-2(9)*** , Scholastic Pr.) Scholastic, Inc.

Vail, Rachel. What Are Friends For? Olivia. (Friendship Ring Ser.: No. 4). (J). (gr. 4-8). 2000. pap. 59.88 (978-0-439-05981-7(X)); 1999. 240p. pap. 3.99 (978-0-590-37454-5(0)) Scholastic, Inc.

Valdes, Leslie. Meet Diego! Hall, Susan T., illus. 2003. (Dora the Explorer Ser.). 24p. (J). pap. 3.50 (978-0-689-85993-9(7) , Simon Spotlight/Nickelodeon) Simon & Schuster Children's Publishing.

—Meet Diego! 2003. (ps-2). lib. bdg. 11.25 (978-0-613-73344-1(4)) Tandem Library Bks.

Van Draanen, Wendelin. Meet the Gecko. 2006. (Shredderman Ser.: Bk. 3). 176p. (J). (gr. 2-5). 5.50 (978-0-440-41914-3(X) , Yearling) Random Hse. Children's Bks.

Van Kersen, Elizabeth. Who's Riley. 2005. (Illus.). 50p. (J). per. 8.99 (978-1-932338-90-4(X)) Lifevest Publishing, Inc.

—Whos' Riley? Stevens, Debra, illus. l.t. ed. 2006. 23p. (J). 15.99 (978-1-59879-173-0(7)) Lifevest Publishing, Inc.

Van Leeuwen, Jean. Amanda Pig & Her Best Friend Lollipop. Schweninger, Ann, illus. 2000. (Puffin-Easy-to-Read Ser.). 48p. (J). (ps-3). pap. 3.99 (978-0-14-037999-0(1) , Puffin) Penguin Group (USA) Inc.

—Amanda Pig & Her Best Friend Lollipop. 2000. (gr. k-3). lib. bdg. 11.80 (978-0-613-28401-1(1)); (Illus.). (J). 10.79 (978-0-606-18832-6(0)) Tandem Library Bks.

Van Lieshout, Elle & Van Os, Erik. Nice Party. 1998. (Illus.). 32p. (J). 15.95 (978-1-886910-89-8(8) , Lemniscaat) Boyds Mills Pr.

van Ommen, Sylvia. Jellybeans. 2006. (Illus.). 56p. (J). pap. 8.95 (978-1-55643-632-1(7)) North Atlantic Bks.

Van Ommen, Sylvia. Jellybeans. Forest-Flier, Nancy, tr. from DUT. Van Ommen, Sylvia, illus. rev. ed. 2005. (Illus.). 48p. (J). 14.95 (978-1-59643-035-8(4)) Roaring Brook Pr.

van Stockum, Hilda. A Day on Skates: 2007 Commemorative Edition. van Stockum, Hilda, illus. 2007. (Illus.). 44p. (J). 19.95 (***978-1-932350-18-0(7)***) Bethlehem Bks.

Van Straaten, Harmen. For Me. 2008. 32p. (J). (ps). 16.95 (***978-0-7358-2163-7(1)***) North-South Bks., Inc.

Vande Velde, Vivian. Companions of the Night. 2002. (Illus.). 224p. (YA). (gr. 7 up). pap. 5.95 (978-0-15-216669-4(6) , Magic Carpet Bks.) Harcourt Children's Bks.

VanderGriend, Pamela. Froggie In Lily Pad Kingdom. Murphy, Sandy et al, eds. Holton, Bob & Reed, Jennifer, illus. 2006. 32p. (J). 17.95 (***978-0-9787456-0-8(4)***) Froggie & Friends, LLC.

Vanier, Jolie. Puwaii Adventures with Joliea & Friends. 2006. 16.95 (***978-0-9787949-1-0(5)***) Puwaii International, LLC.

Vaniko, K. L. Why the Dog Chases the Cat & the Cat C. 2006. 30.99 (***978-1-59926-863-7(9)***) Xlibris Corp.

Varela, Barry. Palmer's Gate. 2006. 112p. (J). 16.95 (978-1-59643-073-0(7)) Roaring Brook Pr.

Varela, Gabrielle Charbonnet & Tiernan, Cate. Strife. 2002. (Sweep Ser.: Vol. 9). 192p. (YA). (gr. 9 up). pap. 6.99 (978-0-14-230107-4(8) , Puffin) Penguin Group (USA) Inc.

Varennes, Monique de. Bibi & the Sad Ballerinas. Juan, Ana, illus. 2006. (J). 16.95 (978-0-689-87665-3(3) , Atheneum) Simon & Schuster Children's Publishing.

Varennes, Monique de. The Jewel Box Ballerinas. Juan, Ana, illus. 2007. 40p. (J). (ps-3). 16.99 (***978-0-375-83605-3(5)*** , Schwartz & Wade Bks.) Random Hse. Children's Bks.

Vaughn Zimmer, Tracie. Reaching for Sun. 2007. 144p. (J). (gr. 7 up). 14.95 (978-1-59990-037-7(8) , Bloomsbury Children) Bloomsbury Publishing.

Vaught, Susan. Fat Tuesday. Hamilton, Dianne, ed. 2004. 249p. (YA). pap. 8.50 (978-0-9700752-3-9(5)) Onstage Publishing, LLC.

Vaupel, Robin. My Contract with Henry. 2003. 256p. (J). (gr. 4-6). tchr. ed. 16.95 (978-0-8234-1701-8(8)) Holiday Hse., Inc.

Veggietales. I Can Be Your Friend. 2007. (Veggie Tales Gift Book Ser.). 32p. (J). 7.99 (978-1-4165-3383-2(4) , Howard Bks.) Simon & Schuster.

—Stand Up! 2005. (Veggie Tales Gift Book Ser.). 32p. (J). 7.99 (978-1-4165-3392-4(3) , Howard Bks.) Simon & Schuster.

Velasquez, Crystal. Neighborhood Friends. 2005. (Maya & Miguel Ser.: No. 1). 96p. (J). (ps-ps). pap. 3.99 (978-0-439-73384-7(7)) Scholastic, Inc.

—Paint the Town. 2006. (Maya & Miguel Ser.). 32p. (J). pap. 3.99 (978-0-439-83008-9(7)) Scholastic, Inc.

Velez-Mitchell, Jane. Bark, Bark, Meow, Tweet, Tweet. 1998. 46p. (J). (gr. k-5). mass mkt. 7.00 (978-1-58193-158-7(1)) Brown Bag Productions.

Vera Viper's Valentine. 2001. (ps-2). lib. bdg. 9.80 (978-0-613-33181-4(8)) Tandem Library Bks.

Veranos, Sandi. David's Friend. Mclean, Mina, illus. 2003. (Pencil Fun Bks.: Vol. 10). 16p. (J). (ps-3). pap., pap. 9.90 (978-1-55513-117-3(4) , 1555131174) Cook, David C. Publishing Co.

Vidal, Cesar. Los Tres Dias del Gladiador. 2002. (SPA.). 190p. (978-84-348-8621-6(9)) SM Ediciones ESP. *Dist:* Lectorum Pubns., Inc.

Viguie, Debbie. Miss O & Friends: Trouble with a Capital O. Brindak, Hermine, illus. 2006. (Miss O & Friends Ser.). 128p. (J). pap. 5.99 (978-0-8230-2946-4(8)) Watson-Guptill Pubns., Inc.

Vilarrubias, Pia. Cua, el Amigo de Tona. (SPA.). 36p. 11.95 (978-84-207-1256-7(6)) Grupo Anaya, S.A. ESP. *Dist:* Distribooks, Inc.

Vili, Fane. Mano: The Awakening. Frakes, Clint, ed. 2006. (YA). per. 19.95 (978-0-9774074-0-8(3)) Plankton Pr.

Villalobos, Ligiah. Save the Elephants. Zalme, Ronald, illus. 2007. (Go, Diego, Go! Ser.). 24p. (J). pap. 3.99 (***978-1-4169-3821-7(4)*** , Simon Spotlight) Simon & Schuster Children's Publishing.

Villanueva Leonard. Hungry Puaa. 2005. 24p. 14.95 (978-1-933067-14-8(4)) Mutual Publishing LLC.

Visitors, 6 Packs. (Literatura 2000 Ser.). (gr. k-1). 28.00 (978-0-7635-0069-6(0)) Rigby Education.

Vivian, Siobhan. A Little Friendly Advice. 2008. 256p. (J). pap. 16.99 (***978-0-545-00404-6(7)*** , PUSH) Scholastic, Inc.

Vogel, Rob & Azarov, Max. Garry the Groundhog. l.t. ed. 2005. (Illus.). 10p. (J). spiral bd. 19.95 incl. DVD (978-0-9768455-0-8(4) , N/A) Vogel, Robert.

Vogelaar, Alie. No Place to Go. Bazen, Edith, tr. from DUT. Visser, Rino, illus. 2001. 114p. (YA). lib. bdg. 10.95 (978-0-9670728-7-6(5)) Early Foundations Pubs.

—Not So High, Margreet!, 5 bks. VanBrugge, J., tr. Kramer, K. J., illus. 2001. 128p. (YA). lib. bdg. 10.95 (978-0-9670728-2-1(4)) Early Foundations Pubs.

—What Are Your Plans, Margreet?, 5 bks. VanBrugge, J., tr. from DUT. Kramer, K. J., illus. 2001. 122p. (YA). lib. bdg. 10.95 (978-0-9670728-3-8(2)) Early Foundations Pubs.

Voigt, Cynthia. Bad, Badder, Baddest. 1999. (Bad Girls Ser.). 272p. (J). (gr. 4-7). pap. 4.99 (978-0-439-08096-5(7) , Scholastic Paperbacks) Scholastic, Inc.

—Bad, Badder, Baddest. 1999. (Bad Girls Ser.). (J). (978-0-606-17038-3(3)) Tandem Library Bks.

—Pero Que Chicas Tan Malas! (Barco de Vapor).Tr. of Bad Girls. (SPA.). 256p. (YA). (gr. 5-8). (978-84-348-6183-1(6) , SM0351) SM Ediciones ESP. *Dist:* Lectorum Pubns., Inc.

—Pero Que Chicas Tan Malas! 2000. Tr. of Bad Girls. (SPA.). (gr. 5-8). lib. bdg. 16.40 (978-0-613-80843-9(6)) Tandem Library Bks.

Voigt, Cynthia & Marcus, Barry David. Bad Girls in Love. (Bad Girls Ser.). 240p. 2003. (Illus.). (J). pap. 5.99 (978-0-689-86620-3(8) , Aladdin); 2002. (YA). (gr. 4-8). 15.95 (978-0-689-82171-5(8) , Atheneum/Anne Schwartz Bks.) Simon & Schuster Children's Publishing.

Voland, Wanda. Ivan Icicle's Wedding. 2007. (J). per. 10.99 (***978-1-60247-064-4(2)***) Tate Publishing & Enterprises, L.L.C.

Volker, Kerstin. Suzie Goes to Sleep. 2003. (Funny Friends Lift-and-Learn Bks.). (Illus.). 14p. (J). 5.99 (978-1-59384-024-2(1)) Parklane Publishing.

Volponi, Paul. Rucker Park Setup. 2007. 208p. (J). 15.99 (978-0-670-06130-3(1) , Viking Juvenile) Penguin Group (USA) Inc.

Von Bergen, Ingri. Friend to Friend. 2006. (J). 12.95 (978-1-59354-177-4(5)) Blue Apple Bks.

von Konigslow, Andrea Wayne. Bing & Chutney. von Konigslow, Andrea Wayne, illus. 1999. (Bing & Chutney Adventures Ser.). (Illus.). 32p. (J). (gr. k-ps). pap. 5.95 (978-1-55037-608-1(X)); lib. bdg. 16.95 (978-1-55037-609-8(8)) Annick Pr., Ltd. CAN. *Dist:* Firefly Bks., Ltd.

—Bing & Chutney. 1999. (ps-2). lib. bdg. 14.10 (978-0-613-53145-0(0)) Tandem Library Bks.

von Konigslow, Andrea Wayne. Bing & Chutney off to Moosonee. von Konigslow, Andrea Wayne, illus. 2001. (Bing & Chutney Adventures Ser.). (Illus.). 24p. (J). (gr. k-ps). pap. 5.95 (978-1-55037-678-4(0)); lib. bdg. 18.95 (978-1-55037-679-1(9)) Annick Pr., Ltd. CAN. *Dist:* Firefly Bks., Ltd.

von Konigslow, Andrea Wayne. Bing Finds Chutney. 2001. (Bing & Chutney Adventures Ser.). (Illus.). 24p. (J). (gr. k-ps). pap. 5.95 (978-1-55037-668-5(3)) Annick Pr., Ltd. CAN. *Dist:* Firefly Bks., Ltd.

—Bing Finds Chutney. von Konigslow, Andrea Wayne, illus. 2001. (Bing & Chutney Adventures Ser.). (Illus.). 24p. (J). (gr. k-ps). lib. bdg. 18.95 (978-1-55037-669-2(1)) Annick Pr., Ltd. CAN. *Dist:* Firefly Bks., Ltd.

von Zennenfels, Skye. Rainbow's Wish: Includes Toy. Aranda, Shane & Cluff, Jon, illus. 2000. (Pixie Tales of the Mystical Forest Ser.). v, 23p. (J). (ps-6). pap. 14.99 (978-0-9678580-0-5(3) , MY9002, IPI Toys) Interstellar Productions, Inc.

—Sunshine's Gift: Includes Toy. Aranda, Shane & Cluff, Jon, illus. 2000. (Pixie Tales of the Mystical Forest Ser.). v, 23p. (J). (ps-6). pap. 14.99 (978-0-9678580-1-2(1) , MY9003, IPI Toys) Interstellar Productions, Inc.

Voss, Fonda. The Bossy Girl. 2005. (Illus.). (J). 31p. per. 9.99 (978-1-932338-96-6(9)); 30p. 15.95 (978-1-932338-44-7(6)) Lifevest Publishing, Inc.

Vrombaut, An. Clarabella's Teeth. 2003. (Illus.). 32p. (J). (gr. k-3). 15.00 (978-0-618-33379-0(7) , Clarion Bks.) Houghton Mifflin Co. Trade & Reference Div.

W. I. T. C. H. The Magic of Friendship Boxed Set, 4 vols., Set. 2004. (W. I. T. C. H. Ser.). (Illus.). 144p. (J). (gr. 3-7). pap. 12.99 (978-0-7868-5242-0(9) , Volo) Hyperion Bks. for Children.

Waaldherr, Kris. Harvest. 1999. (J). pap. 3.25 (978-0-679-88824-6(1) , Random Hse. Bks. for Young Readers) Random Hse. Children's Bks.

Waber, Bernard. Evie & Margie. 2006. (Illus.). 32p. (J). (gr. k-3). reprint ed. pap. 6.95 (978-0-618-69338-2(6)) Houghton Mifflin Co.

—Evie & Margie. Waber, Bernard, illus. 2003. (Illus.). 32p. (J). (gr. k-3). 15.00 (978-0-618-34124-5(2) , Walter Lorraine) Houghton Mifflin Co. Trade & Reference Div.

—Ira Says Goodbye. Waber, Bernard, illus. unabr. ed. 2005. (Illus.). (J). (gr. k-3). pap. 16.95 incl. audio (978-0-87499-138-3(2)) BBC Audiobooks America.

—Quique Duerme Fuera de Casa. Mlawer, Teresa, tr. 2003. (SPA., Illus.). (J). (gr. k-2). pap. (978-968-6579-15-4(X) , SI6510) Sistemas Tecnicos de Edicion, S.A. de C.V. MEX. *Dist:* Lectorum Pubns., Inc.

Waddell, Martin. Hi, Harry! The Moving Story of How One Slow Tortoise Slowly Made a Friend. Firth, Barbara, illus. 2003. 56p. (J). (ps-1). 14.99 (978-0-7636-1802-5(0)) Candlewick Pr.

Wade, Ellen A. Sarah's Friend Peanuts. Schneider, Rex, illus. 1999. 28p. (J). (gr. 2-4). pap. 8.00 (978-0-9653635-1-8(1)) LNA Publishing.

Wagner, Karen. Bravo, Mildred & Ed! Pedersen, Janet, illus. 2000. 32p. (J). (gr. k-3). 16.95 (978-0-8027-8734-7(7)); lib. bdg. 17.85 (978-0-8027-8735-4(5)) Walker & Co.

—A Friend Like Ed. Pedersen, Janet, illus. 1998. 32p. (J). (gr. k-3). 15.95 (978-0-8027-8662-3(6)) Walker & Co.

Waite, Judy. Shopaholic. 224p. (YA). 2003. (Illus.). 16.95 (978-0-689-85138-4(3) , Atheneum); 2004. reprint ed. pap. 6.99 (978-0-689-85139-1(1) , Simon Pulse) Simon & Schuster Children's Publishing.

Waldron, Kathleen Cook. Rough Day at Loon Lake. 2002. (ps-2). lib. bdg. 15.25 (978-0-613-57782-3(5)) Tandem Library Bks.

The Walkathon: Individual Title Six-Packs. (gr. 3 up). 35.00 (978-0-7635-9667-5(1)) Rigby Education.

Walker, Mildred. A Piece of the World. 2001. (Illus.). 218p. pap. 12.95 (978-0-8032-9823-1(4) , WALPIX, Bison Bks.) Univ. of Nebraska Pr.

Walker, Pamela. In Gold & Jade, No. 2. 2006. (Kung Fu Princess Ser.). (Illus.). 224p. (J). (gr. 7). pap. 6.99 (978-0-448-44140-5(3) , Grosset & Dunlap) Penguin Group (USA) Inc.

Walker, Peter. The Magic Airplane. 2006. (ENG.). 160p. per. 12.95 (***978-1-59526-416-9(7)***) Media Creations, Inc.

Wallace, Barbara Brooks. Hello, Claudia! 2001. 160p. (gr. 4-7). pap. 10.95 (978-0-595-15335-0(6)) iUniverse, Inc.

—The Secret Summer of L. E. B. 2000. (Illus.). 196p. (gr. 4-7). pap. 12.95 (978-0-595-09572-8(0) , Backinprint.com) iUniverse, Inc.

—Sparrows in the Scullery. 1999. (978-0-606-15943-2(6)) Tandem Library Bks.

Wallace, Bill. No Dogs Allowed! 2004. 214p. (J). (gr. 4-6). tchr. ed. 16.95 (978-0-8234-1818-3(9)) Holiday Hse., Inc.

—Running Wild: Upchuck & the Rotten Willy. 1998. (Upchuck & the Rotten Willy Ser.). (Illus.). 112p. (J). (gr. 4-7). pap. 5.99 (978-0-671-01415-5(3) , Aladdin) Simon & Schuster Children's Publishing.

Wallace, Carol. One Nosy Pup. Bjorkman, Steve, illus. 40p. (J). 15.95 (978-0-8234-1917-3(7)) Holiday Hse., Inc.

Wallace, Ian. Mavis & Merna. 2005. (Illus.). 40p. (J). (gr. k-3). 16.95 (978-0-88899-647-3(0)) Groundwood Bks. CAN. *Dist:* Perseus Distribution.

Wallace, Ivy. Pookie. (Illus.). 32p. 2002. pap. 9.99 (978-0-00-664731-7(6)); 2001. (J). 19.99 (978-0-00-198377-9(6)) HarperCollins Pubs. Ltd. GBR. *Dist:* Trafalgar Square Publishing.

Wallace, Karen. Ooh la la, Lottie! Parsons, Garry, illus. 2004. (I Am Reading Ser.). 48p. (J). (gr. k-3). pap. 3.95 (978-0-7534-5716-0(4) , Kingfisher) Houghton Mifflin Co. Trade & Reference Div.

—Raspberries on the Yangtze. 2002. 160p. (YA). pap. 8.99 (978-0-689-83699-2(6)) Simon & Schuster, Ltd. GBR. *Dist:* Independent Pubs. Group.

Wallace, Kim. Erik & Isabelle Freshman Year at Foresthill High. 2004. 235p. (YA). per. 12.00 (978-0-9755848-0-4(4)) Foglight Pr.

Wallace, Nikki. Stubby & the Puppy Pack to the Rescue. Gurney, John Steven, illus. 144p. (J). 2003. pap. 4.99 (978-0-7434-2695-4(9) , Aladdin); 2002. (gr. 3-6). 16.00 (978-0-7434-2694-7(0)) Simon & Schuster Children's Publishing.

—Stubby & the Puppy Pack to the Rescue. 2003. (gr. 3-6). lib. bdg. 13.00 (978-0-613-66546-9(5)) Tandem Library Bks.

Wallace, Rich. Double Fake. 2005. (Winning Season Ser.: No. 4). 128p. (J). (gr. 3-7). 14.99 (978-0-670-05943-0(9) , Viking Juvenile) Penguin Group (USA) Inc.

E
F
G

—Second String Center. 2007. (Winning Season Ser.). 128p. (J). (gr. 4). 14.99 (***978-0-670-06150-1(6)*** , Viking Juvenile) Penguin Group (USA) Inc.

Wallace, Rich. Shots on Goal. 1998. 160p. (YA). (gr. 7-11). pap. 5.99 (978-0-679-88671-6(0) , Laurel Leaf) Random Hse. Children's Bks.

Wallace, Rich & Warner, Sally. Not-So-Weird Emma: Double Fake. Harper, Jamie, illus. 2005. 128p. (J). (gr. 3-7). 14.99 (978-0-670-06005-4(4) , Viking Adult) Penguin Group (USA) Inc.

Wallen, Virginia. Sonny & Sammy. 2006. 17.00 (978-0-8059-9809-2(8)) Dorrance Publishing Co., Inc.

Walling, Lani. Clyde-Fred & the Color of Friendship. 2005. 23p. (J). 9.98 (978-1-4116-6091-5(9)) Lulu.com.

Wallington, Aury. Bait & Switch. novel ed. 2005. (O. C. Ser.: No. 6). 264p. (J). pap. 6.99 (978-0-439-74570-3(5)) Scholastic, Inc.

Walsh, Ann. By the Skin of His Teeth. 2005. (Illus.). 144p. (YA). pap., tchr. ed. 6.95 (978-0-88878-448-3(1)) Beach Holme Pubs., Ltd. CAN. *Dist:* Literary Pr. Group of Canada.

Walsh, Ellen Stoll. For Pete's Sake. Walsh, Ellen Stoll, illus. 2002. (Illus.). (J). 20.85 (978-0-7587-2528-8(0)) Book Wholesalers, Inc.

—For Pete's Sake. 1998. (J). (ps-3). 13.95 (978-0-15-200325-8(8)) Harcourt Trade Pubs.

Walsh, Joanna. Amos Jellybean Gets It Right. 2005. (Illus.). (J). 17.95 (978-0-340-88222-1(0) , Hodder & Stoughton) Hodder General Publishing Division GBR. *Dist:* Trafalgar Square Publishing.

Walsh, Sheila. The Purple Ponies. Johnson, Meredith, illus. 2008. (Gigi, God's Little Princess Ser.). 32p. (J). 12.99 (***978-1-4003-1124-8(1))*** Nelson, Thomas Inc.

Walsh, Sheila. The Royal Tea Party. 2006. (Gigi, God's Little Princess Ser.). (Illus.). 32p. (J). 12.99 (978-1-4003-0800-2(3)) Nelson, Thomas Inc.

Walsh, Vivian & Seibold, J. Otto. Olive, My Love. 2004. (Illus.). 40p. (J). 15.00 (978-0-15-204720-7(4)) Harcourt Children's Bks.

Walter, Debbie. Introducing Russell. Walter, Debbie, illus. 2007. (Illus.). 68p. (J). per. 6.95 (***978-0-9766315-2-1(0))*** Moose Run Productions.

Walters, Celeste. The Glass Mountain. 2003. 280p. (YA). pap. 17.00 (978-0-7022-3297-8(1)) Univ. of Queensland Pr. AUS. *Dist:* International Specialized Bk. Services.

Walters, Eric. House Party. 2007. (Orca Soundings Ser.). 112p. (YA). (gr. 7 up). (***978-1-55143-743-9(0))*** Orca Bk. Pubs.

Walters, Eric. Three on Three. 1999. (Young Reader Ser.). (Illus.). 144p. (J). (gr. 3-6). pap. 4.99 (978-1-55143-170-3(X)) Orca Bk. Pubs. USA.

—Three on Three. (J). 2000. (Illus.). 122p. (gr. 2-6). lib. bdg. 13.00 (978-0-613-36704-2(9)); 1999. (978-0-606-19479-2(7)) Tandem Library Bks.

Walters, Jennie. Caz's Birthday Blues. Eckel, Jessie, illus. 2003. 128p. (J). pap. 7.99 (978-0-340-79586-6(7) , Hodder & Stoughton) Hodder General Publishing Division GBR. *Dist:* Trafalgar Square Publishing.

—Caz's Confetti Crisis. 2002. (Illus.). mass mkt. 7.99 (978-0-340-85413-6(8) , Hodder & Stoughton) Hodder General Publishing Division GBR. *Dist:* Trafalgar Square Publishing.

—Jess: Rave Reporter. 2002. (Illus.). 128p. (J). pap. 7.99 (978-0-340-85410-5(3) , Hodder & Stoughton) Hodder General Publishing Division GBR. *Dist:* Trafalgar Square Publishing.

—Jess's Disco Disaster. Eckel, Jessie, illus. 2003. (J). mass mkt. 7.99 (978-0-340-79587-3(5) , Hodder & Stoughton) Hodder General Publishing Division GBR. *Dist:* Trafalgar Square Publishing.

—Lauren: Seeing Stars. 2002. (Illus.). 128p. (J). pap. 7.99 (978-0-340-85412-9(X) , Hodder & Stoughton) Hodder General Publishing Division GBR. *Dist:* Trafalgar Square Publishing.

—Lauren's Spooky Sleepover. 2003. (Illus.). 128p. (J). pap. 7.99 (978-0-340-79591-0(3) , Hodder & Stoughton) Hodder General Publishing Division GBR. *Dist:* Trafalgar Square Publishing.

—Michelle: Centre Stage. 2002. (Illus.). 128p. pap. 7.99 (978-0-340-85411-2(1) , Hodder & Stoughton) Hodder General Publishing Division GBR. *Dist:* Trafalgar Square Publishing.

—Michelle's Big Break. 2003. (Illus.). 128p. (J). pap. 7.99 (978-0-340-79589-7(1) , Hodder & Stoughton) Hodder General Publishing Division GBR. *Dist:* Trafalgar Square Publishing.

—Nikki's Treasure Trail. Eckel, Jessie, illus. 2003. 128p. (J). pap. 7.50 (978-0-340-79590-3(5) , Hodder & Stoughton) Hodder General Publishing Division GBR. *Dist:* Trafalgar Square Publishing.

Walton, Rick. The Remarkable Friendship of Mr. Cat & Mr. Rat. McCue, Lisa, illus. 2006. 32p. (J). (ps-3). 14.99 (978-0-399-23899-4(9) , Putnam Juvenile) Penguin Group (USA) Inc.

Wang, Margaret. Teddy Bear's Picnic. 2008. 12p. (J). (ps-2). 16.99 (***978-0-7641-6069-1(9))*** Barron's Educational Series, Inc.

Ward, Ervin D. The Grump with a Bump. 2005. 48p. pap. 12.95 (978-1-4137-7681-2(7)) PublishAmerica, Inc.

Ward, Heather P. I Promise I'll Find You. McGraw, Sheila, illus. 2005. 32p. (J). (ps-2). pap. 5.95 (978-1-55209-094-7(9)) Firefly Bks., Ltd.

Ward, Helen. Little Moon Dog. Anderson, Wayne, illus. 2007. 32p. (J). (ps-3). 16.99 (978-0-525-47727-3(6) , Dutton Juvenile) Penguin Group (USA) Inc.

Ward, Helen. Moon Dog. 2005. (Illus.). 40p. (J). (***978-1-84011-864-3(4))*** Templar Publishing, Dorking.

Ward, Nick. The Ice Child. Bailey, Peter, illus. 2004. 32p. (J). (978-1-84458-038-5(5)) Chrysalis Children's Bks.

Warde, Margaret. Betty Wales, Sophomore. 2006. 63.99 (***978-1-4219-9626-4(X));*** pap. 57.99 (***978-1-4219-9627-1(8))*** IndyPublish.com.

Warner, Gertrude Chandler, creator. Benny's New Friend. 1998. (Adventures of Benny & Watch: No. 3). (J). (gr. 1-3). 10.75 (978-0-606-13217-6(1)) Tandem Library Bks.

Warner, Sally. Bad Girl Blues. 2001. 224p. (YA). (gr. 5-9). 15.95 (978-0-06-028274-5(6)) HarperCollins Pubs.

—Best Friend Emma. Harper, Jamie, illus. 2007. 112p. (J). (gr. 2-4). 14.99 (978-0-670-06173-0(5) , Viking Juvenile) Penguin Group (USA) Inc.

—Leftover Lily. 2000. (Illus.). (J). (978-0-606-18238-6(1)) Tandem Library Bks.

—Not-So-Weird Emma. Jaten, Harper, illus. 2007. 144p. (J). 5.99 (978-0-14-240807-0(7) , Puffin) Penguin Group (USA) Inc.

—Sort of Forever. 1998. (J). (gr. 3-6). pap. (978-0-679-88649-5(4) , Random Hse. Bks. for Young Readers) Random Hse. Children's Bks.

—Sort of Forever. 1999. (978-0-606-17153-3(3)) Tandem Library Bks.

Warnes, Tim. Can't You Sleep, Dotty? Warnes, Tim, illus. 2003. (Illus.). 32p. (J). pap. 5.95 (978-1-58925-376-6(0) , tiger tales) ME Media LLC.

—Can't You Sleep, Dotty? 2001. (Illus.). 28p. (J). tchr. ed. 14.95 (978-1-58925-010-9(9) , tiger tales) ME Media LLC.

—Can't You Sleep, Dotty? 2003. (ps-2). lib. bdg. 14.10 (978-0-613-84706-3(7)) Tandem Library Bks.

Warnes, Tim. Chalk & Cheese. 2008. (J). (***978-1-4169-1378-8(5)*** , Simon & Schuster Children's Publishing) Simon & Schuster Children's Publishing.

Warren, Rick. Made for a Purpose AMS. 2004. (J). 287.82 (978-0-310-60329-0(3)) Zonderkidz.

Warren, Sandra & Pfleger, Deborah Bel. Arlie the Alligator. Thomas, Deborah, illus. 2000. 48p. (J). 23.90 incl. audio compact disk (978-1-880175-16-3(9)) Arlie Enterprises.

Wartik, David J. The Vonnesta Project. 2006. 140p. (J). (gr. 3-6). pap. 12.95 (978-1-59113-938-6(4)) Booklocker-.com, Inc.

Washington, Donna. The Big Spooky House: Picture Book. Rogers, Jacqueline, illus. 2006. 32p. (gr. k-4). pap. 4.99 (978-0-7868-1231-8(1)) Hyperion Pr.

Wasserman, Robin. Clikits: Friendship Box. 2005. (Lego Ser.). (Illus.). 32p. (J). 9.99 (978-0-439-74567-3(5)) Scholastic, Inc.

—Envy. 2005. (Seven Deadly Sins Ser.). 256p. (YA). pap. 7.99 (978-0-689-87783-4(8) , Simon Pulse) Simon & Schuster Children's Publishing.

—Greed. 2007. (Seven Deadly Sins Ser.). 256p. (YA). pap. 8.99 (***978-1-4169-0720-6(3)*** , Simon Pulse) Simon & Schuster Children's Publishing.

—Hacking Harvard. 2007. 336p. (YA). (gr. 9 up). pap. 8.99 (***978-1-4169-3633-6(5)*** , Simon Pulse) Simon & Schuster Children's Publishing.

—Teenick. 2005. (Teenick Ser.). (Illus.). 120p. (J). (gr. 4-7). pap. 4.99 (978-0-439-80179-9(6) , Scholastic Paperbacks) Scholastic, Inc.

—Winx Club Pass Book. 2006. 50p. (J). pap. 7.99 (978-0-439-78782-6(3)) Scholastic, Inc.

Wasserman, Robin & Pyle, Howard. Lust. 2005. (Seven Deadly Sins Ser.). 256p. (YA). pap. 8.99 (978-0-689-87782-7(X) , Simon Pulse) Simon & Schuster Children's Publishing.

Wasserman, Veronica. The Dinosaur Dig. 2008. 32p. (J). (ps-k). pap. 3.99 (***978-0-448-44710-0(X)*** , Grosset & Dunlap) Penguin Group (USA) Inc.

Waters, Aubrey. Thirteen & Surviving. 2006. pap. 14.49 (***978-1-4259-4644-9(5))*** AuthorHouse.

Watkins, Greg. A Big Beaked, Big Bellied Bird Named Bill. 2006. 32p. 15.99 (978-1-58980-441-8(4)) Pelican Publishing Co., Inc.

Watkins, Kate. Dooley Makes Friends. 2002. (Illus.). 24p. (J). (gr. k-5). pap. 2.99 (978-1-57759-472-7(X)) Dalmatian Pr.

Watson-Dubisch, Carolyn. Bug-a-boo, 1. l.t. ed. 2006. (Illus.). 32p. (J). per. 9.95 (978-0-9779295-1-1(5)) Medusa Road Pr.

Watson, Peter & Watson, Mary. Heart of the Lion. Watson, Peter, illus. 2005. (Illus.). 32p. 15.95 (978-0-9726614-1-6(7)) Shenanigan Bks.

Watson, Richard Jesse. The Magic Rabbit. Watson, Richard Jesse, illus. 2005. (Illus.). 40p. (J). pap. 15.95 (978-0-590-47964-6(4) , Blue Sky Pr., The) Scholastic, Inc.

Watson, Stephanie. Elvis & Olive. 2008. 240p. (J). 15.99 (***978-0-545-03183-7(4)*** , Scholastic) Scholastic, Inc.

Watt, Mélanie. Scaredy Squirrel Makes a Friend. Watt, Mélanie, illus. 2007. (Illus.). 32p. (J). (ps-3). (***978-1-55453-181-3(0))*** Kids Can Pr., Ltd.

Waucaush, Clair. Pokey's World. 2004. 72p. pap. 14.95 (978-1-4137-3923-7(7)) PublishAmerica, Inc.

Wax, Wendy. Phonics Comics: Sugar & Spice. 2007. 24p. (J). (gr. 1). pap. 3.99 (***978-1-58476-614-8(X)*** , IKIDS) Innovative Kids.

Wax, Wendy. What Zebra Likes. Terry, Michael, illus. 2006. (Puppet & Story Book Ser.). 12p. (J). 12.99 (978-0-7944-1043-8(X)) Reader's Digest Assn., Inc., The.

Wayans, Kim & Knotts, Kevin. Amy Hodgepodge 01: All Mixed Up! All Mixed Up! 2008. 112p. (J). (gr. 2-4). 4.99 (***978-0-448-44854-1(8)*** , Grosset & Dunlap) Penguin Group (USA) Inc.

—Happy Birthday to Me. 2008. 112p. (J). (gr. 2-4). 4.99 (***978-0-448-44855-8(6)*** , Grosset & Dunlap) Penguin Group (USA) Inc.

Wayne-von Konigslow, Andrea. Bing Finds Chutney. 2001. (ps-2). lib. bdg. 14.10 (978-0-613-53147-4(7)) Tandem Library Bks.

Weatherall, Barry. Jay & the Worm Save the Day. 2005. 40p. 14.28 (978-1-4116-4717-6(3)) Lulu.com.

Weathers, Anah D. Secrets of the Cave. Weathers, Luther, illus. Weathers, Luther, photos by. unabr. ed. 2000. (Treasures from the Past Ser.). x, 104p. (J). (gr. 4-8). pap. 7.98 (978-0-9702584-0-3(2)) Creative Services.

Weaver, Ann. A Wiggly Spider a Slug a Salamander & the Bug! Hildebrand, Sharon, illus. 2000. 16p. (J). pap. 5.95 (978-0-87012-649-9(0)) McClain Printing Co.

Weaver, Anna E. Birds at My Window. 2004. (Illus.). 231p. 9.35 (978-0-7399-2301-6(3) , 2138) Rod & Staff Pubs., Inc.

Webb, Janeen. Tales from Beyond. 2005. (Thrillogy Ser.). (Illus.). 48p. (gr. 4-8). 17.50 (978-0-7910-8891-3(X)) Facts On File, Inc.

Weber, Judith Eichler. Seeking Safety. Martin, John F., illus. 2006. (Adventures in America Ser.). (J). (978-1-893110-46-5(X)) Silver Moon Pr.

Weber, Lenora Mattingly. The More the Merrier. 1999. (Beany Malone Ser.). 246p. (J). reprint ed. pap. 12.95 (978-1-930009-00-4(3)) Image Cascade Publishing.

—Welcome Stranger. 1999. (Beany Malone Ser.). 291p. (J). reprint ed. pap. 12.95 (978-1-930009-02-8(X)) Image Cascade Publishing.

Weber, Lou, ed. Elmo Best Friends Sing a Long. 2005. 14p. (J). bds. 15.98 (978-1-4127-3373-1(1) , 7251300) Publications International, Ltd.

A Weekend with Wendell. 2004. 29.95 incl. cd-rom (978-1-55592-129-3(9)); (J). 24.95 incl. audio (978-1-56008-003-9(5)); (J). pap. 18.95 incl. audio compact disk (978-1-55592-116-3(7)); (J). pap. 32.75 incl. audio (978-1-55592-329-7(1)) Weston Woods Studios, Inc.

A Weekend with Wendell. 2004. (J). pap. 38.75 incl. audio compact disk (978-1-55592-647-2(9)) Weston Woods Studios, Inc.

Weeks, Sarah. Beware of Mad Dog! 2006. (Boyds Will Be Boyds Ser.: No. 1). 128p. (J). pap. 4.99 (978-0-439-57469-3(2)) Scholastic, Inc.

—Fink's Funk. 2006. (Boyds Will Be Boyds Ser.: No. 4). 144p. (J). pap. 4.99 (978-0-439-57472-3(2) , Scholastic Paperbacks) Scholastic, Inc.

—Guy Wire. 2002. 144p. (J). (gr. 3-7). 16.99 (978-0-06-029492-2(2) , Geringer, Laura Book) HarperCollins Pubs.

—If I Were a Lion. Solomon, Heather M., illus. 2007. 40p. (J). (ps-2). pap. 6.99 (***978-1-4169-3837-8(0)*** , Aladdin) Simon & Schuster Children's Publishing.

—Oggie Cooder #1. 2008. 176p. (J). pap. 16.99 (***978-0-439-92791-8(9)*** , Scholastic) Scholastic, Inc.

Weeks, Sarah. Pip Squeak. Manning, Jane, illus. 2007. (I Can Read Bks.). 32p. (J). lib. bdg. 16.89 (978-0-06-075637-6(3)); 15.99 (978-0-06-075635-2(7)) HarperCollins Pubs. (Geringer, Laura Book).

Weigelt, Udo. Super Guinea Pig to the Rescue. Spranger, Nina, illus. 2007. 32p. (J). 17.85 (***978-0-8027-9706-3(7));*** 16.95 (***978-0-8027-9705-6(9))*** Walker & Co.

Weinberger, Kimberly. Be-a-Good-Friend Sticker Book. 2001. (Clifford, the Big Red Dog Ser.). (Illus.). 24p. (J). (gr. k-2). 5.99 (978-0-439-22945-6(6)) Scholastic, Inc.

Weiner, Brian. Toad Catchers' Creek. Weintraub, Claudia & Frederick, Robin, eds. Cannon, Martin, illus. 2005. 40p. (J). lib. bdg. 17.99 (978-1-932949-58-2(5)) Illusion Factory, The.

Weinmann, Julianne. The Mis-Adventures of Frissue the Tissue. 2005. 48p. (J). pap. 15.69 (978-1-4116-5310-8(6)) Lulu.com.

Weiss, David & Weiss, Bobbi. Foster's Home for Imaginary Friends 8x8, No. 1. 2006. (Illus.). 24p. (J). pap. 3.99 (978-0-439-77580-9(9) , Scholastic) Scholastic, Inc.

Weiss, Ellen. Fruit Salad: A Touch & Learn Book. Jourdan, Jason, illus. 2006. (PBS Kids(R) Ser.). 14p. (J). 6.95 (***978-1-57791-314-6(0))*** Brighter Minds Children's Publishing.

—New Friend, Blue Friend. Di Fiori, Lawrence, illus. 1999. (Road to Reading Ser.). 32p. (J). (ps-3). pap. 3.99 (978-0-307-26210-3(3) , Golden Bks.) Random Hse. Children's Bks.

—Scary, Scary Monsters. DiFiori, Larry, illus. 1999. (Road to Reading Ser.). 32p. (J). (ps-3). 10.99 (978-0-307-46210-7(2) , Golden Bks.) Random Hse. Children's Bks.

Weiss, M. Jerry & Weiss, Helen S., eds. Lost & Found. 2001. 224p. 5.99 (978-0-8125-6866-0(4) , Forge Bks.) Doherty, Tom Assocs., LLC.

Welles, Lee. Gaia Girls Enter the Earth. 2006. (Gaia Girls Ser.). (Illus.). 336p. (YA). 18.95 (978-1-933609-00-3(1)) Daisyworld Pr.

Wells, Carolyn. Patty at Home. 2007. (ENG.). 204p. per. 12.95 (***978-1-4218-3321-7(2))*** 1st World Publishing, Inc.

Wells, Carolyn & E. C. CASWELL. Two Little Women on a Holiday. l.t. ed. 2006. 178p. pap. 14.99 (978-1-4264-2807-4(3)) BiblioBazaar.

Wells, Pamela. Heartbreakers. 2007. 304p. (YA). (gr. 9 up). pap. 16.99 (***978-0-439-02691-8(1))*** Scholastic, Inc.

Wells, Rosemary. Bubble Gum Radar. Wheeler, Jody & Nez, John, illus. 2002. (Yoko & Friends School Days Ser.: Bk. 9). 32p. (gr. k-2). pap. 3.99 (978-0-7868-1528-9(0) , Volo) Hyperion Bks. for Children.

—Lucas y Virginia. 1999. Orig. Title; Benjamin & Tulip. (SPA., Illus.). (J). (ps-3). lib. bdg. 12.95 (978-0-88272-321-1(9)) Santillana USA Publishing Co., Inc.

—Make New Friends. Wheeler, Jody, illus. 2003. (Yoko & Friends School Days Ser.: Bk. 11). 32p. (gr. k-2). pap. 3.99 (978-0-7868-1536-4(1)); 9.99 (978-0-7868-0730-7(X)) Hyperion Bks. for Children. (Volo).

—Make New Friends. Wheeler, Jody, illus. 2003. 31p. (J). (ps-ps). lib. bdg. 11.80 (978-0-613-74980-0(4)) Tandem Library Bks.

—McDuff's New Friend with Plush Box Set. 2003. (Illus.). 28p. (J). 14.99 (978-0-7868-1866-2(2) , Disney Editions) Disney Pr.

—Only You (Solo Tu) Wells, Rosemary, illus. 2004. (SPA., Illus.). 32p. (J). (ps-k). 14.99 (978-0-670-03692-9(7) , Viking Juvenile) Penguin Group (USA) Inc.

Weltman, June. Mystery of the Missing Candlestick. 2004. 216p. (J). 23.95 (978-1-878044-98-3(2)) Mayhaven Publishing.

Wenger, Brahm. Dewey Doo-It at the Jingle Jangle Jamboree: A Musical Storybook Inspired by Arnold Schwarzenegger to Benefit Inner-City Games. 2006. 32p. 18.95 (978-0-9745143-4-5(9)) RandallFraser Publishing.

Wenger, Brahm & Green, Alan. Dewey Doo-It Builds a House: A Children's Story about Habitat for Humanity. 2006. (Illus.). 32p. 17.95 (978-0-9745143-2-1(2)) RandallFraser Publishing.

Weninger, Brigitte. Don't Fight, Davy. Tharlet, Eve, illus. 2003. 16p. (J). bds. 6.95 (978-0-7358-1753-1(7)) North-South Bks., Inc.

—Why Are You Fighting, Davy? Lanning, Rosemary, tr. from GER. Tharlet, Eve, illus. 2002. 32p. (J). pap. 6.95 (978-0-7358-1601-5(8)) North-South Bks., Inc.

—Why Are You Fighting, Davy? 2002. (gr. k-3). lib. bdg. 15.25 (978-0-613-87277-5(0)) Tandem Library Bks.

Werner Watson, Jane. My Little Golden Book about God. Wilkin, Eloise, illus. 2000. (Little Golden Bks.). 24p. (J). (gr. k-k). 2.99 (978-0-307-02105-2(X) , 98246, Golden Inspirational) Random Hse. Children's Bks.

Wersba, Barbara. The Dream Watcher. 2004. 128p. (YA). pap. 7.95 (978-1-932425-08-6(X) , Lemniscaat) Boyds Mills Pr.

West, Tracey. Celebi Rescue. 2007. (Pokemon Junior Chapter Bks.: No. 2). 48p. (J). pap. 3.99 (***978-0-545-00560-9(4))*** Scholastic, Inc.

—Deoxys in Danger. 2007. (Pokemon Ser.: No. 4). 48p. (J). pap. 3.99 (***978-0-545-00564-7(7))*** Scholastic, Inc.

—Foster's Home for Imaginary Friends Sticker Storybook: Mix & Match Imaginary Friends. 2006. 18p. (J). pap. 4.99 (978-0-439-74664-9(7) , Scholastic Paperbacks) Scholastic, Inc.

—Game On! 2007. (Yu-gi-oh Ser.: No. 1). (Illus.). 96p. (J). pap. 4.99 (***978-0-439-87394-9(0))*** Scholastic, Inc.

—Power Pals. Marderosian, Marc, illus. 2002. (Powerpuff Girls Ser.: No. 13). 32p. (J). (gr. 4-6). pap. 3.50 (978-0-439-37229-9(1)) Scholastic, Inc.

—Power Pals. 2002. (gr. k-3). lib. bdg. 11.25 (978-0-613-50486-7(0)) Tandem Library Bks.

—Shadow Riders. 2007. (Yu-gi-oh Ser.). (Illus.). 96p. (J). pap. 4.99 (***978-0-439-88831-8(X))*** Scholastic, Inc.

—Yu-Gi-Oh Gx Reader #3 Rescue Duel. 2008. 32p. pap. 3.99 (***978-0-439-88840-0(9)*** , Scholastic) Scholastic, Inc.

Westera, Marleen & Forest, Nancy. Sheep & Goat. Ommen, Sylvia Van, illus. (J). 16.95 (978-1-932425-81-9(0) , Lemniscaat) Boyds Mills Pr.

Westerfeld, Scott. The Uglies Trilogy: Uglies, Pretties, Specials. 2007. 1216p. (YA). pap. 25.99 (***978-1-4169-3640-4(8)*** , Simon Pulse) Simon & Schuster Children's Publishing.

Weston, Carol. The Diary of Melanie Martin: Or How I Survived Matt the Brat, Michelangelo & the Leaning Tower of Pizza. 2001. 11.64 (978-0-606-21144-4(6)) Tandem Library Bks.

—Melanie in Manhattan. 288p. (J). (gr. 3-7). 2006. 5.99 (978-0-440-42040-8(7) , Yearling); 2005. (Illus.). 15.95 (978-0-375-83028-0(6) , Knopf Bks. for Young Readers) Random Hse. Children's Bks.

—Melanie Martin Goes Dutch: The Private Diary of My Almost Bummer Summer with Cecily, Matt the Brat, & Vincent van Go Go Go. 2003. (Illus.). 240p. (J). (gr. 3-7). 5.99 (978-0-440-41899-3(2) , Yearling) Random Hse. Children's Bks.

—Melanie Martin Goes Dutch: The Private Diary of My Almost Bummer Summer with Cecily, Matt the Brat, & Vincent van Go Go Go. 2003. (gr. 3-6). lib. bdg. 25.70 (978-0-613-62527-2(7)) Tandem Library Bks.

Weston, Martha & Greene, Stephanie. Owen Foote, Super Spy. Weston, Martha, illus. 2001. (Illus.). 96p. (J). (gr. 4-6). tchr. ed. 15.00 (978-0-618-11752-9(0) , Clarion Bks.) Houghton Mifflin Co. Trade & Reference Div.

Weyland, Jack. Ashley & Jen. 2000. (Illus.). 287p. (YA). 16.95 (978-1-57345-803-0(1)) Deseret Bk. Co.

Whalen, Sharla Scannell. Best Friends under the Sun. 2000. (Faithful Friends Ser.). (Illus.). 64p. (J). (gr. 4). lib. bdg. 21.35 (978-1-57765-228-1(2) , ABDO & Daughters) ABDO Publishing Co.

—Meet the Friends. 2000. (Faithful Friends Ser.). (Illus.). 64p. (J). (gr. 4). lib. bdg. 21.35 (978-1-57765-226-7(6) , ABDO & Daughters) ABDO Publishing Co.

What Tommy Did: Individual Title, 6 packs. (Literatura 2000 Ser.). (gr. 1-2). 28.00 (978-0-7635-0152-5(2)) Rigby Education.

Wheeler, Kathryn. No Room for Neighbors: A Tale in Which Two Strangers Become Friends. Myers, Darcy, illus. 2000. (Stories to Grow By Ser.). 19p. (J). 3.95 (978-1-56822-594-4(6) , Instructional Fair) Schaffer, Frank Pubns.

Wheeler, Lisa. Invasion of the Pig Sisters. Ansley, Frank, illus. 2006. (Fitch & Chip Ser.). 48p. (J). pap. 3.99 (978-0-689-84958-9(3)) Simon & Schuster Children's Publishing.

—One Dark Night. Bates, Ivan, illus. 2006. 32p. (J). reprint ed. pap. 6.00 (978-0-15-205888-3(5) , Voyager Bks./ Libros Viajeros) Harcourt Children's Bks.

Wheeler, Lisa & Ansley, Frank. New Pig in Town. 2003. (Ready-to-Read Ser.). (Illus.). 48p. (J). 14.95 (978-0-689-84950-3(8) , Atheneum/Richard Jackson Bks.) Simon & Schuster Children's Publishing.

Wheelock, Ann. The Angel of Camp Courageous. 2005. 89p. pap. 14.95 (978-1-4137-8239-4(6)) PublishAmerica, Inc.

Whelan, Gloria. That Wild Berries Should Grow. 2003. (gr. 3-6). lib. bdg. 16.45 (978-0-613-75569-6(3)) Tandem Library Bks.

—A Time to Keep Silent. 2004. 144p. (J). pap. 8.00 (978-0-8028-5255-7(6)) Eerdmans, William B. Publishing Co.

—Time to Keep Silent. 2003. (gr. 5-8). lib. bdg. 16.45 (978-0-613-75511-5(1)) Tandem Library Bks.

Where the Leprechauns Hide. 2007. pap. 12.99 (***978-0-9792258-9-5(2)***) Bezalel Bks.

Whitaker, Marti. Sock-A-Nina. Kurtz Hubbard, Nancy, illus. 2005. (ENG.). 28p. (J). per. 18.00 (978-1-4208-4256-2(0)) AuthorHouse.

White, Carolyn. The Adventure of Louey & Frank. Dronzek, Laura, illus. 2001. 24p. (J). (ps). 14.95 (978-0-688-16503-1(6)) HarperCollins Pubs.

White, E. B. Charlotte's Web. Williams, Garth, illus. 2006. 192p. (J). 15.99 (978-0-06-088261-7(1)); 8.99 (978-0-06-112495-2(8)) HarperCollins Pubs.

—Charlotte's Web/Stuart Little Slipcase, Set. Williams, Garth, illus. collector's gif. ed. 2004. (J). 49.99 (978-0-06-073940-9(1)) HarperCollins Pubs.

—Wilbur's Adventure. Kneen, Maggie, illus. 2008. (Charlotte's Web Ser.). 32p. (J). (gr. k-2). 16.99 (***978-0-06-078164-4(5)***) HarperCollins Pubs.

—Wilbur's Adventure: A Charlotte's Web Picture Book. Kneen, Maggie, illus. 2008. (Charlotte's Web Ser.). 32p. (J). 17.89 (***978-0-06-078165-1(3)***) HarperCollins Pubs.

White, Linda. Too Many Pumpkins. Lloyd, Megan, illus. 32p. (J). (gr. k-3). tchr. ed. 17.95 (978-0-8234-1245-7(8)) Holiday Hse., Inc.

White, Michelle Renee. Jason's Wild Sister. 2002. 108p. (gr. 4-7). pap. 9.95 (978-0-595-21417-4(7) , Writers Club Pr.) iUniverse, Inc.

Whitfield, Willie. Pig Pen Willie's Inheritance. 2007. (J). 12.95 (***978-1-56167-958-4(5)***) American Literary Pr.

Whybrow, Ian. Miss Wire's Christmas Surprise. Clark, E., illus. 2007. 48p. (J). (ps-3). pap. 3.95 (***978-0-7534-6136-5(6)*** , Kingfisher) Houghton Mifflin Co. Trade & Reference Div.

—The Unvisibles. 2005. 184p. (J). 16.95 (978-0-8234-1972-2(X)) Holiday Hse., Inc.

—Whiff, or, How the Beautiful Big Fat Smelly Baby Found a Friend. Ayto, Russell, illus. 2002. 24p. pap. 11.99 (978-0-552-54615-7(1) , Corgi) Transworld Publishers Ltd. GBR. *Dist:* Trafalgar Square Publishing.

—Wish, Change, Friend. Beeke, Tiphanie, illus. 2002. 32p. (J). (ps-3). 16.00 (978-0-689-84930-5(3) , McElderry, Margaret K.) Simon & Schuster Children's Publishing.

Whyman, Matt. Boy Kills Man. 160p. (J). 2006. pap. 6.99 (978-0-06-074665-0(3)); 2005. 15.99 (978-0-06-074663-6(7)); 2005. lib. bdg. 16.89 (978-0-06-074664-3(5)) HarperCollins Pubs. (HarperTeen).

Whytock, Cherry. My Scrumptious Scottish Dumplings: The Life of Angelica Cookson Potts. Whytock, Cherry, illus. 2006. 192p. (YA). mass mkt. 5.99 (978-0-689-86552-7(X) , Simon Pulse) Simon & Schuster Children's Publishing.

Whytock, Cherry, illus. My Scrumptious Scottish Dumplings: The Life of Angelica Cookson Potts. 2004. 176p. (YA). 14.95 (978-0-689-86549-7(X)) Simon & Schuster Children's Publishing.

Wiesner, David. Tuesday. Wiesner, David, illus. 2002. (Illus.). (J). 14.74 (978-0-7587-0080-3(6)) Book Wholesalers, Inc.

Wiess, Laura. Leftovers. 2008. 256p. pap. 12.00 (***978-1-4165-4662-7(6)*** , MTV) Simon & Schuster.

Wigglesworth, Penny. Penny Bear's Gift of Love: A Story of Friendship Between a Grieving Young Boy & a Magical Little Bear. Eager, Michiko, illus. l.t. ed. 2005. 84p. pap. 7.95 (978-0-9675532-5-2(3)) Quality of Life Publishing Co.

Wilbourne, David. Summers Diary. 2002. (Illus.). 288p. (J). pap. 14.99 (978-0-00-710007-1(8)) HarperCollins Pubs. Ltd. GBR. *Dist:* Trafalgar Square Publishing.

Wild, Margaret. Fox. Brooks, Ron, illus. 2000. 40p. (J). (978-1-86448-465-6(9)); mass mkt. (978-1-86448-933-0(2)) Allen & Unwin.

—Fox. Brooks, Ron, illus. 2006. 32p. (J). pap. 7.95 (978-1-933605-15-9(4)) Kane/Miller Bk. Pubs., Inc.

Wild, Robyn. Benjamin's Basket. Cullen, Elizabeth, illus. 1999. (J). (ps-4). 12.95 (978-0-944576-17-5(6)) Rocky River Pubs., LLC.

Wilde, Oscar. El Joven Rey y Otros Cuentos. 1998. (SPA.). 208p. (gr. 6-8). (978-84-239-2781-4(4)) Espasa Calpe, S.A.

Wilhelm, Doug. The Revealers. 224p. (J). 2003. 16.00 (978-0-374-36255-3(6) , Farrar, Straus & Giroux (BYR)); 2005. reprint ed. pap. 6.95 (978-0-374-46243-7(7) , Sunburst) Farrar, Straus & Giroux.

Wilhelm, Hans. Friends Around the World. 2006. (Hans Wilhelm Lift-the-Flap Bks.). (Illus.). 16p. (J). 9.99 (978-0-7641-5891-9(0)) Barron's Educational Series, Inc.

—Seamos Amigos Otra Vez. (J). 13.95 (978-84-261-2514-9(X)) Juventud, Editorial ESP. *Dist:* AIMS International Bks., Inc.

—What Are Friends For? 2006. (Hans Wilhelm Lift-the-Flap Bks.). (Illus.). 16p. (J). 9.99 (978-0-7641-5890-2(2)) Barron's Educational Series, Inc.

Wilkes, Maria D. Brookfield Friends. Andreasen, Dan, illus. 2000. (Little House Chapter Bks.: No. 4). 80p. (J). (gr. 3-6). 14.89 (978-0-06-028552-4(4)) HarperCollins Pubs.

Wilkins, Harry. Rachael's Way. 2002. (gr. 7-12). lib. bdg. 18.75 (978-0-613-78043-8(4)) Tandem Library Bks.

Will I Have a Friend. 2004. (J). pap. 18.95 incl. audio compact disk (978-0-7882-0994-9(9)); pap. 32.75 incl. audio (978-0-7882-0996-3(5)); pap. 38.75 incl. audio compact disk (978-0-7882-0997-0(3)); pap. 14.95 incl. audio (978-0-7882-0993-2(0)) Weston Woods Studios, Inc.

Willard, Eliza. Totally Crushed. 2008. (Candy Apple Ser.). 160p. (J). pap. 4.99 (***978-0-545-02814-1(0)*** , Scholastic Paperbacks) Scholastic, Inc.

Willems, Mo. My Friend Is Sad. 2007. 64p. (ps-3). 8.99 (978-1-4231-0297-7(5)) Hyperion Bks. for Children.

—Today I Will Fly! 2007. 64p. (ps-3). 8.99 (978-1-4231-0295-3(9)) Hyperion Bks. for Children.

Willey, Margaret. The Bigger Book of Lydia. 2001. 228p. (YA). pap. 16.95 (978-0-595-17700-4(X) , Backinprint.com) iUniverse, Inc.

—Finding David Dolores. 2001. (gr. 7-12). lib. bdg. 23.40 (978-0-613-85102-2(1)) Tandem Library Bks.

—Finding David Dolores. 2001. 164p. (YA). (gr. 7-12). pap. 13.95 (978-0-595-19641-8(1)) iUniverse, Inc.

—If Not for You. 2002. 164p. (YA). pap. 13.95 (978-0-595-25572-6(8) , Backinprint.com) iUniverse, Inc.

—Saving Lenny. 2002. 162p. (YA). pap. 12.95 (978-0-595-21930-8(6) , Backinprint.com) iUniverse, Inc.

Williams, Carol. Dickey. 2005. 16.00 (978-0-8059-9830-6(6)) Dorrance Publishing Co., Inc.

Williams, Dar. Amalee. (J). 2006. 208p. pap. 5.99 (978-0-439-39564-9(X) , Scholastic Paperbacks); 2004. 192p. pap. 16.95 (978-0-439-39563-2(1)) Scholastic, Inc.

Williams-Garcia, Rita. No Laughter Here. 144p. (J). (gr. 7 up). 2007. pap. 6.99 (978-0-06-440992-6(9) , Amistad); 2004. 15.99 (978-0-688-16247-4(9)); 2004. lib. bdg. 16.89 (978-0-688-16248-1(7)) HarperCollins Pubs.

Williams, Jacklyn. Make a New Friend, Gus! Cushman, Doug, illus. 2006. (Read-It! Readers Ser.). (J). 19.93 (978-1-4048-2711-0(0)) Picture Window Bks.

Williams, Josie. Hoppy Finds Friends. 2004. 33p. pap. 17.95 (978-1-4137-1461-6(7)) PublishAmerica, Inc.

Williams, Larry. The League of Clique. Williams, Larry, illus. 2007. (ENG., Illus.). 80p. per. 19.95 (***978-1-4241-5976-5(8)***) PublishAmerica, Inc.

Williams, Mark London. Trail of Bones: Danger Boy Episode 3. 2007. (Illus.). 320p. (J). (gr. 4-8). 5.99 (***978-0-7636-3410-0(7)***) Candlewick Pr.

Williams, Patricia de Belloy. Pioneers-1937. 2003. (Illus.). 409p. (J). per. 14.99 (978-1-932176-00-1(4)) Beluga-Duga Pr.

Williams, Rozanne Lanczak. Two Stories, Two Friends. Maio, Barbara, ed. Allen, Joy, illus. 2006. (Learn to Write Ser.). 16p. (J). pap. 2.99 (978-1-59198-295-1(2) , 6186) Creative Teaching Pr., Inc.

Williams, Sam. Angel's Christmas Cookies. Williams, Sam, illus. 2002. (Angel & Elf Ser.). (Illus.). 32p. (J). (ps-3). 9.99 (978-0-06-029651-3(8) , Harper Festival) HarperCollins Pubs.

Williams, Suzanne. The Gigantic, Genuine Genie. Gonzales, Chuck, illus. 2007. (Princess Power Ser.: No. 6). 128p. (J). 15.99 (***978-0-06-078309-9(5));*** (gr. 3-7). pap. 4.99 (***978-0-06-078308-2(7)*** , Harper Trophy) HarperCollins Pubs.

—The Stubbornly Secretive Servant. Gonzales, Chuck, illus. 2007. (Princess Power Ser.). 128p. (J). 15.99 (***978-0-06-078307-5(9));*** pap. 4.99 (***978-0-06-078306-8(0)*** , Harper Trophy) HarperCollins Pubs.

Williamson, Greg. What's the Recipe for Friends? Abele, Greg, illus. 1999. 24p. pap. 7.99 (978-0-9666076-0-4(0)) Peerless Publishing, L.L.C.

Williamson, Stafford. Puppyfish. 2005. 48p. (J). pap. 18.49 (978-1-4116-3836-5(0)) Lulu.com.

Willis, Jeanne. Misery Moo. Ross, Tony, illus. rev. ed. 2005. 32p. (J). 16.95 (978-0-8050-7672-1(7)) Holt, Henry & Co.

—The Wind in the Willows. Ross, Tony, illus. 1998. 32p. (J). (ps-1). 15.99 (978-0-86264-782-7(7)) Andersen GBR. *Dist:* Trafalgar Square Publishing.

Willis, Jeanne & Jossen, Penelope. When Stephanie Smiled. 2003. (Illus.). 32p. (J). 16.00 (978-1-84270-075-4(8)) Andersen GBR. *Dist:* Trafalgar Square Publishing.

Willis, Tammy A. I Can Work With My Friends. 2006. (J). pap. (978-1-57332-441-0(8)) HighReach Learning, Inc.

—I Can Work with My Friends. ed. 2006. (J). pap. (978-1-57332 442-7(6)) HighReach Learning, Inc.

Willner-Pardo, Gina. Figuring Out Frances. 1999. (Illus.). 144p. (J). (gr. 4-6). tchr. ed. 14.00 (978-0-395-91510-3(4) , Clarion Bks.) Houghton Mifflin Co. Trade & Reference Div.

—Spider Storch, Rotten Runner. Sharratt, Nick, illus. 2001. 88p. (J). (gr. 2-5). lib. bdg. 11.95 (978-0-8075-7594-9(1)) Whitman, Albert & Co.

Willson, Sarah. Be Nice, Nanette! Brandt, Elizabeth, illus. 2001. (Angela Anaconda Ser.: Vol. 2). 64p. (J). (gr. 4-7). pap. 3.99 (978-0-689-83997-9(9) , Simon Spotlight) Simon & Schuster Children's Publishing.

Wilson, Jacqueline. Bad Girls. Sharratt, Nick, illus. 2002. 176p. (gr. 3-7). pap. 5.50 (978-0-440-41806-1(2) , Yearling) Random Hse. Children's Bks.

—Bad Girls. 2002. (gr. 3-6). lib. bdg. 12.40 (978-0-613-83529-9(8)) Tandem Library Bks.

—Bad Girls. Sharratt, Nick, illus. 2000. (Yearling Book Ser.). 192p. pap. 9.99 (978-0-440-86356-4(2) , Corgi); 177p. (J). (gr. 3-7). 16.95 (978-0-385-40702-1(5)) Transworld Publishers Ltd. GBR. *Dist:* Trafalgar Square Publishing.

—Best Friends. 2008. (J). (***978-1-59643-278-9(0)***) Roaring Brook Pr.

—Mr. Cool. Lewis, Stephen, illus. 2004. (I Am Reading Ser.). 48p. (J). (gr. 1-3). pap. 3.95 (978-0-7534-5822-8(5) , Kingfisher) Houghton Mifflin Co. Trade & Reference Div.

—Secrets. l.t. ed. 2003. (Illus.). 208p. (J). 16.95 (978-0-7540-7854-8(X) , Galaxy Children's Large Print) BBC Audiobooks America.

—Vicky Angel. l.t. ed. 2001. (Illus.). 232p. (J). 16.95 (978-0-7540-6165-6(5) , Galaxy Children's Large Print) BBC Audiobooks America.

—Vicky Angel. 2003. (Illus.). 176p. (gr. 3-7). reprint ed. 5.50 (978-0-440-41808-5(9) , Yearling) Random Hse. Children's Bks.

—Vicky Angel. 2003. (gr. 3-6). lib. bdg. 13.00 (978-0-613-88328-3(4)) Tandem Library Bks.

Wilson, Jacqueline & Sharratt, Nick. Candyfloss. 2007. (Illus.). 352p. (J). (gr. 4-7). 14.95 (***978-1-59643-241-3(1)***) Roaring Brook Pr.

Wilson, Jenine. My Familiar. 2007. (YA). per. 9.99 (***978-0-9794414-0-0(4)***) Jensonbooks.

Wilson, Kevin. Brown Spot. 2006. 60p. (J). pap. 12.00 (978-1-4116-8059-3(6)) Lulu.com.

Wilson, Linda Miller. A Few Days Journey. 1998. 124p. (YA). (gr. 4-8). 9.99 (978-0-88092-402-3(0) , 4020) Royal Fireworks Publishing Co.

Wilson, Rosalee. Meet Mushy Mouse. 2003. 27 p. pap. 14.95 (978-1-4137-0714-4(9)) PublishAmerica, Inc.

Wilson, Sarah. Friends & Pals & Brothers, Too. Landry, Leo, illus. 2008. 32p. (J). 16.95 (***978-0-8050-7643-1(3)***) Holt, Henry & Co.

Wilson, Vickie. Friends Club. Turrentine, Jan, ed. 1999. (Illus.). 24p. (J). (gr. 4-6). pap. 19.99 (978-1-56309-298-5(0)) Woman's Missionary Union.

Wilt's on Stilts! 2000. 30p. (J). 14.95 (978-0-9708080-0-4(3)) Stilts.

The Wind & Little Cloud. 2006. (J). 17.95 (978-0-9741743-3-4(5)) Perlycross Pubs.

Wing, Natasha. The Night Before First Grade. Zemke, Deborah, illus. 2005. 32p. (J). (ps-4). 3.99 (978-0-448-43747-7(3) , Grosset & Dunlap) Penguin Group (USA) Inc.

Winget, Susan. Tucker's Four-Carrot School Day. Winget, Susan, illus. 2005. (Illus.). 40p. (J). (ps-k). 12.99 (978-0-06-054642-7(5)); lib. bdg. 13.89 (978-0-06-054643-4(3)) HarperCollins Pubs.

Wingfield, Albert B. Best Friends. Ramey, Lisa L., illus. 2000. 16p. (J). pap. 7.95 (978-1-930260-05-4(9)) CTS Family Pr.

Wings: A Tale of Two Chickens. 2004. (J). pap. 14.95 incl. audio (978-1-56008-045-9(0)); pap. 14.95 incl. audio (978-1-56008-082-4(5)) Weston Woods Studios, Inc.

Winick, Judd. Pedro & Me: Friendship, Loss & What I Learned. 2001. (Illus.). (J). (978-0-606-20504-7(7)) Tandem Library Bks.

Winkler, Henry & Oliver, Lin. Barfing in the Backseat: How I Survived My Family Road Trip. Watson, Jesse Joshua, illus. 2007. (Hank Zipzer Ser.: No. 12). 160p. (J). 13.99 (978-0-448-44329-4(5)); pap. 4.99 (978-0-448-44328-7(7)) Penguin Group (USA) Inc. (Grosset & Dunlap).

—Day of the Iguana. 2006. (Hank Zipzer Ser.: No. 3). (J). (gr. 3-8). 24.21 (978-1-59961-102-0(3)) Spotlight.

—My Secret Life as a Ping-Pong Wizard. Heyer, Carol, illus. 2005. (Hank Zipzer Ser.: No. 9). 160p. (J). (gr. 3-7). 13.99 (978-0-448-43877-1(1) , Grosset & Dunlap) Penguin Group (USA) Inc.

—My Secret Life as a Ping-Pong Wizard. Watson, Jesse Joshua & Heyer, Carol, illus. 2005. (Hank Zipzer Ser.: No. 9). 160p. (J). (gr. 3-7). pap. 4.99 (978-0-448-43749-1(X) , Grosset & Dunlap) Penguin Group (USA) Inc.

Winkler, Henry & Oliver, Lin. Who Ordered This Baby Brother? Definitely Not Me! Watson, Jesse Joshua, illus. 2007. (Hank Zipzer Ser.: No. 13). 160p. (J). (gr. 3-7). 13.99 (***978-0-448-44375-1(9));*** pap. 4.99 (***978-0-448-44374-4(0)***) Penguin Group (USA) Inc. (Grosset & Dunlap).

Winn, Christine M. & Walsh, David. Clover's Secret. Winn, Christine M., illus. 2004. (Illus.). 28p. (J). (gr. k-4). reprint ed. 15.00 (978-0-7567-7653-4(8)) DIANE Publishing Co.

Winstead, Rosie. Ruby & Bubbles. 2006. (Illus.). 32p. (J). (ps). 15.99 (978-0-8037-3024-3(1) , Dial) Penguin Group (USA) Inc.

Winthrop, Elizabeth. Counting on Grace. 240p. (J). (gr. 3-7). 2007. pap. 6.50 (***978-0-553-48783-1(3)*** , Yearling); 2006. (Illus.). 15.95 (978-0-385-74644-1(X) , Lamb, Wendy); 2006. (Illus.). lib. bdg. 17.99 (978-0-385-90878-8(4) , Lamb, Wendy) Random Hse. Children's Bks.

Wisbauer, Cortney. Rodney, the Ice Dragon. Wisbauer, Cortney, illus. 2006. (Illus.). 48p. (J). 22.95 (***978-1-59879-215-7(6)***) Lifevest Publishing, Inc.

Wishinsky, Frieda. A Bee in Your Ear. Laliberte, Louise-Andree, illus. 2004. 64p. (J). lib. bdg. 20.00 (***978-1-4242-1255-2(3)***) Fitzgerald Bks.

—Dimples Delight. Laliberte, Louise-Andree, illus. 2005. (Orca Echoes Ser.). 64p. (J). (gr. 2-3). pap. 4.99 (978-1-55143-362-2(1)) Orca Bk. Pubs. USA.

—Each One Special. ed. 2004. (Illus.). (J). (gr. k-3). spiral bd. (978-0-616-01814-9(2)); spiral bd. (978-0-616-01815-6(0)) Canadian National Institute for the Blind/Institut National Canadien pour les Aveugles.

—Each One Special. Zimmermann, H. Werner, illus. 32p. (J). (ps-2). 2004. 7.95 (978-1-55143-124-6(6)); 1999. 14.95 (978-1-55143-122-2(X)) Orca Bk. Pubs. USA.

—Each One Special. 2001. (gr. k-3). lib. bdg. 16.40 (978-0-613-33891-2(X)) Tandem Library Bks.

—Jennifer Jones Won't Leave Me Alone. Layton, Neal, illus. 2005. 32p. (gr. k-2). 15.95 (978-0-87614-921-8(2)) Lerner Publishing Group.

—Just Mabel. Heap, Sue, illus. (I Am Reading Ser.). (J). 2004. 48p. (gr. 1-3). pap. 3.95 (978-0-7534-5742-9(3)); 2001. 3.95 (978-0-7534-5353-7(3)) Houghton Mifflin Co. Trade & Reference Div. (Kingfisher).

—Nothing Scares Us. Layton, Neal, illus. (Carolrhoda Picture Books Ser.). 32p. (gr. k-2). 2005. pap. 6.25 (978-1-57505-669-2(0)); 2003. (J). 15.95 (978-1-57505-490-2(6) , Carolrhoda Bks.) Lerner Publishing Group.

—So Long Stinky Queen. 2000. (gr. 3-6). lib. bdg. 11.80 (978-0-613-88778-6(6)) Tandem Library Bks.

Wishnisky, Frieda. Jennifer Jones Won't Leave Me Alone. Layton, Neal, illus. 2005. 32p. (J). (gr. k-2). pap. 6.95 (978-1-57505-921-1(5)) Lerner Publishing Group.

Wiskur, Darrell, told to. Dinky Dinosaur - Who's My Friend? 2001. (Illus.). 16p. (J). 6.99 (978-0-89051-362-0(7)) Master Bks.

Wisler, G. Clifton. All for Texas: A Story of Texas Liberation. 2001. (American Portraits Ser.). 140p. (gr. 5-8). 15.32 (978-0-8092-0588-2(2) , 9780809205882) Jamestown.

—All for Texas: A Story of Texas Liberation. 2004. (Jamestown's American Portraits Ser.). (Illus.). 144p. (J). (gr. 5-7). pap. 4.95 (978-0-7696-3428-9(1) , Waterbird Bks.) School Specialty Publishing.

—All for Texas: A Story of Texas Liberation. 2000. (gr. 5-8). lib. bdg. 15.70 (978-0-613-36169-9(5)) Tandem Library Bks.

Wisler, G. Clifton & McGraw-Hill Staff. All for Texas: A Story of Texas Liberation. 2001. (Jamestown Classics Ser.). 140p. (C). (gr. 5-8). pap. 10.00 (978-0-8092-0629-2(3) , 9780809206292) Jamestown.

Wisniewski, David. Tough Cookie. 1999. (Illus.). 32p. (J). (gr. 1-4). 15.93 (978-0-688-15338-0(0)); 16.99 (978-0-688-15337-3(2)) HarperCollins Pubs.

Withers, Pam. Adrenalin Ride. 2004. (Take It to the Extreme Ser.). 176p. (YA). (gr. 7-11). pap. 6.95 (978-1-55285-604-8(6)) Whitecap Bks., Ltd. CAN. *Dist:* Firefly Bks., Ltd.

—Daredevil Club. 2006. 112p. (J). pap. 8.95 (978-1-55143-614-2(0)); lib. bdg. 14.95 (978-1-55143-618-0(3)) Orca Bk. Pubs. USA.

Withrow, Sarah. Box Girl. 2002. 184p. (J). pap. 5.95 (978-0-88899-436-3(2)) Groundwood Bks. CAN. *Dist:* Perseus Distribution.

—Box Girl. 2001. (gr. 5-8). lib. bdg. 14.10 (978-0-613-67071-5(X)) Tandem Library Bks.

—What Gloria Wants. 2006. 176p. pap. 6.95 (978-0-88899-692-3(6)) Groundwood Bks. CAN. *Dist:* Perseus Distribution.

Wittlinger, Ellen. Razzle. 256p. 2003. (YA). pap. 7.99 (978-0-689-85600-6(8) , Simon Pulse); 2001. (Illus.). (J). (gr. 7-10). 17.00 (978-0-689-83565-0(5)) Simon & Schuster Children's Publishing.

—Razzle. 2003. (gr. 7-12). lib. bdg. 16.45 (978-0-613-61811-3(4)) Tandem Library Bks.

—Sandpiper. 2007. 288p. (YA). (gr. 7 up). pap. 6.99 (978-1-4169-3651-0(3) , Simon Pulse) Simon & Schuster Children's Publishing.

Wojciechowski, Susan. Beany & the Dreaded Wedding. Natti, Susanna, illus. ed. 2005. 128p. (J). (gr. 1-4). pap. 4.99 (978-0-7636-2569-6(8)) Candlewick Pr.

—Beany & the Meany. Natti, Susanna, illus. 112p. (J). (gr. 1-4). 2006. pap. 4.99 (978-0-7636-2974-8(X)); 2005. 15.99 (978-0-7636-2630-3(9)) Candlewick Pr.

—Beany Goes to Camp. Natti, Susanna, illus. ed. 2005. (Beany Ser.). 112p. (J). (gr. 1-4). pap. 4.99 (978-0-7636-2570-2(1)) Candlewick Pr.

—The Christmas Miracle of Jonathan Toomey. Lynch, P. J., illus. 1998. 40p. (J). (ps-3). 18.99 incl. cd-rom (978-0-8499-5905-9(5)) Nelson, Thomas Inc.

Wojtowycz, David. Come on Dudley! Friends. 2002. (Dudley! Ser.). (Illus.). (J). 3.95 (978-1-58925-668-2(9) , tiger tales) ME Media LLC.

Wolf, Carla. Moving Towards a Dream. 2006. 91p. pap. 14.95 (***978-1-4241-5444-9(8)***) PublishAmerica, Inc.

Wolf, P. Secrets in the Darkness. 2005. 345p. pap. 24.95 (978-1-4137-6246-4(8)) PublishAmerica, Inc.

Wolfer, Dianne. Border Line. 1998. 190p. (J). pap. 11.95 (978-1-86368-208-4(2)) Fremantle Pr. AUS. *Dist:* International Specialized Bk. Services.

Wolff, Ferida. Watch Out for Bears! The Adventures of Henry & Bruno. 1999. (Step into Reading Ser.). (978-0-606-16893-9(1)) Tandem Library Bks.

Wolff, Virginia Euwer. Make Lemonade. unabr. ed. 2004. (Young Adult Cassette Librariestm Ser.). 200p. (J). (gr. 7 up). pap. 36.00 incl. audio (978-0-8072-0793-2(4) , S YA 348 SP, Listening Library) Random Hse. Audio Publishing Group.

—True Believer. 2004. (Make Lemonade Trilogy Ser.). 272p. (J). (gr. 7 up). pap. 38.00 incl. audio (978-0-8072-2283-6(6) , Listening Library) Random Hse. Audio Publishing Group.

—True Believer. Gordon, Russell, illus. 2002. 272p. (YA). pap. 8.99 (978-0-689-85288-6(6) , Simon Pulse) Simon & Schuster Children's Publishing.

—True Believer. 2001. (Make Lemonade Trilogy Ser.). 272p. (J). (gr. 7 up). 17.00 (978-0-689-82827-0(6) , Atheneum) Simon & Schuster Children's Publishing.

—True Believer. 2002. (gr. 7-12). lib. bdg. 16.45 (978-0-613-60942-5(5)) Tandem Library Bks.

Wolkstein, Diane. Little Mouse's Painting. 2002. (gr. k-3). lib. bdg. 14.10 (978-0-613-63049-8(1)) Tandem Library Bks.

Woloson, Eliza. My Friend Isabelle. Gough, Bryan, tr. Gough, Bryan, illus. 2003. 28p. (J). 14.95 (978-1-890627-50-8(X)) Woodbine Hse.

Wong, Janet S. The Dumpster Diver. Roberts, David, illus. 2007. 32p. (J). (gr. k-3). 16.99 (978-0-7636-2380-7(6)) Candlewick Pr.

—Minn & Jake. Cote, Genevieve, illus. 2003. 160p. (J). (gr. 2-5). 16.00 (978-0-374-34987-5(8) , Farrar, Straus & Giroux (BYR)) Farrar, Straus & Giroux.

Wood, Jamie Martinez. Rogelia's House of Magic. 2008. 320p. (J). (gr. 7). 15.99 (***978-0-385-73477-6(8)*** , Delacorte Bks. for Young Readers) Random Hse. Children's Bks.

Wood, June Rae. About Face. 2001. (J). (978-0-606-21014-0(8)) Tandem Library Bks.

Wood, Kim Marie, ed. Heart, Hoof & Soul. Spatrisano-Graham, Kimberly, illus. 1999. 64p. (YA). (gr. 4-9). pap. 7.95 (978-0-9671978-6-9(4)) Syncopated Pr.

Wood, Lena. The Ancient Omen. 2006. 192p. (J). pap. 6.99 (978-0-7847-1590-1(4) , 42152) Standard Publishing.

EFG

—The Angel of Fire. 2006. 192p. (J). pap. 6.99 (978-0-7847-1530-7(0)) Standard Publishing.

—Carpet of Bones. 2006. (Illus.). 192p. (J). pap. 6.99 (978-0-7847-1535-2(1)) Standard Publishing.

—Elijah Creek & the Armor of Gift Set. 2006. 576p. (J). Bks. 1-3. 17.99 (978-0-7847-1966-4(7)); Bks. 4-6. 17.99 (978-0-7847-1967-1(5)) Standard Publishing.

—The Haunted Soul, Vol. 5. 2005. (Elijah Creek & the Armor of God Ser.: 5). (Illus.). 189p. (J). (gr. 3-7). pap. 6.99 (978-0-7847-1760-8(5) , 42155) Standard Publishing.

—The Path of Shadows, Vol. 4. 2005. (Elijah Creek & the Armor of God Ser.: 4). (Illus.). 189p. (J). (gr. 3-7). pap. 6.99 (978-0-7847-1759-2(1) , 42154) Standard Publishing.

—The Raven's Curse. 2006. 192p. (J). pap. 6.99 (978-0-7847-1592-5(0) , 42153) Standard Publishing.

—The Severed Head. 2006. 192p. (J). pap. 6.99 (978-0-7847-1583-3(1) , 42151) Standard Publishing.

Wood, Phyllis. Pass Me a Pine Cone, Please. 2006. pap. 12.50 (*978-1-4259-7445-9(7)) AuthorHouse.

Woodruff, Elvira. Dear Levi: Letters from the Overland Trail. Peck, Beth, illus. 1998. 128p. (J). (gr. 5-8). 5.50 (978-0-679-88558-0(7) , Yearling) Random Hse. Children's Bks.

Woods, Linda J. The Story of Child, Pebble & Friend. 2007. 27p. pap. 7.95 (*978-0-533-15639-9(4)) Vantage Pr., Inc.

Woodson, Jacqueline. After Tupac & D Foster. 2008. 160p. (YA). (gr. 5). 15.99 (*978-0-399-24654-8(1) , Putnam Juvenile) Penguin Group (USA) Inc.

—Between Madison & Palmetto. 2002. 128p. (J). pap. 5.99 (978-0-698-11958-1(4)); (YA). 16.99 (978-0-399-23757-7(7)) Penguin Group (USA) Inc. (Putnam Juvenile).

—Between Madison & Palmetto. 2002. (gr. 5-8). lib. bdg. 14.15 (978-0-613-50092-0(X)) Tandem Library Bks.

—Feathers. 2007. 128p. (J). (gr. 3-7). 15.99 (978-0-399-23989-2(8) , Putnam Juvenile) Penguin Group (USA) Inc.

—I Hadn't Meant to Tell You This. 2006. (YA). 176p. (gr. 4). 17.99 (978-0-399-24499-5(9) , Putnam Juvenile); 128p. (gr. 7). pap. 5.99 (978-0-14-240555-0(8) , Puffin) Penguin Group (USA) Inc.

—Last Summer with Maizon. 2002. 112p. (J). 17.99 (978-0-399-23755-3(0)); (Illus.). (gr. 3-7). pap. 5.99 (978-0-698-11929-1(0)) Penguin Group (USA) Inc. (Putnam Juvenile).

—Last Summer with Maizon. 2002. (gr. 3-6). lib. bdg. 13.00 (978-0-613-45286-1(0)) Tandem Library Bks.

—The Other Side. Lewis, Earl, illus. 2001. 1p. (J). (gr. k up). 16.99 (978-0-399-23116-2(1) , Putnam Juvenile) Penguin Group (USA) Inc.

Woodworth, Chris. Georgie's Moon. 2006. 176p. (J). 16.00 (978-0-374-33306-5(8)) Farrar, Straus & Giroux.

Woolf, Paula. Old Ladies with Brooms Aren't Always Witches. 1998. 154p. (YA). (gr. 4-6). 9.99 (978-0-88092-395-8(4) , 3954) Royal Fireworks Publishing Co.

Woolley, Barbara B. Freedom West. 2006. 22.99 (*978-1-4257-0124-6(8)); pap. 15.99 (*978-1-4257-0123-9(X)) Xlibris Corp.

Wordshop Editorial Staff. Twink 'n' Twinkle: The Beginning. 1999. (Illus.). 28p. (J). (ps-4). 19.95 (978-0-9668469-0-4(7)) WordSHOP, Inc.

Wormell, Christopher. In the Woods. 2004. (Illus.). 32p. (J). (ps). pap., pap. 9.99 (978-0-09-941767-5(7) , Red Fox) Random Hse. Children's Bks. GBR. *Dist:* Trafalgar Square Publishing.

Wormell, Mary. Why Not? Wormell, Mary, illus. 2003. (Illus.). 32p. (J). (ps-1). pap. 5.95 (978-0-374-48384-5(1) , Sunburst) Farrar, Straus & Giroux.

Worth, Bonnie. Way to Go, Chipmunk Cheeks. (Full House Ser.). 96p. (J). (gr. 4-6). pap. 3.25 (978-0-938753-57-5(6) , PP1) Parachute Publishing, LLC.

Wright, Dare. Edith & Mr. Bear. 2000. (Lonely Doll Story Ser.). (Illus.). 64p. (J). (gr. k-3). tchr. ed. 16.00 (978-0-618-00332-7(0)); pap. 6.95 (978-0-618-04253-1(9)) Houghton Mifflin Co. Trade & Reference Div.

Wright, Sue. Davey & Goliath Blind Mans Bluff. 2005. (Davey & Goliath Storybook #2 Ser.). (Illus.). 40p. (J). 3.99 (978-0-439-69832-0(4) , Scholastic Paperbacks) Scholastic, Inc.

Wurtz, K. D. Digby Finds a Friend. Carrier, Tracey Dahle, illus. 2001. (Digby in Disguise Ser.: Vol. 2). (J). (978-0-9712840-2-9(4) , Bear & Co.) Bear & Co.

Wynne-Jones, Tim. The Maestro. 2004. 224p. (J). pap. 6.95 (978-0-88899-637-4(3)) Groundwood Bks. CAN. *Dist:* Perseus Distribution.

—Rex Zero & the End of the World. 2007. (J). (Illus.). 192p. (gr. 3-7). 16.00 (978-0-374-33467-3(6)); 186p. (*978-1-4287-3318-3(3)) Farrar, Straus & Giroux.

Wyre, Yvonne. The Further Adventures of Cuthbert the Coal Lorry & all His Friends. 2007. (Illus.). 204p. pap. (*978-1-84401-801-7(6)) Athena Pr.

Wyss, Thelma Hatch. A Tale of Gold. 2007. 160p. (J). (gr. 3-7). 16.99 (*978-1-4169-4212-2(2) , McElderry, Margaret K.) Simon & Schuster Children's Publishing.

Yaccarino, Dan. Unlovable. rev. ed. 2004. (Illus.). 32p. (J). reprint ed. pap. 6.95 (978-0-8050-7532-8(1) , Owlet Paperbacks for Young Readers) Holt, Henry & Co.

Yackle, Deanne. Jenny & Me. 2005. (J). lib. bdg. 15.95 (978-0-9725485-4-0(8)) Waterfall Ridge.

Yacobi, Lily & Yacobi, Diana. The Aleph Bet Story: Featuring Sarah & David & Friends. 2004. (J). per. 10.95 (978-0-9761648-0-7(9)) Sarah & David LLC.

Yaeger, Stephen S. Ian & the Woodins. 2001. 152p. (Orig.). pap. 11.95 (978-0-595-18366-1(2) , Writers Club Pr.) iUniverse, Inc.

Yamamura, Anji. Hannah Duck. Yamamura, Anji, illus. 2008. (Illus.). 24p. (J). 15.95 (*978-1-933605-74-6(X)) Kane/Miller Bk. Pubs., Inc.

Yang, Dori Jones. The Secret Voice of Gina Zhang. 2000. (978-0-606-21790-3(8)) Tandem Library Bks.

Yang, Huan. Artie & Julie. Chen, Zhiyuan & Huang, Hsiao-Yen, illus. 2007. 32p. (J). 15.95 (978-0-9787550-0-3(6)) Heryin Publishing Corp.

Yates, Janet Lee. Skeeter Bug Loves Sarah. 2007. (ENG.). 88p. per. 11.99 (*978-1-4141-0820-9(6)) Pleasant Word.

Yates, Patty Fee, told to. Friends. 2004. pap. 8.00 (978-0-8059-6459-2(2)) Dorrance Publishing Co., Inc.

Yeager, Graham. Diablo: The Third Millersburg Novel. 2006. 145p. (YA). per. 7.99 (*978-0-9765478-4-6(8)) Stone Acres Publishing Co.

Yee, Lisa. Millicent Min, Girl Genius. 256p. 2003. (YA). (gr. 5-8). 16.95 (978-0-439-42519-3(0)); 2004. (J). (gr. 4-7). reprint ed. pap. 4.99 (978-0-439-42520-9(4)) Scholastic, Inc. (Levine, Arthur A. Bks.).

—So Totally Emily Ebers. 2008. 304p. (J). 5.99 (978-0-439-83848-1(7) , Levine, Arthur A. Bks.) Scholastic, Inc.

—So Totally Emily Embers. 2007. 304p. (J). (gr. 4-7). pap. 16.99 (978-0-439-83847-4(9) , Levine, Arthur A. Bks.) Scholastic, Inc.

—Stanford Wong Flunks Big Time. (Illus.). (J). 2007. 320p. pap. 5.99 (978-0-439-62248-6(4)); 2005. 304p. (gr. 5-7). pap. 16.99 (978-0-439-62247-9(6)) Scholastic, Inc. (Levine, Arthur A. Bks.).

Yee, Paul. The Boy in the Attic. 1998. (Illus.). (J). (gr. 2-5). 15.95 (978-0-88899-330-4(7) , Libros Tigrillo) Groundwood Bks. CAN. *Dist:* Transition Vendor.

Yee, Wong Herbert. Did You See Chip? Ovresat, Laura, illus. 2004. (Green Light Readers Level 2 Ser.). 24p. (J). 12.95 (978-0-15-205095-5(7)); pap. 3.95 (978-0-15-205096-2(5)) Harcourt Children's Bks. (Green Light Readers).

—Did You See Chip? 2004. (gr. k-3). lib. bdg. 11.80 (978-0-613-81965-7(9)) Tandem Library Bks.

Yep, Laurence. The Traitor: Golden Mountain Chronicles: 1885. (Golden Mountain Chronicles). 320p. (J). (gr. 5 up). 2004. pap. 6.99 (978-0-06-000831-4(8) , Harper Trophy); 2003. 17.99 (978-0-06-027522-8(7)) HarperCollins Pubs.

Yin. Brothers. Soentpiet, Chris, illus. 2006. 32p. (J). (gr. k). 16.99 (978-0-399-23406-4(3) , Philomel) Penguin Group (USA) Inc.

Ylvisaker, Anne. Little Klein. 2007. (Illus.). 192p. (J). (gr. 3-7). 15.99 (*978-0-7636-3359-2(3)) Candlewick Pr.

Yolen, Jane. Boots & Seven Leaguers: A Rock-and-Troll Novel. 2003. (gr. 5-8). lib. bdg. 14.10 (978-0-613-59881-1(4)) Tandem Library Bks.

—Dimity Duck. Braun, Sebastian, illus. 2006. 32p. (J). (ps). 15.99 (978-0-399-24632-6(0) , Philomel) Penguin Group (USA) Inc.

—Dragon's Boy. 2001. (gr. 3-6). lib. bdg. 13.00 (978-0-613-34680-1(7)) Tandem Library Bks.

—Owl Moon. 2002. (Illus.). (J). 23.64 (978-0-7587-0064-3(4)) Book Wholesalers, Inc.

—Tam Lin. 1998. (978-0-606-13836-9(6)) Tandem Library Bks.

Yost-Filgate, Susan. Rip Squeak & His Friends. Filgate, Leonard, illus. 2005. 32p. (J). (ps-3). 14.99 (978-0-9747825-0-8(5)) Rip Squeak, Inc.

—Rip Squeak & His Friends: An Introduction to the Roaring Adventures of Rip Squeak. Filgate, Leonard, illus. 2nd deluxe collector's gif. ed. 1999. (GER.). 64p. 35.00 (978-0-9672422-0-0(7)) Rip Squeak, Inc.

You My Friend. 2007. (J). bds. 21.95 (*978-0-9745191-4-2(6)) Lynn Tyner Mitchum & James Rogers.

Young, Diane. See No Evil. 2006. (Orca Currents Ser.). 112p. (J). pap. (978-1-55143-619-7(1)) Orca Bk. Pubs.

—See No Evil. 2006. 112p. (J). lib. bdg. 14.95 (978-1-55143-664-7(7)) Orca Bk. Pubs. USA.

Young, Kristi. The Secret Club - the Powder Puff Club Book 1. 2007. 140p. (J). per. 12.95 (*978-1-59594-070-4(7) , Wingspan Pr.) WingSpan Publishing.

Young, Lauren. Ally M. & Ally G. Rooney, Sandra, illus. 2006. 20p. (J). (*978-1-4120-8518-2(7)) Trafford Publishing.

Young, Martha & McQuilkin, John A. The Legend of the Land of Caelumen, Pt. 1. 2005. per. 29.95 (978-0-9773523-0-2(7)) Whimble Designs.

Youree, Barbara. Senegal Sleuths. 2006. 56p. 7.75 (978-0-8341-2226-0(X)) Beacon Hill Pr. of Kansas City.

Yumi & Her Best-Forever Friend. 2000. (J). mass mkt. 3.49 (978-0-89610-448-8(6)) Island Heritage Publishing.

Yumoto, Kazumi. The Friends. Hirano, Cathy, tr. 2005. 176p. (J). (gr. 5-9). pap. 6.95 (978-0-374-42461-9(6) , Farrar, Straus & Giroux (BYR)) Farrar, Straus & Giroux.

—The Friends. 1998. (J). (978-0-606-13103-2(5)) Tandem Library Bks.

Zalben, Jane Breskin. Brenda Berman, Wedding Expert. Chess, Victoria, illus. 2007. (J). (*978-0-618-31321-1(4) , Clarion Bks.) Houghton Mifflin Co. Trade & Reference Div.

Zalben, Jane Breskin. Leap. 2007. 272p. (J). (gr. 5). 15.99 (978-0-375-83871-2(6)); lib. bdg. 18.99 (978-0-375-93871-9(0)) Random Hse. Children's Bks. (Knopf Bks. for Young Readers).

Zapata, Elizabeth. You Say Hola, I Say Hello. Johnson, Cathy Ann, illus. 2006. (SPA.). 24p. (J). (gr. k-2). pap. 4.95 (978-0-516-25018-2(3) , Children's Pr.) Scholastic Library Publishing.

—You Say Hola, I Say Hello. Johnson, Cathy Ann, illus. 2005. (Rookie Reader Ser.). 24p. (J). 19.50 (978-0-516-24859-2(6) , Children's Pr.) Scholastic Library Publishing.

Zarchi, Nurit. No Echeis A Nanny! 2002. 90p. (978-84-85334-87-2(6)) Loguez Ediciones ESP. *Dist:* Lectorum Pubns., Inc.

Zarins, Kimberly. Playful Bunny. Pons, Bernadette, illus. 2006. (Cartwheel Books). 32p. (J). pap. 5.99 (978-0-439-72538-5(0) , Cartwheel Bks.) Scholastic, Inc.

Zarr, Sara. Sweethearts. 2008. 224p. (J). 16.99 (*978-0-316-01455-7(9)) Little, Brown Bks. for Young Readers.

Zehler, Antonia. Two Fine Ladies: Tea for Three. Zehler, Antonia, illus. 2002. (Step into Reading Ser.: Vol. 2). (Illus.). 32p. (J). (ps-1). pap. 3.99 (978-0-375-81105-0(2) , Random Hse. Bks. for Young Readers) Random Hse. Children's Bks.

—Two Fine Ladies: Tea for Three. 2002. (ps-2). lib. bdg. 11.80 (978-0-613-84579-3(X)) Tandem Library Bks.

Zemser, Amy Bronwen. Beyond the Mango Tree. 1998. (Illus.). 156p. (YA). (gr. 5 up). 14.95 (978-0-688-16005-0(0)) HarperCollins Pubs.

—Beyond the Mango Tree. 2000. (978-0-606-17879-2(1)) Tandem Library Bks.

Zevin, Gabrielle. Memoirs of a Teenage Amnesiac. 2007. 288p. (YA). (gr. 9 up). 17.00 (*978-0-374-34946-2(0) , Farrar, Straus & Giroux (BYR)) Farrar, Straus & Giroux.

Ziefert, Harriet. 39 Uses for a Friend. Doughty, Rebecca, illus. 2001. 32p. (J). (gr. k-4). 11.99 (978-0-399-23616-7(3) , Putnam Juvenile) Penguin Group (USA) Inc.

Zimmerman, George G. Dougie & the Dane: Chelsea the Great Dane. 2004. (Illus.). 36p. 21.99 (978-1-4134-4139-0(4)) Xlibris Corp.

Zindel, Paul. The Pigman. 2005. (Illus.). 192p. (J). (gr. 7 up). pap. 6.99 (978-0-06-075735-9(3) , Harper Trophy) HarperCollins Pubs.

—The Pigman. Date not set. (Scholastic Bookfiles Ser.). 64p. (J). pap. 4.99 (*978-0-439-53831-2(9)) Scholastic, Inc.

Zindel, Paul. The Pigman's Legacy. 2005. 176p. (J). (gr. 7 up). pap. 5.99 (978-0-06-075970-4(4) , Harper Trophy) HarperCollins Pubs.

Zoehfeld, Kathleen Weidner. Pooh's Friends. Studio Orlando Staff, illus. 1998. (Chunky Roly-Poly Book Ser.). 18p. (J). (ps-3). bds. 3.99 (978-1-57082-991-8(8) , RH/Disney) Random Hse. Children's Bks.

Zoller, Jayson D. The Laziest Duck. l.t. ed. 2004. (Illus.). 13p. (J). lib. bdg. 12.95 (978-1-932338-55-3(1)); per. 7.99 (978-1-932338-52-2(7)) Lifevest Publishing, Inc.

Zollman, Pam. Don't Bug Me! 2001. (Illus.). 144p. (J). (gr. 4-6). tchr. ed. 15.95 (978-0-8234-1584-7(8)) Holiday Hse., Inc.

Zolotow, Charlotte. If It Weren't for You. Karas, G. Brian, illus. 2006. 32p. (J). (ps-3). lib. bdg. 16.89 (978-0-06-027876-2(5)) HarperCollins Pubs.

—The Three Funny Friends. Bronson, Linda, illus. 2006. 27p. (J). (gr. k-4). reprint ed. 16.00 (978-0-7567-9860-4(4)) DIANE Publishing Co.

—The Three Funny Friends. Bronson, Linda, illus. 2003. 32p. (J). (gr. k-3). 15.95 (978-0-7624-1553-3(3) , Running Pr. Kids) Running Pr. Bk. Pubs.

Zolty, H. Calli the Bear: the Story of a Little Bear Who Teaches Children about the Power of Friendship. 2005. 36p. 16.19 (978-1-4116-7135-5(X)) Lulu.com.

Zondervan & Focus on the Family Staff. Froggy World: Where All Your Dreams Come True. 2003. (J). 12.99 incl. VHS (978-0-310-70569-7(X)) Zonderkidz.

Zondervan & Kenney, Cindy. Veggie Tales - Yo Puedo y Tu Tambien, 4 Books, Pack. 2005. (SPA.). 18p. (J). 12.99 (978-0-8297-4361-6(8)) Zondervan.

FRIENDSHIP—POETRY

Martin, Susana. Mi Joven y Romantico Corazon (My Young Romantic Heart) Merino, Vladimiro, illus. 2000. (SPA.). 72p. (YA). pap. (978-950-11-1509-3(7)) Sigmar.

Moses, Brian, contrib. by. My Gang: Poems about Friendship. 2003. (Illus.). 65p. (J). pap. 6.99 (978-0-330-37061-5(8) , Pan) Pan Macmillan GBR. *Dist:* Trafalgar Square Publishing.

Pacilio, V. J. Ling Cho & his Three Friends. Cook, Scott, illus. 2000. 32p. (J). (ps-3). 16.00 (978-0-374-34545-7(7) , Farrar, Straus & Giroux (BYR)) Farrar, Straus & Giroux.

Quattlebaum, Mary. Winter Friends. Nakata, Hiroe, illus. 2005. 32p. (J). (gr. k-k). 15.95 (978-0-385-74626-7(1)); lib. bdg. 17.99 (978-0-385-90868-9(7)) Random Hse. Children's Bks. (Doubleday Bks. for Young Readers).

FROG AND TOAD (FICTITIOUS CHARACTERS)—FICTION

Book Company Staff. Hoppity Hop. 2003. (Novelty Bks.). (Illus.). (J). 15.95 (978-1-74047-233-3(0)) Book Co. Publishing Pty, Ltd., The AUS. *Dist:* Penton Overseas, Inc.

Hood, Karen Jean Matsko. There's A Toad in the Hole - English/French Bilingual Translation: A Big Fat Toad in the Hole. 2005. (J). 24.95 (978-1-59649-795-5(5)) Whispering Pine Pr., Inc.

—There's A Toad in the Hole - English/Spanish Bilingual Translation: A Big Fat Toad in the Hole. 2005. (J). 15.95 (978-1-59649-789-4(0)); spiral bd. 15.95 (978-1-59649-790-0(4)) Whispering Pine Pr., Inc.

Lobel, Arnold. The Adventures of Frog & Toad. 1998. (Illus.). (J). 12.95 (978-0-06-028043-7(3)) HarperCollins Pubs.

—Frog & Toad All Year. Lobel, Arnold, illus. 2002. (Frog & Toad Ser.). (Illus.). (J). 12.34 (978-0-7587-1198-4(0)) Book Wholesalers, Inc.

—Frog & Toad Are Friends. Lobel, Arnold, illus. 2002. (Frog & Toad Ser.). (J). 12.34 (978-0-7587-6105-7(8)) Book Wholesalers, Inc.

—Frog & Toad Together. Lobel, Arnold, illus. 1999. (I Can Read Bks.). (Illus.). 64p. (J). (ps-3). 16.99 (978-0-694-01298-5(X) , Harper Festival) HarperCollins Pubs.

—Une Paire d'Amis. 2000. Tr. of Frog & Toad Are Friends. (FRE.). (J). pap. 14.95 (978-2-211-03651-1(1)) Archimede Editions FRA. *Dist:* Distribooks, Inc.

—Sapo y Sepo Inseparables. Lobel, Arnold, illus. 2003. (SPA., Illus.). 68p. (J). (ps-3). 12.95 (978-84-204-3047-8(1)) Alfaguara, Ediciones, S.A.- Grupo Santillana ESP. *Dist:* Lectorum Pubns., Inc., Santillana USA Publishing Co., Inc.

Plessix, Michel. Viento en los Sauces. Gasol, Anna, tr. 2005. 136p. (J). 21.95 (978-84-607-9015-0(0)) Ediciones Norte, Inc.

FROGMEN

see Skin Diving

FROGS

see also Tadpoles

Aloian, Molly & Kalman, Bobbie. Endangered Frogs. 2006. (Illus.). 32p. (J). (gr. 2-8). pap. (978-0-7787-1918-2(9)); (978-0-7787-1872-7(7)) Crabtree Publishing Co.

Arnosky, Jim. All about Frogs. Arnosky, Jim, illus. 2002. (Illus.). 32p. (J). (ps-5). pap. 16.95 (978-0-590-48164-9(9) , Scholastic Pr.) Scholastic, Inc.

Bailey, Jill. Frogs & Toads. 2003. (Secret World Of... Ser.). (Illus.). 48p. (J). lib. bdg. 27.14 (978-0-7398-7022-8(X)) Raintree.

Bakken, Aimee. Uncover a Frog: Take a Three Dimensional Look Inside a Frog. 2006. (Uncover Bks.). (Illus.). 16p. (J). 18.95 (978-1-59223-456-1(9) , Silver Dolphin Bks.) Advantage Pubs. Group.

Barnard, Edward S. Frogs. 2006. (J). (978-1-59939-074-1(4) , Reader's Digest Young Families, Inc.) Reader's Digest Children's Publishing, Inc.

Benton, Celia. How a Frog Grows. 2003. (Compass Point Phonics Readers Ser.). (Illus.). 16p. (J). (gr. 1 up). 13.26 (978-0-7565-0509-7(7)) Compass Point Bks.

—How a Frog Grows Set B, 6 vols. (Phonics Readers Ser.). (gr. k-2). 17.50 (978-0-7368-3196-3(7)) Red Brick Learning.

Berger, Melvin & Berger, Gilda. De Renacuajo a Rana: Tadpole to Frog. 2006. (SPA & ENG., Illus.). (J). (*978-0-439-82864-2(3)) Scholastic, Inc.

Berger, Melvin & Berger, Gilda. Frogs Live on Logs. 2003. (Illus.). 16p. (J). (978-0-439-47176-3(1)) Scholastic, Inc.

Berman, Ruth. Climbing Tree Frogs. Netherton, John, photos by. 1998. (Pull Ahead Bks.). (Illus.). 32p. (gr. k-2). (J). pap. 5.95 (978-0-8225-3611-6(0)); lib. bdg. 22.60 (978-0-8225-3605-5(6)) Lerner Publishing Group.

Bevington, Kate. A Frog's Life. Herb, Eileen, illus. 2002. (J). vinyl bd., act. bk. ed. 5.99 (978-1-883043-40-7(9)) Straight Edge Pr., The.

Bishop, Nic. Nic Bishop Frogs. 2008. 48p. (J). pap. 17.99 (*978-0-439-87755-8(5)) Scholastic, Inc.

Block, Larry. All about Frogs. 3rd ed. 1998. (Illus.). 48p. (J). (ps-3). reprint ed. pap. 6.95 (978-1-891929-13-7(5) , Manatee Publishing) Four Seasons Pubs.

Book Company Staff. Frog Gets Lost. 2004. (Pond Sparkle Bks.). (Illus.). 10p. (J). bds. 4.95 (978-1-74047-493-1(7)) Book Co. Publishing Pty, Ltd., The AUS. *Dist:* Penton Overseas, Inc.

Bredeson, Carmen. Fun Facts about Frogs! 2007. (I Like Reptiles & Amphibians Ser.). (Illus.). 24p. (J). (gr. 1-3). lib. bdg. 21.26 (978-0-7660-2788-6(0) , Enslow Elementary) Enslow Pubs., Inc.

Burns, Diane L. Frogs, Toads & Turtles. Garrow, Linda, illus. 1999. (Young Naturalist Field Guides Ser.). 40p. (J). (gr. 3 up). lib. bdg. 24.67 (978-0-8368-2145-1(9)) Stevens, Gareth Inc.

—Frogs, Toads & Turtles. Garrow, Linda, illus. 2004. (Take-Along Guide Ser.). 48p. (J). (gr. 2-5). pap. 7.95 (978-1-55971-593-5(6) , NorthWord Bks. for Young Readers) T&N Children's Publishing.

Burns, Kate. Jump Like a Frog! 1999. (Lift-the-Flap Bk.). (Illus.). 12p. (J). (ps-k). 6.95 (978-1-899607-35-8(8)) Sterling Publishing Co., Inc.

Canizares, Susan & Moreton, Daniel. Frogs. 1998. (Science Emergent Readers Ser.). (J). 2.50 (978-0-590-76159-8(5)) Scholastic, Inc.

—Frogs: Ranas. 2002. (Science Emergent Readers Ser.). (ENG & SPA., Illus.). (J). pap. (978-0-439-41158-5(0)) Scholastic, Inc.

Chang, Maria L. Early Themes: Life Cycles Butterflies, Chicks, Frogs & More!, 1. 1999. 48p. pap. 9.95 (978-0-590-68572-6(4)) Scholastic, Inc.

Chrustowski, Rick. Hop Frog. rev. ed. 2003. (Illus.). 32p. (J). (ps-2). 15.95 (978-0-8050-6688-3(8) , Holt, Henry & Co. Bks. For Young Readers) Holt, Henry & Co.

Cooper, Jason. Bullfrog. 2002. (Illus.). 24p. (J). lib. bdg. 25.64 (978-1-58952-353-1(9)) Rourke Publishing, LLC.

Cowley, Joy. The Red-Eyed Tree Frog. Bishop, Nic, illus. 1999. (J). pap. (978-0-590-87176-1(5)); 32p. pap. 16.95 (978-0-590-87175-4(7)) Scholastic, Inc.

—Red-eyed Tree Frog. Bishop, Nic, illus. 2006. 32p. (J). pap. 5.99 (978-0-439-78221-0(X) , Scholastic Paperbacks) Scholastic, Inc.

Craats, Rennay. Caring for Your Frog. 2004. (Caring for Your Pet Ser.). (Illus.). (J). pap. (978-1-59036-218-1(7)); lib. bdg. 16.95 (978-1-59036-198-6(9)) Weigl Pubs., Inc.

Crawford, Tracey. Frogs. 2006. (Illus.). 24p. (J). (978-1-4034-8453-6(8)); pap. (978-1-4034-8460-4(0)) Heinemann Library.

Davis, Jeffrey G. & Menze, Scott A. Frogs & Toads. 2000. (In Ohio's Backyard Ser.: Vol. 3). (Illus.). 150p. (J). (gr. 6 up). 15.00 (978-0-86727-139-3(6)) Ohio Biological Survey.

Del renacuajo a la rana (from Tadpole to Frog) 2007. (J). pap. 4.95 (978-0-8225-6634-2(6) , Ediciones Lerner) Lerner Publishing Group.

Del Renacuajo a la Rana (From Tadpole to Frog) 2006. (De Principio a Fin Ser.). (SPA.). 24p. (J). 18.60 (978-0-8225-6497-3(1) , Ediciones Lerner) Lerner Publishing Group.

Dell'Oro, Suzanne Paul. Hiding Toads. 1999. (gr. k-3). lib. bdg. 14.10 (978-0-613-43832-2(9)) Tandem Library Bks.

Dewey, Jennifer Owings. Poison Dart Frogs. Dewey, Jennifer Owings, illus. 2003. (Illus.). 32p. (J). (gr. k-2). pap. 10.95 (978-1-56397-945-3(4)) Boyds Mills Pr.

—Poison Dart Frogs. 1998. (Illus.). 32p. (J). (gr. k-5). 15.95 (978-1-56397-655-1(2)) Boyds Mills Pr.

—Poison Dart Frogs. 2001. (gr. 3-6). lib. bdg. 18.75 (978-0-613-36607-6(7)); (Illus.). (J). (978-0-606-20858-1(5)) Tandem Library Bks.

Dicks, Ian & Watton, Nick, illus. God's Fantastic Frogs. 1999. (Zoomers Ser.). 4p. (J). (gr. 3-7). 2.99 (978-0-7847-1124-8(0) , 03534, Bean Sprouts) Standard Publishing.

Dickstein, Leslie. Storms! Storms! 2006. (Time for Kids Science Scoops Ser.). (J). pap. (978-978-006-078-7(2)) HarperCollins Pubs.

Dingles, Molly. Green as a Frog. Velez, Walter, illus. 2002. (Community of Color Ser.). 32p. (J). lib. bdg. 20.65 (978-1-891997-21-1(1)) Dingles & Co.

Do Frogs Have Fur? (Animals All Around Ser.). 24p. (J). 7.95 (978-1-4048-1125-6(7)) Picture Window Bks.

Dominquez, Amalia. Happy, Hopping Frog. 2004. (Illus.). 24p. bds. 8.95 (978-1-932915-00-6(1)) Sandvik Publishing.

Dorling Kindersley Publishing Staff. Frog. (See How They Grow Ser.). 24p. (J). (ps-1). 2007. pap. 3.99 (978-0-7566-3016-4(9)); 2006. pap. 4.99 (978-0-7566-2213-8(1)); 2003. (Illus.). pap. 7.99 (978-0-7894-9629-4(1)) Dorling Kindersley Publishing, Inc.

Driscoll, Laura. Frogs. Moffatt, Judith, illus. 1998. (All Aboard Science Reader Station Stop Ser.: No. 1). 32p. (J). (ps-1). pap. 3.99 (978-0-448-41839-1(8) , Grosset & Dunlap) Penguin Group (USA) Inc.

Feely, Jenny. Tadpoles & Frogs. 1999. (ps-2). lib. bdg. 11.80 (978-0-613-30770-3(4)) Tandem Library Bks.

French, Vivian. Growing Frogs. Bartlett, Alison, illus. 2003. (Big Books! Ser.). 32p. (J). (gr. k-3). pap. 19.99 (978-0-7636-2232-9(X)); pap. 6.99 (978-0-7636-2052-3(1)) Candlewick Pr.

—Growing Frogs. 2003. (gr. k-3). lib. bdg. 14.15 (978-0-613-74826-1(3)) Tandem Library Bks.

Fridell, Ron. The Search for Poison-Dart Frogs. 2001. (Wildlife Conservation Society Bks.). (Illus.). 48p. (J). (gr. 4-6). 24.50 (978-0-531-11888-7(6)); pap. 6.95 (978-0-531-16570-6(1)) Scholastic Library Publishing. (Watts, Franklin).

—Search for Poison-Dart Frogs. 2001. (gr. 3-6). lib. bdg. 15.25 (978-0-613-54647-8(4)) Tandem Library Bks.

Frog. 2004. (Peek-A-Boo Coloring Pads Ser.). 48p. (J). act. bk. ed. 3.99 (978-1-85997-394-3(9)) Byeway Bks.

Frog Life Cycle. 2001. (Animal Kingdom Ser.). (J). (gr. k up). vinyl bd. 4.95 (978-1-58845-101-9(1)) School Specialty Publishing.

The Frog Report: Individual Title Six-Packs. (Rigby Focus Ser.). 16p. (gr. 1 up). 28.00 (978-0-7578-5326-5(9)); 30.00 (978-0-7578-5558-0(X)) Rigby Education.

Frogs: Level M, 6 vols. (Wonder Worldtm Ser.). 16p. 34.95 (978-0-7802-4573-0(3)) Wright Group, The.

Frogs & Toads. 2002. (Illus.). (J). pap. 5.43 (978-0-7398-5923-0(4)) Steck-Vaughn.

Frost, Helen. Tree Frogs. Saunders-Smith, Gail, ed. 2002. (Rain Forest Animals Ser.). (Illus.). 24p. (J). (gr. k-1). lib. bdg. 15.93 (978-0-7368-1196-5(6) , Pebble Bks.) Capstone Pr., Inc.

Funtastic Frogs. 2002. (J). (gr. k-2). act. bk. ed. School Specialty Publishing.

Ganeri, Anita. Frogs & Tadpoles. 2007. (J). (***978-1-58340-809-4(6)***) Smart Apple Media.

Ganeri, Anita. From Tadpole to Frog. 2006. (Heinemann First Library). (Illus.). 32p. (J). 25.36 (978-1-4034-7859-7(7)); pap. (978-1-4034-7868-9(6)) Heinemann Library.

Gareth Stevens Publishing Staff, contrib. by. Frogs. 2004. (All about Wild Animals Ser.). (Illus.). 32p. (J). lib. bdg. 23.33 (978-0-8368-4184-8(0)) Stevens, Gareth Inc.

Glaser, Linda. Fabulous Frogs. Krupinski, Loretta, illus. 2000. 1. 32p. (ps-1). pap. 8.95 (978-0-7613-0448-7(7) , Millbrook Pr.) Lerner Publishing Group.

—Fabulous Frogs. 1999. (Linda Glaser's Classic Creatures Ser.). (Illus.). 32p. (ps-3). lib. bdg. 22.90 (978-0-7613-0424-1(X) , Millbrook Pr.) Lerner Publishing Group.

—Fabulous Frogs. 1999. (gr. k-3). lib. bdg. 17.60 (978-0-613 25111-2(3)), (Illus.). (J). (978-0-606-18289-8(6)) Tandem Library Bks.

Godwin, Sam. The Trouble with Tadpoles: A First Look at the Life Cycle of a Frog. Abel, Simone, illus. 2004. (First Look Science Ser.). 32p. (C). (gr. k-3). 22.60 (978-1-4048-0654-2(7)) Picture Window Bks.

Graham, Pamela. A Frog Has a Sticky Tongue. 2001. (Windows on Literacy Ser.). (Illus.). 24p. (J). (gr. k-2). (978-0-7922-8928-9(5)) National Geographic Society.

Green, John. Frogs Stained Glass Coloring Book. 2000. (Illus.). 8p. (J). pap. 1.50 (978-0-486-41258-0(X)) Dover Pubns., Inc.

Greenberg, Daniel A. Frogs. 2000. (Animal Ways Ser.). (Illus.). 112p. (J). (gr. 5 up). lib. bdg. 31.36 (978-0-7614-1138-3(0) , Benchmark Bks.) Cavendish, Marshall Corp.

Grenouille. 1999. (Pocket Pals Ser.). (FRE.). (J). (ps-1). pap. 1.99 (978-0-85953-734-6(X)) Child's Play International Ltd. GBR. *Dist:* Child's Play-International.

Grolier Educational Staff. Toads. 2001. (Nature's Children Ser.). (Illus.). 48p. (J). (978-0-7172-5549-8(2) , Grolier) Scholastic Library Publishing.

Group/McGraw-Hill, Wright. Crabs & Frogs: Decodable Books, 6 vols. (Fasttrack Reading Ser.). 24p. (gr. 4-8). 40.95 (978-0-322-05989-4(5)) Wright Group, The.

Hamilton, Garry. Frog Rescue: Changing the Future for Endangered Wildlife. 2004. (Firefly Animal Rescue Ser.). (Illus.). 64p. (J). (gr. 5-8). pap. 9.95 (978-1-55297-596-1(7)) Firefly Bks., Ltd.

Harcourt School Publishers Staff. Frog or Toad? Advanced Level. 3rd ed. 2002. (Trophies Reading Program Ser.). (Illus.). pap. 5.10 (978-0-15-323104-9(1)) Harcourt Schl. Pubs.

—Frogs, Below Level. 3rd ed. 2002. (Trophies Reading Program Ser.). (Illus.). (J). pap. 3.20 (978-0-15-322948-0(9)) Harcourt Schl. Pubs.

—Ranas: Below Level. 3rd ed. 2002. (Trofeos Ser.). (SPA., Illus.). (J). pap. 4.10 (978-0-15-323859-8(3)) Harcourt Schl. Pubs.

Hawes, Judith. Why Frogs Are Wet. Fraser, Mary Ann, illus. 2000. (Let's-Read-and-Find-Out Ser.). (J). (978-0-606-20007-3(X)) Tandem Library Bks.

Hawes, Judy. Why Frogs Are Wet. Fraser, Mary Ann, illus. 2000. (Let's-Read-and-Find-Out Science Ser.). 40p. (J). (gr. k-4). 15.89 (978-0-06-028162-5(6)) HarperCollins Pubs.

—Why Frogs Are Wet. 2000. (gr. k-3). lib. bdg. 12.95 (978-0-613-31917-1(6)) Tandem Library Bks.

Heinrichs, Ann. Frogs. 2003. (Nature's Friends Ser.). (Illus.). 32p. (J). (gr. 2 up). lib. bdg. 21.26 (978-0-7565-0436-6(8)) Compass Point Bks.

Heller, Ruth. How to Hide a Meadow Frog: And Other Amphibians. 2001. (How to Hide Ser.). (Illus.). (J). (gr. k-3). pap. 14.45 incl. audio (978-0-8045-6572-1(4) , 6572) Spoken Arts, Inc.

Hewitt, Sally. Life Cycles from Tadpole to Frog, 8 vols. 2005. (QEB Readers). (Illus.). 24p. (J). (ps-3). lib. bdg. 15.95 (978-1-59566-068-8(2)) QEB Publishing Inc.

Hibbert. Life of a Frog 6-Pack. 2004. (Life Cycles Ser.). pap. 40.50 (978-1-4109-0827-8(5)) Harcourt Schl. Pubs.

Hibbert, Clare. The Life of a Frog. 2004. (Raintree Perspectives Ser.). (Illus.). 32p. (J). pap. 7.50 (978-1-4109-0820-9(8)) Harcourt Schl. Pubs.

—The Life of a Frog. 2004. (Life Cycles (Perspectives) Ser.). (Illus.). 32p. (J). (gr. 3-5). lib. bdg. 26.36 (978-1-4109-0544-4(6)) Raintree.

Hickman, Pamela. A New Frog: The Life Cycle of an Amphibian. Collins, Heather, illus. unabr. ed. 1999. (My First Look at Nature Ser.). 20p. (J). (gr. k-3). (978-1-55074-615-0(4)) Kids Can Pr., Ltd.

Himmelman, John. A Wood Frog's Life. 1999. (Nature Upclose Ser.). (Illus.). 32p. (J). (gr. k-2). pap. 6.95 (978-0-516-26403-5(6) , Children's Pr.) Scholastic Library Publishing.

Hinshaw Patent, Dorothy. Flashy, Fantastic Rain Forest Frogs. 1999. (J). 13.75 (978-0-606-17073-4(1)) Tandem Library Bks.

—Flashy, Fantastic Rain Forest Frogs. Jubb, Kendahl Jan, illus. 1999. 32p. (J). (gr. k-3). reprint ed. pap. 6.95 (978-0-8027-7536-8(5)) Walker & Co.

Hubbell. Frogs Know It Alls. 2001. (Illus.). 24p. (J). pap. 2.79 (978-0-7681-0230-7(8) , 57092) Learning Horizons, Inc.

Hunt, Joni Phelps. A Chorus of Frogs: The Risky Life of an Ancient Amphibian. Leon, Vicki, ed. 2nd ed. 2005. (Jean-Michel Cousteau Presents Ser.). (Illus.). 48p. pap. 7.95 (978-0-9766134-1-(7)) London Town Pr.

Jacobs, Lee. Toad. 2002. (Illus.). 24p. (J). 24.94 (978-1-56711-646-5(9) , Blackbirch Pr., Inc.) Thomson Gale.

Kalman, Bobbie. Frogs & Other Amphibians. 2005. (What Kind of Animal Is It? Ser.). (Illus.). 32p. (J). (978-978-077-872-9(1)); (978-0-7787-2159-8(0)); pap. (978-0-7787-2217-5(1)) Crabtree Publishing Co.

—Life Cycle of a Frog. 2002. (gr. 3-6). lib. bdg. 14.10 (978-0-613-52971-6(5)) Tandem Library Bks.

Kalman, Bobbie. Ranas y otros Anfibios. 2007. (SPA.). 32p. (J). (gr. 1-2). (***978-0-7787-8837-9(7)); pap. (*978-0-7787-8873-7(3)***) Crabtree Publishing Co.

Kalman, Bobbie & Smithyman, Kathryn. The Life Cycle of a Frog. Rouse, Bonna, illus. 2001. (Life Cycle Ser.). 32p. (J). (gr. 2-3). (978-0-7787-0651-9(6)); pap. (978-0-7787-0681-6(8)) Crabtree Publishing Co.

Kalman, Bobbie, et al. Les Grenouilles: Life Cycle of a Frog. 2006. (FRE., Illus.). 32p. pap. (978-2-89579-080-8(9)) Crabtree Publishing Co.

Kitchen, Bert & Tagholm, Sally. The Frog. 2000. (Animal Lives Ser.). (Illus.). 32p. (J). (gr. k-3). tchr. ed. 9.95 (978-0-7534-5215-8(4) , Kingfisher) Houghton Mifflin Co. Trade & Reference Div.

Lakeshore Learning Materials Staff, contrib. by. From Tadpole to Frog Learning Kit. 2000. (J). pap. 12.95 (978-1-929255-76-4(4)) Lakeshore Learning Materials.

Lever, E., et al. Frogs. Parish, Steve, photos by. 1999. (Animals Are Fun! Ser.). (Illus.). 16p. (J). (ps up). lib. bdg. 19.33 (978-0-8368-2613-5(2)) Stevens, Gareth Inc.

The Life Cycle of a Frog, Vol. 2. 2005. (Animals, Animals, Animals Ser.). (YA). (gr. k-3). (978-0-7368-3395-0(1) , Pebble Bks.) Capstone Pr., Inc.

Livesey, Claire. Our Polliwogs. Wordsworth, Viki, illus. 1999. (Books for Young Learners). 12p. (J). (gr. k-2). pap. 5.00 (978-1-57274-276-5(3)) Owen, Richard C. Pubs., Inc.

Llewellyn, Claire. Frog. Mendez, Simon, illus. 2003. (Starting Life Ser.). 24p. (ps-3). 16.95 (978-1-55971-869-1(2) , NorthWord Bks. for Young Readers) T&N Children's Publishing.

Markle, Sandra. Slippery, Slimy Baby Frogs. 2006. (Illus.). 32p. (J). 17.85 (978-0-8027-8063-8(6)); 16.95 (978-0-8027-8062-1(8)) Walker & Co.

McNab, Chris. Frogs, Toads & Salamanders. 2006. (Nature's Monsters Ser.). (Illus.). 32p. (J). lib. bdg. 23.33 (978-0-8368-6172-3(8)) Stevens, Gareth Inc.

Milbourne, A. Tadpoles & Frogs. 2004. (Beginners Ser.). 32p. (J). (gr. 1 up). lib. bdg. 12.95 (978-1-58086-465-7(1)); (Illus.). pap. 4.95 (978-0-7945-0164-8(8) , Usborne) EDC Publishing.

Milbourne, Anna. Tadpoles & Frogs - Internet Referenced (Level 1) 2007. 32p. (J). 4.99 (978-0-7945-1345-0(X) , Usborne) EDC Publishing.

Miles, Elizabeth. Watching Tree Frogs in South America. 2006. (Heinemann First Library). (Illus.). 32p. (J). (978-1-4034-7228-1(9)); pap. (978-1-4034-7241-0(6)) Heinemann Library.

Miller, Sara Swan. Frogs & Toads: The Leggy Leapers. 2001. (Animals in Order Ser.). (Illus.). 48p. (gr. 4-6). pap. 6.95 (978-0-531-16495-2(0) , Watts, Franklin) Scholastic Library Publishing.

Milton, Ann. Ask Me If I'm a Frog. Chambers, Jill, illus. 1998. (Curious Little Critters Ser.). 40p. (J). (ps-3). pap. 8.95 (978-0-88045-143-7(2)); 16.95 (978-0-88045-140-6(8)) Stemmer Hse. Pubs., Inc. (International Design Library).

Mitchell, Melanie S. Frogs. (First Step Nonfiction Ser.). (Illus.). (gr. k-2). 2005. 24p. lib. bdg. 17.27 (978-0-8225-4600-9(0)); 2003. 23p. (J). pap. 5.95 (978-0-8225-4601-6(9) , Lerner Pubns.) Lerner Publishing Group.

Morgan, Sally. Frogs & Other Amphibians. 2001. (Illus.). 32p. (J). lib. bdg. 24.25 (978-1-930643-45-1(4)) Chrysalis Education.

—From Tadpole to Frog. 2002. (How Things Grow Ser.). (Illus.). 32p. (J). lib. bdg. (978-1-930643-85-7(3)) Chrysalis Education.

Murphy, Patricia J. A Frog's Life. 2006. (Rosen Publishing Group's Reading Room Collection). (J). lib. bdg. (978-1-4042-3334-8(2) , PowerKids Pr.) Rosen Publishing Group, Inc., The.

Murray, Julie. Frogs. (Life Cycles Ser.). 24p. (J). (gr. k-4). 2007. lib. bdg. 21.35 (***978-1-59928-707-2(2)*** , Buddy Bks.); 2005. (Illus.). lib. bdg. 21.35 (978-1-59197-315-7(5)) ABDO Publishing Co.

Murray, Julie. Toads. 2002. (Buddy Book Ser.). (Illus.). 24p. (J). (gr. k-4). lib. bdg. 21.35 (978-1-57765-719-4(5)) ABDO Publishing Co.

Murray, Peter. Frogs. 2006. (New Naturebooks). (Illus.). 32p. (J). (gr. 1-5). 27.07 (978-1-59296-638-7(1)) Child's World, Inc.

Nelson, Robin. Pet Frog. (First Step Nonfiction). (J). (gr. k-2). 2003. (Illus.). 24p. lib. bdg. 18.60 (978-0-8225-1271-4(8)); 2002. pap. 3.95 (978-0-8225-1315-5(3)) Lerner Publishing Group.

Netherton, John. Red-Eyed Tree Frogs. 2000. (Early Bird Nature Bks.). (Illus.). 48p. (J). (gr. 2-4). lib. bdg. 25.26 (978-0-8225-3037-4(6) , Lerner Pubns.) Lerner Publishing Group.

Noonan, Diana. The Frog. 2002. (Life Cycle Ser.). (Illus.). 32p. (gr. k-2). 23.00 (978-0-7910-6966-0(4) , Chelsea Hse.) Facts On File, Inc.

O'Connor, Rebecca K. Frogs & Toads. 2003. (Endangered Animals & Habitats Ser.). (Illus.). 112p. (J). 29.95 (978-1-56006-919-5(8) , Lucent Bks.) Thomson Gale.

Owen, Leslie E. Pacific Tree Frogs. Juhasz, George, illus. 2002. 32p. (J). (gr. 2-5). pap. (978-1-896580-42-5(4)) Tradewind Bks.

Parker, Victoria. Life as a Frog. 2003. (Raintree Sprouts Ser.). (Illus.). 24p. (J). 18.56 (978-1-4109-0627-4(2)); pap. 5.50 (978-1-4109-0653-3(1)) Raintree.

—Life as a Frog. 2003. (ps-2). lib. bdg. 13.55 (978-0-613-78262-3(3)) Tandem Library Bks.

Patent, Dorothy Hinshaw. Flashy, Fantastic Rain Forest Frogs. 1999. (gr. k-3). lib. bdg. 15.25 (978-0-613-17798-6(3)) Tandem Library Bks.

Pugliano-Martin, Carol. Watch a Frog Grow. 2006. (Early Explorers Ser.). (J). 34.00 (***978-1-4108-6098-9(1)***) Benchmark Education Co.

Raintree Steck-Vaughn Staff. Las Ranas. (SPA.). (J). 2000. pap. 19.24 (978-0-7398-0811-5(7)); 1999. pap., stu. ed. 21.50 (978-0-7398-0823-8(0)) Steck-Vaughn.

Las Ranas y los Sapos. (Fascinante Mundo de... Ser.).Tr. of Fascinating World of Frogs & Toads. (Illus.). 8.95 (978-958-04-2597-7(3)) Norma S.A. COL. *Dist:* Distribuidora Norma, Inc.

Rau, Dana Meachen. The Frog in the Pond. 2006. (Nature Ser.). (Illus.). 24p. (J). lib. bdg. 22.79 (***978-0-7614-2310-2(9)*** , Benchmark Bks.) Cavendish, Marshall Corp.

—Guess Who Jumps. 2008. (J). (***978-0-7614-2908-1(5)***) Cavendish, Marshall Bks., Ltd.

Rizzati, Lorella. Frog. 1998. (Portable Pets Ser.). (Illus.). 12p. (J). (ps). bds. 6.95 (978-0-8109-5676-6(4)) Abrams, Harry N., Inc.

Robinson, Fay. Fantastic Frogs! Cassels, Jean, illus. 2000. (Hello Reader! Science Ser.). 32p. (J). (gr. k-2). pap. 3.99 (978-0-590-52269-4(8)) Scholastic, Inc.

—Fantastic Frogs! 2000. (Hello Reader! Ser.). (Illus.). (J). 10.79 (978-0-606-18542-4(9)) Tandem Library Bks.

—Fantastic Frogs. 1999. (gr. k-3). lib. bdg. 11.80 (978-0-613-25128-0(8)) Tandem Library Bks.

Roche, Hannah & Pratt, Pierre. Have You Ever Seen a Frog Leap? 1999. (Illus.). 16p. (J). (978-1-84089-158-4(0)); (978-1-84089-159-1(9)) Evans Publishing Group. (Zero to Ten, Limited).

Royston, Angela. Ciclo de Vida de la Rana. 2003. Tr. of Frog. (SPA.). 32p. (J). pap. 6.95 (978-1-4034-3038-0(1)) Heinemann Library.

—The Frog. 2001. (J). (978-0-606-22324-9(X)) Tandem Library Bks.

—Frog. Ling, Mary, ed. 2001. (See How They Grow Ser.). (Illus.). 24p. (J). (ps-3). pap. 4.99 (978-0-7894-7656-2(8)) Dorling Kindersley Publishing, Inc.

—Frog. 2002. (Life Cycle of a... Ser.). (Illus.). 32p. (J). (gr. k-2). pap. 6.95 (978-1-57572-536-9(3) , 90488) Heinemann Library.

—La Rana. Abello, Patricia, tr. 2003. (Ciclo de la Vida de... Ser.).Tr. of Frog. (SPA & ENG., Illus.). 32p. (J). lib. bdg. 22.79 (978-1-4034-3015-1(2)) Heinemann Library.

Santillo, LuAnn. Mole. Santillo, LuAnn, ed. 2003. (Half-Pint Kids Readers Ser.). (Illus.). 7p. (J). (ps-1). pap. (978-1-59256-111-7(X)) Half-Pint Kids, Inc.

Satterfield, Kathryn Hoffman. Frogs! 2006. 32p. (J). lib. bdg. 15.00 (***978-1-4242-0397-0(X)***) Fitzgerald Bks.

Saunders-Smith, Gail. Frogs. 1998. (Illus.). 24p. (J). (ps-3). pap. 13.25 (978-0-516-21231-9(1) , Children's Pr.) Scholastic Library Publishing.

Savage, Stephen. Toad. 2005. (Illus.). (J). (978-0-7502-4661-3(8) , Hodder Wayland) Hodder Children's Division.

Schaefer, Lola M. Frogs: Leaping Amphibians. 2001. (Wild World of Animals Ser.). (Illus.). 24p. (J). (gr. 1-2). lib. bdg. 18.60 (978-0-7368-0827-9(2) , Bridgestone Bks.) Capstone Pr., Inc.

—Horned Toad. 2003. (Heinemann Read & Learn Ser.). (Illus.). 24p. (J). lib. bdg. 18.50 (978-1-4034-3243-8(0)) Heinemann Library.

Schuepbach, Lynnette. Froggy Hollow. Schuepbach, Lynnette, illus. l.t. ed. 2004. (Illus.). 32p. (J). 7.00 net. (978-0-9759613-0-8(6)) Creative Sources.

Schwartz, David M. La Rana de Bosque. Kuhn, Dwight, photos by. 2001. (Springboards into Science Ser.). (SPA., Illus.). 24p. (J). (gr. 1 up). lib. bdg. 20.67 (978-0-8368-3000-2(8)) Stevens, Gareth Inc.

—Wood Frog. Kuhn, Dwight, photos by. (Life Cycles Ser.). (Illus.). 16p. (J). (gr. 1-3). pap. 2.99 (978-1-57471-552-1(6) , 3062) Creative Teaching Pr., Inc.

—Wood Frog. Kuhn, Dwight, photos by. 2001. (Springboards into Science Ser.). (Illus.). 24p. (J). (gr. 1 up). lib. bdg. 20.67 (978-0-8368-2981-5(6)) Stevens, Gareth Inc.

Slater, Patrick. Australian Frogs & Reptiles. 2002. (Nature Kids Ser.). (Illus.). 52p. (J). (gr. 3 up). lib. bdg. (978-1-59084-216-4(2)) Mason Crest Pubs.

Spilsbury, Louise. Frog. 2005. (Heinemann Read & Learn Ser.). (Illus.). 24p. (J). 20.64 (978-1-4034-6772-0(2)); (978-1-4034-6777-5(3)) Heinemann Library.

Stewart, David. How a Tadpole Grows into a Frog. (Amaze Ser.). 32p. (J). 2008. pap. 8.95 (***978-0-531-20454-2(5)); 2007. spiral bd. 26.00 (*978-0-531-20443-6(X)***) Scholastic Library Publishing. (Children's Pr.).

Stewart, David E. & Scrace, Carolyn. From Tadpole to Frog. 1998. (Lifecycles Ser.). (J). 20.00 (978-0-516-20817-6(9) , Children's Pr.) Scholastic Library Publishing.

Stone, Tanya Lee. Frogs. 2003. (Wild Wild World Ser.). 24p. (YA). 24.94 (978-1-56711-813-1(5) , Blackbirch Pr., Inc.) Thomson Gale.

Swanson, Diane. Frogs & Toads. 2004. (Welcome to the World of Animals Ser.). (Illus.). 32p. (J). (gr. 3 up). lib. bdg. 23.33 (978-0-8368-4023-0(2)) Stevens, Gareth Inc.

—Frogs & Toads. 2002. (gr. k-3). lib. bdg. 14.10 (978-0-613-78517-4(7)) Tandem Library Bks.

—Welcome to the World of Frogs & Toads. 2002. (Welcome to the World Ser.). (Illus.). 32p. (J). (ps-2). pap. 5.95 (978-1-55285-354-2(3)) Whitecap Bks., Ltd. CAN. *Dist:* Firefly Bks., Ltd.

Tagholm, Sally. Frog. Kitchen, Bert, illus. 2003. (Animal Lives Ser.). 32p. (J). (gr. k-3). pap. 4.95 (978-0-7534-5601-9(X) , Kingfisher) Houghton Mifflin Co. Trade & Reference Div.

—Frog. 2003. (gr. k-3). lib. bdg. 12.95 (978-0-613-90773-6(6)) Tandem Library Bks.

Thompson. Theme Pack: Frogs. 2002. (Pair-It Bks.). (Illus.). (J). pap. (978-0-7398-6367-1(3)) Steck-Vaughn.

Thomson, Ruth. Frog. 2007. (J). lib. bdg. (***978-1-4042-3711-7(9)*** , PowerKids Pr.) Rosen Publishing Group, Inc., The.

Time for Kids Editors. Frogs! 2006. (Time for Kids Science Scoops Ser.). (Illus.). 32p. (J). 14.99 (978-0-06-078222-1(6)) HarperCollins Pubs.

Time for Kids Editors & Satterfield, Kathryn Hoffman. Frogs! 2006. (Time for Kids Science Scoops Ser.). (Illus.). 32p. (J). pap. 3.99 (978-0-06-078221-4(8) , Harper Trophy) HarperCollins Pubs.

Trumbauer, Lisa. The Life Cycle of a Frog. 2002. (Life Cycles Ser.). (Illus.). 24p. (J). (gr. k-1). lib. bdg. 15.93 (978-0-7368-1185-9(0) , Pebble Bks.) Capstone Pr., Inc.

University Of Portsmouth, prod. The Frog: A Functional Anatomy. (Multimedia Dissection Library). (YA). cd-rom 149.95 (978-0-7365-3853-4(4)) Films Media Group.

Vern, Alex. Where Do Frogs Come From? 2003. (Green Light Readers Level 2 Ser.). (Illus.). 24p. (J). 11.95 (978-0-15-204884-6(7)); pap. 3.95 (978-0-15-204844-0(8)) Harcourt Children's Bks. (Green Light Readers).

—Where Do Frogs Come From? 2001. (J). (978-0-606-22610-3(9)); lib. bdg. 11.80 (978-0-613-63369-7(5)) Tandem Library Bks.

Wade, Barrie. Frog. Watts, Barrie, illus. 2005. (Reading Corner Ser.). 24p. (J). (gr. k-3). lib. bdg. 22.80 (978-1-59771-004-6(0)) Sea-To-Sea Pubns.

Wallace, Karen. Tale of a Tadpole. 1998. (Eyewitness Readers). (Illus.). 32p. (J). (gr. 5-1). pap. 3.99 (978-0-7894-3437-1(7)) Dorling Kindersley Publishing, Inc.

Wallace, Karen & Dorling Kindersley Publishing Staff. Tale of a Tadpole. 1998. (Eyewitness Readers). (Illus.). 32p. (J). (ps-3). 14.99 (978-0-7894-3761-7(9)) Dorling Kindersley Publishing, Inc.

Walls, Jerry G. Keeping Poison Frogs. 1998. (Basic Domestic Reptile & Amphibian Library). (Illus.). (J). (gr. 2-5). lib. bdg. 17.95 (978-0-7910-5079-8(3) , Chelsea Hse.) Facts On File, Inc.

Watts, Barrie. Frog. 2004. (Illus.). 32p. (J). (ps-17). lib. bdg. 24.25 (978-1-58340-233-7(0)) Smart Apple Media.

Wechsler, Doug. Bullfrogs. 2002. (Really Wild Life of Frogs Ser.). (Illus.). 24p. (J). (gr. 3-6). lib. bdg. 18.75 (978-0-8239-5855-9(8)) Rosen Publishing Group, Inc., The.

—Glass Frogs. 2002. (Really Wild Life Of... Ser.). (Illus.). 24p. (J). lib. bdg. 18.75 (978-0-8239-5857-3(4) , PowerKids Pr.) Rosen Publishing Group, Inc., The.

—Leopard Frogs. 2002. (Really Wild Life of Frogs Ser.). (Illus.). 24p. (J). (gr. 3-6). lib. bdg. 18.75 (978-0-8239-5856-6(6) , PowerKids Pr.) Rosen Publishing Group, Inc., The.

—Poison Dart Frogs. 2002. (Really Wild Life Of... Ser.). 24p. (J). lib. bdg. 18.75 (978-0-8239-5858-0(2) , PowerKids Pr.) Rosen Publishing Group, Inc., The.

E
F
G

—Really Wild Life of Frogs, 3 vols., set. (Illus.). 80.70 (978-0-8239-7186-2(4)) Rosen Publishing Group, Inc., The.

—Treefrogs. 2002. (Really Wild Life Of... Ser.). (Illus.). 24p. (J). (gr. 3-6). lib. bdg. 18.75 (978-0-8239-5859-7(0) , PowerKids Pr.) Rosen Publishing Group, Inc., The.

—Wood Frogs. 2002. (Really Wild Life Ser.). (Illus.). 24p. (J). (gr. 3-6). lib. bdg. 18.75 (978-0-8239-5854-2(X) , PowerKids Pr.) Rosen Publishing Group, Inc., The.

Weir, Diana Loiewski. Tree Frogs. (Let's Investigate Ser.). (Illus.). 32p. (J). 2001. (gr. 3). pap. 8.95 (978-0-89812-325-8(9) , Creative Paperbacks); 1999. (gr. 1-4). pap. 18.95 (978-0-88682-493-8(1) , Creative Education) Creative Co., The.

Whitecap Books Staff. Frogs & Toads. 2000. (Investigate Ser.). (Illus.). 64p. (J). (gr. 1-7). pap. 3.95 (978-1-55285-130-2(3)) Whitecap Bks., Ltd. CAN. *Dist:* Firefly Bks., Ltd.

Whiting, Jim. Frogs in Danger. 2007. (On the Verge of Extinction Ser.). (Illus.). 32p. (J). (gr. 1-4). lib. bdg. 25.70 (***978-1-58415-585-0(X)***) Mitchell Lane Pubs., Inc.

Winer, Yvonne. Frogs Sing Songs. Oliver, Tony, illus. 2003. 32p. (J). pap. 6.95 (978-1-57091-549-9(0)); 16.95 (978-1-57091-548-2(2)) Charlesbridge Publishing, Inc.

World Book, Inc. Staff, contrib. by. Frogs & Other Amphibians. 2005. (World Book's Animals of the World Ser.). (Illus.). 64p. (J). (978-0-7166-1269-8(0)) World Bk., Inc.

Yolen, Jane. Hoptoad. Schmidt, Karen Lee, illus. 2003. 32p. (J). 16.00 (978-0-15-216352-5(2) , Silver Whistle) Harcourt Trade Pubs.

Zemlicka, Shannon. From Tadpole to Frog. (From Start to Finish Ser.). (J). 2003. (Illus.). 24p. 18.60 (978-0-8225-0399-6(9) , Lerner Pubns.); 2002. pap. 4.95 (978-0-8225-0671-3(8)) Lerner Publishing Group.

Zoehfeld, Kathleen Weidner. From Tadpole to Frog. 2001. (Science Readers Ser.). (Illus.). (J). (978-0-439-20549-8(2)) Scholastic, Inc.

Zollman, Pam. A Tadpole Grows Up. 2005. (Scholastic News Nonfiction Readers Ser.). (Illus.). 24p. (J). (gr. 1-2). 19.00 (978-0-516-24947-6(9) , Children's Pr.) Scholastic Library Publishing.

FROGS—FICTION

Adventures of Grandfather Frog. 2000. mass mkt. 3.99 (978-1-55902-935-3(8) , Aerie) Doherty, Tom Assocs., LLC.

Allchin, Rosalind. The Frog Princess. Allchin, Rosalind, illus. 2001. (Illus.). 32p. (J). (gr. k-3). (978-1-55337-000-0(7)) Kids Can Pr., Ltd.

—Frog Princess. 2003. (gr. k-3). lib. bdg. 14.10 (978-0-613-89644-3(0)) Tandem Library Bks.

—The Frog Princess. ed. 2004. (Illus.). (J). (gr. k-3). spiral bd. (978-0-616-14557-9(8)) Canadian National Institute for the Blind/Institut National Canadien pour les Aveugles.

Allchin, Rosalind, illus. The Frog Princess. 2003. 32p. (J). (gr. k-3). (978-1-55337-526-5(2)) Kids Can Pr., Ltd.

Alllen, Katherine. Gloves down Under. Alllen, Katherine, illus. 2005. (Illus.). 32p. (J). 15.95 (978-0-9747278-9-9(X)) Diakonia Publishing.

Alvarez, Lourdes M. La Leyenda del Coqui. Bauta, Susan, illus. 2005. (SPA.). 29p. (J). (gr. k-12). bds. 12.95 (978-1-58173-256-6(2)) Sweetwater Pr.

Anderson, Peggy Perry. Joe on the Go. 2007. (Illus.). 32p. (J). (gr. 3-5). 16.00 (978-0-618-77331-2(8)) Houghton Mifflin Co.

—Let's Clean Up! (Illus.). 32p. (J). (gr. k-3). 2005. 5.95 (978-0-618-55523-9(4)); 2002. 15.00 (978-0-618-19602-9(1)) Houghton Mifflin Co. Trade & Reference Div. (Walter Lorraine).

Animal I Can Hear S/s -Frog. 2005. (J). bds. (978-1-4194-0058-2(4)) Paradise Pr., Inc.

Asch, Frank. Moonbear's Pet. Asch, Frank, illus. 2002. (Moonbear Ser.). (Illus.). (J). 14.47 (978-1-4046-0167-3(8)) Book Wholesalers, Inc.

Asher, Sandy. Too Many Frogs! Graves, Keith, illus. 2005. 32p. (J). (ps-1). 15.99 (978-0-399-23978-6(2) , Philomel) Penguin Group (USA) Inc.

—What a Party! Graves, Keith, illus. 2007. 32p. (J). (ps-1). 15.99 (978-0-399-24496-4(4) , Philomel) Penguin Group (USA) Inc.

Austin, K. B. Old Mother Turtle & the Three Frogs. 2005. (J). lib. bdg. (978-0-9772027-0-6(4)) Dream Star Productions.

Azore, Barbara. Wanda & the Frogs. Graham, Georgia, illus. 2007. 32p. (J). (ps-2). 18.95 (978-0-88776-761-6(3)) Tundra Bks., Inc./Livres Toundra, Inc. CAN. *Dist:* Random Hse., Inc.

Baby Moses Frog. 2004. bds. 6.99 (978-0-8254-7281-7(4)) Kregel Pubns.

Bachand, Stephen. Floater the Frog. Bachand, Stephen, illus. 1999. (Booktime Buddies Ser.). (Illus.). (J). (ps-2). pap. 5.00 (978-1-928972-04-4(7)) Critter Pubns.

Baker, E. D. Dragon's Breath. 2005. (Tales of the Frog Princess Ser.: Bk. 2). (Illus.). 304p. (J). (gr. 3-7). reprint ed. pap. 6.95 (978-1-58234-666-3(6) , Bloomsbury Children) Bloomsbury Publishing.

—The Frog Princess. (J). 2002. 200p. (gr. 3-9). 15.95 (978-1-58234-799-8(9)); 2004. 224p. reprint ed. pap. 6.95 (978-1-58234-923-7(1)) Bloomsbury Publishing. (Bloomsbury Children).

—The Frog Princess. 2005. (J). 55.95 incl. audio (978-1-4193-2955-5(3) , 42014) Recorded Bks., LLC.

Baker, E. D. Tales of the Frog Princess, Set. 2007. (Tales of the Frog Princess Ser.). 784p. (J). pap. 20.85 (***978-1-59990-152-7(8)*** , Bloomsbury Children) Bloomsbury Publishing.

Baker, Harriet Lila. Boyduck Goose: His Life & Times, Bk. II. 2005. (J). pap. 9.00 (978-0-8059-6694-7(3)) Dorrance Publishing Co., Inc.

Banks, Joan. Song of La Selva: A Story of a Costa Rican Rain Forest. Bond, Higgins, illus. 1998. (Habitat Ser.: No. 9). 36p. (J). (gr. 1-4). 15.95 (978-1-56899-586-1(5) , B7009); 19.95 incl. audio (978-1-56899-588-5(1) , BC7009); pap. 6.95 (978-1-56899-587-8(3)); pap. 10.95 incl. audio (978-1-56899-589-2(X)) Soundprints.

—Song of La Selva: A Story of a Costa Rican Rain Forest, Incl. toy. Higgins-Bond, illus. 1998. (Habitat Ser.: Vol. 9). 36p. (J). (gr. 1-4). 26.95 (978-1-56899-590-8(3)) Soundprints.

—Song of La Selva: A Story of a Costa Rican Rain Forest, Incl. toy. Bond, Higgins, illus. 1998. (Habitat Ser.: Vol. 9). 36p. (J). (gr. 1-4). 31.95 incl. audio (978-1-56899-592-2(X)) Soundprints.

—Song of La Selva: A Story of a Costa Rican Rain Forest, Incl. toy. Bond, Higgins & Kaye, Randye, illus. 1998. (Habitat Ser.: Vol. 9). 36p. (J). (gr. 1-4). pap. 19.95 incl. audio (978-1-56899-593-9(8)) Soundprints.

Barchers, Suzanne I. Leap Hops, Pops & Mops. Yakovetic Productions Staff, illus. 12p. (J). (978-1-58605-017-7(6)) LeapFrog Enterprises, Inc.

Barry, Maureen. Freddie the Frog's Adventure. 2007. (J). pap. 10.00 net. (***978-1-60402-177-6(2)***) Independent Pub.

Been, Sherry. If I Were a Frog. 2001. (Illus.). 42p. (J). (gr. k-3). 14.95 (978-0-9705693-0-1(0)) SherMar Pubns.

Beers, Steven. Bumpy the Frog. 2006. (Illus.). 32p. (J). pap. 5.25 (978-1-57874-106-9(8)) Kaeden Corp.

Bender and Bender Staff. Ribbit! Flip & See Who Froggy Can Be. 2007. 40p. (J). (ps-1). 16.99 (***978-0-06-113820-1(7)***) HarperCollins Pubs.

Bennett, Debra J. Hip, Hop & Flop's Many Adventures. 2007. (ENG.). 60p. per. 12.95 (***978-1-4241-6564-3(4)***) PublishAmerica, Inc.

Bennett, Kimberly. The Tale of A Tadpole. 2003. 26p. pap. 14.95 (978-1-4137-1458-6(7)) PublishAmerica, Inc.

Bentley, Dawn. The Icky Sticky Frog. Yoon, Salina, illus. 18p. (J). (ps-k). 2001. 5.95 (978-1-58117-049-8(1)); 1999. 9.95 (978-1-58117-042-9(4)) Dalmatian Pr. (Intervisual/Piggy Toes).

Berkes, Marianne Collins. Marsh Music. Noreika, Robert, illus. 2000. 3. 32p. (J). (gr. k-3). 14.95 (978-0-7613-1850-7(X) , Millbrook Pr.) Lerner Publishing Group.

Billout, Guy. The Frog Who Wanted to See the Sea. 2007. 32p. (J). (gr. 2 up). 17.95 (***978-1-56846-188-5(7)*** , Creative Editions) Creative Co., The.

Birney, Betty G. Friendship According to Humphrey. (J). (gr. 2-4). 2006. 176p. pap. 5.99 (978-0-14-240633-5(3) , Puffin); 2005. 160p. 14.99 (978-0-399-24264-9(3) , Putnam Juvenile) Penguin Group (USA) Inc.

Blair, Eric. El Principe Encantado: Version del Cuento de los Hermanos Grimm. Ouren, Todd, illus. 2006. (Read-It! Readers en Espanol Ser.).Tr. of Frog Prince: A Retelling of the Grimm's Fairy Tale. (SPA.). 32p. (J). (ps-3). 19.95 (978-1-4048-1631-2(3)) Picture Window Bks.

Blake, Quentin. Ten Frogs. 2000. (Michael di Capua Bks.). (Illus.). 24p. (J). 12.95 (978-0-06-205200-1(4)) HarperCollins Pubs.

Bodrogi, Michael. Herbert the Tadpole in the Big Change. La Beree, Brian, illus. 2003. 48p. (J). (ps-4). 15.95 (978-1-878398-61-1(X) , Blue Note Bks.) Blue Note Pubns.

Boelts, Maribeth. Big Daddy, Frog Wrestler. Huang, Benrei, illus. 2004. 29p. (J). (gr. k-4). reprint ed. (978-0-7567-7797-5(6)) DIANE Publishing Co.

Bollen, Christine. Frogs by the Dozen. Matyschenko, Tanya, illus. l.t. ed. 2006. 24p. (J). per. 9.99 (978-1-59879-115-0(X)) Lifevest Publishing, Inc.

Bonnell, Kris. Frog Fun. 2006. (J). 3.95 (***978-1-933727-39-4(X)***) Reading Reading Bks., LLC.

Book Buddy: Frog with Story Book. Orig. Title: Child's Play. (Illus.). 10p. (J). (ps-3). reprint ed. (978-1-881469-80-3(8)) Safari, Ltd.

Book Company Staff. Are You a Frog? 2003. (Novelty Bks.). (Illus.). (J). 12.95 (978-1-74047-318-7(3)) Book Co. Publishing Pty, Ltd., The AUS. *Dist:* Penton Overseas, Inc.

—Froggy & Friends. 2003. (Novelty Bks.). (J). 15.95 (978-1-74047-323-1(X)) Book Co. Publishing Pty, Ltd., The AUS. *Dist:* Penton Overseas, Inc.

—Who Am I: Frog. 2003. (Board Bks.). (Illus.). (J). bds. 10.95 (978-1-74047-306-4(X)) Book Co. Publishing Pty, Ltd., The AUS. *Dist:* Penton Overseas, Inc.

Bosco, Michael. Roodee: The River's End. 2004. 94p. pap. 14.95 (978-1-4137-2137-9(0)) PublishAmerica, Inc.

Boyd, Lizi. I Love Daddy. Boyd, Lizi, illus. 2004. (Super Sturdy Picture Bookstm Ser.). (Illus.). 24p. (J). (gr. k-ps). 8.99 (978-0-7636-2217-6(6)) Candlewick Pr.

—I Love Mommy. Boyd, Lizi, illus. 2004. (Super Sturdy Picture Bookstm Ser.). (Illus.). 24p. (J). (gr. k-ps). 8.99 (978-0-7636-2216-9(8)) Candlewick Pr.

Brandon, Wendy. The Frog Prince: Imagination in a Box. Beckes, Shirley, illus. 2004. 10p. (J). bds. 17.99 (978-1-883043-49-0(2)) Straight Edge Pr., The.

Breen, Steve. Stick. 2007. (Illus.). 40p. (J). (ps). 16.99 (978-0-8037-3124-0(8) , Dial) Penguin Group (USA) Inc.

Brightwood, Laura, illus. I Am A Frog. Brightwood, Laura, . 2007. (J). DVD (***978-1-934409-02-2(2)***) 3-C Institute for Social Development.

Bronson, Tammy Carter. Polliwog. Bronson, Tammy Carter, illus. 2006. (ENG & SPA.). (J). 7.99 (***978-0-9678167-5-3(0)***) Bookaroos Publishing, Inc.

—Polliwog. Davi, Annou, tr. Bronson, Tammy Carter, illus. 2004. (SPA., Illus.). 32p. (J). lib. bdg. 17.00 (978-0-9678167-4-6(2)) Bookaroos Publishing, Inc.

Brooke, Samantha. Portraits from the Pipes. Simpson, Fiona, ed. 2006. (Flushed Away Ser.). 32p. (J). pap. 3.99 (978-0-439-90080-5(8)) Scholastic, Inc.

Brookes, Diane. Kailee & the Frog Prince. Brookes, Shelley, illus. 1999. 16p. (J). (ps-5). pap. (978-0-9683640-2-4(0)) Raven Rock Publishing.

Brookes, Diane & Baird, Alison. A Novel Study for Grades Three & Four Based on The Dragon's Egg. 1998. (J). pap., tchr. ed. (978-0-9683234-7-2(2)) Raven Rock Publishing.

Brookes, Diane & Lobel, Arnold. A Novel Study for Grades One & Two Based on Frog & Toad Are Friends, 25 vols. 1998. (J). pap., tchr. ed. (978-0-9683234-2-7(1)) Raven Rock Publishing.

Brown, Ruth. Toad. 1999. (978-0-606-16767-3(6)) Tandem Library Bks.

Brumett, Jonas O. A Real Fishing Experience: Froginhood & Friends. Johnson, Sandra L., illus. l.t. ed. 2002. 64p. (J). (ps-3). 16.95 (978-1-892812-00-1(2)) Froginhood & Friends, Inc.

Bunting, Eve. Some Frog! Medlock, Scott, illus. 2002. 48p. (J). (gr. 1-4). pap. 6.00 (978-0-15-216384-6(0) , Voyager Bks./Libros Viajeros) Harcourt Children's Bks.

—Some Frog! 2002. (gr. 3-6). lib. bdg. 14.15 (978-0-613-53865-7(X)) Tandem Library Bks.

Burch, Sharon. Freddie the Frog & the Bass Clef Monster: 2nd Adventure: Bass Clef Monster. Harris, Tiffany, illus. 2006. (J). 23.95 (978-0-9747454-8-0(0)) Mystic Publishing.

—Freddie the Frog & the Thump in the Night. 2004. (Illus.). (J). 23.95 incl. audio compact disk (978-0-9747454-9-7(9)) Mystic Publishing.

Burgess, Thornton W. The Adventures of Old Mr. Toad. 1998. (Illus.). 80p. (J). (gr. 3-6). pap. 1.50 (978-0-486-40385-4(8)) Dover Pubns., Inc.

—Big Book of Animal Stories. 2001. (Illus.). 208p. (J). (gr. 4-7). pap. 7.95 (978-0-486-41980-0(0)) Dover Pubns., Inc.

Burns, Joanne. Frog's Dog Days. 2005. 30p. 9.99 (978-1-4116-4829-6(3)) Lulu.com.

Butterfield, Moira. Do Frogs Fly? Canals, Sonia, illus. 2007. (Animal Flappers Bks.). 16p. (J). (gr. k-k). 7.99 (978-0-7641-6027-1(3)) Barron's Educational Series, Inc.

Butterworth, MyLinda & Day, Linda S. Frogazoom! Day, Linda S., illus. l.t. ed. 2003. (Illus.). 32p. (J). (gr. k-3). 16.95 (978-1-890905-03-3(8) , Eco Fiction Bks.) Day to Day Enterprises.

Bynum, Janie. Otis. 2003. (Illus.). 40p. (J). pap. 7.00 (978-0-15-204604-0(6) , Voyager Bks./Libros Viajeros) Harcourt Children's Bks.

—Otis. 2003. (gr. k-3). lib. bdg. 14.15 (978-0-613-70501-1(7)) Tandem Library Bks.

Calmenson, Stephanie. The Frog Principal. Brunkus, Denise, illus. 2006. 32p. (J). pap. 5.99 (978-0-439-81217-7(8) , Scholastic Paperbacks) Scholastic, Inc.

Cannery Row. 2000. (J). 11.95 (978-1-56137-507-3(1)) Novel Units, Inc.

Carle, Eric. Hello Red Fox. (J). (gr. k-3). 2000. (Illus.). 26p. per. (978-0-689-83492-9(6)); 1998. per. (978-0-689-00581-7(4)) Simon & Schuster Children's Publishing. (Simon & Schuster Children's Publishing).

—Hello Red Fox. Carle, Eric & Beneduce, Ann, illus. 1998. 32p. (J). (ps-3). 19.95 (978-0-689-81775-5(4)) Simon & Schuster Children's Publishing.

—Hello, Red Fox. Carle, Eric, illus. 2001. (Illus.). 32p. (J). pap. 8.99 (978-0-689-84431-7(X) , Aladdin) Simon & Schuster Children's Publishing.

Carlson, Lavelle. The Frog Who Could Not Croak: Phonemic Awareness Tale #4. 2004. (Illus.). 32p. (J). per. 16.95 (978-0-9725803-3-5(6)) Children's Publishing.

Carlson, Nancy. Smile a Lot! Carlson, Nancy, illus. 2003. (Words Are Categorical Ser.). (Illus.). 32p. (J). (gr. k-2). 15.95 (978-0-87614-869-3(0) , Carolrhoda Bks.) Lerner Publishing Group.

Carlson, Nancy. ¡Sonríe! (Smile a Lot!) Carlson, Nancy, illus. 2007. (Ediciones Lerner Single Titles Ser.). (SPA., Illus.). 32p. (J). (gr. k-2). 15.95 (***978-0-8225-7817-8(4)*** , Ediciones Lerner) Lerner Publishing Group.

Carmack, Lisa. Philippe in Monet's Garden. 1998. (Illus.). (J). (ps-1). 10.95 (978-0-87846-456-2(5)) Museum of Fine Arts, Boston.

Cassidy, Anne. Jumping Josie. Julian, Sean, illus. 2005. (Reading Corner Ser.). 24p. (J). (gr. k-3). lib. bdg. 22.80 (978-1-59771-014-5(8)) Sea-To-Sea Pubns.

Cassidy, Sean. Gummytoes. (Illus.). 32p. (J). (ps-3). 2007. pap. (***978-1-55041-826-2(2)***); 2004. (978-1-55041-824-8(6)) Fitzhenry & Whiteside, Ltd.

Catalano, Dominic. The Frog Went A-Courting: A Musical Play in Six Acts. 2003. (Illus.). 32p. (J). (gr. k-2). 15.95 (978-1-56397-637-7(4)) Boyds Mills Pr.

Cherrington, Janelle. Drawing the Line. Goldberg, Barry, illus. 2000. (Wild Thornberrys Ready-to-Read Ser. : Vol. 2). 32p. (J). (gr. 4-6). pap. 3.99 (978-0-689-83231-4(1) , Simon Spotlight/Nickelodeon) Simon & Schuster Children's Publishing.

—Drawing the Line. 2000. (gr. k-3). lib. bdg. 11.80 (978-0-613-24899-0(6)) Tandem Library Bks.

Chidvilasananda, Gurumayi & Chidvilasananda, Swami. The Frogs & Their Monster. Martinot, Claude, illus. 2000. 36p. (J). (gr. k-2). 14.00 (978-0-911307-83-2(4)); reprint ed. 14.00 (978-0-911307-91-7(5) , 205200, Siddha Yoga Pubn.) SYDA Foundation.

Chima, Ahiru & Misu, Max. Ellena_- Ellen meets Frog King - 2005. 32p. pap. 14.99 (978-1-4116-4050-4(0)) Lulu.com.

Clarke, Jane. Only Tadpoles Have Tails. Gray, Jane, illus. 2004. (Flying Foxes Ser.). (J). 46p. (978-0-7787-1484-2(5)); 48p. pap. (978-0-7787-1530-6(2)) Crabtree Publishing Co.

Clymer, Susan. There's a Frog in My Sleeping Bag. 1998. (Illus.). (J). (gr. 2-5). pap. 3.99 (978-0-590-88026-8(8) , Scholastic Paperbacks) Scholastic, Inc.

Cofreros, Felipe A. The Hungry Frog. 2005. (J). per. (978-0-9768251-6-6(3)) Dramatic Improvements Publishing.

Cohlene, Terri. Something Special. Keith, Doug, illus. 2005. 32p. (J). (ps-k). 15.95 (978-0-9740190-1-7(1)) Illumination Arts Publishing Co., Inc.

Coplans, Peta & Williams, Dylan. Syniad Da Gwenlli Gwydd. 2005. (WEL., Illus.). 24p. (978-1-84512-015-3(9)) Cymdeithas Lyfrau Ceredigion.

Corazza, Joe, illus. The Frog Prince: A Story about Keeping Your Word. 2006. (J). 6.99 (978-1-59939-008-6(6) , Reader's Digest Young Families, Inc.) Reader's Digest Children's Publishing, Inc.

Coville, Bruce. Jennifer Murdley's Toad. Lippincott, Gary A., illus. 2002. (Magic Shop Bks.). 176p. (YA). (gr. 3-7). 17.00 (978-0-15-204613-2(5)) Harcourt Children's Bks.

—Jennifer Murdley's Toad. 159p. (J). pap. 3.99 (978-0-8072-1483-1(3) , Listening Library) Random Hse. Audio Publishing Group.

Coville, Bruce. Jennifer Murdley's Toad: A Magic Shop Book. Lippincott, Gary A., illus. 2007. (Magic Shop Book Ser.). 176p. (J). (gr. 3-7). pap. 5.95 (***978-0-15-206246-0(7)*** , Magic Carpet Bks.) Harcourt Children's Bks.

Cowan, Charlotte. Peeper Has a Fever. 2008. (Illus.). 32p. 17.95 (978-0-9753516-2-8(1)) Hippocratic Pr., The.

Cox, Phil Roxbee. Frog on A Log. Cartwright, Stephen, illus. rev. ed. 2006. 16p. (J). pap. 6.99 (978-0-7945-1504-1(5) , Usborne) EDC Publishing.

—Toad Makes A Road. Cartwright, Stephen, illus. rev. ed. 2006. 16p. (J). pap. 6.99 (978-0-7945-1512-6(6) , Usborne) EDC Publishing.

Cox, Phil Roxbee & Cartwright, S. Toad Makes a Road. 2004. (Phonics Board Bks.). 10p. (J). 4.99 (978-0-7945-0062-7(5) , Usborne) EDC Publishing.

Cox, Phil Roxbee & Cartwright, Stephen. Frog on a Log. 2004. (Easy Words to Read Ser.). (Illus.). 16p. (J). (gr. 1 up). pap. 6.95 (978-0-7945-0114-3(1) , Usborne) EDC Publishing.

—Ted's Shed. 2004. (Phonics Board Bks.). (Illus.). 10p. (J). 4.95 (978-0-7945-0304-8(7) , Usborne) EDC Publishing.

Cox, Tiffany. Amy, the Frog Who Loved to Sing. 2006. 9.00 (***978-0-8059-8806-2(8)***) Dorrance Publishing Co., Inc.

Cutler, Jane. Leap, Frog. Pearson, Tracey Campbell, illus. 2005. 208p. (J). (gr. 3-7). pap. 6.95 (978-0-374-44320-7(3) , Farrar, Straus & Giroux (BYR)) Farrar, Straus & Giroux.

Cyrus, Kurt. Tadpole Rex. 2008. (J). (***978-0-15-205990-3(3)***) Harcourt Trade Pubs.

Dad's Bathtime: Individual Title Six-Packs. (Literatura 2000 Ser.). (gr. 1-2). 28.00 (978-0-7635-0128-0(X)) Rigby Education.

Dahl, Michael. Frog Pajama Party. Schultz, Sara, illus. 2005. (Read-It! Readers Ser.). 32p. (J). (ps). lib. bdg. 18.60 (978-1-4048-1170-6(2)) Picture Window Bks.

David, Erica. Plumbing Problems. Simpson, Fiona, ed. 2006. (Flushed Away Ser.). 32p. (J). pap. 3.99 (978-0-439-90077-5(8)) Scholastic, Inc.

Davidson, Susanna. Frog Prince. 2005. 48p. (J). (gr. 2 up). 8.95 (978-0-7945-0969-9(X) , Usborne) EDC Publishing.

Davidson, Susanna. Frog Prince Cd Pack. rev. ed. 2007. (Young Reading CD Packs Ser.). 48p. (J). 9.99 (***978-0-7945-1868-4(0)*** , Usborne) EDC Publishing.

Day, Robert O. & Day, Linda S. There's a Frog on a Log in the Bog. Day, Linda S., illus. (Just So Wild Ser.: Vol. 1). (Illus.). (J). 2003. 212p. (gr. 3-6). pap. 8.95 (978-1-890905-50-7(X) , Eco Fiction Bks.); 2003. (gr. 3-6). 14.95 (978-1-890905-51-4(8) , Eco Fiction Bks.); 2002. 112p. (gr. 4-6). pap. 8.95 (978-1-890905-20-0(8)) Day to Day Enterprises.

De Audrade, Norma. The Frog, the Princess, the Purpurine, & the Silk Threads. 2005. (J). pap. 8.00 (978-0-8059-6524-7(6)) Dorrance Publishing Co., Inc.

de Paola, Tomie. Four Friends at Christmas. de Paola, Tomie, illus. 2002. (Illus.). 32p. (J). 14.95 (978-0-689-85282-4(7)) Simon & Schuster Children's Publishing.

Degen, Bruce, illus. Commander Toad & the Space Pirates. 2002. (Commander Toad Ser.). (J). 13.19 (978-0-7587-1080-2(1)) Book Wholesalers, Inc.

—Commander Toad & the Voyage Home. 2002. (Commander Toad Ser.). (J). 13.19 (978-0-7587-1077-2(1)) Book Wholesalers, Inc.

Delacre, Lulu. Rafi & Rosi. 2004. (Illus.). 64p. (J). lib. bdg. 13.85 (***978-1-4242-0596-7(4)***) Fitzgerald Bks.

—Rafi & Rosi. Delacre, Lulu, illus. (I Can Read Bks.). 64p. (J). (gr. k-3). 2005. pap. 3.99 (978-0-06-009897-1(X) , Rayo); 2004. (Illus.). lib. bdg. 16.89 (978-0-06-009896-4(1)) HarperCollins Pubs.

—Rafi & Rosi: Carnival! Delacre, Lulu, illus. 2008. (I Can Read Bks.). 64p. (J). 3.99 (***978-0-06-073599-9(6)*** , Rayo) HarperCollins Pubs.

—Rafi y Rosi. Delacre, Lulu, illus. 2006. (I Can Read Bks.). (SPA.). 64p. (J). 15.99 (978-0-06-087277-9(2)); pap. 3.99 (978-0-06-087278-6(0)) HarperCollins Pubs. (Rayo).

—Rafi y Rosi: Carnival! Delacre, Lulu, illus. 2006. (I Can Read Bks.). 64p. (J). (SPA.). 15.99 (978-0-06-113134-9(2)); (SPA.). pap. 3.99 (978-0-06-113135-6(0)); (Illus.). 15.99 (978-0-06-073597-5(X)); (Illus.). lib. bdg. 16.89 (978-0-06-073598-2(8)) HarperCollins Pubs. (Rayo).

Dell'Oro, Suzanne Paul. Hiding Toads. (Pull Ahead Bks.). (Illus.). 32p. (J). (gr. k-2). 2003. pap. 5.95 (978-0-8225-3630-7(7)); 1999. lib. bdg. 22.60 (978-0-8225-3626-0(9) , Lerner Pubns.) Lerner Publishing Group.

Dennard, Deborah. Bullfrog at Magnolia Circle. Kest, Kristin, illus. 2005. (Smithsonian's Backyard Ser.). 32p. (J). (ps-2). 9.95 (978-1-931465-09-0(6) , PB5072); pap. 6.95 (978-1-931465-39-7(8) , S5022); 4.95 (978-1-931465-05-2(3) , B5072); 15.95 (978-1-931465-04-5(5) , B5022) Soundprints.

—Bullfrog at Magnolia Circle. 2002. (gr. k-3). lib. bdg. 15.25 (978-0-613-61062-9(8)) Tandem Library Bks.

Dexter, Anthony. The Adventures of Manny the Manatee. 2004. 45p. pap. 19.95 (978-1-4137-2751-7(4)) PublishAmerica, Inc.

Di Maggio, Joyce. There's a Frog up Top My Head. Mauro, Ray, illus. 1999. 64p. (J). (ps-5). pap. 7.95 (978-1-928970-04-0(4)) GWR Pr.

Diego, Rapi. El Sapo Hechizado. (SPA.). (J). pap. (978-968-7791-20-3(9)) SM Ediciones ESP. *Dist:* Lectorum Pubns., Inc.

Dooley, Sarah. Wilfred & Harold's Dinner Party Disaster. 2004. 35p. pap. 17.95 (978-1-4137-1585-9(0)) PublishAmerica, Inc.

Drachman, Eric. A Frog Thing. Muscarello, James, illus. 2006. 32p. 18.95 (978-0-9703809-3-7(3)) Kidwick Bks.

Dragon, Granny. Marsh Frog Story Books. 2000. cd-rom 9.95 (978-1-58338-347-6(6)) CrossroadsPub.com.

Dubarle-Bossy, Philippe. Flutter the Bird. Rinaldo, Luana, illus. 2005. (Playful Puppet Bks.). 10p. (J). 6.95 (978-0-7641-3045-8(5)) Barron's Educational Series, Inc.

Ducharme, Huguette. Enquete Tres Speciale. Caron, Romi, illus. 2004. (Collection des 6 Ans : Vol. 32). (FRE.). 68p. (YA). 7.95 (978-2-922565-94-2(7)) Editions de la Paix CAN. *Dist:* World of Reading, Ltd.

Duchesne. Edmund the Terrible Raccoon, Edmund Series. 2000. (Illus.). 32p. (J). (ps-3). pap. (978-1-894363-31-0(0)) Dominique & Friends.

Durkee, Sarah. Movie Storybook. Simpson, Fiona, ed. 2006. (Flushed Away Ser.). 48p. (J). pap. 6.99 (978-0-439-90079-9(4)) Scholastic, Inc.

Eagle, Golden. It's Okay to Cry (Frog Medicine) l.t. ed. 2004. (Illus.). 16p. (J). per. 9.95 (978-1-932338-37-9(3)) Lifevest Publishing, Inc.

Easton, Patricia Harrison. Davey's Blue-Eyed Frog. Wohnoutka, Mike, illus. 2003. 112p. (J). (gr. 3-5). tchr. ed. 14.00 (978-0-618-18185-8(7) , Clarion Bks.) Houghton Mifflin Co. Trade & Reference Div.

Edwards, Frank B. Frogger. Bianchi, John, illus. 2000. (Bug & Frogger Ser.). 120p. (J). (gr. 4-6). 14.95 (978-1-894323-20-8(3)); pap. 4.95 (978-1-894323-19-2(X)) Pokeweed Pr. CAN. *Dist:* Fitzhenry & Whiteside, Ltd.

Enriquez, Jose. Saving the Mango Farm. 2006. 23p. (J). 10.98 (978-1-4116-5917-9(1)) Lulu.com.

Erdman & Perez. Mitos y Leyendas Indigenas. 2005. (SPA.). 72p. 13.99 (978-84-241-8013-3(5)) Everest de Ediciones y Distribucion, S.L. ESP. *Dist:* Lectorum Pubns., Inc.

Erickson, Russell. A Toad for Tuesday. 64p. (J). (gr. 1-3). pap. 3.99 (978-0-8072-1329-2(2) , Listening Library) Random Hse. Audio Publishing Group.

Erickson, Russell E. A Toad for Tuesday. Di Fiori, Lawrence, illus. rev. ed. 1998. 64p. (J). (ps-3). reprint ed. pap. 4.99 (978-0-688-16325-9(4) , Harper Trophy) HarperCollins Pubs.

Escriva, Viví. El Principe de las Ranas. Date not set. (SPA., Illus.). 32p. (J). (gr. k-6). 17.50 (978-1-56492-218-2(9)) Laredo Publishing Co., Inc.

Ethan Finds a Frog. 2003. (Illus.). per. 14.95 (978-0-9721948-5-3(1)) New Dawn Publishing.

Faine, Edward Allan. How the Frog Got His Bree-Dup. Hunt, Jim, illus. 2002. 24p. (J). 3.95 (978-0-9654651-9-9(5)) IM Pr.

Flodin, Louise E. Sherman the Frog Meets the Snow Princess. l.t. ed. 2006. (Illus.). 24p. 15.95 (978-0-9745052-5-1(0) , 1) Tree Of Life Publishing.

Focus On The Family Staff. Hero of Hoppers Landing. 2002. (J). 12.99 incl. VHS (978-0-310-70507-9(X)) Zonderkidz.

Fogerty, Ramona. Froggie Sang Tenor. Nurullah, Seitu, illus. 2005. (FRE.). (J). per. 15.00 (978-0-9759889-0-9(5)) Potenial Psychotherapy Counseling & Remedial Serv.

Fontes, Justine. Leap Tries Again. Yakovetic Productions Staff, illus. 24p. (J). (gr. k-2). (978-1-58605-006-1(0)) LeapFrog Enterprises, Inc.

Foote, Norman. Spider Dan. Mitchell, Charlie, illus. 2001. 32p. (J). (ps). pap. 4.95 (978-1-55285-276-7(8)) Whitecap Bks., Ltd. CAN. *Dist:* Firefly Bks., Ltd.

Fornof, John. I Can Hop, I Just Can't Stop. Adnet, Bernard, illus. 2004. 12p. (J). 7.99 (978-0-310-70715-8(3)) Zonderkidz.

—Tad Meets the Grumbly Grumblebee. Adnet, Bernard, illus. 2004. (Ribbits Ser.). 24p. (J). 9.99 (978-0-310-70716-5(1)) Zonderkidz.

Fox, Stephen. Kim the Frog. Bowman, Brent, illus. 2003. (Little Lagoon Ser.). 22p. (J). bds. 6.95 (978-0-9729197-0-8(8) , Gom Foxtail) Gom Publishing, LLC.

Franco, Betsy. Why the Frog Has Big Eyes. Kim, Joung Un, illus. 2003. (Green Light Readers Level 2 Ser.). 24p. (J). 11.95 (978-0-15-204874-7(X)); pap. 3.95 (978-0-15-204834-1(0)) Harcourt Children's Bks. (Green Light Readers).

—Why the Frog Has Big Eyes. 2000. (Green Light Readers Ser.). (978-0-606-20337-1(0)); (J). (978-0-606-20175-9(0)); lib. bdg. 11.80 (978-0-613-64618-5(5)) Tandem Library Bks.

Frankel, Alona. The Family of Tiny White Elephants. Frankel, Alona, illus. rev. ed. 1999. (Illus.). 48p. (J). (ps-6). 5.95 (978-1-888509-09-0(0)) Baby Matters, Inc.

Frankel, Zygmunt. Freddy the Frog & His Childhood. Frankel, Zygmunt, illus. 1999. (Freddy the Frog Ser.: Vol. 3). (Illus.). 48p. (J). (ps up). 5.95 (978-1-888509-03-8(1) , BMR1002) Baby Matters, Inc.

—Freddy the Frog & His Enemies. Frankel, Zygmunt, illus. 1998. (Freddy the Frog Ser.: Vol. 2). (Illus.). 48p. (J). (ps up). pap. 5.95 (978-1-888509-07-6(4) , BMR1006) Baby Matters, Inc.

—Freddy the Frog & the Princess. Frankel, Zygmunt, illus. 1998. (Freddy the Frog Ser.: Vol. 1). (Illus.). 48p. (J). (ps up). pap. 5.95 (978-1-888509-08-3(2) , BMR1007) Baby Matters, Inc.

Freddie the Frog: Set C Individual Title Six-Packs. (gr. k-3). 29.00 (978-0-7635-0545-5(5)) Rigby Education.

Freddy Frog. 2002. 12p. bds. 2.50 (978-1-56021-401-4(5)) W.J. Fantasy, Inc.

Freddy Frog's Note. (Little Book Practice Reader Ser.). (J). (978-0-8136-0835-8(X)) Modern Curriculum Pr.

Freddy the Frog. Date not set. 5.95 (978-0-89868-311-0(4)) ARO Publishing Co.

Frog & Skunk. 1998. (Fisher-Price Phonics Storybooks Ser.: Vol. 2). (Illus.). (J). pap. (978-0-7666-0172-7(2) , Honey Bear Bks.) Modern Publishing.

A Frog on a Log. 2004. (J). per. (978-1-57657-471-3(7)) Paradise Pr., Inc.

The Frog Prince: 6 Small Books. (gr. k-2). 23.00 (978-0-7635-8511-2(4)) Rigby Education.

The Frog Who Thought He Was a Horse: Individual Title Six-Packs. (Literatura 2000 Ser.). (gr. 2-3). 33.00 (978-0-7635-0225-6(1)) Rigby Education.

Frogs in the House: Individual Title Six-Packs. (Sails Literacy Ser.). (gr. 1-2). 36.00 (978-0-7578-6724-8(3)) Rigby Education.

Garis, Howard Roger. Buddy & Brighteyes Pigg. 2004. reprint ed. pap. 15.95 (978-1-4191-1107-5(8)); pap. 1.99 (978-1-4192-1107-2(2)) Kessinger Publishing, LLC.

Garis, Howard Roger. Bully & Bawly Notail. 2006. 95.99 ***(978-1-4280-4019-9(6));*** pap. 88.99 (***978-1-4280-4015-1(3)***) IndyPublish.com.

Gertein, Sherry & Fleet, Mara Van. My Great Aunt Phibian. 2007. 10p. (J). bds. 6.99 (978-0-7944-1281-4(5)) Reader's Digest Assn., Inc., The.

Gill, Janice. Freddy the Frog. 1998. (ps-3). pap. 4.95 (978-0-89868-372-1(6)); lib. bdg. 10.95 (978-0-89868-310-3(6)) ARO Publishing Co.

Glass, Sue. Helping Hop. 2nd ed. 2004. Orig. Title: What's Wrong with Hop?. (J). spiral bd. 10.99 (978-0-9763593-0-2(8)) Closer Looks Bks.

Gleitzman, Morris. Toad Away. 2007. 208p. (J). (gr. 3-7). 4.99 (978-0-375-82767-9(6) , Yearling) Random Hse. Children's Bks.

—Toad Heaven. 2006. 208p. (J). (gr. 3-7). reprint ed. 4.99 (978-0-375-82765-5(X) , Yearling) Random Hse. Children's Bks.

—Toad Rage. 2005. 176p. (J). (gr. 3-7). 5.50 (978-0-375-82763-1(3) , Yearling) Random Hse. Children's Bks.

Godon, Ingrid. In, Out & Other Places. 2000. (Nelly & Caesar Picture Bks.). (Illus.). 24p. (J). 6.95 (978-0-7641-5255-9(6)) Barron's Educational Series, Inc.

—Jump, Dance & Other Adventures. 2000. (Nelly & Caesar Picture Bks.). (Illus.). 24p. (J). 6.95 (978-0-7641-5257-3(2)) Barron's Educational Series, Inc.

—Neli y Gus: Tocar, Probar y Otras Sensaciones. (SPA.). 96p. (J). (978-84-246-8834-9(1)) La Galera, S.A. Editorial ESP. *Dist:* Lectorum Pubns., Inc.

Gorbachev, Valeri. Ms. Turtle the Babysitter. Gorbachev, Valeri, illus. 2005. (I Can Read Bks.). (Illus.). 64p. (J). (gr. k-3). 15.99 (978-0-06-058073-5(9)); lib. bdg. 16.89 (978-0-06-058074-2(7)) HarperCollins Pubs.

Grobler, Piet. Hey, Frog! 1998. (Illus.). 32p. (J). (ps-k). 15.95 (978-1-886910-84-3(7) , Lemniscaat) Boyds Mills Pr.

Gross, Daisy. Where Is Your Residence? 2004. 38p. per. 14.95 (978-1-59453-153-8(6) , 1832) Airleaf Publishing & Bookselling.

Gross, S. D. Blue Frog. l.t. ed. 2006. (Illus.). 24p. (J). per. 11.99 (978-1-59879-207-2(5)) Lifevest Publishing, Inc.

Guardado, Maria. The Frog That Went to the Moon. Valentin, Jeannette, illus. 32p. (J). (gr. 3 up). 16.00 (978-0-9710860-6-7(0)) Libros, Encouraging Cultural Literacy.

Gunson, Christopher. Little Frog. 2000. (Illus.). 25p. (J). pap. 9.99 (978-0-552-54504-4(X) , Corgi) Transworld Publishers Ltd. GBR. *Dist:* Independent Pubs. Group.

—Little Frog. Gunson, Christopher, illus. 2000. (Illus.). 25p. (J). 19.99 (978-0-385-40785-4(8)) Transworld Publishers Ltd. GBR. *Dist:* Trafalgar Square Publishing.

Hachler, Bruno. Farley Farts. Muller, Birte, illus. 2003. 32p. (J). (gr. k-3). 15.95 (978-0-7358-1847-7(9)) North-South Bks., Inc.

Hachler, Bruno, et al. Farley Farts. 2004. (Illus.). 32p. (J). pap. 6.95 (978-0-7358-1969-6(6)) North-South Bks., Inc.

Hahn, Victor H. The Adventures of Frank the Friendly Frogasaurus & Family. Twiner, Stacy, illus. 2000. (Frank the Friendly Frogasaurus Ser.). 32p. (J). (ps-3). 15.95 (978-0-929765-76-1(1) , Papa & Noelle Stories) Seven Locks Pr.

Hall, Susan', illus. Diego Saves the Tree Frogs. 2006. (Go, Diego, Go! Ser.). 24p. (J). pap. 3.99 (978-1-4169-1574-4(5) , Simon Spotlight/Nickelodeon) Simon & Schuster Children's Publishing.

Hamilton, Martha. A Tale of Two Frogs. 2006. (Illus.). 32p. (J). pap. 3.95 (978-0-87483-812-1(6)) August Hse. Pubs., Inc.

Hansle, Chauline. Mr Frog & Kitty Robin. 2006. (ENG., Illus.). 28p. per. 15.49 (***978-1-4259-6920-2(8)***) AuthorHouse.

Harbo, Gary. The Northern Woods Adventure: Early Reader. Harbo, Gary, illus. l.t. ed. 2004. (If You Want to Succeed, You Need to Read! Ser.: 6). (Illus.). 33p. (J). 10.95 (978-1-884149-16-0(2)) Kutie Kari Bks., Inc.

Harcourt School Publishers Staff. How the Frog Lost His Croak: Take-Home Book. 1999. (Signatures Ser.). (Illus.). (J). pap. 1.90 (978-0-15-313913-0(7)) Harcourt Schl. Pubs.

—I Took My Frog To... Library Book. 1999. (Collections Ser.). (Illus.). pap. 14.90 (978-0-15-313407-4(0)) Harcourt Schl. Pubs.

—"Pardon" Said... Giraffe. 99th ed. 1998. (Signatures Ser.). (Illus.). pap. 60.70 (978-0-15-310894-5(0)) Harcourt Schl. Pubs.

—Renacuajo Curioso: Take-Home Book. 1999. (Vamos Ser.). (SPA., Illus.). (J). pap. 2.50 (978-0-15-318847-3(2)) Harcourt Schl. Pubs.

—Sing for the King: Advanced Level, 6 Packs. 3rd ed. 2002. (Trophies Reading Program Ser.). (Illus.). (gr. 1). pap. 20.10 (978-0-15-326866-3(2)) Harcourt Schl. Pubs.

—Sing for the King Advanced Level. 3rd ed. 2002. (Trophies Reading Program Ser.). (Illus.). (J). pap. 3.70 (978-0-15-323016-5(9)) Harcourt Schl. Pubs.

—Slim Grows Up: On Level. 3rd ed. 2002. (Trophies Reading Program Ser.). (Illus.). (J). pap. 4.10 (978-0-15-322982-4(9)) Harcourt Schl. Pubs.

—Slim Grows Up 5-Pack, On Level. 3rd ed. 2002. (Trophies Reading Program Ser.). (Illus.). (gr. 1). pap. 20.10 (978-0-15-326832-8(8)) Harcourt Schl. Pubs.

—Trofeos Advanced Level: Que Sucide, Rancejo? 3rd ed. 2002. (SPA., Illus.). pap. 5.50 (978-0-15-323927-4(1)) Harcourt Schl. Pubs.

—What the Frog Needed: Take-Home Book. 1999. (Signatures Ser.). (Illus.). (J). pap. 1.70 (978-0-15-313850-8(5)) Harcourt Schl. Pubs.

Harrison, Paul. Hmm, que rica mosca, Level P. Worsley, Belinda, illus. 2006. (Lightning Readers Ser.). 32p. (J). pap. 3.95 (978-0-7696-4228-4(4) , Gingham Dog Pr.) School Specialty Publishing.

—Yummy, Yummy Fly. Worsley, Belinda, illus. 2006. (Lightning Readers Ser.). 32p. (J). (ps-k). pap. 3.95 (978-0-7696-4198-0(9) , Gingham Dog Pr.) School Specialty Publishing.

Hausman, Sid. One Bullfrog. Hausman, Sid, illus. 2002. (Illus.). 32p. (YA). 18.95 (978-1-929115-05-1(9)) Azro Pr., Inc.

Hawes, Judy. Why Frogs Are Wet. Fraser, Mary Ann, illus. 2000. (Let's-Read-and-Find-Out Science Ser.). 40p. (J). (gr. k-4). pap. 5.99 (978-0-06-445195-6(X) , Harper Trophy) HarperCollins Pubs.

Hazen, Barbara Shook. That Toad Is Mine! Floca, Brian & Manning, Jane, illus. 1998. (Growing Tree Ser.). 24p. (J). (ps up). 9.95 (978-0-694-01035-6(9) , Harper Festival) HarperCollins Pubs.

Heo, Yumi. The Green Frogs: A Korean Folktale. 2004. (Illus.). 32p. (J). (gr. k-3). reprint ed. 5.95 (978-0-618-43228-8(0)) Houghton Mifflin Co. Trade & Reference Div.

Hiebert, Elfrieda H. & Juel, Connie. Little Frog's Monster Story. (Little Book Practice Reader Ser.). (J). (978-0-8136-0807-5(4)) Modern Curriculum Pr.

Higginson, Sheila. Look Before You Leap! Disney Storybook Artists Staff, illus. 2007. 24p. (ps-k). pap. 3.99 (***978-1-4231-0646-3(6)***) Disney Pr.

Hilario. Yuck!! A Toad. 2006. (Stories for Smaller Kids Ser.). (Illus.). 16p. (J). bds. 5.95 (978-9974-7925-4-8(1)) Hardenville SA URY. *Dist:* Independent Pubs. Group.

Hip Hop Criminal. 1998. (Illus.). 68p. (J). pap. 12.00 (978-0-9702945-1-7(4)) Vezun.

Hood, Karen Jean Matsko. There's a Toad in the Hole: A Big Fat Toad in the Hole. 2005. (J). 15.95 (978-1-930948-25-9(5)); 24.95 (978-1-930948-24-2(7)) Whispering Pine Pr., Inc.

—Wilbur's Great Adventure: Large Print Edition. l.t. ed. 2006. spiral bd. 22.95 (978-1-59434-730-6(1)) Whispering Pine Pr., Inc.

—Wilbur's Great Adventure - Braille Edition. braille ed. 2006. spiral bd. 22.95 (978-1-59434-732-0(8)) Whispering Pine Pr., Inc.

Hope. The Frog Who Couldn't Jump. Anders, Tim, ed. Pinson, Richard, illus. 2000. (Life Lessons Ser.). 36p. (J). (gr. k-3). 16.95 (978-1-885624-57-4(3)) Alpine Publishing.

Hopkins, Jackie Mims. The Horned Toad Prince. Austin, Michael, illus. 2000. 32p. (J). (ps-3). 15.95 (978-1-56145-195-1(9) , Q28670) Peachtree Pubs., Ltd.

Horowitz, Jeanine. Toady Toad's Move. 2006. (Illus.). 32p. (J). lib. bdg. 17.95 (***978-1-934190-03-6(9)***) Ocean Front Bk. Publishing, Inc.

How Clarence Found Harmony. 2004. (J). pap. 5.00 (978-0-9747734-5-2(X)) Neal, Ann-Marie F.

Hughes, Frieda. Thing in the Sink Storybook. Riddell, Chris, illus. 48p. (J). pap. 9.99 (978-0-340-86579-8(2) , Hodder & Stoughton) Hodder General Publishing Division GBR. *Dist:* Trafalgar Square Publishing.

Hupp, Sarah M. Tad's Messy Day. Adnet, Bernard, illus. 2004. (Ribbits Ser.). 24p. (J). 9.99 (978-0-310-70567-3(3)) Zonderkidz.

Hutta, K. Emily. A Tad Too Much. Yakovetic Productions Staff, illus. 24p. (J). (gr. k-2). (978-1-58605-007-8(9)) LeapFrog Enterprises, Inc.

The Icky Sticky Frog. 2003. (Illus.). 17p. (J). 4.95 (978-1-58117-219-5(2) , Intervisual/Piggy Toes) Dalmatian Pr.

Impey, Rose. Wanda Witch & Too Many Frogs. McEwen, Katharine, illus. 2006. (Scholastic Reader Ser.). 32p. (J). pap. 3.99 (978-0-439-78451-1(4) , Cartwheel Bks.) Scholastic, Inc.

Irvin, Christine. Isaac the Frog. Less, Sally, illus. 2004. 14p. (J). 7.95 (978-0-9706654-9-2(0)) Sprite Pr.

Irvin, Christine M. Isaac the Frog. Less, Sally, illus. l.t. ed. 2002. 20p. (J). 3.95 (978-0-9706654-4-7(X)) Sprite Pr.

Isherwood, Shirley. Flora the Frog. Leplar, Anna C., illus. 2000. 32p. (J). (ps-3). 16.95 (978-1-56145-223-1(8)) Peachtree Pubs., Ltd.

Jackson's Plan: Evaluation Guide. 2006. (J). (978-1-55942-410-3(9)) Marsh Media.

Jamison, Jocelyn. Hoppy Feet. Gévry, Claudine, illus. 2003. 12p. (J). (ps-k). bds. 9.99 (978-0-8431-0240-6(3) , Price Stern Sloan) Penguin Group (USA) Inc.

Johnson, Cindy B. Frantic the Frog. Lane, Cody R., illus. 2004. 27p. pap. 14.95 (978-1-4137-2954-2(1)) PublishAmerica, Inc.

Johnson, Suzanne C. Fribbity Ribbit! 1999. (J). 16.00 (978-0-517-70982-5(1)) Crown Publishing Group.

Kalan, Robert. Jump, Frog, Jump! 2002. Tr. of Salta, Ranita, Salta!. (Illus.). (J). 14.47 (978-0-7587-2910-1(3)) Book Wholesalers, Inc.

—Jump, Frog, Jump! Barton, Byron, illus. 2003. Tr. of Salta, Ranita, Salta!. 34p. (J). (ps-3). 6.99 (978-0-06-008819-4(2) , Harper Entertainment) HarperCollins Pubs.

—Jump, Frog, Jump! 2001. Tr. of Salta, Ranita, Salta!. (Illus.). (J). (ps-2). pap. 16.95 incl. audio (978-0-87499-786-6(0)) Live Oak Media.

—Jump, Frog, Jump! Barton, Byron, illus. 2001. Tr. of Salta, Ranita, Salta!. 28.95 incl. audio compact disk (978-1-59112-728-4(9)); pap. 35.95 incl. audio compact disk (978-1-59112-729-1(7)); (J). 25.95 incl. audio (978-0-87499-787-3(9)); (J). pap. 33.95 incl. audio (978-0-87499-788-0(7)) Live Oak Media.

—Jump, Frog, Jump. 2001. (Illus.). (J). pap. 18.95 incl. audio compact disk (978-1-59112-727-7(0)) Live Oak Media.

—Jump, Frog, Jump! & the Salta Ranita Salta. Barton, Byron, illus. 2001. pap. 33.95 incl. audio (978-0-87499-804-7(2)) Live Oak Media.

Kale, Ann Stephanian. Artie - The Ugly Frog. Kale, Ann Stephanian, illus. 2004. (Illus.). 20p. (J). pap. 10.00 (978-0-9704131-6-1(5)) Abril BookStore & Publishing.

Kalin, Julia. Pickles the Frog: A Picture-It Storybook - A Reader Illustrated Storybook. 1999. (Illus.). 12p. (J). (ps-6). pap. 12.95 (978-0-9672430-6-1(8)) Stay, Play & Learn.

Kasza, Keiko. Grandpa Toad's Secrets. Kasza, Keiko, illus. 2002. (Illus.). (J). 13.19 (978-0-7587-2644-5(9)) Book Wholesalers, Inc.

—Grandpa Toad's Secrets. 1998. (J). (978-0-606-12954-1(5)) Tandem Library Bks.

Kellogg, Steven. The Mysterious Tadpole. Kellogg, Steven, illus. 2002. (Illus.). (J). 14.04 (978-0-7587-3233-0(3)) Book Wholesalers, Inc.

—The Mysterious Tadpole. Kellogg, Steven, illus. 25th anniv. ed. (Illus.). 40p. (J). 2002. (gr. k-3). 16.99 (978-0-8037-2788-5(7) , Dial); 2004. (gr. 1 up). reprint ed. pap. 6.99 (978-0-14-240140-8(4) , Puffin) Penguin Group (USA) Inc.

Kim the Frog. 2004. (J). 7.95 (978-0-9729197-5-3(9) , Gom Foxtail) Gom Publishing, LLC.

Kimmel, Eric A. I Took My Frog to the Library. Sims, Blanche, illus. 2002. (J). 12.34 (978-0-7587-2817-3(4)) Book Wholesalers, Inc.

—I Took My Frog to the Library. Sims, Blanche, illus. 2000. (J). pap. 19.97 incl. audio (978-0-7366-9223-6(1)) Books on Tape, Inc.

Kimura, Ken. 999 Tadpoles. Murakami, Yasunari, illus. 2006. 40p. (J). 14.95 (978-1-74126-433-3(2)) R.I.C. Pubns. AUS. *Dist:* SCB Distributors.

Kline, Trish & Donev, Mary. Coming Home: KA Reader 8. 2007. (Illus.). 32p. (J). per. 20.00 (***978-1-934307-01-4(7)***) Ghost Hunter Productions.

Knudsen, Michelle. Fish & Frog. Petrone, Valeria, illus. 2005. 8p. (J). (ps-2). pap. 5.99 (978-0-7636-2457-6(8)) Candlewick Pr.

Kochalka, James. Fancy Froglin Vol. 1: Sexy Forest. 2003. (Illus.). 96p. (gr. 11 up). pap. 12.95 (978-1-891867-47-7(4)) Alternative Comics.

Kompelien, Tracy. Leap Frog. Haberstroh, Anne, illus. (Fact & Fiction Ser.). 24p. (J). 2007. 21.35 (978-1-59928-448-4(0)); 2006. (978-1-59928-449-1(9)) ABDO Publishing Co.

Kopelke, Lisa. Excuse Me! Kopelke, Lisa, illus. 2003. (Illus.). 32p. (J). (gr. k-3). 16.95 (978-0-689-85111-7(1)) Simon & Schuster Children's Publishing.

—Tissue, Please! Kopelke, Lisa, illus. 2004. (Illus.). 32p. (J). 15.95 (978-0-689-86248-9(2)) Simon & Schuster Children's Publishing.

Lamm, C. Drew. The Prog Frince: A Mixed-Up Tale. McClintock, Barbara, illus. 1999. 32p. (J). (gr. k-4). pap. 16.95 (978-0-531-30135-7(4) , Orchard Bks.) Scholastic, Inc.

The Last Coqui. 2002. (J). 16.00 (978-0-9675413-4-1(4)) Libros, Encouraging Cultural Literacy.

Laurel, Hylton. The Cowboy Frog. Laurel, Hylton, illus. 2003. (Illus.). 24p. (J). pap. 4.95 (978-1-875641-85-7(8)) Magabala Bks. AUS. *Dist:* International Specialized Bk. Services.

Law, Felicia. Rumble Meets Todd Toad. Pak, Yoon Mi, illus. 2006. (Read-It! Readers Ser.). 32p. (J). (gr. 2-4). 18.60 (978-1-4048-1340-3(3)) Picture Window Bks.

LeapFrog Staff, compiled by. Leap Scrubs Up. 2001. (J). (ps-2). spiral bd. 10.95 (978-1-58605-020-7(6)) LeapFrog Enterprises, Inc.

—Leap to the Moon: MFLP. 2001. (J). (ps-2). spiral bd. 12.99 (978-1-58605-110-5(5)) LeapFrog Enterprises, Inc.

—Leap's Big Day: MFLP. 2001. (J). (ps-2). spiral bd. (978-1-58605-109-9(1)) LeapFrog Enterprises, Inc.

—Leap's Snack. 2001. (J). (ps-2). spiral bd. 11.95 (978-1-58605-025-2(7)) LeapFrog Enterprises, Inc.

—Tad Goes Shopping. 2001. (J). (ps-1). spiral bd. 14.99 (978-1-58605-086-3(9)) LeapFrog Enterprises, Inc.

—Tad's Counting Day on the Farm. 2001. (YA). (ps up). spiral bd. 9.99 (978-1-58605-096-2(6)) LeapFrog Enterprises, Inc.

Lechner, John. A Froggy Fable. Lechner, John, illus. 2005. (Illus.). 32p. (J). (ps up). 14.99 (978-0-7636-2123-0(4)) Candlewick Pr.

Ledbetter, Penny. Frog's Lily Pad. 2006. (J). 9.95 (***978-1-59712-048-7(0)***) Catawba Publishing Co.

Leeson, Robert. One Frog Too Many. (Illus.). 48p. (J). 13.95 (978-0-241-13106-0(5) , Hamilton, Hamish) Penguin Bks., Ltd. GBR. *Dist:* Trafalgar Square Publishing.

LeLeu, Lisa. Frenchy the Frog Story Starter: Puppet Show Book Story Starter. 2004. (Puppet Show Bks.). (Illus.). 14p. 1.50 (978-0-9710537-7-9(4)) LeLeu, Lisa Studios! Inc.

Leslie, Amanda, illus. Jumping Frog. 2001. 14p. (J). (ps-k). bds. 5.95 (978-1-58925-657-6(3) , tiger tales) ME Media LLC.

E
F
G

Lewis, Cynthia C. Dilly's Summer Camp Diary. 2000. 4. (Illus.). 32p. (J). (gr. 2-4). pap. 6.95 (978-0-7613-0990-1(X), First Avenue Editions) Lerner Publishing Group.
—Dilly's Summer Camp Diary. 1999. (gr. 3-6). lib. bdg. 15.25 (978-0-613-28464-6(X)) Tandem Library Bks.
Lewis, Paul Owen. Frog Girl. Lewis, Paul Owen, illus. 1999. (Illus.). 32p. (J). (gr. 2 up). lib. bdg. 24.67 (978-0-8368-2228-1(5)) Stevens, Gareth Inc.
—Frog Girl. 2001. (gr. k-3). lib. bdg. 15.25 (978-0-613-37144-5(5)) Tandem Library Bks.
—Frog Girl. 2004. (Illus.). (J). 38p. tchr. ed., tchr.'s planning gde. ed. 2.95 (978-1-58246-009-3(4)); 32p. 14.95 (978-1-58246-003-1(5)); 32p. pap. 6.95 (978-1-58246-048-2(5)) Ten Speed Pr. (Tricycle Pr.).
—Frog Girl. (Illus.). 32p. (J). (ps-5). 18.95 (978-1-55110-658-8(2)); pap. 8.95 (978-1-55285-193-7(1)) Whitecap Bks., Ltd. CAN. *Dist:* Graphic Arts Ctr. Publishing Co.
Lionni, Leo. An Extraordinary Egg. Lionni, Leo, illus. 1998. (Illus.). 32p. (J). (gr. k-ps). pap. 6.99 (978-0-679-89385-1(7), Dragonfly Bks.) Random Hse. Children's Bks.
—Fish Is Fish. Lionni, Leo, illus. 2002. (Illus.). (J). 13.83 (978-0-7587-2509-7(4)) Book Wholesalers, Inc.
—It's Mine! Lionni, Leo, illus. 2002. (Illus.). (J). 13.83 (978-0-7587-6976-3(8)) Book Wholesalers, Inc.
Little Frog, Big Pond: Short Vowel review: Level C, 6 vols. (Wright Skills Ser.). 16p. (gr. k-3). 26.50 (978-0-322-01492-3(1)) Wright Group, The.
Livingston, Irene. Finklehopper Frog. Lies, Brian, illus. 2004. 30p. (J). (ps-2). 14.95 (978-1-58246-075-8(2), Tricycle Pr.) Ten Speed Pr.
—Finklehopper Frog Cheers. Lies, Brian, illus. 2005. 32p. (J). 14.95 (978-1-58246-138-0(4), Tricycle Pr.) Ten Speed Pr.
Lobel, Arnold. The Adventures of Frog & Toad. 1998. (Illus.). (J). 12.95 (978-0-06-028043-7(3)) HarperCollins Pubs.
—Days with Frog & Toad. Lobel, Arnold, illus. 2002. (Frog & Toad Ser.). (Illus.). (J). 12.34 (978-0-7587-6065-4(5)) Book Wholesalers, Inc.
—Dias con Sapo y Sepo. (Sapo Y Sepo Ser.). (SPA., Illus.). 68p. (J). (gr. k-3). pap. 8.95 (978-1-56014-588-2(9)) Santillana USA Publishing Co., Inc.
—Frog & Toad All Year. Lobel, Arnold, illus. 2002. (Frog & Toad Ser.). (Illus.). (J). 12.34 (978-0-7587-1198-4(0)) Book Wholesalers, Inc.
—Frog & Toad Are Friends. Lobel, Arnold, illus. 2002. (Frog & Toad Ser.). (J). 12.34 (978-0-7587-6105-7(8)) Book Wholesalers, Inc.
—The Frog & Toad Collection, Set. Lobel, Arnold, illus. 2004. (I Can Read Bks.). (Illus.). 13p. (J). (gr. k-3). pap., pap. 11.99 (978-0-06-058086-5(0), Harper Trophy) HarperCollins Pubs.
—Frog & Toad Together. Lobel, Arnold, illus. 1999. (I Can Read Bks.). (Illus.). 64p. (J). (ps-3). 16.99 (978-0-694-01298-5(X), Harper Festival) HarperCollins Pubs.
—Sapo y Sepo Inseparables. Lobel, Arnold, illus. 2003. (SPA., Illus.). 68p. (J). (ps-3). 12.95 (978-84-204-3047-8(1)) Alfaguara, Ediciones, S.A.- Grupo Santillana ESP. *Dist:* Lectorum Pubns., Inc., Santillana USA Publishing Co., Inc.
Lobel, Gillian. Little Bear's Special Wish. Hansen, Gaby, illus. 2004. 32p. (J). tchr. ed. 16.95 (978-1-58925-034-5(6), tiger tales) ME Media LLC.
London, Jonathan. Froggy Apprende a Nadar. 2003. (Froggy Ser.). (SPA., Illus.). (J). (gr. k-2). pap. 3.16 net. (978-0-439-20435-4(6), SO30917) Scholastic, Inc.
—Froggy Bakes a Cake. Remkiewicz, Frank, illus. 2000. (Reading Railroad Bks.). 32p. (J). (ps-3). pap. 3.99 (978-0-448-42153-7(4), Grosset & Dunlap) Penguin Group (USA) Inc.
—Froggy Bakes a Cake. 2000. (ps-2). lib. bdg. 11.25 (978-0-613-25269-0(1)); (Illus.). (J). 10.29 (978-0-606-21801-6(7)) Tandem Library Bks.
—Froggy Eats Out. ed. 2004. (Illus.). (J). (ps up). spiral bd. (978-0-616-11117-8(7)); spiral bd. (978-0-616-11118-5(5)) Canadian National Institute for the Blind/Institut National Canadien pour les Aveugles.
—Froggy Eats Out. Remkiewicz, Frank, illus. 32p. (J). (gr. k-2). 2003. pap. 5.99 (978-0-14-250061-3(5), Puffin); 2001. 15.99 (978-0-670-89686-8(1), Viking Juvenile) Penguin Group (USA) Inc.
—Froggy Eats Out. 2003. (gr. k-3). lib. bdg. 14.15 (978-0-613-67453-9(7)) Tandem Library Bks.
—Froggy Gets Dressed. 2007. (Puffin Storytime Ser.). 32p. (J). (ps). pap. 9.99 (978-0-14-240870-4(0), Puffin) Penguin Group (USA) Inc.
—Froggy Goes to Bed. Remkiewicz, Frank, illus. (Froggy Ser.). 32p. (J). (gr. k-3). 2002. pap. 5.99 (978-0-14-056657-4(0), Puffin); 2000. 15.99 (978-0-670-88860-3(5), Viking Juvenile) Penguin Group (USA) Inc.
—Froggy Goes to Bed. 2002. (gr. k-3). lib. bdg. 14.15 (978-0-613-45265-6(8)) Tandem Library Bks.
—Froggy Goes to School. Remkiewicz, Frank, illus. 1998. 32p. (J). (ps-1). pap. 5.99 (978-0-14-056247-7(8), Puffin) Penguin Group (USA) Inc.
—Froggy Goes to the Doctor. ed. 2004. (Illus.). (J). (gr. k-3). spiral bd. (978-0-616-14585-2(3)); spiral bd. (978-0-616-14586-9(1)) Canadian National Institute for the Blind/Institut National Canadien pour les Aveugles.
—Froggy Goes to the Doctor. Remkiewicz, Frank, illus. (Froggy Ser.). 32p. (J). 2004. pap. 5.99 (978-0-14-240193-4(5), Puffin); 2002. 15.99 (978-0-670-03578-6(5), Viking Juvenile) Penguin Group (USA) Inc.
—Froggy Juega al Futbol. 2003. (Froggy Ser.). (SPA., Illus.). (J). (gr. k-2). pap. 3.16 net. (978-0-439-24321-6(1), SO30406) Scholastic, Inc.
—Froggy Plays in the Band. Remkiewicz, Frank, illus. (Froggy Ser.). 32p. (J). 2004. pap. 5.99 (978-0-14-240051-7(3), Puffin); 2002. 15.99 (978-0-670-03532-8(7), Viking Juvenile) Penguin Group (USA) Inc.
—Froggy Plays Soccer. Remkiewicz, Frank, illus. 32p. (J). (ps-3). 2001. pap. 5.99 (978-0-14-056809-7(3), Puffin); 1999. 15.99 (978-0-670-88257-1(7), Viking Juvenile) Penguin Group (USA) Inc.
—Froggy Plays Soccer. 2001. (gr. k-3). lib. bdg. 14.15 (978-0-613-35949-8(6)); (Illus.). (J). 12.79 (978-0-606-21204-5(3)) Tandem Library Bks.
—Froggy Plays T-Ball. Remkiewicz, Frank, illus. 2007. (Froggy Ser.). 32p. (J). (ps-1). 15.99 (978-0-670-06187-7(5), Viking Juvenile) Penguin Group (USA) Inc.
—Froggy Rides a Bike. Remkiewicz, Frank, illus. (Froggy Ser.). 32p. (J). (ps). 2008. pap. 5.99 (***978-0-14-241067-7(5)***, Puffin); 2006. 15.99 (978-0-670-06099-3(2), Viking Adult) Penguin Group (USA) Inc.
—Froggy's Baby Sister. Remkiewicz, Frank, illus. (Froggy Ser.). 32p. (J). 2005. pap. 5.99 (978-0-14-240342-6(3), Puffin); 2003. 15.99 (978-0-670-03659-2(5), Viking Juvenile) Penguin Group (USA) Inc.
—Froggy's Day with Dad. Remkiewicz, Frank, illus. (Froggy Ser.). 32p. (J). (ps). 2006. pap. 5.99 (978-0-14-240634-2(1), Puffin); 2004. 15.99 (978-0-670-03596-0(3), Viking Juvenile) Penguin Group (USA) Inc.
—Froggy's First Kiss. Remkiewicz, Frank, illus. 1999. (Viking Easy-to-Read Ser.). 32p. (J). (ps-1). pap. 5.99 (978-0-14-056570-6(1), Puffin) Penguin Group (USA) Inc.
—Froggy's First Kiss. 2000. (YA). pap. 97.30 incl. audio (978-0-7887-4169-2(1), 47101); pap. 97.30 incl. audio (978-0-7887-4170-8(5), 47101) Recorded Bks., LLC.
—Froggy's First Kiss. (gr. k-3). 2000. lib. bdg. 14.15 (978-0-613-22989-0(4)); 1999. (Illus.). (J). 12.79 (978-0-606-18404-5(X)) Tandem Library Bks.
—Froggy's Halloween. Remkiewicz, Frank, illus. 1999. (Froggy Ser.). 32p. (J). (ps-1). 15.99 (978-0-670-88449-0(9), Viking Juvenile) Penguin Group (USA) Inc.
—Froggy's Halloween. 2002. (gr. k-3). lib. bdg. 14.15 (978-0-613-45266-3(6)) Tandem Library Bks.
—Froggy's Sleepover. Remkiewicz, Frank, illus. (Froggy Ser.). 32p. (J). 2007. pap. 5.99 (978-0-14-240750-9(X), Puffin); 2005. 15.99 (978-0-670-06004-7(6), Viking Juvenile) Penguin Group (USA) Inc.
—Helloooo Froggy! Remkiewicz, Frank, illus. 2001. (Sticker Stories Ser.). 1p. (J). (ps-3). mass mkt. 4.99 (978-0-448-42491-0(6), Grosset & Dunlap) Penguin Group (USA) Inc.
—Let's Go, Froggy! unabr. ed. 1999. (J). (ps up). pap., stu. ed. 24.24 incl. audio (978-0-7887-3647-6(7), 41013X4) Recorded Bks., LLC.
—El Primer Beso de Froggy. 2003. (Froggy Ser.). (SPA., Illus.). (J). (gr. k-2). pap. 3.16 net. (978-0-439-26024-4(8), SO30356) Scholastic, Inc.
London, Jonathan & Remkiewicz, Frank. Froggy's Halloween. rev. ed. 2001. (Illus.). 1p. (J). pap. 5.99 (978-0-14-230068-8(3), Puffin) Penguin Group (USA) Inc.
Luce, Philip. Gotno Tale. 2007. 24p. (J). per. 11.99 (***978-1-59886-754-1(7)***) Tate Publishing & Enterprises, L.L.C.
Lyles, Tanya. The Frog That Needed an Umbrella. 2006. 17.00 (978-0-8059-9906-8(X)) Dorrance Publishing Co., Inc.
Madison, Deborah L. A Slimy Frog Who Went to School. 1999. (J). (gr. k-3). pap. 5.95 (978-0-533-13013-9(1)) Vantage Pr., Inc.
Mann, Pamela. The Frog Princess? (Illus.). (J). 2002. (TUR & ENG.). 24p. 15.95 (978-1-85269-324-4(X)); 2000. (BEN & ENG., 24p. 19.95 (978-1-85269-317-6(7)); 2000. (GUJ & ENG., 25p. 19.95 (978-1-85269-322-0(3)); 2000. (PAN & ENG., 24p. 17.95 (978-1-85269-323-7(1)); 2000. (SOM & ENG., 24p. 15.95 (978-1-85269-319-0(3)); 2000. (URD & ENG., 24p. 17.95 (978-1-85269-321-3(5)) Mantra Publishing, Ltd. GBR. *Dist:* AIMS International Bks., Inc.
Marsoli, Lisa Ann. Leap's Friends A-Z. Yakovetic Productions Staff, illus. 24p. (J). (gr. k-2). (978-1-58605-008-5(7)) LeapFrog Enterprises, Inc.
Martin, David. Lucy & Bob: Brand New Readers. Martin, David, illus. 2006. 48p. (J). (ps-2). pap. 5.99 (978-0-7636-2722-5(4)); (Illus.). 14.99 (978-0-7636-2723-2(2)) Candlewick Pr.
Martín Larrañaga, Ana. Big Wide-Mouthed Frog: A Traditional Tale. 1999. (Illus.). (J). (978-0-606-21641-8(3)) Tandem Library Bks.
—La Gran Rana Bocona. 2003. (SPA., Illus.). (J). (gr. k-2). pap. 3.16 net. (978-0-439-23148-0(5), SO30447) Scholastic, Inc.
Mayer, Mercer. A Boy, a Dog & a Frog. Mayer, Mercer, illus. 2003. (Illus.). 32p. (J). (ps). 5.99 (978-0-8037-2880-6(8), Dial) Penguin Group (USA) Inc.
—Frog Goes to Dinner. Mayer, Mercer, illus. 2003. (Illus.). 32p. (J). (gr. k-1). 6.99 (978-0-8037-2884-4(0), Dial) Penguin Group (USA) Inc.
—Frog on His Own. Mayer, Mercer, illus. 2003. (Illus.). 32p. (J). (gr. k-1). 5.99 (978-0-8037-2883-7(2), Dial) Penguin Group (USA) Inc.
—Frog, Where Are You? Mayer, Mercer, illus. 2003. (Illus.). 32p. (J). (ps). 6.99 (978-0-8037-2881-3(6), Dial) Penguin Group (USA) Inc.
Mayer, Mercer & Mayer, Marianna. One Frog Too Many. Mayer, Mercer & Mayer, Marianna, illus. 2003. (Illus.). 32p. (J). (gr. k-1). 6.99 (978-0-8037-2885-1(9), Dial) Penguin Group (USA) Inc.
McBratney, Sam. When I'm Big. Jeram, Anita, illus. 2007. (Guess How Much I Love You Ser.). 24p. (J). (gr. k-ps). bds. 7.99 (***978-0-7636-3546-6(4)***) Candlewick Pr.
McBride, R. J. Temple of the Rainbow. 2004. 151p. pap. 19.95 (978-1-4137-1934-5(1)) PublishAmerica, Inc.
McCartney, Paul, et al. High in the Clouds. 2005. (Illus.). 96p. (J). (gr. 1-5). 19.99 (978-0-525-47733-4(0), Dutton Juvenile) Penguin Group (USA) Inc.
McLellan, Stephanie Simpson. Leon's Song. Bonder, Dianna, illus. 2004. 32p. (J). (ps-3). (978-1-55041-813-2(0)) Fitzhenry & Whiteside, Ltd.
—Leon's Song. Bonder, Dianna, illus. 2006. 32p. pap. 7.95 (978-1-55041-815-6(7)) Fitzhenry & Whiteside, Ltd. CAN. *Dist:* F & W Pubns., Inc.
McOmber, Rachel B., ed. McOmber Phonics Storybooks: Boe E. Toad. rev. ed. (Illus.). (J). (978-0-944991-54-1(8)) Swift Learning Resources.
McVeity, Jen. The Frogs of Betts. Denton, Terry, illus. 1999. (Supa Doopers Ser.). 64p. (J). (978-0-7608-1932-6(7)) Sundance/Newbridge Educational Publishing.
—Frogs of Betts. 1999. (gr. 3-6). lib. bdg. 12.60 (978-0-613-19363-4(6)) Tandem Library Bks.
Melton, Holly. The Day Leap Are Olives. Yakovetic Productions Staff, illus. 24p. (J). (gr. k-2). (978-1-58605-011-5(7)) LeapFrog Enterprises, Inc.
—Tad's Good Night. Yakovetic Productions Staff, illus. 24p. (J). (gr. k-2). (978-1-58605-009-2(5)) LeapFrog Enterprises, Inc.
Michaels, J. C. Firebelly: A Journey into the Heart of Thinking. 2005. 254p. pap. 18.00 (978-0-9726173-1-4(0)); 50.00 (978-0-9726173-0-7(2)) Cascade, Inc. (Philograph).
Michaels, Kat. Willow's Bend. 2006. 24p. 15.95 (978-0-9745052-6-8(9)) Tree Of Life Publishing.
Miller, Ruth. I Went to the Bay. Gourbault, Martine, illus. unabr. ed. 2002. 24p. (J). (gr. k-3). (978-1-55074-789-8(4)) Kids Can Pr., Ltd.
—I Went to the Bay. 1999. (ps-2). lib. bdg. 14.10 (978-0-613-44525-2(2)) Tandem Library Bks.
Missing Hog. 2004. (J). per. (978-1-57657-374-7(5)) Paradise Pr., Inc.
Mitton, Tony. Down by the Cool of the Pool. Parker-Rees, Guy, illus. 2002. 32p. (J). (ps-k). pap. 15.95 (978-0-439-30915-8(8), Orchard Bks.) Scholastic, Inc.
Montes, Graciela. Cuentos del Sapo. 2003. (SPA.). (978-950-07-1900-1(2), SA31240) Editorial Sudamericana S.A. ARG. *Dist:* Lectorum Pubns., Inc.
Moody-Luther, Jacqui. Word World Frog. 2005. NAp. 11.95 (978-0-7624-2463-4(X)) Running Pr. Bk. Pubs.
Mora, Pat. The Race of Toad & Deer. Domi, illus. 2001. 32p. (J). (ps-k). 15.95 (978-0-88899-434-9(6)) Groundwood Bks. CAN. *Dist:* Perseus Distribution.
Mora, Pat, et al. La Carrera del Sapa y el Venado. Domi, illus. 2001. (SPA.). (J). (ps-k). 15.95 (978-0-88899-435-6(4), GRO30719) Groundwood Bks. CAN. *Dist:* Lectorum Pubns., Inc., Transition Vendor.
Morse, Mary. Frankie Frog's Small Problem. 2004. 20p. pap. 14.95 (978-1-4137-1244-5(4)) PublishAmerica, Inc.
Moser, Erwin. La Rana Solitaria. Moser, Erwin, illus. 2002. (SPA., Illus.). 96p. (J). (gr. 3-5). pap. 8.95 (978-84-204-3695-1(X)) Santillana USA Publishing Co., Inc.
Muller, Birte. Farley Farts BB W/sound. 2007. (Illus.). 18p. (J). bds. 9.95 (978-0-7358-2115-6(1)) North-South Bks., Inc.
My Frog Log: Third Grade Guided Reading Level N. (On Our Way to English Ser.). (gr. 3 up). 34.50 (978-0-7578-7138-2(0)) Rigby Education.
Nanette. Blue the Frog. 2004. (Life on Granny's Farm Ser.). (J). 12.95 (978-0-9741269-2-0(6)) St. Bernard Publishing, LLC.
Napoli, Donna Jo. Gracie: The Pixie of the Puddle. Schachner, Judith B., illus. 2004. 160p. (J). (gr. 3). 16.99 (978-0-525-47264-3(9), Dutton Juvenile) Penguin Group (USA) Inc.
Neel, Leason. Matt & Jeffery: A Children's Story. 2003. pap. 7.95 (978-0-533-14505-8(8)) Vantage Pr., Inc.
Nino y las Ranas. (SPA.). pap. 7.95 (978-88-8148-796-7(9)) European Language Institute ITA. *Dist:* Distribooks, Inc.
Northey, Lawrence. I'm a Hop Hop Hoppity Frog. Northey, Julie, illus. 2002. 28p. (J). (ps-2). 15.95 (978-0-7737-3335-0(3)) Stoddart Kids CAN. *Dist:* Fitzhenry & Whiteside, Ltd.
Novak, Matt. My Froggy Valentine. 2008. (Illus.). 16p. (J). (ps-1). 7.95 (***978-1-59643-204-8(7)***) Roaring Brook Pr.
Olds, Dorri, illus. Irving Goes to Town. 1999. (J). (978-0-9668607-0-2(5)) Norman, Iris A.
Ormerod, Jan & Damon, Emma. Frog Princess. (Illus.). 2005. (J). pap. 9.99 (978-0-340-87372-4(8)); 2004. 32p. 17.95 (978-0-340-87371-7(X)) Hodder General Publishing Division GBR. (Hodder & Stoughton). *Dist:* Trafalgar Square Publishing.
Ouren, Todd, illus. The Frog Prince: A Retelling of the Grimms' Fairy Tale. 2004. (Read-It! Readers Ser.). 32p. (C). (gr. k-3). 18.60 (978-1-4048-0313-8(0)) Picture Window Bks.
Parenteau, Shirley. One Frog Sang. Jabar, Cynthia, illus. 2007. (Read & Wonder Ser.). 32p. (J). (gr. k). pap. 6.99 (978-0-7636-3285-4(6)); 15.99 (978-0-7636-2394-4(6)) Candlewick Pr.
Parish, Steve, illus. Tree Frog Hears a Sound. 2005. 24p. (J). lib. bdg. 20.67 (978-0-8368-5976-8(6)) Stevens, Gareth Inc.
Payne, Tony & Payne, Jan. Plummet. Bolam, Emily, illus. 2004. 32p. (J). 12.95 (978-0-7641-5798-1(1)) Barron's Educational Series, Inc.
Pepin, Rebecca. Bobby Dog & the Flying Frog. Fuller, Cari, illus. 2004. (J). (gr. 4 up). 16.99 (978-0-9760684-0-2(0)); pap. 11.99 (978-0-9760684-1-9(9)) FullofPep Pubns.
Perera, Hilda. Rana Ranita. 1999. (SPA., Illus.). 32p. (J). (gr. k-2). 12.95 (978-84-241-3330-6(7)) Everest de Ediciones y Distribucion, S.L. ESP. *Dist:* Lectorum Pubns., Inc.
—Rana Ranita. Escriva, Viví, illus. 2nd ed. 2001. (SPA.). 32p. (J). 8.99 (978-84-241-3329-0(3)) Everest de Ediciones y Distribucion, S.L. ESP. *Dist:* Lectorum Pubns., Inc.
Pigman, Shari. Little Frog Finds Jesus. 2005. 23p. (J). 12.67 (978-1-4116-5779-3(9)) Lulu.com.
Pinczes, Elinor J. My Full Moon Is Square. Enos, Randall, illus. 2002. 32p. (J). (gr. k-3). tchr. ed. 15.00 (978-0-618-15489-0(2)) Houghton Mifflin Co. Trade & Reference Div.
Post, Jim. Frog in the Kitchen Sink. Vasconsellos, Daniel, illus. 2001. 28p. bds. 9.99 (978-1-57939-098-3(6)) Accord Publishing, Ltd.
Potter, Beatrix. Mr. Jeremy Fisher. 2007. (Potter Shaped Board Book Ser.). 12p. (J). bds. 3.99 (978-0-7232-5858-2(9), Warne) Penguin Group (USA) Inc.
—The Tale of Mr. Jeremy Fisher. Potter, Beatrix, illus. 2002. (Illus.). (J). 15.23 (978-0-7587-6802-5(8)) Book Wholesalers, Inc.
—The Tale of Mr. Jeremy Fisher. 2002. (Illus.). 64p. (J). 6.99 (978-0-7232-4776-0(5), Warne) Penguin Group (USA) Inc.
—The Tale of Mr. Jeremy Fisher. Jorgensen, David, illus. 2006. (J). (gr. 2-6). 25.65 (978-1-59197-753-7(3)) Spotlight.
—The Tale of Mr. Jeremy Fisher. (Beatrix Potter Bookmark Board Book Ser.). (Illus.). 6p. (J). bds. 3.95 (978-1-58989-202-6(X)) Thurman Hse., LLC.
—The Tale of Mr. Toad. Potter, Beatrix, illus. 2002. (Illus.). (J). 15.23 (978-0-7587-3748-9(3)) Book Wholesalers, Inc.
Powell, Patricia Hruby. Frog Brings Rain. Ruffenach, Jessie, ed. Thomas, Peter, tr. Benally, Kendrick, illus. 2006. (NAV & ENG.). 32p. 17.95 (978-1-893354-08-1(3)) Salina Bookshelf.
Powell, Richard. Down the Drain! A Moving Picture Storybook. Hendra, Sue, illus. 2002. (J). bds. 7.95 (978-1-58925-677-4(8), tiger tales) ME Media LLC.
Powers, Paul. Tales of the Swamp Creatures. 2003. 71p. pap. 11.95 (978-1-4137-0160-9(4)) PublishAmerica, Inc.
Preller, James. Jigsaw Jones: Case of the Frog-Jumping Contest. 2005. (Jigsaw Jones Ser.: No. 27). (Illus.). 80p. (J). pap. 3.99 (978-0-439-67805-6(6), Scholastic Paperbacks) Scholastic, Inc.
Prelutsky, Jack. The Frogs Wore Red Suspenders. Mathers, Petra, illus. 64p. (J). (ps-3). 2002. 16.99 (978-0-688-16719-6(5)); 2002. lib. bdg. 17.89 (978-0-688-16720-2(9)); 2005. reprint ed. pap. 6.99 (978-0-06-073776-4(X), Harper Trophy) HarperCollins Pubs.
Price, Mathew. Polo y la Rana. (SPA.). pap. 7.95 (978-950-07-1979-7(7)) Editorial Sudamericana S.A. ARG. *Dist:* Distribooks, Inc.
Princess & Frog. (Ladybird Bks.). (Illus.). 52p. (J). 12.95 incl. audio (978-0-86685-634-8(X)) International Bk. Ctr., Inc.
Pugliano-Martin, Carol. A Frog Someday. 2006. (Early Explorers Ser.). (J). 34.00 (***978-1-4108-6099-6(X)***) Benchmark Education Co.
Rae, Jennifer. Gilbert de la Frogponde: A Swamp Story. braille ed. 2004. (Illus.). (J). (gr. k-3). spiral bd. (978-0-616-03054-7(1)); spiral bd. (978-0-616-04561-9(1)) Canadian National Institute for the Blind/Institut National Canadien pour les Aveugles.
—Gilbert de la Frogponde: A Swamp Story. Cowles, Rose, illus. 2000. 32p. (J). (ps-12). pap. 9.95 (978-1-55285-087-9(0)) Whitecap Bks., Ltd. CAN. *Dist:* Firefly Bks., Ltd.
Rai, Lori. Princess Sheron & the Frog. l.t. ed. 2004. (Illus.). 20p. (J). 10.00 (978-0-9717419-5-9(6)) Law Offices of Harry Glick.
Raintree Steck-Vaughn Staff. Rosita la Rana. 1999. (Coleccion en Parejas). (SPA.). (J). pap., stu. ed. 21.50 (978-0-7398-0822-1(2)) Steck-Vaughn.
Rainy Rainbow & Freta Frog: Lost & Found. 2001. (Rainy Rainbow & Freta Frog: Lost & Found). 52p. (J). (978-1-930130-61-6(9)) Nature's Nest Bks.
Ratnavira, Natalie Ann. Even Frogs Care. Gornik, Joe & Albright, Lisa, eds. Ratnavira, Gamini, illus. 2000. 18p. (J). (ps-7). pap. 12.50 (978-0-9673036-0-4(5)) Purple Hse. Productions.
Reader's Digest Children's Books, creator. Little Cricket & Friends 3 Volume Boxed Set. 2007. (Illus.). 36p. (J). (ps-k). bds., bds. 16.99 (***978-0-7944-1359-0(5)***) Reader's Digest Assn., Inc., The.
Remkiewicz, Frank, illus. Froggy Bakes a Cake. 2002. (Froggy Ser.). (J). 11.06 (978-0-7587-5541-4(4)) Book Wholesalers, Inc.
—Froggy Eats Out. 2002. (Froggy Ser.). (J). 22.72 (978-0-7587-9786-5(9)) Book Wholesalers, Inc.
—Froggy Gets Dressed. 2002. (Froggy Ser.). (J). 13.19 (978-0-7587-2550-9(7)) Book Wholesalers, Inc.
—Froggy Goes to Bed. 2002. (Froggy Ser.). (J). 13.19 (978-1-4046-0751-4(X)) Book Wholesalers, Inc.
—Froggy Goes to School. 2002. (Froggy Ser.). (J). 13.19 (978-0-7587-5334-2(9)) Book Wholesalers, Inc.
—Froggy Learns to Swim. 2002. (Froggy Ser.). (J). 13.19 (978-0-7587-2553-0(1)) Book Wholesalers, Inc.
—Froggy Plays Soccer. 2002. (Froggy Ser.). (J). 13.19 (978-0-7587-5111-9(7)) Book Wholesalers, Inc.
—Froggy's Best Christmas. 2002. (Froggy Ser.). 13.19 (978-1-4046-1700-1(0)) Book Wholesalers, Inc.
—Froggy's Halloween. 2002. (J). 13.19 (978-0-7587-5112-6(5)) Book Wholesalers, Inc.
—Let's Go, Froggy! 2002. (Froggy Ser.). (J). 13.19 (978-0-7587-2975-0(8)) Book Wholesalers, Inc.
Rigby Education Staff. Frog. (Sails Literacy Ser.). (Illus.). 16p. (gr. k-1). 27.00 (978-0-7635-9875-4(5), 698755C99) Rigby Education.
—A Frog at Home. (Illus.). 16p. (J). pap. 30.00 (978-0-7635-6470-4(2), 764702C99) Rigby Education.
—Frog Prince: Jumbled Tumble. (gr. k-2). 26.00 (978-0-7635-2417-3(4)) Rigby Education.
Rip Squeak & His Friends Discover the Treasure. 2003. Tr. of Rip Squeak y Sus Amigos Descubren un Tesoro. per. 16.95 (978-0-9672422-5-5(8)) Rip Squeak, Inc.

Robleda, Margarita. Sana Ranita, Sana. Suarez, Maribel, illus. (Rana, Rema, Rimas Ser.). (SPA.). 16p. (J). (gr. k-3). 7.95 (978-1-59437-820-1(7)) Santillana USA Publishing Co., Inc.

Rondon, Javier. The Absent-Minded Toad. Cabrera, Marcela, illus. 2002. 28p. (J). pap. 6.95 (978-1-929132-39-3(5)) Kane/Miller Bk. Pubs., Inc.

Rong, Yu. A Lovely Day for Amelia Goose. Rong, Yu, illus. 2004. (Illus.). 32p. (J). (gr. k-k). 14.99 (978-0-7636-2309-8(1)) Candlewick Pr.

Ross, Dev. We Both Read-Frank & the Balloon. Reinhart, Larry, illus. 2008. (We Both Read Ser.). 44p. (J). 7.99 ***978-1-60115-011-0(3)** **);* pap. 3.99 (***978-1-60115-012-7(1))*** Treasure Bay, Inc.

—We Both Read-Frank & the Giant. Reinhart, Larry, illus. 2005. (We Both Read Ser.). 44p. (J). (gr. k-1). 7.99 (978-1-891327-59-9(3)); pap. 3.99 (978-1-891327-60-5(7)) Treasure Bay, Inc.

Ross, Dev. We Both Read-Frank & the Giant (Picture Book Edition) Reinhart, Larry, illus. 2007. (We Both Read Ser.). 44p. (J). 14.95 (***978-1-60115-006-6(7))*** Treasure Bay, Inc.

Roth, Susan L. The Biggest Frog in Australia. 2000. (Illus.). (J). (978-0-606-21611-1(1)) Tandem Library Bks.

Rouss, Sylvia A. The Littlest Frog. Hannon, Holly, illus. 2005. 32p. (J). pap. 9.95 (978-1-930143-13-5(3)); 14.95 (978-1-930143-12-8(5)) Pitspopany Pr. (Devora Publishing).

Rovetch, Lissa. Frog Went A-Dancing. Berry, Holly, illus. 2006. (J). (978-1-58987-008-6(5)) Kindermusik International.

Ruddock, Evie. Mozart the Singing Frog. 2006. 7p. (J). 10.58 (978-1-4116-8530-7(X)) Lulu.com.

Rundstrom, T. S. The Adventures of Tommy Toad. Marshall, Setsu, illus. 2002. 34p. (J). per. 16.00 (978-1-932062-03-8(3)) Hability Solution Services, Inc.

Sakairi, Masao. Vietnamese Fables of Frogs & Toads. Kojima, Shoko, illus. 2006. (Asian Folktales Retold Ser.). 32p. (J). 16.95 (978-0-89346-947-4(5)) Heian International Publishing, Inc.

Salzman, Joanne. The Amazing Frogs of Pine Forest Pond. 2004. pap. 8.95 (978-0-533-14714-4(X)) Vantage Pr., Inc.

Sang, Franchesca Ho, compiled by. Wisdom of Frogs. 2006. (Illus.). 128p. (J). (978-1-59258-251-8(6)) Hylas Publishing.

Santillo, LuAnn. The Kiss. Santillo, LuAnn, ed. 2003. (Half-Pint Kids Readers Ser.). (Illus.). 7p. (J). (ps-1). pap. (978-1-59256-053-0(9)) Half-Pint Kids, Inc.

—Look at Me. Santillo, LuAnn, ed. 2003. (Half-Pint Kids Readers Ser.). (Illus.). 7p. (J). (ps-1). pap. (978-1-59256-052-3(0)) Half-Pint Kids, Inc.

—Mole. Santillo, LuAnn, ed. 2003. (Half-Pint Kids Readers Ser.). (Illus.). 7p. (J). (ps-1). pap. (978-1-59256-111-7(X)) Half-Pint Kids, Inc.

—Toad. Santillo, LuAnn, ed. 2003. (Half-Pint Kids Readers Ser.). (Illus.). 7p. (ps-1). pap. (978-1-59256-107-0(1)) Half-Pint Kids, Inc.

El sapo que fue a la Luna. (SPA.). (J). (978-0-9710860-7-4(9)) Libros, Encouraging Cultural Literacy.

Sargent, Dave & Sargent, Pat. Do Frogs Have Tails?, 10, 15. Robinson, Laura, illus. 2004. (Learn to Read Ser.: 10). Tr. of Tienen Colas las Ranas?. 18p. (J). pap. 9.95 (978-1-56763-826-4(0)); lib. bdg. 19.95 (978-1-56763-825-7(2)) Ozark Publishing.

—Do Frogs Have Tails?/Tienen Colas las Ranas?, 10 vols. Robinson, Laura, illus. 2004. (Learn to Read Ser.: 10). Tr. of Tienen Colas las Ranas?. (ENG & SPA.). 18p. (J). lib. bdg. 19.95 (978-1-56763-989-6(5)); 15. pap. 9.95 (978-1-56763-990-2(9)) Ozark Publishing.

Sastrias, Martha. El Sapo Que No Queria Comer. Bouchain, Francisco Nava, illus. 2000. (SPA.). 24p. (J). (ps-k). (978-968-16-5758-1(6) , FC3771) Fondo de Cultura Economica MEX. *Dist:* Lectorum Pubns., Inc.

Schecter, Ellen. Diamonds & Toads. Blackshear, Ami, illus. 1999. (Bank Street Reader Collection). (J). (gr. 2-4). lib. bdg. 22.60 (978-0-8368-1781-2(8)) Stevens, Gareth Inc.

Schnetzler, Pattie L. Fast 'n Snappy. Manning, Jane K., tr. Manning, Jane K., illus. 2004. (Carolrhoda Picture Books Ser.). 32p. (J). (gr. k-3). 16.95 (978-1-57505-539-8(2)) Lerner Publishing Group.

Scholastic, Inc. Staff. Murphy & Myrtle Beanbag. 2002. (Sidekicks Ser.). (J). 9.99 (978-0-439-40397-9(9) , Sidekicks TM) Scholastic, Inc.

Scieszka, Jon. The Frog Prince, Continued. 2002. (Illus.). (J). 14.04 (978-0-7587-2547-9(7)) Book Wholesalers, Inc.

—The Frog Prince, Continued. Johnson, Steve, illus. 2003. pap. 39.95 incl. audio compact disk (978-1-59112-522-8(7)) Live Oak Media.

Silver, Rita. Best Friends. 2006. 17.00 (978-0-8059-9932-7(9)) Dorrance Publishing Co., Inc.

Silvermetz, Marcia A. Gertrude the Albino Frog & Her Friend Rupert the Turtle. Doyel, Ginger, illus. 2003. 48p. (J). (gr. 2-3). 19.95 (978-0-9718724-0-0(6)) Hiccup Cottage Pubns.

Simon, Francesca. Hugo & the Bully Frogs. Church, Caroline Jayne, illus. 2000. 32p. (J). (ps-2). pap. (978-1-86233-173-0(1) , Gullane Children's Bks.) Pinwheel.

—Hugo & the Bully Frogs. Church, Caroline Jayne, illus. 1999. 32p. (J). (ps-2). 14.95 (978-1-86233-093-1(X)) Sterling Publishing Co., Inc.

Simon, Gabriel. Og & His Frogs. Finch, Dianne, illus. l.t. ed. 1998. 32p. (J). (ps-3). lib. bdg. 12.95 (978-0-935343-72-4(5)) Peartree.

Small, David. Eulalie & the Hopping Head. Small, David, illus. 2001. (Illus.). 32p. (J). 16.00 (978-0-374-32230-4(9) , Farrar, Straus & Giroux (BYR)) Farrar, Straus & Giroux.

—Eulalie & the Hopping Head. (Illus.). (J). 2005. pap. 18.95 incl. audio compact disk (978-1-59112-509-9(X)); 2003. 28.95 incl. audio compact disk (978-1-59112-510-5(3)) Live Oak Media.

—Eulalie & the Hopping Head. Small, David, illus. 2003. (Illus.). pap. 35.95 incl. audio compact disk (978-1-59112-520-4(0)) Live Oak Media.

—Eulalie & the Hopping Head. Small, David, illus. l.t. ed. 2001. (Illus.). 32p. (J). pap. 5.95 (978-0-374-42202-8(8) , Sunburst) Farrar, Straus & Giroux.

Snyder, Susan. There's a Frog Trapped in the Bathroom. McCabe, Susan, ed. Johanson, Anna, illus. 2005. 24p. (J). (ps-ps). 9.95 (978-0-9715411-0-8(8)) Kotzig Publishing, Inc.

Spika, Jana. Locket & the Mask. 2004. 12.99 (978-0-9727103-0-5(2)) Tree of Life Pr.

Spotty Frogs' First Number Fun. 2002. (J). bds. 4.98 (978-0-7525-8863-6(X)) Parragon, Inc.

Sprecher, John. Eric & the Angrrry Frog, Vol. 2. Forrest, James, illus. l.t. ed. Date not set. (Special Kids "Special Message" Book Ser.). 32p. (J). (gr. k-4). pap. 10.00 (978-1-892186-01-0(2)) Anythings Possible, Inc.

Star, Nancy. The Case of the April Fool's Frogs. 2006. 77p. (978-0-439-67266-5(X)) Scholastic, Inc.

Stockham, Jess, et al, illus. The Frog Prince. 2007. 24p. pap. 5.99 (***978-1-84643-077-0(1))*** Child's Play International Ltd. GBR. *Dist:* Child's Play-International.

Stratford, Ann. Tara Toad Meets Roman the Robot Soldier. 2005. (ENG., Illus.). pap. (***978-1-84401-465-1(7))*** Athena Pr.

Strawberry Frog's Family. 2002. (Animal's Around the World Mini Bks.). (Illus.). 32p. (J). (978-1-59069-176-2(8) , H4012) Studio Mouse LLC.

Sullivan, William J. Kelly Blue Frog. 2000. 32p. (J). pap. 4.95 (978-0-9708066-2-8(0)) Painted Horse Pubns., Inc.

Sunderland, Margot & Hancock, Nicky. Helping Children Who Yearn for Someone They Love & the Frog Who Longed for the Moon to Smile, 2 vols. Armstrong, Nicky, tr. Armstrong, Nicky, illus. 76p. (978-0-86388-502-0(0) , 002-4776) Speechmark Publishing Ltd.

Swedeen, Staci. Phoebe & the Flame-Bellied Toad: An Original Fairy Tale. 2006. spiral bd. 42.00 (***978-1-4108-7153-4(3))*** Benchmark Education Co.

—The Toad Bridegroom: A Fairy Tale from Korea. 2006. spiral bd. 42.00 (***978-1-4108-7152-7(5))*** Benchmark Education Co.

—Tombi-Ende & the Frog: A Fairy Tale from South Africa. 2006. spiral bd. 42.00 (***978-1-4108-7151-0(7))*** Benchmark Education Co.

Sweeney, Jacqueline. Homesick. Hart, G. K. & Empey, Mark, illus. 2000. (We Can Read! Ser.). 32p. (J). (gr. 1-2). lib. bdg. 21.36 (978-0-7614-1117-8(8) , Benchmark Bks.) Cavendish, Marshall Corp.

Swift, Louie. The Froggie Who Flunked Jumping School, 4 vols. 2000. (J). (ps-3). lib. bdg. 19.95 incl. audio (978-0-9675577-2-4(0)) Puddleduck Music & Publishing.

t, Randolph (Il. Frog He Would AWooing Go Illustrated Edi. 2006. pap. (***978-1-4065-1224-3(9))*** Dodo Pr.

Talley, Linda. Jackson's Plan. Chase, Andra, illus. 1998. (Key Concepts in Personal Development Ser.). 32p. (J). (gr. k-4). 17.95 (978-1-55942-104-1(5) , 7665) Marsh Media.

—Toad in Town. Maeno, Itoko, illus. 2001. (Key Concepts in Personal Development Ser.). (gr. k-4). 30p. (J). 89.95 incl. VHS (978-1-55942-165-2(7)); 32p. pap., tchr. ed. 89.95 incl. VHS (978-1-55942-168-3(1) , 9387K3) Marsh Media.

Tarcov, Edith H. The Frog Prince. Marshall, James, illus. 2004. 40p. (J). lib. bdg. 15.00 (978-1-59054-506-5(0)) Fitzgerald Bks.

Tashiro, Chisato. Five Nice Mice. Uchida, Sayako, tr. from JPN. Tashiro, Chisato, illus. 2007. 36p. (J). (ps-2). 16.99 (***978-0-698-40058-0(5)*** , Minedition) Penguin Group (USA) Inc.

Taylor, Bonnie H. Barnaby Bullfrog. Lee, Jiyoung, illus. 1998. 8p. (J). (ps-2). pap. 3.75 (978-1-880612-84-2(4) , Seedling Pubns.) Continental Pr., Inc.

Teddy Bear Frog. 2003. (J). per. (978-1-57657-161-3(0)) Paradise Pr., Inc.

Thomas, Charolette. Franklin Finds a Friend. 2006. (ENG.). 40p. per. 16.99 (***978-1-4259-6209-8(2))*** AuthorHouse.

Thomas, Peggy. Joshua & the Giant Frog. 2005. (Illus.). 32p. (J). 15.95 (978-1-58980-267-4(5)) Pelican Publishing Co., Inc.

Thompson, Lauren. Little Quack's New Friend. Anderson, Derek, illus. (Classic Board Bks.). (J). 2008. 34p. bds. 7.99 (***978-1-4169-4923-7(2)*** , Little Simon); 2006. 32p. 14.95 (978-0-689-86893-1(6)) Simon & Schuster Children's Publishing.

Thomson, Pat. Share a Story: Thank You for the Tadpole. (Illus.). 32p. (J). pap. 7.95 (978-0-14-038880-0(X)) Penguin Bks., Ltd. GBR. *Dist:* Trafalgar Square Publishing.

Thumbelina. 2002. (Classic Tales Mini Bks.). (Illus.). 32p. (J). (978-1-59069-036-9(2) , T1005); incl. audio compact disk (978-1-59069-103-8(2) , T1105) Studio Mouse LLC.

Toad in Town - Teaching Guide. 2000. 17.95 (978-1-55942-167-6(3)) Marsh Media.

Toad, please use your Manners! 2005. (YA). per. (978-1-59872-302-1(2)) Instantpublisher.com.

Tobey, Carole. If Frogs Could Talk. 2003. (Illus.). 74p. (J). per. 12.00 (978-0-9773648-2-4(8)) Legend eXpress Publishing.

Tobey, Carole A. The Frog Olympics. 2005. (Illus.). 70p. (J). per. 12.00 (978-0-9773648-3-1(6)) Legend eXpress Publishing.

Tribuani, Tammy Desmond. Joe-Joe the Bull Frog. 2000. (J). 10.10 (978-0-533-13265-2(7)) Vantage Pr., Inc.

Tripp, Paul. Tubby the Tuba. Cole, Henry, illus. 2006. 32p. (J). (ps). pap. 16.99 (978-0-525-47717-4(9) , Dutton Juvenile) Penguin Group (USA) Inc.

Trujillo, Rafael E. Mirando y Mirando. Liu, Kimi, illus. 2005. (SPA.). (J). 16.00 (978-0-9765007-0-4(1)) Big Head Fish.

Twain, Mark. The Celebrated Jumping Frog of Calaveras County. Kisner, Don, ed. rev. ed. 1999. (Read-Along Radio Dramas Ser.). 43p. (YA). (gr. 7 up). ring bd. 38.00 incl. audio (978-1-878298-18-8(6)) Balance Publishing Co.

Ulrich, George. Mrs. Picasso's Polliwog: A Mystery. Ulrich, George, illus. 2003. (Illus.). 32p. pap. 7.95 (978-1-891577-84-0(0)); (J). lib. bdg. 15.95 (978-1-891577-83-3(2)) Images Pr.

Umansky, Kaye. The Fwog Pwince: The Twuth! Williamson, Gwyneth, illus. l.t. ed. 1998. 88p. (J). pap. (978-0-7540-6030-7(6) , CLP 235) BBC Audio.

Van Fleet, Matthew. Monday the Bullfrog. 2006. (J). (978-978-141-691-0(2) , Simon & Schuster Children's Publishing) Simon & Schuster Children's Publishing.

—Monday the Bullfrog. Van Fleet, Matthew, illus. 2006. (Illus.). 20p. (J). 17.99 (978-1-4169-1231-6(2)) Simon & Schuster Children's Publishing.

VanderGriend, Pamela. Froggie In Lily Pad Kingdom. Murphy, Sandy et al, eds. Holton, Bob & Reed, Jennifer, illus. 2006. 32p. (J). 17.95 (***978-0-9787456-0-8(4))*** Froggie & Friends, LLC.

Vasconsellos, Daniel. Frog in the Kitchen Sink: And Hand Puppet. gif. ed. 2004. (Illus.). (J). bds. 16.99 (978-1-57939-169-0(9)) Accord Publishing, Ltd.

Vecchione, Glen & Worms, Penny. Movie Novel. 2006. (Flushed Away Ser.). (Illus.). 128p. (J). pap. 4.99 (978-0-439-90078-2(6)) Scholastic, Inc.

Velthuijs, Max. Frog & Hare. (Illus.). 16p. (J). 6.99 (978-0-86264-995-1(1)) Andersen GBR. *Dist:* Trafalgar Square Publishing.

—Frog & Rat. 2000. (Illus.). 16p. (J). 7.50 (978-0-86264-996-8(X)) Andersen GBR. *Dist:* Independent Pubs. Group.

—Frog & the Stranger. ed. 2006. (Illus.). 32p. (J). 8.99 (***978-1-84270-466-0(4))*** Andersen GBR. *Dist:* Independent Pubs. Group.

—Frog & the Stranger. Iqbal, Gulshan, tr. 2005. (Frog Ser.). (URD, ENG, VIE, CHI & BEN., Illus.). 32p. (J). 13.50 (978-1-84059-190-3(0)) Milet Publishing.

—Frog & the Stranger. 2000. (Frog Ser.). (Illus.). 32p. (J). (BEN, ENG, VIE, CHI & URD.). 13.50 (978-1-84059-187-3(0)); (VIE, ENG, CHI, BEN & URD., 13.50 (978-1-84059-191-0(9)); (ALB & ENG., 13.50 (978-1-84059-186-6(2)); (VIE, CHI, BEN, ENG & URD., 13.50 (978-1-84059-189-7(7)) Milet Publishing.

—Frog & the Wide World. (Frog Ser.). (Illus.). 28p. (J). (ps-3). 2005. (VIE, CHI, BEN, GUJ & ENG.). 13.50 (978-1-84059-198-9(6)); 2000. (VIE, CHI, BEN, GUJ & ENG., 13.50 (978-1-84059-193-4(5)); 2000. (VIE, CHI, BEN, GUJ & ENG., 13.50 (978-1-84059-195-8(1)); 2000. (VIE, CHI, BEN, GUJ & ENG., 13.50 (978-1-84059-197-2(8)); 2000. (CHI, VIE, BEN, GUJ & ENG., 13.50 (978-1-84059-199-6(4)) Milet Publishing.

—Frog & the Wide World. Tsai, David, tr. 2000. (Frog Ser.). (VIE, CHI, BEN, GUJ & ENG., Illus.). 28p. (J). (ps-3). 13.50 (978-1-84059-192-7(7)) Milet Publishing.

—Frog & the Wide World. Bhardwaj, Usha, tr. 2000. (Frog Ser.). (VIE, CHI, BEN, GUJ & ENG., Illus.). 28p. (J). (ps-3). 13.50 (978-1-84059-210-8(9)) Milet Publishing.

—Frog in Winter. 2006. (Illus.). 32p. (J). 8.99 (***978-1-84270-447-9(8))*** Andersen GBR. *Dist:* Independent Pubs. Group.

—Frog Is a Hero. 1998. (Illus.). 32p. (J). (ps-1). pap. 9.95 (978-0-86264-761-2(4)) Andersen GBR. *Dist:* Trafalgar Square Publishing.

—Frog Is a Hero. 2000. (Frog Ser.). (Illus.). 28p. (J). (URD, ENG, VIE, CHI & BEN.). 13.50 (978-1-84059-206-1(0)); (TUR, ENG, VIE, CHI & BEN., 13.50 (978-1-84059-205-4(2)); (VIE, CHI, BEN, GUJ & ENG., 13.50 (978-1-84059-200-9(1)); (VIE & ENG., 13.50 (978-1-84059-207-8(9)) Milet Publishing.

—Frog Is a Hero. Bhardwaj, Usha, tr. 2000. (Frog Ser.). (VIE, CHI, BEN, GUJ & ENG., Illus.). 28p. (J). (ps-3). 13.50 (978-1-84059-202-3(8)) Milet Publishing.

—Frog Is a Hero. Dave, Pratima, tr. 2000. (Frog Ser.). (VIE, CHI, BEN, GUJ & ENG., Illus.). 28p. (J). (ps-3). 13.50 (978-1-84059-185-9(4)) Milet Publishing.

—Frog Is Frog. (Frog Ser.). (Illus.). 2005. (URD, ENG, BEN & SOM.). 40p. (J). 13.50 (978-1-84059-214-6(1)); 2005. (SOM, ENG, BEN & URD., 28p. pap. 13.50 (978-1-84059-212-2(5)); 2000. (VIE, ENG, CHI, BEN & URD., 40p. (J). 13.50 (978-1-84059-215-3(X)); 2000. (ALB & ENG., 40p. (J). 13.50 (978-1-84059-211-5(7)) Milet Publishing.

—Frog Is Frog. Datta, Kanai, tr. 2000. (Frog Ser.). (BEN, ENG, URD & SOM., Illus.). 40p. (J). 13.50 (978-1-84059-208-5(7)) Milet Publishing.

—Frog Is Frog. Erdogan, Faith, tr. 2000. (Frog Ser.). (VIE, CHI, BEN, ENG & URD., Illus.). 40p. (J). (ps-3). 13.50 (978-1-84059-213-9(3)) Milet Publishing.

—Sapo y un Dia Especial. 2001. (Frog Ser.). (SPA.). 28p. (J). 14.95 (978-980-257-259-5(4) , EK7849) Ekare, Ediciones VEN. *Dist:* Lectorum Pubns., Inc.

Velthuijs, Max & Bell, Anthea. Frog in Love. Farrell, Kate, ed. rev. ed. 2005. (Illus.). 32p. (J). 5.99 (978-0-8050-7654-7(9) , Holt, Henry & Co. Bks. For Young Readers) Holt, Henry & Co.

A Very Funny Act, 6 Packs. (gr. k-1). 23.00 (978-0-7635-9050-5(9)) Rigby Education.

Viviani, Luisa. There Is Something Special Inside of Me. 2004. 25p. pap. 14.95 (978-1-4137-2372-4(1)) PublishAmerica, Inc.

Waddell, Martin. Bee Frog. Firth, Barbara, illus. 2007. 32p. (J). (ps-2). 14.99 (978-0-7636-3310-3(0)) Candlewick Pr.

Walker, Raynn. Toadina: The Story of a Lady Toad. 2005. (J). pap. 15.00 (978-0-8059-6726-5(5)) Dorrance Publishing Co., Inc.

Walsh, Ellen Stoll. Hop Jump. Walsh, Ellen Stoll, illus. 2002. (Illus.). (J). 13.19 (978-0-7587-2747-3(X)) Book Wholesalers, Inc.

Walton, Rick. Bullfrog Pops! McAllister, Chris, illus. 1999. 32p. (J). (ps-3). 15.95 (978-0-87905-903-3(6)) Gibbs Smith, Publisher.

—Bullfrog Pops. McAllister, Chris, illus. 2005. 32p. pap. 6.95 (978-1-58685-840-7(8)) Gibbs Smith, Publisher.

—Once There Was a Bull... Frog. 1998. (Illus.). 32p. (J). (ps-3). pap. 6.99 (978-0-698-11607-8(0) , Putnam Juvenile) Penguin Group (USA) Inc.

—Once There Was a Bull... Frog. 1998. (978-0-606-13679-2(7)) Tandem Library Bks.

—One There Was a Bull... Frog! Hally, Greg, illus. 10th anniv. ed. 2005. 32p. 15.95 (978-1-58685-862-9(9)) Gibbs Smith, Publisher.

Waltz, Dan Hall. Freckles the Frog: A Read-a-Long/Sing-a-Long Story Book. Waltz, Dan Hall, illus. l.t. ed. 2003. (Illus.). 24p. (J). 19.95 (978-0-9741774-0-3(7)) D. W. Publishing.

Waring, Geoff. Oscar & the Frog: A Book about Growing. Waring, Geoff, illus. 2007. (Illus.). 32p. (J). (ps). 11.99 (***978-0-7636-3558-9(8))*** Candlewick Pr.

Watson, Jacqueline. Six Frogs on a Log! 2004. 43p. pap. 19.95 (978-1-4137-2986-3(X)) PublishAmerica, Inc.

Weare, Tim. I'm a Little Frog. 2004. (Illus.). 12p. (J). (ps-3). 6.95 (978-1-904613-08-4(X) , Buster Bks.) O'Mara, Michael Bks., Ltd. GBR. *Dist:* Ingram Pub. Services.

Weiner, Brian. Toad Catchers' Creek. Weintraub, Claudia & Frederick, Robin, eds. Cannon, Martin, illus. 2005. 40p. (J). lib. bdg. 17.99 (978-1-932949-58-2(5)) Illusion Factory, The.

Welch, Christopher Shiveley. Christopher Bullfrog Catcher. 2006. (J). pap. (978-1-894936-46-0(9)) Saga Bks.

Westphal, Hugo, illus. Tad Pole & Dr. Frog: A Self Help Book for Little Ones. 2002. 60p. (J). (gr. 1-7). 19.95 (978-1-893672-07-9(7)) Johnson, Michael Presentations.

Weyn, Suzanne. Water Song: A Retelling of "The Frog Prince" 2006. (Once upon a Time Ser.). 208p. (YA). (gr. 5 up). pap. 5.99 (978-1-4169-4013-5(8) , Simon Pulse) Simon & Schuster Children's Publishing.

Wildes, Shirley Ann. The Life of Old Big Daddy, the Bullfrog. 2006. 52p. per. 9.95 (978-1-59453-929-9(4) , Airleaf Publishing) Airleaf Publishing & Bookselling.

Williams, Rozanne Lanczak. Leap's Big, Big Bag. Yakovetic Productions Staff, illus. 12p. (J). (gr. 2). (978-1-58605-012-2(5)) LeapFrog Enterprises, Inc.

Wilsdon, Christina. A New York Sailing Adventure. Hockerman, Dennis, illus. 2006. 26p. (J). 7.99 (978-1-59939-014-7(0) , Reader's Digest Young Families, Inc.) Reader's Digest Children's Publishing, Inc.

Wilson, Karma. A Frog in the Bog. Rankin, Joan, illus. 2003. 32p. (J). 16.95 (978-0-689-84081-4(0) , McElderry, Margaret K.) Simon & Schuster Children's Publishing.

Wilson, Karma & Rankin, Joan. A Frog in the Bog. 2007. 32p. (J). pap. 6.99 (978-1-4169-2727-3(1) , Aladdin) Simon & Schuster Children's Publishing.

Wilson, Nancy Hope. Old People, Frogs, & Albert. Ramsey, Marcy Dunn, illus. 1999. 64p. (J). (gr. 2-4). pap. 5.95 (978-0-374-45615-3(1) , Sunburst) Farrar, Straus & Giroux.

—Old People, Frogs, & Albert. Ramsey, Marcy D., illus. 1999. 58p. (J). (ps-ps). lib. bdg. 12.95 (978-0-613-22910-4(X)) Tandem Library Bks.

—Old People, Frogs, & Albert. 1999. (978-0-606-17354-4(4)) Tandem Library Bks.

Wishinsky, Frieda. No Frogs for Dinner. Hendry, Linda, illus. 1999. (First Flight Ser.). 40p. (J). (gr. 1-3). pap. (978-1-55041-521-6(2)) Fitzhenry & Whiteside, Ltd.

Wood, Audrey. Jubal's Wish. Wood, Don, illus. 2000. 32p. (J). (ps up). pap. 17.99 (978-0-439-16964-6(X)) Scholastic, Inc.

Woodberry, Robert Lee. Gruffy, the Lonely Frog. 2003. (J). pap. 9.00 (978-0-8059-9241-0(3) , RoseDog Bks.) Dorrance Publishing Co., Inc.

Woods, Emmett L. The Black Frog. 2004. 38p. (J). (gr. k-7). 6.95 (978-0-615-12589-3(1)) Woods, Emmett L.

Yogananda, Paramhansa. Two Frogs in Trouble: Based on a Fable Told by Paramahansa Yogananda. 1998. (Illus.). 30p. (J). (ps-3). pap. 6.50 (978-0-87612-351-5(5)) Self-Realization Fellowship Pubs.

Yolen, Jane. Commander Toad & the Voyage Home. Degen, Bruce, illus. 1998. 64p. (J). (gr. 2-5). pap. 5.99 (978-0-698-11602-3(X) , Putnam Juvenile) Penguin Group (USA) Inc.

—Commander Toad & the Voyage Home. 1999. (Illus.). (J). (978-0-606-15489-5(2)) Tandem Library Bks.

—Dimity Duck. Braun, Sebastien, illus. 2008. 30p. (J). (ps). bds. 6.99 (***978-0-399-25060-6(3)*** , Philomel) Penguin Group (USA) Inc.

—Dimity Duck. Braun, Sebastian, illus. 2006. 32p. (J). (ps). 15.99 (978-0-399-24632-6(0) , Philomel) Penguin Group (USA) Inc.

Yoshizaki, Mine, illus. & creator. Sgt. Frog. Yoshizaki, Mine, creator. rev. ed. 2005. 192p. Vol. 7. pap. 9.99 (978-1-59532-448-1(8)); Vol. 8. pap. 9.99 (978-1-59532-449-8(6)) TOKYOPOP, Inc. (Tokyopop Adult).

Yost-Filgate, Susan. Rip Squeak & His Friends. Filgate, Leonard, illus. 2004. 32p. (J). 16.95 (978-1-59384-058-7(6)) Parklane Publishing.

—Rip Squeak & His Friends. Filgate, Leonard, illus. 2004. 32p. (J). 16.95 (978-0-9672422-3-1(1)) Rip Squeak, Inc.

—The Treasure. Filgate, Leonard, illus. 2005. 32p. (J). (ps-3). 14.99 (978-0-9747825-1-5(3)) Rip Squeak, Inc.

Yost-Filgate, Susan & Filgate, Leonard. Rip Squeak & His Friends. 1999. 32p. (J). pap. (978-1-931290-01-2(6)) Tallfellow Pr.

Zondervan & Focus on the Family Staff. Froggy World: Where All Your Dreams Come True. 2003. (J). 12.99 incl. VHS (978-0-310-70569-7(X)) Zonderkidz.

FROGS—POETRY

Ryder, Joanne. Toad by the Road: A Year in the Life of These Amazing Amphibians. Kneen, Maggie, illus. 2007. 37p. (*978-1-4287-3975-8(0)) Holt, Henry & Co.

FRONTIER AND PIONEER LIFE

see also Cowboys; Indians of North America—Captivities; Overland Journeys to the Pacific; Ranch Life

Adil, Janeen. Johnny Appleseed. 2003. (Folk Heroes Ser.). (Illus.). 24p. (J). lib. bdg. 15.95 (978-1-59036-075-0(3)) Weigl Pubs., Inc.

Allen, Charles F. David Crockett: Scout, Small Boy, Pilgrim, Mountaineer, Soldier, Bear-Hunter, & Congressman, Defender of the Alamo. (Illus.). 308p. reprint ed. lib. bdg. 98.00 (978-0-7222-4856-0(3)) Library Reprints, Inc.

—David Crockett, Scout: Small Boy, Pilgrim, Mountaineer, Soldier, Bear-Hunter & Congressman: Defender of the Alamo. McKernan, Frank, illus. 2000. (J). (978-0-89526-228-8(2)) Regnery Publishing, Inc., An Eagle Publishing Co.

Alphin, Elaine Marie. Davy Crockett. (History Maker Bios Ser.). (Illus.). (J). 2003. 48p. (gr. 3-5). lib. bdg. 26.60 (978-0-8225-0393-4(X)); 2002. 47p. pap. 6.95 (978-0-8225-1564-7(4) , Lerner Pubns.) Lerner Publishing Group.

Alter, Judy. Daniel Boone: Frontiersman. 2002. (Spirit of America: Our People Ser.). (Illus.). 32p. (J). (gr. 2-6). 27.07 (978-1-56766-162-0(9)) Child's World, Inc.

American Frontier Era, 7 titles, Set. 2005. (Signature Lives Ser.). 214.20 (978-0-7565-1005-3(8)) Compass Point Bks.

Anderson, William. Laura Ingalls Wilder: A Biography. 2007. (Little House Ser.). 256p. (J). pap. 6.99 (978-0-06-088552-6(1) , Harper Trophy) HarperCollins Pubs.

Armentrout, David & Armentrout, Patricia. Daniel Boone. 2002. (People Who Made a Difference Ser.). (Illus.). 24p. (gr. 2-5). 14.95 (978-1-58952-052-3(1)) Rourke Publishing, LLC.

—Daniel Boone. Sarfatti, Esther & de la Vega, Eida, trs. from ENG. 2001. (Personas que Cambiaron la Historia Ser.). (SPA., Illus.). 24p. (J). (gr. 1-4). lib. bdg. 19.27 (978-1-58952-166-7(8) , RK7295) Rourke Publishing, LLC.

Bair, Diane. Leyendas del Oeste & Western Legends. 2005. spiral bd. 88.00 (*978-1-4108-5735-4(2)) Benchmark Education Co.

Balcziak, Bill. Johnny Appleseed. 2003. (Tall Tales Ser.). (Illus.). 32p. (C). (gr. 3-5). 22.60 (978-0-7565-0458-8(9)) Compass Point Bks.

Bannatyne-Cugnet, Jo. A Prairie Year. Moore, Yvette, illus. 2001. 32p. (J). (gr. 1). pap. 9.95 (978-0-88776-569-8(6)) Tundra Bks., Inc./Livres Toundra, Inc. CAN. *Dist:* Random Hse., Inc.

Barkan, Joanne. A Libro de actividades del Oeste & Western Activity Book. 2005. spiral bd. 88.00 (*978-1-4108-5734-7(4)) Benchmark Education Co.

Benge, Janet & Benge, Geoff. Daniel Boone: Frontiersman. 2004. pap. 8.99 (978-1-932096-09-5(4)) Emerald Bks.

Berger, Donna, illus. Davy Crockett. 2004. (Imagination Ser.). 32p. (J). (gr. 3 up). 22.60 (978-0-7565-0603-2(4)) Compass Point Bks.

Berne, Emma Carlson. Laura Ingalls Wilder. 2007. (Essential Lives Ser.). (ENG., Illus.). 112p. (J). (gr. 6-8). lib. bdg. 32.79 (*978-1-59928-843-7(5) , Essential Library) ABDO Publishing Co.

Berton, Pierre. Sterling Point Books: Stampede for Gold: the Story of the Klondike Rush. 2007. (Sterling Point Bks.). 180p. (J). pap. 6.95 (*978-1-4027-5121-9(4)) Sterling Publishing Co., Inc.

Bial, Raymond. The Forts: Building America. 2001. (Building America Ser.). (Illus.). 56p. (J). (gr. 4 up). lib. bdg. 27.07 (978-0-7614-1334-9(0) , Benchmark Bks.) Cavendish, Marshall Corp.

—Frontier Settlements. 2004. (American Community Ser.). (Illus.). 48p. (J). (gr. 2-5). 29.00 (978-0-516-23705-3(5) , Children's Pr.) Scholastic Library Publishing.

Blackstock, Laurie, et al. Discovering Canadian Pioneers. 1999. (Discovery Ser.). (Illus.). 64p. stu. ed. 12.95 (978-0-19-541325-0(3)) Skyline Pr.

Blair, Eric. Johnny Appleseed's Fruitful Adventure: A Retelling of the Classic Traditional Tale. Muehlenhardt, Amy Bailey, illus. 2005. (Read-It! Readers Ser.). 32p. (C). (gr. k-3). 18.60 (978-1-4048-0971-0(6)) Picture Window Bks.

—The Legend of Daniel Boone: A Retelling of the Classic Traditional Tale. Chambers-Goldbert, Micah, illus. 2005. (Read-It! Readers Ser.). 32p. (J). (gr. k-3). 18.60 (978-1-4048-0974-1(0)) Picture Window Bks.

Boraas, Tracey. Daniel Boone: Frontier Scout. 2002. (Let Freedom Ring Ser.). (Illus.). 48p. (J). (gr. 3-4). lib. bdg. 22.60 (978-0-7368-1347-1(0) , Bridgestone Bks.) Capstone Pr., Inc.

Boskey, Madeline. Johnny Appleseed. Petruccio, Steven James, illus. 2001. (Hello Reader! Ser.). (J). (978-0-439-31705-4(3)) Scholastic, Inc.

Brownstone, David M. & Franck, Irene M. Frontier America, 10 vols. 2004. (Illus.). (J). (978-0-7172-5991-5(9)); (978-0-7172-5992-2(7)); (978-0-7172-5993-9(5)); (978-0-7172-5994-6(3)); (978-0-7172-5995-3(1)); (978-0-7172-5996-0(X)); (978-0-7172-5997-7(8)); (978-0-7172-5998-4(6)); (978-0-7172-5999-1(4)); (978-0-7172-6000-3(3)) Scholastic Library Publishing. (Grolier).

Bush, Karen Elizabeth. Marie-Therese Guyon, Mme. Cadillac: First Lady of Detroit. 2001. (Detroit Biography Series for Young Readers). (Illus.). 191p. (J). (gr. 5 up). 27.95 (978-0-8143-2983-2(7) , Great Lakes Bks.) Wayne State Univ. Pr.

Caswell, Maryanne. Pioneer Girl. Grater, Lindsay, illus. 2001. 88p. (J). (gr. 5 up). 16.95 (978-0-88776-550-6(5)) Tundra Bks., Inc./Livres Toundra, Inc. CAN. *Dist:* Random Hse., Inc.

Collard, Sneed B., III. David Crockett: Fearless Frontiersman. 2006. (American Heroes Ser.). (Illus.). 48p. (J). lib. bdg. 28.50 (978-0-7614-2160-3(2) , Benchmark Bks.) Cavendish, Marshall Corp.

Collins, Carolyn Strom & Eriksson, Christina Wyss. My Little House Crafts Book: 18 Projects from Laura Ingalls Wilder's. Collier, Mary, illus. 1998. (Little House Ser.). 64p. (J). (gr. 3 up). pap. 12.99 (978-0-06-446204-4(8) , Harper Trophy) HarperCollins Pubs.

Cook, Diane. Pathfinders of the American Frontier. 2002. (Exploration & Discovery Ser.). (Illus.). 64p. (YA). (gr. 5 up). lib. bdg. (978-1-59084-045-0(3)) Mason Crest Pubs.

Davis, Kenneth C. Don't Know Much about the Pioneers & Indians. 48p. (J). Date not set. (gr. 1-4). pap. 5.99 (978-0-06-446232-7(3)); 2003. (Picture Bks.: No. 6). (Illus.). (ps-1). 16.89 (978-0-06-028618-7(0)) HarperCollins Pubs.

De Capua, Sarah. Great Women of Pioneer America. 2005. (We the People Ser.). (Illus.). 48p. (J). (gr. 4-6). (978-0-7565-1269-9(7) , 1244091) Compass Point Bks.

—The Wilderness Road. 2006. (We the People Ser.). (Illus.). 48p. (J). (gr. 4-6). 23.93 (978-0-7565-1637-6(4)) Compass Point Bks.

Dean, Arlan. The Mormon Pioneer Trail: From Nauvoo, Illinois to the Great Salt Lake, Utah. 2003. (Reading Power Ser.). (Illus.). 24p. (J). lib. bdg. 17.25 (978-0-8239-6476-5(0) , PowerKids Pr.) Rosen Publishing Group, Inc., The.

—The Oregon Trail: From Independence, Missouri to Oregon City, Oregon. 2003. (Reading Power Ser.). (Illus.). 24p. (J). lib. bdg. 17.25 (978-0-8239-6478-9(7) , PowerKids Pr.) Rosen Publishing Group, Inc., The.

—The Overland Trail: From Atchison, Kansas, to Fort Bridger, Wyoming. 2003. (Reading Power Ser.). (Illus.). 24p. (J). lib. bdg. 17.25 (978-0-8239-6479-6(5) , PowerKids Pr.) Rosen Publishing Group, Inc., The.

—The Wilderness Road: From the Shenandoah Valley to the Ohio River. 2003. (Reading Power Ser.). (Illus.). 24p. (J). lib. bdg. 17.25 (978-0-8239-6477-2(9) , PowerKids Pr.) Rosen Publishing Group, Inc., The.

Ditchfield, Christin. Johnny Appleseed. 2003. (Rookie Biographies Ser.). (Illus.). 32p. (J). (gr. 1-2). 20.50 (978-0-516-22853-2(6) , Children's Pr.) Scholastic Library Publishing.

Doherty, Kieran. Ranchers, Homesteaders & Traders: Frontiersmen of the South-Central States. Johnson, Sylvia A. & Anderson, Jenna, eds. 2001. (Shaping America Ser.: Vol. No. 4). (Illus.). 176p. (J). (gr. 7 up). lib. bdg. 22.95 (978-1-881508-53-3(6)) Oliver Pr., Inc.

Dolan, Edward F., Jr. Beyond the Frontier: The Story of the Trails West. 2000. (Great Journeys Ser.). (Illus.). 112p. (J). (gr. 5 up). lib. bdg. 32.79 (978-0-7614-0969-4(6) , Benchmark Bks.) Cavendish, Marshall Corp.

Donlan, Leni. Strike It Rich in Cripple Creek: Gold Rush. 2006. (American History Through Primary Sources Ser.). (Illus.). 32p. (J). (978-1-4109-2419-3(X)); pap. (978-1-4109-2430-8(0)) Steck-Vaughn.

Downie, Mary Alice. A Pioneer ABC. Gerber, Mary Jane, illus. 2005. 32p. (J). (gr. k-2). 15.95 (978-0-88776-688-6(9)) Tundra Bks., Inc./Livres Toundra, Inc. CAN. *Dist:* Random Hse., Inc.

Dutch Colonies in the Americas, 6 Pks. (On Deck Ser.: Vol. 2). 24p. (gr. 4-5). 35.00 (978-0-7578-5800-0(7)) Rigby Education.

Epstein, Dwayne. Lawmen of the Old West. 2004. (History Makers Ser.). (Illus.). 96p. (J). (gr. 7-10). 29.95 (978-1-59018-560-5(9) , Lucent Bks.) Thomson Gale.

Famous Figures of the American Frontier. 2005. 64p. pap. 250.00 (978-0-7910-6501-3(4) , Chelsea Hse.) Facts On File, Inc.

Feinstein, Stephen. Read about Johnny Appleseed. 2006. (I Like Biographies! Ser.). (Illus.). 24p. (J). lib. bdg. 21.26 (978-0-7660-2599-8(3) , Enslow Elementary) Enslow Pubs., Inc.

Fischer, Jeff, illus. Johnny Appleseed. 2006. (Famous Fables Ser.). (J). 6.99 (978-1-59939-028-4(0)) Reader's Digest Young Families, Inc.

Franck, Irene M. & Brownstone, David M. Frontier America, 10 vols. 2004. (Illus.). (J). 369.00 (978-0-7172-5990-8(0) , Grolier) Scholastic Library Publishing.

Freedman, Russell. In the Days of the Vaqueros: America's First True Cowboys. 2001. (Illus.). 80p. (J). (gr. 7-7). tchr. ed. 18.00 (978-0-395-96788-1(0) , Clarion Bks.) Houghton Mifflin Co. Trade & Reference Div.

Fritz, Jean. The Cabin Faced West. 2001. (gr. 3-6). lib. bdg. 14.15 (978-0-613-51439-2(4)) Tandem Library Bks.

Furbee, Mary Rodd. Anne Bailey: Frontier Scout. 2004. (Women of the Frontier Ser.). (Illus.). 112p. (J). (gr. 3 up). 21.95 (978-1-883846-70-1(6)) Reynolds, Morgan Inc.

—Shawnee Captive: The Story of Mary Draper Ingles. 2003. (Illus.). 112p. (YA). per. 9.95 (978-1-891852-29-9(9)) Quarrier Pr.

—Shawnee Captive: The Story of Mary Draper Ingles. 2004. (Women of the Frontier Ser.). (Illus.). 112p. (J). (gr. 6-12). 23.95 (978-1-883846-69-5(2) , First Biographies) Reynolds, Morgan Inc.

Gillis, Jennifer Blizin. William Penn. 2004. (Illus.). 32p. (J). lib. bdg. 25.64 (978-1-4034-5963-3(0)) Heinemann Library.

Glasscock, Sarah. Pioneer. ed. 2004. 80p. pap. 12.99 (978-0-439-31751-1(7) , Teaching Resources) Scholastic, Inc.

Glasthal, Jacqueline B. Great Migration. 2002. (Instant Social Studies Activities Folders Ser.). (Illus.). 6p. (gr. 4-8). 3.95 (978-0-439-37091-2(4)) Scholastic, Inc.

Graham, Amy. The Oregon Trail & the Daring Journey West by Wagon. 2006. (Wild History of the American West Ser.). (Illus.). 128p. (J). lib. bdg. 33.27 (978-1-59845-021-7(2) , MyReportLinks.com Bks.) Enslow Pubs., Inc.

Graves, Kerry A. Going to School in Pioneer Times. 2001. (Blue Earth Books). (Illus.). 32p. (J). (gr. 3-4). lib. bdg. 22.60 (978-0-7368-0804-0(3) , Bridgestone Bks.) Capstone Pr., Inc.

Green, Carl R. Blazing the Wilderness Road with Daniel Boone in American History. 2000. (In American History Ser.). (Illus.). 128p. (YA). (gr. 5-12). lib. bdg. 26.60 (978-0-7660-1346-9(4)) Enslow Pubs., Inc.

—The Mission Trails in American History. 2001. (In American History Ser.). (Illus.). 128p. (YA). (gr. 5-12). lib. bdg. 26.60 (978-0-7660-1349-0(9)) Enslow Pubs., Inc.

Greenwood, Barbara. A Pioneer Christmas: Celebrating in the Backwoods in 1841. Collins, Heather, illus. 2004. 48p. (J). (gr. 4-6). (978-1-55074-955-7(2)); (978-1-55074-953-3(6)) Kids Can Pr., Ltd.

—A Pioneer thanksgiving: A story of harvest celebrations in 1841. Collins, Heather, illus. 1999. (History Comes Alive Ser.). 48p. (J). (gr. 4-6). (978-1-55074-574-0(3)); (978-1-55074-744-7(4)) Kids Can Pr., Ltd.

Haley, James L. Stephen F. Austin & the Founding of Texas. 2005. (Library of American Lives & Times). (Illus.). 112p. (YA). (gr. 4-8). lib. bdg. 31.95 (978-0-8239-5738-5(1)) Rosen Publishing Group, Inc., The.

Harcourt School Publishers Staff. Home on the Plains. 3rd ed. 2002. (Horizons Ser.). (Illus.). (J). pap. 5.50 (978-0-15-333411-5(8)) Harcourt Schl. Pubs.

—Pioneer Living. 3rd ed. 2002. (Horizons Ser.). (Illus.). (J). (gr. 3). pap. 5.50 (978-0-15-333246-3(8)) Harcourt Schl. Pubs.

Harness, Cheryl. The Tragic Tale of Narcissa Whitman & a Faithful History of the Oregon Trail. Harness, Cheryl, illus. 2006. (Illus.). 144p. (J). (gr. 5-9). 16.95 (978-0-7922-5920-6(3) , National Geographic Children's Bks.) National Geographic Society.

Harrison, David L. Johnny Appleseed: My Story. 2001. (gr. k-3). lib. bdg. 11.80 (978-0-613-36831-5(2)) Tandem Library Bks.

Hopkins, Ellen H. Tarnished Legacy: The Story of the Comstock Lode. 2001. (Cover-to-Cover Bks.). (Illus.). 64p. (J). (gr. 4-7). lib. bdg. 17.95 (978-0-7807-9702-4(7)) Perfection Learning Corp.

Hubalek, Linda K. Cultivating Hope: Homesteading on the Great Plains. 1998. (Planting Dreams Ser.: No. 2). (Illus.). 124p. (J). pap. 9.95 (978-1-886652-12-5(0) , BUT013) Butterfield Bks., Inc.

Ichord, Loretta Frances & Millbrook Press. Skillet Bread, Sourdough, & Vinegar Days: Cooking in Pioneer Days. Ellis, Jan Davey, illus. 2005. 64p. (J). (gr. 4-8). pap. 8.95 (978-0-7613-9521-8(0) , First Avenue Editions) Lerner Publishing Group.

Isaacs, Sally Senzell. Life on a Pioneer Homestead. (Picture the Past Ser.). (Illus.). 32p. (J). 2002. (gr. k-3). pap. 7.50 (978-1-58810-300-0(5) , 91066); 2000. (gr. 2-4). lib. bdg. 21.36 (978-1-57572-313-6(1)) Heinemann Library.

—Life on a Pioneer Homestead. 2001. (gr. k-3). lib. bdg. 15.90 (978-0-613-86820-4(X)) Tandem Library Bks.

—Life on the Oregon Trail. (Picture the Past Ser.). (Illus.). 32p. 2003. pap. 7.50 (978-1-58810-302-4(1)); 2000. (J). (gr. 2-4). lib. bdg. 21.36 (978-1-57572-317-4(4)) Heinemann Library.

—Life on the Oregon Trail. 2001. (Picture the Past Ser.). (Illus.). (J). (978-0-606-22007-1(0)) Tandem Library Bks.

Johnston, Charles H. L. Famous Frontiersmen & Heroes of the Border: Their Adventurous. 2006. (ENG.). 420p. per. 34.95 (*978-1-4286-4118-1(1)) Kessinger Publishing, LLC.

Kallen, Stuart A. Life on the American Frontier. 1998. (Way People Live Ser.). (Illus.). 112p. (YA). (gr. 7-10). 29.95 (978-1-56006-366-7(1) , LML00902-177751, Lucent Bks.) Thomson Gale.

—Women of the American Frontier. 2004. (Illus.). 111p. (J). (gr. 7-10). 32.45 (978-1-59018-471-4(8) , Lucent Bks.) Thomson Gale.

Kalman, Bobbie. Bandanas, Chaps & Ten-Gallon Hats. 1998. (Life in the Old West Ser.). (Illus.). 32p. (J). (gr. 3-4). pap. (978-0-7787-0105-7(0)) Crabtree Publishing Co.

—Boomtowns of the West. 1999. (J). (978-0-606-16431-3(6)) Tandem Library Bks.

—Homes of the West. 1998. (Life in the Old West Ser.). (Illus.). 32p. (J). (gr. 3-4). pap. (978-0-7787-0106-4(9)); lib. bdg. (978-0-7787-0074-6(7)) Crabtree Publishing Co.

—Life on the Trail. 1998. (Life in the Old West Ser.). (Illus.). 32p. (J). (gr. 3-4). pap. (978-0-7787-0104-0(2)) Crabtree Publishing Co.

—Pioneer Dictionary. 2000. (gr. 3-6). lib. bdg. 16.40 (978-0-613-22180-1(X)) Tandem Library Bks.

—Pioneer Recipes. 2001. (gr. 3-6). lib. bdg. 16.40 (978-0-613-32950-7(3)); 2000. (J). (978-0-606-20111-7(4)) Tandem Library Bks.

—Travel in the Early Days. 2001. (gr. 3-6). lib. bdg. 16.40 (978-0-613-33160-9(5)) Tandem Library Bks.

—A Visual Dictionary of a Pioneer Community. 2007. (Visual Dictionaries Ser.). (Illus.). 32p. (J). (gr. 1-7). pap. (*978-0-7787-3524-3(9)) Crabtree Publishing Co.

Kalman, Bobbie. The Wagon Train. 1998. (Life in the Old West Ser.). (Illus.). 32p. (J). (gr. 3-4). pap. (978-0-7787-0102-6(6)); lib. bdg. (978-0-7787-0070-8(4)) Crabtree Publishing Co.

Kalman, Bobbie & Brown, Ellen. The Colonial Cook. 2001. (Colonial People Ser.). (Illus.). 32p. (J). (gr. 3). (978-0-7787-0748-6(2)); pap. (978-0-7787-0794-3(6)) Crabtree Publishing Co.

Kalman, Bobbie & Calder, Kate. Travel in the Early Days. 2000. (Historic Communities Ser.). (Illus.). 32p. (J). (gr. 3). pap. (978-0-86505-472-1(X)); lib. bdg. (978-0-86505-442-4(8)) Crabtree Publishing Co.

Kalman, Bobbie & Lewis, Jane. Pioneer Dictionary. 1999. (AlphaBasiCs Ser.). (Illus.). 32p. (J). (gr. 2-3). pap. (978-0-86505-420-2(7)); lib. bdg. (978-0-86505-390-8(1)) Crabtree Publishing Co.

Kalman, Bobbie, et al. Pioneer Recipes. 2000. (Historic Communities Ser.). (Illus.). 32p. (J). (gr. 3). pap. (978-0-86505-468-4(1)); lib. bdg. (978-0-86505-438-7(X)) Crabtree Publishing Co.

Kamma, Anne. If You Were a Pioneer on the Prairie. 2003. (gr. 3-6). lib. bdg. 14.15 (978-0-613-66641-1(0)) Tandem Library Bks.

Kamma, Anne & Watling, James. If You Were a Pioneer on the Prairie. 2003. (If You Were_ Ser.). (Illus.). 64p. (J). 5.99 (978-0-439-41428-9(8) , Scholastic Nonfiction) Scholastic, Inc.

Kent, Deborah. In Colonial New England. 1999. (How We Lived Ser.). (Illus.). 72p. (J). (gr. 4-8). lib. bdg. 28.50 (978-0-7614-0905-2(X) , Benchmark Bks.) Cavendish, Marshall Corp.

—In the Middle Colonies. 1999. (How We Lived Ser.). (Illus.). 72p. (J). (gr. 4-8). lib. bdg. 28.50 (978-0-7614-0907-6(6) , Benchmark Bks.) Cavendish, Marshall Corp.

Kimball, Violet T. Stories of Young Pioneers: In Their Own Words. rev. ed. 2000. (Illus.). 225p. (J). (gr. 4-11). pap. 14.00 (978-0-87842-423-8(7) , 655) Mountain Pr. Publishing Co., Inc.

—Stories of Young Pioneers: In Their Own Words. 2000. (gr. 5-8). lib. bdg. 23.45 (978-0-613-84455-0(6)) Tandem Library Bks.

Klobuchar, Lisa. The History & Activities of the Wagon Trail. 2004. (Hands-On American History Ser.). (Illus.). 32p. (J). pap. (978-1-4034-6062-2(0)) Heinemann Library.

—Pioneer Days. 2004. (Hands-On American History Ser.). (Illus.). 32p. (J). 24.22 (978-1-4034-6056-1(6)) Heinemann Library.

Knowlton, MaryLee & Riehecky, Janet. The Settling of Jamestown. 2002. (Events That Shaped America Ser.). (Illus.). 32p. (J). (gr. 3 up). lib. bdg. 24.67 (978-0-8368-3225-9(6)) Stevens, Gareth Inc.

Knudsen, Anders. Antoine de la Mothe Cadillac: French Settlements at Detroit & Louisiana. 2006. (In the Footsteps of Explorers Ser.). (Illus.). 32p. (J). (gr. 3-9). (978-0-7787-2429-2(8)); pap. (978-0-7787-2465-0(4)) Crabtree Publishing Co.

Kozar, Richard. Fort Duquesne & Fort Pitt. 2004. (American Forts & Their Strategic Importance Ser.). (J). (978-1-59084-719-0(9)) Mason Crest Pubs.

Kramer, Sydelle. Who Was Daniel Boone? Ulrich, George, illus. 2006. (Who Was... ? Ser.). 112p. (J). (gr. 2-5). pap. 4.99 (978-0-448-43902-0(6) , Grosset & Dunlap) Penguin Group (USA) Inc.

Krensky Stephen. Calamity Jane. Carlson, Lisa, illus. 2007. (On My Own Folklore Ser.). (J). pap. 6.95 (*978-0-8225-6480-5(7) , First Avenue Editions) Lerner Publishing Group.

Krohn, Katherine. Women of the Wild West. 2000. (gr. 7-12). lib. bdg. 16.40 (978-0-613-68395-1(1)) Tandem Library Bks.

Kunstler, James Howard. Johnny Appleseed. Olson, Stan, illus. 2005. (Rabbit Ears-A Classic Tale Ser.). 40p. (J). (gr. k-5). 25.65 (978-1-59197-765-0(7)) Spotlight.

Kurtz, Jane & Haverfield, Mary. Johnny Appleseed. 2004. (Ready-to-Read Ser.). (Illus.). 32p. (J). pap. 3.99 (978-0-689-85958-8(9) , Aladdin) Simon & Schuster Children's Publishing.

Landau, Elaine. The Mormon Trail. 2006. 48p. (YA). (gr. 3-5). pap. 6.95 (978-0-516-27904-6(1) , Children's Pr.) Scholastic Library Publishing.

—The Oregon Trail. 2006. 48p. (gr. 3-5). (YA). pap. 6.95 (978-0-516-27903-9(3)); (Illus.). (J). 25.00 (978-0-516-25871-3(0)) Scholastic Library Publishing. (Children's Pr.).

Lange, Karen E. 1607: A New Look at Jamestown. Block, Ira, photos by. 2007. (Illus.). 48p. (J). (gr. 3-7). 17.95 (978-1-4263-0012-7(3)); lib. bdg. 27.90 (978-1-4263-0013-4(1)) National Geographic Society. (National Geographic Children's Bks.).

Lemke, Donald B. The Schoolchildren's Blizzard. Hoover, Dave & Barnett, Charles, illus. 2008. (J). (*978-1-4296-0157-3(4)) Capstone Pr., Inc.

Lisa Klobuchar. The History & Activities of the Frontier. 2006. (Hands-On American History Ser.). (Illus.). 32p. pap. (*978-1-4034-6063-9(9)) Heinemann Library.

Loeper, John J. Meet the Drakes on the Kentucky Frontier. 1998. (Early American Family Ser.). (Illus.). 64p. (J). (gr. 3 up). lib. bdg. 25.64 (978-0-7614-0845-1(2) , Benchmark Bks.) Cavendish, Marshall Corp.

Lowery, Linda. Aunt Clara Brown: Official Pioneer. Porter, Janice Lee, illus. 2003. (On My Own Biographies Ser.). 48p. (J). (gr. 1-3). 5.95 (978-1-57505-416-2(7)) Lerner Publishing Group.

—Aunt Clara Brown: Official Pioneer. 1999. (gr. 3-6). lib. bdg. 14.10 (978-0-613-68191-9(6)) Tandem Library Bks.

Mara, Wil. Laura Ingalls Wilder. 2003. (YA). lib. bdg. 12.95 (978-0-613-67639-7(4)) Tandem Library Bks.

Marcovitz, Hal. Fort Clatsop. 2004. (American Forts & Their Strategic Importance Ser.). (J). (978-1-59084-706-0(7)) Mason Crest Pubs.

Marsh, Carole. Calamity Jane: An Ohio Experience Reader. 2001. (J). (gr. k-5). pap. 1.95 (978-0-635-00425-3(9)) Gallopade International.

Masso, Phyllis H. Never the Same Again . . . A Young Woman's Story of Life in the Blackstone Valley in the 1820s. 1998. 150p. (YA). (gr. 5-12). pap. 14.95 (978-1-57960-046-4(8)) History Compass, LLC.

Mattern, Joanne. Grace Hopper: Computer Pioneer: Individual Title Six-Packs. (On Deck Ser.: Vol. 2). 24p. (gr. 4-5). 35.00 (978-0-7578-5844-4(9)) Rigby Education.

Maynard, Charles W. Fort Clatsop. 2002. (Famous Forts Throughout American History Ser.). (Illus.). 24p. (J). (gr. 3). lib. bdg. 18.75 (978-0-8239-5837-5(X) , PowerKids Pr.) Rosen Publishing Group, Inc., The.

McCall, Edith. Adventures of Pioneer Show People. 2001. (Adventures on the American Frontiers Ser.). (Illus.). 128p. (J). (gr. 3-7). pap. 9.99 (978-0-89824-307-9(6)) Royal Fireworks Publishing Co.

—Adventures of Pioneering on the Plains, 20 vols. 2000. (Adventures on the American Frontiers Ser.: Vol. 4). (Illus.). 128p. (J). (gr. 8-10). pap. 9.99 (978-0-89824-302-4(5) , 3025) Royal Fireworks Publishing Co.

—Adventures of Taking Wagons over the Mountains. 2001. (Adventures on the American Frontier Ser.: Bk. 19). (Illus.). 127p. (J). (gr. 3-6). pap. 9.99 (978-0-89824-318-5(1) , 3181) Royal Fireworks Publishing Co.

McCarthy, Pat. Daniel Boone: Frontier Legend. 2000. (Historical American Biographies Ser.). (Illus.). 128p. (YA). (gr. 6-12). lib. bdg. 26.60 (978-0-7660-1256-1(5)) Enslow Pubs., Inc.

Moore, Eva. Johnny Appleseed. 2000. (J). (ps-3). pap. 4.99 (978-0-590-40297-2(8)) Scholastic, Inc.

Nelson, Sheila. From the Atlantic to the Pacific: Canadian Expansion, 1867-1909. 2005. (Illus.). 87p. (J). (gr. 3-7). lib. bdg. 21.95 (978-1-4222-0005-6(1) , 1247971) Mason Crest Pubs.

—The Settlement of New France & Acadia, 1524-1701. 2005. (Illus.). 87p. (J). (gr. 3-7). lib. bdg. 21.95 (978-1-4222-0002-5(7)) Mason Crest Pubs.

Nemerson, Roy. Daniel Boone. 2005. (Heroes of America Ser.). (Illus.). 240p. (J). (gr. 3-8). lib. bdg. 21.35 (978-1-59679-256-2(6)) ABDO Publishing Co.

Nextext Staff, contrib. by. How America Grew, 1775-1914. 2004. (Stories in History Ser.). (Illus.). 208p. (gr. 6-12). (978-0-618-22196-7(4) , 2-00295) McDougal Littell Inc.

Noble, Marty. Pioneer Life Sticker Picture. 1999. (Illus.). (J). pap. 5.95 (978-0-486-40586-5(9)) Dover Pubns., Inc.

Parker, Lewis K. Dutch Colonies in the Americas. 2003. (Reading Power Ser.). (Illus.). 24p. (J). lib. bdg. 17.25 (978-0-8239-6472-7(8) , PowerKids Pr.) Rosen Publishing Group, Inc., The.

—English Colonies in the Americas. 2003. (Reading Power Ser.). (Illus.). 24p. (J). lib. bdg. 17.25 (978-0-8239-6475-8(2) , PowerKids Pr.) Rosen Publishing Group, Inc., The.

—French Colonies in the Americas. 2003. (Reading Power Ser.). (Illus.). 24p. (J). lib. bdg. 17.25 (978-0-8239-6473-4(6) , PowerKids Pr.) Rosen Publishing Group, Inc., The.

—Spanish Colonies in the Americas. 2003. (Reading Power Ser.). (Illus.). 24p. (J). lib. bdg. 17.25 (978-0-8239-6471-0(X) , PowerKids Pr.) Rosen Publishing Group, Inc., The.

Patchett, Kaye. Laura Ingalls Wilder. 2005. (Inventors & Creators Ser.). (Illus.). 48p. (J). (gr. 4-8). 26.20 (978-0-7377-3159-0(1) , Greenhaven Pr., Inc.) Thomson Gale.

Paul, Ann Whitford. The Seasons Sewn: A Year in Patchwork. 2000. (978-0-606-18189-1(X)) Tandem Library Bks.

Peckham, Linda R. & Heuft, Lori E. Saw Mills & Sleigh Bells. 1999. (Illus.). xv, 103p. (J). (gr. 2-5). pap. 11.95 (978-0-9671616-1-7(4)) Catalpa Pubns.

Petrick, Neila Skinner. Jane Wilkinson Long: Texas Pioneer. Haynes, Joyce, illus. 2004. 32p. (J). pap. 15.95 (978-1-58980-147-9(4)) Pelican Publishing Co., Inc.

Petrie, Kristin. Daniel Boone. 2004. (Explorers Set I Ser.). (J). (gr. k-6). lib. bdg. 22.78 (978-1-59197-592-2(1)) ABDO Publishing Co.

Pioneer Families. (Rosen Real Readers Big Bookstm Ser.). 16p. (J). (gr. 2-3). 38.75 (978-1-4042-6222-5(9)) Rosen Publishing Group, Inc., The.

Raabe, Emily. The Gold Rush: California or Bust! 2003. (Reading Power Ser.). (Illus.). 24p. (J). lib. bdg. 17.25 (978-0-8239-6494-9(9) , PowerKids Pr.) Rosen Publishing Group, Inc., The.

—Pioneers: Life as a Homesteader. 2003. (Reading Power Ser.). (Illus.). 24p. (J). lib. bdg. 17.25 (978-0-8239-6498-7(1) , PowerKids Pr.) Rosen Publishing Group, Inc., The.

Radevsky, Anton. The Wild West Pop-Up Book. 2007. (Illus.). 8p. (gr. 3-7). 24.95 ***978-1-4027-4628-4(8))** Sterling Publishing Co., Inc.

Ransom, Candice. Daniel Boone. 2006. (History Maker Bios Ser.). (Illus.). 48p. (J). (gr. 3-7). 26.60 (978-0-8225-2941-5(6) , Lerner Pubns.) Lerner Publishing Group.

Rauzi, Kelly Emerling. Fearless John. 2006. 32p. 19.95 ***(*978-0-9774831-3-6(4))*** Singing River Pubns.

Riehecky, Janet. The Settling of Jamestown. 2002. (Landmark Events in American History Ser.). (Illus.). 48p. (J). (gr. 5 up). pap. 14.60 (978-0-8368-5355-1(5)); lib. bdg. 30.00 (978-0-8368-5341-4(5)) Stevens, Gareth Inc. (World Almanac Library).

Roberts, Russell. The Life & Times of Stephen F. Austin. 2007. (Profiles in American History Ser.). (Illus.). 48p. (J). lib. bdg. 29.95 ***(*978-1-58415-531-7(0))*** Mitchell Lane Pubs., Inc.

Robertson, Theda Robinson. Journey to a Free Land: The Story of Nicodemus, the First All Black Town West of the Mississippi. 2006. (Illus.). (J). (978-0-9705721-6-5(6)) Written Images, Inc.

Rosa, Joseph G. Wild Bill Hickok: Sharpshooter & U.S. Marshal of the Wild West. 2005. (Library of American Lives & Times). (Illus.). 112p. (J). (gr. 4-8). lib. bdg. 31.95 (978-0-8239-6632-5(1)) Rosen Publishing Group, Inc., The.

Salas, Laura Purdie. The Wilderness Road 1775. 2003. (Let Freedom Ring Ser.). (Illus.). 48p. (J). (gr. 3-4). lib. bdg. 22.60 (978-0-7368-1561-1(9) , Bridgestone Bks.) Capstone Pr., Inc.

Santella, Andrew. Daniel Boone & the Cumberland Gap. (Cornerstones of Freedomtrade;, Second Ser.). 48p. (J). 2007. 5.95 ***(*978-0-531-18687-9(3));*** 2002. (Illus.). (gr. 4-6). 26.00 (978-0-516-22526-5(X)) Scholastic Library Publishing. (Children's Pr.).

Seidman, Laurence I. Once in the Saddle: The Cowboy's Frontier 1866-1896. 1999. 158p. (J). lib. bdg. 21.95 (978-0-7351-0221-7(X)) Replica Bks.

Signature Lives: Colonial America Era. 2006. (Illus.). (YA). (gr. 5-7). 153.00 (978-0-7565-1710-6(9)) Compass Point Bks.

Signature Lives: Modern America. 2006. (Illus.). (YA). (gr. 5-7). 336.60 (978-0-7565-1713-7(3)) Compass Point Bks.

Signature Lives: Modern World. 2006. (Illus.). (YA). (gr. 5-7). 244.80 (978-0-7565-1709-0(5)) Compass Point Bks.

Signature Lives: Reformation Era. 2006. (Illus.). (YA). (gr. 5-7). 153.00 (978-0-7565-1712-0(5)) Compass Point Bks.

Signature Lives Series: Revolutionary War Era, 13 bks. 2006. (Illus.). (YA). (gr. 5-7). 397.80 (978-0-7565-1711-3(7)) Compass Point Bks.

Sioux, Tracee. Immigrants & the Westward Expansion. 2004. (Primary Sources of Immigration & Migration in America Ser.). (Illus.). 24p. (J). lib. bdg. (978-0-8239-8950-8(X)); lib. bdg. 19.95 (978-0-8239-6824-4(3)) Rosen Publishing Group, Inc., The. (PowerKids Pr.).

Spence, Clark C. For Wood River or Bust: Idaho's Silver Boom of the 1880s. 2004. (Idaho Legacy Ser.). (Illus.). 278p. 29.95 (978-0-89301-215-1(7)) Univ. of Idaho Pr.

Stanley, George Edward. The European Settlement of North America (1492-1754) 2005. (Illus.). 48p. (J). pap. (978-0-8368-5833-4(6)); lib. bdg. 30.00 (978-0-8368-5824-2(7)) Stevens, Gareth Inc. (World Almanac Library).

Steele, Christy. Famous Wagon Trails. 2005. (Illus.). 48p. (J). pap. (978-0-8368-5795-5(X)); lib. bdg. 30.00 (978-0-8368-5788-7(7)) Stevens, Gareth Inc. (World Almanac Library).

—Pioneer Life in the American West. 2005. (Illus.). 48p. (J). pap. (978-0-8368-5797-9(6)); lib. bdg. 30.00 (978-0-8368-5790-0(9)) Stevens, Gareth Inc. (World Almanac Library).

Stefoff, Rebecca. Exploration & Settlement. 2007. (Colonial Life Ser.). (Illus.). 96p. (gr. 6 up). 37.95 ***(*978-0-7656-8108-9(0))*** Sharpe, M.E. Inc.

Stefoff, Rebecca. The Opening of the West. 2002. (American Voices From Ser.). (Illus.). xxii, 105p. (J). 34.21 (978-0-7614-1201-4(8) , Benchmark Bks.) Cavendish, Marshall Corp.

Stotter, Mike. The Wild West. 1999. (Single Subject References Ser.). (Illus.). 64p. (J). (gr. 4-8). pap. 10.95 (978-0-7534-5249-3(9) , Kingfisher) Houghton Mifflin Co. Trade & Reference Div.

Streissguth, Thomas. Daniel Boone. Chantland, Loren, illus. 2005. (On My Own Biographies Ser.). 48p. (J). (gr. 2-5). lib. bdg. 23.93 (978-1-57505-520-6(1)) Lerner Publishing Group.

Strom Collins, Carolyn. My Little House Crafts Book: 18 Projects from Laura Ingalls Wilder's Little House Stories. 1998. (Little House Ser.). (978-0-606-13635-8(5)) Tandem Library Bks.

Swain, Gwenyth. Johnny Appleseed. Porter, Janice Lee, illus. 2001. (On My Own Biographies Ser.). 48p. (J). (gr. 1-3). lib. bdg. 23.93 (978-1-57505-519-0(8) , Carolrhoda Bks.) Lerner Publishing Group.

Thompson, Linda. Los Grandes Lagos. 2005. (ENG & SPA., Illus.). 48p. (J). (978-1-59515-661-7(5)) Rourke Publishing, LLC.

—The Great Lakes. 2006. (Expansion of America II Ser.). (Illus.). 48p. (gr. 4-8). 20.95 (978-1-59515-512-2(0)) Rourke Publishing, LLC.

—The Mississippi & West. 2005. (Expansion of America Ser.). (Illus.). 48p. (gr. 4-8). 20.95 (978-1-59515-224-4(5)) Rourke Publishing, LLC.

Townsley, Janet Howe. Dakota Dreams: Fannie Sabra Howe's Own Story, 1881-1884. 2003. (Illus.). 77p. (J). 19.95 (978-0-9715171-4-1(2)) South Dakota State Historical Society.

Unlocking the Secrets of Science: Set of 10 Pioneers. (Illus.). 31p. (gr. 4-10). lib. bdg. (978-1-58415-234-7(6)) Mitchell Lane Pubs., Inc.

Warren, Andrea. Pioneer Girl: Growing up on the Prairie. 1998. (Illus.). 96p. (J). (gr. 3 up). 15.95 (978-0-688-15438-7(7)) HarperCollins Pubs.

Wawrychuk, Carol & McSweeney, Cherie. Wild West: Active Learning about Pioneers. Chalk, Philip, illus. 1999. 48p. (J). (ps-1). pap. 7.95 (978-1-57612-073-6(2) , MM2087) Monday Morning Bks., Inc.

Welveart, Scott R. The Donner Party. Frenz, Ron & Barnett, Charles, illus. 2006. (Graphic Library). 32p. (J). (978-0-7368-5479-5(7)) Capstone Pr., Inc.

Whitman, Sylvia. Children of the Frontier. 1998. (Picture the American Past Ser.). (Illus.). 48p. (gr. 2-5). lib. bdg. 22.60 (978-1-57505-240-3(7)) Lerner Publishing Group.

Winders, Richard Bruce. Davy Crockett: The Legend of the Wild Frontier. 2005. (Library of American Lives & Times). (Illus.). 112p. (YA). (gr. 4-8). lib. bdg. 31.95 (978-0-8239-5747-7(0)) Rosen Publishing Group, Inc., The.

Winters, Kay. John Appleseed: A Trail of Trees. Pullen, Zachary, illus. 2007. (J). (978-1-4263-0101-8(4)) National Geographic Society.

Worth, Richard. Independence for Latino America. 2006. (Latino-American History Ser.). 112p. (J). (gr. 5-8). 35.00 (978-0-8160-6441-0(5) , Chelsea Hse.) Facts On File, Inc.

Zronik, John Paul. Daniel Boone: Woodsman of Kentucky. 2006. (In the Footsteps of Explorers Ser.). (Illus.). 32p. (J). (gr. 3-9). pap. (978-0-7787-2464-3(6) , 1253442); (978-0-7787-2428-5(X) , 1253442) Crabtree Publishing Co.

FRONTIER AND PIONEER LIFE—ALASKA

Haigh, Jane. Gold Rush Dogs. 2001. (gr. 7-12). lib. bdg. 26.85 (978-0-613-58217-9(9)) Tandem Library Bks.

Marsh, Kenneth L. A River Between Us: The Upper Susitna River Valley of Alaska, a Historical Story Collection. 2nd ed. 2002. (Illus.). 268p. per. 19.95 (978-0-9718302-0-2(7) , 001) Trapper Creek Museum Sluice Box Productions.

Parker, Lewis K. Russian Colonies in the Americas. 2003. (Reading Power Ser.). (Illus.). 24p. (J). lib. bdg. 17.25 (978-0-8239-6470-3(1) , PowerKids Pr.) Rosen Publishing Group, Inc., The.

Russian Colonies in the Americas, 6 Packs. (On Deck Ser.: Vol. 2). 24p. (gr. 4-5). 35.00 (978-0-7578-5803-1(1)) Rigby Education.

FRONTIER AND PIONEER LIFE—BIOGRAPHY

Alter, Judy. Laura Ingalls Wilder: Pioneer & Author. 2003. (Spirit of America). (Illus.). 32p. (J). (gr. 2-6). 27.07 (978-1-59296-007-1(3)) Child's World, Inc.

Anderson, William. Laura's Album: A Remembrance Scrapbook of Laura Ingalls Wilder. 1998. (Little House Ser.). (Illus.). 80p. (J). (gr. 3 up). 21.99 (978-0-06-027842-7(0)) HarperCollins Pubs.

Anderson, William T. Pioneer Girl: The Story of Laura Ingalls Wilder. Andreasen, Dan, illus. (Little House Ser.). 32p. (J). (gr. 2 up). 2000. pap. 6.99 (978-0-06-446234-1(X) , Harper Trophy); 1998. 15.89 (978-0-06-027244-9(9)) HarperCollins Pubs.

—Pioneer Girl: The Story of Laura Ingalls Wilder. 2000. (978-0-606-18712-1(X)) Tandem Library Bks.

Armentrout, David & Armentrout, Patricia. Laura Ingalls Wilder. 2004. (Discover the Life of an American Legend Ser.). (Illus.). 24p. (gr. 2-5). 14.95 (978-1-58952-663-1(5)) Rourke Publishing, LLC.

Bailey, Tom. Sam Dale: Alabama Frontiersman. 2001. (Alabama Roots Biography Ser.). (Illus.). 107p. (J). (978-1-878561-82-4(0)) Seacoast Publishing, Inc.

Blair, Eric. La Leyenda de Daniel Boone. Chambers-Goldberg, Micah, illus. 2006. (Read-It! Readers en Español Ser.).Tr. of Legend of Daniel Boone. (SPA.). 32p. (J). (ps-3). 19.95 (978-1-4048-1656-5(9)) Picture Window Bks.

Chipman, Donald & Joseph, Harriett Denise. Explorers & Settlers of Spanish Texas: Men & Women of Spanish Texas. 2001. (Illus.). 272p. (J). (gr. 7-12). pap. 19.95 (978-0-292-71231-7(6)) Univ. of Texas Pr.

Deangelis, Gina. The Wild West. 1998. (Costume, Tradition & Culture). (Illus.). 64p. (YA). 19.75 (978-0-7910-5169-6(2) , Chelsea Hse.) Facts On File, Inc.

Doherty, Kieran. Voyageurs, Lumberjacks & Farmers: Pioneers of the Midwest. 2003. (Shaping America Ser.: Vol. 5). (Illus.). 176p. (gr. 7 up). lib. bdg. 22.95 (978-1-881508-54-0(4)) Oliver Pr., Inc.

Ford, Carin T. Laura Ingalls Wilder: Real-Life Pioneer of the Little House Books. 2003. (People to Know Ser.). (Illus.). 112p. (J). lib. bdg. 26.60 (978-0-7660-2105-1(X)) Enslow Pubs., Inc.

Furbee, Mary Rodd. Outrageous Women of the American Frontier. 2002. (Outrageous Women Ser.: Vol. 6). (Illus.). 120p. pap. 12.95 (978-0-471-38300-0(7) , Wiley) Wiley, John & Sons, Inc.

Furstinger, Nancy. Davy Crockett. 2003. (Folk Heroes Ser.). (Illus.). 24p. (J). lib. bdg. 15.95 (978-1-59036-073-6(7)) Weigl Pubs., Inc.

Gormley, Beatrice. Laura Ingalls Wilder: Young Pioneer. Henderson, Meryl, illus. 2001. (Childhood of Famous Americans Ser.). 224p. (J). (gr. 3-7). pap. 5.99 (978-0-689-83924-5(3) , Aladdin) Simon & Schuster Children's Publishing.

—Laura Ingalls Wilder: Young Pioneer. 2001. (Childhood of Famous Americans Ser.). (Illus.). (J). (978-0-606-21290-8(6)) Tandem Library Bks.

Gosda, Randy T. Daniel Boone. 2002. (First Biographies Ser.). (Illus.). 32p. (J). (gr. k-4). lib. bdg. 22.78 (978-1-57765-735 4(7) , Buddy Bks.) ABDO Publishing Co.

Greenhaven Staff. Pioneers. 2002. (gr. 7-12). lib. bdg. 33.25 (978-0-613-73861-3(6)) Tandem Library Bks.

Harness, Cheryl. The Tragic Tale of Narcissa Whitman & a Faithful History of the Oregon Trail. Harness, Cheryl, illus. 2006. (Illus.). 144p. (J). (gr. 5-9). lib. bdg. 25.90 (978-0-7922-5921-3(1) , National Geographic Children's Bks.) National Geographic Society.

Harper, Jo. Big Foot Wallace: A Hero of Early Texas. Roeder, Virginia M., illus. 1999. 48p. (gr. 1-3). 14.95 (978-1-57168-223-9(6)) Eakin Pr.

Horton, Casey. The French. 2000. (J). 15.75 (978-0-606-22833-6(0)) Tandem Library Bks.

Kelly Allen, Nancy. Daniel Boone: Trailblazer. Waites, Joan C., illus. 2005. 32p. (J). (gr. 2-4). 15.95 (978-1-58980-212-4(8)) Pelican Publishing Co., Inc.

Krohn, Katherine E. Women of the Wild West. 2000. (Biography Ser.). (Illus.). 112p. (J). (gr. 6-12). lib. bdg. 27.93 (978-0-8225-4980-2(8) , Lerner Pubns.) Lerner Publishing Group.

Kundiger, Marion S. & Garretson, Jerri. Izzie: Growing up on the Plains in the 1880s. Kundiger, Marion S. & Garretson, Jerri, illus. 1998. (Illus.). 48p. (J). (ps-4). pap. 5.95 (978-0-9659712-1-8(X)) Ravenstone Pr.

Lightfoot, D. J. Trail Fever: The Life of a Texas Cowboy. Bobbish, John, illus. exp. ed. 2003. 88p. (J). (gr. 3 up). pap. 12.95 (978-0-9728768-0-3(4)) Seven Rivers Publishing.

Mara, Wil. Laura Ingalls Wilder. 2003. (Rookie Biographies Ser.). (gr. 1-2). pap. 4.95 (978-0-516-27840-7(1)); (Illus.). 32p. (J). 20.50 (978-0-516-22855-6(2)) Scholastic Library Publishing. (Children's Pr.).

Marsh, Carole. John Rolfe. 2002. (One Thousand Readers Ser.). (Illus.). 12p. (J). (gr. k-4). 2.95 (978-0-635-01505-1(6) , 15056) Gallopade International.

Martinucci-Marsh, Licia. Laura: A Story about Laura Ingalls Wilder. 2002. (Illus.). 16p. (J). (978-0-439-35118-8(9)) Scholastic, Inc.

Maynard, Charles W. Jedediah Smith: Mountain Man of the American West. 2003. (Famous Explorers of the American West Ser.). (Illus.). 24p. (J). lib. bdg. 18.75 (978-0-8239-6287-7(3) , PowerKids Pr.) Rosen Publishing Group, Inc., The.

—Jim Bridger: Frontiersman & Mountain Guide. 2003. (Famous Explorers of the American West Ser.). (Illus.). 24p. (J). lib. bdg. 18.75 (978-0-8239-6288-4(1) , PowerKids Pr.) Rosen Publishing Group, Inc., The.

McCall, Edith. Adventures of Early Trappers & Traders. 2000. (Adventures on the American Frontiers Ser.). (Illus.). 128p. (J). (gr. 3-5). pap. 9.99 (978-0-89824-300-0(9) , 3009) Royal Fireworks Publishing Co.

McCaslin, Nellie. Johnny Appleseed. 2003. (Players Press Nellie McCaslin Ser.). (Illus.). 16p. (J). (gr. 1-8). pap. 5.00 (978-0-88734-447-3(X)) Players Pr., Inc.

McKain, Mark, ed. Pioneers. 2002. (History Firsthand Ser.). (Illus.). 256p. (J). (gr. 7-10). pap. 24.95 (978-0-7377-1077-9(2)); lib. bdg. 36.20 (978-0-7377-1078-6(0)) Thomson Gale. (Greenhaven Pr., Inc.).

Raatma, Lucia. Laura Ingalls Wilder: Teacher & Author. 2001. (Career Biographies Ser.). (Illus.). 128p. (J). (gr. 6-12). 25.00 (978-0-89434-375-9(0) , F418, Ferguson Publishing Co.) Facts On File, Inc.

Rau, Margaret. Belle of the West: The True Story of Belle Starr. 2004. (Women of the Frontier Ser.). (Illus.). 160p. (YA). (gr. 6-12). 23.95 (978-1-883846-68-8(4) , First Biographies) Reynolds, Morgan Inc.

Riehecky, Janet. Daniel Boone. 2002. (Raintree Biographies Ser.). (Illus.). 32p. (J). lib. bdg. 25.69 (978-0-7398-5672-7(3)) Raintree.

San Souci, Robert D. Larger Than Life: The Adventures of American Legendary Heroes. Colon, Raul, illus. 2000. (978-0-15-200398-2(3)) Harcourt Trade Pubs.

Santella, Andrew. Daniel Boone & the Cumberland Gap. 2002. (Cornerstones of Freedom). (Illus.). 48p. (J). (gr. 4-6). 26.00 (978-0-516-22526-5(X) , Children's Pr.) Scholastic Library Publishing.

Schaefer, Lola M. Johnny Appleseed. Saunders-Smith, Gail, ed. 2003. (First Biographies Ser.). (Illus.). 24p. (J). (gr. k-1). lib. bdg. 15.93 (978-0-7368-1645-8(3) , Pebble Bks.) Capstone Pr., Inc.

Spinner, Stephanie. Who Was Annie Oakley? Day, Larry & Harrison, Nancy, illus. 2002. (Who Was...? Ser.). 112p. (J). (gr. 3-5). pap. 4.99 (978-0-448-42497-2(5) , Grosset & Dunlap) Penguin Group (USA) Inc.

—Who Was Annie Oakley? 2002. (gr. 3-6). lib. bdg. 13.00 (978-0-613-43653-3(9)) Tandem Library Bks.

Spradlin, Mike. Texas Rangers: Legendary Lawmen. Munro, Roxie, illus. 2008. 32p. (J). 17.85 ***(*978-0-8027-8097-3(0));*** 16.95 ***(*978-0-8027-8096-6(2))*** Walker & Co.

Strudwick, Leslie. Laura Ingalls Wilder. 2002. (My Favorite Writer Ser.). (Illus.). 32p. (J). lib. bdg. 18.20 (978-1-59036-027-9(3)) Weigl Pubs., Inc.

Sullivan, George. Davy Crockett. 2001. (gr. 3-6). lib. bdg. 12.40 (978-0-613-50786-8(X)) Tandem Library Bks.

Tyler, Ann Spann. Torry Island Boy of the Everglades. 2000. (Illus.). 119p. (J). (978-0-9679351-0-2(5)); pap. (978-0-9679351-1-9(3)) Tyler Reproductions.

Wadsworth, Ginger. Laura Ingalls Wilder. Haas, Shelly O., illus. (On My Own Biographies Ser.). 48p. (J). (gr. 1-3). 2003. pap. 5.95 (978-1-57505-423-0(X)); 1999. lib. bdg. 23.93 (978-1-57505-266-3(0) , Carolrhoda Bks.) Lerner Publishing Group.

—Laura Ingalls Wilder. 2000. (gr. 3-6). lib. bdg. 14.10 (978-0-613-68249-7(1)); (Illus.). (J). (978-0-606-21947-1(1)) Tandem Library Bks.

Walker, Pamela. Laura Ingalls Wilder. 2001. (Real People Ser.). (Illus.). 24p. (J). (ps-2). 17.00 (978-0-516-23435-9(8)); pap. 4.95 (978-0-516-23589-9(3)) Scholastic Library Publishing. (Children's Pr.).

—Laura Ingalls Wilder. 2001. (gr. k-3). lib. bdg. 12.95 (978-0-613-58846-1(0)) Tandem Library Bks.

Ward, S. Meet Laura Ingalls Wilder. 2001. (About the Author Ser.). (Illus.). 24p. (J). (gr. 3). lib. bdg. 18.75 (978-0-8239-5712-5(8) , PowerKids Pr.) Rosen Publishing Group, Inc., The.

Warren, Andrea. Pioneer Girl. 2000. (gr. 3-6). lib. bdg. 12.95 (978-0-613-28606-0(5)) Tandem Library Bks.

Woods, Mae. Laura Ingalls Wilder. 2000. (Children's Authors Ser.). (Illus.). 24p. (J). (gr. k-6). lib. bdg. 21.35 (978-1-57765-113-0(8) , Checkerboard Library) ABDO Publishing Co.

FRONTIER AND PIONEER LIFE—CALIFORNIA

Aykroyd, Clarissa. Exploration of the California Coast. 2002. (Exploration & Discovery Ser.). (Illus.). 64p. (J). (gr. 5 up). lib. bdg. (978-1-59084-043-6(7)) Mason Crest Pubs.

Balmes, Kathy. Thunder on the Sierra. Catapano, Vicki, illus. 2001. (Adventures in America Ser.). 96p. (J). (gr. 3-7). lib. bdg. 14.95 (978-1-893110-10-6(9)) Silver Moon Pr.

Blashfield, Jean F. The California Gold Rush. 2000. (We the People Ser.). (Illus.). 48p. (J). (gr. 4 up). lib. bdg. 22.60 (978-0-7565-0041-2(9)) Compass Point Bks.

Brown, Rachel K. Sacramento: Daily Life in Western Mining Town. 2003. (J). lib. bdg. (978-1-58417-015-0(8)) Lake Street Pubs.

Burger, James P. The Quest for California's Gold. 2002. (Library of the Westward Expansion). (Illus.). 24p. (J). (gr. 3). lib. bdg. 19.95 (978-0-8239-5849-8(3) , PowerKids Pr.) Rosen Publishing Group, Inc., The.

Cassanos, Lynda Cohen. Sutter's Fort. 2004. (American Forts & Their Strategic Importance Ser.). (J). (978-1-59084-709-1(1)) Mason Crest Pubs.

Craats, Rennay. Gold Rush. 2003. (Real Life Stories Ser.). (Illus.). 24p. (J). lib. bdg. 15.95 (978-1-59036-078-1(8)) Weigl Pubs., Inc.

E
F
G

Crewe, Sabrina & Uschan, Michael V. The California Gold Rush. 2003. (Events That Shaped America Ser.). (Illus.). 32p. (J). (gr. 3 up). lib. bdg. 24.67 (978-0-8368-3393-5(7)) Stevens, Gareth Inc.

Dolan, Edward F., Jr. The California Gold Rush. 2002. (Kaleidoscope - American History Ser.). (Illus.). 48p. (J). 25.64 (978-0-7614-1456-8(8) , Benchmark Bks.) Cavendish, Marshall Corp.

Dunn, Joeming W. California Gold Rush. Dunn, Ben, illus. 2007. (Graphic History Ser.). 32p. (J). (gr. 3-6). lib. bdg. 27.07 (***978-1-60270-076-5(1)*** , Graphic Planet) Magic Wagon.

Goff, Elizabeth Hudson & Uschan, Michael V. The California Gold Rush. 2006. (Graphic Histories Ser.). (Illus.). (J). pap. (978-0-8368-6254-6(6)); 32p. lib. bdg. 26.00 (978-0-8368-6202-7(3)) Stevens, Gareth Inc. (World Almanac Library).

Goldsmith, Connie. Lost in Death Valley: The True Story of Four Families in California's Gold Rush. 2001. (Single Titles Ser.: up). (Illus.). 144p. (J). (gr. 7-12). lib. bdg. 24.90 (978-0-7613-1915-3(8) , Millbrook Pr.) Lerner Publishing Group.

Jordan, Shirley. California Gold Rush: Moments in History. 2003. (Cover-To-Cover Books). (Illus.). 64p. (J). pap. (978-0-7891-5554-2(0)); (gr. 4-7). lib. bdg. 17.95 (978-0-7569-0633-7(4)) Perfection Learning Corp.

Kallen, Stuart A. California Gold Country. 2002. (Traveler's Guide To). (Illus.). 112p. (J). 29.95 (978-1-59018-144-7(1)) Thomson Gale.

Kay, Verla. Rough, Tough Charley. Gustavson, Adam, illus. 2006. 32p. (J). (ps-3). 15.95 (***978-1-58246-184-7(8)*** , Tricycle Pr.) Ten Speed Pr.

Keremitsis, Eileen. Life in a California Mission. 2002. (Way People Live Ser.). (Illus.). 112p. (J). (gr. 7-10). 29.95 (978-1-59018-159-1(X) , Lucent Bks.) Thomson Gale.

Meter, Larry Van. Yerba Buena. 2007. (Colonial Settlements in America Ser.). 104p. (J). (gr. 5-8). 30.00 (***978-0-7910-9338-2(7)*** , Chelsea Hse.) Facts On File, Inc.

Monroe, Judy. The California Gold Rush. 2002. (Let Freedom Ring Ser.). (Illus.). 48p. (J). (gr. 3-4). lib. bdg. 22.60 (978-0-7368-1098-2(6) , Bridgestone Bks.) Capstone Pr., Inc.

Phelan, Regina V. They Came Around the Horn, Vol. 5. Champy, Al, illus. l.t. ed. 1999. (History of California for the Young Reader Ser.). 64p. (J). lib. bdg. 15.00 (978-0-87062-292-2(7) , Clark, Arthur H. Co., The) Univ. of Oklahoma Pr.

Quasha, Jennifer. Gold Rush: Hands-On Projects about Mining the Riches of California. 2001. (Great Social Studies Projects Ser.). (Illus.). 24p. (J). (gr. 3). lib. bdg. 19.95 (978-0-8239-5705-7(5) , PowerKids Pr.) Rosen Publishing Group, Inc., The.

Raum, Elizabeth. The California Gold Rush: An Interactive History Adventure. 2008. (You Choose Bks.). 112p. (J). (gr. 3-7). lib. bdg. 27.23 (***978-1-4296-0160-3(4)*** Capstone Pr., Inc.

Richter, Glenda. The Stories of Juana Briones: Alta California Pioneer. Heywood, Della, illus. 2002. 64p. (J). (gr. 3-6). 14.95 (978-0-9700379-0-9(2)); pap. 7.95 (978-0-9700379-1-6(0)) Bookhandler Pr.

Roop, Connie & Roop, Peter, eds. The Diary of David R. Leeper: Rushing for Gold. 2000. (In My Own Words Ser.). (Illus.). 78p. (J). (gr. 5 up). lib. bdg. 27.07 (978-0-7614-1011-9(2) , Benchmark Bks.) Cavendish, Marshall Corp.

Somervill, Barbara A. The Gold Rush: Buried Treasure. 2005. (Trailblazers of the West Ser.). (Illus.). 48p. (J). (ps-7). 24.00 (978-0-516-25129-5(5)); (YA). (gr. 7-12). pap. 6.95 (978-0-516-25099-1(X)) Scholastic Library Publishing. (Children's Pr.).

Thompson, Gare. Missions & Ranchos: Early California Life. 2004. (National Geographic Reading Expeditions Ser.). (Illus.). 40p. (J). pap. (978-0-7922-4548-3(2)) National Geographic Society.

—When the Mission Padre Came to the Rancho: The Early California Adventures of Rosalinda & Simon Delgado. 2004. (I Am American Ser.). (Illus.). 40p. (J). (gr. 3-7). pap. 6.99 (978-0-7922-6945-8(4) , National Geographic Children's Bks.) National Geographic Society.

Tracy, Kathleen. Mariano Guadalupe Vallejo. 2002. (Latinos in American History). (Illus.). 56p. (gr. 4-8). lib. bdg. 29.95 (978-1-58415-152-4(8)) Mitchell Lane Pubs., Inc.

Uschan, Michael V. The California Gold Rush. 2003. (Landmark Events in American History Ser.). (Illus.). 48p. (J). (gr. 5 up). pap. 14.95 (978-0-8368-5402-2(0)); lib. bdg. 30.00 (978-0-8368-5374-2(1)) Stevens, Gareth Inc. (World Almanac Library).

Werther, Scott P. The Donner Party. 2002. (Survivors Ser.). (Illus.). 48p. (YA). (gr. 7-12). 24.00 (978-0-516-23901-9(5) , Children's Pr.) Scholastic Library Publishing.

Williams, Jack S. & Davis, Thomas L. Sailors, Merchants, & Muleteers. 2004. (People of the California Missions Ser.). (Illus.). 64p. (J). lib. bdg. 25.50 (978-0-8239-6282-2(2)) Rosen Publishing Group, Inc., The.

—Soldiers & Their Families of the California Mission Frontier. 2004. (People of the California Missions Ser.). (Illus.). 64p. (J). lib. bdg. 25.50 (978-0-8239-6285-3(7)) Rosen Publishing Group, Inc., The.

—Townspeople & Ranchers of the California Mission Frontier. 2004. (People of the California Missions Ser.). (Illus.). 64p. (J). lib. bdg. 25.50 (978-0-8239-6284-6(9) , PowerKids Pr.) Rosen Publishing Group, Inc., The.

FRONTIER AND PIONEER LIFE—FICTION

Ackerman, Karen. Araminta's Paint Box. Lewin, Betsy, illus. 1998. 32p. (J). (gr. 1-3). 6.99 (978-0-689-82091-5(7) , Aladdin) Simon & Schuster Children's Publishing.

Aksomitis, Linda. Adeline's Dream. 2006. (From Many Peoples Ser.). 272p. (J). pap. 7.95 (978-1-55050-323-4(5)) Coteau Bks. CAN. *Dist:* F & W Pubns., Inc.

Alef, Daniel. Centennial Stories: A Living History of San Francisco. 2nd ed. 2000. (Illus.). 227p. (J). pap. 15.95 (978-0-9700174-2-0(1)) Maxit Publishing, Inc.

Alter, Judy. Sam Houston Is My Hero. 2003. (Chaparral Book for Young Readers Ser.). 140p. (J). pap. 15.95 (978-0-87565-277-1(8)) Texas Christian Univ. Pr.

Altsheler, A. Joseph. Forest Runners A Story of the Great War. 2006. pap. 72.99 (***978-1-4280-3186-9(3)***) Indy-Publish.com.

Anderson, Launi K. Clarissa's Heart. 1998. (Latter-Day Daughters Ser.). 5.95 (978-1-57345-416-2(8)) Deseret Bk. Co.

Anderson, Rian B. A Christmas Prayer. 2004. pap. 2.95 (978-1-57734-900-6(8)) Covenant Communications, Inc.

Applegate, Katherine. The Buffalo Storm. Ormerod, Jan, illus. 2007. 32p. (J). (ps-3). 16.00 (978-0-618-53597-2(7) , Clarion Bks.) Houghton Mifflin Co. Trade & Reference Div.

Applegate, Stan. The Devil's Highway. Watling, James, illus. 1998. 224p. (J). (gr. 3-7). pap. 8.95 (978-1-56145-184-5(3) , Q21196) Peachtree Pubs., Ltd.

—Natchez Under-the-Hill. Watling, James, illus. 1999. 186p. (J). (gr. 3-7). pap. 8.95 (978-1-56145-191-3(6) , 51916) Peachtree Pubs., Ltd.

—Natchez Under-the-Hill. 1999. (gr. 3-6). lib. bdg. 17.60 (978-0-613-46156-6(8)) Tandem Library Bks.

Arrington, Frances. Bluestem. 2001. (J). (978-0-606-22050-7(X)) Tandem Library Bks.

—Prairie Whispers. 2005. 192p. (J). (gr. 5). pap. 6.99 (978-0-14-240306-8(7) , Puffin) Penguin Group (USA) Inc.

Ayres, Katherine. Silver Dollar Girl. 2002. (Illus.). 208p. (gr. 3-7). pap. 5.50 (978-0-440-41705-7(8) , Yearling) Random Hse. Children's Bks.

—Silver Dollar Girl. 2002. (gr. 3-6). lib. bdg. 13.00 (978-0-613-64685-7(1)) Tandem Library Bks.

Ballantyne, R. M. Silver Lake. 2004. reprint ed. pap. 15.95 (978-1-4191-4729-6(3)); pap. 1.99 (978-1-4192-4729-3(8)) Kessinger Publishing, LLC.

Balmes, Kathy. Thunder on the Sierra. Catapano, Vicki, illus. 2001. (Adventures in America Ser.). 96p. (J). (gr. 3-7). lib. bdg. 14.95 (978-1-893110-10-6(9)) Silver Moon Pr.

Barker, Jane Valentine. Building Up. pap. 7.95 (978-1-878611-07-9(0)) Silver Rim Pr.

Barth, Jeff. The Homesteaders. Barth, Marge, ed. 2002. (Illus.). 304p. pap. (978-1-891484-04-9(4)) Barth Family Ministries.

Bauer, Marion Dane. Land of the Buffalo Bones: The Diary of Mary Elizabeth Rodgers, an English Girl in Minnesota. 2003. (Dear America Ser.). (Illus.). 224p. (J). pap. 12.95 (978-0-439-22027-9(0)) Scholastic, Inc.

Bender, Esther. Elisabeth & the Windmill. 2003. (Lemon Tree Ser.). 112p. (J). (gr. 3-7). pap. 6.99 (978-0-8361-9204-9(4)) Herald Pr.

—Virginia & the Tiny One. Keenan, Joy Dunn, illus. 1998. (Lemon Tree Ser.: Vol. 2). 104p. (J). (gr. 3-7). pap. 6.99 (978-0-8361-9090-8(4)) Herald Pr.

Benton, Amanda. Silent Stranger. 1998. pap. 3.99 (978-0-380-79222-1(2)) HarperCollins Pubs.

Blakeslee, Ann R. A Different Kind of Hero. 2005. 144p. (YA). pap. 5.95 (978-0-7614-5147-1(1)) Cavendish, Marshall Corp.

Blanc, Esther Silverstein & Eagle, Godeane. Long Johns for a Small Chicken. Dixon, Tennessee, illus. 2003. (J). 16.95 (978-1-884244-23-0(8)) Volcano Pr.

Bloomfield, Susanne George & Reed, Melvin, eds. Adventures in the West: Stories for Young Readers. 2007. (Illus.). 302p. (gr. 3 up). pap. 19.95 (***978-0-8032-5974-4(3)*** , Bison Bks.) Univ. of Nebraska Pr.

Bly, Stephen A. The Buffalo's Last Stand. 2002. (Retta Barre's Oregon Trail Ser.: 2). 111p. pap. 5.99 (978-1-58134-392-2(2)) Crossway Bks.

—Dangerous Ride Across Humboldt Flats. 2005. (Adventures of the American Frontier Ser.). 128p. pap. 6.99 (978-1-58134-472-1(4) , Crossway Bibles) Crossway Bks.

—Daring Rescue at Sonora Pass. 2005. (Adventures of the American Frontier Ser.). 144p. pap. 6.99 (978-1-58134-471-4(6) , Crossway Bibles) Crossway Bks.

—The Lost Wagon Train. 2005. (Retta Barre's Oregon Trail Ser.: Vol. 1). 110p. pap. 5.99 (978-1-58134-391-5(4) , Crossway Bibles) Crossway Bks.

Boonstra, Jean Elizabeth. Miss Button & the Schoolboard: Sarah 1842-1844. 2002. 95p. (J). (978-0-8163-1874-2(3)) Pacific Pr. Publishing Assn.

—Sarah's Disappointment: Sarah 1842-1844. 2002. 95p. (J). (978-0-8163-1888-9(3)) Pacific Pr. Publishing Assn.

—Secret in the Family A: Sarah 1842-1844. 2002. 95p. (J). (978-0-8163-1887-2(5)) Pacific Pr. Publishing Assn.

—Song for Grandfather A: Sarah 1842-1844. 2002. 95p. (J). (978-0-8163-1873-5(5)) Pacific Pr. Publishing Assn.

Boutwell, Florence. Love According to Teresa. Ivie, Janet, illus. 2000. 190p. (J). (978-0-87062-298-4(6) , Clark, Arthur H. Co., The) Univ. of Oklahoma Pr.

—Teresa of Northwood Prairie: An Historical Adventure Story for Young & Old. Haff, Monica, illus. 1998. 175p. (J). 17.95 (978-0-87062-284-7(6) , Clark, Arthur H. Co., The) Univ. of Oklahoma Pr.

Bradley, Kimberly Brubaker. Weaver's Daughter. l.t. ed. 2002. 173p. (J). 21.95 (978-0-7862-3763-0(5)) Thomson Gale.

Brandis, Marianne. The Quarter-Pie Window. 2003. (Illus.). 232p. (J). (gr. 6-9). pap. 9.95 (978-0-88776-624-4(2)) Tundra Bks., Inc./Livres Toundra, Inc. CAN. *Dist:* Random Hse., Inc.

Breault, Christie Merriman. Logan West, Printer's Devil. Archembault, Matthew, illus. 2006. 142p. (J). pap. (978-1-59336-762-6(7)) Mondo Publishing.

Brink, Carol Ryrie. Caddie Woodlawn. Hyman, Trina Schart, illus. 2002. (J). 13.94 (978-0-7587-0174-9(8)) Book Wholesalers, Inc.

—Caddie Woodlawn. 288p. (J). 2007. pap. 2.99 (***978-1-4169-4818-6(X)***); 2006. pap. 6.99 (978-1-4169-4028-9(6)) Simon & Schuster Children's Publishing. (Aladdin).

—Caddie Woodlawn. 2001. (Illus.). (J). 12.64 (978-0-606-20588-7(8)) Tandem Library Bks.

—Caddie Woodlawn. l.t. ed. 2003. 260p. pap. 10.95 (978-0-7862-6182-6(X)) Thorndike Pr.

Buckey, Sarah Masters. Enemy in the Fort. 2001. (American Girl Collection). (Illus.). (J). 12.60 (978-0-606-21180-2(2)) Tandem Library Bks.

Buel, Hubert & Erskine, Dorothy Ward. North with de Anza. 2004. (Illus.). 234p. (J). (gr. 6-10). pap. 9.95 (978-0-8263-3631-6(0)) Univ. of New Mexico Pr.

Byars, Betsy. The Golly Sisters Go West. 2002. (Illus.). (J). 12.30 (978-0-7587-6115-6(5)) Book Wholesalers, Inc.

—The Golly Sisters Go West. 2000. (YA). pap. 23.20 incl. audio (978-0-7887-4335-1(X) , 41130) Recorded Bks., LLC.

—The Golly Sisters Ride Again: An I Can Read Book. 2002. (Illus.). (J). 12.34 (978-0-7587-6116-3(3)) Book Wholesalers, Inc.

—Trouble River. l.t. ed. 2004. (Beeler Mystery Ser.). 28.95 (978-1-58118-120-3(5)) LRS.

Calvert, Patricia. Betrayed! 2004. (gr. 5-8). lib. bdg. 13.00 (978-0-613-88652-9(6)) Tandem Library Bks.

—Bigger. 2003. 144p. (J). pap. 8.95 (978-0-689-86003-4(X) , Aladdin) Simon & Schuster Children's Publishing.

Carbone, Elisa. Last Dance on Holladay Street. 208p. (gr. 7-11). 2006. (YA). mass mkt. 5.99 (978-0-553-49426-6(0) , Laurel Leaf); 2005. (J). 15.95 (978-0-375-82896-6(6) , Knopf Bks. for Young Readers) Random Hse. Children's Bks.

Carey, Mary. Two for Texas: The Extraordinary Story of Kian & Jane Long. Finney, Pat, illus. 1999. 88p. 14.95 (978-1-57168-292-5(9)) Eakin Pr.

Carson, William C. Peter Becomes a Trail Man: The Story of a Boy's Journey on the Santa Fe Trail. Oliphant, Pat, illus. 2002. 192p. (J). (gr. 6 up). 12.95 (978-0-8263-2895-3(4)) Univ. of New Mexico Pr.

Cheek, Roland. Lincoln County Crucible, 6 vols. 2003. 288p. pap. 14.95 (978-0-918981-10-3(7) , 3) Skyline Publishing.

Citra, Becky. Danger at the Landings. 2002. (Orca Young Readers Ser.). (Illus.). 96p. (J). (gr. 3-6). pap. 4.99 (978-1-55143-232-8(3)) Orca Bk. Pubs. USA.

—Danger at the Landings. 2002. (gr. 3-6). lib. bdg. 13.00 (978-0-613-84753-7(9)) Tandem Library Bks.

—The Freezing Moon. McCallum, Stephen, illus. 2001. (Young Reader Ser.). 112p. (J). (gr. 3-6). pap. 4.99 (978-1-55143-181-9(5)) Orca Bk. Pubs. USA.

—Runaway. 2003. (Young Reader Ser.). (Illus.). 96p. (J). (gr. 3-6). pap. 4.99 (978-1-55143-276-2(5)) Orca Bk. Pubs. USA.

Clifford, Eth. The Year of the Three-Legged Deer. Cuffari, Richard, tr. Cuffari, Richard, illus. 2003. (Library of Indiana Classics). 176p. (YA). 32.95 (978-0-253-34251-5(1)); pap. 14.95 (978-0-253-21604-5(4)) Indiana Univ. Pr.

Clifton Wisler, G. All for Texas. 2004. 140p. (J). lib. bdg. 16.92 (***978-1-4242-0767-1(3)***) Fitzgerald Bks.

Connor, Leslie. Miss Bridie Chose a Shovel. Azarian, Mary, tr. Azarian, Mary, illus. 2004. 32p. (J). (gr. k-3). tchr. ed. 16.00 (978-0-618-30564-3(5)) Houghton Mifflin Co. Trade & Reference Div.

—Miss Bridie Chose a Shovel. Azarian, Mary, illus. unabr. ed. 2005. (J). (gr. k-3). 27.95 incl. audio (978-0-8045-6936-1(3) , SAC6936); 29.95 incl. audio compact disk (978-0-8045-4135-0(3) , SACD4135) Spoken Arts, Inc.

Cooper, James Fenimore. The Leatherstocking Saga. (J). (gr. 5-6). 44.95 (978-0-8488-0059-8(1)) Amereon LTD.

Couloumbis, Audrey. Maude March on the Run! 2007. (Illus.). 320p. (J). (gr. 3-7). 15.99 (978-0-375-83246-8(7) , Random Hse. Bks. for Young Readers) Random Hse. Children's Bks.

—Maude March on the Run!, or, Trouble Is Her Middle Name. 2007. (Illus.). 309p. (J). pap. (978-0-375-83248-2(3)) Random Hse., Inc.

—Maude March on the Run!, Or, Trouble Is Her Middle Name. 2007. (Illus.). 320p. (J). (gr. 3-7). lib. bdg. 17.99 (978-0-375-93246-5(1) , Random Hse. Bks. for Young Readers) Random Hse. Children's Bks.

—The Misadventures of Maude March: Or Trouble Rides a Fast Horse. 2005. (Illus.). 304p. (J). (gr. 5-9). 15.95 (978-0-375-83245-1(9)); lib. bdg. 17.99 (978-0-375-93245-8(3)) Random Hse. Children's Bks. (Random Hse. Bks. for Young Readers).

—The Misadventures of Maude Marche. 2007. (Illus.). 320p. (J). (gr. 3-7). 6.50 (978-0-375-83247-5(5) , Yearling) Random Hse. Children's Bks.

Crawford, Neil. The Journeyers. 2006. (J). pap. (***978-0-9778205-4-2(8)***) Helm Publishing.

Creel, Ann Howard. Water at the Blue Earth. 1998. (Illus.). 148p. (gr. 5-9). pap. 8.95 (978-1-57098-224-8(4)) Rinehart, Roberts Pubs.

Crook, Connie Brummel. The Perilous Year. 2004. 200p. (J). (gr. 4 up). (978-1-55041-818-7(1)); 2003. 197p. (YA). (978-1-55041-816-3(5)) Fitzhenry & Whiteside, Ltd.

Cullen, Lynn. Diary of Nelly Vandorn. (gr. 3 up). Date not set. 128p. mass mkt. 4.99 (978-0-06-440926-1(0)); 2002. 192p. (J). 15.95 (978-0-06-029133-4(8)) HarperCollins Pubs.

Cynthia DeFelice. Bringing Ezra Back: A Sequel to Weasel. l.t. ed. 2006. (J). 21.95 (978-0-7862-9043-7(9)) Thorndike Pr.

Dalgliesh, Alice. The Courage of Sarah Noble. Weisgard, Leonard, illus. 2002. (J). 13.40 (978-0-7587-0249-4(3)) Book Wholesalers, Inc.

Davis, Tim. More Tales from Dust River Gulch. 2002. (Tales from Dust River Gulch Ser.). (Illus.). 108p. (J). (gr. 4-7). 7.49 (978-1-57924-855-0(1)) Jones, Bob Univ. Pr.

Dearen, Patrick. Comanche Peace Pipe. 2001. (gr. k-3). lib. bdg. 17.60 (978-0-613-86879-2(X)) Tandem Library Bks.

—Comanche Peace Pipe. 2001. (Lone Star Heroes Ser.). 128p. (ps-3). pap. 8.95 (978-1-55622-831-5(7) , Republic of Texas Pr.) Wordware Publishing, Inc.

DeFelice, Cynthia C. Bringing Ezra Back. 2006. 160p. (J). 16.00 (978-0-374-39939-9(5)) Farrar, Straus & Giroux.

Dell, Pamela. Tag-along Tay: A Story about Annie Oakley & Buffalo Bill's Wild West Show. 2003. (Scrapbooks of America Ser.). (Illus.). 48p. (J). (gr. 2-6). 28.50 (978-1-59187-039-5(9)) Child's World, Inc.

Domnick, Howard. Danny on the Pioneer Trail. 2001. (Illus.). 93p. (YA). pap. 10.00 (978-0-9715419-3-1(0)) Domnick, Howard.

Downie, Mary Alice. Scared Sarah. Wood, Muriel, illus. 2002. 65p. pap. (978-1-55041-714-2(2)) Fitzhenry & Whiteside, Ltd.

Duey, Kathleen. Celou Sudden Shout: Idaho, 1826. 1998. (American Diaries Ser.: No. 9). (J). (gr. 3-7). (978-0-606-13121-6(3)) Tandem Library Bks.

Duey, Kathleen. Margret & Flynn 1875. 2008. 160p. (J). (gr. 3). 5.99 (***978-0-14-241019-6(5)*** , Puffin) Penguin Group (USA) Inc.

Durbin, William. Song of Sampo Lake. 2004. 224p. (J). (gr. 5). reprint ed. pap. 5.50 (978-0-440-22899-8(9) , Yearling) Random Hse. Children's Bks.

—Song of Sampo Lake. 2004. (gr. 5-8). lib. bdg. 13.55 (978-0-613-85112-1(9)) Tandem Library Bks.

Durrant, Lynda. The Sun, the Rain, & the Apple Seed: A Novel of Johnny Appleseed's Life. 2003. 208p. (J). (gr. 5-9). tchr. ed. 15.00 (978-0-618-23487-5(X) , Clarion Bks.) Houghton Mifflin Co. Trade & Reference Div.

Ellsworth, Loretta. Shrouding Woman. 2007. 160p. (YA). pap. 6.95 (***978-0-8050-8185-5(2)*** , Holt, Henry & Co. Bks. For Young Readers) Holt, Henry & Co.

Ellsworth, Loretta. The Shrouding Woman. rev. ed. 2002. 160p. (J). (gr. 5-8). 16.95 (978-0-8050-6651-7(9) , Holt, Henry & Co. Bks. For Young Readers) Holt, Henry & Co.

Embry-Litchman, Kristin. All Is Well. 1999. (J). (978-0-606-16714-7(5)) Tandem Library Bks.

Erdman, Loula Grace. The Wind Blows Free: A Tale of the Texas Panhandle. 2006. (Living History Library). 288p. (J). pap. 12.95 (***978-1-932350-09-8(8)***) Bethlehem Bks.

Fahey, Effie. Patience of Dearing Bay. unabr. ed. (Illus.). 152p. (J). (978-0-920576-57-1(5)) Caitlin Pr., Inc.

Finley, Martha. Elsie at Nantucket. 1998. (Elsie Bks.: Vol. 10). (J). (gr. 7-12). pap. 6.99 (978-1-888306-46-0(7)) Holly Hall Pubns., Inc.

—Elsie Dinsmore. 2006. (ENG.). pap. 13.95 (***978-1-4218-3092-6(2)***) 1st World Publishing, Inc.

—Elsie's Kith & Kin. 2001. (Elsie Books: Vol. 12). 228p. (J). (gr. 4-7). mass mkt. 5.99 (978-1-931343-03-9(9)) Hibbard Pubns., Inc.

—Elsie's Kith & Kin. 1998. (Elsie Bks.: Vol. 12). pap. 6.99 (978-1-888306-48-4(3)) Holly Hall Pubns., Inc.

—Elsie's New Relations. 1998. (Elsie Bks.: Vol. 9). (J). (gr. 7-12). pap. 6.99 (978-1-888306-45-3(9)) Holly Hall Pubns., Inc.

—The Two Elsies. 1998. (Elsie Bks.: Vol. 11). (J). (gr. 7-12). pap. 6.99 (978-1-888306-47-7(5)) Holly Hall Pubns., Inc.

Finley, Martha & Mission City Press Staff. Millie Keith, 4 vols., Boxed Set 1-4. 2002. (Life of Faith Ser.). 224p. (YA). 44.99 (978-1-928749-65-3(8)) Mission City Pr., Inc.

Finley, Mary Pearce. Meadow Lark. 2003. (Santa Fe Trail Trilogy Ser.). (Illus.). 199p. (J). 15.95 (978-0-86541-070-1(4)) Filter Pr., LLC.

—White Grizzly. 2000. (gr. 5-9). (Illus.). 215p. (J). 15.95 (978-0-86541-053-4(4)); 216p. (YA). pap. 8.95 (978-0-86541-058-9(5)) Filter Pr., LLC.

Freeman, Bill. Ambush in the Foothills. 2000. (Bains Ser.). (Illus.). 163p. (gr. 3-8). 6.95 (978-1-55028-716-5(8)); (***978-1-55028-717-2(6)***) Lorimer, James & Co., Ltd., Pubs. CAN. *Dist:* Casemate Pubs. & Bk. Distributors, LLC.

Freeman, Marcia S. The Gift. Kennedy, Patrice, illus. 2001. 31p. (J). 14.95 (978-0-929895-51-2(7)) Maupin Hse. Publishing.

Gagliano, Eugene. The Secret of the Black Widow. 2002. 67p. (J). pap. 5.95 (978-1-57249-286-8(4) , White Mane Kids) White Mane Publishing Co., Inc.

Gerrard, Roy. Wagons West! Gerrard, Roy, illus. 2000. (Illus.). 32p. (J). (ps-3). pap. 5.95 (978-0-374-48210-7(1) , Sunburst) Farrar, Straus & Giroux.

—Wagons West! 2000. (J). (ps-ps). (Illus.). lib. bdg. 14.10 (978-0-613-30179-4(X)); (978-0-606-20138-4(6)); (Illus.). (978-0-606-20401-9(6)) Tandem Library Bks.

Giblin, James Cross. The Boy Who Saved Cleveland: Based on a True Story. Dooling, Michael, illus. rev. ed. 2006. 80p. (J). 15.95 (978-0-8050-7355-3(8) , Holt, Henry & Co. Bks. For Young Readers) Holt, Henry & Co.

Gilson, Jamie. Wagon Train 911. 1998. (J). (978-0-606-13090-5(X)) Tandem Library Bks.

Gingold, Katharine Kendzy. Ruth by Lake & Prairie: True Stories of Early Naperville, Illinois. 2006. (J). per. 12.95 (***978-0-9792419-0-1(1)***) Gnu Ventures Co.

Glass, Andrew. Bewildered for Three Days: As to Why Daniel Boone Never Wore His Coonskin Cap. Glass, Andrew, illus. 2000. (Illus.). 32p. (J). (gr. k-3). tchr. ed. 16.95 (978-0-8234-1446-8(9)) Holiday Hse., Inc.

—Folks Call Me Appleseed John. unabr. ed. 1998. (J). Class Set. 102.70 incl. audio (978-0-7887-2552-4(1) , 46722); Homework. 27.24 incl. audio (978-0-7887-2247-9(6) , 40731) Recorded Bks., LLC.

—Folks Call Me Appleseed John. 1998. (978-0-606-13393-7(3)) Tandem Library Bks.

Glaze, Lynn. Seasons of the Trail. Archambault, Matthew, illus. 2000. (Adventures in America Ser.). 96p. (J). (gr. 3-7). lib. bdg. 14.95 (978-1-893110-20-5(6)) Silver Moon Pr.

Graef, Renee, illus. Laura & Mr. Edwards. 1999. (Little House Ser.: No. 13). 80p. (J). (gr. 3-6). 14.89 (978-0-06-027949-3(4)) HarperCollins Pubs.

—Laura & Nellie. 1998. (Little House Chapter Bks.: No. 5). (J). (gr. 3-6). (978-0-606-12979-4(0)) Tandem Library Bks.

—Laura's Ma. 1999. (Little House Ser.: No. 11). 80p. (J). (gr. 3-6). 14.89 (978-0-06-027897-7(8)) HarperCollins Pubs.

—Little House Friends. 1998. (Little House Chapter Bks.: No. 9). 80p. (J). (gr. 3-6). 14.89 (978-0-06-027894-6(3)) HarperCollins Pubs.

—Little House Parties. 1999. (Little House Ser.: No. 14). 80p. (J). (gr. 3-6). 14.89 (978-0-06-027951-6(6)) HarperCollins Pubs.

Graham, Christine. When Pioneer Wagons Rumbled West. Meidell, Sherry, illus. 1998. 32p. (J). (ps-3). 14.95 (978-1-57345-272-4(6) , Shadow Mountain) Deseret Bk. Co.

Gray, Dianne. Holding up the Earth. 2006. 224p. (J). (gr. 5-9). pap. 6.95 (978-0-618-73747-5(2)) Houghton Mifflin Co. Trade & Reference Div.

Gray, Dianne E. Holding up the Earth. 2000. 224p. (J). (gr. 5-9). tchr. ed. 15.00 (978-0-618-00703-5(2)) Houghton Mifflin Co. Trade & Reference Div.

—Holding up the Earth. l.t. ed. 2002. 198p. (J). 22.95 (978-0-7862-3889-7(5)) Thomson Gale.

Gregory, Kristiana. The Great Railroad Race: The Diary of Libby West, Utah Territory, 1868. 1999. (Dear America Ser.). (Illus.). 208p. (J). (gr. 4-9). pap. 10.95 (978-0-590-10991-8(X)) Scholastic, Inc.

—Winter Tidings. 2004. (Prairie River Ser.: No. 3). 192p. (J). (gr. 4-7). pap. 4.99 (978-0-439-44001-1(7) , Scholastic Paperbacks) Scholastic, Inc.

Gregory, Kristinana. Hope Springs Eternal. 2005. (Prairie River Ser.: No. 4). 176p. (J). pap. 4.99 (978-0-439-44003-5(3) , Scholastic Paperbacks) Scholastic, Inc.

Grossman, Bill. Cowboy Ed. Wint, Florence, illus. 2004. 28p. (J). (ps-3). reprint ed. (978-0-7567-7851-4(4)) DIANE Publishing Co.

Hahn, Mary Downing. The Gentleman Outlaw & Me: A Story of the Old West. 2007. 224p. (YA). (gr. 7-9). pap. 6.95 (978-0-618-83000-8(6) , Clarion Bks.) Houghton Mifflin Co. Trade & Reference Div.

Harcourt School Publishers Staff. Wagon Wheels. 3rd ed. 2002. (Trophies English Language Learners Ser.). (Illus.). pap. 5.10 (978-0-15-327776-4(9)) Harcourt Schl. Pubs.

Harper, Jo. Como los Perros de la Pradera. 2000. (SPA.). (gr. k-3). lib. bdg. 17.60 (978-0-613-32422-9(6)) Tandem Library Bks.

Harper, Jo & Harper, Josephine. Prairie Dog Pioneers. Spearing, Craig, illus. 48p. (J). (ps-3). 2000. pap. 8.95 (978-1-890515-23-2(X)); 1998. (SPA.). 16.95 (978-1-890515-10-2(8)) Turtle Bks.

Harper, Jo & Harper, Josephine L. Prairie Dog Pioneers. Spearing, Craig, illus. 2000. 44p. (J). (ps-3). lib. bdg. 17.60 (978-0-613-32966-8(X)) Tandem Library Bks.

Hartson. Willa's New World: The Novel Study. 124p. stu. ed. 29.95 (978-1-55378-058-8(2)) Edmonton Public Schls. Centre for Education CAN. *Dist:* Coteau Bks.

Hemphill, Kris. Ambush in the Wilderness. 2003. (Adventures in America Ser.). (Illus.). 90p. (J). 14.95 (978-1-893110-34-2(6)) Silver Moon Pr.

Henson, Heather. Christmas Stories. 2000. (Little House Chapter Bks.: No. 9). (Illus.). (J). (gr. 3-6). 11.05 (978-0-606-20475-0(X)) Tandem Library Bks.

—Christmas Stories: Adapted from the Little House Books by Laura Ingalls Wilder. Graef, Renee, illus. 1998. (Little House Chapter Bks.: No. 9). 80p. (J). (gr. 3-6). 14.89 (978-0-06-027895-3(1)) HarperCollins Pubs.

Henty, G. A. In the Heart of the Rockies. 2002. 370p. 29.95 (978-1-59087-073-0(5) , GAH073); per. 19.95 (978-1-59087-072-3(7) , GAH072) Althouse Pr.

—In the Heart of the Rockies. l.t. ed. 2006. 322p. pap. 17.99 (978-1-4264-3253-8(4)) BiblioBazaar.

—In the Heart of the Rockies. 2003. (ENG.). pap. 15.99 (***978-1-4142-0081-1(1)***) IndyPublish.com.

—In the Heart of the Rockies. 2004. reprint ed. pap. 27.95 (978-1-4191-2600-0(8)) ; pap. 1.99 (978-1-4192-2600-7(2)) Kessinger Publishing, LLC.

—In the Heart of the Rockies. Hindley, G. C., illus. 1998. 388p. (YA). (gr. 8-12). reprint ed. per. 16.95 (978-1-890623-08-1(3)) Lost Classics Bk. Co.

—In the Heart of the Rockies. collector's ed. 2002. (Illus.). im. lthr. 38.85 (978-1-4115-1341-9(X)); pap. 19.95 (978-1-4115-0577-3(8)); 25.95 (978-1-4115-0949-8(8)); pap. 17.95 (978-1-4115-0174-4(8)) Polyglot Pr., Inc.

—A Tale of the Western Plains. 2006. (Dover Value Editions Ser.). (Illus.). 352p. pap. 8.95 (978-0-486-45261-6(1)) Dover Pubns., Inc.

Hermes, Patricia. Calling Me Home. (J). 1999. 448p. pap. 3.99 (978-0-380-79100-2(5) , Harper Trophy); 1998. 144p. (gr. 4-7). 15.00 (978-0-380-97451-1(7)) HarperCollins Pubs.

—Calling Me Home. 1999. (Illus.). (J). (978-0-606-17961-4(5)) Tandem Library Bks.

—A Perfect Place Bk. 2: Joshua's Oregon Trail Diary. 2002. (My America Ser.: Bk. 2). 112p. (J). (gr. 2-5). pap. 10.95 (978-0-439-19999-5(9) , Scholastic Pr.) Scholastic, Inc.

—A Perfect Place Bk. 2: Joshua's Oregon Trail Diary. 2002. (gr. 3-6). lib. bdg. 13.00 (978-0-613-57261-3(0)) Tandem Library Bks.

—Westward to Home Bk. 1: Joshua's Oregon Trail Diary. 2002. (Joshua's Oregon Trail Diary Ser.: Bk. 1). 112p. (J). (gr. 2-5). 4.99 (978-0-439-38899-3(6) , Scholastic Pr.) Scholastic, Inc.

—Westward to Home Bk. 1: Joshua's Oregon Trail Diary. 2002. (gr. 3-6). lib. bdg. 13.00 (978-0-613-60738-4(4)) Tandem Library Bks.

Holm, Jennifer L. An Adventure. 2002. (Boston Jane Ser.). 288p. (J). (gr. k-17). pap. 6.99 (978-0-06-440849-3(3)) HarperCollins Pubs.

—Boston Jane. 2002. (gr. 3-6). lib. bdg. 15.30 (978-0-613-56251-5(8)) Tandem Library Bks.

—Boston Jane: The Claim. l.t. ed. 2005. (Boston Jane Ser.). 288p. 22.95 (978-0-7862-7392-8(5) , Large Print Pr.) Thorndike Pr.

—Our Only May Amelia. (Harper Trophy Bks.). (Illus.). (J). 2001. 272p. (gr. 4 up). pap. 5.99 (978-0-06-440856-1(6) , Harper Trophy); 1999. 253p. (gr. k-9). per. 15.89 (978-0-06-028354-4(8)); 1999. 272p. (gr. 4 up). 18.99 (978-0-06-027822-9(6)) HarperCollins Pubs.

—Our Only May Amelia. unabr. ed. 2004. 253p. (J). (gr. 5-9). pap. 36.00 incl. audio (978-0-8072-8366-0(5) , YA191SP, Listening Library) Random Hse. Audio Publishing Group.

—Our Only May Amelia. 2001. (Illus.). 251p. (J). (gr. k-9). lib. bdg. 14.15 (978-0-613-35995-5(X)) Tandem Library Bks.

—Our Only May Amelia. l.t. ed. 2000. (Illus.). 261p. (J). (ps up). 21.95 (978-0-7862-2742-6(7)) Thorndike Pr.

—Wilderness Days. (Boston Jane Ser.). 256p. (J). (gr. 5 up). 2004. pap. 5.99 (978-0-06-440881-3(7) , Harper Trophy); 2002. 16.99 (978-0-06-029043-6(9)); 2002. lib. bdg. 18.89 (978-0-06-029044-3(7)) HarperCollins Pubs.

Hopkinson, Deborah. A Packet of Seeds. Andersen, Bethanne, illus. 2004. 32p. (J). 15.99 (978-0-06-009089-0(8)) HarperCollins Pubs.

—Prairie Skies: Cabin in the Snow. 2002. (gr. 3-6). lib. bdg. 11.80 (978-0-613-63224-9(9)) Tandem Library Bks.

—Prairie Skies: Pioneer Summer. 2002. (gr. 3-6). lib. bdg. 11.80 (978-0-613-45093-5(0)) Tandem Library Bks.

Hopkinson, Deborah & Carpenter, Nancy. Apples to Oregon: Being the (Slightly) True Narrative of How a Brave Pioneer Father Brought Apples, Peaches, Pears, Plums, Grapes, & Cherries (And Children) Across the Plains. 2004. (Illus.). 40p. (J). 16.95 (978-0-689-84769-1(6) , Atheneum) Simon & Schuster Children's Publishing.

Hopkinson, Deborah & Faricy, Patrick. Cabin in the Snow. 2002. (Prairie Skies Ser.). 80p. (J). pap. 3.99 (978-0-689-84351-8(8) , Aladdin) Simon & Schuster Children's Publishing.

Horne, Constance. Papa's Surprise. Hansen, Mia, illus. 2005. 60p. (J). 5.95 (978-0-9730831-1-8(5)) Hodgepog Bks. CAN. *Dist:* Coteau Bks., Fitzhenry & Whiteside, Ltd.

Howard, Ellen. The Log Cabin Christmas. Himler, Ronald, illus. 2000. 32p. (J). (gr. k-3). tchr. ed. 16.95 (978-0-8234-1381-2(0)) Holiday Hse., Inc.

—The Log Cabin Church. Himler, Ronald, illus. 2002. 32p. (J). (gr. k-3). tchr. ed. 16.95 (978-0-8234-1740-7(9)) Holiday Hse., Inc.

—The Log Cabin Wedding. Himler, Ronald, illus. 2006. 64p. (J). 15.95 (978-0-8234-1989-0(4)) Holiday Hse., Inc.

Hudson, Jan. Sweetgrass. 1999. 168p. (J). (gr. 5-9). pap. 5.99 (978-0-698-11763-1(8) , Putnam Juvenile) Penguin Group (USA) Inc.

—Sweetgrass. 2002. (J). (gr. 5-10). 20.50 (978-0-8446-7209-0(2)) Smith, Peter Pub., Inc.

—Sweetgrass. 1999. (978-0-606-16851-9(6)) Tandem Library Bks.

Hughes, Dean. As Wide As the River. 2005. 156p. (J). pap. (978-1-59038-450-3(4)) Deseret Bk. Co.

—Facing the Enemy. 2005. (Illus.). 153p. (J). pap. (978-1-59038-449-7(0)) Deseret Bk. Co.

—Under the Same Stars. 2005. viii, 152p. (J). pap. (978-1-59038-448-0(2)) Deseret Bk. Co.

Hulme, Joy N. Climbing the Rainbow. 2004. 224p. (J). 15.99 (978-0-380-81572-2(9)); lib. bdg. 16.89 (978-0-06-054304-4(3)) HarperCollins Pubs.

—Through the Open Door. 2000. 176p. (J). (gr. 4-6). 14.95 (978-0-380-97870-0(9)) HarperCollins Pubs.

Hurst, Carol Otis & Otis, Rebecca. A Killing in Plymouth Colony. 2003. 160p. (YA). (gr. 5-9). tchr. ed. 15.00 (978-0-618-27597-7(5) , Walter Lorraine) Houghton Mifflin Co. Trade & Reference Div.

Hutchinson, Emily. Last of the Mohicans. abr. ed. 2001. (gr. 7-12). lib. bdg. 15.25 (978-0-613-36461-4(9)) Tandem Library Bks.

Ingle, Sheila C. Courageous Kate: A Daughter of the American Revolution. 2006. (J). (***978-1-891885-52-5(9)***) Hub City Writers Project.

Ingold, Jeanette. The Big Burn. 2003. (Illus.). 320p. (YA). pap. 6.95 (978-0-15-204924-9(X) , Harcourt Paperbacks) Harcourt Children's Bks.

—The Big Burn. 2003. (gr. 5-8). lib. bdg. 15.25 (978-0-613-55148-9(6)) Tandem Library Bks.

—Mountain Solo. 320p. (YA). 2005. (gr. 7-17). pap. 6.95 (978-0-15-205358-1(1) , Harcourt Paperbacks); 2003. 17.00 (978-0-15-202670-7(3)) Harcourt Children's Bks.

Isaacs, Anne. Swamp Angel. Zelinsky, Paul O., illus. 2002. (J). 14.04 (978-0-7587-0152-7(7)) Book Wholesalers, Inc.

—Swamp Angel. Zelinsky, Paul O., illus. 2000. 48p. (J). (ps-3). pap. 6.99 (978-0-14-055908-8(6) , Puffin) Penguin Group (USA) Inc.

—Swamp Angel. 2000. (978-0-606-18453-3(8)); lib. bdg. 15.30 (978-0-613-23041-4(8)) Tandem Library Bks.

James, Will. Cowboy in the Making. rev. ed. (Illus.). 104p. (gr. 4-6). pap. 15.00 (978-0-87842-439-9(3) , 811) Mountain Pr. Publishing Co., Inc.

Johnston, Tony. The Sunsets of the West. Lewin, Ted, illus. 2002. 32p. (J). (gr. k up). 16.99 (978-0-399-22659-5(1) , Putnam Juvenile) Penguin Group (USA) Inc.

Jones, Veda Boyd. Adventure in the Wilderness: The Journey to Cincinnati's Frontier, 1999. (American Adventure Ser.: No. 13). (Illus.). 143p. (J). (gr. 3-7). 11.95 (978-0-7910-5587-8(6) , Chelsea Hse.) Facts On File, Inc.

Karim, Roberta. Kindle Me a Riddle: A Pioneer Story. Andersen, Bethanne, illus. 1999. 32p. (J). (gr. k-3). 16.89 (978-0-688-16204-7(5)) HarperCollins Pubs.

Kay, Verla. Covered Wagons, Bumpy Trails. Schindler, S. D., illus. 2000. 1p. (J). (ps-3). 15.99 (978-0-399-22928-2(0) , Putnam Juvenile) Penguin Group (USA) Inc.

Kelley, Nancy J. The Whispering Rod: A Tale of Old Massachusetts. 2002. 160p. (J). lib. bdg. 17.95 (978-1-57249-248-6(1) , White Mane Kids) White Mane Publishing Co., Inc.

Ketteman, Helen. Shoeshine Whittaker. Goto, Scott, illus. 1999. 32p. (J). (gr. k-3). lib. bdg. 16.85 (978-0-8027-8715-6(0)) Walker & Co.

Kierstead-Farber, Vera M. America Is My Country. 2007. 170p. pap. 11.95 (***978-0-533-15643-6(2)***) Vantage Pr., Inc.

Kimmel, Cody E. In the Eye of the Storm. Snow, Scott, illus. 2003. (Adventures of Young Buffalo Bill Ser.). 144p. (J). (gr. 3-7). 15.99 (978-0-06-029115-0(X)) HarperCollins Pubs.

Kimmel, E. Cody. In the Eye of the Storm. Snow, Scott, illus. 2003. (Adventures of Young Buffalo Bill Ser.). 144p. (J). (gr. 3-7). lib. bdg. 16.89 (978-0-06-029116-7(8)) HarperCollins Pubs.

Kimmel, Elizabeth Cody. One Sky above Us. Bernardin, James & Snow, Scott, illus. 2002. (Adventures of Young Buffalo Bill Ser.). 192p. (J). (gr. 3-6). 15.99 (978-0-06-029119-8(2)) HarperCollins Pubs.

—To the Frontier. Snow, Scott, illus. 2002. (Adventures of Young Buffalo Bill Ser.). 192p. (J). (gr. 4-7). 15.95 (978-0-06-029117-4(6)) HarperCollins Pubs.

Kirby, Susan E. Ellen's Story. 2000. (gr. 3-6). lib. bdg. 13.00 (978-0-613-31156-4(6)) Tandem Library Bks.

—Hattie's Story. 2000. (American Quilts Ser.: Vol. 2). (J). 11.64 (978-0-606-20080-6(0)) Tandem Library Bks.

Kirkpatrick, Katherine. The Voyage of the Continental. 2002. (Illus.). 256p. (J). (gr. 7 up). tchr. ed. 16.95 (978-0-8234-1580-9(5)) Holiday Hse., Inc.

LaFaye, A. Worth. unabr. ed. 2006. (Live Oak Histories Ser.). (J). (gr. 3-6). pap. 24.95 incl. audio (***978-1-59519-766-5(4)***); pap. 28.95 incl. audio compact disk (***978-1-59519-767-2(2)***) Live Oak Media.

—Worth. 160p. (J). (gr. 4-7). 2004. (Illus.). 16.99 (978-0-689-85730-0(6)); 2006. reprint ed. pap. 5.99 (978-1-4169-1624-6(5) , Aladdin) Simon & Schuster Children's Publishing.

Lane, Rose Wilder. Young Pioneers. Andreasen, Dan, illus. 1998. (Little House Ser.). 192p. (J). (gr. 3 up). pap. 6.99 (978-0-06-440698-7(9) , Harper Trophy) HarperCollins Pubs.

Larson, Kirby. Hattie Big Sky. 2006. 304p. (J). (gr. 7). 15.95 (978-0-385-73313-7(5)); lib. bdg. 17.99 (978-0-385-90332-5(4)) Random Hse. Children's Bks. (Delacorte Bks. for Young Readers).

—Hattie Big Sky. l.t. ed. 2007. 400p. (YA). 23.95 (***978-0-7862-9697-2(6)***) Thorndike Pr.

Lawlor, Laurie. Down the Rio Grande, Eighteen Twenty-Nine. 2001. (gr. 3-6). lib. bdg. 12.40 (978-0-613-51210-7(3)) Tandem Library Bks.

Lawton, Wendy. Ransom's Mark: A Story Based on the Life of the Pioneer Olive Oatman. 2003. (Daughters of the Faith Ser.: Bk. 4). 144p. (J). (gr. k-3). pap. 6.99 (978-0-8024-3638-2(2)) Moody Pubs.

Levine, Ellen. The Journal of Jedediah Barstow: An Emigrant on the Oregon Trail. 2002. (My Name Is America Ser.). (Illus.). 176p. (J). (gr. 4-9). pap. 10.95 (978-0-439-06310-4(8) , Scholastic Pr.) Scholastic, Inc.

Levinson, Nancy Smiler. Prairie Friends. Schuett, Stacey, illus. 2003. (I Can Read Bks.). 64p. (J). (gr. k-3). 15.99 (978-0-06-028001-7(8)) HarperCollins Pubs.

Levitin, Sonia. Boom Town. Smith, Cat Bowman, illus. 1998. 32p. (J). (gr. k-4). pap. 16.95 (978-0-531-30043-5(9) , Orchard Bks.) Scholastic, Inc.

—Clem's Chances. 2001. (Illus.). 208p. (J). (gr. 2-7). pap. 17.95 (978-0-439-29314-3(6) , Orchard Bks.) Scholastic, Inc.

—Nine for California. Smith, Cat Bowman, illus. 2001. 40p. (J). (ps-3). pap. 6.95 (978-0-531-07176-2(6) , Orchard Bks.) Scholastic, Inc.

Liles, Maurine W. Dona Maria, la Ranchera. 2000. (Illus.). 144p. 15.95 (978-1-57168-381-6(X)) Eakin Pr.

Lottridge, Celia Barker & Gerber, Mary Jane. Wings to Fly. 1999. (Illus.). 216p. (J). (gr. 3-7). pap. 5.95 (978-0-88899-346-5(3) , Libros Tigrillo) Groundwood Bks. CAN. *Dist:* Perseus Distribution.

Love, D. Anne. A Year Without Rain. 2000. (Illus.). 128p. (J). (gr. 4-6). tchr. ed. 15.95 (978-0-8234-1488-8(4)) Holiday Hse., Inc.

Lytle, Robert A. Three Rivers Crossing. 2000. 161p. (J). pap. 8.95 (978-0-938682-60-8(1)); (gr. 4-8). 15.95 (978-0-938682-55-4(5)) River Road Pubns., Inc.

MacBride, Roger Lea. Bachelor Girl. Gilleece, David, illus. 1999. (Little House). 256p. (J). (gr. 3-6). 15.89 (978-0-06-028434-3(X)) HarperCollins Pubs.

—Bachelor Girl. Andreasen, Dan, illus. 1999. (Little House Ser.). 256p. (J). (gr. 3-6). 15.95 (978-0-06-027755-0(6)); (gr. 5 up). pap. 6.99 (978-0-06-440691-8(1) , Harper Trophy) HarperCollins Pubs.

—Bachelor Girl. 1999. (gr. 3-6). lib. bdg. 14.15 (978-0-613-21154-3(5)); (Illus.). (J). 12.64 (978-0-606-18676-6(X)) Tandem Library Bks.

—Little Farm in the Ozarks Bk. 2: The Rose Years. 2007. (Little House Ser.). 176p. (J). pap. 5.99 (***978-0-06-114810-1(5)*** , Harper Trophy) HarperCollins Pubs.

—Little House on Rocky Ridge. 2007. (Little House Ser.). 176p. (J). pap. 5.99 (***978-0-06-114809-5(1)*** , Harper Trophy) HarperCollins Pubs.

—Missouri Bound. 1999. (Little House Chapter Bks.: No. 1). (J). (gr. 3-6). (978-0-606-18717-6(0)) Tandem Library Bks.

—Missouri School Days. 2001. (Little House Chapter Bks.). (Illus.). (J). (gr. 2-5). (978-0-606-20892-5(5)) Tandem Library Bks.

MacLachlan, Patricia. Caleb's Story. 2001. (Sarah, Plain & Tall Ser.). 128p. (J). (gr. 3-5). 16.99 (978-0-06-023605-2(1) , Cotler, Joanna Books) HarperCollins Pubs.

—Grandfather's Dance. 5th ed. 2006. (Sarah, Plain & Tall Ser.). 96p. (J). (gr. 3-6). 14.99 (978-0-06-027560-0(X) , Cotler, Joanna Books) HarperCollins Pubs.

—More Perfect than the Moon. 2004. (Sarah, Plain & Tall Ser.). 96p. (J). 14.99 (978-0-06-027558-7(8) , Cotler, Joanna Books) HarperCollins Pubs.

—Sarah, Plain & Tall. l.t. ed. 1999. (LRS Large Print Cornerstone Ser.). 72p. (J). (gr. 3-8). lib. bdg. 19.95 (978-1-58118-049-7(7) , 22773) LRS.

—Sarah, Plain & Tall. l.t. ed. 2005. 82p. (YA). pap. 10.95 (978-0-7862-8064-3(6)) Thorndike Pr.

Major, Charles. Bears of Blue River. reprint ed. lib. bdg. 23.95 (978-0-88411-094-1(X)) Amereon LTD.

Martin, Gayle. Gunfight at the O. K. Corral: Luke & Jenny Visit Tombstone. 2006. (J). per. 14.95 net. (978-1-58985-050-7(5)) Five Star Pubns., Inc.

Mccabe, Jr. Planting the Wilderness or, the Pioneer Boys: a Story of Frontier Life. 2007. pap. 27.95 (***978-1-4304-8187-4(0)***) Kessinger Publishing, LLC.

McCaughrean, Geraldine. Stop the Train! (J). (gr. 5 up). 2003. 304p. 16.99 (978-0-06-050749-7(7)); 2005. 384p. reprint ed. pap. 6.99 (978-0-06-050751-0(9) , Harper Trophy) HarperCollins Pubs.

McCully, Emily Arnold. Squirrel & John Muir. 2004. (Illus.). 40p. (J). 16.00 (978-0-374-33697-4(0) , Farrar, Straus & Giroux (BYR)) Farrar, Straus & Giroux.

McMullan, Kate. As Far As I Can See Bk. 1: Meg's Prairie Diary. (My America Ser.). 112p. (J). 2002. (gr. 3-5). pap. 10.95 (978-0-439-42517-9(4)); 2001. (Illus.). (gr. 2-5). pap. 10.95 (978-0-439-18895-1(4)) Scholastic, Inc. (Scholastic Pr.).

—For This Land Bk. 2: Meg's Prairie Diary. 2003. (My America Ser.). (Illus.). 112p. (J). pap. 10.95 (978-0-439-37059-2(0) , Scholastic Pr.) Scholastic, Inc.

—For This Land Bk. 2: Meg's Prairie Diary. 2003. (gr. 3-6). lib. bdg. 19.90 (978-0-613-63038-2(6)) Tandem Library Bks.

Meigs, Cornelia & Holm, Jennifer. Swift Rivers. 2004. (Newbery Honor Roll Ser.). 288p. (J). pap. 6.95 (978-0-8027-7703-4(1)) Walker & Co.

Mercati, Cynthia. Wagons Ho! A Diary of the Oregon Trail. Kabel, Larassa, illus. 2000. (Cover-to-Cover Bks.). 56p. (J). pap. (978-0-7891-5039-4(5)); (gr. 1-4). lib. bdg. 16.95 (978-0-7807-9011-7(1)) Perfection Learning Corp.

Miller, Nelson. Little Lake Saga. Bedard, Kathy, illus. unabr. ed. 32p. (J). (978-0-920576-58-8(3)) Caitlin Pr., Inc.

Moeri, Louise. The Devil in Ol' Rosie. l.t. ed. 2002. (Juvenile Ser.). 161p. (J). 21.95 (978-0-7862-3808-8(9)) Thomson Gale.

Morehead, Don & Morehead, Ann. A Short Season: Story of a Montana Childhood. 1998. (Illus.). 190p. pap. 13.00 (978-0-8032-8244-5(3) , MORSHX, A Bison Original) Univ. of Nebraska Pr.

Morey, Walt. Year of the Black Pony. 2006. (Living History Library). 172p. (J). pap. 11.95 (***978-1-932350-08-1(X)***) Bethlehem Bks.

Moss, Marissa. Rachel's Journal: The Story of A Pioneer Girl. 2001. (gr. 3-6). lib. bdg. 15.30 (978-0-613-35560-5(1)) Tandem Library Bks.

Mullin, Penn. Along the Santa Fe Trail. 1999. (gr. 7-12). lib. bdg. 11.60 (978-0-613-23075-9(2)) Tandem Library Bks.

—Gold Rush Fever. 1999. (gr. 7-12). lib. bdg. 11.60 (978-0-613-28855-2(6)) Tandem Library Bks.

—Off to Oregon. 1999. (gr. 7-12). lib. bdg. 11.60 (978-0-613-28988-7(9)) Tandem Library Bks.

Newman, Pamela Lillie. Lissie at Lincoln Lake: Book 2 of Lissie's Series. 2003. 92p. (J). per. 6.95 (978-1-59196-234-2(X)) Instantpublisher.com.

Nixon, Hershell. The Long Way West. 2003. (Illus.). 176p. (J). 16.95 (978-0-89672-508-9(1)) Texas Tech Univ. Pr.

Osborne, Mary Pope. Ghost Town at Sundown. unabr. ed. 2004. (Magic Tree House Ser.: No. 10). 73p. (J). (gr. k-3). pap. 17.00 incl. audio (978-0-8072-0535-8(4) , Listening Library) Random Hse. Audio Publishing Group.

—Twister on Tuesday, Vol. 23. 2004. (Magic Tree House Ser. : No. 23). 70p. (J). (gr. k-3). pap. 17.00 incl. audio (978-0-8072-9932-6(4) , Listening Library) Random Hse. Audio Publishing Group.

—Twister on Tuesday. Murdocca, Sal, illus. 2001. (Magic Tree House Ser.: No. 23). 96p. (J). (gr. k-3). 11.99 (978-0-679-99069-7(0)); 23. pap. 3.99 (978-0-679-89069-0(6)) Random Hse. Children's Bks. (Random Hse. Bks. for Young Readers).

—Twister on Tuesday. 2001. (Magic Tree House Ser.: No. 23). (J). (gr. k-3). lib. bdg. 11.80 (978-0-613-35706-7(X)); (Illus.). (978-0-606-21498-8(4)) Tandem Library Bks.

Otten, Charlotte. Home in a Wilderness Fort: Copper Harbor 1844. 2006. (J). pap. 14.95 (978-0-9766104-5-8(0)) Arbutus Pr.

Patchin, Gee Frank. Pony Rider Boys in New Mexico. 2006. pap. 19.99 (***978-1-4280-3254-5(1)***) IndyPublish.com.

Patneaude, David. The Last Man's Reward. 1998. (J). (978-0-606-13564-1(2)) Tandem Library Bks.

Paulsen, Gary. Tucket's Gold. 2001. (Tucket Adventures Ser.). (Illus.). 112p. (J). (gr. 4-7). pap. 5.50 (978-0-440-41376-9(1) , Yearling) Random Hse. Children's Bks.

—Tucket's Gold. 2001. (J). (978-0-606-20958-8(1)); (gr. 5-8). lib. bdg. 12.40 (978-0-613-33781-6(6)) Tandem Library Bks.

Pearsall, Shelley. Crooked River. (J). (gr. 5-9). 2007. 272p. pap. 6.50 (978-0-440-42101-6(2) , Yearling); 2005. 256p. 15.95 (978-0-375-82389-3(1) , Knopf Bks. for Young Readers); 2005. 256p. lib. bdg. 17.99 (978-0-375-92389-0(6) , Knopf Bks. for Young Readers) Random Hse. Children's Bks.

Peterson, Sara Budinger. Alice Meets Inupiat Eskimos. 2000. (Illus.). 68p. 11.95 (978-0-9665282-1-3(2)) Saranjon Publishing.

Pryor, Bonnie. Luke: 1849 - On the Golden Trail. Dodson, Bert, illus. 1999. (American Adventures Ser.). 272p. (J). (gr. 3-7). 15.00 (978-0-688-15670-1(3)) HarperCollins Pubs.

—Luke: 1849—On the Golden Trail. 2000. (American Adventures Ser.). (Illus.). 176p. (J). (gr. 3-7). pap. 4.50 (978-0-380-73102-2(9) , Harper Trophy) HarperCollins Pubs.

—Luke: 1849-On the Golden Trail. 2000. (Illus.). (J). (978-0-606-17977-5(1)) Tandem Library Bks.

Rees, Celia. Witch Child. 272p. (YA). (gr. 7 up). 2002. pap. 8.99 (978-0-7636-1829-2(2)); 2001. (Illus.). 15.99 (978-0-7636-1421-8(1)) Candlewick Pr.

—Witch Child. unabr. ed. 2004. (Young Adult Cassette Librariestm Ser.). 304p. (J). (gr. 5-9). pap. 40.00 incl. audio (978-0-8072-1198-4(2) , S YA 343 SP, Listening Library) Random Hse. Audio Publishing Group.

—Witch Child. 2002. (gr. 7-12). lib. bdg. 16.45 (978-0-613-60740-7(6)) Tandem Library Bks.

—Witch Child. l.t. ed. 2002. 284p. (J). 22.95 (978-0-7862-3896-5(8)) Thomson Gale.

Rees, Shirley. Hannah Stands Tall. 2002. 130p. (J). pap. 10.95 (978-1-55517-652-5(6) , 76526, Bonneville Bks.) Cedar Fort, Inc./CFI Distribution.

Reiss, Kathryn. Riddle of the Prairie Bride. 2001. (American Girl Collection). (Illus.). (J). (978-0-606-21400-1(3)) Tandem Library Bks.

Reynolds, Marilynn. The Prairie Fire. Kilby, Don, illus. 2001. 32p. (J). (ps-2). 6.95 (978-1-55143-175-8(0)) Orca Bk. Pubs. USA.

Richter, Conrad. The Light in the Forest. (YA). (gr. 7 up). 21.95 (978-0-89190-333-8(X)) Amereon LTD.

Riefe, Barbara. Amelia Dale Archer Story. 1998. 304p. (YA). (gr. 8 up). 22.95 (978-0-312-86077-6(3) , Forge Bks.) Doherty, Tom Assocs., LLC.

Rinaldi, Ann. The Second Bend in the River. 1999. 288p. (J). (gr. 5-9). pap. 4.99 (978-0-590-74259-7(0)) Scholastic, Inc.

Rizzo, Kay D. Wagon Train West. 2003. 96p. (J). (978-0-8163-1986-2(3)) Pacific Pr. Publishing Assn.

Roberts, Sally A. The Legend of Crystal Lake. (Illus.). 2001. vi, 135p. (J). pap. 10.95 (978-1-57168-557-5(X) , Eakin Pr.); 2000. 136p. 16.95 (978-1-57168-369-4(0)) Eakin Pr.

Robinette, Joseph. Sarah, Plain & Tall. 2003. 84p. (YA). (gr. 6 up). pap. 6.50 (978-1-58342-161-1(0) , SG8) Dramatic Publishing Co.

Rogers, Lisa Waller. Remember the Alamo! The Runaway Scrape Diary of Belle Wood. 2003. (Lone Star Journals: Bk. 3). 208p. (J). 15.95 (978-0-89672-497-6(2)) Texas Tech Univ. Pr.

Rudolph, Marian. Lovina's Song: A Pioneer Girl's Journey with the Donner Party. Cole, Christopher, illus. 1998. 192p. (J). pap. 11.95 (978-1-883965-43-3(8)) Rattle OK Pubns.

Rylant, Cynthia. Old Town in the Green Groves: Laura Ingalls Wilder's Lost Little House Years. 2007. (Little House Ser.). 192p. (J). pap. 6.99 (978-0-06-088546-5(7) , Harper Trophy) HarperCollins Pubs.

—Old Town in the Green Groves: Laura Ingalls Wilder's Lost Little House Years. LaMarche, Jim, illus. (Little House Ser.). 176p. (J). 2004. pap. 5.99 (978-0-06-440990-2(2) , Harper Trophy); 2002. 15.99 (978-0-06-029561-5(9)) HarperCollins Pubs.

Sanders, Scott R. Aurora Means Dawn. 1998. (978-0-606-13155-1(8)) Tandem Library Bks.

Sanders, Scott Russell. A Place Called Freedom. 2001. (J). (978-0-606-20854-3(2)) Tandem Library Bks.

Sandin, Joan. At Home in a New Land. 2007. (I Can Read Bks.). 64p. (J). (ps-3). lib. bdg. 16.89 (***978-0-06-058078-0(X)***) HarperCollins Pubs.

—At Home in a New Land. Sandin, Joan, illus. 2007. (I Can Read Bks.). (Illus.). 64p. (J). (ps-3). 15.99 (***978-0-06-058077-3(1)***) HarperCollins Pubs.

Santillo, LuAnn. Pioneer Days, 6 vols. Santillo, LuAnn, ed. 2003. (Half-Pint Kids Readers Ser.). (Illus.). 42p. (J). (ps-1). pap. 6.99 (978-1-59256-070-7(9)) Half-Pint Kids, Inc.

Sargent, Dave & Sargent, Pat. Ben. Lenoir, Jane, illus. 2001. (Saddle Up Ser.). 36p. (J). pap. 6.95 (978-1-56763-644-4(6)) Ozark Publishing.

—Ben: (Bay Sabino) Help Others, 30. Lenoir, Jane, illus. 2001. (Saddle Up Ser.: 2). 36p. (J). lib. bdg. 22.60 (978-1-56763-643-7(8)) Ozark Publishing.

—Pete: (Pink-skinned Palomino) Be a Hero, 30, 46. Lenoir, Jane, illus. 2003. (Saddle Up Ser.: Vol. 46). 42p. (J). lib. bdg. 22.60 (978-1-56763-707-6(8)) Ozark Publishing.

—Pete: Pink-skinned Palomino) Be a Hero, 30, 46. Lenoir, Jane, illus. 2003. (Saddle Up Ser.: Vol. 46). 42p. (J). pap. 6.95 (978-1-56763-708-3(6)) Ozark Publishing.

—Stinky: (Sorrel) Don't Be Mischievous, 25, 56. Lenoir, Jane, illus. 2001. (Saddle Up Ser.: 56). 36p. (J). pap. (978-1-56763-666-6(7)); lib. bdg. 22.60 (978-1-56763-665-9(9)) Ozark Publishing.

Schulte, Elaine. Suzannah & the Secret Coins. 2001. (gr. 3-6). lib. bdg. 14.70 (978-0-613-85515-0(9)) Tandem Library Bks.

Schulte, Elaine L. Daniel Colton Kidnapped. 2002. (Colton Cousins Adventure Ser.: Bk. 4). (Illus.). 138p. (J). (gr. 4-7). 7.49 (978-1-57924-566-5(8)) Jones, Bob Univ. Pr.

—Daniel Colton under Fire. 2001. (Illus.). 137p. (J). (gr. 4-7). pap. 7.49 (978-1-57924-564-1(1)) Jones, Bob Univ. Pr.

—Suzannah & the Secret Coins. 2001. (Colton Cousins Adventure Ser.). (Illus.). 130p. (J). (gr. 4-7). 7.49 (978-1-57924-563-4(3)) Jones, Bob Univ. Pr.

—Suzannah Strikes Gold. 2001. (Illus.). 144p. (J). (gr. 4-7). pap. 7.49 (978-1-57924-565-8(X)) Jones, Bob Univ. Pr.

Schultz, Jan Neubert. Battle Cry. 2006. (Illus.). 240p. (J). 15.95 (978-1-57505-928-0(2) , Carolrhoda Bks.) Lerner Publishing Group.

Scillian, Devin. Pappy's Handkerchief. Ellison, Chris, illus. rev. ed. 2007. (Tales of Young Americans Ser.). 40p. (J). (gr. 3-7). 17.95 (***978-1-58536-316-2(2)***) Sleeping Bear Pr.

Shaw, Marilyn Bishop. Solomon. 2006. 203p. (J). 14.95 (978-1-56164-349-3(1)) Pineapple Pr., Inc.

Sibley, Linda. David Joins the California Gold Rush. 2004. 96p. (***978-0-7891-6002-7(1)***) Perfection Learning Corp.

Silverthorne, Judith. The Secret of the Stone House. 2006. (From Many Peoples Ser.). (Illus.). 192p. (J). pap. 7.95 (978-1-55050-325-8(1)) Coteau Bks. CAN. *Dist:* F & W Pubns., Inc.

Simmons, Marc. Billy Blackfeet in the Rockies: A Story from History. Kil, Ronald R., illus. 2006. 56p. (J). 18.95 (978-0-8263-4105-1(5)) Univ. of New Mexico Pr.

Skinner, Constance Lindsay. Becky Landers: Frontier Warrior. 2006. (Living History Library). 200p. (J). pap. 13.95 (978-1-932350-06-7(3)) Bethlehem Bks.

Smith, Debra. Hattie Marshall & the Dangerous Fire. 2007. 144p. (J). pap. 7.95 (***978-1-58980-492-0(9)***) Pelican Publishing Co., Inc.

Smith, Janice Lee. Jess & the Stinky Cowboys. Thiesing, Lisa, illus. 2004. (Dial Easy-to-Read Ser.). 48p. (J). (gr. k-3). 14.99 (978-0-8037-2641-3(4) , Dial) Penguin Group (USA) Inc.

Snelling, Lauraine. Tender Mercies. 1999. (gr. 5-8). lib. bdg. 19.95 (978-0-613-55672-9(0)) Tandem Library Bks.

Sommer, Carl. Light Your Candle. 2003. (Another Sommer-Time Story Ser.). (Illus.). 48p. (J). (gr. k-4). lib. bdg. 23.95 incl. audio compact disk (978-1-57537-768-1(3)); 16.95 incl. audio compact disk (978-1-57537-567-0(2)); 16.95 incl. audio compact disk (978-1-57537-518-2(4)); lib. bdg. 23.95 incl. audio compact disk (978-1-57537-718-6(7)) Advance Publishing, Inc.

—Light Your Candle. James, Kennon, illus. 2000. (Another Sommer-Time Story Ser.). 48p. (J). (ENG.). (gr. 1-4). 9.95 (978-1-57537-019-4(0)); (ps-4). lib. bdg. 16.95 (978-1-57537-068-2(9)) Advance Publishing, Inc.

Sommerdorf, Norma. Red River Girl. 2006. (Illus.). 192p. (J). 16.95 (978-0-8234-1903-6(7)) Holiday Hse., Inc.

Sperry, Armstrong. Wagons Westward: The Old Trail to Santa Fe. Sperry, Armstrong, illus. 2005. (Illus.). 200p. (YA). (gr. 6-11). reprint ed. pap. 15.00 (978-0-7567-9693-8(8)) DIANE Publishing Co.

—Wagons Westward: The Old Trail to Santa Fe. 2000. (Illus.). 224p. (J). pap. 14.95 (978-1-56792-128-1(0)) Godine, David R. Pub.

Spooner, Michael. Daniel's Walk. rev. ed. 176p. 2004. (J). pap. 7.95 (978-0-8050-7543-4(7)); 2001. (Illus.). (YA). (gr. 7 up). 16.95 (978-0-8050-6750-7(7)) Holt, Henry & Co. (Holt, Henry & Co. Bks. For Young Readers).

Stanley, Diane. Roughing It on the Oregon Trail. Berry, Holly, illus. 2001. (Time-Traveling Twins Ser.: No. 1). 48p. (J). (gr. k-5). pap. 6.99 (978-0-06-449006-1(8) , Harper Trophy) HarperCollins Pubs.

—Roughing It on the Oregon Trail. 2001. (gr. 3-6). lib. bdg. 14.10 (978-0-613-44250-3(4)) Tandem Library Bks.

Steele, William O. The Buffalo Knife. 2004. (Illus.). 144p. (J). 17.00 (978-0-15-205214-0(3) , Harcourt Young Classics); pap. 5.95 (978-0-15-205215-7(1) , Odyssey Classics) Harcourt Children's Bks.

—Flaming Arrows. 2004. (Illus.). 160p. (J). pap. 5.95 (978-0-15-205213-3(5) , Odyssey Classics) Harcourt Children's Bks.

—Winter Danger. 2004. (Illus.). 144p. (J). 17.00 (978-0-15-205205-8(4) , Harcourt Young Classics); pap. 5.95 (978-0-15-205206-5(2) , Odyssey Classics) Harcourt Children's Bks.

Steig, Jeanne. Tales from Gizzard's Grill. Turner, Sandy, illus. 2004. 80p. (J). 17.89 (978-0-06-000960-1(8)); 16.99 (978-0-06-000959-5(4)) HarperCollins Pubs. (Cotler, Joanna Books).

Stites, Clara. Lixia of Gold Mountain: A Story of Early California. 2003. (Illus.). 64p. (J). pap. 8.95 (978-1-56474-421-0(3)) Fithian Pr.

Stone, B. J. Girl on the Bluff. (Illus.). 160p. 8.95 (978-1-57168-297-0(X)); 1999. 124p. (J). (gr. 4-6). 14.95 (978-1-57168-280-2(5)) Eakin Pr.

Stratemeyer, Edward. On the Trail of Pontiac or the Pioneer B. 2006. 63.99 (***978-1-4219-9636-3(7)***); pap. 57.99 (***978-1-4219-9640-0(5)***) IndyPublish.com.

Stumpff, April D. & Johnston, Cassandra. Frontier Fun: A Children's Activity Book. 2007. 96p. (J). pap. 9.95 (***978-1-933337-21-0(4)***) State Hse. Pr.

Stutson, Caroline. Prairie Primer: A to Z. Lamb, Susan Condie, illus. 2006. 29p. (J). (ps-2). reprint ed. 16.00 (978-1-4223-5585-5(3)) DIANE Publishing Co.

—Prairie Primer A to Z. 1999. (978-0-606-16783-3(8)) Tandem Library Bks.

Sullivan, Arlene R. The Journey of Hanna Heart: You Never Know Where the Wind Will Blow. Sullivan, Arlene R., illus. 1998. (Illus.). 16p. (J). (gr. k-5). pap. 12.95 (978-0-9665793-0-7(5)) Changing Images Art Foundation, Inc.

Susi, Geraldine Lee. My Father, My Companion: Life at the Hollow, Chief Justice John Marshall's Boyhood Home in Virginia. 2001. (Illus.). 96p. (J). (gr. 4-9). pap. 10.95 (978-1-889324-22-7(1)) EPM Pubns., Inc.

Thomas, Carroll. Riding by Starlight: A Matty Trescott Novel. 2002. (Illus.). ix, 173p. (J). 9.95 (978-1-57525-315-2(1)) Smith and Kraus Publishers, Incorporated.

—The Town on Rambling Creek: A Matty Trescott Novel. 2004. (Illus.). ix, 185p. (J). (978-1-57525-376-3(3)) Smith and Kraus Publishers, Incorporated.

Thomas, Joyce Carol. I Have Heard of a Land. Cooper, Floyd, illus. 2000. (Trophy Picture Bk.). 32p. (J). (gr. k-3). pap. 6.99 (978-0-06-443617-5(9) , Harper Trophy) HarperCollins Pubs.

—I Have Heard of a Land. 1998. (Illus.). 32p. (J). (gr. 2-6). 15.95 (978-0-06-023477-5(6) , Cotler, Joanna Books) HarperCollins Pubs.

—I Have Heard of a Land. Cooper, Floyd, illus. 1998. 32p. (J). (gr. 3 up). lib. bdg. 14.89 (978-0-06-023478-2(4) , Cotler, Joanna Books) HarperCollins Pubs.

Thomasma, Kenneth. Doe Sia: Bannock Girl & the Handcart Pioneer. 1999. (Amazing Indian Children: Vol. 8). (J). (gr. 3-8). 12.99 (978-1-880114-21-6(6)) Grandview Publishing Co.

—Doe Sia: Bannock Girl & the Handcart Pioneers. 1999. (Illus.). (J). 14.64 (978-0-606-21884-9(X)) Tandem Library Bks.

Thompson, Gare. Our Journey West: An Adventure on the Oregon Trail. 2003. 40p. (J). pap. 6.99 (978-0-7922-5199-6(7)) National Geographic Society.

—Our Journey West: The Oregon Trail Adventures of Sarah Marshall. 2003. (I Am American Ser.). (Illus.). 40p. (J). (gr. 3-7). pap. 6.99 (978-0-7922-5178-1(4) , National Geographic Children's Bks.) National Geographic Society.

Trottier, Maxine. Prairie Willow. 1999. (gr. k-3). lib. bdg. 15.25 (978-0-613-28614-5(6)) Tandem Library Bks.

Turner, Ann Warren. Grasshopper Summer. Meltzer, Erika, illus. 2000. 176p. (J). (gr. 4-7). pap. 4.99 (978-0-689-83522-3(1) , Aladdin) Simon & Schuster Children's Publishing.

—Grasshopper Summer. 2000. (Illus.). (J). (978-0-606-17921-8(6)) Tandem Library Bks.

Turner, Nancy E. These Is My Words: The Diary of Sarah Agnes Prine, 1881-1902 Arizona Territories. 1999. (978-0-606-17597-5(0)) Tandem Library Bks.

Urban, Betsy. Waiting for Deliverance. 2000. (Illus.). iv, 186p. (J). (gr. 7-12). 18.99 (978-0-531-33310-5(8)); pap. 17.95 (978-0-531-30310-8(1)) Scholastic, Inc. (Orchard Bks.).

Van Leeuwen, Jean. Cabin on Trouble Creek. 2004. 224p. (J). (gr. 4). 16.99 (978-0-8037-2548-5(5) , Dial) Penguin Group (USA) Inc.

—Hannah of Fairfield. Diamond, Donna, illus. 2000. (Pioneer Daughters Ser.: No. 1). 96p. (J). (gr. 2-5). pap. 5.99 (978-0-14-130499-1(5) , Puffin) Penguin Group (USA) Inc.

—Hannah of Fairfield. 2000. (Puffin Chapters Ser.). 11.79 (978-0-606-17867-9(8)); (gr. 3-6). lib. bdg. 13.00 (978-0-613-25446-5(5)) Tandem Library Bks.

—Hannah's Helping Hands. Diamond, Donna, illus. 2000. (Pioneer Daughters Ser.: No. 2). 96p. (J). (gr. 2-5). pap. 5.99 (978-0-14-130500-4(2) , Puffin) Penguin Group (USA) Inc.

—Hannah's Helping Hands. 2000. (Puffin Chapters Ser.). 12.79 (978-0-606-18842-5(8)); (gr. 3-6). lib. bdg. 14.15 (978-0-613-28514-8(X)) Tandem Library Bks.

—Papa & the Pioneer Quilt. Bond, Rebecca, illus. 2007. (J). (gr. k-3). 32p. 16.99 (978-0-8037-3028-1(4)); (***978-1-4287-3972-7(6)***) Penguin Group (USA) Inc. (Dial).

Wallace, Bill. Red Dog. 2002. 192p. (J). pap. 5.99 (978-0-689-85394-4(7) , Aladdin) Simon & Schuster Children's Publishing.

—Red Dog. 2002. (gr. 3-6). lib. bdg. 13.00 (978-0-613-64447-1(6)) Tandem Library Bks.

Warring, Molly-Ann. Paradise Acres. 2005. 518p. (978-0-88887-312-5(3)) Borealis Pr.

Watts, Leander. Wild Ride to Heaven. 2003. 176p. (YA). (gr. 5-9). tchr. ed. 16.00 (978-0-618-26805-4(7)) Houghton Mifflin Co. Trade & Reference Div.

Whelan, Gloria. Return to the Island. 192p. (J). (gr. 4-7). 2002. pap. 5.95 (978-0-06-440761-8(6)); 2000. 15.89 (978-0-06-028254-7(1)) HarperCollins Pubs.

Wilder, Laura Ingalls. Animal Adventures. 2004. (Little House Chapter Bks.: No. 3). (Illus.). 48p. (J). (gr. 3-6). (978-0-7666-0608-1(2) , 99170) Modern Publishing.

—Animal Adventures. 2000. (Little House Chapter Bks.). (Illus.). 80p. (J). (gr. 3-6). Teaching Resource Ctr.

—By the Shores of Silver Lake. (Little House Ser.). (J). (gr. 3-6). lib. bdg. 23.95 (978-0-8488-2117-3(3)) Amereon LTD.

—By the Shores of Silver Lake. 2007. (Little House Ser.). 384p. (J). pap. 6.99 (978-0-06-088541-0(6) , Harper Trophy) HarperCollins Pubs.

—By the Shores of Silver Lake. Williams, Garth, illus. 2004. (Little House Ser.). 304p. (J). pap. 8.99 (978-0-06-058184-8(0) , Harper Trophy) HarperCollins Pubs.

—By the Shores of Silver Lake. Williams, Garth, illus. l.t. ed. 2002. (LRS Large Print Cornerstone Ser.). (J). lib. bdg. 35.95 (978-1-58118-098-5(5)) LRS.

—By the Shores of Silver Lake. 2003. (gr. 3-6). lib. bdg. 14.15 (978-0-613-71429-7(6)) Tandem Library Bks.

—County Fair. Wheeler, Jody, illus. 1998. (My First Little House Bks.). 32p. (J). (ps-3). pap. 6.99 (978-0-06-443493-5(1) , Harper Trophy) HarperCollins Pubs.

—The Deer in the Wood. Graef, Renee, illus. 1999. (My First Little House Bks.). 32p. (J). (ps-3). pap. 6.99 (978-0-06-443498-0(2) , Harper Trophy) HarperCollins Pubs.

—The Deer in the Wood. 1999. (My First Little House Bks.). (J). 12.79 (978-0-606-15841-1(3)) Tandem Library Bks.

—The First Four Years. 2007. (Little House Ser.). 160p. (J). pap. 6.99 (978-0-06-088545-8(9) , Harper Trophy) HarperCollins Pubs.

—The First Four Years. Williams, Garth, illus. (Little House Ser.). (J). 2004. 160p. pap. 8.99 (978-0-06-058188-6(3) , Harper Trophy); 2003. 144p. pap. 5.99 (978-0-06-052243-8(7)) HarperCollins Pubs.

—The First Four Years. Williams, Garth, illus. l.t. ed. 2002. (LRS Large Print Cornerstone Ser.). (J). lib. bdg. 27.95 (978-1-58118-103-6(5) , 25535) LRS.

—The First Four Years. 2003. (gr. 3-6). lib. bdg. 14.15 (978-0-613-71430-3(X)) Tandem Library Bks.

—El Largo Invierno.Tr. of Long Winter. (SPA.). 224p. (J). (gr. 4-5). 8.99 (978-84-279-3231-9(6) , NG0108) Noguer y Caralt Editores, S. A. ESP. *Dist:* Lectorum Pubns., Inc.

—El Largo Invierno. 2002. Tr. of Long Winter. (SPA.). (gr. 3-6). lib. bdg. 17.60 (978-0-613-80731-9(6)) Tandem Library Bks.

—Laura & Mr. Edwards. 1999. (Little House Chapter Bks.: No. 13). (J). (gr. 3-6). (978-0-606-16685-0(8)) Tandem Library Bks.

—Laura's Ma. 1999. (Little House Chapter Bks.: No. 11). (J). (gr. 3-6). (978-0-606-15839-8(1)) Tandem Library Bks.

—Laura's Pa. 1999. (Little House Chapter Bks.: No. 12). (J). (gr. 3-6). (978-0-606-15840-4(5)) Tandem Library Bks.

—A Little House Christmas Treasury: Festive Holiday Stories. Williams, Garth, illus. 2005. (Little House Ser.). 144p. (J). 12.99 (978-0-06-076918-5(1)) HarperCollins Pubs.

—The Little House Collection, Set. Williams, Garth, illus. 2004. (Little House Ser.). (J). pap. 44.99 (978-0-06-075428-0(1) , Harper Trophy) HarperCollins Pubs.

—Little House "History Comes to Life" Event Kit. 2000. (J). (978-0-06-028839-6(6)) HarperCollins Pubs.

—Little House in the Big Woods. 2007. (Little House Ser.). 224p. (J). pap. 6.99 (978-0-06-088537-3(8) , Harper Trophy) HarperCollins Pubs.

—Little House in the Big Woods. Williams, Garth, illus. (Little House Ser.). 256p. (J). 2004. pap. 8.99 (978-0-06-058180-0(8) , Harper Trophy); 2001. 19.95 (978-0-06-029647-6(X)); 2007. 19.99 (***978-0-06-128980-4(9)***) HarperCollins Pubs.

—Little House in the Big Woods. Williams, Garth, illus. l.t. ed. 2000. (Little House Ser.). 244p. (J). (gr. 3-6). lib. bdg. 28.95 (978-1-58118-078-7(0) , 24070) LRS.

—Little House in the Big Woods A Special Read Aloud Edition. Williams, Garth, illus. 2001. (Little House Ser.). 256p. (J). (gr. 3-5). 19.89 (978-0-06-029648-3(8)) HarperCollins Pubs.

—Little House on the Prairie. 2007. (Little House Ser.). 336p. (J). pap. 6.99 (978-0-06-088539-7(4) , Harper Trophy) HarperCollins Pubs.

—Little House on the Prairie. Williams, Garth, illus. (Little House Ser.). (J). 2004. 352p. pap. 8.99 (978-0-06-058181-7(6) , Harper Trophy); 2003. 272p. pap. 5.99 (978-0-06-052237-7(2)); 1999. 320p. (gr. 3-6). 29.95 (978-0-06-028244-8(4)) HarperCollins Pubs.

—Little House on the Prairie. Williams, Garth, illus. l.t. ed. 1999. (Little House Ser.). 420p. (J). (gr. 3-6). lib. bdg. 35.95 (978-1-58118-051-0(9) , 22771) LRS.

—Little House on the Prairie. 1999. (Little House Ser.). (J). (gr. 3-6). 11.95 (978-1-56137-834-0(8)) Novel Units, Inc.

—Little House on the Prairie Book & Charm. Williams, Garth, illus. 2002. (Charming Classics). 352p. (J). 6.99 (978-0-06-000046-2(5) , Harper Festival) HarperCollins Pubs.

—Little House Parties. 1999. (gr. 3-6). lib. bdg. 12.10 (978-0-613-15883-1(0)); (Little House Chapter Bks.: No. 14). (J). (978-0-606-16686-7(6)) Tandem Library Bks.

—A Little Prairie House. Graef, Renée, illus. 1999. (My First Little House Bks.). 32p. (J). (ps-3). pap. 6.99 (978-0-06-443526-0(1) , Harper Trophy) HarperCollins Pubs.

—A Little Prairie House. Graef, Renee, illus. adapted ed. 1998. (Little House Picture Bks.). 40p. (J). (ps-3). 13.89 (978-0-06-025908-2(6)) HarperCollins Pubs.

—Little Town on the Prairie. 2007. (Little House Ser.). 320p. (J). pap. 6.99 (978-0-06-088543-4(2) , Harper Trophy) HarperCollins Pubs.

—Little Town on the Prairie. Williams, Garth, illus. (Little House Ser.). 320p. (J). 2004. pap. 8.99 (978-0-06-058186-2(7) , Harper Trophy); 2003. pap. 5.99 (978-0-06-052242-1(9)) HarperCollins Pubs.

—Little Town on the Prairie. 2000. (Little House Ser.). (J). (gr. 3-6). pap. 9.90 (978-0-06-449101-3(3) , Harper Trophy) HarperCollins Pubs.

—Little Town on the Prairie. Williams, Garth, illus. l.t. ed. 2002. (LRS Large Print Cornerstone Ser.). (J). lib. bdg. 35.95 (978-1-58118-101-2(9) , 25533) LRS.

—Little Town on the Prairie. 2003. (gr. 3-6). lib. bdg. 14.15 (978-0-613-71425-9(3)) Tandem Library Bks.

—The Long Winter. 2007. (Little House Ser.). 352p. (J). pap. 6.99 (978-0-06-088542-7(4) , Harper Trophy) HarperCollins Pubs.

—The Long Winter. Williams, Garth, illus. 2004. (Little House Ser.). 352p. (J). pap. 8.99 (978-0-06-058185-5(9) , Harper Trophy) HarperCollins Pubs.

—The Long Winter. Williams, Garth, illus. l.t. ed. 2002. (LRS Large Print Cornerstone Ser.). (J). lib. bdg. 35.95 (978-1-58118-100-5(0)) LRS.

—My Little House Book of Animals. Graef, Renee, illus. 1998. (My First Little House Bks.). (J). (ps). lib. bdg. (978-0-06-025993-8(0)) HarperCollins Pubs.

—My Little House Book of Family. Graef, Renee, illus. 1998. (My First Little House Bks.). (J). (ps). lib. bdg. (978-0-06-025989-1(2)) HarperCollins Pubs.

—On the Banks of Plum Creek. 2007. (Little House Ser.). 384p. (J). pap. 6.99 (978-0-06-088540-3(8) , Harper Trophy) HarperCollins Pubs.

—On the Banks of Plum Creek. Williams, Garth, illus. 2004. (Little House Ser.). 352p. (J). pap. 8.99 (978-0-06-058183-1(2) , Harper Trophy) HarperCollins Pubs.

—On the Banks of Plum Creek. l.t. ed. 2002. (LRS Large Print Cornerstone Ser.). (Illus.). (J). lib. bdg. 35.95 (978-1-58118-099-2(3) , 25531) LRS.

—On the Banks of Plum Creek. 2003. (gr. 3-6). lib. bdg. 14.15 (978-0-613-71423-5(7)) Tandem Library Bks.

—Prairie Day. Graef, Renee, illus. adapted ed. 1998. (My First Little House Bks.). 32p. (J). (ps-3). pap. 6.99 (978-0-06-443504-8(0) , Harper Trophy) HarperCollins Pubs.

—Prairie Day. Graef, Renee, illus. 1998. (My First Little House Bks.). (J). (ps-1). (978-0-606-13719-5(X)) Tandem Library Bks.

—Santa Comes to Little House. Graef, Renee, illus. 2004. (Little House Ser.). 32p. (J). (ps-3). pap. 5.99 (978-0-06-058694-2(X) , Harper Trophy) HarperCollins Pubs.

—Summertime in the Big Woods. Graef, Renee, illus. 2000. (My First Little House Bks.). 40p. (J). (ps-3). pap. 6.99 (978-0-06-443497-3(4) , Harper Trophy) HarperCollins Pubs.

—These Happy Golden Years. 2007. (Little House Ser.). 304p. (J). pap. 6.99 (978-0-06-088544-1(0) , Harper Trophy) HarperCollins Pubs.

—These Happy Golden Years. Williams, Garth, illus. (Little House Ser.). (J). 2004. 304p. pap. 8.99 (978-0-06-058187-9(5) , Harper Trophy); 2003. 336p. pap. 5.99 (978-0-06-052315-2(8)) HarperCollins Pubs.

—These Happy Golden Years. l.t. ed. (J). (gr. 3-6). 35.95 (978-1-58118-102-9(7)) LRS.

—These Happy Golden Years. 2003. (gr. 3-6). lib. bdg. 14.15 (978-0-613-71434-1(2)) Tandem Library Bks.

Wiley, Melissa. Little House Chapter Book, No. 26. 2001. (J). pap. (978-0-06-442112-6(0) , Harper Trophy) HarperCollins Pubs.

Wilkes, Maria. Little Clearing in the Woods. 2008. (Little House Ser.). 160p. (J). pap. 5.99 (***978-0-06-114823-1(7)*** , Harper Trophy) HarperCollins Pubs.

Wilkes, Maria D. Brookfield Days. Ettlinger, Doris, illus. 1999. (Little House Chapter Bks.: No. 1). 80p. (J). (gr. 3-6). 14.89 (978-0-06-027952-3(4)) HarperCollins Pubs.

—Brookfield Days. 1999. (Little House Chapter Bks.: No.1). (Illus.). (J). (gr. 3-6). 11.05 (978-0-606-18680-3(8)) Tandem Library Bks.

—Brookfield Friends. Andreasen, Dan, illus. 2000. (Little House Chapter Bks.: No. 4). 80p. (J). (gr. 3-6). 14.89 (978-0-06-028552-4(4)) HarperCollins Pubs.

—Little Clearing in the Woods. Andreasen, Dan, illus. 1998. (Little House Ser.). 336p. (J). (gr. 3-7). 15.95 (978-0-06-026997-5(9) ; 15.89 (978-0-06-026998-2(7)) HarperCollins Pubs.

—Little House in Brookfield. 2007. (Little House Ser.). 144p. (J). pap. 5.99 (***978-0-06-114821-7(0)*** , Harper Trophy) HarperCollins Pubs.

—Little Town at the Crossroads Bk. 2: The Caroline Years. 2007. (Little House Ser.). 176p. (J). pap. 5.99 (***978-0-06-114822-4(9)*** , Harper Trophy) HarperCollins Pubs.

—A New Little Cabin. Ettlinger, Doris, illus. 2001. (Little House Chapter Bks.: Vol. 5). 80p. (J). (gr. 2-5). 14.89 (978-0-06-028554-8(0)) HarperCollins Pubs.

—A New Little Cabin. 2001. (Little House Chapter Bks.). (Illus.). (J). (gr. 2-5). (978-0-606-20592-4(6)) Tandem Library Bks.

—On Top of Concord Hill. Andreasen, Dan, illus. 2000. (Little House Ser.). 288p. (J). (gr. 3-7). 15.89 (978-0-06-027003-2(9)) HarperCollins Pubs.

Wilkes, Maria D., et al. The Little House Pioneer Girls, 3 vols. 1998. (J). (gr. 3-7). pap. 14.85 (978-0-06-440709-0(8) , Harper Trophy) HarperCollins Pubs.

Wilkins, Celia. Across the Rolling River. Andreasen, Dan, illus. 2001. (Little House Ser.). 272p. (J). 16.95 (978-0-06-027004-9(7)); 16.89 (978-0-06-027005-6(5)); (gr. 5 up). pap. 6.99 (978-0-06-440734-2(9) , Harper Trophy) HarperCollins Pubs.

—Across the Rolling River. Andreasen, Dan, illus. 2001. (gr. 3-6). lib. bdg. 14.15 (978-0-613-51524-5(2)) Tandem Library Bks.

Williams, Heather. Nellie Oleson Meets Laura Ingalls. 2007. (Little House Ser.). 240p. (J). lib. bdg. 16.89 (***978-0-06-124249-6(7));*** (gr. 3-7). 15.99 (***978-0-06-124248-9(9))*** HarperCollins Pubs.

Wilson, Diane Lee. Black Storm Comin'. (J). 2006. 240p. pap. 5.99 (978-0-689-87138-2(4) , Aladdin); 2005. 304p. (gr. 5-9). 17.99 (978-0-689-87137-5(6) , McElderry, Margaret K.) Simon & Schuster Children's Publishing.

Wilson, Laura. How I Survived the Oregon Trail: The Journal of Jesse Adams. 2006. (Illus.). 37p. (J). (gr. 4-8). reprint ed. pap. 10.00 (978-0-7567-9925-0(2)) DIANE Publishing Co.

—How I Survived the Oregon Trail: The Journal of Jesse Adams. 1999. (Time Travellers Ser.). (Illus.). 38p. (J). (gr. 4-7). pap. 9.95 (978-0-688-17276-3(8)) HarperCollins Pubs.

Winston, Annie. Admiral Wright's Heroical Storicals: Daniel Boone & the Battle of Boonesborough. 3rd ed. 2007. (Illus.). 288p. (J). 12.99 (***978-0-9779535-4-7(8)*** , Sonship Pr.) 21st Century Pr.

Wishinsky, Frieda. Pioneer Kids. Griffiths, Dean, illus. 2007. (Canadian Flyer Adventures Ser.: No. 6). 96p. (J). (gr. 1-4). 16.95 (***978-1-897349-04-5(1));*** pap. 6.95 (***978-1-897349-05-2(X))*** Maple Tree Pr. CAN. *Dist:* Perseus Distribution.

Yep, Laurence. When the Circus Came to Town. Wang, Suling, illus. 2001. 128p. (J). (ps-1). 14.99 (978-0-06-029325-3(X)); lib. bdg. 15.89 (978-0-06-029326-0(8)) HarperCollins Pubs.

—When the Circus Came to Town. 2004. (gr. 3-6). lib. bdg. 14.15 (978-0-613-86716-0(5)) Tandem Library Bks.

Yep, Laurence & Yep, Laurence. When the Circus Came to Town. Wang, Suling, illus. 2004. 128p. (J). (ps-k). pap. 5.99 (978-0-06-440965-0(1) , Harper Trophy) HarperCollins Pubs.

FRONTIER AND PIONEER LIFE—SOUTHWEST

Brown, Rachel K. Santa Fe: Daily Life in a Western Trading Center. 2003. (J). lib. bdg. (978-1-58417-011-2(5)) Lake Street Pubs.

Dean, Arlan. The Old Spanish Trail: From Santa Fe, New Mexico to Los Angeles, California. 2003. (Reading Power Ser.). (Illus.). 24p. (J). lib. bdg. 17.25 (978-0-8239-6480-2(9)) Rosen Publishing Group, Inc., The.

Harmon, Daniel E. Billy the Kid. 2001. (Famous Figures of the American Frontier Ser.). (Illus.). 64p. (J). pap. 25.00 (978-0-7910-6484-9(0)); 25.00 (978-0-7910-6483-2(2)) Facts On File, Inc. (Chelsea Hse.).

—Billy the Kid. 2002. (gr. 5-8). lib. bdg. 17.60 (978-0-613-50869-8(6)) Tandem Library Bks.

Isaacs, Sally Senzell. Life at the Alamo. 2003. (Picture the Past Ser.). (Illus.). 32p. (J). (gr. 2-4). lib. bdg. (978-1-58810-695-7(0)); pap. 7.50 (978-1-4034-0523-4(9)) Heinemann Library.

The Old Spanish Trail, 6 Packs. (On Deck Ser.: Vol. 2). 24p. (gr. 4-5). 35.00 (978-0-7578-5812-3(0)) Rigby Education.

Randolph, Ryan P. The Santa Fe Trail. 2003. (Library of the Westward Expansion). (Illus.). 24p. (J). lib. bdg. 19.95 (978-0-8239-6292-1(X) , PowerKids Pr.) Rosen Publishing Group, Inc., The.

Stein, R. Conrad. In the Spanish West. 1999. (How We Lived Ser.). (Illus.). 72p. (J). (gr. 4-8). lib. bdg. 27.07 (978-0-7614-0906-9(8) , Benchmark Bks.) Cavendish, Marshall Corp.

FRONTIER AND PIONEER LIFE—WEST (U.S.)

Alter, Judy. Great Women of the Old West. 2001. (We the People Ser.). (Illus.). 48p. (J). (gr. 4 up). lib. bdg. 22.60 (978-0-7565-0099-3(0)) Compass Point Bks.

Arruda, Suzanne Middendorf. The Girl He Left Behind: The Life & Times of Libbie Custer. 2004. (Avisson Young Adult Ser.). (Illus.). 136p. (J). pap. 19.95 (978-1-888105-67-4(4)) Avisson Pr., Inc.

Bard, Jessica. Lawmen & Outlaws: The Wild, Wild West. 2005. (Trailblazers of the West Ser.). (Illus.). 48p. (J). (ps-7). 24.00 (978-0-516-25130-1(9)); (YA). (gr. 7-12). pap. 6.95 (978-0-516-25085-4(X)) Scholastic Library Publishing. (Children's Pr.).

Binns, Tristan Boyer. Fort Laramie. 2001. (Visiting the Past Ser.). 32p. (J). (gr. 5-7). lib. bdg. 24.22 (978-1-58810-271-3(8)) Heinemann Library.

Bork, Rhoda. Pioneering: Activities to Live History. 2007. (J). (***978-0-9786018-6-7(6))*** Sparrow Media Group, Inc.

Bryant, Jill. John Henry Holliday. 2003. (Folk Heroes Ser.). (Illus.). 24p. (J). lib. bdg. 15.95 (978-1-59036-077-4(X)) Weigl Pubs., Inc.

—Wagon Train. 2003. (Real Life Stories Ser.). (Illus.). 24p. (J). lib. bdg. 15.95 (978-1-59036-082-8(6)) Weigl Pubs., Inc.

—Women in the West. 2003. (Real Life Stories Ser.). (Illus.). 24p. (J). lib. bdg. 15.95 (978-1-59036-083-5(4)) Weigl Pubs., Inc.

Buffalo Soldiers & the Western Frontier Vol. 2: Individual Title Six-Packs. (On Deck Ser.: Vol. 2). 24p. (gr. 4-5). 35.00 (978-0-7578-5805-5(8)) Rigby Education.

Burger, James P. The Mountain Men of the West. 2002. (Library of the Westward Expansion). (Illus.). 24p. (J). (gr. 3). lib. bdg. 19.95 (978-0-8239-5853-5(1) , PowerKids Pr.) Rosen Publishing Group, Inc., The.

—The Oregon Trail. 2002. (Library of the Westward Expansion). (Illus.). 24p. (J). (gr. 3). lib. bdg. 19.95 (978-0-8239-5850-4(7) , PowerKids Pr.) Rosen Publishing Group, Inc., The.

Burke, Rick. James Beckwourth. 2003. (American Lives Ser.). 32p. pap. 6.95 (978-1-4034-4199-7(5)) Heinemann Library.

Burnett, Linda. Pioneers: Adventure in a New Land. 2005. (Trailblazers of the West Ser.). (Illus.). 48p. (J). (ps-7). 24.00 (978-0-516-25127-1(9)); (YA). (gr. 7-12). pap. 6.95 (978-0-516-25097-7(3)) Scholastic Library Publishing. (Children's Pr.).

Calvert, Patricia. Kit Carson: He Led the Way. 2006. (Great Explorations Ser.). (Illus.). 80p. (J). lib. bdg. 32.79 (978-0-7614-2223-5(4) , Benchmark Bks.) Cavendish, Marshall Corp.

Carlson, Laurie M. Westward Ho! An Activity Guide to the Wild West. 2003. (Kid's Guide Ser.). (Illus.). 160p. (J). (gr. k-7). pap. 14.95 (978-1-55652-271-0(1)) Chicago Review Pr., Inc.

Cheney, Martha. History Pockets: Moving West. McClain, Lynn, illus. 2003. (History Pockets Ser.). 96p. (J). (gr. 4-6). suppl. ed. 12.99 (978-1-55799-902-3(3) , EMC 3704) Evan-Moor Educational Pubs.

Collins, Kathleen. Jesse James: Western Bank Robber. 2003. (Famous People in American History Ser.). (Illus.). 32p. (J). pap. (978-0-8239-4184-1(1)) Rosen Publishing Group, Inc., The.

Crewe, Sabrina & Uschan, Michael V. The Oregon Trail. 2004. (Events That Shaped America Ser.). (Illus.). 32p. (J). lib. bdg. 24.67 (978-0-8368-3405-5(4)) Stevens, Gareth Inc.

Danneberg, Julie. Amidst the Gold Dust: Women Who Forged the West. 2004. (Illus.). 96p. (gr. 5 up). pap. 12.95 (978-1-55591-997-9(9)) Fulcrum Publishing.

Demund, Tom. From Slave to Superstar of the Wild West: The Awesome Story of Jim Beckwourth. 2007. 160p. (YA). 18.95 (***978-0-9786904-0-3(0))*** Legends of the West Publishing Co.

Dickinson, Rachel. Great Pioneer Projects You Can Build Yourself. 2007. (Build It Yourself Ser.). 128p. (J). (gr. 4 up). pap. 14.95 (***978-0-9785037-6-5(7))*** Nomad Pr.

DiVito, Anna. Annie Oakley Saves the Day! DiVito, Anna, illus. 2004. (Ready-to-Read Cofa Ser.). 32p. (J). pap. 3.99 (978-0-689-86520-6(1) , Aladdin) Simon & Schuster Children's Publishing.

—Annie Oakley Saves the Day. DiVito, Anna, illus. 2004. (Illus.). 29p. (J). (ps-7). lib. bdg. 10.79 (978-0-606-32656-8(1)) Tandem Library Bks.

Etulain, Richard W. With Badges & Bullets: Lawmen & Outpaws in the Old West. 1999. (gr. 7-12). lib. bdg. 28.00 (978-0-613-37077-6(5)) Tandem Library Bks.

Favor, Lesli J. A Historical Atlas of America's Manifest Destiny. 2005. (United States, Historical Atlases of the Growth of a New Nation Ser.). (Illus.). 64p. (J). (gr. 7-12). lib. bdg 30.60 (978-1-4042-0201-6(3)) Rosen Publishing Group, Inc., The.

Flanagan, Alice K. The Buffalo Soldiers. 2004. (We the People Ser.). (Illus.). 48p. (J). 22.60 (978-0-7565-0833-3(9)) Compass Point Bks.

Foran, Jill. Homesteading. 2003. (Real Life Stories Ser.). (Illus.). 24p. (J). lib. bdg. 15.95 (978-1-59036-079-8(6)) Weigl Pubs., Inc.

Frisch, Aaron. Jesse James. 2005. (Illus.). 48p. (gr. 5-9). 21.95 (978-1-58341-338-8(3) , Creative Education) Creative Co., The.

Gibbons, Gail. Cowboys & Cowgirls: Yippee-Yay! Gibbons, Gail, illus. 2003. (Illus.). 32p. (J). (gr. 1-4). pap. 7.99 (978-0-316-16859-5(9)) Little, Brown Bks. for Young Readers.

—Yippee-Yay! A Book about Cowboys & Cowgirls. Gibbons, Gail, illus. 1998. (Illus.). 32p. (J). (ps-3). 15.95 (978-0-316-30944-8(3)) Little Brown & Co.

Gintzler, A. S. Rough & Ready Homesteaders. Brigman, Chris, illus. 1998. (Rough & Ready Ser.). 46p. (J). lib. bdg. 16.95 (978-1-887238-08-3(5)) Fitzgerald Bks.

Glaser, Jason. The Buffalo Soldiers & the American West. Smith, Tod & Barnett, Charles, illus. 2005. (Graphic Library). 32p. (J). (gr. 3-7). lib. bdg. 25.26 (978-0-7368-4966-1(1)) Capstone Pr., Inc.

Glass, Andrew. Bad Guys: True Stories of Legendary Gunslingers. 2000. (Illus.). (J). (978-0-606-18781-7(2)) Tandem Library Bks.

Goodman, Michael E. Buffalo Bill. 2005. (Illus.). 48p. (gr. 5-9). 21.95 (978-1-58341-336-4(7) , Creative Education) Creative Co., The.

Goodman, Susan E. Brave Kids: Cora Frear. 2002. (gr. 3-6). lib. bdg. 11.80 (978-0-613-45014-0(0)) Tandem Library Bks.

Gregson, Susan R. James Beckwourth: Mountaineer, Scout & Pioneer. 2005. (Signature Lives Ser.). (Illus.). 112p. (J). (gr. 5-7). (978-0-7565-1000-8(7)) Compass Point Bks.

Gunderson, Mary. Cooking on the Lewis & Clark Expedition. 2000. (Blue Earth Books). (Illus.). 32p. (J). (gr. 3-4). lib. bdg. 22.60 (978-0-7368-0354-0(8) , Bridgestone Bks.) Capstone Pr., Inc.

—Cooking on the Lewis & Clark Expedition. 1999. (Exploring History Through Simple Recipes Ser.). (Illus.). 32p. (J). (gr. 2-7). pap. 14.60 (978-0-516-21865-6(4) , Children's Pr.) Scholastic Library Publishing.

—Oregon Trail Cooking. 2000. (Blue Earth Books). (Illus.). 32p. (J). (gr. 3-4). lib. bdg. 22.60 (978-0-7368-0355-7(6) , Bridgestone Bks.) Capstone Pr., Inc.

—Oregon Trail Cooking. 1999. (Exploring History Through Simple Recipes Ser.). (Illus.). 32p. (J). (gr. 2-7). pap. 14.60 (978-0-516-21866-3(2) , Children's Pr.) Scholastic Library Publishing.

Harcourt School Publishers Staff. On the Wild Frontier Below Level. 3rd ed. 2002. (Trophies Reading Program Ser.). (Illus.). pap. 5.10 (978-0-15-323051-6(7)) Harcourt Schl. Pubs.

Hicks, Peter. You Wouldn't Want to Live in a Wild West Town! Antram, David, illus. 2002. (You Wouldn't Want to Ser.). 32p. (J). (gr. 2-5). 28.50 (978-0-531-14606-4(5)); pap. 9.95 (978-0-531-16367-2(9)) Scholastic Library Publishing. (Watts, Franklin).

—You Wouldn't Want to Live in a Wild West Town! 2002. (gr. 3-6). lib. bdg. 18.75 (978-0-613-53888-6(9)) Tandem Library Bks.

Hopkins, Ellen H. Tarnished Legacy: The Story of the Comstock Lode. 2001. (Cover-to-Cover Bks.). (Illus.). 64p. (J). pap. (978-0-7891-1003-9(2)) Perfection Learning Corp.

Hunsaker, Joyce Badgley. Seeing the Elephant: Voices from the Oregon Trail. 2003. (Illus.). 272p. (J). 24.95 (978-0-89672-504-1(9)) Texas Tech Univ. Pr.

Jaffe, Elizabeth Dana. The Oregon Trail. 2002. (Let Freedom Ring Ser.). (Illus.). 48p. (J). (gr. 3-4). lib. bdg. 22.60 (978-0-7368-1101-9(X) , Bridgestone Bks.) Capstone Pr., Inc.

Johmann, Carol A. Going West! Journey on a Wagon Train to Settle a Frontier Town. 2000. (J). 17.60 (978-0-606-22459-8(9)) Tandem Library Bks.

Johmann, Carol A. & Rieth, Elizabeth J. Going West! Journey on a Wagon Train to Settle a Frontier Town. Kline, Michael P., illus. 2000. (Kaleidoscope Kids Bks.). 96p. (J). (gr. 2-8). pap. 12.95 (978-1-885593-38-2(4) , Williamson Bks.) Ideals Pubns.

—Going West! Journey on a Wagon Train to Settle a Frontier Town. 2000. (Illus.). 96p. (J). (gr. 2-7). per. 19.90 (978-0-613-27857-7(7)) Tandem Library Bks.

Jones, Charlotte Foltz. Westward Ho! Eleven Explorers of the American West. 2005. (Illus.). 240p. (J). (gr. 4-6). tchr. ed. 22.95 (978-0-8234-1586-1(4)) Holiday Hse., Inc.

Jordan, Shirley. Pioneer Days: Moments in History. 1999. (Cover-to-Cover Bks.). (Illus.). 64p. (J). pap. (978-0-7891-2912-3(4)); (gr. 4-7). lib. bdg. 17.95 (978-0-7807-8160-3(0)) Perfection Learning Corp.

Kalman, Bobbie. Homes of the West. 1998. (Life in the Old West Ser.). (Illus.). 32p. (J). (gr. 3-4). pap. (978-0-7787-0106-4(9)) Crabtree Publishing Co.

—Life in the Old West, 11 bks. Incl. Bandanas, Chaps & Ten-Gallon Hats. 1998. lib. bdg. (978-0-7787-0073-9(9)); Boomtowns of the West. 1999. lib. bdg. (978-0-7787-0078-4(X)); Gold Rush. 1999. lib. bdg. (978-0-7787-0079-1(8)); Homes of the West. 1998. lib. bdg. (978-0-7787-0074-6(7)); Life of a Miner. Calder, Kate. 1999. lib. bdg. (978-0-7787-0077-7(1)); Life on the Ranch. 1998. lib. bdg. (978-0-7787-0071-5(2)); Life on the Trail. 1998. lib. bdg. (978-0-7787-0072-2(0)); Railroad. 1999. lib. bdg. (978-0-7787-0076-0(3)); Wagon Train. 1998. lib. bdg. (978-0-7787-0070-8(4)); Who Settled the West? 1999. lib. bdg. (978-0-7787-0075-3(5)); Women of the West. Lewis, Jane. 1999. lib. bdg. (978-0-7787-0080-7(1)); 32p. (J). (gr. 3-4). (Illus.). 1999. (978-0-7787-0066-1(6)); Set pap. (978-0-7787-0098-2(4)) Crabtree Publishing Co.

—Wagon Train. 1999. (gr. 3-6). lib. bdg. 16.40 (978-0-613-12241-2(0)) Tandem Library Bks.

—Who Settled the West. 1999. (gr. 3-6). lib. bdg. 16.40 (978-0-613-12276-4(3)) Tandem Library Bks.

King, David C. Wild West Days: Discover the Past with Fun Projects, Games, Activities, & Recipes. 1998. (American Kids in History Ser.: Vol. 5). (Illus.). 128p. (gr. 3-7). pap. 12.95 (978-0-471-23919-2(4) , Wiley-Interscience) Wiley, John & Sons, Inc.

Klobuchar, Lisa. History & Activities of the Wagon Trail. 2004. (Hands-On American History Ser.). (Illus.). 32p. (J). 27.07 (978-1-4034-6055-4(8)) Heinemann Library.

Koestler-Grack, Rachel A. Daily Life in a Southwestern Settlement: San Antonio. 2003. (J). (978-1-58417-012-9(3)); pap. (978-1-58417-075-4(1)) Lake Street Pubs.

Krohn, Katherine E. Women of the Wild West. 2003. (Biography Ser.). (Illus.). 112p. (YA). (gr. 6 up). pap. 7.95 (978-0-8225-9690-5(3) , Carolrhoda Bks.) Lerner Publishing Group.

Landau, Elaine. The Homestead Act. 2006. 48p. (gr. 3-5). (YA). pap. 6.95 (978-0-516-27902-2(5)); (Illus.). (J). 25.00 (978-0-516-25870-6(2)) Scholastic Library Publishing. (Children's Pr.).

—The Mormon Trail. 2006. (True Book - Westward Expansion Ser.). (Illus.). 48p. (J). (gr. 3-5). 25.00 (978-0-516-25872-0(9) , Children's Pr.) Scholastic Library Publishing.

Langley, Andrew. 100 Things You Should Know about the Wild West. 2003. (Illus.). 48p. (J). (gr. 3 up). lib. bdg. (978-1-59084-458-8(0)) Mason Crest Pubs.

Lawrence, Jennie. Fort Laramie. 2004. (American Forts & Their Strategic Importance Ser.). (J). (978-1-59084-713-8(X)) Mason Crest Pubs.

Life on a Wagon Train. (Rosen Real Readers Big Bookstm Ser.). 16p. (J). (gr. 2-3). 38.75 (978-1-4042-6224-9(5)) Rosen Publishing Group, Inc., The.

Link, Theodore. Annie Oakley: Wild West Sharpshooter. 2003. (Primary Sources of Famous People in American History Ser.). (Illus.). 32p. (J). pap. (978-0-8239-4174-2(4)) Rosen Publishing Group, Inc., The.

Littlefield, Holly. Children of the Trail West. 1999. (Picture the American Past Ser.). (Illus.). 48p. (J). (gr. 2-5). lib. bdg. 22.60 (978-1-57505-304-2(7)) Lerner Publishing Group.

Loeper, John J. Meet the Wards on the Oregon Trail. 1998. (Early American Family Ser.). (Illus.). 64p. (J). (gr. 2-4). lib. bdg. 25.64 (978-0-7614-0844-4(4) , Benchmark Bks.) Cavendish, Marshall Corp.

Lowery, Linda. Aunt Clara Brown: Official Pioneer. Porter, Janice Lee, illus. 1999. (On My Own Biographies Ser.). 48p. (J). (gr. 2-5). lib. bdg. 23.93 (978-1-57505-045-4(5)) Lerner Publishing Group.

Manheimer, Ann S. James Beckwourth: Legendary Mountain Man. 2006. (Trailblazer Biography Ser.). (Illus.). 112p. (J). (ps-7). 30.60 (978-1-57505-892-4(8) , Twenty-First Century Bks.) Lerner Publishing Group.

Markel, Rita J. Your Travel Guide to America's Old West. 2005. (Passport to History Ser.). (Illus.). 96p. lib. bdg. 26.60 (978-0-8225-3074-9(0)) Lerner Publishing Group.

Maynard, Charles W. Fort Laramie. 2002. (Famous Forts Throughout American History Ser.). (Illus.). 24p. (J). (gr. 3). lib. bdg. 18.75 (978-0-8239-5839-9(6) , PowerKids Pr.) Rosen Publishing Group, Inc., The.

McCall, Edith. Adventures along the Cumberland Gap, Vol. 6. 2001. (Adventures on the American Frontiers Ser.). (Illus.). 127p. (J). (gr. 3-7). pap. 9.99 (978-0-89824-305-5(X) , 305-x) Royal Fireworks Publishing Co.

McKain, Mark, ed. Pioneers. 2002. (History Firsthand Ser.). (Illus.). 256p. (J). (gr. 7-10). pap. 24.95 (978-0-7377-1077-9(2)); lib. bdg. 36.20 (978-0-7377-1078-6(0)) Thomson Gale. (Greenhaven Pr., Inc.).

McPherson, James M. Into the West: From Reconstruction to the Final Days of the American Frontier. 2006. 96p. (J). (gr. 4-9). 22.95 (978-0-689-86543-5(0) , Atheneum) Simon & Schuster Children's Publishing.

Miller, Steven G. The Legend of Jessie James. 2001. (History Channel History Guides Ser.). (Illus.). 40p. (J). pap. 9.99 (978-0-86730-845-7(1)) Lebhar-Friedman Bks.

Morley, Jacqueline. You Wouldn't Want to Be an American Pioneer! Antram, David, illus. 2002. (You Wouldn't Want to Ser.). 32p. (J). (gr. 2-5). 28.50 (978-0-531-14608-8(1)); pap. 9.95 (978-0-531-16369-6(5)) Scholastic Library Publishing. (Watts, Franklin).

—You Wouldn't Want to Be an American Pioneer! 2002. (gr. 3-6). lib. bdg. 18.75 (978-0-613-53886-2(2)) Tandem Library Bks.

Murdock, S. Reed. Gideon: The Youngest Wagon Driver. unabr. ed. 2002. (Illus.). 32p. (J). (gr. 1-6). 11.95 (978-1-930980-71-6(X) , 8071X) Granite Publishing & Distribution.

Nelson, Sharlene P. & Nelson, Ted W. Jedediah Smith. 2004. (Watts Library). (Illus.). 64p. (J). 25.50 (978-0-531-12287-7(5) , Watts, Franklin) Scholastic Library Publishing.

Oregon Trail. (Exploring the West Ser.). 48p. (YA). 7.95 (978-0-7368-4508-3(9)) Capstone Pr., Inc.

The Oregon Trail, 6 Packs. (On Deck Ser.: Vol. 2). 24p. (gr. 4-5). 35.00 (978-0-7578-5813-0(9)) Rigby Education.

The Overland Trail: Individual Title Six-Packs. (On Deck Ser.: Vol. 2). 24p. (gr. 4-5). 35.00 (978-0-7578-5814-7(7)) Rigby Education.

Patent, Dorothy Hinshaw. Homesteading: Settling America's Heartland. Munoz, William, photos by. 1998. (Illus.). 32p. (J). (gr. 2-5). lib. bdg. 17.85 (978-0-8027-8665-4(0)); (gr. 3-7). 16.95 (978-0-8027-8664-7(2)) Walker & Co.

Porterfield, Jason. The Homestead ACT of 1862. 2005. (Illus.). 64p. (J). (gr. 5-8). lib. bdg. 29.25 (978-1-4042-0178-1(5)) Rosen Publishing Group, Inc., The.

Price, Sean. Crooks, Cowboys, & Characters: The Wild West. 2007. (J). (*978-1-4109-2695-1(8)); pap. (*978-1-4109-2706-4(7)) Steck-Vaughn.

Quasha, Jennifer. Covered Wagons: Hands-On Projects about America's Westward Expansion. 2001. (Great Social Studies Projects Ser.). (Illus.). 24p. (J). (gr. 3). lib. bdg. 19.95 (978-0-8239-5704-0(7) , PowerKids Pr.) Rosen Publishing Group, Inc., The.

Raabe, Emily. Buffalo Soldiers & the Western Frontier. 2003. (Reading Power Ser.). (Illus.). 24p. (J). lib. bdg. 17.25 (978-0-8239-6495-6(7) , PowerKids Pr.) Rosen Publishing Group, Inc., The.

Randolph, Ryan P. Black Cowboys. 2003. (Library of the Westward Expansion). (Illus.). 24p. (J). lib. bdg. 19.95 (978-0-8239-6294-5(6)) Rosen Publishing Group, Inc., The.

—Frontier Schools & Schoolteachers. 2003. (Library of the Westward Expansion). (Illus.). 24p. (J). lib. bdg. 19.95 (978-0-8239-6295-2(4) , PowerKids Pr.) Rosen Publishing Group, Inc., The.

—Frontier Women Who Helped Shape the American West. 2003. (Library of the Westward Expansion). (Illus.). 24p. (J). lib. bdg. 19.95 (978-0-8239-6297-6(0) , PowerKids Pr.) Rosen Publishing Group, Inc., The.

—Wild West Lawmen & Outlaws. 2003. (Library of the Westward Expansion). (Illus.). 24p. (J). lib. bdg. 19.95 (978-0-8239-6293-8(8) , PowerKids Pr.) Rosen Publishing Group, Inc., The.

Raum, Elizabeth. Wild West Legends. 2007. (J). (*978-1-4109-2968-6(X)); pap. (*978-1-4109-2989-1(2)) Steck-Vaughn.

Rea, Thelma. Pioneer Families. 2006. (Illus.). 16p. (J). lib. bdg. (978-1-4042-3346-1(6) , PowerKids Pr.) Rosen Publishing Group, Inc., The.

Reece, Paula. Settling the West: Adventures in Pioneering & Westward Expansion. 2002. (Skill-Based Reading Anthology Ser.). (Illus.). 124p. (978-0-7891-5582-5(6)) Perfection Learning Corp.

Robinson, J. Dennis. Jesse James: Legendary Rebel & Outlaw. 2006. (J). (978-0-7565-1871-4(7)) Compass Point Bks.

Roop, Connie & Roop, Peter, eds. The Diary of David R. Leeper: Rushing for Gold. 2000. (In My Own Words Ser.). (Illus.). 78p. (J). (gr. 5 up). lib. bdg. 27.07 (978-0-7614-1011-9(2) , Benchmark Bks.) Cavendish, Marshall Corp.

Rubin, Rick. Naked Against the Rain: The People of the Lower Columbia River, 1770-1830. 1999. (Illus.). 431p. (YA). (gr. 10 up). 29.95 (978-1-883287-00-9(6)) Far Shore Pr.

Savage, Candace. Born to Be a Cowgirl. 2001. (gr. 3-6). lib. bdg. 18.75 (978-0-613-49287-4(0)) Tandem Library Bks.

Savage, Candace C. Born to Be a Cowgirl: A Spirited Ride Through the Old West. 2001. 16.75 (978-0-606-22827-5(6)) Tandem Library Bks.

Schaefer, Ted. Westward to the Pacific. 2006. (Making a New Nation Ser.). (Illus.). 48p. (J). (978-1-4034-7829-0(5)); pap. (978-1-4034-7836-8(8)) Heinemann Library.

Shields, Charles J. Buffalo Bill Cody. 2001. (Famous Figures of the American Frontier Ser.). (Illus.). 64p. (J). (gr. 3-6). pap. 8.95 (978-0-7910-6498-6(0)); 25.00 (978-0-7910-6497-9(2)) Facts On File, Inc. (Chelsea Hse.).

Sinnott, Susan. Welcome to Kirsten's World, 1854: Growing up in Pioneer America. 1999. (American Girls Collection). (Illus.). 64p. (J). (gr. 2 up). 16.95 (978-1-56247-770-7(6)) American Girl Publishing, Inc.

Slovey, Christine & Pendergast, Sara, contrib. by. Westward Expansion: Almanac. 2000. (Illus.). xlvi, 254p. (J). 66.00 (978-0-7876-4862-6(0) , GML00502-114906, UXL) Thomson Gale.

Sonneborn, Liz. The Mormon Trail. 2005. (Watts Library). (Illus.). 63p. (J). (gr. 5-8). 25.50 (978-0-531-12317-1(0) , Watts, Franklin) Scholastic Library Publishing.

—Women of the American West. 2005. (Watts Library). (Illus.). 63p. (J). (gr. k-7). 25.50 (978-0-531-12318-8(9) , Watts, Franklin) Scholastic Library Publishing.

Stefoff, Rebecca. Texas & the Far West. 2002. (North American Historical Atlases Ser.). (Illus.). 48p. (J). 27.07 (978-0-7614-1345-5(6) , Benchmark Bks.) Cavendish, Marshall Corp.

Stotter, Mike. Wild West. 1999. (gr. 3-6). lib. bdg. 19.90 (978-0-613-86949-2(4)) Tandem Library Bks.

Suen, Anastasia. Trappers & Mountain Men. 2007. (Events in American History Ser.). (Illus.). 48p. (J). (gr. 4-6). lib. bdg. 29.93 (978-1-60044-134-9(3)) Rourke Publishing, LLC.

Sundling, Charles W. Explorers of the Frontier. 2000. (Frontier Land Ser.). (Illus.). 32p. (J). (gr. 3-8). lib. bdg. 24.21 (978-1-57765-044-7(1) , ABDO & Daughters) ABDO Publishing Co.

—Mountain Men of the Frontier. 2000. (Frontier Land Ser.). (Illus.). 32p. (J). (gr. 3-8). lib. bdg. 24.21 (978-1-57765-043-0(3) , ABDO & Daughters) ABDO Publishing Co.

—Pioneers of the Frontier. 2000. (Frontier Land Ser.). (Illus.). 32p. (J). (gr. 3-8). lib. bdg. 24.21 (978-1-57765-047-8(6) , ABDO & Daughters) ABDO Publishing Co.

—Women of the Frontier. 2000. (Frontier Land Ser.). (Illus.). 32p. (J). (gr. 3-8). lib. bdg. 24.21 (978-1-57765-046-1(8) , ABDO & Daughters) ABDO Publishing Co.

Swanson, Wayne. Why the West Was Wild. 2004. (Illus.). 48p. (J). (gr. 5). 24.95 (978-1-55037-837-5(6)); pap. 12.95 (978-1-55037-836-8(8)) Annick Pr., Ltd. CAN. *Dist:* Firefly Bks., Ltd.

Thompson, Gare. Our Journey West: The Oregon Trail Adventures of Sarah Marshall. 2003. (gr. 3-6). lib. bdg. 15.30 (978-0-613-67111-8(2)) Tandem Library Bks.

Torr, James D. Westward Expansion. 2002. (gr. 7-12). lib. bdg. 33.25 (978-0-613-73610-7(9)) Tandem Library Bks.

Torr, James D., ed. Westward Expansion. 2003. (Interpreting American History Through Primary Documents Ser.x). (Illus.). 208p. (J). 32.45 (978-0-7377-1134-9(5) , Greenhaven Pr., Inc.) Thomson Gale.

Two-Can Publishing Ltd. Staff & Martin, Alex. The Trail West. 2004. (Picture That! Ser.). (Illus.). 64p. (gr. 3 up). 19.95 (978-1-58728-442-7(1) , Two Can Publishing) T&N Children's Publishing.

Uschan, Michael V. A Mountain Man of the American Frontier. 2005. (Working Life Ser.). (Illus.). 111p. (J). (gr. 5-8). lib. bdg. 29.95 (978-1-59018-582-7(X) , Lucent Bks.) Thomson Gale.

Wadsworth, Ginger. Words West: The Voices of Young Pioneers. 2003. (Illus.). 208p. (J). (gr. 5-9). tchr. ed. 18.00 (978-0-618-23475-2(6) , Clarion Bks.) Houghton Mifflin Co. Trade & Reference Div.

Walker, Paul Robert. True Tales of the Wild West. 2002. (Illus.). 128p. (J). (gr. 3). 17.95 (978-0-7922-8218-1(3) , National Geographic Children's Bks.) National Geographic Society.

Warren, Andrea. Growing up on the Prairie. 2000. (978-0-606-17883-9(X)) Tandem Library Bks.

Winter, Jonah. Wild Women of the Wild West. Morgan, Mary, illus. 2002. (J). (978-0-8234-1601-1(1)) Holiday Hse., Inc.

FROST, ROBERT, 1874-1963

Bloom, Harold, ed. Robert Frost. 2002. (Bloom's BioCritiques Ser.). (Illus.). 112p. (gr. 9-13). 35.00 (978-0-7910-6183-1(3) , 000864, Chelsea Hse.) Facts On File, Inc.

Caravantes, Peggy. Deep Woods: The Story of Robert Frost. 2006. (World Writers Ser.). (Illus.). 160p. (J). (gr. 6 up). lib. bdg. 26.95 (978-1-931798-92-1(3)) Reynolds, Morgan Inc.

Whiting, Jim. Blue Banner Biographies-Pop Entertainers III. 2006. (J). lib. bdg. 282.70 (978-1-58415-428-0(4)) Mitchell Lane Pubs., Inc.

Wooten, Sara McIntosh. Robert Frost: The Life of America's Poet. 2006. (People to Know Today Ser.). (Illus.). 128p. (YA). lib. bdg. 31.93 (978-0-7660-2627-8(2)) Enslow Pubs., Inc.

FRUIT

see also Fruit Culture

also names of fruits, e.g. Apple, etc.

Anderson, Sara & Handprint Books Staff. Fruits. 2007. 32p. (J). bds. 8.95 (*978-1-59354-188-0(0)) Handprint Bks.

Ayers, Patricia. A Kids Guide to How Fruits Grow. 2000. (Digging in the Dirt Ser.). 24p. (J). (gr. k-4). lib. bdg. 18.75 (978-0-8239-5466-7(8) , PowerKids Pr.) Rosen Publishing Group, Inc., The.

Ball, Jacqueline A. Bite into an Apple. 2003. (Step Back Science Ser.). (Illus.). 48p. (J). 24.95 (978-1-56711-675-5(2) , Blackbirch Pr., Inc.) Thomson Gale.

Barbaresi, Nina. Funny Fruits & Vegetables Stickers. 2003. (Dover Little Activity Bks.). (Illus.). 4p. (J). pap. 1.50 (978-0-486-43004-1(9)) Dover Pubns., Inc.

Benduhn, Tea. Fruit. 2007. (J). pap. (*978-0-8368-8258-2(X)); 24p. lib. bdg. 19.93 (*978-0-8368-8251-3(2)) Stevens, Gareth Inc. (Weekly Reader Early Learning Library).

—Fruit: Fruta. 2007. (SPA & ENG.). (J). pap. (*978-0-8368-8462-3(0) , Weekly Reader Early Learning Library) Stevens, Gareth Inc.

—Fruit/Fruta. 2007. (Find Out about Food/Conoce la Comida Ser.). (SPA & ENG.). 24p. (J). (gr. k-2). lib. bdg. 19.93 (*978-0-8368-8455-5(8) , Weekly Reader Early Learning Library) Stevens, Gareth Inc.

Bodach, Vijaya. Fruit. 2007. (Illus.). 24p. (J). 19.93 (978-0-7368-6343-8(5) , Pebble Bks.) Capstone Pr., Inc.

Boyston, Angela. Flowers, Fruits & Seeds. 1999. (Plants Ser.). (Illus.). 32p. (J). (gr. k-3). lib. bdg. 21.36 (978-1-57572-822-3(2)) Heinemann Library.

Branigan, Carrie & Dunne, Richard. Fruits & Vegetables. 2005. (World of Plants Ser.). (Illus.). 31p. (J). (gr. 2-5). lib. bdg. 27.10 (978-1-58340-613-7(1)) Smart Apple Media.

Chandler, Lynda E. Fruits & Vegetables Coloring Book. 2001. (Illus.). 48p. (J). pap. 3.95 (978-0-486-41543-7(0)) Dover Pubns., Inc.

Charney, Steve & Goldbeck, David. The ABC's of Fruits & Vegetables & Beyond: Delicious Alphabet Poems plus Food, Facts & Fun for Eveyrone. Goldbeck, Nikki, ed. Larson, Maria Burgaleta, illus. 2007. 112p. (J). (ps-7). per. 16.95 (978-1-886101-07-4(8)) Ceres Pr.

Dawson, Susan H. & Norton, Susan R. Pyramid Pal - Fruits: Eating Should Always Be Fun for Kid. O'Hare, Mark, illus. 2000. (Adventures in Eating with the Nutrition Champion of Kids Ser.). 16p. (J). pap. 3.00 (978-1-58000-066-6(5)) Griffin Publishing Group.

Deal, Darlene. Play with Your Food & Learn How to Eat Right: Nutritional Book about Fruits & Vegetables. 2004. (ENG & SPA., Illus.). 22p. (J). (gr. 1-4). pap. 9.95 (978-0-9747299-0-9(6)) Deal, Darlene.

DePrisco, Dorothea. Orange. Taxali, Gary, illus. 2005. (Plush Learning Books Ser.). 10p. (J). bds. 6.95 (978-1-58117-192-1(7) , Intervisual/Piggy Toes) Dalmatian Pr.

Derkazarian, Susan. Fruits & Vegetables. 2005. (Rookie Read-About Health Ser.). (Illus.). 32p. (J). 20.50 (978-0-516-23673-5(3) , Children's Pr.) Scholastic Library Publishing.

DerKazarian, Susan. Fruits & Vegetables. 2006. 32p. (J). (gr. k-2). pap. 5.95 (978-0-516-25926-0(1) , Children's Pr.) Scholastic Library Publishing.

Driscoll, Laura. Apples: And How They Grow. Smith, Tammy, illus. 2003. (All Aboard Science Reader Ser.). 32p. (J). (ps-2). pap. 3.99 (978-0-448-43275-5(7) , Grosset & Dunlap) Penguin Group (USA) Inc.

Dwyer, Jacqueline. Fruits. 2001. (PowerKids Readers Ser.). (Illus.). 24p. (J). (gr. 1). lib. bdg. 16.00 (978-0-8239-5678-4(4) , PKFRUI, PowerKids Pr.) Rosen Publishing Group, Inc., The.

Edwards, Nicola. Fruit. 2007. lib. bdg. (978-1-4042-3701-8(1) , PowerKids Pr.) Rosen Publishing Group, Inc., The.

Ehlert, Lois. Eating the Alphabet: Fruits & Vegetables from A to Z Lap-Sized Board Book. 2006. (Illus.). 28p. (J). bds. 10.95 (978-0-15-205688-9(2) , Red Wagon Bks.) Harcourt Children's Bks.

Farndon, John. Fruits. 2005. (Illus.). 24p. (J). (gr. 2-4). 23.70 (978-1-4103-0424-7(8) , Blackbirch Pr., Inc.) Thomson Gale.

Flagg, Ann. Apples, Pumpkins & Harvest. 1998. (Illus.). 48p. pap. 9.95 (978-0-590-03316-9(6)) Scholastic, Inc.

Flowers & Fruit Sets: 1 Each of 3 Big Books. (Sunshinetm Science Ser.). (gr. 1-2). 111.50 (978-0-7802-2818-4(9)) Wright Group, The.

Flowers & Fruit Sets: 1 Each of 3 Student Books. (Sunshinetm Science Ser.). (gr. 1-2). 20.95 (978-0-7802-2819-1(7)) Wright Group, The.

Franck, Irene M. & Brownstone, David M. Tomatoes. 2003. (Illus.). 32p. (J). (978-0-7172-5726-3(6) , Grolier) Scholastic Library Publishing.

Frost, Helen. The Fruit Group. Saunders-Smith, Gail, ed. 2000. (Food Guide Pyramid Ser.). (Illus.). 24p. (J). (gr. k-1). lib. bdg. 15.93 (978-0-7368-0537-7(0) , Pebble Bks.) Capstone Pr., Inc.

Fruit: 6 Each of 1 Student Book, 6 vols. (Sunshinetm Science Ser.). 24p. (gr. 1-2). 41.95 (978-0-7802-2682-1(8)) Wright Group, The.

Fruit: Big Book. (Sunshinetm Science Ser.). 24p. (gr. 1-2). 37.50 (978-0-7802-2775-0(1)) Wright Group, The.

The Fruit Group, 6 vols. (gr. k-2). 28.95 (978-0-7368-8745-8(8)) Red Brick Learning.

Fruits New Food Guide Pyramid. 2006. (Illus.). 24p. (J). (gr. k-2). 18.50 (*978-0-531-17850-8(1)) Scholastic Library Publishing.

Frutas. 2003. (SPA.). (J). (978-84-246-0692-3(2) , GL30334) La Galera, S.A. Editorial ESP. *Dist:* Lectorum Pubns., Inc.

Ganeri, Anita. From Seed to Apple. 2006. (Illus.). 32p. (J). 25.36 (978-1-4034-7862-7(7)); pap. (978-1-4034-7871-9(6)) Heinemann Library.

Green, Emily K. Fruits. 2006. (Blastoff! Readers Ser.). (Illus.). 24p. (J). lib. bdg. 19.95 (978-1-60014-005-1(X)) Bellwether Media.

Harcourt School Publishers Staff. Funny Fruit On Level. 3rd ed. 2002. (Trophies Reading Program Ser.). (Illus.). pap. 5.10 (978-0-15-323084-4(3)) Harcourt Schl. Pubs.

Harris, Calvin. Apple Harvest. 2008. (J). (*978-1-4296-0023-1(3)) Capstone Pr., Inc.

Heurtelou, Maude. Mwen Pito Fwi. Hippolyte, Johanne & Corbett, Kecia, illus. 2001. (Big Book Ser.).Tr. of I Prefer Fruit. (CRP.). 14p. (J). (gr. k-2). 19.50 (978-1-58432-085-2(0)) Educa Vision.

—Mwen Pito Mango. Hippolyte, Johanne & Corbett, Kecia, illus. 2001. (Big Book Ser.).Tr. of I Prefer Mango. (CRP.). 14p. (J). (gr. k-2). 19.50 (978-1-58432-081-4(8)) Educa Vision.

—Tropical Fruit: Fwi Twopikal. 1999. (Big Book Ser.). (CRP & ENG.). (Illus.). 8p. (J). (gr. k-2). 19.50 (978-1-58432-066-1(4)) Educa Vision.

—Tropical Fruits/Fwi Twopikal. 1999. (CRP & ENG., Illus.). 8p. (J). (gr. k-2). pap. 4.50 (978-1-58432-010-4(9)) Educa Vision.

Hughes, Meredith Sayles. Yes, We Have Bananas! Fruits from Shrubs & Vines. 1999. (Plants We Eat Ser.). (Illus.). 104p. (gr. 6-9). 26.60 (978-0-8225-2836-4(3)) Lerner Publishing Group.

Hughes, Meredith Sayles & Hughes, E. Thomas. Cool as a Cucumber, Hot as a Pepper: Fruit Vegetables. 1998. (Plants We Eat Ser.). (Illus.). 80p. (J). (gr. 5-7). 26.60 (978-0-8225-2832-6(0) , Lerner Pubns.) Lerner Publishing Group.

Jeunesse, Gallimard. In the Garden. Heliadore, illus. 2003. (First Discovery Look-and-Learn Bks.). 24p. (J). bds. 6.95 (978-0-439-33637-6(6) , Cartwheel Bks.) Scholastic, Inc.

Kalz, Jill. Fruits. 2003. 24p. (J). lib. bdg. 21.35 (978-1-58340-299-3(3)) Smart Apple Media.

Klingel, Cynthia Fitterer & Noyed, Robert B. Fruit. Andersen, Gregg, photos by. 2002. (Weekly Reader Early Learning Library). (Illus.). 24p. (J). (ps up). pap. 5.95 (978-0-8368-3146-7(2)); lib. bdg. 19.33 (978-0-8368-3057-6(1)) Stevens, Gareth Inc. (Weekly Reader Early Learning Library).

Landau, Elaine. Apples. 2000. (Illus.). 47p. (J). (gr. 3-5). lib. bdg. 15.25 (978-0-613-37272-5(7)) Tandem Library Bks.

Lee, Frances. Fruit Salad. 1999. (ps-2). lib. bdg. 11.10 (978-0-613-30420-7(9)) Tandem Library Bks.

Martineau, Susan. Healthy Eating. 2006. (Illus.). 32p. (J). (978-1-58340-896-4(7)) Smart Apple Media.

Maurer, Tracy. Growing Fruit. 2000. (Green Thumb Guides Ser.). (Illus.). 24p. (J). (gr. 2-6). lib. bdg. 23.93 (978-1-55916-252-4(X)) Rourke Publishing, LLC.

Mayr, Diane. Out & About at the Apple Orchard. McMullen, Anne, illus. 2004. (Field Trips Ser.). 24p. (C). (gr. k-3). 23.93 (978-1-4048-0036-6(0)) Picture Window Bks.

McMillan, Bruce. Growing Colors. McMillan, Bruce, illus. 2002. (Illus.). (J). 14.43 (978-0-7587-2664-3(3)) Book Wholesalers, Inc.

Mitchell, Judy, ed. More Than One - Fruits & Vegetables. Rojas, Mary Galan, illus. 2001. (Pictures to Color Ser.). 32p. (J). (ps-k). pap. 4.95 (978-1-57310-264-3(4)) Teaching & Learning Co.

El mural de Frutas: 6 Softcover Books. (Saludos Ser.: Vol. 1). (SPA.). (gr. 3-5). 31.00 (978-0-7635-1799-1(2)) Rigby Education.

Nelson, Robin. Fruits. 2003. (First Step Nonfiction Ser.). (Illus.). 24p. (J). (gr. k-2). lib. bdg. 18.60 (978-0-8225-4624-5(8)) Lerner Publishing Group.

—Las Frutas. 2003. (First Step Nonfiction Ser.). (SPA., Illus.). 24p. (J). (gr. k-2). lib. bdg. 18.60 (978-0-8225-5062-4(8)) Lerner Publishing Group.

¿Qué Fruta es ésa? 2004. (SPA.). 16p. (J). (978-968-494-160-1(9)) Centro de Informacion y Desarrollo de la Comunicacion y la Literatura MEX. *Dist:* AIMS International Bks., Inc., Lectorum Pubns., Inc., Iaconi, Mariuccia Bk. Imports.

Richards, Jean. A Fruit Is a Suitcase for Seeds. 2006. (Illus.). (J). pap. 6.95 (978-0-8225-5991-7(9) , First Avenue Editions) Lerner Publishing Group.

—A Fruit Is a Suitcase for Seeds. Hariton, Anca, illus. 2002. (Our World Ser.). 32p. (ps-1). lib. bdg. 21.90 (978-0-7613-1622-0(1) , Millbrook Pr.) Lerner Publishing Group.

Rondeau, Amanda. Fruits Are Fun. 2003. (What Should I Eat? Ser.). (Illus.). 23p. (J). (ps-3). lib. bdg. 19.93 (978-1-57765-834-4(5)) ABDO Publishing Co.

Rosa-Mendoza, Gladys, creator. Fruits & Vegetables. 2004. (English-Spanish Foundations Ser.: Vol. 10). Tr. of Frutas y Vegetales. (SPA & ENG., Illus.). 22p. (J). bds. 6.95 (978-1-931398-10-7(0)) Me+Mi Publishing.

Saunders-Smith, Gail. From Blossom to Fruit. 1998. (J). pap. 13.25 (978-0-516-21244-9(3) , Children's Pr.) Scholastic Library Publishing.

—Picking Apples. 1998. (J). pap. 13.25 (978-0-516-21245-6(1) , Children's Pr.) Scholastic Library Publishing.

Schaefer, Lola M. Fruits. 2007. (J). (*978-1-4329-0143-1(5)); pap. (*978-1-4329-0150-9(8)) Heinemann Library.

Schaefer, Lola M. Pick, Pull, Snap! Where Once a Flower Bloomed. George, Lindsay B., illus. 2003. 32p. (J). 15.99 (978-0-688-17834-5(0)) HarperCollins Pubs.

Schuette, Sarah L. Eating Pairs: Counting Fruits & Vegetables by Twos. 2003. (A+ Counting Books). (Illus.). 16p. (J). (gr. k-1). 22.60 (978-0-7368-1676-2(3) , Aplus Bks.) Capstone Pr., Inc.

Schuh, Mari C. The Fruit Group. 2006. (Illus.). 24p. (J). (978-0-7368-5370-5(7) , Pebble Bks.) Capstone Pr., Inc.

Scratch N Sniff Staff. Scratch N Sniff Fruit. 2005. 12p. 6.95 (978-0-9762524-7-4(3)) Gimme Gimme Toys & Games Inc.

Shepard, Daniel. All Kinds of Farms. 2003. (Illus.). 17p. (J). 15.93 (978-0-7368-2912-0(1)); pap. (978-0-7368-2871-0(0)) Yellow Umbrella Pr.

Shofner, Shawndra. Apples. 2001. (Let's Investigate Ser.). (Illus.). 32p. (J). (978-1-58341-192-6(5)) Creative Co., The.

Snyder, Inez. Cranberries. 2004. (Harvesttime Ser.). (Illus.). 24p. (J). 18.00 (978-0-516-27592-5(5)); pap. 4.95 (978-0-516-25912-3(1)) Scholastic Library Publishing. (Children's Pr.).

—Grapes to Raisins. 2005. (How Things Are Made Ser.). (Illus.). 24p. (J). (ps-2). pap. 4.95 (978-0-516-25528-6(2)); 18.00 (978-0-516-25198-1(8)) Scholastic Library Publishing. (Children's Pr.).

—Tomatoes. 2004. (Harvesttime Ser.). (J). 18.00 (978-0-516-27594-9(1)); pap. 4.95 (978-0-516-25914-7(8)) Scholastic Library Publishing. (Children's Pr.).

Southwater Staff. Look & Learn about Flowers, Fruits & Veg. 2001. (Look & Learn Ser.). (Illus.). 32p. (ps). 7.95 (978-1-84215-283-6(1) , Southwater) Anness Publishing GBR. *Dist:* National Bk. Network.

Spilsbury, Louise. Apples. (Food Ser.). 32p. pap. 6.95 (978-1-4034-4045-7(X)); 2001. (Illus.). (J). lib. bdg. 21.36 (978-1-58810-142-6(8)) Heinemann Library.

Stone, Lynn M. Fruit. 2008. (J). (*978-1-60044-552-1(7)) Rourke Publishing, LLC.

Takaya, Natsuki. Fruits Basket Vol. 6: Fruits Basket DVD: Episodes 1 & 2; Fruits Basket Manga. collector's ltd. ed. 2004. pap. 27.99 (978-1-59532-735-2(5) , Tokyopop Adult) TOKYOPOP, Inc.

Thomas, Ann. Fruits. 2002. (Food Ser.). (Illus.). 32p. (gr. k-2). 23.00 (978-0-7910-6976-9(1) , Chelsea Hse.) Facts On File, Inc.

Tofts, Hannah. I Eat Fruit! 1998. (Things I Eat Ser.). 20p. (J). (ps-1). (978-1-84089-000-6(2) , Zero to Ten, Limited) Evans Publishing Group.

—One Cool Watermelon. 2006. (Things I Eat Ser.). (Illus.). 24p. (J). 12.95 (978-1-84089-450-9(4) , Zero to Ten, Limited) Evans Publishing Group GBR. *Dist:* Independent Pubs. Group.

Tofts, Hannah, illus. I Eat Fruit! rev. ed. 2001. (Things I Eat Ser.). 24p. (J). (ps up). 11.95 (978-1-84089-027-3(4) , Zero to Ten, Limited) Evans Publishing Group GBR. *Dist:* Independent Pubs. Group.

Tropical Twist, 6 vols. (Let's Read about... Ser.). (Illus.). 10p. (J). (978-2-7643-0030-5(1)) Phidal Publishing, Inc./Editions Phidal, Inc.

Tuxworth, Nicola & Lorenz Editors. Fruit. 2003. (Illus.). 20p. 5.99 (978-0-7548-1197-8(2)) Anness Publishing GBR. *Dist:* National Bk. Network.

Vize, Dania. Fruity Fun. 2006. (High Chair Buddy Ser.). (Illus.). 10p. (ps-ps). bds. 6.95 (978-1-84610-015-4(1)) Make Believe Ideas GBR. *Dist:* Ingram Pub. Services.

E F G

Weiss, Ellen. From Pit to Peachtree. 2007. (Scholastic News Nonfiction Readers Ser.). (Illus.). 24p. (J). (gr. 1-2). lib. bdg. 20.00 (***978-0-531-18538-4(9)*** , Children's Pr.) Scholastic Library Publishing.

Weninger, Brigitte. Little Apple, a Book of Thanks. 2002. (ps-2). lib. bdg. 14.10 (978-0-613-84070-5(4)) Tandem Library Bks.

Yummy Yummy Fruits. 2004. (J). per. 15.99 (978-0-9744205-3-0(0)) Golden Eagle Publishing Hse., Inc.

Zemlicka, Shannon. From Fruit to Jelly. 2004. (Start to Finish Ser.). (J). pap. 4.95 (978-0-8225-0748-2(X)); (Illus.). 24p. 18.60 (978-0-8225-0942-4(3) , Lerner Pubns.) Lerner Publishing Group.

FRUIT—CANNING

see Canning and Preserving

FRUIT—MARKETING

see Farm Produce—Marketing

FRUIT CULTURE

see also Plant Propagation

Anderson, Catherine. Apple Orchard. 2004. (Field Trip! Ser.). (Illus.). 24p. (J). pap. 5.50 (978-1-4034-6166-7(X)); lib. bdg. 20.64 (978-1-4034-6159-9(7)) Heinemann Library.

Driscoll, Laura. Apples & How They Grow. 2003. (gr. k-3). lib. bdg. 11.80 (978-0-613-70544-8(0)) Tandem Library Bks.

Hubbell, Patricia. Every Orchard Tree. Broxon, Janet, illus. 2008. (J). (***978-1-55971-986-5(9)*** , NorthWord Bks. for Young Readers) T&N Children's Publishing.

La Huerta: Individual Title Two-Packs. (Chiquilibros Ser.). (SPA.). (ps-1). 12.00 (978-0-7635-8558-7(0)) Rigby Education.

Maurer, Tracy. Growing Fruit. 2000. (Green Thumb Guides Ser.). (Illus.). 24p. (J). (gr. 2-6). lib. bdg. 23.93 (978-1-55916-252-4(X)) Rourke Publishing, LLC.

Minden, Cecilia. Gardening by the Numbers. 2008. (J). lib. bdg. 25.26 (***978-1-60279-008-7(6)***) Cherry Lake Publishing.

Murphy, Patricia J. The Apple Orchard. 2004. (Visit To Ser.). (Illus.). 24p. (J). lib. bdg. 19.93 (978-0-7368-2579-5(7) , Pebble Bks.) Capstone Pr., Inc.

Ryan, Pam Muñoz. How Do You Raise a Raisin? 2003. (gr. k-3). lib. bdg. 15.25 (978-0-613-82657-0(4)) Tandem Library Bks.

Wolfman, Judy. Life on an Apple Orchard. Winston, David Lorenz, illus. Winston, David Lorenz, photos by. 2004. (Life on a Farm Ser.). 48p. (J). (gr. 2-5). lib. bdg. 23.93 (978-1-57505-193-2(1)) Lerner Publishing Group.

FRUIT CULTURE—FICTION

Cheripko, Jan. Brother Bartholomew: And the Apple Grove. Kasparavicius, Kestutis, illus. 2004. 32p. (J). (gr. k-2). 15.95 (978-1-59078-096-1(5)) Boyds Mills Pr.

Cherry Laminated Book. 2005. (J). per. 15.95 (978-1-59649-306-3(2)) Whispering Pine Pr., Inc.

Hazelwood, Drema. The Apple Orchard Gang Featuring Red Delicious. 1999. (Illus.). 20p. (J). (ps-3). pap. 5.95 (978-0-9700157-0-9(4)) Orchard Gang Publishing.

Hood, Karen Jean Matsko. Apple Laminated Book. 2006. per. 19.95 (978-1-59649-305-6(4)) Whispering Pine Pr., Inc.

Houghton, Eric. The Crooked Apple Tree. Gold, Caroline, illus. 2000. 32p. (J). (ps-3). 15.95 (978-1-902283-59-3(7)) Barefoot Bks., Inc.

Klingel, Cynthia Fitterer & Noyed, Robert B. Anna & the Letter A. 2003. (Alphaphonics Ser.). (Illus.). 24p. (J). (ps-2). 21.36 (978-1-59296-091-0(X)) Child's World, Inc.

Madison, Alan. The Littlest Grape Stomper. Potter, Giselle, illus. 2007. 40p. (J). (ps-3). lib. bdg. 18.99 (978-0-375-93675-3(0)); 16.99 (978-0-375-83675-6(6)) Random Hse. Children's Bks. (Schwartz & Wade Bks.).

Ponko, Cindy A. Olive Fingers. 2006. (J). (978-0-9768230-0-1(4)) Some Kids I Know.

Schaub, Michelle. The Bee Puzzle. 2006. (Early Explorers Ser.). (J). 36.00 (***978-1-4108-6123-8(6)***) Benchmark Education Co.

Si, Artists. Peek-a-Boo in the Berry Patch. Si, Artists, illus. 2006. (Strawberry Shortcake Baby Ser.). (Illus.). 10p. (J). (ps-ps). bds. 5.99 (978-0-448-44351-5(1) , Grosset & Dunlap) Penguin Group (USA) Inc.

Wellington, Monica. Apple Farmer Annie/ Anna Cultiva Manzanas. Del Risco, Eida, tr. Wellington, Monica, illus. 2004. (ENG & SPA., Illus.). 32p. (J). (ps). 10.99 (978-0-525-47252-0(5) , Dutton Juvenile) Penguin Group (USA) Inc.

FRUSTRATION

see Attitude (Psychology); Emotions

FUDGE (FICTITIOUS CHARACTER)—FICTION

Blume, Judy. Double Fudge. 2002. (Fudge Ser.). 224p. (gr. 3-7). 15.99 (978-0-525-46926-1(5) , Dutton Juvenile) Penguin Group (USA) Inc.

—Double Fudge. (Fudge Ser.). (SPA.). 250p. (J). (gr. 5-8). pap. 9.95 (978-1-59437-814-0(2)) Santillana USA Publishing Co., Inc.

—Fudge-a-Mania. 2002. (Fudge Ser.). (Illus.). (J). 13.40 (978-0-7587-0013-1(X)) Book Wholesalers, Inc.

—Fudge-a-Mania. 2002. (Fudge Ser.). (Illus.). 160p. (J). 15.99 (978-0-525-46927-8(3) , Dutton Juvenile) Penguin Group (USA) Inc.

—Superfudge. 2002. (Fudge Ser.). (Illus.). (J). 13.40 (978-0-7587-6668-7(8)) Book Wholesalers, Inc.

—Superfudge. 2002. (Fudge Ser.). (Illus.). 176p. (J). 15.99 (978-0-525-46930-8(3) , Dutton Juvenile) Penguin Group (USA) Inc.

—Tales of a Fourth Grade Nothing. 2002. (Fudge Ser.). (Illus.). 128p. (J). 15.99 (978-0-525-46931-5(1) , Dutton Juvenile) Penguin Group (USA) Inc.

FUEL

see also Petroleum As Fuel; Wood

Bernardy, Catherine J. Fuel. 1998. (Let's Investigate Ser.: Vol. 12). (Illus.). 32p. (J). (ps-3). lib. bdg. (978-0-88682-989-6(5) , Creative Education) Creative Co., The.

Fossil Fuel Power. (Energy at Work Ser.). 32p. (J). 7.95 (978-0-7368-5190-9(9)) Capstone Pr., Inc.

Graham, Ian. Fossil Fuels: A Resource Our World Depends On. 2004. (J). pap. 7.50 (978-1-4034-5623-6(2)); lib. bdg. 24.22 (978-1-4034-5615-1(1)) Heinemann Library.

Lippman, David. Energy from Hydrogen. 2008. (J). pap. 7.95 (***978-1-60279-095-7(7)***) Cherry Lake Publishing.

—Hydrogen Energy. 2008. (J). lib. bdg. 25.26 (***978-1-60279-048-3(5)***) Cherry Lake Publishing.

Morris, Neil. Fossil Fuels. 2006. (Energy Sources Ser.). (Illus.). 32p. (J). (978-1-58340-905-3(X)) Smart Apple Media.

Oxlade, Chris. Fossil Fuels. 2004. (Raintree Freestyle Ser.). (Illus.). 48p. (J). 29.93 (978-1-4109-0495-9(4)) Raintree.

—Fossil Fuels 6-Pack. 2004. (Illus.). (J). lib. bdg. 42.90 (978-1-4109-0807-0(0)) Raintree.

—How We Use Coal. 2004. (Illus.). 32p. (J). (ps-ps). pap. 7.50 (978-1-4109-0991-6(3)) Raintree.

Povey, Karen D. Biofuels. 2006. (Our Environment Ser.). 48p. (J). (gr. 4-8). 26.20 (978-0-7377-3560-4(0) , Kidhaven) Thomson Gale.

Saunders, N. & Chapman, Steven. Fossil Fuel. 2005. (Freestyle Express Ser.). (Illus.). 48p. (J). lib. bdg. (978-1-4109-1693-8(6)) Steck-Vaughn.

Saunders, Nigel & Chapman, Steven. Fossil Fuel. 2005. (Freestyle Express Ser.). (Illus.). 48p. (J). (978-1-4109-1698-3(7)) Steck-Vaughn.

—Fossil Fuel. 2004. (Illus.). 48p. (J). (gr. 3-5). pap. 7.95 (978-1-4109-0501-7(2)) Raintree.

Sherman, Josepha. Fossil Fuel Power. 2004. (Fact Finders Ser.). (Illus.). 32p. (J). 16.95 (978-0-7368-2470-5(7)) Capstone Pr., Inc.

Snedden, Robert. Energy from Fossil Fuels. 2006. (Illus.). 48p. (J). (978-1-4034-8732-2(4)); 2nd ed. pap. (978-1-4034-8737-7(5)) Heinemann Library.

Walker, Niki. Biomass: Fueiling Change. 2006. (Energy Revolution Ser.). (Illus.). 32p. (J). (gr. 3-9). pap. (978-0-7787-2928-0(1) , 1259460) Crabtree Publishing Co.

—Hydrogen: Running on Water. 2006. (Energy Revolution Ser.). (Illus.). 32p. (J). (gr. 3-9). pap. (978-0-7787-2929-7(X)); lib. bdg. (978-0-7787-2915-0(X)) Crabtree Publishing Co.

FUEL, LIQUID

see Gasoline; Petroleum As Fuel

FUEL OIL

see Petroleum As Fuel

FULTON, ROBERT, 1765-1815

Boothroyd, Jennifer. Robert Fulton: A Life of Innovation. 2007. (Pull Ahead Books-Biographies Ser.). (J). 22.60 (978-0-8225-6458-4(0) , Lerner Pubns.) Lerner Publishing Group.

Flammang, James M. Robert Fulton: Inventor & Steamboat Builder. 1999. (Historical American Biographies Ser.). (Illus.). 128p. (YA). (gr. 6-12). lib. bdg. 26.60 (978-0-7660-1141-0(0)) Enslow Pubs., Inc.

Ford, Carin T. Robert Fulton: The Steamboat Man. 2004. (Famous Inventors Ser.). (Illus.). 32p. (J). lib. bdg. 22.60 (978-0-7660-2248-5(X)) Enslow Pubs., Inc.

Gillis, Jennifer Blizin. Robert Fulton. 2004. (Illus.). 32p. (J). pap. 6.50 (978-1-4034-5336-5(5)); lib. bdg. 22.79 (978-1-4034-5328-0(4)) Heinemann Library.

Harcourt School Publishers Staff. Robert Fulton. 3rd ed. 2002. (Horizons Ser.). (Illus.). (J). pap. 3.70 (978-0-15-333224-1(7)) Harcourt Schl. Pubs.

Kroll, Steven. Robert Fulton: From Submarine to Steamboat. Farnsworth, Bill, illus. 1999. 32p. (J). (gr. 4-6). tchr. ed. 16.95 (978-0-8234-1433-8(7)) Holiday Hse., Inc.

McLeese, Don. Robert Fulton. 2006. (Rourke Discovery Library). (Illus.). 24p. (gr. 2-5). 14.95 (978-1-59515-434-7(5) , 1244323) Rourke Publishing, LLC.

Parks, Peggy J. Robert Fulton: Innovator with Steam Power. 2003. (Giants of Science Ser.). (Illus.). 64p. (J). 26.20 (978-1-56711-492-8(X) , Blackbirch Pr., Inc.) Thomson Gale.

Pierce, Morris A. Robert Fulton & the Development of the Steamboat. 2005. (Library of American Lives & Times). (Illus.). 112p. (YA). (gr. 4-8). lib. bdg. 31.95 (978-0-8239-5737-8(3)) Rosen Publishing Group, Inc., The.

Robert Fulton, 6 vols. (gr. k-2). 28.95 (978-0-7368-8755-7(5)) Red Brick Learning.

Rosenberg, Pam. Robert Fulton: Engineer & Inventor. 2003. (Spirit of America: Our People Ser.). (Illus.). 32p. (J). (gr. 2-6). 27.07 (978-1-56766-448-5(2)) Child's World, Inc.

Schaefer, Lola M. Robert Fulton. 2005. (Transportation Ser.). 24p. (YA). (gr. k-3). pap. (978-0-7368-8731-1(8) , Pebble Bks.) Capstone Pr., Inc.

—Robert Fulton. 2000. (Famous People in Transportation Ser.). (Illus.). 24p. (J). (gr. k-1). lib. bdg. 15.93 (978-0-7368-0547-6(8) , Pebble Bks.) Capstone Pr., Inc.

Whiting, Jim. Robert Fulton. 2006. (What's So Great About... ? Ser.). (Illus.). 32p. (J). (gr. 1-4). lib. bdg. (978-1-58415-478-5(0)) Mitchell Lane Pubs., Inc.

FUND RAISING

Brownlie, Alison. Charities: Do They Work? 1999. (Talking Points Ser.). (Illus.). 64p. (J). (gr. 4-7). lib. bdg. 27.12 (978-0-8172-5319-6(X)) Raintree.

Haydon, Julie. Fundraising. 2006. (Illus.). 32p. (J). (978-1-58340-785-1(5)) Smart Apple Media.

Kent, Renee Holmes. Robyn to the Rescue, Vol. 5. 2004. (Adventures in Misty Falls Ser.: Vol. 5). (Illus.). 100p. (J). (gr. 4-7). pap. 4.99 (978-1-56309-451-4(7) , N007109) New Hope Pubs.

FUNDS

see Finance

FUNERAL RITES AND CEREMONIES

Briscoe, Diana. King Tut: Tales from the Tomb. 2002. (High Five Reading Ser.). (Illus.). 48p. (J). (gr. 3-4). lib. bdg. 22.60 (978-0-7368-9553-8(1) , Capstone High-Interest Bks.); pap. (978-0-7368-9531-6(0)) Capstone Pr., Inc.

Broadbent, Lynne & Chaplin, Denise. Life's End. Sloan, Frank, ed. 2001. (Ceremonies & Celebrations Ser.). (Illus.). 32p. (J). (ps-3). lib. bdg. 25.69 (978-0-7398-3270-7(0)) Raintree.

Gogerly, Liz. Look Around an Egyptian Tomb: By Liz Gogerly. 2007. (J). (***978-1-84193-719-9(3)***) Smart Apple Media.

Joseph, Judith C. I Hate Strawberry Jam. Spitzer, Hillary, illus. 2002. 120p. (YA). (gr. 3 up). pap. 14.95 (978-0-9715420-0-6(7)) JCJoseph, Ltd.

O'Keefe, Susan Heyboer. My Life & Death, by Alexandra Canarsie. 2002. 217p. (YA). (gr. 7-10). 14.95 (978-1-56145-264-4(5) , Q32889) Peachtree Pubs., Ltd.

Onyefulu, Ifeoma. Saying Goodbye: A Special Farewell to Mama Nkwelle. 2001. (Around the World Ser.). (Illus.). 32p. (gr. 2-4). lib. bdg. 22.90 (978-0-7613-1965-8(4) , Millbrook Pr.) Lerner Publishing Group.

Perl, Lila & Heweston, Nicholas. Dying to Know: About Death, Funeral Customs, & Final Resting Places. 2001. (Single Titles Ser.). (Illus.). 96p. (gr. 5-7). lib. bdg. 25.90 (978-0-7613-1564-3(0) , Millbrook Pr.) Lerner Publishing Group.

Ross, Mandy. Funerals. 2003. (Rites of Passage Ser.). (Illus.). 32p. (J). pap. (978-1-4034-4596-4(6)); lib. bdg. 24.22 (978-1-4034-3987-1(7)) Heinemann Library.

—Funerals. 2003. (gr. k-3). lib. bdg. 15.90 (978-0-613-88219-4(9)) Tandem Library Bks.

Shuter, Jane. Pharaohs & Priests. 1999. (Ancient Egypt Ser.). 32p. (J). (gr. 3-5). lib. bdg. 22.79 (978-1-57572-731-8(5)) Heinemann Library.

Tanaka, Shelley. Mummies: The Newest, Coolest & Creepiest from Around the World. 2005. (Illus.). 48p. (J). (gr. k-4). 16.95 (978-0-8109-5797-8(3) , Abrams Bks. for Young Readers) Abrams, Harry N. , Inc.

Wilcox, Charlotte. Mummies, Bones & Body Parts. 2000. (Photo Bks.). (Illus.). 64p. (J). (gr. 4-7). 25.26 (978-1-57505-428-5(0) , Carolrhoda Bks.) Lerner Publishing Group.

World Book, Inc. Staff, contrib. by. End-of-Life Rituals. 2003. (World Book's Celebrations & Rituals Around the World Ser.). (Illus.). 46p. (J). (978-0-7166-5014-0(2)) World Bk., Inc.

FUNGI

see also Bacteriology; Mushrooms

Brock, David. Infectious Fungi. 2006. (Deadly Diseases & Epidemics Ser.). (Illus.). (J). (gr. 9-12). 31.95 (978-0-7910-8680-3(1) , Chelsea Hse.) Facts On File, Inc.

Fantastic Fungi: Individual Title, 6 pack. (Rigby Focus Ser.). 24p. (gr. 2 up). 30.00 (978-0-7578-5573-3(3)) Rigby Education.

Fantastic Fungi: Individual Title Six-Packs. (Rigby Focus Ser.). 24p. (gr. 2 up). 28.00 (978-0-7578-5343-2(9)) Rigby Education.

Fowler, Allan. Science, Rookie Read-About Science: Plants & Fungi. 2004. (Illus.). 304.00 (978-0-516-29318-9(4)) Scholastic Library Publishing.

Gareth Stevens Publishing Staff, contrib. by. Protists & Fungi. 2003. (Discovery Channel School Science Ser.). (Illus.). 32p. (J). (gr. 5 up). lib. bdg. 24.67 (978-0-8368-3371-3(6)) Stevens, Gareth Inc.

Holt, Rinehart and Winston Staff. Holt Science & Technology Chapter 11: Life Science: Protists & Fungi. 5th ed. 2004. (Illus.). pap. 12.86 (978-0-03-030211-4(0)) Holt, Rinehart & Winston.

—Holt Science & Technology Chptr. 6: Protists & Fungi: Chapter Resources - Tennessee Edition. 3rd ed. 2003. (YA). pap. 11.40 (978-0-03-069136-2(2)) Holt, Rinehart & Winston.

Pascoe, Elaine. Fungi. 2003. (Kids Guide to the Classification of Living Things Ser.). 32p. (J). lib. bdg. 21.25 (978-0-8239-6313-3(6) , PowerKids Pr.) Rosen Publishing Group, Inc., The.

—Slime, Molds & Fungi. Kuhn, Dwight, photos by. 1998. (Nature Close-Up Ser.). (Illus.). 48p. (J). (gr. 4-8). 23.70 (978-1-56711-182-8(3) , Blackbirch Pr., Inc.) Thomson Gale.

Silverman, Buffy. Molds & Fungi. 2004. (Kidhaven Science Library). (Illus.). 48p. (J). (gr. 4-7). 26.20 (978-0-7377-2075-4(1) , Greenhaven Pr., Inc.) Thomson Gale.

Snedden, Robert. Plants & Fungi: Multicelled Life. 2003. (Cells & Life Ser.). (Illus.). 48p. (gr. 6-8). (J). lib. bdg. 27.86 (978-1-58810-675-9(6)); (YA). pap. 8.50 (978-1-58810-937-8(2)) Heinemann Library.

Souza, Dorothy M. What Is a Fungus? 2002. (Watts Library). (Illus.). 63p. (J). (gr. 5-7). pap. 8.95 (978-0-531-16223-1(0) , Watts, Franklin) Scholastic Library Publishing.

Stefoff, Rebecca. The Fungus Kingdom. 2007. (Family Trees Ser.). 96p. (J). lib. bdg. 32.79 (***978-0-7614-2696-7(5)*** , Benchmark Bks.) Cavendish, Marshall Corp.

FUNNIES

see Comic Books, Strips, etc.

FUR-BEARING ANIMALS

see also names of fur-bearing animals, e.g. Beavers, etc.

Dubovoy, Silvia. Pieles. 2002. (SPA.). (gr. k-3). lib. bdg. 15.25 (978-0-613-64577-5(4)) Tandem Library Bks.

Miles, Elizabeth. Fur & Feathers. 2003. (Animal Parts Ser.). (Illus.). 32p. pap. 6.95 (978-1-4034-0425-1(9)) Heinemann Library.

FUR SEALS

see Seals (Animals)

FUR TRADE

Bailey, Katie. Radisson & Groseilliers: Fur Traders of the North. 2006. (In the Footsteps of Explorers Ser.). (Illus.). 32p. (J). (gr. 3-14). pap. (978-0-7787-2458-2(1) , 1253444); (978-0-7787-2422-3(0) , 1253444) Crabtree Publishing Co.

Parker, Lewis K. John Jacob Astor & the Fur Trade: Individual Title Six-Packs. (On Deck Ser.: Vol. 2). 24p. (gr. 4-5). 35.00 (978-0-7578-5852-9(X)) Rigby Education.

Stone, Lynn M. Beaver. 2003. (Animals in U.S. History Ser.). (Illus.). 24p. (J). 25.64 (978-1-58952-697-6(X)) Rourke Publishing, LLC.

Suen, Anastasia. Trappers & Mountain Men. 2007. (Events in American History Ser.). (Illus.). 48p. (J). (gr. 4-6). lib. bdg. 29.93 (978-1-60044-134-9(3)) Rourke Publishing, LLC.

Sundling, Charles W. Mountain Men of the Frontier. 2000. (Frontier Land Ser.). (Illus.). 32p. (J). (gr. 3-8). lib. bdg. 24.21 (978-1-57765-043-0(3) , ABDO & Daughters) ABDO Publishing Co.

Uschan, Michael V. A Mountain Man of the American Frontier. 2005. (Working Life Ser.). (Illus.). 111p. (J). (gr. 5-8). lib. bdg. 29.95 (978-1-59018-582-7(X) , Lucent Bks.) Thomson Gale.

FUR TRADERS

Burger, James P. The Mountain Men of the West. 2002. (Library of the Westward Expansion). (Illus.). 24p. (J). (gr. 3). lib. bdg. 19.95 (978-0-8239-5853-5(1) , PowerKids Pr.) Rosen Publishing Group, Inc., The.

—The Rocky Mountain Fur Trade. 2002. (Library of the Westward Expansion). (Illus.). 24p. (J). (gr. 3). lib. bdg. 19.95 (978-0-8239-5851-1(5) , PowerKids Pr.) Rosen Publishing Group, Inc., The.

Smith, James K. David Thompson. 2001. (Canadians Ser.). (Illus.). 64p. (978-1-55041-493-6(3)) Fitzhenry & Whiteside, Ltd.

FUR TRADERS—FICTION

Durbin, William. The Broken Blade. 1998. (Illus.). 176p. (J). (gr. 5-9). reprint ed. 5.50 (978-0-440-41184-0(X) , Yearling) Random Hse. Children's Bks.

—The Broken Blade. 1998. (J). 11.64 (978-0-606-13228-2(7)) Tandem Library Bks.

Ernst, Kathleen. Trouble at Fort la Pointe. 2000. (American Girl Collection). (Illus.). (J). (978-0-606-20956-4(5)) Tandem Library Bks.

Pendziwol, Jean E. The Red Sash. Debon, Nicolas, illus. 2005. 40p. (J). (ps-7). 16.95 (978-0-88899-589-6(X)) Groundwood Bks. CAN. *Dist:* Perseus Distribution.

Wargin, Kathy-Jo. The Voyageur's Paddle. Geister, David, illus. rev. ed. 2007. 40p. (J). (ps-5). 17.95 (978-1-58536-007-9(4)) Sleeping Bear Pr.

FURNITURE

see also Cabinet Work; Wood-Carving

also names of articles of furniture, e.g. Chairs; Mirrors; etc.

Braithwaite, Jill. From Tree to Table. (Start to Finish Ser.). (J). 2004. (Illus.). 24p. 18.60 (978-0-8225-0947-9(4)); 2002. pap. 4.95 (978-0-8225-0751-2(X)) Lerner Publishing Group. (Lerner Pubns.).

Clyde, Addie M. Sophie the Sofa. l.t. ed. 2004. 40p. (J). per. (978-1-59196-744-6(9)) Instantpublisher.com.

Getty, J. Paul, Museum Staff. 1 to 10 & Back Again: A Getty Museum Counting Book. 1999. (Books for Young Readers Ser.). (Illus.). 52p. (ps-1). 16.95 (978-0-89236-525-8(0)) Oxford Univ. Pr., Inc.

Nelson, Esther. Chairs Are to Sit. Hirsch, Davida, ed. Behr, Joyce, illus. l.t. ed. 1999. 28p. (Orig.). (J). (gr. k-1). pap. 7.95 (978-0-945110-14-9(6)) Granny Pr.

Sundance, ed. My Desk. 2000. (ps-2). lib. bdg. 11.65 (978-0-613-37626-6(9)) Tandem Library Bks.

Taylor, Audilee B. Where Did My Feather Pillow Come From? Dillon, Sharon S., illus. 1998. 32p. (J). (ps-3). reprint ed. 15.95 (978-0-942250-00-8(1)) Castlemarsh Pubns.

FURNITURE, AMERICAN

Congdon-Martin, Douglas. The Gustav Stickley Photo Archives. 2002. (Illus.). 272p. (gr. 10-13). 69.95 (978-0-7643-1661-6(3)) Schiffer Publishing, Ltd.

FURNITURE, COLONIAL

see Furniture, American

FURNITURE—HISTORY

Pressler, Rudolf, et al. Antique Biedermeier Furniture. 2002. (Schiffer Book for Collectors Ser.). (Illus.). 256p. 39.95 (978-0-7643-1648-7(6)) Schiffer Publishing, Ltd.

FUTURE LIFE

Anderson, Joel. Big Topics for Little Kids: Tell Me about Eternity. Smith, Kristi Carter, illus. 2005. 32p. (J). 9.99 (978-1-4003-0598-8(5)) Nelson, Thomas Inc.

Collison, Catherine Wilde, et al, eds. Yaklennium: A Kid's Guide to the Future. Westman, Marty, illus. 1999. 64p. (J). (gr. 1-8). pap. 9.95 (978-0-937247-30-3(8)) Detroit Free Pr., Inc.

Hoffman, Nancy. Life after Death. 2004. (Illus.). 112p. (J). 29.95 (978-1-59018-129-4(8) , Lucent Bks.) Thomson Gale.

Holford, Karen. I Miss Grandpa: A Story to Help Your Child Understand Death— & Eternal Life. 2004. (Illus.). 32p. (J). (978-0-8163-2030-1(6)) Pacific Pr. Publishing Assn.

Libby, Larry. Someday Heaven. McLoughlin, Wayne, illus. 2001. 40p. (J). 12.99 (978-0-310-70105-7(8)) Zonderkidz.

Lynette, Rachel. The after Life. 2007. (Mysterious Encounters Ser.). 48p. (J). (gr. 4-8). 23.70 (***978-0-7377-3642-7(9)*** , Kidhaven) Thomson Gale.

Rock, Lois. When Goodbye Is Forever. Moxley, Sheila, illus. 2004. 32p. (J). (ps-3). 7.95 (978-0-56148-449-2(0)) Good Bks.

E
F
G

E
F
G

FUTURE LIFE—FICTION

Anderson, Jodi Lynn. May Bird among the Stars, Bk. 2. 272p. (J). 2007. pap. 5.99 (978-1-4169-0608-7(8) , Aladdin); 2006. 16.95 (978-0-689-86924-2(X) , Atheneum) Simon & Schuster Children's Publishing.

Basye, Dale E. Heck: Where the Bad Kids Go. Dob, Bob, illus. 2008. (J). (****978-0-375-84075-3(3)***); pap. (****978-0-375-84076-0(1)***); lib. bdg. (****978-0-375-94075-0(8)***) Random Hse., Inc.

Bernard, Patricia. Techno Terror. 2000. (gr. 7-12). lib. bdg. 12.10 (978-0-613-29093-7(3)) Tandem Library Bks.

Black, Robert A. Lunar Pioneers. 2008. 280p. (YA). pap. 14.99 (978-1-59092-397-9(9) , Blue Works) Windstorm Creative.

Brooke, Lauren. New Beginnings. 2005. (Heartland Ser.: Vol. 18). 176p. (J). pap. 4.99 (978-0-439-65366-4(5) , Scholastic Paperbacks) Scholastic, Inc.

Connor, Leslie. Dead on Town Line. Triplett, Gina, illus. 2006. 144p. (YA). (gr. 6). pap. 6.99 (978-0-14-240697-7(X) , Puffin) Penguin Group (USA) Inc.

Crutcher, Chris. The Sledding Hill. 2005. 240p. (J). (gr. 7 up). 16.99 (978-0-06-050243-0(6)); lib. bdg. 17.89 (978-0-06-050244-7(4)) HarperCollins Pubs.

—Sledding Hill. 2006. 256p. (J). pap. 6.99 (978-0-06-050245-4(2) , HarperTeen) HarperCollins Pubs.

—The Sledding Hill. l.t. ed. 2005. 181p. (YA). 20.95 (978-0-7862-8091-9(3)) Thorndike Pr.

Doggett, Julie. Families Are Families Forever. 2005. (Illus.). 39p. pap. 14.95 (978-1-4116-3064-2(5)) Lulu.com.

Flesh, Chris P. Me So Pretty! 2007. (Pretty Freekin Scary Ser.: No. 2). 176p. (J). (gr. 3). pap. 4.99 (****978-0-448-44683-7(9)*** , Grosset & Dunlap) Penguin Group (USA) Inc.

—You Smell Dead. 2007. (Pretty Freekin Scary Ser.: No. 1). 176p. (J). (gr. 3). pap. 4.99 (****978-0-448-44682-0(0)*** , Grosset & Dunlap) Penguin Group (USA) Inc.

Kennedy, Mike. The Language of Chaos. 2003. (Lone Wolf 2100 Ser.: Vol. 2). (Illus.). 120p. (gr. 11 up). pap. 12.95 (978-1-56971-997-8(7)) Dark Horse Comics.

Lincoln, Christopher. Billy Bones. 2007. 208p. (J). (978-0-316-01473-1(7)) Little Brown & Co.

Mathison, Tarver. Rebel Fortunes. 2002. 130p. (YA). pap. 10.95 (978-0-595-25413-2(6) , Writers Club Pr.) iUniverse, Inc.

McGowan, Anthony. Hellbent. 2006. 272p. (YA). pap. 8.99 (978-1-4169-0814-2(5) , Simon & Schuster Children's Publishing) Simon & Schuster Children's Publishing.

Nevins, Paul. Dante's War. 2003. 168p. (YA). pap. 12.95 (978-0-595-26743-9(2) , Writers Club Pr.) iUniverse, Inc.

Pastor, Melanie Joy. Wishes for One More Day. Grantford, Jacqui, illus. 2006. 32p. (J). 15.95 (978-0-9729225-7-9(1)) Flashlight Pr.

Peel, John. Firestorm. 2000. (Twenty Ninety-Nine Ser.: Bk. 6). (Illus.). 160p. (J). (gr. 3-7). pap. 4.99 (978-0-439-06035-6(4)) Scholastic, Inc.

Plante, Raymond. Marilou Forecasts the Future. Favreau, Marie-Claude & Cummins, Sarah, trs. Favreau, Marie-Claude, illus. 2003. (First Novel Ser.). 64p. (J). (gr. 2-5). 4.95 (978-0-88780-614-8(7)); (****978-0-88780-615-5(5)***) Formac Publishing Co., Ltd. CAN. *Dist:* Casemate Pubs. & Bk. Distributors, LLC.

Rosenbloom, Eileen. Stuck Down. 2005. 240p. pap. 8.95 (978-0-7387-0658-0(2)) Llewellyn Pubns.

Rylant, Cynthia. The Heavenly Village: A Novel. 1999. 96p. (J). (gr. 5-9). pap. 15.95 (978-0-439-04096-9(5) , Blue Sky Pr., The) Scholastic, Inc.

—The Heavenly Village: A Novel. 2000. (gr. 5-8). lib. bdg. 13.00 (978-0-613-53819-0(6)) Tandem Library Bks.

Shearer, Alex. The Great Blue Yonder. 2002. 192p. (YA). (gr. 5-9). 15.00 (978-0-618-21257-6(4) , Clarion Bks.) Houghton Mifflin Co. Trade & Reference Div.

Shusterman, Neal. Everlost. 2007. 384p. (YA). mass mkt. 6.99 (****978-0-689-87238-9(0)*** , Simon Pulse); 2006. 320p. (J). (gr. 7 up). 16.95 (978-0-689-87237-2(2)) Simon & Schuster Children's Publishing.

Sleator, William. Hell Phone. 2007. 288p. (J). (gr. 7-17). pap. 6.95 (****978-0-8109-9360-0(0)***); 2006. 252p. (YA). (gr. 8-11). 16.95 (978-0-8109-5479-3(6) , Amulet Bks.) Abrams, Harry N. , Inc.

Springer, Nancy. Sky Rider. 2000. 128p. (J). (gr. 7 up). pap. 4.95 (978-0-380-79565-9(5) , Harper Trophy) HarperCollins Pubs.

Sternthal, Sherry. How Do You Get to Heaven? Thornton-Haas, Barbara, illus. 2000. 36p. (J). (gr. 3-9). pap. 11.95 (978-0-9700375-0-3(3)) Schlifer, Sherry.

Thompson, Kate. Origins. 2007. (Missing Link Trilogy Ser.: Bk. 3). 320p. (YA). (gr. 7 up). 17.95 (****978-1-58234-652-6(6)*** , Bloomsbury Children) Bloomsbury Publishing.

Whitcomb, Laura. A Certain Slant of Light. 2005. 288p. (YA). (gr. 7). pap. 8.99 (978-0-618-58532-8(X) , Graphia) Houghton Mifflin Co. Trade & Reference Div.

Zevin, Gabrielle & McGhee, Alison. Elsewhere. 2005. 288p. (YA). (gr. 7-17). 16.00 (978-0-374-32091-1(8)) Farrar, Straus & Giroux.

—Elsewhere. 2007. 304p. (YA). pap. 6.95 (****978-0-312-36746-6(5)***) Square Fish.

G

G.I.S

see Soldiers—United States

GAGARIN, YURI ALEKSEEVICH, 1934-1968

Cullen, David. The First Man in Space. 2004. (Days That Changed the World Ser.). (Illus.). 48p. (J). (gr. 5 up). pap. 11.95 (978-0-8368-5577-7(9)); lib. bdg. 30.00 (978-0-8368-5570-8(1)) Stevens, Gareth Inc. (World Almanac Library).

Feldman, Heather. Yuri Gagarin: The First Man in Space. 2003. (Space Firsts Ser.). (Illus.). 24p. (J). lib. bdg. 19.95 (978-0-8239-6245-7(8) , PowerKids Pr.) Rosen Publishing Group, Inc., The.

GALAPAGOS ISLANDS

Banting, Erinn. Galapagos Islands. 2006. (J). (978-1-59036-455-0(4)); lib. bdg. (978-1-59036-449-9(X)) Weigl Pubs., Inc.

Barter, James E. The Galapagos Islands. 2002. (Endangered Animals & Habitats Ser.). (Illus.). 112p. (J). (gr. 4-12). (978-1-56006-920-1(1) , Lucent Bks.) Thomson Gale.

Corwin, Jeff. Into Wild Galapagos. Pascoe, Elaine, ed. 2003. (Jeff Corwin Experience Ser.). (Illus.). 48p. (J). 24.95 (978-1-56711-857-5(7)); 11.20 (978-1-4103-0173-4(7)) Thomson Gale. (Blackbirch Pr., Inc.).

Harper, Judith. Unique Places. 2005. (Real Deal - Green Plus Ser.). (Illus.). 32p. (gr. 4-8). 19.00 (978-0-7910-8903-3(7)) Facts On File, Inc.

Harper, Judith E. Unique Places. 2005. (Real Deal Ser.). (Illus.). 32p. (J). pap. (978-0-7608-9635-8(6)) Sundance/Newbridge Educational Publishing.

Heller, Ruth. Galapagos Means Tortoises. Heller, Ruth, illus. 2000. (Books for Children). (Illus.). 40p. (J). (gr. k-4). 14.95 (978-0-87156-917-2(5)) Sierra Club Bks. for Children.

Kras, Sara Louise. The Galapagos Islands. 2008. (J). (****978-0-7614-2856-5(9)***) Cavendish, Marshall Bks., Ltd.

Mastorakis, Michael. We're off... to the Galapagos. Baker, Georgette & Tidwell, Patty, photos by. 2001. (We're Off... Ser.). (Illus.). (J). (ps-8). 12.99 (978-1-892306-03-6(4)) Cantemos-Bilingual Books and Music.

—We're off... to the Galapagos. Baker, Georgitti, ed. Mastorakis, Andreas, photos by. l.t. ed. 2000. (SPA & ENG., Illus.). (J). (gr. 1-8). lib. bdg. 18.95 (978-1-892306-02-9(6)) Cantemos-Bilingual Books and Music.

Roza, Greg. The Galapagos Islands. 2003. (Reading Room Collection). (Illus.). 24p. (J). lib. bdg. 18.75 (978-0-8239-3714-1(3)) Rosen Publishing Group, Inc., The.

Sovak, Jan. Galapagos Islands Coloring Book. 2006. 32p. (J). pap. 3.95 (978-0-486-44886-2(X)) Dover Pubns., Inc.

Tagliaferro, Linda. Galapagos Islands: Nature's Delicate Balance at Risk. 2005. (Discovery! Ser.). (Illus.). 120p. (gr. 5-12). lib. bdg. 27.93 (978-0-8225-0648-5(3)) Lerner Publishing Group.

GALES

see Winds

GALILEI, GALILEO, 1564-1642

Bendick, Jeanne. Along Came Galileo. Bendick, Jeanne, illus. 1999. (Illus.). 99p. (J). (gr. 4-8). pap. 9.95 (978-1-893103-01-6(3)) Beautiful Feet Bks.

Boekhoff, P. M. Galileo. 2003. (Inventors & Creators Ser.). (Illus.). 48p. (J). 23.70 (978-0-7377-1891-1(9) , Greenhaven Pr., Inc.) Thomson Gale.

Boothroyd, Jennifer. Galileo Galilei: A Life of Curiosity. 2007. (Pull Ahead Books-Biographies Ser.). (J). 22.60 (978-0-8225-6460-7(2) , Lerner Pubns.) Lerner Publishing Group.

Doak, Robin S. Galileo: Astronomer & Physicist. 2004. (Signature Lives Ser.). (Illus.). 112p. (J). 30.60 (978-0-7565-0813-5(4)) Compass Point Bks.

Don Nardo. The Trial of Galileo. 2004. (Famous Trials Ser.). (Illus.). 112p. (J). 29.95 (978-1-59018-423-3(8)) Thomson Gale.

Foelker, Rita. Erase Una Vez Galileo Galilei. Abs, Renata, illus. 2004. 24p. pap. 2.95 (978-85-7416-192-1(6)) Callis Editora Ltda BRA. *Dist:* Independent Pubs. Group.

Goldsmith, Mike. Galileo Galilei. 2001. (Scientists Who Made History Ser.). (Illus.). 48p. (J). (gr. 4-6). lib. bdg. 27.12 (978-0-7398-4416-8(4)) Raintree.

Hightower, Paul. Galileo: Astronomer & Physicist. 2008. (J). (****978-0-7660-3008-4(3)***) Enslow Pubs., Inc.

Hightower, Paul W. Galileo: Astronomer & Physicist. 2001. (Great Minds of Science Ser.). (Illus.). 128p. (YA). (gr. 4-10). pap. 10.95 (978-0-7660-1870-9(9)) Enslow Pubs., Inc.

Hilliam, Rachel. Galileo Galilei: Father of Modern Science. 2004. (Rulers, Scholars, & Artists of Renaissance Europe Ser.). (Illus.). 112p. (J). lib. bdg. 31.95 (978-1-4042-0314-3(1)) Rosen Publishing Group, Inc., The.

Mason, Paul. Galileo. (Groundbreakers Ser.). (Illus.). 48p. (J). (gr. 5-7). 2002. pap. 8.50 (978-1-58810-991-0(7) , 91466); 2001. lib. bdg. 25.64 (978-1-58810-052-8(9)) Heinemann Library.

Michael White. Galileo Galilei. 2005. (Gigantes de Ciencia Ser.). (gr. 5-7). 28.70 (978-1-4103-0503-9(1) , Blackbirch Pr., Inc.) Thomson Gale.

O'Donnell, Kerri. Galileo: Man of Science. 2003. (Reading Room Collection). (Illus.). 24p. (J). lib. bdg. 18.75 (978-0-8239-3700-4(3) , Reading Room Collection) Rosen Publishing Group, Inc., The.

Panchyk, Richard. Galileo for Kids: His Life & Ideas, 25 Activities. 2005. (For Kids Ser.). (Illus.). 184p. (J). pap. 16.95 (978-1-55652-566-7(4)) Chicago Review Pr., Inc.

Puerta, German. Galileo Galilei - Y Sin Embargo se Mueve. 2005. 108p. pap. (978-958-30-1700-1(0)) Panamericana Editorial.

Signature Lives: Renaissance Era, 6 titles, Set. 2005. (YA). (gr. 5-7). lib. bdg. 183.60 (978-0-7565-0875-3(4)) Compass Point Bks.

Sis, Peter. Starry Messenger. 2000. (gr. 3-6). lib. bdg. 15.25 (978-0-8085-0262-3(X)) Tandem Library Bks.

—Starry Messenger: Galileo Galilei. Sis, Peter, illus. 2002. (Illus.). 15.49 (978-0-7587-3698-7(3)) Book Wholesalers, Inc.

—Starry Messenger: Galileo Galilei. Sis, Peter, illus. 2000. (Illus.). 40p. (J). (ps-3). pap. 6.95 (978-0-374-47027-2(8) , Sunburst) Farrar, Straus & Giroux.

—Starry Messenger: Galileo Galilei. Sis, Peter, illus. 2000. (J). (978-0-606-19399-3(5)) Tandem Library Bks.

Steele, Philip. Galileo: The Genius Who Faced the Inquisition. 2005. (World History Biographies Ser.). (Illus.). 64p. (J). (gr. 3-7). 17.95 (978-0-7922-3656-6(4)); 27.90 (978-0-7922-3657-3(2)) National Geographic Society. (National Geographic Children's Bks.).

Whiting, Jim. Galileo. 2007. (What's So Great About... ? Ser.). (J). lib. bdg. 25.70 (****978-1-58415-575-1(2)***) Mitchell Lane Pubs., Inc.

GALLERIES (ART)

see Art Museums

GAMA, VASCO DA, 1469-1524

Bailey, Katharine. Vasco da Gama: Quest for the Spice Trade. 2007. (Illus.). 32p. (J). (gr. 3-9). (****978-0-7787-2421-6(2)***); pap. (****978-0-7787-2457-5(3)***) Crabtree Publishing Co.

Calvert, Patricia. Vasco Da Gama: So Strong a Spirit. 2003. (Great Explorations Ser.). (Illus.). 96p. (J). 29.93 (978-0-7614-1611-1(0) , Benchmark Bks.) Cavendish, Marshall Corp.

Compass Point Books, contrib. by. Da Gama. (Exploring the World Ser.). 48p. (YA). pap. 8.95 (978-0-7565-1142-5(9)) Compass Point Bks.

Doak, Robin S. Da Gama: Vasco Da Gama Sails Around the Cape of Good Hope. 2001. (Exploring the World Ser.). (Illus.). 48p. (J). (gr. 4 up). lib. bdg. 22.60 (978-0-7565-0124-2(5)) Compass Point Bks.

Gallagher, Jim. Vasco da Gama & the Portuguese Explorers. 1999. (Explorers of the New World Ser.). (Illus.). 63p. (J). (gr. 4 up). 31.00 (978-0-7910-5514-4(0) , Chelsea Hse.) Facts On File, Inc.

Goodman, Joan Elizabeth. A Long & Uncertain Journey: The 27,000 Mile Voyage of Vasco Da Gama. McNeely, Tom, illus. 2001. (Great Explorers Ser.). 48p. (ps-12). 22.95 (978-0-9650493-7-5(X)) Mikaya Pr.

Koestler-Grack, Rachel A. Vasco Da Gama: And the Sea Route to India. Goetzmann, William H., ed. 2005. (Explorers of New Lands Ser.). (Illus.). 146p. (J). (ps-8). lib. bdg. 30.00 (978-0-7910-8611-7(9) , Chelsea Hse.) Facts On File, Inc.

Larkin, Tanya. Vasco da Gama. 2001. (Famous Explorers Ser.). (Illus.). 24p. (J). (gr. 3). lib. bdg. 18.75 (978-0-8239-5555-8(9) , PowerKids Pr.) Rosen Publishing Group, Inc., The.

Mattern. Earth's Explorers: Vasco de Gama. 2000. (SPA., Illus.). (J). pap. (978-0-7398-3335-3(9)) Steck-Vaughn.

Mattern, Joanne. The Travels of Vasco da Gama. 1999. (Explorers & Exploration Ser.). (Illus.). 48p. (J). (gr. 4-7). lib. bdg. 22.83 (978-0-7398-1490-1(7)) Raintree.

McFarren, Kathleen. Vasco Da Gama. 2004. (Fact Finders Ser.). (Illus.). 32p. (J). 16.95 (978-0-7368-2491-0(X)) Capstone Pr., Inc.

Morey, Allan. Vasco Da Gama. 2003. (Explorers of the Unknown Ser.). (J). (978-1-58417-033-4(6)); pap. (978-1-58417-096-9(4)) Lake Street Pubs.

Petrie, Kristin. Vasco Da Gama. 2004. (Explorers Ser.). (Illus.). 32p. (J). (gr. k-6). lib. bdg. 22.78 (978-1-59197-603-5(0) , Checkerboard Library) ABDO Publishing Co.

GAME PROTECTION

Jackson, Donna M. The Wildlife Detectives: How Forensic Scientists Fight Crimes Against Nature. Shattil, Wendy & Rozinski, Bob, photos by. (Scientists in the Field Ser.). (Illus.). 48p. (J). (gr. 4-6). 2002. pap. 6.95 (978-0-618-19683-8(8)); 2000. tchr. ed. 17.00 (978-0-395-86976-5(5)) Houghton Mifflin Co. Trade & Reference Div.

GAME WARDENS

see Game Protection

GAMES

see also Amusements; Bible Games and Puzzles; Cards; Games for Travelers; Kindergarten; Olympics; Play; Singing Games; Sports

also names of games, e.g. Chess; Tennis; etc.

Aaseng, Nathan. Business Builders in Toys. 2003. (Business Builders Ser.). (Illus.). 160p. (gr. 5 up). lib. bdg. 22.95 (978-1-881508-81-6(1)) Oliver Pr., Inc.

Aboff, Marcie. Rainy Day Games. Cardona, Jose Maria, illus. 2005. (Clifford Ser.). 32p. (J). 3.99 (978-0-439-69044-7(7) , Cartwheel Bks.) Scholastic, Inc.

Acorn's Gold Mine. 2004. (J). cd-rom 39.00 (****978-1-890265-12-0(8)***) Janelle Pubns., Inc.

Acorn's Tree House. 2002. (J). cd-rom 39.00 net. (978-1-890265-09-0(8)) Janelle Pubns., Inc.

Adam, Winky. Playground Fun Sticker Activity Book. 2003. (Dover Little Activity Bks.). (Illus.). 4p. (J). (ps-3). pap. 1.50 (978-0-486-42625-9(4)) Dover Pubns., Inc.

Adams, Carol J., et al. Journey to Gameland: How to Make a Board Game from Your Favorite Children's Book. 2001. (Illus.). 112p. 12.95 (978-1-930051-51-5(4)) Lantern Bks.

Adams, Ken. Bring Out the Genius in Your Child: Fun Activities to Stretch Young Minds from 0 - 11 Years. 2006. (Illus.). 144p. pap. 14.95 (978-0-600-61435-7(2) , Hamlyn) Octopus Publishing Group GBR. *Dist:* Sterling Publishing Co., Inc.

Aigner-Clark, Julie. Animal Discovery Cards: Beautiful Nature Photographs & Animals Facts to Delight Your Tots. 2003. (Baby Einstein Ser.). 29p. (ps-17). 9.99 (978-1-892309-80-8(7)) Hyperion Bks. for Children.

Ainsworth, Ken. Building a Solitaire Game & a Pegboard, 2 vols., Set. Holdcroft, Tina, illus. 1998. (Building Together Ser.: No. 1). 24p. (J). (gr. 3-8). pap. 5.95 (978-1-55037-512-1(1)) Annick Pr., Ltd. CAN. *Dist:* Firefly Bks., Ltd.

Ajmera, Maya. Come Out & Play. 2001. (ps-2). lib. bdg. 15.25 (978-0-613-51238-1(3)); (Illus.). (J). 13.75 (978-0-606-20613-6(2)) Tandem Library Bks.

Ajmera, Maya & Ivanko, John D. Come Out & Play. Shakti for Children Staff, ed. 2004. (It's Kid's World Ser.). (Illus.). 32p. (J). (ps-1). 15.95 (978-1-57091-385-3(4)); pap. 6.95 (978-1-57091-386-0(2)) Charlesbridge Publishing, Inc.

Alipio, Byron P. Jambo Nation Board Game 1st Edition: The game of wild animal Football. 2006. (Illus.). (YA). 25.00 (****978-0-9794647-0-6(6)***) Idyllworks, LLC.

Allen, Miles. Christmas Lore & Legend. 2003. 40p. 8.96 (978-0-9710448-3-8(X) , 1) Momentpoint Media.

Allen, Robert, et al. Mensa Challenge Your IQ. 2002. (Mensa Word Games for Kids Ser.). (Illus.). 224p. pap. 7.95 (978-1-85868-311-9(4)) Carlton Bks., Ltd. GBR. *Dist:* Ingram Pub. Services, Simon & Schuster, Inc.

Allen, Toi Lynn. Game Day/Test Day: Who's Keeping Score? l.t. ed. 2004. (Illus.). (YA). pap. 14.95 (978-0-9753787-0-0(8)) Allen, Toi Operations.

Allyson, Jackie. Antonio "The Magician" Esfandiari. 2008. (J). (****978-1-4222-0217-3(8)***) Mason Crest Pubs.

—Howard "The Professor" Lederer. 2008. (J). (****978-1-4222-0223-4(2)***) Mason Crest Pubs.

—Phil "Unabomber" Laak. 2008. (J). (****978-1-4222-0222-7(4)***) Mason Crest Pubs.

Amazing Card Tricks & Games. 2004. (How 2 Kits Ser.). (Illus.). 48p. (J). (978-1-84229-934-0(4)) Top That! Publishing PLC.

Ambrosek, Renee. Team Roping. 2005. (World of Rodeo Ser.). (Illus.). 48p. (J). lib. bdg. 26.50 (978-1-4042-0548-2(9)) Rosen Publishing Group, Inc., The.

American Girl Editorial Staff, ed. Kits Mystery Party Game. 2005. (American Girls Collection). (Illus.). N/Ap. (J). pap. 16.95 (978-1-59369-004-5(5) , American Girl) American Girl Publishing, Inc.

—Mollys Mystery Party Game. 2005. (American Girls Collection). (Illus.). N/Ap. (J). pap. 16.95 (978-1-59369-003-8(7) , American Girl) American Girl Publishing, Inc.

—Samanthas Mystery Party Game. 2005. (American Girls Collection). (Illus.). N/Ap. (J). pap. 16.95 (978-1-58485-986-4(5) , American Girl) American Girl Publishing, Inc.

American Heritage Dictionary Editors, ed. What Am I Playing?/Qué Juego? Zagarenski, Pamela, illus. 2004. (Good Beginnings Ser.). (SPA & ENG.). 4p. (J). (gr. k-ps). bds. 3.95 (978-0-618-44375-8(4)) Houghton Mifflin Co. Trade & Reference Div.

Ancona, George. Mis Juegos. 32p. (J). 2006. (SPA.). (gr. 1-3). pap. 8.95 (978-0-516-25498-2(7)); 2005. (ENG & SPA.). 21.00 (978-0-516-25293-3(3)) Scholastic Library Publishing. (Children's Pr.).

Anderson, Karen C., ed. Games Magazine Junior Kids' Big Book of Games. 1999. (Illus.). 176p. (J). (gr. 4-7). pap. 9.95 (978-0-89480-657-5(2) , 1657) Workman Publishing Co., Inc.

Angel, R. P. G. Angel: Investigator's Casebook. 2005. 160p. (YA). 30.00 (978-1-891153-43-3(9)) Eden Studios, Inc.

Animal Antics. 2002. (J). 15.95 (978-1-74047-159-6(8)) Book Co. Publishing Pty, Ltd., The AUS. *Dist:* Penton Overseas, Inc.

Animal Soundtracks. 2003. (YA). (ps up). pap. 15.99 (978-0-7424-1528-7(7)) School Specialty Publishing.

Anthony, Mary. Let's Go! Vamonos! Electronic Adventure Game Book. 2005. (Nick Jr. Dora the Explorer Ser.). (Illus.). 10p. (J). (ps-17). bds. 19.99 (978-0-7944-0690-5(4)) Reader's Digest Assn., Inc., The.

Apples to Apples - Core Game - Expansion Set - 1: The Game of Hilarious Comparisons. 2000. 12.95 (978-0-9664517-3-3(2)) Out of the Box Publishing, Inc.

Apples to Apples - Core Game - Expansion Set - 2: The Game of Hilarious Comparisons. 2000. 12.95 (978-0-9664517-7-1(5)) Out of the Box Publishing, Inc.

Apples to Apples - Core Game - Expansion Set - 3: The Game of Hilarious Comparisons. 2001. 12.95 (978-0-9664517-8-8(3)) Out of the Box Publishing, Inc.

Apples to Apples - Core Game - Expansion Set - 4: The Game of Hilarious Comparisons. 2002. 12.95 (978-0-9708554-4-2(3)) Out of the Box Publishing, Inc.

Apples to Apples - Customizable Cards - Carton: The Game of Hilarious Comparisons. 2000. 3.95 (978-0-9664517-5-7(9)) Out of the Box Publishing, Inc.

Apples to Apples - Customizable Cards - Ink Jet: The Game of Hilarious Comparisons. 2002. 6.95 (978-0-9708554-5-9(1)) Out of the Box Publishing, Inc.

Apples to Apples - Customizable Cards - Laser: The Game of Hilarious Comparisons. 2002. 4.95 (978-0-9664517-9-5(1)) Out of the Box Publishing, Inc.

Apples to Apples Junior: The Game of Funny Comparisons. 2000. 15.95 (978-0-9664517-4-0(0)) Out of the Box Publishing, Inc.

Apples to Apples Junior 9+ The Game of Funny Comparisons. 2001. 15.95 (978-0-9708554-0-4(0)) Out of the Box Publishing, Inc.

Avner & Brachot- Islands of Blessings. 2000. cd-rom 29.95 (978-1-931711-16-6(X)) Torah Educational Software.

Avner Travels in Time- Jerusalem 164 B. C. E. Real-Time 3D Jewish Educational Adventure Game. 2002. cd-rom 29.95 (978-1-931711-26-5(7)) Torah Educational Software.

Baker, Sue. Peep-O! Stockham, Jess, illus. 2006. (Blanket Babies Ser.). 12p. (J). 6.99 (978-1-904550-88-4(6)) Child's Play-International.

Bamaopoly. 2002. (C). bds. 24.95 (978-1-932150-00-1(5)) Late For The Sky Production Co.

Bany-Winters, Lisa. Funny Bones: Comedy Games & Activities for Kids. 2002. (Illus.). 176p. (J). (gr. 4-7). pap. 14.95 (978-1-55652-444-8(7)) Chicago Review Pr., Inc.

Barcelo, Josefina. Vamos a Jugar. Alvarez, Mrinalí, illus. 2006. (SPA.). (J). 8.95 (978-0-8477-1560-2(4)) Univ. of Puerto Rico Pr.

Barkan, Joanne. Games We Play. 2005. (Real Deal Ser.). (Illus.). 32p. (J). pap. (978-0-7608-9632-7(1)) Sundance/Newbridge Educational Publishing.

Barker, Cicely Mary. How to Host a Flower Fairy Tea Party. 2004. (Flower Fairies Ser.). (Illus.). 48p. (J). (ps). 7.99 (978-0-7232-5360-0(9) , Warne) Penguin Group (USA) Inc.

Barron's Educational Editorial Staff & Perez, Eulalia. 100 Best Games. Rius, María, illus. 2000. 136p. (J). 12.95 (978-0-7641-1343-7(7)) Barron's Educational Series, Inc.

Barsaive at War. 2001. (YA). 18.00 (978-0-9704191-0-1(4)) Living Room Games.

Bartl, Alison. 101 Pep-up Games for Children: Refreshing, Recharging, Refocusing. 2007. (SmartFun Activity Bks.). (Illus.). 160p. pap. 14.95 (***978-0-89793-495-4(4))** Hunter Hse., Inc.

—101 Pep-up Games for Children: Refreshing, Recharging, Refocusing. Puth, Klaus, illus. 2007. (SmartFun Activity Bks.). 160p. spiral bd. 19.95 (***978-0-89793-496-1(2))** Hunter Hse., Inc.

—101 Relaxation Games for Children: Finding a Little Peace & Quiet in Between. Puth, Klaus, illus. 2007. (SmartFun Activity Bks.). 160p. pap. 14.95 (***978-0-89793-493-0(8)**); spiral bd. 19.95 (***978-0-89793-494-7(6))** Hunter Hse., Inc.

Basari. 2002. 19.95 (978-0-9716729-0-1(3)) Out of the Box Publishing, Inc.

Basic Skills Games. (My First Homework Booklets Ser.). 80p. 2.99 (978-1-56822-762-7(0) , IF0312) School Specialty Publishing.

Battles & Leaders Event Kit. 2003. (Illus.). (978-0-7894-9988-2(6) , D K Ink) Dorling Kindersley Publishing, Inc.

Beatty, Sarah. On the Farm (Full-Color) (Prek-K) 2006. pap. 16.99 (978-1-4206-8144-4(3)) Teacher Created Resources, Inc.

Beaulieu, Jeannine. Caillou Butterfly. (Illus.). 24p. (J). pap. (978-2-89450-292-1(3)) Chouette Publishing.

Becker, Helaine. Boredom Blasters: Brain Bogglers, Awesome Activities, Cool Comics, Tasty Treats, & More... Davila, Claudia, illus. 2004. 160p. (J). 21.95 (978-1-897066-02-7(3)); pap. 9.95 (978-1-897066-03-4(1)) Maple Tree Pr. CAN. *Dist:* Perseus Distribution.

Beginning Fractions. (Math Minders Ser.). 32p. (gr. 1-2). 5.99 (978-0-7682-0029-4(6) , FS12013) Schaffer, Frank Pubns.

Beginning Fractions. 2003. (Illus.). (gr. k up). 9.99 (978-0-7682-1900-5(0) , J41010) School Specialty Publishing.

Berendes, Mary. Sports & Games/Los Deportes y Los Juegos. 2007. (WordBooks/Libros de Palabras Ser.). (SPA & ENG.). 24p. (J). 19.93 (***978-1-59296-802-2(3))** Child's World, Inc.

Berger, Loretta Oleck. Calm down & Play: Activities to Help Impulsive Children. 2003. 76p. (J). pap. 17.95 (978-1-58815-055-4(0) , 63565) Childswork/Childsplay.

Berger, Samantha. Games. 1999. (J). pap. 2.50 (978-0-439-04566-7(5)) Scholastic, Inc.

—Games. 1999. (ps-2). lib. bdg. 10.10 (978-0-613-21574-9(5)) Tandem Library Bks.

Bernhard, Emery. Time to Play: Children's Games Around the World. Bernhard, Durga, illus. 1999. (J). 14.99 (978-0-525-67553-2(1) , Dutton Juvenile) Penguin Group (USA) Inc.

Beylon, Cathy. Animal Ballerinas Stickers. 2002. (Illus.). 4p. (J). pap. 1.50 (978-0-486-42340-1(9)) Dover Pubns., Inc.

—Camping Fun Sticker Activity Book. 2003. (Dover Little Activity Bks.). (Illus.). 4p. (J). (ps-3). pap. 1.50 (978-0-486-42626-6(2)) Dover Pubns., Inc.

—My Clubhouse Sticker Activity Book. 1999. (Dover Little Activity Bks.). (Illus.). 4p. (J). pap. 1.50 (978-0-486-40746-3(2)) Dover Pubns., Inc.

Bieri, Peter. Action Games. rev. ed. 1999. (Illus.). 56p. (J). (gr. k-6). pap. 7.95 (978-1-58107-021-7(7)) New Forums Pr.

The Big Book of Games & Activities for Young Children. (Big Book Ser.). 276p. pap. 19.99 (978-0-8307-2882-4(1) , Gospel Light) Gospel Light Pubns.

Bingham, Jane. Look Around a Roman Amphitheater. 2007. (***978-1-84193-721-2(5))** Smart Apple Media.

Birlew, Dan & Walsh, Doug. Metal Gear Solid 3: Snake Eater: Official Strategy Guide. 2004. (Illus.). 224p. (YA). pap. 16.99 (978-0-7440-0477-9(2)) Brady GAMES.

The Birthday Bug, 6 Pack. (Story Steps Ser.). (gr. k-2). 29.00 (978-0-7635-9575-3(6)) Rigby Education.

Birthday Puzzles & Games. 2002. (Home Workbooks Ser.). 64p. pap. 2.49 (978-0-88724-698-2(2) , CD-4500) Carson-Dellosa Publishing Co., Inc.

Blackstone, Stella. You & Me. Manna, Giovanni, illus. 2000. 32p. (J). (ps-1). 15.99 (978-1-84148-263-7(3)) Barefoot Bks., Inc.

Blair, Beth. The Everything Kids' Gross Hidden Pictures Book. 2006. (Everything Kids' Ser.). (Illus.). 144p. (J). pap. 7.95 (978-1-59337-615-4(4)) Adams Media Corp.

Blakey, Nancy. More Mudpies: 101 Alternatives to Television. Watts, Melissah, illus. 2004. 144p. (J). (ps-7). 9.95 (978-1-883672-11-9(2) , Tricycle Pr.) Ten Speed Pr.

—The Mudpies Activity Book: Recipes for Invention. Watts, Melissah, illus. 2004. 144p. (J). (ps-7). 9.95 (978-1-883672-19-5(8) , Tricycle Pr.) Ten Speed Pr.

Blink: The World's Fastest Game. 2001. 9.95 (978-0-9708554-1-1(9)) Out of the Box Publishing, Inc.

Boase, Petra. I Can Play Games. 2000. (Show Me How Ser.). (Illus.). 48p. (ps-2). pap. 7.95 (978-0-7548-0225-9(6)) Anness Publishing GBR. *Dist:* National Bk. Network.

Bowman-Kruhm, Mary. Fun Facts & Games: New York. Harris, Phyllis, illus. 2000. (Fun Facts & Games Activity Book Ser.). 64p. (J). (gr. 1-5). pap. 5.95 (978-1-892920-49-2(2)) GHB Publishers, LLC.

Boyd, Anne, ed. Games 411. 2003. 200p. spiral bd. 49.00 (978-1-931625-21-0(2)) LA 411 Publishing Co.

Bozulich, Richard. Get Strong at the Joseki 1. 1998. (Beginner & Elementary Go Bks.). (Illus.). 184p. (J). pap. 15.00 (978-4-906574-52-0(1)) KISEIDO.

BradyGames Staff. Advent Rising Official Strategy Guide. 2005. (Illus.). 128p. pap. 14.99 (978-0-7440-0420-5(9)) Brady GAMES.

—Darkwatch Official Strategy Guide. 2005. (Illus.). 128p. pap. 14.99 (978-0-7440-0517-2(5)) Brady GAMES.

—Haunting Ground Official Strategy Guide. 2005. (Illus.). 160p. pap. 14.99 (978-0-7440-0525-7(6)) Brady GAMES.

BradyGames Staff & Deats, Adam. Prince of Persia: Warrior Within Official Strategy Guide. 2004. (BradyGames Signature Ser.). (Illus.). 176p. pap. 15.99 (978-0-7440-0482-3(9)) Brady GAMES.

BradyGames Staff & Lummis, Michael. Mega Man Zero 3 Official Strategy Guide. 2004. (Illus.). 112p. pap. 14.99 (978-0-7440-0422-9(5)) Brady GAMES.

BradyGames Staff & Marcus, Phillip. Rumble Roses(TM) Official Strategy Guide. 2004. (Illus.). 112p. pap. 14.99 (978-0-7440-0474-8(8)) Brady GAMES.

Brain Teasers from the World Almanac(R) for Kids, Book 1. 2003. pap. 12.99 (978-0-7439-3782-5(1)); pap. 12.99 (978-0-7439-3788-7(0)); pap. 12.99 (978-0-7439-3785-6(6)) Teacher Created Materials, Inc.

Brain Teasers from the World Almanac(R) for Kids, Book 2. 2003. pap. 12.99 (978-0-7439-3783-2(X)); pap. 12.99 (978-0-7439-3789-4(9)); pap. 12.99 (978-0-7439-3786-3(4)) Teacher Created Materials, Inc.

Brain Teasers from the World Almanac(R) for Kids, Book 3. 2003. pap. 12.99 (978-0-7439-3784-9(8)); pap. 12.99 (978-0-7439-3790-0(2)); pap. 12.99 (978-0-7439-3787-0(2)) Teacher Created Materials, Inc.

Braman, Arlette N. Kids Around the World Play! The Best Fun & Games from Many Lands. 2002. (Kids Around the World Ser.: Vol. 4). (Illus.). 128p. pap. 12.95 (978-0-471-40984-7(7) , Wiley) Wiley, John & Sons, Inc.

Brian, Sarah Jane. Brainiac's Mindbenders: Fun Activities for Geniuses of All Ages. 2005. (Activity Journal Ser.). (Illus.). 128p. (J). act. bk. ed. 12.99 (978-0-88088-591-1(2)) Peter Pauper Pr. Inc.

Brighter Vision Publishing Staff. Look & Find Activity Book. 2000. (Illus.). 32p. (J). (ps). pap. 1.39 (978-1-55254-149-4(5)) Brighter Vision Pubns.

Brilliant Board Games. 2004. (How 2 Kits Ser.). (Illus.). 48p. (J). (978-1-84229-930-2(1)) Top That! Publishing PLC.

Brooks, Felicity. Messy Baby. 2005. (Busy Baby Board Books Ser.). 10p. (J). 8.95 (978-0-7945-0964-4(9) , Usborne) EDC Publishing.

—Playtime Baby. 2005. (Busy Baby Board Books Ser.). 10p. (J). 8.95 (978-0-7945-0965-1(7) , Usborne) EDC Publishing.

Bruce, Linda. Entertainment Technology. 2006. (How Does It Work? Ser.). (Illus.). 32p. (J). (978-1-58340-792-9(8)) Smart Apple Media.

Bruzzone, Catherine & Beaton, Clare. Action French! A Lively Activity Starter Pack for Adults & Children. 2000. (Illus.). 20p. (J). (ps-5). pap., suppl. ed. 14.95 incl. audio (978-0-658-00448-3(4) , 004484) McGraw-Hill/Contemporary.

Bruzzone, Catherine, et al. Action Spanish! A Lively Activity Starter Pack for Adults & Children. 2000. (ENG & SPA., Illus.). 12p. (J). (ps-5). pap. 14.95 incl. audio (978-0-658-00443-8(3) , 004433) McGraw-Hill/Contemporary.

Bryant, Nick & Summers, Renan. Amazing Spot What! (Illus.). 32p. (J). (978-1-86515-727-6(9)) Hinkler Bks. Pty, Ltd. AUS. *Dist:* Hinkler Bks. Pty, Ltd.

Buchanan, Ben. My Year with Harry Potter: How I Discovered My Own Magical World. 2001. (Illus.). 112p. (ps-3). 12.95 (978-1-930051-50-8(6)) Lantern Bks.

Buck, Nola. Santa's Short Suit Shrunk: And Other Christmas Tongue Twisters. 1998. (I Can Read Bks.). (Illus.). 32p. (J). (gr. k-3). pap. 3.75 (978-0-06-444247-3(0)) HarperCollins Pubs.

Bucken, Hajo. Button, Button, Who's Got the Button? (Illus.). 80p. pap. 15.95 (978-0-86315-214-6(7) , 1915) Floris Bks. GBR. *Dist:* Gryphon Hse., Inc., Steiner-Books, Inc.

Buddy & Belle's Winter Fun. 1998. (Wipe-Off Activity Bks.). (Illus.). 16p. (J). (ps-1). wbk. ed. 3.79 (978-1-889319-25-4(2)) Trend Enterprises, Inc.

Budget City Game. 2005. (gr. 3-6). suppl. ed. 39.00 (978-1-57861-059-4(1) , BC-01E, IEP RESOURCES) Attainment Co., Inc.

BudgetTown: Budget Town. 2005. (J). mass mkt. 29.00 (978-0-934731-67-6(5) , IEP RESOURCES) Attainment Co., Inc.

Buffy, R. P. G. Military Monster Squad: Initiative Sourcebook. 2005. 128p. (YA). pap. 27.00 (978-1-891153-69-3(2)) Eden Studios, Inc.

Bug's Life Fun & Game Book. 1999. (J). 12.99 (978-0-7364-0168-5(7)) Mouse Works.

Bullimore, Tom. Sherlock Holmes Whodunits. 2002. (gr. 5-8). lib. bdg. 15.25 (978-0-613-75663-1(0)) Tandem Library Bks.

Bulloch, Ivan & James, Diane. Un Cow-Boy. 2000. (I Wish I Were Ser.). (FRE., Illus.). 24p. (J). (ps-2). pap. 7.95 (978-1-58728-204-1(6) , Two Can Publishing) T&N Children's Publishing.

—Une Fee. 2000. (I Wish I Were Ser.). (FRE., Illus.). 24p. (J). (ps-2). pap. 7.95 (978-1-58728-206-5(2) , Two Can Publishing) T&N Children's Publishing.

—Un Pirate. 2000. (I Wish I Were Ser.). (Illus.). 24p. (J). (ps-2). pap. 7.95 (978-1-58728-205-8(4) , Two Can Publishing) T&N Children's Publishing.

—Une Princesse. 2000. (I Wish I Were Ser.). (Illus.). 24p. (J). (ps-2). pap. 7.95 (978-1-58728-207-2(0) , Two Can Publishing) T&N Children's Publishing.

Bumper Activity Fun. 2002. 576p. (J). pap. 6.98 (978-0-7525-8926-8(1)) Parragon, Inc.

Bunny Days. (Happy Days Ser.). 48p. 5.99 (978-1-57029-271-2(X) , WPH28007, Totline Pubns.) Schaffer, Frank Pubns.

Burton, Phil. Can Do, Serious Fun: Games for 4-9 Year Olds. 2002. (Illus.). 80p. (C). pap. 15.95 (978-1-86152-838-4(8)) CENGAGE Learning.

—Serious Fun: Games for 10-14 Year Olds. 2002. (Can Do Ser.). (Illus.). 80p. (C). pap. 15.95 (978-1-86152-839-1(6)) CENGAGE Learning.

Butterfield, Moira. Peek-a-Who? 2006. 10p. (J). 6.99 (978-0-439-78534-1(0) , Cartwheel Bks.) Scholastic, Inc.

Cabrera, Jane, illus. If You're Happy & You Know It! 2005. 32p. (J). 16.95 (978-0-8234-1881-7(2)) Holiday Hse., Inc.

Calaboose. 2005. 12.95 (978-0-9764394-2-4(5)) Live Oak Games.

Campaign Map Packs: Village. 2005. (YA). 9.95 (978-0-9770071-7-2(0)) Paizo Publishing, LLC.

Candyland Surprize Ink! Book & Marker. 2004. 24p. (J). 5.99 (978-1-932125-81-8(7)) Giddy Up, LLC.

Care Bears: Caring & Sharing. 2005. (Illus.). 100p. (YA). (978-1-59524-046-0(2)) Giddy Up, LLC.

Care Bears Water Wow! Book. 2005. (J). per. 6.99 (978-1-59524-055-2(1)) Giddy Up, LLC.

Carella, C. J. Buffy the Vampire Slayer Revised Corebook. 2005. 288p. (YA). 40.00 (978-1-933105-10-9(0)) Eden Studios, Inc.

Carmona, Lisa. Games & Puzzles. 2002. (Activity Zone Workbooks Ser.). (Illus.). 64p. (J). pap., wbk. ed. 3.79 (978-1-58947-055-2(9) , 02349) School Zone Publishing Co.

Carter, David A. Blue 2: A Pop-up Book for Children of All Ages. Carter, David A., illus. ltd. ed. 2006. 18p. (J). 250.00 (978-1-4169-2717-4(4) , Little Simon) Simon & Schuster Children's Publishing.

—Blue 2 Vol. 2: A Pop-up Book for Children of All Ages. Carter, David A., illus. 2006. 18p. (J). (gr. 2-5). 19.95 (978-1-4169-1781-6(0) , Little Simon) Simon & Schuster Children's Publishing.

Cartoon Network Staff, contrib. by. Sticker Shock Activities. 2000. (Illus.). 48p. (J). (ps-3). pap. 3.99 (978-0-307-10541-7(5) , Golden Bks.) Random Hse. Children's Bks.

Cartwright, Stephen, illus. Ludo. 2004. (Farmyard Tales Card Games Ser.). (J). 12.95 (978-0-7945-0310-9(1) , Usborne) EDC Publishing.

Cartwright, Stephen & Blundell, Kim, illus. Snakes & Ladders. 2004. (Farmyard Tales Card Games Ser.). (J). 12.95 (978-0-7945-0312-3(8) , Usborne) EDC Publishing.

Cassidy, Maura A. Go Ask Your Father! 2003. (YA). mass mkt. (978-0-9742866-0-0(5)) Go Ask Anyone, Inc.

Cassone, Chris, creator. The Great Central Park Treasure Hunt: Interactive Orienteering Map of NYC's Famous Park. 2004. (YA). 24.95 (978-0-9749809-0-4(0)) Treasure Hunt Adventures, Inc.

Cast, John. Hide & Seek. 1999. (Let's Play Ser.). (Illus.). 24p. (J). (ps-3). pap. 3.99 (978-0-85953-566-3(5)) Child's Play-International.

Castaldo, Nancy F. Rainy Day Play: Explore, Create, Discover, Pretend. 2005. (Illus.). 144p. (J). pap. 12.95 (978-1-55652-563-6(X)) Chicago Review Pr., Inc.

Cat-Opoly. 2002. bds. 24.95 (978-1-932150-87-2(0)) Late For The Sky Production Co.

Cat's Cradle. 2004. (Whizz Kits Ser.). (Illus.). 48p. (J). (978-1-84229-949-4(2)) Top That! Publishing PLC.

Caulson, Kathleen. Power Reading: Games. Caulson, Kathleen, illus. 2005. (Illus.). (J). 76p. (gr. 2-4). 29.95 (978-1-883186-98-2(6) , PPMXG2-3); 88p. (gr. 4-5). 79.95 (978-1-883186-99-9(4) , PPMXG45) National Reading Styles Institute, Inc.

—Power Reading: Games/Mixed P1. 2005. (Illus.). 76p. (J). (gr. k-2). 29.95 (978-1-883186-97-5(8) , PPMXGP1) National Reading Styles Institute, Inc.

Chadwick, Frank. Soldier's Companion. 2001. 192p. per. 24.95 (978-1-930658-10-3(9)) Heliograph, Inc.

Challenging Puzzles & Games. 2004. (Gel Pen Activity Bks.). (Illus.). 24p. (J). (gr. 2-5). act. bk. ed. (978-0-7666-0598-5(1) , 66000) Modern Publishing.

Chambers, Veronica. Double Dutch: A Celebration of Jump Rope, Rhyme, & Sisterhood. 2007. (Illus.). 64p. (J). 19.00 (***978-1-4223-6701-8(0))** DIANE Publishing Co.

Changing Seasons Matching Game. 2005. (J). 14.99 (978-0-7353-0623-3(0)) Galison.

Charlton, Coleman, et al. Rolemaster Fantasy Role Playing. 1999. (Illus.). 256p. (YA). (gr. 7 up). 30.00 (978-1-55806-550-5(4) , 5800) Iron Crown Enterprises, Inc.

—10,000,000 Ways to Die. 1999. (Rolemaster Standard System Ser.). (Illus.). 112p. (YA). (gr. 7 up). pap. 16.00 (978-1-55806-374-7(9) , 5705) Iron Crown Enterprises, Inc.

Chevat, Richie. The Marble Book. Cooper, Martha, photos by. 2004. (Illus.). 186p. (J). (gr. k-4). reprint ed. pap. 10.00 (978-0-7567-7776-0(3)) DIANE Publishing Co.

Chutes & Ladders Suprize Ink! Book & Marker. 2004. 24p. (J). 5.99 (978-1-932125-80-1(9)) Giddy Up, LLC.

Clark, Diane C. & Chernick, Miriam. A Kid's Guide to Washington, D.C. Brown, Richard E., illus. 2008. (J). pap. (***978-0-15-206125-8(8))** Harcourt Trade Pubs.

Clarke, Phillip. Seas & Oceans Game Kid Kit. 2004. (Kid Kits Ser.). 64p. (J). 15.99 (978-1-58086-728-3(6) , Usborne); 15.99 (978-1-58086-730-6(8)) EDC Publishing.

Cloud 9. 2003. mass mkt. 9.95 (978-1-932359-06-0(0)) Out of the Box Publishing, Inc.

Coast-to-Coast Games. (Backseat Bks.). 80p. (J). pap. 3.95 (978-0-528-96548-7(4)) Rand McNally.

Cobb, Rebecca. Tongue Twisters to Tangle Your Tongue. 2006. (Illus.). 32p. pap. 8.95 (978-0-7145-3301-8(7)) Consortium Bk. Sales & Distribution.

Code Buster Fun. 2002. 192p. (J). pap. 3.98 (978-0-7525-7915-3(0)) Parragon, Inc.

Coffin, Bill. Rifts Dimension Book Five: Anvil Galaxy. Zeleznik, John et al, illus. 2002. (Rifts Dimension Bk.: No. 5). (YA). pap. 17.95 (978-1-57457-019-9(6)) Palladium Bks., Inc.

Coffin, Bill & Siembieda, Kevin. Western Empire. Marciniszyn, Alex et al, eds. Dubisch, Mike et al, illus. 1998. (Sourcebook Ser.: Vol. 8). 224p. (YA). (gr. 8 up). pap. 20.95 (978-1-57457-015-1(3) , 462) Palladium Bks., Inc.

Cohen, Todd R. Ultimate Conquest: Games for a New Generation. Flaig, Donald W., ed. 1998. (Illus.). 260p. (YA). (gr. 7 up). pap. 39.95 (978-0-9667921-1-9(4)) Tribute Publishing.

Cole, Joanna. Hopscotch & Sidewalk Game. 2000. (J). (978-0-688-17709-6(3)) HarperCollins Pubs.

Complete Set. (Games Around the World Ser.). (Illus.). (gr. 2-4). 271.20 (978-0-7565-0732-9(4)) Compass Point Bks.

Compound Word Memory Match. 2003. (Language Arts Card Games Ser.). (Illus.). (gr. 1-2). 9.99 (978-0-7682-2088-9(2) , J801300) School Specialty Publishing.

Connally, Dale. Games with a Purpose 2. 2001. (Illus.). 128p. (J). (gr. 7-12). 12.95 (978-0-7673-9447-5(X)) LifeWay Christian Resources.

Conner, Bobbi. Unplugged Play. 2007. (Illus.). 516p. (J). 27.95 (***978-0-7611-4114-3(6))** Workman Publishing Co., Inc.

Cool Designs & Games. 2004. (Gel Pen Activity Bks.). (Illus.). 24p. (J). (gr. 2-5). act. bk. ed. (978-0-7666-0597-8(3) , 66000) Modern Publishing.

Copeland, Cynthia L. Fun on the Run for Kids: 324 Instant Family Activities. Hoffman, Sanford, illus. 2004. 352p. pap. 8.95 (978-0-7611-3448-0(4) , 13448) Workman Publishing Co., Inc.

Correr, Saltar y Brincar. (SPA., Illus.). (J). pap. 6.95 (978-950-11-0123-2(1) , SGM123) Sigmar ARG. *Dist:* Continental Bk. Co., Inc.

Corrie, William E., 3rd & Corrie, Linda D. Another Man's Treasure: A Guide to Shadazar. Breed, Jessica & Corrie, Linda D., eds. 2003. (Illus.). 64p. (YA). per. 15.00 (978-0-9740096-1-2(X) , HWE1100) HinterWelt Enterprises, LLC.

—Shades of Earth: Earth History with a Twist, Breed, Jessica & Corrie, Linda D., eds. 2003. (Illus.). 240p. (YA). per. 30.00 (978-0-9740096-2-9(8) , HWE2000) HinterWelt Enterprises, LLC.

Covey, Dominic, creator. Darwin's World. 2002. (Illus.). 128p. (YA). 19.95 (978-0-9724826-0-8(1)) RPG Objects.

Cranium Inc. Staff. Cranium Big Book of Outrageous Fun! The Write-It, Draw-It, Sculpt-It, Act-It Game-in-a-Book-in-a-Game! Baseman Staff, illus. 2005. 56p. (J). (gr. 2-17). 19.99 (978-0-316-01193-8(2)) Little, Brown Bks. for Young Readers.

Crick, Stephanie. Peek-a-Boo Moon. DeFazio, Deborah, illus. 2004. 16p. (J). per. 9.95 (978-0-9746397-3-4(7)) Pinefield Publishing.

Crist, Nancy & Sheedy, Rose. Bubble Pop Game Sheet. Duncan, Karla et al, eds. 2001. (Illus.). (J). (ps-5). spiral bd. 32.95 (978-1-58650-200-3(X)) Super Duper Pubns.

Curtis, William D. Periculum Latinum. 1998. 87p. (J). spiral bd. 13.50 (978-0-939507-53-5(6) , L8) American Classical League, The.

Dahlstrom, Kathryn. Street Games. Date not set. (Good News Club Ser.). (J). pap. 4.99 (978-1-55976-829-0(0)) CEF Pr.

Dalmatian Press Staff. Boo Games Hidden Picture. 2004. 32p. pap. 2.99 (978-1-4037-0835-9(5)) Dalmatian Pr.

—Cartoon Network Puzzles & Games! 2004. (Cartoon Network Ser.). 64p. (J). pap. 2.99 (978-1-4037-0767-3(7)) Dalmatian Pr.

—Lisa Frank: All Star Rodeo Days. 2005. (Illus.). 32p. (J). pap. 3.49 (978-1-4037-1151-9(8)) Dalmatian Pr.

—Pencil Me In: Cartoon Network Puzzles & Games! (Cartoon Network Ser.). 96p. (J). pap. 2.99 (978-1-4037-0765-9(0)) Dalmatian Pr.

—Saban's Power Rangers Lost Galaxy Mega Maze & Puzzle Book. 1999. (Illus.). (J). (ps-3). pap. 2.99 (978-1-57759-252-5(2)) Dalmatian Pr.

Dalmatian Press Staff, ed. Go-o-o Games! Cartoon Network Puzzles & Games! (Cartoon Network Ser.). 96p. (J). pap. 2.99 (978-1-4037-0766-6(9)) Dalmatian Pr.

Dalmatian Press Staff & School Zone Publishing Interactive Staff. Same or Different. 2000. (On-Track Software Ser.). 32p. (J). (ps). wbk. ed. 13.99 incl. cd-rom (978-0-88743-926-1(8) , 08802) School Zone Publishing Co.

Daniel, Andy. Diangle! Board Game. Wong, Valerie, illus. 2nd rev. ed. 1998. (J). (gr. 3). 24.95 (978-1-929645-06-0(6)) Enginuity, LLC.

—3 Stones Board Game. Daniel, Sara Ellen, ed. Gutierrez, Godi, illus. Jansons, Robert, photos by. 2000. (gr. 3). 29.95 (978-1-929645-08-4(2)) Enginuity, LLC.

Daniel, Andy & Daniel, Sara Ellen. Doubles Wild Solid WOod Board Game. Gutierrez, Godi, illus. 2001. 29.95 (978-1-929645-11-4(2)) Enginuity, LLC.

E
F
G

Danks, Fiona & Schofield, Jo. Nature's Playground: Activities, Crafts, & Games to Encourage Children to Get Outdoors. 2007. 192p. (J). (gr. 2-4). pap. 16.95 (***978-1-55652-723-4(3)***) Chicago Review Pr., Inc.

Danson, Lesley. Fairy Snap. Danson, Lesley, illus. 2007. 52p. (J). 8.99 (978-0-7945-1434-1(0) , Usborne) EDC Publishing.

Daronco, Mickey & Ohanesian, Diane. The Game. 2nd rev. ed. 2004. (BuildUp Ser.). (J). pap. 22.00 (978-1-4108-1533-0(1)) Benchmark Education Co.

Darsie, Richard. String Games. (Illus.). 96p. 2005. (J). pap. 7.95 (978-1-4027-2787-0(9)); 2003. 14.95 (978-1-4027-0089-7(X)) Sterling Publishing Co., Inc.

De Ballon, N. V., contrib. by. Alphabet Dot to Dot. 2004. (Illus.). 64p. pap. 4.95 (978-1-4027-1835-9(7)) Sterling Publishing Co., Inc.

Dino-Mite! 2003. (Science Card Games Ser.). (gr. 2-3). 9.99 (978-0-7682-1977-7(9) , J53005) School Specialty Publishing.

Dinoffer, Joe. 101 Fun Skill Builders for Kids. 1999. 121p. (J). pap. 16.95 (978-1-58518-245-9(1)) Coaches Choice.

Disney Press Staff. Cars - Start Your Engines! Disney Storybook Artists Staff, illus. 2006. 8p. (ps-17). 12.99 (978-0-7868-4921-5(5)) Disney Pr.

DK Publishing. Playtime. 2008. 14p. (J). (ps-k). bds. 5.99 (***978-0-7566-3834-4(8)***) Dorling Kindersley Publishing, Inc.

DK Publishing Staff & Stoppard, Miriam. Baby Games. 2007. (Let's Play Ser.). 16p. (J). (ps-1). ring bd. 9.99 (978-0-7566-2596-2(3)) Dorling Kindersley Publishing, Inc.

Do You Want to Play? (Pebble Soup Explorations Ser.). 16p. (ps up). 31.00 (978-0-7578-1655-0(X)) Rigby Education.

Do You Want to Play? Small Book. (Pebble Soup Explorations Ser.). 16p. (ps up). 5.00 (978-0-7578-1695-6(9)) Rigby Education.

Dodd, Lynley. Gold Star First Readers, 21 bks. Incl. Dragon in a Wagon. Dodd, Lynley, illus. 2000. lib. bdg. 22.00 (978-0-8368-2687-6(6)); Find Me a Tiger. Dodd, Lynley, illus. 2001. lib. bdg. 22.00 (978-0-8368-2781-1(3)); Hairy Maclary & Zachary Quack. Dodd, Lynley, illus. 2000. lib. bdg. 22.00 (978-0-8368-2676-0(0)); Hairy Maclary from Donaldson's Dairy. Dodd, Lynley, illus. 2000. lib. bdg. 21.26 (978-0-8368-2688-3(4)); Hairy Maclary Scattercat. Dodd, Lynley, illus. 2000. lib. bdg. 22.00 (978-0-8368-2689-0(2)); Hairy Maclary, Sit. Dodd, Lynley, illus. 2001. lib. bdg. 22.00 (978-0-8368-2808-5(9)); Hairy Maclary's Bone. Dodd, Lynley, illus. 2001. lib. bdg. 22.00 (978-0-8368-2782-8(1)); Hairy Maclary's Caterwaul Caper. Dodd, Lynley, illus. 2000. lib. bdg. 22.00 (978-0-8368-2690-6(6)); Hairy Maclary's Rumpus at the Vet. Dodd, Lynley, illus. 2000. lib. bdg. 21.26 (978-0-8368-2691-3(4)); Hairy Maclary's Showbusiness. Dodd, Lynley, illus. 1992. lib. bdg. 21.27 (978-0-8368-0763-9(4)); Scarface Claw. Dodd, Lynley, illus. 2002. lib. bdg. 22.00 (978-0-8368-3161-0(6)); Schnitzel Von Krumm, Dogs Never Climb Trees. 2004. lib. bdg. 22.00 (978-0-8368-4092-6(5)); Schnitzel Von Krumm Forget-Me-Not. Dodd, Lynley, illus. 1998. lib. bdg. 21.27 (978-0-8368-2094-2(0)); Schnitzel Von Krumm's Basketwork. Dodd, Lynley, illus. 2001. lib. bdg. 22.00 (978-0-8368-2783-5(X)); Slinky Malinki. Dodd, Lynley, illus. 2001. lib. bdg. 22.00 (978-0-8368-2784-2(8)); Slinky Malinki Catflaps. Dodd, Lynley, illus. 1999. lib. bdg. 22.00 (978-0-8368-2249-6(8)); Slinky Malinki, Open the Door. Dodd, Lynley, illus. 2001. lib. bdg. 22.00 (978-0-8368-2785-9(6)); Smallest Turtle. Dodd, Lynley, illus. 2000. lib. bdg. 22.00 (978-0-8368-2692-0(2)); Sniff-Snuff-Snap! Dodd, Lynley, illus. 2000. lib. bdg. 22.00 (978-0-8368-2677-7(9)); Wake up, Bear. Dodd, Lynley, illus. 2001. lib. bdg. 22.00 (978-0-8368-2786-6(4)); 32p. (J). (gr. 1 up). Set lib. bdg. 418.00 (978-0-8368-4167-1(0)) Stevens, Gareth Inc.

Dog-Opoly. 2002. bds. (978-1-932150-88-9(9)) Late For The Sky Production Co.

Dolby, Karen & Fischel, Emma. Spooks' Surprise. 2004. (Young Puzzle Adventures Ser.). (Illus.). 32p. (J). (gr. 2 up). pap. 4.95 (978-0-7945-0234-8(2) , Usborne) EDC Publishing.

—Usborne Young Puzzle Adventure Stories. Bates, Michelle, ed. (Young Puzzle Adventures Ser.). (Illus.). 96p. (J). pap. 11.95 (978-0-7460-3454-5(7)) EDC Publishing.

Dora the Explorer ColorBlast. 2004. 24p. (J). 7.99 (978-1-932125-98-6(1)) Giddy Up, LLC.

Dora Water Wow! Book. 2005. (J). per. 6.99 (978-1-59524-088-0(8)) Giddy Up, LLC.

Dorling Kindersley Publishing Staff. I Spy! 2006. (DK Toys & Games Ser.). (J). 9.99 (978-0-7566-2234-3(4)) Dorling Kindersley Publishing, Inc.

Douglas, Julie. Fun Facts & Games: California. Nolte, Larry, illus. 2000. (Fun Facts & Games Ser.). 64p. (J). (ps-3). pap. 5.95 (978-1-892920-22-5(0)) GHB Publishers, LLC.

Douglas, Vincent & School Specialty Publishing Staff. Backyard Discoveries. 2004. (Playful Learning Ser.). (Illus.). 128p. (J). (gr. k-k). pap. 10.95 (978-0-7696-3300-8(5) , American Education Publishing) School Specialty Publishing.

—The Complete Book of Travel Games. American Education Publishing Staff, ed. 2000. (Complete Book Ser.). (Illus.). 352p. (J). (gr. k-6). pap. 14.95 (978-1-56189-546-5(6) , 31243, American Education Publishing) School Specialty Publishing.

—Dot-to-Dots, Puzzles, & Games. 2003. (Homework Helpers Ser.). (Illus.). 32p. (J). (gr. k-1). pap. 2.99 (978-0-7696-2914-8(8) , American Education Publishing) School Specialty Publishing.

—Hagamos Cuadritos. EduSlate, ed. 2006. (Edu-Slates Ser.). (Illus.). 1p. (J). 2.99 (978-0-7696-4979-5(3) , Brighter Child) School Specialty Publishing.

—Here We Go Games. 2003. (Travel Games Ser.). (Illus.). 64p. (J). (gr. 1-5). pap. 3.99 (978-1-57768-545-6(8) , Brighter Child) School Specialty Publishing.

—A Jugar Tres en Raya! EduSlate, ed. 2006. (Edu-Slates Ser.). (Illus.). 1p. (J). bds. 2.99 (978-0-7696-4989-4(0) , Brighter Child) School Specialty Publishing.

—Let's Play Box It Up! EduSlate, ed. 2006. (Edu-Slates Ser.). (Illus.). 1p. (J). 2.99 (978-0-7696-4909-2(2) , Brighter Child) School Specialty Publishing.

—Let's Play Tic-Tac-Toe. EduSlate, ed. 2006. (Edu-Slates Ser.). (Illus.). 1p. (J). 2.99 (978-0-7696-4919-1(X) , Brighter Child) School Specialty Publishing.

—Memory. 2003. (Brighter Child Flash Cards Ser.). (Illus.). 54p. (J). (ps up). 2.99 (978-0-7696-2377-1(8) , Brighter Child) School Specialty Publishing.

—Ocean Dot-to-Dot. 2003. (Homework Helpers Ser.). (Illus.). 32p. (J). (gr. k-1). pap. 2.99 (978-0-7696-2918-6(0) , American Education Publishing) School Specialty Publishing.

—On the Way Games. 2003. (Travel Games Ser.). (Illus.). 64p. (J). (gr. 1-5). pap. 3.99 (978-1-57768-543-2(1) , Brighter Child) School Specialty Publishing.

—Rhymes, Songs, & Games. 2004. (Playful Learning Ser.). (Illus.). 128p. (J). (gr. k-k). pap. 10.95 (978-0-7696-3301-5(3) , American Education Publishing) School Specialty Publishing.

—Vacation Travel Games. 2003. (Travel Games Ser.). (Illus.). 64p. (J). (gr. 1-5). pap. 3.99 (978-1-57768-544-9(X) , Brighter Child) School Specialty Publishing.

Dower, Laura. Road Trippin' Back-Seat Shrek-Tivity Book. Henderson, Bill, illus. 2004. (Shrek 2 Ser.). 64p. (J). act. bk. ed. 14.99 (978-0-439-64134-0(9) , Tangerine Pr.) Scholastic, Inc.

Dowswell, Paul. Entertainment. 2002. (Great Inventions Ser.). (Illus.). 48p. (YA). (gr. 6-8). lib. bdg. 25.64 (978-1-58810-211-9(4)) Heinemann Library.

Doyle, Richard. Fairyland Notebook. 2003. (Dover Little Activity Bks.). 64p. (J). pap. 1.50 (978-0-486-42643-3(2)) Dover Pubns., Inc.

Drake, Jane. The Kids Summer Games Book. Collins, Heather, illus. unabr. ed. 2004. (Fun for All Seasons Ser.). 176p. (J). (gr. 4-6). (978-1-55074-469-0(0)) Kids Can Pr., Ltd.

Drake, Jane & Love, Ann. The Kids Summer Games Book. Collins, Heather, illus. unabr. ed. 2004. (Fun for All Seasons Ser.). 176p. (J). (gr. 4-6). (978-1-55074-465-1(8)) Kids Can Pr., Ltd.

Drake, Jennifer & Drake, Aaron. Travel Fun with Towty: A Color & Activity. 2003. (Illus.). 80p. (J). 4.99 (978-1-56251-798-4(8)) AAA.

Driscoll, Laura. Quiz & Game Book. 2003. (Illus.). 64p. (J). pap. 14.99 (978-0-7868-4522-4(8)) Disney Pr.

Dunn, Opal. Acka Backa Boo! Playground Games from Around the World. Winter, Susan, illus. 2000. 46p. (J). (gr. k-4). reprint ed. 17.00 (978-0-7567-6106-6(9)) DIANE Publishing Co.

—Acker Backa Boo! Games to Say & Play from Around the World. Winter, Susan, illus. 2006. 40p. (J). pap. 7.95 (978-1-84507-515-6(3)) Lincoln, Frances Ltd. GBR. *Dist:* Perseus Distribution.

Dunn, Phoebe, illus. Guess Who I Am... gif. ed. 2005. 5p. (J). (ps). per. 7.99 (978-1-57791-175-3(X)) Brighter Minds Children's Publishing.

Duplacey, James. Wingers. 1999. (Hockey's Hottest Ser.). (Illus.). 118p. (J). (gr. 2-5). (978-1-55074-596-2(4)) Kids Can Pr., Ltd.

Easterling, Lisa. Games. 2007. (Illus.). 24p. (J). (***978-1-4034-9403-0(7)***); pap. (***978-1-4034-9412-2(6)***) Heinemann Library.

Eckdahl, Judith & Eckdahl, Kathryn. A Collection of Street Games. O'Regan, Lucy, ed. Miranda, Pedro, illus. 2005. 42p. pupil's gde. ed. 13.95 (978-0-9767200-0-3(0)) Lesen Pub.

Eden Odyssey D20 Staff. Waysides: The Book of Taverns. 2005. (YA). pap. 30.00 (978-1-891153-54-9(4)) Eden Studios, Inc.

Edmunds, Tracy. In the Ocean (Full-Color) (Prek-K) 2006. pap. 16.99 (978-1-4206-8145-1(1)) Teacher Created Resources, Inc.

Einon, D. Juegos para Aprender. (SPA.). 178p. 18.00 (978-84-95456-37-3(0) , 86756) Ediciones Oniro S.A. ESP. *Dist:* Bilingual Pubns. Co., The, Lectorum Pubns., Inc., Libros Sin Fronteras.

Einon, Dorothy, et al, contrib. by. Brilliant Brain Games for Kids to Enjoy: More Than 300 Brain-Boosting Activities for Toddlers to Five Year Olds. 2006. (Illus.). 256p. pap. 12.95 (978-0-600-61335-0(6) , Hamlyn) Octopus Publishing Group GBR. *Dist:* Sterling Publishing Co., Inc.

Eisenberg, Rebecca & Frailey, Cheris. Webber' Functional Communication Games. 2006. (J). 64.95 (***978-1-58650-689-6(7)***) Super Duper Pubns.

Elliott, Lynne. Children & Games in the Middle Ages. 2004. (Medieval World Ser.). (Illus.). 32p. (J). (978-0-7787-1349-4(0)); pap. (978-0-7787-1381-4(4)) Crabtree Publishing Co.

Elton, Candice & Elton, Richard. Every Kid Needs a Marshmallow Launcher. 2005. (Illus.). 50p. (J). spiral bd. 19.95 (978-1-58685-708-0(8)) Gibbs Smith, Publisher.

—Every Kid Needs a Treasure Hunt. 2006. (Illus.). 48p. (J). spiral bd. 19.95 (978-1-58685-710-3(X)) Gibbs Smith, Publisher.

Elton, Richard & Elton, Candice. Every Kid Needs a Rubber Band Launcher. 2007. (J). (***978-1-4236-0268-2(4)***) Gibbs Smith, Publisher.

Erlbach, Arlene. Sidewalk Games Around the World. Holm, Sharon Lane, illus. 1998. 64p. (J). (gr. 2-5). pap. 8.95 (978-0-7613-0178-3(X) , Millbrook Pr.) Lerner Publishing Group.

—Sidewalk Games Around the World. 1998. (gr. 3-6). lib. bdg. 17.60 (978-0-613-88981-0(9)) Tandem Library Bks.

Erwin, Vicki B. Fun Facts & Games: Canada. Thurman, Mark, illus. 2000. (Fun Facts & Games Ser.). 64p. (J). (ps-3). pap. 5.95 (978-1-892920-25-6(5)) GHB Publishers, LLC.

Esparza, Thomas, Jr., prod. Esther's Playhouse, 2 Disk Set. 2004. (Illus.). (J). cd-rom 39.95 (978-1-879817-49-4(7) , Children) Star Light Pr.

—Esther's Playhouse, Disk 1. 2004. (J). cd-rom 39.95 (978-1-879817-40-1(3) , Children) Star Light Pr.

—Esther's Playhouse, Disk 2. 2004. (Illus.). (J). cd-rom (978-1-879817-41-8(1) , Children) Star Light Pr.

—Esther's Playhouse, Disk D. 2004. (Illus.). (J). cd-rom (978-1-879817-45-6(4) , Children) Star Light Pr.

Eubanks, Toni & Lombardi, Janet. Let's Play! 2005. (Illus.). 80p. (J). (978-0-88441-691-3(7)) Girl Scouts of the USA.

Familyarcade—Cracking the Character Code. 2003. (J). (gr. 1-6). cd-rom 12.99 (978-0-633-09040-1(9)) LifeWay Christian Resources.

Farmer, Karen. I Love to Laugh: A Book of Fun & Giggles. 2007. (Illus.). 16p. (J). (gr. 1-5). bds. 9.95 (***978-1-59125-808-7(1)*** , Penton Kids) Penton Overseas, Inc.

Faughn, Jackie. More Fun Around the World. 1998. 48p. (ps). pap. 6.99 (978-1-56309-260-2(3) , N987103) New Hope Pubs.

Felix the Cat/el Gato Felix: A Fun Surprise. 2005. 32p. (J). pap. (978-0-9762071-1-5(7)) Big City Publishing.

Ferri, Francesca, illus. Peek-A-Boo. 2005. 10p. (J). 7.95 (978-0-7641-5851-3(1)) Barron's Educational Series, Inc.

Feyyaz. Das F Prinzip. aut. ltd. num. ed. 2007. (ENG, FRE & GER.). 32p. (J). (978-3-937718-91-0(5)) daab gmbh.

Filella, Nacho & Garcia, Gloria. Los Juegos. 2005. (SPA.). 6p. 5.99 (978-84-272-6683-4(9)) Molino, Editorial ESP. *Dist:* Santillana USA Publishing Co., Inc.

Filipowich, Bob & Ikids. My Purse. 2003. (Illus.). (J). (ps-ps). 9.99 (978-1-58476-213-3(6)) Innovative Kids.

Finkel, Irving. Ancient Board Games. 1999. (Illus.). 19.95 (978-1-56649-072-6(3)) Welcome Rain Pubs.

Fish Eat Fish. 2003. mass mkt. 19.95 (978-1-932359-11-4(7)) Out of the Box Publishing, Inc.

Fleagle, Gail S. Play Ball! Henry, Marilyn, illus. 1998. (Books for Young Learners). 8p. (J). (gr. k-2). pap. 5.00 (978-1-57274-138-6(4) , A2183) Owen, Richard C. Pubs., Inc.

Flip-Flash Signing: Basic Vocabulary. 2002. (J). (gr. k up). 7.99 (978-1-56451-396-0(3) , ID2440) School Specialty Publishing.

Forbeck, Matt & Barrett, Kevin. Silent Death - The Next Millennium. Dennis, Donald G., ed. deluxe ed. 2000. 168p. (YA). (gr. 7 up). reprint ed. 50.00 (978-1-55806-236-8(X) , 7200) Iron Crown Enterprises, Inc.

Four Ace Reverse. 2004. (Formula Fun Ser.). (Illus.). 48p. (J). (978-1-84229-583-0(7)) Top That! Publishing PLC.

Freeman, Christopher M. Nim: Serious Math with a Simple Game. 2nd ed. 2001. 64p. (J). per., wbk. ed. 11.95 net. (978-1-883055-40-0(7)) Dandy Lion Pubns.

Fremont, Victoria & Beylon, Cathy. Nutcracker. 1999. (Illus.). 64p. (J). (ps-5). pap., act. bk. ed. 1.50 (978-0-486-40494-3(3)) Dover Pubns., Inc.

Frost & Fur: The Explorer's Guide to the Frozen Lands. 2004. (Illus.). (YA). lib. bdg. 32.95 (978-0-9728197-5-6(4) , MKY2201) MonkeyGod Enterprises.

Fun, Games, & Mind-Bogglers! 2004. (Gel Pen Activity Bks.). (Illus.). 24p. (J). (gr. 2-5). act. bk. ed. (978-0-7666-0595-4(7) , 66000) Modern Publishing.

Gabriel, Jamie, et al. 1001 Creative Things to Make. 2005. (Illus.). 640p. per. (978-0-7853-7209-7(1) , 3447800) Publications International, Ltd.

Game Day. (C). 180.80 (978-1-4048-1520-9(1)) Picture Window Bks.

Games. 2005. (Emergent/Early (Prek-2) Social Studies Package Ser.). 12p. (YA). (gr. k-1). 25.20 (978-0-8215-7834-6(0)) Sadlier, William H. Inc.

Games: KinderWords Individual Title Six-Packs. (Kinderstarters Ser.). 8p. (ps-1). 21.00 (978-0-7635-8692-8(7)) Rigby Education.

Games for Theater Class. 2001. 150p. (YA). per. 47.00 net. (978-1-889510-46-0(7)) Championship Debate Enterprises.

Gannon, Joe. Fun & Games: How to Play More Than 70 of the World's Greatest Games for Two or More Players. 2006. (Illus.). 80p. pap. (***978-1-59412-154-8(0)***) Mud Puddle, Inc.

Gave, Marc. Number Games Around the World/Juegos de numeros alrededor del Mundo: English/Spanish Pair, ed. 2004. (Navigators Ser.). (J). pap., instr.'s gde. ed. 84.00 (978-1-4108-1765-5(2)) Benchmark Education Co.

Gavitt's Stock Exchange. 2003. mass mkt. 12.95 (978-1-932359-10-7(9)) Out of the Box Publishing, Inc.

Gensicke, Mary Ann. Fun Facts & Games: Iowa. Griffin, Sandra Ure, illus. 2000. (Fun Facts & Games Ser.). 64p. (J). (gr. 1-5). pap. 5.95 (978-1-892920-46-1(8)) GHB Publishers, LLC.

Geyer, Beth & Geyer, Frank. Teaching Early Concepts with Photos of Kids: Easy Activities Using Snapshots of Students to Build Early Skills, Self-Esteem & Classroom Community. 2005. (Illus.). 48p. (J). pap. 10.99 (978-0-439-51770-6(2) , Teaching Resources) Scholastic, Inc.

Gibson, Ray. I Can Cut & Stick, I Can Crayon, I Can Finger Paint, I Can Draw Animals, I Can Count, I Can Add up & Fun with Numbers. 2004. (Playtime Ser.). (Illus.). 224p. (J). pap., act. bk. ed. 17.95 (978-0-7945-0369-7(1) , Usborne) EDC Publishing.

—Things That Move Kid Kit. 2004. (Playtime Ser.). 32p. (J). lib. bdg. 12.95 (978-1-58086-593-7(3)) EDC Publishing.

Gill, Bill. Pojo's Unofficial Yu-Gi-Oh! Guide to Legacy of Darkness. 2003. (Illus.). 80p. (J). pap. 9.95 (978-1-57243-611-4(5)) Triumph Bks.

Gill, Bill Pojo. Pojo's Magic: The Gathering. 2003. 96p. pap. 9.95 (978-1-57243-595-7(X)) Triumph Bks.

—Pojo's Yu-Gi-Oh! 2nd ed. 2003. (Illus.). 96p. (J). pap. 9.95 (978-1-57243-599-5(2)) Triumph Bks.

—Pojo's Yu-Gi-Oh! Annual 2005. 2005. (Illus.). 144p. pap. 12.95 (978-1-57243-739-5(1)) Triumph Bks.

Glassman, Jackie. Candy Land Big Bad Lord Licorice. Edwards, Ken, illus. 2001. (My First Games Ser.). 32p. (J). (gr. 3). pap. 3.99 (978-0-439-32180-8(8)) Scholastic, Inc.

Gob of Games. Date not set. (J). Vol. 1. pap. 2.95 (978-1-57122-062-2(3)); Vol. 2. pap. 2.95 (978-1-57122-063-9(1)) Nickel Pr.

Gold Digger. 2002. 9.95 (978-0-9708554-9-7(4)) Out of the Box Publishing, Inc.

Golden Books Staff. Reindeer Games. 2005. (Illus.). 32p. (J). (ps-2). pap. 3.99 (978-0-375-83183-6(5) , Golden Bks.) Random Hse. Children's Bks.

—Snowflake Dance. 2003. (Illus.). 12p. (J). (ps-2). pap. 3.99 (978-0-307-10639-1(X) , Golden Bks.) Random Hse. Children's Bks.

Goldowsky, Jill. Silly Word Families. Grayson, illus. 5p. (J). bds. 7.99 (978-0-7944-0100-9(7)) Reader's Digest Children's Publishing, Inc.

Goldsack, Gaby. The Ultimate Sleepover Pack. Reeves, Sue, illus. 24p. (J). 79.60 (978-0-7641-7662-3(5)) Barron's Educational Series, Inc.

Gorman, Carol. Games. 2007. 288p. (J). (gr. 6-9). 16.99 (978-0-06-057027-9(X)); lib. bdg. 17.89 (978-0-06-057028-6(8)) HarperCollins Pubs.

Gould, Marilyn. Playground Sports: A Book of Ball Games. rev. ed. 1999. (Illus.). 64p. (J). (gr. 2 up). pap. 10.95 (978-0-9632305-2-2(2)) Allied Crafts Pr.

Gow, Kailin. Activities Guide for 365 Days of the Year! Fun Things to Do for Kids & Grown-Ups That'll Help Develop Creativity, Social Skills, & Self-confidence! 2003. (Gifted Girls Ser.). 167p. (YA). pap., act. bk. ed. 19.95 (978-0-9714776-6-7(3)) Sparklesoup Studios, Inc.

Graham, Noel. Games & Activities with Dice. 2001. 32p. (J). (gr. k-4). pap. 10.00 (978-1-871098-43-3(2)) Claire Pubns. GBR. *Dist:* Parkwest Pubns., Inc.

Grammar & Literature Games: Making Learning Fun through Friendly Classroom Competition. 2003. 48p. (gr. 5-8). 8.99 (978-0-7682-0656-2(1) , GA13089) School Specialty Publishing.

Greaves, Sheldon. Q'Raj Void Protectorate: Silent Death House Book. Dennis, Donald G., ed. 1999. (Silent Death - The Next Millennium Ser.). (Illus.). 112p. (YA). (gr. 7 up). pap. 18.00 (978-1-55806-381-5(1) , 7224) Iron Crown Enterprises, Inc.

Green, Yuko. Anastasia from Russia Sticker Paper Doll. 1998. (Dover Little Activity Bks.). (Illus.). 4p. (J). (gr. k-5). pap. 1.50 (978-0-486-40514-8(1)) Dover Pubns., Inc.

GridWorks: The Fun Game of Logical Deduction. 2004. (YA). spiral bd. 9.99 (978-0-9755330-0-0(2)) ThinkFun, Inc.

Griffin, Margot. The Sleepover Book. Kurisu, Jane, illus. 2001. 144p. (J). (gr. 4-6). (978-1-55074-522-1(0)) Kids Can Pr., Ltd.

—The Sleepover Book. Kurisu, Jane, illus. 2001. 144p. (J). (978-0-439-35642-8(3)) Scholastic, Inc.

Grimm, Gary. I Love America Jingo. Schwab, Vanessa, illus. 1999. 32p. (YA). (gr. 3 up). 12.95 (978-1-56490-123-1(8)) Grim, Gary & Assocs.

—Thanksgiving Jingo. Schwab, Vanessa, illus. 1999. 32p. (YA). (gr. 3 up). 12.95 (978-1-56490-122-4(X)) Grim, Gary & Assocs.

—World Geography Jingo. Schwab, Vanessa, illus. 1999. (YA). (gr. 5 up). 12.95 (978-1-56490-127-9(0)) Grim, Gary & Assocs.

Grolier Educational Staff, contrib. by. Crafts for Kids, 16 vols. 2003. (Illus.). (J). (978-0-7172-5760-7(6) , Grolier) Scholastic Library Publishing.

Gryski, Camilla. Camilla Gryski's Favorite String Games. Sankey, Tom, illus. 2005. 48p. (978-0-439-77939-5(1)) Scholastic, Inc.

—Let's Play: Traditional Games of Childhood. Petricic, Dusan, illus. 2000. 48p. (J). (gr. k-3). (978-1-55074-817-8(3)) Kids Can Pr., Ltd.

—Let's Play: Traditional Games of Childhood. Petricic, Dusan, illus. unabr. ed. 1998. 48p. (J). (gr. k-3). (978-1-55074-497-2(6)) Kids Can Pr., Ltd.

Gunter, Veronika. The Ultimate Indoor Games Book: The 200 Best Boredom Busters Ever! Meyer, Clay, illus. 2005. 128p. 19.95 (978-1-57990-625-2(7) , 1249645) Lark Bks.

Gunter, Veronika. The Ultimate Indoor Games Book: The Best Boredom Busters Ever! Meyer, Clay, illus. 2007. 208p. (J). pap. 7.95 (***978-1-60059-198-3(1)***) Lark Bks.

Gunzi, Christiane. Bears Love Honey. 2004. (Animal Pairs Ser.). (Illus.). 12p. (J). (ps-k). bds. 5.95 (978-1-58728-241-6(0) , Two Can Publishing) T&N Children's Publishing.

—Pigs in Pink. 2004. (Animal Pairs Ser.). (Illus.). 12p. (J). (ps-k). bds. 5.95 (978-1-58728-240-9(2) , Two Can Publishing) T&N Children's Publishing.

Hagarty, Pat. Pet Chase. Hudson, Brett, illus. 2007. (Rollerball Races Ser.). 12p. (J). (gr. 1-3). bds. 4.99 (978-0-7641-6016-5(8)) Barron's Educational Series, Inc.

—Space Chase. Hudson, Brett, illus. 2007. (Rollerball Races Ser.). 12p. (J). (gr. 1-3). bds. 4.99 (978-0-7641-6017-2(6)) Barron's Educational Series, Inc.

Hall, Godfrey. Games. 1999. (J). (gr. 4-7). lib. bdg. 24.26 (978-0-7398-1408-6(7)) Raintree.

Hall, Margaret C. Games. 2002. (Around the World Ser.). (Illus.). 32p. (J). (gr. k-2). lib. bdg. 22.79 (978-1-58810-476-2(1)) Heinemann Library.

Hands on Crafts for Kids Staff. Perfect Kids' Parties: 12 Fantastic Theme Celebrations. 2006. (Illus.). 128p. pap. 9.95 (978-1-4027-3620-9(7)) Sterling Publishing Co., Inc.

—Super Fun Brain Challenges. 2002. (Illus.). 48p. (gr. 3-7). pap. 3.95 (978-1-4027-0099-6(7) , Balloon Bks.) Sterling Publishing Co., Inc.

Hanrahan, Abigail & McSweeny, Catherine. 50 Quick Play Reading Games. 2004. (J). per. 34.95 (978-0-7606-0535-6(1)) LinguiSystems, Inc.

Hanson, Erik A. & Hanson, Jeanne K. The Everything Kids' Travel Activity Book: Games to Play, Songs to Sing, Fun Stuff to Do - Guaranteed to Keep You Busy the Whole Ride! 2002. (Illus.). 144p. (J). 6.95 (978-1-58062-641-5(6)) Adams Media Corp.

Hanson, Sue & Hanson, Jon. All about Mancala: Its History & How to Play. 2003. (Illus.). pap. 17.95 (978-0-9740175-0-1(7)) Happy Viking Crafts.

Hantman, Clea. Hey, Day! 2001. 74.75 (978-0-06-000169-8(0)) HarperCollins Pubs.

Harcourt School Publishers Staff. A Time for Playing: Library Book. 3rd ed. 2002. (Trophies Reading Program Ser.). (Illus.). pap. 14.00 (978-0-15-326530-3(2)) Harcourt Schl. Pubs.

—What Children Play On Level. 3rd ed. 2002. (Trophies Reading Program Ser.). (Illus.). (gr. 2). pap. 5.10 (978-0-15-323078-3(9)) Harcourt Schl. Pubs.

Harlick, Bruce & Sweeney, Patrick. Monster Island: The Game of Giant Monster Combat. Nakagawa, Bryce, illus. 2002. pap. 9.95 (978-1-890305-37-6(5) , FG1001, Gold Rush Games) Gold Rush Entertainment.

HarperCollins Children's Books. Animal Antics. 2007. (Word Play Ser.). 208p. (J). pap. 5.95 (***978-0-00-724335-8(9)***) HarperCollins Pubs. Ltd. GBR. *Dist:* Independent Pubs. Group.

Harpster, Steve. A-Z Dot-to-Dots. 2003. (Illus.). 64p. (J). pap. 4.95 (978-1-4027-0715-5(0)) Sterling Publishing Co., Inc.

—1-100 Dot-to-Dots: Connect the Dots & Learn to Count. 2003. (Illus.). 64p. (J). pap. 4.95 (978-1-4027-0714-8(2)) Sterling Publishing Co., Inc.

Harvey, Ken. The 'Fridge Games. Hermes, Mary Sue, illus. 2003. (Life in the 'Fridge Ser.). (J). 14.95 (978-1-930093-20-1(9)) Brookfield Reader, Inc., The.

Hawkins, Jason & Johansen, Buck. All Hands on Deck. 1999. (Run Out the Guns Ser.). (Illus.). 32p. (YA). (gr. 7 up). pap. 8.00 (978-1-55806-372-3(2) , 4011) Iron Crown Enterprises, Inc.

Hayhurst, Chris. Lacrosse. 2005. (Sports from Coast to Coast Ser.). (Illus.). 48p. (J). (gr. 5-8). lib. bdg. 26.50 (978-1-4042-0183-5(1)) Rosen Publishing Group, Inc., The.

Hazan, Maurice, creator. Resto Presto French. 2000. (FRE.). (J). 120.00 (978-1-932770-58-2(5) , FC3) Symtalk, Inc.

Head, Jason. Sui Companion Set. 2003. 241p. (YA). per. 14.99 (978-1-4116-0371-4(0)) Lulu.com.

Heller, Sarah E. Raichu Shows Off. 2000. (Pokemon Junior Chapter Bks.: No. 6). (Illus.). 44p. (J). (ps-3). pap. 3.99 (978-0-439-20095-0(4)) Scholastic, Inc.

Hello Kitty ColorBlast. 2004. 24p. (J). 7.99 (978-1-932125-96-2(5)) Giddy Up, LLC.

Hello Kitty Water Wow! Book. 2005. (J). per. 6.99 (978-1-59524-054-5(3)) Giddy Up, LLC.

Henley, Ralph. Action Rhymes & Active Games: Over 200 Bible Story Activities for Ages 2 To 5. 2004. (J). tchr. ed., per. 19.99 (978-1-933803-02-9(9)) Child Sensitive Communication, LLC.

Herd, Meg. Learn & Play in the Garden Vol. 7: Games, Crafts & Activities for Children. 1999. (Environmental Bks.). (Illus.). 128p. (J). (ps-6). lib. bdg. 18.95 (978-1-56674-242-9(0) , HTS Bks.) Forest Hse. Publishing Co., Inc.

Herman, Gail. Candy Land: A Surprise Adventure. 2003. (Hasbro Children's Book Collection Ser.). (Illus.). 12p. (J). pap. 9.95 (978-0-7624-1564-9(9) , Running Pr. Kids) Running Pr. Bk. Pubs.

Hershenhorn, Esther. Illinois Fun Facts & Games. Balcom-Vetillo, Eileen, illus. 2000. (Fun Facts & Games Ser.). 64p. (J). (gr. 1-5). pap. 5.95 (978-1-892920-45-4(X)) GHB Publishers, LLC.

Hide & Seek in Hawaii 2. 2000. (Illus.). 32p. (J). bds. 9.95 (978-1-56647-345-3(4)) Booklines Hawaii, Ltd.

Highlights for Children Editorial Staff. The Super Colossal Book of Hidden Pictures, Vol. 4. 2004. (Illus.). 192p. (J). (gr. 6-9). pap., act. bk. ed. 9.95 (978-1-59078-199-9(6)) Boyds Mills Pr.

—What Fun! Over 150 Activities & Puzzles. 2003. (Illus.). 160p. (YA). (gr. 5-7). pap., stu. ed. 7.95 (978-1-56397-653-7(6)) Boyds Mills Pr.

Hill, Linda. Connecting Kids: Exploring Deversity Together. 2001. (Illus.). 192p. pap. (978-0-86571-431-1(2)) New Society Pubs., Ltd.

Hite, Kenneth. Nightmares of Mine: RPG Sourcebook. 1999. (Illus.). 176p. (YA). (gr. 7 up). pap. 14.00 (978-1-55806-367-9(6) , 5704) Iron Crown Enterprises, Inc.

Hjelmeland, Andy. Legalized Gambling: Solution or Illusion? 1998. (Pro/Con Ser.). (Illus.). 128p. (YA). (gr. 7-12). lib. bdg. (978-0-8225-2615-5(8) , Lerner Pubns.) Lerner Publishing Group.

Hoffman, Joan. Word Searches. 2002. (Activity Zone Workbooks Ser.). 64p. (J). pap., wbk. ed. 3.79 (978-1-58947-056-9(7) , 02350) School Zone Publishing Co.

Hopkins, Jane & Gillespie, Ian. Hide & Seek in Hawaii: A Picture Game for Keiki. 1999. (Illus.). 32p. (J). 12.95 (978-1-56647-278-4(4)) Mutual Publishing LLC.

Hopler, John. Warhounds: Silent Death Tech Book. Dennis, Donald G., ed. 2nd rev. ed. 2000. (Silent Death - The Next Millennium Ser.). 112p. (YA). (gr. 7 up). pap. 18.00 (978-1-55806-249-8(1) , 7212) Iron Crown Enterprises, Inc.

Hovanec, Helene. Tough Trivia for Kids. 2005. (Mensa Ser.). (Illus.). 96p. (J). (gr. 3-7). pap. 5.95 (978-1-4027-2136-6(6)) Sterling Publishing Co., Inc.

Hovanec, Helene & Merrell, Patrick. Country Fun Games & Puzzles. 2007. 144p. (J). pap. 9.95 (978-1-58017-679-8(8)) Storey Publishing, LLC.

Huber, Joe M., des. Ice Cream. 2004. (DUT, FRE, GER, JPN & KOR.). (J). 18.00 (978-0-9761156-0-1(3)) Face 2 Face Games Publishing.

Hughes, Francine. Memory: Two of a Kind. Adelman, Dawn, illus. 2001. (My First Games Novelty Ser.). 6p. (J). (ps-1). bds. 5.99 (978-0-439-26467-9(7)) Scholastic, Inc.

—Sweets & Treats. Kulka, Joe, illus. 2001. (My First Games Novelty Ser.). 6p. (J). (ps-1). pap. 5.99 (978-0-439-26466-2(9)) Scholastic, Inc.

Hughes, Melissa & Lenzo, Caroline. Full Color File Folder Games, Grade 3. 2006. 160p. (J). pap. (978-1-59441-090-1(9) , CD-104051) Carson-Dellosa Publishing Co., Inc.

Hughes, Sarah. Let's Jump Rope. 2000. (gr. k-3). lib. bdg. 12.95 (978-0-613-58848-5(7)) Tandem Library Bks.

—Let's Play Hopscotch. 2000. (gr. k-3). lib. bdg. 12.95 (978-0-613-58850-8(9)) Tandem Library Bks.

—Let's Play Jacks. 2000. (Welcome Bks.). (Illus.). 24p. (J). (ps-2). pap. 4.95 (978-0-516-23038-2(7) , Children's Pr.) Scholastic Library Publishing.

—Let's Play Tag. 2000. (Welcome Bks.). (Illus.). 24p. (J). (ps-2). pap. 4.95 (978-0-516-23041-2(7) , Children's Pr.) Scholastic Library Publishing.

—Let's Play Tug-of-War. 2000. (Welcome Bks.). (Illus.). 24p. (J). (ps-2). pap. 4.95 (978-0-516-23040-5(9) , Children's Pr.) Scholastic Library Publishing.

Hunt, Rhian G. Acrohelion Campaign Setting. 2004. (Illus.). 284p. per. 24.99 (978-0-9759166-0-5(2) , GMC-04-1) Great Mastiff Corp.

Hunt, Sara, ed. Girl Talk: Games to Get the Gab Going-at Home, at School, or Anywhere Girls Go! 2005. (American Girl Library). (Illus.). 32p. (J). 17.95 (978-1-58485-845-4(1) , American Girl) American Girl Publishing, Inc.

Hunter, Dette. 38 Ways to Entertain Your Babysitter. MacEachern, Stephen, illus. 2003. 48p. (J). (ps-4). pap., act. bk. ed. 9.95 (978-1-55037-794-1(9)); lib. bdg., act. bk. ed. 19.95 (978-1-55037-795-8(7)) Annick Pr., Ltd. CAN. *Dist:* Firefly Bks., Ltd.

—38 Ways to Entertain Your Grandparents. Betteridge, Deirdre, illus. 2002. 48p. (J). (ps-4). pap., act. bk. ed. 9.95 (978-1-55037-748-4(5)); lib. bdg., act. bk. ed. 19.95 (978-1-55037-749-1(3)) Annick Pr., Ltd. CAN. *Dist:* Firefly Bks., Ltd.

Hurley, Jo. Secret Spy Super Ear. Baumann, Marty, illus. 2003. 32p. (J). pap. 8.99 (978-0-439-52484-1(9) , Tangerine Pr.) Scholastic, Inc.

Ice Lake: Skate Circles Around Your Friends. 2003. (YA). 19.95 (978-0-9764394-0-0(9)) Live Oak Games.

Ideal. Division, 90 Cards. 1999. (Vertical Flash Cards Ser.). (J). (gr. 4-9). 7.99 (978-1-56451-554-4(0) , ID7239) School Specialty Publishing.

IllusionWorks Staff, contrib. by. Amazing Optical Illusions. 2004. (Illus.). 32p. (J). (gr. 1-3). pap. 5.95 (978-1-55297-962-4(8)); lib. bdg. 16.95 (978-1-55297-961-7(X)) Firefly Bks., Ltd.

The Incredibles: Interactive Book & Cartidge. 2004. (978-1-59319-150-4(2)) LeapFrog Enterprises, Inc.

Isaacs, Ron. Kids Love Jewish Holiday Games. Horton, Mike, photos by. 2001. (Kids Love Ser.). 128p. (J). spiral bd. 18.95 (978-1-930143-32-6(X)); (Illus.). pap. 16.95 (978-1-930143-19-7(2)) Pitspopany Pr.

Isaak, Betty. Cheap & Easy Games for Skill-Building. Amerikaner, Kate, ed. Armstrong, Beverly, illus. rev. ed. 2001. Orig. Title: Garbage Games. 128p. (J). (gr. 1-4). pap. 13.99 (978-0-88160-211-1(6) , LW-101, Learning Works, The) Creative Teaching Pr., Inc.

Isono, Tadanobu, et al. The World of Disgaea: Character Collection. Seto, Dietrich, ed. Tajii, Koji et al, trs. from JPN. Harada, Takehito, illus. 2007. (Disgaea Ser.). Orig. Title: Disgaea Character Collection. 176p. 19.99 (978-1-59741-112-7(4)) Broccoli International USA, Inc.

Jackson, Stephen. Mirrorworld. Broadbent, Stephanie, ed. 2004. (Illus.). 32p. 16.99 (978-0-09-176929-1(9) , Hutchinson) Random Hse. GBR. *Dist:* Independent Pubs. Group.

Jaffe, Elizabeth Dana. Dominoes. 2001. (Games Around the World Ser.). (Illus.). 32p. (J). (gr. 3 up). lib. bdg. 21.26 (978-0-7565-0132-7(6)) Compass Point Bks.

—Hopscotch. 2001. (Games Around the World Ser.). (Illus.). 32p. (J). (gr. 3 up). lib. bdg. 21.26 (978-0-7565-0133-4(4)) Compass Point Bks.

—Jacks. 2001. (Games Around the World Ser.). (Illus.). 32p. (J). (gr. 3 up). lib. bdg. 21.26 (978-0-7565-0134-1(2)) Compass Point Bks.

Jaffe, Elizabeth Dana & Flanagan, Alice K. Marbles. 2001. (Holidays & Festivals Ser.). (Illus.). 32p. (J). (gr. 3 up). lib. bdg. 21.26 (978-0-7565-0135-8(0)) Compass Point Bks.

Jenkins, Emily S. Quicketty Splits, Original Edition. 2007. (J). spiral bd. 12.95 (***978-0-9752657-0-3(9)***) Wisecracker Press, Inc.

Jimenez, Olga Lucia. Ronda que Ronda la Ronda. 2003. (SPA.). 144p. (978-958-30-0673-9(4) , PV30130) Panamericana Editorial COL. *Dist:* Lectorum Pubns., Inc.

John, Scott, text. Becoming A Student of the Game. 2004. (YA). pap. 60.00 (978-1-879498-84-6(7)) SportAmerica.

Johnson, Paul F. & Halfman, Patti. 50 Quick Play Vocabulary Games. 2004. (YA). per. 34.95 (978-0-7606-0539-4(4)) LinguiSystems, Inc.

Johnson, Sarah. Barbie: Princess Story. Lloyd, Jeremy, illus. Lloyd, Jeremy, photos by. 2003. 24p. (J). 15.98 (978-0-7853-8090-0(6) , 7181100) Publications International, Ltd.

Joly, Kimberly. Unfold Your Future: With 13 Amazing Origami Fortune Finders. 2004. (Illus.). (J). pap. (978-0-7641-5736-3(1)) Barron's Educational Series, Inc.

Jones, Betty M. A Child's Seasonal Treasury. Jones, Betty M. & Crowther, Catherine R., illus. 2004. 154p. (J). (ps-2). 24.95 (978-1-883672-30-0(9) , Tricycle Pr.) Ten Speed Pr.

Jorgenson, Karen. Making Room in Your Family & Coloring Books, 11. ldr.'s ed. 2002. (Illus.). (J). 40.00 (978-1-892194-28-2(7)) Northwest Media, Inc.

Journey to the Planets. 2003. (Science Card Games Ser.). (gr. 2-3). 9.99 (978-0-7682-1978-4(7) , J53006) School Specialty Publishing.

Judy/Instructo. Food Groups Roundup. 2001. (Science Card Games Ser.). (J). (gr. 1-2). 3.99 (978-0-7682-1976-0(0) , J53004) School Specialty Publishing.

Juegos de Playa: Individual Title Six-Packs. (Coleccion Pm Ser.).Tr. of Teasing dad. (SPA.). 16p. (gr. 1 up). 26.00 (978-0-7578-3020-4(X)) Rigby Education.

Juegos Recreativos para Ninos. 2003. Tr. of Fun Activities for Children. (SPA.). 184p. 35.00 (978-84-494-2464-9(X) , GML07104-192212) Oceano Grupo Editoria, S.A. ESP. *Dist:* Thomson Gale.

Julio, Susan. Great Map Games: 20 Super Fun, Easy Reproducible Games That Build Key Map & Geography Skills-And Help Kids Navigate Their World. 2000. (Illus.). 80p. pap. 11.95 (978-0-439-07753-8(2)) Scholastic, Inc.

—15 Fun & Easy Games for Young Learners: Favorite Themes. 2001. 48p. (J). pap. 9.95 (978-0-439-20254-1(X)) Scholastic, Inc.

—15 Fun & Easy Games for Young Learners: Reading. 2001. 48p. pap. 9.95 (978-0-439-20255-8(8)) Scholastic, Inc.

Kalman, Bobbie. Classroom Games. 2001. (gr. 3-6). lib. bdg. 16.40 (978-0-613-32409-0(9)) Tandem Library Bks.

—Schoolyard Games. 2001. (gr. 3-6). lib. bdg. 16.40 (978-0-613-33028-2(5)) Tandem Library Bks.

Kalman, Bobbie & Levigne, Heather. Classroom Games. (Historic Communities Ser.). (Illus.). 32p. (J). (gr. 3). 2001. pap. (978-0-86505-470-7(3)); 2000. (978-0-86505-440-0(1)) Crabtree Publishing Co.

Kalman, Bobbie, et al. Schoolyard Games. 2000. (Historic Communities Ser.). (Illus.). 32p. (J). (gr. 3). pap. (978-0-86505-471-4(1)); lib. bdg. (978-0-86505-441-7(X)) Crabtree Publishing Co.

Kalnes, Stephanie, creator. Viking Adventure: History-in-a-Box-Board-Game, 2. 2004. (Illus.). (YA). 69.95 (978-0-9761274-0-6(7)) Great Lakes Design.

Katz, Alan. Stinky Thinking: The Big Book of Gross Games & Brain Teasers. Keller, Laurie, illus. 2005. 112p. (J). (gr. 1-5). pap. 6.99 (978-0-689-87188-7(0) , Aladdin) Simon & Schuster Children's Publishing.

—That's Right, That's Wrong!: Level Four, Set Three. 2009. (That's Right, That's Wrong! Ser.). 100p. (J). 9.99 (***978-1-4169-0682-7(7)*** , Little Simon) Simon & Schuster Children's Publishing.

—That's Right, That's Wrong!: Level One, Set Three. 2009. (That's Right, That's Wrong! Ser.). 100p. (J). 9.99 (***978-1-4169-0679-7(7)*** , Little Simon) Simon & Schuster Children's Publishing.

—That's Right, That's Wrong!: Level Three, Set Three. 2009. (That's Right, That's Wrong! Ser.). 100p. (J). 9.99 (***978-1-4169-0681-0(9)*** , Little Simon) Simon & Schuster Children's Publishing.

—That's Right, That's Wrong!: Level Two, Set Three. 2009. (That's Right, That's Wrong! Ser.). 100p. (J). 9.99 (***978-1-4169-0680-3(0)*** , Little Simon) Simon & Schuster Children's Publishing.

Katz, Karen. Donde Esta el Ombliguito? (Where Is Baby's Belly Button?) Ziegler, Argentina Palacios, tr. Katz, Karen, illus. 2004. (SPA., Illus.). 14p. (J). bds. 5.99 (978-0-689-86977-8(0) , Libros Para Ninos) Simon & Schuster Children's Publishing.

Kearney, Tom. Bruins Big Game. 2005. (Illus.). (J). bds. 8.95 (978-0-9745454-3-1(0)) Timberwood Pr.

—Buckeyes Big Game. 2005. (Illus.). (J). bds. 10.95 (978-0-9745454-5-5(7)) Timberwood Pr.

—Trojans Big Game. 2005. (Illus.). (J). bds. 8.95 (978-0-9745454-2-4(2)) Timberwood Pr.

—Wolverines Big Game. 2005. (Illus.). (J). bds. 8.95 (978-0-9745454-4-8(9)) Timberwood Pr.

Keith, Sarah A. Chalk-It-up: 22 Awesome Outdoor Games Kids Draw with Chalk. MacLeod, Kit, ed. 2004. (Illus.). (J). mass mkt. 12.00 (978-0-9665124-1-0(3) , 014) Bible-4-Life.com.

Kelleher, Pat & Twist, Clint. Puzzle Quest Through History. Dennis, Peter, illus. 2006. (Puzzle Quest Ser.). 22p. (J). bds., bds. 22.95 (978-0-7696-4876-7(2) , Brighter Child) School Specialty Publishing.

Kelley, Jennifer A. & Lugo, Miguel. The Little Giant Book of Dominoes. Sterling Publishing Company Staff, ed. 2003. (Illus.). 352p. pap. 6.95 (978-1-4027-0290-7(6)) Sterling Publishing Co., Inc.

Kemp, Jane & Walters, Clare. Pencil & Paper Games for Kids: Over 100 Activities for 3-11 Year Olds. 2006. (Illus.). 128p. (J). pap. 7.95 (978-0-600-61483-8(2) , Hamlyn) Octopus Publishing Group GBR. *Dist:* Sterling Publishing Co., Inc.

Kemp, Marion, et al. All Together. Barnes-Murphy, Rowan, illus. Date not set. (Whizz Bang Bumper Bk.). 63p. (J). pap. 129.15 (978-0-582-18258-5(1)) Addison-Wesley Longman, Ltd. GBR. *Dist:* Trans-Atlantic Pubns., Inc.

Kern. Kern Alphabet Deck & Book Set. (Illus.). 15.00 (978-1-57281-115-7(3) , AZS99) U. S. Games Systems, Inc.

Kids: Bays & Estuaries. 2005. (J). (978-1-888631-33-3(3)) Watercourse, The.

Kimble, Evan & Kimble, Lael. Super Cars Dot-to-Dot. 2004. (Illus.). 80p. (J). pap. 5.95 (978-1-4027-0786-5(X)) Sterling Publishing Co., Inc.

King, Daniel. Games: Learn to Play, Play to Win. Buckley, Mike & Hartigan, Julie, illus. 2003. 64p. (J). (gr. 5-9). tchr. ed. 16.95 (978-0-7534-5581-4(1) , Kingfisher) Houghton Mifflin Co. Trade & Reference Div.

King, David C. World War II Days: Discover the Past with Exciting Projects, Games, Activities A. 2000. (gr. 3-6). lib. bdg. 22.20 (978-0-613-84559-5(5)) Tandem Library Bks.

Klingel, Cynthia Fitterer & Noyed, Robert B. Yo-Yo Tricks. 2002. (Games Around the World Ser.). (Illus.). 32p. (J). (gr. 3 up). lib. bdg. 21.26 (978-0-7565-0193-8(8)) Compass Point Bks.

Klutz Press Staff. The Amazing Booka-Ma-Thing for the Backseat: Thousands of Miles Worth of Hands-On Games & Activities. 1998. (Illus.). 20p. (J). (gr. 4-7). spiral bd. 16.95 (978-1-57054-169-8(8)) Klutz.

—Eat This Book. 2002. 20p. (J). (ps-3). 9.95 (978-1-57054-754-6(8)) Klutz.

—Klutz the Cootie Catcher Book. 1998. (Illus.). 58p. (J). (gr. 4-7). pap. 9.95 (978-1-57054-131-5(0)) Klutz.

Klutz Press Staff, creator. Shadow Games. 2005. (Illus.). 24p. (YA). (gr. 4-7). spiral bd. 9.95 (978-1-59174-160-2(2)) Klutz.

Klutz Press Staff, ed. Magnetic A to Z. 2005. (Chicken Socks Ser.). (Illus.). 12p. (J). 12.95 (978-1-59174-359-0(1)) Klutz.

Knizia, Reiner, des. Rheinlander. 2005. (FRE, GER, JPN, KOR & SPA.). (YA). (978-0-9761156-1-8(1)) Face 2 Face Games Publishing.

Kuffner, Trish. The Wiggle & Giggle Busy Book: 365 Fun, Physical Activities for Toddlers & Preschoolers. McGinnis, Megan, ed. 2005. (Busy Bks.). (Illus.). 400p. pap. 9.95 (978-0-684-03135-4(3)) Meadowbrook Pr.

Kumon Publishing Staff, ed. My Book of Alphabet Games. 2007. 80p. pap. 6.95 (***978-1-933241-36-4(5)***) Kumon Publishing North America, Inc.

Kvale, Anthony, creator & concept. Head1Liners board Game. Kvale, Anthony, concept. 2006. 38.99 (***978-0-9793583-0-2(2)*** , H1L) Kvale Good Natured Games LLC.

Lalicki, Tom. Grierson's Raid: A Daring Cavalry Strike Through the Heart of the Confederacy. 2004. (Illus.). 208p. (J). 18.00 (978-0-374-32787-3(4) , Farrar, Straus & Giroux (BYR)) Farrar, Straus & Giroux.

Lankford, Mary D. Dominoes Around the World. 1998. (Illus.). 40p. (J). (gr. 1 up). 16.00 (978-0-688-14051-9(3)); 15.89 (978-0-688-14052-6(1)) HarperCollins Pubs.

Laredo, Elizabeth. The Jump Rope Book. Cooper, Martha, photos by. 2004. (Illus.). 284p. (J). (gr. k-4). reprint ed. pap. 10.00 (978-0-7567-7775-3(5)) DIANE Publishing Co.

Last Unicorn Games Staff & Hite, Kenneth. Star Trek: Core Game Book. 1999. (Star Trek Ser.). (Illus.). 288p. (J). 35.00 (978-0-671-04014-7(6)) Wizards of the Coast.

LeapFrog Staff, compiled by & des. Thinking Games. LeapFrog Staff, des. 2002. (J). lib. bdg. 9.99 (978-1-58605-797-8(9)) LeapFrog Enterprises, Inc.

Learning Games Panorama Book. 2006. (J). spiral bd. 8.99 (***978-1-59545-052-4(1)***) Learning Horizons, Inc.

Learning Horizons, ed. Games & Puzzles: Grade 2. 2004. (Learn on the GOTM Workbooks Ser.). (Illus.). 64p. (gr. 2 up). pap. 2.95 (978-1-58610-708-6(9) , 61056) Learning Horizons, Inc.

Ledbetter, Mary Ellen. You Say I Say. 2005. per. 19.95 (978-1-888237-61-0(9)) Baxter Pr.

Lee, Helen, ed. PowerGuide Logbook 2: Fun-Filled, Grace-Growing Activities. 2002. 96p. (YA). pap. 3.99 (978-0-8280-1592-9(9)) Review & Herald Publishing Assn.

Lerner, Adam & Charpentier, Cliff. Fantasy Football: Playing to Win. 1998. (J). 19.93 (978-0-8225-7778-2(X)) Lerner Publishing Group.

Libal, Joyce. Folk Games. 2003. (North American Folklore Ser.). (Illus.). 112p. (YA). (gr. 7 up). lib. bdg. (978-1-59084-339-0(8)) Mason Crest Pubs.

Lidbert, Paul A. Big Damn Space Battles. Lidbert, Paul A., illus. 1998. (Illus.). 16p. (YA). 4.95 (978-1-929332-03-8(3) , CFE0101) Crunchy Frog Enterprises.

—Madworld: The Battle Game. Morrissey, Phil et al, illus. 1998. 20p. (J). 4.95 (978-1-929332-07-6(6) , CFE0201) Crunchy Frog Enterprises.

Limona, Mercedes. Juegos/Canciones. 2000. Tr. of Games & Songs. (SPA.). (J). 18.95 incl. audio (978-84-85546-04-6(0)) Servicios Editoriales, S.A. ESP. *Dist:* AIMS International Bks., Inc.

Lin, Chuan. Jadeclaw: Anthropomorphic Fantasy Role-Play. 2002. (YA). pap. 29.95 (978-0-9704583-5-3(5)) Sanguine Productions, Ltd.

Lingo, Susan L. Collect-n-Play Games for Kids. Stoker, Bruce, ed. Carter, Paula Becker, illus. 2006. 112p. (YA). (gr. 1-7). 15.99 (978-0-7847-1199-6(2) , 02433) Standard Publishing.

—Play-It-Again Games. 2001. 64p. (J). (gr. 2-5). pap. 12.99 (978-0-570-05264-7(5) , 12-4077) Concordia Publishing Hse.

Linking Cubes. (Illus.). 24p. (J). (gr. k-2). pap. 6.95 (978-1-55254-046-6(4) , BV25004) Brighter Vision Pubns.

Litchfield, Jo & Dobbie, Meg. First Picture Playground Games. 2007. (First Picture Board Bks). (Illus.). 16p. (J). bds. 11.99 (***978-0-7945-1611-6(4)*** , Usborne) EDC Publishing.

Littlefield, Cindy A. Sea Life Games & Puzzles. 2006. (Illus.). 144p. (J). pap. 9.95 (978-1-58017-624-8(0)) Storey Publishing, LLC.

Livingstone, Ian. Mudworm Swamp No. 3: Adventures of Goldhawk. 2000. (Illus.). 64p. (J). pap. (978-0-14-037069-0(2) , Puffin) Penguin Group (USA) Inc.

Lo, Ginnie. Mahjong All Day Long. Lo, Beth, illus. 2005. 32p. (J). 16.95 (978-0-8027-8941-9(2)) Walker & Co.

Lo, Ginnie & Lo, Beth. Mahjong All Day Long. Lo, Beth, illus. 2005. (Illus.). 32p. (J). 17.85 (978-0-8027-8942-6(0)) Walker & Co.

Long, Cathryn J. & Douglas, Vincent. The Complete Book of American Facts & Games. 2002. (Complete Book Ser.). (Illus.). 352p. (J). (gr. k-6). pap. 14.95 (978-1-56189-208-2(4) , American Education Publishing) School Specialty Publishing.

Looney, Andrew, et al. Playing with Pyramids: 12 Games for Icehouse Pieces. Looney, Andrew, illus. 2002. (Illus.). 128p. per. 12.00 (978-1-929780-28-0(1) , LOO-014) Looney Laboratories, Inc.

Lore, Mark & Lore, Matthew. Rubberneckers, Jr. Fun for Backseat Travelers. Zimmerman, Robert, illus. 2003. 68p. (J). 12.95 (978-0-8118-3733-0(5)) Chronicle Bks. LLC.

Lorenz Books Staff. Food & Drink. 2000. (Sticker Fun Ser.). (Illus.). 16p. (ps-k). pap. 5.00 (978-0-7548-0540-3(9) , Lorenz Bks.) Anness Publishing GBR. *Dist:* National Bk. Network.

—Playtime: With Over 50 Reusable Stickers. 1999. (Sticker Fun Ser.). (Illus.). 16p. (ps-k). pap. 4.95 (978-0-7548-0048-4(2) , Lorenz Bks.) Anness Publishing GBR. *Dist:* National Bk. Network.

Lorenz Books Staff & Tuxworth, Nicola. Hop, Skip, Jump. 1999. (Very First Picture Bks.). (Illus.). 12p. (ps). bds. 4.95 (978-0-7548-0383-6(X)) Anness Publishing, Inc.

Lou Weber Staff, ed. The Incredibles: Look & Find. 2004. (Look & Find Books). (Illus.). 24p. (J). 7.98 (978-1-4127-3223-9(9) , 7235900) Publications International, Ltd.

Lyons, Michelle. Trigun Ultimate Fan Guide, No. 2. 2002. 104p. (YA). pap. 24.95 (978-1-894525-43-5(4)) Guardians of Order CAN. *Dist:* LPC Group.

MacColl, Gail. The Book of Card Games for Little Kids. 2000. (Illus.). 128p. (J). (ps up). pap. 12.95 (978-0-7611-0708-8(8) , 10708) Workman Publishing Co., Inc.

Macken, JoAnn Early. After-School Fun. 24p. (YA). 115.98 (978-0-8368-4510-5(2)) Stevens, Gareth Inc.

Maison, Karen M. The Maison System Bk. I: Games. 1999. (J). (978-0-9671421-3-5(X)) Maison, Karen M.

—The Maison System Bk. II: Games. 1999. (J). (gr. k-6). (978-0-9671421-4-2(8)) Maison, Karen M.

—The Maison System Bk. III: Games. 1999. (J). (gr. k-6). (978-0-9671421-5-9(6)) Maison, Karen M.

Maizels, Jennie. Things to Do Book. Maizels, Jennie, illus. 2007. (Illus.). 20p. (J). (gr. k-3). 15.99 (978-0-7636-3371-4(2)) Candlewick Pr.

Manning, Jane, illus. My First Baby Games. 2001. (Growing Tree Ser.). 16p. (J). (ps up). 6.99 (978-0-694-01435-4(4) , Harper Festival) HarperCollins Pubs.

Marino, Ricardo. El Libro de la Risa. 2002. (SPA.). 104p. (J). pap. (978-1-4000-0036-4(X)) Editorial Sudamericana S.A.

Marrion, Thom & Ward, Kyla. Buffy the Vampire Slayer: Welcome to Sunnydale Supplement. 2005. 128p. (YA). pap. 27.00 (978-1-891153-95-2(1)) Eden Studios, Inc.

Marsh, Carole. Alabama Jeopardy! Answers & Questions about Our State! 2001. (Carole Marsh Alabama Bks.). (Illus.). 32p. (J). (gr. 3-8). pap. 7.95 (978-0-7933-9789-1(8)) Gallopade International.

—Alabama Jography. 2001. (Carole Marsh Alabama Bks.). (Illus.). 32p. (J). (gr. 3-8). pap. 7.95 (978-0-7933-9818-8(5)) Gallopade International.

—Alabama Wheel of Fortune: Game Book. 2001. 32p. (J). (gr. 3-8). pap., act. bk. ed. 9.95 (978-0-7933-9618-4(2)) Gallopade International.

—Alaska Jeopardy! Answers & Questions about Our State! 2001. (Carole Marsh Alaska Bks.). (Illus.). 32p. (J). (gr. 3-8). pap. 7.95 (978-0-7933-9790-7(1)) Gallopade International.

—Alaska "Jography" A Fun Run Thru Our State! 2001. (Carole Marsh Alaska Bks.). (Illus.). 32p. (J). (gr. 3-8). pap. 7.95 (978-0-7933-9819-5(3)) Gallopade International.

—Alaska Wheel of Fortune: Game Book. (Orig.). pap. 9.95 (978-0-7933-9621-4(2)); 2001. (Illus.). 32p. (J). (gr. 3-8). pap. 9.95 (978-0-7933-9620-7(4)) Gallopade International.

—Arizona Jeopardy! Answers & Questions about Our State! 2001. (Carole Marsh Arizona Bks.). (Illus.). 32p. (J). (gr. 3-8). pap. 7.95 (978-0-7933-9791-4(X)) Gallopade International.

—Arizona "Jography" A Fun Run Thru Our State! 2001. (Carole Marsh Arizona Bks.). 32p. (J). (gr. 3-8). pap. 7.95 (978-0-7933-9820-1(7)) Gallopade International.

—Arizona Wheel of Fortune: Game Book. 2001. (Illus.). 32p. (J). (gr. 3-8). pap., act. bk. ed. 9.95 (978-0-7933-9622-1(0)) Gallopade International.

—Arkansas Jeopardy! Answers & Questions about Our State! 2004. (Illus.). 32p. (J). (gr. 3-8). pap. 7.95 (978-0-7933-9792-1(8)) Gallopade International.

—Arkansas "Jography" A Fun Run Thru Our State! 2004. (Carole Marsh Arkansas Bks.). (Illus.). 32p. (J). (gr. 3-8). pap. 7.95 (978-0-7933-9821-8(5)) Gallopade International.

—Arkansas Survivor: Game Book. 2001. (Carole Marsh Arkansas Bks.). (Illus.). 32p. (J). (gr. 3-8). pap., act. bk. ed. 9.95 (978-0-635-00525-0(5)) Gallopade International.

—Arkansas Wheel of Fortune: Game Book. 2001. (Illus.). 32p. (J). (gr. 3-8). pap., act. bk. ed. 9.95 (978-0-7933-9624-5(7)) Gallopade International.

—California Wheel of Fortune: Game Book. 2001. (Illus.). 32p. (J). (gr. 3-8). pap., act. bk. ed. 9.95 (978-0-7933-9626-9(3)) Gallopade International.

—Canada Survivor. 2001. (GameBook Ser.). (Illus.). 32p. (J). (gr. 3-8). pap., act. bk. ed. 9.95 (978-0-635-00698-1(7)) Gallopade International.

—Colorado Wheel of Fortune: Game Book. 2001. (Illus.). 32p. (J). (gr. 3-8). pap., act. bk. ed. 9.95 (978-0-7933-9628-3(X)) Gallopade International.

—Connecticut Millionaire: Game Book. 2001. (Illus.). 32p. (gr. 3-8). pap., act. bk. ed. 9.95 (978-0-635-00030-9(X)) Gallopade International.

—Connecticut Survivor: Game Book. 2001. (Illus.). 32p. (J). (gr. 3-8). pap., act. bk. ed. 9.95 (978-0-635-00528-1(X)) Gallopade International.

—Connecticut Wheel of Fortune: Game Book. 2001. (Illus.). 32p. (J). (gr. 3-8). pap., act. bk. ed. 9.95 (978-0-7933-9630-6(1)) Gallopade International.

—Delaware Jeopardy! Answers & Questions about Our State! 2001. (Illus.). 32p. (J). (gr. 3-8). pap. 7.95 (978-0-7933-9793-8(6)) Gallopade International.

—Delaware "Jography" A Fun Run Thru Our State! 2001. (Carole Marsh Delaware Bks.). (Illus.). 32p. (J). (gr. 3-8). pap. 7.95 (978-0-7933-9822-5(3)) Gallopade International.

—Delaware Wheel of Fortune: Game Book. 2001. (Illus.). 32p. (J). (gr. 3-8). pap., act. bk. ed. 9.95 (978-0-7933-9632-0(8)) Gallopade International.

—Florida Wheel of Fortune: Game Book. 2001. (Illus.). 32p. (J). (gr. 3-8). pap., act. bk. ed. 9.95 (978-0-7933-9634-4(4)) Gallopade International.

—Georgia Survivor: Game Book. 2001. (Illus.). 32p. (J). (gr. 3-8). pap., act. bk. ed. 9.95 (978-0-635-00531-1(X)) Gallopade International.

—Georgia Wheel of Fortune: Game Book. 2001. (Illus.). 32p. (J). (gr. 3-8). pap., act. bk. ed. 9.95 (978-0-7933-9636-8(0)) Gallopade International.

—Hawaii Jeopardy. 2001. (Carole Marsh Hawaii Bks.). (Illus.). 32p. (J). (gr. 3-8). pap. 7.95 (978-0-7933-9794-5(4)) Gallopade International.

—Hawaii "Jography" A Fun Run Thru Our State! 2001. (Illus.). 32p. (J). (gr. 3-8). pap. 7.95 (978-0-7933-9823-2(1)) Gallopade International.

—Hawaii Wheel of Fortune: Game Book. 2001. (Illus.). 32p. (J). (gr. 3-8). pap., act. bk. ed. 9.95 (978-0-7933-9638-2(7)) Gallopade International.

—Idaho Jeopardy! Answers & Questions about Our State! 2001. (Carole Marsh Idaho Bks.). (Illus.). 32p. (J). (gr. 3-8). pap. 7.95 (978-0-7933-9795-2(2)) Gallopade International.

—Idaho "Jography" A Fun Run Thru Our State! 2001. (Carole Marsh Idaho Bks.). (Illus.). 32p. (J). (gr. 3-8). pap. 7.95 (978-0-7933-9824-9(X)) Gallopade International.

—Idaho Survivor: Game Book. 2001. (Carole Marsh Idaho Bks.). (Illus.). 32p. (J). (gr. 3-8). pap., act. bk. ed. 9.95 (978-0-635-00533-5(6)) Gallopade International.

—Idaho Wheel of Fortune: Game Book. 2001. (Illus.). 32p. (J). (gr. 3-8). pap., act. bk. ed. 9.95 (978-0-7933-9640-5(9)) Gallopade International.

—Illinois Survivor: Game Book. 2001. (Carole Marsh Illinois Bks.). (Illus.). 32p. (J). (gr. 3-8). pap., act. bk. ed. 9.95 (978-0-635-00534-2(4) , Marsh, Carole Bks.) Gallopade International.

—Illinois Wheel of Fortune: Game Book. 2001. (Illus.). 32p. (J). (gr. 3-8). pap., act. bk. ed. 9.95 (978-0-7933-9642-9(5)) Gallopade International.

—Indiana Millionaire: Game Book. 2001. (Illus.). 32p. (J). (gr. 3-8). pap., act. bk. ed. 9.95 (978-0-635-00044-6(X)) Gallopade International.

—Indiana Wheel of Fortune: Game Book. 2001. (Illus.). 32p. (J). (gr. 3-8). pap., act. bk. ed. 9.95 (978-0-7933-9644-3(1)) Gallopade International.

—Iowa Jeopardy! Answers & Questions about Our State! 2001. (Carole Marsh Iowa Bks.). (Illus.). 32p. (J). (gr. 3-8). pap. 7.95 (978-0-7933-9797-6(9)) Gallopade International.

—Iowa "Jography" A Fun Run Thru Our State! 2001. (Carole Marsh Iowa Bks.). (Illus.). 32p. (J). (gr. 3-8). pap. 7.95 (978-0-7933-9826-3(6)) Gallopade International.

—Iowa Wheel of Fortune: Game Book. 2001. (Illus.). 32p. (J). (gr. 3-8). pap., act. bk. ed. 9.95 (978-0-7933-9646-7(8)) Gallopade International.

—Kansas Jeopardy! Answers & Questions about Our State! 2004. (Carole Marsh Kansas Bks.). (Illus.). 32p. (J). (gr. 3-8). pap. 7.95 (978-0-7933-9798-3(7)) Gallopade International.

—Kansas "Jography" A Fun Run Thru Your State! 2004. 32p. (J). (gr. 3-8). pap. 7.95 (978-0-7933-9827-0(4)) Gallopade International.

—Kansas Survivor: Game Book. 2001. (Carole Marsh Kansas Bks.). (Illus.). 32p. (J). (gr. 3-8). pap., act. bk. ed. 9.95 (978-0-635-00537-3(9)) Gallopade International.

—Kansas Wheel of Fortune: Game Book. 2001. (Illus.). 32p. (J). (gr. 3-8). pap., act. bk. ed. 9.95 (978-0-7933-9648-1(4)) Gallopade International.

—Kentucky Survivor: Game Book. 2001. (Carole Marsh Kentucky Bks.). (Illus.). 32p. (J). (gr. 3-8). pap., act. bk. ed. 9.95 (978-0-635-00538-0(7)) Gallopade International.

—Kentucky Wheel of Fortune: Game Book. 2001. (Illus.). 32p. (J). (gr. 3-8). pap., act. bk. ed. 9.95 (978-0-7933-9650-4(6)) Gallopade International.

—Louisiana Survivor: Game Book. 2001. (Carole Marsh Louisiana Bks.). (Illus.). 32p. (J). (gr. 3-8). pap., act. bk. ed. 9.95 (978-0-635-00539-7(5)) Gallopade International.

—Louisiana Wheel of Fortune: Game Book. 2001. (Illus.). 32p. (J). (gr. 3-8). pap., act. bk. ed. 9.95 (978-0-7933-9652-8(2)) Gallopade International.

—Maine Jeopardy! Answers & Questions about Our State! 2001. (Illus.). 32p. (J). (gr. 3-8). pap. 7.95 (978-0-7933-9799-0(5)) Gallopade International.

—Maine Wheel of Fortune: Game Book. 2001. (Illus.). 32p. (J). (gr. 3-8). pap., act. bk. ed. 9.95 (978-0-7933-9654-2(9)) Gallopade International.

—Maryland Millionaire: Game Book. 2001. (Carole Marsh Maryland Bks.). (Illus.). 32p. (J). (gr. 3-8). pap., act. bk. ed. 9.95 (978-0-635-00056-9(3)) Gallopade International.

—Maryland Survivor: Game Book. 2001. (Carole Marsh Maryland Bks.). (Illus.). 32p. (J). (gr. 3-8). pap., act. bk. ed. 9.95 (978-0-635-00541-0(7)) Gallopade International.

—Maryland Wheel of Fortune: Game Book. 2001. (Illus.). 32p. (J). (gr. 3-8). pap., act. bk. ed. 9.95 (978-0-7933-9656-6(5)) Gallopade International.

—Massachusetts Jeopardy! Answers & Questions about Our State! 2001. (Carole Marsh Massachusetts Bks.). (Illus.). 32p. (J). (gr. 3-8). pap. 7.95 (978-0-7933-9800-3(2)) Gallopade International.

—Massachusetts Millionaire: Game Book. 2001. (Illus.). 32p. (J). (gr. 3-8). pap., act. bk. ed. 9.95 (978-0-635-00058-3(X)) Gallopade International.

—Massachusetts Wheel of Fortune: Game Book. 2001. (Illus.). 32p. (J). (gr. 3-8). pap., act. bk. ed. 9.95 (978-0-7933-9658-0(1)) Gallopade International.

—Michigan Wheel of Fortune: Game Book. 2001. (Illus.). 32p. (J). (gr. 3-8). pap., act. bk. ed. 9.95 (978-0-7933-9660-3(3)) Gallopade International.

—Minnesota Survivor: Game Book. 2001. (Carole Marsh Montana Bks.). (Illus.). 32p. (J). (gr. 3-8). pap., act. bk. ed. 9.95 (978-0-635-00544-1(1)) Gallopade International.

—Minnesota Wheel of Fortune: Game Book. 2001. (Illus.). 32p. (J). (gr. 3-8). pap., act. bk. ed. 9.95 (978-0-7933-9662-7(X)) Gallopade International.

—Mississippi Survivor: Game Book. 2001. (Illus.). 32p. (J). (gr. 3-8). pap., act. bk. ed. 9.95 (978-0-635-00545-8(X)) Gallopade International.

—Mississippi Wheel of Fortune: Game Book. 2001. (Illus.). 32p. (J). (gr. 3-8). pap., act. bk. ed. 9.95 (978-0-7933-9664-1(6)) Gallopade International.

—Missouri Survivor: Game Book. 2001. (Carole Marsh Missouri Bks.). (Illus.). 32p. (J). (gr. 3-8). pap., act. bk. ed. 9.95 (978-0-635-00546-5(8)) Gallopade International.

—Missouri Wheel of Fortune: Game Book. 2001. (Illus.). 32p. (J). (gr. 3-8). pap., act. bk. ed. 9.95 (978-0-7933-9666-5(2)) Gallopade International.

—Montana Jeopardy! Answers & Questions about Our State! 2001. (Carole Marsh Montana Bks.). 32p. (J). (gr. 3-8). pap. 7.95 (978-0-7933-9802-7(9)) Gallopade International.

—Nevada Jeopardy! Answers & Questions about Our State! Line Art Staff, illus. 2001. 32p. (J). (gr. 3-8). pap. 7.95 (978-0-7933-9804-1(5)) Gallopade International.

—New Hampshire Jeopardy! Answers & Questions about Our State! Line Art Staff, illus. 2001. 32p. (J). (gr. 3-8). pap. 7.95 (978-0-7933-9805-8(3)) Gallopade International.

—New Mexico Jeopardy! Answers & Questions about Our State! Line Art Staff, illus. 2001. 32p. (J). (gr. 3-8). pap. 7.95 (978-0-7933-9806-5(1)) Gallopade International.

—North Dakota Jeopardy! Answers & Questions about Our State! Line Art Staff, illus. 2001. 32p. (J). (gr. 3-8). pap. 7.95 (978-0-7933-9807-2(X)) Gallopade International.

—Oregon Jeopardy! Answers & Questions about Our State! 2001. (Carole Marsh Oregon Bks.). (Illus.). 32p. (J). (gr. 3-8). pap. 7.95 (978-0-7933-9808-9(8)) Gallopade International.

—Rhode Island Jeopardy! Answers & Questions about Our State! 2001. (Carole Marsh Rhode Island Bks.). (Illus.). 32p. (J). (gr. 3-8). pap. 7.95 (978-0-7933-9809-6(6)) Gallopade International.

—South Carolina Jeopardy! Answers & Questions about Our State! Line Art Staff, illus. 2001. 32p. (J). (gr. 3-8). pap. 7.95 (978-0-7933-9810-2(X)) Gallopade International.

—South Dakota Jeopardy! Answers & Questions about Our State! Line Art Staff, illus. 2001. 32p. (J). (gr. 3-8). pap. 7.95 (978-0-7933-9811-9(8)) Gallopade International.

—The Survivor: A Class Challenge. 2001. (Carole Marsh Georgia Bks.). lib. bdg. 29.95 (978-0-635-00656-1(1)); lib. bdg. 29.95 (978-0-635-00659-2(6)); lib. bdg. 29.95 (978-0-635-00697-4(9)) Gallopade International.

—Tennessee Jeopardy! Answers & Questions about Our State! Line Art Staff, illus. 2004. 32p. (J). (gr. 3-8). pap. 7.95 (978-0-7933-9812-6(6)) Gallopade International.

—Utah Jeopardy! Answers & Questions about Our State! Line Art Staff, illus. 2001. 32p. (J). (gr. 3-8). pap. 7.95 (978-0-7933-9813-3(4)) Gallopade International.

—Vermont Jeopardy! Answers & Questions about Our State! Line Art Staff, illus. 2001. 32p. (J). (gr. 3-8). pap. 7.95 (978-0-7933-9814-0(2)) Gallopade International.

—Washington D. C. Millionaire. (GameBook Ser.). (Illus.). 32p. (J). pap., act. bk. ed. 9.95 (978-0-635-00864-0(5)) Gallopade International.

—Washington D. C. Survivor. (GameBook Ser.). (Illus.). 32p. (J). pap., act. bk. ed. 9.95 (978-0-635-00866-4(1)) Gallopade International.

—Washington D. C. Wheel of Fortune. (GameBook Ser.). (Illus.). 32p. (J). pap., act. bk. ed. 9.95 (978-0-635-00865-7(3)) Gallopade International.

—Washington Jeopardy! Line Art Staff, illus. 2001. 32p. (J). (gr. 3-8). pap. 7.95 (978-0-7933-9815-7(0)) Gallopade International.

—Washington Survivor. 2001. (GameBook Ser.). (Illus.). 32p. (J). (gr. 3-8). pap., act. bk. ed. 9.95 (978-0-635-00568-7(9)) Gallopade International.

—West Virginia Jeopardy! Answers & Questions about Our State! Line Art Staff, illus. 2001. 32p. (J). (gr. 3-8). pap. 7.95 (978-0-7933-9816-4(9)) Gallopade International.

—Wisconsin Millionaire. 2001. (GameBook Ser.). (Illus.). 32p. (J). (gr. 3-8). pap., act. bk. ed. 9.95 (978-0-635-00114-6(4)) Gallopade International.

—Wyoming Wheel of Fortune. 2001. (GameBook Ser.). (Illus.). 32p. (J). (gr. 3-8). pap., act. bk. ed. 9.95 (978-0-635-00016-3(4)) Gallopade International.

Martin, Rob & Sellmeyer, Mark, des. Seasons: The Calendar Rummy Game. 2004. mass mkt. 24.95 (978-0-9747833-0-7(7)) Dust Bunny Games LLC.

Martin, Sam. The Curious Boy's Book of Exploration. 2008. 160p. pap. 15.00 (***978-1-59514-207-8(X)*** , Razorbill) Penguin Group (USA) Inc.

Marx, Mandy. Paintball. 2006. (Blazers—To the Extreme Ser.). (Illus.). 32p. (J). (978-0-7368-5463-4(0)) Capstone Pr., Inc.

Marzollo, Jean. I Spy Gold Challenger! Wick, Walter, illus. 2005. (I Spy Ser.). 40p. (J). 9.95 (978-0-439-78728-4(9) , Cartwheel Bks.) Scholastic, Inc.

—I Spy Year-Round Challenger! A Book of Picture Riddles. Wick, Walter, illus. 2005. (I Spy Ser.). 40p. (J). 9.95 (978-0-439-78726-0(2) , Cartwheel Bks.) Scholastic, Inc.

—Treasure Hunt. Wick, Walter, illus. 2005. (I Spy Ser.). 40p. (J). 9.95 (978-0-439-78725-3(4) , Cartwheel Bks.) Scholastic, Inc.

—Ultimate Challenger! A Book of Picture Riddles. Wick, Walter, illus. 2005. (I Spy Ser.). 40p. (J). 9.95 (978-0-439-78727-7(0) , Cartwheel Bks.) Scholastic, Inc.

Mattern, Joanne. Playing at School. 2006. (Illus.). 24p. (J). pap. (978-0-8368-6795-4(5)); lib. bdg. (978-0-8368-6788-6(2)) Stevens, Gareth Inc.

—Playing at School: Juego en la Escuela. 2006. (ENG & SPA., Illus.). 24p. (J). pap. (978-0-8368-7369-6(6)); lib. bdg. (978-0-8368-7362-7(9)) Stevens, Gareth Inc. (Weekly Reader Early Learning Library).

McCafferty, Catherine. Elmo: Look & Find. 2002. (Illus.). 24p. (J). 7.98 (978-0-7853-5990-6(7) , 7145000) Publications International, Ltd.

McCarthy, Rebecca. The Great Galactic Marble Kit. 2007. (Illus.). 32p. (J). (gr. 1 up). pap. 9.95 (***978-0-7624-3062-8(1)*** , Running Pr. Kids) Running Pr. Bk. Pubs.

McCoy, M. M. Where Is Cecil? Maximilian Press Publishers Staff, ed. Brunner, Terry, illus. unabr. l.t. ed. 2005. 28p. (J). lib. bdg. 12.50 (978-1-930211-68-1(6)) Maximilian Pr. Pubs.

McDonald, Heidi. Bully Buster Bingo. Lardner, Walter, illus. 2001. 32p. (J). (gr. 2-7). pap., suppl. ed. 13.95 (978-1-57543-089-8(4)) MAR*CO Products, Inc.

McGillian, Jamie Kyle. Sidewalk Chalk: Outdoor Fun & Games. Sims, Blanche, illus. 2006. 80p. (J). (gr. k-4). reprint ed. 18.00 (978-1-4223-5580-0(2)) DIANE Publishing Co.

McGraw-Hill Staff & Schaffer, Frank. Mazes, Puzzles, & Games. 2001. (Homework Helpers Activity Bks.). (Illus.). 56p. (J). (gr. 2-2). pap., act. bk. ed. 2.99 (978-0-7682-0711-8(8) , FS109040, Schaffer, Frank) Schaffer, Frank Pubns.

McGuire, Nancy. Xtreme Math Football: Taking Math to the Extreme. 2001. 121p. spiral bd. 29.95 (978-0-9728148-0-5(9) , f-1, Extreme Math) McGuire, Nancy.

Miles Kelly Staff. Animals: Family Flip Quiz. 2003. (Flip Quiz Ser.). (Illus.). 152p. (J). spiral bd. 12.95 (978-1-84236-099-6(X)) Miles Kelly Publishing, Ltd. GBR. *Dist:* Independent Pubs. Group.

—Animals: Flip Quiz. 2003. (Flip Quiz Ser.). (Illus.). 38p. (J). spiral bd. 5.95 (978-1-84236-078-1(7)); spiral bd. 5.95 (978-1-84236-076-7(0)); spiral bd. 5.95 (978-1-84236-079-8(5)); spiral bd. 5.95 (978-1-84236-077-4(9)) Miles Kelly Publishing, Ltd. GBR. *Dist:* Independent Pubs. Group.

—Bible: Family Flip Quiz. 2003. (Flip Quiz Ser.). (Illus.). 152p. (J). spiral bd. 12.95 (978-1-84236-124-5(4)) Miles Kelly Publishing, Ltd. GBR. *Dist:* Independent Pubs. Group.

—Geography. 2003. (Flip Quiz Ser.). (Illus.). 152p. (J). spiral bd. 12.95 (978-1-84236-146-7(5)) Miles Kelly Publishing, Ltd. GBR. *Dist:* Independent Pubs. Group.

—Geography Age 10-11: Flip Quiz. 2003. (Flip Quiz Series Ser.). (Illus.). 38p. (J). spiral bd. 5.95 (978-1-84236-102-3(3)) Miles Kelly Publishing, Ltd. GBR. *Dist:* Independent Pubs. Group.

—Geography Age 11-12: Flip Quiz. 2003. (Flip Quiz Ser.). (Illus.). 38p. (J). spiral bd. 5.95 (978-1-84236-103-0(1)) Miles Kelly Publishing, Ltd. GBR. *Dist:* Independent Pubs. Group.

—Geography Age 7-9: Flip Quiz. 2003. (Flip Quiz Ser.). (Illus.). 38p. (J). spiral bd. 5.95 (978-1-84236-100-9(7)) Miles Kelly Publishing, Ltd. GBR. *Dist:* Independent Pubs. Group.

—Geography Age 9-10: Flip Quiz. 2003. (Flip Quiz Ser.). (Illus.). 38p. (J). spiral bd. 5.95 (978-1-84236-101-6(5)) Miles Kelly Publishing, Ltd. GBR. *Dist:* Independent Pubs. Group.

—History. 2003. (Flip Quiz Ser.). (Illus.). 38p. (J). spiral bd. 5.95 (978-1-902947-70-9(3)); spiral bd. 5.95 (978-1-902947-65-5(7)); spiral bd. 5.95 (978-1-902947-68-6(1)) Miles Kelly Publishing, Ltd. GBR. *Dist:* Independent Pubs. Group.

—History: Family Flip Quiz. 2003. (Flip Quiz Ser.). (Illus.). 152p. (J). spiral bd. 12.95 (978-1-84236-052-1(3)) Miles Kelly Publishing, Ltd. GBR. *Dist:* Independent Pubs. Group.

—History Age. 2003. (Flip Quiz Ser.). (Illus.). 38p. (J). spiral bd. 5.95 (978-1-902947-69-3(X)) Miles Kelly Publishing, Ltd. GBR. *Dist:* Independent Pubs. Group.

—Mix-Ups. 2003. (Illus.). 14p. 9.95 (978-1-902947-83-9(5)) Miles Kelly Publishing, Ltd. GBR. *Dist:* Independent Pubs. Group.

—Noises: Let's Learn. Nilsen, Anna, ed. 2003. (Let's Learn Ser.). (Illus.). 20p. (J). 7.95 (978-1-84236-139-9(2)) Miles Kelly Publishing, Ltd. GBR. *Dist:* Independent Pubs. Group.

—Opposites: Let's Learn. Nilsen, Anna, ed. 2003. (Let's Learn Ser.). (Illus.). 20p. (J). 7.95 (978-1-84236-138-2(4)) Miles Kelly Publishing, Ltd. GBR. *Dist:* Independent Pubs. Group.

—Rock & Pop. 2003. (Flip Quiz Ser.). (Illus.). 152p. (J). spiral bd. 12.95 (978-1-84236-145-0(7)) Miles Kelly Publishing, Ltd. GBR. *Dist:* Independent Pubs. Group.

—Science: Family Flip Quiz. 2003. (Flip Quiz Ser.). (Illus.). 152p. (J). spiral bd. 12.95 (978-1-84236-073-6(6)) Miles Kelly Publishing, Ltd. GBR. *Dist:* Independent Pubs. Group.

—Science & Maths. 2003. (Flip Quiz Ser.). (Illus.). 38p. (J). (gr. 10-11). spiral bd. 5.95 (978-1-84236-032-3(9)); (gr. 11-12). spiral bd. 5.95 (978-1-84236-033-0(7)); (gr. 7-9). spiral bd. 5.95 (978-1-84236-030-9(2)); (gr. 9-10). spiral bd. 5.95 (978-1-84236-031-6(0)) Miles Kelly Publishing, Ltd. GBR. *Dist:* Independent Pubs. Group.

Miles Kelly Staff & Nilsen, Anna. Actions: Let's Learn. 2003. (Let's Learn Ser.). (Illus.). 20p. (J). 7.95 (978-1-84236-137-5(6)) Miles Kelly Publishing, Ltd. GBR. *Dist:* Independent Pubs. Group.

—Numbers: Let's Learn. 2003. (Let's Learn Ser.). (Illus.). 20p. (J). 7.95 (978-1-84236-018-7(3)) Miles Kelly Publishing, Ltd. GBR. *Dist:* Independent Pubs. Group.

—Shapes: Let's Learn. 2003. (Let's Learn Ser.). (Illus.). 20p. (J). 7.95 (978-1-84236-016-3(7)) Miles Kelly Publishing, Ltd. GBR. *Dist:* Independent Pubs. Group.

Miller, Anne, et al. Infinity Feng Shui Fortune Telling Game. 2002. (J). 29.99 (978-0-9716419-0-7(0)) Empress3 Publishing.

Miller, Ray. Beat the Clock Sports. Crabtree, Andrew, illus. 1999. 24p. (J). pap. 6.95 (978-1-58295-014-3(8) , Beehive Bk.) Pace Products, Inc.

Milord, Susan. Hands Around the World. Milord, Susan, illus. 1999. (Williamson Kids Can! Ser.). (Illus.). 160p. (J). (gr. 3 up). lib. bdg. 25.26 (978-0-8368-2231-1(5)) Stevens, Gareth Inc.

Mind Bogglers. 2003. (Middle School Mastery Ser.). 64p. (gr. 5-8). 3.99 (978-1-56822-635-4(7) , IF2746) School Specialty Publishing.

Miss O, Harlie, Justine, and Isabella, with Devra Newberger Speregen, Juliette. Miss O & Friends Book of Fabulous Fun: Cool Stuff to make, recipes, quizzes, & More! 2006. (Miss O & Friends Ser.). (Illus.). 96p. (J). pap. 9.95 (978-0-8230-2943-3(3)) Watson-Guptill Pubns., Inc.

Mitchell, Loretta. One, Two, Three... Echo Me! Ready-to-Use Songs, Games & Activities to Help Children Sing in Tune. 2003. (Illus.). 203p. pap. 29.95 (978-0-89328-157-1(3) , 30/1800H) Heritage Music Pr.

Modern Publishing Staff, ed. No Place Like Celesteville. 2005. 12p. pap. 3.99 (978-0-7666-1944-9(3)) Modern Publishing.

—Welcome to the Kingdom. 2005. 12p. pap. 3.99 (978-0-7666-1943-2(5)) Modern Publishing.

Moen, Christine Boardman. 25 Fun & Fabulous Literature Response Activities & Rubrics. 2002. 80p. (J). 11.95 (978-0-439-28235-2(7)) Scholastic, Inc.

Monin, Margie. Candy Corn Bingo. 2006. (Illus.). 32p. pap. 6.95 (978-0-7624-2817-5(1)) Running Pr. Bk. Pubs.

Montaldo, Stuart. Cogno: The Alien Adventure Game. 2003. (J). 29.95 (978-0-9742558-0-4(7)) DoubleStar, LLC.

—Cogno: the Alien Legends: Synapse. 2004. (Cogno the Alien Legends Ser.: Bk. 1). (Illus.). 238p. (J). per. 7.99 (978-0-9742558-2-8(3)) DoubleStar, LLC.

Montaldo, Stuart, creator. Cogno: Deep Worlds. 2004. (J). 29.95 (978-0-9742558-1-1(5)) DoubleStar, LLC.

Montgomery, R. A. The Race Forever. 1999. (Illus.). 116p. mass mkt. (978-0-553-23290-5(8)) Bantam Bks.

Moog, Bob. Made You Laugh for Kids: Truth or Dare! 2005. (Illus.). 96p. pap. (978-1-57528-927-4(X)) University Games.

—Spinner Books: Two-Book Set. 2005. 480p. (978-1-57528-970-0(9)) University Games.

—Spinner Books for Kids Sleeve: Two-Book Set. 2005. (Illus.). 320p. (978-1-57528-971-7(7)) University Games.

Moog, Robert. Spinner Books Junior: 20 Questions for Kids. 2004. (Spinner Books for Kids). (Illus.). 160p. (J). pap. 7.95 (978-1-57528-918-2(0)) University Games.

—Spinner Books Junior: 30 Second Mysteries for Kids. 2004. (Spinner Books for Kids). (Illus.). 160p. (J). pap. 7.95 (978-1-57528-919-9(9)) University Games.

—Spinner Books Junior: Kids Battle the Grown-Ups. 2004. (Spinner Books for Kids). (Illus.). 160p. pap. 7.95 (978-1-57528-921-2(0)) University Games.

—Spinner Books Junior: Totally Gross. 2004. (Illus.). 160p. (J). pap. 7.95 (978-1-57528-920-5(2)) University Games.

Moon, Alan R. & Borg, Richard, des. Dragon Hordes: Warriors Expansion #1. 2005. (JPN & KOR.). (YA). pap. 19.95 (978-0-9728197-9-4(7)) Face 2 Face Games Publishing.

—Warriors. 2005. (JPN & KOR.). (YA). pap. 19.95 (978-0-9728197-8-7(9)) Face 2 Face Games Publishing.

Moore, Suzanne & Henry, Lucia Kemp. Toss & Learn Games: Around the Year. 2003. (Toss & Learn Games Ser.). (Illus.). 48p. (ps-k). pap. 10.99 (978-0-439-47117-6(6) , Teaching Resources) Scholastic, Inc.

—Toss & Learn Games: Science. 2003. (Toss & Learn Games Ser.). (Illus.). 48p. (ps-k). 10.99 (978-0-439-47118-3(4) , Teaching Resources) Scholastic, Inc.

Moran, Paul, illus. World's Scariest Monster Games & Stories. 2003. (World's Ser.). 112p. (J). pap. 3.99 (978-0-603-56103-0(9)) Egmont Bks., Ltd. GBR. *Dist:* Independent Pubs. Group.

More Time for Bible Puzzles & Games. (Illus.). 32p. (YA). (gr. 5 up). pap. 2.25 (978-0-87162-664-6(0) , E9706) Warner Pr. Pubs.

Moreau, Roger. Treasure Hunt Mazes: An A-Maze-Ing Colorful Journey! 2001. (Illus.). 80p. (J). (gr. 2-7). pap. 7.95 (978-0-8069-6633-5(5)) Sterling Publishing Co., Inc.

Morgan, Thane. Armies of Arcana, 1. 4th ed. 2002. (Illus.). 88p. per. 29.99 (978-0-9719404-0-6(1)) Thane's Games.

Morin, Virginia K. Fun to Grow On: Engaging Play Activities for Kids, Teachers, Parents & Grandparents. Sokoloff, David, illus. 2nd rev. ed. 1999. (J). (ps-6). pap. 12.95 (978-1-890374-01-3(6)) Magnolia Street Pubs.

Morton's List: The End to Boredom. 2001. 402p. (YA). per. 36.00 (978-0-9710905-1-4(3)) Dark Carnival Games, L.L.C.

Mosher, Geraldine. A Madcap Mother Goose. Rocque, Rose, illus. 2003. pap. 9.95 (978-0-9726311-4-3(3)) Top Quality Pubns.

Mouse Works Staff. My First Peek-a-Boo Game. 1998. (Disney Babies Ser.). (J). 4.98 (978-1-57082-713-6(3)) Mouse Works.

Muggli, Glorianne. Gospel Games: I Love Bible Stories. 2000. (Illus.). 72p. (J). 7.95 (978-1-57665-067-7(7)) Muggli Graphics.

—Gospel Games: I'm a Latter-Day Saint! 2000. (Illus.). 72p. (J). pap. 7.95 (978-1-57665-068-4(5)) Muggli Graphics.

—Gospel Games: Letters & Numbers for Little Ones. 2000. 72p. (J). pap. 7.95 (978-1-57665-069-1(3)) Muggli Graphics.

—Gospel Games: My Little Book of God's Creations. 2000. (Illus.). 72p. (J). pap. 7.95 (978-1-57665-070-7(7)) Muggli Graphics.

—Visual Aids for Choosing Time. 2003. (J). pap. (978-1-57665-086-8(3)) Muggli Graphics.

Mullarkey, Lisa. Splashing by the Shore: Beach Activities for Kids. Dixon, Debra Spina, illus. 2007. 64p. (J). (gr. 1-3). pap. 9.95 (978-1-58685-884-1(X)) Gibbs Smith, Publisher.

Multiplication 0-12. 2003. (Math Card Games Ser.). (Illus.). (gr. 3 up). 9.99 (978-0-7682-1987-6(6) , J53015) School Specialty Publishing.

Murphy, Stuart J. Game Time! Jabar, Cynthia, illus. 2000. (MathStart Ser.). 40p. (J). (gr. 2 up). pap. 5.99 (978-0-06-446732-2(5) , Harper Trophy); 15.95 (978-0-06-028024-6(7)); 15.89 (978-0-06-028025-3(5)) HarperCollins Pubs.

—Game Time! 2000. (gr. k-3). lib. bdg. 13.00 (978-0-613-31230-1(9)) Tandem Library Bks.

My Book of Number Games 1-150. 2004. (Illus.). 80p. (J). per. 6.95 (978-4-7743-0760-2(2)) Kumon Publishing North America, Inc.

My Little Pony Surprize Ink! Clipboard I. 2004. 24p. (J). 9.99 (978-1-932125-92-4(2)) Giddy Up, LLC.

My Little Pony Water Wow! Book. 2005. (J). per. 6.99 (978-1-59524-056-9(X)) Giddy Up, LLC.

My Word! Fast & Fun Wordplay. 2001. 9.95 (978-0-9708554-2-8(7)) Out of the Box Publishing, Inc.

Nardo, Don. Games of Ancient Rome. 2005. (Daily Life Ser.). (Illus.). 48p. (J). (gr. 4-8). 26.20 (978-0-7377-2345-8(9) , Greenhaven Pr., Inc.) Thomson Gale.

Nelson, Robin. Toys & Games. 2003. (First Step Nonfiction Ser.). (Illus.). 24p. (J). (gr. k-2). lib. bdg. 18.60 (978-0-8225-4644-3(2)) Lerner Publishing Group.

Nero International Holding Company, Inc. Staff. NERO Rule Book. (Illus.). (YA). (gr. 9 up). pap. 10.00 (978-0-9700563-0-6(3)) NERO International Holding Co., Inc.

Newbery, John & Thomas, Isaiah. Little Pretty Pocket-Book. 2006. (Illus.). 122p. (J). (gr. 4-7). per. 8.95 (978-1-55709-990-7(1)) Applewood Bks.

Nicholaus, Bret & Lowrie, Paul. Kidchat: 222 Creative Questions to Spark Conversations. 2nd rev. ed. 2004. (Illus.). 128p. (J). pap. 9.95 (978-0-9755801-0-3(8) , KCR) Questmarc Publishing.

—KidChat Oh, the Places to Go! 204 Creative Questions to Let the Imagination Travel. 2007. (KidChat Ser.). (Illus.). 128p. (J). (gr. 3 up). pap. 6.99 (*978-1-59643-317-5(5)) Roaring Brook Pr.

Nicholaus, Bret & Lowrie, Paul. KidChat Too! All-New Questions to Fuel Young Minds & Mouths. 2004. (Illus.). 128p. (J). pap. 9.95 (978-0-9755801-1-0(6) , KCT) Questmarc Publishing.

Nicholls, Shawn. Sports Gamer: The Best Games, Gear, & Tips. 2004. (YA). 3.99 (978-1-930623-36-1(4)) Sports Illustrated For Kids.

Niederman, Derrick, et al. The Secret Clubhouse Game Book. 2004. (Illus.). 128p. (J). pap. 4.95 (978-1-4027-1107-7(7)) Sterling Publishing Co., Inc.

Nitz, Kristin Wolden. Play-by-Play Track. 2004. (Play-by-Play Ser.). (Illus.). 80p. (J). (gr. 4-8). lib. bdg. 23.93 (978-0-8225-3936-0(5)) Lerner Publishing Group.

—Play-by-Play Track. 2004. (gr. 5-8). lib. bdg. 16.40 (978-0-613-76645-6(8)) Tandem Library Bks.

Norton, Frances Maree. The Victorian Tea Spirit: A Girl's Guide to Her Secret Self, 1. 100th ed. 2003. (Illus.). 230p. (YA). per. 19.95 (978-0-9632938-1-7(8)) Norton, Frances M.

Nunan, David. Go for It, Tests & Games Resource, Bk. 2. 1999. (Adult ESL Ser.). (J). pap. 42.95 (978-0-8384-7972-8(3)) Thomson Heinle.

The Nutcracker Music Game. 2004. (J). (gr. 2-8). 24.95 incl. audio (978-1-55592-175-0(2)) Weston Woods Studios, Inc.

Odom, Mel. Unlock the Secrets of Oddworld: Official Strategy Guide. (J). pap. 12.95 (978-1-56893-960-5(4)) GT Interactive Software.

Off, Greg, et al. Ratchet & Clank: Up Your Arsenal Official Strategy Guide. 2004. (Illus.). 176p. pap. 14.99 (978-0-7440-0500-4(0)) Brady GAMES.

Ogawa, Tomoko. Endgame. 2000. (Elementary Go Ser.). (Illus.). (J). pap. 15.00 (978-4-906574-15-5(7)) KISEIDO.

O'Hare, Jeff. Secret Codes & Hidden Messages. 2003. (Illus.). 48p. (YA). (gr. 5-7). pap. 4.95 (978-1-56397-652-0(8)) Boyds Mills Pr.

Olson, Debra. Colorful File-Fldr Game Gr K. 2006. 160p. (J). pap. (978-0-88724-269-4(3) , CD-104048) Carson-Dellosa Publishing Co., Inc.

Omishi, Denichiro. Otedama: Traditional Japanese Juggling Toys & Games. 2004. (Illus.). 32p. (gr. 4-7). bds. 15.95 (978-0-89346-936-8(X)) Heian International Publishing, Inc.

O'Neill, Amanda. Marble Madness. 2002. 64p. (J). pap. 9.98 (978-0-7525-6295-7(9)) Parragon, Inc.

Onyefulu, Ifeoma. Ebele's Favourite: A Book of African Games. 1999. (Illus.). 32p. (J). (gr. k-3). (978-0-7112-1279-4(1)) Lincoln, Frances Ltd.

—Ebele's Favourite: A Book of African Games. 2001. (Illus.). 32p. (J). (gr. k-3). pap. 8.99 (978-0-7112-1471-2(9)) Lincoln, Frances Ltd. GBR. *Dist:* Antique Collectors' Club.

O'Reilly, Wenda. Amazing places natl Parks. 2007. n/ap. pap. 119.40 (*978-1-59960-014-7(5)) Birdcage Pr.

—Go fish wildlife Mammals. 2007. n/ap. pap. 119.40 (*978-1-59960-016-1(1)) Birdcage Pr.

—GO FISH WILDLIFE REPTILES & AMPHIBIANS. 2007. n/ap. pap. 119.40 (*978-1-59960-018-5(8)) Birdcage Pr.

—Go fish wildlife sea Creatures. 2007. n/ap. pap. 119.40 (*978-1-59960-020-8(X)) Birdcage Pr.

—Wild Cards. 2007. n/ap. pap. 119.40 (*978-1-59960-012-3(9)) Birdcage Pr.

Orr, Julie. Dot-to-Dot. 2002. (Activity Zone Workbooks Ser.). (Illus.). 64p. (J). pap., wbk. ed. 3.79 (978-1-58947-052-1(4) , 02346) School Zone Publishing Co.

Oxenbury, Helen. Clap Hands. Oxenbury, Helen, illus. 1999. (Oxenbury Board Bks.). (Illus.). 10p. (J). (ps-k). bds. 6.99 (978-0-689-81984-1(6) , Little Simon) Simon & Schuster Children's Publishing.

Packard, Edward. The Phantom Submarine. 1999. (Illus.). 111p. mass mkt. (978-0-553-23635-4(0)) Bantam Bks.

Parks, Peggy J. Entertainment. 2005. (Yesterday & Today Ser.). (Illus.). 32p. (J). (ps-7). lib. bdg. 23.70 (978-1-56711-830-8(5) , Blackbirch Pr., Inc.) Thomson Gale.

Pearson, Debora. Kids Do, Animals Too: A Book of Playground Opposites. Hilb, Nora, illus. 2005. 24p. (J). (gr. k-ps). pap. 5.95 (978-1-55037-922-8(4)); lib. bdg. 17.95 (978-1-55037-923-5(2)) Annick Pr., Ltd. CAN. *Dist:* Firefly Bks., Ltd.

Pena, Evelyn. Fun Facts & Games: Michigan. Dieterichs, Shelley, illus. 2000. (Fun Facts & Games Activity Book Ser.). 64p. (J). (gr. 1-5). pap. 5.95 (978-1-892920-48-5(4)) GHB Publishers, LLC.

Penton Overseas, Inc. Staff. U. S. Presidents. 2002. (Smart Kids Flippers Ser.). (Illus.). (J). pap. 7.95 (978-1-59125-165-1(6)) Penton Overseas, Inc.

Perez, Jessica. Spin & Spell: A Book & Game in One! Gevry, Claudine, illus. 2005. 12p. (J). 14.95 (978-1-58117-332-1(6) , Intervisual/Piggy Toes) Dalmatian Pr.

Petelinsek, Kathleen & Primm, E. Russell. At Play/En el Juego. 2006. (Talking Hands Ser.). (ENG & SPA., Illus.). 24p. (J). 21.36 (978-1-59296-683-7(7)) Child's World, Inc.

Petty, Kate. Playtime. 2006. (Illus.). 32p. (J). 8.95 (978-1-58728-546-2(0)); 14.95 (978-1-58728-549-3(5)) T&N Children's Publishing. (Two Can Publishing).

Phillips, Sarah. Jump Rope. 2005. (Play It! Ser.). (Illus.). 24p. (J). (gr. k-3). 12.95 (978-1-905051-57-1(3)) Make Believe Ideas GBR. *Dist:* Ingram Pub. Services.

Picture Window Books, contrib. by. Score! (Game Day Ser.). 24p. (J). pap. 7.95 (978-1-4048-0513-2(3)) Picture Window Bks.

Piekart, Ferry. Playing with Stuff: Outrageous Games with Ordinary Objects. Deltrap, Lars, illus. 2004. 48p. (J). pap. 9.95 (978-1-929132-62-1(X)) Kane/Miller Bk. Pubs., Inc.

Pilkey, Dav. The All New Captain Underpants Extra-Crunchy Book O' Fun 2. 2002. (Captain Underpants Ser.). (gr. 3-6). lib. bdg. 11.80 (978-0-613-49472-4(5)) Tandem Library Bks.

PIN - Balancing Aliens. 2002. mass mkt. 29.95 (978-1-932359-13-8(3)) Out of the Box Publishing, Inc.

PIN - Cityscape. 2002. pap. 29.95 (978-0-9716729-4-9(6)) Out of the Box Publishing, Inc.

PIN - Columns. 2002. mass mkt. 29.95 (978-1-932359-12-1(5)) Out of the Box Publishing, Inc.

PIN - Octiles. 2002. pap. 29.95 (978-0-9716729-5-6(4)) Out of the Box Publishing, Inc.

PIN - Quadtria. 2002. pap. 29.95 (978-0-9716729-2-5(X) , 00801) Out of the Box Publishing, Inc.

Play the Game You Know. 2005. (Book Treks Ser.). (J). 37.95 (978-0-7652-3258-8(8)) Celebration Pr.

Power Pak of Games. 1998. 104p. (J). tchr. ed., per. 12.99 (978-1-57405-001-1(X)) CharismaLife Pubs.

Prater, John. Oh Where, Oh Where? 1998. (Illus.). 24p. (J). bds. 6.95 (978-0-7641-5109-5(6)) Barron's Educational Series, Inc.

Preller, James. Crazy for Crazy Bones, Vol. 1. 1999. (Illus.). 48p. (J). (gr. k-3). pap. 5.99 (978-0-439-14980-8(0)) Scholastic, Inc.

—Fantasy Football. 2003. (NFL Ser.). (Illus.). 32p. (J). pap. 5.99 (978-0-439-53812-1(2)) Scholastic, Inc.

—Fantasy Football. 2003. (gr. 3-6). lib. bdg. 14.15 (978-0-613-87589-9(3)) Tandem Library Bks.

—The Table Top Sports. Davis, Billy, illus. 2004. (3-in-1 Ser.). 32p. (J). pap. 7.99 (978-0-439-55132-8(3) , Tangerine Pr.) Scholastic, Inc.

Pressnall, Deb. Full Color File Folder Games, Grade 1. 2006. 160p. (J). pap. (978-1-59441-089-5(5) , CD-104049) Carson-Dellosa Publishing Co., Inc.

Pressnall, Debra. Full Color File Folder Games PK-K. 2006. 160p. (J). pap. (978-0-88724-268-7(5) , CD-104047) Carson-Dellosa Publishing Co., Inc.

Pressnall, Debra Olson. The Big Book of Music Games. 1999. (Illus.). 320p. (J). (gr. 1-5). pap. 22.99 (978-1-56822-673-6(X) , IF20453) School Specialty Publishing.

Price, Roger. Alphabet Mad Libs Junior. 2004. (Mad Libs Junior Ser.). 48p. (J). (gr. k-3). pap. 3.99 (978-0-8431-0769-2(3) , Price Stern Sloan) Penguin Group (USA) Inc.

—American Idol Mad Libs. 2005. 48p. (J). (gr. 3). pap. 3.99 (978-0-8431-1391-4(X) , Price Stern Sloan) Penguin Group (USA) Inc.

—Once upon a Mad Libs Junior. 2004. (Mad Libs Junior Ser.). 48p. (J). (gr. k-3). pap. 3.99 (978-0-8431-0768-5(5) , Price Stern Sloan) Penguin Group (USA) Inc.

—Sports Star Mad Libs Junior. 2004. 48p. (J). (gr. k-3). pap. 3.99 (978-0-8431-0770-8(7) , Price Stern Sloan) Penguin Group (USA) Inc.

—Summer Fun Mad Libs Junior. 2004. (Mad Libs Junior Ser.). 48p. (J). pap. 3.99 (978-0-8431-0759-3(6) , Price Stern Sloan) Penguin Group (USA) Inc.

—Super Silly Mad Libs Junior. 2004. (Mad Libs Junior Ser.). 48p. (J). (gr. k-3). pap. 3.99 (978-0-8431-0758-6(8) , Price Stern Sloan) Penguin Group (USA) Inc.

Price, Roger & Stern, Leonard. Curious George Mad Libs Junior. 2006. (Mad Libs Junior Ser.). 48p. (J). (gr. k-3). pap. 3.99 (978-0-8431-1828-5(8) , Price Stern Sloan) Penguin Group (USA) Inc.

—Family Guy Mad Libs. 2007. (Mad Libs Ser.). 48p. (J). pap. 3.99 (978-0-8431-2190-2(4) , Price Stern Sloan) Penguin Group (USA) Inc.

—Fear Factor Mad Libs. 2003. (Mad Libs Ser.). 48p. (J). (gr. 3). mass mkt. 3.99 (978-0-8431-0664-0(6) , Price Stern Sloan) Penguin Group (USA) Inc.

—Halloween Mad Libs Junior. 2005. (Mad Libs Junior Ser.). 48p. (J). (gr. k-3). pap. 3.99 (978-0-8431-1589-5(0) , Price Stern Sloan) Penguin Group (USA) Inc.

—Prehistoric Mad Libs Junior. 2004. (Mad Libs Junior Ser.). 48p. (gr. k-3). pap. 3.99 (978-0-8431-0767-8(7) , Price Stern Sloan) Penguin Group (USA) Inc.

—Winter Games Mad Libs. 2005. (Mad Libs Ser.). 48p. (J). (gr. 3). pap. 3.99 (978-0-8431-1651-9(X) , Price Stern Sloan) Penguin Group (USA) Inc.

Price, Stern, Sloan Publishing Staff. The Crazy Dinosaur Game. 2000. (Crazy Games Ser.). (Illus.). 1p. (J). 3.99 (978-0-8431-7589-9(3) , Price Stern Sloan) Penguin Group (USA) Inc.

Princesses Games & Spinner Activities & Crafts. 2000. (Golden Book Ser.). (Illus.). 32p. (J). (ps-3). pap. 4.99 (978-0-307-30157-4(5) , Golden Bks.) Random Hse. Children's Bks.

Publications International Staff. Lion King Look & Find. (J). pap. 6.98 (978-0-7853-1189-8(0)) Publications International, Ltd.

Pulver, David L. & MacKinnon, Mark C. Big Eyes, Small Mouth Third Edition Core Rulebook. 2005. 256p. (YA). 39.95 (978-1-894938-21-1(6)) Guardians of Order CAN. *Dist:* PSI (Publisher Services, Inc.).

Pulver, David L., et al. CyborGladiators. 2003. per. 14.95 (978-0-9747671-0-9(7)) Firefly Games.

Puzzles & Games. 2002. (Home Workbooks Ser.). 64p. pap. 2.49 (978-0-88724-734-7(2) , CD-4536); pap. 2.49 (978-0-88724-722-4(9) , CD-4524) Carson-Dellosa Publishing Co., Inc.

Pyne, Lynette. Full Color File Folder Games 1-2. 2006. (J). pap. (978-0-88724-270-0(7) , CD-104050) Carson-Dellosa Publishing Co., Inc.

Qwitch. 2002. 9.95 (978-0-9708554-8-0(6)) Out of the Box Publishing, Inc.

Radtke, Becky. Circus. 2003. (Dover Little Activity Bks.). (Illus.). 64p. (J). pap., act. bk. ed. 1.50 (978-0-486-42768-3(4)) Dover Pubns., Inc.

Rainfall Staff. Bible Charades Game. 2001. (None Ser.). (J). pap. 29.99 (978-983-45501-3-4(8) , 9834550138) Cook, David C. Publishing Co.

Rand McNally Staff. Are We There Yet? (Backseat Bks.). 64p. (J). pap. 3.95 (978-0-528-96543-2(3)) Rand McNally.

—Kids' Road Atlas. (Backseat Bks.). 80p. (J). pap. 3.95 (978-0-528-96544-9(1)) Rand McNally.

Randinelli, Tracy & Prokos, Anna. Secrets of Space. Snow, Alan, illus. 2002. (Crash Course Ser.). 68p. (J). (gr. 2-17). spiral bd. 16.99 (978-1-58476-137-2(7)) Innovative Kids.

Random House Beginners Books Staff. Seek & Find Fun. Zimmerman, Jerry, illus. 2002. (Thomas & Friends Ser.). 16p. (J). (ps-2). pap. 2.99 (978-0-375-81496-9(5) , Golden Bks.) Random Hse. Children's Bks.

Random House Disney Staff. The Tank Gang. 2003. (Illus.). 32p. (J). (ps-3). pap. 3.99 (978-0-7364-2121-8(1) , Golden/Disney) Random Hse. Children's Bks.

Random House Staff. Pat-a-Cake & Other First Baby Games. 2002. (Sesame Beginnings Ser.). (Illus.). 26p. (J). (gr. k). bds. 7.99 (978-0-375-81557-7(0) , Random Hse. Bks. for Young Readers) Random Hse. Children's Bks.

Random House Staff & Disney Staff. Swim Team. 2003. (Illus.). 64p. (J). (ps-2). pap. 3.99 (978-0-307-10587-5(3) , Golden/Disney) Random Hse. Children's Bks.

Rankin, Hugh. Psi Soldiers. 2004. (Illus.). 200p. (YA). per. 14.95 (978-0-9746817-0-2(9) , 9746917090001) Treadway, Scott.

Rasmussen, Greta & Rasmussen, Ted. Gotta Think! An Entertaining Assortment of Thinking Activities. 2000. (Illus.). 112p. (J). (gr. 2-6). pap. 12.95 (978-0-936110-23-3(6)) Tin Man Pr.

Rathjen, Don. Lego Crazy Action Contraptions. Klutz Press Staff, ed. 1998. (Illus.). 68p. (J). (gr. 4-7). spiral bd. 19.95 (978-1-57054-157-5(4)) Klutz.

Rau, Dana Meachen. Card Games. 2004. (Games Around the World Ser.). 32p. (J). (gr. 3 up). lib. bdg. 22.60 (978-0-7565-0675-9(1)) Compass Point Bks.

—Spinning Toys. 2004. (Games Around the World Ser.). 32p. (J). (gr. 3 up). lib. bdg. 22.60 (978-0-7565-0676-6(X)) Compass Point Bks.

—Toys, Games, & Fun in American History. 2006. (Illus.). 24p. (J). pap. (978-0-8368-7216-3(9)); lib. bdg. (978-0-8368-7209-5(6)) Stevens, Gareth Inc.

RBA. El libro del aprendíz de Brujo. 144p. 21.95 (978-84-7901-783-5(X)) RBA Libros, S.A. ESP. *Dist:* Santillana USA Publishing Co., Inc.

Reitzes, Fretta & Teitelman, Beth. Wonderplay, Too: Games, Crafts, & Creative Activities for 3- to 6-year Olds. 2007. (Illus.). 112p. pap. 12.95 (***978-0-7624-2863-2(5)*** , Running Pr.) Running Pr. Bk. Pubs.

Rhatigan, Joe & Newcomb, Rain. Run, Jump, Hide, Slide, Splash: The 200 Best Outdoor Games Ever. (Illus.). 128p. (ps-6). 2005. (J). pap. 9.95 (978-1-57990-754-9(7)); 2004. 19.95 (978-1-57990-509-5(9)) Lark Bks.

Richards, Karen C. Mulan Puzzlers. 1998. (Illus.). 176p. (J). (gr. 3-7). pap. 9.95 (978-0-7868-4224-7(5)) Little Brown & Co.

Rigby, Christopher & Sail, Nicola. Let's Have a Christmas: Flip Quiz. 2003. (Family Flip Quiz Ser.). (Illus.). 152p. (J). spiral bd. 12.95 (978-1-902947-96-9(7)) Miles Kelly Publishing, Ltd. GBR. *Dist:* Independent Pubs. Group.

Ring, Susan. Gross Anatomy. Snow, Alan, illus. 2002. (Crash Course Ser.). 68p. (J). (gr. 2-17). spiral bd. 16.99 (978-1-58476-136-5(9)) Innovative Kids.

Ripoll & Rovira. Hace un Buen Dia? Ideal Para Jugar! 2004. (SPA.). 36p. (978-84-272-6143-3(8)) Molino, Editorial.

Ripoll, Oriol. Play with Us: 100 Games from Around the World. 2005. (Illus.). 128p. (J). (gr. k-12). pap. 16.95 (978-1-55652-594-0(X)) Chicago Review Pr., Inc.

Roehlkepartain, Jolene L. 101 Great Games for Infants, Toddlers, & Preschoolers: Active, Bible-Based Fun for Christian Education. 2004. (Illus.). 160p. pap. 15.00 (978-0-687-00814-8(X)) Abingdon Pr.

Rogers. What Can You See. 2000. (Illus.). 20p. (J). pap. 8.95 (978-0-552-54588-4(0)) Transworld Publishers Ltd. GBR. *Dist:* Trafalgar Square Publishing.

Rogers, A., contrib. by. Ship Shape. 2004. (Little Giants Ser.). (Illus.). 16p. (ps-k). 5.95 (978-1-58728-155-6(4) , Two Can Publishing) T&N Children's Publishing.

Rohrer, Neal. Rohrer's Fun Coloring & Games. Rohrer, Neal, illus. 2003. (Illus.). 28p. 3.95 (978-0-9721138-0-9(0)) Rohrer Design.

Rooyackers, Paul. 101 More Drama Games for Children: New Fun & Learning with Acting & Make-Believe. Marix Evans, Amina, tr. from DUT. Hofland, Margreet, illus. 2002. (Hunter House Smartfun Book Ser.). 144p. (J). (gr. 4-7). pap. 14.95 (978-0-89793-367-4(2)) Hunter Hse., Inc.

—101 More Drama Games for Children: New Fun & Learning with Acting & Make-Believe. Marix Evans, Amina, tr. from DUT. Hofland, Margareet, illus. 2002. (Hunter House Smartfun Book Ser.). 144p. (J). (ps up). spiral bd. 19.95 (978-0-89793-368-1(0)) Hunter Hse., Inc.

Ross, Kathy. The Best Birthday Parties Ever! A Kid's Do-It-Yourself Guide. 1999. (Illus.). 80p. (J). (gr. 3-6). pap. 9.95 (978-0-7613-0989-5(6) , Millbrook Pr.) Lerner Publishing Group.

—The Best Birthday Parties Ever! A Kid's Do-it-Yourself Guide. Holm, Sharon Lane, illus. 1999. (Crafts from Kathy Ross Ser.). 80p. (gr. 3-6). lib. bdg. 24.90 (978-0-7613-1410-3(5) , Millbrook Pr.) Lerner Publishing Group.

Rossignoli, Marco. The Complete Pinball Book: Collecting the Game & Its History. 2nd rev. ed. 2002. (Schiffer Book for Collectors Ser.). (Illus.). 256p. (gr. 10-13). 59.95 (978-0-7643-1586-2(2)) Schiffer Publishing, Ltd.

Royals, Susan. Fun Facts & Games: Missouri. Nolte, Larry, illus. 2000. (Fun Facts & Games Ser.). 64p. (J). (gr. 1-5). pap. 5.59 (978-1-892920-21-8(2)) GHB Publishers, LLC.

Roycroft, Mitch. Jennifer Harman. 2008. (J). (***978-1-4222-0227-2(5)***) Mason Crest Pubs.

—Johnny "Orient Express" Chan. 2008. (***978-1-4222-0224-1(0)***) Mason Crest Pubs.

—Phil "The Poker Brat" Hellmuth. 2008. (***978-1-4222-0220-3(8)***) Mason Crest Pubs.

—Phil "Tiger Woods of Poker" Ivey. 2008. (***978-1-4222-0221-0(6)***) Mason Crest Pubs.

Royston, Angela. Plastico: Miremos un Frisbee. 2005. (Heinemann Lee y Aprende Ser.). (ENG & SPA., Illus.). 24p. (978-1-4034-7545-9(8)); pap. (978-1-4034-7554-1(7)) Heinemann Library.

Rudisill, J. J., et al, illus. Jonas's Puzzles & Games. 1999. 32p. (J). pap. 2.99 (978-0-88724-484-1(X) , CD-4852) Carson-Dellosa Publishing Co., Inc.

—LouLou's Dot-to-Dot. 1999. 32p. (J). pap. 2.99 (978-0-88724-485-8(8)) Carson-Dellosa Publishing Co., Inc.

—Wimzie's Birthday Fun & Games. 1999. (Wimzie's House Bks.). 32p. (J). pap. 2.99 (978-0-88724-514-5(5) , CD-4855) Carson-Dellosa Publishing Co., Inc.

Running Press Staff. The Scooby Doo Mystery Solver's Handbook. 2007. 128p. 4.95 (978-0-7624-2983-7(6) , Running Pr. Minature Editions) Running Pr. Bk. Pubs.

Rutman, Shereen Gertel. My First Amazing Game. Clough, Julie, illus. 2002. 36p. (J). (ps-1). bds. 19.99 (978-1-58476-094-8(X)) Innovative Kids.

S. I. Artists Staff, illus. Fun & Games. 2003. 40p. (J). 3.95 (978-0-9729026-1-8(9)) Midwest Cylinder Management, Inc.

—Fun & Games. 2003. (J). per. (978-1-57657-854-4(2)) Paradise Pr., Inc.

Saint-Exupery, Antoine De. The Little Prince Book of Fun & Adventure. Bent, Lucinda, tr. from FRE. 2006. (Illus.). 64p. (J). 18.95 (978-0-15-205705-3(6) , Red Wagon Bks.) Harcourt Children's Bks.

Salmon Migration Game. 2000. (Illus.). 2p. (gr. k-5). 10.00 (978-1-56612-065-4(9)) Alaska Sea Grant College Program.

Samuel, Charlie. Entertainment in Colonial America. 2003. (Primary Sources of Everyday Life in Colonial America Ser.). (Illus.). 24p. (J). lib. bdg. 21.25 (978-0-8239-6600-4(3) , PowerKids Pr.) Rosen Publishing Group, Inc., The.

Santillo, LuAnn. Fun with Phonemes. Santillo, LuAnn, ed. 2004. (Half - Pint Readers Ser.). (Illus.). 36p. (J). (ps-1). pap. 14.99 (978-1-59256-129-2(2)) Half-Pint Kids, Inc.

—Lots More Fun with Phonemes. Santillo, LuAnn, ed. 2004. (Half-Pint Readers Ser.). (Illus.). 36p. (J). (ps-1). pap. 14.99 (978-1-59256-131-5(4)) Half-Pint Kids, Inc.

—More Fun with Phonemes. Santillo, LuAnn, ed. 2004. (Half-Pint Readers Ser.). (Illus.). 36p. (J). (ps-1). pap. 14.99 (978-1-59256-130-8(6)) Half-Pint Kids, Inc.

Scamander, Newt, pseud & Rowling, J. K. Harry Potter Schoolbooks: Quidditch Through the Ages & Fantastic Beasts & Where to Find Them, 2 vols., Set. Incl. Fantastic Beasts & Where to Find Them. (Illus.). 64p. (J). (gr. 3 up). 2001. mass mkt. 3.99 (978-0-439-29501-7(7)); (Harry Potter Ser.). (Illus.). 2001. Set mass mkt. 7.98 (978-0-439-28403-5(1) , Levine, Arthur A. Bks.) Scholastic, Inc.

Scarbro, Maxine. One Room Schoolgames: Children's Games of Yesteryear. 2003. (Illus.). 64p. per. 9.95 (978-0-938985-05-1(1) , Mountain Memories Bks.) Quarrier Pr.

Scelsa, Greg & Millang, Steve. Fun & Games. 2001. (J). cd-rom 13.99 (978-1-57471-836-2(3) , YM 018-CD) Creative Teaching Pr., Inc.

Scholastic, Inc. Staff. Gladiator Spinners. 2004. (Illus.). 24p. (J). (gr. 3 up). spiral bd. 4.99 (978-0-439-61501-3(1)) Scholastic, Inc.

—Metru Nui: A Guide to the City of Legends. Simpson, Fiona, ed. 2004. (Bionicle Ser.). 80p. (J). pap. 6.99 (978-0-439-60734-6(5)) Scholastic, Inc.

—The 50 Great States Game. 2003. (J). pap. 12.95 (978-0-439-22252-5(4) , Teaching Resources) Scholastic, Inc.

Scholastic, Inc. Staff & Farshtey, Greg. Tales of Masks, Vol. 4. 2003. (Bionicle Chronicles). 96p. (J). 4.99 (978-0-439-60706-3(X)) Scholastic, Inc.

School Specialty Publishing. Crazy Eights. 2006. (Brighter Child Flash Cards Ser.). 54p. (J). 2.99 (978-0-7696-4699-2(9) , Brighter Child) School Specialty Publishing.

—Easy Picture Recognition. 2001. (Phonics Flash Cards Ser.). 104p. (C). 6.99 (978-0-86734-406-6(7) , Schaffer, Frank) Schaffer, Frank Pubns.

—Old Maid. 2006. (Brighter Child Flash Cards Ser.). 54p. (J). 2.99 (978-0-7696-4848-4(7) , Brighter Child) School Specialty Publishing.

—1-2-3 Ordering & Sequencing. 2003. (1-2-3 Ser.). 80p. (J). pap. 10.99 (978-1-57029-468-6(2) , WPH99019, Totline Pubns.) Schaffer, Frank Pubns.

School Zone Publishing Co. Make-A-Word Bingo Game. 2006. (J). 5.99 (***978-1-58947-496-3(1)***) School Zone Publishing Co.

School Zone Publishing Company Staff. Japanese Numbers Game. (Illus.). (J). 6.99 (978-0-88743-526-3(2)) School Zone Publishing Co.

—Mazes. 2002. (Activity Zone Workbooks Ser.). (Illus.). 64p. (J). pap., wbk. ed. 3.79 (978-1-58947-053-8(2) , 02347) School Zone Publishing Co.

—Old Maid. rev. ed. 1999. (Game Cards Ser.). 56p. (J). 2.79 (978-0-88743-272-9(7) , 05015) School Zone Publishing Co.

School Zone Staff. Old Maid. 2004. (J). 2.79 (978-1-58947-992-0(0)) School Zone Publishing Co.

Scott, Foresman and Company Staff. Up & over, Thrills & Spills. (J). 31.63 (978-0-673-21375-4(7) , Scott Foresman) Addison Wesley Schl.

Scratch N Sniff Staff. Scratch N Sniff Gang. 2005. 12p. 6.95 (978-0-9762524-9-8(X)) Gimme Gimme Toys & Games Inc.

The Secret of the Digimon Emperor. 2001. (Digimon 2nd Season Ultimate Adventures Ser.: No. 4). 96p. (gr. 1-4). pap. 4.50 (978-0-06-107208-6(7) , Harper Entertainment) HarperCollins Pubs.

Seelig, Tina L. Games for Your Brain: Cars. 2007. (Illus.). 61p. (J). 9.95 (978-0-8118-5707-9(7)) Chronicle Bks. LLC.

—Games for Your Brain: Extreme. 2007. (Illus.). 61p. (J). 9.95 (978-0-8118-5708-6(5)) Chronicle Bks. LLC.

Serfozo, Mary. What's What? A Guessing Game. Narahashi, Keiko, illus. 2000. 32p. (J). (ps-3). 6.99 (978-0-689-83322-9(9) , Aladdin) Simon & Schuster Children's Publishing.

—What's What? A Guessing Game. 2000. (978-0-606-17944-7(5)) Tandem Library Bks.

Sesame Street Elmo's Winter Games. 2006. (J). 3.99 (***978-1-59545-119-4(6)***) Learning Horizons, Inc.

Sesame Street Water Wow! Book. 2005. (J). per. 6.99 (978-1-59524-089-7(6)) Giddy Up, LLC.

SGI-USA Kids Fun Book. 1999. (Illus.). 48p. (J). (gr. k-3). 4.95 (978-0-915678-65-5(9) , Treasure Tower Bks.) World Tribune Pr.

Sherman, Josepha. Barrel Racing. (Rodeo Ser.). (Illus.). 32p. (J). (gr. 3-6). 2002. pap. 6.95 (978-1-58810-357-4(9) , 91116); 2000. lib. bdg. 21.36 (978-1-57572-503-1(7)) Heinemann Library.

Sherman, Michael. Suction Cup Critters 6 W/Display. 2005. 20p. (J). 89.70 (978-1-57054-269-5(4)) Klutz.

Shipwrecked: The Wild Game of Bidding, Bluffing, & Survival. 2000. 15.95 (978-0-9664517-6-4(7)) Out of the Box Publishing, Inc.

Shulman, Mark. Secret Hiding Places: (For Clever Kids) 2001. (Illus.). 96p. (gr. 1-4). pap. 4.95 (978-0-8069-6853-7(2)) Sterling Publishing Co., Inc.

SiegeStones. 2004. (YA). 24.95 (978-0-9764394-1-7(7) , LOG002) Live Oak Games.

Siembieda, Kevin. Rifter Number Three. Smith, Wayne & Osten, James, eds. Breaux, Wayne, Jr. et al, illus. 1998. (Rifter Ser.: Vol. 3). (YA). (gr. 8 up). pap. 7.95 (978-1-57457-013-7(7) , 103) Palladium Bks., Inc.

—Rifter Number Two. Smith, Wayne & Osten, James, eds. Breaux, Wayne, Jr. et al, illus. 1998. (Rifter Ser.: Vol. 2). 112p. (YA). (gr. 8 up). pap. 7.95 (978-1-57457-012-0(9) , 102) Palladium Bks., Inc.

—Warlords of Russia. Marciniszyn, Alex et al, eds. Perez, Ramon et al, illus. 1998. (Rifts Worldbook Ser.: Vol. 17). 224p. (YA). (gr. 8 up). pap. 20.95 (978-1-57457-010-6(2) , 832) Palladium Bks., Inc.

Siembieda, Kevin, et al. Rifter Number Nine & a Half. Smith, Wayne & Marciniszyn, Alex, eds. Johnson, Scott et al, illus. 2000. (Rifter Ser.: Vol. 9.5). 112p. (YA). (gr. 8 up). pap. 7.95 (978-1-57457-042-7(0)) Palladium Bks., Inc.

—Rifter Number Ten. Smith, Wayne, ed. Johnson, Scott et al, illus. 2000. (Rifter Ser.: Vol. 10). 112p. (YA). (gr. 8 up). pap. 7.95 (978-1-57457-039-7(0) , 110) Palladium Bks., Inc.

Sierra, Judy. Schoolyard Rhymes: Kids' Own Rhymes for Rope-Skipping, Hand Clapping, Ball Bouncing, & Just Plain Fun. Sweet, Melissa, illus. 2005. 40p. (J). (gr. 1-7). 15.95 (978-0-375-82516-3(9) , Knopf Bks. for Young Readers) Random Hse. Children's Bks.

—Schoolyard Rhymes: Kids' Own Rhymes for Rope Skipping, Hand Clapping, Ball Bouncing, & Just Plain Fun. Sweet, Melissa, illus. 2005. 40p. (J). (gr. 1-7). lib. bdg. 17.99 (978-0-375-92516-0(3) , Knopf Bks. for Young Readers) Random Hse. Children's Bks.

Sievert, Terri. Paintball. 2004. (Edge Books, X-Sports). (Illus.). 32p. (J). lib. bdg. 22.60 (978-0-7368-2711-9(0)) Capstone Pr., Inc.

Silver, Lynette. Great Kids Games. 1999. (Illus.). 112p. (gr. 3-7). pap. 12.95 (978-1-86351-233-6(0)) Milner, Sally Publishing Pty, Ltd. AUS. *Dist:* Sterling Publishing Co., Inc.

—Great Kids Games. 1999. (gr. 3-6). lib. bdg. 22.20 (978-0-613-80103-4(2)) Tandem Library Bks.

Simon & Barklee in Mexico. 2002. (Another Country Calling Ser.). 48p. (J). 7.50 (978-0-9714502-1-9(8) , Explorer Media) Simon & Barklee, Inc./ExplorerMedia.

Sklansky, Amy E. ZoomFun with Friends: 50+ Great Games, Parties, Recipes, Jokes & More from the Hit PBS TV Show. 1999. (Illus.). 64p. (J). (gr. 1-7). pap. 7.95 (978-0-316-95275-0(3)) Little Brown & Co.

—ZoomZingers: 50+ Amazing Activities from the Hit PBS TV Show. 1999. (Illus.). 64p. (J). (gr. 1-7). pap. 7.95 (978-0-316-95261-3(3)) Little Brown & Co.

Slovacek, Cindy. Trek Across America: A Game to Teach American History & Government. 2nd ed. 2001. 80p. (J). per. 15.95 net. (978-1-883055-39-4(3)) Dandy Lion Pubns.

Small, Lily B. Gems: Precious Words for Children. 1998. (Illus.). 32p. (J). pap. 9.95 (978-0-9662971-0-2(5)) Enhance Educational Services.

Smith, Elwood, illus. Jump Rope Rhymes. 1998. 48p. (YA). (gr. 4-7). spiral bd. 10.95 (978-1-57054-166-7(3)) Klutz.

Smolinski, Jill. 60 Super Simple More Travel Games. Abbett, Leo, illus. 1998. (Sixty Super Simple Ser.). 80p. (J). (gr. 3-7). pap. 6.95 (978-1-56565-918-6(X) , 09189W) Lowell Hse. Juvenile.

Snorta. 2003. mass mkt. 19.95 (978-1-932359-14-5(1)) Out of the Box Publishing, Inc.

Sobey, Edwin J. C. Just Plane Smart! Activities for Kids in the Air & on the Ground. 1998. (Illus.). 96p. (gr. 3-12). pap. 7.95 (978-0-07-059598-9(4) , 9780070595989) McGraw-Hill Cos., The.

Sokoloff, David. The New Jewish Holiday. 2003. (Illus.). 96p. pap. 6.95 (978-1-56171-949-5(8)) SPI Bks.

Solomon, Iris L. & Solomon, Ron. Friendz Pakz: Showbiz. 2003. (YA). (gr. 3 up). 4.99 (978-1-930680-06-7(6) , SSP-08SB) Swingset Pr., LLC.

Southwater Books Staff. Playschool. 2000. (Superstickers Ser.). (Illus.). 64p. (ps-2). pap. 7.95 (978-1-84215-152-5(5) , Southwater) Anness Publishing GBR. *Dist:* National Bk. Network.

—Playtime. 2000. (Superstickers Ser.). (Illus.). 64p. (ps-2). pap. 7.95 (978-1-84215-153-2(3) , Southwater) Anness Publishing GBR. *Dist:* National Bk. Network.

Southwater Staff. Outdoor Play: Look & Learn. 2000. (Look & Learn Ser.). (Illus.). 32p. (ps). 7.95 (978-1-84215-168-6(1) , Southwater) Anness Publishing GBR. *Dist:* National Bk. Network.

—Playday. 2000. (Superstickers Ser.). (Illus.). 64p. (ps-k). pap. 7.95 (978-1-84215-279-9(3) , Southwater) Anness Publishing GBR. *Dist:* National Bk. Network.

Speca, Robert. Championship Domino Toppling Set: Includes 112 Dominoes. gif. ed. 2004. (Illus.). 128p. pap. 14.95 (978-1-4027-0659-2(6)) Sterling Publishing Co., Inc.

Spiderman: Heroes & Adventures. 2005. (Illus.). (YA). (978-1-59524-044-6(6)) Giddy Up, LLC.

Spongebob Water Wow! Book. 2005. (J). per. 6.99 (978-1-59524-053-8(5)) Giddy Up, LLC.

Spooky Fun. 2002. 64p. (YA). 7.98 (978-0-7525-8692-2(0)) Parragon, Inc.

Squareman, Clarence. My Book of Indoor Games. 2006. pap. (***978-1-4068-0699-1(4)***) Echo Library.

Squint. 2002. 19.95 (978-0-9708554-6-6(X)) Out of the Box Publishing, Inc.

Squint Junior. 2002. 15.95 (978-0-9708554-7-3(8)) Out of the Box Publishing, Inc.

Stagnitti, Karen. Playthings: 101 Used for Everyday Objects. Treffry, Teresa, illus. (J). (gr. k-3). pap. (978-1-876367-61-9(X)) Wizard Bks.

Standke, Linda. Play & Learn Bible Games: 16 Reproducible Games to Help Children Grow in Their Faith. 2003. 160p. (J). per. 10.99 (978-0-88724-873-3(X)) Carson-Dellosa Publishing Co., Inc.

Staples, Edna. Wolf over the Ridge: Games We Used to Play. 2003. (Illus.). 228p. per. 15.00 (978-1-932621-16-7(4)) Open Bk. Publishing.

Stegall, Amelia. From Your Fingers to Your Toes. Im, Angel, ed. 2005. (J). 9.99 (978-0-439-74123-1(8) , Tangerine Pr.) Scholastic, Inc.

Steig, William. C D B! Steig, William, illus. 2000. (Illus.). 48p. (J). 16.95 (978-0-689-83160-7(9)) Simon & Schuster Children's Publishing.

Stein, David & Klutz Press Staff. How to Make Monstrous, Huge, Unbelievably Big Bubbles. 2005. (Illus.). 38p. (YA). (gr. 3 up). spiral bd. 16.95 (978-1-57054-257-2(0)) Klutz.

Sterling Publishing Co., Inc., ed. A Little Giant Book: Dominoes. 2007. (Illus.). 360p. (J). pap. 6.95 (***978-1-4027-4986-5(4)***) Sterling Publishing Co., Inc.

Sterling Publishing Company Staff, ed. First Learning Games. 2000. (Billy the Bear Activity Bks.). (Illus.). 16p. (ps-k). pap. 3.95 (978-0-8069-5595-7(3)) Sterling Publishing Co., Inc.

—First Thinking Games. 2000. (Billy the Bear Activity Bks.). (Illus.). 16p. (J). (ps-k). pap. 3.95 (978-0-8069-5597-1(X)) Sterling Publishing Co., Inc.

—First Writing Games. 2000. (Billy the Bear Activity Bks.). (Illus.). 16p. (J). (ps-k). pap. 3.95 (978-0-8069-5593-3(7)) Sterling Publishing Co., Inc.

Stern, Leonard & Price, Roger. Go, Diego, Go! Mad Libs Junior. 2007. 48p. (J). pap. 3.99 (978-0-8431-2136-0(X) , Price Stern Sloan) Penguin Group (USA) Inc.

—The Mad Libs Worst-Case Scenario Survival Handbook 2, Vol. 2. 2004. (Mad Libs Ser.). 48p. (J). mass mkt. 3.99 (978-0-8431-1063-0(5) , Price Stern Sloan) Penguin Group (USA) Inc.

—Shrek the Third Mad Libs. 2007. (Mad Libs Ser.). 48p. (J). (gr. 3). pap. 3.99 (978-0-8431-2134-6(3) , Price Stern Sloan) Penguin Group (USA) Inc.

Stern, Leonard, et al. Summer Camp Mad Libs Junior. 2005. 48p. (J). (gr. k-3). mass mkt. 3.99 (978-0-8431-1363-1(4) , Price Stern Sloan) Penguin Group (USA) Inc.

Stetson, Emily & Congdon, Vicky. Little Hands Fingerplays & Action Songs: Seasonal Rhymes & Creative Play for 2 to 6 Year-Olds. Day, Betsy, illus. 2001. (Little Hands Bks.). 128p. (J). (ps-3). pap. 12.95 (978-1-885593-53-5(8) , Williamson Bks.) Ideals Pubns.

Stevens, Beth Dvergsten. Games Galore! 2001. (Cover-To-Cover Books). (Illus.). (J). 64p. pap. (978-0-7891-5429-3(3)); 56p. (gr. 1-4). lib. bdg. 16.95 (978-0-7569-0077-9(8)) Perfection Learning Corp.

Stott, Dorothy. Big Book of Games. 2000. 64p. (J). pap. 5.99 (978-0-14-038470-3(7) , Puffin) Penguin Group (USA) Inc.

Strang Communications Company Staff, ed. Ages 2-3 Activities: Summer 2002. 2002. (J). pap., act. bk. ed. 3.29 (978-1-57405-956-4(4)) CharismaLife Pubs.

—Grades 1-2 Activities: Spring 2002. 2002. (J). (gr. 1-2). pap., act. bk. ed. 3.29 (978-1-57405-934-2(3)) CharismaLife Pubs.

—Grades 1-2 Activities: Summer 2002. 2002. (J). (gr. 1-2). pap., act. bk. ed. 3.29 (978-1-57405-972-4(6)) CharismaLife Pubs.

—Kidz Chat: Summer 2002. 2002. (J). pap. 14.99 (978-1-57405-979-3(3)) CharismaLife Pubs.

—Live Wire: Spring 2002. 2002. (J). pap. 14.99 (978-1-57405-927-4(0)) CharismaLife Pubs.

—Live Wire: Summer 2002. 2002. (J). pap. 14.99 (978-1-57405-965-6(3)) CharismaLife Pubs.

Strawberry Shortcake Old Maid. 2005. (J). 2.95 (***978-1-59545-001-2(7)***) Learning Horizons, Inc.

Sullivan, Carolyn Rose, illus. The Music Box: Songs, Rhymes, & Games for Young Children, 1 box. 2006. 200p. (J). 49.95 (978-0-9772717-1-9(4)) ELZ Publishing.

Taggar, Sam. Great Games: Old & New, Indoor-Outdoor, Board, Card, Ball, & Word. 2004. (Kids Can Bks.). (Illus.). 128p. (J). (gr. 2-9). pap. 12.95 (978-1-885593-72-6(4) , Williamson Bks.) Ideals Pubns.

Takemiya, Masaki. Imagination of a Go Master: Logic-Shattering Cosmic Style. Bianchi, Leslie, ed. Terry, Robert J., tr. 2004. (Illus.). 222p. spiral bd. 23.95 (978-0-9713230-0-1(3) , 323003) NEMESIS Enterprises.

Tallarico. Block Book. (J). 15.95 (978-0-89828-375-4(2)) Penguin Group (USA) Inc.

Tallarico, Tony. Blocks: Block Book. (J). (978-0-89828-377-8(9)) Penguin Group (USA) Inc.

Taylor, Jody, illus. Hidden Pictures 2006-#1. 2006. 48p. (J). pap. 5.95 (978-1-59078-391-7(3)) Boyds Mills Pr.

—Hidden Pictures 2006-#2. 2006. 48p. (J). pap. 5.95 (978-1-59078-392-4(1)) Boyds Mills Pr.

—Hidden Pictures 2006-#3. 2006. 48p. (J). pap. 5.95 (978-1-59078-393-1(X)) Boyds Mills Pr.

—Hidden Pictures 2006-#4. 2006. 48p. (J). pap. 5.95 (978-1-59078-394-8(8)) Boyds Mills Pr.

Taylor, Michael. Now You See It... Bk. 2: String Games & Stories. 2002. (Storytelling Ser.). (Illus.). 128p. pap. 16.95 (978-1-903458-21-1(8)) Hawthorn Pr. GBR. *Dist:* SteinerBooks, Inc.

Teora, ed. Activity & Game BK. 2004. 96p. Vol. 1. pap. 7.95 (978-1-59496-030-7(5)); Vol. 2. pap. 7.95 (978-1-59496-031-4(3)); Vol. 3. pap. 7.95 (978-1-59496-004-8(6)); Vol. 4. pap. 7.95 (978-1-59496-005-5(4)) Teora USA LLC.

—Amazing Games. 2005. 108p. pap. 7.95 (978-1-59496-007-9(0)) Teora USA LLC.

—400 Funny Games for Smart Kids. 2005. 136p. pap. 7.95 (978-1-59496-008-6(9)) Teora USA LLC.

—500 Games for Smart Kids. 2005. 112p. pap. 7.95 (978-1-59496-006-2(2)) Teora USA LLC.

Theisen, Michael. Ready-to-Go Game Shows (That Teach Serious Stuff) Bible Edition. 2003. (Illus.). 128p. (YA). pap. 24.95 (978-0-88489-689-0(7)) St. Mary's Pr.

—Ready-to-Go Game Shows (That Teach Serious Stuff) Catholic Teachings & Practices Edition. 2003. (Illus.). 144p. (YA). 19.95 (978-0-88489-757-6(5)) St. Mary's Pr.

Thomas, Mack. Fun & Games in Colonial America. 2002. (Welcome Bks.). (Illus.). 24p. (J). (ps-2). pap. 4.95 (978-0-516-23492-2(7) , Children's Pr.) Scholastic Library Publishing.

Thomas, Mark. Fun & Games in Colonial America. 2002. (Welcome Books). (Illus.). 24p. (J). (ps-2). 18.00 (978-0-516-23935-4(X) , Children's Pr.) Scholastic Library Publishing.

—Fun & Games in Colonial America. 2002. (gr. k-3). lib. bdg. 12.95 (978-0-613-58774-7(X)) Tandem Library Bks.

Thomson, Dave, ed. The Pool Hustler's Handbook: The Fifty Best Billiard Brain Teasers. Pauchon, Sebastien, illus. 2001. 128p. (YA). pap. 14.95 (978-0-9716026-0-1(3)) Tricks of the Trade, Inc.

Time for Bible Puzzles & Games. (Illus.). 32p. (YA). (gr. 5 up). pap. 2.25 (978-0-87162-662-2(4) , E9705) Warner Pr. Pubs.

Timothy's Special Delivery. 2002. (Let's Start! Play Alongs Ser.). 32p. (J). (ps-1). 15.95 (978-1-57145-696-0(1) , Silver Dolphin Bks.) Advantage Pubs. Group.

Titus, David. Native Alaskan String Figures. 2007. (Illus.). 32p. (J). 5.99 (***978-0-9744562-7-0(6)***) WRDSMTH Productions.

Top That Publishing Staff, ed. Rude Cocktails. 2004. 48p. pap. (978-1-84510-215-9(0)) Top That! Publishing PLC.

—Sidewalk Chalks. 2004. (Creative Studios Ser.). (Illus.). 48p. (J). (978-1-84510-250-0(9)) Top That! Publishing PLC.

—Strip Poker. 2004. (Naughty Shenanigans Ser.). (Illus.). 48p. (978-1-84510-214-2(2)) Top That! Publishing PLC.

Touch & Feel Playtime. braille ed. 2004. (J). (ps up). bds. (978-0-616-14614-9(0)) Canadian National Institute for the Blind/Institut National Canadien pour les Aveugles.

Trago Publishing Staff. The Dinosaur Travel Kit. 1999. (My Art Ser.). 35p. (J). (ps-3). pap. 4.95 (978-0-9683883-5-8(3)) Sterling Publishing Co., Inc.

Tremaine, Jon. Backgammon. 2002. 64p. (J). pap. 9.98 (978-0-7525-5968-1(0)) Parragon, Inc.

Trimble, Richard M. Dice & Spinners. 2001. 32p. (J). (gr. k-7). pap. 12.00 (978-1-871098-34-1(3)) Claire Pubns. GBR. *Dist:* Parkwest Pubns., Inc.

Tronick, Ed, contrib. by. Learn, Practice & Play Set: Different or Same. (Home Learning Tools(R) Ser.). 32p. (J). pap. 3.99 (978-1-4037-0777-2(4)) Dalmatian Pr.

Tully, M. Richard. A Brief Discourse on 18th-Century Games. 2002. 3.50 (978-1-893832-06-0(6)) Ballindalloch Pr.

Turner, Dona, illus. The Itsy Bitsy Spider. 1999. 20p. (J). reprint ed. 16.95 (978-1-892374-29-5(3)) Weldon Owen, Inc.

Tutankhamen. 2003. mass mkt. 9.95 (978-1-932359-07-7(9)) Out of the Box Publishing, Inc.

Tuttle, Cheryl Gerson & Paquette, Penny Hutchins. Thinking Games for Kids. 3rd rev. ed. 2005. 208p. pap. 12.95 (978-0-07-145542-8(6) , 9780071455428) McGraw-Hill Cos., The.

Tuxworth, Nicola. Mix & Match, 12 vols. 2006. (Learn-A-Word Picture Bks.). (Illus.). 12p. bds. 6.99 (978-0-7548-1465-8(3) , Lorenz Bks.) Anness Publishing GBR. *Dist:* National Bk. Network.

—Peek-a-Boo: A Very First Picture Book. 2000. (Illus.). 12p. bds. 4.95 (978-0-7548-0064-4(4)) Anness Publishing, Inc.

Tyler, Jenny. Duck's Bathtime. 2005. (Illus.). 4p. (J). (ps-ps). vinyl bd. 7.95 (978-0-7945-0570-7(8) , Usborne) EDC Publishing.

Tynes, Rick & Whittemore, Diane. Monster Dot-to-Dot. 2003. (Illus.). 80p. (J). pap. 5.95 (978-1-4027-0298-3(1)) Sterling Publishing Co., Inc.

The Ultimate Alphabet Games & Puzzles Workbook. 2002. (Illus.). 158p. (J). (gr. k-1). wbk. ed. 4.97 (978-1-57759-125-2(9)) Dalmatian Pr

Unisystem Staff. Eden Studios Presents, Vol. 3. 2005. 69p. (YA). pap. 15.00 (978-1-891153-64-8(1)) Eden Studios, Inc.

United States Bingo. 2005. (J). pap. (978-1-59461-069-1(X)) eeBoo Corp.

University Games Staff. Made You Laugh for Kids! Books So Fun You'll Pee Your Pants! 2005. (Illus.). 224p. (J). (ps-3). pap. 14.95 (978-1-57528-995-3(4)) University Games.

University Games Staff, compiled by. i-Ballers: Secrret Messages. 2004. 48p. pap. (978-1-57528-954-0(7)) University Games.

Van Rynbach, Iris. Pilgrim House Sticker Activity Book. 2003. (Dover Little Activity Bks.). (Illus.). 4p. (J). 1.50 (978-0-486-42628-0(9)) Dover Pubns., Inc.

Vandawalker, Marianne. Character Fun Box: 20 Character Building Games & Activities. 1999. 32p. (J). (gr. 3-7). pap. 26.95 (978-1-57543-074-4(6)) MAR*CO Products, Inc.

Vargas, Pat & Herrera, Sharon. Character Card Games & Activities. Norcross, Harry, illus. 2001. 32p. (J). (gr. 2-5). pap. 12.95 (978-1-57543-093-5(2)) MAR*CO Products, Inc.

Vecchione, Glen. Kids' Games. 2007. (Illus.). 360p. (J). pap. 6.95 (***978-1-4027-4989-6(9)***) Sterling Publishing Co., Inc.

Vecchione, Glen. Sidewalk Games. Sims, Blanche, illus. 2005. 80p. pap. 7.95 (978-1-4027-2240-0(0)) Sterling Publishing Co., Inc.

Vietro, Lee. Letter Hunt. Delice, Shelly Meredith, illus. 2003. (Memory Match Game Ser.). 10p. (J). (ps-2). bds. 9.99 (978-1-58476-205-8(5)) Innovative Kids.

Vincent, Cindy. The Mystery of the Haunted Mansion. 2002. (Daisy Diamond Detective Ser.: Vol. 3). pap. 24.97 (978-1-932169-17-1(2)) Mysteries by Vincent, LLC.

—The Mystery of the Missing Necklace. 2001. (Daisy Diamond Detective Ser.: Vol. 1). 24.97 (978-1-932169-13-3(X)) Mysteries by Vincent, LLC.

—The Time Machine Mystery. 2001. (Daisy Diamond Detective Ser.: Vol. 2). pap. 24.97 (978-1-932169-14-0(8)) Mysteries by Vincent, LLC.

Viverito, Philip J., et al. Classical Hack Second Edition: Ancient Warfare 600 B. C. to 600 A. D. Cholewa, Thomas H., ed. Connolly, Peter, illus. 2nd exp. ed. 2002. 38p. 24.00 (978-1-889584-07-2(X) , 011802) LMW Works.

Volke, Gordon, et al, illus. Panda Patrol Big Activity Book. 2004. 24p. 6.00 (978-1-84161-111-2(5)) Ravette Publishing, Ltd. GBR. *Dist:* Parkwest Pubns., Inc.

—Panda Patrol Travel Games with Stickers. 2004. 16p. pap., act. bk. ed. 6.00 (978-1-84161-110-5(7)) Ravette Publishing, Ltd. GBR. *Dist:* Parkwest Pubns., Inc.

Wade, Lee. The Cheerios Animal Play Book. Wade, Lee, illus. 1999. (Illus.). 14p. (J). bds. 7.99 (978-0-689-83014-3(9) , Little Simon) Simon & Schuster Children's Publishing.

Wade, Mary Dodson. Fun Facts & Games: Massachusetts. Roader, Virginia, illus. 2000. (Fun Facts & Games Ser.). 64p. (J). (gr. 1-5). pap. 5.95 (978-1-892920-47-8(6)) GHB Publishers, LLC.

—Fun Facts & Games: Texas. Roeder, Virginia M., illus. 2000. (Fun Facts & Games Ser.). 64p. (J). (ps-3). pap. 5.95 (978-1-892920-23-2(9)) GHB Publishers, LLC.

Wai, Joan. 100+ Baby Shower Games. 2006. (100+ Ser.). (Illus.). 128p. pap. 14.00 (978-0-9728354-1-1(5)) Brainstorm Co., The.

Walker, Niki & Dann, Sarah. Badminton in Action. 2003. (Sports in Action Ser.). (Illus.). 32p. (J). (gr. 1-4). (978-0-7787-0334-1(7)); pap. (978-0-7787-0354-9(1)) Crabtree Publishing Co.

Wallace, Paula S. The World of Sports. 2003. (Life Around the World Ser.). (Illus.). 48p. (J). (gr. 2 up). lib. bdg. 24.67 (978-0-8368-3662-2(6)) Stevens, Gareth Inc.

Walton, Rick. The Book of Treasure Hunts: Ready-to-Cut Clues for 40 Hide-and-Seek Games. 2008. (Illus.). 64p. (J). pap. 12.95 (978-1-933317-59-5(0)) Silverleaf Pr.

Ward, Beck & Nicholson, Sue, eds. Play & Learn. Giraffe, Red, illus. 2002. (My First Write & Wipe Ser.). 26p. (J). (ps-k). 14.95 (978-1-57145-726-4(7) , Silver Dolphin Bks.) Advantage Pubs. Group.

Warmachine: Escalation. 2004. (YA). per. 34.99 (978-0-9706970-8-0(2) , PIP 1002) Privateer Pr., Inc.

Warmachine: Prime. (YA). 2004. (GER.). 224p. per. (978-0-9706970-9-7(0)); 2003. 200p. per. 19.99 (978-0-9706970-7-3(4)) Privateer Pr., Inc.

Warner Brothers Staff. Creatures of the Forbidden Forest: A Search & Find with Keepsake Keychain. 1998. (Quest for Camelot Ser.). (Illus.). (J). pap. 5.98 (978-0-590-02437-2(X)) Scholastic, Inc.

Warshaw, Hallie & Brown, Julie. Get Out! Outdoor Activities Kids Can Enjoy Anywhere (Except Indoors) 2003. (Illus.). 128p. pap. 9.95 (978-1-4027-0169-6(1)) Sterling Publishing Co., Inc.

Waschak, Jay, et al. Wars of the Boltians & Kuissians. Watson, Travis & Lohr, Tyrel, illus. 2004. per. 25.00 (978-0-9764048-1-1(8)) Victory by Any Means Games.

Waters, J. Tic Tac ABC. 2002. (Illus.). 16p. (J). (gr. 1-5). pap. (978-1-57579-253-8(2)) Pine Hill Pr., Inc.

Webb, Phila H. & Corby, Jane. The Little Book of Hand Shadows. 2001. (Miniature Editions Ser.). (Illus.). 80p. (J). (ps-3). 4.95 (978-0-89471-852-6(5) , Running Pr. Minature Editions) Running Pr. Bk. Pubs.

Webber, Sharon & Bradburn, Ryan, concepts. Holiday & Seasonal Chipper Chat. 2007. (J). 59.95 (***978-1-58650-789-3(3)***) Super Duper Pubns.

Weber, Bruce. You Can Yo-Yo! 25 Tricks to Try. 1999. (J). 7.95 (978-0-439-08828-2(3)) Scholastic, Inc.

—You Can Yo-Yo! Twenty-Five Tricks to Try. 1998. (Illus.). 48p. (J). (gr. 3-7). pap. 4.50 (978-0-590-81294-8(7)) Scholastic, Inc.

Weber, Lou. Elmo Loves Words Active Point. 2006. 24p. (J). 19.98 (978-1-4127-3173-7(9) , 7232900) Publications International, Ltd.

Weber, Lou, ed. Little People on the Farm My First Look & Find. 2005. 18p. (J). bds. 7.98 (978-1-4127-3315-1(4) , 7241600) Publications International, Ltd.

Wee Sing Staff. Games, Games, Games. (J). 7.98 incl. audio NewSound, LLC.

Weedin, Chris. Horror Worlds. 2006. (Illus.). 107p. (YA). (gr. 5 up). per. 17.99 (978-0-9778263-0-8(9)) Crucifiction Games.

Wells, H. G. Little Wars & Floor Games (A companion piece to Little Wars) 2006. 56p. pap. (978-1-84637-799-0(4)) Echo Library.

Western New York Trivia Quotient. 7.95 (978-0-9620314-0-3(2)) Western New York Wares, Inc.

Whad Ya Know? 2003. mass mkt. 19.95 (978-1-932359-02-2(8)) Out of the Box Publishing, Inc.

What's Next? A First Sequencing Game. 2003. (Illus.). (J). pap. 12.99 (978-0-7424-1519-5(8)) School Specialty Publishing.

Wheedle. 2002. 9.95 (978-0-9716729-1-8(1)) Out of the Box Publishing, Inc.

Whisp, Kennilworthy, pseud & Scamander, Newt. Harry Potter Schoolbooks: Quidditch Through the Ages & Fantastic Beasts & Where to Find Them, 2 vols., Set. braille ed. 2001. (Harry Potter Ser.). (YA). (gr. 3 up). pap. 8.00 (978-0-939173-47-1(6)) National Braille Pr.

Whitmore, John. Piximon's Training Ground. 2001. (Digimon Ser.: No. 8). 96p. (J). (gr. 1-6). pap. 4.50 (978-0-06-107205-5(2) , Harper Entertainment) HarperCollins Pubs.

Whose Baby Are You? 2003. (Science Card Games Ser.). (gr. k-1). 9.99 (978-0-7682-1973-9(6) , J53001) School Specialty Publishing.

Wilcox, Charlotte. Games & Leisure in Colonial America. 2004. (Everyday Life Long Ago Ser.). (J). (978-0-7368-2162-9(7) , Blue Earth Bks.) Capstone Pr., Inc.

WildSide! 2003. mass mkt. 9.95 (978-1-932359-05-3(2)) Out of the Box Publishing, Inc.

Williams, Archibald. Things to Make. 2006. 42.99 (***978-1-4280-2644-5(4)***) IndyPublish.com.

Williams, Carol Lynch. Every Kid Needs New Checkerboard Games. 2007. (Illus.). 64p. (J). pap. 19.95 (978-1-4236-0011-4(8)) Gibbs Smith, Publisher.

Windham, Ryder. Star Wars: Episode I: Adventures. 1999. 108p. (J). (978-0-439-12987-9(7)) Scholastic, Inc.

Witkowski, Teri, ed. The American Girls Pencil Play. 2004. (American Girls Collection(R) Ser.). (Illus.). 64p. (J). pap. 5.95 (978-1-58485-866-9(4)) American Girl Publishing, Inc.

Wood, Sharron. Baby Shower Games. Imasa-Stukuls, Maybelle, illus. 2007. 254p. 12.95 (978-0-8118-5677-5(1)) Chronicle Bks. LLC.

Woolsey, M. Lynn. Target Practice. 1998. 108p. (YA). (gr. 7-12). stu. ed., spiral bd. 29.00 (978-1-884362-30-9(3)) Butte Pubns., Inc.

Word Puzzles & Games. 2002. (Home Workbooks Ser.). 64p. pap. 2.49 (978-0-88724-736-1(9) , CD-4538) Carson-Dellosa Publishing Co., Inc.

Word Puzzles & Games: CD-4525. 2002. (Learning Fun for Little Ones Ser.). 64p. pap. 2.49 (978-0-88724-723-1(7)) Carson-Dellosa Publishing Co., Inc.

Wujcik, Erick. After the Bomb Rpg. Marciniszyn, Alex & Siembieda, Kevin, eds. Laird, Peter, illus. 2001. 48p. (Orig.). (YA). (gr. 8 up). pap. 20.95 (978-0-916211-15-8(0) , 503) Palladium Bks., Inc.

Young, Ian. X Games: Action Sports Grab the Spotlight, 6 vols. (gr. 4 up). 49.95 (978-0-7368-9535-4(3) , High Five) Red Brick Learning.

Young, Judy. Lazy Days of Summer. O'Malley, Kathy, illus. rev. ed. 2007. 32p. (J). (gr. 3-6). 15.95 (978-1-58536-241-7(7)) Sleeping Bear Pr.

Younie, Bradford. Now Playing: Roleplaying in Every TV Genre, 2004. (Illus.). 224p. (YA). 35.00 (978-0-9749150-0-5(9) , CAR1000) Carnivore Games.

Zaslavsky, Claudia. More Math Games & Activities from Around the World. 2003. 160p. (J). pap. 14.95 (978-1-55652-501-8(X)) Chicago Review Pr., Inc.

—More Math Games & Activities from Around the World. 2003. (gr. 7-12). lib. bdg. 24.55 (978-0-613-70817-3(2)) Tandem Library Bks.

Zellnik, Miriam. Barrel of Monkeys. 2002. (Illus.). 32p. (J). pap. 19.95 (978-0-7624-1331-7(X)) Running Pr. Bk. Pubs.

Zoom Travel Games & Activities. 2004. (J). (gr. 2-6). 1.99 (978-0-8066-4979-5(8)); (ps-1). 1.99 (978-0-8066-4975-7(5)) Augsburg Fortress, Pubs.

10 Days in Africa. 2003. mass mkt. 19.95 (978-1-932359-08-4(7)) Out of the Box Publishing, Inc.

10 Days in the USA. 2003. mass mkt. 19.95 (978-1-932359-09-1(5)) Out of the Box Publishing, Inc.

101 after School Activities. 2003. (Illus.). 72p. per. (978-0-7853-9333-7(1)) Publications International, Ltd.

300 Wishes Game: Wish Big. Share Dreams. Friends Forever. 2005. (American Girl Library). (Illus.) (J). (gr. 3). 24.99 (978-1-59369-063-2(0) , American Girl) American Girl Publishing, Inc.

1000 Games for Smart Kids. 2004. (Illus.). 384p. (J). pap. 14.95 (978-1-59496-001-7(1)) Teora USA LLC.

43 Degrees North LLC Staff. Tailgate Trivia National Parks, 2003. (Illus.). 60p. (YA). ring bd. 6.99 (978-0-9744444-0-6(5)) 43 Degrees North LLC.

GAMES—FICTION

Agard, John & Paul, Korky. Brer Rabbit & the Great Tug-O-War. 1998. (Illus.). 32p. (J). (ps-2). 13.95 (978-0-7641-5077-1(4)) Barron's Educational Series, Inc.

Albee, Sarah. Blue's Opposites Game. Style Guide Staff, illus. 2006. (Blue's Clues Ser.). 26p. (J). bds. 5.99 (978-1-4169-0663-6(0) , Simon Spotlight/Nickelodeon) Simon & Schuster Children's Publishing.

Allosso, Dan. Outside the Box. 2007. 148p. 21.95 (***978-0-595-68621-6(4)***); per. 11.95 (***978-0-595-44295-9(1)***) iUniverse, Inc.

Amery, H. & Cartwright, S. The Tournament. 2004. (First Stories Ser.). 16p. (J). pap. 4.95 (978-0-7945-0520-2(1)); lib. bdg. 12.95 (978-1-58086-571-5(2)) EDC Publishing.

Anastasio, Dina. The la tortuga magica & Magic Turtle. 2005. spiral bd. 66.00 (***978-1-4108-5650-0(X)***) Benchmark Education Co.

Anderson, M. T. The Game of Sunken Places. (J). 2004. 272p. pap. 16.95 (978-0-439-41660-3(4)); 2005. 288p. reprint ed. pap. 5.99 (978-0-439-41661-0(2) , Scholastic Paperbacks) Scholastic, Inc.

—The Game of Sunken Places. l.t. ed. 2004. 331p. 23.95 (978-0-7862-7064-4(0) , Large Print Pr.) Thorndike Pr.

Arena, Felice & Kettle, Phil. Battle of the Games. Gordon, Gus, illus. 2004. (J). pap. (978-1-59336-372-7(9)) Mondo Publishing.

Axelrod, Amy. Pigs at Odds: Fun with Math & Games. McGinley-Nally, Sharon, illus. 2000. 40p. (J). (gr. 2-4). 15.95 (978-0-689-81566-9(2)) Simon & Schuster Children's Publishing.

—Pigs at Odds: Fun with Math & Games. 2003. (gr. k-3). lib. bdg. 15.30 (978-0-613-67156-9(2)) Tandem Library Bks.

Axelrod, Amy & McGinley-Nally, Sharon. Pigs at Odds. 2003. (Illus.). 40p. (J). pap. 6.99 (978-0-689-86144-4(3) , Aladdin) Simon & Schuster Children's Publishing.

Baker, Alan. Los Conejitos Aprenden los Numeros. 2003. (Little Rabbit Bks.). (SPA.). 32p. (J). (ps-k). pap. 4.95 (978-0-7534-5595-1(1) , Kingfisher) Houghton Mifflin Co. Trade & Reference Div.

Barbour, Ralph Henry. Left Tackle Thayer. 2007. 196p. pap. 11.99 (***978-1-4264-7077-6(0)***); 216p. pap. 15.99 (***978-1-4264-7153-7(X)***) BiblioBazaar.

—Left Tackle Thayer. 2006. pap. 72.99 (***978-1-4280-1193-9(5)***) IndyPublish.com.

Bauer, Joan. Sticks. 2002. 192p. (YA). 18.99 (978-0-399-23752-2(6) , Putnam Juvenile) Penguin Group (USA) Inc.

Beckwith, Kathy. Playing War. Lyons, Lea, illus. 2005. 32p. (J). (gr. 3-6). 16.95 (978-0-88448-267-3(7)) Tilbury Hse. Pubs.

Bentley, Dawn. The Big Race: A Pop-Up Race Track with 2 Wind-Up Race Cars. Welply, Michael, illus. 1999. (J). (ps-3). 16.95 (978-1-58117-038-2(6) , Intervisual/Piggy Toes) Dalmatian Pr.

Berenstain, Stan & Berenstain, Jan. The Berenstain Bears Play T-Ball. Berenstain, Stan & Berenstain, Jan, illus. Berenstain, Michael, illus. 2005. (Berenstain Bears Ser.). 32p. (J). (gr. k-3). 15.99 (978-0-06-058337-8(1)); pap. 3.99 (978-0-06-058338-5(X)) HarperCollins Pubs.

Bishop, Jane, et al. The Amazing Museum Adventure of Thomas Maxim Moore. 2000. (Illus.). 112p. (J). pap. 12.00 (978-1-57921-268-1(9)) WinePress Publishing.

Blackaby, Susan. Juanita Juega. Cole, Mernie Gallagher, illus. 2006. (Read-It! Readers en Espanol Ser.).Tr. of Jen Plays. (SPA.). 32p. (J). (ps-3). 19.95 (978-1-4048-1652-7(6)) Picture Window Bks.

—Pat Picks Up. Haugen, Ryan, illus. 2005. (Read-It! Readers Ser.). 32p. (C). (gr. k-3). 18.60 (978-1-4048-1059-4(5)) Picture Window Bks.

Bloom, Suzanne. Treasure. 2007. (Illus.). 32p. (J). (ps-1). 15.95 (***978-1-59078-457-0(X)***) Boyds Mills Pr.

Braybrooks, Ann. Tiggers Hate to Lose. 1999. (Winnie the Pooh First Readers Ser.: No. 8). (Illus.). 40p. (J). (gr. k-3). pap. 3.99 (978-0-7868-4266-7(0)) Disney Pr.

Brooke, Susan Rich, adapted by. Finding Nemo. 2003. (Interactive Play-A-Sound Ser.). (Illus.). (J). (978-0-7853-8916-3(4)); 24p. 15.98 (978-0-7853-8420-5(0) , 7184400) Publications International, Ltd.

Brouillet, Chrystine. The Chinese Puzzle. Gaboriau, Linda, tr. Gagnon, Nathalie, illus. 1998. 116p. (J). (gr. 3-7). pap. 6.95 (978-0-921556-60-2(8)) Ragweed Pr. CAN. *Dist:* Univ. of Toronto Pr.

Bryant-Mole, Karen & Tyler, Jenny. Dot-to-Dot Book: Combined Volume. Round, Graham, illus. 2004. (Dot to Dot Ser.). 168p. (J). pap. 12.95 (978-0-7945-0699-5(2) , Usborne) EDC Publishing.

Bury, Laurie D. The Adventures of Dalbert Juan: Playing Hide & Seek. Gallo, Karen A., illus. 2000. 30p. (J). (ps-2). 12.95 (978-0-9702319-0-1(3)) Rhette Enterprises, Inc.

Campbell, Joanna. Derby Day. 1999. (gr. 3-6). lib. bdg. 12.40 (978-0-613-21428-5(5)) Tandem Library Bks.

Carman, Debby. Kittywimpuss, Got Game. 2006. (J). (978-0-9777340-4-7(8)) Faux Paw Media Group.

Castle, Kathryn. Games Rule. Ramirez, Michael, illus. 1998. (Think-Kids Book Collection). 16p. (J). (gr. 1-4). pap. 2.95 (978-1-58237-020-0(6)) Creative Thinkers, Inc.

—Reglas para Juegos. Alvarado, Ana María, tr. Ramirez, Michael, illus. 2000. (Think-Kids Book Collection).Tr. of Games Rule. (SPA.). 16p. (J). pap. 2.95 (978-1-58237-047-7(8)) Creative Thinkers, Inc.

Child, Lauren, illus. I've Won, No I've Won, No I've Won. 2006. (Charlie & Lola Ser.). 32p. (J). (ps-2). pap. 5.99 (978-0-448-44350-8(3) , Grosset & Dunlap) Penguin Group (USA) Inc.

Childs, Rob. Big Prize. 2000. (Illus.). 99p. (J). pap. 7.99 (978-0-552-52823-8(4)) Transworld Publishers Ltd. GBR. *Dist:* Independent Pubs. Group.

Christenson, Lisa. Harley Hippo & the Crane Game. Christenson, Lisa, illus. 2005. (J). per. (978-0-9725311-0-8(6)) Pickled Eggs Pr.

Clean up Game & the Adventures Book. 1999. (J). 4.99 (978-0-689-83053-2(X) , Simon & Schuster Children's Publishing) Simon & Schuster Children's Publishing.

Colfer, Eoin. Benny & Babe. 2007. 288p. (gr. 5-17). 18.95 (***978-1-4231-0283-0(5)***); pap. 7.95 (***978-1-4231-0284-7(3)***) Miramax Bks.

Cooney, Caroline B., et al. Freeze Tag. 2004. 176p. (J). (gr. 6 up). pap. 5.99 (978-0-590-45681-4(4)) Scholastic, Inc.

Curriculum Corporation. Tai Hao Le! 2005. pap. 79.95 incl. audio compact disk (978-1-86366-402-8(5)) Curriculum Corporation AUS. *Dist:* Cheng & Tsui Co.

Dadey, Debbie. The Slime Wars. Basso, Bill, illus. 2003. 80p. (J). 3.99 (978-0-439-42442-4(9)) Scholastic, Inc.

—The Slime Wars. 2003. (gr. k-3). lib. bdg. 11.80 (978-0-613-65059-5(X)) Tandem Library Bks.

Disney Publishing Staff. A Sense of Fun, 15 vols. 2003. (It's Fun to Learn Ser.). (Illus.). 32p. (J). (ps-3). 3.99 (978-1-57973-140-3(6)) Advance Pubs. LLC.

Disney Staff. Toy Story 2: Pull-Out Posters & Game Card. 2000. (Toy Story 2 Ser.). (Illus.). 32p. (J). (ps-3). pap. 7.99 (978-0-7364-0229-3(2) , RH/Disney) Random Hse. Children's Bks.

Dixon, Franklin W. Warehouse Rumble. 2004. (Hardy Boys Ser.). (Illus.). 160p. (J). pap. 4.99 (978-0-689-86455-1(8) , Aladdin) Simon & Schuster Children's Publishing.

Dolby, Karen. Dragon in the Cupboard. 2004. (Young Puzzle Adventures Ser.). 32p. (J). (gr. 2 up). pap. 4.95 (978-0-7945-0232-4(6)); lib. bdg. 12.95 (978-1-58086-461-9(9)) EDC Publishing.

Durant, Alan. Gamer. Mason, Sue, illus. 2008. (J). pap. (***978-1-59889-908-5(2)***); lib. bdg. (***978-1-59889-872-9(8)***) Stone Arch Bks.

E F G

—Gamer: Next Level. Mason, Sue, illus. 2008. (J). pap. (*978-1-59889-909-2(0)); lib. bdg. (*978-1-59889-873-6(6)) Stone Arch Bks.

Duvall, Deborah L. Rabbit Goes to Kansas. 2007. (Illus.). 32p. (J). (gr. 1 up). 16.95 (*978-0-8263-4181-5(0)) Univ. of New Mexico Pr.

Ebl, Donna. The Adventures of Salamander Sam. 2004. (J). pap. 9.00 (978-0-8059-6165-2(8)) Dorrance Publishing Co., Inc.

Einhorn, Edward. A Very Improbable Story. Gustavson, Adam, illus. 2007. (J). (*978-1-57091-871-1(6)); pap. (*978-1-57091-872-8(4)) Charlesbridge Publishing, Inc.

Erlings, Fridrik. Benjamin Dove. 2007. 224p. (YA). (gr. 5-9). pap. 7.95 (*978-0-7358-2149-1(6)) North-South Bks., Inc.

Feldman, Jody. The Gollywhopper Games. Jamieson, Victoria, illus. 2008. 336p. (J). 16.99 (*978-0-06-121450-9(7)); lib. bdg. 17.89 (*978-0-06-121451-6(5)) HarperCollins Pubs. (Greenwillow Bks.).

Flam, Chanie. Make Believe. (Goldie Gold Board Book Ser.: Vol. 3). (Illus.). (J). (ps-1). bds. 4.95 (978-1-58330-027-5(9)) Feldheim Pubs.

Fletcher, Ralph J. Tommy Trouble & the Magic Marble. Caldwell, Benjamin H., Jr., illus. rev. ed. 2000. 64p. (J). (gr. 2-5). 16.00 (978-0-8050-6387-5(0) , Holt, Henry & Co. Bks. For Young Readers) Holt, Henry & Co.

Foon, Dennis. Double or Nothing. 2000. 144p. (YA). (gr. 7 up). 17.95 (978-1-55037-627-2(6)); pap. 6.95 (978-1-55037-626-5(8)) Annick Pr., Ltd. CAN. Dist: Firefly Bks., Ltd.

—Double or Nothing. 2000. (gr. 7-12). lib. bdg. 15.25 (978-0-613-51820-8(9)) Tandem Library Bks.

Frantz, Jennifer. Hide-and-Seek: My Little Pony. Thompson Brothers Staff, illus. 2005. (Festival Reader Ser.). 24p. (J). (ps-1). pap. 3.99 (978-0-06-073270-7(9) , Harper Festival) HarperCollins Pubs.

Freeze Tag: Individual Title Six-Packs. (ps-2). 27.00 (978-0-7635-9449-7(0)) Rigby Education.

Freisleben, Verena. Boing. 2000. (Illus.). 28p. (J). 14.50 (978-1-84059-226-9(5)) Milet Publishing.

Fuchs, Menucha. Hide & Go Sleep. 2004. (Illus.). 20p. (J). 6.95 (978-1-932443-13-4(4) , HGSH) Judaica Pr., Inc., The.

Fun in the Park. 1999. (Tami & Moishy Ser.: Vol. 3). (J). bds. 6.95 (978-1-58330-378-8(2)) Feldheim Pubs.

Gaydos, Nora. The Big Race, Level 2. Becker, Paula, illus. 2006. (innovativeKids readers ser.: level 2). 24p. (J). (gr. k-2). pap. 6.99 (978-1-58476-477-9(5) , IKIDS) Innovative Kids.

Gerver, Jane E. The Big Red Sled. Burris, Priscilla, illus. 2001. (Hello Reader! Ser.). 32p. (J). (ps-1). 3.99 (978-0-439-20434-7(8) , Cartwheel Bks.) Scholastic, Inc.

—The Big Red Sled. 2001. 10.79 (978-0-606-22227-3(8)) Tandem Library Bks.

Glaser, Shirley. The Big Race. Glaser, Milton & Glaser, Shirley, illus. 2005. 32p. (ps-2). 16.99 (978-0-7868-1821-1(2)) Hyperion Bks. for Children.

Grace, Kathryn Diane. On with the Race!, No. 2. Rolden de Moras, Gladys, illus. 1998. (Carita & Her Friends Ser.). 96p. (J). (gr. 2-6). pap. 5.95 (978-0-9653414-1-7(0)) Your Bks.

Gresh, Lois H. & Gresh, Danny. Chuck Farris & the Labyrinth of Doom: An Action Story about PlayStation 2. 2001. (PlayStation2 Ser.). 220p. (J). pap. 6.95 (978-1-55022-460-3(3)) ECW Pr. CAN. Dist: Independent Pubs. Group.

Griggs, Terry. Cat's Eye Corner. 2003. (Cat's Eye Corner Ser.). (Illus.). 168p. (J). pap. 7.95 (978-1-55192-350-5(5)) Raincoast Bk. Distribution CAN. Dist: Perseus Distribution.

—Cat's Eye Corner. 2003. (gr. 3-6). lib. bdg. 16.40 (978-0-613-78641-6(6)) Tandem Library Bks.

Grosset & Dunlap Staff, contrib. by. We Play Outside. 2005. (Dick & Jane Ser.). (Illus.). 144p. (J). (ps-2). 7.99 (978-0-448-43616-6(7) , Grosset & Dunlap) Penguin Group (USA) Inc.

Gym Shoe Salad. 2007. (J). pap. 15.00 (*978-0-9779207-7-8(1)) Text 4m Publishing.

Hall, Kirsten. Duck, Duck, Goose! Rader, Laura, illus. 2003. (My First Reader Ser.). 32p. (J). 18.50 (978-0-516-22925-6(7) , Children's Pr.) Scholastic Library Publishing.

—Tug-of-War: All about Balance. Luedecke, Bev, illus. (Beastieville Ser.). (J). (gr. k-1). 2005. 32p. pap. 3.95 (978-0-516-25523-1(1)); 2004. 31p. 19.50 (978-0-516-22899-0(4)) Scholastic Library Publishing. (Children's Pr.).

Hamburger, Carole. The Star Pupil: A Dot's Quest to Find His Place in the World. 2005. (J). 16.95 (978-0-9764921-0-8(5)) Cherry Street Pr.

Handford, Martin. Where's Waldo: The Wonder Book Mini Edition with Magnifier. Handford, Martin, illus. ed. 2005. (Where's Waldo? Ser.). (Illus.). 32p. (J). (gr. 1). 5.99 (978-0-7636-2700-3(3)) Candlewick Pr.

Haneberg, Janet. Mighty Mitt. 2006. 36p. (J). pap. 14.99 (978-1-4116-4168-6(X)) Lulu.com.

Harcourt School Publishers Staff. A Change of Plans: Take-Home Book. 1999. (Collections Ser.). (Illus.). (J). pap. 1.90 (978-0-15-317211-3(8)) Harcourt Schl. Pubs.

—Game Day: Take-Home Book. 1999. (Signatures Ser.). (Illus.). (J). pap. 1.70 (978-0-15-313838-6(6)) Harcourt Schl. Pubs.

—Girl Detectives: On Level. 3rd ed. 2002. (Trophies Reading Program Ser.). (Illus.). pap. 5.10 (978-0-15-323002-8(9)) Harcourt Schl. Pubs.

—Inside & Outside Together. 3rd ed. 2002. (Trophies English Language Learners Ser.). (Illus.). pap. 5.10 (978-0-15-327758-0(0)) Harcourt Schl. Pubs.

—Trophies On Level. 3rd ed. 2002. (Trophies Reading Program Ser.). (Illus.). pap. 5.10 (978-0-15-323433-0(4)) Harcourt Schl. Pubs.

—Where Is Sam: Take-Home Book. rev. ed. 2001. (Collections Ser.: Vol. 2). (Illus.). (J). pap. 1.90 (978-0-15-317814-6(0)) Harcourt Schl. Pubs.

Harrison, Kevin. I Know a Rhino. 2nd rev. ed. 2007. 44p. (J). pap. 10.99 (978-1-59092-223-1(9) , Little Blue Works) Windstorm Creative.

Hautman, Pete, ed. Full House: 10 Stories about Poker. 2007. (Illus.). 161p. (YA). (gr. 7-12). 17.99 (*978-0-399-24528-2(6) , Putnam Juvenile) Penguin Group (USA) Inc.

Ho, Minfong. Peek! A Thai Hide-and-Seek. Ho, Minfong & Meade, Holly, illus. 2004. 40p. (J). (ps-1). 16.99 (978-0-7636-2041-7(6)) Candlewick Pr.

Howells, Graham, illus. I Saw a Ship A-Sailing. 2001. 32p. pap. 12.95 (978-1-85902-908-4(6)) Beekman Bks., Inc.

Hutchins, Pat. What Game Shall We Play? Hutchins, Pat, illus. 2002. (Illus.). (J). 14.43 (978-0-7587-3959-9(1)) Book Wholesalers, Inc.

Jahn, Jazmine. Sneakers. 2006. (ENG.). 32p. per. 19.99 (*978-1-4259-3098-1(0)) AuthorHouse.

James, Simon. Little One Step. James, Simon, illus. 2007. (Illus.). 24p. (J). (gr. k-ps). bds. 6.99 (*978-0-7636-3520-6(0)) Candlewick Pr.

Jenkins, Susan. The Franklin Annual. 2002. (Franklin Annual Ser.). (Illus.). 96p. (J). (gr. k-3). (978-1-55337-481-7(9)) Kids Can Pr., Ltd.

Jinkins, Jim. Hide & Seek Hunny Pot. 1999. (P B & J Otter Noodle Stories Ser.). (Illus.). 10p. (J). (ps). 4.99 (978-0-7364-0067-1(2)) Mouse Works.

John Brown Publishing Ltd. Diego's Rescue Games: Follow the Reader Level 1. 2007. (Go, Diego, Go! Ser.). 24p. (J). 24.99 (*978-1-4169-4989-3(5) , Simon Scribbles) Simon & Schuster Children's Publishing.

Johns, Geoff. A Kid's Game. rev. ed. 2004. (Teen Titans Go! Ser.). (Illus.). 192p. pap. 9.99 (978-1-4012-0308-5(6)) DC Comics.

Jolin, Dominique. A Friend for Washington. Jolin, Dominique, illus. 1999. (Tickle Ser.). (Illus.). 16p. (J). (ps). bds. (978-1-894363-14-3(0)) Dominique & Friends.

—Washington Dresses Up. Jolin, Dominique, illus. 1999. (Tickle Ser.). (Illus.). 16p. (J). (ps). bds. (978-1-894363-12-9(4)) Dominique & Friends.

—Washington Goes for a Walk. Jolin, Dominique, illus. 2000. (Illus.). 16p. (J). (ps-k). bds. (978-1-894363-28-0(0)) Dominique & Friends.

—Washington Plays Hide-and-Seek. Jolin, Dominique, illus. 1999. (Tickle Ser.). (Illus.). 16p. (J). (ps). bds. (978-1-894363-13-6(2)) Dominique & Friends.

—Washington Tells a Story. Jolin, Dominique, illus. 2000. (Illus.). 16p. (J). (ps-k). bds. (978-1-894363-27-3(2)) Dominique & Friends.

—Washington Wants to Play. Jolin, Dominique, illus. 1999. (Tickle Ser.). (Illus.). 16p. (J). (ps). bds. (978-1-894363-11-2(6)) Dominique & Friends.

Jones, Jasmine, adapted by. The Importance of Being Gordo. 2005. (Illus.). 138p. (J). (*978-1-4155-7362-4(X)) Disney Pr.

—Importance of Being Gordo. 2005. 138p. (J). lib. bdg. 16.92 (*978-1-4242-0688-9(X)) Fitzgerald Bks.

Jones, Marcia Thornton & Dadey, Debbie. Dracula Doesn't Play Kickball. 2004. (Baily School Kids Ser.). 80p. (J). pap. 3.99 (978-0-439-56000-9(4) , Scholastic Paperbacks) Scholastic, Inc.

Katz, Karen. Where Is Baby's Belly Button? Katz, Karen, illus. 2000. (Lift-the-Flap Bks.). (Illus.). 14p. (J). bds. 5.99 (978-0-689-83560-5(4) , Little Simon) Simon & Schuster Children's Publishing.

Kinsella, Sheralyn Mary. Ven a Colorear Con Los Amigos de Villa Coral: Los Amigos de Villa Coral en Una Adventura de Colores Los Colores Veraderos, Una Odisea en el Mar Libro Para Iluminar Con Actividades. Davis, Bob, illus. 2002. (SPA.). 38p. (J). spiral bd. (978-0-9666841-3-1(3)) Odyssey Tales, LLC.

Kirk, Rhina. Burton Barton Bennington Boggs. Wise, Noreen, ed. Bouman, Sharon, illus. 2000. 32p. (YA). (ps up). pap. 5.95 (978-1-58584-350-3(4)) Huckleberry Pr.

Korman, Gordon. The Sixth Grade Nickname Game. 2000. (978-0-606-20309-8(5)) Tandem Library Bks.

Kostick, Conor. Epic. 2007. 384p. (YA). (gr. 7 up). 17.99 (978-0-670-06179-2(4) , Viking Juvenile) Penguin Group (USA) Inc.

Kostick, Conor. Saga. 2008. 368p. (YA). (gr. 7). 18.99 (*978-0-670-06280-5(4) , Viking Juvenile) Penguin Group (USA) Inc.

Kushner, Ellen. The Golden Dreydl. Winn-Lederer, Ilene, illus. 2007. 128p. (J). (gr. 3-6). 15.95 (978-1-58089-135-6(7)) Charlesbridge Publishing, Inc.

Labatt, Mary. Franklin's Trading Cards. 2003. (gr. k-3). lib. bdg. 11.80 (978-0-613-86543-2(X)) Tandem Library Bks.

LeapFrog Staff, compiled by. What Do You Do? 2001. (J). (ps-2). spiral bd. 14.95 (978-1-58605-058-0(3)) LeapFrog Enterprises, Inc.

Levine, Abby. This Is the Dreidel. Billin-Frye, Paige, tr. Billin-Frye, Paige, illus. 2003. 24p. (J). (ps-1). 15.95 (978-0-8075-7884-1(3)) Whitman, Albert & Co.

Lewis, Sian. I Saw a Ship A-Sailing. Howells, Graham, illus. 2001. 32p. pap. 24.95 (978-1-85902-994-7(9)) Beekman Bks., Inc.

Lewison, Wendy Cheyette. Peekaboo! I See You! Moroney, Christopher, illus. 2002. (Sesame Beginnings Ser.). 14p. (J). (gr. k). bds. 7.99 (978-0-375-81512-6(0) , Random Hse. Bks. for Young Readers) Random Hse. Children's Bks.

Lidbert, Paul A. Battle for Fruitcake Hell: Battle #1 of the Christmas Wars. Lincoln, D. B., ed. Lidbert, Paul A., illus. 1999. (Illus.). 24p. (J). 5.95 (978-1-929332-11-3(4) , CFE0701) Crunchy Frog Enterprises.

—Beer Bash. Lincoln, D. B., ed. 1999. (Illus.). 24p. (J). 5.95 (978-1-929332-09-0(2) , CFE0203) Crunchy Frog Enterprises.

—Big Damn Robots. Lidbert, Paul A., illus. 1999. (Illus.). 24p. (J). 5.95 (978-1-929332-06-9(8) , CFE0104) Crunchy Frog Enterprises.

—Full Metal Santa: Battle #3 of the Christmas Wars. Lincoln, D. B., ed. Lidbert, Paul A., illus. 1999. (Illus.). 24p. (J). 5.95 (978-1-929332-13-7(0) , CFE0703) Crunchy Frog Enterprises.

—A Line in the Snow: Battle #4 of the Christmas Wars. Lincoln, D. B., ed. Lidbert, Paul A., illus. 1999. (Illus.). 24p. (YA). 5.95 (978-1-929332-14-4(9) , CFE0704) Crunchy Frog Enterprises.

—10 Minutes over Toyland: Battle #2 of the Christmas Wars. Lidbert, Paul A., illus. 1999. (Illus.). 24p. (J). 5.95 (978-1-929332-12-0(2) , CFE0702) Crunchy Frog Enterprises.

Lidbert, Paul A. & Lincoln, D. B. Happy Farm. 1999. (Illus.). 12p. (J). 5.95 (978-1-929332-08-3(4) , CFE0202) Crunchy Frog Enterprises.

Lubar, David. Wizards of the Game. 2004. 176p. (J). (gr. 5). pap. 5.99 (978-0-14-240215-3(X) , Puffin) Penguin Group (USA) Inc.

Luna Rising Staff, ed. Elmo's Guessing Game about Colors. 2006. (SPA & ENG., Illus.). 12p. (J). 5.95 (978-0-87358-905-5(X) , Luna Rising) Northland Publishing.

MacHado, Ana Maria. El Juego del Cambia-Cambia. Valverde, Mikel, illus. 2004. Tr. of Change-Change Game. (SPA.). (J). 6.50 (978-84-348-8716-9(9)) SM Ediciones ESP. Dist: Lectorum Pubns., Inc.

Maddox, Jake. Paintball Blast. Tiffany, Sean, illus. 2007. (J). 72p. (*978-1-59889-322-9(X)); 65p. pap. (*978-1-59889-417-2(X)) Stone Arch Bks.

Martin, Ann M. Karen's Field Day. 1999. (Baby-Sitters Little Sister Ser.: No. 108). 112p. (J). (gr. 3-7). pap. 3.99 (978-0-590-50060-9(0)) Scholastic, Inc.

Mayer, Mercer. Surprise. 2001. (gr. k-3). lib. bdg. 11.80 (978-0-613-90238-0(6)) Tandem Library Bks.

McKee, David. Hide-and-Seek Elmer. McKee, David, illus. 1998. (Elmer Bks.). (Illus.). 32p. (J). (ps-k). 14.95 (978-0-688-16127-9(8) , Harper Festival) HarperCollins Pubs.

McNeece, Alexander. Sam Iver: Imminent Threat. 2007. 140p. per. 11.95 (*978-0-595-43260-8(3)) iUniverse, Inc.

Meade, Holly, illus. Inside, Inside, Inside. 2005. 32p. (J). 16.95 (978-0-7614-5125-9(0)) Cavendish, Marshall Corp.

Meister, Cari. Game Day. Hicks, Mark A., illus. 2002. (Rookie Reader Espanol Ser.). 24p. (J). (gr. k-2). pap. 4.95 (978-0-516-25964-2(4) , Children's Pr.) Scholastic Library Publishing.

—Game Day. 2001. (gr. k-3). lib. bdg. 12.95 (978-0-613-54226-5(6)) Tandem Library Bks.

Most, Bernard. Catch Me If You Can. 2003. (Green Light Readers Level 2 Ser.). (Illus.). 24p. (J). 11.95 (978-0-15-204879-2(0)); pap. 3.95 (978-0-15-204839-6(1)) Harcourt Children's Bks. (Green Light Readers).

—Catch Me If You Can. 2003. (gr. k-3). lib. bdg. 11.80 (978-0-613-64465-5(4)) Tandem Library Bks.

Murphy, Frank. Ben Franklin & the Magic Squares. Walz, Richard, illus. 2001. (Step into Reading Ser.). 48p. (J). (gr. k-3). pap. 3.99 (978-0-375-80621-6(0)); lib. bdg. 11.99 (978-0-375-90621-3(5)) Random Hse. Children's Bks. (Random Hse. Bks. for Young Readers).

Murphy, Stuart J. Tally O'Malley. Jabar, Cynthia, illus. 2004. (MathStart Ser.). 40p. (J). (gr. 1 up). 15.99 (978-0-06-053162-1(2)); pap. 5.99 (978-0-06-053164-5(9)) HarperCollins Pubs.

Newman, Lesléa. Runaway Dreidel! Brooker, Kyrsten, illus. 2007. 32p. (J). pap. 6.99 (*978-0-312-37142-5(X)) Square Fish.

Newman, Lesléa. Where Is Bear? Gorbachev, Valeri, illus. 2004. 44p. (J). 16.00 (978-0-15-204936-2(3) , Gulliver Bks.) Harcourt Children's Bks.

Newman, Lesléa & Gorbachev, Valeri. Where Is Bear? 2006. (Illus.). 44p. (J). pap. 6.00 (978-0-15-205918-7(0) , Voyager Bks./Libros Viajeros) Harcourt Children's Bks.

Norman, Tony. Terror World. Savage, Paul, illus. 2006. (Pathway Books). 33p. (J). 21.26 (978-1-59889-008-2(5)) Stone Arch Bks.

O'Malley, Kevin. Lucky Leaf. O'Malley, Kevin, illus. (Illus.). (J). (ps-2). 2007. 40p. pap. 6.95 (*978-0-8027-9647-9(8)); 2004. 32p. 16.85 (978-0-8027-8925-9(0)); 2004. 32p. 15.95 (978-0-8027-8924-2(2)) Walker & Co.

Ostrow, Kim & Burnett, Mark. Marquesas. 2005. (Survivor—Outwit, Outplay, Outlast Ser.: Vol. 2). 143p. (J). (978-1-4155-7990-9(3) , Simon Spotlight) Simon & Schuster Children's Publishing.

Packard, Mary. Where Is Jake? 2004. (My First Reader Ser.). (J). (gr. k-1). pap. 3.95 (978-0-516-24641-3(0) , Children's Pr.) Scholastic Library Publishing.

Pass, Erica. The Scavenger Hunt. Marantz, Larissa & DiPaolo, Katharine, illus. 2006. (All Grown Up! Ser.). 24p. (J). pap. 3.99 (978-1-4169-0791-6(2) , Simon Spotlight/Nickelodeon) Simon & Schuster Children's Publishing.

Petrillo, Genevieve & Lyon, Lea. Keep Your Ear on the Ball. 2007. (Illus.). 32p. (J). (gr. 3-7). 16.95 (*978-0-88448-296-3(0)) Tilbury Hse. Pubs.

Pingry, Patricia A. Noses & Toes. Rose, Drew, illus. 2005. (J). (978-0-8249-6594-5(9) , Candy Cane Pr.) Ideals Pubns.

Pollack, Pam, et al. Let's Bowl. 2006. (Foster's Home for Imaginary Friends Ser.: No. 2). 64p. (J). pap. 3.99 (978-0-439-87471-7(8) , Scholastic Paperbacks) Scholastic, Inc.

Price, Margaret Evans. The Angora Twinnies. Price, Margaret Evans, illus. 2005. (Illus.). 16p. (J). (ps-3). 9.00 (978-1-59583-046-3(4)) Laughing Elephant.

Price, Mathew. Peekaboo Collection. 2004. 40p. (J). bds. 19.95 (978-0-7696-3459-3(1)) School Specialty Publishing.

Price, Roger & Stern, Leonard. Candy Land Mad Libs Junior. 2005. (Mad Libs Junior Ser.). 48p. (J). (gr. k-3). pap. 3.99 (978-0-8431-1652-6(8) , Price Stern Sloan) Penguin Group (USA) Inc.

Richards, Kitty. Bowling Twins. 2000. (Rugrats Ser.). (Illus.). 16p. (J). (ps-2). pap. 3.99 (978-0-7434-0801-1(2) , Simon & Schuster Children's Publishing) Simon & Schuster Children's Publishing.

Rizzon, Roberto. Tug of War. 1999. (Let's Play Series 2 Ser.). (Illus.). 24p. (J). (ps-3). pap. 3.99 (978-0-85953-713-1(7)) Child's Play-International.

Robberecht, Thierry. Sam Is Not a Loser. Goossens, Philippe, illus. 2008. (J). (ps-1). 12.00 (*978-0-618-99210-2(3) , Clarion Bks.) Houghton Mifflin Co. Trade & Reference Div.

Romans, William D. Fred, the Foul Ball. 2003. pap. 7.95 (978-0-533-14293-4(8)) Vantage Pr., Inc.

Rosensweig, Jay B. & Repka, Janice. The Stupendous Dodgeball Fiasco. Dibley, Glin, illus. 2004. 192p. (J). (gr. 3). 16.99 (978-0-525-47346-6(7) , Dutton Juvenile) Penguin Group (USA) Inc.

Rovetch, L. Bob. Hot Dog & Bob & the Exceptionally Eggy Attack of the Game Gators. Whamond, Dave, illus. 2007. 96p. (J). pap. 4.95 (978-0-8118-5604-1(6)) Chronicle Bks. LLC.

Rovetch, Lissa. Hot Dog & Bob & the Exceptionally Eggy Attack of the Game Gators. Whamond, Dave, illus. 2007. 96p. (J). 15.50 (978-0-8118-5603-4(8)) Chronicle Bks. LLC.

Sanschagrin, Joceline. Le Visage Masqué. Brignaud, Pierre, illus. 2004. (Mon Roman Ser.). (FRE.). 160p. (J). (gr. 2). pap. (978-2-89021-651-8(9)) Diffusion du livre Mirabel.

Sarafati, Sonia. Tricot, Piano et Jeu Video. 2002. (Premier Roman Ser.). (FRE.). 64p. (J). (gr. 2-5). pap. (978-2-89021-181-0(9)) Diffusion du livre Mirabel.

Scruggs, Afi. Jump Rope Magic. Diaz, David, illus. 2000. 40p. (J). (ps-4). pap. 16.95 (978-0-590-69327-1(1) , Blue Sky Pr., The) Scholastic, Inc.

Sharmat, Marjorie Weinman. Dirty Tricks. Jones, Veronica, illus. 2000. (Duz Shedd Ser.: Vol. 4). (J). (978-0-606-19894-3(6)) Tandem Library Bks.

Shaskan, Trisha. The Treasure Map. Muehlenhardt, Amy Bailey, illus. 2006. (Read-It! Readers Ser.). (J). 19.93 (978-1-4048-2416-4(2)) Picture Window Bks.

Shulman, Mark. Mom & Dad Are Palindromes: A Dilemma for Words... & Backwards. McCauley, Adam, illus. 2006. 36p. (J). 15.95 (978-0-8118-4328-7(9)) Chronicle Bks. LLC.

Slater, Teddy. 98, 99, 100! Ready or Not Here I Come! Fiammenghi, Gioia, illus. 1999. (Hello Reader! Math Ser.: Level 2). 32p. (J). (gr. k-2). pap. 3.99 (978-0-590-12009-8(3) , Cartwheel Bks.) Scholastic, Inc.

—98, 99, 100! Ready or Not Here I Come! 1999. (Hello Reader! Ser.). (978-0-606-17538-8(5)) Tandem Library Bks.

—98, 99, 100, Ready or Not, Here I Come! 1999. (gr. k-3). lib. bdg. 11.80 (978-0-613-19021-3(1)) Tandem Library Bks.

Sleator, William. Parasite Pig. 2002. 192p. (J). 15.99 (978-0-525-46918-6(4) , Dutton Juvenile) Penguin Group (USA) Inc.

Smith, Linda. Sir Cassie to the Rescue. Patkau, Karen, tr. Patkau, Karen, illus. 2003. 32p. (J). (ps-2). 16.95 (978-1-55143-243-4(9)) Orca Bk. Pubs. USA.

Snicket, Lemony, pseud. Volunteer Training: The Puzzling Puzzles. 2006. (Series of Unfortunate Events Ser.). (Illus.). 96p. (J). pap. 3.99 (978-0-06-075730-4(2) , Harper Trophy) HarperCollins Pubs.

Snyder, Zilpha Keatley. The Egypt Game. 2002. (Illus.). (J). 14.47 (978-0-7587-0259-3(0)) Book Wholesalers, Inc.

Spelvin, George. Jumanji. 2000. (SPA., Illus.). 240p. (J). 11.95 (978-84-406-6197-5(5)) Ediciones B ESP. Dist: Distribooks, Inc.

Stainton, Sue. Christmas Magic. Melhuish, Eva, illus. 2007. 32p. (J). lib. bdg. 16.89 (*978-0-06-078572-7(1)); 15.99 (*978-0-06-078571-0(3)) HarperCollins Pubs. (Tegen, Katherine Bks).

Stamper, Judith Bauer, et al. Tic-Tac-Toe: Three in a Row. Wilson-Max, Ken, illus. 1998. (Hello Reader! Math Ser.). 32p. (J). (ps-1). 3.99 (978-0-590-39963-0(2)) Scholastic, Inc.

Stern, Leonard. The Mad Libs Worst-Case Scenario Survival Handbook: Travel. 2004. (Mad Libs Ser.). (Illus.). 48p. (J). (gr. 3). pap. 3.99 (978-0-8431-1033-3(3) , Price Stern Sloan) Penguin Group (USA) Inc.

Stickels, Terry. Pirate Word-Doku. 2007. 240p. (J). pap. 4.99 (978-0-06-125481-9(9)) HarperCollins Pubs.

Stilton, Geronimo. A Fabumouse Vacation for Geronimo. 2004. (Geronimo Stilton Ser.: No. 9). (Illus.). 113p. (J). (gr. 2-5). lib. bdg. 13.94 (978-0-606-33272-9(3)) Tandem Library Bks.

Sula, Sondra. Mr. Fred & Ted: A Game for All Season. 2000. mass mkt. 4.50 (978-1-931179-27-0(1)) Long Hill Productions, Inc.

—Mr. Fred & Ted: A Game for All Seasons. 2000. mass mkt. 8.95 (978-1-931179-38-6(7)) Long Hill Productions, Inc.

Swan, Bill. Mud Run. 2003. (Sports Stories Ser.). 104p. (J). (gr. 3-8). 7.95 (978-1-55028-786-8(9)); (*978-1-55028-787-5(7)) Lorimer, James & Co., Ltd., Pubs. CAN. Dist: Casemate Pubs. & Bk. Distributors, LLC.

—Mud Run. 2003. (gr. 5-8). lib. bdg. 13.55 (978-0-613-78327-9(1)) Tandem Library Bks.

Sweeney, Jacqueline. Critter Day. Hart, G. K. & Empey, Mark, illus. 2000. (We Can Read! Ser.). 32p. (J). (gr. 1-2). lib. bdg. 21.36 (978-0-7614-1119-2(4) , Benchmark Bks.) Cavendish, Marshall Corp.

Takhar, Jodi. What Can I Do Today? Takhar, Jodi & Jones, Paul, illus. 14p. (J). (ps-3). 19.95 (978-1-886000-03-2(4)) Takhar's, Jodi Spilt Milk Collection.

Tanner, Jane. Playmates. Tanner, Jane, illus. 2005. (Illus.). 32p. (J). pap. 10.00 (978-0-14-054147-2(0) , Penguin Global) Penguin Group (USA) Inc.

Things We Like to Do. 1999. (Tami & Moishy Ser.: Vol. 5). (J). bds. 6.95 (978-0-87306-966-3(8)) Feldheim Pubs.

Thompson, Lauren. Little Quack's Hide & Seek. Anderson, Derek, illus. 2004. 32p. (J). 14.95 (978-0-689-85722-5(5)) Simon & Schuster Children's Publishing.

Thorpe, Kiki. Where Is Boots? A Lift-the-Flap Story. Savitsky, Steve, illus. 2002. (Dora the Explorer Ser.). 16p. (J). (ps-1). pap. 5.99 (978-0-689-84775-2(0) , Simon Spotlight/Nickelodeon) Simon & Schuster Children's Publishing.

The three-legged Race, 6 Packs. (gr. 1-2). 25.00 (978-0-7635-9131-1(9)) Rigby Education.

Tigger & Pooh 100 Acre Woods Friends. 2007. 48p. pap. 3.99 (***978-1-4037-3227-9(2)***) Dalmatian Pr.

Tomko, Diana. The Ten-Second Race, Vol. 4465. Kupperstein, Joel, ed. Cochrane, Tom, illus. 1998. (Learn to Read Math Ser.). 16p. (J). pap. 2.75 (978-1-57471-372-5(8) , 4465) Creative Teaching Pr., Inc.

The Tug of War: Individual Title Six-Pack. (Story Steps Ser.). (gr. k-2). 23.00 (978-0-7635-9620-0(5)) Rigby Education.

Van Allsburg, Chris. Zathura: A Space Adventure. Van Allsburg, Chris, illus. 2002. (Illus.). 32p. (J). (gr. k-3). 18.00 (978-0-618-25396-8(3)) Houghton Mifflin Co. Trade & Reference Div.

Vande Velde, Vivian. Heir Apparent. 2004. (gr. 5-8). lib. bdg. 15.25 (978-0-613-71642-0(6)) Tandem Library Bks.

Volponi, Paul. The Hand You're Dealt. 2008. 256p. (YA). (***978-1-4169-3989-4(X)***) Simon & Schuster Children's Publishing.

Voss, Fonda. The Bossy Girl. 2005. (Illus.). 31p. (J). per. 9.99 (978-1-932338-96-6(9)) Lifevest Publishing, Inc.

Weeks, Sarah. Fink's Funk. 2006. (Boyds Will Be Boyds Ser.: No. 4). 144p. (J). pap. 4.99 (978-0-439-57472-3(2) , Scholastic Paperbacks) Scholastic, Inc.

Wells, Rosemary. McDuff's Hide-and-Seek. Jeffers, Susan, illus. 2004. 12p. (ps-ps). 9.99 (978-0-7868-1935-5(9)) Hyperion Bks. for Children.

The Westing Game. (J). 1999. 9.95 (978-1-56137-464-9(4)); 1998. 11.95 (978-1-56137-465-6(2)) Novel Units, Inc.

The Westing Game. 2000. (Novel Vocabulary Ser.). 40p. (J). pap., stu. ed., tchr.'s training gde. ed. 21.95 (978-1-58303-109-4(X)) Pathways Publishing.

White, Rosemary. Kupuckaryaraq. Shantz, Joy, illus. Swope, Dean, photos by. 1998. Tr. of How to Play Hand Darts. (ESK.). 16p. (J). (gr. k-3). pap. 6.00 (978-1-58084-041-5(8)) Lower Kuskokwim Schl. District.

Wilkes, Angela. Animales de la Selva Tropical. 2004. (Ladders Ser.).Tr. of Rain Forest Animals. (SPA., Illus.). 32p. (J). (ps-3). pap. 6.95 (978-1-58728-409-0(X) , Two Can Publishing) T&N Children's Publishing.

Williams, Dylan, et al. Pawb Yn Cuddio. 2005. (WEL., Illus.). 14p. (978-1-84512-021-4(3)) Cymdeithas Lyfrau Ceredigion.

Williams, Rozanne Lanczak. Dan's Game. Yakovetic Productions Staff, illus. 12p. (J). (gr. k-2). (978-1-58605-013-9(3)) LeapFrog Enterprises, Inc.

Willson, Sarah. Simon Says. Ulrich, George, illus. 2006. (Step-By-Step Readers Ser.). (J). pap. (978-1-59939-057-4(4) , Reader's Digest Young Families, Inc.) Reader's Digest Children's Publishing, Inc.

Witzy Plays Hide & Seek. 2001. (Little Suzy's Zoo Ser.). 14p. (J). bds. 5.99 (978-1-58668-155-5(9)) Lyrick Studios.

Wolf, Jackie. Picture Me Peek-A-Boo Farm. 2002. (Peek-a-Boo Ser.). (Illus.). 10p. (J). (ps up). bds. 4.99 (978-1-57151-595-7(X)) Playhouse Publishing.

Wong, Janet S. Hide & Seek. Chodos-Irvine, Margaret, illus. 2005. 40p. (J). 16.00 (978-0-15-204934-8(7)) Harcourt Trade Pubs.

Yee, Wong Herbert. Who Likes Rain? 2007. (Illus.). (J). (***978-1-4287-3979-6(3));*** 32p. 14.95 (978-0-8050-7734-6(0)) Holt, Henry & Co.

YOE! Studio Staff. The Backyardigans Easy Sudoku Puzzles, No. 2. 2007. (Backyardigans Ser.). 32p. (J). pap. 5.99 (***978-1-4169-3557-5(6)*** , Simon Spotlight) Simon & Schuster Children's Publishing.

—Go, Diego, Go! Easy Sudoku Puzzles #2. 2007. (Go, Diego, Go! Ser.). 32p. (J). pap. 5.99 (***978-1-4169-3555-1(X)*** , Simon Spotlight) Simon & Schuster Children's Publishing.

York, Carol Beach. Takers & Returners: A Novel of Suspense. 2005. 128p. (J). pap. 11.95 (978-0-929093-18-5(6) , Taylor Productions) GRM Assocs.

GAMES FOR TRAVELERS

Anastasio, Dina, et al. The Mighty Big Book of Travel Games. Latta, Richard et al, illus. 2002. 288p. (J). (gr. 3-7). pap. 6.99 (978-0-8431-7733-6(0) , Price Stern Sloan) Penguin Group (USA) Inc.

Blair, Beth L. Jumbo Travel Activity Book: Hundreds of Puzzles & Mazes for Fun on the Go. 2006. 384p. pap. 8.95 (978-1-59869-047-7(7)) Adams Media Corp.

Bree, Loris Theovin & Bree, Marlin. Kid's Travel Fun Book: Play Games. Make Things Out of Paper & String. You'll Have a Ball. 2003. (Illus.). 96p. (J). (gr. 1-7). pap. 6.95 (978-1-892147-01-1(7)) Marlor Pr., Inc.

Calkhoven, Laurie. Miles of Smiles. 2007. 80p. (J). pap. 9.95 (***978-1-59369-170-7(X)*** , Pleasant Co.) American Girl Publishing, Inc.

Copeland, Cynthia L. Fun on the Run for Kids: 324 Instant Family Activities. Hoffman, Sanford, illus. 2004. 352p. pap. 8.95 (978-0-7611-3448-0(4) , 13448) Workman Publishing Co., Inc.

Douglas, Vincent & School Specialty Publishing Staff. Fun Time Travel Games. 2002. (Travel Games Ser.). (Illus.). 64p. (J). (gr. 1-5). pap. 3.99 (978-1-57768-864-8(3) , Brighter Child) School Specialty Publishing.

—Have Fun Travel Games. 2003. (Travel Games Ser.). (Illus.). 64p. (J). (gr. 1-5). pap. 3.99 (978-1-57768-546-3(6) , Brighter Child) School Specialty Publishing.

—On the Go Games. 2002. (Travel Games Ser.). (Illus.). 64p. (J). (gr. 1-5). pap. 3.99 (978-1-57768-865-5(1) , Brighter Child) School Specialty Publishing.

—Take a Trip Games. 2002. (Travel Games Ser.). (Illus.). 64p. (J). (gr. 1-5). pap. 3.99 (978-1-57768-866-2(X) , Brighter Child) School Specialty Publishing.

—Travel Fun Kit. 2005. (Book Notes Ser.). (Illus.). 64p. (J). pap. 17.95 (978-0-7696-3888-1(0) , American Education Publishing) School Specialty Publishing.

—Travel Game Mania. 2002. (Travel Games Ser.). (Illus.). 64p. (J). (gr. 1-5). pap. 3.99 (978-1-57768-867-9(8) , Brighter Child) School Specialty Publishing.

G and R Publishing Staff. Games for the Car. 2001. 128p. (J). pap. 7.00 (978-1-56383-120-1(1)) G&R Publishing.

Galvin, Laura Gates. Disney Princess Learning Travel Pack. rev. ed. 2006. 10 x 6p. 12.99 (978-1-59069-479-4(1)) Studio Mouse LLC.

Games on the Go. (Illus.). (J). pap. 6.99 (978-1-55254-193-7(2) , BV24022) Brighter Vision Pubns.

Gilpin, Rebecca. 50 Travel Games & Activities. 2006. 50p. (J). 9.99 (978-0-7945-1319-1(0) , Usborne) EDC Publishing.

Hill, Taven. My Travel Book. 2006. (Illus.). 105p. (J). 19.95 (***978-0-9765321-1-8(5)***) MC123.

Houssin, Frédéric & Ramadier, Cédric. The Big Book of Car Games. 2003. (Illus.). 120p. spiral bd. 12.95 (978-1-57912-276-8(0) , 81276) Black Dog & Leventhal Pubs., Inc.

Klutz Press Staff. Books-in-a-Cup: Lime. 2005. 20p. (J). pap. 9.95 (978-1-57054-274-9(0)) Klutz.

—Books-in-a-Cup: Orange. 2005. (Klutz to Go Ser.). 20p. (J). pap. 9.95 (978-1-57054-271-8(6)) Klutz.

Kuch, K. D. 50 Nifty Super More Travel Games. Yamamoto, Neal, illus. 1999. (Fifty Nifty Ser.). 80p. (J). (gr. 3-7). pap. 6.95 (978-0-7373-0060-4(4) , 00604W) McGraw-Hill/Contemporary.

My Totally Awesome Travel Fun Book. 2000. (Illus.). 64p. (J). pap. 6.95 (978-1-882663-52-1(7)) Plymouth Toy & Book.

O'Hare, Jeffrey A., ed. Travel Puzzles & Games from Highlights U. S. A. 2003. (Illus.). 96p. (YA). (gr. 1-9). pap., act. bk. ed. 9.95 (978-1-59078-016-9(7)) Boyds Mills Pr.

Pryor, Joanne. I Spy... the Next Stop: Kids Camping the Coast from Maine to Georgia. 2004. (Illus.). 164p. (J). spiral bd. (978-0-9735907-1-5(8)) Destination Publishing.

Rand McNally Staff. Kids' Road Atlas. (Backseat Bks.). 80p. (J). pap. 3.95 (978-0-528-96544-9(1)) Rand McNally.

Schiller, David. All American Car-I-Oke. 2003. (Illus.). 64p. (J). 14.95 (978-0-7611-3068-0(3) , 13068) Workman Publishing Co., Inc.

Taylor, Kevin & Taylor, Joan C. 50 Nifty Super Travel Games. Yamamoto, Neal, illus. 1998. (Fifty Nifty Super Ser.). 80p. (J). (gr. 3-7). pap. 6.95 (978-1-56565-926-1(0) , 09260W) Lowell Hse. Juvenile.

Trago Publishing Staff. The Alphabet 1 Travel Kit. 1999. (My Art Ser.). 35p. (J). (ps-3). pap. 4.95 (978-0-9683883-2-7(9)) Sterling Publishing Co., Inc.

—The Zoo Animal Travel Kit. 1999. (My Art Ser.). 35p. (J). (ps-3). pap. (978-0-9683883-8-9(8)) Sterling Publishing Co., Inc.

Travel Games, 6 bks. 2002. (Travel Games Ser.). 64p. (J). (gr. 1-5). pap. 95.76 (978-1-57768-356-8(0)) School Specialty Publishing.

Travel Games: Fun & Games on the Go! 2007. (J). 8.99 (***978-0-439-90351-6(3)***) Scholastic, Inc.

Universal Map Enterprises Inc., Staff, ed. Kid's Travel Activities. 1998. (Little Passengers Ser.). (Illus.). 48p. (ps-1). pap. 3.95 (978-0-7625-0597-5(4)) Universal Map Enterprises, Inc.

—Kid's Travel Fun & Games. 1998. (Little Passengers Ser.). (Illus.). 48p. (ps-1). pap. 3.95 (978-0-7625-0598-2(2)) Universal Map Enterprises, Inc.

Wise, Leonard. The Way Cool License Plate Book. 2002. (Illus.). 64p. (J). (gr. 1-3). 19.95 (978-1-55297-686-9(6)); pap. 9.95 (978-1-55297-563-3(0)) Firefly Bks., Ltd.

—Way Cool License Plate Book. 2002. (gr. k-3). lib. bdg. 18.75 (978-0-613-78599-0(1)) Tandem Library Bks.

GAMES, OLYMPIC

see Olympics

GANDALF (FICTITIOUS CHARACTER)—FICTION

Tolkien, J. R. R. The Hobbit. 2002. 16.60 (978-0-7587-7961-8(5)) Book Wholesalers, Inc.

—The Hobbit. 1999. (YA). 9.95 (978-1-56137-253-9(6)) Novel Units, Inc.

—El Hobbit. 2003. (Lord of the Rings Ser.). (SPA.). 320p. (YA). 17.95 (978-84-450-7141-0(6) , MQ9001) Minotauro Ediciones ESP. *Dist:* Distribooks, Inc., Lectorum Pubns., Inc., Planeta Publishing Corp.

—The Hobbit. adapted ed. 2001. (J). 23.50 (978-0-606-21234-2(5)) Tandem Library Bks.

—Hobbit: An Illustrated Edition of the Fantasy Classic. Wenzel, David, illus. 2001. 144p. reprint ed. pap. 17.95 (978-0-345-44560-5(0) , Del Rey) Random House Publishing Group.

—The Hobbit: Or There & Back Again. 2002. (Illus.). 365p. (YA). (gr. 5). pap. 10.00 (978-0-618-26030-0(7)) Houghton Mifflin Co. Trade & Reference Div.

—The Hobbit: Or There & Back Again. Sis, Peter, illus. 2001. 320p. (YA). (gr. 7 up). pap. 10.00 (978-0-618-15082-3(X)) Houghton Mifflin Co. Trade & Reference Div.

—The Hobbit: Or There & Back Again. 1999. (Illus.). 320p. pap. 12.00 (978-0-618-00221-4(9)) Houghton Mifflin Co. Trade & Reference Div.

—The Hobbit: Or, There & Back Again. 2001. (Illus.). 330p. (YA). (gr. 7 up). 18.00 (978-0-618-16221-5(6)) Houghton Mifflin Co. Trade & Reference Div.

—The Lord of the Rings. unabr. ed. 2000. 1216p. (YA). pap. 80.00 incl. audio (978-0-8072-8344-8(4) , LL0187, Listening Library) Random Hse. Audio Publishing Group.

—The Return of the King. 2002. (J). 16.60 (978-0-7587-5212-3(1)) Book Wholesalers, Inc.

GANDHI, INDIRA, 1917-1984

Dommermuth-Costa, Carol. Indira Gandhi: Daughter of India. 2001. (Lerner Biographies Ser.). (Illus.). 128p. (YA). (gr. 6-12). 6.95 (978-0-8225-4963-5(8) , Lerner Pubns.) Lerner Publishing Group.

Ganeri, Anita. Indira Gandhi. 2003. (Leading Lives Ser.). (Illus.). 64p. (J). lib. bdg. 28.50 (978-1-4034-0833-4(5)) Heinemann Library.

Somervill, Barbara A. Indira Gandhi: Political Leader in India. (Illus.). 112p. (J). 2007. pap. (***978-0-7565-2207-0(2));*** 2006. (978-0-7565-1885-1(7)) Compass Point Bks.

Wheeler, Jill C. Indira Gandhi. 2004. (Women of the World Ser.). (J). (978-1-59197-614-1(6)) ABDO Publishing Co.

GANDHI, MAHATMA, 1869-1948

Attenborough, Richard. Words of Gandhi. 2000. (gr. 7-12). lib. bdg. 21.05 (978-0-613-45353-0(0)) Tandem Library Bks.

Clayborne, Anna. Mahatma Gandhi. 2002. (Famous Lives Ser.). (Illus.). 48p. (J). lib. bdg. 27.12 (978-0-7398-5521-8(2)) Raintree.

Demi. Gandhi. Demi, illus. 2001. (Illus.). 40p. (J). (gr. 2-5). 21.99 (978-0-689-84149-1(3) , McElderry, Margaret K.) Simon & Schuster Children's Publishing.

Downing, David. Mohandas Gandhi. 2002. (Leading Lives Ser.). (Illus.). 64p. (J). (gr. 5-7). lib. bdg. 28.50 (978-1-58810-581-3(4)); pap. (978-1-4034-0124-3(1) , 91615) Heinemann Library.

Heinrichs, Ann. Mahatma Gandhi. 2001. (Trailblazers of the Modern World Ser.). (Illus.). 48p. (J). (gr. 5 up). pap. 14.95 (978-0-8368-5224-0(9)); lib. bdg. 30.00 (978-0-8368-5064-2(5)) Stevens, Gareth Inc. (World Almanac Library).

Judge for Yourself New Releases: Martin Luther King, Jr.; Mahatma Gandhi, 2 bks. 2004. (Illus.). (J). (gr. 5 up). lib. bdg. 58.53 (978-0-8368-5560-9(4) , World Almanac Library) Stevens, Gareth Inc.

Kudlinski, Kathleen. Gandhi: Young Nation Builder. 2006. (Childhood of World Figures Ser.). 192p. (J). pap. 5.99 (978-1-4169-1283-5(5) , Aladdin) Simon & Schuster Children's Publishing.

Malaspina, Ann. Mahatma Gandhi & India's Independence in World History. 2000. (In World History Ser.). (Illus.). 128p. (YA). (gr. 5-12). lib. bdg. 26.60 (978-0-7660-1398-8(7)) Enslow Pubs., Inc.

Martin, Christopher. Mohandas Gandhi. 2000. (Biography Ser.). (Illus.). 112p. (YA). (gr. 6-12). lib. bdg. 27.93 (978-0-8225-4984-0(0) , Lerner Pubns.) Lerner Publishing Group.

Nicholson, Michael. Mahatma Gandhi. (Pacificadores Mundiales Ser.). 64p. (gr. 5-8). 28.70 (978-1-4103-0541-1(4) , Blackbirch Pr., Inc.) Thomson Gale.

Pastan, Amy. Gandhi. 2006. (Biography Ser.). (Illus.). 128p. (J). 14.99 (978-0-7566-2112-4(7)); pap. 4.99 (978-0-7566-2111-7(9)) Dorling Kindersley Publishing, Inc.

The Power of Ghandi. 2003. (Illus.). pap. 5.60 (978-0-7398-7512-4(4)) Steck-Vaughn.

Rivera, Sheila. Mohandas Gandhi: A Life of Integrity. 2007. (Pull Ahead Books). (Illus.). 32p. (J). 22.60 (978-0-8225-6383-9(5) , Lerner Pubns.) Lerner Publishing Group.

Rollason, Jane. Gandhi: Level 2. 2004. (Illus.). iv, 27p. (C). pap. 9.00 (978-0-582-81983-2(0)) Pearson ESL.

Schuldt, Lori Meek. Martin Luther King, Jr: With Profiles of Mohandas K. Gandhi & Nelson Mandela. 2006. (Biographical Connections Ser.). (Illus.). 112p. (J). (978-0-7166-1822-5(2)) World Bk., Inc.

Shaw, Maura D. Gandhi: India's Great Soul. Marchesi, Stephen, illus. 2003. (Spiritual Biographies for Young Readers Ser.). 32p. (J). (gr. 1-3). 12.95 (978-1-893361-91-1(8)) SkyLight Paths Publishing.

Shields, Charles J. Mohandas K. Gandhi. 2001. (Overcoming Adversity Ser.). (Illus.). 106p. (J). 30.00 (978-0-7910-6301-9(1)); pap. (978-0-7910-6302-6(X)) Facts On File, Inc. (Chelsea Hse.).

Todd, Anne M. Mohandas Gandhi. 2004. (Spiritual Leaders & Thinkers Ser.). (Illus.). 120p. (gr. 9-13). (J). 30.00 (978-0-7910-7864-8(7)); 30.00 (978-0-7910-7865-5(5)) Facts On File, Inc. (Chelsea Hse.).

Wheeler, Jill C. Gandhi. 2003. (Breaking Barriers Ser.). 64p. (J). (gr. 3-8). lib. bdg. 25.65 (978-1-57765-906-8(6)) ABDO Publishing Co.

Wilkinson, Philip. Gandhi: The Young Protestor Who Founded a Nation. 2005. (World History Biographies Ser.). (Illus.). 64p. (J). (gr. 3-7). 27.90 (978-0-7922-3648-1(3)); 17.95 (978-0-7922-3647-4(5)) National Geographic Society. (National Geographic Children's Bks.).

Wilkinson, Philip. World History Biographies: Gandhi: The Young Protester Who Founded a Nation. 2007. (NG World History Biographies Ser.). (Illus.). 64p. (J). (gr. 3-7). pap. 6.95 (***978-1-4263-0132-2(4)*** , National Geographic Children's Bks.) National Geographic Society.

YKids Staff. Gandhi. 2007. (Great Figures in History Ser.). 148p. (J). (gr. 4-7). pap. 14.95 (***978-981-05-4945-9(8)***) Youngjin (Singapore) Pte Ltd. SGP. *Dist:* Independent Pubs. Group.

GANDHI, MOHANDAS KARAMCHAND, 1869-1948

see Gandhi, Mahatma, 1869-1948

GANGES RIVER (INDIA AND BANGLADESH)

Bowden, Rob. The Ganges. 2003. (River Journey Ser.). (Illus.). 48p. (J). lib. bdg. 28.56 (978-0-7398-6070-0(4)) Raintree.

Cumming, David. The Ganges. 2003. (Great Rivers of the World Ser.). (Illus.). 48p. (gr. 5 up). (J). pap. 14.95 (978-0-8368-5450-3(0)); (YA). lib. bdg. 30.00 (978-0-8368-5443-5(8)) Stevens, Gareth Inc. (World Almanac Library).

—The Ganges: Rivers of the World. Ashley, Rosemary, ed. 2000. (Illus.). 48p. (J). (gr. 4-6). reprint ed. 17.00 (978-0-7881-9511-2(5)) DIANE Publishing Co.

Lewin, Ted. Sacred River: The Ganges of India. Lewin, Ted, illus. 2003. (Illus.). 40p. (J). (gr. 4-6). 5.95 (978-0-618-37839-5(1) , Clarion Bks.) Houghton Mifflin Co. Trade & Reference Div.

—Sacred River: The Ganges of India. 2003. (gr. 3-6). lib. bdg. 14.10 (978-0-613-70993-4(4)) Tandem Library Bks.

Parker. The Ganges. 2003. pap. 35.10 (978-1-4109-0240-5(4)) Raintree.

Parker, Victoria. The Ganges. 2003. (Holy Places Ser.). (Illus.). 32p. (J). 24.28 (978-0-7398-6078-6(X)) Raintree.

Pyers. River Explorer. 2004. (Habitat Explorer Ser.). (Illus.). pap. 7.50 (978-1-4109-0908-4(5)) Raintree.

Pyers, Greg. River Explorer. 2004. (Habitat Explorer Ser.). (Illus.). 32p. (J). lib. bdg. 25.70 (978-1-4109-0512-3(8)) Raintree.

Simon, Charnan. The Sacred Ganges. 2004. (Geography of the World Ser.). 32p. (J). (gr. 2-6). 27.07 (978-1-59296-338-6(2)) Child's World, Inc.

Spilsbury, Richard. Settlements of the Ganges River. 2005. (Rivers Through Time Ser.). (Illus.). 48p. (J). (gr. 3-7). lib. bdg. 31.43 (978-1-4034-6526-9(6)); pap. (978-1-4034-6527-6(4)) Heinemann.

GANGS

see also Crime and Criminals; Juvenile Delinquency

Dailey, D. C. Use Your Brains Stay Out of Gangs. Boudreau, Dawn, photos by. 1999. (Illus.). 37p. (J). (gr. 1-3). pap. 3.75 (978-1-929662-02-9(5)) Brighter Horizons Publishing.

Daniels, Peggy. Gangs. 2007. (Issues that Concern You Ser.). (Illus.). 144p. (gr. 7-10). 33.70 (***978-0-7377-3815-5(4)*** , Greenhaven Pr., Inc.) Thomson Gale.

Gifford, Clive. Gangs. 2006. (Illus.). 48p. (J). (978-1-58340-984-8(X)) Smart Apple Media.

Johnson, Julie. Why Do People Join Gangs? Sloan, Frank, ed. 2001. (Exploring Tough Issues Ser.). (Illus.). 48p. (J). (gr. 4-7). lib. bdg. 25.69 (978-0-7398-3236-3(0)) Raintree.

Neri, Greg. Yummy: The Last Days of a Southside Shorty. DuBurke, Randy, illus. 2007. (J). (978-1-58430-266-7(6)); pap. (978-1-58430-267-4(4)) Lee & Low Bks., Inc.

Robbins-Turner, Darlene. Wake up & Recognize: Life of a Stepdaughter. Hendricks, Tracey, illus. Date not set. (YA). 16.95 (978-1-889506-09-8(5)) Kendar Publishing, Inc.

Stark, Evan. Pandillas Juveniles en Guayaquil. 2002. (Todo lo Que Necesitas Saber Ser.). (SPA & ENG., Illus.). 64p. (YA). lib. bdg. 26.50 (978-0-8239-3584-0(1) , Buenas Letra) Rosen Publishing Group, Inc., The.

Watkins, Christi. How Can Gang Violence Be Prevented? 2006. (Illus.). 128p. (J). (gr. 10-12). 21.20 (978-0-7377-2381-6(5)); pap. 29.95 (978-0-7377-2380-9(7)) Thomson Gale. (Greenhaven Pr., Inc.).

Worth, Richard. Gangs & Crime. 2001. (Crime, Justice & Punishment Ser.). (Illus.). 80p. (J). 30.00 (978-0-7910-5767-4(4) , Chelsea Hse.) Facts On File, Inc.

GANGS—FICTION

Allred, Alexandra Powe. The Code. 2002. 167p. (J). pap. 5.95 (978-0-7569-0692-4(X)); (gr. 3-6). lib. bdg. 13.95 (978-0-7569-0693-1(8)) Perfection Learning Corp.

Anfousse, Ginette. A Terrible Secret. Hutchison, Jennifer, tr. from FRE. 2000. (SideStreets Ser.). (gr. 7-12). 112p. 7.95 (978-1-55028-704-2(4)); 108p. (YA). (***978-1-55028-705-9(2)***) Lorimer, James & Co., Ltd., Pubs. CAN. *Dist:* Casemate Pubs. & Bk. Distributors, LLC.

—Terrible Secret. 2001. (gr. 7-12). lib. bdg. 13.00 (978-0-613-42804-0(8)) Tandem Library Bks.

Arrigan, Mary & Paul, Korky. The Mummy Family Find Fame. 2006. (Red Bananas Ser.). (Illus.). 48p. (J). pap. (978-0-7787-1090-5(4)) Crabtree Publishing Co.

Ashley, Bernard. Little Soldier: A Novel. 2002. (Illus.). 240p. (J). (gr. 9 up). pap. 16.95 (978-0-439-22424-6(1) , Scholastic Pr.) Scholastic, Inc.

Bateman, Colin. Bring Me the Head of Oliver Plunkett. 2005. 272p. (gr. 4-7). lib. bdg. 17.99 (978-0-385-90269-4(7) , Delacorte Bks. for Young Readers) Random Hse. Children's Bks.

—Running with the Reservoir Pups. 2005. 272p. (J). (gr. 5-9). lib. bdg. 17.99 (978-0-385-90268-7(9) , Delacorte Bks. for Young Readers) Random Hse. Children's Bks.

Big Bad Bully. 2005. 32p. (J). 12.99 (978-0-9758709-1-4(2) , A.W.A. Gang) Journey Stone Creations, LLC.

Bock, Suzanne, illus. Meet the Angels, lt. ed. 2004. 10p. (J). bds. 12.99 (978-0-9758709-4-5(7) , 13401) Journey Stone Creations, LLC.

Brouwer, Sigmund. Hurricane Power. 2007. (Orca Sports Ser.). 176p. (YA). (gr. 5 up). pap. (***978-1-55143-865-8(8)***) Orca Bk. Pubs.

Brouwer, Sigmund. Sewer Rats. 2006. 112p. (gr. 5-10). lib. bdg. 14.95 (978-1-55143-527-5(6)); (J). pap. 7.95 (978-1-55143-488-9(1)) Orca Bk. Pubs. USA.

Bunting, Eve. Your Move. Ransome, James E., illus. 1998. 32p. (J). (gr. 1-5). 17.00 (978-0-15-200181-0(6)) Harcourt Children's Bks.

Coleman, James. The Circle. 2000. 120p. (YA). (gr. 7-12). pap. 9.95 (978-0-595-01081-3(4)) iUniverse, Inc.

Collier, James Lincoln. Chipper. 2001. (Illus.). 144p. (J). (gr. 5-9). 14.95 (978-0-7614-5084-9(X) , Cavendish Children's Bks.) Cavendish, Marshall Corp.

Collins, Anthony. Rip Power: Reading gave him the strength to fight Back! 2006. 178p. per. 12.99 (978-1-59886-469-4(6)) Tate Publishing & Enterprises, L.L.C.

Cooper, Susan. Dawn of Fear. Gill, Margery, illus. 2007. 176p. (J). pap. 5.95 (*978-0-15-206106-7(1)* , Harcourt Paperbacks) Harcourt Children's Bks.

Cross, Gillian. Tightrope. 1999. 224p. (J). (gr. 7 up). 16.95 (978-0-8234-1512-0(0)) Holiday Hse., Inc.

—Tightrope. 1999. 210p. (YA). (978-0-19-271804-4(5)) Oxford Univ. Pr., Inc.

Doder, Joshua. Grk & the Pelotti Brothers. 2006. 240p. (J). pap. (978-1-84270-527-8(X)) Andersen.

Doyle, Jenna. Phoenix Fire. 2005. 51p. pap. 12.95 (978-1-4137-6965-4(9)) PublishAmerica, Inc.

Draper, Sharon M. Romiette & Julio. Lowenbein, Adam, illus. (YA). (gr. 7-12). 2001. 336p. mass mkt. 6.99 (978-0-689-84209-2(0) , Simon Pulse); 1999. 240p. 18.99 (978-0-689-82180-6(8) , Atheneum) Simon & Schuster Children's Publishing.

Elster, Jean Alicia. I'll Do the Right Thing. Tadgell, Nicole, illus. 2003. (Joe Joe in the City Ser.). 32p. (gr. 1-5). 12.00 (978-0-8170-1408-7(X)) Judson Pr.

Ennis, Garth. The Slavers, Vol. 5. 2006. (Illus.). 144p. pap. 15.99 (978-0-7851-1899-2(3)) Marvel Enterprises, Inc.

Ewing, Lynne. Drive-By. 1998. 96p. (J). (gr. 5 up). pap. 4.99 (978-0-06-440649-9(0) , Harper Trophy) HarperCollins Pubs.

—Party Girl. 1999. 128p. (YA). (gr. 9-11). pap. 5.50 (978-0-375-80210-2(X) , Laurel Leaf) Random Hse. Children's Bks.

—Party Girl. 1999. (978-0-606-17373-5(0)); (gr. 7-12). lib. bdg. 13.00 (978-0-613-23023-0(X)) Tandem Library Bks.

—The Prophecy. rev. ed. 2004. (Daughters of the Moon Ser.: No. 11). 288p. (J). (gr. 7-17). 9.99 (978-0-7868-1891-4(3) , Volo) Hyperion Bks. for Children.

Ghose, Sanjoy. The Bodhisa TVA & the Gang. 1998. (Illus.). 48p. (J). pap. 50.00 (978-81-86982-25-9(6)) Business Pubns. Inc. IND. *Dist:* State Mutual Bk. & Periodical Service, Ltd.

Green, Jim. Shadows of the Moon... Dancing. 2007. (YA). pap. 14.95 (*978-1-59705-872-8(6))* Wings ePress, Inc.

Griffin, Peni R. The Music Thief. rev. ed. 2002. 160p. (YA). (gr. 5-8). 16.95 (978-0-8050-7055-2(9) , Holt, Henry & Co. Bks. For Young Readers) Holt, Henry & Co.

—The Music Thief. l.t. ed. 2003. 190p. (J). 21.95 (978-0-7862-5606-8(0)) Thorndike Pr.

Harris, Loretta. Who Did It & Why? 2006. (YA). (*978-0-9786681-1-2(1))* Children's Heart Publishing Co.

Henighan, Tom. Demon in My View. 2007. 176p. (J). pap. 12.99 (*978-1-55002-656-6(9)* , Boardwalk Bks.) Dundurn Group, The CAN. *Dist:* Univ. of Toronto Pr.

Hinton, S. E. The Outsiders. 2002. (YA). 14.04 (978-0-7587-7753-9(1)) Book Wholesalers, Inc.

—The Outsiders. l.t. ed. 2002. (LRS Large Print Cornerstone Ser.). (J). lib. bdg. 32.95 (978-1-58118-089-3(6) , 24874) LRS.

—The Outsiders. 2006. (Penguin Classics Ser.). 160p. (J). (gr. 12). pap. 13.00 (978-0-14-303985-3(7) , Penguin Classics); 208p. (YA). pap. 10.00 (978-0-14-240733-2(X) , Puffin) Penguin Group (USA) Inc.

—The Outsiders. 156p. (YA). (gr. 7 up). pap. 5.99 (978-0-8072-1430-5(2) , Listening Library) Random Hse. Audio Publishing Group.

—The Outsiders. 1999. (J). pap. 19.00 (978-0-88103-039-6(2)) Tandem Library Bks.

—The Outsiders. l.t. ed. 2005. 264p. pap. 10.95 (978-0-7862-7362-1(3) , Large Print Pr.) Thorndike Pr.

Hutchens, Paul. The Blue Cow. rev. ed. 1998. (Sugar Creek Gang Ser.: No. 30). 144p. (J). (gr. 4-7). 4.99 (978-0-8024-7034-8(3)) Moody Pubs.

—The Brown Box Mystery. rev. ed. 1998. (Sugar Creek Gang Ser.: No. 27). 128p. (J). (gr. 4-7). 4.99 (978-0-8024-7031-7(9)) Moody Pubs.

—The Case of the Missing Calf. rev. ed. 1999. (Sugar Creek Gang Ser.: No. 36). 96p. (J). (gr. 4-7). 4.99 (978-0-8024-7040-9(8)) Moody Pubs.

—The Cemetery Vandals. rev. ed. 1999. (Sugar Creek Gang Ser.: Vol. 32). 96p. (J). (gr. 4-7). 4.99 (978-0-8024-7037-9(8)) Moody Pubs.

—The Cemetery Vandals. 1999. (gr. 3-6). lib. bdg. 13.00 (978-0-613-90331-8(5)) Tandem Library Bks.

—Lost in the Blizzard. rev. ed. 1998. (Sugar Creek Gang Ser.: Vol. 17). 96p. (J). (gr. 4-7). 4.99 (978-0-8024-7021-8(1)) Moody Pubs.

—On the Mexican Border. rev. ed. 1998. (Sugar Creek Gang Ser.: Vol. 18). 94p. (J). (gr. 4-7). 4.99 (978-0-8024-7022-5(X)) Moody Pubs.

—Runaway Rescue. rev. ed. 1999. (Sugar Creek Gang Ser.: No. 34). 96p. (J). (gr. 4-7). 4.99 (978-0-8024-7038-6(6)) Moody Pubs.

—Runaway Rescue. 1999. (gr. 3-6). lib. bdg. 13.00 (978-0-613-90555-8(5)) Tandem Library Bks.

—The Trapline Thief. rev. ed. 1998. (Sugar Creek Gang Ser.: No. 29). 144p. (J). (gr. 4-7). 4.99 (978-0-8024-7033-1(5)) Moody Pubs.

—The Watermelon Mystery. rev. ed. 1998. (Sugar Creek Gang Ser.: No. 28). 160p. (J). (gr. 4-7). 4.99 (978-0-8024-7032-4(7)) Moody Pubs.

—The White Boat Rescue. rev. ed. 1998. (Sugar Creek Gang Ser.: No. 26). 128p. (J). (gr. 4-7). 4.99 (978-0-8024-7030-0(0)) Moody Pubs.

Inagaki, Riichiro. Eyeshield 21, Volume 12. 2007. (Eyeshield 21 Ser.). 208p. (YA). pap. 7.99 (978-1-4215-1061-3(8)) Viz Media.

—Eyeshield 21, Volume 13. 2007. (Eyeshield 21 Ser.). 216p. (YA). pap. 7.99 (978-1-4215-1062-0(6)) Viz Media.

Kir-On, Calanitte. The Adventures of the Gimmel Gang I: The Fake Mezuza. 2002. 75p. (YA). pap. 8.95 (978-1-931681-21-6(X)) Israel Bk. Shop.

Kline, Trish. The Fang Gang: KA Reader 4. 2007. (Illus.). 32p. (J). pr. 20.00 (*978-0-9717234-6-7(X))* Ghost Hunter Productions.

Kroll, Steven. Sweet America. 2004. 172p. (J). lib. bdg. 16.92 (*978-1-4242-0773-2(8))* Fitzgerald Bks.

Leblanc, Louise. Maddie Needs Her Own Life. Cummins, Sarah, tr. from FRE. Gay, Marie-Louise, illus. 2001. (First Novels Ser.: Vol. 40). 64p. (gr. 1-5). (J). (978-0-88780-551-6(5)); 4.95 (978-0-88780-550-9(7)) Formac Publishing Co., Ltd. CAN. *Dist:* Casemate Pubs. & Bk. Distributors, LLC.

Lee, Stan. Essential Fantastic Four, Vol. 5. 2006. (Marvel Essentials Ser.). (Illus.). 568p. pap. 16.99 (978-0-7851-2162-6(5)) Marvel Enterprises, Inc.

Lee, Sun-Hee, creator. Neck & Neck, Vol. 5. 5th rev. ed. 2006. (Illus.). 192p. (YA). pap. 9.99 (978-1-59816-099-4(0) , Tokyopop Kids) TOKYOPOP, Inc.

Lisle, Janet Taylor. How I Became a Writer & Oggie Learned to Drive. 2003. (Illus.). 160p. (YA). (ps-17). pap. 5.99 (978-0-14-250167-2(0) , Puffin) Penguin Group (USA) Inc.

Malton, Mel. The Drowned Violin: An Alan Dearing Mystery. 2006. 152p. (J). pap. 8.95 (978-1-894917-23-0(5)) Napoleon Publishing/Rendezvous Pr. CAN. *Dist:* Atlas-Books Distribution.

Marks, Burton. Tanya Tinker & the Gizmo Gang. Smath, Jerry, illus. 2003. 20p. (J). (ps-3). reprint ed. 22.00 (978-0-7567-6760-0(1)) DIANE Publishing Co.

Martinez, Agnes. Poe Park. 2004. 128p. (J). (ps-7). tchr. ed. 16.95 (978-0-8234-1834-3(0)) Holiday Hse., Inc.

Martinez, Victor. El Loro en el Horno: Mi Vida. 2003. (SPA., Illus.). 189p. (YA). (gr. 5-8). (978-84-279-3238-8(3) , NG9012) Noguer y Caralt Editores, S. A. ESP. *Dist:* Lectorum Pubns., Inc.

Mowry, Jess. Voodu Dawgz. 2007. 280p. (YA). pap. 14.99 (978-1-59092-359-7(6) , Blue Works) Windstorm Creative.

Murphy, Barbara Beasley & Wolkoff, Judie. Ace Hits Rock Bottom. 2003. (Can't Stop Ace Ser.: No. 2). 204p. (J). pap. 16.95 (978-0-86534-408-2(6)) Sunstone Pr.

—Ace Hits the Big Time. 2003. (Can't Stop Ace Ser.: No. 1). 184p. (J). pap. 16.95 (978-0-86534-407-5(8)) Sunstone Pr.

Myers, Walter Dean. Autobiography of My Dead Brother. Myers, Christopher, illus. 2006. 224p. (J). pap. 6.99 (978-0-06-058293-7(6) , Amistad) HarperCollins Pubs.

—Autobiography of My Dead Brother. Myers, Christopher, illus. 2005. 224p. (J). 15.99 (978-0-06-058291-3(X)); lib. bdg. 16.89 (978-0-06-058292-0(8)) HarperCollins Pubs. (Amistad).

—Los Escorpiones. (SPA.). (YA). (gr. 5-8). pap. (978-958-04-4381-0(5) , NR8278) Norma S.A. COL. *Dist:* Lectorum Pubns., Inc.

Nutrition Adventures with the Nutri Gang, Race Day, Issue #1: The Nutri Gang. 2007. (J). 2.99 (*978-0-9792383-0-7(7))* KJ Pubns.

Platt. Organized Crime, 6 Packs. 2004. (Illus.). pap. 45.90 (978-1-4109-1178-0(0)) Harcourt Schl. Pubs.

Rai, Bali. The Crew. 2003. 309p. pap. (978-0-552-54739-0(5) , Corgi) Transworld Publishers Ltd.

Randle, Kristen D. Breaking Rank. 2002. (gr. 7-12). lib. bdg. 15.25 (978-0-613-44511-5(2)) Tandem Library Bks.

Rodda, Emily. Dead End. 2006. (Emily Rodda's Raven Hill Mysteries Ser.: Vol. 6). (Illus.). 128p. (J). pap. 4.99 (978-0-439-79572-2(9) , Scholastic Paperbacks) Scholastic, Inc.

Rodriguez, Luis. It Doesn't Have to Be This Way. Galvez, Daniel, illus. 1999. 32p. (J). pap. 21.27 (978-0-516-21698-0(8) , Children's Pr.) Scholastic Library Publishing.

Rose, Gerald. Captain Cool & the Robogang. 1998. (Cambridge Reading Ser.). (Illus.). 64p. (gr. 2-6). pap. 12.00 (978-0-521-55648-4(1)) Cambridge Univ. Pr.

Said, S. F. The Outlaw Varjak Paw. McKean, Dave, illus. 2007. 272p. (J). (gr. 3-7). 6.50 (978-0-440-42172-6(1) , Yearling) Random Hse. Children's Bks.

Sandoval, Victor. Roll over, Big Toben. 128p. (YA). pap. 9.95 (978-1-55885-401-7(0) , Piñata Books) Arte Publico Pr.

Shusterman, Neal. Red Rider's Hood. 2006. (Dark Fusion Ser.). 192p. (YA). (gr. 7). pap. 6.99 (978-0-14-240678-6(3) , Puffin) Penguin Group (USA) Inc.

Sloan, Glenna. Stealing Time. 1998. 126p. (YA). (gr. 7-17). pap. 9.99 (978-0-88092-266-1(4) , 2664) Royal Fireworks Publishing Co.

Stamper, Norm. Breaking Rank: A Top Cop's Street-Smart Approch to Making America a Safe Place - for Everyone. 2005. 384p. 26.00 (978-1-56025-693-9(1) , Nation Bks.) Basic Bks.

Stern, Jacqueline. Dangerous Games, Vol. 4. Eckhardt, Jason C., illus. 2002. (Hollow Tree Mystery Ser.). 160p. 16.95 (978-1-57168-701-2(7)); 12.95 (978-1-57168-702-9(5)) Eakin Pr.

Stork, Francisco X. Behind the Eyes. 2006. 256p. (YA). (gr. 9). 16.99 (978-0-525-47735-8(7) , Dutton Adult) Penguin Group (USA) Inc.

Taylor, Theodore. Lord of the Kill. 2004. 256p. (J). pap. 5.99 (978-0-439-55956-0(1) , Scholastic Paperbacks) Scholastic, Inc.

Urrea, Lourdes, et al. Te Dije Que No Miraras. rev. ed. 2003. (Ediciones Castillo Castillo Del Terror Ser.).Tr. of I Told You Not to Look. (SPA.). 100p. (J). (gr. 2-6). pap. 6.95 (978-970-20-0308-3(3)) Castillo, Ediciones, S. A. de C. V. MEX. *Dist:* Macmillan.

Van Draanen, Wendelin. Sammy Keyes & the Search for Snake Eyes. VanDraanen, Wendelin, illus. 2003. (Sammy Keyes Ser.: Bk. 7). pap. 36.95 incl. audio (978-1-59112-273-9(2)); pap. 54.95 incl. audio compact disk (978-1-59112-281-4(3)) Live Oak Media.

—Sammy Keyes & the Search for Snake Eyes. (Sammy Keyes Ser.: Bk. 7). (gr. 5). 2003. 320p. (J). pap. 5.99 (978-0-440-41900-6(X) , Yearling); 2002. 272p. lib. bdg. 17.99 (978-0-375-91175-0(8) , Knopf Bks. for Young Readers) Random Hse. Children's Bks.

Watt, Kammile. The Adventures of the Box Canyon Gang. 2002. 64p. pap. 12.95 (978-1-59286-114-9(8)) PublishAmerica, Inc.

Weber, Richard D. Elvis & Me. 2004. 511p. (YA). per. 17.41 (978-1-4116-0549-7(7)) Lulu.com.

Wicke, Ed. Mattie & the Highwaymen. Warne, Tom, illus. 2003. 232p. (J). per. 8.99 (978-0-9677652-1-1(8) , BlacknBlue Pr. UK) Blacknblue Pr.

Windle, Jeanette. Jana's Journal: A Novel for Teens. 2002. 256p. pap. 12.99 (978-0-8254-4117-2(X)) Kregel Pubns.

—Secret of the Dragon Mark, Vol. 5. 2002. (Parker Twins Ser.: No. 5). 160p. (gr. 3-8). pap. 5.99 (978-0-8254-4149-3(8)) Kregel Pubns.

Wishinsky, Frieda. Just Call Me Joe. 2003. (Orca Young Readers Ser.). (Illus.). 112p. (J). (gr. 3-6). pap. 4.99 (978-1-55143-249-6(8)) Orca Bk. Pubs. USA.

Young, Diane. See No Evil. 2006. (Orca Currents Ser.). 112p. (J). pap. (978-1-55143-619-7(1)) Orca Bk. Pubs.

—See No Evil. 2006. 112p. (J). lib. bdg. 14.95 (978-1-55143-664-7(7)) Orca Bk. Pubs. USA.

Zephaniah, Benjamin. Gangsta Rap. 2004. 200p. (J). (gr. 9 up). pap. 7.95 (978-1-58234-886-5(3) , Bloomsbury Children) Bloomsbury Publishing.

GANNETT, DEBORAH (SAMPSON) 1760-1827

Burke, Rick. Deborah Sampson. 2003. (American Lives Ser.). (Illus.). 32p. (J). lib. bdg. 24.22 (978-1-4034-0729-0(0)); pap. 6.50 (978-1-4034-3104-2(3)) Heinemann Library.

McDonnell, Peter. A Soldier in Disguise. Tormey, Carlotta, illus. 2005. 16p. (J). pap. (*978-0-7367-2909-3(7))* Zaner-Bloser, Inc.

GARAGES

Dorling Kindersley Publishing Staff. Garage. 2005. (Illus.). 16p. (J). (ps-3). pap. 6.99 (978-0-7566-1330-3(2)) Dorling Kindersley Publishing, Inc.

Hiner, Mark. Village Garage. Thatcher, Fran, illus. 2001. 3p. (J). 16.95 (978-1-902413-62-4(8)) Van der Meer, a Div. of PHPC GBR. *Dist:* Abbeville Pr., Inc.

GARAGES—FICTION

Bienert, Kristin, ed. Monster Nation Jr. 2007. 32p. (J). pap. 6.99 (*978-0-696-23688-4(5))* Meredith Bks.

GARBAGE

see Refuse and Refuse Disposal

GARDEN PESTS

see Insects, Injurious and Beneficial

GARDENING

Here are entered works on the practical operations in the cultivation of fruits, vegetables, flowers and ornamental plants.

see also Flower Gardening; Fruit Culture; Gardens; Insects, Injurious and Beneficial; Organiculture; Plant Propagation; Plants; Plants, Cultivated; Vegetable Gardening; Weeds

Akmon, Nancy C. In My Garden. Akmon, Roni, illus. 2000. 84p. (J). (ps-3). 18.95 (978-1-884807-48-0(8) , EC748) Blushing Rose Publishing.

Aldrich, William & Williamson, Don. Gardening Month by Month in Illinois, Vol. 1. rev. ed. 2004. (Illus.). 160p. (J). (gr. 4). pap. 15.95 (978-1-55105-375-2(6)) Lone Pine Publishing USA.

—Tree & Shrub Gardening for Illinois, Vol. 1. rev. ed. 2004. (Illus.). 352p. (gr. 4). pap. 18.95 (978-1-55105-404-9(3)) Lone Pine Publishing USA.

Amateis, Carole & Amateis-Marsh, Melissa. Benjamin Bean: Planting, Growing, Harvesting. Sides, Randy, illus. 2000. 42p. (YA). pap. (978-0-7392-0505-1(6) , PO4148) Morris Publishing.

Applewood Books Staff. Floral Birthday Book: Flowers & Their Emblems. 2000. (Illus.). 133p. 13.95 (978-1-55709-385-1(7)) Applewood Bks.

Ayers, Patricia. A Kids Guide to How Herbs Grow. 2000. (Digging in the Dirt Ser.). 24p. (J). (gr. k-4). lib. bdg. 18.75 (978-0-8239-5464-3(1) , PowerKids Pr.) Rosen Publishing Group, Inc., The.

Azarian, Mary. A Gardener's Alphabet. 2005. (Illus.). 32p. (J). (gr. k-3). reprint ed. 5.95 (978-0-618-54881-1(5)) Houghton Mifflin Co. Trade & Reference Div.

Barker, Cicely Mary. Gardener's Year. rev. ed. 2004. (Illus.). 112p. (J). (ps). 12.00 (978-0-7232-4938-2(5) , Warne) Penguin Group (USA) Inc.

Beck, Alison. Gardening Month by Month in Ontario. rev. ed. 2003. (Illus.). 160p. (gr. 4). pap. 15.95 (978-1-55105-361-5(6)) Lone Pine Publishing USA.

Beck, Alison & Binetti, Marianne. Gardening Month by Month in British Columbia. rev. ed. 2003. (Illus.). 160p. (J). (gr. 4). pap. 15.95 (978-1-55105-357-8(8)) Lone Pine Publishing USA.

Beck, Alison & Kelbaugh, Duncan. Gardening Month by Month in the Maritimes, Vol. 1. rev. ed. 2004. (Illus.). 160p. (J). (gr. 4). pap. 15.95 (978-1-55105-408-7(6)) Lone Pine Publishing USA.

Beck, Alison & Knapke, Debra. Gardening Month by Month in Ohio, Vol. 1. rev. ed. 2004. (Illus.). 160p. (gr. 4). pap. 15.95 (978-1-55105-406-3(X)) Lone Pine Publishing USA.

Beck, Alison & Szerlag, Nancy. Annual for Michigan, Vol. 1. Kubish, Shelagh, ed. rev. ed. 2002. (Illus.). 296p. (J). (gr. 4). pap. 18.95 (978-1-55105-346-2(2)) Lone Pine Publishing USA.

Beck, Alison & Wood, Tim. Gardening Month by Month in Michigan, Vol. 1. rev. ed. 2004. (Illus.). 160p. (J). (gr. 4). pap. 15.95 (978-1-55105-363-9(2)) Lone Pine Publishing USA.

Beck, Alison, et al. Gardening Month by Month in Washington & Oregon. rev. ed. 2003. (Illus.). 160p. (gr. 4). pap. 15.95 (978-1-55105-359-2(4)) Lone Pine Publishing USA.

Betanzos, Sue, illus. My New Backyard Garden. 2006. Tr. of Mi Nuevo Jardin del Traspatio. (SPA & ENG.). (J). (*978-0-9792253-0-7(2))* Tucson Botanical Gardens.

Blackaby, Susan. Growing Things, 6 bks. DeLage, Charlene, illus. Incl. Buds & Blossoms : A Book about Flowers. 22.60 (978-1-4048-0112-7(X)); Catching Sunlight : A Book about Leaves. 22.60 (978-1-4048-0111-0(1)); Green & Growing : A Book about Plants. 22.60 (978-1-4048-0107-3(3)); Plant Packages : A Book about Seeds. 22.60 (978-1-4048-0108-0(1)); Plant Plumbing : A Book about Roots & Stems. 22.60 (978-1-4048-0109-7(X)); World's Largest Plants : A Book about Trees. 22.60 (978-1-4048-0110-3(3)); 24p. (C). (gr. k-2). 2004. (Illus.). 2003. 135.60 (978-1-4048-0106-6(5)) Picture Window Bks.

Buczacki, Stefan & Buczacki, Beverley. Young Gardener. Sieveking, Anthea, photos by. 2006. (Illus.). 120p. (J). (gr. 1 up). 19.95 (978-1-84507-295-7(2)) Lincoln, Frances Ltd. GBR. *Dist:* Perseus Distribution.

Bull, Jane. The Gardening Book. 2003. (Illus.). 48p. (J). pap. 12.99 (978-0-7894-9216-6(4)) Dorling Kindersley Publishing, Inc.

Bulloch, Ivan. Watch It Grow. James, Diane, illus. rev. ed. 2004. (I Can Do It Ser.). 32p. (gr. 2-5). (J). pap. 5.95 (978-1-58728-501-1(0)); 12.95 (978-1-58728-500-4(2)) T&N Children's Publishing. (Two Can Publishing).

Burns, Kate & Apperley, Dawn. How Does Your Garden Grow? A Pop-Up & Pull-Tab Garden. 1998. (Illus.). 12p. (J). (ps-k). 10.95 (978-1-899607-51-8(X)) Sterling Publishing Co., Inc.

Canizares, Susan, et al. Garden. 2000. (Placebook Ser.). (Illus.). (J). pap. (978-0-439-15376-8(X)) Scholastic, Inc.

Carlson, Laurie M. Green Thumbs: A Kid's Activity Guide to Indoor & Outdoor Gardening. 2003. (Kid's Guide Ser.). (Illus.). 144p. (J). (gr. k-7). pap. 12.95 (978-1-55652-238-3(X)) Chicago Review Pr., Inc.

Chalmers, Michelle. Passages: A Journal for Growing Home. 1999. (Illus.). 151p. (YA). (gr. 7 up). 15.00 (978-0-9637696-4-0(2)) Growing Home.

Chasek, Ruth. Essential Gardening for Teens. 2000. (High Interest Bks.). (Illus.). 48p. (YA). (gr. 7-12). 23.00 (978-0-516-23356-7(4) , Children's Pr.); (YA). (gr. 7-12). pap. 6.95 (978-0-516-23556-1(7) , Children's Pr.); (J). pap. (978-0-531-17644-3(4) , Watts, Franklin) Scholastic Library Publishing.

Chasek, Ruth, contrib. by. Essential Gardening for Teens. 2000. (High Interest Bks.). (Illus.). 48p. (YA). (978-0-531-12144-3(5) , Watts, Franklin) Scholastic Library Publishing.

Comer, Arthur L., Jr. The Beginner's Guide to Successfully Growing Tillandsias - Commonly known as Air Plants. 2003. (Illus.). 10p. (YA). 3.95 (978-0-9752760-0-6(X)) ALCJR Enterprises.

Congdon, Vicky. Garden Fun! Indoors & Out, in Pots & Small Spots. Barberie, Heather, illus. 2002. (Quick Starts for Kids! Ser.). 64p. (J). (gr. 2-5). pap. 8.95 (978-1-885593-69-6(4) , Williamson Bks.) Ideals Pubns.

—Garden Fun! Indoors & Out, in Pots & Small Spots. 2002. (gr. 3-6). lib. bdg. 16.40 (978-0-613-57602-4(0)) Tandem Library Bks.

Culen, Gerald R., et al. Organics - A Wasted Resource? An Extended Case Study for the Investigation & Evaluation of Composting Other Organic Waste Management Issues. 2001. 114p. (YA). (gr. 6-12). stu. ed., spiral bd. 13.80 (978-1-58874-046-5(3)) Stipes Publishing L.L.C.

Danz, Cassandra. Mrs. Greenthumbs Plows Ahead: Five Steps to the Drop-Dead Gorgeous Garden of Your Dreams, 2. 1999. (J). pap. 12.70 (978-0-676-58495-0(0)) Random Hse., Inc.

Davies, Gill. In My Garden. Guile, Gill, illus. 2005. 20p. (J). (gr. k-4). reprint ed. 20.00 (978-0-7567-8702-8(5)) DIANE Publishing Co.

DK Publishing. Grow It, Cook It. 2008. 80p. (J). (gr. 2-5). 16.99 (*978-0-7566-3367-7(2))* Dorling Kindersley Publishing, Inc.

Dorling Kindersley Publishing Staff. Learn to Garden. 2005. (Illus.). 272p. 30.00 (978-0-7566-0916-0(X)) Dorling Kindersley Publishing, Inc.

Dunn, S. K. Grow for It! 2006. (Illus.). 48p. (978-0-439-80306-9(3)) Scholastic, Inc.

Eames-Sheavly, Marcia. The Appealing Apple. 2000. (Illus.). 28p. (YA). (gr. 4-9). pap. 8.00 (978-1-57753-271-2(6) , 142LM19) Resource Centre, The.

Eggleton, Jill. My Garden: Emergent Level Satellite Individual Title Six-Packs. (Sails Literacy Ser.). (gr. k-1). 27.00 (978-0-7578-7909-8(8)) Rigby Education.

Ehlert, Lois. Como Plantar un Arco Iris. Campoy, F. Isabel, tr. 2006. (SPA., Illus.). 32p. (J). bds. 6.95 (978-0-15-205723-7(4) , Voyager Bks./Libros Viajeros) Harcourt Children's Bks.

Fryer, Jane E. The Mary Frances Garden Book. fac. ed. 2000. (Illus.). 394p. pap. 22.95 (978-1-4021-9848-9(5) , Elibron Classics) Adamant Media.

Garden, Nancy. Garden. 2005. 128p. (J). 14.99 (978-0-7868-0376-7(2)) Disney Pr.

Gardening, Set. Incl. Flower Gardens. Pupeza, Lori K. lib. bdg. 22.78 (978-1-57765-031-7(X)); Indoor Gardens. Kinstad-Pupeza, Lori. lib. bdg. 22.78 (978-1-57765-035-5(2)); Organic Gardens. Pupeza, Lori K. lib. bdg. 22.78 (978-1-57765-748-4(9)); Patio Gardens. Pupeza, Lori K. lib. bdg. 22.78 (978-1-57765-034-8(4)); Vegetable Gardens. Kinstad-Pupeza, Lori. lib. bdg. 22.78 (978-1-57765-030-0(1)); Wildlife Gardens. Pupeza, Lori K.

lib. bdg. 22.78 (978-1-57765-032-4(8)); 32p. (J). (gr. k-6). (Illus.). 2002. Set lib. bdg. 136.68 (978-1-57765-525-1(7) , Checkerboard Library) ABDO Publishing Co.

Gibson, R. What Shall I Grow? 2004. (What Shall I Do Today? Ser.). 32p. (J). pap. 7.95 (978-0-7945-0388-8(8)); lib. bdg. 15.95 (978-1-58086-548-7(8)) EDC Publishing.

Golluch, Norbert & Kerp, Theo. Muriels Garten: Eine Paradiso-Geschichte. 1999. (GER., Illus.). 56p. (J). (978-3-257-00855-5(4)) Diogenes Verlag AG CHE. *Dist:* International Bk. Import Service, Inc.

Green Thumb Guides. 2001. (J). (gr. 2-6). lib. bdg. 95.72 (978-1-55916-250-0(3)) Rourke Publishing, LLC.

Greg's Guide to Common Sense Gardening in the Northwest. 2004. 29.95 (978-0-9639495-8-5(6)) Moore, Greg Publishing.

Haig-Brown, Roderick L. How to Get Your Lawn off Grass: A North American Guide to Turning off the Water. 2002. (gr. 7-12). lib. bdg. 24.55 (978-0-613-86085-7(3)) Tandem Library Bks.

Halfmann, Janet. Life in a Garden. 2000. (Lifeviews Ser.). (Illus.). 32p. (J). (gr. 5-7). lib. bdg. (978-1-58341-072-1(4) , Creative Education) Creative Co., The.

Harcourt School Publishers Staff. Cultivar y Jardin: Take-Home Book. 2001. (Vamos Ser.). (SPA., Illus.). (J). pap. 2.80 (978-0-15-319932-5(6)) Harcourt Schl. Pubs.

—Growing a City Garden: Take-Home Book. 2001. (Collections Ser.). (Illus.). (J). pap. 1.90 (978-0-15-319489-4(8)) Harcourt Schl. Pubs.

—Growing a City Garden Below Level. 3rd ed. 2002. (Trophies Reading Program Ser.). (Illus.). pap. 5.10 (978-0-15-323229-9(3)) Harcourt Schl. Pubs.

—How Does a Garden Grow. 3rd ed. 2002. (Trophies English Language Learners Ser.). (Illus.). pap. 5.10 (978-0-15-327644-6(4)) Harcourt Schl. Pubs.

—How to Grow a Garden On Level. 3rd ed. 2002. (Trophies Reading Program Ser.). (Illus.). pap. 5.10 (978-0-15-323082-0(7)) Harcourt Schl. Pubs.

Hardesty, Constance. Grow Your Own Pizza: Gardening Plans & Recipes for Kids. McClung, Jeff, illus. 2004. 128p. (gr. 4-7). pap. 16.95 (978-1-55591-398-4(9)) Fulcrum Publishing.

Herd, Meg. Learn & Play in the Garden Vol. 7: Games, Crafts & Activities for Children. 1999. (Environmental Bks.). (Illus.). 128p. (J). (ps-6). lib. bdg. 18.95 (978-1-56674-242-9(0) , HTS Bks.) Forest Hse. Publishing Co., Inc.

Horticultural Science: Compentency-Based Student Handbook & Planning Guide. 2003. 52p. (YA). pap., stu. ed. 12.95 (978-0-913163-34-4(1) , 978) Hobar Pubns.

Houle, Michelle. Lindsey Williams: Gardening for Impoverished Families. 2007. (Young Heroes Ser.). (Illus.). 64p. (J). (gr. 4-8). 24.95 (***978-0-7377-3867-4(7)*** , Kidhaven) Thomson Gale.

Hower, Fred & Beck, Alison. Tree & Shrub Gardening for Ohio, Vol. 1. rev. ed. 2004. (Illus.). 360p. (gr. 4). pap. 18.95 (978-1-55105-402-5(7)) Lone Pine Publishing USA.

Ichikawa, Satomi. Rosy's Garden. (Illus.). (J). (978-0-399-22388-4(6) , Philomel) Penguin Group (USA) Inc.

Johnson, S. & Evans, C. Starting Gardening. 2004. (First Skills Ser.). (Illus.). 32p. (J). lthr. 12.95 (978-1-58086-543-2(7)); pap. 4.95 (978-0-7945-0445-8(0) , Usborne) EDC Publishing.

Johnson, Sue. Usborne Starting Gardening. 2003. (gr. 3-6). lib. bdg. 12.95 (978-0-613-75364-7(X)) Tandem Library Bks.

Kate, M. Old Time Gardening Notebook. 1999. (Illus.). 64p. pap. 1.00 (978-0-486-40837-8(X)) Dover Pubns., Inc.

Kent, Lorna, illus. In the Garden. 2004. 8p. (J). bds. 3.99 (978-1-85854-088-7(7)) Brimax Books Ltd. GBR. *Dist:* Byeway Bks.

Kids' Gardening: 30 Great Gardening Project for Kids of All Ages. 2002. 64p. (J). pap. 14.98 (978-0-7525-8872-8(9)) Parragon, Inc.

Kindersley, Dorling. 1St Garden Act Bk. 2008. 48p. (J). (gr. 3). ring bd. 9.99 (***978-0-7566-3504-6(7)*** Dorling Kindersley Publishing, Inc.

Kinstad-Pupeza, Lori. Indoor Gardens. 2002. (Gardening Ser.). (Illus.). 32p. (J). (gr. k-6). lib. bdg. 22.78 (978-1-57765-035-5(2) , Checkerboard Library) ABDO Publishing Co.

Krezel, Cindy. Kid's Container Gardening: Year-Round Projects for Inside & Out. Curtis, Bruce, photos by. 2005. (Illus.). 88p. (J). (gr. 1-7). pap. 14.95 (978-1-883052-43-0(2)) Ball Publishing.

Lang, Gail M. Horticulture. 2007. (Green World Ser.). (Illus.). 136p. (J). (gr. 6-12). 37.50 (978-0-7910-8961-3(4) , Chelsea Hse.) Facts On File, Inc.

Lerner, Carol. My Indoor Garden. 1999. (Illus.). 48p. (J). (ps-3). 16.00 (978-0-688-14753-2(4)); 15.89 (978-0-688-14754-9(2)) HarperCollins Pubs.

Lindley, Nancy & Peters, Laura. Roses for Michigan, Vol. 1. rev. ed. 2004. (Illus.). 272p. (gr. 4). pap. 18.95 (978-1-55105-367-7(5)) Lone Pine Publishing USA.

Little, Brenda. The Secrets of Companion Planting: Restoring Nature's Balance. 2008. 144p. pap. 14.95 (***978-1-933317-93-9(0)***) Silverleaf Pr.

Loreno, Rose. In the Garden. 2002. (Windows on Literacy Ser.). (Illus.). 12p. (J). (978-0-7922-8492-5(5)) National Geographic Society.

Lovejoy, Sharon. Sunflower Houses: Inspiration from the Garden. 2001. (Illus.). 144p. (J). (gr. 4-7). pap. 13.95 (978-0-7611-2386-6(5) , 12386) Workman Publishing Co., Inc.

MacLeod, Elizabeth. Grow It Again. Price, Caroline, illus. unabr. ed. 1999. (Kids Can Do It Ser.). 40p. (J). (gr. 4-6). (978-1-55074-558-0(1)) Kids Can Pr., Ltd.

—Grow It Again. Price, Carolyn, illus. 1999. 40p. (J). (ps-ps). lib. bdg. 14.10 (978-0-613-16358-3(3)) Tandem Library Bks.

—Grow It Again: Kids Can Do It. 1999. (J). (978-0-606-16548-8(7)) Tandem Library Bks.

Make a Bottle Garden: Individual Title Six-Pack Pouch - Level L. (Lighthouse Ser.). 16p. (gr. 2 up). 28.00 (978-0-7578-0876-0(X)) Rigby Education.

Maurer, Tracy. Growing Herbs. 2000. (Green Thumb Guides Ser.). (Illus.). 24p. (J). (gr. 2-6). lib. bdg. 23.93 (978-1-55916-253-1(8)) Rourke Publishing, LLC.

—Growing House Plants. 2000. (Green Thumb Guides Ser.). (Illus.). 24p. (J). (gr. 2-6). lib. bdg. 23.93 (978-1-55916-254-8(6)) Rourke Publishing, LLC.

—Growing Vegetables. 2000. (Green Thumb Guides Ser.). (Illus.). 24p. (J). (gr. 2-6). lib. bdg. 23.93 (978-1-55916-256-2(2)) Rourke Publishing, LLC.

Morris, Karyn. Kids Can Press Jumbo Book of Gardening. 2000. (gr. k-3). lib. bdg. 24.55 (978-0-613-89107-3(4)) Tandem Library Bks.

—The Kids Can Press Jumbo Book of Gardening. Kurisu, Jane, illus. unabr. ed. 2000. (Jumbo Bks.). 240p. (J). (gr. 4-6). (978-1-55074-690-7(1)) Kids Can Pr., Ltd.

Morris, Ting & Morris, Neil. Growing Things. Levy, Ruth, illus. 2006. (J). (978-1-59771-026-8(1)) Sea-To-Sea Pubns.

The New Gardener. Date not set. (Essential Gardening Ser.). 96p. 6.98 (978-0-7525-9645-7(4)) Parragon, Inc.

Oliver, Clare. Life in a Flowerbed. 2002. (Microhabitats Ser.). (Illus.). 32p. (J). lib. bdg. 25.69 (978-0-7398-4329-1(X)) Raintree.

Otten, Jack. Watch Me Plant a Garden. (Welcome Bks.). (Illus.). 24p. (J). (ps-2). 2002. pap. 4.95 (978-0-516-23593-6(1)); 2001. 18.00 (978-0-516-23945-3(7)) Scholastic Library Publishing. (Children's Pr.).

—Watch Me Plant a Garden. 2002. (gr. k-3). lib. bdg. 12.95 (978-0-613-58814-0(2)) Tandem Library Bks.

Papazoglu, Paula. I Plant a Garden with My Mom. Gumm, Susan Kathleen, illus. 2005. (J). per. 15.00 (978-0-9754298-9-1(2) , Ithaca Pr.) Authors & Artists Publishers of New York, Inc.

Pattou, Edith. Mrs. Spitzer's Garden. Tusa, Tricia, illus. 2001. 32p. (J). (ps-2). 17.00 (978-0-15-201978-5(2)) Harcourt Children's Bks.

Pease, Pamela. The Garden Is Open. 1999. (Illus.). 32p. (J). (gr. k-6). 20.00 (978-0-9669433-1-3(7) , No. 9901) Paintbox Pr.

—The Garden Is Open: Signed Artist's Pop-Up Edition. Pease, Pamela, illus. 1999. (Illus.). 32p. (J). (gr. k-6). 24.00 (978-0-9669433-0-6(9) , 9901) Paintbox Pr.

Peters, Laura. Indoor Plants for Canada, Vol. 1. rev. ed. 2004. (Illus.). 264p. (J). (gr. 4). pap. (978-1-55105-389-9(6)) Lone Pine Publishing.

Peters, Laura & Didur, Dean. Gardening Month by Month in Manitoba, Vol. 1. rev. ed. 2003. (Illus.). 160p. (J). (gr. 4). pap. 15.95 (978-1-55105-400-1(0)) Lone Pine Publishing USA.

Peters, Laura & Hanbidge, Patricia. Gardening Month by Month in Saskatchewan, Vol. 1. rev. ed. 2003. (Illus.). 160p. (J). (gr. 4). pap. 15.95 (978-1-55105-398-1(5)) Lone Pine Publishing USA.

Pipe, Jim. Growing Plants. 2007. (J). (***978-1-59604-140-0(4)***) Stargazer Bks.

Planting a Garden. (Little Book Practice Reader). (J). (978-0-8136-2052-7(X)) Modern Curriculum Pr.

Planting & Growing: First Grade Guided Reading Level D. (On Our Way to English Ser.). (gr. 1 up). 27.75 (978-0-7578-7042-2(2)) Rigby Education.

Publishing Edc. Staff, Publishing. What Shall I Grow. 2003. (gr. 3-6). lib. bdg. 16.40 (978-0-613-75425-5(5)) Tandem Library Bks.

Pupeza, Lori K. Flower Gardens. 2002. (Gardening Ser.). (Illus.). 32p. (J). (gr. k-6). lib. bdg. 22.78 (978-1-57765-031-7(X) , Checkerboard Library) ABDO Publishing Co.

—Organic Gardens. 2002. (Gardening Ser.). (Illus.). 32p. (J). (gr. k-6). lib. bdg. 22.78 (978-1-57765-748-4(9) , Checkerboard Library) ABDO Publishing Co.

—Patio Gardens. 2002. (Gardening Ser.). (Illus.). 32p. (J). (gr. k-6). lib. bdg. 22.78 (978-1-57765-034-8(4) , Checkerboard Library) ABDO Publishing Co.

—Wildlife Gardens. 2002. (Gardening Ser.). (Illus.). 32p. (J). (gr. k-6). lib. bdg. 22.78 (978-1-57765-032-4(8) , Checkerboard Library) ABDO Publishing Co.

Quin, Caroline & Pearce, Sue. Gardening. 2004. (Activities for 3-5 Year Olds Ser.). (Illus.). 32p. pap. 11.00 (978-1-897675-40-3(2)) Brilliant Pubns. GBR. *Dist:* Parkwest Pubns., Inc.

Royston, Angela. Tierra: Miremos un Jardin. 2006. (Illus.). 24p. (J). 21.36 (978-1-4034-7547-3(4)); pap. 6.00 (978-1-4034-7556-5(3)) Heinemann Library.

Rushing, Felder. Dig, Plant, Grow: A Kid's Guide to Gardening. 2004. (Illus.). 160p. (J). (gr. 3-7). per. 16.99 (978-1-59186-093-8(8)) Cool Springs Pr.

Schwartz, David M. In the Garden. Kuhn, Dwight, photos by. 1999. (Springboards into Science Ser.). (Illus.). 24p. (J). (gr. 1 up). lib. bdg. 19.93 (978-0-8368-2242-7(0)) Stevens, Gareth Inc.

Shepherd, Matthew, et al. Pollinator Conservation Handbook: A Guide to Understanding, Protecting, & Providing Habitat for Native Pollinator Insects, 2003. (Illus.). 145p. pap. 19.95 (978-0-9744475-0-6(1)) Xerces Society, The.

Snyder, Inez. Gardening Tools. 2002. (Welcome Bks.). (Illus.). 24p. (J). (ps-2). pap. 4.95 (978-0-516-24037-4(4) , Children's Pr.) Scholastic Library Publishing.

Southwater Staff. Fun with Gardening. 2000. (Illus.). 96p. 12.95 (978-1-84215-138-9(X) , Southwater) Anness Publishing GBR. *Dist:* National Bk. Network.

Spohn, Rebecca. Ready Set Grow. 2007. 96p. pap. (***978-1-59647-132-0(8)***) Good Year Bks.

Storey Publishing Staff. Dinner from Dirt: Ten Meals Kids Can Grow & Cook. 1998. pap. 10.00 (978-0-676-57342-8(8)) Random Hse., Inc.

Synder, Inez. Gardening Tools. 2002. (gr. k-3). lib. bdg. 12.95 (978-0-613-58834-8(7)) Tandem Library Bks.

Talmadge, Ellen. Unearthing Garden Mysteries Vol. 1: Experiments for Kids. Curtis, Bruce, photos by. 2004. (Illus.). 96p. (gr. 4-7). 17.95 (978-1-55591-993-1(6)) Fulcrum Publishing.

Tanem, Bob & Williamson, Don. Gardening Month by Month in Northern California, Vol. 1. rev. ed. 2004. (Illus.). 160p. (J). (gr. 4). pap. 15.95 (978-1-55105-365-3(9)) Lone Pine Publishing USA.

Taylor, "Grandma" Mary. Randy Grows a Garden for Julia. Lawson, Keri, photos by. 2005. (J). 12.50 (978-1-58597-321-7(1)) Leathers Publishing.

Texas Agricultural Extension Service Staff, contrib. by. Junior Master Gardener Handbook. 2002. (SPA., Illus.). 192p. pap. 20.00 (978-0-9672990-8-2(X)) Texas Cooperative Extension.

Texas Cooperative Extension Staff, contrib. by. Operation Thistle: Seeds of Despair. 2002. (Junior Master Gardener Ser.). (Illus.). 204p. (J). lib. bdg. 29.50 (978-0-9672990-9-9(8)) Texas Cooperative Extension.

Tommes, Susanne & Ross, Thea. Wally's Big Book of Gardening. 2002. (Illus.). 42p. (J). pap. 14.95 (978-0-7892-0741-8(9)) Abbeville Pr., Inc.

Totilo, Rebecca Park. The Christian Kids' Gardening Guide: Cool Stuff for You to Make & Grow. 2004. (Illus.). 168p. (J). pap. 12.99 (978-1-58411-034-7(1) , Legacy Pr.) Rainbow Pubs. & Legacy Pr.

Tucker, Patrick & Minter, Brian. Gardening in Toronto. rev. ed. 2000. 160p. (J). (gr. 3). pap. 9.95 (978-0-919433-68-7(5)) Lone Pine Publishing USA.

Walker and Company Staff & Rockwell, Anne F. One Bean. Halsey, Megan, illus. 1999. 32p. (J). (ps-3). reprint ed. pap. 6.95 (978-0-8027-7572-6(1)) Walker & Co.

Wally's Big Book of Gardening. 2001. (Illus.). 42p. (J). pap. 16.95 (978-0-7892-0742-5(7) , Abbeville Kids) Abbeville Pr., Inc.

Walpole, Brenda. Funstation Let's Grow It!, 5 vols., Set. 1998. (Funstations Ser.). (Illus.). 48p. (J). (gr. 3-7). 17.95 (978-1-57145-348-8(2) , Silver Dolphin Bks.) Advantage Pubs. Group.

Walton, Sally & Donaldson, Stephanie. I Can Grow Things: How-to-Grow Activity Projects for the Very Young. 2000. (Show Me How Ser.). (Illus.). 48p. (ps-3). pap. 7.95 (978-0-7548-0221-1(3) , Lorenz Bks.) Anness Publishing GBR. *Dist:* National Bk. Network.

What Fine Gardeners: Second Grade. (On Our Way to English Ser.). (gr. 2 up). 29.95 (978-0-7578-1419-8(0)) Rigby Education.

What Fine Gardeners: Small Versions. (On Our Way to English Ser.). (gr. 2 up). 29.00 (978-0-7578-7240-2(9)) Rigby Education.

What Makes Plants Grow? Second Grade Newcomer Books. (On Our Way to English Ser.). (gr. 2 up). 29.50 (978-0-7578-7212-9(3)) Rigby Education.

Whitehouse, Patricia. Plant & Prune. 2007. (Illus.). 24p. (J). (978-1-60044-210-0(2)) Rourke Publishing, LLC.

Whittlesey, Lisa. Junior Master Gardener Level One Handbook. Winn, Judy, ed. Price, Jackson, illus. 1999. 196p. (J). (gr. 3-5). pap., stu. ed. 20.00 (978-0-9672990-0-6(4) , B-6082) Texas Cooperative Extension.

Who Lives in the Garden? 2004. (Who Lives... Ser.). 12p. (J). bds. 4.99 (978-1-85854-643-8(5)) Brimax Books Ltd. GBR. *Dist:* Byeway Bks.

Williamson, Don. Organic Lawns in Canada, Vol. 1. rev. ed. 2005. (Illus.). 160p. (J). (gr. 4). pap. (978-1-55105-485-8(X)) Lone Pine Publishing.

Winckler, Suzanne. Planting the Seed: A Guide to Gardening. (Illus.). 64p. 2005. (gr. 5-12). 25.76 (978-0-8225-0081-0(7)); 2003. (J). (gr. 6-12). pap. 7.95 (978-0-8225-0471-9(5)) Lerner Publishing Group.

—Planting the Seed: A Guide to Gardening. 2002. (gr. 7-12). lib. bdg. 16.40 (978-0-613-46159-7(2)) Tandem Library Bks.

Yoon, Salina. Spring Fever! A Petal Tab Book. Yoon, Salina, illus. 2005. (Illus.). 12p. (J). bds. 6.99 (978-0-689-87424-6(3) , Little Simon) Simon & Schuster Children's Publishing.

GARDENING—FICTION

Aardvark, E. Gartner Jake. 2005. Orig. Title: Jake, the Gardener. (DAN.). 18.95 (978-0-9766859-6-8(5)) Macaronic Pr.

—Giacco il Giardiniere. 2005. Orig. Title: Jake, the Gardener. (ITA.). 18.95 (978-0-9766859-3-7(0)) Macaronic Pr.

—Jakke, den Traedgaardaren. 2005. (SWE.). 18.95 (978-0-9766859-7-5(3)) Macaronic Pr.

Aardvark, E. S. Jacques, le Jardinier: Chien D'Aveugle Trouve des Tresors. Zimmer, Dirk, illus. 2006. Orig. Title: Jake, the Gardener. (FRE.). 32p. 14.95 (978-0-9766859-1-3(4)) Macaronic Pr.

—Jake, der Gaertner. Zimmer, Dirk, illus. 2006. Orig. Title: Jake, the Gardener. (GER.). 32p. 14.95 (978-0-9766859-2-0(2)) Macaronic Pr.

—Jake, the Gardener: Guide Dog Digs Treasure. Zimmer, Dirk, illus. 2006. (Many Tongue Tales Ser.). Orig. Title: Jake, the Gardener. 14.95 (978-0-9766859-0-6(6)) Macaronic Pr.

—Jakke Puutarhurinna. 2005. (FIN.). 18.95 (978-0-9766859-8-2(1)) Macaronic Pr.

—Joao o Jardineiro. 2005. (POR.). 18.95 (978-0-9766859-5-1(7)) Macaronic Pr.

—Juan el Jardinero: El Perro Guia Excavador del Tesoro. 2005. (SPA.). 32p. 18.85 (978-0-9766859-4-4(9)) Macaronic Pr.

Aardvark, Esperanza. Jaap de Tuinman. Zimmer, Dirk, illus. 2006. (DUT.). 14.95 (978-0-9766859-9-9(X)) Macaronic Pr.

Argueta, Jorge. Xochitl & the Flowers / Xochitl, la Nina de Las Flores. Angel, Carl, illus. 2003. Tr. of Xochitl, la Nina de Las Flores. (ENG & SPA.). 32p. (J). 16.95 (978-0-89239-181-3(2)) Children's Bk. Pr.

Arnold, Marliese. Ghost Park Bks. 1 & 2: The Vanishing Gate & The Imposter. Spry, Alexis L., tr. from GER. Scholz, Barbara, illus. 2007. 215p. (J). (gr. 4-6). 12.95 (978-0-7358-2099-9(6)) North-South Bks., Inc.

Ayres, Katherine. Up, Down, & Around. Westcott, Nadine Bernard, illus. 2007. 32p. (J). (gr. k). 16.99 (978-0-7636-2378-4(4)) Candlewick Pr.

Bess, Stacey. Planting More Than Pansies: A Fable about Love. Ricks, Melissa, illus. 2003. (J). 14.95 (978-1-57008-893-3(4) , Shadow Mountain) Deseret Bk. Co.

Blackaby, Susan. Ann Plants a Garden. Collier-Morales, Roberta, illus. 2005. (Read-It! Readers Ser.). 32p. (J). (gr. k-3). 18.60 (978-1-4048-1010-5(2)) Picture Window Bks.

Boyden, Linda. The Blue Roses. Cordova, Amy, illus. 2002. 32p. (J). (gr. 1-5). 16.95 (978-1-58430-037-3(X)) Lee & Low Bks., Inc.

Brennan, Martin. I Saw It in the Garden. Monroe, Michael Glenn, illus. 2006. 32p. (J). 17.95 (978-1-58726-296-8(7) , Mitten Pr.) Ann Arbor Media Group, LLC.

Bronn, Charles Heil. The Sun, the Moon, & the Gardener's Son. Kami, Y. Z., illus. 2006. 30p. (J). (gr. 4-12). reprint ed. 16.00 (978-1-4223-5222-9(6)) DIANE Publishing Co.

Brown, Alan. Humbugs. 1998. (Illus.). 25p. (J). 22.99 (978-0-340-70960-3(X)); pap. 11.99 (978-0-340-70961-0(8)) Hodder General Publishing Division GBR. (Hodder & Stoughton). *Dist:* Trafalgar Square Publishing.

Brown, Margaret Wise & Hurd, Edith Thacher. Two Little Gardeners. Elliot, Gertrude, illus. 2006. 24p. (J). (gr. k-k). 2.99 (978-0-375-83529-2(6) , Golden Bks.) Random Hse. Children's Bks.

Bunting, Eve. Flower Garden. 2002. (Illus.). (J). 13.19 (978-0-7587-2519-6(1)) Book Wholesalers, Inc.

—Flower Garden. Hewitt, Kathryn, illus. 2000. 32p. (J). (ps-3). pap. 7.00 (978-0-15-202372-0(0)) Harcourt Children's Bks.

—Flower Garden. Hewitt, Kathryn, illus. 1999. 32p. (J). (ps-3). 25.95 (978-0-15-201968-6(5)) Harcourt Trade Pubs.

—Flower Garden. Hewitt, Kathryn, illus. 2000. (J). (ps-ps). lib. bdg. 14.15 (978-0-613-28490-5(9)) Tandem Library Bks.

—Flower Garden. 2000. 12.80 (978-0-606-17842-6(2)) Tandem Library Bks.

Bunting, Eve. Flower Garden: Lap-Sized Board Book. Hewitt, Kathryn, illus. 2008. 30p. (J). bds. 10.95 (***978-0-15-206516-4(4)*** , Red Wagon Bks.) Harcourt Children's Bks.

Care, Bears. Care Bears: Plant A Garden. 2008. 24p. pap. 3.99 (***978-0-545-00908-9(1)*** , Scholastic) Scholastic, Inc.

Cherry, Lynne. How Groundhog's Garden Grew. Cherry, Lynne, illus. 2003. (Illus.). 40p. (J). (ps up). pap. 15.95 (978-0-439-32371-0(1) , Blue Sky Pr., The) Scholastic, Inc.

Clark, Brenda, illus. Franklin Forgets. 2002. (Franklin Ser.). (J). 12.40 (978-0-7587-6588-8(6)) Book Wholesalers, Inc.

Corey, Irene. The Magic Garden. 2000. (J). (gr. k-3). pap. 7.00 (978-0-87602-376-1(6)) Anchorage Pr.

Ehlert, Lois. Growing Vegetable Soup. Ehlert, Lois, illus. 2002. (Illus.). (J). 27.74 (978-0-7587-2667-4(8)) Book Wholesalers, Inc.

—Growing Vegetable Soup. (Illus.). (J). (ps). 2007. 32p. bds. 10.95 (***978-0-15-206176-0(2)***); 2004. 30p. bds. 6.95 (978-0-15-205055-9(8)) Harcourt Children's Bks. (Red Wagon Bks.).

—Planting a Rainbow. Ehlert, Lois, illus. 2003. (Illus.). 32p. (J). bds. 6.95 (978-0-15-204633-0(X) , Red Wagon Bks.) Harcourt Children's Bks.

Ehlert, Lois. Planting a Rainbow: Lap-Sized Board Book. 2008. (Illus.). 32p. (J). bds. 10.95 (***978-0-15-206304-7(8)*** , Red Wagon Bks.) Harcourt Children's Bks.

Ellis, A. G. A Trellis for Mr. Ellis: Or How I Saved the World from Global Warming. Ellis, A. G. & Deaton, T. K., illus. l.t. ed. 2002. 32p. (J). per. 8.95 (978-0-9717451-1-7(0) , Louisa May Allcat Children's Bks.) Allcat Pr.

Elvgren, Jennifer Riesmeyer. Josias, Hold the Book. Tadgell, Nicole, illus. 2006. 32p. (J). 15.95 (978-1-59078-318-4(2)) Boyds Mills Pr.

Fisher, Valorie. When Ruby Tried to Grow Candy. 2008. (J). (***978-0-375-84015-9(X)***); 40p. lib. bdg. 19.99 (***978-0-375-94015-6(4)***) Random Hse. Children's Bks. (Schwartz & Wade Bks.).

Fleischman, Paul. Weslandia. 2002. (Illus.). (J). 23.40 (978-0-7587-3948-3(6)) Book Wholesalers, Inc.

—Weslandia. braille ed. 2004. (Illus.). (J). (gr. k-3). spiral bd. (978-0-616-01641-1(7)) Canadian National Institute for the Blind/Institut National Canadien pour les Aveugles.

—Weslandia. Hawkes, Kevin, illus. 40p. (J). (ps-3). 2002. pap. 6.99 (978-0-7636-1052-4(6)); 1999. 15.99 (978-0-7636-0006-8(7)) Candlewick Pr.

—Weslandia. Hawkes, Kevin, illus. 2001. (J). (gr. k-4). 26.95 incl. audio (978-0-8045-6869-2(3) , 6869) Spoken Arts, Inc.

—Weslandia. 2002. (gr. k-3). lib. bdg. 14.15 (978-0-613-63531-8(0)) Tandem Library Bks.

Fleming, Candace. Muncha! Muncha! Muncha! Karas, G. Brian, illus. pap. 16.95 incl. audio (978-1-59112-463-4(8)); pap. incl. audio (978-1-59112-465-8(4)); pap. 18.95 incl. audio compact disk (978-1-59112-923-3(0)); pap. incl. audio compact disk (978-1-59112-925-7(7)) Live Oak Media.

—Muncha! Muncha! Muncha! Karas, G. Brian, illus. 2002. 32p. (J). (ps-2). 17.99 (978-0-689-83152-2(8) , Atheneum/Anne Schwartz Bks.) Simon & Schuster Children's Publishing.

Florian, Douglas. Vegetable Garden. Florian, Douglas, illus. 2002. (Illus.). (J). 13.19 (978-0-7587-3896-7(X)) Book Wholesalers, Inc.

—Vegetable Garden. 2000. (Illus.). 31p. (J). (gr. 2-3). reprint ed. pap. 20.00 (978-0-7881-9459-7(3)) DIANE Publishing Co.

Freeman, Don & Inches, Alison. Corduroy's Garden. Freeman, Don & Eitzen, Allan, illus. 2004. (Easy-to-Read, Puffin Ser.). 32p. (J). (gr. k-3). pap. 3.99 (978-0-14-240131-6(5) , Puffin) Penguin Group (USA) Inc.

Friedlander, Eleanor. Mrs. Digger's Roots. Traverso, Laura, illus. 1999. 44p. (J). (ps-3). 17.95 (978-0-9672124-0-1(5)) Jadeda Pr.

Fry, Stella. Grandpa's Garden. Jago, illus. 2007. (J). ***978-1-84686-053-9(9))** Barefoot Bks., Inc.

Garland, Sarah. Eddie's Garden & How to Make Things Grow. 2004. (Illus.). 40p. (J). 15.95 (978-1-84507-015-1(1)) Lincoln, Frances Ltd. GBR. *Dist:* Perseus Distribution.

Garrigue, Sheila. The Eternal Spring of Mr. Ito. 1998. (J). pap. 3.95 (978-0-87628-340-0(7)) Ctr. for Applied Research in Education, The.

Gibson, B. J. Grannie's World Record Collard Greens. 2004. (J). pap. 10.00 (978-0-8059-5951-2(3)) Dorrance Publishing Co., Inc.

Gliori, Debi. Flora's Surprise! 2003. (Illus.). 32p. (J). (ps-1). pap. 15.95 (978-0-439-45590-9(1) , Orchard Bks.) Scholastic, Inc.

Grant, Judyann. Chicken Said Cluck. Date not set. (My First I Can Read Bks.). (J). lib. bdg. 16.89 (978-0-06-028724-5(1)) HarperCollins Pubs.

—My First I Can Read. Truesdell, Sue, illus. 2002. (My First I Can Read Bks.). 32p. (J). (ps up). 12.95 (978-0-06-028723-8(3)) HarperCollins Pubs.

Guest, C. Z. Tiny Green Thumbs. Krupinski, Loretta, illus. 2000. 32p. (ps-2). 15.99 (978-0-7868-0516-7(1)) Hyperion Bks. for Children.

Hafner, Marylin. Molly & Emmett's Surprise Garden. 2003. (Molly & Emmett Ser.). (Illus.). 32p. (J). (ps up). 12.95 (978-1-57768-895-2(3) , Cricket) School Specialty Publishing.

Hall, Kirsten. Green Thumbs. Burnett, Lindy, illus. 2002. (J). 3.99 (978-0-439-32095-5(X)) Scholastic, Inc.

Hall, Zoe. It's Pumpkin Time! Halpern, Shari, illus. 1999. 40p. (J). (ps-2). pap. 5.99 (978-0-590-55849-5(8)) Scholastic, Inc.

—It's Pumpkin Time. 1999. (J). 12.79 (978-0-606-17270-7(X)) Tandem Library Bks.

Hamsa, Bobbie. Larry, el Sucio. Catanese, Donna, illus. rev. ed. 2002. (Rookie Readers - Spanish Ser.).Tr. of Dirty Larry. (SPA.). 24p. (J). (gr. k-2). 19.50 (978-0-516-22690-3(8) , Children's Pr.) Scholastic Library Publishing.

—Larry, el Sucio. 2002. Tr. of Dirty Larry. (gr. k-3). lib. bdg. 12.95 (978-0-613-59505-6(X)) Tandem Library Bks.

Harcourt School Publishers Staff. Homegrown Advanced Level. 3rd ed. 2002. (Trophies Reading Program Ser.). (Illus.). pap. 5.10 (978-0-15-323289-3(7)) Harcourt Schl. Pubs.

—Jasper's Beanstalk: Little Book. 2000. (Collections Ser.). (Illus.). (J). pap. 10.20 (978-0-15-314504-9(8)) Harcourt Schl. Pubs.

—Kenny's Tomatoes Below Level. 3rd ed. 2002. (Trophies Reading Program Ser.). (Illus.). (gr. 4). pap. 5.10 (978-0-15-323221-3(8)) Harcourt Schl. Pubs.

—Kenny's Tomatos: Take-Home Book. 2001. (Collections Ser.). (Illus.). (J). (gr. 4). pap. 1.90 (978-0-15-319483-2(9)) Harcourt Schl. Pubs.

—Kids Can! 3rd ed. 2002. (Trophies English Language Learners Ser.). (Illus.). pap. 5.10 (978-0-15-327874-7(9)) Harcourt Schl. Pubs.

—Steff Grows an Apple: Take-Home Book. 1999. (Collections Ser.). (Illus.). (J). pap. 1.90 (978-0-15-317197-0(9)) Harcourt Schl. Pubs.

Harris, Ruth Elwin. Gwen's Story. 2002. (gr. 7-12). lib. bdg. 14.15 (978-0-613-74775-2(5)) Tandem Library Bks.

—Gwen's Story: Sisters of the Quantock Hills. 2002. (Quantock's Quartet Ser.). (Illus.). 288p. (YA). (gr. 7 up). pap. 5.99 (978-0-7636-1705-9(9)) Candlewick Pr.

Harwood, Beth. Amazing Baby Picture Pairs! 2007. (Amazing Baby Ser.). (Illus.). 16p. (J). bds. 5.95 (978-1-59223-596-4(4) , Silver Dolphin Bks.) Advantage Pubs. Group.

Hearn, Diane Dawson. Anna in the Garden. 2006. (Illus.). 29p. (J). (gr. k-4). reprint ed. 15.00 (978-1-4223-5087-4(8)) DIANE Publishing Co.

Henderson, Kathy. And the Good Brown Earth. Henderson, Kathy, illus. 2004. (Illus.). 40p. (J). (ps up). 15.99 (978-0-7636-2301-2(6)) Candlewick Pr.

Higgs, Liz Curtis. The Sunflower Parable. 10th anniv. ed. 2007. 32p. (J). 7.99 (978-1-4003-0845-3(3)) Nelson, Thomas Inc.

Hill, Eric. Spot's Little Book of Fun in the Garden. Hill, Eric, illus. 2003. (Spots Little Book of Fun Ser.). (Illus.). 10p. (J). (ps-k). 5.99 (978-0-399-23894-9(8) , Putnam Juvenile) Penguin Group (USA) Inc.

Hinman, Bonnie. Jennie's War: The Home Front in World War 2. 2005. (Sisters in Time Ser.). 144p. (J). pap. 4.97 (978-1-59310-659-1(9)) Barbour Publishing, Inc.

Hoffman, Alice. Green Angel. 128p. (J). 2003. (gr. 6 up). pap. 16.95 (978-0-439-44384-5(9) , Scholastic Pr.); 2004. reprint ed. pap. 5.99 (978-0-439-44385-2(7) , Scholastic Paperbacks) Scholastic, Inc.

Holub, Joan. The Garden That We Grew. Nakata, Hiroe, illus. 2001. 32p. (J). pap. 3.99 (978-0-14-131198-2(3) , Puffin) Penguin Group (USA) Inc.

—The Garden That We Grew. Nakata, Hiroe, illus. 2001. (J). (ps-3). lib. bdg. 11.80 (978-0-613-35612-1(8)) Tandem Library Bks.

—The Garden That We Grew. 2001. (Puffin Easy-to-Read Ser.). (Illus.). (J). 10.79 (978-0-606-21207-6(8)) Tandem Library Bks.

Holub, Joan. Spring Time! A Story about Seeds. Terry, Will, illus. 2008. (Ant Hill Ser.). 24p. (J). 13.89 ***978-1-4169-5132-2(6)**); pap. 3.99 ***978-1-4169-5131-5(8))** Simon & Schuster Children's Publishing. (Aladdin).

Hopkinson, Deborah. Bluebird Summer. Andersen, Bethanne, illus. 2001. 32p. (J). (gr. 1 up). 15.95 (978-0-688-17398-2(5)) HarperCollins Pubs.

Hopsalot's Garden. 2001. (Jumpstart Ser.). (Illus.). 32p. (ps-3). pap. 3.99 (978-0-439-20319-7(8)) Scholastic, Inc.

Hopsalot's Garden. 2000. (gr. k-3). lib. bdg. 11.80 (978-0-613-35615-2(2)) Tandem Library Bks.

Icanberry, Mark & Mount, Arthur. Super Salads. 1999. (Look, Learn & Do Ser.). (Illus.). 48p. (J). (gr. 3-5). 14.95 (978-1-893327-01-6(9)) Look, Learn & Do Pubns.

Janovitz, Marilyn. Can I Help? 1998. (Illus.). 32p. (J). (ps-3). pap. 5.95 (978-1-55858-904-9(X)) North-South Bks., Inc.

Jeffers, Dawn. Vegetable Dreams/Huerto Soñado. Schneider, Claude, illus. 2006. Tr. of Huerto Soñado. (SPA & ENG.). (J). pap. 4.99 (978-0-9770906-0-0(4) , 626999); 32p. lib. bdg. 16.95 (978-0-9741992-9-0(X) , 626999) Raven Tree Pr.

Kennedy, Marlane. Me & the Pumpkin Queen. 2007. 192p. (J). (gr. 3-7). 15.99 (978-0-06-114022-8(3)); lib. bdg. 16.89 (978-0-06-114023-5(6)) HarperCollins Pubs.

Klinting, Lars. Harvey the Gardener. 2006. (Handy Harvey Ser.). (Illus.). 40p. (J). (ps-k). pap. 4.95 (978-0-7534-5954-6(X) , Kingfisher) Houghton Mifflin Co. Trade & Reference Div.

Krauss, Ruth. The Carrot Seed. Johnson, Crockett, illus. 2000. 28p. (J). (ps-3). pap. 6.95 (978-1-931016-01-8(1) , MHC-1-1) Minnesota Humanities Commission.

LaReau, Kara. Rabbit & Squirrel. Magoon, Scott, illus. 2008. (J). ***978-0-15-206307-8(2))** Harcourt Trade Pubs.

Law, Felicia. Rumble Meets Randy Rabbit. Pak, Yoon Mi, illus. 2006. (Read-It! Readers Ser.). 32p. (J). (gr. 2-4). 18.60 (978-1-4048-1337-3(3)) Picture Window Bks.

Lin, Grace. The Ugly Vegetables. 2001. (Illus.). 32p. (J). pap. 6.95 (978-1-57091-491-1(5)) Charlesbridge Publishing, Inc.

—The Ugly Vegetables. Lin, Grace, illus. 1999. (Illus.). 32p. (J). (ps-3). 15.95 (978-0-88106-336-3(3)) Charlesbridge Publishing, Inc.

—The Ugly Vegetables. 2001. (978-0-606-22628-8(1)) Tandem Library Bks.

The Little Squash Seed. 2003. 32p. (J). 9.95 (978-1-57072-238-7(2)) Overmountain Pr.

Mattern, Joanne. The Tricky Garden. 2005. 22.00 ***978-1-4108-4191-9(X))** Benchmark Education Co.

McDonald, Erin Melodie. This Is My Garden. Hanrahan, Denise, illus. 2002. 24p. per. 9.95 (978-0-9721427-2-4(X)) Talking Hands, Inc.

McKissack, Patricia C. El Jardin de Bessey, la Desordenada. 2002. Tr. of Messy Bessey's Garden. (SPA.). (gr. k-3). lib. bdg. 12.95 (978-0-613-59503-2(3)) Tandem Library Bks.

—Messy Bessey's Garden. 2002. (gr. k-3). lib. bdg. 12.95 (978-0-613-53836-7(6)) Tandem Library Bks.

McKissack, Patricia C. & McKissack, Fredrick L. Messy Bessey's Garden. Regan, Dana, illus. rev. ed. 2002. (Rookie Reader Espanol Ser.). 32p. (J). (gr. k-2). pap. 4.95 (978-0-516-27386-0(8) , Children's Pr.) Scholastic Library Publishing.

—Messy Bessey's Garden Level C. Regan, Dana, illus. rev. ed. 2002. (Rookie Readers Ser.). 32p. (J). (gr. 1-2). 19.50 (978-0-516-22491-6(3) , Children's Pr.) Scholastic Library Publishing.

McLeod, Elaine. Lessons from Mother Earth. Wood, Colleen, illus. 2002. (J). (ps-1). 15.95 (978-0-88899-312-0(9)) Groundwood Bks. CAN. *Dist:* Transition Vendor.

Michael's Garden. 1998. (PNI Healing Stories for Children Ser.). 24p. (J). (gr. k-6). 6.95 (978-1-893351-02-8(5)) Asclepian Pr.

Mills, Susan & Shara, Diana. Frankie & Her Little Pals - Save the Watermelons. 2007. 32p. (J). ***978-0-9790690-3-1(3))** Lucky Red Pr., LLC.

Moncure, Jane Belk. Word Bird's Rainy-Day Dance. 2002. (New Word Bird Library). (Illus.). 32p. (J). (ps-3). 22.79 (978-1-56766-893-3(3)) Child's World, Inc.

Nettrour, Nelani. Jodi's Garden. 2006. (Illus.). 100p. (J). per. 14.95 (978-1-932657-63-0(0)) Third Millennium Pubns.

Ochiltree, Dianne. Sunflowers Measure Up! 2003. (Hello Math Reader Ser.). (Illus.). (J). (978-0-439-24228-8(2)) Scholastic, Inc.

Pak, Soyung. A Place to Grow. Truong, Marcellino, illus. 2002. (J). pap. (978-0-439-13017-2(4) , Levine, Arthur A. Bks.) Scholastic, Inc.

—A Place to Grow. Truong, Marcelino, illus. 2002. 32p. (J). (ps-5). pap. 16.95 (978-0-439-13015-8(8) , Levine, Arthur A. Bks.) Scholastic, Inc.

Pattou, Edith. Mrs. Spitzer's Garden. Tusa, Tricia, illus. 2007. 32p. (J). 9.95 (978-0-15-205802-9(8)) Harcourt Children's Bks.

Pellegrino, Marjorie White, ed. Too Nice. Matthews, Bonnie, illus. 2002. 48p. (YA). (gr. 4-7). 14.95 (978-1-55798-917-8(6)); pap. 8.95 (978-1-55798-918-5(4)) American Psychological Assn. (Magination Pr.).

Puttock, Simon. Pig's Prize. 2004. (Illus.). 32p. (J). 17.99 (978-1-4052-0538-2(5)); pap. 17.99 (978-1-4052-0880-2(5)) Egmont Bks., Ltd. GBR. *Dist:* Independent Pubs. Group.

Quattlebaum, Mary. Jackson Jones & the Curse of the Outlaw Rose. 2006. 112p. (J). (gr. 3-7). 14.95 (978-0-385-73349-6(6)); lib. bdg. 16.99 (978-0-385-90365-3(0)) Random Hse. Children's Bks. (Delacorte Bks. for Young Readers).

Raintree Steck-Vaughn Staff, contrib. by. Planting a Rainbow. 1999. (J). (ps-3). pap. 22.00 (978-0-8172-9787-9(1)) Steck-Vaughn.

Ray, Mary Lyn. Christmas Farm. Root, Barry, illus. 2008. (J). ***978-0-15-216290-0(9))** Harcourt Trade Pubs.

Rock, Maria. MiMi's Garden, It's a Kid Thing! A Guide for Beginning Gardeners. l.t. ed. 2003. (Illus.). 45p. (J). 12.95 (978-0-9726979-0-3(X)) Rock Ink.

Ross, Thea. Molly Mole Loves to Garden. 2004. (Lift-the-Flap Surprise on Every Spread! Ser.). 12p. (J). 5.99 (978-1-59384-044-0(6)) Parklane Publishing.

Rubel, Nicole. No More Vegetables! Rubel, Nicole, illus. 2002. (Illus.). 32p. (J). (gr. k-2). 16.00 (978-0-374-36362-8(5) , Farrar, Straus & Giroux (BYR)) Farrar, Straus & Giroux.

Saltzberg, Barney. Mrs. Morgan's Lawn. Saltzberg, Barney, illus. 1999. (Illus.). 32p. (gr. k-3). pap. 4.95 (978-0-7868-1294-3(X)) Hyperion Bks. for Children.

Saltzman, Ruth E. Poppy Bear: The Garden That Overslept. Deeter, Catherine, illus. 2001. 32p. (J). (gr. k-2). 16.95 (978-1-58270-042-7(9)) Beyond Words Publishing, Inc.

Sarmonpol, Paulette. Where Are My Onions? Vignale, Silvia, illus. 2000. 32p. (J). (ps-3). (978-1-896580-08-1(4)) Tradewind Bks.

Schatzer, Jeffery. The Runaway Garden. Ebbeler, Jeffrey, illus. 2007. 32p. (J). 17.95 ***978-1-58726-436-8(6)** , Mitten Pr.) Ann Arbor Media Group, LLC.

Segal, John. Carrot Soup. Segal, John, illus. 2006. (Illus.). 32p. (J). (ps-1). 12.95 (978-0-689-87702-5(1) , McElderry, Margaret K.) Simon & Schuster Children's Publishing.

Shinju, Mariko. A Pumpkin Story. Shinju, Mariko, illus. 1998. (Illus.). 32p. (J). (ps-4). 16.95 (978-1-880851-36-4(9)) Greene Bark Pr., Inc.

Smith, Maggie. This Is Your Garden. 2001. (978-0-606-21488-9(7)) Tandem Library Bks.

Spalding, Andrea. Me & Mr. Mah. Wilson, Janet, illus. 2000. 32p. (J). (ps-3). 14.95 (978-1-55143-168-0(8)) Orca Bk. Pubs. USA.

Stephens, Monique Z. Spring for Strawberry Shortcake. Yee, Josie, tr. Yee, Josie, illus. 2004. (Strawberry Shortcake Ser.). 32p. (J). (ps-2). mass mkt. 3.99 (978-0-448-43373-8(7) , Grosset & Dunlap) Penguin Group (USA) Inc.

—Spring for Strawberry Shortcake. 2004. (gr. k-3). lib. bdg. 11.25 (978-0-613-72570-5(0)) Tandem Library Bks.

Stewart, Sarah. The Gardener. Small, David, illus. 2002. (J). 15.49 (978-0-7587-2567-7(1)) Book Wholesalers, Inc.

—The Gardener. Small, David, illus. 2000. (J). pap. 19.97 incl. audio (978-0-7366-9203-8(7)) Books on Tape, Inc.

—The Gardener. Small, David, illus. (J). 2005. pap. 18.95 incl. audio compact disk (978-1-59112-312-5(7)); 1999. pap. 16.95 incl. audio (978-0-87499-431-5(4)) Live Oak Media.

—The Gardener. Small, David, illus. 2007. 40p. (J). pap. 6.95 ***978-0-312-36749-7(X))** Square Fish.

—The Gardener. 2000. 13.75 (978-0-606-17840-2(6)) Tandem Library Bks.

—Gardener. 2000. (gr. k-3). lib. bdg. 15.25 (978-0-613-29173-6(5)) Tandem Library Bks.

—The Gardener. Small, David, illus. unabr. ed. 1999. (J). (gr. k-3). pap., tchr. ed. 37.95 incl. audio (978-0-87499-432-2(2)) Live Oak Media.

Waddell, Martin. Something So Big. Canty, Charlotte, illus. 2004. 24p. (J). lib. bdg. 22.65 ***978-1-59646-706-4(1))** Dingles & Co.

Wellington, Monica. Zinnia's Flower Garden. Wellington, Monica, illus. 2007. 32p. (J). pap. 5.99 (978-0-14-240787-5(9) , Puffin) Penguin Group (USA) Inc.

Zunshine, Tatiana. A Little Story about a Big Turnip. Antonenkov, Evgeny, illus. 2004. 32p. (J). 15.95 (978-0-9646010-0-0(1)) Pumpkin Hse., Ltd.

GARDENING—POETRY

Havill, Juanita. I Heard It from Alice Zucchini: Poems about the Garden. Davenier, Christine, illus. 2006. 32p. (J). (gr. k-6). 15.95 (978-0-8118-3962-4(1)) Chronicle Bks. LLC.

Shannon, George. Busy in the Garden. Williams, Sam, illus. 2006. 40p. (J). 15.99 (978-0-06-000464-4(9)); lib. bdg. 16.89 (978-0-06-000465-1(7)) HarperCollins Pubs.

GARDENS

Appel, Dee. The Friends in My Garden. Francour, Kathleen, photos by. Date not set. (Tiny Times Board Book Ser.). (Illus.). 10p. (J). bds. 5.99 (978-0-7369-0564-0(2)) Harvest Hse. Pubs.

Barlowe, Dot. Flower Gardens to Paint or Color. 2007. 48p. pap., pap. 4.95 ***978-0-486-46204-2(8))** Dover Pubns., Inc.

Bauld, Jane Scoggins. The Story of MotherTree. l.t. ed. 2000. (J). 12.95 (978-1-929701-03-2(9)) Under the Green Umbrella.

Chalmers, Michelle. Passages: A Journal for Growing Home. 1999. (Illus.). 151p. (YA). (gr. 7 up). 15.00 (978-0-9637696-4-0(2)) Growing Home.

Eames-Sheavly, Marcia. The Three Sisters: Exploring an Iroquois Garden. Eames-Sheavly, Marcia, illus. 2000. (Illus.). 24p. (J). (gr. 4-7). pap. 5.50 (978-1-57753-269-9(4) , 142LM15) Resource Centre, The.

Emberley, Rebecca. My Garden/ Mi Jardin. 2005. (SPA & ENG., Illus.). 10p. (J). (ps-ps). bds. 6.99 (978-0-316-00049-9(3)) Little Brown & Co.

Loreno, Rose. In the Garden. 2002. (Windows on Literacy Ser.). (Illus.). 12p. (J). (978-0-7922-8492-5(5)) National Geographic Society.

Mary, Mary: 6 Small Books. (gr. k-2). 23.00 (978-0-7635-8499-3(1)) Rigby Education.

McKendry, Sam. A Little Whale Tale. Castillon, Carly, illus. 2005. (Stories to Share Ser.). 18p. (J). (ps-k). 9.95 (978-1-58117-146-4(3) , Intervisual/Piggy Toes) Dalmatian Pr.

Mr Kean's Garden: Fourth Grade Guided Comprehension Level O. (On Our Way to English Ser.). (gr. 4 up). 34.50 (978-0-7578-7166-5(6)) Rigby Education.

Nichol, Barbara. One Small Garden. Moser, Barry, illus. 2004. 56p. (J). (gr. 3-7). pap. 9.95 (978-0-88776-687-9(0)) Tundra Bks., Inc./Livres Toundra, Inc. CAN. *Dist:* Random Hse., Inc.

Raintree Steck-Vaughn Staff. Los Colores del Jardín. (SPA.). (J). (-k). 2000. pap. 19.24 (978-0-7398-0808-5(7)); 1999. pap., stu. ed. 21.50 (978-0-7398-0818-4(4)) Steck-Vaughn.

Royston, Angela. Tierra: Miremos un Jardin. 2006. (Illus.). 24p. (J). 21.36 (978-1-4034-7547-3(4)); pap. 6.00 (978-1-4034-7556-5(3)) Heinemann Library.

Sarkisian, Kevin. I Go to the Garden: Learning the Hard G Sound. (PowerPhonics Ser.). (Illus.). (J). 2002. 24p. (gr. 1). lib. bdg. 18.50 (978-0-8239-5907-5(4)); 2001. 23p. lib. bdg. 26.40 (978-0-8239-8252-3(1)) Rosen Publishing Group, Inc., The. (PowerKids Pr.).

School Specialty Publishing. In the Garden. 2004. (Brighter Child Activity Bks.). 32p. (J). (ps-1). pap. 2.99 (978-0-7696-3223-0(8) , Brighter Child) School Specialty Publishing.

Wickings, Ruth. Round the Garden. 2006. (World at Your Feet Ser.). (Illus.). 10p. 9.95 (978-1-84560-025-9(8)) Mercury Bks. Ltd. GBR. *Dist:* International Publishers Marketing.

Woodward, John. What Lives in the Garden? 2002. (What Lives...? Ser.). (Illus.). 48p. (J). (gr. 3 up). pap. 7.95 (978-0-7641-2108-1(1)) Barron's Educational Series, Inc.

GARDENS—FICTION

Ahlberg, Allan. It Was a Dark & Stormy Night. Ahlberg, Janet, illus. 1999. 32p. (J). (ps-3). 13.99 (978-0-670-85159-1(0) , Viking Juvenile) Penguin Group (USA) Inc.

Akley, Jason. Sweet Pea & the Bumblebee. 2007. (ENG.). 36p. (J). per. 16.95 ***978-1-4327-0341-7(2))** Outskirts Press, Inc.

Alexander, Carmen. Garden Stories: Rosemarie's Garden, Rosemarie's Roof Garden & Rosemarie Returns to Her Garden. Roswell, Stacey, illus. 2006. 60p. (J). pap. 14.99 (978-1-886383-55-5(3) , Little Blue Works) Windstorm Creative.

Alonso, Fernando. La Estatua y el Jardincito. (Superbks./Superlibros).Tr. of Statue & the Little Garden. (Illus.). 16p. (J). (gr. k-3). pap. 6.95 (978-0-88272-509-3(2)) Santillana USA Publishing Co., Inc.

Anholt, Laurence. The Magical Garden of Claude Monet. (Anholt's Artists Books for Children Ser.). 32p. (J). (ps-3). 2007. pap. 7.99 ***978-0-7641-3855-3(3));** 2003. (Illus.). 14.95 (978-0-7641-5574-1(1)) Barron's Educational Series, Inc.

Annabelle Alpaca Plants a Garden. 2002. (J). 7.99 (978-0-9746409-0-7(5)) O'Neill, Jan.

Arnold, Caroline. Wiggle & Waggle. Peterson, Mary, illus. 2007. 48p. (J). (gr. k-3). 12.95 ***978-1-58089-306-0(6))** Charlesbridge Publishing, Inc.

Ashman, Sarah & Parent, Nancy. Holly Bloom's Garden. Mitchell, Lori, illus. 2004. 32p. (J). 15.95 (978-0-9729225-0-4(4)) Flashlight Pr.

Auerbach, Annie. Dizzy & Muck Work It Out. 2002. (gr. k-3). lib. bdg. 11.25 (978-0-613-51299-2(5)) Tandem Library Bks.

Baglio, Ben M. Goat in the Garden. McNicholas, Shelagh, illus. 1998. (Animal Ark Ser.: No. 4). (J). (gr. 3-5). 10.64 (978-0-606-13132-2(9)) Tandem Library Bks.

Barker, Cicely Mary. Sweet Pea's Garden: Special Things to Make & Do a Flower Fairies Friends Book. 2005. 32p. (J). 7.99 (978-0-7232-5670-0(5) , Warne) Penguin Group (USA) Inc.

Beames, Margaret. Night Cat. Hitchcock, Sue, illus. 2003. 40p. (J). (gr. k-2). pap. 15.95 (978-0-439-38576-3(8) , Orchard Bks.) Scholastic, Inc.

Berry, Eileen M. Buttercup Hill. Harrald-Pilz, Marilee, illus. 2006. 39p. (J). (978-1-59166-667-7(8)) Jones, Bob Univ. Pr.

Blackaby, Susan. Ann Plants a Garden. Collier-Morales, Roberta, illus. 2005. (Read-It! Readers Ser.). 32p. (J). (gr. k-3). 18.60 (978-1-4048-1010-5(2)) Picture Window Bks.

Bogacki, Tomek. Mi Primer Jardin. 2003. (Picture Bks.). (SPA., Illus.). (J). (978-970-690-649-6(5)) Planeta Mexicana Editorial S. A. de C. V.

Bond, Michael. Paddington Bear in the Garden. Alley, R. W., illus. 2002. (Paddington Bear Ser.). 40p. (J). (ps-3). 15.99 (978-0-06-029696-4(8)) HarperCollins Pubs.

Bonnell, Kris. A Garden Is Fun. 2006. (J). 3.95 ***978-1-933727-37-0(3))** Reading Reading Bks., LLC.

Brenner, Barbara. Good Morning, Garden. Ortakales, Denise, illus. 2004. 32p. (ps up). 15.95 (978-1-55971-888-2(9) , NorthWord Bks. for Young Readers) T&N Children's Publishing.

Briggs-Ward, Barbara. Snarly Sally's Garden of ABC. (Illus.). 32p. 14.95 (978-1-890621-30-8(7)) Landauer Corp.

Brisson, Pat. The Summer My Father Was Ten. 2003. (Illus.). 32p. (J). (gr. k-2). 15.95 (978-1-56397-435-9(5)) Boyds Mills Pr.

—The Summer My Father Was Ten. Shine, Andrea, illus. 2003. 32p. (J). (gr. k-2). pap. 9.95 (978-1-56397-829-6(6)) Boyds Mills Pr.

—The Summer My Father Was Ten. 1999. (978-0-606-18015-3(X)) Tandem Library Bks.

Bryant, Jennifer. Into Enchanted Woods. Browne, James, illus. 2001. (Winterthur Book for Children Ser.). (J). (978-0-912724-59-1(5)) Winterthur, Henry Francis du-Pont Museum, Inc.

Buffie, Margaret. Dark Garden. 2001. (gr. 7-12). lib. bdg. 15.25 (978-0-613-87662-9(8)) Tandem Library Bks.

Bug in the Garden. Date not set. (Illus.). (J). bds. 1.98 (978-0-7525-9839-0(2)) Parragon, Inc.

Bumpy Slide Books Staff. Blue's Garden. Nickelodeon/Viacom International Staff, ed. 2000. (Blue's Clues: No. 6). (Illus.). 32p. (J). (ps-1). 3.49 (978-1-57973-072-7(8)) Advance Pubs. LLC.

Burnett, Frances Hodgson. El Jardin Secreto. 2001. (Illus.). (J). 16.60 (978-0-606-20735-5(X)) Tandem Library Bks.

—The Secret Garden. McKowen, Scott, illus. 2004. (Unabridged Classics Ser.). 248p. 9.95 (978-1-4027-1459-7(9)) Sterling Publishing Co., Inc.

—The Secret Garden. 2008. (Puffin Classics Ser.). 368p. (J). (gr. 3). pap. 4.99 (***978-0-14-132106-6(7)***, Puffin) Penguin Group (USA) Inc.

—The Secret Garden. 2002. (Illustrated Children's Library Ser.). (Illus.). 288p. (J). 12.99 (978-0-517-22115-0(2), Gramercy) Random Hse. Value Publishing.

—The Secret Garden. Corvino, Lucy, illus. 2005. (Classic Starts Ser.). 160p. 4.95 (978-1-4027-1319-4(3)) Sterling Publishing Co., Inc.

—The Secret Garden. Engelbreit, Mary, illus. 2007. (Mary Engelbreit's Classic Library). 368p. (J). (gr. 3-7). 9.99 (***978-0-06-008136-2(8)***, Harper Festival) HarperCollins Pubs.

—The Secret Garden: A Young Reader's Edition of the Classic Story. 2005. 332p. 29.95 (978-1-4218-0619-8(3), 1st World Library - Literary Society) 1st World Publishing, Inc.

—The Secret Garden: A Young Reader's Edition of the Classic Story. Kaster, Shelley Austin, illus. 2002. (Great Illustrated Classics Ser.). 240p. (J). (gr. 3-8). 21.35 (978-1-57765-809-2(4), ABDO & Daughters) ABDO Publishing Co.

—The Secret Garden: A Young Reader's Edition of the Classic Story. (J). 22.95 (978-0-8488-0692-7(1)) Amereon LTD.

—The Secret Garden: A Young Reader's Edition of the Classic Story. ed. 2004. (Illus.). (J). (gr. 1-4). spiral bd. (978-0-616-14565-4(9)); spiral bd. (978-0-616-14566-1(7)) Canadian National Institute for the Blind/Institut National Canadien pour les Aveugles.

—The Secret Garden: A Young Reader's Edition of the Classic Story. Moore, Inga, illus. 2008. 272p. (J). (gr. 1). 21.99 (***978-0-7636-3161-1(2)***) Candlewick Pr.

—The Secret Garden: A Young Reader's Edition of the Classic Story. 2005. 132p. per. 5.95 (978-1-4209-2229-5(7)) Digireads.com.

—The Secret Garden: A Young Reader's Edition of the Classic Story. 1999. (Illus.). 256p. (J). (gr. 4-7). pap. 3.00 (978-0-486-40784-5(5)) Dover Pubns., Inc.

—The Secret Garden: A Young Reader's Edition of the Classic Story. Tudor, Tasha, illus. 1998. 368p. (gr. 4 up). (YA). 17.99 (978-0-397-32165-0(1)); (J). reprint ed. pap. 6.99 (978-0-06-440188-3(X), Harper Trophy) HarperCollins Pubs.

—The Secret Garden: A Young Reader's Edition of the Classic Story. Cockcroft, Jason, illus. 2002. (Kingfisher Classics Ser.). 384p. (J). (gr. k-3). tchr. ed. 15.95 (978-0-7534-5479-4(3), Kingfisher) Houghton Mifflin Co. Trade & Reference Div.

—The Secret Garden: A Young Reader's Edition of the Classic Story. 2004. reprint ed. pap. 28.95 (978-1-4179-2544-5(2)); pap. 1.99 (978-1-4192-8193-8(3)) Kessinger Publishing, LLC.

—The Secret Garden: A Young Reader's Edition of the Classic Story. (English As a Second Language Bk.). (Illus.). 92p. pap. 4.46 net. (978-0-582-53417-9(8)) Longman Publishing Group.

—The Secret Garden: A Young Reader's Edition of the Classic Story. 1998. 248p. (J). reprint ed. lib. bdg. 25.00 (978-1-58287-069-4(1)) North Bks.

—The Secret Garden: A Young Reader's Edition of the Classic Story. 2002. (Oxford World's Classics Ser.). (Illus.). 368p. 8.95 (978-0-19-283596-3(3)) Oxford Univ. Pr., Inc.

—The Secret Garden: A Young Reader's Edition of the Classic Story. 2003. 288p. (gr. 12). mass mkt. 3.95 (978-0-451-52883-4(2), Signet Classics) Penguin Group (USA) Inc.

—The Secret Garden: A Young Reader's Edition of the Classic Story. 2003. (Modern Library Classics Ser.). 288p. pap. 7.95 (978-0-8129-6998-6(7), Modern Library) Random House Publishing Group.

—The Secret Garden: A Young Reader's Edition of the Classic Story. 304p. (J). (gr. 3-5). pap. 4.95 (978-0-8072-1412-1(4), Listening Library) Random Hse. Audio Publishing Group.

—The Secret Garden: A Young Reader's Edition of the Classic Story. Sauber, Robert G., illus. 2001. 56p. (J). (ps up). 9.98 (978-0-7624-0572-5(4), Courage Bks.) Running Pr. Bk. Pubs.

—The Secret Garden: A Young Reader's Edition of the Classic Story. 2006. (Scholastic Classics Ser.). vi, 222p. (J). (gr. 9-12). 25.00 (978-0-531-16960-5(X), Watts, Franklin) Scholastic Library Publishing.

—The Secret Garden: A Young Reader's Edition of the Classic Story. 1999. (Illus.). 320p. (J). (gr. 4-7). pap. 4.99 (978-0-439-09939-4(0)) Scholastic, Inc.

—The Secret Garden: A Young Reader's Edition of the Classic Story. Rust, Graham, illus. 1999. (J). pap. 22.95 (978-0-590-24077-2(3)) Scholastic, Inc.

—The Secret Garden: A Young Reader's Edition of the Classic Story. 1999. (Aladdin Classics Ser.). (Illus.). 416p. (J). (gr. 4-7). pap. 5.99 (978-0-689-83141-6(2), Aladdin) Simon & Schuster Children's Publishing.

—The Secret Garden: A Young Reader's Edition of the Classic Story. 2003. (gr. 3-6). lib. bdg. 11.80 (978-0-613-83894-8(7)); 1999. (978-0-606-17320-9(X)); 1999. (gr. 3-6). lib. bdg. 11.80 (978-0-613-63230-0(3)) Tandem Library Bks.

—The Secret Garden: A Young Reader's Edition of the Classic Story. 2005. (ENG.). 24.95 (***978-1-55742-519-5(1)***); pap. 15.95 (***978-1-55742-524-9(8)***) Wildside Pr.

—The Secret Garden: A Young Reader's Edition of the Classic Story. 1998. (Children's Classics). (ENG.). 224p. (YA). (gr. 8-12). pap. (978-1-85326-104-6(1), 1041WW) Wordsworth Editions, Ltd.

—The Secret Garden: With a Discussion of Compassion. Lauter, Richard, illus. 2003. (Values in Action Illustrated Classics Ser.). 191p. (J). (978-1-59203-037-8(8)) Learning Challenge, Inc.

—The Secret Garden Book & Charm. Tudor, Tasha, illus. deluxe ed. 2005. (Charming Classics). 368p. (J). 9.99 (978-0-06-075771-7(X), Harper Festival) HarperCollins Pubs.

Burnett, Frances Hodgson, ed. The Secret Garden: A Young Reader's Edition of the Classic Story. rev. ed. 2004. (Great Classics for Children Ser.). (Illus.). 192p. (J). 5.99 (978-1-4037-0798-7(7)) Dalmatian Pr.

Burnett, Frances Hodgson & Cockcroft, Jason. The Secret Garden: A Young Reader's Edition of the Classic Story. 2002. (Kingfisher Classics Ser.). (Illus.). 384p. (J). (978-0-7534-0602-1(0), Kingfisher) Houghton Mifflin Co. Trade & Reference Div.

Burnett, Frances Hodgson & Rust, Graham. The Secret Garden: A Young Reader's Edition of the Classic Story. 2000. (Illus.). 224p. (YA). (gr. 5 up). reprint ed. 18.95 (978-0-87923-649-6(3)) Godine, David R. Pub.

Carlson, Nancy L., tr. & illus. Harriet & the Garden. Carlson, Nancy L., illus. 2nd rev. ed. (Nancy Carlson's Neighborhood Ser.). 32p. (gr. k-2). 2005. 15.95 (978-1-57505-710-1(7)); 2004. (J). pap. (978-1-57505-612-8(7)) Lerner Publishing Group.

A City Garden, 6 Packs. (ps-2). 27.00 (978-0-7635-9441-1(5)) Rigby Education.

Cohn, Diana. Mr. Goethe's Garden. Mirocha, Paul, illus. 2003. 32p. 17.95 (978-0-88010-521-7(6)) SteinerBooks, Inc.

Colorful Garden: A Feelings Coloring Book. 2005. (Illus.). 17p. (J). 6.99 (978-0-9769150-0-3(6)) Bright Spots.

Curry, Kelli. Strawberry Shortcake & the Butterfly Garden. 2005. (All Aboard Reading Ser.). (Illus.). 32p. (J). (ps-2). mass mkt. 3.99 (978-0-448-43643-2(4), Grosset & Dunlap) Penguin Group (USA) Inc.

—Strawberry Shortcake & the Butterfly Garden. Artful Doodlers Limited Staff, illus. 2005. 31p. (J). (ps-ps). lib. bdg. 10.79 (978-0-606-33096-1(8)) Tandem Library Bks.

Curry, Peter. Millie in the Garden. 2004. (First Words with Millie Ser.). (Illus.). 12p. (J). bds. 3.99 (978-1-85854-507-3(2)) Brimax Books Ltd. GBR. *Dist:* Byeway Bks.

Dalmatian Press Staff, adapted by. The Secret Garden. 2002. (Spot the Classics Ser.). (Illus.). 180p. (J). (gr. k-5). 4.99 (978-1-57759-555-7(6)) Dalmatian Pr.

—The Secret Garden. (Illus.). (J). 9.95 (978-1-56156-312-8(9)) Kidsbooks, Inc.

—The Secret Garden. 1999. (978-0-14-771399-5(4), Penguin Classics) Penguin Group (USA) Inc.

Dannenmaier, Molly. Child's Garden. 1998. 35.00 (978-0-676-57282-7(0), Random Hse. Bks. for Young Readers) Random Hse. Children's Bks.

Davis, Maggie Steincrohn. Garden of Whales. 2000. (gr. k-3). lib. bdg. 15.25 (978-0-613-77755-1(7)) Tandem Library Bks.

—A Garden of Whales. O'Connell, Jennifer Barrett, illus. 2000. 32p. (J). (ps-2). reprint ed. pap. 6.95 (978-0-944475-35-5(3)) Camden Hse. Publishing CAN. *Dist:* Firefly Bks., Ltd.

Disney Staff. Pooh's Garden. 1999. (Pooh's Learn & Grow Ser.: Vol. 11). (Illus.). 12p. (J). 3.49 (978-1-57973-045-1(0)) Advance Pubs. LLC.

Dodee. That Big Old Round Orange Thing: A Mrs. Tockalocka Adventure. 2006. 64p. (J). per. 9.95 (978-1-60002-129-9(8), 3931, Airleaf Publishing) Airleaf Publishing & Bookselling.

Eakle, Kit. In My Grandmother's Garden. Eakle, Laura Jean, illus. l.t. ed. 2001. 32p. (J). (gr. k-5). 21.95 (978-0-9713194-0-0(5), MusicTales) MusicKit.COM.

Eggleton, Jill. The Hole in the Garden: Early Level Satellite Individual Title Six-Packs. (Sails Literacy Ser.). 16p. (gr. 1-2). 27.00 (978-0-7578-2932-1(5)) Rigby Education.

Erlich, Bev. Pink Roses Everywhere. gif. ed. 2004. (Illus.). 64p. (J). 14.95 (978-0-9743913-0-4(1)) Snojoy Publishing.

Eves, Sue. Hic. 2003. (Illus.). 32p. (J). 19.99 (978-0-370-32645-0(8)) Random Hse. GBR. *Dist:* Trafalgar Square Publishing.

Ficklin, Jonene H. The Garden Gate. 2005. (YA). 14.95 (978-0-9761188-2-4(3)) Victor's Crown Publishing.

Fitzl, Richelle Kristi, illus. Grandma's Garden. 2004. (J). (978-0-9741657-1-4(9)) Galaxia Publishing Group, LLC.

Fleischman, Paul. Seedfolks. Pedersen, Judy, illus. 1999. (Joanna Cotler Bks.). 112p. (J). (gr. 5 up). pap. 5.99 (978-0-06-447207-4(8), Harper Trophy) HarperCollins Pubs.

—Seedfolks. Pedersen, Judy, illus. 1999. 102p. (J). (gr. k-9). lib. bdg. 13.00 (978-0-613-18276-8(6)) Tandem Library Bks.

—Seedfolks. 1999. (978-0-606-16732-1(3)) Tandem Library Bks.

Ford, Miela. My Day in the Garden. Lobel, Anita, illus. 1999. 24p. (J). (ps-3). 17.99 (978-0-688-15541-4(3)) HarperCollins Pubs.

Foreman, Michael. Evie & the Man Who Helped God. 2003. (Illus.). 32p. (J). 18.00 (978-1-84270-219-2(X)) Andersen GBR. *Dist:* Independent Pubs. Group.

Francis, Pauline & Burnett, Frances Hodgson. The Secret Garden. 2003. (Fast Track Classics Ser.). (Illus.). 48p. (YA). pap. 9.99 (978-0-237-52535-4(6), Evans Brothers, Limited) Evans Publishing Group GBR. *Dist:* Independent Pubs. Group.

Gambrell, Linda B. & Dorling Kindersley Publishing Staff. Garden Friends. 2003. (Readers Ser.). (Illus.). (J). 32p. 12.99 (978-0-7894-9993-6(2)); 1p. pap. 3.99 (978-0-7894-9991-2(6)) Dorling Kindersley Publishing, Inc.

Garfield, Valerie. Harold & the Purple Crayon: The Giant Garden. 2002. (ps-2). lib. bdg. 11.80 (978-0-613-50439-3(9)) Tandem Library Bks.

Garis, Howard Roger. Daddy Takes Us to the Garden. 2006. 77.99 (***978-1-4280-3218-7(5)***) IndyPublish.com.

Garland, Sarah. Doing the Garden. 2008. (Illus.). 32p. (J). 9.95 (***978-1-84507-721-1(0)***) Lincoln, Frances Ltd. GBR. *Dist:* Perseus Distribution.

George, Lindsay Barrett. In the Garden: Who's Been Here? George, Lindsay Barrett, illus. 2006. (Illus.). 48p. (J). 16.99 (978-0-06-078762-2(7)); lib. bdg. 17.89 (978-0-06-078763-9(5)) HarperCollins Pubs.

Gershator, Phillis. Sky Sweeper. Meade, Holly, illus. 2007. 40p. (J). (gr. k). 16.00 (978-0-374-37007-7(9)) Farrar, Straus & Giroux.

Gilkey, Gail. Seashell Garden. 2005. (J). per. 9.95 (978-0-9662983-6-9(5)) Windy Hill Pr.

Gilmore, Rachna. Roses for Gita. Priestley, Alice, illus. 2004. 24p. (J). (CHI, ENG, TUR, PAN & GUJ.). (978-1-85269-367-1(3)); (GUJ, CHI, ENG, PAN & TUR.). (978-1-85269-369-5(X)) Mantra Publishing, Ltd.

—Roses for Gita. 2001. (gr. k-3). lib. bdg. 16.40 (978-0-613-53301-0(1)) Tandem Library Bks.

—Roses for Gita. Priestley, Alice, illus. 2005. 24p. (J). (gr. 3-6). pap. 7.95 (978-0-88448-224-6(3)) Tilbury Hse. Pubs.

Gingerich, Neeltje & Peterson, Joyce. The Secret Garden. 1999. 38p. (gr. 1-12). pap. 10.00 (978-0-88734-045-1(8)) Players Pr., Inc.

Godden, Rumer. An Episode of Sparrows. 2004. (New York Review Children's Collection). 256p. (J). reprint ed. 16.95 (978-1-59017-124-0(1), NYR Children's Collection) New York Review of Bks., Inc., The.

Greenburg, J. C. In the Garden. 2003. (Andrew Lost Ser.: Bk. 4). (Illus.). 96p. (J). (gr. 2-5). pap. 3.99 (978-0-375-81280-4(6), Random Hse. Bks. for Young Readers) Random Hse. Children's Bks.

Gugler, Laurel Dee. There's a Billy Goat in the Garden. Beaton, Clare, illus. 2003. 32p. (J). (ps-2). 14.99 (978-1-84148-089-3(4)) Barefoot Bks., Inc.

Hall, Zoe. The Surprise Garden. Halpern, Shari, illus. 1998. (J). (978-0-590-10076-2(9)) Scholastic, Inc.

Hall, Zoe & Halpern, Shari. The Surprise Garden. 1998. (Illus.). 32p. (J). (gr. k-4). pap. 15.95 (978-0-590-10075-5(0), Blue Sky Pr., The) Scholastic, Inc.

Harcourt School Publishers Staff. A Garden Grows On Level. 3rd ed. 2002. (Trophies Reading Program Ser.). (Illus.). (gr. 4). pap. 5.10 (978-0-15-323251-0(X)) Harcourt Schl. Pubs.

—In the Garden. 3rd ed. 2002. (Trophies English Language Learners Ser.). (Illus.). pap. 5.10 (978-0-15-327716-0(5)) Harcourt Schl. Pubs.

—My Enormous Turnip On Level. 3rd ed. 2002. (Trophies Reading Program Ser.). (Illus.). pap. 5.10 (978-0-15-323076-9(2)) Harcourt Schl. Pubs.

Harris, Sue. Butterfly Garden. Boey, Stephanie, illus. 2006. 20p. (J). 15.95 (978-0-8118-5247-0(4)) Chronicle Bks. LLC.

Harshman, Marc & Ryan, Cheryl. Red Are the Apples. Zahares, Wade, illus. 32p. (J). 2007. pap. 6.00 (***978-0-15-206065-7(0)***, Voyager Bks./Libros Viajeros); 2001. 17.00 (978-0-15-201917-4(0)) Harcourt Children's Bks.

Heap, Sue. Four Friends in the Garden. Heap, Sue, illus. 2004. (Illus.). 32p. (J). (gr. k-ps). 15.99 (978-0-7636-2371-5(7)) Candlewick Pr.

Henderson, Malcolm. Katie & Her Friends. Moss, P. Buckley, illus. 1998. 32p. (J). (ps-3). 15.95 (978-0-9665198-0-8(9), 0998001000) Moss Portfolio, The.

Hendrickson-Foy, Alyssa. The Mysterious Garden of Maude M. Mcnutt. Bachand, Stephen, illus. 2002. 22p. (J). pap. 6.00 (978-1-928972-07-5(1)) Critter Pubns.

Hill, Eric. Spot en el Jardin. (SPA.). pap. 4.95 (978-950-07-1967-4(3)) Editorial Sudamericana S.A. ARG. *Dist:* Distribooks, Inc.

Hirashima, Jean. Hello Kitty's House & Garden: Reusable Sticker Book. Henry, Allison, illus. 2003. 12p. (J). (ps-3). 13.95 (978-0-8109-4230-1(5)) Abrams, Harry N., Inc.

Hoberman, Mary Ann. Whose Garden Is It? Dyer, Jane, illus. 2004. 40p. (J). 16.00 (978-0-15-202631-8(2), Gulliver Bks.) Harcourt Children's Bks.

Hoffman, Eric. Play Lady - La Senora Juguentona. 2004. (Anti-Bias Books for Kids). (ENG & SPA., Illus.). 32p. (J). (ps-3). pap. 11.95 (978-1-884834-61-5(2)) Redleaf Pr.

Hopkinson, Deborah. A Packet of Seeds. Andersen, Bethanne, illus. 2004. 32p. (J). 15.99 (978-0-06-009089-0(8)) HarperCollins Pubs.

Hughes, Shirley. Enchantment in the Garden. 2007. (Illus.). 64p. (J). pap. 12.95 (***978-0-09-964441-5(X)***, Red Fox) Random Hse. Children's Bks. GBR. *Dist:* Independent Pubs. Group.

In the Garden, 6 Packs. (Literatura 2000 Ser.). (gr. 1-2). 28.00 (978-0-7635-0138-9(7)) Rigby Education.

In the Garden: Individual Title Six-Packs. (Sails Literacy Ser.). 16p. (gr. k up). 27.00 (978-0-7635-4416-4(7)) Rigby Education.

Inches, Alison. A Surprise for Wendy. Dubreuil, Diane, illus. 2002. (Bob the Builder Ready-to-Read Ser.: Vol. 4). 24p. (J). pap. 3.99 (978-0-689-84754-7(8), Simon Spotlight) Simon & Schuster Children's Publishing.

Inches, Alison & Freeman, Don. Corduroy's Garden. Eitzen, Allan, illus. 2002. (Viking Easy-to-Read Ser.). 32p. (J). (gr. k-3). 13.99 (978-0-670-03547-2(5), Viking Juvenile) Penguin Group (USA) Inc.

Island, Fiona. Wishbone's Magic Garden. 2006. 120p. pap. (***978-1-84401-733-1(8)***) Athena Pr.

Johnson, Rhonda & Paladin, Frank. The Little Garden. Amber, Holly & Davidsson, Ashton, illus. l.t. ed. 2004. 48p. (J). per. 16.95 (978-0-9763635-7-6(7), TLG01) Beyond the Stars Pubns.

Johnson, Sandi. Jades Garden. Johnson, Britt, ed. Perritt, Jordona, illus. 2000. (Sunflowers Ser.). 16p. (J). (ps-6). 8.99 (978-1-929063-53-6(9), 152) Moons & Stars Publishing For Children.

Jordan's Zoo: Individual Title, 6 packs. (ps-2). 27.00 (978-0-7635-9456-5(3)) Rigby Education.

Joslin, Mary. The Tale of the Heaven Tree. So, Meilo, illus. 1999. 32p. (J). (ps-3). 16.00 (978-0-8028-5190-1(8), Eerdmans Bks For Young Readers) Eerdmans, William B. Publishing Co.

Joyce, William. The Leaf Men & the Brave Good Bugs. 2001. (Illus.). (J). (978-0-606-21291-5(4)) Tandem Library Bks.

—Leaf Men & the Brave Good Bugs. 2001. (gr. k-3). lib. bdg. 15.25 (978-0-613-35969-6(0)) Tandem Library Bks.

Kindergarden: El Jardin del Arco Iris, 3 vols. 2002. Tr. of Kindergarden: El Jardin del Arco Iris. (SPA., Illus.). 192p. 50.00 incl. audio compact disk (978-84-494-2025-2(3), GML07104-186055) Oceano Grupo Editoria, S.A. ESP. *Dist:* Thomson Gale.

King, Dorothea. Teddybears' Garden. King, Dorothea, illus. 1999. (Teddybears Ser.). (Illus.). 8p. (J). bds. 3.95 (978-1-57717-105-8(5)) New Line Bks.

Kipling, Rudyard. Rikki Tikki Tavi & the Mystery in the Garden. Madsen, Jim, illus. 2006. (Easy Reader Classics Ser.: No. 2). 32p. (J). pap. 3.95 (978-1-4027-3290-4(2)) Sterling Publishing Co., Inc.

Kochenderfer, Lee. The Victory Garden. 2003. 176p. (J). (gr. 3-7). pap. 5.99 (978-0-440-41703-3(1), Yearling) Random Hse. Children's Bks.

La Montagne Secrete/Secret Mountain. A Treasure in My Gardem. 2007. 36p. 16.95 incl. DVD (***978-2-923163-14-7(1)***) La Montagne Secrete CAN. *Dist:* National Bk. Network.

Ladd, Frances Ann. How Does Your Garden Grow? Johnson, Jay, illus. 2004. (Care Bears Ser.). 32p. (J). 3.99 (978-0-439-54962-2(0)) Scholastic, Inc.

LaDeane, Symone. The Caterpillar That Would Be A Rainbow. 2007. 24p. (J). per. 11.99 (***978-1-59886-691-9(5)***) Tate Publishing & Enterprises, L.L.C.

Lakin, Patricia. Harold & the Purple Crayon: The Giant Garden. 2002. (Festival Reader Ser.). (Illus.). 32p. (J). (ps-2). pap. 3.99 (978-0-694-01641-9(1), Harper Festival) HarperCollins Pubs.

Larsen, Kirsten, et al. Lily's Pesky Plant. Clarke, Judith, illus. 2006. (Stepping Stone Bks.). 128p. (J). (gr. 2-4). 5.99 (978-0-7364-2374-8(5), RH/Disney) Random Hse. Children's Bks.

Lascurain, Anna. Apollo in the Moon House. 2006. Orig. Title: The Moonboy. (J). per. 7.99 (978-0-9769612-3-9(7), Pixiefire) Darker Intentiona Pr.

Lea, Laura. One Last Garden. 2007. (J). pap. 15.95 (***978-1-934603-00-0(7)***) Terracopiae Press, Inc.

LeapFrog Staff, compiled by. The Secret Garden. 2001. (J). spiral bd. 14.99 (978-1-58605-043-6(5)) LeapFrog Enterprises, Inc.

—Secret Garden. 2002. (J). (gr. 3-7). 14.95 (978-1-58605-917-0(3), LeapFrog Schl. Hse.) LeapFrog Enterprises, Inc.

Leppard, Lois Gladys. The Secret Garden. 2003. 160p. (J). mass mkt. 4.99 (978-1-889893-04-4(8), Ambassador-Emerald, International) Emerald Hse. Group, Inc.

Lin, Grace. The Ugly Vegetables. 2001. (Illus.). 32p. (J). pap. 6.95 (978-1-57091-491-1(5)) Charlesbridge Publishing, Inc.

—The Ugly Vegetables. Lin, Grace, illus. 1999. (Illus.). 32p. (J). (ps-3). 15.95 (978-0-88106-336-3(3)) Charlesbridge Publishing, Inc.

—The Ugly Vegetables. 2001. (978-0-606-22628-8(1)) Tandem Library Bks.

—Ugly Vegetables. 2001. (gr. k-3). lib. bdg. 15.25 (978-0-613-79134-2(7)) Tandem Library Bks.

Lisle, Janet Taylor. The Lost Flower Children. Ichikawa, Satomi, illus. 2001. 112p. (J). (ps-7). pap. 5.99 (978-0-698-11880-5(4), Putnam Juvenile) Penguin Group (USA) Inc.

—Lost Flower Children. 2001. (gr. 3-6). lib. bdg. 14.15 (978-0-613-35975-7(5)) Tandem Library Bks.

—The Lost Flower Children. l.t. ed. 2000. (Illus.). 188p. (J). 21.95 (978-0-7862-2890-4(3)) Thorndike Pr.

Londonderry, School. A Visit to Monet's Garden. Londonderry, School, illus. 2002. (J). bds. 12.00 (978-0-9676717-4-1(4)) Freet Publishing.

Look at the Garden: Individual Title, 6 Packs. (gr. 1-2). 22.00 (978-0-7635-9112-0(2)) Rigby Education.

Loye, David. Grandfather's Garden: Bedtime Stories for Little & Big Folk. 2008. (J). pap. 18.95 (***978-0-9795257-7-3(2)***) Benjamin Franklin Pr.

Lucado, Max. Hermie y sus Amigos del Jardín: Hermie & His Garden Friends. 2005. (Max Lucado's Hermie & Friends Ser.). (SPA.). 96p. (J). 14.99 (978-0-88113-853-5(3)) Grupo Nelson.

Mandy, et al. George's Garden. (Illus.). 16p. 2005. (URD, ENG, VIE, CHI & BEN.). 9.95 (978-1-84059-168-2(4)); 2000. (TUR, ENG, URD, VIE & CHI., (J). pap. 9.95 (978-1-84059-167-5(6)); 2000. (VIE, ENG, URD, TUR & CHI., (J). pap. 9.95 (978-1-84059-169-9(2)) Milet Publishing.

—George's Garden. Datta, Kanai, tr. from ENG. 2000. (Senses Ser.). (BEN, ENG, VIE, GUJ & URD., Illus.). 16p. (J). pap. 9.95 (978-1-84059-164-4(1)) Milet Publishing.

—George's Garden. Dave, Pratima, tr. Ford, Shaun, photos by. 2000. (Senses Ser.). (GUJ, ENG, VIE, CHI & BEN., Illus.). 16p. (J). pap. 9.95 (978-1-84059-166-8(8)) Milet Publishing.

Mansfield, Howard. Hogwood Steps Out. 2008. (Illus.). 32p. (J). 16.95 (***978-1-59643-269-7(1)***) Roaring Brook Pr.

Marie, Evelyn. Pick Your Own Strawberries. Stewart, Todd W., illus. 1998. 32p. (J). (gr. k-3). reprint ed. pap. 3.50 (978-0-9614746-3-8(7)) Berry Bks.

Martin-Larranaga, Ana, illus. Butterfly in the Garden. 2007. (J). bds. 5.95 (978-1-58925-803-7(7) , tiger tales) ME Media LLC.

Martin, Mary. Miss Lilly & the Hollyhock Garden. 2001. (Illus.). 48p. (J). 24.95 (978-1-58597-107-7(3)) Leathers Publishing.

Mayer, Mercer. Grandma's Garden. 2002. (Little Critter First Readers Ser.). (Illus.). 24p. (J). (gr. k-1). pap. 3.95 (978-1-57768-846-4(5)) School Specialty Publishing.

—Grandma's Garden. 2001. (gr. k-3). lib. bdg. 11.80 (978-0-613-67625-0(4)) Tandem Library Bks.

McCue, Dick. Bunny's Numbers. McCue, Lisa, illus. 2000. 14p. (J). (ps-3). bds. 4.99 (978-0-689-83086-0(6) , Little Simon) Simon & Schuster Children's Publishing.

McDonald, Erin Melodie. This Is My Garden. Hanrahan, Denise, illus. 2002. 24p. per. 9.95 (978-0-9721427-2-4(X)) Talking Hands, Inc.

McGraw-Hill - Jamestown Education Staff. Aliens & UFOs. 1999. (Wordsworth Classics Ser.). (gr. 6-12). pap. 16.64 (978-0-89061-104-3(1) , 9780890611043) Jamestown.

McGuire, Heather Ridgway. The Vegetable Garden. 2006. 17.00 (978-0-8059-9093-5(3)) Dorrance Publishing Co., Inc.

McKissack, Patricia C. El Jardin de Bessey, la Desordenada. 2002. Tr. of Messy Bessey's Garden. (SPA.). (gr. k-3). lib. bdg. 12.95 (978-0-613-59503-2(3)) Tandem Library Bks.

Metz, Lorijo. Floridius Bloom & the Planet of Gloom. Phelan, Matt, illus. 2007. 32p. (J). (gr. 1-3). 16.99 (978-0-8037-3084-7(5) , Dial) Penguin Group (USA) Inc.

Miller, Olive Beaupr. The Magic Garden of My Book House. 2005. reprint ed. pap. 24.95 (978-1-4191-4169-0(4)) Kessinger Publishing, LLC.

Montenegro, Laura Nyman. A Poet's Bird Garden. 2007. (Illus.). 32p. (J). (ps-3). 16.00 (978-0-374-36038-2(3)) Farrar, Straus & Giroux.

More Than a Meal. (Early Intervention Levels Ser.). 28.56 (978-0-7362-1049-2(0)) Hampton-Brown Bks.

Mullican, Judy. Bugs in the Garden. 2006. (J). pap. (978-1-57332-419-9(1)) HighReach Learning, Inc.

Murawski, Kevin, illus. Harold & the Purple Crayon: The Giant Garden. 128p. (J). (978-0-06-059705-4(4)) HarperCollins Pubs.

My Vegetable Garden. 2003. (J). per. (978-1-57657-896-4(8)) Paradise Pr., Inc.

Narvaez, Concha Lopez. El Arbol de los Pajaros Sin Vuelo. (SPA.). 128p. (YA). (gr. 5-8). (978-84-207-2905-3(1)) Grupo Anaya, S.A. ESP. *Dist:* Lectorum Pubns., Inc.

Noguchi, Rick & Jenks, Deneen. Flowers from Mariko. Kumata, Michelle Reiko, illus. 2001. 32p. (J). (gr. 1 up). 16.95 (978-1-58430-032-8(9)) Lee & Low Bks., Inc.

Our Garden: Second Grade Guided Reading Level L. (On Our Way to English Ser.). (gr. 2 up). 34.50 (978-0-7578-7102-3(X)) Rigby Education.

Owls in the Garden: Individual Title Six-Packs. 16p. (gr. 2 up). 35.00 (978-0-7635-9374-2(5)) Rigby Education.

Parent, Nancy. A Surprise Garden, 15 vols. Harchy, Atelier Philippe, illus. 2003. (It's Fun to Learn Ser.). 32p. (J). (ps-3). 3.99 (978-1-57973-126-7(0)) Advance Pubs. LLC.

Park, Linda Sue. What Does Bunny See? A Book of Colors & Flowers. Smith, Maggie, illus. 2005. 32p. (J). (ps-k). 15.00 (978-0-618-23485-1(3) , Clarion Bks.) Houghton Mifflin Co. Trade & Reference Div.

Parker, Kim. Counting in the Garden. 2005. (Illus.). 32p. (J). pap. 16.95 (978-0-439-69452-0(3) , Orchard Bks.) Scholastic, Inc.

Peters, Lisa Westberg. We're Rabbits! Mack, Jeff, illus. 2004. 32p. (J). 16.00 (978-0-15-204671-2(2)) Harcourt Children's Bks.

Pochocki, Ethel. The Gazebo. Owens, Mary Beth, illus. 2002. 30p. (gr. 3-6). 15.95 (978-0-89272-516-8(3)) Down East Bks.

Podoshen, Lois. Paco's Garden. Buket, illus. 1999. (Books for Young Learners). 12p. (J). (gr. k-2). pap. 5.00 (978-1-57274-235-2(6)) Owen, Richard C. Pubs., Inc.

Poole, Amy Lowry, illus. & retold by. The Pea Blossom. Poole, Amy Lowry, retold by. 2006. 32p. reprint ed. 6.95 (978-0-8234-2018-6(3)) Holiday Hse., Inc.

Potter, Beatrix. Peter Rabbit's Giant Storybook. 2000. (Illus.). 192p. (J). (ps-3). 15.99 (978-0-7232-4583-4(5) , Warne) Penguin Group (USA) Inc.

—The Tale of Peter Rabbit. Potter, Beatrix, illus. 2004. (Wee Books for Wee Folks). (Illus.). 64p. (J). (ps-3). reprint ed. 6.95 (978-1-55709-412-4(8)) Applewood Bks.

—The Tale of Peter Rabbit. Hague, Michael, illus. 2003. 29p. (J). (gr. 2-5). reprint ed. 16.00 (978-0-7567-6968-0(X)) DIANE Publishing Co.

—The Tale of Peter Rabbit. 1999. (Illus.). 12p. (J). (ps-k). bds. 6.99 (978-0-7232-4432-5(4) , Warne) Penguin Group (USA) Inc.

—The Tale of Peter Rabbit. (Illus.). 12p. 4.95 (978-1-58989-271-2(2)) Thurman Hse., LLC.

Potter, Beatrix, et al. The Tale of Peter Rabbit. Andersen, Alan, illus. 2001. (Little Golden Bks.). 24p. (gr. k-k). 2.99 (978-0-307-03071-9(7) , 98039, Golden Bks.) Random Hse. Children's Bks.

Quattlebaum, Mary. Jackson Jones & Mission Greentop. 2005. 112p. (gr. 3-7). 5.50 (978-0-440-41957-0(3) , Yearling) Random Hse. Children's Bks.

—Jackson Jones & the Curse of the Outlaw Rose. 2006. 112p. (J). (gr. 3-7). 14.95 (978-0-385-73349-6(6) , Delacorte Bks. for Young Readers) Random Hse. Children's Bks.

Quinones, Laura-Ann. Rainbow Flowers. 2006. 16p. (J). 10.68 (978-1-4116-6873-7(1)) Lulu.com.

Ray, Jane. Adan y Eva y el Jardin del Eden. Rodriguez, Maite, tr. 2005. (SPA., Illus.). 32p. (J). 12.95 (978-84-95939-84-5(3)) Blume ESP. *Dist:* Independent Pubs. Group.

Ready Reader Staff. The City Cat & the Country Cat, 6 bks., set, Level 8, Bk. 18. 2003. (J). (ps-3). pap. 33.50 (978-0-8136-2038-1(4)) Modern Curriculum Pr.

Rechkemmer, Jaime Marie. Caillou's Friends in the Garden. Storch, Ellen N., illus. 2006. (J). pap. (978-1-57332-373-4(X)) HighReach Learning, Inc.

Richards, Lucy. Little Garden. 2007. (Illus.). 10p. (J). bds. 4.99 (***978-1-84458-363-8(5)***) Anova Bks. GBR. *Dist:* Independent Pubs. Group.

The rock Garden: Individual Title Six-Packs. (gr. 1-2). 25.00 (978-0-7635-9195-3(5)) Rigby Education.

Rowlands, Avril. Animals to the Rescue & Other Stories. 2002. (Illus.). 128p. (J). pap. 7.99 (978-0-7459-4764-8(6) , Lion) Lion Hudson plc GBR. *Dist:* Independent Pubs. Group.

Ruck, Susan. Jonathan's Garden. Joyce, Susan, illus. 1998. 48p. (J). (gr. k-4). reprint ed. 17.35 incl. audio (978-0-9662934-1-8(X)) Sunflower Promotions, L.L.C.

Rylant, Cynthia. Annie & Snowball & the Pink Surprise. Stevenson, Sucie, illus. 2008. (Annie & Snowball Ser.). (J). (***978-1-4169-0941-5(9)*** , Simon & Schuster Children's Publishing) Simon & Schuster Children's Publishing.

Rylant, Cynthia. This Year's Garden. Szilagyi, Mary, illus. 1998. (J). pap. 4.95 (978-0-87628-397-4(0)) Ctr. for Applied Research in Education, The.

—This Year's Garden. 1999. (Illus.). (J). (ps-2). lib. bdg. 12.95 (978-0-8085-9240-2(8)) Tandem Library Bks.

Scott, Nathan Kumar. Mangoes & Bananas. Balaji, T., illus. 2006. 32p. 16.95 (978-81-86211-06-9(3)) Consortium Bk. Sales & Distribution.

Scraper, Katherine. Garden Lunch. 2006. (Early Explorers Ser.). (J). 30.00 (***978-1-4108-6027-9(2)***) Benchmark Education Co.

Scratch & Sniff: Garden. braille ed. 2004. (J). spiral bd., bds. (978-0-616-11141-3(X)) Canadian National Institute for the Blind/Institut National Canadien pour les Aveugles.

Seider, Sharon J. The Door in the Garden Wall. 2003. 139p. (J). pap. 13.95 (978-0-7414-1712-1(X)) Infinity Publishing.

Sekarski, Dan. Bemba's Secret Garden. 2006. (Illus.). 57p. (J). per. 16.95 (***978-0-9790110-0-9(0)***) Tpprince Esquire.

The Selfish Giant: Individual Title Six-Packs. (Literatura 2000 Ser.). (gr. 2-3). 33.00 (978-0-7635-0239-3(1)) Rigby Education.

Shaw, Irene. Cosy Cottage. 2006. (Illus.). 48p. pap. (***978-1-84401-792-8(3)***) Athena Pr.

Sleator, William. The Last Universe. (J). (gr. 7-11). 2006. 240p. pap. 6.95 (978-0-8109-9213-9(2)); 2005. 224p. 16.95 (978-0-8109-5858-6(9) , Amulet Bks.) Abrams, Harry N., Inc.

Smith, Jeremy. Lily's Garden of India. Hefferan, Rob, illus. 2003. 32p. (J). 15.95 (978-1-57768-491-6(5)) School Specialty Publishing.

Spalding, Andrea. Me & Mr. Mah. Wilson, Janet, illus. 32p. (J). (ps-2). 2001. 7.95 (978-1-55143-177-2(7)); 2000. 14.95 (978-1-55143-168-0(8)) Orca Bk. Pubs. USA.

St. John, Patricia. Rainbow Garden. 2002. (gr. 3-6). lib. bdg. 15.30 (978-0-613-88836-3(7)) Tandem Library Bks.

Stevenson, Linda Walton. The Baby Elephant's Painted Face. Julich, Jennifer, illus. 2001. 16p. (J). (gr. k-3). 12.95 (978-0-9748725-0-6(4)) Bubbi's Touch Pr.

Stuefloten, Helen. There's A Giant in the Garden. Janguay, Patricia, illus. l.t. ed. 2006. 35p. (J). per. 11.99 (978-1-59879-161-7(3)) Lifevest Publishing, Inc.

Thomas, Frances. Little Monster's Book of Numbers. Collins, Ross, illus. 2005. 10p. (J). (ps-k). bds. 5.95 (978-1-58234-979-4(7)) Bloomsbury Publishing.

Tildes, Phyllis L. The Garden Wall. Tildes, Phyllis L., illus. 2005. (Illus.). (J). pr. 7.95 (978-0-9723729-1-6(1)) Imagination Stage, Inc.

Trooboff & Bucher, Cecile. Ben, the Bells & the Peacocks. 2007. 36p. pap. 15.00 (***978-0-9773536-0-6(5)***) Tenley Circle Pr.

Trottier, Maxine. Flags. Morin, Paul, illus. l.t. ed. 1999. 27p. (ps-3). 16.95 (978-0-7737-3136-3(9)) Stoddart Kids CAN. *Dist:* Fitzhenry & Whiteside, Ltd.

—Mr Hiroshis Garden. Morin, Paul, illus. 2006. 32p. (J). pap. 7.95 (978-1-55005-152-0(0)) Fitzhenry & Whiteside, Ltd. CAN. *Dist:* F & W Pubns., Inc.

Tutt, Ann Chamberlain. Red Wings & Fairy Things. 2006. 78p. pap. 14.95 (978-1-4241-2219-6(8)) PublishAmerica, Inc.

Waldherr, Kris. Harvest. 2001. (Illus.). 32p. (J). 16.85 (978-0-8027-8793-4(2)) ; 15.95 (978-0-8027-8792-7(4)) Walker & Co.

Wellington, Monica. Zinnia's Flower Garden. Wellington, Monica, illus. 2007. 32p. (J). pap. 5.99 (978-0-14-240787-5(9) , Puffin) Penguin Group (USA) Inc.

What's in the Garden? 2003. (J). pap. (978-1-57657-931-2(X)) Paradise Pr., Inc.

Wheeler, Leslie. Dolly's Day in the Garden. 2006. 18p. (J). per. 10.99 (***978-1-59886-708-4(3)***) Tate Publishing & Enterprises, L.L.C.

Wimbiscus, Robin. Somewhere in the Garden. 2007. 72p. (J). 19.95 (978-0-9772692-9-7(9)) Historical Pages Co.

Winter, Jeanette. September Roses. 2004. (Illus.). 40p. (J). 14.00 (978-0-374-36736-7(1) , Farrar, Straus & Giroux (BYR)) Farrar, Straus & Giroux.

Workman Publishing Company Staff, ed. Secret Garden. 1999. (J). 11.95 (978-1-56137-526-4(8)) Novel Units, Inc.

Yep, Laurence. Sea Glass: Golden Mountain Chronicles. 2002. (gr. 5-8). lib. bdg. 15.25 (978-0-613-89808-9(7)) Tandem Library Bks.

Yoon, Salina. Maggie's Colorful Garden: A Touchy, Feely Lift-the-Flap Colors Book. 1999. 10p. (J). 7.95 (978-1-58117-057-3(2) , Intervisual/Piggy Toes) Dalmatian Pr.

Zebrowski, Marianne. Babka's Serenade. Teis, Kyra, illus. 2002. 9.95 (978-1-56123-161-4(4) , BASC) Centering Corp.

GARFIELD, JAMES A. (JAMES ABRAM), 1831-1881

Brunelli, Carol. James A. Garfield: Our Twentieth President. 2001. (Spirit of America: Our Presidents Ser.). (Illus.). 48p. (J). (gr. 2-6). 28.50 (978-1-56766-857-5(7)) Child's World, Inc.

Doak, Robin S. James A. Garfield. 2003. (Profiles of the Presidents Ser.). (Illus.). 64p. (J). (gr. 4 up). lib. bdg. 23.93 (978-0-7565-0267-6(5)) Compass Point Bks.

Feldman, Ruth Tenzer. James A. Garfield. 2005. (Presidential Leaders Ser.). (Illus.). 112p. (J). (gr. 6-12). 29.27 (978-0-8225-1398-8(6)) Lerner Publishing Group.

Joseph, Paul. James A. Garfield. 2000. (United States Presidents Ser.). (Illus.). 32p. (J). (gr. k-6). lib. bdg. 22.78 (978-1-57765-242-7(8) , Checkerboard Library) ABDO Publishing Co.

Kent, Deborah. James A. Garfield. 2004. (Encyclopedia of Presidents Ser.). (Illus.). 110p. (J). 34.00 (978-0-516-22886-0(2) , Children's Pr.) Scholastic Library Publishing.

Marsh, Carole. James A. Garfield: An Ohio Experience Reader. 2001. (J). (gr. k-5). pap. 1.95 (978-0-635-00444-4(5)) Gallopade International.

Parker, Lewis K. How to Draw the Life & Times of James A. Garfield. 2006. (Kid's Guide to Drawing the Presidents of the United States of America Ser.). (J). 25.25 (978-1-4042-2997-6(3) , PowerKids Pr.) Rosen Publishing Group, Inc., The.

Venezia, Mike. James A. Garfield. 2006. (Illus.). 32p. (YA). (gr. 3-4). pap. 7.95 (978-0-516-25403-6(0) , Children's Pr.) Scholastic Library Publishing.

Venezia, Mike, illus. James A. Garfield. 2006. (Getting to Know the U. S. Presidents Ser.). 32p. (J). (gr. 3-4). 27.00 (978-0-516-22625-5(8) , Children's Pr.) Scholastic Library Publishing.

Young, Jeff C. James A. Garfield: A MyReportLinks.com Book. 2003. (Presidents Ser.). (Illus.). 48p. (J). (gr. 5-10). lib. bdg. 25.26 (978-0-7660-5100-3(5) , MyReportLinks.com Bks.) Enslow Pubs., Inc.

GARFIELD, JAMES A. (JAMES ABRAM), 1831-1881—FICTION

Alger, Horatio. From Canal Boy to President. 2006. pap. (***978-1-4068-0665-6(X)***) Echo Library.

—From Canal Boy to President: Or, The Boyhood & Manhood of James A. Garfield. 2006. 78.99 (***978-1-4280-3197-5(9)***) IndyPublish.com.

GARMENT MAKING

see Dressmaking

GARRISON, WILLIAM LLOYD, 1805-1879

Fauchald, Nick. William Lloyd Garrison: Abolitionist & Journalist. 2004. (Signature Lives Ser.). (Illus.). 112p. (J). 30.60 (978-0-7565-0819-7(3) , 1240146) Compass Point Bks.

Lilley, Stephen R. Fighters Against American Slavery. 1998. (History Makers Ser.). (Illus.). 128p. (YA). (gr. 7-10). 27.45 (978-1-56006-036-9(0) , Lucent Bks.) Thomson Gale.

GAS COMPANIES

see Public Utilities

GAS STATIONS

see Service Stations

GASES

Blashfield, Jean F. Hydrogen. 1999. (Sparks of Life Ser.). (Illus.). 64p. (YA). (gr. 7-8). lib. bdg. 27.12 (978-0-8172-5038-6(7)) Raintree.

—Nitrogen. 1999. (Sparks of Life Ser.). (Illus.). 64p. (YA). (gr. 7-8). lib. bdg. 27.12 (978-0-8172-5039-3(5)) Raintree.

—Oxygen. 1999. (Sparks of Life Ser.). (Illus.). 64p. (YA). (gr. 7-8). lib. bdg. 27.12 (978-0-8172-5037-9(9)) Raintree.

Boothroyd, Jennifer. What Is a Gas? 2007. (First Step Nonfiction Ser.). 24p. (J). (gr. k-3). 18.60 (978-0-8225-6837-7(3) , Lerner Pubns.) Lerner Publishing Group.

Brannon, Barbara. Discover Gases. 2005. 39.00 (***978-1-4108-5119-2(2)***) Benchmark Education Co.

Brown, Mark. Solids, Liquids, & Gases. 2005. (J). per. 14.99 (978-1-59441-699-6(0) , K04027) Carson-Dellosa Publishing Co., Inc.

Cesa, Irene, ed. Chemistry of Gases, 28 vols., Vol. 8. 2003. (ChemTopic Labs Ser.: 8). (Illus.). 84p. (YA). 11.95 (978-1-877991-76-9(7)) Flinn Scientific, Inc.

—The Gas Laws, 28 vols., Vol. 9. 2003. (ChemTopic Labs Ser.: 9). (Illus.). 96p. (YA). pap. 11.95 (978-1-877991-77-6(5)) Flinn Scientific, Inc.

Farndon, John. Nitrogen. 1999. (Elements Ser.). (Illus.). 32p. (J). (gr. 3-5). lib. bdg. 25.64 (978-0-7614-0877-2(0) , Benchmark Bks.) Cavendish, Marshall Corp.

—Oxygen. 1999. (Elements Ser.). (Illus.). 32p. (J). (gr. 3-5). lib. bdg. 25.64 (978-0-7614-0879-6(7) , Benchmark Bks.) Cavendish, Marshall Corp.

Fleisher, Paul. Liquids & Gases: Principles of Fluid Mechanics. 2005. (Secrets of the Universe Ser.). (Illus.). 80p. (gr. 6-12). 25.26 (978-0-8225-2988-0(2)) Lerner Publishing Group.

Frank, Marjorie Slavick, et al. Science Instant Readers Bk. 9: Solids, Liquids, & Gases. 1999. (Harcourt Science Ser.). (gr. 2 up). pap. 15.50 (978-0-15-316219-0(8)) Harcourt Schl. Pubs.

Frost, Helen. Water as a Gas, Vol. 5. 2005. (Our Seasons & Weather Ser.). 24p. (YA). (gr. k-3). pap. (978-0-7368-8636-9(2) , Pebble Bks.) Capstone Pr., Inc.

Hasan, Heather. Nitrogen. 2005. (Interpreting the Periodic Table Ser.). (Illus.). 48p. (J). (gr. 5-8). lib. bdg. 26.50 (978-1-4042-0158-3(0)) Rosen Publishing Group, Inc., The.

Holt, Rinehart and Winston Staff. Holt Chemistry Chptr. 12: Gases. 4th ed. Date not set. pap. 11.20 (978-0-03-068137-0(5)) Holt, Rinehart & Winston.

Kjelle, Marylou Morano. The Properties of Gases. 2007. (Library of Physical Science). (Illus.). 24p. (J). (978-1-4042-2360-8(6)); pap. (978-1-4042-2170-3(0)); lib. bdg. (978-1-4042-3423-9(3)) Rosen Publishing Group, Inc., The. (PowerKids Pr.).

Merrill, Amy French. Everyday Physical Science Experiments with Gases. 2002. (Science Surprises Ser.). (Illus.). 24p. (J). lib. bdg. 19.95 (978-0-8239-5803-0(5) , PowerKids Pr.) Rosen Publishing Group, Inc., The.

Mezzanotte, Jim. Gases. 2006. (States of Matter Ser.). (Illus.). 24p. (J). pap. (978-0-8368-6802-9(1)); lib. bdg. (978-0-8368-6797-8(1)) Stevens, Gareth Inc.

Morrison, Yvonne. Take a Deep Breath: What Is CO? 2007. (Shockwave: Earth & Physical Science Ser.). (Illus.). 36p. (J). (gr. 4-6). lib. bdg. 25.00 (***978-0-531-17790-7(4)*** , Children's Pr.) Scholastic Library Publishing.

Nelson, Robin. Gases. 2005. (First Step Nonfiction Ser.). (Illus.). 23p. (J). (ps-7). 18.60 (978-0-8225-2616-2(6) , Lerner Pubns.) Lerner Publishing Group.

O'Daley, Anne. Gases. 2003. (Illus.). 24p. (J). 22.45 (978-1-4103-0083-6(8) , Blackbirch Pr., Inc.) Thomson Gale.

Oxlade, Chris. How We Use Gases. 2004. (Illus.). 25.70 (978-1-4109-0601-4(9)) Raintree.

Parker, Steve. Oil & Gas. 2004. (Science Files Ser.). (Illus.). 32p. (J). (gr. 3 up). lib. bdg. 24.37 (978-0-8368-4031-5(3)) Stevens, Gareth Inc.

Randolph, Joanne. Gases in My World. 2006. (My World of Science Ser.). (J). 16.00 (978-1-4042-3284-6(2) , PowerKids Pr.) Rosen Publishing Group, Inc., The.

—Gases in My World: Los Gases en Mi Mundo. 2006. (My World of Science/ Mi mundo y la Ciencia Ser.). (ENG & SPA.). (J). 16.00 (978-1-4042-3315-7(6) , PowerKids Pr.) Rosen Publishing Group, Inc., The.

Riley, Peter D. All about Gases. 2007. (J). (***978-1-59920-022-4(8)***) Smart Apple Media.

Saunders, N. Oxygen & the Group 16 Elements. 2003. (Periodic Table Ser.). (Illus.). 64p. (J). pap. 8.95 (978-1-4034-3520-0(0)); lib. bdg. 28.50 (978-1-4034-0874-7(2)) Heinemann Library.

Sian Gases. 2004. (J). (978-1-59242-035-3(4)) Delta Education, LLC.

Slade, Suzanne. The Nitrogen Cycle. 2007. (Illus.). 24p. (J). (978-1-4042-2390-5(8)); pap. (978-1-4042-2200-7(6)) Rosen Publishing Group, Inc., The. (PowerKids Pr.).

Sullivan, Erin Ash. Liquids & Gases. 2005. (Navigators Ser.). (J). pap. 38.00 (***978-1-4108-5071-3(4)***) Benchmark Education Co.

Tocci, Salvatore. Experiments with Solids, Liquids, & Gases. 2002. 13.75 (978-0-606-22879-4(9)) Tandem Library Bks.

—Hydrogen & Noble Gases. 2004. (True Book Ser.). (J). 25.00 (978-0-516-22830-3(7) , Children's Pr.) Scholastic Library Publishing.

—Hydrogen & the Noble Gases. 2005. (True Bks.). (Illus.). 48p. (J). (gr. 3-5). pap. 6.95 (978-0-516-27849-0(5) , Children's Pr.) Scholastic Library Publishing.

—Nitrogen. (True Bks.). (J). 2005. (Illus.). 48p. (gr. 3-5). pap. 6.95 (978-0-516-27850-6(9)); 2004. 25.00 (978-0-516-22831-0(5)) Scholastic Library Publishing. (Children's Pr.).

—Oxygen. (True Bks.). (J). 2005. (Illus.). 48p. (gr. 3-5). pap. 6.95 (978-0-516-27851-3(7)); 2004. 25.00 (978-0-516-22832-7(3)) Scholastic Library Publishing. (Children's Pr.).

Willett, Edward. Neon. 2006. (Understanding the Elements of the Periodic Table Ser.). (Illus.). 48p. (J). (gr. 5-8). lib. bdg. 26.50 (978-1-4042-1008-0(3)) Rosen Publishing Group, Inc., The.

Williams, Zella. Experiments with Solids, Liquids, & Gases. 2007. (Do-It-Yourself Science Ser.). (Illus.). 24p. (J). (gr. 2-5). lib. bdg. 23.95 (978-1-4042-3658-5(9) , PowerKids Pr.) Rosen Publishing Group, Inc., The.

GASES, RARE

Saunders, N. Neon & the Noble Gases. 2003. (Periodic Table Ser.). (Illus.). 64p. (J). pap. 8.95 (978-1-4034-3519-4(7)); lib. bdg. 28.50 (978-1-4034-0875-4(0)) Heinemann Library.

Thomas, Jens. The Noble Gases. 2002. (Elements Ser.). (Illus.). 32p. (J). 25.64 (978-0-7614-1462-9(2) , Benchmark Bks.) Cavendish, Marshall Corp.

GASOLINE

Cunningham, Kevin. Gasoline. 2008. (J). lib. bdg. 25.26 (***978-1-60279-121-3(X)***) Cherry Lake Publishing.

Murray, Julie. Oil to Gas. 2007. (J). 21.35 (978-1-59679-913-4(7) , Buddy Bks.) ABDO Publishing Co.

Sloan, Peter. Gasoline for the Car. 1999. (gr. k-3). lib. bdg. 11.80 (978-0-613-30424-5(1)) Tandem Library Bks.

GASTRONOMY

see Cookery; Food; Menus

GAUCHOS

see Cowboys

GAUGUIN, PAUL, 1848-1903

Anderson, Poul. Paul Gauguin. 2003. (gr. 5-8). lib. bdg. 15.25 (978-0-613-59536-0(X)) Tandem Library Bks.

Anderson, Robert. Paul Gauguin. 2003. (Artists in Their Time Ser.). (Illus.). 48p. (J). 23.50 (978-0-531-12239-6(5)); (gr. 5-7). pap. 6.95 (978-0-531-16647-5(3)) Scholastic Library Publishing. (Watts, Franklin).

Becker, Christoph. Paul Gauguin: A Journey to Tahiti. Jackson, Rosie, tr. from GER. 2001. (Adventures in Art Ser.). (Illus.). 30p. (gr. 5-8). 14.95 (978-3-7913-2572-9(8)) Prestel Publishing.

De Magalhaes, Roberto Carvalho. Paul Gauguin. 2003. (Great Artists Ser.). (Illus.). 40p. (J). 15.95 (978-1-59270-010-3(1)) Enchanted Lion Bks., LLC.

de Salvia, Maria Siponta. Paul Gauguin. 2005. (Great Artists Ser.). (Illus.). 40p. (J). (gr. 5). pap. 7.95 (978-1-59270-051-6(9)) Enchanted Lion Bks., LLC.

Flux, Paul. The Life & Work of Paul Gauguin, Set 2. 2002. (Illus.). 32p. (J). (gr. k-2). pap. 6.50 (978-1-4034-0004-8(0) , 91622) Heinemann Library.

—Paul Gauguin. 2002. (Life & Work of. . . Ser.). (Illus.). 32p. (J). (gr. k-2). lib. bdg. 22.79 (978-1-58810-605-6(5)) Heinemann Library.

Gauguin, Paul & Noble, Marty. Color Your Own Gaugin Paintings. 2001. (Illus.). 32p. (J). pap. 3.95 (978-0-486-41325-9(X)) Dover Pubns., Inc.

Klein, Adam G. & Gauguin, Paul. Paul Gauguin. 2007. (Great Artists Ser.). (Illus.). 32p. (J). (gr. 2-5). lib. bdg. 22.78 (978-1-59679-729-1(0)) ABDO Publishing Co.

Merberg, Julie & Bober, Suzanne. On an Island with Gauguin. 2007. (Illus.). 22p. (J). (ps). bds. 6.95 (978-0-8118-5711-6(5)) Chronicle Bks. LLC.

Rubin, Susan Goldman. The Yellow House: Vincent Van Gogh & Paul Gauguin Side by Side. Smith, Joseph A., illus. 2001. 40p. (J). (gr. k-4). 17.95 (978-0-8109-4588-3(6)) Abrams, Harry N. , Inc.

GAULLE, CHARLES DE, 1890-1970

Jackson, Julian. De Gaulle. 2005. (Life & Times Ser.). (Illus.). 192p. pap. 15.95 (978-1-904341-44-4(6)) Haus Publishing GBR. *Dist:* International Publishers Marketing.

GAUTAMA BUDDHA

Buddhist Text Translation Society Staff, et al, contrib. by. Under the Bodhi Tree. 2002. 76p. (J). 15.00 (978-0-88139-319-4(3)) Buddhist Text Translation Society.

Carew-Miller, Anna. Buddha. 2002. (Great Names Ser.). (Illus.). 32p. (J). (gr. 3 up). lib. bdg. (978-1-59084-137-2(9)) Mason Crest Pubs.

Duran, Magdelena, illus. The Jewel of Friendship: A Jataka Tale. 2001. (Jataka Tales Ser.). (J). pap. 7.95 (978-0-89800-319-2(9)) Dharma Publishing.

—The King Who Understood Animals: A Jataka Tale. 2001. (Jataka Tales Ser.). (J). pap. 7.95 (978-0-89800-318-5(0)) Dharma Publishing.

Foran, Jill. Buddha Day. 2003. (Celebrating Cultures Ser.). (Illus.). 24p. (J). lib. bdg. 15.95 (978-1-59036-090-3(7)) Weigl Pubs., Inc.

Ganeri, Anita. Buddhist Stories. Fennell, Tracey, illus. 2006. (Traditional Religious Tales Ser.). 32p. (J). (gr. 4-6). 23.95 (978-1-4048-1311-3(X)) Picture Window Bks.

Gedney, Mona K. The Life & Times of Buddha. 2005. (Biography from Ancient Civilizations Ser.). (Illus.). 48p. (J). (ps-7). lib. bdg. 29.95 (978-1-58415-342-9(3)) Mitchell Lane Pubs., Inc.

Hsuan Hua. Buddha's Wisdom. Yeh, Alicia, illus. 2004. (ENG & CHI.). (J). (978-0-88139-867-0(5)) Buddhist Text Translation Society.

Kandahsari, Tara & Kandahsari, Cintya, illus. No Words: The Teachings of the Buddha. 2001. (J). (978-0-88139-426-9(2)) Buddhist Text Translation Society.

Landaw, Jonathan. Prince Siddhartha: The Story of Buddha. Brooke, Janet, illus. 2nd ed. 2005. 144p. (J). pap. 18.95 (978-0-86171-375-2(3)) Wisdom Pubns.

Mantell, Paul. Buddha: Young Seeker. 2007. (Childhood of World Figures Ser.). 208p. (J). pap. 5.99 (978-1-4169-1543-0(5) , Aladdin) Simon & Schuster Children's Publishing.

Nestorowich, Sherri, illus. The Spade Sage: A Jataka Tale. 2002. (Jataka Tales Ser.). (J). pap. 7.95 (978-0-89800-321-5(0)) Dharma Publishing.

Ross, Mandy. Bodh Gaya. 2003. (Holy Places Ser.). (Illus.). 32p. (J). 24.28 (978-0-7398-6077-9(1)) Raintree.

Stewart, Whitney. Becoming Buddha: The Story of Siddhartha. Rippin, Sally, illus. 2005. 32p. (ps-3). 16.95 (978-0-89346-946-7(7)) Heian International Publishing, Inc.

GAZELLES—FICTION

Pirotta, Saviour & Marks, Alan. The Enchanted Gazelle. 2007. (J). (***978-1-59771-081-7(4)***) Sea-To-Sea Pubns.

Temple, Frances. The Beduins' Gazelle. 1998. 150p. (YA). (gr. 7-12). lib. bdg. 14.15 (978-0-613-07324-0(X)) Tandem Library Bks.

—Beduins' Gazelle. 1998. (Harper Trophy Bks.). (978-0-606-12887-2(5)) Tandem Library Bks.

Wilson, George H. The Legend of Thompson the Gazelle. 2008. (Illus.). 50p. (J). 14.99 (***978-0-9778477-4-7(8)***) Storyplus, Inc., A.

GEESE

Bradley, James V. The Canada Goose. 2006. (Nature Walk Ser.). (Illus.). 64p. (J). 28.00 (978-0-7910-9113-5(9) , Chelsea Hse.) Facts On File, Inc.

Cooper, Jason. Canada Goose. 2003. (Life Cycles Ser.). (Illus.). 24p. (J). (gr. 1-4). 17.95 (978-1-58952-351-7(2)) Rourke Publishing, LLC.

Endres, Hollie. Geese. 2007. (Illus.). 24p. (J). lib. bdg. 19.95 (978-1-60014-084-6(X)) Bellwether Media.

Hills, Tad. What's up Duck? Hills, Tad, illus. 2008. (Illus.). 22p. (J). bds. (***978-0-375-84738-7(3)*** , Schwartz & Wade Bks.) Random Hse. Children's Bks.

Kallgren, Beverly H. A Duck Named Goose. 2004. (Illus.). 48p. (J). per. 10.00 (978-1-930648-90-6(1)) Goose River Pr.

Miller, Sara Swan. Waterfowl: From Swans to Screamers. 1999. (Animals in Order Ser.). (Illus.). 48p. (J). (gr. 4-6). 26.50 (978-0-531-11584-8(4) , Watts, Franklin) Scholastic Library Publishing.

Schuh, Mari. Geese on the Farm. (On the Farm Ser.). 24p. (J). pap. 5.95 (978-0-7368-3424-7(9)) Capstone Pr., Inc.

Schuh, Mari C. Geese on the Farm. 2003. (On the Farm Ser.). (Illus.). 24p. (J). (gr. k-1). lib. bdg. 15.93 (978-0-7368-1662-5(3) , Pebble Bks.) Capstone Pr., Inc.

GEESE—FICTION

Baglio, Ben M. Goose on the Loose. McNicholas, Shelagh, illus. 2000. (Animal Ark Ser.: No. 14). 160p. (J). (gr. 3-6). pap. 3.99 (978-0-439-09699-7(5)) Scholastic, Inc.

Baker, Harriet Lila. Book III: Boyduck Goose: His Life & Times. 2005. (J). pap. 9.00 (978-0-8059-6803-3(2)) Dorrance Publishing Co., Inc.

Bang, Molly Garrett. Dawn. Bang, Molly Garrett, illus. 2002. (Illus.). 32p. (J). (gr. k-3). reprint ed. pap. 5.95 (978-1-58717-188-8(0) , SeaStar Bks.) Chronicle Bks. LLC.

—Dawn. 2002. (gr. k-3). lib. bdg. 14.10 (978-0-613-62742-9(3)) Tandem Library Bks.

—Goose. Bang, Molly Garrett, illus. 2002. (Illus.). (J). 19.72 (978-0-7587-2626-1(0)) Book Wholesalers, Inc.

Bea, Holly. Lucy Goose Goes to Texas. Boddy, Joe, illus. 2005. 32p. (J). 15.95 (978-1-932073-15-7(9)) New World Library.

Becker, Helaine. Mother Goose Unplucked: Crazy Comics, Zany Activities, Nutty Facts, & Other Twisted Takes on Childhood Favorites. Davila, Claudia, illus. 2007. 160p. (J). (gr. 3-7). 22.95 (978-1-897066-83-6(X)); pap. 10.95 (978-1-897066-84-3(8)) Maple Tree Pr. CAN. *Dist:* Perseus Distribution.

Bedtime with Mothergoose. 2005. (J). bds. (978-1-4194-0089-6(4)) Paradise Pr., Inc.

Best, Cari. Goose's Story. Meade, Holly, illus. 2002. 32p. (J). 16.00 (978-0-374-32750-7(5) , Farrar, Straus & Giroux (BYR)) Farrar, Straus & Giroux.

Bloom, Suzanne. Splendid Friend Indeed Big BK. 2007. (Illus.). 32p. pap. 24.95 (***978-1-59078-532-4(0)***) Boyds Mills Pr.

—Treasure. 2007. (Illus.). 32p. (J). (ps-1). 15.95 (***978-1-59078-457-0(X)***) Boyds Mills Pr.

Bloom, Suzanne, illus. A Splendid Friend, Indeed. 2007. 32p. (J). 15.95 (978-1-59078-286-6(0)) Boyds Mills Pr.

Bowman, Eddie. Gilbert the Goose. Prater, Howard, illus. 1998. (J). pap. 6.95 (978-1-56763-428-0(1)); lib. bdg. 19.95 (978-1-56763-427-3(3)) Ozark Publishing.

Braun, Trudi. My Goose Betsy. Bendall-Brunello, John, illus. 2002. (Read & Wonder Ser.). 32p. (J). (ps-3). pap. 5.99 (978-0-7636-1714-1(8)) Candlewick Pr.

—My Goose Betsy. 2002. (gr. k-3). lib. bdg. 14.15 (978-0-613-74764-6(X)) Tandem Library Bks.

Brennan-Nelson, Denise. Grady the Goose. Monroe, Michael Glenn, illus. rev. ed. 2006. 32p. (J). 16.95 (978-1-58536-282-0(4)) Sleeping Bear Pr.

Brenner, Barbara. Good News. Duke, Kate, illus. 1999. (Bank Street Reader Collection). 48p. (J). (ps-2). lib. bdg. 22.60 (978-0-8368-1775-1(3)) Stevens, Gareth Inc.

Brothers Grimm Staff. The Golden Goose/ la oca de Oro. 2004. (Illus.). (J). (978-1-933530-22-2(7)) Bingo Bks., Inc.

Brown, Cathy. The World's Most Forgotten Grandmother, Granny Goose. Island, Sylvester, Jr., illus. 1998. (J). (ps-4). 10.95 (978-1-892089-55-7(6)); pap. 5.95 (978-1-892089-52-6(1)) Our Kids Pubn., Inc.

Burningham, John. Borka. 40th anniv. ed. 2004. (Illus.). 32p. 16.99 (978-0-224-06494-1(0) , Jonathan Cape) Random Hse. Children's Bks. GBR. *Dist:* Trafalgar Square Publishing.

Cameron, Anne. The Gumboot Geese. Huber, June, illus. unabr. ed. 26p. (Orig.). (J). (978-1-55017-063-4(5)) Harbour Publishing Co., Ltd.

Childress, Mildred Tickfer. Esmerelda, the Silly Goose. Zipperer, Susan Johnson, illus. 2004. 64p. (J). lib. bdg. 11.95 (978-1-887774-17-8(3) , Wynden) Canmore Pr.

Church, Caroline Jane. One Smart Goose. 2005. (Illus.). 32p. (J). 16.95 (978-0-439-68765-2(9) , Orchard Bks.) Scholastic, Inc.

Coplans, Peta & Williams, Dylan. Syniad Da Gwenlli Gwydd. 2005. (WEL., Illus.). 24p. (978-1-84512-015-3(9)) Cymdeithas Lyfrau Ceredigion.

Cox, Phil Roxbee & Cartwright, S. Goose on the Loose. 2004. (Easy Words to Read Ser.). 16p. (J). (gr. 1 up). pap. 6.95 (978-0-7945-0036-8(6) , Usborne) EDC Publishing.

Cox, Phil Roxbee & Cartwright, Stephen. Goose on the Loose. 2004. (Phonics Board Bks.). (Illus.). 10p. (J). 4.99 (978-0-7945-0305-5(5) , Usborne) EDC Publishing.

—Ted's Shed. 2004. (Phonics Board Bks.). (Illus.). 10p. (J). 4.95 (978-0-7945-0304-8(7) , Usborne) EDC Publishing.

Cox, Phil Roxbee & Grant, Marlynne. Goose on the Loose. Tyler, Jenny, ed. Cartwright, Stephen, illus. 10p. (J). pap. 4.95 (978-0-7460-4486-5(0) , Usborne) EDC Publishing.

Cuffe-Perez, Mary. Skylar. Liwska, Renata, illus. 2008. 144p. (J). (gr. 3). 14.99 (***978-0-399-24543-5(X)*** , Philomel) Penguin Group (USA) Inc.

Demarest, Chris L. Honk! Demarest, Chris L., illus. 2003. (Illus.). 16p. (J). (ps up). 11.95 (978-1-56397-221-8(2)) Boyds Mills Pr.

DePaola, Tomie. More Mother Goose Favorites. 2007. (Illus.). 32p. (J). pap. 3.99 (978-0-448-44494-9(1) , Grosset & Dunlap) Penguin Group (USA) Inc.

Doudna, Kelly. Goose Down. Haberstroh, Anne, illus. 2006. (Fact & Fiction Ser.). 24p. (J). 21.35 (978-1-59679-941-7(2) , SandCastle); pap. (978-1-59679-942-4(0)) ABDO Publishing Co.

Dunbar, Joyce. Gander's Pond. Craig, Helen, illus. 1998. (Panda & Gander Stories Ser.). (J). pap. (978-0-7636-0721-0(5)) Candlewick Pr.

—Pomegranate Seeds. Craig, Helen, illus. 1998. (Panda & Gander Stories Ser.). (J). pap. (978-0-7636-0707-4(X)) Candlewick Pr.

—The Secret Friend. Craig, Helen, illus. 1998. (Panda & Gander Stories Ser.). (J). pap. (978-0-7636-0719-7(3)) Candlewick Pr.

Dunrea, Olivier. Boo Boo. 2008. (Illus.). 32p. (J). (gr. k-ps). bds. 6.95 (***978-0-618-75505-9(5)***) Houghton Mifflin Co. Trade & Reference Div.

—BooBoo. 2004. (Illus.). 32p. (J). (gr. k-ps). tchr. ed. 9.95 (978-0-618-35654-6(1)) Houghton Mifflin Co. Trade & Reference Div.

—Gossie. 2007. (Illus.). 16p. (J). (ps-k). bds. 6.95 (978-0-618-74791-7(5)) Houghton Mifflin Co. Trade & Reference Div.

—Gossie. Dunrea, Olivier, illus. 2002. (Illus.). 32p. (J). (gr. k-ps). tchr. ed. 9.95 (978-0-618-17674-8(8)) Houghton Mifflin Co. Trade & Reference Div.

—Gossie & Gertie. 2007. (Illus.). 16p. (J). (ps-k). bds. 6.95 (978-0-618-74793-1(1)) Houghton Mifflin Co. Trade & Reference Div.

—Gossie & Gertie. Dunrea, Olivier, illus. 2002. (Illus.). 32p. (J). (gr. k-ps). tchr. ed. 9.95 (978-0-618-17676-2(4)) Houghton Mifflin Co. Trade & Reference Div.

—Gossie's Busy Day. 2007. (Illus.). 10p. (J). (ps-k). 11.99 (***978-0-618-82148-8(1)***) Houghton Mifflin Co. Trade & Reference Div.

—Ollie. 2007. (Illus.). 16p. (J). bds. 6.95 (***978-0-618-75503-5(9)***) Houghton Mifflin Co. Trade & Reference Div.

—Ollie. Dunrea, Olivier, illus. 2003. (Illus.). 32p. (J). (gr. k-ps). tchr. ed. 9.95 (978-0-618-33928-0(0)) Houghton Mifflin Co. Trade & Reference Div.

—Ollie the Stomper. (Illus.). (J). 2007. 16p. bds. 6.95 (***978-0-618-75504-2(7)***); 2003. 32p. tchr. ed. 9.95 (978-0-618-33930-3(2)) Houghton Mifflin Co. Trade & Reference Div.

—Ollie's Eggs. 2006. (J). (978-0-618-53243-8(9)) Houghton Mifflin Co.

Dunrea, Olivier. Peedie. (Illus.). 32p. (J). (ps-k). 2008. bds. 6.95 (***978-0-618-75506-6(3)***); 2004. tchr. ed. 9.95 (978-0-618-35652-2(5)) Houghton Mifflin Co. Trade & Reference Div.

Dunrea, Olivier, illus. Goslings on the Prowl! 2005. (J). (978-0-618-53241-4(2)) Houghton Mifflin Co.

—Merry Christmas, Ollie! 2005. (J). (978-0-618-53242-1(0)) Houghton Mifflin Co.

Duvoisin, Roger. Petunia. 2002. (Illus.). 32p. (J). (ps-3). reprint ed. pap. 6.99 (978-0-440-41754-5(6) , Dragonfly Bks.) Random Hse. Children's Bks.

Ehrlich, H. M. Louie's Goose. Bolam, Emily, illus. 32p. (J). (gr. k-3). 2002. pap. 5.95 (978-0-618-26008-9(0)); 2000. tchr. ed. 15.00 (978-0-618-03023-1(9)) Houghton Mifflin Co. Trade & Reference Div. (Walter Lorraine).

—Louie's Goose. 2002. (gr. k-3). lib. bdg. 14.10 (978-0-613-72913-0(7)) Tandem Library Bks.

Engelbreit, Mary. Mary Engelbreit's Happy Mother Goose. Engelbreit, Mary, illus. 2007. 16p. (J). 6.99 (978-0-06-008126-3(0) , Harper Festival) HarperCollins Pubs.

—Mary Engelbreit's Silly Mother Goose. Engelbreit, Mary, illus. 2007. 16p. (J). 6.99 (978-0-06-008127-0(9) , Harper Festival) HarperCollins Pubs.

Fox, Mem. Boo to a Goose. 2001. (gr. k-3). lib. bdg. 14.15 (978-0-613-35910-8(0)) Tandem Library Bks.

Fox, Mem & Miller, David. Boo to a Goose. Bonnell, J., ed. 2001. (Illus.). 32p. (J). (ps-3). pap. 6.99 (978-0-14-056766-3(6) , Puffin) Penguin Group (USA) Inc.

Freedman, Claire. Gooseberry Goose. Cabban, Vanessa, illus. 2005. 32p. (J). 6.95 (978-1-58925-392-6(2) , tiger tales) ME Media LLC.

Freedman, Claire & Cabban, Vanessa. Gooseberry Goose. 2003. (Illus.). 32p. (J). (ps-2). tchr. ed. 15.95 (978-1-58925-030-7(3) , tiger tales) ME Media LLC.

Freeman, Don. Will's Quill: Or How a Goose Saved Shakespeare. ed. 2004. (Illus.). 32p. (J). (ps-k). 16.99 (978-0-670-03686-8(2) , Viking Juvenile) Penguin Group (USA) Inc.

George, Jean Craighead. Goose & Duck. Lamont, Priscilla, illus. 2008. (I Can Read Bks.). 48p. (J). 16.99 (***978-0-06-117076-8(3)***); lib. bdg. 17.89 (***978-0-06-117077-5(1)***) HarperCollins Pubs. (Geringer, Laura Book).

Goodspeed, Judy. Perky Turkey Finds a Friend. 2006. (Illus.). 24p. (J). lib. bdg. 24.95 (978-0-9778651-2-3(6)) Dragonfly Publishing, Inc.

The Goose, the Chick & the Duck. 1998. (Fisher-Price Phonics Storybooks Ser.: Vol. 4). (Illus.). (J). pap. (978-0-7666-0173-4(0) , Honey Bear Bks.) Modern Publishing.

Greenfield, Giles. The World of Mother Goose. 2008. (Illus.). 56p. (J). 9.98 (978-0-7624-2312-5(9)) Running Pr. Bk. Pubs.

Grimm, Jacob W. The Golden Goose. 1998. (J). (978-0-606-13434-7(4)) Tandem Library Bks.

Grimm, Wilhelm K. & Grimm, Jacob W. The Golden Goose. Shulevitz, Uri, illus. 1998. 32p. (J). (gr. k-3). pap. 6.95 (978-0-374-42748-1(8) , Sunburst) Farrar, Straus & Giroux.

Grindley, Sally. Silly Goose & Dizzy Duck & the Colorful Day. Reynolds, Adrian, illus. 2001. (Toddlers Ser.). 24p. (J). (ps). pap. 5.95 (978-0-7894-7860-3(9) , D K Ink) Dorling Kindersley Publishing, Inc.

Gruetzke, Mary, ed. Real Mother Goose. 2006. (Scholastic Hands-on Learning Ser.). (J). 9.99 (978-0-439-81223-8(2) , Cartwheel Bks.) Scholastic, Inc.

Halfmann, Janet. Canada Goose at Cat Tail Lane. Stegos, Daniel, illus. 2005. 32p. (J). (ps-2). 9.95 (978-1-59249-499-6(4) , PB5079) Soundprints.

Halfmann, Janet & Stegos, Daniel. Canada Goose at Cat Tail Lane. 2005. (Smithsonian's Backyard Ser.). (Illus.). 32p. (J). (gr. k-2). 15.95 (978-1-59249-494-1(3) , B5029); 4.95 (978-1-59249-496-5(X) , B5079); pap. 6.95 (978-1-59249-495-8(1) , S5029) Soundprints.

Hall, Kirsten. Duck, Duck, Goose! 2004. (My First Reader Ser.). (Illus.). 31p. (J). (gr. k-1). pap. 3.95 (978-0-516-24627-7(5) , Children's Pr.) Scholastic Library Publishing.

Hamilton, Martha & Weiss, Mitch. How Fox Became Red. O'Malley, Kathy, illus. 2005. 12p. (J). pap. 5.00 (978-1-57274-717-3(X) , 2749, Bks. for Young Learners) Owen, Richard C. Pubs., Inc.

Harcourt School Publishers Staff. Why Geese Fly in Teams Advanced Level. 3rd ed. 2002. (Trophies Reading Program Ser.). (Illus.). pap. 5.10 (978-0-15-323377-7(X)) Harcourt Schl. Pubs.

Hardinge, Frances. Fly by Night. (J). 2008. 512p. pap. 7.99 (***978-0-06-087630-2(1)*** , Harper Trophy); 2006. 496p. (gr. 5-9). 16.99 (978-0-06-087627-2(1)) HarperCollins Pubs.

Harper, Charise Mericle. When Randolph Turned Rotten. 2007. 40p. (J). (gr. k-3). 16.99 (***978-0-375-84071-5(0)***); lib. bdg. 19.99 (***978-0-375-94071-2(5)***) Random Hse. Children's Bks. (Knopf Bks. for Young Readers).

Hay, Jerry M. & Pollema-Cahill, Phyllis. A Goose Named Gilligan. 2004. (Illus.). 32p. 15.95 (978-1-932073-09-6(4)) Kramer, H.J. Inc.

Hayward, Linda. The King's Chorus. Goldfinger, Jennifer P., illus. 2006. 32p. (J). (ps-k). 16.00 (978-0-618-51618-6(2) , Clarion Bks.) Houghton Mifflin Co. Trade & Reference Div.

Hernandez, Norberto, tr. The Goose with the Golden Eggs: A Fable by Aesop. Leonard, Card, illus. 2000. Tr. of Ganso con los Huevos de Oro: Una Fabula de Esopo. (ENG & SPA.). (J). (gr. 1-4). pap. 12.95 incl. audio (978-0-9678821-0-9(9)) Libie Alone Pubns.

Hills, Tad. Duck & Goose. Hills, Tad, illus. 2006. 40p. (J). (ps-2). lib. bdg. 16.99 (978-0-375-93611-1(4)); (Illus.). 14.95 (978-0-375-83611-4(X)) Random Hse. Children's Bks. (Schwartz & Wade Bks.).

—Duck, Duck, Goose. 2007. (Illus.). 40p. (J). (ps-2). 15.99 (978-0-375-84068-5(0)); lib. bdg. 18.99 (978-0-375-94068-2(5)) Random Hse. Children's Bks. (Schwartz & Wade Bks.).

Horacek, Petr. Silly Suzy Goose. Horacek, Petr, illus. 2006. (Illus.). 40p. (J). (gr. k-k). 14.99 (978-0-7636-3040-9(3)) Candlewick Pr.

How the Geese Saved Rome: Individual Title Six-Packs. (Story Steps Ser.). (gr. k-2). 32.00 (978-0-7635-9801-3(1)) Rigby Education.

Hutchins, Pat. We're Going on a Picnic! Hutchins, Pat, illus. 2002. (Illus.). 32p. (J). 16.99 (978-0-688-16799-8(3)) HarperCollins Pubs.

Jensen, Lillian. A Treasury of Modern Mother Goose Rhymes, Vol. 1. 2003. 54p. pap. 9.00 (978-0-8059-5981-9(5)) Dorrance Publishing Co., Inc.

Jobling, Brenda. Goose on the Loose. Briggs, Valerie, illus. 1998. (Animal Tales Ser.). 131p. (J). (gr. 3-7). pap. 3.95 (978-0-7641-0602-6(3)) Barron's Educational Series, Inc.

—Goose on the Loose. 1998. (Animal Tales Ser.). (978-0-606-13438-5(7)) Tandem Library Bks.

Johnson, Paul Brett. The Goose Who Had Blueberry Pie. 2001. (Illus.). (J). lib. bdg. (978-0-531-33317-4(5) , Orchard Bks.) Scholastic, Inc.

—The Goose Who Went off in a Huff. Johnson, Paul Brett, illus. 2001. (Illus.). 40p. (J). (ps-1). pap. 15.95 (978-0-531-30317-7(9) , Orchard Bks.) Scholastic, Inc.

Johnson, Sandi. Peppermint Goose & Baby Giki: Fantasy Land. Johnson, Britt, ed. Zalrey, C. J., illus. 1998. (Little Choo-Choo Bks.). 12p. (J). (ps-6). 8.99 (978-1-929063-14-7(8) , 114) Moons & Stars Publishing For Children.

Keller, Holly. Farfallina & Marcel. Keller, Holly, illus. (Illus.). 32p. (J). 2002. 16.99 (978-0-06-623932-3(X)); 2005. reprint ed. pap. 6.99 (978-0-06-443872-8(4) , Harper Trophy) HarperCollins Pubs.

—Farfallina & Marcel. 2004. (Illus.). 26p. (J). (ps-ps). lib. bdg. 12.79 (978-0-606-32617-9(0)) Tandem Library Bks.

Kelly, John & Tincknell, Cathy. The Mystery of Eatum Hall. Kelly, John & Tincknell, Cathy, illus. 2004. (Illus.). 32p. (J). (gr. k-3). 15.99 (978-0-7636-2594-8(9)) Candlewick Pr.

Kerr, Judith. Goose in a Hole. Kerr, Judith, illus. 2006. (Illus.). 40p. (J). (ps). pap. 9.99 (978-0-00-720794-7(8) , HarperCollins Children's Bks.) HarperCollins Pubs. Ltd. GBR. *Dist:* Independent Pubs. Group.

—Goose in a Hole. 2005. (Illus.). 40p. (J). 15.99 (978-0-00-720793-0(X)) HarperCollins Pubs. Ltd. GBR. *Dist:* Independent Pubs. Group.

—The Other Goose. (Illus.). 32p. (J). 2002. pap. 8.99 (978-0-00-712735-1(9)); 2001. 15.99 (978-0-00-712119-9(9)) HarperCollins Pubs. Ltd. GBR. *Dist:* Independent Pubs. Group.

Kick, J. D. A Goose Tale—Downside Up. Just, John, illus. 2000. (Owl Creek Farm Book Ser.: No. 1). vi, 71p. (J). (gr. k-7). pap. 16.95 (978-1-929424-10-8(8)) Owl Tree Pr.

—A Goose Tale—Downside up. Just, John, illus. 2nd l.t. ed. 2003. 80p. (J). per. 16.95 (978-1-929424-13-9(2) , Owl Creek Farm Bks.) Owl Tree Pr.

E F G

Kindermans, Martine. You & Me. Quinton, Sasha, tr. from GER. Kindermans, Martine, illus. 2006. (Illus.). 32p. (J). (ps-3). 15.99 (978-0-399-24471-1(9) , Philomel) Penguin Group (USA) Inc.

Kindl, Patrice. Goose Chase. 2001. 224p. (J). (gr. 5-9). tchr. ed. 16.00 (978-0-618-03377-5(7)) Houghton Mifflin Co. Trade & Reference Div.

—Goose Chase. 2002. 224p. (YA). pap. 5.99 (978-0-14-230208-8(2) , Puffin) Penguin Group (USA) Inc.

—Goose Chase. 2002. (gr. 5-8). lib. bdg. 14.15 (978-0-613-60805-3(4)) Tandem Library Bks.

King, Deborah. The Flight of the Snow Geese. 1998. (Illus.). 32p. (J). (ps-2). pap. 15.95 (978-0-531-30088-6(9) , Orchard Bks.) Scholastic, Inc.

King-Smith, Dick. The Golden Goose. 2006. 128p. (J). (gr. 4-7). 5.50 (978-0-440-42030-9(X) , Yearling) Random Hse. Children's Bks.

—The Golden Goose. Kronheimer, Ann, illus. 2005. 128p. (J). (gr. 3-7). 15.95 (978-0-375-82984-0(9) , Knopf Bks. for Young Readers) Random Hse. Children's Bks.

Korba, Joanne. Two Golden Geese. 2005. 40.00 (***978-1-4108-4201-5(0)***) Benchmark Education Co.

Kubik, Dorothy. The Adventures of Elbert & Leopoldina. James, Annie, illus. 2006. 104p. (J). per. 15.00 (***978-0-9790775-1-7(6)***) Touchstone Communications.

Lagerlof, Selma. The Wonderful Adventures of Nils. 2004. reprint ed. pap. 34.95 (978-1-4191-8845-9(3)); pap. 1.99 (978-1-4192-8845-6(8)) Kessinger Publishing, LLC.

Langton, Jane. The Fledgling. unabr. ed. 2004. 192p. (J). (gr. 4-7). pap. 36.00 incl. audio (978-0-8072-8779-8(2) , YA265SP, Listening Library) Random Hse. Audio Publishing Group.

Leeson, Christine. Snow Angel. Chapman, Jane, illus. 2007. 32p. (J). (ps-2). 15.95 (***978-1-58925-068-0(0)*** , tiger tales) ME Media LLC.

Lurie, Alison. Baba Yaga & the Stolen Baby. Souhami, Jessica, illus. ed. 2008. 32p. (J). pap. 7.95 (***978-1-84507-753-2(9))*** Lincoln, Frances Ltd. GBR. *Dist:* Perseus Distribution.

Mackinnon, Mairi. Goose That Laid the Golden Eggs. Howarth, Daniel, illus. 2006. 48p. (J). 8.99 (978-0-7945-1378-8(6) , Usborne) EDC Publishing.

Macy-Mills, Phyllis. Murphy Moose & Garrett Goose. Russell, Kay, illus. 2003. (J). spiral bd. (978-1-932303-48-3(0) , Llumina Pr.) Media Creations, Inc.

Maestro, Giulio. Geese Find the Missing Piece: School Time Riddle Rhymes. Maestro, Giulio, illus. 2000. (I Can Read Bks.). (Illus.). 48p. (J). (ps-1). pap. 4.99 (978-0-06-443707-3(8) , Harper Trophy) HarperCollins Pubs.

McBratney, Sam. Just You & Me. Bates, Ivan, illus. 2000. 32p. (J). (gr. k-1). pap. 5.99 (978-0-7636-1078-4(X)) Candlewick Pr.

—Just You & Me. 2000. (J). (978-0-606-19318-4(9)); lib. bdg. 14.15 (978-0-613-28545-2(X)) Tandem Library Bks.

McDermott, Dennis & Grimm, Jacob W. The Golden Goose. 2000. (Illus.). 32p. (J). (ps-3). 15.95 (978-0-688-11402-2(4)); 15.89 (978-0-688-11403-9(2)) HarperCollins Pubs.

McPhail, David M. A Girl, a Goat & a Goose. 2000. (Hello Reader! Ser.). (Illus.). (J). 10.79 (978-0-606-18875-3(4)) Tandem Library Bks.

—A Girl, a Goat, & a Goose. 2004. 32p. (J). lib. bdg. 15.00 (978-1-59054-669-7(5)) Fitzgerald Bks.

—A Girl, a Goat, & a Goose, & the Storm. 2002. (SPA., Illus.). (J). (978-0-439-41152-3(1)) Scholastic, Inc.

McWilliams Pittard, Irene. Goose Dreams. Kiplinger Pandy, Lori, illus. 2005. (J). 10.00 (978-1-59971-142-3(7)) Aardvark Global Publishing.

Mother Goose Barnyard. 2003. (J). per. (978-1-57657-164-4(5)) Paradise Pr., Inc.

Mothergoose-Feathered. 2003. (J). per. (978-1-57657-165-1(3)) Paradise Pr., Inc.

Newton, Jill. Gordon in Charge. Newton, Jill, illus. 2003. (Illus.). 32p. (J). 15.95 (978-1-58234-823-0(5) , Bloomsbury Children) Bloomsbury Publishing.

O'Kelley, Jeff. Sam Finds the Way. 2006. (Early Explorers Ser.). (J). 34.00 (***978-1-4108-6107-8(4))*** Benchmark Education Co.

Petunia. 2004. 24.95 incl. audio (978-1-56008-237-8(2)); pap. 14.95 incl. audio (978-0-7882-0603-0(6)) Weston Woods Studios, Inc.

Pilkey, Dav. The Silly Gooses. Pilkey, Dav, illus. 2000. (Illus.). 40p. (J). (ps-3). pap. 5.99 (978-0-590-95735-9(X)) Scholastic, Inc.

—The Silly Gooses. 2000. (978-0-606-18890-6(8)) Tandem Library Bks.

Polacco, Patricia. I Can Hear the Sun. Polacco, Patricia, illus. 1999. (Illus.). 40p. (J). (ps-3). pap. 5.99 (978-0-698-11857-7(X) , Putnam Juvenile) Penguin Group (USA) Inc.

—I Can Hear the Sun. 1999. (J). (978-0-606-17412-1(5)); lib. bdg. 14.15 (978-0-613-22873-2(1)) Tandem Library Bks.

—Rechenka's Eggs. Polacco, Patricia, illus. 2002. (Illus.). (J). 14.04 (978-0-7587-3502-7(2)) Book Wholesalers, Inc.

Prentice, Amy. The Gray Goose's Story. 2004. reprint ed. pap. 15.95 (978-1-4191-6454-5(6)); pap. 1.99 (978-1-4192-6454-2(0)) Kessinger Publishing, LLC.

Pyle, Howard. Twilight Land. 2004. reprint ed. pap. 22.95 (978-1-4191-9142-8(X)); pap. 1.99 (978-1-4192-9142-5(4)) Kessinger Publishing, LLC.

Rapson, Helen. One Lucky Goose. 2005. 31p. pap. 17.95 (978-1-4137-2852-1(9)) PublishAmerica, Inc.

Rogers, Jacqueline. Goose on the Loose at School. Rogers, Jacqueline, illus. 2006. (Scholastic Reader Ser.: 1). 32p. (J). pap. 3.99 (978-0-439-72501-9(1) , Cartwheel Bks.) Scholastic, Inc.

Rong, Yu. A Lovely Day for Amelia Goose. Rong, Yu, illus. 2004. (Illus.). 32p. (J). (gr. k-k). 14.99 (978-0-7636-2309-8(1)) Candlewick Pr.

Running Press Staff. Silly Goose's Lost Easter Eggs. 2006. (Illus.). 8p. (J). 4.95 (978-0-7624-2632-4(2) , Running Pr. Kids) Running Pr. Bk. Pubs.

Rylant, Cynthia. Henry & Mudge & the Wild Goose Chase. Bracken, Carolyn, illus. ed. 2005. (Henry & Mudge Ser.). 40p. (J). lib. bdg. 15.00 (978-1-59054-946-9(5)) Fitzgerald Bks.

—Henry & Mudge & the Wild Goose Chase. Bracken, Carolyn, illus. 2004. (Henry & Mudge Ser.). 40p. (J). pap. 3.99 (978-0-689-83450-9(0) , Aladdin) Simon & Schuster Children's Publishing.

—Henry & Mudge & the Wild Goose Chase. Bracken, Carolyn, illus. 2004. (Henry & Mudge Ser.). 40p. (J). (gr. k-2). lib. bdg. 12.10 (978-1-4176-4340-0(4)) Tandem Library Bks.

Rylant, Cynthia & Bracken, Carolyn. Henry & Mudge & the Wild Goose Chase. 2003. (Henry & Mudge Ser.). (Illus.). 40p. (J). (gr. k-3). 14.95 (978-0-689-81172-2(1)) Simon & Schuster Children's Publishing.

Sansone, Adele. The Little Green Goose. 2001. (Illus.). (J). (978-0-606-20768-3(6)) Tandem Library Bks.

—The Little Green Goose. James, J. Alison, tr. Marks, Alan, illus. 2001. (J). (ps-ps). lib. bdg. 15.25 (978-0-613-36468-3(6)) Tandem Library Bks.

—Pequeno Ganso Verde. 2001. (SPA.). (gr. k-3). lib. bdg. 15.25 (978-0-613-36002-9(8)) Tandem Library Bks.

Scholastic, Inc. Staff. The Real Mother Goose. 2005. (Humpty Dumpty Musical Toy Ser.). (J). pap. 24.99 (978-0-439-72694-8(8) , SideKicks TM Baby) Scholastic, Inc.

Silverman, Erica. Don't Fidget a Feather. Schindler, S. D., illus. 1998. 32p. (J). (ps-2). 6.99 (978-0-689-81967-4(6) , Aladdin) Simon & Schuster Children's Publishing.

—Don't Fidget a Feather. 1998. 12.79 (978-0-606-13340-1(2)) Tandem Library Bks.

Simmons, Jane. Ebb & Flo & the Greedy Gulls. 2003. (gr. k-3). lib. bdg. 15.30 (978-0-613-66401-1(9)) Tandem Library Bks.

—Ebb & Flo & the New Friend. Simmons, Jane, illus. 2002. (Illus.). 32p. (J). (ps-2). 6.99 (978-0-689-84890-2(0) , Aladdin) Simon & Schuster Children's Publishing.

—Ebb & Flo & the New Friend. 2002. (ps-2). lib. bdg. 15.30 (978-0-613-50532-1(8)) Tandem Library Bks.

Simmons, Jane, illus. Ebb & Flo & the Greedy Gulls. 2003. 32p. (J). pap. 6.99 (978-0-689-85810-9(8) , Aladdin) Simon & Schuster Children's Publishing.

Simont, Marc. The Goose That Almost Got Cooked. 2001. (Illus.). 40p. (J). (gr. 4). pap. 5.99 (978-0-439-24399-5(8)) Scholastic, Inc.

Soundprints. Here We Go Round the Mulberry Bush: And Other Favorites. 2002. (Illus.). 36p. (J). bds. 8.95 (978-1-931465-26-7(6)); bds. 10.95 incl. audio compact disk (978-1-931465-32-8(0)) Soundprints. (Little Soundprints).

—Humpty Dumpty: And Other Favorites. 2005. (Meet Mother Goose Ser.). (Illus.). 36p. (J). bds. 14.95 incl. audio compact disk (978-1-931465-49-6(5) , MPD1101) Soundprints.

—Humpty Dumpty: And Other Favorites. (Meet Mother Goose Ser.). (Illus.). 36p. (J). 2005. bds. 10.95 incl. audio compact disk (978-1-931465-29-8(0) , MD1101); 2002. bds. 8.95 (978-1-931465-23-6(1)) Soundprints.

Tafuri, Nancy. Blue Goose. Tafuri, Nancy, illus. 2008. 32p. (J). 15.99 (***978-1-4169-2834-8(0)*** , Simon & Schuster Children's Publishing) Simon & Schuster Children's Publishing.

Tafuri, Nancy. Silly Little Goose! 2001. (Illus.). (J). 15.95 (978-0-439-06305-0(1)) Scholastic, Inc.

Tattersfield, Nigel, intro. Mother Goose's Melody. 2005. (Illus.). 118p. 19.00 (978-1-85124-072-2(1)) Bodleian Library GBR. *Dist:* Chicago Distribution Ctr.

Van Scoyoc, Pam. The Ballerina with Webbed Feet/la Bailarina Palmipeda. Teichman, Diane E., tr. Lewis, R. J., illus. l.t. ed. 2004. (ENG & SPA.). 40p. (J). (gr. k-2). lib. bdg. 16.98 (978-0-9663629-2-3(6)) By Grace Enterprises.

Vande Velde, Vivian. Three Good Deeds. (Illus.). 160p. 2007. (YA). pap. 5.95 (***978-0-15-205455-7(3)*** , Magic Carpet Bks.); 2005. (J). (gr. 3-7). 16.00 (978-0-15-205382-6(4)) Harcourt Children's Bks.

Walker, Sally. 18 Penny Goose. 1999. (gr. k-3). lib. bdg. 11.80 (978-0-613-15776-6(1)) Tandem Library Bks.

Walker, Sally M. The 18 Penny Goose. Beier, Ellen, illus. 1998. (I Can Read Bks.). 64p. (J). (gr. k-3). 15.89 (978-0-06-027557-0(X)) HarperCollins Pubs.

Whitaker, Margaret. Goose Lake. Whitaker, Margaret, illus. 2005. (Illus.). 36p. (J). 12.95 (978-0-9768051-0-6(3)) RoseFountain Pr., LLC.

White, Mark. La Gansa de los Huevos de Oro: Version de la Fabula de Esopo. Rojo, Sara, illus. 2006. (Read-It! Readers en Espanol Ser.).Tr. of Goose that Laid the Golden Egg: A Retelling of Aesop's Fable. (SPA.). 32p. (J). (ps-3). 19.95 (978-1-4048-1622-0(4)) Picture Window Bks.

Wiggin, Kate Douglas. The Diary of a Goose Girl. 2006. (ENG.). pap. (***978-1-4250-2104-7(2))*** Assistedreading-books.com Inc.

—The Diary of a Goose Girl. 2004. reprint ed. pap. 1.99 (978-1-4192-5922-7(9)) Kessinger Publishing, LLC.

—The Diary of a Goose Girl. Shepperson, Claude A., illus. 2004. reprint ed. pap. 20.95 (978-1-4179-1501-9(3)) Kessinger Publishing, LLC.

Wingfield, David. Little Goose. Apple, Margot, illus. 2007. (J). (***978-1-58246-190-8(2)*** , Tricycle Pr.) Ten Speed Pr.

Wu, Liz. Rosa Farm. Phelan, Matt, illus. 2006. 144p. (J). (gr. 2-7). 15.95 (978-0-375-83681-7(0)); lib. bdg. 17.99 (978-0-375-93681-4(5)) Random Hse. Children's Bks. (Knopf Bks. for Young Readers).

Zalben, Jane Breskin. Hey, Mama Goose. Chollat, Emilie, illus. 2005. 32p. (J). (ps). 15.99 (978-0-525-47097-7(2) , Dutton Juvenile) Penguin Group (USA) Inc.

GEHRIG, LOU, 1903-1941

Abramovitz, Melissa. Lou Gehrigs Disease. 2006. (Illus.). 112p. (J). (gr. 7-10). 32.45 (978-1-59018-676-3(1) , Lucent Bks.) Thomson Gale.

Adler, David A. Lou Gehrig: The Luckiest Man. Widener, Terry, illus. 2001. 32p. (J). (gr. 1-4). pap. 7.00 (978-0-15-202483-3(2) , Harcourt Paperbacks) Harcourt Children's Bks.

—Lou Gehrig: The Luckiest Man. 2001. (978-0-606-21307-3(4)); lib. bdg. 14.15 (978-0-613-35534-6(2)) Tandem Library Bks.

Boothroyd, Jennifer. Lou Gehrig: A Life of Dedication. 2008. (Pull Ahead Books-Biographies Ser.). (J). lib. bdg. 22.60 (***978-0-8225-8587-9(1)*** , Lerner Pubns.) Lerner Publishing Group.

Moss, Marissa. Mighty Jackie: The Strike-Out Queen. Payne, C. F., tr. Payne, C. F., illus. 2004. 32p. (J). 16.95 (978-0-689-86329-5(2) , Simon & Schuster/Paula Wiseman Bks.) Simon & Schuster Children's Publishing.

Patrick Jean L. S. La niña que poncho a Babe Ruth (the Girl Who Struck Out Babe Ruth) Reeves, Jeni, illus. 2007. (Yo solo Historia (on My Own History) Ser.). (J). pap. 6.95 (***978-0-8225-7788-1(7)*** , Ediciones Lerner) Lerner Publishing Group.

Patrick, Jean L. S. La Niña Que Poncho a Babe Ruth (The Girl Who Struck Out Babe Ruth) Reeves, Jeni, illus. 2007. (Yo Solo - Historia (on My Own - History) Ser.). (SPA.). 48p. (J). (gr. 2-4). 25.26 (***978-0-8225-7785-0(2)*** , Ediciones Lerner) Lerner Publishing Group.

Reis, Ronald A. Lou Gehrig. 2007. (Baseball Superstars Ser.). 136p. (J). (gr. 6-12). 30.00 (***978-0-7910-9423-5(5)*** , Chelsea Hse.) Facts On File, Inc.

Viola, Kevin. Lou Gehrig. (Sports Heroes & Legends Ser.). (J). 2005. (Illus.). 112p. (gr. 6-12). lib. bdg. 27.93 (978-0-8225-1794-8(9)); 2004. pap. 8.95 (978-0-8225-5311-3(2) , LernerSports) Lerner Publishing Group.

GEMINI PROJECT

see Project Gemini

GEMS

Here are entered antiquarian or artistic works on engraved stones and jewels. Mineralogical and technological works on potential and actual engraved stones and jewels are entered under Precious Stones.

see also Precious Stones

Dorling Kindersley Publishing Staff & Foa, Emma. Gemstones. 2nd rev. ed. 2003. (DK Pockets Ser.). (Illus.). 128p. (J). pap. 6.99 (978-0-7894-9596-9(1)) Dorling Kindersley Publishing, Inc.

Gems: Individual Title Six-Packs. (On Deck Ser.: Vol. 2). 24p. (gr. 4-5). 35.00 (978-0-7578-5818-5(X)) Rigby Education.

Pellant, Christopher. Collecting Gems & Minerals. 1998. (Illus.). 80p. (YA). (gr. 5 up). 14.95 (978-0-8069-9760-5(5)) Sterling Publishing Co., Inc.

Phelan, Glen. Rocks & Minerals. 2004. (National Geographic Reading Expeditions Ser.). (Illus.). 32p. (J). pap. (978-0-7922-4571-1(7)) National Geographic Society.

Symes, R. F., et al. Crystal & Gem. Keates, Colin, illus. 2004. (Eyewitness Books). 72p. (J). lib. bdg. 19.99 (978-0-7566-0663-3(2)) Dorling Kindersley Publishing, Inc.

GENDARMERIE ROYALE DU CANADA

see Royal Canadian Mounted Police

GENEALOGY

see also Biography; Heraldry

Baugrud, Kim J. Searching for Your Family: Practical Genealogy. 2002. (YA). cd-rom 13.00 (978-0-9715922-1-6(7)); 3rd rev. l.t. ed. 140p. 13.00 net. (978-0-9715922-0-9(9)) Baugrud, Kim.

Benchmark Education Staff, compiled by. Family Album & Ancestors. 2005. spiral bd. 225.00 (***978-1-4108-5821-4(9))*** Benchmark Education Co.

—Our Family Stories & Las historias de nuestras Familias. 2005. 52.00 (***978-1-4108-4493-4(5))*** Benchmark Education Co.

Day, Reed B. Two Families: A History of the Lives & Times of the Families of Isaac Newton Day & Lucilla Caroline Blachly 1640-1940. 2004. (Illus.). 285p. per. 29.95 (978-0-9760563-1-7(3) , 7796) Mechling Bookbindery.

Dunbar, James. When I Was Young. Remphry, Martin, illus. 1999. (Picture Bks.). 32p. (J). (ps-3). lib. bdg. 15.95 (978-1-57505-359-2(4) , Carolrhoda Bks.) Lerner Publishing Group.

EchoHawk, Terry. Call Me Little Echo Hawk. 2005. (Illus.). 22p. (J). 15.99 (978-1-55517-804-8(9) , Cedar Fort, Inc.) Cedar Fort, Inc./CFI Distribution.

Goudge, Elizabeth. The Little White Horse. 2001. 240p. (YA). (gr. 3-6). pap. 5.99 (978-0-14-230027-5(6) , Puffin) Penguin Group (USA) Inc.

Harcourt School Publishers Staff. All in the Family. 3rd ed. 2002. (Trophies English Language Learners Ser.). (Illus.). pap. 5.10 (978-0-15-327876-1(5)) Harcourt Schl. Pubs.

Hill, George. The Fall of Irish Chiefs & Clans & the Plantation of Ulster: Including the Names of Irish Catholics, & Protestant Settlers. 2004. Orig. Title: An Historical Account of the Plantation in Ulster at the Commencement of the 17th Century. (Illus.). 276p. lib. bdg. 39.00 (978-0-940134-42-3(X)) Irish Genealogical Foundation.

Hood, Karen Jean Matsko. Hood & Matsko Family Tree & Heritage: Annual Edition 2002. 2002. 15.95 (978-1-59210-657-8(9)); cd-rom 13.95 (978-1-59210-658-5(7)) Whispering Pine Pr., Inc.

Hubbs, Susan H. Dig Up Your Roots & Find Your Branches: A Child's Guide to Genealogy. 2000. (Illus.). 108p. (gr. 4-7). pap. 9.95 (978-0-595-13162-4(X)) iUniverse, Inc.

Leavitt, Caroline. The Kids' Family Tree Book. Phillips, Ian, illus. 96p. (J). 2007. pap. 5.95 (978-1-4027-4715-1(2)); 2005. 14.95 (978-1-4027-0942-5(0)) Sterling Publishing Co., Inc.

Maley Yamamoto, Barbara. Family Tapestry: An Examination of Family Histories, Immigration, Personal Choices & Heredity. 2005. 64p. 11.95 (978-1-59363-071-3(9)) Prufrock Pr.

Peyton, Denyce Porter. Learn to Harvest Your Family History. 2005. 41p. spiral bd. 14.96 (978-1-4116-3350-6(4)) Lulu.com.

Roca, Nuria. Tu arbol Genealogico: Your Family Tree (Spanish Edition) Curto, Rosa M., illus. 2007. (What Do You Know about? Bks.). 36p. (J). (gr. k-1). pap. 6.99 (978-0-7641-3580-4(5)) Barron's Educational Series, Inc.

—Your Family Tree. Curto, Rosa M., illus. 2007. (What Do You Know about? Bks.). 36p. (J). (gr. k-1). pap. 6.99 (978-0-7641-3579-8(1)) Barron's Educational Series, Inc.

Sebring, Ellen & Rudder, Mary. When I Was a Boy: Based on the Real Life Story of Shigeru Miyagawa & His Family. Miyagawa, Shigeru, ed. Ferreira, Melissa, illus. 2000. 20p. (J). (gr. 1-6). pap. 40.00 (978-1-929724-15-4(2)) StarFestival, Inc.

Shepherdson, Nancy. Ancestor Hunt: Finding Your Family Online. 2003. (Single Title: Social Studies). (Illus.). 144p. (J). 30.50 (978-0-531-15454-0(8) , Watts, Franklin) Scholastic Library Publishing.

Sweeney, Joan. Me & My Family Tree. Cable, Annette, illus. 2000. (Me Ser.). 32p. (J). (gr. k-3). 6.99 (978-0-517-88597-0(2) , Dragonfly Bks.) Random Hse. Children's Bks.

—Me & My Family Tree. 2000. (978-0-606-18091-7(5)); lib. bdg. 15.30 (978-0-613-26171-5(2)) Tandem Library Bks.

Taylor, Maureen. Through the Eyes of Your Ancestors: A Step-by-Step Guide to Uncovering Your Fami. 1999. (gr. 3-6). lib. bdg. 17.60 (978-0-613-15233-4(6)) Tandem Library Bks.

Walker, Richard. Genes & DNA. 2003. (Kingfisher Knowledge Ser.). (Illus.). 64p. (J). (gr. 4-8). tchr. ed. 12.95 (978-0-7534-5621-7(4) , Kingfisher) Houghton Mifflin Co. Trade & Reference Div.

Williams, Jeffrey Lewis. The Cheek Family Chronicles: Of America, England & Australia, a 700 Year History. 2004. (Illus.). 1104p. lib. bdg. 79.95 (978-0-9712564-5-3(4)) Kinfolk Research Pr.

Wolfman, Ira. Climbing Your Family Tree: Online & off-Line Genealogy for Kids. 2002. (gr. 3-6). lib. bdg. 23.40 (978-0-613-53417-8(4)) Tandem Library Bks.

—Climbing Your Family Tree: Online & off-Line Genealogy for Kids. 2001. (Illus.). 240p. (J). (gr. 3-7). pap. 13.95 (978-0-7611-2539-6(6) , 12539) Workman Publishing Co., Inc.

GENERALS

Aaseng, Nathan. Strategic Battles. 2002. (American War Library). (Illus.). 112p. (J). 29.95 (978-1-59018-221-5(9) , Lucent Bks.) Thomson Gale.

Adelson, Bruce. Baron Von Steuben. 2001. (Revolutionary War Leaders Ser.). (Illus.). 80p. (J). pap. 27.50 (978-0-7910-6393-4(3)); 27.50 (978-0-7910-6392-7(5)) Facts On File, Inc. (Chelsea Hse.).

—William Howe: British General. 2002. (gr. 5-8). lib. bdg. 17.60 (978-0-613-50852-0(1)) Tandem Library Bks.

Allen, Thomas B. George Washington, Spymaster: How the Americans Outspied the British & Won the Revolutionary War. 2007. (Illus.). 192p. (J). (gr. 5). pap. 5.95 (978-1-4263-0041-7(7) , National Geographic Children's Bks.) National Geographic Society.

Aller, Susan Bivin. Ulysses S. Grant. 2005. (History Maker Bios Ser.). (Illus.). 48p. (J). 26.60 (978-0-8225-2438-0(4) , Lerner Pubns.) Lerner Publishing Group.

Anderson, Dale. Leaders of the American Revolution. 2005. (World Almanac Library of the American Revolution). (J). pap. (978-0-8368-5940-9(5)); lib. bdg. 30.00 (978-0-8368-5931-7(6)) Stevens, Gareth Inc. (World Almanac Library).

—The Patriots Win the American Revolution. 2005. (World Almanac Library of the American Revolution). (J). pap. (978-0-8368-5937-9(5)); lib. bdg. 30.00 (978-0-8368-5928-7(6)) Stevens, Gareth Inc. (World Almanac Library).

Aronson, Billy. Ulysses S. Grant. 2007. (Presidents & Their Times Ser.). 96p. (J). lib. bdg. 32.79 (978-0-7614-2430-7(X) , Benchmark Bks.) Cavendish, Marshall Corp.

Aronson, Marc. John Winthrop, Oliver Cromwell, & the Land of Promise. 2004. (Illus.). 224p. (J). (gr. 5-9). tchr. ed. 20.00 (978-0-618-18177-3(6) , Clarion Bks.) Houghton Mifflin Co. Trade & Reference Div.

Ashby, Ruth. Lee vs. Grant: The Major Battles. 2002. (Illus.). 48p. (J). lib. bdg. 28.50 (978-1-58340-184-2(9)) Smart Apple Media.

Bankston, John. The Life & Times of Alexander the Great. 2004. (Biography of Ancient Civilizations Ser.). (Illus.). 48p. (J). lib. bdg. (978-1-58415-235-4(4)) Mitchell Lane Pubs., Inc.

Behnke, Alison. The Conquests of Alexander the Great. 2007. (Pivotal Moments in History Ser.). 160p. (YA). (gr. 9-12). lib. bdg. 38.60 (978-0-8225-5920-7(X) , Twenty-First Century Bks.) Lerner Publishing Group.

Benge, Janet & Benge, Geoff. Douglas MacArthur: What Greater Honor. 2005. (Illus.). 205p. (J). 6.99 (978-1-932096-15-6(9)) Emerald Bks.

Blohm, Craig E. Leaders & Generals. 2001. (American War Library). (Illus.). 112p. (J). (gr. 4-12). lib. bdg. 29.95 (978-1-56006-839-6(6) , LML00902-178171, Lucent Bks.) Thomson Gale.

Bodie, Idella. Light-Horse Harry. 2004. (Illus.). 86p. (J). pap. 6.95 (978-0-87844-172-3(7)) Sandlapper Publishing Co., Inc.

—The Old Wagoner. 2002. (Illus.). 82p. (J). 5.95 (978-0-87844-165-5(4)) Sandlapper Publishing Co., Inc.

—The Wizard Owl. 2003. (Illus.). 86p. (J). pap. 6.95 (978-0-87844-167-9(0)) Sandlapper Publishing Co., Inc.

Boomhower, Ray E. The Sword & the Pen: A Life of Lew Wallace. 2005. (Illus.). x, 164p. (J). (978-0-87195-185-4(1)) Indiana Historical Society.

Brager, Bruce L. There He Stands: The Story of Stonewall Jackson. 2005. (Civil War Leaders Ser.). (Illus.). 176p. (J). (gr. 6-12). 26.95 (978-1-931798-44-0(3)) Reynolds, Morgan Inc.

Brown, Warren. Colin Powell: Soldier & Statesman. (Black Americans of Achievement Ser.). (Illus.). 112p. (J). (gr. 6-12). 2005. pap. 13.25 (978-0-7910-8373-4(X)); 2004. 30.00 (978-0-7910-8254-6(7)) Facts On File, Inc. (Chelsea Hse.).

Burgan, Michael. Alexander the Great: World Conqueror. 2006. (J). (978-0-7565-1872-1(5)) Compass Point Bks.

—George Rogers Clark. 2001. (Revolutionary War Leaders Ser.). (Illus.). 80p. (J). pap. 27.50 (978-0-7910-6395-8(X)); 27.50 (978-0-7910-6394-1(1)) Facts On File, Inc. (Chelsea Hse.).

Carter, E. J. Robert E. Lee. 2004. (American War Biographies Ser.). (Illus.). 48p. (J). pap. 8.50 (978-1-4034-5088-3(9)); lib. bdg. 27.07 (978-1-4034-5081-4(1)) Heinemann Library.

—Ulysses S. Grant. 2004. (American War Biographies Ser.). (Illus.). 48p. (J). pap. 8.50 (978-1-4034-5087-6(0)); lib. bdg. (978-1-4034-5080-7(3)) Heinemann Library.

Cawthorne, Nigel. Military Commanders: The 100 Greatest Throughout History. 2004. (Illus.). 208p. 18.95 (978-1-59270-029-5(2)) Enchanted Lion Bks., LLC.

Chrisp, Peter, contrib. by. Alexander the Great. 2000. (Illus.). 48p. (YA). 14.95 (978-0-7894-6109-4(9)) Dorling Kindersley Publishing, Inc.

Civil War Generals. 1998. (Illus.). 32p. (YA). (gr. 6 up). pap. 4.00 (978-1-890541-11-8(7)) Americana Souvenirs & Gifts.

Coleman, Wim & Perrin, Pat. George Washington: Creating a Nation. 2004. (America's Founding Fathers Ser.). (Illus.). 128p. (J). lib. bdg. 26.60 (978-0-7660-2290-4(0)) Enslow Pubs., Inc.

Cornelius, Kay. Francis Marion: The Swamp Fox. 2001. (gr. 5-8). lib. bdg. 17.60 (978-0-613-32583-7(4)) Tandem Library Bks.

Crannell, Karl. John Stark: Live Free or Die. 2006. (Forgotten Heroes of the American Revolution Ser.). (Illus.). 80p. (J). (gr. 5-11). lib. bdg. 23.95 (978-1-59556-016-2(5)) OTTN Publishing.

—John Stark: Live Free or Die! 2006. (J). pap. (978-1-59556-021-6(1)) OTTN Publishing.

Crompton, Samuel Willard. Alexander the Great. 2003. (Ancient World Leaders Ser.). (Illus.). 112p. (gr. 6-12). (J). 30.00 (978-0-7910-7219-6(3)); pap. 30.00 (978-0-7910-7493-0(5)) Facts On File, Inc. (Chelsea Hse.).

—Ariel Sharon. 2nd rev. ed. 2007. (Modern World Leaders Ser.). 112p. (J). (gr. 6-12). 30.00 (***978-0-7910-9263-7(1)*** , Chelsea Hse.) Facts On File, Inc.

—Julius Caesar. 2003. (Ancient World Leaders Ser.). (Illus.). 112p. (gr. 6-12). 30.00 (978-0-7910-7220-2(7)); pap. 30.00 (978-0-7910-7494-7(3)) Facts On File, Inc. (Chelsea Hse.).

—100 Military Leaders Who Changed the World. 2003. (People Who Changed the World Ser.). (Illus.). 112p. (J). (gr. 5 up). lib. bdg. 30.00 (978-0-8368-5470-1(5) , World Almanac Library) Stevens, Gareth Inc.

Darby, Jean. Dwight D. Eisenhower. 2004. (Presidential Leaders Ser.). (Illus.). 112p. (J). (gr. 6-12). lib. bdg. 29.27 (978-0-8225-0813-7(3)) Lerner Publishing Group.

Doak, Robin S. Thomas "Stonewall" Jackson: Confederate General. 2005. (Signature Lives Ser.). (Illus.). 112p. (J). (gr. 5-7). (978-0-7565-0987-3(4)) Compass Point Bks.

Faber, Harold. John Charles Fremont: Pathfinder to the West. 2002. (Great Explorations Ser.). (Illus.). 79p. (J). 29.93 (978-0-7614-1481-0(9) , Benchmark Bks.) Cavendish, Marshall Corp.

Firth, Rachel & Parkhouse, Stephen. Julius Caesar. 2007. (Famous Lives Gift Bks). 64p. (J). 8.99 (978-0-7945-1595-9(9) , Usborne) EDC Publishing.

Flanagan, Alice K. Colin Powell: U. S. Army General & Secretary of State. 2001. (Career Biographies Ser.). (Illus.). 128p. (J). (gr. 6-12). 25.00 (978-0-89434-372-8(6) , F415, Ferguson Publishing Co.) Facts On File, Inc.

Fritz, Jean. Why Not, Lafayette? 2001. (J). (978-0-606-21526-8(3)); (gr. 5-8). lib. bdg. 14.15 (978-0-613-36030-2(3)) Tandem Library Bks.

Fryer, Mary Beacock. Bold, Brave, & Born to Lead: Major General Isaac Brock & the Canadas. 2004. (Illus.). 200p. pap. 9.99 (978-1-55002-501-9(5)) Dundurn Group, The CAN. *Dist:* Univ. of Toronto Pr.

Galford, Ellen. Julius Caesar: The Boy Who Conquered an Empire. 2007. (World History Biographies Ser.). (Illus.). 64p. (J). (gr. 3-7). 17.95 (978-1-4263-0064-6(6)); lib. bdg. 27.90 (978-1-4263-0065-3(4)) National Geographic Society. (National Geographic Children's Bks.).

Gallagher, Jim. Daniel Morgan: Fighting Frontiersman. 2006. (J). pap. (978-1-59556-020-9(3)); (Illus.). 88p. (gr. 5-11). lib. bdg. 23.95 (978-1-59556-015-5(7)) OTTN Publishing.

Ganeri, Anita. Alexander the Great: The Life of a King & Conqueror. 2005. (Graphic Nonfiction Ser.). (Illus.). 48p. (J). lib. bdg. 26.50 (978-1-4042-0238-2(2) , 1241094) Rosen Publishing Group, Inc., The.

Generals at Gettysburg. 2000. (Illus.). 32p. (YA). (gr. 5 up). pap. 5.00 (978-1-890541-24-8(9)) Americana Souvenirs & Gifts.

George C. Marshall, Reporting for Duty. 2001. (YA). (gr. 6-10). pap. 12.00 (978-0-9661582-2-9(9)) Blue Valley Bks.

Gillis, Jennifer Blizin. Robert E. Lee: Confederate Commander. 2004. (Signature Lives Ser.). (Illus.). 112p. (J). 30.60 (978-0-7565-0821-0(5) , 1240144) Compass Point Bks.

Gimpel, Lee. Fighting Wars, Planning for Peace: The Story of George C. Marshall. 2005. (World Leaders Ser.). (Illus.). 176p. (J). (gr. 8 up). lib. bdg. 26.95 (978-1-931798-66-2(4)) Reynolds, Morgan Inc.

Grabowski, Patricia A. General "Mad" Anthony Wayne. 2001. (Revolutionary War Leaders Ser.). (Illus.). 80p. (J). pap. 27.50 (978-0-7910-6383-5(6)); 27.50 (978-0-7910-6382-8(8)) Facts On File, Inc. (Chelsea Hse.).

Granger, Stacey. Colin Powell. l.t. ed. 2002. (Real-Life Reader Biography Ser.). (Illus.). 32p. (J). (gr. 3-8). lib. bdg. 15.95 (978-1-58415-144-9(7)) Mitchell Lane Pubs., Inc.

Green, Carl R. & Sanford, William R. Confederate Generals of the Civil War. 1998. (Collective Biographies Ser.). (Illus.). 112p. (YA). (gr. 6-12). lib. bdg. 26.60 (978-0-7660-1029-1(5)) Enslow Pubs., Inc.

—Union Generals of the Civil War. 1998. (Collective Biographies Ser.). (Illus.). 112p. (YA). (gr. 6-12). lib. bdg. 26.60 (978-0-7660-1028-4(7)) Enslow Pubs., Inc.

Greenblatt, Miriam. Julius Caesar & the Roman Republic. 2005. (Rulers & Their Times Ser.). (Illus.). 96p. (J). (gr. 3-7). lib. bdg. 29.93 (978-0-7614-1836-8(9) , Benchmark Bks.) Cavendish, Marshall Corp.

Gunther, John. Sterling Point Books: Alexander the Great. 2007. (Sterling Point Bks.). (Illus.). 176p. (J). 12.95 (978-1-4027-4519-5(2)); pap. 6.95 (978-1-4027-4139-5(1)) Sterling Publishing Co., Inc.

Hale, Sarah Elder, ed. Stonewall Jackson: Spirit of the South. 2005. (Cobblestone the Civil War Ser.). (Illus.). 48p. (J). 17.95 (978-0-8126-7907-6(5)) Cobblestone Publishing Co.

Hatch, Alden. General George Patton: Old Blood & Guts. 2006. (Sterling Point Bks.). (Illus.). 208p. (J). 12.95 (978-1-4027-3186-0(8)); pap. 6.95 (978-1-4027-3614-8(2)) Sterling Publishing Co., Inc.

Haugen, Brenda. Douglas MacArthur: America's General. 2005. (Illus.). 112p. (J). (gr. 5-7). (978-0-7565-0994-1(7)) Compass Point Bks.

—Ulysses S. Grant: Union General & U.S. President. 2004. (Signature Lives Ser.). (Illus.). 112p. (J). 30.60 (978-0-7565-0820-3(7) , 1240145) Compass Point Bks.

Havelin, Kate. Ulysses S. Grant. 2004. (Presidential Leaders Ser.). (Illus.). 112p. (J). 29.27 (978-0-8225-0814-4(1) , Lerner Pubns.) Lerner Publishing Group.

Hill, Mary. Colin Powell. 2003. (gr. k-3). lib. bdg. 12.95 (978-0-613-67704-2(8)) Tandem Library Bks.

Hinman, Bonnie. General Thomas Gage. 2001. (Revolutionary War Leaders Ser.), 80p. (J). pap. 27.50 (978-0-7910-6385-9(2)); 27.50 (978-0-7910-6384-2(4)) Facts On File, Inc. (Chelsea Hse.).

Hoogenboom, Lynn. William Tecumseh Sherman: The Fight to Preserve the Union. 2005. (Library of American Lives & Times). (Illus.). 112p. (J). (gr. 4-8). lib. bdg. 31.95 (978-0-8239-6625-7(9)) Rosen Publishing Group, Inc., The.

Horn, Geoffrey M. Colin Powell. 2004. (Trailblazers of the Modern World Ser.). (Illus.). 48p. (J). pap. 11.95 (978-0-8368-5267-7(2)); (YA). lib. bdg. 30.00 (978-0-8368-5498-5(5)) Stevens, Gareth Inc. (World Almanac Library).

Hughes, Libby. Colin Powell: A Man of Quality. 2000. (Illus.). 188p. (gr. 4-7). pap. 12.95 (978-0-595-00734-9(1) , Backinprint.com) iUniverse, Inc.

—Norman Schwartzkopf: Hero with a Heart. 2002. 148p. pap. 12.95 (978-0-595-25570-2(1) , Backinprint.com) iUniverse, Inc.

Jeffrey, Gary & Petty, Kate. Julius Caesar: The Life of a Roman General. 2005. (Illus.). 48p. (J). lib. bdg. 26.50 (978-1-4042-0239-9(0) , 1241097) Rosen Publishing Group, Inc., The.

Kauffman, Scott. Francis Marion: Swamp Fox of South Carolina. 2006. (Forgotten Heroes of the American Revolution Ser.). (Illus.). 88p. (YA). (gr. 5-11). lib. bdg. 23.95 (978-1-59556-014-8(9)) OTTN Publishing.

Keller, Kristin Thoennes. George Washington. 2000. (Let Freedom Ring Ser.). (Illus.). 48p. (J). (gr. 3-4). lib. bdg. 22.60 (978-0-7368-1034-0(X) , Bridgestone Bks.) Capstone Pr., Inc.

Kennedy, Robert F. Robert F. Kennedy, Jr.'s American Heroes: Joshua Chamberlain & the American Civil War. Andreev, Nikita, illus. rev. ed. 2007. 48p. (gr. 3-7). 16.99 (***978-1-4231-0771-2(3)***) Hyperion Pr.

Kent, Zachary. Julius Caesar: Ruler of the Roman World. 2006. (Rulers of the Ancient World Ser.). (Illus.). 160p. (J). lib. bdg. 27.93 (978-0-7660-2563-9(2)) Enslow Pubs., Inc.

Knapp, Ron, et al. American Generals of World War II. 1998. (Collective Biographies Ser.). (Illus.). 128p. (YA). (gr. 6-12). lib. bdg. 26.60 (978-0-7660-1024-6(4)) Enslow Pubs., Inc.

Lace, William W. Leaders & Generals. 1999. (American War Library). (Illus.). 112p. (YA). (gr. 4-12). 28.70 (978-1-56006-664-4(4) , LML00902-178016, Lucent Bks.) Thomson Gale.

Leaders of the American Revolution Set, 11-Volumes. 2006. (Leaders of the American Revolution Ser.). 100p. (gr. 5-8). 330.00 (978-0-7910-9320-7(4) , Chelsea Hse.) Facts On File, Inc.

Mara, Wil. Colin Powell. 2004. (Rookie Biographies Ser.). (Illus.). 31p. (J). (gr. 1-2). pap. 4.95 (978-0-516-27918-3(1) , Children's Pr.) Scholastic Library Publishing.

Marcovitz, Hal. George a Custer. 2002. (gr. 5-8). lib. bdg. 17.60 (978-0-613-50916-9(1)) Tandem Library Bks.

Maynard, Charles W. John Charles Fremont: The Pathfinder. 2003. (Famous Explorers of the American West Ser.). (Illus.). 24p. (J). lib. bdg. 18.75 (978-0-8239-6289-1(X) , PowerKids Pr.) Rosen Publishing Group, Inc., The.

McCarthy, Pat. Famous Union Generals & Leaders of the North: A MyReportLinks. com Book. 2004. (American Civil War Ser.). (Illus.). 48p. (J). lib. bdg. 25.26 (978-0-7660-5188-1(9) , MyReportLinks.com Bks.) Enslow Pubs., Inc.

McElroy, Lisa Tucker. Alberto Gonzalez. 2006. (J). pap. 6.95 (978-0-8225-6058-6(5) , First Avenue Editions) Lerner Publishing Group.

McGowen, Tom. Alexander the Great: Conqueror of the Ancient World. 2006. (Rulers of the Ancient World Ser.). (Illus.). 160p. (J). lib. bdg. 27.93 (978-0-7660-2560-8(8)) Enslow Pubs., Inc.

McLeese, Don. George Meade. 2005. (Civil War Military Leaders Ser.). (Illus.). 32p. (J). (ps-6). lib. bdg. 6.45 (978-1-59515-480-4(9)) Rourke Publishing, LLC.

—Jeb Stuart. 2006. (Civil War Military Leaders Ser.). (Illus.). 32p. (gr. 3-6). 19.95 (978-1-59515-479-8(5)) Rourke Publishing, LLC.

—Robert E. Lee. 2006. (Civil War Military Leaders Ser.). (Illus.). 32p. (gr. 3-6). 19.95 (978-1-59515-476-7(0)) Rourke Publishing, LLC.

—Stonewall Jackson. 2006. (Civil War Military Leaders Ser.). (Illus.). 32p. (gr. 3-6). 19.95 (978-1-59515-477-4(9)) Rourke Publishing, LLC.

—Ulysses S. Grant. 2006. (Civil War Military Leaders Ser.). (Illus.). 32p. (gr. 3-6). 19.95 (978-1-59515-475-0(2)) Rourke Publishing, LLC.

—William Tecumseh Sherman. 2006. (Civil War Military Leaders Ser.). (Illus.). 32p. (gr. 3-6). 19.95 (978-1-59515-478-1(7)) Rourke Publishing, LLC.

McNeese, Tim. H. Norman Schwarzkopf. 2003. (Great Military Leaders of the Twentieth Century Ser.). (Illus.). 112p. (gr. 6-12). 30.00 (978-0-7910-7406-0(4) , Chelsea Hse.) Facts On File, Inc.

McPherson, Stephanie Sammartino. Douglas MacArthur. 2005. (History Maker Bios Ser.). (Illus.). 48p. (J). 26.60 (978-0-8225-2434-2(1)) Lerner Publishing Group.

Mierka, Gregg A. Nathanael Greene: The General Who Saved the Revolution. 2006. (J). pap. (978-1-59556-017-9(3)); (Illus.). 88p. (gr. 5-11). lib. bdg. 23.95 (978-1-59556-012-4(2)) OTTN Publishing.

Miller, Brandon Marie. George Washington for Kids: His Life & Times with 21 Activities. 2007. (For Kids Ser.). 144p. (J). pap. 14.95 (***978-1-55652-655-8(5)***) Chicago Review Pr., Inc.

Miller, Roger G. Billy Mitchell: Evangelist of Airpower. 2007. (Illus.). 152p. (YA). (gr. 10 up). lib. bdg. 25.95 (***978-1-59556-025-4(4)***) OTTN Publishing.

Murphy, Frank. George Washington & the General's Dog. Walz, Richard, illus. 2002. (Step into Reading Ser.). 48p. (J). (gr. 1-3). pap. 3.99 (978-0-375-81015-2(3)); lib. bdg. 11.99 (978-0-375-91015-9(8)) Random Hse. Children's Bks. (Random Hse. Bks. for Young Readers).

Murphy, Jim. The Real Benedict Arnold. 2007. (Illus.). 272p. (YA). (gr. 5 up). 20.00 (***978-0-395-77609-4(0)*** , Clarion Bks.) Houghton Mifflin Co. Trade & Reference Div.

Pancella, Peggy. Alexander the Great. 2003. (Historical Biographies Ser.). (Illus.). 32p. (J). pap. 7.50 (978-1-4034-3707-5(6)); lib. bdg. 22.79 (978-1-4034-3699-3(1)) Heinemann Library.

Parker, Lewis K. Lord Charles Cornwallis. 2002. (Triangle History of the American Revolution Ser.). (Illus.). 104p. (J). 28.70 (978-1-56711-608-3(6) , Blackbirch Pr., Inc.) Thomson Gale.

Petrie, Kristin. John C. Fremont. 2004. (Explorers Ser.). (Illus.). 32p. (J). (gr. k-6). lib. bdg. 22.78 (978-1-59197-602-8(2) , Checkerboard Library) ABDO Publishing Co.

Pflueger, Lynda. Jeb Stuart: Confederate Cavalry General. 1998. (Historical American Biographies Ser.). (Illus.). 128p. (YA). (gr. 6-12). lib. bdg. 20.95 (978-0-7660-1013-0(9)) Enslow Pubs., Inc.

Pingry, Patricia A. Meet George Washington. 2001. (Meet Ser.). (Illus.). 32p. (J). (ps-3). 9.95 (978-0-8249-4131-4(4)) Ideals Pubns.

—Meet Robert E. Lee. Johnson, Meredith, illus. 2004. (J). 9.95 (978-0-8249-5465-9(3) , Ideals Pr.) Ideals Pubns.

Price Hossell, Karen. Benedict Arnold. 2004. (American War Biographies Ser.). (J). pap. 8.50 (978-1-4034-5085-2(4)); lib. bdg. 29.93 (978-1-4034-5078-4(1)) Heinemann Library.

—John C. Fremont. (Groundbreakers Ser.). (Illus.). 48p. (J). 2003. (gr. 5-7). lib. bdg. 27.07 (978-1-4034-0244-8(2)); 2002. pap. 8.50 (978-1-4034-0480-0(1)) Heinemann Library.

Rau, Dana Meachen. George Armstrong Custer. 2003. (Compass Point Early Biographies Ser.). (Illus.). 32p. (J). (gr. 2 up). lib. bdg. 21.26 (978-0-7565-0419-9(8)) Compass Point Bks.

Redgrave, Roy. The adventures of colonel Daffodil. 2007. (Illus.). 208p. 45.00 (***978-1-84415-525-5(0)***) Pen & Sword Bks. Ltd. GBR. *Dist:* Casemate Pubs. & Bk. Distributors, LLC.

Remstein, Henna. William Sherman. 2001. (gr. 5-8). lib. bdg. 17.60 (978-0-613-33253-8(9)) Tandem Library Bks.

Rice, Earle, Jr. Claire Chennault. 2003. (Famous Flyers Ser.). (Illus.). 112p. (gr. 6-12). 30.00 (978-0-7910-7217-2(7)); pap. 30.00 (978-0-7910-7499-2(4)) Facts On File, Inc. (Chelsea Hse.).

Rice, Earle. Claire Chennault: Flying Tigers. 2003. (gr. 5-8). lib. bdg. 18.75 (978-0-613-65196-7(0)) Tandem Library Bks.

Rice, Earle, Jr. Ulysses S. Grant: Defender of the Union. 2005. (Civil War Leaders Ser.). (Illus.). 176p. (J). (gr. 6-12). 26.95 (978-1-931798-48-8(6)) Reynolds, Morgan Inc.

Robertson, James I., Jr. Robert E. Lee: Virginian Soldier, American Citizen. 2005. (Illus.). 176p. (YA). (gr. 7 up). 21.95 (978-0-689-85731-7(4) , Atheneum) Simon & Schuster Children's Publishing.

Robertson, James I. Standing Like a Stone Wall: The Life of General Thomas J. Jackson. 2001. (Illus.). 192p. (YA). (gr. 6 up). 22.00 (978-0-689-82419-7(X) , Atheneum) Simon & Schuster Children's Publishing.

Rockwell, Anne. Open the Door to Liberty! A Biography of Toussaint L'Ouverture. Christie, Gregory, illus. 2008. (J). (***978-0-618-60570-5(3)***) Houghton Mifflin Co.

Sapp, Richard. Ulysses S. Grant & the Road to Appomattox. 2006. (In the Footsteps of American Heroes Ser.). (Illus.). 64p. (J). pap. (978-0-8368-6436-6(0)); lib. bdg. 32.67 (978-0-8368-6431-1(X)) Stevens, Gareth Inc. (World Almanac Library).

Saunders, Nicholas. The Life of Alexander the Great. 2006. (Stories from History Ser.). 48p. (J). 14.95 (978-0-7696-4713-5(8)) School Specialty Publishing.

—The Life of Julius Caesar. 2006. (Stories from History Ser.). 48p. (J). 14.95 (978-0-7696-4717-3(0)); pap. 6.95 (978-0-7696-4697-8(2)) School Specialty Publishing.

Schanzer, Rosalyn. George vs. George: The American Revolution As Seen from Both Sides. 2007. (Illus.). 64p. (J). (gr. 4-9). pap. 6.95 (978-1-4263-0042-4(5) , National Geographic Children's Bks.) National Geographic Society.

Shecter, Vicky Alvear. Alexander the Great Rocks the World. Naughton, Terry, illus. 2006. 128p. (J). (gr. 6 up). 18.95 (978-1-58196-045-7(X)) Darby Creek Publishing.

Sonneborn, Liz. Benedict Arnold: Hero & Traitor. 2005. (Leaders of the American Revolution Ser.). (Illus.). 130p. (J). (ps-8). lib. bdg. 30.00 (978-0-7910-8617-9(8) , Chelsea Hse.) Facts On File, Inc.

Souza, Dorothy M. John C. Fremont. 2004. (Watts Library). (Illus.). 64p. (J). (gr. 5-7). pap. 8.95 (978-0-531-16652-9(X)); 25.50 (978-0-531-12288-4(3)) Scholastic Library Publishing. (Watts, Franklin).

Spivey, Mark. A Spot in the Road: My Personal Adventu. 2005. 52p. pap. 12.95 (978-1-4137-8806-8(8)) PublishAmerica, Inc.

Stanley, George E. George S. Patton: War Hero. Henderson, Meryl, illus. 2007. (Childhood of Famous Americans Ser.). 192p. (J). pap. 5.99 (***978-1-4169-1547-8(8)*** , Aladdin) Simon & Schuster Children's Publishing.

Strong, Mike. Colin Powell: It Can Be Done! 2002. (High Five Reading Ser.). (Illus.). 48p. (J). (gr. 3-4). lib. bdg. 22.60 (978-0-7368-9551-4(5) , Capstone High-Interest Bks.); pap. (978-0-7368-9529-3(9)) Capstone Pr., Inc.

Strum, Richard. Henry Knox: Washington's Artilleryman. 2006. (Forgotten Heroes of the American Revolution Ser.). (Illus.). 88p. (J). (gr. 5-11). lib. bdg. 23.95 (978-1-59556-013-1(0)) OTTN Publishing.

Strum, Richard M. Henry Knox: Washington's Artilleryman. 2006. (J). pap. (978-1-59556-018-6(1)) OTTN Publishing.

Sutcliffe, Jane. George S. Patton Jr. 2005. (History Maker Bios Ser.). (Illus.). 48p. (J). 26.60 (978-0-8225-2436-6(8) , Lerner Pubns.) Lerner Publishing Group.

Thorne, James. Julius Caesar: Conqueror & Dictator. 2003. (Leaders of Ancient Rome Ser.). (Illus.). 112p. (YA). (gr. 5-8). lib. bdg. 31.95 (978-0-8239-3595-6(7) , Rosen Central) Rosen Publishing Group, Inc., The.

Trumbauer, Lisa. Life in the Time of George Washington & the Revolutionary War. 2007. (J). (***978-1-4034-9667-6(6)***); pap. (***978-1-4034-9675-1(7)***) Heinemann Library.

Van Steenwyck, Elizabeth. Seneca Chief, Army General: A Story about Ely Parker. 2001. (gr. 3-6). lib. bdg. 15.25 (978-0-613-68385-2(4)) Tandem Library Bks.

Venezia, Mike, illus. Ulysses S. Grant. 2005. 32p. (J). 27.00 (978-0-516-22623-1(1) , Children's Pr.) Scholastic Library Publishing.

Warrick, Karen Clemens. Hannibal: Great General of the Ancient World. 2006. (Rulers of the Ancient World Ser.). (Illus.). 160p. (J). lib. bdg. 27.93 (978-0-7660-2564-6(0)) Enslow Pubs., Inc.

Waryncia, Lou. Robert E. Lee: Duty & Honor. Hale, Sarah Elder, ed. 2005. (Civil War Ser.). (Illus.). 48p. (J). 17.95 (978-0-8126-7905-2(9)) Cobblestone Publishing Co.

—Ulysses S. Grant: Confident Leaders & Hero. Hale, Sarah Elder, ed. 2005. (Civil War Ser.). (Illus.). 48p. (J). 17.95 (978-0-8126-7906-9(7)) Cobblestone Publishing Co.

Waxman, Laura Hamilton. Colin Powell. 2005. (History Maker Bios Ser.). 48p. (J). pap. 6.95 (978-0-8225-5463-9(1)); (Illus.). 26.60 (978-0-8225-2433-5(3) , Lerner Pubns.) Lerner Publishing Group.

Weil, Ann. Great Warriors. 2006. (Atomic Ser.). (Illus.). 31p. (J). (gr. 4-6). lib. bdg. 28.21 (978-1-4109-2525-1(0)) Raintree.

—Great Warriors. 2006. (Illus.). 32p. (J). pap. (978-1-4109-2530-5(7)) Steck-Vaughn.

Welch, Catherine A. George C. Marshall. 2005. (History Maker Bios Ser.). 48p. (J). pap. 6.95 (978-0-8225-5460-8(7)); (Illus.). 26.60 (978-0-8225-2435-9(X) , Lerner Pubns.) Lerner Publishing Group.

Whiting, Jim. The Life & Times of Julius Caesar. 2005. (Biography from Ancient Civilizations Ser.). (Illus.). 48p. (J). (ps-7). lib. bdg. 29.95 (978-1-58415-337-5(7)) Mitchell Lane Pubs., Inc.

Williams, Jean Kinney. Ulysses S. Grant. 2002. (Profiles of the Presidents Ser.). (Illus.). 64p. (J). (gr. 4 up). lib. bdg. 23.93 (978-0-7565-0265-2(9)) Compass Point Bks.

Witteman, Barbara. John Charles Fremont: Western Pathfinder. 2002. (Let Freedom Ring Ser.). (Illus.). 48p. (J). (gr. 3-4). lib. bdg. 22.60 (978-0-7368-1348-8(9) , Bridgestone Bks.) Capstone Pr., Inc.

Worth, Richard. Ariel Sharon. 2003. (Major World Leaders Ser.). (Illus.). 112p. (gr. 6-12). 30.00 (978-0-7910-7653-8(9) , Chelsea Hse.) Facts On File, Inc.

Yancey, Diane. Leaders & Generals. 2003. (American War Library). (Illus.). 112p. (J). 29.95 (978-1-59018-328-1(2) , Lucent Bks.) Thomson Gale.

Young, Jeff C. Dwight D. Eisenhower: Soldier & President. 2004. (Notable Americans Ser.). (Illus.). 128p. (YA). (gr. 6-12). 23.95 (978-1-883846-76-3(5) , First Biographies) Reynolds, Morgan Inc.

GENERATION

see Reproduction

GENETIC ENGINEERING

see also Biotechnology; Cloning

Barbour, Scott. Genetic Engineering. 2005. (Introducing Issues with Opposing Viewpoints Ser.). (Illus.). 126p. (YA). (gr. 10-13). lib. bdg. 33.70 (978-0-7377-3223-8(7) , Greenhaven Pr., Inc.) Thomson Gale.

Cefrey, Holly. Cloning & Genetic Engineering. 2002. (High Interest Bks.). (Illus.). 48p. (YA). (gr. 7-12). pap. 6.95 (978-0-516-24006-0(4) , Children's Pr.) Scholastic Library Publishing.

—Cloning & Genetic Engineering. 2002. (gr. 7-12). lib. bdg. 15.25 (978-0-613-58693-1(X)) Tandem Library Bks.

Cobb, Allan B. Scientifically Engineered Foods: The Debate over What's on Your Plate. 2000. (Focus on Science & Society Ser.). (Illus.). 64p. (J). (gr. 4-6). lib. bdg. 26.50 (978-0-8239-3208-5(7) , FSENFO) Rosen Publishing Group, Inc., The.

Cohen, Daniel. Cloning. rev. ed. 2002. (Single Titles Ser.). (Illus.). 160p. (gr. 7 up). lib. bdg. 25.90 (978-0-7613-2802-5(5) , Twenty-First Century Bks.) Lerner Publishing Group.

Dowswell, Paul. Genetic Engineering. 2004. (21st Century Issues Ser.). (J). pap. 11.95 (978-0-8368-5660-6(0)); lib. bdg. 30.00 (978-0-8368-5643-9(0)) Stevens, Gareth Inc. (World Almanac Library).

—Genetics: The Impact on Our Lives. 2001. (Twenty-First Century Debates Ser.). (Illus.). 64p. (YA). (gr. 6-8). lib. bdg. 27.12 (978-0-7398-3174-8(7)) Raintree.

Fridell, Ron. Genetic Engineering. 2006. (Cool Science Ser.). (Illus.). 48p. (J). (gr. 4-8). lib. bdg. 26.60 (978-0-8225-2633-9(6) , Lerner Pubns.) Lerner Publishing Group.

Friedman, Lauri S. Genetic Engineering. 2007. (Writing the Critical Essay Ser.). (Illus.). 128p. (gr. 6-10). 29.95 (***978-0-7377-3857-5(X)*** , Greenhaven Pr., Inc.) Thomson Gale.

Fritz, Sandy. Genomics & Cloning. 2003. (Hot Science Ser.). (J). lib. bdg. 28.50 (978-1-58340-365-5(5)) Smart Apple Media.

Hunnicut, Susan C. World Hunger. 2006. (Illus.). 128p. (J). (gr. 10-12). pap. 29.95 (978-0-7377-2761-6(6) , Greenhaven Pr., Inc.) Thomson Gale.

Jefferis, David. Cloning: Frontiers of Genetic Engineering. 1999. (Megatech Ser.). (Illus.). 32p. (J). (gr. 4-5). pap. (978-0-7787-0058-6(5)); lib. bdg. (978-0-7787-0048-7(8)) Crabtree Publishing Co.

—Cloning: Frontiers of Genetic Engineering. 1999. 15.75 (978-0-606-17480-0(X)) Tandem Library Bks.

Kowalski, Kathiann M. The Debate over Genetically Engineered Foods: Healthy or Harmful? 2002. (Issues in Focus Ser.). (Illus.). 128p. (YA). (gr. 6-12). lib. bdg. 26.60 (978-0-7660-1686-6(2)) Enslow Pubs., Inc.

McGee, Glenn. Perfect Baby: Parenthood in the New World of Cloning & Genetics. 2000. (gr. 7-12). lib. bdg. 26.85 (978-0-613-64759-5(9)) Tandem Library Bks.

Nardo, Don. DNA Testing. 2007. (Crime Scene Investigations Ser.). (Illus.). 128p. (J). (gr. 7-10). 31.20 (***978-1-59018-951-1(5)*** , Lucent Bks.) Thomson Gale.

Parker, Steve. Genetic Engineering. 2002. (World Issues Ser.). (Illus.). 57p. (J). lib. bdg. 28.50 (978-1-931983-28-0(3)) Chrysalis Education.

—Genetic Engineering. 2004. (Face the Facts Ser.). (Illus.). 56p. (J). 31.36 (978-1-4109-1069-1(5)) Harcourt Schl. Pubs.

Snedden, Robert. DNA & Genetic Engineering. 2003. (Cells & Life Ser.). (Illus.). 48p. (gr. 6-8). (J). lib. bdg. 27.86 (978-1-58810-674-2(8)); (YA). pap. 8.50 (978-1-58810-936-1(4)) Heinemann Library.

Stanley, Debbie. Genetic Engineering: The Cloning Debate. 2000. (Focus on Science & Society Ser.). (Illus.). 64p. (YA). (gr. 4-6). lib. bdg. 26.50 (978-0-8239-3211-5(7) , FSGEEN) Rosen Publishing Group, Inc., The.

Stoyles, Pennie, et al. Genetic Engineering. 2003. 32p. (J). lib. bdg. 24.25 (978-1-58340-330-3(2)) Smart Apple Media.

Tracy, Kathleen. Barbara Mcclintock: Pioneering Geneticist. l.t. ed. 2002. (Unlocking the Secrets of Science Ser.). (Illus.). 56p. (gr. 4-10). lib. bdg. 25.70 (978-1-58415-111-1(0)) Mitchell Lane Pubs., Inc.

Yount, Lisa. Modern Genetics: Engineering Life. 2006. (Milestones in Discovery & Invention Ser.). (Illus.). 224p. (gr. 6-12). 35.00 (978-0-8160-5744-3(3)) Facts On File, Inc.

GENETICS

see also Adaptation (Biology); Evolution; Life (Biology); Natural Selection; Reproduction

Allan, Tony. Understanding DNA: A Breakthrough in Medicine. 2002. (Point of Impact Ser.). 32p. (J). (gr. 5-7). pap. 7.50 (978-1-4034-0074-1(1) , 91555) Heinemann Library.

—Understanding DNA: A Breakthrough in Science Medicine. 2002. (Point of Impact Ser.). (Illus.). 32p. (J). (gr. 5-7). lib. bdg. 25.64 (978-1-58810-557-8(1)) Heinemann Library.

Baeuerle, Patrick A. & Landa, Norbert. Ingenious Genes Vol. 3: Microexplorers. 1999. (Microexplorers Ser.). (Illus.). 42p. (J). (gr. k up). lib. bdg. 18.95 (978-1-56674-237-5(4)) Forest Hse. Publishing Co., Inc.

Balkwill, Fran & Rolph, Mic. Gene Machines. 2002. (Enjoy Your Cells Ser.: Vol. 4). (Illus.). 32p. (J). 13.95 (978-0-87969-616-0(8)); pap. 8.95 (978-0-87969-611-5(7)) Cold Spring Harbor Laboratory Pr.

Bankston, John. Francis Crick & James Watson: Pioneers in DNA Research. l.t. ed. 2002. (Unlocking the Secrets of Science Ser.). (Illus.). 56p. (gr. 4-10). lib. bdg. 17.95 (978-1-58415-122-7(6)) Mitchell Lane Pubs., Inc.

—Gregor Mendel & the Discovery of the Gene. 2004. (Uncharted, Unexplored, & Unexplained Ser.). (Illus.). 48p. (J). (gr. 4-8). lib. bdg. 29.95 (978-1-58415-266-8(4)) Mitchell Lane Pubs., Inc.

Beatty, Richard. Genetics. 2001. (Science Fact Files Ser.). (Illus.). 48p. (J). (gr. 4-7). lib. bdg. 27.12 (978-0-7398-1015-6(4)) Raintree.

Blackwood, Gary L. Secrets of the Unexplained - Group 2, 3 bks., Set. Incl. Extraordinary Events & Oddball Occurrences. lib. bdg. 29.93 (978-0-7614-0748-5(0)); Long-Ago Lives. lib. bdg. 28.50 (978-0-7614-0747-8(2)); Spooky Spectres. lib. bdg. 29.93 (978-0-7614-0746-1(4)); 80p. (J). (gr. 5-9). 1999. (Illus.). 2000. Set lib. bdg. 85.50 (978-0-7614-0745-4(6) , Benchmark Bks.) Cavendish, Marshall Corp.

Boon, Kevin Alexander. The Human Genome Project: What Does Decoding DNA Mean for Us? 2002. (Issues in Focus Ser.). (Illus.). 128p. (YA). (gr. 8-12). lib. bdg. 26.60 (978-0-7660-1685-9(4)) Enslow Pubs., Inc.

Butterfield, Moira. Genetics. 2003. (21st Century Science Ser.). 48p. (J). lib. bdg. 27.10 (978-1-58340-350-1(7)) Smart Apple Media.

Claybourne, A. Introduction to Genes & DNA. 2004. (Genes & Dna Ser.). (Illus.). 64p. (J). lib. bdg. 19.95 (978-1-58086-546-3(1)) EDC Publishing.

Claybourne, Anna. Genetics. 2006. (Science in Focus Ser.). (Illus.). 48p. (J). 27.00 (978-0-7910-8860-9(X) , Chelsea Hse.) Facts On File, Inc.

Cullen, J. Heather. Barbara McClintock. 2003. (Women in the Science Ser.). (Illus.). 122p. pap. 30.00 (978-0-7910-7522-7(2)); 112p. (gr. 6-12). 30.00 (978-0-7910-7248-6(7)) Facts On File, Inc. (Chelsea Hse.).

Day, Trevor, rev. Genetics. 2004. (Routes of Science Ser.). (J). 11.20 (978-1-4103-0300-4(4)); (Illus.). 40p. (gr. 4-7). 24.95 (978-1-4103-0301-1(2)) Thomson Gale. (Blackbirch Pr., Inc.).

Doak, Robin. Genetic Disorders. 2006. (Navigators Ser.). (J). pap. 44.00 (***978-1-4108-6239-6(9)***) Benchmark Education Co.

Doeden, Matthew. Advances in Genetics. 2006. (Navigators Ser.). (J). pap. 44.00 (***978-1-4108-6240-2(2)***) Benchmark Education Co.

Edelson, Edward. Francis Crick & James Watson: And the Building Blocks of Life. 1998. (Oxford Portraits in Science Ser.). (Illus.). 112p. (YA). (gr. 9 up). 30.00 (978-0-19-511451-5(5)) Oxford Univ. Pr., Inc.

Eskeland, N. Lucia. Fun with Gene. 2001. 48p. (YA). (gr. 5-8). stu. ed., wbk. ed. 10.95 (978-0-9673811-3-8(4)) Science2Discover, Inc.

Eskeland, N. Lucia & Bailey, N. Celeste. My Name Is Gene. 2nd l.t. ed. 2002. 110p. (J). per. 19.95 (978-0-9673811-5-2(0)) Science2Discover, Inc.

Fine, Edith Hope. Barbara McClintock: Nobel Prize Geneticist. 1998. (People to Know Ser.). (Illus.). 128p. (YA). (gr. 6-12). lib. bdg. 26.60 (978-0-89490-983-2(5)) Enslow Pubs., Inc.

Freedman, Jeri. How Do We Know about Genetics & Heredity? 2005. (Great Scientific Questions & the Scientists Who Answered Them Ser.). (Illus.). 112p. (J). (gr. 7-12). lib. bdg. 26.50 (978-1-4042-0074-6(6)) Rosen Publishing Group, Inc., The.

Fridell, Ron. Decoding Life: Unraveling the Mysteries of the Genome. 2005. (Discovery! Ser.). (Illus.). 120p. (J). (gr. 5-12). lib. bdg. 29.27 (978-0-8225-1196-0(7)) Lerner Publishing Group.

Fullick, Ann. Inheritance & Selection. 2005. (Life Science In-Depth Ser.). (Illus.). 64p. (J). pap. (978-1-4034-7531-2(8)); lib. bdg. (978-1-4034-7523-7(7)) Heinemann Library.

Gallant, Roy A. The Treasure of Inheritance. 2002. (Story of Science Ser.). (Illus.). 78p. (J). 29.93 (978-0-7614-1426-1(6) , Benchmark Bks.) Cavendish, Marshall Corp.

Gardner, Robert. Genetics & Evolution Science Fair Projects: Using Skeletons, Cereal, Earthworms, & More. 2005. (Biology! Best Science Projects Ser.). (Illus.). 128p. (J). (gr. 6-13). lib. bdg. 26.60 (978-0-7660-1175-5(5)) Enslow Pubs., Inc.

—Health Science Projects about Heredity. 2001. (Science Projects Ser.). (Illus.). 128p. (YA). (gr. 6-12). lib. bdg. 26.60 (978-0-7660-1438-1(X)) Enslow Pubs., Inc.

Gareth Stevens Publishing Staff, contrib. by. Genetics. 2003. (Discovery Channel School Science Ser.). (Illus.). 32p. (J). (gr. 5 up). lib. bdg. 24.67 (978-0-8368-3370-6(8)) Stevens, Gareth Inc.

Genetik: Fachliche Inhalte und Uebungsaufgaben. 2nd ed. (Duden Abiturhilfen Ser.). (GER.). 112p. (YA). (gr. 12-13). (978-3-411-05472-5(7)) Bibliographisches Institut & F. A. Brockhaus AG DEU. *Dist:* International Bk. Import Service, Inc.

George, Linda. Gene Therapy. 2003. (Science on the Edge Ser.). (Illus.). 48p. (J). 24.95 (978-1-56711-786-8(4) , Blackbirch Pr., Inc.) Thomson Gale.

Gleason, Katherine. Awesome Science: A Chapter Book. (True Tales Ser.). (Illus.). 48p. (J). 2005. (gr. 2-4). pap. 4.95 (978-0-516-24681-9(X)); (J). 2004. 22.50 (978-0-516-23727-5(6)) Scholastic Library Publishing. (Children's Pr.).

Glimm, Adele. Gene Hunter: The Story of Neuropsychologist Nancy Wexler. 2006. (Women's Adventures in Science Ser.). 128p. pap. 9.95 (978-0-309-09558-7(1) , Joseph Henry Pr.) National Academies Pr.

Graham, Ian. Genetics: The Study of Heredity. 2002. (Investigating Science Ser.). (Illus.). 36p. (J). (gr. 4 up). lib. bdg. 24.67 (978-0-8368-3231-0(0)) Stevens, Gareth Inc.

Hasan, Heather. Mendel & the Laws of Genetics. 2004. (Primary Sources of Revolutionary Scientific Discoveries & Theories Ser.). (Illus.). 64p. (J). lib. bdg. 29.25 (978-1-4042-0309-9(5)) Rosen Publishing Group, Inc., The.

Holt, Rinehart and Winston Staff. Holt Science & Technology Chapter 6: Life Science: Genes & DNA. 5th ed. 2004. (Illus.). pap. 12.86 (978-0-03-030186-5(6)) Holt, Rinehart & Winston.

—Holt Science & Technology Chptr. 3: Genes & Techniques: Chapter Resources - Tennessee Edition. 3rd ed. 2003. (YA). pap. 11.40 (978-0-03-069161-4(3)) Holt, Rinehart & Winston.

Innes, Brian. DNA & Body Evidence. 2007. (Forensic Evidence Ser.). (Illus.). 96p. (gr. 6 up). 39.95 (***978-0-7656-8115-7(3)***) Sharpe, M.E. Inc.

Jacobs, Marian B. Coping with Hereditary Diseases. 1999. (Coping Ser.). (Illus.). 152p. (YA). (gr. 7-12). lib. bdg. 26.50 (978-0-8239-2823-1(3) , COHEDI) Rosen Publishing Group, Inc., The.

Johnson, Rebecca L. Genetics. 2006. (Great Ideas of Science Ser.). (Illus.). 80p. (J). (ps-7). 27.93 (978-0-8225-2910-1(6) , Twenty-First Century Bks.) Lerner Publishing Group.

—You & Your Genes. 2003. (Life Science Ser.). (Illus.). 32p. (J). pap. (978-0-7922-8866-4(1)) National Geographic Society.

Kafka, Tina. DNA on Trial. 2004. (Overview Ser.). (Illus.). 112p. (J). (gr. 7-10). 29.95 (978-1-59018-337-3(1) , Lucent Bks.) Thomson Gale.

Kidd, J. S. & Kidd, Renee A. New Genetics: The Study of Life Lines. 2nd rev. ed. 2006. (Science & Society Ser.). 224p. (J). (gr. 6-12). 35.00 (978-0-8160-5604-0(8)) Facts On File, Inc.

Klare, Roger. Gregor Mendel: Father of Genetics. 2001. (Great Minds of Science Ser.). (Illus.). 128p. (YA). (gr. 4-10). pap. 10.95 (978-0-7660-1871-6(7)) Enslow Pubs., Inc.

Knowles, Johanna. Huntington's Disease. 2006. (Genetic Diseases Ser.). (Illus.). 64p. (J). (978-1-4042-0694-6(9)) Rosen Publishing Group, Inc., The.

Leech, Bonnie Coulter. Gregor Mendel's Genetic Theory: Understanding & Applying Concepts of Probability. 2006. (Math for the Real World Ser.). (Illus.). 32p. (J). pap. (978-1-4042-6063-4(3)); lib. bdg. (978-1-4042-3355-3(5)) Rosen Publishing Group, Inc., The.

Marsh, Carole. Is One Enough? Are Two Too Many? 1998. (Cloning for Kids! Ser.). (Illus.). pap., tchr. ed. 19.95 (978-0-7933-8995-7(X)); (J). (gr. 3-6). pap. 19.95 (978-0-7933-8991-9(7)); (J). (gr. 3-6). pap. 19.95 (978-0-7933-8994-0(1)); (J). (gr. 3-6). lib. bdg. 29.95 (978-0-7933-8990-2(9)) Gallopade International. (Marsh, Carole Family CD-Rom).

The Mechanisms of Genetics: An Anthology of Current Thought. 2005. (Contemporary Discourse in the Field of Biology Ser.). (Illus.). 206p. (J). (ps-7). lib. bdg. 30.60 (978-1-4042-0402-7(4)) Rosen Publishing Group, Inc., The.

Meredith, Susan. Genes & Dna - Internet Linked. rev. ed. 2006. 64p. (J). pap. 11.99 (978-0-7945-1562-1(2) , Usborne) EDC Publishing.

Miller-Schroeder, Patricia, ed. The Revolution in Genetics: Understanding Global Issues. 2002. (Understanding Global Issues). (Illus.). 56p. (YA). (gr. 10-12). lib. bdg. 19.95 (978-1-58340-171-2(7)) Weigl Pubs., Inc.

Morgan, Sally. From Mendel's Peas to Genetic Fingerprinting: Discovering Inheritance. 2006. (Chain Reactions Ser.). (Illus.). 64p. (YA). (gr. 6-9). lib. bdg. 34.29 (978-1-4034-8837-4(1)) Heinemann Library.

Morris, Jonathan, et al. Genetics in the News. 2007. (Science News Flash Ser.). 112p. (J). (gr. 6-12). 31.95 (***978-0-7910-9255-2(0)*** , Chelsea Hse.) Facts On File, Inc.

Nicolson, Cynthia Pratt. Baa! The Most Interesting Book You'll Ever Read about Genes & Cloning. 2001. (gr. 5-8). lib. bdg. 15.25 (978-0-613-83949-5(8)) Tandem Library Bks.

—Baa! The most interesting book you'll ever read about genes & cloning. Cowles, Rose, illus. 2004. (Mysterious You Ser.). 40p. (J). (gr. 4-6). (978-1-55074-886-4(6)) Kids Can Pr., Ltd.

—Baa! The Most Interesting Book You'll Ever Read About Genes & Cloning. Cowles, Rose, illus. 2004. (Mysterious You Ser.). 40p. (J). (gr. 4-6). (978-1-55074-856-7(4)) Kids Can Pr., Ltd.

Our Genes, Our Selves Complete Materials Package W/Teacher's Guide & Student Books. 2001. (Illus.). (YA). ring bd. (978-1-887725-56-9(3)) Lab-Aids, Inc.

Parker, Steve. In Your Genes! Genetics & Reproduction. 2006. (Illus.). 48p. (J). (978-1-4109-1876-5(9)); pap. (978-1-4109-1883-3(1)) Steck-Vaughn.

Rainis, Kenneth G. Blood & DNA Evidence: Crime-Solving Science Experiments. 2006. (Forensic Science Projects Ser.). (Illus.). 104p. (J). lib. bdg. 31.93 (978-0-7660-1958-4(6)) Enslow Pubs., Inc.

Sheen, Barbara. Birth Defects. 2005. (Diseases & Disorders Ser.). (Illus.). 112p. (YA). (gr. 7-10). lib. bdg. 32.45 (978-1-59018-406-6(8) , Lucent Bks.) Thomson Gale.

Sian revision one&only You. 2004. (Science in A Nutshell(R) Ser.). (J). (978-1-59242-051-3(6)) Delta Education, LLC.

Silverman, Buffy. Blame Your Parents. 2007. (J). (***978-1-4109-2841-2(1)***); (***978-1-4109-2875-7(6)***) Steck-Vaughn.

Silverstein, Alvin & Silverstein, Virginia. DNA. 2002. (Science Concepts Ser.). (Illus.). 64p. (gr. 5-8). lib. bdg. 26.90 (978-0-7613-2257-3(4) , Twenty-First Century Bks.) Lerner Publishing Group.

Silverstein, Alvin & Silverstein, Virginia B. The Code of Life. Gosner, Kenneth L., illus. 2004. 96p. (gr. 5-8). pap. 5.95 (978-0-486-43944-0(5)) Dover Pubns., Inc.

Snedden, Robert. Cell Division & Genetics. 2003. (Cells & Life Ser.). (Illus.). 48p. (gr. 6-8). (J). lib. bdg. 27.86 (978-1-58810-672-8(1)); (YA). pap. 8.50 (978-1-58810-934-7(8)) Heinemann Library.

Solway, Andrew. Genetics in Medicine. 2006. (Illus.). 64p. (J). lib. bdg. (***978-0-8368-7865-3(5)*** , World Almanac Library) Stevens, Gareth Inc.

Stille, Darlene R. Genetics: A Living Blueprint. 2006. (Exploring Science Ser.). (Illus.). 48p. (J). (gr. 5-7). 25.27 (978-0-7565-1618-5(8)) Compass Point Bks.

Taylor, Robert. Genetics. 2003. (Lucent Library of Science). (Illus.). 112p. (J). 29.95 (978-1-59018-103-4(4) , Lucent Bks.) Thomson Gale.

Toriello, James. The Human Genome Project. 2005. (Library of Future Medicine). (Illus.). 64p. (YA). (gr. 7-12). lib. bdg. 26.50 (978-0-8239-3671-7(6)) Rosen Publishing Group, Inc., The.

Yannuzzi, Della. Gregor Mendel: Genetics Pioneer. 2004. (Great Life Stories Ser.). (Illus.). 111p. (J). 30.50 (978-0-531-12263-1(8) , Watts, Franklin) Scholastic Library Publishing.

Yount, Lisa. Modern Genetics: Engineering Life. 2006. (Milestones in Discovery & Invention Ser.). (Illus.). 224p. (gr. 6-12). 35.00 (978-0-8160-5744-3(3)) Facts On File, Inc.

GENGHIS KHAN, 1162-1227

Greenblatt, Miriam. Genghis Khan & the Mongol Empire. 2001. (Rulers & Their Times Ser.). (Illus.). 80p. (J). (gr. 6-8). lib. bdg. 29.93 (978-0-7614-1027-0(9) , Benchmark Bks.) Cavendish, Marshall Corp.

Kent, Zachary. Genghis Khan: Invincible Ruler of the Mongol Empire. 2007. (Rulers of the Middle Ages Ser.). (Illus.). 160p. (YA). (gr. 6). lib. bdg. 34.60 (***978-0-7660-2715-2(5)***) Enslow Pubs., Inc.

Lange, Brenda. Genghis Khan. 2003. (Ancient World Leaders Ser.). (Illus.). 112p. (gr. 6-12). 30.00 (978-0-7910-7222-6(3)); pap. 30.00 (978-0-7910-7496-1(X)) Facts On File, Inc. (Chelsea Hse.).

Rice, Earle, Jr. Empire in the East: The Story of Genghis Khan. 2005. (World Leaders Ser.). (Illus.). 160p. (J). (ps-7). per. 26.95 (978-1-931798-62-4(1)) Reynolds, Morgan Inc.

Streissguth, Thomas. Genghis Khan's Mongol Empire. 2005. (Lost Civilizations Ser.). (Illus.). 112p. (J). (gr. 5-8). lib. bdg. 29.95 (978-1-59018-436-3(X) , Lucent Bks.) Thomson Gale.

Whiting, Jim. The Life & Times of Genghis Khan. 2005. (Biography from Ancient Civilizations Ser.). (Illus.). 48p. (J). (gr. 4-8). lib. bdg. 29.95 (978-1-58415-348-1(2)) Mitchell Lane Pubs., Inc.

GENIUS—FICTION

Beechen, Adam. No More Mr Smart Guy. 2003. (gr. k-3). lib. bdg. 11.80 (978-0-613-66370-0(5)) Tandem Library Bks.

Boczkowski, Tricia. Jimmy's Backpack Book. 2003. (Jimmy Neutron Boy Genius Ser.). (Illus.). 16p. (J). 6.99 (978-0-689-85978-6(3) , Simon Spotlight/Nickelodeon) Simon & Schuster Children's Publishing.

Clements, Andrew. The Report Card. (Illus.). (J). 2004. 176p. (gr. 3-7). 15.95 (978-0-689-84515-4(4)); 2005. 192p. reprint ed. pap. 5.99 (978-0-689-84524-6(3) , Aladdin) Simon & Schuster Children's Publishing.

Greenland, Shannon. Model Spy. 2007. (Specialists Ser.). 224p. (YA). pap. 6.99 (978-0-14-240849-0(2) , Puffin) Penguin Group (USA) Inc.

Greenland, Shannon. The Winning Element. 2008. (Specialists Ser.). 224p. (J). (gr. 5). 6.99 (***978-0-14-241052-3(7)*** , Puffin) Penguin Group (USA) Inc.

Henderson, J. A. Bunker 10. 2007. (Illus.). 272p. (YA). (gr. 7 up). 17.00 (***978-0-15-206240-8(8)***) Harcourt Children's Bks.

Jinks, Catherine. Evil Genius. 2008. (Illus.). 512p. (YA). pap. 7.95 (***978-0-15-206185-2(1)*** , Harcourt Paperbacks) Harcourt Children's Bks.

—Evil Genius. 2007. (Illus.). 496p. (YA). (gr. 7 up). 17.00 (978-0-15-205988-0(1)); 486p. (J). (***978-1-4287-3510-1(0)***) Harcourt Trade Pubs.

Lithgow, John. The Remarkable Farkle McBride. Payne, C. F., illus. 2003. 40p. (J). pap. 7.99 (978-0-689-83541-4(8) , Aladdin) Simon & Schuster Children's Publishing.

Walden, Mark. The Overlord Protocol. 2008. (H. I. V. E. Ser.). 384p. (J). 15.99 (***978-1-4169-3573-5(8)***) Simon & Schuster Children's Publishing.

Walters, Jennie. Michelle's Big Break. 2003. (Illus.). 128p. (J). pap. 7.99 (978-0-340-79589-7(1) , Hodder & Stoughton) Hodder General Publishing Division GBR. *Dist:* Trafalgar Square Publishing.

Yee, Lisa. Millicent Min, Girl Genius. 256p. 2003. (YA). (gr. 5-8). 16.95 (978-0-439-42519-3(0)); 2004. (J). (gr. 4-7). reprint ed. pap. 4.99 (978-0-439-42520-9(4)) Scholastic, Inc. (Levine, Arthur A. Bks.).

GENOCIDE

see also Holocaust, Jewish (1939-1945)

Agbabian, Alidz. Dzalabadig: A Photographic Journey into Diaspora's First Armenian Community. Derounian, Vartan, photos by. 2002. 32p. (J). (gr. 3-6). pap. 15.00 (978-0-9655507-5-8(3)) Dziludzar.

Chippendale, Neil. Crimes Against Humanity. 2002. (gr. 7-12). lib. bdg. 18.75 (978-0-613-70610-0(2)) Tandem Library Bks.

Downing, David. Toward Genocide. 2005. (World Almanac Library of the Holocaust). (Illus.). 48p. pap. (978-0-8368-5952-2(9)); (YA). (gr. 10-12). lib. bdg. 30.00 (978-0-8368-5945-4(6)) Stevens, Gareth Inc. (World Almanac Library).

Fisanick, Christina. Genocide. 2007. (Opposing Viewpoints Ser.). 240p. (gr. 10-12). 34.95 (***978-0-7377-3321-1(7)***); pap. 23.70 (***978-0-7377-3322-8(5)***) Thomson Gale. (Greenhaven Pr., Inc.).

Grant, R. G. Genocide. 1999. (Talking Points Ser.). (Illus.). 64p. (YA). (gr. 4-7). lib. bdg. 27.12 (978-0-8172-5314-1(9)) Raintree.

Innes, Brian. The History & Methods of Torture. 2002. (Crime & Detection Ser.). (Illus.). 96p. (J). (gr. 7 up). lib. bdg. 22.95 (978-1-59084-376-5(2)) Mason Crest Pubs.

Sheehan, Sean. Genocide. 2004. (Face the Facts Ser.). (Illus.). 56p. (J). 31.36 (978-1-4109-1070-7(9)) Harcourt Schl. Pubs.

Spangenburg, Ray & Moser, Kit. The Crime of Genocide: Terror Against Humanity. 2000. (Issues in Focus Ser.). (Illus.). 128p. (YA). (gr. 6-12). lib. bdg. 26.60 (978-0-7660-1249-3(2)) Enslow Pubs., Inc.

Springer, Jane. Genocide. 2007. (Groundwork Guides). (Illus.), 144p. pap. 9.95 ***(978-0-88899-682-4(9))** Groundwood Bks. CAN. *Dist:* Perseus Distribution.

Woolf, Alex. Genocide. (Illus.). 64p. (YA). (gr. 5 up). lib. bdg. 29.95 (978-1-931983-81-5(X)) Chrysalis Education.

GEOGRAPHICAL ATLASES

see Atlases

GEOGRAPHICAL DISTRIBUTION OF ANIMALS AND PLANTS

see also Animals—Migration; Birds—Migration; Desert Animals; Desert Plants; Fresh-Water Animals; Fresh-Water Plants; Marine Animals; Marine Plants

Bertolucci, Cristiano, et al. Hot & Cold. Cucchiariani, Fer, illus. 2004. (Contrasts Ser.). 32p. (J). (gr. 1-4). 14.95 (978-1-57768-526-5(1) , Waterbird Bks.) School Specialty Publishing.

Butterfield, Moira. Animals in Cold Places. 1999. (Looking at...Ser.). (Illus.). 32p. (J). (gr. 1-4). lib. bdg. 24.26 (978-0-7398-0111-6(2)) Raintree.

Harcourt School Publishers Staff. Don't Go There Advanced Level. 3rd ed. 2002. (Trophies Reading Program Ser.). (Illus.). pap. 5.10 (978-0-15-323295-4(1)) Harcourt Schl. Pubs.

Llewellyn, Claire. Animal Atlas. 2004. (Atlases Ser.). (Illus.). 48p. (gr. 3-6). 13.95 (978-1-58728-099-3(X) , Two Can Publishing) T&N Children's Publishing.

—Animal Atlas. 2001. (gr. 3-6). lib. bdg. 16.40 (978-0-613-53698-1(3)) Tandem Library Bks.

—Animal Atlas, 2 vols., Set. 1999. (Illus.). 48p. (J). (gr. 5-8). 14.95 (978-0-7166-9602-5(9)) World Bk., Inc.

Of the World, 9 vols., Set. Incl. Rodents of the World. Alderton, David. Tanner, Bruce, photos by. 192p. 1996. 32.95 (978-0-8160-3229-7(7)); Seals & Sea Lions of the World. Bonner, Nigel. 224p. (J). 1994. 32.95 (978-0-8160-2955-6(5)); Spiders of the World. Preston-Mafham, Rod & Preston-Mafham, Ken. 191p. (J). 1984. 32.95 (978-0-87196-996-5(3)); Wild Bears of the World. Ward, Paul & Kynaston, Suzanne. 192p. 1995. 32.95 (978-0-8160-3245-7(9)); (Illus.). 1998. 210.90 o.p. (978-0-8160-3837-4(6)) Facts On File, Inc.

Squire, Ann O. African Animals. 2002. (True Bks.). (J). (gr. 3-5). pap. 6.95 (978-0-516-25994-9(6) , Children's Pr.) Scholastic Library Publishing.

—African Animals. 2001. (gr. 3-6). lib. bdg. 15.25 (978-0-613-51608-2(7)) Tandem Library Bks.

GEOGRAPHICAL DISTRIBUTION OF HUMANS

see Ethnology; Human Geography

GEOGRAPHICAL NAMES

see Names, Geographical

GEOGRAPHY

Here are entered works on geography as a branch of learning. Works limited to descriptive information including those derived from travel narratives or intended to assist travelers are entered under the names of countries, cities, etc. with the subdivision Description and Travel or Guidebooks.

see also Atlases; Commercial Geography; Discoveries in Geography; Ethnology; Human Geography; Maps; Physical Geography; Surveying; Voyages and Travels

also subdivision Maps under names of countries, cities, etc.

Aberg, Rebecca. Latitude & Longitude. 2003. (Rookie Read-About Geography Ser.). (gr. 1-2). pap. 5.95 (978-0-516-27765-3(0) , Children's Pr.) Scholastic Library Publishing.

—Latitude & Longitude. 2003. (gr. k-3). lib. bdg. 14.10 (978-0-613-67906-0(7)) Tandem Library Bks.

Abitz, Diana & LaRoy, Susan. Know-the-Facts Review Game: 100 Must-Know Facts in a Q&A Game Format to Help Kids Really Remember Standards-Based Social Studies Information. 2005. (U. S. & World Geography Ser.). 48p. pap. 14.99 (978-0-439-37433-0(2) , Teaching Resources) Scholastic, Inc.

Adamson, Heather. In My Continent. 2005. (Illus.). 24p. (J). (978-0-7368-4235-8(7)) Capstone Pr., Inc.

—In My Country. 2005. (Illus.). 24p. (J). (978-0-7368-4236-5(5)) Capstone Pr., Inc.

—In My World. 2005. (Illus.). 24p. (J). (978-0-7368-4242-6(X)) Capstone Pr., Inc.

All about Our World, 6 vols., Set. 2000. 240p. (J). 49.95 (978-0-7525-4375-8(X)) Parragon, Inc.

American Education Staff. Complete Book of Map & Geography. 1998. (ps-2). lib. bdg. 24.55 (978-0-613-82802-4(X)) Tandem Library Bks.

Ariganello, Lisa. Henry the Navigator: Prince of Portuguese Exploration. 2006. (In the Footsteps of Explorers Ser.). (Illus.). 32p. (J). (gr. 3-9). (978-0-7787-2433-9(6)); pap. (978-0-7787-2469-8(7)) Crabtree Publishing Co.

Arundale, Jackie, et al. Investigating Geography. 2002. (Illus.). 132p. pap. 33.50 ***(978-0-340-80377-6(0)** , Hodder Murray) Hodder Education GBR. *Dist:* Trans-Atlantic Pubns., Inc.

—Investigating Geography B. 2002. (Illus.). 132p. pap. 33.50 ***(978-0-340-80376-9(2)** , Hodder Murray) Hodder Education GBR. *Dist:* Trans-Atlantic Pubns., Inc.

Ashcroft, Minnie. Geography. 2003. (5-Minute Daily Practice Ser.). (Illus.). 64p. pap., tchr. ed. 11.95 (978-0-439-27178-3(9) , Teaching Resources) Scholastic, Inc.

Aten, Jerry. Understanding Our World Through Geography. 2003. (Illus.). 208p. (gr. 4 up). 18.99 (978-0-86653-592-2(6) , GA1309) School Specialty Publishing.

Atlas del mundo para estudiantes de nivel Primario: Aqui Estoy! 2000. (Aventuras A Traves Del Tiempo Ser.). (ENG & SPA.). (gr. k-3). (978-0-02-148511-6(9)) Macmillan/McGraw-Hill Schl. Div.

Atlas del mundo para niveles Primarios. 2003. (MacMillan/McGraw-Hill. Estudios Sociales Ser.). (ENG & SPA.). (gr. k-3). (978-0-02-149475-0(4)) Macmillan/McGraw-Hill Schl. Div.

Atrapados en el Artico 16: Leveled Books. 2001. (McGraw-Hill. Lectura Ser.). (ENG & SPA.). (gr. 5 up). (978-0-02-188264-9(9)) Macmillan/McGraw-Hill Schl. Div.

Audiocasete de la Antologia: Aqui Estoy! 2000. (Aventuras A Traves Del Tiempo Ser.). (ENG & SPA.). (gr. 1 up). (978-0-02-148488-1(0)) Macmillan/McGraw-Hill Schl. Div.

Audiocasete de la Antologia: Comunidades. 2000. (Aventuras A Traves Del Tiempo Ser.). (ENG & SPA.). (gr. 3 up). (978-0-02-148491-1(0)) Macmillan/McGraw-Hill Schl. Div.

Audiocasete de la Antologia: Gente. 2000. (Aventuras A Traves Del Tiempo Ser.). (ENG & SPA.). (gr. 2 up). (978-0-02-148489-8(9)) Macmillan/McGraw-Hill Schl. Div.

Ayllon Torres, Maria Teresa. Geografia Economica para las Escuelas Preparatorias. 9th ed. 1999. (SPA., Illus.). 268p. (C). (978-968-18-5867-4(0) , Limusa) Noriega Editores.

Beck, Roger B. World History: Patterns of Interaction: Pupil's Edition. l.t. ed. 2005. (YA). (gr. 9-12). 86.64 (978-0-618-18774-4(X) , 2-01396) McDougal Littell Inc.

Bednarz, Robert, et al. TIME for Kids Readers: Across the Wide Oceans. 3rd ed. 2002. (Harcourt Horizons Ser.). (gr. k-7). pap. 38.10 (978-0-15-335277-5(9)) Harcourt Schl. Pubs.

Beers, Bonnie. Earth's Land & Water. 2000. (Yellow Umbrella Books). (Illus.). 16p. (J). (gr. 1). lib. bdg. 14.60 (978-0-7368-0737-1(3) , Pebble Bks.) Capstone Pr., Inc.

Bell, Athena. The Continents: Test Your Global Knowledge. 2002. 14p. (C). spiral bd. 15.00 (978-0-9714936-5-0(0)) International Fitness Professionals Assn.

Bell, Neil. Brown Paper School Book: The Book of Where. 2007. 128p. (J). pap. 12.99 (978-0-316-05982-4(X)) Little Brown & Co.

Benchmark Education Staff, compiled by. Engish Explorers Social Studies Levels 2, 3, 4 (CAN) 2006. spiral bd. 95.00 ***(978-1-4108-6045-3(0))** Benchmark Education Co.

—Geography. 2006. spiral bd. 85.00 ***(978-1-4108-7045-2(6))**; spiral bd. 119.00 ***(978-1-4108-7114-5(2))** Benchmark Education Co.

—Native Land & Geography. 2005. spiral bd. 225.00 ***(978-1-4108-5811-5(1))** Benchmark Education Co.

—This State Is Mine & Geography. 2005. spiral bd. 110.00 ***(978-1-4108-5818-4(9))** Benchmark Education Co.

—World Geography. 2006. spiral bd. 125.00 ***(978-1-4108-7141-1(X))** Benchmark Education Co.

Benenson, Gary & Neujahr, James L. Mapping. 2002. (Stuff That Works! Ser.). 176p. (J). (ps-1). pap. 19.00 (978-0-325-00467-9(6) , E00467) Heinemann.

Berryhill, Judy. Chuckle & Giggle Vol. 2: Exploring the Natchez Trace. l.t. ed. 1998. (Illus.). 30p. (J). (ps-4). 14.00 (978-0-9653872-4-8(0)) Hartford Pubns.

Big Book Atlas 3-6. 2003. (gr. 3-6). (978-0-328-04179-4(3) , Scott Foresman) Addison-Wesley Educational Pubs., Inc.

Blain, Theresa A. Visualize World Geography in 7 Minutes a Day: Let Pictography Take You from Clueless to Knowing the World. Blain, Theresa A., illus. 2003. (Illus.). 302p. per. 19.95 (978-0-9741401-0-0(4)) Tender Heart Pr.

Boehm, Richard G. & McGraw-Hill Staff. Glencoe World Geography. 2002. (C). (gr. 9-12). stu. ed. 91.33 (978-0-02-664173-9(9) , 9780026641739) Glencoe/McGraw-Hill.

Boehm, Richard G., et al. Daily Geography: Communities. 2003. (Harcourt Brace Social Studies). (gr. k-7). 33.90 (978-0-15-310427-5(9)) Harcourt Schl. Pubs.

Daily Geography: Grades K-2. 2003. (Harcourt Brace Social Studies). (gr. k-2). 33.90 (978-0-15-310426-8(0)) Harcourt Schl. Pubs.

—Daily Geography: States & Regions. 1999. (Harcourt Brace Social Studies). (gr. k-7). pap. 41.00 (978-0-15-312216-3(1)) Harcourt Schl. Pubs.

—Daily Geography: The World. 1999. (Harcourt Brace Social Studies). (gr. k-7). pap. 41.00 (978-0-15-312223-1(4)) Harcourt Schl. Pubs.

—Daily Geography: United States. 2003. (Harcourt Brace Social Studies). (gr. k-7). 33.90 (978-0-15-312218-7(8)) Harcourt Schl. Pubs.

—Daily Geography: United States in Modern Times. 1999. (Harcourt Brace Social Studies). (gr. k-7). pap. 41.00 (978-0-15-312217-0(X)) Harcourt Schl. Pubs.

Boone, Melvin, Jr. JD Mc Doil What's up with Oil. l.t. ed. 2003. (Illus.). 32p. (J). 19.95 (978-0-9741750-0-3(5)) Never Stop Reading Never Stop Learning.

Boyle. Your Geography. Date not set. (Illus.). 48p. (J). Bk. A. pap. 129.15 (978-0-582-18799-3(0)); Bk. B. pap. 129.15 (978-0-582-18800-6(8)) Addison-Wesley Longman, Ltd. GBR. *Dist:* Trans-Atlantic Pubns., Inc.

Bramwell, Martyn J. Our World: An In-Depth Guide to Countries Around the World. 1999. (J). (978-1-84100-262-0(3)) Quadrillion Publishing.

Brimson, Samuel. Nations of the World, 8 bks. Incl. Afghanistan-Botswana. lib. bdg. 30.00 (978-0-8368-5485-5(3)); Brazil-East Timor. lib. bdg. 30.00 (978-0-8368-5486-2(1)); Ecuador-Honduras. lib. bdg. 30.00 (978-0-8368-5487-9(X)); Hungary-Kiribati. lib. bdg. 30.00 (978-0-8368-5488-6(8)); Korea, North-Nicaragua. lib. bdg. 30.00 (978-0-8368-5489-3(6)); Niger-Seychelles. lib. bdg. 30.00 (978-0-8368-5490-9(X)); Sierra Leone-United Arab Emirates. lib. bdg. 30.00 (978-0-8368-5491-6(8)); United Kingdom-Zimbabwe. lib. bdg. 30.00 (978-0-8368-5492-3(6)); 64p. (J). (gr. 5 up). (Illus.). 2003. Set lib. bdg. 240.00 (978-0-8368-5484-8(5) , World Almanac Library) Stevens, Gareth Inc.

British Library Staff, prod. The Image of the World. (YA). cd-rom 99.95 (978-0-7365-0396-9(X)) Films Media Group.

Brun, Henry. Reviewing Global History & Geography. 2003. pap. (978-1-56765-614-5(5) , R674W) AMSCO Schl. Pubns., Inc.

Bushell, Tony. Key Geography: Basics Pupils' Book. 1999. (Illus.). 112p. (J). (gr. 6-9). pap., stu. ed. 19.95 (978-0-7487-4310-0(3)) Nelson Thornes Ltd. GBR. *Dist:* Trans-Atlantic Pubns., Inc.

—Skills. 2003. (Illus.). 112p. (J). (gr. 2-4). pap. 22.50 (978-0-7487-7091-5(7)) Nelson Thornes Ltd. GBR. *Dist:* Trans-Atlantic Pubns., Inc.

Callella, Trisha. Integrating Maps & Money with Reading Instruction, 2830. Walter, LaDawn, ed. Campbell, Jenny, illus. 2002. 72p. (J). (gr. 3-4). pap. 10.99 (978-1-57471-905-5(X) , 2830) Creative Teaching Pr., Inc.

Canetti, Yanitzia. Our World of Wonders. 2000. (Pair-It Books). (Illus.). 40p. (J). pap. (978-0-7398-0887-0(7)) Steck-Vaughn.

Casef, et al. Countries of the World Set, 6 vols. 2003. (Countries of the World Ser.). (Illus.). 64-64p. (gr. 9-12). 180.00 (978-0-8160-5379-7(0)) Facts On File, Inc.

Cave, Kathryn. W Is for World: A Round-the-World ABC. 2004. (World Alphabets Ser.). (Illus.). 36p. (J). pap. 7.95 (978-1-84507-314-5(2)) Lincoln, Frances Ltd. GBR. *Dist:* Perseus Distribution.

—W Is for World: Around the World ABC. 1999. (J). (978-0-382-42113-6(2)); (978-0-382-42114-3(0)) Silver Pr. Co.

Center for Learning Network Staff. The Environment. 1998. (Social Studies Ser.). 84p. (YA). (gr. 9-12). tchr. ed., spiral bd. 20.95 (978-1-56077-513-3(0)) Ctr. for Learning, The.

The Changing Face of... Series, 4 vols., Set. 2003. (Illus.). (J). 114.24 (978-0-7398-5492-1(5)) Raintree.

Chicola, Nancy A. & English, Eleanor B. Discovering World Geography with Books Kids Love. 1999. (Learning with Books Kids Love Ser.). (Illus.). 175p. (gr. 2-3). pap. 17.95 (978-1-55591-965-8(0)) Fulcrum Publishing.

Chin-Lee, Cynthia & De la Pena, Terri. A Is for the Americas. Sanchez, Enrique O., illus. 1999. 32p. (J). (gr. 1-5). 15.95 (978-0-531-30194-4(X) , Orchard Bks.) Scholastic, Inc.

Claybourne, A. Encyclopedia of Planet Earth. 2004. (Geography Ser.). (Illus.). 160p. (J). 19.95 (978-0-7945-0534-9(1)) EDC Publishing.

Clinch, Mike, et al. Allwedd Daearyddiaeth: Cyfnod Allweddol 3. 2005. (WEL., Illus.). 176p. (978-1-85644-677-8(8)) Univ. of Wales, Aberystwyth, Centre for Educational Studies.

CNN Staff, prod. Issues in Science. 2000. (Primary Source Science Collection). (YA). (gr. 5-8). pap. incl. VHS (978-0-7398-3215-8(8)) Raintree.

Cole, Ronda, et al. My Worldwide GeoJourney. 2002. (Illus.). 48p. (J). (gr. 3-6). pap., wbk. ed. 2.85 (978-1-56762-168-6(6)) Modern Learning Pr.

Collins. Geography. 5th ed. 2002. (Illus.). 256p. pap. 7.95 (978-0-00-713803-6(2)) HarperCollins Pubs. Ltd. GBR. *Dist:* Trafalgar Square Publishing.

Continentes: Atlas de Geografia e Historia. (SPA.). (J). 25.00 (978-958-04-6482-2(0)) Norma S.A. COL. *Dist:* Distribuidora Norma, Inc.

Continents, 7 bks. Incl. Africa. Graf, Mike. 18.60 (978-0-7368-1414-0(0)); Antarctica. Bagley, Katie. 18.60 (978-0-7368-1415-7(9)); Asia. Graf, Mike. 18.60 (978-0-7368-1416-4(7)); Australia. Bagley, Katie. 18.60 (978-0-7368-1417-1(5)); Europe. Graf, Mike. 18.60 (978-0-7368-1418-8(3)); North America. Bagley, Katie. 18.60 (978-0-7368-1419-5(1)); South America. Graf, Mike. 18.60 (978-0-7368-1421-8(3)); 79p. (J). (gr. 1-2). 2002. (Illus.). 2002. Set lib. bdg. 130.20 (978-0-7368-1422-5(1) , Bridgestone Bks.) Capstone Pr., Inc.

Continents of the World. 196.02 (978-0-8368-5909-6(X)) Stevens, Gareth Inc.

Countries of the World, 42 bks. Incl. Argentina. Dubois, Muriel L. 126p. 2001. 18.60 (978-0-7368-0811-8(6)); Australia. Dahl, Michael. 24p. 1997. lib. bdg. 18.60 (978-1-56065-521-3(6)); Brazil. Dahl, Michael. 24p. 1997. lib. bdg. 18.60 (978-1-56065-522-0(4)); Cambodia. Nobleman, Marc Tyler. 126p. 2002. 18.60 (978-0-7368-1370-9(5)); Canada. Dahl, Michael. 24p. 1997. lib. bdg. 18.60 (978-1-56065-565-7(8)); China. Dahl, Michael. 126p. 1997. 18.60 (978-1-56065-566-4(6)); Cuba. Mara, W. P. 126p. 1998. 18.60 (978-0-7368-0068-6(9)); Denmark. Murphy, Patricia J. 24p. 2002. lib. bdg. 18.60 (978-0-7368-1371-6(3)); Dominican Republic. Dubois, Muriel L. 126p. 2001. 18.60 (978-0-7368-0812-5(4)); Egypt. Deady, Kathleen W. 126p. 2000. 18.60 (978-0-7368-0626-8(1)); El Salvador. Deady, Kathleen W. 24p. 2001. lib. bdg. 18.60 (978-0-7368-0941-2(4)); England. Deady, Kathleen W. 126p. 2000. 18.60 (978-0-7368-0627-5(X)); Ethiopia. Dubois, Muriel L. 126p. 2001. 18.60 (978-0-7368-0813-2(2)); France. Dahl, Michael. 126p. 1998. 18.60 (978-1-56065-737-8(5)); Germany. Dahl, Michael. 24p. 1997. lib. bdg. 18.60 (978-1-56065-523-7(2)); Ghana. Davis, Lucile. 126p. 1998. 18.60 (978-0-7368-0069-3(7)); Greece. Riehecky, Janet. 126p. 2000. 18.60 (978-0-7368-0628-2(8)); Guatemala. Dahl, Michael. 126p. 1998. 18.60 (978-1-56065-738-5(3)); Haiti. Dell'Oro, Suzanne Paul. 126p. 2001. 18.60 (978-0-7368-0942-9(2)); India. Dahl, Michael. 126p. 1997. 18.60 (978-1-56065-567-1(4)); Indonesia. Riehecky, Janet. 126p. 2002. 18.60 (978-0-7368-1106-4(0)); Ireland. Deady, Kathleen W. 126p. 2001. 18.60 (978-0-7368-0814-9(0)); Israel. Thoennes, Kristin. 126p. 1999. 18.60 (978-0-7368-0152-2(9)); Italy. Thoennes, Kristin. 126p. 1999. 18.60 (978-0-7368-0153-9(7)); Japan. Dahl, Michael. 24p. 1997. lib. bdg. 18.60 (978-1-56065-524-4(0)); Kenya. Dahl, Michael. 126p. 1997. 18.60 (978-1-56065-475-9(9)); Mexico. Dahl, Michael. 126p. 1997. 18.60 (978-1-56065-476-6(7)); Netherlands. Dahl, Michael. 126p. 1997. 18.60 (978-1-56065-568-8(2)); Nicaragua. Riehecky, Janet. 24p. 2002. lib. bdg. 18.60 (978-0-7368-1107-1(9)); Nigeria. Thoennes, Kristin. 126p. 1999. 18.60 (978-0-7368-0154-6(5)); Norway. Deady, Kathleen W. 24p. 2001. lib. bdg. 18.60 (978-0-7368-0943-6(0)); Pakistan. Dubois, Muriel L. 126p. 2001. 18.60 (978-0-7368-0815-6(9)); Panama. Nobleman, Marc Tyler. 126p. 2002. 18.60 (978-0-7368-1372-3(1)); Peru. Thoennes, Kristin. 126p. 1999. 18.60 (978-0-7368-0155-3(3)); Philippines. Davis, Lucile. 24p. 1998. lib. bdg. 18.60 (978-0-7368-0071-6(9)); Poland. Dell'Oro, Suzanne Paul. 24p. 2001. lib. bdg. 18.60 (978-0-7368-0944-3(9)); Russia. Thoennes, Kristin. 126p. 1999. 18.60 (978-0-7368-0156-0(1)); Somalia. Graf, Mike. 24p. 2002. lib. bdg. 18.60 (978-0-7368-1108-8(7)); South Africa. Dahl, Michael. 24p. 1998. lib. bdg. 18.60 (978-1-56065-739-2(1)); South Korea. Davis, Lucile. 126p. 1998. 18.60 (978-0-7368-0070-9(0)); Spain. Deady, Kathleen W. 126p. 2001. 18.60 (978-0-7368-0816-3(7)); Sweden. Riehecky, Janet. 126p. 2000. 18.60 (978-0-7368-0629-9(6)); Switzerland. Graf, Mike. 24p. 2002. lib. bdg. 18.60 (978-0-7368-1109-5(5)); Tanzania. Murphy, Patricia J. 126p. 2002. 18.60 (978-0-7368-1373-0(X)); Thailand. Thoennes, Kristin. 126p. 1999. 18.60 (978-0-7368-0157-7(X)); Vietnam. Dahl, Michael. 24p. 1998. lib. bdg. 18.60 (978-1-56065-740-8(5)); (J). (gr. 2-3). (Illus.). Set lib. bdg. 855.60 (978-0-7368-1374-7(8) , Bridgestone Bks.) Capstone Pr., Inc.

Countries of the World: A Primary Source Journey: Set 3. (Illus.). (J). (gr. k-5). 119.70 (978-1-4042-2952-5(3)) Rosen Publishing Group, Inc., The.

Countries of the World: A Primary Source Journey: Set 4. (Illus.). (J). (gr. k-5). 119.70 (978-1-4042-2951-8(5)) Rosen Publishing Group, Inc., The.

Countries of the World New Releases: Bangladesh, Bolivia, Czech Republic, Dominican Republic, Libya, Uganda, 6 bks. 2004. (Illus.). (J). (gr. 6 up). lib. bdg. 175.60 (978-0-8368-3106-1(3)) Stevens, Gareth Inc.

Countries of the World New Releases: Jamaica; Jordan; Liberia; Romania; Taiwan; Venezuela, 6 bks. 2003. (Illus.). (J). (gr. 6 up). lib. bdg. 175.60 (978-0-8368-2363-9(X)) Stevens, Gareth Inc.

Countries of the World Set. 2004. (Countries of the World Ser.). (gr. 9-12). 360.00 (978-0-8160-6118-1(1)) Facts On File, Inc.

Countries of the World Set 2. 2004. (Countries of the World Ser.). 61-64p. (gr. 9-12). 180.00 (978-0-8160-5500-5(9)) Facts On File, Inc.

Countries of the World Set 4. 2005. 61p. 180.00 (978-0-8160-6503-5(9)) Facts On File, Inc.

Countries Set V. 2004. (J). (gr. k-6). lib. bdg. 227.80 (978-1-59197-289-1(2) , Checkerboard Library) ABDO Publishing Co.

Country Studies, 4 bks., Set 1. 1999. 64p. (YA). lib. bdg. 108.28 (978-1-57572-897-1(4)) Heinemann Library.

Crespi, Jess. Exploring Jamaica with the Five Themes of Geography. 2005. (Library of the Western Hemisphere). (Illus.). 24p. 19.95 (978-1-4042-2674-6(5) , PowerKids Pr.); pap. (978-0-8239-4646-4(0)); (Illus.). 24p. pap. (978-0-8239-4634-1(7)) Rosen Publishing Group, Inc., The.

Cunha, Stephen F. National Geographic Bee. rev. ed. 2005. (Illus.). 128p. (J). (gr. 3-9). stu. ed. 26.90 (978-0-7922-7997-6(2) , National Geographic Children's Bks.) National Geographic Society.

—National Geographic Bee Official. rev. ed. 2005. (Illus.). 128p. (J). (gr. 3-9). stu. ed. 9.95 (978-0-7922-7983-9(2) , National Geographic Children's Bks.) National Geographic Society.

Cunningham, Patricia. Making Places. 2005. (Four-Blocks Ser.). (J). per. 24.99 (978-1-59441-199-1(9) , CD-104108) Carson-Dellosa Publishing Co., Inc.

De Capua, Sarah. We Need Directions! (Rookie Read-About Geography Ser.). (Illus.). 32p. (J). (gr. 1-2). 2002. pap. 5.95 (978-0-516-27380-8(9)); 2001. 20.50 (978-0-516-22574-6(X)) Scholastic Library Publishing. (Children's Pr.).

DK Publishing. My World. 2008. 16p. (J). (ps-k). bds. 9.99 ***(978-0-7566-3833-7(X))** Dorling Kindersley Publishing, Inc.

Dobson, James C., et al. Living Geography: Homework & Assessment. 2001. (Illus.). 112p. (YA). (gr. 6-9). Bk. 2. pap. 22.50 (978-0-17-434324-0(8)); Bk. 3. pap. 22.50 (978-0-17-434325-7(6)) Nelson Thornes Ltd. GBR. *Dist:* Trans-Atlantic Pubns., Inc.

—Living Geography Bk. 1: Homework & Assessment. 2000. (Illus.). 112p. (YA). (gr. 6-9). pap. 22.50 (978-0-17-434323-3(X)) Nelson Thornes Ltd. GBR. *Dist:* Trans-Atlantic Pubns., Inc.

Doherty, Gillian. Encyclopedia of World Geography: With Complete World Atlas. 2004. (Geography Encyclopedias Ser.). (Illus.). 400p. (J). 39.99 (978-0-7945-0108-2(7) , Usborne); lib. bdg. 47.99 (978-1-58086-390-2(6)) EDC Publishing.

Donaldson, Madeline. Europe. 2005. (Pull Ahead Bks.). (Illus.). 32p. (J). (gr. k-3). lib. bdg. 22.60 (978-0-8225-4719-8(8)) Lerner Publishing Group.

Dorling Kindersley Publishing Staff. Around the World. 2005. (Barbie sticker Bks.). 20p. (J). pap. 6.99 (978-0-7566-1179-8(2)) Dorling Kindersley Publishing, Inc.

Douglas, Vincent. Science And Social Studies Fun Fact Cards. 2004. (Flash Card Collection). 324p. (C). 16.95 (978-1-58845-664-9(1)) School Specialty Publishing.

E F G

Douglas, Vincent & School Specialty Publishing Staff. Geography, Grade 3. 2004. (Brighter Child Workbook Ser.). (Illus.). 40p. (J). (gr. 3-3). pap. 2.99 (978-0-7696-3683-2(7) , Brighter Child) School Specialty Publishing.

—Geography, Grade 4. 2004. (Brighter Child Workbook Ser.). (Illus.). 40p. (J). (gr. 4-4). pap. 2.99 (978-0-7696-3684-9(5) , Brighter Child) School Specialty Publishing.

—Geography, Grade 5. 2004. (Brighter Child Workbook Ser.). (Illus.). 40p. (J). (gr. 5-5). pap. 2.99 (978-0-7696-3685-6(3) , Brighter Child) School Specialty Publishing.

—Geography, Grade 6. 2004. (Brighter Child Workbook Ser.). (Illus.). 40p. (J). (gr. 6-6). pap. 2.99 (978-0-7696-3686-3(1) , Brighter Child) School Specialty Publishing.

—Spectrum Geography, Grade 3: Communities. 2002. (Starburst Spectrum Workbook Ser.). (Illus.). 160p. (J). (gr. 3 up). pap. 8.95 (978-1-56189-963-0(1) , American Education Publishing) School Specialty Publishing.

—Spectrum Geography, Grade 4: Regions of the U. S. A. 2002. (Starburst Spectrum Workbook Ser.). (Illus.). 160p. (J). (gr. 4 up). pap. 8.95 (978-1-56189-964-7(X) , American Education Publishing) School Specialty Publishing.

—Spectrum Geography, Grade 5: United States of America. 2002. (Starburst Spectrum Workbook Ser.). (Illus.). 160p. (J). (gr. 5 up). pap. 8.95 (978-1-56189-965-4(8) , American Education Publishing) School Specialty Publishing.

—Spectrum Geography, Grade 6: World. 2002. (Starburst Spectrum Workbook Ser.). (Illus.). 160p. (J). (gr. 6 up). pap. 8.95 (978-1-56189-966-1(6) , American Education Publishing) School Specialty Publishing.

Edwards, John & Webber, Peter. Essential GCSE Geography: Current Issues, Future Scenarios. 2001. (Illus.). 288p. (YA). (gr. 9-11). pap. 34.50 (978-0-7487-6040-4(7)) Nelson Thornes Ltd. GBR. *Dist:* Trans-Atlantic Pubns., Inc.

Enchantment of the World Series, 94 bks., Set. Incl. Afghanistan. Foster, Leila Merrell. (Illus.). 172p. (J). (gr. 5-9). 1996. pap. 32.00 (978-0-516-20017-0(8)); Algeria. Brill, Marlene Targ. (Illus.). 128p. (J). (gr. 4-7). 1990. pap. 32.00 (978-0-516-02717-3(4)); Angola. Laure, Jason. (Illus.). 128p. (J). (gr. 4-7). 1994. pap. 32.00 (978-0-516-02721-0(2)); Antarctica. Billings, Henry. (Illus.). 128p. (J). (gr. 6-9). 1994. pap. 32.00 (978-0-516-02624-4(0)); Bangladesh. Laure, Jason. (Illus.). 128p. (J). (gr. 6-9). 1992. pap. 32.00 (978-0-516-02609-1(7)); Belize. Morrison, Marion. (Illus.). 172p. (J). (gr. 5-9). 1996. pap. 32.00 (978-0-516-02639-8(9)); Bolivia. Morrison, Marion. (Illus.). 128p. (J). (gr. 4-7). 1988. pap. 32.00 (978-0-516-02705-0(0)); Botswana. Laure, Jason. (Illus.). 128p. (J). (gr. 4-7). 1993. pap. 32.00 (978-0-516-02616-9(X)); Brunei. Wright, David K. (Illus.). 128p. (J). (gr. 4-7). 1991. pap. 32.00 (978-0-516-02602-2(X)); Bulgaria. Resnick, Abraham. (Illus.). 172p. (J). (gr. 4-7). 1995. pap. 32.00 (978-0-516-02631-2(3)); Burma. Wright, David K. (Illus.). 128p. (J). (gr. 4-7). 1991. pap. 32.00 (978-0-516-02725-8(5)); Cambodia. Greenblatt, Mariam. (Illus.). 172p. (J). (ps-3). 1995. pap. 32.00 (978-0-516-02632-9(1)); Canada. Shepherd, J. (Illus.). 128p. (J). (gr. 6-9). 1992. pap. 32.00 (978-0-516-02757-9(3)); Chile. Hintz, Martin. (Illus.). 128p. (J). (gr. 6-9). 1994. pap. 32.00 (978-0-516-02755-5(7)); China : A History to 1949. McLenighan, Valjean. (Illus.). 128p. (J). (gr. 6-9). 1983. pap. 32.00 (978-0-516-02754-8(9)); Commonwealth of Independent States. Resnick, Abraham. (Illus.). 128p. (J). (gr. 4-7). 1993. pap. 32.00 (978-0-516-02613-8(5)); Cote d'Ivoire (Ivory Coast) Kummer, Patricia K. (Illus.). 172p. (J). (gr. 6-9). 1996. pap. 32.00 (978-0-516-02641-1(0)); Cyprus. Fox, Mary Virginia. (Illus.). 128p. (J). (ps-3). 1993. pap. 32.00 (978-0-516-02617-6(8)); Denmark. Hintz, Martin. (Illus.). 128p. (J). (gr. 4-7). 1994. pap. 32.00 (978-0-516-02620-6(8)); El Salvador. Bachelis, Faren M. (Illus.). 128p. (J). (gr. 6-9). 1990. pap. 32.00 (978-0-516-02718-0(2)); Ethiopia. Fradin, Dennis Brindell. (Illus.). 128p. (J). (gr. 4-7). 1994. pap. 32.00 (978-0-516-02706-7(9)); France. Moss, Peter & Palmer, Thelma. (Illus.). 128p. (J). (gr. 6-9). 1986. lib. bdg. 32.00 (978-0-516-02761-6(1)); French Guiana. Morrison, Marion. (Illus.). 172p. (J). (gr. 7 up). 1995. pap. 32.00 (978-0-516-02633-6(X)); Gambia. Zimmerman, Robert. (Illus.). 128p. (J). (gr. 6-9). 1994. pap. 32.00 (978-0-516-02625-1(9)); Germany. Hargrove, Jim. (Illus.). 128p. (J). (gr. 4-7). 1994. pap. 32.00 (978-0-516-02601-5(1)); Greece. Stein, R. Conrad. (Illus.). 128p. (J). (gr. 4-7). 1987. pap. 32.00 (978-0-516-02759-3(X)); Guatemala. Brill, Marlene Targ & Targ, Harry R. (Illus.). 128p. (J). (gr. 4-7). 1993. pap. 32.00 (978-0-516-02614-5(3)); Guyana. Brill, Marlene Targ & Dunn, James. (Illus.). 128p. (J). (gr. 7 up). 1994. pap. 32.00 (978-0-516-02626-8(7)); Honduras. Targ, Harry R. & Brill, Marlene Targ. (Illus.). 172p. (J). (gr. 4-7). 1995. pap. 32.00 (978-0-516-02635-0(6)); Iceland. Lepthien, Emilie U. (Illus.). 128p. (J). (gr. 4-7). 1994. pap. 32.00 (978-0-516-02775-3(1)); India. McNair, Sylvia. (Illus.). 128p. (J). (gr. 4-7). 1990. pap. 32.00 (978-0-516-02719-7(0)); Indonesia. McNair, Sylvia. (Illus.). 128p. (J). (gr. 4-7). 1993. pap. 32.00 (978-0-516-02618-3(6)); Iran. Fox, Mary Virginia. (Illus.). 128p. (J). (gr. 4-7). 1991. pap. 32.00 (978-0-516-02727-2(1)); Jordan. Foster, Leila Merrell. (Illus.). 128p. (J). (gr. 4-7). 1994. pap. 32.00 (978-0-516-02603-9(8)); Korea. McNair, Sylvia. (Illus.). 127p. (J). (gr. 4-7). 1986. pap. 32.00 (978-0-516-02771-5(9)); Mongolia. Brill, Marlene Targ. (Illus.). 128p. (J). (gr. 4-7). 1992. pap. 32.00 (978-0-516-02605-3(4)); Mozambique. Laure, Jason & Blauer, Ettagale. (Illus.). 172p. (J). (gr. 4-7). 1995. pap. 32.00 (978-0-516-02636-7(4)); Namibia. Laure, Jason. (Illus.). 128p. (J). (gr. 4-7). 1993. pap. 32.00 (978-0-516-02615-2(1)); Nepal. Heinrichs, Ann. (Illus.). 172p. (J). (gr. 5-9). 1996. pap. 32.00 (978-0-516-02642-8(9)); New Zealand. Fox, Mary Virginia. (Illus.). 128p. (J). (gr. 4-7). 1991. pap. 32.00 (978-0-516-02728-9(X)); Nigeria. Sutherland, Dorothy B. (Illus.). 172p. (J). (gr. 7 up). 1995. pap. 32.00 (978-0-516-02634-3(8)); Norway. Hintz, Martin. (Illus.). 128p. (J). (gr. 6-9). 1994. pap. 32.00 (978-0-516-02780-7(8)); Panama. Vazquez, Ana M. (Illus.). 128p. (J). (gr. 4-7). 1991. pap. 32.00 (978-0-516-02604-6(6)); Papua New Guinea. Fox, Mary Virginia. (Illus.). 128p. (J). (gr. 4-7). 1994. pap. 32.00 (978-0-516-02621-3(6)); Paraguay. Morrison, Marion. (Illus.). 128p. (J). (gr. 4-7). 1993. pap. 32.00 (978-0-516-02619-0(4)); Peru. Lepthien, Emilie U. (Illus.). 128p. (J). (gr. 6-9). 1992. pap. 32.00 (978-0-516-02610-7(0)); Philippines. Lepthien, Emilie U. (Illus.). 128p. (J). (gr. 6-9). 1994. pap. 32.00 (978-0-516-02782-1(4)); Republic of Ireland. Fradin, Dennis Brindell. (Illus.). 128p. (J). (gr. 4-7). 1994. pap. 32.00 (978-0-516-02767-8(0)); Romania. Carran, Betty B. (Illus.). 124p. (J). (gr. 4-7). 1988. pap. 32.00 (978-0-516-02703-6(4)); Saudi Arabia. Foster, Leila Merrell. (Illus.). 128p. (J). (gr. 4-7). 1993. pap. 32.00 (978-0-516-02611-4(9)); Scotland. Sutherland, Dorothy B. (Illus.). 128p. (J). (gr. 4-7). 1985. pap. 32.00 (978-0-516-02787-6(5)); Senegal. Beaton, Margaret. (Illus.). 144p. (YA). (gr. 6-9). 1997. pap. 32.00 (978-0-516-20304-1(5)); Singapore. Brown, Marion M. (Illus.). 128p. (J). (gr. 4-7). 1992. pap. 28.70 (978-0-516-02715-9(8)); Somalia. Fox, Mary Virginia. (Illus.). 128p. (J). (gr. 5-9). 1996. pap. 32.00 (978-0-516-20019-4(4)); Spain. Cross, Wilbur L. & Cross, Esther. (Illus.). 128p. (J). (gr. 4-7). 1985. pap. 32.00 (978-0-516-02786-9(7)); Sri Lanka. Zimmermann, Robert. 128p. (J). (gr. 6-9). 1992. pap. 32.00 (978-0-516-02606-0(2)); Suriname. Lieberg, Carolyn S. (Illus.). 172p. (J). (gr. 4-7). 1995. pap. 32.00 (978-0-516-02638-1(0)); Swaziland. Blauer, Ettagale & Laure, Jason. (Illus.). 128p. (J). (gr. 6-9). 1996. pap. 32.00 (978-0-516-20020-0(8)); Switzerland. Hintz, Martin. (Illus.). 128p. (J). (gr. 4-7). 1994. pap. 32.00 (978-0-516-02790-6(5)); Syria. Beaton, Margaret. (Illus.). 128p. (J). (gr. 4-7). 1988. pap. 32.00 (978-0-516-02708-1(5)); Taiwan. Cromie, Alice. (Illus.). 128p. (J). (gr. 4-7). 1994. pap. 32.00 (978-0-516-02627-5(5)); Tanzania. Blauer, Ettagale & Laure, Jason. (Illus.). 128p. (J). (gr. 4-7). 1994. pap. 32.00 (978-0-516-02622-0(4)); Tibet. Heinrichs, Ann. (Illus.). 128p. (J). (gr. 4-7). 1996. lib. bdg. 32.00 (978-0-516-20155-9(7)); Tunisia. Fox, Mary Virginia. (Illus.). 128p. (J). (gr. 4-7). 1994. pap. 32.00 (978-0-516-02724-1(7)); Turkey. Baralt, Luis A. (Illus.). 144p. (YA). (gr. 6-9). 1997. pap. 32.00 (978-0-516-20305-8(3)); Uganda. Blauer, Ettagale & Laure, Jason. (Illus.). 144p. (YA). (gr. 6-9). 1997. pap. 32.00 (978-0-516-20306-5(1)); United States of America. Stein, R. Conrad. (Illus.). 128p. (J). (gr. 4-7). 1994. pap. 32.00 (978-0-516-02623-7(2)); Uruguay. Morrison, Marion. (Illus.). 128p. (J). (gr. 4-7). 1992. pap. 36.00 (978-0-516-02607-7(0)); Venezuela. Morrison, Marion. (Illus.). 128p. (J). (gr. 4-7). 1989. pap. 32.00 (978-0-516-02711-1(5)); Vietnam. Wright, David K. (Illus.). 128p. (J). (gr. 4-7). 1989. pap. 32.00 (978-0-516-02712-8(3)); Wales. Sutherland, Dorothy B. (Illus.). 128p. (J). (gr. 4-7). 1987. pap. 32.00 (978-0-516-02794-4(8)); Zambia. Laure, Jason. (Illus.). 128p. (J). (gr. 4-7). 1989. pap. 32.00 (978-0-516-02716-6(6)); Zimbabwe. Laure, Jason. (Illus.). 128p. (J). (gr. 4-7). 1994. pap. 32.00 (978-0-516-02704-3(2)); Set. Bahrain. Fox, Mary Virginia. (Illus.). 128p. (J). (gr. 6-9). 1992. pap. 32.00 (978-0-516-02608-4(9)); Set. Qatar. Augustin, Byron & Augustin, Rebecca. (Illus.). 144p. (YA). (gr. 6-9). 1997. lib. bdg. 32.00 (978-0-516-20303-4(7)); (Illus.). 1999. Set pap. 3008.00 (978-0-516-02750-0(6) , Children's Pr.) Scholastic Library Publishing.

Enciclopedia Mega - Benjamin. (SPA.). 159p. 12.95 (978-970-607-203-0(9) , LA039) Larousse, Ediciones, S. A. de C. V. MEX. *Dist:* Continental Bk. Co., Inc.

English, Kim & Feaster, Laura S. Community Geography: GIS in Action. 2003. (Illus.). 350p. per. 24.95 (978-1-58948-023-0(6) , ESRI Pr.) ESRI, Inc.

Extreme Survival 6-Pack (30 Books), Set. 2004. (Illus.). pap. 214.65 (978-1-4109-1252-7(3)) Raintree.

Facts on File, Inc. Staff. Geography on File. rev. ed. 2005. (Geography on File Ser.). (Illus.). 326p. (gr. 9-12). 195.00 (978-0-8160-5941-6(1)) Facts On File, Inc.

—Geography on File, 2005 Update. 2005. (Geography on File Ser.). 36p. (gr. 9-12). ring bd. 55.00 (978-0-8160-5942-3(X)) Facts On File, Inc.

Falstein, Mark. World Geography Mysteries, Grades 4-6: Research-Based Mysteries for Super Sleuths to Solve. Clark Editorial and Design Staff, ed. Kennedy, Kelly, illus. 1998. 96p. pap., tchr. ed. 11.99 (978-0-88160-261-6(2) , LW-382, Learning Works, The) Creative Teaching Pr., Inc.

Farndon, John. Amazing Planet Earth: The Story of Our World & the Forces That Shaped It With. 2001. (gr. 3-6). lib. bdg. 30.35 (978-0-613-84237-2(5)) Tandem Library Bks.

Fetty, Maurice A. The Central Plains & Southwest. 1999. pap. 11.95 (978-0-7398-1318-8(8)) Steck-Vaughn.

Find It on the Map. 2002. (Illus.). pap. 3.74 (978-0-7398-5851-6(3)) Steck-Vaughn.

Fof. Geography on File: 2001 Update. 2001. (Illus.). 312p. (YA). (gr. 8-12). ring bd. 55.00 (978-0-8160-4495-5(3)) Facts On File, Inc.

Foster, Leila Merrell & Fox, Mary Virginia. Continents: First Lessons in Geography, 8 bks., Set 2001. (Illus.). (J). (gr. k-2). lib. bdg. 149.52 (978-1-58810-000-9(6)) Heinemann Library.

Fowler, Allan. Living in the Arctic. 2001. (Rookie Read-About Geography Ser.). (Illus.). 32p. (J). (gr. 1-2). pap. 5.95 (978-0-516-27084-5(2) , Children's Pr.) Scholastic Library Publishing.

—Living in the Arctic. 2000. (gr. k-3). lib. bdg. 14.10 (978-0-613-54733-8(0)) Tandem Library Bks.

From Sea to Shining Sea, Second Series. 2004. 885.00 (978-0-516-24709-0(3)); 885.00 (978-0-516-27711-0(1)) Scholastic Library Publishing.

Gakken Co. Ltd. Editors. Famous Places. Time-Life Books Editors, tr. 1999. (Illus.). 88p. (J). (gr. 1-4). 14.95 (978-0-8094-4893-7(9)) Time-Life, Inc.

Gall, Timothy L. & Gall, Susan B. Junior Worldmark Encyclopedia of the Nations/[edited By] Timothy L. Gall & Susan Bevan Gall. 5th ed. 2007. (***978-1-4144-1096-8(4)**); (***978-1-4144-1097-5(2)**); (***978-1-4144-1098-2(0)**); (***978-1-4144-1099-9(9)**); (***978-1-4144-1100-2(6)**); (***978-1-4144-1101-9(4)**); (***978-1-4144-1102-6(2)**); (***978-1-4144-1103-3(0)**); (***978-1-4144-1104-0(9)**); (***978-1-4144-1105-7(7)**) Thomson Gale.

Gall, Timothy L. & Gall, Susan B., eds. Junior Worldmark Encyclopedia of the Nations, 9 vols. 2nd ed. 1999. (Illus.). (J). (978-0-7876-3804-7(8)); (978-0-7876-3805-4(6)) Thomson Gale.

Gardner, David, et al. Geography, Bks. 11-14. (Illus.). 128p. 2006. (YA). pap., stu. ed. 27.50 (978-0-7487-9051-7(9)); 2005. (J). pap., stu. ed. 27.50 (978-0-7487-9050-0(0)) Nelson Thornes Ltd. GBR. *Dist:* Trans-Atlantic Pubns., Inc.

Gardner, David Knill, et al. Horizons, Bk. 1. 2004. (Illus.). 128p. (J). pap., stu. ed. 27.50 (978-0-7487-9049-4(7)) Nelson Thornes Ltd. GBR. *Dist:* Trans-Atlantic Pubns., Inc.

Garton, Keith & Cutler, Nelida Gonzalez, eds. Time for Kids World Atlas. 2007. (Illus.). 176p. (J). reprint ed. pap. 11.00 (***978-1-4223-6807-7(6)***) DIANE Publishing Co.

Geo Libro: Aqui Estoy! 2000. (Aventuras A Traves Del Tiempo Ser.). (ENG & SPA.). (gr. k-1). (978-0-02-147879-8(1)) Macmillan/McGraw-Hill Schl. Div.

Geo Libro: Gente. 2000. (Aventuras A Traves Del Tiempo Ser.). (ENG & SPA.). (gr. 2-3). (978-0-02-147881-1(3)) Macmillan/McGraw-Hill Schl. Div.

Die Geographie. (Duden-Schuelerduden Ser.). (GER., Illus.). 468p. (YA). (978-3-411-04223-4(0)) Bibliographisches Institut & F. A. Brockhaus AG DEU. *Dist:* International Bk. Import Service, Inc.

Geography, Set. 2004. (Illus.). (gr. 9-12). pap. 23.95 (978-0-86717-682-7(2) , ES3015, Lifepac) Alpha Omega Pubns., Inc.

Geography. 2005. (Quick Study Academic Ser.). (Illus.). 4p. 4.95 (978-1-57222-843-6(1)) Barcharts, Inc.

Geography Centers. 2005. (Take It to Your Seat Ser.). 192p. (gr. 1-2). 19.99 (978-1-55799-995-5(3) , EMC 3716); (gr. 2-3). 19.99 (978-1-55799-996-2(1) , EMC 3717); (gr. 3-4). 19.99 (978-1-55799-997-9(X) , EMC 3718); (gr. 4-5). 19.99 (978-1-55799-998-6(8) , EMC 3719) Evan-Moor Educational Pubs.

Geography Riddles & Puzzles. 32p. (gr. 6-8). 6.99 (978-0-7682-0215-1(9) , GA13015) School Specialty Publishing.

Geography; Rookie Read-About Geography: Bodies of Water. 2004. (Illus.). 57.00 (978-0-516-29659-3(0)) Scholastic Library Publishing.

Geography; Rookie Read-About Geography: Continents. 2004. (Illus.). 133.00 (978-0-516-29188-8(2)) Scholastic Library Publishing.

Geography, Rookie Read-About Geography: Landforms & Landmarks. 2004. (Illus.). 57.00 (978-0-516-29651-7(5)) Scholastic Library Publishing.

Geography, Rookie Read-About Geography: Peoples & Places. 2004. (Illus.). 228.00 (978-0-516-29566-4(7)) Scholastic Library Publishing.

Geography Starts Here, 8 bks., Set. 2000. (J). (978-0-7398-3528-9(9)) Raintree.

George, Michael. Antarctica: Land of Endless Water. 2001. (Life on Earth Ser.). (Illus.). 32p. (J). lib. bdg. (978-1-58341-025-7(2) , Creative Education) Creative Co., The.

Gildea, Ray Y. Letters Home: Children Learn Geography Through Communication with Parents Traveling/ Working Abroad. 2005. (J). per. (978-0-9721032-4-4(4)) Parlance Publishing.

Gordon, Juli A., ed. Monopoly Geography Grades 4-5. 2002. 32p. (YA). 3.99 (978-1-58792-029-5(8)) Trend Enterprises, Inc.

Gordon, Patricia. Kids Learn America! Bringing Geography to Life with People, Places & History. 1999. (J). (gr. k-3). lib. bdg. 22.20 (978-0-613-16370-5(2)) Tandem Library Bks.

Gordon, Patricia & Snow, Reed C. Kids Learn America! Bringing Geography to Life with People, Places & History. 2nd rev. ed. 1999. (Kids Can Bks.). (Illus.). 173p. (J). (gr. 2-7). pap. 12.95 (978-1-885593-31-3(7) , Williamson Bks.) Ideals Pubns.

Graham, Leland & McCoy, Isabelle. World Geography. 2004. 128p. (J). pap. (978-0-88724-255-7(3) , CD-4347) Carson-Dellosa Publishing Co., Inc.

Grahame, Deborah. Asia. 2003. (Continents Ser.). (Illus.). 32p. (J). (gr. 2-6). 27.07 (978-1-59296-058-3(8)) Child's World, Inc.

Gravois, Michael. Comic Strip Map Skills: 30 Reproducible, Rib-Tickling Cartoons with Related Maps & Questions That Build Map Skills. 2001. 64p. pap. 10.95 (978-0-439-21557-2(9)) Scholastic, Inc.

Green, David. The Geography of the World. Parsons, Jayne, ed. 2003. (Illus.). 304p. (J). 29.99 (978-0-7894-8594-6(X)) Dorling Kindersley Publishing, Inc.

Grolier Educational Staff. Lands & Peoples, 6 vols. 2000. (Illus.). (J). (978-0-7172-8022-3(5) , Grolier) Scholastic Library Publishing.

Grolier Educational Staff, contrib. by. Lands & Peoples, 6 vols. 2003. (Illus.). 1088p. (J). (978-0-7172-8023-0(3) , Grolier) Scholastic Library Publishing.

Group/McGraw-Hill, Wright. Canada Coast to Coast, 6 vols. (Book2WebTM Ser.). (gr. 4-8). 36.50 (978-0-322-04444-9(8)) Wright Group, The.

Guinness, Paul & Nagle, Garrett. Advanced Geography: Concepts & Cases. rev. ed. 2002. (Illus.). 544p. pap. 94.00 (978-0-340-85826-4(5)) Hodder Education GBR. *Dist:* Trans-Atlantic Pubns., Inc.

Harcourt, Mike, et al. Tomorrow's Geography for Edexcel GCSE Specification A. 2001. (Illus.). 190p. pap. 52.00 (***978-0-340-79965-9(X)*** , Hodder Murray) Hodder Education GBR. *Dist:* Trans-Atlantic Pubns., Inc.

Harcourt School Publishers Staff. Flat or Round? Advanced Level: Early Discoveries about Our Planet. 3rd ed. 2002. (Trophies Reading Program Ser.). pap. 5.10 (978-0-15-323490-3(3)) Harcourt Schl. Pubs.

—Horizons: Time for Kids: Postsale 18 Packages, 5 Collections. 2nd ed. 2003. (Harcourt Horizons Ser.). (gr. k up). 272.50 (978-0-15-336168-5(9)) Harcourt Schl. Pubs.

—My World, Unit 6. 3rd ed. 2003. (Harcourt Brace Social Studies). pap. 76.00 (978-0-15-341063-5(9)) Harcourt Schl. Pubs.

—Preparation Book of TAKS: World Regions. 2nd ed. 2002. (Horizons Ser.). pap. 12.00 (978-0-15-336577-5(3)) Harcourt Schl. Pubs.

—Social Studies: FL Daily Geography. 2nd ed. 2002. (Illus.). (J). pap. 31.40 (978-0-15-319433-7(2)) Harcourt Schl. Pubs.

—States & Regions. 97th ed. 1999. (Stories in Time Ser.). (Illus.). (gr. 4). 70.40 (978-0-15-302040-7(7)) Harcourt Schl. Pubs.

—TIME for Kids: State & Region. 3rd ed. 2002. (Horizontes (Social Studies) Ser.). Bk. 1. (SPA.). pap. 7.00 (978-0-15-333856-4(3)); Bk. 3. (SPA.). pap. 7.00 (978-0-15-333860-1(1)); Bk. 4. (SPA.). pap. 7.00 (978-0-15-333862-5(8)); Bk. 5. (SPA.). pap. 7.00 (978-0-15-333864-9(4)); Bk. 6. pap. 7.00 (978-0-15-333866-3(0)); Bk. 7. (SPA.). pap. 7.00 (978-0-15-333868-7(7)); Bk. 8. (SPA.). pap. 7.00 (978-0-15-333870-0(9)); Bk. 9. (SPA.). pap. 7.00 (978-0-15-333872-4(5)); Bk. 10. (SPA.). pap. 7.00 (978-0-15-333874-8(1)); Bk. 11. (SPA.). pap. 7.00 (978-0-15-333876-2(8)); Bk. 12. (SPA.). pap. 7.00 (978-0-15-333878-6(4)) Harcourt Schl. Pubs.

—World Regions Horizons. 3rd ed. 2001. (Harcourt Horizons Ser.). (gr. k-7). pap., tchr. ed. 23.30 (978-0-15-322615-1(3)) Harcourt Schl. Pubs.

Hart, Greg & Arundale, Jackie. Investigating Geography. 2003. (Illus.). 132p. pap. 33.50 (***978-0-340-84634-6(8)***); pap. 33.50 (***978-0-340-84633-9(X)***) Hodder Education GBR. (Hodder Murray). *Dist:* Trans-Atlantic Pubns., Inc.

Haslam, Andrew. Living Geography. 2001. (Make It Work! Geography Ser.). 192p. (J). (gr. 4-7). pap. 19.95 (978-1-58728-285-0(2) , Two Can Publishing) T&N Children's Publishing.

Helgren, David M. World Geography Today: Online Edition. 3rd ed. 2003. 79.06 (978-0-03-072539-5(9)) Holt, Rinehart & Winston.

Henderson, Felicity. The World Around Us. Donnelly, Strawberrie, illus. 2002. (Pop-Up Prayers Ser.). 16p. (ps-3). 3.99 (978-0-8066-4370-0(6) , Augsburg Bks.) Augsburg Fortress, Pubs.

Hirsch, E. D., ed. Early Explorers & Settlers. 2003. tchr. ed. 9.95 (978-0-7690-5041-6(7)); stu. ed. 49.95 (978-0-7690-2946-7(9)) Pearson Learning.

—Geography of the Americas. 2003. stu. ed. 49.95 (978-0-7690-2959-7(0)) Pearson Learning.

—Geography of the United States, Level 5. tchr. ed. 9.95 (978-0-7690-5084-3(0)); stu. ed. 49.95 (978-0-7690-2849-1(7)) Pearson Learning.

History & Geography. (Switched on Schoolhouse Ser.). 2004. (YA). (gr. 7). cd-rom 69.95 (978-0-7403-0587-0(5)); 2000. (Illus.). (J). (gr. 3-7). pap., stu. ed. 66.95 incl. cd-rom (978-0-7403-0223-7(X) , SOS300H); Set. 2004. (Illus.). (gr. 5). tchr. ed., stu. ed. 47.95 (978-1-58095-651-2(3) , HIS05015, Lifepac) Alpha Omega Pubns., Inc.

History & Geography: Government & Economics. 2004. (Illus.). (gr. 12). tchr. ed., stu. ed. 47.95 (978-1-58095-672-7(6) , HIS1215, Lifepac) Alpha Omega Pubns., Inc.

History & Geography: U. S. History, 12 vols., Set. 2004. (Illus.). (gr. 11-12). tchr. ed., stu. ed. 47.95 (978-1-58095-669-7(6) , HIS1115, Lifepac) Alpha Omega Pubns., Inc.

Hogan & Wiggers. Ultimate Geography & Timeline. 2004. pap. 34.95 (978-0-9663722-0-5(4)) Coffee Hse. Ink.

Hogan, Maggie S. Hands-on Geography. Ulrich-Bonk, Ivy, ed. Shaffer, Christy, illus. 2001. pap. 10.99 (978-1-892427-03-8(6)) Bright Ideas! Educational Resources.

Holiday, Jane. Exploring Argentina with the Five Themes of Geography. (Library of the Western Hemisphere). (J). 2005. (Illus.). 24p. 19.95 (978-1-4042-2678-4(8) , PowerKids Pr.); 2003. (978-0-8239-4650-1(9)); 2003. (Illus.). 24p. pap. (978-0-8239-4638-9(X)) Rosen Publishing Group, Inc., The.

—Exploring Brazil with the Five Themes of Geography. 2005. (Library of the Western Hemisphere). (Illus.). 24p. (J). 19.95 (978-1-4042-2679-1(6) , PowerKids Pr.); pap. (978-0-8239-4639-6(8)) Rosen Publishing Group, Inc., The.

Holt, Rinehart and Winston Staff. American Nation: Geography Activities. 3rd ed. 2001. pap. 25.80 (978-0-03-065329-2(0)) Holt, Rinehart & Winston.

—American Nation: Modern Era: Geography Activities. 3rd ed. 2001. pap. 25.80 (978-0-03-065396-4(7)) Holt, Rinehart & Winston.

—People, Places & Change: Western Hemisphere: Main Idea Activities. 5th ed. 2005. (SPA.). pap. 25.80 (978-0-03-040198-5(4)) Holt, Rinehart & Winston.

—Social Studies: Readings in World Geography with Answer Key. 2001. pap. 37.53 (978-0-03-054911-3(6)) Holt, Rinehart & Winston.

—Texas Connections to World Geography. 3rd ed. 2002. pap. 24.60 (978-0-03-065442-8(4)) Holt, Rinehart & Winston.

—World Geography Today: Chapter & Unit Tests for English Language Students. 3rd ed. 2001. pap. 25.80 (978-0-03-065422-0(X)) Holt, Rinehart & Winston.

—World Geography Today: Chapter & Unit Tests with Answer Key. 2000. pap. 22.40 (978-0-03-054476-7(9)); 3rd ed. 2001. pap. 45.13 (978-0-03-065412-1(2)) Holt, Rinehart & Winston.

—World Geography Today: Critical Thinking Activities with Answer Key. 2000. pap. 15.06 (978-0-03-054472-9(6)); 3rd ed. 2001. pap. 25.80 (978-0-03-065411-4(4)) Holt, Rinehart & Winston.

—World Geography Today: Geography for Life Activities. 3rd ed. 2001. pap. 25.80 (978-0-03-065416-9(5)) Holt, Rinehart & Winston.

—World Geography Today: Guided Reading Strategies. 3rd ed. 2001. pap. 25.80 (978-0-03-065418-3(1)); 5th ed. 2005. pap. 25.80 (978-0-03-038874-3(0)) Holt, Rinehart & Winston.

—World Geography Today: Guided Reading Strategies - Answer Key. 3rd ed. 2001. pap. 25.80 (978-0-03-066686-5(4)) Holt, Rinehart & Winston.

—World Geography Today: Standard Test Preparation: Virginia Edition. 3rd ed. 2003. (YA). pap., wbk. ed. 10.60 (978-0-03-070171-9(6)) Holt, Rinehart & Winston.

—World Geography Today: Virginia Edition. 3rd annot. ed. 2003. (YA). tchr. ed. 109.20 (978-0-03-070153-5(8)) Holt, Rinehart & Winston.

In Neighbourhoods. (J). (gr. 2). (978-0-8374-1456-0(3) , 204) Weekly Reader Corp.

Instructional Fair. Blank Map Outlines. 1999. 96p. (J). (gr. 3-6). pap. 10.99 (978-0-88012-668-7(X) , IF8554) School Specialty Publishing.

Jarrell, Jane & Saathoff, Deborah. Address: Planet Earth. 2004. 48p. pap., act. bk. ed. 6.99 (978-0-8054-0824-9(X)) B&H Publishing Grp.

Jeffus, Sharon & Jeffus, Richard. Teaching Geography Through Art. 2001. (Illus.). 120p. (YA). (gr. 4-11). 19.95 (978-0-9715970-1-3(4)) Visual Manna.

Jenkins, Steve. Hottest, Coldest, Highest, Deepest. 32p. (J). (gr. k-3). 2004. pap. 6.95 (978-0-618-49488-0(X)); 1998. (Illus.). tchr. ed. 16.00 (978-0-395-89999-1(0)) Houghton Mifflin Co. Trade & Reference Div.

Jones, David & Kimpton, Laurence. Quick Revision KS3 Geography. 2007. 46p. pap. 9.95 (***978-0-340-94310-6(6)*** , Hodder Murray) Hodder Education GBR. *Dist:* Trans-Atlantic Pubns., Inc.

Jones, Janice C. Geography Fun Facts! A Historical Trip Across the U. S. A., in Poetry. Struble, John H., illus. 1999. (Geography Makes Sense Ser.). 224p. (gr. 4-8). pap. 29.95 (978-0-9669638-0-9(6)) Think, Ink!.

Kaplan, Leslie C. Land & Resources in Ancient Egypt. 2004. (Primary Sources of Ancient Civilizations Ser.). (Illus.). 24p. (J). lib. bdg. 19.95 (978-0-8239-6781-0(6) , PowerKids Pr.) Rosen Publishing Group, Inc., The.

—Land & Resources of Ancient Egypt. 2004. (Primary Sources of Ancient Civilizations Ser.). (Illus.). 24p. (J). lib. bdg. (978-0-8239-8931-7(3) , PowerKids Pr.) Rosen Publishing Group, Inc., The.

Klingel, Cynthia Fitterer. Africa. 2003. (Continents Ser.). (Illus.). 32p. (J). (gr. 2-6). 27.07 (978-1-59296-059-0(6)) Child's World, Inc.

—Europe. 2003. (Continents Ser.). (Illus.). 32p. (J). (gr. 2-6). 27.07 (978-1-59296-060-6(X)) Child's World, Inc.

Lasseter, Rollin, ed. History: All Ye Lands. (Illus.). 360p. (J). (gr. 6). 55.00 (978-0-89870-944-5(X)) Ignatius Pr.

Leedy, Loreen. Blast off to Earth! A Look at Geography. 1998. (Illus.). 32p. (J). (gr. k-3). 6.95 (978-0-8234-1409-3(4)) Holiday Hse., Inc.

Lerner Publishing Group Staff. Continents: Classroom Set. 2005. (Pull Ahead Bks.). (Illus.). (J). (gr. 1-3). 40.95 (978-0-8225-2410-6(4)) Lerner Publishing Group.

Let's Investigate Series, 8 vols., Set. Incl. Australia. Richardson, Adele D. pap. 10.60 (978-0-89812-002-8(0)); Bats. Shaw, Nancy J. pap. 10.60 (978-0-89812-003-5(9)); Fossils. Shaw, Nancy J. & Gish, Melissa. pap. 10.60 (978-0-89812-004-2(7)); Japan. Richardson, Adele D. pap. 10.60 (978-0-89812-005-9(5)); Mexico. Richardson, Adele D. pap. 10.60 (978-0-89812-006-6(3)); Russia. Richardson, Adele D. pap. 10.60 (978-0-89812-007-3(1)); Seashells. Richardson, Adele D. pap. 10.60 (978-0-89812-008-0(X)); Snakes. Gish, Melissa. pap. 10.60 (978-0-89812-009-7(8)); 32p. (J). 2000. (Illus.). Set pap. 84.80 (978-0-89812-011-0(X) , Creative Paperbacks) Creative Co., The.

Lewis, Sian. Dilyn Declan. 2005. (978-1-901862-58-4(5)) FBA Pubns.

El Libro de los Acertijos Geograficos. (Coleccion Acertijos). (SPA.). (YA). (gr. 5-8). pap. (978-950-724-973-0(7) , LMA6983) Lumen ARG. *Dist:* Lectorum Pubns., Inc.

Lubawy, Susan. World View: A Global Study of Geography, History & Culture, Bk. 1. (J). stu. ed. 8.95 (978-0-916591-30-4(1)) Linmore Publishing, Inc.

MacDonald, Fiona. Travel, War & Exploration. 2001. (Illus.). 64p. (gr. 3-7). 12.95 (978-0-7548-0849-7(1)) Anness Publishing GBR. *Dist:* National Bk. Network.

Mara, Wil. The Seven Continents. 2005. (Rookie Read-about Geography Ser.). (Illus.). (J). (gr. 1-2). 31p. pap. 5.95 (978-0-516-22534-0(0)); 32p. 20.50 (978-0-516-22748-1(3)) Scholastic Library Publishing. (Children's Pr.).

Marsh, Carole. Geo Bingo: 38 Must Know State Geographay Facts. rev. ed. 2001. (Kansas Experience! Ser.). 9.95 (978-0-635-00343-0(0)) Gallopade International.

—Jography. 2004. (New York Experience! Ser.). 32p. (J). (gr. 3-8). pap. 7.95 (978-0-635-00162-7(4)) Gallopade International.

Marx, David F. Geography, Rookie Read-About Geography: Countries. 2004. (Illus.). 57.00 (978-0-516-29189-5(0)) Scholastic Library Publishing.

McClish, Bruce. Earth & Its Continents. 2003. (Illus.). 32p. (J). 24.22 (978-1-4034-2986-5(3)) Heinemann Library.

—Island Continents & Super Continents. 2003. (Continents Ser.). (Illus.). 32p. pap. 7.50 (978-1-4034-4245-1(2)) Heinemann Library.

—Island Continents & Super Continents: Australia & Antarctica. 2003. (Illus.). 32p. (J). lib. bdg. 24.22 (978-1-4034-2989-6(8)) Heinemann Library.

—Land Bridges & New World Continents: North & South America. 2003. (Illus.). 32p. (J). lib. bdg. 24.22 (978-1-4034-2988-9(X)) Heinemann Library.

—Old World Continents. 2003. (Continents Ser.). (Illus.). 32p. pap. 7.50 (978-1-4034-4247-5(9)) Heinemann Library.

—Old World Continents: Europe, Asia, & Africa. 2003. (Illus.). 32p. (J). 24.22 (978-1-4034-2987-2(1)) Heinemann Library.

McCoy, Isabelle & Graham, Leland. Hands-on Geography. 2005. 128p. (J). pap. (978-1-59441-183-0(2) , CD-104099); pap. (978-1-59441-184-7(0) , CD-104100) Carson-Dellosa Publishing Co., Inc.

McGraw-Hill Staff. Geography: The World & Its People, Interactive Student Edition. 2002. cd-rom 81.61 (978-0-07-827936-2(4) , 9780078279362) Glencoe/McGraw-Hill.

—Geography: The World & Its People, Student Edition. 2001. 82.35 (978-0-07-821540-7(4) , 9780078215407) Glencoe/McGraw-Hill.

—Geography: The World & Its People, Terra Nova Test Prep, Grade 7. 2001. pap., stu. ed. 12.60 (978-0-07-827134-2(7) , 9780078271342) Glencoe/McGraw-Hill.

—Geography: The World & Its People, Terra Nova Test Prep, Grade 8. 2001. pap., stu. ed. 12.60 (978-0-07-827136-6(3) , 9780078271366) Glencoe/McGraw-Hill.

—Geography Vol. 1: The World & Its People. 2001. stu. ed. 55.82 (978-0-07-827938-6(0) , 9780078279386); stu. ed. 56.06 (978-0-07-824940-2(6) , 9780078249402) Glencoe/McGraw-Hill.

—Geography Vol. 2: The World & Its People. 2001. stu. ed. 56.06 (978-0-07-824941-9(4) , 9780078249419) Glencoe/McGraw-Hill.

—Geography Vol. 2: The World & Its People, Interactive. 2001. (C). stu. ed. 55.82 incl. cd-rom (978-0-07-827940-9(2) , 9780078279409) Glencoe/McGraw-Hill.

—Glencoe World Geography. 8th ed. 2004. stu. ed. 93.32 (978-0-07-860699-1(3) , 9780078606991) Glencoe/McGraw-Hill.

—Glencoe World Geography: Reading Essentials. 2003. pap., stu. ed. 29.18 (978-0-07-860602-1(0) , 9780078606021) Glencoe/McGraw-Hill.

—Glencoe World Geography: Spanish Reading Essentials. 8th ed. 2004. (SPA.). pap., stu. ed., wbk. ed. 26.64 (978-0-07-865328-5(2) , 9780078653285) Glencoe/McGraw-Hill.

—Glencoe World Geography, Active Reading Note-Taking Guide. 8th ed. 2004. pap., stu. ed. 18.00 (978-0-07-867989-6(3) , 9780078679896) Glencoe/McGraw-Hill.

—Glencoe World Geograpy, Reading Essentials. 8th ed. 2004. (C). pap., stu. ed., wbk. ed. 18.00 (978-0-07-865326-1(6) , 9780078653261) Glencoe/McGraw-Hill.

—World & Its People: Eastern Hemisphere. 2004. stu. ed. 69.32 (978-0-07-865472-5(6) , 9780078654725) Glencoe/McGraw-Hill.

—The World & Its People: Standardized Test Practice. 2004. pap., stu. ed., wbk. ed. 10.00 (978-0-07-865523-4(4) , 9780078655234) Glencoe/McGraw-Hill.

—World & Its People: Western Hemisphere, Europe, & Russia. 2004. stu. ed. 69.32 (978-0-07-865475-6(0) , 9780078654756) Glencoe/McGraw-Hill.

—World Geography & Cultures, Interactive Tutor Self-Assessment. 2007. (C). cd-rom 93.32 (***978-0-07-878573-3(1)*** , 9780078785733) Glencoe/McGraw-Hill.

—World Geography & Cultures, Spanish Reading Essentials & Note-Taking Guide. 2007. (C). pap. 18.00 (***978-0-07-878391-3(7)*** , 9780078783913) Glencoe/McGraw-Hill.

—World Geography & Cultures, Standardized Test Practice Workbook. 2007. (C). pap. 14.00 (***978-0-07-878564-1(2)*** , 9780078785641) Glencoe/McGraw-Hill.

—World Geography & Cultures, Student Edition. 2007. (C). 93.32 (***978-0-07-874529-4(2)*** , 9780078745294) Glencoe/McGraw-Hill.

—World Geography & Cultures, StudentWorks Plus. 2007. (C). cd-rom 122.00 (***978-0-07-878394-4(1)*** , 9780078783944) Glencoe/McGraw-Hill.

Miles Kelly Staff. Geography. 2003. (Info Bank Ser.). (Illus.). 96p. (J). 7.95 (978-1-84236-055-2(8)) Miles Kelly Publishing, Ltd. GBR. *Dist:* Independent Pubs. Group.

—Geography Age 10-11: Flip Quiz. 2003. (Flip Quiz Series Ser.). (Illus.). 38p. (J). spiral bd. 5.95 (978-1-84236-102-3(3)) Miles Kelly Publishing, Ltd. GBR. *Dist:* Independent Pubs. Group.

—Geography Age 11-12: Flip Quiz. 2003. (Flip Quiz Ser.). (Illus.). 38p. (J). spiral bd. 5.95 (978-1-84236-103-0(1)) Miles Kelly Publishing, Ltd. GBR. *Dist:* Independent Pubs. Group.

—Geography Age 7-9: Flip Quiz. 2003. (Flip Quiz Ser.). (Illus.). 38p. (J). spiral bd. 5.95 (978-1-84236-100-9(7)) Miles Kelly Publishing, Ltd. GBR. *Dist:* Independent Pubs. Group.

—Geography Age 9-10: Flip Quiz. 2003. (Flip Quiz Ser.). (Illus.). 38p. (J). spiral bd. 5.95 (978-1-84236-101-6(5)) Miles Kelly Publishing, Ltd. GBR. *Dist:* Independent Pubs. Group.

Miller, Millie. Our World: A Country-by-Country Guide. 2006. (Our World Ser.). (Illus.). 112p. (J). (gr. 3-6). pap. 16.99 (978-0-439-55004-8(1) , Scholastic Reference) Scholastic, Inc.

Morter, Peter. Atlas Visual de los Descubrimientos. (SPA., Illus.). 412p. (YA). (gr. 5-8). (978-84-216-1814-1(8) , BU4892) Bruño, Editorial ESP. *Dist:* Lectorum Pubns., Inc.

My American Geography Student. 2004. pap. 2.65 (978-0-8388-6275-9(6)) Educators Publishing Service, Inc.

My World. 2005. (Pebble Ser.). (Illus.). (J). (gr. k-1). lib. bdg. 111.51 (978-0-7368-4401-7(5)) Capstone Pr., Inc.

Nagle, Garrett. Thinking Geography: KS3 Higher Ability Text. 2000. (Illus.). 144p. pap. 36.50 (***978-0-340-74283-9(6)*** , Hodder Murray) Hodder Education GBR. *Dist:* Trans-Atlantic Pubns., Inc.

Nagle, Garrett & Spencer, Kris. Geographical Enquiries: Skills & Techniques for Geography. 2nd ed. 2000. (Illus.). 128p. (J). pap. 22.50 (978-0-7487-5318-5(4)) Nelson Thornes Ltd. GBR. *Dist:* Trans-Atlantic Pubns., Inc.

Nations of the World, 6 vols. 1999. (J). (Illus.). 205.56 (978-0-8172-5788-0(8)); 137.00 (978-0-7398-1294-5(7)); (Illus.). 274.00 (978-0-7398-1295-2(5)) Raintree.

Nations of the World, 18 bks., Set. Incl. Argentina. Dalai, Anita. (YA). 2000. lib. bdg. 34.26 (978-0-7398-1279-2(3)); Australia. Darlington, Robert A. (J). 2000. lib. bdg. 34.26 (978-0-7398-1280-8(7)); Brazil. Dalal, Anita. Kossmann, Walter, ed. (YA). 2001. lib. bdg. 34.26 (978-0-7398-1284-6(X)); Canada. Nickles, Greg & Walker, Niki. (YA). 2000. lib. bdg. 34.26 (978-0-8172-5780-4(2)); China. Fields, Catherine. (YA). 2000. lib. bdg. 34.26 (978-0-8172-5781-1(0)); Egypt. Wilson, Neil. (J). 2001. lib. bdg. 34.26 (978-0-7398-1283-9(1)); France. Ingham, Richard. (YA). 2000. lib. bdg. 34.26 (978-0-8172-5782-8(9)); Germany. Nickles, Greg & Walker, Niki. (J). 2001. lib. bdg. 34.26 (978-0-7398-1285-3(8)); India. Dalal, Anita. (YA). 2001. lib. bdg. 34.26 (978-0-7398-1289-1(0)); Israel. Green, Jen. (YA). 2001. lib. bdg. 34.26 (978-0-7398-1286-0(6)); Italy. Cassidy, Picot. (YA). 2001. lib. bdg. 34.26 (978-0-7398-1287-7(4)); Japan. Green, Jen. (YA). 2000. lib. bdg. 34.26 (978-0-8172-5783-5(7)); Kenya. Giles, Bridget. (YA). 2001. lib. bdg. 34.26 (978-0-7398-1290-7(4)); Mexico. Green, Jen. (YA). 2000. lib. bdg. 34.26 (978-0-8172-5779-8(9)); Russia. Wilson, Neil. (J). 2000. lib. bdg. 34.26 (978-0-7398-1281-5(5)); South Africa. Green, Jen. (J). 2000. lib. bdg. 34.26 (978-0-7398-1282-2(3)); Sweden. Butler, Roberta. (J). 2000. lib. bdg. 34.26 (978-0-8172-5784-2(5)); United Kingdom. Innes, Brian. (YA). 2001. lib. bdg. 34.26 (978-0-7398-1288-4(2)); 128p. (gr. 6-8). (Illus.). 2001. Set lib. bdg. 616.68 (978-0-7398-4327-7(3)) Raintree.

Nations of the World Series, 4 vols., Set. 2003. pap. 137.12 (978-0-7398-7002-0(5)); 2000. (Illus.). 342.60 (978-0-7398-4182-2(3)) Steck-Vaughn.

Neighborhoods, Level B. 2003. (Maps, Charts & Graphs Ser.). suppl. ed. 8.95 (978-0-8136-2133-3(X)) Modern Curriculum Pr.

Nelson, Robin. Where Is My Continent? (First Step Nonfiction Ser.). (gr. k-2). 2005. (Illus.). 24p. lib. bdg. 17.27 (978-0-8225-0193-0(7)); 2001. (J). pap. 3.95 (978-0-8225-1982-9(8) , Lerner Pubns.) Lerner Publishing Group.

—Where Is My Country? (First Step Nonfiction Ser.). (gr. k-2). 2005. (Illus.). 24p. lib. bdg. 17.27 (978-0-8225-0192-3(9)); 2001. (J). pap. 3.95 (978-0-8225-1981-2(X) , Lerner Pubns.) Lerner Publishing Group.

—Where Is My State? (First Step Nonfiction Ser.). (gr. k-2). 2005. (Illus.). 24p. lib. bdg. 17.27 (978-0-8225-0191-6(0)); 2001. (J). pap. 3.95 (978-0-8225-1980-5(1) , Lerner Pubns.) Lerner Publishing Group.

New York Public Library Staff & Sutcliffe, Andrea. The New York Public Library Amazing U. S. Geography: A Book of Answers for Kids. 2002. (New York Public Library Books for Kids: Vol. 12). (Illus.). 176p. pap. 12.95 (978-0-471-39294-1(4) , Wiley) Wiley, John & Sons, Inc.

—The New York Public Library Amazing World Geography: A Book of Answers for Kids. 2002. (New York Public Library Books for Kids: Vol. 13). (Illus.). 176p. pap. 12.95 (978-0-471-39296-5(0) , Howell Bk. Hse.) Wiley, John & Sons, Inc.

Osbourne, David. The World of Waters or A Peaceful Progress O'er the Unpathed Sea. 2004. reprint ed. pap. 1.99 (978-1-4192-8870-8(9)) Kessinger Publishing, LLC.

Our World. Date not set. (Questions & Answers Ser.). 176p. (J). 7.98 (978-0-7525-9624-2(1)) Parragon, Inc.

Our World Set. (gr. k-2). 346.95 (978-0-7368-9396-1(2)) Red Brick Learning.

Parsons, Jayne, ed. Geography of the World. 2006. (Illus.). 304p. (J). pap. 19.99 (978-0-7566-1952-7(1)) Dorling Kindersley Publishing, Inc.

Penton Overseas, Inc. Staff. States & Capitals. (Social Studies Ser.). (J). incl. audio NewSound, LLC.

—States & Capitals. 2002. (Smart Kids Flippers Ser.). (Illus.). (J). pap. 7.95 (978-1-59125-126-2(X)); pap. 7.95 (978-1-59125-127-9(3) , Smart Kids) Penton Overseas, Inc.

People & Places. 1999. pap. 169.80 (978-0-8172-4683-9(5)) Raintree.

People Communities. (J). (gr. 3). (978-0-8374-1457-7(1) , 205) Weekly Reader Corp.

Petty, Kate. The Amazing Pop-Up Geography Book. Maizels, Jennie, illus. 2000. 1p. (J). (gr. 3 up). 24.99 (978-0-525-46438-9(7) , Dutton Juvenile) Penguin Group (USA) Inc.

Pickering, Mel, contrib. by. Childrensatlas.com. 2004. (Interfact Ser.). (Illus.). 48p. (J). (gr. 3-6). 24.95 incl. cd-rom (978-1-58728-403-8(0) , Two Can Publishing) T&N Children's Publishing.

Practor, Jodie. Geography Brain Teasers. 1998. (Brain Teasers Ser.). (Illus.). 80p. (YA). (gr. 5-8). pap., tchr. ed. 9.99 (978-1-57690-213-4(7) , TCA2213) Teacher Created Materials, Inc.

Priddy, Roger. My Big World Book. rev. ed. 2002. (Illus.). 12p. (J). bds. 5.95 (978-0-312-49122-2(0) , Priddy Bks.) St. Martin's Pr.

Race the States: Travel Games with Press & Peel Clings. 1999. (J). (ps-3). pap. 4.29 (978-0-88743-734-2(6)) School Zone Publishing Co.

Raintree Steck-Vaughn Staff. Country Fact Files. 1999. (J). 759.36 (978-0-8172-5409-4(9)) Raintree.

—Our World of Wonders. 1999. (Illus.). (J). pap. 35.60 (978-0-7398-0918-1(0)) Steck-Vaughn.

—Wide World, 6 bks. 1998. (Illus.). (gr. 3-7). 113.88 (978-0-8172-5066-9(2)) Raintree.

Rau, Dana Meachen. North America. 2003. (Continents Ser.). (Illus.). 32p. (J). (gr. 2-6). 27.07 (978-1-59296-061-3(8)) Child's World, Inc.

Readman, Jo & Roberts, Ley H. The World Came to My Place Today. 2003. (Illus.). 32p. 19.99 (978-1-903919-01-9(0) , Eden Project Books) Transworld Publishers Ltd. GBR. *Dist:* Trafalgar Square Publishing.

Regional Geography on File, 6 vols., Set. 2001. (YA). (gr. 6-12). 1110.00 (978-0-8160-4838-0(X)) Facts On File, Inc.

Ritchie, Scot. Up, up & Away: A Round-the-World Puzzle Adventure. Ritchie, Scot, illus. 2006. (Illus.). 32p. (J). 16.95 (978-1-897066-59-1(7)) Maple Tree Pr. CAN. *Dist:* Perseus Distribution.

—Up, up & Away: A Round-the-World Puzzle Adventure. 2006. (Illus.). 32p. (J). pap. 6.95 (978-1-897066-60-7(0)) Maple Tree Pr. CAN. *Dist:* Perseus Distribution.

Rockwell, Anne F. Our Earth. 2000. (gr. k-3). lib. bdg. 14.15 (978-0-613-28598-8(0)) Tandem Library Bks.

Rookie Read-About Geography. 2004. 627.00 (978-0-516-27717-2(0)) Scholastic Library Publishing.

Rookie Read-About Geography: General, 4 Bks. 2004. 76.00 (978-0-516-23748-0(9) , Children's Pr.) Scholastic Library Publishing.

Rookie Read-About Geography: States, 10 bks., Set. Incl. Hawaii. Taylor-Butler, Christine. (Illus.). 2007. 20.50 (978-0-531-12571-7(8)); Indiana. Hyde, Judith Jensen. (Illus.). 2006. 20.50 (978-0-516-21846-5(8)); Louisiana. Hyde, Judith Jensen. (Illus.). 2007. 20.50 (978-0-516-21848-9(4)); Mississippi. Trueit, Trudi Strain. (Illus.). 2007. 20.50 (978-0-531-12572-4(6)); Nebraska. Zollman, Pam. 2006. 20.50 (978-0-516-25466-1(9)); Nevada. Labella, Susan. (Illus.). 2006. 20.50 (978-0-516-25467-8(7)); Ohio. Taylor-Butler, Christine. (Illus.). 2007. 20.50 (978-0-531-12573-1(4)); Oklahoma. LaBella, Susan. (Illus.). 2006. 20.50 (978-0-516-25468-5(5)); Utah. Trueit, Trudi Strain. (Illus.). 2007. 20.50 (978-0-531-12574-8(2)); Vermont. Taylor-Butler, Christine. (Illus.). 2007. 20.50 (978-0-531-12593-9(9)); 32p. (J). (gr. 1-2). 2007. 205.00 (***978-0-531-17737-2(8));*** 97.50 (978-0-516-25415-9(4)) Scholastic Library Publishing. (Children's Pr.).

Rosenberg, Matthew T. The Handy Geography Answer Book. (Illus.). 462p. (YA). pap. (978-1-57859-105-3(8)) Visible Ink Pr.

Santella, Andrew. All Around Illinois: Regions & Resources. 2002. (Heinemann State Studies). (Illus.). 48p. (J). (gr. 3-5). lib. bdg. 27.07 (978-1-4034-0007-9(5)); pap. 8.50 (978-1-4034-0568-5(9) , 91872) Heinemann Library.

Sapp, Eric. World Geography. 2003. (Illus.). stu. ed., per., wbk. ed. (978-1-931680-38-7(8) , Expert Systems for Teachers) Teaching Point, Inc.

Scholastic Library Publishing Staff, ed. Rookie Read-About Geography, 2. 2004. 418.00 (978-0-516-24707-6(7)) Scholastic Library Publishing.

—True Books Social Studies Geography, 2. 2004. 752.00 (978-0-516-22902-7(8)) Scholastic Library Publishing.

School Specialty Publishing. Continents. 1999. (Learning Cards Ser.). 7p. (J). (gr. 3-8). 7.99 (978-0-7424-0633-9(4) , Instructional Fair) Schaffer, Frank Pubns.

Scillian, Devin. P Is for Passport: A World Alphabet. 2003. (Illus.). 56p. (J). 19.95 (978-1-58536-157-1(7)) Sleeping Bear Pr.

Sepheri, Sandy. The Seven Continents. 2008. (J). (***978-1-60044-548-4(9)***) Rourke Publishing, LLC.

Sharíatí, Karen Allíson. Meet Arzeen, Citizen of the World. Kím, Jay Jíyeon, illus. 2006. 45p. (J). (***978-0-9770475-0-5(4)***) Arzana, Inc.

Somervill, Barbara A. Australia. 2003. (Continents Ser.). (Illus.). 32p. (J). (gr. 2-6). 27.07 (978-1-59296-063-7(4)) Child's World, Inc.

Spyglass Books - Geography, 8 bks. Incl. Continents. Waters, Jennifer. lib. bdg. 18.60 (978-0-7565-0378-9(7)); Mapping Our World. Scott, Janine. lib. bdg. 18.60 (978-0-7565-0362-8(0)); Welcome to Brazil. Auch, Alison. lib. bdg. 18.60 (978-0-7565-0370-3(1)); Welcome to Canada. Auch, Alison. lib. bdg. 18.60 (978-0-7565-0372-7(8)); Welcome to Japan. Auch, Alison & Stewart, Joan. lib. bdg. 18.60 (978-0-7565-0368-0(X)); Welcome to Kenya. Auch, Alison. lib. bdg. 18.60 (978-0-7565-0369-7(8)); Welcome to Mexico. Auch, Alison. lib. bdg. 18.60 (978-0-7565-0373-4(6)); Welcome to Russia. Auch, Alison. lib. bdg. 18.60 (978-0-7565-0371-0(X)); 24p. (J). (gr. 1 up). 2002. (Illus.). 2003. Set lib. bdg. 148.80 (978-0-7565-0782-4(0)) Compass Point Bks.

States. 2004. (Illus.). 323.00 (978-0-516-29324-0(9)) Scholastic Library Publishing.

States & Nations. (J). (gr. 4). (978-0-8374-1458-4(X) , 206) Weekly Reader Corp.

Steck-Vaughn Staff. Geography. 2000. (Illus.). (J). (gr. 1). pap. (978-0-7398-3409-1(6)); (gr. 2). pap. (978-0-7398-3410-7(X)); (gr. 3). pap. (978-0-7398-3411-4(8)); (gr. 4). pap. (978-0-7398-3412-1(6)); (gr. 5). pap. (978-0-7398-3413-8(4)) Steck-Vaughn.

—So Many Places to Go. 2000. pap. (978-0-7398-4462-5(8)); (Illus.). (J). bds. (978-0-7398-4452-6(0)) Steck-Vaughn.

—Social Studies: US & World History, Geography. 2002. (Illus.). pap. (978-0-7398-5426-6(7)) Steck-Vaughn.

E F G

—Weekly Geography Practice. (Illus.). (J). 2002. (gr. 2). pap. 12.99 (978-0-7398-5357-3(0)); 2002. (gr. 6). pap. (978-0-7398-5358-0(9)); 2000. (gr. 3). pap. (978-0-7398-3432-9(0)); 2000. (gr. 4). pap. (978-0-7398-3433-6(9)); 2000. (gr. 5). pap. (978-0-7398-3434-3(7)) Steck-Vaughn.

Sullivan, Erin Ash. Matematicas alrededor del mundo & Math Around the Globe. 2005. spiral bd. 84.00 (***978-1-4108-5689-0(5)***) Benchmark Education Co.

Sumner, Ray, ed. World Geography, 8 vols., Vol. 8. Incl. World Geography, Volume 1 Vol. 1 : The World. lib. bdg. (978-0-89356-276-2(9)); World Geography, Volume 2 Vol. 2 : North America & the Caribbean. lib. bdg. (978-0-89356-277-9(7)); World Geography, Volume 3 Vol. 3 : South & Central America. lib. bdg. (978-0-89356-335-6(8)); World Geography, Volume 4 Vol. 4 : Africa. lib. bdg. (978-0-89356-336-3(6)); World Geography, Volume 4 Vol. 5 : Europe. lib. bdg. (978-0-89356-399-8(4)); World Geography, Volume 6 Vol. 6 : Asia. lib. bdg. (978-0-89356-650-0(0)); World Geography, Volume 7 Vol. 7 : Antarctica, Australia, & the Pacific. lib. bdg. (978-0-89356-699-9(3)); World Geography, Volume 8 Vol. 8 : Glossary, Bibliography, Appendices. lib. bdg. (978-0-89356-723-1(X)); (YA). (Illus.). 2379p. 2001. Set lib. bdg. 499.00 (978-0-89356-024-9(3) , 608) Salem Pr., Inc.

—World Geography, Volume 1 Vol. 1: The World, 8 vols. 2001. (Illus.). (YA). lib. bdg. (978-0-89356-276-2(9)) Salem Pr., Inc.

—World Geography, Volume 2 Vol. 2: North America & the Caribbean, 8 vols. 2001. (Illus.). (YA). lib. bdg. (978-0-89356-277-9(7)) Salem Pr., Inc.

—World Geography, Volume 3 Vol. 3: South & Central America, 8 vols. 2001. (Illus.). (YA). lib. bdg. (978-0-89356-335-6(8)) Salem Pr., Inc.

—World Geography, Volume 4 Vol. 4: Africa, 8 vols. 2001. (Illus.). (YA). lib. bdg. (978-0-89356-336-3(6)) Salem Pr., Inc.

—World Geography, Volume 4 Vol. 5: Europe, 8 vols. 2001. (Illus.). (YA). lib. bdg. (978-0-89356-399-8(4)) Salem Pr., Inc.

—World Geography, Volume 6 Vol. 6: Asia, 8 vols. 2001. (Illus.). (YA). lib. bdg. (978-0-89356-650-0(0)) Salem Pr., Inc.

—World Geography, Volume 7 Vol. 7: Antarctica, Australia, & the Pacific, 8 vols. 2001. (Illus.). (YA). lib. bdg. (978-0-89356-699-9(3)) Salem Pr., Inc.

—World Geography, Volume 8 Vol. 8: Glossary, Bibliography, Appendices, 8 vols. 2001. (Illus.). (YA). lib. bdg. (978-0-89356-723-1(X)) Salem Pr., Inc.

Sutcliffe, Andrea. The New York Public Library Amazing World Geography: A Book of Answers for Kids. 2002. (gr. 5-8). lib. bdg. 22.20 (978-0-613-82482-8(2)) Tandem Library Bks.

Take Five Minutes: Fascinating Facts about Geography. 2003. 176p. (YA). (gr. 5-8). 16.99 (978-0-7439-3290-5(0)) Teacher Created Materials, Inc.

Taylor, Barbara. The Earth: The Geography of Our World. 2001. (Discover & Learn Ser.). (Illus.). 96p. (J). (gr. 3-5). pap. 10.95 (978-0-7534-5425-1(4) , Kingfisher) Houghton Mifflin Co. Trade & Reference Div.

Tetro, Marc. Where Are You from Little Goose? 2006. (Illus.). 6.99 (978-1-55278-433-4(9)) McArthur & Co. CAN. *Dist:* National Bk. Network.

Texas, 6 bks., Set. 2003. (Heinemann State Studies). (Illus.). (J). lib. bdg. 162.42 (978-1-4034-0692-7(8)) Heinemann Library.

Texas. 2003. (World Almanac Biblioteca de los Estados). (SPA., Illus.). 48p. (J). (gr. 5 up). pap. 11.95 (978-0-8368-5554-8(X) , World Almanac Library) Stevens, Gareth Inc.

Tomlinson, Jodi. Character under Pressure: What You Leave Behind. 2002. (Illus.). 74p. (YA). spiral bd. 15.95 (978-1-931397-13-1(9)) Geography Matters, Inc.

Toth, J. A. Those Fabulous 50 States (Esos 50 Estados Fabulosos) (ENG & SPA.). (YA). (gr. 4 up). pap. 14.95 (978-1-883986-04-9(4) , SPC6044) Imprints.

Treays, Rebecca. My Street. Wells, R., illus. 1999. (Young Geography Ser.). (SPA.). 24p. (J). (gr. 1 up). pap. 8.95 (978-0-7460-3077-6(0) , EDC0770) EDC Publishing.

—My Town. 1998. (Young Geography Ser.). (Illus.). 24p. (J). (ps up). lib. bdg. 16.95 (978-1-58086-129-8(6)) EDC Publishing.

—My Town. Wells, R., illus. 1998. (Young Geography Ser.). 24p. (J). (gr. 1 up). pap. 8.95 (978-0-7460-3079-0(7) , EDC0797) EDC Publishing.

True Books: Social Studies - Geography, 32 bks., Vol. 1. 2004. pap. 752.00 (978-0-516-29708-8(2) , Children's Pr.) Scholastic Library Publishing.

Two-Can Publishing Ltd. Staff. Living Geography. 2004. (Illus.). 192p. (gr. 3-6). 24.95 (978-1-58728-254-6(2) , Two Can Publishing) T&N Children's Publishing.

Unidad 2 Superlibro: Geografia: Superlibros. 2003. (MacMillan/McGraw-Hill. Estudios Sociales Ser.). (ENG & SPA.). (gr. 1 up). (978-0-02-149435-4(5)) Macmillan/McGraw-Hill Schl. Div.

Unidad 2 Superlibro: Geografia: Vivimos Juntos: Superlibros (Big Books) 2003. (MacMillan/McGraw-Hill. Estudios Sociales Ser.). (ENG & SPA.). (gr. 2 up). (978-0-02-149442-2(8)) Macmillan/McGraw-Hill Schl. Div.

United States Geography. 2004. 128p. (J). per. 11.99 (978-0-88724-254-0(5) , CD-4346) Carson-Dellosa Publishing Co., Inc.

US Geoboard Geography: Hands-on Coordinate Activity Cards. 2001. (J). 17.95 (978-1-56911-020-1(4)) Learning Resources, Inc.

USA - UDSSR: Die Geographischen Aspekte der USA und der Ehemaligen zweiten Weltmacht UDSSR. (Duden Abiturhilfen Ser.). (GER.). 96p. (YA). (gr. 12-13). (978-3-411-02626-5(X)) Bibliographisches Institut & F. A. Brockhaus AG DEU. *Dist:* International Bk. Import Service, Inc.

Volpe, Theresa. All about Continents. 2006. (Early Explorers Ser.). (J). 36.00 (***978-1-4108-6128-3(7)***) Benchmark Education Co.

Wade, Mary Dodson. Map Scales. 2003. (Rookie Read-About Geography Ser.). (gr. 1-2). pap. 5.95 (978-0-516-27767-7(7) , Children's Pr.) Scholastic Library Publishing.

—Map Scales. 2003. (gr. k-3). lib. bdg. 14.10 (978-0-613-67912-1(1)) Tandem Library Bks.

Waters, Jennifer. The Continents. 2002. (Spyglass Books). (Illus.). 24p. (J). (gr. 1 up). lib. bdg. 18.60 (978-0-7565-0378-9(7)) Compass Point Bks.

Waugh, David. Key Geography for GCSE Bk. 1: Pupil's Book, New Edition. 2nd ed. 1998. (Illus.). 176p. pap. 32.00 (978-0-7487-3603-4(4)) Nelson Thornes Ltd. GBR. *Dist:* Trans-Atlantic Pubns., Inc.

—The New Wider World. 2nd rev. ed. 2005. (Illus.). 328p. pap. 47.50 (978-0-7487-7376-3(2)) Nelson Thornes Ltd. GBR. *Dist:* Trans-Atlantic Pubns., Inc.

Waugh, David & Bushell, Tony. Foundations. 2nd ed. 2006. (Illus.). 144p. (YA). pap., stu. ed. 32.50 (978-0-7487-9701-1(7)) Nelson Thornes Ltd. GBR. *Dist:* Trans-Atlantic Pubns., Inc.

—Key Geography: Places. 2nd ed. 2000. (Illus.). 136p. (YA). (gr. 6-9). pap. 29.50 (978-0-7487-5439-7(3)) Nelson Thornes Ltd. GBR. *Dist:* Trans-Atlantic Pubns., Inc.

—New Connections. 3rd ed. 2001. (Key Geography Ser.). (Illus.). 120p. (YA). pap. 29.50 (978-0-7487-6074-9(1)) Nelson Thornes Ltd. GBR. *Dist:* Trans-Atlantic Pubns., Inc.

—New Interactions. 3rd ed. 2001. (Key Geography Ser.). (Illus.). 128p. (YA). pap. 29.50 (978-0-7487-6076-3(8)) Nelson Thornes Ltd. GBR. *Dist:* Trans-Atlantic Pubns., Inc.

Welcome to My Country New Releases: Denmark; Haiti; Pakistan; South Korea; Sri Lanka; Ukraine, 6 bks. 2003. (Illus.). (J). (gr. 2 up). lib. bdg. 151.60 (978-0-8368-2549-7(7)) Stevens, Gareth Inc.

Whitling, Matt. Elementary State Facts Geography Program. 2000. 31p. (J). spiral bd. 10.00 (978-1-930443-32-7(3)) Logos Schl.

Widdowson, John. Geography for Common Entrance. 2003. (Illus.). 160p. pap. 36.50 (***978-0-7195-7572-3(9)*** , Hodder Murray) Hodder Education GBR. *Dist:* Trans-Atlantic Pubns., Inc.

—This Is Geography, Bk. 1. 2006. (Illus.). 144p. pap., pupil's gde. ed. (***978-0-340-91219-5(7)***) Hodder General Publishing Division.

—This Is Geography Book, Vol. 2. 2006. (Illus.). 144p. pap., pupil's gde. ed. (***978-0-340-90742-9(8)***) Hodder General Publishing Division.

—This Is Geography Book 3 Pupil's, Vol. 3. 2007. (Illus.). 144p. pap., pupil's gde. ed. (***978-0-340-90743-6(6)***) Hodder General Publishing Division.

Wilson, John. Map Reading for GCSE. 1999. (Illus.). 48p. (YA). (gr. 9-11). pap. 33.00 (978-0-7217-1072-3(7)) Schofield & Sims Ltd. GBR. *Dist:* State Mutual Bk. & Periodical Service, Ltd.

Wolfman, Ira. My World & Globe. Meisel, Paul, illus. rev. ed. 2003. 64p. (Orig.). (J). pap. 13.95 (978-0-7611-3069-7(1) , 13069) Workman Publishing Co., Inc.

Woodworth, Viki. World of Mazes. 2007. 48p. (J). pap. 4.95 (***978-0-486-45640-9(4)***) Dover Pubns., Inc.

World Cities, 8 vols., Set. Incl. Beijing. Hatt, Christine. 1999. lib. bdg. 16.95 (978-1-929298-28-0(5)); Berlin. Hatt, Christine. 1999. lib. bdg. 16.95 (978-1-929298-27-3(7)); London. Hatt, Christine. 2000. lib. bdg. 16.95 (978-1-929298-29-7(3)); Moscow. Hatt, Christine. 1999. lib. bdg. 16.95 (978-1-929298-25-9(0)); New York. Hatt, Christine. 2000. lib. bdg. 16.95 (978-1-929298-31-0(5)); Paris. Hatt, Christine. 2000. lib. bdg. 16.95 (978-1-929298-30-3(7)); Rome. Barber, Nicola. 2000. lib. bdg. 16.95 (978-1-929298-32-7(3)); Sydney. Hatt, Christine. 1999. lib. bdg. 16.95 (978-1-929298-26-6(9)); 48p. (J). (gr. 2-6). (Illus.). 2000. Set lib. bdg. 180.80 (978-1-929298-33-4(1)) Chrysalis Education.

World Cultures & Geography. 2005. (gr. 6-12). stu. ed. (978-0-618-16841-5(9) , 2-00408) McDougal Littell Inc.

World Geography. 2005. (gr. 6-12). stu. ed. (978-0-618-08721-1(4) , 2-00400) McDougal Littell Inc.

World Geography: Building a Global Perspective. 1998. (J). (gr. 7-9). stu. ed. 79.50 (978-0-13-435990-8(9)) Prentice Hall PTR.

World Geography: EEdition Plus Online Parent Purchase. 2005. (gr. 6-12). (978-0-618-21296-5(5) , 2-00433) McDougal Littell Inc.

World Geography: EEdition Plus Online with purchase of print Pupil's Edition-1 Year. 2005. (gr. 6-12). (978-0-618-25856-7(6) , 2-00435) McDougal Littell Inc.

World Geography: EEdition Plus Online with purchase of print Pupil's Edition-2 Year. 2005. (gr. 6-12). (978-0-618-25857-4(4) , 2-00436) McDougal Littell Inc.

World Geography: EEdition Plus Online with purchase of print Pupil's Edition-3 Year. 2005. (gr. 6-12). (978-0-618-25858-1(2) , 2-00437) McDougal Littell Inc.

World Geography: EEdition Plus Online with Purchase of Print Pupil's Edition-4 Year. 2005. (gr. 6-12). (978-0-618-25859-8(0) , 2-00438) McDougal Littell Inc.

World Geography: EEdition Plus Online with Purchase of Print Pupil's Edition-5 Year. 2005. (gr. 6-12). (978-0-618-25860-4(4) , 2-00439) McDougal Littell Inc.

World Geography: EEdition Plus Online with purchase of print Pupil's Edition-6 Year. 2005. (gr. 6-12). (978-0-618-34785-8(2) , 2-90229) McDougal Littell Inc.

World Geography Syllabus. 1999. 18p. (J). ring bd. 2.50 (978-1-57896-057-6(6) , 2801, Hewitt Homeschooling Resources) Hewitt Research Foundation, Inc.

World View: A Global Study of Geography, History & Culture, Bk. 2. stu. ed. 21.95 (978-0-916591-45-8(X)) Linmore Publishing, Inc.

Wough, David & Bushell, Tony. Key Geography for GCSE Pupil's, Bk. 2. 2nd ed. 1998. (Illus.). 160p. pap. 24.00 (978-0-7487-3649-2(2)) State Mutual Bk. & Periodical Service, Ltd.

York, Michaela D. Mr. Oodle MaDoodle's Time Around the World. 2002. 15.95 (978-0-9704457-0-4(9)) Chef John Folse & Co.

Zarate, Antonio & Sanchez Sanchez, José. Atlas Geografico (Geographical Atlas) (SPA., Illus.). 160p. (J). (gr. 5-7). (978-84-348-4114-7(2) , SM6162) SM Ediciones ESP. *Dist:* i.b.d., Ltd.

50 Nifty States. 2nd ed. 320p. (gr. 4-8). 22.99 (978-0-7682-2457-3(8) , GA15016) School Specialty Publishing.

1000 Things You Should Know about Geography. (Illus.). 64p. (YA). (gr. 5 up). lib. bdg. (978-1-59084-465-6(3)) Mason Crest Pubs.

GEOGRAPHY, BIBICAL

see Bible—Geography

GEOGRAPHY, COMMERCIAL

see Commercial Geography

GEOGRAPHY—DICTIONARIES

Countries - Set II, Set. Incl. Brazil. Furlong, Kate A. lib. bdg. 22.78 (978-1-57765-491-9(9)); China. Italia, Bob. lib. bdg. 22.78 (978-1-57765-492-6(7)); Egypt. Italia, Bob. lib. bdg. 22.78 (978-1-57765-493-3(5)); England. Britton, Tamara L. lib. bdg. 22.78 (978-1-57765-499-5(4)); France. Italia, Bob. lib. bdg. 22.78 (978-1-57765-494-0(3)); Iran. Italia, Bob. lib. bdg. 22.78 (978-1-57765-495-7(1)); Ireland. Italia, Bob. lib. bdg. 22.78 (978-1-57765-496-4(X)); Israel. Italia, Bob. lib. bdg. 22.78 (978-1-57765-497-1(8)); Poland. Furlong, Kate A. lib. bdg. 22.78 (978-1-57765-498-8(6)); Sweden. Furlong, Kate A. lib. bdg. 22.78 (978-1-57765-550-3(8)); 40p. (J). (gr. k-6). 2001. (Illus.). 2001. Set lib. bdg. 227.80 (978-1-57765-500-8(1) , Checkerboard Library) ABDO Publishing Co.

Doherty, Gillian & Claybourne, Anna. Encyclopedia of World Geography Internet Linked. 2004. 400p. (J). pap. 19.95 (978-0-7945-0805-0(7) , Usborne) EDC Publishing.

Gall, Timothy L. & Gall, Susan B. Junior Worldmark Encyclopedia of the Nations, 10 vols., Set. 5th rev. ed. 2007. 520.00 (978-1-4144-1095-1(6) , UXL) Thomson Gale.

—Junior Worldmark Encyclopedia of the Nations, 9 vols. 3rd ed. Incl. Junior Worldmark Encyclopedia of the Nations Vol. 1 : Afghanistan to Brunei Darussalam. (978-0-7876-5367-5(5)); Junior Worldmark Encyclopedia of the Nations Vol. 2 : Bulgaria to Czech Republic. (978-0-7876-5368-2(3)); Junior Worldmark Encyclopedia of the Nations Vol. 3 : Denmark to Guyana. (978-0-7876-5369-9(1)); Junior Worldmark Encyclopedia of the Nations Vol. 4 : Haiti to Kyrgyzstan. (978-0-7876-5370-5(5)); Junior Worldmark Encyclopedia of the Nations Vol. 5 : Laos to Myanmar. (978-0-7876-5371-2(3)); Junior Worldmark Encyclopedia of the Nations Vol. 6 : Nambia to Portugal. (978-0-7876-5372-9(1)); Junior Worldmark Encyclopedia of the Nations Vol. 7 : Qatar to South Africa. (978-0-7876-5373-6(X)); Junior Worldmark Encyclopedia of the Nations Vol. 8 : Spain to Tuvalu. (978-0-7876-5374-3(8)); Junior Worldmark Encyclopedia of the Nations Vol. 9 : Uganda to Zimbabwe. (978-0-7876-5375-0(6)); (J). (Illus.). 2200p. 2001. lib. bdg. (978-0-7876-5366-8(7) , GML00502-173512, UXL) Thomson Gale.

—Junior Worldmark Encyclopedia of the Nations Vol. 1: Afghanistan to Brunei Darussalam, 9 vols. 3rd ed. 2001. (Illus.). (J). (978-0-7876-5367-5(5) , UXL) Thomson Gale.

—Junior Worldmark Encyclopedia of the Nations Vol. 2: Bulgaria to Czech Republic, 9 vols. 3rd ed. 2001. (Illus.). (J). (978-0-7876-5368-2(3) , UXL) Thomson Gale.

—Junior Worldmark Encyclopedia of the Nations Vol. 3: Denmark to Guyana, 9 vols. 3rd ed. 2001. (Illus.). (J). (978-0-7876-5369-9(1) , UXL) Thomson Gale.

—Junior Worldmark Encyclopedia of the Nations Vol. 4: Haiti to Kyrgyzstan, 9 vols. 3rd ed. 2001. (Illus.). (J). (978-0-7876-5370-5(5) , UXL) Thomson Gale.

—Junior Worldmark Encyclopedia of the Nations Vol. 5: Laos to Myanmar, 9 vols. 3rd ed. 2001. (Illus.). (J). (978-0-7876-5371-2(3) , UXL) Thomson Gale.

—Junior Worldmark Encyclopedia of the Nations Vol. 6: Nambia to Portugal, 9 vols. 3rd ed. 2001. (Illus.). (J). (978-0-7876-5372-9(1) , UXL) Thomson Gale.

—Junior Worldmark Encyclopedia of the Nations Vol. 7: Qatar to South Africa, 9 vols. 3rd ed. 2001. (Illus.). (J). (978-0-7876-5373-6(X) , UXL) Thomson Gale.

—Junior Worldmark Encyclopedia of the Nations Vol. 8: Spain to Tuvalu, 9 vols. 3rd ed. 2001. (Illus.). (J). (978-0-7876-5374-3(8) , UXL) Thomson Gale.

—Junior Worldmark Encyclopedia of the Nations Vol. 9: Uganda to Zimbabwe, 9 vols. 3rd ed. 2001. (Illus.). (J). (978-0-7876-5375-0(6) , UXL) Thomson Gale.

Ganeri, Anita. Esos Destructores Terremotos. (Coleccion Esa Horrible Geografia). (SPA.). 128p. (YA). (gr. 5-8). 9.95 (978-84-272-2156-7(8) , ML31293) Molino, Editorial ESP. *Dist:* Lectorum Pubns., Inc.

Haggett, Peter, ed. Encyclopedia of World Geography, 24 vols. 2nd ed. 2001. (Illus.). (J). Vol. 1. (978-0-7614-7290-2(8)); Vol. 2. (978-0-7614-7291-9(6)); Vol. 3. (978-0-7614-7292-6(4)); Vol. 4. (978-0-7614-7293-3(2)); Vol. 5. (978-0-7614-7294-0(0)); Vol. 6. (978-0-7614-7295-7(9)); Vol. 7. (978-0-7614-7296-4(7)); Vol. 8. (978-0-7614-7297-1(5)); Vol. 9. (978-0-7614-7298-8(3)); Vol. 10. (978-0-7614-7299-5(1)); Vol. 11. (978-0-7614-7300-8(9)); Vol. 12. (978-0-7614-7301-5(7)); Vol. 13. (978-0-7614-7302-2(5)); Vol. 14. (978-0-7614-7303-9(3)); Vol. 15. (978-0-7614-7304-6(1)); Vol. 16. (978-0-7614-7305-3(X)); Vol. 17. (978-0-7614-7306-0(8)); Vol. 18. (978-0-7614-7307-7(6)); Vol. 19. (978-0-7614-7308-4(4)); Vol. 20. (978-0-7614-7309-1(2)); Vol. 21. (978-0-7614-7310-7(6)); Vol. 22. (978-0-7614-7311-4(4)); Vol. 23. (978-0-7614-7312-1(2)); Vol. 24. 3456p. (978-0-7614-7313-8(0)) Cavendish, Marshall Corp.

—Encyclopedia of World Geography, 24 vols., Set. 2nd ed. Incl. Vol. 1. (978-0-7614-7290-2(8)); Vol. 2. (978-0-7614-7291-9(6)); Vol. 3. (978-0-7614-7292-6(4)); Vol. 4. (978-0-7614-7293-3(2)); Vol. 5. (978-0-7614-7294-0(0)); Vol. 6. (978-0-7614-7295-7(9)); Vol. 7. (978-0-7614-7296-4(7)); Vol. 8. (978-0-7614-7297-1(5)); Vol. 9. (978-0-7614-7298-8(3)); Vol. 10. (978-0-7614-7299-5(1)); Vol. 11. (978-0-7614-7300-8(9)); Vol. 12. (978-0-7614-7301-5(7)); Vol. 13. (978-0-7614-7302-2(5)); Vol. 14. (978-0-7614-7303-9(3)); Vol. 15. (978-0-7614-7304-6(1)); Vol. 16. (978-0-7614-7305-3(X)); Vol. 17. (978-0-7614-7306-0(8)); Vol. 18. (978-0-7614-7307-7(6)); Vol. 19. (978-0-7614-7308-4(4)); Vol. 20. (978-0-7614-7309-1(2)); Vol. 21. (978-0-7614-7310-7(6)); Vol. 22. (978-0-7614-7311-4(4)); Vol. 23. (978-0-7614-7312-1(2)); Vol. 24. 3456p. (978-0-7614-7313-8(0)); (J). (Illus.). 3,000p. 2001. 657.07 (978-0-7614-7289-6(4) , Cavendish, Marshall Reference Bks.) Cavendish, Marshall Corp.

Knowlton, Jack. Geography from A to Z: A Picture Glossary. ed. 2004. (Illus.). (J). (gr. k-3). spiral bd. (978-0-616-03042-4(8)) Canadian National Institute for the Blind/Institut National Canadien pour les Aveugles.

Oxford Editorial Staff. Oxford Essential Geographical Dictionary. 1999. (978-0-606-16391-0(3)) Tandem Library Bks.

Porras, Carlos & D'Andrea, Patricia, trs. World Almanac Biblioteca de los Estados, 6 bks. Incl. California. Ingram, Scott. lib. bdg. 30.00 (978-0-8368-5542-5(6)); Florida. Chui, Patricia. lib. bdg. 30.00 (978-0-8368-5543-2(4)); Illinois. Feeley, Kathleen. lib. bdg. 30.00 (978-0-8368-5544-9(2)); Nueva Jersey. Holtz, Eric Siegfried. lib. bdg. 30.00 (978-0-8368-5545-6(0)); Nueva York. Ball, Jackie & Behrens, Kristen. lib. bdg. 30.00 (978-0-8368-5546-3(9)); Texas. Barenblat, Rachel. lib. bdg. 30.00 (978-0-8368-5547-0(7)); 48p. (J). (gr. 5 up). (SPA., Illus.). 2003. Set lib. bdg. 175.60 (978-0-8368-5541-8(8) , World Almanac Library) Stevens, Gareth Inc.

Stathis, Roberta, et al. Explore Geography Picture Dictionary. 2nd ed. 2002. (Illus.). 60p. (J). (978-1-55501-549-`7(2)) Ballard & Tighe Pubs.

Sterling Publishing Co., Inc., ed. Philip's Geography Dictionary. 2nd ed. 2000. (Illus.). 240p. (J). pap. (978-0-540-07824-0(7) , Philip's) Octopus Publishing Group.

The United States, 52 bks. Incl. Alabama. Welsbacher, Anne. (Illus.). 32p. lib. bdg. 22.78 (978-1-56239-851-4(2)); Alaska. Italia, Bob. (Illus.). 32p. lib. bdg. 22.78 (978-1-56239-855-2(5)); Arizona. Joseph, Paul. (Illus.). 32p. lib. bdg. 22.78 (978-1-56239-859-0(8)); Arkansas. Welsbacher, Anne. (Illus.). 32p. lib. bdg. 22.78 (978-1-56239-852-1(0)); California. Welsbacher, Anne. (Illus.). 32p. lib. bdg. 22.78 (978-1-56239-862-0(8)); Colorado. Welsbacher, Anne. (Illus.). 32p. lib. bdg. 22.78 (978-1-56239-850-7(4)); Connecticut. Welsbacher, Anne. (Illus.). 32p. lib. bdg. 22.78 (978-1-56239-866-8(0)); Delaware. Welsbacher, Anne. (Illus.). 32p. lib. bdg. 22.78 (978-1-56239-865-1(2)); Florida. Joseph, Paul. (Illus.). 32p. lib. bdg. 22.78 (978-1-56239-853-8(9)); Georgia. Joseph, Paul. 32p. lib. bdg. 22.78 (978-1-56239-854-5(7)); Hawaii. Italia, Bob. (Illus.). 32p. lib. bdg. 22.78 (978-1-56239-856-9(3)); Idaho. Joseph, Paul. (Illus.). 32p. lib. bdg. 22.78 (978-1-56239-857-6(1)); Illinois. Joseph, Paul. (Illus.). 32p. lib. bdg. 22.78 (978-1-56239-858-3(X)); Indiana. Welsbacher, Anne. (Illus.). 32p. lib. bdg. 22.78 (978-1-56239-873-6(3)); Iowa. Welsbacher, Anne. (Illus.). 32p. lib. bdg. 22.78 (978-1-56239-872-9(5)); Kansas. Welsbacher, Anne. (Illus.). 32p. lib. bdg. 22.78 (978-1-56239-879-8(2)); Kentucky. Welsbacher, Anne. (Illus.). 32p. lib. bdg. 22.78 (978-1-56239-874-3(1)); Louisiana. Welsbacher, Anne. (Illus.). 32p. lib. bdg. 22.78 (978-1-56239-880-4(6)); Maine. Joseph, Paul. (Illus.). 32p. lib. bdg. 22.78 (978-1-56239-861-3(X)); Maryland. Joseph, Paul. (Illus.). 32p. lib. bdg. 22.78 (978-1-56239-881-1(4)); Massachusetts. Joseph, Paul. (Illus.). 32p. lib. bdg. 22.78 (978-1-56239-882-8(2)); Michigan. Joseph, Paul. (Illus.). 32p. lib. bdg. 22.78 (978-1-56239-860-6(1)); Minnesota. Joseph, Paul. (Illus.). 32p. lib. bdg. 22.78 (978-1-56239-863-7(6)); Mississippi. Joseph, Paul. (Illus.). 32p. lib. bdg. 22.78 (978-1-56239-883-5(0)); Missouri. Welsbacher, Anne. (Illus.). 32p. lib. bdg. 22.78 (978-1-56239-884-2(9)); Montana. Joseph, Paul. (Illus.). 32p. lib. bdg. 22.78 (978-1-56239-864-4(4)); Nebraska. Welsbacher, Anne. (Illus.). 32p. lib. bdg. 22.78 (978-1-56239-887-3(3)); Nevada. Joseph, Paul. (Illus.). 32p. lib. bdg. 22.78 (978-1-56239-867-5(9)); New Hampshire. Welsbacher, Anne. (Illus.). 32p. lib. bdg. 22.78 (978-1-56239-888-0(1)); New Jersey. Welsbacher, Anne. (Illus.). 32p. lib. bdg. 22.78 (978-1-56239-892-7(X)); New Mexico. Joseph, Paul. (Illus.). 32p. lib. bdg. 22.78 (978-1-56239-868-2(7)); New York. Welsbacher, Anne. (Illus.). 32p. lib. bdg. 22.78 (978-1-56239-891-0(1)); North Carolina. Joseph, Paul. (Illus.). 32p. lib. bdg. 22.78 (978-1-56239-869-9(5)); North Dakota. Welsbacher, Anne. (Illus.). 32p. lib. bdg. 22.78 (978-1-56239-896-5(2)); Ohio. Joseph, Paul. (Illus.). 32p. lib. bdg. 22.78 (978-1-56239-870-5(9)); Oklahoma. Joseph, Paul. (Illus.). 32p. lib. bdg. 22.78 (978-1-56239-871-2(7)); Oregon. Joseph, Paul. (Illus.). 32p. lib. bdg. 22.78 (978-1-56239-878-1(4)); Pennsylvania. Welsbacher, Anne. (Illus.). 32p. lib. bdg. 22.78 (978-1-56239-893-4(8)); Puerto Rico. Welsbacher, Anne. (Illus.). 32p. lib. bdg. 22.78 (978-1-56239-897-2(0)); Rhode Island. Joseph, Paul. (Illus.). 32p. lib. bdg. 22.78 (978-1-56239-877-4(6)); South Carolina. Joseph, Paul. (Illus.). 32p. lib. bdg. 22.78 (978-1-56239-876-7(8)); South Dakota. Welsbacher, Anne. (Illus.). 32p. lib. bdg. 22.78 (978-1-56239-898-9(9)); Tennessee. Joseph, Paul. (Illus.). 32p. lib. bdg. 22.78 (978-1-

56239-875-0(X)); Texas. Welsbacher, Anne. (Illus.). 32p. lib. bdg. 22.78 (978-1-56239-899-6(7)); Utah. Joseph, Paul. (Illus.). 32p. lib. bdg. 22.78 (978-1-56239-890-3(3)); Vermont. Joseph, Paul. (Illus.). 32p. lib. bdg. 22.78 (978-1-56239-886-6(5)); Virginia. Joseph, Paul. (Illus.). 32p. lib. bdg. 22.78 (978-1-56239-889-7(X)); Washington. Joseph, Paul. (Illus.). 23p. lib. bdg. 22.78 (978-1-56239-895-8(4)); Washington, D. C. Welsbacher, Anne. (Illus.). 32p. lib. bdg. 22.78 (978-1-56239-800-2(8)); West Virginia. Joseph, Paul. (Illus.). 32p. lib. bdg. 22.78 (978-1-56239-894-1(6)); Wisconsin. Joseph, Paul. (Illus.). 32p. lib. bdg. 22.78 (978-1-56239-801-9(6)); Wyoming. Joseph, Paul. (Illus.). 32p. lib. bdg. 22.78 (978-1-56239-802-6(4)); (J). (gr. k-6). 1998. (Illus.). Set lib. bdg. 1184.56 (978-1-56239-944-3(6) , Checkerboard Library) ABDO Publishing Co.

World Book, Inc. Staff, ed. The World Book Encyclopedia of People & Places. (Illus.). (gr. 4 up). 1999. 1579p. (YA). (978-0-7166-3797-4(9)); Vol. 6. 2001. 1,579p. (J). (978-0-7166-3750-9(2) , 20073) World Bk., Inc.

GEOGRAPHY, ECONOMIC

see Economic Geography

GEOGRAPHY, HISTORICAL

see Historical Geography

GEOGRAPHY, PHYSICAL

see Physical Geography

GEOGRAPHY—PICTORIAL WORKS

see Views

GEOGRAPHY, SOCIAL

see Human Geography

GEOLOGICAL PHYSICS

see Geophysics

GEOLOGISTS

Guidici, Cynthia. Adriana Ocampo. 2005. (Hispanic-American Biographies Ser.). (Illus.). 64p. (J). (gr. 6-9). lib. bdg. 32.86 (978-1-4109-1297-8(3)); pap. 9.50 (978-1-4109-1305-0(8)) Raintree.

Hammonds, Heather. Geologists. 2004. (J). lib. bdg. 27.10 (978-1-58340-543-7(7)) Smart Apple Media.

Hartzog, Brooke. Iguanodon & Dr. Gideon Mantell. 1999. (Dinosaurs & Their Discoverers Ser.). (Illus.). 24p. (J). (gr. k-4). lib. bdg. 18.75 (978-0-8239-5325-7(4) , PowerKids Pr.) Rosen Publishing Group, Inc., The.

Mason, Paul. Into the Fire: Volcanologists. 2007. (J). ***(978-1-4034-9950-9(0));*** pap. ***(978-1-4034-9957-8(8))*** Heinemann Library.

—Scientists at Work: Into the Fire: Volcanologists Hardback. 2007. (Illus.). 32p. (J). ***(978-0-431-14926-4(7))*** Heinemann Library.

—Scientists at Work: Into the Fire: Volcanologists Paperback. 2007. (Illus.). 32p. (J). ***(978-0-431-14933-2(X))*** Heinemann Library.

Parks, Peggy. The Earth. 2007. (KidHaven Science Library Ser.). (Illus.). 48p. (J). (gr. 4-8). 23.70 ***(978-0-7377-3776-9(X)*** , Kidhaven) Thomson Gale.

Ross, Michael Elsohn. Exploring the Earth with John Wesley Powell. Smith, Wendy, illus. 2006. 48p. (J). (gr. 4-10). reprint ed. 19.00 (978-1-4223-5581-7(0)) DIANE Publishing Co.

—Exploring the Earth with John Wesley Powell. Smith, Wendy, illus. 2005. (Naturalist's Apprentice Biographies Ser.). 48p. (gr. 3-6). lib. bdg. 19.93 (978-1-57505-254-0(7)) Lerner Publishing Group.

Souza, Dorothy M. John Wesley Powell. 2004. (Watts Library). (Illus.). 64p. (J). (gr. 5-7). pap. 8.95 (978-0-531-16653-6(8)); 25.50 (978-0-531-12289-1(1)) Scholastic Library Publishing. (Watts, Franklin).

GEOLOGY

see also Coral Reefs and Islands; Creation; Earth; Earthquakes; Glaciers; Mineralogy; Mountains; Oceanography; Physical Geography; Rocks; Submarine Geology; Volcanoes

Adams, Colleen. Exploring the Grand Canyon. 2002. (Reading Room Collection). (Illus.). 24p. (J). pap. (978-0-8239 8163 2(0)); lib. bdg. 18.75 (978-0-8239-3726-4(7)) Rosen Publishing Group, Inc., The.

Ball, Jackie. Earth's History. 2004. (Discovery Channel School Science Ser.). (Illus.). 32p. (J). (gr. 5 up). lib. bdg. 24.67 (978-0-8368-3379-9(1)) Stevens, Gareth Inc.

Bellamy, David. The Rockpool. Dow, Jill, illus. 1999. (Our Changing World Ser.). 32p. (J). (gr. 1-5). pap. 7.99 (978-0-7112-1386-9(0)) Lincoln, Frances Ltd. GBR. *Dist:* Transition Vendor.

Benchmark Education Staff, compiled by. Our Environment. 2006. spiral bd. 165.00 ***(978-1-4108-7088-9(X));*** spiral bd. 109.00 ***(978-1-4108-7102-2(9))*** Benchmark Education Co.

Berger, Melvin & Berger, Gilda. Do Bears Sleep All Winter? Questions & Answers about Bears. Osti, Roberto, illus. 2002. (Question & Answer Ser.). 48p. (J). pap. 5.95 (978-0-439-26671-0(8) , Scholastic Reference) Scholastic, Inc.

Blay, Chuck & Siemers, Robert. Kauai's Geologic History: A Simplified Guide. 2003. (Illus.). 15.00 (978-0-9744723-0-0(1)) Siemers, Robert.

Blobaum, Cindy. Geology Rocks! 50 Hands-on Activities to Explore the Earth. 1999. (J). 19.60 (978-0-606-22461-1(0)) Tandem Library Bks.

—Geology Rocks! 50 Hands-on Activities to Explore the Earth. 1999. (gr. 3-6). lib. bdg. 19.90 (978-0-613-27849-2(6)) Tandem Library Bks.

Bramwell, M. Rocks & Fossils. 2003. (gr. 5-8). lib. bdg. 15.25 (978-0-613-74357-0(1)) Tandem Library Bks.

Calvetti, Leonello & Massini, Luca, illus. Caudipteryx. 2004. (J). (gr. 2-4). 23.70 (978-1-4103-0333-2(0) , Blackbirch Pr., Inc.) Thomson Gale.

Clifford, Tim. Geology. 2008. (J). ***(978-1-60044-623-8(X))*** Rourke Publishing, LLC.

Cole, Joanna. The Magic School Bus Inside the Earth. 2001. (Early Readers Ser.: Vol. 1). (J). lib. bdg. (978-1-59054-523-2(0)) Fitzgerald Bks.

Colson, Mary. Crumbling Earth Erosion & Landslides. 2005. (Turbulent Planet Ser.). pap. (978-1-4109-1751-5(7)); lib. bdg. (978-1-4109-1741-6(X)) Steck-Vaughn.

—Shaky Ground: Earthquakes. 2005. (Turbulent Planet Ser.). (J). (978-1-4109-1736-2(3)); pap. (978-1-4109-1746-1(0)) Steck-Vaughn.

Dayton, Connor. Rock Formations. 2007. (Rocks & Minerals Ser.). (Illus.). 24p. (J). (gr. 2-5). lib. bdg. 21.25 ***(978-1-4042-3690-5(2)*** , PowerKids Pr.) Rosen Publishing Group, Inc., The.

Desonie, Dana. Geosphere. 2007. (Our Fragile Planet Ser.). 216p. (gr. 6-12). 35.00 ***(978-0-8160-6217-1(X)*** , Chelsea Hse.) Facts On File, Inc.

Edwards, John. Plate Tectonics & Continental Drift. 2005. (Looking at Landscapes Ser.). (Illus.). 47p. (J). (gr. 6-9). lib. bdg. 29.95 (978-1-58340-730-1(8)) Smart Apple Media.

Elda, Doug & Elda, Dorry. Lyrical Earth Science: Geology. Raskauskas, Sally, illus. 2003. 116p. (YA). (gr. 5-10). pap. 25.50 incl. audio (978-0-9741635-2-9(X)) Lyrical Learning.

Elda, Doug & Elda, Dory. Lyrical Earth Science: Geology. Raskauskas, Sally, illus. 2003. 116p. (YA). (gr. 5-10). pap. 19.95 incl. audio (978-0-9741635-7-4(0)) Lyrical Learning.

Eldon, Doug & Eldon, Dorry. Lyrical Earth Science: Geology. Raskavskas, Sally, illus. 2003. 116p. (YA). (gr. 5-10). pap. 23.95 incl. audio compact disk (978-0-9741635-8-1(9)) Lyrical Learning.

Erickson, Jon. Lost Creatures of the Earth: Mass Extinction in the History of Life. 2001. (Living Earth Ser.). (Illus.). 272p. (YA). (gr. 6-12). 55.00 (978-0-8160-4337-8(X)) Facts On File, Inc.

Fredette, Nathalie & Lafleur, Claude. Inside the Earth. 2001. (Twenty-First Century Science Ser.). (Illus.). 64p. (J). (gr. 5 up). lib. bdg. 32.67 (978-0-8368-5002-4(5) , World Almanac Library) Stevens, Gareth Inc.

Frost, Helen. Tigre Dientes de Sable: Sabertooth Cat. 2006. (SPA & ENG.). (J). 19.93 (978-0-7368-6685-9(X)) Capstone Pr., Inc.

Gallant, Roy A. Dance of the Continents. 1999. (Story of Science Ser.). (Illus.). 80p. (YA). (gr. 5 up). lib. bdg. 29.93 (978-0-7614-0962-5(9)) Cavendish, Marshall Corp.

—Geysers: When Earth Roars. 1998. (First Bks.). (Illus.). 64p. (J). (gr. 5-7). pap. 6.95 (978-0-531-15838-8(1) , Watts, Franklin) Scholastic Library Publishing.

—Geysers: When Earth Roars. 1998. (Illus.). 64p. (J). (ps-7). lib. bdg. 15.25 (978-0-613-12688-5(2)) Tandem Library Bks.

—Structure: Exploring Earth's Interior. 2002. (Earthworks Ser.). (Illus.). 80p. (J). 29.93 (978-0-7614-1368-4(5) , Benchmark Bks.) Cavendish, Marshall Corp.

Ganeri, Anita. The Crumbling Earth. 2004. (Turbulent Planet Ser.). (Illus.). pap. 8.50 (978-1-4109-1024-0(5)) Raintree.

—Shaky Ground. 2004. (Turbulent Planet Ser.). (Illus.). 48p. (J). 28.56 (978-1-4109-0589-5(6)); pap. 8.50 (978-1-4109-1027-1(X)) Raintree.

Gerwitz, Felice, creator. Geology & Creation Science: Experiments, Games, Activities & Puzzles: Hands-on Science Experiment & Activity Pack. 1999. 81p. pap. 12.95 (978-0-9700385-7-9(7)) Media Angels, Inc.

Gerwitz, Felice & Whitlock, Jill. Creation Geology: A Study Guide to Fossils, Formations & the Flood. 2004. 206p. (YA). per. 18.95 ***(978-1-931941-09-9(2))*** Media Angels, Inc.

Gilbert, Miquel Angel. The Land. 2002. (Living Planet Ser.). (Illus.). 32p. (J). 23.70 (978-1-56711-668-7(X) , Blackbirch Pr., Inc.) Thomson Gale.

Green, Jen. Geology. 2004. (Routes of Science Ser.). (Illus.). 40p. (J). pap. 11.20 (978-1-4103-0299-1(7) , Blackbirch Pr., Inc.) Thomson Gale.

Hiscock, Bruce. The Big Rock. 1vol. Hiscock, Bruce, illus. 1999. (Illus.). 32p. (J). (gr. 2-5). 5.99 (978-0-689-82958-1(2) , Aladdin) Simon & Schuster Children's Publishing.

—The Big Rock. 1999. (J). 12.79 (978-0-606-17197-7(5)) Tandem Library Bks.

—Big Rock. 1999. (gr. 3-6). lib. bdg. 14.15 (978-0-613-22969-2(X)) Tandem Library Bks.

Hocker, Katherine M. Frozen in Motion: Alaska's Glaciers. Brubaker, Jill, ed. Lepley, Kathy, illus. 2006. 54p. (J). spiral bd. 8.95 (978-0-930931-76-6(9)) Alaska Natural History Assn.

Holmes & Thom. Early Humans: The Pleistocene & Holocene Periods. 2008. (Prehistoric Earth Ser.). 208p. (gr. 6-12). 35.00 ***(978-0-8160-5966-9(7)*** , Chelsea Hse.) Facts On File, Inc.

—Early Life: The Cambrian Period. 2008. (Prehistoric Earth Ser.). 208p. (gr. 6-12). 35.00 ***(978-0-8160-5957-7(8)*** , Chelsea Hse.) Facts On File, Inc.

—Time of the Giants. 2008. (Prehistoric Earth Ser.). 208p. (gr. 6-12). 35.00 ***(978-0-8160-5961-4(6)*** , Chelsea Hse.) Facts On File, Inc.

Holt, Rinehart and Winston Staff. Holt Science & Technology Chapter 3: Earth Science: Minerals & Earth's Crust. 5th ed. 2004. (Illus.). pap. 12.86 (978-0-03-030276-3(5)) Holt, Rinehart & Winston.

—Holt Science & Technology Chapter 4: Earth Science: Rocks - Mineral Mixtures. 5th ed. 2004. (Illus.). pap. 12.86 (978-0-03-030281-7(1)) Holt, Rinehart & Winston.

—Holt Science & Technology Chapter 6: Earth Science: Rocks & Fossils. 5th ed. 2004. (Illus.). pap. 12.86 (978-0-03-030291-6(9)) Holt, Rinehart & Winston.

—Holt Science & Technology Chapter 7: Earth Science: Plate Tectonics. 5th ed. 2004. (Illus.). pap. 12.86 (978-0-03-030296-1(X)) Holt, Rinehart & Winston.

—Holt Science & Technology Chptr. 11: Plate Tectonics: Chapter Resources - Tennessee Edition. 3rd ed. 2003. (YA). pap. 11.40 (978-0-03-069171-3(0)) Holt, Rinehart & Winston.

Hooper, Meredith & De Leiris, Lucia. The Island That Moved: The Forces That Shape Our Earth. 2004. (Illus.). 32p. (J). (978-1-84507-003-8(8)) Lincoln, Frances Ltd.

Hopping, Lorraine Jean. Space Rocks: The Story of Planetary Geologist Adriana Ocampo. 2006. (Women's Adventures in Science Ser.). (Illus.). 128p. pap. 9.95 (978-0-309-09555-6(7) , Joseph Henry Pr.) National Academies Pr.

Jackson, Kay. Plate Tectonics. 2005. (Lucent Library of Science & Technology). (Illus.). 112p. (YA). (gr. 7-10). lib. bdg. 29.95 (978-1-59018-105-8(0) , Lucent Bks.) Thomson Gale.

Johnson, Rebecca L. Plate Tectonics. 2006. (Great Ideas of Science Ser.). (Illus.). 80p. (J). (gr. 9-12). 27.93 (978-0-8225-3056-5(2) , Twenty-First Century Bks.) Lerner Publishing Group.

Kingsley, Charles. Madam How & Lady Why. 2006. pap. ***(978-1-4250-0631-0(0))*** Assistedreadingbooks.com Inc.

Kosek, Jane Kelly. What's Inside Earth? 1999. (What's Inside Library). 24p. (J). (gr. k-4). lib. bdg. 18.75 (978-0-8239-5277-9(0) , PowerKids Pr.) Rosen Publishing Group, Inc., The.

Lawrence, Debbie & Lawrence, Richard. Our Planet Earth. 2004. (Illus.). vi, 134p. (gr. 1-6). pap. 18.00 (978-0-9725365-3-0(1)) R & D Educational Ctr.

Loeschnig, L. V. Experimentos Sencillos de Geologia y Biologia. 2004. (Juego de la Ciencia Ser.). (SPA.). 128p. (gr. 5-8). 9.99 (978-84-95456-60-1(5) , 87804) Ediciones Oniro S.A. ESP. *Dist:* Bilingual Pubns. Co., The, Lectorum Pubns., Inc., Libros Sin Fronteras.

Lunis, Natalie & White, Nancy. Investigating Rocks. Date not set. (Thinking Like a Scientist Ser.). (Illus.). 20p. (J). pap. 16.95 (978-1-58273-081-3(4)) Sundance/Newbridge Educational Publishing.

Manning, Mick. Que Hay Debajo de la Cama? Cortes, Eunice, tr. Granstrom, Brita, illus. 2003. (Descubriendo Mi Mundo Ser.). (SPA.). 32p. (J). (978-970-690-588-8(X)) Planeta Mexicana Editorial S. A. de C. V.

Marsh, Carole. Kentucky's Big Activity Book. 2004. (Kentucky Experience! Ser.). (Illus.). 96p. (J). (gr. 2-6). pap. 9.95 (978-0-7933-9461-6(9)) Gallopade International.

Martin, Michael. Earth Evidence. 2007. 32p. (J). (978-0-7368-6787-0(2)) Capstone Pr., Inc.

Mattern, Joanne. Sand, Silt, & Mud & the Rock Cycle. 2006. (J). lib. bdg. (978-1-4042-3197-9(8) , PowerKids Pr.) Rosen Publishing Group, Inc., The.

Moor, Jo Ellen. Geology. Evans, Marilyn, ed. Robison, Don, illus. 1998. (ScienceWorks for Kids Ser.: Vol. 5). 80p. (J). (gr. 1-3). pap., tchr. ed. 9.95 (978-1-55799-686-2(5) , EMC 857) Evan-Moor Educational Pubs.

Morris, John D. The Geology Book. 2000. (Wonders of Creation Ser.). (Illus.). 80p. (J). (gr. 4-7). 15.99 (978-0-89051-281-4(7)) Master Bks.

—The Geology Book- Study Guide. 2005. pap. 3.99 (978-1-893345-60-7(2)) Answers in Genesis Ministries.

Murck. Computerized Test Bank to Accompany Geology Today. 1999. (YA). (978-0-471-19975-5(3)) Wiley, John & Sons, Inc.

—Geology Today & Take Note!, Set. 1999. 848p. (YA). 76.00 net. (978-0-471-33091-2(4)) Wiley, John & Sons, Inc.

Nicolson, Cynthia Pratt. The Earth. Slavin, Bill, illus. unabr. ed. 1999. (Starting with Space Ser.). 40p. (J). (gr. 4-6). (978-1-55074-327-2(9)) Kids Can Pr., Ltd.

O'Neill Grace, Catherine. Forces of Nature: The Awesome Power of Volcanoes, Earthquakes, & Tornadoes. 2004. (Illus.). 64p. (J). (gr. 3-7). 17.95 (978-0-7922-6328-9(6) , National Geographic Children's Bks.) National Geographic Society.

Ostopowich, Melanie. The Rock Cycle. 2004. (Science Matters Ser.). (Illus.). 24p. (J). lib. bdg. 24.45 (978-1-59036-209-9(8)) Weigl Pubs., Inc.

—Rocks. 2004. (Science Matters Ser.). (Illus.). 24p. (J). lib. bdg. 24.45 (978-1-59036-210-5(1)) Weigl Pubs., Inc.

Parks, Peggy. The Earth. 2007. (KidHaven Science Library Ser.). (Illus.). 48p. (J). (gr. 4-8). 23.70 ***(978-0-7377-3776-9(X)*** , Kidhaven) Thomson Gale.

Patent, Dorothy Hinshaw. Shaping the Earth. Munoz, William, photos by. 2000. (Illus.). 96p. (J). (gr. 4-6). tchr. ed. 18.00 (978-0-395-85691-8(4) , Clarion Bks.) Houghton Mifflin Co. Trade & Reference Div.

Pluckrose, Henry. Earth. 2001. (Let's Explore Ser.). (Illus.). 32p. (J). (gr. 1 up). lib. bdg. 23.33 (978-0-8368-2960-0(3)) Stevens, Gareth Inc.

Pluckrose, Henry Arthur. Earth. 2006. (Illus.). 32p. (J). (978-1-59771-036-7(9)) Sea-To-Sea Pubns.

Reed, W. Maxwell. The Earth for Sam the Story of Mountains. 2005. reprint ed. pap. 34.95 (978-0-7661-9449-6(3)) Kessinger Publishing, LLC.

Ross, Michael. Earth Cycles. 2003. (Illus.). 32p. (J). (gr. 2-5). pap. 7.95 (978-0-7613-1977-1(8) , First Avenue Editions) Lerner Publishing Group.

Ross, Michael Elsohn. Exploring the Earth with John Wesley Powell. Smith, Wendy, illus. 2006. 48p. (J). (gr. 4-10). reprint ed. 19.00 (978-1-4223-5581-7(0)) DIANE Publishing Co.

Science stories foss spanish pebbles sand & silt ea Cr05. 2005. (J). (978-1-59242-585-3(2)) Delta Education, LLC.

Silverstein, Alvin, et al. Plate Tectonics. 1998. (Science Concepts Ser.: 8). (Illus.). 64p. (gr. 5-8). lib. bdg. 26.90 (978-0-7613-3225-1(1) , Twenty-First Century Bks.) Lerner Publishing Group.

Spilsbury, Louise & Spilsbury, Richard. Thundering Landslides. 2004. (Heinemann Infosearch Ser.). (Illus.). 32p. (J). pap. 7.50 (978-1-4034-5444-7(2)); lib. bdg. (978-1-4034-4786-9(1)) Heinemann Library.

Stewart, Melissa. Igneous Rocks. 2002. (Rocks & Minerals Ser.). (Illus.). 32p. (J). (gr. 4-6). lib. bdg. 24.22 (978-1-58810-256-0(4)); pap. 7.50 (978-1-4034-0092-5(X) , 91659) Heinemann Library.

—Metamorphic Rocks. 2002. (Rocks & Minerals Ser.). (Illus.). 32p. (J). (gr. 4-6). lib. bdg. 24.22 (978-1-58810-257-7(2)); pap. 7.50 (978-1-4034-0093-2(8) , 91660) Heinemann Library.

—Sedimentary Rocks. 2002. (Rocks & Minerals Ser.). (Illus.). 32p. (J). (gr. 4-6). lib. bdg. 24.22 (978-1-58810-259-1(9)); pap. 7.50 (978-1-4034-0095-6(4) , 91662) Heinemann Library.

Stille, Darlene R. Plate Tectonics: Earth's Moving Crust. 2006. (J). lib. bdg. 26.60 (978-0-7565-1957-5(8)) Compass Point Bks.

Thompson, David. Processes That Shape the Earth. 2007. (Physics in Action Ser.). 120p. (J). (gr. 9). 30.00 ***(978-0-7910-8932-3(0)*** , Chelsea Hse.) Facts On File, Inc.

VanCleave, Janice Pratt. Janice VanCleave's A+ Projects in Earth Science: Winning Experiments for Science Fairs & Extra Credit. 1998. (Illus.). 234p. (YA). (gr. 7-12). lib. bdg. 22.20 (978-0-613-16516-7(0)) Tandem Library Bks.

West, Krista. Hands-On Projects about Changes in the Earth. 2002. (Great Earth Science Projects Ser.). (Illus.). 24p. (J). lib. bdg. 19.95 (978-0-8239-5844-3(2) , PowerKids Pr.) Rosen Publishing Group, Inc., The.

Whiting, Jim. The Volcanic Eruption on Santorini, 1500 BCE. 2007. (Natural Disasters Ser.). (J). lib. bdg. 25.70 ***(978-1-58415-568-3(X))*** Mitchell Lane Pubs., Inc.

Williams, Zella. Experiments on Rocks & the Rock Cycle. 2007. (Do-It-Yourself Science Ser.). (Illus.). 24p. (J). (gr. 2-5). lib. bdg. 23.95 (978-1-4042-3660-8(0)) Rosen Publishing Group, Inc., The.

Wilson, John. Dancing Elephants & Floating Continents: The Story of the Land Beneath Your Feet. 2003. (Illus.). 48p. 19.95 ***(978-1-55263-200-0(8))*** Key Porter Bks. CAN. *Dist:* Perseus Distribution.

Woods, Michael & Woods, Mary B. Mudflows & Landslides. 2007. (Disasters up Close Ser.). (J). 27.93 ***(978-0-8225-6574-1(9)*** , Lerner Pubns.) Lerner Publishing Group.

World Book, Inc Staff, contrib. by. Forces of Nature. 2007. (J). ***(978-0-7166-9806-7(4))*** World Bk., Inc.

Ylvisaker, Anne. Landslides. 2003. (Natural Disasters Ser.). (Illus.). 48p. (J). (gr. 3-4). lib. bdg. 21.26 (978-0-7368-1507-9(4) , Capstone High-Interest Bks.) Capstone Pr., Inc.

GEOLOGY, DYNAMIC

see Geophysics

GEOLOGY, HISTORICAL

see Geology, Stratigraphic

GEOLOGY—NORTH AMERICA

Alt, David D. & Hyndman, Donald W. Roadside Geology of Montana. rev. ed. (Roadside Geology Ser.). (Illus.). 435p. (J). (gr. 4). pap. 20.00 (978-0-87842-202-9(1) , 212) Mountain Pr. Publishing Co., Inc.

Blashfield, Jean F. & Jacobs, Richard P. When Dinosaurs Ruled: The Mesozoic Era. 2005. (Illus.). 80p. (J). 37.14 (978-1-4034-7660-9(8)) Heinemann Library.

—When Giant Mammals Thundered: The Cenozoic Era. 2005. (Illus.). 80p. (J). (978-1-4034-7661-6(6)) Heinemann Library.

—When Giant Mammals Thundered: The Cenozoic Era. 2004. (J). 35.64 (978-1-4109-1292-3(2)) Raintree.

—When Ice Threatened Living Things: The Pleistocene. 2005. (Illus.). 80p. (J). 37.14 (978-1-4034-7662-3(4)) Heinemann Library.

—When Ice Threatened Living Things: The Pleistocene. 2004. (J). 35.64 (978-1-4109-1293-0(0)) Raintree.

Frye, Keith. Roadside Geology of Virginia. Alt, David & Hyndman, Donald W., eds. Venkatakrishnan, Rames, illus. rev. ed. (Roadside Geology Ser.). 256p. (gr. 4). pap. 16.00 (978-0-87842-199-2(8) , 211) Mountain Pr. Publishing Co., Inc.

Hartz, Wilson H., Jr., et al. Kids Rock: A Geologic Coloring Guide from Cody to Yellowstone. 2002. (Illus.). 32p. (YA). (gr. 6-9). pap. 6.95 (978-0-9652942-7-0(7)) WordsWorth.

Weintraub, Aileen. The Grand Canyon: Widest Canyon. 2001. (Great Record Breakers in Nature Ser.). (Illus.). 24p. (J). (gr. 2-5). lib. bdg. 18.75 (978-0-8239-5641-8(5) , PowerKids Pr.) Rosen Publishing Group, Inc., The.

GEOLOGY, STRATIGRAPHIC

see also Fossils

Blashfield, Jean F. & Jacobs, Richard P. When Giant Mammals Thundered: The Cenozoic Era. 2004. (J). 35.64 (978-1-4109-1292-3(2)) Raintree.

—When Ice Threatened Living Things: The Pleistocene. 2005. (Illus.). 80p. (J). 37.14 (978-1-4034-7662-3(4)) Heinemann Library.

—When Ice Threatened Living Things: The Pleistocene. 2004. (J). 35.64 (978-1-4109-1293-0(0)) Raintree.

—When Life Took Root on Land. 2004. (J). 35.64 (978-1-4109-1290-9(6)) Raintree.

Gallant, Roy A. History: Journey Through Time. 2002. (Earthworks Ser.). (Illus.). 80p. (J). 29.93 (978-0-7614-1367-7(7) , Benchmark Bks.) Cavendish, Marshall Corp.

Holmes & Thom. Primates & Human Ancestors: The Pliocene Climates. 2008. (Prehistoric Earth Ser.). 208p. (gr. 6-12). 35.00 ***(978-0-8160-5965-2(9)*** , Chelsea Hse.) Facts On File, Inc.

—Rise of the Mammals: The Paleocene & Eocene Periods. 2008. (Prehistoric Earth Ser.). 208p. (gr. 6-12). 35.00 ***(978-0-8160-5963-8(2)*** , Chelsea Hse.) Facts On File, Inc.

E F G

Prehistoric World - Group 1, 5 bks., Set. 128.21 (978-0-7614-1021-8(X) , Benchmark Bks.) Cavendish, Marshall Corp.

Williams, Brian. Earth Time. 2002. (Illus.). 32p. (J). lib. bdg. 24.25 (978-1-58340-210-8(1)) Smart Apple Media.

Williams, Colleen Madonna Flood. My Adventure in the Triassic Period: Advanced My Adventure. 2007. 44p. (J). pap. 8.99 (978-1-59092-437-2(1) , Orchard Academy Pr.) Windstorm Creative.

GEOLOGY, SUBMARINE

see Submarine Geology

GEOLOGY—VOCATIONAL GUIDANCE

Firestone, Mary. Volcanologist. 2005. (Weird Careers in Science Ser.). (Illus.). 77p. (J). (gr. 4-8). lib. bdg. 25.00 (978-0-7910-8702-2(6) , Chelsea Hse.) Facts On File, Inc.

Hammonds, Heather. Geologists. 2004. (J). lib. bdg. 27.10 (978-1-58340-543-7(7)) Smart Apple Media.

GEOMETRICAL DRAWING

see also Graphic Methods; Mechanical Drawing; Perspective

Bishop, Jennifer Lynn. Geometrix Coloring Book. 2006. (Illus.). 32p. pap. 3.95 (***978-0-486-45672-0(2)*** Dover Pubns., Inc.

Constructions: Creating Geometric Figures. (Studies in Geometry). (J). pap., wbk. ed. 9.95 (978-1-930820-43-2(7)) Garlic Pr.

Heller, Ruth. Geometrics. 1998. (Ruth Heller's Stained Glass Designs for Coloring Ser.). (Illus.). 32p. (J). (ps-3). pap. 6.99 (978-0-448-41853-7(3) , Grosset & Dunlap) Penguin Group (USA) Inc.

Horemis, Spyros. Geometrical Design Coloring Book. 1998. (Illus.). 48p. (J). pap. 3.95 (978-0-486-20180-1(5)) Dover Pubns., Inc.

Randolph, Joanne. Let's Draw a Bird with Shapes: Vamos a Dibujar un Ave Usando Figuras. Muschinske, Emily, illus. 2005. (Let's Draw with Shapes/ Vamos a dibujar con Figuras Ser.). (J). 17.25 (978-1-4042-7555-3(X) , PowerKids Pr.) Rosen Publishing Group, Inc., The.

Smith, A. G. Little Geometric Stained Glass Coloring Book. 2000. (Illus.). 8p. (J). (gr. k-5). pap. 1.50 (978-0-486-41256-6(3)) Dover Pubns., Inc.

Smith, Christine. Art Smart, 8 bks. Smith, Christine, illus. Incl. How to Draw Cartoons. 1997. lib. bdg. 22.00 (978-0-8368-1709-6(5)); How to Draw Dinosaurs. 1996. lib. bdg. 22.00 (978-0-8368-1609-9(9)); How to Draw Insects. 1997. lib. bdg. 22.00 (978-0-8368-1710-2(9)); How to Draw Pets. 1996. lib. bdg. 22.00 (978-0-8368-1610-5(2)); How to Draw Trucks & Cars. 1996. lib. bdg. 22.00 (978-0-8368-1611-2(0)); How to Draw Wild Animals. 1996. lib. bdg. 22.00 (978-0-8368-1612-9(9)); How to Have Fun with Letters. 1997. lib. bdg. 22.00 (978-0-8368-1711-9(7)); How to Have Fun with Paper. 1997. lib. bdg. 22.00 (978-0-8368-1712-6(5)); 24p. (J). (gr. 1 up). (Illus.). Set lib. bdg. 154.00 (978-0-8368-1905-2(5)) Stevens, Gareth Inc.

GEOMETRY

see also Geometrical Drawing; Trigonometry

Accelerated Math West Virginia State Tagged Geometry Library. 2004. cd-rom 1199.00 (978-1-59455-115-4(4)) Renaissance Learning, Inc.

Activities for Geometric Solids. 32p. (gr. 3-6). 4.99 (978-1-56451-330-4(0) , ID78541) School Specialty Publishing.

Aigner-Clark, Julie. Baby Einstein: Puzzling Shapes, Spanish-Language Edition. Zaidi, Nadeem, illus. 2005. (Baby Einstein: Libros de Carton Ser.). (SPA.). 12p. (J). bds. 6.95 (978-970-718-303-2(9) , Silver Dolphin en Español) Advanced Marketing, S. de R. L. de C. V. MEX. *Dist:* Perseus Distribution.

Barber, Patti. First Shape Book. Stanley, Mandy, illus. 2002. (First Bks.). 48p. (J). (gr. k-ps). tchr. ed. 12.95 (978-0-7534-5433-6(5) , Kingfisher) Houghton Mifflin Co. Trade & Reference Div.

Basic Geometry. 1999. (Illus.). (YA). (gr. 5-8). pap. 7.95 (978-1-58037-105-6(1)) Twain, Mark Media, Inc. Pubs.

Benchmark Education Staff, compiled by. Geometry. 2005. spiral bd. 110.00 (***978-1-4108-3885-8(4));*** spiral bd. 55.00 (***978-1-4108-3886-5(2));*** spiral bd. 180.00 (***978-1-4108-3893-3(5));*** spiral bd. 60.00 (***978-1-4108-3894-0(3));*** spiral bd. 50.00 (***978-1-4108-3909-1(5));*** spiral bd. 165.00 (***978-1-4108-4511-5(7));*** spiral bd. 350.00 (***978-1-4108-5451-3(5));*** spiral bd. 160.00 (***978-1-4108-5862-7(6))*** Benchmark Education Co.

Boothroyd, Jennifer. Cone. 2008. (J). pap. (***978-0-8225-8850-4(1))*** Lerner Publishing Group.

—Cube. 2008. (J). pap. (***978-0-8225-8852-8(8))*** Lerner Publishing Group.

—Cylinder. 2008. (J). pap. (***978-0-8225-8851-1(X))*** Lerner Publishing Group.

—Pyramid. 2008. (J). pap. (***978-0-8225-8855-9(2))*** Lerner Publishing Group.

—Rectangular Prism. 2008. (J). pap. (***978-0-8225-8854-2(4))*** Lerner Publishing Group.

—Sphere. 2008. (J). pap. (***978-0-8225-8853-5(6))*** Lerner Publishing Group.

Brian, Sarah J. Measurement & Geometry. 1998. (Funtastic Math Ser.). (Illus.). 64p. pap. 9.95 (978-0-590-37370-8(6)) Scholastic, Inc.

Brown, Margery W. Afro-Bets Book of Shapes. Blair, Culverson & Simpson, Howard, illus. 2nd ed. 2004. (Afro-Bets Ser.). 24p. (J). (ps-1). pap. 3.95 (978-0-940975-58-3(0) , Sankofa Bks.) Just Us Bks., Inc.

Bulloch, Ivan. Formas Geometriques. 2001. (Action Math Ser.). (Illus.). 32p. (J). (ps-3). pap. 5.95 (978-1-58728-146-4(5) , Two Can Publishing) T&N Children's Publishing.

Burstein, John. Calculating Area: Space Rocket! Destiny Images Staff, illus. 2003. (Math Monsters Ser.). 24p. (YA). (gr. 1 up). lib. bdg. 19.33 (978-0-8368-3804-6(1) , Weekly Reader Early Learning Library) Stevens, Gareth Inc.

—Calculating Area: Space Rocket! 2003. (Weekly Reader Early Learning Library). (Illus.). 24p. (J). (gr. 1 up). pap. 7.93 (978-0-8368-3819-0(X) , Weekly Reader Early Learning Library) Stevens, Gareth Inc.

—Geometry: Looking Down on Monster Town. Destiny Images Staff, illus. 2003. (Math Monsters Ser.). 24p. (YA). (gr. 1 up). lib. bdg. 19.33 (978-0-8368-3809-1(2) , Weekly Reader Early Learning Library) Stevens, Gareth Inc.

—Geometry: Looking Down on Monster Town. 2003. (Weekly Reader Early Learning Library). (Illus.). 24p. (J). (gr. 1 up). pap. 7.93 (978-0-8368-3824-4(6) , Weekly Reader Early Learning Library) Stevens, Gareth Inc.

Cambridge Educational, prod. Angles & Lines; Shapes in Two Dimensions; & Shapes in Three Dimensions. 1999. (Multimedia Applied Math Ser.). (YA). cd-rom 149.95 (978-0-7365-3116-0(5)) Films Media Group.

Caron, Lucille & St. Jacques, Philip M. Geometry. 2001. (Math Success Ser.). (Illus.). 64p. (YA). (gr. 4-10). lib. bdg. 22.60 (978-0-7660-1433-6(9)) Enslow Pubs., Inc.

Carroll, Danielle. Tiling with Shapes. 2005. (Illus.). 16p. (J). (978-0-7368-5287-6(5)); (978-0-7368-5323-1(5)) Capstone Pr., Inc.

Chappell, Rachel M. Geometría en Cada Vuelta. 2007. (ENG & SPA., Illus.). 24p. (J). (***978-1-60044-281-0(1))*** Rourke Publishing, LLC.

Chappell, Rachel M. Geometry at Every Turn. 2007. (Illus.). 24p. (J). (978-1-59515-974-8(6)) Rourke Publishing, LLC.

Circles: Relationships with Segments & Angles. (Studies in Geometry). (J). pap., wbk. ed. 9.95 (978-1-930820-45-6(3)) Garlic Pr.

Cognitive Tutor (R) Geometry. 2002. tchr. ed., per. (978-1-930804-93-7(8)); stu. ed., per. (978-1-930804-94-4(6)) Carnegie Learning.

Diggins, Julia E. String, Straightedge & Shadow: The Story of Geometry. Diggins, Julia E. & Bell, Corydon, illus. 2003. (J). per. 16.95 (978-1-892857-07-1(3)) Whole Spirit Pr.

Dingles, Molly. Rectangle Ranch. Dobson, Len, illus. 2005. (Community of Shapes Ser.). 32p. (J). pap. 9.95 (978-1-59646-244-1(2)); lib. bdg. 20.65 (978-1-59646-035-5(0)); per. 9.95 (978-1-59646-245-8(0)) Dingles & Co.

—Rectangle Ranch/Rancho Rectangular. Dobson, Len, illus. 2005. (Community of Shapes Ser.).Tr. of Rancho Rectangular. (ENG & SPA.). 32p. (J). pap. 9.95 (978-1-59646-246-5(9)); lib. bdg. 20.65 (978-1-59646-036-2(9)); per. 9.95 (978-1-59646-247-2(7)) Dingles & Co.

—Seaside Circles. Brodie, Neale, illus. 2006. (Community of Shapes Ser.). 32p. (J). pap. 9.95 (978-1-59646-256-4(6)); lib. bdg. 20.65 (978-1-59646-033-1(4)); per. 9.95 (978-1-59646-257-1(4)) Dingles & Co.

—Seaside Circles/Círculos a la orilla del Mar. Brodie, Neale, illus. 2006. (Community of Shapes Ser.).Tr. of Círculos a la orilla del Mar. (ENG & SPA.). 32p. (J). pap. 9.95 (978-1-59646-258-8(2)); lib. bdg. 20.60 (978-1-59646-034-8(2)) Dingles & Co.

—Seaside Circles/Círculos a la orilla del Mar. Brodie, Neal, illus. 2006. (Community of Shapes Ser.).Tr. of Círculos a la orilla del Mar. (ENG & SPA.). 32p. (J). per. 9.95 (978-1-59646-259-5(0)) Dingles & Co.

—Town Squares. Brodie, Neale, illus. 2006. (Community of Shapes Ser.). 32p. (J). pap. 9.95 (978-1-59646-264-9(7)); lib. bdg. 20.65 (978-1-59646-041-6(5)); per. 9.95 (978-1-59646-265-6(5)) Dingles & Co.

—Town Squares/Cuadrados en la Plaza. Brodie, Neale, illus. 2006. (Community of Shapes Ser.).Tr. of Cuadrados en la Plaza. (ENG & SPA.). 32p. (J). pap. 9.95 (978-1-59646-266-3(3)); lib. bdg. 20.65 (978-1-59646-042-3(3)); per. 9.95 (978-1-59646-267-0(1)) Dingles & Co.

Dorling Kindersley Publishing Staff. Shapes. 2000. (Touch & Feel Ser.). (Illus.). 12p. (J). (ps). bds. 6.99 (978-0-7894-5222-1(7)) Dorling Kindersley Publishing, Inc.

—Shapes. 2001. (ps-2). lib. bdg. 11.80 (978-0-613-75083-7(7)) Tandem Library Bks.

Dot Paper Geometry: With or Without a Geoboard. 2000. (J). pap. 10.95 (978-1-56911-095-9(6)) Learning Resources, Inc.

Dotlich, Rebecca Kai. What Is a Triangle? 2000. (Growing Tree Ser.). (Illus.). 24p. (J). (ps). pap. 9.95 (978-0-694-01392-0(7) , Harper Festival) HarperCollins Pubs.

—What Is Square? Ferrari, Maria, illus. 1999. (Growing Tree Ser.). 24p. (J). (ps up). 9.95 (978-0-694-01207-7(6) , Harper Festival) HarperCollins Pubs.

Douglas, Vincent & School Specialty Publishing Staff. The Complete Book of Algebra & Geometry. 2005. (Complete Book Ser.). (Illus.). 352p. (J). pap. 14.95 (978-0-7696-4330-4(2) , American Education Publishing) School Specialty Publishing.

Ellis, Julie. What's Your Angle, Pythagoras? A Math Adventure. Hornung, Phyllis, illus. 2004. (Math Adventures Ser.). 32p. (J). pap. 6.95 (978-1-57091-150-7(9)); 16.95 (978-1-57091-197-2(5)) Charlesbridge Publishing, Inc.

Encycbrita. Looking at an Angle Mic 2006 G. 6th ed. 2005. pap. 10.60 (978-0-03-038569-8(5)) Harcourt Schl. Pubs.

—Packages & Polygons Mic 2006. 6th ed. 2005. pap. 10.60 (978-0-03-039632-8(8)) Harcourt Schl. Pubs.

Evans, Henry. Cubeworld: An Adventure in Solid Geometry. 2004. (Illus.). 110p. per. 11.95 (978-0-9754699-2-7(4)) Gross, H. H.

Figures in Space Student: Foundations of Advanced Mathematics. 2003. 5.00 (978-1-932230-37-6(8)) National Ctr. on Education & The Economy.

Freeman, Christopher. Drawing Stars & Building Polyhedra. 2003. per. 11.95 (978-1-883055-59-2(8) , 153) Dandy Lion Pubns.

Freudenthal. Looking at Angles. 3rd ed. 2003. (Math in Context Ser.). (Illus.). 8.33 (978-0-03-071524-2(5)) Holt, Rinehart & Winston.

—Triangles & Patchwork. 3rd ed. 2003. (Math in Context Ser.). (Illus.). 7.86 (978-0-03-071711-6(6)) Holt, Rinehart & Winston.

Gateways to Algebra & Geometry, an Integrated Approach: Multi-Language Glossary. 2003. (gr. 11-12). (978-0-618-10650-9(2) , 2-61315) McDougal Littell Inc.

Geometric Measure Student: Foundations of Advanced Mathematics. 2002. spiral bd. 5.00 (978-1-932230-04-8(1)) National Ctr. on Education & The Economy.

Geometry: Answer Key, Tests. 2000. (gr. 9-11). (978-0-395-47071-8(4) , 2-28945) McDougal Littell Inc.

Geometry: Concepts & Skills. 2003. (gr. 6-12). stu. ed. (978-0-618-08758-7(3) , 2-05500); stu. ed., wbk. ed. (978-0-618-14048-0(4) , 2-01360) McDougal Littell Inc.

Geometry: Explorations & Applications. 2001. (gr. 9-11). tchr. ed. (978-0-395-93165-3(7) , 2-99442); wbk. ed. (978-0-395-93788-4(4) , 2-78792) McDougal Littell Inc.

Geometry: Foundations of Advance Mathematics: in Three Dimensions Student's Edition. 2002. stu. ed., spiral bd. 5.00 (978-1-931954-66-2(6)) National Ctr. on Education & The Economy.

Geometry: Foundations of Advanced Mathematics: in Two Dimensions Student's Edition. 2002. (Foundations of Advance Mathematics Ser.). lib. bdg., stu. ed. 5.00 (978-1-931954-82-2(8)) National Ctr. on Education & The Economy.

Geometry: Overhead Visuals. 2000. (gr. 9-11). (978-0-395-51072-8(4) , 2-28955) McDougal Littell Inc.

Geometry: Practice Masters (Blackline) 2000. (gr. 9-11). (978-0-395-52259-2(5) , 2-28967) McDougal Littell Inc.

Geometry: Pupil's Edition (c)1997. 2000. (gr. 9-11). (978-0-395-77120-4(X) , 2-29050) McDougal Littell Inc.

Geometry: Test Bank & User's Guide. 2000. (gr. 9-11). (978-0-395-55597-2(3) , 2-28976) McDougal Littell Inc.

Geometry: Tests (Blackline) 2000. (gr. 9-11). (978-0-395-57332-7(7) , 2-28939) McDougal Littell Inc.

Geometry Brainteasers with Pattern Blocks. 2003. 48p. (gr. 1-3). 8.99 (978-1-56451-369-4(6) , ID7848) School Specialty Publishing.

Geometry Brainteasers with Tangrams. 48p. (gr. 4-6). 8.99 (978-1-56451-370-0(X) , ID7849) School Specialty Publishing.

Geometry: Concepts & Skills: EEdition. 2003. (gr. 6-12). cd-rom (978-0-618-43975-1(7) , 2-05844) McDougal Littell Inc.

Geometry: Concepts & Skills: Multi-Language Glossary. 2003. (gr. 6-12). (978-0-618-15357-2(8) , 2-12135) McDougal Littell Inc.

Geometry: Concepts & Skills: Notetaking Guide, PE. 2003. (gr. 6-12). (978-0-618-41063-7(5) , 2-05719) McDougal Littell Inc.

Geometry: Explorations & Applications. 2001. (gr. 9-11). (SPA.). (978-0-395-83607-1(7) , 2-29076); stu. ed. (978-0-395-83592-0(5) , 2-29061) McDougal Littell Inc.

Geometry: Explorations & Applications: Answer Key. 2001. (gr. 9-11). stu. ed. (978-0-395-83593-7(3) , 2-29062) McDougal Littell Inc.

Geometry: Explorations & Applications: Assessment Book & Answer Key. 2001. (gr. 9-11). (978-0-395-91786-2(7) , 99430); (SPA.). (978-0-395-83608-8(5) , 2-29077) McDougal Littell Inc.

Geometry: Explorations & Applications: Challenge Problems. 2001. (gr. 9-11). (978-0-395-84613-1(7) , 2-29083) McDougal Littell Inc.

Geometry: Explorations & Applications: Course Guides. 2001. (gr. 9-11). (978-0-395-83600-2(X) , 2-29069) McDougal Littell Inc.

Geometry: Explorations & Applications: Explorations Lab Manual. 2001. (gr. 9-11). (978-0-395-83594-4(1) , 2-29063) McDougal Littell Inc.

Geometry: Explorations & Applications: Multi-Language Glossary. 2001. (gr. 9-11). (978-0-395-83609-5(3) , 2-29078) McDougal Littell Inc.

Geometry: Explorations & Applications: Overhead Visuals. 2001. (gr. 9-11). (978-0-395-83598-2(4) , 2-29067) McDougal Littell Inc.

Geometry: Explorations & Applications: Portfolio Project Book. 2001. (gr. 9-11). (978-0-395-83596-8(8) , 2-29065) McDougal Littell Inc.

Geometry: Explorations & Applications: Practice Bank. 2001. (gr. 9-11). (978-0-395-83595-1(X) , 2-29064) McDougal Littell Inc.

Geometry: Explorations & Applications: Preparing for College Entrance Tests. 2001. (gr. 9-11). (978-0-395-83603-3(4) , 2-29072) McDougal Littell Inc.

Geometry: Explorations & Applications: Professional Handbook. 2001. (gr. 9-11). (978-0-395-83602-6(6) , 2-29071) McDougal Littell Inc.

Geometry: Explorations & Applications: Solutions Manual. 2001. (gr. 9-11). (978-0-395-83606-4(9) , 2-29075) McDougal Littell Inc.

Geometry: Explorations & Applications: Technology Book. 2001. (gr. 9-11). (978-0-395-83597-5(6) , 2-29066) McDougal Littell Inc.

Geometry-Flip Chart. 2003. (J). (gr. k-12). spiral bd. 14.95 (978-1-58845-185-9(2)) School Specialty Publishing.

George, Lynn. Teotihuacan: Designing an Ancient Mexican City: Calculating Perimeters & Areas of Squares & Rectangles. 2004. (PowerMath Ser.). (Illus.). 32p. (J). lib. bdg. (978-0-8239-8876-1(7)); lib. bdg. 22.50 (978-0-8239-8983-6(6)) Rosen Publishing Group, Inc., The. (PowerKids Pr.).

Ginsburg, Herbert P., et al. Favorite Shapes. 2003. (Illus.). 9.95 (978-0-7690-3043-2(2)) Seymour, Dale Pubns.

Gold, Kari Jenson. Parts of a Whole. Date not set. (Early Math Big Bks.). (Illus.). 16p. (J). (ps-2). pap. 16.95 (978-1-56784-426-9(X)) Sundance/Newbridge Educational Publishing.

Graham, Noel. Mathematics with Geoshapes. South, Jacqueline, illus. 2001. 32p. (J). (gr. 3-8). pap. 13.00 (978-1-871098-41-9(6)) Claire Pubns. GBR. *Dist:* Parkwest Pubns., Inc.

Granowsky, Alvin. Shapes. 2001. (978-0-606-22368-3(1)) Tandem Library Bks.

Greenes, Carol, et al. Geometry & Measurements. 2003. (Illus.). 60p. (J). (gr. 4-7). 16.95 (978-0-7690-0019-0(3)) Seymour, Dale Pubns.

Hall, Pamela. Rectangles. Holm, Sharon Lane, illus. 2007. (Shapes Ser.). 24p. (J). (ps-2). lib. bdg. 25.65 (***978-1-60270-046-8(X)*** , Looking Glass Library) Magic Wagon.

—Squares. Holm, Sharon Lane, illus. 2007. (Shapes Ser.). 24p. (J). (ps-2). lib. bdg. 25.65 (***978-1-60270-047-5(8)*** , Looking Glass Library) Magic Wagon.

Hanson, Anders. What in the World Is a Cone? 2007. (3-D Shapes Ser.). (ENG., Illus.). 24p. (J). (ps-3). lib. bdg. 19.93 (***978-1-59928-886-4(9)*** , SandCastle) ABDO Publishing Co.

—What in the World Is a Cube? 2007. (3-D Shapes Ser.). (ENG., Illus.). 24p. (J). (ps-3). lib. bdg. 19.93 (***978-1-59928-887-1(7)*** , SandCastle) ABDO Publishing Co.

—What in the World Is a Cylinder? 2007. (3-D Shapes Ser.). (ENG., Illus.). 24p. (J). (ps-3). lib. bdg. 19.93 (***978-1-59928-888-8(5)*** , SandCastle) ABDO Publishing Co.

—What in the World Is a Prism? 2007. (3-D Shapes Ser.). (ENG., Illus.). 24p. (J). (ps-3). lib. bdg. 19.93 (***978-1-59928-889-5(3)*** , SandCastle) ABDO Publishing Co.

—What in the World Is a Pyramid? 2007. (3-D Shapes Ser.). (ENG., Illus.). 24p. (J). (ps-3). lib. bdg. 19.93 (***978-1-59928-890-1(7)*** , SandCastle) ABDO Publishing Co.

—What in the World Is a Sphere? 2007. (3-D Shapes Ser.). (ENG., Illus.). 24p. (J). (ps-3). lib. bdg. 19.93 (***978-1-59928-891-8(5)*** , SandCastle) ABDO Publishing Co.

Harris, Nancy. Taking Sides: Exploring Geometry. 2008. (J). (***978-1-60044-644-3(2))*** Rourke Publishing, LLC.

Hein, Marilyn B. Math Phonic(tm) Pre-Geometry. 2003. (Illus.). 96p. pap. 10.95 (978-1-57310-406-7(X)) Teaching & Learning Co.

Heinze, Monica Bacon. A Day with Shapes. Dow, S. B., illus. 2004. (J). (***978-0-9761710-0-3(7))*** Paisley Publishing.

Holt, Rinehart and Winston Staff. Geometry: Student Technical Guide. 2001. pap. 22.73 (978-0-03-054337-1(1)) Holt, Rinehart & Winston.

—Geometry: Transparencies wiht Answer Key. 2000. trans. 227.26 (978-0-03-064688-1(X)) Holt, Rinehart & Winston.

—Holt Geometry 2003: South Carolina Practice Workbook. 3rd ed. 2003. pap. 9.60 (978-0-03-069036-5(6)) Holt, Rinehart & Winston.

—Standart Test Practice Workbook: South Carolina Edition - Geometry. 3rd ed. 2003. pap. 13.26 (978-0-03-069032-7(3)) Holt, Rinehart & Winston.

HSP. Geometry, Bk. E. 2nd ed. 2002. (First-Place Math Ser.). (gr. 3 up). pap. 12.60 (978-0-15-334625-5(6)); (gr. 4 up). pap. 12.60 (978-0-15-334631-6(0)) Harcourt Schl. Pubs.

—Geometry & Measurement, Bk. E. 2nd ed. 2002. (First-Place Math Ser.). (gr. 5 up). pap. 12.60 (978-0-15-334637-8(X)); (gr. 6 up). pap. 12.60 (978-0-15-334643-9(4)) Harcourt Schl. Pubs.

—Measurement, Geometry, & Fractions, Bk. F. 2nd ed. 2002. (First-Place Math Ser.). (gr. 1 up). pap. 12.60 (978-0-15-334614-9(0)); (gr. 2 up). pap. 12.60 (978-0-15-334620-0(5)) Harcourt Schl. Pubs.

In Step with the Standards - Geometry Concept. 2005. (J). spiral bd. 15.95 (978-1-58123-379-7(5)) Larson Learning, Inc.

In Three Diimensions: CA Math Series II. 2004. stu. ed. 6.00 (978-1-932230-69-7(6)) National Ctr. on Education & The Economy.

In Two Dimensions Student's Edition: CA Math Series II. 2004. 6.00 (978-1-932230-67-3(X)) National Ctr. on Education & The Economy.

Instructional Fair. Rectangle. 1999. (Blank Books for Young Authors Ser.). 16p. (J). (gr. k-3). pap. 1.49 (978-0-7424-0388-6(2) , IF81); pap. 16.99 (978-0-7424-0389-5(0) , IF81B) School Specialty Publishing.

Investigating with Power Solids. 2000. (J). pap. 11.95 (978-1-56911-062-1(X)) Learning Resources, Inc.

Irvin, Barbara. Geometry & Measurement: Up-to-Speed Math. 2001. (Illus.). 96p. per. 8.95 (978-1-56254-367-9(9) , SP 3679) Saddleback Educational Publishing.

Islamic Art: Recognizing Geometric Ideas in Art. (Math Big Bookstm Ser.). 32p. (YA). (gr. 6-7). 53.25 (978-1-4042-6367-3(5)) Rosen Publishing Group, Inc., The.

Johnson, Rebecca L. Sizing up Shapes. 2004. (Math Behind the Science Ser.). (Illus.). 24p. (J). pap. (978-0-7922-4589-6(X)) National Geographic Society.

Jones, Christianne C. Around the Park: A Book about Circles. Rooney, Ronnie, illus. 2006. 24p. (J). (ps-2). 22.60 (978-1-4048-1572-8(4)) Picture Window Bks.

—Four Sides the Same: A Book about Squares. Rooney, Ronnie, illus. 2006. 24p. (J). (ps-2). 22.60 (978-1-4048-1574-2(0)) Picture Window Bks.

—Party of Three: A Book about Triangles. Rooney, Ronnie, illus. 2006. 24p. (J). (ps-2). 22.60 (978-1-4048-1575-9(9)) Picture Window Bks.

—Two Short, Two Long: A Book about Rectangles. Rooney, Ronnie, illus. 2006. 24p. (J). (ps-2). 22.60 (978-1-4048-1573-5(2)) Picture Window Bks.

Jurgensen, Ray C. & Brown, Richard G. Geometry. 2000. (gr. 9-11). 74.28 (978-0-395-97727-9(4) , 2-13331) McDougal Littell Inc.

Kalman, Bobbie. What Shape Is It? 2007. (Looking at Nature Ser.). (Illus.). 24p. (J). (ps-2). lib. bdg. (***978-0-7787-3320-1(3))*** Crabtree Publishing Co.

Kassirir, Sue. Math Fair Blues. 2001. (Math Matters Ser.). (Illus.). (J). (978-0-606-20786-7(4)) Tandem Library Bks.

Kautza, Jeremy. Geometry. Matthews, Douglas L., ed. 2003. (Illus.). stu. ed., per., act. bk. ed. (978-1-931680-49-3(3) , 25, Expert Systems for Teachers) Teaching Point, Inc.

Kingfisher Editors, ed. Puzzling Puzzles: What Shape Is This? Book + 2004. (J). pap. 7.95 (978-0-7534-5644-6(3)) Kingfisher Bks.

Kirkby, David. Patterns. 1998. (Mini Math Ser.). (Illus.). 24p. (J). (978-1-57572-003-6(5)) Heinemann Library.

Kishel, Ann-Marie. Hexagon. 2007. (First Step Nonfiction Ser.). (J). lib. bdg. (978-0-8225-6857-5(8)) Lerner Publishing Group.

—Oval. 2007. (First Step Nonfiction Ser.). (J). lib. bdg. (978-0-8225-6858-2(6)) Lerner Publishing Group.

—Trapezoid. 2007. (First Step Nonfiction Ser.). (Illus.). 8p. (J). lib. bdg. (978-0-8225-6856-8(X)) Lerner Publishing Group.

Koizim, Jessica. Geometry. 2004. 48p. pap. 6.95 (978-1-4042-8529-3(6)) Rosen Publishing Group, Inc., The.

Kompelien, Tracy. 2-D Shapes Are Behind the Drapes! (Math Made Fun Ser.). (Illus.). 24p. (J). 2007. 19.93 (978-1-59928-507-8(X)); 2006. (978-1-59928-508-5(8)) ABDO Publishing Co.

—3-D Shapes are Like Green Grapes! 2007. (Math Made Fun Ser.). (Illus.). 24p. (J). 19.93 (978-1-59928-509-2(6) , SandCastle) ABDO Publishing Co.

—3-D Shapes Are Like Green Grapes! 2006. (Math Made Fun Ser.). (Illus.). 24p. (J). pap. (978-1-59928-510-8(X)) ABDO Publishing Co.

Koomen, Michele. Shapes: Discovering Flats & Solids. 2001. (Exploring Math Ser.). (Illus.). 24p. (J). (gr. 1-2). lib. bdg. 18.60 (978-0-7368-0820-0(5) , Bridgestone Bks.) Capstone Pr., Inc.

Larson, Roland E. Passport to Algebra & Geometry: (c)2004. l.t. ed. 2004. (YA). (gr. 6-9). stu. ed. (978-0-618-37422-9(1) , 2-05530) McDougal Littell Inc.

Leake, Diyan. Circles. 2005. (Illus.). 24p. (J). (ps-1). pap. 6.00 (978-1-4034-7479-7(6)); lib. bdg. 21.36 (978-1-4034-7474-2(5)) Steck-Vaughn.

—Circulos. 2005. (SPA & ENG., Illus.). 24p. (J). (978-1-4034-7489-6(3)); pap. (978-1-4034-7494-0(X)) Heinemann Library.

—Rectangulos. 2005. (SPA & ENG., Illus.). 24p. (J). (978-1-4034-7490-2(7)); pap. (978-1-4034-7496-4(6)) Heinemann Library.

—Squares. 2005. (Illus.). 24p. (J). (ps-1). pap. 6.00 (978-1-4034-7481-0(8)); lib. bdg. 21.36 (978-1-4034-7476-6(1)) Steck-Vaughn.

—Triangles. 2005. (Illus.). 24p. (J). (ps-1). lib. bdg. 21.36 (978-1-4034-7477-3(X)) Steck-Vaughn.

Leech, Bonnie Coulter. Geometry's Great Thinkers: The History of Geometry. 2006. (Math for the Real World Ser.). (Illus.). 32p. (J). pap. (978-1-4042-6073-3(0)); lib. bdg. (978-1-4042-3360-7(1)) Rosen Publishing Group, Inc., The.

Levy, Janey. Islamic Art: Recognizing Geometric Ideas in Art. 2006. (Math for the Real World Ser.). (Illus.). 32p. (J). pap. (978-1-4042-6081-8(1)); lib. bdg. (978-1-4042-3364-5(4)) Rosen Publishing Group, Inc., The.

Linde, Barbara M. Building Washington, D. C. Measuring the Area of Rectangular Spaces. 2004. (PowerMath Ser.). (Illus.). 32p. (J). lib. bdg. (978-0-8239-8867-9(8) , PowerKids Pr.) Rosen Publishing Group, Inc., The.

—Building Washington, DC: Measuring the Area of Rectangular Shapes. 2004. (PowerMath Ser.). (Illus.). 32p. (J). lib. bdg. 22.50 (978-0-8239-8980-5(1) , PowerKids Pr.) Rosen Publishing Group, Inc., The.

—Origami: Identifying Right Angles in Geometric Figures. 2004. (PowerMath Ser.). (Illus.). 24p. (J). lib. bdg. (978-0-8239-8882-2(1)); lib. bdg. 21.25 (978-0-8239-8968-3(2)) Rosen Publishing Group, Inc., The. (PowerKids Pr.).

Long, Lynette. Painless Geometry. Kerr, Tom, illus. 2001. (Barron's Painless Ser.). 307p. pap. 8.99 (978-0-7641-1773-2(4)) Barron's Educational Series, Inc.

Painless Geometry. 2001. (gr. 5-8). lib. bdg. 17.60 (978-0-613-52775-0(5)) Tandem Library Bks.

Lorbiecki, Marybeth. Circles. Holm, Sharon Lane, illus. 2007. (Shapes Ser.). 24p. (J). (ps-2). lib. bdg. 25.65 (*978-1-60270-043-7(5) , Looking Glass Library) Magic Wagon.

—Triangles. Holm, Sharon Lane, illus. 2007. 24p. (J). (ps-2). lib. bdg. 25.65 (*978-1-60270-048-2(6) , Looking Glass Library) Magic Wagon.

Lorenz Editors. Shapes & Patterns, 4 vols., Set 4. 2001. (Mini Board Bks.). (Illus.). 12p. bds. 12.95 (978-0-7548-0873-2(4)) Anness Publishing GBR. *Dist:* National Bk. Network.

MacKall, Dandi Daley. The Shape of Things. Newton, Jill, illus. 2004. (Imagination Ser.). 12p. 6.99 (978-0-8066-4384-7(6) , Augsburg Bks.) Augsburg Fortress, Pubs.

Margaritas, Aki. Investigations in Geometry Using Cabri(r) Jr. & the Graphing Calculator. 2004. 50p. pap. 14.95 net. (978-1-58108-048-3(4) , 1-58108-048-4) Pencil Point Pr., Inc.

Martin, Elena. So Many Circles. 2006. (Yellow Umbrella Books for Early Readers). (Illus.). 18p. (J). (978-0-7368-5979-0(9)); (ENG & SPA., (978-0-7368-6015-4(0)) Yellow Umbrella Pr.

Math Core Assignments: Geometric Measurement. 1999. 65p. (J). pap., stu. ed. 6.00 (978-1-889630-09-0(8)) National Ctr. on Education & The Economy.

Math Forum Staff. Dr. Math Presents More Geometry: Learning Geometry Is Easy! Just Ask Dr. Math. 2004. (Illus.). 192p. pap. 14.95 (978-0-471-22553-9(3) , Wiley) Wiley, John & Sons, Inc.

Mathematics: Structure & Method. 2004. (gr. 6-12). cd-rom (978-0-618-01300-5(8) , 2-99708) McDougal Littell Inc.

MathQueue. Using the Standards—Geometry, Grade 1. 2005. (100+ Ser.). (Illus.). 128p. (C). pap. 12.99 (978-0-7424-2981-9(4) , Instructional Fair) Schaffer, Frank Pubns.

—Using the Standards—Geometry, Grade 2. 2005. (100+ Ser.). (Illus.). 128p. (C). pap. 12.99 (978-0-7424-2982-6(2) , Instructional Fair) Schaffer, Frank Pubns.

—Using the Standards—Geometry, Grade 3. 2005. (100+ Ser.). (Illus.). 128p. (C). pap. 12.99 (978-0-7424-2983-3(0) , Instructional Fair) Schaffer, Frank Pubns.

—Using the Standards—Geometry, Grade 4. 2005. (100+ Ser.). (Illus.). 128p. (C). pap. 12.99 (978-0-7424-2984-0(9) , Instructional Fair) Schaffer, Frank Pubns.

—Using the Standards—Geometry, Grade 5. 2005. (100+ Ser.). (Illus.). 128p. (C). pap. 12.99 (978-0-7424-2985-7(7) , Instructional Fair) Schaffer, Frank Pubns.

McDougal Littell Geometry: EEdition Plus Online - Parent Purchase. 2004. (gr. 6-12). (978-0-618-39819-5(8) , 2-05649) McDougal Littell Inc.

McDougal Littell Geometry: EEdition Plus Online with Print Purchase - 1 Year. 2004. (gr. 6-12). (978-0-618-39820-1(1) , 2-05650) McDougal Littell Inc.

McDougal Littell Geometry: EEdition Plus Online with Print Purchase - 2 Years. 2004. (gr. 6-12). (978-0-618-39821-8(X) , 2-05651) McDougal Littell Inc.

McDougal Littell Geometry: EEdition Plus Online with Print Purchase - 3 Years. 2004. (gr. 6-12). (978-0-618-39822-5(8) , 2-05652) McDougal Littell Inc.

McDougal Littell Geometry: EEdition Plus Online with Print Purchase - 4 Years. 2004. (gr. 6-12). (978-0-618-39823-2(6) , 2-05653) McDougal Littell Inc.

McDougal Littell Geometry: EEdition Plus Online with Print Purchase - 5 Years. 2004. (gr. 6-12). (978-0-618-39824-9(4) , 2-05654) McDougal Littell Inc.

McDougal Littell Geometry: EEdition Plus Online with Print Purchase - 6 Years. 2004. (gr. 6-12). (978-0-618-39825-6(2) , 2-05655) McDougal Littell Inc.

McDougal Littell Geometry: EEdition Plus Online without print purchase - 6 Years. 2004. (gr. 6-12). (978-0-618-39643-6(8) , 2-05630) McDougal Littell Inc.

McDougal Littell Geometry: Exercises in Spanish. 2004. (gr. 6-12). (978-0-618-37053-5(6) , 2-06337) McDougal Littell Inc.

McGraw-Hill Staff. Geometry: Concepts & Applications. 2005. stu. ed. 84.92 (978-0-07-868172-1(3) , 9780078681721) Glencoe/McGraw-Hill.

—Glencoe Geometry. 2005. stu. ed. 84.92 (978-0-07-865106-9(9) , 9780078651069); 2003. 962p. (gr. 9-12). stu. ed. 83.96 (978-0-07-829637-6(4) , 9780078296376) Glencoe/McGraw-Hill.

—Glencoe Geometry: Concepts & Applications. 3rd ed. 2003. (gr. 6-12). stu. ed. 81.32 (978-0-07-845773-9(4) , 9780078457739) Glencoe/McGraw-Hill.

McGuire, Leslie. Circles at the Circus: My First Book of Shapes. Haskamp, Steven, illus. 1999. (Gymboree Book Ser.). 16p. (J). reprint ed. 5.95 (978-1-892374-20-2(X)) Weldon Owen, Inc.

McLean, Kerry. 501 Geometry Questions: Master This Math Skill & Score Higher! 2002. (Illus.). 288p. pap. 12.95 (978-1-57685-425-9(6)) LearningExpress, LLC.

Measurement & Geometry. 2003. Level C. tchr. ed. 19.50 (978-0-7652-1317-4(6)); Level C. stu. ed. 14.50 (978-0-7652-1305-1(2)); Level D. tchr. ed. 19.50 (978-0-7652-1321-1(4)); Level D. stu. ed. 14.50 (978-0-7652-1309-9(5)); Level E. tchr. ed. 19.50 (978-0-7652-1325-9(7)); Level E. stu. ed. 14.50 (978-0-7652-1313-6(3)) Modern Curriculum Pr.

Measurement & Geometry. 2003. 16.95 (978-0-7690-0836-3(4)) Seymour, Dale Pubns.

Merrell, Patrick, illus. Colors & Shapes: Fun Color & Shape Activities! 2001. (My Wipe-Off Book Ser.). (J). (978-0-7853-5861-9(7)) Publications International, Ltd.

Migachyov, Dina & Migachyov, Larisa. Equations in Geometry: How to Make Your Child Successful in Math. Migachyov, Larisa, ed. 2004. (Illus.). 267p. per. 29.99 (978-0-9672535-4-1(3)) Quatemion Pr.

Murphy. Captain Invincible. 2002. (Illus.). pap. (978-0-7398-6791-4(1)) Steck-Vaughn.

—The Greatest Gymnast of All: Opposites Big Book. 2002. (Illus.). pap. (978-0-7398-6780-8(6)) Steck-Vaughn.

Murphy, Chuck. Shapes. Murphy, Chuck, illus. 2001. (Slide 'n' Seek Ser.: Vol. 3). (Illus.). 12p. (J). bds. 5.99 (978-0-689-84477-5(8) , Little Simon) Simon & Schuster Children's Publishing.

Murphy, Stuart J. Captain Invincible & the Space Shapes. Simard, Remy, illus. 2001. (MathStart Ser.). 40p. (J). (gr. 1 up). 16.89 (978-0-06-028023-9(9)); pap. 5.99 (978-0-06-446731-5(7) , Harper Trophy) HarperCollins Pubs.

—Captain Invincible & the Space Shapes. 2001. (gr. k-3). lib. bdg. 12.95 (978-0-613-59231-4(X)) Tandem Library Bks.

—The Greatest Gymnast of All. Jabar, Cynthia, illus. 1998. (MathStart Ser.). 40p. (J). (ps up). 15.95 (978-0-06-027608-9(8)); 15.89 (978-0-06-027609-6(6)) HarperCollins Pubs.

—Hamster Champs. Martin, Pedro, illus. 2005. (MathStart Ser.). 40p. (J). 15.99 (978-0-06-055772-0(9)); pap. 5.99 (978-0-06-055773-7(7)) HarperCollins Pubs.

Nelson, Robin. Playing Safely. 2006. (Pull Ahead Bks.). (Illus.). 32p. (J). (ps-7). 22.60 (978-0-8225-2632-2(8) , Lerner Pubns.) Lerner Publishing Group.

Neuschwander, Cindy. Mummy Math: An Adventure in Geometry. Langdo, Bryan, illus. rev. ed. 2005. 32p. (J). 16.95 (978-0-8050-7505-2(4) , Holt, Henry & Co. Bks. For Young Readers) Holt, Henry & Co.

—Sir Cumference & the Great Knight of Angleland: A Math Adventure. Geehan, Wayne, illus. 2004. (Make the Math-Literature Connection Ser.). 32p. (J). (gr. 4-7). 16.95 (978-1-57091-170-5(3)); pap. 6.95 (978-1-57091-169-9(X)) Charlesbridge Publishing, Inc.

—Sir Cumference & the Isle of Immeter. Geehan, Wayne, illus. 2006. (Math Adventures Ser.). 32p. (J). 16.95 (978-1-57091-680-9(2)); pap. 6.95 (978-1-57091-681-6(0)) Charlesbridge Publishing, Inc.

Novick, Mary. Colors & Shapes. Harlin, Sybel, illus. 2002. (Double Delight Ser.). 24p. (J). (ps-k). 9.95 (978-1-57145-782-0(8) , Silver Dolphin Bks.) Advantage Pubs. Group.

Olenych, Bob, et al. Geometry & Measurement. 2003. (Rtg Reproducibles Ser.). 48p. pap., tchr. ed. 10.95 (978-0-439-38526-8(1) , Teaching Resources) Scholastic, Inc.

Olson, Nathan. Cones. 2008. (J). (*978-1-4296-0048-4(9)) Capstone Pr., Inc.

—Cubes. 2008. (J). (*978-1-4296-0049-1(7)) Capstone Pr., Inc.

—Cylinders. 2008. (J). (*978-1-4296-0050-7(0)) Capstone Pr., Inc.

—Ovals Around Town. 2007. (Illus.). 32p. (J). 23.93 (978-0-7368-6369-8(9)) Capstone Pr., Inc.

—Pyramids. 2008. (J). (*978-1-4296-0051-4(9)) Capstone Pr., Inc.

—Spheres. 2008. (J). (*978-1-4296-0052-1(7)) Capstone Pr., Inc.

Olson, Nathan. Triangles Around Town. 2007. (Illus.). 32p. (J). 23.93 (978-0-7368-6373-5(7)) Capstone Pr., Inc.

Onyefulu, Ifeoma. Triangle for Adaora: An African Book of Shapes. 2007. (Illus.). 32p. (J). pap. 7.95 (978-1-84507-738-9(5)) Lincoln, Frances Ltd. GBR. *Dist:* Perseus Distribution.

Osborne, J. E. Graph It! Date not set. (Early Math Big Books). (Illus.). 16p. (J). (ps-2). pap. 16.95 (978-1-58273-186-5(1)) Sundance/Newbridge Educational Publishing.

Page, David A., et al. Maneuvers with Rectangles. 2001. (Maneuvers with Mathematics Ser.). 124p. (YA). (gr. 5-9). pap., stu. ed., lab manual ed. 23.50 (978-0-86651-592-4(5)) Seymour, Dale Pubns.

Passaporte a las Algebra y a la Geometria. 2004. Tr. of Passport to Algebra & Geometry. (SPA.). (gr. 6-12). (978-0-395-91854-8(5) , 2-80510) McDougal Littell Inc.

Passport to Algebra & Geometry. 2004. (gr. 6-12). stu. ed. (978-0-618-18596-2(8) , 2-05508); stu. ed. (978-0-395-87988-7(4) , 2-77610) McDougal Littell Inc.

Passport to Algebra & Geometry: Answer Masters. 2004. (gr. 6-12). (978-0-395-89679-2(7) , 2-77751) McDougal Littell Inc.

Passport to Algebra & Geometry: Complete Solutions Manual. 2004. (gr. 6-12). (978-0-395-89681-5(9) , 2-77753) McDougal Littell Inc.

Passport to Algebra & Geometry: Daily Cumulative Review. 2004. (gr. 6-12). (978-0-395-89674-7(6) , 2-77746) McDougal Littell Inc.

Passport to Algebra & Geometry: Enrichment Copymasters. 2004. (gr. 6-12). (978-0-395-89678-5(9) , 2-77750) McDougal Littell Inc.

Passport to Algebra & Geometry: Math Log. 2004. (gr. 6-12). (978-0-395-89676-1(2) , 2-77748) McDougal Littell Inc.

Passport to Algebra & Geometry: Practice Workbook. 2004. (gr. 6-12). (SPA.). (978-0-395-90160-1(X) , 2-77865); stu. ed., wbk. ed. (978-0-395-89670-9(3) , 2-77742) McDougal Littell Inc.

Passport to Algebra & Geometry: Problem of the Day. 2004. (gr. 6-12). (978-0-395-89677-8(0) , 2-77749) McDougal Littell Inc.

Passport to Algebra & Geometry: Reteaching Copymasters. 2004. (gr. 6-12). (978-0-395-89669-3(X) , 2-77741) McDougal Littell Inc.

Passport to Algebra & Geometry: Warm-up Exercises. 2004. (gr. 6-12). (978-0-395-89680-8(0) , 2-77752) McDougal Littell Inc.

Patilla, Peter. Shapes. 1999. (Math Links Ser.). 32p. (J). (gr. k-2). lib. bdg. 21.36 (978-1-57572-968-8(7)) Heinemann Library.

Pistoia, Sara. Shapes. 2006. (MathBooks Ser.). (Illus.). 24p. (J). 24.21 (978-1-59296-691-2(8)) Child's World, Inc.

Pluckrose, Henry Arthur. What Shape Is It? 2006. (Illus.). 32p. (J). (978-1-59771-039-8(3)) Sea-To-Sea Pubns.

Proofs: Reasoning with Mathematics. (Studies in Geometry). (J). pap., wbk. ed. 9.95 (978-1-930820-46-3(1)) Garlic Pr.

Radunsky, Vladimir. Square, Triangle, Round, Skinny: 4 Little Books, 4 vols. 2002. (Illus.). (J). (978-0-7636-1533-8(1)) Candlewick Pr.

Rau, Dana Meachen. Circle City. Miller, Susan, illus. 2000. (Rookie Readers Ser.). (J). (978-0-516-21690-4(2) , Children's Pr.) Scholastic Library Publishing.

—Circle City. 1999. (gr. k-3). lib. bdg. 12.95 (978-0-613-54130-5(8)) Tandem Library Bks.

—Circles. 2006. (Bookworms Ser.). (Illus.). 24p. (J). lib. bdg. 22.79 (*978-0-7614-2280-8(3) , Benchmark Bks.) Cavendish, Marshall Corp.

—Many-Sided Shapes. 2006. (Bookworms Ser.). (Illus.). 24p. (J). lib. bdg. 22.95 (*978-0-7614-2279-2(X) , Benchmark Bks.) Cavendish, Marshall Corp.

—Ovals. 2006. (Bookworms Ser.). (Illus.). 24p. (J). (ps-k). lib. bdg. 22.79 (*978-0-7614-2281-5(1) , Benchmark Bks.) Cavendish, Marshall Corp.

—Rectangles. 2006. (Bookworms Ser.). (Illus.). 24p. (J). (ps-k). lib. bdg. 22.79 (*978-0-7614-2282-2(X) , Benchmark Bks.) Cavendish, Marshall Corp.

—Squares. 2006. (Bookworms Ser.). (Illus.). 24p. (J). (ps-k). lib. bdg. 22.79 (*978-0-7614-2284-6(6) , Benchmark Bks.) Cavendish, Marshall Corp.

—A Star in My Orange: Looking for Nature's Shapes. (Illus.). 2006. (J). pap. 6.95 (978-0-8225-5992-4(7) , First Avenue Editions); 2002. 32p. lib. bdg. 22.90 (978-0-7613-2414-0(3) , Millbrook Pr.) Lerner Publishing Group.

Rau, Dana Meachen. Triangles. 2006. (Bookworms Ser.). (Illus.). 24p. (J). (ps-k). lib. bdg. 22.79 (*978-0-7614-2286-0(2) , Benchmark Bks.) Cavendish, Marshall Corp.

Realtime Associates and Mazer Corporation Staff & LeapFrog Staff, compiled by. Identify Right, Acute, & Obtuse Angles. 2002. (J). (gr. 4). 66.75 (978-1-58605-462-5(7) , LeapFrog Schl. Hse.) LeapFrog Enterprises, Inc.

Rectangles. (Shapes Ser.). 32p. (J). 7.95 (978-0-7368-5060-5(0)) Capstone Pr., Inc.

Ribke, Simone T. The Shapes We Eat. (Rookie Read-About Math Ser.). (J). 2005. (Illus.). 32p. (gr. 1-2). pap. 5.95 (978-0-516-25848-5(6)); 2004. 20.50 (978-0-516-24431-0(0)) Scholastic Library Publishing. (Children's Pr.).

Rigby Education Staff. Shapes. (Illus.). 8p. (J). bds. 3.95 (978-0-7635-6440-7(0) , 764400C99) Rigby Education.

Rivera, Sheila. Compass. 2007. (First Step Nonfiction Ser.). (Illus.). 8p. (J). lib. bdg. (978-0-8225-6852-0(7)) Lerner Publishing Group.

—Pentagon. 2007. (First Step Nonfiction Ser.). (J). lib. bdg. (978-0-8225-6859-9(4)) Lerner Publishing Group.

—Rhombus. 2007. (First Step Nonfiction Ser.). (Illus.). 8p. (J). lib. bdg. (978-0-8225-6860-5(8)) Lerner Publishing Group.

—What Shape Is It? 2004. (First Step Nonfiction Ser.). (J). pap. (978-0-8225-5407-3(0) , Lerner Pubns.) Lerner Publishing Group.

Robinson, C. L. MATH1on1 Geometry Foundation. 2006. (YA). per. 9.99 (978-0-9786767-6-6(9)) Robinson, Consuelo.

Robleda, Maria. Jugando con Geometria.Tr. of Playing with Geometry. (SPA.). (J). 4.95 (978-968-6579-18-5(4)) Sistemas Tecnicos de Edicion, S.A. de C.V. MEX. *Dist:* AIMS International Bks., Inc.

Rock, Nathaniel. Math for Everyone Geometry I. 2007. pap. 99.99 (*978-1-59980-003-5(9)) Nathaniel Max Rock.

Ross, Kathy. Kathy Ross Crafts Triangles, Rectangles, Circles, & Squares. Barger, Jan, illus. 2002. (Crafts from Kathy Ross Ser.). 48p. (ps-1). lib. bdg. 23.90 (978-0-7613-2104-0(7) , Millbrook Pr.) Lerner Publishing Group.

Roy, Jennifer Rozines & Roy, Gregory. Shapes in Transportation. 2006. (Math All Around Ser.). (Illus.). 32p. (J). lib. bdg. 28.50 (978-0-7614-2265-5(X) , Benchmark Bks.) Cavendish, Marshall Corp.

Roza, Greg. Geometry. 2004. 48p. pap. 6.95 (978-1-4042-8538-5(5)) Rosen Publishing Group, Inc., The.

—Where We Play Sports: Measuring the Perimeters of Polygons. 2004. (PowerMath Ser.). (Illus.). 24p. (J). lib. bdg. (978-0-8239-8895-2(3)); lib. bdg. 21.25 (978-0-8239-8972-0(0)) Rosen Publishing Group, Inc., The. (PowerKids Pr.).

Running Press Staff. Shapes: Fit-a-shape. 2000. (Fit-a-Shape Ser.). (Illus.). 10p. (J). (ps-k). pap. 6.95 (978-0-7624-0814-6(6) , Running Pr. Kids) Running Pr. Bk. Pubs.

Schaefer, Lola M. Shapes to Go. 2003. (Wheels, Wings, & Water Ser.). (Illus.). 24p. (J). lib. bdg. 18.50 (978-1-4034-0886-0(6)); pap. (978-1-4034-3622-1(3)) Heinemann Library.

—Shapes to Go. 2003. (gr. k-3). lib. bdg. 13.30 (978-0-613-67433-1(2)) Tandem Library Bks.

Schlein, Miriam. Round & Square. Bronson, Linda, illus. 1999. 32p. (J). (gr. k-4). 15.95 (978-1-57255-719-2(2)) Mondo Publishing.

School Mathematics Project Staff. SMP 16-19 Pure 2: Co-Ordinate Geometry, Trigonometry & Further Calculus. rev. ed. 2002. (School Mathematics Project 16-19 Ser.). (Illus.). 172p. pap. 19.00 (978-0-521-78798-7(X)) Cambridge Univ. Pr.

—SMP 16-19 Pure 3: Vectors & Applications of Calculus. rev. ed. 2002. (School Mathematics Project 16-19 Ser.). (Illus.). 158p. pap. 19.80 (978-0-521-78799-4(8)) Cambridge Univ. Pr.

School Specialty Publishing. Geometry at Home: It's Everyplace You Are! 2004. (It's Everyplace You Are! Ser.). 48p. (J). (gr. k up). pap. 6.99 (978-0-7682-2890-8(5) , FS99293); (gr. 1 up). pap. 6.99 (978-0-7682-2891-5(3) , FS99288); (gr. 3 up). pap. 6.99 (978-0-7682-2893-9(X) , FS99290); (gr. 4 up). pap. 6.99 (978-0-7682-2894-6(8) , FS99291); (gr. 5 up). pap. 6.99 (978-0-7682-2895-3(6) , FS99292) Schaffer, Frank Pubns.

—Introductory Geometry Gr 6. 2005. (Math 2 Master Ser.). 32p. (J). pap. 3.99 (978-0-7696-3926-0(7) , Brighter Child) School Specialty Publishing.

—Introductory Geometry, Grade 6. 2006. (Skills for Scholars Ser.). 80p. (C). pap. 4.99 (*978-0-7696-4976-4(9) , Schaffer, Frank) Schaffer, Frank Pubns.

—Mathematics: A Step-by-Step Approach. 1999. (Practice Drills Ser.). 86p. (YA). (gr. 8-8). pap. 2.99 (978-0-88012-487-4(3) , IF0180, Instructional Fair) Schaffer, Frank Pubns.

—Step-by-Step Homework Booklets: Geometry. 2003. (Homework Booklets Ser.). 80p. (C). pap. 2.99 (978-0-7682-2637-9(6) , IFG99147) School Specialty Publishing.

School Zone Publishing Company Staff. Colors, Shapes & More. rev. ed. 1999. (Flash Cards Ser.). (Illus.). (J). 2.79 (978-0-938256-96-0(3) , 04011) School Zone Publishing Co.

Schultz. Geometry: Premier Online Edition. 4th ed. 2003. 19.93 (978-0-03-040423-8(1)) Holt, Rinehart & Winston.

Scott, Janine. The Shape of Things. 2003. (Spyglass Books). (Illus.). 24p. (J). (gr. 1 up). lib. bdg. 18.60 (978-0-7565-0453-3(8)) Compass Point Bks.

Senisi, Ellen B. A 3-D Birthday Party. 2006. (Rookie Read-About Math Ser.). (Illus.). 31p. (J). (978-0-516-29828-3(3)) Children's Pr., Ltd.

Sesame Street Rosita's Holiday of Colors & Patterns. 2006. (J). 3.99 (*978-1-59545-118-7(8)) Learning Horizons, Inc.

E F G

Shepard, Daniel. Solid Shapes. (Yellow Umbrella Books for Early Readers). (J). (gr. k-2). 2006. (Illus.). 16p. 15.93 (978-0-7368-5853-3(9) , Yellow Umbrella Bks.); 2005. (978-0-7368-5319-4(7)); 2005. (Illus.). 17p. (978-0-7368-5283-8(2)) Capstone Pr., Inc.

Shields, Charles. Succeed in Geometry. 2000. (Math "How To" Ser.). (Illus.). 48p. (gr. 5-8). pap. 7.99 (978-1-57690-958-4(1)) Teacher Created Materials, Inc.

Siede Preis Photography (Firm) Staff & Brian Warling Photography (Firm) Staff, contrib. by. Colors & Shapes. 2004. (Active Minds Ser.). (Illus.). 12p. (J). bds. (978-1-4127-0540-0(1) , 3970905) Publications International, Ltd.

Simard, Remy. Captain Invincible & the Space Shapes: Three-Dimensional Shapes. 2001. 11.79 (978-0-606-22288-4(X)) Tandem Library Bks.

So Many Circles. 2006. (Yellow Umbrella Math Ser.). 8,16p. (J). 6.50 (978-0-7368-1696-0(8)) Red Brick Learning.

Steck-Vaughn Staff. Focus on Math Level C: Geometry. 2005. pap. 2.99 (978-1-4190-0270-0(8)) Harcourt Schl. Pubs.

—Focus on Math Level C 10-pack: Geometry. 2005. pap. 29.95 (978-1-4190-0294-6(5)) Harcourt Schl. Pubs.

—Focus on Math Level D: Geometry. 2005. pap. 2.99 (978-1-4190-0276-2(7)) Harcourt Schl. Pubs.

—Focus on Math Level D 10-pack: Geometry. 2005. pap. 29.95 (978-1-4190-0300-4(3)) Harcourt Schl. Pubs.

—Focus on Math Level E: Geometry. 2005. pap. 2.99 (978-1-4190-0281-6(3)) Harcourt Schl. Pubs.

—Focus on Math Level E 10-pack: Geometry. 2005. pap. 29.95 (978-1-4190-0305-9(4)) Harcourt Schl. Pubs.

—Focus on Math Level F: Geometry. 2005. pap. 2.99 (978-1-4190-0286-1(4)) Harcourt Schl. Pubs.

—Focus on Math Level F 10-pack: Geometry. 2005. pap. 29.95 (978-1-4190-0310-3(0)) Harcourt Schl. Pubs.

—Geometry. 1999. (Illus.). (J). pap. (978-0-7398-1297-6(1)); (gr. 5). pap. (978-0-7398-1298-3(X)); (gr. 6). pap. (978-0-7398-1299-0(8)) Steck-Vaughn.

—Geometry for Primary Grade 1. 1999. (Illus.). (J). pap. (978-0-8172-5805-4(1)) Steck-Vaughn.

—Geometry for Primary Grade 2. 1999. (Illus.). pap. (978-0-8172-5806-1(X)) Steck-Vaughn.

—Geometry for Primary Grade 3. 1999. (Illus.). pap. (978-0-8172-5807-8(8)) Steck-Vaughn.

—Math: Data Analysis, Measurement, Geometry. 2002. (Illus.). pap. (978-0-7398-5429-7(1)) Steck-Vaughn.

—Measurement & Geometry. 2004. pap. 14.95 (978-0-7398-9855-0(8)) Harcourt Schl. Pubs.

—Middle School Geometry: Basic Concepts. 1999. (Illus.). (J). pap. (978-0-7398-2930-1(0)) Steck-Vaughn.

—Middle School Geometry: Polygons. 1999. (Illus.). (J). pap. (978-0-7398-2931-8(9)) Steck-Vaughn.

—Middle School Geometry: Solids. 1999. (Illus.). (J). pap. (978-0-7398-2932-5(7)) Steck-Vaughn.

—Top Line Math: Geometry. 2005. pap. 5.49 (978-1-4190-0373-8(9)) Steck-Vaughn.

—Top Line Math 10-Pack: Geometry. 2005. pap. 54.95 (978-1-4190-0394-3(1)) Harcourt Schl. Pubs.

Sterling, Kristin. Subtraction. 2008. (J). pap. ***978-0-8225-8845-0(5))** Lerner Publishing Group.

Succeed in Geometry. 2004. (Math "How To" Ser.). (Illus.). 48p. (J). (gr. 3-5). 7.99 (978-1-57690-957-7(3)) Teacher Created Materials, Inc.

Triangles: Calculating Measurments & Rations. (Studies in Geometry). (J). pap., wbk. ed. 9.95 (978-1-930820-44-9(5)) Garlic Pr.

Triangles 2. 2001. (Early Math Ser.). (J). (gr. k-12). vinyl bd. 4.95 (978-1-58845-106-4(2)) School Specialty Publishing.

Triola, Chris. Geometreats. 2001. 127p. pap., wbk. ed., act. bk. ed. 12.95 (978-1-58123-184-7(9)) Larson Learning, Inc.

Tucker, Shirley & Rambo, Jane. Looking at Shapes. 2002. (Yellow Umbrella Books). (Illus.). 16p. (J). (gr. 1). lib. bdg. 14.60 (978-0-7368-1284-9(9) , Pebble Bks.) Capstone Pr., Inc.

Tuxworth, Nicola & Lorenz Editors. Mix & Match. 2004. (Let's Look at... Ser.). (Illus.). 20p. 5.99 (978-0-7548-1278-4(2)) Anness Publishing GBR. *Dist:* National Bk. Network.

Using Cuisenaire Rods: Geometry & Measurement. 2001. (J). pap. 7.95 (978-1-56911-739-2(X)) Learning Resources, Inc.

Vivian, Mary Lee, et al. Geometry, Grades 5-8. 2003. (100+ Seriestm Ser.). (Illus.). 128p. (J). (gr. 5-8). pap. 12.99 (978-0-7424-1776-2(X) , IFG99037, Instructional Fair) Schaffer, Frank Pubns.

—Intro to Geometry, Grades 5-8. 2003. (100+ Seriestm Ser.). (Illus.). 128p. (J). (gr. 5-8). pap. 12.99 (978-0-7424-1777-9(8) , IFG99036, Instructional Fair) Schaffer, Frank Pubns.

Vogel, Julia. Crescents. Holm, Sharon Lane, illus. 2007. (Shapes Ser.). 24p. (J). (ps-2). lib. bdg. 25.65 ***978-1-60270-044-4(3)** , Looking Glass Library) Magic Wagon.

—Ovals. Holm, Sharon Lane, illus. 2007. (Shapes Ser.). 24p. (J). (ps-2). lib. bdg. 25.65 ***978-1-60270-045-1(1)** , Looking Glass Library) Magic Wagon.

Weekly Reader Early Learning Library (Firm) Staff, contrib. by. I Know Shapes. 2006. (I'm Ready for Math Ser.). (Illus.). 16p. (J). pap. (978-0-8368-6482-3(4)); lib. bdg. 16.67 (978-0-8368-6477-9(8)) Stevens, Gareth Inc.

—I Know Shapes: Las Figuras. 2006. (ENG & SPA., Illus.). 16p. (J). pap. 4.50 (978-0-8368-6492-2(1)); lib. bdg. 16.67 (978-0-8368-6487-8(5)) Stevens, Gareth Inc.

What Are? Colors & Shapes. 1998. (Illus.). 8p. (J). bds. 4.99 (978-1-929174-05-8(5)) Oshkosh B'Gosh, Inc.

Wiltshire, Alan. Creativity Through Design: Challenges in Art & Mathematics Using the Anglemaster. 64p. pap. 12.50 (978-1-871098-25-9(4)) Claire Pubns. GBR. *Dist:* Parkwest Pubns., Inc.

Wingard-Nelson, Rebecca. Trigonometry. 2004. (Math Success Ser.). (Illus.). 64p. (J). lib. bdg. 22.60 (978-0-7660-2568-4(3)) Enslow Pubs., Inc.

Wright, Elena Dworkin & Shapero, Susan. Round Table Geometry: 30 Activities to Connect Math & Literature. 1998. (Illus.). 32p. (J). (gr. 1-5). pap., tchr. ed. 9.95 (978-1-57091-155-2(X) , MA15) Charlesbridge Publishing, Inc.

Yates, Irene. Shape. 2002. (All about Ser.). (Illus.). 32p. (J). lib. bdg. 24.25 (978-1-930643-98-7(5)) Chrysalis Education.

Yoon, Salina, illus. Foil Fun Shapes. 2000. (Foil Fun Board Bks.). 10p. (J). (ps). bds. 4.95 (978-1-58117-064-1(5) , Intervisual/Piggy Toes) Dalmatian Pr.

Youngs, Michelle. Paper Square Geometry: The Mathematics of Origami. Cordel, Betty, ed. Pocock, Margo, illus. 2000. 235p. (J). 18.95 (978-1-881431-90-9(8)) AIMS Education Foundation.

Zuravicky, Orli. Exploring Pyramids Around the World: Making Models of Geometric Solids. 2004. (PowerMath Ser.). (Illus.). 32p. (J). lib. bdg. (978-0-8239-8908-9(9)); lib. bdg. 22.50 (978-0-8239-8992-8(5)) Rosen Publishing Group, Inc., The. (PowerKids Pr.).

GEOMETRY, ANALYTIC

Calculus with Analytic Geometry. 7th ed. 2001. (YA). (gr. 11-12). stu. ed. 3.96 incl. cd-rom (978-0-618-21333-7(3) , 332381) Houghton Mifflin College Div.

Calculus with Analytic Geometry. 7th ed. 2002. (gr. 11-12). (978-0-618-14928-5(7) , 3-32364); (978-0-618-14939-1(2) , 3-32375); tchr. ed. (978-0-618-14931-5(7) , 3-32367); tchr. ed. (978-0-618-14932-2(5) , 3-32368); tchr. ed. (978-0-618-14933-9(3) , 3-32369); tchr. ed. (978-0-618-14926-1(0) , 3-32362); instr.'s gde. ed. (978-0-618-14930-8(9) , 3-32366) McDougal Littell Inc.

Larson. Calculus: High School. 7th ed. 2001. (YA). (gr. 11-12). stu. ed. 165.96 (978-0-618-14918-6(X) , 332352) Houghton Mifflin College Div.

—Calculus with Analytic Geometry. 7th ed. 2002. (gr. 11-12). pap., stu. ed. (978-0-618-23973-3(1) , 3-84365) McDougal Littell Inc.

Larson, Roland, et al. Calculus with Analytic Geometry. 6th alt. ed. 1998. 1123p. (YA). 165.96 (978-0-395-88902-2(2) , 331030) Houghton Mifflin College Div.

Larson, Ron, et al. Calculus of a Single Variable with Learning. 7th ed. 2002. 713p. (YA). (gr. 11-12). 144.36 incl. cd-rom (978-0-618-23974-0(X) , 384366) Houghton Mifflin College Div.

Levy, Benjamin N. & Larson, Ron. Graphing Technology Guide for Calculus & Precalculus. 5th ed. 2000. (YA). (gr. 6-12). 22.36 (978-0-618-07287-3(X) , 330431) Houghton Mifflin College Div.

Lineare Algebra und Analytische Geometrie I: Leistungskurs. (Duden Abiturhilfen Ser.). (GER.). 96p. (YA). (gr. 12-13). (978-3-411-04601-0(5)) Bibliographisches Institut & F. A. Brockhaus AG DEU. *Dist:* International Bk. Import Service, Inc.

Lineare Algebra und Analytische Geometrie II: Leistungskurs. (Duden Abiturhilfen Ser.). (GER.). 96p. (YA). (gr. 12-13). (978-3-411-04631-7(7)) Bibliographisches Institut & F. A. Brockhaus AG DEU. *Dist:* International Bk. Import Service, Inc.

GEOMETRY, PLANE

see Geometry

GEOMETRY, SOLID

see Geometry

GEOPHYSICS

see also Meteorology; Oceanography

DK Publishing. Rainbow Colors. 2008. 12p. (J). (ps-ps). bds. 6.99 ***978-0-7566-3760-6(0))** Dorling Kindersley Publishing, Inc.

Ganeri, Anita. I Wonder Why the Wind Blows: And Other Questions about Our Planet. 2003. (I Wonder Why Ser.). 32p. (J). (gr. k-3). pap. 6.95 (978-0-7534-5664-4(8) , Kingfisher) Houghton Mifflin Co. Trade & Reference Div.

—I Wonder Why the Wind Blows: And Other Questions about Our Planet. 2003. (gr. k-3). lib. bdg. 14.10 (978-0-613-90899-3(6)) Tandem Library Bks.

Gardner, Robert. Earth-Shaking Science Projects about Planet Earth. LaBaff, Tom, illus. 2007. (Rockin' Earth Science Experiments Ser.). 48p. (J). (gr. 3-4). lib. bdg. 23.93 ***978-0-7660-2733-6(3)** , Enslow Elementary) Enslow Pubs., Inc.

Sherman, Josepha. Geothermal Power. 2004. (Fact Finders Ser.). (Illus.). 32p. (J). 16.95 (978-0-7368-2471-2(5)) Capstone Pr., Inc.

GEORGE, SAINT, D. 303—FICTION

Grahame, Kenneth. The Reluctant Dragon. Moore, Inga, illus. 2004. 64p. (J). (ps-3). 17.99 (978-0-7636-2199-5(4)) Candlewick Pr.

—The Reluctant Dragon Me. 2003. (J). cd-rom (978-0-9724995-6-9(3)) Alcazar AudioWorks.

Hightman, Jason. The Saint of Dragons. (gr. 7 up). 2004. (J). 16.99 (978-0-06-054011-1(7)); 2004. 304p. (J). lib. bdg. 17.89 (978-0-06-054012-8(5)); 2005. 340p. (YA). reprint ed. pap. 6.99 (978-0-06-054013-5(3)) HarperCollins Pubs.

—Samurai. 2006. 320p. (J). 15.99 (978-0-06-054014-2(1)); lib. bdg. 16.89 (978-0-06-054015-9(X)) HarperCollins Pubs.

GEORGE AND MARTHA (FICTITIOUS CHARACTERS)—FICTION

Marshall, James. George & Martha Back in Town. Marshall, James, illus. 2002. (George & Martha Ser.). (Illus.). (J). 14.74 (978-0-7587-2569-1(8)) Book Wholesalers, Inc.

—George & Martha Encore. Marshall, James, illus. 2002. (George & Martha Ser.). (Illus.). (J). 14.74 (978-0-7587-2570-7(1)) Book Wholesalers, Inc.

—George & Martha One Fine Day. Marshall, James, illus. 2002. (George & Martha Ser.). (Illus.). (J). 14.74 (978-0-7587-2571-4(X)) Book Wholesalers, Inc.

—George & Martha Rise & Shine. Marshall, James, illus. 2002. (George & Martha Ser.). (Illus.). (J). 14.74 (978-0-7587-2572-1(8)) Book Wholesalers, Inc.

—George & Martha Round & Round. Marshall, James, illus. 2002. (George & Martha Ser.). (Illus.). (J). 14.74 (978-0-7587-2573-8(6)) Book Wholesalers, Inc.

—George & Martha: Round & Round Early Reader #3. 2008. 32p. (J). (ps-3). 15.00 ***978-0-618-98505-0(0))** Houghton Mifflin Co. Trade & Reference Div.

—George & Martha: the Best of Friends Early Reader #4. 2008. 24p. (J). (ps-3). 15.00 ***978-0-618-98451-0(8))** Houghton Mifflin Co. Trade & Reference Div.

Marshall, James. George & Martha Tons of Fun. Marshall, James, illus. 2002. (George & Martha Ser.). (Illus.). (J). 14.74 (978-0-7587-2574-5(4)) Book Wholesalers, Inc.

GEORGIA

BHB International Staff. Savannah. 1998. (Here We Go Round Ser.). (J). (978-2-215-06178-6(2)) Editions Fleurus.

Bograd, Larry. Uniquely Georgia. (Heinemann State Studies). (Illus.). 48p. (J). (ps-k). 2004. pap. 8.50 (978-1-4034-4504-9(4)); 2003. 27.07 (978-1-4034-4489-9(7)) Heinemann Library.

Bredeson, Carmen. Georgia. (Rookie Read-About Geography Ser.). (Illus.). 32p. (J). (gr. 1-2). 2003. pap. 5.95 (978-0-516-27497-3(X)); 2002. 20.50 (978-0-516-22670-5(3)) Scholastic Library Publishing. (Children's Pr.).

—Georgia. 2002. (gr. k-3). lib. bdg. 14.10 (978-0-613-59487-5(8)) Tandem Library Bks.

Capstone Press Staff, contrib. by. Georgia. rev. ed. 2002. (One Nation Ser.). (Illus.). 48p. (J). (gr. 3-4). lib. bdg. 22.60 (978-0-7368-1234-4(2) , Bridgestone Bks.) Capstone Pr., Inc.

Coleman, Wim & Perrin, Pat. Martin Luther King, Jr. National Historic Site: A MyReportLinks.com Book. 2005. (Virtual Field Trips Ser.). (Illus.). 48p. (J). (gr. 4-10). lib. bdg. 25.26 (978-0-7660-5225-3(7) , MyReportLinks.com Bks.) Enslow Pubs., Inc.

Crane, Carol. Georgia Number. Braught, Mark, illus. rev. ed. 2007. (State Counting Ser.). 40p. (J). 17.95 ***978-1-58536-177-9(1))** Sleeping Bear Pr.

Crane, Carol. P Is for Peach: A Georgia Alphabet. Braught, Mark, illus. rev. ed. 2002. 40p. (J). 17.95 (978-1-58536-046-8(5)) Sleeping Bear Pr.

Glaser, Jason. California. 2003. (Land of Liberty Ser.). (Illus.). 64p. (J). (gr. 3-4). lib. bdg. 23.93 (978-0-7368-1573-4(2) , Bridgestone Bks.) Capstone Pr., Inc.

Harcourt School Publishers Staff. Social Studies: Georgia Copying Masters. 2000. (gr. 3-5). pap. 15.70 (978-0-15-316133-9(7)) Harcourt Schl. Pubs.

Haywood, Karen Diane. Georgia. 2005. (It's My State! Ser.). (Illus.). 79p. (J). 27.07 (978-0-7614-1862-7(8) , Benchmark Bks.) Cavendish, Marshall Corp.

Heinrichs, Ann. Georgia. 2005. (Welcome to the USA Ser.). 40p. (J). (gr. 1-5). 27.07 (978-1-59296-373-7(0)) Child's World, Inc.

—Georgia. 2003. (This Land Is Your Land Ser.). (Illus.). 48p. (J). (gr. 3 up). lib. bdg. 22.60 (978-0-7565-0321-5(3)) Compass Point Bks.

Holtz, Eric Siegfried. Georgia: Empire State of the South. 2002. (World Almanac Library of the States). (Illus.). 48p. (J). (gr. 5 up). lib. bdg. 30.00 (978-0-8368-5132-8(3)); pap. 14.95 (978-0-8368-5302-5(4)) Stevens, Gareth Inc. (World Almanac Library).

Jackson, Edwin L. & Carl Vinson Institute of Government Staff. The Georgia Studies Book: Our State & the Nation. 1998. (Illus.). 512p. (YA). (gr. 8). 28.50 (978-0-89854-192-2(1)) Univ. of Georgia, Carl Vinson Institute of Government.

Jackson, Edwin L. & Stakes, Mary E. The Georgia Studies Book: Our State & the Nation. 2nd ed. 2004. (J). (978-0-89854-210-3(3)) Univ. of Georgia, Carl Vinson Institute of Government.

Kalman, Bobbie. A Savanna Habitat. 2006. (Illus.). 32p. (J). (gr. 2). pap. (978-0-7787-2980-8(X)) Crabtree Publishing Co.

Kalman, Bobbie & Dyer, Hadley. Savanna Food Chains. 2006. (Food Chains Ser.). (Illus.). 32p. (J). (gr. 3-5). pap. (978-0-7787-1998-4(7)) Crabtree Publishing Co.

Kent, Deborah. Atlanta. 2001. (Cities of the World Ser.). (Illus.). 64p. (YA). (gr. 4-9). pap. 9.95 (978-0-516-27282-5(9) , Children's Pr.) Scholastic Library Publishing.

LaDoux, Rita C. Georgia. 2nd rev. exp. ed. 2002. (Hello U. S. A. Ser.). (Illus.). 84p. (J). (gr. 3-6). lib. bdg. 25.26 (978-0-8225-4076-2(2)) Lerner Publishing Group.

—Georgia. 2002. (gr. 3-6). lib. bdg. 15.25 (978-0-613-46070-5(7)) Tandem Library Bks.

Marsh, Carole. Georgia Classic Christmas Trivia. 2002. (Carole Marsh Georgia Bks.). (Illus.). 32p. pap. 6.95 (978-0-635-01387-3(8)); lib. bdg. 21.95 (978-0-635-01388-0(6) , 13886) Gallopade International. (Marsh, Carole Bks.).

—Georgia Current Events Projects: 30 Cool, Activities, Crafts, Experiments & More for Kids to Do to Learn about Your State! 2003. (Georgia Experience Ser.). 32p. (gr. k-5). pap. 5.95 (978-0-635-02029-1(7) , Marsh, Carole Bks.) Gallopade International.

—The Georgia Experience Pocket Guide. 2001. (Georgia Experience! Ser.). (Illus.). 96p. (J). (gr. 3-8). pap. 6.95 (978-0-7933-9449-4(X)) Gallopade International.

—Georgia Geography Projects: 30 Cool, Activities, Crafts, Experiments & More for Kids to Do to Learn about Your State! 2003. (Georgia Experience Ser.). 32p. (gr. k-5). pap. 5.95 (978-0-635-01829-8(2) , Marsh, Carole Bks.) Gallopade International.

—Georgia Government Projects: 30 Cool, Activities, Crafts, Experiments & More for Kids to Do to Learn about Your State! 2003. (Georgia Experience Ser.). 32p. (gr. k-5). pap. 5.95 (978-0-635-01929-5(9) , Marsh, Carole Bks.) Gallopade International.

—Georgia Jeopardy! Answers & Questions about Our State! 2000. (Georgia Experience! Ser.). (Illus.). 32p. (J). (gr. 3-8). pap. 7.95 (978-0-7933-9510-1(0)) Gallopade International.

—Georgia "Jography" A Fun Run Thru Our State! 2000. (Georgia Experience! Ser.). (Illus.). 32p. (J). (gr. 3-8). pap. 7.95 (978-0-7933-9511-8(9)) Gallopade International.

—Georgia Millionaire: Game Book. 2001. (Carole Marsh Georgia Bks.). (Illus.). 32p. (J). (gr. 3-8). pap., act. bk. ed. 9.95 (978-0-635-00036-1(9)) Gallopade International.

—Georgia People Projects: 30 Cool, Activities, Crafts, Experiments & More for Kids to Do to Learn about Your State! 2003. (Georgia Experience Ser.). 32p. (gr. k-5). pap. 5.95 (978-0-635-01979-0(5) , Marsh, Carole Bks.) Gallopade International.

—Georgia Symbols & Facts Projects: 30 Cool, Activities, Crafts, Experiments & More for Kids to Do to Learn about Your State! 2003. (Georgia Experience Ser.). 32p. (gr. k-5). pap. 5.95 (978-0-635-01879-3(9) , Marsh, Carole Bks.) Gallopade International.

—Georgia's Big Activity Book. 2004. (Georgia Experience! Ser.). (Illus.). 96p. (J). (gr. 2-6). pap. 9.95 (978-0-7933-9459-3(7)) Gallopade International.

—The Groovy Georgia Coloring Book. 2000. (Georgia Experience! Ser.). (Illus.). 32p. (J). (gr. k-2). pap. 3.95 (978-0-7933-9469-2(4)) Gallopade International.

—My First Book about Georgia. 2000. (Georgia Experience! Ser.). (Illus.). 32p. (J). (gr. k-4). pap. 7.95 (978-0-7933-9509-5(7)) Gallopade International.

—The Survivor: A Class Challenge. 2001. (Carole Marsh Florida Bks.). lib. bdg. 29.95 (978-0-635-00655-4(3)) Gallopade International.

Masters, Nancy R. Georgia. 2000. (Switched on Schoolhouse Ser.). (Illus.). (YA). (gr. 7-12). pap. 24.95 incl. cd-rom (978-0-7403-0262-6(0) , SOSGA) Alpha Omega Pubns., Inc.

McAuliffe, Emily. Georgia: Facts & Symbols. 1999. (J). lib. bdg. 14.00 (978-0-531-11801-6(0)) Capstone Pr., Inc.

—Georgia Facts & Symbols. (States & Their Symbols Ser.). 24p. (J). 1999. (Illus.). (gr. 2-3). lib. bdg. 18.60 (978-0-7368-0215-4(0) , Bridgestone Bks.); 2003. lib. bdg. 19.93 (978-0-7368-2240-4(2)) Capstone Pr., Inc.

Murphy, Andrea. Georgia. 2005. (Portraits of the States Ser.). (Illus.). 32p. (J). pap. (978-0-8368-4642-3(7)); lib. bdg. 23.33 (978-0-8368-4623-2(0)) Stevens, Gareth Inc.

Murray, Julie. Georgia. 2006. (Illus.). 32p. (J). (gr. k-4). 22.78 (978-1-59197-669-1(3) , Buddy Bks.) ABDO Publishing Co.

Nault, Jennifer. A Guide to Georgia. 2001. (American States Ser.). (Illus.). 32p. (J). lib. bdg. 16.95 (978-1-930954-28-1(X)); per. 7.95 (978-1-930954-71-7(9)) Weigl Pubs., Inc.

Otfinoski, Steven, ed. Georgia. 2000. (Celebrate the States Ser.). (Illus.). 144p. (J). (gr. 4-8). lib. bdg. 37.07 (978-0-7614-1062-1(7) , Benchmark Bks.) Cavendish, Marshall Corp.

Peach Tree Street, Vol. 2. 2005. (Early Library). (YA). (ps-3). 23.94 (978-0-8215-8949-6(0)) Sadlier, William H. Inc.

Piddock, Charles. Republic of Georgia. 2006. (Illus.). 48p. (J). pap. (978-0-8368-6717-6(3)); lib. bdg. (978-0-8368-6710-7(6)) Stevens, Gareth Inc. (World Almanac Library).

Prentzas, G. S. Georgia. 2007. (America the Beautiful, Third Ser.). 144p. (J). spiral bd. 38.00 ***978-0-531-18572-8(9)** , Children's Pr.) Scholastic Library Publishing.

The Republic of Georgia Updated Ed. 2005. 150p. 30.00 (978-0-7910-8784-8(0) , Chelsea Hse.) Facts On File, Inc.

Savage, Jeff. Georgia: A MyReportLinks. Com Book. 2003. (States Ser.). (Illus.). 48p. (J). lib. bdg. 25.26 (978-0-7660-5114-0(5) , MyReportLinks.com Bks.) Enslow Pubs., Inc.

Schumacher, Tyler. Georgia: Land & People. 2006. (J). (978-0-7368-5826-7(1)) Capstone Pr., Inc.

Shofner, Shawndra. Georgia. 2008. (J). ***978-1-58341-635-8(X)** , Creative Education) Creative Co., The.

Stechschulte, Pattie. Georgia. 80p. (J). 2008. (From Sea to Shining Sea, Second Ser.). pap. 7.95 ***978-0-531-18803-3(5));** 2001. (From Sea to Shining Sea Ser.: 2). (Illus.). (gr. 3-5). 30.50 (978-0-516-22311-7(9)) Scholastic Library Publishing. (Children's Pr.).

Stefoff, Rebecca. Furman v. Georgia: Debating the Death Penalty. 2007. (Supreme Court Milestones Ser.). 144p. (J). (gr. 9 up). lib. bdg. 39.93 ***978-0-7614-2583-0(7)** , Benchmark Bks.) Cavendish, Marshall Corp.

Stout, Mary. Atlanta. 2005. (Great Cities of the World Ser.). (Illus.). 48p. (J). pap. (978-0-8368-5202-8(8)); (YA). lib. bdg. 30.00 (978-0-8368-5042-0(4)) Stevens, Gareth Inc. (World Almanac Library).

Sullivan, Jody. Georgia. 2003. (Land of Liberty Ser.). (Illus.). 64p. (J). (gr. 3-4). lib. bdg. 23.93 (978-0-7368-1578-9(3) , Bridgestone Bks.) Capstone Pr., Inc.

GEORGIA—FICTION

Anderson, Jodi. Peaches. 2005. 320p. (J). (gr. 7 up). lib. bdg. 16.89 (978-0-06-073306-3(3)) HarperCollins Pubs.

Anderson, Jodi & Anderson, Jodi Lynn. Peaches. 2005. 320p. (YA). (gr. 7-12). 15.99 (978-0-06-073305-6(5)) HarperCollins Pubs.

Anderson, Jodi Lynn. Peaches. 2006. 320p. (J). reprint ed. pap. 8.99 (978-0-06-073307-0(1) , Harper Trophy) HarperCollins Pubs.

—The Secrets of Peaches. 2006. 304p. (YA). (gr. 9 up). 16.99 (978-0-06-073308-7(X) , HarperTeen) HarperCollins Pubs.

Angle, Kimberly Greene. Hummingbird. 2008. 256p. (J). 16.95 (***978-0-374-33376-8(9)***) Farrar, Straus & Giroux.

Armstrong, William H. Sounder. Barkley, James, illus. l.t. ed. 1999. (LRS Large Print Cornerstone Ser.). 230p. (YA). (gr. 6-12). lib. bdg. 27.95 (978-1-58118-054-1(3) , 22768) LRS.

As Orange As Marmalade: Tan naranja como Mermelada. 2007. (ENG & SPA.). (J). per. 10.00 (***978-0-9749876-8-2(9)***) Doggie In The Window Pubns.

Bauer Mueller, Pamela. An Angry Drum Echoed: Mary Musgrove, Queen of the Creeks. 2007. (Illus.). 296p. (J). (978-0-9685097-7-7(0)) Pinata Publishing.

Booth, A. Fran. Singing Violet: The Decade Between Georgia's Gold Rush & the Trail of Tears. 2002. 132p. (J). (gr. 4-7). pap. 16.95 (978-1-59129-299-9(9)) PublishAmerica, Inc.

Burch, Robert. Ida Early Comes over the Mountain. 2001. (J). (gr. 3-6). 20.75 (978-0-8446-7171-0(1)) Smith, Peter Pub., Inc.

Charbonneau, Eileen. The Connor Emerald. Williams, Lori, ed. 1999. 170p. (YA). pap. 9.99 (978-1-58365-753-9(3) , Timeless Romance) Sierra Raconteur Publishing.

Cofer, Amadeus. Mystery of the Golden Pearls: A Halloween Adventure in Clarkesville, 1. l.t. ed. 2004. (Illus.). 36p. (J). 14.00 (978-1-932957-02-0(2)) Legacy Pubs.

Coleman, Evelyn. Freedom Train. Riley, David, illus. 2008. 160p. (J). 15.99 (***978-0-689-84716-5(5)*** , McElderry, Margaret K.) Simon & Schuster Children's Publishing.

Dudley, David L. The Bicycle Man. 2005. 256p. (J). (gr. 5-9). 16.00 (978-0-618-54233-8(7) , Clarion Bks.) Houghton Mifflin Co. Trade & Reference Div.

Felcoski, Victoria. Secret of the Scotchpottle Farm. 2006. 21.99 (***978-1-4259-8117-4(8)***); pap. 12.99 (***978-1-4259-8118-1(6)***) AuthorHouse.

Gamble, Adam. Good Night Atlanta. Veno, Joe, illus. 2007. (Good Night Our World Ser.). 20p. (J). bds. 9.95 (***978-1-60219-001-6(1)***) Our World of Books.

Gibbons, Faye. The Day the Picture Man Came. Meidell, Sherry, illus. 2003. 32p. (YA). (gr. k-2). 16.95 (978-1-56397-161-7(5)) Boyds Mills Pr.

—Full Steam Ahead. Meidell, Sherry, illus. 2003. 32p. (J). (gr. k-2). 15.95 (978-1-56397-858-6(X)) Boyds Mills Pr.

GSUSA Staff. Octavia's Girl Scout Journey Activity Guide. 2001. (978-0-88441-624-1(0)) Girl Scouts of the USA.

Hahn, Stephen. Pike McCallister. 1998. 253p. (YA). (gr. 6 up). per. 14.95 (978-1-888125-29-0(2)) Publication Consultants.

Hantman, Clea. Goddesses No.3: Muses on the Move. 2002. (gr. 5-8). lib. bdg. 13.00 (978-0-613-71476-1(8)) Tandem Library Bks.

Hewett, Lorri. Lives of Our Own. 2000. (J). (978-0-606-19695-6(1)) Tandem Library Bks.

Holmes, Lynda. Spring Cleaning. 2006. 55p. pap. 12.95 (978-1-4241-4324-5(1)) PublishAmerica, Inc.

Huff, Barb. Perfect Girl. 2003. (gr. 3-6). lib. bdg. 11.80 (978-0-613-79653-8(5)) Tandem Library Bks.

Jacobs, Jimmy. Moonlight Through the Pines: Tales of the Georgia Evenings. Ward, Calvin H., illus. 2000. x, 116p. (J). (gr. 7-12). pap. 11.95 (978-0-9637477-3-0(8)) Franklin-Sarrett Pubs.

Kadohata, Cynthia. Kira-Kira. 2004. (Illus.). 256p. 16.95 (978-0-689-85639-6(3) , Atheneum); 2006. 272p. (J). reprint ed. pap. 6.99 (978-0-689-85640-2(7) , Aladdin) Simon & Schuster Children's Publishing.

—Kira-Kira. l.t. ed. 2005. 201p. 23.95 (978-0-7862-7616-5(9) , Large Print Pr.) Thorndike Pr.

Krisher, Trudy B. Kinship. 1999. (J). (978-0-606-16170-1(8)) Tandem Library Bks.

Kytle, Calvin. Like a Tree. 2007. 430p. 28.95 (***978-1-58838-220-7(6)*** , NewSouth Bks.) NewSouth, Inc.

Lasky, Kathryn. Georgia Rises. 2008. (J). (978-0-374-32529-9(4) , Farrar, Straus & Giroux (BYR)) Farrar, Straus & Giroux.

Love, Judy. Praise Be & Rainbows. 2006. 51p. pap. 12.95 (978-1-4241-0333-1(9)) PublishAmerica, Inc.

Matthews, Kezi. Scorpio's Child. 2001. 160p. (YA). (gr. 6-8). 16.95 (978-0-8126-2890-6(X)) Cricket Bks.

McDaniel, Lurlene. Garden of Angels. 2005. 288p. (YA). (gr. 7). pap. 5.50 (978-0-553-49432-7(5) , Laurel Leaf) Random Hse. Children's Bks.

—Letting Go of Lisa. (YA). (gr. 7). 2007. 176p. mass mkt. 6.50 (***978-0-440-23868-3(4)*** , Laurel Leaf); 2006. 192p. 10.95 (978-0-385-73159-1(0) , Delacorte Bks. for Young Readers); 2006. 192p. lib. bdg. 12.99 (978-0-385-90196-3(8) , Delacorte Bks. for Young Readers) Random Hse. Children's Bks.

Mickles Sr., Robert T. S. Blood Kin, a Savannah Story. 2007. 108p. per. 9.95 (***978-0-595-45129-6(2)***) iUniverse, Inc.

Miller, Mitzi & Millner, Denene. Hotlanta #1. 2008. 288p. (J). 8.99 (***978-0-545-00308-7(3)*** , Scholastic Paperbacks) Scholastic, Inc.

Mosley, Walter. 47. 240p. (gr. 7-17). 2005. (YA). 16.99 (978-0-316-11035-8(3)); 2006. (J). reprint ed. pap. 7.99 (978-0-316-01635-3(7)) Little Brown & Co.

Murphy, Rita. Black Angels. 2002. 176p. (J). (gr. 4). pap. 4.99 (978-0-440-22934-6(0) , Yearling) Random Hse. Children's Bks.

—Black Angels. 2002. (gr. 3-6). lib. bdg. 13.00 (978-0-613-57701-4(9)) Tandem Library Bks.

Myracle, Lauren. Thirteen. 2008. 224p. (J). (gr. 5). 15.99 (***978-0-525-47896-6(5)*** , Dutton Juvenile) Penguin Group (USA) Inc.

Norman, Will. Tignall Gold. 2004. 152p. (YA). pap. 13.95 (978-1-58736-359-7(3) , Starbound Bks.) Wheatmark.

O'Connor, Barbara. Moonpie & Ivy. 160p. (J). 2001. (gr. 5 up). 16.00 (978-0-374-35059-8(0) , Farrar, Straus & Giroux (BYR)); 2004. (Illus.). reprint ed. pap. 7.95 (978-0-374-45320-6(9) , Sunburst) Farrar, Straus & Giroux.

Oughton, Jerrie. The War in Georgia. 1999. (978-0-606-16444-3(8)) Tandem Library Bks.

Scampering Through Savannah. 2007. (YA). lib. bdg., act. bk. ed. (***978-0-9787589-2-9(7)***) ON Words Publishing, LLC.

Schick, Alice & Schick, Joel. The Penguin Child & the Albatross Child. 2007. (J). bds. 13.95 (***978-1-59692-228-0(1)***) MacAdam/Cage Publishing, Inc.

Schunk, Laurel. Black & Secret Midnight. 1998. 238p. (gr. 6-8). 24.99 (978-0-9661879-0-8(3) , SKP98-41) St Kitts Pr.

Stroud, Bettye. The Patchwork Path: A Quilt Map to Freedom. Bennett, Erin Susanne, illus. 2007. 32p. (J). (gr. k-3). pap. 7.99 (***978-0-7636-3519-0(7)***) Candlewick Pr.

Taylor, Mildred D. The Land. 2003. (gr. 7-12). lib. bdg. 15.30 (978-0-613-86520-3(0)) Tandem Library Bks.

Woods, Brenda. My Name Is Sally Little Song. 192p. (J). 2007. (gr. 2). 5.99 (***978-0-14-240943-5(X)*** , Puffin); 2006. (gr. 3-6). 15.99 (978-0-399-24312-7(7) , Putnam Juvenile) Penguin Group (USA) Inc.

Young, Ronder Thomas. Moving Mama to Town: Class Set. unabr. ed. 1998. (J). pap. 106.70 incl. audio (978-0-7887-2560-9(2) , 46730) Recorded Bks., LLC.

—Moving Mama to Town: Homework Set. unabr. ed. 1998. (J). 58.24 incl. audio (978-0-7887-1936-3(X) , 40643) Recorded Bks., LLC.

Zalonis, C. B. Strangers in the Forest. 2006. (J). pap. 8.00 (978-0-8059-6820-0(2)) Dorrance Publishing Co., Inc.

GEORGIA—HISTORY

Bednarz, Robert, et al. TIME for Kids Readers: Atlanta. 3rd ed. 2002. (Harcourt Horizons Ser.). (gr. k-7). pap. 38.10 (978-0-15-335268-3(X)) Harcourt Schl. Pubs.

Berendt, John. Midnight in the Garden of Good & Evil: A Savannah Story. 1999. (gr. 7-12). lib. bdg. 23.45 (978-0-613-19397-9(0)) Tandem Library Bks.

Britton, Tamara L. The Georgia Colony. 2001. (Colonies Ser.). (Illus.). 32p. (J). (gr. k-6). lib. bdg. 22.78 (978-1-57765-583-1(4) , Checkerboard Library) ABDO Publishing Co.

Brown, Vanessa. Georgia. 2005. (Bilingual Library of the United States of America: Set 1). (ENG & SPA., Illus.). 32p. (J). (ps-k). lib. bdg. 22.50 (978-1-4042-3075-0(0) , Buenas Letra) Rosen Publishing Group, Inc., The.

Coleman, Brooke. The Colony of Georgia. 2000. (Library of the Thirteen Colonies & the Lost Colony). (Illus.). 24p. (J). (gr. 3). lib. bdg. 19.95 (978-0-8239-5474-2(9) , PowerKids Pr.) Rosen Publishing Group, Inc., The.

Doak, Robin. Voices from Colonial America: Georgia 1629-1776. 2006. (Voices from Colonial America Ser.). (Illus.). 112p. (J). (gr. k-3). 21.95 (978-0-7922-6389-0(8)); 32.90 (978-0-7922-6858-1(X)) National Geographic Society. (National Geographic Children's Bks.).

Doherty, Craig A. & Doherty, Katherine M. Georgia. 2005. (Thirteen Colonies Ser.). (Illus.). 144p. (J). (gr. 4-9). 35.00 (978-0-8160-5419-0(3)) Facts On File, Inc.

Harkins, Susan Sales & Harkins, William H. Georgia: The Debtors Colony. 2006. (Building America Ser.). (Illus.). 48p. (J). (gr. 4-8). lib. bdg. 20.95 (978-1-58415-465-5(9)) Mitchell Lane Pubs., Inc.

Haskins, Jim. Delivering Justice: W. W. Law & the Fight for Civil Rights. Andrews, Benny, illus. 2005. 32p. (J). (gr. k-3). 17.99 (978-0-7636-2592-4(2)) Candlewick Pr.

Kaeter, Margaret. The Caucasian Republics. 2004. (Nations in Transition Ser.). (Illus.). 176p. (YA). (gr. 6-12). 40.00 (978-0-8160-5268-4(9)) Facts On File, Inc.

Marsh, Carole. Georgia History Projects: 30 Cool, Activities, Crafts, Experiments & More for Kids to Do to Learn about Your State! 2003. (Georgia Experience Ser.). 32p. (gr. k-5). pap. 5.95 (978-0-635-01779-6(2) , Marsh, Carole Bks.) Gallopade International.

—My First Pocket Guide Georgia. 2000. (Georgia Experience! Ser.). (Illus.). 96p. (J). (gr. 3-8). 12.95 (978-0-635-01300-2(2) , 13002) Gallopade International.

—The New Georgia Flag. 2001. (Illus.). (J). pap., tchr. ed. 7.95 (978-0-635-00506-9(9)) Gallopade International.

Mis, Melody S. The Colony of Georgia: A Primary Source History. 2007. (Primary Source Library of the Thirteen Colonies & the Lost Colony). (Illus.). 24p. (J). lib. bdg. (978-1-4042-3433-8(0) , PowerKids Pr.) Rosen Publishing Group, Inc., The.

Niland, Kurt, Sr. Gwinnett: Success Lives Here. 2003. 256p. bds. 64.95 (978-0-9748034-0-1(5)) Intaglio, Inc.

Quasha, Jennifer. How to Draw Georgias Sights & Symbols. 2002. (Kids Guide to Drawing America Ser.). 32p. (J). lib. bdg. 25.25 (978-0-8239-6065-1(X) , PowerKids Pr.) Rosen Publishing Group, Inc., The.

Schumacher, Tyler. The Georgia Colony. 2006. (Fact Finders Ser.). (Illus.). 32p. (J). (gr. 2-4). 22.60 (978-0-7368-2674-7(2) , Fact Finders) Capstone Pr., Inc.

Sonneborn, Liz. A Primary Source History of the Colony of Georgia. 2005. (Primary Sources of the Thirteen Colonies & the Lost Colony Ser.). (Illus.). 64p. (J). (gr. 3-7). pap. 14.60 (978-1-4042-0674-8(4)); (YA). (gr. 5-8). lib. bdg. 29.25 (978-1-4042-0426-3(1)) Rosen Publishing Group, Inc., The.

Steele, Christy & Todd, Anne M. A Confederate Girl: The Diary of Carrie Berry, 1864. 1999. (Diaries, Letters & Memoirs Ser.). (Illus.). 32p. (J). (gr. 2-7). pap. 21.00 (978-0-516-21338-5(5) , Children's Pr.) Scholastic Library Publishing.

Walsh, Kieran. James Oglethorpe. (Discover the Life of a Colonial American Ser.). 24p. 2005. (Illus.). (gr. 2-5). 14.95 (978-1-59515-138-4(9)); 2004. pap. 4.95 (978-1-59515-339-5(X)) Rourke Publishing, LLC.

Weitzel, Kelley G. The Timucua Indians: A Native American Detective Story. 2000. (UPF Young Readers Library). (Illus.). 176p. (gr. 4-7). pap. 12.95 (978-0-8130-1738-9(6)) Univ. Pr. of Florida.

Wiener. The 13 Colonies Pack: Georgia, 6. 2004. (Illus.). 48.30 (978-1-4109-0366-2(4)) Harcourt Schl. Pubs.

Wiener, Roberta & Arnold, James R. Georgia. 2004. (Illus.). 64p. (J). 28.56 (978-0-7398-6879-9(9)) Harcourt Schl. Pubs.

—The 13 Colonies: Georgia. 2004. (Illus.). 64p. (J). 8.95 (978-1-4109-0303-7(6)) Harcourt Schl. Pubs.

GEOSCIENCE

see Geology

GERBILS

Coppendale, Jean. Gerbils & Hamsters. 2004. (QEB You & Your Pet Ser.). (Illus.). 32p. (J). lib. bdg. 18.95 (978-1-59566-055-8(0)) QEB Publishing Inc.

Head, Honor. Hamsters & Gerbils. Burton, Jane, photos by. 2000. (My Pet Ser.). (Illus.). 32p. (J). (gr. 3-5). lib. bdg. 25.69 (978-0-7398-2886-1(X)) Raintree.

—Hamsters & Gerbils. 2000. (My Pet Ser.). (Illus.). 32p. (J). (gr. 3-5). pap. 8.95 (978-0-7398-3010-9(4)) Steck-Vaughn.

Hinds, Kathryn. Hamsters & Gerbils. 2000. (Perfect Pets Ser.). (Illus.). 32p. (J). (gr. 3-5). lib. bdg. 25.64 (978-0-7614-1104-8(6) , Benchmark Bks.) Cavendish, Marshall Corp.

Howell, Laura. Gerbils - internet Linked. 2005. 32p. (J). (gr. 1 up). pap. 5.95 (978-0-7945-1116-6(3) , Usborne) EDC Publishing.

Koopmans, Carol. Caring for Your Gerbil. 2006. (J). (978-1-59036-469-7(4)); lib. bdg. (978-1-59036-468-0(6)) Weigl Pubs., Inc.

Kotter, Engelbert. My Gerbil & Me. Steimer, Christine, photos by. 2002. (For the Love of Animals Ser.). (Illus.). 64p. pap. 6.99 (978-0-7641-1923-1(0)) Barron's Educational Series, Inc.

Landau, Elaine. Your Pet Gerbil. rev. ed. 2006. (True Book Ser.). (Illus.). 47p. (J). (978-0-531-16768-7(2)) Children's Pr., Ltd.

—Your Pet Gerbil. 1998. (True Bks.). (Illus.). 48p. (J). (gr. 3-5). pap. 6.95 (978-0-516-26264-2(5) , Children's Pr.) Scholastic Library Publishing.

Petty, Kate. Gerbil. 2005. (Illus.). 24p. (J). (gr. 2-5). lib. bdg. 22.80 (978-1-59604-030-4(0)) Stargazer Bks.

Rockwell, Anne F. My Pet Hamster. Lum, Bernice, illus. 2002. (Let's-Read-and-Find-Out Science Ser.). 40p. (J). (ps-1). 15.99 (978-0-06-028564-7(8)); 17.89 (978-0-06-028565-4(6)) HarperCollins Pubs.

Sjonger, Rebecca & Kalman, Bobbie. Gerbils. Crabtree, Marc, illus. Crabtree, Marc, photos by. 2004. (Pet Care Ser.). 32p. (J). pap. (978-0-7787-1784-3(4)); (978-0-7787-1752-2(6)) Crabtree Publishing Co.

GERBILS—FICTION

Adler, David A. The Many Troubles of Andy Russell. Hillenbrand, Will, illus. 2005. (Andy Russell Ser.). 144p. (J). pap. 5.95 (978-0-15-205440-3(5) , Gulliver Bks.) Harcourt Children's Bks.

Daniels, Lucy & Baglio, Ben M. Gerbil Genius. Howard, Paul, illus. 2000. (Animal Ark Pets Ser.: No. 9). 128p. (J). (gr. 3-6). pap. 3.99 (978-0-439-05166-8(5)) Scholastic, Inc.

Fine, Anne & Trimmer, Tony. Countdown. 2006. (Yellow Bananas Ser.). (Illus.). 44p. (J). (978-0-7787-0958-9(2)) Crabtree Publishing Co.

Jane, Pamela. Winky Blue Goes Wild! Tilley, Debbie, illus. 2003. 64p. (J). 13.95 (978-1-59034-588-7(6)); pap. (978-1-59034-589-4(4)) Mondo Publishing.

Levy, Elizabeth. Night of the Living Gerbil. Basso, Bill, illus. 2001. 96p. (J). (gr. 2-5). lib. bdg. 15.89 (978-0-06-028589-0(3)); (gr. k-4). 14.95 (978-0-06-028588-3(5)) HarperCollins Pubs.

Pearce, Philippa. The Firework-Maker's Daughter. unabr. ed. 2003. (Read-Along Ser.). (J). (gr. 3-6). pap. 24.95 incl. audio (978-0-7540-6217-2(1) , Galaxy Children's Large Print) BBC Audiobooks America.

Pearson, Mary E. Donde Esta Max? Cordova, Jacqueline, tr. Walker, Samantha L., illus. (Rookie Reader Espanol Ser.). (SPA.). 24p. (J). (gr. k-2). 2001. pap. 4.95 (978-0-516-27011-1(7)); 2000. 19.50 (978-0-516-22023-9(3)) Scholastic Library Publishing. (Children's Pr.).

—Donde Esta Max? 2000. (SPA.). (gr. k-3). lib. bdg. 12.95 (978-0-613-54176-3(6)) Tandem Library Bks.

—Where Is Max? Walker, Samantha L., illus. 2001. (Rookie Reader Espanol Ser.: Level A). 24p. (J). (gr. k-2). pap. 4.95 (978-0-516-27077-7(X) , Children's Pr.) Scholastic Library Publishing.

—Where Is Max? 2000. (gr. k-3). lib. bdg. 12.95 (978-0-613-54777-2(2)) Tandem Library Bks.

Schroeder, Judith, illus. Melvil & Dewey in the Chips. 2004. 48p. (J). (gr. 2-4). pap. 12.00 (978-1-59158-150-5(8) , LU1508) Libraries Unlimited, Inc.

—Melvil & Dewey in the Fast Lane. 2004. 48p. (J). (gr. 2-4). pap. 12.00 (978-1-59158-151-2(6) , LU1516) Libraries Unlimited, Inc.

Swallow, Pamela Curtis. Melvil & Dewey Gone Fishing. Eliasen, Lorena, illus. 2004. 56p. (J). pap. 12.00 (978-1-59158-153-6(2) , LU1532) Libraries Unlimited, Inc.

GERMAN LANGUAGE—CONVERSATION AND PHRASE BOOKS

Auf Deutsch! 2003. (978-0-618-02995-2(8)); (978-0-618-02996-9(6)); tchr. ed. (978-0-618-02964-8(8)); tchr. ed. (978-0-618-02965-5(6)); stu. ed. (978-0-618-02962-4(1)); stu. ed. (978-0-618-02961-7(3)); stu. ed., wbk. ed. (978-0-618-02967-9(2)); stu. ed., wbk. ed. (978-0-618-02968-6(0)); Level 3. (978-0-618-02997-6(4)); Level 3. stu. ed. (978-0-618-02963-1(X)); Level 3. stu. ed., wbk. ed. (978-0-618-02969-3(9)) McDougal Littell Inc.

Davis, Carla Norman. German Made Fun. 1999. (GER.). (J). Vol. 1, Bk. 1. (gr. 1-3). wbk. ed. 15.00 (978-1-930272-08-8(1)); Vol. 1, Bk. 2. (gr. 4-5). wbk. ed. 15.00 (978-1-930272-09-5(X)) Queen Enterprises, Inc.

Funk, Hermann, et al. Geni@l: Deutsch Fremdsprache fuer Jugendliche. (GER.). (YA). Level A1. 2005. pap. 22.95 (978-3-468-96709-2(8)); Level A2. 2005. 192p. pap., tchr. ed. 34.95 (978-3-468-47572-6(1)); Level A2. 2003. wbk. ed. 14.95 (978-3-468-96712-2(8)); Level B1. 2005. pap., tchr. ed. 34.75 (978-3-468-47532-0(2)); Level B1. 2005. 112p. pap., wbk. ed. 18.25 (978-3-468-47531-3(4)); Level B1. 2005. pap., wbk. ed. 16.50 (978-3-468-47536-8(5)) Langenscheidt Pubs Inc.

—Geni@l: Deutsch Fremdsprache fuer Jugendliche - Intensive Trainer. 2005. (GER & ENG.). (YA). Level A2. 94p. pap. 12.75 (978-3-468-47579-5(9)); Level B1. pap. 12.75 (978-3-468-47539-9(X)) Langenscheidt Pubs Inc.

—Geni@l: Deutsch Fremdsprache fuer Jugendliche - Test Booklet with CD-ROM. 2005. (GER & ENG.). (YA). Level A1. 48p. pap. 27.50 (978-3-468-47558-0(6)); Level A2. 56p. pap. 29.25 incl. audio compact disk (978-3-468-47578-8(0)); Level B1. 56p. pap. 27.50 incl. audio compact disk (978-3-468-47538-2(1)) Langenscheidt Pubs Inc.

Litchfield, J. Everyday Words German Sticker Book. 2004. (GER.). 32p. (J). pap. 8.95 (978-0-7945-0479-3(5)) EDC Publishing.

Litchfield, J. & Brooks, F. Everyday Words in German. rev. ed. 2004. (Computer Guide Ser.). (GER.). 48p. (J). 12.95 (978-0-7945-0424-3(8)) EDC Publishing.

Litchfield, Jo. Everyday Words in German. 1999. (Everyday Words Ser.). (GER & ENG., Illus.). 48p. (J). (ps-3). 12.95 (978-0-7460-2770-7(2)) EDC Publishing.

Lovik. Student In-Text Audio: Used with ... Lovik-Vorsprung: An Introduction to the German Language & Culture for Communication. rev. ed. 2002. (YA). cd-rom 45.16 (978-0-618-14254-5(1) , 333155) Houghton Mifflin College Div.

Passport Books Staff, ed. German Picture Dictionary. Goodman, Marlene, illus. 2003. (Let's Learn... Picture Ser.). (GER.). 72p. (J). (gr. 4-7). pap. 9.95 (978-0-8442-2167-0(8) , 21678, Passport Bks.) McGraw-Hill Trade.

Pirz, Therese S. & Hobson, Mark. Kids' Stuff German: Easy German Phrases to Teach Your Kids (and Yourself) 1999. (Bilingual Kids Ser.: Vol. 3). (ENG & GER., Illus.). 177p. (J). (ps-8). pap. 18.95 (978-0-9606140-4-2(4)) Chou-Chou Pr.

GERMAN LANGUAGE—DICTIONARIES—ENGLISH

Bedeutungswoerterbuch. 3rd ed. (Duden-Schuelerduden Ser.). (GER.). 496p. (YA). 26.95 (978-3-411-05963-8(X)) Bibliographisches Institut & F. A. Brockhaus AG DEU. *Dist:* International Bk. Import Service, Inc.

Berlitz Publishing Staff. German: Picture Dictionary. Demarest, Chris L., illus. 2nd ed. 2004. (Berlitz Picture Dictionaries Ser.). (ENG, GER & GRE.). 128p. (ps-4). pap. 12.95 (978-981-246-388-3(7) , 463887) Berlitz Publishing.

Davies, H. German Dictionary for Beginners. 2004. (Beginner's Dictionaries Ser.). (GER.). 128p. (J). pap. 12.95 (978-0-7945-0289-8(X)); lib. bdg. 20.95 (978-1-58086-487-9(2)) EDC Publishing.

Funk, Hermann, et al. Geni@l: Deutsch Fremdsprache fuer Jugendliche - Learning Glossary German-English. (GER & ENG.). (YA). 2005. 64p. pap. 11.50 (978-3-468-47560-3(8)); Level A2. 2005. 64p. pap. 10.95 (978-3-468-47580-1(2)); Level A2. 2003. 18.95 (978-3-468-96711-5(X)); Level B1. 2004. 72p. 9.95 (978-3-468-47540-5(3)) Langenscheidt Pubs Inc.

Goodman, Marlene. Let's Learn German Dictionary. 2003. (ENG & GER., Illus.). 80p. 10.95 (978-0-07-140824-0(X) , 9780071408240) McGraw-Hill Cos., The.

Hippocrene Books Staff. Children's Illustrated German Dictionary: English-German, German-English. 2003. (Hippocrene Children's Illustrated Foreign Language Dictionaries Ser.). (ENG & GER., Illus.). 122p. pap. 11.95 (978-0-7818-0986-3(X)) Hippocrene Bks., Inc.

Hippocrene Books Staff, ed. Children's Illustrated German Dictionary: English-German, German-English. 1998. (Children's Illustrated Foreign Language Dictionaries Ser.). (ENG & GER., Illus.). 122p. (gr. k-5). 14.95 (978-0-7818-0722-7(0)) Hippocrene Bks., Inc.

Hochstatter, Daniel J. Just Look 'n Learn German Picture Dictionary. 2003. (ENG & GER., Illus.). 96p. 11.95 (978-0-07-140831-8(2) , 9780071408318) McGraw-Hill Cos., The.

Kuehn. Mein Erstes Schul-Woerterbuch. 2000. (GER., Illus.). 144p. (J). (978-3-427-31951-1(2) , 3195) Dummler's Ferd., Verlagsbuchhandlung DEU. *Dist:* International Bk. Import Service, Inc.

—Mein Schul-Woerterbuch. 2000. (GER., Illus.). 416p. (J). (978-3-427-31913-9(X) , 3191) Dummler's Ferd., Verlagsbuchhandlung DEU. *Dist:* International Bk. Import Service, Inc.

—Woerterbuch-Training. 2000. (GER., Illus.). 88p. (J). pap., wbk. ed. (978-3-427-31922-1(9) , 3192) Dummler's Ferd., Verlagsbuchhandlung DEU. *Dist:* International Bk. Import Service, Inc.

Lipton, Gladys C. & Losoncy, Renata. German Bilingual Dictionary. 1998. (Barron's Bilingual Dictionaries Ser.). (ENG & GER., Illus.). 180p. (gr. 4-7). pap. 10.99 (978-0-7641-0340-7(7)) Barron's Educational Series, Inc.

Litchfield, J. & Brooks, F. Everyday Words in German. rev. ed. 2004. (What Shall I Do Today? Ser.). (GER.). 48p. (J). lib. bdg. 20.95 (978-1-58086-547-0(X)) EDC Publishing.

WrightGroup/McGraw-Hill. German. 2003. (Just Look 'n Learn Picture Dictionary Ser.). (GER & ENG., Illus.). 96p. (J). (gr. 4-7). 11.95 (978-0-8442-2058-1(2) , 20582, Passport Bks.) McGraw-Hill Trade.

GERMAN LANGUAGE—GRAMMAR

Amery, H. First Thousand Words in German. 2004. (First Thousand Words Ser.). 64p. (J). lib. bdg. 20.95 (978-1-58086-625-5(5) , Usborne) EDC Publishing.

Derkow-Disselbeck, Barbara & Kirsch, Dieter. Anna, Schmidt und Oskar, Level 2. 2005. (GER.). 64p. (J). pap., tchr. ed. 19.25 (978-3-468-96853-2(1)) Langenscheidt Pubs Inc.

Duden. Kennst du Das? Das ABC. (Duden Ser.). (GER., Illus.). 16p. (J). (978-3-411-70631-0(7)) Bibliographisches Institut & F. A. Brockhaus AG DEU. *Dist:* International Bk. Import Service, Inc.

—Kennst du Das? Lastwagen. (Duden Ser.). (GER., Illus.). 16p. (J). (978-3-411-70641-9(4)) Bibliographisches Institut & F. A. Brockhaus AG DEU. *Dist:* International Bk. Import Service, Inc.

Funk, Hermann, et al. Geni@l: Deutsch Fremdsprache fuer Jugendliche. 2005. (GER & ENG.). (YA). pap. 16.50 (978-3-468-47555-9(1)); (YA). pap. 16.50 (978-3-468-47576-4(4)); Level A1. 168p. pap., tchr. ed. 34.75 (978-3-468-47552-8(7)); Level A1. (YA). pap. 43.00 (978-3-468-47557-3(8)); Level A1. (YA). pap. 16.50 (978-3-468-47556-6(X)); Level A1. (YA). pap. 22.50 (978-3-468-47553-5(5)); Level A1. (YA). pap. 22.50 (978-3-468-47554-2(3)); Level A2. (YA). pap. 43.00 (978-3-468-47577-1(2)); Level A2. (YA). pap. 22.50 (978-3-468-47574-0(8)); Level A2. (YA). pap. 22.50 (978-3-468-47573-3(X)); Level A2. (YA). pap. 16.50 (978-3-468-47575-7(6)); Level B1. (YA). pap., tchr. ed. 22.50 (978-3-468-47534-4(9)); Level B1. (YA). pap., tchr. ed. 22.50 (978-3-468-47533-7(0)); Level B1. (YA). pap., wbk. ed. 16.50 (978-3-468-47535-1(7)) Langenscheidt Pubs Inc.

—Geni@l: Deutsch Fremdsprache fuer Jugendliche - Intensive Trainer, Level A1. 2005. (GER.). 96p. pap. 10.95 (978-3-468-47559-7(4)) Langenscheidt Pubs Inc.

Grammatik. (Duden-Schuelerduden Ser.). (GER.). 522p. (YA). (978-3-411-05634-7(7)); 96p. (J). (gr. 4-5). (978-3-411-04441-2(1)) Bibliographisches Institut & F. A. Brockhaus AG DEU. *Dist:* International Bk. Import Service, Inc.

Holt, Rinehart and Winston Staff. Komm Mit! Level 1: Grammatikheft. 3rd ed. 2003. (GER.). pap., tchr. ed. 21.46 (978-0-03-065009-3(7)) Holt, Rinehart & Winston.

—Komm Mit! Level 1: Practice & Activities Book. 1998. pap. 18.53 (978-0-03-032524-3(2)) Holt, Rinehart & Winston.

—Komm Mit! Level 1: Ubungsheft. 3rd ed. 2003. (GER.). pap., tchr. ed. 22.66 (978-0-03-065012-3(7)) Holt, Rinehart & Winston.

Morris, Kelly. German - Elementary. 2000. (100+ Seriestm Ser.). (FRE & GER.). 128p. (J). (gr. k-12). pap. 12.99 (978-1-56822-916-4(X) , IF8788) School Specialty Publishing.

—German - Middle/High School. 2000. (100+ Seriestm Ser.). (FRE & GER.). 128p. (J). (gr. k-12). pap. 12.99 (978-1-56822-917-1(8) , IF8789) School Specialty Publishing.

Teichert. Student in-text Audio Cd: Used with ... Teichert-Allerlei zum Lesen. 2nd ed. 2004. (YA). cd-rom 3.96 (978-0-618-55993-0(0) , 355332) Houghton Mifflin College Div.

Uebungen zur Deutschen Rechtschreibung I. (Duden-Schuelerduden Ser.). (GER.). 304p. (YA). (978-3-411-05243-1(0)) Bibliographisches Institut & F. A. Brockhaus AG DEU. *Dist:* International Bk. Import Service, Inc.

Uebungen zur Deutschen Rechtschreibung II. (Duden-Schuelerduden Ser.). (GER.). 160p. (YA). (978-3-411-05593-7(6)) Bibliographisches Institut & F. A. Brockhaus AG DEU. *Dist:* International Bk. Import Service, Inc.

GERMAN LANGUAGE—READERS

Die Abenteuer der Seefahrt.Tr. of Adventure of Seafares. (GER., Illus.). (YA). 31.95 (978-3-411-09141-6(X) , MY9141E) Bibliographisches Institut & F. A. Brockhaus AG DEU. *Dist:* Continental Bk. Co., Inc.

Das Aegyptische Grab. (GER.). (978-3-411-09301-4(3)) Bibliographisches Institut & F. A. Brockhaus AG DEU. *Dist:* i.b.d., Ltd.

Am Himmel und im Weltall. (GER.). 19.95 (978-3-411-09311-3(0)) Bibliographisches Institut & F. A. Brockhaus AG DEU. *Dist:* Distribooks, Inc., i.b.d., Ltd.

Auf der Suche Nach Ihrem Freund. 2000. (GER., Illus.). 70p. (YA). (gr. 6-8). pap. 12.95 (978-88-8148-322-8(X)) European Language Institute ITA. *Dist:* Distribooks, Inc., Midwest European Pubns.

Aufsatz. (Duden-Schuelerhilfen Ser.). (GER.). 79p. (J). (gr. 2-3). (978-3-411-02616-6(2)) Bibliographisches Institut & F. A. Brockhaus AG DEU. *Dist:* International Bk. Import Service, Inc.

Aufsatz 2. (Duden-Schuelerhilfen Ser.). (GER.). 96p. (J). (gr. 3-4). (978-3-411-02633-3(2)) Bibliographisches Institut & F. A. Brockhaus AG DEU. *Dist:* International Bk. Import Service, Inc.

Aufsatz/Bericht. (Duden-Schuelerhilfen Ser.). (GER.). 112p. (YA). (gr. 8-10). (978-3-411-05731-3(9)) Bibliographisches Institut & F. A. Brockhaus AG DEU. *Dist:* International Bk. Import Service, Inc.

Aufsatz/Beschreibung. (Duden-Schuelerhilfen Ser.). (GER.). 112p. (YA). (gr. 7-10). (978-3-411-05761-0(0)) Bibliographisches Institut & F. A. Brockhaus AG DEU. *Dist:* International Bk. Import Service, Inc.

Aufsatz/Eroerterung. (Duden-Schuelerhilfen Ser.). (GER.). 112p. (YA). (gr. 8-10). (978-3-411-05741-2(6)) Bibliographisches Institut & F. A. Brockhaus AG DEU. *Dist:* International Bk. Import Service, Inc.

Aufsatz/Erzaehlen. (Duden-Schuelerhilfen Ser.). (GER.). 112p. (J). (gr. 5-7). (978-3-411-05821-1(8)) Bibliographisches Institut & F. A. Brockhaus AG DEU. *Dist:* International Bk. Import Service, Inc.

Aufsatz/Inhaltsangabe. (Duden-Schuelerhilfen Ser.). (GER.). 112p. (YA). (gr. 7-9). (978-3-411-05801-3(3)) Bibliographisches Institut & F. A. Brockhaus AG DEU. *Dist:* International Bk. Import Service, Inc.

Blair, Robert. Power-Glide German Children's Course, 2 bks. l.t. rev. ed. 2001. (Illus.). 206p. (J). pap. 59.95 incl. audio compact disk (978-1-58204-212-1(8)) Power-Glide Foreign Language Courses.

—Power-Glide German Children's Workbook Upgrade, 2. l.t. ed. 2002. (Illus.). 206p. (J). pap. 29.95 (978-1-58204-225-1(X)) Power-Glide Foreign Language Courses.

—Power-Glide German Lower Elementary, 4 vols. l.t. ed. 2002. (Illus.). 524p. pap. 99.95 incl. cd-rom, audio compact disk (978-1-58204-208-4(X)) Power-Glide Foreign Language Courses.

—Power-Glide German Ultimate Additional Learner Package, 2 bks. 2002. (Illus.). 482p. (YA). pap. 39.95 (978-1-58204-215-2(2)) Power-Glide Foreign Language Courses.

—Power-Glide German Ultimate Adventure Course, 2 bks. 2002. (Illus.). 482p. (YA). pap. 149.95 incl. cd-rom, audio compact disk (978-1-58204-202-2(0)) Power-Glide Foreign Language Courses.

Blair, Robert W. Power-Glide German Lower Elementary, 3 vols. l.t. ed. 2002. (Illus.). 355p. (J). pap. 119.95 incl. cd-rom, audio compact disk (978-1-58204-221-3(7)) Power-Glide Foreign Language Courses.

Boldt. Politik und Gesellschaft. (Duden-Schuelerduden Ser.). (GER., Illus.). 460p. (YA). 27.95 (978-3-411-04723-9(2)) Bibliographisches Institut & F. A. Brockhaus AG DEU. *Dist:* Continental Bk. Co., Inc., International Bk. Import Service, Inc.

Bour, Laura. Am Fluss. 2005. (Meyers Klein Kinderbibliothek). (GER.). 24p. (J). spiral bd. 14.25 (978-3-411-08591-0(6)) Langenscheidt Pubs Inc.

Bourgoing, Pascale de. Der Apfel. 2005. (Meyers Klein Kinderbibliothek).Tr. of Apple. (GER., Illus.). 24p. (J). spiral bd. 14.25 (978-3-411-08541-5(X)) Langenscheidt Pubs Inc.

Broeger, Achim. Meyers Grosses Kinderlexikon. (GER., Illus.). 348p. (978-3-411-07693-2(3)) Bibliographisches Institut & F. A. Brockhaus AG DEU. *Dist:* i.b.d., Ltd.

Burke, David. Goldilocks (English to German - Level 2) Learn GERMAN Through Fairy Tales. 2007. (Learn German Through Fairy Tales Ser.). (ENG & GER., Illus.). (J). per. 14.95 incl. audio compact disk (***978-1-891888-83-0(8)***) Slangman Publishing.

Cooper-Pete, Beverly. Tootie Fruity Bear's Sing-A-Long Tunes. 4th l.t. ed. 2000. Tr. of Para que cantes junto con el oso Tootie Fruity. (ENG & GER.). 32p. pap. (978-0-9714093-1-6(5)) Trey-Ish & Co.

Delafosse, Claude. Das Haus. 2005. (Meyers Klien Kinderbibliothek). (GER.). 24p. (J). spiral bd. 14.25 (978-3-411-08561-3(4)) Langenscheidt Pubs Inc.

Delafosse, Claude & Mettler, Réne. Die Maus. 2005. (Meyers Klien Kinderbibliothek). (GER., Illus.). 24p. (J). spiral bd. 14.25 (978-3-411-08551-4(7)) Langenscheidt Pubs Inc.

—Der Vogel. 2005. (Meyers Klein Kinderbibliothek).Tr. of Bird. (GER.). 24p. (J). spiral bd. 14.25 (978-3-411-08531-6(2)) Langenscheidt Pubs Inc.

Der Deutsche Aufsatz. (Duden Abiturhilfen Ser.). (GER.). 96p. (YA). (gr. 12-13). (978-3-411-04641-6(4)) Bibliographisches Institut & F. A. Brockhaus AG DEU. *Dist:* International Bk. Import Service, Inc.

Ferienspass Deutsch. 2000. (GER & ENG., Illus.). (J). (gr. k-5). Vol. 1. pap., wbk. ed. 14.95 (978-88-8148-365-5(3)); Vol. 2. pap., wbk. ed. 14.95 (978-88-8148-366-2(1)); Vol. 3. pap., wbk. ed. 14.95 (978-88-8148-367-9(X)) European Language Institute ITA. *Dist:* Distribooks, Inc., Midwest European Pubns.

Geheimnis bei der Wassersport-Olympiade. 2000. (GER., Illus.). 70p. (YA). (gr. 6-8). pap. 12.95 (978-88-8148-455-3(2)) European Language Institute ITA. *Dist:* Distribooks, Inc., Midwest European Pubns.

Hannas Tagebuch. 2000. (GER., Illus.). 70p. (YA). (gr. 7-9). pap. 11.95 (978-88-8148-327-3(0)) European Language Institute ITA. *Dist:* Distribooks, Inc., Midwest European Pubns.

Holt, Rinehart and Winston Staff. Elements of Literature: Terra Nova Test Preparation with Answer Key. 5th ed. 2005. pap. 13.46 (978-0-03-037789-1(7)) Harcourt Schl. Pubs.

—Komm Mitt! Level 1: Storytelling Book. 3rd ed. 2003. (GER.). pap. 14.60 (978-0-03-065479-4(3)) Holt, Rinehart & Winston.

Im Zirkus. (GER.). (978-3-411-09341-0(2)) Bibliographisches Institut & F. A. Brockhaus AG DEU. *Dist:* i.b.d., Ltd.

In den Nestern der Insekten. (GER.). (978-3-411-09281-9(5)) Bibliographisches Institut & F. A. Brockhaus AG DEU. *Dist:* i.b.d., Ltd.

In Hoehlen und Grotten. (GER.). (978-3-411-09291-8(2)) Bibliographisches Institut & F. A. Brockhaus AG DEU. *Dist:* i.b.d., Ltd.

Die Kleine Seejungfer: Family, The Weather, Gardens, Underwater Life. 2000. (GER & ENG., Illus.). 24p. (J). (ps-5). pap. 7.95 (978-88-8148-362-4(9)) European Language Institute ITA. *Dist:* Distribooks, Inc., Midwest European Pubns.

Literatur. 3rd ed. (Duden-Schuelerduden Ser.). (GER.). 432p. (YA). (978-3-411-05403-9(4)) Bibliographisches Institut & F. A. Brockhaus AG DEU. *Dist:* International Bk. Import Service, Inc.

Meyer-Hullmann, Kerstin, illus. Das Grundschulwoerterbuch. (Duden Ser.). (GER.). 224p. (J). (978-3-411-06061-0(1)) Bibliographisches Institut & F. A. Brockhaus AG DEU. *Dist:* International Bk. Import Service, Inc.

Meyers Editors. Der Bauernhof. 2005. (Meyers Klien Kinderbibliothek). (GER.). 24p. (J). spiral bd. 14.25 (978-3-411-08581-1(9)) Langenscheidt Pubs Inc.

—Das Schiff. 2005. (Meyers Klien Kinderbibliothek). (GER.). 24p. (J). spiral bd. 14.25 (978-3-411-08571-2(1)) Langenscheidt Pubs Inc.

Moerike, Eduard. Mozart Auf der Reise Nach Prag. 2006. (GER.). pap. (***978-1-4068-0825-4(3)***) Echo Library.

Na Klar 2 (Lower) 2005. (Illus.). (J). pap., stu. ed. 32.50 (978-0-7487-9160-6(4)) Nelson Thornes Ltd. GBR. *Dist:* Trans-Atlantic Pubns., Inc.

Naoura, Salah. Auf dem Bauernhof. (GER., Illus.). 24p. pap. (978-3-411-08241-4(0)) Bibliographisches Institut & F. A. Brockhaus AG DEU. *Dist:* i.b.d., Ltd.

—Im Eis. (GER., Illus.). 24p. pap. (978-3-411-08251-3(8)) Bibliographisches Institut & F. A. Brockhaus AG DEU. *Dist:* i.b.d., Ltd.

—Im Regenwald. (GER., Illus.). 24p. pap. (978-3-411-08231-5(3)) Bibliographisches Institut & F. A. Brockhaus AG DEU. *Dist:* i.b.d., Ltd.

—In der Savanne. (GER., Illus.). 24p. pap. (978-3-411-08261-2(5)) Bibliographisches Institut & F. A. Brockhaus AG DEU. *Dist:* i.b.d., Ltd.

Raths, Angelika. Ein Bisschen Panik. 2000. (GER.). 80p. (YA). pap. 31.00 (978-3-468-49818-3(7)) Langenscheidt Pubs Inc.

Robinson, Bryan, ed. Bilingual Baby Vol. 3: Introduce Your Child to German. 2000. (GER.). (J). pap., stu. ed. 16.95 incl. VHS (978-1-892703-11-8(4)) Small Fry Productions.

Rosler, O'Sullivan. It Could Be Worse-Oder? (GER.). 8.95 (978-3-499-20374-9(X) , RW374E) Rowohlt Taschenbuch Verlag GmbH DEU. *Dist:* Continental Bk. Co., Inc.

Schaetze und Wracks. (GER.). (978-3-411-09331-1(5)) Bibliographisches Institut & F. A. Brockhaus AG DEU. *Dist:* i.b.d., Ltd.

Scholz, Barbara, illus. Der Abc-Duden. 2nd ed. (Duden Ser.). (GER.). 96p. (J). (978-3-411-70772-0(0)) Bibliographisches Institut & F. A. Brockhaus AG DEU. *Dist:* International Bk. Import Service, Inc.

Semper, Lothar. Auf Einer Harley Davidson Mochte Ich Sterben, Grades 7-12. 2005. (GER.). 104p. (YA). (gr. 7-12). pap. 9.00 (978-3-468-49697-4(4)) Langenscheidt Pubs Inc.

Ein Sprung Ins Unbekannte. 2000. (GER., Illus.). 70p. (YA). (gr. 8-10). pap. 11.95 (978-88-8148-332-7(7)) European Language Institute ITA. *Dist:* Distribooks, Inc., Midwest European Pubns.

Trim, John & Kohl, Katrin M. Deutsch Direkt. (J). (gr. 9-12). suppl. ed. 84.00 (978-0-8219-0227-1(X) , 45033) EMC/Paradigm Publishing.

—Deutsch Direkt! (J). (gr. 9-12). wbk. ed. 19.95 (978-0-8219-0240-0(7) , 45659) EMC/Paradigm Publishing.

—Deutsch Direkt! Answer Key. (J). (gr. 9-12). 11.95 (978-0-8219-0354-4(3) , 45826) EMC/Paradigm Publishing.

Verdet, Jean-Pierre. Das Weltall. 2005. (Meyers Klien Kinderbibliothek Ser.). (GER.). (J). spiral bd. 14.25 (978-3-411-09791-3(4)) Langenscheidt Pubs Inc.

Wesson, Alan & Spencer, J. Michael. Na Klar 2 (Higher) 2005. (Illus.). (J). pap., stu. ed. 32.50 (978-0-7487-9159-0(0)) Nelson Thornes Ltd. GBR. *Dist:* Trans-Atlantic Pubns., Inc.

Wesson, Alan & Spencer, Michael. Na Klar! 1. 2004. (GER., Illus.). 160p. (J). pap., stu. ed. 32.50 (978-0-7487-7838-6(1)) Nelson Thornes Ltd. GBR. *Dist:* Trans-Atlantic Pubns., Inc.

Der Zinnsoldat: Toys, In Town, At the Market, Prepositions of Place. 2000. (GER & ENG., Illus.). 24p. (J). (ps-5). pap. 7.95 (978-88-8148-292-4(4)) European Language Institute ITA. *Dist:* Distribooks, Inc., Midwest European Pubns.

GERMAN SHEPHERD DOG

Fiedler, Julie. German Shepherd Dogs. 2006. (Illus.). 24p. (J). lib. bdg. (978-1-4042-3121-4(8) , PowerKids Pr.) Rosen Publishing Group, Inc., The.

Gray, Susan H. German Shepherds. 2008. (Domestic Dogs Ser.). 32p. (J). (gr. k-4). 27.07 (***978-1-59296-965-4(8)***) Child's World, Inc.

Loewen, Nancy. German Shepherds. 2003. (Dog Breeds Ser.). 24p. (J). lib. bdg. 21.35 (978-1-58340-313-6(2)) Smart Apple Media.

Miller, Connie Colwell. German Shepherds. 2007. (Illus.). 24p. (J). 15.93 (978-0-7368-6327-8(3)) Capstone Pr., Inc.

Stone, Lynn M. German Shepherds. 2003. (Eye to Eye with Dogs Ser.). (Illus.). 24p. (gr. 2-5). 17.95 (978-1-58952-327-2(X)) Rourke Publishing, LLC.

GERMANS—UNITED STATES

Ashbrock, Peg. The German Americans. 2002. (Welcome to America Ser.). (Illus.). 64p. (J). (gr. 5 up). lib. bdg. (978-1-59084-107-5(7)) Mason Crest Pubs.

Boyer Binns, Tristan. German Americans. (We Are America Ser.). (Illus.). 32p. (J). 2003. (gr. 2-4). lib. bdg. (978-1-4034-0165-6(9)); 2002. pap. 6.95 (978-1-4034-0420-6(8)) Heinemann Library.

Fitterer, C. Ann. German Americans. 2002. (Spirit of America: Our Cultural Heritage Ser.). (Illus.). 32p. (J). (gr. 2-6). 27.07 (978-1-56766-151-4(3)) Child's World, Inc.

Frost, Helen. German Immigrants, 1820-1920. 2001. (Blue Earth Books). (Illus.). 32p. (J). (gr. 3-4). lib. bdg. 22.60 (978-0-7368-0794-4(2) , Bridgestone Bks.) Capstone Pr., Inc.

Nickles, Greg. The Germans. 2001. (We Came to North America Ser.). (Illus.). 32p. (J). (gr. 4). (978-0-7787-0191-0(3)); pap. (978-0-7787-0205-4(7)) Crabtree Publishing Co.

Parker, Lewis K. Why German Immigrants Came to America. 2003. (Reading Power Ser.). (Illus.). 24p. (J). lib. bdg. 17.25 (978-0-8239-6458-1(2) , PowerKids Pr.) Rosen Publishing Group, Inc., The.

Sonneborn, Liz. German Americans. 2003. (Immigrants in America Ser.). (Illus.). 112p. (gr. 6-12). 30.00 (978-0-7910-7127-4(8)); pap. 30.00 (978-0-7910-7512-8(5)) Facts On File, Inc. (Chelsea Hse.).

Ueda, Reed & Stotsky, Sandra, eds. German-American Answer Book. 1999. (Ethnic Answer Book Ser.). (Illus.). 136p. (YA). (gr. 5 up). pap. 9.95 (978-0-7910-4794-1(6)); lib. bdg. 19.75 (978-0-7910-4793-4(8)) Facts On File, Inc. (Chelsea Hse.).

GERMANS—UNITED STATES—FICTION

Bender, Esther. Virginia & the Tiny One. Keenan, Joy Dunn, illus. 1998. (Lemon Tree Ser.: Vol. 2). 80p. (J). (gr. 3-7). pap. 6.99 (978-0-8361-9090-8(4)) Herald Pr.

Doty, Kathryn Adams. Wild Orphan. 2006. 144p. pap. 14.95 (978-1-889020-20-4(6)) Edinborough Pr.

Hubbard, Coleen. Christmas in Silver Lake, Rabinowitz, Sandy & Keiffer, Christa, illus. l.t. ed. 1999. (Treasured Horses Collection). 128p. (J). (gr. 4 up). lib. bdg. 23.33 (978-0-8368-2400-1(8)) Stevens, Gareth Inc.

O Little Town (Germans) 76p. (YA). (gr. 6-12). pap. 9.95 (978-0-8224-3681-2(7)) Globe Fearon Educational Publishing.

GERMANY

Allison, Amy. Germany. 2001. (Dropping in on Ser.). (Illus.). 32p. (J). lib. bdg. 28.50 (978-1-55916-284-5(8)) Rourke Publishing, LLC.

Blashfield, Jean F. Germany. 2003. (Enchantment of the World, Second Ser.). (Illus.). 144p. (J). (gr. 5-9). 36.00 (978-0-516-22376-6(3) , Children's Pr.) Scholastic Library Publishing.

Boast, Clare. Germany. 1998. (Next Stop! Ser.). 32p. (J). lib. bdg. 19.92 (978-1-57572-566-6(5)) Heinemann Library.

Byers, Ann. Germany: A Primary Source Cultural Guide. 2005. (Primary Sources of World Cultures Ser.). (Illus.). 128p. (J). (gr. 4-8). lib. bdg. 34.60 (978-1-4042-2910-5(8)) Rosen Publishing Group, Inc., The.

Cartlidge, Cherese & Clark, Charles. Life in Berlin. 2001. (Way People Live Ser.). (Illus.). 96p. (YA). (gr. 7-10). 28.70 (978-1-56006-870-9(1) , LML00902-178194, Lucent Bks.) Thomson Gale.

Costain, Meredith & Collins, Paul. Welcome to Germany. 2001. (Countries of the World Ser.). (Illus.). 32p. (J). (gr. 4 up). 28.00 (978-0-7910-6546-4(4) , 010204, Chelsea Hse.) Facts On File, Inc.

Davis, Kevin A. Look What Came from Germany. 1999. (J). (978-0-606-20144-5(0)); (gr. 3-6). lib. bdg. 15.25 (978-0-613-29680-9(X)) Tandem Library Bks.

Dolan, Sean. Germany. 1999. (Major World Nations Ser.). (Illus.). 144p. (YA). (gr. 4-7). 29.95 (978-0-7910-4752-1(0) , Chelsea Hse.) Facts On File, Inc.

Flint, David. Focus on Germany. 2006. (Illus.). 64p. (J). pap. 11.95 (978-0-8368-6237-9(6)); lib. bdg. 32.67 (978-0-8368-6218-8(X)) Stevens, Gareth Inc. (World Almanac Library).

Frank, Nicole & Lord, Richard. Welcome to Germany. 1999. (Welcome to My Country Ser.). (Illus.). 48p. (J). (gr. 2 up). lib. bdg. 26.00 (978-0-8368-2496-4(2)) Stevens, Gareth Inc.

Frost, Helen. A Look at Germany. Saunders-Smith, Gail, ed. 2002. (Our World Ser.). (Illus.). 24p. (J). (gr. k-1). lib. bdg. 15.93 (978-0-7368-1430-0(2) , Pebble Bks.) Capstone Pr., Inc.

—A Look at Germany. 2005. (One World, Many Cultures Ser.). 24p. (YA). (gr. k-3). pap. (978-0-7368-9392-3(X) , Pebble Bks.) Capstone Pr., Inc.

Ganeri, Anita. Germany & the Germans. 2004. (Focus on Europe Ser.). (J). lib. bdg. 28.50 (978-1-932799-17-0(6)) Stargazer Bks.

Gordon, Sharon. Germany. 2004. (Discovering Cultures Ser.). (J). 25.64 (978-0-7614-1792-7(3) , Benchmark Bks.) Cavendish, Marshall Corp.

Gray, Shirley W. Germany. 2001. (First Reports). (Illus.). 48p. (J). (gr. 3 up). 22.60 (978-0-7565-0128-0(8)) Compass Point Bks.

Gray, Susan Heinrichs. England. 2001. (First Reports). (Illus.). 48p. (J). (gr. 3 up). lib. bdg. 22.60 (978-0-7565-0127-3(X)) Compass Point Bks.

—Germany. 2003. (True Book Ser.). (Illus.). 48p. (J). 25.00 (978-0-516-22673-6(8) , Children's Pr.) Scholastic Library Publishing.

—Germany. 2003. (gr. 3-6). lib. bdg. 15.25 (978-0-613-67963-3(6)) Tandem Library Bks.

Harris, Nathaniel. The Rise of Hitler. 2004. (Illus.). 56p. (J). pap. 8.95 (978-1-4034-5526-0(0)); lib. bdg. 27.07 (978-1-4034-4866-8(3)) Heinemann Library.

Hiemen, Sara. Germany ABCs: A Book about the People & Places of Germany. Miller, Jason, illus. 2004. (Country ABCs Ser.). 32p. (gr. k-5). 23.93 (978-1-4048-0020-5(4)) Picture Window Bks.

Hirst, Mike. Germany. 1999. (Food & Festivals Ser.). (Illus.). 32p. (J). (gr. 1-4). lib. bdg. 25.69 (978-0-7398-1372-0(2)) Raintree.

Horne, Reginald. Germany. 2002. (Modern World Nations Ser.). (Illus.). 150p. (gr. 6-12). 30.00 (978-0-7910-6936-3(2) , Chelsea Hse.) Facts On File, Inc.

Hurst, Mike. Germany. 1999. (We Come from Ser.). (Illus.). 32p. (J). (gr. 1-4). lib. bdg. 25.69 (978-0-8172-5218-2(5)) Raintree.

Italia, Bob. Germany. 2002. (Countries Ser.). (Illus.). 40p. (J). (gr. k-6). lib. bdg. 22.78 (978-1-57765-753-8(5) , Checkerboard Library) ABDO Publishing Co.

Kelly, Nigel. The Fall of the Berlin Wall Set 1: The Cold War Ends. 2002. (Point of Impact Ser.). (Illus.). 32p. (J). (gr. 5-7). pap. 7.50 (978-1-58810-355-0(2) , 91114) Heinemann Library.

Lane, Kathryn. Germany: The Culture. 2001. (gr. 3-6). lib. bdg. 16.40 (978-0-613-43445-4(5)) Tandem Library Bks.

—Germany: The Land. 2001. (gr. 3-6). lib. bdg. 16.40 (978-0-613-43446-1(3)) Tandem Library Bks.

—Germany: The People. 2001. (gr. 3-6). lib. bdg. 16.40 (978-0-613-43447-8(1)) Tandem Library Bks.

A Look at Germany, 6 vols. (gr. k-2). 28.95 (978-0-7368-9393-0(8)) Red Brick Learning.

Lord, Richard. Germany. 1999. (Countries of the World Ser.). (Illus.). 96p. (J). (gr. 6 up). lib. bdg. 30.00 (978-0-8368-2261-8(7)) Stevens, Gareth Inc.

Miller, Raymond H. The Brothers Grimm. 2005. (Inventors & Creators Ser.). (Illus.). 48p. (J). (gr. 4-8). lib. bdg. 26.20 (978-0-7377-3157-6(5) , Greenhaven Pr., Inc.) Thomson Gale.

Mills, Clifford W. Angela Merkel. 2007. (Modern World Leaders Ser.). 120p. (J). (gr. 6-12). 30.00 (***978-0-7910-9496-9(0)*** , Chelsea Hse.) Facts On File, Inc.

Mitten, Christopher. Germany. 2002. (Steadwell Books World Tour). (Illus.). 48p. (J). lib. bdg. 24.26 (978-0-7398-5754-0(1)) Raintree.

Morris, Ting & Wright, Rachel. Germany. 2005. (Illus.). 32p. (J). (978-1-932889-95-6(7)) Sea-To-Sea Pubns.

Nations of the World: Germany. (Time Traveler Ser.). 32p. (gr. 3-6). 6.99 (978-1-56822-788-7(4) , IF23797) School Specialty Publishing.

Nations of the World: Includes: Brazil, Egypt, Germany, Israel, 4 bks., Set. 2001. (Illus.). (YA). (gr. 5-9). lib. bdg. 95.92 (978-0-7398-4289-8(7)) Raintree.

Nickles, Greg. The Germans. 2001. (J). 15.75 (978-0-606-21209-0(4)) Tandem Library Bks.

Park. Taking Your Camera To..., 6 vols., Set 3. 2000. pap. (978-0-7398-4136-5(X)) Steck-Vaughn.

Park, Ted. Taking Your Camera To..., Set 3. 2000. pap., tchr. ed. (978-0-7398-4135-8(1)) Steck-Vaughn.

—Taking Your Camera to Germany. Sloan, Frank, ed. 2001. (Taking Your Camera to Ser.). (Illus.). 32p. (J). (gr. 4-7). lib. bdg. 22.83 (978-0-7398-3569-2(6)) Raintree.

—Taking Your Camera to Germany. 2000. (Illus.). (J). pap. (978-0-7398-4131-0(9)) Steck-Vaughn.

Pavlovic, Zoran & Horne, William R. Germany. 2nd rev. ed. 2007. (Modern World Nations Ser.). 120p. (gr. 6-12). 30.00 (***978-0-7910-9512-6(6)*** , Chelsea Hse.) Facts On File, Inc.

Pluckrose, Henry Arthur. Germany. 1999. (Picture a Country Ser.). (Illus.). 32p. (J). (gr. k-2). pap. 6.95 (978-0-531-15363-5(0) , Watts, Franklin) Scholastic Library Publishing.

Popper, Garry. Lena & Peter in Germany. Johnson, Andi, illus. 2004. 36p. (ps-7). 4.00 (978-1-84161-060-3(7)) Ravette Publishing, Ltd. GBR. *Dist:* Parkwest Pubns., Inc.

Regenberg, Werner. Armored Vehicles & Units of the German Order Police, 1936-1945. 2002. (Illus.). 288p. (gr. 10-13). 39.95 (978-0-7643-1555-8(2)) Schiffer Publishing, Ltd.

Reynolds, Jeff. Germany. 2005. (to Z Ser.). (Illus.). 40p. (J). (gr. 2-4). pap. 6.95 (978-0-516-25071-7(X) , Children's Pr.) Scholastic Library Publishing.

Reynolds, Jeff E. Germany. 2004. (to Z Ser.). (Illus.). 40p. (J). 24.50 (978-0-516-23654-4(7) , Children's Pr.) Scholastic Library Publishing.

Ruth, Angie. My Adventure in Germany. 2007. 44p. (J). 8.99 (978-1-59092-429-7(0) , Orchard Academy Pr.) Windstorm Creative.

Schanz, Sonja & Donaldson, Gerry. Germany. 2004. (Countries of the World Ser.). (Illus.). 64p. (J). (gr. 6-12). 30.00 (978-0-8160-5501-2(7)) Facts On File, Inc.

Senker, Cath. Germany. Schurpf, Christof, photos by. 2005. (Letters from Around the World Ser.). (Illus.). 32p. (J). (gr. 3-7). lib. bdg. (978-1-84234-352-4(1) , Cherrytree Books) Evans Publishing Group.

Spengler, Kremena. Germany: A Question & Answer Book. 2004. (Fact Finders Ser.). (Illus.). 32p. (J). lib. bdg. 22.60 (978-0-7368-2690-7(4)) Capstone Pr., Inc.

Taking Your Camera To... Includes: Argentina, China, Germany, India, South Africa, Vietnam, 6 bks., Set. 2001. (Taking Your Camera to Ser.). (Illus.). (J). (gr. 4-7). 136.98 (978-0-7398-3573-9(4)) Raintree.

Thoennes, Kristin. Christmas in Germany. 1998. (Christmas Around the World Ser.). (Illus.). 24p. (J). (gr. 2-3). lib. bdg. 19.93 (978-0-7368-0089-1(1) , Bridgestone Bks.) Capstone Pr., Inc.

Trumbauer, Lisa. King Ludwig's Castle: Germany's Neuschwanstein. 2005. (Castles, Palaces, & Tombs Ser.). (J). lib. bdg. 25.27 (978-1-59716-002-5(4)) Bearport Publishing Co., Inc.

Walsh, Kieran. Germany. 2005. (Countries in the News Ser.). (Illus.). 24p. (gr. 1-4). 17.95 (978-1-59515-173-5(7)) Rourke Publishing, LLC.

Wukovits, John F. World War II in Europe. 2004. (World History Ser.). (Illus.). 112p. (gr. 7-10). 32.45 (978-1-59018-185-0(9) , Lucent Bks.) Thomson Gale.

Zocchi, Judy. In Germany. Brodie, Neale, illus. 2005. (Global Adventures II Ser.). 32p. (J). per. 9.95 (978-1-59646-181-9(0)) Dingles & Co.

—In Germany/en Alemania. Brodie, Neale, illus. 2005. (Global Adventures II Ser.).Tr. of En Alemania. (ENG & SPA.). 32p. (J). per. 9.95 (978-1-59646-183-3(7)) Dingles & Co.

Zuehlke, Jeffrey. Germany in Pictures. 2nd ed. 2003. (Visual Geography Ser.). (Illus.). 80p. (J). (gr. 5-12). 27.93 (978-0-8225-4681-8(7)) Lerner Publishing Group.

GERMANY—FICTION

Alma, Ann. Skateway to Freedom. 2008. 136p. (YA). pap. 11.99 (***978-1-55002-719-8(0)*** , Sandcastle Bks.) Dundurn Group, The CAN. *Dist:* Univ. of Toronto Pr.

Balaguae, Lin & Long, Robert, contrib. by. Hansel y Gretel: Hansel & Gretel. 2000. (Cuentos y Leyendas Bilingues Ser.). (ENG & SPA.). (J). 21.20 (978-0-658-01037-8(9) , National Textbook Co.) McGraw-Hill/Contemporary.

Balague, Lin & Long, Robert. Hansel y Gretel (Hansel & Gretel) 2000. (Cuentos y Leyendas Bilingues Ser.). (SPA & ENG., Illus.). (J). 19.88 (978-0-658-01038-5(7)) McGraw-Hill/Contemporary.

Bell, Michele Ashman. Spyhunt: A Heart-Pounding Adventure: A Novel. 2004. 187p. (J). (978-1-59156-457-7(3)) Covenant Communications.

Bryant, Megan E. Rapunzel: Berry Fairy Tales. Huxtable, John & Huxtable, Tonja, illus. 2007. (Strawberry Shortcake Ser.). 32p. (J). (ps-2). 6.99 (978-0-448-44556-4(5) , Grosset & Dunlap) Penguin Group (USA) Inc.

Cassidy, Anne. Snow White. 2006. (First Fairy Tales Ser.). (Illus.). 32p. (J). (978-1-59771-074-9(1)) Sea-To-Sea Pubns.

Celenza, Anna Harwell. Bach's Goldberg Variations. Kitchel, JoAnn E., illus. 2005. 32p. (J). 19.95 incl. audio compact disk (978-1-57091-510-9(5)) Charlesbridge Publishing, Inc.

Chotjewitz, David & Orgel, Doris. Crazy Diamond. 2008. 272p. (YA). 17.99 (***978-1-4169-1176-0(6)***) Simon & Schuster Children's Publishing.

Christmas in Bavaria. 2005. (YA). per. 16.95 (978-0-9763572-7-8(5)) English Garden Talk Pr.

Chronicle Books LLC Staff. Pied Piper (Bilingual) 2008. (SPA & ENG.). (J). 14.95 (978-0-8118-6028-4(0)); pap. 6.95 (978-0-8118-6029-1(9)) Chronicle Bks. LLC.

Du Bist Spat Aufgewacht, Mein Schatz: Eine Abenteuergeschichte. 2003. (Illus.). 284p. (YA). 15.00 (978-0-9712545-0-3(8)) Privatgaeste Verlag.

Fraser, Christine Marion. Rhanna at War. 2000. (Illus.). 320p. pap. 13.99 (978-0-340-76567-8(4) , Hodder & Stoughton) Hodder General Publishing Division GBR. *Dist:* Trafalgar Square Publishing.

French, Simon. Where in the World. 2003. 208p. (J). (gr. 3-6). 14.95 (978-1-56145-292-7(0) , Q34443) Peachtree Pubs., Ltd.

Friedrich, Joachim. The Disappearing Bio Teacher, Bk. 2. 2001. (4 1/2 Friends Mysteries Ser.). (Illus.). 160p. (gr. 3-7). 14.99 (978-0-7868-0698-0(2) , Volo) Hyperion Bks. for Children.

—4 1/2 Friends: And the Disappearing Bio Teacher. Crawford, Elizabeth D., tr. from GER. 2001. 144p. (J). lib. bdg. 15.49 (978-0-7868-2588-2(X) , Volo) Hyperion Bks. for Children.

Glatshteyn, Yankev. Emil & Karl. Shandler, Jeffrey, tr. 2008. 208p. (YA). pap. 6.99 (***978-0-312-37387-0(2)***) Square Fish.

Grimm. The Musicians of Bremen. Puttapipat, Niroot, illus. 2005. 32p. (J). (gr. k-3). 15.99 (978-0-7636-2758-4(5)) Candlewick Pr.

Grimm, Jacob W. & Grimm, Wilhelm K. The Elves & the Shoemaker. Chelushkin, Kirill, illus. 2007. (Classic Fairy Tale Collection). 24p. (J). (gr. 1-4). 14.95 (978-1-4027-3067-2(5)) Sterling Publishing Co., Inc.

Holub, Josef. The Robber & Me. 1999. (J). (gr. 4-7). 19.25 (978-0-8446-7007-2(3)) Smith, Peter Pub., Inc.

—The Robber & Me. 1999. (978-0-606-15909-8(6)) Tandem Library Bks.

Hoobler, Dorothy & Hoobler, Thomas. The 1930s: Directions. Hoffman, Robin, illus. 2000. (Century Kids Ser.). 160p. (J). (gr. 5-8). lib. bdg. 22.90 (978-0-7613-1603-9(5) , Twenty-First Century Bks.) Lerner Publishing Group.

Howell, Trisha Adelena. The Stinky Shepherd. Marshall, Jamie, illus. 2005. 32p. (J). 15.95 (978-1-931210-25-6(X)) Howell Canyon Pr.

Hutsell-Manning, Linda. Jason & the Wonder Horn. Gardos, Susan, illus. 2005. (In the Same Boat Ser.). 328p. (J). 8.95 (978-1-55050-214-5(X)) Coteau Bks. CAN. *Dist:* Fitzhenry & Whiteside, Ltd.

Ketcham, Sallie. Bach's Big Adventure. Bush, Timothy, illus. 1999. 32p. (J). (gr. k-4). 17.99 (978-0-531-33140-8(7) , Orchard Bks.) Scholastic, Inc.

Lang, George. Pixy's Holiday Journey. 2006. 33.99 (***978-1-4280-4243-8(1)***); pap. 26.99 (***978-1-4280-4261-2(X)***) IndyPublish.com.

Morel, Alicia. Los Viajeros Invisibles. 2002. (J). (978-956-240-360-3(2)) Arrayan Editores S.A.

Napoli, Donna Jo. Stones in Water. 1999. 224p. (J). (gr. 5-9). reprint ed. pap. 5.99 (978-0-14-130600-1(9) , Puffin) Penguin Group (USA) Inc.

—Stones in Water. 1999. (978-0-606-17262-2(9)) Tandem Library Bks.

Nelson, Suzanne. The Sound of Munich. Henderson, Jeanine, illus. 2006. (S. A. S. S. (Students Across the Seven Seas) Ser.). 224p. (J). (gr. 7). pap. 6.99 (978-0-14-240576-5(0) , Puffin) Penguin Group (USA) Inc.

Newbery, Linda. Sisterland. 2006. 384p. (YA). (gr. 7). reprint ed. mass mkt. 6.50 (978-0-553-49450-1(3) , Laurel Leaf) Random Hse. Children's Bks.

Osborne, Mary Pope & Potter, Giselle. The Brave Little Seamstress. 2006. (Illus.). 40p. (J). (ps-3). reprint ed. pap. 6.99 (978-1-4169-1620-8(2) , Aladdin) Simon & Schuster Children's Publishing.

Pausewang, Gudrun. Dark Hours. Brownjohn, John, tr. from GER. 2006. (Illus.). 212p. (YA). (gr. 7-12). 21.95 (978-1-55451-042-9(2)) Annick Pr., Ltd. CAN. *Dist:* Firefly Bks., Ltd.

Pausewang, Gudrun & Ward, Rachel. Traitor. 2006. 224p. (YA). 16.95 (978-0-8225-6195-8(6) , Carolrhoda Bks.) Lerner Publishing Group.

Pinkney, Jerry. Little Red Riding Hood. 2007. 40p. (J). (ps-3). 16.99 (***978-0-316-01355-0(2)***) Little Brown & Co.

Pirotta, Saviour & Marks, Alan. The Glass Palace. 2007. (J). (***978-1-59771-078-7(4)***) Sea-To-Sea Pubns.

Prose, Francine. Leopold: The Liar of Leipzig. Aviram, Einav, illus. 2005. 32p. (J). 15.99 (978-0-06-008075-4(2) , Cotler, Joanna Books) HarperCollins Pubs.

Randall, Homer. Army Boys on German Soil Our Doughboys Q. 2006. 62.99 (***978-1-4280-2321-5(6)***) IndyPublish.com.

Richter, Jutta. The Cat, or, How I Lost Eternity. Brailovsky, Anna, tr. from GER. 2007. (Illus.). 80p. (J). (gr. 3 up). 14.00 (***978-1-57131-676-9(0)***) Milkweed Editions.

Richter, Jutta. The Summer of the Pike. Brailovsky, Anna, tr. from GER. Buchholz, Quint, illus. 2006. 132p. (J). pap. 6.95 (978-1-57131-672-1(8)); 16.95 (978-1-57131-671-4(X)) Milkweed Editions.

Savery, Constance. Enemy Brothers. 2001. (Living History Library). (Illus.). 304p. (J). (gr. 5-12). reprint ed. pap. 13.95 (978-1-883937-50-8(7) , 50-7) Bethlehem Bks.

Schalk, Marian. A Great Miracle in a Small Mountain Village. VanBrugge, Marinus, tr. from DUT. Kramer, Jaap, illus. l.t. ed. 2002. 48p. (J). pap. 6.95 (978-0-9670728-9-0(1)) Early Foundations Pubs.

Simon & Barklee in Germany. 2001. (Another Country Calling Ser.). (Illus.). 64p. (J). (gr. 3-5). per. 15.00 (978-0-9704661-2-9(9) , Explorer Media) Simon & Barklee, Inc./ExplorerMedia.

Smith, Annie Laura. The Legacy of Bletchley Park. 2004. (YA). mass mkt. 6.99 (***978-0-9753367-1-7(1)***) Onstage Publishing, LLC.

Steinhofel, Andreas. The Center of the World. 2007. 480p. (YA). (gr. 9). pap. 7.99 (978-0-440-22932-2(4) , Laurel Leaf) Random Hse. Children's Bks.

Taylor, Mary Ann. Spies: A Gander's Cove Mystery. Casteel, Kay, illus. 2006. (J). mass mkt. 5.99 (***978-0-9753367-7-9(0)***) Onstage Publishing, LLC.

Walters, Jennie. Shelter from the Storm. 2007. (Swallowcliffe Hall Trilogy: Book 3 Ser.). (Illus.). 240p. (J). pap. 9.99 (***978-0-689-87528-1(2)***) Simon & Schuster, Ltd. GBR. *Dist:* Independent Pubs. Group.

Watts, Irene N. Good-Bye Marianne: A Story of Growing up in Nazi Germany. 1998. 112p. (J). (gr. 3-7). pap. 7.95 (978-0-88776-445-5(2)) Tundra Bks., Inc./Livres Toundra, Inc. CAN. *Dist:* Random Hse., Inc.

Weisleder, Stanley. Wings of the Panther. 2004. 224p. 15.00 (978-0-936783-38-3(9)) Merril Pr.

Wildner, Martina & Skofield, James. Shooting Stars Everywhere. 2006. 192p. (J). (gr. 7). 15.95 (978-0-385-73250-5(3) , Delacorte Bks. for Young Readers) Random Hse. Children's Bks.

Wilson, John. Flames of the Tiger. 2004. 176p. (YA). (gr. 13 up). (978-1-55337-618-7(8)); (Illus.). (978-1-55337-619-4(6)) Kids Can Pr., Ltd.

GERMANY—HISTORY

Beyer, Mark. Heinrich Muller: Gestapo Chief. 2005. (Holocaust Biographies Ser.). (Illus.). 112p. (YA). (gr. 7-12). lib. bdg. 26.50 (978-0-8239-3376-1(8)) Rosen Publishing Group, Inc., The.

Davis, Kevin A. Look What Came from Germany. 2000. (Look What Came from Ser.). (Illus.). 32p. (J). (gr. 2-4). pap. 6.95 (978-0-531-16435-8(7) , Watts, Franklin) Scholastic Library Publishing.

Downing, David. Persecution & Emigration. 2005. (World Almanac Library of the Holocaust). (Illus.). 48p. (978-0-8368-5951-5(0)); (YA). (gr. 5 up). lib. bdg. 30.00 (978-0-8368-5944-7(8)) Stevens, Gareth Inc. (World Almanac Library).

Fischer, Sue. The Mother of Eagles: The War Diary of Baroness Von Richthofen. 2001. (Schiffer Military History Ser.). (Illus.). 208p. (gr. 10-13). 29.95 (978-0-7643-1307-3(X)) Schiffer Publishing, Ltd.

Fleischer, Wolfgang. An Illustrated Guide to German Panzers, 1935-1945. 2002. (Illus.). 160p. (gr. 10-13). 19.95 (978-0-7643-1556-5(0)) Schiffer Publishing, Ltd.

Haugen, Brenda. Adolf Hitler: Dictator of Nazi Germany. 2006. (Signature Lives Ser.). (Illus.). 112p. (J). (gr. 5-7). 30.60 (978-0-7565-1589-8(0)) Compass Point Bks.

Kelly, Nigel. The Fall of the Berlin Wall: The Cold War Ends. 2006. (Point of Impact Ser.). (Illus.). 32p. (J). (***978-1-4034-9139-8(9)***) Heinemann Library.

Lawson, Dorothea von Schwanenfluegel. Laughter Wasn't Rationed: A Personal Journey Through Germany's World Wars & Postwar Years, 1. 2nd ed. 2001. 527p. pap. 24.95 (978-0-9673830-4-0(8)) Tricor Pr.

Marcovitz, Hal. The Munich Olympics. 2002. (Great Disasters, Reforms & Ramifications Ser.). (Illus.). 112p. (J). 30.00 (978-0-7910-6737-6(8)); pap. 13.25 (978-0-7910-6911-0(7)) Facts On File, Inc. (Chelsea Hse.).

Nickles, Greg & Walker, Niki. Germany. 2001. (Nations of the World Ser.). (Illus.). 128p. (J). (gr. 6-8). lib. bdg. 34.26 (978-0-7398-1285-3(8)) Raintree.

Prien, Jochen & Stemmer, Gerhard. Jagdgeswader 3 Udet in WWII: II. /Jg 3 in Action with the Messerschmitt Bf 109. 2003. (Illus.). 408p. (gr. 10-13). 69.95 (978-0-7643-1774-3(1)) Schiffer Publishing, Ltd.

Ramen, Fred. Hermann Goering: Hitler's Second in Command. 2005. (Holocaust Biographies Ser.). (Illus.). 112p. (YA). (gr. 7-12). lib. bdg. 26.50 (978-0-8239-3307-5(5) , HBGORI) Rosen Publishing Group, Inc., The.

Richard Tames. The Fall of the Berlin Wall. 2nd ed. 2006. (Point of Impact Ser.). (Illus.). 32p. (J). pap. (***978-1-4034-9148-0(8)***) Heinemann Library.

Roberts, Jeremy. Joseph Goebbels: Nazi Propaganda Minister. 2005. (Holocaust Biographies Ser.). (Illus.). 112p. (J). (gr. 7-12). lib. bdg. 26.50 (978-0-8239-3309-9(1) , HBGOEB) Rosen Publishing Group, Inc., The.

Russell, Henry. Germany. 2007. (Countries of the World Ser.). (Illus.). 64p. (YA). (gr. 5 up). lib. bdg. 27.90 (***978-1-4263-0059-2(X)*** , National Geographic Children's Bks.) National Geographic Society.

Schanz, Sonja & Donaldson, Gerry. Germany. 2006. (Destination Detectives Ser.). (Illus.). 48p. (J). (978-1-4109-2337-0(1)); pap. (978-1-4109-2348-6(7)) Steck-Vaughn.

Schiel, Katy. Inside Germany's BND: The Federal Intelligence Service. 2005. (Illus.). 63p. (YA). (gr. 4-8). reprint ed. 20.00 (978-0-7567-8669-4(X)) DIANE Publishing Co.

Smith, Frank Dabba. Elsie's War: A Story of Courage in Nazi Germany. 2005. (Illus.). 32p. (J). reprint ed. pap. 7.95 (978-1-84507-006-9(2)) Lincoln, Frances Ltd. GBR. *Dist:* Perseus Distribution.

Somervill, Barbara A. Martin Luther: Father of the Reformation. 2006. (Signature Lives Ser.). (Illus.). 112p. (J). (gr. 5-7). 30.60 (978-0-7565-1593-5(9)) Compass Point Bks.

Uschan, Michael V. German Americans. 2006. (World Almanac Library of American Immigration). (Illus.). 48p. (J). pap. (978-0-8368-7323-8(8)); lib. bdg. (978-0-8368-7310-8(6)) Stevens, Gareth Inc. (World Almanac Library).

Walker, Ida. Germany. 2006. (European Union Ser.). (Illus.). 88p. (J). (gr. 5 up). lib. bdg. (978-1-4222-0048-3(5) , 1248000) Mason Crest Pubs.

Zocchi, Judy. In Germany. Brodie, Neale, illus. 2005. (Global Adventures II Ser.). 32p. (J). pap. 9.95 (978-1-59646-180-2(2)); lib. bdg. 20.65 (978-1-59646-089-8(X)) Dingles & Co.

—In Germany/en Alemania. Brodie, Neale, illus. 2005. (Global Adventures II Ser.).Tr. of En Alemania. (ENG & SPA.). (J). 32p. pap. 9.95 (978-1-59646-182-6(9)); 28p. lib. bdg. 20.65 (978-1-59646-090-4(3)) Dingles & Co.

GERMANY—HISTORY—FICTION

Bartoletti, Susan Campbell. The Boy Who Dared. 2008. 192p. (J). pap. 16.99 (***978-0-439-68013-4(1)*** , Scholastic Pr.) Scholastic, Inc.

Benary-Isbert, Margot. Under a Changing Moon. 1998. (Young Adult Historical Library). 326p. (J). (gr. 9-12). reprint ed. pap. 14.95 (978-1-883937-33-1(7) , 33-7) Bethlehem Bks.

Bessey, Sian Ann. Escape from Germany. 2004. 183p. (J). (978-1-59156-436-2(0)) Covenant Communications.

Charles, Elizabeth. From Dark to Dawn: A Tale of Martin Luther & the Reformation. James and Stacy McDonald & Marilyn Rockett, eds. Johannah Bluedorn, illus. 2003. Orig. Title: Chronicles of the Schonburg Cotta Family. xxi, 370p. 19.99 (978-0-9743390-0-9(8)) Books on the Path.

Chetkowski, Emily. Gooseman. 2001. (J). 11.95 (978-1-880158-32-6(9)) Townsend, J.N. Publishing.

Chotjewitz, David. Daniel Half Human. Orgel, Doris, tr. 2006. 336p. (YA). reprint ed. mass mkt. 5.99 (978-0-689-85748-5(9) , Simon Pulse) Simon & Schuster Children's Publishing.

—Daniel, Half Human: And the Good Nazi. Orgel, Doris, tr. from GER. 2004. (Illus.). 304p. (YA). 17.95 (978-0-689-85747-8(0) , Atheneum) Simon & Schuster Children's Publishing.

Chotjewitz, David & Orgel, Doris. Daniel, Half Human: And the Good Nazi. 2004. 298p. (J). (978-3-551-58045-0(6)) Carlsen Verlag DEU. *Dist:* Distribooks, Inc.

French, Jackie. Hitler's Daughter. 2003. 128p. (J). 15.99 (978-0-06-008652-7(1)) HarperCollins Pubs.

Harris, Ruth Elwin. Gwen's Story. 2002. (gr. 7-12). lib. bdg. 14.15 (978-0-613-74775-2(5)) Tandem Library Bks.

—Gwen's Story: Sisters of the Quantock Hills. 2002. (Quantock's Quartet Ser.). (Illus.). 288p. (YA). (gr. 7 up). pap. 5.99 (978-0-7636-1705-9(9)) Candlewick Pr.

Ibbotson, Eva. The Star of Kazan. 2006. (Illus.). 416p. (J). (gr. 3). reprint ed. 6.99 (978-0-14-240582-6(5) , Puffin) Penguin Group (USA) Inc.

Innocenti, Roberto. Rosa Blanca. 2nd ed. 2003. (Rosa y Manzana Ser.). (SPA., Illus.). 32p. (978-84-85334-52-0(3) , LG2811) Loguez Ediciones ESP. *Dist:* Lectorum Pubns., Inc.

Jung, Reinhardt. Dreaming in Black & White. Bell, Anthea, tr. from GER. 2003. 112p. (J). (gr. 6). 15.99 (978-0-8037-2811-0(5) , Dial) Penguin Group (USA) Inc.

Leeds, Constance & Bennett, Constance. The Silver Cup. 2007. 240p. (YA). (gr. 6-9). 16.99 (978-0-670-06157-0(3) , Viking Adult) Penguin Group (USA) Inc.

Napoli, Donna Jo. Breath. 2003. (Illus.). 272p. (YA). 17.95 (978-0-689-86174-1(5) , Atheneum) Simon & Schuster Children's Publishing.

—Breath. l.t. ed. 2005. 251p. 21.95 (978-0-7862-7420-8(4) , Large Print Pr.) Thorndike Pr.

Robertson, Barbara. Rosemary Meets Rosemarie Bk. 1: Berlin in 1870. 2001. (Hourglass Adventures Ser.: Bk. 1). (Illus.). 128p. (J). (gr. 4-6). pap. 5.95 (978-1-890817-55-8(4)) Winslow Pr.

Tingle, Rebecca. The Edge on the Sword. 2003. (gr. 5-8). lib. bdg. 15.30 (978-0-613-67451-5(0)) Tandem Library Bks.

Wulffson, Don L. Soldier X. 2003. 240p. (YA). pap. 6.99 (978-0-14-250073-6(9) , Puffin); 2001. 244p. (J). (gr. 5-9). 16.99 (978-0-670-88863-4(X) , Viking Juvenile) Penguin Group (USA) Inc.

—Soldier X. 2003. (gr. 7-12). lib. bdg. 15.30 (978-0-613-67163-7(5)) Tandem Library Bks.

Zusak, Markus. The Book Thief. (YA). (gr. 7 up). 2007. 576p. pap. 11.99 (***978-0-375-84220-7(9)***); 2006. 560p. 16.95 (978-0-375-83100-3(2)); 2006. 560p. lib. bdg. 18.99 (978-0-375-93100-0(7)) Random Hse. Children's Bks. (Knopf Bks. for Young Readers).

GERMANY—HISTORY, MILITARY

O'Connor, Neal W. Aviation Awards of Imperial Germany in WWI & the Men Who Earned Them, Vol. 7. 2002. (Illus.). 528p. (gr. 10-13). 69.95 (978-0-7643-1626-5(5)) Schiffer Publishing, Ltd.

GERMANY—HISTORY—1866-1918

Holmes, Burton. Berlin. Schlesinger, Arthur M., Jr. & Isreal, Fred L., eds. 1999. (World 100 Years Ago Ser.). (Illus.). 144p. (YA). (ps-3). 29.95 (978-0-7910-4664-7(8) , Chelsea Hse.) Facts On File, Inc.

E
F
G

GERMANY—HISTORY—20TH CENTURY

Burgan, Michael. The Berlin Wall: Barrier to Freedom. 2007. (J). lib. bdg. (***978-0-7565-3330-4(9)***) Compass Point Bks.

Radovic, Branislav. German Helmets of the Second World War. 2002. (Schiffer Military History Ser.). (Illus.). (gr. 10-13). Vol. 1. 328p. 79.95 (978-0-7643-1447-6(5)); Vol. 2. 304p. 79.95 (978-0-7643-1448-3(3)) Schiffer Publishing, Ltd.

Smith, Bob, illus. & photos by. Germany. Smith, Bob, photos by. 2002. (Changing Face Of... Ser.). 48p. (J). lib. bdg. 27.12 (978-0-7398-5489-1(5)) Raintree.

Tracy, Kathleen. The Fall of the Berlin Wall. 2005. (Illus.). 48p. (J). lib. bdg. 29.95 (978-1-58415-405-1(5)) Mitchell Lane Pubs., Inc.

GERMANY—HISTORY—1918-1933

Banham, Dale, et al. Essential Germany, 1918-1945: A Study in Depth. 2004. (Illus.). 96p. pap., stu. ed. 32.50 (***978-0-7195-7753-6(5)***, Hodder Murray) Hodder Education GBR. *Dist:* Trans-Atlantic Pubns., Inc.

Clare, John D. Germany 1919-45. 2nd ed. 2004. (Illus.). 64p. pap. 26.50 (***978-0-340-81478-9(0)***, Hodder Murray) Hodder Education GBR. *Dist:* Trans-Atlantic Pubns., Inc.

Freeman, Charles. The Rise of the Nazis. 1998. (New Perspectives Ser.). (Illus.). 80p. (J). (gr. 4-7). 28.54 (978-0-8172-5015-7(8)) Raintree.

—The Rise of the Nazis. 2005. (How Did It Happen? Ser.). (Illus.). 48p. (J). (gr. 7-10). lib. bdg. 29.95 (978-1-59018-608-4(7), Lucent Bks.) Thomson Gale.

Woolf, Alex. The Rise of Nazi Germany. 2004. (Questioning History Ser.). (J). lib. bdg. 28.50 (978-1-58340-442-3(2)) Smart Apple Media.

GERMANY—HISTORY—1933-1945

Altman, Linda Jacobs. Adolf Hitler: Evil MasterMind of the Holocaust. 2005. (Holocaust Heroes & Nazi Criminals Ser.). (Illus.). 160p. (YA). (gr. 7-13). lib. bdg. 27.93 (978-0-7660-2533-2(0)) Enslow Pubs., Inc.

—Hitler's Rise to Power & the Holocaust. 2003. (Holocaust in History Ser.). (Illus.). 128p. (J). (gr. 5-12). lib. bdg. 26.60 (978-0-7660-1991-1(8)) Enslow Pubs., Inc.

—The Holocaust, Hitler & Nazi Germany. 1999. (Holocaust Remembered Ser.). (Illus.). 112p. (YA). (gr. 6-12). lib. bdg. 26.60 (978-0-7660-1230-1(1)) Enslow Pubs., Inc.

—The Jewish Victims of the Holocaust. 2003. (Holocaust in History Ser.). (Illus.). 128p. (J). (gr. 5-12). lib. bdg. 26.60 (978-0-7660-1992-8(6)) Enslow Pubs., Inc.

—Resisters & Rescuers: Standing up Against the Holocaust. 2003. (Holocaust in History Ser.). (Illus.). 104p. (J). (gr. 5-12). lib. bdg. 26.60 (978-0-7660-1994-2(2)) Enslow Pubs., Inc.

Axelrod, Toby. Hans & Sophie Scholl: German Resisters of the White Rose. 2005. (Holocaust Biographies Ser.). (Illus.). 112p. (YA). (gr. 7-12). lib. bdg. 26.50 (978-0-8239-3316-7(4), HBHOBI) Rosen Publishing Group, Inc., The.

Banham, Dale, et al. Essential Germany, 1918-1945: A Study in Depth. 2004. (Illus.). 96p. pap., stu. ed. 32.50 (***978-0-7195-7753-6(5)***, Hodder Murray) Hodder Education GBR. *Dist:* Trans-Atlantic Pubns., Inc.

Clare, John D. Germany 1919-45. 2nd ed. 2004. (Illus.). 64p. pap. 26.50 (***978-0-340-81478-9(0)***, Hodder Murray) Hodder Education GBR. *Dist:* Trans-Atlantic Pubns., Inc.

Davenport, John. The Nuremberg Trials. 2006. (World History Ser.). 112p. (J). (gr. 7-10). 32.45 (978-1-59018-634-3(6), Lucent Bks.) Thomson Gale.

Dufner, Annette. The Rise of Adolf Hitler. 2003. (Illus.). 144p. (YA). pap. 23.70 (978-0-7377-1519-4(7)); lib. bdg. 33.70 (978-0-7377-1518-7(9)) Thomson Gale. (Greenhaven Pr., Inc.).

Garner, Eleanor Ramrath. Eleanor's Story: An American Girl in Hitler's Germany. 288p. (YA). 2003. (gr. 6-10). pap. 8.95 (978-1-56145-296-5(3), Q19196); 1999. (Illus.). (gr. 7-11). 15.95 (978-1-56145-193-7(2), Q19196) Peachtree Pubs., Ltd.

—Eleanor's Story: An American Girl in Hitler's Germany. 2003. (gr. 7-12). lib. bdg. 16.40 (978-0-613-78736-9(6)) Tandem Library Bks.

Gogerly, Liz. Adolf Hitler. 2003. (Twentieth Century History Makers Ser.). (Illus.). 112p. (J). lib. bdg. 32.85 (978-0-7398-5256-9(6)) Raintree.

Gottfried, Ted. Martyrs to Madness: The Victims of the Nazis. Alcorn, Stephen, illus. 2000. (Holocaust Ser.: up). 128p. (gr. 7). lib. bdg. (978-0-7613-1715-9(5), Twenty-First Century Bks.) Lerner Publishing Group.

Grabowski, John F. Josef Mengele. 2003. (Heroes & Villains Ser.). (Illus.). 112p. (YA). 29.95 (978-1-59018-425-7(4), Lucent Bks.) Thomson Gale.

Hay, Jeff. Personalities, 4 vols. 2003. (History of the Third Reich Ser.). (Illus.). 292p. (J). 78.70 (978-0-7377-1120-2(5), Greenhaven Pr., Inc.) Thomson Gale.

Ramen, Fred. Albert Speer: Hitler's Architect. 2005. (Holocaust Biographies Ser.). (Illus.). 112p. (YA). (gr. 7-12). lib. bdg. 26.50 (978-0-8239-3372-3(5)) Rosen Publishing Group, Inc., The.

—Reinhard Heydrich: Hangman of the Third Reich. 2005. (Holocaust Biographies Ser.). (Illus.). 112p. (YA). (gr. 7-12). lib. bdg. 26.50 (978-0-8239-3379-2(2)) Rosen Publishing Group, Inc., The.

Rice, Earle, Jr. Adolf Hitler & Nazi Germany. 2005. (World Leaders Ser.). (Illus.). 176p. (J). (gr. 3-7). lib. bdg. 26.95 (978-1-931798-78-5(8)) Reynolds, Morgan Inc.

Shuter, Jane. Prelude to the Holocaust. 2003. (Holocaust Ser.). (Illus.). 56p. (J). lib. bdg. 28.50 (978-1-4034-0813-6(0)); pap. 8.95 (978-1-4034-3205-6(8)) Heinemann Library.

—Resistance to the Nazis. 2003. (Holocaust Ser.). (Illus.). 56p. (J). lib. bdg. 28.50 (978-1-4034-0814-3(9)); pap. 8.95 (978-1-4034-3206-3(6)) Heinemann Library.

Soumerai, Eve Nussbaum & Schulz, Carol D. A Voice from the Holocaust. 2003. (Voices of the Twentieth Century Conflict Ser.). (Illus.). 160p. 39.95 (978-0-313-32358-4(5), GR2358, Greenwood Pr.) Greenwood Publishing Group, Inc.

Stalcup, Brenda. Adolf Hitler. (People Who Made History Ser.). (Illus.). 202p. (YA). (gr. 9-12). 2000. lib. bdg. 32.45 (978-0-7377-0223-1(0)); 1999. 21.20 (978-0-7377-0222-4(2)) Thomson Gale. (Greenhaven Pr., Inc.).

Woolf, Alex. The Rise of Nazi Germany. 2004. (Questioning History Ser.). (J). lib. bdg. 28.50 (978-1-58340-442-3(2)) Smart Apple Media.

GERMANY—HISTORY—1945-

Raven, Margot Theis. Mercedes & the Chocolate Pilot: A True Story of the Berlin Airlift & the Candy That Dropped from the Sky. van Frankenhuyzen, Gijsbert, illus. 2002. 48p. (J). (gr. k-5). 17.95 (978-1-58536-069-7(4)) Sleeping Bear Pr.

Smith, Jeremy. The Fall of the Berlin Wall. 2004. (Days That Changed the World Ser.). (Illus.). 48p. (J). (gr. 5 up). pap. 11.95 (978-0-8368-5576-0(0)); lib. bdg. 30.00 (978-0-8368-5569-2(8)) Stevens, Gareth Inc. (World Almanac Library).

GERMS

see Bacteriology; Microorganisms

GERONIMO, 1829-1909

Bruchac, Joseph. Geronimo. 2006. 240p. (J). (gr. 7 up). pap. 16.99 (978-0-439-35360-1(2)) Scholastic, Inc.

Feinstein, Stephen. Read about Geronimo. 2006. (I Like Biographies! Ser.). (Illus.). 24p. (J). lib. bdg. 21.26 (978-0-7660-2598-1(5), Enslow Elementary) Enslow Pubs., Inc.

Geronimo. 1999. (SmartReader Ser.). (J). Level 1. pap., tchr. ed. 19.95 incl. audio (978-0-7887-0764-3(7), 79348T3); Level 2. pap., tchr. ed. 19.95 incl. audio (978-0-7887-0127-6(4), 79315T3) Recorded Bks., LLC.

Haugen, Brenda. Geronimo: Apache Warrior. 2005. (Signature Lives Ser.). (Illus.). 112p. (J). (gr. 5-7). 30.60 (978-0-7565-1002-3(2)) Compass Point Bks.

Moody, Ralph. Geronimo: Wolf of the Warpath. 2006. (Sterling Point Bks.). (Illus.). 192p. (J). 12.95 (978-1-4027-3184-6(1)); pap. 6.95 (978-1-4027-3612-4(6)) Sterling Publishing Co., Inc.

Moskal, Greg. An Apache Indian Community. 2002. (Reading Room Collection). (J). (978-0-8239-8156-4(8)); (978-0-8239-8558-6(X)); (Illus.). 24p. lib. bdg. 18.75 (978-0-8239-3719-6(4)) Rosen Publishing Group, Inc., The.

Stanley, George Edward. Geronimo: Young Warrior. Henderson, Meryl, illus. 2001. (Childhood of Famous Americans Ser.). 176p. (J). pap. 5.99 (978-0-689-84455-3(7), Aladdin) Simon & Schuster Children's Publishing.

—Geronimo: Young Warrior. 2001. 11.64 (978-0-606-22097-2(6)); (gr. 3-6). lib. bdg. 13.00 (978-0-613-63409-0(8)) Tandem Library Bks.

Thompson, William & Thompson, Dorcas. Geronimo. 2001. (Famous Figures of the American Frontier Ser.). (Illus.). 64p. (J). (gr. 5 up). pap. 8.95 (978-0-7910-6492-4(1)); 25.00 (978-0-7910-6491-7(3)) Facts On File, Inc. (Chelsea Hse.).

Welch, Catherine A. Geronimo. 2004. (History Maker Bios Ser.). (J). pap. 6.95 (978-0-8225-2069-6(9)) Lerner Publishing Group.

—Geronimo. Parlin, Tim, tr. Parlin, Tim, illus. 2004. (History Maker Bios Ser.). 47p. (J). 26.60 (978-0-8225-0698-0(X), Carolrhoda Bks.) Lerner Publishing Group.

GERONTOLOGY

see Old Age

GERSHWIN, GEORGE, 1898-1937

Reef, Catherine. George Gershwin: American Composer. 2004. (Masters of Music Ser.). (Illus.). 112p. (YA). (gr. 6-12). 23.95 (978-1-883846-58-9(7), First Biographies) Reynolds, Morgan Inc.

Whiting, Jim. The Life & Times of George Gershwin. 2004. (Masters of Music Ser.). (Illus.). 48p. (gr. 4-8). lib. bdg. 20.95 (978-1-58415-279-8(6)) Mitchell Lane Pubs., Inc.

GETTYSBURG (PA.), BATTLE OF, 1863

see Gettysburg, Battle of, Gettysburg, Pa., 1863

GETTYSBURG, BATTLE OF, GETTYSBURG, PA., 1863

Abnett, Dan. The Battle of Gettysburg: Spilled Blood on Sacred Ground. 2007. (Graphic Battles of the Civil War Ser.). (Illus.). 48p. (J). lib. bdg. (978-1-4042-0777-6(5)) Rosen Publishing Group, Inc., The.

Anderson, Dale. The Battle of Gettysburg. 2003. (Landmark Events in American History Ser.). (Illus.). 48p. (J). (gr. 5 up). pap. 14.95 (978-0-8368-5400-8(4)); lib. bdg. 30.00 (978-0-8368-5372-8(5)) Stevens, Gareth Inc. (World Almanac Library).

Ashby, Ruth. Gettysburg. 2002. (Illus.). 48p. (J). lib. bdg. 28.50 (978-1-58340-186-6(5)) Smart Apple Media.

Burgan, Michael. The Battle of Gettysburg. Erwin, Steve et al, illus. 2006. (Graphic Library). 32p. (J). (978-0-7368-5491-7(6)) Capstone Pr., Inc.

—The Battle of Gettysburg. 2001. (We the People Ser.). (Illus.). 48p. (J). (gr. 4 up). lib. bdg. 22.60 (978-0-7565-0098-6(2)) Compass Point Bks.

Capstone Press, contrib. by. Battle of Gettysburg: Turning Point of the Civil War. (Civil War Ser.). 48p. (YA). pap. 7.95 (978-0-7368-4516-8(X)) Capstone Pr., Inc.

Crewe, Sabrina & Anderson, Dale. The Battle of Gettysburg. 2003. (Events That Shaped America Ser.). (Illus.). 32p. (J). (gr. 3 up). lib. bdg. 24.67 (978-0-8368-3391-1(0)) Stevens, Gareth Inc.

De Angelis, Gina. The Battle of Gettysburg: Turning Point of the Civil War. 2002. (Let Freedom Ring Ser.). (Illus.). 48p. (J). (gr. 3-4). lib. bdg. 22.60 (978-0-7368-1340-2(3), Bridgestone Bks.) Capstone Pr., Inc.

Elish, Dan. The Battle of Gettysburg. 2005. (Cornerstones of Freedom Ser.). (Illus.). 48p. (J). (gr. 4-6). 26.00 (978-0-516-23623-0(7), Children's Pr.) Scholastic Library Publishing.

Ernst, Kathleen. Retreat from Gettysburg. 2000. (Illus.). viii, 141p. (J). (gr. 4-12). lib. bdg. 17.95 (978-1-57249-187-8(6), White Mane Kids) White Mane Publishing Co., Inc.

Ford, Carin T. The Battle of Gettysburg & Lincoln's Gettysburg Address. 2004. (Civil War Library Ser.). (Illus.). 48p. (J). lib. bdg. 23.93 (978-0-7660-2253-9(6)) Enslow Pubs., Inc.

Fradin, Dennis B. The Battle of Gettysburg. 2007. (Turning Points in U. S. History Ser.). (J). lib. bdg. (978-0-7614-2043-9(6), Benchmark Bks.) Cavendish, Marshall Corp.

Gaines, Ann Graham. The Battle of Gettysburg in American History. 2001. (In American History Ser.). (Illus.). 128p. (J). (gr. 5-12). lib. bdg. 26.60 (978-0-7660-1455-8(X)) Enslow Pubs., Inc.

The Gettysburg Collection. 1999. (Illus.). 22p. (YA). (gr. 6 up). pap. 3.00 (978-1-890541-19-4(2)) Americana Souvenirs & Gifts.

High, Linda Oatman. The Cemetery Keepers of Gettysburg. Filippucci, Laura Francesca, illus. 2007. 32p. (J). 17.85 (978-0-8027-8095-9(4)); 16.95 (978-0-8027-8094-2(6)) Walker & Co.

Hughes, Christopher. Gettysburg. 1998. (Battlefields Across America Ser.: 8). (Illus.). 64p. (gr. 5-8). lib. bdg. 26.90 (978-0-7613-3012-7(7), Twenty-First Century Bks.) Lerner Publishing Group.

January, Brendan. Gettysburg: July 1-3 1863. 2004. (American Battlefields Ser.). (Illus.). 32p. (J). 14.95 (978-1-59270-025-7(X)) Enchanted Lion Bks., LLC.

McNamara, Margaret. The Battle of Gettysburg. 2006. pap. 39.00 (***978-1-4108-6445-1(6)***) Benchmark Education Co.

—Discover the Battle of Gettysburg. 2006. pap. 39.00 (***978-1-4108-6448-2(0)***) Benchmark Education Co.

Murphy, Jim. The Long Road to Gettysburg. 2000. (Illus.). 128p. (J). (gr. 4-6). pap. 8.95 (978-0-618-05157-1(0), Clarion Bks.) Houghton Mifflin Co. Trade & Reference Div.

—The Long Road to Gettysburg. 2000. (J). (978-0-606-19362-7(6)) Tandem Library Bks.

O'Hern, Kerri & Anderson, Dale. The Battle of Gettysburg. 2006. (Graphic Histories Ser.). (Illus.). 32p. (J). lib. bdg. 26.00 (978-0-8368-6204-1(X), World Almanac Library) Stevens, Gareth Inc.

—Gettysburg. 2006. (Graphic Histories Ser.). (Illus.). (J). pap. (978-0-8368-6256-0(2), World Almanac Library) Stevens, Gareth Inc.

Olson, Steven P. Lincoln's Gettysburg Address: A Primary Source Investigation. 2004. (Great Historic Debates & Speeches Ser.). (Illus.). 64p. (J). lib. bdg. 29.25 (978-1-4042-0151-4(3)) Rosen Publishing Group, Inc., The.

Rice, Earle. The Battle of Gettysburg. 2002. (Battles That Changed the World Ser.). (Illus.). (J). 118p. pap. 30.00 (978-0-7910-7108-3(1)); 112p. 30.00 (978-0-7910-6684-3(3)) Facts On File, Inc. (Chelsea Hse.).

Sinnott, Susan. Charley Waters Goes to Gettysburg. Handelman, Dorothy, photos by. 2003. (Illus.). 48p. (J). (gr. 4-7). pap. 8.95 (978-0-7613-1887-3(9), Millbrook Pr.) Lerner Publishing Group.

—Charley Waters Goes to Gettysburg. 2003. (gr. 3-6). lib. bdg. 17.60 (978-0-613-88855-4(3)) Tandem Library Bks.

Sinnott, Susan, illus. Charley Waters Goes to Gettysburg. Handelman, Dorothy, photos by. 2000. 48p. (gr. 3-6). lib. bdg. (978-0-7613-1567-4(5), Millbrook Pr.) Lerner Publishing Group.

The Story of Gettysburg. 2003. (Illus.). 26p. (J). (ps-k). 6.95 (978-0-8249-6503-7(5)) Ideals Pubns.

Tackach, James, ed. The Battle of Gettysburg. 2002. (At Issue in History Ser.). (Illus.). 122p. (YA). (gr. 7-10). lib. bdg. 33.70 (978-0-7377-0817-2(4), Greenhaven Pr., Inc.) Thomson Gale.

Vierow, Wendy. The Battle of Gettysburg: The Civil War's Biggest Battle. 2004. (Headlines from History Ser.). (Illus.). 24p. (J). lib. bdg. 19.95 (978-0-8239-6225-9(3), PowerKids Pr.) Rosen Publishing Group, Inc., The.

Warrick, Karen Clemens. Gettysburg National Military Park: A MyReportLinks.com Book. 2005. (Virtual Field Trips Ser.). (Illus.). 48p. (J). (gr. 4-10). lib. bdg. 25.26 (978-0-7660-5223-9(0), MyReportLinks.com Bks.) Enslow Pubs., Inc.

Warynica, Lou & Hale, Sarah Elder. Gettysburg: Bold Battle in the North. 2005. (Civil War Ser.). (Illus.). 43p. (J). 17.95 (978-0-8126-7903-8(2)) Cobblestone Publishing Co.

GETTYSBURG, BATTLE OF, GETTYSBURG, PA., 1863—FICTION

Brown, Philip. Franky Franklyn's Fantastic Adventure. 2007. 118p. (J). pap. 10.99 (***978-1-60247-322-5(6)***) Tate Publishing & Enterprises, L.L.C.

Crist-Evans, Craig. Moon over Tennessee: A Boy's Civil War Journal. Christensen, Bonnie, illus. 64p. (J). (gr. 4-6). 2003. pap. 6.95 (978-0-618-31107-1(6)); 1999. tchr. ed. 15.00 (978-0-395-91208-9(3)) Houghton Mifflin Co. Trade & Reference Div.

—Moon over Tennessee: A Boy's Civil War Journal. 1999. (gr. 3-6). lib. bdg. 15.25 (978-0-613-60819-0(4)) Tandem Library Bks.

Gauch, Patricia Lee. Thunder at Gettysburg. 2003. (Illus.). 48p. (YA). (gr. 4-6). pap. 9.95 (978-1-59078-186-9(4)) Boyds Mills Pr.

Gibboney, Douglas Lee. Stonewall Jackson at Gettysburg. 2002. (Illus.). 132p. pap. 12.95 (978-1-57249-317-9(8), Burd Street Pr.) White Mane Publishing Co., Inc.

Gutman, Dan. Abner & Me. (Baseball Card Adventures Ser.). 176p. (J). 2007. pap. 5.99 (978-0-06-053445-5(1), Harper Trophy); 2005. (Illus.). 16.99 (978-0-06-053443-1(5)); 2005. (Illus.). lib. bdg. 17.89 (978-0-06-053444-8(3)) HarperCollins Pubs.

Hopkinson, Deborah. Billy & the Rebel. Floca, Brian, illus. 2005. 44p. (J). lib. bdg. 15.00 (***978-1-4242-1148-7(4)***) Fitzgerald Bks.

Hopkinson, Deborah. Billy & the Rebel: Based on a True Civil War Story. Floca, Brian, illus. 2006. (Ready-to-Reads Ser.). 48p. (J). pap. 3.99 (978-0-689-83396-0(2), Aladdin) Simon & Schuster Children's Publishing.

—Billy & the Rebel: Based on a True Civil War Story. Anderson, Bethanne & Floca, Brian, illus. 2005. (Ready-to-Read Ser.). 48p. (J). 14.95 (978-0-689-83964-1(2), Atheneum) Simon & Schuster Children's Publishing.

Kay, Alan N. Crossroads at Gettysburg. 2005. (Young Heroes of History: 6). (Illus.). 166p. (J). (gr. 3-7). pap. 7.95 (978-1-57249-359-9(3), White Mane Kids) White Mane Publishing Co., Inc.

Sykes, Shelley & Szymanski, Lois. The Ghost Comes Out. 2001. (Gettysburg Ghost Gang Ser.: Vol. 1). 96p. (J). pap. 5.95 (978-1-57249-266-0(X), White Mane Kids) White Mane Publishing Co., Inc.

—The Soldier in the Cellar. 2004. (Gettysburg Ghost Gang Ser.: Vol. 5). 96p. (J). pap. 5.95 (978-1-57249-299-8(6), White Mane Kids) White Mane Publishing Co., Inc.

Venner, Thomas. Young Heroes of Gettysburg. 2000. (White Mane Kids Ser.: Vol. 10). (Illus.). vi, 172p. (J). (gr. 4-7). pap. 8.95 (978-1-57249-200-4(7), White Mane Kids) White Mane Publishing Co., Inc.

GHANA

Ahiagble, Gilbert & Meyer, Louise. Master Weaver from Ghana. Hernandez, Nestor, photos by. 1998. (Illus.). 32p. (YA). (gr. 2-8). 18.00 (978-0-940880-61-0(X)) Open Hand Publishing, LLC.

Armentrout, David & Armentrout, Patricia. Ghana, Mali & Songhay. 2003. (Timelines of Ancient Civilizations Ser.). (Illus.). 32p. (J). 28.50 (978-1-58952-721-8(6)) Rourke Publishing, LLC.

Barnett, Jeanie M. Ghana. 1999. (Major World Nations Ser.). (Illus.). 144p. (YA). (gr. 4-7). lib. bdg. 21.95 (978-0-7910-4739-2(3), Chelsea Hse.) Facts On File, Inc.

Conrad, David C. Empires of Medieval West Africa: Ghana, Mali, & Songhay. 2005. (Great Empires of the Past Ser.). (Illus.). 128p. (J). (gr. 6-12). 35.00 (978-0-8160-5562-3(9)) Facts On File, Inc.

Davis, Lucile. Ghana. 1998. (Countries of the World Ser.). (Illus.). 126p. (J). (gr. 2-3). 18.60 (978-0-7368-0069-3(7), Bridgestone Bks.) Capstone Pr., Inc.

Ghana. (Countries of the World Ser.). 24p. (J). 6.95 (978-0-7368-8372-6(X)) Capstone Pr., Inc.

Ghana, 6 vols. (gr. 2-5). 36.95 (978-0-7368-8393-1(2)) Red Brick Learning.

La Pierre, Yvette. Ghana in Pictures. 2nd rev. expurg. ed. 2004. (Visual Geography Ser.). (Illus.). 80p. (J). (gr. 5-12). 27.93 (978-0-8225-1997-3(6)) Lerner Publishing Group.

Levy, P. Ghana. 1999. (Cultures of the World Ser.). (Illus.). 128p. (gr. 5-12). lib. bdg. 37.07 (978-0-7614-0952-6(1), Benchmark Bks.) Cavendish, Marshall Corp.

Littlefield, Holly. Colors of Ghana. Knutson, Barbara, illus. 1999. (Colors of the World Ser.). 24p. (gr. 3-6). 19.93 (978-1-57505-354-7(3)); (J). (gr. 1-4). 5.95 (978-1-57505-374-5(8)) Lerner Publishing Group.

—Colors of Ghana. Knutson, Barbara, illus. 1999. 24p. (J). (ps-3). lib. bdg. 14.10 (978-0-613-68204-6(1)) Tandem Library Bks.

Oppong, Joseph R. Ghana. 2003. (Modern World Nations Ser.). (Illus.). 150p. (gr. 6-12). 30.00 (978-0-7910-7378-0(5), Chelsea Hse.) Facts On File, Inc.

Poisson, Barbara Aoki. Ghana. 2004. (Africa Ser.). (Illus.). 79p. (J). lib. bdg. (978-1-59084-814-2(4)) Mason Crest Pubs.

Provencal, Francis & McNamara, Catherine. A Child's Day in a Ghanaian City. 2001. (Child's Day Ser.). (Illus.). 32p. (J). (gr. k-2). lib. bdg. 25.64 (978-0-7614-1223-6(9), Benchmark Bks.) Cavendish, Marshall Corp.

Quigley, Mary. Ancient West African Kingdoms. 2002. (Understanding People in the Past Ser.). (Illus.). 64p. (J). (gr. 4-6). pap. 8.95 (978-1-4034-0098-7(9), 91673) Heinemann Library.

—Ancient West African Kingdoms: Ghana, Mali, & Songhai. 2002. (Understanding People in the Past Ser.). (Illus.). 64p. (J). (gr. 4-6). lib. bdg. 28.50 (978-1-58810-425-0(7)) Heinemann Library.

GHANA—BIOGRAPHY

Currie-McGhee, Leanne K. Emmanuel Osofu Yeboah: Champion for Ghana's Disabled. 2006. (Young Heroes Ser.). (Illus.). 64p. (J). (gr. 4-8). lib. bdg. 27.45 (978-0-7377-3614-4(3), Kidhaven) Thomson Gale.

Tessitore, John. Kofi Annan: The Peacekeeper. 2000. (Book Report Biographies Ser.). (Illus.). 112p. (YA). (gr. 6-8). pap. 6.95 (978-0-531-16458-7(6), Watts, Franklin) Scholastic Library Publishing.

GHANA—CIVILIZATION

Nelson, Julie. Great African Kingdoms. 2001. (Ancient Civilizations Ser.). (Illus.). 48p. (J). lib. bdg. 22.83 (978-0-7398-3581-4(5)) Raintree.

Provencal, Francis & McNamara, Catherine. A Child's Day in a Ghanaian City. 2001. (Child's Day Ser.). (Illus.). 32p. (J). (gr. k-2). lib. bdg. 25.64 (978-0-7614-1223-6(9), Benchmark Bks.) Cavendish, Marshall Corp.

GHANA—FICTION

Boadu, Therson, illus. Fati & the Honey Tree. 2002. 28p. (978-9988-550-78-3(2)) Sub-Saharan Pubs. & Traders.

Glasser, Margaret D. Kofi's Story. 1999. (Illus.). 28p. (J). (gr. k-3). pap. 8.95 (978-1-58521-003-9(X)) Books for Black Children, Inc.

Hewins, Shirley, illus. Rainy Brown & the Seven Midgets. l.t. ed. 2006. (J). (gr. k-3). pap. 11.95 (978-1-884242-24-3(3) , RB1STED); 44p. lib. bdg. 19.95 (978-1-884242-25-0(1) , RB1STED) Multicultural Pubns.

Jarman, Julia. The Magic Backpack. Gon, Adriano, illus. 2004. (Flying Foxes Ser.). 48p. (J). (978-0-7787-1487-3(X)); pap. (978-0-7787-1533-7(7)) Crabtree Publishing Co.

Medearis, Angela Shelf. Seven Spools of Thread: A Kwanzaa Story. Minter, Daniel, illus. 2000. 40p. (J). (gr. 2-5). 15.95 (978-0-8075-7315-0(9)); pap. 6.95 (978-0-8075-7316-7(7)) Whitman, Albert & Co.

GHOST STORIES

Ada, Alma Flor. What Are Ghosts Afraid Of? (Stories the Year 'Round Ser.). (Illus.). 16p. (J). (gr. k-3). pap. 8.95 (978-1-58105-210-7(3)) Santillana USA Publishing Co., Inc.

—What Are Ghosts Afraid Of? 2000. (gr. k-3). lib. bdg. 30.40 (978-0-613-79388-9(9)) Tandem Library Bks.

Adler, David A. The Mystery at the Haunted House. Natti, Susanna, illus. 2004. (Cam Jansen Ser.: No. 13). 64p. (J). (gr. 2-4). pap. 3.99 (978-0-14-240210-8(9) , Puffin) Penguin Group (USA) Inc.

Anzaldua, Gloria. Prietita & the Ghost Woman (Prietita y la Llorona) ed. 2004. (ENG & SPA., Illus.). (J). (gr. k-3). spiral bd. (978-0-616-07273-8(2)) Canadian National Institute for the Blind/Institut National Canadien pour les Aveugles.

—Prietita & the Ghost Woman (Prietita y la Llorona) Gonzalez, Maya Christina, illus. 2001. (ENG & SPA.). 32p. (J). (gr. 1 up). pap. 7.95 (978-0-89239-167-7(7)) Children's Bk. Pr.

Arkle, Phyllis. Railway Cat & the Ghost. (Illus.). 56p. (J). pap. 6.99 (978-0-340-69993-5(0) , Hodder & Stoughton) Hodder General Publishing Division GBR. *Dist:* Trafalgar Square Publishing.

Arnold, Louise. Golden & Grey: the Nightmares That Ghosts Have. 2007. 304p. (J). pap. 5.99 (***978-0-689-87587-8(8)*** , Aladdin) Simon & Schuster Children's Publishing.

Asfar, Dan. Ghost Stories of Old West. rev. ed. 2003. (Ghost Stories Ser.: 28). (Illus.). 88p. (J). 10.95 (978-1-55105-332-5(2)) Lone Pine Publishing USA.

Asquith, R. Nora Normal Great Ghost Adventure. (Illus.). 64p. (J). pap. 6.99 (978-0-340-68071-1(7) , Hodder & Stoughton) Hodder General Publishing Division GBR. *Dist:* Trafalgar Square Publishing.

Atungsiri's Ghost & Other Tales. 2002. (J). pap. 5.95 net. (978-0-620-29636-6(4)) African Artistic Ventures.

Baglio, Ben M. Wolf at the Window. Baum, Ann, illus. 2003. (Animal Ark Hauntings Ser.: Vol. 7). 144p. (J). pap. 3.99 (978-0-439-44896-3(4) , Scholastic Paperbacks) Scholastic, Inc.

Bellairs, John. The Ghost in the Mirror. 2002. (J). (gr. 3 up). 20.75 (978-0-8446-7205-2(X)) Smith, Peter Pub., Inc.

Bennett, Cherie. The Haunted Heart. 1999. (J). (978-0-606-16362-0(X)) Tandem Library Bks.

Berenstain, Stan & Berenstain, Jan. The Berenstain Bear Scouts Scream Their Heads Off. 1998. (Berenstain Bear Scouts Ser.). (Illus.). 32p. (J). (gr. 3-6). pap. 3.99 (978-0-590-94484-7(3) , Scholastic Paperbacks) Scholastic, Inc.

—The Berenstain Bear Scouts Scream Their Heads Off. 1998. (Berenstain Bear Scouts Ser.). (J). (gr. 3-6). (978-0-606-13194-0(9)) Tandem Library Bks.

—The Haunted Lighthouse. 2001. (Berenstain Bears Ser.). (J). (gr. k-3). lib. bdg. 11.80 (978-0-613-33814-1(6)); (Illus.). 10.79 (978-0-606-21058-4(X)) Tandem Library Bks.

Betancourt, Jeanne. The Ghost Pony. 2000. (Pony Pals Super Special Ser.: No. 3). (J). (gr. 2). (978-0-606-19920-9(9)) Tandem Library Bks.

Black, Theodor, illus. Ghosts & Golems: Haunting Tales of the Supernatural. 2003. (Jps Young Adult Story Collections). 128p. pap. 9.95 (978-0-8276-0763-7(6)) Jewish Pubn. Society.

Bodkin, Odds. The Ghost of the Southern Belle: A Sea Tale. Fuchs, Bernie, illus. 1999. 32p. (J). (gr. 3-7). 15.95 (978-0-316-02608-6(5)) Little Brown & Co.

Bond, Ruskin. A Season of Ghosts. 1999. xi, 210p. (J). (978-0-670-88852-8(4) , Viking Adult) Penguin Group (USA) Inc.

Boniface, William. The Five Little Ghosts. Smath, Jerry, illus. 2002. 16p. (J). pap. 5.99 (978-0-8431-4907-4(8) , Price Stern Sloan) Penguin Group (USA) Inc.

Bouton, Warren Hussey. Sea Chest in the Attic: A Spooky Tale from Nantucket. Locke, Barbara K., illus. 2000. 86p. (J). (gr. 2-6). pap. 5.95 (978-0-9700555-0-7(1)) Hither Creek Pr.

Bryant, M. Ghosts in the Cloisters. (Illus.). x, 307p. (J). pap. 15.00 (978-0-340-71376-1(3) , Hodder & Stoughton) Hodder General Publishing Division GBR. *Dist:* Trafalgar Square Publishing.

Burchett, J. & Vogler, S. Tower Block Blowdown. Sharpe, Caroline, illus. 1998. (Cambridge Reading Ser.). 32p. (gr. 2-6). pap. 9.00 (978-0-521-63746-6(5)) Cambridge Univ. Pr.

Burchett, Janet & Vogler, Sara. Bones & Groans. 2003. (Illus.). 107p. (J). pap. (978-0-330-36814-8(1) , Pan) Pan Macmillan.

—Creep from the Deep. Brown, Judy, illus. 10th ed. 96p. (J). pap. (978-0-330-37607-5(1) , Pan) Pan Macmillan.

—Gruesome Twosome. Brown, Judy, illus. 89p. (J). pap. 6.99 (978-0-330-37605-1(5) , Pan) Pan Macmillan GBR. *Dist:* Trafalgar Square Publishing.

—Hector the Spectre. 2003. (Illus.). 86p. (J). pap. 6.99 (978-0-330-36812-4(5) , Pan) Pan Macmillan GBR. *Dist:* Trafalgar Square Publishing.

—Shiver & Deliver. Brown, Judy, illus. 2003. 87p. (J). pap. (978-0-330-37604-4(7) , Pan) Pan Macmillan.

Cabot, Meg. Twilight. 2006. (Mediator Ser.: Bk. 6). 336p. (J). pap. 6.99 (978-0-06-072469-6(2)) HarperCollins Pubs.

Carroll, Jenny, pseud. Ninth Key. 2005. (Mediator Ser.: Bk. 2). 304p. (YA). (gr. 7 up). pap. 7.99 (978-0-06-072512-9(5)) HarperCollins Pubs.

—Shadowland. 2005. (Mediator Ser.: Bk. 1). 304p. (YA). (gr. 7 up). pap. 7.99 (978-0-06-072511-2(7)) HarperCollins Pubs.

Carter, David A. In a Dark, Dark Wood: An Old Tale with a New Twist. 2002. (Illus.). 24p. (J). (ps-2). 10.95 (978-0-689-85280-0(0) , Little Simon) Simon & Schuster Children's Publishing.

Carus, Marianne. 13 Scary Ghost Stories. Xuan, Yong-Sheng, illus. 2002. 144p. (J). pap. 4.99 (978-0-439-34021-2(7)) Scholastic, Inc.

—13 Scary Ghost Stories. 2002. (gr. 3-6). lib. bdg. 12.40 (978-0-613-72025-0(3)) Tandem Library Bks.

Charles, Veronika Martenova. Don't Open the Door! Franson, Leanne, illus. 2001. (Easy-to-Read Spooky Tales Ser.). 56p. (J). (gr. 1-4). pap. (978-0-7737-6137-7(3)) Stoddart Kids.

Christensen, Jo-Anne. Haunted Christmas: A Collection of Ghost Stories, Vol. 1. rev. ed. 2002. (Ghost Stories Ser.). (Illus.). 208p. (J). (gr. 4). pap. (978-1-894877-15-2(2)) Lone Pine Publishing.

—Haunted Halloween Stories Vol. 1: A Collection of Ghost Stories. rev. ed. 2003. (Ghost Stories Ser.). (Illus.). 208p. (J). (gr. 4). pap. (978-1-894877-34-3(9)) Lone Pine Publishing.

Chrsitensen, Jo-Anne. Ghost Stories of Christmas. rev. ed. 2001. (Ghost Stories Ser.). (Illus.). 224p. (J). (gr. 4). pap. 10.95 (978-1-55105-334-9(9)) Lone Pine Publishing USA.

Clifford, Eth. Ghost School. 1998. (Illus.). (J). (gr. 1-4). pap. 3.99 (978-0-590-35032-7(3)) Scholastic, Inc.

Comer, O. B. Chile & Co. Mrs. Fable's Ghost & the Kidnappers. 1998. 105p. (J). (gr. 4-6). pap. 4.95 (978-0-9662064-9-4(5)) Paige Publishing.

Cook, Vivian E. Trapped in Haunted Castle. Nelson, Grace I., illus. 1999. (Adventures of Spencer, Private Eye & His Psychic Sister, Tiffany Ser.: No. 5). 58p. (J). (gr. 3-5). pap. 8.95 (978-1-928659-04-4(7)) Two Sisters Publishing.

Cool, Kim. Ghost Stories of Clearwater & St. Petersburg. 2004. (YA). pap. 12.95 (978-0-9721655-4-9(1)) Cool, Kim @ Historic Venice Pr.

Cooper, Louise. Demon Crossing. 2003. 208p. pap. (978-0-340-85399-3(9) , Hodder Children's Books) Hodder Children's Division.

—Short & Scary! A Book of Very Short Scary Stories. 2002. (Illus.). 96p. (978-0-19-278190-1(1)) Oxford Univ. Pr., Inc.

Coville, Bruce. The Ghost Saw Red. 1998. (J). (978-0-385-32215-7(1) , Dell Books for Young Readers) Random Hse. Children's Bks.

Crews, Nina. A Ghost Story. 2001. (Illus.). 48p. (J). 15.89 (978-0-688-17674-7(7)) HarperCollins Pubs.

Crowley, Bridget. Step into the Dark. 2002. (J). mass mkt. 9.99 (978-0-340-84416-8(7) , Hodder & Stoughton) Hodder General Publishing Division GBR. *Dist:* Trafalgar Square Publishing.

Cullen, Lynn. The Backyard Ghost. 2000. 164p. (YA). (gr. 4-7). pap. 11.95 (978-0-595-14410-5(1) , Backinprint-.com) iUniverse, Inc.

Dadey, Debbie & Jones, Marcia Thornton. Phantoms Don't Drive Sports Cars. Gurney, John Steven, illus. 1998. (Adventures of the Bailey School Kids Ser.: No. 32). 80p. (J). (gr. 2-4). pap. 3.99 (978-0-590-18982-8(4) , Scholastic Paperbacks) Scholastic, Inc.

—Phantoms Don't Drive Sports Cars. 1998. (Adventures of the Bailey School Kids Ser.: No. 32). (J). (gr. 2-4). (978-0-606-13702-7(5)) Tandem Library Bks.

de Brunhoff, Laurent. Babar Raconte le Fantome. (Babar Ser.). (FRE., Illus.). 48p. (J). (ps-3). 19.95 (978-0-7859-8819-9(X)) French & European Pubns., Inc.

del Sur, Duendes, illus. Pizza Place Ghost. 2001. (Scooby-Doo! Picture Clue Book Ser.: No. 4). 32p. (J). (gr. 5). pap. 3.99 (978-0-439-20495-8(X)) Scholastic, Inc.

Dunlop, Eileen. A Flute in Mayferry Street. 2000. 256p. (YA). (gr. 5 up). pap. (978-0-86315-328-0(3)) Floris Bks. GBR. *Dist:* SteinerBooks, Inc.

Eckett, Sean, illus. Ghost Stories. 2003. (Red Hot Reads Ser.). 256p. (J). (gr. 4-8). pap. 6.95 (978-0-7534-5675-0(3) , Kingfisher) Houghton Mifflin Co. Trade & Reference Div.

Elboz, Stephen. Ghostlands. l.t. ed. 2005. 200p. (J). pap. (978-0-7540-7849-4(3) , CLP 439) BBC Audio.

Enderle, Dotti. The Ghost of Shady Lane. 2005. (Fortune Tellers Club Ser.: book 7). (Illus.). 160p. pap. 4.99 (978-0-7387-0590-3(X) , 1241933) Llewellyn Pubns.

Fienberg, Anna & Fienberg, Barbara. Tashi & the Ghosts. Gamble, Kim, illus. 2003. (Tashi Ser.). 64p. (J). (gr. 1-4). pap. 4.95 (978-1-86448-090-0(4)) Allen & Unwin AUS. *Dist:* Independent Pubs. Group.

Fink Inc. Staff. Post, the Ghost. 2000. (Fink, Inc. Presents Ser.: Vol. 2). (Illus.). (J). 2.50 (978-1-930281-04-2(8)) FINK, Inc.

Fleischman, Sid. The Ghost in the Noonday Sun. 1999. (J). (978-0-606-18960-6(2)) Tandem Library Bks.

—McBroom's Ghost. Wummer, Amy, illus. 1998. 62p. lib. bdg. 11.79 (978-0-606-15963-0(0)) Tandem Library Bks.

Forrestal, Elaine. Straggler's Reef. 1999. 176p. (J). pap. 12.95 (978-1-86368-254-1(6)) Fremantle Pr. AUS. *Dist:* International Specialized Bk. Services.

Foster, Tony. Manor Spirits. 1998. 158p. (YA). (gr. 4-9). pap. 7.95 (978-1-85594-184-7(8)) Attic Pr. IRL. *Dist:* Dufour Editions, Inc., International Specialized Bk. Services.

Gallagher, Diana G. Spark & Burn. 2005. (Buffy the Vampire Slayer Ser.). 256p. (YA). pap. 6.99 (978-1-4169-0056-6(X) , Simon Spotlight Entertainment) Simon & Schuster.

Garton, Kevan. The Cockleton Mystery. 2006. 68p. pap. (***978-1-84401-788-1(5)***) Athena Pr.

Gaskin, Jack. The Ghostman's Halloween. Cassidy, Christina, illus. 1998. 12p. (J). (gr. k-4). pap. 5.95 (978-0-9668560-0-2(7)) Equity Research Corp.

Gliori, Debi. Pure Dead Trouble. 2005. (Illus.). 288p. (J). (gr. 5 up). 15.95 (978-0-375-83311-3(0) , Knopf Bks. for Young Readers) Random Hse. Children's Bks.

Golden, Christopher & Gilmore, Ford Lytle. Enemies, No. 4. 2006. (Hollow Ser.: No. 4). 240p. (YA). (gr. 7-12). mass mkt. 6.99 (978-1-59514-027-2(1) , Razorbill) Penguin Group (USA) Inc.

Gordon, Lawrence. User Friendly; The Ghost Chronicles, Vol. 1. 1998. 162p. (YA). (gr. 5-7). pap. 11.95 (978-0-9653966-0-8(6)) Karmichael Pr.

Greenburg, Dan. This Body's Not Big Enough for the Both of Us, Vol. 22. Davis, Jack E., illus. 2000. (Zack Files Ser.: No. 22). 64p. (J). (gr. 2-5). pap. 4.99 (978-0-448-42176-6(3) , Grosset & Dunlap) Penguin Group (USA) Inc.

Guiberson, Brenda Z. Tales of the Haunted Deep. Godwin, Laura, ed. Guiberson, Brenda Z., illus. rev. ed. 2000. (Redfeather Chapter Bk.). (Illus.). 80p. (J). (gr. 3-6). 16.95 (978-0-8050-6057-7(X) , Holt, Henry & Co. Bks. For Young Readers) Holt, Henry & Co.

Hahn, Mary Downing. Time for Andrew: A Ghost Story. 2007. 176p. (J). (gr. 4-6). pap. 5.95 (***978-0-618-87316-6(3)*** , Clarion Bks.) Houghton Mifflin Co. Trade & Reference Div.

Harper, Meg. The Ghost in the Gallery. 2001. 176p. (J). pap. 8.99 (978-0-7459-4589-7(9) , Lion) Lion Hudson plc GBR. *Dist:* Independent Pubs. Group.

Haskins, James. Moaning Bones: African-American Ghost Stories. Marshall, Felicia, illus. 1998. 64p. (YA). (gr. 2 up). 14.00 (978-0-688-16021-0(2)) HarperCollins Pubs.

Herman, Gail. The Haunted Ski Lodge. del Sur, Duendes, illus. 2001. (Scooby-Doo Ser.: No. 9). 32p. (J). pap. 3.99 (978-0-439-33493-8(4)) Scholastic, Inc.

Hoffman, Mallory. Touched by a Vampire. 2005. 70p. pap. 14.95 (978-1-4137-6583-0(1)) PublishAmerica, Inc.

Holder, Nancy. Queen of the Slayers. 2005. (Buffy the Vampire Slayer Ser.). 352p. (YA). pap. 9.99 (978-1-4169-0241-6(4) , Simon Spotlight Entertainment) Simon & Schuster.

Hutchens, Paul. The Ghost Dog. rev. ed. 1998. (Sugar Creek Gang Ser.: No. 25). 128p. (J). (gr. 4-7). 4.99 (978-0-8024-7029-4(7)) Moody Pubs.

—The Haunted House. rev. ed. 1998. (Sugar Creek Gang Ser.: Vol. 16). 112p. (J). (gr. 4-7). 4.99 (978-0-8024-7020-1(3)) Moody Pubs.

Irving, Washington. The Legend of Sleepy Hollow & Other Stories. 1999. (Penguin Classics Ser.). (Illus.). 368p. (gr. 12). pap. 8.95 (978-0-14-043769-0(X) , Penguin Classics) Penguin Group (USA) Inc.

—Washington Irving's the Legend of Sleepy Hollow: And Other Stories. 1999. (Illustrated Junior Library). (Illus.). 256p. (J). (gr. 4-7). 16.99 (978-0-448-42074-5(0) , Grosset & Dunlap) Penguin Group (USA) Inc.

Jacques, Brian. Seven Strange & Ghostly Tales. 1999. (Illus.). 144p. (J). (gr. 4-7). pap. 5.99 (978-0-698-11808-9(1) , Putnam Juvenile) Penguin Group (USA) Inc.

James, Henry. The Turn of the Screw. 310p. reprint ed. pap. 75.00 (978-1-4047-3418-0(X)) Classic Textbooks.

Johnson, Sandi. Haunted Dog House. Stillwell, Heath, illus. 2000. (Spooky Ser.). 12p. (J). (ps-6). spiral bd. 5.99 (978-1-929063-50-5(4) , 149) Moons & Stars Publishing For Children.

Johnson, Sandi, et al. Haunted Doghouse II: Halloween Night, 3 vols. Brundige, Britt, ed. Stargeon, Bobbi, illus. l.t. ed. 2005. 15p. (J). (gr. k-5). spiral bd. 6.99 (978-1-929063-27-7(X) , 351) Moons & Stars Publishing For Children.

Johnston, Tony. Boo! Croll, Carolyn, illus. 1998. (Hello Reader! Ser.). (J). 3.99 (978-0-590-37998-4(4)) Scholastic, Inc.

Jones, Marcia Thornton & Dadey, Debbie. Ghost Class. 2003. (gr. 3-6). lib. bdg. 11.80 (978-0-613-72126-4(8)) Tandem Library Bks.

—Happy Boo Day. 2000. (Bailey City Monsters Ser.: No. 9). (Illus.). (J). (gr. 2-4). 10.79 (978-0-606-18515-8(1)) Tandem Library Bks.

—Spooky Spells. 1999. (Bailey City Monsters Ser.: No. 6). (Illus.). 80p. (J). (gr. 2-4). pap. 3.99 (978-0-439-05871-1(6)) Scholastic, Inc.

—Spooky Spells. 1999. (Bailey City Monsters Ser.: No. 6). (J). (gr. 2-4). (978-0-606-16656-0(4)) Tandem Library Bks.

—Vampire Baby. 1999. (Bailey City Monsters Ser.: No. 7). (Illus.). 80p. (J). (gr. 2-4). pap. 3.99 (978-0-439-05872-8(4)) Scholastic, Inc.

—Vampire Baby. 1999. (Bailey City Monsters Ser.: No. 7). (J). (gr. 2-4). (978-0-606-17059-8(6)) Tandem Library Bks.

Joosse, Barbara M. Ghost Trap. Truesdell, Sue, illus. 1998. (Wild Willie Mystery Ser.). 80p. (J). (gr. 4-6). tchr. ed. 15.00 (978-0-395-66587-9(6) , Clarion Bks.) Houghton Mifflin Co. Trade & Reference Div.

Katz, Welwyn W. Time Ghost. 2002. (Illus.). (J). (gr. 4-7). pap. (978-0-88899-275-8(0)) Groundwood Bks.

—Time Ghost. 2002. 172p. (J). (gr. 4-7). 16.95 (978-0-88899-216-1(5) , Libros Tigrillo) Groundwood Bks. CAN. *Dist:* Perseus Distribution.

—Time Ghost. 2002. (gr. 3-6). lib. bdg. 15.25 (978-0-613-88591-1(0)) Tandem Library Bks.

Keene, Carolyn. The Haunted Bridge. 2000. (Nancy Drew Mystery Stories: Vol. 15). (Illus.). 220p. (J). (gr. 4-7). per. 14.95 (978-1-55709-261-8(3)) Applewood Bks.

Kimmel, Eric A. Hayyim's Ghost. 2005. (Illus.). 40p. (J). pap. 9.95 (978-1-932687-03-3(3) , Devora Publishing) Pitspopany Pr.

—Hayyim's Ghost. Binus, Ari, illus. 2005. 40p. (J). 16.95 (978-1-932687-02-6(5) , Devora Publishing) Pitspopany Pr.

Kipling, Rudyard. The Room in the Tower & Other Stories: Penguin Reading Lab, Level 2. 2001. 48p. pap. 7.66 (978-0-582-41667-3(1)) Longman Publishing Group.

Kiwak, Barbara, illus. Classic Ghost Stories II. 1998. (Classic Ghost Stories Ser.). 128p. (J). (gr. 3-7). pap. 5.95 (978-1-56565-893-6(0) , 08930W) Lowell Hse. Juvenile.

Labatt, Mary. The Ghost of Captain Briggs. Hill-Jackson, Troy, illus. 1999. (Sam Ser.). 120p. (J). (gr. 4-6). (978-1-55074-636-5(7)) Kids Can Pr., Ltd.

—The Ghost of Captain Briggs. Jackson, Troy, illus. 1999. (Sam Ser.). 120p. (J). (gr. 4-6). (978-1-55074-638-9(3)) Kids Can Pr., Ltd.

—The Ghost of Captain Briggs. 1999. (J). 11.60 (978-0-606-19016-9(3)) Tandem Library Bks.

Lawson, Julie. The Ghost of Avalanche Mountain. 2000. (Goldstone Trilogy Ser.). (Illus.). 232p. (YA). (gr. 5-9). pap. 7.95 (978-0-7737-6091-2(1)) Stoddart Kids CAN. *Dist:* Fitzhenry & Whiteside, Ltd.

—Ghost of Avalanche Mountain. 2000. (gr. 5-8). lib. bdg. 16.40 (978-0-613-34731-0(5)) Tandem Library Bks.

Leavitt, Caroline. The Haunted Clubhouse. l.t. ed. 1999. (Wishbone Mysteries Ser.: No. 2). 144p. (J). (gr. 4 up). lib. bdg. 22.60 (978-0-8368-2383-7(4)) Stevens, Gareth Inc.

Lee, Brian. Ghost Hunters. Lee, Brian, illus. 1999. (Illus.). 4p. (J). (gr. 2-7). 15.99 (978-0-7636-0889-7(0)) Candlewick Pr.

Lerangis, Peter. Boo! Ghosts in the School. 2001. (gr. 3-6). lib. bdg. 11.80 (978-0-613-53484-0(0)) Tandem Library Bks.

LeVitt, J. A. Ghsots of Whitner. LeVitt, Mike, illus. 2004. 84p. (J). per. 10.95 (978-1-932196-47-4(1)) Word-Wright.biz, Inc.

Loughead, Deb. Time & Again. 2005. 192p. (J). pap. 9.95 (978-1-894549-39-4(2)) Sumach Pr. CAN. *Dist:* Orca Bk. Pubs. USA.

Lubar, David. Gloomy Ghost. 1998. (Accidental Monsters Ser.: Vol. 4). (J). (gr. 3-7). pap. 3.99 (978-0-590-90721-7(2)) Scholastic, Inc.

Mahy, Margaret. The Horribly Haunted School. unabr. ed. 1998. (J). pap. 24.95 incl. audio (978-0-7540-6207-3(4)) BBC Audiobooks America.

Maitland, Barbara. The Bookstore Burglar. 2001. (Easy-to-Read Ser.). (Illus.). (J). 10.79 (978-0-606-21079-9(2)) Tandem Library Bks.

—The Bookstore Ghost. Westcott, Nadine Bernard, photos by. 1998. (Puffin Chapters Ser.). (Illus.). 29p. lib. bdg. 10.79 (978-0-606-16144-2(9)) Tandem Library Bks.

Maitland, Barbara & Funnell, Barbara E. The Bookstore Ghost. Westcott, Nadine Bernard, illus. 1998. (Puffin Easy-to-Read Program Ser.). 32p. (J). (gr. k-3). pap. 3.99 (978-0-14-130084-9(1) , Puffin) Penguin Group (USA) Inc.

Martin, Ann M. Karen's Black Cat. 1998. (Baby-Sitters Little Sister Ser.: No. 102). (J). (gr. 3-7). pap. 3.99 (978-0-590-50054-8(6)) Scholastic, Inc.

Mayer, Mercer. You're the Scaredy-Cat. 2002. (Mercer Mayer Picture Bks.). (Illus.). 32p. (J). pap. 5.95 (978-1-57768-859-4(7) , Mercer Mayer First Readers) School Specialty Publishing.

—You're the Scaredy-Cat. 2001. (gr. k-3). lib. bdg. 14.10 (978-0-613-84264-8(2)) Tandem Library Bks.

McCormick, Maggie. Spooky Stories: Super-Scary Tales to Chill Your Spine. 1999. (J). (978-1-84100-266-8(6)) Quadrillion Publishing.

McKay, Hilary. The Amber Cat. 1999. (YA). pap., stu. ed. 41.00 incl. audio (978-0-7887-3635-3(3) , 41000) Recorded Bks., LLC.

—The Amber Cat. 1999. [illegible]p. (J). 11.64 (978-0-606-16326-2(3)) Tandem Library Bks.

McKenna, Colleen O'Shaughnessy. Third Grade Ghouls! Roth, Stephanie, illus. 2001. 96p. (J). (gr. 4-6). tchr. ed. 15.95 (978-0-8234-1652-3(6)) Holiday Hse., Inc.

McNaughton, Colin. Boo! 1999. (Illus.). (J). (978-0-606-18169-3(5)) Tandem Library Bks.

Moerbeck, Kees. The Spooky Scrapbook. Moerbeck, Kees, illus. 2003. (Illus.). 15p. (J). (gr. 1-6). reprint ed. 17.00 (978-0-7567-6880-5(2)) DIANE Publishing Co.

Monte, Emily C. The Lost Sword of the Confederate Ghost: A Mystery in Two Centuries. 1999. 116p. (J). (gr. 4-7). 5.99 (978-1-57249-132-8(9)) White Mane Publishing Co., Inc.

Moses, Will & Irving, Washington. The Legend of Sleepy Hollow. 1999. (Illus.). 48p. (J). (gr. 4-7). pap. 6.99 (978-0-698-11648-1(8) , Putnam Juvenile) Penguin Group (USA) Inc.

Myers, Arthur & Rau, Margaret. Scary Stories for Campfires. 2005. (Illus.). 96p. (ps-7). pap. 5.95 (978-1-4027-2170-0(6)) Sterling Publishing Co., Inc.

Naylor, Phyllis Reynolds. Jade Green: A Ghost Story. 2001. (gr. 5-8). lib. bdg. 13.00 (978-0-613-36438-6(4)); (Illus.). (J). 11.64 (978-0-606-20732-4(5)) Tandem Library Bks.

Noyes, Deborah, ed. The Restless Dead: Ten Original Stories of the Supernatural. 2007. (Illus.). 256p. (YA). (gr. 7). 16.99 (***978-0-7636-2906-9(5)***) Candlewick Pr.

Olin, Sean. Killing Britney. 2005. 240p. (YA). (gr. 9 up). pap. 8.99 (978-0-689-87778-0(1) , Simon Pulse) Simon & Schuster Children's Publishing.

Pike, Christopher, pseud. Bury Me Deep. 2001. 224p. (YA). reprint ed. mass mkt. 5.99 (978-0-7434-2424-0(7) , Simon Pulse) Simon & Schuster Children's Publishing.

E
F
G

—Bury Me Deep. 2001. (gr. 7-12). lib. bdg. 14.15 (978-0-613-74176-7(5)); (J). 12.64 (978-0-606-21093-5(8)) Tandem Library Bks.

—The Last Story. 2002. (Remember Me Ser.: No. 3). 256p. (YA). mass mkt. 5.99 (978-0-689-85459-0(5) , Simon Pulse) Simon & Schuster Children's Publishing.

Pippen, Scottie. Out of the Shadows. 2001. mass mkt. (978-0-7868-8982-2(9)) Hyperion Pr.

Plourde, Josee & Dagenais, Sofi. Les Fantcomes d'Elia. 1999. (Roman Jeunesse Ser.). 96p. (YA). (gr. 4-7). pap. (978-2-89021-378-4(1)) Diffusion du livre Mirabel.

Price, Susan. Can Yr Ysbrydion. 2005. (WEL.). 172p. pap. (978-1-85596-217-0(9)) Dref Wen.

Rand, Johnathan. Aliens Attack Alpena. 1999. (Michigan Chillers: Vol. 4). 208p. (YA). pap. 5.99 (978-1-893699-09-0(9)) AudioCraft Publishing, Inc.

—American Chillers: Nebraska Night Crawlers, 15. 2004. (American Chillers Ser.: 15). 208p. (J). pap. 5.99 (978-1-893699-67-0(6)) AudioCraft Publishing, Inc.

—Gargoyles of Gaylord. 2000. (Michigan Chillers: Vol. 5). 204p. (YA). pap. 5.99 (978-1-893699-10-6(2)) AudioCraft Publishing, Inc.

—Ghost in the Graveyard. 2001. 297p. (YA). pap. 6.99 (978-1-893699-16-8(1)) AudioCraft Publishing, Inc.

Random House Disney Staff. Haunted Mansion: The Junior Novelization. 2003. (gr. 3-6). lib. bdg. 13.00 (978-0-613-73704-3(0)) Tandem Library Bks.

Reasoner, Charles. Boo! 1999. (Halloween Ser.). (Illus.). 14p. (J). bds. 4.99 (978-0-8431-7513-4(3) , Price Stern Sloan) Penguin Group (USA) Inc.

Rees, C. Haunts Vol. 4: N Is for Nightmare. 137p. (J). pap. (978-0-340-71525-3(1) , Hodder & Stoughton) Hodder General Publishing Division.

Rees, Celia. A Is for Apparition. (Haunts Ser.: Vol. 2). 122p. (J). pap. (978-0-340-71488-1(3) , Hodder & Stoughton) Hodder General Publishing Division.

—Host Rides Out. 2002. (Celia Rees Supernatural Trilogy: Bk. 3). (J). (gr. 3-6). mass mkt. 7.99 (978-0-340-81802-2(6) , Hodder & Stoughton) Hodder General Publishing Division GBR. *Dist:* Trafalgar Square Publishing.

Reeser, Tim. Ghost Stories of Ocean City, NJ. 2003. 122p. per. 11.99 (978-0-9729265-0-8(X)) 1stSight Pr.

—Ghost Stories of St. Petersburg, FL. 2004. 140p. per. 11.99 (978-0-9729265-2-2(6)) 1stSight Pr.

—Ghost Stories of Tampa, Fl. 2004. 142p. per. 11.99 (978-0-9729265-3-9(4)) 1stSight Pr.

Rehnert, Anne M. Witchworks Perilous Journeys. 2002. 235p. (YA). pap. 9.95 (978-1-892614-36-0(7)) Briarwood Pubns.

Roberts, David & Fletcher, Corina. Ghoul School. Roberts, David & Fletcher, Corina, illus. 2000. (Illus.). 10p. (J). (ps-3). 17.95 (978-0-8109-4140-3(6)) Abrams, Harry N. , Inc.

Roberts, David & Fletcher, Corina, illus. Ghoul School. 2003. 10p. (J). (gr. k-4). reprint ed. 18.00 (978-0-7567-7028-0(9)) DIANE Publishing Co.

Rogers, Jacqueline, illus. Even More Short & Shivery: Thirty Spine-Tingling Tales. 2003. 162p. (J). (gr. k-7). lib. bdg. 13.00 (978-0-613-72191-2(8)) Tandem Library Bks.

Rose, Sherrie. A Girl, A Guy & A Ghost. 2003. (YA). mass mkt. 5.99 (978-0-8439-5276-6(8)) Dorchester Publishing Co., Inc.

—Girl, a Guy & a Ghost. 2003. (gr. 7-12). lib. bdg. 14.15 (978-0-613-76907-5(4)) Tandem Library Bks.

Rosselson, Leon. Somewhere Else. (Illus.). 121p. (J). pap. 8.99 (978-0-340-72264-0(9) , Hodder & Stoughton) Hodder General Publishing Division GBR. *Dist:* Trafalgar Square Publishing.

Roxbury Park Staff. Best of Scary Stories for Stormy Nights. 2000. (Illus.). v, 151p. (J). pap. 5.95 (978-0-7373-0431-2(6) , Roxbury Park) Lowell Hse.

Rushby, Pamela. Footsteps. 2000. (gr. 7-12). lib. bdg. 12.25 (978-0-613-28844-6(0)) Tandem Library Bks.

—Shadows in the Garden. 2000. (gr. 7-12). lib. bdg. 12.25 (978-0-613-29063-0(1)) Tandem Library Bks.

San Souci, Robert D. Even More Short & Shivery: Thirty Spine-Tingling Stories. Rogers, Jacqueline, illus. 2003. 176p. (J). (gr. 5-7). pap. 5.99 (978-0-440-41877-1(1) , Yearling) Random Hse. Children's Bks.

—Short & Shivery: Thirty Chilling Tales. Coville, Katherine, illus. 2001. 192p. (J). (gr. 5). pap. 5.50 (978-0-440-41804-7(6) , Yearling) Random Hse. Children's Bks.

—Short & Shivery: Thirty Chilling Tales. 2001. (gr. 5-8). lib. bdg. 13.00 (978-0-613-85704-8(6)) Tandem Library Bks.

—A Terrifying Taste of Short & Shivery: Thirty Creepy Tales. Coville, Katherine, illus. 2004. 176p. (gr. 3-7). 5.99 (978-0-440-41878-8(X) , Yearling) Random Hse. Children's Bks.

Sansouci. Boy & the Ghost. 1998. (J). pap. 5.95 (978-0-87628-333-2(4)) Ctr. for Applied Research in Education, The.

Scholastic, Inc. Staff, et al. Scooby-Doo & the Witch's Ghost. 1999. (Scooby-Doo Movie Storybooks). (Illus.). 32p. (J). (ps-3). pap. 3.50 (978-0-439-08786-5(4)) Scholastic, Inc.

Schwartz, Alvin. Ghosts! Ghostly Tales from Folklore. 2002. (Illus.). (J). 11.87 (978-0-7587-6110-1(4)) Book Wholesalers, Inc.

—Scary Stories 3: More Tales to Chill Your Bones. 2002. (Illus.). (J). 14.47 (978-0-7587-6725-7(0)) Book Wholesalers, Inc.

—Scary Stories 3: More Tales to Chill Your Bones. Gammell, Stephen, illus. 2001. (Scary Stories Ser.). 128p. (J). (gr. 4 up). 16.99 (978-0-06-021794-5(4)) HarperCollins Pubs.

Sefton, Catherine. Ghost Ship. (Illus.). 32p. (J). 13.95 (978-0-241-11596-1(5) , Hamilton, Hamish) Penguin Bks., Ltd. GBR. *Dist:* Trafalgar Square Publishing.

—Ghosts of Cobweb & the TV Battle. (Illus.). 48p. (J). 11.95 (978-0-241-00199-8(4) , Hamilton, Hamish) Penguin Bks., Ltd. GBR. *Dist:* Trafalgar Square Publishing.

Shan, Darren, pseud. The Vampire Prince. 2005. (Cirque du Freak: Bk. 6). 208p. (J). (gr. 5-17). mass mkt. 6.99 (978-0-316-00097-0(3)) Little Brown & Co.

—The Vampire Prince. 2004. (Cirque du Freak: Bk. 6). 208p. (J). (gr. 5-17). pap. 7.99 (978-0-316-60274-7(4)) Little, Brown Bks. for Young Readers.

Shreve, Susan Richards. Ghost Cats. 2001. (Illus.). (J). (978-0-606-21211-3(6)) Tandem Library Bks.

Singer, Marilyn. Deal with a Ghost. 1999. 192p. (J). pap. 6.99 (978-0-380-73183-1(5) , HarperTeen) HarperCollins Pubs.

Skidmore, Steve & Barlow, Steve. Knyghtmare: Tales of the Dark Forest, Bk. 4. 2004. (Tales of the Dark Forest Ser.). (Illus.). 256p. (J). pap. 11.00 (978-0-00-710866-4(4) , HarperSport) HarperCollins Pubs. Ltd. GBR. *Dist:* Independent Pubs. Group.

Smith, Barbara. Ghost Stories of the Sea, Vol. 1. rev. ed. 2003. (Ghost Stories Ser.). (Illus.). 224p. (J). (gr. 4). pap. (978-1-894877-23-7(3)) Lone Pine Publishing.

Smith, L. J. Strange Fate. 1998. (Night World Ser.). 224p. (J). pap. 4.50 (978-0-671-01478-0(1) , Simon Pulse) Simon & Schuster Children's Publishing.

Smithley, Amanda. Mary's Next Encounter. 2004. 81p. pap. 14.95 (978-1-4137-4210-7(6)) PublishAmerica, Inc.

Snyder, Zilpha Keatley. Gib & the Gray Ghost. 2001. 240p. (gr. 3-7). 5.99 (978-0-440-41518-3(7) , Yearling) Random Hse. Children's Bks.

—Gib & the Gray Ghost. 2001. 12.15 (978-0-606-22418-5(1)) Tandem Library Bks.

—Gib & the Gray Ghost. 2003. (Juvenile Ser.). (Illus.). 22.95 (978-0-7862-5018-9(6)) Thorndike Pr.

Soileau, Hodges, illus. The Mystery of the Haunted Boxcar, Vol. 100. 2004. (Boxcar Children Mysteries Ser.: 100). 128p. (J). (gr. 2-7). mass mkt. 4.50 (978-0-8075-5554-5(1)) Whitman, Albert & Co.

Souhami, Jessica. In the Dark Dark Wood. 2004. (Illus.). 24p. (J). 15.95 (978-1-84507-199-8(9)) Lincoln, Frances Ltd. GBR. *Dist:* Perseus Distribution.

Stamper, Judith Bauer. Five Haunted Houses. 2001. (Hello Reader! Ser.). (Illus.). (J). (978-0-606-21190-1(X)) Tandem Library Bks.

Stanley, George Edward. Ghost Horse. 2000. (gr. 3-6). lib. bdg. 11.80 (978-0-613-27851-5(8)) Tandem Library Bks.

Stark, Kirt. Campfire Chills: 13 Haunting Ghost Tales. 1998. 405p. (YA). pap. 14.95 (978-0-9665002-3-3(7)) Dark Woods Publishing.

Stine, R. L. All-Night Party. 2005. (Fear Street Ser.). 160p. (YA). pap. 5.99 (978-1-4169-0321-5(6) , Simon Pulse) Simon & Schuster Children's Publishing.

—Darkest Dawn. 2005. (Fear Street Nights Ser.). 192p. (YA). pap. 5.99 (978-0-689-87866-4(4) , Simon Pulse) Simon & Schuster Children's Publishing.

—Ghost Beach. 2003. (Goosebumps Ser.). 144p. mass mkt. 4.99 (978-0-439-56830-2(7) , 53655424, Scholastic Paperbacks) Scholastic, Inc.

—Ghost Beach. 2003. (gr. 5-8). lib. bdg. 13.00 (978-0-613-70848-7(2)) Tandem Library Bks.

—Goosebumps: The Beast from the East. 2005. (Goosebumps Ser.). 144p. 4.99 (978-0-439-72403-6(1)) Scholastic, Inc.

—Goosebumps: The Curse of Camp Cold Lake. 2005. (Goosebumps Ser.). 144p. pap. 4.99 (978-0-439-72404-3(X)) Scholastic, Inc.

—The Haunted Car. 1999. (Goosebumps Series 2000: No. 21). (Illus.). (J). (gr. 3-7). (978-0-606-18552-3(6)) Tandem Library Bks.

—Killer's Kiss. 2005. (Fear Street Ser.). 160p. (YA). pap. 5.99 (978-1-4169-0320-8(8) , Simon Pulse) Simon & Schuster Children's Publishing.

—Little Camp of Horrors. 2005. 144p. (J). (gr. 2-5). 6.95 (978-0-385-74666-3(0)); lib. bdg. 8.99 (978-0-385-90916-7(0)) Random Hse. Children's Bks. (Delacorte Bks. for Young Readers).

—Midnight Games. 2005. (Fear Street Nights Ser.). 160p. (YA). pap. 5.99 (978-0-689-87865-7(6) , Simon Pulse) Simon & Schuster Children's Publishing.

—El Monstruo del Club Laguna. 2000. (Fear Street Ser.). (SPA.). (YA). (gr. 7 up). pap. 6.36 net. (978-950-04-1904-8(1) , EM4472) Lectorum Pubns., Inc.

—Moonlight Secrets. 2005. (Fear Street Nights Ser.). 160p. (YA). pap. 5.99 (978-0-689-87864-0(8) , Simon Pulse) Simon & Schuster Children's Publishing.

—Nightmare Hour. 2000. (Illus.). 160p. (J). (gr. 5 up). pap. 5.99 (978-0-06-440842-4(6) , Avon) HarperCollins Pubs.

—Nightmare Hour: Time for Terror. 1999. (Illus.). 160p. (J). (gr. 3 up). 16.99 (978-0-06-028688-0(1)) HarperCollins Pubs.

—Nightmare Hour: Time for Terror. 2000. (gr. 5-8). lib. bdg. 14.15 (978-0-613-71481-5(4)) Tandem Library Bks.

—The Nightmare Room Vol. 1-2-3: The Nightmare Begins! 2001. (Nightmare Room Ser.). 432p. (gr. 5 up). pap. 7.99 (978-0-06-076674-0(3)) HarperCollins Pubs.

—La Noche del Muneco Viviente II. 1999. (Escalofrios/Goosebumps Ser.: Vol. 31). (SPA.). 110p. (J). (gr. 3-7). pap. 3.99 (978-0-439-06627-3(1) , SO31217) Scholastic, Inc.

—La Noche del Muneco Viviente II. 1999. (SPA., Illus.). (J). (978-0-606-16955-4(5)) Tandem Library Bks.

—Por Que No Asustan los Fantasmas. (Fear Street Ser.). (SPA.). (YA). (gr. 7 up). pap. 7.95 (978-950-04-1929-1(7) , EM4372) Emecé Editores S.A. ARG. *Dist:* Lectorum Pubns., Planeta Publishing Corp.

—Return to Ghost Camp. 1999. (Goosebumps Series 2000: No. 19). 112p. (gr. 3-7). pap. 3.99 (978-0-590-68523-8(6)) Scholastic, Inc.

—Ship of Ghouls. 1999. (Give Yourself Goosebumps Ser.: No. 36). 144p. (gr. 3-7). pap. 3.99 (978-0-590-51723-2(6)) Scholastic, Inc.

—The Stepsister. 2005. (Fear Street Ser.). 176p. (YA). pap. 5.99 (978-1-4169-0029-0(2) , Simon Pulse) Simon & Schuster Children's Publishing.

—Welcome to Dead House. 2003. (Goosebumps Ser.). 144p. (J). pap. 4.99 (978-0-439-56847-0(1) , 53657974, Scholastic Paperbacks) Scholastic, Inc.

—Welcome to Dead House. 2003. (gr. 3-6). lib. bdg. 13.00 (978-0-613-70766-4(4)) Tandem Library Bks.

Sullivan, Sullivan. Can I Be the Ghost? 1998. (YA). (gr. 3 up). pap. 8.95 (978-0-8464-4931-7(5)) Beekman Bks., Inc.

Sutton, Margaret & Bolton, Judy. Haunted Attic. 2004. (Judy Bolton Mystery Ser.). 224p. (J). (gr. 4-7). reprint ed. 24.95 (978-1-55709-251-9(6)) Applewood Bks.

Taylor, Cora. Ghost Voyages III: Endeavour & Resolution. 2004. (Ghost Voyages Fantasy Ser.: Vol. 3). (Illus.). 176p. (J). (gr. 3-5). pap. 6.95 (978-1-55050-305-0(7)) Coteau Bks. CAN. *Dist:* Fitzhenry & Whiteside, Ltd.

Thuma, Cynthia & Lower, Catherine. Creepy Colleges & Haunted Universities: True Ghost Stories. 2003. (Illus.). 128p. (gr. 10-13). pap. 16.95 (978-0-7643-1805-4(5)) Schiffer Publishing, Ltd.

Tjong Khing Staff, Tjong Khing, illus. Don't Read This! And Other Tales of the Unnatural. Date not set. 214p. (J). (gr. 5-10). pap. 9.95 (978-0-88899-325-0(0) , Libros Tigrillo) Groundwood Bks. CAN. *Dist:* Transition Vendor.

Tolan, Stephanie S. The Face in the Mirror. 2000. (Harper Trophy Bks.). 224p. (J). (gr. 3-7). pap. 4.95 (978-0-380-73263-0(7) , Harper Trophy) HarperCollins Pubs.

—The Face in the Mirror. 2000. (J). (978-0-606-19968-1(3)) Tandem Library Bks.

Triple-Decker, 3 vols., Set. pap. 20.00 (978-0-9657367-4-9(1)) Less Pr.

Tunnell, Michael O. Halloween Pie. Highlights Staff, ed. Omalley, Kevin, illus. 2004. 32p. (J). (gr. k-2). pap. 9.95 (978-1-59078-250-7(X)) Boyds Mills Pr.

—School Spirits. 2005. 201p. (J). (ps-7). pap. 10.95 (978-1-59078-376-4(X)) Boyds Mills Pr.

Turner, Anthea. Ghost of Knightsbridge. Hunt, Andy, illus. 48p. (J). pap. 7.95 (978-0-14-056388-7(1)) Penguin Bks., Ltd. GBR. *Dist:* Trafalgar Square Publishing.

Turner, Barbara F. Ghost Fire. 1998. (J). pap. 6.00 (978-1-892614-08-7(1)) Briarwood Pubns.

Tyrrell, David. Kim & the Witch's Tomb. 2003. 48 p. pap. 12.95 (978-1-4137-0850-9(1)) PublishAmerica, Inc.

Van Belkom, Edo. Lone Wolf. 2005. 184p. (J). (gr. 5-9). pap. 8.95 (978-0-88776-741-8(9)) Tundra Bks., Inc./Livres Toundra, Inc. CAN. *Dist:* Random Hse., Inc.

Van de Velde, Vivian. There's a Dead Person Following My Sister Around. 2001. (Illus.). (J). (978-0-606-21485-8(2)) Tandem Library Bks.

Vandersteen, Willy. The Circle of Power. Geerts, Paul, illus. 1998. (Greatest Adventures of Spike & Suzy Ser.: Vol. 2). 56p. (J). (gr. 2-9). 11.95 (978-0-9533178-1-3(1)) Intes International (UK) Ltd. GBR. *Dist:* Diamond Comic Distributors, Inc.

Wallace, Karen. Creakie Hall: Ace Ghosts. Ross, Tony, illus. l.t. ed. 1998. 72p. (J). pap. (978-0-7540-6034-5(9) , CLP 237) BBC Audio.

Warner, Gertrude Chandler, creator. The Mystery of the Haunted Boxcar, Vol. 100. 2004. (Boxcar Children Mysteries Ser.: 100). 128p. (J). (gr. 2-7). 14.95 (978-0-8075-5553-8(3)) Whitman, Albert & Co.

Westall, Robert. Ghost Stories. 2003. (gr. 3-6). lib. bdg. 15.25 (978-0-613-90167-3(3)) Tandem Library Bks.

—Shades of Darkness. 1999. 313p. (YA). (gr. 7 up). (978-0-330-35318-2(7) , Macmillan Children's Bks.) Pan Macmillan.

Wilde, Oscar. El Fantasma de Canterville y Otros Cuentos. (Clasicos Juveniles Coleccion). (SPA.). (YA). (gr. 5-8). pap. (978-950-11-1264-1(0) , SG8742) Sigmar ARG. *Dist:* Lectorum Pubns., Inc.

Wingo, W. There Grows a Crooked Tree. 2003. 188p. pap. 13.95 (978-0-595-28903-5(7)) iUniverse, Inc.

—There Grows a Crooked Tree. 2003. 188p. 23.95 (978-0-595-75271-3(3)) iUniverse, Inc.

Winters, Kay. The Teeny Tiny Ghost. Munsinger, Lynn, illus. 2002. (J). 14.43 (978-0-7587-3770-0(X)) Book Wholesalers, Inc.

—The Teeny Tiny Ghost. Munsinger, Lynn, illus. 1999. 32p. (J). (ps-3). pap. 6.99 (978-0-06-443590-1(3) , Harper Trophy) HarperCollins Pubs.

—The Teeny Tiny Ghost & the Monster, Vol. 3. Munsinger, Lynn, illus. 2004. 32p. (J). (ps-3). 14.99 (978-0-06-028884-6(1)); lib. bdg. 15.89 (978-0-06-028885-3(X)) HarperCollins Pubs.

Woodbury, Mary. The Ghost in the Machine. 2005. 222p. (J). (gr. 6-9). pap. 7.95 (978-1-55050-227-5(1)) Coteau Bks. CAN. *Dist:* Fitzhenry & Whiteside, Ltd.

Woodruff, Elvira. Ghost of Lizard Light. Clayton, Elaine, illus. 2001. 176p. (J). (ps-7). per. 11.64 (978-0-606-22076-7(3)) Tandem Library Bks.

Wright, Betty Ren. Christina's Ghost. unabr. ed. 2002. (Illus.). (J). (ps-3). 39.95 incl. audio (978-0-87499-937-2(5)) Live Oak Media.

—Haunted Summer. 2001. (J). (978-0-606-21228-1(0)) Tandem Library Bks.

Yee, Paul. The Bone Collector's Son. 2005. 144p. (YA). 15.95 (978-0-7614-5242-3(7)) Cavendish, Marshall Corp.

—Dead Man's Gold & Other Stories. Chan, Harvey, illus. 2004. 112p. (YA). pap. 7.95 (978-0-88899-587-2(3)); 2002. (J). (gr. 6 up). 14.95 (978-0-88899-475-2(3)) Groundwood Bks. CAN. *Dist:* Perseus Distribution, Transition Vendor.

—Ghost Train. Chan, Harvey, illus. 2004. 29p. (J). (gr. k-4). reprint ed. 16.00 (978-0-7567-9083-7(2)) DIANE Publishing Co.

Yep, Laurence. The Case of the Goblin Pearls. Krenitsky, Nicholas, illus. 1998. (Chinatown Mystery Ser.: Vol. 1). 192p. (J). (gr. 3-7). pap. 5.99 (978-0-06-440552-2(4) , Harper Trophy) HarperCollins Pubs.

13 Ghosts Strange but True. 2003. pap. 2.50 (978-0-590-41690-0(1)) Scholastic, Inc.

GHOST TOWNS

see Cities and Towns, Ruined, Extinct, Etc.

GHOSTS

see also Apparitions; Superstition

Asfar, Dan. Ghost Stories of Old West, Vol. 1. rev. ed. 2003. (Ghost Stories Ser.). (Illus.). 216p. (gr. 4). pap. (978-1-894877-17-6(9)) Lone Pine Publishing.

—Ghost Stories of Pennsylvania, Vol. 1. rev. ed. 2002. (Ghost Stories Ser.). (Illus.). 208p. (gr. 4). pap. (978-1-894877-08-4(X)) Lone Pine Publishing.

Asfar, Dan & Thay, Edrick. Ghost Stories of America, 2 vols., Vol. 1. rev. ed. 2002. (Ghost Stories Ser.). (Illus.). 248p. (J). (gr. 4). pap. (978-1-894877-11-4(X)) Lone Pine Publishing.

Asfar, Dan, et al. Ghost Stories of America, 2 vols., Vol. 2. rev. ed. 2003. (Ghost Stories Ser.). (Illus.). 248p. (gr. 4). pap. (978-1-894877-31-2(4)) Lone Pine Publishing.

Bada, Kathleen. Ghosts: Glow in the Dark Sticker Book. 2001. (Ultimate Sticker Bks.). (Illus.). 16p. (J). pap. 6.99 (978-0-7894-7868-9(4)) Dorling Kindersley Publishing, Inc.

Blackwood, Gary L. Spooky Spectres. 1999. (Secrets of the Unexplained Ser.). (Illus.). 80p. (J). (gr. 5-9). lib. bdg. 29.93 (978-0-7614-0746-1(4) , Benchmark Bks.) Cavendish, Marshall Corp.

Brucken, Kelli M. Ghosts. 2006. (Encounters with Ser.). (Illus.). 48p. (J). (gr. 4-8). 26.20 (978-0-7377-3474-4(4) , Greenhaven Pr., Inc.) Thomson Gale.

Burtinshaw, Julie. Romantic Ghost Stories, Vol. 1. rev. ed. 2003. (Ghost Stories Ser.). (Illus.). 224p. (gr. 4). pap. (978-1-894877-28-2(4)) Lone Pine Publishing.

Christensen, Jo-Anne. Haunted Hotels, Vol. 1. rev. ed. 2002. (Ghost Stories Ser.). (Illus.). 216p. (J). (gr. 4). pap. (978-1-894877-03-9(9)) Lone Pine Publishing.

Claybourne, Anna, ed. Ghosts & Hauntings. 2000. (Ghosts & Hauntings Ser.). (Illus.). 96p. (YA). (gr. 3-7). pap. 13.95 (978-0-7460-3716-4(3)) EDC Publishing.

—Poltergeists. 1998. (Usborne Paranormal Guides Ser.). (Illus.). 48p. (YA). (gr. 4 up). pap. 5.95 (978-0-7460-3058-5(4)) EDC Publishing.

Cohen, Daniel. Civil War Ghosts. 1999. (Illus.). 105p. (J). (gr. 3-7). pap. 4.50 (978-0-439-05387-7(0)) Scholastic, Inc.

—Civil War Ghosts. 1999. (Illus.). (J). (gr. 3-7). (978-0-606-18532-5(1)) Tandem Library Bks.

Costain, Meredith. It's True! Hauntings Happen & Ghosts Get Grumpy. Smith, Craig, illus. 2006. (It's True! Ser.). 96p. (J). (gr. 5-8). 19.95 (978-1-55451-022-1(8)); pap. 5.95 (978-1-55451-021-4(X)) Annick Pr., Ltd. CAN. *Dist:* Firefly Bks., Ltd.

Deary, Terry. True Ghost Stories. Waytt, David, illus. l.t. ed. 1998. (J). pap. (978-0-7540-6022-2(5) , CLP 221) BBC Audio.

—True Ghost Stories. l.t. ed. 2003. (J). pap. 29.95 incl. audio (978-0-7540-6212-7(0) , Galaxy Children's Large Print) BBC Audiobooks America.

Doherty, Gillian. Ghosts? 1999. (Usborne Paranormal Guides Ser.). (Illus.). 48p. (gr. 4-7). pap. 5.95 (978-0-7460-3056-1(8)) EDC Publishing.

Donkin, Andrew. Spooky Spinechillers. 2000. (Eyewitness Readers Ser.). (J). (978-0-606-20127-8(0)); lib. bdg. 11.80 (978-0-613-33085-5(4)) Tandem Library Bks.

Duffield, Katy. Poltergeists. 2007. (Mysterious Encounters Ser.). (Illus.). 48p. (J). (gr. 4-8). 26.20 ***978-0-7377-3665-6(8)** , Kidhaven) Thomson Gale.

Elborough, Travis. Ghosts, Ghouls, & Phantoms of London. 2004. (Illus.). 96p. 8.99 (978-1-904153-02-3(X)) Watling St., Ltd. GBR. *Dist:* Trafalgar Square Publishing.

Everett, Lawrence. Ghosts & Legends of Southeastern Ohio & Beyond: Tales of Legends, Hauntings & the Unexplained, 2. 2003. 124p. (YA). pap. 11.95 (978-0-7414-1760-2(X)) Infinity Publishing.

Farman, John. The Short & Bloody History of Ghosts. 2005. (Short & Bloody Histories Ser.). (Illus.). 96p. (gr. 6-12). lib. bdg. 19.93 (978-0-8225-0837-3(0)) Lerner Publishing Group.

Floyd, E. Randall. In the Realm of Ghosts & Hauntings. 2002. 190p. pap. 16.95 (978-1-891799-06-8(1)) Harbor Hse.

Galashan, Kathy. Livewire Investigates Ghosts. 2nd rev. ed. 2004. (Livewires Ser.). (Illus.). 32p. pap. (978-0-340-81126-9(9)) Cambridge Univ. Pr.

Gee, Joshua. Encyclopedia Horrifica: The Terrifying Truth! about Vampires, Ghosts, Monsters & More. 2007. (Encyclopedia Horrifica Ser.). (Illus.). 144p. (J). (gr. 4-7). pap. 14.99 (***978-0-439-92255-5(0)**) Scholastic, Inc.

Ghost Sticker Book. 2003. (Illus.). 16p. (J). 2.98 (978-1-84273-120-8(3) , Exclusive Editions) Parragon, Inc.

Gorman, Jacqueline Laks. Ghosts. 2002. (X Science Ser.). (Illus.). 24p. (YA). (gr. 2 up). lib. bdg. 22.00 (978-0-8368-3199-3(3)) Stevens, Gareth Inc.

Grohsmeyer, Janeen K. Moll Dyer: She Still Walks This Land - A Legend of Southern Maryland. Grohsmeyer, Ryan, illus. 2000. 40p. (YA). (gr. 4 up). pap. (978-1-892573-06-3(7) , 0007) Campanile Pr., Inc.

Guy, John. Ghosts. 2006. (Illus.). 36p. (J). lib. bdg. 24.67 (978-0-8368-6265-2(1)) Stevens, Gareth Inc.

Hamilton, Sue L. Ghosts & Goblins. 2007. (ENG., Illus.). 32p. (J). lib. bdg. 24.21 (***978-1-59928-767-6(6)** , ABDO & Daughters) ABDO Publishing Co.

Harvey, Gill. Poltergeists? 1998. (Paranormal Guides Ser.). (Illus.). 48p. (J). lib. bdg. 13.95 (978-1-58086-198-4(9)) EDC Publishing.

Haskins, Lori. Spooky America: Four Real Ghost Stories. Diaz, Viviana, illus. 2003. 48p. (J). (gr. 1-4). pap. 3.99 (978-0-375-82500-2(2) , Random Hse. Bks. for Young Readers) Random Hse. Children's Bks.

—Spooky America: Four Real Ghost Stories. 2003. (gr. k-3). lib. bdg. 11.80 (978-0-613-82987-8(5)) Tandem Library Bks.

Hausman, Gerald. Duppy Talk: West Indian Tales of Mystery & Magic. Hausman, Mariah, illus. rev. ed. 1999. 102p. (YA). (gr. 5 up). pap. 10.00 (978-0-9709112-0-9(3)) Irie Bks.

Hepplewhite, Peter. Unexplained: Hauntings. 1998. (Unexplained Ser.). (Illus.). 48p. (J). (gr. 4-7). 7.95 (978-0-8069-3883-7(8)) Sterling Publishing Co., Inc.

Horner, William. Wisconsin's Ridgeway Ghost. Schneider, Beth, illus. 2001. 32p. (J). (gr. 2-4). lib. bdg. 24.95 (978-1-931765-02-2(2)) Badger Hse., LLC.

Innes, Brian. Ghosts of Flight 401. 1999. (Unsolved Mysteries Ser.). (Illus.). 48p. (J). (gr. 3-7). lib. bdg. 25.69 (978-0-8172-5475-9(7)) Raintree.

—The Ghosts of Flight 401. 1998. (Unsolved Mysteries Ser.). (Illus.). 48p. (J). (gr. 3-7). pap. 8.05 (978-0-8172-4272-5(4)) Steck-Vaughn.

Jennings, Linda & Gardner, Louise. Ghosts. 1999. (Spooky Pop-Ups Ser.). (Illus.). 12p. 4.95 (978-1-899607-21-1(8)) Sterling Publishing Co., Inc.

Kallen, Stuart A. Ghosts. 2003. (Illus.). 112p. (J). 29.95 (978-1-59018-290-1(1) , Lucent Bks.) Thomson Gale.

—Haunted Houses. 2007. (J). lib. bdg. (***978-1-60152-026-5(3)***) ReferencePoint Pr., Inc.

Kallen, Stuart A. Poltergeists. 2005. (Mystery Library). (Illus.). 112p. (J). (gr. 7-10). 29.95 (978-1-59018-321-2(5) , Lucent Bks.) Thomson Gale.

Kidslabel Staff. Spot 7 Spooky. 2007. (Illus.). 40p. (J). (gr. 1-6). 12.95 (978-0-8118-5723-9(9)) Chronicle Bks. LLC.

Krensky, Stephen. Ghosts. 2007. (Monster Chronicles Ser.). 48p. (J). (gr. 4-8). lib. bdg. 26.60 (***978-0-8225-6762-2(8)*** , Lerner Pubns.) Lerner Publishing Group.

Krohn, Katherine E. Haunted Houses. 2006. (Edge Books, the Unexplained). 32p. (J). (978-0-7368-5450-4(9)) Capstone Pr., Inc.

Lanigan-Schmidt, Therese. Ghosts of New York City. 2003. (Illus.). 224p. (gr. 10-13). pap. 16.95 (978-0-7643-1714-9(8)) Schiffer Publishing, Ltd.

Mac Iver, Kathi, told to. Ghosts of Bennett Avenue. 2000. (Illus.). 74p. 9.95 (978-0-9651272-7-1(3)) Columbine Pr.

MacDonald, Janice E. The Ghouls' Night Out. Currie, Pamela B., illus. 1998. 50p. (J). (gr. 1-5). pap. 8.95 (978-0-921870-58-6(2)) Ronsdale Pr. CAN. *Dist:* Literary Pr. Group of Canada.

Martin, Michael. Ghosts. 2004. (Unexplained Ser.). 32p. (J). lib. bdg. 22.60 (978-0-7368-2717-1(X)) Capstone Pr., Inc.

Marts, Michael. Ghosts in Amityville: The Haunted House. 2007. (Graphic Mysteries Ser.). (Illus.). 24p. (J). (978-1-4042-2345-5(2)); pap. (978-1-4042-2155-0(7)); (gr. 2-6). lib. bdg. 21.25 (978-1-4042-3402-4(0)) Rosen Publishing Group, Inc., The. (PowerKids Pr.).

Mendoza, Patrick M. Between Midnight & Morning: Historic Hauntings from the Frontier, Hispanic, & Native American Traditions. 2001. 128p. (gr. 4-9). pap. 8.95 (978-0-87483-607-3(7)) August Hse. Pubs., Inc.

Mott, A. S. Fireside Ghost Stories, Vol. 1. rev. ed. 2003. (Ghost Stories Ser.). 216p. (J). (gr. 4). pap. (978-1-894877-40-4(3)) Lone Pine Publishing.

Mott, Allan. Haunted Schools, Vol. 1. rev. ed. 2003. (Ghost Stories Ser.). (Illus.). 216p. (J). (gr. 4). pap. (978-1-894877-32-9(2)) Lone Pine Publishing.

My Big Spooky Sticker Activity Book. 2003. (Illus.). 48p. (J). 5.98 (978-1-4054-1219-3(4)) Parragon, Inc.

Netzley, Patricia D. Haunted Houses. 2000. (Mystery Library). (Illus.). 96p. (J). (gr. 4-12). 29.95 (978-1-56006-685-9(7) , Lucent Bks.) Thomson Gale.

Nobleman, Marc Tyler. Detective Notebook: Ghost Hunting Handbook. 2007. (Illus.). 96p. (J). pap., pap., spiral bd. 4.95 (978-1-4027-3123-5(X)) Sterling Publishing Co., Inc.

—Ghosts. 2006. (Illus.). 32p. (J). (978-1-4109-2523-7(4)); pap. (978-1-4109-2528-2(5)) Steck-Vaughn.

O'Donnell, Kerri. Ghosts & Poltergeists. 2006. (Tony Stead Nonfiction Independent Reading Collection). (J). pap. (978-1-4042-5677-4(6)) Rosen Publishing Group, Inc., The.

Oxlade, Chris. The Mystery of Haunted Houses. 2006. (Can Science Solve? Ser.). (Illus.). 32p. (J). 29.29 (978-1-4034-8334-8(5)); 2nd ed. pap. 7.85 (978-1-4034-8343-0(4)) Heinemann Library.

Pipe, Jim. Ghosts. 2006. (Tales of Horror Ser.). (Illus.). 32p. (J). lib. bdg. 25.27 (978-1-59716-203-6(5)) Bearport Publishing Co., Inc.

—Zombies. 2007. (Tales of Horror Ser.). (Illus.). 32p. (J). (gr. 3-6). lib. bdg. 25.27 (978-1-59716-207-4(8)) Bearport Publishing Co., Inc.

Raum, Elizabeth. Fusion: On the Move. 2007. (Illus.). 32p. (J). pap. (***978-1-4062-0505-3(2)***) Steck-Vaughn.

Smith, Barbara. Animal Phantoms: Fin, Fur & Feather Ghosts, 3 vols., Vol. 1. rev. ed. 2004. (Haunted Kids Ser.). (Illus.). 144p. (J). (gr. 4). pap. (978-1-894877-52-7(7)) Lone Pine Publishing.

—Ghost Riders: Planes, Trains & Automobiles, Vol. 1. rev. ed. 2004. (Haunted Kids Ser.). (Illus.). 144p. (J). (gr. 4-6). pap. (978-1-894877-56-5(X)) Lone Pine Publishing.

—Haunted Theaters, Vol. 1. rev. ed. 2002. (Ghost Stories Ser.). (Illus.). 224p. (J). (gr. 4). pap. (978-1-894877-04-6(7)) Lone Pine Publishing.

Smitten, Susan. Canadian Ghost Stories, 2 vols., Vol. 2. rev. ed. 2003. (Ghost Stories Ser.). (Illus.). 240p. (J). (gr. 4). pap. (978-1-894877-24-4(1)) Lone Pine Publishing.

—Ghost Stories of New England, Vol. 1. Wangler, Chris, ed. rev. ed. 2003. (Ghost Stories Ser.). (Illus.). 224p. (J). (gr. 4). pap. (978-1-894877-12-1(8)) Lone Pine Publishing.

—Ghost Stories of Oregon, Vol. 1. rev. ed. 2002. (Ghost Stories Ser.). (Illus.). 216p. (J). (gr. 4). pap. (978-1-894877-13-8(6)) Lone Pine Publishing.

Teel, Gina. Ghost Stories of Minnesota, Vol. 1. Dykstra, Denise & Kubish, Shelagh, eds. rev. ed. 2002. (Ghost Stories Ser.). (Illus.). 208p. (J). (gr. 4). pap. (978-1-894877-07-7(1)) Lone Pine Publishing.

Teitelbaum, Michael. Famous Ghosts. 2006. (Boys Rock! Ser.). (Illus.). 32p. (J). (gr. 1-5). 24.21 (978-1-59296-729-2(9)) Child's World, Inc.

—Ghosts: Real-Life Ghost Hunter Investigations. 2007. (24/7 - Science Behind the Scenes Ser.). 64p. (J). (gr. 8-12). 26.00 (978-0-531-12077-4(5) , Watts, Franklin) Scholastic Library Publishing.

Teitelbaum, Michael. Ghosts: Real-life Ghost Hunters. 2008. (24/7: Science Behind the Scenes: Mystery Files Ser.). 64p. (J). pap. 7.95 (***978-0-531-18740-1(3)*** , Watts, Franklin) Scholastic Library Publishing.

Thay, Edrick. Ghost Stories of Indiana, Vol. 1. rev. ed. 2002. (Ghost Stories Ser.). (Illus.). 200p. (J). (gr. 4). pap. (978-1-894877-06-0(3)) Lone Pine Publishing.

—Ghost Stories of Ohio, Vol. 1. rev. ed. 2002. (Ghost Stories Ser.). (Illus.). 192p. (J). (gr. 4). pap. (978-1-894877-09-1(8)) Lone Pine Publishing.

Top That Publishing Staff, ed. Freaky Fredas Ghost. 2004. (Wicked Tattoos Ser.). (Illus.). 16p. (J). pap. (978-1-84510-110-7(3)) Top That! Publishing PLC.

Townsend. Mysterious Signs. 2004. (Out There Ser.). (Illus.). pap. 8.95 (978-1-4109-0967-1(0)) Raintree.

Townsend, John. Mysterious Signs. 2004. (Illus.). 56p. (J). lib. bdg. 28.56 (978-1-4109-0566-6(7)) Raintree.

True Ghost Stories of Alameda. 2005. (YA). per. (978-1-59872-163-8(1)) Instantpublisher.com.

Watkins, Graham. Ghosts & Poltergeists. 2005. (Unsolved Mysteries Ser.). (Illus.). 48p. (YA). (gr. 5-8). lib. bdg. 25.25 (978-0-8239-3563-5(9)) Rosen Publishing Group, Inc., The.

Wood, Ted. Ghosts of the West Coast: The Lost Souls of the Queen Mary & Other Real-Life Hauntings. 1999. (Haunted America Ser.: Vol. 2). (Illus.). 48p. (YA). 16.95 (978-0-8027-8668-5(5)); (gr. 3). lib. bdg. 17.85 (978-0-8027-8669-2(3)) Walker & Co.

Xlade, Chris. The Mystery of Haunted Houses, Set 1. 2002. (Can Science Solve? Ser.). (Illus.). 32p. (J). (gr. 4-7). pap. 7.50 (978-1-58810-456-4(7) , 91157) Heinemann Library.

GHOSTS—FICTION

Abnett, Dan & Williams, Anthony. This Ghost Is Toast! 2007. (Real Ghostbusters Ser.). (Illus.). 96p. pap. 8.95 (***978-1-84576-143-1(X)***) Titan Bks. Ltd. GBR. *Dist:* Random Hse., Inc.

Adler, David A. Cam Jansen & the Ghostly Mystery. Natti, Susanna, illus. 2005. (Cam Jansen Ser.: No. 16). 64p. (J). (gr. 2-4). pap. 3.99 (978-0-14-240287-0(7) , Puffin) Penguin Group (USA) Inc.

Ahlberg, Allan. My Brother's Ghost. l.t. ed. 2005. (Illus.). 64p. (J). pap. (978-0-7540-6181-6(7) , CLP 372) BBC Audio.

Aldridge, Janet. Meadow Brook Girls Afloat. l.t. ed. 2006. 156p. pap. 14.99 (978-1-4264-0859-5(5)) BiblioBazaar.

—Meadow Brook Girls Afloat: Or the Stormy Cruise of the Red Rover. 2006. 160p. pap. 11.99 (978-1-4264-0878-6(1)) BiblioBazaar.

Aldridge, Janet. The Meadow-Brook Girls under Canvas (Ill. 2006. pap. (***978-1-4065-0695-2(8)***) Dodo Pr.

Alexander, E. M. Death at Deacon Pond. 2006. 192p. (J). (gr. 8-12). pap. (978-1-897073-42-1(9)) Lobster Pr.

Alexander, Jenny. Surfers Haunting for Beginners. 1998. (Illus.). 112p. (J). 7.95 (978-0-14-037580-0(5)) Penguin Bks., Ltd. GBR. *Dist:* Trafalgar Square Publishing.

Alexander, Wilma E. The William Ghost. 2001. (Illus.). 120p. (J). (gr. 3-7). pap. 6.95 (978-1-896184-92-0(8)) Roussan Pubs., Inc./Roussan Editeur, Inc. CAN. *Dist:* Orca Bk. Pubs. USA.

Allison, Jennifer. Gilda Joyce: Psychic Investigator. 2005. 208p. (YA). 12.99 (978-0-525-47375-6(0) , Dutton Juvenile); 2006. 336p. (J). (gr. 5). reprint ed. pap. 6.99 (978-0-14-240698-4(8) , Puffin) Penguin Group (USA) Inc.

—Gilda Joyce: The Ghost Sonata. 2007. 288p. (J). (gr. 5-8). 15.99 (***978-0-525-47808-9(6)*** , Dutton Juvenile) Penguin Group (USA) Inc.

—Gilda Joyce & the Ladies of the Lake. 2006. 352p. (J). (gr. 5). 15.99 (978-0-525-47693-1(8) , Dutton Juvenile) Penguin Group (USA) Inc.

Allison, Jennifer. The Ladies of the Lake: Gilda Joyce. 2007. 352p. (J). (gr. 5). 7.99 (***978-0-14-240907-7(3)*** , Puffin) Penguin Group (USA) Inc.

Almond, David. Kit's Wilderness. l.t. ed. 2000. 263p. (J). pap. 16.95 (978-0-7540-6115-1(9) , Galaxy Children's Large Print) BBC Audiobooks America.

—Kit's Wilderness. unabr. ed. 2004. 240p. (J). (gr. 7 up). pap. 36.00 incl. audio (978-0-8072-8216-8(2) , Listening Library) Random Hse. Audio Publishing Group.

—Kit's Wilderness. (YA). (gr. 7). 2001. (Illus.). 256p. mass mkt. 5.99 (978-0-440-41605-0(1) , Laurel Leaf); 2000. 240p. 15.95 (978-0-385-32665-0(3) , Delacorte Bks. for Young Readers) Random Hse. Children's Bks.

—Kit's Wilderness. 2001. 229p. (YA). (gr. 8-12). lib. bdg. 13.00 (978-0-613-36836-0(3)); (978-0-606-22406-2(8)) Tandem Library Bks.

—Kit's Wilderness. l.t. ed. 2001. (Illus.). 272p. (J). (gr. 4-7). 22.95 (978-0-7862-2772-3(9)) Thorndike Pr.

Alter, Stephen. The Phantom Isles. 2007. (Illus.). 244p. (J). (gr. 4-6). 16.95 (978-1-58234-738-7(7) , Bloomsbury Children) Bloomsbury Publishing.

Amsden, Janet. Grizzly Pete & the Ghosts. Beder, John, illus. 2002. 32p. (J). (gr. 1-2). pap. 7.95 (978-1-55037-718-7(3)); lib. bdg. 19.95 (978-1-55037-719-4(1)) Annick Pr., Ltd. CAN. *Dist:* Firefly Bks., Ltd.

—Grizzly Pete & the Ghosts. 2002. (gr. k-3). lib. bdg. 16.40 (978-0-613-56404-5(9)) Tandem Library Bks.

Anderson, Jodi Lynn. May Bird among the Stars, Bk. 2. 272p. (J). 2007. pap. 5.99 (978-1-4169-0608-7(8) , Aladdin); 2006. 16.95 (978-0-689-86924-2(X) , Atheneum) Simon & Schuster Children's Publishing.

Anderson, M. T. Thirsty. 2005. 256p. (YA). (gr. 9 up). pap. 5.99 (978-0-7636-2750-8(X)) Candlewick Pr.

Anderson, Scoular, illus. Spookball Champions. 2005. (Read-It! Chapter Bks.). 48p. (J). (gr. 2-4). lib. bdg. 19.95 (978-1-4048-1278-9(4)) Picture Window Bks.

Arnold, Louise. Golden & Grey: An Unremarkable Boy & a Rather Remarkable Ghost. 2005. 272p. (J). 15.95 (978-0-689-87473-4(1) , McElderry, Margaret K.) Simon & Schuster Children's Publishing.

—Golden & Grey: (an Unremarkable Boy & a Rather Remarkable Ghost) l.t. ed. 2006. 317p. 22.95 (978-0-7862-8290-6(8)) Thorndike Pr.

—Golden & Grey: The Nightmares That Ghosts Have. 2006. 304p. (J). (gr. 3-7). 16.99 (978-0-689-87586-1(X) , McElderry, Margaret K.) Simon & Schuster Children's Publishing.

—Golden & Grey (an Unremarkable Boy & a Rather Remarkable Ghost) 2006. (Illus.). 272p. (J). reprint ed. pap. 5.99 (978-0-689-87585-4(1) , Aladdin) Simon & Schuster Children's Publishing.

Arnold, Marliese. Ghost Park Bks. 1 & 2: The Vanishing Gate & The Imposter. Spry, Alexis L., tr. from GER. Scholz, Barbara, illus. 2007. 215p. (J). (gr. 4-6). 12.95 (978-0-7358-2099-9(6)) North-South Bks., Inc.

Arrigan, Mary. Ghost Bird. 2001. (Illus.). 64p. (J). pap. 8.99 (978-0-09-940287-9(4)) Random Hse. GBR. *Dist:* Independent Pubs. Group.

—Grimstone's Ghost. 2003. 159p. (J). (gr. 3-6). pap. 6.99 (978-0-00-675480-0(5) , Collins) HarperCollins Pubs. Ltd. GBR. *Dist:* Trafalgar Square Publishing.

—The Spirits of the Attic. 2001. 128p. (J). pap. 9.95 (978-1-901737-27-1(6)) Anvil Bks., Ltd. IRL. *Dist:* Dufour Editions, Inc.

Asfar, Dan. Dylan Mcbryde. 2005. 240p. (gr. 4). (978-1-894877-62-6(4)) Lone Pine Publishing.

Ashkenas, Bruce. Auntie's Ghost. 2007. 108p. 34.50 (***978-1-4303-1929-0(1)***) Lulu.com.

Avery, Harold. The Triple Alliance (Its Trials & Triu. 2006. 42.99 (***978-1-4219-7265-7(4)***); pap. 36.99 (***978-1-4219-1014-7(4)***) IndyPublish.com.

Avi. Midnight Magic. 2001. (978-0-606-22158-0(1)); (gr. 5-8). lib. bdg. 13.00 (978-0-613-54286-9(X)) Tandem Library Bks.

Ballard, Mignon F. Aunt Matilda's Ghost. 2000. (Illus.). vii, 136p. (J). 22.50 (978-1-57072-116-8(5)); pap. 12.50 (978-1-57072-132-8(7)) Overmountain Pr.

Banerjee, Anjali & Emesse, Tea. Rani & the Wedding Ghost. 2007. (Star Sisterz Ser.). 144p. (J). (gr. 3-7). pap. 4.99 (978-0-7869-4165-0(0) , Mirrorstone) Wizards of the Coast.

Banks, Steven. The Big Halloween Scare. Martinez, Heather, illus. 2005. (Ready-to-Read Ser. Level 2: 1). 32p. (J). lib. bdg. 15.00 (978-1-59054-987-2(2)) Fitzgerald Bks.

—The Big Halloween Scare. Martinez, Heather, illus. 2003. (SpongeBob SquarePants Ready-To-Read Ser.: Vol. 1). 32p. (J). (gr. k-2). pap. 3.99 (978-0-689-84196-5(5) , Simon Spotlight/Nickelodeon) Simon & Schuster Children's Publishing.

—The Big Halloween Scare. Martinez, Heather, illus. 2003. 32p. (J). (gr. k-2). lib. bdg. 11.80 (978-0-613-73339-7(8)) Tandem Library Bks.

Banscherus, Jurgen & Baron, Daniel C. After School Ghosthunter. Butschkow, Ralf, illus. 2007. 63p. (J). (***978-1-59889-342-7(4)***); pap. (***978-1-59889-441-7(2)***) Stone Arch Bks.

Barrett, Tracy. Cold in Summer. rev. ed. 2003. (Illus.). 208p. (YA). (gr. 5-9). 16.95 (978-0-8050-7052-1(4) , Holt, Henry & Co. Bks. For Young Readers) Holt, Henry & Co.

Barrows, Ann F. Ivy & Bean & the Ghost That Had to Go. Blackall, Sophie, illus. 2006. (Ivy + Bean Ser.: Bk. 2). 136p. (J). (gr. 1-5). 14.95 (978-0-8118-4910-4(4)) Chronicle Bks. LLC.

Baudet, Stephanie. New Library of Horror: Dracula. 128p. (J). pap. 7.95 (978-0-233-99578-6(1)) Andre Deutsch GBR. *Dist:* Trans-Atlantic Pubns., Inc.

Bauer, Joan. Peeled. 2008. 256p. (YA). (gr. 7). 16.99 (***978-0-399-23475-0(6)*** , Putnam Juvenile) Penguin Group (USA) Inc.

Bauer, Marion Dane. The Blue Ghost. Wang, Suling, illus. 2006. (Stepping Stones Ser.). 96p. (J). (gr. 3-7). pap. 3.99 (978-0-375-83339-7(0) , Random Hse. Bks. for Young Readers) Random Hse. Children's Bks.

—The Blue Ghost. 2005. (Illus.). 96p. (J). (gr. 3-7). 11.95 (978-0-375-83179-9(7)); lib. bdg. 13.99 (978-0-375-93179-6(1)) Random Hse. Children's Bks. (Random Hse. Bks. for Young Readers).

Beardsley, Martyn. Sir Gadabout & the Ghost. 2nd ed. 2007. (Sir Gadabout Ser.). (Illus.). 96p. (J). pap. 6.95 (***978-1-85881-072-0(8)***) Orion Publishing Group, Ltd. GBR. *Dist:* Independent Pubs. Group.

Berenstain, Stan & Berenstain, Jan. The Berenstain Bears Go on a Ghost Walk. 2005. (Berenstain Bears Ser.). (Illus.). 32p. (J). (ps-2). 8.99 (978-0-06-057399-7(6)); pap. 3.99 (978-0-06-057383-6(X)) HarperCollins Pubs. (Harper Festival).

Beresford, Elisabeth. Wombles Ghost of Wimbledon Common. (Illus.). 15p. (J). (gr. k-6). pap. (978-0-340-73579-4(1) , Hodder & Stoughton) Hodder General Publishing Division.

Beth, Hodder. The Ghost of Schafer Meadows. 2007. (J). per. 7.99 (***978-0-9793963-0-4(1)***) Grizzly Ridge Publishing.

Bial, Raymond. The Ghost of Honeymoon Creek. Bial, Anna, illus. 1999. 169p. (J). (gr. 4-7). pap. 13.95 (978-1-883953-27-0(8)) Midwest Traditions, Inc.

—Shadow Island: A Tale of Lake Superior. 2006. 176p. (J). (gr. 3-7). 18.95 (978-1-883953-37-9(5)); (gr. 4-7). pap. 12.95 (978-1-883953-36-2(7)) Midwest Traditions, Inc. (Blue Horse Bks.).

Biro, Val. Gumdrop Finds a Ghost. (Illus.). 27p. (J). (978-0-340-71062-3(4)); pap. (978-0-340-71063-0(2)) Hodder General Publishing Division. (Hodder & Stoughton).

Bloom, Carol A. The Wishing Closet. (Magic Mansion Mystery Ser.: Bk. 2). 124p. (J). (gr. 3-6). 9.99 (978-0-88092-476-4(4)) Royal Fireworks Publishing Co.

Bloor, Edward. Story Time. 2005. (Illus.). 444p. (YA). (gr. 7-12). reprint ed. pap. 7.95 (978-0-15-205222-5(4) , Harcourt Paperbacks) Harcourt Children's Bks.

—Story Time. 2004. (Illus.). 432p. (YA). 17.00 (978-0-15-204670-5(4)) Harcourt Trade Pubs.

Bodi, Sari. The Ghost in Allie's Pool. 2007. 192p. (YA). (gr. 5 up). pap. 8.95 (***978-0-9768126-6-1(5)***) Brown Barn Bks.

Bourgeois, Paulette. Franklin's Halloween. Clark, Brenda, illus. 2002. (Franklin Ser.). 12.40 (978-1-4046-0326-4(3)) Book Wholesalers, Inc.

Bourgeois, Paulette, et al. Franklin y el Día de Halloween. Clark, Brenda, illus. 1999. (SPA.). (J). pap. (978-1-880507-45-2(5)) Lectorum Pubns., Inc.

Bouton, Warren Hussey. The Ghost of Ichabod Paddack: A Spooky Tale from Nantucket. Locke, Barbara K., illus. l.t. ed. 2002. 86p. (J). per. 5.95 (978-0-9700555-2-1(8)) Hither Creek Pr.

—Oliver's Ghost: A Spooky Tale from Nantucket. Locke, Barbara K., illus. 2003. (J). per. 5.95 (978-0-9700555-3-8(6)) Hither Creek Pr.

Bowvayne, A. E. Turn in the Grave. Snow, Alan, illus. 2006. 144p. (J). pap. 4.99 (978-0-7945-1292-7(5) , Usborne) EDC Publishing.

The Boy Who Tricked the Ghosts. 2003. (J). 14.99 (978-0-89610-769-4(8)) Island Heritage Publishing.

Boyd, David. Spellbound. 2002. (gr. 3-6). lib. bdg. 12.95 (978-0-613-77599-1(6)) Tandem Library Bks.

Bradman, Tony & Chatterton, Martin. Final Cut. 2004. (Illus.). 85p. (J). pap. 7.50 (978-1-4052-1125-3(3)) Egmont Bks., Ltd. GBR. *Dist:* Independent Pubs. Group.

—Voodoo Child. 2004. (Illus.). 88p. (J). pap. 7.50 (978-1-4052-1126-0(1)) Egmont Bks., Ltd. GBR. *Dist:* Independent Pubs. Group.

Brewster, Joy. The Roller Ghoster. del Sur, Duendes, illus. 2004. (Scooby-Doo Mysteries Ser.). 48p. (J). (gr. 1 up). pap. 3.99 (978-0-439-70128-0(7)) Scholastic, Inc.

Bright, Robert. Georgie. 2000. (J). pap. 2.50 (978-0-590-42126-3(3)) Scholastic, Inc.

Brightwood, Laura, illus. The Ghost House. Brightwood, Laura, . 2006. (J). (978-0-9779290-1-6(9)) 3-C Institute for Social Development.

Brin, Susannah. Haunted Beach House. 2000. (gr. 5-8). lib. bdg. 11.80 (978-0-613-51214-5(6)) Tandem Library Bks.

Brodeur, Tom. Regina Silsby's Phantom Militia. 2005. (Illus.). 267p. (J). (ps-7). 7.49 (978-1-59166-385-0(7)) Jones, Bob Univ. Pr.

—Regina Silsby's Secret War. 2004. 248p. (J). 7.49 (978-1-59166-235-8(4)) Jones, Bob Univ. Pr.

Brooks, Walter R. Jimmy Takes Vanishing Lessons. Bolognese, Don, illus. 2007. 26p. (gr. 1). 16.95 (978-1-58567-895-2(3)) Overlook Pr., The.

Brown, Marc. Arthur & the Goalie Ghost. Brown, Marc, illus. 5th ed. 2001. (Arthur Good Sports Ser.: Bk. 5). (Illus.). 64p. (J). (gr. 2-4). 14.95 (978-0-316-12042-5(1)); pap. 3.95 (978-0-316-12146-0(0)) Little, Brown Bks. for Young Readers.

Bruchac, Joseph. The Return of Skeleton Man. Comport, Sally Wern, illus. 2006. 144p. (J). lib. bdg. 16.89 (978-0-06-058091-9(7)) HarperCollins Pubs.

Buchanan, Steve. More True Tales of Shorty Stevens the le. 2006. pap. 15.50 (***978-1-4259-8161-7(5)***) AuthorHouse.

Buffie, Margaret. Who Is Frances Rain? 20th ed. 2007. 184p. pap. (***978-1-55453-209-4(4)***) Kids Can Pr., Ltd.

Bunce, Elizabeth. A Curse Dark As Gold. 2008. 400p. (J). pap. 17.99 (***978-0-439-89576-7(6)*** , Levine, Arthur A. Bks.) Scholastic, Inc.

Burchett, Janet & Vogler, Sara. Scare Fair, Vol. 9. Brown, Judy, illus. 96p. (J). pap. 6.99 (978-0-330-37606-8(3) , Pan) Pan Macmillan GBR. *Dist:* Trafalgar Square Publishing.

—Shiver & Deliver. Brown, Judy, illus. 2003. 87p. (J). pap. (978-0-330-37604-4(7) , Pan) Pan Macmillan.

Burchett, Loni R. Bear & Katie in a Day with Friends, Vol. 3. l.t. ed. 2005. (Illus.). 68p. (J). per. 11.95 (978-0-9742815-2-0(2) , bk003) Black Lab Publishing LLC.

Burgess, Melvin. El Fantasma tras la Pared. (SPA.). (J). 8.95 (978-958-04-6483-9(9)) Norma S.A. COL. *Dist:* Distribuidora Norma, Inc.

Burke, Morgan. After Hours. 2005. (Party Room Ser.: No. 2). 256p. (YA). (gr. 11 up). mass mkt. 5.99 (978-0-689-87226-6(7) , Simon Pulse) Simon & Schuster Children's Publishing.

Burrows, Roger. The Haunted House. 2004. (Illus.). 10p. bds. 9.95 (978-1-932915-05-1(2)) Sandvik Publishing.

Butler, Charles, Jr. Lychfont Ghosts. 2006. (Illus.). 202p. (J). pap. 9.99 (978-0-00-712858-7(4) , HarperCollins Children's Bks.) HarperCollins Pubs. Ltd. GBR. *Dist:* Independent Pubs. Group.

Cabarga, Leslie & Beck, Jerry. Harvey Comics Classics Volume 1: Casper: Casper. 2007. (Illus.). 480p. pap. 19.95 (***978-1-59307-781-5(5)***) Dark Horse Comics.

Cabot, Meg. Haunted. 2004. (Mediator Ser.: Bk. 5). 288p. (J). (gr. 7 up). pap. 6.99 (978-0-06-447278-4(7) , Harper Trophy) HarperCollins Pubs.

—Twilight. 2005. (Mediator Ser.: Bk. 6). 256p. (J). 15.99 (978-0-06-072467-2(6)); (gr. 7 up). lib. bdg. 16.89 (978-0-06-072468-9(4)) HarperCollins Pubs.

Cabot, Meg, et al. Prom Nights from Hell. 2007. (YA). (gr. 9 up). 320p. 16.99 (***978-0-06-125310-2(3));*** 240p. pap. 9.99 (***978-0-06-125309-6(X))*** HarperCollins Pubs. (HarperTeen).

Carlee: The Ghost of the Black Forest. 2004. per. 13.00 (978-0-8059-9996-9(5)) Dorrance Publishing Co., Inc.

Carris, Joan D. A Ghost of a Chance. 2003. (Legends of the Carolinas Ser.). 155p. (J). 8.95 (978-1-928556-40-4(X)) Coastal Carolina Pr.

Carroll, Betty J. The Mystery of the Red Brick House. 2002. 137p. pap. 10.95 (978-0-595-20562-2(3) , Writers Club Pr.) iUniverse, Inc.

Carroll, Jenny, pseud & Cabot, Meg. Young Blood. 4th ed. 2005. (Mediator Ser.: No. 4). 336p. (J). (gr. 7 up). pap. 7.99 (978-0-06-072514-3(1)) HarperCollins Pubs.

Carter, Dean Vincent. The Hand of the Devil. 2006. 288p. (YA). (gr. 9). pap. 7.95 (978-0-385-73371-7(2)); lib. bdg. 9.99 (978-0-385-90386-8(3)) Random Hse. Children's Bks. (Delacorte Bks. for Young Readers).

Carus, Marianne, ed. That's Ghosts for You: 13 Scary Stories. Xuan, Yong-Sheng, illus. 2000. viii, 134p. (J). (gr. 4-7). 15.95 (978-0-8126-2675-9(3)) Cricket Bks.

Cary, Kate. Bloodline. 2005. 336p. (J). (gr. 7-12). 16.99 (978-1-59514-012-8(3) , Razorbill) Penguin Group (USA) Inc.

Cassandra's Ghost. 2002. (J). pap. 4.99 (978-1-58608-566-7(2)) New Concepts Publishing.

Cazet, Denys. The Perfect Pumpkin Pie. Cazet, Denys, illus. 2005. (Illus.). 32p. (J). (gr. k-3). 16.99 (978-0-689-86467-4(1) , Atheneum/Richard Jackson Bks.) Simon & Schuster Children's Publishing.

Chapman, Linda. Starlight Surprise. 2007. (My Secret Unicorn Ser.: No. 4). (Illus.). 144p. (J). pap. 4.99 (978-0-439-81385-3(9) , Scholastic Paperbacks) Scholastic, Inc.

Chase, Mary. The Wicked, Wicked Ladies in the Haunted House. Sis, Peter, illus. 2003. 144p. (J). (gr. 2-5). lib. bdg. 17.99 (978-0-375-92572-6(4) , Knopf Bks. for Young Readers) Random Hse. Children's Bks.

A Christmas Carol. 2004. (J). cd-rom 7.99 (978-0-9740847-9-4(4)) GiGi Bks.

A Christmas Carol. 2003. (Illus.). 32p. (J). 9.98 (978-1-4054-0997-1(5)); 4.98 (978-1-4054-0980-3(0)) Parragon, Inc.

Citra, Becky. Never to Be Told: Becky Citra. 2006. 224p. (J). pap. 7.95 (978-1-55143-567-1(5)) Orca Bk. Pubs. USA.

Clapp, Patricia. Jane-Emily: And Witches' Children. 2007. 304p. pap. 12.95 (***978-0-06-124501-5(1))*** HarperCollins Pubs.

Clarke, Judith. Starry Nights. 2004. 148p. (YA). 15.95 (978-1-886910-82-9(0) , Lemniscaat) Boyds Mills Pr.

Colfer, Eoin. The Legend of Captain Crow's Teeth. McCoy, Glenn, illus. 2006. 112p. (gr. 2-6). pap. 4.99 (978-0-7868-5505-6(3)) Miramax Bks.

Collier, James Lincoln. The Empty Mirror. 192p. 2006. (YA). pap. 6.95 (978-1-58234-904-6(5)); 2004. (J). 16.95 (978-1-58234-949-7(5)) Bloomsbury Publishing. (Bloomsbury Children).

Compestine, Ying Chang. Boy Dumplings. Yamasaki, James, illus. 2007. (J). (978-0-8234-1955-5(X)) Holiday Hse., Inc.

Cooper, Douglas Anthony. Milrose Munce & the Den of Professional Help. 2007. 240p. (gr. 6). 14.50 (***978-0-385-66080-8(4)*** , Doubleday Can) Doubleday Canada, Ltd. CAN. *Dist:* Random Hse., Inc.

Cormier, Robert. El Sindrome de la Ternura. Palmer, Magdalena, tr. 2005. (Escritura desatada Ser.). (SPA.). 208p. (YA). pap. 11.95 (978-84-666-0160-3(0)) Ediciones B ESP. *Dist:* Independent Pubs. Group.

Corrigan, Eireann. Ordinary Ghosts. 2007. 380p. (J). (gr. 7 up). pap. 16.99 (978-0-439-83243-4(8) , Scholastic Pr.) Scholastic, Inc.

Craig, Stephen. Ghost Walkers of Shadow Canyon. 2001. (gr. 7-12). lib. bdg. 24.55 (978-0-613-74543-7(4)) Tandem Library Bks.

Cramer, Jon. Ghost! The Adventures of Horace & His Jungle Friends. 2005. (Illus.). 48p. (978-1-86074-183-8(5)) Sanctuary Publishing, Ltd.

Creech, Sharon. El Fantasma del Tio Roco. 2003. (SPA.). (J). 8.95 (978-958-04-6026-8(4) , NR30564) Norma S.A. COL. *Dist:* Distribuidora Norma, Inc., Lectorum Pubns., Inc.

Crowe, Carole. Sharp Horns on the Moon. 2003. 128p. (YA). (gr. 4-6). 14.95 (978-1-56397-671-1(4)) Boyds Mills Pr.

Crowson, Andrew. Flip Flap Spooky. Crowson, Andrew, illus. 2003. (Illus.). 12p. (J). bds. (978-1-85602-475-4(X)) Chrysalis Children's Bks.

Culbertson, Jan E. The Legend of Dunsmoor Manor. 2006. 88p. pap. 13.95 (978-1-58909-348-5(8)) Bookstand Publishing.

Cunningham, Scott. Scooby Doo & the Hungry Ghost. del Sur, Duendes, illus. 2005. 12p. (J). (ps-3). pap. 8.99 (978-0-439-74882-7(8)) Scholastic, Inc.

Cursed Creatures. 2006. (Ghost Stories Ser.). (Illus.). 128p. (J). lib. bdg. (978-0-8368-6821-0(8)) Stevens, Gareth Inc.

Cusick, Richie Tankersley. The House Next Door. 2002. (gr. 7-12). lib. bdg. 13.00 (978-0-613-74151-4(X)) Tandem Library Bks.

—Sin & Salvation Pt. 4. 2006. 384p. (YA). (gr. 7). pap. 6.99 (978-0-14-240584-0(1) , Puffin) Penguin Group (USA) Inc.

Cusick, Richie Tankersley. Walk of the Spirits. 2008. 336p. (YA). (gr. 7). pap. 8.99 (***978-0-14-241050-9(0)*** , Puffin) Penguin Group (USA) Inc.

Cuyler, Margery. Skeleton Hiccups. Schindler, S. D., illus. 2002. 32p. (J). 14.95 (978-0-689-84770-7(X) , McElderry, Margaret K.) Simon & Schuster Children's Publishing.

Dadey, Debbie & Jones, Marcia Thornton. Beware of the Blabbermouth! 2005. (Ghostville Elementary Ser.: No. 9). (Illus.). 96p. (J). pap. 3.99 (978-0-439-68120-9(0) , Scholastic Paperbacks) Scholastic, Inc.

—Ghosts Be Gone! Francis, Guy, illus. 8th ed. 2005. (Ghostville Elementary Ser.). 96p. (J). 3.99 (978-0-439-56004-7(7) , Scholastic Paperbacks) Scholastic, Inc.

—Ghosts Be Gone! Francis, Guy, illus. 2005. 79p. (J). (gr. 2-5). lib. bdg. 11.19 (978-0-606-33841-7(1)) Tandem Library Bks.

—The Treasure Haunt. Francis, Guy, illus. 2005. (Ghostville Elementary Ser.: No. 11). 96p. (J). (gr. 2-5). pap. 3.99 (978-0-439-67810-0(2) , Scholastic Paperbacks) Scholastic, Inc.

Dalmatian Press Staff, ed. Ghostly Fun. 2006. 48p. pap. 2.99 (978-1-4037-2429-8(6)) Dalmatian Pr.

Davidson, Susannah, retold by. Canterville Ghost. 2005. (Young Reading Series 2 Ser.). 64p. (J). (gr. 2 up). pap. 5.95 (978-0-7945-0877-7(4) , Usborne) EDC Publishing.

de Brunhoff, Laurent. Babar & the Ghost. 2001. (Babar Ser.). (Illus.). 40p. (J). (ps-3). 16.95 (978-0-8109-4398-8(0)) Abrams, Harry N. , Inc.

—Babar & the Ghost. de Brunhoff, Laurent, illus. 2002. (Babar Ser.). (Illus.). (J). 26.13 (978-0-7587-6816-2(8)) Book Wholesalers, Inc.

—Babar & the Ghost. ed. 2004. (Illus.). (J). (gr. k-3). spiral bd. (978-0-616-14570-8(5)); spiral bd. (978-0-616-14571-5(3)) Canadian National Institute for the Blind/Institut National Canadien pour les Aveugles.

De Lint, Charles. The Blue Girl. 2006. 384p. (YA). (gr. 7). reprint ed. pap. 7.99 (978-0-14-240545-1(0) , Puffin) Penguin Group (USA) Inc.

Deary, Terry. The Ghosts of Batwing Castle. l.t. ed. 2005. (Illus.). 88p. (J). pap. incl. audio (978-0-7540-7869-2(8) , CLP 451) BBC Audio.

—The Phantom & the Fisherman. Flook, Helen, illus. 2005. (Read-It! Chapter Bks.). 64p. (J). (ps-k). lib. bdg. 19.95 (978-1-4048-1272-7(5)) Picture Window Bks.

DeCandido, Keith R. A. Blackout. 2006. (Buffy the Vampire Slayer Ser.). 256p. (YA). pap. 6.99 (978-1-4169-1917-9(1) , Simon Spotlight Entertainment) Simon & Schuster.

DeFelice, Cynthia. The Ghost of Cutler Creek. 2006. (Ghost Mysteries Ser.). 192p. (J). pap. 5.95 (978-0-374-40004-0(0) , Farrar, Straus & Giroux (BYR)) Farrar, Straus & Giroux.

DeFelice, Cynthia C. The Ghost & Mrs. Hobbs. 2001. (Ghost Mysteries Ser.). (Illus.). 192p. (J). (gr. 3-7). 16.00 (978-0-374-38046-5(5) , Farrar, Straus & Giroux (BYR)) Farrar, Straus & Giroux.

—The Ghost & Mrs. Hobbs. 2003. 192p. (J). pap. 5.99 (978-0-06-001172-7(6) , Harper Trophy) HarperCollins Pubs.

—The Ghost & Mrs. Hobbs. 2003. (gr. 3-6). lib. bdg. 14.15 (978-0-613-85155-8(2)) Tandem Library Bks.

—The Ghost of Cutler Creek. 2004. (Ghost Mysteries Ser.). 192p. (J). 16.00 (978-0-374-38058-8(9)) Farrar, Straus & Giroux.

—The Ghost of Cutler Creek. l.t. ed. 2005. 20.95 (978-0-7862-7190-0(6)) Thorndike Pr.

—The Ghost of Fossil Glen. 1998. (Ghost Mysteries Ser.). 176p. (J). (gr. 3-7). 16.00 (978-0-374-31787-4(9) , Farrar, Straus & Giroux (BYR)) Farrar, Straus & Giroux.

—The Ghost of Fossil Glen. 1999. 160p. (J). (gr. 3-7). pap. 5.99 (978-0-380-73175-6(4) , Harper Trophy) HarperCollins Pubs.

—The Ghost of Fossil Glen. 2000. (YA). (gr. 6 up). pap. 52.00 incl. audio (978-0-7887-4334-4(1) , 41129) Recorded Bks., LLC.

—The Ghost of Fossil Glen. 1999. (J). 11.60 (978-0-606-16359-0(X)); (gr. 5-8). lib. bdg. 14.15 (978-0-7857-0557-4(0)) Tandem Library Bks.

—The Ghost of Fossil Glen. l.t. ed. 2000. (Juvenile Ser.). (Illus.). 185p. (J). (gr. 4-7). 21.95 (978-0-7862-2768-6(0)) Thorndike Pr.

DeFelice, Cynthia C. The Ghost of Poplar Point. 2007. (Ghost Mysteries Ser.). (Illus.). 192p. (J). (gr. 3-7). 16.00 (***978-0-374-32540-4(5))*** Farrar, Straus & Giroux.

deGroat, Diane. Good Night, Sleep Tight, Don't Let the Bed Bugs Bite! deGroat, Diane, illus. 2006. (Illus.). 27p. (J). (gr. k-4). reprint ed. 16.00 (978-0-7567-9991-5(0)) DIANE Publishing Co.

—Good Night, Sleep Tight, Don't Let the Bedbugs Bite! deGroat, Diane, illus. 2002. (Illus.). 32p. (J). (gr. k-3). 16.50 (978-1-58717-129-1(5) , SeaStar Bks.) Chronicle Bks. LLC.

Del Negro, Janice. Passion & Poison: Tales of Shape-Shifters, Ghosts, & Spirited Women. 2007. 64p. (YA). (gr. 6 up). 16.99 (***978-0-7614-5361-1(X))*** Cavendish, Marshall Corp.

Diamond, Bobby. What's Waiting at Wellington Mansion. 2002. 244p. (J). per. 18.00 (978-1-58982-026-5(6) , Bedside Bks.) American Bk. Publishing Group.

Dickens, Charles. Charles Dickens/A Christmas Carol. Lo Famia, Jon, illus. 2005. 48p. (gr. 5-8). 25.50 (978-0-7910-9108-1(2)) Facts On File, Inc.

—A Christmas Carol. Blake, Quentin, illus. 2001. 160p. (J). pap. 8.99 (978-1-86205-130-0(5) , Pavilion Bks., Ltd.) Anova Bks. GBR. *Dist:* Trafalgar Square Publishing.

—A Christmas Carol. Date not set. (C). pap. (978-0-7593-9886-3(0) , Thomson Learning) CENGAGE Learning.

—A Christmas Carol. Wheatcroft, Andrew, illus. 2006. (Read & Listen Bks.). 64p. (J). 9.99 (978-0-7566-1831-5(2)) Dorling Kindersley Publishing, Inc.

—A Christmas Carol. Morrissey, Dean, illus. 2001. 80p. (J). (gr. 2-5). 17.89 (978-0-06-028578-4(8)) HarperCollins Pubs.

—A Christmas Carol. Zwerger, Lisbeth, illus. 2001. (ENG & GER.). 72p. (J). (ps up). 19.95 (978-0-7358-1259-8(4)) North-South Bks., Inc.

—A Christmas Carol. 1999. (Saddleback Classics). (Illus.). (J). 13.75 (978-0-606-21547-3(6)) Tandem Library Bks.

—A Christmas Carol. 2005. (Great Illustrated Classics Ser.). (Illus.). 238p. (J). (gr. 3-8). 21.35 (978-1-59679-237-1(X) , ABDO & Daughters) ABDO Publishing Co.

—A Christmas Carol. Lynch, P. J., illus. 2006. 160p. (J). (gr. 5). 19.99 (978-0-7636-3120-8(5)) Candlewick Pr.

—A Christmas Carol, Level 2. 2001. (Illus.). v, 38p. (C). pap. 9.00 (978-0-582-42120-2(9)) Longman Publishing Group.

Dickens, Charles & Moore, Clement C. A Christmas Carol & the Night Before Christmas. Rackham, Arthur, illus. deluxe ed. 2006. 192p. 14.99 (978-0-517-22927-9(7) , Gramercy) Random Hse. Value Publishing.

Dickens, Charles & Sims, L. A Christmas Carol. (Young Reading Ser.: Vol. 2). 64p. (J). (gr. 2 up). lib. bdg. 13.95 (978-1-58086-790-0(1) , Usborne) EDC Publishing.

Doherty, Berlie. Jinnie Ghost. Ray, Jane, illus. 2005. 40p. (J). (ps-7). 16.95 (978-1-84507-292-6(8)) Lincoln, Frances Ltd. GBR. *Dist:* Perseus Distribution.

Dolby, Karen. House of Shadows. 2005. (Young Reading Series 2 Ser.). 64p. (J). (gr. 2 up). pap. 5.95 (978-0-7945-0929-3(0) , Usborne) EDC Publishing.

Donkin, Andrew. Spooky Spinechillers, Vol. 4. 2000. (Eyewitness Readers). (Illus.). 48p. (J). (gr. 2-4). pap. 3.99 (978-0-7894-6523-8(X)) Dorling Kindersley Publishing, Inc.

Donkin, Andrew & Dorling Kindersley Publishing Staff. Spooky Spinechillers. 2000. (Dk Readers Ser.). (Illus.). 32p. (J). (gr. 2-4). 12.95 (978-0-7894-6522-1(1)) Dorling Kindersley Publishing, Inc.

The Doomed & the Dead. 2006. (Ghost Stories Ser.). (Illus.). 128p. (J). (gr. 7-9). lib. bdg. 25.27 (978-0-8368-6822-7(6)) Stevens, Gareth Inc.

Dorling Kindersley Publishing Staff & Darling, Andrew. Ghost Rider Visual Guide. 2006. (Illus.). 128p. (ps-12). 19.99 (978-0-7566-2148-3(8)) Dorling Kindersley Publishing, Inc.

Dowswell, P. & Allan, Tony. True Ghost Stories. 2004. (True Adventure Stories Ser.). 144p. (J). pap. 4.95 (978-0-7945-0274-4(1)); lib. bdg. 12.95 (978-1-58086-601-9(8)) EDC Publishing.

Doyle, Patrick H. T. Edgar Font's Hunt for a House to Haunt: Adventure One: the Castle Tower Lighthouse. 2006. (Illus.). 232p. (J). per. 6.99 (978-0-9786132-0-4(1)) Armadillo Bks.

Doyle, Patrick H. T. Edgar Font's Hunt for a House to Haunt: Adventure Two: the Fakersville Power Station. 2007. (J). per. 7.99 (***978-0-9786132-1-1(X))*** Armadillo Bks.

Dubowski, Cathy East. Family Reunion. 2000. (gr. 3-6). lib. bdg. 13.00 (978-0-613-25123-5(7)) Tandem Library Bks.

—Family Reunion: Junior Novel. Richardson, Julia, ed. 2000. (So Weird Ser.: No. 1). (Illus.). 144p. (gr. 3-7). pap. 4.99 (978-0-7868-1397-1(0)) Disney Pr.

Dunwoodie, Helen. Ghost on the Loose! l.t. ed. 2005. 176p. (J). pap. (978-0-7540-7830-2(2) , CLP 421) BBC Audio.

—Ghost on the Loose! l.t. ed. 2003. (Illus.). (J). pap. 24.95 incl. audio (978-0-7540-6264-6(3) , Galaxy Children's Large Print) BBC Audiobooks America.

Duquennoy, Jacques. Operation Ghost. 1999. (J). (978-0-606-19002-2(3)) Tandem Library Bks.

Durant. Team on Tour. 2003. (Illus.). 86p. (J). pap. 6.99 (978-0-330-35131-7(1) , Pan) Pan Macmillan GBR. *Dist:* Trafalgar Square Publishing.

Ellerbee, Linda. Ghoul Reporter Digs up Zombies! 2000. (Get Real Ser.: No. 5). 208p. (J). (gr. 3-7). 14.89 (978-0-06-028249-3(5)); No. 5. pap. 4.99 (978-0-06-440759-5(4) , Avon) HarperCollins Pubs.

Enderle, Dotti. Hidden. Gentry, T. Kyle, illus. 2007. 120p. (YA). (gr. 5-9). pap. 8.95 (***978-1-58980-481-4(3))*** Pelican Publishing Co., Inc.

Eno, Paul F. The Kitleys & the Gate of the Poltergeist. 2006. (ENG.). (YA). pap. 12.95 (978-1-891724-04-6(5) , 5,000) New River Pr.

Entara Ltd. Staff, photos by. Spooky Storytellers. 2006. (Jakers! Ser.: Vol. 2). (Illus.). 24p. (J). pap. 3.99 (978-0-689-87712-4(9) , Simon Spotlight) Simon & Schuster Children's Publishing.

Escondete y Grita, Vol. II. (Fantasmas de Fear Street Coleccion: No. 1). (SPA.). (J). (gr. 4-7). pap. 7.95 (978-950-04-1999-4(8) , EM4474) Emecé Editores S.A. ARG. *Dist:* Lectorum Pubns., Inc., Planeta Publishing Corp.

Even Little Ghosts Get Boo-Boo's. 2005. (J). per. 8.95 (***978-1-930154-17-9(8))*** Whitline Ink, Inc.

Fairbanks, Randy. The Weird Club: The Search for the Jersey Devil. 2007. (Weird Ser.). (Illus.). 144p. (J). (gr. 3-7). 12.95 (978-1-4027-4228-6(2)) Sterling Publishing Co., Inc.

El Fantasma: Individual Title Six-Packs. (Literatura 2000 Ser.). (SPA.). (gr. k-1). 28.00 (978-0-7635-1022-0(X)) Rigby Education.

Farley, Terri. Free Again, Vol. 5. 2003. (Phantom Stallion Ser.: No. 5). (Illus.). 224p. (J). (gr. 5 up). pap. 4.99 (978-0-06-441089-2(7) , Avon) HarperCollins Pubs.

—Free Again. 2003. (gr. 5-8). lib. bdg. 13.00 (978-0-613-66706-7(9)) Tandem Library Bks.

Fedele, Mario. Stories for a Stormy Night II: Featuring Two Novellas: Bugs: Runaway. 2005. 165p. pap. 19.95 (978-1-4137-4745-4(0)) PublishAmerica, Inc.

Ferguson, Donald. Chums of Scranton High on the Cinder Pat. 2006. 40.99 (***978-1-4280-2658-2(4));*** pap. 34.99 (***978-1-4280-2660-5(6))*** IndyPublish.com.

Fienberg, Anna & Fienberg, Barbara. The Big Big Big Book of Tashi. Gamble, Kim, illus. 2002. (Tashi Ser.). 448p. (J). (gr. 1-5). pap. 15.95 (978-1-86508-563-0(4)) Allen & Unwin AUS. *Dist:* Independent Pubs. Group.

Fischel, Emma. Midnight Ghosts. 2005. (Young Reading Series 2 Ser.). 64p. (J). (gr. 2 up). pap. 5.95 (978-0-7945-0930-9(4) , Usborne) EDC Publishing.

—The Midnight Ghosts. (Young Reading Ser.: Vol. 2). 64p. (J). (gr. 2 up). lib. bdg. 13.95 (978-1-58086-777-1(4) , Usborne) EDC Publishing.

Flanagan, Jim. The School of Scary Stories. 2006. (Illus.). 125p. (J). per. 12.95 (978-0-9766666-5-3(0)) Arcadian Hse.

Fleischman, Sid. The Entertainer & the Dybbuk. 2007. 192p. (J). (gr. 4-9). 16.99 (***978-0-06-134445-9(1));*** lib. bdg. 17.89 (***978-0-06-134446-6(X))*** HarperCollins Pubs. (Greenwillow Bks.).

Flynn, M. H. The Shadow City Ghost Hunters Vol. 1: The Mystery of Mapleshade Manor. 2006. 48p. pap. 12.95 (978-1-4241-2002-4(0)) PublishAmerica, Inc.

Fort, Gloria. Grabatruenos. 2000. (Dulces Suenos Collection). (SPA., Illus.). 10p. (J). 7.95 (978-84-348-6256-2(5)) SM Ediciones ESP. *Dist:* Distribooks, Inc.

Foster, Kelli C. & Erickson, Gina Clegg. Whiptail of Blackshale Trail. Gifford, Kerri, illus. 2004. 18p. (J). (gr. k-3). lib. bdg. 11.15 (978-0-606-30085-8(6)) Tandem Library Bks.

Franco, Mercedes. Vuelven los Fantasmas! 2000. Tr. of Ghosts Are Back!. (SPA.). (gr. 5-8). lib. bdg. 15.90 (978-0-613-84811-4(X)) Tandem Library Bks.

Frazier, J. E. Starlight Laser Express. 2003. 192p. pap. 8.95 (978-1-56315-303-7(3)) SterlingHouse Pubs., Inc.

Fred, Anthony. Meet Heinie Goblins. Primavera, Elise, illus. rev. ed. 2008. 128p. 14.99 (***978-0-7868-3681-9(4))*** Hyperion Bks. for Children.

Fred, Anthony & Primavera, Elise. Meet Heinie Goblins. Primavera, Elise, illus. rev. ed. 2008. 128p. pap. 4.99 (***978-0-7868-3682-6(2))*** Hyperion Bks. for Children.

Freeman, Martha. Who Stole Halloween? 224p. (J). (ps-7). 16.95 (978-0-8234-1962-3(2)) Holiday Hse., Inc.

Freese, Thomas, reader. Fog Swirler & 11 Other Ghost Stories. 2006. (J). Pt. 1. cd-rom 13.95 (***978-0-9789511-0-8(7));*** Pt. 2. cd-rom 13.95 (***978-0-9789511-1-5(5));*** Pt. 3. cd-rom 13.95 (***978-0-9789511-2-2(3))*** Illumination Pubns.

—Shaker Ghost Stories from Pleasant Hill, KY Audio Book/cd. 2006. (J). cd-rom 17.95 (***978-0-9789511-3-9(1))*** Illumination Pubns.

From the Grave. 2007. (Ghost Stories Ser.). 128p. (YA). (gr. 7-9). lib. bdg. 25.27 (978-0-8368-6823-4(4)) Stevens, Gareth Inc.

Funke, Cornelia. Ghosthunters & the Gruesome Invincible Lightning Ghost. 2006. (Ghosthunters Ser.). 192p. (J). pap. 4.99 (978-0-439-83309-7(4) , Scholastic Paperbacks); (Illus.). pap. 16.99 (978-0-439-84962-3(4) , Chicken Hse., The) Scholastic, Inc.

—Ghosthunters & the Incredibly Revolting Ghost! 2006. (Ghosthunters Ser.: Bk. 1). (Illus.). 192p. (J). pap. 4.99 (978-0-439-83308-0(6) , Chicken Hse., The) Scholastic, Inc.

—Ghosthunters & the Incredibly Revolting Ghost! Ragg-Kirkby, Helena, tr. from GER. 2006. (Ghosthunters Ser.: Bk. 1). (Illus.). 144p. (J). pap. 16.99 (978-0-439-84958-6(6) , Chicken Hse., The) Scholastic, Inc.

—Ghosthunters & the Incredibly Revolting Ghost. 2007. (Ghosthunters Ser.: No. 1). 144p. (J). pap. 2.99 (***978-0-545-01033-7(0))*** Scholastic, Inc.

—Ghosthunters & the Muddy Monster of Doom! 2007. (Ghosthunters Ser.: No. 4). 176p. (J). (gr. 2-5). pap. 16.99 (978-0-439-86268-4(X) , Chicken Hse., The) Scholastic, Inc.

—Ghosthunters & the Totally Moldy Baroness! 2007. (Ghosthunters Ser.). 144p. (J). pap. 4.99 (978-0-439-86267-7(1)); (Illus.). (gr. 2-5). pap. 16.99 (978-0-439-86266-0(3)) Scholastic, Inc. (Chicken Hse., The).

—Muddy Monster of Doom. 2007. (Ghosthunters Ser.: No. 4). 176p. (J). pap. 4.99 (978-0-439-86269-1(8) , Chicken Hse., The) Scholastic, Inc.

Fuqua, Jonathon Scott. Catie & Josephine. Parke, Steven, illus. 2003. 72p. (J). (gr. 3-5). 16.00 (978-0-618-39403-6(6)) Houghton Mifflin Co. Trade & Reference Div.

Furie, Peter. Cyber Screams: Numchuks' Curse. 2005. 189p. (J). per. 12.95 (978-0-9772927-0-7(3)) Bangzoom Pubs.

Gallego García, Laura & Peden, Margaret Sayers. The Valley of the Wolves. 2006. 247p. (J). pap. (978-0-439-58554-5(6) , Levine, Arthur A. Bks.) Scholastic, Inc.

Gapanowicz, Delores. The Finchley House Mystery. 2005. 112p. (J). per. 13.95 (978-1-933449-06-7(3)) Nightengale Pr.

Garcia, Laura Gallego. The Valley of the Wolves. 2006. 336p. (J). (gr. 4-7). pap. 16.99 (978-0-439-58553-8(8) , Levine, Arthur A. Bks.) Scholastic, Inc.

Garcia, Randolph. The Steamer Trunk Adventures #2: The Ghosts of Machu Picchu. 2006. (ENG.). 88p. per. 14.95 (***978-1-4241-1843-4(3))*** PublishAmerica, Inc.

Garretson, Jerri. The Secret of Whispering Springs. 2002. 208p. (J). per. 6.99 (978-0-9659712-4-9(4)) Ravenstone Pr.

Gelsey, James. The Baseball Boogeyman. 2004. (Illus.). 44p. (J). (***978-0-439-55713-9(5))*** Scholastic, Inc.

—Scooby-Doo! & the Gruesome Goblin. 2004. (Illus.). 60p. (J). lib. bdg. 15.00 (***978-1-4242-0303-1(1))*** Fitzgerald Bks.

Gelsey, James. Sunken Ship: Scooby-Doo y el Barco Hundido. 2004. (Scooby-Doo Ser.). (ENG & SPA.). 64p. (J). mass mkt. 3.99 (978-0-439-55116-8(1) , Scholastic en Espanol) Scholastic, Inc.

The Ghost on Main Street: A Spooky Tale from Nantucket. 2001. 87p. (J). per. 5.95 (978-0-9700555-1-4(X)) Hither Creek Pr.

Gil, Carmen. Un Fantasma con Asma. Webster, Sarah, illus. 2004. (Libros para Sonar Ser.). (SPA.). 40p. (J). 15.99 (978-84-8464-186-5(4)) Kalandraka Editora, S.L. ESP. *Dist:* Lectorum Pubns., Inc.

Gillieron, Rebecca. Spooky Sums & Counting Horrors. Cobb, Rebecca, illus. 2006. 32p. (J). 14.95 (978-0-7145-3307-0(6)) Boyars, Marion Pubs., Inc.

Givens, Steven J. Stony Point: A Triangle Club Adventure. 2001. 106p. pap. 5.95 (978-1-889658-21-6(9)) New Canaan Publishing Co. LLC.

Gliori, Debi. Pure Dead Trouble. 2005. (Illus.). 288p. (J). (gr. 5 up). 15.95 (978-0-375-83311-3(0) , Knopf Bks. for Young Readers) Random Hse. Children's Bks.

Glover, Sandra. It Didn't Happen. 2006. 160p. (J). pap. 9.99 (***978-1-84270-077-8(4)***) Andersen GBR. *Dist:* Independent Pubs. Group.

Golden, Christopher & Sniegoski, Thomas E. Ghostfire. 2005. (OutCast Ser.). 240p. (J). pap. 5.99 (978-0-689-86663-0(1) , Aladdin) Simon & Schuster Children's Publishing.

Gonzalez, Eladia. El Misterio de las Damas Chinas. 2000. (SPA.). 30p. (J). (gr. 2-4). (978-968-494-094-9(7) , CI30454) Centro de Informacion y Desarrollo de la Comunicacion y la Literatura MEX. *Dist:* AIMS International Bks., Inc., Continental Bk. Co., Inc., Lectorum Pubns., Inc.

Goodhart, Pippa. Three Little Ghosties. Cantone, Anna-Laura, illus. 2007. 32p. (J). (ps-1). 16.95 (***978-1-58234-711-0(5)***) Bloomsbury Publishing.

Gordon, Lawrence. Haunted High: The Ghost Chronicles. 2000. (gr. 7-12). lib. bdg. 21.05 (978-0-613-87684-1(9)) Tandem Library Bks.

—Haunted High Vol. 2: The Ghost Chronicles. 2000. 162p. (YA). (gr. 6-9). pap. 11.95 (978-0-9653966-1-5(4)) Karmichael Pr.

Gorey, Edward. The Haunted Looking Glass: Ghost Stories. 2001. (gr. 3-6). lib. bdg. 22.20 (978-0-613-56413-7(8)) Tandem Library Bks.

Grabenstein, Chris. The Crossroads. 2008. 368p. (J). (gr. 4-7). 16.99 (***978-0-375-84697-7(2)*** , Random Hse. Bks. for Young Readers) Random Hse. Children's Bks.

Graham-Barber, Lynda. Say Boo. Lehman, Barbara, illus. 2002. 16p. (J). (ps-k). bds. 4.99 (978-0-7636-1890-2(X)) Candlewick Pr.

—Say Boo! Sticker Book. Lehman, Barbara, illus. 2006. 24p. (J). (ps). pap. 3.99 (978-0-7636-2911-3(1)) Candlewick Pr.

Graham, Denise R. Curse of the Lost Grove. 2005. (Knights of the Silver Dragon Ser.: Bk. 10). (Illus.). 177p. (J). (***978-1-4156-3841-5(1)*** , Mirrorstone) Wizards of the Coast.

Grant, John & Stocks, Mike. Classic Horror. 2004. 432p. (J). 12.95 (978-0-7945-0616-2(X) , Usborne) EDC Publishing.

Grant, Steven, et al. Ghost Rider Team-up TPB. 2007. (Illus.). 144p. pap. 15.99 (978-0-7851-2257-9(5)) Marvel Enterprises, Inc.

Graves, Damien. Liar. 2007. (Midnight Library: No. 5). 160p. (J). pap. 5.99 (***978-0-439-89392-3(5)*** , Scholastic Paperbacks) Scholastic, Inc.

—Midnight Library #7 I Can See You. 2007. (Midnight Library). 176p. (J). pap. 5.99 (***978-0-439-89394-7(1)*** , Scholastic Paperbacks) Scholastic, Inc.

—Shut Your Mouth. 2007. (Midnight Library: No. 6). 192p. (J). pap. 5.99 (***978-0-439-89393-0(3)***) Scholastic, Inc.

Green, Jim. The Ghost Dancer. 2007. (YA). pap. 15.95 (***978-1-59705-923-7(4)***) Wings ePress, Inc.

Greenwood, Kerry. Alien Invasions. 2005. (Thrillogy Ser.). (Illus.). 48p. (gr. 4-8). 17.50 (978-0-7910-8865-4(0)) Facts On File, Inc.

Griffin, Peni R. The Ghost Sitter. (J). 2002. 144p. pap. 5.99 (978-0-14-230216-3(3) , Puffin); 2001. (Illus.). 128p. (gr. 4-6). 14.99 (978-0-525-46676-5(2) , Dutton Juvenile) Penguin Group (USA) Inc.

—The Ghost Sitter. 2002. (gr. 3-6). lib. bdg. 14.15 (978-0-613-53815-2(3)) Tandem Library Bks.

Grigsby, Cynthia. Hollow Creek: A Haunted Beginning, 01. 2006. 163p. (J). 14.95 (978-0-9786840-0-6(1)) Grigsby, Cynthia.

Grow, Mary L. Chester Meets the Walker House Ghost, No. 1. Richel, Jean - Marc, illus. 2000. 72p. (Orig.). (J). (gr. 8-12). pap. 12.00 (978-0-9700777-0-7(X)) Studio 17.

Guard, Dominic. Spooky Fun. Howard, Colin, illus. 2007. (Fun Packs Ser.). 24p. (J). (gr. k-3). pap. 19.99 (***978-0-7641-9342-2(2)***) Barron's Educational Series, Inc.

Gunther, Joseph. The Bluff, 1. Sabiston, Susan, illus. l.t. ed. 2006. 28p. (J). 14.95 (***978-0-9789525-0-1(2)***) Young Readers Publications.

Gutteridge, Rene. Ghost Writer. 2000. (gr. 5-8). lib. bdg. 21.10 (978-0-613-55597-5(X)) Tandem Library Bks.

Hahn, Mary Downing. Deep & Dark & Dangerous: A Ghost Story. 2007. 192p. (J). (gr. 5-9). 16.00 (***978-0-618-66545-7(5)*** , Clarion Bks.) Houghton Mifflin Co. Trade & Reference Div.

—The Doll in the Garden: A Ghost Story. 2002. (J). 14.47 (978-0-7587-9541-0(6)) Book Wholesalers, Inc.

Hahn, Mary Downing. The Old Willis Place: A Ghost Story. 208p. (gr. 4-7). 2007. (J). pap. 5.95 (***978-0-618-89741-4(0)***); 2004. (Illus.). (YA). 16.00 (978-0-618-43018-5(0)) Houghton Mifflin Co. Trade & Reference Div. (Clarion Bks.).

Hall, Traci. Rhiannon, Goddess in Training. 2006. 350p. (YA). pap. (978-1-932815-58-0(9) , Bronze Medallion) Medallion Pr., Inc.

Hamilton, Martha. Scared Witless: Thirteen Eerie Tales to Tell. 2006. (Illus.). 64p. (J). 15.95 (978-0-87483-796-4(0)) August Hse. Pubs., Inc.

Hamilton, Martha & Weiss, Mitch. The Ghost Catcher: A Bengali Folktale. Balouch, Kristen, illus. 2008. 32p. (***978-0-87483-835-0(5)*** , August Hse. Little Folk) August Hse. Pubs., Inc.

Harness, Cheryl. Ghosts of the Civil War. Harness, Cheryl, illus. 2004. (Illus.). 48p. (J). 7.99 (978-0-689-86992-1(4) , Aladdin) Simon & Schuster Children's Publishing.

Harris, Mark. Dario Figg & the Phantom of Murk. 2001. 192p. pap. 13.95 (978-0-595-18933-5(4) , Writers Club Pr.) iUniverse, Inc.

Haunted. 2006. (Ghost Stories Ser.). (Illus.). 128p. (J). lib. bdg. (978-0-8368-6824-1(2)) Stevens, Gareth Inc.

Hawes, Louise. Rosey in the Present Tense. 1999. (Illus.). (J). (978-0-606-20488-0(1)) Tandem Library Bks.

—Rosey in the Present Tense. l.t. ed. 2002. 186p. (J). 22.95 (978-0-7862-4418-8(6)) Thorndike Pr.

—Rosey in the Present Tense. 1999. 176p. (YA). (gr. 7). 16.95 (978-0-8027-8685-2(5)) Walker & Co.

Hawthorne, Nathaniel. The House of the Seven Gables. 1999. reprint ed. pap. 28.00 (978-1-4047-1350-5(6)) Classic Textbooks.

Hayes, Joe. Ghost Fever.Tr. of Mal de Fantasma. (J). 2006. (SPA.). 90p. pap. 8.95 (978-1-933693-03-3(7)); 2004. (ENG & SPA., Illus.). 80p. (gr. 3-6). 14.95 (978-0-938317-83-8(0)) Cinco Puntos Pr.

Hendry, Diana. Harvey Angel y la Nina Fantasma. Alban, Rafael Segovia, tr. Morin, Mauricio Gomez, illus. 2003. (la Orilla Del Viento Ser.). (SPA.). 166p. (J). reprint ed. pap. 4.99 (978-968-16-6723-8(9)) Fondo de Cultura Economica USA.

—Harvey Angell & the Ghost Child. 1999. 242p. (J). 16.95 (978-0-7540-6074-1(8) , Galaxy Children's Large Print) BBC Audiobooks America.

—Harvey Angell & the Ghost Child. 2002. (Harvey Angell Ser.: Vol. 2). (Illus.). 160p. (J). pap. 4.99 (978-0-7434-2829-3(3) , Aladdin) Simon & Schuster Children's Publishing.

—Harvey Angell & the Ghost Child. 2002. (gr. 3-6). lib. bdg. 13.00 (978-0-613-57904-9(6)) Tandem Library Bks.

Henn, Pamela. Nick & Slim: The Legend of the Falcon Mine. 2006. (Illus.). 472p. (YA). 19.95 (978-0-9760654-0-1(1)) White Wolf Studio, Inc.

Hicks, John B. The Ghost of Fire Company 18. 2005. 149p. (J). per. 6.50 (978-0-9742829-2-3(8)) Quiet Man Publishing.

Hill, David. Ghosts & Ghoulies. 2005. (Thrillogy Ser.). (Illus.). 48p. (gr. 4-8). 17.50 (978-0-7910-8888-3(X)) Facts On File, Inc.

Hill, Susan. The Woman in Black. Lawrence, John, illus. 2002. 144p. (J). pap. 15.95 (978-1-56792-189-2(2)) Godine, David R. Pub.

—The Woman in Black. 2001. (gr. 7-12). lib. bdg. 25.70 (978-0-613-78975-2(X)) Tandem Library Bks.

Hoh, Diane. Train. 2000. (gr. 7-12). lib. bdg. 21.05 (978-0-613-84104-7(2)) Tandem Library Bks.

Holmes, Fay. The Happy Little Ghost: A Halloween Tale. Holmes, Fay, illus. 2003. (Illus.). 20p. (J). (gr. 1-3). pap. 5.00 (978-0-9674241-4-9(3)) IZA Publishing Co.

Hoshino, Katsura. D. Gray-Man, Vol. 4. 2007. (D. Gray-man Ser.). 200p. (YA). pap. 7.99 (978-1-4215-1052-1(9)) Viz Media.

Howe, James. The Fright Before Christmas. Mack, Jeff, illus. 2006. (Bunnicula & Friends Ser.). 48p. (J). 14.95 (978-0-689-86939-6(8) , Atheneum) Simon & Schuster Children's Publishing.

Howe, James & Howe, James. The Fright Before Christmas. Mack, Jeff, illus. 2007. (Bunnicula & Friends Ser.). 42p. (J). (gr. 1-3). per. 3.99 (***978-0-689-86941-9(X)*** , Aladdin) Simon & Schuster Children's Publishing.

Hurst, Carol Otis. The Wrong One. 2003. 160p. (YA). (gr. 4-6). tchr. ed. 15.00 (978-0-618-27599-1(1) , Walter Lorraine) Houghton Mifflin Co. Trade & Reference Div.

Hutchens, Paul. The Ghost Dog. 1998. (gr. 3-6). lib. bdg. 13.00 (978-0-613-90866-5(X)) Tandem Library Bks.

Ibbotson, Eva. Beasts of Clawstone Castle. 2005. 192p. (J). (***978-1-4050-4889-7(1)*** , Macmillan Children's Bks.) Pan Macmillan.

—The Beasts of Clawstone Castle. Hawkes, Kevin, illus. (J). 2007. 256p. (gr. 3 up). 6.99 (***978-0-14-240931-2(6)*** , Puffin); 2006. 192p. (gr. 5). 16.99 (978-0-525-47719-8(5) , Dutton Juvenile) Penguin Group (USA) Inc.

—Dial-a-Ghost. Hawkes, Kevin, illus. 2003. 224p. (J). (gr. 3-6). pap. 5.99 (978-0-14-250018-7(6) , Puffin) Penguin Group (USA) Inc.

—Dial-a-Ghost. Hawkes, Kevin, illus. l.t. ed. 2002. 212p. (J). 22.95 (978-0-7862-3927-6(1)) Thomson Gale.

—The Great Ghost Rescue. 2002. (J). pap. 29.95 incl. audio (978-0-7540-6253-0(8)) BBC Audiobooks America.

—The Great Ghost Rescue. Hawkes, Kevin, illus. (J). (gr. 3-7). 2003. 192p. pap. 5.99 (978-0-14-250087-3(9) , Puffin); 2002. 144p. 15.99 (978-0-525-46769-4(6) , Dutton Juvenile) Penguin Group (USA) Inc.

—Great Ghost Rescue. 2003. (gr. 3-6). lib. bdg. 14.15 (978-0-613-67277-1(1)) Tandem Library Bks.

—Island of the Aunts. 2002. (Illus.). (YA). 13.19 (978-1-4046-0936-5(9)) Book Wholesalers, Inc.

—Island of the Aunts. 2001. (J). 12.64 (978-0-606-21782-8(7)); (gr. 3-6). lib. bdg. 14.15 (978-0-613-44394-4(2)) Tandem Library Bks.

Ireland, Kenneth. Noises in the Night. 2004. 126p. (J). 5.00 (978-1-84161-031-3(3)) Ravette Publishing, Ltd. GBR. *Dist:* Parkwest Pubns., Inc.

Irving, Washington. The Legend of Sleepy Hollow. Van Nutt, Robert, illus. 2005. (Rabbit Ears Ser.). 40p. (J). (gr. k-5). 25.65 (978-1-59679-225-8(6)) Spotlight.

—The Legend of Sleepy Hollow. Flint, Russ, illus. 2004. 64p. (J). (gr. 4-8). reprint ed. 17.00 (978-0-7567-8304-4(6)) DIANE Publishing Co.

—Washington Irving. Hall, Tracy, illus. 2004. (Great American Short Stories Ser.). 80p. (J). lib. bdg. 23.33 (978-0-8368-4253-1(7)) Stevens, Gareth Inc.

Jacques, Brian. Seven Strange & Ghostly Tales. 1999. (gr. 5-8). lib. bdg. 14.15 (978-0-613-64214-9(7)) Tandem Library Bks.

Jaffrey, Alizeh. The Silly Ghost, 2004. (Illus.). 24p. (J). per. 10.00 (978-0-9753673-0-8(7)) Jaffrey, Kamal.

James, Brian. I'm No Fraidy Cat. Woodman, Ned, illus. 2007. (Catkid Ser.: Bk. 1). 96p. (J). pap. 3.99 (***978-0-439-88854-7(9)***) Scholastic, Inc.

Jarman, Julia. Ollie & the Bogle. 2001. (Illus.). 144p. (J). pap. 8.99 (978-1-84270-039-6(1)) Andersen GBR. *Dist:* Independent Pubs. Group.

Jenkins, A. M. Beating Heart: A Ghost Story. 2006. 256p. (YA). 16.99 (978-0-06-054607-6(7)); (Illus.). (J). lib. bdg. 16.89 (978-0-06-054608-3(5)) HarperCollins Pubs.

Jenkins, A. M. Repossessed. 2007. 224p. (J). lib. bdg. 16.89 (***978-0-06-083569-9(9));*** (gr. 7 up). 15.99 (***978-0-06-083568-2(0)***) HarperCollins Pubs. (HarperTeen).

Jennings, Richard W. Scribble: A Dog Story, a Ghost Story, a Love Story. 2004. 160p. (YA). (gr. 5-9). tchr. ed. 15.00 (978-0-618-43367-4(8) , Walter Lorraine) Houghton Mifflin Co. Trade & Reference Div.

Jennings, Sharon. Franklin's Pond Phantom. McIntyre, Sasha et al, illus. 2005. 32p. (J). lib. bdg. 15.38 (***978-1-4242-1181-4(6)***) Fitzgerald Bks.

Jensen, Dorothea. The Riddle of Penncroft Farm. 2001. (Great Episodes Ser.). 272p. (YA). (gr. 5-9). pap. 6.00 (978-0-15-216441-6(3) , Gulliver Bks.) Harcourt Children's Bks.

Jinks, Catherine. Eloise: A Ghost Story. 2007. (Allie's Ghost Hunters Ser.). 180p. (J). (gr. 4-7). pap. 7.95 (***978-1-74114-659-2(3)***) Allen & Unwin AUS. *Dist:* Independent Pubs. Group.

—Eustace: A Ghost Story. 2007. (Allie's Ghost Hunters Ser.). 168p. (J). (gr. 4-7). pap. 7.95 (***978-1-74114-660-8(7)***) Allen & Unwin AUS. *Dist:* Independent Pubs. Group.

Johnson, Emily Rhoads. Write Me If You Dare! 2000. (Illus.). 176p. (J). (gr. 3-6). 15.95 (978-0-8126-2944-6(2)) Cricket Bks.

Johnson, Pete. The Frighteners. l.t. ed. 2005. (Illus.). 200p. (J). pap. incl. audio (978-0-7540-7857-9(4) , CLP 446) BBC Audio.

—The Frighteners. 2004. (J). 24.95 incl. audio (978-0-7540-6270-7(8) , Chivers Children's Audio Bks.) BBC Audiobooks America.

—The Ghost Dog. l.t. ed. 2005. pap. 16.95 (978-1-4056-6028-0(7)) BBC Audio GBR. *Dist:* BBC Audiobooks America.

Johnson, Sandi, et al. Haunted Doghouse II: Halloween Night, 3 vols. Brundige, Britt, ed. Stargeon, Bobbi, illus. l.t. ed. 2005. 15p. (J). (gr. k-5). spiral bd. 6.99 (978-1-929063-27-7(X) , 351) Moons & Stars Publishing For Children.

Johnston, Norma. Feather in the Wind. 2001. (Illus.). 172p. (J). (gr. 5-9). 14.95 (978-0-7614-5063-4(7) , Cavendish Children's Bks.) Cavendish, Marshall Corp.

Johnstone. Horror: Spook Files Omnibus Two. 1999. 384p. (J). pap. 11.99 (978-0-233-99688-2(5)) Andre Deutsch GBR. *Dist:* Independent Pubs. Group.

—Horror: The Spook Files Omnibus One. 1999. 384p. (J). pap. 11.99 (978-0-233-99687-5(7)) Andre Deutsch GBR. *Dist:* Independent Pubs. Group.

Johse, Jill Taylor. Beyond the Third Floor. 2003. (gr. 7-12). lib. bdg. 22.20 (978-0-613-86202-8(3)) Tandem Library Bks.

—Beyond the Third Floor. 2003. 166p. (YA). pap. 12.95 (978-0-595-28006-3(4)) iUniverse, Inc.

—Wanted a Friend, Got an Alien. 2003. 58p. pap. 8.95 (978-0-595-30459-2(1)) iUniverse, Inc.

Jones, Diana Wynne. The Time of the Ghost. 2002. 304p. (J). (gr. 7 up). 16.99 (978-0-06-029887-6(1)) HarperCollins Pubs.

Jones, Ivan. Ghost Hunter at Chillwood Castle. l.t. ed. 2005. 176p. (J). pap. (978-0-7540-6136-6(1) , CLP 329) BBC Audio.

Jones, Marcia Thornton & Dadey, Debbie. Beware of the Blabbermouth! Francis, Guy, illus. 2005. 81p. (J). (gr. 2-5). lib. bdg. 11.19 (978-0-606-33813-4(6)) Tandem Library Bks.

—Frights! Camera! Action! 2006. (Ghostville Elementary Ser.: No. 12). 96p. (J). pap. 3.99 (978-0-439-67811-7(0) , Scholastic Paperbacks) Scholastic, Inc.

—Ghost Game, Vol. 2. Tugeau, Jeremy, illus. 2003. (Ghostville Elementary Ser.). 96p. (J). 3.99 (978-0-439-42438-7(0) , Scholastic Paperbacks) Scholastic, Inc.

—Hide-and-Spook. Tugeau, Jeremy, illus. 2004. 86p. (J). (gr. 2-5). lib. bdg. 11.19 (978-0-606-32926-2(9)) Tandem Library Bks.

—New Ghoul in School. 2004. (Ghostville Elementary Ser.). (Illus.). 96p. mass mkt. 3.99 (978-0-439-42439-4(9) , Scholastic Paperbacks) Scholastic, Inc.

—New Ghoul in School. 2003. (gr. 3-6). lib. bdg. 11.80 (978-0-613-72127-1(6)) Tandem Library Bks.

Jones, Marcia Thornton, et al. Ghost Class. Tugeau, Jeremy, illus. 2003. (Ghostville Elementary Ser.). 96p. (J). 3.99 (978-0-439-42437-0(2) , 53616146, Scholastic Paperbacks) Scholastic, Inc.

Kasischke, Laura. Boy Heaven. 288p. (J). 2008. pap. 7.99 (***978-0-06-081316-1(4));*** 2006. 16.99 (978-0-06-081314-7(8)); 2006. lib. bdg. 17.89 (978-0-06-081315-4(6)) HarperCollins Pubs. (HarperTeen).

Katchke, Judy. Full House No.1: Dear Michelle. 2003. (gr. 3-6). lib. bdg. 13.00 (978-0-613-71410-5(5)) Tandem Library Bks.

Katschke, Judy, et al. Help! There's a Ghost in My Room! 2003. (Full House Ser.: No. 1). (Illus.). 96p. mass mkt. 4.99 (978-0-06-054083-8(4) , 53751756, Harper Entertainment) HarperCollins Pubs.

Keane, Dave. The Haunted Toolshed. Keane, Dave, illus. 2006. (Joe Sherlock Ser.). 128p. (J). pap. 3.99 (978-0-06-076188-2(1) , Harper Trophy) HarperCollins Pubs.

Kee, James & Dunne, Robin. The Roxy Hunter Files: Case #1 the Mystery of the Moody Ghost: Case #1 the Mystery of the Moody Ghost. 2007. 64p. (J). (gr. 2-5). pap. 5.99 (***978-0-8431-2664-8(7)*** , Price Stern Sloan) Penguin Group (USA) Inc.

Keeley, Catherine. The Secrets of Phantom Valley. 2003. 101p. (YA). pap. 10.95 (978-0-7414-1831-9(2)) Infinity Publishing.

Keep, Linda Lowery. Truth & Salsa. 2006. 176p. (J). 14.95 (978-1-56145-366-5(8) , Peachtree Junior) Peachtree Pubs., Ltd.

Kehret, Peg. The Ghost's Grave. 224p. 2007. pap. 5.99 (***978-0-14-280819-1(9)*** , Puffin); 2007. (YA). (gr. 5). 5.99 (978-0-14-240819-3(0) , Puffin); 2005. (J). (gr. 5). 16.99 (978-0-525-46162-3(0) , Dutton Juvenile) Penguin Group (USA) Inc.

Kerr, P. B. The Day of the Djinn Warriors. 2008. (Scholastic First Discovery Ser.). 400p. (J). pap. 17.99 (***978-0-439-93214-1(9)*** , Orchard Bks.) Scholastic, Inc.

King-Smith, Dick. The Roundhill. Bailey, Sian, illus. 2002. 96p. (YA). (gr. 5-8). 4.99 (978-0-440-41844-3(5) , Yearling) Random Hse. Children's Bks.

—Roundhill. 2002. (gr. 5-8). lib. bdg. 13.00 (978-0-613-62501-2(3)) Tandem Library Bks.

—The Roundhill. l.t. ed. 2001. (Illus.). 112p. (J). 16.95 (978-0-7540-6168-7(X) , Galaxy Children's Large Print) BBC Audiobooks America.

Kingfisher Editors, ed. Seriously Spooky Stories. 2007. (Super Shorts Ser.). 160p. (J). (gr. k-3). pap. 6.95 (978-0-7534-6074-0(2) , Kingfisher) Houghton Mifflin Co. Trade & Reference Div.

Kline, C. A. The Fright Night Series: Elizabeth Kind & the Strange Things. 2007. pap. 10.00 (***978-0-8059-8619-8(7)***) Dorrance Publishing Co., Inc.

Kline, Trish. The Ghost Hunter & the Ghost of Gettysburg. 2002. 92p. (J). per. 7.50 (978-0-9717234-0-5(0)) Ghost Hunter Productions.

Kline, Trish & Donev, Mary. The Ghost Hunter & the Ghost of the Amazon Warrior. Droney, John, illus. 2003. 96p. (J). per. 7.50 (978-0-9717234-1-2(9)) Ghost Hunter Productions.

Koeppel, Ruth & Sander, Sonia. Let's Spell. 2006. (Clifford Ser.). 8p. (J). bds. 12.99 (978-0-439-73376-2(6) , Scholastic) Scholastic, Inc.

Krishnaswami, Uma. The Closet Ghosts. Bhabha, Shiraaz, illus. 2005. 32p. (J). 16.95 (978-0-89239-208-7(8)) Children's Bk. Pr.

Lanagan, Margo. Red Spikes. 2007. 176p. (gr. 9). (J). 16.99 (***978-0-375-84320-4(5));*** (YA). lib. bdg. 19.99 (***978-0-375-94577-9(6)***) Random Hse. Children's Bks. (Knopf Bks. for Young Readers).

Landy, Derek. Landy Mid Grade: Raising Cain. 2006. (Skulduggery Pleasant Ser.). 384p. (J). pap. 7.99 (978-0-06-124090-4(7) , Harper Trophy) HarperCollins Pubs.

Lasky, Kathryn. Born to Rule. Walton, Tony, illus. 2006. (Camp Princess Ser.: No. 1). 160p. (J). pap. 4.99 (978-0-06-058763-5(6) , Harper Trophy); 15.99 (978-0-06-058761-1(X)) HarperCollins Pubs.

Lassiter, Rhiannon. Ghosts. 2002. (Hex Ser.: Bk. 3). (Illus.). 288p. (J). (gr. 5 up). mass mkt. 4.99 (978-0-7434-2213-0(9) , Simon Pulse) Simon & Schuster Children's Publishing.

—Ghosts. 2002. (gr. 5-8). lib. bdg. 13.00 (978-0-613-74159-0(5)) Tandem Library Bks.

Lawson, Julie. Ghost of Avalanche Mountain. 2000. (gr. 5-8). lib. bdg. 16.40 (978-0-613-34731-0(5)) Tandem Library Bks.

Le Fanu, J. Sheridan. Madam Crowl's Ghost & the Dead Sexton. 2004. reprint ed. pap. 15.95 (978-1-4191-3188-2(5)); pap. 1.99 (978-1-4192-3188-9(X)) Kessinger Publishing, LLC.

Lectorum Publications Staff, contrib. by. Comodin Embrujado. 2000. (Fantasmas de Fear Street Coleccion). (SPA.). (YA). (gr. 5-8). pap. 7.95 (978-950-04-1892-8(4) , EM4471) Emecé Editores S.A. ARG. *Dist:* Lectorum Pubns., Inc., Planeta Publishing Corp.

Lehr, Norma. Haunting at Black Water Cove. 2000. (Illus.). (J). (978-0-606-18311-6(6)) Tandem Library Bks.

Lemire, Jeff. Essex County Vol. 2: Ghost Stories. 2007. (Illus.). 112p. (YA). pap. 14.95 (***978-1-891830-94-5(5)***) Top Shelf Productions.

Leon McCann, Jesse. Haunted Halloween: Sticker Storybook. del Sur, Duendes, illus. 2004. (Scooby-Doo Ser.). 24p. (J). pap. 5.99 (978-0-439-60699-8(3) , Scholastic Paperbacks) Scholastic, Inc.

Levithan, David. Marly's Ghost. Selznick, Brian, illus. 176p. 2007. (YA). (gr. 7). 6.99 (***978-0-14-240912-1(X)*** , Puffin); 2005. (J). 14.99 (978-0-8037-3063-2(2) , Dial) Penguin Group (USA) Inc.

Levy, Robert Joseph. Go Ask Malice: A Slayer's Diary. 2006. (Buffy the Vampire Slayer Ser.). 256p. (YA). pap. 9.99 (978-1-4169-1587-4(7) , Simon Spotlight Entertainment) Simon & Schuster.

Lincoln, Christopher. Billy Bones. 2007. 208p. (J). (978-0-316-01473-1(7)) Little Brown & Co.

Lindsay, Elizabeth. Ghost in the House. Eastwood, John, illus. 2003. 92p. (J). (978-0-439-44652-5(X)) Scholastic, Inc.

Lockwood, Penny, et al. Ghost for Rent / the Newfie Ghost. 2002. (Twin Spins Ser.: No. 6). 168p. (YA). pap. 10.95 (978-0-7599-1005-8(7)) Hard Shell Word Factory.

Lorey, Dean. Nightmare Academy. Wyatt, David, illus. 2007. (Nightmare Academy Ser.). 320p. (J). (gr. 5 up). 16.99 (***978-0-06-134042-0(1)***) HarperCollins Pubs.

Lorimer, Janet. The Woman Who Loved a Ghost, Set 3. 2002. 32p. (YA). 2.95 (978-1-56254-434-8(9) , SP 4349) Saddleback Educational Publishing.

E F G

Lowenstein, Sallie. Waiting for Eugene. Lowenstein, Sallie, illus. 2005. (Illus.). 208p. (J). 19.00 (978-0-9658486-5-7(5)) Lion Stone Bks.

Luke, Eric, et al. Black October. 1999. (Ghost Ser.). 144p. (YA). (gr. 9 up). pap. 14.95 (978-1-56971-377-8(4)) Dark Horse Comics.

—Painful Music. 1999. (Ghost Ser.). (Illus.). 96p. (YA). (gr. 9 up). pap. 9.95 (978-1-56971-422-5(3)) Dark Horse Comics.

Lunn, John. The Mariner's Curse. 2004. (gr. 3-6). lib. bdg. 18.75 (978-0-613-77349-2(7)) Tandem Library Bks.

Mac Iver, Kathi. Ghosts of the Mining District. 2003. (Illus.). 60p. 9.95 (978-0-9651272-1-9(4)) Columbine Pr.

MacHado, Ana Maria. Del otro Mundo. (SPA.). (YA). 8.95 (978-958-04-7071-7(5)) Norma S.A. COL. *Dist:* Distribuidora Norma, Inc.

MacPhail, Catherine. Dark Waters. 2005. 176p. (YA). pap. 6.95 (978-1-58234-986-2(X)); 2003. 177p. (J). (gr. 5 up). 15.95 (978-1-58234-846-9(4)) Bloomsbury Publishing. (Bloomsbury Children).

—Get That Ghost to Go! Donnelly, Karen, illus. 2006. (Pathway Books). 83p. (J). 21.26 (978-1-59889-004-4(2)) Stone Arch Bks.

Madrzak, Carole. In the Shadows of Bington Manor. 2006. (ENG.). 132p. per. 19.95 (*978-1-4241-5168-4(6)) PublishAmerica, Inc.

Maguire, Gregory. Six Haunted Hairdos. 1999. (978-0-606-17470-1(2)) Tandem Library Bks.

—Six Haunted Hairdos. l.t. ed. 2002. 178p. (J). 21.95 (978-0-7862-4421-8(6)) Thorndike Pr.

Mahy, Margaret. Don't Read This! And Other Tales of the Unnatural. 2004. (Illus.). 208p. (J). reprint ed. pap. 7.95 (978-1-932425-25-3(X) , Lemniscaat) Boyds Mills Pr.

Mahy, Margaret, et al. Don't Read This! And Other Tales of the Unnatural. 2004. (Illus.). 208p. (J). (gr. 4-7). per. 15.00 (978-0-606-33200-2(6)) Tandem Library Bks.

Mantell, Paul. Sacrifice. 2000. (gr. 3-6). lib. bdg. 13.00 (978-0-613-26807-3(5)) Tandem Library Bks.

Mariotti, Celine Rose. Olivia Macallister, Who Are You? A Ghost Mystery Set in Maine. Tango-Schurmann, Ann, illus. 2004. 85p. (YA). (gr. 3-6). pap. 12.95 (978-0-9721389-6-3(X)) Rock Village Publishing.

Marquardt, Marsha, illus. Little Ghost Goes to the Zoo. 2001. 8p. (J). pap. 3.00 (978-1-882225-21-7(X)) Tott Pubns.

Marr, Andrew. Born in the Darkest Time of Year: Stories for the Season of the Christ Child. 2004. 180p. (J). pap. 13.95 (978-0-595-32633-4(1)) iUniverse, Inc.

Marrone, Amanda. Uninvited. 2007. 224p. (YA). (gr. 9 up). pap. 8.99 (*978-1-4169-3978-8(4) , Simon Pulse) Simon & Schuster Children's Publishing.

Marsh, Carole. The Ghost of Pickpocket Plantation. 2006. 128p. (gr. 3-5). pap. 5.99 (*978-0-635-06233-8(X)); (gr. 7-14). 14.95 (*978-0-635-06237-6(2)) Gallopade International.

—The Mystery of the Alamo Ghost. 2003. (Carole Marsh Mysteries Ser.). 160p. (J). (gr. 2-8). 14.95 (978-0-635-01654-6(0)); pap. 5.95 (978-0-635-01652-2(4)) Gallopade International.

—The Mystery of the Ghost of the Grand Canyon. 2001. 160p. (J). (gr. 2-8). pap. 5.95 (978-0-635-02395-7(4)) Gallopade International.

Marsh, Carole. The Phantom of Thunderbolt Fort. 2007. 128p. (gr. 3-5). pap. 5.99 (*978-0-635-06235-2(6)); (gr. 7-14). 14.95 (*978-0-635-06239-0(9)) Gallopade International.

Martin, Gayle. Gunfight at the O. K. Corral: Luke & Jenny Visit Tombstone. 2006. (J). per. 14.95 net. (978-1-58985-050-7(5)) Five Star Pubns., Inc.

Mason, Janet. The Legend of Sleepy Hollow. 2002. (Scholastic Junior Classics Ser.). 80p. (J). pap. 3.99 (978-0-439-22510-6(8)) Scholastic, Inc.

Masters, Elaine. Kalani & the Night Marchers. Croci, Ronald, illus. 2002. pap. 3.49 (978-0-89610-359-7(5)) Island Heritage Publishing.

Matthews, Derek. Snappy Sounds Boo! 2005. (Snappy Sounds Ser.). (Illus.). 10p. (J). (ps-ps). 12.95 (978-1-59223-452-3(6) , Silver Dolphin Bks.) Advantage Pubs. Group.

McCLure, Beverly Stowe. Listen to the Ghost. 2005. (J). per. 16.95 (978-1-933353-51-7(1) , Paladin Timeless) Twilight Times Bks.

McCracken, Hugh. Grandfather & the Ghost. 2002. (gr. 7-12). lib. bdg. 19.00 (978-0-613-80450-9(3)) Tandem Library Bks.

McLean, Alan C. Ghost of the Glen. Date not set. (Knockout Ser.). 123p. 44.77 (978-0-582-25082-6(X)) Addison-Wesley Longman, Ltd. GBR. *Dist:* Trans-Atlantic Pubns., Inc.

McMullan, Kate. The Ghost of Sir Herbert Dungeonstone. 2006. (Dragon Slayers' Academy Ser.: No. 12). (J). (gr. 1-6). 24.21 (978-1-59961-124-2(4)) Spotlight.

McNicoll, Sylvia. Grave Secrets. l.t. ed. 1999. (Illus.). 176p. (J). (gr. 7-9). pap. 8.95 (978-0-7737-6015-8(6)) Stoddart Kids CAN. *Dist:* Fitzhenry & Whiteside, Ltd.

—Grave Secrets. 1999. (J). 228p. (gr. 3-7). per. 17.60 (978-0-613-28858-3(0)); (978-0-606-19641-3(2)) Tandem Library Bks.

McNish, Cliff. Breathe: A Ghost Story. 2006. 264p. (J). 15.95 (978-0-8225-6443-0(2) , Carolrhoda Bks.) Lerner Publishing Group.

McRae, David. Blood of the Donnellys. 2008. 152p. (YA). pap. 9.99 (*978-1-55002-754-9(9) , Sandcastle Bks.) Dundurn Group, The CAN. *Dist:* Univ. of Toronto Pr.

Messer, Celeste M. The Ghost of Piper's Landing. Hoeffner, Deb, illus. 2004. 82-92p. 4.95 (978-0-9702171-7-2(X)) AshleyAlan Enterprises.

Metz, Melinda. Ravens Point. 2005. pap. (978-0-06-052373-2(5)) HarperCollins Canada, Ltd.

Metzger, Steve. Five Spooky Ghosts Playing Tricks at School. Harrald-Pilz, Marilee, illus. 2005. (J). (*978-0-439-80381-6(0)) Scholastic, Inc.

Milord, Susan. The Ghost on the Hearth. Dabcovich, Lydia, illus. 2003. (Family Heritage Ser.). 36p. (J). (gr. 1-5). 15.95 (978-0-916718-18-3(2)) Vermont Folklife Ctr.

Mind Grabber. 64p. (YA). (gr. 6-12). pap. (978-0-8224-2335-5(9)) Globe Fearon Educational Publishing.

Miyazaki, Hayao. Miyazaki's Spirited Away. Miyazaki, Hayao, illus. 2002. (Spirited Away Ser.). (Illus.). 17.51 (978-1-4046-2807-6(X)); 17.51 (978-1-4046-2808-3(8)); 17.51 (978-1-4046-2809-0(6)); 17.51 (978-1-4046-2789-5(8)); 17.51 (978-1-4046-2587-7(9)) Book Wholesalers, Inc.

Moloney, James. Trapped. Tan, Shaun, illus. 2008. 80p. (J). pap. (*978-1-59889-919-1(8)); (YA). (gr. 5-9). lib. bdg. 16.95 (*978-1-59889-863-7(9)) Stone Arch Bks.

Montgomery, R. A. The Haunted House. 2007. (Choose Your Own Adventure Ser.). (Illus.). 64p. (J). pap. 5.99 (*978-1-933390-51-2(4)) Chooseco LLC.

Morgan, Allen. Quackadack Duck. Beder, John, illus. 2003. 32p. (J). (ps-2). lib. bdg. 18.95 (978-1-55037-761-3(2)) Annick Pr., Ltd. CAN. *Dist:* Firefly Bks., Ltd.

Moro, Robin, et al, illus. Read Aloud Spooky Stories. 320p. 15.98 (978-0-7853-6338-5(6) , 7159100) Publications International, Ltd.

Morris, Tony, illus. The Kingfisher Treasury of Ghost Stories. 2005. (Kingfisher Treasury of Stories Ser.). 160p. (gr. k-3). pap. 5.95 (978-0-7534-5890-7(X) , Kingfisher) Houghton Mifflin Co. Trade & Reference Div.

Moser, Barry, illus. Scary Stories. 2006. 96p. (J). (gr. 6-9). 16.95 (978-0-8118-5414-6(0) , SeaStar Bks.) Chronicle Bks. LLC.

Moses, Antoinette. The Girl at the Window: Starter/Beginner. 2007. (Cambridge English Readers Ser.). 32p. pap. 5.00 (*978-0-521-70585-1(1)) Cambridge Univ. Pr.

—The Girl at the Window Book: Starter/Beginner. 2007. (Cambridge English Readers Ser.). (Illus.). 32p. pap. 9.00 (*978-0-521-70586-8(X)) Cambridge Univ. Pr.

Moses, Will. Legend of Sleepy Hollow. 1999. (gr. k-3). lib. bdg. 15.30 (978-0-613-19385-6(7)) Tandem Library Bks.

Mott, A. S. & Dean, Jessica Casey. Gothic Ghost Stories, Vol. 1. rev. ed. 2004. (Ghost Stories Ser.). (Illus.). 216p. (J). (gr. 4). pap. (978-1-894877-39-8(X)) Lone Pine Publishing.

Mould, Chris. Dust n Bones. 2007. 96p. (J). (gr. 2-4). 17.95 (*978-0-340-89326-5(5)) Hodder Children's Division GBR. *Dist:* Independent Pubs. Group.

Mowry, Jess. Voodu Dawgz. 2007. 280p. (YA). pap. 14.99 (978-1-59092-359-7(6) , Blue Works) Windstorm Creative.

Murray, Guillermo. Que, Miedo! rev. ed. 2006. (Castillo del Terror Ser.). (SPA.). 112p. (J). (gr. 2-6). pap. 6.95 (978-970-20-0338-0(5)) Castillo, Ediciones, S. A. de C. V. MEX. *Dist:* Macmillan.

Mutis, Alvaro. La Mansion de Araucaima: Diario de Lecumberri. (SPA.). (J). 8.00 (978-958-04-6975-9(X)) Norma S.A. COL. *Dist:* Distribuidora Norma, Inc.

Nagler, Michelle H. Surf Scare. 2003. (gr. k-3). lib. bdg. 11.80 (978-0-613-72204-9(3)) Tandem Library Bks.

Naylor, Phyllis Reynolds. Bernie Magruder & the Haunted Hotel. l.t. ed. 2001. 127p. (J). 20.95 (978-0-7862-3600-8(0)) Thorndike Pr.

—The Boys Return. 2003. 144p. (gr. 4-7). pap. 5.50 (978-0-440-41675-3(2) , Yearling); 2001. (Illus.). 132p. (J). (978-0-385-32734-3(X) , Delacorte Bks. for Young Readers) Random Hse. Children's Bks.

—The Boys Return. 2003. (gr. 3-6). lib. bdg. 13.00 (978-0-613-88332-0(2)) Tandem Library Bks.

—The Boys Return. l.t. ed. 2003. 170p. (J). 23.95 (978-0-7862-5822-2(5)) Thorndike Pr.

—Jade Green: A Ghost Story. 2001. 176p. (YA). (gr. 4-7). mass mkt. 5.99 (978-0-689-82002-1(X) , Simon Pulse) Simon & Schuster Children's Publishing.

—Jade Green: A Ghost Story. Elliott, Mark, illus. 2000. 176p. (YA). (gr. 5-9). 16.95 (978-0-689-82005-2(4) , Atheneum) Simon & Schuster Children's Publishing.

—Jade Green: A Ghost Story. l.t. ed. 2000. 174p. (J). (gr. 4-7). 21.95 (978-0-7862-2886-7(5)) Thorndike Pr.

Newbery, Linda. Lost Boy. 2008. (J). (*978-0-375-84574-1(7)); lib. bdg. (*978-0-375-93617-3(3)) Random Hse. Children's Bks. (Fickling, David Bks.).

Nickel, Scott. Night of the Homework Zombies. Harpster, Steve, illus. 2006. (Graphic Sparks Ser.). 33p. (J). 19.93 (978-1-59889-035-8(2)) Stone Arch Bks.

Nixon, Joan Lowery. Ghost Town: Seven Ghostly Stories. Horowitz, Beverly, ed. 2000. 160p. (gr. 3-7). 14.95 (978-0-385-32681-0(5) , Delacorte Bks. for Young Readers) Random Hse. Children's Bks.

—The Haunting. 2000. (gr. 7-12). lib. bdg. 13.00 (978-0-613-28370-0(8)) Tandem Library Bks.

Nugent, Matthew. Nightmares on Goose Rocks Beach in Kennebunkport, Maine: Book 4 of the Goose Rocks Tales. 2003. (Illus.). 204p. (J). per. 14.95 (978-0-9705812-3-5(8)) CBI Pr.

Nye, Alex. Chill. 2006. 176p. (YA). 11.95 (978-0-86315-546-8(4)) Floris Bks. GBR. *Dist:* SteinerBooks, Inc.

O'Connell, Jennifer. Ten Timid Ghosts. O'Connell, Jennifer, illus. 2000. (Read with Me Paperbacks Ser.). (Illus.). 32p. (J). (ps-3). 3.99 (978-0-439-15804-6(4)) Scholastic, Inc.

—Ten Timid Ghosts. 2000. (ps-2). lib. bdg. 10.95 (978-0-613-27197-4(1)) Tandem Library Bks.

Ogburn, Jacqueline K. The Bake Shop Ghost. Priceman, Marjorie, illus. 2005. 32p. (J). (gr. k-3). 16.00 (978-0-618-44557-8(9)) Houghton Mifflin Co. Trade & Reference Div.

Olivia MacAllister, Who Are You? ed. 2006. (J). 12.95 (978-0-615-13155-9(7)) CRM Enterprises.

Olliver, Jane. Kingfisher Treasury of Spooky Stories. 2003. (gr. k-3). lib. bdg. 14.10 (978-0-613-90575-6(X)) Tandem Library Bks.

Olsen, Mary-Kate, et al. The Case of the Giggling Ghost. 2002. (New Adventures of Mary-Kate & Ashley Ser.: No. 31). (Illus.). 96p. mass mkt. 4.50 (978-0-06-106653-5(2)) HarperCollins Pubs.

O'Reilly, Sean. Kade: Identity. 2005. (YA). 9.95 (978-0-9763095-1-2(3)) Arcana Studio, Inc.

Orr, Wendy. Spook's Shack. Millard, Kerry, illus. 2005. 120p. (J). (ps-ps). pap. 6.95 (978-1-86508-645-3(2)) Allen & Unwin AUS. *Dist:* Independent Pubs. Group.

O'Shaughnessy, J. M. Summersville: One Flight Fiction(UNKNOWN CHARACTER). 2007. 105p. pap. 9.95 (978-0-9773175-2-3(8) , 004) Banda Pr. International, Inc.

Papp, Robert, illus. The Ghost of the Chattering Bones, Vol. 102. 2005. (Boxcar Children Mysteries Ser.: 102). 128p. (J). pap. 4.50 (978-0-8075-0874-9(8)) Whitman, Albert & Co.

Parry, Glyn. Last Gasp. 2005. (Thrillogy Ser.). (Illus.). 48p. (gr. 4-8). 17.50 (978-0-7910-8890-6(1)) Facts On File, Inc.

Patneaude, David. Haunting at Home Plate. 2000. (gr. 3-6). lib. bdg. 15.25 (978-0-613-61848-9(3)) Tandem Library Bks.

—Haunting at Home Plate. 2000. 192p. (J). (gr. 4-8). 15.95 (978-0-8075-3181-5(2)); pap. 6.95 (978-0-8075-3182-2(0)) Whitman, Albert & Co.

Patschke, Steve. The Spooky Book. McElligott, Matthew, illus. 2001. (J). (gr. k-3). 26.90 incl. audio (978-0-8045-6871-5(5) , 6871) Spoken Arts, Inc.

Peck, Richard. The Ghost Belonged to Me. 2005. 176p. (YA). 21.00 (978-0-8446-7275-5(0) , 3590) Smith, Peter Pub., Inc.

—Ghosts I Have Been. November, S., ed. 2001. 224p. (J). (gr. 4-7). pap. 6.99 (978-0-14-131096-1(0) , Puffin) Penguin Group (USA) Inc.

—Ghosts I Have Been. 2002. 22.00 (978-0-8446-7211-3(4)) Smith, Peter Pub., Inc.

—Ghosts I Have Been. 2001. (J). 12.64 (978-0-606-21213-7(2)); (gr. 5-8). lib. bdg. 14.15 (978-0-613-35952-8(6)) Tandem Library Bks.

Peebles, Joseph. The Stickman & the Crow. 2004. (ENG.). (YA). 10.95 (978-0-9644758-4-7(7)) Peebco Publishing Hse., The.

Peifer, Meighan. The Chocolate Chip Ghost. French, Phyllis, illus. 2004. (J). 14.95 (978-1-58597-245-6(2)) Leathers Publishing.

Penn, Audrey. Mystery at Blackbeard's Cove. 2006. (Illus.). 200p. (J). 14.95 (978-0-9749303-1-2(8)) American Media Intl.

—Mystery at Blackbeard's Cove. 2007. 347p. pap. 7.95 (*978-1-933718-09-5(9)) Tanglewood Pr.

Pepper, Dennis. New Young Oxford Book of Ghost Stories. 2000. (gr. 7-12). lib. bdg. 22.20 (978-0-613-58672-6(7)) Tandem Library Bks.

Peretti, Frank E. The Legend of Annie Murphy. 2005. (Cooper Kids Adventure Ser.: Vol. 7). 160p. (J). pap. 6.99 (978-1-4003-0576-6(4)) Nelson, Thomas Inc.

Perkins, T J. In the Grand Scheme of Things: A Kim & Kelly Mystery. 2007. (Illus.). 151p. (YA). 10.99 (*978-0-9777538-4-0(0)) GumShoe Press.

Perkins, T J. Mystery of the Attic. 2006. (Illus.). 113p. (YA). 10.99 (978-0-9777538-6-4(7)) GumShoe Press.

Peyton, K. M. The Boy Who Wasn't There. 2000. 192p. (J). pap. 5.95 (978-0-552-52717-0(3) , Corgi Bks. Ltd.) Random Hse. Children's Bks. GBR. *Dist:* Trafalgar Square Publishing.

—Stealaway. Wyatt, David, illus. 2004. 96p. (J). 12.95 (978-0-8126-2722-0(9)) Cricket Bks.

Pfeffer, Susan Beth. Ghostly Tales: Four Stories. 2002. (Portraits of Little Women Ser.). (gr. 3-6). lib. bdg. 12.40 (978-0-613-85700-0(3)) Tandem Library Bks.

Pienkowski, Jan. Haunted House. Pienkowski, Jan, illus. 2005. (Illus.). 12p. (J). (ps up). 14.99 (978-0-7636-2818-5(2)) Candlewick Pr.

Pierson, Jan. Ghost of Nighthawk (Nighthawk, Washington) 2002. (Ghostowners Ser.: Vol. 2). (Illus.). 109p. (Orig.). pap. 10.00 (978-0-9721800-1-6(X)) WildWest Publishing.

—Shadow of Shaniko (Shaniko, Oregon) 2002. (Ghostowners Ser.: Vol. 3). (Illus.). 105p. (Orig.). pap. 10.00 (978-0-9721800-2-3(8)) WildWest Publishing.

Pike, Christopher, pseud. The Last Story. 2002. (Remember Me Ser.: No. 3). (gr. 3-6). lib. bdg. 14.15 (978-0-613-73362-5(2)) Tandem Library Bks.

Plum-Ucci, Carol. The She. 2005. (Illus.). 372p. (YA). (gr. 9-17). reprint ed. pap. 6.95 (978-0-15-205453-3(7) , Harcourt Paperbacks) Harcourt Children's Bks.

Poe, Edgar Allan. The Raven & Other Writings. 2003. (Aladdin Classics Ser.). 448p. pap. 4.99 (978-0-689-86352-3(7) , Aladdin) Simon & Schuster Children's Publishing.

Potter, Ellen. Olivia Kidney & the Exit Academy. Reynolds, Peter H., illus. 2005. 256p. (J). (gr. 4-6). 15.99 (978-0-399-24162-8(0) , Philomel) Penguin Group (USA) Inc.

—Olivia Kidney & the Secret Beneath the City. 2007. 336p. (YA). (gr. 4 up). 16.99 (978-0-399-24701-9(7) , Philomel) Penguin Group (USA) Inc.

Powling, Chris. On the Ghost Trail. Peterson, Shaunna, illus. 2006. (Read-It! Chapter Books). 48p. (J). (*978-1-4048-3125-4(8) , 1265811) Picture Window Bks.

Pratchett, Terry. Johnny & the Dead. 224p. (J). 2007. pap. 5.99 (978-0-06-054190-3(3) , Harper Trophy); 2006. 15.99 (978-0-06-054188-0(1)); 2006. (gr. 5-7). lib. bdg. 16.89 (978-0-06-054189-7(X)) HarperCollins Pubs.

Preller, James. Case of the Ghost Writer. 2001. (Jigsaw Jones Mystery Ser.). (Illus.). (J). 10.79 (978-0-606-20740-9(6)) Tandem Library Bks.

—The Case of the Groaning Ghost. 2007. (Jigsaw Jones Ser.: No. 32). 96p. (J). pap. 3.99 (*978-0-439-89624-5(X)) Scholastic, Inc.

—Case of the Spooky Sleepover. 1999. (gr. 3-6). lib. bdg. 11.80 (978-0-613-16907-3(7)) Tandem Library Bks.

Preller, James. Ghost Cat & Other Spooky Tales. 2007. (Illus.). 80p. (J). (gr. 2-5). pap. 3.99 (*978-0-439-79398-8(X)) Scholastic, Inc.

Price, Susan. Olly Spellmaker & the Sulky Smudge. 2005. (Read-along Ser.). (Illus.). (J). audio (978-0-7540-6287-5(2)) BBC Audio.

Prins, Piet. The Flying Phantom. 2006. (Illus.). 142p. (J). pap. (978-1-894666-45-9(3)) Inheritance Pubns.

Ransom, Candice. Rider in the Night: A Tale of Sleepy Hollow. 2007. 128p. (J). (gr. 1-5). pap. 4.99 (*978-0-7869-4354-8(8) , Mirrorstone) Wizards of the Coast.

Ransom, Candice F. Key to the Griffon's Lair. Fiegenshuh, Emily, illus. 2005. (Knights of the Silver Dragon Ser.: Bk. 9). 182p. (J). (*978-1-4156-3032-7(1) , Mirrorstone) Wizards of the Coast.

Rao, Cheryl. Mixed Score: Ghost & Other Stories. 2004. 122p. 15.00 (978-81-291-0401-4(6)) Rupa & Co. IND. *Dist:* South Asia Bks.

Reber, Jack. The Ghost form the Schenectady Massacre: A Haunting from the Dutch Settlers. 121p. (J). (gr. 4-5). 9.99 (978-0-88092-547-1(7)) Royal Fireworks Publishing Co.

Rees, C. Haunts: H Is for Haunting. 136p. (J). pap. (978-0-340-71487-4(5) , Hodder & Stoughton) Hodder General Publishing Division.

—Haunts Vol. 3: U Is for Unbeliever. 120p. (J). pap. (978-0-340-71524-6(3) , Hodder & Stoughton) Hodder General Publishing Division.

Rees, Celia. City of Shadows. 2003. (Celia Rees Supernatural Trilogy: Bk. 1). 256p. (J). (gr. 3-6). pap. 7.99 (978-0-340-81800-8(X) , Hodder & Stoughton) Hodder General Publishing Division GBR. *Dist:* Trafalgar Square Publishing.

—City of Shadows. 2002. (gr. 7-12). lib. bdg. 16.40 (978-0-613-71846-2(1)) Tandem Library Bks.

Reiche, Dietlof. Ghost Ship. 2006. 320p. (J). pap. 5.99 (978-0-439-59705-0(6)) Scholastic, Inc.

—Ghost Ship. Brownjohn, John, tr. from GER. 2005. 320p. (J). pap. 16.95 (978-0-439-59704-3(8)) Scholastic, Inc.

Reiche, Dietlof & Brownjohn, John. The Haunting of Freddy. Cepeda, Joe, illus. 2006. (Golden Hamster Saga Ser.: Bk. 4). 320p. (J). pap. 16.99 (978-0-439-53159-7(4) , Scholastic Pr.) Scholastic, Inc.

Reiss, Kathryn. Sweet Miss Honeywell's Revenge: A Ghost Story. 2005. 444p. (J). (gr. 7-17). pap. 6.95 (978-0-15-205471-7(5) , Harcourt Paperbacks); 2004. (Illus.). 448p. (YA). 17.00 (978-0-15-216574-1(6)) Harcourt Children's Bks.

Rice, Bebe Faas. The Place at the Edge of the Earth. 2002. 192p. (YA). (gr. 5-9). tchr. ed. 15.00 (978-0-618-15978-9(9) , Clarion Bks.) Houghton Mifflin Co. Trade & Reference Div.

Richardson, Bill. Sally Dog Little. Malepart, Celine, illus. 2002. 24p. (J). (ps-2). lib. bdg. 14.95 (978-1-55037-759-0(0)) Annick Pr., Ltd. CAN. *Dist:* Firefly Bks., Ltd.

Riddell, J. H. The Open Door. 2004. reprint ed. pap. 15.95 (978-1-4191-7623-4(4)); pap. 1.99 (978-1-4192-7623-1(9)) Kessinger Publishing, LLC.

Riddle, Waide. The Chocolate Man: A Children's Horror Tale. 2003. 24p. (J). 9.95 (978-0-9724619-1-7(4)) Passage Publishing.

Roberts, Laura Peyton. Ghost of a Chance. 2006. 208p. (YA). (gr. 7). mass mkt. 5.99 (978-0-553-49498-3(8) , Laurel Leaf) Random Hse. Children's Bks.

—Ghost of a Chance. 1999. (J). (978-0-606-16448-1(0)) Tandem Library Bks.

Rochester & Merle. A Day at the Carnival. 2000. 32p. (J). pap. (978-0-9701450-5-5(5)) Long Hill Productions, Inc.

Roy, Ron. The Haunted Hotel. Gurney, John Steven, illus. 1999. (A to Z Mysteries Ser.: No. 8). (J). (gr. k-3). lib. bdg. 11.80 (978-0-613-16122-0(X)) Tandem Library Bks.

Ruby, Laura. Lily's Ghosts. 272p. (J). (gr. 5 up). 2005. pap. 5.99 (978-0-06-051831-8(6) , Harper Trophy); 2003. 16.99 (978-0-06-051829-5(4)) HarperCollins Pubs.

Rushby, Pamela. Footsteps. 2000. (gr. 7-12). lib. bdg. 12.25 (978-0-613-28844-6(0)) Tandem Library Bks.

—Midnight Children. 2000. (gr. 7-12). lib. bdg. 12.25 (978-0-613-28957-3(9)) Tandem Library Bks.

Sage, Angie. Frognapped. Pickering, Jimmy, illus. 2007. (Araminta Spookie Ser.: Bk. 3). (J). (gr. 2-5). 128p. 8.99 (*978-0-06-077487-5(8)); 208p. lib. bdg. 14.89 (*978-0-06-077488-2(6)) HarperCollins Pubs. (Tegen, Katherine Bks).

—My Haunted House. Pickering, Jimmy, illus. 2006. (Araminta Spookie Ser.: Bk. 1). 144p. (J). (gr. 2-5). 8.99 (978-0-06-077481-3(9) , Tegen, Katherine Bks); lib. bdg. 14.89 (978-0-06-077482-0(7)) HarperCollins Pubs.

—The Sword in the Grotto. Pickering, Jimmy, illus. 2006. (Araminta Spookie Ser.: Bk. 2). 160p. (J). (gr. 2-5). 8.99 (978-0-06-077484-4(3) , Tegen, Katherine Bks); lib. bdg. 14.89 (978-0-06-077485-1(1)) HarperCollins Pubs.

Sage, Angie. Vampire Brat. 2007. (Araminta Spookie Ser.: Bk. 4). (Illus.). 208p. (J). (gr. 2-5). lib. bdg. 14.89 (*978-0-06-077491-2(6)) HarperCollins Pubs.

—Vampire Brat, No. 4. Pickering, Jimmy, illus. 2007. (Araminta Spookie Ser.: Bk. 4). 128p. (J). (gr. 2-5). 8.99 (*978-0-06-077490-5(8)) HarperCollins Pubs.

San Souci, Robert D. More Short & Shivery. 2002. (gr. 5-8). lib. bdg. 15.30 (978-0-613-86685-9(1)) Tandem Library Bks.

Sargent, Dave, et al. Keeping Ghosts Away Vol. 8: (Creek) Be Respectful, 20. Lenoir, Jane, illus. l.t. ed. 2003. (Story Keeper Ser.: Vol. 8). 42p. (J). pap. 6.95 (978-1-56763-918-6(6) , 1228135); lib. bdg. 22.60 (978-1-56763-917-9(8) , 1228135) Ozark Publishing.

Sauer, Cat. Gwendolyn the Ghost. Jankowski, Dan, illus. l.t. ed. 2003. (Brown Bag Bedtime Bks.: 1). 29p. (YA). spiral bd. 16.95 (978-0-9704460-9-1(8)) Writer's Ink. Studios, Inc.

Saunders, Joanne D. Secret at the Winthrop House. 2007. 192p. per. 12.99 (*978-1-59886-622-3(2)) Tate Publishing & Enterprises, L.L.C.

Scarry, Richard. Richard Scarry's Books on the Go. Scarry, Richard, illus. 2006. (Illus.). 24p. (J). (gr. k-ps). bds. 12.95 (978-0-375-87522-9(0) , Golden Bks.) Random Hse. Children's Bks.

Schkolnik, Saul. Cuentos de Terror, de Magia y de Otras Cosas Extranas. (SPA.). (YA). (gr. 5-8). pap. (978-956-13-1319-4(7) , AB0160) Bello, Andres CHL. *Dist:* Lectorum Pubns., Inc.

Scholastic, Inc. Staff & Krovatin, Christopher. The Best Ghost Stories Ever. 2004. (Scholastic Classics Ser.). 192p. (J). (gr. 4 up). pap. 3.99 (978-0-439-57426-6(9) , Scholastic Paperbacks) Scholastic, Inc.

Schwegler, Tomas. Cuentos de Barcos Fantasma para Ninos. 1999. (Stories for Children Ser.).Tr. of Stories of Haunted Boats for Kids. (SPA.). 125p. (J). 7.95 (978-970-643-156-1(X)) Selector, S.A. de C.V. MEX. *Dist:* Libros Sin Fronteras.

Scooby-Doo & the Hex Files. 1999. (gr. k-3). lib. bdg. 11.25 (978-0-613-22339-3(X)) Tandem Library Bks.

Scooby Doo & the Pirate Ghost. 2001. (Illus.). (J). 15.98 (978-0-7853-4875-7(1)) Publications International, Ltd.

Scooby-Doo & the Witch's Ghost. 1999. (gr. k-3). lib. bdg. 11.25 (978-0-613-22340-9(3)) Tandem Library Bks.

Scroggs, Kirk Brandon. Hair Ball from Outer Space. 6th ed. 2007. (Wiley & Grampa Ser.: No. 6). 112p. (J). (gr. 3-7). pap. 3.99 (*978-0-316-05951-0(X)); 12.99 (*978-0-316-05950-3(1)) Little, Brown Bks. for Young Readers.

Senate, Richard. Ghosts of the Ojai: California's Most Haunted Valley. 2002. (Illus.). per. 8.95 (978-0-9722936-0-0(4)) Del Sol Pubns.

Shadow, Nick & Graves, Damien. Voices. 2006. (Apple Ser.: Vol. 1). (Illus.). 176p. (J). pap. 5.99 (978-0-439-86356-8(2)) Scholastic, Inc.

Shearer, Alex. The Great Blue Yonder. 2004. 192p. (J). (ps-7). mass mkt. 4.99 (978-0-439-56127-3(2) , Scholastic Paperbacks) Scholastic, Inc.

Shiozu, Shuri, creator. Eerie Queerie!, 4 vols., Vol. 4. rev. ed. 2004. (Illus.). 200p. pap. 9.99 (978-1-59182-861-7(9) , Tokyopop Adult) TOKYOPOP, Inc.

Showell, Ellen Harvey. The Ghost of Tillie Jean Cassaway. 2000. (Illus.). 128p. (YA). (gr. 4-7). pap. 9.95 (978-0-595-14292-7(3) , Backinprint.com) iUniverse, Inc.

Shreve, Susan Richards. Ghost Cats. 1999. 162p. (J). (gr. 3-7). pap. 14.95 (978-0-590-37131-5(2) , Levine, Arthur A. Bks.) Scholastic, Inc.

Shusterman, Neal. Darkness Creeping: Twenty Twisted Tales. 2007. 304p. (YA). (gr. 5 up). pap. 7.99 (978-0-14-240721-9(6) , Puffin) Penguin Group (USA) Inc.

Singleton, Linda Joy. Last Dance. 2005. (Seer Ser.: Book 2). 264p. pap. 6.99 (978-0-7387-0638-2(8)) Llewellyn Pubns.

—Sword Play. 2006. 288p. pap. 6.99 (978-0-7387-0880-5(1)) Llewellyn Pubns.

Sinykin, Sheri Cooper. Giving up the Ghost. 2007. 224p. (J). (gr. 4-7). 14.95 (*978-1-56145-423-5(0) , Peachtree Junior) Peachtree Pubs., Ltd.

Slammin' Ghost of the Boys Club. 2002. (Illus.). (J). (978-0-7868-2579-0(0)) Hyperion Pr.

Sleator, William. The Boy Who Couldn't Die. 2005. 184p. (YA). (gr. 7-17). pap. 6.95 (978-0-8109-8790-6(2)) Abrams, Harry N. , Inc.

Smith, Jeff. Bone Vol. 7: Ghost Circles. Smith, Jeff, illus. 2002. (Bone Ser.). (Illus.). 27.19 (978-1-4046-2805-2(3)) Book Wholesalers, Inc.

Smitten, Susan. Guardian Angels, Vol. 1. Norell, Aaron, illus. rev. ed. 2004. (Ghost Stories Ser.). 224p. (J). (gr. 4). pap. (978-1-894877-59-6(4)) Lone Pine Publishing.

Soileau, Hodges, illus. The Mystery of the Runaway Ghost, Vol. 98. 2004. (Boxcar Children Mysteries Ser.: 98). 128p. (J). (gr. 2-7). pap. 4.50 (978-0-8075-5551-4(7)) Whitman, Albert & Co.

Something Upstairs. 2002. (Avi Ser.). (Illus.). (J). 13.40 (978-0-7587-9129-0(1)) Book Wholesalers, Inc.

Soto, Gary. The Afterlife: A Novel. 2003. 176p. (J). (gr. 6 up). 17.00 (978-0-15-204774-0(3) , 53597422) Harcourt Children's Bks.

Souhami, Jessica. In the Dark, Dark Wood. 2007. (Illus.). 24p. (J). 7.95 (*978-1-84507-755-6(5)) Lincoln, Frances Ltd. GBR. *Dist:* Perseus Distribution.

Spenceley, Annabel, illus. The Kingfisher Treasury of Spooky Stories. 2003. (Kingfisher Treasury of Stories Ser.). 160p. (J). (gr. k-3). pap. 5.95 (978-0-7534-5634-7(6) , Kingfisher) Houghton Mifflin Co. Trade & Reference Div.

St. George, Judith. The Ghost, the White House, & Me. 2007. 128p. (J). (gr. 3-7). 16.95 (978-0-8234-2045-2(0)) Holiday Hse., Inc.

Stahler, David, Jr. Gathering of Shades. 2006. pap. (978-0-06-052296-4(8)) HarperCollins Canada, Ltd.

—A Gathering of Shades. 2005. 304p. (J). 15.99 (978-0-06-052294-0(1)); lib. bdg. 16.89 (978-0-06-052295-7(X)) HarperCollins Pubs. (HarperTeen).

Stamper, Judith Bauer. Five Haunted Houses. Raglin, Tim, illus. 2001. (Hello Reader! Ser.). 48p. (J). (gr. 2-4). pap. 3.99 (978-0-439-20546-7(8) , Cartwheel Bks.) Scholastic, Inc.

Stanley, George Edward. Ghost Horse. 2000. (gr. 3-6). lib. bdg. 11.80 (978-0-613-27851-5(8)) Tandem Library Bks.

Steiber, Ellen. Fantasmas Hambrientos. 1998. (SPA.). (gr. 7-12). lib. bdg. 15.70 (978-0-613-80642-8(5)) Tandem Library Bks.

Stein, Mathilde. Mine! Hout, Mies van, illus. 2007. 28p. (J). (ps-1). 16.95 (*978-1-59078-506-5(1)) Boyds Mills Pr.

Stem, Jacqueline. The Ghosts of Goliad. 2003. iii, 165p. (J). 17.95 (978-1-57168-785-2(8) , Eakin Pr.) Eakin Pr.

Stengel, Joyce A. Mystery of the Island Jewels. 2002. 208p. (J). (gr. 3-7). pap. 4.99 (978-0-689-85049-3(2) , Aladdin) Simon & Schuster Children's Publishing.

—Mystery of the Island Jewels. 2002. (gr. 3-6). lib. bdg. 13.00 (978-0-613-70940-8(3)) Tandem Library Bks.

Stevenson, Robert Louis. The Strange Case of Dr. Jekyll & Mr. Hyde. Akib, Jamel, illus. 2006. (Classic Starts Ser.). 160p. 4.95 (978-1-4027-2667-5(8) , 1252057) Sterling Publishing Co., Inc.

Stilton, Geronimo. The Phantom of the Subway. Wolf, Matt, illus. 2004. (Geronimo Stilton Ser.: No. 13). 112p. (J). lib. bdg. 10.00 (*978-1-4242-0282-9(5)) Fitzgerald Bks.

—The Phantom of the Subway. 2004. (Geronimo Stilton Ser.: No. 13). (Illus.). 112p. (J). (gr. 2-5). lib. bdg. 13.94 (978-0-606-33276-7(6)) Tandem Library Bks.

Stine, R. L. Como Consegui Mi Cabeza Humana Reducida: Escalofrios: Como consegui mi cabeza Humana. 2004. (Goosebumps Ser.).Tr. of How I Got My Shrunken Head. (SPA.). 128p. (J). (gr. 4-7). pap. 4.99 (978-0-439-67051-7(9) , Scholastic Paperbacks) Scholastic, Inc.

—The Confession. 2005. (Fear Street Ser.). 160p. (YA). pap. 5.99 (978-1-4169-0322-2(4) , Simon Pulse) Simon & Schuster Children's Publishing.

—Don't Close Your Eyes! 2006. 144p. (J). (gr. 2-5). 8.99 (978-0-385-90933-4(0)); (Mostly Ghostly Ser.: No. 8). 6.95 (978-0-385-74695-3(4)) Random Hse. Children's Bks. (Delacorte Bks. for Young Readers).

—Ghouls Gone Wild. 2005. 144p. (J). (gr. 2-5). lib. bdg. 8.99 (978-0-385-90930-3(6)); (Mostly Ghostly Ser.: Bk. 5). 6.95 (978-0-385-74692-2(X)) Random Hse. Children's Bks. (Delacorte Bks. for Young Readers).

—Goosebumps: Be Careful What You Wish For. 2005. (Goosebumps Ser.). 144p. (J). pap. 4.99 (978-0-439-66990-0(1) , Scholastic Paperbacks) Scholastic, Inc.

—Gritos en el Campo de Juego. 2000. (Fantasmas de Fear Street Coleccion). (SPA.). (YA). (gr. 5-8). pap. 7.95 (978-950-04-1903-1(3) , EM4473) Emecé Editores S.A. ARG. *Dist:* Lectorum Pubns., Inc., Planeta Publishing Corp.

—Halloween Party. 2006. (Fear Street Ser.). 160p. (YA). pap. 5.99 (978-1-4169-1811-0(6) , Simon Pulse) Simon & Schuster Children's Publishing.

—The Haunted School. 2005. (Goosebumps Ser.). 128p. (J). (gr. 3-7). pap. 4.99 (978-0-439-77475-8(6)) Scholastic, Inc.

—Have You Met My Ghoulfriend? 2004. (Mostly Ghostly Ser.). 144p. (J). (gr. 2-5). 6.95 (978-0-385-74664-9(4)); lib. bdg. 8.99 (978-0-385-90914-3(4)) Random Hse. Children's Bks. (Delacorte Bks. for Young Readers).

—Headless Ghost. rev. ed. 2004. (Goosebumps Ser.). 134p. (J). (gr. 4-7). pap. 4.99 (978-0-439-66987-0(1) , Scholastic Paperbacks) Scholastic, Inc.

—It Came from Beneath the Sink: Escalofrios: Lo Encontramos Debajo del Fregadero! 2004. (Goosebumps Ser.). (SPA.). 128p. (J). (gr. 4-7). mass mkt. 4.99 (978-0-439-67050-0(0) , Scholastic Paperbacks) Scholastic, Inc.

—Let's Get This Party Haunted! 2005. 144p. (J). (gr. 2-5). lib. bdg. 8.99 (978-0-385-90931-0(4)); (Mostly Ghostly Ser.: No. 6). 6.95 (978-0-385-74693-9(8)) Random Hse. Children's Bks. (Delacorte Bks. for Young Readers).

—Los Monstruos Oviparos de Marte. 2004. (Goosebumps Ser.).Tr. of Egg Monsters from Mars. (SPA.). 128p. (J). (gr. 4-7). pap. 4.99 (978-0-439-67053-1(5) , Scholastic Paperbacks) Scholastic, Inc.

STINE, R. L. My Best Friend Is Invisible. 2007. (Goosebumps Ser.). 144p. (J). pap. 4.99 (*978-0-439-92220-3(8)) Scholastic, Inc.

Stine, R. L. One Night in Doom House. 2005. (Mostly Ghostly Ser.). 144p. (gr. 2-5). lib. bdg. 8.99 (978-0-385-90915-0(2)); Vol. 3. (J). 6.95 (978-0-385-74665-6(2)) Random Hse. Children's Bks. (Delacorte Bks. for Young Readers).

—The Perfect Date. 2005. (Fear Street Ser.). 160p. (YA). pap. 5.99 (978-1-4169-0323-9(2) , Simon Pulse) Simon & Schuster Children's Publishing.

—The Rich Girl. 2005. (Fear Street Ser.). 144p. (YA). pap. 5.99 (978-1-4169-0324-6(0) , Simon Pulse) Simon & Schuster Children's Publishing.

—Scary Summer. 2007. (Goosebumps Graphix Ser.: No. 3). 144p. (J). pap. 8.99 (*978-0-439-85782-6(1)) Scholastic, Inc.

—Secret Admirer. 2005. (Fear Street Ser.). 160p. (YA). pap. 5.99 (978-1-4169-0820-3(X) , Simon Pulse) Simon & Schuster Children's Publishing.

—Sitter. 2003. (gr. 7-12). lib. bdg. 22.20 (978-0-613-71731-1(7)) Tandem Library Bks.

—Terror Trips. 2007. (Goosebumps Graphix Ser.). 144p. (J). pap. 16.99 (978-0-439-85777-2(5)); (Illus.). pap. 8.99 (978-0-439-85780-2(5)) Scholastic, Inc. (Graphix).

—When Good Ghouls Go Bad. 2001. (Nightmare Room Ser.: No. 11). 144p. (J). (gr. 4-6). pap. 3.99 (978-0-06-441082-3(X) , Avon) HarperCollins Pubs.

—When Good Ghouls Go Bad. 2001. (gr. 3-6). lib. bdg. 11.80 (978-0-613-54448-1(X)) Tandem Library Bks.

—Who Let the Ghosts Out? 2004. (Mostly Ghostly Ser.). 144p. (J). (gr. 2-5). 6.95 (978-0-385-74663-2(6)); lib. bdg. 8.99 (978-0-385-90913-6(6)) Random Hse. Children's Bks. (Delacorte Bks. for Young Readers).

Stine, R. L., ed. Midnight Games. 2005. 183p. (YA). (978-1-4156-1074-9(6) , Simon Pulse) Simon & Schuster Children's Publishing.

Stine, R.L. Midnight Games. 2005. 183p. (YA). lib. bdg. 20.00 (*978-1-4242-1119-7(0)) Fitzgerald Bks.

Stocks, Mike. Victorian horror Stories. 2005. 144p. (J). pap. 4.95 (978-0-7945-0237-9(7) , Usborne) EDC Publishing.

Storrie, Paul D. Terror in Ghost Mansion. Carruthers, Sandy, illus. 2007. (Twisted Journeys Ser.). 112p. (J). (gr. 4-7). lib. bdg. 27.93 (*978-0-8225-6776-9(8) , Graphic Universe) Lerner Publishing Group.

Strachan, Linda. Ghost of Glamis. 2005. (Illus.). 32p. pap. 9.00 (978-0-9546701-9-1(1)) GW Publishing GBR. *Dist:* Wilson & Assocs.

Strangway, Melissa. 56 Water Street. 2007. 104p. per. 9.95 (*978-0-595-42429-0(5)) iUniverse, Inc.

Strategy Guide: Ghost Dogs of Moon Lake. 2002. 9.99 (978-0-9672618-9-8(9)) Her Interactive, Inc.

Surrell, Jason. The Haunted Mansion: From the Magic Kingdom to the Movies. 2003. (Illus.). 132p. (J). 19.95 (978-0-7868-5419-6(7)) Disney Pr.

Swoish, Tammy. Hot Scots, Castles, & Kilts. 2008. (YA). (gr. 7). 208p. pap. 7.99 (*978-0-385-73447-9(6)); 224p. lib. bdg. 10.99 (*978-0-385-90450-6(9)) Random Hse. Children's Bks. (Delacorte Bks. for Young Readers).

Sykes, Shelley & Szymanski, Lois. The Ghost Comes Out. 2001. (Gettysburg Ghost Gang Ser.: Vol. 1). 96p. (J). pap. 5.95 (978-1-57249-266-0(X) , White Mane Kids) White Mane Publishing Co., Inc.

—Ghost on Board. 2001. (Gettysburg Ghost Gang Ser.: Vol. 2). (Illus.). 96p. (J). pap. 5.95 (978-1-57249-267-7(8) , White Mane Kids) White Mane Publishing Co., Inc.

—The Soldier in the Cellar. 2004. (Gettysburg Ghost Gang Ser.: Vol. 5). 96p. (J). pap. 5.95 (978-1-57249-299-8(6) , White Mane Kids) White Mane Publishing Co., Inc.

—A Whisper of War. 2003. (J). 5.95 (978-1-57249-327-8(5) , White Mane Kids) White Mane Publishing Co., Inc.

Tabori, Lena & Tabori-Fried, Natasha, eds. The Little Big Book of Chills & Thrills. (Illus.). 352p. (J). (ps-7). 24.95 (978-1-932183-85-6(X) , Welcome Bks.) Welcome Enterprises, Inc.

Tan, Shaun, illus. The Haunted Playground. 2008. (J). lib. bdg. (*978-1-59889-860-6(4)); 80p. pap. (*978-1-59889-916-0(3)) Stone Arch Bks.

Taylor, Sean. Purple Class & the Skelington. Bate, Helen & Dunbar, Polly, illus. 2006. 98p. pap. 7.95 (978-1-84507-377-0(0)) Lincoln, Frances Ltd. GBR. *Dist:* Perseus Distribution.

Teitelbaum, Michael. The Scary States of America. 2007. 416p. (J). (gr. 4-7). pap. 7.99 (978-0-385-73331-1(3)); lib. bdg. 12.99 (*978-0-385-90348-6(0)) Random Hse. Children's Bks. (Delacorte Bks. for Young Readers).

Terasaki, Stanley Todd. Ghosts for Breakfast. Shinjo, Shelly, illus. 2002. 32p. (J). (gr. k-4). 16.95 (978-1-58430-046-5(9)) Lee & Low Bks., Inc.

Thay, Edrick. Haunted Cemeteries, Vol. 1. rev. ed. 2004. (Ghost Stories Ser.). (Illus.). 200p. (gr. 4). pap. (978-1-894877-60-2(8)) Lone Pine Publishing.

Theriault, Francis. Just Another Ghost Story: A critical thinking Novel. 2007. 68p. (J). per. 8.95 (*978-0-595-45258-3(2)) iUniverse, Inc.

Thieman, Linda. Katie & Kimble: A Ghost Story. l.t. ed. 2007. (Illus.). 148p. (J). pap. 12.48 (*978-0-9794396-0-5(4)) Pale Silver Rainplop Pr.

Thomas, Teri. The Barge Ghost. 2004. (Illus.). 32p. (YA). 2.95 (978-1-56254-737-0(2) , SP7372) Saddleback Educational Publishing.

Thompson, B. B. Strangetales: A Book of Beginning. Cuce, Thomas A. & Sutphin, Eric, illus. 2002. (Strangetales Ser.). 172p. pap. 4.95 (978-0-9725614-0-2(4)) Tricorner Publishing.

Tibbetts, Peggy. The Road to Weird. 2003. 12.00 (978-1-869942-59-5(0)) Zumaya Pubns. LLC.

Tingle, Tim & Moore. Spooky Texas Tales. Miller, Gina, illus. 2005. x, 85p. (J). pap. (978-0-89672-566-9(9)) Texas Tech Univ. Pr.

Trasler, Janee. Ghost Eats It All: Little Boo Books. 2006. (Illus.). 24p. (J). (ps-1). 5.99 (978-0-316-01844-9(9)) Little Brown & Co.

Trasler, Janee. Ghost Gets Dressed! 2007. (Little Boo! Bks.). 24p. (J). (ps-1). 5.99 (*978-0-316-06530-6(7)) Little, Brown Bks. for Young Readers.

Turner, Rosa M. The Ghost of Willow Hill. 2000. (J). cd-rom 9.95 (978-1-58338-390-2(5)) CrossroadsPub.com.

Twigg, Aeres. The Green Hawk. 2003. (Illus.). 87p. (J). pap. 12.95 (978-1-85902-787-5(3)) Beekman Bks., Inc.

Ure, Jean. Little Daisy. 2002. (Illus.). 96p. pap. 7.99 (978-0-00-713369-7(3)) HarperCollins Pubs. Ltd. GBR. *Dist:* Independent Pubs. Group.

Vail, Emily Blake. The Grey Ghost of the Pharaoh. Barbra K. Mudd, illus. 2004. 176p. (YA). per. 8.99 (978-0-935087-27-7(3)) Wright Publishing, Inc.

Van de Velde, Vivian. There's a Dead Person Following My Sister Around. 2001. (Illus.). (J). (978-0-606-21485-8(2)) Tandem Library Bks.

Vande Velde, Vivian. Ghost of a Hanged Man. 96p. (J). 2005. pap. 5.95 (978-0-7614-5154-9(4)); 1998. (gr. 3-7). 14.95 (978-0-7614-5015-3(7) , Cavendish Children's Bks.) Cavendish, Marshall Corp.

—There's a Dead Person Following My Sister Around. 2001. 160p. (J). pap. 5.99 (978-0-14-131281-1(5) , Puffin) Penguin Group (USA) Inc.

—There's a Dead Person Following My Sister Around. 2001. (gr. 5-8). lib. bdg. 13.00 (978-0-613-43899-5(X)) Tandem Library Bks.

Vaughan, Marcia. We're Going on a Ghost Hunt. Schweninger, Ann, illus. 2001. 32p. (J). (gr. k-2). 15.00 (978-0-15-202353-9(4)) Harcourt Children's Bks.

Wallin, Luke. The Slavery Ghosts. 2001. 132p. (YA). pap. 11.95 (978-0-595-19277-9(7)) iUniverse, Inc.

Warner, Gertrude Chandler. Ghost Town Mystery. 1999. (gr. 3-6). lib. bdg. 11.80 (978-0-613-16266-1(8)) Tandem Library Bks.

—Mystery of the Midnight Dog. 2001. (gr. 3-6). lib. bdg. 11.80 (978-0-613-35789-0(2)) Tandem Library Bks.

—The Mystery of the Midnight Dog, Vol. 81. 2004. (Boxcar Children Ser.: No. 81). (Illus.). 122p. (J). (gr. 2-7). pap. 4.50 (978-0-8075-5476-0(6)) Whitman, Albert & Co.

—Mystery on Blizzard Mountain. 2002. (gr. 3-6). lib. bdg. 11.80 (978-0-613-53287-7(2)) Tandem Library Bks.

Warner, Gertrude Chandler, creator. The Mystery on Blizzard Mountain, Vol. 86. 2004. (Boxcar Children Ser.: No. 86). (Illus.). 122p. (J). (gr. 2-7). 14.95 (978-0-8075-5493-7(6)); pap. 4.50 (978-0-8075-5494-4(4)) Whitman, Albert & Co.

Warren, Celia. The Ghost Dog. Smith, Pete, illus. 2008. (J). pap. (*978-1-59889-899-6(X)); 33p. (YA). (gr. 5-9). lib. bdg. 21.26 (*978-1-59889-847-7(7)) Stone Arch Bks.

Warren, Samuel. The Spectre Smitten. 2004. reprint ed. pap. 15.95 (978-1-4191-8323-2(0)); pap. 1.99 (978-1-4192-8323-9(5)) Kessinger Publishing, LLC.

Wasserman, Robin. Ghost School. 2003. (gr. k-3). lib. bdg. 11.80 (978-0-613-72194-3(2)) Tandem Library Bks.

Wasserman, Robin, et al. Ghost School. del Sur, Duendes, illus. 2003. (Scooby-Doo Ser.: No. 17). 32p. (J). pap. 3.99 (978-0-439-44227-5(3) , Scholastic Paperbacks) Scholastic, Inc.

Watson. The Ghosts of Izieu, Level 3. 2000. (Illus.). v, 41p. (C). pap. 9.00 (978-0-582-42654-2(5)) Longman Publishing Group.

Watson Martin, JoAn. Goodnight Mrs. Dinglewall. Sleep Tight! 2006. (YA). per. (978-0-9777996-0-2(3)) Great American Pr.,The.

Welsh, T. K. Resurrection Men. 2007. 214p. (J). (gr. 9 up). 16.99 (978-0-525-47699-3(7) , Dutton Juvenile) Penguin Group (USA) Inc.

—The Unresolved. 2006. 160p. (YA). (gr. 9). 16.99 (978-0-525-47731-0(4) , Dutton Juvenile) Penguin Group (USA) Inc.

West, Tracey. Hoothoot's Haunted Forest. 2001. (Pokemon Junior Chapter Bks.: No. 13). (Illus.). 48p. (J). (gr. k-4). pap. 3.99 (978-0-439-32066-5(6)) Scholastic, Inc.

—Mario & the Incredible Rescue. 2006. 76p. (J). pap. (*978-0-439-84366-9(9)) Scholastic, Inc.

—Roxy Hunter & the Mystery of the Moody Ghost. 2007. 128p. (J). (gr. 2-5). 4.99 (*978-0-8431-2663-1(9) , Price Stern Sloan) Penguin Group (USA) Inc.

Westall, Robert, compiled by. Spinetinglers: Ghoulish Ghost Stories. 2007. 272p. (J). pap. 6.95 (*978-0-7534-6140-2(4) , Kingfisher) Houghton Mifflin Co. Trade & Reference Div.

Westmoreland, Ann. Aunt Annie's Ghost. 2005. 66p. pap. 14.95 (978-1-4137-6693-6(5)) PublishAmerica, Inc.

Weston, Joanna M. The Willow Tree Girl. 2003. (ENG.). 84p. pap. (*978-1-55352-073-3(4)) Treeside Pr.

Wharton, Edith. Edith Wharton. McConnell, James, illus. 2004. (Great American Short Stories Ser.). 74p. (J). lib. bdg. 23.33 (978-0-8368-4256-2(1)) Stevens, Gareth Inc.

Whitcomb, Laura. A Certain Slant of Light. 2005. 288p. (YA). (gr. 7). pap. 8.99 (978-0-618-58532-8(X) , Graphia) Houghton Mifflin Co. Trade & Reference Div.

Whybrow, Ian. Little Wolf's Haunted Hall for Small Horrors. Ross, Tony, illus. (Middle Grade Fiction Ser.). 132p. (J). 2005. (gr. 3-6). 14.95 (978-1-57505-412-4(4)); 2004. (gr. 2-6). pap. 6.95 (978-1-57505-794-1(8)) Lerner Publishing Group.

Wiesner, David, adapted by. Gonna Roll the Bones. 2004. 32p. 16.95 (978-1-59687-176-2(8) , Milk & Cookies) ibooks, Inc.

Wight, Eric. My Dead Girlfriend. 2007. (Illus.). pap. 9.99 (*978-1-59816-996-6(3) , Tokyopop Adult) TOKYOPOP, Inc.

Wilde, Oscar. The Canterville Ghost. Date not set. (Nelson Readers Ser.). (J). pap. (978-0-17-557035-5(3)) Addison-Wesley Longman, Inc.

—The Canterville Ghost. 2nd ed. 2000. (Reading & Training Ser.). 112p. (YA). pap. (978-1-57159-012-1(9)) Los Andes Publishing Co.

—El Fantasma de Canterville. 2005. (Clasicos de la literatura Ser.). (SPA., Illus.). 184p. pap. 5.95 (978-84-9764-458-7(1)) Edimat Libros, S. A. ESP. *Dist:* Independent Pubs. Group.

—El Fantasma de Canterville. 2000. (SPA.). 112p. (978-950-03-6274-0(0) , 1060) Losada.

Wilde, Terry Lee. Ghostly Liaisons. 2006. 350p. (YA). pap. (978-1-932815-37-5(6) , Bronze Medallion) Medallion Pr., Inc.

Wilhelm, Hans. I'm Not Scared! 2005. (Illus.). 32p. (J). (ps-ps). pap. 3.99 (978-0-439-44334-0(2) , Cartwheel Bks.) Scholastic, Inc.

Williams, Jacklyn. The Haunted Schoolhouse: A Spooky. Cushman, Doug, illus. 2007. 16p. (J). pap. 6.99 (*978-0-689-87150-4(3) , Little Simon) Simon & Schuster Children's Publishing.

Williams, Kethette. The Ghosts on the Hill. 2007. (ENG.). 56p. per. 12.95 (*978-1-4241-6767-8(1)) PublishAmerica, Inc.

Wilson, Eric G. The Ghost of Lunenburg Manor. 1999. (Tom & Liz Austen Mysteries Ser.). (Illus.). 117p. (J). (gr. 3-6). mass mkt. 5.95 (978-0-7736-7484-4(5)) Stoddart Kids CAN. *Dist:* Fitzhenry & Whiteside, Ltd.

Wilson, Jacqueline. Vicky Angel. l.t. ed. 2001. (Illus.). 232p. (J). 16.95 (978-0-7540-6165-6(5) , Galaxy Children's Large Print) BBC Audiobooks America.

—Vicky Angel. 2003. (Illus.). 176p. (gr. 3-7). reprint ed. 5.50 (978-0-440-41808-5(9) , Yearling) Random Hse. Children's Bks.

—Vicky Angel. 2003. (gr. 3-6). lib. bdg. 13.00 (978-0-613-88328-3(4)) Tandem Library Bks.

Wilson, Troy. Frosty Is a Stupid Name. Griffiths, Dean, illus. 2005. 32p. (J). (ps-2). 17.95 (978-1-55143-382-0(6)) Orca Bk. Pubs. USA.

Wimmer, Mary. Reaching Shore. 2007. 280p. (YA). per. 14.95 (***978-1-59598-063-2(6))** Goblin Fern Pr., Inc.

Winters, Kay. Teeny Tiny Ghost. 1999. (gr. k-3). lib. bdg. 14.10 (978-0-613-22943-2(6)) Tandem Library Bks.

—Teeny Tiny Ghost & the Monster. Munsinger, Lynn, illus. 2006. 32p. (J). pap. 6.99 (978-0-06-443662-5(4), Harper Trophy) HarperCollins Pubs.

—Whooo's Haunting the Teeny Tiny Ghost? Munsinger, Lynn, illus. 32p. (J). (ps-3). 2001. pap. 5.95 (978-0-06-443784-4(1), Harper Trophy); Bk. 2. 2000. (Teeny Tiny Ghost Ser.: Vol. 2). 14.89 (978-0-06-027359-0(3)); Bk. 2. 1999. (Teeny Tiny Ghost Ser.: Vol. 2). 14.95 (978-0-06-027358-3(5)) HarperCollins Pubs.

—Whooo's Haunting the Teeny Tiny Ghost? 2001. (gr. k-3). lib. bdg. 14.10 (978-0-613-89285-8(2)) Tandem Library Bks.

Witches, Wizards, Ghosts & the Beast of Nyiragongo. 2002. (YA). mass mkt. 7.95 net. (978-0-620-31122-9(3)) African Artistic Ventures.

Woodruff, Elvira. The Ghost of Lizard Light. Clayton, Elaine, illus. 2001. 192p. (gr. 3-7). pap. 4.99 (978-0-440-41655-5(8), Yearling) Random Hse. Children's Bks.

—The Ghost of Lizard Light. 2001. (gr. 3-6). lib. bdg. 13.00 (978-0-613-36814-8(2)) Tandem Library Bks.

Wright, Betty Ren. Crandall's Castle. 2005. 184p. (YA). (gr. 4-6). tchr. ed. 16.95 (978-0-8234-1726-1(3)) Holiday Hse., Inc.

—A Ghost in the Family. 2002. 96p. (J). (gr. 3-7). pap. 3.99 (978-0-590-02953-7(3), Scholastic Paperbacks) Scholastic, Inc.

—Princess for a Week. Rogers, Jacqueline, illus. 160p. (J). (gr. 2-5). 16.95 (978-0-8234-1945-6(2)) Holiday Hse., Inc.

Yolen, Jane. The Bagpiper's Ghost. 2003. (Tartan Magic Ser.: Bk. 3). (Illus.). 144p. (J). pap. 5.95 (978-0-15-204913-3(4), Magic Carpet Bks.) Harcourt Children's Bks.

—Bagpiper's Ghost. 2003. (gr. 3-6). lib. bdg. 6.95 (978-0-613-70524-0(6)) Tandem Library Bks.

Yoon, Salina. Five Spooky Ghosts. Yoon, Salina, illus. 2005. (Illus.). 10p. (J). (ps-1). bds. 5.99 (978-0-8431-1443-0(6), Price Stern Sloan) Penguin Group (USA) Inc.

Youngquist, D. M. Ghosts of Interstate 80. 2007. (Illus.). 180p. (YA). per. 9.95 (***978-1-57166-459-4(9))** Quixote Pr.

Zindel, Paul. The Phantom of 86th Street. 2002. (gr. 3-6). lib. bdg. 13.00 (978-0-613-62914-0(0)) Tandem Library Bks.

Zucker, Jonny. The Phantom Striker. Tavares, Victor, illus. 2008. (J). pap. (***978-1-59889-901-6(5)**); 33p. (YA). (gr. 5-9). lib. bdg. 21.26 (***978-1-59889-849-1(3))** Stone Arch Bks.

The 13 Pet Geists. 2005. (Illus.). (J). 15.99 (978-0-9755889-0-1(7)); lib. bdg. 15.99 (978-0-9755889-1-8(5)) Rose-Knows, Inc.

GIANTS

Andreasen, Dan. The Giant of Seville: A "Tall" Tale Based on a True Story. 2007. (Illus.). 32p. (J). (ps-3). 15.95 (978-0-8109-0988-5(X), Abrams Bks. for Young Readers) Abrams, Harry N., Inc.

Busquets, Jordi. Leo y Veo, los Gigantes.Tr. of I Read & See, the Giants. (SPA.). 24p. (J). 3.48 (978-84-305-9409-2(4)) Susaeta Ediciones, S.A. ESP. *Dist:* AIMS International Bks., Inc., Giron Bks.

Hamilton, John. Ogres And Giants. 2005. (Fantasy & Folklore Ser.). (Illus.). 32p. (J). (gr. 4-8). lib. bdg. 24.21 (978-1-59197-714-8(2)) ABDO Publishing Co.

The Story of David. 2000. (Illus.). 24p. (J). (ps-k). bds. 6.95 (978-0-8249-4171-0(3)) Ideals Pubns.

GIANTS—FICTION

Anderson, Brian. The Adventures of Commander Zack Proton & the Red Giant. Holgate, Doug, illus. 2006. (Adventures of Commander Zack Proton Ser.). 128p. (J). (gr. 2-5). pap. 3.99 (978-1-4169-1364-1(5), Aladdin) Simon & Schuster Children's Publishing.

Appleton, Victor. Tom Swift in Captivity or A Daring Escap. 2006. pap. (***978-1-4065-0914-4(0))** Dodo Pr.

Balian, Lorna. A Sweetheart for Valentine. Balian, Lorna, illus. 2005. (Illus.). 40p. (J). 15.95 (978-1-932065-14-5(8)) Star Bright Bks., Inc.

Beamish, Diane. Gentle Jack. 2006. 25p. (J). 10.25 (978-1-4116-5553-9(2)) Lulu.com.

Beaty, Andrea. When Giants Come to Play. Hawkes, Kevin, illus. 2006. 32p. (J). (ps-3). 16.95 (978-0-8109-5759-6(0)) Abrams, Harry N., Inc.

Becker, Shari. Horris Grows Down. Petrone, Valeria, illus. 2007. 32p. (J). (ps). 15.99 (978-0-399-24358-5(5), Putnam Juvenile) Penguin Group (USA) Inc.

Beer, Barbara Vagnozzi. Jack & the Beanstalk. (Illus.). 24p. pap. (978-1-904550-20-4(7)) Child's Play-International.

Birdseye, Tom. Look Out Jack! Giant Is Back! Hillenbrand, Will, illus. 2005. 32p. (J). (gr. k-3). 6.95 (978-0-8234-1776-6(X)) Holiday Hse., Inc.

Brookes, Diane & Leonard, Marcia. A Novel Study for Grades One & Two Based on When the Giants Came to Town, 25 vols. 1998. (J). pap., tchr. ed. (978-0-9683234-5-8(6)) Raven Rock Publishing.

Casey & the Amazing, Giant, Green Shirt: The Greatly Loved, Special, Brave, Smart, Kind, Fast, Patriotic American Kid! Lt. ed. 2001. (Kamaron Concept Book). 32p. 9.99 (978-0-9715713-0-3(9)) Kamaron Institute Pr.

Cole, Brock. The Giant's Toe. Cole, Brock, illus. 2001. (Sunburst Ser.). (Illus.). 32p. (J). (ps-3). pap. 6.95 (978-0-374-42557-9(4), Sunburst) Farrar, Straus & Giroux.

Cote, Denis. Les Géants de Blizzard. 2002. (Roman Jeunesse Ser.). (FRE.). 96p. (YA). (gr. 4-7). pap. (978-2-89021-126-1(6)) Diffusion du livre Mirabel.

Coville, Bruce. Thor's Wedding Day: By Thialfi, the goat boy, as told to & translated by Bruce Coville. Cogswell, Matthew, illus. 2008. 144p. (J). pap. 5.95 (978-0-15-205872-2(9), Magic Carpet Bks.) Harcourt Children's Bks.

Cross, Frances. Mystery of the Green Elephant. 2007. (Blobber Trilogy Ser.). 96p. pap. 7.95 (***978-1-84167-559-6(8))** Ransom Publishing Ltd. GBR. *Dist:* International Publishers Marketing.

Dahl, Roald. The BFG. Blake, Quentin, illus. 2007. 208p. (J). (gr. 2). 6.99 (***978-0-14-241038-7(1)**, Puffin) Penguin Group (USA) Inc.

Dahl, Roald. James y el Melocoton Gigante. Blake, Quentin, illus. 2003. (SPA.). 184p. pap. 9.95 (978-968-19-0625-2(X)) Aguilar, Altea, Taurus, Alfaguara, S.A. de C.V MEX. *Dist:* Santillana USA Publishing Co., Inc.

The David & Goliath, Beginner's Biblereg; 2007. 24p. (J). 5.99 (978-0-8297-4937-3(3)) Vida Pubs.

Daynes, Katie. Jack & the Beanstalk. 2006. 48p. (J). 8.99 (978-0-7945-1238-5(0), Usborne) EDC Publishing.

dela Pena, Alba. The Tales of Gorba the Crafty Giant of Loomsville. 2006. (J). 6.95 (978-1-56167-925-6(9)) American Literary Pr.

Desimini, Lisa. The Sun & Moon: A Giant Love Story. 1999. (Illus.). 40p. (YA). (ps-3). pap. 16.95 (978-0-590-18720-6(1), Blue Sky Pr., The) Scholastic, Inc.

Doherty, B. Jack the Giant Killer. (Illus.). 139p. pap. 8.99 (978-0-340-76452-7(X), Hodder & Stoughton) Hodder General Publishing Division GBR. *Dist:* Trafalgar Square Publishing.

Donaldson, Julia. The Giants & the Joneses. Swearingen, Greg, illus. 2005. 224p. (J). (gr. 3-5). 14.95 (978-0-8050-7805-3(3)) Holt, Henry & Co.

—The Giants & the Joneses. Swearingen, Greg, illus. 2008. 240p. (J). pap. 6.99 (***978-0-312-37961-2(7))** Square Fish.

Eggleton, Jill. The Giant's Ice Cream: 3-in-1 Package. Hawley, Kelvin, illus. (Sails Literacy Ser.). 24p. (gr. k up). 57.00 (978-0-7578-3195-9(8)) Rigby Education.

—The Giant's Ice Cream: 6 Small Books. Hawley, Kelvin, illus. (Sails Literacy Ser.). 24p. (gr. k up). 25.00 (978-0-7578-3171-3(0)) Rigby Education.

—The Giant's Ice Cream: Big Book Only. Hawley, Kelvin, illus. (Sails Literacy Ser.). 24p. (gr. k up). 27.00 (978-0-7635-6986-0(0)) Rigby Education.

Evans, Latonya, adapted by. Jack & the Beanstalk. l.t. ed. 2005. (Fairy Tales of Special Children Ser.: Book 1). (Illus.). 25p. (J). (978-0-9767258-0-0(0)) Diversity Ink Publishing.

Fairy Tales- Jack & the Beanstalk. 2005. (J). bds. (978-1-4194-0040-7(1)) Paradise Pr., Inc.

Farley, Jacqui. Giant Hiccups. Venus, Pamela, illus. 2001. (Selected Children's Multicultural Stories). 32p. (J). lib. bdg. 15.95 (978-1-56674-312-9(5)) Forest Hse. Publishing Co., Inc.

Fienberg, Anna & Fienberg, Barbara. The Big Big Big Book of Tashi. Gamble, Kim, illus. 2002. (Tashi Ser.). 448p. (J). (gr. 1-5). pap. 15.95 (978-1-86508-563-0(4)) Allen & Unwin AUS. *Dist:* Independent Pubs. Group.

Fitzpatrick, Marie-Louise. The Sleeping Giant. 2001. (Illus.). 32p. (J). (ps-3). pap. 7.95 (978-0-86327-643-9(1)) Interlink Publishing Group, Inc.

Garcia Sanchez, J. L. El Nino Gigante (The Giant Child) (Derechos del Nino Ser.). (SPA., Illus.). 32p. (J). (gr. 3-5). pap. 8.95 (978-1-56014-580-6(3)) Santillana USA Publishing Co., Inc.

Gelsey, James. The Summer Camp Cyclops. 2007. (Scooby-Doo Case Files Ser.: No. 2). 80p. (J). pap. 3.99 (***978-0-439-91592-2(9))** Scholastic, Inc.

Gerstein, Mordecai. Carolinda Clatter! unabr. ed. 2007. (Illus.). (J). (ps-2). 28.95 incl. audio compact disk (***978-1-59519-958-4(6))** Live Oak Media.

A Giant in the Forest, Level 18. 1999. (J). (gr. k-3). 3.95 (978-0-673-61481-0(6)) Addison-Wesley Longman, Inc.

The Giant's Day Out: Set D Individual Title Six-Packs. (Smart Start Ser.). (gr. k-1). 23.00 (978-0-7635-0454-0(8)) Rigby Education.

El gigante Egoista: Individual Title Six-Packs. (Literatura 2000 Ser.). (SPA.). (gr. 2-3). 33.00 (978-0-7635-1261-3(3)) Rigby Education.

Gill, Janie S. A Tall, Tall Giant. Lambson, Elizabeth, illus. 1999. 23p. (J). pap. 3.95 (978-0-89868-432-2(3)); lib. bdg. 10.95 (978-0-89868-431-5(5)); 5.95 (978-0-89868-433-9(1)) ARO Publishing Co.

Glynn, Gower. Stories Told in the Wigwam. 2006. pap. 24.95 (***978-1-4254-9966-2(X))** Kessinger Publishing, LLC.

Grindley, Sally & Utton, Peter. Shhh! (Illus.). 32p. (J). pap. 13.95 (978-0-340-74662-2(9), Hodder & Stoughton) Hodder General Publishing Division GBR. *Dist:* Trafalgar Square Publishing.

Hall, Amanda. Giant Tales from Around the World. Waters, Fiona, illus. 2004. 96p. (J). 17.95 (978-1-84458-143-6(8)) Chrysalis Children's Bks. GBR. *Dist:* Transition Vendor.

Hall, Amanda, tr. & illus. Giant Tales. Hall, Amanda, illus. 2003. 96p. (YA). (978-1-84365-017-1(7)) Chrysalis Children's Bks.

Harcourt School Publishers Staff. The Baker & the Rings: On Level. 3rd ed. 2002. (Trophies Reading Program Ser.). (Illus.). pap. 5.10 (978-0-15-323185-8(8)) Harcourt Schl. Pubs.

—Trofeos On Level: Panadera/Anillos. 3rd ed. 2002. (SPA., Illus.). pap. 6.80 (978-0-15-324096-6(2)) Harcourt Schl. Pubs.

Harrison, David L. Book of Giant Stories. 2001. (gr. 3-6). lib. bdg. 19.90 (978-0-613-56248-5(8)) Tandem Library Bks.

Hillman, Jack. There Are Giants in This Valley. 2005. 256p. (YA). 26.99 (978-1-59507-096-8(6), ArcheBooks) ArcheBooks Publishing.

Hoffmire, A. B. The Ogre Bully. 2007. 32p. (J). pap. 3.95 (***978-0-87483-803-9(7))** August Hse. Pubs., Inc.

Holub, Joan. Jack & the Jellybeanstalk. 2002. (gr. k-3). lib. bdg. 11.25 (978-0-613-72447-0(X)) Tandem Library Bks.

Hughes, Ted. The Iron Giant. 1999. (Illus.). 96p. (gr. 3-5). pap. 5.50 (978-0-375-80153-2(7), Yearling) Random Hse. Children's Bks.

—The Iron Giant: A Story in Five Nights. Davidson, Andrew, illus. 1999. 79p. (J). (ps-7). per. 13.00 (978-0-613-21772-9(1)) Tandem Library Bks.

Hutchins, Hazel J. Two So Small. Ohi, Ruth, illus. 2000. 32p. (J). (ps-1). pap. 7.95 (978-1-55037-650-0(0)) Annick Pr., Ltd. CAN. *Dist:* Firefly Bks., Ltd.

—Two So Small. 2000. (gr. k-3). lib. bdg. 16.40 (978-0-613-50386-0(4)) Tandem Library Bks.

Jacques et le Haricot Magique.Tr. of Jack & the Bean Stalk. (FRE.). 48p. (J). pap. 12.95 incl. audio compact disk (978-2-89558-069-0(3)) Coffragants CAN. *Dist:* Penton Overseas, Inc.

Jarman, Julia. Molly & the Giant. Sholto, Walker, illus. 2005. 24p. (J). lib. bdg. 22.65 (***978-1-59646-746-0(0))** Dingles & Co.

Jill & the Beanstalk. 2004. (J). (ENG & ITA.). (978-1-84444-480-9(5)); (ALB & ENG.). (978-1-84444-492-2(9)); (ARA & ENG.). (978-1-84444-486-1(4)); (BEN & ENG.). (978-1-84444-478-6(3)); (CHI & ENG.). (978-1-84444-488-5(0)); (SBC & ENG.). (978-1-84444-483-0(X)); (ENG & PER.). (978-1-84444-491-5(0)); (ENG & FRE.). (978-1-84444-489-2(9)); (ENG & GUJ.). (978-1-84444-479-3(1)); (ENG & PAN.). (978-1-84444-494-6(5)); (ENG & POR.). (978-1-84444-481-6(3)); (ENG & RUS.). (978-1-84444-482-3(1)); (ENG & SOM.). (978-1-84444-487-8(2)); (ENG & SPA.). (978-1-84444-490-8(2)); (ENG & TAM.). (978-1-84444-484-7(8)); (ENG & TUR.). (978-1-84444-495-3(3)); (ENG & URD.). (978-1-84444-485-4(6)); (ENG & VIE.). (978-1-84444-496-0(1)); E-Book incl. cd-rom (978-1-84444-463-2(5)) Mantra Publishing, Ltd.

Johnson, Richard, tr. & illus. Jack & the Beanstalk. Johnson, Richard, illus. 2004. 31p. (J). (978-1-84444-108-2(3)) Mantra Publishing, Ltd.

Kasza, Keiko. The Mightiest. 2003. (Picture Puffin Ser.). (Illus.). 32p. (J). pap. 5.99 (978-0-14-250185-6(9), Puffin) Penguin Group (USA) Inc.

—The Mightiest. Kasza, Keiko, illus. 2001. (Illus.). 32p. (J). 16.99 (978-0-399-23586-3(8), Putnam Juvenile) Penguin Group (USA) Inc.

Kennedy, Kim. Pirate Pete's Giant Adventure. Kennedy, Doug, illus. 2006. 36p. (J). (ps-3). 15.95 (978-0-8109-5965-1(8)) Abrams, Harry N., Inc.

Ketteman, Helen. Waynetta & the Cornstalk: A Texas Fairy Tale. Greenseid, Diane, illus. 2007. 32p. (J). 16.95 (978-0-8075-8687-7(0)) Whitman, Albert & Co.

Kielty, Derek. Back up the Beanstalk. Myler, Terry, illus. 2003. 64p. (YA). pap. 8.95 (978-1-901737-45-5(4)) Anvil Bks., Ltd. IRL. *Dist:* Dufour Editions, Inc.

King-Smith, Dick. The Twin Giants. Grey, Mini, illus. 2008. 80p. (J). (gr. 1-4). 16.99 (***978-0-7636-3529-9(4))** Candlewick Pr.

Kirk, Daniel. Moondogs. 1999. (Illus.). 1p. (J). (ps-3). 16.99 (978-0-399-23128-5(5), Putnam Juvenile) Penguin Group (USA) Inc.

Kurtz, John. Jack & the Beanstalk. Kurtz, John, illus. 2004. (Illus.). 24p. (J). lib. bdg. 8.00 (***978-1-4242-0636-0(7))** Fitzgerald Bks.

Larcombe, Jennifer Rees. The Terrible Giant. Bjorkman, Steve, illus. 2004. (Best Bible Stories Ser.). 24p. (ps-3). 2.99 (978-1-58134-054-9(0)) Crossway Bks.

Lewin, Ted. Elephant Quest. Lewin, Betsy, illus. 2000. 48p. (J). (gr. 1 up). lib. bdg. 15.89 (978-0-688-14112-7(9)) HarperCollins Pubs.

Lewin, Ted & Lewin, Betsy. Elephant Quest. 2000. (Illus.). 48p. (J). (gr. 1 up). 15.95 (978-0-688-14111-0(0)) HarperCollins Pubs.

Light, Steve. The Shoemaker Extraordinaire. 2003. (Illus.). 32p. (J). (ps-3). 14.95 (978-0-8109-4236-3(4)) Abrams, Harry N., Inc.

Limke, Jeff. Thor & Loki: In the Land of Giants. Randall, Ron, illus. 2007. (Graphic Myths & Legends Ser.). 48p. (YA). (gr. 4-9). pap. 8.95 (***978-0-8225-6481-2(5))** Lerner Publishing Group.

Limke Jeff. Thor y Loki (Thor & Loki) En la tierra de los gigantes (in the Land of Giants) Randall, Ron, illus. 2007. (Mitos y leyendas en viñetas (Graphic Myths & Legends) Ser.). (J). pap. 8.95 (***978-0-8225-7969-4(3)**, Ediciones Lerner) Lerner Publishing Group.

The Lonely Giant: Individual Title Six-Packs. (Literatura 2000 Ser.). (gr. 2-3). 33.00 (978-0-7635-0175-4(1)) Rigby Education.

Maccarone, Grace. Magic Matt & the Jack O' Lantern. 2003. (ps-2). lib. bdg. 11.80 (978-0-613-72183-7(7)) Tandem Library Bks.

Mackenzie, Robert, illus. Jack & the Beanstalk. 2008. (Classic Fairy Tale Collection). 32p. (J). 14.95 (***978-1-4027-3064-1(0))** Sterling Publishing Co., Inc.

Mayes, Walter M. Walter the Giant Storyteller's Giant Book of Giant Stories. O'Malley, Kevin, illus. 2005. 48p. (J). (gr. 1-5). 18.95 (978-0-8027-8974-7(9)) Walker & Co.

McCaughrean, Geraldine. Fig's Giant. (Illus.). 40p. (J). (ps-2). 10.99 (978-0-19-279130-6(3)) Oxford Univ. Pr., Inc.

McCaughrean, Geraldine & Jago. Fig's Giant. (Illus.). 40p. (978-0-19-272569-1(6)) Oxford Univ. Pr., Inc.

McConnell, G. Robert. Norbert Nipkin. Pilcher, Steve, illus. 3rd ed. 2005. 40p. (J). pap. 14.95 (978-1-894917-29-2(4)) Napoleon Publishing/Rendezvous Pr. CAN. *Dist:* AtlasBooks Distribution.

McMullan, Kate. Little Giant—Big Trouble, No. 19. Basso, Bill, illus. 2007. (Dragon Slayers' Academy Ser.). 112p. (J). pap. 4.99 (978-0-448-44448-2(8), Grosset & Dunlap) Penguin Group (USA) Inc.

Mora, Pat. Dona Flor: A Tall Tale about a Giant Lady with a Great Big Heart. Colon, Raul, illus. 2005. 40p. (J). (ps-3). lib. bdg. 17.99 (978-0-375-92337-1(3), Knopf Bks. for Young Readers) Random Hse. Children's Bks.

—Dona Flor: A Tall Tale about a Giant Woman with a Great Big Heart. Colon, Raul, illus. 2005. 40p. (J). (ps-3). 15.95 (978-0-375-82337-4(9), Knopf Bks. for Young Readers) Random Hse. Children's Bks.

—Dona Flor: Un Cuento de una Mujer Gigante con un Gran Corazon. Mora, Pat & Mlawer, Teresa, trs. Colon, Raul, illus. 2005. 32p. (J). (ps-3). lib. bdg. 15.19 (978-0-606-33665-9(6)) Tandem Library Bks.

Moran, Edna Cabcabin, illus. & retold by. The Sleeping Giant: A Tale from Kauai. Moran, Edna Cabcabin, retold by. 2006. (J). (978-1-933067-20-9(9)) Beachhouse Publishing, LLC.

Morgan, Gwyn & Owen, Dai. Babi Ben. 2005. (WEL., Illus.). 64p. (978-1-85596-611-6(5)) Dref Wen.

Morpurgo, Michael. Gentle Giant. Foreman, Michael, illus. 2006. 28p. (J). (gr. 4-8). reprint ed. 19.00 (978-1-4223-5398-1(2)) DIANE Publishing Co.

—Gentle Giant. 2005. (Illus.). 32p. (J). pap. 9.99 (978-0-00-711192-3(4)) HarperCollins Pubs. Ltd. GBR. *Dist:* Trafalgar Square Publishing.

—Gentle Giant. Foreman, Michael, illus. 2003. 32p. (J). 16.95 (978-0-00-711064-3(2), HarperSport) HarperCollins Pubs. Ltd. GBR. *Dist:* Trafalgar Square Publishing.

Mortimer, Sheila. Finn & the Magic Harp. Catchpole, Diana, illus. 2004. (J). 10.95 (978-0-7171-3767-1(8)) Gill & MacMillan, Ltd. IRL. *Dist:* Irish Bks. & Media, Inc.

Nesbit, E. Jack & the Beanstalk. Tavares, Matt, illus. 2006. 48p. (J). (ps-1). 16.99 (978-0-7636-2124-7(2)) Candlewick Pr.

Nolen, Jerdine. Hewitt Anderson's Great Big Life. Nelson, Kadir A., illus. 2005. 40p. (J). 16.95 (978-0-689-86866-5(9), Simon & Schuster/Paula Wiseman Bks.) Simon & Schuster Children's Publishing.

Norac, Carl. My Daddy Is a Giant. Godon, Ingrid, illus. 2004. (ENG & IRI.). 32p. (J). pap. 12.95 (978-1-84444-719-0(7)) Mantra Lingua GBR. *Dist:* Mantra Publishing, Ltd.

Northland Publishing Staff, ed. Jack & the Giant/Cowboy Billy. 1998. (J). pap. 15.95 (978-0-87358-696-2(4), Rising Moon Bks. for Young Readers) Northland Publishing.

Offen, Hilda. There Might Be Giants. (Illus.). 25p. (J). pap. (978-0-340-68149-7(7), Hodder & Stoughton) Hodder General Publishing Division.

O'Malley, Kevin. Once upon a Cool Motorcycle Dude. O'Malley, Kevin et al, illus. 2005. 32p. (J). 16.95 (978-0-8027-8947-1(1)) Walker & Co.

Oram, Hiawyn. The Giant Surprise: A Narnia Story. Humphries, Tudor, illus. 2005. (Step into Narnia Ser.). 40p. (J). (ps-2). lib. bdg. 16.89 (978-0-06-001360-8(5)) HarperCollins Pubs.

Oram, Hiawyn & Brown, Ken. Little Giant & Jabber-Jabber. 1998. (Illus.). 32p. (J). (ps-3). 19.99 (978-0-86264-798-8(3)) Andersen GBR. *Dist:* Independent Pubs. Group.

Oram, Hiawyn & Lewis, C. S. The Giant Surprise: A Narnia Story. Humphries, Tudor, illus. 2005. (Step into Narnia Ser.). 40p. (J). (ps-2). 15.99 (978-0-06-008361-8(1)) HarperCollins Pubs.

Ottolenghi, Carol. Jack & the Beanstalk. Porfirio, Guy, illus. 2002. (Brighter Child Keepsake Stories Ser.). 32p. (J). (ps-3). pap. 3.99 (978-1-57768-377-3(3), Brighter Child) School Specialty Publishing.

Page, Nick & Page, Claire. David & Goliath. Loy, Nikki, illus. 2006. (Read with Me (Make Believe Ideas) Ser.). 31p. (J). (gr. k-2). 3.95 (978-1-84610-173-1(5)) Make Believe Ideas GBR. *Dist:* Ingram Pub. Services.

Page, Nick & Claire. Jack & the Beanstalk. 2006. (Read with Me (Make Believe Ideas) Ser.). (Illus.). (J). (gr. k-2). 32p. 3.95 (978-1-84610-164-9(6)); 12p. pap. 4.95 (978-1-84610-180-9(8)) Make Believe Ideas GBR. *Dist:* Ingram Pub. Services.

Pelley, Kathleen. The Giant King. Manning, Maurie, tr. Manning, Maurie, illus. 2003. (New Child & Family Press Titles Ser.). 32p. (ps-4). 14.95 (978-0-87868-880-7(3), 8803, Child & Family Pr.) Child Welfare League of America, Inc.

Picard, Anne M. Peace & Pancakes. 2006. 48p. bds. 25.00 (978-1-59298-149-6(6)) Beaver's Pond Pr., Inc.

Priddy, Roger. My Giant Sticker Coloring Book. 2007. 38p. (J). pap. 12.95 (***978-0-312-50033-7(5)**, Priddy Bks.) St. Martin's Pr.

Quinlan, Janet, adapted by. Love: The Selfish Giant. 2005. (Illus.). (***978-1-4127-3758-6(3))** Publications International, Ltd.

Rawson, C. Stories of Giants. 2004. (Young Reading Ser.: Vol. 1). 48p. (J). (gr. 2 up). pap. 5.95 (978-0-7945-0646-9(1)) EDC Publishing.

Reader's Digest Staff. Dream Works Shrek Magnetic. 2007. 16p. (J). bds. 14.99 (***978-0-7944-1356-9(0))** Reader's Digest Assn., Inc., The.

Rigby Education Staff. The Big Giant. (Sails Literacy Ser.). (Illus.). 16p. (gr. k-1). 27.00 (978-0-7635-9880-8(1), 698801C99) Rigby Education.

Ritz, Joyce. I Am but A Giant. 2004. 32p. pap. 17.95 (978-1-4137-1114-1(6)) PublishAmerica, Inc.

Roberts, Esyllt Nest & Owen, Carys Eurwen. Rhita Gawr. 2005. (WEL., Illus.). 35p. (978-0-86381-624-6(X)) Gwasg Carreg Gwalch.

Rogers, Alan. Bright & Breezy. 1999. (Little Giants Ser.). (Illus.). 16p. (YA). (ps). pap. 2.95 (978-0-7166-4417-0(7)) World Bk., Inc.

Ross, Dev. We Both Read-Frank & the Giant (Picture Book Edition) Reinhart, Larry, illus. 2007. (We Both Read Ser.). 44p. (J). 14.95 (***978-1-60115-006-6(7)***) Treasure Bay, Inc.

Russell, P. Craig. Fairy Tales of Oscar Wilde: The Selfish Giant & the Star Child, Vol. 1. Russell, P. Craig, illus. 2003. (Fairy Tales of Oscar Wilde Ser.: No. 1). (Illus.). 48p. 7.95 (978-1-56163-375-3(5)) NBM Publishing Co.

Ruzzier, Sergio. The Little Giant. 2004. (Illus.). 32p. (J). (ps-2). 16.89 (978-0-06-052952-9(0) , Geringer, Laura Book) HarperCollins Pubs.

Salan, Felipe Lopez, illus. Jack & the Beanstalk. 2006. 32p. (J). 15.95 (978-1-933327-11-2(1)) Purple Bear Bks., Inc.

Scholastic, Inc. Staff & Blade, Adam. Cypher the Mountain Giant. 2007. (Beast Quest Ser.: No. 3). 80p. (J). pap. 4.99 (***978-0-439-92225-8(9)***) Scholastic, Inc.

Seeger, Pete & Jacobs, Paul DuBois. Abiyoyo Returns. Hays, Michael, illus. 2004. (J). (ps-3). lib. bdg. 14.19 (978-0-606-32677-3(4)) Tandem Library Bks.

The Selfish Giant: Individual Title Six-Packs. (Literatura 2000 Ser.). (gr. 2-3). 33.00 (978-0-7635-0239-3(1)) Rigby Education.

Seomeng, Judah. Dimo & the Little Bush Doctor. 2004. (Illus.). 24p. 9.95 (978-99912-5-551-4(6)) Pyramid Publishing (PTY), Ltd. BWA. *Dist:* Michigan State Univ. Pr.

Smith, Sherri L. Lucy the Giant. l.t. ed. 2002. 236p. 23.95 (978-0-7862-4751-6(7)) Thorndike Pr.

Stanley, Diane. The Giant & the Beanstalk. Stanley, Diane, illus. 2004. (Illus.). 32p. (J). (gr. k-3). 16.99 (978-0-06-000010-3(4)); lib. bdg. 17.89 (978-0-06-000011-0(2)) HarperCollins Pubs.

Sullivan, Joe E. Giant Tales. 1999. (Illus.). 109p. (J). mass mkt. (978-0-7541-0873-3(2)) Minerva Pr. GBR. *Dist:* Unity Distribution.

Swope, Sam. Jack & the Seven Deadly Giants. Cneut, Carll, illus. 2004. 112p. (J). 16.00 (978-0-374-33670-7(9) , Frances Foster Bks.) Farrar, Straus & Giroux.

Umansky, Kaye. Jealous Giant. (Illus.). 32p. (J). pap. 7.95 (978-0-14-038840-4(0)) Penguin Bks., Ltd. GBR. *Dist:* Trafalgar Square Publishing.

—The Jealous Giant. Weir, Doffy, illus. 2005. 32p. (J). (ps-ps). pap. 6.95 (978-1-903015-41-4(3)) Barn Owl Bks, London GBR. *Dist:* Independent Pubs. Group.

—Romantic Giant. (Illus.). 32p. (J). pap. 7.95 (978-0-14-038160-3(0)) Penguin Bks., Ltd. GBR. *Dist:* Trafalgar Square Publishing.

Walker, Raven. The Feather Giant. 2004. 92p. pap. 9.95 (978-0-595-30484-4(2)) iUniverse, Inc.

Wallace, Karen. Prince Marvin's Great Moment. Flook, Helen, illus. 2007. (J). lib. bdg. (***978-1-4048-3707-2(8)***) Picture Window Bks.

Watch Out! Individual Title Six-Packs. (Literatura 2000 Ser.). (ps-1). 28.00 (978-0-7635-0016-0(X)) Rigby Education.

Watson-Dubisch, Carolyn. The Giant's Playground. 2001. (Illus.). 36p. (J). (ps-1). 11.95 (978-0-9714740-0-0(1)) Fantastic Visions Studio.

Where Is the Giant? Early Level Satellite Individual Title Six-Packs. (Sails Literacy Ser.). 16p. (gr. 1-2). 27.00 (978-0-7578-2912-3(0)) Rigby Education.

Wilde, Oscar. The Selfish Giant: A Tale about Being Unselfish. Ebert, Len, illus. 2006. (J). (978-1-59939-085-7(X) , Reader's Digest Young Families, Inc.) Reader's Digest Children's Publishing, Inc.

Wisniewski, David, illus. & retold by. Golem. Wisniewski, David, retold by. 2007. 32p. (J). (gr. 1-5). 6.95 (***978-0-618-89424-6(1)*** , Clarion Bks.) Houghton Mifflin Co. Trade & Reference Div.

Wood, Audrey. Rude Giants. Wood, Audrey, illus. 2002. (Illus.). (J). 19.96 (978-0-7587-3542-3(1)) Book Wholesalers, Inc.

—Rude Giants. 1998. (Illus.). 32p. (J). (ps-2). pap. 7.00 (978-0-15-201889-4(1) , Voyager Bks./Libros Viajeros) Harcourt Children's Bks.

—Rude Giants. 1998. (J). (978-0-606-13752-2(1)) Tandem Library Bks.

Yorinks, Arthur. The Miami Giant. Sendak, Maurice, illus. 1999. 36p. (J). (gr. 5-8). 16.00 (978-0-7881-6464-4(3)) DIANE Publishing Co.

Zeman, Ludmila, illus. & retold by. Sinbad's Secret. Zeman, Ludmila, retold by. 2003. 32p. (J). (gr. 1 up). 17.95 (978-0-88776-462-2(2)) Tundra Bks., Inc./Livres Toundra, Inc. CAN. *Dist:* Random Hse., Inc.

Zeman, Ludmila & Levesque, Suzanne. Sinbad et les Geants. 2001. (FRE & SPA., Illus.). 32p. (J). (gr. 1). 19.95 (978-0-88776-525-4(4) , Livres Toundra) Tundra Bks., Inc./Livres Toundra, Inc. CAN. *Dist:* Random Hse., Inc.

GIBSON, ALTHEA, 1927-2003

Benson, Michael. Althea Gibson: Tennis Player. 2005. (Ferguson Career Biographies Ser.). (Illus.). 144p. (J). (gr. 6-12). 25.00 (978-0-8160-5889-1(X) , Ferguson Publishing Co.) Facts On File, Inc.

Deans, Karen. Playing to Win: The Story of Althea Gibson. Brown, Elbrite, illus. 2007. 32p. (J). (ps-3). 16.95 (978-0-8234-1926-5(6)) Holiday Hse., Inc.

Gormley, Beatrice. Althea Gibson: Young Tennis Player. Henderson, Meryl, illus. 2005. (Childhood of Famous Americans Ser.). 224p. (J). pap. 4.99 (978-0-689-87187-0(2) , Aladdin) Simon & Schuster Children's Publishing.

—Althea Gibson: Young Tennis Player. Henderson, Meryl, illus. 2005. 214p. (J). (gr. 3-7). lib. bdg. 12.04 (978-0-606-33374-0(6)) Tandem Library Bks.

Stauffacher, Sue. Nothing but Trouble: The Story of Althea Gibson. Couch, Greg, illus. 2007. 40p. (J). (gr. k-3). lib. bdg. 19.99 (978-0-375-93408-7(1)); 16.99 (978-0-375-83408-0(7)) Random Hse. Children's Bks. (Knopf Bks. for Young Readers).

GIDEON, CLARENCE EARL

Prentzas, G. S. Gideon V. Wainwright: The Right to Free Legal Counsel. 2007. (Great Supreme Court Decisions Ser.). 120p. (J). (gr. 5-8). 30.00 (978-0-7910-9383-2(2) , Chelsea Hse.) Facts On File, Inc.

GIFTED CHILDREN

Here are entered works on talented elementary and secondary school students.

Almukahhal, Raja. Physics Laboratory Experiments for the Gifted: Middle & High School. 2005. (Illus.). 90p. (978-0-910609-51-7(9)) Gifted Education Pr.

Galbraith, Judy. The Gifted Kids' Survival Guide for Ages 10 & Under. 2nd rev. ed. 1998. (Illus.). 104p. (J). (ps-5). pap. 10.95 (978-1-57542-053-0(8)) Free Spirit Publishing, Inc.

Sganga, Francis. Introducing Gifted Students to the Wonders of Mathematics: Preparation for High School & Higher Mathematics, Grades 4 ¿ 8. 2004. (Illus.). 75p. (978-0-910609-47-0(0)) Gifted Education Pr.

Wood, Mark. Beyond Classroom Enrichment: Creative Units for Gifted Students. 2004. (Illus.). 80p. (978-0-910609-48-7(9)) Gifted Education Pr.

GIFTED CHILDREN—FICTION

Besser, Kenneth/R. Arnie Carver & the Plague of Demeverde. 2007. (Illus.). x, 338p. (J). (***978-1-934316-02-3(4)***) RTMC Organization, LLC.

Burton, Jennifer. Christopher's Dilemma. 2003. (Topeka Heights Ser.). (YA). (gr. 9-12). pap. 10.99 (978-0-9724733-1-6(9)) Allen Publishing, USA.

Evangelista, Beth. Gifted. 192p. (J). 2007. pap. 6.95 (***978-0-8027-9644-8(3)***); 2005. (gr. 5-9). 16.95 (978-0-8027-8994-5(3)) Walker & Co.

Holmes, Sarah. Letters from Rapunzel. 2007. 192p. (J). (gr. 5-8). 15.99 (978-0-06-078073-9(8)); lib. bdg. 16.89 (978-0-06-078074-6(6)) HarperCollins Pubs.

Huws, Emily. Nid Fy Mai I. 2005. (WEL., Illus.). 62p. (978-1-84512-025-2(6)) Cymdeithas Lyfrau Ceredigion.

Kiernan, Kristy. Catching Genius. 2007. 384p. pap. 14.00 (978-0-425-21435-0(4) , Berkley Trade) Penguin Group (USA) Inc.

McDonald, Janet. Brother Hood. 2004. 176p. (YA). 16.00 (978-0-374-30995-4(7) , Frances Foster Bks.) Farrar, Straus & Giroux.

—Brother Hood. l.t. ed. 2005. 179p. 20.95 (978-0-7862-7334-8(8) , Large Print Pr.) Thorndike Pr.

Morris, Gilbert. Too Smart Jones & the Pool Party Thief: A Gilbert Morris Mystery. 1999. (Gilbert Morris Mysteries Ser.: Vol. 1). (Illus.). 115p. (J). (gr. 2-7). pap. 5.99 (978-0-8024-4025-9(8)) Moody Pubs.

Nolan, Allia. What I Do Best! 2006. (Illus.). 14p. (J). 14.99 (978-0-7944-1131-2(2)) Reader's Digest Assn., Inc., The.

Petcoff, Desmond Onyx. The Gift of Silliness: A Collection of 20 Silly Stories. 2003. (J). (978-0-9701184-9-3(X)) Onoma Enterprises.

Ryan, Margaret. Beat the Bully. Slater, Nicola, illus. 2002. (J). mass mkt. (978-0-340-80605-0(2) , Hodder & Stoughton) Hodder General Publishing Division.

—Missing Moggy Mystery. Slater, Nicola, illus. 2002. (J). mass mkt. 8.99 (978-0-340-81706-3(2) , Hodder & Stoughton) Hodder General Publishing Division GBR. *Dist:* Trafalgar Square Publishing.

Selzer, Adam. Pirates of the Retail Wasteland. 2008. 208p. (YA). (gr. 7). 15.99 (***978-0-385-73482-0(4)*** , Delacorte Bks. for Young Readers) Random Hse. Children's Bks.

Stanley, Diane. The Mysterious Case of the Allbright Academy. 2008. 272p. (J). lib. bdg. 17.89 (***978-0-06-085818-6(4)***); (gr. 3-7). 16.99 (***978-0-06-085817-9(6)***) HarperCollins Pubs.

Tolan, Stephanie S. Welcome to the Ark. 2000. (gr. 5-8). lib. bdg. 15.30 (978-0-613-10539-2(7)) Tandem Library Bks.

Woodson, Jacqueline. Maizon at Blue Hill. 2002. 160p. (J). pap. 5.99 (978-0-698-11957-4(6)); 144p. (YA). 16.99 (978-0-399-23756-0(9)) Penguin Group (USA) Inc. (Putnam Juvenile).

—Maizon at Blue Hill. 2002. (gr. 3-6). lib. bdg. 14.15 (978-0-613-50098-2(9)) Tandem Library Bks.

Yee, Lisa. Millicent Min, Girl Genius. 256p. 2003. (YA). (gr. 5-8). 16.95 (978-0-439-42519-3(0)); 2004. (J). (gr. 4-7). reprint ed. pap. 4.99 (978-0-439-42520-9(4)) Scholastic, Inc. (Levine, Arthur A. Bks.).

Yoo, Paula. Good Enough. 2008. 336p. (J). 16.99 (***978-0-06-079085-1(7)***); lib. bdg. 17.89 (***978-0-06-079089-9(X)***) HarperCollins Pubs. (HarperTeen).

Yoo, Paula & Dereske, Jo. Good Enough. 2008. 272p. mass mkt. 6.99 (***978-0-06-079086-8(5)*** , HarperTeen) HarperCollins Pubs.

GIFTS

Craig, Rebecca. EcoCrafts. 2007. (Illus.). 48p. (J). (***978-1-4287-3452-4(X)*** , Kingfisher) Houghton Mifflin Co. Trade & Reference Div.

—Gorgeous Gifts. 2007. (EcoCrafts Ser.). (Illus.). 48p. (J). (gr. 3-5). pap. 7.95 (***978-0-7534-5967-6(1)*** , Kingfisher) Houghton Mifflin Co. Trade & Reference Div.

G and R Publishing Staff. Gifts in a Jar, for Kids. 2002. (Illus.). 128p. (J). pap. 10.00 (978-1-56383-135-5(X)) G&R Publishing.

Gilpin, Rebecca. Things to Make for Dads. MEREDITH SAMANTHA ET AL, illus. 2006. 32p. (J). pap. 8.99 (978-0-7945-1272-9(0) , Usborne) EDC Publishing.

Hantman, Clea. I Wanna Make Gifts. Houshyar, Azadeh, illus. 2006. 144p. (J). pap. 9.99 (978-0-689-87464-2(2) , Aladdin) Simon & Schuster Children's Publishing.

It's a Gift: Individual Title Six-Pack Pouch - Level I. (Lighthouse Ser.). 16p. (gr. 1 up). 26.00 (978-0-7578-0848-7(4)) Rigby Education.

Johnson, Kristin & Cummins, Mimi. Christmas Cookies Are for Giving: Recipes, Stories & Tips for Making Heart-warming Gifts. 2003. (Illus.). 208p. 16.95 (978-0-9723473-9-6(9)) Tyr Publishing.

The Liberty Bell. 2001. (Illus.). 32p. (YA). (gr. 5 up). pap. 5.00 (978-1-890541-76-7(1)) Americana Souvenirs & Gifts.

Lodien, Jennie, des. Cat Tales. 2004. (Illus.). 48p. (YA). ring bd. 16.95 (978-0-9746341-8-0(2)) Chin & A Pr.

MacLeod, Elizabeth. Gifts to Make & Eat. Bradford, June, illus. 2001. (Kids Can Do It Ser.). 40p. (J). (gr. 4-6). (978-1-55074-958-8(7)) Kids Can Pr., Ltd.

—Gifts to Make & Eat. Bradford, June et al, illus. 2001. (Kids Can Do It Ser.). 40p. (J). (gr. 4-6). (978-1-55074-956-4(0)) Kids Can Pr., Ltd.

—Gifts to Make & Eat. 2001. (gr. 3-6). lib. bdg. 14.10 (978-0-613-50798-1(3)) Tandem Library Bks.

Mecham, Janeal A. Christmas Gifts. Mecham, Janeal A., illus. l.t. unabr. ed. 2003. (Illus.). 32p. (J). (gr. k-3). 12.95 (978-1-932280-16-6(2) , 80162) Granite Publishing & Distribution.

Souter, Gillian. Great Gifts. Watson, Clare, illus. Martin, Andre, photos by. 2001. (Handy Crafts Ser.). 48p. (J). (gr. 2 up). lib. bdg. 24.67 (978-0-8368-2820-7(8)) Stevens, Gareth Inc.

Wright, Rachel. Presents. (Illus.). 32p. (YA). (gr. 1 up). lib. bdg. 27.10 (978-1-932889-25-3(6)) Sea-To-Sea Pubns.

GIFTS—FICTION

Adair, Amy. Jay Jay's Special Delivery. 2003. (Illus.). (J). 15.98 (978-0-7853-8625-4(4)) Publications International, Ltd.

Adler, David A. Bones & the Birthday Mystery. Newman, Barbara Johansen, illus. 2007. (Jeffrey Bones Mystery Ser.: No. 5). 32p. (J). (gr. k). 13.99 (978-0-670-06164-8(6) , Viking Adult) Penguin Group (USA) Inc.

Ameen, Judith. Harold & the Magic Books. 2005. 40p. pap. 8.95 (978-1-933265-42-1(6)) Wasteland Pr.

Anderson, Laurie Halse. No Time for Mother's Day. Donohue, Dorothy, illus. 2004. 32p. (J). (gr. k-3). pap. 6.95 (978-0-8075-4956-8(8)) Whitman, Albert & Co.

Appel, Cindy. The Best Christmas Gift. Collier, Kevin Scott, illus. 2005. (J). E-Book 6.00 incl. cd-rom (978-1-933090-19-1(7)) Guardian Angel Publishing, Inc.

Appelt, Kathi. The Best Kind of Gift. 2003. (Illus.). 32p. (J). 17.89 (978-0-688-15393-9(3)) HarperCollins Pubs.

Atkinson, Juliette. I'm Sorry. Atkinson, John, illus. 2008. 32p. (J). (ps-k). 16.99 (***978-0-698-40079-5(8)*** , Minedition) Penguin Group (USA) Inc.

Auger, Dale. Mwakwa Talks to the Loon: A Cree Story for Children. 2007. (Illus.). 32p. (J). pap. 9.95 (***978-1-894974-32-5(8)***) Heritage Hse. Publishing Co., Ltd. CAN. *Dist:* Midpoint Trade Bks., Inc.

Bailey, Debbie. Happy Birthday. Huszar, Susan, photos by. 1999. (Talk-about-Bks.: Vol. 14). (Illus.). 14p. (J). (gr. k-ps). bds. 5.95 (978-1-55037-559-6(8)) Annick Pr., Ltd. CAN. *Dist:* Firefly Bks., Ltd.

Bailey's Birthday - Evaluation Guide: Evaluation Guide. 2006. (J). (978-1-55942-399-1(4)) Marsh Media.

Balfour, Melissa. The Magic Footprints. Julian, Russell, illus. 2005. (Green Bananas Ser.). 48p. (J). (978-0-7787-1023-3(8)) Crabtree Publishing Co.

—The Magic Footprints. 2005. (Green Bananas Ser.). (Illus.). 48p. (J). (ps). pap. (978-0-7787-1039-4(4)) Crabtree Publishing Co.

Balfour, Melissa, et al. Yr Olion Traed Hud. 2005. (WEL., Illus.). 47p. (978-1-85596-677-2(8)) Dref Wen.

Batt Tanya Robyn. Faeries Gift. Ceccoli Nicoletta, illus. 2006. 0032p. pap. 6.99 (978-1-905236-73-2(5)) Barefoot Bks., Inc.

Bauld, Jane S. The Gift of the Gold Coin. Carpenter, Christina D., ed. Newsome, Andy, illus. Date not set. 32p. (J). (ps-5). 15.95 (978-1-886440-03-6(4)) Portunus Publishing Co.

Bellingham, Brenda. Lilly's Special Gift. 2005. (Illus.). 59p. (J). lib. bdg. 12.00 (***978-1-4242-1204-0(9)***) Fitzgerald Bks.

Benjamin, Ruth. My Little Pony: A Secret Gift. Middleton, Gayle, illus. 2006. 24p. (J). lib. bdg. 15.00 (***978-1-4242-1536-2(6)***) Fitzgerald Bks.

Benjamin, Ruth. A Secret Gift/el regalo Secreto. Middleton, Gayle, illus. 2006. (I Can Read Bks.). (SPA.). 24p. (J). pap. 3.99 (978-0-06-112391-7(9) , Rayo) HarperCollins Pubs.

The Best Birthday Present: Individual Title Six-Packs. (Literatura 2000 Ser.). (gr. 2-3). 33.00 (978-0-7635-0216-4(2)) Rigby Education.

Best, Cari. Three Cheers for Catherine the Great! 2003. (gr. k-3). lib. bdg. 15.25 (978-0-613-71883-7(6)) Tandem Library Bks.

Best, Cari & Potter, Giselle. Three Cheers for Catherine the Great! 2003. (Illus.). 32p. (J). pap. 6.95 (978-0-374-47551-2(2) , Sunburst) Farrar, Straus & Giroux.

The Best Gift. 1998. (Fisher-Price Phonics Storybooks Ser.: Vol. 5). (Illus.). (J). pap. (978-0-7666-0170-3(6) , Honey Bear Bks.) Modern Publishing.

The Best Gift of All. 2003. (J). per. (978-1-57657-803-2(8)) Paradise Pr., Inc.

Black, Sonia W. Jumping the Broom. Wright and Hu, Cornelius Van and Ying-Hwa, illus. 2004. 32p. (J). lib. bdg. 15.00 (***978-1-4242-0234-8(5)***) Fitzgerald Bks.

Blackaby, Susan. Greg Gets a Hint. Trover, Zachary, illus. 2006. (Read-It! Readers Ser.). (J). 19.93 (978-1-4048-2411-9(1)) Picture Window Bks.

Bogart, JoEllen. Regalos. Reid, Barbara, illus. 2001. (SPA.). 40p. (J). (gr. 1-3). 12.95 (978-84-241-2610-0(6)) Everest de Ediciones y Distribucion, S.L. ESP. *Dist:* Lectorum Pubns., Inc.

Bogart, JoEllen & Reid, Barbara. Cadeaux.Tr. of Gifts. (Illus.). 32p. (J). pap. 8.99 (978-0-590-24682-8(8)) Scholastic, Inc.

Borden, Louise. The Last Day of School. Gustavson, Adam, illus. 2006. 40p. (J). (gr. 2-5). 15.95 (978-0-689-86869-6(3) , McElderry, Margaret K.) Simon & Schuster Children's Publishing.

Bosworth, Evelyn. A Christmas Gift for Michael. 2005. 17.00 (978-0-8059-9013-3(5)) Dorrance Publishing Co., Inc.

Bourgeois, Paulette. Franklin Says I Love You. Clark, Brenda, illus. 2004. (Franklin the Turtle Ser.). 32p. (J). (gr. k-3). (978-1-55337-035-2(X)) Kids Can Pr., Ltd.

—Franklin y el Regalo de Navidad. Clark, Brenda, illus. 1999. (Franklin Ser.). (SPA.). (J). (ps-3). pap. 5.95 (978-1-880507-56-8(0) , LC2911) Lectorum Pubns., Inc.

Brouwer, Sigmund. Fly Trap. 2003. (Watch Out for Joel Ser.). (Illus.). 32p. (J). (gr. 1-3). pap. 3.99 (978-0-7642-2583-3(9)) Bethany Hse. Pubs.

—Fly Trap. 2003. (gr. k-3). lib. bdg. 11.80 (978-0-613-87753-4(5)) Tandem Library Bks.

Brown, Marc. D. W.'s Perfect Present. Brown, Marc, illus. 2004. (Athur's 8 x 8 Bks.). (Illus.). 24p. (J). (ps-3). pap. 3.99 (978-0-316-73386-1(5) , Tingley, Megan Bks.) Little, Brown Bks. for Young Readers.

Brown, Marc & Schulman, Lester. Arthur Breaks the Bank. 2004. (Arthur Ser.). (Illus.). 24p. (J). (gr. k-3). pap. 3.99 (978-0-375-81002-2(1)); lib. bdg. 11.99 (978-0-375-91002-9(6)) Random Hse. Children's Bks. (Random Hse. Bks. for Young Readers).

Brumbeau, Jeff. The Quiltmaker's Gift. Marcken, Gail De, illus. 2001. 56p. (J). (gr. k-3). pap. 17.95 (978-0-439-30910-3(7)) Scholastic, Inc.

Bryant, Kathleen. Kokopelli's Gift. Sisneros, Michelle Tsosie, illus. 2002. 32p. (J). 15.95 (978-1-885772-29-9(7)) Kiva Publishing, Inc.

Buckley, Ray. Christmas Moccasins. Buckley, Ray, illus. 2003. (Illus.). 32p. 18.00 (978-0-687-02738-5(1)) Abingdon Pr.

Butcher, Sam. Blessings for Your Birthday. 2005. 48p. (J). 10.99 (978-1-4003-0564-3(0)) Nelson, Thomas Inc.

Callahan, Thera S. Un Regalo Bien Envuelto: All Wrapped Up. Gordon, Mike, illus. 2003. (Rookie Readers - Spanish Ser.). (SPA.). (J). 19.50 (978-0-516-25885-0(0) , Children's Pr.) Scholastic Library Publishing.

Calmenson, Stephanie. Birthday at the Panda Palace. Cushman, Doug, illus. 2007. 32p. (J). (ps-1). 15.99 (978-0-06-052663-4(7)); lib. bdg. 16.89 (978-0-06-052664-1(5)) HarperCollins Pubs.

Cameron, Ann. Julian, Dream Doctor. 2002. (J). 12.32 (978-0-7587-6155-2(4)) Book Wholesalers, Inc.

Capucilli, Alyssa Satin. Biscuit Gives a Gift. Schories, Pat, illus. 2004. 16p. (J). (ps-1). 4.99 (978-0-06-009467-6(2) , Harper Festival) HarperCollins Pubs.

Chen, Chih-Yuan. The Best Christmas Ever. 2006. (Illus.). 48p. (J). 15.95 (978-0-9762056-2-3(9)) Heryin Publishing Corp.

Christensen, Lichelle. Santa's Last Delivery. 2005. pap. 8.95 (978-1-933265-81-0(7)) Wasteland Pr.

Ciletti, Barbara. I Want It All! Morrison, Cathy, illus. 2005. 32p. (J). 14.95 (978-0-7696-4376-2(0) , Gingham Dog Pr.) School Specialty Publishing.

Clark, Emma Chichester. Merry Christmas to You, Blue Kangaroo! Clark, Emma Chichester, illus. 2004. (Illus.). 32p. (J). (gr. k-k). lib. bdg. 17.99 (978-0-385-90918-1(7) , Doubleday Bks. for Young Readers) Random Hse. Children's Bks.

Clarke, Jane. Prince Albert's Birthday. Chatterton, Martin, illus. 2005. 24p. (J). lib. bdg. 22.65 (***978-1-59646-748-4(7)***) Dingles & Co.

Climo. Pandora's Gift. Date not set. (Illus.). 64p. (J). (gr. 3-4). 15.99 (978-0-06-028632-3(6)) HarperCollins Pubs.

Conrad, Pam. The Rooster's Gift. 1998. (978-0-606-13750-8(5)) Tandem Library Bks.

Cooney, Caroline B. What Child Is This? A Christmas Story. 1999. 160p. (YA). (gr. 7-12). mass mkt. 5.50 (978-0-440-22684-0(8) , Laurel Leaf) Random Hse. Children's Bks.

—What Child Is This? A Christmas Story. 1999. (978-0-606-17218-9(1)) Tandem Library Bks.

Cooper, Wendy. Isaiah's Big Surprise. Mobley, Elizabeth, illus. 2007. (J). per. 11.95 (***978-0-9792074-5-7(2)***) Kingdom Publishing Group, Inc.

Cousins, Lucy. With Love from Maisy: Mini Edition. Cousins, Lucy, illus. 2007. (Maisy Ser.). (Illus.). 16p. (J). (ps). 4.99 (***978-0-7636-3539-8(1)***) Candlewick Pr.

Danneberg, Julie. Last Day Blues. Love, Judy, illus. 2006. 32p. (J). pap. 6.95 (978-1-58089-104-2(7)) Charlesbridge Publishing, Inc.

Davis, Aubrey. Bagels from Benny. Petricic, Dusan, illus. 2005. 32p. (J). (gr. 3). (978-1-55337-749-8(4)) Kids Can Pr., Ltd.

—Bagels from Benny. Petriecic, Duesan, illus. 2004. 32p. (J). (gr. k-3). (978-1-55337-417-6(7)) Kids Can Pr., Ltd.

de Brunhoff, Laurent. Babar Raconte le Plus Beau Cadeau du Monde. (Babar Ser.). (FRE., Illus.). 48p. (J). (ps-3). 19.95 (978-0-7859-8821-2(1)) French & European Pubns., Inc.

de Tena, Torcuato Luca. El Fabricante de Suenos. (SPA.). 112p. (J). (978-84-348-4787-3(6)) SM Ediciones ESP. *Dist:* Lectorum Pubns., Inc.

deGroat, Diane. Happy Birthday to You, You Belong in a Zoo. deGroat, Diane, illus. 2007. 32p. (J). pap. 6.99 (978-0-06-001029-4(0) , Harper Trophy) HarperCollins Pubs.

—Happy Birthday to You, You Belong in a Zoo. 1999. (Illus.). 32p. (J). (ps-3). 15.00 (978-0-688-16544-4(3)) HarperCollins Pubs.

—Happy Birthday to You, You Belong in a Zoo. deGroat, Diane, illus. 1999. (Illus.). 32p. (J). (ps-3). lib. bdg. 16.89 (978-0-688-16545-1(1)) HarperCollins Pubs.

Dewan, Ted. Bing: Something for Daddy. 2004. (Illus.). 24p. (J). (gr. k-ps). 5.99 (978-0-385-75046-2(3) , Fickling, David Bks.) Random Hse. Children's Bks.

E F G

Dickinson, Peter. The Gift. 2001. 176p. (YA). (gr. 4-7). pap. 12.00 (978-0-375-89501-2(9) , Delacorte Bks. for Young Readers) Random Hse. Children's Bks.

Dillard, Mary Gregory. Finding Betsyanna. 2006. (ENG.). 48p. per. 12.95 (*978-1-4241-5492-0(8)) PublishAmerica, Inc.

Dinse, James. Thistlefoot's Gift. Wise, Noreen, ed. Smith, Philip, illus. 2000. (Book-a-Day Collection). 32p. (YA). (ps up). pap. 5.95 (978-1-58584-397-8(0)) Huckleberry Pr.

Donahue, Jill L. Benny & the Birthday Gift. 2007. (Illus.). 24p. (J). (*978-1-4048-0590-3(7)) Picture Window Bks.

—Benny & the Birthday Gift. Senturk, Burak, illus. 2006. (Read It! Readers Ser.). 24p. (J). (gr. 1-2). 19.93 (*978-1-4048-3164-3(9)) Picture Window Bks.

Donahue, Jill L. Urban. Danny's Birthday. Rooney, Ronnie, illus. 2007. (Read-It! Readers Ser.). (J). 19.93 (978-1-4048-2408-9(1)) Picture Window Bks.

Dooley, Norah. Everybody Serves Soup. Thornton, Peter J., illus. 2004. (Picture Bks.). 40p. (J). (ps-3). 15.95 (978-1-57505-422-3(1)); pap. 6.95 (978-1-57505-791-0(3)) Lerner Publishing Group.

Edwards, Pamela Duncan. Rosie's Roses. Cole, Henry, illus. 2003. 32p. (J). (ps-1). 16.99 (978-0-06-028997-3(X)) HarperCollins Pubs.

Elya, Susan Middleton. Tooth on the Loose. Mattheson, Jenny, illus. 2008. (SPA & ENG.). 32p. (J). (ps-k). 16.99 (*978-0-399-24459-9(X) , Putnam Juvenile) Penguin Group (USA) Inc.

Engelbreit, Mary. Queen of Christmas. Engelbreit, Mary, illus. 2003. (Ann Estelle Stories Ser.). (J). 32p. 16.99 (978-0-06-058608-9(7)); 159.90 (978-0-06-056902-0(6)); 127.92 (978-0-06-056903-7(4)); (Illus.). 32p. 15.99 (978-0-06-008175-1(9)) HarperCollins Pubs.

—Queen of Christmas. Engelbreit, Mary, illus. 2006. (Ann Estelle Stories Ser.). 32p. (J). pap. 6.99 (978-0-06-008177-5(5) , Harper Trophy) HarperCollins Pubs.

Evans, Cambria. Martha Moth Makes Socks. 2006. (Illus.). 40p. (J). (gr. k-3). 16.00 (978-0-618-55745-5(8)) Houghton Mifflin Co.

Fagan, Cary. My New Shirt. Petricic, Dusan, illus. 2007. 32p. (J). (ps-2). 18.95 (*978-0-88776-715-9(X)) Tundra Bks., Inc./Livres Toundra, Inc. CAN. *Dist:* Random Hse., Inc.

For My Birthday: Individual Title Six-Pack Pouch - Level B. (Lighthouse Ser.). 12p. (gr. k-1). 24.00 (978-0-7578-0815-9(8)) Rigby Education.

Foster, Kinsley. Kitty in the City. McGaren, Kari, illus. 1999. 28p. (J). (gr. k-4). 15.95 (978-0-9667634-0-9(8)) What's Inside Pr.

Frazee, Marla. Santa Claus: The World's Number One Toy Expert. 2005. (Illus.). 40p. (J). (ps-ps). 16.00 (978-0-15-204970-6(3) , Harcourt Children's Bks) Harcourt Children's Bks.

Frei, Greg. Magical Gift. 2007. 44p. (J). 10.99 (978-1-59092-254-5(9) , Little Blue Works) Windstorm Creative.

French, Vivian. Present for Mom. Kubick, Dana, illus. 32p. (J). (ps up). 2002. 13.99 (978-0-7636-1587-1(0)); 2005. reprint ed. pap. 5.99 (978-0-7636-2692-1(9)) Candlewick Pr.

Fromental, Jean-Luc. 365 Penguins. Jolivet, Joelle, illus. 2006. 48p. (J). (ps-3). 17.95 (978-0-8109-4460-2(X)) Abrams, Harry N. , Inc.

Fry, Sonali. Clifford's Christmas Presents. Kurtz, John, illus. 2002. (Clifford, the Big Red Dog Ser.). 7p. (J). bds. 8.99 (978-0-439-39451-2(1) , Cartwheel Bks.) Scholastic, Inc.

Gadot, A. S. The First Gift. Lafrance, Marie, illus. 2006. 24p. (J). pap. 6.95 (978-1-58013-149-0(2)) Kar-Ben Publishing.

Gago, Jenny. Perfect Gift. 2001. (gr. k-3). lib. bdg. 11.80 (978-0-613-82082-0(7)) Tandem Library Bks.

Gaines, Isabel. Pooh's Christmas Gift. 1999. 40p. (J). pap. 3.99 (978-0-7868-4402-9(7)) Disney Pr.

Gallegos, Patrick M. Meno's Gift. Russell, Ginger, illus. deluxe ed. 1999. 64p. (YA). (gr. 1-12). 19.95 (978-0-9675742-0-2(X)) Wiggly's Pubns.

Gardella, Tricia & Coalson, Glo. Blackberry Booties. 2000. (Illus.). 32p. (J). (ps-2). 16.99 (978-0-531-33184-2(9) , Orchard Bks.) Scholastic, Inc.

Garvey, Linda K. Doug's Twelve Days of Christmas. 1998. (Doug Ser.). (Illus.). 32p. (J). (ps-2). 8.95 (978-0-7868-3197-5(9)) Disney Pr.

Gauthier, Gilles. Le Gros Cadeau du Petit Marcus. 2003. (Premier Roman Ser.). (FRE., Illus.). 64p. (J). (gr. 2-5). pap. (978-2-89021-255-8(6)) Diffusion du livre Mirabel.

Genechten, Guido van. Snowy's Special Secret. 2005. (Illus.). 32p. (J). (ps-ps). 15.95 (978-1-58925-049-9(4) , tiger tales) ME Media LLC.

Gerlach-Babb nee Maines, Mary & Gerlach, Susan. Best Christmas Gift. 2007. (ENG.). 52p. per. 12.95 (*978-1-4241-6389-2(7)) PublishAmerica, Inc.

The Gift. l.t. ed. 2003. 360p. per. (978-0-9725719-5-1(7)) 21st Century Pr.

The Gift, 6 vols. (Multicultural Programs Ser.). 16p. (gr. 1-6). 31.95 (978-0-7802-8309-1(0)) Wright Group, The.

Gillmor, Don. Yuck, a Love Story. Gay, Marie-Louise, illus. 2001. 26p. (ps-3). 7.95 (978-0-7737-6209-1(4)) Stoddart Kids CAN. *Dist:* Fitzhenry & Whiteside, Ltd.

Gilmore, Rachna. A Gift for Gita. Priestley, Alice, illus. 2004. (TAM, ARA, BEN, GUJ & ENG.). 24p. (J). (978-1-85269-403-6(3)); (978-1-85269-407-4(6)); (978-1-85269-408-1(4)); (978-1-85269-409-8(2)) Mantra Publishing, Ltd.

—A Gift for Gita. Priestley, Alice, illus. 1999. 24p. (J). (gr. k-3). 12.95 (978-1-896764-12-2(6)); pap. 5.95 (978-1-896764-10-8(X)) Second Story Pr. CAN. *Dist:* Orca Bk. Pubs. USA, Univ. of Toronto Pr., Orca Bk. Pubs. USA.

—A Gift for Gita. Priestley, Alice, illus. 2005. 24p. (J). (gr. 3-6). pap. 7.95 (978-0-88448-239-0(1)) Tilbury Hse. Pubs.

Goldin, Barbara Diamond. The Best Hanukkah Ever. Katz, Avi, illus. 2007. 32p. (J). (gr. k-3). 16.99 (*978-0-7614-5355-0(5)) Cavendish, Marshall Corp.

Gordon, Fran & Tischler, Faye. Dutch Double. 2007. (Illus.). 88p. pap. 15.95 (*978-1-59299-242-3(0)) Inkwater Pr.

Gorgas, Paula Blais. The Perfect Purple Present. l.t. ed. 2007. (Illus.). 24p. (J). 24.99 (*978-0-9794660-4-5(0)); per. 12.99 (*978-0-9794660-5-2(9)) Dragonfly Publishing, Inc.

Greenberger, Tehilla. Gifts to Treasure. Toron, Eli, illus. 2007. (Fun to Read Book). 224p. (J). per. 10.95 (*978-1-929628-32-2(3)) Hachai Publishing.

Griek, Susan Vande & Gerber, Mary J. A Gift for Ampato. 1999. (Illus.). (J). (gr. 3-7). pap. (978-0-88899-359-5(5)) Groundwood Bks.

Gutman, Anne. Gaspard & Lisa's Christmas Surprise. Hallensleben, Georg, illus. 2002. 32p. (J). (ps-3). 9.95 (978-0-375-82229-2(1) , Knopf Bks. for Young Readers) Random Hse. Children's Bks.

Hallwood, Cheri L. The Curious Polka-Dot Present. 2007. (J). 16.99 (*978-0-9774422-1-8(7)) Forever Young Pubs.

Hamilton, Martha & Weiss, Mitch. Priceless Gifts: A Folktale from Italy. Kanzler, John, illus. 2007. 32p. (gr. k-3). 16.95 (978-0-87483-788-9(X)) August Hse. Pubs., Inc.

Hanson, Bonnie Compton. The Impossible Christmas Present. 2004. (Ponytail Girls Ser.). (Illus.). 208p. (J). pap. 7.99 (978-1-58411-030-9(9) , Legacy Pr.) Rainbow Pubs. & Legacy Pr.

Harcourt School Publishers Staff. The Gift - Grade 3. 3rd ed. 2002. (Trophies English Language Learners Ser.). pap. 5.10 (978-0-15-327712-2(2)) Harcourt Schl. Pubs.

—Gloria's Gift: Take-Home Book. 1999. (Signatures Ser.). (Illus.). (J). pap. 1.90 (978-0-15-313963-5(3)) Harcourt Schl. Pubs.

—The Lad Who Went with the North Wind On Level. 3rd ed. 2002. (Illus.). pap. 5.10 (978-0-15-323268-8(4)) Harcourt Schl. Pubs.

Haston, Meg. The Thanksgiving Gift. Fletcher, Lyn, illus. 2007. (My Little Pony Ser.). 24p. (J). (ps-2). pap. 4.99 (*978-0-06-123446-0(X) , Harper Festival) HarperCollins Pubs.

Henry, O. The Gift of the Magi. Zwerger, Lisbeth, illus. 2006. 32p. (J). 15.99 (978-1-4169-3586-5(X)) Simon & Schuster Children's Publishing.

—Gift of the Magi. Zwerger, Lisbeth & Gooden, Stephen, illus. 2007. 32p. 12.95 (*978-1-59583-191-0(6)) Laughing Elephant.

—The Gift of the Magi: A Story about Giving. Jaekel, Susan M., illus. 2006. (J). (978-1-59939-084-0(1) , Reader's Digest Young Families, Inc.) Reader's Digest Children's Publishing, Inc.

—Gift of the Magi/the Purple Dress. 2006. (Wonderfully Illustrated Short Pieces Ser.). (Illus.). 48p. 14.95 (978-0-06-113880-5(0) , Collins Design) HarperCollins Pubs.

Henry, Rohan. The Perfect Gift. 2007. (Illus.). 32p. 8.95 (*978-1-58479-658-9(8)) Abrams, Harry N. , Inc.

Henson, John, illus. Sarah Lynn's Christmas Present. 2002. (J). 24.95 (978-0-9711706-8-1(1)) Waiver Publishing.

Higashi/Glaser Design Inc. Staff. Hello Kitty, Hello Love! Red Heart Secret Drawer Locked Diary. 2005. 128p. 12.95 (978-0-8109-8807-1(0) , Abrams Gifts and Stationery) Abrams, Harry N. , Inc.

Higgs, Liz Curtis. The Parable of the Lily. 10th anniv. ed. 2007. 32p. (J). 7.99 (978-1-4003-0844-6(5)) Nelson, Thomas Inc.

Hobbie, Holly. A Present for Toot. Hobbie, Holly, illus. 1998. (Toot & Puddle Ser.). (Illus.). 32p. (J). (ps-3). 15.99 (978-0-316-36556-7(4)) Little Brown & Co.

Holabird, Katharine. The Nutcracker—Sticker Stories. Craig, Helen, illus. 2007. 16p. (J). (ps-1). pap. 5.99 (*978-0-448-44681-3(2) , Grosset & Dunlap) Penguin Group (USA) Inc.

Hollis, Ginger. The Pumpkin Gift. Scarborough, Casey, illus. 28p. (J). 2006. 16.95 (*978-1-933660-04-2(X) , Tadpole Pr. 4 Kids); 2005. 24.95 (*978-1-933660-05-9(8)) Smooth Sailing Pr.

Hughes, Shirley. Giving. Hughes, Shirley, illus. 2002. (Illus.). (J). 11.91 (978-0-7587-2602-5(3)) Book Wholesalers, Inc.

Hutchins, Hazel. The List. Van Lieshout, Maria, illus. 2007. 32p. (J). (ps-1). pap. 7.95 (*978-1-55451-063-4(5)); lib. bdg. 19.95 (*978-1-55451-064-1(3)) Annick Pr., Ltd. CAN. *Dist:* Firefly Bks., Ltd.

Idle, Molly Schaar. Emma's Gift. 2004. (Illus.). 32p. bds. 14.00 (978-0-687-02294-6(0)) Abingdon Pr.

Jackson, Ellen B. The Precious Gift. 1998. (J). 16.00 (978-0-671-89725-3(X) , Simon & Schuster Children's Publishing) Simon & Schuster Children's Publishing.

Jacono, Mary Kaye. Lenny's Gift. 2005. 27p. pap. 10.95 (978-0-7414-2602-4(1)) Infinity Publishing.

James, Sabrina & Scognamiglio, John. Secret Santa. 2007. 368p. (J). (gr. 7 up). pap. 6.99 (*978-0-439-02695-6(4)) Scholastic, Inc.

Johnson, Michael. A Gift for Ida & Bell. l.t. ed. 2002. 32p. (J). 19.95 (978-1-893672-08-6(5)) Johnson, Michael Presentations.

Kaaberbol, Lene. The Serpent Gift. 3rd rev. ed. 2006. (Shamer Chronicles Ser.). Orig. Title: Slangens Gave. (Illus.). 384p. (J). 18.95 (978-0-8050-7770-4(7)) Holt, Henry & Co.

Kimmel, Elizabeth Cody. My Penguin Osbert. Lewis, H. B., illus. 2004. 40p. (J). (ps-3). 16.99 (978-0-7636-1699-1(0)) Candlewick Pr.

Knudsen, Michelle. A Slimy Story. Billin-Frye, Paige, illus. 2004. 32p. (J). lib. bdg. 20.00 (*978-1-4242-1150-0(6)) Fitzgerald Bks.

—A Slimy Story. Billin-Frye, Paige, illus. 2004. (Science Solves It! Ser.). 32p. (J). (ps-3). pap. 4.99 (978-1-57565-144-6(0)) Kane Pr., The.

La Borde, Roger & Biddulph, Robert. Hello Kitty, Hello Love! 2003. (Illus.). 24p. (J). (ps-3). 12.95 (978-0-8109-8538-4(1)) Abrams, Harry N. , Inc.

Langlois, Florence. The Extraordinary Gift. Goodman, John, tr. from FRE. Langlois, Florence, illus. 2005. (Illus.). 48p. (J). (ps-2). reprint ed. 15.00 (978-0-7567-8942-8(7)) DIANE Publishing Co.

Leeson, Christine. Snow Angel. Chapman, Jane, illus. 2007. 32p. (J). (ps-2). 15.95 (*978-1-58925-068-0(0) , tiger tales) ME Media LLC.

Little, Jean. Pippin the Christmas Pig. Zimmermann, H. Werner, illus. 2004. 40p. (J). (ps-3). 16.95 (978-0-439-65062-5(3) , Scholastic Pr.) Scholastic, Inc.

Lobel, Gillian. Little Bear's Special Wish. Hansen, Gaby, illus. 2004. 32p. (J). tchr. ed. 16.95 (978-1-58925-034-5(6) , tiger tales) ME Media LLC.

Loomis, Christine. The Best Father's Day Present Ever. Paparone, Pam, illus. 2007. 32p. (J). (gr. k-3). 15.99 (978-0-399-24253-3(8) , Putnam Juvenile) Penguin Group (USA) Inc.

Loter, Darlene. Santa's Promise. 2004. 25p. pap. 9.95 (978-1-4137-1238-4(X)) PublishAmerica, Inc.

Louie, Therese On. Raymond's Perfect Present. Wang, Suling, illus. 2002. (J). (gr. 2-4). 16.95 (978-1-58430-055-7(8)) Lee & Low Bks., Inc.

Lucado, Max. Punchinello & the Most Marvelous Gift. Martinez, Sergio, illus. 2005. (Tales of Wemmicksville Ser.: Bk. 5). 32p. (J). 15.99 (978-1-58134-546-9(1) , Crossway Bibles); 2003. 28p. bds. 6.99 (978-1-58134-562-9(3)) Crossway Bks.

—Punchinello & the Most Marvelous Gift: And, Your Special Gift. Martinez, Sergio, illus. 2007. (J). (*978-1-58134-877-4(0)) Crossway Bks.

Lucado, Max. Your Special Gift. Wenzel, David, illus. 2006. 31p. (J). 15.99 (978-1-58134-698-5(0)) Crossway Bks.

MacKall, Dandi Daley. Gift Horse. 2003. (Winnie the Horse Gentler Ser.). (Illus.). 224p. (J). mass mkt. 5.99 (978-0-8423-5547-6(2)) Tyndale Hse. Pubs.

Mackall, Dandi Daley. My Christmas Gift to Jesus. O'Neill, Rachael, illus. 2005. (Carry Me Along Ser.). 24p. (J). (ps). 6.99 (978-0-310-70938-1(5)) Zonderkidz.

Marzollo, Jean. Ten Little Christmas Presents. 2008. (J). (*978-0-545-02791-5(8)) Scholastic, Inc.

Mathias, B. J. Jeffrey William & The Little Prince. 2002. 10.00 (978-0-9711320-9-2(7)) Electronic Publishing Services.

McCain, Steve. A Christmas Tale: The Precious Gift. l.t. ed. 2002. 36p. per. 7.95 (978-0-9719597-1-2(4)) Thornton Publishing.

McDonnell, Patrick. The Gift of Nothing. 2005. (Illus.). 52p. (J). (ps-1). 14.99 (978-0-316-11488-2(X)) Little Brown & Co.

McKee, David. El Principe Pedro y el oso de Peluche. (SPA.). (J). 7.95 (978-958-04-6258-3(5)) Norma S.A. COL. *Dist:* Distribuidora Norma, Inc.

McKissack, Patricia C. & McKissack, Frederick. Miami Gets It Straight. Chesworth, Michael, illus. 2004. 89p. (J). (gr. 4-7). lib. bdg. 11.80 (978-0-613-27975-8(1)) Tandem Library Bks.

McOmber, Rachel B., ed. McOmber Phonics Storybooks: A Box. rev. ed. (Illus.). (J). (978-0-944991-13-8(0)) Swift Learning Resources.

Mitchelhill, Barbara. Eric & the Green-Eyed God. (Illus.). (J). 2003. 80p. pap. 8.99 (978-1-84270-224-6(6)); 2001. 79p. 14.99 (978-1-84270-006-8(5)) Andersen GBR. *Dist:* Independent Pubs. Group.

Mitchell, Margaree King. Granddaddy's Gift. 1998. (978-0-606-13449-1(2)) Tandem Library Bks.

Molnar, Gwen. No Presents Please. Clark, Dan, illus. 2001. (Early Chapters Bks.). 48p. (J). (gr. 2-5). pap. (978-1-896184-86-9(3)) Roussan Pubs., Inc./Roussan Editeur, Inc.

Mooney, E. S. Snow Fun. 2002. (gr. k-3). lib. bdg. 11.80 (978-0-613-58168-4(7)) Tandem Library Bks.

Mora, Pat. A Birthday Basket for Tia. 1998. (J). pap. 4.99 (978-0-87628-395-0(4)) Ctr. for Applied Research in Education, The.

—Una Cesta de Cumpleanos para Tia Abuela. Lang, Cecily, illus. (SPA.). (J). (gr. k-2). pap. 3.16 net. (978-0-395-78817-2(X) , HMS088) Houghton Mifflin Co.

Moser, Kay. David's Gift. 2000. 260p. (YA). pap. 11.99 (978-1-890236-16-8(0)) Seton St. Clare Bks.

Moulton, Mark. Travelers Gift. Sherwood, Stewart, illus. 2001. 32p. 18.00 (978-0-7412-0867-5(9)) Lang Graphics, Ltd.

Munsch, Robert. Ribbon Rescue. Fernandes, Eugenie, illus. 1999. 32p. (J). (ps-1). pap. 11.95 (978-0-590-89012-0(3)) Scholastic, Inc.

Murail, Marie-Aude & Murail, Elvire. Santa's Last Present. Blake, Quentin, illus. 2004. 32p. (J). 12.95 (978-1-56145-319-1(6)) Peachtree Pubs., Ltd.

Nicholson, William. The Wind on Fire Trilogy, 3 bks., Set. 2004. 288p. (J). (gr. 7-17). pap. 30.00 (978-0-7868-0927-1(2)) Hyperion Paperbacks for Children.

Nolan, Janet. A Father's Day Thank You. Ember, Kathi, illus. 2007. 32p. (J). 15.95 (978-0-8075-2291-2(0)) Whitman, Albert & Co.

Olsen, Mary-Kate. Perfect Gift. 2002. (gr. 3-6). lib. bdg. 13.00 (978-0-613-58163-9(6)) Tandem Library Bks.

O'Neil, Amy. Just for You. Silver, Pattie, illus. 2002. (Read-To-Me Ser.). 24p. (J). (978-0-7665-1225-2(8)) Abrams, Harry N. , Inc.

Pachela, Czes, illus. The Birthday Present. 2001. 24p. (J). pap. 3.50 (978-1-58925-363-6(9) , tiger tales) ME Media LLC.

Park, Barbara. Junie B., First Grader: Jingle Bells, Batman Smells! (P. S. So Does May.) Brunkus, Denise, illus. 2005. (Junie B. Jones Ser.: No. 25). 118p. (J). (gr. k-3). pap. (978-0-375-82809-6(5)) Random Hse., Inc.

Paterson, Katherine. Marvin's Best Christmas Present Ever. Brown, Jane Clark, illus. 2002. (J). 11.91 (978-0-7587-6200-9(3)) Book Wholesalers, Inc.

—Marvin's Best Christmas Present Ever. 1999. (I Can Read Bks.). (J). (978-0-606-17299-8(8)); lib. bdg. 11.80 (978-0-613-22890-9(1)) Tandem Library Bks.

Paul, Ann Whitford. Fiesta Fiasco. Long, Ethan, illus. 2007. 32p. (J). (ps-3). 16.95 (978-0-8234-2037-7(X)) Holiday Hse., Inc.

Phillips, Sheila Starks. The Eggstra-Ordinary Surprise. Alderson, Lynnett G., illus. 2000. 40p. (J). (ps-4). lib. bdg. 16.95 (978-0-9679195-0-8(9)) RWP Interests, LLC.

Pike, Christopher, pseud. The Witch's Gift. 1999. (Spooksville Ser.). (gr. 3-6). lib. bdg. 11.80 (978-0-613-85085-8(8)) Tandem Library Bks.

Pittar, Gill. Milly, Molly & the Secret Scarves/CD-ROM. 28p. 2006. cd-rom (978-1-877337-68-0(4)); 2004. pap. incl. cd-rom (978-1-877337-67-3(6)) Milly Molly Bks.

Polden, William. The Best Present I Ever Had. 2005. 59p. pap. 12.95 (978-1-4137-5937-2(8)) PublishAmerica, Inc.

The Presents: Individual Title Six-Packs. (Sails Literacy Ser.). 16p. (gr. k up). 27.00 (978-0-7635-4444-7(2)) Rigby Education.

Rempt, Fiona. Snail's Birthday Wish. Smit, Noelle, illus. 2007. 32p. (J). (ps-1). 14.95 (*978-1-905417-52-0(7)) Boxer Bks., Ltd. GBR. *Dist:* Sterling Publishing Co., Inc.

Richardson, Linda. The Gift. 2003. (J). 6.95 (978-1-59094-021-1(0) , Jawbreakers for Kids) Jawbone Publishing Corp.

Rinck, Maranke. The Prince Child. Linden, Martijn van der, illus. 2004. (ENG & GER.). 32p. (J). 16.95 (978-1-932425-15-4(2) , Lemniscaat) Boyds Mills Pr.

Ritchie, Joseph R. Peter Cottontail's Easter Surprise. Rasmussen, Wendy, illus. 2006. 18p. (J). bds. 9.95 (978-0-8249-6627-0(9) , Candy Cane Pr.) Ideals Pubns.

Rocklin, Joanne & Burns, Marilyn. The Incredibly Awesome Box. Pillo, Cary, illus. 2000. (Hello Reader! Math Ser.). (J). pap. 3.99 (978-0-439-09955-4(2)) Scholastic, Inc.

Rovetch, Lissa. TLC Grow with Me! McLeod, Chum, illus. 2005. (J). (978-1-58987-114-4(6)) Kindermusik International.

Rumford, James. Nine Animals & the Well. 2003. (Illus.). 32p. (J). (gr. k-3). tchr. ed. 16.00 (978-0-618-30915-3(2)) Houghton Mifflin Co. Trade & Reference Div.

Sage, Angie. Molly & the Birthday Party. 2001. (Illus.). 12p. (J). (ps-1). 9.95 (978-1-56145-248-4(3)) Peachtree Pubs., Ltd.

Saltis, Nicki. Mailbox. 1999. (ps-2). lib. bdg. 11.55 (978-0-613-30580-8(9)) Tandem Library Bks.

Santat, Dan. The Guild of Geniuses. 2004. (Illus.). (J). pap. (978-0-439-29810-0(5) , Levine, Arthur A. Bks.) Scholastic, Inc.

Santiago, Esmeralda. A Doll for Navidades. Sanchez, Enrique O., illus. 2005. 32p. (J). (ps-3). pap. 16.99 (978-0-439-55398-8(9) , Scholastic Pr.) Scholastic, Inc.

Scamell, Ragnhild. Toby's Doll's House. Reynolds, Adrian, illus. 1999. 32p. (J). (ps-3). 14.95 (978-1-86233-026-9(3)) Sterling Publishing Co., Inc.

Scamell, Ragnhild & Reynolds, Adrian. Toby's Doll's House. 2000. (Illus.). 32p. (J). (ps-1). pap. 6.95 (978-1-86233-067-2(0)) Sterling Publishing Co., Inc.

Schoenherr, Ian. Pip & Squeak. Schoenherr, Ian, illus. 2007. (Illus.). 32p. (J). (ps-1). 16.99 (978-0-06-087253-3(5)); lib. bdg. 17.89 (978-0-06-087254-0(3)) HarperCollins Pubs.

Scholastic, Inc. Staff & Black, Sonia. Just for You! Jumping the Broom. 2004. (Just for You! Ser.). (Illus.). 32p. pap. 3.99 (978-0-439-56878-4(1) , Teaching Resources) Scholastic, Inc.

Schwartz, Betty. Santa's Magic Gifts. Pickering, Jimmy, illus. 2006. 16p. (J). 9.99 (978-0-689-87469-7(3) , Little Simon) Simon & Schuster Children's Publishing.

Scraper, Katherine. The Gift-Guessing Kid. 2005. 22.00 (*978-1-4108-4211-4(8)) Benchmark Education Co.

Segal, Lore. Morris the Artist. Kulikov, Boris, illus. 2003. 32p. (J). (gr. k-4). 16.00 (978-0-374-35063-5(9) , Farrar, Straus & Giroux (BYR)) Farrar, Straus & Giroux.

Seymour, Jane & Keach, James. The Other One: You Make Me Happy Gift Book. Planer, Geoffrey, illus. gif. ed. 2007. (This One & That One Ser.). 16p. 5.99 (978-1-932431-57-5(8) , Angel Ede) Left Field Ink.

Shannon, George & Dronzek, Laura. Rabbit's Gift. 2007. (Illus.). 32p. (J). (ps-2). 16.00 (978-0-15-206073-2(1)) Harcourt Trade Pubs.

Sheets, Judy. The Gift. Nausley, Kathy, illus. 2005. 40p. (J). lib. bdg. 24.00 (978-0-9726451-2-6(8)) Sheets, Judy.

Shepard. Los Regalos de Wali Dad. 1999. (J). per. 16.00 (978-0-689-80419-9(9) , Atheneum) Simon & Schuster Children's Publishing.

Simont, Marc, illus. Nate the Great & the Snowy Trail. 2002. (Nate the Great Ser.). (J). 12.87 (978-0-7587-0709-3(6)) Book Wholesalers, Inc.

Speirs, John. Little Boys Christmas Gift. 2001. (Illus.). 32p. (J). (ps-3). 16.95 (978-0-8109-4399-5(9)) Abrams, Harry N. , Inc.

Spiradellis, Gregg. Jibjab Santa Book. Spiridellis, Evan, illus. 2007. 40p. (ps-17). 15.99 (*978-1-4231-0193-2(6)) Hyperion Pr.

St-Onge, Claire. Caillou: L'anniversaire. (FRE., Illus.). 32p. pap. 11.95 (978-2-89450-263-1(X)) Chouette Publishing CAN. *Dist:* Distribooks, Inc.

Staenberg, Bonnie. A Present for Mama Bear. Bratun, Katy, illus. 1999. (Hello Reader! Ser.). 32p. (J). (gr. 1-3). pap. 3.99 (978-0-590-28154-6(2)) Scholastic, Inc.

—Present for Mama Bear. 1999. (Hello Reader! Ser.). (978-0-606-16633-1(5)) Tandem Library Bks.

Stahel, Merry Kesner. Jennifer's Christmas Gift. 2005. 48p. pap. 8.93 (978-1-4116-4029-0(2)) Lulu.com.
Steptoe, Javaka. The Jones Family Express. Steptoe, Javaka, illus. 2005. (Illus.). 40p. (J). 7.95 (978-1-58430-262-9(3)) Lee & Low Bks., Inc.
—The Jones Family Express. 2003. (Illus.). 40p. (J). (ps-4). 17.95 (978-1-58430-047-2(7)) Lee & Low Bks., Inc.
Stewart, Paul. Un Regalo de Cumpleanos. Riddell, Chris, illus. (SPA.). 30p. (J). (gr. k-2). (978-84-348-6840-3(7) , SM30935) SM Ediciones ESP. *Dist:* Lectorum Pubns., Inc.
Stewart, Paul & Henry, O. The Gift of the Magi, Level 1. 2001. (Illus.). 32p. (C). pap. 9.27 (978-0-582-43286-4(3)) Pearson ESL.
Strelitski, Mies & Hartog, Arnold. Woobie Dreams Hc. 2006. (Illus.). 32p. (J). 16.95 (978-1-59249-554-2(0)) Soundprints.
Tagg, Christine. A Very Special Valentine. Kneen, Maggie, illus. 2003. (J). 15.95 (978-0-8118-4073-6(5)) Chronicle Bks. LLC.
Taylor, Jennifer. Dragon Sitter. 2005. 36p. (J). 14.99 (978-1-4116-6449-4(3)) Lulu.com.
Tews, Susan. The Gingerbread Doll. 2001. (gr. k-3). lib. bdg. 14.10 (978-0-613-35518-6(0)) Tandem Library Bks.
Thomas, Joan M. Mimi's Gift. 2004. (Illus.). 112p. (J). (ps-4). pap. 14.95 (978-1-57921-482-1(7)) WinePress Publishing.
Titonis, George, illus. The Gift of the Giggles. 2005. 24p. (J). 16.95 (978-0-9765398-0-3(2)) Bellaboozle Books, Inc.
Treadaway, Angie. Banah for Kids&. The Master's Workshop. 2003. 25 p. pap. 14.95 (978-1-59286-866-7(5)) PublishAmerica, Inc.
Walker, Susan Eileen. Maura's Trunk. 2004. 171p. pap. 19.95 (978-1-4137-3793-6(5)) PublishAmerica, Inc.
Walsh, Sheila. Gigi & the Perfect Christmas Gift. 2006. (Gigi, God's Little Princess Ser.). (Illus.). 32p. (J). 12.99 (978-1-4003-0801-9(1)) Nelson, Thomas Inc.
Walton, Rick. The Remarkable Friendship of Mr. Cat & Mr. Rat. McCue, Lisa, illus. 2006. 32p. (J). (ps-3). 14.99 (978-0-399-23899-4(9) , Putnam Juvenile) Penguin Group (USA) Inc.
Warner, Gertrude Chandler, creator. A Present for Grandfather. 1998. (Adventures of Benny & Watch: No. 2). (J). (gr. 1-3). (978-0-606-13216-9(3)) Tandem Library Bks.
Watts, Jeri Hanel. Keepers. Marshall, Felicia, illus. 2000. 32p. (gr. k up). (YA). 15.95 (978-1-880000-58-8(X)); (J). 6.95 (978-1-58430-013-7(2)) Lee & Low Bks., Inc.
—Keepers. 2000. (J). (978-0-606-19832-5(6)) Tandem Library Bks.
Weiss, Nicki. The World Turns Round & Round. Weiss, Nicki, illus. 2000. (Illus.). 32p. (J). (ps-3). 17.99 (978-0-688-17213-8(X)) HarperCollins Pubs.
Wells, Rosemary. Yoko's Paper Cranes. Wells, Rosemary, illus. 2001. (Illus.). 32p. (ps-2). 15.99 (978-0-7868-0737-6(7)) Hyperion Bks. for Children.
Wilder, Alice. It's Present Day. Levy, David B., illus. 1999. (Blue's Clues Ser.). 16p. (J). (ps-k). pap. 5.99 (978-0-689-82898-0(5) , Simon Spotlight/Nickelodeon) Simon & Schuster Children's Publishing.
Williams, Barbara. Albert's Gift for Grandmother. Cushman, Doug, illus. 2006. 32p. (J). (ps-1). 16.99 (978-0-7636-2097-4(1)) Candlewick Pr.
Williams, Jacklyn. Happy Valentine's Day, Gus! Cushman, Doug, illus. 2005. (Read-It! Readers Ser.). 32p. (J). (gr. k-3). 18.60 (978-1-4048-0962-8(7)) Picture Window Bks.
Williams, Vera B. Algo Especial Para Mi. Williams, Vera B., illus. 2006. (SPA.). 32p. (J). pap. 6.99 (978-0-06-088707-0(9)) HarperCollins Pubs.
Wooters, Duane. The Unnamed Manuscript. 2003. 70p. (YA). pap. 8.95 (978-0-595-29612-5(2)) iUniverse, Inc.
Wright, Dare. Gift from the Lonely Doll. 2001. (gr. k-3). lib. bdg. 15.25 (978-0-613-35517-9(2)) Tandem Library Bks.
Wurst, Thomas Scott. Pearl's Christmas Present. Wurst, Thomas Scott, illus. 2006. (Illus.). 40p. (J). 20.00 ***(978-0-9772441-1-9(3))*** Pearl & Dotty.
Ziefert, Harriet. Hey Irma! It's Mother's Day. 2004. (Illus.). 36p. pap. 7.95 (978-1-59354-027-2(2)) Blue Apple Bks.
—Presents for Santa. Rader, Laura, illus. 2000. (Easy-to-Read Ser.). 32p. (J). (gr. k-3). 13.89 (978-0-670-88390-5(5) , Viking Juvenile) Penguin Group (USA) Inc.
Zondervan. 2:52 Laptop 1 Reality Shift/Laptop 2 Double Take - Focus on the Family: 52 Laptop 1 Reality Shift/ Laptop 2 Double Take - Focus on the Family. 2004. (J). pap. 9.98 (978-0-310-70934-3(2)) Zonderkidz.

GILBERT, W. S. (WILLIAM SCHWENCK), 1836-1911

Dark, Sidney. W. S. Gilbert, His Life & Letters. 2001. 269p. (YA). reprint ed. 98.00 (978-0-7222-5537-7(3)) Library Reprints, Inc.
Goldberg, Isaac. Sir William S. Gilbert: A Study in Modern Satire. 2001. 156p. (YA). reprint ed. 88.00 (978-0-7222-5542-1(X)) Library Reprints, Inc.

GILBRETH FAMILY

Gilbreth, Frank B., Jr. Cheaper by the Dozen. 2000. (YA). (gr. 7 up). (978-0-606-19692-5(7)) Tandem Library Bks.
Gilbreth, Frank B., Jr. & Carey, Ernestine Gilbreth. Cheaper by the Dozen. 188p. (YA). (gr. 7 up). reprint ed. lib. bdg. 24.95 (978-0-88411-289-1(6)) Amereon LTD.
—Cheaper by the Dozen. 2002. (Perennial Classics Ser.). 224p. (gr. 7 up). pap. 11.95 (978-0-06-008460-8(X)) HarperCollins Pubs.
—Cheaper by the Dozen. 180p. (YA). (gr. 7 up). pap. 5.50 (978-0-8072-8308-0(8)); 2004. (J). (gr. 4-7). pap. 38.00 incl. audio (978-0-8072-8307-3(X) , YA157SP) Random Hse. Audio Publishing Group. (Listening Library).

GILDS

see Guilds

GILGAMESH

Bryson, Bernarda. Gilgamesh: Man's First Story. 2000. (J). per. 19.95 (978-1-892857-01-9(4)) Whole Spirit Pr.
George, Andrew. The Epic of Gilgamesh. 2003. (gr. 7-12). lib. bdg. 17.65 (978-0-613-64275-0(9)) Tandem Library Bks.
Zeman, Ludmila. La Derniere Quete de Gilgamesh. 2000. (Gilgamesh Trilogy Ser.). (FRE & SPA.). 24p. (J). (gr. 3). pap. 9.95 (978-0-88776-528-5(9) , Livres Toundra) Tundra Bks., Inc./Livres Toundra, Inc. CAN. *Dist:* Random Hse., Inc.
—Gilgamesh the King. Zeman, Ludmila, illus. 1998. (Epic of Gilgamesh Ser.: Vol. 1). (Illus.). 24p. (J). (gr. 3-7). reprint ed. pap. 8.95 (978-0-88776-437-0(1)) Tundra Bks., Inc./Livres Toundra, Inc. CAN. *Dist:* Random Hse., Inc.
—The Last Quest of Gilgamesh, Book 3. Zeman, Ludmila, illus. 1998. (Epic of Gilgamesh Ser.: Vol. 3). (Illus.). 24p. (J). (gr. 3-7). reprint ed. pap. 8.95 (978-0-88776-380-9(4)) Tundra Bks., Inc./Livres Toundra, Inc. CAN. *Dist:* Random Hse., Inc.
—The Revenge of Ishtar, Bk. 2. Zeman, Ludmila, illus. 1998. (Epic of Gilgamesh Ser.: Vol. 2). (Illus.). 24p. (J). (gr. 3-7). reprint ed. pap. 8.95 (978-0-88776-436-3(3)) Tundra Bks., Inc./Livres Toundra, Inc. CAN. *Dist:* Random Hse., Inc.
Zeman, Ludmila, illus. & narrated by. Gilgamesh. Zeman, Ludmila, narrated by. 2005. (SPA.). (J). 29.95 (978-968-7381-51-0(5)); pap. 21.95 (978-968-7381-47-3(7)) Tecolote, Ediciones, S.A. de C.V. MEX. *Dist:* Iaconi, Mariuccia Bk. Imports.
Zeman, Ludmila, illus. & retold by. The Revenge of Ishtar. Zeman, Ludmila, retold by. 1998. (J). (ps-7). lib. bdg. 17.60 (978-0-613-09466-5(2)) Tandem Library Bks.
Zeman, Ludmila & Boileau, Michele. La Revanche D'Ishtar. 2000. (Gilgamesh Trilogy Ser.). (FRE & SPA., Illus.). 24p. (J). (gr. 3). pap. 9.95 (978-0-88776-527-8(0) , Livres Toundra) Tundra Bks., Inc./Livres Toundra, Inc. CAN. *Dist:* Random Hse., Inc.

GIOTTO, 1266?-1337

Venezia, Mike. Giotto. 2000. (Getting to Know the World's Greatest Artists Ser.). (Illus.). 32p. (J). (gr. 3-4). pap. 6.95 (978-0-516-27040-1(0)); 27.00 (978-0-516-21592-1(2)) Scholastic Library Publishing. (Children's Pr.).
—Giotto. 2000. (gr. 3-6). lib. bdg. 15.25 (978-0-613-37362-3(6)) Tandem Library Bks.

GIPSIES

see Gypsies

GIRAFFES

Albee, Sarah. Giraffes. 2006. (J). 7.99 (978-1-59939-034-5(5) , Reader's Digest Young Families, Inc.) Reader's Digest Children's Publishing, Inc.
Allin, Michael. Zarafa: A Giraffe's True Story, from Deep in Africa to the Heart of Paris. 1998. (Illus.). 224p. 22.00 (978-0-8027-1339-1(4)) Walker & Co.
Anderson, Jill. Giraffes. 2005. (Wild Ones Ser.). (Illus.). 24p. (ps-1). 12.95 (978-1-55971-928-5(1)); (J). pap. 6.95 (978-1-55971-929-2(X)) T&N Children's Publishing. (NorthWord Bks. for Young Readers).
Butterfield, Moira. Giraffe. (Who Am I? Ser.). (Illus.). 32p. (J). lib. bdg. 25.25 (978-1-930643-92-5(6)) Chrysalis Education.
Craft, Sarah S. Mother Giraffes & Their Babies. 1999. (Zoo Life Book Ser.). 24p. (J). (gr. k-4). lib. bdg. 18.75 (978-0-8239-5316-5(5) , PowerKids Pr.) Rosen Publishing Group, Inc., The.
Gareth Stevens Publishing Staff, contrib. by. Giraffes. 2004. (All about Wild Animals Ser.). (Illus.). 32p. (J). (gr. 2 up). lib. bdg. 23.33 (978-0-8368-4116-9(6)) Stevens, Gareth Inc.
The Giraffe: Individual Title Six-Packs. (On Deck Ser.). 24p. (gr. 4-5). 35.00 (978-0-7578-1069-5(1)) Rigby Education.
Giraffes. 2006. (Critters Up Close Ser.). (J). bds. 5.95 ***(978-1-932396-16-4(0))*** Wildlife Education, Ltd.
Goldish, Meish. Giraffe: The World's Tallest Mammal. 2007. (SuperSized! Ser.). (Illus.). 24p. (J). lib. bdg. 21.28 (978-1-59716-374-3(0) , 1265932) Bearport Publishing Co., Inc.
—Giraffes & Other Hoofed Mammals, Vol. 4. World Book, Inc. Staff, ed. 2001. (World Book's Animals of the World Ser.: Set 2). (Illus.). 64p. (J). (978-0-7166-1213-1(5)) World Bk., Inc.
Helget, Nicole Lea. Giraffes. 2008. (J). ***(978-1-58341-654-9(4)*** , Creative Education) Creative Co., The.
Hewett, Richard, illus. & photos by. A Giraffe Calf Grows Up. Hewett, Richard, photos by. Hewett, Joan, photos by. 2004. (Baby Animals Ser.). 32p. (J). (gr. k-3). lib. bdg. 21.27 (978-1-57505-197-0(4)) Lerner Publishing Group.
Hillard, Leith. A Giraffe for France. Blackall, Sophie, illus. 2000. 42p. (J). 13.95 (978-0-949284-41-9(6)) Watermark Pr., The AUS. *Dist:* Antique Collectors' Club.
Hodgson, Mona Gansberg. I Wonder Who Stretched the Giraffe's Neck. 1999. (I Wonder Ser.). (Illus.). 32p. (J). (ps-2). 6.99 (978-0-570-05065-0(0)) Concordia Publishing Hse.
Jango-Cohen, Judith. Giraffes. 2001. (Animals Animals Ser.). (Illus.). 48p. (J). (gr. 3-5). lib. bdg. 25.64 (978-0-7614-1258-8(1) , Benchmark Bks.) Cavendish, Marshall Corp.
La Jirafa: Individual Title Six-Packs. (On Deck en Espanol Ser.).Tr. of Giraffe. (SPA.). 24p. (gr. 4-5). 35.00 (978-0-7578-6440-7(6)) Rigby Education.
Kalz, Jill. Giraffes. 2005. (Wild World of Animals Ser.). (Illus.). 32p. (gr. 2-5). 18.95 (978-1-58341-350-0(2) , Creative Education) Creative Co., The.
Kendell, Patricia. Giraffes. 2003. (In the Wild Ser.). (Illus.). 32p. (J). lib. bdg. 25.70 (978-0-7398-6634-4(6)) Raintree.
Kennaway, Adrienne. Baby Giraffe: A Lift-the-Flap Book. Kennaway, Adrienne, illus. 1999. (Illus.). 20p. (J). (ps-k). 7.95 (978-1-887734-76-9(7)) Star Bright Bks., Inc.
Leach, Michael. Giraffe: Habitats, Life Cycles, Food Chains, Threats. 2001. (Natural World Ser.). (Illus.). 48p. (J). lib. bdg. 27.12 (978-0-7398-4435-9(0)) Raintree.
Leigh, Autumn. Giant Giraffes: Learning the Soft G Sound. (PowerPhonics Ser.). (Illus.). (J). 2002. 24p. (gr. 1). lib. bdg. 18.50 (978-0-8239-5919-8(8)); 2001. 23p. pap. 26.40 (978-0-8239-8264-6(5)) Rosen Publishing Group, Inc., The. (PowerKids Pr.).
Lockwood, Sophie. Giraffes. 2005. (World of Mammals Ser.). 40p. (J). (gr. 2-6). 29.93 (978-1-59296-496-3(6)) Child's World, Inc.
Macken, JoAnn Early. Giraffes. 2002. (Weekly Reader Early Learning Library). (Illus.). 24p. (J). (ps up). pap. 5.95 (978-0-8368-3282-2(5)); lib. bdg. 19.33 (978-0-8368-3269-3(8)) Stevens, Gareth Inc. (Weekly Reader Early Learning Library).
—Giraffes/Las Jirafas. Coffey, Colleen & Carrillo, Consuelo, trs. from SPA. 2003. (Weekly Reader Early Learning Library). (ENG & SPA., Illus.). 24p. (J). (ps up). lib. bdg. 19.33 (978-0-8368-4000-1(3) , Weekly Reader Early Learning Library) Stevens, Gareth Inc.
—Giraffes/Las Jirafas. 2003. (Weekly Reader Early Learning Library). (ENG & SPA., Illus.). 24p. (J). (ps up). pap. (978-0-8368-4005-6(4) , Weekly Reader Early Learning Library) Stevens, Gareth Inc.
Marie, Christian. Little Giraffes. Lantier, Patricia, tr. from FRE. 2005. (Born to Be Wild Ser.). (Illus.). 24p. (J). (gr. 1-3). lib. bdg. 22.00 (978-0-8368-4436-8(X)) Stevens, Gareth Inc.
—La pequena Jirafa. 2005. (Quien eres tu? Ser.). 24p. (J). 7.95 (978-84-7864-249-6(8)) Combel Editorial, S.A. ESP. *Dist:* Independent Pubs. Group.
Morgan, Sally. Giraffes. 2006. (QEB Animal Lives Ser.). (Illus.). 32p. (J). lib. bdg. 19.95 (978-1-59566-201-9(4)) QEB Publishing Inc.
Murray, Julie. Giraffes. 2002. (Buddy Book Ser.). (Illus.). 24p. (J). (gr. k-4). lib. bdg. 21.35 (978-1-57765-722-4(5)) ABDO Publishing Co.
Paige, Joy. The Giraffe: World's Tallest Animal. 2002. (Reading Power Ser.). (Illus.). 24p. (J). (gr. 1). lib. bdg. 17.25 (978-0-8239-5964-8(3) , PowerKids Pr.) Rosen Publishing Group, Inc., The.
—La Jirafa: El Animal Mas Alto Del Mundo. 2004. (Campeones Del Mundo Animal Ser.). (SPA & ENG., Illus.). 24p. (J). (gr. 3-6). lib. bdg. 17.25 (978-0-8239-6895-4(2) , Buenas Letra) Rosen Publishing Group, Inc., The.
Parker, Barbara Keevil. Giraffes. (Early Bird Nature Bks.). (Illus.). (J). 2005. (gr. 2-4). lib. bdg. 25.26 (978-0-8225-2419-9(8)); 2004. 48p. 25.26 (978-1-57505-346-2(2) , Carolrhoda Bks.) Lerner Publishing Group.
Pingry, Patricia A. Baby Giraffe. 2003. (San Diego Zoo Animal Library: Vol. 4). (Illus.). 26p. (J). bds. 6.95 (978-0-8249-6529-7(9)) Ideals Pubns.
Schaefer, Lola M. Giraffes: Long-Necked Leaf-Eaters. 2001. (Wild World of Animals Ser.). (Illus.). 24p. (J). (gr. 1-2). lib. bdg. 18.60 (978-0-7368-0965-8(1) , Bridgestone Bks.) Capstone Pr., Inc.
Steele, Christy. Okapis. 2003. (Animals of the Rain Forest Ser.). (Illus.). 32p. (J). 24.28 (978-0-7398-6839-3(X)) Raintree.
Tourville, Amanda Doering. A Giraffe Grows Up. 2007. (Illus.). 24p. (J). ***(978-1-4048-3565-8(2)*** , 1265740) Picture Window Bks.
—A Giraffe Grows Up. Denman, Michael & Huiett, William J., illus. 2006. (Wild Animals Ser.). 24p. (J). (gr. 1-3). 25.26 (978-1-4048-3158-2(4) , 1265740) Picture Window Bks.
Underwood, Deborah. Watching Giraffes in Africa. 2006. (Heinemann First Library). (Illus.). 32p. (J). 25.36 (978-1-4034-7230-4(0)); pap. (978-1-4034-7243-4(2)) Heinemann Library.
Watt, Melanie. Giraffes. 2002. (Untamed World Ser.). (Illus.). 64p. (J). lib. bdg. 28.54 (978-0-7398-4971-2(9)) Raintree.
Wexo, John Bonnett. Giraffes. (Illus.). 24p. (J). (gr. 1-7). 2003. 10.95 (978-1-888153-92-7(X) , Zoo Bks.); 2001. 15.95 (978-1-888153-47-7(4)) Wildlife Education, Ltd.
—Jirafas. Rountree, Monica, tr. 2003. (Zoobooks). Orig. Title: Giraffes. (SPA., Illus.). 24p. (J). (gr. k-6). lib. bdg. 15.95 (978-1-888153-74-3(1)) Wildlife Education, Ltd.
Whitehouse, Patricia. Giraffe. 2003. (Zoo Animals Ser.). (Illus.). 24p. (ps-1). (J). lib. bdg. 17.08 (978-1-58810-898-2(8)); pap. 5.25 (978-1-4034-0644-6(8)) Heinemann Library.
—La Jirafa. 2003. (Animales del Zoologico (Zoo Animals) Ser.). (SPA., Illus.). 24p. (ps-1). (J). lib. bdg. 17.08 (978-1-4034-0405-3(4)); pap. 5.25 (978-1-4034-0653-8(7)) Heinemann Library.
Wildlife Education, Ltd. Staff & Wexo, John Bonnett. Giraffes. Francis, John et al, illus. 2001. (Zoobooks Ser.). 18p. (Orig.). (YA). (gr. 5 up). pap. 2.95 (978-0-937934-09-8(7)) Wildlife Education, Ltd.
Zumbusch, Amelie von. Giraffes. 2007. (Safari Animals Ser.). (Illus.). 24p. (J). (gr. k-3). lib. bdg. 21.25 (978-1-4042-3615-8(5) , PowerKids Pr.) Rosen Publishing Group, Inc., The.

GIRAFFES—FICTION

Andreae, Giles. Giraffes Can't Dance. Parker-Rees, Guy, illus. (J). (ps-1). 2001. 32p. pap. 16.95 (978-0-439-28719-7(7) , Orchard Bks.); 2007. 29.95 incl. audio compact disk ***(978-0-439-02734-2(9));*** 2007. 24.95 incl. audio ***(978-0-439-02733-5(0))*** Scholastic, Inc.
Bailey, Elinor Peace. What Wilhelmina Sees. 2002. (J). 9.50 (978-0-9716586-6-0(8)) Fairfield Processing Corp.
Blight, Peter. Lonely Giraffe. Terry, Michael, illus. 32p. (J). (ps-k). pap. 12.99 (978-0-7475-7144-5(9)) Bloomsbury Publishing Plc GBR. *Dist:* Trafalgar Square Publishing.
—Lonely Giraffe. Matthewson, Emma, ed. Terry, Michael, illus. 2005. 32p. 19.99 (978-0-7475-6894-0(4)) Bloomsbury Publishing Plc GBR. *Dist:* Independent Pubs. Group.
Brovelli, Tito Alberto. Ely, la Jirafa Inconforme. 2001. Tr. of Ely, the Upset Giraffe. (SPA & ENG., Illus.). 32p. (J). (gr. k up). pap. 10.95 (978-0-9673032-3-9(0)) Sweet Dreams Bilingual Pubs.
Carter, Herbert. The, Boy Scouts on Sturgeon Island. rev. ed. 2006. (ENG.). 212p. 27.95 (978-1-4218-2084-2(6) , 1st World Library - Literary Society) 1st World Publishing, Inc.
Corner, K. K. The Gawky Giraffe. Richert, Sharon L., illus. 2005. (ENG.). 40p. (J). (ps-3). per. 16.99 (978-1-4141-0477-5(4)) Pleasant Word.
Dahl, Roald. The Giraffe, the Pelly & Me. Blake, Quentin, illus. 1998. 80p. (Orig.). (J). (gr. 2-6). pap. 5.99 (978-0-14-130228-7(3) , Puffin) Penguin Group (USA) Inc.
—La Jirafa, el Pelicano y el Mono, Level 4.7. 2001. (SPA.). 96p. (J). 7.95 (978-84-204-4430-7(8)) Alfaguara, Ediciones, S.A.- Grupo Santillana ESP. *Dist:* Santillana USA Publishing Co., Inc.
Dartez, C. Jenny Giraffe Discovers the French Quarter. 2nd ed. 160p. (J). 17.95 (978-1-56554-819-0(1)) Pelican Publishing Co., Inc.
Eduar, Gilles. Gigi & Zachary's Around-the-World Adventure: A Seek-and-Find Game. Eduar, Gilles, illus. 2003. (Illus.). 56p. (J). 16.95 (978-0-8118-3909-9(5)) Chronicle Bks. LLC.
Faulkner, Keith. The Giraffe Who Cock-a-Doodle-Doo'd. Lambert, Jonathan, illus. 2002. 16p. (J). (ps-1). 13.99 (978-0-8037-2739-7(9) , Dial) Penguin Group (USA) Inc.
—Tanglefoot Giraffe. Holmes, Stephen, illus. 2002. (Slot-to-Slot Model Ser.). 16p. (J). 9.95 (978-1-931411-00-4(X)) CPG Publishing, Inc.
Galvin, Laura Gates. Kakuda the Giraffe. Denman, Michael & Huiett, William, illus. 2005. (Meet Africa's Animals Ser.). 32p. (J). (ps-2). 8.95 incl. cd-rom (978-1-59249-206-0(1) , SD6501); 2.95 incl. cd-rom (978-1-59249-187-2(1) , S6551); 9.95 (978-1-59249-188-9(X) , PS6551) Soundprints.
—Kakuda the Giraffe. Denman, Michael L. & Huiett, William J., trs. Denman, Michael L. & Huiett, William J., illus. 2005. (Meet Africa's Animals Ser.). 36p. (J). (ps-2). 6.95 (978-1-59249-186-5(3) , S6501); 14.95 incl. cd-rom (978-1-59249-185-8(5) , H6501) Soundprints.
Garber, Linda. Sy, the Mile-High Giraffe. Feig, Harriet, illus. 1998. 35p. (J). (gr. 2-5). pap. 9.95 (978-1-892218-01-8(1)) Murlin Pubns.
Gates-Galvin, Laura. New Baby Giraffe. Cohen, Jessie, photos by. 1999. (Let's Go to the Zoo! Ser.: Vol. 3). (Illus.). 16p. (J). (ps-k). bds. 5.95 (978-1-56899-798-8(1) , B9003) Soundprints.
Georgie Giraffe, the Detective. 2005. (J). (978-1-932570-41-0(1)) Literacy Footprints Inc.
Gilda the Giraffe. (C). 158.20 (978-1-4048-1531-5(7)) Picture Window Bks.
Green, Mary. What Am I? 1999. (gr. k-3). lib. bdg. 18.75 (978-0-613-35376-2(5)) Tandem Library Bks.
Grindley, Sally. Archie's Amazing Adventure. Bendall-Brunello, John, tr. Bendall-Brunello, John, illus. 2003. 32p. (YA). (978-1-84365-026-3(6)) Chrysalis Children's Bks.
Hagin, Karen. Jeremy, the Giraffe Who Was Afraid of Heights. 2005. (J). lib. bdg. 19.95 ***(978-0-9754728-8-0(7)*** , Bear Hug Bks.) MidAmerica Publishing Co.
Hamilton, Elizabeth L. Georgey Giraffe's Giant Respect: Character Critter Series #6. 2004. (Character Critters Ser.: No. 6). (Illus.). 32p. (J). per. 5.95 (978-0-9754629-1-1(1) , Character-in-Action) Quiet Impact, Inc.
Harcourt School Publishers Staff. Collections: Pardon Said the Giraffe: Grade Level Library. 1999. (Illus.). (J). pap. 4.70 (978-0-15-315202-3(8)) Harcourt Schl. Pubs.
—"Pardon" Said... Giraffe. 99th ed. 1998. (Signatures Ser.). (Illus.). pap. 60.70 (978-0-15-310894-5(0)) Harcourt Schl. Pubs.
Harder Tangvald, Christine. Jessica Giraffe's Long Neck. Gambill, Henrietta, ed. Fletcher, Rusty, illus. 1998. (Shaped Paperback Bks.). 24p. (J). (ps-k). pap. 3.99 (978-0-7847-0834-7(7) , 03994, Bean Sprouts) Standard Publishing.
Hellings, Collete. Un Bebe Caido del Cielo. Jacobs, Nadine, illus. 2003. (SPA.). 32p. (J). (gr. k-1). 16.95 (978-84-95150-10-3(7) , COR4033) Corimbo, Editorial S.L. ESP. *Dist:* Distribooks, Inc., Lectorum Pubns., Inc.
Hillard, Leith. A Giraffe for France. Blackall, Sophie, illus. 2000. 42p. (J). 13.95 (978-0-949284-41-9(6)) Watermark Pr., The AUS. *Dist:* Antique Collectors' Club.
Horowitz, Dave. A Monkey among Us. Horowitz, Dave, illus. 2004. (Illus.). 40p. (J). (ps-1). 14.99 (978-0-06-054335-8(3) , Harper Festival) HarperCollins Pubs.
Hurst, Valerie. The Giraffe That Wore a Necklace: Mister Giraffe Bow Tie & Long Gold Chain! One Flip-Flop Books. 2002. 48p. 19.99 (978-0-9716882-3-0(0) , 661-392-0867) Giraffe Family Pr.
Hurwitz, Andy Blackman. Philly Joe Giraffe's Jungle Jazz: Baby Loves Jazz. Cunningham, Andrew, illus. 2007. 16p. (J). bds. 7.99 (978-0-8431-2193-3(9) , Price Stern Sloan) Penguin Group (USA) Inc.
Jeremy Can't Drink Milk. 2006. (Illus.). 24p. (J). 5.99 ***(978-0-9725593-2-4(9))*** by shayne.
Kennaway, Adrienne. Baby Giraffe: A Lift-the-Flap Book. 2000. (Illus.). 32p. (J). (ps-k). 13.95 (978-1-899248-13-1(7)) Happy Cat Bks. GBR. *Dist:* Star Bright Bks., Inc.
Louise, T. Paula. Imposibus Rhinoceros, Giraffe & Gnu. Wood, Ashley, illus. 2002. 32p. (J). (gr. 1-5). pap. 7.99 (978-0-9712282-4-5(8)) Idea & Design Works, LLC.
Mayfield, Sue & Padua, Rochelle. I Can, You Can, Toucan! 2006. (Green Bananas Ser.). (Illus.). 47p. (J). (978-0-7787-1032-5(7)) Crabtree Publishing Co.

Napoli, Donna Jo. On Her Own. 1999. (Angelwings Ser.: No. 3). Orig. Title: Room to Grow. (Illus.). 96p. (J). (gr. 2-5). pap. 7.95 (978-0-689-82985-7(X) , Aladdin) Simon & Schuster Children's Publishing.

—On Her Own. 1999. (Angelwings Ser.: No. 3). Orig. Title: Room to Grow. (Illus.). (J). (978-0-606-17906-5(2)) Tandem Library Bks.

Nirgad, Lia. A Kiss for Lily. Aboulafia, Yossi, illus. 2006. 28p. (J). 12.95 (978-1-59692-163-4(3)) MacAdam/Cage Publishing, Inc.

Ommen, Sylvia Van. The Surprise. 2007. 24p. (J). (ps). 15.95 (978-1-932425-85-7(3) , Front Street) Boyds Mills Pr.

Papineau, Lucie. No Bananas for This Giraffe. 2000. (Adventures of Gilda Ser.). (Illus.). 32p. (J). (ps-3). pap. (978-1-894363-29-7(9)) Dominique & Friends.

—No Bananas for This Giraffe. Sarrazin, Marisol, illus. 2005. (Gilda the Giraffe Ser.). 32p. (J). 22.60 (978-1-4048-1292-5(X)) Picture Window Bks.

—No Spots for This Giraffe! Fischman, Sheila, tr. from FRE. Sarrazin, Marisol, illus. 1999. (Adventures of Gilda Ser.). 32p. (J). (ps up). pap. (978-1-894363-25-9(6)) Dominique & Friends.

—No Spots for This Giraffe. Sarrazin, Marisol, illus. 2005. (Gilda the Giraffe Ser.). 32p. (J). 22.60 (978-1-4048-1291-8(1)) Picture Window Bks.

—Pas de Taches Pour une Girafe. ed. 2004. (FRE., Illus.). (J). (gr. k-3). spiral bd. (978-0-616-03075-2(4)) Canadian National Institute for the Blind/Institut National Canadien pour les Aveugles.

Pigni, Guido & Hermsen, Ronald. The Story of Giraffe. Pigni, Guido, illus. 2007. (Illus.). 32p. (J). (ps-2). 16.95 (978-1-932425-87-1(X) , Front Street) Boyds Mills Pr.

Piper, William Bowman. Giraffe of Montana, Volume I, 1. Megenhardt, William, illus. ed. 2005. 152p. (J). 19.95 (978-0-9763359-4-8(8) , 0-9763359) Little Pemberley Pr.

Platt, Kin. Big Max & the Mystery of the Missing Giraffe. Cravath, Lynne, illus. (I Can Read Bks.). 64p. (J). 2006. pap. 3.99 (978-0-06-009920-6(8) , Harper Trophy); 2005. 15.99 (978-0-06-009918-3(6)); 2005. lib. bdg. 17.89 (978-0-06-009919-0(4)) HarperCollins Pubs.

Randel, Jackie. Calendar Friends. l.t. ed. 2005. (Illus.). 34p. (J). per. 9.99 (978-1-59879-018-4(8)) Lifevest Publishing, Inc.

Reviejo, Carlos. La Jirafa Curiosa. 3rd ed. 2000. (Cuentos de Ahora Ser.).Tr. of Curious Giraffe. (SPA., Illus.). 32p. (J). 12.95 (978-84-348-5162-7(8)) SM Ediciones ESP. *Dist:* Distribooks, Inc.

Rey, H. A., illus. Cecily G. & the 9 Monkeys. 2007. (Curious George Ser.). 48p. (J). (gr. 3-5). 16.00 (***978-0-618-80066-7(2)***) Houghton Mifflin Co.

Rosario, Joann. Happy- Go -Lucky Giraffe!! Rosario, Joann, illus. 2004. (Illus.). 20p. (J). (gr. k-5). pap. 10.00 (978-0-9758746-7-7(5) , 1246169) J.G.R. Enterprises.

Salem, Lynn & Stewart, Josie. My Giraffe. Brock, LaShara, illus. 2000. 8p. (J). (gr. k-2). pap. 3.75 (978-1-58323-006-0(8) , Seedling Pubns.) Continental Pr., Inc.

Scheer, Ruth. Giraffe at the Zoo. 2000. (Illus.). (J). pap. 9.95 (978-0-9671761-1-6(5)) Scheer Delight Publishing.

Sharratt, Nick. A Giraffe with a Scarf: Buggy Buddies. 1999. (Illus.). 10p. (J). bds. 3.99 (978-1-58048-059-8(4)) Sandvik Publishing.

Sheehan, Jennifer E. Griffy Giraffe's Accident. 2001. 32p. (J). 15.95 (978-0-9700952-1-3(X)) Bumples.

Spanyol, Jessica. Carlo & the Really Nice Librarian. Spanyol, Jessica, illus. 2004. (Illus.). 32p. (J). (gr. k-k). 15.99 (978-0-7636-2526-9(4)) Candlewick Pr.

—Carlo Likes Reading. Spanyol, Jessica, illus. 2005. (Illus.). 24p. (J). (ps-2). reprint ed. 15.00 (978-0-7567-8660-1(6)) DIANE Publishing Co.

Tate, Cynthia Wagoner. Gordy's Grimy but Groovy Adventure. 2006. 24p. 12.98 (978-1-4116-6297-1(0)) Lulu-.com.

Ufer, David A. The Giraffe Who Was Afraid of Heights. Carlson, Kirsten, illus. (J). 2007. 1p. 8.95 (***978-1-934359-05-1(X)***); 2006. 32p. 15.95 (978-0-9768823-0-5(2)) Sylvan Dell Pubng.

Underhill, Marjorie Fay. Jeremiah. Garrett, Caroline S., tr. Garrett, Caroline S., illus. 2003. (J). 12.00 (978-1-887905-75-6(8)) Parkway Pubs., Inc.

Weare, Tim, illus. I'm a Little Giraffe: A Finger-Puppet Pal. 2002. (I'm A Little Ser.). 12p. (J). (ps-k). bds. 6.95 (978-0-439-40641-3(2) , Cartwheel Bks.) Scholastic, Inc.

Winnard, Rebecca Victoria & Winnard, Linda. Giraffe Liberation: An Act of Freedom. 2006. 53p. pap. 12.95 (978-1-4241-0552-6(8)) PublishAmerica, Inc.

Yates, Gene, illus. The Giraffe Numbers Book. 2006. (J). (***978-1-58865-364-2(1)***) Kidsbooks, Inc.

GIRL SCOUTS

Aller, Susan Bivin. Juliette Low. 2007. (History Maker Biographies Ser.). (J). 26.60 (978-0-8225-6580-2(3) , Lerner Pubns.) Lerner Publishing Group.

Brown, Fern. Daisy & the Girl Scouts: The Story of Juliette Gordon Low. Dejohn, Marie, illus. 2005. 111p. (J). (gr. 3-6). lib. bdg. 15.90 (978-0-606-33708-3(3)) Tandem Library Bks.

Eubanks, Toni. Let's Celebrate! Girl Scout Ceremonies. 2004. (Illus.). 48p. (J). (978-0-88441-688-3(7)) Girl Scouts of the USA.

Girl Scout Gold Award Insert. 2004. (YA). (978-0-88441-674-6(7)) Girl Scouts of the USA.

Girl Scout Silver Award Insert. 2004. (YA). (978-0-88441-675-3(5)) Girl Scouts of the USA.

Parks Matter! 2004. (YA). (978-0-88441-673-9(9)) Girl Scouts of the USA.

Studio 2b: Focus - Express It. 2004. (YA). pap. (978-0-88441-671-5(2)) Girl Scouts of the USA.

Studio 2b Focus - Don't Sweat It. 2004. (YA). pap. (978-0-88441-669-2(0)) Girl Scouts of the USA.

Studio 2b Focus - Express It. 2004. (YA). (978-0-88441-670-8(4)) Girl Scouts of the USA.

Studio 2B Focus - On the Money. 2004. (YA). (978-0-88441-687-6(9)) Girl Scouts of the USA.

STUDIO 2B Guide for Councils Phase II: Strategies & Models. 2004. (YA). (978-0-88441-686-9(0)) Girl Scouts of the USA.

GIRL SCOUTS—FICTION

Garis, C. Lillian. The Girl Scout Pioneers or Winning the F. 2006. 25.99 (***978-1-4280-1682-8(1)***) IndyPublish.com.

GSUSA Staff. Octavia's Girl Scout Journey Activity Guide. 2001. (978-0-88441-624-1(0)) Girl Scouts of the USA.

Higgins, Helen Boyd. Juliette Low, Girl Scout Founder. Underdown, Harold, ed. Morrison, Cathy, illus. 2nd ed. 2002. (Young Patriots Ser.: Vol. 4). (J). 112p. 15.95 (978-1-882859-08-5(1)); 124p. (gr. 3-7). pap. 9.95 (978-1-882859-09-2(X)) Patria Pr., Inc.

—Juliette Low, Girl Scout Founder. 2002. (gr. 3-6). lib. bdg. 18.75 (978-0-613-80165-2(2)) Tandem Library Bks.

McKenzie, Lyn. Betsy, Girl Scout of Woodward Center 1935. 2007. 244p. (YA). pap. 17.95 net. (***978-0-9722839-0-8(0)***) Just Write Bks.

Warner, Penny. Mystery of the Haunted Cave. 2001. 102p. (J). (978-0-88166-390-7(5)) Meadowbrook Pr.

Wesley, Valerie Wilson. How to Lose Your Cookie Money. Roos, Maryn, illus. 2004. 105p. (J). lib. bdg. 15.00 (***978-1-4242-0644-5(8)***) Fitzgerald Bks.

GIRL SCOUTS—HANDBOOKS, MANUALS, ETC

Algranati, Melissa. Junior Girl Scout Badgebook. 2001. (Illus.). 237p. (J). pap. 10.95 (978-0-88441-620-3(8)) Girl Scouts of the USA.

Hoxie, W. J. How Girls Can Help Their Country: The Original Girl Scout Handbook. 2001. 180p. (J). (gr. 4-7). per. 8.00 (978-1-55709-522-0(1)) Applewood Bks.

GIRLS

Abingdon. Promises for Girls Living Faithfully with God & Neighbor. 2006. 64p. 4.00 (978-0-687-49385-2(4)) Abingdon Pr.

Adelman, Penina, et al. The JGirl's Guide: The Young Jewish Woman's Handbook for Coming of Age. 2005. 240p. (J). pap. 14.99 (978-1-58023-215-9(9)) Jewish Lights Publishing.

Ajmera, Maya. Extraordinary Girls. 2000. (J). 14.75 (978-0-606-19326-9(X)) Tandem Library Bks.

Ajmera, Maya, et al. Extraordinary Girls: A Celebration of Girlhood Around the World. 2004. (Illus.). 48p. (YA). (ps-3). 16.95 (978-0-88106-065-2(8)) Charlesbridge Publishing, Inc.

Al-Windawi, Thura. Thura's Diary. 2004. (Illus.). 144p. (J). (gr. 3-7). 15.99 (978-0-670-05886-0(6) , Viking Juvenile) Penguin Group (USA) Inc.

Albregts, Lisa & Cape, Elizabeth. Best Friends: Tons of Crazy, Cool Things to Do with Your Girlfriends. 1998. (Illus.). 152p. (J). (gr. 3-7). pap. 12.95 (978-1-55652-326-7(2)) Chicago Review Pr., Inc.

Allenbaugh, Kay. Chocolate for a Teen's Spirit: Inspiring Stories for Young Women about Hope. Str. 2002. (gr. 7-12). lib. bdg. 21.10 (978-0-613-56962-0(8)) Tandem Library Bks.

AMA, et al. The Girl's Guide to Becoming a Teen. Middleman, Amy B., ed. 2006. (Illus.). 128p. pap. 12.95 (978-0-7879-8344-4(6) , Jossey-Bass) Wiley, John & Sons, Inc.

Arredia, Joni. Sex, Boys, & You: Be Your Own Best Girlfriend. 1998. (Illus.). 192p. (YA). pap. 15.95 (978-0-9653203-2-0(4)) Perc Publishing.

Billinghurst, Jane. Hey Girl! A Journal of My Life. Cowles, Rose, illus. 2001. 128p. (J). (gr. 4-9). spiral bd. 14.95 (978-1-55037-684-5(5)) Annick Pr., Ltd. CAN. *Dist:* Firefly Bks., Ltd.

Birkemoe, Karen. Strike a Pose: The Planet Girl Guide to Yoga. Collett, Heather, illus. 2007. (Planet Girl Ser.). 96p. (YA). (gr. 5-10). (***978-1-55337-004-8(X)***) Kids Can Pr., Ltd.

Blackstone, Margaret. Girl Stuff: A Survival Guide to Growing Up. 2000. (J). 15.60 (978-0-606-19417-4(7)) Tandem Library Bks.

Blatt, Jessica. The Teen Girl's Gotta-Have-It Guide to Money: Getting Smart about Making It, Saving It, & Spending It! Frenette, Cynthia, illus. 2007. (Teen Girl's Gotta-Have-It Guides). 96p. (YA). pap. 8.95 (***978-0-8230-1727-0(3)***) Watson-Guptill Pubns., Inc.

Bonnell, Jennifer. Stylin' Salon 'n' Spa: Spa Tips, Beauty Tricks, & Recipes for Feelin' Good! 2003. (Bratz Ser.). (Illus.). 1p. pap. 8.40 (978-0-14-131750-2(7) , Putnam Juvenile) Penguin Group (USA) Inc.

Borlenghi, Patricia. Dear Aunty. 2001. 128p. (J). pap. 10.99 (978-0-7475-4735-8(1)) Bloomsbury Publishing Plc GBR. *Dist:* Independent Pubs. Group.

Brooks, Annie, compiled by. The Little Girls Treasury of Precious Things. unabr. ed. 1998. (Children's Heritage Ser.). (Illus.). 143p. (J). (ps-6). pap. 7.50 (978-1-58339-125-9(8) , 2D25) Grace & Truth Bks.

Brooks, Susan. Any Girl Can Rule the World. 1998. 224p. (gr. 8-12). pap. 12.95 (978-1-57749-068-5(1)) Fairview Pr.

Bryant, Sharon & Hood, Dana. Beautiful in God's Eyes: Building Character, Wisdom, & Faith in Young Women. 2004. (Illus.). 64p. (J). (gr. 4-6). pap. 15.00 (978-0-687-09344-1(9)) Abingdon Pr.

Buchan, Molly. Take It from Me: Straight Talk about Life from a Teen Who's Been There. 2002. (gr. 3-6). lib. bdg. 16.45 (978-0-613-71678-9(7)) Tandem Library Bks.

Buckley, Annie. Hero Girls. 2006. (Girls Rock! Ser.). (Illus.). 32p. (J). (gr. 1-5). 24.21 (978-1-59296-744-5(2)) Child's World, Inc.

Bull, Dave. What Every Girl Should Know: An A to Z of Health - From Allergies to Zits. 1999. (Illus.). 160p. (YA). (gr. 4 up). pap. 5.95 (978-1-902618-18-0(1)) Element Children's Bks.

Bullock, Jocelyn, illus. I Can Do Anyhting! Melpomen Institutes Activity Book for Girls. 1998. 45p. (J). (ps-6). pap. 6.00 (978-0-9651137-1-7(X)) Melpomene Institute.

Bundschuh, Rick, et al. Secret Power for Girls Video Devotionals. 2003. (YA). 19.99 incl. VHS (978-0-310-24771-5(3)) Zondervan.

Bunting, Eve. Girls A to Z. Bloom, Suzanne, illus. 2003. 32p. (J). (gr. k-2). 15.95 (978-1-56397-147-1(X)) Boyds Mills Pr.

Busby, Cylin & Licensing Company Staff. Stylin' Slumber Party. 2003. (Bratz Ser.). (Illus.). 48p. 8.40 (978-0-14-131751-9(5) , Putnam Juvenile) Penguin Group (USA) Inc.

Buttler, Elizabeth, illus. Girls & Their Dogs. 2007. 64p. (YA). (gr. 3 up). pap. 8.95 (***978-1-59369-169-1(6)***) American Girl Publishing, Inc.

Cabot, Meg. Princess Lessons. McLaren, Chesley, illus. 2003. (Princess Diaries). 144p. (J). (gr. 7 up). 12.99 (978-0-06-052677-1(7)) HarperCollins Pubs.

Caldwell, Micheala. The Girls' Yoga Book: Stretch Your Body, Open Your Mind, & Have Fun! D#0225;vila, Claudia, illus. 2005. (Girl Zone Ser.). 64p. 16.95 (978-1-897066-24-9(4)) Maple Tree Pr. CAN. *Dist:* Perseus Distribution.

—The Girls' Yoga Book: Stretch Your Body, Open Your Mind, & Have Fun! Davila, Claudia, illus. 2005. (Girl Zone Ser.). 64p. pap. 9.95 (978-1-897066-25-6(2)) Maple Tree Pr. CAN. *Dist:* Perseus Distribution.

Canfield, Jack L. Chicken Soup for the Teenage Soul Letters. 2001. (gr. 7-12). lib. bdg. 22.20 (978-0-613-30314-9(8)) Tandem Library Bks.

Carlson, Dale B. & Carlson, Hannah. Girls Are Equal Too: The Teenage Girls How-to-Survive Book. Nicklaus, Carol, illus. 2nd rev. ed. 2000. (Psychology for Teenagers Ser.: Vol. 1). 231p. (gr. 5-12). pap. 14.95 (978-1-884158-18-6(8)) Bick Publishing Hse.

Casey, Karen. Girls Only! A Daily Thoughts for Young Girls, Ages 7 to 10. 2004. (Illus.). 388p. (gr. 4-7). pap. 12.00 (978-0-930100-92-6(1)) Holy Cow! Pr.

Cattrall, Kim. Being a Girl: Navigating the Ups & Downs of Teen Life. Briamonte, Amy, illus. 2006. 128p. (J). (gr. 7-17). 18.99 (978-0-316-01102-0(9)) Little Brown & Co.

Clark, Sondra. Snap 2 It! A Real Girl's Guide to Keeping a Positive Outlook (even when you're having a bad hair day, just got a pimple on your nose & you & your best friend are fighting) 2007. 128p. pap. 7.95 (***978-1-4022-0954-3(1)***) Sourcebooks, Inc.

Clark, Travis & Ziff, Jane. A Guys' Guide to Stress; A Girls' Guide to Stress. 2008. (Flip-It-over Guides to Teen Emotions Ser.). (Illus.). 128p. (J). (gr. 5 up). lib. bdg. 31.93 (***978-0-7660-2857-9(7)***) Enslow Pubs., Inc.

Cole, Sheila. To Be Young in America: Growing up with the Country, 1776-1940. 2005. (Illus.). 160p. (J). (gr. 8-17). 19.99 (978-0-316-15196-2(3)) Little Brown & Co.

Colman, Penny. Girls: History of Growing up Female in America. (Girls Ser.). (Illus.). 192p. (J). (gr. 3 up). 2003. pap. 12.95 (978-0-590-37130-8(4) , Scholastic Nonfiction); 2000. pap. 18.95 (978-0-590-37129-2(0) , Scholastic Reference) Scholastic, Inc.

Coon, Nora E. It's Your Rite: Girls' Coming-of-Age Stories. 2002. (gr. 7-12). lib. bdg. 18.75 (978-0-613-67097-5(3)) Tandem Library Bks.

CosmoGIRL! Editors. All about Guys. Cosmopolitan Editors, ed. 2004. (CosmoGIRL Quiz Book Ser.). (Illus.). 128p. pap. 5.95 (978-1-58816-382-0(2)) Hearst Bks.

—All about You. Cosmopolitan Editors, ed. 2004. (CosmoGIRL Quiz Book Ser.). (Illus.). 128p. pap. 5.95 (978-1-58816-381-3(4)) Hearst Bks.

Courtney, Vicki. BeTween: A Preteen Girl's Guide to Life. 2006. (Illus.). 160p. (J). pap. 14.99 (978-0-8054-4193-2(X)) B&H Publishing Grp.

Courtney, Vicki. TeenVirtue Confidential: Your Questions Answered about Guys, God, & Getting Older. 2007. (Illus.). 160p. (YA). pap. 14.99 (***978-0-8054-4192-5(1)*** , B&H Bks.) B&H Publishing Grp.

Criswell, Patti. Friends: Making Them & Keeping Them. Watkins, Michelle, ed. 2006. 80p. (J). pap. (978-1-59369-154-7(8)) American Girl Publishing, Inc.

Criswell, Patti Kelley. What Would You Do? Quizzes About Real-Life Problems. Bendell, Norm, illus. 2004. (Americangirl Library(R) Ser.). 64p. (J). pap. 8.95 (978-1-58485-874-4(5)) American Girl Publishing, Inc.

—What Would You Do? Quizzes About Real-Life Problems. 2004. (gr. 3-6). lib. bdg. 17.60 (978-0-613-83321-9(X)) Tandem Library Bks.

Cross, Mandy. Goal Power: A Real-Life Girls' Soccer Story. 1999. (Illus.). 128p. (J). (gr. 3-9). pap. 4.95 (978-1-902618-46-3(7)) Element Children's Bks.

Dellasega, Cheryl. The Girl's Friendship Journal: A Guide to Relationshps. 2005. 128p. (J). (gr. 4-7). pap. 16.00 (978-1-932783-59-9(8)) Champion Pr., Ltd.

Delmege, Sarah. Pink Pages. 2004. (Illus.). 158p. (J). (978-0-439-67992-3(3)) Scholastic, Inc.

Dickerson, Karle. Girl Chat: The Fine Art of Talk, Talk, Talk. 2001. (Illus.). 105p. (J). (978-0-439-18745-9(1)) Scholastic, Inc.

Doudna, Kelly. Boys & Girls Around the World. 2004. (Around the World Ser.). (Illus.). 23p. (J). (ps-3). lib. bdg. 19.93 (978-1-59197-564-9(6)) ABDO Publishing Co.

Douglas, Ann & Douglas, Julie. Body Talk: The Straight Facts on Fitness, Nutrition, & Feeling Great about Yourself! Davila, Claudia, illus. 2nd ed. 2006. (Girl Zone Ser.). 64p. (J). 19.95 (978-1-897066-62-1(7)); pap. 9.95 (978-1-897066-61-4(9)) Maple Tree Pr. CAN. *Dist:* Perseus Distribution.

Dower, Laura. For Girls Only: Everything Great about Being a Girl. 2008. (Illus.). 192p. (J). 14.95 (***978-0-312-38205-6(7)***) Feiwel & Friends.

Drill, Esther, et al. Deal with It! A Whole New Approach to Your Body, Brain & Life as a GURL. 1999. (Illus.). 320p. (YA). (gr. 7-12). pap. 19.95 (978-0-671-04157-1(6) , Pocket) Simon & Schuster.

Driscoll, Anne M. Friends & You! 2000. (Girl to Girl Ser.). (Illus.). 160p. (J). (gr. 3-7). 5.95 (978-1-902618-06-7(8)) Element Children's Bks.

DuJardin, Rosamond & DuJardin, Judy. Junior Year Abroad. 2003. (YA). pap. 12.95 (978-1-930009-80-6(1) , 800-691-7779) Image Cascade Publishing.

Eastwood, Kay. Women & Girls in the Middle Ages. 2003. (Medieval World Ser.). (Illus.). 32p. (J). (gr. 5). (978-0-7787-1346-3(6)); pap. (978-0-7787-1378-4(4)) Crabtree Publishing Co.

Evans, Denise K. Graduating Girlhood: A Teenage Girl's Guide to Success in Relationships & Life. 2002. 123p. pap. 11.95 (978-0-9722720-0-1(3)) Life-Enhancing Publishing.

Fast, Suellen M. America's Daughters. Fast, Suellen M., photos by. (Illus.). 100p. (Orig.). (J). (gr. k up). pap. 19.00 (978-0-935281-13-2(4)) Daughter Culture Pubns.

Finnis, Anne & Bond, Denis. It's A Boy/Girl Thing. 2003. (Illus.). 144p. (J). pap. 10.95 (978-0-09-943212-8(9) , Red Fox) Random Hse. Children's Bks. GBR. *Dist:* Random Hse. of Canada, Ltd.

Foster, Juliana. The Girls' Book: How to Be the Best at Everything. Enright, Amanda, illus. 2007. (Girls' Book Ser.). 128p. (J). (gr. 4-7). 9.99 (***978-0-545-01629-2(0)*** , Scholastic Pr.) Scholastic, Inc.

Gallagher, Jim & Cavenaugh, Dorothy. A Guys' Guide to Conflict; A Girls' Guide to Conflict. 2008. (Flip-It-over Guides to Teen Emotions Ser.). (Illus.). 128p. (J). (gr. 5 up). lib. bdg. 31.93 (***978-0-7660-2852-4(6)***) Enslow Pubs., Inc.

George, Elizabeth. A Young Woman after God's Own Heart: A Teen's Guide to Friends, Faith, Family, & the Future. 2003. 224p. (YA). pap. 9.99 (978-0-7369-0789-7(0) , 6907890) Harvest Hse. Pubs.

Girls Can Do Christian Adventures in Learning Book. 2005. (J). 19.95 (978-1-59649-223-3(6)) Whispering Pine Pr., Inc.

Girls Can Do Hood Christian Educational Curriculum Book. 2005. (J). 19.95 (978-1-59210-365-2(0)) Whispering Pine Pr., Inc.

Girls' Guides. 2005. (Illus.). 48p. (gr. 5-8). lib. bdg. 215.40 (978-0-8239-3919-0(7)) Rosen Publishing Group, Inc., The.

Girls' Life Magazine Editors. The Girls' Life Guide to Growing Up. 2000. (J). (978-0-606-19485-3(1)) Tandem Library Bks.

Graves, Kerry, ed. Nineteenth-Century Schoolgirl: The Diary of Caroline Cowles Richards, 1852-1854. 1999. (Diaries, Letters & Memoirs Ser.). 32p. (J). (gr. 2-7). pap. 21.00 (978-0-516-21853-3(0) , Children's Pr.) Scholastic Library Publishing.

Green, Mischa P. Sacred: 100 Affirmations for Girls. 2004. (YA). per. 12.00 (978-0-9754191-3-7(7)) Morals & Values Pr.

Greenberg, Judith. Girl's Guide to Growing Up: Making the Right Choices. 2000. (gr. 7-12). lib. bdg. 18.75 (978-0-613-34230-8(5)) Tandem Library Bks.

Griffin, Starla. Girl, 13: A Global Snapshot of Generation E. 2004. (Illus.). 240p. (J). pap. (978-1-59258-112-2(9)) Hylas Publishing.

Guest, Elissa Haden & Blackstone, Margaret. Girl Stuff: A Survival Guide to Growing Up. Pollak, Barbara, illus. 2006. 192p. (J). pap. 8.95 (978-0-15-205679-7(3) , Harcourt Paperbacks) Harcourt Children's Bks.

Haberman, Lia. About Face: Beauty Tricks & Tips. 2005. (Illus.). 48p. (J). (***978-0-439-80297-0(0)***) Scholastic, Inc.

Hainer, Michelle & Rainer, Michelle. Quiz Zone. 2006. (Girl World Ser.). (Illus.). 96p. (J). pap. 8.99 (978-0-7566-2347-0(2)) Dorling Kindersley Publishing, Inc.

Hamilton, Bethany. Ask Bethany: FAQ's: Surfing, Faith & Friends. 2007. (Soul Surfe Ser.). (Illus.). 192p. (J). pap. 9.99 (978-0-310-71227-5(0)) Zonderkidz.

Hantman, Clea. Hey, Day! 2001. 74.75 (978-0-06-000169-8(0)) HarperCollins Pubs.

Harrison, Emma. From Head to Toe: The Girls' Life Guide to Taking Care of You. Montagna, Frank, illus. 2004. 124p. (J). (978-0-439-44983-0(9)) Scholastic, Inc.

Haski, Pierre & Ma, Yan. The Diary of Ma Yan: The Struggles & Hopes of a Chinese Schoolgirl. Appignanesi, Lisa & Yanping, He, trs. from CHI. 2005. (Illus.). 176p. (J). (gr. k-17). 15.99 (978-0-06-076496-8(1)) HarperCollins Pubs.

Hearst Books (Firm) Staff. CosmoGirl! Secrets of Success. 2007. (Illus.). 176p. (J). (gr. 7 up). pap. 7.95 (***978-1-58816-666-1(X)***) Hearst Bks.

Hodgson, Mona. Real Girls of the Bible. 2008. 192p. (J). pap. 9.99 (***978-0-310-71338-8(2)***) Zondervan.

Holl, Kristi. Shine on Girl: Devotions to Keep You Sparkling. 2006. (Faithgirlz Ser.). (Illus.). 192p. (J). pap. 9.99 (978-0-310-71144-5(4)) Zonderkidz.

Holmes, Melisa & Hutchinson, Patricia. Girlology: A Girl's Guide to Stuff That Matters. Eldridge, Emily, illus. 2005. 240p. (YA). (gr. 7-12). pap. 12.95 (978-0-7573-0295-4(5)) Health Communications, Inc.

Holyoke, Nancy. A Smart Girl's Guide to Boys: Surviving Crushes, Staying True to Yourself & Other Stuff! Timmons, Bonnie, illus. 2001. (American Girl Library). 112p. (J). (gr. 3 up). 9.95 (978-1-58485-368-8(9)) American Girl Publishing, Inc.

—A Smart Girl's Guide to Boys: Surviving Crushes, Staying True to Yourself & Other Stuff! 2001. (gr. 3-6). lib. bdg. 18.75 (978-0-613-50064-7(4)) Tandem Library Bks.

Hovsepian, Ann-Margaret. The One Year Designer Genes Devo. 2007. 320p. (J). pap. 13.99 (***978-1-4143-1359-7(4)*** , Tyndale Kids) Tyndale Hse. Pubs.

Hurley, Jo. My Stylebook. Martini, Angela, illus. 2004. 48p. (J). pap. 9.99 (978-0-439-55131-1(5) , Tangerine Pr.) Scholastic, Inc.

Jaha, Niambi. Project Butterfly: Supporting Young Women & Girls of African Descent Through the Transitions of Life. 2003. 360p. (YA). per. 19.95 (978-0-9720854-1-0(6)) Perfect Bks.

Jernegan, Laura. A Whaling Captain's Daughter: The Diary of Laura Jernegan, 1868-1871. O'Hara, Megan, ed. 2000. (Blue Earth Books). (Illus.). 32p. (J). (gr. 3-4). lib. bdg. 22.60 (978-0-7368-0346-5(7) , Bridgestone Bks.) Capstone Pr., Inc.

Johnston, Andrea. Girls Speak Out: Finding Your True Self. 1999. (J). (978-0-606-16591-4(6)) Tandem Library Bks.

Karnes, Frances A. & Bean, Suzanne M. Adventures & Challenges: Real Life Stories by Girls & Young Women. 2000. (Illus.). 208p. (YA). 12.95 (978-0-910707-35-0(9)) Great Potential Pr., Inc.

Kauchak, Therese. Real Beauty: 101 Ways to Feel Great about You. Yoshizumi, Carol, illus. 2004. (American Girl Library(R) Ser.). 120p. (J). pap. 9.95 (978-1-58485-908-6(3)) American Girl Publishing, Inc.

Kelly, Dorothy A. Developing a Sense of Self: A Workbook of Tenets & Tactics for Adolescent Girls. 2006. (Illus.). 146p. (J). pap. 29.99 (978-0-87101-366-8(5) , NASW Pr.) National Assn. of Social Workers/NASW Pr.

Khidekel, Marina. The Quiz Life. 2008. 224p. (J). lib. bdg. (***978-0-375-94063-7(4)***); (YA). (gr. 5). pap. 6.99 (***978-0-375-84263-4(2)***) Dell Publishing. (Delacorte Pr.).

King, Bart. The Big Book of Girl Stuff. Kalis, Jennifer, illus. 2006. 320p. (J). (gr. 3-9). reprint ed. 19.95 (978-1-58685-819-3(X)) Gibbs Smith, Publisher.

Kirkpatrick, Katherine. The Snow Baby: The Arctic Childhood of Robert E. Peary's Daring Daughter. 2006. (Illus.). 48p. (J). 16.95 (978-0-8234-1973-9(8)) Holiday Hse., Inc.

Klutz Press Staff. My Life According to Me. 1999. (Illus.). 66p. (YA). (gr. 4-7). spiral bd. 14.95 (978-1-57054-354-8(2)) Klutz.

Krulik, Nancy E. & Ladybird Books Staff. Cloe: Angel with Attitude! 2003. (Bratz Ser.). (Illus.). 32p. pap. 2.99 (978-1-84422-186-8(5) , Putnam Juvenile) Penguin Group (USA) Inc.

—Sasha: Hip-Hop Hot! 2003. (Bratz Ser.). (Illus.). 32p. pap. 2.99 (978-1-84422-187-5(3) , Putnam Juvenile) Penguin Group (USA) Inc.

Ladybird Books Staff. Hangin' with the Lil' Bratz. 2004. (Lil' Bratz Ser.). 32p. pap. 5.43 (978-1-84422-521-7(6) , Grosset & Dunlap) Penguin Group (USA) Inc.

LaFlamme, Linda M. Rites of Passage: A Celebration of Menarche. 2001. (Moontime Ser.). (Illus.). 80p. (J). (gr. 3-9). 19.95 (978-0-9673449-0-4(5)) Synchronicity Pr.

Legacy Press Staff. God's Girls! Fun & Faith for Ages 9-12. 2004. (God's Girls Ser.: Vol. 1). (Illus.). (J). (gr. 4-7). 176p. pap. 12.99 (978-1-58411-020-0(1)); Vol. 2. 192p. pap. 12.99 (978-1-58411-021-7(X)) Rainbow Pubs. & Legacy Pr. (Legacy Pr.).

Lessons in Responsibility for Girls: Level One. 2006. Orig. Title: Home Economics for Home Schoolers Level One. (J). per., pupil's gde. ed. 18.95 (***978-0-9792446-2-9(5)***) Messiah Publishing - Pearables.

Lessons in Responsibility for Girls: Level Three, 3. 2005. Orig. Title: Home Economics for Home Schoolers Level Three. (J). per., pupil's gde. ed. (***978-0-9792446-4-3(1)***) Messiah Publishing - Pearables.

Lessons in Responsibility for Girls: Level Two, 2. 2006. Orig. Title: Home Economics for Home Schoolers Level Two. (J). per., pupil's gde. ed. 18.95 (***978-0-9792446-3-6(3)***) Messiah Publishing - Pearables.

Levchuck, Leslie. Fuel Up! A Girl's Guide to Eating Well. 1999. (Girls' Guides). (Illus.). 48p. (YA). (gr. 5-8). lib. bdg. 23.95 (978-0-8239-2981-8(7) , GGFUUP, Rosen Central) Rosen Publishing Group, Inc., The.

Loulan, Joann & Worthen, Bonnie. Periodo: Guina de una Joven. 2nd ed. 2003. (Lansky, Vicki Ser.). (SPA., Illus.). 92p. pap. 9.99 (978-0-916773-99-1(X)) Book Peddlers.

Lugovskaya, Nina. I Want to Live: The Diary of a Young Girl in Stalin's Russia. Bromfield, Andrew, tr. from RUS. 2007. (Illus.). 304p. (YA). (gr. 7 up). 17.00 (***978-0-618-60575-0(4)***) Houghton Mifflin Co. Trade & Reference Div.

Lundsten, Apryl. The Girls' Life Guide to Being a Style Superstar! Parett, Lisa, illus. 2004. 124p. (J). (978-0-439-44984-7(7)) Scholastic, Inc.

Madaras, Lynda. Ready, Set, Grow! A What's Happening to My Body? Book for Younger Girls. Davick, Linda, tr. Davick, Linda, illus. 2003. 128p. (YA). (gr. 3 up). 22.00 (978-1-55704-587-4(9)); pap. 12.00 (978-1-55704-565-2(8)) Newmarket Pr. (Newmarket Shooting Scripts).

—Ready, Set, Grow! A What's Happening to My Body? Book for Younger Girls. 2003. (gr. 3-6). lib. bdg. 21.10 (978-0-613-68537-5(7)) Tandem Library Bks.

Madaras, Lynda & Madaras, Area. My Body, My Self for Girls. 3rd rev. ed. 2007. (Illus.). 128p. (YA). pap. 12.95 (***978-1-55704-766-3(9)***) Newmarket Pr.

—The What's Happening to My Body Book for Girls. 3rd rev. ed. 2007. (Illus.). 304p. (YA). 24.95 (***978-1-55704-768-7(5)***); pap. 12.95 (***978-1-55704-764-9(2)***) Newmarket Pr.

Magruder, Trula, ed. True Stories: Girls' Inspiring Stories of Courage & Heart. Haley, Amanda, illus. 2003. (American Girl Library). 80p. pap. 7.95 (978-1-58485-744-0(7)) American Girl Publishing, Inc.

Marcovitz, Hal & Snyder, Gail. A Guys' Guide to Anger; A Girls' Guide to Anger. 2008. (Flip-It-over Guides to Teen Emotions Ser.). (Illus.). 128p. (J). (gr. 5 up). lib. bdg. 31.93 (***978-0-7660-2853-1(4)***) Enslow Pubs., Inc.

Martin, Dawn. Fast Girls Finish Last: A Girl's Guide to Becoming a Virgin with Attitude! 2nd rev. ed. 2006. (Illus.). 248p. (YA). (gr. 7-13). per. 19.95 (978-0-9668718-0-7(4)) Eos Publishing.

McMahon, Patricia. Chi-Hoon: A Korean Girl. 2003. (Illus.). 48p. (YA). (gr. 4-6). pap. 10.95 (978-1-56397-720-6(6)) Boyds Mills Pr.

Mission City Press Inc. Staff. Dear Elsie. 2001. (Elsie Dinsmore). 208p. (YA). (gr. 5-9). 12.99 (978-1-928749-55-4(0)) Zonderkidz.

Mo, Potato. Fries & Rice: My Treasured Memories. 2002. 157p. (YA). pap. 11.95 (978-0-595-24963-3(9) , Writers Club Pr.) iUniverse, Inc.

Moka & Daly, Melissa. Just Us Girls: Secrets to Feeling Good about Yourself, Inside & Out, 4 vols. Heliot, Eric, illus. 2004. (Sunscreen Ser.). 112p. (J). (gr. 6-11). pap. 9.95 (978-0-8109-9161-3(6)) Abrams, Harry N. , Inc.

Monson-Burton, Marianne, compiled by. Girls Know Best Vol. 2: Tips on Life & Fun Stuff to Do. l.t. ed. 1999. (Girls Know Best Ser.). (Illus.). (J). (gr. 3 up). lib. bdg. 23.33 (978-0-8368-2453-7(9)) Stevens, Gareth Inc.

Morina, Barbara. Girls Only: A Teen Journal. 2000. (Write It down Ser.: Vol. 21). (Illus.). 202p. (YA). (gr. 6-12). 19.95 (978-1-892033-19-2(4)) Journals Unlimited, Inc.

Mulcahy, Lisa, et al. Bye Bye Boredom! The Girl's Life Big Book of Fun. 2003. (Illus.). 124p. (J). (978-0-439-44976-2(6)) Scholastic, Inc.

Musgrave, Susan. You Be Me: Friendship in the Lives of Teen Girls. 2002. (gr. 7-12). lib. bdg. 16.40 (978-0-613-78373-6(5)) Tandem Library Bks.

Musgrave, Susan, ed. You Be Me: Friendship in the Lives of Teen Girls. 2002. 128p. (YA). (gr. 10 up). 18.95 (978-1-55037-739-2(6)); pap. 7.95 (978-1-55037-738-5(8)) Annick Pr., Ltd. CAN. *Dist:* Firefly Bks., Ltd.

Naylor, Caroline. Beauty Trix for Cool Chix: Easy-to-Make Lotions, Potions, & Spells to Bring out a Beautiful You. 2003. (Cool Chix Ser.). (Illus.). 96p. (gr. 5 up). pap. 9.95 (978-0-8230-6957-6(5)) Watson-Guptill Pubns., Inc.

Norac, Carl & Dubois, Claude K. Las Palabras Dulces. 2003. (SPA.). 32p. (978-84-95150-18-9(2)) Corimbo, Editorial S.L.

Norris, Teresa Rae. Beauty, Brains & Talent: A Workbook for Girls on Self Esteem, Well Being & Safety. Norris, Tresseca M., photos by. 2001. (Illus.). 160p. pap. 24.95 (978-0-9713685-0-7(3)) Morning Star.

O'Hara, Megan, ed. A Whaling Captain's Daughter: The Diary of Laura Jernegan, 1868-1871. 1999. (Diaries, Letters & Memoirs Ser.). (Illus.). 32p. (J). (gr. 2-7). pap. 21.00 (978-0-516-21851-9(4) , Children's Pr.) Scholastic Library Publishing.

Olsen, Mary-Kate & Olsen, Ashley. Mary-Kate & Ashley: Our Story. rev. ed. 2003. 96p. mass mkt. 4.99 (978-0-06-056848-1(8) , Harper Entertainment) HarperCollins Pubs.

—Mary-Kate & Ashley Our Story: The Official Biography. 2003. (gr. 5-8). lib. bdg. 13.00 (978-0-613-68449-1(4)) Tandem Library Bks.

Peters, Diane. Girlness: Body & Soul. Murray, Steven, illus. 2005. (Deal with It Ser.). 32p. (J). (gr. 4-8). pap. 12.95 (978-1-55028-891-9(1)) Lorimer, James & Co., Ltd., Pubs. CAN. *Dist:* Casemate Pubs. & Bk. Distributors, LLC.

Phidal Publishing Staff, ed. Girls World: My Best Friends. (Illus.). 64p. (J). pap. (978-2-7643-0145-6(6)) Phidal Publishing, Inc./Editions Phidal, Inc.

Plaisted, Caroline. Totally Secret: Every Girl's Guide to Keeping & Sharing Secrets. 2000. (Illus.). 128p. (J). (gr. 3 up). pap. (978-1-902618-08-1(4)) Element Children's Bks.

Pleasant Company Staff. Girls & Their Horses: True Tales from American Girls. 2000. (J). 14.75 (978-0-606-20219-0(6)) Tandem Library Bks.

Powell, Rebecca. Wise up! Experience the Power of Proverb. 2005. 210p. pap. 19.95 (978-1-4141-0399-0(9)) Pleasant Word.

Raica-Klotz, Helen. Journal Me! A Pocketbook for Girls. 1999. 96p. (J). (gr. 4-7). pap. 9.95 (978-0-89390-449-4(X)) Resource Pubns., Inc.

Raine, Alison. Ultimate You! 365 Days to a More Daring, Deep, & Adorable You. 2001. (gr. 7-12). lib. bdg. 13.00 (978-0-613-33175-3(3)) Tandem Library Bks.

Rainer, Michelle. Quiz Zone 2. 2007. (Girl World Ser.). 96p. (J). pap. 8.99 (978-0-7566-2670-9(6)) Dorling Kindersley Publishing, Inc.

Rau, Margaret. Young Women in China. 2001. (Illus.). 168p. (YA). pap. 11.95 (978-0-595-16033-4(6)) iUniverse, Inc.

Reader, Jenny. Girl 2 Girl: The Swap Book You Share with Your Friends. Martin, Caroline & Davies, Nic, illus. 2003. 96p. (J). pap. (978-0-439-56743-5(2)) Scholastic, Inc.

Rice, Ashley. Adelante, niñA... Sigue soñando (You Go, Girl Keep Dreaming) Un libro especial sobre Como. 2006. (SPA & ENG., Illus.). 64p. (J). pap. 9.95 (978-1-59842-162-0(X) , Blue Mountain Pr.) Blue Mountain Arts Inc.

—Friends Rule: A Very Special Book of Friendship Especially for Girls. 2003. (Illus.). 64p. (J). pap. (978-0-88396-772-0(3) , Blue Mountain Pr.) Blue Mountain Arts Inc.

—Girls Rule: A Very Special Book Created Especially for Girls. Rice, Ashley, illus. (Illus.). 64p. (J). pap. 9.95 (978-0-88396-627-3(1) , Blue Mountain Pr.) Blue Mountain Arts Inc.

—You Are an Amazing Girl: A very special book about being you & making your dreams come True. (Illus.). 64p. (J). pap. 9.95 (978-1-59842-066-1(6) , Blue Mountain Pr.) Blue Mountain Arts Inc.

—You Go, Girl Keep Dreaming. (Illus.). 56p. (J). 5.95 (978-1-59842-101-9(8) , Blue Mountain Pr.) Blue Mountain Arts Inc.

Richards, Caroline Cowles. A Nineteenth-Century Schoolgirl: The Diary of Caroline Cowles Richards, 1852-1855. Graves, Kerry A., ed. 2000. (Blue Earth Books). (Illus.). 32p. (J). (gr. 3-4). lib. bdg. 22.60 (978-0-7368-0342-7(4) , Bridgestone Bks.) Capstone Pr., Inc.

Roderick, Stacey & Warwick, Ellen. Centsibility: The Planet Girl Guide to Money. Melnychuk, Monika, illus. 2008. 80p. (***978-1-55453-208-7(6)***) Kids Can Pr., Ltd.

Roehm, Michelle. Girls Who Rocked the World, Vol. 2. 2000. (YA). (978-0-606-19486-0(X)) Tandem Library Bks.

Roehm, Michelle, compiled by. Girls Knows Best: Advice for Girls from Girls on Just about Everything. 1999. (Girls Know Best Ser.). (Illus.). 160p. (J). (gr. 3 up). lib. bdg. 23.33 (978-0-8368-2452-0(0)) Stevens, Gareth Inc.

Rue, Nancy N. The Fun-Finder Book: It's a God Thing! 2003. (YWOF Library). 112p. (J). pap. 7.99 (978-0-310-70258-0(5)) Zondervan.

—The Walk-the-Walk Book: It's a God Thing! Boyer, Lyn, illus. 2003. (YWOF Library). 128p. (J). pap. 7.99 (978-0-310-70259-7(3)) Zonderkidz.

Schoenberg, Jill. Journal Buddies: A Girl's Journal for Sharing & Celebrating Magnificence (2nd Edition) 2007. (J). per. 16.95 (***978-0-9768623-0-7(1)***) Blue Sky at Night Publishing.

Schwager, Tina & Schuerger, Michele. The Right Moves to Getting Fit & Feeling Great! Verdick, Elizabeth, ed. Gordon, Mike & Heinlen, Marieka, illus. 1998. Orig. Title: The Right Moves: a Girl's Guide to Getting Fit & Feeling Good. 280p. (YA). (gr. 7 up). pap. 15.95 (978-1-57542-035-6(X)) Free Spirit Publishing, Inc.

Smith, Liz. A Girl's Guide to Growing up - Booklet, 10 per packet. Perry, Gala, illus. 2005. (J). 63.95 (978-1-55942-207-9(6)) Marsh Media.

Steele, Christy & Todd, Anne M. A Confederate Girl: The Diary of Carrie Berry, 1864. 1999. (Diaries, Letters & Memoirs Ser.). (Illus.). 32p. (J). (gr. 2-7). pap. 21.00 (978-0-516-21338-5(5) , Children's Pr.) Scholastic Library Publishing.

Stern, Zoe. Protect This Girl: Words of Inspiration from Girl to Girl. 2004. (Illus.). 32p. (gr. 7-13). 9.95 (978-1-883672-81-2(3) , Tricycle Pr.) Ten Speed Pr.

Stoppard, Miriam. Every Girl's Life Guide. 1999. (J). (978-0-606-16987-5(3)) Tandem Library Bks.

Swain, Claudia. What's a Girl to Do? 2004. 128p. pap. 6.99 (978-1-56309-440-8(1)) New Hope Pubs.

Swann, Elaine. Girls Have Style... at School! A Glam Girl's Guide to Taking on the Day with Grace & Style. 2005. (Illus.). (YA). pap. 8.95 (978-0-9773520-0-5(5)) W S Publishing.

Tym, Kate. Totally You! Every Girl's Guide to Looking Good. 1999. (Illus.). 160p. (YA). (gr. 7-9). pap. 5.95 (978-1-902618-44-9(0)) Element Children's Bks.

Villegas, Maria & Kent, Jennie. Girl to Girl. Salom Safi, Ivette, illus. 2007. 336p. (J). spiral bd. 16.00 (***978-958-8306-03-2(5)***) Villegas Editores S.A. COL. *Dist:* Independent Pubs. Group.

Weschler, Toni. Cycle Savvy: The Smart Teen's Guide to the Mysteries of Her Body. 2006. (Illus.). 224p. pap. 14.95 (978-0-06-082964-3(8)) HarperCollins Pubs.

Weston, Carol. For Girls Only: Wise Words, Good Advice. 2004. 208p. (J). (gr. 5 up). pap. 8.99 (978-0-06-058318-7(5) , Harper Trophy) HarperCollins Pubs.

—For Girls Only: Wise Words, Good Advice. 1998. (978-0-606-13396-8(8)) Tandem Library Bks.

—Girltalk: All the Stuff Your Sister Never Told You. 4th ed. 2004. 448p. pap. 14.95 (978-0-06-058575-4(7)) HarperCollins Pubs.

White, Kelly. The Girls' Life Big Book of Quizzes: Your Secret Self Revealed! Montagna, Frank, illus. 2003. 124p. (YA). (978-0-439-44979-3(0)) Scholastic, Inc.

White, Kelly & Stacy, Lori. Ask Lucky! The Girls'life Guide to Dealing with Dilemmas. 2003. (Illus.). 120p. (J). (978-0-439-44982-3(0)) Scholastic, Inc.

Wong, A. & Tabori, Lena. The Little Big Book for Girls. (Illus.). 352p. 24.95 (978-0-941807-81-4(9) , Welcome Bks.) Welcome Enterprises, Inc.

Yaconelli, Mike. A Gift for My Daughter. 2nd ed. 2002. (Illus.). 64p. (J). pap. 6.99 (978-0-7459-4786-0(7) , Lion) Lion Hudson plc GBR. *Dist:* Independent Pubs. Group.

Yan, Adrianne. It's a Money Thing. 2008. 96p. (YA). 12.99 (978-0-8118-4427-7(7)) Chronicle Bks. LLC.

Yan, Ma. The Diary of Ma Yan: The Life of a Chinese School Girl. Haski, Pierre, ed. 2006. (Illus.). 208p. reprint ed. pap. 22.00 (978-1-4223-5712-5(0)) DIANE Publishing Co.

Zimmerman, Jill. Picture Perfect: What You Need to Feel Better about Your Body. 2007. 256p. (YA). pap. 14.95 (***978-0-7573-0607-5(1)***) Health Communications, Inc.

GIRLS—EDUCATION

see Women—Education

GIRLS—EMPLOYMENT

see Children—Employment

GIRLS—FICTION

Abbot, Belle K. Leah Mordecai. 2006. pap. (***978-1-4065-0341-8(X)***) Dodo Pr.

Abdo Publishing Staff, contrib. by. Flower Girl Friends. 2000. (Faithful Friends Ser.). (Illus.). 64p. (J). (gr. 4). lib. bdg. 21.35 (978-1-57765-229-8(0) , ABDO & Daughters) ABDO Publishing Co.

Abdul-Rauf, Muhammad. The Story of Tawaddud: A Brilliant & Beautiful Girl & a Model of Good Moral Conduct. 2005. xx, 185p. (978-983-9184-66-2(0)) Institut Perkembangan Minda.

Abrahamson, Deborah. Brittany's Big Surprise. 1998. 112p. (J). (gr. 5-8). pap. 3.99 (978-0-87406-891-7(6) , Willowisp Pr.) Darby Creek Publishing.

Ada, Alma Flor. Me Encantan los Saturdays y los Domingos. Savadier, Elivia, illus. 2006. Tr. of I Love Saturdays y Domingos. (SPA.). (J). (gr. 1-2). 11.95 (978-1-59437-576-7(3) , AF33204) Santillana USA Publishing Co., Inc.

—Rosa Alada. (Cuentos para Todo el Ano Ser.). (SPA., Illus.). 16p. (J). (gr. k-3). pap. 8.95 (978-1-58105-186-5(7)) Santillana USA Publishing Co., Inc.

Adams, D. J. Rachel Beats the Blizzard. 1998. 64p. (J). (gr. 1-6). pap. 5.95 (978-0-9659630-1-5(2)) Tomorrow's Girl.

Adams, Denise H. Annabelle's Angels. 2007. (J). per. 11.99 (***978-1-59879-386-4(1)***) Lifevest Publishing, Inc.

Adams, Kendall. Don't Do Anything I Wouldn't Do. 2007. (Hook up or Break Up Ser.: No. 4). 256p. (J). pap. 8.99 (***978-0-06-088566-3(1)*** , HarperTeen) HarperCollins Pubs.

Advantage Publishers Group. Clara Goes to School. 2000. (Let's Start! Teacher's Pets Ser.). (Illus.). 32p. (J). (ps-1). 6.95 (978-1-57145-437-9(3) , Silver Dolphin Bks.) Advantage Pubs. Group.

Ahlberg, Allan. Janet's Last Book. (Illus.). 64p. (J). (gr. k-6). pap. 19.95 (978-0-14-026872-0(3)) Penguin Bks., Ltd. GBR. *Dist:* Penguin Group (USA) Inc.

—Miss Dirt the Dustman's Daughter. (Illus.). 24p. (J). pap. 6.95 (978-0-14-037882-5(0)) Penguin Bks., Ltd. GBR. *Dist:* Trafalgar Square Publishing.

Aikins, Dave, illus. At the Carnival. 2005. (J). (***978-1-4156-0769-5(9)*** , Simon Spotlight/Nickelodeon) Simon & Schuster Children's Publishing.

Ajmera, Maya. Extraordinary Girls. 1999. (gr. 3-6). lib. bdg. 16.40 (978-0-613-35113-3(4)) Tandem Library Bks.

Ajmera, Maya, et al. Extraordinary Girls. 2004. (Illus.). 48p. (YA). (ps-3). reprint ed. pap. 7.95 (978-0-88106-066-9(6)) Charlesbridge Publishing, Inc.

Alcott, Louisa May. Eight Cousins. 2005. 300p. pap. 14.95 (978-1-59540-676-7(X) , 1st World Library - Literary Society) 1st World Publishing, Inc.

—Eight Cousins. 2005. 120p. per. 4.95 (978-1-4209-2569-2(5)) Digireads.com.

—Eight Cousins. 2007. (Dover Evergreen Classics Ser.). 224p. pap. 4.95 (***978-0-486-45559-4(9)***) Dover Pubns., Inc.

—Eight Cousins. 2003. (ENG.). pap. 13.99 (***978-1-4043-6290-1(8)***) IndyPublish.com.

—Eight Cousins. 2004. reprint ed. pap. 1.99 (978-1-4192-1740-1(2)) Kessinger Publishing, LLC.

—A Garland for Girls. 2006. pap. (***978-1-4065-0587-0(0)***) Dodo Pr.

—Kitty's Class Day. l.t. ed. 2005. 424p. pap. (978-1-84637-055-7(8)) Echo Library.

—Little Women: Juvenile Classic. 2005. (Illus.). 192p. (J). 5.99 (978-1-4037-1440-4(1)) Dalmatian Pr.

—An Old-Fashioned Girl. 1999. (J). 25.01 (978-0-316-03809-6(1)) Little Brown & Co.

—Les Quatre Filles du Docteur March.Tr. of Little Women. (FRE.). (J). pap. 19.95 (978-2-07-051516-5(8)) Gallimard, Editions FRA. *Dist:* Distribooks, Inc.

Aldridge, Janet. The Meadow-Brook Girls Afloat. rev. ed. 2006. 208p. 27.95 (978-1-4218-1766-8(7)); pap. 12.95 (978-1-4218-1866-5(3)) 1st World Publishing, Inc. (1st World Library - Literary Society).

Aldridge, Janet. The Meadow-Brook Girls Afloat or the Sto. 2006. 33.99 (***978-1-4280-0789-5(X)***); pap. 26.99 (***978-1-4280-0811-3(X)***) IndyPublish.com.

Alegria, Malin. Sofi Mendoza's Guide to Getting Lost in Mexico. 2007. 304p. (YA). (gr. 9 up). 15.99 (978-0-689-87811-4(7)) Simon & Schuster Children's Publishing.

Aleman Lascurain, Guadalupe. La Domadora de Miedos. Diseno, Tane Arte y, illus. rev. ed. 2006. (SPA.). 232p. (J). pap. 8.95 (978-970-20-0182-9(X)) Castillo, Ediciones, S. A. de C. V. MEX. *Dist:* Macmillan.

Alessi, Alberto. Alessi. 1998. (Illus.). 130p. pap. 4.95 (978-3-8290-1377-2(9) , 520754) Konemann.

Alexander, Samantha. Against the Clock, Vol. 6. 133p. (J). mass mkt. 6.99 (978-0-330-34538-5(9) , Pan) Pan Macmillan GBR. *Dist:* Trafalgar Square Publishing.

Alma, Ann. Under Emily's Sky. 2005. (Sandcastle Book Ser.). 96p. (YA). (gr. 3-8). pap., tchr. ed. (978-0-88878-379-0(5) , Sandcastle Bks.) Dundurn Group, The.

Alsius, Lourdes. Unos Padres Para Aruna. 2005. (SPA.). 32p. (J). 18.95 (978-84-8418-096-8(4)) Zendrera Zariquiey, Editorial ESP. *Dist:* Iaconi, Mariuccia Bk. Imports.

Amelio-Ortiz, Osvaldo Pastor. He Loves Me, He Loves Me Not: Margarita's Story. Ballester, Juan P., tr. 2006. (Magical Stories Ser.). (Illus.). 28p. (J). 16.95 (978-9974-7896-9-2(9)) Hardenville SA URY. *Dist:* Independent Pubs. Group.

American Girl Magazine: Jan/Feb 2004. (J). 19.75 (978-1-58485-925-3(3)) American Girl Publishing, Inc.

American Girl Magazine: July/Aug 2004 Jumbo Issue. (J). 24.75 (978-1-58485-928-4(8)) American Girl Publishing, Inc.

American Girl Magazine: March/April 2004. (J). 19.75 (978-1-58485-926-0(1)) American Girl Publishing, Inc.

American Girl Magazine: May/June 2004. (J). 19.75 (978-1-58485-927-7(X)) American Girl Publishing, Inc.

American Girl Magazine: Sept/Oct 2004. (J). 19.75 (978-1-58485-929-1(6)) American Girl Publishing, Inc.

Anastasio, Dina. The Case of the Grand Canyon Eagle. Saflund, Birgitta, illus. 2000. (Juliet Stone Mystery Ser.: No. 1). 73p. (Orig.). (gr. 5 up). pap. 6.95 (978-1-879373-84-6(X)) Rinehart, Roberts Pubs.

Andersen, Hans Christian. The Little Match Girl. Bell, Anthea, tr. from DAN. Pacovska, Kveta, illus. 2005. 40p. (J). (ps-3). 18.99 (978-0-698-40027-6(5) , Minedition) Penguin Group (USA) Inc.

—The Little Match Seller. 2005. 12p. pap. (978-958-30-1509-0(1)) Panamericana Editorial.

Anderson, Ho Che. The No-Boys Club. 1998. (J). (gr. 4-7). pap. 5.95 (978-0-88899-321-2(8)) Groundwood Bks. CAN. *Dist:* Transition Vendor.

Anderson, Jodi Lynn. May Bird & the Ever After, Bk. 1. Gore, Leonid, illus. 2006. 352p. (J). (gr. 5-9). reprint ed. pap. 5.99 (978-1-4169-0607-0(X) , Aladdin) Simon & Schuster Children's Publishing.

Anderson, Laurie Halse. No Time for Mother's Day. 2001. (978-0-606-21356-1(2)); 1999. lib. bdg. 15.25 (978-0-613-37020-2(1)) Tandem Library Bks.

Anderson, Pamela. My New School: Brunette Girl. Lee, Han & Wu, Stacie, illus. 2004. (J). 12.95 (978-1-932555-06-6(4)) Watch Me Grow Kids.

Andrews, Carol. The Giggle Wind. 2003. (Illus.). 40p. 17.95 (978-0-9725609-2-4(0)) Diakonia Publishing.

Andrews, V. C. Orphans. 2000. (gr. 7-12). lib. bdg. 16.45 (978-0-613-33602-4(X)) Tandem Library Bks.

Anfousse, Ginette. Le Grand Reve de Rosalie. 2002. (Roman Jeunesse Ser.). (FRE.). 96p. (YA). (gr. 4-7). pap. (978-2-89021-182-7(7)) Diffusion du livre Mirabel.

—Mon Ami Pichou. ed. 2004. (FRE.). (J). (ps-1). spiral bd. (978-0-616-01824-8(X)) Canadian National Institute for the Blind/Institut National Canadien pour les Aveugles.

—Rosalie S'En Va-T-En Guerre. 2002. (Roman Jeunesse Ser.). (FRE.). 96p. (YA). (gr. 4-7). pap. (978-2-89021-093-6(6)) Diffusion du livre Mirabel.

—Les Vacances de Rosalie. 2002. (Roman Jeunesse Ser.). (FRE.). 96p. (YA). (gr. 4-7). pap. (978-2-89021-116-2(9)) Diffusion du livre Mirabel.

Anholt, Laurence. El Jardin Magico de Claude Monet. 2004. (SPA., Illus.). 28p. (J). 19.99 (978-84-8488-101-8(6)) Serres, Ediciones, S. L. ESP. *Dist:* Lectorum Pubns., Inc.

Annette: The Desert Inn Mystery. 2003. (Illus.). pap. 15.99 (978-0-7868-4559-0(7)) Disney Pr.

Annette & the Mystery at Smugglers' Cove. 2003. (Illus.). pap. 15.99 (978-0-7868-4558-3(9)) Disney Pr.

Answer Why for Mee Mee: Work & Play Book. 2006. (J). (978-0-9748715-3-0(2)) Vision Harmony Publishing.

Antillano, Laura. Diana en la Tierra Wayuu. Armas, Lourdes, illus. 2003. (SPA.). 121p. (YA). (gr. 5-8). pap. 9.95 (978-958-24-0180-1(X)) Santillana COL. *Dist:* Santillana USA Publishing Co., Inc.

Apostolina, M. Dark Cindy. 2006. 336p. (YA). pap. 8.99 (978-1-4169-1769-4(1) , Simon Pulse) Simon & Schuster Children's Publishing.

Applegate, Katherine. Don't Tell Zoey. 1999. (Making Out Ser.: No. 13). 176p. (YA). (gr. 7 up). pap. 3.99 (978-0-380-80869-4(2)) HarperCollins Pubs.

—Lara Gets Lucky. 2000. (Making Out Ser.: No. 23). 176p. (YA). (gr. 7-12). pap. 3.99 (978-0-380-81527-2(3)) HarperCollins Pubs.

—Zoey Speaks Out. 1999. (Making Out Ser.: No. 18). 192p. (YA). (gr. 7-12). pap. 3.99 (978-0-380-81120-5(0)) HarperCollins Pubs.

Arai, Kiyoko. Beauty Pop, Vol. 1. 2006. (Beauty Pop Ser.). (Illus.). 200p. (YA). pap. 8.99 (978-1-4215-0575-6(4)) Viz Media.

Archer, Lily. The Poison Apples. 2007. 288p. (YA). (gr. 6 up). 16.95 (***978-0-312-36762-6(7)***) Feiwel & Friends.

Argueta, Jorge & Alvarez, Cecilia Concepcion. Moony Luna. Gomez, Elizabeth, illus. 2005. (ENG & SPA.). 32p. (J). 16.95 (978-0-89239-205-6(3)) Children's Bk. Pr.

Ariano, Tara. Untitled: A Bad Teen Novel. 2002. 154p. pap. 11.95 (978-0-595-22478-4(4) , Writers Club Pr.) iUniverse, Inc.

Arlen, Richard. Girls' Boarding School. 320p. pap. 6.95 (978-0-7472-4039-6(6)) Headline Bk. Publishing GBR. *Dist:* Trafalgar Square Publishing.

Armstrong, Bill. Letters from Ozo, 1. 2005. (Illus.). 190p. (J). per. (978-0-9771676-0-9(7)) Rubicon Bks.

Arnold, Shauna. Baa. Hines, Irene, illus. 2004. 19p. (J). (ps-3). 12.00 (978-0-9743669-0-6(0)) Trinity Bks.

Arnold, Tedd. Catalina Magdalina Hoopensteiner Wallendiner Hogan Logan Bogan Was Her Name. Arnold, Tedd, illus. 2004. (Illus.). 40p. (J). pap. 10.95 (978-0-590-10994-9(4) , Cartwheel Bks.) Scholastic, Inc.

Asai, Carrie. Book of the Flame. 2004. lib. bdg. 15.30 (978-0-613-73423-3(8)) Tandem Library Bks.

—The Book of the Pearl. Verhoye, Annabelle & Alarcao, Renato, illus. 2003. (Samurai Girl Ser.: Bk. 3). 240p. (YA). pap. 6.99 (978-0-689-86432-2(9) , Simon Pulse) Simon & Schuster Children's Publishing.

—Book of the Pearl. 2003. lib. bdg. 15.30 (978-0-613-73440-0(8)) Tandem Library Bks.

Asai, Carrie & Gray, Mitchel. The Book of the Wind. Verhoye, Annabelle & Alarcao, Renato, illus. 2003. (Samurai Girl Ser.). 224p. (YA). pap. 6.99 (978-0-689-86433-9(7) , Simon Pulse) Simon & Schuster Children's Publishing.

Asner, Anne-Marie. Shluffy Girl. l.t. ed. 2005. (Illus.). 32p. (J). per. 6.95 (978-0-9753629-2-1(5)) Matzah Ball Bks.

—Shmutzy Girl. Asner, Anne-Marie, illus. l.t. ed. 2004. (Illus.). 32p. (J). per. 6.95 (978-0-9753629-0-7(9)) Matzah Ball Bks.

Atkins, Jeannine. Get Set! Swim! Lee, Hector Viveros, illus. 1998. 32p. (J). (ps up). 15.95 (978-1-880000-66-3(0)) Lee & Low Bks., Inc.

—Preparadas... Listas... Ya! ed. 2004. (SPA., Illus.). (J). (gr. k-3). spiral bd. (978-0-616-07274-5(0)) Canadian National Institute for the Blind/Institut National Canadien pour les Aveugles.

—Preparadas... Listas... Ya! Sarfatti, Esther, tr. from ENG. Lee, Hector Viveros, illus. 1998. (SPA.). 32p. (J). (gr. 1-3). 15.95 (978-1-880000-77-9(6) , LW(8473)); pap. 6.95 (978-1-880000-78-6(4) , LW(8474)) Lee & Low Bks., Inc.

Aumann, Jane & Ladage, Cindy. The Christmas Tractor. Freitag, Charles, illus. 2003. 30p. (J). (gr. k-4). pap. 8.95 (978-0-9703319-2-2(4)) Roots & Wings.

Avey, F. M. Girl Gifts. Duit, Kirk, photos by. 2001. 32p. (YA). per. 18.95 (978-1-930758-86-5(3)) Yeva Corp.

Avi. The Secret School. 2003. (Illus.). 168p. (J). (gr. 3-6). pap. 5.95 (978-0-15-204699-6(2) , 53582853, Harcourt Paperbacks) Harcourt Children's Bks.

—The True Confessions of Charlotte Doyle. 1999. (Masterpiece Series Access Editions). xvii, 187p. (J). 10.95 (978-0-8219-1983-5(0)) Paradigm Publishing, Inc.

Azuma, Kiyohiko. Azumanga Daioh, Vol. 3. 2004. (Illus.). 172p. (YA). pap. 9.99 (978-1-4139-0030-9(5)) ADV Manga.

—Azumanga Daioh: The Manga, Vol. 1. 2003. (Illus.). 172p. (YA). pap. 9.99 (978-1-4139-0000-2(3)) A. D. Vision, Inc.

—Azumanga Daioh: The Manga, Vol. 2. 2003. (Illus.). 168p. (YA). pap. (978-1-4139-0023-1(2)) ADV Manga.

Babcock, Bruce. Christmas with the Little People. Babcock, Bruce, illus. unabr. ed. 1998. (Illus.). 46p. (J). (ps-6). pap. 7.95 (978-1-892161-04-8(4)) Babcock Publishing Co.

—I Wished upon a Falling Star. Babcock, Bruce, illus. unabr. ed. 1998. (Illus.). 54p. (J). (ps-6). pap. 7.95 (978-1-892161-03-1(6)) Babcock Publishing Co.

Bailey, Helen. Takes a Break. 2007. (Topaz Ser.: Vol. 4). (Illus.). 144p. pap. 7.95 (***978-0-340-91733-6(4)***) Hodder Children's Division GBR. *Dist:* Independent Pubs. Group.

Bakas, Tita. Black-Eyed Susan. 1999. (Illus.). 32p. (J). (gr. 1-5). pap. 7.95 (978-0-9662431-2-3(9)) Viewpoint Pr., Inc.

Baldacci, David. Wish You Well. 2001. (gr. 5-8). lib. bdg. 16.45 (978-0-613-57333-7(1)) Tandem Library Bks.

Balzola, Asun. Babi es Barbara. (SPA.). 72p. 8.95 (978-84-392-8113-9(7)) Baker & Taylor Bks.

—Munia y Sra. Piltronera (Munia & Mrs. Piltronera) (SPA.). 36p. (J). 16.95 (978-84-233-1290-0(9)) Ediciones Destino ESP. *Dist:* AIMS International Bks., Inc.

Banks, Lynne Reid. Alice-by-Accident. 2000. (Avon Camelot Bks.). 144p. (J). (gr. 4-7). 14.95 (978-0-380-97865-6(2)) HarperCollins Pubs.

Bannon, Kay Thorpe. Curious One: A Cherokee Story. Sneed, Ravina Rene, illus. 2001. 38p. (J). (ps-5). pap. 12.95 (978-0-9669946-3-6(9)) Lobster Cove Publishing Co.

Banting, Celia. I only said I was telling the Truth. 2006. 240p. (YA). per. 14.99 (***978-0-9786648-4-8(1)***) Wighita Pr.

—I Only Said Yes So That They'd Like Me. 2006. 224p. (YA). per. 14.99 (***978-0-9786648-1-7(7)***) Wighita Pr.

Barber, Antonia. Dancing Shoes: Lucy's Next Step. (Illus.). 96p. (J). 6th ed. 5.95 (978-0-14-130150-1(3)); Vol. 4. 5.95 (978-0-14-038685-1(8)) Penguin Bks., Ltd. GBR. *Dist:* Trafalgar Square Publishing.

Barber, Barbara E. Allie's Basketball Dream. Ligasan, Darryl, illus. 1998. 32p. (J). (ps-5). 6.95 (978-1-880000-72-4(5)) Lee & Low Bks., Inc.

Bardwell, Harrison. Roberta's Flying Courage. 2003. 248p. (J). pap. 13.95 (978-1-55753-335-7(0)) Purdue Univ. Pr.

Barham, Lisa. A Girl Like Moi: The Fashion-Forward Adventures of Imogene. Rim, Sujean, illus. 2006. (Fashion-Forward Adventures of Imogene Ser.). 272p. (YA). (gr. 6-10). pap. 8.99 (978-1-4169-1443-3(9) , Simon Pulse) Simon & Schuster Children's Publishing.

Bates, Cynthia. Mikayla's Victory. 1999. (978-0-606-17712-2(4)); (gr. 7-12). lib. bdg. 13.55 (978-0-613-18220-1(0)) Tandem Library Bks.

Baum, L. Frank. The Patchwork Girl of Oz. rev. ed. 2006. Tr. of 220. 272p. 28.95 (978-1-4218-1793-4(4)); pap. 13.95 (978-1-4218-1893-1(0)) 1st World Publishing, Inc. (1st World Library - Literary Society).

—The Patchwork Girl of Oz. 2002. Tr. of 220. (ENG.). pap. 19.99 (***978-1-4043-2379-7(1)***) IndyPublish.com.

—The Patchwork Girl of Oz. 2004. Tr. of 220. reprint ed. pap. 22.95 (978-1-4191-7678-4(1)); pap. 1.99 (978-1-4192-7678-1(6)) Kessinger Publishing, LLC.

—The Patchwork Girl of Oz. 2004. (Twelve-Point Ser.).Tr. of 220. lib. bdg. 24.00 (978-1-58287-275-9(9)) North Bks.

Beacon Street Girls Staff. Meet the Beacon Street Girls. 2004. (Illus.). 36p. (J). 3.99 (978-0-9746587-5-9(8) , Beacon Street Girls) B*tween Productions, Inc.

Beale, Fleur. Walking Lightly. Sangl, Michaela, illus. 2006. 72p. (J). 12.95 (978-1-894965-37-8(X)) Simply Read Bks. CAN. *Dist:* Perseus Distribution.

Beatty, Patricia. Lupita Manana. 2000. (Harper Trophy Bks.). (SPA.). 192p. (J). (gr. 3-7). pap. 5.99 (978-0-380-73247-0(5) , Harper Trophy) HarperCollins Pubs.

—Turn Homeward, Hannalee. 1999. 208p. (J). (gr. 3-7). pap. 5.99 (978-0-688-16676-2(8)) HarperCollins Pubs.

—Turn Homeward, Hannalee. 1999. (978-0-606-16763-5(3)) Tandem Library Bks.

Because of Walter, 6 Packs. (Action Packs Ser.). 104p. (gr. 3-5). 44.00 (978-0-7635-8402-3(9)) Rigby Education.

Beechwood, Beth. Crush-Tastic! 6th rev. ed. 2007. (Hannah Montana Ser.: No. 6). 128p. (gr. 3-7). pap. 4.99 (***978-1-4231-0461-2(7)***) Disney Pr.

Beeke, Joel & Kleyn, Diana. How God Used a Snowdrift. Anderson, Jeff, illus. (Building on the Rock Ser.). 176p. (J). pap. (978-1-85792-817-4(2) , Christian Focus) Christian Focus Pubns. GBR. *Dist:* Riverside.

Behr, Ashley F. Nailah's Surprise. O'Neill, Terry, ed. Karn, George, illus. 1998. 32p. (J). (ps-3). per. 5.95 (978-0-9660533-1-9(1)) Behr, D. J. Co.

Bellante, V. I Did It Myself. (Illus.). 29p. (J). (978-1-85863-502-6(0)) Minerva Pr. GBR. *Dist:* Unity Distribution.

Bellingham, Brenda. Lilly Plays Her Part. Owen, Elizabeth, illus. 2000. (New First Novels Ser.: Vol. 12). 58p. (gr. 1-5). 4.95 (978-0-88780-500-4(0)) Formac Publishing Co., Ltd. CAN. *Dist:* Casemate Pubs. & Bk. Distributors, LLC.

—Lilly Takes the Lead. MacDonald, Clarke, illus. 2006. (First Novels Ser.: Vol. 34). 64p. (gr. 2-5). (***978-0-88780-703-9(8)***); (J). 4.95 (978-0-88780-701-5(1)) Formac Publishing Co., Ltd. CAN. *Dist:* Casemate Pubs. & Bk. Distributors, LLC.

Bellingham, Brenda. Lilly's Special Gift. MacDonald, Clarke, illus. 2005. (First Novel Ser.). 64p. (gr. 2-5). (***978-0-88780-665-0(1)***); 4.95 (978-0-88780-664-3(3)) Formac Publishing Co., Ltd. CAN. *Dist:* Casemate Pubs. & Bk. Distributors, LLC.

Bemelmans, Ludwig. Madeline in London. Bemelmans, Ludwig, illus. deluxe ed. 2000. (Madeline Ser.). (Illus.). 64p. (J). (ps-3). pap. 7.99 (978-0-14-056649-9(X) , Viking Juvenile) Penguin Group (USA) Inc.

Benge, Judy. My Name Is Sandy. 2004. 152p. pap. 19.95 (978-1-4137-1947-5(3)) PublishAmerica, Inc.

Bennett, Donna I. Jessica's Bear. Dippold, Jane, illus. 2003. 32p. pap. 9.95 (978-1-878044-57-0(5)) Mayhaven Publishing.

Berg, R. J. Jenny Martin & the Unexpected Gift. 2004. (Illus.). 139p. (YA). per. 9.95 (978-0-9666104-2-0(3)) Ziert, Paul Assocs., Inc.

Bevin, Teresa. Tina Springs into Summer/Tina se Lanza al Verano. Rodríguez, Perfecto, illus. 2005. (ENG & SPA.). 114p. (J). pap. 21.00 (978-1-928589-28-0(6)) Gival Pr., LLC.

The Big Rain. 2003. (Illus.). 32p. (J). mass mkt. (978-0-9740599-2-1(7) , 3) Omnibus Publishing.

Bishop, Benita. Escape from el Monte. 2005. 155p. pap. 7.64 (978-1-4116-1415-4(1)) Lulu.com.

A Bit Haywire. 2006. (YA). per. 11.95 (978-0-9777883-5-4(0)) Viper Comics.

Blackmore, R. D. Lorna Doone. 1999. lib. bdg. 21.95 (978-1-56723-172-4(1)) Yestermorrow, Inc.

Blackmore, Richard D. Lorna Doone: A Romance of Exmoor. Shuttleworth, Sally, ed. 1999. (Oxford World's Classics Ser.). (Illus.). 720p. 13.95 (978-0-19-283627-4(7)) Oxford Univ. Pr., Inc.

Blackwell North America Staff. Matilda. (FRE., Illus.). (J). pap. (978-2-07-033555-8(0)) Gallimard, Editions.

Blanca Nieves y los Siete Enanitos. 2001. Tr. of Snow White & the Seven Dwarfs. (SPA.). (978-968-6347-31-9(3)) Larousse, Ediciones, S. A. de C. V.

Blegvad, Lenore. Ana Banana y Yo. 1999. (SPA., Illus.). (J). (978-0-606-16025-4(6)) Tandem Library Bks.

Blegvad, Lenore, et al, trs. Ana Banana y Yo. Blegvad, Erik, illus. 2003. (SPA.). 56p. (J). (gr. k-3). pap. 9.95 (978-84-204-4375-1(1)) Santillana USA Publishing Co., Inc.

Block, Francesca Lia. Girl Goddess: Nine Stories, 1998. (YA). (gr. 7 up). (978-0-606-12944-2(8)) Tandem Library Bks.

—Nine Stories. Scott, Steve, illus. 1998. (Girl Goddess Ser.: No. 9). 192p. (J). (gr. 12 up). pap. 7.99 (978-0-06-447187-9(X) , Harper Trophy) HarperCollins Pubs.

—Violet & Claire. 2000. (Illus.). 176p. (J). (gr. 8-12). pap. 6.99 (978-0-06-447253-1(1) , Harper Trophy) HarperCollins Pubs.

—Violet & Claire. 2000. (gr. 7-12). lib. bdg. 15.30 (978-0-613-30177-0(3)) Tandem Library Bks.

Blueberries for Sal. 2004. (J). 24.95 incl. audio (978-0-89719-860-8(3)); pap. 18.95 incl. audio compact disk (978-1-55592-799-8(8)); pap. 18.95 incl. audio compact disk (978-1-55592-767-7(X)); pap. 38.75 incl. audio compact disk (978-1-55592-816-2(1)); pap. 38.75 incl. audio compact disk (978-1-55592-782-0(3)) Weston Woods Studios, Inc.

Blume, Judy. Best of Judy Blume Set: Are You There God? It's Me, Margaret; Blubber; Iggie's House; Starring Sally J. Freedman as Herself, 4 vols. 2004. (gr. 3-7). pap. 23.47 (978-0-440-42022-4(9) , Yearling) Random Hse. Children's Bks.

—Blubber. 2002. (J). 13.40 (978-0-7587-9341-6(3)) Book Wholesalers, Inc.

—Blubber. unabr. ed. 2004. 153p. (J). (gr. 3-7). pap. 29.00 incl. audio (978-0-8072-1709-2(3) , S YA 1016 SP, Listening Library) Random Hse. Audio Publishing Group.

—Blubber. 2002. 168p. (J). 17.99 (978-0-689-84974-9(5) , Atheneum/Richard Jackson Bks.) Simon & Schuster Children's Publishing.

—Deenie. 143p. (YA). (gr. 7 up). pap. 3.99 (978-0-8072-1360-5(8) , Listening Library) Random Hse. Audio Publishing Group.

—Double Fudge. 2004. (Fudge Ser.). 192p. (gr. 12). mass mkt. 5.99 (978-0-425-19647-2(X) , Berkley) Penguin Group (USA) Inc.

—Estas Ahi Dios? Soy Yo, Margaret. rev. ed. 2001. Tr. of Are You There God? It's Me, Margaret. (SPA.). 176p. (J). (gr. 4-6). 17.00 (978-0-689-84688-5(6) , Atheneum/Richard Jackson Bks.) Simon & Schuster Children's Publishing.

—Otherwise Known As Sheila the Great. (Fudge Ser.). 166p. (J). pap. 4.99 (978-0-8072-1497-8(3) , Listening Library) Random Hse. Audio Publishing Group.

—Starring Sally J. Freedman As Herself. 2000. 296p. (YA). (gr. 4-7). 18.99 (978-0-689-84089-0(6) , Atheneum/Richard Jackson Bks.) Simon & Schuster Children's Publishing.

—Tales of a Fourth Grade Nothing. 1998. (Fudge Ser.). (J). 9.95 (978-1-56137-271-3(4)) Novel Units, Inc.

Blyton, Enid. The Naughtiest Girl Again. (Illus.). 192p. (J). mass mkt. 6.95 (978-0-09-915911-7(2)) Random Hse. GBR. *Dist:* Trafalgar Square Publishing.

—The Naughtiest Girl in the School. (Illus.). 160p. (J). 6.95 (978-0-09-945500-4(5)) Random Hse. GBR. *Dist:* Trafalgar Square Publishing.

—The Naughtiest Girl Is a Monitor. (Illus.). 160p. (J). pap. 6.95 (978-0-09-945490-8(4)) Random Hse. GBR. *Dist:* Trafalgar Square Publishing.

Boadu, Therson, illus. Fati & the Honey Tree. 2002. 28p. (978-9988-550-78-3(2)) Sub-Saharan Pubs. & Traders.

Boase, Wendy. Caperucita Roja. Puncel, María, tr. Philpot, Heather, illus. (Primeros Cuentos Ser.). (SPA.). 28p. (J). (gr. k-3). pap. 7.95 (978-1-56014-458-8(0)) Santillana USA Publishing Co., Inc.

Bogunya, Angels. El Maiz Amargo. 2004. (SPA.). 144p. (J). (978-84-263-5237-8(5)) Vives, Luis Editorial (Edelvives) ESP. *Dist:* Lectorum Pubns., Inc.

Bolden-Thompson, Angela. When Company Comes. 2007. 224p. pap. 19.95 (***978-0-615-14774-1(7)***) Thompson, Angela.

Bolme, Edward Sarah. Jesus Heals a Little Girl. Gillette, Tim, illus. l.t. ed. 2003. 20p. (J). bds. 6.99 (978-0-9725546-1-9(0)) CREST Pubns.

Boss, Sarah. Mary's Story. Cann, Helen, photos by. 2000. (Illus.). 48p. (J). (ps up). 16.95 (978-1-901223-44-6(2)) Barefoot Bks., Inc.

Bossley, Michele Martin. Queen of the Court. 2000. (Sports Stories Ser.). (Illus.). 89p. (gr. 3-8). (J). (***978-1-55028-703-5(6)***); 7.95 (978-1-55028-702-8(8)) Lorimer, James & Co., Ltd., Pubs. CAN. *Dist:* Casemate Pubs. & Bk. Distributors, LLC.

—Queen of the Court. 2001. (gr. 5-8). lib. bdg. 13.55 (978-0-613-78314-9(X)) Tandem Library Bks.

Boucles d'Or et les Trois Ours.Tr. of Goldilocks & the Three Bears. (FRE.). 48p. pap. 12.95 incl. audio compact disk (978-2-89558-061-4(8)) Coffragants CAN. *Dist:* Penton Overseas, Inc.

Bournea, R. C. Chloe. 1999. 752p. (J). 24.95 (978-0-9673723-0-3(5)) Mousetrap Bks.

Bowdish, Lynea. A Friend for Caitlin. 1998. (Illus.). 48p. (J). (gr. 3-5). pap. 3.50 (978-0-87406-894-8(0) , Willowisp Pr.) Darby Creek Publishing.

Boynton, Cara. Sam's Secret World. 2006. (ENG.). 48p. per. 12.95 (***978-1-4241-4529-4(5)***) PublishAmerica, Inc.

Bradley, Alex. 24 Girls in 7 Days. 2006. 272p. (YA). (gr. 7). reprint ed. pap. 5.99 (978-0-14-240543-7(4) , Puffin) Penguin Group (USA) Inc.

Brawn, Janyce, illus. Compassion in the City: An Amish Child Finds Love & Friendship. 2000. 38p. (J). (gr. 1-5). pap. 5.00 (978-0-9650519-1-0(9)) Moriarty, Timothy K.

Brenner, Barbara. Annie's Pet. Ziegler, Jack, illus. 1999. (Bank Street Reader Collection). (J). (gr. 1-3). lib. bdg. 22.60 (978-0-8368-2419-3(9)) Stevens, Gareth Inc.

Brooke, Lauren. Making Strides. 2005. (Chestnut Hill Ser.: No. 2). 224p. (J). (gr. 4-7). pap. 4.99 (978-0-439-73855-2(5) , Scholastic Paperbacks) Scholastic, Inc.

—The New Class. 2005. (Chestnut Hill Ser.: No. 1). 224p. (J). (ps-7). pap. 4.99 (978-0-439-73854-5(7) , Scholastic Paperbacks) Scholastic, Inc.

Brooks, Jillian. The New Girl. 2002. (Wondergirls Ser.: No. 1). (Illus.). 141p. (J). (gr. 3-7). pap. 4.99 (978-0-439-35200-0(2) , Scholastic Paperbacks) Scholastic, Inc.

Brophy, Mary-Beth. The Last Stop Before Home. 2004. 166p. (YA). pap. 12.95 (978-0-595-30436-3(2)) iUniverse, Inc.

Brouillet, Chrystine. Les Pieges de Clementine. 2002. (Premier Roman Ser.). (Illus.). 64p. (J). (gr. 2-5). pap. (978-2-89021-358-6(7)) Diffusion du livre Mirabel.

Brown, Alan. Nikki & the Rocking Horse. Utton, Peter, illus. 1999. 30p. (J). (ps-3). pap. 9.95 (978-0-00-664517-7(8)) Zondervan.

Brown, Amanda. Beach Blonde. 2006. (Legally Elle Woods Ser.: Vol. 1). 240p. (gr. 7-17). pap. 6.99 (978-0-7868-3843-1(4)); 2nd rev. ed. (gr. 3-7). pap. 6.99 (978-0-7868-3844-8(2)) Hyperion Pr.

Brown, Marc. D. W.'s Perfect Present. Brown, Marc, illus. 2004. (Athur's 8 x 8 Bks.). (Illus.). 24p. (J). (ps-3). pap. 3.99 (978-0-316-73386-1(5) , Tingley, Megan Bks.) Little, Brown Bks. for Young Readers.

Brugman, Alyssa. Walking Naked. 2005. 208p. (YA). (gr. 7-11). pap. 5.99 (978-0-440-23832-4(3) , Laurel Leaf) Random Hse. Children's Bks.

Brumbeau, Jeff. The Quiltmaker's Journey. De Marcken, Gail, illus. ed. 2005. 56p. (J). pap. 17.95 (978-0-439-51219-0(0) , Orchard Bks.) Scholastic, Inc.

Bruna, Dick. Miffy in the Snow: A Storybook. 1999. (Miffy Ser.). (Illus.). 28p. (J). (ps-k). 4.95 (978-1-56836-296-0(X)) Kodansha America, Inc.

—Miffy Rides a Bike. Bruna, Dick, illus. 1999. (Miffy Ser.). (Illus.). 28p. (ps-k). 4.95 (978-1-56836-280-9(3)) Kodansha America, Inc.

—Miffy's Busy Morning: A Flip Book. Bruna, Dick, illus. 1999. (Miffy Ser.). (Illus.). 16p. (ps-k). bds. 5.95 (978-1-56836-288-5(9)) Kodansha America, Inc.

—Miffy's Counting Book. Bruna, Dick, illus. 1999. (Miffy Ser.). (Illus.). 20p. (ps-k). bds. 7.95 (978-1-56836-281-6(1)) Kodansha America, Inc.

—Miffy's First Sleepover. Bruna, Dick, illus. 1999. (Miffy Ser.). (Illus.). 28p. (ps-k). 4.95 (978-1-56836-279-3(X)) Kodansha America, Inc.

Bryant, Annie. Freestyle with Avery. 2007. (Beacon Street Girls Ser.). 240p. (J). (gr. 4-8). pap. 7.99 (***978-1-933566-01-6(9)***) B*tween Productions, Inc.

Bryant, Annie. Out of Bounds. 2005. (Beacon Street Girls Ser.). 255p. (J). 7.99 (978-0-9746587-9-7(0) , Beacon Street Girls) B*tween Productions, Inc.

Buckey, Sarah Masters & Ross, Peg. Stolen Sapphire: A Samantha Mystery. 2006. 192p. (J). pap. 6.95 (978-1-59369-099-1(1) , American Girl) American Girl Publishing, Inc.

Buffie, Margaret. Angels Turn Their Backs. 1998. (Margaret Buffie Ser.). 240p. (YA). (gr. 13 up). (978-1-55074-415-6(1)) Kids Can Pr., Ltd.

Bulla, Clyde Robert. Shoeshine Girl. 1999. (Illus.). (J). (gr. 3-6). lib. bdg. 13.00 (978-0-8335-2660-1(X)) Tandem Library Bks.

Bunting, Eve. Blackwater. 2000. (gr. 5-8). lib. bdg. 14.15 (978-0-613-29889-6(6)) Tandem Library Bks.

—Blackwater. l.t. ed. 2000. 128p. (J). (gr. 8-12). 20.95 (978-0-7862-2753-2(2)) Thorndike Pr.

—Two Different Girls. 2001. 32p. (YA). (gr. 6-12). pap. (978-0-8224-3535-8(7)) Globe Fearon Educational Publishing.

Burge, Constance M. Seasons of the Witch, Vol. 1. Simon and Schuster Children's Staff, ed. 2003. (Charmed Ser.). 192p. (YA). pap. 7.99 (978-0-689-86545-9(7), Simon Pulse) Simon & Schuster Children's Publishing.

Burke, Tina. Fly Little Bird. Burke, Tina, illus. 2006. (Illus.). 32p. (J). 14.95 (978-1-933605-02-9(2)) Kane/Miller Bk. Pubs., Inc.

Burkett, Larry. Sarah & the Art Contest. 2000. (Great Smoky Mountain Storybook Ser.). (Illus.). 32p. (J). (ps-3). 7.99 (978-0-8024-0984-3(9)) Moody Pubs.

Burks, Catherine. Hi! Let's Meet Bertha, Vol. 4. Lee, Rudolph, illus. 1998. (J). (gr. 1-5). pap. 6.95 (978-1-892750-03-7(1)) Different Friends.

—Hi! Let's Meet Doris, Vol. 5. Lee, Rudolph, illus. 1998. (J). (gr. 1-5). pap. 6.95 (978-1-892750-05-1(8)) Different Friends.

Burleigh, Robert. Edna. Yardley, Joanna, illus. 2000. 32p. (J). (gr. k-4). 16.99 (978-0-531-33246-7(2), Orchard Bks.) Scholastic, Inc.

Burnett, Frances Hodgson. The Secret Garden: A Young Reader's Edition of the Classic Story. 1999. (978-0-606-17320-9(X)) Tandem Library Bks.

Burnham, Niki. Royally Jacked. 2005. (Romantic Comedies Ser.). 208p. (YA). mass mkt. 3.99 (978-1-4169-0519-6(7), Simon Pulse) Simon & Schuster Children's Publishing.

—Royally Jacked. 2004. (gr. 7-12). lib. bdg. 14.15 (978-0-613-73454-7(8)) Tandem Library Bks.

—Scary Beautiful. 2005. (Romantic Comedies Ser.). 272p. (YA). pap. 6.99 (978-0-689-87619-6(X), Simon Pulse) Simon & Schuster Children's Publishing.

—Sticky Fingers. 2005. 278p. (YA). (gr. 7 up). pap. 6.99 (978-0-689-87649-3(1), Simon Pulse) Simon & Schuster Children's Publishing.

Burnham, Niki & Saidens, Amy. Royally Jacked. 2003. (Romantic Comedies Ser.). 208p. (YA). pap. 6.99 (978-0-689-86668-5(2), Simon Pulse) Simon & Schuster Children's Publishing.

Burningham, John. Come Away from the Water, Shirley. 2004. (Red Fox Picture Book Ser.). (Illus.). 24p. (J). pap. 8.99 (978-0-09-989940-2(X), Red Fox) Random Hse. Children's Bks. GBR. *Dist:* Trafalgar Square Publishing.

—Courtney. 2004. (Illus.). 32p. (J). pap. 8.95 (978-0-09-966681-3(2), Red Fox) Random Hse. Children's Bks. GBR. *Dist:* Trafalgar Square Publishing.

—Time to Get Out of the Bath, Shirley. 2004. (Red Fox Picture Book Ser.). (Illus.). 24p. (J). pap. 8.99 (978-0-09-920051-2(1), Red Fox) Random Hse. Children's Bks. GBR. *Dist:* Trafalgar Square Publishing.

Burns, Joanne. Abigail Is a Big Girl Now. 2005. 20p. (J). 8.99 (978-1-4116-2042-1(9)) Lulu.com.

—Annibelle Is a Big Girl Now Weaning Two Year-Olds. 2005. 20p. 8.99 (978-1-4116-2044-5(5)) Lulu.com.

Burris, Barbara. Callie & Zora. Halstead, Wendy, illus. 1998. 96p. (Orig.). (J). (gr. 4-5). 15.95 (978-0-9654197-3-4(8)) PennyRoyal Bks.

Byars, Betsy. Tarot Says Beware. 2006. (Herculeah Jones Mystery Ser.). 160p. (J). (gr. 3). pap. 5.99 (978-0-14-240593-2(0), Puffin) Penguin Group (USA) Inc.

Cabot, Meg. The Princess Diaries Box Set Vols. I-III: Princess in Love; Princess in the Spotlight; The Princess Diaries. 2003. (Princess Diaries). 304p. (gr. 7 up). pap. 19.99 (978-0-06-058745-1(8)) HarperCollins Pubs.

—Teen Idol. (J). (gr. 7 up). 2004. 304p. 15.99 (978-0-06-009616-8(0)); 2005. (Illus.). 320p. reprint ed. pap. 8.99 (978-0-06-009618-2(7), Harper Trophy) HarperCollins Pubs.

Caffee, Tammie Jenks. The Summer of Snail. 2007. (J). per. 12.95 ***(978-1-934345-24-5(5))*** SouthWest Pubns.

Cage, Elizabeth. Spy Girls. Date not set. (Spy Girls Ser.: No. 7). (YA). (gr. 7 up). mass mkt. (978-0-671-03637-9(8)); mass mkt. (978-0-671-03638-6(6)) Simon & Schuster Children's Publishing. (Simon Pulse).

Callahan, Thera S. All Wrapped Up. 2004. (Rookie Reader Espanol Ser.). (Illus.). 31p. (J). (gr. k-2). pap. 4.95 (978-0-516-21949-3(9), Children's Pr.) Scholastic Library Publishing.

—All Wrapped Up. Gordon, Mike, illus. 2003. (Rookie Reader - Level C Ser.). 32p. (J). 19.50 (978-0-516-22844-0(7), Children's Pr.) Scholastic Library Publishing.

—Sara Joins the Circus. McLeod, Chum, illus. 2002. (Rookie Reader Skill Set Ser.). 32p. (J). (gr. k-2). pap. 4.95 (978-0-516-27384-6(1), Children's Pr.) Scholastic Library Publishing.

—Sara Joins the Circus. 2002. (gr. k-3). lib. bdg. 12.95 (978-0-613-53862-6(5)) Tandem Library Bks.

Cameron, Nancy Scott. Bad Hair Day: A Guide to Dealing with Everyday Stress. 2000. (Illus.). 128p. (J). (gr. 4-7). pap. 5.95 (978-1-902618-15-9(7)) Element Children's Bks.

Campbell, Ellen Langas. Will Stephanie Get the Story? 2004. (Girls Know How Ser.: #1 - Journalism). (Illus.). 112p. (J). pap. 4.95 (978-0-9743604-0-9(6), GIRLS KNOW HOW) NouSoma Communications, Inc.

Campbell, Joanna. Faith in a Long Shot. 2003. (Thoroughbred Ser.: Vol. 57). 176p. mass mkt. 4.99 (978-0-06-009049-4(9), Harper Entertainment) HarperCollins Pubs.

—Faith in a Long Shot. 2003. (gr. 3-6). lib. bdg. 13.00 (978-0-613-67192-7(9)) Tandem Library Bks.

—Samantha's Irish Luck. 2004. (Thoroughbred Ser.: No. 66). 176p. mass mkt. 4.99 (978-0-06-059525-8(6), Harper Entertainment) HarperCollins Pubs.

—Stardust's Foal. 2003. (gr. 3-6). lib. bdg. 13.00 (978-0-613-67226-9(7)) Tandem Library Bks.

—Star's Inspiration. 2003. (Thoroughbred Ser.: No. 59). (Illus.). 176p. mass mkt. 4.99 (978-0-06-009051-7(0), Harper Entertainment) HarperCollins Pubs.

—Star's Inspiration. 2003. (gr. 3-6). lib. bdg. 13.00 (978-0-613-66737-1(9)) Tandem Library Bks.

—Thoroughbred Box Set, Nos. 1-4. 2003. (Thoroughbred Ser.). (Illus.). pap. 19.96 (978-0-06-055585-6(8), Harper Entertainment) HarperCollins Pubs.

Canals, Sonia. Maraca. 1999. (Music Time Ser.). (Illus.). 8p. (J). (ps). 6.95 (978-1-899607-72-3(2)) Sterling Publishing Co., Inc.

Cano, Robin B. Lucita Regresa a Oaxaca (Lucita Comes Home to Oaxaca) Ricardez, Rafael E., tr. Smith, Kerry, illus. 1998. (ENG & SPA.). 32p. (J). (gr. 3-6). 16.95 (978-1-56492-111-6(5)) Laredo Publishing Co., Inc.

Cano, Robin B., et al. Ramona Viaja Al Norte (North with Ramona) 1998. (Tales in Two Languages, LS Ser.). (ENG & SPA.). (J). (gr. 3-6). 16.95 (978-1-56492-254-0(5)) Laredo Publishing Co., Inc.

Cappucceto Rosso. 1999. Tr. of Little Red Riding Hood. (ITA., Illus.). 24p. (J). (ps-5). pap. 7.95 (978-88-8148-254-2(1)) European Language Institute ITA. *Dist:* Distribooks, Inc., Midwest European Pubns.

Carbone, Elisa. Sarah & the Naked Truth. 2005. (J). per. 10.95 (978-0-9769404-8-7(5), 0-9769404-8-5) Cloonfad Pr.

Carey, Elizabeth Doyle. Together Again. 4th ed. 2006. (Callahan Cousins Ser.: No. 4). (Illus.). 272p. (J). (gr. 3-7). 10.99 (978-0-316-73695-4(3)) Little Brown & Co.

Carey, Rosa Nouchette. Esther: a Book for Girls. 2007. pap. ***(978-1-4065-1267-0(2))*** Dodo Pr.

Carlson, Melody. Bad Connection. 2006. 256p. pap. 11.99 (978-1-59052-692-7(9), Multnomah) WaterBrook Pr.

—Charlene's Grumpy Day: A Scoozie Tale about Patience. Fincher, Kathryn Andrews, illus. Date not set. 32p. (J). 9.99 (978-0-7369-0734-7(3)) Harvest Hse. Pubs.

—Just Ask. 2005. (Diary of a Teenage Girl Ser.). 256p. (J). pap. 12.99 (978-1-59052-321-6(0), Multnomah) WaterBrook Pr.

Carpenter, Ann. The Slumber Girls & the Mystical Dollhouse. 2006. (J). per. 8.99 (978-0-9771030-0-3(5)) Kidz By Dezign Pr., Inc.

Carroll, Jenny, pseud. Code Name Cassandra. 2007. (1-800-Where-R-You Ser.: No. 2). 272p. (YA). mass mkt. 6.99 (978-1-4169-2704-4(2), Simon Pulse) Simon & Schuster Children's Publishing.

—When Lightning Strikes. 2007. (1-800-Where-R-You Ser.: No. 1). 272p. (YA). mass mkt. 6.99 (978-1-4169-2705-1(0), Simon Pulse) Simon & Schuster Children's Publishing.

Carroll, Lewis, pseud. Alice Through the Looking-Glass. Reed, Jeremy, ed. Brown, Trevor R., illus. 2000. (Classic Portables Ser.). 192p. (J). reprint ed. 10.95 (978-1-84068-021-8(0)) Creation Bks. GBR. *Dist:* Subterranean Co.

—Alice's Adventures in Wonderland. 2000. (Aladdin Classics Ser.). (Illus.). 176p. (J). (gr. 3-7). pap. 3.99 (978-0-689-83375-5(X), Aladdin) Simon & Schuster Children's Publishing.

—Alice's Adventures in Wonderland. 1998. (Classics Ser.). (ENG., Illus.). 288p. pap. (978-1-85326-002-5(9), 0029WW) Wordsworth Editions, Ltd.

—Alicia en el Pais de las Maravillas. (SPA., Illus.). (YA). 11.95 (978-84-7281-081-5(X), AF1081) Auriga, Ediciones S.A. ESP. *Dist:* Continental Bk. Co., Inc.

—Alicia en el Pais de las Maravillas. (Coleccion Cuentos Universales). (SPA.). 128p. (YA). (gr. 4 up). (978-84-261-0267-6(0), JV30114) Juventud, Editorial ESP. *Dist:* Lectorum Pubns., Inc.

—Alicia en el Pais de las Maravillas. 4th ed. 2002. (Clover Ser.). (SPA., Illus.). 192p. (YA). 11.50 (978-84-392-8004-0(1), EV5541) Lectorum Pubns., Inc.

Carroll, Lewis, pseud & Baker, Kyle. Through the Looking Glass. (Classics Illustrated Ser.). (Illus.). 52p. (YA). pap. 4.95 (978-1-57209-002-6(2)) Classics International Entertainment, Inc.

Cary. Rosa Nouchette. Esther: A book for Girls. 2006. 208p. pap. 12.99 ***(978-1-4264-5023-5(0));*** 230p. pap. 15.99 ***(978-1-4264-5324-3(8))*** BiblioBazaar.

Casanova, Mary. Jess: Girl of the Year. 2005. 136p. (J). pap. 6.95 (978-1-59369-016-8(9)) American Girl Publishing, Inc.

Castor, Harriet. Milly of the Rovers. 1998. (Illus.). 96p. (J). 7.95 (978-0-14-037839-9(1)) Penguin Bks., Ltd. GBR. *Dist:* Trafalgar Square Publishing.

Caudill, Rebecca. Up & down the River. Merwin, Decie, illus. 2005. 143p. (J). (ps-17). pap. 11.95 (978-1-883937-81-2(7)) Bethlehem Bks.

Center for Learning Network Staff. The House on Mango Street: Curriculum Unit. 2005. (Novel Ser.). (YA). tchr. ed., spiral bd. 19.95 (978-1-56077-783-0(4)) Ctr. for Learning, The.

Cernyar, Anne C. In the Shadow of the Mountains. 2002. 276p. (YA). pap. 15.95 (978-0-595-24886-5(1), Writers Club Pr.) iUniverse, Inc.

Chambers, Aidan. This Is All: The Pillow Book of Cordelia Kenn. 2006. 816p. (J). (gr. 8-17). 19.95 (978-0-8109-7060-1(0), Amulet Bks.) Abrams, Harry N., Inc.

Chandler, Andrew and Amanda. Gertrude & Abigail (the Adventures Thereof) 2006. 35p. (J). 18.90 (978-1-4116-7572-8(X)) Lulu.com.

Chase, Diana. Chloe's Wish. 2001. (Illus.). 112p. (J). pap. 11.95 (978-1-86368-309-8(7)) Fremantle Pr. AUS. *Dist:* International Specialized Bk. Services.

Chen, Ming & Chen, Wah. Sassparilla's New Shoes. 1999. (Illus.). 40p. (J). (ps-3). 19.95 (978-1-880664-26-1(7)) E. M. Productions.

Cheva, Cherry. She's So Money. 2008. 304p. (J). 16.99 ***(978-0-06-128855-5(1));*** lib. bdg. 17.89 ***(978-0-06-128852-4(7))*** HarperCollins Pubs. (HarperTeen).

Ch'iao, Xiao. Patti & the Weegors. (Illus.). 32p. (J). pap. 4.99 (978-1-85792-557-9(2), Christian Focus) Christian Focus Pubns. GBR. *Dist:* Riverside.

Chick, Sandra. Don't Look Back. 2000. (Livewire Ser.). 100p. (J). pap. 11.99 (978-0-7043-4958-2(2)) Women's Pr., Ltd., The GBR. *Dist:* Independent Pubs. Group.

Child, Lauren. Soy Demasiado Pequeña para Ir Al Colegio: Protagonizado Por Juan y Totola. 2004. (SPA., Illus.). (J). 17.99 (978-84-8488-111-7(3)) Serres, Ediciones, S. L. ESP. *Dist:* Lectorum Pubns., Inc.

Child, Lauren & Rubio, Esther. Nunca Jamas Comeré Tomates. 2004. (ESP & SPA., Illus.). 28p. (J). 17.99 (978-84-8488-092-9(3)) Serres, Ediciones, S. L. ESP. *Dist:* Lectorum Pubns., Inc.

Children in Different Times & Places Theme Pack, 7 vols. 2001. (Illus.). (J). (gr. 8-9). 54.95 (978-1-56762-148-8(1)) Modern Learning Pr.

Chima, Ahiru & Misu, Max. Ellena_- Ellen meets Frog King - 2005. 32p. pap. 14.99 (978-1-4116-4050-4(0)) Lulu.com.

Chinchinian, Harry. Holly Brown & the Dragon Dingle. 1998. (Heather & Hally Brown Ser.). (Illus.). 134p. (J). (gr. k-3). pap. 9.95 (978-0-9653535-9-5(1), 1883697) Plum Tree Pr.

Chittenden, E. Charl. What Two Children Did. 2006. 77.99 ***(978-1-4280-4815-7(4));*** pap. 70.99 ***(978-1-4280-4817-1(0))*** IndyPublish.com.

Chomiak, Joseph N. & Swanson, Matt. Mookie: A Girl in Maximsubornia. Tremlin, Nathan A., illus. 2000. 48p. (J). 17.95 (978-0-9676688-0-2(8)) Tremiak Publishing.

Choung, Eun-hee. Minji's Salon. Choung, Eun-hee, illus. 2008. (Illus.). 32p. (J). 15.95 ***(978-1-933605-67-8(7))*** Kane/Miller Bk. Pubs., Inc.

Choyce, Lesley. Go for It, Carrie. 1998. (gr. k-3). lib. bdg. 11.80 (978-0-613-88931-5(2)) Tandem Library Bks.

Christin, Dominique. Girlz Rock: The Go-Girl Kit with Attitude. Cider Mill Press Staff, ed. gif. ed. 2006. (Magnetic Wisdom Ser.). (Illus.). 96p. pap. 9.95 (978-1-933662-26-8(3)) Cider Mill Pr. Bk. Pubs. LLC.

Christopher, Lawrence. The Tickle Fingers: Where Is Pinky? Christopher, Lawrence, illus. 2006. (ENG., Illus.). 24p. (J). (ps up). 9.95 (978-0-9712278-3-5(7)) MF Unlimited.

Ciencin, Scott & Burge, Constance M. High Spirits. 2007. (Charmed Ser.). 240p. (YA). pap. 6.99 (978-1-4169-3668-8(8), Simon Spotlight Entertainment) Simon & Schuster.

Circle of Blue. 2006. (J). (978-1-933343-37-2(0), PONY) Stabenfeldt Inc.

Cisneros. The House on Mango Street. 2000. (J). 12.81 (978-0-07-243517-7(8), McGraw-Hill Humanities, Social Sciences & World Languages) McGraw-Hill Higher Education.

Clairmont, Patsy, et al. Extravagant Grace. 2000. 224p. 14.99 (978-0-310-23125-7(6)) Zondervan.

Clark, Catherine. The Alison Rules. 2004. 272p. (J). 15.99 (978-0-06-055980-9(2)); lib. bdg. 16.89 (978-0-06-055981-6(0)) HarperCollins Pubs. (HarperTeen).

Clark, Clara. Nellie Bishop. Shine, Andrea, illus. 2003. 128p. (YA). (gr. 4-6). pap. 12.95 (978-1-56397-642-1(0)) Boyds Mills Pr.

Clark, Kathy. Summertime Secrets. 2000. (gr. 3-6). lib. bdg. 11.80 (978-0-613-28093-8(0)) Tandem Library Bks.

Clarke, Nicole. Vips. 2006. (Flirt Ser.: No. 6). (Illus.). 224p. (J). (gr. 7). pap. 6.99 (978-0-448-44395-9(3), Grosset & Dunlap) Penguin Group (USA) Inc.

Clarke, Nicole & Katsuda, Kiyoko. Spin City. 2006. (Flirt Ser.: No. 4). 224p. (J). (gr. 7). pap. 6.99 (978-0-448-44123-8(3), Grosset & Dunlap) Penguin Group (USA) Inc.

Cleary, Beverly. Ellen Tebbits. 160p. (J). (gr. 2-4). pap. 4.99 (978-0-8072-1397-1(7), Listening Library) Random Hse. Audio Publishing Group.

—Muggie Maggie. 2000. (J). pap., stu. ed. 24.24 incl. audio (978-0-7887-4344-3(9), 41138) Recorded Bks., LLC.

—Ramona y Su Padre. 10th ed. 2003. (SPA., Illus.). 136p. (J). (gr. 3-5). 15.95 (978-84-239-9020-7(6), EC1443) Espasa Calpe, S.A. ESP. *Dist:* Distribooks, Inc., Lectorum Pubns., Inc., Planeta Publishing Corp.

—Ramona's World. Tiegreen, Alan & Dockray, Tracy, illus. 2001. (Ramona Quimby Ser.). 240p. (J). (gr. 3-5). 16.99 (978-0-688-16816-2(7)) HarperCollins Pubs.

—Ramona's World. 2000. (Ramona Ser.). (J). (gr. 3-5). tchr. ed. 9.95 (978-1-58130-664-4(4)); stu. ed. 11.95 (978-1-58130-665-1(2)) Novel Units, Inc.

—Ramona's World. unabr. ed. 2004. (Ramona Quimby Ser.). 194p. (J). (gr. 3-7). pap. 29.00 incl. audio (978-0-8072-8169-7(7), Listening Library) Random Hse. Audio Publishing Group.

—Ramona's World. (gr. 3-6). 2001. lib. bdg. 14.15 (978-0-613-35794-4(9)); 2000. (J). (978-0-606-19464-8(9)) Tandem Library Bks.

—Troton Mi Perro. 2nd ed. 2003. (Ramona Collection). (SPA., Illus.). 128p. (J). (gr. 5-8). 9.95 (978-84-239-9017-7(6), EC4693) Espasa Calpe, S.A. ESP. *Dist:* Lectorum Pubns., Inc., Planeta Publishing Corp.

—Viva Ramona. 4th ed. 2003. (Ramona Collection: Vol. 23). (SPA., Illus.). 152p. (J). (gr. 4-7). 15.95 (978-84-239-8877-8(5), EC3784) Espasa Calpe, S.A. ESP. *Dist:* Distribooks, Inc., Lectorum Pubns., Inc., Planeta Publishing Corp.

Cloci, Gabriella. Minda's Happily Ever After. 2003. (J). pap. 9.95 (978-0-7414-1501-1(1)) Infinity Publishing.

Clugston, Chynna. The Kids Are Alright. 2nd ed. 2003. (Blue Monday Ser.: Vol. 1). (Illus.). 136p. pap. 11.95 (978-1-929998-62-3(7)) Oni Pr., Inc.

—Queen Bee. 2005. (Illus.). 112p. (J). pap. 16.99 (978-0-439-71572-0(5), Graphix) Scholastic, Inc.

Coerr, Eleanor. The Josefina Story Quilt. Degen, Bruce, illus. 2002. 12.34 (978-0-7587-6153-8(8)) Book Wholesalers, Inc.

Cole, Brock. Celine. 2003. 224p. (YA). (gr. 7-12). pap. 6.95 (978-0-374-41082-7(8), Sunburst) Farrar, Straus & Giroux.

Cole, Joanna. Get Well, Gators! 1998. (Gator Girls Ser.: Vol. 4). (Illus.). 64p. (J). (gr. 1-4). 15.89 (978-0-688-14787-7(9)) HarperCollins Pubs.

Cole, Michelle. Lilla Belle the First Stages. 2002. 118p. 21.99 (978-0-9722173-2-3(0)) Write World, Inc.

Coleman, Wim & Perrin, Pat. Sister Anna: A Story of Shaker Life. 2000. 232p. (J). (gr. 5-12). pap. 10.95 (978-1-57960-059-4(X)) History Compass, LLC.

Collidge, Susan. What Katy Did Next. 1998. (Children's Library). 192p. (J). pap. 3.95 (978-1-85326-150-3(5), 1505WW) Wordsworth Editions, Ltd. GBR. *Dist:* Combined Publishing.

Collins-Ludwick, Anne. Nancy Drew: Ghost Dogs of Moon Lake. 2002. (YA). cd-rom 19.99 (978-0-9672618-7-4(2)) Her Interactive, Inc.

Comer, James E. Katie of Oak Point. 1998. 142p. (YA). (gr. 5-12). pap. 11.00 (978-0-9650690-2-1(8)) Lyndel Pubns.

Conkin, Barbara. Lisa's Story. Steinrock, Larry, illus. 2001. 16p. (J). (gr. k-10). pap. 4.95 (978-0-9674662-4-8(5)) Hycliffe Publishing.

Conklin, Jennie Maria. Miss Prudence: A Story of Two Girls' Lives. l.t. ed. 2006. 308p. pap. 14.99 ***(978-1-4264-4041-0(3));*** 346p. pap. 18.99 ***(978-1-4264-4100-4(2))*** BiblioBazaar.

Conklin, Jennie Maria. Miss Prudence A Story of Two Girls' Lives. 2004. reprint ed. pap. 30.95 (978-1-4191-3464-7(7)); pap. 1.99 (978-1-4192-3464-4(1)) Kessinger Publishing, LLC.

Cook, Lisa Broadie. The Author on My Street. Friar, Joanne, illus. 2001. (Books for Young Learners). 16p. (J). pap. 5.00 (978-1-57274-245-1(3), 2725) Owen, Richard C. Pubs., Inc.

Coombs, Patricia. Dorrie & the Haunted Schoolhouse. Coombs, Patricia, illus. 2001. (Illus.). 32p. (J). (gr. k-3). 5.95 (978-0-618-13053-5(5), Clarion Bks.) Houghton Mifflin Co. Trade & Reference Div.

—Dorrie & the Haunted Schoolhouse. 2001. (gr. k-3). lib. bdg. 14.10 (978-0-613-44203-9(2)) Tandem Library Bks.

Cooper, Helen. Ella & the Rabbit. 1999. (Illus.). 32p. (J). (ps-k). pap. 6.99 (978-0-7112-0635-9(X)) Lincoln, Frances Ltd. GBR. *Dist:* Antique Collectors' Club.

Corbella, Piedad. El Cuento de las Montanas Azules. (SPA.). 160p. (YA). (gr. 5-8). (978-84-321-2457-0(5), RP6165) Rialp, Ediciones, S.A. ESP. *Dist:* Lectorum Pubns., Inc.

Cordova, Isabel. La Caja Tonta de Laura y Manolo. 2nd ed. 1998. (Espasa Juvenil Ser.: Vol. 43). (SPA., Illus.). 168p. (gr. 5-7). 6.95 (978-84-239-8898-3(8)) i.b.d., Ltd.

Corey, Shana. Players in Pigtails. Gibbon, Rebecca, illus. 2003. 40p. (J). pap. 16.95 (978-0-439-18305-5(7)) Scholastic, Inc.

Cory, Kim Delmar. Lilly's Way. Austin, Jane G., ed. 1998. 187p. (YA). (gr. 4-6). 9.99 (978-0-88092-363-7(6), 3636) Royal Fireworks Publishing Co.

Cosby, Andrew. Mary Scary. 2007. 56p. (YA). 9.95 (978-1-59307-730-3(0)) Dark Horse Comics.

Coste, Marion. Wild Beach. Gray, Cissy, illus. 2005. 32p. (J). pap. 8.25 (978-0-89317-062-2(3), WW-623); lib. bdg. 17.95 (978-0-89317-061-5(5), WW-0615) Finney Co., Inc. (Windward Publishing).

Courage of Sarah Noble. 1999. (J). 9.95 (978-1-56137-239-3(0)) Novel Units, Inc.

Coville, Bruce. Juliet Dove, Queen of Love. 2005. (Magic Book Shop Ser.). 208p. (J). pap. 5.95 (978-0-15-205217-1(8), Magic Carpet Bks.) Harcourt Children's Bks.

Cowsert, Sami. Tammi & Her Dragon. 2006. 48p. pap. 12.95 ***(978-1-4241-5211-7(9))*** PublishAmerica, Inc.

Cozzolino, Ann Yards. The Girl's of St. Mary's. 2001. (Illus.). 116p. (YA). (gr. 6-12). pap. 8.95 (978-0-9603108-2-1(7)) Yards, A.

Crane, Dede. The 25 Pains of Kennedy Baines. 2007. 176p. (J). pap. 8.95 (978-1-55192-979-8(1)) Raincoast Bk. Distribution CAN. *Dist:* Perseus Distribution.

Crary, Elizabeth. Amy's Disappearing Pickle. Avishai, Susan, illus. 2000. (Kids Can Choose Book Ser.). 32p. (J). (gr. 1-5). lib. bdg. 17.95 (978-1-884734-60-1(X)); (ps-5). pap. 7.95 (978-1-884734-59-5(6)) Parenting Pr., Inc.

—Heidi's Irresistible Hat. Avishai, Susan, illus. 2000. (Kids Can Choose Book Ser.). 32p. (J). (gr. 1-5). lib. bdg. 17.95 (978-1-884734-56-4(1)); (ps-5). pap. 7.95 (978-1-884734-55-7(3)) Parenting Pr., Inc.

Craven, Tracy Leininger. Life of Faith/Kathleens Dreams. 2006. (Life of Faith': Kathleen Mckenzie Ser.). 160p. (YA). pap. 6.99 (978-1-928749-25-7(9)) Mission City Pr., Inc.

Craze, Galaxy. By the Shore. 1999. (gr. 7-12). lib. bdg. 21.10 (978-0-613-28778-4(9)) Tandem Library Bks.

Creel, Ann Howard. A Ceiling of Stars. 1999. (gr. 5-8). lib. bdg. 14.10 (978-0-613-24514-2(8)) Tandem Library Bks.

—Nicki. 2006. 136p. (J). pap. 6.95 ***(978-1-59369-259-9(5)***, Pleasant Co.) American Girl Publishing, Inc.

—Thanks to Nicki. 2007. (J). pap. 6.95 ***(978-1-59369-290-2(0)***, Pleasant Co.) American Girl Publishing, Inc.

Cresswell, Helen. Sophie & the Sea Wolf. (Illus.). 32p. (J). (978-0-340-65608-2(5), Hodder & Stoughton) Hodder General Publishing Division.

Crook, Connie Brummel. Meyers' Creek. 293p. (J). (gr. 3-6). mass mkt. 5.95 (978-0-7736-7436-3(5)) Stoddart Kids CAN. *Dist:* Fitzhenry & Whiteside, Ltd.

—Nellie's Quest. 1998. 193p. (YA). (gr. 7-12). mass mkt. 5.95 (978-0-7736-7469-1(1)) Stoddart Kids CAN. *Dist:* Fitzhenry & Whiteside, Ltd.

Cruikshank, Margrit & Harvey, Amanda. Don't Dawdle Dorothy. 2004. (Illus.). 32p. (J). pap. 7.95 (978-1-84507-182-0(4)) Lincoln, Frances Ltd. GBR. *Dist:* Perseus Distribution.

Crystalene, the Rainbow Snow Girl. rev. ed. 2002. (J). per. (978-0-9724174-1-9(9)) Jung, Loretta.

Cunha, Francisco. My Very Own Lighthouse. 2006. (Picture books from around the World Seri Ser.). (Illus.). 32p. (J). 16.95 (978-1-905341-01-6(6)) WingedChariot Pr. GBR. *Dist:* Independent Pubs. Group.

Currey, A. Albertine. (Illus.). 25p. (J). pap. (978-0-340-68325-5(2) , Hodder & Stoughton) Hodder General Publishing Division.

Curtis. Tell Me a Girl Story. 2000. (J). (ps-1). 32p. 16.89 (978-0-06-029019-1(6)); 48p. pap. 6.95 (978-0-06-443697-7(7)) HarperCollins Pubs.

Curtis, Alice Turner. A Little Maid of Provincetown. 2004. (Little Maid Ser.). (Illus.). 192p. (J). (gr. 2-7). reprint ed. per. 9.95 (978-1-55709-331-8(8)) Applewood Bks.

—A Yankee Girl at Gettysburg. Garner, Charles, illus. 2004. (Yankee Girl Ser.). 204p. (J). (gr. 4-7). per. 12.95 (978-1-55709-526-8(4)) Applewood Bks.

Cushman, Karen. Aprendiz de Comadrona. 2003. (SPA.). 96p. (YA). (gr. 5-8). (978-84-236-4773-6(0) , ED3133) Edebé ESP. *Dist:* Lectorum Pubns., Inc.

—The Ballad of Lucy Whipple. 1998. (J). 12.64 (978-0-606-13177-3(9)) Tandem Library Bks.

Czernecki, Stefan. Beastly Boys & Ghastly Girls. 2000. (Illus.). 48p. (J). (gr. 2-5). 14.95 (978-0-06-024952-6(8)) HarperCollins Pubs.

Dale, Mitzi. The Sky's the Limit. 2001. 153p. (YA). (gr. 8-11). pap. 5.95 (978-0-88899-244-4(0)) Groundwood Bks. CAN. *Dist:* Perseus Distribution.

Dalmatian Press Staff. Charming Tales for Little Girls: Keepsake Treasury. rev. ed. 2004. (Keepsake Treasuries Ser.). (Illus.). 224p. (J). 10.99 (978-1-4037-0791-8(X)) Dalmatian Pr.

—Power Play: Glitter Paint Box Book. 2002. (Powerpuff Girls Ser.). (Illus.). 32p. (J). 3.99 (978-1-57759-870-1(9)) Dalmatian Pr.

Dancing Dilemma. 2005. 46p. (J). 3.99 (978-0-9763213-1-6(9)) OHC Group LLC.

Danziger, Paula. Forever Amber Brown. unabr. ed. 1998. (Amber Brown Ser.: No. 5). 101p. (J). (gr. 2-4). pap. 17.00 incl. audio (978-0-8072-0366-8(1) , FTR185SP, Listening Library) Random Hse. Audio Publishing Group.

—It's Justin Time, Amber Brown. Ross, Tony, illus. 2001. 48p. (J). pap. 3.99 (978-0-698-11907-9(X) , Putnam Juvenile) Penguin Group (USA) Inc.

David, Lawrence. The Good Little Girl. 1999. (YA). pap., wbk. ed. 100.70 incl. audio (978-0-7887-3021-4(5) , 46838) Recorded Bks., LLC.

Davidson, Ellen. Ruby's Hair. Wise, Noreen, ed. Pickard, Ann, illus. 2000. (Book-a-Day Collection). 32p. (YA). pap. 5.95 (978-1-58584-368-8(7)) Huckleberry Pr.

Davis, Daniel M. & Davis, Dawna Jo. Klawberry: Good Girl. Bad World. McClellan, Sara, ed. ltd. ed. 2007. per. 20.00 (***978-0-9774173-3-9(6)***) Steam Crow Pr.

Davis, Richard Harding. The Red Cross Girl & Other Stories. 2004. reprint ed. pap. 1.99 (978-1-4192-7996-6(3)) Kessinger Publishing, LLC.

Day, Roselie. Ruby, the Little Girl Who Loved Trains, 10 chapters. 2004. (Illus.). 170p. (J). (ps-7). per. 12.95 (978-0-9749826-0-1(1)) Next Page Pr., The.

De Horne, George. Pixie O'shaughnessy. 2004. reprint ed. pap. 24.95 (978-1-4191-4172-0(4)) Kessinger Publishing, LLC.

—Pixie O'Shaughnessy. 2004. reprint ed. pap. 1.99 (978-1-4192-4172-7(9)) Kessinger Publishing, LLC.

De La Croix, Alice. Mattie's Whisper. 2000. (gr. 7-12). lib. bdg. 22.20 (978-0-613-81389-1(8)) Tandem Library Bks.

de la Cruz, Melissa. Skinny-dipping. 2005. (Au Pairs Ser.: No. 2). 304p. (YA). (gr. 9 up). 15.95 (978-1-4169-0382-6(8)) Simon & Schuster Children's Publishing.

de Paola, Tomie. Strega Nona Meets Her Match. de Paola, Tomie, illus. 2002. (Illus.). (J). 14.04 (978-0-7587-3718-2(1)) Book Wholesalers, Inc.

Dean, Zoey. The A-List Collection. 2005. (J). (gr. 10-17). pap. 29.99 (978-0-316-15445-1(8) , Poppy) Little, Brown Bks. for Young Readers.

—Girls on Film. 2004. (A-List Ser.: Bk. 2). 256p. (YA). (gr. 9-17). pap. 9.99 (978-0-316-73475-2(6) , Poppy) Little, Brown Bks. for Young Readers.

Dean, Zoey. Heart of Glass. 8th ed. 2007. (A-List Ser.: No. 8). 320p. (J). (gr. 9 up). pap. 9.99 (***978-0-316-01096-2(0)*** , Poppy) Little, Brown Bks. for Young Readers.

Debris, Cosmic. Emily the Strange. 2001. (Illus.). 64p. 12.95 (978-0-8118-3147-5(7)) Chronicle Bks. LLC.

Deen, Ron. Annabelle Rides Her Bike on an Iowa Farm. 2005. (J). 6.95 (978-1-57166-261-3(8)) Quixote Pr.

DeFalco, Tom. Spider-Girl Battles the Deadly Dragon King. 2006. (Illus.). (J). (gr. 2-6). 21.35 (978-1-59961-025-2(6)) Spotlight.

—Touch of Venom. 2006. (Illus.). (J). (gr. 2-6). 21.35 (978-1-59961-026-9(4)) Spotlight.

Delton, Judy. Angel's Mother's Wedding. Weber, Jill, illus. 2001. 176p. (J). (gr. 4-6). pap. 4.95 (978-0-618-11118-3(2)) Houghton Mifflin Co. Trade & Reference Div.

Dematteis, J. M. The Dream Thief. Ploog, Mike, illus. 2nd rev. ed. 2006. (Abadazad Ser.: Bk. 2). 144p. (gr. 4-7). 9.99 (978-1-4231-0064-5(6)) Hyperion Pr.

DeMatteis, J. M. & Ploog, Mike. The Road to Inconceivable. Ploog, Mike, illus. 2006. (Abadazad Ser.: Bk. 1). (Illus.). 144p. (gr. 4-7). 9.99 (978-1-4231-0062-1(X)) Hyperion Pr.

Dembkoski, Kacey. Believe. 2004. 60p. (YA). pap. 8.95 (978-0-595-30549-0(0)) iUniverse, Inc.

Demers, Barbara. Willa's New World. Demers-Bryan, Debra, illus. 2005. 320p. (J). (gr. 6-12). pap. 7.95 (978-1-55050-150-6(X)) Coteau Bks. CAN. *Dist:* Fitzhenry & Whiteside, Ltd.

—Willa's New World. 2000. (gr. 7-12). lib. bdg. 16.40 (978-0-613-78439-9(1)) Tandem Library Bks.

DeMeyer, Patricia. Little Horsey Little Lessons: A Young Girl & Her Special Horse Help Teach Skills for Life. Christie, Terri, illus. 1999. 40p. (J). (gr. 1-6). pap. 9.95 (978-0-9666433-0-5(5)) Saddle Tree Pr.

Denitz Smith, Jane & Johnson, Stephen. Mary by Myself. 1999. (Illus.). 240p. (YA). (gr. 3 up). pap. 4.95 (978-0-06-440568-3(0) , Harper Trophy) HarperCollins Pubs.

Dent, Grace. LBD: It's a Girl Thing. 2004. 288p. (J). (gr. 7 up). reprint ed. pap. 6.99 (978-0-14-240182-8(X) , Puffin) Penguin Group (USA) Inc.

—LBD: The Great Escape. 2004. 176p. (J). pap. (978-0-14-131627-7(6) , Puffin) Penguin Group (USA) Inc.

Dernoga, Lenora. The Girl Who Loved Juice. Kay, Sue, illus. 1998. 32p. (J). (ps-2). pap. 6.99 (978-1-891043-03-1(X)) Perry Publishing.

Desrosiers, Sylvie. La Jeune Fille Venue du Froid. Sylvestre, Daniel, illus. 2002. (Roman Jeunesse Ser.). (FRE.). 96p. (YA). (gr. 4-7). pap. (978-2-89021-283-1(1)) Diffusion du livre Mirabel.

Dessen, Sarah. Keeping the Moon. 2004. 240p. (YA). (gr. 7 up). pap. 7.99 (978-0-14-240176-7(5) , Puffin) Penguin Group (USA) Inc.

—Someone Like You. ed. 2004. 288p. (YA). (gr. 7 up). pap. 7.99 (978-0-14-240177-4(3) , Puffin) Penguin Group (USA) Inc.

—That Summer. 208p. (YA). (gr. 7). 2006. 16.99 (978-0-670-06110-5(7) , Viking Juvenile); 2004. pap. 7.99 (978-0-14-240172-9(2) , Puffin) Penguin Group (USA) Inc.

Las Desventuras de Sofia. (SPA., Illus.). (YA). 14.95 (978-84-7281-169-0(7) , AF1169) Auriga, Ediciones S.A. ESP. *Dist:* Continental Bk. Co., Inc.

Devereux, Jan. Poe the Crow. Devereux, Jan, ed. Vanslette, Roxy, illus. 2004. 139p. (J). per. (978-0-9749677-0-7(X)) Lakeview Pr.

Devlin, Wende & Devlin, Harry. The Trouble with Henriette! Devlin, Wende & Devlin, Harry, illus. 1999. (Illus.). 30p. (J). (ps-2). reprint ed. 15.00 (978-0-7881-6637-2(9)) DIANE Publishing Co.

Devoto, Pat Cunningham. My Last Days As Roy Rogers. 2000. (gr. 7-12). lib. bdg. 23.40 (978-0-613-27988-8(3)) Tandem Library Bks.

Dewin, Howie. Little Miss Pokey Oaks. 2002. lib. bdg. 11.80 (978-0-613-50457-7(7)) Tandem Library Bks.

—Sand Hassle. 2001. (gr. k-3). lib. bdg. 11.80 (978-0-613-43877-3(9)) Tandem Library Bks.

Diaz, Enrique Perez. Los Pelusos, Cuentos Policiacos. Martinez, Enrique, illus. 2003. (SPA.). 95p. (J). (gr. 3-5). pap. 8.95 (978-968-19-1018-1(4)) Santillana USA Publishing Co., Inc.

DiCamillo, Kate. Because of Winn-Dixie. 2002. (Illus.). (J). 13.83 (978-0-7587-6512-3(6)) Book Wholesalers, Inc.

—Because of Winn-Dixie. braille ed. 2003. (J). (gr. 2). spiral bd. (978-0-616-15263-8(9)) Canadian National Institute for the Blind/Institut National Canadien pour les Aveugles.

—Because of Winn-Dixie. unabr. ed. 2004. 192p. (J). (gr. 4-7). pap. 29.00 incl. audio (978-0-8072-0707-9(1) , Listening Library) Random Hse. Audio Publishing Group.

—Gracias a Winn-Dixie. 2005. (SPA.). 154p. 13.99 (978-84-279-5002-3(0)) Noguer y Caralt Editores, S. A. ESP. *Dist:* Lectorum Pubns., Inc.

Diersch, Sandra. Alecia's Challenge. 1999. (Sports Stories Ser.: Vol. 32). 101p. (J). (gr. 3-8). 7.95 (978-1-55028-650-2(1)) Lorimer, James & Co., Ltd., Pubs. CAN. *Dist:* Casemate Pubs. & Bk. Distributors, LLC.

DiGiacomo, Anthony W. Girls of Power. DiGiacomo, Rachel Alison, illus. 2000. 50p. (YA). (gr. 5-8). pap. 6.99 (978-1-58265-018-0(7) , 00020) Orphan Pr.

Dinosaur Girl: Individual Title, 6 packs. (Action Packs Ser.). 120p. (gr. 3-5). 44.00 (978-0-7635-8394-1(4)) Rigby Education.

Discussion Guide for Imani in Young Love & Deception. 2002. 16p. (YA). pap., wbk. ed. 4.00 (978-0-9706226-1-7(9)) Enlighten Pubns.

Disney Press Staff & Alfonsi, Alice. House Party: Junior Novel. 17th rev. ed. 2006. 144p. (gr. 3-7). pap. 4.99 (978-0-7868-3837-0(X)) Disney Pr.

Disney Press Staff & Jones, Jasmine. Queen of Hearts. 18th rev. ed. 2006. 144p. (gr. 3-7). pap. 4.99 (978-0-7868-3838-7(8)) Disney Pr.

Doggett, Julie. Families Are Families Forever. 2005. (Illus.). 39p. pap. 14.95 (978-1-4116-3064-2(5)) Lulu.com.

Dokey, Cameron. Truth & Consequences. 2003. (gr. 7-12). lib. bdg. 14.15 (978-0-613-73389-2(4)) Tandem Library Bks.

Dokey, Cameron & Burge, Constance M. Truth & Consequences. 2003. (Charmed Ser.). (Illus.). 208p. (YA). pap. 6.99 (978-0-689-85791-1(8) , Simon Pulse) Simon & Schuster Children's Publishing.

Donnell, Annie Hamilton. Four Girls & a Compact. 2005. 76p. pap. 10.95 (978-1-59540-606-4(9) , 1st World Library - Literary Society) 1st World Publishing, Inc.

—Four Girls & A Compact. 2005. 26.95 (978-1-4218-0906-9(0) , 1st World Library - Literary Society) 1st World Publishing, Inc.

—Four Girls & A Compact. 2004. reprint ed. pap. 15.95 (978-1-4191-2048-0(4)); pap. 1.99 (978-1-4192-2048-7(9)) Kessinger Publishing, LLC.

Donovan, Stacey. Dive. 2000. (gr. 7-12). lib. bdg. 25.70 (978-0-613-87317-8(3)) Tandem Library Bks.

—Dive. 2001. 256p. (gr. 7-12). pap. 15.95 (978-0-595-16557-5(5) , Backinprint.com) iUniverse, Inc.

Dorris, Michael. Tainos. Escriva, Viví, illus. 97th ed. 2003. Tr. of Morning Girl. (SPA.). 112p. (gr. 5-8). pap. 26.30 (978-84-204-4757-5(9) , AF1929) Harcourt Schl. Pubs.

Dowell, Frances O'Roark. The Secret Language of Girls. (Illus.). 256p. (J). (gr. 3-7). 2005. pap. 5.99 (978-1-4169-0717-6(3) , Aladdin); 2004. 16.95 (978-0-689-84421-8(2) , Atheneum) Simon & Schuster Children's Publishing.

Dower, Laura. Bought & Scold. 2001. (gr. k-3). lib. bdg. 11.25 (978-0-613-43920-6(1)) Tandem Library Bks.

—Boy, Oh Boy!, Bk. 2. Powers, Stephanie, illus. rev. ed. 2001. (From the Files of Madison Finn Ser.: Bk. 2). 176p. (J). (gr. 3-7). pap. 4.99 (978-0-7868-1554-8(X) , Volo) Hyperion Bks. for Children.

—Bubbles Bedazzled. 2003. (gr. k-3). lib. bdg. 11.80 (978-0-613-64695-6(9)) Tandem Library Bks.

—From the Files of Madison Finn, Bks. 4-6. 2006. 528p. (gr. 3-7). pap. 9.99 (978-1-4231-0287-8(8)) Hyperion Pr.

—From the Files of Madison Finn: Double Dare. 2003. (gr. 3-6). lib. bdg. 13.00 (978-0-613-68230-5(0)) Tandem Library Bks.

—From the Files of Madison Finn: Give & Take. 2002. (gr. 3-6). lib. bdg. 13.00 (978-0-613-75024-0(1)) Tandem Library Bks.

—From the Files of Madison Finn: Heart to Heart. 2003. (gr. 3-6). lib. bdg. 13.00 (978-0-613-75026-4(8)) Tandem Library Bks.

—From the Files of Madison Finn: Only the Lonely. 2001. (gr. 3-6). lib. bdg. 13.00 (978-0-613-44497-2(3)) Tandem Library Bks.

—From the Files of Madison Finn Bk. 19: Keep It Real. rev. ed. 2005. (From the Files of Madison Finn Ser.: Bk. 19). 176p. (J). (gr. 3-7). pap. 4.99 (978-0-7868-5687-9(4) , Volo) Hyperion Bks. for Children.

—From the Files of Madison Finn No.8: Picture-Perfect. 2002. (gr. 3-6). lib. bdg. 13.00 (978-0-613-75025-7(X)) Tandem Library Bks.

—From the Files of Madison Finn No.15: Off the Wall. 2004. (gr. 3-6). lib. bdg. 13.00 (978-0-613-91008-8(7)) Tandem Library Bks.

—From the Files of Madison Finn Bind Up, Bks. 1-3. 2006. 528p. (gr. 3-7). pap. 9.99 (978-1-4231-0040-9(9)) Hyperion Pr.

—Give Me a Break. 2004. 166p. (J). lib. bdg. 16.92 (***978-1-4242-0649-0(9)***) Fitzgerald Bks.

—Give Me a Break. 2004. 166p. (J). (978-1-4155-7364-8(6) , Volo) Hyperion Bks. for Children.

—Hit the Beach. 2nd rev. ed. 2006. (From the Files of Madison Finn Ser.: Bk. 2). 272p. (gr. 3-7). pap. 5.99 (978-0-7868-3780-9(2)) Hyperion Pr.

—Keep It Real. 2005. 171p. (J). (978-1-4156-1057-2(6) , Volo) Hyperion Bks. for Children.

—Let the Fur Fly. 2002. (gr. k-3). lib. bdg. 11.25 (978-0-613-64743-4(2)) Tandem Library Bks.

—Only the Lonely, Bk. 1. Powers, Stephanie, illus. 2001. (From the Files of Madison Finn Ser.). 176p. (J). (gr. 3-7). pap. 4.99 (978-0-7868-1553-1(1) , Volo) Hyperion Bks. for Children.

—Three Girls & a Monster. 2002. (gr. k-3). lib. bdg. 11.25 (978-0-613-43964-0(3)) Tandem Library Bks.

Doyle, Brian. Up to Low. (J). 2004. 115p. pap. 6.95 (978-0-88899-622-0(5)); 2002. (gr. 5-7). pap. 5.95 (978-0-88899-264-2(5) , Libros Tigrillo) Groundwood Bks. CAN. *Dist:* Perseus Distribution, Transition Vendor.

Doyle, Malachy. Who Is Jesse Flood. 2004. 176p. (J). pap. 6.95 (978-1-58234-922-0(3) , Bloomsbury Children) Bloomsbury Publishing.

Drachman, Eric. It's Me! Isabelle, Decenciere, illus. 2004. 32p. 18.95 (978-0-9703809-2-0(5)) Kidwick Bks.

Drawson, Blair. Mary Margaret's Tree. (Illus.). 32p. (J). 16.95 (978-0-88899-259-8(9)) Groundwood Bks. CAN. *Dist:* Transition Vendor.

Dreliozis-Abon, Fotini. Franchesca's Journey. 2000. 132p. (YA). (gr. 5-12). pap. 15.95 (978-1-930002-16-6(5)) I & L Publishing.

Du Jardin, Rosamond. Marcy Catches Up. 2003. (YA). pap. 12.95 (978-1-930009-75-2(5) , 800-691-7779) Image Cascade Publishing.

Dubé, Pierrette. Sticks & Stones! Jolin, Dominique, illus. 1998. 24p. (J). (gr. k-3). pap. 4.95 (978-1-55209-234-7(8)) Firefly Bks., Ltd.

—Sticks & Stones. Jolin, Dominique, illus. 1998. 24p. (J). (gr. k-3). 14.95 (978-1-55209-284-2(4)) Firefly Bks., Ltd.

Duey, Kathleen. Hoofbeats Bk. 4: Lara & the Silent Place. 2005. 144p. (gr. 4-7). pap. 4.99 (978-0-14-240233-7(8) , Puffin) Penguin Group (USA) Inc.

—Lara & the Moon-Colored Filly, Vol. 2. 2005. (Hoofbeats Ser.: Bk. 2). 144p. (J). (gr. 4). pap. 4.99 (978-0-14-240231-3(1) , Puffin) Penguin Group (USA) Inc.

Durrant, Sabine. Cross Your Heart, Connie Pickles. 2007. 272p. (J). (gr. 7 up). 16.99 (978-0-06-085479-9(0)); lib. bdg. 17.89 (978-0-06-085480-5(4)) HarperCollins Pubs. (HarperTeen).

DuVall, Nell. The Bucket. Less, Sally, illus. 2000. 32p. (J). 7.95 (978-0-9706654-1-6(5)) Sprite Pr.

Dyer, Heather. The Girl with the Broken Wing. Bailey, Peter, illus. 2005. 160p. (J). pap. 15.99 (978-0-439-74827-8(5) , Chicken Hse., The) Scholastic, Inc.

Echo of Hooves. 2005. (J). (978-1-933343-10-5(9) , PONY) Stabenfeldt Inc.

Echols, Jennifer. The Boys Next Door. 2007. (Romantic Comedies Ser.). 336p. (YA). mass mkt. 6.99 (***978-1-4169-1831-8(0)*** , Simon Pulse) Simon & Schuster Children's Publishing.

Eglin, Lorna. A Girl of Two Worlds. (Illus.). 176p. (YA). mass mkt. 5.99 (978-1-85792-839-6(3) , Christian Focus) Christian Focus Pubns. GBR. *Dist:* Riverside.

Elder. Beauty & the Beast: Belle's Story. 1998. (Disney Chapters Ser.). (Illus.). 64p. (J). (gr. 2-4). pap. 3.95 (978-0-7868-4182-0(6)) Disney Pr.

Elizabeth, Ann. Little Annie Fountainhead. Larson, Karl, ed. Miskov, Kathy, illus. (J). 1998. 14.95 (978-0-9654436-3-0(9)); 1999. 32p. pap. 8.95 (978-0-9654436-5-4(5)) Honey Creek Publishing, Inc.

Elliot, Greg & Burge, Constance M. Demon Doppelgangers. 2005. (Charmed Ser.). 256p. (YA). pap. 5.99 (978-1-4169-0026-9(8) , Simon Spotlight Entertainment) Simon & Schuster.

Elliot, Jessie. Girls' Dinner Club. 2005. 256p. (gr. 7 up). 15.99 (978-0-06-059539-5(6)) HarperCollins Pubs.

—Girls Dinner Club. 2005. (Illus.). 256p. (J). (gr. 7 up). lib. bdg. 16.89 (978-0-06-059540-1(X)) HarperCollins Pubs.

Elliott, Patricia. Murkmere. 2007. 352p. (J). (gr. 7-17). pap. 7.99 (978-0-316-01044-3(8)) Little Brown & Co.

Eloise French. (J). (978-2-07-056179-7(8)) Gallimard, Editions.

Emerson, Alice. Ruthfielding at Snow Camp. 2002. 216p. pap. 29.95 (978-1-932080-54-4(6)) Ross & Perry, Inc.

Emerson, Charlotte. Beth's Snow Dancer. 1999. (Little Women Journals Ser.). (J). (978-0-606-16347-7(6)) Tandem Library Bks.

Emerson, Charlotte & Alcott, Louisa May. Beth's Snow Dancer. Wasden, Kevin, illus. 1999. (Little Women Journals). 128p. (J). (gr. 3-7). pap. 3.99 (978-0-380-79704-2(6)) HarperCollins Pubs.

—Jo's Troubled Heart. Wasden, Kevin, illus. 1999. (Little Women Journals). 128p. (J). (gr. 3-7). pap. 3.99 (978-0-380-79669-4(4)) HarperCollins Pubs.

Emesse, Tea. Nova Rocks. 2005. (Star Sisterz Ser.: Bk. 1). (Illus.). 192p. (J). pap. 5.99 (978-0-7869-3625-0(8)) Wizards of the Coast.

Emmert, Christine. Titania's Mountain. 1998. (Illus.). 22p. (J). (978-1-86106-945-0(6)) Minerva Pr. GBR. *Dist:* Unity Distribution.

England, Tamara, ed. Samantha - An American Girl Holiday: The Complete Script Book. 2004. (American Girls Collection). (Illus.). 140p. (J). pap. 9.95 (978-1-58485-968-0(7)) American Girl Publishing, Inc.

English, Karen. Francie. 1999. (Illus.). 208p. (J). (gr. 5-9). 17.00 (978-0-374-32456-8(5) , Farrar, Straus & Giroux (BYR)) Farrar, Straus & Giroux.

—Speak English for Us, Marisol! Sanchez, Enrique O., illus. 2000. (Concept Book Ser.). 32p. (J). (gr. 1-4). 15.95 (978-0-8075-7554-3(2)) Whitman, Albert & Co.

Epstein, Robin. First Pajama Party: Slumberrific Six. 2005. (Groovy Girls Ser.). (Illus.). 80p. (J). pap. 3.99 (978-0-439-81431-7(6)) Scholastic, Inc.

—The Great Outdoors: Take a Hike. 2005. (Groovy Girls Sleepover Club Ser.: Vol. 6). 58p. (J). (978-0-439-65794-5(6)) Scholastic, Inc.

—Groovy Girls #4 Rock & Roll Divas Supreme. 2005. (Groovy Girls Ser.). 80p. (J). pap. 3.99 (978-0-439-81434-8(0)) Scholastic, Inc.

—Pranks A Lot: Girls vs Boys. 2005. (Little Apple Ser.). (Illus.). 80p. (J). pap. 3.99 (978-0-439-81432-4(4)) Scholastic, Inc.

—Sleepover Surprise: A Twin-sational Birthday. 2005. (Groovy Girls Ser.). (Illus.). 80p. (J). pap. 3.99 (978-0-439-81433-1(2)) Scholastic, Inc.

Ericson, Helen. Harriet Spies Again. 2004. 240p. (J). (gr. 3-7). pap. 36.00 incl. audio (978-0-8072-2091-7(4) , Listening Library) Random Hse. Audio Publishing Group.

—Harriet Spies Again. 2003. 256p. (J). (gr. 5). mass mkt. 6.50 (978-0-440-41688-3(4) , Yearling) Random Hse. Children's Bks.

Ericson, Helen & Fitzhugh, Louise. Harriet Spies Again. 2002. 240p. (gr. 5 up). 15.95 (978-0-385-32786-2(2)); lib. bdg. 17.99 (978-0-385-90022-5(8)) Random Hse. Children's Bks. (Delacorte Bks. for Young Readers).

Ernst, Lisa Campbell. Sylvia Jean, the Drama Queen. 2005. (Illus.). 32p. (J). (ps). 16.99 (978-0-525-46962-9(1) , Dutton Juvenile) Penguin Group (USA) Inc.

Escott, John. Hannah & the Hurricane. abr. ed. 1998. (Illus.). 16p. (C). pap. 9.00 (978-0-582-35290-2(8)) Pearson ESL.

Evans, Pamela. Tina Queen of the Dragons. 2006. 101p. pap. 14.95 (978-1-4241-3356-7(4)) PublishAmerica, Inc.

Fabra, Jordi Sierra. Las Chicas de Alambre. 2003. (SPA., Illus.). 224p. (J). (gr. 8-12). pap. 8.95 (978-84-204-4915-9(6)) Santillana USA Publishing Co., Inc.

Falconer, Ian. Olivia. (Olivia Ser.). (FRE.). pap. 29.95 (978-2-02-041087-8(7)) Editions du Seuil FRA. *Dist:* Distribooks, Inc.

—Olivia. (Olivia Ser.). pap. 27.95 (978-85-250-3380-2(4)) Globo, Editora SA BRA. *Dist:* Distribooks, Inc.

—Olivia. (Olivia Ser.). (978-3-7891-6504-7(2)) Oetinger, Friedrich GmbH Verlag.

—Olivia. Falconer, Ian, illus. 2000. (Olivia Ser.). (Illus.). 33p. (J). (gr. k-3). per. 17.00 (978-0-689-83495-0(0) , Simon & Schuster Children's Publishing) Simon & Schuster Children's Publishing.

Farley, Terri. Phantom Stallion Box Set: The Wild One; Mustang Moon; Dark Sunshine. Call, Greg, illus. 2004. (Phantom Stallion Ser.). 704p. (J). (gr. 5 up). pap. 14.99 (978-0-06-059504-3(3) , HarperCollins) HarperCollins Pubs.

Feely, Jenny. Annie & the Pirates. 2001. (gr. k-3). lib. bdg. 11.65 (978-0-613-33328-3(4)) Tandem Library Bks.

Feld, Ellen F. Blackjack. 2001. 179p. (J). (gr. 4-7). pap. 7.95 (978-0-9709002-0-3(1)) Willow Bend Publishing.

Feltrin, Elise. That Curly-Haired Girl. Pavanel, Jane, ed. Cheung, Aries, illus. 2000. 32p. (J). (ps-2). pap. 8.95 (978-1-894222-14-3(8)) Lobster Pr. CAN. *Dist:* Univ. of Toronto Pr.

Ferguson, Sarah. Little Red. Williams, Sam, illus. 2006. 40p. (J). 6.99 (978-1-4169-1853-0(1) , Aladdin) Simon & Schuster Children's Publishing.

Fernandez, Laura. Pajaros en la Cabeza. 2001. (SPA., Illus.). (J). (gr. k-2). pap. (978-968-24-1554-8(3), TR7471) Trillas Editorial, S. A. MEX. *Dist:* Lectorum Pubns., Inc.

Ferrone, John M. Margo & the Secret Pond. Ferrone, John M., photos by. Date not set. (Illus.). 36p. (J). (ps-5). pap. 16.95 (978-1-928811-03-9(5)) Story Stuff, Inc.

Fiddler, Carol. Girl of Beauty. 1999. (Illus.). 91p. (J). pap. 12.99 (978-0-8474-1428-4(0)) Back to the Bible Publishing.

Fielding, Sarah. The Governess or the Little Female Academy. 2004. reprint ed. pap. 19.95 (978-1-4191-6442-2(2)); pap. 1.99 (978-1-4192-6442-9(7)) Kessinger Publishing, LLC.

Fifteen at Last. 2003. (J). pap. 2.75 (978-0-590-43526-0(4)) Scholastic, Inc.

Finley, Martha. Elsie at Nantucket, Vol. 10. 2000. (Elsie Bks.: Vol. 10). 272p. (J). (gr. 4-7). pap. 5.95 (978-1-58182-102-4(6)) Cumberland Hse. Publishing.

—Elsie at Nantucket. 1998. (Elsie Bks.: Vol. 10). (J). (gr. 7-12). pap. 6.99 (978-1-888306-46-0(7)) Holly Hall Pubns., Inc.

—Elsie Dinsmore. 2006. (ENG.). pap. 13.95 (***978-1-4218-3092-6(2)***) 1st World Publishing, Inc.

—Elsie's Great Hope, Bk. 8. 2001. (Elsie Dinsmore: Bk. 8). 224p. (J). (gr. 5-9). 12.99 (978-1-928749-08-0(9)) Vida Pubs.

—Elsie's Kith & Kin. 1998. (Elsie Bks.: Vol. 12). pap. 6.99 (978-1-888306-48-4(3)) Holly Hall Pubns., Inc.

—Elsie's New Relations. 1998. (Elsie Bks.: Vol. 9). (J). (gr. 7-12). pap. 6.99 (978-1-888306-45-3(9)) Holly Hall Pubns., Inc.

—Mildred's Boys & Girls. 1999. (Mildred Keith Collection Ser.: vol. 6). (J). reprint ed. 14.00 (978-1-889128-36-8(8)) Mantle Ministries.

—The Two Elsies. 1998. (Elsie Bks.: Vol. 11). (J). (gr. 7-12). pap. 6.99 (978-1-888306-47-7(5)) Holly Hall Pubns., Inc.

Finley, Martha & Mission City Press Staff. Violet's Hidden Doubts, Bk. 1. 2004. (Life of Faith Ser.: Bk. 1). 224p. (YA). 12.99 (978-1-928749-17-2(8)) Zonderkidz.

Firelight Secrets Vol. 28: Individual Chapter Book Title Six-Packs. Vol. 28. 32p. (gr. 4 up). 44.00 (978-0-7635-4499-7(X)) Rigby Education.

Fisher, Norma Grusy. Kira. Retana, Maria Luisa, tr. Steiner, Trisha, illus. 1999. (SPA & ENG.). 32p. (J). (gr. 3-5). pap. 7.95 (978-0-9664797-8-2(5)) Roaninn Pubns.

Fleischman, Paul. Semillas. De Hernandez, Isaac, illus. 2000. (la Orilla Del Viento Ser.). (SPA.). 69p. (J). (ps-7). pap. 6.99 (978-968-16-6072-7(2), 127) Fondo de Cultura Economica USA.

Fleming, Candace. Gabriella's Song. Potter, Giselle, illus. 2001. 40p. (J). (gr. k-3). reprint ed. pap. 6.99 (978-0-689-84175-0(2), Aladdin) Simon & Schuster Children's Publishing.

Flower, Graham Jessie. Grace Harlowes Return to Overton Campus. 2006. 63.99 (***978-1-4280-2335-2(6)***) IndyPublish.com.

Flower, Jessie Graham. Grace Harlowe's Overland Riders on the Great American Desert. 2006. 132p. pap. 10.99 (978-1-4264-1676-7(8)) BiblioBazaar.

—Grace Harlowe's Overland Riders on the Great American Desert. 2004. reprint ed. pap. 20.95 (978-1-4191-2221-7(5)); pap. 1.99 (978-1-4192-2221-4(X)) Kessinger Publishing, LLC.

Flower, Jessie Graham. Grace Harlowe's Return to Overton Campus. l.t. ed. 2006. 154p. pap. 11.99 (***978-1-4264-3783-0(8)***); 174p. pap. 14.99 (***978-1-4264-3853-0(2)***) BiblioBazaar.

Foglio, Phil & Foglio, Kaja. Agatha Heterodyne & the Clockwork Princess. 2006. (Girl Genius Ser.: Vol. 5). (Illus.). 112p. (YA). pap. 19.95 (978-1-890856-39-7(8)) Studio Foglio, LLC.

Forrest, Emma. Namedropper. 2000. 240p. pap. 12.00 (978-0-684-86538-6(6) , Touchstone) Simon & Schuster.

Forrester, Emma. Heart-to-Heart. Riley, Kellee, illus. 2007. (Holly Hobbie & Friends Ser.). 96p. (J). 2.99 (***978-1-4169-3422-6(7)*** , Simon Scribbles) Simon & Schuster Children's Publishing.

Forte, Joyce. The Brave Little Girl. 2004. 37p. pap. 17.95 (978-1-4137-1833-1(7)) PublishAmerica, Inc.

Forte, Lauren. Go, Girl! Cardona, Jose Maria, illus. 2007. (Groovy Girls Ser.). 400p. (J). 5.99 (***978-1-4169-3552-0(5)*** , Simon Scribbles) Simon & Schuster Children's Publishing.

Francia, Silvia. El Regreso a Clases de Roberta. 2000. (SPA.). 32p. (J). (ps-3). pap. 6.99 (978-980-257-257-1(8)) Ekare, Ediciones VEN. *Dist:* Kane/Miller Bk. Pubs., Inc., Lectorum Pubns., Inc.

Francis, Stella M. Campfire Girls in the Allegheny Mountains. rev. ed. 2006. (ENG.). 136p. 25.95 (978-1-4218-2100-9(1) , 1st World Library - Literary Society) 1st World Publishing, Inc.

Franklin, Emily. Off the Trails: Chalet Girls. 2008. 256p. (gr. 12 up). pap. 9.99 (***978-0-451-22300-5(4)*** , N A L Trade) Penguin Group (USA) Inc.

Franz, Kevin. The Princess Sisters & the Underwater City. Stigler, Marilyn, illus. 2004. 112p. (J). per. 7.99 (978-0-9747774-1-2(2)) Starbell Bks.

Fraser, Christine Marion. Rhanna at War. 2000. (Illus.). 320p. pap. 13.99 (978-0-340-76567-8(4) , Hodder & Stoughton) Hodder General Publishing Division GBR. *Dist:* Trafalgar Square Publishing.

Frechette, Carole. Do Pour Dolores. 1999. (Roman Plus Ser.). (Illus.). 160p. (YA). (gr. 8 up). pap. (978-2-89021-356-2(0)) Diffusion du livre Mirabel.

French, Vivian. Princess Alice & the Magical Mirror. Gibb, Sarah, illus. 2007. (Tiara Club Ser.: Vol. 4). 80p. (J). pap. 3.99 (978-0-06-112439-6(7) , Harper Trophy) HarperCollins Pubs.

—The Princess Alice & the Magical Mirror. Gibb, Sarah, illus. 2007. (Tiara Club Ser.: Vol. 4). 80p. (J). 15.99 (978-0-06-112440-2(0) , Tegen, Katherine Bks) HarperCollins Pubs.

—Princess Charlotte & the Birthday Ball. Gibb, Sarah, illus. 2007. (Tiara Club Ser.). 80p. (J). (gr. 1-4). pap. 3.99 (978-0-06-112428-0(1) , Harper Trophy); 15.99 (978-0-06-112431-0(1) , Tegen, Katherine Bks) HarperCollins Pubs.

—Princess Charlotte & the Enchanted Rose. Gibb, Sarah, illus. 2007. (Tiara Club Ser.: No. 7). 80p. (J). pap. 3.99 (***978-0-06-112441-9(9)*** , Harper Trophy) HarperCollins Pubs.

—Princess Daisy & the Dazzling Dragon. Gibb, Sarah, illus. 2007. (Tiara Club Ser.: No.3). 80p. (J). (gr. 1-4). 15.99 (978-0-06-112434-1(6) , Tegen, Katherine Bks); pap. 3.99 (978-0-06-112433-4(8) , Harper Trophy) HarperCollins Pubs.

—Princess Katie & the Silver Pony. Gibb, Sarah, illus. 2007. (Tiara Club Ser.: No.2). 80p. (J). (gr. 1-4). pap. 3.99 (978-0-06-112430-3(3) , Harper Trophy) HarperCollins Pubs.

—Princess Sophia & the Sparkling Surprise. Gibb, Sarah, illus. 2007. (Tiara Club Ser.: Vol. 5). 80p. (J). pap. 3.99 (978-0-06-112437-2(0) , Harper Trophy) HarperCollins Pubs.

French, Vivian. Tiara Club at Ruby Mansions 2: Princess Jessica & the Best-Friend Bracelet, T. Gibb, Sarah, illus. 2008. (Tiara Club Ser.). 80p. (J). pap. 3.99 (***978-0-06-143485-3(X)*** , Harper Trophy) HarperCollins Pubs.

French, Vivian & Ayliffe, Alex. Not Again Anna! (Illus.). (J). 1999. 32p. pap. 6.95 (978-1-86233-077-1(8)); 1998. 24p. 14.95 (978-1-899607-96-9(X)) Sterling Publishing Co., Inc.

Frenkel, Yetti. Libby & the Cat. Frenkel, Yetti, illus. 2005. (Illus.). 32p. 16.95 (978-0-9749006-2-9(1)) Snow Tree Bks.

Frey, G. Hildegard. The Camp Fire Girls at Camp Keeway-din or. 2006. 41.99 (***978-1-4280-0526-6(9)***); pap. 35.99 (***978-1-4280-0521-1(8)***) IndyPublish.com.

Frey, Hildegard G. The Camp Fire Girls at School or the Woleho Weavers. 2004. reprint ed. pap. 21.95 (978-1-4191-5575-8(X)); pap. 1.99 (978-1-4192-5575-5(4)) Kessinger Publishing, LLC.

—The Camp Fire Girls Do Their Bit. 2004. reprint ed. pap. 20.95 (978-1-4191-5577-2(6)); pap. 1.99 (978-1-4192-5577-9(0)) Kessinger Publishing, LLC.

—The Camp Fire Girls Go Motoring. 2004. reprint ed. pap. 20.95 (978-1-4191-5583-3(0)); pap. 1.99 (978-1-4192-5583-0(5)) Kessinger Publishing, LLC.

Frink-Hunter, Chene I. Britney's Rough Day. Smith, Kevin, Jr., illus. 2001. 34p. (J). (ps-7). pap. 19.95 (978-0-9654185-0-8(2)) Hunter Pubns.

Funke, Cornelia. Pirate Girl. Meyer, Kerstin, illus. 2005. (Pirate Girl Ser.). 32p. (J). (ps-ps). pap. 15.95 (978-0-439-71672-7(1)) Scholastic, Inc.

Gaetz, Dayle Campbell. Living Freight. 1998. (On Time's Wing Ser.). 176p. (J). (gr. 4-7). pap. 8.95 (978-1-896184-32-6(4)) Roussan Pubs., Inc./Roussan Editeur, Inc. CAN. *Dist:* Orca Bk. Pubs. USA.

Gag, Wanda. The Funny Thing. 2003. (Illus.). 32p. 14.95 (978-0-8166-4241-0(9)) Univ. of Minnesota Pr.

Gage, Jenny, photos by. Hotel Andromeda: Fiction by Heidi Julavits & Photographs by Jenny Gage. 2004. (Illus.). 90p. (YA). (gr. 13 up). 20.00 (978-1-891273-04-9(3)) Artspace Bks.

Gaiman, Neil. Blueberry Girl. Vess, Charles, illus. 2008. (J). (***978-0-06-083808-9(6)***) HarperCollins Pubs.

Gallagher, Diana G. & Burge, Constance M. Hurricane Hex. 2006. (Charmed Ser.). 224p. (YA). pap. 6.99 (978-1-4169-1467-9(6) , Simon Spotlight Entertainment) Simon & Schuster.

—Mystic Knoll. 2005. 217p. (J). (978-1-4155-8004-2(9) , Simon Spotlight) Simon & Schuster Children's Publishing.

Gallardo, Adam. Grunts Vol. 1, Vol. 1. Demong, Todd, illus. 2008. (YA). 17.95 (978-0-9763095-3-6(X)) Arcana Studio, Inc.

Garcia, Jerry & Grisman, David. What Will You Wear, Jenny Jenkins? Kelley, True, illus. 2000. 40p. (J). (ps-3). 15.95 (978-0-06-028263-9(0)) HarperCollins Pubs.

Gardner, Sally. Magical Kids: The Strongest Girl in the World & the Invisible Boy. 2007. (Illus.). 224p. (J). (gr. 2-5). 15.99 (978-0-8037-3158-5(2) , Dial) Penguin Group (USA) Inc.

Garland, Sarah. Ellie's Breakfast. 2001. (Illus.). 32p. (J). pap. 9.99 (978-0-09-969261-4(9)) Random Hse. GBR. *Dist:* Trafalgar Square Publishing.

Garrett, Caroline S. Sarah's Bead. 2000. (Illus.). 32p. (J). (gr. k-4). 18.00 (978-0-9678780-8-9(X) , Divine Mirror Pr.) Remington Literary Assn., Inc.

Gauch, Patricia Lee. Baila, Tanya. Ichikawa, Satomi, illus. 2002. Tr. of Dance, Tanya. (SPA.). 32p. (J). (ps-3). 16.99 (978-84-8488-032-5(X) , RR31515) Serres, Ediciones, S. L. ESP. *Dist:* Lectorum Pubns., Inc.

—Christina Katerina & the Box. 1998. (J). (978-0-606-13272-5(4)) Tandem Library Bks.

Gauthier, Bertrand. Une Chanson pour Gabriella. 2001. (Roman Plus Ser.). (FRE.). 160p. (YA). (gr. 8 up). pap. (978-2-89021-134-6(7)) Diffusion du livre Mirabel.

Geis, Patricia. Pequena Tamazigh. 2005. (Ninos y ninas del mundo Ser.). (SPA., Illus.). 32p. (J). 5.95 (978-84-7864-882-5(8)) Combel Editorial, S.A. ESP. *Dist:* Independent Pubs. Group.

Geldart, Thomas. Emilie the Peacemaker. 2004. reprint ed. pap. 15.95 (978-1-4191-1769-5(6)); pap. 1.99 (978-1-4192-1769-2(0)) Kessinger Publishing, LLC.

Geller, Rita. Victoria's Smile. 2002. (Illus.). 32p. (YA). (gr. 7 up). pap. 5.99 (978-0-439-31905-8(6)) Scholastic, Inc.

George, Jean Craighead. The Julie Trilogy. 1999. (Julie of the Wolves Ser.). (Illus.). (J). (gr. 5 up). pap. 17.97 (978-0-06-449350-5(4)) HarperCollins Pubs.

Get Together Girls - Fashion Show. 2005. (J). bds. (978-1-4194-0086-5(X)) Paradise Pr., Inc.

Get Together Girls - Girl Band. 2005. (J). bds. (978-1-4194-0084-1(3)) Paradise Pr., Inc.

Get Together Girls - Going to the Mall. 2005. (J). bds. (978-1-4194-0087-2(8)) Paradise Pr., Inc.

Get Together Girls - Hanging Out. 2005. (J). bds. (978-1-4194-0085-8(1)) Paradise Pr., Inc.

Ghent, Natale. Piper. 2001. (J). (978-0-606-21772-9(X)); (gr. 5-8). lib. bdg. 15.25 (978-0-613-36600-7(X)) Tandem Library Bks.

Giff, Patricia Reilly. All about Stacy. 79p. (J). (gr. 1-2). pap. 3.99 (978-0-8072-1280-6(6) , Listening Library) Random Hse. Audio Publishing Group.

—Not-So-Perfect Rosie, No. 4. Durrell, Julie, illus. 1998. (Ballet Slippers Ser.: Vol. 4). 80p. (J). (gr. 2-5). pap. 4.99 (978-0-14-130060-3(4) , Puffin) Penguin Group (USA) Inc.

—Stacy Says Good-Bye. 75p. (J). (gr. 1-2). pap. 3.99 (978-0-8072-1278-3(4) , Listening Library) Random Hse. Audio Publishing Group.

—Starring Rosie. Durrel, Julie, illus. 1998. (Ballet Slippers Ser.: Vol. 3). 80p. (J). (gr. 2-5). pap. 4.99 (978-0-14-038967-8(9) , Puffin) Penguin Group (USA) Inc.

—Starring Rosie. 1998. (Puffin Chapters Ser.). (978-0-606-13813-0(7)) Tandem Library Bks.

Gil, Alejandra & Magnasco, Carlos. Misterio en la profundidad de mi Cama. 2005. (SPA., Illus.). 28p. (J). 14.95 (978-9974-7799-3-8(6)) Hardenville SA URY. *Dist:* Independent Pubs. Group.

Gilbert, Sheri. The Legacy of Gloria Russell. 2004. 224p. (J). (gr. 3-7). 15.95 (978-0-375-82823-2(0)); lib. bdg. 17.99 (978-0-375-92823-9(5)) Random Hse. Children's Bks. (Knopf Bks. for Young Readers).

Gilbert, Virginia R. Letitia's Home in the Valley. 2000. (Illus.). 83p. (J). (ps-7). pap. 9.99 (978-0-88092-449-8(7)) Royal Fireworks Publishing Co.

Gilmore, Rachna. Ellen's Terrible TV Troubles. Mardon, John, illus. 2000. (First Flight Ser.). 38p. (J). (gr. 1-3). (978-1-55041-526-4(5)) Fitzhenry & Whiteside, Ltd.

—Ellen's Terrible TV Troubles. 2000. (gr. k-3). lib. bdg. 11.80 (978-0-613-90273-1(4)) Tandem Library Bks.

—A Gift for Gita. Priestley, Alice, illus. 2004. (TAM, ARA, BEN, GUJ & ENG.). 24p. (J). (978-1-85269-403-6(3)); (978-1-85269-407-4(6)); (978-1-85269-408-1(4)); (978-1-85269-409-8(2)) Mantra Publishing, Ltd.

—A Gift for Gita. Priestley, Alice, illus. 1999. 24p. (J). (gr. k-3). 12.95 (978-1-896764-12-2(6)); pap. 5.95 (978-1-896764-10-8(X)) Second Story Pr. CAN. *Dist:* Orca Bk. Pubs. USA, Univ. of Toronto Pr., Orca Bk. Pubs. USA.

—A Gift for Gita. Priestley, Alice, illus. 2005. 24p. (J). (gr. 3-6). pap. 7.95 (978-0-88448-239-0(1)) Tilbury Hse. Pubs.

—Lights for Gita. (Illus.). 24p. (J). 2002. (TUR & ENG.). 15.95 (978-1-85269-298-8(7)); 2000. (BEN & ENG., 15.50 (978-1-85269-283-4(9)); 2000. (GUJ & ENG., 15.95 (978-1-85269-288-9(X)) Mantra Publishing, Ltd. GBR. *Dist:* AIMS International Bks., Inc.

—Lights for Gita. Priestley, Alice, illus. 2005. 24p. (J). (gr. 3-6). pap. 7.95 (978-0-88448-151-5(4)) Tilbury Hse. Pubs.

—Lights for Gita. 2000. (CHI & ENG., Illus.). 24p. (J). 15.50 (978-1-85269-284-1(7)) Yuan-liou Publishing Co., Ltd. TWN. *Dist:* AIMS International Bks., Inc.

—When-I-Was-A-Little-Girl. Benoit, Renné, illus. 2006. 28p. 12.95 (978-1-897187-12-8(2)) Second Story Pr. CAN. *Dist:* Orca Bk. Pubs. USA.

Gilmour, H. B. & Reisfeld, Randi. Oh Baby! 2005. 336p. (J). (gr. 7). pap. 8.99 (978-0-439-67705-9(X) , Scholastic Paperbacks) Scholastic, Inc.

Gin, Courtney. The Shape of Miss. 2003. 206p. (YA). 24.95 (978-0-595-66052-0(5)); pap. 14.95 (978-0-595-29783-2(8)) iUniverse, Inc.

A Girl Named Pants. 2004. (J). per. 7.99 (978-0-9755959-0-9(3)) Girl Named Pants, Inc., A.

Girls Can Do Story Book. 2005. (J). 15.95 (978-1-59649-421-3(2)) Whispering Pine Pr. Inc.

Gist, Clark. Alice in God's Wonderland. Gist, Clark, illus. 1998. (Illus.). 80p. (J). (gr. 2-6). 19.95 (978-0-9644622-4-3(9)) Zeppelin.

Gittemeier, Tausha. Hmmm, I was Thinking... What If? 2004. 20p. pap. 14.95 (978-1-4137-3429-4(4)) PublishAmerica, Inc.

Givner, Joan. Ellen Fremedon: Journalist. 2005. 219p. (J). (ps-7). pap. 5.95 (978-0-88899-640-4(3) , Libros Tigrillo) Groundwood Bks. CAN. *Dist:* Perseus Distribution.

Glamour Girls. 2002. (Illus.). (J). 12.95 (978-0-448-43169-7(6) , Putnam Juvenile) Penguin Group (USA) Inc.

Glasser, Sophie. I've Known since I Was Eight. 2003. 126p. (YA). pap. 10.95 (978-0-595-29333-9(6)) iUniverse, Inc.

Glatzer, Jenna. Hattie, Get a Haircut! Kendall, Monica, illus. 2005. 32p. 19.95 (978-0-9724853-0-2(9) , Moo Pr.) Keene Publishing.

Glitz, Angelika & Swoboda, Annette. El Secreto de Mili. 2001. Tr. of Mili's Secret. (SPA.). 32p. (J). 12.76 (978-84-261-3086-0(0)) Juventud, Editorial ESP. *Dist:* Lectorum Pubns., Inc.

Glover, Sandra. The Girl Who Knew. 2000. (Illus.). 132p. (J). 17.99 (978-0-86264-962-3(5)) Andersen GBR. *Dist:* Independent Pubs. Group.

Goble, Paul. The Girl Who Loved Wild Horses. unabr. ed. 2001. (Illus.). (J). (ps-2). pap. 16.95 incl. audio (978-0-87499-762-0(3)) Live Oak Media.

—The Girl Who Loved Wild Horses. 2001. 32p. (J). 17.99 (978-0-689-84504-8(9) , Atheneum/Richard Jackson Bks.) Simon & Schuster Children's Publishing.

Godfrey, Rebecca. Torn Skirt. 2002. (gr. 7-12). lib. bdg. 21.05 (978-0-613-60626-4(4)) Tandem Library Bks.

Golden Books Staff. Barbie: The Nutcracker. 2002. (Illus.). 16p. (J). (gr. k-k). 2.99 (978-0-307-99512-4(7) , Golden Bks.) Random Hse. Children's Bks.

—Barbie As Ballerina. 2001. (Illus.). (J). (ps-2). pap. 1.00 (978-0-307-20016-7(7) , Golden Bks.) Random Hse. Children's Bks.

—Barbie Picture Frame. 1999. (Illus.). 70p. (J). pap. 0.99 (978-0-307-20018-1(3) , Golden Bks.) Random Hse. Children's Bks.

—Barbie with Gold Earrings. 1999. (Illus.). 70p. (J). pap. 0.99 (978-0-307-20020-4(5) , Golden Bks.) Random Hse. Children's Bks.

—Barbie with Pets. 1999. (Illus.). 70p. (J). pap. 0.99 (978-0-307-20019-8(1) , Golden Bks.) Random Hse. Children's Bks.

—Dora: Going to a Party. 2001. (Illus.). 32p. (J). (ps-2). pap. 3.99 (978-0-307-20216-1(X) , Golden Bks.) Random Hse. Children's Bks.

—Fun on the Go! 2006. (Illus.). 32p. (J). (ps-3). 4.99 (978-0-375-83661-9(6) , Golden Bks.) Random Hse. Children's Bks.

—It's a Colorful World. 2000. (Illus.). 48p. (J). (ps-3). pap. 3.99 (978-0-307-25217-3(5) , 25217, Golden Bks.) Random Hse. Children's Bks.

—Stories to Share. 2004. (Illus.). 176p. (J). (ps-2). 9.99 (978-0-375-82758-7(7) , Golden Bks.) Random Hse. Children's Bks.

—Who's the Boss? 2000. (Dear Barbie Ser.). (Illus.). 24p. (J). (gr. k-k). pap. 0.99 (978-0-307-17789-6(0) , Golden Bks.) Random Hse. Children's Bks.

—Wonderful Wedding. 2000. (Dear Barbie Ser.). (Illus.). 24p. (J). (gr. k-k). pap. 0.99 (978-0-307-17786-5(6) , Golden Bks.) Random Hse. Children's Bks.

Goldilocks & the Three Bears. 2004. (My First Fairy Tales Ser.). (Illus.). 24p. (J). pap. 3.99 (978-1-85854-686-5(9)) Brimax Books Ltd. GBR. *Dist:* Byeway Bks.

Goldilocks & the Three Bears. 2002. (Puppy Tales Ser.). (Illus.). 24p. (J). (gr. k-3). 1.49 (978-1-57759-219-8(0)); pap. 2.99 (978-1-57759-479-6(7)) Dalmatian Pr.

Goldilocks & the Three Bears. (Ladybird Bks.). (ARA., Illus.). 52p. (J). 12.95 incl. audio (978-0-86685-254-8(9) , LDL109C) International Bk. Ctr., Inc.

Goobie, Beth. Something Girl. 2005. (Orca Soundings Ser.). 112p. (J). (gr. 7-12). pap. 7.95 (978-1-55143-347-9(8)) Orca Bk. Pubs. USA.

Good NighMare. 2007. (J). lib. bdg. 13.25 (***978-1-59616-001-9(2)***) Caballo Bks.

Goodyear-Brown, Paris. Gabby the Gecko. 2003. per. (978-1-932203-54-7(0)) Sundog, Ltd.

Gordon, Lorell Cynthia. Tilly's Birthday: A Young Girl's Introduction to Menstruation. 2005. (Illus.). 64p. (J). per. 6.99 (978-0-9763961-0-9(6)) Learning All About Me, LLC.

Gourley, Catherine. Good Girl Work. 1999. (Single Titles Ser.: up). (Illus.). 96p. (gr. 7 up). lib. bdg. 26.90 (978-0-7613-0951-2(9) , Millbrook Pr.) Lerner Publishing Group.

Gow, Kailin. Reborn #1: Queen B Superheroine Series. 2005. 168p. (YA). per. 7.99 (978-1-59748-855-6(0)) Sparklesoup Studios, Inc.

Graef, Renee, illus. Hard Times on the Prairie. 1998. (Little House Chapter Bks.: No. 8). (J). (gr. 3-6). 11.05 (978-0-606-13458-3(1)) Tandem Library Bks.

—Laura & Nellie. 1998. (Little House Chapter Bks.: No. 5). (J). (gr. 3-6). (978-0-606-12979-4(0)) Tandem Library Bks.

Grambling, Lois G. Daddy Will Be There. Kessell, Walter G., illus. 1998. 24p. (J). (ps-3). 15.99 (978-0-688-14983-3(9)) HarperCollins Pubs.

Graver, Elizabeth. Honey Thief. 2000. (gr. 7-12). lib. bdg. 22.25 (978-0-613-36404-1(X)) Tandem Library Bks.

The Green Dragons: Individual Title Six-Packs. 16p. (gr. 2 up). 35.00 (978-0-7635-9232-5(3)) Rigby Education.

Green, John. Terdellaline: A Free-Spirited, Energeti. 2005. 48p. pap. 12.95 (978-1-4137-9528-8(5)) PublishAmerica, Inc.

Greenberg, Joanne. I Never Promised You a Rose Garden. 2004. 288p. (gr. 12). pap. 13.95 (978-0-451-21120-0(0) , N A L Trade) Penguin Group (USA) Inc.

—I Never Promised You a Rose Garden. 256p. (YA). (gr. 7 up). pap. 5.99 (978-0-8072-1362-9(4) , Listening Library) Random Hse. Audio Publishing Group.

Greene, Brenda. Dog Gone: Boomer's Story. Cheryl H. Hahn, illus. 2005. 127p. (YA). per. 8.99 (978-0-9770279-0-3(2)) Three Willows Pr.

Greene, Constance C. A Girl Called Al. 127p. (J). (gr. 4-6). pap. 5.99 (978-0-8072-1410-7(8) , Listening Library) Random Hse. Audio Publishing Group.

Greene, Janice. The Girl Who Had Everything. 2003. (Illus.). 80p. (YA). per. (978-1-56254-702-8(X)) Saddleback Educational Publishing.

Greenwood, Barbara. Secret Garden. 2001. (Young Reader's Classics Ser.). (Illus.). 94p. (J). 16.95 (978-1-55013-548-0(1) , Key Porter kids) Key Porter Bks. CAN. *Dist:* Firefly Bks., Ltd.

Gregory, Deborah. Off the Hook! 2005. 672p. (gr. 3-7). pap. 9.99 (978-0-7868-5654-1(8) , Jump at the Sun) Hyperion Bks. for Children.

—Showdown at the Okie Dokie. 2000. (Cheetah Girls Ser.: Bk. 9). 160p. (J). (gr. 3-7). pap. 3.99 (978-0-7868-1475-6(6) , Jump at the Sun) Hyperion Bks. for Children.

—Showdown at the Okie Dokie. 2001. (gr. 3-6). lib. bdg. 11.80 (978-0-613-31700-9(9)) Tandem Library Bks.

—Who's Bout to Bounce, Baby? 3rd rev. ed. 1999. (Cheetah Girls Ser.: No. 3). 160p. (gr. 3-7). pap. 3.99 (978-0-7868-1386-5(5)) Hyperion Bks. for Children.

—Wishing on a Star. Brown, Trevor, illus. 1999. (Cheetah Girls Ser.: No. 1). 144p. (gr. 3-7). pap. 3.99 (978-0-7868-1384-1(9)) Hyperion Bks. for Children.

—Wishing on a Star. 1999. (gr. 3-6). lib. bdg. 11.80 (978-0-613-22642-4(9)) Tandem Library Bks.

E F G

Gregory, Deborah & Alfonsi, Alice. The Cheetah Girls, Vol. 2. 2nd rev. ed. 2006. (Illus.). 128p. (gr. 3-7). pap. 4.99 (978-1-4231-0080-5(8)) Disney Pr.

Grenon, Macha. Charlotte Porte Bonheur. Despres, Genevieve, illus. 2000. (FRE.). 64p. (J). pap. 7.95 (978-2-921997-89-8(4)) Coffragants CAN. *Dist:* Penton Overseas, Inc.

Griese, Arnold A. Anna's Athabaskan Summer. Ragins, Charles, illus. 2003. 32p. (J). (gr. k-2). pap. 9.95 (978-1-56397-650-6(1)) Boyds Mills Pr.

Griffin, Marcia. Debbie's Letter to God. Davies, Michelle, illus. 2005. (J). pap. 8.00 (978-0-8059-6409-7(6)) Dorrance Publishing Co., Inc.

Grimes, Martha. Biting the Moon. 2000. (gr. 7-12). lib. bdg. 22.25 (978-0-613-34018-2(3)) Tandem Library Bks.

Grimes, Nikki. Aneesa Lee & the Weaver's Gift. Bryan, Ashley, illus. 1999. 32p. (J). (gr. 3 up). 17.99 (978-0-688-15997-9(4)) HarperCollins Pubs.

Grimm, Jacob W. & Grimm, Wilhelm K. The Goose Girl. (Illus.). 32p. (J). pap. 15.95 (978-0-86315-182-8(5) , 1751) Floris Bks. GBR. *Dist:* SteinerBooks, Inc.

Grimm, Jacob W., et al. Little Red Riding Hood/Caperucita Roja: A Bilingual Book. Surges, James, tr. from CAT. Estrada, Pau, illus. 1999. (ENG & SPA.). 32p. (J). (ps-3). 12.95 (978-0-8118-2561-0(2)) Chronicle Bks. LLC.

Grimn. Caperucita Roja. 2001. Tr. of Little Red Ridinghood. (SPA.). (978-968-6347-35-7(6)) Larousse, Ediciones, S. A. de C. V.

Grogan, Marijo. As Strong As the Wind, As Deep As a Canyon: A Girl's Adventure Story. 1999. (Illus.). 127p. (YA). (gr. 5-8). 24.95 (978-0-9678801-0-5(6)) Acorn Publishing.

Grosch, Greta & Grosch, Heidi. What We Did Last Summer Bk. 1: Some Silly Sisters' Summer Stories. Grosch, Heidi, illus. 1998. (Illus.). 70p. (J). (ps-6). pap. 8.95 (978-0-9668728-0-4(0)) Oh, You Girls!.

Guenther, James. Turnagain, Ptarmigan! Where Did You Go? A Story about the Alaska State Bird. Cartwright, Shannon, illus. 2003. (J). (ps-2). lib. bdg. 17.60 (978-0-613-79147-2(9)) Tandem Library Bks.

Gunn, Robin Jones. A Promise Is Forever. rev. ed. 1999. (Christy Miller Ser.: Bk. 12). 160p. (J). (gr. 7-12). pap. (978-1-56179-733-2(2)) Focus on the Family Publishing.

—Seventeen Wishes. rev. ed. 1999. (Christy Miller Ser.: Bk. 9). 160p. (J). (gr. 7-12). pap. (978-1-56179-730-1(8)) Focus on the Family Publishing.

—Sweet Dreams. rev. ed. 1999. (Christy Miller Ser.: Bk. 11). 160p. (J). (gr. 7-12). pap. (978-1-56179-732-5(4)) Focus on the Family Publishing.

—A Time to Cherish. rev. ed. 1999. (Christy Miller Ser.: Bk. 10). 176p. (J). (gr. 7-12). pap. (978-1-56179-731-8(6)) Focus on the Family Publishing.

Gurney, Stella & Sparklington, Madame. Princess: A Glittering Guide for Young Ladies. Allsop, Sophie et al, illus. 2006. (Genuine & Moste Authentic Gdes Ser.). 32p. (J). (gr. 1-4). 17.99 (978-0-7636-3430-8(1)) Candlewick Pr.

Ha, Thu Huong. Hail Caesar. 2007. 304p. (J). pap. 7.99 (978-0-439-89026-7(8) , PUSH) Scholastic, Inc.

Haldeman, Myrtle L. Cassie after Antietam. 2004. 109p. (J). pap. 7.99 (978-0-8280-1782-4(4) , 30-665) Review & Herald Publishing Assn.

Hale, Stephanie. Revenge of the Homecoming Queen. 2007. 272p. (YA). (gr. 6 up). pap. 9.99 (***978-0-425-21615-6(2)*** , Berkley Trade) Penguin Group (USA) Inc.

Hamilton, Bethany. Surfer Girl Rise above 90 Day Devotional. 2007. (Soul Surfer#8482; Ser.). 192p. (J). pap. 9.99 (978-0-310-71226-8(2)) Zonderkidz.

Hamilton, Harriet. Ribbons of the Sun. 2006. (YA). pap. 8.95 (978-0-9768126-2-3(2)) Brown Barn Bks.

Hanel, Wolfram. Abby. Marks, Alan, illus. 1998. 64p. (J). (gr. 2-4). pap. 5.95 (978-1-55858-908-7(2)) North-South Bks., Inc.

—Abby. Lanning, Rosemary, tr. Marks, Alan, illus. 1998. 60p. (J). (ps-ps). lib. bdg. 14.10 (978-0-613-09440-5(9)) Tandem Library Bks.

—Mary & the Mystery Dog. 2000. (gr. 3-6). lib. bdg. 14.10 (978-0-613-30020-9(3)) Tandem Library Bks.

Hankey, Sandy. Sweet Little Girl. Gay, Maria T., illus. 2004. 20p. pap. 14.95 (978-1-4137-3329-7(8)) PublishAmerica, Inc.

Hapka, Catherine. Supernova. 2004. (Star Power Ser.: No. 1). 144p. (J). pap. 4.99 (978-0-689-86787-3(5) , Aladdin) Simon & Schuster Children's Publishing.

Hapka, Cathy. My Sparkle Purse. 2003. (Sparkle Shape Bks.). (Illus.). 10p. (J). (ps up). bds. 6.99 (978-1-57151-714-2(6)) Playhouse Publishing.

—Picture MeTM Sparkle Princess. Hill, Heather C. & Roush, April, illus. 2002. (Role Play Ser.). 10p. (J). (ps up). bds. 6.99 (978-1-57151-560-5(7)) Playhouse Publishing.

Harcourt School Publishers Staff. Ann Gets a Map 5-Pack, Below Level. 3rd ed. 2002. (Trophies Reading Program Ser.). (Illus.). (gr. 1). pap. 20.10 (978-0-15-326808-3(5)) Harcourt Schl. Pubs.

—F Is for Found. 3rd ed. 2002. (Trophies English Language Learners Ser.). (Illus.). pap. 5.10 (978-0-15-327692-7(4)) Harcourt Schl. Pubs.

—Full Count Advanced Level. 3rd ed. 2002. (Trophies Reading Program Ser.). (Illus.). pap. 5.10 (978-0-15-323481-1(4)) Harcourt Schl. Pubs.

—Fun with Paper Advanced Level. 3rd ed. 2002. (Trophies Reading Program Ser.). (Illus.). pap. 5.10 (978-0-15-323296-1(X)) Harcourt Schl. Pubs.

—The Girl Who Spoke Dog Below Level. 3rd ed. 2002. (Illus.). pap. 5.10 (978-0-15-323408-8(3)) Harcourt Schl. Pubs.

—The Guest That Forgot to Leave: Take-Home Book. 2001. (Collections Ser.). (Illus.). (J). pap. 1.90 (978-0-15-319494-8(4)) Harcourt Schl. Pubs.

—The Guest That Forgot to Leave Below Level. 3rd ed. 2002. (Trophies Reading Program Ser.). (Illus.). pap. 5.10 (978-0-15-323232-9(3)) Harcourt Schl. Pubs.

—Hello! - Grade 3. 3rd ed. 2002. (Trophies English Language Learners Ser.). pap. 5.10 (978-0-15-327710-8(6)) Harcourt Schl. Pubs.

—Historias Que Contaba Mi Abuelo On Level. 3rd ed. 2002. (Trofeos Ser.). (SPA., Illus.). pap. 6.80 (978-0-15-324188-8(8)) Harcourt Schl. Pubs.

—Jump! Advanced Level. 3rd ed. 2002. (Trophies Reading Program Ser.). (Illus.). pap. 5.10 (978-0-15-323205-3(6)) Harcourt Schl. Pubs.

—The Keeper On Level. 3rd ed. 2002. (Trophies Reading Program Ser.). (Illus.). pap. 5.10 (978-0-15-323436-1(9)) Harcourt Schl. Pubs.

—My Friend, Boots Advanced Level. 3rd ed. 2002. (Trophies Reading Program Ser.). (Illus.). (J). pap. 3.70 (978-0-15-323014-1(2)) Harcourt Schl. Pubs.

—My Friend, Boots 5-Pack, Advanced Level. 3rd ed. 2002. (Trophies Reading Program Ser.). (Illus.). (gr. 12). pap. 20.10 (978-0-15-326864-9(6)) Harcourt Schl. Pubs.

—Stacy's Surprise: Take-Home Book. 1999. (Collections Ser.). (Illus.). (J). pap. 1.90 (978-0-15-317298-4(3)) Harcourt Schl. Pubs.

—Stop the Presses: Take-Home Book. 1999. (Collections Ser.). (Illus.). (J). (gr. 3). pap. 1.90 (978-0-15-317267-0(3)) Harcourt Schl. Pubs.

—Taming the Land: Take-Home Book. 2001. (Collections Ser.). (Illus.). (J). pap. 1.90 (978-0-15-319528-0(2)) Harcourt Schl. Pubs.

—Taming the Land Below Level. 3rd ed. 2002. (Trophies Reading Program Ser.). (Illus.). pap. 5.10 (978-0-15-323326-5(5)) Harcourt Schl. Pubs.

—That Reminds Me of a Story Advanced Level. 3rd ed. 2002. (Trophies Reading Program Ser.). (Illus.). pap. 5.10 (978-0-15-323392-0(3)) Harcourt Schl. Pubs.

—That's Terrific Debbie: Take-Home Book. 1999. (Collections Ser.). (Illus.). (J). pap. 1.90 (978-0-15-317280-9(0)) Harcourt Schl. Pubs.

—Trofeos Below Level: El Mapa de Ana. 3rd ed. 2002. (SPA., Illus.). pap. 5.50 (978-0-15-323869-7(0)) Harcourt Schl. Pubs.

—Walking Thru the Jungle: Little Book. 2000. (Collections Ser.). (Illus.). (J). pap. 10.20 (978-0-15-314502-5(1)) Harcourt Schl. Pubs.

Harding, Kitchener L. Little Miss Priss: Flying Kites & Kisses Not for the Misses. Harding, Kitchener L., illus. l.t. ed. 1999. 10p. (J). (gr. 1-5). spiral bd. 4.95 (978-1-930503-00-7(8)) Office Max.

Hardrick, Jackie. Imani in Young Love & Deception. 2002. 304p. (J). per. 15.00 (978-0-9706226-0-0(0)) Enlighten Pubns.

Hargreaves, Roger. Little Miss Bossy. 1998. (Mr. Men & Little Miss Ser.). (Illus.). 32p. (J). (gr. k up). pap. 3.99 (978-0-8431-7423-6(4) , Price Stern Sloan) Penguin Group (USA) Inc.

—Little Miss Contrary. Hargreaves, Roger, illus. 2000. (Mr. Men & Little Miss Ser.). (Illus.). 32p. (J). (gr. k-3). pap. 3.99 (978-0-8431-7619-3(9) , Price Stern Sloan) Penguin Group (USA) Inc.

—Little Miss Ditzy. Hargreaves, Roger, illus. 2001. (Mr. Men & Little Miss Ser.). (Illus.). 32p. (J). pap. 2.99 (978-0-8431-7690-2(3) , Price Stern Sloan) Penguin Group (USA) Inc.

—Little Miss Shy. 1998. (Mr. Men & Little Miss Ser.). (Illus.). 32p. (J). (gr. k up). pap. 3.99 (978-0-8431-7425-0(0) , Price Stern Sloan) Penguin Group (USA) Inc.

—Little Miss Trouble. 1998. (Mr. Men & Little Miss Ser.). (Illus.). 32p. (J). (gr. k-3). pap. 3.99 (978-0-8431-7426-7(9) , Price Stern Sloan) Penguin Group (USA) Inc.

Harkes, Willy. Little Dutch Girl in World War II. Blair, Jocelyn, illus. l.t. ed. 2004. 22p. (J). pap. 13.95 (978-0-9741627-1-3(X)) Write Designs, Ltd.

Harper. St. Jenni. 2004. (Illus.). (J). 96p. pap. 8.99 (978-0-7459-4895-9(2)); 80p. pap. 8.99 (978-0-7459-4894-2(4)) Lion Hudson plc GBR. (Lion). *Dist:* Independent Pubs. Group.

Harper, Charise Mericle. Amy & Ivan: What's in That Truck? 2006. (Illus.). 24p. (J). 12.95 (978-1-58246-134-2(1) , Tricycle Pr.) Ten Speed Pr.

Harper, Meg. Chilling Out. 2005. (Illus.). 96p. (J). pap. 9.99 (978-0-7459-4896-6(0) , Lion) Lion Hudson plc GBR. *Dist:* Independent Pubs. Group.

Harpster, Steve, illus. Debra Doesn't Take the Dare: An Emotional Literacy Book. 2004. 54p. (J). 14.95 (978-0-9747789-3-8(1) , 20705) CTC Publishing.

Harrah, Madge. Honey Girl. 2001. (Illus.). 120p. (J). (gr. 3-6). reprint ed. pap. 7.95 (978-0-9709152-1-4(7)) Trailway Bks.

Harris, Cynthia. Three of Hearts. 2003. 12p. (J). pap. 4.99 (978-1-4037-0185-5(7)) Dalmatian Pr.

Harris, Joe. Narda. 2005. (J). (978-0-9772259-0-3(9)) Character Arts.

Harris, Robert & Yolen, Jane. Girl in a Cage. 2004. 240p. (J). (gr. 5 up). pap. 6.99 (978-0-14-240132-3(3) , Puffin) Penguin Group (USA) Inc.

Harrison, Emma. The Queen's Curse. 2005. (Charmed Ser.). 224p. (YA). pap. 5.99 (978-1-4169-0024-5(1) , Simon Spotlight Entertainment) Simon & Schuster.

Harrison, Emma & Burge, Constance M. Phoebe Who? 2006. (Charmed Ser.). 208p. (YA). pap. 6.99 (978-1-4169-2532-3(5) , Simon Spotlight Entertainment) Simon & Schuster.

Harrison, Jean & Cristnogol, Cymorth. Shompa o India. 2005. (978-0-904379-43-3(4)) Christian Aid.

Harrison, Lisi. The Pretty Committee Strikes Back. 2006. (Clique Ser.: No. 5). 272p. (J). (gr. 7-12). pap. 9.99 (978-0-316-11500-1(2) , Poppy) Little, Brown Bks. for Young Readers.

Hartley, Susan. Stephanie Investigates. ed. 2004. (Shared Connections Ser.). (J). pap. 27.00 (978-1-4108-1642-9(7)) Benchmark Education Co.

—Stephanie Investigates (Big Book) ed. 2004. (Shared Connections Ser.). (J). pap., instr.'s gde. ed. 27.00 (978-1-4108-1618-4(4)) Benchmark Education Co.

Hartley, Susan & Schieber, Jennifer. Red Riding Hood. ed. 2004. (Shared Connections Ser.). (J). pap. 27.00 (978-1-4108-1635-1(4)) Benchmark Education Co.

—Red Riding Hood (Big Book) ed. 2004. (Shared Connections Ser.). (J). pap., instr.'s gde. ed. 27.00 (978-1-4108-1611-5(7)) Benchmark Education Co.

Hartry, Nancy. Jocelyn & the Ballerina. Hendry, Linda, illus. (J). (ps-k). 2000. 36p. (978-1-55041-649-7(9)); 2nd ed. 32p. pap. (978-1-55041-803-3(3)) Fitzhenry & Whiteside, Ltd.

Haubegger, Christy. Latina Beauty. 2002. (J). pap. (978-0-7868-8585-5(8)) Disney Pr.

Havill, Juanita. El Hallazgo de Jamaica. Mlawer, Teresa, tr. O'Brien, Anne Sibley, illus. 2000. (SPA.). (J). (gr. k-2). pap. 6.95 (978-1-880507-82-7(X) , LC6975) Lectorum Pubns., Inc.

Hawes, Louise. Nelson Malone Saves Flight 942. Rogers, Jacqueline, illus. 2001. 164p. (YA). (gr. 4-7). pap. 11.95 (978-0-595-16721-0(7)) iUniverse, Inc.

Hawkins-Rodgers, Donzella. No Bulley Destroy's Chloe's Hairdo. Hewins, Shirley, illus. 2003. 32p. (J). (gr. 3 up). lib. bdg. 16.95 (978-1-884242-56-4(1)) Multicultural Pubns.

Hayes, Joe. Little Gold Star (Estrellita de Oro) A Cinderella Cuento. 2002. (SPA & ENG.). 32p. (J). pap. 7.95 (978-0-938317-68-5(7)) Cinco Puntos Pr.

—Little Gold Star (Estrellita de Oro) A Cinderella Cuento. Perez, Gloria Osuna & Perez, Lucia Angela, illus. 2000. (SPA & ENG.). 32p. (ps-3). 15.95 (978-0-938317-49-4(0) , CPP7490) Cinco Puntos Pr.

Hébert, Marie-Francine. La Petite Fille Qui Detestait l'Heure du Dodo. ed. 2004. (FRE., Illus.). (J). (gr. k-3). spiral bd. (978-0-616-01834-7(7)) Canadian National Institute for the Blind/Institut National Canadien pour les Aveugles.

Hedderwick, Mairi. The Big Katie Morag Storybook. 2000. (Katie Morag Stories Ser.). (Illus.). 48p. (J). (gr. 1-4). pap. 11.00 (978-0-09-940371-7(0) , Red Fox) Random Hse. Children's Bks. GBR. *Dist:* Trafalgar Square Publishing.

—Katie Morag & the Big Boy Cousins. 1999. (Katie Morag Stories Ser.). (Illus.). 32p. (J). pap. 9.99 (978-0-09-911891-6(2)) Random Hse. GBR. *Dist:* Independent Pubs. Group.

—Katie Morag & the Grand Concert. 1999. (Katie Morag Stories Ser.). (Illus.). 32p. (J). pap. 10.99 (978-0-09-926275-6(4)) Random Hse. GBR. *Dist:* Independent Pubs. Group.

—Katie Morag & the New Pier. 2005. (Illus.). 32p. (J). pap. 10.99 (978-0-09-922082-4(2) , Red Fox) Random Hse. Children's Bks. GBR. *Dist:* Trafalgar Square Publishing.

—Katie Morag & the Tiresome Ted. 1999. (Illus.). 32p. (J). (gr. 1-4). pap. 9.99 (978-0-09-911881-7(5)) Random Hse. GBR. *Dist:* Independent Pubs. Group.

—Katie Morag Delivers the Mail. 2005. (Illus.). 32p. (J). pap. 9.99 (978-0-09-922072-5(5) , Red Fox) Random Hse. Children's Bks. GBR. *Dist:* Trafalgar Square Publishing.

—Katie Morag's Island Stories. 2002. (Illus.). 112p. pap. 14.99 (978-0-09-943856-4(9) , Red Fox) Random Hse. Children's Bks. GBR. *Dist:* Trafalgar Square Publishing.

—The Second Katie Morag Storybook. 2000. (Katie Morag Stories Ser.). (Illus.). 48p. (J). pap. 11.99 (978-0-09-926474-3(9)) Random Hse. GBR. *Dist:* Independent Pubs. Group.

Heller, Sarah & Reader's Digest Staff. Disney Tinker Bell Music Player & Storybook. 2008. (RD Innovative Book & Player Format Ser.). 36p. (J). 24.99 (***978-0-7944-1300-2(5)***) Reader's Digest Assn., Inc., The.

Helmso, Candy Grant. Lakeside. Taylor, Stephen, illus. 2003. (Books for Young Learners). 16p. (J). pap. 5.00 net. (978-1-57274-250-5(X) , 2727) Owen, Richard C. Pubs., Inc.

Henderson, Dianne. The Frightening Old Mansion. 2006. 116p. pap. 16.95 (978-1-4241-2486-2(7)) PublishAmerica, Inc.

Henderson, Tim. Butterflies & Magic Dreams. Hansen, Melissa, illus. l.t. ed. 2003. 28p. (J). (978-0-9728691-0-2(7)) Logan Bks.

Henkes, Kevin. Lilly's Chocolate Heart. Henkes, Kevin, illus. 2003. (Illus.). 24p. (J). (ps up). 6.99 (978-0-06-056066-9(5)) HarperCollins Pubs.

—Lily y Su Bolso de Plastico Morado. 2nd ed. 1998. (SPA., Illus.). 32p. (J). (gr. k-2). 13.99 (978-84-241-3366-5(8) , EV7781) Everest de Ediciones y Distribucion, S.L. ESP. *Dist:* Lectorum Pubns., Inc.

—Lily y Su Bolso de Plastico Morado. Henkes, Kevin, illus. (Illus.). 2005. (SPA.). (J). pap. 18.95 incl. audio compact disk (978-1-59519-177-9(1)); 2001. 28.95 incl. audio compact disk (978-1-59519-179-3(8)); 2001. 25.95 incl. audio (978-0-87499-812-2(3)); 2001. pap. 41.95 incl. audio (978-0-87499-813-9(1)); 2001. pap. 43.95 incl. audio compact disk (978-1-59519-178-6(X)) Live Oak Media.

Henshon, Suzanna. Mildew on the Wall. (J). pap. 9.99 (978-0-88092-484-9(5)) Royal Fireworks Publishing Co.

Herman, Debbie. Carla's Sandwich. Bailey, Sheila, illus. 2004. 32p. (J). 15.95 (978-0-9729225-2-4(0)) Flashlight Pr.

Herman, Gail. Little Star. 2000. (Fairy School Ser.). (Illus.). (J). (978-0-606-21634-0(0)) Tandem Library Bks.

Herrera, Juan Felipe. Cinnamon Girl: Letters Found Inside a Cereal Box. 2005. 176p. (J). 15.99 (978-0-06-057984-5(6) , Cotler, Joanna Books); lib. bdg. 16.89 (978-0-06-057985-2(4) , HarperTeen) HarperCollins Pubs.

Hesse, Karen. The Cats in Krasinski Square. Watson, Wendy, illus. 2004. 32p. (J). (gr. 2-5). pap. 16.95 (978-0-439-43540-6(4) , Scholastic Pr.) Scholastic, Inc.

Hest, Amy. When Jessie Came Across the Sea. Lynch, P. J., illus. 2003. 40p. (J). (gr. 1-7). pap. 6.99 (978-0-7636-1274-0(X)) Candlewick Pr.

Heyde, Christiane. The Happy Girl. Hawkins, Linda, illus. 2003. 48p. 14.95 (978-0-87516-618-6(0) , Devorss Pubns.) DeVorss & Co.

Hickman, Janet. Susannah. 2000. (Illus.). 192p. (J). (gr. 5 up). mass mkt. 4.95 (978-0-380-73224-1(6) , Harper Trophy) HarperCollins Pubs.

Hill, Janet Muirhead. Starlight's Courage: (the Starlight Books, 2), 6 vols. Lehmkuhl, Pat, illus. 2002. (Starlight Bks.: Bk. 2). 180p. (J). (gr. 4-7). pap. 9.00 (978-0-9714161-1-6(7)) Raven Publishing Inc. of Montana.

Hill, Nancy J. The Magical Spree of Katie McGee. Roberts, Amylyn, illus. 1999. 32p. (J). (ps-k). pap. 10.95 (978-0-9669436-0-3(0)) Serenity Pr.

Hillary, Robert, told to. Angel Girl. 2005. 21p. per. 9.95 (978-1-59453-708-0(9) , 2816) Airleaf Publishing & Bookselling.

Hillert, Margaret. Little Red Riding Hood. (Illus.). (J). 6.00 (978-0-87895-680-7(8)) Modern Curriculum Pr.

Hines, Stephen. "I Remember Laura", 1. 1999. 10.99 (978-1-57866-047-6(5) , Galahad Bks.) BBS Publishing Corp.

Hirt, Kelly K. Lucy & the Leprechaun Seekers. Laurie, Kane A., illus. 2001. (J). (gr. k-4). pap. 14.95 (978-0-9708027-0-5(6) , 14009) Passion Works, LLC.

Hobbie, Holly. Just Like You. Workman, Lisa, illus. 2006. (Holly Hobbie & Friends Ser.). 16p. (J). 8.99 (978-1-4169-2797-6(2) , Little Simon) Simon & Schuster Children's Publishing.

Hoestlandt, Jo. Emile bille de Clown. pap. 14.95 (978-2-7470-0822-8(3)) Bayard Editions FRA. *Dist:* Distribooks, Inc.

Hofer, Nelly & Hofer, Ernst, illus. Clever Katarina: A Tale in Six Parts. 2006. 40p. (J). (gr. 3-5). 17.95 (978-0-88776-764-7(8)) Tundra Bks., Inc./Livres Toundra, Inc. CAN. *Dist:* Random Hse., Inc.

Hoffman, Alice. Incantation. 2006. 176p. (J). (gr. 7 up). 16.99 (978-0-316-01019-1(7)) Little Brown & Co.

Hofmeister, Alan, et al. It Is Ann. (Reading for All Learners Ser.). (Illus.). (J). pap. (978-1-56861-084-9(X)) Swift Learning Resources.

—Nan & the Man. (Reading for All Learners Ser.). (Illus.). (J). pap. (978-1-56861-086-3(6)) Swift Learning Resources.

—Nan Sits. (Reading for All Learners Ser.). (Illus.). (J). pap. (978-1-56861-092-4(0)) Swift Learning Resources.

Hogan, Mary. Perfect Girl. 2007. 208p. (J). 16.99 (978-0-06-084108-9(7)); lib. bdg. 17.89 (978-0-06-084109-6(5)) HarperCollins Pubs. (HarperTeen).

Holl, Kristi. Chick Chat: More Devotions for Girls. 2006. (Faithgirlz Ser.). (Illus.). 192p. (J). pap. 9.99 (978-0-310-71143-8(6)) Zonderkidz.

Holm, Jennifer L. Claim No. 3. 2004. (Boston Jane Ser.). 240p. (J). (gr. 5 up). lib. bdg. 16.89 (978-0-06-029046-7(3)); 15.99 (978-0-06-029045-0(5)) HarperCollins Pubs.

Holohan, Maureen. Sideline Blues. 2001. (Broadway Ballplayers Ser.). (Illus.). (J). (978-0-606-21433-9(X)) Tandem Library Bks.

Holub, Joan, et al. Girls Will Be Girls. Smath, Jerry, illus. 2003. (All Aboard Reading Ser.). 224p. (J). (ps-2). 9.99 (978-0-448-43334-9(6) , Grosset & Dunlap) Penguin Group (USA) Inc.

Hooks, William H. Where's Lulu? Alley, R. W., illus. 1998. (Bank Street Reader Collection). 48p. (J). (ps-2). lib. bdg. 22.60 (978-0-8368-1768-3(0)) Stevens, Gareth Inc.

Hope, Laura Lee. Outdoor Girls at Ocean View or the Box T. 2007. 95.99 (***978-1-4280-5332-8(8)***); pap. 89.99 (***978-1-4280-5327-4(1)***) IndyPublish.com.

—The Outdoor Girls at the Hostess House: Or, doing their best for the Soldiers. 2007. 138p. pap. 10.99 (***978-1-4264-7589-4(6)***) BiblioBazaar.

—The Outdoor Girls at the Hostess House O. 2006. 77.99 (***978-1-4280-2008-5(X)***) IndyPublish.com.

—Outdoor Girls in Florida or Wintering in. 2007. 95.99 (***978-1-4280-5353-3(0)***); pap. 88.99 (***978-1-4280-5357-1(3)***) IndyPublish.com.

—Outdoor Girls in the Saddle or the Girl. 2007. 95.99 (***978-1-4280-5359-5(X)***); pap. 88.99 (***978-1-4280-5368-7(9)***) IndyPublish.com.

—The Outdoor Girls of Deepdale or Camping. 2006. 41.99 (***978-1-4280-0232-6(4)***); pap. 35.99 (***978-1-4280-0258-6(8)***) IndyPublish.com.

—Outdoor Girls on Pine Island or A Cave A. 2007. 95.99 (***978-1-4280-5320-5(4)***); pap. 89.99 (***978-1-4280-5317-5(4)***) IndyPublish.com.

Hopkins, Cathy. All Mates Together. 2007. (Truth or Dare Ser.: No. 8). 240p. (YA). (gr. 7 up). mass mkt. 5.99 (978-1-4169-2722-8(0) , Simon Pulse) Simon & Schuster Children's Publishing.

—Mates, Dates & Chocolate Cheats. 2005. (Mates, Dates Ser.). (Illus.). 224p. (YA). mass mkt. 5.99 (978-0-689-87696-7(3) , Simon Pulse) Simon & Schuster Children's Publishing.

—Mates, Dates & Cosmic Kisses. 2003. (Mates, Dates Ser.). (Illus.). 208p. (YA). mass mkt. 5.99 (978-0-689-85545-0(1) , Simon Pulse) Simon & Schuster Children's Publishing.

—Mates, Dates & Sizzling Summers. 2006. (Mates, Dates Ser.). 224p. (YA). mass mkt. 5.99 (978-0-689-87698-1(X) , Simon Pulse) Simon & Schuster Children's Publishing.

—The Princess of Pop. 2004. (Truth or Dare Ser.: No. 2). 191p. (YA). (gr. 7-17). per. 14.45 (978-1-4176-2894-0(4)) Tandem Library Bks.

Hopkins, David. Emily Edison. Rizy, Brock, illus. 2006. 144p. (YA). (gr. 8 up). per. 12.95 (978-0-9777883-2-3(6)) Viper Comics.

Hopkinson, Deborah. Girl Wonder: A Baseball Story in Nine Innings. Widener, Terry, illus. 2006. 40p. (J). reprint ed. pap. 6.99 (978-1-4169-1393-1(9) , Aladdin) Simon & Schuster Children's Publishing.

Horan, Evelyn. Jeannie, a Texas Frontier Girl. 2002. 149p. pap. 14.95 (978-1-59129-750-5(8)) PublishAmerica, Inc.

Hornburg, Michael. Downers Grove. 2001. (gr. 7-12). lib. bdg. 21.10 (978-0-613-36949-7(1)) Tandem Library Bks.

Horniman, Joanne. Secret Scribbled Notebooks. 2005. 228p. (Orig.). (YA). (gr. 7-17). pap. 7.95 (978-1-74114-406-2(X)) Allen & Unwin AUS. *Dist:* Independent Pubs. Group.

Horwitz, Elinor Lander. When the Sky Is Like Lace. Cooney, Barbara, illus. 2004. 32p. (J). (ps-3). reprint ed. 16.99 (978-0-670-05909-6(9) , Viking Juvenile) Penguin Group (USA) Inc.

Howard, Joanne. Not So Long Ago. 2005. 48p. pap. 12.95 (978-1-4137-6324-9(3)) PublishAmerica, Inc.

Howard, Josh. Dead@17: Blood of Saints. Howard, Josh, illus. 2004. 112p. (YA). per. 14.95 (978-0-9754193-1-1(5)) Viper Comics.

Hrdlitschka, Shelley. Sun Signs. 2005. 208p. (J). (gr. 7-12). pap. 7.95 (978-1-55143-338-7(9)); lib. bdg. 16.95 (978-1-55143-388-2(5)) Orca Bk. Pubs. USA.

Hudson, Cheryl Willis. Glo' Goes Shopping. 1998. (Afro-Bets Ser.). (Illus.). 32p. (J). (ps-2). pap. 5.95 (978-0-940975-84-2(X) , Sankofa Bks.) Just Us Bks., Inc.

Hughes, Sananjaleen June. Joanna's World. 44p. (J). spiral bd. (978-1-880757-01-7(X)) Reverence for Life.

Hunt, Thorpe. Mary the Lamb Gets Lost. 1998. (Illus.). 16p. (J). 6.99 (978-1-85608-285-3(7)) Hunt, John Publishing Ltd. GBR. *Dist:* APG Sales and Fulfillment.

Hurwitz, Johanna. Busybody Nora. Tilley, Debbie, illus. 2001. (Riverside Kids Ser.). 96p. (J). (gr. 1-4). pap. 4.99 (978-0-06-442143-0(0) , Harper Trophy) HarperCollins Pubs.

—Busybody Nora. 2001. (gr. 3-6). lib. bdg. 12.10 (978-0-613-34624-5(6)) Tandem Library Bks.

—Elisa in the Middle. Hoban, Lillian, illus. 1998. 96p. (J). (gr. 2-5). pap. 5.99 (978-0-14-038783-4(8) , Puffin) Penguin Group (USA) Inc.

—Ever-Clever Elisa. Tilley, Debbie, illus. 2002. (Riverside Kids Ser.). 128p. (J). pap. 4.99 (978-0-06-441096-0(X)) HarperCollins Pubs.

—New Shoes for Silvia. 1999. (Illus.). 32p. (J). (ps-3). pap. 5.95 (978-0-688-17115-5(X) , Harper Trophy) HarperCollins Pubs.

Hutchins, Hazel J. Tess. Ohi, Ruth, illus. 2003. 32p. (J). (gr. 2-5). pap. 5.95 (978-1-55037-394-3(3)) Annick Pr., Ltd. CAN. *Dist:* Firefly Bks., Ltd.

Hutchinson, Hanna. Caperucita Roja. Nofziger, Edward, illus. 1998. (Interlingo Ser.). (SPA.). 20p. (J). (ps-2). pap. 2.95 (978-0-922852-54-3(5)) Another Language Pr.

Hyppolite, Joanne. Ola Shakes It Up. Chang, Warren, illus. 2001. 176p. (gr. 4-7). pap. 12.00 (978-0-375-89509-8(4) , Yearling) Random Hse. Children's Bks.

I Spy: Individual Title Six-Packs. (Story Steps Ser.). (gr. k-2). 29.00 (978-0-7635-9571-5(3)) Rigby Education.

Ilogienboh, Caroline. Jayda's Story: Lost at the Crossroads. 2001. 114p. (YA). pap. 5.99 (978-0-9712781-0-3(5)) Sun Rose Pubs.

The Imaginer: Individual Title Six-Packs. (Bookweb Ser.). 32p. (gr. 6 up). 34.00 (978-0-7578-0900-2(6)) Rigby Education.

Innocenti, Roberto. Rosa Blanca. 2nd ed. 2003. (Rosa y Manzana Ser.). (SPA., Illus.). 32p. (978-84-85334-52-0(3) , LG2811) Loguez Ediciones ESP. *Dist:* Lectorum Pubns., Inc.

—Rose Blanche. Innocenti, Roberto, illus. 2003. (Illus.). 32p. (YA). (gr. 4 up). 17.95 (978-1-56846-189-2(5)) Creative Co., The.

Inoue, Kazurou. Midori Days. 2006. (Midori Days Ser.). 208p. (YA). Vol. 6. pap. 9.99 (978-1-4215-0495-7(2)); Vol. 7. pap. 9.99 (978-1-4215-0496-4(0)) Viz Media.

Isabella's Rainbow & Grandma's Teapots. 2000. vi, 126p. (YA). (gr. 7-12). pap. 9.95 (978-0-9707575-0-0(6)) Slator, Laraine.

Jablonski, Carla. Silent Echoes. 2007. 288p. (J). (gr. 9 up). 16.99 (978-1-59514-082-1(4) , Razorbill) Penguin Group (USA) Inc.

Jackson, Gwendolyn. The Adventures of Super T: The Missing Blanket. Scott-Daniel, Toni, illus. 2004. 32p. (J). lib. bdg. 15.95 (978-0-9753434-0-1(8)) LeTay Publishing.

Jacobs, Breena. Daddy's Girl. Austrew, Neva, illus. ed. 2006. 32p. (J). 15.95 (978-0-9749423-2-2(4)) Bookworm Bks.

Jacobs, John. I Wanna Be. 2006. (Illus.). 144p. 9.95 (978-0-9774659-6-5(9)) Cameo Pubns., LLC.

Jacobs, Sheila. This New Life. 144p. (YA). mass mkt. 5.99 (978-1-85792-661-3(7) , Christian Focus) Christian Focus Pubns. GBR. *Dist:* Riverside.

Jam, Teddy. Ttum. Chan, Harvey, illus. 2001. (Charlotte Stories). 110p. (J). (gr. 2-4). pap. 5.95 (978-0-88899-374-8(9)) Groundwood Bks. CAN. *Dist:* Perseus Distribution.

James, Annabelle. Abigail's Ballet Class. 2003. (J). per. (978-1-57657-956-5(5)) Paradise Pr., Inc.

—Abigail's Ballet Class. Beckes, Shirley, illus. 2004. 10p. (J). (ps-k). 12.49 (978-1-883043-54-4(9)) Straight Edge Pr., The.

James, Catherine. Bobby Cottontail's Gift. Collier, Kevin Scott, illus. 2006. 32p. (J). E-Book 9.95 incl. cd-rom (978-1-933090-24-5(3)) Guardian Angel Publishing, Inc.

James, Leah. Always after It Rains. 2002. 170p. (YA). pap. 12.95 (978-0-595-23611-4(1) , Writer's Showcase Pr.) iUniverse, Inc.

James, Sara & Ruckdeschel, Liz. What If ... All the Boys Wanted You. 2006. 288p. (YA). (gr. 7). pap. 8.95 (978-0-385-73297-0(X) , Delacorte Bks. for Young Readers) Random Hse. Children's Bks.

Janie. 2001. 32p. (YA). (gr. 6-12). pap. (978-0-8224-3461-0(X)) Globe Fearon Educational Publishing.

Jarrell, Pamela R. Jennifer & Danny. Linke, Don, Jr., illus. l.t. ed. 1999. (Cuddle Bks.). 7p. (J). (ps-k). pap. 10.95 (978-1-57332-124-2(9)) HighReach Learning, Inc.

Jay, Alison. 1-2-3: A Child's First Counting Book. 2007. 40p. (J). (ps-3). 15.99 (***978-0-525-47836-2(1)*** , Dutton Juvenile) Penguin Group (USA) Inc.

Jeanne-Marie in Gay Paris. 2003. (Illus.). 32p. (J). mass mkt. 9.99 (978-0-9740599-1-4(9) , 2) Omnibus Publishing.

Jenny's Yellow Ribbon. Date not set. 5.95 (978-0-89868-365-3(3)) ARO Publishing Co.

Jeremy Can't Drink Milk. 2006. (Illus.). 24p. (J). 5.99 (***978-0-9725593-2-4(9)***) by shayne.

Jewett, Sarah Orne. Betty Leicester: A Story for Girls. 2004. reprint ed. pap. 20.95 (978-1-4191-0978-2(2)); pap. 1.99 (978-1-4192-0978-9(7)) Kessinger Publishing, LLC.

Jimenez, Angeles. Macarena la Anguila. Gil, Sabina, illus. 2004. 26p. pap. 8.00 (978-84-931888-0-1(8)) Editorial Brief ESP. *Dist:* Independent Pubs. Group.

Johansen, K. V. & Lum, Bernice. Pippin Takes a Bath. 1999. (Pippin & Mabel Ser.). (Illus.). 32p. (J). (gr. k-3). (978-1-55074-627-3(8)) Kids Can Pr., Ltd.

Johns, Linda. Carmen Dives In. 2005. (Star Sisterz Ser.: Bk. 2). (Illus.). 192p. (J). pap. 5.99 (978-0-7869-3714-1(9)) Wizards of the Coast.

Johnson, Andi. Rollerskate Kate. 2004. (Illus.). 16p. 9.00 (978-1-84161-115-0(8)) Ravette Publishing, Ltd. GBR. *Dist:* Parkwest Pubns., Inc.

Johnson, Janet. Hallie & Grace- in the Beginning, God... 2007. (Illus.). 24p. (J). per. 6.99 (***978-1-59886-696-1(0)***) Tate Publishing & Enterprises, L.L.C.

Johnson, Julia. Cheetah's Tale. Keeble, Suzie, illus. 2004. 56p. pap. 16.95 (978-1-900988-87-2(9)) Stacey International Pubs. GBR. *Dist:* Interlink Publishing Group, Inc.

Johnson, Maureen. 13 Little Blue Envelopes. (Illus.). (J). 2005. 336p. (gr. 7 up). 16.99 (978-0-06-054141-5(5)); 2005. 336p. (gr. 7 up). lib. bdg. 17.89 (978-0-06-054142-2(3)); 2006. 352p. reprint ed. pap. 8.99 (978-0-06-054143-9(1) , HarperTeen) HarperCollins Pubs.

Johnson, Maureen G. The Key to the Golden Firebird. 2004. 304p. (J). (gr. 7 up). 15.99 (978-0-06-054138-5(5)) HarperCollins Pubs.

Johnston, Annie Fell. Georgina of the Rainbows (Illustrated Ed. 2006. pap. (***978-1-4065-1134-5(X)***) Dodo Pr.

Johnston, Annie Fellows. The Giant Scissors. Barry, Etheldred B., illus. 2005. reprint ed. pap. 22.95 (978-1-4179-0341-2(4)) Kessinger Publishing, LLC.

Johnston, Norma. Lotta's Progress. 1998. (gr. 3-7). pap. 3.99 (978-0-380-78916-0(7)) HarperCollins Pubs.

—Lotta's Progress. 1998. (978-0-606-13584-9(7)) Tandem Library Bks.

Jones, Elizabeth Orton. Twig. Jones, Elizabeth Orton, illus. anniv. ed. 2002. (Illus.). 152p. (J). (gr. 1-6). 18.95 (978-1-930900-05-9(8)) Purple Hse. Pr.

Joosse, Barbara M. Three Little Girls. Date not set. 32p. (J). (978-0-8050-6671-5(3) , Holt, Henry & Co. Bks. For Young Readers) Holt, Henry & Co.

Jordan, Apple. Stuck on You! 2006. (Illus.). 24p. (J). (gr. 1-5). pap. 5.99 (978-0-7364-2431-8(8) , RH/Disney) Random Hse. Children's Bks.

Jordan, Evora. Annie Love: A Hannah Gray Dog Story. 2003. (Hannah Gray Mysteries). (J). per. (978-0-9725071-2-7(4)) EvoraBooks, LLC.

Jukes, Mavis. Es Cosa de Chicas. (SPA.). 120p. (978-84-7927-422-1(0)) Robinbk., Ediciones S.L. ESP. *Dist:* Lectorum Pubns., Inc.

Julie of the Wolves. 1999. (J). (gr. 4-7). 11.95 (978-1-56137-821-0(6)) Novel Units, Inc.

Kacer, Kathy. The Secret of Gabi's Dresser. 2005. (Illus.). 128p. (YA). (gr. 3-6). pap. 4.95 (978-1-896764-15-3(0)) Second Story Pr. CAN. *Dist:* Orca Bk. Pubs. USA, Univ. of Toronto Pr.

Kakinouchi, Narumi. Juline, 5 vols. 168p. Vol. 1. 2001. (gr. 7-12). pap. 12.99 (978-1-892213-63-1(X)); Vol. 3. 3rd rev. ed. 2002. pap. 12.99 (978-1-931514-03-3(8)) TOKYOPOP, Inc.

Kallok, Emma. The Diary of Chickabiddy Baby. 2004. (Illus.). 128p. (YA). (gr. 4-7). pap. 4.95 (978-1-883672-90-4(2) , Tricycle Pr.) Ten Speed Pr.

Kamio, Yoko. Boys over Flowers. 2006. (Boys over Flowers Ser.).Tr. of Hana Yori Dango. 208p. (YA). Vol. 18. pap. 9.99 (978-1-4215-0532-9(0)); Vol. 19. pap. 9.99 (978-1-4215-0533-6(9)) Viz Media.

—Boys over Flowers: Hana Yori Dango, Vol. 1. 2003. (Boys over Flowers ~ Hana Yori Dango Ser.). (Illus.). 208p. (YA). pap. 9.95 (978-1-56931-996-3(0)) Viz Media.

Kaneyoshi, Izumi. Doubt!!, Vol. 4. Kaneyoshi, Izumi, illus. 2005. (Doubt Ser.). 192p. (YA). pap. 9.99 (978-1-59116-984-0(4)) Viz Media.

Kantor, Melissa. Confessions of a Not it Girl. 2004. 256p. (gr. 7-17). 15.99 (978-0-7868-1837-2(9)) Hyperion Bks. for Children.

Kantor, Melissa. If I Have a Wicked Stepmother, Where's My Prince? 2007. 320p. (gr. 7 up). pap. 8.99 (***978-0-7868-0961-5(2)***) Hyperion Pr.

Kaplan-Taylor, Maeve. At the Movies with Maeve. 2004. (Illus.). 36p. (J). 3.99 (978-0-9746587-4-2(X) , Beacon Street Girls) B*tween Productions, Inc.

Katchke, Judy. Full House No.3: Dear Michelle. 2004. (gr. 3-6). lib. bdg. 13.00 (978-0-613-71412-9(1)) Tandem Library Bks.

—Full House No.4: Dear Michelle. 2004. (gr. k-3). lib. bdg. 13.00 (978-0-613-71556-0(X)) Tandem Library Bks.

Katschke, Judy. A Day in the Life of a Princess: Storybook & Dress-Up Kit. 2006. 24p. (J). pap. 18.99 (978-0-7944-1106-0(1)) Reader's Digest Assn., Inc., The.

Katz, Jennifer A. The Era of Courting. 2006. 119p. pap. 16.95 (978-1-4241-3321-5(1)) PublishAmerica, Inc.

Kazuo, Umezu. Reflections. 2006. (Scary Book Ser.: Vol. 1). 232p. (YA). pap. 13.95 (978-1-59307-476-0(X)) Dark Horse Comics.

Keehn, Sally M. I Am Regina. 2001. (Novels Ser.). 240p. (J). (gr. 5-7). pap. 6.99 (978-0-698-11920-8(7) , Putnam Juvenile) Penguin Group (USA) Inc.

—I Am Regina. 2002. (gr. 3-6). lib. bdg. 14.15 (978-0-613-45282-3(8)) Tandem Library Bks.

Keene, Carolyn. Action! ed. 2005. (Nancy Drew Ser.: 6). 138p. (J). lib. bdg. 15.00 (978-1-59054-809-7(4)) Fitzgerald Bks.

—Case of the Sneaky Snowman. Pamintuan, Macky, illus. 2006. (Nancy Drew & the Clue Crew Ser.: No. 5). 96p. (J). pap. 3.99 (978-1-4169-1254-5(1) , Aladdin) Simon & Schuster Children's Publishing.

—The Cinderella Ballet Mystery. Pamintuan, Macky, illus. 2006. (Nancy Drew & the Clue Crew Ser.: No. 4). 96p. (J). pap. 3.99 (978-1-4169-1256-9(8) , Aladdin) Simon & Schuster Children's Publishing.

—False Notes. 2004. (Nancy Drew Ser.: No. 3). 160p. (J). pap. 4.99 (978-0-689-86568-8(6) , Aladdin) Simon & Schuster Children's Publishing.

—Framed. 2005. (Nancy Drew Ser.). 160p. (J). pap. 4.99 (978-0-689-87863-3(X) , Aladdin) Simon & Schuster Children's Publishing.

—Lights, Camera ... Cats! Pamintuan, Macky, illus. 2007. (Nancy Drew & the Clue Crew Ser.: No. 8). 96p. (J). pap. 3.99 (978-1-4169-3957-3(1) , Aladdin) Simon & Schuster Children's Publishing.

—Mystery on Maui. 1998. (Nancy Drew Mystery Stories: No. 143). 160p. (gr. 3-6). mass mkt. 4.99 (978-0-671-00753-9(X) , Aladdin) Simon & Schuster Children's Publishing.

—Pit of Vipers. 2006. (Nancy Drew Ser.: No. 18). 160p. (J). pap. 4.99 (978-1-4169-1180-7(4) , Aladdin) Simon & Schuster Children's Publishing.

—A Race Against Time. ed. 2005. (Nancy Drew Ser.: 2). 154p. (J). lib. bdg. 15.00 (978-1-59054-808-0(6)) Fitzgerald Bks.

—The Singing Suspects. Jones, Jan Naimo, illus. Frost, Michael, photos by. 2005. (Nancy Drew Notebooks: No. 67). 80p. (J). (ps). pap. 3.99 (978-1-4169-0087-0(X) , Aladdin) Simon & Schuster Children's Publishing.

—Space Case. Jones, Jan Naimo, illus. 2004. (Nancy Drew Notebooks: No. 6). 80p. (J). pap. 3.99 (978-0-689-86536-7(8) , Aladdin) Simon & Schuster Children's Publishing.

—A Taste of Danger. 2003. (Nancy Drew Mystery Stories: No. 174). 176p. (J). pap. 4.99 (978-0-689-86154-3(0) , Aladdin) Simon & Schuster Children's Publishing.

—Uncivil Acts. 2005. (Nancy Drew Ser.). 160p. (J). pap. 4.99 (978-0-689-86937-2(1) , Aladdin) Simon & Schuster Children's Publishing.

—Valentine's Day Secret. 2007. (Nancy Drew & the Clue Crew Ser.). 96p. (J). pap. 3.99 (***978-1-4169-4944-2(5)*** , Aladdin) Simon & Schuster Children's Publishing.

Keene, Carolyn. The Wild Cat Crime. 1998. (Nancy Drew Mystery Stories: No. 141). (J). (gr. 3-6). (978-0-606-13643-3(6)) Tandem Library Bks.

Kehret, Peg. Don't Tell Anyone. 2000. (Illus.). 144p. (YA). (gr. 5-9). 15.99 (978-0-525-46388-7(7) , Dutton Juvenile) Penguin Group (USA) Inc.

Kelly, Everett. Tiny Tom. 2007. 56p. (J). per. 15.95 (***978-1-58939-983-9(8)***) Virtualbookworm.com Publishing, Inc.

Kelly, Katy. Lucy Rose: Busy Like You Can't Believe. 2007. 192p. (J). (gr. 3-7). pap. 5.99 (978-0-440-42108-5(X) , Yearling) Random Hse. Children's Bks.

Kendall, Cassie. Laurel & the Sprites' Mischief. Rodriguez, Robert, illus. 1999. (Stardust Classics: Vol. 4). 114p. (J). (gr. 2-5). 12.95 (978-1-889514-29-1(2)); pap. 5.95 (978-1-889514-30-7(6)) Dolls Corp.

Kennemore, Tim. Alice's World Record. 2006. (Illus.). 86p. (J). (gr. 3-4). 8.99 (978-1-84270-238-3(6)) Andersen GBR. *Dist:* Independent Pubs. Group.

Kern, Merilee A. It's Not Your Fault That You're Overweight: A Story of Enlightenment, Empowerment, & Accomplishment for Overweight & Obese Kids: Girls' Edition. DeCrotie, Jerry, illus. 2005. 72p. (J). (gr. 3-5). pap. 11.95 (978-1-58736-567-6(7) , Starbound Bks.) Wheatmark.

Kerven, Rosalind & Marks, Alan. Enchanted Forest. 2004. (Illus.). 32p. (J). pap. 7.95 (978-1-84507-192-9(1)) Lincoln, Frances Ltd. GBR. *Dist:* Perseus Distribution.

Kidd, Erin. Cowgirl. 2004. 32p. (J). per. 9.95 (978-1-59094-072-3(5)) Jawbone Publishing Corp.

Kieffer, Eduardo Gudino. Giraluna. (SPA.). (J). (gr. 3-5). pap. 6.95 (978-1-930332-18-8(1) , LC2158) Lectorum Pubns., Inc.

Kikuchi, Hideyuki. Azumanga Daioh Vol. 4: The Manga. 2004. (Illus.). 198p. (YA). pap. (978-1-4139-0048-4(8)) ADV Manga.

King, Jan. It's a Girl Thing. 2003. 96p. 5.99 (978-0-7407-3355-0(9)) Andrews McMeel Publishing.

King, Susan. Amy & the Christmas Party/Amy & the New Year's Goals. King, Susan, illus. 2001. (Illus.). 75p. (J). (ps-6). 7.00 (978-0-9714446-1-4(7)) King RIT - ACKS Pubs.

Kinsey-Warnock, Natalie. Nora's Ark. McCully, Emily Arnold, illus. 2005. 32p. (J). 16.99 (978-0-688-17244-2(X)); lib. bdg. 17.89 (978-0-06-029517-2(1)) HarperCollins Pubs.

Kirby, Susan E. Daniel's Story. Andreasen, Dan, illus. 2001. (American Quilts Ser.: Vol. 3). 208p. (J). (gr. 4-7). mass mkt. 9.95 (978-0-689-80971-2(9) , Aladdin) Simon & Schuster Children's Publishing.

—Ellen's Story. Andreasen, Dan, illus. 2000. (American Quilts Ser.: Vol. 1). 192p. (J). (gr. 4-7). pap. 9.95 (978-0-689-80969-9(7) , Aladdin) Simon & Schuster Children's Publishing.

—Hattie's Story. 2000. (American Quilts Ser.: Vol. 2). 192p. (J). (gr. 3-6). pap. 9.95 (978-0-689-80970-5(0) , Aladdin) Simon & Schuster Children's Publishing.

—Sunbonnet Girls. 2000. (J). Bk. 3. 15.00 (978-0-689-80976-7(X)); Bk. 4. 15.00 (978-0-689-80977-4(8)) Simon & Schuster Children's Publishing. (Simon & Schuster Children's Publishing).

Kirchel, Karen. Irrepressible Lucie Archer. 2006. 147p. pap. 19.95 (***978-1-4241-3400-7(5)***) PublishAmerica, Inc.

Kirk, Heather. A Drop of Rain. 2004. 215p. (YA). pap. 8.95 (978-1-894917-10-0(3)) Napoleon Publishing/ Rendezvous Pr. CAN. *Dist:* AtlasBooks Distribution.

Klages, Ellen. The Green Glass Sea. 2006. 272p. (YA). (gr. 5). 16.99 (978-0-670-06134-1(4) , Viking Juvenile) Penguin Group (USA) Inc.

Klar, Elizabeth. Ella Enchanted. Robbins, Dawn Michelle, ed. 2000. (J). 9.95 (978-1-58130-626-2(1)); 11.95 (978-1-58130-627-9(X)) Novel Units, Inc.

Klar, Elizabeth & Trim, Cheryl Klar. Shabanu: Daughter of the Wind. Robbins, Dawn Michelle, ed. 2000. (YA). 9.95 (978-1-58130-632-3(6)); 11.95 (978-1-58130-633-0(4)) Novel Units, Inc.

Klearman-Cooper, Mel. The Dirty Little Orphan Girl. 2005. 50p. pap. 12.95 (978-1-4137-5891-7(6)) PublishAmerica, Inc.

Knight, Caitlyn. Anastasia: the Tapestry of the Silver Unicorns. 2007. 386p. pap. 19.98 (***978-0-615-15145-8(0)***) Neugard, S.L.

Knoebel, Suzanne B. Dr. Tootsie: A Young Girl's Dream. Armour, Steven & Kennard, Thomas, illus. 2003. 100p. (J). per. 12.97 (978-0-9679416-1-5(X)) Alexie Bks.

Komaiko, Leah. Annie Bananie & the Pain Sisters. 2000. (978-0-606-17890-7(2)) Tandem Library Bks.

Korba, Joanna. Rough-Face Girl: A Native AMER Cinderella Story. 2006. 42.00 (***978-1-4108-6163-4(5)***) Benchmark Education Co.

Koski, Mary B. Impatient Pamela Asks: Why Are My Feet So Huge? Brown, Dan, illus. (Impatient Pamela Ser.). 32p. (J). (ps-3). 2003. pap. 4.95 (978-1-930650-02-2(7)); 2000. pap. 7.95 (978-0-9663281-3-4(2)) Trellis Publishing, Inc.

—Impatient Pamela Calls 9-1-1. Brown, Dan, illus. 2003. (Impatient Pamela Ser.). 32p. (J). (ps-3). 15.95 (978-0-9663281-9-6(1)) Trellis Publishing, Inc.

Krensky, Stephen. Sacagawea & the Bravest Deed. Magnuson, illus. 2002. (Ready-to-Read Cofa Ser.). 32p. (J). pap. 3.99 (978-0-689-84803-2(X) , Aladdin) Simon & Schuster Children's Publishing.

—Sacagawea & the Bravest Deed. 2002. (gr. k-3). lib. bdg. 11.80 (978-0-613-57582-9(2)) Tandem Library Bks.

Kriesel, Mae. Aggi Pursued. 2007. per. 12.99 (***978-1-59886-534-9(X)***) Tate Publishing & Enterprises, L.L.C.

Kroll, Steven. When I Dream of Heaven: Angelina's Story. 2000. (978-0-606-21879-5(3)) Tandem Library Bks.

Kroll, Virginia L. She Is Born: A Celebration of Daughters. Rowe, John, illus. 2000. 32p. (J). (gr. 9 up). 15.95 (978-1-885223-94-4(3)) Beyond Words Publishing, Inc.

Krulik, Nancy E. Who's Afraid of Fourth Grade? 2004. (Katie Kazoo, Switcheroo Ser.). (Illus.). 160p. (J). (gr. 2-6). mass mkt. 4.99 (978-0-448-43555-8(1) , Grosset & Dunlap) Penguin Group (USA) Inc.

Kyber, Manfred. The Three Candles of Little Veronica. 2003. (Illus.). 194p. 19.95 (978-0-913098-84-4(1)) Orion Society, The.

LaBate, Jim. Let's Go, Gaels: A Novella by Jim LaBate. Mosher, Jeff, illus. 1998. 60p. (YA). (gr. 7-12). pap. 5.95 (978-0-9662100-4-0(2)) Mohawk River Pr.

Lablanc, Louise. Sophie Fait des Folies. 2002. (Premier Roman Ser.). (FRE., Illus.). 64p. (J). (gr. 2-5). pap. (978-2-89021-244-2(0)) Diffusion du livre Mirabel.

Laird, Elisabeth. Anitas Big Day. 1998. (Illus.). 16p. (C). pap. 9.00 (978-0-582-35289-6(4)) Pearson ESL.

Lambert, Janet. First of All: A Campbell Story. 2002. (J). per. 9.95 (978-1-930009-60-8(7) , 800-691-7779) Image Cascade Publishing.

—Five's a Crowd: A Campbell Story. 2002. (J). per. 9.95 (978-1-930009-59-2(3)) Image Cascade Publishing.

Lamere, Jill. Upside Down. Lamere, Jill, illus. 2005. (J). bds. 12.95 (978-0-9772320-0-0(X)) Minikin Pr.

Lampman, Annette. Nicole's Wish. 2006. 23.00 (***978-0-8059-9146-8(8)***) Dorrance Publishing Co., Inc.

Lance, Kathryn. Going to See Grassy Ella. 2000. 148p. (gr. 4-7). pap. 10.95 (978-0-595-09070-9(2) , Backinprint-.com) iUniverse, Inc.

Landolf, Diane Wright. Hooray for Halloween! Wolcott, Karen, illus. 2004. (Barbie Ser.). 24p. (J). (ps-2). 3.99 (978-0-375-82757-0(9) , Golden Bks.) Random Hse. Children's Bks.

Landon, Lucinda. Meg Mackintosh & the Mystery on Main Street: A Solve-It-Yourself Mystery. Murrray, Wendy, ed. Landon, Lucinda, illus. 2000. (Meg Mackintosh Mystery Ser.). (Illus.). 48p. (J). pap. 5.95 (978-1-888695-06-9(4)) Secret Passage Pr.

Langlois, Annie. Victorine et la Pièce D'or. Beshwaty, Steve, tr. 2003. (Picture Bks.). (FRE., Illus.). 32p. (J). (ps). pap. (978-2-89021-658-7(6)) Diffusion du livre Mirabel.

Lansky, Bruce. Chicas Al Rescate. 2001. (SPA.). lib. bdg. 15.70 (978-0-613-80581-0(X)) Tandem Library Bks.

—Girls to the Rescue, Bk. 7. 2000. (Illus.). 120p. (J). (gr. 3-7). pap. 3.95 (978-0-689-84079-1(9)) Meadowbrook Pr.

—Girls to the Rescue, No. 6. 1999. (978-0-606-17665-1(9)) Tandem Library Bks.

—Girls to the Rescue: Folk Tales from Around the World. 1999. (Illus.). (J). 78.00 (978-0-684-81211-3(8)) Meadowbrook Pr.

—When Grandma Was a Girl: What Her Life Was Like As a Child. 2002. (Illus.). 22p. 9.95 (978-0-7432-3694-2(7)) Meadowbrook Pr.

Lansky, Bruce, ed. The Best of Girls to the Rescue. 2002. (Girls to the Rescue Ser.). 250p. (J). pap. 5.95 (978-0-689-02468-9(1)) Meadowbrook Pr.

—Girls to the Rescue. 1998. (J). Bk. 1. 3.95 (978-0-88166-314-3(X)); Bk. 4. 112p. (gr. 3-6). pap. 3.95 (978-0-88166-301-3(8)) Meadowbrook Pr.

Lansky, Bruce & Johnson, Martha. Girls to the Rescue, Bk. 5. 108p. (J). pap. (978-0-88166-315-0(8)) Meadowbrook Pr.

LaRose, Linda. Jessica Takes Charge. Franson, Leanne, illus. 1999. 24p. (J). (ps-1). pap. 5.95 (978-1-55037-562-6(8)) Annick Pr., Ltd. CAN. *Dist:* Firefly Bks., Ltd.

Lasky, Kathryn. Starring Lucille. Hafner, Marylin, illus. 2003. 32p. (J). (ps-2). pap. 6.99 (978-0-440-41796-5(1) , Dragonfly Bks.) Random Hse. Children's Bks.

Lasser, Olivier. Charlotte et l'nle du Destin. ed. 2004. (FRE., Illus.). (J). (gr. k-3). spiral bd. (978-0-616-07262-2(7)) Canadian National Institute for the Blind/Institut National Canadien pour les Aveugles.

Laurens, Jennifer. Magic Hands. 2007. (YA). per. 12.95 (978-1-933963-97-6(2)) Grove Creek Publishing, LLC.

Lavender, William. Just Jane: A Daughter of England Caught in the Struggle of the American Revolution. 2005. (Great Episodes Ser.). 336p. (YA). pap. 6.95 (978-0-15-205472-4(3) , Gulliver Bks.) Harcourt Children's Bks.

Lawrence, Josephine. Rainbow Hill. 2005. pap. 30.95 (978-1-4179-9852-4(0)) Kessinger Publishing, LLC.

Lawrence, Mike. The Macaroni Disaster! 2006. 44p. pap. 12.00 (978-1-4116-8613-7(6)) Lulu.com.

Lawson, Julie. Emma & the Silk Train. Mombourquette, Paul, illus. 32p. (J). (gr. k-3). 2002. (978-1-55074-651-8(0)); 1998. (978-1-55074-388-3(0)) Kids Can Pr., Ltd.

—Emma & the Silk Train. 2002. (gr. k-3). lib. bdg. 14.10 (978-0-613-83948-8(X)) Tandem Library Bks.

Lay, Eddie. Mystery of the Hats. 2006. 61p. pap. 12.95 (978-1-4241-2649-1(5)) PublishAmerica, Inc.

Le Guin, Ursula K. Jane on Her Own. Schindler, S. D., illus. (Catwings Ser.: No. 4). 48p. (J). (gr. 1-4). 2001. pap. 3.95 (978-0-531-07180-9(4)); 1999. 15.99 (978-0-531-33133-0(4)) Scholastic, Inc. (Orchard Bks.).

—Jane on Her Own. 2001. (Catwings Ser.: No. 4). (Illus.). (J). (978-0-606-21260-1(4)) Tandem Library Bks.

Leather. Birthday Girl. (Illus.). (J). mass mkt. (978-0-671-88667-7(3) , Pocket) Simon & Schuster.

Leblanc, Louise. Ca Suffit, Sophie! 2003. (Premier Roman Ser.). (FRE.). 64p. (J). (gr. 2-5). pap. (978-2-89021-131-5(2)) Diffusion du livre Mirabel.

—Ca Va Mal Pour Sophie. 2002. (Premier Roman Ser.). (FRE.). 64p. (J). (gr. 2-5). pap. (978-2-89021-177-3(0)) Diffusion du livre Mirabel.

—Maddie Tries to Be Good. Cummins, Sarah, tr. Gay, Marie-Louise, illus. 1999. 61p. (gr. 1-5). (First Novel Ser.). 4.95 (978-0-88780-482-3(9)); (First Novels Ser.: Vol. 33). (J). (978-0-88780-483-0(7)) Formac Publishing Co., Ltd. CAN. *Dist:* Casemate Pubs. & Bk. Distributors, LLC.

—Sophie Devient Sage. Gay, Marie-Louise, illus. 2001. (Premier Roman Ser.). (FRE.). 64p. (J). (gr. 1-4). pap. (978-2-89021-466-8(4)) Diffusion du livre Mirabel.

—Sophie Est en Danger. Gay, Marie-Louise, illus. 2001. (Premier Roman Ser.). (FRE.). 64p. (J). pap. (978-2-89021-464-4(8)) Diffusion du livre Mirabel.

—Sophie Lance et Compte. 2002. (Premier Roman Ser.). (FRE.). 64p. (J). (gr. 2-5). pap. (978-2-89021-158-2(4)) Diffusion du livre Mirabel.

—Sophie Part en Voyage. 2002. (Premier Roman Ser.). (FRE.). 64p. (J). (gr. 2-5). pap. (978-2-89021-195-7(9)) Diffusion du livre Mirabel.

—Sophie Vit un Cauchemar. Gay, Marie-Louise, illus. 2001. (Premier Roman Ser.). (FRE.). 64p. (J). (gr. 1-4). pap. (978-2-89021-465-1(6)) Diffusion du livre Mirabel.

Leblanc, Louise & Gay, Marie-Louise. Sophie Decouvre l'Envers du Decor. 2002. (Premier Roman Ser.). (FRE., Illus.). 64p. (J). (gr. 1-4). pap. (978-2-89021-569-6(5)) Diffusion du livre Mirabel.

—Sophie Prend les Grands Moyens. 2001. (Premier Roman Ser.). (FRE., Illus.). 64p. (J). pap. (978-2-89021-463-7(X)) Diffusion du livre Mirabel.

Leedy, Loreen. Measuring Penny. rev. ed. 2000. (Illus.). 32p. (J). (gr. 2-4). pap. 7.95 (978-0-8050-6572-5(5) , Holt, Henry & Co. Bks. For Young Readers) Holt, Henry & Co.

—Measuring Penny. 2000. (gr. 3-6). lib. bdg. 15.25 (978-0-613-30024-7(6)) Tandem Library Bks.

Leeson, Robert. Geraldine Gets Lucky. (Illus.). 32p. (J). 13.95 (978-0-241-00234-6(6) , Hamilton, Hamish); pap. 7.95 (978-0-14-038615-8(7)) Penguin Bks., Ltd. GBR. *Dist:* Trafalgar Square Publishing.

Lehman, Barbara. The Red Book. Lehman, Barbara, illus. 2004. (Illus.). 32p. (J). (gr. k-3). 12.95 (978-0-618-42858-8(5)) Houghton Mifflin Co. Trade & Reference Div.

Lembcke, Marjaleena & Martínez, Eduardo. Tiempo de Secretos. Steffens, Klaus & Martínez, Eduardo, trs. Steffens, Klaus, illus. 2002. (SPA.). 144p. (978-84-89804-58-6(3)) Loguez Ediciones ESP. *Dist:* Lectorum Pubns., Inc.

Lemieux, Michele. Noche de Tormenta. Lopez, L. Rodriquez, tr. from GER. Lemieux, Michele, illus. 2nd ed. 2002. (SPA., Illus.). 186p. (J). (gr. 3-5). 23.95 (978-84-89804-27-2(3)) Loguez Ediciones ESP. *Dist:* Baker & Taylor Bks., Lectorum Pubns., Inc.

L'Engle, Madeleine. Camilla. 278p. (YA). (gr. 7 up). pap. 4.95 (978-0-8072-1359-9(4) , Listening Library) Random Hse. Audio Publishing Group.

Lenhard, Elizabeth, et al. The Power of Five. 2004. (W. I. T. C. H. Ser.: Bk. 1). (Illus.). 158p. (J). (gr. 3-7). pap. 4.99 (978-0-7868-5257-4(7) , Volo) Hyperion Bks. for Children.

Leppard, Lois Gladys. New Girl. 1999. (Young Mandie Mystery Ser.). (978-0-606-20314-2(1)) Tandem Library Bks.

Lester, Helen. La Mochila de Lin, Level 2. Ada, Alma Flor, tr. Munsinger, Lynn, illus. 3rd ed. 2003. (Dejame Leer Ser.). (SPA.). 8p. (J). (ps-1). 6.50 (978-0-673-36291-9(4) , Good Year Bks.) Celebration Pr.

Levine, Gail Carson. Ella Enchanted. movie tie-in ed. 2004. 288p. (J). (gr. 7 up). pap. 6.99 (978-0-06-055886-4(5)) HarperCollins Pubs.

—Ella Enchanted. 2004. (gr. 7-12). lib. bdg. 15.30 (978-0-613-71408-2(3)); 1998. 238p. (J). (ps-7). lib. bdg. 14.75 (978-0-613-07691-3(5)) Tandem Library Bks.

Levinson, Robin K. Shoshana & the Native Rose. Kehl, Drusilla, illus. 2006. 103p. (J). (gr. 3-5). per. 12.00 (978-0-9773673-2-0(0)) Gali Girls, Inc.

Lewis, Beverly. A Perfect Match. 1999. (Girls Only (Go!) Ser.: Vol. 3). 128p. (J). (gr. 3-8). pap. 6.99 (978-0-7642-2060-9(8)) Bethany Hse. Pubs.

—Reach for the Stars. 1999. (Girls Only (Go!) Ser.: Vol. 4). 128p. (J). (gr. 3-8). pap. 6.99 (978-0-7642-2061-6(6)) Bethany Hse. Pubs.

Lewis, Kim. A Puppy for Annie. Lewis, Kim, illus. 2006. (Illus.). 32p. (J). (ps). 15.99 (978-0-7636-3200-7(7)) Candlewick Pr.

Lewis, Megan. The Girl Who Could Fly. l.t. ed. 2005. (Illus.). 30p. (J). per. 9.99 (978-1-59879-029-0(3)) Lifevest Publishing, Inc.

Lewis, Wendy. Graveyard Girl & Other Stories. 2004. 176p. (YA). (gr. 9 up). pap. 7.95 (978-0-88995-202-7(7)) Red Deer Pr. CAN. *Dist:* Fitzhenry & Whiteside, Ltd.

Li, Zeru. Boyero/Muchacha. 2000. Tr. of Oxherd/Weaver. (CHI & SPA.). (J). 5.95 (978-7-5032-0120-2(7)) China Travel Books Pr. CHN. *Dist:* AIMS International Bks., Inc.

Libhart, Virginia B. Carrie's Dream. 2005. (978-0-9652963-7-3(7)) Harborseal Publishing Co.

Lichtman, Wendy. Do the Math: Secrets, Lies, & Algebra: Secrets, Lies, & Algebra. 2007. 192p. (J). 16.99 (***978-0-06-122955-8(5)***); lib. bdg. 17.89 (***978-0-06-122956-5(3)***) HarperCollins Pubs. (HarperTeen).

Liebig, Nelda J. Carrie & the Apple Pie. 1999. 122p. (J). (gr. 3-7). pap. (978-1-883953-30-0(8)) Midwest Traditions, Inc.

Light, John. Julie's Problem. 2005. (Illus.). 24p. (978-1-897968-13-0(2)) Photon Pr.

Lillian's First Day. 2003. (J). 12.00 (978-0-9724442-3-1(8)) LightHouse Pr.

Limb, Sue. Girl, 15, Charming but Insane. 2005. (Girl, 15 Ser.). 240p. (J). (gr. 5). reprint ed. pap. 8.95 (978-0-385-73215-4(5) , Delacorte Bks. for Young Readers) Random Hse. Children's Bks.

Lindgren, Astrid. Pippi Goes to the Circus. Chesworth, Michael, illus. 2000. (Pippi Longstocking Storybooks). 32p. (J). (gr. k-2). pap. 6.99 (978-0-14-130243-0(7) , Puffin) Penguin Group (USA) Inc.

—Pippi Longstocking. Nunally, Tina, tr. from SWE. 2007. 208p. (J). (gr. k). 25.00 (***978-0-670-06276-8(6)*** , Viking Juvenile) Penguin Group (USA) Inc.

—Pippi Longstocking. (Pippi Longstocking Ser.). 160p. (J). (gr. 3-5). pap. 4.99 (978-0-8072-1431-2(0) , Listening Library) Random Hse. Audio Publishing Group.

—Pippi's Extraordinary Ordinary Day. 1999. (Pippi Longstocking Storybooks). (Illus.). 64p. (J). (gr. k-2). 14.99 (978-0-670-88073-7(6) , Viking Juvenile) Penguin Group (USA) Inc.

Linhart, Sandra Miller. What Does a Hero Look Like? 2007. 44p. (J). pap. 16.99 (978-1-59092-576-8(9) , Little Blue Works) Windstorm Creative.

Linn, Margot. The Big Red Blanket. Jacobson, David, illus. 2005. (I'm Going to Read Ser.). 28p. (J). 11.95 (978-1-4027-2069-7(6)) Sterling Publishing Co., Inc.

Lisa's Ices: Individual Title Six-Packs. (ps-2). 27.00 (978-0-7635-9459-6(8)) Rigby Education.

Lisle, Rebecca. Amethyst. 2007. 176p. (J). (gr. 4-7). pap. 7.95 (***978-1-84270-541-4(5)***) Andersen GBR. *Dist:* Independent Pubs. Group.

Literature Connections English: My Antonia. 2004. (gr. 6-12). (978-0-395-77539-4(6) , 2-80108) McDougal Littell Inc.

Literature Connections English: Nervous Conditions. 2004. (gr. 6-12). (978-0-395-77560-8(4) , 2-80129) McDougal Littell Inc.

Literature Connections English: The Friends. 2004. (gr. 6-12). (978-0-395-77541-7(8) , 2-80110) McDougal Littell Inc.

Literature Connections Spanish: Tuck para Siempre (Tuck Everlasting) 2004. (gr. 6-12). (978-0-395-80046-1(3) , 2-70465) McDougal Littell Inc.

The Little Girl & Her Beetle: Individual Title Six-Packs. (Literatura 2000 Ser.). (gr. 2-3). 33.00 (978-0-7635-0174-7(3)) Rigby Education.

Little, Jean. Emma's Magic Winter. Plecas, Jennifer, illus. (I Can Read Bks.). 64p. (J). (ps-3). 2000. pap. 3.99 (978-0-06-443706-6(X) , Harper Trophy); 1998. 15.95 (978-0-06-025389-4(9)); 1998. 15.89 (978-0-06-025390-5(8)) HarperCollins Pubs.

—His Banner over Me. 1999. 224p. (J). mass mkt. 6.99 (978-0-14-037761-3(1)) Penguin Group (USA) Inc.

—Somebody Else's Summer. 2007. 192p. (J). 16.00 (978-0-670-04466-5(0) , Penguin Global) Penguin Group (USA) Inc.

Lizzie McGuire Movie Scrapbook. 2003. (Illus.). 48p. (J). pap. 6.99 (978-0-7868-4583-5(X)) Disney Pr.

London, Victoria. Emily Cobbs & the Naked School Bk. 1: A Gifted Girls Series. 2005. (Gifted Girls Ser.). (J). per. 7.99 (978-1-59748-857-0(7)) Sparklesoup Studios, Inc.

Look Out the Window: Individual Title Six-Packs. (Story Steps Ser.). (gr. k-2). 29.00 (978-0-7635-9587-6(X)) Rigby Education.

Lopez, C. Pellicer. Julieta y Su Caja de Colores. (SPA., Illus.). (J). (gr. k-2). pap. 3.96 net. (978-0-395-79735-8(7) , HMS033) Houghton Mifflin Co.

Lorimer, Janet. Ruby's Terrible Secret. 2004. (Illus.). 32p. (YA). 2.95 (978-1-56254-744-8(5) , SP7445) Saddleback Educational Publishing.

Lost in the Wilderness. 2006. (J). (978-1-933343-39-6(7) , PONY) Stabenfeldt Inc.

Loughrey, Eithne. Annie Moore: First in Line for America. 1999. (Illus.). 143p. (YA). (gr. 5-10). pap. 7.95 (978-1-85635-245-1(5)) Mercier Pr., Ltd., The IRL. *Dist:* Irish Bks. & Media, Inc.

—Annie Moore: The Golden Dollar Girl. 1999. (Illus.). 160p. (YA). (gr. 5-10). pap. 7.95 (978-1-85635-296-3(X)) Mercier Pr., Ltd., The IRL. *Dist:* Irish Bks. & Media, Inc.

Lovelace, Maud Hart. Emily of Deep Valley. Neville, Vera, illus. 2000. 304p. (YA). (gr. 3 up). 16.89 (978-0-06-028873-0(6)) HarperCollins Pubs.

—Emily of Deep Valley. 2000. (gr. 3-6). lib. bdg. 15.25 (978-0-613-31157-1(4)) Tandem Library Bks.

Lowe, Lana. The Three Little Girls & the Giant Sea Turtle. Beaumont, Peter, illus. 2006. (J). (978-0-9777274-0-7(8)) Lone Star Publishing Co.

Lueck, Andrew. Chicabee. 2006. 32p. 16.95 (978-0-9774547-0-9(3)) Lueck Studios.

Luke, Michelle. Victoria Elizabeth's Magical Dream Paper Dolls. Luke, Michelle, illus. 1998. (Illus.). 32p. (J). (gr. 2-5). 7.99 (978-0-9660672-2-4(3)) It's a Girl Pubns.

Lum, Bernice, illus. Pippin Takes a Bath. 2002. (Pippin Ser.). 32p. (J). (gr. k-3). (978-1-55337-420-6(7)) Kids Can Pr., Ltd.

Luria, Paul. Magda Rose. l.t. ed. 1999. 150p. (J). (gr. 4-5). pap. 12.95 (978-0-943864-98-3(4)) Davenport, May Pubs.

Lurie, Dana. Mackey Mack: The Makings of a Tomgirl. ed. 2005. (J). pap. 5.95 (978-0-9768012-2-1(1)) Tomgirlz Enterprises LLC.

Lutz, Norma Jean. Maggie's Choice: Jonathan Edwards & the Great Awakening. 1999. (American Adventure Ser.: No. 8). (Illus.). 144p. (J). (gr. 3-7). lib. bdg. 15.95 (978-0-7910-5048-4(3) , Chelsea Hse.) Facts On File, Inc.

Lyon, George Ella. Borrowed Children. 1999. 176p. (J). (gr. 7-12). pap. 9.95 (978-0-8131-0972-5(8)) Univ. Pr. of Kentucky.

Lyon, Tammie, illus. Eloise at the Wedding. 2006. (Ready-to-Reads Ser.). 32p. (J). (ps-1). lib. bdg. 11.89 (978-1-4169-2457-9(4) , Aladdin Library) Simon & Schuster Children's Publishing.

Lyons, Suzanne. Oops! Why Did I Do That? ed. 2003. (Early Connections Ser.). (J). pap. 35.00 (978-1-4108-1550-7(1)) Benchmark Education Co.

MacDonald, George. The Golden Key. 2006. pap. (***978-1-4250-0937-3(9)***) Assistedreadingbooks.com Inc.

Machalek, Jan. Eva's Summer Vacation: A Story of the Czech Republic. Machalek, Jan, illus. 1999. (Multi-National Ser.). (Illus.). 32p. (J). (gr. k-3). 15.95 (978-1-56899-802-2(3) , B8003); pap. 5.95 (978-1-56899-803-9(1) , S8003) Soundprints.

Maclean, Christine. Mary Margaret Meets Her Match. 2007. 176p. (J). (gr. 3-5). 15.99 (978-0-525-47775-4(6) , Dutton Juvenile) Penguin Group (USA) Inc.

MacLean, Kerry Lee. Sophie's Not Afraid! A Bubble-Bug Book. 1999. (Illus.). 32p. (J). (gr. k-4). 16.95 (978-0-9652998-2-4(1)) On the Spot! Bks.

MacLeod, Jean. At Home in This World: A China Adoption Story. 2003. (Illus.). 32p. (J). lib. bdg. 15.95 (978-0-9726244-1-1(4)) EMK Pr.

Madden, Avery. Sport Talk with Avery. 2004. (Illus.). 36p. (J). 3.99 (978-0-9746587-2-8(3) , Beacon Street Girls) B*tween Productions, Inc.

Madden, Kerry. Gentle's Holler. 2005. 256p. (YA). (gr. 5). 16.99 (978-0-670-05998-0(6) , Viking Juvenile) Penguin Group (USA) Inc.

Maendel, Rachel. Rachel, a Hutterite Girl. Marsden, Hannah, illus. 1999. 48p. (J). (ps-4). pap. 12.99 (978-0-8361-9119-6(6)) Herald Pr.

Malcolm, Jahnna N. Dolt! We're Rats! 2000. (Bad News Ballet Ser.). Orig. Title: The Terrible Tryouts. 160p. (J). (gr. 4-6). pap. 3.95 (978-0-9700164-0-9(9)) Starcatcher Pr.

Malkin, Nina. Orange Is the New Pink. 2007. 272p. (YA). (gr. 7 up). 8.99 (***978-0-439-89965-9(6)***) Scholastic, Inc.

Man-Kong, Mary. High Fashion: Cool & Casual, No. 2. 2007. (Illus.). 32p. (J). (ps-2). 4.99 (978-0-375-83548-3(2) , Golden Bks.) Random Hse. Children's Bks.

—High Fashion Glam & Glitz, No. 1. 2007. (Illus.). 32p. (J). (ps-2). 4.99 (978-0-375-83547-6(4) , Golden Bks.) Random Hse. Children's Bks.

Mancusi, Mari. Sk8er Boy. 2005. (YA). (gr. 8-12). mass mkt. 5.99 (978-0-8439-5604-7(6) , SMOOCH) Dorchester Publishing Co., Inc.

Mancusi, Marianne. Boys That Bite. 2006. 224p. (YA). (gr. 12). pap. 9.99 (978-0-425-20942-4(3) , Berkley Trade) Penguin Group (USA) Inc.

Mann, Seymour. The Purple Automobile & the Newspaper Girl. 2003. 112p. 20.95 (978-0-595-66076-6(2)); pap. 10.95 (978-0-595-29907-2(5)) iUniverse, Inc.

Manos, John. Samantha Saves the Stream. 2006. (Early Explorers Ser.). (J). 36.00 (***978-1-4108-6125-2(2)***) Benchmark Education Co.

Marchetta, Melina. Saving Francesca. 2004. 256p. (gr. 7). (J). lib. bdg. 17.99 (978-0-375-92982-3(7)); (YA). 15.95 (978-0-375-82982-6(2)) Random Hse. Children's Bks. (Knopf Bks. for Young Readers).

—Saving Francesca. l.t. ed. 2005. 343p. 22.95 (978-0-7862-7309-6(7) , Large Print Pr.) Thorndike Pr.

Marie, E. The Porcupine Connection: The Story of a Young Girl's Journey from Tragedy to Healing, with the Help of Her Forest Friends. 2004. 48p. pap. 19.95 (978-1-4137-3480-5(4)) PublishAmerica, Inc.

Marineau, Michèle. Cinderella. Pratt, Mylène, illus. 2007. 32p. (J). (ps-2). 10.95 (***978-0-88776-825-5(3)***) Tundra Bks., Inc./Livres Toundra, Inc. CAN. *Dist:* Random Hse., Inc.

Markle, Sandra. The Fledglings. 2003. 144p. (YA). (gr. 4-6). pap. 9.95 (978-1-56397-696-4(X)) Boyds Mills Pr.

Marraffino, Liz. Escape. 2000. (gr. 3-6). lib. bdg. 13.00 (978-0-613-25040-5(0)) Tandem Library Bks.

Marsh, Carole. The Puzzle of the Shark Surfer Girl. 2006. 64p. (gr. 1-3). 14.95 (***978-0-635-06204-8(6)***) Gallopade International.

—The Riddle of the Missing Puppies. 2006. 64p. (gr. 1-3). 14.95 (***978-0-635-06203-1(8)***) Gallopade International.

Marshall, Catherine. Christy Juvenile Fiction Series: The Bridge to Cutter Gap/Silent Superstitions/the Angry Intruder. 2005. (Christy Juvenile Ser.). 384p. (J). (ps-7). pap. 9.99 (978-1-4003-0772-2(4)) Nelson, Thomas Inc.

Marshall, James. Goldilocks & the Three Bears. Marshall, James, illus. 2002. (Illus.). (J). 14.04 (978-0-7587-2613-1(9)) Book Wholesalers, Inc.

—Goldilocks & the Three Bears. 1998. (J). 13.79 (978-0-606-12946-6(4)) Tandem Library Bks.

Marshall, Peter, et al. Mercy Clifton: Pilgrim Girl. 2007. 208p. (J). pap. 9.99 (***978-0-8054-4395-0(9)*** , B&H Bks.) B&H Publishing Grp.

Marsoli, Lisa Ann. Ask Fickle Fairy. 2007. 16p. (J). (gr. 2-4). 9.99 (978-0-7641-6010-3(9)) Barron's Educational Series, Inc.

Martin, Ann M. Abby's Un-Valentine. 1999. (Baby-Sitters Club Ser.: No. 127). 160p. (J). (gr. 3-7). pap. 4.50 (978-0-590-50350-1(2)) Scholastic, Inc.

—The All-New Mallory Pike, No. 126. 1999. (Baby-Sitters Club Ser.: No. 126). 138p. (J). (gr. 3-7). pap. 4.50 (978-0-590-50349-5(9)) Scholastic, Inc.

—Amalia: Diary Three. 2000. (California Diaries: Bk. 14). (Illus.). 144p. (YA). (gr. 6-8). pap. 4.99 (978-0-439-09548-8(4)) Scholastic, Inc.

—Amalia: Diary Three. 1999. (California Diaries: Bk. 14). (Illus.). (YA). (gr. 6-8). (978-0-606-18525-7(9)) Tandem Library Bks.

—Amalia: Diary Two. 1998. (California Diaries: Bk. 9). (Illus.). 10p. (YA). (gr. 6-8). pap. 4.50 (978-0-590-02385-6(3)) Scholastic, Inc.

—Belle Teale. 2001. 224p. (J). (gr. 5-9). pap. 16.95 (978-0-439-09823-6(8)) Scholastic, Inc.

—Dawn: Diary Two. 1998. (California Diaries: Bk. 7). (YA). (gr. 6-8). pap. 4.99 (978-0-590-01846-3(9)) Scholastic, Inc.

—Dawn: Diary Two. 1998. (California Diaries: Bk. 7). (YA). (gr. 6-8). (978-0-606-13238-1(4)) Tandem Library Bks.

—Ducky. 1998. (California Diaries Ser.: Bk 5). 10p. (YA). (gr. 6-8). pap. 4.50 (978-0-590-29839-1(9)) Scholastic, Inc.

—Ducky: Diary Three. 15th ed. 2000. (California Diaries: Bk. 15). 144p. (YA). (gr. 6-8). pap. 4.99 (978-0-439-09549-5(2) , Scholastic Paperbacks) Scholastic, Inc.

—Ducky: Diary Three. 2000. (California Diaries: Bk. 15). (Illus.). (YA). (gr. 6-8). (978-0-606-18866-1(5)) Tandem Library Bks.

—Ducky: Diary Two. 1998. (California Diaries: Bk. 10). (YA). (gr. 6-8). pap. 71.82 (978-0-590-63083-2(0)) Scholastic, Inc.

—Ducky No. 10: Diary Two. 1998. (California Diaries: Bk. 10). 144p. (YA). (gr. 6-8). pap. 3.99 (978-0-590-02387-0(X)) Scholastic, Inc.

—Karen's Big City Mystery. 1998. (Baby-Sitters Little Sister Ser.: No. 99). (J). (gr. 3-7). (978-0-606-13175-9(2)) Tandem Library Bks.

—Karen's Big Move. 1998. (Baby-Sitters Little Sister Ser.: No. 96). (J). (gr. 3-7). (978-0-606-13172-8(8)) Tandem Library Bks.

—Karen's Chain Letter. 1998. (Baby-Sitters Little Sister Ser.: No. 101). (J). (gr. 3-7). pap. 3.99 (978-0-590-50053-1(8)) Scholastic, Inc.

—Karen's Fishing Trip. 1998. (Baby-Sitters Little Sister Ser.: No. 98). (J). (gr. 3-7). (978-0-606-13174-2(4)) Tandem Library Bks.

—Karen's Mistake. 2000. (Baby-Sitters Little Sister Ser.: No. 117). (Illus.). 112p. (J). (gr. 3-7). pap. 3.99 (978-0-590-52467-4(4)) Scholastic, Inc.

—Karen's Paper Route. 1998. (Baby-Sitters Little Sister Ser.: No. 97). (J). (gr. 3-7). (978-0-606-13173-5(6)) Tandem Library Bks.

—Karen's President. 1999. (Baby-Sitters Little Sister Ser.: No. 106). 112p. (J). (gr. 3-7). pap. 3.99 (978-0-590-50058-6(9)) Scholastic, Inc.

—Karen's Promise. 1998. (Baby-Sitters Little Sister Ser.: No. 95). (J). (gr. 3-7). pap. 3.99 (978-0-590-06593-1(9) , Scholastic Paperbacks) Scholastic, Inc.

—Karen's Promise. 1998. (Baby-Sitters Little Sister Ser.: No. 95). (J). (gr. 3-7). (978-0-606-13171-1(X)) Tandem Library Bks.

—Karen's Reindeer. 1999. (Baby-Sitters Little Sister Ser.: No. 116). (Illus.). 128p. (J). (gr. 3-7). pap. 3.99 (978-0-590-52454-4(2)) Scholastic, Inc.

—Karen's Runaway Turkey. 1999. (Baby-Sitters Little Sister Ser.: No. 115). (Illus.). 112p. (J). (gr. 3-7). pap. 3.99 (978-0-590-52392-9(9)) Scholastic, Inc.

—Karen's Show & Share. 1999. (Baby-Sitters Little Sister Ser.: No. 109). 112p. (J). (gr. 3-7). pap. 3.99 (978-0-590-50061-6(9)) Scholastic, Inc.

—Karen's Snow Princess. 1998. (Baby-Sitters Little Sister Ser.: No. 94). (J). (gr. 3-7). (978-0-606-13170-4(1)) Tandem Library Bks.

—Kristy at Bat. 1999. (Baby-Sitters Club Ser.: No. 129). (Illus.). 160p. (J). (gr. 3-7). pap. 4.50 (978-0-590-50352-5(9)) Scholastic, Inc.

—Kristy Power! 1999. (Baby-Sitters Club Friends Forever Ser.: No. 5). (Illus.). 144p. (J). (gr. 3-7). pap. 4.50 (978-0-590-52332-5(5)) Scholastic, Inc.

—Kristy Thomas, Dog Trainer. 1998. (Baby-Sitters Club Ser.: No. 118). (J). (gr. 3-7). (978-0-606-13162-9(0)) Tandem Library Bks.

—Kristy's Big News. 1999. (Baby-Sitters Club Friends Forever Ser.: No. 1). (J). (gr. 3-7). 54.00 (978-0-439-09611-9(1)); 136p. pap. 4.50 (978-0-590-52313-4(9)) Scholastic, Inc.

—Maggie: Diary Two. 1998. (California Diaries: Bk. 8). (YA). (gr. 6-8). pap. 3.99 (978-0-590-02383-2(7)) Scholastic, Inc.

—Maggie: Diary Two. 1998. (California Diaries: Bk. 8). (YA). (gr. 6-8). (978-0-606-13239-8(2)) Tandem Library Bks.

—Mary Anne's Big Breakup. 1999. (Baby-Sitters Club Friends Forever Ser.: No. 3). (J). (gr. 3-7). pap. 54.00 (978-0-439-11739-5(9)) Scholastic, Inc.

—Mary Anne's Revenge. 2000. (Baby-Sitters Club Friends Forever Ser.: No. 8). (Illus.). 144p. (J). (gr. 3-7). pap. 4.50 (978-0-590-52340-0(6)) Scholastic, Inc.

—Stacey vs. Claudia. 1999. (Baby-Sitters Club Friends Forever Ser.: No. 2). (J). (gr. 3-7). pap. 54.00 (978-0-439-10721-1(0)); 121p. pap. 4.50 (978-0-590-52318-9(X)) Scholastic, Inc.

—Sunny. 1999. (California Diaries: Bk. 2). (YA). (gr. 6-8). pap. 54.00 (978-0-439-09614-0(6)) Scholastic, Inc.

—Sunny: Diary Two. 1998. (California Diaries: Bk. 6). (YA). (gr. 6-8). pap. 3.99 (978-0-590-29840-7(2)); pap. 71.82 (978-0-590-65607-8(4)) Scholastic, Inc.

—Sunny: Diary Two. 1998. (California Diaries: Bk. 6). (YA). (gr. 6-8). (978-0-606-13237-4(6)) Tandem Library Bks.

Martin, Rafe. The Rough-Face Girl. Shannon, David, illus. 1998. 32p. (J). (ps-3). pap. 6.99 (978-0-698-11626-9(7) , Putnam Juvenile) Penguin Group (USA) Inc.

—The Rough-Face Girl. 1998. (978-0-606-13751-5(3)) Tandem Library Bks.

Martin, Rebella. Joanna's Journey. Yoder, Laura, illus. 2006. 168p. (YA). pap. 10.99 (978-1-933753-01-0(3)) Carlisle Pr.- Walnut Creek.

Martinez, Vendrell. Yo Las Queria (I Loved Them) (SPA.). 40p. (J). 18.95 (978-84-233-1289-4(5)) Ediciones Destino ESP. *Dist:* AIMS International Bks., Inc.

Mary Emme. Date not set. (978-0-517-80135-2(3)) Random Hse. Value Publishing.

Mary Mccowski Was Not a Pretty Girl: About a Girl Who Isn't Pretty, & Never Will Be Pretty but Finds Success Anyway. 2005. (J). 3.99 (978-0-9754420-0-5(7)) www.underdogpublishing.com.

Mason, Jane & Stephens, Sarah. Zoey 101 Bk. 1: Girls Got Game. 2005. (Teenick Ser.). 112p. (J). pap. 4.99 (978-0-439-79665-1(2) , Scholastic Paperbacks) Scholastic, Inc.

—Zoey 101 Bk. 2: Dramarama. 2005. (Teenick Ser.). 120p. (J). pap. 4.99 (978-0-439-80177-5(X) , Scholastic Paperbacks) Scholastic, Inc.

Masurel, Claire & Bond, Barbara Higgins. Sticker Stories Penguins. Calitri, Susan & Bond, Barbara Higgins, illus. 2003. (Giant Lift-the-Flap Ser.). 16p. (J). pap. 4.99 (978-0-448-42527-6(0) , Grosset & Dunlap) Penguin Group (USA) Inc.

Matthews, Caitlin. The Barefoot Book of Princesses. Whelan, Olwyn, illus. 2004. 64p. (J). 14.99 (978-1-84148-172-2(6)) Barefoot Bks., Inc.

Mauner, Claudia & Smalley, Elisa. Zoe Sophia's Scrapbook. Mauner, Claudia, illus. 2006. (Illus.). 40p. (J). reprint ed. pap. 6.95 (978-0-8118-5304-0(7)) Chronicle Bks. LLC.

Maurer, Donna. Annie, Bea & Chi Chi Dolores. Cazet, Denys, illus. 1998. 32p. (J). (ps-k). pap. 6.95 (978-0-531-07092-5(1) , Orchard Bks.) Scholastic, Inc.

Maxwell, Katie. Eyeliner of the Gods. 2004. (YA). mass mkt. 5.99 (978-0-8439-5378-7(0)) Dorchester Publishing Co., Inc.

Maxwell, Ruth. Eighteen Roses Red: A Young Girl's Heroic Mission in the Revolutionary War. 2006. (YA). pap. 8.95 (978-1-57249-380-3(1) , White Mane Kids) White Mane Publishing Co., Inc.

May, Kyla. Kyla May Miss. Behaves: Around the World. 2005. (Illus.). 64p. (J). (gr. 4-7). pap. 4.99 (978-0-8431-1371-6(5) , Price Stern Sloan) Penguin Group (USA) Inc.

—Kyla May Miss. Behaves: Live Onstage. 2005. (Illus.). 64p. (J). (gr. 3-6). pap. 4.99 (978-0-8431-1396-9(0) , Price Stern Sloan) Penguin Group (USA) Inc.

Mayer, Melody. All Night Long: A Nannies Novel. 2008. 256p. (YA). lib. bdg. 12.99 (***978-0-385-90506-0(8)*** , Delacorte Bks. for Young Readers) Random Hse. Children's Bks.

Mazer, Anne. Every Cloud Has a Silver Lining. Gesue, Monica, illus. 2000. (Amazing Days of Abby Hayes Ser.: No. 1). 128p. (gr. 4-7). mass mkt. 4.99 (978-0-439-14977-8(0)) Scholastic, Inc.

—Every Cloud Has a Silver Lining. 2000. (Amazing Days of Abby Hayes Ser.: No. 1). (J). 11.79 (978-0-606-19559-1(9)); (gr. 3-6). lib. bdg. 12.40 (978-0-613-25048-1(6)) Tandem Library Bks.

—Home Is Where the Heart Is. 2006. (Amazing Days of Abby Hayes Ser.: no. 17). 118p. (J). lib. bdg. 16.92 (***978-1-4242-1518-8(8)***) Fitzgerald Bks.

—Home Is Where the Heart Is. 2006. (Amazing Days of Abby Hayes Ser.: No. 17). 128p. (J). pap. 4.99 (978-0-439-82924-3(0) , Scholastic Paperbacks) Scholastic, Inc.

—Now You See It, Now You Don't. 2005. (Amazing Days of Abby Hayes Ser.: No. 15). (Illus.). 126p. (J). (978-1-4156-0511-0(4)) Scholastic, Inc.

—That's the Way the Cookie Crumbles. 2005. (Amazing Days of Abby Hayes Ser.: No. 16). (Illus.). 128p. (J). (gr. 3-7). pap. 4.99 (978-0-439-68067-7(0) , Scholastic Paperbacks) Scholastic, Inc.

Mazetti, Katerina. God & I Broke Up. Lundin, Maria, tr. from SWE. 2005. 128p. (J). pap. 6.95 (978-0-88899-617-6(9) , Libros Tigrillo) Groundwood Bks. CAN. *Dist:* Perseus Distribution.

Mazur, ed. Miss O & Friends Write On: The Miss O & Friends Collection of Rockin' Fiction. Brindak, Hermine, illus. rev. ed. 2006. (Miss O & Friends Ser.). 64p. (J). pap. 4.99 (978-0-8230-2940-2(9)) Watson-Guptill Pubns., Inc.

McBratney, Sam. Lo Siento. 2003. (SPA.). 32p. (J). 13.95 (978-84-241-8020-1(8)) Everest de Ediciones y Distribucion, S.L. ESP. *Dist:* Lectorum Pubns., Inc.

McBrier, Page. Beatrice's Goast. unabr. ed. 2005. (J). (ps-3). 27.95 incl. audio (978-0-8045-6938-5(X)) Spoken Arts, Inc.

McClear, Preston. Frannie & Pickles. Dollak, Nicholas, illus. 1999. 29p. (J). (gr. k-5). 16.95 (978-1-929084-04-3(8)); pap. 12.95 (978-1-929084-05-0(6)) Malibu Bks. for Children.

McClintock, Barbara, illus. Goldilocks & the Three Bears. 2003. 32p. (J). (ps-2). pap. 15.95 (978-0-439-39545-8(3) , Scholastic Pr.) Scholastic, Inc.

McCorkle, Mark & Schooley, Bob. Grudge Match. 2005. (Illus.). 80p. (J). (978-1-4155-9100-0(8)) Disney Pr.

McCormick, Patricia. Sold. 2006. 272p. (gr. 7 up). 15.99 (978-0-7868-5171-3(6)) Hyperion Pr.

McCourt, Lisa & Grant-Porter, Pat. Della Splatnuk, Birthday Girl. 1999. (Chicken Soup for Little Souls Ser.). (Illus.). 32p. (J). (gr. 4-7). tchr. ed. 14.95 (978-1-55874-600-8(5)) Health Communications, Inc.

McDaniel, Lurlene. A Horse for Mandy. 2004. 80p. (J). (gr. 3-5). pap. 4.99 (978-1-58196-011-2(5)) Darby Creek Publishing.

McDaniel, Lurlene. Sometimes Love Isn't Enough. 2007. (J). pap. 4.99 (***978-1-58196-048-8(4)***) Darby Creek Publishing.

McDonald, Ann-Eve. I Can't Go to School Today, My Horses Might Escape. 2004. (J). (978-0-9770158-0-1(7)) BeachWalk Bks. Inc.

McDonald, Megan. Changes for Julie, Bk. 6. McAliley, Susan, illus. 2007. 104p. (YA). (gr. 3 up). 12.95 (***978-1-59369-355-8(9)***) American Girl Publishing, Inc.

—Changes for Julie, Bk. 6. McAliley, Susan & Hunt, Robert, illus. 2007. 104p. (YA). (gr. 3 up). pap. 6.95 (***978-1-59369-354-1(0)***) American Girl Publishing, Inc.

—Daisy Jane, Best-Ever Flower Girl. Gévry, Claudine, illus. 2007. (Step into Reading Ser.). 48p. (J). (gr. k-3). 3.99 (978-0-375-83110-2(X) , Random Hse. Bks. for Young Readers) Random Hse. Children's Bks.

—Daisy Jane, Best-Ever Flower Girl! Gévry, Claudine, illus. 2007. (Step into Reading Ser.). 48p. (J). (gr. k-3). lib. bdg. 11.99 (978-0-375-93110-9(4) , Random Hse. Bks. for Young Readers) Random Hse. Children's Bks.

—The Judy Moody Star-Studded Collection: Judy Moody; Judy Moody Gets Famous!; Judy Moody Saves the World! Reynolds, Peter H., illus. 2004. (Judy Moody Ser.). 464p. (J). (gr. 1-5). pap. 17.97 (978-0-7636-2563-4(9)) Candlewick Pr.

—Julie & the Eagles, Bk. 4. McAliley, Susan, illus. 2007. 88p. (YA). (gr. 3 up). 12.95 (***978-1-59369-351-0(6)***) American Girl Publishing, Inc.

—Julie & the Eagles, Bk. 4. McAliley, Susan & Hunt, Robert, illus. 2007. 88p. (YA). (gr. 3 up). pap. 6.95 (***978-1-59369-350-3(8)***) American Girl Publishing, Inc.

—Julie Tells Her Story, Bk. 2. McAliley, Susan, illus. 2007. 104p. (YA). (gr. 3 up). 12.95 (***978-1-59369-289-6(7)***) American Girl Publishing, Inc.

—Julie Tells Her Story, Bk. 2. McAliley, Susan & Hunt, Robert, illus. 2007. 104p. (YA). (gr. 3 up). pap. 6.95 (***978-1-59369-288-9(9)***) American Girl Publishing, Inc.

—Julie's Journey, Bk. 5. McAliley, Susan, illus. 2007. 88p. (YA). (gr. 3 up). 12.95 (***978-1-59369-353-4(2)***) American Girl Publishing, Inc.

McElroy, Laurie. Hold on Tight. Disney Press Staff, ed. rev. ed. 2007. (Hannah Montana Ser.: No. 5). 128p. (gr. 3-7). pap. 4.99 (***978-1-4231-0460-5(9)***) Disney Pr.

McGowan, Sharlene. Macaroni Monday. 2007. 112p. (YA). per. 10.95 (***978-0-595-45984-1(6)***) iUniverse, Inc.

McKay, Amanda. Sally Marshall's Not an Alien! 1999. 88p. (J). reprint ed. pap. 13.95 (978-0-7022-3108-7(8)) Univ. of Queensland Pr. AUS. *Dist:* International Specialized Bk. Services.

McKay, Sindy. We Both Read-June's Tune. Staake, Bob, illus. 2000. (We Both Read Ser.). 44p. (J). (gr. 1 up). 7.99 (978-1-891327-25-4(9)); pap. 3.99 (978-1-891327-26-1(7)) Treasure Bay, Inc.

McKee, David. Charlotte's Piggy Bank. 2004. (Illus.). 32p. (J). pap. 11.00 (978-1-84270-331-1(5)) Andersen GBR. *Dist:* Independent Pubs. Group.

—Mary's Secret. 1999. (Illus.). 32p. (J). 19.99 (978-0-86264-909-8(9)) Andersen GBR. *Dist:* Independent Pubs. Group.

McKeever, Sean. Loyalty Thing. 2006. (Illus.). (J). (gr. 2-6). 21.35 (978-1-59961-037-5(X)) Spotlight.

—Real Thing. 2006. (Illus.). (J). (gr. 2-6). 21.35 (978-1-59961-039-9(6)) Spotlight.

McKenna, K. J. Take Three Girls. 2005. 96p. pap. 10.00 (978-1-4116-6290-2(3)) Lulu.com.

McKissack, Fredrick L. & McKissack, Patricia C. Messy Bessey's School Desk. Rau, Dana, ed. Regan, Dana, illus. 1998. (Rookie Reader Skill Set Ser.). 32p. (J). (gr. k-2). pap. 4.95 (978-0-516-26361-8(7) , Children's Pr.) Scholastic Library Publishing.

McKissack, Patricia C. Loved Best. Marshall, Felicia, illus. ed. 2005. 57p. (J). lib. bdg. 15.00 (978-1-59054-905-6(8)) Fitzgerald Bks.

McLaughlin, Vicki. The Dancer of Her Dreams. 2006. 48p. pap. 12.95 (978-1-4241-2723-8(8)) PublishAmerica, Inc.

McMillen, Charlotte Palmer. The Little Sea Rock & His Friend Arena. 2005. (Illus.). 32p. (J). per. 14.95 (978-0-9771939-4-3(2) , 003) New World Publishing.

McPhate, Paul. The Puggles: The Adventures of Carly & Vinigin. 2006. (ENG.). 48p. per. 12.95 (***978-1-4241-4481-5(7)***) PublishAmerica, Inc.

Meade, L. T. Red Rose & Tiger Lily or in a Wider Wo. 2004. reprint ed. pap. 28.95 (978-0-7661-8345-2(9)) Kessinger Publishing, LLC.

Meade, T. L. Palace Beautiful. 2006. 35.99 (***978-1-4280-3419-8(6)***); pap. 29.99 (***978-1-4280-3423-5(4)***) Indy-Publish.com.

Meddaugh, Susan. Martha & Skits. 2000. (Illus.). 32p. (J). (gr. k-3). tchr. ed. 15.00 (978-0-618-05776-4(5) , Walter Lorraine) Houghton Mifflin Co. Trade & Reference Div.

—Martha Calling. Meddaugh, Susan, illus. 2002. (Martha Ser.). (Illus.). (J). 13.79 (978-0-7587-3095-4(0)) Book Wholesalers, Inc.

Meik, Mitchell. Molly the Milkmaid. Muggli, Glorianne, illus. 2003. (J). pap. 7.95 (978-1-57665-089-9(8)) Muggli Graphics.

Meissner, Susan. A Window to the World. 2005. 320p. pap. 11.99 (978-0-7369-1414-7(5)) Harvest Hse. Pubs.

Melas, Elizabeth Murphy. The Girl with No Hair: A Story about Alopecia Areata. Hernandez, Alex, illus. 2003. 32p. (J). pap. 14.95 (978-0-929173-40-5(6)) Health Pr. NA, Inc.

Merz, Marisa. The Land of Keep-Still. 2004. (Illus.). 66p. (gr. 13 up). 16.00 (978-88-7757-168-7(3)) Hopefulmonster Editore ITA. *Dist:* D.A.P./Distributed Art Pubs.

Metzger, Steve. No Girls Allowed! Wilhelm, Hans, illus. 2000. (Dinofours Ser.: No. 19). (J). (ps-1). 20.01 (978-0-439-06328-9(0)) Scholastic, Inc.

Meyer, Louis A. Bloody Jack: Being an Account of the Curious Adventures of Mary Jacky Faber, Ship's Boy. 2004. (Bloody Jack Adventures Ser.). (Illus.). 320p. (YA). reprint ed. pap. 6.95 (978-0-15-205085-6(X) , Harcourt Paperbacks) Harcourt Children's Bks.

Mihelic, Mira. Come My Gentle Ariel. MacKinnon, Alasdair, tr. from SLV. Abaza, Dasa, illus. 2002. 132p. (YA). 34.95 net. (978-961-6463-02-7(0)) Bks. of Slovenia.

Miller, Heather. Lost in Alaska: A Texas Girl & an Aleut Boy. 2001. (J). pap. 9.95 (978-0-89992-149-5(3)) Council for Indian Education.

Miller, William. The Bus Ride. Ward, John, illus. 1998. 32p. (YA). (gr. k up). 15.95 (978-1-880000-60-1(1)) Lee & Low Bks., Inc.

—The Piano. Keeter, Susan, illus. 2005. 32p. (gr. 1-4). 7.95 (978-1-58430-242-1(9)) Lee & Low Bks., Inc.

Millman, M. C. Always Something Else: The whimsical adventures of Elisheva Raskin. 2005. (Illus.). 160p. (J). 14.95 (978-1-932443-23-3(1) , ASEH) Judaica Pr., Inc., The.

—Always Something Else 2. 2006. (Illus.). 160p. (J). 14.95 (978-1-932443-43-1(6) , ASE2H) Judaica Pr., Inc., The.

Minter, J. Girls We Love. 2006. (Insiders Novel Ser.). 256p. (YA). pap. 8.95 (978-1-58234-742-4(5) , Bloomsbury Children) Bloomsbury Publishing.

Mitchell, Joni. Chelsea Morning. Froud, Brian, illus. 2004. 32p. 17.95 (978-1-59687-178-6(4) , Milk & Cookies) ibooks, Inc.

Mohr, Nicholasa. Felita, Vol. 1. Cruz, Ray, illus. 1999. 112p. (J). (gr. 3-7). reprint ed. pap. 5.99 (978-0-14-130643-8(2) , Puffin) Penguin Group (USA) Inc.

Mol, Alien. The Hasty Promise. 2002. (Illus.). 120p. (YA). lib. bdg. 10.95 (978-0-9670728-8-3(3)) Early Foundations Pubs.

Molesworth, Mary Louisa. Carrots, Just a Little Boy. Oldham, Marion, illus. 2004. reprint ed. pap. 22.95 (978-1-4179-3800-1(5)) Kessinger Publishing, LLC.

—Rosy. 2004. reprint ed. pap. 15.95 (978-1-4191-4549-0(5)); pap. 1.99 (978-1-4192-4549-7(X)) Kessinger Publishing, LLC.

Montanari, Eva. My First... 2007. (Illus.). 32p. (J). (ps-k). 17.00 (***978-0-618-64644-9(2)***) Houghton Mifflin Co.

Montgomery Gibson, Jane. Gracie Got Glasses. Montgomery Gibson, Jane, illus. 2005. (J). bds. 8.99 (978-1-4183-0039-5(X)) Christ Inspired, Inc.

Montgomery, L. M. Anne d'Avonlea. 1998. (Avonlea Ser.: No. 2). Tr. of Anne of Avonlea. (FRE.). 194p. (YA). (gr. 5-8). pap. 10.95 (978-0-920304-88-4(5)) Ragweed Pr. CAN. *Dist:* Univ. of Toronto Pr.

—Anne, la Maison aux Pignons Verts. 1998. (Avonlea Ser.: No. 1). Tr. of Anne of Green Gables. (FRE.). 262p. (YA). (gr. 5-8). pap. 10.95 (978-0-920304-50-1(8)) Ragweed Pr. CAN. *Dist:* Univ. of Toronto Pr.

—Anne of Green Gables. 2004. 400p. per. 16.95 (978-1-59540-110-6(5)) 1st World Publishing, Inc.

—Anne of Green Gables. 349p. (978-1-58726-053-7(0)) Ann Arbor Media Group, LLC.

—Anne of Green Gables. 2007. per. 6.99 (***978-1-4209-2922-5(4)***) Digireads.com.

—Anne of Green Gables. 2003. 276p. pap. 15.99 (***978-1-4043-6066-2(2)***) IndyPublish.com.

—Anne of Green Gables. Stemach, Jerry, ed. Ham, Jeff, illus. 2000. 65.00 incl. audio, cd-rom (978-1-58702-311-8(3)); 50.00 (978-1-58702-502-0(7)) Johnston, Don Inc.

—Anne of Green Gables. 2004. (Oxford Bookworms Ser.). 8.50 (978-0-19-423273-9(5)) Oxford Univ. Pr., Inc.

—Anne of Green Gables. 2003. 320p. (gr. 12). 4.95 (978-0-451-52882-7(4) , Signet Classics) Penguin Group (USA) Inc.

—Christmas with Anne & Other Holiday Stories. Wilmshurst, Rea, ed. 2001. (Illus.). 224p. (YA). (gr. 5 up). pap. 4.99 (978-0-553-57100-4(1) , Starfire) Random Hse. Children's Bks.

—The Complete Anne of Green Gables: Anne of Green Gables; Anne of the Island; Anne of Avonlea; Anne of Windy Poplars; Anne's House of Dreams; Anne of Ingleside; Rainbow Valley; Rilla of Ingleside, 8 vols. gif. ed. 1998. (J). (gr. 4-7). mass mkt. 40.43 (978-0-553-60941-7(6) , Starfire) Random Hse. Children's Bks.

—Further Chronicles of Avonlea. 1999. (Avonlea Ser.: No. 7). 256p. (YA). (gr. 5-8). 3.99 (978-0-14-036774-4(8) , Puffin) Penguin Group (USA) Inc.

—Further Chronicles of Avonlea. 2004. 152p. (YA). pap. 7.95 (978-1-57646-892-0(5)) Quiet Vision Publishing.

—Kilmeny of the Orchard. 2004. 100p. (YA). pap. 7.95 (978-1-57646-894-4(1)) Quiet Vision Publishing.

—Rainbow Valley. 2004. 184p. (YA). pap. 8.95 (978-1-57646-890-6(9)) Quiet Vision Publishing.

Montgomery, Mary Ann. Bonnie la Abejita. Norby, Carey, illus. 2001. Tr. of Bonnie the Baby Bumble Bee. (SPA.). 32p. (J). (ps-3). pap. 7.50 (978-1-59134-000-3(4)) Maval Publishing, Inc.

Moon, Nicola. Happy Birthday, Amelia. Jones, Jenny, illus. 1999. 32p. (J). reprint ed. 17.99 (978-1-86205-208-6(5) , Pavilion Bks., Ltd.) Anova Bks. GBR. *Dist:* Trafalgar Square Publishing.

Mooney, E. S. Mojo Mayhem. 2002. (gr. k-3). lib. bdg. 11.80 (978-0-613-43852-0(3)) Tandem Library Bks.

Moore, Bradley. Introducing Serina K. , Ph. D. & Future Famous Person. 2006. (ENG.). 60p. per. 12.95 (***978-1-4241-5631-3(9)***) PublishAmerica, Inc.

Moore, Diane. Sophie's Sojourn in Persia. 2004. 143p. pap. 19.95 (978-1-4137-4458-3(3)) PublishAmerica, Inc.

Moore, Ishbel. Annilea. 2001. (Illus.). 180p. (J). (gr. 4-7). pap. (978-1-896184-80-7(4)) Roussan Pubs., Inc./ Roussan Editeur, Inc.

—Annilea. 2000. (gr. 3-6). lib. bdg. 15.25 (978-0-613-62886-0(1)) Tandem Library Bks.

—Xanthe's Pyramid. 1998. 120p. (YA). (gr. 7-12). pap. 6.95 (978-1-896184-34-0(0)) Roussan Pubs., Inc./Roussan Editeur, Inc. CAN. *Dist:* Orca Bk. Pubs. USA.

Moore-Mallinos, Jennifer. It's Hard Being a Kid. Fabrega, Marta, illus. 2007. (Live & Learn Ser.). 36p. (J). (gr. k-2). pap. 6.99 (978-0-7641-3586-6(4)) Barron's Educational Series, Inc.

—Ser un nino es Dificil: It's Hard Being a Kid (Spanish Edition) Fabrega, Marta, illus. 2007. (Live & Learn Ser.). 36p. (J). (gr. k-2). pap. 6.99 (978-0-7641-3587-3(2)) Barron's Educational Series, Inc.

Moore, Martha A. Under the Mermaid Angel. 2001. (Illus.). 176p. (YA). (gr. 7). pap. 12.00 (978-0-375-89507-4(8) , Laurel Leaf) Random Hse. Children's Bks.

Moree, Cody. Her Senior Year: A One-Act Play. 1998. (Illus.). 17p. (YA). (gr. 9-12). pap. 3.50 (978-0-88680-453-4(1) , C4531) Clark, I. E. Pubns.

Morgan, Melissa J. Hide & Shriek No. 14: Super Special. 2007. (Camp Confidential Ser.). 256p. (J). pap. 5.99 (978-0-448-44452-9(6) , Grosset & Dunlap) Penguin Group (USA) Inc.

—Winter Games. 2006. (Camp Confidential Ser.: Vol. 12). 160p. (J). (gr. 4-7). pap. 4.99 (978-0-448-44392-8(9) , Grosset & Dunlap) Penguin Group (USA) Inc.

Moriyama, Daisuke. Chrono Crusade. 2004. (Illus.). (YA). Vol. 1. 190p. pap. (978-1-4139-0084-2(4)); Vol. 2. 200p. pap. (978-1-4139-0104-7(2)); Vol. 3. 198p. pap. (978-1-4139-0045-3(3)) ADV Manga.

Morris, Robert. Grandma Ursu, Think Blue. 2003. (Illus.). 32p. (J). 15.95 (978-0-9741634-0-6(6)) Ursu Pubns.

Morton, Elizabeth. Anne & the Hunt for the Golden Crown: The Animated Series. 2001. (J). (gr. 2-5). pap. 4.99 (978-0-06-442161-4(9)) HarperCollins Pubs.

Moskin, Marietta D. I Am Rosemarie. 1999. 258p. (J). pap. 12.95 (978-0-7351-0226-2(0)); lib. bdg. 24.95 (978-0-7351-0225-5(2)) Replica Bks.

—I Am Rosemarie. 2000. (J). pap. 1.95 (978-0-590-04278-9(5)) Scholastic, Inc.

Moulton, Mark Kimball. Twisted Sistahs. Good, Karen Hillard, illus. 2006. 32p. (J). (gr. 2-3). 14.95 (978-0-8249-8676-6(8)) Ideals Pubns.

Mowery, Julia. Little Nessie. Ray, Marleen K., illus. 2001. vi, 87p. (J). (gr. 1-7). mass mkt. 7.95 (978-0-9710529-0-1(5)) Dobie Bk. Publishing.

Moyer, Bess. Gypsies of the Air. 2004. reprint ed. pap. 19.95 (978-1-4179-9112-9(7)) Kessinger Publishing, LLC.

Muldrow, Diane. Sweet-and-Sour Summer. 2003. (gr. 3-6). lib. bdg. 13.00 (978-0-613-72478-4(X)) Tandem Library Bks.

—Truth Without the Trimmings. 2002. (gr. 3-6). lib. bdg. 13.00 (978-0-613-72484-5(4)) Tandem Library Bks.

Murphy, Jill. On the Way Home. 2003. (Illus.). 32p. (J). pap. 9.99 (978-0-333-37572-3(6)) Macmillan Publishers Ltd. GBR. *Dist:* Independent Pubs. Group.

Murphy, Pat. The Wild Girls. 2007. 272p. (J). (gr. 5 up). 16.99 (***978-0-670-06226-3(X)*** , Viking Juvenile) Penguin Group (USA) Inc.

Murray, Millie. Jade. 2000. 122p. (J). pap. 9.99 (978-0-7043-4967-4(1)) Women's Pr., Ltd., The GBR. *Dist:* Independent Pubs. Group.

Mysak, Mary. Little Train! Stickley, Kelly, illus. 2004. 16p. (J). 7.50 (978-0-9762274-0-3(1)) Helping Hands Children's Bks.

Nabb, Magdalen. Josie Smith. Vainio, Pirkko, illus. l.t. ed. 2005. 96p. (J). pap. (978-0-7540-6154-0(X) , CLP 346) BBC Audio.

—Josie Smith. 2000. (Illus.). 80p. pap. 6.95 (978-0-00-673744-5(7)) HarperCollins Pubs. Ltd. GBR. *Dist:* Trafalgar Square Publishing.

—Josie Smith at the Market. 2000. (Illus.). 125p. (J). 6.95 (978-0-00-675064-2(8)) Zondervan.

—Josie Smith in Summer. l.t. ed. 2005. (Illus.). 112p. (J). pap. (978-0-7540-6164-9(7) , CLP 356) BBC Audio.

—Josie Smith in the Hospital. 2000. (Illus.). 126p. (J). pap. 7.99 (978-0-00-674720-8(5)) HarperCollins Pubs. Ltd. GBR. *Dist:* Independent Pubs. Group.

Namioka, Lensey. Yang the Second & Her Secret Admirers. 2000. (978-0-606-18794-7(4)) Tandem Library Bks.

Napoli, Donna Jo. New Voices. 2000. (Angelwings Ser.: No. 12). (Illus.). 80p. (J). (gr. 2-5). pap. 7.95 (978-0-689-83573-5(6) , Aladdin) Simon & Schuster Children's Publishing.

EFG

—New Voices. 2000. (Angelwings Ser.: No. 12). (Illus.). (J). (978-0-606-21617-3(0)) Tandem Library Bks.

—Spinners. 2001. (978-0-606-20924-3(7)) Tandem Library Bks.

Narahashi, Keiko. Two Girls Can! 2000. Orig. Title: Friends. (Illus.). 32p. (ps-3). 16.00 Simon & Schuster Children's Publishing.

Nash, Naomi. Chloe, Queen of Denial. 2004. (YA). mass mkt. 5.99 (978-0-8439-5377-0(2)) Dorchester Publishing Co., Inc.

Natlie, Jeffrey Michael. Emily Gets Angry. 2006. (J). 9.95 (978-0-9779822-0-2(3)) ErieKIDS, Inc.

Naylor, Phyllis Reynolds. Alice in Rapture, Sort Of. Mak, Kam, illus. 1999. (Alice Ser.). 176p. (J). (gr. 5-9). pap. 4.99 (978-0-689-81687-1(1) , Aladdin) Simon & Schuster Children's Publishing.

—Alice in Rapture, Sort Of. 1999. (Alice Ser.). (YA). (gr. 5-9). 11.64 (978-0-606-16333-0(6)); (gr. 7-12). lib. bdg. 13.00 (978-0-8335-5028-6(4)) Tandem Library Bks.

—I Can't Take You Anywhere! Kaminsky, Jef, illus. 2001. 32p. (J). (ps-3). 6.99 (978-0-689-84116-3(7) , Aladdin) Simon & Schuster Children's Publishing.

Naylor, Phyllis Reynolds & Naylor, Magdalena R. Achingly Alice. 1998. (Alice Ser.). 128p. (J). (gr. 5-9). 15.95 (978-0-689-80355-0(9) , Atheneum) Simon & Schuster Children's Publishing.

Nelson, Dorothy N. God Spoke to a Girl. Gorunoff, Oleg, illus. 1998. 32p. (J). (ps-2). pap. 1.97 (978-0-8163-1655-7(4)) Pacific Pr. Publishing Assn.

Ness, Evaline. Sam, Bangs y Hechizo de Luna. (SPA.). (J). (gr. 3-5). pap. 6.95 (978-1-880507-81-0(1) , LC0231) Lectorum Pubns., Inc.

Newmark, Rachel J. Fearless Faith: And the New School. Specialty Publishing Company, illus. 2006. (J). pap. 7.95 (978-0-9755199-4-3(8)) Specialty Publishing Co.

Newton, Samantha. Being Nine Isn't So Bad. 2006. 52p. pap. 12.95 (978-1-4241-1902-8(2)) PublishAmerica, Inc.

Nicholas, J. B. The Waving Girl. Waites, Joan C., illus. 2004. 32p. (J). pap. 7.95 (978-1-58980-185-1(7)) Pelican Publishing Co., Inc.

Nielsen, Virginia. Batty Hattie. 1999. (Accelerated Reader Bks.). 144p. (YA). (gr. 3-7). 14.95 (978-0-7614-5047-4(5) , Cavendish Children's Bks.) Cavendish, Marshall Corp.

Niland, Deborah. When I Was a Baby. Niland, Deborah, illus. 2007. (Illus.). 24p. (J). (ps). pap. 4.99 (***978-1-933605-49-4(9)**) Kane/Miller Bk. Pubs., Inc.

Nilsson, Per. You & You & You. Chace, Tara, tr. from SWE. 2005. 301p. (978-1-932425-19-2(5) , Lemniscaat) Boyds Mills Pr.

Nivola, Claire A. Elisabeth. 2001. (978-0-606-22620-2(6)) Tandem Library Bks.

Noonan, Rosalind. Turning Seventeen: Any Guy You Want, Bk. 1. 2000. (Turning Seventeen Ser.: No. 1). 208p. (YA). (gr. 7 up). pap. 4.95 (978-0-06-447237-1(X)) HarperCollins Pubs.

Norling, Beth. The Stone Baby. Norling, Beth, illus. 2004. (Illus.). 32p. (J). (gr. k-2). (978-0-7344-0353-7(4) , Lothian Bks.) Hachette Livre Australia.

Nostlinger, Christine. Rosalinde Tiene Ideas en la Cabeza. Balzola, Sofia, illus. 2003. (SPA.). 80p. (J). (gr. 3-5). 11.95 (978-84-204-4804-6(4)) Alfaguara, Ediciones, S.A.- Grupo Santillana ESP. *Dist:* Santillana USA Publishing Co., Inc.

—Rosalinde Tiene Ideas en la Cabeza, Level 4.2. 1998. (SPA.). 80p. (J). (gr. 4-7). 5.95 (978-84-204-3136-9(2)) Alfaguara, Ediciones, S.A.- Grupo Santillana ESP. *Dist:* Santillana USA Publishing Co., Inc.

Nowak, Linda Y. Cinnamon: A Teen's Survival & Romance on the Appalachian Trail. 2005. 169p. (YA). per. 11.95 (978-0-9762392-0-8(5)) Harmony Spirit Publishing Co., Inc.

Nunes, Lygia Bojunga. La Cuerda Floja. (SPA.). 136p. (YA). (gr. 5-8). (978-84-204-3122-2(2) , AF1749) Alfaguara, Ediciones, S.A.- Grupo Santillana ESP. *Dist:* Lectorum Pubns., Inc.

Oates, Joyce Carol. Big Mouth & Ugly Girl. 2003. 288p. pap. 7.99 (978-0-06-447347-7(3)) HarperCollins Pubs.

Obrien, Elaime F. Anita of Ranch Del Mar. 2005. 171p. (J). (gr. 5-6). reprint ed. pap. 995.00 (978-1-885375-14-8(X) , Shore Line Pr.) Pacific Bks.

O'Dell, Scott. La Isla de los Delfines Azules. (SPA., Illus.). (YA). (gr. 5-8). (978-1-56137-541-7(1) , NU5722) Noguer y Caralt Editores, S. A. ESP. *Dist:* Lectorum Pubns., Inc.

—No Me Llamo Angelica. (SPA.). 192p. (YA). (gr. 5-8). (978-84-279-3222-7(7) , NG5801) Noguer y Caralt Editores, S. A. ESP. *Dist:* Lectorum Pubns., Inc.

Odgers, Sally. Translations in Celadon. 1999. 140p. (J). (gr. 7-12). 7.95 (978-0-7322-5908-2(8)) HarperCollins Pubs.

—Translations in Celadon. 1999. (gr. 7-12). lib. bdg. 16.40 (978-0-613-73234-5(0)) Tandem Library Bks.

O'Dwyer, Bridget. A Celtic Night: A fifteen-year old girl's modern retelling of Shakespeare's A Midsummer Night's Dream. 2006. 160p. (J). pap. 5.95 (978-1-932802-94-8(0) , Holy Macro! Bks.) MrExcel.com Publishing.

Offerman, Lynn. Where Is It? Hers. Chambers, Sally, illus. 1998. (Nuk Bks.). 8p. (J). 6.95 (978-0-7641-7233-5(6)) Barron's Educational Series, Inc.

O'Kelley, Jeff. Sharing Our Stories. 2006. (Early Explorers Ser.). (J). 36.00 (***978-1-4108-6127-6(9)**) Benchmark Education Co.

Okimoto, Jean Davies. Molly by Any Other Name. 2000. (gr. 3-6). lib. bdg. 28.00 (978-0-613-86208-0(2)) Tandem Library Bks.

—Molly by Any Other Name. 2000. 288p. (gr. 4-7). pap. 17.95 (978-0-595-00796-7(1) , Backinprint.com) iUniverse, Inc.

Olagunju, Elizabeth Olufunlayo Bose. Tasha. 2004. 48p. pap. 12.95 (978-1-4137-3349-5(2)) PublishAmerica, Inc.

Oldfield, J. Sophie Show Off, Bk. 15. (Illus.). 121p. (J). pap. 7.99 (978-0-340-69987-4(6) , Hodder & Stoughton) Hodder General Publishing Division GBR. *Dist:* Trafalgar Square Publishing.

Oldfield, Jenny. Drop Dead, Danielle. Layton, Neal, illus. mass mkt. (978-0-340-85106-7(6) , Coronet) Hodder General Publishing Division.

—Get Lost, Lola! Layton, Neal, illus. mass mkt. 7.99 (978-0-340-85104-3(X) , Coronet) Hodder General Publishing Division GBR. *Dist:* Trafalgar Square Publishing.

—What's the Matter, Maya? Child, Lauren, illus. 106p. (J). pap. (978-0-340-78503-4(9) , Hodder & Stoughton) Hodder General Publishing Division.

—When I Won a Prize. (Illus.). (J). mass mkt. 8.99 (978-0-340-85076-3(0) , Hodder & Stoughton) Hodder General Publishing Division GBR. *Dist:* Independent Pubs. Group.

—When Shah Went Weird. (Illus.). (J). mass mkt. 8.99 (978-0-340-85077-0(9) , Hodder & Stoughton) Hodder General Publishing Division GBR. *Dist:* Independent Pubs. Group.

Oldham, Mary. Alwena's Garden. 1998. (YA). (gr. 6-12). pap. 17.95 (978-0-8464-4604-0(9)) Beekman Bks., Inc.

Olds, Sara V. Anna - a Farewell to Juarez. Roy, T. M., illus. 2003. Orig. Title: Hanne's Farewell to Juarez. (J). pap. 10.50 (978-0-9715433-7-9(2) , AFJ-TP) Zapstone Productions.

Olsen, Ashley, et al. The Case of the Hollywood Who-Done-It. 2003. (New Adventures of Mary-Kate & Ashley Ser.: No. 33). (Illus.). 96p. mass mkt. 4.50 (978-0-06-009331-0(5) , Harper Entertainment) HarperCollins Pubs.

Olsen, Mary-Kate. All That Glitters. 2003. (gr. 5-8). lib. bdg. 13.00 (978-0-613-68397-5(8)) Tandem Library Bks.

—Secret Crush. 2002. (gr. 5-8). lib. bdg. 13.00 (978-0-613-64768-7(8)) Tandem Library Bks.

Olsen, Mary-Kate & Olsen, Ashley. Mary-Kate & Ashley Sweet 16 No.12: Dream Holiday. 2003. (gr. 3-6). lib. bdg. 13.00 (978-0-613-71958-2(1)) Tandem Library Bks.

—Two of a Kind No. 32: Santa Girls. 2003. (gr. 3-6). lib. bdg. 13.00 (978-0-613-85153-4(6)) Tandem Library Bks.

Olson, Mildred Thompson. Diamondola: A Little Diamond. 2003. (Illus.). 192p. (J). reprint ed. per. 11.95 (978-1-57258-251-4(0) , 945-6106) TEACH Services, Inc.

On the Job: Individual Title Six-Packs. (ps-2). 27.00 (978-0-7635-9468-8(7)) Rigby Education.

O'Neill, Alexis. Loud Emily. 2001. (gr. k-3). lib. bdg. 15.30 (978-0-613-73313-7(4)) Tandem Library Bks.

O'Neill, Alexis & Carpenter, Nancy. Loud Emily. 2001. (Illus.). 40p. (J). pap. 6.99 (978-0-689-84669-4(X) , Aladdin) Simon & Schuster Children's Publishing.

O'Neill, Joan. Daisy Chain Days. 2004. (Daisy Chain War Bks.: Bk. 4). (J). pap. (978-0-340-88178-1(X) , Hodder Children's Books) Hodder Children's Division.

O'Neill, Joan. Dream Chaser. 2007. 272p. pap. 10.95 (***978-0-340-91148-8(4)**) Hodder Children's Division GBR. *Dist:* Independent Pubs. Group.

Optometrist: Individual Title Six-Packs. (Bookweb Ser.). 32p. (gr. 3 up). 34.00 (978-0-7635-3946-7(5)) Rigby Education.

Orgel, Doris. Sarah's Room. Sendak, Maurice, illus. 2003. (Sendak Reissues Ser.). 48p. (J). (gr. 5 up). 14.95 (978-0-06-029727-5(1)) HarperCollins Pubs.

Orliac, Catherine. Te Tumu o Rapa Nui: El Arbolito de Rapa Nui. the Little Tree of Rapa Nui. le Petit Arbre de Rapa Nui. Haoa Cardinali, Viki et al, trs. Willemin, Veronique, illus. 2005. (FRE, SPA & ENG.). 40p. (J). spiral bd. 12.00 (978-1-880636-02-2(6)) Easter Island Foundation.

Orme, Helen. Horsing Around. 2008. (Siti's Sisters Ser.). 36p. pap. 7.95 (***978-1-84167-685-2(3)**) Ransom Publishing Ltd. GBR. *Dist:* International Publishers Marketing.

—Odd One Out. 2007. (Siti's Sisters Ser.). (Illus.). 36p. pap. 7.95 (***978-1-84167-597-8(0)**) Ransom Publishing Ltd. GBR. *Dist:* International Publishers Marketing.

—Stalker. 2007. (Siti's Sisters Ser.). (Illus.). 36p. pap. 7.95 (***978-1-84167-595-4(4)**) Ransom Publishing Ltd. GBR. *Dist:* International Publishers Marketing.

—Trouble with Teachers. 2007. (Siti's Sisters Ser.). (Illus.). 36p. pap. 7.95 (***978-1-84167-599-2(7)**) Ransom Publishing Ltd. GBR. *Dist:* International Publishers Marketing.

Orsini, Marina. The Nutcracker. 2001. 48p. (J). (ps up). pap. 12.95 incl. audio compact disk (978-2-89517-065-5(7)) Coffragants CAN. *Dist:* Penton Overseas, Inc.

Ostrander, Jennifer. Wild Frontier. 2004. 254p. pap. 21.95 (978-1-4137-2717-3(4)) PublishAmerica, Inc.

Oswald, Nancy. Nothing Here but Stones: A Jewish Pioneer Story. rev. ed. 2004. (Illus.). 224p. (C). 16.95 (978-0-8050-7465-9(1) , Holt, Henry & Co. Bks. For Young Readers) Holt, Henry & Co.

Page, Marion. Dirty Mary No More. l.t. ed. 1999. 176p. (J). (gr. 5-7). pap. 10.95 (978-0-943864-96-9(8)) Davenport, May Pubs.

Palatini, Margie. Lab Coat Girl in My Triple Decker Hero, Bk. 3. 2000. (L.A.F. Ser.). 112p. (gr. 2-6). pap. 4.99 (978-0-7868-1348-3(2)) Disney Pr.

Pansy. Ester Ried. 2007. 206p. pap. 12.99 (***978-1-4264-6875-9(X)**); 228p. pap. 15.99 (***978-1-4264-6957-2(8)**) BiblioBazaar.

Pants Makes the Swim Team. 2004. (J). per. 7.99 (978-0-9755959-2-3(X)) Girl Named Pants, Inc., A.

Papineau, Lucie. Casse-Noisette. Jorisch, Stephane, illus. 2000. (Best-Sellers Ser.).Tr. of Nutcracker. (FRE.). (J). (ps-2). audio, audio compact disk 9.95 (978-2-921997-40-9(1) , PS8581 A6658) Coffragants CAN. *Dist:* Penton Overseas, Inc.

Parish, Herman. Bravo, Amelia Bedelia! Sweat, Lynn, illus. 2002. 45p. (J). (ps-ps). lib. bdg. 11.80 (978-0-613-62133-5(6)) Tandem Library Bks.

Parish, Margaret. Adventures of Amelia Bedelia, 2 vols., Vol. 2. 2001. 27.65 (978-0-06-001318-9(4)) HarperCollins Pubs.

Parish, Peggy. Amelia Bedelia & the Surprise Shower. Thomas, Barbara Siebel, illus. 1999. (I Can Read Bks.). (J). (gr. 1-3). 11.55 (978-0-88103-911-5(X)) Tandem Library Bks.

—Amelia Bedelia Helps Out. Sweat, Lynn, illus. 2005. (I Can Read Bks.). 64p. (J). (gr. k-3). pap. 3.99 (978-0-06-051111-1(7) , Harper Trophy) HarperCollins Pubs.

—Come Back, Amelia Bedelia. Tripp, Wallace, illus. 1999. (I Can Read Bks.). (J). (gr. 1-3). 11.55 (978-0-88103-918-4(7)) Tandem Library Bks.

—Merry Christmas, Amelia Bedelia. Sweat, Lynn, illus. 2002. (I Can Read Bks.). 64p. (J). pap. 3.99 (978-0-06-009945-9(3) , Harper Trophy) HarperCollins Pubs.

—Merry Christmas, Amelia Bedelia. 2002. (gr. k-3). lib. bdg. 11.80 (978-0-613-68450-7(8)) Tandem Library Bks.

—Play Ball, Amelia Bedelia. Tripp, Wallace, illus. 1999. (I Can Read Bks.). (J). (gr. 1-3). 11.50 (978-0-88103-913-9(6)) Tandem Library Bks.

—Teach Us, Amelia Bedelia. Sweat, Lynn, illus. 2004. 48p. (J). lib. bdg. 15.00 (978-1-59054-537-9(0)) Fitzgerald Bks.

—Teach Us, Amelia Bedelia. Sweat, Lynn, illus. 2004. (I Can Read Bks.). 64p. (J). (gr. k-3). pap. 3.99 (978-0-06-051114-2(1) , Harper Trophy) HarperCollins Pubs.

Parish, Peggy & Brookes, Diane. A Novel Study for Grade One & Two Based on Amelia Bedelia & the Surprise Shower Novel Study, 25 vols. 1998. (J). pap., tchr. ed. (978-0-9683234-4-1(8)) Raven Rock Publishing.

Park, Barbara. Junie B. Jones & That Meanie Jim's Birthday, Vol. 6. unabr. ed. 2004. (Junie B. Jones Ser.: No. 6). 85p. (J). (gr. k-3). pap. 17.00 incl. audio (978-0-8072-0642-3(3) , Listening Library) Random Hse. Audio Publishing Group.

—Junie B. Jones & the Yucky Blucky Fruitcake. unabr. ed. 2004. (Junie B. Jones Ser.: No. 5). 71p. (J). (gr. k-3). pap. 17.00 incl. audio (978-0-8072-0641-6(5) , Listening Library) Random Hse. Audio Publishing Group.

—Junie B. Jones Has a Monster under Her Bed. unabr. ed. 2004. (Junie B. Jones Ser.: No. 8). 69p. (J). (gr. k-3). pap. 17.00 incl. audio (978-0-8072-0644-7(X) , Listening Library) Random Hse. Audio Publishing Group.

—Junie B. Jones Has a Peep in Her Pocket. unabr. ed. 2004. (Junie B. Jones Ser.: No. 15). 80p. (J). (gr. k-3). pap. 17.00 incl. audio (978-0-8072-0336-1(X) , Listening Library) Random Hse. Audio Publishing Group.

—Junie B. Jones Has a Peep in Her Pocket. Brunkus, Denise, illus. 2000. (Junie B. Jones Ser.: No. 15). 80p. (J). (gr. k-3). lib. bdg. 11.99 (978-0-375-90040-2(3)); pap. 3.99 (978-0-375-80040-5(9)) Random Hse. Children's Bks. (Random Hse. Bks. for Young Readers).

—Junie B. Jones Is (Almost) a Flower Girl. unabr. ed. 2004. (Junie B. Jones Ser.: No. 13). 68p. (J). (gr. k-3). pap. 17.00 incl. audio (978-0-8072-0334-7(3) , Listening Library) Random Hse. Audio Publishing Group.

—Junie B. Jones Is (Almost) a Flower Girl. Brunkus, Denise, illus. 1999. (Junie B. Jones Ser.: No. 13). 80p. (J). (gr. 1-4). lib. bdg. 11.99 (978-0-375-90038-9(1)); (gr. k-3). pap. 3.99 (978-0-375-80038-2(7)) Random Hse. Children's Bks. (Random Hse. Bks. for Young Readers).

—Junie B. Jones Is (Almost) a Flower Girl. 1999. (Junie B. Jones Ser.: No. 13). (J). (gr. k-3). 10.79 (978-0-606-16840-3(0)) Tandem Library Bks.

—Junie B. Jones Is Captain Field Day. unabr. ed. 2004. (Junie B. Jones Ser.: No. 16). 80p. (J). (gr. k-3). pap. 17.00 incl. audio (978-0-8072-0337-8(8) , Listening Library) Random Hse. Audio Publishing Group.

—Junie B. Jones Is Captain Field Day. Brunkus, Denise, illus. 2001. (Junie B. Jones Ser.: No. 16). 80p. (J). (gr. k-3). pap. 3.99 (978-0-375-80291-1(6)); lib. bdg. 11.99 (978-0-375-90291-8(0)) Random Hse. Children's Bks. (Random Hse. Bks. for Young Readers).

—Junie B. Jones Loves Handsome Warren. unabr. ed. 2004. (Junie B. Jones Ser.: No. 7). 71p. (J). (gr. k-3). pap. 17.00 incl. audio (978-0-8072-0643-0(1) , Listening Library) Random Hse. Audio Publishing Group.

—Junie B. Jones Smells Something Fishy. unabr. ed. 2004. (Junie B. Jones Ser.: No. 12). 66p. (J). (gr. k-3). pap. 17.00 incl. audio (978-0-8072-0533-4(8) , Listening Library) Random Hse. Audio Publishing Group.

—Junie B. Jones Smells Something Fishy. Brunkus, Denise & Silverpin Studio Staff, illus. 1998. (Junie B. Jones Ser.: No. 12). 80p. (J). (gr. k-3). lib. bdg. 11.99 (978-0-679-99130-4(1) , Random Hse. Bks. for Young Readers) Random Hse. Children's Bks.

—Junie B. Jones Smells Something Fishy. Brunkus, Denise, illus. 1998. (Junie B. Jones Ser.: No. 12). 80p. (J). (gr. 1-4). pap. 3.99 (978-0-679-89130-7(7) , Random Hse. Bks. for Young Readers) Random Hse. Children's Bks.

Parker, Neal. Captain Annabel. Harris, Emily, illus. 2005. 32p. 15.95 (978-0-89272-653-0(9)) Down East Bks.

Parra, Kelly. Graffiti Girl. 2007. 256p. pap. 9.95 (978-1-4165-3461-7(X) , MTV) Simon & Schuster.

Partridge, Elizabeth. Annie & Bo & the Big Surprise. Weston, Martha, illus. 2002. (Easy-to-Read Ser.). 48p. (J). pap. 3.99 (978-0-14-230071-8(3) , Puffin) Penguin Group (USA) Inc.

Pascal, Francine. Chicos Contra Chicas. 2000. (Gemelas de Sweet Valley Ser.: No. 17). Tr. of Boys Against Girls. (SPA.). 136p. (J). (gr. 3-7). 7.50 (978-84-272-3787-2(1)) Molino, Editorial ESP. *Dist:* AIMS International Bks., Inc.

—Esa Clase de Chica.Tr. of Wrong Kind of Girl. (SPA.). 168p. (J). 7.95 (978-84-272-3880-0(0)) Molino, Editorial ESP. *Dist:* AIMS International Bks., Inc.

—Fearless. 2003. (Fearless Ser.: No. 25). Tr. of Lost. lib. bdg. 14.15 (978-0-613-73397-7(5)) Tandem Library Bks.

—Fearless Nos. 4 & 28: Twisted & Chase. 2003. (Fearless Ser.: No. 4). lib. bdg. 14.15 (978-0-613-68861-1(9)) Tandem Library Bks.

—Gaia Abducted. 2003. (Fearless Super Edition Ser.). (gr. 7-12). lib. bdg. 15.30 (978-0-613-66504-9(X)) Tandem Library Bks.

—Nueva Mirada de Jessica. Orig. Title: Jessica's New Look. (SPA.). 160p. (J). 6.95 (978-84-272-4647-8(1)) Molino, Editorial ESP. *Dist:* AIMS International Bks., Inc.

—Wrong Kind of Girl. 1999. mass mkt. (978-0-553-24182-2(6)) Random Hse., Inc.

Payne, Emmy. Katy No Tiene Bolsa. Canetti, Yanitzia, tr. Rey, H. A., illus. 1999. (SPA.). 32p. (J). (gr. k-3). pap. 5.95 (978-0-395-97911-2(0) , HM4909) Houghton Mifflin Co. Trade & Reference Div.

Pearson, Kit. A Handful of Time. 2003. (Illus.). 208p. (gr. 3-7). pap. 6.99 (978-0-14-032268-2(X) , Penguin Global) Penguin Group (USA) Inc.

Pearson, S. & Ellis, Sarah. Next Door Neighbours. (J). pap. 7.95 (978-0-88899-084-6(7)) Groundwood Bks. CAN. *Dist:* Transition Vendor.

Peck, Harry Thurston. The Adventures of Mabel. Rountree, Harry, illus. 2000. 236p. (J). (gr. k-5). reprint ed. 25.00 (978-0-9616844-0-2(2)) Greenhouse Publishing Co.

Peck, Richard. Amanda/Miranda. 2001. 176p. (YA). (gr. 8-12). pap. 5.99 (978-0-14-131217-0(3) , Puffin) Penguin Group (USA) Inc.

Peek, Merle. Mary Wore Her Red Dress & Henry Wore His Green Sneakers. 1998. (Illus.). 11p. (J). (gr. k-ps). bds. 5.95 (978-0-395-90022-2(0) , Clarion Bks.) Houghton Mifflin Co. Trade & Reference Div.

Peep for Keeps. 2005. 43p. (J). 3.99 (978-0-9763213-4-7(3)) OHC Group LLC.

Peirce-Bale, Mary. Twinkle, Twinkle Little Girl. 2005. (J). 6.95 (978-0-9743869-9-7(5)) Mother's Hse. Publishing.

Pelham, P.J. Hanna Searches for "Me!" 2004. 24p. (J). pap. (978-1-4120-3208-7(3)) Trafford Publishing.

Pelletier, Marthe. Elle S'appelle Elodie. Sottolichio, Rafael, illus. 2002. 107. (FRE.). 96p. (J). pap. (978-2-89021-544-3(X)) Diffusion du livre Mirabel.

Penguin Books Staff, ed. Heidi. (Classics Ser.). (Illus.). 56p. (J). 3.50 (978-0-7214-1751-6(5) , Dutton Juvenile) Penguin Group (USA) Inc.

Penrose, Margaret. Dorothy Dale. rev. ed. 2006. 196p. 26.95 (978-1-4218-1801-6(9)); pap. 11.95 (978-1-4218-1901-3(5)) 1st World Publishing, Inc. (1st World Library - Literary Society).

—The Motor Girls. 2006. 152p. pap. 11.99 (978-1-4264-1903-4(1)) BiblioBazaar.

—The Motor Girls. 2004. reprint ed. pap. 21.95 (978-1-4191-7466-7(5)); pap. 1.99 (978-1-4192-7466-4(X)) Kessinger Publishing, LLC.

—The Motor Girls on Waters Blue. rev. ed. 2006. 228p. 27.95 (978-1-4218-1802-3(7)); pap. 12.95 (978-1-4218-1902-0(3)) 1st World Publishing, Inc. (1st World Library - Literary Society).

—The Motor Girls on Waters Blue. 2006. 164p. pap. 11.99 (978-1-4264-2184-6(2)) BiblioBazaar.

—The Motor Girls on Waters Blue. 2004. reprint ed. pap. 22.95 (978-1-4191-7467-4(3)); pap. 1.99 (978-1-4192-7467-1(8)) Kessinger Publishing, LLC.

Peris, Carme. Goldilocks & the Three Bears. 1998. (Fairy Tale Theater Ser.). (Illus.). 32p. (J). (gr. k-3). pap. 8.95 (978-0-7641-5116-3(9)) Barron's Educational Series, Inc.

Perkins, Lynne Rae. All Alone in the Universe. (Illus.). (J). (gr. 5 up). 1999. 144p. 16.99 (978-0-688-16881-0(7)); 2001. 224p. reprint ed. 5.99 (978-0-380-73302-6(1) , Harper Trophy) HarperCollins Pubs.

Perl, Lila. Dumb Like Me, Olivia Potts. (J). 19.95 (978-0-8164-3178-6(7)) Houghton Mifflin Co.

Perrault, Charles. Le Petit Chaperon Rouge. Barrington, Lara, illus. adapted ed. 2000. (Best-Sellers Ser.). Orig. Title: Little Red Riding Hood. (FRE.). (J). (ps-2). audio 9.95 (978-2-921997-00-3(2)) Coffragants CAN. *Dist:* Penton Overseas, Inc.

Perry, Kate. Girls Like You: Sophie. 1999. (Illus.). 160p. (J). pap. 7.99 (978-1-85881-656-2(4)) Orion Children's Bks. GBR. *Dist:* Independent Pubs. Group.

Perry, Sarah Catherine. Clara's Test. 2006. (J). per. (978-1-55452-022-0(3)) Essence Publishing.

Person, Sarah. A Book for Betsy. DeGrood, Therese, illus. 1998. 24p. (J). (gr. k-6). pap. 3.95 (978-0-9668635-0-5(X)) Greater Mankato Area United Way.

Peters, Elizabeth T. Through the Eyes of Friendship. 2002. (gr. 7-12). lib. bdg. 23.40 (978-0-613-74593-2(0)) Tandem Library Bks.

Peters, Julie Anne. Grl2Grl. 2007. 160p. (YA). (gr. 10 up). pap. 11.99 (***978-0-316-01343-7(9)**) Little, Brown Bks. for Young Readers.

Petersen, Elise. Tracy's Mess. Trapani, Iza, illus. 1998. 32p. (J). (ps-2). pap. 5.95 (978-1-58089-003-8(2)) Charlesbridge Publishing, Inc.

—Tracy's Mess. 1998. (ps-2). lib. bdg. 14.10 (978-0-613-85270-8(2)) Tandem Library Bks.

Petrucha, Stefan. Writ in Stone. 2006. (J). (gr. 3-8). 24.21 (978-1-59961-058-0(2)) Spotlight.

Pettersson, Aline. Renata y Sus Curitas. Ochoa, Ana, illus. 2003. Tr. of Renata & Her Bandages. (SPA.). 24p. (J). (gr. k-3). pap. 7.95 (978-968-19-0745-7(0)) Santillana USA Publishing Co., Inc.

Petty. Girls Like You: Charlotte. 1999. 160p. (J). pap. 6.99 (978-1-85881-659-3(9)) Orion Children's Bks. GBR. *Dist:* Independent Pubs. Group.

—Girls Like You: Hannah. 1999. 160p. (J). pap. 7.99 (978-1-85881-657-9(2)) Orion Children's Bks. GBR. *Dist:* Independent Pubs. Group.

—Girls Like You: Maddy. 1999. 160p. (J). pap. 7.99 (978-1-85881-658-6(0)) Orion Children's Bks. GBR. *Dist:* Independent Pubs. Group.

Pfeffer, Susan Beth. Justice for Emily. 1998. (978-0-606-13549-8(9)) Tandem Library Bks.

Pfister, Ashley. Cindy Makes A Difference. 2005. 21p. (J). 13.93 (978-1-4116-3348-3(2)) Lulu.com.

Philipson, Sandra. Annie Loses Her Leg but Finds Her Way. Takatch, Robert, illus. 1999. 38p. (J). (gr. 1-6). 17.95 (978-1-929821-00-6(X)) Chagrin River Publishing Co.

Pickford, Susan B. Roxy's Gift. 1999. (Illus.). 16p. (Orig.). (YA). (gr. 4-8). pap. 6.95 (978-1-889664-06-4(5)) SBP Collaboratioin Works.

Pielichaty, Helena. Starring Sammie ... 2006. (Girls of Avenue Z Ser.). 128p. (J). pap. 4.99 (978-1-4169-0061-0(6) , Aladdin) Simon & Schuster Children's Publishing.

Pietri, Annie. The Orange Trees of Versailles. 2005. 144p. (J). (gr. 3-7). pap. 5.99 (978-0-440-41948-8(4) , Yearling) Random Hse. Children's Bks.

Pike, Christopher, pseud. Remember Me. ed. 2001. (Remember Me Ser.: No. 1). 240p. (YA). (gr. 8 up). reprint ed. mass mkt. 5.99 (978-0-7434-2801-9(3) , Simon Pulse) Simon & Schuster Children's Publishing.

—Remember Me. 2002. (Remember Me Ser.: No. 1). (gr. 7-12). lib. bdg. 14.15 (978-0-613-52993-8(6)) Tandem Library Bks.

Pinkett-Smith, Jada. Girls Hold up This World. Kennedy-McCullough, Donyelle, photos by. 2005. (Illus.). 40p. (J). 16.95 (978-0-439-08793-3(7) , Cartwheel Bks.) Scholastic, Inc.

—Girls Hold up This World. 2003. (Illus.). (J). pap. (978-0-439-11332-8(6)) Scholastic, Inc.

Pittar, Gill. Basura No, Gracias! Rioja, Alberto Jiménez, tr. Morrell, Cris, illus. 2003. (Milly Molly Ser.). (SPA.). 24p. (J). pap. (978-84-241-8695-1(8)) Everest de Ediciones y Distribucion, S.L. ESP. *Dist:* Lectorum Pubns., Inc.

—Las Ciruelas de Isa Bela. Rioja, Alberto Jiménez, tr. Morrell, Cris, illus. 2003. (Milly Molly Ser.). (SPA.). 24p. (J). pap. (978-84-241-8687-6(7)) Everest de Ediciones y Distribucion, S.L. ESP. *Dist:* Lectorum Pubns., Inc.

—Milly, Molly & the Runaway Bean. Morrell, Cris, illus. 2005. 28p. (ps-ps). pap. (978-1-86972-049-0(0)) Milly Molly Bks.

—De Quien es Este Sombrero? Rioja, Alberto Jiménez, tr. Morrell, Cris, illus. 2003. (Milly Molly Ser.). 24p. (J). pap. (978-84-241-8679-1(6)) Everest de Ediciones y Distribucion, S.L. ESP. *Dist:* Lectorum Pubns., Inc.

Plante, Raymond. Un Dromadaire Chez Marilou Polaire. Favreau, Marie-Claude, illus. 2003. (Premier Roman Ser.). (FRE.). 64p. (J). (gr. 1-4). pap. (978-2-89021-608-2(X)) Diffusion du livre Mirabel.

—Marilou on Stage. Cummins, Sarah, tr. Favreau, Marie-Claude, illus. 1999. 59p. (gr. 1-5). (Early Readers Ser.). 4.95 (978-0-88780-480-9(2)); (First Novels Ser.: Vol. 30). (J). (978-0-88780-481-6(0)) Formac Publishing Co., Ltd. CAN. *Dist:* Casemate Pubs. & Bk. Distributors, LLC.

—Marilou Polaire Crie au Loup. 2000. (Premier Roman Ser.). (FRE.). 64p. (J). (gr. 2-5). pap. (978-2-89021-396-8(X)) Diffusion du livre Mirabel.

Plante, Raymond & Favreau, Marie-Claude. Le Long Nez de Marilou Polaire. 2002. (Premier Roman Ser.). 64p. (J). (gr. 2-5). pap. (978-2-89021-307-4(2)) Diffusion du livre Mirabel.

Platt, Chris. Stardust's Foal. 2003. (Ashleigh Ser.). 176p. pap. 4.99 (978-0-06-009146-0(0) , Harper Entertainment) HarperCollins Pubs.

Pockets Learning Staff. Samantha's Alaska Adventure. 1998. (Illus.). 2p. (J). (ps-1). 15.00 (978-1-888074-90-1(6)) Pockets of Learning.

—Samantha's California Adventure. 1998. (Illus.). 2p. (ps-1). 15.00 (978-1-888074-91-8(4)) Pockets of Learning.

Poer, Nancy Jewel. Mia's Apple Tree. Poer, Nancy Jewel, illus. 2004. (Illus.). 34p. (J). 21.95 (978-0-9740413-1-5(9)) White Feather Publishing.

Pohl-Weary, Emily. Strange Times at Western High. Cowles, Rose, illus. 2006. (Natalie Fuentes Mystery Ser.). 219p. (YA). (gr. 7-12). 19.95 (978-1-55451-040-5(6)); pap. 9.95 (978-1-55451-039-9(2)) Annick Pr., Ltd. CAN. *Dist:* Firefly Bks., Ltd.

Polak, Monique. On the Game. 2005. (SideStreets Ser.). 184p. (YA). (gr. 7-12). ***(978-1-55028-877-3(6));*** 7.95 (978-1-55028-876-6(8)) Lorimer, James & Co., Ltd., Pubs. CAN. *Dist:* Casemate Pubs. & Bk. Distributors, LLC.

The Pony Winter. 2007. (J). (978-1-933343-42-6(7) , PONY) Stabenfeldt Inc.

Poole-Carter, Rosemary. Juliette Ascending. 2007. (YA). pap. 14.00 (***978-1-929976-41-6(0)*** , TOP) Top Pubns., Ltd.

Porter, Eleanor H. Pollyanna Book & Charm. 2001. (J). (gr. 4-7). 6.99 (978-0-694-01588-7(1) , Harper Festival) HarperCollins Pubs.

Poulin, Stephane. Agarren Esa Gata! (SPA., Illus.). 24p. (J). (gr. 1-4). pap. 6.99 (978-980-257-233-5(0)) Ekare, Ediciones VEN. *Dist:* Kane/Miller Bk. Pubs., Inc.

—Agarren Esa Gata (Can You Catch Josephine?) (SPA., Illus.). 24p. (J). (gr. 1-4). pap. 8.95 (978-980-257-116-1(4)) Ekare, Ediciones VEN. *Dist:* Kane/Miller Bk. Pubs., Inc.

Pound, Emily. Angel Shoes. 2007. (Illus.). 32p. (J). (ps-k). pap. 9.95 (***978-0-7459-4974-1(6)***) Lion Hudson plc GBR. *Dist:* Independent Pubs. Group.

A Prairie Heart. 2007. (Illus.). (J). per. 19.95 (***978-0-9793668-0-2(1)***) Prairie Heart Publishing.

Pratts, Christine. Tabby Wise for School Secretary. 2005. 61p. pap. 8.99 (978-1-4116-4935-4(4)) Lulu.com.

Priddy, Roger. Baby Gund Baby Girl. 2006. 22p. (J). bds. 5.95 (978-0-312-49703-3(2) , Priddy Bks.) St. Martin's Pr.

Prom Girl. 2nd ed. 2003. (J). pap. 8.95 (978-0-9726917-0-3(7)) Prom Girl Publishing. Inc.

Pryor, Bonnie. Toenails, Tonsils, & Tornadoes. 1999. (Illus.). 176p. (J). (gr. 3-7). pap. 4.95 (978-0-688-16675-5(X) , Harper Trophy) HarperCollins Pubs.

Puerto, Carlos. No Mires Ahora. 1999. Tr. of Don't Look Now. (978-0-606-17722-1(1)) Tandem Library Bks.

Pugh, Tracey D. A Show & Tell Lesson. McCracken, Jaime, photos by. l.t. ed. 2006. (Illus.). 32p. (J). 12.95 (978-1-59879-105-1(2)) Lifevest Publishing, Inc.

Pugh, Tracey D. & McCracken, Jaime, photos by. A Show & Tell Lesson. l.t. ed. 2006. (Illus.). 32p. (J). per. 12.95 (978-1-59879-134-1(6)) Lifevest Publishing, Inc.

Pullman, Philip. Der Goldene Kompass. (GER.). pap. 27.95 (978-3-453-13744-8(2)) Verlag Wilhelm Heyne DEU. *Dist:* Distribooks, Inc.

Pure. 2005. 245p. (YA). pap. 7.95 (978-1-896764-96-2(7)) Second Story Pr. CAN. *Dist:* Orca Bk. Pubs. USA.

Puttock, Simon. A Ladder to the Stars. Jay, Alison, illus. 2006. 32p. (J). pap. 7.95 (978-1-84507-512-5(9)) Lincoln, Frances Ltd. GBR. *Dist:* Perseus Distribution.

Pyatt, Susan. Call Me Madame President. Gaston, Keith, illus. 2003. 32p. (J). 17.00 (978-0-9742575-0-1(8)) Imagination Station Pr.

Quindlen, Anna. Happily Ever After. Stevenson, James, illus. 1999. 64p. (J). (gr. 2-5). pap. 4.99 (978-0-14-038706-3(4) , Puffin) Penguin Group (USA) Inc.

Radford, Sheri. Penelope & the Humongous Burp. Tripp, Christine, illus. 2005. 32p. pap. (978-1-897073-33-9(X)) Lobster Pr.

Rainey, L. E. Sad Sam, Glad Sam. 2006. (Illus.). 32p. (J). 16.95 (978-0-9785521-0-7(5)) Shoetree Publishers, Inc.

Rainville, Doris I., creator. The Girl Who Never Let Her Mother Brush Her Hair. l.t. ed. 2003. (Illus.). 24p. (J). per. 7.95 (978-0-9744879-0-8(2)) Magical Creations.

Ramona Empieza el Curso. 1999. (SPA.). (J). 9.95 (978-1-56137-546-2(2) , NU6106) Novel Units, Inc.

Ramsey, Charlotte. Go Global with Charlotte. 2004. (Illus.). 36p. (J). 3.99 (978-0-9746587-1-1(5) , Beacon Street Girls) B*tween Productions, Inc.

Randall, David. Sorrel. 2007. 304p. (YA). (gr. 7 up). 16.99 (***978-0-689-87872-5(9)*** , McElderry, Margaret K.) Simon & Schuster Children's Publishing.

Random House Disney Staff. Cinderella. 2005. (Illus.). 48p. (J). (ps-2). pap. 2.99 (978-0-375-83069-3(3) , Golden/Disney) Random Hse. Children's Bks.

—Cinderella's Secret. Harchy, Atelier Philippe, illus. 2005. (Princess Secrets Ser.). 32p. (J). (ps-2). 4.99 (978-0-7364-2325-0(7) , RH/Disney) Random Hse. Children's Bks.

—Snow White's Secret. Artful Doodlers Limited Staff, illus. 2005. 32p. (J). (ps-2). 4.99 (978-0-7364-2326-7(5) , RH/Disney) Random Hse. Children's Bks.

Random House Value Publishing Staff & Burnett, Frances Hodgson. Secret Garden. 1998. (Children's Classics Ser.). 288p. (J). (gr. 5-9). 5.99 (978-0-517-18960-3(7) , Children's Classics) Random Hse. Value Publishing.

Random House Value Publishing Staff & Spyri, Johanna. Heidi. 1998. (Children's Classics Ser.). (Illus.). 352p. (J). (gr. 5-9). 5.99 (978-0-517-18967-2(4) , Children's Classics) Random Hse. Value Publishing.

Ransom, Candice F. Goldilocks & the Three Bears. Bryant, Laura J., illus. 2002. (Brighter Child Keepsake Stories Ser.). 32p. (J). (ps-3). pap. 3.99 (978-1-57768-178-6(9) , Brighter Child) School Specialty Publishing.

—Little Red Riding Hood. Lyon, Tammie Speer, illus. 2002. (Brighter Child Keepsake Stories Ser.). 32p. (J). (ps-3). pap. 3.99 (978-1-57768-198-4(3) , Brighter Child) School Specialty Publishing.

Rathmann, Peggy. Ruby the Copycat Library. 2007. (J). 18.95 (***978-0-545-00583-8(3)***) Scholastic, Inc.

Rattigan, Jama Kim. Dumpling Soup. Hsu-Flanders, Lillian, illus. 1998. 32p. (J). (ps-3). pap., pap. 6.99 (978-0-316-73047-1(5)) Little, Brown Bks. for Young Readers.

Ray, Anna Chapin. Half A Dozen Girls. 2004. reprint ed. pap. 24.95 (978-1-4191-2264-4(9)); pap. 1.99 (978-1-4192-2264-1(3)) Kessinger Publishing, LLC.

Razzell, Mary. Snow Apples. 2006. 216p. (J). pap. 6.95 (978-0-88899-728-9(0)) Groundwood Bks. CAN. *Dist:* Perseus Distribution.

Rea, Ba. Monarch! Come Play with Me. Rea, Ba, illus. 2006. (Illus.). 32p. (J). per. 10.95 (978-0-9657472-5-7(5)) Bas Relief Publishing.

Reader's Digest Staff. Hannah Montana Storybook & Microphone. 2007. (RD Innovative Book & Player Format Ser.). (J). 24.99 (***978-0-7944-1364-4(1)***) Reader's Digest Assn., Inc., The.

RealBuzz Studios Staff. Girl Overboard Frankensteins Monster: Life Camera Action Book 4. 2007. 128p. (YA). pap. 4.97 (978-1-59789-580-4(6) , Barbour Bks.) Barbour Publishing, Inc.

—Hits & Misses. 2007. 128p. (YA). No. 1. pap. 4.97 (978-1-59789-569-9(5)); No. 2. pap. 4.97 (978-1-59789-570-5(9)); No. 3. pap. 4.97 (978-1-59789-571-2(7)); No. 4. pap. 4.97 (978-1-59789-572-9(5)) Barbour Publishing, Inc. (Barbour Bks.).

—Serenity—You Shall Love..., Vol. 6. 2006. 96p. (YA). pap. 7.97 (978-1-59310-875-5(3) , Barbour Bks.) Barbour Publishing, Inc.

—When Dolphins Fly. 2007. (Goofyfoot Gurl Ser.: No. 2). 96p. (YA). pap. 4.97 (978-1-59789-574-3(1) , Barbour Bks.) Barbour Publishing, Inc.

Reeve, Phyllis Cardoze. One for Sorrow, Two for Joy. 2002. 150p. (YA). (gr. 6-9). pap. 14.95 (978-0-9725590-0-3(0)) Reeve, Phyllis.

Regan, Dian Curtis. The World According to Kaley. 2005. (Illus.). 112p. (J). (gr. 4-7). per. 14.99 (978-1-58196-039-6(5)) Darby Creek Publishing.

Rennison, Louise. Away Laughing on a Fast Camel: Even More Confessions of Georgia Nicolson. (Confessions of Georgia Nicolson Ser.). 2004. (Illus.). 288p. (J). lib. bdg. 16.89 (978-0-06-058935-6(3)); 2005. 304p. reprint ed. pap. 7.99 (978-0-06-058936-3(1)) HarperCollins Pubs. (HarperTeen).

Reno, I. N. Applecores. 2002. 546p. (YA). pap. 26.95 (978-0-595-23456-1(9) , Writers Club Pr.) iUniverse, Inc.

Rey, H. A. Elizabite: Adventures of a Carnivorous Plant. Rey, H. A., illus. 1999. (Illus.). 32p. (J). (gr. k-3). pap. 5.95 (978-0-395-97704-0(5)) Houghton Mifflin Co. Trade & Reference Div.

Reynolds, Peter H. El Punto. 2004. (SPA., Illus.). 48p. (J). 16.99 (978-84-8488-110-0(5)) Serres, Ediciones, S. L. ESP. *Dist:* Lectorum Pubns., Inc.

Reza, Connie. Leah Ann Adopta un Perico. 2006. (Illus.). 32p. (J). 19.99 incl. audio compact disk (978-0-9714533-2-6(2)) Yo Puedo Publishing.

Ricci, Christine. Dora's Costume Party. 2006. (J). (ps-2). 21.35 (978-1-59961-071-9(X)) Spotlight.

Rice, Sheila. The Night Watchers. 2005. 88p. pap. 14.95 (978-1-4137-7663-8(9)) PublishAmerica, Inc.

Richards, J. Kirk. I'll Be There with Belzon. 2004. (Illus.). 32p. (J). per. 19.95 (978-0-9752553-0-8(4)) Bright-Brights Media Co., The.

Richardson, Beverly J. Timbs. Lilly & Me. (Illus.). 2006. (ENG.). 36p. per. 12.95 (978-1-59800-459-5(X)); 2005. 29p. 26.99 (978-1-59800-121-1(3)) Outskirts Press, Inc.

Riding High: Individual Title Six-Packs. 16p. (gr. 2 up). 35.00 (978-0-7635-9243-1(9)) Rigby Education.

Rigby Education Staff, ed. Going to the Doctor. (Illus.). 8p. (J). bds. 3.95 (978-0-7635-6427-8(3) , 764273C99) Rigby Education.

Rinaldi, Ann. The Last Silk Dress. 1999. 352p. (YA). (gr. 7). mass mkt. 6.50 (978-0-440-22861-5(1) , Laurel Leaf) Random Hse. Children's Bks.

Risk, Mary, et al. Hurry up Molly/English-Spanish: Apurate, Molly. Scriven, Gill, illus. 2000. (I Can Read Bks.).Tr. of Hurry Up, Molly. (SPA, ENG & FRE.). 28p. (J). (ps up). 8.99 (978-0-7641-5286-3(6)) Barron's Educational Series, Inc.

Roberts, Barbara A. Phoebe's Tree House Secrets. Sternberg, Kate, tr. Sternberg, Kate, illus. 2002. 59p. pap. 5.95 (978-0-9714609-0-4(6)) National Bk. Network.

Roberts, Laura Peyton. Heart & Soul. 1998. (Clearwater Crossing Ser.: No. 3). (YA). (gr. 5-8). (978-0-606-13280-0(5)) Tandem Library Bks.

Roberts, Rachel. All That Glitters. 2001. (Avalon Ser.: Bk. 2). (J). (978-0-606-22175-7(1)) Tandem Library Bks.

Robertson, Elysia Hill. Toley's Sleep over Learning Party. Robertson, Elysia Hill, illus. 2005. (Illus.). 118p. (J). per. 12.95 (978-0-9764444-4-2(5) , EJWV-005) E. J. Publishing.

Robleda, Margarita. Este Soy Yo. Suarez, Maribel, illus. 2006. (SPA.). 10p. (J). 7.95 (978-1-59820-207-6(3) , Alfaguara) Santillana USA Publishing Co., Inc.

—Maria: Una Nina Latina en Estados Unidos. Ramirez, Danilo, illus. 2005. (SPA.). 36p. pap. 10.95 (978-1-59437-557-6(7) , Alfaguara) Santillana USA Publishing Co., Inc.

—Muñeca de Trapo. Suarez, Maribel, illus. 2006. (SPA.). 10p. (J). 7.95 (978-1-59820-209-0(X) , Alfaguara) Santillana USA Publishing Co., Inc.

—Patito, Donde Estas? Suarez, Maribel, illus. 2006. (SPA.). 10p. (J). 7.95 (978-1-59820-208-3(1) , Alfaguara) Santillana USA Publishing Co., Inc.

Robshaw, Brandon. Georgina & the Dragon. (Illus.). 96p. (J). 7.95 (978-0-14-038370-6(0)) Penguin Bks., Ltd. GBR. *Dist:* Trafalgar Square Publishing.

The Rocket, 6 Packs. (ps-2). 27.00 (978-0-7635-9471-8(7)) Rigby Education.

Rocks!, Misako. Biker Girl. 2006. (Illus.). 160p. (gr. 5-17). pap. 7.99 (978-0-7868-3676-5(8)) Hyperion Pr.

Rockwell, D. R. The Jessicas: The Adventures of Five City Girls. 2005. (J). pap. 9.95 (978-0-9767711-0-4(1)) CLOJ Publishing.

Rodrigues, Carmen. Not Anything. 2008. 224p. pap. 9.99 (***978-0-425-21928-7(3)*** , Berkley Trade) Penguin Group (USA) Inc.

Rodriguez, Edarissa. The Girl Who Took a Shower. Santiago, Claribel, ed. Rodriguez, Edarissa, illus. 2003. (J). pap. 13.99 (978-0-9744726-0-7(3)) Santiago, Claribel.

Rodriguez, Robert, et al. The Day Dreamer. Toader, Alex, illus. 2005. (Shark Boy & Lava Girl Adventures Ser.: Bk. 1). 162p. (J). (ps-7). per. (978-1-933104-04-1(X)) Troublemaker Publishing, LP.

Rogers, Amy. All Chalked Up. 2000. (gr. k-3). lib. bdg. 11.80 (978-0-613-24133-5(9)) Tandem Library Bks.

Rogers, Scott. The Little Red Boat. 2001. (Illus.). 78p. (J). (gr. k-3). pap. 9.95 (978-0-9705237-2-3(6)) 1stCoBooks.

Romero, Sensi. La familia de Nieve. 2004. (Cuentos con miga Ser.). 47p. (J). pap. 11.00 (978-84-95895-22-6(6)) Editorial Brief ESP. *Dist:* Independent Pubs. Group.

Rorby, Ginny. Hurt Go Happy. 2006. 272p. (J). 17.95 (978-0-7653-1442-0(8) , Starscape) Doherty, Tom Assocs., LLC.

Rosa-Leigh. The Briar & the Rose. 2006. 62p. pap. 12.95 (978-1-4137-7230-2(7)) PublishAmerica, Inc.

Rosenbaum, Bev Katz. Beyond Cool. 2007. 320p. (YA). (gr. 6 up). pap. 9.99 (***978-0-425-21563-0(6)*** , Berkley Trade) Penguin Group (USA) Inc.

Rosenbluth, Roz. Nettie's Spaghetti. Dillard, Kristine, illus. 1999. 12p. (J). (ps-2). pap. 3.75 (978-1-880612-88-0(7) , Seedling Pubns.) Continental Pr., Inc.

Rosenfeld, Dina. A Little Girl Named Miriam. Winn-Lederer, Ilene, illus. 2001. (Little Greats Ser.). (J). (ps-1). 9.95 (978-0-922613-79-3(6)) Hachai Publishing.

Ross, Jillian. Alissa & the Dungeons of Grimrock. Backes, Nick, illus. 1998. (Stardust Classics). 106p. (J). (gr. 2-6). 12.95 (978-1-889514-15-4(2)) Dolls Corp.

Roter, Jordan. Camp Rules. 2007. 272p. (YA). (gr. 6-9). 15.99 (978-0-525-47803-4(5) , Dutton Juvenile) Penguin Group (USA) Inc.

Roth, Matthue. Candy in Action. 2007. 224p. (YA). (gr. 9 up). 15.95 (978-1-933368-63-4(2)) Counterpoint.

Rowan, Paula S. Remember This. Mueller-Brown, Julie, illus. 1998. (World Tree Ser.). (J). (gr. 2-5). 18.95 (978-0-9654682-5-1(9)) Savannah College of Art & Design.

Roy, Jacqueline. Daughter Like Me. (Illus.). 192p. (J). 9.95 (978-0-14-037927-3(4) , N A L Trade) Penguin Group (USA) Inc.

Roy, James. Full Moon Racing. 1998. 208p. (YA). reprint ed. pap. 16.95 (978-0-7022-2974-9(1)) Univ. of Queensland Pr. AUS. *Dist:* International Specialized Bk. Services.

Roy, Lillian. Polly & Her Friends Abroad. 2002. 320p. pap. 34.95 (978-1-932080-49-0(X)) Ross & Perry, Inc.

Ruben, Pamela J. Don't Pick on Pepper! Take a Journey with Pepper as She Takes on a Schoolyard Bully with Brainpower, Humor, & a Dash of Spice! Ruben, Anthony R., ed. 2004. 31p. (J). 12.95 (978-0-9764813-1-7(6)) Peppery Pr.

Rubio, Carlos. Bullwhip. 2003. (gr. 7-12). lib. bdg. 30.35 (978-0-613-84760-5(1)) Tandem Library Bks.

Ruckdeschel, Liz & James, Sara. What If ... All the Boys Wanted You. 2006. 288p. (YA). (gr. 7-10). 10.99 (978-0-385-90318-9(9) , Delacorte Bks. for Young Readers) Random Hse. Children's Bks.

Ruditis, Paul. Ready to Glow. Choi Sung Hwan, Aragon Noel, illus. 2005. (Trollz Ser.). 80p. (J). pap. 5.99 (978-0-439-80313-7(6)) Scholastic, Inc.

Ruditis, Paul & Burge, Constance M. As Puck Would Have It. 2006. (Charmed Ser.). 240p. (YA). pap. 6.99 (978-1-4169-1468-6(4) , Simon Spotlight Entertainment) Simon & Schuster.

Rudolph, Marian. Lovina's Song: A Pioneer Girl's Journey with the Donner Party. Cole, Christopher, illus. 1999. 187p. (YA). (gr. 5-8). pap. 11.95 (978-1-928595-01-4(4)) Citron Bay Pr.

—Lovina's Song: A Pioneer Girl's Journey with the Donner Party. Cole, Christopher, illus. 1998. 192p. (J). pap. 11.95 (978-1-883965-43-3(8)) Rattle OK Pubns.

Rue, Nancy N. Here's Lily! 2000. (gr. 7-12). lib. bdg. 10.65 (978-0-613-71716-8(3)) Tandem Library Bks.

—Here's Lily. 2003. pap. 2.99 (978-0-310-70590-1(8)) Zondervan.

—Horse Crazy Lily. 2003. (Young Women of Faith Ser.). 128p. (J). pap. 5.99 (978-0-310-70263-4(1)) Zonderkidz.

—Rough & Rugged Lily. 2002. (gr. 3-6). lib. bdg. 13.00 (978-0-613-71713-7(9)) Tandem Library Bks.

Rushton, Rosie. Friends, Enemies. 2006. 240p. (gr. 5-17). pap. 5.99 (978-0-7868-5178-2(3)) Hyperion Pr.

Ruurs, Margriet. Emma & the Coyote. Spurll, Barbara, illus. 2001. 24p. (J). pap. 8.95 (978-0-7737-6205-3(1)) Stoddart Kids CAN. *Dist:* Fitzhenry & Whiteside, Ltd.

—Emma & the Coyote. 1999. (gr. k-3). lib. bdg. 16.40 (978-0-613-65091-5(3)) Tandem Library Bks.

Ryherd, Tim. My Hurricane Book. 2006. (J). 12.95 (978-0-9749974-1-4(2)) Ryherd, Tim Publishing.

Sachs, Marilyn. Amy & Laura. 2001. 180p. (gr. 4-7). pap. 13.95 (978-0-595-17592-5(9)) iUniverse, Inc.

Sackin, Jacob. Islands. 2008. 280p. (YA). pap. 14.99 (978-1-59092-392-4(8) , Blue Works) Windstorm Creative.

Sakura's Never-Ending Day. 2001. (gr. 3-6). lib. bdg. 11.80 (978-0-613-33016-9(1)) Tandem Library Bks.

Samantha's Arizona Adventure. 1998. (Illus.). 2p. (J). (ps-1). 15.00 (978-1-888074-84-0(1)) Pockets of Learning.

Samantha's Colorado Adventure. 1998. (Illus.). 2p. (J). (ps-1). 15.00 (978-1-888074-85-7(X)) Pockets of Learning.

Samantha's Florida Adventure. 1998. (Illus.). 2p. (J). (ps-1). 15.00 (978-1-888074-86-4(8)) Pockets of Learning.

Samantha's Hawaii Adventure. 1998. (Illus.). 2p. (J). (ps-1). 15.00 (978-1-888074-87-1(6)) Pockets of Learning.

Samantha's New York Adventure. 1998. (Illus.). 2p. (J). (ps-1). 15.00 (978-1-888074-88-8(4)) Pockets of Learning.

Samantha's Travel Adventure Starter Kit. 1998. (Illus.). 2p. (J). (ps-1). 30.00 (978-1-888074-83-3(3)) Pockets of Learning.

Samantha's Vermont Adventure. 1998. (Illus.). 2p. (J). (ps-1). 15.00 (978-1-888074-89-5(2)) Pockets of Learning.

Samton, Sheila W. Rosa Loves to Walk. 2000. (Illus.). (J). (978-0-7636-1123-1(9)) Candlewick Pr.

Samuels, Gertrude. Run, Shelley, Run! 2000. (gr. 7-12). lib. bdg. 22.20 (978-0-613-86204-2(X)) Tandem Library Bks.

—Run, Shelley, Run. 2000. 192p. (gr. 7-12). pap. 12.95 (978-0-595-12145-8(4) , Backinprint.com) iUniverse, Inc.

—Yours, Brett. 2000. 180p. (YA). (gr. 4-7). pap. 13.95 (978-0-595-00806-3(2)) iUniverse, Inc.

Sandberg, Rosemary, ed. The Kingfisher Book of Great Girl Stories: A Treasury of Classics from Children's Literature. Blake, Quentin, illus. 2006. (Story Collections). 160p. (J). (gr. k-3). tchr. ed. 19.95 (978-0-7534-5207-3(3) , Kingfisher) Houghton Mifflin Co. Trade & Reference Div.

Sandoval, Lynda. Chicks Ahoy. 2006. 224p. (YA). pap. 7.99 (978-0-689-86441-4(8) , Simon Pulse) Simon & Schuster Children's Publishing.

—Who's Your Daddy? 2004. 320p. (YA). pap. 6.99 (978-0-689-86440-7(X) , Simon Pulse) Simon & Schuster Children's Publishing.

—Who's Your Daddy? 2004. 318p. (YA). (gr. 7). lib. bdg. 15.60 (978-1-4176-4527-5(X)) Tandem Library Bks.

Sanschagrin, Joceline. La Fille aux Cheveux Rouges. 1998. (Roman Jeunesse Ser.). (FRE., Illus.). 96p. (J). (gr. 4-7). pap. (978-2-89021-096-7(0)) Diffusion du livre Mirabel.

Sarah Bishop. 1999. (J). 9.95 (978-1-56137-486-1(5)) Novel Units, Inc.

Sarah Bishop. 2003. pap. 2.50 (978-0-590-41407-4(0)) Scholastic, Inc.

Sarah, Plain & Tall. 1999. (J). 11.95 (978-1-56137-632-2(9)); 9.95 (978-1-56137-247-8(1)) Novel Units, Inc.

Sargent, Dave & Sargent, Pat. Amy Armadillo: Mind Your Mama, 15 vols. Huff, Jeane, illus. 2003. (Animal Pride Ser.: 15). 42p. (J). pap. 6.95 (978-1-56763-788-5(4)); lib. bdg. 19.95 (978-1-56763-787-8(6)) Ozark Publishing.

—Valley Oak Acorns: (Maidu) Be Helpful, 20, Vol. 20. Lenoir, Jane, illus. l.t. ed. 2005. (Story Keeper Ser.: 20). 42p. (J). (ps-ps). lib. bdg. 22.60 (978-1-56763-941-4(0)) Ozark Publishing.

Sargent, Dave, et al. The Bundle Keeper: (Pawnee) Be Responsible, 20, Vol. 18. Lenoir, Jane, illus. l.t. ed. 2004. (Story Keeper Ser.: 18). 48p. (J). pap. 6.95 (978-1-56763-938-4(0)) Ozark Publishing.

—On the Banks of the Wallowa River: (Nez Perce) Use Your Talent, 20, 13. Lenoir, Jane, illus. l.t. ed. 2004. (Story Keeper Ser.: 13). 48p. (J). pap. 6.95 (978-1-56763-928-5(3)) Ozark Publishing.

—Rays of the Sun Vol. 15: (shoshone) Learn Lessons, 20 vols. Lenoir, Jane, illus. l.t. ed. 2004. (Story Keeper Ser.: 15). 48p. (J). pap. 6.95 (978-1-56763-932-2(1)) Ozark Publishing.

—Rays of the Sun Vol. 15: (Shoshone) Learn Lessons, 20 vols. Lenoir, Jane, illus. l.t. ed. 2004. (Story Keeper Ser.: 15). 48p. (J). lib. bdg. 22.60 (978-1-56763-931-5(3)) Ozark Publishing.

—Valley Oaks Acorns Vol. 20: (Maidu) Be Helpful, 20. Lenoir, Jane, illus. l.t. ed. 2004. (Story Keeper Ser.: 20). 48p. (J). pap. 6.95 (978-1-56763-942-1(9)) Ozark Publishing.

Sasso, Sandy Eisenberg. For Heaven's Sake. Finney, Kathryn Kunz, illus. 1999. 32p. (J). (ps-3). 16.95 (978-1-58023-054-4(7)) Jewish Lights Publishing.

Sathre, Vivian. Slender Ella & Her Fairy Hogfather. 1999. (Illus.). (J). (978-0-606-16212-8(7)) Tandem Library Bks.

Satterfield, Barbara. Answer Why for Mee Mee. 2004. (Illus.). 32p. (J). pap. 11.50 (978-0-9748715-1-6(6) , 314-004) Vision Harmony Publishing.

Savage, Deborah. Summer Hawk. 1999. 304p. (YA). (gr. 7-12). tchr. ed. 16.00 (978-0-395-91163-1(X)) Houghton Mifflin Co. Trade & Reference Div.

Savage, Tawanna. Anna Mischievous: The Early Years. 2005. Orig. Title: ANNA MISCHIEVOUS: the Early Years. (J). spiral bd. (978-0-9754147-9-8(8)) ASP Corp. Entertainment Group, Inc.

Saxild, Elizabeth. Katie Visits a Monastery. 1998. (Illus.). 50p. (YA). (gr. 4-12). pap. 6.00 (978-0-913026-47-2(6)) St. Nectarios Pr.

Say, Allen. Allison. 2004. (Illus.). 32p. (J). (gr. k-3). reprint ed. pap. 6.95 (978-0-618-49537-5(1) , Walter Lorraine) Houghton Mifflin Co. Trade & Reference Div.

Schick, Doris. The Summer of Missandra. Schulte, Mary K., illus. 1998. 208p. (Orig.). (J). (gr. 5-9). pap. 12.95 (978-1-880090-35-0(X)) Galde Pr., Inc.

Schindler, Nina. An Order of Amelie, Hold the Fries. Barrett, Robert, tr. from GER. 2004. (Illus.). 136p. (YA). (gr. 8). 18.95 (978-1-55037-861-0(9)); pap. 8.95 (978-1-55037-860-3(0)) Annick Pr., Ltd. CAN. *Dist:* Firefly Bks., Ltd.

Schraff, Anne. Black Widow Beauty, Set 1. 2002. 32p. (YA). 2.95 (978-1-56254-405-8(5) , SP 4055) Saddleback Educational Publishing.

Schrecengost, Maity. Panther Girl. Salazar, Sal, illus. 1999. 128p. (J). (gr. 3-5). pap. 5.95 (978-0-929895-29-1(0) , Hoot Owl Bks.) Maupin Hse. Publishing.

Scorcia, Yvonne M. Cindy Goes to Camp. 1998. 64p. (J). (gr. k-4). pap. 8.00 (978-0-8059-4521-8(0)) Dorrance Publishing Co., Inc.

Scott, James. Julie of the Wolves: Reproducible Teaching Unit. 1999. 20p. (YA). (gr. 7-12). ring bd. 29.50 (978-1-58049-096-2(4) , TU92) Prestwick Hse., Inc.

Scudamore, Beverly. Ready to Run. 2006. (Sports Stories Ser.). 96p. (J). (gr. 3-8). ***(978-1-55028-915-2(2));*** 7.95 (978-1-55028-914-5(4)) Lorimer, James & Co., Ltd., Pubs. CAN. *Dist:* Casemate Pubs. & Bk. Distributors, LLC.

Sculthorp, Jeffrey A. Heidi's Hike. Wingate, Lynae & Kober, John R., eds. Walter, Lorin, illus. 2000. (Wickleville Woods Ser.). 28p. (J). (ps-2). pap. 4.99 (978-1-889319-72-8(4) , Wickleville Woods) Trend Enterprises, Inc.

—Shelly's Race. Wingate, Lynae & Kober, John R., eds. Walter, Lorin, illus. 2000. (Wickleville Woods Ser.). 28p. (J). (ps-2). pap. 4.99 (978-1-889319-74-2(0) , Wickleville Woods) Trend Enterprises, Inc.

Seidler, Tor. Mean Margaret. Agee, Jon, illus. 2001. 176p. (J). (gr. 3 up). pap. 8.99 (978-0-06-441039-7(0) , Harper Trophy) HarperCollins Pubs.

Semel, Nava & Silveira, Carlos. Clases de Vuelo. Silveira, Carlos, tr. 2002. (Joven Coleccion Ser.). (SPA., Illus.). 206p. (978-84-89804-06-7(0)) Loguez Ediciones ESP. *Dist:* Lectorum Pubns., Inc.

Sendak, Jack. Circus Girl. 2002. (Sendak Reissues Ser.). (Illus.). 32p. (J). 13.89 (978-0-06-028784-9(5)) HarperCollins Pubs.

—Circus Girl. Sendak, Maurice, illus. 2002. (Sendak Reissues Ser.). 32p. reprint ed. 17.95 (978-0-06-028783-2(7)) HarperCollins Pubs.

Serros, Michele. Honey Blonde Chica. 2006. 304p. (YA). (gr. 9 up). 14.95 (978-1-4169-1591-1(5) , Simon Pulse) Simon & Schuster Children's Publishing.

Sewell, Anna. Black Beauty. (Great Classics for Children Ser.). (Illus.). 192p. (J). 5.99 (978-1-4037-0592-1(5)) Dalmatian Pr.

—Black Beauty. Aldous, Kate, illus. 2003. 288p. (J). 9.98 (978-1-4054-1675-7(0)) Parragon, Inc.

Seymour, Dorothy Z. & Mills, Dorothy. Ann Likes Red. Meyerhoff, Nancy, illus. 2001. 28p. (J). (ps-1). 8.95 (978-1-930900-12-7(0)) Purple Hse. Pr.

Shaw, Susan. Black-Eyed Suzie. (YA). (gr. 6-9). 2003. 176p. 15.95 (978-1-56397-729-9(X)); 2002. 167p. pap. 4.95 (978-1-56397-701-5(X)) Boyds Mills Pr.

Sheldon, Dyan. Confessions of a Teenage Drama Queen. braille ed. 2003. (J). (gr. 2). spiral bd. (978-0-616-15873-9(4)) Canadian National Institute for the Blind/Institut National Canadien pour les Aveugles.

—Confessions of a Teenage Drama Queen. 2002. (Illus.). 272p. (YA). (gr. 7-12). pap. 7.99 (978-0-7636-1848-3(9)) Candlewick Pr.

Sheth, Kashmira. Blue Jasmine. 2006. (Illus.). 192p. (gr. 4-7). reprint ed. pap. 5.99 (978-0-7868-5565-0(7)) Hyperion Pr.

Sheth, Kashmira. Keeping Corner. 2007. 288p. (YA). (gr. 7 up). 15.99 ***(978-0-7868-3859-2(0))*** Hyperion Pr.

Shi, Sharon. Arula's Special Day. Casillas, Roman, illus. rev. ed. 2000. 23p. (J). (ps-2). pap. 4.99 (978-0-9678636-3-4(5) , B004, Tattootles Bks.) Tattoo Manufacturing.

—Girlfriends. Sohn, Catherine Jung, illus. rev. ed. 2000. 15p. (J). (ps-2). pap. 4.99 (978-0-9678636-5-8(1) , B006, Tattootles Bks.) Tattoo Manufacturing.

Shofner, Myra. Kristina, New Girl on the Scene: A Christ Girl Book. 1999. 70p. (J). (gr. 4-7). pap. 4.95 (978-1-929228-03-4(1)) Southern Pub.

Shull, Megan. Amazing Grace. 2006. 256p. (gr. 6-9). pap. 6.99 (978-0-7868-5691-6(2)) Hyperion Pr.

Shull, Megan. Penelope. 2007. (J). (gr. 6-9). 15.99 ***(978-0-7868-3730-4(6))*** Hyperion Pr.

Shyamalan, M. Night. The Lady in the Water. 2006. (Illus.). 64p. (J). (ps-1). 17.99 (978-0-316-01734-3(5)) Little Brown & Co.

Sidney's Saddest Sunday. 2007. (J). per. 14.95 ***(978-0-9787913-4-6(7))*** Urban Moon Publishing.

Siefken, Paul. Smashing Lumpkins. 2001. (gr. k-3). lib. bdg. 11.80 (978-0-613-43890-2(6)) Tandem Library Bks.

Sills, Elizabeth & Patrice, Elena. Nana Star Book. Saker, Linda, illus. 2004. 15p. (J). 17.99 (978-0-9753843-0-5(9)) ee publishing & productions, inc.

Silva, Cheryl. Marni's Mirror. 1999. 115p. (J). (gr. 4-7). pap. 8.95 (978-0-87159-230-9(4)) Unity Schl. of Christianity.

Silver Dolphin en Español Staff. Imanes Magicos: Girlfriends: Magnets on the Move: Girlfriends, Spanish-Language Edition. 2006. (Illus.). 8p. (J). bds. 12.95 (978-970-718-371-1(3) , Silver Dolphin en Español) Advanced Marketing, S. de R. L. de C. V. MEX. *Dist:* Perseus Distribution.

Silverman, Erica. Cowgirl Kate & Cocoa. Lewin, Betsy, illus. 2005. (Cowgirl Kate & Cocoa Ser.). 44p. (J). 15.00 (978-0-15-202124-5(8)) Harcourt Trade Pubs.

—Partners. Lewin, Betsy, illus. 2006. (Cowgirl Kate & Cocoa Ser.). 44p. (J). 15.00 (978-0-15-202125-2(6)) Harcourt Children's Bks.

Simms, Jory. Scout's Honor #4. 2006. (Darcy's Wild Life Ser.: Vol. 4). 160p. (J). (gr. 2-4). pap. 4.99 (978-0-448-44261-7(2) , Grosset & Dunlap) Penguin Group (USA) Inc.

Simpson, Carolie. Allie Applebee — Can't Wait for Eight. 2003. 40p. pap. 9.95 (978-1-4137-0104-3(3)) PublishAmerica, Inc.

Simpson, Dorothy. A Lesson for Janie. Date not set. 190p. (J). 20.95 (978-0-8488-2617-8(5)) Amereon LTD.

Singh, Amrit Kaur & Singh, Rabindra Kaur. Bindhu's Weddings. Singh, Amrit Kaur & Singh, Rabindra Kaur, illus. 1999. (Illus.). 40p. (J). (ps-4). 12.95 (978-0-9700363-2-2(9)) Sikh Foundation.

Sinke, Janet Mary. Priscilla McdoodleNutMcDoodleMcMae Asks Why. Pennington, Craig, illus. 2007. 40p. (J). 17.95 (978-0-9742732-8-0(7)) My Grandma & Me Pubs.

Skolsky, Mindy Warshaw. Love from Your Friend, Hannah. 1999. (Illus.). 256p. (J). (gr. 3-7). pap. 6.99 (978-0-06-440746-5(2) , Harper Trophy) HarperCollins Pubs.

—Welcome to the Grand View, Hannah! 2000. (978-0-606-18727-5(8)) Tandem Library Bks.

Slater, David Michael. Flour Girl: A Recipe for Disaster. Brooks, S. G., illus. 2007. (Missy Swiss & More Ser.). 32p. (J). (ps-4). lib. bdg. 27.07 ***(978-1-60270-009-3(5)*** , Looking Glass Library) Magic Wagon.

Slater, Teddy. In-O Es No! 2003. Tr. of N-O Spells No!. (SPA.). (gr. k-3). lib. bdg. 11.80 (978-0-613-89264-3(X)) Tandem Library Bks.

Sleator, William. The Boy Who Reversed Himself. 1998. 176p. (J). (gr. 5-9). pap. 5.99 (978-0-14-038965-4(2) , Puffin) Penguin Group (USA) Inc.

Small, David. Ruby Mae Has Something to Say. 1999. (978-0-606-17345-2(5)) Tandem Library Bks.

Smith. Wanda Jean's Face. Date not set. 240p. (J). pap. 4.99 (978-0-06-440826-4(4)) HarperCollins Pubs.

Smith, Debra West. Hattie Marshall & the Hurricane. 2000. 144p. (J). (gr. 4-7). pap. 7.95 (978-1-56554-675-2(X)) Pelican Publishing Co., Inc.

Smith, George Harmon. Dark Delta Deep, Blue Goodbye. 2002. (ENG.). 156p. 21.95 ***(978-0-595-65454-3(1));*** 152p. (YA). pap. 11.95 (978-0-595-25946-5(4)) iUniverse, Inc. (Writers Club Pr.).

Smith, Kirsten. The Geography of Girlhood. 2007. 192p. (J). (gr. 7-17). pap. 7.99 (978-0-316-01735-0(3)) Little Brown & Co.

Smith, Linda. Wanda Jean's Face. 2000. (Illus.). 240p. (J). (gr. 3-7). 14.95 (978-0-06-028526-5(5)); lib. bdg. 14.89 (978-0-06-028525-8(7)) HarperCollins Pubs.

Smith, Sherwood. Crown Duel. 2002. (Firebird Ser.). (Illus.). 480p. (YA). pap. 7.99 (978-0-14-230151-7(5) , Puffin) Penguin Group (USA) Inc.

—Crown Duel. 2002. (gr. 5-8). lib. bdg. 16.45 (978-0-613-45255-7(0)) Tandem Library Bks.

Smucker, Barbara. Selina & the Bear Paw Quilt. Wilson, Janet, illus. 2002. 24p. (J). (978-0-7737-2992-6(5)) Stoddart Kids.

—Selina & the Bear Paw Quilt. Wilson, Janet, illus. 2002. 24p. 8.95 (978-0-7737-5837-7(2)) Stoddart Kids CAN. *Dist:* Fitzhenry & Whiteside, Ltd.

Snead, Shawn A. Dragon's Egg. 2002. 220p. pap. 14.95 (978-0-595-20964-4(5) , Writers Club Pr.) iUniverse, Inc.

Snyder, Zilpha Keatley. Janie's Private Eyes. 2001. 220p. (gr. 4-7). pap. 12.00 (978-0-375-89514-2(0) , Yearling) Random Hse. Children's Bks.

Soci Et E de La Faune Et Des Parcs Du Qu Ebec. Sarah de Cordoba. Sanchez, Andres & Tagle, illus. 2003. (SPA.). 130p. (J). pap. 4.99 (978-968-16-7020-7(5)) Fondo de Cultura Economica USA.

Sokoloff, David. Here I Am: For Girls. Sokoloff, David, illus. 1999. (Illus.). 10p. (J). (ps-3). 6.00 (978-1-889655-01-7(5)) Jewish Educational Toys.

Sophia, Constance. Wisdom of the Swan. 2002. 24p. (J). 3.95 (978-1-59094-019-8(9) , 1590940199) Jawbone Publishing Corp.

Sorensen, Virginia. Plain Girl. Geer, Charles, illus. 2003. 168p. (J). pap. 6.95 (978-0-15-204725-2(5) , Odyssey Classics) Harcourt Children's Bks.

—Plain Girl. 2003. (gr. 3-6). lib. bdg. 14.10 (978-0-613-84140-5(9)) Tandem Library Bks.

Soto, Gary. The Afterlife. 2005. 168p. (YA). reprint ed. pap. 6.95 (978-0-15-205220-1(8) , Harcourt Paperbacks) Harcourt Children's Bks.

Soulsby, H. M. Lucy. Stray Thoughts for Girls. 2006. 32.99 ***(978-1-4280-2808-1(0))*** IndyPublish.com.

Sparks, Beatrice. Annie's Baby: The Diary of Anonymous, a Pregnant Teenager. 1998. 12.64 (978-0-606-13145-2(0)) Tandem Library Bks.

Spinelli, Eileen. Lizzie Logan, Second Banana. 2000. (978-0-606-17827-3(9)) Tandem Library Bks.

Spinelli, Jerry. There's a Girl in My Hammerlock. 2002. (YA). 13.40 (978-0-7587-9582-3(3)) Book Wholesalers, Inc.

Spinelli, Patti. Mackenzie & Emma Visit York Beach. Spinelli, Patti, illus. 2003. (J). (978-0-9742328-0-5(7)) Spinelli, Patti.

The Spirited Philadelphia Adventure. 2000. (Illus.). 32p. (J). (gr. k-2). (978-0-9626959-1-9(2)) Junior League of Philadelphia, Inc.

Spyri, Johanna. Heidi. (J). 24.95 (978-0-8488-1179-2(8)) Amereon LTD.

—Heidi. 1999. (Andre Deutsch Classics). 316p. (J). 9.95 (978-0-233-99227-3(8)) Andre Deutsch GBR. *Dist:* Trafalgar Square Publishing.

—Heidi. 2001. (Young Reader's Classics Ser.). 94p. (J). pap. 9.95 (978-1-55013-971-6(1) , Key Porter kids) Key Porter Bks. CAN. *Dist:* Firefly Bks., Ltd.

—Heidi. 1998. (Children's Classics). (ENG., Illus.). 240p. (J). pap. (978-1-85326-125-1(4) , 1254WW) Wordsworth Editions, Ltd.

—Heidi Book & Charm. 2000. (Charming Classics). (J). (gr. 3-7). pap. 6.99 (978-0-694-01453-8(2) , Harper Festival) HarperCollins Pubs.

Stahl, Hilda. The Dangerous Double. 2001. (Elizabeth Gail Ser.: Vol. 4). (Illus.). 160p. (J). (gr. 4-7). mass mkt. 5.99 (978-0-8423-4070-0(X)) Tyndale Hse. Pubs.

Stanaszek, Mary Jane. Sara Wants to Know. 2005. 32p. (J). lib. bdg. 17.95 (978-1-59298-123-6(2)) Beaver's Pond Pr., Inc.

Stanley, John. Little Lulu Volume 13: Too Much Fun: Too Much Fun. 2006. (Illus.). 208p. pap. 9.95 (978-1-59307-621-4(5)) Dark Horse Comics.

Starks, Kimberly. Real Girls, Inc. 2005. 68p. pap. 14.95 (978-1-4137-7133-6(5)) PublishAmerica, Inc.

Staunton, Ted. Trouble with Girls. 2003. (gr. 3-6). lib. bdg. 12.95 (978-0-613-84452-9(1)) Tandem Library Bks.

Stegall, Billy Mark. Pat & Pea Soup. Archambault, Matthew, illus. 2003. (Books for Young Learners). 12p. (J). pap. 5.00 net. (978-1-57274-278-9(X) , 2757) Owen, Richard C. Pubs., Inc.

Steptoe, John L. Las Bellas Hijas de Mufaro. Kohen, Clarita, tr. Steptoe, John L., illus. unabr. ed. 1998. Tr. of Mufaro's Beautiful Daughters: An African Tale. (SPA., Illus.). (J). (gr. k-3). pap. 16.95 incl. audio (978-0-87499-461-2(6)) BBC Audiobooks America.

—Las Bellas Hijas de Mufaro. Kohen, Clarita, tr. Steptoe, John L., illus. 1998. Tr. of Mufaro's Beautiful Daughters: An African Tale. (SPA., Illus.). pap., tchr. ed. 41.95 incl. audio (978-0-87499-463-6(2)) Live Oak Media.

Sterling Publishing Co., Inc. & Fernleigh Books Staff. Snow White: A Magic 3-Dimensional Fairy-Tale World. 2006. (Step Inside Ser.). (Illus.). 12p. (J). 9.95 (978-1-4027-3656-8(8)) Sterling Publishing Co., Inc.

Sternberg, Libby. Uncovering Sadie's Secrets. 2005. (YA). (gr. 8-12). mass mkt. 5.99 (978-0-8439-5497-5(3) , SMOOCH) Dorchester Publishing Co., Inc.

Stewart, Dawn. Harriet's Horrible Hair Day. White, Michael, illus. 2000. 32p. (J). (ps-3). 15.95 (978-1-56145-165-4(7)) Peachtree Pubs., Ltd.

Stewart, Jane L. The Camp Fire Girls at Long Lake. rev. ed. 2006. (ENG.). 140p. 25.95 (978-1-4218-2057-6(9) , 1st World Library - Literary Society) 1st World Publishing, Inc.

—The Camp Fire Girls at Long Lake or Bessie King in Summer Camp. 2004. reprint ed. pap. 15.95 (978-1-4191-5574-1(1)); pap. 1.99 (978-1-4192-5574-8(6)) Kessinger Publishing, LLC.

—A Campfire Girl's Test of Friendship. 2004. reprint ed. pap. 26.95 (978-1-4179-3874-2(9)) Kessinger Publishing, LLC.

Stewart, Melanie. Hitting the Slopes. 1999. (gr. 3-6). lib. bdg. 11.80 (978-0-613-27877-5(1)) Tandem Library Bks.

—Pushing the Limits. 1999. (gr. 3-6). lib. bdg. 11.80 (978-0-613-28030-3(X)) Tandem Library Bks.

—Stage Fright. 1999. (gr. 3-6). lib. bdg. 11.80 (978-0-613-28086-0(5)) Tandem Library Bks.

Stine, R. L. Dangerous Girls. 2004. 320p. (YA). (gr. 7 up). pap. 6.99 (978-0-06-053082-2(0)) HarperCollins Pubs.

Stoeke, Janet Morgan. A Hat for Minerva Louise. Stoeke, Janet Morgan, illus. 2002. (Minerva Louise Ser.). (Illus.). (J). 13.19 (978-0-7587-2701-5(1)) Book Wholesalers, Inc.

—A Hat for Minerva Louise. 2nd ed. 2002. (Illus.). (978-0-525-46875-2(7) , Dutton Juvenile) Penguin Group (USA) Inc.

—Minerva Louise at School. Stoeke, Janet Morgan, illus. 2002. (Minerva Louise Ser.). (Illus.). (J). 13.19 (978-0-7587-3139-5(6)) Book Wholesalers, Inc.

—Minerva Louise at School. Stoeke, Janet Morgan, illus. 2nd ed. 2002. (Illus.). (978-0-525-46876-9(5) , Dutton Juvenile) Penguin Group (USA) Inc.

—Minerva Louise at School. 1999. (978-0-606-17420-6(6)) Tandem Library Bks.

Stone, Phoebe. Go Away, Shelley Boo! Stone, Phoebe, illus. 1999. (Illus.). 32p. (J). (ps-3). 15.95 (978-0-316-81677-9(1)) Little, Brown Bks. for Young Readers.

Storad, Conrad J. Don't Call Me Pig: A Javelina Story. 1999. (Illus.). 32p. (J). 15.95 (978-1-891795-03-9(1)) RGU Group, The.

Stories for Girls. 2007. 512p. pap. 14.95 ***(978-1-84236-586-1(X))*** Miles Kelly Publishing, Ltd. GBR. *Dist:* National Bk. Network.

The Story of Jacqueline. 2004. (Illus.). 36p. (J). per. 12.95 (978-0-9762911-0-7(X)) Ameeramac Reporting, Inc.

Stouffer, N. K. Lilly Laughs. Stouffer, N. K., illus. 2001. (Larry Potter Storybks.). (Illus.). 22p. (J). (ps-2). 7.95 (978-1-58989-301-6(8)) Thurman Hse., LLC.

Strategy Guide: Secret of the Scarlet Hand. 2002. 9.99 (978-0-9672618-8-1(0)) Her Interactive, Inc.

Strong, Jeremy. It's a Tough Life. l.t. ed. 2005. (J). pap. (978-0-7540-7933-0(3) , CLP 487) BBC Audio.

Stroschin, Jane H. Emma Lou & the Reindeer Flu. Stroschin, Jane H., illus. 1998. (Illus.). 32p. (J). (ps-6). lib. bdg. 15.00 (978-1-883960-15-5(0)) Henry Quill Pr.

Stuve-Bodeen, Stephanie. Muneca de Elizabeti. 2000. (SPA.). (gr. k-3). lib. bdg. 15.25 (978-0-613-27986-4(7)) Tandem Library Bks.

Suarez, Maribel, illus. Rebecca. (Rowing Frog's Rhymes Ser.). 16p. (J). (gr. k-3). 7.95 (978-1-59437-840-9(1)) Santillana USA Publishing Co., Inc.

Summers, Katani. Style in with Katani. 2004. (Illus.). 36p. (J). 3.99 (978-0-9746587-3-5(1) , Beacon Street Girls) B*tween Productions, Inc.

Sunderland, Margot & Hancock, Nicky. How Hattie Hated Kindness: A Story for Children Locked in Rage or Hate. Armstrong, Nicky, tr. Armstrong, Nicky, illus. 30p. pap. (978-0-86388-461-0(X) , 002-5145) Speechmark Publishing Ltd.

Surget, Alain. Tirya y el Complot del Nilo. 2004. Tr. of Tirya & the Conspiracy in the Nile. (SPA.). 208p. (978-84-95618-50-4(8) , Umbriel) Ediciones Urano S. A.

Swain, Gwenyth. I Wonder As I Wander. Himler, Ronald, illus. 2005. 32p. (J). (gr. k-17). pap. 8.00 (978-0-8028-5298-4(X) , Eerdmans Bks For Young Readers) Eerdmans, William B. Publishing Co.

Sweetser, Kate Dickinson. Boys & girls from Thackeray. l.t. ed. 2006. 264p. pap. 13.99 ***(978-1-4264-3943-8(1))*** BiblioBazaar.

Swensen, Karen. Catherine the Great & Her Teatime Tagalongs. Kirkman, Kelly, illus. 2005. 28p. (J). (gr. k-3). per. 15.95 (978-1-58980-343-5(4)) Pelican Publishing Co., Inc.

Swindells, Jacqueline Hyde. 2000. (Illus.). 159p. (J). 16.95 (978-0-385-40508-9(1)) Transworld Publishers Ltd. GBR. *Dist:* Trafalgar Square Publishing.

Sydor, Colleen. Smarty pants. Langlois, Suzane, illus. 2nd rev. ed. 2003. 32p. (J). (gr. 1-5). (978-1-894222-62-4(8)) Lobster Pr.

Sydow, Dena J. A Day of Smiles with Marlee: A Story Told Using American Sign Language. Bock, Jane M., illus. 1998. 32p. (J). (ps-6). pap. 8.95 (978-0-9661631-0-0(9)) Pumpkin Pr.

Tada, Joni Eareckson & Jensen, Steve. The Amazing Secret. 2000. (Darcy & Friends Ser.: Vol. 1). 127p. (J). (gr. 4-7). pap. 5.99 (978-1-58134-197-3(0) , Crossway Bibles) Crossway Bks.

Takahashi, Rumiko. Inu Yasha Animanga. 2007. (Inuyasha Ani-Manga Ser.). 216p. (YA). Vol. 19. pap. 11.99 (978-1-4215-0903-7(2)); Vol. 20. pap. 11.99 (978-1-4215-0904-4(0)) Viz Media.

—Inuyasha, Vol. 29. 2007. (Inuyasha Ser.). 192p. (YA). pap. 8.95 (978-1-4215-0900-6(8)) Viz Media.

Takemoto, Novala. Kamikaze Girls. 2006. (Kamikaza Girls Novel Ser.). (Illus.). 208p. (YA). pap. 8.99 (978-1-4215-0268-7(2)) Viz Media.

—Kamikaze Girls Novel, Vol. 1. 2006. (Kamikaza Girls Novel Ser.). 208p. (YA). 17.99 (978-1-4215-0269-4(0)) Viz Media.

Takeuchi, Naoko. Sailor Moon, 11 vols. (Illus.). 184p. (gr. 7-12). Vol. 2. 2nd rev. ed. 1998. (Sailor Moon Ser.: Vol. 2). pap. 9.99 (978-1-892213-05-1(2)); Vol. 3. 3rd rev. ed. 1999. pap. 9.99 (978-1-892213-06-8(0)) TOKYOPOP, Inc.

—Sailor Moon Supers, Vol. 3. 3rd rev. ed. 2000. (Illus.). 160p. (gr. 7-12). pap. 9.99 (978-1-892213-26-6(5)) TOKYOPOP, Inc.

Taniguchi, Tomoko. Just a Girl, 2 bks., Bk. 1. Pannone, Frank, ed. Hiroe, Ikoi, tr. from JPN. Taniguchi, Tomoko, illus. 2004. (Illus.). 184p. (YA). pap. 9.99 (978-1-58664-911-1(6) , CMX 64801G, CPM Manga) Central Park Media Corp.

Tashjian, Janet. Multiple Choice. 1999. (J). (gr. 5-10). 16.95 (978-0-8050-6114-7(2) , Holt, Henry & Co. Bks. For Young Readers) Holt, Henry & Co.

—Multiple Choice. 2001. 192p. (YA). (gr. 5-9). pap. 4.99 (978-0-439-17484-8(8)) Scholastic, Inc.

Tate, Nikki. No Cafes in Narnia: A Mystery on Tarragon Island. 2001. 174p. (J). (gr. 3-7). pap. 7.95 (978-1-55039-107-7(0)) Sono Nis Pr. CAN. *Dist:* Orca Bk. Pubs. USA.

Tate, Susan, illus. Pentalia. 2002. 109p. (Orig.). (J). (gr. 3-7). pap. 13.95 (978-0-9647783-0-6(0)) Sunflower Pr.

Taylor, Kim. Bowery Girl. 2006. 240p. (YA). (gr. 9). 16.99 (978-0-670-05966-9(8) , Viking Juvenile) Penguin Group (USA) Inc.

—Cissy Funk. Date not set. 224p. (YA). (gr. 5 up). mass mkt. 4.99 (978-0-06-440880-6(9)) HarperCollins Pubs.

Teacher Talk: Individual Title Six-Packs. (ps-2). 27.00 (978-0-7635-9477-0(6)) Rigby Education.

Thal, Michael I. The Legend of Koolura. 2002. 176p. (J). pap. (978-1-55313-179-3(7)) Adventure Bk. Pubs.

Thesman, Jean. Meredith. 1998. (Elliott Cousins Ser.: No. 2). (YA). (gr. 7 up). pap. 3.99 (978-0-380-78682-4(6)) HarperCollins Pubs.

This & That, 6 Packs. (ps-2). 23.00 (978-0-7635-8812-0(1)) Rigby Education.

Thomas, Alisa. Anne of Green Gables. 2001. 72p. (J). stu. ed., ring bd. 12.99 (978-1-58609-179-8(4)) Progeny Pr.

Thomas, Jane Resh. Maggie & Ruby. 1999. (J). (978-0-7868-0188-6(3)) Hyperion Pr.

Thompson, Kay. Eloise the Absolutely Essential Edition. Knight, Hilary, illus. 1999. 80p. (J). (ps-3). 19.95 (978-0-689-82703-7(2)) Simon & Schuster Children's Publishing.

—Eloise the Ultimate Edition. Knight, Hilary, illus. 2000. 304p. (J). (ps-3). 39.99 (978-0-689-83990-0(1)) Simon & Schuster Children's Publishing.

—Eloise's Guide to Life: Or, How to Eat, Dress, Travel, Behave, & Stay Six Forever. Knight, Hilary, illus. 2000. (Eloise Ser.). 48p. (J). (ps-3). 9.95 (978-0-689-83310-6(5)) Simon & Schuster Children's Publishing.

—Kay Thompson's Eloise: A Book for Precocious Grown-Ups. Knight, Hilary, illus. 2000. 65p. (J). per. (978-0-689-82795-2(4) , Simon & Schuster Children's Publishing) Simon & Schuster Children's Publishing.

Thompson, Kay & Knight, Hilary. Eloise at Christmastime. 1999. (Illus.). 56p. (J). (ps-3). 17.95 (978-0-689-83039-6(4)) Simon & Schuster Children's Publishing.

—Eloise in Moscow. 40th ed. 2000. (Illus.). 80p. (J). (ps-3). 17.00 (978-0-689-83211-6(7)) Simon & Schuster Children's Publishing.

Thong, Roseanne. Tummy Girl. Williams, Sam, illus. rev. ed. 2007. 32p. (J). (ps-k). 15.95 (978-0-8050-7609-7(3) , Holt, Henry & Co. Bks. For Young Readers) Holt, Henry & Co.

Thorpe and Hunt Staff. Merry the Lamb Sails with Noah. 1998. (Illus.). 16p. (978-1-85608-286-0(5)) Hunt, John Publishing Ltd.

Tich, Jan. Pope & Ba. 2006. (Adventures in Unusual Places Ser.). (Illus.). 28p. (J). 12.95 (978-9974-7925-8-6(4)) Hardenville SA URY. *Dist:* Independent Pubs. Group.

Tilley, Jessica. You Have to Be Smart If You're Going to be Tall. Evans, Leslie, illus. 2006. 46p. (J). per. 16.99 ***(*978-1-59879-217-1(2))*** Lifevest Publishing, Inc.

Tinkler, David. Revenge of the Dinner Ladies. l.t. ed. 2005. (J). pap. (978-0-7540-7804-3(3) , CLP 185) BBC Audio.

Tisdell, Wendy & Takhar, Jodi. Angela Goes to Daycare. 14p. (J). (ps-3). 19.95 (978-1-886000-01-8(8)) Takhar's, Jodi Spilt Milk Collection.

Tomarelli, Patti Rae & Cowper-Thomas, Wendy. Maggie Celebrates Ayybam-I-Ha. 1999. (Illus.). (J). (978-0-87743-276-0(7)) Baha'i Publishing Trust, U.S.

Tomasi, Joseph. Miss Wheezer Comes to Stay. 2006. 48p. pap. 12.95 (978-1-4241-3703-9(9)) PublishAmerica, Inc.

Too Many Clothes: Individual Title Six-Packs. (Literatura 2000 Ser.). (gr. k-1). 28.00 (978-0-7635-0068-9(2)) Rigby Education.

Torba, Ed. The Magic Trip. Hansen, Kate, illus. 2002. (YA). per. 15.00 (978-0-9765748-0-4(2)) Torba Publishing.

Torres, Melissa & A&J Studios Staff. Under the Sea. 2006. (Dora the Explorer Ser.). 8p. (J). 6.99 (978-1-4169-1427-3(7) , Simon Spotlight/Nickelodeon) Simon & Schuster Children's Publishing.

Torrey, Michele. Sisters unto Death. 1999. 222p. (YA). (gr. 7-17). pap. 9.99 (978-0-88092-371-2(7) , 3717) Royal Fireworks Publishing Co.

Towell, Katy. The Little Girl Who Was Forgotten by Absolutely Everyone (Even the Postman) 2005. 56p. (YA). pap. 16.99 (978-1-4116-5919-3(8)) Lulu.com.

Towles, LaRhonda. Ginger & Cocoa Island. Kirkpatrick, Philip, illus. 1998. i, 16p. (J). (ps-k). pap. 5.95 (978-0-9667894-0-9(7)) Towles, LaRhonda.

Tracey & the Sun: Individual Title, 6 packs. (Sails Literacy Ser.). 16p. (gr. 2-3). 27.00 (978-0-7578-0710-7(0)) Rigby Education.

Traffic Jam: Individual Title Six-Packs. (ps-2). 27.00 (978-0-7635-9479-4(2)) Rigby Education.

Trayer, Edward H. Struggles of Felicity Brady: Articulus Quest. 2005. (YA). per. 14.95 (978-1-59571-091-8(4)) Word Association Pubs.

Trebi-Ollennu, Flora. A Big Christmas Surprise for Sweetie Awo. Burgesson, Kate & Adu Nyarko, Margaret M., illus. 2000. (Sunbeamy Kids Ser.). 90p. (J). (gr. 4-6). pap. (978-1-894718-00-4(3)) Amerley Treb Bks.

Tregebov, Rhea. What-If Sara. Franson, Leanne, illus. 2000. 12p. (J). (ps-3). 10.95 (978-1-896764-22-1(3)); pap. 4.95 (978-1-896764-20-7(7)) Second Story Pr. CAN. *Dist:* Orca Bk. Pubs. USA.

Tremlin, Nathan, et al. Mookie: A Girl in Maximsubornia. Tremlin, Nathan & Chomiak, Joseph, illus. 2004. 48p. (J). (gr. 4-8). reprint ed. 18.00 (978-0-7567-9081-3(6)) DIANE Publishing Co.

Tripp, Valerie. Brave Emily. 2006. (Illus.). 85p. (J). 12.95 ***(*978-1-59369-211-7(0)*** , American Girl) American Girl Publishing, Inc.

—Brave Emily. Backes, Nick, illus. 2006. (American Girl Ser.). 85p. (J). (gr. 2-4). pap. 6.95 (978-1-59369-210-0(2) , American Girl) American Girl Publishing, Inc.

—Cambios para Josefina: Un Cuento de Invierno. 1998. (American Girls Collection: Bk. 6). (SPA.). (YA). (gr. 2 up). 12.75 (978-0-606-13241-1(4)) Tandem Library Bks.

—Josefina Entra en Accion: Un Cuento de Verano. Tibbles, Jean-Paul, illus. 1998. (American Girls Collection: Bk. 5). Tr. of Josefina Saves the Day. (SPA.). (YA). (gr. 2 up). 12.75 (978-0-606-13540-5(5)) Tandem Library Bks.

—Josefina's Boxed Set: Meet Josefina; Josefina Learns a Lesson; Josefina's Surprise; Happy Birthday, Josefina; Josefina Saves the Day; Changes for Josefina, 6 bks. Tibbles, Jean-Paul & McAliley, Susan, illus. 1998. (American Girls Collection: Bks. 1-6). (J). 39.95 (978-1-56247-675-5(0)); 432p. (gr. 2-7). 74.95 (978-1-56247-676-2(9)) American Girl Publishing, Inc.

—Josefina's Craft Book: A Look at Crafts from the Past with Projects You Can Make Today. 1998. (American Girls Collection). (YA). (gr. 2 up). (978-0-606-13543-6(X)) Tandem Library Bks.

—Very Funny, Elizabeth! Andreasen, Dan, illus. 2005. (American Girls Collection). 81p. (J). (gr. 3). pap. 6.95 (978-1-59369-061-8(4) , American Girl) American Girl Publishing, Inc.

Trombley, Cyndi. According to Abbey. 2005. (J). 22.00 (978-1-59858-087-7(6)); (YA). per. 14.00 (978-1-59858-014-3(0)) Dog Ear Publishing, LLC.

Troulis, Jennifer. Penelope & Prisilla & the Enchanted House of Whispers, 2004. 240p. (YA). per. 13.95 (978-0-9741805-5-7(6)) American LaserTechnic.

Trudel, Sylvain. Les Dimanches de Julie. Langlois, Suzane, illus. 2002. (Premier Roman Ser.). (FRE.). 64p. (J). (gr. 2-5). pap. (978-2-89021-317-3(X)) Diffusion du livre Mirabel.

Trump, Fred. Lincoln's Little Girl: A True Story. 2003. (Illus.). 184p. (YA). (gr. 4-6). pap. 11.95 (978-1-56397-852-4(0)) Boyds Mills Pr.

—Lincoln's Little Girl: A True Story. 1999. (gr. 7-12). lib. bdg. 19.90 (978-0-613-28926-9(9)) Tandem Library Bks.

Try Again, Emma: Individual Title Six-Pack Pouch - Level J. (Lighthouse Ser.). 16p. (gr. 2 up). 28.00 (978-0-7578-0859-3(X)) Rigby Education.

Turcotte, Elise. La Legon d'Annette. 1999. (La Courte Echelle Premier Roman Ser.). (FRE., Illus.). 64p. (J). (gr. 2-5). pap. (978-2-89021-338-8(2)) Diffusion du livre Mirabel.

Turcotte, Elise & Barrette, Doris. Les Cahiers d'Annette. 2002. (Premier Roman Ser.). (FRE., Illus.). 64p. (J). (gr. 2-5). pap. (978-2-89021-325-8(0)) Diffusion du livre Mirabel.

Turner Curtis, Alice. Little Maid of Mohawk Valley. 2004. (Little Maid Ser.). 192p. (J). (gr. 1-3). per. 9.95 (978-1-55709-337-0(7)) Applewood Bks.

Turner, Deirdre. Lilac Sky. 2005. 60p. pap. 12.95 (978-1-4137-9316-1(9)) PublishAmerica, Inc.

Two Smart Cookies. 2005. 44p. (J). 3.99 (978-0-9763213-5-4(1)) OHC Group LLC.

Tytler, Sarah. Girlhood & Womanhood the Story of Some. 2007. 43.99 ***(*978-1-4280-5160-7(0))***; pap. 36.99 ***(*978-1-4280-5161-4(9))*** IndyPublish.com.

Ueda, Miwa. Change of Heart. Yoshimoto, Ray, tr. from JPN. rev. ed. 2003. (Peach Girl Ser.: Vol. 2). (Illus.). 192p. (gr. 7 up). pap. 9.99 (978-1-59182-195-3(9) , Tokyopop Adult) TOKYOPOP, Inc.

—Change of Heart, 1. 2003. (Illus.). 192p. (gr. 7 up). pap. 9.99 (978-1-931514-19-4(4) , Tokyopop Adult) TOKYOPOP, Inc.

—Change of Heart, 11 , 8. Yoshimoto, Ray, tr. rev. ed. 2004. (Illus.). 192p. pap. 9.99 (978-1-59182-497-8(4) , Tokyopop Adult) TOKYOPOP, Inc.

—Change of Heart, 11. rev. ed. (Illus.). 192p. 9. 2004. pap. 9.99 (978-1-59182-498-5(2)); Vol. 3. 2003. (gr. 7 up). pap. 9.99 (978-1-59182-196-0(7)) TOKYOPOP, Inc. (Tokyopop Adult).

—Peach Girl. 2002. Vol. 3. 3rd rev. ed. 184p. (gr. 8-12). pap. 9.99 (978-1-931514-13-2(5)); Vol. 4. 4th rev. ed. 184p. (gr. 8-12). pap. 9.99 (978-1-931514-14-9(3)); Vol. 5. 5th rev. ed. 184p. pap. 9.99 (978-1-931514-15-6(1)); Vol. 6. 6th rev. ed. 176p. pap. 9.99 (978-1-931514-16-3(X)); Vol. 7. 7th rev. ed. 184p. pap. 9.99 (978-1-931514-17-0(8)) TOKYOPOP, Inc.

Ueda, Miwa, creator. Peach Girl: Limited Collector's Edition, 2 Vols., Vol. 5-8. collector's ltd. ed. 2004. (Illus.). 768p. pap. 39.99 (978-1-59532-170-1(5) , Tokyopop Adult) TOKYOPOP, Inc.

Umansky, Kaye. Wilma's Wicked Revenge. l.t. ed. 2000. (Illus.). 264p. (J). pap. (978-0-7540-6124-3(8) , CLP 318) BBC Audio.

Ungerer, Tomi. Adelaide. 1999. (Illus.). 40p. (J). (ps-4). pap. 5.95 (978-1-57098-296-5(1)) Rinehart, Roberts Pubs.

Unobagha, Uzo. Grandma, How Do You Say I Love You? Krassa, Victoria, illus. 2007. 28p. (J). 16.95 (978-0-9773180-0-1(1)) Adonoke Inc.

Uram, Maggie. Good Night Good Knight. 2004. (Illus.). 39p. (J). per. (978-1-932077-38-4(3)) Athena Pr.

Ure, Jean. Boys on the Brain. l.t. ed. 2005. (Illus.). 184p. (J). pap. incl. audio (978-0-7540-7859-3(0) , CLP 450) BBC Audio.

—Boys on the Brain. 2002. (Diary Ser.). (Illus.). 208p. (J). pap. 9.99 (978-0-00-711373-6(0)) HarperCollins Pubs. Ltd. GBR. *Dist:* Independent Pubs. Group.

—The Secret Life of Sally Tomato. l.t. ed. 2006. pap. 16.95 (978-1-4056-6018-1(X)) BBC Audio GBR. *Dist:* BBC Audiobooks America.

Uslan, Michael E. Chatterbox: The Bird Who Wore Glasses. Gurney, John Steven, illus. 2006. 34p. (J). 17.99 (978-0-9753843-2-9(5)) ee publishing & productions, inc.

Ustaris, Steven, illus. Lannett Runs Off. 2000. (It's up to You Ser.). 109p. (YA). per. 8.95 (978-0-9726099-3-7(8)) BurnsBooks.

Vallejo-Nagera, Alejandra. Los Bigotes de Chocolate. 2003. (SPA., Illus.). 27p. (J). (gr. k-1). 8.95 (978-968-19-1020-4(6)) Santillana USA Publishing Co., Inc.

Van Draanen, Wendelin. How I Survived Being a Girl. (J). 2003. (Illus.). 176p. pap. 5.99 (978-0-06-054073-9(7)); 1998. 288p. (gr. 3-7). pap. 4.95 (978-0-06-440725-0(X) , Harper Trophy) HarperCollins Pubs.

Van Dyne, Edith. Mary Louise. 2006. 148p. pap. 10.99 (978-1-4264-1952-2(X)); 144p. pap. 13.99 (978-1-4264-2063-4(3)) BiblioBazaar.

Van Horne, Mary Anne. Genevieve. 2000. 350p. (YA). (gr. 9 up). pap. 12.95 (978-1-893221-03-1(2)) Pendleton Bks.

Van Leeuwen, Jean. Hannah of Fairfield. Diamond, Donna, illus. 2000. (Pioneer Daughters Ser.: No. 1). 96p. (J). (gr. 2-5). pap. 5.99 (978-0-14-130499-1(5) , Puffin) Penguin Group (USA) Inc.

—Hannah of Fairfield. 2000. (Puffin Chapters Ser.). 11.79 (978-0-606-17867-9(8)); (gr. 3-6). lib. bdg. 13.00 (978-0-613-25446-5(5)) Tandem Library Bks.

—Hannah's Helping Hands. Diamond, Donna, illus. 2000. (Pioneer Daughters Ser.: No. 2). 96p. (J). (gr. 2-5). pap. 5.99 (978-0-14-130500-4(2) , Puffin) Penguin Group (USA) Inc.

—Hannah's Helping Hands. 2000. (Puffin Chapters Ser.). 12.79 (978-0-606-18842-5(8)); (gr. 3-6). lib. bdg. 14.15 (978-0-613-28514-8(X)) Tandem Library Bks.

Vandercook, Margaret. The Camp Fire Girls at Sunrise Hill. 2005. 26.95 (978-1-4218-0977-9(X) , 1st World Library - Literary Society) 1st World Publishing, Inc.

—The Camp Fire Girls at Sunrise Hill. 2004. reprint ed. pap. 19.95 (978-1-4191-5576-5(8)); pap. 1.99 (978-1-4192-5576-2(2)) Kessinger Publishing, LLC.

Vandercook, Margaret. Camp Fire Girls at Sunrise Hill, the (Fi. 2006. pap. 55.99 ***(*978-1-4219-9140-5(3))*** IndyPublish.com.

Varela, Gabrielle. Disney Girls: Untitled - Book #13. 2005. 128p. (J). pap. 3.99 (978-0-7868-4277-3(6)) Disney Pr.

Vaughan, Marcia. Abbie Against the Storm: The True Story of a Young Heroine & a Lighthouse. Farnsworth, Bill, illus. 1999. 30p. (J). (gr. 1-3). 15.95 (978-1-58270-007-6(9)) Beyond Words Publishing, Inc.

Vicary, Tim & Hedge, Tricia. Grace Darling, Level 2. 2000. (Bookworms Ser.). (Illus.). 64p. 6.50 (978-0-19-422974-6(2)) Oxford Univ. Pr., Inc.

Vick, Helen Hughes. Charlotte. 1999. (Courage of the Stone Ser.: Vol. 2). (Illus.). 128p. (gr. 4-7). pap. 9.95 (978-1-57098-282-8(1)) Rinehart, Roberts Pubs.

Vilcoq, Marianne. Espero un Hermanito. (SPA.). 24p. (J). (978-84-8470-013-5(5)) Corimbo, Editorial S.L. ESP. *Dist:* Lectorum Pubns., Inc.

Vogelaar, Alie. No Place to Go. Bazen, Edith, tr. from DUT. Visser, Rino, illus. 2001. 114p. (YA). lib. bdg. 10.95 (978-0-9670728-7-6(5)) Early Foundations Pubs.

Vogl, Nancy & Strange, David. Grandma Loves Her Harley Too. Gibson, Nichoel, illus. ed. 2006. (J). per. 16.95 (978-0-9772771-1-7(9)) Cherry Tree Pr. LLC.

Voigt, Cynthia. Elske: A Novel of the Kingdom. Vermeer, Jan, illus. 2003. (Kingdom Ser.). 320p. (YA). mass mkt. 5.99 (978-0-689-86438-4(8) , Simon Pulse) Simon & Schuster Children's Publishing.

—Elske: A Novel of the Kingdom. 2001. (Kingdom Ser.). (gr. 7-12). lib. bdg. 18.80 (978-0-613-73327-4(4)) Tandem Library Bks.

—It's Not Easy Being Bad. 2002. (Bad Girls Ser.). 256p. (J). (gr. 4-7). pap. 4.99 (978-0-689-85115-5(4) , Aladdin) Simon & Schuster Children's Publishing.

—It's Not Easy Being Bad. 2002. (Bad Girls Ser.). (gr. 3 6). lib. bdg. 13.00 (978-0-613-45069-0(8)) Tandem Library Bks.

—Izzy, Willy-Nilly. unabr. ed. 2004. 280p. (J). (gr. 7 up). pap. 46.00 incl. audio (978-0-8072-8763-7(6) , YA260SP, Listening Library) Random Hse. Audio Publishing Group.

von Ziegesar, Cecily. Don't You Forget about Me. 11th ed. 2007. 304p. (YA). (gr. 9 up). pap. 10.99 ***(*978-0-316-01184-6(3)*** , Poppy) Little, Brown Bks. for Young Readers.

—Unforgettable. 2007. (It Girl Ser.: No. 4). 288p. (YA). (gr. 10-17). pap. 9.99 ***(*978-0-316-11348-9(4)*** , Poppy) Little, Brown Bks. for Young Readers.

von Ziegesar, Cecily. You Know You Love Me. 2nd ed. 2002. (Gossip Girl Ser.: Bk. 2). (Illus.). 240p. (YA). (gr. 10-17). pap. 10.99 (978-0-316-91148-1(8) , Poppy) Little, Brown Bks. for Young Readers.

—You Know You Love Me. 2002. (Gossip Girl Ser.: No. 2). (YA). (gr. 7-12). lib. bdg. 17.35 (978-0-613-56955-2(5)) Tandem Library Bks.

Voss, Fonda. The Bossy Girl. l.t. ed. 2005. (Illus.). 30p. (J). 15.95 (978-1-932338-44-7(6)) Lifevest Publishing, Inc.

Wacik-Lynch, Rosemary. Round Maureen. 1999. (J). (gr. 1-4). pap. 7.95 (978-0-533-12867-9(6)) Vantage Pr., Inc.

Waddell, Martin. Mimi & the Dream House. 2002. (Illus.). (J). 12.34 (978-0-7587-3136-4(1)) Book Wholesalers, Inc.

—Mimi & the Picnic. 2002. (Illus.). (J). 12.34 (978-0-7587-3137-1(X)) Book Wholesalers, Inc.

Wade, Ellen A. Sarah's Friend Peanuts. Schneider, Rex, illus. 1999. 28p. (J). (gr. 2-4). pap. 8.00 (978-0-9653635-1-8(1)) LNA Publishing.

Waghorn. Message for the Media. 1999. 144p. (J). pap. 11.99 (978-0-7043-4950-6(7)) Women's Pr., Ltd., The GBR. *Dist:* Independent Pubs. Group.

Waite, Judy. Forbidden. 2006. 256p. (YA). 16.95 (978-0-689-87642-4(4) , Atheneum) Simon & Schuster Children's Publishing.

Walker, Craig, ed. Mystery Stories for Girls. 2006. 432p. (J). pap. 5.99 (978-0-439-85858-8(5) , Scholastic) Scholastic, Inc.

Wallace, Barbara Brooks. Claudia. 2000. 196p. (gr. 4-7). pap. 12.95 (978-0-595-15338-1(0) , Backinprint.com) iUniverse, Inc.

Walsh, Suella. The Case of Erica's Weird Behavior. 79p. (J). (gr. 3-6). 9.99 (978-0-88092-093-3(9)) Royal Fireworks Publishing Co.

Walters, Eric. Elixir. 2007. 192p. (J). pap. 6.99 (978-0-14-301641-0(5) , Penguin Global) Penguin Group (USA) Inc.

Walters, Jennie. Shelter from the Storm. 2007. (Swallowcliffe Hall Trilogy: Book 3 Ser.). (Illus.). 240p. (J). pap. 9.99 ***(*978-0-689-87528-1(2))*** Simon & Schuster, Ltd. GBR. *Dist:* Independent Pubs. Group.

Walton, O. F. A Peep Behind the Scenes: A Little Girl's Journey of Discovery. 1999. 256p. (J). mass mkt. (978-1-85792-524-1(6) , Christian Heritage) Christian Focus Pubns.

Ward, Barbara Briggs. The Really REALLY Hairy Flight of Snarly Sally. (Illus.). 32p. (ps-3). 14.95 (978-1-890621-23-0(4)) Landauer Corp.

Ward, Cindy. Cookie's Week. de Paola, Tomie, illus. 2002. (J). 13.19 (978-0-7587-2273-7(7)) Book Wholesalers, Inc.

Warner, Sally. Finding Hattie: A Novel. 2004. 227p. (YA). (gr. 4-8). reprint ed. 16.00 (978-0-7567-8107-1(8)) DIANE Publishing Co.

—Hattie's Year. (J). Date not set. 160p. pap. 4.99 (978-0-06-440793-9(4)); 2001. 240p. (gr. 5 up). 15.95 (978-0-06-028464-0(1)) HarperCollins Pubs.

—Private Lily. 1999. (978-0-606-16569-3(X)) Tandem Library Bks.

—Quinney Novel, 2. Date not set. 224p. (J). (gr. 3-7). 4.99 (978-0-06-440763-2(2)) HarperCollins Pubs.

—Sweet & Sour Lily. 1999. (978-0-606-16570-9(3)) Tandem Library Bks.

Watanabe, Taeko. Kaze Hikaru, Vol. 4. 2007. (Kaze Hikaru Ser.). 200p. (YA). pap. 8.99 (978-1-4215-1017-0(0)) Viz Media.

Watase, Yuu. Genbu Kaiden, Vol. 4. Watase, Yuu, illus. 2006. (Fushigi Yugi Ser.). 208p. (YA). pap. 8.99 (978-1-4215-0579-4(7)) Viz Media.

Watch Out, Sara! 2006. (J). (978-1-933343-35-8(4) , PONY) Stabenfeldt Inc.

Waterton, Betty. Pettranella. Waterton, Betty & Blades, Ann, illus. 2003. (J). pap. 5.95 (978-0-88899-108-9(8)) Groundwood Bks. CAN. *Dist:* Transition Vendor.

—Pettranella. Blades, Ann, illus. 3rd ed. 2003. 32p. (J). pap. 5.95 (978-0-88899-560-5(1)) Groundwood Bks. CAN. *Dist:* Perseus Distribution.

Weatherill, Stephen & Weatherill, Sue. Little Red Riding Hood: A Puzzling Version. 1999. (Illus.). 24p. pap. (978-1-874735-28-1(X)) B Small Publishing.

Weaver, Lisa D. Praying with Our Feet. Hess, Ingrid, illus. 2005. 40p. (J). pap. 12.99 (978-0-8361-9306-0(7)) Herald Pr.

Weber, Lynda. The Adventures of Little Bit. Billac, Pete, ed. Young, Rudy, illus. 1998. 48p. (J). (ps-3). pap. 9.95 (978-1-888224-03-0(7)) Prestige Pubns.

Weiss, Bobbi J. G. Prom Time. 1999. (gr. 7-12). lib. bdg. 13.00 (978-0-613-73077-8(1)) Tandem Library Bks.

Weiss, David Cody. Now & Again. 2003. (gr. 5-8). lib. bdg. 13.00 (978-0-613-73348-9(7)) Tandem Library Bks.

Weitzman, Jacqueline Preiss. Mi Globo Paseando por Nueva York: Yo en el Metropolitan Museum. Glasser, Robin Preiss, illus. 2000. (SPA.). 32p. (J). (gr. k-2). 17.95 (978-84-95040-49-7(2) , RR1515) Serres, Ediciones, S. L. ESP. *Dist:* Lectorum Pubns., Inc.

Wells, Carolyn. Patty at Home. 2004. reprint ed. pap. 21.95 (978-1-4191-4032-7(0)); pap. 1.99 (978-1-4192-4032-4(3)) Kessinger Publishing, LLC.

Wells, Rosemary. Julieta, Estate Quieta! (SPA.). 43p. (J). 5.50 (978-84-372-1523-5(4)) Santillana USA Publishing Co., Inc.

—Julieta, Estate Quieta! Wells, Rosemary, illus. 2003. (SPA., Illus.). 38p. (J). (gr. k-3). 5.95 (978-0-88272-433-1(9)) Santillana USA Publishing Co., Inc.

—Leave Well Enough Alone. 2002. 224p. (J). pap. 5.99 (978-0-14-230149-4(3) , Puffin) Penguin Group (USA) Inc.

—Noisy Nora. 32p. (J). (ps-2). 2000. (Pied Piper Bks.: Vol. 1). (Illus.). pap. 6.99 (978-0-14-056728-1(3) , Puffin); 1999. 15.99 (978-0-670-88722-4(6) , Viking Juvenile) Penguin Group (USA) Inc.

—Noisy Nora. 2000. (978-0-606-18437-3(6)) Tandem Library Bks.

West, Cathy. Unlucky in Lunch. 2000. (gr. 3-6). lib. bdg. 11.80 (978-0-613-28119-5(5)) Tandem Library Bks.

West, Elizabeth. The ARUN Project. 2002. 184p. (YA). per. 9.99 (978-0-9720919-0-9(4)) West, Elizabeth.

West, Tracey. Hi Hi Puffy Amiyumi World Tour Sticker Storybook. 2006. 18p. (J). pap. 4.99 (978-0-439-79387-2(4) , Scholastic Paperbacks) Scholastic, Inc.

—Liz Makes a Rainbow. Durk, Jim, illus. 1999. (Magic School Bus Ser.). 24p. (J). (gr. 1-4). pap. 3.50 (978-0-590-66232-1(5)) Scholastic, Inc.

—Liz Takes Flight. Enik, Ted, illus. 1999. (Magic School Bus Ser.). 24p. (J). (gr. 1-4). pap. 3.50 (978-0-439-08207-5(2)) Scholastic, Inc.

—No Girls Allowed. Morrow, Cindy, illus. 2001. (Powerpuff Girls Readers: No. 4). 32p. (J). pap. 3.99 (978-0-439-29588-8(2)) Scholastic, Inc.

EFG

—No Girls Allowed. 2001. (gr. k-3). lib. bdg. 11.80 (978-0-613-43857-5(4)) Tandem Library Bks.

Westaway, Jane. Reliable Friendly Girls. 2001. 128p. pap. 13.00 (978-0-9583405-8-8(7)) Longacre Pr. NZL. *Dist:* Pacific Island Bks.

Westerfeld, Scott. Specials. 2006. (YA). (978-1-4169-2165-3(6)); 384p. (gr. 7 up). 15.95 (978-0-689-86540-4(6) , Simon Pulse) Simon & Schuster Children's Publishing.

Westerfeld, Scott. The Uglies Trilogy: Uglies, Pretties, Specials. 2007. 1216p. (YA). pap. 25.99 (***978-1-4169-3640-4(8)*** , Simon Pulse) Simon & Schuster Children's Publishing.

Weyn, Suzanne & Gonzalez, Diana. South Beach Sizzle. 2005. 249p. (YA). (978-1-4155-7724-0(2) , Simon Pulse) Simon & Schuster Children's Publishing.

Weyn, Suzanne & Gonzalez, Diana. South Beach Sizzle. 2005. 249p. (YA). (gr. 9-12). per. 14.45 (978-1-4176-6059-9(7)) Tandem Library Bks.

Wheeler, D. Janet. Billie Bradley & Her Inheritance or Th. 2006. 95.99 (***978-1-4280-1535-7(3)***); pap. 89.99 (***978-1-4280-1550-0(7)***) IndyPublish.com.

Whitehouse, Howard. The Strictest School in the World: Being the Tale of a Clever Girl, a Rubber Boy & a Collection of Flying Machines,Mostly Broken. Slavin, Bill, illus. 2006. 256p. (978-1-55337-883-9(0)); (978-1-55337-882-2(2)) Kids Can Pr., Ltd.

Whitney, D. T. A. Faith Gartneys Girlhood. 2006. 97.99 (***978-1-4280-4990-1(8)***); pap. 90.99 (***978-1-4280-4999-4(1)***) IndyPublish.com.

Wi', Raven. Inky the Raven: An Alaska Tale Based on a True Story. 2005. (J). per. 14.95 net. (978-1-59433-037-7(9)) Publication Consultants.

Wick, Elaine. It's MY Future: Should I Be a Nurse Practitioner? Tremaine, Michele, illus. 2004. 64p. (J). lib. bdg. 12.95 (978-0-9749769-0-7(3)) NAPNAP.

Wiggin, Eric. Hannah's Island Gift Set, 6 vols. 1998. 35.94 (978-1-883002-56-5(7)) Emerald Bks.

Wiggin, Kate Douglas. New Chronicles of Rebecca. 2006. 128p. pap. (978-1-84637-648-1(3)) Echo Library.

—New Chronicles of Rebecca. 2004. reprint ed. pap. 28.95 (978-1-4179-2096-9(3)); pap. 15.95 (978-1-4179-9994-1(2)); pap. 1.99 (978-1-4179-9944-6(6)) Kessinger Publishing, LLC.

—New Chronicles of Rebecca. 2006. (ENG.). 300p. per. 21.45 (978-1-59462-367-7(8) , 403); per. 21.45 (978-1-59462-368-4(6) , 404) Standard Pubns., Inc. (Book Jungle).

—Polly Oliver's Problem. 2006. 77.99 (***978-1-4280-4811-9(1)***); pap. 71.99 (***978-1-4280-4818-8(9)***) IndyPublish.com.

Wiggin, Kate Douglas. Rebecca of Sunnybrook Farm. reprint ed. (J). lib. bdg. 48.00 (978-0-7426-1139-9(6)); 2001. pap. 28.00 (978-0-7426-6139-4(3)) Classic Bks.

—Rebecca of Sunnybrook Farm. McClintock, Barbara, illus. anniv. ed. 2006. 290p. (J). (gr. 4-8). reprint ed. 22.00 (978-1-4223-5332-5(X)) DIANE Publishing Co.

—Rebecca of Sunnybrook Farm. 1999. (978-0-606-18653-7(0)) Tandem Library Bks.

Wight, Tamra. The Three Grumpies. Collins, Ross, illus. 2005. 32p. (J). pap. 6.95 (978-1-58234-985-5(1) , Bloomsbury Children) Bloomsbury Publishing.

Wiley, Debra D. Peanut Butter Boogers. 2006. 24p. per. 11.99 (***978-1-59886-730-5(X)***) Tate Publishing & Enterprises, L.L.C.

Wiley, Melissa. Across the Puddingstone Dam. Andreasen, Dan, illus. (J). 2004. (Little House Ser.: No. 4). 224p. 16.99 (978-0-06-027021-6(7)); 7. Date not set. (gr. 3-7). pap. 5.99 (978-0-06-440743-4(8)) HarperCollins Pubs.

Wilkes, Maria D., et al. The Little House Pioneer Girls, 3 vols. 1998. (J). (gr. 3-7). pap. 14.85 (978-0-06-440709-0(8) , Harper Trophy) HarperCollins Pubs.

Wilkins, Harry. Rachael's Way. 2002. (gr. 7-12). lib. bdg. 18.75 (978-0-613-78043-8(4)) Tandem Library Bks.

Williams, Cynthia G. Enid & the Church Fire. Harper, Betty, illus. 1999. (Our Neighborhood Ser.). 32p. (J). (ps-5). 11.99 (978-0-8054-1885-9(7)) B&H Publishing Grp.

—Enid & the Dangerous Discovery. Harper, Betty, illus. 1999. (Our Neighborhood Ser.). 32p. (J). (ps-5). 11.99 (978-0-8054-1884-2(9)) B&H Publishing Grp.

—Enid & the Homecoming. Harper, Betty, illus. 2000. (Our Neighborhood Ser.). 32p. (J). (ps-5). 11.99 (978-0-8054-1887-3(3)) B&H Publishing Grp.

Williams, Joyce Hall. Can Cousin Kunju Cut a Kanga? 1999. (Illus.). 16p. (J). pap. 8.95 (978-0-7414-0190-8(8)) Infinity Publishing.

Williams, Laura E. Champion Rose. 1999. (Magic Attic Club Ser.). (J). (gr. 2-6). 12.75 (978-0-606-16945-5(8)) Tandem Library Bks.

Williams, Leslie L. Assassin Queen. 2004. 157p. pap. 19.95 (978-1-4137-1944-4(9)) PublishAmerica, Inc.

Williams, Lori Aurelia. When Kambia Elaine Flew in from Neptune. unabr. ed. 2004. 246p. (J). (gr. 7 up). pap. 50.00 incl. audio (978-0-8072-8851-1(9) , Listening Library) Random Hse. Audio Publishing Group.

—When Kambia Elaine Flew in from Neptune. Louth, Jack, illus. 2001. 256p. (YA). pap. 10.00 (978-0-689-84593-2(6) , Simon Pulse) Simon & Schuster Children's Publishing.

—When Kambia Elaine Flew in from Neptune. 2002. (978-0-606-22109-2(3)); 2001. (gr. 7-12). lib. bdg. 18.80 (978-0-613-73307-6(X)) Tandem Library Bks.

Williams, Rozanne Lanczak. Emily Santos, Star of the Week. Maio, Barbara, ed. Burris, Priscilla, illus. 2006. (Learn to Write Ser.). 16p. (J). pap. 2.99 (978-1-59198-298-2(7) , 6194) Creative Teaching Pr., Inc.

—Tess Builds a Snowman. Maio, Barbara & Faulkner, Stacey, eds. Harris, Jenny B., illus. 2006. (Learn to Write Ser.). 8p. (J). pap. 1.99 (978-1-59198-286-9(3) , 6180) Creative Teaching Pr., Inc.

Wills, Morgan B. Mulright Island. 2004. (Illus.). 417p. (YA). per. 14.95 (978-0-9762768-0-7(1)) Williams, Morgan.

Willson, Sarah. My Dress-up Party. Oxley, Jennifer, illus. ed. 2005. 22p. (J). lib. bdg. 15.00 (978-1-59054-971-1(6)) Fitzgerald Bks.

Wilson, Jacqueline. The Diamond Girls. 2004. (Illus.). 229p. (J). (978-0-385-60607-3(9) , Doubleday) Transworld Publishers Ltd.

—Girls under Pressure. 2003. 224p. (YA). (gr. 7). pap. 5.50 (978-0-440-22958-2(8) , Laurel Leaf) Random Hse. Children's Bks.

—Girls under Pressure. 2003. (gr. 7-12). lib. bdg. 13.00 (978-0-613-72337-4(6)) Tandem Library Bks.

Wilson, Linda Miller. A Few Days Journey. 1998. 124p. (YA). (gr. 4-8). 9.99 (978-0-88092-402-3(0) , 4020) Royal Fireworks Publishing Co.

The Wishing Star. ed. 2006. (J). bds. 16.95 (978-0-9772320-1-7(8)) Minikin Pr.

Wojciechowski, Susan. Patty Dillman of Hot Dog Fame. 1999. 180p. (J). (gr. 5-8). pap. 5.99 (978-0-9673794-0-1(7)) Small Miracles Pr.

Wolf, Joan M. Someone Named Eva. 2007. 208p. (J). (gr. 5-9). 16.00 (978-0-618-53579-8(9) , Clarion Bks.) Houghton Mifflin Co. Trade & Reference Div.

Wong, Joyce Lee. Seeing Emily. 2007. 288p. (J). (gr. 5-10). pap. 6.95 (***978-0-8109-9258-0(2)*** , Amulet Bks.) Abrams, Harry N. , Inc.

Wood, Frances M. Becoming Rosemary. 2001. 256p. (J). (gr. 5-9). pap. 12.00 (978-0-375-89504-3(3) , Delacorte Bks. for Young Readers) Random Hse. Children's Bks.

Wood, Gail. Lizzie & the Prairie Fire: Girl Pioneer in the American Midwest. 2006. (Illus.). (J). pap. 7.95 (978-1-57249-381-0(X) , White Mane Kids) White Mane Publishing Co., Inc.

Wood, Maryrose. Why I Let My Hair Grow Out. 2007. 272p. (J). pap. 9.99 (978-0-425-21380-3(3) , Berkley Trade) Penguin Group (USA) Inc.

Woodbury. Where in the World is Jenny Parker. (J). 6.95 (978-0-88894-813-7(1)) Douglas & McIntyre, Ltd. CAN. *Dist:* Transition Vendor.

Woodbury, Mary. The Intrepid Polly McDoodle. 1999. (Polly McDoodle Ser.: Vol. 2). 180p. (J). (gr. 3 up). pap. 6.95 (978-1-55050-133-9(X)) Coteau Bks. CAN. *Dist:* Fitzhenry & Whiteside, Ltd.

Wooden, Thomas James, Jr. Four-Hundred Meter Champion. Winston, Dennis, illus. 2003. 103p. (J). mass mkt. 12.00 (978-0-9740195-0-5(X)) New Castle Publishing Co.

Woolf, Paula. Old Ladies with Brooms Aren't Always Witches. 1998. 154p. (YA). (gr. 4-6). 9.99 (978-0-88092-395-8(4) , 3954) Royal Fireworks Publishing Co.

Wormell, Chris. The Wild Girl. Wormell, Chris, illus. 2006. (Illus.). 32p. (J). 17.00 (978-0-8028-5311-0(0) , Eerdmans Bks For Young Readers) Eerdmans, William B. Publishing Co.

Wright, Jill. Minnie's Tea Party. Boyd, Anthony, ed. David, Simon, illus. 1999. (Minnie's Adventures Ser.). 32p. (J). (gr. k-2). pap. (978-0-9672839-1-3(4)) Starry Puddle Publishing.

Wrightman, Stephen. Guardian Angel. 1998. (YA). (gr. 7-12). pap. 9.95 (978-1-892403-00-1(5)) StarMist Development, Inc.

Ye, Ting-Xing. White Lily. 2002. (Illus.). 48p. (J). pap. 5.95 (978-0-385-25913-2(1)) Doubleday Publishing.

Ylitalo, Gail. Blackberry Summer. 2003. 153p. pap. 16.95 (978-1-59286-784-4(7)) PublishAmerica, Inc.

Yolen, Jane. The Girl in the Golden Bower. 1998. (978-0-606-13429-3(8)) Tandem Library Bks.

Yoon, Salina. Maggie's Colorful Garden: A Touchy, Feely Lift-the-Flap Colors Book. 1999. 10p. (J). 7.95 (978-1-58117-057-3(2) , Intervisual/Piggy Toes) Dalmatian Pr.

—My Princess Essentials. 2007. 10p. (J). pap. 8.99 (978-0-8431-2180-3(7) , Price Stern Sloan) Penguin Group (USA) Inc.

Young, Amy. Belinda in Paris. 2005. (Illus.). 32p. (J). 15.99 (978-0-670-03693-6(5) , Viking Juvenile) Penguin Group (USA) Inc.

The Young Girl. 2002. 14.95 (978-0-7893-0690-6(5)) Universe Publishing.

Young, K. A. Man in the Moon. 2001. (Illus.). 120p. (J). per. 10.00 (978-0-9708999-5-8(5)) Whyte Dove Pr.

You're the Best, Hannah! 2000. (J). pap., tchr. ed. (978-0-06-449250-8(8) , Harper Trophy) HarperCollins Pubs.

Yoxen, Jackie. Hannah's Sunday Hats. Francis, Lauren, illus. l.t. ed. 2006. 32p. (J). 19.95 (***978-1-59879-184-6(2)***) Lifevest Publishing, Inc.

Zabel, Alanna. The Seven Doors. 2006. 59p. pap. 18.50 (978-1-4116-4369-7(0)) Lulu.com.

Zagwyn, Deborah Turney. Turtle Spring. Zagwyn, Deborah Turney, illus. 2004. (Illus.). 32p. (J). (gr. k-3). 15.95 (978-1-883672-53-9(8) , Tricycle Pr.) Ten Speed Pr.

Zendrera, Concepcion. Yaci y Su Muneca. (SPA.). 16p. (J). 9.95 (978-84-261-5604-4(5) , JV3576) Juventud, Editorial ESP. *Dist:* AIMS International Bks., Inc., Lectorum Pubns., Inc.

Ziefert, Harriet. The Snow Child. Zanes, Julia, illus. 2000. (J). (gr. k-3). lib. bdg. 11.80 (978-0-613-31724-5(6)) Tandem Library Bks.

GIRLS—POETRY

De la Garza, Phyllis. Charissa of the Overland. 1999. 284p. (YA). (gr. 8 up). 9.99 (978-0-88092-370-5(9) , 3709) Royal Fireworks Publishing Co.

George, Kristine O'Connell. Swimming Upstream: Middle School Poems. Tilley, Debbie, illus. 2002. 80p. (J). (gr. 4-6). tchr. ed. 14.00 (978-0-618-15250-6(4) , Clarion Bks.) Houghton Mifflin Co. Trade & Reference Div.

Nye, Naomi Shihab. A Maze Me: Poems for Girls. Maher, Terre, illus. 2005. 128p. (YA). (gr. 7 up). 16.99 (978-0-06-058189-3(1)); lib. bdg. 17.89 (978-0-06-058190-9(5)) HarperCollins Pubs.

Richards, Beah E. Keep Climbing, Girls. Christie, R. Gregory, illus. 2006. 32p. (J). (ps-3). 15.95 (978-1-4169-0264-5(3)) Simon & Schuster Children's Publishing.

Yeagle, Gary. Angels Footprints. 2007. per. 24.95 (***978-1-59633-011-5(2)***) Goose Creek Pubs.

GIRLS' CLUBS—FICTION

Bowen, Debralee. The Little Yellow Clubhouse Diary. 2004. 38p. pap. 17.95 (978-1-4137-1073-1(5)) PublishAmerica, Inc.

Bryant, Bonnie. Dude Ranch. 2007. (Saddle Club Ser.: No. 6). 144p. (J). (gr. 4-6). lib. bdg. 11.99 (978-0-385-90422-3(3) , Yearling) Random Hse. Children's Bks.

Perry, Chrissie. The Secret Club. Oswald, Ash, illus. 2007. (Go Girl! Ser.: Bk. 1). 96p. (Orig.). (J). (gr. 2 up). pap. 3.99 (***978-0-312-34652-2(2)***) Feiwel & Friends.

Richards, Alex. Back Talk. 2007. 264p. (J). (gr. 7 up). pap. 8.95 (***978-0-7387-1017-4(2)*** , Flux) Llewellyn Pubns.

GIST, TAD (FICTITIOUS CHARACTER)—FICTION

Charbonneau, Eileen. The Connor Emerald. Williams, Lori, ed. 1999. 170p. (YA). pap. 9.99 (978-1-58365-753-9(3) , Timeless Romance) Sierra Raconteur Publishing.

GLACIAL EPOCH

Bailey, Linda. Adventures in the Ice Age. Slavin, Bill, illus. 2005. (Good Times Travel Agency Ser.). 48p. (YA). (gr. 3-7). (978-1-55337-503-6(3)) Kids Can Pr., Ltd.

Dixon, Dougal. Frozen Mammoth. 2003. (History Hunters Ser.). (Illus.). 32p. (J). (gr. 3 up). lib. bdg. 24.67 (978-0-8368-3740-7(1)) Stevens, Gareth Inc.

Donnelly, Karen J. Ice Ages of the Past & the Future. 2003. (Earths Changing Weather & Climate Ser.). (Illus.). 24p. (J). lib. bdg. 18.75 (978-0-8239-6219-8(9) , PowerKids Pr.) Rosen Publishing Group, Inc., The.

Kimble, Evan & Kimble, Lael. Ice Age Creatures Dot-to-Dot. 2004. (Illus.). 80p. pap. 5.95 (978-1-4027-0994-4(3)) Sterling Publishing Co., Inc.

Meierhenry, Mark V. & Volk, David. The Mystery of the Round Rocks. 2007. (J). (***978-0-9777955-3-6(5)*** , South Dakota State Historical Society Pr.) South Dakota State Historical Society.

Nardo, Don. The Ice Ages. 2005. (KidHaven Science Library). (Illus.). 48p. (J). (gr. 4-8). 26.20 (978-0-7377-3055-5(2) , Greenhaven Pr., Inc.) Thomson Gale.

Osborne, Mary Pope & Boyce, Natalie Pope. Sabertooths & the Ice Age. Murdocca, Sal, illus. 2005. (Magic Tree House Research Guide Ser.: No. 12). 128p. (J). (gr. k-3). pap. 4.99 (978-0-375-82380-0(8) , Random Hse. Bks. for Young Readers) Random Hse. Children's Bks.

—Sabertooths & the Ice Age: A Nonfiction Companion to Sunset of the Sabertooth. Murdocca, Sal, illus. 2005. (Magic Tree House Research Guide Ser.: No. 12). 128p. (J). (gr. k-3). lib. bdg. 11.99 (978-0-375-92380-7(2) , Random Hse. Bks. for Young Readers) Random Hse. Children's Bks.

Patent, Dorothy Hinshaw. Secrets of the Ice Man. 1999. (Frozen in Time Ser.). (Illus.). 72p. (J). (gr. 5-9). lib. bdg. 28.50 (978-0-7614-0782-9(0) , Benchmark Bks.) Cavendish, Marshall Corp.

Stein, Paul. Ice Ages in the Future. 2001. (Library of Future Weather & Climate). (Illus.). 64p. (YA). (gr. 4-6). lib. bdg. 26.50 (978-0-8239-3415-7(2)) Rosen Publishing Group, Inc., The.

GLACIAL EPOCH—FICTION

Greenburg, J. C. In the Ice Age. Gerardi, Jan, illus. 2005. (Andrew Lost Ser.: Bk. 12). 96p. (J). (gr. 2-5). pap. 3.99 (978-0-375-82952-9(0)); lib. bdg. 11.99 (978-0-375-92952-6(5)) Random Hse. Children's Bks. (Random Hse. Bks. for Young Readers).

Griffin, Peni R. 11,000 Years Lost. (J). (gr. 5-9). 2006. 368p. pap. 7.95 (978-0-8109-9251-1(5)); 2004. (Illus.). 336p. 18.95 (978-0-8109-4822-8(2)) Abrams, Harry N. , Inc.

Harrison, Troon. Eye of the Wolf. 212p. 2004. pap. (978-1-55005-073-8(7)); 2003. (Illus.). (YA). (978-1-55005-072-1(9)) Fitzhenry & Whiteside, Ltd.

Layton, Neal. Hot Hot Hot. Layton, Neal, illus. 2004. (Illus.). 32p. (J). (ps-3). 15.99 (978-0-7636-2148-3(X)) Candlewick Pr.

Weston, Martha. Dr. Clock-Sicle: A Holiday House Reader, Level 1. (Illus.). 32p. (J). (gr. k-3). tchr. ed. 14.95 (978-0-8234-1825-1(1)) Holiday Hse., Inc.

GLACIER NATIONAL PARK (MONT.)

Aretha, David. Glacier National Park. 2008. (J). (***978-1-59845-088-0(3)*** , MyReportLinks.com Bks.) Enslow Pubs., Inc.

Christian, Peggy. Chocolate, a Glacier Grizzly. Cottone-Kolthoff, Carol, illus. (Humane Society of the United States Animal Tales Ser.). 32p. (J). (gr. 1-5). 34.95 incl. audio (978-1-882728-64-0(5)); pap. 9.95 incl. audio (978-1-882728-67-1(X)); pap. 19.95 incl. audio (978-1-882728-69-5(6)) Benefactory, Inc., The.

Graf, Mike. Glacier National Park. 2003. (National Parks Ser.). (Illus.). 24p. (J). lib. bdg. 19.93 (978-0-7368-2220-6(8) , Bridgestone Bks.) Capstone Pr., Inc.

Hall, M. C. Glacier National Park. 2005. (Symbols of Freedom Ser.). (Illus.). 32p. (J). (gr. k-2). lib. bdg. 25.36 (978-1-4034-6698-3(X)) Heinemann Library.

Hall, Margaret. Glacier National Park. 2005. (Heinemann First Library). (Illus.). 32p. (J). pap. (978-1-4034-6705-8(6)) Heinemann Library.

Higgins, Nadia. Welcome to Glacier National Park. 2006. (Visitor Guides Ser.). (Illus.). 32p. (J). (gr. 1-5). 27.07 (978-1-59296-696-7(9)) Child's World, Inc.

Leftridge, Alan. Going to Glacier. 2006. (J). (978-1-56037-340-7(7)) Farcountry Pr.

Robinson, Gary D. Who Pooped in the Park: Glacier. 2004. 48p. pap. 9.95 (978-1-56037-279-0(6)) Farcountry Pr.

Vernon, Tannis & Longmore, Rich, illus. Glacier National Park Wildlife. 2004. (Postcard Book Ser.). 40p. 9.95 (978-0-7627-2903-6(1) , Falcon) Globe Pequot Pr., The.

Wade, Linda R. Glacier National Park. 2005. (National Parks Ser.). (Illus.). 32p. (J). (gr. 3-8). lib. bdg. 24.21 (978-1-59197-425-3(9)) ABDO Publishing Co.

GLACIER NATIONAL PARK (MONT.)—FICTION

Ferguson, Alane & Skurzynski, Gloria. The Hunted. 2007. (Mysteries in Our National Park Ser.). (Illus.). 160p. (J). (gr. 3-7). 4.99 (***978-1-4263-0095-0(6)*** , National Geographic Children's Bks.) National Geographic Society.

Skurzynski, Gloria. The Hunted. 2001. 12.60 (978-0-606-22147-4(6)); (gr. 3-6). lib. bdg. 14.10 (978-0-613-62422-0(X)) Tandem Library Bks.

Skurzynski, Gloria & Ferguson, Alane. The Hunted. (National Parks Mysteries Ser.: No. 5). 160p. (J). (gr. 3-7). 2000. (Illus.). 15.95 (978-0-7922-7053-9(3)); 5th ed. 2001. pap. 5.95 (978-0-7922-7665-4(5)) National Geographic Society. (National Geographic Children's Bks.).

GLACIERS

Benchmark Education Staff. Glaciers. 2005. 2.00 (***978-1-4108-4655-6(5)***) Benchmark Education Co.

Bodden, Valerie. Glaciers. 2006. (Our World Ser.). (Illus.). 24p. 16.95 (978-1-58341-462-0(2) , Creative Education) Creative Co., The.

Brannon, Barbara. Discover Glaciers. 2005. 39.00 (***978-1-4108-5134-5(6)***) Benchmark Education Co.

Brimner, Larry Dane. Glaciers. 2001. (True Bks.). (Illus.). 48p. (J). (gr. 3-5). pap. 6.95 (978-0-516-27191-0(1) , Children's Pr.) Scholastic Library Publishing.

—Glaciers. 2001. (J). 13.75 (978-0-606-22875-6(6)); 2000. (gr. 3-6). lib. bdg. 15.25 (978-0-613-54510-5(9)) Tandem Library Bks.

Carruthers, Margaret W. Glaciers. 2005. (Watts Library). (Illus.). 64p. (J). 25.50 (978-0-531-12285-3(9) , Watts, Franklin) Scholastic Library Publishing.

Fowler, Allan. Icebergs, Ice Caps, & Glaciers. 1998. (Rookie Read-About Science Ser.). (Illus.). 32p. (J). (gr. 1-2). pap. 4.95 (978-0-516-26257-4(2) , Children's Pr.) Scholastic Library Publishing.

Gallant, Roy A. Glaciers. 1999. (First Bks.). (Illus.). 64p. (J). (gr. 5-7). 22.00 (978-0-531-20390-3(5) , Watts, Franklin) Scholastic Library Publishing.

George, Michael. Glaciers: Rivers of Ice. 2003. (LifeViews Ser.). (Illus.). 32p. (J). lib. bdg. (978-1-58341-253-4(0) , Creative Education) Creative Co., The.

Gordon, John. Glaciers. Stock Photographers Staff, photos by. rev. ed. 2001. (WorldLife Library). (Illus.). 72p. (J). pap. 17.95 (978-0-89658-559-1(X)) Voyageur Pr., Inc.

Harcourt School Publishers Staff. Glaciers Change the Earth. 3rd ed. 2002. (Horizons Ser.). (Illus.). (J). pap. 5.50 (978-0-15-333288-3(3)) Harcourt Schl. Pubs.

Harrison David. Glaciers. 2006. (Earthworks (Honesdale, Pa.)). (Illus.). 32p. (J). 15.95 (978-1-59078-372-6(7)) Boyds Mills Pr.

Hocker, Katherine M. Frozen in Motion: Alaska's Glaciers. Brubaker, Jill, ed. Lepley, Kathy, illus. 2006. 54p. (J). spiral bd. 8.95 (978-0-930931-76-6(9)) Alaska Natural History Assn.

Ice on the Move, 6 Packs. (Rigby Focus Ser.). 24p. (gr. 2 up). 30.00 (978-0-7578-5571-9(7)) Rigby Education.

Ice on the Move: Individual Title, 6 Packs. (Rigby Focus Ser.). 24p. (gr. 2 up). 28.00 (978-0-7578-5341-8(2)) Rigby Education.

Johnson, Rebecca L. Surviving Volcanoes & Glaciers. 2003. (National Geographic Reading Expeditions Ser.). (Illus.). 32p. (J). (978-0-7922-8448-2(8)) National Geographic Society.

Leathers, Dan. The Snows of Kilimanjaro. 2007. (On the Verge of Extinction Ser.). (Illus.). 32p. (J). (gr. 1-4). lib. bdg. 25.70 (***978-1-58415-584-3(1)***) Mitchell Lane Pubs., Inc.

Lindeen, Mary. Glaciers. 2007. (Illus.). 24p. (J). lib. bdg. 19.95 (978-1-60014-113-3(7)) Bellwether Media.

Llewellyn, Claire. Glaciers. 2000. (Heinemann First Library). (Illus.). 32p. (J). (gr. k-2). lib. bdg. 21.36 (978-1-57572-205-4(4)) Heinemann Library.

Llewellyn, Claire, et al. Glaciers. 2002. (Geography Starts Ser.). (Illus.). 32p. (J). (gr. k-2). pap. 6.95 (978-1-58810-973-6(9) , 91456) Heinemann Library.

Mattern, Joanne. Antarctica: World's Biggest Glacier. 2002. (Reading Power Ser.). (Illus.). 24p. (J). lib. bdg. 17.25 (978-0-8239-6017-0(X) , PowerKids Pr.) Rosen Publishing Group, Inc., The.

Nadeau, Isaac. Glaciers. 2006. (Illus.). 24p. (J). lib. bdg. (978-1-4042-3124-5(2) , PowerKids Pr.) Rosen Publishing Group, Inc., The.

—Water in Glaciers. 2003. (Water Cycle Ser.). (Illus.). 24p. (J). lib. bdg. 18.75 (978-0-8239-6265-5(2) , PowerKids Pr.) Rosen Publishing Group, Inc., The.

Osborne, Mary Pope & Boyce, Natalie Pope. Sabertooths & the Ice Age. Murdocca, Sal, illus. 2005. (Magic Tree House Research Guide Ser.: No. 12). 128p. (J). (gr. k-3). pap. 4.99 (978-0-375-82380-0(8) , Random Hse. Bks. for Young Readers) Random Hse. Children's Bks.

—Sabertooths & the Ice Age: A Nonfiction Companion to Sunset of the Sabertooth. Murdocca, Sal, illus. 2005. (Magic Tree House Research Guide Ser.: No. 12). 128p. (J). (gr. k-3). lib. bdg. 11.99 (978-0-375-92380-7(2) , Random Hse. Bks. for Young Readers) Random Hse. Children's Bks.

—Sabertooths & the Ice Age: A Nonfiction Companion to Sunset of the Sabertooth. Murdocca, Salvatore, illus. 2005. (Magic Tree House Research Guide Ser.: No. 12). 121p. (J). (gr. k-3). lib. bdg. 12.94 (978-0-606-33233-0(2)) Tandem Library Bks.

Sepheri, Sandy. Glaciers. 2008. (J). (***978-1-60044-544-6(6)***) Rourke Publishing, LLC.

Simon, Seymour. Icebergs & Glaciers. 1999. (Illus.). 32p. (J). (ps-3). pap. 6.99 (978-0-688-16705-9(5) , Harper Trophy) HarperCollins Pubs.

—Icebergs & Glaciers. 1999. (J). 13.79 (978-0-606-16760-4(9)); lib. bdg. 15.25 (978-0-613-18255-3(3)) Tandem Library Bks.

Trumbauer, Lisa. Glaciers. 2005. 42.00 (***978-1-4108-4607-5(5)***) Benchmark Education Co.

Walker, Sally M. Glaciers. 2007. (Early Bird Earth Science Ser.). (J). 26.60 (***978-0-8225-6737-0(7)*** , Lerner Pubns.) Lerner Publishing Group.

Webster, Christine. Glaciers. 2005. (Science Matters Ser.). (Illus.). 24p. (J). (ps-7). pap. 6.95 (978-1-59036-309-6(4)); lib. bdg. 24.45 (978-1-59036-303-4(5)) Weigl Pubs., Inc.

GLADSTONE, WILLIAM EWART, 1809-1898

Lee, Stephen J. Gladstone & Disraeli. 2005. (Questions & Analysis in History Ser.). (Illus.). 208p. 20.95 (978-0-415-32357-4(6)); 90.00 (978-0-415-32356-7(8)) Routledge.

GLANDS

Woodward, John. Stinkers. 2005. (Planet's Most Extreme Ser.). (Illus.). 48p. (J). (gr. 3-7). 24.95 (978-1-4103-0397-4(7) , Blackbirch Pr., Inc.) Thomson Gale.

GLASS

Cackett, Susan. Glass & the Environment. Nevett, Louise, illus. 2004. (J). lib. bdg. (978-1-932799-37-8(0)) Stargazer Bks.

Ellis, William. Glass: From the First Mirror to Fiber Optics. 1999. (gr. 7-12). lib. bdg. 23.45 (978-0-613-25339-0(6)) Tandem Library Bks.

Firestone, Mary. Glass. 2004. (First Facts Ser.). 24p. (J). lib. bdg. 21.26 (978-0-7368-2650-1(5)) Capstone Pr., Inc.

Glass: Individual Title Six-Packs. (Rigby Focus Ser.). 16p. (gr. 1 up). 28.00 (978-0-7578-5306-7(4)); 30.00 (978-0-7578-5538-2(5)) Rigby Education.

Harcourt School Publishers Staff. Making Glass Advanced Level. 3rd ed. 2002. (Trophies Reading Program Ser.). (Illus.). pap. 5.10 (978-0-15-323301-2(X)) Harcourt Schl. Pubs.

Kassinger, Ruth. Glass: From Cinderella's Slipper to Fiber Optics. 2003. (Material World Ser.). (Illus.). 80p. (gr. 6-8). lib. bdg. 25.90 (978-0-7613-2109-5(8) , Twenty-First Century Bks.) Lerner Publishing Group.

Koscielniak, Bruce. Looking at Glass Through the Ages. 2006. (Illus.). 40p. (J). (gr. 3-5). 16.00 (978-0-618-50750-4(7)) Houghton Mifflin Co.

Levete, Sarah. Glass. 2005. (Illus.). 32p. (J). (gr. 3-7). lib. bdg. 27.10 (978-1-59604-044-1(0)) Stargazer Bks.

Oxlade, Chris. Glass. (Materials, Materials, Materials Ser.). 32p. pap. 6.95 (978-1-4034-4097-6(2)); 2001. (Illus.). (J). lib. bdg. 21.36 (978-1-58810-154-9(1)) Heinemann Library.

—How We Use Glass. 2004. (Illus.). 32p. (J). (ps-ps). pap. 7.50 (978-1-4109-0993-0(X)); 25.70 (978-1-4109-0594-9(2)) Raintree.

Parker, Steve. Glass. 2002. (Science Files Ser.). (Illus.). 32p. (J). (gr. 3 up). lib. bdg. 24.67 (978-0-8368-3082-8(2)) Stevens, Gareth Inc.

Pina, Leslie, et al. Purple Glass: 20th Century American & European. 2002. (Schiffer Book for Collectors Ser.). (Illus.). 160p. (gr. 10-13). 29.95 (978-0-7643-1515-2(3)) Schiffer Publishing, Ltd.

Rivera, Sheila. Magnifying Glass. 2006. (First Step Nonfiction Ser.). (Illus.). 8p. pap. (978-0-8225-5713-5(4) , Lerner Pubns.) Lerner Publishing Group.

Royston, Angela. Glass: Let's Look at a Marble. 2005. (Illus.). 24p. (J). (978-1-4034-7678-4(0)); pap. (978-1-4034-7687-6(X)) Heinemann Library.

—Glass: Let's Look at a Marble. 2005. (J). (978-1-4109-1825-3(4)); pap. (978-1-4109-1834-5(3)) Steck-Vaughn.

—Vidrio: Miremos unas Canicas. 2005. (Heinemann Lee y Aprende Ser.). (ENG & SPA., Illus.). 24p. (978-1-4034-7542-8(3)); pap. (978-1-4034-7551-0(2)) Heinemann Library.

Snyder, Inez. Sand to Glass. 2005. (How Things Are Made Ser.). (Illus.). 24p. (J). (ps-2). pap. 4.95 (978-0-516-25529-3(0)); 18.00 (978-0-516-25199-8(6)) Scholastic Library Publishing. (Children's Pr.).

Thomson, Ruth. Glass. 2006. (Illus.). 29p. (J). (978-1-58340-942-8(4)) Smart Apple Media.

Walker, Kate. Glass. 2004. (Recycle, Reduce, Reuse, Rethink Ser.). (J). lib. bdg. 27.10 (978 1 58340 557 4(7)) Smart Apple Media.

Wallace, Holly. Glass. 2007. (J). (***978-1-59920-002-6(3)*** Smart Apple Media.

GLASS, STAINED

see Glass Painting and Staining

GLASS MANUFACTURE

Branse, J. L. A Day in the Life of a Colonial Glassblower. 2002. (Library of Living & Working in Colonial Times). (Illus.). 24p. (J). (gr. 3). lib. bdg. 18.75 (978-0-8239-5820-7(5) , PowerKids Pr.) Rosen Publishing Group, Inc., The.

Cackett, Susan. Glass & the Environment. Nevett, Louise, illus. 2004. (J). lib. bdg. (978-1-932799-37-8(0)) Stargazer Bks.

Firestone, Mary. Glass. 2004. (First Facts Ser.). 24p. (J). lib. bdg. 21.26 (978-0-7368-2650-1(5)) Capstone Pr., Inc.

Hallock, Marilyn R. Central Glass Company: The First Thirty Years, 1863-1893. 2003. (Illus.). 176p. 39.95 (978-0-7643-1762-0(8)) Schiffer Publishing, Ltd.

Levete, Sarah. Glass. 2005. (Illus.). 32p. (J). (gr. 3-7). lib. bdg. 27.10 (978-1-59604-044-1(0)) Stargazer Bks.

Ridley, Sarah. A Glass Jar. 2006. (Illus.). 32p. (J). lib. bdg. (978-0-8368-6701-5(7)) Stevens, Gareth Inc.

Snyder, Inez. Sand to Glass. 2005. (How Things Are Made Ser.). (Illus.). 24p. (J). (ps-2). pap. 4.95 (978-0-516-25529-3(0)); 18.00 (978-0-516-25199-8(6)) Scholastic Library Publishing. (Children's Pr.).

Zemlicka, Shannon. From Sand to Glass. 2004. (Start to Finish Ser.). (Illus.). 24p. (J). 18.60 (978-0-8225-0945-5(8) , Lerner Pubns.) Lerner Publishing Group.

GLASS PAINTING AND STAINING

Abbey, Rita Deanin. Isaiah Stained-Glass Windows. Sanders, Laura, ed. Preston, Gregory, photos by. 2002. (ENG & HEB., Illus.). 40p. (J). pap. (978-0-9652870-1-2(7)) Gan Or.

Araujo, Paige Krul & Dakota, Heather. Glass Art: Window Clings & Other Things. Im, Angela, ed. 2004. (Glass Art Ser.). (Illus.). 48p. (J). (gr. 3 up). lthr. 9.99 (978-0-439-63536-3(5)) Scholastic, Inc.

The Art of Glass Painting. 2004. (Classic Craft Cases Ser.). (Illus.). 64p. (978-1-84229-801-5(1)) Top That! Publishing PLC.

Butterflies & Moths: Stained Glass Art. 2001. (Illus.). 16p. (gr. 3-7). pap. 4.99 (978-0-439-11681-7(3)) Scholastic, Inc.

Eaton, Connie Clough. Easy Victorian Florals Stained Glass Pattern Book. 2005. (Pictorial Archive Ser.). (Illus.). 64p. pap. 8.95 (978-0-486-44174-0(1)) Dover Pubns., Inc.

Green, John. Frogs Stained Glass Coloring Book. 2000. (Illus.). 8p. (J). pap. 1.50 (978-0-486-41258-0(X)) Dover Pubns., Inc.

—Heavenly Snowflakes Stained Glass Coloring Book. 2006. (Dover Little Activity Bks.). 8p. (J). pap. 1.50 (978-0-486-44923-4(8)) Dover Pubns., Inc.

Klutz Press Staff & Kane, Barbara. Window Art. 2001. (Illus.). 64p. (J). spiral bd. 19.95 (978-1-57054-643-3(6)) Klutz.

Lafontaine, Bruce. Construction Trucks Stained Glass Coloring Book. 2004. 8p. (J). pap. 1.50 (978-0-486-44106-1(7)) Dover Pubns., Inc.

Noble, Marty. Book of Kells Stained Glass Colouring Book. 2006. 16p. pap. 5.95 (978-0-486-44810-7(X)) Dover Pubns., Inc.

—Easter Ornaments Stained Glass Coloring Book. 1998. (Illus.). 8p. (J). pap. 1.50 (978-0-486-40304-5(1)) Dover Pubns., Inc.

—Fairy Babies Stained Glass Coloring Book. 2006. (Dover Little Activity Bks.). 8p. (J). pap. 1.50 (978-0-486-44916-6(5)) Dover Pubns., Inc.

—Japanese Designs Stained Glass Coloring Book. 2006. 16p. pap. 5.95 (978-0-486-45175-6(5)) Dover Pubns., Inc.

—Victorian Fashions Stained Glass Coloring Book. 2001. (Illus.). 32p. (J). pap. 5.95 (978-0-486-41555-0(4)) Dover Pubns., Inc.

Palmer, Michael & Palmer, Lori. The Charleton Line: Decoration on Glass & Porcelain. 2002. (Schiffer Book for Collectors Ser.). (Illus.). 176p. (gr. 10-13). 29.95 (978-0-7643-1645-6(1)) Schiffer Publishing, Ltd.

Pomaska, Anna. Same & Different. 2007. pap. 2.95 (***978-0-486-46107-6(6)*** Dover Pubns., Inc.

Relei, Carolyn. Arts & Crafts Stained Glass Coloring Book. 2002. (Illus.). 16p. (J). pap. 5.95 (978-0-486-42387-6(5)) Dover Pubns., Inc.

Smith, A. G. Arabic Patterns Stained Glass Coloring Book. 2006. 16p. (J). pap. 5.95 (978-0-486-44839-8(8)) Dover Pubns., Inc.

—Boats Stained Glass Coloring Book. 1999. 8p. (J). pap. 1.50 (978-0-486-40737-1(3)) Dover Pubns., Inc.

—Celtic Knotwork Stained Glass Colouring Book. 2006. 16p. pap. 5.95 (978-0-486-44816-9(9)) Dover Pubns., Inc.

—Chinese Designs Stained Glass Coloring Book. 2006. 16p. pap. 5.95 (978-0-486-45172-5(0)) Dover Pubns., Inc.

—Classic Posters Stained Glass Coloring Book. 2004. (Pictorial Archive Ser.). (Illus.). 16p. (J). (gr. 3). pap. 5.95 (978-0-486-43343-1(9)) Dover Pubns., Inc.

—Southwest Indians Stained Glass Coloring Book. 2002. (Illus.). 8p. (J). (gr. k-5). pap. 1.50 (978-0-486-42338-8(7)) Dover Pubns., Inc.

Stewart, Pat L. Nutcracker Stained Glass Coloring Book. 1998. (Illus.). 8p. (J). (ps-5). pap. 1.50 (978-0-486-40260-4(6)) Dover Pubns., Inc.

Tropical Fish: Stained Glass Art. 2001. (Illus.). 16p. (J). (gr. 3-7). pap. 4.99 (978-0-439-21739-2(3)) Scholastic, Inc.

Waldrep, Mary Carolyn. Traditional Patchwork Designs Stained Glass Coloring Book. 2006. (Illus.). 16p. (J). pap. 5.95 (978-0-486-44842-8(8)) Dover Pubns., Inc.

GLASSWARE

Coe-McRitchie, Tara. Fenton Glass Cats & Dogs. 2001. (Schiffer Book for Collectors Ser.). (Illus.). 112p. (gr. 10-13). pap. 19.95 (978-0-7643-1489-6(0)) Schiffer Publishing, Ltd.

G and R Publishing Staff. Gifts in a Jar, for Kids. 2002. (Illus.). 128p. (J). pap. 10.00 (978-1-56383-135-5(X)) G&R Publishing.

Gardner, Paul V. The Glass of Frederick Carder. 2001. (Illus.). 373p. (gr. 10-13). 75.00 (978-0-7643-1318-9(5)) Schiffer Publishing, Ltd.

Hopper, Philip. Anchor Hocking Decorated Pitchers & Glasses: The Fire King Years. 2001. (Illus.). 128p. (gr. 10-13). pap. 24.95 (978-0-7643-1488-9(2)) Schiffer Publishing, Ltd.

Ketchum, Marshall. Frederick Carder's Steuben Glass: Guide to Shapes, Numbers, Colors, Finishes & Values. 2002. (Illus.). 192p. (gr. 10-13). pap. 29.95 (978-0-7643-1506-0(4)) Schiffer Publishing, Ltd.

Marsh, Thomas E. The Official Guide to Collecting Applied Color Soda Bottles, Vol. II. 105p. (J). (ps up). pap. (978-0-9633682-1-8(4)) Marsh, Thomas E. Inc.

Mauzy, Barbara E. Sour Cream Glasses. 2002. (Illus.). 92p. (gr. 10-13). pap. 12.95 (978-0-7643-1566-4(8)) Schiffer Publishing, Ltd.

Pina, Leslie. Blenko Catalogs Then & Now: 1959-1961, 1984-2001. 2002. (Schiffer Book for Collectors Ser.). (Illus.). 160p. (gr. 10-13). 29.95 (978-0-7643-1651-7(6)) Schiffer Publishing, Ltd.

—Fostoria American Line 2056. 2nd rev. exp. ed. 2002. (Illus.). 160p. (gr. 10-13). 29.95 (978-0-7643-1532-9(3)) Schiffer Publishing, Ltd.

Pina, Leslie & Vigier, Lorenzo. Scandinavian Glass, 1930-2000: Smoke & Ice. 2002. (Illus.). 224p. (gr. 10-13). 59.95 (978-0-7643-1653-1(2)) Schiffer Publishing, Ltd.

Torsiello, Paul, et al. Paden City Glassware. 2002. (Schiffer Book for Collectors Ser.). (Illus.). 160p. (gr. 10-13). pap. 29.95 (978-0-7643-1493-3(9)) Schiffer Publishing, Ltd.

Walk, John. The Big Book of Fenton Glass: 1940-1970. Gates, Joseph, photos by. 3rd rev. ed. 2001. (Illus.). 208p. (gr. 10-13). pap. 19.95 (978-0-7643-1470-4(X)) Schiffer Publishing, Ltd.

—The Big Book of Fenton Milk Glass: 1940-1985. 2002. (Schiffer Book for Collectors Ser.). (Illus.). 160p. (gr. 10-13). pap. 29.95 (978-0-7643-1596-1(X)) Schiffer Publishing, Ltd.

—Fenton Glass Compendium: 1940-1970. 2001. (Illus.). 224p. (gr. 10-13). 29.95 (978-0-7643-1408-7(4)) Schiffer Publishing, Ltd.

—Fenton Rarities, 1940-1985. 2002. (Schiffer Book for Collectors Ser.). (Illus.). 208p. (gr. 10-13). pap. 29.95 (978-0-7643-1595-4(1)) Schiffer Publishing, Ltd.

—Fenton Special Orders: 1980-Present: QVC; Mary Walrath; Martha Stewart; Cracker Barrel; JC Penney; National Fenton Glass Society; & Fenton Art Glass Club of America. 2003. (Schiffer Book for Collectors Ser.). (Illus.). 240p. 29.95 (978-0-7643-1813-9(6)) Schiffer Publishing, Ltd.

GLENN, JOHN, 1921-

Ashby, Ruth. Rocket Man: The Mercury Adventure of John Glenn. Hunt, Robert, illus. 2004. 144p. (J). 12.95 (978-1-56145-323-8(4)) Peachtree Pubs., Ltd.

Bredeson, Carmen. John Glenn Returns to Orbit: Life on the Space Shuttle. 2000. (Countdown to Space Ser.). (Illus.). 48p. (YA). (gr. 4-10). lib. bdg. 23.93 (978-0-7660-1304-9(9)) Enslow Pubs., Inc.

Burgan, Michael. John Glenn: Young Astronaut. Brown, Robert S., illus. 2000. (Childhood of Famous Americans Ser.). 192p. (J). (gr. 4-6). pap. 5.99 (978-0-689-83397-7(0) , Aladdin) Simon & Schuster Children's Publishing.

—John Glenn: Young Astronaut. 2000. (gr. 3-6). lib. bdg. 13.00 (978-0-613-31379-7(8)) Tandem Library Bks.

Cole, Michael D. John Glenn: Astronaut & Senator. rev. ed. 2000. (People to Know Ser.). (Illus.). 112p. (YA). (gr. 6-12). lib. bdg. 26.60 (978-0-7660-1532-6(7)) Enslow Pubs., Inc.

Dunn, Herb. John Glenn: Young Astronaut. Brown, Robert S., illus. 2000. (Childhood of Famous Americans Ser.). (J). 11.64 (978-0-606-19714-4(1)) Tandem Library Bks.

Green, Robert. John Glenn: Astronaut & U. S. Senator. 2000. (Career Biographies Ser.). (Illus.). 128p. (YA). (gr. 6-12). 25.00 (978-0-89434-341-4(6) , F403, Ferguson Publishing Co.) Facts On File, Inc.

Harcourt School Publishers Staff. J. Glenn in Space: Take-Home Book. 1999. (Collections Ser.). (Illus.). (J). pap. 1.90 (978-0-15-317214-4(2)) Harcourt Schl. Pubs.

—The Three Orbits of John Glenn Below Level. 3rd ed. 2002. (Trophies Reading Program Ser.). (Illus.). pap. 5.10 (978-0-15-323428-6(8)) Harcourt Schl. Pubs.

—The 3 Orbits of John Glenn: Take-Home Book. 2001. (Collections Ser.). (Illus.). (J). pap. 1.90 (978-0-15-319668-3(8)) Harcourt Schl. Pubs.

Hilliard, Richard. Godspeed, John Glenn. 2006. (Illus.). (J). 16.95 (978-1-59078-384-9(0)) Boyds Mills Pr.

Holden, Henry M. Trailblazing Astronaut John Glenn: A MyReportLinks. com Book. 2004. (Space Flight Adventures & Disasters Ser.). (Illus.). 48p. (J). lib. bdg. 25.26 (978-0-7660-5166-9(8) , MyReportLinks.com Bks.) Enslow Pubs., Inc.

Kramer, Barbara. John Glenn: A Space Biography. 1998. (Countdown to Space Ser.). (Illus.). 48p. (YA). (gr. 4-10). lib. bdg. 23.93 (978-0-89490-964-1(9)) Enslow Pubs., Inc.

Marsh, Carole. John Glenn. 2002. (One Thousand Readers Ser.). (Illus.). 12p. (J). (gr. k-4). 2.95 (978-0-635-01564-8(1) , 15641) Gallopade International.

—John Glenn: An Ohio Experience Reader. 2001. (J). (gr. k-5). pap. 1.95 (978-0-635-00440-6(2)) Gallopade International.

Mitchell, Don. Liftoff: A Photobiography of John Glenn. 2006. (Illus.). 64p. (J). (gr. 4-8). lib. bdg. 27.90 (978-0-7922-5900-8(9)); (gr. 5-9). pap. 17.95 (978-0-7922-5899-5(1)) National Geographic Society. (National Geographic Children's Bks.).

Raum, Elizabeth. John Glenn. 2005. (American Lives Ser.). (Illus.). 32p. (J). (978-1-4034-6940-3(7)); pap. (978-1-4034-6947-2(4)) Heinemann Library.

Streissguth, Thomas. John Glenn. 2003. (Explore Space! Ser.). (Illus.). 24p. (J). (gr. 1-2). lib. bdg. 18.60 (978-0-7368-1625-0(9) , Bridgestone Bks.) Capstone Pr., Inc.

—John Glenn. 2003. (Biography Ser.). (Illus.). 112p. (J). (gr. 6 up). pap. 7.95 (978-0-8225-9685-1(7)) Lerner Publishing Group.

—John Glenn. 1999. (Illus.). (J). (978-0-606-18822-7(3)) Tandem Library Bks.

Streissguth, Tom. John Glenn. 2005. (Bios for Challenged Readers Ser.). (Illus.). 112p. (J). (gr. 6-12). lib. bdg. 27.93 (978-0-8225-2274-4(8)) Lerner Publishing Group.

—John Glenn. 1999. (gr. 7-12). lib. bdg. 16.40 (978-0-613-81316-7(2)) Tandem Library Bks.

Tilton, Rafael. John Glenn. 2000. (Importance of Ser.). (Illus.). 120p. (J). (gr. 7-10). 27.45 (978-1-56006-689-7(X) , Lucent Bks.) Thomson Gale.

Vogt, Greg. John Glenn's Return to Space. 2000. (Illus.). 72p. (gr. 5-8). lib. bdg. 24.90 (978-0-7613-1614-5(0) , Millbrook Pr.) Lerner Publishing Group.

Zelon, Helen. The Mercury 6 Mission: The First American Astronaut to Orbit Earth. 2002. (Space Missions Ser.). (Illus.). 24p. (J). (gr. 2-4). lib. bdg. 19.95 (978-0-8239-5770-5(5) , PowerKids Pr.) Rosen Publishing Group, Inc., The.

GLIDERS (AERONAUTICS)

Clark, Nancy Lawrence, ed. Gliders Soaring: The Sport of Motorless Flight with Pioneer Larry Lawrence. 2003. (Illus.). 120p. (J). pap. 15.00 (978-0-9641197-2-7(2)) Clark Pubs.

Loves, June. Balloons, Kites, Airships & Gliders. 2001. (Flight Ser.). (Illus.). (J). (gr. 5 up). 27.00 (978-0-7910-6563-1(4) , 010302, Chelsea Hse.) Facts On File, Inc.

GLIDERS (AERONAUTICS)—FICTION

Appleton, Victor. Tom Swift & His Air Glider or Seeking. 2006. pap. (***978-1-4065-0895-6(0)*** Dodo Pr.

GLIDING AND SOARING

Billings, Henry & Billings, Melissa. Hang Gliding: Livewire Investigates. 1999. (Livewires Ser.). (Illus.). 32p. pap. (978-0-340-74719-3(6) , Hodder Arnold) Hodder Education.

Clark, Nancy Lawrence, ed. Gliders Soaring: The Sport of Motorless Flight with Pioneer Larry Lawrence. 2003. (Illus.). 120p. (J). pap. 15.00 (978-0-9641197-2-7(2)) Clark Pubs.

Rigby Education Staff. Gliders & Sliders. (Sails Literacy Ser.). (Illus.). 16p. (gr. 1-2). 27.00 (978-0-7635-9922-5(0) , 699220C99) Rigby Education.

Schindler, John E. Hang Gliding & Parasailing. 2005. (Extreme Sports Ser.). (Illus.). 24p. (J). pap. 5.95 (978-0-8368-4547-1(1)); (YA). lib. bdg. 22.00 (978-0-8368-4540-2(4)) Stevens, Gareth Inc.

GLOBAL SATELLITE COMMUNICATIONS SYSTEMS

see Artificial Satellites in Telecommunication

GLOBAL WARMING

Biskup, Agnieszka. Understanding Global Warming with Max Axiom, Super Scientist. Martin, Cynthia & Anderson, Bill, illus. 2008. (J). (***978-1-4296-0139-9(6)*** Capstone Pr., Inc.

Bradley, Suzannah. Global Warming. 2005. (Your Environment Ser.). (Illus.). 32p. (J). (978-1-59604-063-2(7)) Stargazer Bks.

El Calentamiento Global. 2003. (Essential Science Ser.). (SPA.). (J). pap. (978-970-690-602-1(9)) Planeta Mexicana Editorial S. A. de C. V.

Capstone Press Editors. Global Warming. 2002. (Our Planet in Peril Ser.). (Illus.). 48p. (J). (gr. 3-4). lib. bdg. 22.60 (978-0-7368-1361-7(6) , Bridgestone Bks.) Capstone Pr., Inc.

—Our Planet in Peril, 4 bks. Incl. Acid Rain. lib. bdg. 22.60 (978-0-7368-1360-0(8)); Global Warming. lib. bdg. 22.60 (978-0-7368-1361-7(6)); Nuclear Waste. lib. bdg. 22.60 (978-0-7368-1362-4(4)); Oil Spills. lib. bdg. 22.60 (978-0-7368-1363-1(2)); 48p. (J). (gr. 3-4). 2002. (Illus.). 2002. Set lib. bdg. 90.40 (978-0-7368-1364-8(0) , Bridgestone Bks.) Capstone Pr., Inc.

Cheel, Richard. Global Warming Alert! 2007. (Disaster Alert! Ser.). (Illus.). 32p. (J). (gr. 2-9). (***978-0-7787-1587-0(6)***); pap. (***978-0-7787-1619-8(8)*** Crabtree Publishing Co.

Cohen, Judith Love & Friend, Robyn C. A Clean Sky: The Global Warming Story. Katz, David A., illus. 2007. (J). pap. 7.00 (***978-1-880599-81-5(3)*** Cascade Pass, Inc.

—A clean Sky: The Global Warming Story. Katz, David A., illus. l.t. ed. 2007. 42p. (J). 13.95 (***978-1-880599-82-2(1)*** Cascade Pass, Inc.

Dan Minkel. Global Warming. 2006. (Introducing Issues with Opposing Viewpoints Ser.). (Illus.). 244p. (J). (gr. 7-10). 33.70 (978-0-7377-3564-2(3) , Greenhaven Pr., Inc.) Thomson Gale.

David, Laurie & Gordon, Cambria. The Down-to-Earth Guide to Global Warming. 2007. (Illus.). 128p. (J). (gr. 4-7). pap. 15.99 (***978-0-439-02494-5(3)*** , Orchard Bks.) Scholastic, Inc.

Donnelly, Karen. Rising Temperatures of the Past & the Future. 2003. (Earths Changing Weather & Climate Ser.). (Illus.). 24p. (J). lib. bdg. 18.75 (978-0-8239-6214-3(8) , PowerKids Pr.) Rosen Publishing Group, Inc., The.

Donnelly, Karen J. Floods of the Past & Future. 2003. (Earths Changing Weather & Climate Ser.). (Illus.). 24p. (J). lib. bdg. 18.75 (978-0-8239-6218-1(0)) Rosen Publishing Group, Inc., The.

—Ice Ages of the Past & the Future. 2003. (Earths Changing Weather & Climate Ser.). (Illus.). 24p. (J). lib. bdg. 18.75 (978-0-8239-6219-8(9) , PowerKids Pr.) Rosen Publishing Group, Inc., The.

Evans, Kate. Weird Weather: Everything You Didn't Want to Know about Climate Change but Probably Should Find Out. 2007. (Illus.), 96p. (YA). (gr. 7 up). 15.95 (***978-0-88899-838-5(4)***); pap. 9.95 (***978-0-88899-841-5(4)*** Groundwood Bks. CAN. *Dist:* Perseus Distribution.

Farrar, Amy. Global Warming. 2007. (Essential Viewpoints Ser.). (ENG., Illus.). 112p. (YA). (gr. 7-9). lib. bdg. 32.79 (***978-1-59928-859-8(1)*** , Essential Library) ABDO Publishing Co.

Fretwell, Holly. The Sky's Not Falling! Why It's Ok to Chill about Global Warming. 2007. (Illus.). 126p. (J). (gr. 4-7). per. (***978-0-9767269-4-4(7)*** World Ahead Media.

Friedman, Katherine. What If the Polar Ice Caps Melted? 2002. (What If Ser.). (Illus.). 48p. (YA). (gr. 7-12). 24.00 (978-0-516-23914-9(7)); pap. 6.95 (978-0-516-23477-9(3)) Scholastic Library Publishing. (Children's Pr.).

—What If the Polar Ice Caps Melted? 2002. (gr. 7-12). lib. bdg. 15.25 (978-0-613-58817-1(7)) Tandem Library Bks.

Global Warming. (Our Planet in Peril Ser.). 24p. (YA). 7.95 (978-0-7368-3295-3(5)) Capstone Pr., Inc.

Gore, Al. An Inconvenient Truth: The Crisis of Global Warming. 2007. (Illus.). 192p. (J). (gr. 5-8). 23.00 (978-0-670-06271-3(5)); pap. 16.00 (978-0-670-06272-0(3)) Penguin Group (USA) Inc. (Viking Juvenile).

E F G

Green, Kenneth. Global Warming: Understanding the Debate. 2002. (Issues in Focus Ser.). (Illus.). 128p. (YA). (gr. 6-12). lib. bdg. 26.60 (978-0-7660-1691-0(9)) Enslow Pubs., Inc.

Haugen, David & Musser, Susan. Is Global Warming a Threat. 2007. (At Issue Ser.). (Illus.). 128p. (YA). (gr. 10-12). 28.70 (***978-0-7377-3687-8(9)**); pap. 19.95 (***978-0-7377-3688-5(7)*** Thomson Gale. (Greenhaven Pr., Inc.).

Johnson, Kirk R. Gas Trees & Car Turds: A Kids' Guide to the Roots of Global Warming. Bonnell, Mary Ann, illus. (YA). (gr. 3 up). pap. 16.95 (***978-1-55591-666-4(X)*** Fulcrum Publishing.

Johnson, Rebecca L. Global Warming. 2002. (Science Issues Today Ser.). (Illus.). 32p. (J). (978-0-7922-8873-2(4)) National Geographic Society.

Leathers, Dan. The Snows of Kilimanjaro. 2007. (On the Verge of Extinction Ser.). (Illus.). 32p. (J). (gr. 1-4). lib. bdg. 25.70 (***978-1-58415-584-3(1)*** Mitchell Lane Pubs., Inc.

Maslin, Mark. Global Warming: Causes, Effects, & the Future. rev. ed. 2007. (Illus.). 72p. pap. 17.95 (978-0-7603-2965-8(6)) Voyageur Pr., Inc.

Morgan, Sally. Changing Climate. 2007. (Illus.). 32p. (J). (***978-1-59771-067-1(9)*** Sea-To-Sea Pubns.

Morgan, Sally. Global Warming. 2003. (Science at the Edge Ser.). (Illus.). 64p. (J). (gr. 6-8). lib. bdg. 27.86 (978-1-4034-0324-7(4)) Heinemann Library.

Morris, Neil. Global Warming. 2006. (Illus.). 48p. (J). pap. (***978-0-8368-7762-5(4)***); pap. (***978-0-8368-8155-4(9)***); lib. bdg. (***978-0-8368-7755-7(1)*** Stevens, Gareth Inc. (World Almanac Library).

Parks, Peggy J. Global Warming. (Our Environment Ser.). (Illus.). (J). (ps-7). 2004. 48p. lib. bdg. 26.20 (978-0-7377-1822-5(6) , Greenhaven Pr., Inc.); 2003. 111p. 29.95 (978-1-59018-319-9(3) , Lucent Bks.) Thomson Gale.

Pringle, Laurence P. Global Warming: Assessing the Greenhouse Threat. 2003. (Illus.). 48p. (J). (gr. 3-7). pap. 6.95 (978-1-58717-228-1(3) , SeaStar Bks.) Chronicle Bks. LLC.

—Global Warming: The Threat of Earth's Changing Climate. 2001. (Illus.). 48p. (J). (gr. 5-8). 16.95 (978-1-58717-009-6(4) , SeaStar Bks.) Chronicle Bks. LLC.

Puay, Lim Cheng. The Warming Planet. 2004. (Green Alert Ser.). (Illus.). 24p. (J). lib. bdg. 28.56 (978-0-7398-7014-3(9)) Raintree.

Robinson, Matthew. Global Warming: Crisis or Myth? 2007. (J). (***978-1-4042-1925-0(0)*** Rosen Publishing Group, Inc., The.

Rockwell, Anne F. Why Are the Ice Caps Melting? The Dangers of Global Warming. Meisel, Paul, illus. 2006. (Let's-Read-and-Find-Out Science Ser.). 40p. (J). (gr. 2-4). 15.99 (978-0-06-054669-4(7)); pap. 5.99 (978-0-06-054671-7(9)) HarperCollins Pubs.

Royston, Angela. Buildings of the Future. 2007. (J). pap. (***978-1-4329-0131-8(1)***); lib. bdg. (***978-1-4329-0126-4(5)*** Heinemann Library.

—Consumerism of the Future. 2007. (J). (***978-1-4329-0128-8(1)*** Heinemann Library.

—Energy of the Future. 2007. (J). pap. (***978-1-4329-0134-9(6)***); lib. bdg. (***978-1-4329-0129-5(X)*** Heinemann Library.

—Travel of the Future. 2007. (J). pap. (***978-1-4329-0132-5(X)***); lib. bdg. (***978-1-4329-0127-1(3)*** Heinemann Library.

Shaw, Jane S., ed. Global Warming. 2002. (Critical Thinking about Environmental Issues Ser.). (Illus.). 112p. (J). 33.70 (978-0-7377-1270-4(8) , Greenhaven Pr., Inc.) Thomson Gale.

Silverstein, Alvin, et al. Global Warming. 2003. (Science Concepts Ser.). (Illus.). 64p. (gr. 5-8). lib. bdg. 26.90 (978-0-7613-2256-6(6) , Twenty-First Century Bks.) Lerner Publishing Group.

Stein, Paul. Global Warming: A Threat to Our Future. 2001. (Library of Future Weather & Climate). (Illus.). 64p. (YA). (gr. 4-6). lib. bdg. 26.50 (978-0-8239-3414-0(4)) Rosen Publishing Group, Inc., The.

—Storms of the Future. 2001. (Library of Future Weather & Climate). (Illus.). 64p. (YA). (gr. 4-6). lib. bdg. 26.50 (978-0-8239-3417-1(9)) Rosen Publishing Group, Inc., The.

Stoyles, Pennie, et al. Global Warming. 2003. 32p. (J). lib. bdg. 24.25 (978-1-58340-328-0(0)) Smart Apple Media.

Tara, Stephanie/Tara. Snowy White World. Walton, Alex, illus. 2007. (J). 16.95 (***978-1-933285-89-4(3)*** Brown Bks. Publishing Group.

Taylor, Barbara. How to Save the Planet. Anderson, Scoular, illus. 2001. (How to Ser.). 96p. (J). (gr. 5-7). 16.00 (978-0-531-14640-8(5)); pap. 4.95 (978-0-531-14821-1(1)) Scholastic Library Publishing. (Watts, Franklin).

—How to Save the Planet. 2001. (gr. 5-8). lib. bdg. 12.95 (978-0-613-54552-5(4)) Tandem Library Bks.

Tesar, Jenny. Global Warming. 1999. (Illus.). 114p. (YA). (gr. 7-12). lib. bdg. 23.95 (978-0-7351-0214-9(7)) Replica Bks.

Thornhill, Jan. This Is My Planet: The Kids' Guide to Global Warming. 2007. (Illus.). 64p. (J). (gr. 4-8). 21.95 (***978-1-897349-06-9(8)***); pap. 10.95 (***978-1-897349-07-6(6)*** Maple Tree Pr. CAN. *Dist:* Perseus Distribution.

Unwin, Mike. Climate Change. 2006. (Planet under Pressure Ser.). (Illus.). 48p. (YA). (gr. 6-8). lib. bdg. 31.43 (***978-1-4034-8216-7(0)*** Heinemann Library.

Vogel, Carole G. Human Impact. 2003. (Restless Sea Ser.). (Illus.). 96p. (J). (gr. 5-8). 30.50 (978-0-531-12323-2(5) , Watts, Franklin) Scholastic Library Publishing.

—Human Impact. 2003. (gr. 5-8). lib. bdg. 22.20 (978-0-613-67817-9(6)) Tandem Library Bks.

Woodward, John. Climate Change. 2008. (DK Eyewitness Bks.). 72p. (J). (gr. 3-8). lib. bdg. 19.99 (***978-0-7566-3770-5(8)*** Dorling Kindersley Publishing, Inc.

GLOBE THEATRE (SOUTHWARK, LONDON, ENGLAND)

Aliki. William Shakespeare & the Globe. Aliki, illus. 1999. (Illus.). 48p. (J). (gr. 7 up). lib. bdg. 17.89 (978-0-06-027821-2(8)) HarperCollins Pubs.

—William Shakespeare & the Globe. 2000. (J). (978-0-606-20008-0(8)) Tandem Library Bks.

Allison, Amy. Shakespeare's Globe. 1999. (Building History Ser.). (Illus.). 96p. (YA). (gr. 6-9). 27.45 (978-1-56006-526-5(5) , Lucent Bks.) Thomson Gale.

Chrisp, Peter. Welcome to the Globe! The Story of Shakespeare's Theater. Martin, Linda, ed. 2000. (Readers Ser.). (Illus.). 48p. (J). (gr. 3-5). pap. 3.99 (978-0-7894-6640-2(6)) Dorling Kindersley Publishing, Inc.

—Welcome to the Globe! The Story of Shakespeare's Theater. 2000. (Eyewitness Readers Ser.). (J). (978-0-606-20130-8(0)) Tandem Library Bks.

—Welcome to the Globe! the Story of Shakespeare's Theater. 2000. (gr. k-3). lib. bdg. 11.80 (978-0-613-33212-5(1)) Tandem Library Bks.

Chrisp, Peter & Dorling Kindersley Publishing Staff. Welcome to the Globe! The Story of Shakespeare's Theater. 2000. (Eyewitness Readers). (Illus.). 48p. (J). (gr. 2-4). 12.99 (978-0-7894-6641-9(4)) Dorling Kindersley Publishing, Inc.

Langley, Andrew. Shakespeare's Theatre. 2000. (978-0-606-20908-3(5)) Tandem Library Bks.

GLOBE THEATRE (SOUTHWARK, LONDON, ENGLAND)—FICTION

Blackwood, Gary L. Shakespeare's Spy. 2005. 288p. (J). (gr. 5-9). pap. 6.99 (978-0-14-240311-2(3) , Puffin) Penguin Group (USA) Inc.

Cooper, Susan. King of Shadows. Clapp, John, illus. 192p. (J). (gr. 5-9). 2001. mass mkt. 5.99 (978-0-689-84445-4(X) , Aladdin); 1999. 16.00 (978-0-689-82817-1(9) , McElderry, Margaret K.) Simon & Schuster Children's Publishing.

—King of Shadows. l.t. ed. 2000. (Thorndike Press Large Print Juvenile Ser.). (Illus.). 246p. (J). (gr. 8-12). 21.95 (978-0-7862-2706-8(0)) Thorndike Pr.

GLOBES

Aberg, Rebecca. Latitude & Longitude. 2003. (Rookie Read-About Geography Ser.). (Illus.). 32p. (J). (gr. 1-2). 20.50 (978-0-516-22723-8(8) , Children's Pr.) Scholastic Library Publishing.

Bredeson, Carmen. Looking at Maps & Globes. 2002. (Rookie Read-About Geography Ser.). (Illus.). 32p. (J). (gr. 1-2). pap. 5.95 (978-0-516-25982-6(2) , Children's Pr.) Scholastic Library Publishing.

—Looking at Maps & Globes. 2001. (gr. k-3). lib. bdg. 14.10 (978-0-613-54284-5(3)) Tandem Library Bks.

—Mapas y Globos Terraqueos. (J). (gr. k-2). 2006. (SPA.). 32p. pap. 5.95 (978-0-516-25043-4(4)); 2005. (ENG & SPA., Illus.). 31p. 19.50 (978-0-516-25241-4(0)) Scholastic Library Publishing. (Children's Pr.).

Edson, Ann & Insel, Eunice. Reading Maps, Globes, Charts, Graphs. (J). (gr. 4-6). stu. ed., instr.'s gde. ed. 39.00 incl. audio (978-0-89525-175-6(2) , AKC 356) Educational Activities, Inc.

Geography, Rookie Read-About Geography: Maps & Globes. 2004. (Illus.). 114.00 (978-0-516-29652-4(3)) Scholastic Library Publishing.

Nelson, Robin. Globes. 2004. (First Step Nonfiction Ser.). (J). pap. (978-0-8225-5391-5(0)) Lerner Publishing Group.

GLOSSARIES

see also names of language or subject with the subdivision dictionaries, e.g. English Language—Dictionaries; Chemistry—Dictionaries

Stojic, Manya. Hello World! Greetings in 42 Languages Around the Globe! Stojic, Manya, illus. 2002. (ENG & MUL., Illus.). 40p. (J). (ps-2). pap. 14.95 (978-0-439-36202-3(4) , Cartwheel Bks.) Scholastic, Inc.

GLOVES

Salas, Laura Purdie. Whose Gloves Are These? A Look at Gloves Workers Wear—Leather, Cloth, & Rubber. Muehlenhardt, Amy Bailey, illus. 2006. (Whose Is It? Ser.). 24p. (J). (ps-2). 22.60 (978-1-4048-1599-5(6)) Picture Window Bks.

Warren, Jean. Mittens. Cubley, Kathleen, ed. 1998. (Sticker Book Ser.). (Illus.). 32p. (J). (ps). pap. 3.95 (978-1-57029-222-4(1) , WPH 3712, Totline Pubns.) Schaffer, Frank Pubns.

GNOMES

see Fairies

GO KARTS

see Karts and Karting

GOATS

Bregoli, Jane. The Goat Lady. 2005. 32p. (J). (gr. 3-6). 16.95 (978-0-88448-260-4(X)) Tilbury Hse. Pubs.

Ciovacco, Justine. Goats. 2007. (J). (***978-1-59939-121-2(X)*** , Reader's Digest Young Families, Inc.) Reader's Digest Children's Publishing, Inc.

Damerow, Gail. Your Goats: A Kid's Guide to Raising & Showing. 2003. (Illus.). 176p. (gr. 4-7). pap. 14.95 (978-0-88266-825-3(0) , 66825) Storey Publishing, LLC.

The Goat: KinderReaders Individual Title Six-Packs. (Kinderstarters Ser.). 8p. (ps-1). 21.00 (978-0-7635-8658-4(7)) Rigby Education.

Goats: Individual Title Six-Packs. 16p. (gr. 2 up). 36.00 (978-0-7635-9213-4(7)) Rigby Education.

The Goats: Individual Title Six-Packs. (Sails Literacy Ser.). 16p. (gr. k up). 27.00 (978-0-7635-4408-9(6)) Rigby Education.

Goats on the Farm, 6 vols. (gr. k-2). 28.95 (978-0-7368-9381-7(4)) Red Brick Learning.

Green, Emily. Goats. 2007. (Blastoff! Readers Ser.). 24p. (J). (gr. k-2). 18.50 (***978-0-531-17552-1(9)*** , Children's Pr.) Scholastic Library Publishing.

Green, Emily K. Goats. 2007. (Illus.). 24p. (J). lib. bdg. 16.95 (978-1-60014-066-2(1)) Bellwether Media.

Hudak, Heather C. Goats. 2006. (J). (978-1-59036-424-6(4)); (978-1-59036-431-4(7)) Weigl Pubs., Inc.

Ketel, Debbie M. One Baby Mountain Goat. Horstman, Lisa, illus. 2005. (J). bds. 6.99 (978-0-9752617-3-6(8)) Mount Rushmore History Assn.

Macken, JoAnn Early. Goats. 2004. (Illus.). 24p. (J). pap. (978-0-8368-4280-7(4)); (YA). lib. bdg. 19.33 (978-0-8368-4273-9(1)) Stevens, Gareth Inc.

—Goats: Las Cabras. 2004. (ENG & SPA., Illus.). 24p. (J). pap. (978-0-8368-4294-4(4)); lib. bdg. 19.33 (978-0-8368-4287-6(1)) Stevens, Gareth Inc.

—Mountain Goats. 2006. (Illus.). 24p. (J). pap. 5.95 (978-0-8368-6327-7(5)); lib. bdg. 19.33 (978-0-8368-6320-8(8)) Stevens, Gareth Inc.

Miller, Heather. My Goats. 2000. (Welcome Bks.). (Illus.). 24p. (J). (ps-3). 17.00 (978-0-516-23107-5(3) , Children's Pr.) Scholastic Library Publishing.

—My Goats. 2000. (gr. k-3). lib. bdg. 12.95 (978-0-613-58862-1(2)) Tandem Library Bks.

Miller, Sara Swan. Goats. 2001. (True Bks.). (Illus.). 48p. (J). (gr. 3-5). pap. 6.95 (978-0-516-27182-8(2) , Children's Pr.) Scholastic Library Publishing.

—Goats. 2000. (gr. 3-6). lib. bdg. 15.25 (978-0-613-54514-3(1)) Tandem Library Bks.

Morgan, Sally. Goats. 2007. (QEB Down on the Farm Ser.). (J). lib. bdg. 15.95 (***978-1-59566-389-4(4)*** QEB Publishing Inc.

Mr Magee's Goats: Individual Title Six-Packs. (Sails Literacy Ser.). (gr. 1-2). 36.00 (978-0-7578-6713-2(8)) Rigby Education.

Murray, Julie. Goats. 2002. (Buddy Book Ser.). (Illus.). 24p. (J). (gr. k-4). lib. bdg. 21.35 (978-1-57765-700-2(4)) ABDO Publishing Co.

Roumain, Marika. Kabrit Mawon. 2000. Tr. of Brown Goat. (CRP., Illus.). 24p. (J). (gr. k-2). pap. 8.50 (978-1-58432-016-6(8)); (gr. 3-5). 19.50 (978-1-58432-063-0(X)) Educa Vision.

—Kabrit Nwa Kisa ou Tnde? Roumain, Marika, illus. 2000. (Big Book Ser.). (Illus.). (J). (gr. k-2). pap. 19.50 (978-1-58432-036-4(2)) Educa Vision.

—Kabrit Peyi Kabrit Peyi. 2000. (Big Book Ser.). (CRP., Illus.). 14p. (J). (gr. 3-5). 19.50 (978-1-58432-064-7(8)) Educa Vision.

Schuh, Mari C. Goats on the Farm. 2002. (On the Farm Ser.). (Illus.). 24p. (J). (gr. k-1). lib. bdg. 15.93 (978-0-7368-1188-0(5) , Pebble Bks.) Capstone Pr., Inc.

—Goats on the Farm. (On the Farm Ser.). 24p. (J). pap. 5.95 (978-0-7368-9380-0(6)) Capstone Pr., Inc.

Top That Publishing Staff, ed. Wacky Goat. 2004. (Wacky Animals Ser.). (Illus.). 10p. (J). pap. (978-1-84510-087-2(5)) Top That! Publishing PLC.

Whitehouse, Patricia. La Cabra Montes. 2003. (Animales del Zoologico (Zoo Animals) Ser.). (SPA., 24p. (ps-1). Illus.). (J). lib. bdg. 17.08 (978-1-4034-0333-9(3)); pap. 5.25 (978-1-4034-0551-7(4)) Heinemann Library.

—Mountain Goat. 2003. (Zoo Animals Ser.). (Illus.). 24p. (J). (ps-1). lib. bdg. 17.08 (978-1-58810-890-6(2)); pap. 5.75 (978-1-4034-0541-8(7)) Heinemann Library.

—Mountain Goat. 2002. (ps-2). lib. bdg. 13.30 (978-0-613-88918-6(5)) Tandem Library Bks.

Wolfman, Judy. Life on a Goat Farm. Winston, David Lorenz, photos by. 2005. (Life on a Farm Ser.). (Illus.). 48p. (gr. 2-5). lib. bdg. 23.93 (978-1-57505-515-2(5)) Lerner Publishing Group.

Wood, Ramona. The Goat Woman of Smackover: An Arkansas Legend. Wood, Ramona, . 2006. (Illus.). 32p. (J). 11.00 (978-0-9758622-1-6(9)) ABC Pr.

GOATS—FICTION

Abedi & Neuendorf. No Quiero Verte Mas! 2004. (SPA., Illus.). 196p. (J). 17.99 (978-84-261-3303-8(7)) Juventud, Editorial ESP. *Dist:* Lectorum Pubns., Inc.

Alakija, Polly. Catch That Goat! (Illus.). 32p. (J). 2004. pap. 6.99 (978-1-84148-161-6(0)); 2002. 16.99 (978-1-84148-908-7(5)) Barefoot Bks., Inc.

Amery, Heather. Grumpy Goat. Cartwright, Stephen, illus. 2004. 16p. (J). pap. 5.95 (978-0-7945-0788-6(3) , Usborne) EDC Publishing.

Artigas de Sierra, Ione M. La Chivita del Cebollar. (Superbks./Superlibros). (J). (gr. k-1). 21.95 (978-0-88272-486-7(X)); (Illus.). 16p. pap. 6.95 (978-0-88272-487-4(8)); Big Book. (SPA.). 21.95 (978-0-88272-484-3(3)) Santillana USA Publishing Co., Inc.

B Small Publishing Staff. Three Billy Goats Gruff. 1999. (Illus.). 24p. pap. (978-1-874735-29-8(8)) B Small Publishing.

Baglio, Ben M. Goat in the Garden. McNicholas, Shelagh, illus. 1998. (Animal Ark Ser.: No. 4). (J). (gr. 3-5). 10.64 (978-0-606-13132-2(9)) Tandem Library Bks.

Ballesteros, Xose. Los Siete Cabritos. (SPA.). 32p. (J). (978-84-8464-020-2(5)) Kalandraka Editora, S.L. ESP. *Dist:* Lectorum Pubns., Inc.

Barkow, Henriette. Three Billy Goats Gruff. Johnson, Richard, illus. 2004. 24p. (J). (TAM, CZE, SPA, GUJ & PER.). (978-1-85269-611-5(7)); (TAM, CZE, SPA, GUJ & PER.). (978-1-85269-612-2(5)); (TAM, CZE, SPA, GUJ & PER.). (978-1-85269-614-6(1)); (TAM, CZE, SPA, GUJ & PER.). (978-1-85269-615-3(X)); (TAM, CZE, SPA, GUJ & PER.). (978-1-85269-616-0(8)); (TAM, CZE, SPA, GUJ & PER.). (978-1-85269-617-6(6)); (TAM, CZE, SPA, GUJ & PER.). (978-1-85269-618-4(4)); (TAM, CZE, SPA, GUJ & PER.). (978-1-85269-619-1(2)); (TAM, CZE, SPA, GUJ & PER.). (978-1-85269-620-7(6)); (TAM, CZE, SPA, GUJ & PER.). (978-1-85269-621-4(4)); (TAM, CZE, SPA, GUJ & PER.). (978-1-85269-622-1(2)); (CZE, TAM, SPA, GUJ & PER.). (978-1-85269-623-8(0)); (TAM, CZE, SPA, GUJ & PER.). (978-1-85269-624-5(9)); (TAM, CZE, SPA, GUJ & PER.). (978-1-85269-625-2(7)); (TAM, CZE, SPA, GUJ & SER.). (978-1-85269-627-6(3)); (ENG & GER.). (978-1-85269-785-3(7)) Mantra Publishing, Ltd.

Bendro Bach. 2005. (WEL., Illus.). 30p. (978-1-902416-84-7(8)) Cymdeithas Lyfrau Ceredigion.

Benningfield, Cece. Angora Kidd. Arnold, Dan, illus. 2000. 32p. 16.95 (978-1-57168-378-6(X)); 8.95 (978-1-57168-394-6(1)) Eakin Pr.

Bester, Maryanne. Three Friends & a Taxi. Bester, Shayle, illus. 2007. 24p. (J). pap. 12.00 (***978-1-77009-265-5(X)*** Jacana Media ZAF. *Dist:* Independent Pubs. Group.

Bingham, Jane. Billy Goat's Gruff Cd Pack. rev. ed. 2007. (Young Reading CD Packs Ser.). 48p. (J). 9.99 (***978-0-7945-1867-7(2)*** , Usborne) EDC Publishing.

Bingham, Jane, retold by. Billy Goats Gruff. 2005. (Young Reading Gift Books Ser.). 48p. (J). (gr. 2 up). 8.95 (978-0-7945-0889-0(8) , Usborne) EDC Publishing.

Blyton, Enid. Don't Be Silly Mr Twiddle! (Illus.). 111p. (J). pap. 7.95 (978-0-7475-3858-5(1)) Bloomsbury Publishing Plc GBR. *Dist:* Trafalgar Square Publishing.

Bonning, Tony. Poli el Granjero. Hobson, Sally, illus. 2nd ed. 2001. (SPA.). 32p. (J). (gr. k-2). (978-84-89675-87-2(2) , ZZ1087) Zendrera Zariquiey, Editorial ESP. *Dist:* Lectorum Pubns., Inc.

Brewer, Dottie A. Jessie's Walk. Naenix, Robin, illus. 2004. 20p. (J). 4.95 (978-0-9707945-7-4(6)) Billion $ Baby Pubns.

Brightwood, Laura, illus. Bully Goat Grim. Brightwood, Laura, . 2006. (J). (978-0-9779290-2-3(7)) 3-C Institute for Social Development.

Brooks, Yvonne & Grant, Steven. The Goat Kids Explore the Woods. 2006. (Illus.). 32p. (J). 14.95 (***978-0-9791021-1-0(1)*** Lotus Pond Media.

—Meet the Goat Kids. l.t. ed. 2006. (Illus.). 32p. (J). 14.95 (***978-0-9791021-0-3(3)*** , 978-0-9791021-0-3) Lotus Pond Media.

Broome, Errol. What a Goat! Thompson, Sharon, illus. 2004. (Annick Chapter Bks.). 72p. (J). (gr. 2-4). 16.95 (978-1-55037-869-6(4)) Annick Pr., Ltd. CAN. *Dist:* Firefly Bks., Ltd.

Capdevila, Roser. El Lobo y los Siete Cabritos. 2002. (Cuentos Fantasticos de las Tres Mellizas Coleccion: Vol. 2). (SPA.). (J). (gr. k-2). pap. 5.95 (978-1-930332-36-2(X)) Lectorum Pubns., Inc.

—El Loby Y Los Siete Cabritos. 2002. (SPA.). (gr. k-3). lib. bdg. 14.10 (978-0-613-64537-9(5)) Tandem Library Bks.

Capriola, Arlene & Swenson, Rigmor. The Three Billy Goats Gruff. Mastry, Cherisse, ed. Burns, Kathy, illus. 1998. (Once upon a Time Ser.). (J). (gr. k-2). pap., wbk. ed. incl. audio (978-1-57022-169-9(3)) ECS Learning Systems, Inc.

La Chevre de Monsieur Seguin. 2000. (Musicontes Ser.). (FRE.). (J). 24.95 incl. audio (978-2-09-230431-0(3)) Nathan, Fernand FRA. *Dist:* Distribooks, Inc.

Church, Caroline Jayne, illus. Little Apple Goat. 2007. 28p. (J). (ps-2). 16.00 (***978-0-8028-5320-2(X)*** , Eerdmans Bks For Young Readers) Eerdmans, William B. Publishing Co.

Cook, Sherry & Johnson, Terri. Gilbert Gas, 26 vols. Kuhn, Jesse, illus. l.t. ed. 2006. (Quirkles—Exploring Phonics through Science Ser.: 7). 32p. (J). 7.99 (978-1-933815-06-0(X) , Quirkles, The) Creative 3, LLC.

Coville, Bruce. Thor's Wedding Day: By Thialfi, the goat boy, as told to & translated by Bruce Coville. Cogswell, Matthew, illus. 2008. 144p. (J). pap. 5.95 (978-0-15-205872-2(9) , Magic Carpet Bks.) Harcourt Children's Bks.

Crummel, Susan Stevens. Ten-Gallon Bart. Donohue, Dorothy, illus. 2006. 32p. (J). 16.95 (978-0-7614-5246-1(X)) Cavendish, Marshall Corp.

Cunliffe, John. Postman Pat & the Goat's Supper. (Illus.). 20p. (J). (978-0-340-71437-9(9) , Hodder & Stoughton) Hodder General Publishing Division.

Daniels, Lucy. Animal Ark: Goat in the Garden. l.t. ed. 1999. (Illus.). 232p. (J). pap. (978-0-7540-6089-5(6) , CLP 287) BBC Audio.

Las Dos Cabritas. (Coleccion Fabulas y Cuentos Populares). (SPA.). (J). (gr. 2-4). lib. bdg. (978-84-246-1554-3(9) , GL3091) La Galera, S.A. Editorial ESP. *Dist:* Lectorum Pubns., Inc.

Doudna, Kelly. Goat Cheese. Haberstroh, Anne, illus. 2006. (Fact & Fiction Ser.). 24p. (J). 21.35 (978-1-59679-937-0(4) , SandCastle); pap. (978-1-59679-938-7(2)) ABDO Publishing Co.

Edwards, Julie Andrews & Hamilton, Emma Walton. Dumpy to the Rescue! Walton, Tony, illus. 2004. (My First I Can Read Bks.). 32p. (J). (ps up). 14.99 (978-0-06-052689-4(0)); pap. 3.99 (978-0-06-052691-7(2)); lib. bdg. 15.89 (978-0-06-052690-0(4)) HarperCollins Pubs.

Edwards, Julie Andrews & Hamilton, Emma Walton. Dumpy to the Rescue. Walton, Tony, illus. 2004. 24p. (J). lib. bdg. 13.85 (***978-1-4242-0707-7(X)*** Fitzgerald Bks.

Eggleton, Jill. The Rock Boss: Early Level Satellite Individual Title Six-Packs. (Sails Literacy Ser.). 16p. (gr. 1-2). 27.00 (978-0-7578-2934-5(1)) Rigby Education.

Ellis, Deborah. Jakeman. 2007. 195p. (J). (gr. 3-7). (***978-1-55041-573-5(5)*** Fitzhenry & Whiteside, Ltd.

Ellis, Tacy. Goat Tales: Stories of Izzy & Her Friends. Collins, Don, illus. 2006. 128p. (J). 17.95 (978-1-931721-78-3(5)) Bright Sky Pr.

Elschner, Geraldine. Pashmina the Little Christmas Goat. Kehlenbeck, Angela, illus. 2006. 32p. (J). (ps-3). 16.99 (978-0-698-40046-7(1) , Minedition) Penguin Group (USA) Inc.

Emerson, Carl. Falling Freddy, the Fainting Goat. Tresize, Zachary, illus. 2007. (Animal Underdogs Ser.). 32p. (J). (ps-4). lib. bdg. 27.07 (***978-1-60270-015-4(X)*** , Looking Glass Library) Magic Wagon.

The Fight on the Hill: Individual Title Six-Pack. (Story Steps Ser.). (gr. k-2). 23.00 (978-0-7635-9837-2(2)) Rigby Education.

Finch, Mary. Los Tres Chivitos Gruff. 2003. (SPA.). (gr. k-3). lib. bdg. 15.30 (978-0-613-67169-9(4)) Tandem Library Bks.

Florence, Nancy L. Harold the Goat. 2004. 30p. pap. 14.95 (978-1-4137-3941-1(5)) PublishAmerica, Inc.

Ford, Carolyn. The Paper Bag. Diez-Luckie, Cathy, illus. 2005. 8p. (J). pap. 5.00 (978-1-57274-756-2(0) , 2494, Bks. for Young Learners) Owen, Richard C. Pubs., Inc.

French, Vivian. Cat in a Coat. Bartlett, Alison, illus. 2005. 32p. (J). (ps-k). lib. bdg. 11.15 (978-0-606-33583-6(8)) Tandem Library Bks.

French, Vivian & Lewis, Jan. Big Fat Hen & the Hairy Goat. 1999. (Illus.). 24p. (J). pap. 7.95 (978-1-86233-000-9(X)) Sterling Publishing Co., Inc.

—Big Fat Hen & the Red Rooster. 1999. (Illus.). 24p. (J). pap. 7.95 (978-1-86233-005-4(0)) Sterling Publishing Co., Inc.

Galdone, Paul. The Three Billy Goat's Gruff. 2006. 32p. (J). (ps-k). 25.00 (978-0-618-83685-7(3)) Houghton Mifflin Co. Trade & Reference Div.

—Los Tres Chivitos Gruff. Fiol, María A., tr. 2003. (SPA., Illus.). (J). (gr. k-3). pap. 7.95 (978-1-880507-62-9(5) , LC0249) Lectorum Pubns., Inc.

El Gnomo Pelusa y las tres Cabras Grunonas 9: Leveled Books. 2001. (McGraw-Hill. Lectura Ser.). (ENG & SPA.). (gr. 2 up). (978-0-02-188058-4(1)) Macmillan/McGraw-Hill Schl. Div.

The Goat & the Rock: a Tale from Tibet: Fifth Grade Guided Comprehension Level O. (On Our Way to English Ser.). (gr. 5 up). 34.50 (978-0-7578-6604-3(2)) Rigby Education.

The Goat's Beard: Early Level Satellite Individual Title Six-Packs. (Sails Literacy Ser.). 16p. (gr. 1-2). 27.00 (978-0-7578-3158-4(3)) Rigby Education.

Gorbachev, Valeri. The Big Trip. Gorbachev, Valeri, illus. 2004. (Illus.). 32p. (J). 15.99 (978-0-399-23965-6(0) , Philomel) Penguin Group (USA) Inc.

—That's What Friends Are For. Gorbachev, Valeri, illus. 2005. (Illus.). 32p. (J). (ps-3). 15.99 (978-0-399-23966-3(9) , Philomel) Penguin Group (USA) Inc.

Grandma's Pie: Individual Title Six-Packs. (Story Steps Ser.). (gr. k-2). 32.00 (978-0-7635-9816-7(X)) Rigby Education.

Grimm, Jacob W. & Grimm, Wilhelm K. The Wolf & the Seven Little Kids. Routiaux, Claudine, illus. 2001. (Little Pebbles Ser.).Tr. of Wolf und die Sieben Jungen Geisslein. 32p. 6.95 (978-0-7892-0735-7(4)) Abbeville Pr., Inc.

Hamilton, John. The Army. 2007. (Defending the Nation Ser.). (Illus.). 32p. (J). (gr. 3-5). lib. bdg. 22.78 (978-1-59679-754-3(1)) ABDO Publishing Co.

Hamilton, Martha & Weiss, Mitch. Two Fables of Aesop. MacDonald, Bruce, illus. 2005. 16p. (J). pap. 5.00 (978-1-57274-718-0(8) , 2788, Bks. for Young Learners) Owen, Richard C. Pubs., Inc.

Harcourt School Publishers Staff. The Best Food: On Level. 3rd ed. 2002. (Trophies Reading Program Ser.). (Illus.). (J). pap. 4.10 (978-0-15-322990-9(X)) Harcourt Schl. Pubs.

Heurtelou, Maude. Konpe Kabrit ak Konpe Kodenn. Louissaint, Louis, illus. 1999. Tr. of Turkey & Goat. (CRP.). 26p. (J). (gr. 3-5). pap. 19.00 incl. audio (978-1-881839-94-1(X)) Educa Vision.

Hiebert, Elfrieda H. & Juel, Connie. Eric & the Three Goats. (Little Book Practice Reader Ser.). (J). (978-0-8136-0987-4(9)) Modern Curriculum Pr.

—Nanny Goat's Nap. (Little Book Practice Reader Ser.). (J). (978-0-8136-0692-7(6)) Modern Curriculum Pr.

Hillert, Margaret. The Boy & the Goats. Miyake, Yoshi, illus. rev. exp. ed. 2007. (Beginning to Read Ser.). 32p. (J). lib. bdg. (978-1-59953-053-6(8)) Norwood Hse. Pr.

—The Three Goats. Pekarsky, Mel, illus. rev. ed. 2006. (Beginning to Read Ser.). 30p. (J). lib. bdg. 18.60 (978-1-59953-027-7(9)) Norwood Hse. Pr.

The Hungry Goat. (Early Intervention Levels Ser.). 23.10 (978-0-7362-0010-3(X)) Hampton-Brown Bks.

Hutchins, Hazel J. Two So Small. Ohi, Ruth, illus. 2000. 32p. (J). (ps-1). pap. 7.95 (978-1-55037-650-0(0)) Annick Pr., Ltd. CAN. *Dist:* Firefly Bks., Ltd.

Jespersen, Amanda. The Little Lost Goat. Tadjo, Veronique, tr. from ENG. 1998. (Cambridge African Language Library). (FRE., Illus.). 16p. pap. 3.75 (978-0-521-64792-2(4)) Cambridge Univ. Pr.

—The Little Lost Goat: Luganda Version. Lubega, Bonnie, tr. 1998. (Cambridge African Language Library Ser.). (LUG., Illus.). 16p. pap. 3.65 (978-0-521-63795-4(3)) Cambridge Univ. Pr.

Johnson, Richard, illus. The Three Billy Goats Gruff. 2004. (TAM, CZE, SPA, GUJ & PER.). 24p. (J). (978-1-85269-613-9(3)) Mantra Publishing, Ltd.

—Three Billy Goats Gruff: English Big Book. 2004. (J). (978-1-85269-784-6(9)) Mantra Publishing, Ltd.

Johnston, Tony. Desert Dog. Weatherford, Robert, illus. 2001. 32p. (J). (gr. 1-5). 15.95 (978-0-87156-979-0(5)) Gibbs Smith, Publisher.

Jordan, Rosa. The Goatnappers. 2007. 224p. (J). (gr. 5-7). 14.95 (***978-1-56145-400-6(1)*** , Peachtree Junior) Peachtree Pubs., Ltd.

Jordan, Rosa. Lost Goat Lane. 2004. 192p. (J). 14.95 (978-1-56145-325-2(0)) Peachtree Pubs., Ltd.

Keffer, Lois. Fancy the Filly's Not Selfish or Silly. 1999. (J). 9.99 (978-1-57673-442-1(0)) Zondervan.

The Kids from Quiller's Bend: Individual Title Six-Packs. (Action Packs Ser.). 120p. (gr. 3-5). 44.00 (978-0-7635-8432-0(0)) Rigby Education.

Kimmel, Eric A. & Asbjornsen, Peter Christen. The Three Cabritos. Gilpin, Stephen, illus. 2007. (J). (***978-1-4287-3709-9(X)*** , Cavendish Children's Bks.) Cavendish, Marshall Corp.

Kimura & North, Lucy. One Stormy Night. Abe, Hiroshi, illus. 2005. 48p. (J). (gr. 1-3). 16.00 (978-4-7700-2970-6(5)) Kodansha International JPN. *Dist:* Cheng & Tsui Co.

—One Sunny Day, 2 vols., Vol. 2. Abe, Hiroshi, illus. 2005. 48p. (J). 16.00 (978-4-7700-2971-3(3)) Kodansha International JPN. *Dist:* Cheng & Tsui Co.

Kitamura, Satoshi. Por el Hilo se Saca el Ovillo. Kitamura, Satoshi, illus. 2003. (Picture Books Collection). (SPA., Illus.). 32p. (J). (gr. k-3). 14.95 (978-84-372-2357-5(1)) Altea, Ediciones, S.A. - Grupo Santillana ESP. *Dist:* Santillana USA Publishing Co., Inc.

Krailing, Tessa. Jilly the Kid. Lewis, Jan & Eastwood, John, illus. 1998. (Petsitters Club Ser.: No. 1). 96p. (J). (gr. 1-4). pap. 4.50 (978-0-7641-0569-2(8)) Barron's Educational Series, Inc.

Kroll, Virginia L. & Jones, Dawn L. Bluffy's Mighty Mountain. Maydak, Michael S., illus. 2001. (J). (978-0-9712840-3-6(2)) Boyds Collection Ltd., The.

Little Goat's Coat. (Sails Literacy Ser.). 24p. (gr. k up). 27.00 (978-0-7635-6990-7(9)) Rigby Education.

Little Goat's Coat: 3-in-1 Package. (Sails Literacy Ser.). 24p. (gr. k up). 57.00 (978-0-7578-3200-0(8)) Rigby Education.

Little Goat's Coat: 6 Small Books. (Sails Literacy Ser.). 24p. (gr. k up). 25.00 (978-0-7578-3176-8(1)) Rigby Education.

Littler, Jody. The Little Goat on the Roof. Jablonski, Jan, illus. 1998. 32p. (J). (ps-3). pap. 8.95 (978-1-57534-029-6(1)) Skandisk, Inc.

Mancini, Kitty. Goatina Goes to New York. Piccolo, Rina, illus. 1999. 72p. (J). (gr. k-3). pap. 10.00 (978-0-9648010-7-3(8)) Hypertext Publishing Group.

Maruca, Mary. Joy at Mount Rushmore. 2000. (Illus.). pap. 6.99 (978-0-9646798-4-9(1)) Mount Rushmore History Assn.

Mason, Jo-Anne. Paddy, the Goat That Saved Rainbow Island. 2003. 48p. (ps-3). 13.95 (978-0-333-97062-1(4)) Macmillan Caribbean GBR. *Dist:* Interlink Publishing Group, Inc.

McBrier, Page. Beatrice's Goat. Lohstoeter, Lori, illus. 40p. (J). (ps-3). 2001. 17.99 (978-0-689-82460-9(2) , Atheneum); 2004. reprint ed. 7.99 (978-0-689-86990-7(8) , Aladdin) Simon & Schuster Children's Publishing.

—Beatrice's Goat. unabr. ed. 2005. (J). (ps-3). 29.95 incl. audio compact disk (978-0-8045-4137-4(X)) Spoken Arts, Inc.

—Beatrice's Goat. Lohstoeter, Lori, illus. 2004. 34p. (J). (ps-ps). lib. bdg. 15.60 (978-1-4176-3045-5(0)) Tandem Library Bks.

MCP Staff. Nanny Goat's Nap, Level 3, Bk. 21. (J). (ps-3). 24.50 (978-0-8136-0691-0(8)) Modern Curriculum Pr.

McPhail, David M. A Girl, a Goat & a Goose. 2000. (Hello Reader! Ser.). (Illus.). (J). 10.79 (978-0-606-18875-3(4)) Tandem Library Bks.

—A Girl, a Goat, & a Goose. 2004. 32p. (J). lib. bdg. 15.00 (978-1-59054-669-7(5)) Fitzgerald Bks.

—A Girl, a Goat, & a Goose, & the Storm. 2002. (SPA., Illus.). (J). (978-0-439-41152-3(1)) Scholastic, Inc.

Miller, Edward. 3 Tales Retold & Illustrated: The Three Little Pigs, Goldilocks & the Three Bears, Three Billy Goats Gruff. Miller, Edward, illus. 2007. (Illus.). 48p. (J). (ps-2). 17.95 (978-0-8050-7916-6(5)) Holt, Henry & Co.

Molzahn, Arlene Bourgeois. The Goat Who Wouldn't Come Home. Dillard, Kristine, illus. 1998. 12p. (J). (gr. k-2). pap. 3.75 (978-1-880612-82-8(8) , Seedling Pubns.) Continental Pr., Inc.

Montgomery, Trego Frances. Billy Whiskers the Autobiography of A Go. 2007. 40.99 (***978-1-4280-5180-5(5)***); pap. 34.99 (***978-1-4280-5194-2(5)***) IndyPublish.com.

Moore, Carol H. Marvin the Magnificent Nubian Goat. Harrell, Micheael, illus. 2006. (J). 20.00 (***978-0-9792019-0-5(X)***) iwishyouicecreamandcake.

Mustaine Hettinger, Cynthia. Doc the Pygmy Goat. Ramsey, Jayne, illus. 2003. (Electra's Acres Ser.). 32p. (J). per. 14.95 (978-0-9746330-0-8(3)) Anton Berkshire Publishing.

Newton, Jill. Gordon in Charge. Newton, Jill, illus. 2003. (Illus.). 32p. (J). 15.95 (978-1-58234-823-0(5) , Bloomsbury Children) Bloomsbury Publishing.

Once upon a Time Spanish Version-the Three Billy Goats Gruff. 2005. (J). (978-1-57022-564-2(8)) ECS Learning Systems, Inc.

Page, Nick & Page, Claire. Read with Me Three Billy Goats Gruff: Sticker Activity Book. Saunders, Katie, illus. 2006. (Read with Me (Make Believe Ideas) Ser.). 12p. (J). (gr. k-2). pap. 4.95 (978-1-84610-181-6(6)) Make Believe Ideas GBR. *Dist:* Ingram Pub. Services.

—Three Billy Goats Gruff. 2006. (Read with Me (Make Believe Ideas) Ser.). (Illus.). 32p. (J). (gr. k-2). 3.95 (978-1-84610-165-6(4)) Make Believe Ideas GBR. *Dist:* Ingram Pub. Services.

Paschal Shija. The Proud Kid & the Stream. 2005. (Illus.). 14p. pap. 9.95 (978-9987-686-97-1(4)) Mkuki na Nyoka Pubs. TZA. *Dist:* Michigan State Univ. Pr.

PC Treasures, prod. The Three Billy Goats Gruff. 2007. (J). (***978-1-60072-017-8(X)***) PC Treasures, Inc.

Penguin Books Staff, ed. The Three Billy Goats Gruff. (Fairy Tale Fun Ser.). (J). 3.95 (978-0-7214-5430-6(5) , Dutton Juvenile) Penguin Group (USA) Inc.

Percy, Graham, illus. The Three Billy Goats Gruff. l.t. ed. 2001. (SPA.). 28p. (ps-3). incl. audio compact disk (978-84-8214-088-9(4) , 1622) Peralt Montagut.

—The Three Billy Goats Gruff. l.t. ed. 2001. 28p. (J). (ps-3). 8.99 incl. audio (978-84-86154-89-9(8)) Peralt Montagut ESP. *Dist:* imaJen, Inc.

Plato's Journey: Evaluation Guide. 2006. (J). (978-1-55942-421-9(4)) Marsh Media.

Play Along Fairy Tales. The Three Billy Goats Gruff. 2008. (Illus.). 14p. (J). bds. 9.95 (***978-0-00-722327-5(7)***) HarperCollins Pubs. Ltd. GBR. *Dist:* Independent Pubs. Group.

Polacco, Patricia. G Is for Goat. Gauch, Patricia Lee, ed. Polacco, Patricia, illus. 2003. (Illus.). 32p. (J). (ps-1). 16.99 (978-0-399-24018-8(7) , Philomel) Penguin Group (USA) Inc.

—G Is for Goat. Polacco, Patricia, illus. 32p. (J). 2007. 6.99 (978-0-399-24530-5(8) , Philomel); 2006. (Illus.). reprint ed. pap. 6.99 (978-0-14-240550-5(7) , Puffin) Penguin Group (USA) Inc.

—Oh, Look! Polacco, Patricia, illus. 2004. (Illus.). 32p. (J). (ps-3). 16.99 (978-0-399-24223-6(6) , Philomel) Penguin Group (USA) Inc.

Puttock, Simon. Goat & Donkey in Strawberry Sunglasses. Julian, Russell, illus. 2007. 28p. (J). (ps-2). 16.00 (***978-1-56148-572-7(1)***) Good Bks.

—Goat & Donkey in the Great Outdoors. Julian, Russell, illus. 2007. 28p. (J). (ps-2). 16.00 (***978-1-56148-573-4(X)***) Good Bks.

Rider, Cynthia. Gertie the Goat. Bury, Michael, illus. 2001. (Cambridge Reading Ser.). 16p. pap., stu. ed. 8.00 (978-0-521-01427-4(1)) Cambridge Univ. Pr.

Rigby Education Staff. The Goat. 1999. (Sails Literacy Ser.). (Illus.). 16p. (gr. k-1). 27.00 (978-0-7635-9858-7(5) , 698585C99) Rigby Education.

—The House Sitters. (Sails Literacy Ser.). (Illus.). 16p. (gr. 1-2). 27.00 (978-0-7635-9914-0(X) , 699149C99) Rigby Education.

Rix, Jamie. Giddy Goat. Chapman, Lynne, illus. 2003. 32p. (J). (gr. k-3). 14.95 (978-0-7696-3161-5(4) , Gingham Dog Pr.) School Specialty Publishing.

Roberts, Dannel. Me & Uncle Mike & Billy Goat Bob. Nichols, Brenda, illus. l.t. ed. 2002. (Me & Uncle Mike Children's Book Ser.: Bk. 3). 36p. (J). per. 14.95 (978-1-893459-02-1(0)) Lions & Tigers & Bears Publishing, Inc.

Rosenberg, Jonathan. Behold the Power of Ignorance Vol. IV: Goats. 2001. (Illus.). 132p. per. 17.95 (978-1-59151-041-3(4)) Point E Publishing.

Ross, Tony. Mrs. Goat & Her Seven Little Kids. 2004. (Illus.). 32p. (J). pap. 9.99 (978-1-84270-338-0(2)) Andersen GBR. *Dist:* Independent Pubs. Group.

Rwakasisi, Rose. How Goats Lost Their Beautiful Tails. 2004. (Illus.). 19p. pap. 9.95 (978-9970-02-436-0(1)) Fountain Pubs. Ltd. UGA. *Dist:* Michigan State Univ. Pr.

Sargent, Dave. Storky Stork: Be Trustworthy, 19, 18. Lenoir, Jane, illus. 2003. (Feather Tales Ser.: 18). 42p. (J). pap. 6.95 (978-1-56763-754-0(X)) Ozark Publishing.

Sargent, Dave & Sargent, Julie. Billy Goat: Don't Brag on Yourself, 56 vols., Vol. 23. Huff, Jeane, illus. 2001. (Animal Pride Ser.: Vol. 23). 36p. (J). lib. bdg. 19.95 (978-1-56763-362-7(5)) Ozark Publishing.

Sharmat, Mitchell. Gregory, the Terrible Eater. Aruego, Jose, illus. 2002. (J). 12.87 (978-0-7587-2663-6(5)) Book Wholesalers, Inc.

Sidwell, Larry. Hold to the Dream. 2002. 89p. pap. 10.95 (978-0-7414-1068-9(0)) Infinity Publishing.

Siegal, Aranka. Upon the Head of the Goat: A Childhood in Hungary, 1939-1944. 2003. 224p. (J). pap. 6.95 (978-0-374-48079-0(6) , Sunburst) Farrar, Straus & Giroux.

Singer, Isaac Bashevis. Cuentos Judios de la Aldea de Chelm.Tr. of Zlateh the Goat & Other Stories. (SPA.). 62p. (J). 7.96 (978-84-264-3404-3(5) , LM2595) Editorial Lumen ESP. *Dist:* Lectorum Pubns., Inc.

Smithers, J. Megan, illus. Emma: An Interactive Storybook. 2nd ed. 2005. 60p. (J). (gr. k-4). pap. 9.00 (978-0-9713342-6-7(9)) BV Wespat.

Stevens, Janet. The Three Billy Goats Gruff. Stevens, Janet, illus. 2002. (Illus.). (J). 13.19 (978-0-7587-3798-4(X)) Book Wholesalers, Inc.

Switzer, Vern. Hard Heads Make Soft Bottoms. Connally, Perry L., Sr., illus. 2007. 34p. (J). 15.95 (***978-0-9753542-2-3(1)***) Rural Farm Productions.

Three Billy Goats Gruff. 2005. (J). bds. 3.99 (978-1-933200-12-5(X)) Family Bks. at Home.

Three Billy Goat's Gruff. 2004. (J). E-Book incl. cd-rom (978-1-84444-467-0(8)) Mantra Publishing, Ltd.

Tompert, Ann & Chwast, Jacqueline. The Hungry Black Bag. 1999. (Illus.). 32p. (J). (gr. k-3). tchr. ed. 15.00 (978-0-395-89418-7(2) , Walter Lorraine) Houghton Mifflin Co. Trade & Reference Div.

Westera, Marleen & Forest, Nancy. Sheep & Goat. Ommen, Sylvia Van, illus. (J). 16.95 (978-1-932425-81-9(0) , Lemniscaat) Boyds Mills Pr.

Youngquist, Cathrene Valente. The Three Billygoats Gruff & Mean Calypso Joe. Sorra, Kristin, illus. 2002. 32p. (J). (ps-3). 16.00 (978-0-689-82824-9(1) , Atheneum) Simon & Schuster Children's Publishing.

Ziefert, Harriet. Pumpkin Pie. Dreifuss, Donald, illus. 2000. 32p. (J). (gr. k-3). tchr. ed. 15.00 (978-0-618-04883-0(9) , Walter Lorraine) Houghton Mifflin Co. Trade & Reference Div.

Zyrro, Roggen. Il Goatino. Shields, Ruth, illus. 2004. 32p. (J). 16.95 (978-0-9762580-0-1(5)) Zyrro, Roggen.

GOATS—SONGS

Hoberman, Mary Ann. Bill Grogan's Goat. Westcott, Nadine Bernard, illus. 2002. 32p. (J). (ps-3). 14.95 (978-0-316-36232-0(8)) Little, Brown Bks. for Young Readers.

GOBI DESERT—FICTION

Stilton, Geronimo. Valley of the Giant Skeletons. 2008. (Geronimo Stilton Ser.: No. 32). 128p. (J). pap. 6.99 (***978-0-545-02132-6(4)*** , Scholastic Paperbacks) Scholastic, Inc.

GOBLINS

see Fairies

GOD

see also Christianity; Creation; Jesus Christ; Mythology; Religion; Theology

ABCs of God. 2004. (In Celebration Coloring & Activity Book Ser.). (Illus.). 32p. (J). (gr. k-2). pap. 1.99 (978-0-7647-1016-2(8) , In Celebration) Schaffer, Frank Pubns.

Abraham, Ken & Fitzgerald, Annie. Dear God, Do You Really See Everything? 2003. (Dear God Kids Ser.). (Illus.). 12p. (J). 4.99 (978-0-8254-2646-9(4)) Kregel Pubns.

Abts, Stacey & Kleinman, Bertha A. I Have Two Little Hands. 2004. (Illus.). (J). 9.95 (978-1-59038-182-3(3)) Deseret Bk. Co.

Adams, Patricia E. Detouring off the Road of Oneness: An Inductive Study on Intimacy with God. 2006. (One Heart Ser.: Vol. 3). (Illus.). 175p. pap. 19.95 (978-0-9700976-2-0(X) , Shekinah Publishing Hse.) Shekinah Publishing Hse.

—I & My Father Are One: An Inductive Study on Intimacy with God. 2006. (One Heart Ser.: Vol. 4). (Illus.). 175p. pap. 19.95 (978-0-9700976-3-7(8) , Shekinah Publishing Hse.) Shekinah Publishing Hse.

—Journeying to the Road Called Oneness: An Inductive Study on Intimacy with God. 2006. (One Heart Ser.: Vol. 2). (Illus.). 175p. pap. 19.95 (978-0-9700976-1-3(1) , Shekinah Publishing Hse.) Shekinah Publishing Hse.

—With Oneness of Heart: An Inductive Study on Intimacy with God Vol. 1 of the One Heart Series, 4 vols., Vol. 1. 2004. (One Heart Ser.: Vol. 1). (Illus.). 175p. (gr. 7 up). pap. 19.95 (978-0-9700976-0-6(3) , Shekinah Publishing Hse.) Shekinah Publishing Hse.

All about God, 6 vols., Set. 1999. (J). pap. 1.50 (978-0-87162-808-4(2)) Warner Pr. Pubs.

Allsopp, Sophie, illus. Dear God: Little Letter Prayers for Little People. 2006. 16p. (J). 12.99 (978-1-4169-1216-3(9) , Little Simon Inspirations) Simon & Schuster Children's Publishing.

Anderson, Debby. Every Child Everywhere. 2007. 32p. (J). pap. 9.99 (***978-1-58134-862-0(2)***) Crossway Bks.

Anderson, Debby. God Knows My Name. 2005. (Illus.). 32p. 9.99 (978-1-58134-415-8(5) , Crossway Bibles) Crossway Bks.

The Apostles' Creed. 2004. (Exploring Luther's Small Catechism Ser.). (gr. 3-4). 2.99 (978-0-8066-6780-5(X)) Augsburg Fortress, Pubs.

Ashworth, Leon. Ancient Egypt. (Gods & Goddesses Ser.). (Illus.). 32p. (J). lib. bdg. 24.25 (978-1-58340-196-5(2)) Smart Apple Media.

—Gods & Goddesses of Ancient Greece. (Gods & Goddesses Ser.). (Illus.). 32p. (J). lib. bdg. 24.25 (978-1-58340-195-8(4)) Smart Apple Media.

—Gods & Goddesses of Ancient Greece. 2003. (gr. 5-8). lib. bdg. 35.30 (978-0-613-79421-3(4)) Tandem Library Bks.

—Gods & Goddesses of the Vikings & Northlands. (Gods & Goddesses Ser.). (Illus.). 32p. lib. bdg. 24.25 (978-1-58340-193-4(8)) Smart Apple Media.

Association of Christian Schools International Staff. Kindergarten Bible: God & Me. 2000. (Elementary Bible Ser.). (Illus.). 161p. (gr. k-1). pap., stu. ed. 14.90 (978-1-58331-102-8(5) , 7112) Assn. of Christian Schls. International.

Bagley, Val Chadwick, illus. I Will Trust in Heavenly Father & Jesus. 2006. (J). (978-1-59811-056-2(X)) Covenant Communications.

Bechtel, Faythelma. God's Marvelous Gifts. rev. ed. 2000. (Christian Day School Ser.). (J). (gr. 5). 14.95 (978-0-87813-936-1(2)) Christian Light Pubns., Inc.

Becker, Mary Lee, contrib. by. Living Our Faith God: Revelation & Relationship. 2002. (Living Our Faith Ser.). (Illus.). 112p. pap., stu. ed. 8.95 (978-0-15-900488-3(8)) Harcourt Religion Pubs.

Berg, Rabbi Yehuda. 72 Names of God for Kids. 2005. (Illus.). 200p. 19.95 (978-1-57189-347-5(4)) Research Centre of Kabbalah.

Berg, Yehuda. The 72 Names of God for Kids: A Treasury of Timeless Wisdom. 2006. (Illus.). 192p. 14.95 (978-1-57189-343-1(4)) Research Centre of Kabbalah.

Beveridge, Amy. Let's Thank God for Freedom. 2006. 24p. (J). bds. 6.99 (978-0-7847-1505-5(X) , 04384) Standard Publishing.

Bible Visuals International, compiled by. God (the Trinity) Vol. 43: New Testament. 2006. (Illus.). (J). pap. (978-1-932381-65-8(1) , 1043) Bible Visuals International, Inc.

Bishop, Jennie. Jesus Must Be Really Special. Wummer, Amy, illus. 2007. (J). (***978-0-7847-1988-6(8)***) Standard Publishing.

Borchard, Therese Johnson. Taste & See the Goodness of the Lord. Saroff, Phyllis V., illus. 2000. 32p. (ps-3). 9.95 (978-0-8091-6665-7(8) , 6665-8) Paulist Pr.

Boroson, Martin. Becoming Me: A Story of Creation. Gilvan-Cartwright, Chris, illus. 2000. (SkyLight Lives Ser.). 32p. (J). (ps-3). 16.95 (978-1-893361-11-9(X)) SkyLight Paths Publishing.

Bostrom, Kathleen Long. God Loves You. Kucharik, Elena, illus. 2001. (Little Blessings Ser.). 32p. (J). bds. 6.99 (978-0-8423-5370-0(4)) Tyndale Hse. Pubs.

Bowler, Kathryn C. & Osborne, Rick. I Want to Know, Sam's Club: About God, Jesus, the Bible & Prayer. 2001. 168p. (J). 27.99 (978-0-310-70242-9(9)) Zonderkidz.

Britt, Stephanie M., illus. My Little Bible Promises. 2005. 96p. (J). 5.99 (978-1-4003-0649-7(3)) Nelson, Thomas Inc.

Bruce & Stan. God Is in the Small Stuff for Kids. Smouse, Phil, illus. 2004. 256p. (J). pap. 5.97 (978-1-59310-335-4(2)) Barbour Publishing, Inc.

Burch, Deborah. God's Greatest Gift. Burch, Deborah, illus. l.t. ed. 2007. (Illus.). 32p. (J). lib. bdg. 12.95 (978-0-9779445-3-8(0)) Zoe Life Publishing.

E
F
G

Butt, Sheila K. Does God Love Michael's Two Daddies. Perkins, Ken, illus. 2007. 16p. (J). 7.95 (***978-0-932859-94-5(1)***) Apologetics Pr., Inc.

Catch 22: The Book That Will Change the Way You See Life. 2004. 120p. (C). per. 9.99 (978-0-9759691-0-6(2)) Catch 22 Publishing Inc.

CharismaLife Publishing Staff. Iglesia para Ninos: Guardando la Ley de Dios en Nuestros Corazons. 1998. Tr. of Church for Children: Guarding the Law of God in our Hearts. (SPA.). 160p. (J). (gr. 1-6). 129.99 (978-1-57405-444-6(9)) CharismaLife Pubs.

Chidvilasananda. Good Night, Sweet Dreams, I Love You! 2004. (Illus.). (J). (978-1-930939-01-1(9)) SYDA Foundation.

Chimento, Carmen C. A Vision of God. 2004. per. (978-0-9656847-1-2(7)) Spiritual Hse. Pr., The.

Christ at the Coffee Shop. 2004. lib. bdg. (978-0-9747425-0-2(3) , 09747425) Tranquility Ranch Publishing.

Clarke, Pat. Questions about God. 1999. (Dimensions in Religion Ser.). (Illus.). 194p. (YA). (gr. 11 up). pap. 26.50 (978-0-7487-4340-7(5)) Nelson Thornes Ltd. GBR. *Dist:* Trans-Atlantic Pubns., Inc.

Comella, Angels. Hablemos de Dios. 2003. (SPA.). (J). 11.98 (978-968-13-3508-3(2)) Editorial Diana, S.A. MEX. *Dist:* Giron Bks.

Conan, Sally Ann. God Made Creepy Crawlies. 2005. (Illus.). 40p. (J). 9.99 (978-0-8066-4986-3(0) , Augsburg Bks.) Augsburg Fortress, Pubs.

Cone, Molly. Hello, Hello, Are You There, God? Kaye, Rosalind Charney, illus. rev. ed. 2004. viii, 55p. (gr. k-3). pap. 12.95 (978-0-8074-0648-9(1) , 102553) URJ Pr.

Count Your Blessings 123: My Wipe-off Book. 2003. spiral bd. (978-0-7853-8570-7(3)) Publications International, Ltd.

Crook, Carol. God's Guidance: Being Led by the Spirit. 2000. (Illus.). 94p. (YA). (gr. 10 up). stu. ed., spiral bd. 25.75 (978-0-939399-54-3(7)) Books of Truth.

Daleski, Gil. Is God Sad? Kaufman, Shirley, tr. from HEB. Veinshtein, Debbie, illus. 2006. 40p. 14.95 (978-965-229-372-5(5)) Gefen Publishing Hse., Ltd ISR. *Dist:* Gefen Bks.

Dalmatian Press Staff, ed. God Loves Me. 2005. (Timeless Treasures Ser.). (Illus.). 30p. (J). 7.99 (978-1-4037-0555-6(0) , Spirit Pr.) Dalmatian Pr.

Davis, Mary J. My Answer Journal: What Kids Wonder about God & the Bible. 2004. (Journals Just for Kids Ser.). (Illus.). 136p. (J). (gr. 4-7). pap. 9.99 (978-1-885358-72-1(5) , Legacy Pr.) Rainbow Pubs. & Legacy Pr.

Dayal, Mala. The Ramayana in Pictures. Joshi, Jagdish, illus. 2006. 64p. (J). (***978-81-291-0896-8(8)***) Rupa & Co.

De Graaf, Anne. God Makes the World. Perez-Montero, Jose, illus. 1998. (Little Children's Bible Bks.). 38p. (J). 5.99 (978-0-8054-1782-1(6)) B&H Publishing Grp.

Dear God 2001. 2004. (My First Prayers Ser.). 10p. (J). bds. 3.99 (978-1-85854-406-9(8)) Brimax Books Ltd. GBR. *Dist:* Byeway Bks.

Derico, Laura. God Says I Am: What God Tells Us about Himself in the Bible from A to Z. McLouglin, Wayne, illus. 2002. (Heritage Builders Ser.). 32p. 15.99 (978-0-7847-1378-5(2)) Standard Publishing.

Dobson, Shirley. God Loves You! Coloring Book: A Read-Aloud Coloring Book about God's Plan for Salvation. 1998. 16p. (ps-3). pap. 1.49 (978-0-8307-2329-4(3) , Gospel Light) Gospel Light Pubns.

Dunlap, Irene, ed. True Vol. 1: Real Stories about God Showing up in the Lives of Teens. 2004. (Invert Ser.). (Illus.). 352p. (YA). pap. 12.99 (978-0-310-25268-9(7)) Zondervan.

Egbert, Rebecca A. God & Me. 1999. (Illus.). 48p. (J). (ps-k). 10.00 (978-0-570-05553-2(9)) Concordia Publishing Hse.

Elkins, Stephen. Awesome God: A Very Special Story for Children. Colton, Ellie, illus. 2003. (Dove Award Signature Ser.). 32p. (J). 14.99 (978-0-8054-2664-9(7)) B&H Publishing Grp.

—First Steps to God. Colton, Ellie, illus. 2006. (First Steps Ser.). 32p. (J). 9.99 (978-0-8054-2661-8(2)) B&H Publishing Grp.

—God's Power. O'Connor, Tim, illus. 2002. (Word & Song Ser.: Vol. 1). 32p. (J). 9.99 (978-0-8054-2466-9(0)) B&H Publishing Grp.

England, Don. God, Are You Really There? (YA). pap., stu. ed. 7.99 (978-0-89098-105-4(1)) Twentieth Century Christian Bks.

Feyh, Janelle. Does God Have a Remote Control? Feyh, Alexa & Deghand, Tim, illus. l.t. ed. 2003. 66p. (J). per. 11.95 (978-1-932344-26-4(8)) Thornton Publishing.

Fitch, Florence Mary. A Book about God. Sorensen, Henri, illus. 1999. 24p. (J). (ps-3). 15.89 (978-0-688-16129-3(4)) HarperCollins Pubs.

Freed, Shirley & Moon, Louise. Jesus Hears Me. Morelan, Bill, ed. Harrell, Rob, illus. 2003. 8p. (J). (gr. 1 up). pap. 3.99 (978-1-58938-104-9(1)) Concerned Communications.

—Put God First. Morelan, Bill, ed. Harrell, Rob, illus. 2003. 8p. (J). (gr. 1 up). pap. 3.99 (978-1-58938-106-3(8)) Concerned Communications.

Freed, Shirley Ann & Moon, Louise. God Makes the Sun Shine. Morelan, Bill, ed. Harrell, Rob, illus. l.t. ed. 2002. 8p. (J). (ps-k). pap. 3.99 (978-1-58938-013-4(4)) Concerned Communications.

Ganeri, Anita. Krishna Steals the Butter & Other Stories: Hindu Stories. 2007. (J). lib. bdg. 19.95 (***978-1-59566-377-1(0)***) QEB Publishing Inc.

Gaudrat, Marie-Agnes. What Is God Like. Wensell, Ulises, illus. 1998. (What is God Like Ser.). 40p. (ps-2). 7.95 (978-0-8146-2510-1(X)) Liturgical Pr.

Gellman, Marc. How Do You Spell God? 1998. (J). (978-0-606-13493-4(X)) Tandem Library Bks.

Gemmen, Heather & McNeil, Mary. Who Cares?, Level 4. Taylor, John, tr. Taylor, John, illus. 1999. (Rocket Readers Ser.). 32p. (J). (gr. 4 up). pap., pap. 4.99 (978-0-7814-3980-0(9) , 0781439809) Cook, David C. Publishing Co.

Germano, Jean, illus. God Be in My Heart. 1998. 40p. (J). (ps-ps). pap. 6.95 (978-0-915531-85-1(2)) Oregon Catholic Pr.

Glory Praise & Honor. 7.50 (978-0-8054-5969-2(3)) B&H Publishing Grp.

God Is Color. 2004. (J). spiral bd. 11.97 (978-0-9759551-0-9(1)) Creative Success Works.

God Made Everything Good. 3.50 (978-0-8054-5878-7(6)) B&H Publishing Grp.

God Made Me. 3.50 (978-0-8054-5887-9(5)) B&H Publishing Grp.

God's Wonders. 3.50 (978-0-8054-5877-0(8)) B&H Publishing Grp.

Gold, August. Does God Forgive Me? Waller, Diane Hardy, illus. 2006. 32p. (J). 8.99 (978-1-59473-142-6(X)) SkyLight Paths Publishing.

Gold, August & Perlman, Matthew J. Where Does God Live? 2001. (SkyLight Lives Ser.). (Illus.). 32p. (J). (ps-1). pap. 8.99 (978-1-893361-39-3(X)) SkyLight Paths Publishing.

Green, Jen, et al. In the Daily Life of the Vikings. 2002. (Gods & Goddesses Ser.). (Illus.). 48p. (J). (gr. 4 up). 18.95 (978-0-87226-594-3(3) , Bedrick, Peter Bks.) School Specialty Publishing.

Grimes, Nikki. At Break of Day. Collier, John & Morin, Paul, illus. 2004. 32p. (ps-3). 17.00 (978-0-8028-5104-8(5)) Eerdmans, William B. Publishing Co.

Hahn, Lisa & Nimtz, Wendy. More of God's Seasons Inside: Spring & Summer Bulletin Board Designs. 2000. 64p. (gr. k-3). 9.99 (978-0-570-05223-4(8)) Concordia Publishing Hse.

Hartman, Jill. All about Angels: A Biblical Look at God's Messengers. 1999. 48p. 9.99 (978-0-570-06873-0(8) , 20-2438GJ) Concordia Publishing Hse.

Head, Heno, Jr. God Made the Ocean. Ring, Laura, ed. Fletcher, Rusty, illus. 2000. (Happy Day Bks.). 24p. (J). (ps-2). 2.49 (978-0-7847-1100-2(3) , 04305, Bean Sprouts) Standard Publishing.

—God's World of Weather. Ring, Laura, ed. Fletcher, Rusty, illus. 2000. (Happy Day Bks.). 24p. (J). (ps-2). 2.49 (978-0-7847-1101-9(1) , 04306, Bean Sprouts) Standard Publishing.

Henley, Karyn. Who Is God? 2000. (Tails Activity Bks.). (Illus.). (J). pap. 7.99 (978-0-8054-2288-7(9)) B&H Publishing Grp.

Holder, Greg. God's World. 1998. (Baby Board Bks.). (Illus.). 6p. (J). (ps). bds. 3.99 (978-0-7847-0839-2(8) , 03479, Bean Sprouts) Standard Publishing.

Horner, Susan. Why Do Birds Build Nests? 2004. (Miracle of Creation Ser.). (Illus.). 32p. (J). 9.99 (978-0-8024-0922-5(9)) Moody Pubs.

—Why Do Plants Grow? 2004. (Miracle of Creation Ser.). (Illus.). 32p. (J). 9.99 (978-0-8024-0921-8(0)) Moody Pubs.

Hudson, Wade. God Gave Me: Wade Hudson. Pillo, Cary, illus. 2004. 16p. bds. 8.00 (978-0-687-02590-9(7)) Abingdon Pr.

Iakovina, Theodore. A Special Gift to God. Buchmiller, Therese, illus. 2000. 32p. (J). (gr. k-3). reprint ed. pap. 12.95 (978-1-880971-58-1(5)) Light & Life Publishing Co.

Ingraham, Ronald H. There Is No Telling What God Can Do If You Believe: A 21st Century Spiritual Awakening. 2001. (Illus.). 176p. (YA). (gr. 10 up). mass mkt. 13.95 (978-0-9678741-1-4(4)) R I C C Productions.

Jeffs, Stephanie. My First Picture Book about God. Bishop, Roma, illus. 2001. 32p. (ps up). 14.99 (978-0-8066-4155-3(X) , Augsburg Bks.) Augsburg Fortress, Pubs.

Johari, Harish & Sperling, Vatsala. How Parvati Won the Heart of Shiva. Weltevrede, Pieter, illus. 2004. (Classic Indian Stories for Children Ser.). 32p. (J). 15.95 (978-1-59143-042-1(9) , Bear Cub Bks.) Bear & Co.

Jones, Sally Lloyd. How Big Is God's Love? A Soft-Edges Photo Frame Book. MacLean, Moira, illus. 2000. (Baby Blessings Ser.). 12p. (J). (ps-k). bds. 6.99 (978-0-7847-1136-1(4) , 04316, Bean Sprouts) Standard Publishing.

Jordan, Michael. Dictionary of Gods & Goddesses. (Illus.). 402p. (gr. 9). pap. 19.95 (978-0-8160-6490-8(3) , Checkmark Bks.) Facts On File, Inc.

Josef, Marion. We Thank God Col/Act Bk. 24p. pap. 1.25 (978-0-8198-8303-2(4) , 332-411) Pauline Bks. & Media.

Kaposh, Mosh. The Moon, the Sun & a Hotdog Bun. Toron, Eli, illus. l.t. ed. 2002. (Experience Reading Ser.: Vol. 1). 32p. (J). (gr. k-5). 12.95 (978-0-9723488-0-5(8) , 651-695-9166) Nava Pubns.

Kids in Destiny. 2002. pap. 69.99 (978-1-59185-158-5(0)) CharismaLife Pubs.

Kids in Destiny Manual. 2002. pap. 10.00 (978-1-59185-159-2(9)) CharismaLife Pubs.

Kids in Destiny Transparencies. 2002. 29.99 (978-1-59185-161-5(0)) CharismaLife Pubs.

Kids in Evangelism. 2000. pap. 10.00 (978-1-59185-165-3(3)) CharismaLife Pubs.

Kids in Leadership. 2002. pap. 69.99 (978-1-59185-156-1(4)) CharismaLife Pubs.

Kids in Leadership Cover. 2002. pap. 0.00 (978-1-59185-162-2(9)) CharismaLife Pubs.

Kids in Leadership Manual. 2002. pap. 10.00 (978-1-59185-148-6(3)) CharismaLife Pubs.

Kids in Leadership Transparencies. 2002. 29.99 (978-1-59185-150-9(5)) CharismaLife Pubs.

Kids in Service Cover. 2002. pap. 0.00 (978-1-59185-164-6(5)) CharismaLife Pubs.

Kids in Service Manual. 2002. pap. 10.00 (978-1-59185-145-5(9)) CharismaLife Pubs.

Kraft, Tamera & Colkmire, Lance. Kid Konnection: Kids Entering the Presence of God, Vol. 5. 2003. (Illus.). 112p. ring bd. 69.99 (978-0-87148-383-6(1)) Pathway Pr.

Kripke, Dorothy Karp. Let's Talk about God. Tripp, Christine, tr. Tripp, Christine, illus. 2003. (J). 9.95 (978-1-881283-34-8(8)) Alef Design Group.

Kuhn, Pamela J. God Attitudes Win. 2000. (CPH Teaching Resource Ser.). (Illus.). 64p. (J). (gr. 1-5). pap. 8.99 (978-0-570-05260-9(2)) Concordia Publishing Hse.

Kurth, Steve & Schultz, Barbara. Demeter & Persephone: Spring Held Hostage. 2007. (Graphic Myths & Legends Ser.). (Illus.). 48p. (J). (gr. 4-8). 26.60 (978-0-8225-5966-5(8)) Lerner Publishing Group.

Kushner, Lawrence & Kushner, Karen. Because Nothing Looks Like God: Teacher's Guide. 2002. (SPA., Illus.). 22p. (J). (gr. k-3). tchr. ed. 6.95 (978-1-58023-140-4(3)) Jewish Lights Publishing.

—How Does God Make Things Happen? Majewski, Dawn W., illus. 2001. (Early Childhood Spirituality Ser.). 24p. (J). (ps-k). bds. 7.99 (978-1-893361-24-9(1)) SkyLight Paths Publishing.

—What Does God Look Like? Majewski, Dawn W., illus. 2001. (Early Childhood Spirituality Ser.). 24p. (J). (ps-k). bds. 7.99 (978-1-893361-23-2(3)) SkyLight Paths Publishing.

—Where Is God? Majewski, Dawn W., illus. 2000. (SkyLight Lives Ser.). 24p. (J). (ps-k). bds. 7.99 (978-1-893361-17-1(9)) SkyLight Paths Publishing.

Kushner, Lawrence, et al. Because Nothing Looks Like God. Majewski, Dawn W., illus. 2000. (SPA.). 32p. (J). (ps-2). 16.95 (978-1-58023-092-6(X)) Jewish Lights Publishing.

Lee, Laurel. God's Greatest Day. Harvey, Bonnie C. & Phillips, Cheryl M., eds. Burnett, Lindy, illus. 2003. (My Jesus Pocket Book Ser.). 32p. (J). (ps). pap. 8.90 (978-1-55513-013-8(5) , 1555130135) Cook, David C. Publishing Co.

Lepley, Lynne M. Three in One: A Book about God. 2004. 32p. 14.00 (978-0-687-00710-3(0)) Abingdon Pr.

Let's Thank God for Freedom. 2006. 16p. (J). pap. 1.99 (978-0-7847-1723-3(0) , 04184); pap. 1.99 (978-0-7847-1538-3(6) , 22142) Standard Publishing.

Letters from God for Teens: God's Promises for You. 2001. 192p. (J). (gr. 8-12). 12.99 (978-1-56292-711-0(6)) Cook, David C. Publishing Co.

Levey, Michael. The Book of the Holy Light. 2004. 204p. 17.95 (978-1-59540-987-4(4) , Sunstar Publishing) 1st World Publishing, Inc.

Libby, Larry. Who Made God? And Other Things We Wonder About. Gauthier, Corbert, illus. 2002. 40p. (J). 12.99 (978-0-310-70280-1(1)) Zonderkidz.

Lindahl, Kay. How Does God Listen? Maloney, Cynthia, photos by. 2005. (Illus.). 32p. (J). 8.99 (978-1-59473-084-9(9)) SkyLight Paths Publishing.

Lindbergh, Reeve. On Morning Wings. Meade, Holly, illus. 2002. 32p. (J). (ps-1). 15.99 (978-0-7636-1106-4(9)) Candlewick Pr.

Lingo, Susan L. Discover-N-Do Object Talks That Teach about God: 23 Messages That Teach Kids Ways to Investigate & Find God. Becker, Paula, illus. 2006. 48p. (J). pap. 6.99 (978-0-7847-1371-6(5) , 02901) Standard Publishing.

Long-Bostrom, Kathleen & Kucharik, Elena. What Is God Like? 1998. (Questions from Little Hearts Ser.). (Illus.). 80p. (J). 9.99 (978-0-8423-5118-8(3)) Tyndale Hse. Pubs.

Lopez, Hilda L. Mensajes de Amor Para Mi Pueblo, Creo en Dios. ltd. ed. 2000. (SPA.). 71p. per. 6.00 (978-0-9729299-0-5(8) , 2000-1, Vida Devocional) Lopez, Hilda.

The Lord's Lady Liberty (Children's Book) The Statue of Liberation Through Christ Helping America to Remember God. 2006. (J). pap. 7.00 (978-0-9749019-8-5(9)) Understanding For Life Ministries, Inc.

Lorenz, Jinye. God's Mountain Not the Mountain God. Lorenz, Virginia O., ed. Lorenz, Jacob J., illus. l.t. ed. 1998. 120p. (YA). (gr. 6 up). pap. 12.95 (978-1-888350-09-8(1)) Lighted Lamp Pr.

Mackall, Dandi D. For God So Loved the World. Selivanova, Elen, illus. 2007. 32p. (J). (ps-2). 12.99 (978-1-59145-524-0(3)) Nelson, Thomas Inc.

Mackall, Dandi Daley. God Made Me. Nakata, Hiroe, illus. 2006. 14p. (J). 6.99 (978-1-4169-1499-0(4) , Little Simon Inspirations) Simon & Schuster Children's Publishing.

MacKenzie, Carine. God Has Power. 1999. (Learn about God Ser.). (Illus.). 14p. (J). (ps-k). 3.99 (978-1-85792-477-0(0) , Christian Focus) Christian Focus Pubns. GBR. *Dist:* Riverside.

Mackenzie, Carine. God has Power. 16p. (J). pap., act. bk. ed. 1.50 (978-1-85792-634-7(X) , Christian Focus) Christian Focus Pubns. GBR. *Dist:* Riverside.

MacKenzie, Carine. God Is Everywhere. 1999. (Learn about God Ser.). (Illus.). 14p. (J). (ps-k). 3.99 (978-1-85792-480-0(0) , Christian Focus) Christian Focus Pubns. GBR. *Dist:* Riverside.

—God Is Faithful. 1999. (Learn about God Ser.). (Illus.). 14p. (J). (ps-k). 3.99 (978-1-85792-481-7(9) , Christian Focus) Christian Focus Pubns. GBR. *Dist:* Riverside.

—God Is Kind. 1999. (Learn about God Ser.). (Illus.). 14p. (J). (ps-k). 3.99 (978-1-85792-476-3(2) , Christian Focus) Christian Focus Pubns. GBR. *Dist:* Riverside.

—God Knows Everything. 1999. (Learn about God Ser.). (Illus.). 14p. (J). (ps-k). 3.99 (978-1-85792-479-4(7) , Christian Focus) Christian Focus Pubns. GBR. *Dist:* Riverside.

—God Never Changes. 1999. (Learn about God Ser.). (Illus.). 14p. (J). (ps-k). 3.99 (978-1-85792-478-7(9) , Christian Focus) Christian Focus Pubns. GBR. *Dist:* Riverside.

Mahan, Ben. God's World Letters & Numbers. 1999. (Illus.). 48p. (J). (ps-2). 2.99 (978-0-7847-0757-9(X) , Bean Sprouts) Standard Publishing.

Marxhausen, Joanne. 3 In 1: A Picture of God. 2nd ed. 2004. (Illus.). 48p. (J). (ps-4). 8.99 (978-0-7586-0680-8(X)) Concordia Publishing Hse.

McIntruff, Stephen. Look What God Made! 1999. (Illus.). 48p. (J). (ps-2). pap. 2.49 (978-0-7847-0887-3(8) , 22059, Bean Sprouts) Standard Publishing.

Meadows, James L. God Speaks to Today's Teenagers. (YA). Vol. I. pap. 5.50 (978-0-89098-375-1(5)); Vol. II. pap. 5.50 (978-0-89098-376-8(3)) Twentieth Century Christian Bks.

Mehl, Ron & Taylor, Jeannie St. John. Who Did It? Taylor, Jeannie St. John, illus. 2005. (YA). pap. 12.99 (978-0-8254-3168-5(9)) Kregel Pubns.

Menges, Jeff A. Nordic Gods Tattoos. 2004. (Art Tattoos Ser.). (Illus.). 2p. pap. 1.50 (978-0-486-43526-8(1)) Dover Pubns., Inc.

Moore, Mary A. Hide-and-Seek with God. 2005. 104p. (J). (ps-3). pap. 14.00 (978-1-55896-277-4(8) , Skinner Hse. Bks.) Unitarian Universalist Assn.

Moss, Donna. How I Praise You! 150 Little Psalms in Song. Moss, Rebecca, illus. 1998. 240p. (J). (ps-8). pap. (978-0-9663809-2-7(4)) Apex Publishing Services.

Nappa, Tony & Nappa, Mike. Lunch Box Promises: Over 75 Tear-Out Notes with Promises from God's Word. 2000. (Illus.). 160p. (J). (gr. k-6). pap. 7.99 (978-0-7847-1181-1(X) , 04326) Standard Publishing.

Nee, Watchman. God Is Willing. 2001. (Salvation Ser.). 9p. (gr. 6). 1.00 (978-0-7363-1208-0(0) , 18-086-001) Living Stream Ministry.

—God's Eternal Plan. 2001. 57p. (gr. 6). 5.50 (978-0-7363-0627-0(7) , 08-046-001) Living Stream Ministry.

—El Plan Eterno de Dios. 2001. Tr. of God's Eternal Plan. (SPA & ESP.). 58p. (gr. 6). 5.50 (978-0-7363-0415-3(0) , 08-046-002) Living Stream Ministry.

Nordenstrom, Michael, illus. & adapted by. Hina & the Sea of Stars. Nordenstrom, Michael, adapted by. 2003. 32p. 10.95 (978-1-57306-167-4(0)) Bess Pr., Inc.

Oeltjenbruns, Joni. Where Is God. 2004. (Illus.). 16p. (J). 6.95 (978-0-8198-8307-0(7) , 332-415) Pauline Bks. & Media.

Olsen, Debi W. My Very Own Book about God. 2004. 32p. (J). 10.95 (978-1-931947-03-9(1)) Ink & Scribe.

O'Neal, Claire. Artemis. 2007. (Profiles in Greek & Roman Mythology Ser.). (Illus.). 48p. (J). (gr. 4-9). lib. bdg. 29.95 (***978-1-58415-555-3(8)***) Mitchell Lane Pubs., Inc.

Ortiz, Michelle. You are a Child of God. 2006. (ENG.). 40p. (J). per. 17.99 (978-1-4141-0604-5(1)) Pleasant Word.

Osborne, Rick & Bowler, K. Christie. I Want to Know about God: Who God Is, What He Does & Why He Cares about Me. 1998. (I Want to Know Ser.). (Illus.). 32p. (J). (gr. 2-5). 9.99 (978-0-310-22090-9(4)) Zondervan.

Otis, George K., 3rd & Scotchmer, Paul, told to. The Seal of Faith: A True Story for Children. 2002. (Illus.). 32p. (J). pap. 12.95 (978-1-930612-12-9(5)) Sentinel Group, The.

Parrott, Leslie & Zondervan. God Made You Nose to Toes. Petrone, Valeria, illus. 2002. 18p. (J). bds. 6.99 (978-0-310-70216-0(X)) Zonderkidz.

Paterson, John & Paterson, Katherine. Images of God. 1998. (J). pap. 20.00 (978-0-395-70729-6(3)) Houghton Mifflin Co.

Pingry, Patricia A. The Story of Noah & the Rainbow. Venturi-Pickett, Stacy, illus. 2001. (J). (ps-3). pap. 3.95 (978-0-8249-5414-7(9) , Ideals Children's Bks.) Ideals Pubns.

Pollack-Brichto, Mira. The God Around Us: A Child's Garden of Prayer. Alko, Selina, illus. rev. ed. 2004. (ENG & HEB.). 32p. (J). (ps-1). 13.95 (978-0-8074-0701-1(1) , 101072) URJ Pr.

Poor Man's Heaven: Living for the Goodness of God. 2002. 136p. per. 10.00 (978-0-9712585-7-0(0)) JuDe Publishing.

Praise & Worship. 1998. (Cross Training Ser.: Vol. 1). 64p. (YA). (gr. 10-12). pap., tchr. ed. 15.00 incl. VHS (978-1-57405-009-7(5) , Cross Training) CharismaLife Pubs.

Publications International Staff, contrib. by. Count Your Blessings 123. 2001. (My Wipe-Off Book Ser.). (Illus.). (J). (978-0-7853-5103-0(5)) Publications International, Ltd.

Reeve, Penny. God Made Something Beautiful. 2002. (ps-2). lib. bdg. 11.80 (978-0-613-79989-8(5)) Tandem Library Bks.

Rodgers, Phillip W. How Tall Is God? 2003. (Discovering God Ser.). (Illus.). 32p. (J). 12.99 (978-0-8254-3634-5(6)) Kregel Pubns.

Ruckman, Kathleen. The Tiny Book: God Made Small Things, Too. 2002. (Illus.). 24p. (J). pap. 5.99 (978-0-89051-359-0(7)) Master Bks.

Ryks, Tracy. God Loves You Today! Ryks, Tracy, illus. 2000. (Illus.). 28p. (J). (ps-3). pap. 9.95 (978-0-9677367-0-9(6)) Devoted to You Bks.

Samuels, Ami. How Do I Know God Loves Me? Sholders, Sherri, illus. 2001. 12p. (J). (ps-6). 7.00 (978-0-9715430-0-3(3)) Samuels, Ami.

Sasso, Sandy. God's Paintbrush: Special 10th Anniversary Edition. Compton, Annette, illus. 10th anniv. annot. ed. 2004. (GER.). 32p. (J). 17.95 (978-1-58023-195-4(0)) Jewish Lights Publishing.

Sasso, Sandy Eisenberg. El Nombre de Dios. Sasso, Dennis C., tr. from ENG. Stone, Phoebe, illus. 2002. (SkyLight Lives Ser.). (SPA.). 32p. (J). 16.95 (978-1-893361-63-8(2)) SkyLight Paths Publishing.

Skinas, John Kosmas. Getting to Know God. 2005. (Illus.). (***978-1-888212-73-0(X)***) Conciliar Pr.

Smith, Barbara. Thank You God. Crowdy, Wendy, illus. 1998. 12p. (J). (ps-k). 8.00 (978-0-687-10370-6(3)) Abingdon Pr.

Sperling, Vatsala. Hanuman's Journey to the Medicine Mountain. 2006. (Illus.). 32p. (J). 15.95 (978-1-59143-063-6(1)) Inner Traditions International, Ltd.

Stannard, Russell. The Curious History of God. Davies, Taffy, illus. 1998. 95p. 16.99 (978-0-7459-3964-3(3) , Lion) Lion Hudson plc GBR. *Dist:* Independent Pubs. Group.

—The Curious History of God. Davies, Taffy, illus. 2003. 96p. 7.95 (978-1-932031-27-0(8)) Templeton Foundation Pr.

Steele, Philip. Gods & Gladiators: Everyday Life. 2004. (Illus.). 128p. pap. 17.99 (978-1-84476-032-9(4) , Southwater) Anness Publishing GBR. *Dist:* National Bk. Network.

Stevens, Sherri. Where Is God? Freeman, Patricia, illus. 2005. 24p. (YA). 15.95 (978-0-9769541-0-1(9) , 2005-1) Enlightened Bks.

Stohs, Anita Reith. Hush, Little One: A Lullaby for God's Children. Kanzler, John, tr. Kanzler, John, illus. 2004. 32p. (J). 12.99 (978-0-570-07144-0(5)) Concordia Publishing Hse.

Strang Communications Company Staff, ed. Ages 2-3 Resources: Spring 2002. 2002. (J). pap. 12.99 (978-1-57405-919-9(X)) CharismaLife Pubs.

—Ages 2-3 Resources: Summer 2002. 2002. (J). (gr. 12 up). pap. 12.99 (978-1-57405-957-1(2)) CharismaLife Pubs.

—Grades 1-2 Resources: Spring 2002. 2002. (J). pap. 12.99 (978-1-57405-935-9(1)) CharismaLife Pubs.

—Grades 1-2 Resources: Summer 2002. 2002. (J). (gr. 1-2). pap. 12.99 (978-1-57405-973-1(4)) CharismaLife Pubs.

Strobel, Lee. The Case for a Creator for Kids. 2006. (Illus.). 96p. (J). pap. 7.99 (978-0-310-71148-3(7)) Zonderkidz.

Surprised by God's Grace: Bible Learning Tool. 2004. (Firelight Ser.). (ps-6). 1.99 (978-0-8066-6452-1(5)) Augsburg Fortress, Pubs.

Surprised by God's Grace: Bible Story Flipbook. 2004. (Firelight Ser.). (gr. 3-4). 4.99 (978-0-8066-6460-6(6)) Augsburg Fortress, Pubs.

Surprised by God's Grace: Bible Story Magazine. 2004. (Firelight Ser.). (gr. 5-6). 4.99 (978-0-8066-6462-0(2)) Augsburg Fortress, Pubs.

Surprised by God's Grace: Bible Storybook. 2004. (Firelight Ser.). (gr. 1-2). 4.99 (978-0-8066-6458-3(4)) Augsburg Fortress, Pubs.

Swartz, Nancy Sohn. In Our Image: God's First Creatures. Hall, Melanie, illus. 1998. 32p. (ps-3). 16.95 (978-1-879045-99-6(0)) Jewish Lights Publishing.

Taylor, Jane. God Made Me. 1998. 16p. (J). 3.99 (978-1-85792-289-9(1) , Christian Focus) Christian Focus Pubns. GBR. *Dist:* Riverside, Spring Arbor Distributors, Inc.

—God Made the World. 1998. (Illus.). 16p. (J). (ps-k). 3.99 (978-1-85792-292-9(1) , Christian Focus) Christian Focus Pubns. GBR. *Dist:* Riverside, Spring Arbor Distributors, Inc.

Taylor, Kenneth N. Hablemos un Poquito Acerca de Dios. 1998. (SPA.). (J). 10.99 (978-0-7899-0516-1(7) , 498775) Editorial Unilit.

Traywick-Jones, Andrea. God Loves Me! Thomas, James, illus. 2003. 24p. (J). (978-1-55306-459-6(3) , Guardian Bks.) Essence Publishing.

VanBuskirk, Luegenia. God Loves Me. 2003. 40p. (J). per. 12.95 (978-1-56167-790-0(6)) American Literary Pr.

Vander Klipp, Michael A. God Made Animals. 1999. (God Made Bks.). (Illus.). 12p. (J). (ps). 2.99 (978-0-310-97860-2(2)) Zonderkidz.

—God Made Food. 1999. (God Made Bks.). (Illus.). 12p. (J). (ps). 2.99 (978-0-310-97857-2(2)) Zonderkidz.

Walsch, Neale Donald. Conversations with God for Teens. 2001. 256p. 19.95 (978-1-57174-263-6(8)) Hampton Roads Publishing Co., Inc.

Warnes, Tim, illus. Jesus Loves Me. 2008. 26p. (J). bds. 7.99 (***978-1-4169-5367-8(1)*** , Little Simon Inspirations) Simon & Schuster Children's Publishing.

Watson, Jane Werner. My Big Little Golden Book about God. Wilkin, Eloise, illus. ed. 2006. 32p. (J). (gr. k-k). 8.99 (978-0-375-83551-3(2) , Golden Inspirational) Random Hse. Children's Bks.

Watson, Jane Werner & Wilkin, Eloise. My Little Book about God. 2001. (Golden Book Ser.). (Illus.). 26p. (J). (gr. k-ps). bds. 4.99 (978-0-307-20312-0(3) , 20312, Golden Inspirational) Random Hse. Children's Bks.

Webber, Christopher L. Praise the Lord, My Soul: Psalm 104 for Children. McDaniels, Preston, illus. 2002. 32p. (ps-1). 14.95 (978-0-8192-1889-6(8)) Morehouse Publishing.

—Shout for Joy & Sing! Psalm 65 for Children. McDaniels, Preston, illus. 2003. (Psalms for Children Ser.). 32p. 14.95 (978-0-8192-1934-3(7)) Morehouse Publishing.

Wesleyan Publishing House Staff. Learning about God: Preschool. 2006. pap., stu. ed., act. bk. ed. 15.99 (978-0-89827-340-3(4)) Wesleyan Publishing Hse.

Wiens, Patti. A Child's ABCs of Praise, Spieler, Leah, ed. LeTourneau, Anthony & Carlson, Josh, illus. 2004. 60p. (J). pap. 14.99 (978-0-9761408-0-1(2)) Creative Marketing Concepts, Inc.

Winkler, Jude. God the Father. Catholic Book Publishing Staff, ed. 1998. (St. Joseph Picture Bks.). (Illus.). 32p. (J). (ps-3). 1.25 (978-0-89942-514-6(3) , 511) Catholic Bk. Publishing Co.

Winston, Pat. God Loves Me Just the Way I Am. Allen, Cathy H., illus. 2001. (Earl the EMU Ser.). 24p. (J). (ps-3). 12.95 (978-0-9702821-1-8(7)) Light Way Pubns., The.

Womersley, S. Dios es Bueno: Libro de Colorear. 2000. Tr. of God is Good: Coloring Book. pap. 1.69 (978-0-7899-0256-6(7)) Editorial Unilit.

Zondervan, contrib. by. GNT My Book — God. 2nd ed. 2001. (Illus.). 1440p. (J). pap. 14.99 (978-0-310-92024-3(8)) Zondervan.

—Mom, You're Berry Sweet. 2004. (Illus.). 48p. (J). 7.99 (978-0-310-80512-0(0)) Zondervan.

GOD—FICTION

Adams, Michelle Medlock. Why I Love you, God. 2004. (ENG.). 20p. (J). bds. 4.99 (978-0-570-07187-7(9)) Concordia Publishing Hse.

Atwood, Jeff. Our Big, Big God. Graef, Renee, illus. 2007. 20p. (J). 8.99 (978-1-4169-2520-0(1) , Little Simon Inspirations) Simon & Schuster Children's Publishing.

Baldwin, Christy. Nine Things Nathan Noticed at Night. Barnes, Sarah, illus. 2005. 24p. (J). per. 13.00 (978-0-9765072-1-5(8)) Tribute Bks.

Bea, Holly & Howard, Kim. God Believes in You. 2004. (Illus.). 32p. (J). 15.00 (978-1-932073-08-9(6)) Kramer, H.J. Inc.

Beeke, Joel & Kleyn, Diana. How God Used a Drought & an Umbrella. Anderson, Jeff, illus. (Building on the Rock Ser.). 176p. (J). pap. (978-1-85792-818-1(0) , Christian Focus) Christian Focus Pubns. GBR. *Dist:* Riverside.

Bergren, Lisa Tawn. God Gave Us Christmas. Hohn, David, illus. 2006. 40p. (J). 9.99 (978-1-4000-7175-3(5) , WaterBrook Pr.) WaterBrook Pr.

Bergren, Lisa Tawn. How Big Is God? Bryant, Laura J., illus. 2008. (HarperBlessings Ser.). 32p. (J). 10.99 (***978-0-06-113174-5(1)***) HarperCollins Pubs.

Bernthal, Mark & Exclaim Entertainment Staff. Boz/Good Morning Boz. Jeffords, Brandon, illus. 2006. (BOZ#8482; Ser.). 14p. (J). 4.99 (978-0-310-71207-7(6)) Zondervan.

—Boz/Good Night Boz. Jeffords, Brandon, illus. 2006. (BOZ#8482; Ser.). 14p. (J). 4.99 (978-0-310-71206-0(8)) Zondervan.

—God Loves Your Nose. McKee, Darren, illus. 2006. (BOZ#8482; Ser.). 12p. (J). 5.99 (978-0-310-71152-0(5)) Zonderkidz.

Bjorkman, Steve. Good Night, Little One. Bjorkman, Steve, illus. 1999. (Illus.). 40p. (J). (ps-3). 9.99 (978-1-57856-275-6(9) , WaterBrook Pr.) WaterBrook Pr.

Bluitgen, Kare. A Boot Fell from Heaven. Carrer, Chiara, illus. 2002. 36p. (J). 15.95 (978-1-929132-45-4(X)) Kane/Miller Bk. Pubs., Inc.

Blume, Judy. Are You There God? It's Me, Margaret. 2002. (J). 13.94 (978-0-7587-9131-3(3)) Book Wholesalers, Inc.

—Are You There God? It's Me, Margaret. l.t. ed. 2002. (LRS Large Print Cornerstone Ser.). (J). lib. bdg. 28.95 (978-1-58118-088-6(8) , 24873) LRS.

Bowman, Crystal. My Happy Pumpkin. 2007. (Illus.). 14p. (J). 6.99 (***978-0-310-71160-5(6)***) Zonderkidz.

Bridges, Moire. Sissy & the King. 2007. (J). 19.99 (***978-1-59879-403-8(5)***); per. 13.99 (***978-1-59879-425-0(6)***) Lifevest Publishing, Inc.

—Sissy & the King (Spanish Version) Hermanita y el Rey. 2007. (J). per. 13.99 (***978-1-59879-427-4(2)***) Lifevest Publishing, Inc.

Burningham, John. Whadayamean. 1999. (Illus.). (J). lib. bdg. 20.99 (978-0-375-90177-5(9)) Crown Publishing Group.

—Whadayamean. 1999. (Illus.). (J). 19.00 (978-0-375-80177-8(4)) Knopf, Alfred A. Inc.

Carlson, Melody. God Goes with Me. Banek, Yvette Santiago, illus. 2000. (God Is Here Ser.). 20p. (ps-k). 9.99 (978-1-58134-160-7(1) , Crossway Bibles) Crossway Bks.

—My Happy Heart. Osborn, Jim, illus. 2001. 32p. (J). (ps-5). 12.99 (978-0-8054-2382-2(6)) B&H Publishing Grp.

Cavalli, Frank. Before the Beginning Began. Riley, Kellee, illus. 2005. 56p. (J). per. 19.95 (978-0-9766662-0-2(0)) Star Dome Publishing, LLC.

Children in Action: Agents of God's Love. 2004. 80p. (J). (gr. k-1). pap. 9.99 (978-0-7647-0987-6(9)); (gr. 2-4). pap. 9.99 (978-0-7647-0988-3(7)) School Specialty Publishing.

Coffee, Karen. God, Do You Love Me? Hardison, Buist, illus. 2007. 32p. (ps-1). 14.00 (***978-0-687-49270-1(X)***) Abingdon Pr.

Cohen, Deborah Bodin. The Seventh Day. Hall, Melanie, illus. 2005. 24p. (J). (ps-3). pap. 6.95 (978-1-58013-125-4(5)); 16.95 (978-0-929371-24-5(0)) Kar-Ben Publishing.

Dalmatian Press Staff. Thanks You, God: Board Book with Plush Toy. rev. ed. 2007. 7p. 12.99 (***978-1-4037-3074-9(1)*** , Spirit Pr.) Dalmatian Pr.

Daniel, Patricia A. The Purple Swan. 2007. 12.95 (***978-1-59526-676-7(3)***) Media Creations, Inc.

David C. Cook. God Made Everything with Love, Set. 2007. (Land of Milk & Honey Ser.). (J). (ps). bds. 9.99 (***978-1-4347-0007-0(0)***) Cook, David C. Publishing Co.

—Little Hearts, Little Hands Prayer Set. 2007. (Land of Milk & Honey Ser.). 16p. (J). (ps). bds. 9.99 (***978-1-4347-0008-7(9)***) Cook, David C. Publishing Co.

Davina. Mr. G - Are You Listening? Kat's Diary. 2003. 96p. (J). pap. 7.99 (978-0-7459-4841-6(3) , Lion) Lion Hudson plc GBR. *Dist:* Independent Pubs. Group.

DeBoer, Rondi. God Must Really Love... Numbers. Haskamp, Steve, illus. 2007. 14p. (J). (ps). 6.99 (***978-1-4169-3356-4(5)*** , Little Simon Inspirations) Simon & Schuster Children's Publishing.

DeKok, Joy. It Is Good. 2005. (ENG.). 28p. (J). per. 15.99 (978-1-4141-0390-7(5)) Pleasant Word.

Dougherty, Brittany Luciani. God Is Laughing. 2004. 68p. pap. 14.95 (978-1-4137-4973-1(9)) PublishAmerica, Inc.

Engelhardt, Lisa O. God Is My Friend: A Kid's Guide to God. Alley, R. W., illus. 2002. (J). per. 6.95 (978-0-87029-361-0(3) , 20079) Abbey Pr.

Fedrau, Noel. An Autumn Leaf. Houston, Barbara, illus. 2007. (ENG.). 40p. (J). per. 21.99 (***978-1-4141-0828-5(1)***) Pleasant Word.

Fortuna, Lorna. When God Spoke to Trees. 2006. 17.00 (978-0-8059-9884-9(5)) Dorrance Publishing Co., Inc.

Freed, Shirley & Moon, Louise. God Can See Me. Morelan, Bill, ed. Harrell, Rob, illus. 2003. 8p. (J). (-k). pap. 3.99 (978-1-58938-098-1(3)) Concerned Communications.

Freed, Shirley Ann & Moon, Louise. God's Promise. Morelan, Bill, ed. Butler, Steven, illus. l.t. ed. 2002. 16p. (J). (gr. 5). pap. 3.99 (978-1-58938-021-9(5)) Concerned Communications.

Gemmen, Heather. I Don't Like It. Lagares, Luciano, illus. 2004. (Tough Stuff for Kids Ser.). 36p. (J). (gr. 4-7). pap., pap. 5.99 (978-0-7814-4036-3(X) , 078144036X) Cook, David C. Publishing Co.

Golden Books Staff. Where's God When I'm S-scared? 2007. (Illus.). 24p. (J). (gr. k-k). 2.99 (***978-0-375-83931-3(3)*** , Golden Inspirational) Random Hse. Children's Bks.

Gurley, Nan. Twice Yours: A Parable of God's Gift. Farnsworth, Bill, illus. 2004. 32p. (J). pap. 6.99 (978-0-310-70920-6(2)) Zonderkidz.

Hafer, Todd. In the Chat Room with God. 2002. (gr. 7-12). lib. bdg. 22.25 (978-0-613-81753-0(2)) Tandem Library Bks.

Hafer, Todd & Hafer, Jedd. In the Chat Room with God. 2002. 256p. pap., pap. 12.99 (978-1-58919-970-5(7) , 1589199707) Cook, David C. Publishing Co.

Hickman, Martha Whitmore. Then I Think of God. 2003. (Illus.). 32p. (J). (gr. k-4). 15.95 (978-0-8075-7847-6(9)) Whitman, Albert & Co.

Hodgson, Mona Gansberg. I Wonder Who Hung the Moon in the Sky. 1999. (I Wonder Ser.). (Illus.). 32p. (J). (ps-2). 6.99 (978-0-570-05067-4(7)) Concordia Publishing Hse.

Hunt, Susan & Hunt, Richie. Discovering Jesus in Exodus, Vol. 2. 2005. (Illus.). 176p. pap. 16.99 (978-1-58134-453-0(8) , Crossway Bibles) Crossway Bks.

Huskins, Suzanne Hallier, illus. No Matter What! 2004. (J). (978-1-887905-93-0(6)) Parkway Pubs., Inc.

Jackson, Beverly Lozier. Mommy, Is God a Super Hero? 2007. (J). per. 7.99 (***978-1-59886-903-3(5)***) Tate Publishing & Enterprises, L.L.C.

Jeffs, Stephanie. A Bad Day for Christopher Bear. Thomas, Jacqui, illus. 2004. (Christopher Bear Ser.). 30p. 5.99 (978-0-8066-4367-0(6) , Augsburg Bks.) Augsburg Fortress, Pubs.

—I Love You, Christopher Bear. Thomas, Jacqui, illus. 2004. (Christopher Bear Ser.). 32p. 5.99 (978-0-8066-4366-3(8) , Augsburg Bks.) Augsburg Fortress, Pubs.

Jenkins, Jerry B. & LaHaye, Tim. Breakout! Believers in Danger. 2003. (Left Behind Ser.: Bk. 29). (gr. 5-8). lib. bdg. 14.15 (978-0-613-76887-0(6)) Tandem Library Bks.

Jones, Erik, illus. God Is in the Refrigerator. 2006. 38p. (J). 18.95 (978-0-9771936-4-6(0)) InterWeave Corp.

Koehne, Troy. Death of a Martyr. 2003. 138p. (YA). pap. 11.95 (978-0-595-28031-5(5)) iUniverse, Inc.

Lane, Sondra. Showin' Out to God's Glory. 2004. (Illus.). 28p. (J). 7.95 (978-0-9743874-1-3(X)) Lane, Sondra Corp.

Lester, Julius. Why Heaven Is Far Away. Cepeda, Joe, illus. 2002. 40p. (J). (gr. 1-3). pap. 16.95 (978-0-439-17871-6(1) , Scholastic Pr.) Scholastic, Inc.

Maccabe, Catherine. Teddy Bear, Piglet, Kitten & Me. Scruton, Clive, illus. 2004. 28p. 11.99 (978-0-8066-4148-5(7) , Augsburg Bks.) Augsburg Fortress, Pubs.

Mackall, Dandi Daley. Cinnamon Lake Mysteries Set, 6 vols. (Cinnamon Lake Mysteries Ser.). (J). 33.74 (978-0-7586-0006-6(2)) Concordia Publishing Hse.

McGillicuddy, Barbara. Adventures in the Kingdom of Mim: Buddie Saves the Day. 2006. (J). per. 13.95 (978-0-9774513-7-1(2)) Changing Lives Publishing.

Mooney, Jane-Marie. Wings in Dragon Dance. 2007. (ENG.). 168p. per. (***978-1-84685-551-1(9)*** , Exposure Publishing) Meadow Bks.

O'Day, Joseph E. I Like Rain! Foster, Ron, illus. 2007. (J). (***978-1-929039-39-5(5)***) Ambassador Bks., Inc.

Peckham, Lori, ed. Guide's Greatest Animal Stories. 2006. 144p. (YA). pap. 10.99 (***978-0-8280-1944-6(4)***) Review & Herald Publishing Assn.

Reeves, Nancy Christine, et al. Adventures of the God Detectives. 2006. (Illus.). 94p. (J). pap. 6.95 (***978-1-55145-542-6(0)***) Wood Lake Bks., Inc. CAN. *Dist:* Pilgrim Pr., The/United Church Pr.

Rodgers, Phillip W. When Does God Sleep? 2007. 12.99 (***978-0-8254-3631-4(1)***) Kregel Pubns.

Rylant, Cynthia. God Went to Beauty School. 2003. (J). 64p. 14.99 (978-0-06-009433-1(8)); 80p. lib. bdg. 15.89 (978-0-06-009434-8(6)) HarperCollins Pubs.

Sauro, Joan. Does God Ever Sleep? Sauro, Joan, photos by. 2005. (Illus.). 32p. (J). (ps-3). 8.99 (978-1-59473-110-5(1)) SkyLight Paths Publishing.

Schlessinger, Laura. Dr. Laura Schlessinger's Where's God? McFeeley, Daniel, illus. 2003. 40p. (J). (ps-2). lib. bdg. 16.89 (978-0-06-051910-0(X)) HarperCollins Pubs.

—Where's God? McFeeley, Daniel, illus. l.t. ed. 2003. 40p. (J). (ps-2). 16.99 (978-0-06-051909-4(6)) HarperCollins Pubs.

Smith, Jennifer Lynne. Things I Wonder. Perez, Angela J., ed. Gray, Angela M., illus. 2007. 36p. (J). 17.95 (***978-0-9778328-5-9(6)***) His Work Christian Publishing.

Stannard, Russell. WWW Here-I-Am. 2002. (gr. 7-12). lib. bdg. 18.75 (978-0-613-84233-4(2)) Tandem Library Bks.

—www.Here-I-Am. Pugh, Jonathan, illus. 2002. 160p. (gr. 5-8). 9.95 (978-1-890151-85-0(8)) Templeton Foundation Pr.

Steele, Michael Anthony & Exclaim Entertainment Staff. God Gives You Friends: With Boz the Bear. McKee, Darren, illus. 2006. (Boz Ser.). 12p. (J). 5.99 (978-0-310-71153-7(3)) Zonderkidz.

Stefano, Roberto D. La Magia de Pablo y Otros Cuentos con Poderes. Martin, Silvia, illus. 2000. (Chicos de la Valija Ser.).Tr. of Pablo's Magic Tricks & Other Magical Tales. (SPA.). 61p. (J). (gr. k-2). pap. 8.95 (978-950-739-829-2(5)) Errepar ARG. *Dist:* Baker & Taylor Bks.

Stockton, Lucille. God in a Child's World & King Catfish Roonie & His Neighbors. 2003. 48p. (J). per. (978-1-932077-34-6(0)) Athena Pr.

Stone, Forrest. Loki & the Magic Hammer: A Norse Myth. 2006. 42.00 (***978-1-4108-6178-8(3)***) Benchmark Education Co.

Strong, R. What Difference Does Seven Days Make? 2005. 140p. pap. 19.95 (978-1-4137-7789-5(9)) PublishAmerica, Inc.

Swartz, Nancy Sohn. How Did the Animals Help God? Hall, Melanie, illus. 2004. 24p. (J). bds. 7.99 (978-1-59473-044-3(X)) SkyLight Paths Publishing.

Tada, Joni Eareckson. A Father's Touch. Nelson, Craig, illus. 2005. 48p. (J). pap. 17.99 (978-1-58134-714-2(6) , Crossway Bibles) Crossway Bks.

Thank You, God. 2003. (Illus.). 28p. (J). (ps-k). bds. 7.95 (978-0-8249-5457-4(2)) Ideals Pubns.

The Thirsty Turtle. 2003. 32p. (J). per. 14.95 (978-1-59094-049-5(0)) Jawbone Publishing Corp.

Umina, Lisa. Milo with a Halo. Karcic, Andrea, illus. 2002. 24p. pap. 5.95 (978-0-9718350-0-9(4)) Halo Publishing International.

Veggietales. God Is Bigger! 2007. (Veggie Tales Gift Book Ser.). 32p. (J). 7.99 (978-1-4165-3384-9(2) , Howard Bks.) Simon & Schuster.

Wallace, Michael. You, Mommy & Me. 2006. 22p. spiral bd. 8.50 (978-1-4116-9761-4(8)) Lulu.com.

Walsh, Sheila. Hello, Stars! A Sleepytime Tale of God's Loving Presence. Maze, Deborah, illus. 2001. 40p. (J). 9.95 (978-1-57856-336-4(4) , WaterBrook Pr.) WaterBrook Pr.

Wargin, Kathy-Jo. P Is for Pumpkin. Pang, Ariel Ya-Wen, illus. 2008. (J). (978-0-310-71180-3(0)) Zonderkidz.

Williamson, Marianne. Emma & Mommy Talk to God. Noonan, Julia, illus. 2006. 32p. (J). pap. 6.99 (978-0-06-079926-7(9) , Harper Trophy) HarperCollins Pubs.

Wiskur, Darrell. Dinky Dinosaur: Creation Days. 2002. (Illus.). (J). (ps-1). 6.99 (978-0-89051-361-3(9) , 303-075) Master Bks.

GODDARD, ROBERT HUTCHINGS, 1882-1945

McLeese, Don. Robert Goddard. (Rourke Discovery Library). 2006. (Illus.). 24p. (gr. 2-5). 14.95 (978-1-59515-435-4(3) , 1244322); 2005. (ENG & SPA.). (J). (978-1-59515-675-4(5)) Rourke Publishing, LLC.

Patchett, Kaye. Robert Goddard: Rocket Pioneer. 2005. (Giants of Science Ser.). (Illus.). 64p. (J). (ps-7). lib. bdg. 26.20 (978-1-56711-888-9(7) , Blackbirch Pr., Inc.) Thomson Gale.

Schaefer, Lola M. Robert Goddard. 2005. (Transportation Ser.). 24p. (YA). (gr. k-3). pap. (978-0-7368-8732-8(6) , Pebble Bks.) Capstone Pr., Inc.

GODS—FICTION

Alberti, Robert. Mitlanyal: The Gods of Stability, Vol. 1. 10th ed. 2004. (Illus.). 152p. (YA). pap. 19.95 (978-0-9725880-2-7(7) , mit1) Zottola Publishing, Inc.

Bailey, Sian, illus. Grandfather Mountain: Stories of Gods & Heroes from Many Cultures. 2004. 80p. (J). (gr. 3-6). 19.99 (978-1-84148-789-2(9)) Barefoot Bks., Inc.

Banerjee, Anjali. Maya Running. 2006. 224p. (YA). (gr. 7). reprint ed. mass mkt. 5.99 (978-0-553-49424-2(4) , Laurel Leaf) Random Hse. Children's Bks.

Burciaga, David. Say Cheese, God! Wisner, Luke, illus. l.t. ed. 2006. 24p. (J). per. 11.99 (***978-1-59879-235-5(0)***) Lifevest Publishing, Inc.

La Cancion del Sol. 2001. (Cuentos y Mitos de America Latina Ser.). (SPA., Illus.). 32p. (J). (gr. 2-5). lib. bdg. 26.60 (978-1-58952-192-6(7) , RK7107) Rourke Publishing, LLC.

Climo, Shirley. Atlanta's Race: A Greek Myth. 2000. (J). 13.75 (978-0-606-19360-3(X)) Tandem Library Bks.

Collins Malia. Pele & Poliahu. Peterson Kathleen, illus. 2005. 24p. 14.95 (978-1-933067-13-1(6)) Mutual Publishing LLC.

Corrie, Chad. Gambit's End. 2007. (Divine Gambit Trilogy Ser.: Bk. 3). (Illus.). 492p. pap. 15.99 (***978-0-9776043-5-7(7)***) Aspirations Media, Inc.

Coville, Bruce. Thor's Wedding Day: By Thialfi, the goat boy, as told to & translated by Bruce Coville. Cogswell, Matthew, illus. 2008. 144p. (J). pap. 5.95 (978-0-15-205872-2(9) , Magic Carpet Bks.) Harcourt Children's Bks.

Deary, Terry. The Fire Thief. 2007. 256p. (J). (gr. 5). pap. 5.95 (***978-0-7534-6118-1(8)*** , Kingfisher) Houghton Mifflin Co. Trade & Reference Div.

—The Fire Thief Fights Back. 2007. (Fire Thief Ser.). 224p. (J). (gr. 5-7). 9.95 (978-0-7534-5970-6(1) , Kingfisher) Houghton Mifflin Co. Trade & Reference Div.

—Flight of Fire Thief. 2007. (Fire Thief Ser.). 224p. (J). pap. 5.95 (***978-0-7534-6169-3(2)*** , Kingfisher) Houghton Mifflin Co. Trade & Reference Div.

Deary, Terry. Flight of the Fire Thief. 2006. (Fire Thief Ser.). 240p. (J). (gr. 5). 9.95 (978-0-7534-5819-8(5) , Kingfisher) Houghton Mifflin Co. Trade & Reference Div.

Farfan, Flores & Antonio, Jose. Axolotl: El Ajolote. Celestino, Cleofas Ramirez, illus. 2003. (SPA.). 40p. (J). (978-968-411-569-9(5)) Ediciones Era.

Friesner, Esther. Temping Fate. 2007. 288p. (YA). pap. 6.99 (978-0-14-240848-3(4) , Puffin) Penguin Group (USA) Inc.

Fujishima, Kosuke. Oh My Goddess! (J). Vol. 1. 2005. 192p. pap. 10.95 (978-1-59307-387-9(9)); Vol. 22. 2006. 176p. pap. 10.95 (978-1-59307-400-5(X)); Vol. 25. 2007. 176p. pap. 10.95 (978-1-59307-644-3(4)) Dark Horse Comics.

EFG

—Oh My Goddess! Colors. 2007. 192p. (J). pap. 19.95 (978-1-59307-408-1(5)) Dark Horse Comics.

—Terrible Master Urd. Gleason, Alan et al, trs. 1999. (Oh My Goddess! Ser.: Vol. 4). (Illus.). 176p. (J). (gr. 3 up). pap. 14.95 (978-1-56971-369-3(3)) Dark Horse Comics.

Guilfoyle, Kim. Why Do You Love Me? 2007. (J). per. 9.99 (***978-1-59886-980-4(9)***) Tate Publishing & Enterprises, L.L.C.

Harris, Joanne. Runemarks. 2008. 544p. (J). (gr. 5). lib. bdg. 21.99 (***978-0-375-94444-4(3)*** , Knopf Bks. for Young Readers) Random Hse. Children's Bks.

Jones, Allan Frewin. Blood Stone, Vol. 6. 2003. 176p. (J). mass mkt. (978-0-330-37476-7(1) , Pan) Pan Macmillan.

Limke Jeff. Isis y Osiris (Isis & Osiris) Hasta el fin del mundo (to the Ends of the Earth) Witt, David, illus. 2007. (Mitos y leyendas en viñetas (Graphic Myths & Legends) Ser.). (SPA & ENG.). (J). pap. 8.95 (***978-0-8225-7971-7(5)*** , Ediciones Lerner) Lerner Publishing Group.

Limke, Jeff. Thor & Loki: In the Land of Giants. Randall, Ron, illus. 2007. (Graphic Myths & Legends Ser.). 48p. (YA). (gr. 4-9). pap. 8.95 (***978-0-8225-6481-2(5)***) Lerner Publishing Group.

Limke Jeff. Thor y Loki (Thor & Loki) En la tierra de los gigantes (in the Land of Giants) Randall, Ron, illus. 2007. (Mitos y leyendas en viñetas (Graphic Myths & Legends) Ser.). (J). pap. 8.95 (***978-0-8225-7969-4(3)*** , Ediciones Lerner) Lerner Publishing Group.

Madkins, Doris J. God Made the Sun to Shine. 2004. (J). pap. 8.00 (978-0-8059-6625-1(0)) Dorrance Publishing Co., Inc.

Magee, Kanika. Where Is God at Midnight?? Thomas, Sonya, illus. 2003. (J). 10.00 net. (978-0-9748834-1-0(7)) Ebenezer A.M.E. Church.

Nicholson, Nancy E. Devotional Stories for Little Folks. 2002. (J). per. (978-0-9771236-0-5(X)) For Little Folks.

Novesky, Amy. Elephant Prince: The Story of Ganesh. Wedman, Belgin K., illus. 2004. 32p. (J). 16.95 (978-1-886069-16-9(6) , BK2304HB) Mandala Publishing.

Oeming, Michael Avon. Thor Blood Oath. 2007. (Illus.). 144p. pap. 14.99 (978-0-7851-1852-7(7)) Marvel Enterprises, Inc.

Schlessinger, Laura. Where's God. 2006. pap. (978-0-06-051911-7(8)) HarperCollins Canada, Ltd.

Seow, David. Monkey: The Journey Begins. 2005. (Illus.). 32p. 15.95 (978-0-8048-3517-6(9)) Tuttle Publishing.

Shoup, Andrew J. Toko of Coco Oko. Shoup, Andrew J., illus. l.t. ed. 2002. (Illus.). 32p. (J). 16.95 (978-0-9720436-0-1(8) , SAN: 254-573X) TokoBooks.

Smith, Cheryl Jean. The Offering. 2006. 129p. pap. 11.95 (978-0-7414-3181-3(5)) Infinity Publishing.

Sutherland, Tui. Shadow Falling. 2007. (Avatars Ser.: Bk. 2). 368p. (YA). (gr. 7 up). 16.99 (***978-0-06-085146-0(5)***); (J). lib. bdg. 17.89 (***978-0-06-085147-7(3)***) HarperCollins Pubs. (Eos).

Tchana, Katrin. Changing Woman & Her Sisters: Stories of Goddesses from Around the World. Hyman, Trina Schart, illus. 2006. 80p. (J). (gr. 4 up). 18.95 (978-0-8234-1999-9(1)) Holiday Hse., Inc.

Turtledove, Harry. Between the Rivers. 1999. (J). (978-0-606-16884-7(2)) Tandem Library Bks.

Uberoi, Meera. Lord Ganesha's Feast of Laughter. 2007. 120p. pap. 9.95 (978-0-14-333524-5(3) , Penguin Global) Penguin Group (USA) Inc.

Wheeler, Leslie. Dolly's Day in the Garden. 2006. 18p. (J). per. 10.99 (***978-1-59886-708-4(3)***) Tate Publishing & Enterprises, L.L.C.

Wong, Tony. Weapons of the Gods, Vol. 6. 2003. (Illus.). 120p. (YA). (gr. 8 up). pap. 13.95 (978-1-58899-206-2(3)) ComicsOne Corp./Dr. Masters.

Yolen, Jane. Sister Light, Sister Dark: Book One in the Great Alta Saga. 2003. (gr. 7-12). lib. bdg. 15.30 (978-0-613-74858-2(1)) Tandem Library Bks.

GODZILLA (FICTITIOUS CHARACTER)—FICTION

Bissette, Steve, et al. The Age of Monsters. 1998. (Godzilla Ser.). (Illus.). 272p. (YA). (gr. 5 up). pap. 17.95 (978-1-56971-277-1(8)) Dark Horse Comics.

Cerasini, Marc. Godzilla Saves America: A Monster Showdown In 3-D! Morgan, Tom & Mounts, Paul, illus. 2006. 20p. (J). (gr. k-4). reprint ed. 12.00 (978-1-4223-5409-4(1)) DIANE Publishing Co.

Gilmour, H. B. Godzilla: A Junior Novelization. novel ed. 1998. (Godzilla Ser.). 88p. (J). (gr. 1-4). pap. 3.99 (978-0-590-68091-2(9)) Scholastic, Inc.

Godzilla: Picture Book. 2002. (Illus.). 32p. (J). 16.99 (978-0-7868-0797-0(0)) Disney Pr.

Preller, James. Godzilla Deluxe Storybook. 1998. (Godzilla Ser.). 48p. (J). (gr. 2-5). pap. 5.98 (978-0-590-57213-2(X)) Scholastic, Inc.

Scholastic, Inc. Staff. Godzilla: A Novelization. novel ed. 1998. (Godzilla Ser.). (Illus.). 152p. (J). (gr. 3-7). pap. 3.99 (978-0-590-28243-7(3)) Scholastic, Inc.

—Godzilla Danger Zone: The Ultimate Movie Fact Book. 1998. (Godzilla Ser.). (J). (gr. 3-7). pap. 4.98 (978-0-590-78627-0(X)) Scholastic, Inc.

—Godzillas Scrapbook. 1998. (Godzilla Ser.). 32p. (J). (gr. 2-5). pap. 7.98 (978-0-590-57239-2(3)) Scholastic, Inc.

GOETHE, JOHANN WOLFGANG VON, 1749-1832—FICTION

Cohn, Diana. Mr. Goethe's Garden. Mirocha, Paul, illus. 2003. 32p. 17.95 (978-0-88010-521-7(6)) SteinerBooks, Inc.

GOGH, VINCENT VAN, 1853-1890

Aigner-Clark, Julie. Van Gogh's World of Color. Zaidi, Nadeem, illus. 2001. (Baby Einstein Ser.). 12p. (J). (ps-ps). 7.99 (978-0-7868-0805-2(5)) Hyperion Bks. for Children.

Baby Van Gogh. 2000. (Baby Einstein Ser.). 25p. (J). pap. 19.98 incl. VHS (978-1-892309-33-4(5)) Baby Einstein Co., LLC, The.

Bassil, Andrea & Van Gogh, Vincent. Vincent Van Gogh. 2004. (Lives of the Artists Ser.). (Illus.). 48p. (J). (gr. 5 up). pap. 29.26 (978-0-8368-5607-1(4)); lib. bdg. 30.00 (978-0-8368-5602-6(3)) Stevens, Gareth Inc. (World Almanac Library).

Bevan, Clare. The Story of Vincent Van Gogh. 2002. (Lifetimes Ser.). (Illus.). 48p. (J). lib. bdg. 28.50 (978-1-931983-16-7(X)) Chrysalis Education.

Bowen, Richard. Vincent Van Gogh: Modern Artist. 2002. (Great Names Ser.). (Illus.). 32p. (J). (gr. 3 up). lib. bdg. (978-1-59084-141-9(7)) Mason Crest Pubs.

Claybourne, Anna & Van Gogh, Vincent. Vincent Van Gogh. 2004. (Illus.). 48p. (J). lib. bdg. 28.56 (978-0-7398-6631-3(1)) Raintree.

Connolly, Sean. Vincent Van Gogh. (Heinemann First Library). 32p. (J). 2006. (Illus.). lib. bdg. (***978-1-4034-8497-0(X)***); 1999. lib. bdg. 21.36 (978-1-57572-958-9(X)) Heinemann Library.

—Vincent Van Gogh. 2001. (gr. k-3). lib. bdg. 14.75 (978-0-613-86818-1(8)) Tandem Library Bks.

Crispino, Enrica. Van Gogh. 2008. (YA). lib. bdg. 24.95 net. (***978-1-934545-05-8(8)***) Oliver Pr., Inc.

David, Thomas. Vincent Van Gogh: El Puente de Arles. 2nd ed. 2002. (Coleccion Joven Arte).Tr. of Vincent Van Gogh: The Bridge at Arles. (SPA., Illus.). 128p. (YA). 11.96 (978-84-89804-17-3(6)) Loguez Ediciones ESP. *Dist:* Lectorum Pubns., Inc.

de Bie, Ceciel. My Brother Vincent Van Gogh. Williams, Kate, tr. 2003. (Books for Young Readers Ser.). (Illus.). 64p. 19.95 (978-0-89236-711-5(3)) Oxford Univ. Pr., Inc.

Dorling Kindersley Publishing Staff & Bernard, Bruce. Van Gogh. 1999. (Eyewitness Bks.). (Illus.). 64p. (J). (gr. 3-7). 15.99 (978-0-7894-4878-1(5)) Dorling Kindersley Publishing, Inc.

Flux, Paul. Vincent Van Gogh, Set 1. 2002. (Illus.). 32p. (J). (gr. k-2). pap. 6.50 (978-1-58810-287-4(4) , 91058) Heinemann Library.

Green, Jen. Vincent Van Gogh. Iribarren Berrade, Miguel, tr. 2006. (Los artistas en su mundo Ser.). (SPA., Illus.). 46p. (J). 19.95 (978-84-932442-2-4(8)) Blume ESP. *Dist:* Independent Pubs. Group.

—Vincent Van Gogh. 2002. (Artists in Their Time Ser.). (J). (gr. 5-7). pap. 6.95 (978-0-531-16648-2(1)); (Illus.). 48p. pap. 23.50 (978-0-531-12238-9(7)) Scholastic Library Publishing. (Watts, Franklin).

—Vincent Van Gogh. 2002. (gr. 5-8). lib. bdg. 15.25 (978-0-613-54378-1(5)) Tandem Library Bks.

Greenberg, Jan. Vincent Van Gogh: Portrait of an Artist. 2003. (gr. 5-8). lib. bdg. 15.30 (978-0-613-65100-4(6)) Tandem Library Bks.

Greenberg, Jan & Jordan, Sandra. Vincent Van Gogh: Portrait of an Artist. 2003. (Illus.). 144p. (gr. 5). 6.99 (978-0-440-41917-4(4) , Yearling) Random Hse. Children's Bks.

Holub, Joan. Vincent Van Gogh: Sunflowers & Swirley Stars. 2001. (gr. k-3). lib. bdg. 14.15 (978-0-613-45320-2(4)) Tandem Library Bks.

Hyde, Margaret E., ed. Van Gogh for Kids. 2005. (Great Art for Kids Ser.). (Illus.). 10p. (J). pap. 8.95 (978-1-58980-207-0(1)) Pelican Publishing Co., Inc.

Klein, Adam G. & Van Gogh, Vincent. Vincent Van Gogh. 2007. (Great Artists Ser.). (Illus.). 32p. (J). (gr. 2-5). lib. bdg. 22.78 (978-1-59679-730-7(4)) ABDO Publishing Co.

Martín, Carme. My Name Is Vincent van Gogh. Luciani, Rebeca, illus. 2006. (My Name Is ... Ser.). 64p. (J). pap. 7.99 (978-0-7641-3394-7(2)) Barron's Educational Series, Inc.

Martin, Carmen. Vincent Van Gogh. 2006. (SPA.). 64p. (J). (gr. 4-5). 7.60 (978-84-342-2682-1(0) , PR33292) Parramon Ediciones S.A. ESP. *Dist:* Lectorum Pubns., Inc.

Muhlberger, Richard. What Makes a Van Gogh a Van Gogh? 2002. (Illus.). 48p. (YA). 16.99 (978-0-670-03573-1(4) , Viking Juvenile) Penguin Group (USA) Inc.

Rubin, Susan Goldman. The Yellow House: Vincent Van Gogh & Paul Gauguin Side by Side. Smith, Joseph A., illus. 2001. 40p. (J). (gr. k-4). 17.95 (978-0-8109-4588-3(6)) Abrams, Harry N. , Inc.

Sateren, Shelley Swanson. Van Gogh. 2002. (Masterpieces). (Illus.). 24p. (J). (gr. 2-3). lib. bdg. 18.60 (978-0-7368-1124-8(9) , Bridgestone Bks.) Capstone Pr., Inc.

Soni, Jaymee & Schubert, Charles. A Kid at Art - Vincent Van Gogh. 2003. (J). pap. 14.99 (978-0-9743760-1-1(9)) Little Noggin LLC.

Spence, David. Vincent Van Gogh: Arte y Emocion. (Coleccion Grandes Artistas).Tr. of Vincent Van Gogh: Art & Emotion. (SPA.). (YA). (gr. 5-8). 12.76 (978-84-8211-136-0(1)) Celeste Ediciones, S.A. ESP. *Dist:* Lectorum Pubns., Inc.

Van Gogh, Vincent. Van Gogh Stained Glass Coloring Book. 2007. 16p. pap. 5.95 (***978-0-486-45671-3(4)***) Dover Pubns., Inc.

Van Gogh, Vincent. Vincent's Colors: Words & Pictures by Vincent van Gogh. Metropolitan Museum of Art Staff, ed. 2005. (Illus.). 48p. (J). (ps-3). 14.95 (978-0-8118-5099-5(4)) Chronicle Bks. LLC.

Whiting, Jim. Vincent Van Gogh. 2007. (Art Profiles for Kids Ser.). (Illus.). 48p. (J). lib. bdg. 29.95 (***978-1-58415-564-5(7)***) Mitchell Lane Pubs., Inc.

GOLD

see also Coinage; Gold Mines and Mining; Jewelry; Money

Beck, Gail. Gold. 2006. (Navigators Ser.). (J). pap. 42.00 (***978-1-4108-6236-5(4)***) Benchmark Education Co.

Beers, Jack. Bridges - Gold. 2002. (Metro Math Bridges Ser.). (J). (gr. 7). stu. ed., per. 13.95 (978-1-58830-329-5(2)) Metropolitan Teaching & Learning Co.

Belval, Brian. Gold. 2006. (Understanding the Elements of the Periodic Table Ser.). (Illus.). 48p. (J). lib. bdg. (978-1-4042-0708-0(2)) Rosen Publishing Group, Inc., The.

Biesty, Stephen. Gold: A Treasure Hunt Through Time. Hooper, Meredith, ed. 2002. (Illus.). 48p. (J). 25.00 (978-0-340-78855-4(0) , Hodder & Stoughton) Hodder General Publishing Division GBR. *Dist:* Trafalgar Square Publishing.

Edwards, Ron & Gladstone, James. Gold. 2004. (Rocks, Minerals, & Resources Ser.). (Illus.). 32p. (J). (978-0-7787-1413-2(6)); pap. (978-0-7787-1445-3(4)) Crabtree Publishing Co.

Franck, Irene M. & Brownstone, David M. Gold. 2003. (Illus.). 32p. (J). (978-0-7172-5716-4(9) , Grolier) Scholastic Library Publishing.

Haynes, Betsy. My Adventure Panning for Gold. 2007. 44p. (J). 8.99 (978-1-59092-444-0(4) , Orchard Academy Pr.) Windstorm Creative.

Hooper, Meredith & Biesty, Stephen. Gold Quest: A Treasure Trail Through History. 2005. (Illus.). (J). (ps-7). pap., pap. (978-0-340-78858-5(5) , Hodder Children's Books) Hodder Children's Division.

Jones, Charlotte Foltz. Yukon Gold: The Story of the Klondike Gold Rush. 1998. (Illus.). 112p. (J). (gr. 4-7). tchr. ed. 18.95 (978-0-8234-1403-1(5)) Holiday Hse., Inc.

Morris, Neil. Gold & Silver. 2005. (Earth's Resources Ser.). (Illus.). 32p. (J). (gr. 4-7). lib. bdg. 27.10 (978-1-58340-630-4(1)) Smart Apple Media.

Murray, Peter. Gold. 2001. (From the Earth Ser.). (Illus.). 24p. (J). 21.35 (978-1-58340-108-8(3)) Smart Apple Media.

Tocci, Salvatore. Gold. 2005. (True Bks.). (Illus.). (J). (gr. 3-5). 47p. pap. 6.95 (978-0-516-25570-5(3)); 48p. 25.00 (978-0-516-23694-0(6)) Scholastic Library Publishing. (Children's Pr.).

GOLD—FICTION

Becket, Jim. Inca Gold: Choose Your Own Adventure #20. 2007. (Choose Your Own Adventure Ser.: 20). (Illus.). 144p. (J). per. 6.99 (***978-1-933390-20-8(4)*** , CHCL20) Chooseco LLC.

Carpino, Nancy. The Leprechaun & His Bag of Gold. Carpino, Nancy & McNeilis, Jessica, illus. 2000. 50p. (J). (gr. k-4). 8.95 (978-1-928675-03-7(4)) Carpino Bks.

Dann, Max. Dead Men Don't Walk. 2004. (Illus.). 132p. pap. 5.99 (978-0-14-330065-6(2) , Penguin Global) Penguin Group (USA) Inc.

Dixon, Franklin W. The Secret of the Soldier's Gold. 2003. (gr. 3-6). lib. bdg. 13.00 (978-0-613-90468-1(0)) Tandem Library Bks.

Dixon, Franklin W. & Walker, Jeff. The Secret of the Soldier's Gold. 2003. (Hardy Boys Ser.). (Illus.). 160p. (J). pap. 4.99 (978-0-689-85885-7(X) , Aladdin) Simon & Schuster Children's Publishing.

Harcourt School Publishers Staff. Better Than Gold On Level. 3rd ed. 2002. (Trophies Reading Program Ser.). (Illus.). pap. 5.10 (978-0-15-323167-4(X)) Harcourt Schl. Pubs.

—Gold Rush News Below Level. 3rd ed. 2002. (Trophies Reading Program Ser.). (Illus.). pap. 5.10 (978-0-15-323246-6(3)) Harcourt Schl. Pubs.

Hopkinson, Deborah. Sailing for Gold. Farnsworth, Bill, illus. ed. 2005. 76p. (J). lib. bdg. 15.00 (978-1-59054-915-5(5)) Fitzgerald Bks.

The Hunt for Pirate Gold, 6 vols., Vol. 2. (Woodland Mysteriestm Ser.). 133p. (gr. 3-7). 42.50 (978-0-7802-7934-6(4)) Wright Group, The.

Johnson, Tim. Lost Dutchman in Cochise County? Incidents & Coincidences. 2003. (Illus.). 52p. 19.95 (978-0-9742351-0-3(5)) MCM Prime, Inc.

Kent, Deborah. Blackwater Creek. Kingfisher Editors, ed. 2005. (Saddles, Stars, & Stripes Ser.). 192p. (J). (gr. 4-6). 8.95 (978-0-7534-5885-3(3) , Kingfisher) Houghton Mifflin Co. Trade & Reference Div.

Lorenzen, Margaret Brownell. Petunia Patch Pockets & the Golden Locket. Jocelyn, Sawyer & Liza, Behles, illus. 2005. 76p. (J). per. 12.50 (978-0-9724922-7-0(5)) Authors & Artists Publishers of New York, Inc.

McAfee, Joan K. The Road to el Dorado. 2003. (Illus.). 186p. (YA). pap. 12.95 (978-0-89745-273-1(9)) Sunflower Univ. Pr.

O'Leary, John. En busca del tesoro del Pirata! 2005. (SPA., Illus.). 14p. (J). bds. 13.95 (978-84-7864-794-1(5)) Combel Editorial, S.A. ESP. *Dist:* Independent Pubs. Group.

Santillo, LuAnn. Fred & Ed. Santillo, LuAnn, ed. 2003. (Half-Pint Kids Readers Ser.). (Illus.). 7p. (J). (ps-1). pap. (978-1-59256-074-5(1)) Half-Pint Kids, Inc.

Sommer, Carl. The Richest Poor Kid. Martinez, Jorge, illus. 2007. (J). (***978-1-57537-025-5(5)***); lib. bdg. (***978-1-57537-074-3(3)***) Advance Publishing, Inc.

Thompson, Colin. The Last Alchemist. Thompson, Colin, illus. 2003. (Illus.). 30p. (J). (gr. k-3). reprint ed. 17.00 (978-0-7567-6164-6(6)) DIANE Publishing Co.

Where the Leprechauns Hide. 2007. pap. 12.99 (***978-0-9792258-9-5(2)***) Bezalel Bks.

Wickstrom, Lois June & Lorrah, Jean. Nessie & the Living Stone. Strand, Sara Silvestri, illus. 2001. (J). pap. 13.80 (978-1-58338-616-3(5) , CrossroadsPub.Org) CrossroadsPub.com.

Wilson, David J. Lucky & the Pot of Gold. 2001. (J). pap. 6.95 (978-0-533-13633-9(4)) Vantage Pr., Inc.

GOLD FISH

see Goldfish

GOLD MINES AND MINING

see also Prospecting

Aretha, David. The Gold Rush to California's Riches. 2006. (Wild History of the American West Ser.). (Illus.). 128p. (J). lib. bdg. 33.27 (978-1-59845-012-5(3) , MyReportLinks.com Bks.) Enslow Pubs., Inc.

Bryan, Nichol. Danube: Cyanide Spill. 2003. (Environmental Disasters Ser.). (Illus.). 48p. (gr. 5 up). (YA). lib. bdg. 30.00 (978-0-8368-5505-0(1)); (J). pap. 11.95 (978-0-8368-5512-8(4)) Stevens, Gareth Inc. (World Almanac Library).

Craats, Rennay. Gold Rush. 2003. (Real Life Stories Ser.). (Illus.). 24p. (J). lib. bdg. 15.95 (978-1-59036-078-1(8)) Weigl Pubs., Inc.

Donlan, Leni. Strike It Rich in Cripple Creek: Gold Rush. 2006. (American History Through Primary Sources Ser.). (Illus.). 32p. (J). (978-1-4109-2419-3(X)); pap. (978-1-4109-2430-8(0)) Steck-Vaughn.

Kalman, Bobbie. The Gold Rush. 1999. (Life in the Old West Ser.). (Illus.). 32p. (J). (gr. 3-4). pap. (978-0-7787-0111-8(5)); lib. bdg. (978-0-7787-0079-1(8)) Crabtree Publishing Co.

—The Gold Rush. 1999. (Life in the Old West Ser.). (J). (978-0-606-16430-6(8)) Tandem Library Bks.

—Life of a Miner. 2000. (gr. 3-6). lib. bdg. 16.40 (978-0-613-11777-7(8)) Tandem Library Bks.

Klein, James. Gold Rush! The Young Prospector's Guide to Striking It Rich. Rohani, Michael, illus. 2004. 96p. (J). (gr. 3-7). 9.95 (978-1-883672-64-5(3) , Tricycle Pr.) Ten Speed Pr.

Kraft, Eric. Gold Rush! 2004. (Navigators Ser.). (J). pap. 42.00 (978-1-4108-0423-5(2)) Benchmark Education Co.

Kraft, Eric. ¡la fiebre del oro! & Gold Rush! 2005. spiral bd. 84.00 (***978-1-4108-5699-9(2)***) Benchmark Education Co.

Lyngheim, Linda. California Gold Rush Projects & Activities. Garber, Phyllis, illus. 1998. (California Junior Heritage Ser.). 56p. (J). (gr. 3-12). pap. 9.95 (978-0-915369-07-2(9)) Langtry Pubns.

Mason, Paul. Panning for Gold. 2007. (J). pap. (***978-1-4109-2865-8(9)***) Steck-Vaughn.

—Panning for Gold: Mixtures & Solutions. 2007. (Raintree Fusion: Physical Science Ser.). (Illus.). 32p. (J). lib. bdg. (***978-1-4109-2848-1(9)***) Steck-Vaughn.

Murphy, Claire Rudolf & Haigh, Jane G. Children of the Gold Rush. 1999. (Illus.). 96p. (YA). (gr. 3-7). pap. 14.95 (978-1-57098-257-6(0)) Rinehart, Roberts Pubs.

Nobleman, Marc Tyler. The Klondike Gold Rush. 2006. (We the People Ser.). (Illus.). 48p. (J). (gr. 4-6). 23.93 (978-0-7565-1630-7(7)) Compass Point Bks.

Raabe, Emily. The Gold Rush: California or Bust! 2003. (Reading Power Ser.). (Illus.). 24p. (J). lib. bdg. 17.25 (978-0-8239-6494-9(9) , PowerKids Pr.) Rosen Publishing Group, Inc., The.

Roop, Connie & Roop, Peter, eds. The Diary of David R. Leeper: Rushing for Gold. 2000. (In My Own Words Ser.). (Illus.). 78p. (J). (gr. 5 up). lib. bdg. 27.07 (978-0-7614-1011-9(2) , Benchmark Bks.) Cavendish, Marshall Corp.

Somervill, Barbara A. The Gold Rush: Buried Treasure. 2005. (Trailblazers of the West Ser.). (Illus.). 48p. (J). (ps-7). 24.00 (978-0-516-25129-5(5)); (YA). (gr. 7-12). pap. 6.95 (978-0-516-25099-1(X)) Scholastic Library Publishing. (Children's Pr.).

Uschan, Michael V. The California Gold Rush. 2003. (Landmark Events in American History Ser.). (Illus.). 48p. (J). (gr. 5 up). pap. 14.95 (978-0-8368-5402-2(0)); lib. bdg. 30.00 (978-0-8368-5374-2(1)) Stevens, Gareth Inc. (World Almanac Library).

GOLD MINES AND MINING—FICTION

Addy, Sharon Hart. Lucky Jake. Zahares, Wade, illus. 2007. 40p. (J). (gr. k-3). 17.00 (978-0-618-47286-4(X)) Houghton Mifflin Co.

Alger, Horatio. Joe's Luck: Or, Always Wide Awake. 2007. 172p. pap. 11.99 (***978-1-4264-6426-3(6)***); 2006. 176p. pap. 13.99 (978-1-4264-0883-0(8)); 2007. 186p. pap. 14.99 (***978-1-4264-6500-0(9)***); 2006. 170p. pap. 16.99 (978-1-4264-0864-9(1)) BiblioBazaar.

Altman, Linda Jacobs. The Legend of Freedom Hill. Van Wright, Cornelius, illus. 2003. 32p. (J). (978-1-58430-169-1(4)) Lee & Low Bks., Inc.

—The Legend of Freedom Hill. Van Wright, Cornelius & Hu, Ying-Hwa, illus. 2000. 32p. (J). (ps-up). 15.95 (978-1-58430-003-8(5)) Lee & Low Bks., Inc.

—The Legend of Freedom Hill. Van Wright, Cornelius et al, illus. 2004. 32p. (J). (ps-k). lib. bdg. 13.75 (978-0-606-30127-5(5)) Tandem Library Bks.

Ayres, Katherine. Silver Dollar Girl. 2002. (Illus.). 208p. (gr. 3-7). pap. 5.50 (978-0-440-41705-7(8) , Yearling) Random Hse. Children's Bks.

—Silver Dollar Girl. 2002. (gr. 3-6). lib. bdg. 13.00 (978-0-613-64685-7(1)) Tandem Library Bks.

Balmes, Kathy. Thunder on the Sierra. Catapano, Vicki, illus. 2001. (Adventures in America Ser.). 96p. (J). (gr. 3-7). lib. bdg. 14.95 (978-1-893110-10-6(9)) Silver Moon Pr.

Big Gold Mountain: Individual Title Six-Packs. (Bookweb Ser.). 32p. (gr. 5 up). 34.00 (978-0-7635-3784-5(5)) Rigby Education.

Coren, Alan. Klondike Arthur. 2004. (Illus.). 64p. (978-0-903895-93-4(5) , Robson Bks. Ltd.) Anova Bks.

Dearen, Patrick. Hidden Treasure of the Chisos. 2001. (gr. 3-6). lib. bdg. 17.60 (978-0-613-83165-9(9)) Tandem Library Bks.

—The Hidden Treasure of the Chisos, Bk. 3. 2001. (Lone Star Heroes Ser.). 117p. pap. 8.95 (978-1-55622-829-2(5) , Republic of Texas Pr.) Wordware Publishing, Inc.

Derby, Pat. Away to the Goldfields! 2004. 256p. (J). 18.00 (978-0-374-39961-0(1) , Farrar, Straus & Giroux (BYR)) Farrar, Straus & Giroux.

Elliott, Louise. Mr. Hornbeams Treasure Hunt. (Illus.). 96p. pap. 10.95 (978-0-7022-2587-1(8)) Univ. of Queensland Pr. AUS. *Dist:* International Specialized Bk. Services.

Fleischman, Sid. Bo & Mzzz Mad. 112p. (J). (gr. 3 up). 2002. pap. 6.99 (978-0-06-440972-8(4)); 2001. lib. bdg. 15.89 (978-0-06-029398-7(5)) HarperCollins Pubs.

E F G

—Bo & Mzzz Mad. Hunt, Jonathan, illus. 2001. 112p. (J). (gr. 3 up). 14.99 (978-0-06-029397-0(7)) HarperCollins Pubs.

—Bo & Mzzz Mad. 2002. 103p. (J). (ps-7). lib. bdg. 13.00 (978-0-613-61838-0(6)) Tandem Library Bks.

Getzinger, Donna. For a Speck of Gold. 2002. pap. 8.95 (978-0-87714-828-9(7)) Denlingers Pubs., Ltd.

Gold Mountain. 2002. (Illus.). (J). pap. 6.25 (978-0-7398-6173-8(5)) Steck-Vaughn.

Greenwood, Barbara. Gold Rush Fever: A Story of the Klondike, 1898. Collins, Heather, illus. 2001. (History Comes Alive Ser.). 160p. (J). (gr. 4-6). (978-1-55074-850-5(5)); (978-1-55074-852-9(1)) Kids Can Pr., Ltd.

—Gold Rush Fever: A Story of the Klondike, Eighteen Ninety-Eight. 2001. (gr. 3-6). lib. bdg. 22.20 (978-0-613-50312-9(0)) Tandem Library Bks.

Gregory, Kristiana. Seeds of Hope: The Gold Rush Diary of Susanna Fairchild, 1849. 2001. (Dear America Ser.). (Illus.). 176p. (J). (gr. 5-8). pap. 10.95 (978-0-590-51157-5(2)) Scholastic, Inc.

Gunderson, Jessica. Fire & Snow: A Tale of the Alaskan Gold Rush. Townsend, Shannon, illus. 2007. (J). 56p. 23.93 ***(978-1-59889-310-6(6));*** 47p. pap. ***(978-1-59889-405-9(6))*** Stone Arch Bks.

Harris, Marian. Tuesday in Arizona. Harris, Jim, illus. 1998. 32p. (J). (ps-3). 15.95 (978-1-56554-233-4(9)) Pelican Publishing Co., Inc.

Heisel, Sharon E. Precious Gold, Precious Jade. 2000. 192p. (J). (gr. 7 up). tchr. ed. 16.95 (978-0-8234-1432-1(9)) Holiday Hse., Inc.

Hobbs, William. Jason's Gold. 2000. (Illus.). 240p. (J). (gr. 6 up). pap. 5.99 (978-0-380-72914-2(8)) HarperCollins Pubs.

Hopkins, Jackie. The Gold Miner's Daughter: A Melodramatic Fairytale. Goodell, Jon, illus. 2006. (J). 15.95 (978-1-56145-362-7(5)) Peachtree Pubs., Ltd.

James, Will. Look-See with Uncle Bill. (Illus.). 190p. 26.00 (978-0-87842-459-7(8) , 815); (J). (gr. 4). pap. 14.00 (978-0-87842-458-0(X) , 814) Mountain Pr. Publishing Co., Inc.

Jason's Gold. 2000. (J). pap., tchr. ed. (978-0-06-449242-3(7) , Harper Trophy) HarperCollins Pubs.

Johnson, Tim. Lost Dutchman in Cochise County? Incidents & Coincidences. 2003. (Illus.). 52p. 19.95 (978-0-9742351-0-3(5)) MCM Prime, Inc.

Kay, Verla. Gold Fever. Schindler, S. D., illus. (Picture Puffin Ser.). (J). (gr. k-3). 2003. 32p. pap. 6.99 (978-0-14-250183-2(2) , Puffin); 1999. 1p. 15.99 (978-0-399-23027-1(0) , Putnam Juvenile) Penguin Group (USA) Inc.

—Gold Fever. 2003. (gr. k-3). lib. bdg. 15.30 (978-0-613-89796-9(X)) Tandem Library Bks.

London, Jack. White Fang. 2001. (Classics Ser.). (Illus.). 272p. (J). (gr. 10). pap. 3.99 (978-0-439-23619-5(3)) Scholastic, Inc.

—White Fang. (gr. 7-12). 2001. lib. bdg. 11.80 (978-0-613-39272-3(8)); 1999. lib. bdg. 29.20 (978-0-613-88083-1(8)) Tandem Library Bks.

Luxa, Sue. A Cabin in Cripple Creek. 2004. (Illus.). 99p. (J). pap. 8.95 (978-1-932738-04-9(5) , 1234249) Western Reflections Publishing Co.

Mullin, Penn. Gold Rush Fever. 1999. (gr. 7-12). lib. bdg. 11.60 (978-0-613-28855-2(6)) Tandem Library Bks.

Murphy, Claire Rudolf. Gold Rush Winter. 2002. (gr. 3-6). lib. bdg. 11.80 (978-0-613-50201-6(9)) Tandem Library Bks.

Provensen, Alice. Klondike Gold. Provensen, Alice, illus. 2005. (Illus.). 40p. (J). (gr. 3-6). 17.95 (978-0-689-84885-8(4) , Simon & Schuster Children's Publishing) Simon & Schuster Children's Publishing.

Reichart, George. A Bag of Lucky Rice. Mitchell, Mark, illus. 2004. 160p. pap. 10.95 (978-1-56792-278-3(3)) Godine, David R. Pub.

Sargent, Dave & Sargent, Pat. Stinky: (Sorrel) Don't Be Mischievous, 25, 56. Lenoir, Jane, illus. 2001. (Saddle Up Ser.: 56). 36p. (J). pap. (978-1-56763-666-6(7)); lib. bdg. 22.60 (978-1-56763-665-9(9)) Ozark Publishing.

Schulte, Elaine L. Suzannah Strikes Gold. 2001. (Illus.). 144p. (J). (gr. 4-7). pap. 7.49 (978-1-57924-565-8(X)) Jones, Bob Univ. Pr.

Stites, Clara. Lixia of Gold Mountain: A Story of Early California. 2003. (Illus.). 64p. (J). pap. 8.95 (978-1-56474-421-0(3)) Fithian Pr.

Turner, Ginger. Gold Mine! The California Gold Rush Story. 2004. (Illus.). 46p. (J). per. 15.95 (978-0-9742502-2-9(8)) Gossamer Bks., LLC.

Turner, Ginger & Shimpi, Shekhar. Gold Mine! The California Gold Rush Story. 2004. (Illus.). 44p. (J). pap. 15.95 (978-0-9742502-3-6(6)) Gossamer Bks., LLC.

Walsh, Ann. Your Time, My Time. 2006. 168p. (J). (gr. 3-8). reprint ed. pap., tchr. ed. 5.95 (978-0-88878-219-9(5) , Sandcastle Bks.) Dundurn Group, The CAN. *Dist:* Univ. of Toronto Pr.

Whitehead, Catherine. Skookumchuck. 2002. (Illus.). 156p. (J). (gr. 5-12). pap. 11.95 (978-1-58151-064-5(0)) BookPartners, Inc.

Willingham, Ellie. Wildwood. Willingham, Ellie, illus. 2007. (Illus.). 136p. (J). pap. 10.00 ***(978-0-9792371-0-2(6)*** , Moo Pr.) Keene Publishing.

Wyss, Thelma Hatch. A Tale of Gold. 2007. 160p. (J). (gr. 3-7). 16.99 ***(978-1-4169-4212-2(2)*** , McElderry, Margaret K.) Simon & Schuster Children's Publishing.

Yamada, Debbie Leung. Striking It Rich: Treasures from Gold Mountain. Tang, You-shan, illus. l.t. ed. 2004. 128p. (J). (gr. 4-8). pap. 13.95 (978-1-879965-21-8(6)) Polychrome Publishing Corp.

Yep, Laurence. My Name Is America: The Journal of Wongming-chun, A Chinese Miner. 2000. (My Name Is America Ser.). (Illus.). 224p. (J). (gr. 4-8). pap. 10.95 (978-0-590-38607-4(7)) Scholastic, Inc.

GOLD RUSH

see California—Gold Discoveries

GOLDFISH

Alderton, David. Goldfish. 2003. (Looking after My Pet Ser.). (Illus.). 20p. 7.99 (978-0-7548-1223-4(5)) Anness Publishing GBR. *Dist:* National Bk. Network.

Barnes, Julia. Pet Goldfish. 2006. (Pet Pals Ser.). (Illus.). 32p. (J). (gr. 2-5). lib. bdg. 23.93 (978-0-8368-6778-7(5)) Stevens, Gareth Inc.

Barnes, Julia, et al. 101 Facts about Goldfish. 2002. (One Hundred One Facts about Pets Ser.). (Illus.). 32p. (J). (gr. 3 up). lib. bdg. 23.33 (978-0-8368-3017-0(2)) Stevens, Gareth Inc.

Do Goldfish Gallop? (Animals All Around Ser.). 24p. (J). 7.95 (978-1-4048-0375-6(0)) Picture Window Bks.

Ganeri, Anita. Goldfish. 2003. (Heinemann First Library). (Illus.). 32p. (J). pap. (978-1-4034-4271-0(1)) Heinemann Library.

—A Pet's Life: Goldfish. 2003. (Heinemann First Library). (Illus.). 32p. (J). lib. bdg. 22.79 (978-1-4034-3998-7(2)) Heinemann Library.

Gillis, Jennifer Blizin. Goldfish. 2004. (Heinemann Read & Learn Ser.). (Illus.). 24p. (J). 18.50 (978-1-4034-5053-1(6)); pap. 5.75 (978-1-4034-6021-9(3)) Heinemann Library.

Glass, Spencer. Goldfish. 1999. (Fish). (Illus.). 64p. (YA). (gr. 4-7). 32.00 (978-0-7910-5090-3(4) , Chelsea Hse.) Facts On File, Inc.

MacAulay, Kelley & Kalman, Bobbie. Goldfish. Reiach, Margaret Amy & Crabtree, Marc, illus. Crabtree, Marc, photos by. 2004. (Pet Care Ser.). 32p. (J). (978-0-7787-1759-1(3)); pap. (978-0-7787-1791-1(7)) Crabtree Publishing Co.

Macken, JoAnn Early. Goldfish. 2003. (Let's Read about Pets Ser.). (Illus.). 24p. (J). (ps up). lib. bdg. 19.33 (978-0-8368-3797-1(5)); pap. 7.93 (978-0-8368-3844-2(0)) Stevens, Gareth Inc. (Weekly Reader Early Learning Library).

Miller, M. Goldfish. 2002. (Pets Ser.). (Illus.). 24p. (J). (gr. k-3). pap. 6.50 (978-1-57572-479-9(0) , 90468) Heinemann Library.

Miller, Michaela. Goldfish. 1998. (Pets Ser.). (Illus.). 24p. (J). (gr. 1-3). lib. bdg. 21.36 (978-1-57572-574-1(6)) Heinemann Library.

My Pet: KinderReaders Individual Title Six-Packs. (Kinderstarters Ser.). 8p. (ps-1). 21.00 (978-0-7635-8661-4(7)) Rigby Education.

Page, Gill. I Am Your Goldfish. 2004. (I Am Your Pet Ser.). (Illus.). 48p. (J). pap. 5.95 (978-0-7696-3388-6(9) , Waterbird Bks.) School Specialty Publishing.

Walker, Pam. My Goldfish. 2001. (My Pets Ser.). (Illus.). 24p. (J). (ps-2). 17.00 (978-0-516-23185-3(5) , Children's Pr.) Scholastic Library Publishing.

World Book, Inc Staff, contrib. by. Goldfish & Other Carp. 2007. (World Book's Animals of the World Ser.). (Illus.). 64p. (J). (978-0-7166-1329-9(8)) World Bk., Inc.

GOLDING, WILLIAM, 1911-1993

Bloom, Harold, intro. Lord of the Flies. 2004. (Bloom's Guides Ser.). (Illus.). 80p. (J). (gr. 9-13). 30.00 (978-0-7910-7878-5(7) , Chelsea Hse.) Facts On File, Inc.

Koopmans, Andy. Lord of the Flies. 2003. (Understanding Great Literature Ser.). (Illus.). 112p. (J). 29.95 (978-1-56006-786-3(1) , Lucent Bks.) Thomson Gale.

GOLF

Anderson, Dave. The Story of Golf. 1998. (Illus.). 192p. (J). (gr. 5 up). 16.00 (978-0-688-15796-8(3)) HarperCollins Pubs.

Bratton, Deboral B. & Bigly, Ashley D. Record-a-Sport Golf Organizer. Bratton, Deboral B. & Bigly, Ashley D., eds. Bigly, Ashley D., illus. 2003. (Illus.). (gr. 1 up). 18.95 (978-1-931746-00-7(1)) Sport Your Stuff Corp.

Burby, Liza N. A Day in the Life of a Professional Golfer. 1999. (Kids' Career Library). (Illus.). 24p. (J). (gr. 3). lib. bdg. 18.75 (978-0-8239-5299-1(1) , PowerKids Pr.) Rosen Publishing Group, Inc., The.

Chapleski, Gregory. Getting Started in Golf. 2006. (J). 4.95 ***(978-0-9787759-1-9(0))*** eDimples, Inc.

Chapleski, Gregory, creator. Moving Ahead in Golf. 2006. (J). 4.95 net. ***(978-0-9787759-2-6(9))*** eDimples, Inc.

De Garmo, John & Wiley, Sam. Hey Kids, Start Golf Right! 2002. (Illus.). 128p. 9.95 (978-1-57197-295-8(1)) Pentland Pr., Inc.

Ditchfield, Christin. Golf. 2003. (True Book Ser.). (Illus.). 48p. (J). 25.00 (978-0-516-22590-6(1) , Children's Pr.) Scholastic Library Publishing.

—Golf. 2003. (gr. 3-6). lib. bdg. 15.25 (978-0-613-67964-0(4)) Tandem Library Bks.

Dunn, Nancy. Golf's Greenland, Vol. 1. Mustard, Kirk, ed. Dunn, Nancy, illus. 1999. (Illus.). 28p. (J). (gr. 4). pap. (978-0-9673330-0-7(8)) Swing Play.

Emerick, Don, et al. Tiger's Tips: Beginner's Golf for Kids 6-106. Kebow, Ken, illus. 1998. 144p. (J). (gr. 1-7). pap. 10.95 (978-1-885758-12-5(X)) Quality Sports Pubns.

Emerick, Donald. Tiger's Tips: Beginner's Golf for Kids. 2000. (gr. 3-6). lib. bdg. 19.90 (978-0-613-80255-0(1)) Tandem Library Bks.

Fatzinger, Don. Golf Tips for the Junior Golfer. McKenna, Kathy, ed. 2002. (Illus.). 60p. (YA). (gr. 6-12). pap. 7.95 (978-0-9716326-0-8(X)) Junior Golf of N.E. Pennsylvania.

Fauchald, Nick. Tee Off! You Can Play Golf. 2005. (Game Day Ser.). (Illus.). 24p. (J). (ps). lib. bdg. 22.60 (978-1-4048-1155-3(9)) Picture Window Bks.

Frisch, Aaron. Golf. 2002. (Illus.). 32p. (J). lib. bdg. 24.25 (978-1-58340-161-3(X)) Smart Apple Media.

Golf. 2003. (Quick Kiss Guides Ser.). 160p. (YA). pap. 10.00 (978-0-7894-9310-1(1)) Dorling Kindersley Publishing, Inc.

Golf for Fun! (For Fun Ser.). 48p. (YA). 8.95 (978-0-7565-1155-5(0)) Compass Point Bks.

Gordon, John. The Kids Book of Golf. 2001. (Illus.). 48p. (J). (gr. 4-6). (978-1-55337-017-8(1)); (978-1-55074-617-4(0)) Kids Can Pr., Ltd.

—The Kids Book of Golf. 2001. (Illus.). (J). (978-0-606-21279-3(5)) Tandem Library Bks.

Greene, Susan. Consider It Golf: Golf Etiquette & Safety Tips for Children! Klavins, Dagne Angersbach, illus. l.t. ed. 2000. 40p. (J). (ps-4). 14.95 (978-0-9651100-7-5(9)) Excel Publishing.

Gregory, C. Matt. Golf Secrets 4 U & Me. 2005. (Illus.). 20p. (J). 20.00 (978-0-9766442-1-7(5)) Gregory, Charles Matthew.

Hall, Mary. Golf. 1999. (Composite Guide Ser.). (Illus.). 64p. (YA). (gr. 4-7). lib. bdg. 18.65 (978-0-7910-4726-2(1) , Chelsea Hse.) Facts On File, Inc.

Herzog, Brad. P Is for Putt: A Golf Alphabet. Langton, Bruce, illus. 2005. 40p. (J). 16.95 (978-1-58536-252-3(2)) Sleeping Bear Pr.

Jovenes Golfistas. (SPA.). (YA). (gr. 2 up). 20.76 (978-84-272-4973-8(X)) Molino, Editorial ESP. *Dist:* Lectorum Pubns., Inc.

Kalman, Bobbie. Golf in Action. 2001. (gr. 3-6). lib. bdg. 14.10 (978-0-613-32608-7(3)) Tandem Library Bks.

Key, Cory, illus. Golf Thinking for Kids: On & Off the Course. 1999. 48p. (YA). pap. 10.95 (978-0-9675172-0-9(6)) Privitera, Vincent J.

Leitch, Cecil. Golf for Girls. reprint ed. 150.00 (978-0-7222-1908-9(3)) Library Reprints, Inc.

MacMillan, Daniel Emerson. Golfing in British Columbia. 2003. 400p. per. 16.95 (978-1-878591-14-2(2)) MAC Productions.

—Golfing in Idaho & Montana. 3rd ed. 2003. 270p. per. 12.95 (978-1-878591-60-9(6)) MAC Productions.

—Golfing in Oregon. 12th ed. 2003. 270p. per. 12.95 (978-1-878591-59-3(2)) MAC Productions.

—Golfing in Washington. 17th ed. 2003. 360p. per. 14.95 (978-1-878591-58-6(4)) MAC Productions.

Mitchell, Susan M. Golf Buddies: A Storybook Introduction to the Rules, Etiquette, & Game of Golf. Mitchell, Susan M., illus. 1998. (Illus.). 40p. (J). (ps-5). pap. 8.95 (978-0-9651598-1-4(7)) Busy Buddy Bks.

Montgomerie, Colin. Kiss Guide to Playing Golf. 2000. (gr. 7-12). lib. bdg. 29.20 (978-0-613-32749-7(7)) Tandem Library Bks.

Parks, Peter. How to Improve at Golf. 2007. 48p. (J). (gr. 3-9). pap. ***(978-0-7787-3589-2(3))*** Crabtree Publishing Co.

Resch, Celeste. Alana's 12-Step Guide to Fun Golf: A How-to Book for Kids Who Want to Play Golf & Have Fun Doing It! 2003. (J). 7.99 (978-0-9743851-0-5(7)) Star Write Creations.

Schwartz, Heather E. Girls' Golf. 2008. (J). ***(978-1-4296-0132-0(9))*** Capstone Pr., Inc.

Smith, James D. & Smith, Lauren M. My First Golf Book. Vuong, Tuvinh, illus. 1999. (My First Book Ser.). 44p. (ps-1). 14.95 (978-0-9669116-0-2(1)) C T L Publishing.

Smith, Ryan A. Golf Balls: From Start to Finish. Tolle, Gary, photos by. 2005. (Made in the USA Ser.). (Illus.). 32p. (J). (gr. 3-5). lib. bdg. 23.70 (978-1-4103-0657-9(7) , Blackbirch Pr., Inc.) Thomson Gale.

Sotzek, Hannelore. Golf in Action. 2000. (Sports in Action Ser.). (Illus.). 32p. (J). (gr. 3-4). (978-0-7787-0168-2(9)); pap. (978-0-7787-0180-4(8)) Crabtree Publishing Co.

—Golf in Action. 2000. (J). 12.75 (978-0-606-22834-3(9)) Tandem Library Bks.

Sporting Heroes. 2000. 32p. (YA). 7.49 (978-0-7525-4645-2(7)) Parragon, Inc.

Stanger, Rob. I Love Golf! l.t. ed. 2003. (Illus.). 20p. pap. 7.95 (978-0-9725721-0-1(4)) Club Pro Products.

Swift, Duncan. The Golfer's Reference Vol. 6: Juniors Guide. Copeland, Nicklaus, ed. Anthony, David & Graham, Savelle, illus. Anthony, David, photos by. 2000. 256p. (YA). (gr. 5-12). pap. 16.95 (978-0-9658132-4-2(X) , 7006) Schaefer's Publishing.

Taylor, Lynn Claire & Robb, Debra Ann. Mountain Biking. 2003. (Radsports Guides Ser.). (Illus.). 48p. (gr. 4-8). 20.95 (978-1-58952-277-0(X)) Rourke Publishing, LLC.

Thomas, Ron & Herran, Joe. Getting into Golf. 2005. (Getting Into Ser.). (Illus.). 32p. (J). (ps-8). lib. bdg. 28.00 (978-0-7910-8811-1(1) , Chelsea Clubhouse) Facts On File, Inc.

Wells, Don. For the Love of Golf. 2005. (For the Love of Sports Ser.). (Illus.). 24p. (J). (ps-6). lib. bdg. 24.45 (978-1-59036-296-9(9)) Weigl Pubs., Inc.

—Golf. 2005. (For the Love of Sports Ser.). (Illus.). 24p. (J). (ps-7). pap. 6.95 (978-1-59036-300-3(0)) Weigl Pubs., Inc.

Will, Sandra. Golf for Fun! 2003. (Sports for Fun! Ser.). (Illus.). 48p. (J). (gr. 3 up). 21.26 (978-0-7565-0486-1(4)) Compass Point Bks.

Wright, David F., et al. Wright Balance Focus for Success Series - Relaxation: A Guide to Your Best Golf. 2005. (YA). per. 19.95 (978-0-9767272-0-0(X)) Foundation Pr.

The Young Americans Golf Guide 2004. 2004. (YA). 422p. per. 24.95 (978-0-9727998-1-2(8)); cd-rom 19.95 (978-0-9727998-2-9(6)) i wantz Publishing.

The Young Americans Golf Guide Record of Accomplishments 2004. 2004. 152p. (YA). per. 14.95 (978-0-9727998-3-6(4)) i wantz Publishing.

GOLF—BIOGRAPHY

Armentrout, David & Armentrout, Patricia, trs. Tiger Woods. 2003. (Discover the Life of a Sports Star Ser.). (Illus.). 24p. (J). 20.64 (978-1-58952-656-3(2)) Rourke Publishing, LLC.

Brown, Jonatha A. & Raatma, Lucia. Tiger Woods. 2004. (Illus.). 24p. (J). pap. (978-0-8368-4320-0(7)); (YA). lib. bdg. 19.33 (978-0-8368-4313-2(4)) Stevens, Gareth Inc.

Christopher, Matt. On the Course with... Tiger Woods. rev. ed. 1998. (Matt Christopher Sports Biographies Ser.). (Illus.). 144p. (J). (gr. 3-7). pap. 4.99 (978-0-316-13445-3(7)) Little, Brown Bks. for Young Readers.

—On the Course with... Tiger Woods. 1998. (978-0-606-13676-1(2)) Tandem Library Bks.

Collins, David R. Tiger Woods: Golf Superstar. Nolte, Larry, illus. 1998. 32p. (J). (gr. k-3). pap. 15.95 (978-1-56554-321-8(1)) Pelican Publishing Co., Inc.

—Tiger Woods: Golfing Champion. Nolte, Larry, illus. 1999. 104p. (J). (gr. 3-7). 14.95 (978-1-56554-322-5(X)) Pelican Publishing Co., Inc.

Curtis, Walter J., Sr. History's Master Golfers: The Only Four-Time Champions of the U. S. Open & the Only Four-or-More Time Champions of the British Open. 2003. (Illus.). 272p. 24.95 (978-0-9659419-2-1(2)) Curtis Publishing Co.

Dean, Cynthia A. Michelle Wie: She's Got the Power. 2005. (High Five Reading Ser.). (Illus.). 64p. (J). (gr. 4-5). lib. bdg. incl. audio (978-0-7368-5756-7(7)) Capstone Pr., Inc.

Dean, Cynthia A. & Rasinski, Timothy V. Michelle Wie: She's Got the Power. 2005. (High Five Reading Ser.). (J). (978-0-7368-5746-8(X)); (978-0-7368-5736-9(2)) Capstone Pr., Inc.

Doeden, Matt. Tiger Woods. 2005. (Sports Heroes & Legends Ser.). (Illus.). 106p. (J). (gr. 3-7). 27.93 (978-0-8225-3082-4(1) , Lerner Pubns.) Lerner Publishing Group.

Dougherty, Terri. Tiger Woods. 1999. (Jam Session Ser.). (Illus.). 32p. (J). (gr. 3-8). lib. bdg. 24.21 (978-1-57765-041-6(7) , ABDO & Daughters) ABDO Publishing Co.

Durbin, William. Arnold Palmer. 1999. (Golf Legends Ser.). (Illus.). 64p. (YA). (gr. 4-7). 18.65 (978-0-7910-4562-6(5) , Chelsea Hse.) Facts On File, Inc.

—Tiger Woods: Golf Star. 1999. (Golf Legends Ser.). (Illus.). (YA). 64p. (gr. 4-7). 18.65 (978-0-7910-4563-3(3)); 144p. (gr. 5 up). pap. 30.00 (978-0-7910-4687-6(7)) Facts On File, Inc. (Chelsea Hse.).

Edwards, Nicholas. Tiger Woods: An American Master. rev. ed. 2001. (J). (978-0-606-22872-5(1)) Tandem Library Bks.

Feinstein, Stephen. Lee sobre Tiger Woods/Read about Tiger Woods. 2006. (I Like Biographies! Bilingual Ser.). (ENG & SPA., Illus.). 24p. (J). (gr. 1-3). lib. bdg. 21.26 (978-0-7660-2743-5(0) , Enslow Elementary) Enslow Pubs., Inc.

—Read about Tiger Woods. 2005. (I Like Biographies! Ser.). (Illus.). 24p. (J). lib. bdg. 21.26 (978-0-7660-2594-3(2) , Enslow Elementary) Enslow Pubs., Inc.

Gigliotti, Jim. Great Girl Golfers. 2007. (Girls Rock! Ser.). 32p. (J). (gr. 1-5). 24.21 ***(978-1-59296-868-8(6))*** Child's World, Inc.

Gigliotti, Jim. Michelle Wie. 2006. (World's Greatest Athletes Ser.). 32p. (J). (gr. 1-5). 27.07 (978-1-59296-757-5(4)) Child's World, Inc.

Glaser, Jason. Tiger Woods. 2008. (J). lib. bdg. ***(978-1-4042-4179-4(5)*** , PowerKids Pr.) Rosen Publishing Group, Inc., The.

Golf Legends. 1999. (Illus.). 64p. (J). (gr. 3). 101.70 (978-0-7910-4593-0(5) , Chelsea Hse.) Facts On File, Inc.

Goodman, Michael E. Tiger Woods. 2003. (Ovations Ser.). (Illus.). 32p. (J). (978-1-58341-246-6(8) , Creative Education) Creative Co., The.

Gutelle, Andrew. Tiger Woods. Gutelle, Andrew, illus. 2002. (All Aboard Reading Ser.). (Illus.). 48p. (J). pap. 3.99 (978-0-448-42663-1(3) , Grosset & Dunlap) Penguin Group (USA) Inc.

—Tiger Woods. 2002. (gr. k-3). lib. bdg. 11.80 (978-0-613-43647-2(4)) Tandem Library Bks.

Gutman, Bill. Paul Azinger. 1998. (Overcoming the Odds Ser.). (Illus.). 48p. (J). (gr. 3-8). (978-0-8172-4127-8(2)) Raintree.

Horn, Geoffrey M. Michelle Wie. 2006. (Today's Superstars). (Illus.). 32p. (YA). (gr. 5 up). lib. bdg. 23.33 (978-0-8368-6186-0(8)) Stevens, Gareth Inc.

Hughes, Libby. Tiger Woods: A Biography for Kids. 2000. (Illus.). 70p. (J). pap. 5.95 (978-1-58571-003-4(2)) Kensington Publishing Corp.

—Tiger Woods: A Biography for Kids. 2000. (gr. 3-6). lib. bdg. 14.10 (978-0-613-88468-6(X)) Tandem Library Bks.

Kramer, Sydelle A. Tiger Woods: Golf's Young Master. 1998. (Step into Reading Step 4 Bks.). (J). (gr. 2-4). (978-0-606-13970-0(2)) Tandem Library Bks.

Lace, William W. Tiger Woods: Star Golfer. 1999. (Sports Reports). (Illus.). 104p. (YA). (gr. 4-10). lib. bdg. 20.95 (978-0-7660-1081-9(3)) Enslow Pubs., Inc.

Macnow, Glen. Sports Great Tiger Woods. 2001. (Sports Great Bks.). (Illus.). 64p. (YA). (gr. 4-10). lib. bdg. 22.60 (978-0-7660-1468-8(1)) Enslow Pubs., Inc.

Mooney, Martin. John Daly. 1999. (Golf Legends Ser.). (Illus.). 64p. (YA). (gr. 4-7). 18.65 (978-0-7910-4581-7(1) , Chelsea Hse.) Facts On File, Inc.

Raatma, Lucia. Tiger Woods. 2008. (J). lib. bdg. 26.00 ***(978-1-60279-076-6(0))*** Cherry Lake Publishing.

—Tiger Woods. 2001. (Trailblazers of the Modern World Ser.). (Illus.). 48p. (J). (gr. 5 up). pap. 14.95 (978-0-8368-5226-4(5)); lib. bdg. 30.00 (978-0-8368-5066-6(1)) Stevens, Gareth Inc. (World Almanac Library).

Riner, Dax. Annika Sorenstam. 2007. (J). lib. bdg. ***(978-0-8225-7160-5(9))*** Twenty First Century Bks.

Roberts, Jeremy. Tiger Woods. 2002. (Illus.). 112p. (J). (gr. 6-12). lib. bdg. 16.40 (978-0-613-46178-8(9)) Tandem Library Bks.

—Tiger Woods: Biography A&E Series. 2001. (Biography Ser.). (Illus.). 112p. (YA). (gr. 6-12). 27.93 (978-0-8225-0030-8(2) , Lerner Pubns.) Lerner Publishing Group.

EFG

Savage, Jeff. Michelle Wie. 2007. (J). lib. bdg. (*978-0-8225-7664-8(3) , Lerner Pubns.) Lerner Publishing Group.

Savage, Jeff. Tiger Woods. (Amazing Athletes Ser.). 2007. (J). 23.93 (978-0-8225-6889-6(6) , Lerner Pubns.); 2005. (Illus.). 32p. (gr. 3-4). lib. bdg. 22.60 (978-0-8225-1337-7(4)) Lerner Publishing Group.

Sirak, Ron. Greg Norman. 1999. (Golf Legends Ser.). (Illus.). 64p. (YA). (gr. 4-7). 18.65 (978-0-7910-4561-9(7) , Chelsea Hse.) Facts On File, Inc.

Sirimarco, Elizabeth. Tiger Woods. 2000. (Sports Heroes Ser.). (Illus.). 48p. (J). (gr. 3-4). lib. bdg. 21.26 (978-0-7368-0581-0(8) , Capstone High-Interest Bks.) Capstone Pr., Inc.

Stewart, Mark. Se Ri Pak: The Drive to Win. 2000. (New Wave Ser.). (Illus.). 48p. (gr. 4 up). lib. bdg. 22.90 (978-0-7613-1519-3(5) , Millbrook Pr.) Lerner Publishing Group.

—Tiger Woods: Drive to Greatness. 2001. (Inspiring People Ser.). (Illus.). 64p. (gr. 4 up). lib. bdg. 24.90 (978-0-7613-1966-5(2) , Millbrook Pr.) Lerner Publishing Group.

Stewart, Mark Alan. Se Ri Pak: The Drive to Win. 2000. (J). (978-0-606-19172-2(0)) Tandem Library Bks.

—Tiger Woods: Drive to Greatness. 2001. (Illus.). 64p. (gr. 4-12). pap. 7.95 (978-0-7613-1477-6(6) , Millbrook Pr.) Lerner Publishing Group.

Thomas, Bob. Ben Hogan's Secret: A Literary Portrait. 2002. Orig. Title: Ben Hogan's Secret: A Fictionalized Biography. 208p. pap. 13.95 (978-0-9717682-2-2(6)) Bob Thomas Bks.

Tiger Woods (Revised Edition) 2007. (J). pap. 5.95 (*978-0-8225-6890-2(X) , First Avenue Editions) Lerner Publishing Group.

Torres, John Albert. Tiger Woods. 2001. (Real-Life Reader Biography Ser.). (Illus.). 32p. (J). (gr. 3-8). lib. bdg. 15.95 (978-1-58415-067-1(X)) Mitchell Lane Pubs., Inc.

Uschan, Michael V. Tiger Woods. 2002. (Stars of Sports Ser.). (Illus.). 48p. (J). 26.20 (978-0-7377-1397-8(6) , Greenhaven Pr., Inc.) Thomson Gale.

Wheeler, Jill C. Michelle Wie. 2007. (Awesome Athletes Ser.). (Illus.). 32p. (J). 22.78 (978-1-59928-309-8(3)) ABDO Publishing Co.

Wilner, Barry. Golf Stars of Today. 1999. (Golf Legends Ser.). (Illus.). 64p. (YA). (gr. 4-7). 18.65 (978-0-7910-4585-5(4) , Chelsea Hse.) Facts On File, Inc.

Woods, Bob. Annika Sorenstam. 2007. (World's Greatest Athletes Ser.). 32p. (J). (gr. 1-5). 27.07 (978-1-59296-788-9(4)) Child's World, Inc.

Wukovits, John F. Jack Nicklaus. 1999. (Golf Legends Ser.). (Illus.). 64p. (YA). (gr. 4-7). 18.65 (978-0-7910-4560-2(9) , Chelsea Hse.) Facts On File, Inc.

GOLF—FICTION

Arena, Felice & Kettle, Phil. Golf Legends. Gordon, Gus, illus. 2004. (J). pap. (978-1-59336-367-3(2)) Mondo Publishing.

Axelrod, Amy. Pigs on the Ball: Fun With Math & Sports. 2000. (978-0-606-18800-5(2)) Tandem Library Bks.

Bewitching Golf. 2002. (YA). per. (978-0-9673867-9-9(9)) Pearl Street Publishing, LLC.

Christopher, Matt. Fairway Phenom. ed. 2005. (Sports Classics IV Ser.). 135p. (J). lib. bdg. 15.00 (978-1-59054-756-4(X)) Fitzgerald Bks.

—Fairway Phenom. 2003. 144p. (J). (gr. 5-8). pap. 4.99 (978-0-316-07551-0(5)) Little, Brown Bks. for Young Readers.

—Fairway Phenom. 2003. (gr. 3-6). lib. bdg. 12.40 (978-0-613-71602-4(7)) Tandem Library Bks.

Grader, Argentina. Alli Gator's Tail of Golf. Vickery, Shea, illus. 1999. 28p. (J). pap. 7.95 (978-0-9670529-1-5(2)) Argentina Pubns.

grunion. The Adventures of Poppy the Golf Ball. 2003. (J). pap. 9.00 (978-0-8059-6441-7(X)) Dorrance Publishing Co., Inc.

Gutman, Dan. The Million Dollar Putt. 2006. 176p. (gr. 3-7). 15.99 (978-0-7868-3641-3(5)) Hyperion Bks. for Children.

Gutman, Dan. Million Dollar Putt. 2007. 176p. (gr. 3-7). pap. 5.99 (*978-0-7868-3642-0(3)) Hyperion Pr.

Hayes, Alan. Dad's Golf Story: Coloring Book. Hayes, Alan, illus. 2000. (Illus.). 24p. (J). (ps-2). pap. 4.95 (978-0-615-11424-8(5)) A R T L U Publishing.

Henkes, Kevin. Two under Par. Henkes, Kevin, illus. 2005. (Illus.). 128p. (J). (ps-k). pap. 4.99 (978-0-06-075695-6(0) , Harper Trophy) HarperCollins Pubs.

Henry, Chaz. St. Mulligan & the History of Golf. 2nd l.t. ed. 2003. (Illus.). 26p. (J). 21.95 (978-0-9725355-1-9(9) , 1) Newtonian Golf & Particle Physics, Inc.

Horowitz, Jeanine. My First Playing Lesson. l.t. ed. 2006. (Illus.). 32p. (J). lib. bdg. (*978-1-934190-04-3(7)) Ocean Front Bk. Publishing, Inc.

If Golf Balls Could Talk. 2001. 56p. pap. 7.95 (978-0-9741983-0-9(7)) Frank, Paul.

Jerome, Kate Boehm. Miniature Golf Madness. 2005. (Illus.). 32p. (J). 15.95 (978-0-9769087-3-9(5)) Vertical Connect Pr.

London, Jonathan. Froggy's Day with Dad. Remkiewicz, Frank, illus. (Froggy Ser.). 32p. (J). (ps). 2006. pap. 5.99 (978-0-14-240634-2(1) , Puffin); 2004. 15.99 (978-0-670-03596-0(3) , Viking Juvenile) Penguin Group (USA) Inc.

Marsh, Carole. The Gargoyle Golf Course. 2006. 64p. (gr. 2-4). 14.95 (*978-0-635-06220-8(8)); pap. 3.99 (*978-0-635-06214-7(3)) Gallopade International.

McAllister, Troon, pseud. Foursome. 2001. (gr. 7-12). lib. bdg. 23.40 (978-0-613-36809-4(6)) Tandem Library Bks.

McFarland, Henry O. Ralph & Jimbo's Great Golf Adventure. Vaughn, Patrika, ed. 2002. (Illus.). 32p. (J). (gr. k-5). 13.95 (978-0-9706576-6-4(8) , Advocate Hse.) A Cappela Publishing.

Miller, William. Night Golf. Lucas, Cedric, illus. 32p. 2002. (YA). pap. 6.95 (978-1-58430-056-4(6)); 1999. (J). (gr. 1-4). 15.95 (978-1-880000-79-3(2)) Lee & Low Bks., Inc.

Reichman, Justin. The Green. 2003. (Dream Series Ser.: Vol. 9). 160p. 9.95 (978-0-9708992-9-3(7)) Scobre Pr. Corp.

Villar Liebana, Luisa. Misterio en el Campo de Golf. 2005. (Investigator Big Ears Ser.). (SPA., Illus.). 78p. (J). (gr. 2-3). 8.95 (978-84-348-9424-2(6)) SM Ediciones ESP. *Dist:* Iaconi, Mariuccia Bk. Imports.

Waldron, Kathleen Cook. Rough Day at Loon Lake. 2002. (ps-2). lib. bdg. 15.25 (978-0-613-57782-3(5)) Tandem Library Bks.

GOMPERS, SAMUEL, 1850-1924

Wooten, Sara McIntosh. The Industrial Revolution. 2003. (People at the Center of Ser.). (Illus.). 48p. (J). 24.95 (978-1-56711-766-0(X) , Blackbirch Pr., Inc.) Thomson Gale.

GONZALEZ, PANCHO, 1928-1995

Gonzales, Doreen. Richard "Pancho" Gonzales: Tennis Champion. 1998. (Hispanic Biographies Ser.). (Illus.). 128p. (YA). (gr. 6-12). lib. bdg. 20.95 (978-0-89490-891-0(X)) Enslow Pubs., Inc.

GOOD AND EVIL

Marks, James Lynn. Opposites. 2000. (Education Through Creation Ser.: Bk. 7). (Illus.). 16p. (J). (ps-6). pap. 9.95 (978-0-9706412-6-7(5) , 1007) Seventh Sun Productions.

Pijoan, Teresa. Dark & Evil World. 1999. (gr. 7-12). lib. bdg. 24.55 (978-0-613-80112-6(1)) Tandem Library Bks.

GOOD AND EVIL—FICTION

Aidinoff, Elsie V. The Garden. 2004. (Illus.). 416p. (J). 17.99 (978-0-06-055605-1(6)); lib. bdg. 17.89 (978-0-06-055606-8(4)) HarperCollins Pubs. (HarperTeen).

Alexander, Lloyd. The High King. 5th rev. ed. 2006. (Chronicles of Prydain Ser.: Bk. 5). 272p. (J). (gr. 3-8). pap. 5.99 (978-0-8050-8052-0(X) , Holt, Henry & Co. Bks. For Young Readers) Holt, Henry & Co.

Amano, Shiro. Kingdom Hearts: Chain of Memories, Vol. 2. 2nd rev. ed. 2007. 232p. (gr. 4-7). pap. 9.99 (978-1-59816-638-5(7) , Tokyopop Kids) TOKYOPOP, Inc.

Anderson, Al. Pegasus: Adventures with Bingo Borden. Kurzyca, Krystyna Emilia, illus. 2006. 77p. (J). per. 19.50 (*978-1-887250-46-7(8)) Agora Pubns., Inc.

Baldwin, Stephen. Spirit Warriors: A Graphic Novel. 2006. Vol. 1. (Illus.). 208p. (YA). pap. 9.99 (978-0-8054-4357-8(6)) B&H Publishing Grp.

—Spirit Warriors: Number Three. Simko, Joe et al, illus. 2007. 208p. (YA). pap. 9.99 (978-0-8054-4356-1(8)) B&H Publishing Grp.

—Spirit Warriors: Number Two. 2007. (Illus.). 208p. (YA). pap. 9.99 (978-0-8054-4355-4(X)) B&H Publishing Grp.

Banerjee, Anjali. The Silver Spell. Fiegenshuh, Emily, illus. 2005. (Knights of the Silver Dragon Ser.: Bk. 8). 174p. (J). (*978-1-4156-1645-1(0) , Mirrorstone) Wizards of the Coast.

Beckham, David. Charlie Barker & the Secret of the Deep Dark Woods. 2006. 570p. pap. (*978-1-4120-9264-7(7)) Trafford Publishing.

Benton, Jim. The Good, the Bad, & the Bunny. 2006. (It's Happy Bunny Ser.: No. 4). (Illus.). 72p. (J). pap. 7.99 (978-0-439-70593-6(2) , Scholastic Paperbacks) Scholastic, Inc.

Blenkhorn, Les. The Adventures of Tracker. 2006. 26.99 (*978-1-4259-6605-8(5)); pap. 16.99 (*978-1-4259-6604-1(7)) AuthorHouse.

Brooks, Terry. A Knight of the Word. 1999. (Word & the Void Ser.: Bk. 2). (gr. 7-12). lib. bdg. 15.30 (978-0-613-21872-6(8)) Tandem Library Bks.

Caballero, Erica. Mount Mole. 2006. pap. 10.00 (*978-1-4257-2301-9(2)) Xlibris Corp.

Carman, Patrick. Beyond the Valley of Thorns (Mas Alla Del Valle de Espinos) 2006. (Tierra de Elyon Ser.: Bk. 2). 224p. (J). pap. 6.99 (978-0-439-87480-9(7) , Scholastic en Espanol) Scholastic, Inc.

Chapman, Andrew. Heroic Feats. 2005. (Thrillogy Ser.). (Illus.). 48p. (gr. 4-8). 17.50 (978-0-7910-8889-0(8)) Facts On File, Inc.

—Heroic Feats. 2000. (gr. 7-12). lib. bdg. 12.10 (978-0-613-28872-9(6)) Tandem Library Bks.

Chizuru, Mio. The Pirate & the Princess Volume 1: the Timelight Stone: The Timelight Stone. 2007. 110p. (J). pap. 5.99 (*978-1-933164-43-4(3)) Seven Seas Entertainment, LLC.

—The Pirate & the Princess Volume 2: the Red Crystal: The Red Crystal. 2007. 110p. (J). pap. 5.99 (*978-1-933164-44-1(1)) Seven Seas Entertainment, LLC.

Corlett, William. The Door in the Tree. 2000. 289p. (J). (gr. 5-8). per. 13.00 (978-0-613-74171-2(4)) Tandem Library Bks.

Cormier, Shawn P. NiDemon. 2005. (YA). per. 12.95 (978-0-9740151-1-8(3)) Pine View Pr.

Corwin, Susan Simon. The Cryptic Cat. Corwin, Stuart, illus. 2006. 99p. (YA). (*978-0-9790632-0-6(5)) Lucky Duck Designs.

Craik, Dinah Maria Mulock. Little Lame Prince EasyRead Comfort Edit. 2006. pap. (*978-1-4250-2001-9(1)) Assistedreadingbooks.com Inc.

—Little Lame Prince EasyRead Edition. 2006. pap. (*978-1-4250-1718-7(5)) Assistedreadingbooks.com Inc.

—Little Lame Prince EasyRead Large Editio. 2006. pap. (*978-1-4250-2260-0(X)) Assistedreadingbooks.com Inc.

—Little Lame Prince the. 2006. pap. (*978-1-4250-2683-7(4)) Assistedreadingbooks.com Inc.

Curry, Kenneth. The Return of Gamalok: The Return of Gamalok. 2007. (Illus.). 83p. (J). per. 12.95 (*978-0-9798364-2-8(5)) Curry Brothers Publishing.

DeFalco, Tom & Reader's Digest Staff. Marvel Heroes the Battle Unfolds Fold-Out Flap Book. 2007. 10p. (J). 12.99 (*978-0-7944-1306-4(4)) Reader's Digest Assn., Inc., The.

Doyle, Malachy & Walker, Sholto. Long Gray Norris. 2006. (Yellow Bananas Ser.). (Illus.). 46p. (J). (978-0-7787-0956-5(6)) Crabtree Publishing Co.

Egan, Kate, adapted by. World's Apart. 2005. (W. I. T. C. H. Ser.: Bk. 14). 134p. (J). lib. bdg. 16.92 (*978-1-4242-0788-6(6)) Fitzgerald Bks.

Farshtey, Greg. Bionicle Legends: Island of Doom. 2006. 128p. (J). pap. 4.99 (978-0-439-74560-4(8)) Scholastic, Inc.

—Downfall. 2008. (Bionicle Legends Ser.: No. 8). 128p. (J). pap. 4.99 (*978-0-439-89037-3(3)) Scholastic, Inc.

—Legacy of Evil. 2006. (Bionicle Legends Ser.). 128p. (J). pap. 4.99 (978-0-439-82807-9(4)) Scholastic, Inc.

—Prisoners of the Pit. 2007. (Bionicle Legends Ser.: No. 7). 144p. (J). pap. 4.99 (*978-0-439-89034-2(9)) Scholastic, Inc.

—Shadows in the Sky. 2008. (Bionicle Legends Ser.). 128p. (J). 4.99 (*978-0-439-91641-7(0) , Scholastic) Scholastic, Inc.

Forde, Catherine. Firestarter. 2006. 160p. (J). pap. 8.99 (*978-1-4052-1056-0(7)) Egmont Bks., Ltd. GBR. *Dist:* Independent Pubs. Group.

Frazier, Jan. The Adventures of JC Van Winkler, Vol. 3. 2005. 192p. pap. 8.95 (978-1-56315-374-7(2)) Sterling-House Pubs., Inc.

Fullerton, Charlotte. Battle at Ice Palace. 2006. (Sonic X Ser.). (Illus.). 48p. (J). (gr. 1-3). pap. 4.99 (978-0-448-44409-3(7) , Grosset & Dunlap) Penguin Group (USA) Inc.

—Dr. Eggman Goes to War. 2006. (Sonic X Ser.). (Illus.). 48p. (J). (gr. 1-3). pap. 4.99 (978-0-448-44327-0(9) , Grosset & Dunlap) Penguin Group (USA) Inc.

Goldberg, Dennis. Double Bubble Trouble. 2007. (J). 14.95 (*978-1-933769-19-6(X)) Level 4 Press, Inc.

Golden Books Staff. Spy Race! 2008. (Color Plus Chunky Crayons Ser.). (Illus.). 48p. (J). (ps-2). pap. 3.99 (*978-0-375-84008-1(7) , Golden Bks.) Random Hse., Inc.

Gunson, Jonathan. The Divine Calling. 2006. 289p. 24.30 (978-1-4116-7790-6(0)) Lulu.com.

Hamilton, Tisha. All That Glitters. Noel, Aragon & Hwan, Choi Sung, illus. 2006. (Trollz Ser.). 80p. (J). pap. 3.99 (978-0-439-75309-8(0)) Scholastic, Inc.

Ingelvie, Bodie. Dudleytown Curse. 2007. 320p. pap. 14.99 (*978-1-59554-321-9(X)) Nelson, Thomas Inc.

Inns, Dennis & Kanaan, Salah. Fattish & Fattoush: The Revelation. 2005. 143p. pap. 19.95 (978-1-4137-4397-5(8)) PublishAmerica, Inc.

Irvin, William. The Adventures of Winston & Hazel: Episode 1: the Silver Medallion. 2006. 11.00 (978-0-8059-8220-6(5)) Dorrance Publishing Co., Inc.

Jenkins, Jerry B. Uplink from the Underground: Showtime for Vicki. 2002. (Left Behind Ser.: Bk. 24). (gr. 5-8). lib. bdg. 14.15 (978-0-613-59222-2(0)) Tandem Library Bks.

—Wildfire! Into the Great Tribulation. 2003. (Left Behind Ser.: Bk. 27). (gr. 5-8). lib. bdg. 14.15 (978-0-613-63532-5(9)) Tandem Library Bks.

Jenkins, Jerry B. & Fabry, Chris. The Book of the King. 2007. (Wormling Ser.). 288p. (J). (gr. 5-9). pap. 7.99 (*978-1-4143-0155-6(3)) Tyndale Hse. Pubs.

—The Changeling. 2007. (Wormling Ser.). 336p. (J). (gr. 5-9). pap. 7.99 (*978-1-4143-0157-0(X)) Tyndale Hse. Pubs.

—The Sword of the Wormling. 2007. (Wormling Ser.). 336p. (J). (gr. 5-9). pap. 7.99 (*978-1-4143-0156-3(1)) Tyndale Hse. Pubs.

Jenkins, Jerry B. & LaHaye, Tim. Battling the Commander: The Hidden Cave. 2001. (Left Behind Ser.: Bk. 15). (gr. 5-8). lib. bdg. 14.15 (978-0-613-57389-4(7)) Tandem Library Bks.

—Battling the Commander: The Hidden Cave. 2001. (Left Behind Ser.: Bk. 15). (Illus.). 152p. (J). (gr. 5-9). mass mkt. 5.99 (978-0-8423-4296-4(6)) Tyndale Hse. Pubs.

—The Beast Arises: Unveiling the Plan. 2003. (Left Behind Ser.: Bk. 26). (gr. 3-6). lib. bdg. 14.15 (978-0-613-63496-0(9)) Tandem Library Bks.

—Darkening Skies: Judgment of Ice. 2001. (Left Behind Ser.: Bk. 18). (gr. 5-8). lib. bdg. 14.15 (978-0-613-57402-0(8)) Tandem Library Bks.

—Death at the Gala: History in the Making. 2003. (Left Behind Ser.: Bk. 25). (gr. 3-6). lib. bdg. 14.15 (978-0-613-63501-1(9)) Tandem Library Bks.

—Death Strike: The Young Trib Force Faces War. 2000. (Left Behind Ser.: Bk. 8). (gr. 5-8). lib. bdg. 14.15 (978-0-613-33289-7(X)) Tandem Library Bks.

—Fire from Heaven: Deceiving the Enemy. 2001. (Left Behind Ser.: Bk. 16). (gr. 5-8). lib. bdg. 14.15 (978-0-613-57411-2(7)) Tandem Library Bks.

—Horsemen of Terror: The Unseen Judgment. 2002. (Left Behind Ser.: Bk. 23). (gr. 5-8). lib. bdg. 14.15 (978-0-613-59200-0(X)) Tandem Library Bks.

—The Mark of the Beast: Dilema in New Babylon. 2003. (Left Behind Ser.: Bk. 28). (gr. 5-8). lib. bdg. 14.15 (978-0-613-63524-0(8)) Tandem Library Bks.

—Secrets of New Babylon: The Search for an Impostor. 2002. (Left Behind Ser.: Bk. 21). (gr. 3-6). lib. bdg. 14.15 (978-0-613-59360-1(X)) Tandem Library Bks.

—The Showdown: Behind Enemy Lines. 2001. (Left Behind Ser.: Bk. 13). 132p. (J). (ps-7). lib. bdg. 12.64 (978-0-606-22119-1(0)); (gr. 5-8). lib. bdg. 14.15 (978-0-613-33316-0(0)) Tandem Library Bks.

—Terror in the Stadium: Witnesses under Fire. 2001. (Left Behind Ser.: Bk. 17). (gr. 5-8). lib. bdg. 14.15 (978-0-613-57449-5(4)) Tandem Library Bks.

Jinks, Catherine. Evil Genius. 2008. (Illus.). 512p. (YA). pap. 7.95 (*978-0-15-206185-2(1) , Harcourt Paperbacks) Harcourt Children's Bks.

—Evil Genius. 2007. (Illus.). 496p. (YA). (gr. 7 up). 17.00 (978-0-15-205988-0(1)); 486p. (J). (*978-1-4287-3510-1(0)) Harcourt Trade Pubs.

Jordan, Robert. To the Blight. 2002. (gr. 7-12). lib. bdg. 14.15 (978-0-613-62655-2(9)) Tandem Library Bks.

Juckes, Deborah Sioux. Meesha, Guardian of Grand Mountain: Book One of the Guardian Series. McCleary, Twila, illus. 2005. (YA). 18.95 (978-0-9767748-1-5(X)) Red Earth Publishing.

Kerr, Katharine. The Fire Dragon. 2001. (Dragon Mage Ser.: Bk. 3). (gr. 7-12). lib. bdg. 15.30 (978-0-613-63036-8(X)) Tandem Library Bks.

Kishimoto, Seishi. O-Parts Hunter. 2007. (O-Parts Hunter Ser.). 200p. (YA). Vol. 2. pap. 9.99 (978-1-4215-0856-6(7)); Vol. 3. pap. 9.99 (978-1-4215-0857-3(5)) Viz Media.

Kohlhepp, Michael G. Within the Hearthstone Book 2: The Fountain of Balance. 2007. (ENG.). 184p. per. 19.95 (*978-1-4241-4446-4(9)) PublishAmerica, Inc.

La Fevers, Robin. The Forging of the Blade. 2006. (Lowthar's Blade Ser.: Bk. 1). 144p. (J). (gr. 2). pap. 5.99 (978-0-14-240557-4(4) , Puffin) Penguin Group (USA) Inc.

LaHaye, Tim & Jenkins, Jerry B. Attack of Apollyon: Revenge of the Locusts. 2002. (Left Behind Ser.: Bk. 19). (gr. 5-8). lib. bdg. 14.15 (978-0-613-57388-7(9)) Tandem Library Bks.

Lancett, Peter. Dark Candle. 2007. (Dark Man Ser.). 36p. pap. 6.95 (*978-1-84167-603-6(9)) Ransom Publishing Ltd. GBR. *Dist:* International Publishers Marketing.

—The Dark Fire of Doom. Pedroietta, Jan, illus. 2008. (J). pap. (*978-1-59889-924-5(4)); lib. bdg. (*978-1-59889-864-4(7)) Stone Arch Bks.

—The Dark Never Hides. Pedroietta, Jan, illus. 2008. (J). pap. (*978-1-59889-925-2(2)); (gr. 3-8). lib. bdg. 15.95 (*978-1-59889-865-1(5)) Stone Arch Bks.

—Dark Words. 2007. (Dark Man Ser.). 36p. pap. 6.95 (*978-1-84167-602-9(0)) Ransom Publishing Ltd. GBR. *Dist:* International Publishers Marketing.

—Day Is Dark. 2007. (Dark Man Ser.). 36p. pap. 6.95 (*978-1-84167-606-7(3)) Ransom Publishing Ltd. GBR. *Dist:* International Publishers Marketing.

—Destiny in the Dark. Pedroietta, Jan, illus. 2008. (J). pap. (*978-1-59889-926-9(0)); (gr. 3-8). lib. bdg. 15.95 (*978-1-59889-866-8(3)) Stone Arch Bks.

—Dying for the Dark. 2007. (Dark Man Ser.). 36p. pap. 6.95 (*978-1-84167-604-3(7)) Ransom Publishing Ltd. GBR. *Dist:* International Publishers Marketing.

—Escape from the Dark. Pedroietta, Jan, illus. 2008. (J). pap. (*978-1-59889-927-6(9)); lib. bdg. (*978-1-59889-867-5(1)) Stone Arch Bks.

—The Face in the Dark Mirror. Pedroietta, Jan, illus. 2008. (J). pap. (*978-1-59889-928-3(7)); lib. bdg. (*978-1-59889-868-2(X)) Stone Arch Bks.

—Fear in the Dark. Pedroietta, Jan, illus. 2008. (J). pap. (*978-1-59889-929-0(5)); (gr. 3-8). lib. bdg. 15.95 (*978-1-59889-869-9(8)) Stone Arch Bks.

—Killer in the Dark. 2007. (Dark Man Ser.). 36p. pap. 6.95 (*978-1-84167-605-0(5)) Ransom Publishing Ltd. GBR. *Dist:* International Publishers Marketing.

Lang, Andrew. Prince Prigio. 2004. reprint ed. pap. 19.95 (978-1-4179-0522-5(0)) Kessinger Publishing, LLC.

Lasky, Kathryn. The Hatchling. 2005. (Guardians of Ga'Hoole Ser.: Bk. 7). 222p. (J). (ps-7). per. 12.04 (978-0-606-33802-8(0)) Tandem Library Bks.

—The Outcast. 2005. (Guardians of Ga'Hoole Ser.: Bk. 8). 209p. (J). (gr. 4-7). per. 12.04 (978-0-606-34177-6(3)) Tandem Library Bks.

—The Shattering. 2004. (Guardians of Ga'Hoole Ser.: Bk. 5). (Illus.). 192p. (J). (gr. 3-7). pap. 4.99 (978-0-439-40561-4(0) , Scholastic Paperbacks) Scholastic, Inc.

Layden, Joseph Lyon. The Other Side of Yore. 2007. 156p. pap. 14.95 (*978-1-60145-122-4(9)) Booklocker.com, Inc.

Lecesne, James. Absolute Brightness. 2008. 480p. (J). 17.99 (*978-0-06-125627-1(7)); lib. bdg. 18.89 (*978-0-06-125628-8(5)) HarperCollins Pubs. (HarperTeen).

Lenhard, Elizabeth. Different Path. 2004. (W. I. T. C. H. Ser.: Bk. 13). 158p. (J). lib. bdg. 16.92 (*978-1-4242-0791-6(6)) Fitzgerald Bks.

Lewis, Steven & Parker, Shelley. Return to Allapatria. 2006. 395p. (J). pap. 12.95 (978-0-9547092-9-7(2)) Accent Pr. GBR. *Dist:* Dufour Editions, Inc.

Little Tiny Good Things. 2002. (Illus.). 28p. (978-0-9726611-0-2(7)) New Leaf Communications.

Lutzen, Hanna. Vlad the Undead. 2001. (gr. 7-12). lib. bdg. 14.10 (978-0-613-88930-8(4)) Tandem Library Bks.

MacDonald, George. A Rough Shaking. Parkinson, W., illus. unabr. ed. 1999. (George MacDonald Original Works Ser.: Series I). 384p. (J). reprint ed. lib. bdg. 24.00 (978-1-881084-04-4(3)) Johannesen Printing & Publishing.

Mahy, Margaret. Alchemy. 2004. 207p. (YA). (gr. 7-12). per. 16.75 (978-1-4176-3556-6(8)) Tandem Library Bks.

Matthews, Andrew. Bob Robber & Dancing Jane. Willey, Bee, illus. 2002. 32p. (J). (gr. 1-4). (978-0-224-06465-1(7) , Jonathan Cape) Random Hse. Children's Bks.

McCurdy, J. Fitzgerald. The Serpent's Egg. 2001. (Illus.). 280p. (J). (gr. 9-13). (978-0-9688713-0-0(5)) Saratime, Inc.

McKinstry, J. A. The Adventures of the 31st Street Saints: Book 1: the Eno. 2007. pap. 10.99 (*978-1-59886-892-0(6)) Tate Publishing & Enterprises, L.L.C.

Meadows, Daisy. Weather Fairies: Crystal the Snow Fairy. Ripper, Georgie, illus. 2006. 80p. (J). pap. 4.99 (978-0-439-81387-7(5) , Scholastic Paperbacks) Scholastic, Inc.

Melvin, Anita. What to do with Boogers. Melvin, Anita, illus. 2004. (Illus.). 14p. (J). per. 9.95 (978-0-9760129-8-6(7)) Avant Garde Publishing.

Miller, Christopher & Miller, Allan. The Legend of Gid the Kid & the Black Bean Bandits: Doing the Right Thing Ain't Always Easy. 2007. (Illus.). 32p. (J). (gr. 1-5). 12.99 (***978-1-59317-202-2(8)***) Warner Pr. Pubs.

Milson, Matthew R. Young Arcan & the Garden of Loc. 2007. 240p. pap. 14.95 (***978-1-933770-03-1(1)***) Avari Press.

Mitchell, Chris. The Realm Legends. 2006. pap. 40.99 (***978-1-4208-9129-4(4)***) AuthorHouse.

Mortenson, R. K. Landon Snow & the Shadows of Malus Quidam. 2006. (Landon Now Ser.). 208p. (J). 9.97 (978-1-59789-044-1(8)) Barbour Publishing, Inc.

Nettrour, Nelani. Angels in Training. l.t. ed. 2006. (Illus.). 114p. (J). pap. 12.95 (978-1-932657-57-9(6)) Third Millennium Pubns.

O'Brien, Fitz James. The Wondersmith. 2004. reprint ed. pap. 15.95 (978-1-4191-8848-0(8)); pap. 1.99 (978-1-4192-8848-7(2)) Kessinger Publishing, LLC.

Orme, David. Boffin Boy & the Deadly Swarm. 2007. (Boffin Boy Ser.). (Illus.). 36p. pap. 7.95 (***978-1-84167-625-8(X)***) Ransom Publishing Ltd. GBR. *Dist:* International Publishers Marketing.

—Boffin Boy & the Lost City. 2007. (Boffin Boy Ser.). (Illus.). 36p. pap. 7.95 (***978-1-84167-617-3(9)***) Ransom Publishing Ltd. GBR. *Dist:* International Publishers Marketing.

—Boffin Boy & the Monsters from the Deep. 2007. (Boffin Boy Ser.). (Illus.). 36p. pap. 7.95 (***978-1-84167-615-9(2)***) Ransom Publishing Ltd. GBR. *Dist:* International Publishers Marketing.

—Boffin Boy & the Red Wolf. 2007. (Boffin Boy Ser.). (Illus.). 36p. pap. 7.95 (***978-1-84167-616-6(0)***) Ransom Publishing Ltd. GBR. *Dist:* International Publishers Marketing.

—Boffin Boy & the Time Warriors. 2007. (Boffin Boy Ser.). (Illus.). 36p. pap. 7.95 (***978-1-84167-622-7(5)***) Ransom Publishing Ltd. GBR. *Dist:* International Publishers Marketing.

—Boffin Boy & the Wizard of Edo. 2007. (Boffin Boy Ser.). (Illus.). 36p. pap. 7.95 (***978-1-84167-614-2(4)***) Ransom Publishing Ltd. GBR. *Dist:* International Publishers Marketing.

Oshima, Towa & Aikawa, Yu. Dark Edge, Vol. 3. 2005. (Illus.). 208p. (YA). pap. 9.95 (978-1-59796-030-4(6)) DrMaster Pubns. Inc.

Paver, Michelle. Outcast. Taylor, Geoff, illus. 2008. (Chronicles of Ancient Darkness). 336p. (J). 16.99 (***978-0-06-072834-2(5));*** lib. bdg. 17.89 (***978-0-06-072835-9(3)***) HarperCollins Pubs.

Peacock, Ann & Lewis, C. S. The Chronicles of Narnia. Barbera, Tony et al, illus. Barbera, Tony et al, photos by. 2005. (Narnia Ser.). 64p. (J). (***978-1-4156-3678-7(8)***) HarperCollins Pubs.

Perkins, T J. On Forbidden Ground: Sequel to Mystery of the Attic. 2006. (Illus.). 112p. (YA). 10.99 (978-0-9777538-7-1(5)) GumShoe Press.

Perrin. Rafi's Song & the Stones of Erebrus. 2006. 10.18 (***978-0-9738036-0-0(6)***) Ankh Bks. CAN. *Dist:* Mountain Bk. Co.

Randall, David. Sorrel. 2007. 304p. (YA). (gr. 7 up). 16.99 (***978-0-689-87872-5(9)***, McElderry, Margaret K.) Simon & Schuster Children's Publishing.

Sabin, E. Rose. A School for Sorcery. rev. ed. 2002. 318p. 17.95 (978-0-7653-0289-2(6) , Forge Bks.) Doherty, Tom Assocs., LLC.

Sampson, Fay. Pangur Ban, the White Cat, Vol. 2. 2002. 160p. (J). (gr. 5-8). pap. 7.99 (978-0-7459-4763-1(8) , Lion) Lion Hudson plc GBR. *Dist:* Independent Pubs. Group.

Shaffer, Jeanne E. The Swimmer with a Rope in His Teeth: A Shadow Fable. Cruse, Howard, illus. 2004. 70p. pap. 14.00 (978-1-59102-181-0(2) , Pyr Bks.) Prometheus Bks., Pubs.

Sharpe, Gerald. What Lies Beneath the Bed: Parade of Lights. 2007. 496p. (YA). pap. 11.00 (***978-1-933894-01-0(9)***) IJN Publishing, Inc.

Sheryl the pearl productions, Sheryl Clayton. Teeny the Magic Genie. 2007. (Illus.). 170p. (J). per. 12.95 (***978-0-9795862-0-0(8)***) Sheryl Da Pearl Productions.

Shiro Amano. Kingdom Hearts, 4 vols., Vol. 4. 4th rev. ed. 2006. (Disney Squaresoft Ser.). (Illus.). pap. 5.99 (978-1-59816-220-2(9) , Tokyopop Kids) TOKYOPOP, Inc.

Stevenson, Robert Louis. Dr Jekyll & Mr Hyde. abr. ed. 1999. (gr. 7-12). lib. bdg. 15.25 (978-0-613-32488-5(9)) Tandem Library Bks.

Stine, R. L. Darkest Dawn. 2005. 182p. (YA). (978-1-4156-1459-4(8) , Simon Pulse) Simon & Schuster Children's Publishing.

Stine, R.L. Darkest Dawn. 2005. 182p. (YA). lib. bdg. 20.00 (***978-1-4242-0994-1(3)***) Fitzgerald Bks.

Temperley, Alan. The Magician of Samarkand. l.t. ed. 2005. 216p. (J). pap. (978-0-7540-7883-8(3) , CLP 459) BBC Audio.

—The Magician of Samarkand. 2004. (J). pap. 29.95 incl. audio (978-0-7540-6279-0(1) , Chivers Children's Audio Bks.) BBC Audiobooks America.

Thomas, Blair L. The Sabatini Prophecy. 2008. (ENG.). 496p. (YA). 8.99 (***978-0-9760237-4-6(1)***) Axiom Hse.

Todorov, Boriana & Todorov, Vladimir. The Moon Rock. 2007. (Illus.). 96p. (J). (gr. 7 up). 19.95 (***978-1-894965-77-4(9)***) Simply Read Bks. CAN. *Dist:* Perseus Distribution.

Umezu, Kazuo. The Drifting Classroom, Vol. 8. Roman, Annette, ed. Umezu, Kazuo, illus. 2007. (Drifting Classroom Ser.). 192p. (YA). pap. 9.99 (***978-1-4215-0960-0(1)***) Viz Media.

Walden, Mark. The Overlord Protocol. 2008. (H. I. V. E. Ser.). 384p. (J). 15.99 (***978-1-4169-3573-5(8)***) Simon & Schuster Children's Publishing.

West, Tracey, adapted by. Jack in! MegaMan! 2006. 59p. (J). (***978-0-439-76837-5(3)***) Scholastic, Inc.

Whitlock, Dean. Raven. 2007. (Illus.). 240p. (J). (gr. 5-9). 16.00 (***978-0-618-70224-4(5)***, Clarion Bks.) Houghton Mifflin Co. Trade & Reference Div.

Wilde, Gloria. Lucifer, Good Angel Gone Bad. Bauer, John, illus. 2007. 36p. (J). 14.95 (***978-1-57258-462-4(9)***, 945-6323) TEACH Services, Inc.

Willett, Edward. The Dark Unicorn. 18th ed. 1998. 158p. (YA). (gr. 6 up). 9.99 (978-0-88092-414-6(4) , 4144) Royal Fireworks Publishing Co.

Wood, Brian. The Cramp Twins: Lucien's Little. 2005. (Illus.). 112p. 13.95 (978-1-904674-01-6(1)) Reynolds & Hearn GBR. *Dist:* Trafalgar Square Publishing.

Young, Joseph R. Legend of the Lost Josephine Mine: A Fascinating Adventure. 2001. 221p. (J). pap. 13.95 (978-1-55517-550-4(3) , Bonneville Bks.) Cedar Fort, Inc./CFI Distribution.

GOOD GROOMING

see Beauty, Personal; Grooming for Men

GOOFY (FICTITIOUS CHARACTER)—FICTION

Amano, Shiro. Kingdom Hearts: Chain of Memories, Vol. 2. 2nd rev. ed. 2007. 232p. (gr. 4-7). pap. 9.99 (978-1-59816-638-5(7) , Tokyopop Kids) TOKYOPOP, Inc.

Barks, Carl, et al. Walt Disney's Christmas Parade #5. 2007. 80p. pap. 10.50 (***978-1-60360-005-7(1)***) Gemstone Publishing, Inc.

Shiro Amano. Kingdom Hearts, 4 vols., Vol. 4. 4th rev. ed. 2006. (Disney Squaresoft Ser.). (Illus.). pap. 5.99 (978-1-59816-220-2(9) , Tokyopop Kids) TOKYOPOP, Inc.

GOOSE

see Geese

GOPHERS

Harman, Amanda. Gophers. 2004. (Nature's Children Ser.). (J). (978-0-7172-5966-3(8) , Grolier) Scholastic Library Publishing.

GORDON, KATE (FICTITIOUS CHARACTER)—FICTION

Barron, T. A. The Ancient One. 2003. 320p. (gr. 12). mass mkt. 6.99 (978-0-441-01032-5(6) , Ace Bks.) Penguin Group (USA) Inc.

—Heartlight. 2003. 256p. (gr. 12). mass mkt. 6.99 (978-0-441-01036-3(9) , Ace Bks.) Penguin Group (USA) Inc.

—Heartlight. 2003. (gr. 3-6). lib. bdg. 15.30 (978-0-613-83897-9(1)) Tandem Library Bks.

GORILLA

Ake, Anne. The Gorilla. 1999. (Endangered Animals & Habitats Ser.). (Illus.). 112p. (YA). (gr. 4-12). 27.45 (978-1-56006-492-3(7) , Lucent Bks.) Thomson Gale.

Animal Lives: Gorillas. 2006. pap. 4.99 (978-1-4206-8155-0(9)) Teacher Created Materials, Inc.

Armentrout, David & Armentrout, Patricia. Gorillas. 2008. (J). (***978-1-60044-567-5(5)***) Rourke Publishing, LLC.

Barnes, Julia. The Secret Lives of Gorillas. 2006. (Illus.). 32p. (J). lib. bdg. (***978-0-8368-7658-1(X)***) Stevens, Gareth Inc.

Bender, Lionel. Gorilla. 2005. (Illus.). 32p. (J). 18.95 (978-1-59389-190-9(3)) Chrysalis Education.

Books Are Fun 8 Title Animal Lives Set: Gorilla. 2006. (J). (978-1-59566-307-8(X)) QEB Publishing Inc.

Brend, Stephen. Gorilla: Habitats, Life Cycles, Food Chains, Threats. 2002. (Natural World Ser.). (Illus.). 48p. (J). lib. bdg. 27.12 (978-0-7398-5228-6(0)) Raintree.

Brewer, Stephen. Gorillas. 2007. (J). (***978-1-59939-123-6(6)***, Reader's Digest Young Families, Inc.) Reader's Digest Children's Publishing, Inc.

Costa-Prades, Bernadette. Little Gorillas. 2005. (Born to Be Wild Ser.). (Illus.). 23p. (J). lib. bdg. 22.00 (978-0-8368-4437-5(8)) Stevens, Gareth Inc.

Costain, Meredith. Gorillas. 2000. (gr. k-3). lib. bdg. 11.80 (978-0-613-30441-2(1)) Tandem Library Bks.

Craft, Sarah S. Mother Gorillas & Their Babies. 1999. (Zoo Life Book Ser.). 24p. (J). (gr. k-4). lib. bdg. 18.75 (978-0-8239-5313-4(0) , PowerKids Pr.) Rosen Publishing Group, Inc., The.

De Medeiros, Michael. Gorillas. 2006. (Amazing Animals Ser.). (J). (978-1-59036-390-4(6)); (978-1-59036-396-6(5)) Weigl Pubs., Inc.

Dennard, Deborah. Gorillas. McGee, John F., illus. 2004. (Our Wild World Ser.). 48p. (J). (gr. 2-5). ring bd. 10.95 (978-1-55971-844-8(7)); pap. 7.95 (978-1-55971-843-1(9)) T&N Children's Publishing. (NorthWord Bks. for Young Readers).

—Gorillas. McGee, John F., illus. 2003. 47p. (J). (gr. 4-7). lib. bdg. 16.40 (978-0-613-67965-7(2)) Tandem Library Bks.

Diamond, Claudia C. Gorilla Families. 2002. (Reading Room Collection). (Illus.). 24p. (J). pap. (978-0-8239-8168-7(1)); lib. bdg. 18.75 (978-0-8239-3731-8(3)) Rosen Publishing Group, Inc., The.

Ebersole, Rene. Gorilla Mountain: The Story of Wildlife Biologist Amy Vedder. 2005. (Women's Adventures in Science Ser.). (Illus.). 118p. (YA). (gr. 5-8). 31.00 (978-0-531-16779-3(8) , Watts, Franklin) Scholastic Library Publishing.

Fleisher, Paul. Gorillas. 2000. (Animal Ways Ser.). (Illus.). 112p. (J). (gr. 5 up). lib. bdg. 28.50 (978-0-7614-1140-6(2) , Benchmark Bks.) Cavendish, Marshall Corp.

Frost, Helen. Gorillas. Saunders-Smith, Gail, ed. 2002. (Rain Forest Animals Ser.). (Illus.). 24p. (J). (gr. k-1). lib. bdg. 15.93 (978-0-7368-1192-7(3) , Pebble Bks.) Capstone Pr., Inc.

Gareth Stevens Publishing Staff, contrib. by. Gorillas. 2004. (All about Wild Animals Ser.). (J). lib. bdg. (978-0-8368-4117-6(4)) Stevens, Gareth Inc.

Gogerly, Liz. Dian Fossey. 2002. (Scientists Who Made History Ser.). (Illus.). 48p. (J). lib. bdg. 27.12 (978-0-7398-5225-5(6)) Raintree.

Goldish, Meish. Gorillas. 2007. (Smart Animals! Ser.). (Illus.). 32p. (J). lib. bdg. 25.27 (978-1-59716-369-9(4) , 1265960) Bearport Publishing Co., Inc.

Gorillas & Other Primates. 2002. (Wild, Wild World Ser.). 32p. (J). 9.95 (978-0-7525-4687-2(2)) Parragon, Inc.

Gorilla's New Family. 2002. (Animal's Around the World Mini Bks.). (Illus.). 32p. (J). (978-1-59069-165-6(2) , H4001) Studio Mouse LLC.

Green, Carl R. The Gorilla: A MyReportLinks. com Book. 2004. (Endangered & Threatened Animals Ser.). (Illus.). 48p. (J). lib. bdg. 25.26 (978-0-7660-5060-0(2) , MyReportLinks.com Bks.) Enslow Pubs., Inc.

Hall, Margaret. Gorillas & Their Infants. 2003. (Animal Offspring Ser.). (Illus.). 24p. (J). lib. bdg. 17.26 (978-0-7368-2108-7(2) , Pebble Bks.) Capstone Pr., Inc.

Imbriaco, Alison. The Mountain Gorilla: Help Save This Endangered Species! 2006. (Saving Endangered Species Ser.). (Illus.). 128p. (J). lib. bdg. 33.27 (978-1-59845-035-4(2) , MyReportLinks.com Bks.) Enslow Pubs., Inc.

Jango-Cohen, Judith. Gorillas. 2002. (Animals, Animals Ser.). (Illus.). 47p. (J). 25.64 (978-0-7614-1444-5(4) , Benchmark Bks.) Cavendish, Marshall Corp.

Johnson, Jinny. Gorilla. Woods, Michael, illus. 2005. 32p. (J). (gr. 2-5). lib. bdg. 27.10 (978-1-58340-642-7(5)) Smart Apple Media.

Kalman, Bobbie & Lundblad, Kristina. Endangered Mountain Gorillas. 2004. (Earth's Endangered Animals Ser.). (Illus.). 32p. (J). (978-0-7787-1855-0(7)); pap. (978-0-7787-1901-4(4)) Crabtree Publishing Co.

Kane, Karen. Mountain Gorillas. Ellis, Gerry, photos by. 2001. (Early Bird Nature Bks.). (Illus.). 48p. (J). (gr. 2-4). lib. bdg. 25.26 (978-0-8225-3040-4(6) , Lerner Pubns.) Lerner Publishing Group.

Kendell, Patricia. Gorillas. 2003. (In the Wild Ser.). (Illus.). 32p. (J). lib. bdg. 25.70 (978-0-7398-5497-6(0)) Raintree.

Lewin, Ted & Lewin, Betsy. Gorilla Walk. 1999. (Illus.). 48p. (J). (gr. 1 up). 15.95 (978-0-688-16509-3(5)) HarperCollins Pubs.

—Gorilla Walk. Lewin, Ted & Lewin, Betsy, illus. 1999. (Illus.). 48p. (J). (gr. 1 up). lib. bdg. 17.89 (978-0-688-16510-9(9)) HarperCollins Pubs.

Mara, Wil. Dian Fossey: Among the Gorillas. 2004. (Great Life Stories Ser.). (Illus.). 127p. (J). 30.50 (978-0-531-12059-0(7) , Watts, Franklin) Scholastic Library Publishing.

Martin, Patricia A. Fink. Gorillas. 2000. (True Bks.). (Illus.). 48p. (J). (gr. 3-5). 25.00 (978-0-516-21570-9(1) , Children's Pr.) Scholastic Library Publishing.

Mathews, Tom L. Light Shining Through the Mist: A Photobiography of Dian Fossey. 1998. (Illus.). 64p. (J). (gr. 4-7). 17.95 (978-0-7922-7300-4(1) , T07300C, National Geographic Children's Bks.) National Geographic Society.

McNeil, Niki, et al. HOCPP 1147 King of the Apes: The Gorilla: the Gorilla. 2007. spiral bd. 22.00 (***978-1-60308-147-4(X)***) In the Hands of a Child.

Murray, Julie. Gorillas. 2002. (Animal Kingdom Ser.). (Illus.). 24p. (J). (gr. k-4). lib. bdg. 21.35 (978-1-57765-712-5(8)) ABDO Publishing Co.

Naden, Corinne J. & Blue, Rose. Dian Fossey: At Home with the Giant Gorillas. 2002. (Gateway Greens Ser.). (Illus.). 48p. (gr. 2-4). lib. bdg. 23.90 (978-0-7613-2569-7(7) , Millbrook Pr.) Lerner Publishing Group.

Orme, Helen. Gorillas in Danger. 2007. (Wildlife Survival Ser.). (Illus.). 32p. (J). (gr. 2-4). lib. bdg. 25.27 (978-1-59716-261-6(2)) Bearport Publishing Co., Inc.

Pimm, Nancy Roe. The Heart of the Beast: Eight Great Gorilla Stories. 2007. (J). 18.95 (***978-1-58196-054-9(9)***) Darby Creek Publishing.

Pohl, Kathleen. Gorillas. 2007. (J). pap. (***978-0-8368-8226-1(1));*** 24p. lib. bdg. 19.93 (***978-0-8368-8219-3(9)***) Stevens, Gareth Inc. (Weekly Reader Early Learning Library).

—Gorillas: Gorilas. 2007. (SPA & ENG.). (J). pap. (***978-0-8368-8240-7(7)***, Weekly Reader Early Learning Library) Stevens, Gareth Inc.

—Gorillas/Gorilas. 2007. (Animals I See at the Zoo/ Animales que Veo en el Zoologico Ser.). (SPA & ENG.). 24p. (J). (gr. k-2). lib. bdg. 19.93 (***978-0-8368-8233-9(4)***, Weekly Reader Early Learning Library) Stevens, Gareth Inc.

Prebeg, Rick. Into the Jungle. Prebeg, Rick, photos by. 2005. (J). (978-1-933248-05-9(X)) World Quest Learning.

Redmond, Ian. Gorilas. Anderson, Peter & Brightling, Geoff, illus. 2003. (SPA.). 64p. 14.95 (978-84-372-2323-0(7)) Altea, Ediciones, S.A. - Grupo Santillana ESP. *Dist:* Santillana USA Publishing Co., Inc.

—Gorilla. 2000. (Eyewitness Bks.). (Illus.). 64p. (J). (gr. 4-7). 15.99 (978-0-7894-6036-3(X)) Dorling Kindersley Publishing, Inc.

Redmond, Ian & Dorling Kindersley Publishing Staff. Gorilla. 2000. (Eyewitness Bks.). (Illus.). 64p. (J). (gr. 4-7). lib. bdg. 19.99 (978-0-7894-6613-6(9)) Dorling Kindersley Publishing, Inc.

Simon, Seymour. Gorillas. 2003. 32p. (J). pap. 6.99 (978-0-06-050670-4(9) , Harper Trophy) HarperCollins Pubs.

—Gorillas. 2003. (gr. 3-6). lib. bdg. 15.30 (978-0-613-62448-0(3)) Tandem Library Bks.

Somervill, Barbara A. Mountain Gorilla. 2008. (J). lib. bdg. 25.26 (***978-1-60279-033-9(7)***) Cherry Lake Publishing.

Spilsbury, Louise & Spilsbury, Richard. A Band of Gorillas. 2004. 32p. (J). pap. 6.95 (978-1-4034-5413-3(2)); (Illus.). lib. bdg. 24.22 (978-1-4034-4687-9(3)) Heinemann Library.

—Save the Mountain Gorilla. 2006. (Illus.). 32p. (J). 25.36 (978-1-4034-7808-5(2)); pap. (978-1-4034-7816-0(3)) Heinemann Library.

Stevens, Kathryn. Gorillas. 2007. (New Naturebooks Ser.). 32p. (J). (gr. 1-5). 27.07 (***978-1-59296-846-6(5)***) Child's World, Inc.

Stewart, Josie & Salem, Lynn. Gorillas. Gerner, Kristian, illus. 2000. 12p. (J). (gr. k-2). pap. 3.75 (978-1-58323-033-6(5) , Seedling Pubns.) Continental Pr., Inc.

Stone, Tanya Lee. Gorillas. 2003. (Wild Wild World Ser.). (Illus.). 24p. (J). 24.94 (978-1-56711-814-8(3) , Blackbirch Pr., Inc.) Thomson Gale.

Taylor, Barbara. Why Don't Gorillas Lay Eggs? 2004. (Animal Puzzlers Ser.). (Illus.). 32p. (J). 12.95 (978-1-57768-949-2(6) , Waterbird Bks.) School Specialty Publishing.

Taylor, Marianne. Mountain Gorilla. 2004. (Animals under Threat Ser.). (Illus.). 48p. (J). lib. bdg. 27.07 (978-1-4034-4861-3(2)) Heinemann Library.

—The Mountain Gorilla. 2004. (Animals under Threat Ser.). (Illus.). 48p. (J). pap. 8.50 (978-1-4034-5435-5(3)) Heinemann Library.

Theodorou, Rod. Mountain Gorilla. (Animals in Danger Ser.). (Illus.). 32p. (J). (gr. k-2). 2002. pap. 6.95 (978-1-58810-444-1(3) , 91155); 2000. lib. bdg. 21.36 (978-1-57572-266-5(6)) Heinemann Library.

—Mountain Gorilla. 2001. (gr. k-3). lib. bdg. 14.75 (978-0-613-36111-8(3)) Tandem Library Bks.

Thomson, Sarah L. Amazing Gorillas! (I Can Read Bks.). (Illus.). 32p. (J). 2006. pap. 3.99 (978-0-06-054461-4(9) , Harper Trophy); 2005. 15.99 (978-0-06-054459-1(7)); 2005. lib. bdg. 16.89 (978-0-06-054460-7(0)) HarperCollins Pubs.

Turner, Pamela S. Gorilla Doctors: Saving Endangered Great Apes. 2005. (Scientists in the Field Ser.). (Illus.). 64p. (J). (gr. 4-6). 17.00 (978-0-618-44555-4(2)) Houghton Mifflin Co. Trade & Reference Div.

Welvaert, Scott R. Gorillas. 2005. (Illus.). 24p. (J). 21.26 (978-0-7368-3718-7(3)) Capstone Pr., Inc.

Wexo, John Bonnett. Gorilas. Rountree, Monica, tr. 2003. (Zoobooks). Orig. Title: Gorillas. (SPA., Illus.). 24p. (J). (gr. k-6). lib. bdg. 15.95 (978-1-888153-78-1(4)) Wildlife Education, Ltd.

—Gorillas. rev. ed. 2003. (Illus.). 24p. (J). (gr. 1-7). 10.95 (978-1-932396-04-1(7) , Zoo Bks.) Wildlife Education, Ltd.

Wildlife Education, Ltd. Staff & Wexo, John Bonnett. Gorillas. Orr, Richard & Stuart, Walter, illus. 2001. (Zoobooks Ser.). 24p. (J). 15.95 (978-0-937934-78-4(X)) Wildlife Education, Ltd.

—Gorillas. Orr, Richard et al, illus. 2000. (Zoobooks Ser.). 18p. (J). (gr. 1-8). pap. 2.95 (978-0-937934-28-9(3)) Wildlife Education, Ltd.

Wood, Richard & Barton-Wood, Sara. Dian Fossey. (Groundbreakers Ser.). 48p. pap. 8.50 (978-1-4034-4061-7(1)); 2001. (Illus.). (J). (gr. 5-7). lib. bdg. 25.64 (978-1-58810-049-8(9)) Heinemann Library.

World Book, Inc. Staff, contrib. by. Gorillas & Other Apes. 2005. (World Book's Animals of the World Ser.). (Illus.). 64p. (J). (978-0-7166-1263-6(1)) World Bk., Inc.

GORILLA—FICTION

Anderson, Derek, illus. Gladys Goes Out to Lunch. 2005. 40p. (J). 15.95 (978-0-689-85688-4(1) , Simon & Schuster Children's Publishing) Simon & Schuster Children's Publishing.

Baena, Gloria. Invitacion a la Fiesta del Gran Gorila. Osorno, Laura, illus. 2003. (SPA.). 32p. (J). 8.95 (978-958-04-7072-4(3)) Norma S.A. COL. *Dist:* Distribuidora Norma, Inc., Lectorum Pubns., Inc.

Ballantyne, R. M. Gorilla Hunters A Tale of the Wilds of A. 2006. pap. 36.95 (***978-1-4286-5952-0(8)***) Kessinger Publishing, LLC.

Barbetta, Sue. Nilla's Big Adventure. DeLorimier, Finnette G., illus. 1998. 32p. (J). (gr. k-3). pap. 4.95 (978-1-892774-00-2(3)) Creative Publishing Services.

Bollinger/Papp, illus. King Kong: Journey to Skull Island. 2005. 32p. (J). lib. bdg. 13.85 (***978-1-4242-0614-8(6)***) Fitzgerald Bks.

—King Kong: Meet Kong & Ann. 2005. 32p. (J). lib. bdg. 13.85 (***978-1-4242-0615-5(4)***) Fitzgerald Bks.

Bornstein, Ruth. Little Gorilla. 2000. (Illus.). 32p. (J). (gr. k-ps). bds. 4.95 (978-0-618-05158-8(9) , Clarion Bks.) Houghton Mifflin Co. Trade & Reference Div.

Bornstein, Ruth Lercher. Gorilita. 2004. (SPA., Illus.). 14p. (J). (gr. k-ps). bds. 4.95 (978-0-618-44214-0(6) , Clarion Bks.) Houghton Mifflin Co. Trade & Reference Div.

Boston, Lucy M. Stranger at Green Knowe. 2002. (gr. 3-6). lib. bdg. 14.15 (978-0-613-54691-1(1)) Tandem Library Bks.

—A Stranger at Green Knowe. Boston, Peter, illus. 2002. (Green Knowe Ser.). 208p. (YA). reprint ed. (gr. 3 up). 17.00 (978-0-15-202583-0(9) , Harcourt Young Classics); (gr. 4-7). pap. 6.95 (978-0-15-202589-2(8) , Odyssey Classics) Harcourt Children's Bks.

Browne, Anthony. Voices in the Park. 2001. (gr. 3-6). lib. bdg. 16.45 (978-0-613-75141-4(8)) Tandem Library Bks.

Browne, Anthony & Dorling Kindersley Publishing Staff. Voices in the Park. 2001. 32p. (J). (gr. 2-6). pap. 7.99 (978-0-7894-8191-7(X)) Dorling Kindersley Publishing, Inc.

Castle, Caroline. Funny! 2005. (Illus.). 32p. (J). pap. 11.95 (978-0-09-943302-6(8) , Red Fox) Random Hse. Children's Bks. GBR. *Dist:* Trafalgar Square Publishing.

Fenner Williams, Carol. 2 Picture Books: Tigers in the Cellar & Gorilla Gorilla. 2001. 112p. (J). pap. 14.95 (978-0-595-17555-0(4) , Backinprint.com) iUniverse, Inc.

Gorilla, Be Good! 2001. (ps-2). lib. bdg. 9.80 (978-0-613-32610-0(5)) Tandem Library Bks.

E
F
G

Grey, Chelsea Gillian. Jeshi the Gorilla. Leeper, Christopher J., illus. 2005. (Meet Africa's Animals Ser.). (J). (ps-2). 36p. 14.95 (978-1-59249-415-6(3) , H6504); 32p. 2.95 incl. cd-rom (978-1-59249-418-7(8) , S6554); 36p. pap. 6.95 (978-1-59249-416-3(1) , S6504) Soundprints.

Hall, John. How to Get a Gorilla Out of Your Bathtub. Gilpin, Stephen, illus. 2006. 48p. (J). 14.99 (978-1-59379-070-7(8)) White Stone Bks.

Harvey, Damian. Just the Thing! Chapman, Lynne, illus. 2005. 32p. (J). (ps-ps). 15.95 (978-0-7696-4300-7(0) , Gingham Dog Pr.) School Specialty Publishing.

Howe, James. Day the Teacher Went Bananas. 1999. (Illus.). (J). (gr. k-3). lib. bdg. 14.15 (978-0-8335-0697-9(8)) Tandem Library Bks.

Huxman, K. D. Grizzelda Gorilla. l.t. ed. 2007. (Illus.). 24p. (J). 24.99 (***978-0-9794660-2-1(4)***); per. 12.99 (***978-0-9794660-3-8(2)***) Dragonfly Publishing, Inc.

James, Simon. Jake & the Babysitter. 2002. (gr. 3-6). lib. bdg. 13.00 (978-0-613-53738-4(6)) Tandem Library Bks.

Joyce, William, illus. Buddy. 1999. 48p. (J). (gr. 2-7). pap. 6.95 (978-0-06-440710-6(1)) HarperCollins Pubs.

Komaiko, Leah. Earl's Too Cool for Me. 2003. (gr. k-3). lib. bdg. 14.15 (978-0-613-65690-0(3)) Tandem Library Bks.

Lee, Evelyn. Mountain Mists: A Story of the Virungas. Kratter, Paul, illus. 1999. (Habitat Ser.: No. 14). 36p. (J). (gr. 1-4). 26.95 (978-1-56899-789-6(2)); (ps-3). 15.95 (978-1-56899-785-8(X)); (ps-3). pap. 5.95 (978-1-56899-786-5(8)) Soundprints.

—Mountain Mists: A Story of the Virungas. 1999. (gr. k-3). lib. bdg. 15.25 (978-0-613-56927-9(X)) Tandem Library Bks.

LeLeu, Lisa. Percilla the Gorilla Gift Set: Puppet Book Gift Set with 2 Books. 2004. (J). bds. 19.99 (***978-0-9710537-3-1(1)***) LeLeu, Lisa Studios! Inc.

Lunablau, Jani. Little Snowflake. 2006. (Illus.). 32p. (J). 14.95 (978-1-59692-139-9(0)) MacAdam/Cage Publishing, Inc.

Marchus, Linda. The Gorilla Who Wanted to Dance. Marchus, Linda, illus. 2003. (Illus.). 32p. (J). lib. bdg. 15.95 (978-0-9723122-1-9(8)) Wee Read Publishing.

Mayer. Si Javais Gorille. (FRE.). (J). pap. (978-2-07-050613-2(4)) Gallimard, Editions FRA. *Dist:* Distribooks, Inc.

Mayer, Mercer. If I Had a Gorilla. 2002. (Mercer Mayer Picture Bks.). (Illus.). 32p. (J). pap. 5.95 (978-1-57768-856-3(2) , Mercer Mayer First Readers) School Specialty Publishing.

McFarlane, Arlene. My Name Is Not Magilla Gorilla. Wise, Noreen, ed. Silverman, Karen, illus. 2000. (Lemonade Collection). 48p. (J). (ps up). pap. 5.95 (978-1-58584-210-0(9)) Huckleberry Pr.

McMahon, P. J. The Mystery of the Swimming Gorilla. Manders, John, illus. 2004. (Freaky Joe Club Ser.: No. 1). 112p. (J). pap. 4.99 (978-0-689-86260-1(1) , Aladdin) Simon & Schuster Children's Publishing.

Morozumi, Atsuko. Mi Amigo Gorila. 1999. Tr. of My Friend Gorila. (SPA.). (J). (978-0-606-16477-1(4)); lib. bdg. 14.10 (978-0-613-28956-6(0)) Tandem Library Bks.

—My Friend Gorilla. Morozumi, Atsuko, illus. 2001. (Illus.). 32p. (J). (ps-1). pap. 5.95 (978-0-374-45428-9(0) , Sunburst) Farrar, Straus & Giroux.

—My Friend Gorilla. 2001. (ps-2). lib. bdg. 14.10 (978-0-613-45450-6(2)) Tandem Library Bks.

Oke, Janette. Who's New at the Zoo? Munger, Nancy, illus. rev. ed. 2001. (Animal Friends Ser.). 80p. (J). (gr. 1-5). reprint ed. pap. 6.99 (978-0-7642-2460-7(3)) Bethany Hse. Pubs.

—Who's New at the Zoo? 2001. (gr. k-3). lib. bdg. 14.15 (978-0-613-82432-3(6)) Tandem Library Bks.

Osborne, Mary Pope. Good Morning, Gorillas. Murdocca, Sal, illus. 2002. (Magic Tree House Ser.: No. 26). 96p. (J). (gr. k-3). lib. bdg. 11.99 (978-0-375-90614-5(2)); mass mkt. 3.99 (978-0-375-80614-8(8)) Random Hse. Children's Bks. (Random Hse. Bks. for Young Readers).

—Good Morning, Gorillas. 2003. (Magic Tree House Ser. : No. 26). (J). (gr. k-3). lib. bdg. 11.80 (978-0-613-50441-6(0)) Tandem Library Bks.

Roberts, Dannel. Me & Uncle Mike & the Purple Gorilla, 5 bks, Bk. 5. l.t. ed. 2003. (Me & Uncle Mike Children's Book Ser.: Bk. 5). (Illus.). 32p. (J). per. 14.95 (978-1-893459-04-5(7)) Lions & Tigers & Bears Publishing, Inc.

Smalley, Roger. Gorilla Guardian. Shaw, Charles, illus. 2005. (J). (978-1-933248-14-1(9)) World Quest Learning.

Tomlinson, Jill. The Gorilla Who Wanted to Grow Up. Howard, Paul, illus. 2005. 96p. (J). reprint ed. pap. 6.99 (978-1-4052-1081-2(8)) Egmont Bks., Ltd. GBR. *Dist:* Trafalgar Square Publishing.

Trotter, Stuart, illus. Do You Know about Gorillas? 2002. (Softy Tops Ser.). 18p. (J). bds. 3.95 (978-0-7641-5578-9(4)) Barron's Educational Series, Inc.

Ward, Nick. Charlie Small 1: Gorilla City. 2008. 144p. (J). (gr. 3-7). 15.99 (***978-0-375-84970-1(X)***); lib. bdg. 18.99 (***978-0-375-94970-8(4)***) Random Hse. Children's Bks. (Fickling, David Bks.).

Willis, Jeanne. Gorilla! Gorilla! Ross, Tony, illus. 2006. 32p. (J). (ps-3). 15.95 (978-1-4169-1490-7(0) , Atheneum) Simon & Schuster Children's Publishing.

GOVERNMENT, LOCAL

see Local Government

GOVERNMENT, MUNICIPAL

see Municipal Government

GOVERNMENT, RESISTANCE TO

Grabowski, John F. The Ruby Ridge Scandal. 2005. (American Secrets & Scandals Ser.). (J). (978-1-59018-485-1(8) , Lucent Bks.) Thomson Gale.

Sonder, Ben. Militia Movement: Fighters of the Far Right. 2000. (J). (978-0-606-19786-1(9)) Tandem Library Bks.

GOVERNMENT EMPLOYEES

see Civil Service

GOVERNMENT SERVICE

see Civil Service

GOVERNORS

Alter, Judy. Miriam Ma Ferguson: First Woman Governor of Texas. Messersmith, Patrick, illus. 2006. (Stars of Texas Ser.). 72p. (J). 17.95 (978-1-933337-01-2(X)) State Hse. Pr.

Banks, Joan. Peter Stuyvesant: Dutch Military Leader. 2000. (gr. 5-8). lib. bdg. 17.60 (978-0-613-43365-5(3)) Tandem Library Bks.

Bodie, Idella. Light-Horse Harry. 2004. (Illus.). 86p. (J). pap. 6.95 (978-0-87844-172-3(7)) Sandlapper Publishing Co., Inc.

Boraas, Tracey. Sam Houston: Soldier & Statesman. 2002. (Let Freedom Ring Ser.). (Illus.). 48p. (J). (gr. 3-4). lib. bdg. 22.60 (978-0-7368-1350-1(0) , Bridgestone Bks.) Capstone Pr., Inc.

Burgan, Michael. John Winthrop: First Governor of Massachusetts. 2006. (Signature Lives Ser.). (Illus.). 112p. (J). (gr. 5-7). 30.60 (978-0-7565-1591-1(2)) Compass Point Bks.

Caravantes, Peggy. American in Texas: The Story of Sam Houston. 2004. (Notable Americans Ser.). (Illus.). 144p. (YA). (gr. 6-12). 23.95 (978-1-931798-19-8(2)) Reynolds, Morgan Inc.

Cefrey, Holly. Your Governor: State Government in Action. 2003. (Primary Source Library of American Citizenship). (Illus.). 32p. (J). pap. (978-1-4042-5094-9(8)) Rosen Publishing Group, Inc., The.

Cohen, Daniel. George W. Bush: The Family Business. rev. ed. 2000. (Gateway Biography Ser.). (Illus.). 48p. (gr. 2-4). lib. bdg. 23.90 (978-0-7613-1851-4(8) , Millbrook Pr.) Lerner Publishing Group.

—George W. Bush: The Family Business. 2000. 16.75 (978-0-606-22377-5(0)) Tandem Library Bks.

Cohen, Daniel & Graham, Kevin. Jesse Ventura: The Body, the Mouth, & the Mind. 2001. (Single Titles Ser.: up). (Illus.). 112p. (gr. 7 up). lib. bdg. 25.90 (978-0-7613-1905-4(0) , Twenty-First Century Bks.) Lerner Publishing Group.

Connelly, Elizabeth Russell. John Winthrop. 2001. (gr. 5-8). lib. bdg. 17.60 (978-0-613-32729-9(2)) Tandem Library Bks.

De Capua, Sarah. Being A Governor. 2004. (True Bks.). 48p. (J). (gr. 3-5). pap. 6.95 (978-0-516-27939-8(4) , Children's Pr.) Scholastic Library Publishing.

Decapua, Sarah. Being a Governor. 2004. (True Bks.). 48p. 25.00 (978-0-516-22797-9(1) , Watts, Franklin) Scholastic Library Publishing.

Dube, Jean-Claude. The Chevalier de Montmagny: First Governor of New France. Rapley, Elizabeth, tr. from FRE. 2004. (FRE., Illus.). 430p. (C). 65.00 (978-0-7766-3028-1(8)) Univ. of Ottawa Pr./Presses de l'Universite d'Ottawa CAN. *Dist:* Univ. of Toronto Pr.

Ebon Research Systems Staff. Dare to Be Vol. 4: Luis Munoz Marin. l.t. ed. 2003. Tr. of Atrevete Ser... Un Heroe Luis Munoz Marin. (ENG & SPA., Illus.). 14p. (J). 3.99 (978-0-9648313-7-7(6)) Ebon Research Systems Publishing, LLC.

Firestone, Mary. The State Governor. 2004. (First Facts Ser.). (Illus.). 24p. (J). 15.95 (978-0-7368-2500-9(2)) Capstone Pr., Inc.

Gaff, Jackie. Hernan Cortes: The Life of a Spanish Conquistador. 2005. (Graphic Nonfiction Ser.). (Illus.). 48p. (J). (gr. 4-6). lib. bdg. 26.50 (978-1-4042-0244-3(7)) Rosen Publishing Group, Inc., The.

George, Linda. Luis Munoz Marin: Father of Modern Puerto Rico. 1999. (gr. 3-6). lib. bdg. 15.25 (978-0-613-54744-4(6)) Tandem Library Bks.

George, Linda & George, Charles. Luis Munoz Marin: Father of Modern Puerto Rico. 1999. (Community Builders Ser.). (Illus.). 48p. (J). (gr. 3-5). 25.00 (978-0-516-21586-0(8) , Children's Pr.) Scholastic Library Publishing.

Gorman, Jacqueline Laks. Governor. 2005. (Illus.). 24p. (J). pap. (978-0-8368-4574-7(9)); lib. bdg. 19.33 (978-0-8368-4567-9(6)) Stevens, Gareth Inc.

Greenberg, Keith Elliot. Jesse Ventura. (Biography Ser.). (Illus.). 112p. (gr. 6-12). 2003. (YA). pap. 7.95 (978-0-8225-9680-6(6) , Carolrhoda Bks.); 1999. lib. bdg. 27.93 (978-0-8225-4977-2(8)) Lerner Publishing Group.

—Jesse Ventura. 1999. (A&E Biography Ser.). (Illus.). (J). (978-0-606-18821-0(5)) Tandem Library Bks.

Gregson, Susan R. Sam Houston: Texas Hero. 2005. (Signature Lives Ser.). (Illus.). 112p. (J). (gr. 5-7). (978-0-7565-1004-6(X)) Compass Point Bks.

Harris, Nancy. What's a Governor? 2007. (J). (***978-1-4034-9508-2(4)***); pap. (***978-1-4034-9514-3(9)***) Heinemann Library.

Hinman, Bonnie. General Thomas Gage. 2001. (Revolutionary War Leaders Ser.). 80p. (J). pap. 27.50 (978-0-7910-6385-9(2)); 27.50 (978-0-7910-6384-2(4)) Facts On File, Inc. (Chelsea Hse.).

Hunter, Matt. Jesse Ventura: Story of the Wrestler They Call The Body. 1999. (Pro Wrestling Legends Ser.). (Illus.). 64p. (YA). (gr. 3-7). 25.00 (978-0-7910-5410-9(1) , Chelsea Hse.) Facts On File, Inc.

—Jesse Ventura: The Story of the Wrestler They Call "The Body" 1999. (Pro Wrestling Legends Ser.). (Illus.). 64p. (YA). (gr. 3 up). pap. 25.00 (978-0-7910-5556-4(6) , Chelsea Hse.) Facts On File, Inc.

Jacobstein, Bennett. Profiles of the California Governors. 1999. (California Government Ser.). (Illus.). 48p. (J). (gr. 4-10). pap. 14.95 (978-1-884925-98-6(7)) Toucan Valley Pubns., Inc.

Johnson, Darv. The Reagan Years. 1999. (World History Ser.). (Illus.). 111p. (YA). (gr. 8-11). 27.45 (978-1-56006-592-0(3) , LML00902-177947, Lucent Bks.) Thomson Gale.

Kachurek, Sandra J. Francisco Pizarro: Explorer of South America. 2004. (Explorers! Ser.). (Illus.). 48p. (J). lib. bdg. 23.93 (978-0-7660-2178-5(5)) Enslow Pubs., Inc.

Kiely Miller, Barbara. Sam Houston. 2007. (J). pap. (***978-0-8368-8323-7(3)*** , Weekly Reader Early Learning Library) Stevens, Gareth Inc.

Knudsen, Anders. Antoine de la Mothe Cadillac: French Settlements at Detroit & Louisiana. 2006. (In the Footsteps of Explorers Ser.). (Illus.). 32p. (J). (gr. 3-9). (978-0-7787-2429-2(8)); pap. (978-0-7787-2465-0(4)) Crabtree Publishing Co.

Kovach, John. Bob Ehrlich: His Historical Campaign for Governor & How a Young Girl Made a Difference. 2003. (Illus.). 52p. (J). pap. 9.95 (978-0-7414-1497-7(X)) Infinity Publishing.

Lee, Sally. Arnold Schwarzenegger: From Superstar to Governor. 2006. (People to Know Today Ser.). (Illus.). 128p. (J). lib. bdg. 31.93 (978-0-7660-2625-4(6)) Enslow Pubs., Inc.

Manning, Ruth. Francisco Pizarro. (Groundbreakers Ser.). (Illus.). 48p. (J). (gr. 5-7). 2002. pap. 8.50 (978-1-58810-341-3(2) , 91092); 2000. lib. bdg. 25.64 (978-1-57572-369-3(7)) Heinemann Library.

—Francisco Pizarro. 2001. (gr. 5-8). lib. bdg. 17.05 (978-0-613-87922-4(8)) Tandem Library Bks.

Marsh, Carole. Harry Flood Byrd. 2002. (One Thousand Readers Ser.). (Illus.). 12p. (J). (gr. k-4). 2.95 (978-0-635-01538-9(2) , 15382) Gallopade International.

—L. Douglas Wilder. 2002. (One Thousand Readers Ser.). (Illus.). 12p. (J). (gr. k-4). 2.95 (978-0-635-01532-7(3) , 15323) Gallopade International.

Miller, Barbara Kiely. Sam Houston. 2007. (Great Americans Ser.). 24p. (J). (gr. 2-4). lib. bdg. 19.93 (***978-0-8368-8316-9(0)*** , Weekly Reader Early Learning Library) Stevens, Gareth Inc.

Otfinoski, Steven. Calvin Coolidge. 2008. (J). (***978-0-7614-2836-7(4)***) Cavendish, Marshall Bks., Ltd.

Pell, Ed. John Winthrop: Governor of the Massachusetts Bay Colony. 2004. (Let Freedom Ring Ser.). (Illus.). 48p. (J). 23.93 (978-0-7368-2455-2(3) , Bridgestone Bks.) Capstone Pr., Inc.

Richter, Robert. Cuauhtemoc Cardenas & the Roots of Mexico's New Democracy. 2000. (Contemporary Profiles & Policy Series for the Younger Reader). (Illus.). 75p. (YA). (gr. 8 up). 24.00 (978-0-934272-66-7(2)); pap. 15.00 (978-0-934272-65-0(4)) Burke, John Gordon Pub., Inc.

Sexton, Colleen A. Arnold Schwarzenegger. 2005. (A&E Biography Ser.). (Illus.). 112p. (J). (gr. 6-12). 29.27 (978-0-8225-1634-7(9)); (ENG & SPA., pap., lib. bdg. 27.93 (978-0-8225-5328-1(7)) Lerner Publishing Group.

Solberg, Jessica L. First Dog: Unleashed in the Montana Capitol. Rath, Robert, illus. 2007. (J). (***978-1-56037-419-0(5)***) Farcountry Pr.

Soler Blanch, Carmen. Hernan Cortes. (SPA., Illus.). 160p. (YA). 11.95 (978-84-7281-174-4(3) , AF1174) Auriga, Ediciones S.A. ESP. *Dist:* Continental Bk. Co., Inc.

Uschan, Michael V. Jesse Ventura. 2000. (People in the News Ser.). (Illus.). 112p. (J). (gr. 6-9). (978-1-56006-777-1(2) , Lucent Bks.) Thomson Gale.

Walsh, Kieran. James Oglethorpe. (Discover the Life of a Colonial American Ser.). 24p. 2005. (Illus.). (gr. 2-5). 14.95 (978-1-59515-138-4(9)); 2004. pap. 4.95 (978-1-59515-339-5(X)) Rourke Publishing, LLC.

Watson, Marilyn Myrick. Raul Castro: Arizona's First Hispanic Governor. 2007. (J). (***978-0-9790826-5-8(X)***); (***978-0-9790826-6-5(8)***) Acacia Publishing, Inc.

—Rose Mofford. 2007. (J). per. 6.95 (***978-0-9790826-1-0(7)***) Acacia Publishing, Inc.

—Rose Perica Mofford. 2006. (J). (***978-0-9788283-5-6(6)***) Acacia Publishing, Inc.

Whitehurst, Susan. William Bradford & Plymouth: A Colony Grows. 2002. (Library of the Pilgrims). (Illus.). 24p. (J). (gr. 3). lib. bdg. 19.95 (978-0-8239-5808-5(6) , PowerKids Pr.) Rosen Publishing Group, Inc., The.

Whiting, Jim. The Life & Times of Peter Stuyvesant. 2007. (Profiles in American History Ser.). (Illus.). 48p. (J). lib. bdg. 29.95 (***978-1-58415-526-3(4)***) Mitchell Lane Pubs., Inc.

Wilson, Wayne. Gaspar de Portola. 2002. (Latinos in American History). (Illus.). 56p. (gr. 4-8). lib. bdg. 29.95 (978-1-58415-140-1(4)) Mitchell Lane Pubs., Inc.

Wukovits, John F. George W. Bush. 2000. (People in the News Ser.). (Illus.). 112p. (J). (gr. 6-9). 32.45 (978-1-56006-693-4(8) , Lucent Bks.) Thomson Gale.

Yeager, Alice. George C. Wallace: Alabama Political Power. 2003. (Alabama Roots Biography Ser.). (Illus.). 104p. (J). pap. (978-1-59421-003-7(9)) Seacoast Publishing, Inc.

Young, Jeff C. Arnold Schwarzenegger. 2007. (Political Profiles Ser.). (Illus.). 112p. (YA). (gr. 5 up). lib. bdg. 27.95 (***978-1-59935-050-9(5)***) Reynolds, Morgan Inc.

GOYA, FRANCISCO, 1746-1828

Lectorum Publications Staff & Schiaffino, Mariarosa. Goya: El Arte de la Vida y de la Historia. 2000. (Maestros del Arte Ser.). (SPA., Illus.). 72p. (J). (gr. 4-7). 22.95 (978-84-88061-99-7(4)) Serres, Ediciones, S. L. ESP. *Dist:* Lectorum Pubns., Inc.

GRAAL

see Grail

GRAHAM, BILLY, 1918-

Wellman, Sam. Billy Graham: The Great Evangelist. 1999. (Heroes of the Faith Ser.). (Illus.). 208p. (YA). (gr. 4-7). 14.95 (978-0-7910-5031-6(9) , Chelsea Hse.) Facts On File, Inc.

GRAHAM, MARTHA, 1894-1991

Freedman, Russell. Martha Graham: A Dancer's Life. 1998. (Illus.). 176p. (J). (gr. 4-6). tchr. ed. 19.00 (978-0-395-74655-4(8) , Clarion Bks.) Houghton Mifflin Co. Trade & Reference Div.

Garfunkel, Trudy. Letter to the World: The Life & Dances of Martha Graham. 1999. (Illus.). 92p. (YA). (gr. 7-12). reprint ed. 17.00 (978-0-7881-6064-6(8)) DIANE Publishing Co.

Kessel, Kristin. Martha Graham. 2005. (Library of American Choreographers). (Illus.). 48p. (J). pap. (978-1-4042-0644-1(2)) Rosen Publishing Group, Inc., The.

GRAIL

see also Arthur, King

Church, J. R. Guardians of the Grail: And the Men Who Plan to Rule the World. Griffin, Ralph G. & Stearman, G. G., eds. 2003. (Illus.). 318p. (Orig.). (gr. 12). pap. 11.95 (978-0-941241-02-1(5)) Prophecy Pubns.

McIntosh, Kenneth. The Grail, the Shroud & Other Religious Relics: Secrets & Ancient Mysteries. 2005. (Religion & Modern Culture Ser.). (Illus.). 112p. (J). (gr. 7 up). lib. bdg. 24.95 (978-1-59084-978-1(7) , 1248067) Mason Crest Pubs.

GRAIL—FICTION

O'Neill, Katrina & Thompson, Lisa. Quest for the Cup. Cantell, Brenda, illus. 2005. (Treasure Trackers Ser.). 80p. (gr. 5-9). 19.00 (978-0-7910-8876-0(6)) Facts On File, Inc.

GRAIN

Alexander, Carol. Grains. 32p. (J). (gr. k-2). 2006. pap. 5.95 (978-0-516-24649-9(6)); 2005. 20.50 (978-0-516-23646-9(6)) Scholastic Library Publishing. (Children's Pr.).

Benduhn, Tea. Bread & Cereal. 2007. (J). pap. (***978-0-8368-8257-5(1)***); 24p. lib. bdg. 19.93 (***978-0-8368-8250-6(4)***) Stevens, Gareth Inc. (Weekly Reader Early Learning Library).

—Bread & Cereal: Pan y Cereales. 2007. (SPA & ENG.). (J). pap. (***978-0-8368-8461-6(2)*** , Weekly Reader Early Learning Library) Stevens, Gareth Inc.

—Bread & Cereal/Pan y Cereales. 2007. (Find Out about Food/Conoce la Comida Ser.). (SPA & ENG.). 24p. (J). (gr. k-2). lib. bdg. 19.93 (***978-0-8368-8454-8(X)*** , Weekly Reader Early Learning Library) Stevens, Gareth Inc.

Dawson, Susan H. & Norton, Susan R. Pyramid Pal - Grains: Eating Should Always Be Fun for a Kid. O'Hare, Mark, illus. 2000. (Adventures in Eating with the Nutrition Champion of Kids Ser.). 24p. (J). pap. 3.50 (978-1-58000-064-2(9)) Griffin Publishing Group.

Edwards, Nicola. Cereals. 2007. (J). (978-1-4042-3702-5(X)) Rosen Publishing Group, Inc., The.

Frost, Helen. The Grain Group. Saunders-Smith, Gail, ed. 2000. (Food Guide Pyramid Ser.). (Illus.). 24p. (J). (gr. k-1). lib. bdg. 15.93 (978-0-7368-0538-4(9) , Pebble Bks.) Capstone Pr., Inc.

Grains New Food Guide Pyramid. 2006. (Illus.). 24p. (J). (gr. k-2). 18.50 (***978-0-531-17851-5(X)***) Scholastic Library Publishing.

Green, Emily K. Grains. 2006. (Blastoff! Readers Ser.). (Illus.). 24p. (J). lib. bdg. 16.95 (978-1-60014-003-7(3)) Bellwether Media.

Hughes, Meredith Sayles & Hughes, E. Thomas. Glorious Grasses: The Grains. 1998. (Plants We Eat Ser.). (Illus.). 104p. (gr. 6-9). lib. bdg. 26.60 (978-0-8225-2831-9(2)) Lerner Publishing Group.

Kalz, Jill. Grains. 2003. 24p. (J). lib. bdg. 21.35 (978-1-58340-301-3(9)) Smart Apple Media.

Mattern, Joanne. How Peas Grow: Como Crecen Los Guisantes. 2006. (ENG & SPA., Illus.). 24p. (J). pap. (978-0-8368-6470-0(0) , Weekly Reader Early Learning Library) Stevens, Gareth Inc.

Mayo, Gretchen Will. Cereal. 2004. (Weekly Reader Early Learning Library). (Illus.). 24p. (gr. 2 up). (J). pap. 5.95 (978-0-8368-4072-8(0)); (YA). lib. bdg. 19.33 (978-0-8368-4065-0(8)) Stevens, Gareth Inc. (Weekly Reader Early Learning Library).

Nelson, Robin. Los Cereales. 2003. (First Step Nonfiction Ser.). (SPA., Illus.). 24p. (J). (gr. k-2). lib. bdg. 18.60 (978-0-8225-5063-1(6)) Lerner Publishing Group.

—Grains. 2003. (First Step Nonfiction Ser.). (Illus.). 24p. (J). (gr. k-2). lib. bdg. 18.60 (978-0-8225-4628-3(0)) Lerner Publishing Group.

Rondeau, Amanda. Grains Are Good. 2003. (What Should I Eat? Ser.). (Illus.). 23p. (J). (ps-3). lib. bdg. 19.93 (978-1-57765-833-7(7) , SandCastle) ABDO Publishing Co.

Schaefer, Lola M. Grains. 2007. (J). (***978-1-4329-0141-7(9)***); pap. (***978-1-4329-0148-6(6)***) Heinemann Library.

Schuh, Mari C. The Grain Group. 2006. (Illus.). 24p. (J). (978-0-7368-5371-2(5) , Pebble Bks.) Capstone Pr., Inc.

Snyder, Inez. Grains to Bread. 2005. (How Things Are Made Ser.). (Illus.). 24p. (J). (ps-2). pap. 4.95 (978-0-516-25527-9(4)); 18.00 (978-0-516-25197-4(X)) Scholastic Library Publishing. (Children's Pr.).

Thomas, Ann. Food: Grains. 2002. (Food Ser.). (Illus.). 32p. (gr. k-2). 23.00 (978-0-7910-6975-2(3) , Chelsea Hse.) Facts On File, Inc.

Wrobel, Scott. Grain. 2001. (Let's Investigate Ser.). (Illus.). 32p. (J). (gr. 2 up). 24.25 (978-0-88682-970-4(4) , Creative Education) Creative Co., The.

Yadav, S. S. Chickpea Breeding & Management: Botany, Production & Uses. Redden, R. et al, eds. 2007. (CABI Publishing Ser.). 638p. 198.00 (***978-1-84593-213-8(7)***) CABI GBR. *Dist:* Oxford Univ. Pr., Inc.

GRAMMAR

see also Language and Languages

also names of languages with the subdivision Grammar, e.g. English Language—Grammar

Coppage, Bruce Ali. The Counterpart Case. 2000. 192p. (YA). (gr. 10-12). pap. 12.95 (978-1-930937-00-0(8)) Beyond Infinity Bks., Inc.

Farr, Roger C., et al. Harcourt Electronic Test System: Grammar Practice & Assessment. 2nd ed. 2000. (Harcourt Language Ser.). (gr. 2 up). pap., tchr. ed. 10.90 (978-0-15-322245-0(X)) Harcourt Schl. Pubs.

Glencoe McGraw-Hill Staff. Writer's Choice: Grammar & Composition, Grade 7. 3rd ed. 2000. stu. ed. 75.96 (978-0-02-818148-6(4) , 9780028181486) Glencoe/McGraw-Hill.

—Writer's Choice: Grammar & Composition, Grade 10. 3rd ed. 2000. stu. ed. 80.64 (978-0-02-818149-3(2) , 9780028181493) Glencoe/McGraw-Hill.

—Writer's Choice: Grammar & Composition, Grade 11. 2000. stu. ed. 82.64 (978-0-07-822660-1(0) , 9780078226601) Glencoe/McGraw-Hill.

—Writer's Choice: Grammar & Composition, Grade 12. 2000. stu. ed. 82.64 (978-0-07-822662-5(7) , 9780078226625) Glencoe/McGraw-Hill.

—Writer's Choice: Grammar & Composition, Grade 6. 2000. stu. ed. 73.32 (978-0-07-822652-6(X) , 9780078226526) Glencoe/McGraw-Hill.

—Writer's Choice: Grammar & Composition, Grade 8. 2000. stu. ed. 75.96 (978-0-07-822655-7(4) , 9780078226557) Glencoe/McGraw-Hill.

Grammar for You Student Book 1. 2005. (978-1-56420-468-4(5)) New Readers Pr.

Grammar for You Student Book 2. 2005. (978-1-56420-469-1(3)) New Readers Pr.

Holt, Rinehart and Winston Staff. Allez Viens! Level 2: Grammar & Vocabulary Workbook. 1999. pap., tchr. ed. 21.86 (978-0-03-052764-7(3)) Holt, Rinehart & Winston.

—Elements of Language: Daily Oral Grammar: Texas Edition. 1999. (gr. 11). 145.53 (978-0-03-053764-6(9)); (gr. 12). 145.53 (978-0-03-053767-7(3)); (gr. 9). 145.53 (978-0-03-053762-2(2)) Holt, Rinehart & Winston.

—Elements of Language: Literature & Communication Skills: Media - Grade 6. 2003. (Elements of Language Ser.). 148.73 (978-0-03-057398-9(X)) Holt, Rinehart & Winston.

—Elements of Language: One-Stop Lesson Planner. 2003. (Elements of Language Ser.). 301.00 (978-0-03-057376-7(9)) Holt, Rinehart & Winston.

—Elements of Literature, Grade 11: Daily Oral Grammar: Oklahoma Edition. 2001. pap. 13.86 (978-0-03-066929-3(4)) Holt, Rinehart & Winston.

Jensen, Frode. Jensen's Grammar. (YA). 2001. 200p. per. 30.00 (978-1-886061-28-6(9)); Vol. 1. 4th ed. 2000. 80p. pap. 11.00 (978-1-886061-24-8(6)) Wordsmiths.

The Language of Literature: Grammar, Usage, & Mechanics Book. 2004. (gr. 10 up). (978-0-618-30393-9(6) , 2-04298); 2001. (gr. 7 up). (978-0-618-15376-3(4) , 2-04131); 2001. (gr. 8 up). (978-0-618-15382-4(9) , 2-04137) McDougal Littell Inc.

The Language of Literature: Grammar, Usage, & Mechanics Book Answer Key. 2004. (gr. 10 up). (978-0-618-30799-9(0) , 2-04414); 2001. (gr. 7 up). (978-0-618-15377-0(2) , 2-04132); 2001. (gr. 8 up). (978-0-618-15383-1(7) , 2-04138) McDougal Littell Inc.

Latin Grammar. 2003. stu. ed., ring bd., wbk. ed. (978-1-931680-42-4(6)) Teaching Point, Inc.

Park, Linda Sue & Durango, Julia. Yum! Yuck! A Foldout Book of People Sounds. Rama, Sue, illus. 2005. 36p. (J). (ps-7). per. 9.95 (978-1-57091-659-5(4)) Charlesbridge Publishing, Inc.

Realtime Associates and Mazer Corporation Staff & LeapFrog Staff, compiled by. Identify Letters, Words & Sentences. 2002. (J). (gr. 2). 66.75 (978-1-58605-316-1(7) , LeapFrog Schl. Hse.) LeapFrog Enterprises, Inc.

Shake & Learn Grammar & Usage. 2002. (YA). spiral bd. 119.95 incl. audio compact disk (978-0-9746001-3-0(X)) Salt Productions, Inc.

Sterling-Orth, Angela. Sound Reading: Literature Lists for Phonology & Articulation. 2005. (Illus.). iv, 43p. (J). pap. (978-1-932054-28-6(6)) Super Duper Pubns.

Turrell, Linda. Mastering Adjectives & Adverbs Student Activities Book: Mastering Language Arts Series. Matthews, Douglas L., ed. 2003. (Illus.). tchr. ed., stu. ed. (978-1-931680-63-9(9) , Expert Systems for Teachers) Teaching Point, Inc.

—Mastering Prepositions, Conjunctions, Phrases & Clauses Student Activities Book: Mastering Language Arts Series. Matthews, Douglas L., ed. 2003. (Illus.). stu. ed., wbk. ed. (978-1-931680-65-3(5) , Expert Systems for Teachers) Teaching Point, Inc.

Voyages in English: Writing & Grammar. 2004. (gr. 4 up). (978-0-8294-1305-2(7)); (gr. 5 up). (978-0-8294-1307-6(3)); (gr. 5 up). tchr. ed. (978-0-8294-0989-5(0)); (gr. 5 up). tchr. ed., wbk. ed. (978-0-8294-1323-6(5)); (gr. 5 up). stu. ed. (978-0-8294-0990-1(4)); (gr. 5 up). stu. ed., wbk. ed. (978-0-8294-1322-9(7)); (gr. 6 up). (978-0-8294-1310-6(3)); (gr. 6 up). tchr. ed. (978-0-8294-0991-8(2)); (gr. 6 up). tchr. ed., wbk. ed. (978-0-8294-1325-0(1)); (gr. 6 up). stu. ed. (978-0-8294-0992-5(0)); (gr. 6 up). stu. ed., wbk. ed. (978-0-8294-1324-3(3)); (gr. 7 up). (978-0-8294-1313-7(8)); (gr. 7 up). tchr. ed. (978-0-8294-0993-2(9)); (gr. 7 up). tchr. ed., wbk. ed. (978-0-8294-1328-1(6)); (gr. 7 up). stu. ed. (978-0-8294-0994-9(7)); (gr. 7 up). stu. ed., wbk. ed. (978-0-8294-1327-4(8)); (gr. 8 up). (978-0-8294-1315-1(4)); (gr. 8 up). tchr. ed. (978-0-8294-0995-6(5)); (gr. 8 up). tchr. ed., wbk. ed. (978-0-8294-1330-4(8)); (gr. 8 up). stu. ed. (978-0-8294-0996-3(3)); (gr. 8 up). stu. ed., wbk. ed. (978-0-8294-1329-8(4)) Loyola Pr.

GRAMMAR SCHOOLS

see Education, Elementary; Public Schools

GRAMOPHONE

see Phonograph

GRAND CANYON (ARIZ.)

Adams, Colleen. Exploring the Grand Canyon. 2002. (Reading Room Collection). (Illus.). 24p. (J). pap. (978-0-8239-8163-2(0)); lib. bdg. 18.75 (978-0-8239-3726-4(7)) Rosen Publishing Group, Inc., The.

Bauer, Marion Dane. The Grand Canyon. Wallace, John, illus. 2006. (Ready-To-Read Ser.). 32p. (J). lib. bdg. 11.89 (978-0-689-86947-1(9)); pap. 3.99 (978-0-689-86946-4(0)) Simon & Schuster Children's Publishing. (Aladdin).

Fitzpatrick, Anne, tr. Grand Canyon. 2004. (Natural Wonders of the World Ser.). (Illus.). 32p. (J). lib. bdg. (978-1-58341-323-4(5) , Creative Education) Creative Co., The.

Foster, Lynne. Exploring the Grand Canyon: Adventures in Yesterday & Today. 2003. (Illus.). 150p. (YA). (gr. 4 up). pap. 15.95 (978-0-938216-33-9(3) , 30280) Grand Canyon Assn.

Graf, Mike. Grand Canyon National Park. 2002. (National Parks Ser.). (Illus.). 24p. (J). (gr. 2-3). lib. bdg. 18.60 (978-0-7368-1375-4(6) , Bridgestone Bks.) Capstone Pr., Inc.

Hall, Margaret. Grand Canyon National Park. 2005. (Heinemann First Library). (Illus.). 32p. (J). pap. (978-1-4034-6706-5(4)); lib. bdg. 25.36 (978-1-4034-6699-0(8)) Heinemann Library.

Justesen, Kim Williams. Hey Ranger! Kids Ask Questions about Grand Canyon National Park. Newhouse, Judy, illus. 2005. 48p. (J). pap. 9.95 (978-0-7627-3847-2(2) , Falcon) Globe Pequot Pr., The.

Lomberg, Michelle. Grand Canyon. 2003. (Natural Wonders of the U. S. A. Ser.). (Illus.). 32p. (J). lib. bdg. 18.20 (978-1-59036-038-5(9)) Weigl Pubs., Inc.

—The Grand Canyon. 2004. (Natural Wonders of the U. S. A. Ser.). (J). pap. 7.95 (978-1-59036-161-0(X)) Weigl Pubs., Inc.

Meister, Cari. Grand Canyon. 2000. (Going Places Ser.). (Illus.). 24p. (J). (gr. k-6). lib. bdg. 21.35 (978-1-57765-024-9(7) , Checkerboard Library) ABDO Publishing Co.

Minor, Wendell. Grand Canyon: Exploring a Natural Wonder. Minor, Wendell, illus. (Illus.). (J). 2000. 32p. (ps-3). pap. 5.99 (978-0-439-19278-1(1)); 1998. 40p. (gr. 1-4). pap. 16.95 (978-0-590-47968-4(7) , Blue Sky Pr., The) Scholastic, Inc.

Murray, Julie. Grand Canyon. 2005. (All Aboard America Ser.). (Illus.). 24p. (J). (gr. k-4). lib. bdg. 21.35 (978-1-59197-505-2(0)) ABDO Publishing Co.

National Geographic Society Staff. Experiences in the Grand Canyon. 1999. (Cultural & Geographical Exploration Ser.). (Illus.). x, 107p. (J). (gr. 7-12). 21.95 (978-0-7910-5442-0(X) , Chelsea Hse.) Facts On File, Inc.

Petersen, David. Grand Canyon National Park. 2001. (True Bks.). (Illus.). 48p. (J). (gr. 3-5). pap. 6.95 (978-0-516-27316-7(7) , Children's Pr.) Scholastic Library Publishing.

—Grand Canyon National Park. 2001. (gr. 3-6). lib. bdg. 15.25 (978-0-613-54522-8(2)) Tandem Library Bks.

Peterson, David. Grand Canyon National Park. 2001. (National Parks Ser.). (Illus.). 48p. (J). (gr. 3-5). 25.00 (978-0-516-21664-5(3) , Children's Pr.) Scholastic Library Publishing.

Powell, John Wesley. The Diary of John Wesley Powell: Exploring the Grand Canyon. Roop, Connie & Roop, Peter, eds. 2000. (In My Own Words Ser.). (Illus.). 96p. (J). (gr. 5 up). lib. bdg. 24.21 (978-0-7614-1013-3(9) , Benchmark Bks.) Cavendish, Marshall Corp.

Puzzler's Guide to the Grand Canyon. 2002. (National Parks series). 48p. (J). 4.95 (978-0-9714226-0-5(5)) Puzzler's Guides.

Ross, Michael Elsohn. Exploring the Earth with John Wesley Powell. Smith, Wendy, illus. 2006. 48p. (J). (gr. 4-10). reprint ed. 19.00 (978-1-4223-5581-7(0)) DIANE Publishing Co.

Souza, Dorothy M. John Wesley Powell. 2004. (Watts Library). (Illus.). 64p. (J). 25.50 (978-0-531-12289-1(1) , Watts, Franklin) Scholastic Library Publishing.

Trumbauer, Lisa. The Grand Canyon. 2005. (Rookie Read-About Geography Ser.). (Illus.). 32p. (J). (gr. 1-2). 20.50 (978-0-516-22747-4(5) , Children's Pr.) Scholastic Library Publishing.

—Grand Canyon. 2005. (Rookie Read-about Geography Ser.). (Illus.). 31p. (J). (gr. 1-2). pap. 5.95 (978-0-516-25931-4(8) , Children's Pr.) Scholastic Library Publishing.

Vieira, Linda. Grand Canyon: A Trail Through Time. 2000. (Illus.). (J). (978-0-606-18743-5(X)) Tandem Library Bks.

Wade, Linda R. Grand Canyon National Park. 2005. (National Parks Ser.). (Illus.). 32p. (J). (gr. 3-8). lib. bdg. 24.21 (978-1-59197-426-0(7)) ABDO Publishing Co.

Weintraub, Aileen. The Grand Canyon: Widest Canyon. 2001. (Great Record Breakers in Nature Ser.). (Illus.). 24p. (J). (gr. 2-5). lib. bdg. 18.75 (978-0-8239-5641-8(5) , PowerKids Pr.) Rosen Publishing Group, Inc., The.

GRAND CANYON (ARIZ.)—FICTION

Carole Marsh. The Mystery of the Grand Canyon Ghost. 2001. 160p. (gr. 2-8). 14.95 (978-0-635-02396-4(2)) Gallopade International.

Chandler, Mitzi. I See Something Grand. 2003. (Illus.). 32p. (J). (ps-1). pap. 8.95 (978-0-938216-50-6(3)) Grand Canyon Assn.

Cuyler, Margery. That's Good! That's Bad! In the Grand Canyon. Catrow, David, illus. rev. ed. 2002. 32p. (J). (ps-2). 16.95 (978-0-8050-5975-5(X) , Holt, Henry & Co. Bks. For Young Readers) Holt, Henry & Co.

Harcourt School Publishers Staff. Down in the Grand Canyon Advanced Level. 3rd ed. 2002. (Trophies Reading Program Ser.). (Illus.). pap. 5.10 (978-0-15-323308-1(7)) Harcourt Schl. Pubs.

Hautman, Pete. Hole in the Sky. 2005. (Illus.). 224p. (YA). reprint ed. mass mkt. 5.99 (978-0-689-84428-7(X) , Simon Pulse) Simon & Schuster Children's Publishing.

Henry, Marguerite. Brighty: Of the Grand Canyon. 2002. (Illus.). (YA). 13.40 (978-1-4046-1351-5(X)) Book Wholesalers, Inc.

—Brighty: Of the Grand Canyon. 2001. (J). (gr. 3-6). 21.50 (978-0-8446-7176-5(2)) Smith, Peter Pub., Inc.

Hobbs, Will. River Thunder. 1999. (Learn-Along Board Bks. Ser.). 224p. (YA). (gr. 7-12). pap. 5.99 (978-0-440-22681-9(3) , Laurel Leaf) Random Hse. Children's Bks.

Jenkins, Jerry B. & Fabry, Chris. Canyon Echoes. 2005. (Tyndale Kids Ser.). 240p. (J). pap. 5.99 (978-1-4143-0147-1(2)) Tyndale Hse. Pubs.

Lamote, Lisa Edman. A Day Out for Opus. 2006. (J). 15.99 (978-1-933673-03-5(6) , BookMann Pr.) Mann Publishing Group.

Patchin, Gee Frank. The Pony Rider Boys in the Grand Canyon. 2006. 33.99 (***978-1-4219-7869-7(5)**); pap. 27.99 (***978-1-4219-7871-0(7)***) IndyPublish.com.

Perlman, Rhea. Canyon Catastrophe. Santat, Dan, illus. 2006. (Otto Undercover Ser.). 128p. (J). 14.99 (978-0-06-075498-3(2)); pap. 3.99 (978-0-06-075497-6(4)) HarperCollins Pubs.

Ratnayake, Kumari/Keiko. Monsieur Bagel's War. Ratnayake, Kumari/Keiko, illus. 2007. (Illus.). 25p. (J). spiral bd. 15.00 net. (***978-0-9797015-1-1(1)***) Augustana College Geology Dept. Pr.

Rogers, Christopher M., illus. Homer the Helicopter Grand Canyon Adventures: N/a. 2007. Tr. of N/a. 72p. (J). 18.95 (***978-0-9786352-3-7(X)***) Buscher, Julie W.

GRAND CENTRAL TERMINAL (NEW YORK, N.Y.)

Stanley, Ed. Grand Central Terminal: Gateway to New York City. 2003. (Illus.). 48p. (J). 16.95 (978-1-59034-491-0(X)); pap. (978-1-59034-492-7(8)) Mondo Publishing.

GRAND CENTRAL TERMINAL (NEW YORK, N.Y.)—FICTION

Kalman, Maira. Next Stop, Grand Central. Kalman, Maira, illus. 2001. (Illus.). 40p. (J). (ps-3). pap. 6.99 (978-0-698-11888-1(X) , Putnam Juvenile) Penguin Group (USA) Inc.

—Next Stop Grand Central. 2001. (gr. 5-8). lib. bdg. 15.30 (978-0-613-35991-7(7)) Tandem Library Bks.

GRAND OPERA

see Opera

GRANDPARENTS

Ancona, George. Mis Abuelos/My Grandparents. 32p. (J). 2006. (SPA.). (gr. 1-3). pap. 8.95 (978-0-516-25495-1(2)); 2005. (ENG & SPA.). 21.00 (978-0-516-25294-0(1)) Scholastic Library Publishing. (Children's Pr.).

At My Grandfather's, 6 Pcks. (ps-2). 27.00 (978-0-7635-9435-0(0)) Rigby Education.

Auld, Mary. Mis Abuelos. 2004. (Conoce la Familia Ser.). (SPA., Illus.). 24p. (J). (gr. 1 up). lib. bdg. 20.67 (978-0-8368-3934-0(X)) Stevens, Gareth Inc.

—My Grandparents. 2004. (Meet the Family Ser.). (Illus.). 24p. (J). (gr. 1 up). lib. bdg. 20.67 (978-0-8368-3926-5(9)) Stevens, Gareth Inc.

Bailey, Debbie. La Abuela. Huszar, Susan, photos by. 2001. (Hablemos Ser.). (SPA., Illus.). 14p. (J). (gr. k-ps). bds. 5.95 (978-1-55037-706-4(X)) Annick Pr., Ltd. CAN. *Dist:* Firefly Bks., Ltd.

—El Abuelo. Huszar, Susan, photos by. 2001. (Hablemos Ser.). (SPA., Illus.). 14p. (J). (gr. k-ps). bds. 5.95 (978-1-55037-707-1(8)) Annick Pr., Ltd. CAN. *Dist:* Firefly Bks., Ltd.

Barbara, Diane & Beccaria, Dominique. Grandmother & Me: A Special Book for You & Your Grandmother to Fill in Together & Share with Each Other. 2004. (Illus.). 52p. (J). 16.95 (978-0-8109-4936-2(9)) Abrams, Harry N. , Inc.

Gizicki-Lipson, Coryn & Gizicki, Carlie. An Angel in the Sky. Gizicki-Lipson, Coryn, illus. 2003. (Illus.). 32p. (J). 14.95 (978-0-9740438-0-7(X)) In the Sky Publishing.

Gosselin, Kim. Allie Learns about Alzheimer's Disease: A Family Story about Love, Patience, & Acceptance. Dineen, Tom, illus. 2001. (Special Family & Friends: Vol. 1). 32p. (J). pap. 14.95 (978-1-891383-15-1(9)) JayJo Bks., LLC.

Grandfathers, 6 vols. (gr. k-2). 28.95 (978-0-7368-8268-2(5)) Red Brick Learning.

Grandmother. 2005. (Illus.). 64p. (978-0-7853-3349-4(5) , 3638300) Publications International, Ltd.

Grandmothers, 6 vols. (gr. k-2). 28.95 (978-0-7368-8269-9(3)) Red Brick Learning.

Kelly, Sheila M. Lots of Grandparents! Rotner, Shelley, photos by. 2001. (Contemporary Issues for Young Children Ser.). (Illus.). 32p. (gr. k-3). lib. bdg. 23.90 (978-0-7613-2313-6(9) , Millbrook Pr.) Lerner Publishing Group.

Lakin, Patricia. Grandparents: Around the World. 1999. (We All Share Ser.). (Illus.). 32p. (J). (gr. 3-6). 22.45 (978-1-56711-146-0(7) , Blackbirch Pr., Inc.) Thomson Gale.

McCain, John. Faith of Our Fathers. 2000. (gr. 7-12). lib. bdg. 23.45 (978-0-613-27819-5(4)) Tandem Library Bks.

McElroy, Lisa Tucker. Meeting Grandmother: She's a Supreme Court Justice. 2000. (Grandmothers at Work Ser.: 4). (Illus.). 32p. (J). (gr. 2-4). pap. 7.95 (978-0-7613-1386-1(9) , Millbrook Pr.) Lerner Publishing Group.

Moore-Mallinos, Jennifer. My Grandparents Are Special. 2006. (Let's Talk about It Bks.). (Illus.). 32p. (J). pap. 6.99 (978-0-7641-3507-1(4)) Barron's Educational Series, Inc.

—My Grandparents Are Special. Fabrega, Marta, illus. 2006. (Let's Talk about It Bks.). 32p. (J). pap. 6.99 (978-0-7641-3506-4(6)) Barron's Educational Series, Inc.

Morris, Ann. Grandma Francisca Remembers: A Hispanic-American Family Story. 2002. (Illus.). 32p. (J). (gr. 5 up). pap. 7.95 (978-0-7613-1733-3(3) , Millbrook Pr.) Lerner Publishing Group.

—Grandma Francisca Remembers: A Hispanic-American Family Story. Linenthal, Peter, photos by. 2001. (What Was It Like, Grandma? Ser.). (Illus.). 32p. (gr. k-3). lib. bdg. 22.90 (978-0-7613-2315-0(5) , Millbrook Pr.) Lerner Publishing Group.

—Grandma Hekmat Remembers: An Egyptian - American Family Story. Linenthal, Peter, illus. 2003. (What Was It Like, Grandma? Ser.). 32p. lib. bdg. 22.90 (978-0-7613-2864-3(5) , Millbrook Pr.) Lerner Publishing Group.

—Grandma Hekmat Remembers: An Egyptian - American Family Story. Linenthal, Peter, photos by. 2003. (Illus.). 32p. (J). (gr. 5 up). pap. 7.95 (978-0-7613-1944-3(1) , Millbrook Pr.) Lerner Publishing Group.

North, Merry. My Grandma & Me: A Picture, Play & Tote Book. 2004. 10p. (J). (ps up). bds. 5.99 (978-1-57151-724-1(3)) Playhouse Publishing.

Prince, Sarah. Grandpa's House. 1999. (ps-2). lib. bdg. 11.55 (978-0-613-30445-0(4)) Tandem Library Bks.

Richmond, Marianne R. It's Good to Be Grand. 2005. (Illus.). 40p. (YA). 7.95 (978-0-9770000-2-9(8)) Marianne Richmond Studios, Inc.

Robertson, J. Jean. Meet My Grandparents. 2007. (World Around Me Ser.). (Illus.). 24p. (J). (gr. k-2). lib. bdg. 21.35 (***978-1-59515-990-8(8)***) Rourke Publishing, LLC.

—Les Presento a MIS Abuelos. 2007. (SPA & ENG.). (J). (***978-1-60044-302-2(8)***) Rourke Publishing, LLC.

—Te Presento a MIS Abuelos. 2007. (ENG & SPA.). (J). (***978-1-60044-301-5(X)***) Rourke Publishing, LLC.

Rothburd, Allyson. Grandparents are Special. 2005. pap. 19.00 incl. audio compact disk (978-0-86647-221-0(5)); pap., tchr. ed. 24.00 incl. audio compact disk (978-0-86647-220-3(7)) Pro Lingua Assocs., Inc.

Rotner, Shelley & Kelly, Sheila M. Lots of Grandparents! 2003. (Single Titles Ser.: Vol. 3). (Illus.). 32p. (J). 7.95 (978-0-7613-1896-5(8) , Millbrook Pr.) Lerner Publishing Group.

Ruth, Angie. My Grandma: Early My Adventure. 2007. 44p. (J). 8.99 (978-1-59092-481-5(9) , Orchard Academy Pr.) Windstorm Creative.

—My Grandpa: Early My Adventure. 1999. 44p. (J). 8.99 (978-1-59092-482-2(7) , Orchard Academy Pr.) Windstorm Creative.

Schaefer, Lola M. Grandfathers. 2008. (J). (***978-1-4296-1225-8(8)*** , Pebble Bks.) Capstone Pr., Inc.

—Grandmothers. 2008. (J). (***978-1-4296-1226-5(6)*** , Pebble Bks.) Capstone Pr., Inc.

Sim, David & Rock, Lois. Cos You're My Grandma. 2001. (Illus.). 32p. 6.99 (978-0-7459-4544-6(9) , Lion) Lion Hudson plc GBR. *Dist:* Independent Pubs. Group.

Swainston, Jeani. Grandma Stuff: ... it's what love Is made Of. 2006. (J). (***978-0-9791384-0-9(X)***) Rock Cliff Media.

Thompson, Cheryl. Fun with Grandma: 99 Simple Ways to Spend Memory-Making Time with Your Grandchild. l.t. ed. 2002. 123p. per. 8.95 (978-1-931317-01-6(1)) Clarion Marketing Group, Inc.

Yaconelli, Mike. A Gift for My Grandchild. 2nd ed. 2002. (Illus.). 64p. (J). pap. 6.99 (978-0-7459-4788-4(3) , Lion) Lion Hudson plc GBR. *Dist:* Independent Pubs. Group.

GRANDPARENTS—FICTION

Abeele, Veronique van den. Still My Grandma. Dubois, Claude K., illus. 2007. 28p. (J). (ps-3). 16.00 (***978-0-8028-5323-3(4)*** , Eerdmans Bks For Young Readers) Eerdmans, William B. Publishing Co.

Aber, Linda Williams. Carrie Measures Up! Allen, Joy, illus. 2001. (Math Matters Ser.). 32p. (J). (gr. 1-3). pap. 4.95 (978-1-57565-100-2(9)) Kane Pr., The.

—Carrie Measures Up! 2001. (gr. k-3). lib. bdg. 12.95 (978-0-613-39301-0(5)); (Illus.). (J). 11.75 (978-0-606-20593-1(4)) Tandem Library Bks.

Abrahams, Peter. Into the Dark: An Echo Falls Mystery. 2008. (Echo Falls Ser.). 304p. (J). 15.99 (***978-0-06-073708-5(5)**); lib. bdg. 16.89 (***978-0-06-073709-2(3)***) HarperCollins Pubs. (Geringer, Laura Book).

Abreu, Raquel, illus. Little Ruth Reddingford (and the Wolf) An Old Tale retold by Hank Wesselman, PH. D. 2004. 32p. (J). per. 15.95 (978-0-9740190-0-0(3)) Illumination Arts Publishing Co., Inc.

Ackerman, Karen. By the Dawn's Early Light: Al Amanecer. 1999. (J). (978-0-606-15924-1(X)) Tandem Library Bks.

—Song & Dance Man. Gammell, Stephen, illus. 2002. (J). 14.79 (978-0-7587-4226-1(6)) Book Wholesalers, Inc.

—Song & Dance Man. Gammell, Stephen, illus. 2003. 32p. (J). (ps-2). 17.99 (978-0-394-99330-0(6)); 15.95 (978-0-394-89330-3(1)) Random Hse. Children's Bks. (Knopf Bks. for Young Readers).

Ada, Alma Flor. Celebrate Hannukah with Bubbe's Tales. Epelbaum, Mariano, illus. 2006. 31p. (J). (978-1-59820-134-5(4)) Santillana USA Publishing Co., Inc.

—The Golden Cage. 2000. (gr. k-3). lib. bdg. 17.60 (978-0-613-37387-2(0)) Tandem Library Bks.

—I Love Saturdays y Domingos. 1999. (SPA.). pap. 4.95 (978-0-689-80591-2(8) , Aladdin) Simon & Schuster Children's Publishing.

—I Love Saturdays y Domingos. Savadier, Elivia, illus. 2004. 32p. (J). reprint ed. pap. 6.99 (978-0-689-87409-3(X) , Aladdin) Simon & Schuster Children's Publishing.

—I Love Saturdays y Domingos. Savadier, Elivia, illus. 2004. 32p. (J). (ps-ps). lib. bdg. 14.19 (978-0-606-32672-8(3)) Tandem Library Bks.

—Me Encantan los Saturdays y los Domingos. Savadier, Elivia, illus. 2006. Tr. of I Love Saturdays y Domingos. (SPA.). (J). (gr. 1-2). 11.95 (978-1-59437-576-7(3) , AF33204) Santillana USA Publishing Co., Inc.

Ada, Alma Flor & Savadier, Elivia. I Love Saturdays y Domingos. 2002. (Illus.). 32p. (J). (gr. k-3). 17.99 (978-0-689-31819-1(7) , Atheneum) Simon & Schuster Children's Publishing.

Adams, H. J. The Song of the Blackbirds in the Reeds: In Which Great-Grandpa Nicholas Winslow Applewood Entertains Young Folk with Stories & Fables & Has Some Remarkable Betimes. Adams, Denise, illus. 1998. 168p. (J). lib. bdg. 20.00 (978-0-923687-48-9(3)) Celo Valley Bks.

Addy, Sharon. In Grandpa's Woods. Akins, Tamlyn, illus. 2004. (J). (*978-1-931599-42-9(4)* , Trails Bks.) Big Earth Publishing.

Adler, David A. Bones & the Birthday Mystery. Newman, Barbara Johansen, illus. 2007. (Jeffrey Bones Mystery Ser.: No. 5). 32p. (J). (gr. k). 13.99 (978-0-670-06164-8(6) , Viking Adult) Penguin Group (USA) Inc.

—Cam Jansen & the Birthday Mystery. Natti, Susanna, illus. 2000. (Cam Jansen Ser.: No. 20). 64p. (J). (gr. 3-7). 13.99 (978-0-670-88877-1(X) , Viking Juvenile) Penguin Group (USA) Inc.

The Adventures of Molly. 2004. pap. 13.95 (*978-1-59526-180-9(X)*) Media Creations, Inc.

Agell, Charlotte. Welcome Home or Someplace Like It. rev. ed. 2003. (Illus.). 240p. (J). 16.95 (978-0-8050-7083-5(4) , Holt, Henry & Co. Bks. For Young Readers) Holt, Henry & Co.

Alarid, Carilyn & Markel, Marilyn. Old Grandfather Teaches a Lesson: Mimbres Children Learn Respect. Alarid, Carilyn & Markel, Marilyn, illus. 2004. (Illus.). 116p. (J). pap. 16.95 (978-0-86534-418-1(3)) Sunstone Pr.

Alcantara, Ricardo. Mauro Ojos Brillantes. 9th ed. 2003. (SPA., Illus.). 48p. (978-84-236-2865-0(5) , ED6279) Edebé ESP. *Dist:* Lectorum Pubns., Inc.

Alcorn, Randy & Ben-Ami, Doran. Wait until Then. 2007. (Illus.). 32p. (J). 14.99 (978-1-4143-1041-1(2) , Tyndale Kids) Tyndale Hse. Pubs.

Alda, Arlene. Hurry Granny Annie. 2004. (Illus.). 32p. (J). 6.95 (978-1-58246-067-3(1) , Tricycle Pr.) Ten Speed Pr.

Alexander Greene, Alesia. A Mural for Mamita. Lara, Susana, tr. Teis, Kyra, illus. 2001. Tr. of Mural Para Mamita. (ENG & SPA.). (J). 8.95 (978-1-56123-154-6(1) , MFMC) Centering Corp.

Alexander, Marge. Adventures at the Grandparents' House. 2001. 96p. 9.99 (978-1-58169-064-4(9) , Evergreen Pr.) Genesis Communications, Inc.

Algeo, Kristie. When Daddy Comes Home. 2006. (ENG., Illus.). 36p. per. 21.99 (978-1-4141-0667-0(X)) Pleasant Word.

Alice-by-Accident Bound Galley. 2000. (J). (978-0-06-029056-6(0)) HarperCollins Pubs.

Allende, Isabel. El Bosque de los Pigmeos. 2005. Tr. of Forest of the Pygmies. (SPA.). 304p. pap. 7.99 (978-0-06-081619-3(8) , Rayo) HarperCollins Pubs.

—City of the Beasts. 2005. Tr. of Ciudad de las Bestias. 464p. (J). (gr. 7-17). pap. 7.99 (978-0-06-077645-9(5) , Rayo) HarperCollins Pubs.

—City of the Beasts. Peden, Margaret Sayers, tr. from SPA. 2002. Tr. of Ciudad de las Bestias. 416p. (J). (gr. 5 up). 19.99 (978-0-06-050918-7(X)) HarperCollins Pubs.

—City of the Beasts. l.t. ed. 2002. Tr. of Ciudad de las Bestias. 400p. (J). (gr. 5). pap. 19.99 (978-0-06-051195-1(8)) HarperCollins Pubs.

—City of the Beasts. Peden, Margaret Sayers, tr. from SPA. 2004. Tr. of Ciudad de las Bestias. 432p. (J). (gr. 5 up). reprint ed. pap. 7.99 (978-0-06-053503-2(2)) HarperCollins Pubs.

—City of the Beasts. 2004. Tr. of Ciudad de las Bestias. (gr. 5-8). lib. bdg. 16.45 (978-0-613-71427-3(X)) Tandem Library Bks.

—La Ciudad de las Bestias. 2003. (SPA.). (gr. 5-8). lib. bdg. 16.45 (978-0-613-83866-5(1)) Tandem Library Bks.

—Forest of the Pygmies. Peden, Margaret Sayers, tr. from SPA. 2005. 304p. (J). (gr. 5 up). 19.99 (978-0-06-076196-7(2) , Rayo) HarperCollins Pubs.

—Forest of the Pygmies. l.t. ed. 2005. 304p. (J). (gr. 5 up). pap. 19.99 (978-0-06-076200-1(4) , Rayo) HarperCollins Pubs.

Almond, David. Kit's Wilderness. l.t. ed. 2000. 263p. (J). pap. 16.95 (978-0-7540-6115-1(9) , Galaxy Children's Large Print) BBC Audiobooks America.

—Kit's Wilderness. unabr. ed. 2004. 240p. (J). (gr. 7 up). pap. 36.00 incl. audio (978-0-8072-8216-8(2) , Listening Library) Random Hse. Audio Publishing Group.

—Kit's Wilderness. (YA). (gr. 7). 2001. (Illus.). 256p. mass mkt. 5.99 (978-0-440-41605-0(1) , Laurel Leaf); 2000. 240p. 15.95 (978-0-385-32665-0(3) , Delacorte Bks. for Young Readers) Random Hse. Children's Bks.

—Kit's Wilderness. 2001. 229p. (YA). (gr. 8-12). lib. bdg. 13.00 (978-0-613-36836-0(3)); (978-0-606-22406-2(8)) Tandem Library Bks.

—Kit's Wilderness. l.t. ed. 2001. (Illus.). 272p. (J). (gr. 4-7). 22.95 (978-0-7862-2772-3(9)) Thorndike Pr.

Altman, Linda Jacobs. Singin' with Momma Lou. Johnson, Larry, illus. 2002. 32p. (J). (gr. 1-5). 16.95 (978-1-58430-040-3(X)) Lee & Low Bks., Inc.

Amateau, Gigi. Claiming Georgia Tate. 208p. (YA). (gr. 9). 2007. pap. 7.99 (*978-0-7636-3311-0(9)*); 2005. 15.99 (978-0-7636-2339-5(3)) Candlewick Pr.

Amato, Carol A. On the Trail of the Grizzly, Vol. 9. O'Brien, Patrick & Wenzel, David, illus. 1998. (Young Reader Ser.: No. 9). 48p. (J). (gr. 3-6). lib. bdg. 13.45 (978-1-56674-240-5(4)) Forest Hse. Publishing Co., Inc.

And Then it was Sugar, 6 vols. (Multicultural Programs Ser.). 16p. (gr. 1-6). 31.95 (978-0-7802-8324-4(4)) Wright Group, The.

Anderson, Carolyn D. Granny¿s Favorite Tales. Anderson, Carolyn D. et al, illus. 2006. 156p. (J). per. 39.95 (*978-1-60002-098-8(4)* , 3915, Airleaf Publishing) Airleaf Publishing & Bookselling.

Anderson, Laurie Halse. Time to Fly. 2003. (Wild at Heart Ser.). (Illus.). 113p. (J). (gr. 4 up). lib. bdg. 23.33 (978-0-8368-3262-4(0)) Stevens, Gareth Inc.

Andreae, Giles. Heaven Is Having You. Cabban, Vanessa, illus. (J). (ps-k). 2007. 24p. bds. 7.95 (*978-1-58925-820-4(7)*); 2002. 32p. tchr. ed. 15.95 (978-1-58925-016-1(8)) ME Media LLC. (tiger tales).

Angle, Kimberly Greene. Hummingbird. 2008. 256p. (J). 16.95 (*978-0-374-33376-8(9)*) Farrar, Straus & Giroux.

Anholt, Laurence. Seven for a Secret. Coplestone, Jim, illus. 2006. 36p. (J). 15.95 (978-1-84507-300-8(2)) Lincoln, Frances Ltd. GBR. *Dist:* Perseus Distribution.

Anna, Jennifer. Grandma's Button Box. 2006. (Trutle's Back Bks.). (Illus.). 50p. (Orig.). (J). (gr. k-4). pap. 14.99 (978-1-886383-36-4(7) , Little Blue Works) Windstorm Creative.

Ansley, Frank & Wheeler, Lisa. Who's Afraid of Granny Wolf? Ansley, Frank, tr. 2004. (Fitch & Chip Ser.). (Illus.). 48p. (J). 14.95 (978-0-689-84952-7(4) , Atheneum/Richard Jackson Bks.) Simon & Schuster Children's Publishing.

Appel, Cindy. The Best Christmas Gift. Collier, Kevin Scott, illus. 2005. (J). E-Book 6.00 incl. cd-rom (978-1-933090-19-1(7)) Guardian Angel Publishing, Inc.

Applegate, Katherine. The Buffalo Storm. Ormerod, Jan, illus. 2007. 32p. (J). (ps-3). 16.00 (978-0-618-53597-2(7) , Clarion Bks.) Houghton Mifflin Co. Trade & Reference Div.

Applegate, Stan. Natchez Under-the-Hill. Watling, James, illus. 1999. 186p. (J). (gr. 3-7). pap. 8.95 (978-1-56145-191-3(6) , 51916) Peachtree Pubs., Ltd.

—Natchez Under-the-Hill. 1999. (gr. 3-6). lib. bdg. 17.60 (978-0-613-46156-6(8)) Tandem Library Bks.

Appleton-Smith, Laura. It Is Halloween! Neel, Preston, illus. 1999. (Book to Remember Ser.). (J). (ps-3). pap. 8.95 (978-0-9658246-4-4(0) , Books To Remember) Flyleaf Publishing.

Argueta, Jorge. Talking with Mother Earth/Hablando con Madre Tierra: Poems/Poemas. Perez, Lucia Angela, illus. 2006. (ENG & SPA.). 32p. (J). 15.95 (978-0-88899-626-8(8)) Groundwood Bks. CAN. *Dist:* Perseus Distribution.

Arkin, Alan. One Present from Flekman's. Egielski, Richard, illus. 1999. 32p. (J). (gr. k-3). 15.95 (978-0-06-024530-6(1)) HarperCollins Pubs.

Armistead, John. The $66 Summer. 2000. (978-0-606-21752-1(5)) Tandem Library Bks.

—The $66 Summer: A Novel of the Segregated South. 2nd ed. 2006. (Milkweed Prize for Children's Literature Ser.). 240p. (J). reprint ed. pap. 6.95 (978-1-57131-663-9(9)) Milkweed Editions.

Arnold, Marsha Diane & Pelzel, Vernise Elaine. Hugs on the Wind. Warnick, Elsa, illus. 2006. 32p. (J). (ps-1). 15.95 (978-0-8109-5968-2(2)) Abrams, Harry N. , Inc.

Arnold, Tedd. There Was an Old Lady Who Swallowed Fly Guy. 2007. (Fly Guy Ser.). 32p. (J). pap. 5.99 (*978-0-439-63906-4(9)*) Scholastic, Inc.

Arnosky, Jim. Little Champ. Arnosky, Jim, illus. 2001. (J). pap. 6.95 (978-0-9657144-5-7(4)) Onion River Pr.

Asay, Colleen. What Happened to Grandpa's Hair? 2005. (J). per. 11.95 (978-0-9767658-0-6(2)) Calico Connection, Inc., The.

Ashcraft, Shelly & Hunter, Cheryl. Mamaw & the Girls. 2007. per. 10.99 (*978-1-59886-846-3(2)*) Tate Publishing & Enterprises, L.L.C.

Asher, Sandy. What a Party! Graves, Keith, illus. 2007. 32p. (J). (ps-1). 15.99 (978-0-399-24496-4(4) , Philomel) Penguin Group (USA) Inc.

Aumann, Jane & Ladage, Cindy. Tucker's Surprise. Craig, Christy, illus. 2000. 16p. (J). (ps-7). pap. 8.00 (978-0-9703319-0-8(8)) Roots & Wings.

Avery, Najiyyah. My Grandmother's House Plant. 1999. 16p. (J). (gr. k-6). pap. 7.00 (978-0-8059-4539-3(3)) Dorrance Publishing Co., Inc.

Babbitt, Natalie. Elsie Times Eight. Babbitt, Natalie, illus. 2005. (Illus.). 26p. (J). (gr. k-4). reprint ed. 16.00 (978-0-7567-9640-2(7)) DIANE Publishing Co.

Babbitt, Natalie. The Eyes of the Amaryllis. 2007. 144p. (J). pap. 6.99 (*978-0-312-37008-4(3)*) Square Fish.

Badart, Della. Two Coins. 2007. (Illus.). (J). per. 18.95 (978-0-9788985-2-6(4)) A Better Be Write Pub.

Badoe, Adwoa A. Nana's Cold Days. Junaid, Bushra, illus. 2002. 32p. (J). pap. 15.95 (978-0-88899-479-0(6)) Groundwood Bks. CAN. *Dist:* Transition Vendor.

Baggette, Susan K. Jonathan & Papa. Moriarty, William J., photos by. 1999. (Jonathan Adventures Ser.). (Illus.). 24p. (J). (ps-3). bds. 7.95 (978-0-9660172-7-4(7)) Brookfield Reader, Inc., The.

—Jonathan Goes to the Grocery Store. Moriarty, William J., photos by. 1998. (Jonathan Adventures Ser.). (Illus.). 16p. (J). (ps-k). bds. 5.95 (978-0-9660172-2-9(6)) Brookfield Reader, Inc., The.

—Jonathan Goes to the Library. Moriarty, William J., photos by. 1998. (Jonathan Adventures Ser.). (Illus.). 16p. (J). (ps-k). bds. 5.95 (978-0-9660172-3-6(4)) Brookfield Reader, Inc., The.

Bailey, Linda. When Addie Was Scared. ed. 2004. (Illus.). (J). (gr. k-3). spiral bd. (978-0-616-01535-3(6)); spiral bd. (978-0-616-01537-7(2)) Canadian National Institute for the Blind/Institut National Canadien pour les Aveugles.

—When Addie Was Scared. Bailey, Wendy, illus. unabr. ed. 2002. 32p. (J). (gr. k-3). (978-1-55337-163-2(1)) Kids Can Pr., Ltd.

Bair, Sheila. Rock, Brock, & the Savings Shock. Gott, Barry, illus. 2006. (Way I ACT Ser.). 32p. (J). 15.95 (978-0-8075-7094-4(X)) Whitman, Albert & Co.

Baker, Dierdre. Becca at Sea. 2007. 165p. (J). (gr. 3-7). 16.95 (*978-0-88899-737-1(X)*) Groundwood Bks. CAN. *Dist:* Perseus Distribution.

Balgassi, Haemi. Peacebound Trains. Soentpiet, Chris K., illus. 2000. 48p. (J). (gr. 4-6). 6.95 (978-0-618-04030-8(7) , Clarion Bks.) Houghton Mifflin Co. Trade & Reference Div.

Ballou, Kathy. The Tracks Out Back. l.t. ed. 2005. (Illus.). 24p. (J). per. 10.00 (978-1-932338-50-8(0)) Lifevest Publishing, Inc.

Banerjee, Anjali. Looking for Bapu. 2006. 176p. (J). (gr. 3-6). 15.95 (978-0-385-74657-1(1)); lib. bdg. 17.99 (978-0-385-90894-8(6)) Random Hse. Children's Bks. (Lamb, Wendy).

Banks, Lynne Reid. Alice-by-Accident. 2000. (Avon Camelot Bks.). 144p. (J). (gr. 4-7). 14.95 (978-0-380-97865-6(2)) HarperCollins Pubs.

Barad, Alexis & Pelizzari, Nora. What's in Grandma's Closet? Lyon, Tammie, illus. 2007. 16p. (J). (ps-3). 12.99 (978-0-06-088701-8(X) , Harper Festival) HarperCollins Pubs.

Barasch, Lynne. A Country Schoolhouse. 2004. (Illus.). 40p. (J). 16.00 (978-0-374-31577-1(9) , Farrar, Straus & Giroux (BYR)) Farrar, Straus & Giroux.

Barnes, Peter W. Little Miss Patriot: NFRW Edition. Barnes, Cheryl Shaw, illus. ed. 2007. 32p. (J). 17.95 (*978-1-893622-20-3(7)* , VSP Bks.) Vacation Spot Publishing.

Barnwell, Ysaye M. No Mirrors in My Nana's House. Saint James, Synthia, illus. 1998. 32p. (J). (gr. k-3). 18.00 (978-0-15-201825-2(5)) Harcourt Children's Bks.

—No Mirrors in My Nana's House: Musical CD & Book. Saint James, Synthia, illus. 2005. 32p. (J). reprint ed. 8.00 (978-0-15-205243-0(7) , Voyager Bks./Libros Viajeros) Harcourt Children's Bks.

Barra, Nancy. Natalia y Su Abuelita. Zuman, John, ed. Deming, Linda, illus. 2002. (Sunflower/Girasol Ser.). (SPA.). 20p. tchr. ed., spiral bd. 5.95 (978-1-58332-063-1(6)) Intercultural Center for Research in Education (I N C R E).

—Natalia y Su Abuelita. Deming, Linda, illus. 2002. (Sunflower/Girasol Ser.). (SPA.). 38p. (J). 5.95 (978-1-58332-062-4(8)) Intercultural Center for Research in Education (I N C R E).

Barrett, Judi. Pickles to Pittsburgh: The Sequel to Cloudy with A Chance of Meatballs. (Illus.). (J). 2005. pap. 16.95 incl. audio (978-0-87499-537-4(X)); 2005. pap. 18.95 incl. audio compact disk (978-1-59112-749-9(1)); 1999. (gr. 1-6). 25.95 incl. audio (978-0-87499-538-1(8)) Live Oak Media.

—Pickles to Pittsburgh: The Sequel to Cloudy with A Chance of Meatballs. Barrett, Ron, illus. 1999. 28.95 incl. audio compact disk (978-1-59112-750-5(5)); pap. 37.95 incl. audio (978-0-87499-539-8(6)); pap. 39.95 incl. audio compact disk (978-1-59112-751-2(3)) Live Oak Media.

—Pickles to Pittsburgh: The Sequel to Cloudy with A Chance of Meatballs. Barrett, Ron, illus. 2000. 32p. (J). (ps-3). pap. 6.99 (978-0-689-83929-0(4) , Aladdin) Simon & Schuster Children's Publishing.

—Pickles to Pittsburgh: The Sequel to Cloudy with A Chance of Meatballs. 2000. (J). (978-0-606-20089-9(4)); lib. bdg. 15.30 (978-0-613-30090-2(4)) Tandem Library Bks.

—Pickles to Pittsburgh & Cloudy with a Change of Meatballs. Barrett, Ron, illus. 1999. pap. 30.95 incl. audio (978-0-87499-819-1(0)); pap. 34.95 incl. audio compact disk (978-1-59112-842-7(0)) Live Oak Media.

Barron, T. A. Where is Grandpa? 2000. (978-0-606-22527-4(7)) Tandem Library Bks.

—Where Is Grandpa? Soentpiet, Chris K., illus. (J). (ps-3). 2001. 32p. pap. 6.99 (978-0-698-11904-8(5) , Putnam Juvenile); 2000. 1p. 16.99 (978-0-399-23037-0(8) , Philomel) Penguin Group (USA) Inc.

—Where Is Grandpa? Soentpiet, Chris K., illus. 2001. (J). (ps-3). lib. bdg. 15.30 (978-0-613-44431-6(0)) Tandem Library Bks.

Barwin, Gary. Grandpa's Snowman. Macaulay, Kitty, illus. 2000. 24p. (J). (ps-1). 17.95 (978-1-55037-635-7(7)); pap. 5.95 (978-1-55037-634-0(9)) Annick Pr., Ltd. CAN. *Dist:* Firefly Bks., Ltd.

—Grandpa's Snowman. 2000. (gr. k-3). lib. bdg. 14.10 (978-0-613-62770-2(9)) Tandem Library Bks.

Baskin, Nora Raleigh. The Truth about My Bat Mitzvah. 2008. 144p. (J). 15.99 (*978-1-4169-3558-2(4)* , Simon & Schuster Children's Publishing) Simon & Schuster Children's Publishing.

Basore, Polly M. Santa's Stray in A Piano for Christmas. Williams, Carlene H., illus. 2005. 32p. (J). per. (978-0-9771749-1-1(3)) AngelBooks.

Bateman, Teresa. April Foolishness. Westcott, Nadine Bernard, illus. 32p. (J). 2007. pap. 6.95 (*978-0-8075-0405-5(X)*); 2004. 16.95 (978-0-8075-0404-8(1)) Whitman, Albert & Co.

Bauer, Joan. Stand Tall. 2005. 192p. (YA). (gr. 5). pap. 7.99 (978-0-14-240427-0(6) , Puffin) Penguin Group (USA) Inc.

—Sticks. 192p. (YA). 2005. (Illus.). (gr. 5-7). pap. 7.99 (978-0-14-240428-7(4) , Puffin); 2002. 18.99 (978-0-399-23752-2(6) , Putnam Juvenile) Penguin Group (USA) Inc.

Bauer, Jutta. El Angel Del Abuelo. 2002. (Rosa y Manzana Ser.). (SPA., Illus.). 28p. (978-84-89804-49-4(4)) Loguez Ediciones ESP. *Dist:* Lectorum Pubns., Inc.

—Grandpa's Angel. Bauer, Jutta, illus. 2005. (Illus.). 48p. (J). (ps-ps). 12.99 (978-0-7636-2743-0(7)) Candlewick Pr.

Bauer, Marion Dane. The Blue Ghost. Wang, Suling, illus. 2006. (Stepping Stones Ser.). 96p. (J). (gr. 3-7). pap. 3.99 (978-0-375-83339-7(0) , Random Hse. Bks. for Young Readers) Random Hse. Children's Bks.

—The Blue Ghost. 2005. (Illus.). 96p. (J). (gr. 3-7). 11.95 (978-0-375-83179-9(7)); lib. bdg. 13.99 (978-0-375-93179-6(1)) Random Hse. Children's Bks. (Random Hse. Bks. for Young Readers).

—An Early Winter. 1999. (Illus.). 128p. (J). (gr. 5-9). tchr. ed. 15.00 (978-0-395-90372-8(6) , Clarion Bks.) Houghton Mifflin Co. Trade & Reference Div.

—An Early Winter. 2000. (YA). pap. 42.00 incl. audio (978-0-7887-4328-3(7) , 41123) Recorded Bks., LLC.

Bawden, Nina. Off the Road. 1998. (Illus.). 192p. (J). (gr. 5-9). 16.00 (978-0-395-91321-5(7) , Clarion Bks.) Houghton Mifflin Co. Trade & Reference Div.

—Off the Road. 2001. (J). (978-0-606-21364-6(3)); (gr. 5-8). lib. bdg. 14.15 (978-0-613-35993-1(3)) Tandem Library Bks.

Beamish, Diane. Grandma's Magic Button Necklace. 2006. 25p. 12.16 (978-1-4116-5487-7(0)) Lulu.com.

Beardshaw, Rosalind. Grandpa's Surprise. 2004. (Illus.). 32p. (J). (ps-2). 15.95 (978-1-58234-934-3(7) , Bloomsbury Children) Bloomsbury Publishing.

Bell, Mary Reeves. Sagebrush Rebellion. 1999. (Passport to Danger Ser.: Vol. 2). 208p. (YA). (gr. 7-12). pap. 5.99 (978-1-55661-550-4(7)) Bethany Hse. Pubs.

—Sagebrush Rebellion. 1999. (J). (978-0-606-18973-6(4)) Tandem Library Bks.

Bell, Ossie S. When Grandma Is Not Grandma: Alzheimer's Steals Family's Treasures. 2006. 51p. pap. 12.95 (978-1-4241-2920-1(6)) PublishAmerica, Inc.

Bellante, V. I Did It Myself. (Illus.). 29p. (J). (978-1-85863-502-6(0)) Minerva Pr. GBR. *Dist:* Unity Distribution.

Belton, Sandra. Beauty, Her Basket. Cabrera, Cozbi A., illus. 2004. 32p. (J). 15.99 (978-0-688-17821-5(9)); lib. bdg. 16.89 (978-0-688-17822-2(7)) HarperCollins Pubs.

Bencastro, Mario. A Promise to Keep. Giersbach-Rascon, Susan, tr. from SPA. 2005. 134p. (J). (gr. 3-7). pap. 9.95 (978-1-55885-457-4(6) , Piñata Books) Arte Publico Pr.

—Viaje a la Tierra del Abuelo. 2004. (SPA.). 144p. pap. 9.95 (978-1-55885-404-8(5) , Piñata Books) Arte Publico Pr.

Bender, Esther. Search for a Fawn. Bender, Edna, illus. 1998. 32p. (J). (gr. k-5). pap. 8.99 (978-0-8361-9099-1(8)) Herald Pr.

Benedetti, Marie. Fishing with Grandpapa: The Most Important Rules. 2007. (J). per. 8.99 (*978-1-59886-975-0(2)*) Tate Publishing & Enterprises, L.L.C.

Bennett, W. J., Jr. Sydney & Garrett's Great Arkansas Adventury. 2005. (J). pap. (*978-0-9794044-6-7(0)*) Archeological Assessments, Inc.

Benson, Judith. The Noise in Grandma's Attic. 2005. (Illus.). 48p. (J). 4.95 (978-1-895836-55-4(7)) River Bks. CAN. *Dist:* Fitzhenry & Whiteside, Ltd.

Bercowetz, Cynthia. Grandpa Herman¿s Petting Zoo. 2007. (Illus.). 48p. (J). per. 14.95 (*978-0-9708430-9-8(7)*) Uitti, Daniel.

Bernstein, Susan H. N. E. Pominonous Epstein & Change. l.t. ed. 2003. (E. Pominonous Epstein Ser.: No. 3). (Illus.). 20p. (Orig.). (J). (gr. k-3). pap. 8.95 (978-0-9706596-2-0(8)) Bernstein, Susan.

Besson, Luc. Arthur & the Forbidden City. (Illus.). 192p. (J). 2006. pap. 5.99 (978-0-06-059628-6(7) , Harper Trophy); 2005. 15.99 (978-0-06-059626-2(0)); 2005. lib. bdg. 16.89 (978-0-06-059627-9(9)) HarperCollins Pubs.

Best, Cari. Three Cheers for Catherine the Great! 2003. (gr. k-3). lib. bdg. 15.25 (978-0-613-71883-7(6)) Tandem Library Bks.

—When Catherine the Great & I Were Eight! Potter, Giselle, illus. 2003. 32p. (J). (gr. k-3). 16.00 (978-0-374-39954-2(9) , Farrar, Straus & Giroux (BYR)) Farrar, Straus & Giroux.

Best, Cari & Potter, Giselle. Three Cheers for Catherine the Great! 2003. (Illus.). 32p. (J). pap. 6.95 (978-0-374-47551-2(2) , Sunburst) Farrar, Straus & Giroux.

The Big Rain. 2003. (Illus.). 32p. (J). mass mkt. (978-0-9740599-2-1(7) , 3) Omnibus Publishing.

Birdseye, Tom. A Tough Nut to Crack. 2006. 128p. (J). (gr. 3-7). 16.95 (978-0-8234-1967-8(3)) Holiday Hse., Inc.

Bishop, Mary Harelkin. Tunnels of Tyranny: A Fourth Moose Jaw Adventure. 2005. (Juvenile Novel, Ser.). 312p. (J). (gr. 4-6). pap. 7.95 (978-1-55050-316-6(2)) Coteau Bks. CAN. *Dist:* Fitzhenry & Whiteside, Ltd.

Bjornson, Nancy. Llamas, Ponies & Pyrite. 2007. (J). (*978-1-930596-82-5(0)*) Amherst Pr.

Black, Frank M. Grandma Always Knows What to Do for Me. Moses, Robin, illus. 1999. (J). pap. (978-1-929157-06-8(1)) Inside-OUT Corp.

—Grandpa Knows Everyone. Moses, Robin, illus. 1999. (J). pap. (978-1-929157-07-5(X)) Inside-OUT Corp.

Black, Sonia W. Jumping the Broom. Wright and Hu, Cornelius Van and Ying-Hwa, illus. 2004. 32p. (J). lib. bdg. 15.00 (*978-1-4242-0234-8(5)*) Fitzgerald Bks.

Blackstone, Stella. My Granny Went to Market: A Round-the-World Counting Rhyme. Corr, Christopher, illus. 2005. 24p. (J). 16.99 (978-1-84148-792-2(9)) Barefoot Bks., Inc.

Blake, Edna L. & Boatwright, Edith. Grandma & her Amazing Colt, Dripper! Allen, Kathy, illus. 2005. 50p. (J). 12.00 (978-0-9668906-3-1(9)) Blake, Edna.

Blakeslee, Ann R. Summer Battles. 2000. (Illus.). 128p. (YA). (gr. 5-9). 14.95 (978-0-7614-5064-1(5) , Cavendish Children's Bks.) Cavendish, Marshall Corp.

Blomberg, Dianne L. Sam & Gram & the First Day of School. Ulrich, George, illus. 1999. 32p. (J). (ps-1). (978-1-55798-562-0(6) , 441-5626, Magination Pr.) American Psychological Assn.

Bobic, Marilyn Kay. My Nana My Special Friend. 2006. (J). per. 15.95 (978-0-9748426-9-1(9)) Accent Pubns.

Bodalski, Gerard S. Lucy's Legacy. 2004. 137p. pap. 19.95 (978-1-4137-4692-1(6)) PublishAmerica, Inc.

Boelts, Maribeth. Sarah's Grandma Goes to Heaven: A Book about Grief. Bladholm, Cheri, illus. 2004. (Helping Kids Heal Ser.). 32p. (J). 9.99 (978-0-310-70656-4(4)) Zonderkidz.

Boelts, Maribeth. Those Shoes. Jones, Noah Z., illus. 2007. 40p. (J). (gr. k-3). 15.99 (***978-0-7636-2499-6(3)***) Candlewick Pr.

Bogart, JoEllen. Tomas Aprende a Leer. Fernandez, Laura & Jacobson, Rick, illus. 1998. (SPA.). 40p. (J). (gr. 1-3). 13.56 (978-84-261-3066-2(6)) Juventud, Editorial ESP. *Dist:* Lectorum Pubns., Inc.

Bongiorno, Patti Lynn. Grandma, Does God Make Mistakes? 2nd ed. 2001. (J). spiral bd. 20.00 (978-0-9715819-3-7(2)) Bongiorno Bks.

Boonstra, Jean Elizabeth. Song for Grandfather A: Sarah 1842-1844. 2002. 95p. (J). (978-0-8163-1873-5(5)) Pacific Pr. Publishing Assn.

Booth-Cartwright, Karan. A Grandma's Love. 1999. (Illus.). 30p. (J). (ps-6). 22.95 (978-1-929819-00-3(5)) A+ Bk. Publishing.

Booth, David. The Dust Bowl. Reczuch, Karen, illus. 2002. 32p. (J). (gr. k-3). (978-1-55074-746-1(0)) Kids Can Pr., Ltd.

Bootman, Colin. Fish for the Grand Lady. Bootman, Colin, illus. 2006. (Illus.). 32p. (J). 16.95 (978-0-8234-1898-5(7)) Holiday Hse., Inc.

Borders, Christine Kareem. Gram Makes a House Call. Borders, Christine Kareem, illus. 1999. (Illus.). 77p. (J). (gr. 2-4). pap. 5.95 (978-0-9671160-0-6(7)) Greenhills Pr.

Bosak, Susan V. Para Que No Me Olvides. McGraw, Laurie, illus. (SPA.). 30p. (J). (gr. 3-5). 15.95 (978-1-58105-446-0(7)) Santillana USA Publishing Co., Inc.

—Something to Remember Me By: A Story about Love & Legacies. McGaw, Laurie, illus. 2003. 32p. (gr. 1-6). (978-1-896232-01-0(9) , TCP Pr.) Communication Project, The.

Boston, Lucy M. Children of Green Knowe. 2002. (gr. 3-6). lib. bdg. 14.15 (978-0-613-54457-3(9)) Tandem Library Bks.

—Enemy at Green Knowe. 2002. (gr. 3-6). lib. bdg. 14.15 (978-0-613-54436-8(6)) Tandem Library Bks.

—Stranger at Green Knowe. 2002. (gr. 3-6). lib. bdg. 14.15 (978-0-613-54691-1(1)) Tandem Library Bks.

Bouchard, Dave. The Song Within My Heart. Sapp, Allen, illus. 2003. 32p. (J). (gr. 2 up). 16.95 (978-1-55192-559-2(1)) Raincoast Bk. Distribution CAN. *Dist:* Perseus Distribution.

Bouchard, David. Nokum Was My Teacher. Sapp, Allen, illus. 2007. (CRE & ENG.). 32p. 21.95 incl. audio compact disk (***978-0-88995-367-3(8)***) Red Deer Pr. CAN. *Dist:* Fitzhenry & Whiteside, Ltd.

Bourgeois, Paulette. Oma's Quilt. ed. 2004. (Illus.). (J). (gr. k-3). spiral bd. (978-0-616-11099-7(5)); spiral bd. (978-0-616-11100-0(2)) Canadian National Institute for the Blind/Institut National Canadien pour les Aveugles.

—Oma's Quilt. Jorisch, Stephane, illus. 32p. (J). (gr. k-3). 2003. (978-1-55337-625-5(0)); 2001. (978-1-55074-777-5(0)) Kids Can Pr., Ltd.

—Postal Workers. LaFave, Kim, illus. 2005. 32p. (J). lib. bdg. 15.38 (***978-1-4242-1192-0(1)***) Fitzgerald Bks.

Bourgeois, Paulette. El Principe y el Mendigo. Jorisch, Stephane, illus. 2004. (SPA.). (J). 14.99 (978-84-241-8644-9(3)) Everest de Ediciones y Distribucion, S.L. ESP. *Dist:* Lectorum Pubns., Inc.

Bow, Patricia. The Ruby Kingdom. 2007. 256p. (J). pap. 12.99 (***978-1-55002-667-2(4)*** , Boardwalk Bks.) Dundurn Group, The CAN. *Dist:* Univ. of Toronto Pr.

Bowen, Anne. When You Visit Grandma & Grandpa. Bogacki, Tomasz, tr. Bogacki, Tomasz, illus. 2004. (Carolrhoda Picture Books Ser.). 32p. (J). (ps-3). 15.95 (978-1-57505-610-4(0)) Lerner Publishing Group.

Bowen, Anne M. I Loved You Before You Were Born. Shed, Greg, illus. 32p. (J). (ps-3). 2001. 16.99 (978-0-06-028720-7(9)); 2004. reprint ed. pap. 6.99 (978-0-06-443631-1(4)) HarperCollins Pubs.

—I Loved You Before You Were Born. 2004. (gr. 3-6). lib. bdg. 14.15 (978-0-613-81977-0(2)) Tandem Library Bks.

Bowler, Tim. River Boy. l.t. ed. 2003. (Read-Along Ser.). (Illus.). (J). pap. 29.95 incl. audio (978-0-7540-6214-1(7) , Galaxy Children's Large Print) BBC Audiobooks America.

—River Boy. 2002. (Illus.). 160p. (YA). mass mkt. 4.99 (978-0-689-84804-9(8) , Simon Pulse) Simon & Schuster Children's Publishing.

—River Boy. 2002. (gr. 5-8). lib. bdg. 13.00 (978-0-613-67116-3(3)) Tandem Library Bks.

—River Boy. l.t. ed. 2001. 190p. (J). 22.95 (978-0-7862-3507-0(1)) Thorndike Pr.

Bowman, Andy. The Quilt. Travis, Stephanie, illus. 25p. (J). (gr. 1-6). pap. 6.95 (978-1-931650-04-5(7)); lib. bdg. 14.95 (978-1-931650-05-2(5)) Coastal Publishing Carolina, Inc.

Bowman, Crystal. Windmills & Woodenshoes. Tanis, Joel E., illus. 1999. 40p. (J). (gr. 2-6). 15.00 (978-0-9636050-2-3(X)) Cygnet Publishing Co.

Bowman, Winnie. Grandma's Magic Carpet. 2002. per. 6.95 (978-1-891429-48-4(5)) Armadillo Publishing Corp.

Boyd, Dee. Only the Stars. Rich, Anna, illus. 2004. 32p. (J). lib. bdg. 15.00 (***978-1-4242-0230-0(2)***) Fitzgerald Bks.

Boyden, Linda. The Blue Roses. Cordova, Amy, illus. 2002. 32p. (J). (gr. 1-5). 16.95 (978-1-58430-037-3(X)) Lee & Low Bks., Inc.

Bradman, Tony. Flora the Fairy. 2005. (Green Bananas Ser.). (Illus.). 48p. (J). (ps). pap. (978-0-7787-1038-7(6)) Crabtree Publishing Co.

—Look Out, He's Behind You! Chamberlain, Margaret, illus. 2007. 28p. (J). 7.95 (***978-1-84507-734-1(2)***) Lincoln, Frances Ltd. GBR. *Dist:* Perseus Distribution.

Bradman, Tony. The Surprise Party. 2005. (Red Bananas Ser.). (Illus.). 48p. (J). (ps). pap. (978-0-7787-1084-4(X)) Crabtree Publishing Co.

Brammer, Ethriam Cash. The Rowdy, Rowdy Ranch / Alla en el Rancho Grande. Cruz, D. Nina, illus. (ENG & SPA.). 32p. 15.95 (978-1-55885-409-3(6) , Piñata Books) Arte Publico Pr.

Bray, Jeannine D. How My Grandmother Sees. Kenyatta, Imani, ed. Mitchell, Denise B., illus. 1998. 64p. (J). (gr. k-6). 14.95 (978-1-886580-39-8(1)) Pinnacle-Syatt Pubns.

Bredsdorff, Bodil. The Crow-Girl: The Children of Crow Cove. Ingwersen, Faith, tr. from DAN. 160p. (J). 2004. (Illus.). 16.00 (978-0-374-31247-3(8)); 2006. reprint ed. pap. 5.95 (978-0-374-40003-3(2)) Farrar, Straus & Giroux. (Farrar, Straus & Giroux (BYR)).

Brekke, Nancy Rose. But Grandma Didn't Mind. 2005. (Illus.). (J). (978-0-9766264-0-4(3)) Raven Productions, Inc.

—But That's OK with Grandpa. 2005. (Illus.). (J). (978-0-9766264-1-1(1)) Raven Productions, Inc.

Brennan, Kevin. Jimmy Jammers/Jaimito Pijama. Raven Tree Press, L. L. C., ed. de la Vega, Eida, tr. Driessen, Elizabeth, illus. 2002. Tr. of Jaimito Pijama. (SPA & ENG.). 32p. (J). (gr. k-3). 16.95 (978-0-9701107-9-4(0) , 626999) Raven Tree Pr.

Brennan, Martin. I Saw It in the Garden. Monroe, Michael Glenn, illus. 2006. 32p. (J). 17.95 (978-1-58726-296-8(7) , Mitten Pr.) Ann Arbor Media Group, LLC.

Brett, Jan. On Noah's Ark. 2003. (Illus.). 32p. (J). (ps-3). 16.99 (978-0-399-24028-7(4) , Putnam Juvenile) Penguin Group (USA) Inc.

Brian, Janeen. In a Pickle. 1999. (gr. 3-6). lib. bdg. 12.60 (978-0-613-19376-4(8)) Tandem Library Bks.

Brimner, Larry Dane. Nana's Fiddle. Miller, Susan, illus. 2002. (Rookie Reader Ser.). 32p. (J). (gr. 1-2). 19.50 (978-0-516-22373-5(9) , Children's Pr.) Scholastic Library Publishing.

—Nana's Fiddle. 2002. (gr. k-3). lib. bdg. 12.95 (978-0-613-59521-6(1)) Tandem Library Bks.

—Nana's Hog. Miller, Susan, illus. (Rookie Reader Skill Set Ser.). 32p. (J). 1999. (gr. k-2). pap. 4.95 (978-0-516-26412-7(5)); 1998. (gr. 1-2). 19.50 (978-0-516-20755-1(5)) Scholastic Library Publishing. (Children's Pr.).

—Sammy's Something Sweet. Petelinsek, Kathleen, illus. 2005. (Magic Door to Learning Ser.). 24p. (J). (ps-3). 21.36 (978-1-59296-533-5(4)) Child's World, Inc.

Bringing the Sea Back Home: Individual Title Six-Packs. (Literatura 2000 Ser.). (gr. 2-3). 33.00 (978-0-7635-0218-8(9)) Rigby Education.

Brink, Hazel. The Runaway Little Red Lawnmower. 2005. 32p. (J). 15.95 (978-1-931945-46-2(2)) Expert Publishing, Inc.

Broderick, Damien. Time Zones. 2005. (Thrillogy Ser.). (Illus.). 48p. (gr. 4-8). 17.50 (978-0-7910-8870-8(7)) Facts On File, Inc.

Brodeur, Tom. Regina Silsby's Phantom Militia. 2005. (Illus.). 267p. (J). (ps-7). 7.49 (978-1-59166-385-0(7)) Jones, Bob Univ. Pr.

Bronson, Wilfrid S. Pinto's Journey. 2007. (J). pap. (***978-0-86534-557-7(0)***) Sunstone Pr.

Brooke, Lauren. Heartland: From This Day On. 19th ed. 2005. (Heartland Ser.). 160p. (J). mass mkt. 4.99 (978-0-439-65367-1(3)) Scholastic, Inc.

Brooks, Bruce. Prince. 1998. (Wolfbay Wings Ser.: No. 5). (Illus.). 144p. (J). (gr. 4-7). pap. 4.50 (978-0-06-440600-0(8)) HarperCollins Pubs.

—Prince. 1998. (Wolfbay Wings Ser.: No. 5). (J). (gr. 4-7). (978-0-606-13925-0(7)) Tandem Library Bks.

Brown, Cathy. The World's Most Forgotten Grandmother, Granny Goose. Island, Sylvester, Jr., illus. 1998. (J). (ps-4). 10.95 (978-1-892089-55-7(6)); pap. 5.95 (978-1-892089-52-6(1)) Our Kids Pubn., Inc.

Brown, Erik, illus. Just Like Grandma. 2006. 14p. (J). bds. 6.95 (978-1-4027-3061-0(6) , 1252296) Sterling Publishing Co., Inc.

—Just Like Grandpa. 2006. 14p. (J). bds. 6.95 (978-1-4027-3062-7(4)) Sterling Publishing Co., Inc.

Brown, Monica & Ventura, Gabriela Baeza. Butterflies on Carmen Street/Mariposas en la Calle Carmen. Ward, April, illus. 2007. (SPA & ENG.). 32p. (J). (ps-4). 15.95 (***978-1-55885-484-0(3)*** , Piñata Books) Arte Publico Pr.

Brown, Ruth. Night Time Tale. 2005. (Illus.). 32p. (J). 19.99 (***978-1-84270-344-1(7)***) Transworld Publishers Ltd. GBR. *Dist:* Independent Pubs. Group.

Browne, Anthony. Into the Forest. Browne, Anthony, illus. 2004. (Illus.). 32p. (J). (gr. k-3). 16.99 (978-0-7636-2511-5(6)) Candlewick Pr.

Broyles, Beverly Ashley, illus. Grandmother's Alligator/ Burukenge Wa Nyanya Activity Guide. 2005. (ENG & SWA.). (J). 12.95 (978-0-9703632-7-5(3)) Wakefield Connection, The.

Bruce, Wendy, illus. Grandfather's Ship, The S. S. "United States" 2000. 50p. (J). (gr. 3-5). (978-0-9701870-0-0(9)) Fletcher, Elizabeth Byrd.

Brunett, Rita Ortiz. Actividad de la Abuela. 1999. (SPA.). 24p. (J). pap. 5.95 (978-1-56758-088-4(2)) Editorial Cultural, Inc.

—Cuentos y Aventuras de la Abuela II. 1998. (SPA.). 56p. (J). pap. 15.95 (978-1-56758-071-6(8)) Editorial Cultural, Inc.

Buckley, Helen. Grandfather & I. 2000. (ps-2). lib. bdg. 14.10 (978-0-613-28503-2(4)) Tandem Library Bks.

—Grandmother & I. 2000. (ps-2). lib. bdg. 14.10 (978-0-613-28504-9(2)) Tandem Library Bks.

Buckley, Helen E. Grandfather & I. Ormerod, Jan, illus. 2000. 24p. (J). (ps-3). pap. 6.99 (978-0-688-17526-9(0) , Harper Trophy) HarperCollins Pubs.

—Grandmother & I. Ormerod, Jan, illus. 2000. 24p. (J). (ps-3). pap. 6.99 (978-0-688-17525-2(2) , Harper Trophy) HarperCollins Pubs.

Buckley, Michael. The Fairy Tale Detectives. Ferguson, Peter, illus. 2007. (Sisters Grimm Ser.: Bk. 1). 312p. (J). (gr. 2-8). pap. 5.95 (***978-0-8109-9322-8(8)*** , Amulet Bks.) Abrams, Harry N. , Inc.

—The Problem Child. Ferguson, Peter, illus. (Sisters Grimm Ser.: Bk. 3). 320p. (gr. 3-7). 2007. (YA). pap. 5.95 (***978-0-8109-9359-4(7));*** 2006. (J). 14.95 (978-0-8109-4914-0(8) , Amulet Bks.) Abrams, Harry N. , Inc.

—The Unusual Suspects. Ferguson, Peter, illus. 2007. (Sisters Grimm Ser.: Bk. 2). 320p. (J). (gr. 2-8). pap. 5.95 (***978-0-8109-9323-5(6)*** , Amulet Bks.) Abrams, Harry N. , Inc.

Buckley, Ray. Christmas Moccasins. Buckley, Ray, illus. 2003. (Illus.). 32p. 18.00 (978-0-687-02738-5(1)) Abingdon Pr.

Buffie, Margaret. Who Is Frances Rain? 20th ed. 2007. 184p. pap. (***978-1-55453-209-4(4)***) Kids Can Pr., Ltd.

Bumpus, Gloria. Violee: Legend of Where the Crow's Foot Grows. 2004. 48p. pap. 12.95 (978-1-4137-4983-0(6)) PublishAmerica, Inc.

Bunge, Daniela. The Scarves. Bishop, Kathryn, tr. from GER. Bunge, Daniela, illus. 2006. (Illus.). 32p. (J). (ps-3). 16.99 (978-0-698-40045-0(3) , Minedition) Penguin Group (USA) Inc.

Bunting, Eve. The Butterfly House. Shed, Greg, illus. 1999. 32p. (J). (gr. k-3). pap. 16.95 (978-0-590-84884-8(4)) Scholastic, Inc.

—The Day Before Christmas. 2000. (gr. k-3). lib. bdg. 14.10 (978-0-613-29920-6(5)) Tandem Library Bks.

—The Days of Summer. Low, William, illus. 2001. 40p. (J). (gr. k-3). 16.00 (978-0-15-201840-5(9)) Harcourt Children's Bks.

—A Day's Work. 2002. (Illus.). (J). 13.79 (978-0-7587-2361-1(X)) Book Wholesalers, Inc.

—My Backpack. Cocca-Leffler, Maryann, illus. 2005. 32p. (J). (ps-ps). pap. 9.95 (978-1-59078-369-6(7)) Boyds Mills Pr.

—So Far from the Sea. Soentpiet, Chris K., illus. 1998. 32p. (J). (gr. 4-6). tchr. ed. 16.00 (978-0-395-72095-0(8) , Clarion Bks.) Houghton Mifflin Co. Trade & Reference Div.

—Sunshine Home. De Groat, Diane, illus. 2005. 32p. (J). (gr. k-3). pap. 5.95 (978-0-618-55157-6(3) , Clarion Bks.) Houghton Mifflin Co. Trade & Reference Div.

Burnett, Frances Hodgson. Little Lord Fauntleroy. 2004. (Aladdin Classics Ser.). 288p. (J). pap. 4.99 (978-0-689-86994-5(0) , Aladdin) Simon & Schuster Children's Publishing.

—Little Lord Fauntleroy. Howell, Troy, illus. 2008. (Classic Starts Ser.). 160p. (J). 5.95 (***978-1-4027-4578-2(8)***) Sterling Publishing Co., Inc.

—Little Lord Fauntleroy. unabr. ed. 2002. (Dover Evergreen Classics Ser.). (Illus.). 176p. (J). (gr. 4-7). pap. 2.50 (978-0-486-42368-5(9)) Dover Pubns., Inc.

—Little Lord Fauntleroy Book & Charm. 2004. (Charming Classics). (Illus.). 240p. (J). pap. 6.99 (978-0-06-055990-8(X) , Harper Festival) HarperCollins Pubs.

Burningham, John. Granpa. 2004. (Illus.). 32p. pap. 8.99 (978-0-09-943408-5(3) , Red Fox) Random Hse. Children's Bks. GBR. *Dist:* Trafalgar Square Publishing.

Burrowes, Adjoa J. Grandma's Purple Flowers. ed. 2004. (J). (gr. k-3). spiral bd. (978-0-616-07252-3(X)); spiral bd. (978-0-616-08496-0(X)) Canadian National Institute for the Blind/Institut National Canadien pour les Aveugles.

—Grandma's Purple Flowers. 2000. (Illus.). 32p. (J). (ps-3). 15.95 (978-1-880000-73-1(3)) Lee & Low Bks., Inc.

Busse, Sarah Martin & Martin, Jacqueline Briggs. Banjo Granny. Root, Barry, illus. 2006. 32p. (J). (ps-k). 16.00 (978-0-618-33603-6(6)) Houghton Mifflin Co.

Butcher, Kristin. Gramma War. 2001. (gr. 3-6). lib. bdg. 15.25 (978-0-613-45662-3(9)) Tandem Library Bks.

Butterworth, MyLinda. The Monster Run. Day, Linda S., ed. Mercer, Matthew, illus. l.t. ed. 2004. 32p. (J). (ps-3). 14.95 (978-1-890905-23-1(2)) Day to Day Enterprises.

Butterworth, Nick. My Grandma Is Wonderful. Butterworth, Nick, illus. 2003. (My Relative Series Ser.). (Illus.). 32p. (J). (ps-3). 5.99 (978-0-7636-2051-6(3)) Candlewick Pr.

—My Grandpa Is Amazing. Butterworth, Nick, illus. 2003. (My Relative Ser.). (Illus.). 32p. (J). (ps-3). 5.99 (978-0-7636-2057-8(2)) Candlewick Pr.

Byars, Betsy. A Blossom Promise. (Blossom Ser.). (J). (gr. 4-6). 145p. pap. 4.50 (978-0-8072-1444-2(2)); Set. 2000. pap. 29.00 incl. audio (978-0-8072-7322-7(8) , YA826SP) Random Hse. Audio Publishing Group. (Listening Library).

—La Casa de las Alas. (SPA., Illus.). (YA). (gr. 5-8). pap. (978-84-406-0861-1(6) , EB3416) Ediciones B ESP. *Dist:* Lectorum Pubns., Inc.

Byrd, Sandra. Island Girl. 2005. (Friends for A Season Ser.). 240p. (J). reprint ed. pap. 10.99 (978-0-7642-0020-5(8)) Bethany Hse. Pubs.

Caldwell, V. M. The Ocean Within. Magnus, Erica, illus. 1999. (Milkweed Prize for Children's Literature Ser.). 236p. (J). (gr. 3-8). pap. 6.95 (978-1-57131-624-0(8)) Milkweed Editions.

—The Ocean Within. 1999. (J). (gr. 3-9). (978-0-606-19035-0(X)) Tandem Library Bks.

Cali, Davide. Piano Piano. Rivers, Randi, tr. from FRE. Héliot, Eric, illus. 2007. 28p. (J). (gr. 1-3). 15.95 (***978-1-58089-191-2(8)***) Charlesbridge Publishing, Inc.

Callahan, Sean. The Bear Hug. Bryant, Laura, illus. 2006. 24p. (J). 15.95 (978-0-8075-0596-0(X)) Whitman, Albert & Co.

Cameron, Ann. El Lugar Mas Bonito del Mundo. 2000. (SPA., Illus.). 72p. (J). (ps-3). 15.95 (978-84-204-4449-9(9)) Aguilar, S. A. de Ediciones-Grupo Santillana ESP. *Dist:* Santillana USA Publishing Co., Inc.

—El Lugar Mas Bonito del Mundo. Alonso, Juan Ramon, illus. 2003. (SPA.). 70p. (J). (gr. 3-5). pap. 10.95 (978-968-19-0402-9(8)) Santillana USA Publishing Co., Inc.

Campbell, Tara. The Boy Who Called Heaven. 2006. pap. 32.49 (***978-1-4208-5456-5(9)***) AuthorHouse.

Canales, Viola. Orange Candy Slices & Other Secret Tales. 2001. 128p. (YA). pap. 9.95 (978-1-55885-332-4(4) , Piñata Books) Arte Publico Pr.

Capdevila, Roser. Grandparents! Fournier le Ray, Anne-Laure, illus. 2003. 40p. (J). 10.95 (978-1-929132-46-1(8)) Kane/Miller Bk. Pubs., Inc.

Caplin, Daniel. Grandfather Turtle. 2003. pap. 14.95 (978-0-9726781-0-0(7)) Evening Sun Pr.

Cappucceto Rosso. 1999. Tr. of Little Red Riding Hood. (ITA., Illus.). 24p. (J). (ps-5). pap. 7.95 (978-88-8148-254-2(1)) European Language Institute ITA. *Dist:* Distribooks, Inc., Midwest European Pubns.

Cappuccetto Rosso. pap. 14.95 (978-88-04-44204-2(2)) Mondadori ITA. *Dist:* Distribooks, Inc.

Caraballo, Samuel. Mis abuelos y yo / My Grandparents & I. Brammer, Ethriam Cash, tr. Cruz, D. Nina, illus. (ENG & SPA.). 32p. 15.95 (978-1-55885-407-9(X) , Piñata Books) Arte Publico Pr.

Carabine, Sue. Grandma's Night Before Christmas. Kawasaki, Shauna Mooney, illus. 2000. Vol. 13. 60p. 5.95 (978-0-87905-820-3(X)) Gibbs Smith, Publisher.

Carey, Elizabeth Doyle. The Callahan Cousins: Summer Begins, 1. 2005. 208p. (J). pap. 7.99 (978-0-316-73696-1(1)) Little Brown & Co.

—Keeping Cool. 3rd ed. 2006. (Callahan Cousins Ser.). (Illus.). 226p. (J). (gr. 3-7). 10.99 (978-0-316-73693-0(7)) Little Brown & Co.

—Summer Begins. 2005. (Callahan Cousins Ser.: No. 1). (Illus.). 274p. (J). (gr. 3-7). 10.99 (978-0-316-73690-9(2)) Little Brown & Co.

Carlow, Emma. Flora the Fairy. Carlow, Emma, illus. 2005. (Green Bananas Ser.). (Illus.). 48p. (J). (978-0-7787-1022-6(X)) Crabtree Publishing Co.

Carlson, Nancy. Hooray for Grandparents' Day! Carlson, Nancy, illus. 2002. (Illus.). (YA). 13.19 (978-1-4046-0774-3(9)) Book Wholesalers, Inc.

—Hooray for Grandparents' Day! 2002. (gr. k-3). lib. bdg. 14.15 (978-0-613-45272-4(0)) Tandem Library Bks.

—Hooray for Grandparents Day! Carlson, Nancy, illus. 2002. (Illus.). 32p. (J). pap. 5.99 (978-0-14-230125-8(6) , Puffin) Penguin Group (USA) Inc.

—Hooray for Grandparent's Day. 2000. (Illus.). 32p. (J). (ps-2). 15.99 (978-0-670-88876-4(1) , Viking Juvenile) Penguin Group (USA) Inc.

Carney, Margaret. The Biggest Fish in the Lake. Wilson, Janet, illus. 2003. 32p. (J). (gr. k-3). (978-1-55337-528-9(9)) Kids Can Pr., Ltd.

—Biggest Fish in the Lake. 2003. (Illus.). (gr. k-3). lib. bdg. 14.10 (978-0-613-86544-9(8)) Tandem Library Bks.

—The Biggest Fish in the Lake. Wilson, Janet, illus. unabr. ed. 2003. 32p. (J). (gr. k-3). (978-1-55074-720-1(7)) Kids Can Pr., Ltd.

—Grandpa's Sugar Bush. Wilson, Janet, illus. unabr. ed. 2002. 32p. (J). (gr. k-3). (978-1-55074-671-6(5)) Kids Can Pr., Ltd.

Carr, Pat. Border Ransom. 2006. (Illus.). 146p. (J). pap. 11.95 (978-0-87565-332-7(4)) Texas Christian Univ. Pr.

Carson, Jerry. The Story of Georgie-George. 2002. 32p. pap. 8.00 (978-0-8059-5789-1(8)) Dorrance Publishing Co., Inc.

Carter, Don. Heaven's All-Star Jazz Band. Carter, Don, illus. 2002. (Illus.). 40p. (J). (gr. k-3). 15.95 (978-0-375-81571-3(6) , Knopf Bks. for Young Readers) Random Hse. Children's Bks.

Carter, Dorothy. Grandma's General Store - The Ark. Allen, Thomas B., illus. 2005. 144p. (J). 16.00 (978-0-374-32766-8(1) , Farrar, Straus & Giroux (BYR)) Farrar, Straus & Giroux.

Caruso, Carla. El Secreto de la Abuela Maria. 2003. (ENG & SPA., Illus.). 24p. pap. 6.95 (978-85-7416-187-7(X)) Callis Editora Ltda BRA. *Dist:* Independent Pubs Group.

Caseley, Judith. Beauty Day. 2007. 32p. 15.95 (***978-1-933718-06-4(4)***) Tanglewood Pr.

Caseley, Judith. In Style with Grandma Antoinette. 2005. (Illus.). 32p. (J). (ps-7). 15.95 (978-0-9749303-4-3(2)) Tanglewood Pr.

Cassidy, Anne. Cleo & Leo. Norman, Philip, illus. 2004. (Read-It! Readers Ser.). 32p. (C). (gr. k-3). 18.60 (978-1-4048-0449-6(2)) Picture Window Bks.

Castañeda, Omar S. El Tapiz de Abuela. ed. 2004. Tr. of Abuela's Weave. (SPA., Illus.). (J). (gr. k-3). spiral bd. (978-0-616-03088-2(6)) Canadian National Institute for the Blind/Institut National Canadien pour les Aveugles.

Castleberry, Stephen B., Sr. & Castleberry, Susie. The History Mystery. 2005. (Farm Mystery Ser.). per. 8.50 (978-1-891907-16-6(6)) Castleberry Farms Pr.

Cates, Karin. The Far-Fetched Story Quilt. Carpenter, Nancy, illus. 2002. 32p. (J). 15.95 (978-0-688-15938-2(9)) HarperCollins Pubs.

Cazet, Denys. Grandpa Spanielson's Chicken Pox Stories No. 1: The Octopus. Cazet, Denys, illus. 2005. (I Can Read Bks.). (Illus.). 48p. (J). (ps-3). lib. bdg. 16.89 (978-0-06-051089-3(7)) HarperCollins Pubs.

—Octopus. Cazet, Denys, illus. 2005. (I Can Read Bks.). (Illus.). 48p. (J). (ps-3). 15.99 (978-0-06-051088-6(9)) HarperCollins Pubs.

—Octopus No. 1: Grandpa Spanielson's Chicken Pox Stories. Cazet, Denys, illus. 2006. (I Can Read Bks.). 48p. (J). pap. 3.99 (978-0-06-051092-3(7) , Harper Trophy) HarperCollins Pubs.

—Shrunken Head. Cazet, Denys, illus. 2008. (I Can Read Bks.: No. 3). 48p. (J). pap. 3.99 (***978-0-06-073015-4(3)*** , Harper Trophy) HarperCollins Pubs.

E
F
G

—Shrunken Head No. 3: Grandpa Spanielson's Chicken Pox Stories. Cazet, Denys, illus. 2007. (I Can Read Bks.). (Illus.). 48p. (J). (gr. k-2). 15.99 (978-0-06-073013-0(7)); lib. bdg. 16.89 (978-0-06-073014-7(5)) HarperCollins Pubs.

—Snout for Chocolate: Grandpa Spanielson's Chicken Pox Stories. Cazet, Denys, illus. 2007. (I Can Read Bks.). 48p. (J). pap. 3.99 (978-0-06-051095-4(1) , Harper Trophy) HarperCollins Pubs.

—Snout for Chocolate No. 2: Grandpa Spanielson's Chicken Pox Stories. Cazet, Denys, illus. 2006. (I Can Read Bks.). (Illus.). 48p. (J). 15.99 (978-0-06-051093-0(5)); lib. bdg. 16.89 (978-0-06-051094-7(3)) HarperCollins Pubs.

Cech, John. My Grandmother's Journey. 1998. (978-0-606-13633-4(9)) Tandem Library Bks.

Chambers, Aidan. Postcards from No Man's Land. (gr. 9). 2007. 336p. (YA). pap. 10.00 (978-0-14-240788-2(7)); 2004. 320p. (J). reprint ed. pap. 7.99 (978-0-14-240145-3(5)) Penguin Group (USA) Inc. (Puffin).

Chambers, Veronica. Marisol & Magdalena. 2001. 176p. (gr. 3-7). pap. 5.99 (978-0-7868-1304-9(0)) Hyperion Bks. for Children.

—Marisol & Magdalena: The Sound of Our Sisterhood. 2001. (gr. 5-8). lib. bdg. 14.15 (978-0-613-60642-4(6)) Tandem Library Bks.

Chandler, Elizabeth. Legacy of Lies. 2004. 182p. (YA). (gr. 7-12). per. 11.64 (978-0-606-29817-9(7)) Tandem Library Bks.

Chandler, Mitzi. I See Something Grand. 2003. (Illus.). 32p. (J). (ps-1). pap. 8.95 (978-0-938216-50-6(3)) Grand Canyon Assn.

Chapman, Cynthia. Dog Gone. 2008. 224p. (J). 16.95 (***978-0-312-37123-4(3)***) Feiwel & Friends.

Chapman, Jean. Favourite Live Thing. (Illus.). 62p. pap. 10.95 (978-0-7022-2888-9(5)) Univ. of Queensland Pr. AUS. *Dist:* International Specialized Bk. Services.

Charnan, Simon. To Grandmother's House We Go. 2006. (Rookie Reader Skill Set Ser.). (Illus.). 32p. (J). (gr. k-2). 19.50 (978-0-531-12089-7(9) , Children's Pr.) Scholastic Library Publishing.

Chatterton, Martin. The Surprise Party. Chatterton, Martin, illus. 2005. (Red Bananas Ser.). (Illus.). 48p. (J). (978-0-7787-1068-4(8)) Crabtree Publishing Co.

Chavarria-Chairez, Becky. Magda's Tortillas (Las Tortillas de Magda) Castilla, Julia Mercedes, tr. Vega, Anne, illus. 2000. (SPA & ENG.). 32p. (J). (ps-2). 14.95 (978-1-55885-286-0(7) , Piñata Books) Arte Publico Pr.

Cheaney, J. B. The Middle of Somewhere. 2007. (Illus.). 224p. (J). (gr. 4-6). 15.99 (978-0-375-83790-6(6)); lib. bdg. 18.99 (978-0-375-93790-3(0)) Random Hse. Children's Bks. (Knopf Bks. for Young Readers).

Cheng, Andrea. Goldfish & Chrysanthemums. Chang, Michelle, illus. 2003. 32p. (J). 16.95 (978-1-58430-057-1(4)) Lee & Low Bks., Inc.

—Grandfather Counts. Zhang, Ange, illus. 32p. (J). 2003. (978-1-58430-158-5(9)); 2000. 15.95 (978-1-58430-010-6(8)) Lee & Low Bks., Inc.

—Grandfather Counts. 2000. (gr. k-3). lib. bdg. 15.25 (978-0-613-65692-4(X)) Tandem Library Bks.

—The Key Collection. Choi, Yangsook, illus. rev. ed. 2003. 128p. (J). (gr. 3-6). 16.95 (978-0-8050-7153-5(9) , Holt, Henry & Co. Bks. For Young Readers) Holt, Henry & Co.

Chess, Sharon. Grandma's Ready. 2007. 30p. pap. (***978-1-933916-04-0(4)***) Nelson Publishing & Marketing.

Chichester-Clark, Emma. Mimi's Book of Counting. Chichester-Clark, Emma, illus. 2004. (Illus.). 24p. (J). 9.95 (978-1-57091-573-4(3)) Charlesbridge Publishing, Inc.

Chiu, Esther. The Lobster & the Sea. Takahashi, Mika, illus. 1998. 32p. (J). (gr. 2-5). pap. 14.95 (978-1-879965-14-0(3)) Polychrome Publishing Corp.

Chocolate, Debbi. The Piano Man. 2000. (978-0-606-17886-0(4)) Tandem Library Bks.

Choi, Yangsook. Behind the Mask. 2006. (Illus.). 40p. (J). 16.00 (978-0-374-30522-2(6) , Frances Foster Bks.) Farrar, Straus & Giroux.

Church, Lisa R. & Spyri, Johanna. Heidi. Akib, Jamel, illus. 2007. (Classic Starts Ser.). 152p. (J). (***978-1-4287-4211-6(5)***) Sterling Publishing Co., Inc.

Ciocca, Donna. Tavern Tales. 2005. 136p. per. 14.95 (978-0-9747361-3-6(9)) Oak Manor Publishing, Inc.

Clark, Clara Gillow. Hattie on Her Way. Thompson, John, illus. 2005. 208p. (J). (gr. 5 up). 15.99 (978-0-7636-2286-2(9)) Candlewick Pr.

Clark, Eleanor. Eleanor Jo: The Farmer's Daughter. 2007. (Eleanor Jo Ser.). (J). pap. 14.99 (978-0-9788726-1-8(4)) HonorNet.

—Melanie Ann: A Legacy of Love. 2007. (Eleanor Jo Ser.). (J). pap. 14.99 (978-0-9788726-2-5(2)) HonorNet.

—Sarah Jane: Liberty's Torch. 2007. (Eleanor Jo Ser.). (J). pap. 14.99 (978-0-9753036-9-6(4)) HonorNet.

Clark, Katie. Grandma Drove the Garbage Truck. Huntington, Amy, illus. 2006. 32p. 15.95 (978-0-89272-698-1(9)) Down East Bks.

Clarke, Judith. Kalpana's Dream. 2005. 168p. (J). 16.95 (978-1-932425-22-2(5) , Lemniscaat) Boyds Mills Pr.

Clarke, Judith. One Whole & Perfect Day. 2007. 250p. (YA). (gr. 7 up). 16.95 (***978-1-932425-95-6(0)*** , Front Street) Boyds Mills Pr.

Cleary, Brian P. When I Go to Grandma's House. Schiffman, Jessica, illus. 2002. 24p. (J). (gr. k-2). pap. 5.25 (978-1-57874-034-5(7)) Kaeden Corp.

Clement, Rod. Grandpa's Teeth. Clement, Rod, illus. 2002. (Illus.). (J). 14.43 (978-0-7587-2647-6(3)) Book Wholesalers, Inc.

—Grandpa's Teeth. Clement, Rod, illus. (Trophy Picture Bk.). (Illus.). 32p. (J). (ps-3). 1999. pap. 6.99 (978-0-06-443557-4(1) , Harper Trophy); 1998. 16.99 (978-0-06-027671-3(1)) HarperCollins Pubs.

Clements, Andrew. Things Hoped For. 176p. (gr. 5). 2008. (J). 6.99 (***978-0-14-241073-8(X)*** , Puffin); 2006. (YA). 16.99 (978-0-399-24350-9(X) , Philomel) Penguin Group (USA) Inc.

Cocks, Nancy & Marton, Jirina. Fergie Goes to Grandma's. 2003. (Illus.). 16p. pap. (978-2-89507-312-3(0)) Novalis Publishing.

Coffey, Maria. Cat Adrift. 2002. (gr. k-3). lib. bdg. 15.25 (978-0-613-63025-2(4)) Tandem Library Bks.

Cohen, Caron Lee. Everything Is Different at Nonna's House. Nakata, Hiroe, illus. 2003. 40p. (J). (gr. k-3). tchr. ed. 16.00 (978-0-618-07335-1(3) , Clarion Bks.) Houghton Mifflin Co. Trade & Reference Div.

Cohen, Deborah Bodin. Papa Jethro: A Story of Moses' Interfaith Family. Dippold, Jane, illus. 2007. (Jewish Identity Ser.). (J). (gr. k-3). 17.95 (***978-1-58013-250-3(2));*** pap. 7.95 (***978-1-58013-252-7(9)***) Kar-Ben Publishing.

Cohen, Tish. The Invisible Rules of the Zoe Lama. 2007. 208p. (J). (gr. 4-7). 15.99 (978-0-525-47810-2(8) , Dutton Juvenile) Penguin Group (USA) Inc.

Cola, Arthur. Papa & the Gingerbread Man. 2006. 14.95 (***978-0-9789423-0-4(2)***) Cola, Arthur.

Colato Lainez, Rene. Playing Loteria Mexicana: El Juego de la Loteria Mexicana. Arena, Jillayne, illus. 2005. (ENG & SPA.). 32p. (J). (gr. 1-3). 15.95 (978-0-87358-881-2(9) , Rising Moon Bks. for Young Readers) Northland Publishing.

Cole, Babette. The Trouble with Gran. 2005. (Illus.). 32p. (J). pap. 3.99 (978-1-4052-1123-9(7)) Egmont Bks., Ltd. GBR. *Dist:* Trafalgar Square Publishing.

—The Trouble with Grandad. 2005. (Illus.). 32p. (J). pap. 3.99 (978-1-4052-1124-6(5)) Egmont Bks., Ltd. GBR. *Dist:* Trafalgar Square Publishing.

Cole, Barbara H. Wash Day. Himler, Ronald, illus. 2004. 40p. (J). 15.95 (978-1-932065-36-7(9) , 7187849112) Star Bright Bks., Inc.

Cole, Brock. Fair Monaco. 2004. (Illus.). 32p. (J). 16.95 (978-1-932425-07-9(1) , Lemniscaat) Boyds Mills Pr.

Collard, Sneed B., III. Dog Sense. 2005. 192p. (J). 14.95 (978-1-56145-351-1(X)) Peachtree Pubs., Ltd.

A Collection of Stories Inspired by My Grandchildren. 2005. (YA). per. (978-1-59872-111-9(9)) Instantpublisher.com.

Collins, Ross. Alvie Eats Soup. 2002. (Illus.). (J). (978-0-439-27265-0(3) , Levine, Arthur A. Bks.) Scholastic, Inc.

Comino, Sandra. La Casita Azul. Zeller, Beatriz, tr. (SPA.). 128p. (J). 2004. pap. 6.95 (978-0-88899-540-7(7)); 2003. (Illus.). 15.95 (978-0-88899-504-9(0)) Groundwood Bks. CAN. *Dist:* Perseus Distribution.

—The Little Blue House. Zeller, Beatriz, tr. from SPA. 2004. 128p. (J). pap. 6.95 (978-0-88899-541-4(5) , Libros Tigrillo) Groundwood Bks. CAN. *Dist:* Perseus Distribution.

—The Little Blue House. Zeller, Beatriz & Wald, Susana, trs. from SPA. 2003. (Illus.). 128p. (J). (gr. 4-7). 15.95 (978-0-88899-503-2(2)) Groundwood Bks. CAN. *Dist:* Perseus Distribution.

Connelly, Peg & Kenniger, Harriet. Grannies' Shorts. 2003. per. 14.95 (978-0-9725229-0-8(5)) Schoolyard Pr.

Connelly, Peggy. My Quirky, Oddball, Eccentric, Unpredictable Grandma. 2006. (ENG.). 112p. pr. 16.95 (***978-1-4241-4486-0(8)***) PublishAmerica, Inc.

Cooke, Trish. Full of Love. Howard, Paul, illus. 2003. 32p. (J). (ps). 15.99 (978-0-7636-1851-3(9)) Candlewick Pr.

Cooney, Caroline B. Hit the Road. 2006. 192p. (gr. 7). (J). lib. bdg. 17.99 (978-0-385-90174-1(7)); (YA). 15.95 (978-0-385-72944-4(8)) Random Hse. Children's Bks. (Delacorte Bks. for Young Readers).

Cooper, Wendy. My First Ride with Isaiah. Elizabeth Mobley, illus. 2006. 18p. (J). 11.95 (***978-0-9772964-8-4(2)***) Kingdom Publishing Group, Inc.

Cornwell, Autumn. Carpe Diem. 2007. 368p. (YA). (gr. 7 up). 16.95 (***978-0-312-36792-3(9)***) Feiwel & Friends.

Costales, Amy. Abuelita Llena De Vida. Avilés, Martha, illus. 2007. (ENG & SPA.). 32p. 14.95 (978-0-87358-914-7(9) , Luna Rising) Northland Publishing.

Cotten, Cynthia. Fair Has Nothing to Do with It. 2007. 160p. (J). (gr. 4-7). 16.00 (978-0-374-39935-1(2)) Farrar, Straus & Giroux.

Cottrell, Janet L. Train Ride to Grandma's. 2000. 27p. (J). pap. 8.00 (978-0-8059-5065-6(6)) Dorrance Publishing Co., Inc.

Couch, Joann. Catching Old Catfish Joe. 2003. (Illus.). 27p. pap. 6.95 (978-0-533-14100-5(1)) Vantage Pr., Inc.

Countess, Mary Alice. Cowpath Days. Fallis, Janet M., ed. Daggett, Susan, illus. 2001. 128p. (J). (gr. 4-8). pap. 6.95 (978-0-9662431-1-6(0)) Viewpoint Pr., Inc.

Court, Georgia. Traitor of Bled. 2005. 108p. pap. 16.95 (978-1-4137-9595-0(1)) PublishAmerica, Inc.

Coville, Bruce. I Lost My Grandfather's Brain. unabr. ed. 2004. (I Was a Sixth Grade Alien Ser.). 160p. (J). (gr. 3-6). pap. 29.00 incl. audio (978-0-8072-8385-1(1) , YA180SP, Listening Library) Random Hse. Audio Publishing Group.

—I Lost My Grandfather's Brain. 1999. (I Was a Sixth Grade Alien Ser.). (Illus.). (J). 10.64 (978-0-606-18306-2(X)) Tandem Library Bks.

Covington, Jean. Nanny Planted Love. (J). 2006. per. 11.99 (***978-1-933732-12-1(1));*** 2005. lib. bdg. 19.95 (***978-0-9754728-9-7(5)***) MidAmerica Publishing Co. (Bear Hug Bks.).

—Nanny Planted Love: Color Book. 2006. (J). per. 6.99 (***978-1-933732-13-8(X)*** , Bear Hug Bks.) MidAmerica Publishing Co.

Cowley, Joy. The Rusty, Trusty Tractor. Dunrea, Olivier, illus. 2003. 32p. (J). (gr. k-2). 15.95 (978-1-56397-565-3(3)); pap. 8.95 (978-1-56397-873-9(3)) Boyds Mills Pr.

—Rusty, Trusty Tractor. 1999. (gr. k-3). lib. bdg. 16.40 (978-0-613-29045-6(3)) Tandem Library Bks.

Crabberg, Edna Dookie. Time to Go Home. 2000. (Illus.). 6p. (J). pap. 8.00 (978-0-9667830-5-6(0)) Early Learning Assessment 2000.

Crabtree, Dianne. On the Road to Royalty. 2005. 222p. (YA). pap. 14.95 (978-1-932898-32-3(8) , 98328) Spring Creek Bk. Co.

Craddock, Sonia. Runaway Gran. 2006. (Streetlights Ser.). 168p. (J). (gr. 2-5). 7.95 (***978-1-55028-953-4(5)***) Lorimer, James & Co., Ltd., Pubs. CAN. *Dist:* Casemate Pubs. & Bk. Distributors, LLC.

Crandall, Sharon Olexa. Sick Bay. Kemp, Sue, illus. 2001. 24p. (J). pap. 14.95 incl. audio compact disk (978-0-9662378-5-6(4)) Astoria Productions.

The Creature of Cassidy's Creek: Individual Chapter Book Title Six-Packs. Vol. 26. 32p. (gr. 3-4). 44.00 (978-0-7635-4481-2(7)) Rigby Education.

Creech, Sharon. Entre Dos Lunas. 2003. (SPA., Illus.). 191p. (YA). (gr. 5-8). (978-84-279-3221-0(9) , NG7785) Noguer y Caralt Editores, S. A. ESP. *Dist:* Lectorum Pubns., Inc.

—Granny Torrelli Makes Soup. Raschka, Chris, illus. 160p. (J). 2003. (gr. 3-6). 15.99 (978-0-06-029290-4(3) , HarperChildren's Audio); 2003. (gr. 4-7). lib. bdg. 16.89 (978-0-06-029291-1(1) , Cotler, Joanna Books); 2005. reprint ed. pap. 5.99 (978-0-06-440960-5(0) , Harper Trophy) HarperCollins Pubs.

—Heartbeat. (J). 2005. 208p. pap. 5.99 (978-0-06-054024-1(9)); 2004. 192p. 15.99 (978-0-06-054022-7(2)); 2004. 192p. lib. bdg. 16.89 (978-0-06-054023-4(0)) HarperCollins Pubs.

—Heartbeat. l.t. ed. 2004. 160p. 23.95 (978-0-7862-6902-0(2) , Large Print Pr.) Thorndike Pr.

—Walk Two Moons. 2002. (Illus.). (J). 15.00 (978-0-7587-0223-4(X)) Book Wholesalers, Inc.

—Walk Two Moons. 2004. 304p. (J). (gr. 7 up). pap. 6.99 (978-0-06-056013-3(4) , Harper Trophy) HarperCollins Pubs.

—Walk Two Moons. 1999. (J). 9.95 (978-1-56137-770-1(8)); 11.95 (978-1-56137-771-8(6)) Novel Units, Inc.

—Walk Two Moons. 1998. (Assessment Packs Ser.). 15p. (J). pap., tchr.'s training gde. ed. 15.95 (978-1-58303-067-7(0)) Pathways Publishing.

—Walk Two Moons. 280p. (J). (gr. 4-6). pap. 4.95 (978-0-8072-1509-8(0) , Listening Library) Random Hse. Audio Publishing Group.

—Walk Two Moons. 2004. (gr. 7-12). lib. bdg. 14.75 (978-0-613-81971-8(3)) Tandem Library Bks.

—Walk Two Moons. l.t. ed. 287p. 2003. pap. 10.95 (978-0-7862-6185-7(4)); 2000. (Illus.). (J). 21.95 (978-0-7862-2773-0(7)) Thorndike Pr.

—The Wanderer. Diaz, David, illus. 320p. 2002. (gr. 3-7). pap. 6.99 (978-0-06-441032-8(3)); 2000. (J). (ps-3). 16.99 (978-0-06-027730-7(0) , Cotler, Joanna Books); 2000. (J). (ps-3). lib. bdg. 17.89 (978-0-06-027731-4(9) , Cotler, Joanna Books) HarperCollins Pubs.

—The Wanderer. 2002. (gr. 3-6). lib. bdg. 14.15 (978-0-613-49702-2(3)) Tandem Library Bks.

—The Wanderer. l.t. ed. 2003. 263p. pap. 10.95 (978-0-7862-6186-4(2)) Thorndike Pr.

—The Wanderer. Diaz, David, illus. l.t. ed. 2002. 263p. (J). 24.95 (978-0-7862-4125-5(X)) Thorndike Pr.

Creevy, Anne. Lets Go Birding, You & Me. ed. 2006. (J). pap. (978-0-9785108-0-0(1)) ABC Bks.

Crespin, Paula Lopez. I'm the Only Grandson. 2004. (Illus.). 30p. pap. 14.99 (978-1-4134-2897-1(5)) Xlibris Corp.

Croteau, Marie-Danielle. Fred & the Mysterious Letter. St-Aubin, Bruno, illus. 2005. 61p. (J). lib. bdg. 12.00 (***978-1-4242-1199-9(9)***) Fitzgerald Bks.

Crowe, Carole. Turtle Girl. Postier, Jim, illus. 2007. (J). (***978-1-59078-262-0(3)***) Boyds Mills Pr.

Crowe, Chris. The Mississippi Trial, 1955. 2003. 240p. (YA). pap. 5.99 (978-0-14-250192-4(1) , Puffin) Penguin Group (USA) Inc.

—The Mississippi Trial, 1955. Okamura, Tim, illus. 2002. 240p. (YA). (gr. 6-8). 17.99 (978-0-8037-2745-8(3) , Dial) Penguin Group (USA) Inc.

—The Mississippi Trial, 1955. 2003. (gr. 7-12). lib. bdg. 14.15 (978-0-613-86522-7(7)) Tandem Library Bks.

Crowley, Mary. I Love to Visit My Grammy. 2007. (Illus.). 40p. (J). (ps-3). 19.95 (***978-1-933002-48-4(4)***) PublishingWorks.

Cruise, Robin. Little Mama Forgets. Dressen-McQueen, Stacey, illus. 2006. 40p. (J). 16.00 (978-0-374-34613-3(5) , Farrar, Straus & Giroux (BYR)) Farrar, Straus & Giroux.

Crum, Shutta. My Mountain Song. 2007. (Illus.). 32p. (J). 16.00 (***978-1-4223-6590-8(5)***) DIANE Publishing Co.

—My Mountain Song. Rand, Ted, tr. Rand, Ted, illus. 2004. 32p. (J). (gr. k-3). tchr. ed. 16.00 (978-0-618-15970-3(3) , Clarion Bks.) Houghton Mifflin Co. Trade & Reference Div.

Crunk, Tony. Big Mama. Apple, Margot, illus. 2003. 32p. (J). pap. 5.95 (978-0-374-40634-9(0) , Sunburst) Farrar, Straus & Giroux.

—Big Mama. 2003. (ps-2). lib. bdg. 14.10 (978-0-613-71734-2(1)) Tandem Library Bks.

—Grandpa's Overall. Nash, Scott, illus. 2001. 32p. (J). (ps). pap. 15.95 (978-0-531-30321-4(7) , Orchard Bks.) Scholastic, Inc.

—Grandpa's Overalls. Nash, Scott, illus. 2001. (J). lib. bdg. (978-0-531-33321-1(3) , Orchard Bks.) Scholastic, Inc.

Crystal, Billy. Grandpa's Little One. 2008. 40p. (J). (ps-k). pap. 6.99 (978-0-06-078175-0(0) , Harper Trophy) HarperCollins Pubs.

—Grandpa's Little One. Porfirio, Guy, illus. 2006. 40p. (J). (ps-k). lib. bdg. 17.89 (978-0-06-078174-3(2)) HarperCollins Pubs.

—I Already Know I Love You. Sayles, Elizabeth, illus. 40p. (J). (ps-3). 2007. pap. 6.99 (978-0-06-059393-3(8) , Harper Trophy); 2004. lib. bdg. 17.89 (978-0-06-059392-6(X)); 2004. 16.99 (978-0-06-059391-9(1)) HarperCollins Pubs.

Crystal, Billy. I Already Know I Love You Board Book. Sayles, Elizabeth, illus. 2008. 32p. (J). 7.99 (***978-0-06-145057-0(X)*** , Harper Festival) HarperCollins Pubs.

Cumberbatch, Judy. Can You Hear the Sea? Wilson-Max, Ken, illus. 2006. 32p. (J). (gr. k-3). 15.95 (978-1-58234-703-5(4) , Bloomsbury Children) Bloomsbury Publishing.

Curry, Kenneth. The Legend of the Dancing Trees: An African American Folk Tale. 2007. 111p. (J). per. 14.95 (***978-0-9798364-0-4(9)***) Curry Brothers Publishing.

Curry, Kenneth, et al. The Legend of the Dancing Tees Teachers Resource: The Legend of the Dancing Trees. 2007. Tr. of Teachers Resource. per. 19.95 (***978-0-9798364-1-1(7)***) Curry Brothers Publishing.

Cutler, Jane. Darcy & Gran Don't Like Babies. Ryan, Susannah, illus. rev. ed. 2002. 32p. (J). (ps-2). 16.50 (978-0-374-31696-9(1) , Farrar, Straus & Giroux (BYR)); pap. 6.95 (978-0-374-41686-7(9) , Sunburst) Farrar, Straus & Giroux.

Cuyler, Margery. That's Good! That's Bad! In the Grand Canyon. Catrow, David, illus. rev. ed. 2002. 32p. (J). (ps-2). 16.95 (978-0-8050-5975-5(X) , Holt, Henry & Co. Bks. For Young Readers) Holt, Henry & Co.

Czech, Jan M. The Garden Angel: A Young Child Discovers a Grandparent's Love Grows Even after Death. Johnson, Joy, ed. Aitken, Susan, illus. 2000. 20p. (J). (gr. k-4). 7.95 (978-1-56123-130-0(4)) Centering Corp.

Dagg, Stephanie. Oh Grandad! 2001. (Illus.). 48p. (J). (gr. 1-4). per. (978-1-84210-084-4(X)) Mentor Bks.

Dahl, Roald. George's Marvelous Medicine. Blake, Quentin, illus. 2002. (J). 13.19 (978-0-7587-9421-5(5)) Book Wholesalers, Inc.

—George's Marvelous Medicine. Blake, Quentin, illus. 2007. 96p. (J). (gr. 2). 5.99 (***978-0-14-241035-6(7)*** , Puffin) Penguin Group (USA) Inc.

—George's Marvelous Medicine. Blake, Quentin, illus. 2002. 112p. (J). (gr. 3-7). 15.95 (978-0-375-82206-3(2)); lib. bdg. 17.99 (978-0-375-92206-0(7)) Random Hse. Children's Bks. (Knopf Bks. for Young Readers).

—The Witches. 2002. (J). pap. 29.95 incl. audio (978-0-7540-6247-9(3)) BBC Audiobooks America.

—The Witches. Blake, Quentin, illus. 208p. (J). 2007. (gr. 2). 6.99 (***978-0-14-241011-0(X)*** , Puffin); 1999. (gr. 3-7). pap. 3.95 (978-0-14-031730-5(9) , Viking Juvenile) Penguin Group (USA) Inc.

—The Witches. 1999. (J). (gr. 3-6). lib. bdg. 14.15 (978-0-8085-7491-0(4)) Tandem Library Bks.

Daly, Niki. Not So Fast, Songololo. 1998. (J). pap. 4.95 (978-0-87628-975-4(8)) Ctr. for Applied Research in Education, The.

D'Arcy, Karen Scourby. My Grandmother Is a Singing Yaya. Palmisciano, Diane, illus. 2001. (J). (gr. k-2). 32p. pap. 15.95 (978-0-439-29309-9(X)); lib. bdg. (978-0-531-33323-5(X)) Scholastic, Inc. (Orchard Bks.).

Das, Christina. Swinging under the Stars. l.t. ed. 2005. (Illus.). 32p. (J). 15.95 (978-0-9763082-1-8(5) , A JuneOne Production) JuneOne Publishing Hub.

Davidson, Jean. My Grandma Rides a Harley: She's Cool! Bauknecht, Julie, illus. 2007. (J). (***978-1-930596-79-5(0)***) Amherst Pr.

Davidson, Susanna. Heidi (Picture Book) 2007. (Picture Book Classics Ser.). 24p. (J). 9.99 (***978-0-7945-1716-8(1)*** , Usborne) EDC Publishing.

Davis, Catherine. Abby & Alex Feel Their Hearts' Little. 2006. 57p. pap. 12.95 (***978-1-4241-4586-7(4)***) PublishAmerica, Inc.

Davis, Elaine Sklar. How I Helped My Grandma Rose. 2003. pap. 18.00 (978-0-8059-6293-2(X)) Dorrance Publishing Co., Inc.

Davis, Rachel. My Life at Mapleleaf Cabin. 2nd ed. 2004. (YA). per. 10.00 (978-0-9741176-8-3(4)) Wu Li Turtle Corp.

De Gross, Monalisa. Granddaddy's Street Songs. Cooper, Floyd, illus. 1999. (Jump at the Sun Bks.). 32p. (ps-3). 14.99 (978-0-7868-0160-2(3) , Jump at the Sun) Hyperion Bks. for Children.

De Guzman, Michael. The Bamboozlers. 2005. 176p. (J). (gr. 5-8). 16.00 (978-0-374-30512-3(9)) Farrar, Straus & Giroux.

de Paola, Tomie. Nana Upstairs & Nana Downstairs. 2000. (Illus.). 32p. (J). (ps-3). pap. 6.99 (978-0-698-11836-2(7) , Putnam Juvenile) Penguin Group (USA) Inc.

—Nana Upstairs & Nana Downstairs. unabr. ed. 2006. (J). (gr. k-3). pap. 17.95 incl. audio (978-0-8045-6943-9(6)); pap. 19.95 incl. audio compact disk (978-0-8045-4157-2(4)) Spoken Arts, Inc.

—Nana Upstairs & Nana Downstairs. 2000. (gr. k-3). lib. bdg. 15.30 (978-0-8085-2686-5(3)) Tandem Library Bks.

—Now One Foot, Now the Other. 48p. (J). 2006. pap. 7.99 (978-0-14-240104-0(8) , Puffin); 2005. (Illus.). reprint ed. 14.99 (978-0-399-24259-5(7) , Putnam Juvenile) Penguin Group (USA) Inc.

—Strega Nona. de Paola, Tomie, illus. 2002. (Illus.). (J). 23.64 (978-0-7587-3720-5(3)) Book Wholesalers, Inc.

—Strega Nona. 2000. (978-0-606-20375-3(3)); (J). (978-0-606-20259-6(5)) Tandem Library Bks.

—Strega Nona: Her Story. 2000. (Illus.). 32p. (J). (ps-ps). pap. 6.99 (978-0-698-11814-0(6) , Putnam Juvenile) Penguin Group (USA) Inc.

Dear Abuelita, 6, Pack. (Greetings Ser.: Vol. 2). (gr. 3-5). 31.00 (978-0-7635-1765-6(8)) Rigby Education.

DeFelice, Cynthia C. Old Granny & the Bean Thief. Smith, Cat Bowman, illus. 2003. 32p. (J). 16.00 (978-0-374-35614-9(9) , Farrar, Straus & Giroux (BYR)) Farrar, Straus & Giroux.

Del Canizo, Jose Antonio. Las Cosas del Abuelo. (SPA.). 96p. (J). (gr. 3-5). (978-84-279-3345-3(2) , NG4456) Noguer y Caralt Editores, S. A. ESP. *Dist:* Lectorum Pubns., Inc.

Delgado, Linda D. The Visitors. 2006. 169p. (J). per. (978-0-9767861-1-5(7)) Muslim Writers Publishing.

DeLisa, Patricia, illus. Little Red Riding Hood: A Book for the Thoughtful Parent. 2006. 32p. (J). 14.95 (978-0-88010-571-2(2) , Bell Pond Bks.) SteinerBooks, Inc.

Demers, David & Demers, Lee Ann. My Grandpa Loves Trains: A Picture Storybook for Preschoolers. Demers, David, photos by. l.t. ed. 2005. (Illus.). 76p. (J). 27.95 (978-0-922993-36-9(X)) Marquette Bks., LLC.

—My Grandpa Loves Trains: A Storybook for Preschoolers. Demers, David, photos by. l.t. ed. 2005. (Illus.). 76p. (J). per. 19.95 (978-0-922993-23-9(8)) Marquette Bks., LLC.

Demers, Dominique. Grampy's Bad Day. Dumont, Daniel, illus. 2005. (Read-It! Readers Ser.). 32p. (C). (gr. k-3). 18.60 (978-1-4048-1073-0(0)) Picture Window Bks.

DeMuth, Robert R. Grandpa's Treasures. 2006. (Illus.). 22p. (J). pap. 7.95 (978-1-933255-20-0(X)) DNA Pr.

Denman, K. L. Rebel's Tag. 2007. (Orca Currents Ser.). 112p. (YA). (gr. 5 up). pap. ***978-1-55143-740-8(6));** lib. bdg. (***978-1-55143-742-2(2))** Orca Bk. Pubs.

deRubertis, Barbara. Count on Pablo. Thornburgh, Rebecca McKillip, illus. 1999. (Math Matters Ser.). 32p. (gr. k-2). pap. 4.95 (978-1-57565-090-6(8)) Kane Pr., The.

—Count on Pablo. 1999. (ps-2). lib. bdg. 12.95 (978-0-613-17153-5(3)); (Illus.). (J). 11.75 (978-0-606-18217-1(9)) Tandem Library Bks.

Desplechin, Marie. Poor Little Witch Girl. Rosner, Gillian, tr. 2007. 144p. (J). pap. 6.95 (***978-1-59990-128-2(5)** , Bloomsbury Children) Bloomsbury Publishing.

Devries, Karen. Peekaboo, Pearly Moon. Myers, Stan, illus. 2004. 32p. (ps-2). 12.99 (978-0-8254-2448-9(8)) Kregel Pubns.

DeWitt, Dawn Davis. Searching for Blue Bears. Rolando, Cecilia, tr. Rolando, Cecilia, illus. 2003. (J). (978-0-9677057-5-0(4)) Raven Productions, Inc.

Dickinson, Peter & Dickinson, Peter. Inside Grandad. 2005. 128p. (J). (gr. 4-7). 5.50 (978-0-553-48782-4(5) , Yearling) Random Hse. Children's Bks.

Dilz, Ric. My Grandma Could do Anything in Hawaii. 2006. (J). 7.95 (***978-0-9758704-2-6(4))** Rein Designs, Inc.

Dingles, Molly. Jinka, Jinka Jelly Bean. Bingler, Aimee, illus. 1998. 38p. (J). (ps-6). 23.00 (978-1-891997-03-7(3)) Dingles & Co.

DiSalvo-Ryan, DyAnne. Grandpa's Corner Store. DiSalvo-Ryan, DyAnne, illus. 2000. (Illus.). 40p. (J). (gr. k-3). 16.99 (978-0-688-16716-5(0)) HarperCollins Pubs.

—Grandpa's Corner Store. 2000. (Illus.). 40p. (J). (gr. k-3). 15.89 (978-0-688-16717-2(9)) HarperCollins Pubs.

—Spaghetti Park. DiSalvo-Ryan, DyAnne, illus. 2002. (Illus.). 32p. (J). (gr. k-3). tchr. ed. 16.95 (978-0-8234-1682-0(8)) Holiday Hse., Inc.

Dodd, Anne W. The Story of the Sea Glass. Owens, Mary Beth, illus. 1999. 32p. (gr. k-3). 15.95 (978-0-89272-416-1(1)) Down East Bks.

Dodson, Bert, illus. Super Grandpa. 2nd rev. ed. 2005. 32p. (J). (ps-ps). 18.95 (978-1-889910-33-8(3)) Tortuga Pr.

Dolan, Penny. Plip & Plop. Smith, Lisa, illus. 2004. (Read-It! Readers Ser.). (J). lib. bdg. 18.60 (978-1-4048-0551-4(6)) Picture Window Bks.

Domoslai, Autumn. Grandmother Witch: Samhain at Grandmother's, 10 bks., Vol. 2. Price, Starr, ed. Domoslai, Autumn, illus. l.t. ed. 2005. (Illus.). 44p. (J). pap. 6.49 (978-0-9755403-7-4(8)) Spiral Publishing, Inc.

—Grandmother Witch Vol. I: Springtime. Domoslai, Autumn, illus. l.t. ed. 2004. (Illus.). 44p. (J). pap. 6.49 (978-0-9755403-5-0(1)) Spiral Publishing, Inc.

Doray, Malika. One More Wednesday. Freeman, Suzanne, tr. Doray, Malika, illus. 2001. (Illus.). 32p. (J). (ps up). 15.89 (978-0-06-029590-5(2)) HarperCollins Pubs.

Dorfman, Ariel & Dorfman, Joaquin. The Burning City. 2005. 272p. (J). (gr. 5-9). lib. bdg. 17.95 (978-0-375-93203-8(8) , Random Hse. Bks. for Young Readers) Random Hse. Children's Bks.

—Burning City. (YA). mass mkt. (978-0-375-83205-3(X)); 2006. 288p. (J). (gr. 5-9). reprint ed. pap. 7.95 (978-0-375-83204-8(1) , Random Hse. Bks. for Young Readers) Random Hse. Children's Bks.

Dorros, Arthur. Abuela. Kleven, Elisa, illus. 2002. (J). 14.04 (978-0-7587-1901-0(9)) Book Wholesalers, Inc.

—Isla. Kleven, Elisa, illus. 1999. Orig. Title: The Island. 40p. (J). (ps-1). pap. 6.99 (978-0-14-056505-8(1) , Puffin) Penguin Group (USA) Inc.

—Isla. 1999. Orig. Title: The Island. (J). 12.79 (978-0-606-16810-6(9)); (J). 13.79 (978-0-606-16811-3(7)); lib. bdg. 14.15 (978-0-613-14865-8(7)); (SPA.). lib. bdg. 15.30 (978-0-613-18258-4(8)) Tandem Library Bks.

—La Isla. Kleven, Elisa, illus. 1999. (Picture Puffin Ser.). (SPA.). 40p. (J). (gr. k-3). pap. 6.99 (978-0-14-056541-6(8) , DT8806, Puffin) Penguin Group (USA) Inc.

Dos Santos, Lisa. Grandpa's Bridge. 2004. (Illus.). 32p. (J). (978-0-9708571-1-8(X)) Mango Tree Pr.

Dougherty, Terri. The Flying Fish. Visser, Kristy, illus. 2006. (Read-It! Readers Ser.). (J). 19.93 (978-1-4048-2410-2(3)) Picture Window Bks.

Dowell, F. M. C. The Little Palace. 2004. (YA). per. 14.95 (978-1-932205-48-0(9)) Word Association Pubs.

Dowell, Frances O'Roark. Chicken Boy. Krause, George, photos by. 2007. 208p. (J). (gr. 5 up). pap. 5.99 (978-1-4169-3482-0(0) , Aladdin) Simon & Schuster Children's Publishing.

—Chicken Boy. 2005. (Illus.). 208p. (J). 15.95 (978-0-689-85816-1(7) , Atheneum) Simon & Schuster Children's Publishing.

—Chicken Boy. l.t. ed. 2006. 169p. (YA). 22.95 (978-0-7862-8280-7(0)) Thorndike Pr.

Doyle, Malachy. Antonio on the Other Side of the World, Getting Smaller. Cneut, Carll, illus. 2003. 32p. (J). (ps-3). 15.99 (978-0-7636-2173-5(0)) Candlewick Pr.

—Jody's Beans. Allibone, Judith, illus. 2002. (Read & Wonder Bks.). 32p. (J). (ps-1). pap. 6.99 (978-0-7636-1713-4(X)) Candlewick Pr.

—Jody's Beans. 2002. (gr. k-3). lib. bdg. 14.15 (978-0-613-74776-9(3)) Tandem Library Bks.

—Splash, Joshua, Splash! Max, Ken Wilson, tr. Max, Ken Wilson, illus. 2004. 32p. (J). (ps-1). 15.95 (978-1-58234-837-7(5) , Bloomsbury Children) Bloomsbury Publishing.

Doyle, Malachy, et al. Owain A'r Mynydd. 2005. (WEL., Illus.). 24p. (978-0-86381-738-0(6)) Gwasg Carreg Gwalch.

Doyle, Patrick H. T. Edgar Font's Hunt for a House to Haunt: Adventure One: the Castle Tower Lighthouse. 2006. (Illus.). 232p. (J). per. 6.99 (978-0-9786132-0-4(1)) Armadillo Bks.

Doyle, Patrick H. T. Edgar Font's Hunt for a House to Haunt: Adventure Two: the Fakersville Power Station. 2007. (J). per. 7.99 (***978-0-9786132-1-1(X))** Armadillo Bks.

Dozier, Jennifer. Love, Grandpa. Marczak, Chris, illus. 2002. 27p. (J). 14.95 (978-0-9713985-2-8(6)) CDA Publishing.

Dream Catchers - Evaluation Guide: Evaluation Guide. 2006. (J). (978-1-55942-403-5(6)) Marsh Media.

Dream Catchers - Teaching Guide. 2001. (J). 17.95 (978-1-55942-183-6(5)) Marsh Media.

Duble, Kathleen Benner. Bravo Zulu, Samantha! 2007. 144p. (J). (gr. 4-7). 14.95 (***978-1-56145-401-3(X)** , Peachtree Junior) Peachtree Pubs., Ltd.

Duffy, Daniel M., illus. A Present for Grandfather, Vol. 2. 1998. (Adventures of Benny & Watch: Vol. No. 2). 32p. (J). (ps-2). pap. 3.95 (978-0-8075-6625-1(X)) Whitman, Albert & Co.

Dunbar, James. When I Was Young. Remphry, Martin, illus. 1999. (Picture Bks.). 32p. (J). (ps-3). lib. bdg. 15.95 (978-1-57505-359-2(4) , Carolrhoda Bks.) Lerner Publishing Group.

Dupasquier, Philippe. Sunday with Grandpa. 2000. (Illus.). 33p. (J). pap. 8.99 (978-0-86264-029-3(6)) Andersen GBR. *Dist:* Independent Pubs. Group.

—Sunday with Grandpa. 1998. (Illus.). 33p. (J). 19.99 (978-0-86264-791-9(6)) Random Hse. GBR. *Dist:* Trafalgar Square Publishing.

Durben, Toni. Grandpa Isn't Grandpa Anymore. Mulholland, Bailey, illus. 2006. (J). lib. bdg. (978-1-933556-33-8(1)) Publishers' Graphics, L.L.C.

Durrant, Sabine. Bon Voyage, Connie Pickles. 2008. 240p. (J). 16.99 (***978-0-06-085482-9(0));** lib. bdg. 17.89 (***978-0-06-085483-6(9))** HarperCollins Pubs. (HarperTeen).

Dwyer, Mindy. Quilt of Dreams. 2000. (Illus.). 32p. (J). (gr. 2-4). 15.95 (978-0-88240-522-3(5)); pap. 8.95 (978-0-88240-521-6(7)) Graphic Arts Ctr. Publishing Co. (Alaska Northwest Bks.).

—Quilt of Dreams. 2000. (978-0-606-22817-6(9)); (gr. 3-6). lib. bdg. 17.60 (978-0-613-49764-0(3)) Tandem Library Bks.

Eagle Feathers, 6 vols. (Multicultural Programs Ser.). 16p. (gr. 1-6). 31.95 (978-0-7802-8327-5(9)) Wright Group, The.

Eakle, Kit. In My Grandmother's Garden. Eakle, Laura Jean, illus. l.t. ed. 2001. 32p. (J). (gr. k-5). 21.95 (978-0-9713194-0-0(5) , MusicTales) MusicKit.COM.

Easton, Kelly. Hiroshima Dreams. 2007. 192p. (YA). (gr. 7). 16.99 (***978-0-525-47821-8(3)** , Dutton Juvenile) Penguin Group (USA) Inc.

Eberhart, Nancy. The Adventures of Granny: Granny Goes to the Zoo. 2007. (J). pap. 10.99 (***978-1-59879-372-7(1));** per. 13.99 (***978-1-59879-373-4(X))** Lifevest Publishing, Inc.

Edwards, Julie Andrews & Hamilton, Emma Walton. Dumpy the Dumptruck. Walton, Tony, illus. 2000. (Dumpy Ser.). 32p. (ps-2). 15.99 (978-0-7868-0609-6(5)) Hyperion Bks. for Children.

Edwards, Michelle. Zero Grandparents. 2005. (Jackson Friends Ser.). (Illus.). 64p. (J). (ps-ps). pap., pap. 5.95 (978-0-15-205754-1(4) , Harcourt Paperbacks) Harcourt Children's Bks.

Eenie Meanie Me & the Very Sad Day. 2005. (J). (978-0-9772878-0-2(7)) Bishop, Susan Lynn.

Eggleton, Jill. Granny Groggin: 6 Small Books. (Sails Literacy Ser.). 24p. (gr. 3 up). 25.00 (978-0-7578-6989-1(0)) Rigby Education.

—Granny Groggin: Big Book Only. (Sails Literacy Ser.). 24p. (gr. 3 up). 27.00 (978-0-7578-6981-5(5)) Rigby Education.

Ehrenberg, Pamela. Ethan, Suspended. 2007. 336 Pagesp. 16.00 (***978-0-8028-5317-2(X));** vi, 266p. (J). (gr. 6 up). 16.00 (***978-0-8028-5324-0(2)** , Eerdmans Bks For Young Readers) Eerdmans, William B. Publishing Co.

Elgar, Edward & Briggs, Raymond. The Puddleman. (Illus.). 32p. pap. 7.99 (***978-0-09-945642-1(7)** , Red Fox) Random Hse. Children's Bks. GBR. *Dist:* Trafalgar Square Publishing.

Elliott, Dean. Grampa Dean's Hunting Adventures. 1999. (Grampa Dean Ser.: Vol. 1). (Illus.). 176p. pap. 12.95 (978-0-9671996-0-3(3)) Rascal Publishing.

Ellsworth, Mark R. Grawnma Becky's Bread. 2005. (J). pap. 8.00 (978-0-8059-6631-2(5)) Dorrance Publishing Co., Inc.

Elster, Jean Alicia. I'll Do the Right Thing. Tadgell, Nicole, illus. 2003. (Joe Joe in the City Ser.). 32p. (gr. 1-5). 12.00 (978-0-8170-1408-7(X)) Judson Pr.

Enderle, Dotti & Sansum, Vicki. Grandpa for Sale. Gentry, T. Kyle, illus. 2007. 32p. (J). 15.95 (***978-0-9729225-8-6(X))** Flashlight Pr.

England, Kathryn. Grandfather's Wrinkles. McFarland, Richard, illus. 2007. 32p. (J). (ps-3). 15.95 (***978-0-9729225-9-3(8))** Flashlight Pr.

English, Karen. The Baby on the Way. Qualls, Sean, illus. 2005. 32p. (J). (ps-1). 16.00 (978-0-374-37361-0(2) , Farrar, Straus & Giroux (BYR)) Farrar, Straus & Giroux.

Erdrich, Louise. Grandmother's Pigeon. 1999. (J). (978-0-606-16663-8(7)) Tandem Library Bks.

Erickson, John R. Moonshiner's Gold. 2001. 176p. (J). (gr. 5-9). 15.99 (978-0-670-03502-1(5) , Viking Juvenile) Penguin Group (USA) Inc.

Erickson, Mary Ellen. Snowstorm. 2005. (J). (978-0-9765453-3-0(0)) Dr. Mary's Bks.

Ernst, Lisa Campbell. The Luckiest Kid on the Planet. 1999. (J). (978-0-606-15923-4(1)) Tandem Library Bks.

Esbaum, Jill. Stink Soup. Roth, Roger, illus. 2004. 32p. (J). 16.00 (978-0-374-37252-1(7) , Farrar, Straus & Giroux (BYR)) Farrar, Straus & Giroux.

El estanque del Abuelo. 2000. (McGraw-Hill Ciencias Ser.). (ENG & SPA.). (gr. 3 up). (978-0-02-279636-5(3)) Macmillan/McGraw-Hill Schl. Div.

Evans, Cornelia. Sasha & Babushka: A Story of Russia. (Make Friends Around the World Ser.). (Illus.). 32p. (J). (gr. k-3). 19.95 incl. audio (978-1-59249-445-3(5) , BC8007); 8.95 incl. audio (978-1-59249-446-0(3) , SC8007); 2006. 15.95 (978-1-59249-443-9(9) , B8007) Soundprints.

Evans, Cornilia. Sasha & Babushka: A Story of Russia. 2006. (Make Friends Around the World Ser.). (Illus.). 32p. (J). (gr. k-3). pap. 6.95 (978-1-59249-444-6(7) , S8007) Soundprints.

Fallon, Kevin A. Rest in Peas: What Does that Mean? 2005. per. 12.95 (978-1-59196-943-3(3)) Instantpublisher.com.

Faris, Debi. Kaya & Nannas First Excellent Adventur. 2006. pap. 18.99 (***978-1-4259-7780-1(4))** AuthorHouse.

Farren, Rick. Eliza's Wish. 2005. (J). per. 14.95 (***978-0-9794863-8-8(6))** Summerland Publishing.

—Grandpa & the Pirate. 2003. (J). per. 9.95 (978-0-9728716-4-8(0)) Journey Pubns., LLC.

Farren, Rick. The Secret of the Lighthouse. 2004. (J). per. 12.95 (***978-0-9794863-7-1(8))** Summerland Publishing.

Feely, Jenny. Loudest Sneeze. 2000. (gr. k-3). lib. bdg. 11.80 (978-0-613-29690-8(7)) Tandem Library Bks.

Ferguson, Dwayne. Mess at Loch Ness. 2004. (Kid Caramel). 72p. (J). pap. 4.50 (978-0-940975-74-3(2) , Sankofa Bks.) Just Us Bks., Inc.

Few, Cyndi. Going to Nanna & Poppy's Ranch : for My Grandson-Talon. 2006. (ENG.). 28p. per. 14.00 (***978-1-4259-4179-6(6))** AuthorHouse.

Fietzek, Petra. Trommeln, Trommeln. 2002. (GER.). 128p. pap. 15.00 (978-1-4000-3958-6(4) , New Media German Language) Random House Foreign Language Publishing.

Fine, Arnold & Spielman, Howard. Too Many Toys. (J). 9.99 (978-0-89906-422-2(1) , TOYH) Mesorah Pubns., Ltd.

Finley, Martha. Christmas with Grandma Elsie, Bk. 14. 2001. mass mkt. 5.99 (978-1-931343-23-7(3)) Hibbard Pubns., Inc.

—Christmas with Grandma Elsie. 2006. 79.99 (***978-1-4280-2610-0(X))** IndyPublish.com.

—Elsie at Home, Vol. 22. (Elsie Bks.: Vol. 22). 320p. (gr. 4-7). pap. 5.95 (978-1-58182-175-8(1)) Cumberland Hse. Publishing.

—Elsie at Home. unabr. ed. 1998. (Elsie Dinsmore Collection: Vol. 22). 295p. reprint ed. 15.00 (978-1-889128-22-1(8)) Mantle Ministries.

—Grandmother Elsie. 1998. (Elsie Bks.: Vol. 8). 200p. (J). (gr. 7-12). reprint ed. pap. 6.99 (978-1-888306-41-5(6) , Full Quart Pr.) Holly Hall Pubns., Inc.

Fisher, Phyllis Mae Richardson. Twiglet the Little Christmas Tree. Fisher, Phyllis Mae Richardson & Fisher, Douglas W., illus. 2003. (J). 30.00 (978-0-9745615-1-6(7) , Twiglet The Little Christmas Tree); 186p. 12.00 (978-0-9745615-4-7(1)) PJs Corner.

Fisher, Rick. Unknown Heroes. 2007. (ENG., Illus.). 32p. (J). per. 14.95 (***978-1-59800-899-9(4))** Outskirts Press, Inc.

Fitz-Gibbon, Sally. Pig in the Middle. Wakelin, Kirsti, illus. 2004. 32p. (J). (978-1-55041-894-1(7)) Fitzhenry & Whiteside, Ltd.

Fitzl, Richelle Kristi, illus. Grandma's Garden. 2004. (J). (978-0-9741657-1-4(9)) Galaxia Publishing Group, LLC.

Fleischman, Paul. Lost! A Story in String. Mordan, C. B., illus. rev. ed. 2000. 32p. (J). (ps-3). 16.95 (978-0-8050-5583-2(5) , Holt, Henry & Co. Bks. For Young Readers) Holt, Henry & Co.

Flood, Pansie Hart. Sometimey Friend. Marshall, Felicia, illus. 2005. 128p. (J). (gr. 4-6). 15.95 (978-1-57505-866-5(9)) Lerner Publishing Group.

Ford, Linda. Santa S O S. 1999. (gr. 3-6). lib. bdg. 12.40 (978-0-613-33021-3(8)) Tandem Library Bks.

Foreman, Mark. Grandpa Jack's Tattoo Tales. 2007. (Illus.). 40p. (J). (ps-3). 16.00 (978-0-374-32768-2(8)) Farrar, Straus & Giroux.

Forward, Toby. The Wolf's Story: What Really Happened to Little Red Riding Hood. Cohen, Izhar, illus. 2005. 32p. (J). (ps-3). 15.99 (978-0-7636-2785-0(2)) Candlewick Pr.

Fowler, Zinita. Bubba Bailey & the Farkleberry Bush. 1998. 64p. (gr. 3-4). 14.95 (978-1-57168-187-4(6)) Eakin Pr.

Franco, Betsy. Going to Grandma's Farm. 2004. (Rookie Reader Espanol Ser.). (Illus.). 23p. (J). (gr. k-2). pap. 4.95 (978-0-516-27787-5(1) , Children's Pr.) Scholastic Library Publishing.

—Going to Grandma's Farm. Rueda, Claudia, illus. 2003. (Rookie Reader Ser.). 24p. (J). 19.50 (978-0-516-22875-4(7) , Children's Pr.) Scholastic Library Publishing.

—Going to Grandma's Farm. Rueda, Claudia, illus. 2004. 24p. (ps-ps). lib. bdg. 11.75 (978-0-606-30159-6(3)) Tandem Library Bks.

—Grandpa's Quilt. Bild, Linda, illus. 1999. (Rookie Readers Ser.). 32p. (J). (gr. 1-2). 19.50 (978-0-516-21604-1(X) , Children's Pr.) Scholastic Library Publishing.

—Grandpa's Quilt. 1999. (gr. k-3). lib. bdg. 12.95 (978-0-613-54523-5(0)) Tandem Library Bks.

—Vamos a la Granja de la Abuela. 2004. (Rookie Reader Espanol Ser.). (J). (gr. k-2). pap. 4.95 (978-0-516-24616-1(X) , Children's Pr.) Scholastic Library Publishing.

—Vamos a la Granja de la Abuela. Rueda, Claudia, illus. 2003. (Rookie Reader Espanol Ser.). (SPA.). (J). 19.50 (978-0-516-25889-8(3) , Children's Pr.) Scholastic Library Publishing.

Franco, Betsy & Bild, Linda A. Grandpa's Quilt. 2000. (Rookie Reader Skill Set Ser.). (Illus.). 32p. (J). (gr. k-2). pap. 4.95 (978-0-516-26551-3(2) , Children's Pr.) Scholastic Library Publishing.

Franklin, Daniel. Secret Chest. 2004. 49p. pap. 12.95 (978-1-4137-5631-9(X)) PublishAmerica, Inc.

Frazier, Sundee Tucker. Brendan Buckley's Universe & Everything in It. 2007. 208p. (J). (gr. 4-7). 14.99 (***978-0-385-73439-4(5));** lib. bdg. 17.99 (***978-0-385-90445-2(2))** Random Hse. Children's Bks. (Delacorte Bks. for Young Readers).

Fredericks, Anthony D. The Tsunami Quilt: Grandfather's Story. Yee, Tammy, illus. rev. ed. 2007. 40p. (J). 17.95 (***978-1-58536-313-1(8))** Sleeping Bear Pr.

Freedman, Claire. Good Night, Sleep Tight. Tyger, Rory, illus. 2003. 32p. (J). (ps-1). 14.95 (978-0-8109-4513-5(4)) Abrams, Harry N., Inc.

Freedman, Claire. Good Night, Sleep Tight! Tyger, Rory, illus. 2007. 32p. (J). pap. 6.95 (***978-1-58925-405-3(8)** , tiger tales) ME Media LLC.

Freeman, Martha. The Polyester Grandpa. 1998. 160p. (J). (gr. 4-7). tchr. ed. 15.95 (978-0-8234-1398-0(5)) Holiday Hse., Inc.

French, Simon. Where in the World. 2003. 208p. (J). (gr. 3-6). 14.95 (978-1-56145-292-7(0) , Q34443) Peachtree Pubs., Ltd.

French, Vivian. I Love You, Grandpa. Kubick, Dana, illus. 32p. (J). (ps). 2006. pap. 5.99 (978-0-7636-2748-5(8)); 2004. 15.99 (978-0-7636-2520-7(5)) Candlewick Pr.

—Oliver's Vegetables. 1998. (Illus.). 32p. (J). (ps-1). pap. 6.95 (978-0-531-07104-5(9) , Orchard Bks.) Scholastic, Inc.

French, Vivien. Oliver's Fruit Salad. Bartlett, Alison, illus. 1998. 32p. (J). (ps-1). pap. 14.95 (978-0-531-30087-9(0) , Orchard Bks.) Scholastic, Inc.

Fried, Amelie. Is Grandpa Wearing a Suit? Gleich, Jacky, illus. 2007. 32p. (J). (gr. 4-7). 16.95 (***978-0-9787550-4-1(9))** Heryin Publishing Corp.

Frienz, D. J. Where Will Nana Go Next: An Illustrated Tour of 19 Places to Go & Things to Do Across America & the World. Garber, Sean, illus. 1999. 32p. (J). (ps-3). 15.95 (978-0-9654333-0-3(7)) Howling at the Moon Pr.

Fry, Stella. Grandpa's Garden. Jago, illus. 2007. (J). (***978-1-84686-053-9(9))** Barefoot Bks., Inc.

Fuller, Susan. Grandma's Wisdom: Secure in His Love, Faith & Joy. 2004. 32p. (J). per. 14.95 (978-1-58930-106-1(4)) Selah Publishing Group, LLC.

Funke, Julie Ann & Foekel, Alessandra. Conner's Cubbyhole. 2004. 20p. pap. 14.95 (978-1-4137-3192-7(9)) PublishAmerica, Inc.

Fusillo, Archimede. Let It Rip! David & Nick Have the Smelliest Plan of All! 2006. (Bites Ser.). (Illus.). 84p. (J). (gr. 2-5). pap. 3.95 (978-0-7624-2622-5(5) , Running Pr. Kids) Running Pr. Bk. Pubs.

Gagliano, Eugene M. Falling Stars. 2004. 68p. pap. 14.95 (978-1-58851-419-6(6)) PublishAmerica, Inc.

Galindo, Mary Sue & Howard, Pauline Rodriguez. Icy Watermelon. 2000. Tr. of Sandia Fria. (SPA & ENG., Illus.). 32p. (J). (ps-2). 14.95 (978-1-55885-306-5(5) , Piñata Books) Arte Publico Pr.

Gandolfi, Silvana & Schwartz, Lynne Sharon. Aldabra, or, the Tortoise Who Loved Shakespeare. 2004. 151p. (J). (978-0-439-49744-2(2) , Levine, Arthur A. Bks.) Scholastic, Inc.

Gansle, Sherry. Oops, a Curious Horse Big Book. Light, Carol, illus. 2003. 56p. (J). (978-0-9745803-6-4(8)) Little Big Tomes.

—Oops, a Curious Horse Little Book. Light, Carol, illus. 2003. 52p. (J). (978-0-9745803-7-1(6)) Little Big Tomes.

—Oops, a Curious Horse Story Book Reader. Light, Carol, illus. 2003. 58p. (J). (978-0-9745803-5-7(X)) Little Big Tomes.

Gantos, Jack. What Would Joey Do? 2002. (Joey Pigza Ser.). 240p. (J). (gr. 5-9). 16.00 (978-0-374-39986-3(7) , Farrar, Straus & Giroux (BYR)) Farrar, Straus & Giroux.

—What Would Joey Do? 2004. 240p. (J). (gr. 5 up). reprint ed. pap. 5.99 (978-0-06-054403-4(1) , Harper Trophy) HarperCollins Pubs.

—What Would Joey Do? l.t. ed. 2003. (Juvenile Ser.). 264p. (J). 22.95 (978-0-7862-5468-2(8)) Thorndike Pr.

—What Would Joey Do? A Dazzling Conclusion to the Joey Pigza Trilogy! 2004. 240p. (J). (gr. 5-9). pap. 36.00 incl. audio (978-1-4000-9020-4(2) , Listening Library) Random Hse. Audio Publishing Group.

García, Cristina. I Wanna Be Your Shoebox. 2008. 208p. (J). (***978-1-4169-3928-3(8)** , Simon & Schuster Children's Publishing) Simon & Schuster Children's Publishing.

Garis, Howard Roger. The Curlytops on Star Island or Camping. 2006. 63.99 (***978-1-4280-0922-6(1));** pap. 56.99 (***978-1-4280-0933-2(7))** IndyPublish.com.

Garis, Howard Roger. Johnnie & Billie Bushytail. 2004. reprint ed. pap. 15.95 (978-1-4191-2786-1(1)); pap. 1.99 (978-1-4192-2786-8(6)) Kessinger Publishing, LLC.

Garrett, Ann. El Guardian del Pantano. Chandler, Karen, illus. 2001. (SPA.). 40p. (J). (gr. 3-5). 8.95 (978-1-890515-28-7(0), TK30971) Turtle Bks.

—El Guardian del Pantano. Gutiérrez, Guillermo, tr. Chandler, Karen, illus. 1998. (SPA.). 40p. (J). (gr. 3-5). 16.95 (978-1-890515-13-3(2), TK2991) Turtle Bks.

—Keeper of the Swamp. 1999. (gr. 3-6). lib. bdg. 17.60 (978-0-613-50211-5(6)) Tandem Library Bks.

—Keeper of the Swamp. Chandler, Karen, illus. 40p. (J). 2001. (ps-3). pap. 8.95 (978-1-890515-27-0(2)); 1998. (SPA.). (gr. 1-4). 16.95 (978-1-890515-12-6(4)) Turtle Bks.

Garza, Xavier & Villarroel, Carolina. Juan & the Chupacabras: Juan y la Chupacabras. Ward, April, illus. 2006. (ENG & SPA.). 32p. (J). 15.95 (978-1-55885-454-3(1), Piñata Books) Arte Publico Pr.

Gates, Josephine Scribner. Nannette goes to visit her Grandmother. 2007. (J). lib. bdg. 59.00 (***978-1-60304-021-1(8)**) Dollworks.

Gatty, Alfred. The Fairy Godmothers & Other Tales. 2004. reprint ed. pap. 15.95 (978-1-4191-6178-0(4)); pap. 1.99 (978-1-4192-6178-7(9)) Kessinger Publishing, LLC.

Gavalda, Anna. 95 Pounds of Hope. Rosner, Gill, tr. from FRE. 2003. (Illus.). 112p. (J). (gr. 3). 14.99 (978-0-670-03672-1(2), Viking Juvenile) Penguin Group (USA) Inc.

Geisert, Arthur. The Etcher's Studio. 2005. (Illus.). 32p. (J). (gr. k-3). reprint ed. 5.95 (978-0-618-55614-4(1), Walter Lorraine) Houghton Mifflin Co. Trade & Reference Div.

—Mystery. Geisert, Arthur, illus. 2003. (Illus.). 32p. (J). (gr. k-3). 16.00 (978-0-618-27293-8(3), Walter Lorraine) Houghton Mifflin Co. Trade & Reference Div.

George & His Best Friend. 2003. (Illus.). 32p. (J). 6.99 (978-0-9744520-0-5(9)) Glitter Creek, Inc.

George, Jean Craighead. Charlie's Raven. 2006. 208p. (YA). (gr. 4). reprint ed. pap. 5.99 (978-0-14-240547-5(7), Puffin) Penguin Group (USA) Inc.

—Dear Katie, the Volcano Is a Girl. 32p. (J). pap. (978-0-7868-1178-6(1)) Hyperion Bks. for Children.

—My Side of the Mountain. l.t. ed. 2005. 198p. pap. 10.95 (978-0-7862-7359-1(3), Large Print Pr.) Thorndike Pr.

Georgopolis, Annmarie H. An american flag for their Father. Spellman, Susan, illus. 2005. 80p. (J). per. 14.95 (978-1-933002-06-4(9)) PublishingWorks.

Gerstein, Mordicai. Fox Eyes. 2001. (gr. k-3). lib. bdg. 11.80 (978-0-613-43036-4(0)) Tandem Library Bks.

—The Old Country. 144p. 2006. (J). pap. 7.95 (978-1-59643-192-8(X)); 2005. (YA). 14.95 (978-1-59643-047-1(8)) Roaring Brook Pr.

Giddens, Martha Anne. The Unluckiest Kid in the Universe. 2006. 56p. pap. (***978-1-4120-7935-8(7)**) Trafford Publishing.

Giff, Patricia Reilly. Eleven. 2008. 144p. (J). (***978-0-385-73069-3(1)**, Delacorte Pr.) Dell Publishing.

—Eleven. 2008. 176p. (J). (gr. 3-8). lib. bdg. 18.99 (***978-0-385-90098-0(8)**, Lamb, Wendy) Random Hse. Children's Bks.

Gill, Janie S. When Grandma Comes to Visit. Date not set. 5.95 (978-0-89868-351-6(3)) ARO Publishing Co.

—When Grandma Visits Me. 1998. (Predictable Readers Ser.). (J). (ps-3). lib. bdg. 11.95 (978-0-89868-350-9(5)) ARO Publishing Co.

Gillard, Denise. Music from the Sky. Taylor, Stephen, illus. 2001. 32p. (J). (gr. k-2). 15.95 (978-0-88899-311-3(0)) Groundwood Bks. CAN. *Dist:* Perseus Distribution.

Gilman, Phoebe. Algo de Nada. Roehrich-Rubio, Esther, tr. from ENG. Gilman, Phoebe, illus. 1999. Tr. of Something from Nothing. (SPA., Illus.). 40p. (J). (gr. k-3). lib. bdg. 15.95 (978-1-880507-53-7(6), LC8621) Lectorum Pubns., Inc.

Gilmore, Dorina Lazo. A Stone in the Soup. Hires, Josh, illus. 2006. 39p. per. 15.00 (***978-0-938911-29-6(5)**) Individualized Education Systems/Poppy Lane Publishing.

Gilmore, Rachna. Gift for Gita. 2002. (gr. k-3). lib. bdg. 16.40 (978-0-613-53191-7(4)) Tandem Library Bks.

—Grandpa's Clock. Meissner, Amy, illus. 2006. 32p. (ps-2). 17.95 (978-1-55143-333-2(8)) Orca Bk. Pubs. USA.

—Mina's Spring of Colors. 2000. 150p. (J). (gr. 4-7). (978-1-55041-549-0(2)); (978-1-55041-534-6(4)) Fitzhenry & Whiteside, Ltd.

—Mina's Spring of Colors. 2000. (gr. 3-6). lib. bdg. 17.60 (978-0-613-43201-6(0)) Tandem Library Bks.

—When-I-Was-A-Little-Girl. Benoit, Renné, illus. 2006. 28p. 12.95 (978-1-897187-12-8(2)) Second Story Pr. CAN. *Dist:* Orca Bk. Pubs. USA.

Girling, Brough. Granddad's Dinosaur. Dell, Stephen, illus. 2005. (I Am Reading Ser.). 48p. (J). (gr. k-3). pap. 3.95 (978-0-7534-5897-6(7), Kingfisher) Houghton Mifflin Co. Trade & Reference Div.

Glass, Sue. Remember Me?/¿Te acuerdas de Mí? Alzheimer's Through the Eyes of a Child/la enfermedad de Alzheimer a través de los ojos de un Niño. de la Vega, Eida, tr. Yunker, W., illus. 2003. Tr. of ¿Te acuerdas de mí? la enfermedad de Alzheimer a través de los ojos de un Niño. (SPA & ENG.). 32p. (J). (gr. 4-6). 16.95 (978-0-9720192-5-5(1), 626999) Raven Tree Pr.

Godden, Rumer. The Doll's House. 126p. (J). (gr. 3-5). pap. 4.99 (978-0-8072-1408-4(6), Listening Library) Random Hse. Audio Publishing Group.

Gold-Vukson, Marji & Evans, Leslie. Grandpa & Me on Tu B'Shevat. 2004. (Illus.). 32p. (J). (ps-3). pap. (978-1-58013-122-3(0)) Kar-Ben Publishing.

Golds, Cassandra. Clair de Lune. Blackall, Sophie, illus. 2007. 208p. (J). (gr. 4-7). 5.99 (978-0-440-42089-7(X), Yearling) Random Hse. Children's Bks.

Goode, Diane. Thanksgiving Is Here! Goode, Diane, illus. 2005. 32p. (J). (ps-3). pap. 6.99 (978-0-06-051590-4(2), Harper Trophy) HarperCollins Pubs.

Goodhart, Pippa. Dragon Boy. Ursell, Martin, illus. 2005. (Red Bananas Ser.). 48p. (J). (978-0-7787-1071-4(8)) Crabtree Publishing Co.

—Dragon Boy. 2005. (Red Bananas Ser.). (Illus.). 48p. (J). (ps). pap. (978-0-7787-1087-5(4)) Crabtree Publishing Co.

—Slow Magic. Kelly, John, illus. 2003. (Flying Foxes Ser.). (J). (978-0-7787-1489-7(6)); pap. (978-0-7787-1535-1(3)); 48p. (978-0-7787-1528-3(0)); 48p. pap. (978-0-7787-1482-8(9)) Crabtree Publishing Co.

Gordon, Marie Elaina. My Grand-Mom Told Me... Book 1. 2006. 48p. pap. 12.95 (978-1-4241-2655-2(X)) PublishAmerica, Inc.

Gorgas, Paula Blais. The Perfect Purple Present. l.t. ed. 2007. (Illus.). 24p. (J). 24.99 (***978-0-9794660-4-5(0)***); per. 12.99 (***978-0-9794660-5-2(9)**) Dragonfly Publishing, Inc.

Gormley, Greg. Grandad's Busy Day. 2007. (Fantastic Phones Ser.). (Illus.). 12p. (J). 9.99 (***978-0-7475-8377-6(3)**) Bloomsbury Publishing Plc GBR. *Dist:* Independent Pubs. Group.

—Grandma Goes to Tea. 2007. (Fantastic Phones Ser.). (Illus.). 12p. (J). 9.99 (***978-0-7475-8379-0(X)**) Bloomsbury Publishing Plc GBR. *Dist:* Independent Pubs. Group.

Gossett, Dean L. The Hair Angel. 2006. (ENG.). 32p. per. 15.99 (***978-1-4259-7677-4(8)**) AuthorHouse.

Gower, Catherine. Long-Long's New Year: A Story about the Chinese Spring Festival. Zhihong, He, illus. 2004. 32p. 16.95 (978-0-8048-3666-1(3)) Tuttle Publishing.

Grace, Julie. Echoes of the Heart. 2004. 49p. pap. 12.95 (978-1-4137-3042-5(6)) PublishAmerica, Inc.

Graff, Nancy Price. Taking Wing. Minor, Wendell, illus. 2005. 224p. (YA). (gr. 5-9). 15.00 (978-0-618-53591-0(8), Clarion Bks.) Houghton Mifflin Co. Trade & Reference Div.

Grambling, Lois G. Grandma Tells a Story. Willingham, Fred, illus. 2004. (J). pap. 6.95 (978-1-58089-072-4(5)); 15.95 (978-1-58089-057-1(1)) Charlesbridge Publishing, Inc.

Grandad's Dinosaur: Level M, 6 vols. 128p. (gr. 2-3). 49.95 (978-0-7699-0984-4(1)) Shortland Pubns. (U. S. A.) Inc.

Grandfather's Dream. (Lexile Levels Ser.). 9.09 (978-1-56334-707-8(5)) Hampton-Brown Bks.

Grandma Carol's Plant: Individual Title Six-Packs. (gr. k-1). 23.00 (978-0-7635-9039-0(8)) Rigby Education.

Grandma Comes to Stay: Early Level Satellite Individual Title Six-Packs. (Sails Literacy Ser.). 16p. (gr. 1-2). 27.00 (978-0-7578-2922-2(8)) Rigby Education.

Grandma Comes to Stay Again: Individual Title Six-Packs. (Sails Literacy Ser.). (gr. 1-2). 36.00 (978-0-7578-6706-4(5)) Rigby Education.

Grandma is a Runner. (J). 26.20 (978-0-8136-8449-9(8)); 59.50 (978-0-8136-8020-0(4)) Modern Curriculum Pr.

Grandma Is Now A Butterfly. 2005. (Illus.). 24p. (J). 8.00 (978-0-9767077-0-7(5)) Carson, Tracy.

Grandma Jenny's Trip: Six-Pack. (Greetings Ser.: Vol. 3). (gr. 3-5). 31.00 (978-0-7635-1778-6(X)) Rigby Education.

Grandma Knits A Blanket. 2008. (J). 11.95 (978-1-933872-31-5(4)) Lima Bear Pr LLC, The.

Grandma Moves In: Six-Pack. (Greetings Ser.: Vol. 2). (gr. 2-3). 31.00 (978-0-7635-9429-9(6)) Rigby Education.

Grandma Net's Stories for the Flannelboard. 2005. (Illus.). 130p. (J). 7.50 net. (978-0-9771210-0-7(3)) Graham Bay, Jeanette.

Grandma's Do Best Newsletter Kit. 2000. (J). per. (978-0-689-01658-5(1), Simon & Schuster Children's Publishing) Simon & Schuster Children's Publishing.

Grandma's Memories, 6 Pack. (Literatura 2000 Ser.). (gr. 1-2). 28.00 (978-0-7635-0134-1(4)) Rigby Education.

Grandma's Pictures: Individual Title Six-Packs. (gr. k-1). 23.00 (978-0-7635-8842-7(3)) Rigby Education.

Grandma's Pie: Individual Title Six-Packs. (Story Steps Ser.). (gr. k-2). 32.00 (978-0-7635-9816-7(X)) Rigby Education.

Grandmother & I: Individual Title Six-Packs. (ps-2). 23.00 (978-0-7635-8791-8(5)) Rigby Education.

Grandmother Sparrow: Copyright TXu1-280-697. 2007. (J). (***978-0-9792641-0-8(3)**) Sible, Carole Creative Arts.

Grandpa & Grandma & the Mischievous Kids. 2004. (J). per. 15.99 (978-0-9759122-0-1(8)) Golden Eagle Publishing Hse., Inc.

Grandpa & I: Individual Title Six-Packs. (ps-2). 23.00 (978-0-7635-8792-5(3)) Rigby Education.

Grandpa & Little Guy. 2004. (J). 15.95 (978-0-9764012-0-9(7)) Rockmill Publishing Co.

Grandpa's Back. 1998. (PNI Healing Stories for Children Ser.). 8p. (J). (gr. k-6). 6.95 (978-1-893351-03-5(3)) Asclepian Pr.

Grandpa's Birthday: Individual Title Six-Packs. (Literatura 2000 Ser.). (gr. 2-3). 33.00 (978-0-7635-0199-0(9)) Rigby Education.

Grandpa's Boat. 2001. (J). (978-1-58453-168-5(1)) Pioneer Valley Educational Pr., Inc.

Grandpa's House. (J). 26.20 (978-0-8136-8407-9(2)); 26.20 (978-0-8136-8408-6(0)); 59.50 (978-0-8136-7936-5(2)) Modern Curriculum Pr.

Grandpa's Trains. 2001. (978-1-58453-158-6(4)) Pioneer Valley Educational Pr., Inc.

Gray, Nigel. Little Bear's Grandad. Cabban, Vanessa, illus. 2001. 28p. (J). (ps-k). tchr. ed. 14.95 (978-1-58925-008-6(7), tiger tales) ME Media LLC.

Gray, Rita. Nonna's Porch. Widener, Terry, illus. 2004. 40p. (ps-2). 15.99 (978-0-7868-1613-2(9)) Hyperion Bks. for Children.

Grecco, Paula. My Flying Grandma. 2006. pap. 16.99 (***978-1-4259-7015-4(X)**) AuthorHouse.

Green, Holly. Don't Slam the Door! Scott, Sarah Chamberlin, illus. 2005. (J). 19.95 (978-0-9744803-7-4(1)) PublishingWorks.

Green, Richard G. Skywoman's Granddaughter. 1998. (Darrin Captain Ser.). 128p. (J). (gr. 7 up). pap. 12.95 (978-0-911737-04-2(9)) Ricara Features.

Greenburg, Dan. My Grandma, Major League Slugger. Davis, Jack E., illus. 2001. (Zack Files Ser.: No. 24). 64p. (J). (gr. 2-5). pap. 4.99 (978-0-448-42550-4(5), Grosset & Dunlap) Penguin Group (USA) Inc.

—My Grandma, Major League Slugger. 2001. (gr. 3-6). lib. bdg. 13.00 (978-0-613-58376-3(0)) Tandem Library Bks.

—Yikes! Grandma's a Teenager, Vol. 17. Davis, Jack E., illus. 1999. (Zack Files Ser.: No. 17). 64p. (J). (gr. 2-5). pap. 4.99 (978-0-448-41999-2(8), Grosset & Dunlap) Penguin Group (USA) Inc.

—Yikes! Grandma's a Teenager. Davis, Jack E., illus. 1999. 58p. (J). (ps-k). lib. bdg. 13.00 (978-0-613-22664-6(X)) Tandem Library Bks.

—Yikes! Grandma's a Teenager. 1999. (Zack Files Ser.: No. 17). (J). (gr. 2-5). (978-0-606-17783-2(3)) Tandem Library Bks.

Greene, Rhonda Gowler. At Grandma's. Firehammer, Karla, illus. rev. ed. 2003. 32p. (J). (ps-k). 15.95 (978-0-8050-6336-3(6), Holt, Henry & Co. Bks. For Young Readers) Holt, Henry & Co.

Greene, Stephanie. Falling into Place. 128p. (J). (gr. 4-6). 2006. pap. 5.95 (978-0-618-68928-6(1)); 2002. (Illus.). tchr. ed. 15.00 (978-0-618-17744-8(2)) Houghton Mifflin Co. Trade & Reference Div. (Clarion Bks.).

Greenfield, Eloise. Grandmama's Joy. 1999. (J). 12.79 (978-0-606-16847-2(8)) Tandem Library Bks.

—William & the Good Old Days. Date not set. (Illus.). 32p. (J). (gr. k-3). pap. 4.99 (978-0-06-443453-9(2)) HarperCollins Pubs.

Greenlee, Gale. Grandma Loves You. Jarecki, Angela, illus. 2003. (My First Treasury Ser.). 40p. (J). bds. 7.98 (978-0-7853-8693-3(9), 7191400) Publications International, Ltd.

Gregory, Nan. Wild Girl & Gran. ed. 2004. (Illus.). (J). (gr. k-3). spiral bd. (978-0-616-11112-3(6)) Canadian National Institute for the Blind/Institut National Canadien pour les Aveugles.

—Wild Girl & Gran. Lightburn, Ron, illus. 2004. (Northern Lights Books for Children Ser.). 32p. (J). (ps-3). pap. 16.95 (978-0-88995-221-8(3)) Red Deer Pr. CAN. *Dist:* Fitzhenry & Whiteside, Ltd.

Griessman, Annette. Like a Hundred Drums. Monks, Julie, illus. 2006. 32p. (J). (gr. k-3). 15.00 (978-0-618-55878-0(0)) Houghton Mifflin Co.

Griffin, Marcia. Debbie's Letter to God. Davies, Michelle, illus. 2005. (J). pap. 8.00 (978-0-8059-6409-7(6)) Dorrance Publishing Co., Inc.

Griffith, Helen V. Grandaddy & Janetta. 1999. (Illus.). 32p. (J). (ps-3). pap. 4.95 (978-0-688-17114-8(1)) HarperCollins Pubs.

—Grandaddy & Janetta Together: The Three Stories in One Book. Stevenson, James, illus. 2001. 80p. (gr. 2 up). (YA). 15.95 (978-0-06-029148-8(6)); (J). 15.89 (978-0-06-029238-6(5)) HarperCollins Pubs.

Griggs, Terry. Invisible Ink. Nugent, Cynthia, illus. 2006. (Cat's Eye Corner Ser.). 256p. pap. 7.95 (978-1-55192-833-3(7)) Raincoast Bk. Distribution CAN. *Dist:* Perseus Distribution.

Grimm, Jacob W. Little Red Riding Hood. 1999. (gr. k-3). lib. bdg. 15.25 (978-0-613-89995-6(4)) Tandem Library Bks.

Grimm, Jacob W., et al. Little Red Riding Hood/Caperucita Roja: A Bilingual Book. Surges, James, tr. from CAT. Estrada, Pau, illus. 1999. (ENG & SPA.). 32p. (J). (ps-3). 12.95 (978-0-8118-2561-0(2)) Chronicle Bks. LLC.

Grimm-Richardson, Anne. Granny Grimm, Read Aloud Storybook. 2002. (Illus.). pap. 24.95 (978-0-937953-89-1(X)) Tiptoe Literary Service.

Grimm, Wilhelm K. & Grimm, Jacob W. Little Red Cap. Zwerger, Lisbeth, illus. 37p. (J). (gr. k-2). pap. 5.95 (978-0-8072-1285-1(7), Listening Library) Random Hse. Audio Publishing Group.

Grimm. Caperucita Roja. 2001. Tr. of Little Red Ridinghood. (SPA.). (978-968-6347-35-7(6)) Larousse, Ediciones, S. A. de C. V.

Grindley, Sally. A Little Bit of Trouble. Taylor, Eleanor, illus. 2004. 32p. (J). 16.95 (978-1-58234-882-7(0), Bloomsbury Children) Bloomsbury Publishing.

—No Trouble at All. 2004. (Illus.). 32p. (J). reprint ed. pap. 6.95 (978-1-58234-894-0(4), Bloomsbury Children) Bloomsbury Publishing.

Grisham, John. La Casa Dipinta. pap. 21.95 (978-88-04-50528-0(1)) Mondadori ITA. *Dist:* Distribooks, Inc.

—A Painted House. 2002. (gr. 5-8). lib. bdg. 16.45 (978-0-613-49451-9(2)) Tandem Library Bks.

Grove, Vicki. Rhiannon. 2007. 224p. (YA). (gr. 5). 18.99 (***978-0-399-23633-4(3)**, Putnam Juvenile) Penguin Group (USA) Inc.

Grover, Lorie Ann. On Pointe. 2004. 320p. (J). 17.99 (978-0-689-86525-1(2), McElderry, Margaret K.) Simon & Schuster Children's Publishing.

Gudel, Helen. Dear Alexandra: A Story of Switzerland. Gudel, Helen, illus. 1999. (Make Friends Around the World Ser.). Orig. Title: Leiber Alex. (Illus.). 32p. (J). (gr. k-3). 15.95 (978-1-56899-739-1(6), B8002); pap. 5.95 (978-1-56899-740-7(X), S8002) Soundprints.

Guest, C. Z. Tiny Green Thumbs. Krupinski, Loretta, illus. 2000. 32p. (ps-2). 15.99 (978-0-7868-0516-7(1)) Hyperion Bks. for Children.

Guest, Elissa Haden. Iris & Walter & the Substitute Teacher. Davenier, Christine, tr. Davenier, Christine, illus. 2004. (Iris & Walter Ser.). 44p. (J). 15.00 (978-0-15-205013-9(2), Gulliver Bks.) Harcourt Children's Bks.

Guiffre, William. Gramma's Glasses. Pippin, Barbara, illus. 1998. (J). pap. 6.95 (978-1-56763-347-4(1)); lib. bdg. 19.95 (978-1-56763-346-7(3)) Ozark Publishing.

Guo, Jing Jing. Grandpa's Mask. Wu, Di, illus. 2001. 32p. (J). (978-1-876615-05-5(2)) Benchmark Pubns. Pty, Ltd.

Gurley, Nan. What Color Is Love: A Parable of God's Gifts. Farnsworth, Bill, illus. 2005. 32p. (J). 14.99 (978-0-310-70888-9(5)) Zonderkidz.

Gutman, Dan. The Million Dollar Goal. 2nd ed. 2006. 176p. (J). (gr. 3-7). pap. 5.99 (978-1-4231-0083-6(2)) Hyperion Pr.

Gutteridge, Alex. Oven Chips for Tea. l.t. ed. 2005. 198p. (J). (gr. 4-7). pap. (978-1-4056-6029-7(5)) BBC Audio.

Haas, Jessie. Birthday Pony. Apple, Margot, illus. 2004. 80p. (J). (gr. 2 up). 15.99 (978-0-06-057359-1(7)); lib. bdg. 16.89 (978-0-06-057360-7(0)) HarperCollins Pubs.

Haddix, Margaret Peterson. The House on the Gulf. (Illus.). 208p. (J). 2006. pap. 5.99 (978-1-4169-1406-8(4), Aladdin); 2004. 15.95 (978-0-689-85422-4(6)) Simon & Schuster Children's Publishing.

Hadley, Caroline. Woodside or Look Listen & Learn. 2007. pap. 87.99 (***978-1-4280-5242-0(9)**) IndyPublish.com.

—Woodside; or, Look, Listen & Learn. 2007. (ENG., Illus.). 80p. per. (***978-1-4065-1557-2(4)**) Dodo Pr.

Hagman, Harvey Dixon. Majesty from Assateague. Aiken, David, illus. 2003. 76p. (J). pap. 8.95 (978-0-87033-552-5(9), Tidewater Pubs.) Cornell Maritime Pr., Inc.

Hahn, Betty Brandt. Grandma's House. 2004. 28p. pap. 9.98 (978-1-4116-1077-4(6)) Lulu.com.

Hahnke. Through the Eyes of a Raptor. 2007. 424p. per. 19.95 (***978-0-595-42609-6(3)**) iUniverse, Inc.

Haislip, Phyllis Hall. Anybody's Hero: The Battle of Old Men & Young Boys. 2004. (Illus.). 220p. (J). pap. 8.95 (978-1-57249-343-8(7), White Mane Kids) White Mane Publishing Co., Inc.

Hale, Lisa Soares. Penny Love. Harrald-Pilz, Marilee, illus. 2006. 32p. (J). 16.95 (978-1-57921-844-7(X)) Wine-Press Publishing.

Halfmann, Janet. Bewitching the Chickadees. 2007. 88p. (J). pap. 14.99 (978-1-59092-573-7(4), Orchard Academy Pr.) Windstorm Creative.

Hall, Kirsten. Grandma's House. Calderas, Gloria, illus. 2004. (My First Reader Ser.). 32p. (J). (gr. k-1). pap. 3.95 (978-0-516-25502-6(9), Children's Pr.) Scholastic Library Publishing.

—Grandma's House. Calderas Lim, Gloria, illus. 2004. (My First Reader Ser.). 31p. (J). 18.50 (978-0-516-24411-2(6), Children's Pr.) Scholastic Library Publishing.

Hall, Nancy R. My Grandparents Live in an RV, Hall, Nancy R., illus. l.t. ed. 2005. (Illus.). 32p. (J). 16.95 (978-0-9761759-0-2(8)) Jasnans Publishing Co.

Halley, Marilyn. Apple-Green Eyes. 2005. pap. 8.00 (978-0-8059-6681-7(1)) Dorrance Publishing Co., Inc.

Hallinan, P. K. Christmas at Grandma's House. Hallinan, P. K., illus. 2006. (Illus.). 32p. (J). (ps). 8.95 (978-0-8249-5535-9(8), 1262731, Ideals Children's Bks.) Ideals Pubns.

—We're Very Good Friends, My Grandma & I. 24p. (J). 7.95 (978-0-8249-5379-9(7), Ideals); 5.95 (978-0-8249-5380-5(0)) Ideals Pubns.

—We're Very Good Friends, My Grandpa & I. 24p. (J). 7.95 (978-0-8249-5377-5(0), Ideals); 5.95 (978-0-8249-5378-2(9)) Ideals Pubns.

Hallwood, Cheri L. The Curious Polka-Dot Present. 2007. (J). 16.99 (***978-0-9774422-1-8(7)**) Forever Young Pubs.

Hamanaka, Sheila. Grandparents Song. Hamanaka, Sheila, illus. 2003. (Illus.). 32p. (J). 15.99 (978-0-688-17852-9(9)) HarperCollins Pubs.

Hambrick, Sharon. Arby Jenkins Meets His Match. Thompson, Del, illus. 2000. 120p. (J). (gr. 4-7). 7.49 (978-1-57924-461-3(0)) Jones, Bob Univ. Pr.

Hamilton, Richard. Jack Bolt & the Highwaymen's Hideout. Hearn, Sam, illus. 2007. 192p. (J). (gr. 2-5). 15.95 (***978-1-59990-090-2(4)***); pap. 5.95 (***978-1-59990-091-9(2)**) Bloomsbury Publishing.

Hanson, P. H. My Grandpa's Briefcase. 2005. (Illus.). 12p. (J). bds. 16.95 (978-0-7611-3794-8(7), 13794) Workman Publishing Co., Inc.

—My Granny's Purse. 2003. (Illus.). 14p. (J). (gr. k-3). bds. 16.95 (978-0-7611-2978-3(2), 12978) Workman Publishing Co., Inc.

Hanson, Regina. A Season for Mangoes. Velasquez, Eric, illus. 2005. 40p. (J). (gr. k-3). 15.00 (978-0-618-15972-7(X), Clarion Bks.) Houghton Mifflin Co. Trade & Reference Div.

Hanson, Warren. Grandpa Has a Great Big Face. Elliott, Mark, illus. 2006. 32p. (J). 16.99 (978-0-06-078775-2(9)); lib. bdg. 17.89 (978-0-06-078776-9(7)) HarperCollins Pubs. (Geringer, Laura Book).

Harcourt School Publishers Staff. The Best Thanksgiving On Level. 3rd ed. 2002. (Trophies Reading Program Ser.). (Illus.). pap. 5.10 (978-0-15-323176-6(9)) Harcourt Schl. Pubs.

—The Box: Below Level. 3rd ed. 2002. (Trophies Reading Program Ser.). (Illus.). (J). pap. 3.20 (978-0-15-322943-5(8)) Harcourt Schl. Pubs.

—Coast to Coast Level D: Library Edition. 2001. (Collections Ser.). (Illus.). pap. 13.20 (978-0-15-314434-9(3)) Harcourt Schl. Pubs.

—Dale Lightfoot & the Moon: Take-Home Book. 1999. (Collections Ser.). (Illus.). (J). pap. 1.90 (978-0-15-317231-1(2)) Harcourt Schl. Pubs.

—Dear Grandma. 3rd ed. 2002. (Trophies English Language Learners Ser.). (Illus.). pap. 5.10 (978-0-15-327820-4(X)) Harcourt Schl. Pubs.

—Dear Grandma: Take-Home Book. 2001. (Collections Ser.). (Illus.). (J). pap. 1.90 (978-0-15-319516-7(9)) Harcourt Schl. Pubs.

—Dear Grandma Below Level. 3rd ed. 2002. (Trophies Reading Program Ser.). (Illus.). pap. 5.10 (978-0-15-323314-2(1)) Harcourt Schl. Pubs.

—Grammy & Me: Take-Home Book. 1999. (Collections Ser.). (Illus.). (J). pap. 1.90 (978-0-15-317260-1(6)) Harcourt Schl. Pubs.

—Grandma's Surprise: Take-Home Book. 1999. (Signatures Ser.). (Illus.). (J). pap. 1.90 (978-0-15-313870-6(X)) Harcourt Schl. Pubs.

—Grandpa Takes Me... Library Edition. 1999. (Collections Ser.). (Illus.). (J). 4.70 (978-0-15-314300-7(2)) Harcourt Schl. Pubs.

—Happy Birthday, Grandma. 3rd ed. 2002. (Trophies English Language Learners Ser.). (Illus.). pap. 5.10 (978-0-15-327651-4(7)) Harcourt Schl. Pubs.

—Historias Que Contaba Mi Abuelo On Level. 3rd ed. 2002. (Trofeos Ser.). (SPA., Illus.). pap. 6.80 (978-0-15-324188-8(8)) Harcourt Schl. Pubs.

—In the Garden. 3rd ed. 2002. (Trophies English Language Learners Ser.). (Illus.). pap. 5.10 (978-0-15-327716-0(5)) Harcourt Schl. Pubs.

—Jake Can Read: Take-Home Book. 1999. (Collections Ser.). (Illus.). (J). (gr. 2). pap. 1.90 (978-0-15-317218-2(5)) Harcourt Schl. Pubs.

—Kenny's Tomatoes Below Level. 3rd ed. 2002. (Trophies Reading Program Ser.). (Illus.). (gr. 4). pap. 5.10 (978-0-15-323221-3(8)) Harcourt Schl. Pubs.

—Kenny's Tomatos: Take-Home Book. 2001. (Collections Ser.). (Illus.). (J). (gr. 4). pap. 1.90 (978-0-15-319483-2(9)) Harcourt Schl. Pubs.

—No Problem. 3rd ed. 2002. (Trophies English Language Learners Ser.). (Illus.). pap. 5.10 (978-0-15-327637-8(1)) Harcourt Schl. Pubs.

—No Problem: Take-Home Book. 1999. (Signatures Ser.). (Illus.). (J). pap. 1.90 (978-0-15-313903-1(X)) Harcourt Schl. Pubs.

—The Orphan Train Home Advanced Level. 3rd ed. 2002. (Trophies Reading Program Ser.). (Illus.). pap. 5.10 (978-0-15-323126-1(2)) Harcourt Schl. Pubs.

—Picture a Kite: Below Level. 3rd ed. 2002. (Trophies Reading Program Ser.). (Illus.). (J). (gr. 1). pap. 4.10 (978-0-15-322960-2(8)) Harcourt Schl. Pubs.

—Picture a Kite 5-Pack, Below Level. 3rd ed. 2002. (Trophies Reading Program Ser.). (Illus.). (gr. 1). pap. 20.10 (978-0-15-326810-6(7)) Harcourt Schl. Pubs.

—A Pinch of This & That On Level. 3rd ed. 2002. (Trophies Reading Program Ser.). (Illus.). pap. 5.10 (978-0-15-323079-0(7)) Harcourt Schl. Pubs.

—Pop On Level. 3rd ed. 2002. (Trophies Reading Program Ser.). (Illus.). pap. 5.10 (978-0-15-323450-7(4)) Harcourt Schl. Pubs.

—Side by Side: On Level. 3rd ed. 2002. (Trophies Reading Program Ser.). (Illus.). (J). pap. 4.10 (978-0-15-322994-7(2)) Harcourt Schl. Pubs.

—Side by Side 5-Pack, On Level. 3rd ed. 2002. (Trophies Reading Program Ser.). (Illus.). (gr. 1). pap. 20.10 (978-0-15-326844-1(1)) Harcourt Schl. Pubs.

—Trofeos Below Level: La Cometa. 3rd ed. 2002. (SPA., Illus.). pap. 5.50 (978-0-15-323871-0(2)) Harcourt Schl. Pubs.

—Trofeos Below Level: Sopresa/Filo. 3rd ed. 2002. (SPA., Illus.). (J). pap. 3.50 (978-0-15-323854-3(2)) Harcourt Schl. Pubs.

—Trofeos On Level: Mi Abuelita/Yo. 3rd ed. 2002. (SPA., Illus.). (gr. 1). pap. 5.50 (978-0-15-323905-2(0)) Harcourt Schl. Pubs.

—Why Butterflies Were Made On Level. 3rd ed. 2002. (Trophies Reading Program Ser.). (Illus.). pap. 5.10 (978-0-15-323178-0(5)) Harcourt Schl. Pubs.

Hardcastle, Michael. Soccer Star. Cox, Ken, illus. 2002. (Yellow Bananas Ser.). 48p. (J). (gr. 3-4). pap. (978-0-7787-0979-4(5)); lib. bdg. (978-0-7787-0933-6(7)) Crabtree Publishing Co.

—Soccer Star. 2002. (gr. 3-6). lib. bdg. 12.95 (978-0-613-52909-9(X)) Tandem Library Bks.

Harding, Sandy Bacon. A Stick, a Stone & a Bone. Mickelson, Brenda, illus. 1999. (Farm Adventures Ser.: Vol. 2). 79p. (J). (gr. 1-6). pap. 6.95 (978-1-890609-08-5(0) , Lion's Paw Bks.) Coronet Bks. & Pubns.

Harlow, Joan Hiatt. Shadows on the Sea. (Illus.). 256p. (J). 2005. pap. 4.99 (978-0-689-84927-5(3) , Aladdin); 2003. (gr. 3-6). 17.99 (978-0-689-84926-8(5) , McElderry, Margaret K.) Simon & Schuster Children's Publishing.

—Shadows on the Sea. l.t. ed. 2003. 214p. 20.95 (978-0-7862-6145-1(5) , Large Print Pr.) Thorndike Pr.

Harper, Charise Mericle. The Invisible Mistakecase. 2005. (Illus.). 32p. (J). (gr. k-3). 16.00 (978-0-618-44885-2(3)) Houghton Mifflin Co. Trade & Reference Div.

Harrar, George. Not as Crazy As I Seem. 2003. 208p. (J). (gr. 7). tchr. ed. 15.00 (978-0-618-26365-3(9)) Houghton Mifflin Co. Trade & Reference Div.

—Not As Crazy As I Seem. 2004. 240p. (J). (gr. 7). pap. 6.99 (978-0-618-49480-4(4) , Graphia) Houghton Mifflin Co. Trade & Reference Div.

Harris, E. Lynn. Diaries of a Light Skinned Colored Boy. 2001. (Illus.). 160p. (J). lib. bdg. 16.49 (978-0-7868-2552-3(9)) Hyperion Pr.

Harrison, Troon. Goodbye to Atlantis. 2002. 231p. (YA). (gr. 7 up). pap. 7.95 (978-0-7737-6229-9(9)) Stoddart Kids CAN. *Dist:* Fitzhenry & Whiteside, Ltd.

Harshman, Marc. Roads. DePalma, Mary Newell, illus. 2002. 32p. (J). (ps-2). 16.95 (978-0-7614-5112-9(9)) Cavendish, Marshall Corp.

Hart, James W. Grandpa & the Computer. Kingsley, Steven, ed. Glasbergen, Randy, illus. l.t. ed. 2001. 84p. per. 12.95 (978-1-893798-18-2(6)) AIL Newmedia Publishing.

Hartgraves, Richard. Little Cedar. 2006. 130p. pap. 19.95 ***(978-1-4241-4603-1(8))*** PublishAmerica, Inc.

Hartling, Peter. La Abuela. 1998. (SPA., Illus.). 112p. (gr. 4-7). 9.95 (978-84-204-4768-1(4)) Alfaguara, Ediciones, S.A.- Grupo Santillana ESP. *Dist:* Santillana USA Publishing Co., Inc.

—La Abuela. Mizsenko, Ingrid, illus. 2003. (SPA.). 103p. (J). (gr. 5-8). pap. 9.95 (978-968-19-0730-3(2)) Santillana USA Publishing Co., Inc.

—El Viejo John. Habinger, Renate, illus. 2003. Tr. of Old John. (SPA.). 144p. (YA). (gr. 5-8). 12.95 (978-84-204-4816-9(8)) Alfaguara, Ediciones, S.A.- Grupo Santillana ESP. *Dist:* Santillana USA Publishing Co., Inc.

—El viejo John. Habinger, Renate, illus. (SPA.). 144p. (J). (gr. 5-8). pap. 9.95 (978-968-19-0720-4(5)) Santillana USA Publishing Co., Inc.

Hartnett, Sonya. What the Birds See. 2007. (Illus.). 208p. (YA). (gr. 9). pap. 7.99 ***(978-0-7636-3680-7(0))*** Candlewick Pr.

Hartt-Snowbell, Sarah. Vivian Untangled. 2006. (Illus.). 128p. (J). pap. 8.95 (978-1-894917-25-4(1)) Napoleon Publishing/Rendezvous Pr. CAN. *Dist:* AtlasBooks Distribution.

Hassett, Ann & Hassett, John. Mouse in the House. 2007. (Illus.). 32p. (J). (gr. k-3). 6.95 ***(978-0-618-84064-9(8)*** , Walter Lorraine) Houghton Mifflin Co. Trade & Reference Div.

Hassett, John & Hassett, Ann. Mouse in the House. 2004. (Illus.). 32p. (J). (gr. k-3). tchr. ed. 15.00 (978-0-618-35317-0(8) , Walter Lorraine) Houghton Mifflin Co. Trade & Reference Div.

Hatch, Bee. Grandma Talks to Me. l.t. ed. 2005. (Illus.). 46p. (J). per. 12.99 (978-1-59879-022-1(6)) Lifevest Publishing, Inc.

Haugaard, Kay. The Day the Dragon Danced. Barritt, Carolyn Reed, illus. 2006. (J). (gr. 2-4). 16.95 (978-1-885008-30-5(9)) Shen's Bks.

Hautzig, Esther. A Picture of Grandmother. Peck, Beth, illus. 2002. 80p. (J). (gr. 2-5). 15.00 (978-0-374-35920-1(2) , Farrar, Straus & Giroux (BYR)) Farrar, Straus & Giroux.

Hawkesworth, Asha. Grandma's Roses. Kathie, Gabriel, illus. 2006. (J). per. (978-0-9738442-9-0(9)) Avatar Pubns., Inc. CAN. *Dist:* Baker & Taylor Bks., NACSCORP, Inc.

Hawxhurst, Joan C. Bubbe & Gram: My Two Grandmothers. Bynum-Nwulu, Jane, illus. 2003. 32p. (J). (ps-2). 12.95 (978-0-9651284-2-1(3)) Dovetail Publishing.

Hay, Kathleen. The Quest of Happy Hearts. 2004. reprint ed. pap. 15.95 (978-1-4191-7963-1(2)); pap. 1.99 (978-1-4192-7963-8(7)) Kessinger Publishing, LLC.

Haynes, Max. Grandma's Gone to Live in the Stars. 2000. (Concept Book Ser.). (Illus.). 32p. (J). (ps-3). 15.95 (978-0-8075-3026-9(3)) Whitman, Albert & Co.

Heck, C. S. Memory-Kisses. 2007. 104p. per. 9.95 ***(978-0-595-41514-4(8))*** iUniverse, Inc.

Hedderwick, Mairi. Katie Morag & the Two Grandmothers. 2005. (Illus.). 32p. (J). pap. 9.99 (978-0-09-911871-8(8) , Red Fox) Random Hse. Children's Bks. GBR. *Dist:* Trafalgar Square Publishing.

—Walk with Grannie. 2003. (Illus.). 32p. (J). 19.99 (978-0-340-86642-9(X) , Hodder & Stoughton) Hodder General Publishing Division GBR. *Dist:* Trafalgar Square Publishing.

—A Walk with Grannie. Date not set. (Illus.). pap. (978-0-340-87353-3(1) , Hodder Children's Books) Hodder Children's Division.

Hege, Evelyn. A Letter for Titus. 2004. (Illus.). 24p. (ps-5). 2.70 (978-0-7399-2345-0(5) , 2791) Rod & Staff Pubs., Inc.

Heidi. 2006. 64p. (J). 8.99 (978-0-7945-1237-8(2) , Usborne) EDC Publishing.

Heine, Teresa. Elephant Dance: Remembering India. Moxley, Sheila, illus. 2004. 40p. (J). 16.99 (978-1-84148-917-9(4)) Barefoot Bks., Inc.

Helldorfer, M. C. Got to Dance. Nakata, Hiroe, illus. 2004. 32p. (J). (gr. k-k). lib. bdg. 17.99 (978-0-385-90865-8(2) , Doubleday Bks. for Young Readers) Random Hse. Children's Bks.

Heller, Linda. The Castle on Hester Street. Kulikov, Boris, illus. 2007. 40p. (J). 15.99 (978-0-689-87434-5(0) , Simon & Schuster Children's Publishing) Simon & Schuster Children's Publishing.

Helowicz, Cathy. On Grandpop's Lap. 1. 2004. (Illus.). 32p. (J). 18.95 (978-0-9752684-0-7(6)) Bodkin Pointe Pr.

Hemery, Kathleen Maresh. The Healing Tree. Teis, Kyra, illus. 2001. (J). (978-1-56123-153-9(3) , HTRC) Centering Corp.

Hemphill, Helen. Long Gone Daddy. 2006. 176p. (J). 16.95 (978-1-932425-38-3(1) , Lemniscaat) Boyds Mills Pr.

Henderson, Kathy. And the Good Brown Earth. Henderson, Kathy, illus. 2004. (Illus.). 40p. (J). (ps up). 15.99 (978-0-7636-2301-2(6)) Candlewick Pr.

Henkes, Kevin. Grandpa & Bo. Henkes, Kevin, illus. 2002. (Illus.). 40p. (J). 15.99 (978-0-06-623837-1(4)); lib. bdg. 16.89 (978-0-06-623838-8(2)) HarperCollins Pubs.

—Olive's Ocean. 224p. (J). 2003. (gr. 5 up). 15.99 (978-0-06-053543-8(1) , 53396925); 2003. (gr. 5 up). lib. bdg. 16.89 (978-0-06-053544-5(X)); 2005. (gr. k-9). reprint ed. pap. 6.99 (978-0-06-053545-2(8) , Harper Trophy) HarperCollins Pubs.

Henkes, Kevin. Sun & Spoon. 2007. 144p. (J). pap. 5.99 ***(978-0-06-128875-3(6)*** , Harper Trophy) HarperCollins Pubs.

—Sun & Spoon. 1998. (Puffin Novel Ser.). 144p. (J). (gr. 3-7). pap. 4.99 (978-0-14-130095-5(7) , Puffin) Penguin Group (USA) Inc.

Herman, Charlotte. The Memory Cupboard: A Thanksgiving Story. Stahl, Ben F., illus. 2003. 32p. (J). (gr. 1-4). 16.95 (978-0-8075-5055-7(8)) Whitman, Albert & Co.

Hermes, Patricia. Emma Dilemma & the Two Nannies. 2007. 117p. (J). ***(978-1-4287-3961-1(0))*** Cavendish, Marshall Corp.

Hermes, Patricia. Sweet by & By. 2002. 208p. (J). (gr. 3-6). 15.99 (978-0-380-97452-8(5)) HarperCollins Pubs.

Herrera, Juan Felipe. Grandma & Me at the Flea / Los Meros Meros Remateros. Rohmer, Harriet & Cumpiano, Ina, eds. Lucio-Brock, Anita de, illus. 2002. Tr. of Los Meros Meros Remateros. (ENG & SPA.). 32p. (J). (gr. 1 up). 16.95 (978-0-89239-171-4(5)) Children's Bk. Pr.

Herrick, Steven. Do-Wrong Ron. Magerl, Caroline, illus. 2005. 132p. (J). pap. 6.95 (978-1-86508-661-3(4)) Allen & Unwin AUS. *Dist:* Independent Pubs. Group.

Hesse, Karen. Poppy's Chair. 2000. (Illus.). 32p. (J). (ps-3). pap. 5.99 (978-0-439-16130-5(4)) Scholastic, Inc.

—Poppy's Chair. 2000. (978-0-606-18884-5(3)) Tandem Library Bks.

Hest, Amy. Jamaica Louise James. (gr. k-3). lib. bdg. 14.15 (978-0-613-70961-3(6)) Tandem Library Bks.

—Make the Team, Baby Duck! Barton, Jill, illus. 2002. (Baby Duck Books! Ser.). 32p. (J). (ps-1). 16.99 (978-0-7636-1541-3(2)) Candlewick Pr.

—Off to School, Baby Duck! Barton, Jill, illus. 2002. (J). 26.15 (978-0-7587-3294-1(5)) Book Wholesalers, Inc.

—Off to School, Baby Duck! Barton, Jill, illus. 2007. 32p. (J). (ps-1). pap. 6.99 ***(978-0-7636-3438-4(7))*** Candlewick Pr.

Hest, Amy. You're the Boss, Baby Duck! 2001. (978-0-606-22536-6(6)) Tandem Library Bks.

Hickey, Tony. Granny & the American Witch. 1998. (Illus.). 112p. (YA). (gr. 1 up). pap. 7.95 (978-1-901737-13-4(6)) Anvil Bks., Ltd. IRL. *Dist:* Dufour Editions, Inc.

High, Gracia. I am not going to sleep Now. 2004. 21p. pap. 14.95 (978-1-4137-3000-5(0)) PublishAmerica, Inc.

High, Linda. Lap Talks with Granny at Easter. 2003. (J). pap. 9.95 (978-0-9661186-9-8(3)) Books for Children of the World.

High, Linda Oatman. Beekeepers. 2003. (Illus.). 32p. (J). (gr. 2-4). 15.95 (978-1-56397-486-1(X)) Boyds Mills Pr.

Hill, Eric. Spot Loves His Grandma. Hill, Eric, illus. 2008. 12p. (J). (ps-k). bds. 5.99 ***(978-0-399-24728-6(9)*** , Putnam Juvenile) Penguin Group (USA) Inc.

—Spot Loves His Grandpa. Hill, Eric, illus. 2008. 12p. (J). (ps-k). bds. 5.99 ***(978-0-399-24729-3(7)*** , Putnam Juvenile) Penguin Group (USA) Inc.

Hill, Eric. Spot Visits His Grandparents. 2005. 20p. (J). pap. 6.99 (978-0-14-240360-0(1) , Puffin) Penguin Group (USA) Inc.

Hill, Janet Muirhead. The Many Adventures of Miranda & Starlight: Six Volume Set. Lehmkuhl, Pat, illus. 2007. (J). 49.95 ***(978-0-9772525-7-2(4))*** Raven Publishing Inc. of Montana.

Hill, Karen. Grandmother's Book of Promises. 2002. 48p. (J). 17.95 (978-1-57856-579-5(0)) Random Hse., Inc.

—Grandmother's Book of Promises. Clar, David Austin, illus. 2000. 48p. (J). (ps-2). 9.99 (978-1-57856-221-3(X) , WaterBrook Pr.) WaterBrook Pr.

Hilton, Nette. Web. 1998. (Illus.). 88p. (ps-3). 5.95 (978-0-207-17245-8(5)) HarperCollins Pubs.

Hines, Anna Grossnickle. My Grandma Is Coming to Town. Sweet, Melissa, illus. 2003. 24p. (J). (ps-1). 13.99 (978-0-7636-1237-5(5)) Candlewick Pr.

Hobbie, Holly. Just Like You. Workman, Lisa, illus. 2006. (Holly Hobbie & Friends Ser.). 16p. (J). 8.99 (978-1-4169-2797-6(2) , Little Simon) Simon & Schuster Children's Publishing.

Hoberman, Mary Ann. I'm Going to Grandma's. Beeke, Tiphanie, illus. 2007. 32p. (J). (ps-2). 16.00 (978-0-15-216592-5(4)) Harcourt Trade Pubs.

Hodes, Loren. Too Big, Too Little. . . Just Right! Hodes, Loren, illus. 2002. (Illus.). (J). 9.95 (978-1-880582-72-5(4) , TTTH) Judaica Pr., Inc., The.

Hodge, John. Finding Grandpa Everywhere: A Young Child Discovers Memories of a Grandparent. Aitken, Susan, illus. 1999. (J). 6.95 (978-1-56123-125-6(8)) Centering Corp.

Hoffman, Mary. Starring Grace. Binch, Caroline, illus. (Chapters Ser.). 96p. (J). 2001. (gr. 2-6). pap. 4.99 (978-0-14-230022-0(5) , Puffin); 2000. (gr. k-4). 14.99 (978-0-8037-2559-1(0) , Dial) Penguin Group (USA) Inc.

—Starring Grace. 2001. (gr. 3-6). lib. bdg. 13.00 (978-0-613-44418-7(3)) Tandem Library Bks.

Hojel, Barbara & Guy, Ginger F. A Surprise for Grandpa! 1999. Bk. 3. (Illus.). 16p. (C). pap. 7.66 (978-0-201-35145-3(5)) Longman Publishing Group.

Holman, Sandy Lynne. Grandpa, Is Everything Black Bad? Holman, Sandy Lynne, ed. Kometiani, Lela, illus. 1998. 32p. (J). (gr. 2-6). lib. bdg. 18.95 (978-0-9644655-0-3(7)) Culture C.O.-O.P., The.

Holt, Kimberly Willis. Dancing in Cadillac Light. 2002. 176p. (J). (gr. 5 up). pap. 5.99 (978-0-698-11970-3(3) , Putnam Juvenile) Penguin Group (USA) Inc.

—Dancing in Cadillac Light. 2004. 176p. (J). (gr. 4-7). pap. 36.00 incl. audio (978-0-8072-2095-5(7) , Listening Library) Random Hse. Audio Publishing Group.

—Dancing in Cadillac Light. 2002. (gr. 5-8). lib. bdg. 14.15 (978-0-613-66873-6(1)) Tandem Library Bks.

—My Louisiana Sky. rev. ed. 1998. 176p. (J). (gr. 4-7). 17.95 (978-0-8050-5251-0(8) , Holt, Henry & Co. Bks. For Young Readers) Holt, Henry & Co.

—My Louisiana Sky. 2000. 208p. (YA). (gr. 5 up). 4.99 (978-0-8072-8291-5(X) , Listening Library) Random Hse. Audio Publishing Group.

—My Louisiana Sky. 2000. 200p. (J). (gr. k-9). lib. bdg. 13.55 (978-0-613-22802-2(2)) Tandem Library Bks.

Holub, Joan. Glorious Grandmas. Holub, Joan, illus. 2006. (Sparkle 'n' Shimmer Ser.). (Illus.). 14p. (J). 5.99 (978-1-4169-0623-0(1) , Little Simon) Simon & Schuster Children's Publishing.

Holubitsky, Katherine. The Big Snapper. 2006. (Illus.). 144p. (J). pap. 5.95 (978-1-55143-563-3(2)) Orca Bk. Pubs. USA.

Honeywood, Varnette P., illus. One Dark & Scary Night. 2002. (Little Bill Ser.). (J). 11.91 (978-0-7587-1525-8(0)) Book Wholesalers, Inc.

Hong, Chen Jian. La Leyenda De la Cometa. (SPA.). 32p. (978-84-95150-29-5(8)); (978-84-95150-39-4(5)) Corimbo, Editorial S.L.

Hooper, Meredith. Honey Cookies. Bartlett, Alison, illus. 2005. 32p. (J). 15.95 (978-1-84507-394-7(0)); pap. 7.95 (978-1-84507-395-4(9)) Lincoln, Frances Ltd. GBR. *Dist:* Perseus Distribution.

Hooray for Midsommar! 6 Small Books. (Greetings Ser.: Vol. 1). 24p. (gr. 2-3). 31.00 (978-0-7635-9410-7(5)) Rigby Education.

Hooray for Midsommar! Big Book. (Greetings Ser.: Vol. 1). 24p. (gr. 2-3). 31.00 (978-0-7635-5694-5(7)) Rigby Education.

Hope, Laura Lee. Bunny Brown & His Sister Sue on Grandpa's Farm. 2007. (ENG.). 164p. 95.99 ***(978-1-4280-7438-5(4));*** per. 89.99 ***(978-1-4280-7440-8(6))*** IndyPublish.com.

—Six Little Bunkers at Grandpa Ford's. 2006. 41.99 ***(978-1-4280-1454-1(3));*** pap. 35.99 ***(978-1-4280-1451-0(9))*** IndyPublish.com.

Hopkins, Nicolia. What was Grandma Doing? eVision, ed. Wiggins, Margaret W., illus. 2007. (J). per. 9.99 ***(978-0-9768579-8-3(7))*** eVision, LLC.

Hopkinson, Deborah. Bluebird Summer. Andersen, Bethanne, illus. 2001. 32p. (J). (gr. 1 up). 15.95 (978-0-688-17398-2(5)) HarperCollins Pubs.

Horning, Sandra. The Giant Hug. Gorbachev, Valeri, illus. 2005. 40p. (J). (ps-3). 15.95 (978-0-375-82477-7(4)); lib. bdg. 17.99 (978-0-375-92477-4(9)) Random Hse. Children's Bks. (Knopf Bks. for Young Readers).

Horse, Harry, illus. The Last Polar Bears. 2007. 76p. (J). (gr. 1-5). 12.95 ***(978-1-56145-379-5(X)*** , Peachtree Junior) Peachtree Pubs., Ltd.

Howard, Milly. The Case of the Sassy Parrot. Day, Bruce, illus. 2002. (Crimebusters, Inc Ser.: Bk. 2). 168p. (J). pap. 6.49 (978-1-57924-721-8(0)) Jones, Bob Univ. Pr.

—Case of the Sassy Parrot. 2002. (gr. 3-6). lib. bdg. 14.70 (978-0-613-79328-5(5)) Tandem Library Bks.

Hudspeth, Elly Shafter & Peyton, Barbara. Colt Revolt: Memoirs of Three Mischievous, but Adorable Equine Siblings. Wilkins, Rhett, illus. 2007. 140p. pap. 12.95 ***(978-1-60145-223-8(3))*** Booklocker.com, Inc.

Hull, Maureen. The View from a Kite. 2007. (Illus.). 320p. (YA). (gr. 10 up). pap. ***(978-1-55109-591-2(2)*** , Vagrant Pr.) Nimbus Publishing, Ltd.

The Hundred Penny Box. 1999. (J). 9.95 (978-1-56137-386-4(9)) Novel Units, Inc.

Hunter, Helen W. Turkey Hunting with Grandpa. Rozeboom, Grant, illus. 2000. (Young American Hunting & Fishing Ser.: Vol. 2). (J). (gr. 2-7). pap. 9.99 (978-0-9662769-2-3(2)) Hunter Hse. Pubns.

Hurst, Carol Otis. Terrible Storm. Schindler, S. D., illus. 2007. 32p. (J). (gr. k-3). 16.99 (978-0-06-009001-2(4)); lib. bdg. 17.89 (978-0-06-009002-9(2)) HarperCollins Pubs.

Huskins, T. A. I Am a Whosoever. 2006. 62p. pap. 12.95 (978-1-4241-0308-9(8)) PublishAmerica, Inc.

Hutchins, Pat. Bumpety Bump! Hutchins, Pat, illus. 2006. (Illus.). 32p. (J). 15.99 (978-0-06-055999-1(3)); lib. bdg. 16.89 (978-0-06-056000-3(2)) HarperCollins Pubs.

Hysen, Sylvia. A Very Dairy Christmas. 2005. 312p. (YA). 24.95 (978-0-9763365-6-3(1)) 1st Impression Publishing.

I Love My Grandma. (Early Intervention Levels Ser.). 23.10 (978-0-7362-0020-2(7)) Hampton-Brown Bks.

I Remember Mama. 2004. (J). per. 5.99 (978-0-9760112-0-0(4)) Smith, Tyjauna.

Igus, Toyomi. Two Mrs Gibsons. 2001. (gr. k-3). lib. bdg. 16.40 (978-0-613-65372-5(6)) Tandem Library Bks.

I'm Glad I'm Your Grandma. 2006. 16p. (J). pap. 1.99 (978-0-7847-1686-1(2) , 02988) Standard Publishing.

Ingold, Jeanette. Window. 2003. (gr. 7-12). lib. bdg. 8.10 (978-0-613-70529-5(7)) Tandem Library Bks.

Isabella's Rainbow & Grandma's Teapots. 2000. vi, 126p. (YA). (gr. 7-12). pap. 9.95 (978-0-9707575-0-0(6)) Slator, Laraine.

Isadora, Rachel. Lili Backstage. Isadora, Rachel, illus. 2002. (Illus.). (J). 13.19 (978-0-7587-2987-3(1)) Book Wholesalers, Inc.

—Luke Goes to Bat. Isadora, Rachel, illus. 2005. (Illus.). 32p. (J). (ps-3). 15.99 (978-0-399-23604-4(X) , Putnam Juvenile) Penguin Group (USA) Inc.

—What a Family! A Fresh Look at Family Trees. 2006. (Illus.). (J). ***(978-1-4156-5634-1(7)*** , Putnam Juvenile) Penguin Group (USA) Inc.

Isadora, Rachel. Yo, Jo! 2007. (Illus.). 40p. (J). 16.00 (978-0-15-205783-1(8)) Harcourt Children's Bks.

It's a Zoo! Individual Title, 6 Packs. (ps-2). 27.00 (978-0-7635-9454-1(7)) Rigby Education.

Itterman, Bert. Growing up with Grandpa. 2006. (Illus.). 112p. pap. ***(978-1-57579-330-6(X))*** Pine Hill Pr., Inc.

Ives, Penny. Granny's Quilt. (Illus.). 32p. (J). pap. 9.95 (978-0-14-054560-9(3)) Penguin Bks., Ltd. GBR. *Dist:* Trafalgar Square Publishing.

Jacko, the Dreamer: Early Level Satellite Individual Title Six-Packs. (Sails Literacy Ser.). 16p. (gr. 1-2). 27.00 (978-0-7578-3159-1(1)) Rigby Education.

Jackson, Neta. Grandma Aggie & the Bless You. 2004. 11.99 (978-0-8254-2939-2(0)) Kregel Pubns.

Jackson, Rebecca. Mackenzie & the Baby Robin. 2004. (Illus.). (J). bds. 14.95 (978-1-56469-114-9(4)) Harmony Hse. Pubs.

Jacobson, Jennifer Richard. Andy Shane & the Pumpkin Trick. Carter, Abby, illus. 64p. (J). (gr. k-3). 2007. pap. 4.99 ***(978-0-7636-3306-6(2));*** 2006. 13.99 (978-0-7636-2605-1(8)) Candlewick Pr.

Jardine, Alan. Sloop John B: A Pirate's Tale. Pickering, Jimmy, illus. 2005. 32p. 17.95 (978-1-59687-181-6(4)); 17.95 (978-0-689-03596-8(9)) ibooks, Inc. (Milk & Cookies).

E
F
G

Jennings, Patrick. The Ears of Corn: An Ike & Mem Story. Alter, Anna, illus. 2003. 64p. (J). tchr. ed. 15.95 (978-0-8234-1770-4(0)) Holiday Hse., Inc.

—The Weeping Willow. Alter, Anna, illus. 2002. (Ike & Mem Story Ser.: No. 3). 56p. (J). (gr. k-3). tchr. ed. 15.95 (978-0-8234-1671-4(2)) Holiday Hse., Inc.

Jennings, Sharon. The Bye-Bye Pie. Ohi, Ruth, illus. 1999. 31p. (J). (gr. k-3). (978-1-55041-405-9(4)) Fitzhenry & Whiteside, Ltd.

Jessup, Harley. Grandma Summer. 2001. (Illus.). (J). (978-0-606-21800-9(9)) Tandem Library Bks.

Johnson, Angela. Just Like Josh Gibson. Peck, Beth, illus. 2007. 32p. (J). reprint ed. 6.99 (978-1-4169-2728-0(X), Aladdin) Simon & Schuster Children's Publishing.

—Toning the Sweep. 2002. (J). 13.19 (978-0-7587-0401-6(1)) Book Wholesalers, Inc.

—Toning the Sweep. 2003. 112p. (J). (gr. 7 up). pap. 5.99 (978-0-590-48142-7(8), Scholastic Paperbacks) Scholastic, Inc.

Johnson, Dolores, illus. Grandma's Hands. 1998. (Accelerated Reader Bks.). 32p. (J). (gr. 1-4). 15.95 (978-0-7614-5025-2(4), Cavendish Children's Bks.) Cavendish, Marshall Corp.

Johnson, Lindsay Lee. Soul Moon Soup. 1998. 134p. (J). (gr. 5 up). 15.95 (978-1-886910-87-4(1), Lemniscaat) Boyds Mills Pr.

Johnson, Sandi. Baseball Billy. Johnson, Britt, ed. Nadaskay, Lori, illus. l.t. ed. 2003. 12p. (J). (gr. k-5). spiral bd. 5.99 (978-1-929063-30-7(X), 320) Moons & Stars Publishing For Children.

Johnston, Annie Fell. The Little Colonel. 2005. reprint ed. pap. 21.95 (978-0-7661-9402-1(7)) Kessinger Publishing, LLC.

Johnston, Annie Fell. The Little Colonel (Illustrated Edition) 2006. pap. (*978-1-4065-1132-1(3)) Dodo Pr.

Johnston, Annie Fellows. The Little Colonel. Barry, Etheldred B., illus. 2004. (Little Colonel Ser.). 128p. (J). (gr. 4-7). reprint ed. per. 12.95 (978-1-55709-315-8(6)) Applewood Bks.

Johnston, Fellows Annie. Little Colonel. 2006. pap. 18.99 (*978-1-4280-3283-5(5)) IndyPublish.com.

Johnston, Julie. The Only Outcast. 1999. (J). (978-0-606-19122-7(4)) Tandem Library Bks.

—The Only Outcast. 1999. 248p. (J). (gr. 6-9). reprint ed. pap. 6.95 (978-0-88776-488-2(6)) Tundra Bks., Inc./Livres Toundra, Inc. CAN. *Dist:* Random Hse., Inc.

Jonathan Buys a Present: Individual Title Six-Packs. 16p. (gr. 1-2). 35.00 (978-0-7635-8931-8(4)) Rigby Education.

Jones, Marcia Thornton & Dadey, Debbie. Happy Boo Day. 2000. (Bailey City Monsters Ser.: No. 9). (Illus.). (J). (gr. 2-4). 10.79 (978-0-606-18515-8(1)) Tandem Library Bks.

Jones, Margaret. Nat. 2004. (Illus.). 111p. pap. 13.95 (978-1-84323-327-5(4)) Beekman Bks., Inc.

Jones, Meinir Pierce & Jones, Jac. Taid Ar Binnau. 2005. (WEL., Illus.). 14p. 4.99 (978-1-84323-381-7(9)) Gomer Pr. GBR. *Dist:* Gomer Pr.

Jones, Susan & Jones, Susan. Until We Meet Again. 2007. (Illus.). 64p. 24.95 (*978-0-9778209-4-8(7)) 50/50 Publishing.

Joyce, Jacqueline. Grandma's Rocker. DelMar Communication International Staff, tr. 1998. (Illus.). 36p. (J). (ps-4). pap. 7.95 (978-1-891317-02-6(4), 11145); (ENG & SPA., pap. 7.95 (978-1-891317-03-3(2), 11146) Bear Path, The.

Just Like Grandpa: Individual Title Six-Packs. (Literatura 2000 Ser.). (gr. 1-2). 28.00 (978-0-7635-0093-1(3)) Rigby Education.

Just Like My Grandpa. (Early Intervention Levels Ser.). 23.10 (978-0-7362-0033-2(9)) Hampton-Brown Bks.

Juster, Norton. The Hello, Goodbye Window. Raschka, Chris, illus. 2005. 32p. (J). (ps-17). 15.95 (978-0-7868-0914-1(0)) Hyperion Bks. for Children.

Kaderli, Janet. Patchwork Trail. Arnold, Patricia, illus. 2005. 59p. (J). 9.95 (978-0-9754796-2-9(8)) GASLight Publishing.

Kadono, Eiko. Grandpa's Soup. Ichikawa, Satomi, illus. 2004. 32p. (J). (ps-3). 16.00 (978-0-8028-5195-6(9)) Eerdmans, William B. Publishing Co.

Kakugawa, Frances H. Wordsworth Dances the Waltz. DeSica, Melissa, illus. 2007. 32p. 10.95 (*978-0-9790647-3-9(2)) Watermark Publishing, LLC.

Kalkman, Lora. Grandma Loves You. Fitchwell, Jennifer, illus. 2003. (My First Treasury Ser.). 40p. (J). bds. (978-0-7853-8246-1(1), 7181800) Publications International, Ltd.

Kallevig, Christine P. Please Pass Grandma's Leg: Aka, the Case of the Sacked Potatoes. 2003. (Illus.). 128p. (J). per. 9.95 (978-0-9628769-3-6(3)) Storytime Ink International.

Karim, Roberta. Faraway Grandpa. Rand, Ted, illus. rev. ed. 2004. 40p. (J). 16.95 (978-0-8050-6785-9(X), Holt, Henry & Co. Bks. For Young Readers) Holt, Henry & Co.

Kass, Pnina Moed. Real Time. 2004. 192p. (YA). (gr. 7 up). 15.00 (978-0-618-44203-4(0), Clarion Bks.) Houghton Mifflin Co. Trade & Reference Div.

Kasza, Keiko. Grandpa Toad's Secrets. Kasza, Keiko, illus. 2002. (Illus.). (J). 13.19 (978-0-7587-2644-5(9)) Book Wholesalers, Inc.

—Grandpa Toad's Secrets. 1998. (J). (978-0-606-12954-1(5)) Tandem Library Bks.

—Los Secretos de Abuelo Sapo. (SPA., Illus.). (J). (gr. 1-3). 8.95 (978-958-04-3624-9(X), NR7688) Norma S.A. COL. *Dist:* Distribuidora Norma, Inc., Lectorum Pubns., Inc.

Katz, Karen. Grandma & Me. Katz, Karen, illus. 2002. (Illus.). 14p. (J). 6.99 (978-0-689-84905-3(2), Little Simon) Simon & Schuster Children's Publishing.

Keenan, Carolyn. Annie Belle. 2005. 94p. pap. 14.95 (978-1-4137-8263-9(9)) PublishAmerica, Inc.

Keep, Linda Lowery. Truth & Salsa. 2006. 176p. (J). 14.95 (978-1-56145-366-5(8), Peachtree Junior) Peachtree Pubs., Ltd.

Keller, Laurie S. Grandpa Gazillion's Number Yard. 2005. (Illus.). 32p. (J). (ps-ps). 16.95 (978-0-8050-6282-3(3), Holt, Henry & Co. Bks. For Young Readers) Holt, Henry & Co.

Kemper, Bebe. Seeing Zach. 1999. (Illus.). 32p. (J). 14.95 (978-0-9674363-0-2(3), Rainy Day Bks.) Purple Chickie Pr.

Kennedy, Frances. The Just-Right, Perfect Present. Aldridge, Sheila, illus. 2006. 32p. (J). (gr. k-2). 14.95 (*978-1-58246-199-1(6), Tricycle Pr.) Ten Speed Pr.

Kennedy, Pamela. Granny's Cozy Quilt of Memories. Wummer, Amy, illus. 2006. 32p. (J). (gr. 4-6). 8.95 (978-0-8249-5538-0(2), Guideposts) Ideals Pubns.

Kessler, Cristina. My Great-Grandmother's Gourd. Krudop, Walter Lyon, illus. 2000. 32p. (J). (gr. k-4). 17.99 (978-0-531-33284-9(5), Orchard Bks.) Scholastic, Inc.

King, Emily. Mrs. Twiggenbotham Goes to Town. 2003. (Twiggenbotham Adventure Ser.). (Illus.). 32p. (J). 12.99 (978-0-8254-3064-0(X)) Kregel Pubns.

Kinsey-Warnock, Natalie. Canada Geese Quilt. 2000. 11.79 (978-0-606-20354-8(0)) Tandem Library Bks.

Kippling, Bozenka. Stories from the Inner World: Introducing My Best Friends. Sawatzky, Goranka, illus. l.t. ed. 2002. 48p. (J). per. (978-0-9689096-1-4(2)) Seed Children, Inc.

Klein, Adria F. Max Goes to a Cookout. 2007. (Read-It! Readers Ser.). (Illus.). 24p. (J). (*978-1-4048-3290-9(4), 1265793) Picture Window Bks.

—Max Goes to a Cookout. Gallagher-Cole, Mernie, illus. 2006. (Read-It! Readers Ser.). 24p. (J). (*978-1-4048-3146-9(0), 1265793) Picture Window Bks.

—Max Goes to the Farm. Gallagher-Cole, Mernie, illus. 2007. (J). lib. bdg. (*978-1-4048-3678-5(0)) Picture Window Bks.

Kline, Suzy. Horrible Harry & the Holidaze. Remkiewicz, Frank, illus. 2004. (Horrible Harry Ser.). 80p. (J). pap. 3.99 (978-0-14-240205-4(2), Puffin) Penguin Group (USA) Inc.

—Horrible Harry & the Holidaze. Remkiewicz, Frank, illus. 2004. 67p. (J). (gr. 2-5). per. 11.19 (978-0-606-32710-7(X)) Tandem Library Bks.

Kline, Suzy & Kline, Suzy. Horrible Harry & the Holidaze. Remkiewicz, Frank, illus. 2003. (Horrible Harry Ser.). 64p. (J). (gr. 2-k). 13.99 (978-0-670-03642-4(0), Viking Juvenile) Penguin Group (USA) Inc.

Klingel, Cynthia Fitterer & Noyed, Robert B. Grandma, Grandpa, & the Letter G. 2003. (Alphaphonics Ser.). (Illus.). 24p. (J). (ps-2). 21.36 (978-1-59296-097-2(9)) Child's World, Inc.

Knipe, Floyd P. Forest & Grandpa Go Fishing. Jackson, James K., illus. 2000. (Forest the Huggable Dog Ser.: Vol. 2). 23p. (J). (ps-3). pap. 4.95 (978-1-930130-06-7(6)) Nature's Nest Bks.

—Forest & Grandpa Go Fishing Coloring Book. Jackson, James K., illus. 2000. (Forest the Huggable Dog Ser.: Vol. 2). 23p. (J). (ps-3). pap. 2.00 (978-1-930130-07-4(4)) Nature's Nest Bks.

Knister. Sophie's Dance. Schlundt, Mandy, illus. 2007. 32p. (J). 16.99 (*978-0-698-40056-6(9), Minedition) Penguin Group (USA) Inc.

Knowlton, Laurie Lazzaro. A Young Man's Dance. Johnson, Layne, illus. 2006. 32p. (J). 15.95 (978-1-59078-259-0(3)) Boyds Mills Pr.

Kohlhepp, Michael G. Within the Hearthstone Book 2: The Fountain of Balance. 2007. (ENG.). 184p. per. 19.95 (*978-1-4241-4446-4(9)) PublishAmerica, Inc.

Konigsburg, E. L. Amy Elizabeth Explores Bloomingdale's. 1999. (J). 12.79 (978-0-606-17201-1(7)); lib. bdg. 14.15 (978-0-613-21097-3(2)) Tandem Library Bks.

Korman, Gordon. Schooled. 2007. 224p. (gr. 3-7). 15.99 (*978-0-7868-5692-3(0)) Hyperion Pr.

Kornblatt, Marc. Izzy's Place. 2003. (Illus.). 128p. (J). 16.95 (978-0-689-84639-7(8), McElderry, Margaret K.) Simon & Schuster Children's Publishing.

Koutsky, Jan Dale. My Grandma, My Pen Pal. Koutsky, Jan Dale, illus. 2003. (Illus.). 32p. (J). (gr. k-2). 15.95 (978-1-56397-118-1(6)) Boyds Mills Pr.

Kovalski, Maryann. Jenny & Joanna Album. 2005. (978-1-55041-941-2(2)) Fitzhenry & Whiteside, Ltd.

—Take Me Out to the Ball Game. 2004. (Illus.). 32p. (J). (gr. k-2). (978-1-55041-897-2(1)) Fitzhenry & Whiteside, Ltd.

—Take Me Out to the Ball Game. 2006. (Illus.). 32p. (J). pap. 7.95 (978-1-55041-899-6(8)) Fitzhenry & Whiteside, Ltd. CAN. *Dist:* F & W Pubns., Inc.

Kranich, Jane. The Adventures of Froggie & Grandma: Froggie Visits Grandma's House. Plotner, Robert, illus. 2002. 50p. (J). (ps-3). pap. 7.50 (978-0-9716515-0-0(7)) Crane & Rogers Pubs.

Kroll, Virginia L. Butterfly Boy. Suzan, Gerardo, illus. 2003. 32p. (J). (gr. k-2). pap. 8.95 (978-1-59078-055-8(8)) Boyds Mills Pr.

—Butterfly Boy. 2002. (gr. k-3). lib. bdg. 16.40 (978-0-613-59283-3(2)) Tandem Library Bks.

Kropf, Latifa Berry & Cohen, Tod. It's Hanukkah Time! 2004. (Illus.). 24p. (J). (ps-1). (978-1-58013-120-9(4)) Kar-Ben Publishing.

Kurtz, Carmen. Veva y el Mar.Tr. of Veva & the Sea. (SPA.). 144p. (J). (gr. 3-5). (978-84-279-3129-9(8)) Noguer y Caralt Editores, S. A. ESP. *Dist:* Lectorum Pubns., Inc.

Labrecque, Candida. A Riverside Walk with Grandma. Labrecque, Candida, illus. l.t. ed. 2006. (Illus.). 23p. (J). per. 11.95 (978-1-59879-137-2(0)) Lifevest Publishing, Inc.

Lachtman, Ofelia Dumas. A Good Place for Maggie. 2002. 160p. (YA). pap. 9.95 (978-1-55885-372-0(3), Piñata Books) Arte Publico Pr.

—A Good Place for Maggie. 2002. (gr. 3-6). lib. bdg. 18.75 (978-0-613-85296-8(6)) Tandem Library Bks.

Lacy, Kendra. Drachen. 2007. 188p. per. 13.95 (*978-0-595-43809-9(1)) iUniverse, Inc.

Lake, Julie. Galveston's Summer of the Storm. 2003. (Chaparral Book for Young Readers Ser.). 210p. 16.95 (978-0-87565-272-6(7)) Texas Christian Univ. Pr.

LaMarche, Jim. The Raft. LaMarche, Jim, illus. (Illus.). 40p. (J). (gr. 1 up). 2000. 16.99 (978-0-688-13977-3(9)); 2002. reprint ed. pap. 6.99 (978-0-06-443856-8(2), Harper Trophy) HarperCollins Pubs.

Laminack, Lester. Saturdays & Teacakes. Soentpiet, Chris K., illus. 2004. 32p. (J). (gr. 1-2). 16.95 (978-1-56145-303-0(X)) Peachtree Pubs., Ltd.

Laminack, Lester L. The Sunsets of Miss Olivia Wiggins. Bergum, Constance Rummel, illus. 1998. 32p. (J). (gr. 1-5). 15.95 (978-1-56145-139-5(8)) Peachtree Pubs., Ltd.

Lamote, Lisa Edman. A Day Out for Opus. 2006. (J). 15.99 (978-1-933673-03-5(6), BookMann Pr.) Mann Publishing Group.

—Don't Judge a Book by Its Cover. 2006. (J). 15.99 (978-1-933673-01-1(X), BookMann Pr.) Mann Publishing Group.

The Land Beyond Forever. 2006. 25.00 (*978-0-9785570-0-3(X)) Three Sisters Publishing Hse., Ltd.

Landis, Mary. David & Susan at the Little Green House. 2005. (Illus.). 170p. 8.20 (978-0-7399-2352-8(8), 2185.3) Rod & Staff Pubs., Inc.

Langcaon, Jeff, illus. My Grandpa's Battleship Missouri Tour. 2007. (J). 14.95 (*978-1-56647-831-1(6)) Mutual Publishing LLC.

Langlais, Heather M. Mummy's Home Town: The Curse of the Amulet. Gillespie, P. J., illus. 1999. 144p. (J). (gr. 4-8). pap. 7.95 (978-1-930506-00-8(7)) March Forth Pubns.

Lanqcaon, Jeff. Grandpa's Magic Banyan Tree. 2005. 32p. (J). 12.95 (978-1-56647-740-6(9)) Mutual Publishing LLC.

Lansky, Bruce. When Grandma Was a Girl: What Her Life Was Like as a Child. 2002. (Illus.). 22p. 9.95 (978-0-7432-3694-2(7)) Meadowbrook Pr.

Larbalestier, Justine. Magic or Madness. (gr. 7-12). 2006. 304p. (YA). pap. 7.99 (978-1-59514-070-8(0)); 2005. 288p. (J). 16.99 (978-1-59514-022-7(0)) Penguin Group (USA) Inc. (Razorbill).

Lasky, Kathryn. True North: A Novel of the Underground Railroad. 1998. (J). (978-0-606-13874-1(9)) Tandem Library Bks.

Lavallee, Joosse. Grandma Calls Me Beautiful. 2008. 36p. (J). 16.99 (978-0-8118-5815-1(4)) Chronicle Bks. LLC.

Lawson, Sue. My Gram's different. Magerl, Caroline, illus. 2005. 32p. (J). 16.95 (978-1-894965-16-3(7)) Simply Read Bks. CAN. *Dist:* Perseus Distribution.

Leach, Janet Elliott. Grandma Used to Be a Girl. 2004. pap. 8.95 (978-0-533-14587-4(2)) Vantage Pr., Inc.

Leavell, Chuck & Crovotta, Nicholas. The Tree Farmer. Bleau, Rebecca, illus. 2005. 32p. (J). 16.95 (978-1-893622-16-6(9), VSP Bks.) Vacation Spot Publishing.

Leavitt, Martine. Keturah & Lord Death. 2006. 216p. (YA). (gr. 7 up). 16.95 (978-1-932425-29-1(2), Front Street) Boyds Mills Pr.

Lee, Milly. Nim & the War Effort. Choi, Yangsook, illus. 2002. 40p. (J). pap. 6.95 (978-0-374-45506-4(6), Sunburst) Farrar, Straus & Giroux.

—Nim & the War Effort. 2002. (gr. 3-6). lib. bdg. 14.10 (978-0-613-53846-6(3)) Tandem Library Bks.

Lee, So-Young, illus. & creator. Arcana, Vol. 4. Lee, So-Young, creator. 4th rev. ed. 2006. pap. 9.99 (978-1-59816-200-4(4), Tokyopop Kids) TOKYOPOP, Inc.

Lee, Uk-Bae. Sori's Harvest Moon Day: A Story of Korea. Lee, Uk-Bae, illus. 1999. (Make Friends Around the World Ser.). Orig. Title: Sori's Chu-Suk. (Illus.). 32p. (J). (gr. k-3). 15.95 (978-1-56899-687-5(X), B8001); 5.95 (978-1-56899-688-2(8), S8001) Soundprints.

Leininger, Tracy M. Nothing Can Separate Us: The Story of Nan Harper. Pulley, Kelly & Reed, Lisa, illus. 2000. 63p. (J). 16.00 (978-1-929241-21-7(6)) Vision Forum, Inc., The.

Leiviska, Karen. The War with Grandpa. Chang, Wendy, illus. 1999. (Literature Units Ser.). 48p. (gr. 3-5). pap., tchr. ed. 7.99 (978-1-57690-334-6(6), TCA2334) Teacher Created Materials, Inc.

Lenam, Salva. Kiko en Casa de los Abuelos. Roman, Santi, illus. 2005. (Kiko Ser.). (SPA.). 10p. (J). 3.95 (978-84-95761-81-1(5)) Ediciones Norte, Inc.

Leonard, Marcia. Dan & Dan. Handelman, Dorothy, photos by. 1998. (Real Kids Readers Ser.). (Illus.). 32p. (gr. k-1). (J). pap. 4.99 (978-0-7613-2028-9(8)); lib. bdg. 18.90 (978-0-7613-2003-6(2)) Lerner Publishing Group. (Millbrook Pr.).

Leonard, Nellie M. Grand Daddy Whiskers, M. D. 2004. reprint ed. pap. 15.95 (978-1-4191-2227-9(4)); pap. 1.99 (978-1-4192-2227-6(9)) Kessinger Publishing, LLC.

Leppard, Lois Gladys. Mandie & the Graduation Mystery. 2004. (Mandie Bks.). 160p. (J). reprint ed. mass mkt. 5.99 (978-0-7642-2643-4(6)) Bethany Hse. Pubs.

Less, Emma. My Trip to Grandma's. Ledger, Bill, illus. 2006. 14p. bds. 5.95 (978-1-4027-2175-5(7)) Sterling Publishing Co., Inc.

Levy, Janice. Abuelito Eats with His Fingers. Johnson, Layne, illus. 1998. 32p. 14.95 (978-1-57168-177-5(9)) Eakin Pr.

Levy, Janice. I Remember Abuelito/Yo Recuerdo a Abuelito: A Day of the Dead Story/Un Cuento del Dia de los Muertos. Arisa, Miguel, tr. Lopez, Loretta, illus. 2007. (Albert Whitman Prairie Paperback Ser.). (SPA & ENG.). 32p. (J). (ps-3). 6.95 (*978-0-8075-3517-2(6)); 16.95 (*978-0-8075-3516-5(8)) Whitman, Albert & Co.

Lewin, Ted. The Storytellers. 1998. (Illus.). 40p. (J). (gr. k-3). 16.00 (978-0-688-15178-2(7)) HarperCollins Pubs.

Lewis, Beverly. The Granny Game. 1999. (Cul-de-Sac Kids Ser.: Vol. 20). (Illus.). 80p. (J). (gr. 2-5). pap. 3.99 (978-0-7642-2125-5(6)) Bethany Hse. Pubs.

Lewis, Rob. Grandpa at the Beach. Lewis, Rob, illus. 1998. (Mondo Ser.). (Illus.). 48p. (J). (gr. 1-5). pap. 4.50 (978-1-57255-552-5(1)) Mondo Publishing.

—Too Much Trouble for Grandpa. 1998. (Mondo Ser.). (Illus.). 48p. (J). (gr. 1-5). pap. 4.50 (978-1-57255-551-8(3)) Mondo Publishing.

Lewis, Sian. Josh in the Jungle. Roberts, Gill, illus. 2005. 32p. pap. 12.95 (978-1-84323-462-3(9)) Beekman Bks., Inc.

Life, Kay, illus. The Secret under the Tree, Vol. 7. 2004. (Adventures of Benny & Watch: Vol. No. 7). 32p. (J). (ps-2). pap. 3.95 (978-0-8075-0643-1(5)) Whitman, Albert & Co.

Light, Carol, illus. Oops, a Curious Horse Story Telling Board. 2003. (J). (978-0-9745803-4-0(1)) Little Big Tomes.

Lindbergh, Reeve. My Hippie Grandmother. Carter, Abby, illus. 2003. 24p. (J). (ps). 15.99 (978-0-7636-0671-8(5)) Candlewick Pr.

—My Little Grandmother Often Forgets. Brown, Kathryn, illus. 2007. (J). (ps-1). 32p. 16.99 (978-0-7636-1989-3(2)); (*978-1-4287-3962-8(9)) Candlewick Pr.

Linko, G. J. Tess's Touchstone. 2004. (Seekers Ser.: No. 5). 108p. 5.99 (978-0-8066-4189-8(4), Augsburg Bks.) Augsburg Fortress, Pubs.

Lipp, Frederick J. Bread Song. Gaillard, Jason, tr. Gaillard, Jason, illus. 2004. (J). 15.95 (978-1-59336-000-9(2)); pap. (978-1-59336-001-6(0)) Mondo Publishing.

Lisle, Janet Taylor. The Art of Keeping Cool. 2002. 256p. (J). (gr. 5-9). pap. 5.99 (978-0-689-83788-3(7), Aladdin) Simon & Schuster Children's Publishing.

—The Art of Keeping Cool. Goldstrom, Robert, illus. 2000. 216p. (J). (gr. 5-7). 17.00 (978-0-689-83787-6(9), Atheneum/Richard Jackson Bks.) Simon & Schuster Children's Publishing.

—The Art of Keeping Cool. 2002. (gr. 5-8). lib. bdg. 13.00 (978-0-613-54109-1(X)) Tandem Library Bks.

Little Red Riding Hood: 6 Small Books. (gr. k-2). 23.00 (978-0-7635-8510-5(6)) Rigby Education.

Little Red Riding Hood: Individual Title Six-Packs. (Story Steps Ser.). (gr. k-2). 32.00 (978-0-7635-9841-9(0)) Rigby Education.

Little, Robert. Grandma's Biscuits. Richmond, Jamea, illus. 2004. 32p. (J). (ps-7). 15.95 (978-0-9701863-5-5(5)) Relde Publishing.

Littman, Sarah. Confessions of a Closet Catholic. 2006. 208p. (J). (gr. 5). reprint ed. pap. 5.99 (978-0-14-240597-0(3), Puffin) Penguin Group (USA) Inc.

Lively, Penelope. Dragon Trouble. 2002. (gr. 3-6). lib. bdg. 12.95 (978-0-613-52832-0(8)) Tandem Library Bks.

Lloyd-Jones, Sally. The Ultimate Guide to Grandmas & Grandpas. Emberley, Michael, illus. 2008. 32p. (J). 16.99 (*978-0-06-075687-1(X)); lib. bdg. 17.89 (*978-0-06-075688-8(8)) HarperCollins Pubs.

Lobel, Gillian. Does Anybody Love Me? Beardshaw, Rosalind, illus. 2002. 28p. (J). (gr. k-3). 16.00 (978-1-56148-368-6(0)) Good Bks.

Lombardi, Mary. Grandpa's Chair. l.t. ed. 2005. (Illus.). 17p. (J). per. 9.99 (978-1-59879-016-0(1)) Lifevest Publishing, Inc.

Longoria, Eugene R., Jr. Junior y la Llorona en la Montana de Nieve. 2006. (SPA., Illus.). 40p. (J). 12.00 (*978-0-9796818-0-6(4)) Longoria, Eugene R.

Loof, Jan. Mi Abuelo Es Pirata. 2001. (SPA., Illus.). 40p. (J). 16.76 (978-84-305-7196-3(5), MN3132) Susaeta Ediciones, S.A. ESP. *Dist:* Lectorum Pubns., Inc.

Look, Lenore. Henry's First-Moon Birthday. Heo, Yumi, illus. 2001. 40p. (J). (ps-2). 16.99 (978-0-689-82294-0(4), Atheneum/Anne Schwartz Bks.) Simon & Schuster Children's Publishing.

—Love As Strong As Ginger. Johnson, Stephen T., illus. 1999. 32p. (J). (gr. 1-4). 16.99 (978-0-689-81248-4(5), Atheneum/Anne Schwartz Bks.) Simon & Schuster Children's Publishing.

Looper, Grace W. Great-Grandpa's Hidden Treasure. 2006. (YA). pap. (*978-1-933523-18-7(2)) Bella Rosa Bks.

Loper, Kathleen. Angelina Katrina: Bugs in My Backyard. Waltz, Dan, illus. l.t. ed. 2004. 24p. (J). 17.95 (978-0-9741774-4-1(X)) D. W. Publishing.

Lopez, Lois. Grandpape. 2003. 27p. pap. 9.00 (978-0-8059-6247-5(6)) Dorrance Publishing Co., Inc.

Lord, Janet. Here Comes Grandma! Paschkis, Julie, illus. rev. ed. 2005. 32p. (J). (ps-ps). 12.95 (978-0-8050-7666-0(2)) Holt, Henry & Co.

Lore, Erin, illus. Timmy the Dragon. l.t. ed. 2007. 32p. (J). 8.95 (*978-0-9741562-7-9(2)) Yarrow Pr.

Lorenz, Jinye, Sr. Grandfather, the Tiger & Ryong. Lorenz, Virginia O., Sr., ed. Lorenz, Jinye, Sr., illus. ltd. ed. 2005. (Illus.). 65p. (J). spiral bd. 14.95 (978-1-888350-10-4(5)) Lighted Lamp Pr.

Lorenz, Jinye. Ryong's Story: Extended Version of Grandfather, the Tiger & Ryong. Lorenz, Virginia O., ed. 2006. (Illus.). 135p. (YA). per. 14.95 (978-1-888350-11-1(3)) Lighted Lamp Pr.

Lovell, Patty. Stand Tall, Molly Lou Melon. Catrow, David, illus. 2001. 32p. (J). (ps-3). 15.99 (978-0-399-23416-3(0), Putnam Juvenile) Penguin Group (USA) Inc.

—Stand Tall, Molly Lou Melon. 2002. (J). (gr. k-3). 25.95 incl. audio (978-0-8045-6891-3(X)) Spoken Arts, Inc.

Loye, David. Grandfather's Garden: Bedtime Stories for Little & Big Folk. 2008. (J). pap. 18.95 (*978-0-9795257-7-3(2)) Benjamin Franklin Pr.

Lozano, Neal. Can God See Me in the Dark? Hatke, Ben, illus. 2007. (J). (*978-1-883551-45-2(5)) , Maple Corners Press) Attic Studio Publishing Hse.
Luenn, Nancy. A Gift for Abuelita: Celebrating the Day of the Dead. Chapman, Robert, illus. 1998. Tr. of Un Regalo para Abuelita: En Celebration del Dia de los Muertos. (ENG & SPA.). 32p. (gr. k-3). 15.95 (978-0-87358-688-7(3) , Rising Moon Bks. for Young Readers) Northland Publishing.
Lum, Kate. What! Cried Granny. 2002. (ps-2). lib. bdg. 15.30 (978-0-613-49647-6(7)) Tandem Library Bks.
—What! Cried Granny: An Almost Bedtime Story. Johnson, Adrian, illus. 2002. 14.04 (978-1-4046-0859-7(1)) Book Wholesalers, Inc.
—What! Cried Granny: An Almost Bedtime Story. Johnson, Adrian, illus. 2002. 32p. (J). (ps-2). pap. 6.99 (978-0-14-230092-3(6) , Puffin) Penguin Group (USA) Inc.
Lum, Kate & Johnson, Adrian. What! Cried Granny. 1999. (Illus.). 32p. (J). pap. (978-0-7475-4178-3(7)) Bloomsbury Publishing Plc.
Lundy, Charlotte. Thank You, Jesus. Waldrep, Evelyn L., ed. Claremont, Heather, illus. 2003. 32p. (gr. k-3). 15.95 (978-0-9670280-1-9(9)) Bay Light Publishing.
Ly, Many. Roots & Wings. 2008. 256p. (YA). (gr. 7). lib. bdg. 18.99 (*978-0-385-90494-0(0) , Delacorte Bks. for Young Readers) Random Hse. Children's Bks.
Lynch, Chris. Freewill. 2002. 160p. (J). (gr. 8 up). pap. 6.99 (978-0-06-447202-9(7)) HarperCollins Pubs.
—Freewill. 2002. 148p. (YA). (gr. 8-12). lib. bdg. 15.30 (978-0-613-56380-2(8)) Tandem Library Bks.
MacCaughrean, Geraldine. El Reloj de Mi Abuela. 2004. (SPA., Illus.). 32p. (J). 14.99 (978-84-241-8643-2(5)) Everest de Ediciones y Distribucion, S.L. ESP. *Dist:* Lectorum Pubns., Inc.
MacDonald, Margaret Read. The Squeaky Door. DePalma, Mary Newell, illus. 2006. 40p. (J). (ps-1). 12.99 (978-0-06-028373-5(4)) HarperCollins Pubs.
MacHado, Ana Maria. Bisa Bea, Bisa Bel. (SPA.). (J). (gr. 4-5). 6.00 (978-968-16-5463-4(3) , FC6391) Fondo de Cultura Economica MEX. *Dist:* Lectorum Pubns., Inc.
—De carta en Carta. Basulto, Rita, illus. (SPA.). 44p. (J). (gr. 3-5). pap. 7.95 (978-968-19-1483-7(X)) Santillana USA Publishing Co., Inc.
—Me in the Middle. Unger, David, tr. from POR. Merola, Caroline, illus. 2002. 96p. (J). (gr. 2-6). 14.95 (978-0-88899-463-9(X)) Groundwood Bks. CAN. *Dist:* Perseus Distribution.
MacHado, Ana Maria & Merola, Caroline. Me in the Middle. Unger, David, tr. from POR. 2003. (Illus.). 112p. (J). (gr. 3-6). pap. 4.95 (978-0-88899-467-7(2)) Groundwood Bks. CAN. *Dist:* Perseus Distribution.
MacKall, Dandi Daley. Horse Whispers in the Air, Vol. 3. 2000. (Horsefeathers Ser.: Vol. 3). 192p. (YA). (gr. 7-11). 5.99 (978-0-570-07008-5(2)) Concordia Publishing Hse.
—Horse Whispers in the Air. 2000. (gr. 7-12). lib. bdg. 14.15 (978-0-613-72831-7(9)) Tandem Library Bks.
MacLachlan, Patricia. Caleb's Story. 2001. (Sarah, Plain & Tall Ser.). 128p. (J). (gr. 3-5). 16.99 (978-0-06-023605-2(1) , Cotler, Joanna Books) HarperCollins Pubs.
—Grandfather's Dance. (Sarah, Plain & Tall Ser.). 96p. (J). 2008. pap. 5.99 (*978-0-06-134003-1(0)); 2006. lib. bdg. 15.89 (978-0-06-027561-7(8)); 5th ed. 2006. (gr. 3-6). 14.99 (978-0-06-027560-0(X)) HarperCollins Pubs. (Cotler, Joanna Books).
MacLachlan, Patricia. Two Novels: Baby/Journey. 2007. 224p. (J). (gr. 4-7). 16.99 (978-0-385-73423-3(9)); lib. bdg. 19.99 (978-0-385-90436-0(3)) Random Hse. Children's Bks. (Delacorte Bks. for Young Readers).
MacPhail, Catherine. Granny Nothing. 2005. (Illus.). pap. 29.95 incl. audio (978-0-7540-6289-9(9) , Chivers Children's Audio Bks.) BBC Audiobooks America.
Magrane, Mijares. Grandma Garcia: La Abuela Garcia - An Intimate Journey into the Past. 2004. (SPA & ENG., Illus.). 96p. pap. 13.95 (978-0-9741167-0-9(X)) Magrane, Etna International.
Mahalo e Grandpa. 2002. 5.99 (978-0-89610-395-5(1)) Island Heritage Publishing.
Malanga, Tara & O'Keefe, Susan Heyboer. Sleepy Angel's First Bedtime Story. 2000. (Illus.). 32p. (ps-2). 9.95 (978-0-8091-6670-1(4) , 6670-4) Paulist Pr.
Malkin, Arlene Swinson. Adventures with Grandma & Grandpa: The Secret of the Old Trunk. 2006. 48p. pap. 12.95 (978-1-4241-1621-8(X)) PublishAmerica, Inc.
Malot, Hector & Crewe-Jones, Florence. Nobody's Girl: Companion Story to Nobody's Boy. Gooch, Thelma, illus. 2006. 220p. (J). pap. (978-1-894666-76-3(3)) Inheritance Pubns.
Malyon, Carol. Mixed-up Grandmas. Peacock, David, illus. 1998. 36p. (J). (ps-1). 12.95 (978-0-88984-194-9(2)) Porcupine's Quill, Inc. CAN. *Dist:* Univ. of Toronto Pr.
Mangum, Kay Lynn. A Love Like Lilly. 2006. 336p. (YA). pap. 15.95 (978-1-59038-580-7(2)) Deseret Bk. Co.
Manushkid, Fran. Grandma Beatrice Brings Spring to Minsk. 2005. 32p. (J). (978-0-7868-2147-1(7)) Hyperion Bks. for Children.
—Grandma Beatrice Brings Spring to Minsk. 1999. 32p. (J). (978-0-7868-0175-6(1)) Hyperion Pr.
Manushkin, Fran. Grandma Beatrice Brings Spring to Minsk. Berry, Holly, illus. 2008. 32p. (J). (gr. k). 16.99 (978-0-525-42027-9(4) , Dutton Juvenile) Penguin Group (USA) Inc.
Mariconda, Barbara. Turn the Cup Around. 1998. (978-0-606-13878-9(1)) Tandem Library Bks.
Marie, Evelyn. Grandma from Manhattan or Danger I Carry a "Meshok" Stewart, Todd W., illus. 2001. (YA). (gr. 5 up). pap. 10.50 (978-1-890579-02-9(5)) Berry Bks.
Marino, Jan. The Mona Lisa of Salem Street. 1999. 155p. (J). (gr. 3-6). reprint ed. 15.00 (978-0-7881-6635-8(2)) DIANE Publishing Co.
Markel, Michelle. Dream Town. Reese, Rick, illus. 2006. (J). 15.95 (978-1-59714-022-5(8)) Heyday Bks.
Markle, Sandra. The Fledglings. 2003. 144p. (YA). (gr. 4-6). pap. 9.95 (978-1-56397-696-4(X)) Boyds Mills Pr.
Marsden, Carolyn. Silk Umbrellas. 2007. (Illus.). 144p. (J). (gr. 3-7). 5.99 (*978-0-7636-3376-9(3)) Candlewick Pr.
Marsh, Carole. The Goshawful Gold Rush MYST. 2007. 160p. pap. 5.95 (*978-0-635-06334-2(4)) Gallopade International.
—The Mystery at the Ancient Pyramid. 2006. 144p. (gr. 3-5). 14.95 (*978-0-635-03473-1(5)) Gallopade International.
—The Mystery on the Great Barrier Reef. 2006. 144p. (gr. 3-5). 14.95 (*978-0-635-06210-9(0)); pap. 5.95 (*978-0-635-06206-2(2)) Gallopade International.
—The Mystery on the Great Wall of China. 2006. 144p. (gr. 3-5). 14.95 (*978-0-635-06209-3(7)); pap. 5.95 (*978-0-635-06205-5(4)) Gallopade International.
Marshall, Kenneth L. The Adventures of Maya & Grandpa. 2004. 60p. (J). pap. 9.95 (978-0-7414-2016-9(3)); Bk. II. 2005. 65p. pap. 9.95 (978-0-7414-2238-5(7)) Infinity Publishing.
Marsoli, Lisa Ann. Ask Fickle Fairy. 2007. 16p. (J). (gr. 2-4). 9.99 (978-0-7641-6010-3(9)) Barron's Educational Series, Inc.
Martin, Jacqueline Briggs. Grandmother Bryant's Pocket. Mathers, Petra, illus. 2000. 48p. (J). (gr. k-3). pap. 5.95 (978-0-618-03309-6(2)) Houghton Mifflin Co. Trade & Reference Div.
—Grandmother Bryant's Pocket. 2000. (Illus.). (J). (978-0-606-18209-6(8)) Tandem Library Bks.
—The Water Gift & the Pig of the Pig. Wingerter, Linda S., illus. 2003. 32p. (J). (gr. k-3). tchr. ed. 15.00 (978-0-618-07436-5(8)) Houghton Mifflin Co. Trade & Reference Div.
Martin, Terri L. A Family Trait. 1999. 160p. (J). (gr. 4-6). tchr. ed. 15.95 (978-0-8234-1467-3(1)) Holiday Hse., Inc.
Martinez-Mena, Alfonso. La Tierra de Nadie. (SPA.). 96p. (YA). (gr. 5-8). (978-84-279-3134-3(4) , NG3469) Noguer y Caralt Editores, S. A. ESP. *Dist:* Lectorum Pubns., Inc.
Martone, Ginny. The White Stallion. 2006. (ENG.). 60p. per. 12.95 (*978-1-4241-4332-0(2)) PublishAmerica, Inc.
Marzollo, Jean. Companeros en el Futbol. 1999. (J). lib. bdg. 10.79 (978-0-606-17055-0(3)) Tandem Library Bks.
Massey, Barbara & DeLoach, Sylvia. Darby down Under. Robinson, Amy Giles, illus. 2000. (Child Like Me Ser.: Vol. 4). (J). (gr. 2-5). 6.99 (978-1-56309-766-9(4)) New Hope Pubs.
Masson, Sophie. Sooner or Later. 115p. pap. 11.95 (978-0-7022-2336-5(0)) Univ. of Queensland Pr. AUS. *Dist:* International Specialized Bk. Services.
Masters, Susan Rowan. Summer Song. 2000. 148p. (YA). (gr. 4-7). pap. 9.95 (978-0-595-14407-5(1)) iUniverse, Inc.
Masurel, Claire. Emily's First Sleepover. 2003. (gr. k-3). lib. bdg. 11.25 (978-0-613-72542-2(5)) Tandem Library Bks.
Mateos, Pilar. El Cuento Interrumpido. (SPA.). 128p. (YA). (gr. 5-8). (978-84-279-3149-7(2) , NG0388) Noguer y Caralt Editores, S. A. ESP. *Dist:* Lectorum Pubns., Inc.
Mathis, Sharon Bell. The Hundred-Penny Box. Dillon, Leo & Dillon, Diane, illus. 2006. 48p. (J). (gr. 1). pap. 7.99 (978-0-14-240702-8(X) , Puffin) Penguin Group (USA) Inc.
Matott, Justin. When Did I Meet You Grandpa? McAdam, Laurie, illus. 2000. 32p. (J). (gr. 1-7). 16.95 (978-1-889191-14-0(0)) Clove Pubns.
Matze, Claire Sidhom. The Stars in My Geddoh's Sky. Farnsworth, Bill, illus. 1999. (Concept Book Ser.). 32p. (J). (gr. k-3). pap. 14.95 (978-0-8075-5332-9(8)) Whitman, Albert & Co.
May, Scott. Outer Space Earl: The Trees Have the Blues. 2000. mass mkt. 8.95 incl. audio compact disk (978-1-931179-06-5(9)) Long Hill Productions, Inc.
—Outer Space Earl: The Trees Have the Blues. Fisher, Brian Patrick, illus. 2000. 32p. (J). (gr. 1-3). pap. (978-0-9701450-1-7(2)) Long Hill Productions, Inc.
May, Sophie. Dotty Dimples Flyaway. 2007. 94.99 (*978-1-4280-5295-6(X)); pap. 88.99 (*978-1-4280-5304-5(2)) IndyPublish.com.
Mayer, Mercer. Grandma's Garden. 2002. (Little Critter First Readers Ser.). (Illus.). 24p. (J). (gr. k-1). pap. 3.95 (978-1-57768-846-4(5)) School Specialty Publishing.
—Grandma's Garden. 2001. (gr. k-3). lib. bdg. 11.80 (978-0-613-67625-0(4)) Tandem Library Bks.
—Just Grandma & Me. Mayer, Mercer, illus. 2001. (Little Critter Ser.). (Illus.). 24p. (J). (gr. k-k). reprint ed. pap. 3.29 (978-0-307-11893-6(2) , 11893, Random Hse. Bks. for Young Readers) Random Hse. Children's Bks.
—My Trip to the Farm, Vol. 3. 2002. (Little Critter First Readers Ser.). (Illus.). 24p. (J). (gr. 1-2). pap. 3.95 (978-1-57768-817-4(1)) School Specialty Publishing.
—My Trip to the Farm. 2000. (gr. k-3). lib. bdg. 11.80 (978-0-613-67647-2(5)) Tandem Library Bks.
Mayfield, Sue. The Four Franks. Parsons, Garry, illus. 2005. (Blue Go Bananas Ser.). 38p. (J). (978-0-7787-2629-6(0)) Crabtree Publishing Co.
Mayoral, Juana Aurora. El Rincon de las Lilas. (SPA.). 144p. (YA). (gr. 5-8). (978-84-321-2993-3(3) , RP5998) Rialp, Ediciones, S.A. ESP. *Dist:* Lectorum Pubns., Inc.
Mazer, Norma Fox. After the Rain. l.t. ed. 2005. 359p. (YA). pap. 10.95 (978-0-7862-7913-5(3)) Thorndike Pr.
McAllister, Margaret. Emily & the Lamb. Vince, Dawn, illus. 2005. 24p. (J). lib. bdg. 22.65 (*978-1-59646-756-9(8)) Dingles & Co.
McCafferty, Catherine. Picture Me with My Grandpa. Rasmussen, Wendy, illus. 2000. (Picture Me Ser.). 10p. (J). (ps up). bds. 4.99 (978-1-57151-579-7(8)) Playhouse Publishing.
McCain, Becky Ray. Grandmother's Dreamcatcher. 2001. (Illus.). (J). (978-0-606-21858-0(0)) Tandem Library Bks.
—Grandmother's Dreamcatcher. Schuett, Stacey, illus. 32p. (J). (gr. k-3). 2004. pap. 6.95 (978-0-8075-3032-0(8)); 1998. 15.95 (978-0-8075-3031-3(X)) Whitman, Albert & Co.
McClintock, Barbara, illus. Goldilocks & the Three Bears. 2003. 32p. (J). (ps-2). pap. 15.95 (978-0-439-39545-8(3) , Scholastic Pr.) Scholastic, Inc.
McConduit, Denise Walter. D. J. & the Debutante Ball. Henriquez, Emile F., illus. 2004. 32p. (J). pap. 15.95 (978-1-58980-173-8(3)) Pelican Publishing Co., Inc.
McCracken, Hugh. Grandfather & the Ghost. 2002. (gr. 7-12). lib. bdg. 19.00 (978-0-613-80450-9(3)) Tandem Library Bks.
McCully, Emily Arnold. First Snow. McCully, Emily Arnold, illus. 2004. (Illus.). 32p. (J). (ps-k). 16.99 (978-0-06-623852-4(8)); lib. bdg. 17.89 (978-0-06-623853-1(6)) HarperCollins Pubs.
—Grandmas Trick-or-Treat. McCully, Emily Arnold, illus. 2002. (Illus.). 12.34 (978-1-4046-1307-2(2)) Book Wholesalers, Inc.
—Grandmas Trick-or-Treat. McCully, Emily Arnold, illus. (I Can Read Bks.). (Illus.). 48p. (J). (ps-1). 2002. pap. 3.99 (978-0-06-444277-0(2)); 2001. 14.95 (978-0-06-028730-6(6)) HarperCollins Pubs.
McCutcheon, John. Christmas in the Trenches. Sorensen, Henri, illus. 2006. 32p. (J). 18.95 incl. audio compact disk (978-1-56145-374-0(9) , Peachtree Junior) Peachtree Pubs., Ltd.
McDonald, Diane. Treasure Chest. Halicky, Sandi, illus. 2002. 34p. (J). spiral bd. 12.95 (978-0-9721681-0-6(9)) McDonald, Diane.
McDonald, Megan. Beezy at Bat. Poydar, Nancy, illus. 48p. (J). (gr. 1-4). 2000. pap. 4.95 (978-0-531-07164-9(2)); 1998. pap. 13.95 (978-0-531-30085-5(4)) Scholastic, Inc. (Orchard Bks.).
—Beezy at Bat. 2000. (J). (978-0-606-20453-8(9)) Tandem Library Bks.
McDonald, Megan & Poydar, Nancy. Beezy at Bat. 1998. (Illus.). 48p. (J). (gr. 1-4). 14.99 (978-0-531-33085-2(0) , Orchard Bks.) Scholastic, Inc.
Mcduffee, William. Story Time with Grandpa Bill Collection. 2006. 50p. pap. 12.95 (978-1-4241-4001-5(3)) PublishAmerica, Inc.
McFarlane, Sheryl. Waiting for the Whales. 1998. (gr. k-3). lib. bdg. 16.40 (978-0-613-86453-4(0)) Tandem Library Bks.
McGill, Alice. Here We Go Round. Evans, Shane W., illus. 2002. 128p. (J). (gr. 3-5). 15.00 (978-0-618-16064-8(7)) Houghton Mifflin Co. Trade & Reference Div.
McKay, Hilary. The Exiles in Love. 1999. (J). 11.15 (978-0-606-17315-5(3)) Tandem Library Bks.
McKay, Sindy. We Both Read-My Car Trip. Johnson, Meredith, illus. 2005. (J). (*978-1-4156-3785-2(7)) Book Wholesalers, Inc.
—We Both Read-My Car Trip. Johnson, Meredith, illus. 2005. (We Both Read Ser.). 44p. (J). (gr. k up). 7.99 (978-1-891327-63-6(1)); pap. 3.99 (978-1-891327-64-3(X)) Treasure Bay, Inc.
McKenna, Sharon. Good Morning Sunshine: A Grandpa Story. McKenna, Sharon, illus. 2006. (Illus.). 32p. (J). 15.95 (978-1-60108-003-5(4)) Red Cygnet Pr.
McLaughlin, Kirsten. The Memory Box. Rudolph, Adrienne, illus. 2000. (J). 5.95 (978-1-56123-136-2(3) , MEBC) Centering Corp.
McLeod, Elaine. Lessons from Mother Earth. Wood, Colleen, illus. 2002. (J). (ps-1). 15.95 (978-0-88899-312-0(9)) Groundwood Bks. CAN. *Dist:* Transition Vendor.
McNab, Andy & Rigby, Robert. Meltdown. 2008. 276p. (YA). (gr. 7). 16.99 (*978-0-399-24686-9(X) , Putnam Juvenile) Penguin Group (USA) Inc.
—Payback. 2006. 272p. (YA). (ps-k). 16.99 (978-0-399-24465-0(4) , Putnam Juvenile) Penguin Group (USA) Inc.
—Traitor. 2006. 288p. (YA). (gr. 7). pap. 6.99 (978-0-14-240727-1(5) , Puffin) Penguin Group (USA) Inc.
McNatt, Martha. Grandmother's Face in the Mirror. 2003. (YA). per. 14.00 (978-0-9741294-0-2(2)) Main St Publishing, Inc.
Medlyn, Lynda Lee & Staudenmier, Kelley Anne. The Best Belcher. 2007. (Illus.). 32p. (J). lib. bdg. 15.95 (*978-0-9793738-0-0(8)) Window Box Pr. LLC.
Meik, Mitchell. Grandma & the Troll. Bradbury, Stephanie, illus. 2004. (J). 4.95 (978-1-57665-118-6(5)) Muggli Graphics.
Mendes, Valerie. Look at Me, Grandma! Fletcher, Claire, illus. 2001. 32p. (J). (ps-1). pap. 15.95 (978-0-439-29654-0(4) , Chicken Hse., The) Scholastic, Inc.
—Lost & Found. 2004. 256p. pap. 8.99 (978-0-689-86049-2(8)) Simon & Schuster, Ltd. GBR. *Dist:* Independent Pubs. Group.
Michelson, Richard. Too Young for Yiddish. Waldman, Neil, illus. 2002. 32p. (J). (gr. k-4). 15.95 (978-0-88106-118-5(2)) Charlesbridge Publishing, Inc.
Mills, Claudia. Gus & Grandpa. Stock, Catherine, illus. 1999. (Gus & Grandpa Ser.). 48p. (J). (gr. 1-3). pap. 5.95 (978-0-374-42847-1(6) , Sunburst) Farrar, Straus & Giroux.
—Gus & Grandpa. Stock, Catherine, illus. 1999. 48p. (J). (ps-ps). lib. bdg. 11.75 (978-0-606-16474-0(X)) Tandem Library Bks.
—Gus & Grandpa. 1999. (ps-2). lib. bdg. 12.95 (978-0-613-17805-1(X)) Tandem Library Bks.
—Gus & Grandpa & Show-and-Tell. Stock, Catherine, illus. (Gus & Grandpa Ser.). 48p. (J). 2002. pap. 5.95 (978-0-374-42848-8(4) , Sunburst); 2000. (gr. 1-3). 13.00 (978-0-374-32819-1(6) , Farrar, Straus & Giroux (BYR)) Farrar, Straus & Giroux.
—Gus & Grandpa & the Christmas Cookies. 2000. (J). (978-0-606-20133-9(5)) Tandem Library Bks.
—Gus & Grandpa & the Halloween Costume. Stock, Catherine, illus. 2002. (Gus & Grandpa Ser.). 48p. (J). (gr. 1-3). 15.00 (978-0-374-32816-0(1) , Farrar, Straus & Giroux (BYR)) Farrar, Straus & Giroux.
—Gus & Grandpa & the Piano Lesson. Stock, Catherine, illus. 2004. (Gus & Grandpa Ser.). 48p. (J). 15.00 (978-0-374-32814-6(5) , Farrar, Straus & Giroux (BYR)) Farrar, Straus & Giroux.
—Gus & Grandpa & the Two-Wheeled Bike. Stock, Catherine, illus. Stock, Catherine, photos by. 1999. (Gus & Grandpa Ser.). 48p. (J). (gr. 1-3). 15.00 (978-0-374-32821-4(8) , Farrar, Straus & Giroux (BYR)) Farrar, Straus & Giroux.
—Gus & Grandpa at Basketball. Stock, Catherine, illus. 2001. (Gus & Grandpa Ser.). 48p. (J). (gr. 1-3). 15.00 (978-0-374-32818-4(8) , Farrar, Straus & Giroux (BYR)) Farrar, Straus & Giroux.
—Gus & Grandpa at the Hospital. Stock, Catherine, illus. 2001. (Sunburst Bks.). 48p. (J). (gr. 1-3). pap. 4.95 (978-0-374-42812-9(3) , Sunburst) Farrar, Straus & Giroux.
—Gus & Grandpa at the Hospital. 2001. (Illus.). (J). 11.75 (978-0-606-20686-0(8)) Tandem Library Bks.
—Gus & Grandpa Go Fishing. Stock, Catherine, illus. 2003. (Gus & Grandpa Ser.). 48p. (J). 15.00 (978-0-374-32815-3(3) , Farrar, Straus & Giroux (BYR)) Farrar, Straus & Giroux.
—Gus & Grandpa Ride the Train. Stock, Catherine, illus. 2000. (Gus & Grandpa Ser.). 48p. (J). (ps-3). pap. 5.95 (978-0-374-42813-6(1) , Sunburst) Farrar, Straus & Giroux.
—Gus & Grandpa Ride the Train. 2000. (Illus.). (J). 11.75 (978-0-606-18133-4(4)) Tandem Library Bks.
—The Two Wheeled Bike. Stock, Catherine, illus. 2001. (Gus & Grandpa Ser.). 48p. (J). pap. 4.95 (978-0-374-42816-7(6) , Sunburst) Farrar, Straus & Giroux.
Mills, Judith. The Book of the Sage. 3rd rev. ed. 2004. (Goodfellow Chronicles Ser.). (Illus.). 304p. (J). pap. 9.95 (*978-1-55263-559-9(7)) Key Porter Bks. CAN. *Dist:* Perseus Distribution.
Mills, Susan & Shara, Diana. Frankie & Her Little Pals - Save the Watermelons. 2007. 32p. (J). (*978-0-9790690-3-1(3)) Lucky Red Pr., LLC.
Mitchelhill, Barbara. Eric & the Old Fossil. 2005. (Illus.). 80p. (J). pap. 7.99 (*978-1-84270-430-1(3)) Transworld Publishers Ltd. GBR. *Dist:* Independent Pubs. Group.
Mitchell, Lori. Different Just Like Me. (Illus.). 32p. (J). (ps-3). 2001. pap. 6.95 (978-1-57091-490-4(7)); 1999. 15.95 (978-0-88106-975-4(2)) Charlesbridge Publishing, Inc.
—Different Just Like Me. 2001. (gr. k-3). lib. bdg. 16.40 (978-0-613-79208-0(4)) Tandem Library Bks.
Mitchell, Margaree King. Granddaddy's Gift. 1998. (978-0-606-13449-1(2)) Tandem Library Bks.
Mochizuki, Chiemi. The Promise. Randle, Walt R., ed. Mochizuki, Chiemi, illus. 2003. (Illus.). 38p. (J). (gr. 3-6). 16.99 (978-0-9720691-0-6(0)) Berkeley Major Publishing.
Molloy, Michael. The House on Falling Star Hill. 2004. (Illus.). 384p. (J). pap. 16.95 (978-0-439-57740-3(3) , Chicken Hse., The) Scholastic, Inc.
Moloney, James. Black Taxi. 2005. 272p. (J). (gr. 7 up). 15.99 (978-0-06-055937-3(3)); lib. bdg. 16.89 (978-0-06-055938-0(1)) HarperCollins Pubs.
Momaday, N. Scott. Circle of Wonder: A Native American Christmas Story. 1999. (Illus.). 44p. (gr. 4-7). 19.95 (978-0-8263-2149-7(6)) Univ. of New Mexico Pr.
Monk, Isabell. Blackberry Stew. Porter, Janice Lee, illus. 2005. 32p. (J). (ps-ps). lib. bdg. 15.95 (978-1-57505-605-0(4)) Lerner Publishing Group.
Monroy, Manuel. Rabieta Trebejos. 2000. (Los Especials de A la Orilla Del Viento Ser.). (SPA.). 24p. (J). (ps-ps). per. 13.99 (978-968-16-6080-2(3)) Fondo de Cultura Economica USA.
Moon, Catherine R. & Everette, Maureen C. The Adventures of NanaCat & Her Children: Someone New. Richardson, Kara, illus. 2004. 32p. (J). per. 6.95 (978-0-930507-02-2(9)) Currier Davis Publishing.
Moore, Brenda M. Together on the Mountain. Varnedoe, Catharine E., illus. 1998. 32p. (J). (ps-3). 14.95 (978-1-890326-14-2(3)) First Story Pr.
Moore, Nancy Delano. Kiernan's Jam. Peck, Bill, illus. 2006. (J). 10.00 (978-0-9785775-0-6(7)) Moore, Hullihen.
Moran, Michelle. Nana's Secret Christmas Room. 2006. 80p. per. 8.99 (*978-1-59886-581-3(1)) Tate Publishing & Enterprises, L.L.C.
Moranville, Sharelle Byars. Over the River. rev. ed. 2002. 240p. (J). (gr. 4-9). 16.95 (978-0-8050-7049-1(4) , Holt, Henry & Co. Bks. For Young Readers) Holt, Henry & Co.
—Over the River. 2004. 240p. (gr. 5). 5.99 (978-0-440-41977-8(8) , Yearling) Random Hse. Children's Bks.
Morgan, Michaela. Buffalo Bert: The Cowboy Grandad. Newsham, Ian, illus. 2006. (Read-It! Chapter Books). 48p. (J). (gr. 2-4). 19.95 (978-1-4048-1660-2(7)) Picture Window Bks.
Morpurgo, Michael. The Amazing Story of Adolphus Tips. 2006. 208p. (J). (gr. 2-5). 16.99 (978-0-439-79661-3(X) , Scholastic Pr.) Scholastic, Inc.
—Colly's Barn. Andrew, Ian P., illus. 2002. (Yellow Bananas Ser.). 48p. (J). (gr. 3-4). pap. (978-0-7787-0978-7(7)); lib. bdg. (978-0-7787-0932-9(9)) Crabtree Publishing Co.
—Colly's Barn. 2002. (gr. 3-6). lib. bdg. 12.95 (978-0-613-52822-1(0)) Tandem Library Bks.
—Farm Boy. 2007. (Illus.). 76p. (J). pap. 16.99 (*978-1-84365-090-4(8)) Anova Bks. GBR. *Dist:* Independent Pubs. Group.

E
F
G

—Farm Boy. Foreman, Michael, illus. 1999. 74p. (YA). pap. 16.99 (978-1-86205-192-8(5) , Pavilion Bks., Ltd.) Anova Bks. GBR. *Dist:* Trafalgar Square Publishing.

—Snakes & Ladders. Wilson, Anne, illus. 2006. 46p. (J). (978-0-7787-0952-7(3)) Crabtree Publishing Co.

Morris, Ann. Grandma Lai Goon Remembers: A Chinese-American Family Story. 2002. (Illus.). 32p. (J). (gr. 5 up). pap. 7.95 (978-0-7613-1730-2(9) , Millbrook Pr.) Lerner Publishing Group.

—Grandma Lois Remembers: An African-American Family Story. 2002. (Illus.). 32p. (J). (gr. 5 up). pap. 7.95 (978-0-7613-1729-6(5) , Millbrook Pr.) Lerner Publishing Group.

—Grandma Maxine Remembers: A Native American Family Story. 2002. (Illus.). 32p. (J). (gr. 5 up). pap. 7.95 (978-0-7613-1728-9(7) , Millbrook Pr.) Lerner Publishing Group.

—Grandma Susan Remembers: A British-American Family Story. 2002. (Illus.). 32p. (J). (gr. 5 up). pap. 7.95 (978-0-7613-1732-6(5) , Millbrook Pr.) Lerner Publishing Group.

Morris, Jennifer. Come, Llamas. 2006. 208p. (gr. 3-7). 5.99 (978-0-440-42024-8(5) , Yearling) Random Hse. Children's Bks.

Morris, V. L. Grandma's Soup. Morris, V. L., illus. 2007. (J). per. (***978-0-9773604-1-3(5)***) Wil-Mor Creations, Inc.

Morrissey, Dean. The Monster Trap. Morrissey, Dean, illus. 2006. (Illus.). 40p. (J). reprint ed. pap. 6.99 (978-0-06-052500-2(2) , Harper Trophy) HarperCollins Pubs.

Morrissey, Dean & Krensky, Stephen. The Monster Trap. Morrissey, Dean, illus. 2004. (Illus.). 40p. (J). lib. bdg. 17.89 (978-0-06-052499-9(5)) HarperCollins Pubs.

Moser, Lisa. Watermelon Wishes. Schuett, Stacey, illus. 2006. 32p. (J). (gr. k-3). 16.00 (978-0-618-56433-0(0) , Clarion Bks.) Houghton Mifflin Co. Trade & Reference Div.

Moses, Antoinette. Happy Granny. 2000. (C). pap. 9.00 (978-0-582-34413-6(1)) Longman Publishing Group.

Moses, Shelia P. The Legend of Buddy Bush. unabr. ed. 2005. (J). (gr. 3-7). 55.70 incl. audio (978-1-4193-3575-4(8) , 42043) Recorded Bks., LLC.

—The Legend of Buddy Bush. (Illus.). 224p. 2005. (YA). pap. 5.99 (978-1-4169-0716-9(5) , Simon Pulse); 2003. (J). 15.95 (978-0-689-85839-0(6) , McElderry, Margaret K.) Simon & Schuster Children's Publishing.

—The Legend of Buddy Bush. l.t. ed. 2005. 179p. 22.95 (978-0-7862-7311-9(9)) Thorndike Pr.

Mosher, Eunice D. Olympics, 2004? Ask Yia Yia & Pa Pou. Caso, Adolph, ed. Mosher, Eunice D. & Wenzel, Lauren M., illus. l.t. ed. 1998. 32p. (J). (ps-3). pap. 9.95 (978-0-8283-2033-7(0)) Branden Bks.

Mosher, Richard. Zazoo. (YA). (gr. 7 up). 2001. 256p. tchr. ed. 16.00 (978-0-618-13534-9(0) , Clarion Bks.); 2004. 272p. reprint ed. pap. 6.99 (978-0-618-43904-1(8) , Graphia) Houghton Mifflin Co. Trade & Reference Div.

Moss, Marissa. The Ugly Menorah. 2000. (978-0-606-20400-2(8)); (J). (978-0-606-20137-7(8)) Tandem Library Bks.

Most, Bernard. Catch Me If You Can!/A que no me Alcanzas! Campoy, F. Isabel & Ada, Alma Flor, trs. from ENG. 2007. (Green Light Reader Ser.). (ENG & SPA., Illus.). 28p. (J). 12.95 (978-0-15-205964-4(4)); pap. 3.95 (978-0-15-205967-5(9)) Harcourt Trade Pubs.

Mr. Miyataki's Marvelous Machine. 2004. (J). 10.99 (978-0-931548-68-0(3)) Island Heritage Publishing.

Mueller, Janet. A Star from Grandma. Mueller, Janet, illus. 2004. (Illus.). (J). pap. 8.96 (978-0-9746932-3-1(5)) Stella Bks, Inc.

Mull, Brandon. Fablehaven. 2006. (Illus.). 368p. (J). 16.95 (978-1-59038-581-4(0) , Shadow Mountain) Deseret Bk. Co.

—Fablehaven. Dorman, Brandon, illus. 2007. (Fablehaven Ser.). 368p. (J). pap. 6.99 (***978-1-4169-4720-2(5)*** , Aladdin) Simon & Schuster Children's Publishing.

—Fablehaven: Rise of the Evening Star. 2007. 456p. 17.95 (***978-1-59038-742-9(2)*** , Shadow Mountain) Deseret Bk. Co.

Muller, Birte. Felipa & the Day of the Dead. 2005. (Illus.). 36p. (J). (ps up). reprint ed. pap. 6.95 (978-0-7358-2011-1(2)) North-South Bks., Inc.

—Felipa y el Dia de los Muertos. 2005. (SPA., Illus.). 36p. (J). (ps up). 15.95 (978-0-7358-2009-8(0)) North-South Bks., Inc.

Munro, Ken. Grandfather's Secret. 2004. (Sammy & Brian Mystery Ser.: 16). (J). pap. 5.95 (978-1-932864-04-5(0)) Masthof Pr.

Munsch, Robert. Lighthouse: A Story of Remembrance. Wilson, Janet, illus. 2004. 28p. (J). pap. 5.95 (978-0-439-49032-0(4)) Scholastic, Inc.

Murphy, Yannick. Ahwoooooooo! Muñoz, Claudio, illus. 2006. (J). (gr. k-3). 32p. 16.00 (978-0-618-11762-8(8)); 31p. (978-1-4156-8100-8(7)) Houghton Mifflin Co. Trade & Reference Div. (Clarion Bks.).

My Grandma & I! 2002. (Illus.). 24p. (J). (ps-k). bds. 7.95 (978-0-8249-4220-5(5)) Ideals Pubns.

My Grandma Is Great. 2002. (Great Relatives Ser.). 32p. (J). 11.95 (978-1-84250-575-5(0) , Bright Sparks) Parragon, Inc.

My Grandmother's Hands: First Grade Big Books. (On Our Way to English Ser.). (gr. 1 up). 29.95 (978-0-7578-1503-4(0)) Rigby Education.

My Grandmother's Hands: Small Versions of Big Books. (On Our Way to English Ser.). (gr. 1 up). 29.00 (978-0-7578-7230-3(1)) Rigby Education.

My Grandpa & I! 2002. (Illus.). 24p. (J). (ps-k). bds. 7.95 (978-0-8249-4219-9(1)) Ideals Pubns.

My Grandpa Is Great. 2002. (Great Relatives Ser.). (Illus.). 32p. (J). 11.95 (978-1-84250-576-2(9) , Bright Sparks) Parragon, Inc.

My Great Grandma Clara. 2006. (J). pap. 12.95 (978-0-9677047-8-4(2)) Marble House Editions.

Myott, Lanita. RJ Saves the Day. 2003. 19p. 11.16 (978-1-4116-0354-7(0)) Lulu.com.

The Mystery of October Island. 2003. (Illus.). 50p. (J). per. 12.95 (978-0-9754823-0-8(0)) Pumpkin Patch Publishing.

Namioka, Lensey. April & the Dragon Lady. 2007. (Illus.). 224p. (YA). pap. 6.95 (***978-0-15-205669-8(6)*** , Harcourt Paperbacks) Harcourt Children's Bks.

Nanji, Shenaaz. An Alien in My House. McLeod, Chum, tr. McLeod, Chum, illus. 2005. 24p. (J). (gr. k-3). 11.95 (978-1-896764-77-1(0)) Second Story Pr. CAN. *Dist:* Orca Bk. Pubs. USA.

Nanny & I Meet Odie. 2006. (J). lib. bdg. 18.99 (978-0-9724394-1-1(2)) Sylables.

Napoli, Donna Jo. April Flowers. Ben-Ami, Doren & Klementz-Harte, Lauren, illus. 2000. (Angelwings Ser.: No. 7). 80p. (J). (gr. 2-5). pap. 7.95 (978-0-689-83207-9(9) , Aladdin) Simon & Schuster Children's Publishing.

—April Flowers. 2000. (Angelwings Ser.: No. 7). (Illus.). (J). 10.79 (978-0-606-17910-2(0)) Tandem Library Bks.

Narena, Tammy. This Great Love to Cherish. 1999. (Illus.). 64p. (J). pap. 12.50 (978-1-929319-00-8(2)) Sean & I Publishing.

Naylor, Phyllis Reynolds. Ice. 1998. 256p. (YA). (gr. 7-12). mass mkt. 12.95 (978-0-689-81872-1(6) , Simon Pulse) Simon & Schuster Children's Publishing.

—Ice. 1998. (J). 11.64 (978-0-606-12970-1(7)) Tandem Library Bks.

Neasi, Barbara J. Escucheme. Wummer, Amy, illus. (Rookie Reader Espanol Ser.). (J). (gr. k-2). 2002. pap. 4.95 (978-0-516-26314-4(5)); 2001. (SPA.). 32p. 19.50 (978-0-516-22358-2(5)) Scholastic Library Publishing. (Children's Pr.).

—Escucheme. 2001. (SPA.). (gr. k-3). lib. bdg. 12.95 (978-0-613-54203-6(7)) Tandem Library Bks.

—Listen to Me. Wummer, Amy, illus. 2nd rev. ed. 2001. (Rookie Reader Espanol Ser.). 32p. (J). (gr. k-2). pap. 4.95 (978-0-516-25970-3(9) , Children's Pr.) Scholastic Library Publishing.

—Listen to Me. 2001. (gr. k-3). lib. bdg. 12.95 (978-0-613-46085-9(5)) Tandem Library Bks.

Neitzel, Shirley. The Bag I'm Taking to Grandma's. Parker, Nancy Winslow, illus. 1998. 32p. (J). (ps-3). pap. 6.99 (978-0-688-15840-8(4) , Harper Trophy) HarperCollins Pubs.

—The Bag I'm Taking to Grandma's. Parker, Nancy Winslow, illus. 1998. (J). (978-0-606-13176-6(0)) Tandem Library Bks.

Nelson, S. D. The Star People: A Lakota Story. 2003. (Illus.). 36p. (J). (ps-3). 14.95 (978-0-8109-4584-5(3)) Abrams, Harry N., Inc.

Newbery, Linda. Sisterland. 384p. (gr. 7). 2004. (J). 15.95 (978-0-385-75026-4(9) , Fickling, David Bks.); 2006. (YA). reprint ed. mass mkt. 6.50 (978-0-553-49450-1(3) , Laurel Leaf) Random Hse. Children's Bks.

Newbery, Linda & Ripper, Georgie. A Dog Called Whatnot. 2006. (Red Bananas Ser.). (Illus.). 48p. (J). pap. (978-0-7787-1094-3(7)) Crabtree Publishing Co.

Newman, Dolores A. Papa, How Do You Know? 2000. (Illus.). 32p. (J). pap. 9.95 (978-0-9676438-0-9(5)) Sanctuary Pr.

Newman, Leslea. A Fire Engine for Ruthie. Moore, Cyd, illus. 2004. 32p. (J). (gr. k-3). tchr. ed. 16.00 (978-0-618-15989-5(4) , Clarion Bks.) Houghton Mifflin Co. Trade & Reference Div.

—Matzo Ball Moon. 1998. 15.00 (978-0-395-71519-2(9)) Houghton Mifflin Co.

—Matzo Ball Moon. Greenstein, Elaine, illus. 32p. (J). (gr. k-3). 2006. 5.95 (978-0-618-60481-4(2)); 1998. tchr. ed. 15.00 (978-0-395-71530-7(X)) Houghton Mifflin Co. Trade & Reference Div. (Clarion Bks.).

Newman, Nanette & Cook, Beryl. My Granny. (Illus.). 32p. (YA). 2004. (978-1-84365-058-4(4)); 2003. (978-1-84365-059-1(2)) Chrysalis Children's Bks.

Nicholetti, Terry & Campbell, Annie. Noralee's Adventures on Planet Ifwee. 2002. pap. 10.95 (978-0-9716488-0-7(8)) Goldstar Magic.

Nicholson, Doris. A Day with Grandma. 2006. 9.00 (978-0-8059-9914-3(0)) Dorrance Publishing Co., Inc.

Nickle, John. TV Rex. 2001. (Illus.). 32p. (J). (gr. k-2). pap. 15.95 (978-0-439-12043-2(8)) Scholastic, Inc.

Nicolai, Margaret. Kitaq Goes Ice Fishing. Rubin, David, illus. 32p. (gr. k up). 2002. pap. 8.95 (978-0-88240-569-8(1)); 1998. 15.95 (978-0-88240-504-9(7)) Graphic Arts Ctr. Publishing Co.

Nislick, June Levitt. Zayda Was a Cowboy. 2005. 128p. (J). pap. 9.95 (978-0-8276-0817-7(9)) Jewish Pubn. Society.

Nobisso, Josephine. Grandpa Loved. Hyde, Maureen, illus. 2nd rev. ed. 2000. 32p. (J). (gr. 2 up). pap. 8.95 (978-0-940112-04-9(3)); reprint ed. 16.95 (978-0-940112-01-8(9)) Gingerbread Hse.

—Grandpa Loved. 2000. (gr. k-3). lib. bdg. 17.60 (978-0-613-70807-4(5)) Tandem Library Bks.

Nolan, Han. When We Were Saints. (YA). 2005. 312p. pap. 6.95 (978-0-15-205322-2(0) , Harcourt Paperbacks); 2003. (Illus.). 304p. 17.00 (978-0-15-216371-6(9) , 53586153) Harcourt Children's Bks.

Nora, David, Jr. Happy Balloon to You. 2005. 9.00 (978-0-8059-9870-2(5)) Dorrance Publishing Co., Inc.

Norfolk, Bobby. Anansi & the Pot of Beans. 2006. (Illus.). 32p. (J). pap. 3.95 (978-0-87483-811-4(8)) August Hse. Pubs., Inc.

Norman, Will. Tignall Gold. 2004. 152p. (YA). pap. 13.95 (978-1-58736-359-7(3) , Starbound Bks.) Wheatmark.

Not in a Thousand Years: Individual Chapter Book Title Six-Packs. Vol. 30. 32p. (gr. 5 up). 44.00 (978-0-7578-0979-8(0)) Rigby Education.

Nozick, Betsy. Grandma & Me & Her Secret Recipe. Morgan, Polsky, illus. 2000. 32p. (J). 16.95 (978-1-57168-473-8(5)) Eakin Pr.

Numeroff, Laura Joffe. What Grandmas Do Best What Grandpas Do Best. 2000. (Illus.). 36p. (J). (gr. k-3). per. 14.00 (978-0-689-83491-2(8) , Simon & Schuster Children's Publishing) Simon & Schuster Children's Publishing.

—What Grandmas Do Best What Grandpas Do Best. Munsinger, Lynn, illus. 2000. 40p. (J). (ps-3). 14.95 (978-0-689-80552-3(7)) Simon & Schuster Children's Publishing.

—What Grandpas Do Best. Munsinger, Lynn, illus. gif. ed. 2001. 24p. (J). 6.95 (978-0-689-84701-1(7)) Simon & Schuster Children's Publishing.

Numeroff, Laura Joffe & Munsinger, Lynn. What Grandmas Do Best. gif. ed. 2001. (Illus.). 24p. (J). 6.95 (978-0-689-84700-4(9)) Simon & Schuster Children's Publishing.

Oberman, Sheldon. The Always Prayer Shawl. Lewin, Ted, illus. 2005. 40p. (J). (ps-17). pap. 10.95 (978-1-59078-332-0(8)) Boyds Mills Pr.

O'Connor, Jane. Fancy Nancy: Bonjour, Butterfly. Glasser, Robin Preiss, illus. 2008. (Fancy Nancy Ser.). 32p. (J). 16.99 (***978-0-06-123588-7(1)***); lib. bdg. 17.89 (***978-0-06-123589-4(X)***) HarperCollins Pubs.

Oelschlager, Van. My Grampy Can't Walk. 2006. (Illus.). 40p. 17.95 (978-1-59624-015-5(6)) Cleveland Clinic Pr.

Ohi, Ruth. A Trip with Grandma. Ohi, Ruth, illus. 2007. (Ruth Ohi Picture Book Ser.). (Illus.). 32p. (J). (ps-2). pap. 5.95 (***978-1-55451-071-9(6)***); lib. bdg. 19.95 (***978-1-55451-072-6(4)***) Annick Pr., Ltd. CAN. *Dist:* Firefly Bks., Ltd.

Oke, Janette. Making Memories. Bladholm, Cheri, illus. 1999. 32p. (J). (ps-3). 14.99 (978-0-7642-2190-3(6)) Bethany Hse. Pubs.

Oleson, Susan. Sammy Tails: Finding a Home. 1. ed. 2006. (Illus.). 28p. (J). pap. (978-0-9779251-0-0(2)) Oleson, Susan.

Olshan, Matthew. Finn. 2001. 245p. (YA). (gr. 8-12). 19.95 (978-1-890862-13-8(4)); pap. 14.95 (978-1-890862-14-5(2)) Bancroft Pr.

Onyefulu, Ifeoma. Grandfather's Work: A Traditional Healer in Nigeria. 1998. (Around the World Ser.). (Illus.). 32p. (gr. 2-4). lib. bdg. 22.90 (978-0-7613-0412-8(6) , Millbrook Pr.) Lerner Publishing Group.

Oppenheim, Shulamith Levey. What Is the Full Moon Full Of? Moore, Cyd, illus. 2003. 32p. (J). (ps up). 14.95 (978-1-56397-479-3(7)) Boyds Mills Pr.

—What Is the Moon Full Of? 2000. (978-0-606-18793-0(6)) Tandem Library Bks.

Orr, Wendy. Ark in the Park. pap. 6.95 (978-0-8050-6818-4(X) , Holt, Henry & Co. Bks. For Young Readers) Holt, Henry & Co.

—Ark in the Park. Millard, Kerry, illus. rev. ed. 2000. (Redfeather Book Ser.). 80p. (J). (gr. k-5). 15.95 (978-0-8050-6221-2(1) , Holt, Henry & Co. Bks. For Young Readers) Holt, Henry & Co.

Ortega, Cristina. The Eyes of the Weaver: Los Ojos Del Tejedor. Garcia, Patricio, illus. 2006. 64p. (J). 17.95 (978-0-8263-3990-4(5)) Univ. of New Mexico Pr.

Ortega, Cristina. The Key to Grandpa's House. Ortega, Luis Armando, illus. 2007. 24p. (J). (gr. 1 up). 14.95 (***978-0-8263-4205-8(1)***) Univ. of New Mexico Pr.

Orzak, Carol. Grandpa & the Boys. Jones, Shyrlee, photos by. 2000. (Illus.). 24p. (J). spiral bd. (978-0-9679747-0-5(4)) Details Creative.

Osborne. The Boy who Loved to Shim-sham Shimmy. 2004. (Illus.). 40p. (J). lib. bdg. 14.95 (978-0-9762852-0-5(7)) Wooden Shoe Pr.

Ottolenghi, Carol. Grandparents Love Their Little Ones. Campanella, Marco, illus. 2006. (Tell Me a Story Ser.). 36p. (J). (gr. k-k). bds. 14.95 (978-0-7696-4815-6(0) , Gingham Dog Pr.) School Specialty Publishing.

Overstreet, Marcia Cate. A Day at Gramma's. 2001. (Illus.). 48p. 14.99 (978-0-8254-3471-6(8)) Kregel Pubns.

Owens, Connie S. My Heart Is Sad: When Someone Special Dies. 2005. pap. 7.99 (978-1-59317-088-2(2)) Warner Pr. Pubs.

Oxenbury, Helen. En Casa de los Abuelos. 2002. Tr. of At Grandparents' House. (SPA., Illus.). 24p. (J). (ps-2). 7.50 (978-84-261-2065-6(2)) Juventud, Editorial ESP. *Dist:* AIMS International Bks., Inc.

—En Casa de los Abuelos (At Grandparents' House) (SPA.). 24p. (J). 7.50 (978-84-261-2066-3(0)) Juventud, Editorial ESP. *Dist:* AIMS International Bks., Inc.

Padian, Maria. Brett McCarthy: Work In Progress. 2008. (J). 288p. (***978-0-375-84675-5(1)***); (***978-0-375-94675-2(6)***) Knopf, Alfred A. Inc.

Pak, Soyung. Dear Juno. Hartung, Susan Kathleen, illus. 32p. (J). (ps-2). 2001. pap. 5.99 (978-0-14-230017-6(9) , Puffin); 1999. 17.99 (978-0-670-88252-6(6) , Viking Juvenile) Penguin Group (USA) Inc.

—Dear Juno. 2001. (gr. k-3). lib. bdg. 14.15 (978-0-613-44386-9(1)) Tandem Library Bks.

Pallotta, Jerry. The Hershey's Milk Chocolate Multiplication Book. Bolster, Rob, illus. 2002. 32p. (J). (gr. 1-4). pap. 14.95 (978-0-439-23623-2(1)) Scholastic, Inc.

Pan, Hui-Mei. Que Hay en la Bolsa del Mercdo de la Abuela. Pan, Hui-Mei, illus. 2004. (SPA., Illus.). 16p. (J). bds. 5.95 (978-1-932065-05-3(9)) Star Bright Bks., Inc.

Panagopoulos, Janie Lynn. Mark of the Bear Claw. 2004. (J). 15.95 (978-0-938682-78-3(4)) River Road Pubns., Inc.

Papademetriou, Lisa. Lucky Me! 1999. (Real Kids Readers Ser.). (Illus.). 32p. (J). (gr. 2-4). pap. 4.99 (978-0-7613-2096-8(2) , Millbrook Pr.) Lerner Publishing Group.

—Lucky Me! Handelman, Dorothy, photos by. 1999. (Real Kids Readers Ser.). (Illus.). 48p. (J). (gr. 1-3). lib. bdg. 18.90 (978-0-7613-2071-5(7) , Millbrook Pr.) Lerner Publishing Group.

—Lucky Me! 1999. (J). (978-0-606-19160-9(7)); lib. bdg. 11.80 (978-0-613-18160-0(3)) Tandem Library Bks.

—Lucky Me! Handelman, Dorothy, photos by. 1999. (978-1-58824-805-3(4)) ipicturebooks, LLC.

Park, Barbara. The Graduation of Jake Moon. unabr. ed. 2004. 115p. (J). (gr. 4-7). pap. 29.00 incl. audio (978-0-8072-8722-4(9) , Listening Library) Random Hse. Audio Publishing Group.

—The Graduation of Jake Moon. Colin, Paul, illus. 2000. 128p. (J). (gr. 4-6). 15.00 (978-0-689-83912-2(X) , Atheneum/Anne Schwartz Bks.) Simon & Schuster Children's Publishing.

—The Graduation of Jake Moon. 2002. 128p. (J). (gr. 4-7). reprint ed. pap. 4.99 (978-0-689-83985-6(5) , Aladdin) Simon & Schuster Children's Publishing.

—The Graduation of Jake Moon. 2002. (gr. 3-6). lib. bdg. 13.00 (978-0-613-54234-0(7)) Tandem Library Bks.

—Junie B. Jones Duerme en una Mansion. 2007. (SPA.). 80p. (J). pap. 3.99 (978-0-439-87425-0(4) , Scholastic en Espanol) Scholastic, Inc.

Park, Frances & Park, Ginger. The Have a Good Day Café. Potter, Katherine, illus. 2005. 32p. (J). 16.95 (978-1-58430-171-4(6)) Lee & Low Bks., Inc.

Parker, Gary. Highland Hopes. 2001. (gr. 5-8). lib. bdg. 22.25 (978-0-613-55605-7(4)) Tandem Library Bks.

Parr, Todd. The Grandma Book. 2006. (Illus.). 24p. (J). (ps-1). 9.99 (978-0-316-05802-5(5) , Tingley, Megan Bks.) Little, Brown Bks. for Young Readers.

—The Grandpa Book. 2006. (Illus.). 24p. (J). (ps-1). 9.99 (978-0-316-05801-8(7) , Tingley, Megan Bks.) Little, Brown Bks. for Young Readers.

Parrish, Shelley Berlin. Sharing Grandma's Gift. Petosa-Sigel, Kristi, illus. 2000. 40p. (J). 18.00 (978-0-89716-936-3(0)) Peanut Butter Publishing.

Pastor, Melanie Joy. Wishes for One More Day. Grantford, Jacqui, illus. 2006. 32p. (J). 15.95 (978-0-9729225-7-9(1)) Flashlight Pr.

Paterson, Katherine. The Same Stuff As Stars. 2004. 288p. (J). reprint ed. pap. 6.99 (978-0-06-055712-6(5) , Harper Trophy) HarperCollins Pubs.

Patrick, Denise Lewis. Ma Dear's Old Green House. Sadler, Sonia Lynn, illus. 2004. (J). (gr. k-3). 16.95 (978-0-940975-55-2(6) , Sankofa Bks.) Just Us Bks., Inc.

Paul, Ann Whitford. Everything to Spend the Night: From A to Z. 2001. (978-0-606-22366-9(5)) Tandem Library Bks.

Paulsen, Gary. Alida's Song. 2001. 96p. (J). (gr. 5 up). 5.50 (978-0-440-41474-2(1) , Yearling) Random Hse. Children's Bks.

—Alida's Song. 2001. (J). 12.30 (978-0-606-21019-5(9)); (gr. 5-8). lib. bdg. 13.55 (978-0-613-33744-1(1)) Tandem Library Bks.

—The Cookcamp. 2003. 128p. (J). pap. 4.99 (978-0-439-52357-8(5) , Scholastic Paperbacks) Scholastic, Inc.

—Molly McGinty Has a Good Day. 2004. 112p. (gr. 4-7). lib. bdg. 14.99 (978-0-385-90911-2(X) , Lamb, Wendy) Random Hse. Children's Bks.

—Molly Mcginty Has a Really Good Day. 112p. (gr. 3-7). 2006. 5.50 (978-0-440-41482-7(2) , Yearling); 2004. 12.95 (978-0-385-32588-2(6) , Lamb, Wendy) Random Hse. Children's Bks.

—The Quilt. 96p. (gr. 3-7). 2005. (Illus.). (J). 5.50 (978-0-440-22936-0(7) , Yearling); 2004. (YA). 15.95 (978-0-385-72950-5(2) , Lamb, Wendy); 2004. (YA). lib. bdg. 17.99 (978-0-385-90886-3(5) , Lamb, Wendy) Random Hse. Children's Bks.

PC Treasures, prod. Little Red Riding Hood. 2007. (J). (***978-1-60072-031-4(5)***) PC Treasures, Inc.

Pechero-Loewen, Mariella. I Want to Know How You Found Me. 2004. 39p. pap. 17.95 (978-1-4137-2955-9(X)) PublishAmerica, Inc.

Peck, Richard. A Long Way from Chicago. 2002. (Illus.). (J). 13.19 (978-0-7587-6520-8(7)) Book Wholesalers, Inc.

—A Long Way from Chicago. (Puffin Modern Classics Ser.). 2004. 160p. (gr. 3-6). pap. 6.99 (978-0-14-240110-1(2) , Puffin); 2000. (Illus.). 176p. (J). (gr. 5-9). pap. 6.99 (978-0-14-130352-9(2) , Puffin); 1998. 192p. (J). (gr. 4-7). 16.99 (978-0-8037-2290-3(7) , Dial) Penguin Group (USA) Inc.

—A Long Way from Chicago. 2000. (J). (978-0-606-19769-4(9)) Tandem Library Bks.

—Monster Night at Grandma's House. Freeman, Don, illus. 2003. 32p. (J). (gr. k-3). reprint ed. 12.99 (978-0-8037-2904-9(9) , Dial) Penguin Group (USA) Inc.

—A Year down Yonder. 2002. (Illus.). (YA). 13.19 (978-1-4046-1795-7(7)) Book Wholesalers, Inc.

—A Year down Yonder. 2002. 144p. (gr. 5-8). pap. 6.99 (978-0-14-230070-1(5) , Puffin) Penguin Group (USA) Inc.

—A Year down Yonder. Cieslawski, Steve, illus. 2000. 144p. (J). (gr. 5-9). 16.99 (978-0-8037-2518-8(3) , Dial) Penguin Group (USA) Inc.

—A Year down Yonder. unabr. ed. 2004. (Middle Grade Cassette Librariestm Ser.). 144p. (J). (gr. 5-9). pap. 29.00 incl. audio (978-0-8072-0991-2(0) , S YA 256 SP, Listening Library) Random Hse. Audio Publishing Group.

—A Year down Yonder. 2002. (gr. 5-8). lib. bdg. 14.15 (978-0-613-57934-6(8)) Tandem Library Bks.

—A Year down Yonder. l.t. ed. 2001. 160p. (J). 24.95 (978-0-7862-3282-6(X)) Thorndike Pr.

Peck, Robert Newton. Bro. 2004. 160p. (J). (gr. 7 up). 16.99 (978-0-06-052974-1(1)); lib. bdg. 17.89 (978-0-06-052975-8(X)) HarperCollins Pubs.

Pegram, Laura. Daughter's Day Blues. 2002. (gr. k-3). lib. bdg. 15.30 (978-0-613-49468-7(7)) Tandem Library Bks.

Peirce-Bale, Mary. Noah's Moon. 2006. (J). spiral bd. 10.90 (978-0-9773990-2-4(8)) Mother's Hse. Publishing.

Pellegrino, Marjorie White. My Grandma's the Mayor. Lund, John, illus. 1999. 32p. (J). (gr. 1-7). (978-1-55798-608-5(8) , 441-6088, Magination Pr.) American Psychological Assn.

Pellegrino, Marjorie White, ed. Too Nice. Matthews, Bonnie, illus. 2002. 48p. (YA). (gr. 4-7). 14.95 (978-1-55798-917-8(6)); pap. 8.95 (978-1-55798-918-5(4)) American Psychological Assn. (Magination Pr.).

Pennington, Tony. Fishing with Granddaddy B. 2004. (Illus.). 24p. pap. 8.00 (978-0-687-02570-1(2)) Abingdon Pr.

Pennix, Ladaro, II & Washington-Pennix, Loretha. Granny¿s Helpers. 2006. (Illus.). 22p. (J). per. 10.95 (978-1-59453-974-9(X) , 3186, Airleaf Publishing) Airleaf Publishing & Bookselling.

—Sugar for My Granny. 2006. (Illus.). 17p. (J). per. 10.95 (978-1-59453-807-0(7) , 3185, Airleaf Publishing) Airleaf Publishing & Bookselling.

Penson, Mary. Billy Bardin & the Witness Tree. 2003. 140p. (J). 11.95 (978-0-87565-283-2(2)) Texas Christian Univ. Pr.

Perdomo, Willie. Abuela. Date not set. (J). 16.95 (978-0-8050-7302-7(7) , Holt, Henry & Co. Bks. For Young Readers) Holt, Henry & Co.

Perera, Hilda. Pepin y el Abuelo.Tr. of Pepin & His Grandfather. (SPA., Illus.). 60p. (J). (gr. 2). 7.50 (978-84-241-3271-2(8)) Everest de Ediciones y Distribucion, S.L. ESP. *Dist:* Lectorum Pubns., Inc.

—Pepin y el Abuelo. 2000. Tr. of Pepin & His Grandfather. (SPA.). (gr. k-3). lib. bdg. 16.40 (978-0-613-80619-0(0)) Tandem Library Bks.

Perez, Amada Irma. Nana's Big Surprise/¡Nana, Que Sorpresa! Gonzalez, Maya Christina, tr. Gonzalez, Maya Christina, illus. 2007. (ENG & SPA.). 32p. (J). (gr. 1-2). 16.95 (978-0-89239-190-5(1)) Children's Bk. Pr.

Perkyns, Dorothy. Last Days in Africville. 2005. (Illus.). 144p. (YA). pap., tchr. ed. (978-0-88878-446-9(5) , Sandcastle Bks.) Dundurn Group, The.

—Last Days in Africville. 2006. 120p. (J). pap. 10.99 (***978-1-55002-630-6(5)*** , Dundurn Pr.) Dundurn Group, The CAN. *Dist:* Univ. of Toronto Pr.

Petersen, Patricia. Magali/Magali: An Aztec Legend about Good Fortune (Una Ieyenja Azteca Sobre La Buena Fortuna) Petersen, Sheli, illus. 1998. (Cuentos en Dos Idiomas Ser.). 32p. (J). (gr. 3-6). 16.95 (978-1-56492-250-2(2)) Laredo Publishing Co., Inc.

Pfister, Marcus. The Happy Hedgehog. 2003. (Illus.). 32p. (J). pap. 6.95 (978-0-7358-1816-3(9)) North-South Bks., Inc.

Phoenix, Woodrow & Price, Robin. Count Milkula: A Tale of Milk & Monsters! 2007. 32p. (J). 19.95 (***978-0-9546576-5-9(9)***) Mogzilla GBR. *Dist:* Independent Pubs. Group.

Pinder, Margaret. But I Don't Want to Be a Movie Star. 2006. 256p. (YA). (gr. 6-12). 15.99 (978-0-525-47634-4(2) , Dutton Juvenile) Penguin Group (USA) Inc.

Pitt, Linda. Toddler Gran. 2001. (Illus.). 105p. (J). pap. 8.99 (978-1-84270-027-3(8)) Andersen GBR. *Dist:* Independent Pubs. Group.

Pittar, Gill. Milly, Molly & Grandpa Friday. 2004. 28p. (978-1-86972-029-2(6)) Milly Molly Bks.

—Milly, Molly & Grandpa Friday (book W/dolls) 2006. 28p. pap. (978-1-86972-107-7(1)) Milly Molly Bks.

Pitzer, Susanna & Teis, Kyra. Grandfather Hurant Lives Forever. Pitzer, Susanna & Teis, Kyra, illus. 2001. (Illus.). (J). 9.95 (978-1-56123-159-1(2)) Centering Corp.

Placide, Jaira. Fresh Girl. 2002. 224p. (YA). (gr. 7 up). 15.95 (978-0-385-32753-4(6) , Lamb, Wendy) Random Hse. Children's Bks.

Platt, Randall Beth. Honor Bright. 1998. (978-0-606-13486-6(7)) Tandem Library Bks.

Plourde, Lynn. Thank You Grandpa. Cockroft, Jason, illus. 2003. 32p. (J). (gr. k). 15.99 (978-0-525-46992-6(3) , Dutton Juvenile) Penguin Group (USA) Inc.

Plummer, Joseph. Listening to Crickets. 2006. pap. 10.49 (***978-1-4259-5697-4(1)***) AuthorHouse.

The Poet's Basket. 2006. (J). 10.00 (978-0-9769827-0-8(6)) Wren Song Pr.

Polacco, Ernest L. When Lightning Comes in a Jar. Polacco, Patricia, illus. 2007. 40p. (J). (gr. k). pap. 6.99 (978-0-14-240350-1(4) , Puffin) Penguin Group (USA) Inc.

Polacco, Patricia. Babushka Baba Yaga. 1999. (Illus.). 32p. (J). (ps-3). pap. 6.99 (978-0-698-11633-7(X) , Putnam Juvenile) Penguin Group (USA) Inc.

—Babushka Baba Yaga. 1999. (J). lib. bdg. 13.79 (978-0-606-16844-1(3)); lib. bdg. 15.30 (978-0-613-11296-3(2)) Tandem Library Bks.

—Meteor! 2001. (J). (gr. k-4). pap. 17.95 incl. audio (978-0-8045-6857-9(X) , 6857) Spoken Arts, Inc.

—The Trees of the Dancing Goats. Polacco, Patricia, illus. 2002. (Illus.). (J). 25.11 (978-0-7587-3858-5(7)) Book Wholesalers, Inc.

—The Trees of the Dancing Goats. Polacco, Patricia, illus. 2000. (Illus.). 32p. (J). (gr. k-3). 7.99 (978-0-689-83857-6(3) , Aladdin) Simon & Schuster Children's Publishing.

—The Trees of the Dancing Goats. 2000. (J). (978-0-606-20094-3(0)) Tandem Library Bks.

—Trees of the Dancing Goats. 2000. (gr. k-3). lib. bdg. 15.30 (978-0-613-30164-0(1)) Tandem Library Bks.

—When Lightning Comes in a Jar: Come to a Family Reunion. Polacco, Patricia, illus. 2002. (Illus.). 40p. (J). 16.99 (978-0-399-23164-3(1) , Philomel) Penguin Group (USA) Inc.

Polacco, Patricia & Polacco, Patricia. The Bee Tree. 1998. (Illus.). (J). (ps-ps). lib. bdg. 15.30 (978-0-613-07325-7(8)) Tandem Library Bks.

Polette, Nancy & Shaw, Charles. Grandma's Patchy Pocket. 2004. (Illus.). 16p. (J). (gr. k-3). pap. 4.95 (978-1-57874-075-8(4)) Kaeden Corp.

Porter, Cullen. Grandpa Grumpy Pants. 2006. (Illus.). 32p. (J). 19.95 (978-1-932278-05-7(2)) Mayhaven Publishing.

Poulsen, Kathleen Phillips. Apple Doll. Poulsen, Kathleen Phillips, illus. 2002. (Illus.). 32p. (J). 9.95 (978-1-57072-222-6(6)) Overmountain Pr.

Preller, James. Case of the Race Against Time. 2003. (gr. 3-6). lib. bdg. 11.80 (978-0-613-63389-5(X)) Tandem Library Bks.

Pressler, Mirjam. Let Sleeping Dogs Lie. Macki, Erik J., tr. from GER. 2007. 208p. (YA). (gr. 7 up). 16.95 (***978-1-932425-84-0(5)*** , Front Street) Boyds Mills Pr.

Principe, Hilda. My Red Hat Grandma & Me. 2007. 24p. (J). pap. 8.99 (***978-1-59886-990-3(6)***) Tate Publishing & Enterprises, L.L.C.

Pringle, Nicholas. Silly Billy. 2005. 40p. (J). pap. 9.00 (978-1-4116-4981-1(8)) Lulu.com.

Prokofiev, Sergei & Malone, Peter. Sergei Prokofiev's Peter & the Wolf: With Fully-Orchestrated & Narrated CD. 2004. (Illus.). 40p. (J). 19.95 incl. audio compact disk (978-0-375-82430-2(8) , Knopf Bks. for Young Readers) Random Hse. Children's Bks.

PS, I Love You, Gramps: Individual Title, 6 packs. (Action Packs Ser.). 120p. (gr. 3-5). 44.00 (978-0-7635-8389-7(8)) Rigby Education.

Puckett, Annie Marie. Pedro Learns about Salvation. 2006. 56p. per. 9.95 (***978-1-57258-453-2(X)*** , 945-6314) TEACH Services, Inc.

Pullen, Janis Charlton. Grandma¿s Stories. 2004. 44p. (J). per. 9.95 (***978-1-59453-422-5(5)*** , 2513, Airleaf Publishing) Airleaf Publishing & Bookselling.

Purmell, Ann. Christmas Tree Farm. Weber, Jill, illus. 32p. (J). 16.95 (978-0-8234-1886-2(3)) Holiday Hse., Inc.

Purwin, Patricia. Grampa's a Scientist. Purwin, Patricia, illus. Dawson, John, photos by. 1999. (Illus.). 24p. (J). (ps-6). pap. 12.95 (978-0-9673408-0-7(2)) Collage Storybook Pr.

Quigley, Mary. Granddad's Fishing Buddy. Jorisch, Stephane, illus. 2007. 32p. (J). (ps-3). 16.99 (978-0-8037-2942-1(1) , Dial) Penguin Group (USA) Inc.

Quinn, Zoe. The Caped 6th Grader: Happy Birthday, Hero! 2006. (Illus.). 144p. (J). (gr. 4-7). pap. 4.99 (978-0-440-42079-8(2) , Yearling) Random Hse. Children's Bks.

—The Caped 6th Grader: Happy Birthday, Hero! Spangler, Brie, illus. 2006. 144p. (J). (gr. 4-7). lib. bdg. 11.99 (978-0-385-90304-2(9) , Yearling) Random Hse. Children's Bks.

Rader, Jared. Sandy's Dream. 2007. (J). per. 10.99 (***978-1-59879-398-7(5)***) Lifevest Publishing, Inc.

Ramblin' Rose: The Porcelain Mines in Russia. 2007. 196p. (YA). pap. 8.99 (***978-0-9776043-7-1(3)***) Aspirations Media, Inc.

Ransom, Candice F. Finding Day's Bottom. 2006. 168p. (J). (gr. 4-6). 15.95 (978-1-57505-933-4(9) , Carolrhoda Bks.) Lerner Publishing Group.

—Little Red Riding Hood. Lyon, Tammie Speer, illus. 2002. (Brighter Child Keepsake Stories Ser.). 32p. (J). (ps-3). pap. 3.99 (978-1-57768-198-4(3) , Brighter Child) School Specialty Publishing.

Ransom, Jeanie Franz. Grandma U. Corvino, Lucy, illus. 2002. 32p. (J). 15.95 (978-1-56145-214-9(9)) Peachtree Pubs., Ltd.

Rau, Dana Meachen. Yahoo for You, Level B. Pillo, Cary, illus. 2002. (Compass Point Early Reader Ser.). 32p. (J). (gr. k up). lib. bdg. 18.60 (978-0-7565-0177-8(6)) Compass Point Bks.

Ravel, Edeet. The Secret Journey of Pauline Siddhartha. 2007. 224p. pap. 9.95 (***978-1-55192-974-3(0)***) Raincoast Bk. Distribution CAN. *Dist:* Perseus Distribution.

Raven, Margot Theis. Circle Unbroken. Lewis, E. B., illus. 2004. 48p. (J). 16.00 (978-0-374-31289-3(3) , Farrar, Straus & Giroux (BYR)) Farrar, Straus & Giroux.

—Circle Unbroken. Lewis, E.B., illus. 2007. 48p. (J). pap. 6.99 (***978-0-312-37603-1(0)***) Square Fish.

Read to Me, Grandma: Keepsake Collection. 2004. (Illus.). 96p. (J). (978-1-4127-0459-5(6) , 7217600) Publications International, Ltd.

Reed, Jennifer. The Falling Flowers. Cole, Dick, illus. 2005. (J). 16.95 (978-1-885008-28-2(7)) Shen's Bks.

Refrrolo, C. T. Grandchild of Mine: You & I. 2006. (J). 12.00 (978-0-8059-6845-3(8)) Dorrance Publishing Co., Inc.

Un regalo para Abuelito, 6 Packs. (Coleccion Pm Ser.). (SPA.). 16p. (gr. 1 up). 26.00 (978-0-7578-3049-5(8)) Rigby Education.

Reiser, Lynn W. Cherry Pies & Lullabies. Reiser, Lynn W., illus. 1998. (Illus.). 40p. (J). (ps-3). 18.99 (978-0-688-13391-7(6)) HarperCollins Pubs.

—Cherry Pies & Lullabies. 1998. (Illus.). 40p. (J). (ps-3). 16.89 (978-0-688-13392-4(4)) HarperCollins Pubs.

Renaud, Anne. How the Sea Came to Marissa. Durland, Maud, illus. 2006. 32p. (J). (978-1-58270-129-5(6)) Beyond Words Publishing, Inc.

Renner, Zainabu. My Grandma & I. 1998. 16p. pap. (978-1-57579-107-4(2)) Pine Hill Pr., Inc.

Repp, Gloria. Booklinks, Level 2. 1998. 149p. (J). (gr. 4-7). pap. 7.49 (978-1-57924-000-4(3) , 106484) Jones, Bob Univ. Pr.

—Trouble at Silver Pines Inn. 1998. lib. bdg. 14.70 (978-0-613-86050-5(0)) Tandem Library Bks.

Resau, Laura. What the Moon Saw. 2006. 272p. (gr. 5). (J). 15.95 (978-0-385-73343-4(7)); (YA). lib. bdg. 17.99 (978-0-385-90360-8(X)) Random Hse. Children's Bks. (Delacorte Bks. for Young Readers).

—What the Moon Saw. l.t. rev. ed. 2007. 300p. (YA). 22.95 (***978-0-7862-9278-3(4)***) Thorndike Pr.

Reynolds, Adrian. Pete & Polo's Farmyard Adventure. Reynolds, Adrian, illus. 2002. (Illus.). 32p. (J). (ps-1). pap. 16.95 (978-0-439-30913-4(1) , Orchard Bks.) Scholastic, Inc.

Reynolds, Cynthia Furlong. Across the Reach. 2007. 144p. (J). 16.95 (***978-1-58726-518-1(4)*** , Mitten Pr.) Ann Arbor Media Group, LLC.

—Grammie's Secret Cupboard. Dodson, Bert, illus. 2007. 32p. (J). 17.95 (***978-1-58726-310-1(6)*** , Mitten Pr.) Ann Arbor Media Group, LLC.

Reynolds, Jean. Gwen & the Talking Napkin. 2007. (Grandma Ser.: 4). (J). per. 7.99 (***978-1-59872-897-2(0)***) Instantpublisher.com.

Richards, Justin. The Invisible Detective: Double Life. 2005. 160p. (J). (gr. 4). 10.99 (978-0-399-24313-4(5) , Putnam Juvenile) Penguin Group (USA) Inc.

Richardson, Faith. The Peacock's Stone. 2003. 192p. (J). 21.95 (978-0-9744989-0-4(4)); (Illus.). pap. 12.95 (978-0-9744989-1-1(2)) Fox Song Bks.

Richter, Bernd C. When Grandma & Grandpa Visited Alaska They. . . 1999. 48p. 14.95 (978-0-9663495-6-6(3)) Saddle Pal Creations, Inc.

Richter, Bernd C. & Richter, Susan E. When Grandma & Grandpa Visited Alaska They. . . Richter, Bernd C., illus. 1998. (Illus.). 48p. (ps-6). pap. 9.95 (978-0-9663495-0-4(4)) Saddle Pal Creations, Inc.

Riddle, Jamie. Beach Bum Babies & Sand Sisters Stormy. 2006. 48p. pap. 12.95 (978-1-4241-3600-1(8)) PublishAmerica, Inc.

Riefe, Barbara. Amelia Dale Archer Story. 1998. 304p. (YA). (gr. 8 up). 22.95 (978-0-312-86077-6(3) , Forge Bks.) Doherty, Tom Assocs., LLC.

Rigby Education Staff. Granny. (Sails Literacy Ser.). (Illus.). 16p. (gr. 1-2). 27.00 (978-0-7635-9900-3(X) , 699009C99) Rigby Education.

Riley, Kathryn. The Big Sale. Handelman, Dorothy, photos by. 1999. (Real Kids Readers Ser.). (Illus.). 32p. (gr. k-2). lib. bdg. 18.90 (978-0-7613-2057-9(1)); (J). pap. 4.99 (978-0-7613-2082-1(2)) Lerner Publishing Group. (Millbrook Pr.).

—The Big Sale. 1999. (J). 10.79 (978-0-606-19147-0(X)) Tandem Library Bks.

—Big Sale. 1999. (gr. k-3). lib. bdg. 11.80 (978-0-613-16854-0(2)) Tandem Library Bks.

Rivera-Ashford, Roni Capin. My Nana's Remedies: Los Remedios de Mi Nana. 2002. (SPA.). 32p. (J). (ps-4). 15.95 (978-1-886679-19-1(3)) Arizona Sonora Desert Museum Pr.

Roberts, Barbara A. Phoebe's Lost Treasure. Sternberg, Kate, illus. 1999. (Phoebe Flower's Adventures Ser.). 68p. (gr. 2-4). pap. 5.95 (978-0-9660366-6-4(2)) National Bk. Network.

Roberts, Bethany. Gramps & the Fire Dragon. Iwai, Melissa, illus. 2000. 32p. (J). (gr. k-3). tchr. ed. 15.00 (978-0-395-69849-5(9) , Clarion Bks.) Houghton Mifflin Co. Trade & Reference Div.

Roberts, Lynn. Little Red: A Fizzingly Good Yarn. Roberts, David, illus. 2005. 32p. (J). (ps-3). 16.95 (978-0-8109-5783-1(3) , Abrams Bks. for Young Readers) Abrams, Harry N. , Inc.

Roberts, Willo Davis. Rebel. 160p. (J). 2005. pap. 5.99 (978-0-689-85081-3(6) , Aladdin); 2003. (Illus.). 16.95 (978-0-689-85073-8(5) , Atheneum) Simon & Schuster Children's Publishing.

Robertson, Barbara. Rosemary & the Island Treasure: Back to 1947. 2001. (Hourglass Adventures Ser.: Bk. 4). (Illus.). 128p. (J). (gr. 3-5). pap. 4.95 (978-1-890817-58-9(9)) Winslow Pr.

—Rosemary in Paris: Back to 1889. 2001. (Hourglass Adventures Ser.: Bk. 2). (Illus.). 121p. (J). (gr. 4-7). pap. 4.95 (978-1-890817-56-5(2)) Winslow Pr.

—Rosemary Meets Rosemarie Bk. 1: Berlin in 1870. 2001. (Hourglass Adventures Ser.: Bk. 1). (Illus.). 128p. (J). (gr. 4-6). pap. 5.95 (978-1-890817-55-8(4)) Winslow Pr.

Robinson, Linda. Dear Grandchild: When You Come for a Visit. Larkins, Mona, illus. 2005. (J). 15.99 (978-0-9740841-4-5(X)) K&B Products.

Rochester, B. The Joey Jenkins Mysteries: Something Is Missing at Redding Lake. 2005. 67p. pap. 14.95 (978-1-4241-0065-1(8)) PublishAmerica, Inc.

Rodda, Emily. The Charm Bracelet. Vitale, Raoul, illus. 2003. (Fairy Realm Ser.: No. 1). 128p. (J). (gr. 2-5). 8.99 (978-0-06-009583-3(0)); lib. bdg. 15.89 (978-0-06-009584-0(9)) HarperCollins Pubs.

—The Charm Bracelet. Vitale, Raoul, illus. 2007. (Fairy Realm Ser.). 128p. (J). (gr. 3-6). 25.65 (978-1-59961-323-9(9)) Spotlight.

—The Star Cloak. Vitale, Raoul, illus. 2005. (Fairy Realm Ser.: No. 7). 128p. (J). lib. bdg. 14.89 (978-0-06-077739-3(1)); 8.99 (978-0-06-077758-6(3)) HarperCollins Pubs.

Rodowsky, Colby F. That Fernhill Summer. 2006. 176p. (J). 16.00 (978-0-374-37442-6(2)) Farrar, Straus & Giroux.

Romain, Trevor. Under the Big Sky. Romain, Trevor, illus. 2001. (Illus.). 48p. (J). (gr. 2 up). 14.89 (978-0-06-029495-3(7)) HarperCollins Pubs.

Roman, Sela Anders. Where Are Grandpa's Teeth? Smith, Len, illus. 2007. (Meet the Robinsons Ser.). 20p. (J). pap. 6.99 (978-0-06-112478-5(8)) HarperCollins Pubs.

Root, Phyllis. The Name Quilt. Apple, Margot, illus. 2003. 32p. (J). (gr. k-3). 16.00 (978-0-374-35484-8(7) , Farrar, Straus & Giroux (BYR)) Farrar, Straus & Giroux.

Rose, Simon. The Emerald Curse. Nugent, Cynthia, illus. 2006. 96p. (J). (gr. 3-7). 7.95 (978-1-896580-90-6(4)) Tradewind Bks. CAN. *Dist:* Orca Bk. Pubs. USA.

Rosenbaum, Adnira Warmflash. A Grandma Like Yours/A Grandpa Like Yours. 2006. (J). pap. 6.95 (978-1-58013-168-1(9)) Kar-Ben Publishing.

Rosenbaum, Andria Warmflash. A Grandma Like Yours: A Grandpa Like Yours. Bjornson, Barbara, illus. 2006. (J). 16.95 (978-1-58013-167-4(0)) Kar-Ben Publishing.

Rosenberg, Liz. The Silence in the Mountains. Soentpiet, Chris K., illus. 32p. (J). (gr. k-4). 1999. 16.99 (978-0-531-33084-5(2)); 1998. pap. 15.95 (978-0-531-30084-8(6)) Scholastic, Inc. (Orchard Bks.).

Rosenberry, Vera. Vera's Baby Sister. rev. ed. 2005. (Illus.). 32p. (J). 16.95 (978-0-8050-7126-9(1) , Holt, Henry & Co. Bks. For Young Readers) Holt, Henry & Co.

Rosenbluth, Roz. Getting to Know Ruben Plotnick. Manning, Maurie J., illus. 2005. 32p. (J). 15.95 (978-0-9729225-5-5(5)) Flashlight Pr.

Rosenthal, Betsy R. It's Not Worth Making a Tzimmes Over! Rivers, Ruth, illus. 2006. 32p. (J). 15.95 (978-0-8075-3677-3(6)) Whitman, Albert & Co.

Rosseau, Paul. Lucifer, Mon Grand-Père, Tome 1. Guénette, Geneviève, illus. 2004. (Mon Roman Ser.). (FRE.). 160p. (J). (gr. 2). pap. (978-2-89021-650-1(0)) Diffusion du livre Mirabel.

Rossi. El Chaparron Torrencial. 2000. Tr. of Gullywasher. (SPA.). (J). 14.75 (978-0-606-19852-3(0)) Tandem Library Bks.

Rossi, Joyce. The Gullywasher (El Chaparron Torrencial) 1998. (ENG & SPA., Illus.). 32p. (J). (gr. k-3). 7.95 (978-0-87358-728-0(6) , Rising Moon Bks. for Young Readers) Northland Publishing.

Roth, Susan L. Grandpa Blows His Penny Whistle until the Angels Sing. 2001. (Illus.). 40p. (J). (gr. 3-5). 16.99 (978-1-84148-247-7(1)) Barefoot Bks., Inc.

—Happy Birthday Mr. Kang. 2001. (Illus.). 32p. (J). (ps-3). 16.95 (978-0-7922-7723-1(6) , National Geographic Children's Bks.) National Geographic Society.

Rouse, Marisa K. Hildigarde of Willow Hollow. 2007. 64p. pap. 9.95 (***978-1-4327-0127-7(4)***) Outskirts Press, Inc.

Rovira, Francesca, illus. Caperucita Roja / Little Red Riding Hood. 2006. (Bilingual Tales Ser.). 24p. (J). pap. 3.50 (978-0-439-77375-1(X) , Scholastic en Espanol) Scholastic, Inc.

Ruelle, Karen Gray. Easy As Apple Pie: A Harry & Emily Adventure. (Holiday House Readers Ser.). (Illus.). 32p. (J). (gr. k-3). 4.95 (978-0-8234-1800-8(6)) Holiday Hse., Inc.

—Easy As Apple Pie: A Harry & Emily Adventure. Ruelle, Karen Gray, illus. (Holiday House Reader Ser.). (Illus.). 32p. (J). (gr. k-3). tchr. ed. 14.95 (978-0-8234-1759-9(X)) Holiday Hse., Inc.

Rumford, James. Cloudmakers. 2006. (Illus.). 32p. (J). (gr. k-3). pap. 6.95 (978-0-618-68951-4(6)) Houghton Mifflin Co.

—When Silver Needles Swam: The Story of Tutu's Quilt. 1998. (ENG & HAW., Illus.). 30p. (J). (gr. 1-6). 10.95 (978-1-891839-00-9(4)) Manoa Pr.

Russell, Ching Yeung. Child Bride. 136p. 2003. (YA). (gr. 4-6). pap. 9.95 (978-1-59078-024-4(8)); 1999. (Illus.). (J). (gr. 3-7). 15.95 (978-1-56397-748-0(6)) Boyds Mills Pr.

Ryan, Pam Muñoz. Arroz con Frijoles y unos Amables Ratones. Cepeda, Joe, illus. 2002. (SPA.). 32p. (J). (gr. k-2). pap. 5.99 (978-0-439-31737-5(1) , SO30909, Scholastic en Espanol) Scholastic, Inc.

—Becoming Naomi Leon. (J). (gr. 4-7). 2004. 240p. pap. 16.95 (978-0-439-26969-8(5) , Scholastic Pr.); 2005. 272p. reprint ed. pap. 5.99 (978-0-439-26997-1(0) , Scholastic Paperbacks) Scholastic, Inc.

—Mice & Beans. Cepeda, Joe, illus. 2001. 32p. (J). (ps-2). pap. 16.95 (978-0-439-18303-1(0) , Levine, Arthur A. Bks.) Scholastic, Inc.

Rylant, Cynthia. Henry & Mudge & the Bedtime Thumps. Stevenson, Sucie, illus. 2002. (Henry & Mudge Ser.). (J). 11.91 (978-0-7587-1265-3(0)) Book Wholesalers, Inc.

—Henry & Mudge & the Bedtime Thumps. 2006. (Henry & Mudge Ser.). (J). (gr. 1). 24.21 (978-1-59961-081-8(7)) Spotlight.

—The Islander. 1999. (Illus.). 112p. (J). (gr. 5-17). reprint ed. pap. 5.50 (978-0-440-41542-8(X) , Yearling) Random Hse. Children's Bks.

—The Islander. 1999. (gr. 5-8). lib. bdg. 13.00 (978-0-613-23002-5(7)) Tandem Library Bks.

—The Ticky-Tacky Doll. Stevenson, Harvey, illus. 2002. 32p. (J). (gr. k-2). 16.00 (978-0-15-201078-2(5)) Harcourt Children's Bks.

Sadasivan, Lathika. My First Millennium. Sadasivan, Lathika, illus. 2000. (Illus.). 20p. (J). (ps-3). 14.99 (978-0-9700318-1-5(5)); pap. 7.99 (978-0-9700318-0-8(7)) Peek-A-Bks.

Saenz, Benjamin Alire. Gift from Papa Diego.Tr. of Regalo De Papa Diego. (gr. k-3). lib. bdg. 19.90 (978-0-613-06587-0(5)) Tandem Library Bks.

—A Gift from Papa Diego (Un Regalo de Papa Diego) Garcia, Geronimo, illus. 2004. (ENG & SPA.). 40p. (gr. k-7). pap. 10.95 (978-0-938317-33-3(4)) Cinco Puntos Pr.

—Grandma Fina & Her Wonderful Umbrellas. 2001. (gr. k-3). lib. bdg. 16.40 (978-0-613-77727-8(1)) Tandem Library Bks.

—Grandma Fina & Her Wonderful Umbrellas: La Abuelita Fina y Sus Sombrillas Maravillosas. Garcia, Geronimo, illus. 2001. (SPA.). 32p. (J). pap. 7.95 (978-0-938317-61-6(X)) Cinco Puntos Pr.

Sagel, Jim. Always the Heart. 1998. (Red Crane Literature Ser.).Tr. of Siempre el Corazon. (ENG & SPA., Illus.). 168p. (gr. 8-12). pap. 12.95 (978-1-878610-68-3(6)) Red Crane Bks., Inc.

—Always the Heart. 1998. Tr. of Siempre el Corazon. (gr. 7-12). lib. bdg. 22.20 (978-0-613-80111-9(3)) Tandem Library Bks.

Salisbury, Linda G. No Sisters Sisters Club: A Bailey Fish Adventure. Grotke, Christopher A., illus. 2005. 188p. (J). per. 8.95 (978-1-881539-40-7(0)) Tabby Hse. Bks.

—The Wild Women of Lake Anna: A Bailey Fish Adventure. 2005. (Illus.). 159p. (J). (978-1-881539-37-7(7)) Tabby Hse. Bks.

Sanderson, Brandon. Alcatraz Versus the Evil Librarians. 2007. (Alcatraz Versus the Evil Librarians Ser.). 320p. (J). pap. 16.99 (***978-0-439-92550-1(9)*** , Scholastic Pr.) Scholastic, Inc.

Sanschagrin, Joceline. Caillou' at Grandma & Grandpa's. Lapierre, Claude, illus. 2002. 23p. (J). pap. (978-2-89450-296-9(6)) Chouette Publishing.

Santillana U. S. A. Publishing Co, Inc. Staff. La Abuela. 2003. (SPA.). (gr. 5-8). lib. bdg. 18.75 (978-0-613-71356-6(7)) Tandem Library Bks.

Sarrazin, Marisol. Peppy, Patch, & the Postman. 2005. (Read-It! Readers Ser.). (Illus.). 32p. (C). (gr. k-3). 18.60 (978-1-4048-1034-1(X)) Picture Window Bks.

Sarrazin, Marisol, illus. Peppy, Patch, & the Bath. 2005. (Read-It! Readers Ser.). 32p. (C). (gr. k-3). 18.60 (978-1-4048-1032-7(3)) Picture Window Bks.

Sato, Wakiko. Grandma Baba Wants Sunshine!, Vol. 5. 2004. (Grandma Baba Ser.). (JPN & ENG., Illus.). 32p. (J). 10.95 (978-0-8048-3568-8(3)) Tuttle Publishing.

—Grandma Baba's Amazing Scarf!, Vol. 10. 2004. (Grandma Baba Ser.: Bk. 10). (Illus.). 28p. 12.95 (978-0-8048-3566-4(7)) Tuttle Publishing.

—Grandma Baba's Big Cleanup!, Vol. 6. 2004. (Grandma Baba Ser.). (JPN & ENG., Illus.). 32p. (J). 10.95 (978-0-8048-3569-5(1)) Tuttle Publishing.

—Grandma Baba's Bird's Nest!, Vol. 9. Carpenter, Richard, tr. from JPN. 2004. (Grandma Baba Ser.). (Illus.). 32p. (J). 10.95 (978-0-8048-3571-8(3)) Tuttle Publishing.

—Grandma Baba's Dream Mountain!, Vol. 7. 2004. (Grandma Baba Ser.). (JPN & ENG., Illus.). 32p. (J). 10.95 (978-0-8048-3570-1(5)) Tuttle Publishing.

—Grandma Baba's Magic Watermelon!, Vol. 8. Carpenter, Richard, tr. from JPN. 2004. (Grandma Baba Ser.). (Illus.). 28p. (J). 10.95 (978-0-8048-3567-1(5)) Tuttle Publishing.

Saulsman, Helen L. From Grandma... With Love. Raymer, M. Loys, illus. 1998. (J). (ps-6). pap. 10.00 (978-0-9663051-0-4(8)) Saulsman, Helen L.

Saunders, Susan. Lucky Lady. 2000. 128p. (J). (gr. 4-7). 14.95 (978-0-380-97784-0(2)) HarperCollins Pubs.

Savadier, Elivia. Will Sheila Share? 2008. 24p. (J). 12.95 (*978-1-59643-289-5(6)) Roaring Brook Pr.

Savageau, Cheryl. Muskrat Will Be Swimming. Hynes, Robert, illus. 2006. 32p. (J). pap. (978-0-88448-280-2(4)) Tilbury Hse. Pubs.

Say, Allen. Grandfather's Journey. Say, Allen, illus. 2002. (Illus.). (J). 26.83 (978-0-7587-0050-6(4)) Book Wholesalers, Inc.

Scacco, Linda. Always My Grandpa: A Story for Children about Alzheimer's Disease. Wong, Nicole, illus. 2005. 48p. (J). (gr. 1-3). 14.95 (978-1-59147-311-4(X)); pap. 8.95 (978-1-59147-312-1(8)) American Psychological Assn. (Magination Pr.).

Scaglione, Joseph. My Lucky Penny. Szarko, Kathy, illus. deluxe l.t. ed. 1999. 64p. (J). (ps-4). pap. 24.95 incl. cd-rom (978-0-9675011-0-9(5)) New Day Enterprises, Ltd.

Scelsa, Greg. Granny's Coming 'Round the Mountain' Faulkner, Stacey, ed. Leary, Catherine, illus. 2006. (J). pap. 2.99 (*978-1-59198-350-7(9)) Creative Teaching Pr., Inc.

Schachner, Judith B. The Grannyman. (Illus.). 32p. (J). (gr. k-3). 2003. pap. 6.99 (978-0-14-250062-0(3) , Puffin); 1999. 15.99 (978-0-525-46122-7(1) , Dutton Juvenile) Penguin Group (USA) Inc.

—The Grannyman. unabr. ed. 2000. (YA). pap. 32.99 incl. audio (978-0-7887-3640-7(X) , 41005X4) Recorded Bks., LLC.

Schatzer, Jeffery. The Runaway Garden. Ebbeler, Jeffrey, illus. 2007. 32p. (J). 17.95 (*978-1-58726-436-8(6) , Mitten Pr.) Ann Arbor Media Group, LLC.

Scheer, Julian. A Thanksgiving Turkey. Himler, Ronald, illus. 2001. 32p. (J). (gr. k-3). tchr. ed. 16.95 (978-0-8234-1674-5(7)) Holiday Hse., Inc.

Schirripa, Steve & Fleming, Charles. Nicky Deuce: Welcome to the Family. 2006. 176p. (gr. 5-8). 5.99 (978-0-440-42053-8(9) , Yearling) Random Hse. Children's Bks.

Schlein, Miriam. The Story about Me. Stephenson, Kristina, illus. 2004. 32p. (J). (ps-1). 15.95 (978-0-8075-7631-1(X)) Whitman, Albert & Co.

Schlesinger, Gretchen. Send Me the Soap #1: The Emerald Isle Adventure. Pietila, David, illus. 2006. (J). 11.95 (978-0-9778536-0-1(8)) Eco-thumb Publishing Co.

—Send Me the Soap #1: The Emerald Isle Adventure (lib. Bdg.) Pietila, David, illus. 2006. (J). lib. bdg. (978-0-9778536-1-8(6)) Eco-thumb Publishing Co.

Schlessinger, Laura. Dr. Laura Schlessinger's Where's God? McFeeley, Daniel, illus. 2003. 40p. (J). (ps-2). lib. bdg. 16.89 (978-0-06-051910-0(X)) HarperCollins Pubs.

—Where's God. 2006. pap. (978-0-06-051911-7(8)) HarperCollins Canada, Ltd.

—Where's God? McFeeley, Daniel, illus. l.t. ed. 2003. 40p. (J). (ps-2). 16.99 (978-0-06-051909-4(6)) HarperCollins Pubs.

Schlusberg, Julian S. Who Paints the Sky? Berger, Ethel, illus. l.t. ed. 2002. 40p. (J). (ps-6). pap. (978-0-9720243-0-3(1)) Clover Pubns.

Schneider, Antonie. The Birthday Bear. 2000. (J). 12.75 (978-0-606-19469-3(X)) Tandem Library Bks.

Schofield, S. M. Race to Eagle Mountain. 2007. (ENG.). 184p. (J). per. 16.99 (*978-1-4141-0814-8(1)) Pleasant Word.

Scholastic, Inc. Staff & Black, Sonia. Just for You! Jumping the Broom. 2004. (Just for You! Ser.). (Illus.). 32p. pap. 3.99 (978-0-439-56878-4(1) , Teaching Resources) Scholastic, Inc.

Scholastic, Inc. Staff & Boyd, Dee. Only the Stars. Rich, Anna, illus. 2004. (Just for You! Ser.). 32p. pap. 3.99 (978-0-439-56862-3(5) , Teaching Resources) Scholastic, Inc.

Schumacher, Julie. The Book of One Hundred Truths. 192p. (gr. 4-7). 2008. 5.99 (*978-0-440-42085-9(7) , Yearling); 2006. (J). 15.95 (978-0-385-73290-1(2) , Delacorte Bks. for Young Readers); 2006. (J). lib. bdg. 17.99 (978-0-385-90311-0(1) , Delacorte Bks. for Young Readers) Random Hse. Children's Bks.

Schwartz, David M. Super Grandpa. 1998. (Illus.). 32p. (J). (gr. k-3). pap. 5.95 (978-0-688-16296-2(7)) HarperCollins Pubs.

—Superabuelo. Guzman, Martin Luis, tr. Dodson, Bert, illus. 2005. (SPA.). (J). (ps-4). 32p. pap. 18.95 incl. audio compact disk (978-1-889910-37-6(6)); pap. 6.95 (978-1-889910-38-3(4)) Tortuga Pr.

Scott, C. Anne. Lizard Meets Ivana the Terrible. 2001. (gr. 3-6). lib. bdg. 11.80 (978-0-613-81946-6(2)) Tandem Library Bks.

Scott, C. Anne & Roth, Stephanie. Lizard Meets Ivana the Terrible. 2001. 128p. (J). pap. 3.99 (978-0-439-21999-0(X) , Scholastic Paperbacks) Scholastic, Inc.

Scott, Cynthia A. Lizard Meets Ivana the Terrible. 2001. (978-0-606-22173-3(5)) Tandem Library Bks.

Scraper, Katherine. Garden Lunch. 2006. (Early Explorers Ser.). (J). 30.00 (*978-1-4108-6027-9(2)) Benchmark Education Co.

Scrimger, Richard. Of Mice & Nutcrackers: A Peeler Christmas. 2001. lib. bdg. 16.40 (978-0-613-53630-1(4)) Tandem Library Bks.

—Of Mice & Nutcrackers: A Peeler Christmas. Hendry, Linda, illus. 2001. 232p. (J). (gr. 3-7). pap. 7.95 (978-0-88776-498-1(3)) Tundra Bks., Inc./Livres Toundra, Inc. CAN. *Dist:* Random Hse., Inc.

Scroggs, Kirk. Night of the Living Eggnog. 7th rev. ed. 2007. (Wiley & Grampa Ser.). 112p. (J). (gr. 1). pap. 3.99 (*978-0-316-00685-9(8)) Little, Brown Bks. for Young Readers.

Scroggs, Kirk Brandon. Bigfoot Backpacking Bonanza. 5th ed. 2007. (Wiley & Grampa Ser.: No. 5). 112p. (J). (gr. 3-7). pap. 3.99 (*978-0-316-05949-7(8)); 12.99 (*978-0-316-05948-0(X)) Little, Brown Bks. for Young Readers.

—Dracula vs. Grampa at the Monster Truck Spectacular. 2006. (Wiley & Grampa's Creature Features Ser.: No. 1). (Illus.). 112p. (J). (gr. 3-7). pap. 2.99 (978-0-316-05941-1(2)) Little Brown & Co.

—Grampa's Zombie BBQ. 2nd ed. 2006. (Wiley & Grampa's Creature Features Ser.: No. 2). (Illus.). 112p. (J). (gr. 3-7). 12.99 (978-0-316-05943-5(9)); pap. 3.99 (978-0-316-05942-8(0)) Little Brown & Co.

—Monster Fish Frenzy. 3rd ed. 2006. (Wiley & Grampa's Creature Features Ser.: No. 3). (Illus.). 112p. (J). (gr. 3-7). 12.99 (978-0-316-05944-2(7)); pap. 3.99 (978-0-316-05945-9(5)) Little Brown & Co.

—Super Soccer Freak Show. 4th ed. 2007. (Wiley & Grampa's Creature Features Ser.: No. 4). (Illus.). 112p. (J). (gr. 3-7). 12.99 (978-0-316-05946-6(3)); pap. 3.99 (978-0-316-05947-3(1)) Little Brown & Co.

Secret Soup: Individual Title Six-Packs. (Literatura 2000 Ser.). (gr. 1-2). 28.00 (978-0-7635-0111-2(5)) Rigby Education.

Segal, Lore. More Mole Stories & Little Gopher, Too. Ruzzier, Sergio, illus. 2005. 40p. (J). 16.00 (978-0-374-35026-0(4) , Farrar, Straus & Giroux (BYR)) Farrar, Straus & Giroux.

—Why Mole Shouted & Other Stories. Ruzzier, Sergio, illus. 2004. 40p. (J). 16.00 (978-0-374-38417-3(7) , Farrar, Straus & Giroux (BYR)) Farrar, Straus & Giroux.

Seidler, Tor. The Silent Spillbills. 1998. 224p. (J). (gr. 3-7). 14.95 (978-0-06-205180-6(6)); 14.89 (978-0-06-205181-3(4)) HarperCollins Pubs.

Seltzer, Eric. Granny Doodle Day. Seltzer, Eric, illus. 2006. (Ready-to-Reads Ser.). (Illus.). 32p. (J). pap. 3.99 (978-0-689-85911-3(2) , Aladdin) Simon & Schuster Children's Publishing.

Sendak, Philip. In Grandpa's House. Sendak, Maurice, illus. 2003. (Sendak Reissues Ser.). 48p. reprint ed. 12.95 (978-0-06-028787-0(X)) HarperCollins Pubs.

Seuling, Barbara. Robert Takes a Stand. Brewer, Paul, illus. 2004. (Robert Bks.). 120p. (J). 15.95 (978-0-8126-2712-1(1)) Cricket Bks.

Shahan, Sherry. Death Mountain. 2005. 176p. (J). 15.95 (978-1-56145-353-5(6)) Peachtree Pubs., Ltd.

Shalom, Phylli O. Adopted Grandma. 2006. (Illus.). 36p. (J). 14.95 (*978-1-59299-236-2(6)) Inkwater Pr.

Shanks, Melanie. The Squints. 2007. 116p. per. 10.95 (*978-0-595-44849-4(6)) iUniverse, Inc.

Shawver, Margaret. What's Wrong with Grandma? A Family's Experience with Alzheimer's. Bagby, Jeffrey K., illus. 2004. 62p. pap. 16.00 (978-1-59102-174-2(X)) Prometheus Bks., Pubs.

Shea, Pegi Deitz. Tangled Threads: A Hmong Girl's Story. 2003. 240p. (J). (gr. 5-9). tchr. ed. 15.00 (978-0-618-24748-6(3) , Clarion Bks.) Houghton Mifflin Co. Trade & Reference Div.

Shelton, Jayne C. In Grandmother's Arms. Katz, Karen, illus. 2001. 32p. (J). pap. 3.25 (978-0-439-21314-1(2)) Scholastic, Inc.

Sheth, Kashmira. My Dadima Wears a Sari. Jaeggi, Yoshiko, illus. 2007. 32p. (J). (ps-3). 16.95 (978-1-56145-392-4(7) , Peachtree Junior) Peachtree Pubs., Ltd.

Shetterly, Susan Hand. Shelterwood. 1999. (gr. 3-6). lib. bdg. 16.40 (978-0-613-63530-1(2)) Tandem Library Bks.

—Shelterwood. McCall, Rebecca H., illus. 40p. (J). 2005. (gr. 3-6). 7.95 (978-0-88448-256-7(1)); 1999. (gr. k-3). 16.95 (978-0-88448-210-9(3)) Tilbury Hse. Pubs.

Shields, Carol Diggory. Lucky Pennies & Hot Chocolate. Nakata, Hiroe, illus. 2002. 32p. (J). pap. 5.99 (978-0-14-230190-6(6) , Puffin) Penguin Group (USA) Inc.

—Lucky Pennies & Hot Chocolate. 2002. lib. bdg. 14.15 (978-0-613-60816-9(X)) Tandem Library Bks.

Shipley, Jocelyn. Seraphina's Circle: A Young Adult Novel. 2006. 144p. (YA). (gr. 6-9). pap. 9.95 (978-1-894549-51-6(1)) Sumach Pr. CAN. *Dist:* Orca Bk. Pubs. USA.

Shore, Monica G. The Tale of Grandpa's Hair. 2006. (ENG.). 28p. per. 13.99 (*978-1-4259-2997-8(4)) AuthorHouse.

Shriver, Maria. What's Happening to Grandpa? Speidel, Sandra, illus. 2004. 48p. (J). (gr. 1-4). 15.95 (978-0-316-00101-4(5)) Little, Brown Bks. for Young Readers.

—What's Heaven? ed. 2004. (Illus.). (J). (gr. k-3). spiral bd. (978-0-616-03056-1(8)) Canadian National Institute for the Blind/Institut National Canadien pour les Aveugles.

—What's Heaven? Speidel, Sandra, illus. 1999. (J). 15.00 (978-1-58238-100-8(3)); 10th ed. 32p. reprint ed. 15.00 (978-0-307-44043-3(5) , NHC 0190) St. Martin's Pr. (Golden Bks. Adult Publishing Group).

Shulman, Goldie. Way Too Much Challah Dough. 2006. (Illus.). 30p. (J). 12.95 (978-1-929628-23-0(4)) Hachai Publishing.

Shulman, Lisa. The Moon Might Be Milk. Hillenbrand, Will, illus. 2007. (J). (*978-1-4287-3291-9(8) , Dutton Juvenile) Penguin Group (USA) Inc.

Shuster, Bud. Double Buckeyes: A Story of the Way America Used to Be. (Illus.). vi, 149p. (J). (gr. 4-7). 2000. pap. 7.95 (978-1-57249-177-9(9) , White Mane Kids); 1999. 19.95 (978-1-57249-176-2(0) , White Mane Bks.) White Mane Publishing Co., Inc.

Shusterman, Neal. Red Rider's Hood. (Dark Fusion Ser.). 192p. 2006. (YA). (gr. 7). pap. 6.99 (978-0-14-240678-6(3) , Puffin); 2005. (J). (gr. 5-7). 15.99 (978-0-525-47562-0(1) , Dutton Juvenile) Penguin Group (USA) Inc.

Siegelson, Kim L. In the Time of the Drums. Pinkney, Brian, illus. 1999. (Jump at the Sun Bks.). 32p. (gr. 1-4). 15.99 (978-0-7868-0436-8(X)) Hyperion Bks. for Children.

Silvera, Elvia. Candida. Peli, Peli, illus. 2005. (SPA.). (J). (gr. 2-3). pap. 7.95 (978-980-257-281-6(0)) Ekare, Ediciones VEN. *Dist:* Iaconi, Mariuccia Bk. Imports.

Silverman, Toby. The Garbage Grandma. Strapec, Amy, illus. 2005. 23p. (J). 9.50 (*978-0-9793475-0-4(5)) Silverman, Toby.

Simmons, Martha. Grandma Perkido & Sidney. 2007. (Illus.). 24p. (J). 14.95 (*978-0-9777041-4-9(9)) Third Dimension Publishing.

Simon, Charnan. To Grandmother's House We Go. Gallagher-Cole, Mernie, illus. 2007. (Rookie Reader Ser.). 31p. (J). pap. (*978-0-531-12491-8(6)) Children's Pr., Ltd.

Singleton, Linda Joy. Don't Die, Dragonfly. Karre, Andrew, ed. 2004. 288p. pap. 6.99 (978-0-7387-0526-2(8)) Llewellyn Pubns.

—Fatal Charm. 2007. 384p. pap. 6.99 (*978-0-7387-1153-9(5) , Flux) Llewellyn Pubns.

Singleton, Linda Joy. Last Dance. 2005. (Seer Ser.: Book 2). 264p. pap. 6.99 (978-0-7387-0638-2(8)) Llewellyn Pubns.

Sinke, Janet. Grandma's Treasure Chest. l.t. ed. 2005. (Illus.). 32p. (J). 16.95 (978-0-9742732-3-5(6)) My Grandma & Me Pubs.

—Grandpa's Fishin' Friend. 2005. (Illus.). 50p. (J). (978-0-9742732-2-8(8)) My Grandma & Me Pubs.

—I Wanna Go to Grandma's House. 2003. (Illus.). 50p. (J). (978-0-9742732-0-4(1)) My Grandma & Me Pubs.

Sinke, Janet Mary. Grandpa's Fishin' Friend. Pennington, Craig, illus. 2nd ed. 2006. (J). 16.95 (978-0-9742732-7-3(9)) My Grandma & Me Pubs.

—I Wanna Go to Grandma's House & Grandma's Treasure Chest, 2, Set. Pennington, Craig, illus. 2006. 80p. (J). (978-0-9742732-6-6(0)) My Grandma & Me Pubs.

Sinnott, L. Great Grandfather Was a Pirate. 2005. 77p. pap. 14.95 (978-1-4137-8006-2(7)) PublishAmerica, Inc.

Sinykin, Sheri Cooper. A Matter of Time. 1998. (Accelerated Reader Bks.). 208p. (J). (gr. 5-9). lib. bdg. 14.95 (978-0-7614-5019-1(X) , Cavendish Children's Bks.) Cavendish, Marshall Corp.

Slipperjack, Ruby. Little Voice. Racette, Sherry Farrell, illus. 2005. (In the Same Boat Ser.: No. 4). 256p. (J). (gr. 4-6). pap. 8.95 (978-1-55050-182-7(8)) Coteau Bks. CAN. *Dist:* Fitzhenry & Whiteside, Ltd.

Smalls, Irene. My Nana & Me. Johnson, Cathy Ann, illus. 2005. 24p. (J). (ps-3). 15.99 (978-0-316-16821-2(1)) Little Brown & Co.

Smith, Cynthia Leitich. Indian Shoes. Madsen, Jim, illus. 2002. 80p. (J). (gr. 2-5). 15.99 (978-0-06-029531-8(7)) HarperCollins Pubs.

Smith, Dana Kessimakis. A Wild Cowboy. Freeman, Laura, illus. 2004. 32p. (ps-1). 14.99 (978-0-7868-1931-7(6)) Hyperion Bks. for Children.

Smith, M. J. Kevin Murphy Takes on the Father of Lies. 2005. (Illus.). 311p. (J). (gr. 4-8). pap. 10.95 (978-0-9765066-0-7(2)) B & S Publishing Corp.

Smith, Patricia. Janna & the Kings. Boyd, Aaron, illus. 2003. 32p. (J). 16.95 (978-1-58430-088-5(4)) Lee & Low Bks., Inc.

Smith, Robert Kimmel. The War with Grandpa. 2002. 13.40 (978-0-7587-9609-7(9)) Book Wholesalers, Inc.

—The War with Grandpa. 128p. (J). (gr. 4-6). pap. 4.99 (978-0-8072-1407-7(8) , Listening Library) Random Hse. Audio Publishing Group.

Smith, Roland. The Last Lobo. 2001. (gr. 3-6). lib. bdg. 14.15 (978-0-613-74960-2(X)) Tandem Library Bks.

Smith, Sherri L. Sparrow. 192p. (YA). (gr. 7). 2008. mass mkt. 6.50 (*978-0-440-23945-1(1) , Laurel Leaf); 2006. 15.95 (978-0-385-73324-3(0) , Delacorte Bks. for Young Readers); 2006. lib. bdg. 17.99 (978-0-385-90343-1(X) , Delacorte Bks. for Young Readers) Random Hse. Children's Bks.

Smith, Walter. Grandad's Ashes. 2007. (Illus.). 32p. (J). (*978-1-84310-517-6(9)) Kingsley, Jessica Ltd.

Smothers, Ethel Footman. Moriah's Pond. 2004. 96p. (J). pap. 7.00 (978-0-8028-5249-6(1)) Eerdmans, William B. Publishing Co.

—Moriah's Pond. 2003. (gr. 3-6). lib. bdg. 15.30 (978-0-613-67247-4(X)) Tandem Library Bks.

Smucker, Barbara. Selina & the Shoo-Fly Pie. Wilson, Janet & Holliday, Lucy Anne, illus. 1999. 28p. (J). (ps-3). 15.95 (978-0-7737-3018-2(4)) Stoddart Kids CAN. *Dist:* Fitzhenry & Whiteside, Ltd.

Sneve, Virginia Driving Hawk. Lana's Lakota Moons. 2007. (Illus.). 127p. (J). (gr. 3 up). pap. 12.95 (*978-0-8032-6028-3(8)) Univ. of Nebraska Pr.

Snyder, Jennifer. Grandad's Book. Bruner, Tammy, illus. 2005. (J). 8.99 (978-1-4183-0079-1(9)) Christ Inspired, Inc.

Sommer, A. M. Tucker's Christmas. 2006. pap. 7.95 (978-0-533-15278-0(X)) Vantage Pr., Inc.

Soros, Barbara. Grandmother's Song. Morris, Jackie, illus. 32p. (J). (gr. 3-7). 2000. pap. 6.99 (978-1-902283-09-8(0)); 1998. 15.95 (978-1-902283-02-9(3)) Barefoot Bks., Inc.

Soto, Gary. My Little Car. Sawaya, Linda Dalal & Paparone, Pamela, illus. 2006. Tr. of Mi Carrito. (ENG & SPA.). 32p. (J). (ps-3). 15.99 (978-0-399-23220-6(6) , Putnam Juvenile) Penguin Group (USA) Inc.

Spalding, Andrea. Bottled Sunshine. Ohi, Ruth, illus. 2005. 32p. (J). (gr. 1). (978-1-55041-703-6(7)) Fitzhenry & Whiteside, Ltd.

—Phoebe & the Gypsy. 1999. (Young Reader Ser.). (Illus.). 128p. (J). (gr. 3-6). pap. 4.99 (978-1-55143-135-2(1)) Orca Bk. Pubs. USA.

—Phoebe & the Gypsy. 1999. (Young Reader Ser.). (J). (978-0-606-19478-5(9)); (gr. 3-6). lib. bdg. 13.00 (978-0-8085-8430-8(8)) Tandem Library Bks.

Spinelli, Eileen. Something to Tell the Grandcows. Slavin, Bill, illus. 2004. 32p. 16.00 (978-0-8028-5236-6(X)) Eerdmans, William B. Publishing Co.

Spinelli Eileen. Something to Tell the Grandcows. Slavin Bill, illus. 2006. 32p. (J). pap. 8.00 (978-0-8028-5304-2(8) , Eerdmans Bks For Young Readers) Eerdmans, William B. Publishing Co.

Spinelli, Eileen. Wanda's Monster. Hayashi, Nancy, illus. 2002. 32p. (J). (gr. k-3). 15.95 (978-0-8075-8656-3(0)) Whitman, Albert & Co.

Spinner, Stephanie. It's a Miracle! A Hanukkah Storybook. 2007. (Illus.). 40p. (J). (ps-3). 6.99 (*978-1-4169-5001-1(X) , Aladdin) Simon & Schuster Children's Publishing.

Spinner, Stephanie & McElmurry, Jill. It's a Miracle! A Hanukkah Storybook. 2003. (Illus.). 48p. (J). (gr. k-3). 16.95 (978-0-689-84493-5(X) , Atheneum/Anne Schwartz Bks.) Simon & Schuster Children's Publishing.

Spitz, Mary Y. Mint's Christmas Message. Pierce, Joanne Y., illus. 2003. 32p. 14.95 (978-0-9724570-0-2(3)) Mother Moose Pr.

Spyri, Johanna. Classic Starts: Heidi. Akib, Jamel, illus. 2007. (Classic Starts Ser.). 160p. (J). 4.95 (978-1-4027-3691-9(6)) Sterling Publishing Co., Inc.

—Heidi. 2002. (Great Illustrated Classics Ser.). (Illus.). 240p. (J). (gr. 3-8). 21.35 (978-1-57765-688-3(1) , ABDO & Daughters) ABDO Publishing Co.

—Heidi. unabr. ed. 2000. (Dover Juvenile Classics Ser.). (Illus.). 304p. (J). (gr. 4-7). pap. 3.00 (978-0-486-41235-1(0)) Dover Pubns., Inc.

—Heidi. 2nd ed. (Coleccion Clasicos en Accion). (SPA., Illus.). 80p. (YA). (gr. 5-8). 15.95 (978-84-241-5784-5(2) , EV0790) Everest de Ediciones y Distribucion, S.L. ESP. *Dist:* Lectorum Pubns., Inc.

—Heidi. Rinaldi, Angelo, illus. 2002. (Kingfisher Classics Ser.). 352p. (J). (gr. k-3). tchr. ed. 15.95 (978-0-7534-5494-7(7) , Kingfisher) Houghton Mifflin Co. Trade & Reference Div.

—Heidi. 2002. (Twelve-Point Ser.). lib. bdg. 25.00 (978-1-58287-183-7(3)) North Bks.

—Heidi. 2000. (Aladdin Classics Ser.). (Illus.). 304p. (J). (gr. 4-7). pap. 5.99 (978-0-689-83962-7(6) , Aladdin) Simon & Schuster Children's Publishing.

—Heidi. 1998. (Children's Classics). (ENG., Illus.). 240p. (J). pap. (978-1-85326-125-1(4) , 1254WW) Wordsworth Editions, Ltd.

—Heidi: With a Discussion of Optimism. Clift, Eva, illus. 2003. (Values in Action Illustrated Classics Ser.). 190p. (J). (978-1-59203-030-9(0)) Learning Challenge, Inc.

—Heidi EasyRead Large Edition. 2006. pap. (*978-1-4250-4150-2(7)) Assistedreadingbooks.com Inc.

—What Sami Sings with the Birds. 2006. pap. 87.99 (*978-1-4280-4365-7(9)) IndyPublish.com.

Stafford, Liliana. Grandpa's Gate. Boyer, Susy, illus. 2003. 32p. (YA). 22.50 (978-1-876268-66-4(2)) Univ. of Western Australia Pr. AUS. *Dist:* International Specialized Bk. Services.

Stahl, Hilda. Big Trouble for Roxie. 2003. (Best Friends Ser.: No. 2). 160p. (YA). (gr. 4-7). pap. 4.99 (978-0-89107-658-2(1)) Crossway Bks.

Stang, Debra L. Visiting Grandma. 2003. 136p. (YA). pap. 12.95 (978-1-59113-322-3(X)) Booklocker.com, Inc.

Stanley, George Edward. The Battle of the Bakers. Graves, Linda Dockey, illus. 2000. (Katie Lynn Cookie Company Ser. : Vol. 3). (J). (978-0-606-19900-1(4)) Tandem Library Bks.

—The Secret Ingredient. 1999. (Katie Lynn Cookie Company Ser.). (Illus.). (J). (978-0-606-18500-4(3)) Tandem Library Bks.

—Wedding Cookies: Katie Lynn Cookie Company. Graves, Linda, illus. 2001. (Stepping Stone Book Ser.: Vol. 4). 54p. (J). (gr. k-3). lib. bdg. 11.99 (978-0-679-99223-3(5) , Random Hse. Bks. for Young Readers) Random Hse. Children's Bks.

Staub, Wendy Corsi. Lily Dale: Awakening. 2007. 240p. (YA). (gr. 7 up). 15.95 (*978-0-8027-9654-7(0)) Walker & Co.

Steck-Vaughn Staff. Grandma J. 1998. (Illus.). (J). pap. (978-0-8172-8695-8(0)) Steck-Vaughn.

—Special Friends: Grandma J/Buddy. 1998. (Illus.). (J). pap. (978-0-8172-8649-1(7)) Steck-Vaughn.

Steele, Giselle V. Nicholas & the Magical Wind. 2005. 32p. 23.95 (978-1-58275-093-4(9)) Stuart & Weitz Publishing Group.

Steiner, Lili. Grandparents Around the World. Erlich, Esther, illus. 1998. (My Jewish Family Series with a Bissel Yiddish). 24p. (J). pap. 14.95 (978-1-891397-03-5(6)) Steiner, Lili Pubns.

—My Bubbe - My Grandmother. Epstein, Debby, illus. 1998. 24p. (J). pap. 14.95 (978-1-891397-02-8(8)) Steiner, Lili Pubns.

—My Zaidah - My Grandfather. Epstein, Debby, illus. 1998. (My Jewish Family Series with a Bissel Yiddish). 24p. (J). pap. 14.95 (978-1-891397-01-1(X)) Steiner, Lili Pubns.

Steinmann, Donna. Hello, Grand Mamoon! Guion, Tamara, illus. 2005. 32p. (J). 16.95 (978-0-9663286-4-6(7)) EarthTime Pubns.

Sterling Publishing Company Staff. Benjamin Visits Grandpa & Grandma. 1999. 16p. (ps-3). pap. 4.95 (978-0-8069-3132-6(9)) Sterling Publishing Co., Inc.

Stevens, Carla. Anna, Grandpa, & the Big Storm. Tomes, Margot, illus. 1998. (Puffin Chapters for Readers on the Move Ser.). 64p. (J). (gr. 2-5). pap. 5.99 (978-0-14-130083-2(3) , Puffin) Penguin Group (USA) Inc.

Stilton, Geronimo, text. A Cheese-Colored Camper. 2005. (Geronimo Stilton Ser.: No. 16). (Illus.). 111p. (J). (ps-k). lib. bdg. 12.64 (978-0-606-33281-1(2)) Tandem Library Bks.

Stock, Catherine. Gugu's House. 2001. (Illus.). 32p. (J). (gr. k-3). tchr. ed. 16.00 (978-0-618-00389-1(4) , Clarion Bks.) Houghton Mifflin Co. Trade & Reference Div.

Stock, Catherine, illus. Gus & Grandpa. 2002. (Gus & Grandpa Ser.). (J). 13.36 (978-0-7587-1232-5(4)) Book Wholesalers, Inc.

—Gus & Grandpa & the Christmas Cookies. 2002. (Gus & Grandpa Ser.). (J). 22.19 (978-0-7587-1233-2(2)) Book Wholesalers, Inc.

—Gus & Grandpa & the Two-Wheeled Bike. 2002. (Gus & Grandpa Ser.). (J). 24.36 (978-0-7587-1235-6(9)) Book Wholesalers, Inc.

—Gus & Grandpa at the Hospital. 2002. (Gus & Grandpa Ser.). (J). 22.19 (978-0-7587-1234-9(0)) Book Wholesalers, Inc.

—Gus & Grandpa Ride the Train. 2002. (Gus & Grandpa Ser.). (J). 13.36 (978-0-7587-0576-1(X)) Book Wholesalers, Inc.

Stone Fox. 1998. (J). (gr. 5). pap. 3.95 (978-0-439-04473-8(1)) Scholastic, Inc.

Strange, David. Why Grandpa Rides a Harley. 2005. 16.95 (978-0-9772771-0-0(0)) Cherry Tree Pr. LLC.

Strong, Jeremy. My Granny's Great Escape. (Illus.). 96p. (J). 7.95 (978-0-14-038390-4(5)) Penguin Bks., Ltd. GBR. *Dist:* Trafalgar Square Publishing.

Stuve-Bodeen, Stephanie. Babu's Song. Boyd, Aaron, illus. 2003. 32p. (J). 16.95 (978-1-58430-058-8(2)) Lee & Low Bks., Inc.

Sullivan, Jaqueline Levering. Annie's War. 2007. 190p. (J). (gr. 3-7). 15.00 (***978-0-8028-5325-7(0)*** , Eerdmans Bks For Young Readers) Eerdmans, William B. Publishing Co.

Sullivan, Jean. The Blakely Field Stories. 2005. 58p. pap. 12.95 (978-1-4137-8611-8(1)) PublishAmerica, Inc.

Swanson, Stan. The Misadventures of Hobart Hucklebuck. 2007. (J). 16.95 (***978-0-9787925-3-4(X)***); per. 9.95 (***978-0-9787925-2-7(1)***) Stony Meadow Publishing.

Sweeney, Joyce. Headlock. 2006. 224p. (YA). 16.95 (978-0-8050-8018-6(X) , Holt, Henry & Co. Bks. For Young Readers) Holt, Henry & Co.

—Spirit Window. 1999. (978-0-606-16717-8(X)) Tandem Library Bks.

Sweet, J.H. & Sierra, Holly. Periwinkle & the Cave of Courage: The Fairy Chronicles. 2007. (Fairy Chronicles Ser.). (Illus.). 128p. (J). (gr. 2 up). pap. 6.99 (***978-1-4022-1026-6(4)*** , Sourcebooks Jabberwocky) Sourcebooks, Inc.

Sweet, Melissa. Carmine: A Little More Red. 2005. (Illus.). 40p. (J). (gr. k-3). 16.00 (978-0-618-38794-6(3)) Houghton Mifflin Co. Trade & Reference Div.

Tadjo, Veronique. Grandma Nana. 2000. (Veronique Tadjo Ser.). (Illus.). 24p. (J). (FRE, ENG, VIE, CHI & BEN.). pap. 9.95 (978-1-84059-289-4(3)); (GUJ, ENG, VIE, CHI & BEN., pap. 9.95 (978-1-84059-291-7(5)); (TUR, ENG, VIE, CHI & BEN., pap. 9.95 (978-1-84059-293-1(1)); (ALB, ENG, VIE, CHI & BEN., pap. 9.95 (978-1-84059-286-3(9)); (CHI, ENG, VIE, BEN & URD., pap. 9.95 (978-1-84059-288-7(5)); pap. 7.95 (978-1-84059-285-6(0)); (URD, ENG, VIE, CHI & BEN., pap. 9.95 (978-1-84059-294-8(X)); (VIE, ENG, CHI, BEN & URD., pap. 9.95 (978-1-84059-295-5(8)) Milet Publishing.

—Grandma Nana. Greatorex, Gisela, tr. 2000. (Veronique Tadjo Ser.). (GER, ENG, VIE, CHI & BEN., Illus.). 24p. (J). pap. 9.95 (978-1-84059-290-0(7)) Milet Publishing.

—Grandma Nana. Datta, Kanai, tr. 2000. (Veronique Tadjo Ser.). (BEN, ENG, VIE, CHI & URD., Illus.). 24p. (J). (ps-1). pap. 9.95 (978-1-84059-287-0(7)) Milet Publishing.

Taniguchi, Tomoko. Popcorn Romance. Taniguchi, Tomoko, illus. 2003. Orig. Title: Love & Peace in a Cornfield. (Illus.). 192p. pap. 9.99 (978-1-58664-901-2(9) , CMX 64901G, CPM Manga) Central Park Media Corp.

Tapp, Kathy Kennedy. Deadbolts & Dinkles. 2000. (gr. 3-6). lib. bdg. 11.80 (978-0-613-27788-4(0)) Tandem Library Bks.

Tate, Nikki. Grandparents' Day. Laverdière, Benoit, illus. 2004. 32p. (J). (gr. k-3). pap. 7.95 (978-1-55037-842-9(2)); lib. bdg. 18.95 (978-1-55037-843-6(0)) Annick Pr., Ltd. CAN. *Dist:* Firefly Bks., Ltd.

—Trouble on Tarragon. 2006. 208p. (J). 8.95 (978-1-55039-154-1(2)) Sono Nis Pr. CAN. *Dist:* Orca Bk. Pubs. USA.

Taulbert, Clifton L. Little Cliff's First Day of School. Taulbert, Clifton L. & Lewis, Earl, illus. 2003. 32p. (J). (gr. k-3). pap. 6.99 (978-0-14-250082-8(8) , Puffin) Penguin Group (USA) Inc.

—Little Cliff's First Day of School. Lewis, Earl, illus. 2001. 32p. (J). (ps-3). 15.99 (978-0-8037-2557-7(4) , Dial) Penguin Group (USA) Inc.

—Little Cliff's First Day of School. 2003. (gr. k-3). lib. bdg. 15.30 (978-0-613-67561-1(4)) Tandem Library Bks.

Tavares, Matt. Oliver's Game. Tavares, Matt, illus. 2004. (Illus.). 32p. (J). (gr. 1-5). 15.99 (978-0-7636-1852-0(7)) Candlewick Pr.

Taylor, Cora. Adventure in Istanbul No. 1: The Spy Who Wasn't There. 2005. (Juvenile Novel, Ser.). (Illus.). 176p. (J). (gr. 4-6). pap. 7.95 (978-1-55050-315-9(4)) Coteau Bks. CAN. *Dist:* Fitzhenry & Whiteside, Ltd.

Taylor, Theodore. A Sailor Returns. 2002. 160p. (J). (gr. 3-7). pap. 4.99 (978-0-439-24880-8(9) , Scholastic Paperbacks) Scholastic, Inc.

Testa, Maria. Becoming Joe Dimaggio. Hunt, Scott, illus. 2002. 64p. (J). (gr. 5-9). 14.99 (978-0-7636-1537-6(4)) Candlewick Pr.

—Becoming Joe DiMaggio. Hunt, Scott, illus. 2005. 64p. (J). (gr. 5-9). reprint ed. pap. 5.99 (978-0-7636-2444-6(6)) Candlewick Pr.

Theroux, Phyllis. Serefina under the Circumstances. Priceman, Marjorie, illus. 2004. 30p. (J). (gr. k-4). reprint ed. (978-0-7567-7756-2(9)) DIANE Publishing Co.

—Serefina under the Circumstances. 2000. (J). 16.00 (978-0-689-80450-2(4) , Simon & Schuster Children's Publishing) Simon & Schuster Children's Publishing.

Things Don't Change Much: Individual Title Six-Packs. (gr. k-1). 23.00 (978-0-7635-9055-0(X)) Rigby Education.

Thomas, Maria Jose. Bravo, Rosina. Munoz, Claudio, illus. 2006. Tr. of Bravo, Rosina!. (SPA.). (J). (gr. 4-5). 10.40 (978-980-257-242-7(X) , EK33833) Ekare, Ediciones VEN. *Dist:* Lectorum Pubns., Inc.

Thong, Roseanne. The Wishing Tree. McLennan, Connie, illus. 2004. 32p. (J). 16.95 (978-1-885008-26-8(0)) Shen's Bks.

Thorson, Kristine & Thorson, Robert. Stone Wall Secrets. Moore, Gustav, illus. 2003. (J). (gr. 4-7). lib. bdg. 16.40 (978-0-613-43779-0(9)) Tandem Library Bks.

—Stone Wall Secrets. Moore, Gustav, illus. 2005. 40p. (J). (gr. 3-7). 7.95 (978-0-88448-229-1(4)) Tilbury Hse. Pubs.

Thorson, Robert & Thorson, Kristine. Stone Wall Secrets. Moore, Gustav, illus. 1998. 40p. (J). (gr. 3-7). 16.95 (978-0-88448-195-9(6)) Tilbury Hse. Pubs.

Tierno, Susan F. El Mejor Dia. Alvarado, Ana María, tr. Ramirez, Michael, illus. 2000. (Think-Kids Book Collection).Tr. of Best-Ever Day. (SPA.). 16p. (J). (gr. 1). pap. 2.95 (978-1-58237-045-3(1)) Creative Thinkers, Inc.

—El Plan. Alvarado, Ana María, tr. Ramirez, Michael, illus. 2000. (Think-Kids Book Collection).Tr. of Plan. (SPA.). 16p. (J). pap. 2.95 (978-1-58237-056-9(7)) Creative Thinkers, Inc.

Tischler, Helene & Lockwood, Charlotte. Jamie & the Ducks of August: A Tale of Decoys. Lockwood, Charlotte, illus. 2001. (Illus.). 32p. (J). (ps-2). 6.95 (978-0-9679350-0-3(8)) Parkstone Publishing.

Tobias, Tobi. Wishes for You. Sorensen, Henri, illus. 40p. (J). (ps-2). 2005. pap. 6.99 (978-0-06-443730-1(2)); 2003. 16.99 (978-0-688-10838-0(5)) HarperCollins Pubs.

Tobin, C., adapted by. Maya & Miguel: Family Fix-Up. 2005. (Maya & Miguel Ser.). (Illus.). 80p. (J). 5.99 (978-0-439-69606-7(2)) Scholastic, Inc.

Todorov, Boriana & Todorov, Vladimir. The Moon Rock. 2007. (Illus.). 96p. (J). (gr. 7 up). 19.95 (***978-1-894965-77-4(9)***) Simply Read Bks. CAN. *Dist:* Perseus Distribution.

Tomey, Ingrid. Grandfather's Day. McKay, Robert A., illus. 2003. 64p. (YA). (gr. 4-6). pap. 9.95 (978-1-56397-947-7(0)) Boyds Mills Pr.

—Grandfather's Day. 2001. (J). 16.75 (978-0-606-20682-2(5)); (gr. 3-6). lib. bdg. 18.75 (978-0-613-63598-1(1)) Tandem Library Bks.

—Nobody Else Has to Know. 2000. 240p. (YA). (gr. 7-12). pap. 5.50 (978-0-440-22782 3(8) , Laurel Leaf) Random Hse. Children's Bks.

—Nobody Else Has to Know. 2000. 231p. (YA). (gr. 8-12). lib. bdg. 13.00 (978-0-613-28372-4(4)); 1999. (J). (978-0-606-19744-1(3)) Tandem Library Bks.

Torres, Leyla. Sancocho del Sabado. 1999. Tr. of Saturday Sancocho. (978-0-606-16478-8(2)) Tandem Library Bks.

—Sancocho Del Sabado. 1999. (SPA.). (gr. k-3). lib. bdg. 14.10 (978-0-613-17852-5(1)) Tandem Library Bks.

Tran, Truong. Going Home, Coming Home / Ve Nha Tham Que Hu'O'Ng. Phong, Ann, illus. 2003. Tr. of Ve Nha Tham Que Hu'O'Ng. (ENG & VIE.). 32p. (J). 16.95 (978-0-89239-179-0(0)) Children's Bk. Pr.

Trembath, Don. Bachelors. 2002. (gr. 3-6). lib. bdg. 15.25 (978-0-613-85895-3(6)) Tandem Library Bks.

Trip to Freedom: Six-Pack. (Greetings Ser.: Vol. 3). (gr. 3-5). 31.00 (978-0-7635-1777-9(1)) Rigby Education.

Trooboff & Bucher, Cecile. Ben, the Bells & the Peacocks. 2007. 36p. pap. 15.00 (***978-0-9773536-0-6(5)***) Tenley Circle Pr.

Trotter, Deborah W. A Summer's Trade. Manavi, Lorraine Begay, tr. Toddy, Irving, illus. 2008. (ENG & NAV.). 32p. (gr. 2-5). 17.95 (***978-1-893354-71-5(7)***) Salina Bookshelf.

Truax, Doug. A Good Day for Ducks. Smith, Jack K., illus. 2003. 32p. (gr. k-4). 16.95 (978-1-932052-12-1(7)) Ducks Unlimited, Inc.

Tsubakiyama, Margaret. Mei-Mei Loves the Morning. Van Wright, Cornelius & Hu, Ying-Hwa, illus. 1999. 32p. (J). (ps-3). 15.95 (978-0-8075-5039-7(6)) Whitman, Albert & Co.

Tung, Angela. Song of the Stranger. Artenstein, Michael, ed. 1999. (Roxbury Park Bks.). (J). 192p. (gr. 3-7). pap. 4.95 (978-1-56565-948-3(1) , 09481W); 96p. (gr. 5-8). 12.95 (978-1-56565-774-8(8) , 07748W) Lowell Hse. (Roxbury Park).

Tunnell, Michael. Mailing May. 2000. (gr. k-3). lib. bdg. 15.30 (978-0-613-30016-2(5)) Tandem Library Bks.

Turner-Denstaedt, Melanie. Grandma's Good Hat. Morrison, Frank, illus. 2008. (J). (978-0-374-32794-1(7)) Farrar, Straus & Giroux.

Ueda, Rinko. Tail of the Moon, Volume 4. 2007. (Tail of the Moon Ser.). 200p. (YA). pap. 8.99 (978-1-4215-0816-0(8)) Viz Media.

—Trail of the Moon, Volume 3. 2007. (Tail of the Moon Ser.). 200p. (YA). pap. 8.99 (978-1-4215-0814-6(1)) Viz Media.

Unobagha, Uzo. Grandma, How Do You Say I Love You? Krassa, Victoria, illus. 2007. 28p. (J). 16.95 (978-0-9773180-0-1(1)) Adonoke Inc.

Urdahl, Cathy Nelson. Emma's Question. Dawson, Janine, illus. 2008. (J). (***978-1-58089-145-5(4)***) Charlesbridge Publishing, Inc.

Uslander, Arlene. That's What Grandparents Are For. Levin, Freddie, illus. 2001. 32p. (J). (ps-3). (978-0-939217-60-1(0)) Peel Productions, Inc.

V., Patti. My Na Na Stories. 2005. 18.00 (978-0-8059-9806-1(3)) Dorrance Publishing Co., Inc.

Van Draanen, Wendelin. Sammy Keyes & the Hotel Thief. VanDraanen, Wendelin, illus. 2000. (Sammy Keyes Ser.: Bk. 1). pap. 39.95 incl. audio compact disk (978-0-87499-876-4(X)) Live Oak Media.

—Sammy Keyes & the Hotel Thief. unabr. ed. 2000. (Sammy Keyes Ser.: Bk. 1). (Illus.). (J). (gr. 4-7). 38.95 incl. audio (978-0-87499-694-4(5)); pap. 30.95 incl. audio (978-0-87499-693-7(7)) Live Oak Media.

—Sammy Keyes & the Hotel Thief. 1998. (Sammy Keyes Ser.: Bk. 1). (Illus.). 163p. (J). (gr. k-8). lib. bdg. 13.55 (978-0-613-12062-3(0)) Tandem Library Bks.

Van Dyne, Edith. Mary Louise. 2006. 148p. pap. 10.99 (978-1-4264-1952-2(X)) BiblioBazaar.

Vaughn Zimmer, Tracie. Reaching for Sun. 2007. 144p. (J). (gr. 7 up). 14.95 (978-1-59990-037-7(8) , Bloomsbury Children) Bloomsbury Publishing.

Vaughns, Bertha J. The Backporch: Keep Praying Child One Day You Will Understand. Taylor, Ceola, ed. unabr. ed. 1999. 20p. (YA). (gr. 7-12). pap. 6.99 incl. audio (978-0-9676396-0-4(3) , TBP2) Ahtreb, Inc.

Vedder, G. M. Where Is Grandpa Now. Vedder, G. M., illus. 1999. (Adventures in Learning with Miss Lucy & the Village Children Ser.: Vol. III). (Illus.). 75p. (J). (gr. k-6). spiral bd. 12.95 (978-0-9679091-2-7(0)) A Miracle Cub.

—Why Did Grandpa Die. Vedder, G. M., illus. 1999. (Adventures in Learning with Miss Lucy & the Village Children Ser.: Vol. II). (Illus.). 75p. (J). (gr. k-6). spiral bd. 12.95 (978-0-9679091-1-0(2)) A Miracle Cub.

Velasquez, Eric. Grandma's Records. Velasquez, Eric, illus. 2004. (Illus.). 32p. (J). pap. 7.95 (978-0-8027-7660-0(4)) Walker & Co.

—Grandma's Records. 2004. (Illus.). 32p. (J). (gr. k-3). 16.95 (978-0-8027-8760-6(6)); 17.85 (978-0-8027-8761-3(4)) Walker & Co.

Velasquez, Eric & de la Vega, Eida. Los Discos de Mi Abuela. 2002. (SPA., Illus.). (J). (gr. 1-3). 16.95 (978-1-930332-21-8(1) , LC7246) Lectorum Pubns., Inc.

Vision, David & Vision, Mutiya Sahar. Missing You. Alcantara, Ignacio, illus. 2005. 40p. (J). mass mkt. 17.00 (978-0-9659538-6-3(6)) Soul Vision Works Publishing.

Vogl, Nancy & Strange, David. Grandma Loves Her Harley Too. Gibson, Nichoel, illus. ed. 2006. (J). per. 16.95 (978-0-9772771-1-7(9)) Cherry Tree Pr. LLC.

Vulliamy, Clara. Small. 2002. (Illus.). 32p. (J). (gr. k-ps). 15.00 (978-0-618-19459-9(2) , Clarion Bks.) Houghton Mifflin Co. Trade & Reference Div.

Waboose, Jan Bourdeau. Firedancers. Taylor, C. J., illus. 2000. 26p. (J). (ps-3). 14.95 (978-0-7737-3138-7(5)) Stoddart Kids CAN. *Dist:* Fitzhenry & Whiteside, Ltd.

—Morning on the Lake. Reczuch, Karen, illus. 32p. (J). (gr. k-3). 2002. (978-1-55074-588-7(3)); 1998. (978-1-55074-373-9(2)) Kids Can Pr., Ltd.

—Morning on the Lake. 2002. (gr. k-3). lib. bdg. 14.10 (978-0-613-83962-4(5)) Tandem Library Bks.

Wagner, Dennis. The Grampa Chair. 2006. 30p. (J). per. 13.99 (***978-1-59886-574-5(9)***) Tate Publishing & Enterprises, L.L.C.

Wagner, Sally R. The Grandmother Who Climbed to the Top of the World. 9p. (J). (gr. 1-5). pap. 3.95 (978-1-880589-40-3(0)) Sky Carrier Pr.

Walden, Joseph. Grandpa's Smile. Walden, Joseph, illus. 2000. (Illus.). 32p. (ps-2). 9.95 (978-1-59093-058-8(4)) Warehousing & Fulfillment Specialists, LLC (WFS, LLC).

Walker, Nan. Check It Out! Sims, Blanche, illus. 2006. 32p. (J). lib. bdg. 20.00 (***978-1-4242-1105-0(0)***) Fitzgerald Bks.

—Check It Out! Sims, Blanche, illus. 2006. (Social Studies Connects). 32p. (J). pap. 4.99 (978-1-57565-166-8(1)) Kane Pr., The.

Walker, Russell D. Michelle & the Magic Timepiece. 2006. 108p. pap. 16.95 (978-1-4241-3143-3(X)) PublishAmerica, Inc.

Wallace, Barbara Brooks. Ghosts in the Gallery: My Life with Carlos Castaneda. 2000. (Illus.). (J). (978-0-606-21612-8(X)) Tandem Library Bks.

Wallace, Bill. Beauty. 2007. 192p. (J). pap. 5.99 (***978-1-4169-4942-8(9)*** , Aladdin) Simon & Schuster Children's Publishing.

Wallace, Bill. Pick of the Litter. 2005. 160p. (J). (ps-7). 16.95 (978-0-8234-1921-0(5)) Holiday Hse., Inc.

—Pick of the Litter. 2006. 176p. (J). pap. 4.99 (978-1-4169-2511-8(2) , Aladdin) Simon & Schuster Children's Publishing.

Wallace, Ian. Chin Chiang & the Dragon's Dance. 1998. (Illus.). 32p. (J). (ps-2). pap. 5.95 (978-0-88899-167-6(3)) Groundwood Bks. CAN. *Dist:* Perseus Distribution.

Wallace, Ian, illus. Chin Chiang & the Dragon's Dance. 1998. 32p. (J). (ps-2). 19.95 (978-0-88899-020-4(0)) Groundwood Bks. CAN. *Dist:* Perseus Distribution.

Wallace, Nancy Elizabeth. Seeds! Seeds! Seeds! 2004. (Illus.). 40p. (J). 16.95 (978-0-7614-5159-4(5)) Cavendish, Marshall Corp.

Wallace, Nancy Elizabeth. Seeds Seeds Seeds. 2007. 32p. 5.99 (***978-0-7614-5366-6(0)***) Cavendish, Marshall Corp.

Walley, Diane D. Codger & Baggs. 2004. 78p. (J). per. 9.95 (978-0-9748591-3-2(3) , MSP) Main St Publishing, Inc.

Walter, Mildred Pitts. Justin & the Best Biscuits in the World. Stock, Catherine, illus. 2002. (J). 13.40 (978-0-7587-0371-2(6)) Book Wholesalers, Inc.

—Justin & the Best Biscuits in the World. 1999. (Illus.). 128p. (J). (gr. 3-5). pap. 4.99 (978-0-679-89448-3(9)) Knopf, Alfred A. Inc.

—Ray & the Best Family Reunion Ever. 2001. (Illus.). 128p. (J). (ps-2). 15.95 (978-0-06-623624-7(X) , Amistad) HarperCollins Pubs.

Wangerin, Walter, Jr. I Am My Grandpa's Enkelin. Tate, Don, illus. 2007. (J). (gr. 2-6). 18.95 (***978-1-55725-468-9(0)***) Paraclete Pr., Inc.

Ware, Cheryl. Catty-Cornered. Yalowitz, Paul, illus. 1998. 112p. (J). (gr. 4-8). 16.99 (978-0-531-33067-8(2)); pap. 15.95 (978-0-531-30067-1(6)) Scholastic, Inc. (Orchard Bks.).

Wargin, Kathy-Jo. The Legend of the Loon. van Frankenhuyzen, Gijsbert, illus. (Great Lakes Legend Ser.). 48p. (J). (ps-3). 2000. 17.95 (978-1-886947-97-9(X)); 2003. pap. 7.95 (978-1-58536-167-0(4)) Sleeping Bear Pr.

Warmuth, Donna Akers. Plumb Full of History: A Story of Abingdon, Virginia. Gobble, DeAnna Akers, illus. 2003. 64p. pap. 9.95 (978-1-932158-78-6(2)) Ingalls Publishing Group, Inc.

Warner, Gertrude Chandler. Haunted Clock Tower Mystery. 2001. (gr. 3-6). lib. bdg. 11.80 (978-0-613-49434-2(2)) Tandem Library Bks.

—Secret under the Tree. 2001. (gr. k-3). lib. bdg. 11.80 (978-0-613-35676-3(4)) Tandem Library Bks.

—Stuffed Bear Mystery. 2002. (gr. 3-6). lib. bdg. 11.80 (978-0-613-62574-6(9)) Tandem Library Bks.

Warner, Gertrude Chandler, creator. A Present for Grandfather. 1998. (Adventures of Benny & Watch: No. 2). (J). (gr. 1-3). (978-0-606-13216-9(3)) Tandem Library Bks.

Washington-Pennix, Loretha & Pennix, Ladaro, II. Grandparent¿s Day in September. 2006. (Illus.). 13p. (J). per. 10.95 (978-1-59453-975-6(8) , 3187) Airleaf Publishing & Bookselling.

Waters, Zack C. Blood Moon Rider. 2006. 126p. (J). 13.95 (978-1-56164-350-9(5)) Pineapple Pr., Inc.

Watkins, Dawn L. Chickadee Winter. Dellosso, Gabriela, illus. 1999. (J). (ps-1). pap. 5.49 (978-1-57924-273-2(1) , 120170) Jones, Bob Univ. Pr.

Watts, Jeri Hanel. Keepers. 2000. (J). (978-0-606-19832-5(6)) Tandem Library Bks.

Webb, Kimberly. The Christmas Memory Quilt. Gaskin, Jennifer, illus. 2007. 32p. (J). 17.95 (***978-1-934393-00-0(2)***) Silverleaf Pr.

Weber, Lori. Strange Beauty. 2006. (SideStreets Ser.). 144p. (YA). (gr. 7-12). (***978-1-55028-944-2(6)***); 7.95 (***978-1-55028-941-1(1)***) Lorimer, James & Co., Ltd., Pubs. CAN. *Dist:* Casemate Pubs. & Bk. Distributors, LLC.

Wehmeyer, Betty J. Jesus Goes to Grandma's House. 1998. vi, 8p. (J). (ps-6). pap. 14.95 (978-1-892611-00-0(7)) Wehmeyer, Betty Jean.

Wells, Rosemary. Bunny Mail. 2004. (Max & Ruby Ser.). (Illus.). 32p. (J). (ps-3). 15.99 (978-0-670-03630-1(7) , Viking Juvenile) Penguin Group (USA) Inc.

—Bunny Money. 2000. (gr. k-3). lib. bdg. 14.15 (978-0-613-33681-9(X)) Tandem Library Bks.

—Yoko's Paper Cranes. Wells, Rosemary, illus. 2001. (Illus.). 32p. (ps-2). 15.99 (978-0-7868-0737-6(7)) Hyperion Bks. for Children.

Wendel, Tim. My Man Stan. 2006. (J). 15.95 (978-0-9766104-7-2(7)) Arbutus Pr.

West, Colin. Grandpa's Boneshaker Bicycle. 2006. (Read-It! Chapter Books). (J). 21.26 (978-1-4048-2732-5(3)) Picture Window Bks.

West, L. J. Mr. Blacky & His Palace. lt. ed. 2006. (Illus.). 31p. (J). 19.99 (***978-1-59879-268-3(7)***); per. 13.99 (***978-1-59879-267-6(9)***) Lifevest Publishing, Inc.

Wheelock, Ann. The Angel of Camp Courageous. 2005. 89p. pap. 14.95 (978-1-4137-8239-4(6)) PublishAmerica, Inc.

When I'm Older, 6 Packs. (Literatura 2000 Ser.). (gr. 1-2). 28.00 (978-0-7635-0154-9(9)) Rigby Education.

Where Is Nancy?, 6 Pack. (Literatura 2000 Ser.). (gr. k-1). 28.00 (978-0-7635-0079-5(8)) Rigby Education.

White, Howard. The Airplane Ride. Guzek, Greta, illus. unabr. ed. 2006. 32p. (J). bds. 14.95 (***978-0-88971-224-9(7)***) Harbour Publishing Co., Ltd. CAN. *Dist:* Graphic Arts Ctr. Publishing Co.

White, Kathy. Little Green Riding Hood. 2006. 42.00 (***978-1-4108-6182-5(1)***) Benchmark Education Co.

Whitethorne, Baje, Sr. Father's Boots: Azhe'e bikenidoots'osii. Marvin, Yellowhair & Jerrold, Johnson, eds. Darlene, Redhair, tr. Whitethorne, Baje, Sr., illus. 2001. (ENG & NAV., Illus.). 32p. (gr. 1-6). 17.95 (978-1-893354-29-6(6)) Salina Bookshelf.

Whitethorne, Baje, Sr., illus. Sunpainters: Eclipse of the Navajo Sun. 2002. 32p. 17.95 (978-1-893354-33-3(4)) Salina Bookshelf.

WHO Staff. Grandma's off Her Rocker. 2001. 120p. (J). pap. 10.95 (978-0-595-18922-9(9)) iUniverse, Inc.

E
F
G

Whybrow, Ian. Sammy & the Robots. Reynolds, Adrian, illus. 2001. 32p. (J). (ps-1). pap. 15.95 (978-0-531-30327-6(6) , Orchard Bks.) Scholastic, Inc.

Wiedeman, Connie. Grandma, Do Preachers Lie? A Guide to Truth for Youth. 2005. 273p. pap. 21.95 (978-1-4137-6550-2(5)) PublishAmerica, Inc.

Wigersma, Tanneke. Baby Brother. Talsma, Nynke Mare, illus. 2005. 32p. (J). (ps-ps). 16.95 (978-1-932425-55-0(1) , Lemniscaat) Boyds Mills Pr.

Wiggins, Leah Holder. My Neighbor Is Gone. Wiggins, Margaret W., illus. 2006. 28p. (J). per. 17.99 (*978-0-9768579-5-2(2)) eVision, LLC.

Wilcox, Brian & David, Lawrence. Full Moon. Wilcox, Brian, illus. 2004. (Illus.). 30p. (J). (gr. k-4). reprint ed. 16.00 (978-0-7567-7762-3(3)) DIANE Publishing Co.

Wild, Margaret. Our Granny. Vivas, Julie, illus. 2002. (J). 13.79 (978-0-7587-3344-3(5)) Book Wholesalers, Inc.

—Our Granny. Vivas, Julie, illus. 1998. 32p. (J). (gr. k-3). pap. 5.95 (978-0-395-88395-2(4)) Houghton Mifflin Co. Trade & Reference Div.

Wild, Margaret & Shaw, Peter. Hop, Little Hare! 2008. (Illus.). 0024p. pap. 10.95 (*978-1-921049-68-2(5)) Little Hare Bks. AUS. *Dist:* Independent Pubs. Group.

Wilder, Rae. Soccer Girls. 2000. 252p. (J). (gr. 4-7). pap. 13.95 (978-0-595-00566-6(7)) iUniverse, Inc.

Wiles, Deborah. Love, Ruby Lavender. (Illus.). (J). 2001. 200p. (gr. 3-7). 16.00 (978-0-15-202314-0(3)); 2005. 228p. reprint ed. pap. 5.95 (978-0-15-205478-6(2)) Harcourt Children's Bks. (Gulliver Bks.).

—Love, Ruby Lavender. 2004. 216p. (J). (gr. 3-7). pap. 36.00 incl. audio (978-0-8072-2096-2(5) , Listening Library) Random Hse. Audio Publishing Group.

Williams, Annie Morris. Gwyneth's Secret Grandpa. Doelittle, Linsey, illus. 2001. (Family History Adventures for Young Readers Ser.: Vol. 1). 168p. (J). (gr. 4-7). per. 10.95 (978-0-9645272-7-0(8)) Field Stone Pubs.

Williams, Barbara. Albert's Gift for Grandmother. Cushman, Doug, illus. 2006. 32p. (J). (ps-1). 16.99 (978-0-7636-2097-4(1)) Candlewick Pr.

Williams, Dell. If I Forget, You Remember. 1999. (J). 11.64 (978-0-606-16171-8(6)) Tandem Library Bks.

Williams, Jacklyn. Let's Go Fishing, Gus! Cushman, Doug, illus. 2006. (Read-It! Readers Ser.). (J). 19.93 (978-1-4048-2713-4(7)) Picture Window Bks.

Williams Laura. Best Winds. 2006. (Illus.). 32p. (J). 16.95 (978-1-59078-274-3(7)) Boyds Mills Pr.

Williams, Laura E. The Long Silk Strand: A Grandmother's Legacy to Her Granddaughter. Bochak, Grayce, illus. 2003. 32p. (YA). (gr. 4-6). pap. 8.95 (978-1-56397-856-2(3)) Boyds Mills Pr.

—The Long Silk Strand: A Grandmother's Legacy to Her Granddaughter. 2000. (Illus.). (J). (978-0-606-18013-9(3)) Tandem Library Bks.

—Torch Fishing with the Sun. Broeck, Fabricio Vanden, illus. 2003. 32p. (J). (gr. 4-6). 15.95 (978-1-56397-685-8(4)) Boyds Mills Pr.

Williams, Mardo. Great-Grandpa Fussy & the Little Puckerdoodles. Mishima, Yukiko, illus. 2000. 64p. (J). (ps-4). 17.95 (978-0-9649241-3-0(7)) Calliope Pr.

Williams, Rozanne Lanczak. Grandma's Lists. Maio, Barbara & Faulkner, Stacy, eds. Briles, Patty, illus. 2006. (Learn to Write Ser.). 8p. (J). pap. 1.99 (978-1-59198-284-5(7) , 6178) Creative Teaching Pr., Inc.

—Grandma's Lists. Maio, Barbara & Faulkner, Stacey, eds. Briles, Patty, illus. 2006. (J). per. 4.99 (*978-1-59198-335-4(5)) Creative Teaching Pr., Inc.

Williams, Versey. My Grandma's Dog. l.t. ed. 2004. (Illus.). 50p. 19.00 (978-0-9763357-0-2(0)) Christian Bible Studies.

Willner-Pardo, Gina. Figuring Out Frances. 1999. (Illus.). 144p. (J). (gr. 4-6). tchr. ed. 14.00 (978-0-395-91510-3(4) , Clarion Bks.) Houghton Mifflin Co. Trade & Reference Div.

Wilson, Gina. Grandma's Bears. Howard, Paul, illus. 2004. 40p. (J). (ps-1). 15.99 (978-0-7636-2518-4(3)) Candlewick Pr.

Wilson, Nancy Hope. Mountain Pose. 2001. 240p. (J). (gr. 5 up). 17.00 (978-0-374-35078-9(7) , Farrar, Straus & Giroux (BYR)) Farrar, Straus & Giroux.

Wilson, Rebekah. Grandmother's Hope Chest: Lucie's Snowflakes. l.t. ed. 2004. (Illus.). 80p. (J). 15.00 (978-1-59565-003-0(2)) Hope Chest Legacy, Inc.

—Grandmother's Hope Chest: The Running Rooster. l.t. ed. 2004. (Illus.). 52p. (J). 15.00 (978-1-59565-002-3(4)) Hope Chest Legacy, Inc.

Winkler, Henry & Oliver, Lin. My Secret Life as a Ping-Pong Wizard. 2006. (Hank Zipzer Ser.: No. 9). (J). (gr. 3-8). 24.21 (978-1-59961-110-5(4)) Spotlight.

Winters, Kay. How Will the Easter Bunny Know? 1999. (978-0-606-17670-5(5)); (gr. 3-6). lib. bdg. 12.40 (978-0-613-16128-2(9)) Tandem Library Bks.

Winthrop, Elizabeth. Dancing Granny. Murdocca, Sal, illus. 2003. 32p. (J). 16.95 (978-0-7614-5141-9(2)) Cavendish, Marshall Corp.

Wisnewski, Andrea, illus. & retold by. Little Red Riding Hood. Wisnewski, Andrea, retold by. 2007. 32p. (J). (ps-3). 18.95 (978-1-56792-303-2(8)) Godine, David R. Pub.

Wolf, Claudia. Grandma & Me. Wolf, Claudia, illus. 2006. (Illus.). 24p. (J). per. 2.99 (978-1-59958-024-1(1)) Journey Stone Creations, LLC.

Wong, Janet S. Homegrown House. Lewis, Earl B, illus. 2008. (J). (*978-0-689-84718-9(1) , McElderry, Margaret K.) Simon & Schuster Children's Publishing.

Wood, Douglas. Grandad's Prayers for the Earth. Lynch, P. J., illus. 1999. 32p. (J). (gr. 1-4). 17.99 (978-0-7636-0660-2(X)) Candlewick Pr.

—Grandad's Prayers of the Earth. Lynch, P. J., illus. 2004. 28p. (J). (gr. k-4). reprint ed. 17.00 (978-0-7567-7101-0(3)) DIANE Publishing Co.

—What Grandmas Can't Do. Cushman, Doug, illus. 2005. 32p. (J). 14.95 (978-0-689-84647-2(9) , Simon & Schuster Children's Publishing) Simon & Schuster Children's Publishing.

Wood, June Rae. About Face. 2001. (J). (978-0-606-21014-0(8)) Tandem Library Bks.

Woodruff, Liza. What Time Is It? Woodruff, Liza, illus. 2005. (My First Reader Ser.). (Illus.). 32p. (J). (gr. k-1). 18.50 (978-0-516-25180-6(5) , Children's Pr.) Scholastic Library Publishing.

Woodruff, Liza, illus. What Time Is It? 2005. (My First Reader Ser.). 31p. (J). (gr. k-1). pap. 3.95 (978-0-516-25279-7(8) , Children's Pr.) Scholastic Library Publishing.

Woodson, Jacqueline. Coming on Home Soon. Lewis, Earl, illus. 2004. 32p. (J). (ps). 16.99 (978-0-399-23748-5(8) , Putnam Juvenile) Penguin Group (USA) Inc.

—Visiting Day. Ransome, James E., illus. 2002. 32p. (J). (ps-3). pap. 15.95 (978-0-590-40005-3(3) , Scholastic Pr.) Scholastic, Inc.

Woodson, Jacqueline & Ransome, James E. Visiting Day. 2001. (Illus.). (J). pap. (978-0-590-55262-2(7)) Scholastic, Inc.

Workman, Joan. Scavenger Hunt: The Twokay Kids at the Mall. 2004. 42p. per. 12.95 (978-1-932344-14-1(4)) Thornton Publishing.

Wrenn, Elizabeth. The Christmas Cactus. Aitken, Susan, illus. 2001. (J). (978-1-56123-158-4(4)) Centering Corp.

Wright, Betty Ren. The Wish Master. 2000. (Illus.). 112p. (J). (gr. 4-6). tchr. ed. 15.95 (978-0-8234-1611-0(9)) Holiday Hse., Inc.

Wright, Lynn F. Grandma, Tell Me a Story. Pagliughi, Debbie, illus. 1999. (J). 13.95 (978-1-881519-10-2(4)); pap. 6.95 (978-1-881519-11-9(2)) WorryWart Publishing Co.

Wright, Mary H. Grandma Spoils Me. Megenhardt, Bill, illus. l.t. ed. 2005. 32p. (J). lib. bdg. 16.95 (978-0-9645493-4-0(4)) Bluebonnets, Boots & Bks.

Wyse, Lois, et al. How to Take Your Grandmother to the Museum. 1998. (Illus.). 48p. (J). (gr. k-3). 12.95 (978-0-7611-0990-7(0) , 10990) Workman Publishing Co., Inc.

Yamada, Debbie Leung. Striking It Rich: Treasures from Gold Mountain. Tang, You-shan, illus. l.t. ed. 2004. 128p. (J). (gr. 4-8). pap. 13.95 (978-1-879965-21-8(6)) Polychrome Publishing Corp.

Ye, Ting-Xing. Share the Sky. Langlois, Suzane, illus. 1999. 32p. (J). (ps-2). lib. bdg. 17.95 (978-1-55037-579-4(2)) Annick Pr., Ltd. CAN. *Dist:* Firefly Bks., Ltd.

—Share the Sky. 1999. (gr. k-3). lib. bdg. 15.25 (978-0-613-26907-0(1)) Tandem Library Bks.

Yep, Laurence. Angelfish. 2001. 1p. (J). (gr. 5 up). 16.99 (978-0-399-23041-7(6) , Putnam Juvenile) Penguin Group (USA) Inc.

—Child of the Owl. (J). pap., stu. ed. (978-0-13-053125-4(1)) Prentice Hall (Schl. Div.).

—Child of the Owl. 8.97 (978-0-13-437497-0(5)) Prentice Hall PTR.

—The Cook's Family. 1998. (J). (978-0-03-992907-7(8)) Holt, Rinehart & Winston.

—The Cook's Family. 1999. (J). (978-0-606-18932-3(7)) Tandem Library Bks.

—The Imp That Ate My Homework. 2000. 11.75 (978-0-606-17671-2(3)) Tandem Library Bks.

—The Magic Paintbrush. Wang, Suling, illus. 2003. 96p. (J). (gr. 3-7). pap. 4.99 (978-0-06-440852-3(3)) HarperCollins Pubs.

—The Magic Paintbrush. 2003. (gr. 3-6). lib. bdg. 13.00 (978-0-613-65808-9(6)) Tandem Library Bks.

Yisrael, A'mon. Mr. Jerry's Nap. 2005. (Illus.). 9p. (J). 8.99 (978-0-9772424-0-5(4)) Yisrael, Sean Publishing Co.

Yolen, Jane. Grandma's Hurrying Child. Johnson, Stephen T. & Chorao, Kay, illus. 2005. 32p. (J). 16.00 (978-0-15-201813-9(1) , Gulliver Bks.) Harcourt Children's Bks.

—Off We Go! 2002. (Illus.). (J). 18.89 (978-0-7587-3295-8(3)) Book Wholesalers, Inc.

—Off We Go! Molk, Laurel, illus. 2000. 32p. (J). (ps-1). 14.99 (978-0-316-90228-1(4)) Little Brown & Co.

—Off We Go! Molk, Laurel, illus. 2002. 8p. (J). (ps-k). bds. 5.95 (978-0-316-90972-3(6)) Little, Brown Bks. for Young Readers.

Yuricich, Jillian Grace, illus. What did Grandma See? 2006. (J). lib. bdg. 15.99 (978-0-9774696-0-4(3)) Gilboy Publishing.

Zagwyn, Deborah Turney. The Winter Gift. 2004. (Illus.). 32p. (J). (gr. k-3). 15.95 (978-1-883672-93-5(7) , Tricycle Pr.) Ten Speed Pr.

Zakarin, Debra Mostow. Countdown to Grandma's House. Peterson, Stacy, illus. 2002. (Reading Railroad Bks.). 32p. (J). pap. 3.99 (978-0-448-42813-0(X) , Grosset & Dunlap) Penguin Group (USA) Inc.

—Countdown to Grandma's House. 2002. (ps-2). lib. bdg. 11.25 (978-0-613-52014-0(9)) Tandem Library Bks.

Zaugg, Sandra L. The Rock Slide Rescue. Ford, Mark, illus. 1998. (Shoebox Kids Ser.: Vol. 8). 91p. (J). (gr. 2-5). pap. 6.99 (978-0-8163-1387-7(3)) Pacific Pr. Publishing Assn.

Zepeda, Monique. Las Pinatas. Graullera, Fabiola, illus. Tr. of Pinatas. (SPA.). 26p. (J). (gr. 3-5). pap. 6.95 (978-968-19-0612-2(8)) Santillana USA Publishing Co., Inc.

Zermeno, Mariana. Nuevo Peinado para Abuelitas. 2003. (SPA., Illus.). 24p. (J). (gr. k-5). pap. 7.95 (978-968-19-0678-8(0)) Aguilar, Altea, Taurus, Alfaguara, S.A. de C.V MEX. *Dist:* Santillana USA Publishing Co., Inc.

Ziefert, Harriet. Grandma, Where Are You? Boon, Emilie, illus. 2005. 16p. (J). pap. 5.95 (978-1-4027-1880-9(2)) Sterling Publishing Co., Inc.

—Grandmas Are for Giving Tickles. Plecas, Jennifer, illus. 2000. (Lift-the-Flap Ser.). 16p. (J). (ps-1). pap. 6.99 (978-0-14-056718-2(6) , Puffin) Penguin Group (USA) Inc.

—Grandpa, Will You Play with Me? Boon, Emilie, illus. 2005. 16p. (J). pap. 5.95 (978-1-4027-1897-7(7)) Sterling Publishing Co., Inc.

—Grandpas Are for Finding Worms. Plecas, Jennifer, illus. 2000. (Lift-the-Flap Ser.). 16p. (J). (ps-1). pap. 6.99 (978-0-14-056719-9(4) , Puffin) Penguin Group (USA) Inc.

—My Friend Grandpa. Wurzberg, Robert, illus. 2004. 40p. 15.95 (978-1-59354-063-0(9)) Blue Apple Bks.

—No Kiss for Grandpa. Boon, Emilie, illus. 2001. 32p. (J). (ps-k). pap. 12.95 (978-0-531-30328-3(4) , Orchard Bks.) Scholastic, Inc.

—What's Polite? Brown, Rick & Brown, Richard, illus. 2004. 20p. pap. 6.95 (978-1-4027-1790-1(3)) Sterling Publishing Co., Inc.

—With Love from Grandma. Ray, Deborah Kogan, illus. 2004. 36p. (J). 9.95 (978-1-4027-1703-1(2)) Sterling Publishing Co., Inc.

—40 Uses for Grandpa. Haley, Amanda, illus. 2005. 38p. (ps-ps). 12.95 (978-1-59354-076-0(0)) Blue Apple Bks.

—41 Uses for a Grandma. Haley, Amanda, illus. 2005. 38p. 12.95 (978-1-59354-070-8(1)) Blue Apple Bks.

Zirlin, Sande H. Visits to Gradma's House. 2006. 18.00 (978-0-8059-9920-4(5)) Dorrance Publishing Co., Inc.

Zolotow, Charlotte. My Grandson Lew. rev. ed. 1999. 32p. (J). (ps-1). pap. 5.95 (978-0-06-443549-9(0)); 14.89 (978-0-06-028300-1(9)); 14.95 (978-0-06-028299-8(1)) HarperCollins Pubs.

Zyla, Natalie. Cherie Chipmunk, Aventuriere. 2004. 52p. pap. 12.95 (978-1-4137-3526-0(6)) PublishAmerica, Inc.

GRANT, JULIA (DENT), 1826-1902

Larkin, Tanya. What Was Cooking in Julia Grant's White House? 2001. (Cooking Throughout American History Ser.). (Illus.). 24p. (J). (gr. 3). lib. bdg. 19.95 (978-0-8239-5611-1(3) , PowerKids Pr.) Rosen Publishing Group, Inc., The.

GRANT, ULYSSES S. (ULYSSES SIMPSON), 1822-1885

Aller, Susan Bivin. Ulysses S. Grant. 2005. (History Maker Bios Ser.). (Illus.). 48p. (J). 26.60 (978-0-8225-2438-0(4) , Lerner Pubns.) Lerner Publishing Group.

Alter, Judy. Ulysses S. Grant: A MyReportLinks.com Book. 2002. (Presidents Ser.). (Illus.). 48p. (J). (gr. 4-10). lib. bdg. 25.26 (978-0-7660-5014-3(9) , MyReportLinks.com Bks.) Enslow Pubs., Inc.

Aronson, Billy. Ulysses S. Grant. 2007. (Presidents & Their Times Ser.). 96p. (J). lib. bdg. 32.79 (978-0-7614-2430-7(X) , Benchmark Bks.) Cavendish, Marshall Corp.

Ashby, Ruth. Lee vs. Grant: The Major Battles. 2002. (Illus.). 48p. (J). lib. bdg. 28.50 (978-1-58340-184-2(9)) Smart Apple Media.

Burton, Alma Holman. Four American Patriots: Patrick Henry, Alexander Hamilton, Andrew Jackson, Ulysses S. Grant: A Book for Young Americans. 2000. (Illus.). (J). (978-0-89526-204-2(5)) Regnery Publishing, Inc., An Eagle Publishing Co.

Carter, E. J. Ulysses S. Grant. 2004. (American War Biographies Ser.). (Illus.). 48p. (J). pap. 8.50 (978-1-4034-5087-6(0)); lib. bdg. (978-1-4034-5080-7(3)) Heinemann Library.

Gregson, Susan R. Ulysses S. Grant. 2002. (Let Freedom Ring Ser.). (Illus.). 48p. (J). (gr. 3-4). lib. bdg. 22.60 (978-0-7368-1091-3(9) , Bridgestone Bks.) Capstone Pr., Inc.

Haugen, Brenda. Ulysses S. Grant: Union General & U.S. President. 2004. (Signature Lives Ser.). (Illus.). 112p. (J). 30.60 (978-0-7565-0820-3(7) , 1240145) Compass Point Bks.

Havelin, Kate. Ulysses S. Grant. 2004. (Presidential Leaders Ser.). (Illus.). 112p. (J). 29.27 (978-0-8225-0814-4(1) , Lerner Pubns.) Lerner Publishing Group.

Kantor, MacKinlay. Sterling Point Books: Lee & Grant at Appomattox. 2007. (Sterling Point Bks.). 144p. (J). pap. 6.95 (*978-1-4027-5124-0(9)) Sterling Publishing Co., Inc.

Larkin, Tanya. What Was Cooking in Julia Grant's White House? 2001. (Cooking Throughout American History Ser.). (Illus.). 24p. (J). (gr. 3). lib. bdg. 19.95 (978-0-8239-5611-1(3) , PowerKids Pr.) Rosen Publishing Group, Inc., The.

Marsh, Carole. Ulysses S. Grant. 2002. (One Thousand Readers Ser.). (Illus.). 12p. (J). (gr. k-4). 2.95 (978-0-635-01489-4(0) , 14890) Gallopade International.

—Ulysses S. Grant: An Ohio Experience Reader. 2001. (J). (gr. k-5). pap. 1.95 (978-0-635-00442-0(9)) Gallopade International.

—The Virginia Reader: Ulysses S. Grant. 2001. (Virginia Experience! Ser.). (Illus.). 12p. (J). (gr. k-5). pap. 2.95 (978-0-635-00374-4(0)) Gallopade International.

McLeese, Don. Ulysses S. Grant. 2006. (Civil War Military Leaders Ser.). (Illus.). 32p. (gr. 3-6). 19.95 (978-1-59515-475-0(2)) Rourke Publishing, LLC.

Mcleese, Don. Ulysses S Grant. 2005. 32p. pap. 6.45 (978-1-59515-789-8(1)) Rourke Publishing, LLC.

O'Shei, Tim. Ulysses S. Grant. 2001. (gr. 5-8). lib. bdg. 17.60 (978-0-613-33176-0(1)) Tandem Library Bks.

—Ulysses S. Grant: Military Leader & President. 2000. (Famous Figures of the Civil War Era Ser.). (Illus.). 80p. (J). (gr. 4-7). pap. 25.00 (978-0-7910-6139-8(6) , Chelsea Hse.) Facts On File, Inc.

Patrick, Bethanne Kelly. Ulysses S. Grant. 2003. (Childhoods of the Presidents Ser.). (Illus.). 48p. (J). (gr. 4 up). lib. bdg. (978-1-59084-276-8(6)) Mason Crest Pubs.

Ransom, Candice F. Willie McLean & the Civil War Surrender. Reeves, Jeni, illus. 2005. (On My Own History Ser.). 48p. (J). 25.26 (978-1-57505-588-6(0)) Lerner Publishing Group.

Rice, Earle, Jr. Ulysses S. Grant: Defender of the Union. 2005. (Civil War Leaders Ser.). (Illus.). 176p. (J). (gr. 6-12). 26.95 (978-1-931798-48-8(6)) Reynolds, Morgan Inc.

Riehecky, Janet. Ulysses S. Grant. 2004. (Encyclopedia of Presidents Ser.). (Illus.). 110p. (J). 34.00 (978-0-516-22868-6(4) , Children's Pr.) Scholastic Library Publishing.

Sapp, Richard. Ulysses S. Grant & the Road to Appomattox. 2006. (In the Footsteps of American Heroes Ser.). (Illus.). 64p. (J). pap. (978-0-8368-6436-6(0)); lib. bdg. 32.67 (978-0-8368-6431-1(X)) Stevens, Gareth Inc. (World Almanac Library).

Schuman, Michael A. Ulysses S. Grant. 2004. (United States Presidents Ser.). (Illus.). 128p. (J). lib. bdg. 26.60 (978-0-7660-2038-2(X)) Enslow Pubs., Inc.

Smolinski, Diane. Soldiers of the Civil War. 2002. (Americans at War Ser.). (Illus.). 32p. (J). (gr. 4-6). lib. bdg. (978-1-58810-098-6(7)); pap. 6.95 (978-1-58810-392-5(7) , 91132) Heinemann Library.

Tecco, Betsy Dru. How to Draw the Life & Times of Ulysses S. Grant. 2006. (Kid's Guide to Drawing the Presidents of the United States of America Ser.). (J). 25.25 (978-1-4042-2995-2(7) , PowerKids Pr.) Rosen Publishing Group, Inc., The.

Ulysses S Grant. (Civil War Biographies Ser.). 48p. (YA). 7.95 (978-0-7368-4526-7(7)) Capstone Pr., Inc.

Ulysses Simpson Grant. 1999. (Illus.). 32p. (YA). (gr. 6 up). pap. 4.00 (978-1-890541-17-0(6)) Americana Souvenirs & Gifts.

Venezia, Mike. Ulysses S. Grant. Venezia, Mike, illus. 2006. (Illus.). 32p. (J). (gr. 3-4). pap. 7.95 (978-0-516-25488-3(X) , Children's Pr.) Scholastic Library Publishing.

Venezia, Mike, illus. Ulysses S. Grant. 2005. 32p. (J). 27.00 (978-0-516-22623-1(1) , Children's Pr.) Scholastic Library Publishing.

Warynica, Lou. Ulysses S. Grant: Confident Leaders & Hero. Hale, Sarah Elder, ed. 2005. (Civil War Ser.). (Illus.). 48p. (J). 17.95 (978-0-8126-7906-9(7)) Cobblestone Publishing Co.

Welsbacher, Anne. Ulysses S. Grant. 2001. (United States Presidents Ser.). (Illus.). 32p. (J). (gr. k-6). lib. bdg. 22.78 (978-1-56239-741-8(9) , Checkerboard Library) ABDO Publishing Co.

Williams, Jean Kinney. Ulysses S. Grant. 2002. (Profiles of the Presidents Ser.). (Illus.). 64p. (J). (gr. 4 up). lib. bdg. 23.93 (978-0-7565-0265-2(9)) Compass Point Bks.

GRAPHIC ARTS

see also Drawing; Painting; Printing; Prints

The Animaniacs in a Hip-Hopera Christmas. (Illus.). 32p. (J). (ps up). pap. 5.89 incl. audio (978-1-56826-788-3(6) , KR5) Rhino Entertainment Co, A Warner Music Group Co.

Cooties. 2004. (YA). cd-rom (978-0-9762083-8-9(5)) Go-Know Learning.

Dennis, Kevin A. & Jenkins, John D. Comprehensive Graphic Arts. 3rd ed. 1999. (Illus.). (YA). (gr. 6-12). 633p. stu. ed. 45.35 (978-0-02-681251-1(7)); 167p. stu. ed., wbk. ed. 10.37 (978-0-02-681253-5(3)) Glencoe/McGraw-Hill.

Dombek, Jeff. Caveman Art Teacher. Dombek, Jeff, illus. 2004. (Illus.). 28p. (J). pap. 4.95 (978-0-9752597-0-2(9)) Corn Tassel Pr.

Dover Staff. Whimsical Animals Illustration, Vol. 3. 2000. (Illus.). 64p. pap. 14.95 incl. cd-rom (978-0-486-99973-9(4)) Dover Pubns., Inc.

Eisner, Will. The Will Eisner Sketchbook. 2004. (Illus.). 200p. (YA). 49.95 (978-1-56971-960-2(8)) Dark Horse Comics.

Hart, Christopher. ¡Dibuja Manga! Nivel Basico. Miralles, Charles, tr. 2005. (SPA., Illus.). 64p. pap. 17.95 (978-1-59497-092-4(0)) Public Square Bks.

Miyazaki, Hayao. The Art of Miyazaki's Spirited Away. Miyazaki, Hayao, illus. 2002. (Anime Art Gallery Ser.). (Illus.). 240p. (YA). 34.95 (978-1-56931-777-8(1)) Viz Media.

Page, Phil. Hodder Graphics: Heroes. 2007. (Illus.). 64p. pap. 21.95 (*978-0-340-92749-6(6) , Hodder Murray) Hodder Education GBR. *Dist:* Trans-Atlantic Pubns., Inc.

Page, Phil & Blackmore, Ruth Benton. Hodder Graphics: A Kestrel for a Knave. 2007. (Illus.). 58p. pap. 21.95 (*978-0-340-92748-9(8) , Hodder Murray) Hodder Education GBR. *Dist:* Trans-Atlantic Pubns., Inc.

Plotting Points: Fun Holiday & Seasonal Graph Art. (Basic Skills Ser.). 48p. (gr. 2-4). 5.99 (978-1-56822-921-8(6) , IF5210); (gr. 5-8). 5.99 (978-1-56822-922-5(4) , IF5211) School Specialty Publishing.

Shepard, Tristram & Loft, Andrew. Graphic Products. 2nd rev. ed. 2001. (Design & Make It Ser.). (Illus.). 152p. (YA). pap. 27.50 (978-0-7487-6081-7(4)) Nelson Thornes Ltd. GBR. *Dist:* Trans-Atlantic Pubns., Inc.

Special Effects, 6 vols. 2005. (QEB Learn Art Ser.). (Illus.). 32p. (J). per. 8.95 (978-1-59566-126-5(3)) QEB Publishing Inc.

Special Effects: 6 Each of 1 Anthology, 6 vols. (Wildcats Ser.). 32p. (gr. 2-8). (978-0-322-00593-8(0)) Wright Group, The.

Steck-Vaughn Staff. Graphic Skills. 2002. (Illus.). (J). pap. (978-0-7398-5747-2(9)) Steck-Vaughn.

Thorgerson, Storm & Powell, Aubrey. 100 Best Album Covers. 1999. 160p. (YA). pap. 24.95 (978-0-7894-4615-2(4)) Dorling Kindersley Publishing, Inc.

Torres, Daniel. El arte de Daniel Torres. 2005. (SPA., Illus.). 80p. 14.95 (978-1-59497-051-1(3)) Public Square Bks.

Williams, Cheryl & Williams, Sheila. People of Colour Illustrations: Klip-Klik Art, 2 disc. (J). pap. 39.95 incl. cd-rom (978-1-889926-98-8(1)) TwinAtaa Studio.

Yenawine, Philip. Lines. 2006. (Illus.). 24p. (gr. 13 up). 14.95 (978-0-87070-175-7(4)) D.A.P./Distributed Art Pubs.

GRAPHIC ARTS—VOCATIONAL GUIDANCE

McGuire-Lytle, Erin. Careers in Graphic Arts & Computer Graphics. rev. ed. 1999. (Careers). (Illus.). 192p. (YA). (gr. 7-12). lib. bdg. 26.50 (978-0-8239-2228-4(6) , CAGRAR) Rosen Publishing Group, Inc., The.

GRAPHIC METHODS

see also Statistics—Graphic Methods

Adams, Colleen. The Everglades: Analyzing Graphs, Tables, & Charts. 2005. (PowerMath Ser.). (J). 22.50 (978-1-4042-2933-4(7)); pap. (978-1-4042-5127-4(8)) Rosen Publishing Group, Inc., The. (PowerKids Pr.).

Bader, Bonnie. Graphs. Cole, Mernie Gallagher, illus. 2003. (All Aboard Math Reader Ser.). 48p. (J). (gr. 1-3). pap. 3.99 (978-0-448-42896-3(2) , Grosset & Dunlap) Penguin Group (USA) Inc.

—Graphs. 2003. (gr. k-3). lib. bdg. 11.80 (978-0-613-68345-6(5)) Tandem Library Bks.

Bodach, Vijaya. Pictographs. 2008. (J). (***978-1-4296-0041-5(1)***) Capstone Pr., Inc.

Boothroyd, Jennifer. Graphing. 2007. (First Step Nonfiction Ser.). (J). lib. bdg. (978-0-8225-6830-8(6)) Lerner Publishing Group.

Britt, Murray, et al. Graphs & Rates. 2001. (PreAlgebra Makes Sense Ser.: Bk. 5). 48p. (J). pap., stu. ed. 16.50 (978-0-7690-2525-4(0)) Seymour, Dale Pubns.

Cartland Noble, Mrs, Patricia. Activities for the Graphing Mat. 2000. 32p. (J). (gr. k-3). pap. 5.99 (978-1-56451-325-0(4) , ID7248) School Specialty Publishing.

Cefrey, Holly. Exploring Australia: Using Charts, Graphs, & Tables. 2004. (PowerMath Ser.). (Illus.). 24p. (J). lib. bdg. (978-0-8239-8883-9(X)); lib. bdg. 21.25 (978-0-8239-8969-0(0)) Rosen Publishing Group, Inc., The. (PowerKids Pr.).

Charts & Graphs. 2002. (Illus.). (J). pap. (978-0-7398-5946-9(3)) Steck-Vaughn.

Clarke, Jacqueline. Graphing. 2002. (Best-Ever Activities for Grades 2-3 Ser.). (Illus.). 48p. (J). (gr. 2-3). 10.95 (978-0-439-29645-8(5)) Scholastic, Inc.

Edson, Ann & Insel, Eunice. Reading Maps, Globes, Charts, Graphs. (J). (gr. 4-6). stu. ed., instr.'s gde. ed. 39.00 incl. audio (978-0-89525-175-6(2) , AKC 356) Educational Activities, Inc.

Estigarribia, Diana. Learning about the Effects of Natural Events with Graphic Orgainizers. 2005. (Graphic Organizers in Science Ser.). (Illus.). 24p. (J). (ps). lib. bdg. 19.95 (978-1-4042-2804-7(7) , PowerKids Pr.) Rosen Publishing Group, Inc., The.

—Learning about the Effects of Natural Events with Graphic Organizers. 2005. (Graphic Organizers in Science Ser.). (Illus.). 24p. (J). pap. (978-1-4042-5038-3(7) , PowerKids Pr.) Rosen Publishing Group, Inc., The.

Freudenthal. Graph Equations. 3rd ed. 2002. (Math in Context Ser.). (Illus.). (J). stu. ed. (978-0-85229-902-9(8)) Encyclopaedia Britannica, Inc.

—Graph Equations. 3rd ed. 2003. (Math in Context Ser.). (Illus.). 8.33 (978-0-03-071659-1(4)) Holt, Rinehart & Winston.

Graham, Noel & Blundell, Graham. Graph Pack. (Illus.). 22p. (J). (gr. k-3). 10.00 (978-1-871098-29-7(7)) Claire Pubns. GBR. *Dist:* Parkwest Pubns., Inc.

Hixson, Bryce. Great Graphs in Ten Days. Hixson, Bryce, illus. 2003. (Illus.). (J). 6.95 (978-1-931801-18-8(5)) Loose In The Lab.

Irvin, Barbara B. & School Zone Publishing Company Staff. Classifying & Graphing. 1999. (I Know It! Workbooks Ser.). (Illus.). 32p. (J). (gr. 1-3). pap., wbk. ed. 2.49 (978-0-88743-247-7(6) , 02047) School Zone Publishing Co.

Irvin, Barbara Bando. Classifying & Graphing. 2000. (Teacher Edition Wkbks.). (Illus.). 32p. (J). pap., tchr. ed. 3.99 (978-0-88743-858-5(X) , 02839) School Zone Publishing Co.

Johnson, Rebecca L. Decoding Data. 2004. (Math Behind the Science Ser.). (Illus.). 24p. (J). pap. (978-0-7922-4588-9(1)) National Geographic Society.

Kernan, Elizabeth. Let's Graph It! 2003. (Reading Room Collection). (Illus.). 24p. (J). lib. bdg. 18.75 (978-0-8239-3716-5(X)) Rosen Publishing Group, Inc., The.

Long Windmoeller, Michelle. Graph-A-Day: Building Skills for Collecting & Displaying Data. 2001. 80p. (J). (gr. 2-5). pap. 9.99 (978-0-7424-0148-8(0) , IF19210) School Specialty Publishing.

Mitchell, Cindi. Math Skills Made Fun: Great Graph Art Decimals & Fractions. 2000. (Illus.). 64p. (J). pap. 10.95 (978-0-590-64375-7(4)) Scholastic, Inc.

Nechaev, Michelle Wagner. Making Graphs. Jarrett, Michael, illus. Jarrett, Michael, photos by. 2004. (I Can Do Math Ser.). 24p. (J). (gr. 1 up). lib. bdg. 20.67 (978-0-8368-4111-4(5)) Stevens, Gareth Inc.

Pistoia, Sara. Graphs. 2006. (MathBooks Ser.). (Illus.). 24p. (J). 24.21 (978-1-59296-687-5(X)) Child's World, Inc.

Priestley, Michael. Scholastic Success with Charts, Tables, & Graphs: Grades 5-6. 2002. (Illus.). 48p. pap. 4.95 (978-0-439-29706-6(0) , Teaching Resources) Scholastic, Inc.

QEB Let's Start! Computing National Book Stores Edition: Making Charts. 2006. (J). per. (978-1-59566-297-2(9)) QEB Publishing Inc.

Realtime Associates and Mazer Corporation Staff & LeapFrog Staff, compiled by. Understand & Use Simple Graphs. 2002. (J). (gr. 2). 66.75 (978-1-58605-336-9(1) , LeapFrog Schl. Hse.) LeapFrog Enterprises, Inc.

—Understand Tally Charts & Graphs. 2002. (J). (gr. 3). 66.75 (978-1-58605-398-7(1) , LeapFrog Schl. Hse.) LeapFrog Enterprises, Inc.

—Use or Construct Picture & Bar Graphs. 2002. (J). (gr. 2). 66.75 (978-1-58605-347-5(7)); (gr. 4). 66.75 (978-1-58605-458-8(9)) LeapFrog Enterprises, Inc. (LeapFrog Schl. Hse.).

—Use Picture, Line, Circle & Bar Graphs. 2002. (J). (gr. 5). 66.75 (978-1-58605-523-3(2) , LeapFrog Schl. Hse.) LeapFrog Enterprises, Inc.

Robinson, C. L. MATH1on1 Graphing Foundation. 2006. (YA). per. 9.99 (978-0-9786767-3-7(7)) Robinson, Consuelo.

Roy, Jennifer Rozines & Roy, Gregory. Graphing in the Desert. 2006. (Math All Around Ser.). (Illus.). 32p. (J). lib. bdg. 28.50 (978-0-7614-2262-4(5) , Benchmark Bks.) Cavendish, Marshall Corp.

Steck-Vaughn Staff. Math Level J-M: Graphing the Rain Forest. 2003. (Illus.). pap. (978-0-7398-7700-5(3)) Steck-Vaughn.

Trumbauer, Lisa. Graph It! 2002. (Yellow Umbrella Books). (Illus.). 16p. (J). (gr. 1). lib. bdg. 14.60 (978-0-7368-1282-5(2) , Pebble Bks.) Capstone Pr., Inc.

—Hagamos una Grafica. 2005. Tr. of Let's Graph. (SPA., Illus.). 16p. (J). (gr. k-1). lib. bdg. 15.93 (978-0-7368-4153-5(9)) Capstone Pr., Inc.

—Let's Graph. 2003. (J). 15.93 (978-0-7368-2932-8(6)); pap. (978-0-7368-2891-8(5)) Yellow Umbrella Pr.

Williams & Cohen. Graphing Across the Curriculum. 2nd ed. 2003. (Illus.). 32p. (J). pap. 10.95 (978-0-590-53551-9(X)) Scholastic, Inc.

Wilson, Natashya. The Census & America's People: Analyzing Data Using Line Graphs & Tables. 2004. (PowerMath Ser.). (Illus.). 32p. (J). lib. bdg. (978-0-8239-8903-4(8)); lib. bdg. 22.50 (978-0-8239-8990-4(9)) Rosen Publishing Group, Inc., The. (PowerKids Pr.).

Wingard-Nelson, Rebecca. Data, Graphing, & Statistics. 2004. (Math Success Ser.). (Illus.). 64p. (J). lib. bdg. 22.60 (978-0-7660-2567-7(5)) Enslow Pubs., Inc.

Wirkner, Linda. Learning about the Settlement of the Americas, with Graphic Organizers. 2005. (Graphic Organizers in Social Studies). (J). 19.95 (978-1-4042-2814-6(4) , PowerKids Pr.) Rosen Publishing Group, Inc., The.

Zuravicky, Orli. The Amazon & the Sahara: Using Double Line Graphs & Double Bar Graphs. 2004. (PowerMath Ser.). (Illus.). 32p. (J). lib. bdg. (978-0-8239-8868-6(6)); lib. bdg. 22.50 (978-0-8239-8981-2(X)) Rosen Publishing Group, Inc., The. (PowerKids Pr.).

GRAPHS

see Graphic Methods

GRASSES

see also Feeding and Feeds

Blaisdell, Molly. The Grass Patch Project. Demski, James, illus. 2007. (J). lib. bdg. (***978-1-4048-2292-4(5)***) Picture Window Bks.

Bullock, Linda. Living in the Savannah. 2004. (Rookie Read-About Geography Ser.). (Illus.). 31p. (J). (gr. 1-2). pap. 5.95 (978-0-516-27327-3(2) , Children's Pr.) Scholastic Library Publishing.

Chambers, Catherine. Life in the Grasslands. 2005. (What on Earth? Ser.). (Illus.). 32p. (J). 25.50 (978-0-516-25319-0(0) , Children's Pr.) Scholastic Library Publishing.

Giant Grass: Individual Title Six-Packs. (Story Steps Ser.). (gr. k-2). 32.00 (978-0-7635-9840-2(2)) Rigby Education.

Holmes, Anita. If Grass Could Talk. 2001. (We Can Read about Nature! Ser.). (Illus.). 32p. (J). (gr. 1-2). lib. bdg. 21.36 (978-0-7614-1111-6(9) , Benchmark Bks.) Cavendish, Marshall Corp.

Loves, June. Grasses. 2004. (Plants Ser.). (Illus.). 32p. (J). (gr. 2-4). 23.00 (978-0-7910-8269-0(5) , Chelsea Hse.) Facts On File, Inc.

Mattern, Joanne. How Grass Grows: Como Crece la Hierba. 2006. (ENG & SPA., Illus.). 24p. (J). pap. (978-0-8368-6469-4(7) , Weekly Reader Early Learning Library) Stevens, Gareth Inc.

—How Grass Grows/ Como crece la hierba. 2006. (ENG & SPA., Illus.). 24p. (J). 19.33 (978-0-8368-6462-5(X)) Stevens, Gareth Inc.

Salas, Laura Purdie. Grasslands. 2007. (Amazing Science Ser.). (Illus.). 24p. (J). (***978-1-4048-3470-5(2)*** , 1265691) Picture Window Bks.

Salas, Laura Purdie. Grasslands: Fields of Green & Gold. Yesh, Jeff, illus. 2006. (Amazing Science Ser.). 24p. (J). (978-1-4048-3096-7(0) , 1265691) Picture Window Bks.

Whitehouse, Patricia. Living in a Grassland. 2007. (Illus.). 24p. (J). (978-1-60044-185-1(8)) Rourke Publishing, LLC.

GRASSHOPPERS

see Locusts

GRASSLAND ECOLOGY

Allaby, Michael. Grasslands. Garratt, Richard, illus. 2006. (Biomes of the Earth Ser.). 288p. (J). (gr. 6-12). 39.50 (978-0-8160-5323-0(5)) Facts On File, Inc.

Anderson, Sheila. Plains. 2008. (First Step Nonfiction - Landforms Ser.). (J). lib. bdg. 18.60 (***978-0-8225-8593-0(6)*** , Lerner Pubns.) Lerner Publishing Group.

Bradley, Catherine. Life on the Plains. 2001. (World Book Ecology Ser.). (Illus.). 32p. (J). (978-0-7166-5230-4(7)) World Bk., Inc.

Butterfield, Moira. Who Eats Who in Grasslands? 2007. (Food Chains in Action Ser.). (Illus.). 32p. (J). (***978-1-58340-964-0(5)***) Smart Apple Media.

Cefrey, Holly. Grasslands. 2003. (Reading Power Ser.). (Illus.). 24p. (J). lib. bdg. 17.25 (978-0-8239-6457-4(4) , PowerKids Pr.) Rosen Publishing Group, Inc., The.

Dunphy, Madeleine. Here Is the African Savanna. Leonard, Tom, illus. 2006. (Web of Life Ser.). 32p. (J). 16.95 (978-0-9773795-3-8(1)); pap. 9.95 (978-0-9773795-2-1(3)) Web of Life Children's Bks.

Endres, Hollie. Prairies. 2007. (Illus.). 24p. (J). lib. bdg. 19.95 (978-1-60014-114-0(5)) Bellwether Media.

Erlic, Lily. Grasslands. 2005. (Illus.). 32p. (J). (ps-6). lib. bdg. 24.45 (978-1-59036-346-1(9)); pap. 7.95 (978-1-59036-352-2(3)) Weigl Pubs., Inc.

Finton, Nancy. Ecosystems. 2004. (Life Science Ser.). (Illus.). 32p. (J). pap. (978-0-7922-4578-0(4)) National Geographic Society.

Fleisher, Paul. Grassland Food Webs. 2007. (Early Bird Food Webs Ser.). 48p. (J). (gr. 2-5). 26.60 (***978-0-8225-6730-1(X)*** , Lerner Pubns.) Lerner Publishing Group.

Gilkerson, Patricia. My Adventure in a Meadow. 2006. 44p. (J). 8.99 (978-1-59092-274-3(3) , Orchard Academy Pr.) Windstorm Creative.

Grassland Safari, 6 Pack. (Rigby Infoquest Ser.). 32p. (gr. 4 up). 37.00 (978-0-7578-5729-4(9)) Rigby Education.

Grasslands. (Ecosystems Ser.). 24p. (J). 6.95 (978-0-7368-9163-9(3)) Capstone Pr., Inc.

Grasslands, 6 vols. (gr. 2-5). 36.95 (978-0-7368-9264-3(8)) Red Brick Learning.

Grasslands: Individual Title Six-Packs. (On Deck Ser.: Vol. 2). 24p. (gr. 4-5). 35.00 (978-0-7578-5826-0(0)) Rigby Education.

Gray, Susan Heinrichs. Grasslands. 2000. (First Reports). (Illus.). 48p. (J). (gr. 3 up). lib. bdg. 21.26 (978-0-7565-0020-7(6)) Compass Point Bks.

Haugen, Hayley Mitchell. Life in a Grassland. 2005. (Ecosystems Ser.). (Illus.). 48p. (J). (gr. 4-7). lib. bdg. 26.20 (978-0-7377-3015-9(3) , Greenhaven Pr., Inc.) Thomson Gale.

Hoare. Temperate Grasslands. 2003. (Biomes Atlas Ser.). (Illus.). 64p. pap. 9.50 (978-1-4109-0017-3(7)); pap. 48.30 (978-1-4109-0252-8(8)) Raintree.

Hoare, Ben. Temperate Grasslands. 2002. (Biomes Atlases Ser.). (Illus.). 64p. (J). lib. bdg. 31.42 (978-0-7398-5249-1(3)) Raintree.

—Temperate Grasslands. 2003. (gr. 5-8). lib. bdg. 18.20 (978-0-613-78189-3(9)) Tandem Library Bks.

Johansson, Philip. The Wide Open Grasslands: A Web of Life. 2004. (World of Biomes Ser.). (Illus.). 48p. (J). lib. bdg. 23.93 (978-0-7660-2201-0(3)) Enslow Pubs., Inc.

Kalman, Bobbie. A Savanna Habitat. 2006. (Illus.). 32p. (J). (gr. 2). pap. (978-0-7787-2980-8(X)) Crabtree Publishing Co.

Kalman, Bobbie & Dyer, Hadley. Savanna Food Chains. 2006. (Food Chains Ser.). (Illus.). 32p. (J). (gr. 3-5). pap. (978-0-7787-1998-4(7)); lib. bdg. (978-0-7787-1952-6(9)) Crabtree Publishing Co.

Lalley. Grassland Scientists. 2001. (Scientists of the Biomes Ser.). (Illus.). (J). pap. (978-0-7398-4937-8(9)) Steck-Vaughn.

Lalley, Pat & Lalley, Janet. Grasslands Scientists. 2001. (Scientists of the Biomes Ser.). (Illus.). 48p. (J). (gr. 4-7). lib. bdg. 24.26 (978-0-7398-4753-4(8)) Raintree.

Lambert, David. People of the Grasslands. 1998. (Wide World Ser.). (Illus.). 48p. (J). (gr. 3-7). 18.98 (978-0-8172-5060-7(3)) Raintree.

Levy, Janey. Discovering the Tropical Savanna. 2008. (J). lib. bdg. (***978-1-4042-3783-4(6)*** , PowerKids Pr.) Rosen Publishing Group, Inc., The.

Lynch, Wayne, photos by. Prairie Grasslands. 2006. (Illus.). 64p. 16.95 (978-1-55971-946-9(X)); (J). 8.95 (978-1-55971-947-6(8)) T&N Children's Publishing. (NorthWord Bks. for Young Readers).

MacAulay, Kelley. Un Habitat de Pastizal. 2007. (SPA.). 32p. (J). (gr. 1-2). (***978-0-7787-8334-3(0)***) Crabtree Publishing Co.

MacAulay, Kelley & Kalman, Bobbie. A Grassland Habitat. 2006. (Illus.). 32p. (J). (978-0-7787-2959-4(1)) Crabtree Publishing Co.

MacAulay, Kelley & Kalman, Bobbie. Un Habitat de Pastizal. rev. ed. 2007. (SPA.). 32p. (J). (gr. 1-2). pap. (***978-0-7787-8358-9(8)***) Crabtree Publishing Co.

MacAuley, Kelley. A Grassland Habitat. 2006. (Illus.). 32p. (J). (gr. 2). pap. (978-0-7787-2987-7(7)) Crabtree Publishing Co.

Mayer, Cassie. Prairie. 2007. (J). (***978-1-4034-9428-3(2));*** pap. (***978-1-4034-9434-4(7)***) Heinemann Library.

McKissack, Fredrick, Jr. & McKissack, Lisa Beringer. Counting in the Grasslands. 2008. (J). (***978-0-7660-2991-0(3)***) Enslow Pubs., Inc.

McNeil, Niki, et al. HOCPP 1093 Grassland Habitats. 2006. spiral bd. 24.50 (***978-1-60308-093-4(7)***) In the Hands of a Child.

Morgan. Tropical Grasslands. 2003. (Biomes Atlas Ser.). (Illus.). 64p. pap. 9.50 (978-1-4109-0019-7(3)); pap. 48.30 (978-1-4109-0254-2(4)) Raintree.

Morgan, Ben. Tropical Grasslands. 2002. (Biomes Atlases Ser.). (Illus.). 64p. (J). lib. bdg. 31.42 (978-0-7398-5516-4(6)) Raintree.

Murphy, Patricia J. Grassland Animals, 4 bks. Saunders-Smith, Gail, ed. Incl. Badgers. lib. bdg. 15.93 (978-0-7368-2071-4(X)); Coyotes. lib. bdg. 15.93 (978-0-7368-2072-1(8)); Prairie Dogs. lib. bdg. 15.93 (978-0-7368-2073-8(6)); Red Foxes. lib. bdg. 15.93 (978-0-7368-2074-5(4)); 24p. (J). (gr. k-1). (Illus.). 2004. Set lib. bdg. 63.72 (978-0-7368-2319-7(0) , Pebble Bks.) Capstone Pr., Inc.

Nelson, Julie. Grasslands. Sloan, Frank, ed. 2001. (Biomes Ser.). (Illus.). 32p. (J). (gr. 4-7). lib. bdg. 22.83 (978-0-7398-3562-3(9)) Raintree.

Nichols, Catherine. Grassy Lands. 2002. (We Can Read about Nature! Ser.). (Illus.). 32p. (J). 21.36 (978-0-7614-1435-3(5) , Benchmark Bks.) Cavendish, Marshall Corp.

Pascoe, Elaine. The Ecosystem of a Grassy Field. 2003. (Library of Small Ecosystems Ser.). (Illus.). 24p. (J). lib. bdg. 21.25 (978-0-8239-6305-8(5) , PowerKids Pr.) Rosen Publishing Group, Inc., The.

—The Ecosystem of a Milkweed Patch. 2003. (Library of Small Ecosystems Ser.). (Illus.). 24p. (J). lib. bdg. 21.25 (978-0-8239-6309-6(8)) Rosen Publishing Group, Inc., The.

Patent, Dorothy Hinshaw. Life in a Grassland. Munoz, William, illus. 2003. (Ecosystems in Action Ser.). 72p. (J). (gr. 6-12). 26.60 (978-0-8225-2139-6(3)) Lerner Publishing Group.

Penny, Malcolm. Grasslands. (Illus.). 64p. (YA). (gr. 4 up). lib. bdg. 29.95 (978-1-59389-127-5(X)) Chrysalis Education.

Quigley, Mary. Prairie Explorer. 2004. (Habitat Explorer Ser.). (Illus.). 32p. (J). (ps-ps). lib. bdg. 25.70 (978-1-4109-0513-0(6)) Raintree.

Reid, Greg. Grasslands. 2004. (Ecosystems Ser.). (Illus.). 32p. (J). (gr. 3-5). 23.00 (978-0-7910-7939-3(2) , Chelsea Hse.) Facts On File, Inc.

Schofield, Jennifer. Animal Babies in Grasslands. 2004. (Animal Babies Ser.). (Illus.). 32p. (J). (ps-k). 7.95 (978-0-7534-5789-4(X) , Kingfisher) Houghton Mifflin Co. Trade & Reference Div.

Snedden, Robert. Tropical Grasslands. 2004. (Illus.). 32p. (J). lib. bdg. (978-1-58340-386-0(8)) Smart Apple Media.

Somervill, Barbara A. Our Living World: Earth's Biomes, 7 vols., Set. 2005. (Illus.). (J). (gr. 4-8). 350.00 (978-1-59187-052-4(6)) Tradition Publishing Co.

Spilsbury, Louise & Spilsbury, Richard. Grassland Food Chains. 2004. (Food Webs Ser.). (Illus.). 32p. (J). pap. 7.50 (978-1-4034-5867-4(7)); lib. bdg. 24.22 (978-1-4034-5860-5(X)) Heinemann Library.

Stille, Darlene R. Grasslands. (True Bks.). (Illus.). 48p. (J). (gr. 3-5). 2000. pap. 6.95 (978-0-516-26762-3(0)); 1998. 25.00 (978-0-516-21509-9(4)) Scholastic Library Publishing. (Children's Pr.).

—Grasslands. 1999. (gr. 3-6). lib. bdg. 15.25 (978-0-613-37370-8(7)) Tandem Library Bks.

Stone, Lynn M. Grasslands. 2003. (Rourke Discovery Library). (Illus.). 24p. (J). 20.64 (978-1-58952-685-3(6)) Rourke Publishing, LLC.

Toupin, Laurie Peach. Life in the Temperate Grasslands. 2005. (Biomes & Habitats Ser.). (Illus.). 64p. (J). (gr. 5-7). 24.50 (978-0-531-12385-0(5) , Watts, Franklin) Scholastic Library Publishing.

Wallace, Marianne D. America's Prairies & Grasslands: Guide to Plants & Animals. 2004. (America's EcoSystem Ser.: Vol. 3). (Illus.). 48p. (J). (gr. 3-6). pap. 11.95 (978-1-55591-992-4(8)) Fulcrum Publishing.

Warhol, Tom. Chaparral & Scrub. 2006. (Earth's Biomes Ser.). (Illus.). 80p. (YA). (gr. 5-8). lib. bdg. 32.79 (978-0-7614-2195-5(5) , Benchmark Bks.) Cavendish, Marshall Corp.

—Grassland. 2006. (Earth's Biomes Ser.). (Illus.). 80p. (J). lib. bdg. 32.79 (978-0-7614-2196-2(3) , Benchmark Bks.) Cavendish, Marshall Corp.

Wilkins, Sally. Grasslands. 2001. (Bridgestone Science Library). (Illus.). 24p. (J). (gr. 2-3). lib. bdg. 18.60 (978-0-7368-0837-8(X) , Bridgestone Bks.) Capstone Pr., Inc.

GRAVES

see Cemeteries; Funeral Rites and Ceremonies; Mounds and Mound Builders

GRAVEYARDS

see Cemeteries

GRAVITATION

Bailey, Jacqui. Up, down, All Around: A Story of Gravity. Lilly, Matthew, illus. 2006. 32p. (J). (gr. 3-6). 23.93 (978-1-4048-1597-1(X)) Picture Window Bks.

Bergethon, Peter R. The World of Gravity: Student Science Manual. 1999. (Illus.). 75p. (J). (gr. 5-7). pap., stu. ed. (978-1-58447-033-5(X)) Symmetry Learning Systems.

Branley, Franklyn M. Gravity Is a Mystery. 2nd rev. ed. Date not set. 40p. (J). (gr. k-4). lib. bdg. 16.89 (978-0-06-028533-3(8)) HarperCollins Pubs.

—Gravity Is a Mystery. Miller, Edward, illus. 2nd rev. ed. (Let's-Read-and-Find-Out Science Ser.). 40p. (J). (gr. k-4). 2007. 15.99 (978-0-06-028532-6(X)); 2001. pap. 5.99 (978-0-06-445201-4(8)) HarperCollins Pubs.

Canizares, Susan. Gravity. 1999. (Science Emergent Readers Ser.). (J). pap. 2.50 (978-0-439-08127-6(0)) Scholastic, Inc.

Cobb, Vicki. I Fall Down. Gorton, Julia, illus. 2004. (Science Play Ser.). 40p. (J). (ps-k). 15.99 (978-0-688-17842-0(1)); lib. bdg. 16.89 (978-0-688-17843-7(X)) HarperCollins Pubs.

Conrad, David. All Fall Down. 2002. (Spyglass Books). (Illus.). 24p. (J). (gr. 1 up). lib. bdg. 18.60 (978-0-7565-0224-9(1)) Compass Point Bks.

Dalton, Cindy Devine. Gravity. 2001. (How Can I Experiment With? Ser.). (Illus.). 32p. (gr. 1-4). 19.95 (978-1-58952-013-4(0)) Rourke Publishing, LLC.

Farndon, John. Gravity, Weight & Balance. 2001. (Science Experiments Ser.). (Illus.). 32p. (J). (gr. 3-5). lib. bdg. 25.64 (978-0-7614-1340-0(5) , Benchmark Bks.) Cavendish, Marshall Corp.

Frisch, Joy. Gravity. 2008. (J). (***978-1-58341-576-4(9)*** , Creative Education) Creative Co., The.

Goodstein, Madeline. Science Fair Success Using Newton's Laws of Motion. 2002. (Science Fair Success Ser.). (Illus.). 128p. (YA). (gr. 6-12). lib. bdg. 26.60 (978-0-7660-1628-6(5)) Enslow Pubs., Inc.

Hantula, Richard. Electricity & Forces. 2006. (Real World Science Ser.). (Illus.). 32p. (J). 24.67 (978-0-8368-6305-5(4)) Stevens, Gareth Inc.

Hopwood, James. Cool Gravity Activities: Fun Science Projects about Balance. 2007. (Cool Science Ser.). (Illus.). 32p. (J). (gr. k-6). lib. bdg. 24.21 (***978-1-59928-908-3(3)*** , Checkerboard Library) ABDO Publishing Co.

Jedicke, Peter. Gravity, & How It Works. 2007. (Scientific American Ser.). 72p. (J). (gr. 5-8). 30.00 (***978-0-7910-9051-0(5)*** , Chelsea Hse.) Facts On File, Inc.

Korb, Rena B. Groovy Gravity. Reibeling, Brandon, illus. 2007. (Science Rocks Ser.). 32p. (J). (ps-4). lib. bdg. 27.07 (***978-1-60270-039-0(7)*** , Looking Glass Library) Magic Wagon.

Lilly, Melinda. Gravity. Thompson, Scott M., illus. 2003. (Read & Do Science Ser.). (J). 20.64 (978-1-58952-642-6(2)) Rourke Publishing, LLC.

EFG

A Look at Gravity, 6 vols., Set E. (Phonics Readers Ser.). (gr. k-2). 28.95 (978-0-7368-4072-9(9)) Red Brick Learning.

Lyons, Suzanne. Gravity. ed. 2003. (Early Connections Ser.). (J). pap. 35.00 (978-1-4108-1547-7(1)) Benchmark Education Co.

Merrill, Amy French. Everyday Physical Science Experiments with Gravity. 2002. (Science Surprises Ser.). 24p. (J). lib. bdg. 19.95 (978-0-8239-5805-4(1) , PowerKids Pr.) Rosen Publishing Group, Inc., The.

Murphy, Patricia. Up & Down. 2002. (gr. k-3). lib. bdg. 12.95 (978-0-613-54372-9(6)) Tandem Library Bks.

Murphy, Patricia J. Up & Down. 2002. (Rookie Read-About Science Ser.). (Illus.). 32p. (J). (gr. 1-2). 20.50 (978-0-516-22553-1(7) , Children's Pr.) Scholastic Library Publishing.

Murray, Julie. Gravity. 2007. (Illus.). 24p. (J). 21.35 (978-1-59679-824-3(6)) ABDO Publishing Co.

Nardo, Don. Gravity. 2003. (Kidhaven Science Library). (Illus.). 48p. (J). (gr. 3-5). 26.20 (978-0-7377-1404-3(2) , Kidhaven) Thomson Gale.

Nelson, Robin. La Gravedad (Gravity) 2007. (Mi Primer Paso al Mundo Real - Fuerzas y Movimiento (First Step Nonfiction - Forces & Motion) Ser.). (SPA.). 24p. (J). (gr. k-2). lib. bdg. 18.60 (***978-0-8225-7807-9(7)*** , Ediciones Lerner) Lerner Publishing Group.

Nelson, Robin. Gravity. 2004. (First Step Nonfiction Ser.). (Illus.). 24p. (J). (gr. k-2). lib. bdg. 18.60 (978-0-8225-5133-1(0)) Lerner Publishing Group.

Niz, Ellen Sturm. Gravity. 2005. (First Facts Ser.). (Illus.). 24p. (J). (978-0-7368-5403-0(7)) Capstone Pr., Inc.

O'Daley, Anne. Gravity. 2003. (Illus.). 24p. (J). 22.45 (978-1-4103-0081-2(1) , Blackbirch Pr., Inc.) Thomson Gale.

Oxlade, Chris. Gravity. 2006. (Fantastic Forces Ser.). (Illus.). 32p. (J). pap. (978-1-4034-8177-1(6)); lib. bdg. (978-1-4034-8172-6(5)) Heinemann Library.

Parker, Barry. The Mystery of Gravity. 2002. (Story of Science Ser.). (Illus.). 78p. (J). 29.93 (978-0-7614-1428-5(2) , Benchmark Bks.) Cavendish, Marshall Corp.

Prasad, Kamal S. Why Can't I Jump Very High? A Book about Gravity. Simonnet, Aurore, illus. 2004. 32p. (J). lib. bdg. 14.95 (978-0-9740861-5-6(0)) Science Square Publishing.

Solway, Andrew. 10 Experiments Your Teacher Never Told You About: Gravity. 2005. (Illus.). 32p. (J). (978-1-4109-1921-2(8)); (gr. 4-6). 7.85 (978-1-4109-1952-6(8)) Steck-Vaughn.

Stone, Lynn M. High Tide, Low Tide. 2007. (Illus.). 24p. (J). (978-1-60044-178-3(5)) Rourke Publishing, LLC.

Stringer, John. The Science of Gravity. 1999. (Science World Ser.). (Illus.). 32p. (J). (gr. 2-4). lib. bdg. 25.69 (978-0-7398-1323-2(4)) Raintree.

Tiner, John Hudson. Gravity. 2002. (J). 24.25 (978-1-58340-157-6(1)) Smart Apple Media.

Tocci, Salvatore. Experiments with Gravity. 2002. (True Book Ser.). (Illus.). 48p. (J). (gr. 3-5). pap. 25.00 (978-0-516-22513-5(8) , Children's Pr.) Scholastic Library Publishing.

Trumbauer, Lisa. What Is Gravity? 2004. (Rookie Read about Science Ser.). (Illus.). 31p. (J). 20.50 (978-0-516-23448-9(X) , Watts, Franklin) Scholastic Library Publishing.

—What Is Gravity. 2004. (Rookie Read-About Science Ser.). 32p. (J). (gr. 1-2). pap. 4.95 (978-0-516-25844-7(3) , Children's Pr.) Scholastic Library Publishing.

What Is Gravity? Third Grade Guided Reading Level J. (On Our Way to English Ser.). (gr. 3 up). 34.50 (978-0-7578-7118-4(6)) Rigby Education.

Wilson, Jim. Gravity Rules! Grades 5-12. Cordel, Betty, ed. Mason, Renee, illus. 1998. 170p. (J). pap., tchr. ed., wbk. ed. 18.95 (978-1-881431-75-6(4)) AIMS Education Foundation.

Woodford, Chris. Gravity. 2004. (Routes of Science Ser.). (Illus.). 40p. (J). pap. 11.20 (978-1-4103-0298-4(9) , Blackbirch Pr., Inc.) Thomson Gale.

GRAVITATION—FICTION

Lyons, Suzanne. Pete Discovers Gravity. ed. 2003. (Early Connections Ser.). (J). pap. 35.00 (978-1-4108-1559-0(5)) Benchmark Education Co.

GRAVITY

see Gravitation

GREAT BRITAIN

Blomquist, Christopher. The United Kingdom, a Primary Source Guide. 2005. (Countries of the World, a Primary Source Journey Ser.). (J). 19.95 (978-1-4042-2760-6(1) , PowerKids Pr.) Rosen Publishing Group, Inc., The.

Bowden, Rob. United Kingdom. 2003. (Countries of the World Ser.). (Illus.). 64p. (gr. 6-12). 30.00 (978-0-8160-5383-4(9)) Facts On File, Inc.

—The United Kingdom. 2004. (Changing Face Of... Ser.). (J). 28.56 (978-0-7398-6832-4(2)) Harcourt Schl. Pubs.

Campbell, Kumari. United Kingdom in Pictures. 2nd rev. expurg. ed. 2004. (Visual Geography Ser.). (Illus.). 80p. (J). (gr. 5-12). 27.93 (978-0-8225-1995-9(X)) Lerner Publishing Group.

Copeland, Tim. Investigating Romans. (Illus.). 32p. (J). pap. 8.95 (978-0-7078-0330-2(6)) National Trust, Aylesbury GBR. *Dist:* Trafalgar Square Publishing.

Costain, Meredith & Collins, Paul. Welcome to the United Kingdom. 2001. (Countries of the World Ser.). (Illus.). 32p. (J). (gr. 4 up). 28.00 (978-0-7910-6544-0(8) , 010211, Chelsea Hse.) Facts On File, Inc.

Cruikshank, Dan. The Story of Britain's Best Buildings. Parker, John, photos by. 2003. (Illus.). 240p. (gr. 7-12). pap. 24.95 (978-1-55297-748-4(X)) Firefly Bks., Ltd.

Farm Holiday England, Scotland, Wales, Ireland. 2004. 16.95 (978-1-58843-361-9(7)) Hunter Publishing, Inc.

Foreman, Michael. Memories of Childhood. ltd. ed. 2000. (Illus.). 192p. (J). (gr. 5 up). 35.00 (978-1-86205-408-0(8) , Pavilion Bks., Ltd.) Anova Bks. GBR. *Dist:* Independent Pubs. Group.

Ganeri, Anita. Britain & the British. 2004. (Focus on Europe Ser.). (Illus.). 40p. (J). (ps-7). pap., lib. bdg. 29.95 (978-1-932799-16-3(8)) Stargazer Bks.

Hawthorne, Kate, et al. The Young Person's Guide to the Internet: An Essential Website Reference Book for Young People, Parents, & Teachers. 2nd ed. 2005. (Illus.). 224p. 30.95 (978-0-415-34505-7(7)) Routledge.

Innes, Brian. United Kingdom. 2001. (Nations of the World Ser.). (Illus.). 128p. (YA). (gr. 6-8). lib. bdg. 34.26 (978-0-7398-1288-4(2)) Raintree.

Lister, Maree, et al. Welcome to England. 1999. (Welcome to My Country Ser.). (Illus.). 48p. (J). (gr. 2 up). lib. bdg. 26.00 (978-0-8368-2396-7(6)) Stevens, Gareth Inc.

Myers, Walter Dean. African Princess: At Her Majesty's Request. 1999. (Illus.). 160p. (J). (gr. 4-7). pap. 17.95 (978-0-590-48669-9(1)) Scholastic, Inc.

Oliver, Clare. Great Britain. 2003. (Country Files Ser.). (Illus.). 32p. (J). lib. bdg. 24.25 (978-1-58340-204-7(7)) Smart Apple Media.

Orme, David. The Brontes. 1999. (Writers in Britain Ser.). (Illus.). 32p. 24.99 (978-0-237-51744-1(2) , Evans Brothers, Limited) Evans Publishing Group GBR. *Dist:* Independent Pubs. Group.

Popper, Garry. James & Jemma in Great Britain. Johnson, Andi, illus. 2004. 36p. (ps-7). 4.00 (978-1-84161-054-2(2)) Ravette Publishing, Ltd. GBR. *Dist:* Parkwest Pubns., Inc.

Powell, Jillian. Looking at Great Britain. 2007. (J). pap. (***978-0-8368-8177-6(X)***); 32p. (gr. 2-4). lib. bdg. 25.27 (***978-0-8368-8170-7(2)***) Stevens, Gareth Inc.

Sevier, Marti & Lister, Maree. England. 1998. (Countries of the World Ser.). (Illus.). 96p. (J). (gr. 6 up). lib. bdg. 30.00 (978-0-8368-2125-3(4)) Stevens, Gareth Inc.

Simons, Rae. United Kingdom. 2006. (European Union Ser.). (Illus.). 88p. (YA). (gr. 5 up). lib. bdg. (978-1-4222-0064-3(7)) Mason Crest Pubs.

Tames, Richard & Tames, Sheila. Great Britain. 2005. (Illus.). 32p. (J). (gr. 4-7). lib. bdg. 27.10 (978-1-932889-92-5(2)) Sea-To-Sea Pubns.

Walsh, Kieran. The United Kingdom. 2005. (Countries in the News Ser.). (Illus.). 24p. (gr. 1-4). 17.95 (978-1-59515-174-2(5)) Rourke Publishing, LLC.

Watts, Duncan. Understanding American Government & Politics: A Comparative Guide. 2004. (Understanding Politics Ser.). 352p. pap. 21.95 (978-0-7190-6721-1(9)) Manchester Univ. Pr. GBR. *Dist:* Macmillan.

Woolf, Alex. Focus on the United Kingdom. 2006. (World in Focus (Milwaukee, Wis.) Ser.). (Illus.). 64p. pap. (978-0-8368-6731-2(9)); lib. bdg. (978-0-8368-6724-4(6)) Stevens, Gareth Inc. (World Almanac Library).

GREAT BRITAIN—ANTIQUITIES

Lace, William W. Stonehenge. 2003. (Mystery Library). (Illus.). 104p. (J). 29.95 (978-1-59018-131-7(X) , Lucent Bks.) Thomson Gale.

Nardo, Don. King Arthur. 2002. (Heroes & Villains Ser.). (Illus.). 112p. (J). (gr. 6). 27.45 (978-1-56006-948-5(1) , Lucent Bks.) Thomson Gale.

Petrini, Catherine M. Stonehenge. 2005. (Wonders of the World Ser.). (Illus.). 48p. (J). (gr. 4-8). lib. bdg. 26.20 (978-0-7377-3073-9(0) , Greenhaven Pr., Inc.) Thomson Gale.

Wilcox, Charlotte. Bog Mummies: Preserved in Peat. 2002. (Mummies Ser.). (Illus.). 32p. (J). (gr. 3-4). lib. bdg. 21.26 (978-0-7368-1306-8(3) , Capstone High-Interest Bks.) Capstone Pr., Inc.

Wyly, Michael J. King Arthur. 2001. (Mystery Library). (Illus.). 112p. (YA). (gr. 4-12). 27.45 (978-1-56006-771-9(3) , Lucent Bks.) Thomson Gale.

GREAT BRITAIN—BIOGRAPHY

Adair, Gene. Alfred Hitchcock: Filming Our Fears. 2002. (Oxford Portraits Ser.). (Illus.). 160p. (YA). (gr. 7-10). 28.00 (978-0-19-511967-1(3)) Oxford Univ. Pr., Inc.

Adelson, Bruce. British General William Howe. 2001. (Revolutionary War Leaders Ser.). (Illus.). 80p. (J). pap. 27.50 (978-0-7910-6389-7(5) , Chelsea Hse.) Facts On File, Inc.

—William Howe: British General. 2002. (gr. 5-8). lib. bdg. 17.60 (978-0-613-50852-0(1)) Tandem Library Bks.

Aller, Susan Bivin. Florence Nightingale. 2007. (History Maker Biographies Ser.). (J). 26.60 (***978-0-8225-7609-9(0)*** , Lerner Pubns.) Lerner Publishing Group.

Anderson, Dale. Leaders of the American Revolution. 2005. (World Almanac Library of the American Revolution). (J). pap. (978-0-8368-5940-9(5)); lib. bdg. 30.00 (978-0-8368-5931-7(6)) Stevens, Gareth Inc. (World Almanac Library).

Atkinson, Mary. Genius or Madman? Sir Isaac Newton. 2008. (Shockwave: Life Stories Ser.). 32p. (J). pap. 6.95 (***978-0-531-18840-8(X)*** , Children's Pr.) Scholastic Library Publishing.

Aykroyd, Clarissa. Savage Satire: The Story of Jonathan Swift. 2006. (World Writers Ser.). (Illus.). 160p. (J). (gr. 6-12). lib. bdg. 27.95 (978-1-59935-027-1(0)) Reynolds, Morgan Inc.

Bardhan-Quallen, Sudipta. Up Close: Jane Goodall: Jane Goodall. 2008. (Up Close Ser.). 208p. (YA). (gr. 6). 16.99 (***978-0-670-06263-8(4)*** , Viking Juvenile) Penguin Group (USA) Inc.

Barton-Wood, Sara. Queen Elizabeth II: Monarch of Our Times. 2001. (Famous Lives Ser.). (Illus.). 48p. (J). (gr. 4-6). lib. bdg. 27.12 (978-0-7398-4430-4(X)) Raintree.

Baxter, Roberta. Skeptical Chemist: The Story of Robert Boyle. 2006. (Profiles in Science Ser.). (Illus.). 128p. (YA). (gr. 6-12). lib. bdg. 27.95 (978-1-59935-025-7(4)) Reynolds, Morgan Inc.

Bedesky, Baron. Sir Walter Raleigh: Founding the Virginia Colony. 2006. (In the Footsteps of Explorers Ser.). (Illus.). 32p. (J). (gr. 3-9). (978-0-7787-2424-7(7) , 1253445) Crabtree Publishing Co.

Belmonte, Kevin Charles. A Journey Through the Life of William Wilberforce: The Abolitionist Who Changed the Face of a Nation. 2006. (Illus.). 122p. (J). (***978-0-89221-671-0(9)***) New Leaf Pr., Inc.

Benge, Janet & Benge, Geoff. John Wesley: The World, His Parish. 2007. (J). (***978-1-57658-382-1(1)***) YWAM Publishing.

Billinghurst, Jane. Growing up Royal: Life in the Shadow of the British Throne. 2001. (Illus.). 176p. (J). (gr. 3-7). 22.95 (978-1-55037-623-4(3)); pap. 12.95 (978-1-55037-622-7(5)) Annick Pr., Ltd. CAN. *Dist:* Firefly Bks., Ltd.

Bingham, Jane. Captain Cook's Pacific Explorations. 2007. (J). (***978-1-4034-9756-7(7)***) Heinemann Library.

Briscoe, Diana. Jane Goodall: Finding Hope in the Wilds of Africa. 2004. (High Five Reading Ser.). (J). (978-0-7368-3851-1(1)); 23.93 (978-0-7368-3879-5(1)) Capstone Pr., Inc.

Browning, Oscar. True Stories from English History from T. 2006. pap. 33.95 (***978-1-4254-9960-0(0)***) Kessinger Publishing, LLC.

Burgan, Michael. Robert Hooke: Natural Philosopher & Scientific Explorer. 2007. (J). lib. bdg. (***978-0-7565-3315-1(5)***) Compass Point Bks.

Collier, Bruce & MacLachlan, James. Charles Babbage: And the Engines of Perfection. Gingerich, Owen, ed. 1998. (Oxford Portraits in Science Ser.). (Illus.). 128p. (YA). (gr. 7 up). 30.00 (978-0-19-508997-4(9)) Oxford Univ. Pr., Inc.

Constable, John. Colour Your Own John Constable Paintings. 2007. 32p. pap. 3.95 (***978-0-486-46201-1(3)***) Dover Pubns., Inc.

Dash, Joan. The Longitude Prize: The Race Between the Moon & the Watch-Machine. Petricic, Dusan, illus. 2000. 208p. (J). (gr. 4-7). 17.00 (978-0-374-34636-2(4) , Farrar, Straus & Giroux (BYR)) Farrar, Straus & Giroux.

Davis, Rebecca. George Mueller: A Father to the Fatherless. 2004. (Illus.). 135p. (J). pap. 7.49 (978-1-59166-255-6(9)) Jones, Bob Univ. Pr.

Dougherty, Terri & Dougherty, Denis. Prince William. 2001. (People in the News Ser.). (Illus.). 96p. (YA). (gr. 6-9). 32.45 (978-1-56006-982-9(1) , Lucent Bks.) Thomson Gale.

Edward, Herman. Pink Floyd. 2008. (J). (***978-1-4222-0214-2(3)***) Mason Crest Pubs.

Foreman, Michael. After the War was Over. 2007. (Illus.). 96p. (J). pap. 16.99 (***978-1-84365-088-1(6)***) Anova Bks. GBR. *Dist:* Independent Pubs. Group.

—War Boy. 2006. (Illus.). 96p. (J). pap. 16.99 (***978-1-84365-087-4(8)***) Anova Bks. GBR. *Dist:* Independent Pubs. Group.

Gallagher, Jim. The Beatles. 2008. (J). (***978-1-4222-0186-2(4)***) Mason Crest Pubs.

Goodridge, Catherine. Jane Goodall (Spanish) & Jane Goodall. 2005. spiral bd. 70.00 (***978-1-4108-5658-6(5)***) Benchmark Education Co.

Gow, Mary. Robert Hooke: Creative Genius, Scientist, Inventor. 2006. (Great Minds of Science Ser.). (Illus.). 128p. (J). (gr. 4-10). lib. bdg. 31.93 (978-0-7660-2547-9(0)) Enslow Pubs., Inc.

Graves, Charles L. The Life & Letters of Sir George Grove. 2001. 484p. (YA). reprint ed. 98.00 (978-0-7222-5425-7(3)) Library Reprints, Inc.

Gregory, Peter. Queen. 2008. (J). (***978-1-4222-0193-0(7)***) Mason Crest Pubs.

Hamilton, Sue L. Bartholomew Roberts. 2007. (Illus.). 32p. (J). lib. bdg. 24.21 (***978-1-59928-757-7(9)*** , ABDO & Daughters) ABDO Publishing Co.

—Captain Kidd. 2007. (Pirates! Ser.). (ENG., Illus.). 32p. (J). (gr. 3-6). 24.21 (***978-1-59928-759-1(5)*** , ABDO & Daughters) ABDO Publishing Co.

Hantula, Richard. Alexander Fleming. 2003. (Trailblazers of the Modern World Ser.). (Illus.). 48p. (J). (gr. 5 up). pap. 14.95 (978-0-8368-5243-1(5)); lib. bdg. 30.00 (978-0-8368-5083-3(1)) Stevens, Gareth Inc. (World Almanac Library).

Harmon, Daniel E. Lord Cornwallis. 2001. (Revolutionary War Leaders Ser.). (Illus.). 80p. (J). pap. 27.50 (978-0-7910-6397-2(6)); 27.50 (978-0-7910-6396-5(8)) Facts On File, Inc. (Chelsea Hse.).

Haugen, Brenda. Jane Goodall: Legendary Zoologist. 2006. (Signature Lives Ser.). (Illus.). 112p. (J). (gr. 5-7). 30.60 (978-0-7565-1590-4(4)) Compass Point Bks.

Havelin, Kate. Queen Elizabeth I. 2002. (Biography Ser.). (Illus.). 112p. (J). (gr. 6-12). lib. bdg. 27.93 (978-0-8225-0029-2(9) , Lerner Pubns.) Lerner Publishing Group.

Heims, Neil. J. R. R. Tolkien. 2004. (Great Writers Ser.). (Illus.). 128p. (YA). (gr. 9-13). 31.95 (978-0-7910-7847-1(7) , Chelsea Hse.) Facts On File, Inc.

Hein, Rolland. George MacDonald: Victorian Mythmaker. 2nd rev. ed. 1999. (Illus.). 406p. lib. bdg. 28.00 (978-1-881084-64-8(7)) Johannesen Printing & Publishing.

Ingwe. Ingwe. 2nd ed. 2001. (YA). per. 15.00 (978-1-57994-013-3(7)) Owlink Media.

Kishel, Ann-Marie. Elizabeth Blackwell: A Life of Diligence. 2007. (Pull Ahead Books-Biographies Ser.). (J). 22.60 (978-0-8225-6459-1(9) , Lerner Pubns.) Lerner Publishing Group.

Kittinger, Jo S. Jane Goodall. 2005. (Scholastic News Nonfiction Readers Ser.). (Illus.). 24p. (J). (gr. 1-2). 19.00 (978-0-516-24940-7(1) , Children's Pr.) Scholastic Library Publishing.

Kjelle, Marylou. John Dalton & the Atomic Theory. 2004. (Uncharted, Unexplored, & Unexplained Ser.). (Illus.). 48p. (J). (gr. 4-8). lib. bdg. 29.95 (978-1-58415-308-5(3)) Mitchell Lane Pubs., Inc.

Krull, Kathleen. Isaac Newton. Kulikov, Boris, illus. 2006. (Giants of Science Ser.: No. 2). 128p. (J). (gr. 3-7). 15.99 (978-0-670-05921-8(8) , Viking Juvenile) Penguin Group (USA) Inc.

Larkin, Tanya. Sir Walter Raleigh. 2001. (Famous Explorers Ser.). (Illus.). 24p. (J). (gr. 3). lib. bdg. 18.75 (978-0-8239-5558-9(3) , PowerKids Pr.) Rosen Publishing Group, Inc., The.

Lough, Loree. Lord Baltimore. 2000. (Colonial Leaders Ser.). (Illus.). 80p. (YA). (gr. 3 up). 27.50 (978-0-7910-5349-2(0) , Chelsea Hse.) Facts On File, Inc.

Mattern, Joanne. Orlando Bloom. 2007. (J). (***978-1-4222-0198-5(8)***) Mason Crest Pubs.

McCarthy, Shaun. Sir Walter Raleigh. 2002. (Groundbreakers Ser.). (Illus.). 48p. (J). (gr. 5-7). lib. bdg. 27.07 (978-1-58810-599-8(7)) Heinemann Library.

—Sir Walter Raleigh. 2002. (gr. 5-8). lib. bdg. 16.40 (978-0-613-45831-3(1)) Tandem Library Bks.

McCaughrean, Geraldine. Daredevils & Desperadoes: 20 Stories from British History. Brassey, Richard, illus. 2002. 128p. pap. 9.99 (978-1-84255-059-5(4)) Orion Children's Bks. GBR. *Dist:* Trafalgar Square Publishing.

—Movers, Shakers & Record Breakers. Brassey, Richard, illus. 112p. pap. 9.99 (978-1-85881-895-5(8)) Orion Bks. Ltd. GBR. *Dist:* Trafalgar Square Publishing.

McCracken, Kristin. Prince William. 2000. (High Interest Bks.). (Illus.). 48p. (J). (gr. 7-12). 23.00 (978-0-516-23325-3(4) , Children's Pr.) Scholastic Library Publishing.

Nardo, Don. Charles Darwin. 2004. (Importance of Ser.). (Illus.). 112p. (YA). (gr. 7-10). lib. bdg. 32.45 (978-1-59018-339-7(8) , Lucent Bks.) Thomson Gale.

Neunzig, Hans A. Brahms. Mitchell, Mike, tr. from GER. 2005. (Life & Times Ser.). (Illus.). 192p. pap. 15.95 (978-1-904341-17-8(9)) Haus Publishing GBR. *Dist:* International Publishers Marketing.

Orr, Tamra. Orlando Bloom. 2006. (Blue Banner Biography Ser.). (Illus.). 32p. (J). (gr. 4-8). lib. bdg. (978-1-58415-515-7(9)) Mitchell Lane Pubs., Inc.

Otfinoski, Steven. Bram Stoker: The Man Who Wrote Dracula. 2005. (Great Life Stories Ser.). (Illus.). 111p. (J). 30.50 (978-0-531-16750-2(X) , Watts, Franklin) Scholastic Library Publishing.

Parks, Peggy J. Joseph Lister: Father of Antiseptics. 2005. (Giants of Science Ser.). 64p. (J). (gr. 5-7). 26.20 (978-1-4103-0322-6(5) , Blackbirch Pr., Inc.) Thomson Gale.

Pendleton, Ken. David Beckham. 2007. (J). lib. bdg. (***978-0-8225-7161-2(7)***) Twenty First Century Bks.

Perrin, Pat & Coleman, Wim. The Mystery of the Murdered Playwright. 2004. (Cover-To-Cover Books). (Illus.). 56p. pap. (***978-0-7891-6001-0(3)***); (gr. 4-7). lib. bdg. 17.95 (***978-0-7569-1353-3(5)***) Perfection Learning Corp.

Petrie, Kristin. Sir Walter Raleigh. 2007. (Illus.). 32p. (J). 22.78 (978-1-59679-748-2(7)) ABDO Publishing Co.

Powling, Chris. Quentin Blake. 1999. (Tell Me about Ser.). (Illus.). 22p. (J). 15.99 (978-0-237-51971-1(2) , Evans Brothers, Limited) Evans Publishing Group GBR. *Dist:* Independent Pubs. Group.

Redgrave, Roy. The adventures of colonel Daffodil. 2007. (Illus.). 208p. 45.00 (***978-1-84415-525-5(0)***) Pen & Sword Bks. Ltd. GBR. *Dist:* Casemate Pubs. & Bk. Distributors, LLC.

Robbins, Trina. Florence Nightingale: Lady with the Lamp. Timmons, Anne, illus. 2007. 32p. (J). (978-0-7368-6850-1(X)) Capstone Pr., Inc.

Robinson, Tom. David Beckham: Soccer's Superstar. 2008. (People to Know Today Ser.). 128p. (J). (gr. 6 up). lib. bdg. 31.93 (***978-0-7660-3110-4(1)***) Enslow Pubs., Inc.

Rosenberg, Aaron. Thomas Hobbes: An English Philosopher in the Age of Reason. 2005. (Leaders of the Enlightenment Ser.). (Illus.). 112p. (J). (ps-7). lib. bdg. 31.95 (978-1-4042-0419-5(9)) Rosen Publishing Group, Inc., The.

Ross, Stewart. Will's Dream. Shields, Susan, illus. 28p. pap. 9.99 (978-0-7502-2965-4(9) , Hodder & Stoughton) Hodder General Publishing Division GBR. *Dist:* Trafalgar Square Publishing.

Roth, B. A. David Beckham: Born to Play. 2008. (All Aboard Reading Ser.). 48p. (J). (gr. 1-3). pap. 3.99 (***978-0-448-44788-9(6)*** , Grosset & Dunlap) Penguin Group (USA) Inc.

Roza, Greg. David Beckham: Soccer Superstar. 2006. (Tony Stead Nonfiction Independent Reading Collection). (J). pap. (978-1-4042-5539-5(7)) Rosen Publishing Group, Inc., The.

Sapet, Kerrily. Eleanor of Aquitaine: Medieval Queen. 2006. (European Queens Ser.). (Illus.). 176p. (J). (gr. 6-12). 26.95 (978-1-931798-90-7(7)) Reynolds, Morgan Inc.

Schaefer, Lola M. Jane Goodall. (First Biographies Ser.). 24p. (J). pap. 5.95 (978-0-7368-5085-8(6)) Capstone Pr., Inc.

Sitford, Mikaela. Serial Killer File: The Doctor of Death Investigation. 2008. (J). lib. bdg. (***978-1-59716-551-8(4)***) Bearport Publishing Co., Inc.

Sterling, Kristin. Jane Goodall: A Life of Loyalty. 2008. (Pull Ahead Books-Biographies Ser.). (J). lib. bdg. 22.60 (***978-0-8225-8727-9(0)*** , Lerner Pubns.) Lerner Publishing Group.

Streissguth, Thomas. Richard the Lionheart: Crusader King of England. 2007. (Rulers of the Middle Ages Ser.). (Illus.). 160p. (YA). (gr. 7-9). lib. bdg. 34.60 (978-0-7660-2714-5(7)) Enslow Pubs., Inc.

Trachtenberg, Martha P. Bono: Rock Star Activist. 2008. (People to Know Today Ser.). (Illus.). 112p. (J). (gr. 6 up). lib. bdg. 31.93 (***978-0-7660-2695-7(7)***) Enslow Pubs., Inc.

Tucker, Margaret E. Biography of Richard Bullard: From Shoe Cobbler in England to Minister for Jesus Christ in America. 2003. pap. 6.75 (978-0-9672363-3-9(9)) Heritage Publishing.

Ungs, Tim. Paul McCartney & Stella McCartney. 2004. (Famous Families Ser.). (Illus.). 48p. (J). lib. bdg. 25.25 (978-1-4042-0263-4(3)) Rosen Publishing Group, Inc., The.

Watson, Galadriel Findlay. David Beckham. 2007. (J). ***(978-1-59036-641-7(7)); (978-1-59036-642-4(5))*** Weigl Pubs., Inc.

Waxman, Laura Hamilton. Jane Goodall. Butler, Tad, illus. 2007. (History Maker Biographies Ser.). (J). 26.60 ***(978-0-8225-7610-5(4)*** , Lerner Pubns.) Lerner Publishing Group.

Weaver, Anne H. The Voyage of the Beetle: A Journey Around the World with Charles Darwin & the Search for the Solution to the Mystery of Mysteries, As Narrated by Rosie, an Articulate Beetle. Lawrence, George, illus. 2007. 80p. (YA). (gr. 5 up). 16.95 ***(978-0-8263-4304-8(X))*** Univ. of New Mexico Pr.

Weinberger, Kimberly. Princess Diana - Forever in Our Hearts: A Scrapbook of Memories. 439th ed. 1998. (Illus.). 48p. (gr. 1-4). pap. 5.99 (978-0-439-04529-2(0)) Scholastic, Inc.

Wellman, Sam. John Wesley: Founder of the Methodist Church. 1999. (Heroes of the Faith Ser.). 208p. (YA). (gr. 4-7). lib. bdg. 17.95 (978-0-7910-5036-1(X) , Chelsea Hse.) Facts On File, Inc.

Wood, Richard & Barton-Wood, Sara. The Queen Mother: Grandmother of a Nation. 2000. (Famous Lives Ser.). (Illus.). 48p. (J). (gr. 3-7). lib. bdg. 27.12 (978-0-8172-5715-6(2)) Raintree.

Wyborny, Sheila. Prince William. 2002. (Famous People Ser.). (Illus.). 48p. (J). (gr. 3-5). 26.20 (978-0-7377-1401-2(8) , Kidhaven) Thomson Gale.

Young, Serenity. Richard Francis Burton: Explorer, Scholar, Spy. 2007. (Great Explorations Ser.). (Illus.). 80p. (YA). (gr. 5-9). lib. bdg. 32.79 ***(978-0-7614-2222-8(6)*** , Benchmark Bks.) Cavendish, Marshall Corp.

Yount, Lisa. William Harvey: Discoverer of How Blood Circulates. 2008. (Great Minds of Science Ser.). 128p. (J). (gr. 5 up). lib. bdg. 31.93 ***(978-0-7660-3010-7(5))*** Enslow Pubs., Inc.

Yuan, Margaret Speaker. Beatrix Potter. 2005. (Who Wrote That? Ser.). (Illus.). 114p. (J). (gr. 6-12). lib. bdg. 30.00 (978-0-7910-8655-1(0) , Chelsea Hse.) Facts On File, Inc.

GREAT BRITAIN—CIVILIZATION

Ashby, Ruth. Victorian England. 2002. (Cultures of the Past Ser.). (Illus.). 80p. (YA). (gr. 5-8). 29.93 (978-0-7614-1493-3(2) , Benchmark Bks.) Cavendish, Marshall Corp.

Banting, Erinn. England — The Culture. 2004. (Lands, Peoples, & Cultures Ser.). (Illus.). 32p. pap. (978-0-7787-9691-6(4)) Crabtree Publishing Co.

—England — The Land. 2004. (Lands, Peoples, & Cultures Ser.). (Illus.). 32p. (J). (978-0-7787-9323-6(0)) Crabtree Publishing Co.

Cole, Joanna, et al. Ms. Frizzle's Adventures: Medieval Castle. Degen, Bruce, illus. 2003. (Magic School Bus Ser.). 48p. (J). pap. 15.95 (978-0-590-10820-1(4)) Scholastic, Inc.

Davis, Kevin A. Look What Came from England. 1999. (J). (978-0-606-20143-8(2)); (gr. 3-6). lib. bdg. 15.25 (978-0-613-29678-6(8)) Tandem Library Bks.

Rhys Jones Publishing Ltd, prod. Life in Tudor Times. (YA). cd-rom 89.95 (978-1-56950-574-8(8)) Films Media Group.

GREAT BRITAIN—COLONIES

Burt, Barbara. Eve of Revolutuion: The Colonial Adventures of Benjamin Wilcox. 2003. (gr. 3-6). lib. bdg. 15.30 (978-0-613-67082-1(5)) Tandem Library Bks.

Davies, Gill. The British Colonies. Aronson, Marc, ed. 2005. (National Geographic Timelines Ser.). (Illus.). 64p. (J). lib. bdg. 27.90 (978-0-7922-7980-8(8)) National Geographic Society.

—The Thirteen Colonies 1584 - 1776. Aronson, Marc, ed. 2005. (National Geographic Timelines Ser.). (Illus.). 64p. (J). 17.95 (978-0-7922-7978-5(6)) National Geographic Society.

Harvey, Dan. The English Colonization of North America. 2002. (Exploration & Discovery Ser.). (Illus.). 64p. (J). (gr. 4-7). lib. bdg. (978-1-59084-051-1(8)) Mason Crest Pubs.

Nardo, Don. The Age of Colonialism. 2006. (World History Ser.). (Illus.). 112p. (J). (gr. 7-10). 32.45 (978-1-59018-833-0(0) , Lucent Bks.) Thomson Gale.

Nelson, Sheila. Britain's Canada, 1613-1770. 2005. (Illus.). 87p. (J). (gr. 3-7). lib. bdg. 21.95 (978-1-4222-0003-2(5)) Mason Crest Pubs.

—A Nation Is Born: World War I & Independence, 1910-1929. 2005. (Illus.). 87p. (J). (gr. 3-7). lib. bdg. 21.95 (978-1-4222-0006-3(X) , 1247972) Mason Crest Pubs.

Parker, Lewis K. English Colonies in the Americas. 2003. (Reading Power Ser.). (Illus.). 24p. (J). lib. bdg. 17.25 (978-0-8239-6475-8(2) , PowerKids Pr.) Rosen Publishing Group, Inc., The.

Riley, Michael, et al. Impact of Empire: Colonialism 1500-2000. (Illus.). 2005. 64p. tchr. ed., spiral bd. 62.50 ***(978-0-7195-8562-3(7));*** 2004. 128p. pap. 29.50 ***(978-0-7195-8561-6(9))*** Hodder Education GBR. (Hodder Murray). *Dist:* Trans-Atlantic Pubns., Inc.

GREAT BRITAIN—FICTION

Alcott, Louisa May. The Inheritance. 1998. (Classics Ser.). 208p. pap. 14.00 (978-0-14-043666-2(9) , Penguin Classics) Penguin Group (USA) Inc.

Ashe, Susan & Lawrie, Robin. Cuda of the Celts. 2005. (Yellow Go Bananas Ser.). (Illus.). 48p. (J). pap. (978-0-7787-2742-2(4)) Crabtree Publishing Co.

Austen, Jane. Pride & Prejudice. Miralles, Joseph, illus. 2005. (Great Illustrated Classics Ser.). 236p. (J). (gr. 3-8). 21.35 (978-1-59679-249-4(3) , ABDO & Daughters) ABDO Publishing Co.

Beckham, David. Charlie Barker & the Secret of the Deep Dark Woods. 2006. 570p. pap. ***(978-1-4120-9264-7(7))*** Trafford Publishing.

Beddor, Frank. The Looking Glass Wars. 2007. (Looking Glass Wars Trilogy: Bk. 1). 400p. (J). (gr. 5 up). 8.99 ***(978-0-14-240941-1(3)*** , Puffin) Penguin Group (USA) Inc.

Bird, Helen. Fighting Back. 2005. (Shades Ser.). 64p. (J). pap. 7.99 (978-0-237-52845-4(2) , Evans Brothers, Limited) Evans Publishing Group GBR. *Dist:* Independent Pubs. Group.

Blackwood, Gary L. The Shakespeare Stealer. 2000. (ps-7). 216p. (J). lib. bdg. 14.15 (978-0-613-28638-1(3)); (978-0-606-17870-9(8)) Tandem Library Bks.

Blackwood, Gary L. & Alcorn, Stephen. The Shakespeare Stealer. 1998. 208p. (J). (gr. 4-6). 16.99 (978-0-525-45863-0(8) , Dutton Juvenile) Penguin Group (USA) Inc.

Borden, Louise & Foreman, Michael. The Little Ships. 2003. (Illus.). 32p. (J). (gr. 4 up). pap. 6.99 (978-0-689-85396-8(3) , Aladdin) Simon & Schuster Children's Publishing.

Brighton, Catherine. The Fossil Girl. Brighton, Catherine, illus. 2007. (Illus.). 32p. (J). pap. 7.95 ***(978-1-84507-732-7(6))*** Lincoln, Frances Ltd. GBR. *Dist:* Perseus Distribution.

Brouwer, Sigmund. Barbarians from the Isle. 2002. (Winds of Light Ser.). 202p. (YA). pap. 5.99 (978-1-55305-033-9(9)) Cygnet Publishing Group, Inc./Coolreading.com CAN. *Dist:* Orca Bk. Pubs. USA.

—Wings of an Angel. 2004. (Winds of Light Ser.). 214p. (YA). pap. 5.99 (978-1-55305-032-2(0)) Cygnet Publishing Group, Inc./Coolreading.com CAN. *Dist:* Orca Bk. Pubs. USA.

—Wings of an Angel. 2002. (gr. 5-8). lib. bdg. 14.15 (978-0-613-84971-5(X)) Tandem Library Bks.

Browne, N. M. Warriors of Camlann. 2003. (Illus.). 275p. (J). 16.95 (978-1-58234-817-9(0) , Bloomsbury Children) Bloomsbury Publishing.

Buckland, R. A. The Empire Annual for Girls. 2006. 99.99 ***(978-1-4280-4296-4(2));*** pap. 92.99 ***(978-1-4280-4305-3(5))*** IndyPublish.com.

Cheshire, Simon. Kissing Vanessa. 2006. 144p. (YA). (gr. 7-11). mass mkt. 5.99 (978-0-440-23894-2(3) , Laurel Leaf) Random Hse. Children's Bks.

Cornwell, Nicki. Christophe's Story. Littlewood, Karin, illus. 2007. 96p. (gr. 3 up). pap. 7.95 (978-1-84507-521-7(8)) Lincoln, Frances Ltd. GBR. *Dist:* Perseus Distribution.

Cross, Gillian. Down with the Dirty Danes. (Illus.). 61p. (J). pap. 7.99 (978-0-00-675534-0(8) , HarperSport) HarperCollins Pubs. Ltd. GBR. *Dist:* Trafalgar Square Publishing.

Crossley-Holland, Kevin. The Seeing Stone, Book 1. 2002. (Arthur Trilogy: Bk. 1). 368p. (J). (gr. 4-7). mass mkt. 7.99 (978-0-439-26327-6(1) , Levine, Arthur A. Bks.) Scholastic, Inc.

Crowley, Bridget. Feast of Fools. 2005. (Illus.). (J). (gr. k-9). mass mkt. (978-0-340-85082-4(5) , Hodder Children's Books) Hodder Children's Division.

—Harriet's Ghost. 2006. (J). (gr. 4-6). pap. 9.99 (978-0-340-88156-9(9) , Hodder & Stoughton) Hodder General Publishing Division GBR. *Dist:* Trafalgar Square Publishing.

—Ship's Angel. 2005. (Illus.). (J). pap. (978-0-340-88155-2(0) , Hodder Children's Books) Hodder Children's Division.

Dalton, Annie & Dalton, Maria. Invisible Threads. 2006. 208p. (YA). (gr. 9). 15.95 (978-0-385-73286-4(4)); lib. bdg. 17.99 (978-0-385-90303-5(0)) Random Hse. Children's Bks. (Delacorte Bks. for Young Readers).

De Angeli, Marguerite. The Door in the Wall. 2002. (Illus.). (J). 13.94 (978-0-7587-0181-7(0)) Book Wholesalers, Inc.

—The Door in the Wall. unabr. ed. 2004. 121p. (J). (gr. 4-7). pap. 29.00 incl. audio (978-0-8072-8691-3(5) , YA237SP, Listening Library) Random Hse. Audio Publishing Group.

Dhami, Narinder. Bhangra Babes. 2006. 192p. (J). (gr. 3-7). 14.95 (978-0-385-73318-2(6)); lib. bdg. 16.99 (978-0-385-90337-0(5)) Random Hse. Children's Bks. (Delacorte Bks. for Young Readers).

Dickens, Charles. Oliver Twist. Andreasen, Dan, illus. 2006. (Classic Starts Ser.). 160p. 4.95 (978-1-4027-2665-1(1)) Sterling Publishing Co., Inc.

Elliott, Dorothy. Little Angel Third Class - below Stairs. 2007. 92p. per. ***(978-1-84685-562-7(4)*** , Exposure Publishing) Meadow Bks.

Ewing, Juliana Horatia. We & the World A Book for Boys Part I. 2006. 41.99 ***(978-1-4280-2083-2(7));*** pap. 34.99 ***(978-1-4280-2085-6(3))*** IndyPublish.com.

Fisher, Linda C. A Will of Her Own. 2006. (YA). pap. (978-0-88092-641-6(4)); lib. bdg. (978-0-88092-640-9(6)) Royal Fireworks Publishing Co.

Forde, Catherine. Tug of War: Two Mums, One Girl, One Choice. 2007. 304p. (J). pap. 9.95 ***(978-1-4052-2005-7(8))*** Egmont Bks., Ltd. GBR. *Dist:* Independent Pubs. Group.

Gibbons, Alan. Caught in the Crossfire. 2006. 304p. (J). pap. 11.99 ***(978-1-84255-096-0(9))*** Orion Publishing Group, Ltd. GBR. *Dist:* Independent Pubs. Group.

Groot, Bob de & Turk. The Laughing Thief. 2007. (Illus.). 48p. pap. 9.99 ***(978-1-905460-07-6(4))*** CineBook GBR. *Dist:* Biblio Distribution.

—My Dear Wilkinson. 2007. (Illus.). 48p. pap. 9.99 ***(978-1-905460-06-9(6))*** CineBook GBR. *Dist:* Biblio Distribution.

Hayes, Malcolm. The Dreamcatchers. 2006. 282p. pap. ***(978-1-4120-8320-1(6))*** Trafford Publishing.

Hayes, Rosemary. Bright Horizon. 2004. (J). pap. 11.95 (978-0-340-85471-6(5) , Hodder & Stoughton) Hodder General Publishing Division GBR. *Dist:* Trafalgar Square Publishing.

Henty, G. A. The Dragon & the Raven: Or the Days of King Alfred. 2000. (Illus.). 238p. (J). pap. 14.99 (978-1-887159-31-9(2)) Preston-Speed Pubns.

Horne, Constance. Accidental Orphan. 1998. (gr. 5-8). lib. bdg. 14.10 (978-0-613-77364-5(0)) Tandem Library Bks.

Ibbotson, Eva. Great Ghost Rescue. 2003. (gr. 3-6). lib. bdg. 14.15 (978-0-613-67277-1(1)) Tandem Library Bks.

King, Danny. School for Scumbags. 2008. 288p. pap. 14.95 ***(978-1-85242-972-0(0))*** Serpent's Tail Ltd. GBR. *Dist:* Consortium Bk. Sales & Distribution.

Kirwan, Anna & Yep, Laurence. Victoria, May Blossom of Britannia, England 1829. 2001. (Royal Diaries Ser.). (Illus.). 224p. (J). (gr. 4-9). pap. 10.95 (978-0-439-21598-5(6)) Scholastic, Inc.

MacDonald, Margaret Read. Teeny Weeny Bop. Greenseid, Diane, illus. 2006. 32p. (J). 16.95 (978-0-8075-7992-3(0)) Whitman, Albert & Co.

Malone, Patricia. The Legend of Lady Ilena. 2003. (gr. 7-12). lib. bdg. 13.55 (978-0-613-72280-3(9)) Tandem Library Bks.

Maltby Jr., Richard. Miss Potter. 2006. 196p. (J). pap. 7.99 (978-0-7232-5899-5(6) , Warne) Penguin Group (USA) Inc.

Mathur-Kamat, Ambika. Miss Panda in England & Scotland. Crawford, K. Michael, illus. 2001. (Miss Panda Ser.). 40p. (J). (ps-5). pap. 11.99 (978-1-883573-01-0(7) , Little Blue Works) Windstorm Creative.

McNab, Andy & Rigby, Robert. Meltdown. 2008. 276p. (YA). (gr. 7). 16.99 ***(978-0-399-24686-9(X)*** , Putnam Juvenile) Penguin Group (USA) Inc.

McNab, Andy & Rigby, Robert. Payback. (YA). 2007. 288p. (gr. 7). 7.99 ***(978-0-14-240914-5(6)*** , Puffin); 2006. 272p. (ps-k). 16.99 (978-0-399-24465-0(4) , Putnam Juvenile) Penguin Group (USA) Inc.

Mills, Frank. The Boggarts of Britain. 2000. (Illus.). 1p. (J). 13.99 (978-1-84243-005-7(X)) No Exit Pr. GBR. *Dist:* Independent Pubs. Group.

Morpurgo, Michael. The Wreck of the Zanzibar. l.t. ed. 2003. (J). 16.95 (978-0-7540-7846-3(9) , Galaxy Children's Large Print) BBC Audiobooks America.

Nesbit, E. The Phoenix & the Carpet. l.t. ed. 2005. 352p. pap. (978-1-84637-204-9(6)) Echo Library.

Nesbit, E. Wouldbegoods. 2006. pap. ***(978-1-4068-3508-3(0))*** Echo Library.

Norfolk, Booby. The Great Smelly, Slobbery, Small-Tooth Dog: A Folktale from Great Britain. Paschkis, Julie, illus. 2008. 32p. ***(978-0-87483-831-2(2))*** August Hse. Pubs., Inc.

Paschkis, Julie, illus. The Great Smelly, Slobbery, Small-Tooth Dog: A Folktale from Great Britain. 2007. 32p. (ps-3). 16.95 ***(978-0-87483-808-4(8))*** August Hse. Pubs., Inc.

Pockets Learning Staff. Victorian Advent. 1998. (Illus.). (J). 45.00 (978-1-888074-68-0(X)) Pockets of Learning.

—Victorian Stocking. 1998. (Illus.). (J). 20.00 (978-1-888074-21-5(3)) Pockets of Learning.

Price, Robin. Die Clawdius, Vol. 3. 2007. (Spartapuss Tales Ser.). 192p. (J). pap. 14.95 ***(978-0-9546576-8-0(3))*** Mogzilla GBR. *Dist:* Independent Pubs. Group.

Pyle, Howard. Men of Iron. l.t. ed. 2004. 329p. (J). 29.95 (978-0-7862-6775-0(5) , Large Print Pr.) Thorndike Pr.

Rai, Bali. Dominoes & Other Stories. 2005. 192p. (J). pap. 9.99 (978-0-340-87732-6(4) , Hodder & Stoughton) Hodder General Publishing Division GBR. *Dist:* Trafalgar Square Publishing.

Rosen, Michael. You're Thinking about Tomatoes. 2005. (Illus.). 96p. (J). pap. 5.95 (978-1-903015-44-5(8)) Barn Owl Bks, London GBR. *Dist:* Independent Pubs. Group.

Ross, Stewart. Dear Mum, I Miss You! 2007. (Flashbacks Ser.). (Illus.). 64p. (J). (gr. 4-7). pap. 8.95 ***(978-0-237-53149-2(6)*** , Evans Brothers, Limited) Evans Publishing Group GBR. *Dist:* Independent Pubs. Group.

Scott, Walter, Sr. Ivanhoe. 2nd ed. 2003. (Historias de Siempre Ser.). (SPA., Illus.). 92p. (J). (gr. 5-8). pap. 12.95 (978-84-204-5721-5(3)) Santillana USA Publishing Co., Inc.

Springer, Nancy. Lionclaw. 2002. (Tales of Rowan Hood Ser.: No. 2). 160p. (YA). (gr. 4-7). 16.99 (978-0-399-23716-4(X) , Philomel) Penguin Group (USA) Inc.

—Rowan Hood Returns: The Final Chapter. 2005. (Tales of Rowan Hood Ser.: No. 5). 170p. (YA). (gr. 5). 16.99 (978-0-399-24206-9(6) , Philomel) Penguin Group (USA) Inc.

Stevenson, Robert Louis. The Black Arrow. 1998. (Tor Classics Ser.). 288p. (gr. 7 up). 3.99 (978-0-8125-6562-1(2) , Tor Classics) Doherty, Tom Assocs., LLC.

—The Black Arrow. 2001. (Dover Juvenile Classics Ser.). 240p. (J). (gr. 4-7). pap. 3.00 (978-0-486-41820-9(0)) Dover Pubns., Inc.

Thomas, Jane Resh. The Counterfeit Princess. 2005. 208p. (J). (gr. 5-9). 15.00 (978-0-395-93870-6(8) , Clarion Bks.) Houghton Mifflin Co. Trade & Reference Div.

Tingle, Rebecca. The Edge on the Sword. (Sailing Mystery Ser.). 2003. 288p. (YA). (gr. 8-12). pap. 6.99 (978-0-14-250058-3(5) , Puffin); 2001. (Illus.). 1p. (J). (gr. 7 up). 18.99 (978-0-399-23580-1(9) , Putnam Juvenile) Penguin Group (USA) Inc.

Tomlinson, Theresa. Child of the May. 1998. (Illus.). 128p. (YA). (gr. 5-9). pap. 15.95 (978-0-531-30118-0(4) , Orchard Bks.) Scholastic, Inc.

Twain, Mark. A Connecticut Yankee in King Arthur's Court. 1999. reprint ed. pap. 28.00 (978-1-4047-1121-1(X)) Classic Textbooks.

Umansky, Kaye. Solomon Snow & the Stolen Jewel. Nash, Scott, illus. 2007. 256p. (J). (gr. 2-7). 12.99 (978-0-7636-2793-5(3)) Candlewick Pr.

Uncle Markie. Pigletté & Bobo in the United Kingdom. 2003. (YA). ring bd. 9.95 (978-1-933129-14-3(X)) Studio 403.

Wilson, John. And in the Morning. 2004. 200p. (YA). (gr. 13 up). (978-1-55337-348-3(0)); (978-1-55337-400-8(2)) Kids Can Pr., Ltd.

Yonge, Charlotte. The Little Duke. 2006. pap. ***(978-1-4250-2682-0(6))*** Assistedreadingbooks.com Inc.

GREAT BRITAIN—HISTORY

Abbott, Jacob. History of King Richard the First of England. 2003. 336p. 99.00 (978-0-7950-3593-7(4)) New Library Press.Net.

—History of King Richard the Second of England. 2003. 347p. 99.00 (978-0-7950-3594-4(2)) New Library Press.Net.

—History of William the Conqueror. 2003. 291p. 89.00 (978-0-7950-4508-0(5)) New Library Press.Net.

Abbott, Jacob. King Alfred of England, Makers of Histor. 2006. pap. ***(978-1-4065-0359-3(2))*** Dodo Pr.

Adelson, Bruce. British General William Howe. 2001. (Revolutionary War Leaders Ser.). (Illus.). 80p. (J). 27.50 (978-0-7910-6388-0(7) , Chelsea Hse.) Facts On File, Inc.

Anderson, Dale. Soldiers & Surgeons in the American Revolution. 2005. (World Almanac Library of the American Revolution). (J). pap. (978-0-8368-5938-6(3)); lib. bdg. 30.00 (978-0-8368-5929-4(4)) Stevens, Gareth Inc. (World Almanac Library).

Anon. History Detective Investigates. (Illus.). 32p. pap. (978-0-7502-3750-5(3) , Hodder Wayland) Hodder Children's Division.

—History Detective Investigates: Victorian School. (Illus.). 32p. pap. (978-0-7502-3744-4(9) , Hodder Wayland) Hodder Children's Division.

Ashby, Ruth. Elizabethan England. 1998. (Cultures of the Past Ser.). (Illus.). 80p. (J). (gr. 5 up). lib. bdg. 29.93 (978-0-7614-0269-5(1) , Benchmark Bks.) Cavendish, Marshall Corp.

—Victorian England. 2002. (Cultures of the Past Ser.). (Illus.). 80p. (YA). (gr. 5-8). 29.93 (978-0-7614-1493-3(2) , Benchmark Bks.) Cavendish, Marshall Corp.

Ashworth, Leon. Guy Fawkes. (Illus.). 32p. (978-0-7451-5288-2(0) , Cherrytree Books) Evans Publishing Group.

—Guy Fawkes. (British History Makers Ser.). (Illus.). 32p. 2001. 22.99 (978-1-84234-080-6(8)); 1999. pap. 11.99 (978-0-7540-9011-3(6)) Evans Publishing Group GBR. (Cherrytree Books). *Dist:* Independent Pubs. Group.

—King Henry VIII. 2004. (British History Makers Ser.). (Illus.). 32p. (YA). pap. 9.99 (978-1-84234-283-1(5) , Cherrytree Books) Evans Publishing Group GBR. *Dist:* Independent Pubs. Group.

—Queen Victoria. 1999. (British History Makers Ser.). (Illus.). 32p. pap. 11.99 (978-0-7540-9014-4(0) , Cherrytree Books) Evans Publishing Group GBR. *Dist:* Independent Pubs. Group.

Baker, Gayle. Cambria: A HarborTown History. 2003. (Illus.). 96p. per. 8.95 (978-0-9710984-2-8(5)) HarborTown Histories.

Beller, Susan Provost. Yankee Doodle & the Redcoats: Soldiering in the Revolutionary War. Day, Larry, illus. 2003. (Single Titles Ser.). 96p. (gr. 5 up). lib. bdg. 26.90 (978-0-7613-2612-0(X) , Twenty-First Century Bks.) Lerner Publishing Group.

Bowden, Rob. United Kingdom. 2006. (Destination Detectives Ser.). (Illus.). 48p. (J). pap. (978-1-4109-2343-1(6)); lib. bdg. (978-1-4109-2332-5(0)) Steck-Vaughn.

Brassey, Richard. Queen Elizabeth 1. Brassey, Richard, illus. 2005. (Brilliant Brits Ser.). (Illus.). 24p. (J). pap. 8.99 (978-1-84255-233-9(3)) Orion Children's Bks. GBR. *Dist:* Independent Pubs. Group.

Brimson, Samuel. United Kingdom-Zimbabwe, 8 vols. 2003. (Nations of the World Ser.: Vol. 8). (Illus.). 64p. (J). (gr. 5 up). lib. bdg. 30.00 (978-0-8368-5492-3(6) , World Almanac Library) Stevens, Gareth Inc.

Brocklehurst, Ruth. Roman Britain - Internet Linked. 2006. 48p. (J). pap. 8.99 (978-0-7945-1232-3(1) , Usborne) EDC Publishing.

Browning, Oscar. True Stories from English History from T 2006. pap. 33.95 ***(978-1-4254-9960-0(0))*** Kessinger Publishing, LLC.

Buchanan, Jane. Mary Tudor: Courageous Queen or Bloody Mary? 2007. (Wicked Historytrade; Ser.). 128p. (J). spiral bd. 30.00 ***(978-0-531-12595-3(5)*** , Children's Pr.) Scholastic Library Publishing.

Can't You Make Them Behave, King George? 2002. (978-1-56137-402-1(4)) Novel Units, Inc.

Can't You Make Them Behave, King George? 2004. 24.95 incl. audio (978-1-56008-171-5(6)); 29.95 incl. cd-rom (978-1-55592-378-5(X)); (J). pap. 14.95 incl. audio (978-1-56008-172-2(4)); (J). pap. 18.95 incl. audio compact disk (978-1-55592-377-8(1)); (J). pap. 18.95 incl. audio compact disk (978-1-55592-380-8(1)); (J). pap. 38.75 incl. audio compact disk (978-1-55592-379-2(8)); (J). pap. 38.75 incl. audio compact disk (978-1-55592-381-5(X)); (J). pap. 32.75 incl. audio (978-1-55592-350-1(X)) Weston Woods Studios, Inc.

Capt, E. Raymond. Isle of Iona. 2003. 160p. per. 11.95 (978-0-934666-58-9(X)) Artisan Pubs.

Cawood, Ian. Britain in the Twentieth Century. 2003. (Spotlight History Ser.). (Illus.). 496p. 34.95 (978-0-415-25457-1(4)); 115.00 (978-0-415-25456-4(6)) Routledge.

Chibi, Andrew A. The English Reformation: The Effect on a Nation. 2003. (Studymates Ser.). (Illus.). 98p. pap. (978-1-84285-024-4(5)) Studymates Ltd.

Chrisp, Peter. Victorian Crime. (Illus.). 32p. pap. (978-0-7502-3740-6(6) , Hodder Wayland) Hodder Children's Division.

Clare, John D. Medieval Britain, 1066-1500. 2003. (Illus.). 96p. pap. 29.50 ***(978-0-340-86903-1(8)*** , Hodder Murray) Hodder Education GBR. *Dist:* Trans-Atlantic Pubns., Inc.

Crompton, Samuel Willard. Queen Elizabeth: And England's Golden Age. 2005. (Makers of the Middle Ages & Renaissance Ser.). (Illus.). 148p. (J). (gr. 4-8). lib. bdg. 30.00 (978-0-7910-8632-2(1) , Chelsea Hse.) Facts On File, Inc.

—Thomas More: And His Struggles of Conscience. 2005. (Makers of the Middle Ages & Renaissance Ser.). (Illus.). 140p. (J). (gr. 4-8). lib. bdg. 30.00 (978-0-7910-8636-0(4) , Chelsea Hse.) Facts On File, Inc.

Davis, Kenneth C. Don't Know Much about the Kings & Queens of England. Date not set. 48p. (J). (gr. 1-4). pap. 5.99 (978-0-06-446229-7(3)) HarperCollins Pubs.

—Don't Know Much about the Kings & Queens of England. Schindler, S. D., illus. 2002. (Don't Know Much About Ser.: No. 3). 48p. (J). (gr. 1-4). 15.89 (978-0-06-028612-5(1)) HarperCollins Pubs.

Dawson, Ian. Lost in Time: 1000-2000, Has Life Really Been Getting Better?: Pupil's Book. 2001. (Illus.). 120p. pap. 29.50 (***978-0-7195-8557-9(0)** , Hodder Murray) Hodder Education GBR. *Dist:* Trans-Atlantic Pubns., Inc.

—Lost in Time: 1000-2000, Has Life Really Been Getting Better?: Teachers Book. 2001. (Illus.). 80p. pap. 92.50 (***978-0-7195-8558-6(9)** , Hodder Murray) Hodder Education GBR. *Dist:* Trans-Atlantic Pubns., Inc.

Dickens, Charles. A Child's History of England. fac. ed. 2000. 279p. pap. 18.95 (978-1-4021-8509-0(X)); Vol. 2. 2002. 349p. pap. 15.95 (978-1-4021-6103-2(4)) Adamant Media. (Elibron Classics).

—A Child's History of England. Exams Unlimited, Inc. Staff, ed. 2001. 482p. (YA). reprint ed. cd-rom 7.25 (978-1-885343-20-8(5)) Exams Unlimited, Inc.

Elgin, Kathy. Daily Life. 2004. (Changing Times Ser.). (Illus.). 32p. (J). 26.60 (978-0-7565-0886-9(X)) Compass Point Bks.

Evers, Charlotte & Welbourne, Dave. Britain 1783-1851: From Disaster to Triumph? 2003. (Illus.). 272p. pap. 54.00 (***978-0-7195-7482-5(X)** , Hodder Murray) Hodder Education GBR. *Dist:* Trans-Atlantic Pubns., Inc.

Farman, John. The Short & Bloody History of Highwaymen. 2005. (Short & Bloody Histories Ser.). (Illus.). 96p. (gr. 6-12). lib. bdg. 19.93 (978-0-8225-0839-7(7)) Lerner Publishing Group.

—Short & Bloody History of Highwaymen. 2002. (gr. 5-8). lib. bdg. 14.10 (978-0-613-52496-4(9)) Tandem Library Bks.

Ferguson, Amanda. SAS: British Special Air Service. 2003. (Inside Special Operations Ser.). (Illus.). 64p. (YA). (gr. 5-8). lib. bdg. 26.50 (978-0-8239-3810-0(7) , Rosen Central) Rosen Publishing Group, Inc., The.

Ford, Nick. Henry VIII: The King, His Six Wives & His Court. 2004. (Leaders of the Middle Ages Ser.). (Illus.). 112p. (YA). lib. bdg. 31.95 (978-1-4042-0163-7(1)) Rosen Publishing Group, Inc., The.

Foreman, Stephen. Hylands: The Story on an Essex Country House & Its Owner. Henry, Ian, ed. 2nd unabr. ed. 1999. (Illus.). 128p. (gr. 4-12). pap. 15.00 (978-0-86025-492-8(5)) Henry, Ian Pubns. GBR. *Dist:* Empire Publishing Service.

Fowke, Bob. Victorians. (Illus.). 128p. (J). pap. 9.99 (978-0-340-85184-5(8) , Hodder & Stoughton) Hodder General Publishing Division GBR. *Dist:* Independent Pubs. Group.

Gail, Margaret. Moggie Grows up. 2006. (ENG.). 74p. pap. (***978-0-7552-0227-0(9)**) Authors OnLine, Ltd.

Harmon, Daniel E. Fighting Units of the American Revolution. 1998. (Costume, Tradition & Culture). (Illus.). 64p. (J). 19.75 (978-0-7910-5162-7(5) , Chelsea Hse.) Facts On File, Inc.

Harris, Nathaniel. 19th Century Reform. (Illus.). 32p. (YA). 22.99 (978-0-7502-4185-4(3) , Hodder & Stoughton) Hodder General Publishing Division GBR. *Dist:* Trafalgar Square Publishing.

Hebditch, Felicity. Roman Britain. 2003. (Illus.). 32p. (YA). pap. 12.99 (978-0-237-52636-8(0) , Evans Brothers, Limited) Evans Publishing Group GBR. *Dist:* Independent Pubs. Group.

Heinrichs, Ann. Luxembourg. 2005. (Enchantment of the World, Second Ser.). (Illus.). 144p. (YA). (gr. 5-9). 36.00 (978-0-516-23681-0(4) , Children's Pr.) Scholastic Library Publishing.

Herold, Vickey. Discover the Renaissance in England. 2006. pap. 39.00 (***978-1-4108-6466-6(9)**) Benchmark Education Co.

—The Renaissance in England. 2006. pap. 39.00 (***978-1-4108-6463-5(4)**) Benchmark Education Co.

Hinds, Kathryn. The Church. 2007. (Life in Elizabethan England Ser.). 80p. (J). lib. bdg. 32.79 (***978-0-7614-2545-8(4)** , Benchmark Bks.) Cavendish, Marshall Corp.

—The City. 2007. (Life in Elizabethan England Ser.). 80p. (J). lib. bdg. 32.79 (***978-0-7614-2544-1(6)** , Benchmark Bks.) Cavendish, Marshall Corp.

—The Countryside. 2007. (Life in Elizabethan England Ser.). 80p. (J). lib. bdg. 32.79 (***978-0-7614-2543-4(8)** , Benchmark Bks.) Cavendish, Marshall Corp.

—Elizabeth & Her Court. 2007. (Life in Elizabethan England Ser.). 80p. (J). lib. bdg. 32.79 (***978-0-7614-2542-7(X)** , Benchmark Bks.) Cavendish, Marshall Corp.

HOCPP 1101 the Norman Conquest. 2006. spiral bd. 23.50 (***978-1-60308-101-6(1)**) In the Hands of a Child.

Hynson, Colin. The Tower of London. 2005. (Places in History Ser.). (Illus.). 48p. (J). pap. (978-0-8368-5820-4(4)); lib. bdg. 30.00 (978-0-8368-5813-6(1)) Stevens, Gareth Inc. (World Almanac Library).

Immell, Myra H. Life in Victorian England. 2005. (Way People Live Ser.). (Illus.). 96-128p. (J). (gr. 7-10). 29.95 (978-1-56006-391-9(2) , 1251192, Lucent Bks.) Thomson Gale.

Imperato, Anthony. Henry VII. 1999. (Pathfinder History Ser.). (Illus.). 64p. (YA). (gr. 11 up). pap. 15.95 (978-0-7487-4308-7(1)) Nelson Thornes Ltd. GBR. *Dist:* Trans-Atlantic Pubns., Inc.

Johnson, Emma. Medieval Town & Country Life. (Illus.). 32p. 18.95 (978-1-932889-28-4(0)) Sea-To-Sea Pubns.

Johnson, Robert. British History 1870-1918: The Emergence of a Nation. 2003. (Studymates Ser.). (Illus.). 154p. (C). pap. 27.50 (978-1-84285-026-8(1) , Judith Handbooks) Studymates Ltd. GBR. *Dist:* Trans-Atlantic Pubns., Inc.

Lace, William W. Elizabeth I & Her Court. 2002. (Lucent Library of Historical Eras. Elizabethan England Library). (Illus.). 112p. (J). 28.70 (978-1-59018-098-3(4) , Lucent Bks.) Thomson Gale.

—Elizabethan England. 2005. (World History Ser.). (Illus.). 112p. (YA). (gr. 7-10). lib. bdg. 32.45 (978-1-59018-655-8(9) , Lucent Bks.) Thomson Gale.

Lambers, William. From War to Peace: The Story of Great Britain & the U. S. Clermont, Lisa, illus. 1999. 70p. (YA). (gr. 7-12). pap. 7.50 (978-0-9656520-2-5(5)) Lambers, Bill.

Lee, Stephen J. Gladstone & Disraeli. 2005. (Questions & Analysis in History Ser.). (Illus.). 208p. 20.95 (978-0-415-32357-4(6)) Routledge.

Lynch, Michael. An Introduction to Modern British History, 1900-1999. 2001. (Access to History Ser.). (Illus.). 272p. pap. 44.50 (978-0-340-77525-7(4)) Hodder Education GBR. *Dist:* Trans-Atlantic Pubns., Inc.

Macdonald, Fiona. You wouldn't/be victorian Servant. 2006. (Illus.). 32p. (J). (gr. 2-5). 28.50 (***978-0-531-14972-0(2)**) Scholastic Library Publishing.

Malam, John. The Victorians. (Illus.). 48p. (J). pap. (978-0-7502-2695-0(1) , Hodder Wayland) Hodder Children's Division.

Malam, John. You Wouldn't Want to Be a Victorian Mill Worker! A Grueling Job You'd Rather Not Have. Antram, David, illus. 2007. (You Wouldn't Want to... : History of the World Ser.). 32p. (J). 29.00 (***978-0-531-18747-0(0)**); (gr. 2-5). pap. 9.95 (***978-0-531-13928-8(X)**) Scholastic Library Publishing. (Watts, Franklin).

Marilyn Tower Oliver. Henry VIII. 2004. (Importance of Ser.). (Illus.). 112p. (J). 32.45 (978-1-59018-424-0(6)) Thomson Gale.

Marshall, H. E. Our Island Story. 2005. (Illus.). 512p. 44.95 (978-1-902984-74-2(9)) Galore Park Publishing Ltd. GBR. *Dist:* Coronet Bks.

Marshall, H. E. Our Island Story. 2007. (Phoenix Press Ser.). (Illus.). 496p. per. 14.95 (***978-0-7538-2300-2(4)** , Phoenix) Orion Publishing Group, Ltd. GBR. *Dist:* Sterling Publishing Co., Inc.

Marshall, H.E. Our Island Story (Yesterday's Classics) Forrest, A. S., illus. l.t. ed. 2006. 676p. (J). per. 19.95 (978-1-59915-009-3(3)) Yesterday's Classics.

McCaughrean, Geraldine. Ghosts, Rogues & Highwaymen: 20 Stories from British History. Brassey, Richard, illus. 2003. 128p. (J). pap. 9.99 (978-1-85881-894-8(X)) Orion Bks. Ltd. GBR. *Dist:* Trafalgar Square Publishing.

—Movers, Shakers & Record Breakers. Brassey, Richard, illus. 112p. pap. 9.99 (978-1-85881-895-5(8)) Orion Bks. Ltd. GBR. *Dist:* Trafalgar Square Publishing.

—Rebels & Royals: 20 Stories from British History. Brassey, Richard, illus. 2003. (Britannia Ser.). 128p. (J). pap. 9.99 (978-1-85881-852-8(4)) Orion Bks. Ltd. GBR. *Dist:* Trafalgar Square Publishing.

McCormack, Shaun. Britain's MI6: Military Intelligence 6. 2005. (Inside the World's Most Famous Intelligence Agencies Ser.). (Illus.). 64p. (YA). (gr. 7-12). lib. bdg. 26.50 (978-0-8239-3812-4(3)) Rosen Publishing Group, Inc., The.

McNeil, Niki, et al. HOCPP 1092 Romans in Britain. 2006. spiral bd. 19.50 (***978-1-60308-092-7(9)**) In the Hands of a Child.

Nardo, Don. The Age of Colonialism. 2006. (World History Ser.). (Illus.). 112p. (J). (gr. 7-10). 32.45 (978-1-59018-833-0(0) , Lucent Bks.) Thomson Gale.

National Geographic Society Staff & Bean, Rachel. United Kingdom. 2007. (Countries of the World Ser.). (Illus.). 64p. (YA). (gr. 5 up). lib. bdg. 27.90 (***978-1-4263-0126-1(X)** , National Geographic Children's Bks.) National Geographic Society.

Nelson, Sheila. A Nation Is Born: World War I & Independence, 1910-1929. 2005. (Illus.). 87p. (J). (gr. 3-7). lib. bdg. 21.95 (978-1-4222-0006-3(X) , 1247972) Mason Crest Pubs.

Pollard, Michael. Great Rivers of Britain: The Clyde, Mersey, Severn, Tees, Thames, Trent. (Illus.). 45p. (978-0-237-51829-5(5) , Evans Brothers, Limited) Evans Publishing Group.

—Rivers of Britain & Ireland: The Avon, Yorkshire Ouse, Tyne, Wye, Forth, Liffey, Lagan. (Illus.). 46p. (J). (978-0-237-51805-9(8) , Evans Brothers, Limited) Evans Publishing Group.

Pryor, Francis. Britain Ad: A Quest for Authur, England & the Anglo-Saxon. movie tie-in ed. 2006. (Illus.). 268p. 35.00 (***978-0-00-718186-5(8)**) HarperCollins Pubs. Ltd. GBR. *Dist:* Independent Pubs. Group.

Reynoldson, Fiona. The Home Front. (Illus.). 48p. (J). pap. (978-0-7502-2696-7(X) , Hodder Wayland) Hodder Children's Division.

Rhys Jones Publishing Ltd, prod. Life in Tudor Times. (YA). cd-rom 89.95 (978-1-56950-574-8(8)) Films Media Group.

Riley, Gail Blasser. Tower of London: England's Ghostly Castle. 2006. (Illus.). 32p. (J). lib. bdg. 25.27 (978-1-59716-249-4(3)) Bearport Publishing Co., Inc.

Robson, Pam. The Great Fire of London 1666. Marwood, Dez, illus. 2nd ed. 2003. 48p. pap. (978-0-7500-1935-4(2) , Hodder Wayland) Hodder Children's Division.

Ross, Stewart. God Bless Queen Victoria. Shields, Susan, illus. 2000. 62p. (J). (978-0-237-52030-4(3) , Evans Brothers, Limited) Evans Publishing Group.

—God Bless Queen Victoria. Shields, Susan, illus. 2000. (Coming Alive Ser.). 62p. (YA). pap. 8.99 (978-0-237-52031-1(1) , Evans Brothers, Limited) Evans Publishing Group GBR. *Dist:* Independent Pubs. Group.

—The Home Front in World War II. (Illus.). 32p. 22.99 (978-0-7502-4184-7(5) , Hodder & Stoughton) Hodder General Publishing Division GBR. *Dist:* Trafalgar Square Publishing.

—Princess Elizabeth, Are You a Traitor? Andrews, Gary, illus. 2000. 62p. (J). (978-0-237-52028-1(1) , Evans Brothers, Limited) Evans Publishing Group.

—Princess Elizabeth, Are You a Traitor? Andrews, Gary, illus. 2000. (Coming Alive Ser.). 62p. (J). pap. 8.99 (978-0-237-52029-8(X) , Evans Brothers, Limited) Evans Publishing Group GBR. *Dist:* Independent Pubs. Group.

—Sink the Armada! Sir Francis Drake & the Spanish Armada of 1588. Shields, Susan, illus. 62p. (J). pap. (978-0-237-51959-9(3) , Evans Brothers, Limited) Evans Publishing Group.

—Will's Dream. Shields, Susan, illus. 28p. pap. 9.99 (978-0-7502-2965-4(9) , Hodder & Stoughton) Hodder General Publishing Division GBR. *Dist:* Trafalgar Square Publishing.

Rowe, David J. & Carman, W. Y. Head Dress of the British Lancers, 1816-Present. 2002. (Illus.). 272p. (gr. 10-13). 75.00 (978-0-7643-1446-9(7)) Schiffer Publishing, Ltd.

Sapet, Kerrily. Eleanor of Aquitaine: Medieval Queen. 2006. (European Queens Ser.). (Illus.). 176p. (J). (gr. 6-12). 26.95 (978-1-931798-90-7(7)) Reynolds, Morgan Inc.

Scheuerman, Richard D. & Ellis, Arthur K., eds. Eleanor of Aquitaine & the Crusade of the Kings: A Medieval Journey of Discovery Travelogue. LeGette, James, illus. unabr. ed. 2000. 494p. (YA). (gr. 5-8). ring bd. 69.95 (978-1-885360-19-9(3)) Demco, Inc.

Senior, Kathryn & Salariya, David. You Wouldn't Want to Be Sick in the 16th Century! Diseases You'd Rather Not Catch. Antram, David, illus. 2002. (You Wouldn't Want to Ser.). 32p. (J). (gr. 2-5). 28.50 (978-0-531-14605-7(7) , Watts, Franklin) Scholastic Library Publishing.

Shephard, Colin & Reid, Andy. Re-Discovering Britain 1750-1900. 2001. (Illus.). 120p. pap., stu. ed. 32.50 (***978-0-7195-8546-3(5)** , Hodder Murray) Hodder Education GBR. *Dist:* Trans-Atlantic Pubns., Inc.

Shone, Rob & Ganeri, Anita. Elizabeth I: The Life of England's Renaissance Queen. 2005. (Graphic Nonfiction Ser.). (Illus.). 48p. lib. bdg. 26.50 (978-1-4042-0246-7(3)) Rosen Publishing Group, Inc., The.

Shuter, Jane. Shakespeare's Birthplace. 2003. (Visiting the Past Ser.). (Illus.). 32p. (J). (gr. 5-7). lib. bdg. 25.64 (978-1-58810-708-4(6)) Heinemann Library.

Smith. Age of Aristocracy Volume 3, Eighth Edition, with Britian Yesterday & Today, Volume 4, Eighth Edition. 8th ed. 2000. (YA). pap., pap. 89.16 (978-0-618-13527-1(8) , 382627) Houghton Mifflin College Div.

—Arnstein England. 8th ed. 2002. (YA). Vols. 2-4. pap., pap., pap. 133.56 (978-0-618-30102-7(X) , 385434); Vols. 2&3. pap., pap. 89.16 (978-0-618-34403-1(9) , 385949) Houghton Mifflin College Div.

Stephens, Chris S. A Wartime Scrapbook: The Teachers' Pack. 2004. (Illus.). 32p. pap. 42.95 (978-1-84323-329-9(0)) Beekman Bks., Inc.

Stimpson, Bea. The World of Empire, Industry & Trade. 1999. (Quest History Ser.: No. 3). (Illus.). 128p. (YA). (gr. 6-9). pap., stu. ed. 17.95 (978-0-7487-3660-7(3)) Nelson Thornes Ltd. GBR. *Dist:* Trans-Atlantic Pubns., Inc.

Streissguth, Thomas. Richard the Lionheart: Crusader King of England. 2007. (Rulers of the Middle Ages Ser.). (Illus.). 160p. (YA). (gr. 7-9). lib. bdg. 34.60 (978-0-7660-2714-5(7)) Enslow Pubs., Inc.

Strum, Richard M. Causes of the American Revolution. 2005. (Road to War Ser.). (Illus.). 64p. (J). pap. 12.95 (978-1-59556-005-6(X)); (gr. 4 up). lib. bdg. 22.95 (978-1-59556-001-8(7)) OTTN Publishing.

Swisher, Clarice. Victorian England. 2000. (Turning Points in World History Ser.). (Illus.). (YA). (gr. 9-12). 288p. pap. 24.95 (978-0-7377-0220-0(6)); 220p. lib. bdg. 37.45 (978-0-7377-0221-7(4)) Thomson Gale. (Greenhaven Pr., Inc.).

Timeless Voices, Timeless Themes: The British Tradition. (YA). (gr. 12). 2000. stu. ed. 53.97 (978-0-13-050280-3(4)); 1999. stu. ed. 55.97 (978-0-13-434058-6(2)) Prentice Hall PTR.

Timeless Voices, Timeless Themes: The British Tradition, Standardized Test Preparation Blackline Masters. 2000. (YA). (gr. 11). 19.97 (978-0-13-437473-4(8)) Prentice Hall PTR.

Turnbull, S. Elizabeth I. (Beginners Social Studies). 32p. (J). (gr. 1 up). lib. bdg. 12.95 (978-1-58086-741-2(3) , Usborne) EDC Publishing.

Welby, Rebecca. Hello Britain! 2006. (Illus.), 60p. spiral bd. 16.95 (978-0-9549476-4-4(9)) Beautiful Bks. GBR. *Dist:* International Publishers Marketing.

West, David & Gaff, Jackie. Richard the Lionheart: The Life of a King & Crusader. 2005. (Graphic Nonfiction Ser.). (Illus.). 48p. (J). lib. bdg. 26.50 (978-1-4042-0241-2(2)) Rosen Publishing Group, Inc., The.

Whistler, Charles W. Wulfric the Weapon Thane. 2007. 222p. pap. 12.99 (***978-1-4264-7331-9(1)**); 250p. pap. 16.99 (***978-1-4264-7404-0(0)**) BiblioBazaar.

Whittock, Martyn J. Medieval Britain, 1066-1500. 2003. (Illus.). 96p. pap. 29.50 (***978-0-340-86904-8(6)** , Hodder Murray) Hodder Education GBR. *Dist:* Trans-Atlantic Pubns., Inc.

Williams, Brian. Guide to Great Britain. 1999. (World Guides Ser.). (Illus.). 32p. (J). (gr. 2-6). lib. bdg. 21.27 (978-1-884756-45-0(X)) Davidson Titles, Inc.

Wilson. Investigating Childhood in Tudor England. (Illus.). 32p. (J). pap. 8.95 (978-0-7078-0335-7(7)) National Trust, Aylesbury GBR. *Dist:* Trafalgar Square Publishing.

Yonge, Charlotte. Young Folks History of England. 2006. pap. (***978-1-4250-3476-4(4)**) Assistedreadingbooks.com Inc.

Yonge, Charlotte M. Young Folks' History of England. 2004. reprint ed. pap. 19.95 (978-1-4191-9531-0(X)); pap. 1.99 (978-1-4192-9531-7(4)) Kessinger Publishing, LLC.

GREAT BRITAIN—HISTORY—BIOGRAPHY

Hilliam, David. Eleanor of Aquitaine: The Richest Queen in Medieval Europe. 2004. (Leaders of the Middle Ages Ser.). (Illus.). 112p. (J). lib. bdg. 31.95 (978-1-4042-0162-0(9)) Rosen Publishing Group, Inc., The.

Koestler-Grack, Rachel A. Eleanor of Aquitaine: Heroine of the Middle Ages. 2005. (Makers of the Middle Ages & Renaissance Ser.). (Illus.). 158p. (J). (gr. 4-8). lib. bdg. 30.00 (978-0-7910-8633-9(X) , Chelsea Hse.) Facts On File, Inc.

Lasky, Kathryn. Elizabeth I: Red Rose of the House of Tudor, England 1544. 1999. (Royal Diaries Ser.). (Illus.). 240p. (J). (gr. 4-8). 10.95 (978-0-590-68484-2(1) , Scholastic Pr.) Scholastic, Inc.

GREAT BRITAIN—HISTORY—FICTION

Almond, David. The Fire-Eaters. 2004. 224p. (gr. 3). 15.95 (978-0-385-73170-6(1) , Delacorte Bks. for Young Readers) Random Hse. Children's Bks.

Ardagh, Philip. The Green Men of Gressingham. Phillips, Mike, illus. 2006. 72;88p. (J). (gr. 2-3). lib. bdg. (978-1-59889-000-6(X)) Stone Arch Bks.

Armstrong, Alan W. Raleigh's Page. Jessell, Tim, illus. 2007. (J). 336p. (gr. 1-5). lib. bdg. 19.99 (978-0-375-93319-6(0)); 328p. (gr. 5-7). 16.99 (978-0-375-83319-9(6)) Random Hse. Children's Bks. (Random Hse. Bks. for Young Readers).

Ashe, Susan. Cuda of the Celts. Lawrie, Robin, illus. 2005. (Yellow Go Bananas Ser.). 39p. (J). lib. bdg. (978-0-7787-2720-0(3)) Crabtree Publishing Co.

Augarde, Steve. Celandine. 496p. (J). (gr. 5). 2008. 6.99 (***978-0-440-42216-7(7)** , Yearling); 2006. 16.95 (978-0-385-75048-6(X) , Fickling, David Bks.); 2006. lib. bdg. 18.99 (978-0-385-75049-3(8) , Fickling, David Bks.) Random Hse. Children's Bks.

Avi. Crispin: La Cruz de Plomo. 2004. Tr. of Crispin: The Cross of Lead. (SPA., Illus.). (YA). pap. 7.99 (978-84-348-9601-7(X)) SM Ediciones ESP. *Dist:* Lectorum Pubns., Inc.

—Crispin: The Cross of Lead. 2002. 256p. (gr. 5-9). 16.49 (978-0-7868-2647-6(9)) Disney Pr.

—Crispin: The Cross of Lead. 2002. (Illus.). 272p. (gr. 5-9). 15.99 (978-0-7868-0828-1(4)) Hyperion Bks. for Children.

—Crispin: The Cross of Lead. 2004. 320p. (J). (gr. 3-7). reprint ed. pap. 6.99 (978-0-7868-1658-3(9)) Hyperion Paperbacks for Children.

—Crispin: The Cross of Lead. 2004. (gr. 3-6). lib. bdg. 15.30 (978-0-613-74965-7(0)) Tandem Library Bks.

—Crispin: The Cross of Lead. 2003. 303p. (J). 25.95 (978-0-7862-5501-6(3)) Thorndike Pr.

Avi Staff. Crispin: At the Edge of the World. 2nd rev. ed. 2006. 240p. (gr. 5-9). 16.99 (978-0-7868-5152-2(X)) Hyperion Pr.

Bergen, Lara Rice. Into the Woods. 2000. (Back to Sherwood Ser.: 1). 176p. (J). (gr. 5-9). pap. 3.99 (978-0-440-22853-0(0) , Laurel Leaf) Random Hse. Children's Bks.

Blackwood, Gary L. Shakespeare's Spy. 2005. 288p. (J). (gr. 5-9). pap. 6.99 (978-0-14-240311-2(3) , Puffin) Penguin Group (USA) Inc.

Blaisdell, Robert & Scott, Walter, Sr. Ivanhoe. Green, John, illus. 1998. (Dover Children's Thrift Classics Ser.). 76p. (J). pap. 1.00 (978-0-486-40143-0(X)) Dover Pubns., Inc.

Bond, Douglas. Hostage Lands. 2006. 248p. (YA). per. 9.99 (978-1-59638-027-1(6)) P & R Publishing.

Broach, Elise. Shakespeare's Secret. 2007. 272p. (J). pap. 5.99 (***978-0-312-37132-6(2)**) Square Fish.

Browne, N. M. Warriors of Alavna. (J). 2004. 312p. (gr. 5-10). pap. 7.95 (978-1-58234-916-9(9)); 2002. 319p. 16.95 (978-1-58234-775-2(1)) Bloomsbury Publishing. (Bloomsbury Children).

Buckley-Archer, Linda. Gideon the Cutpurse. 2006. (Gideon Trilogy Ser.). 416p. (J). (gr. 5 up). 17.95 (978-1-4169-1525-6(7)) Simon & Schuster Children's Publishing.

Buckley-Archer, Linda. The Time Thief. 2007. (Gideon Trilogy Ser.). 512p. (J). (gr. 5 up). 17.99 (***978-1-4169-1527-0(3)**) Simon & Schuster Children's Publishing.

Burchett, Jan, et al. Exile. 2006. (Lady Grace Mysteries, from the Daybookes of Lady Grace Cavendish Ser.). 208p. (J). (gr. 3-7). 7.95 (978-0-385-73322-9(4)); lib. bdg. 9.99 (978-0-385-90341-7(3)) Random Hse. Children's Bks. (Delacorte Bks. for Young Readers).

Burnett, Frances Hodgson. A Little Princess. Marcos, Pablo, illus. 2005. (Great Illustrated Classics Ser.). 239p. (J). (gr. 3-8). 21.35 (978-1-59679-246-3(9) , ABDO & Daughters) ABDO Publishing Co.

—A Little Princess: The Story of Sara Crewe. 2006. (Scholastic Classics Ser.). v, 178p. (J). (gr. 9-12). 25.00 (978-0-531-16991-9(X) , Watts, Franklin) Scholastic Library Publishing.

—The Secret Garden. 2008. (Puffin Classics Ser.). 368p. (J). (gr. 3). pap. 4.99 (***978-0-14-132106-6(7)** , Puffin) Penguin Group (USA) Inc.

Burnett, Frances Hodgson. The Secret Garden: A Young Reader's Edition of the Classic Story. Moore, Inga, illus. 2008. 272p. (J). (gr. 1). 21.99 (***978-0-7636-3161-1(2)**) Candlewick Pr.

—The Secret Garden: A Young Reader's Edition of the Classic Story. 2006. (Scholastic Classics Ser.). vi, 222p. (J). (gr. 9-12). 25.00 (978-0-531-16960-5(X) , Watts, Franklin) Scholastic Library Publishing.

Cadnum, Michael. In a Dark Wood. 1999. 11.64 (978-0-606-17596-8(2)) Tandem Library Bks.

—Raven of the Waves. 2004. 208p. (J). (gr. 7 up). pap. 5.99 (978-0-439-62661-3(7)); 2001. 224p. (YA). (gr. 9 up). pap. 17.95 (978-0-531-30334-4(9) , Orchard Bks.) Scholastic, Inc.

Carey, Janet Lee. Dragon's Keep. 2007. 302p. (J). (*978-1-4287-3929-1(7)) Harcourt Trade Pubs.

Cavendish, Grace. The Lady Grace Mysteries: Assassin. l.t. ed. 2006. pap. 16.95 (978-1-4056-6068-6(6)) BBC Audio GBR. *Dist:* BBC Audiobooks America.

Clement-Davies, David. The Telling Pool. (gr. 7-17). 2007. 382p. (YA). pap. 7.95 (*978-0-8109-9257-3(4)); 2005. (Illus.). 376p. (J). 19.95 (978-0-8109-5758-9(2) , Abrams Bks. for Young Readers) Abrams, Harry N. , Inc.

Couch, T. Quiller Art. Splendid Spur. 2006. 63.99 (*978-1-4219-9730-8(4)) IndyPublish.com.

Crake, Augustine David. Alfgar the Dane or the Second Chronicle of Aescendune. 2007. 224p. pap. 12.99 (*978-1-4264-6907-7(1)); 254p. pap. 16.99 (*978-1-4264-6989-3(6)) BiblioBazaar.

Crossley-Holland, Kevin. At the Crossing Places. 2002. (Arthur Trilogy: Bk. 2). 416p. (J). (gr. 9 up). 17.95 (978-0-439-26598-0(3) , Levine, Arthur A. Bks.) Scholastic, Inc.

—At the Crossing-Places. 2004. (Illus.). 394p. (YA). (gr. 7-12). lib. bdg. 13.64 (978-0-606-32761-9(4)) Tandem Library Bks.

—At the Crossing Places. 2004. (Arthur Trilogy: Bk. 2). 416p. (J). (gr. 4-7). reprint ed. pap. 7.99 (978-0-439-26599-7(1) , Levine, Arthur A. Bks.) Scholastic, Inc.

—The Seeing Stone. 2002. (Arthur Trilogy: Vol. 1). 368p. (J). (gr. 5 up). mass mkt. 6.99 (978-0-439-43524-6(2) , Levine, Arthur A. Bks.) Scholastic, Inc.

Curry, Jane Louise. The Black Canary. 2005. (Illus.). 288p. (J). (gr. 5 up). 17.99 (978-0-689-86478-0(7) , McElderry, Margaret K.) Simon & Schuster Children's Publishing.

Dickens, Charles. David Copperfield. Marcos, Pablo, illus. 2002. (Great Illustrated Classics Ser.). 240p. (J). (gr. 3-8). 21.35 (978-1-57765-685-2(7) , ABDO & Daughters) ABDO Publishing Co.

—David Copperfield: Level 5. 2nd ed. 2000. (Bookworms Ser.). (Illus.). 112p. 6.50 (978-0-19-423060-5(0)) Oxford Univ. Pr., Inc.

—Great Expectations. Lynch, Brendan, illus. 2002. (Great Illustrated Classics Ser.). 240p. (J). (gr. 3-8). 21.35 (978-1-57765-687-6(3) , ABDO & Daughters) ABDO Publishing Co.

Duble, Kathleen Benner. Quest. 2008. 256p. (J). 15.99 (*978-1-4169-3386-1(7) , McElderry, Margaret K.) Simon & Schuster Children's Publishing.

Dunkle, Clare B. Hollow Kingdom. 2006. (Hollow Kingdom Trilogy Ser.). 240p. (YA). reprint ed. pap. 6.95 (978-0-8050-8108-4(9) , Holt, Henry & Co. Bks. For Young Readers) Holt, Henry & Co.

Elise Broach. Shakespeare's Secret. l.t. ed. 2006. 350p. (J). 22.95 (978-0-7862-8735-2(7)) Thorndike Pr.

Everett-Green, Evelyn. The Secret Chamber at Chad. 2006. (ENG.). 140p. 77.99 (*978-1-4280-4786-0(7)) IndyPublish.com.

Farenhorst, Christine. A Cup of Cold Water: The Compassion of Nurse Edith Cavell. 2007. (J). pap. (*978-1-59638-026-4(8)) P & R Publishing.

Finney, Patricia & Cavendish, Grace. Deception. 2005. (Lady Grace Mysteries, from the Daybookes of Lady Grace Cavendish Ser.). 224p. (J). (gr. 3-7). 7.95 (978-0-385-73321-2(6)); lib. bdg. 9.99 (978-0-385-90340-0(5)) Random Hse. Children's Bks. (Delacorte Bks. for Young Readers).

French, Allen. The Lost Baron. Wyeth, Andrew, illus. 2001. 320p. (J). (gr. 5-12). reprint ed. pap. 14.95 (978-1-883937-53-9(1) , 53-1) Bethlehem Bks.

Furlong, Monica. Colman. 2005. 288p. (J). (gr. 5). reprint ed. pap. 5.99 (978-0-375-81515-7(5) , Laurel Leaf) Random Hse. Children's Bks.

Garfield, Leon. The Strange Affair of Adelaide Harris. 2001. (978-0-606-22822-0(5)) Tandem Library Bks.

Gilman, Laura Anne. Morgain's Revenge. 2006. (Grail Quest Trilogy Ser.: No. 2). 288p. (J). lib. bdg. 14.89 (978-0-06-077283-3(2)) HarperCollins Pubs.

Grant, K. M. Blaze of Silver. 2007. 272p. 16.95 (978-0-8027-9625-7(7)) Walker & Co.

—Green Jasper. (J). 2007. 272p. pap. 7.95 (978-0-8027-9627-1(3)); 2006. 256p. 16.95 (978-0-8027-8073-7(3)) Walker & Co.

Grant, K. M. How the Hangman Lost His Heart. 2007. 256p. (YA). (gr. 7 up). 16.95 (*978-0-8027-9672-1(9)) Walker & Co.

Harris, Ruth Elwin. Julia's Story. 2002. (gr. 7-12). lib. bdg. 14.15 (978-0-613-74777-6(1)) Tandem Library Bks.

Hayner, Linda K. Ellanor's Exchange. 2005. 195p. (YA). (978-1-59166-462-8(4)) Jones, Bob Univ. Pr.

Hearn, Julie. The Minister's Daughter. 2006. 272p. (YA). pap. 7.99 (978-0-689-87691-2(2) , Simon Pulse) Simon & Schuster Children's Publishing.

Hearn, Julie & Frost, Michael. The Minister's Daughter. 2005. 272p. (YA). (gr. 7 up). 17.99 (978-0-689-87690-5(4) , Atheneum) Simon & Schuster Children's Publishing.

Henty, A. G. Under Drakes Flag A Tale of the Spanish. 2007. 97.99 (*978-1-4280-5259-8(3)); pap. 91.99 (*978-1-4280-5245-1(3)) IndyPublish.com.

Henty, G. A. When London Burned: A Story of Restoration Times & the Great Fire. l.t. ed. 2005. 724p. pap. (978-1-84637-212-4(7)) Echo Library.

Hooper, Mary. At the Sign of the Sugared Plum. 2005. 176p. (J). (gr. 4-7). pap. 6.95 (978-1-58234-695-3(X) , Bloomsbury Children) Bloomsbury Publishing.

—Petals in the Ashes. (J). 2006. 192p. pap. 6.95 (978-1-58234-720-2(4)); 2004. 200p. (gr. 5 up). 16.95 (978-1-58234-936-7(3)) Bloomsbury Publishing. (Bloomsbury Children).

Jeapes, Ben. New World Order. 2006. 448p. (YA). (gr. 7). mass mkt. 6.50 (978-0-553-49491-4(0) , Laurel Leaf) Random Hse. Children's Bks.

Jordan, Sherryl. The Hunting of the Last Dragon. 2002. 192p. (J). (gr. 7 up). 15.99 (978-0-06-028902-7(3)); 15.89 (978-0-06-028903-4(1)) HarperCollins Pubs.

Kolosov, Jacqueline. The Red Queen's Daughter. rev. ed. 2007. 399p. (YA). (gr. 7 up). 16.99 (*978-1-4231-0797-2(7)) Hyperion Pr.

Konigsburg, E. L. A Proud Taste for Scarlet & Miniver. 2001. (978-0-606-22124-5(7)) Tandem Library Bks.

LaFevers, R. L. Theodosia & the Serpents of Chaos. Tanaka, Yoko, illus. 2007. 368p. (J). (gr. 5-7). 16.00 (*978-0-618-75638-4(8)) Houghton Mifflin Co. Trade & Reference Div.

Lake, A. J. The Coming of Dragons. 2006. (Darkest Age Ser.: Bk. 1). (Illus.). 250p. (J). 16.95 (978-1-58234-965-7(7) , Bloomsbury Children) Bloomsbury Publishing.

Lamprey, L. Masters of the Guild. l.t. ed. 2006. 168p. pap. 14.99 (978-1-4264-2076-4(5)) BiblioBazaar.

Lawlor, Laurie. The Two Loves of Will Shakespeare. 2006. 256p. (YA). 16.95 (978-0-8234-1901-2(0)) Holiday Hse., Inc.

Lawton, Wendy. The Tinker's Daughter: A Story Based on the Life of Mary Bunyan. 2002. (Daughters of the Faith Ser.). 144p. (YA). pap. 6.99 (978-0-8024-4099-0(1)) Moody Pubs.

Lee, Tanith. Piratica: Being a Daring Tale of a Singular Girl's Adventure upon the High Seas. 2004. (Piratica Ser.: Vol. 1). (Illus.). 304p. (J). (gr. 6). 17.99 (978-0-525-47324-4(6) , Dutton Juvenile) Penguin Group (USA) Inc.

Limke, Jeff & Randall, Ron. Tristan & Isolde: The Warrior & the Princess: A British Legend: Adapted by Jeff Limke from Celtic Mythology & from Sir Thomas Malory's le Morte D'Arthur: Illustrations by Ron Randall. 2008. (Graphic Myths & Legends Ser.). (J). lib. bdg. 26.60 (*978-0-8225-7526-9(4) , Graphic Universe) Lerner Publishing Group.

Mack, Tracy & Citrin, Michael. The Fall of the Amazing Zalindas. Ruth, Greg, illus. 2006. (Sherlock Holmes & the BSI Ser.). 272p. (J). (gr. 4-7). pap. 16.99 (978-0-439-82836-9(8) , Orchard Bks.) Scholastic, Inc.

Malone, Patricia. Lady Ilena: Way of the Warrior. 2007. 176p. (YA). (gr. 7-11). mass mkt. 5.99 (*978-0-440-23901-7(X) , Laurel Leaf) Random Hse. Children's Bks.

Marryat, Frederick. The Children of the New Forest. fac. ed. 2000. 341p. pap. 15.95 (978-1-4021-9975-2(9) , Elibron Classics) Adamant Media.

—The Children of the New Forest. 2004. reprint ed. pap. 28.95 (978-1-4191-5655-7(1)); pap. 1.99 (978-1-4192-5655-4(6)) Kessinger Publishing, LLC.

McCaughrean, Geraldine. Knights, Kings & Conquerors: 20 Stories from British History. Brassey, Richard, illus. l.t. ed. 2005. 216p. (J). pap. (978-0-7540-7820-3(5) , CLP 410) BBC Audio.

—Knights, Kings & Conquerors: 20 Stories from British History. Brassey, Richard, illus. 2003. 115p. (J). pap. 11.00 (978-1-85881-851-1(6)) Orion Bks. Ltd. GBR. *Dist:* Trafalgar Square Publishing.

McCaughrean, Geraldine & Marks, Alan. King Arthur. 2007. (Illus.). (J). pap. (*978-0-340-89437-8(7) , Hodder Children's Books) Hodder Children's Division.

Meyer, Carolyn. Beware, Princess Elizabeth. (Young Royals Ser.). 2002. (Illus.). 240p. (YA). pap. 5.95 (978-0-15-204556-2(2)); 2001. (J). 17.00 (978-0-15-202639-4(8)) Harcourt Children's Bks. (Gulliver Bks.).

—Loving Will Shakespeare. 2006. 272p. (YA). 17.00 (978-0-15-205451-9(0)) Harcourt Children's Bks.

—Patience, Princess Catherine: A Young Royals Book. 2005. (Young Royals Ser.). 208p. (gr. 7-17). pap. 5.95 (978-0-15-205447-2(2) , Gulliver Bks.) Harcourt Children's Bks.

Michael, Livi. The Whispering Road. 2006. 336p. (J). (gr. 5). pap. 6.99 (978-0-14-240724-0(0) , Puffin) Penguin Group (USA) Inc.

Morpurgo, Michael. Private Peaceful. (J). 2006. 176p. pap. 5.99 (978-0-439-63653-7(1) , Scholastic Paperbacks); 2004. 208p. (gr. 7 up). 16.95 (978-0-439-63648-3(5) , Scholastic Pr.) Scholastic, Inc.

—Private Peaceful. l.t. ed. 2006. 225p. (J). 21.95 (978-0-7862-8946-2(5)) Thorndike Pr.

Nesbit, E. Five Children & IT. Nesbit, E. & Millar, H. R., illus. 2004. 240p. (gr. 12). pap. 10.00 (978-0-14-303915-0(6) , Penguin Classics) Penguin Group (USA) Inc.

—The House of Arden. 2006. (New York Review Children's Collection). 248p. (J). (gr. 3). 17.95 (978-1-59017-202-5(7) , NYR Children's Collection) New York Review of Bks., Inc., The.

—Railway Children. 2004. (ENG.). 580p. (*978-0-9548401-2-9(7)) Shoes & Ships & Sealing Wax Ltd.

—The Railway Children. Brock, C. E., illus. 100th ed. 2005. 240p. (J). (ps-7). 14.95 (978-1-58717-279-3(8)); pap. 9.95 (978-1-58717-280-9(1)) Chronicle Bks. LLC. (SeaStar Bks.).

—The Railway Children. 2004. reprint ed. pap. 22.95 (978-1-4191-7972-3(1)); pap. 1.99 (978-1-4192-7972-0(6)) Kessinger Publishing, LLC.

—The Railway Children. l.t. ed. 2006. (Large Print Ser.). lib. bdg. 26.00 (*978-1-58287-890-4(0)) North Bks.

Newbery, Linda. Set in Stone. 2006. 368p. (YA). (gr. 9). lib. bdg. 18.99 (978-0-385-75103-2(6)) Knopf, Alfred A. Inc.

—Set in Stone. 2006. 368p. (YA). (gr. 9). 16.95 (978-0-385-75102-5(8) , Fickling, David Bks.) Random Hse. Children's Bks.

Ortiz, Michael J. Swan Town: The Secret Journal of Susanna Shakespeare. 2006. 208p. (J). lib. bdg. 16.89 (978-0-06-058127-5(1)); (Illus.). 15.99 (978-0-06-058126-8(3)) HarperCollins Pubs.

Pennington, Kate. Charley Feather. 2007. (J). pap. (*978-0-340-87873-6(8) , Hodder Children's Books) Hodder Children's Division.

Pennington, Kate & Oldfield, Jenny. Tread Softly. 2005. (J). pap. (978-0-340-87343-4(4) , Hodder Children's Books) Hodder Children's Division.

Peyton, K. M. Small Gains. 2004. 368p. (J). pap. 12.95 (*978-0-09-944387-2(2)) Transworld Publishers Ltd. GBR. *Dist:* Independent Pubs. Group.

Prince & the Pauper App Clas. 2003. (J). pap. 2.75 (978-0-590-43283-2(4)) Scholastic, Inc.

Pullman, Philip. Sally y la Sombra del Norte. Miguel, Isabel de, tr. 2002. Tr. of Shadow in the North. (SPA.). 347p. (J). pap. (978-84-95618-46-7(X) , Umbriel) Ediciones Urano S. A.

Pyle, Howard. Men of Iron. unabr. ed. 2003. (General Juvenile Ser.). 224p. (J). (gr. 5-8). pap. 8.95 (978-0-486-42841-3(9)) Dover Pubns., Inc.

Rabin, Staton. Black Powder. 2005. 256p. (J). (gr. 6-9). 16.95 (978-0-689-86876-4(6) , McElderry, Margaret K.) Simon & Schuster Children's Publishing.

Rautenberg, Karen Rita. Lady Lucy's Gallant Knight. 2007. 156p. (J). pap. 7.95 (978-1-933255-22-4(6)) DNA Pr.

Richards, Justin. The Invisible Detective: Ghost Soldiers. 2006. 160p. (J). (gr. 4). 11.99 (978-0-399-24500-8(6) , Putnam Juvenile) Penguin Group (USA) Inc.

Rinaldi, Ann. Mutiny's Daughter. 2005. 224p. (J). (ps-7). pap. 5.99 (978-0-06-441010-6(2) , Harper Trophy) HarperCollins Pubs.

—Nine Days a Queen: The Short Life & Reign of Lady Jane Grey. (J). 2006. 240p. pap. 5.99 (978-0-06-054925-1(4) , Harper Trophy); 2005. 192p. (gr. 7 up). 15.99 (978-0-06-054923-7(8)); 2005. 192p. (gr. 7 up). lib. bdg. 16.89 (978-0-06-054924-4(6)) HarperCollins Pubs.

Rinaldi, Ann. The Redheaded Princess. 2008. 224p. (J). 15.99 (*978-0-06-073374-2(8)); lib. bdg. 16.89 (*978-0-06-073375-9(6)) HarperCollins Pubs.

Russell, Christopher. Hunted. 2007. 272p. (J). (gr. 5-8). 15.99 (978-0-06-084119-5(2)); lib. bdg. 16.89 (978-0-06-084120-1(6)) HarperCollins Pubs.

Sandell, Lisa Ann. Song of the Sparrow. 2007. 416p. (YA). (gr. 7 up). pap. 16.99 (*978-0-439-91848-0(0) , Scholastic Pr.) Scholastic, Inc.

Scott, Walter, Sr. Ivanhoe. Marcos, Pablo, illus. 2002. (Great Illustrated Classics Ser.). 240p. (J). (gr. 3-8). 21.35 (978-1-57765-811-5(6) , ABDO & Daughters) ABDO Publishing Co.

—Ivanhoe. (SPA., Illus.). 176p. (YA). 14.95 (978-84-7281-096-9(8) , AF1096) Auriga, Ediciones S.A. ESP. *Dist:* Continental Bk. Co., Inc.

—Ivanhoe. 2000. (gr. 7-12). lib. bdg. 17.65 (978-0-613-64293-4(7)) Tandem Library Bks.

Sedgwick, Marcus. The Foreshadowing. 2006. 304p. (YA). (gr. 7 up). 16.95 (978-0-385-74646-5(6) , Lamb, Wendy) Random Hse. Children's Bks.

Selbo, Jule & Peters, Laura. Pilgrim Girl: Diaries & Recipes of her First Year in the New World. 2005. (Illus.). 132p. (YA). per. 12.95 (978-1-932993-05-9(3)) Star Publish LLC.

Sewell, Anna. Black Beauty. 2006. (Scholastic Classics Ser.). x, 203p. (J). (gr. 9-12). 25.00 (978-0-531-16981-0(2) , Watts, Franklin) Scholastic Library Publishing.

Shinn, Sharon. The Safe-Keeper's Secret. 2005. (Firebird Ser.). 240p. (YA). (gr. 7). pap. 6.99 (978-0-14-240357-0(1) , Puffin) Penguin Group (USA) Inc.

Springer, Nancy. The Case of the Left-Handed Lady: An Enola Holmes Mystery. 2007. 224p. (YA). (gr. 5-9). 12.99 (978-0-399-24517-6(0) , Philomel) Penguin Group (USA) Inc.

—Rowan Hood Returns: The Final Chapter. 2006. (Tales of Rowan Hood Ser.: No. 5). 176p. (J). (gr. 3). pap. 5.99 (978-0-14-240685-4(6) , Puffin) Penguin Group (USA) Inc.

Stead, Richard. With Marlborough to Malplaquet. 2006. pap. (*978-1-4068-3012-5(7)) Echo Library.

Strang, Herbert. With Marlborough to Malplaquet. 2006. pap. (*978-1-4068-3126-9(3)) Echo Library.

—With Marlborough to Malplaquet (a Story. 2006. 32.99 (*978-1-4280-1761-0(5)) IndyPublish.com.

Sturtevant, Katherine. At the Sign of the Star. 2000. 144p. (YA). (gr. 5 up). 16.00 (978-0-374-30449-2(1) , Farrar, Straus & Giroux (BYR)) Farrar, Straus & Giroux.

—A True & Faithful Narrative. 2006. 256p. (YA). 17.00 (978-0-374-37809-7(6)) Farrar, Straus & Giroux.

Sutcliff, Rosemary. The Shield Ring. 2007. 220p. pap. 10.95 (*978-1-59078-522-5(3)) Boyds Mills Pr.

Thoene, Jake & Thoene, Luke. The Jeweled Peacock of Persia. 2006. (Baker Street Detectives Ser.). 144p. (J). 9.99 (978-1-4143-0368-0(8)) Tyndale Hse. Pubs.

Thomson, Sarah L. The Secret of the Rose. 2006. 304p. (J). 16.99 (978-0-06-087250-2(0)); lib. bdg. 17.89 (978-0-06-087251-9(9)) HarperCollins Pubs.

Tingle, Rebecca. Far Traveler. 2006. 240p. (J). (gr. 4). pap. 6.99 (978-0-14-240630-4(9) , Puffin) Penguin Group (USA) Inc.

Tolhurst, Marilyn. Knights: The Age of Adventure, to Unlock & Discover. 2001. (Treasure Chest Ser.). (Illus.). 32p. (J). (gr. 4-7). pap. 22.95 (978-1-56138-545-4(X) , Running Pr. Kids) Running Pr. Bk. Pubs.

Turnbull, Ann. No Shame, No Fear. 304p. (YA). (gr. 7). 2006. pap. 8.99 (978-0-7636-3190-1(6)); 2004. 15.99 (978-0-7636-2505-4(1)) Candlewick Pr.

Twain, Mark. The Prince & the Pauper. Lynch, Brendan, illus. 2002. (Great Illustrated Classics Ser.). 240p. (J). (gr. 3-8). 21.35 (978-1-57765-698-2(9) , ABDO & Daughters) ABDO Publishing Co.

—The Prince & the Pauper. 1999. reprint ed. pap. 28.00 (978-1-4047-1120-4(1)) Classic Textbooks.

—The Prince & the Pauper. 2003. (Modern Library Classics). (Illus.). 240p. pap. 8.95 (978-0-375-76112-6(8) , Modern Library) Random House Publishing Group.

—The Prince & the Pauper. Akib, Jamel, illus. 2007. (Classic Starts Ser.). 160p. (J). 4.95 (978-1-4027-3687-2(8)) Sterling Publishing Co., Inc.

Updale, Eleanor. Montmorency & the Assassins: Master, Criminal, Spy. 2006. 416p. (J). (gr. 4-7). pap. 16.99 (978-0-439-68343-2(2) , Orchard Bks.) Scholastic, Inc.

—Montmorency on the Rocks: Doctor, Aristocrat, Murderer? 2006. 368p. (J). pap. 6.99 (978-0-439-60677-6(2) , Scholastic Paperbacks) Scholastic, Inc.

—Montmorency on the Rocks: Doctor, Aristocrat, Murderer? Hardcastle, Nick, illus. 2005. (Montmorency Ser.). 368p. (J). pap. 16.95 (978-0-439-60676-9(4) , Orchard Bks.) Scholastic, Inc.

—Montmorency's Revenge. 2007. (Montmorency Ser.: Vol. 4). 304p. (J). (gr. 7 up). pap. 16.99 (978-0-439-81373-0(5) , Orchard Bks.) Scholastic, Inc.

Vandersteen, Willy. The Circle of Power. Geerts, Paul, illus. 1998. (Greatest Adventures of Spike & Suzy Ser.: Vol. 2). 56p. (J). (gr. 2-9). 11.95 (978-0-9533178-1-3(1)) Intes International (UK) Ltd. GBR. *Dist:* Diamond Comic Distributors, Inc.

Wallace, Karen. Wendy. 2003. 320p. (J). (978-0-689-83747-0(X) , Simon & Schuster Children's Publishing) Simon & Schuster Children's Publishing.

Wallace, Karen & Frost, Michael. Wendy. 2003. 320p. (J). 16.95 (978-0-689-86769-9(7)) Simon & Schuster Children's Publishing.

Walters, Jennie. Shelter from the Storm. 2007. (Swallowcliffe Hall Trilogy: Book 3 Ser.). (Illus.). 240p. (J). pap. 9.99 (*978-0-689-87528-1(2)) Simon & Schuster, Ltd. GBR. *Dist:* Independent Pubs. Group.

Whelan, Gloria. Listening for Lions. 208p. (J). 2006. pap. 5.99 (978-0-06-058176-3(X) , Harper Trophy); 2005. (gr. 5 up). 15.99 (978-0-06-058174-9(3)); 2005. (Illus.). (gr. 5 up). lib. bdg. 16.89 (978-0-06-058175-6(1)) HarperCollins Pubs.

Willard, Barbara. If All the Swords in England. Sax, Robert M., illus. 2000. (Living History Library). x, 181p. (J). (gr. 8-12). reprint ed. pap. 12.95 (978-1-883937-49-2(3) , 49-3) Bethlehem Bks.

Wooding, Chris. The Haunting of Alaizabel Cray. 2005. 304p. (YA). (gr. 7-17). reprint ed. pap. 7.99 (978-0-439-59851-4(6)) Scholastic, Inc.

GREAT BRITAIN—HISTORY, NAVAL

Ashworth, Leon. Horatio Nelson. 2000. (British History Makers Ser.). (Illus.). 32p. (J). 22.95 (978-0-7451-5290-5(2) , Cherrytree Books) Evans Publishing Group GBR. *Dist:* Independent Pubs. Group.

Crompton, Samuel Willard. Francis Drake & the Oceans of the World. 2005. (Explorers of New Worlds Ser.). (Illus.). 160p. (J). (gr. 4-8). 30.00 (978-0-7910-8615-5(1) , Chelsea Hse.) Facts On File, Inc.

Hoogenboom, Lynn. Sir Francis Drake: A Primary Source Portrait. 2006. (J). lib. bdg. (978-1-4042-3035-4(1) , PowerKids Pr.) Rosen Publishing Group, Inc., The.

Hynson, Colin. Elizabeth I & the Spanish Armada. 2006. (Stories from History Ser.). 48p. (J). 14.95 (978-0-7696-4703-6(0)); pap. 6.95 (978-0-7696-4629-9(8)) School Specialty Publishing.

Kline, Trish. Sir Francis Drake. (Rourke Discovery Library). 2003. (Illus.). 24p. (gr. 2-5). 14.95 (978-1-58952-295-4(8)); 2002. (J). lib. bdg. 19.27 (978-1-58952-429-3(2)) Rourke Publishing, LLC.

Malam, John. You wouldn't/sail in spanish Armada. 2006. (Illus.). 32p. (J). (gr. 2-5). 28.50 (*978-0-531-14974-4(9)) Scholastic Library Publishing.

GREAT BRITAIN—HISTORY, NAVAL—FICTION

Cooper, Susan. Victory. (J). 2007. 224p. pap. 6.99 (*978-1-4169-1478-5(1) , Aladdin); 2006. (Illus.). 208p. (gr. 4-7). 16.95 (978-1-4169-1477-8(3) , McElderry, Margaret K.) Simon & Schuster Children's Publishing.

Dowswell, Paul. Powder Monkey: Adventures of a Young Sailor. 2006. 288p. (YA). pap. 7.95 (978-1-58234-748-6(4) , Bloomsbury Children) Bloomsbury Publishing.

Molloy, Michael. Peter Raven under Fire. 2007. 512p. (J). 8.99 (*978-0-439-72457-9(0)) Scholastic, Inc.

Styles, Showell. Midshipman Quinn Collection. 1999. (gr. 7-12). lib. bdg. 30.35 (978-0-613-80204-8(7)) Tandem Library Bks.

GREAT BRITAIN—HISTORY—TO 1066

see also Celts

Abbott, Jacob. King Alfred of England. 2006. pap. (*978-1-4068-0240-5(9)) Echo Library.

Crompton, Samuel Willard. Hastings. (Battles That Changed the World Ser.). (J). pap. 30.00 (978-0-7910-7164-9(2)); 2002. (Illus.). 112p. (gr. 7-10). 30.00 (978-0-7910-6680-5(0)) Facts On File, Inc. (Chelsea Hse.).

Jarvie, Frances. The Romans in Scotland. Philip, Carrie, illus. 1999. (Scottie Bks.). 40p. (J). (gr. 3-7). pap. 6.95 (978-0-11-494277-9(3)) Stationery Office, The GBR. *Dist:* Balogh International, Inc.

Nardo, Don. King Arthur. 2002. (Heroes & Villains Ser.). (Illus.). 112p. (J). (gr. 6). 27.45 (978-1-56006-948-5(1) , Lucent Bks.) Thomson Gale.

Roberts, Jeremy. King Arthur. 2005. (How History Is Invented Ser.). (Illus.). 112p. (J). (gr. 6-12). lib. bdg. 23.93 (978-0-8225-4891-1(7)) Lerner Publishing Group.

Ross, Stewart. Down with the Romans. 2007. (Flashbacks Ser.). (Illus.). 64p. (J). (gr. 4-7). pap. 8.95 (*978-0-237-53150-8(X) , Evans Brothers, Limited) Evans Publishing Group GBR. *Dist:* Independent Pubs. Group.

Whistler, W. Charles. Wulfric the Weapon Thane (a Story of the. 2006. 34.99 (*978-1-4280-1745-0(3)) IndyPublish.com.

E F G

GREAT BRITAIN—HISTORY—TO 1066—FICTION

Avi. The Book Without Words: A Fable of Medieval Magic. 2006. 224p. (gr. 5-9). reprint ed. pap. 5.99 (978-0-7868-1659-0(7)) Hyperion Pr.

—The Book Without Words: A Fable of Medieval Magic. l.t. ed. 2005. 220p. (YA). 23.95 (978-0-7862-7940-1(0)) Thorndike Pr.

Duey, Kathleen. Arthur. 2007. (Illus.). 96p. (J). 24.21 (978-1-59961-224-9(0)) Spotlight.

Lake, A. J. The Coming of Dragons Bk. 1: Darkest Age I. 2007. (Illus.). 240p. (YA). pap. 6.95 (978-1-58234-902-2(9) , Bloomsbury Children) Bloomsbury Publishing.

Malone, Patricia. The Legend of Lady Ilena. 2003. (Illus.). 240p. (YA). (gr. 7). mass mkt. 5.50 (978-0-440-22909-4(X) , Laurel Leaf) Random Hse. Children's Bks.

McCaffrey, Anne. Black Horses for the King. 1998. 224p. mass mkt. 6.99 (978-0-345-42257-6(0) , Del Rey) Random House Publishing Group.

Morris, Gerald. The Lioness & Her Knight. 2005. (Squire's Tales Ser.). 352p. (J). (gr. 5-7). 16.00 (978-0-618-50772-6(8)) Houghton Mifflin Co. Trade & Reference Div.

San Souci, Robert D. Young Lancelot. 1998. (J). (978-0-606-13937-3(0)) Tandem Library Bks.

Tingle, Rebecca. Far Traveler. 2005. (Illus.). 10p. (YA). (gr. 4). 18.99 (978-0-399-23890-1(5) , Putnam Juvenile) Penguin Group (USA) Inc.

Vande Velde, Vivian. The Book of Mordred. 2005. (Illus.). 352p. (YA). (gr. 7-7). 18.00 (978-0-618-50754-2(X)) Houghton Mifflin Co. Trade & Reference Div.

Velde, Vivian Vande. The Book of Mordred. 2007. 352p. (YA). (gr. 7). pap. 8.99 (***978-0-618-80916-5(3)*** , Graphia) Houghton Mifflin Co. Trade & Reference Div.

GREAT BRITAIN—HISTORY—MEDIEVAL PERIOD, 1066-1485

Childress, Diana. Chaucer's England. 2000. (Illus.). xvii, 137p. (YA). (gr. 7-12). pap. 25.00 (978-0-208-02489-3(1) , Linnet Bks.) Shoe String Pr., Inc.

Hinds, Kathryn. Medieval England. 2001. (Cultures of the Past Ser.). (Illus.). 80p. (J). lib. bdg. 29.93 (978-0-7614-0308-1(6) , Benchmark Bks.) Cavendish, Marshall Corp.

Shephard, Colin & Large, Alan. Re-Discovering Medieval Realms: Britain 1066-1500. 2000. (Illus.). 112p. pap., stu. ed. 32.50 (***978-0-7195-8542-5(2)*** , Hodder Murray) Hodder Education GBR. *Dist:* Trans-Atlantic Pubns., Inc.

GREAT BRITAIN—HISTORY—NORMAN PERIOD, 1066-1154

Culpin, Christopher & Dawson, Ian. The Norman Conquest. 2002. (Illus.). 64p. 62.50 (***978-0-7195-8556-2(2) ;*** pap., stu. ed. 26.00 (***978-0-7195-8555-5(4)***) Hodder Education GBR. (Hodder Murray). *Dist:* Trans-Atlantic Pubns., Inc.

Hamilton, Janice. The Norman Conquest of England. 2007. (Pivotal Moments in History Ser.). 160p. (YA). (gr. 9-12). lib. bdg. 38.60 (***978-0-8225-5902-3(1)*** , Twenty-First Century Bks.) Lerner Publishing Group.

Henty, G. A. Wulf the Saxon: A Story of the Norman Conquest. (J). 2000. 316p. mass mkt. 7.99 (978-1-887159-70-8(3)); 1998. (Illus.). 361p. pap. 14.99 (978-1-887159-17-3(7)) Preston-Speed Pubns.

—The Young Carthaginian: A Tale of the Times of Hannibal. Preston Speed Publications Staff, ed. Peacock, Ralph, illus. 1998. 361p. (YA). pap. 14.99 (978-1-887159-20-3(7)) Preston-Speed Pubns.

McGowen, Tom. William the Conqueror: Last Invader of England. 2007. (Rulers of the Middle Ages Ser.). (Illus.). 160p. (YA). (gr. 7-9). lib. bdg. 34.60 (978-0-7660-2713-8(9)) Enslow Pubs., Inc.

GREAT BRITAIN—HISTORY—NORMAN PERIOD, 1066-1154—FICTION

Chaucer, Geoffrey. The Canterbury Tales. adapted ed. (YA). (gr. 5-12). 8.50 (978-0-8359-0869-6(0)) Globe Fearon Educational Publishing.

GREAT BRITAIN—HISTORY—PLANTAGENETS, 1154-1399

Brooks, Polly Schoyer. Queen Eleanor: Independent Spirit of the Medieval World. 1999. (Illus.). 192p. (J). (gr. 7-12). pap. 8.95 (978-0-395-98139-9(5)) Houghton Mifflin Co. Trade & Reference Div.

—Queen Eleanor: Independent Spirit of the Medieval World: A Biography of Eleanor of Aquitaine, 1999. (978-0-606-17228-8(9)); (gr. 7-12). lib. bdg. 17.60 (978-0-613-22231-0(8)) Tandem Library Bks.

Plain, Nancy. Eleanor of Aquitaine & the High Middle Ages. 2005. (Rulers & Their Times Ser.). (Illus.). 96p. (J). (gr. 3-7). lib. bdg. 29.93 (978-0-7614-1834-4(2) , Benchmark Bks.) Cavendish, Marshall Corp.

GREAT BRITAIN—HISTORY—PLANTAGENETS, 1154-1399—FICTION

Cadnum, Michael. Forbidden Forest: The Story of Little John & the Robin Hood. 2002. 224p. (J). (gr. 7 up). pap. 17.95 (978-0-439-31774-0(6) , Orchard Bks.) Scholastic, Inc.

—In a Dark Wood: A Novel. 1998. 246p. (YA). (gr. 7-12). 18.99 (978-0-531-33071-5(0) , Orchard Bks.) Scholastic, Inc.

Crossley-Holland, Kevin. King of the Middle March. 432p. (J). 2006. pap. 7.99 (978-0-439-26601-7(7)); Book 3. 2004. (gr. 7 up). 17.95 (978-0-439-26600-0(9) , Levine, Arthur A. Bks.) Scholastic, Inc.

—Seeing Stone. 2002. (gr. 7-12). lib. bdg. 15.30 (978-0-613-50642-7(1)) Tandem Library Bks.

Konigsburg, E. L. A Proud Taste for Scarlet & Miniver. 2001. (gr. 5-8). lib. bdg. 13.00 (978-0-613-88159-3(1)) Tandem Library Bks.

Lasky, Kathryn. Robin Hood: The Boy Who Became a Legend. 1999. (J). (978-0-590-25933-0(4) , Blue Sky Pr., The) Scholastic, Inc.

Mayer, Marianna. Ivanhoe. Rush, John, illus. 2004. 56p. (J). 17.95 (978-1-58717-248-9(8)); 18.50 (978-1-58717-249-6(6)) Chronicle Bks. LLC. (SeaStar Bks.).

Scott, Walter, Sr., et al. Ivanhoe. (Classics Illustrated Ser.). (Illus.). 52p. (YA). pap. 4.95 (978-1-57209-023-1(5)) Classics International Entertainment, Inc.

Tomlinson, Theresa. Child of the May. 1998. (Illus.). 128p. (YA). (gr. 5-9). pap. 15.95 (978-0-531-30118-0(4) , Orchard Bks.) Scholastic, Inc.

GREAT BRITAIN—HISTORY—LANCASTER AND YORK, 1399-1485—FICTION

McAllister, Margaret. High Cragg Linn. 2008. 224p. (YA). pap. 9.95 (***978-0-7459-6062-3(6)***) Lion Hudson plc GBR. *Dist:* Independent Pubs. Group.

Pyle, Howard. Men of Iron. (J). 25.95 (978-0-8488-1131-0(3)) Amereon LTD.

Rose, Simon. The Sorcerer's Letterbox. 2006. 116p. (J). 7.95 (978-1-896580-52-4(1)) Tradewind Bks. CAN. *Dist:* Orca Bk. Pubs. USA.

GREAT BRITAIN—HISTORY—WARS OF THE ROSES, 1455-1485—FICTION

Stevenson, Robert Louis. The Black Arrow. 1998. (Tor Classics Ser.). 288p. (gr. 7 up). 3.99 (978-0-8125-6562-1(2) , Tor Classics) Doherty, Tom Assocs., LLC.

—The Black Arrow. 2001. (Dover Juvenile Classics Ser.). 240p. (J). (gr. 4-7). pap. 3.00 (978-0-486-41820-9(0)) Dover Pubns., Inc.

—The Black Arrow. l.t. ed. 2005. 448p. pap. (978-1-84637-164-6(3)) Echo Library.

GREAT BRITAIN—HISTORY—TUDORS, 1485-1603

Anon. Tudor War. (Illus.). 32p. pap. (978-0-7502-3742-0(2) , Hodder Wayland) Hodder Children's Division.

Ashby, Ruth. Elizabethan England. 1998. (Cultures of the Past Ser.). (Illus.). 80p. (J). (gr. 5 up). lib. bdg. 29.93 (978-0-7614-0269-5(1) , Benchmark Bks.) Cavendish, Marshall Corp.

Fowke, Bob. Tudors. (Illus.). 128p. (J). pap. 9.99 (978-0-340-85185-2(6) , Hodder & Stoughton) Hodder General Publishing Division GBR. *Dist:* Independent Pubs. Group.

Green, Robert. King Henry VIII. 1998. (First Bks.). 64p. (J). 23.00 (978-0-531-20305-7(0) , Watts, Franklin) Scholastic Library Publishing.

Greenblatt, Miriam. Elizabeth I & Tudor England. 2001. (Rulers & Their Times Ser.). (Illus.). 80p. (J). (gr. 6 up). lib. bdg. 29.93 (978-0-7614-1028-7(7) , Benchmark Bks.) Cavendish, Marshall Corp.

Guy, John. Elizabeth I & the Armada. 2004. (Illus.). 32p. (J). (gr. 4-7). pap. (978-1-86007-029-7(9)) Ticktock Media Ltd.

—Tudor & Stuart Life. 2004. (Illus.). 32p. (J). (gr. 4-7). pap. 6.95 (978-1-86007-003-7(5)) Ticktock Media Ltd. GBR. *Dist:* Consortium Bk. Sales & Distribution.

Havelin, Kate. Queen Elizabeth I. 2002. (Biography Ser.). (Illus.). 112p. (J). (gr. 6-12). lib. bdg. 27.93 (978-0-8225-0029-2(9) , Lerner Pubns.) Lerner Publishing Group.

Hebditch, Felicity. Tudors. 2003. (Illus.). 32p. (YA). pap. 9.99 (978-0-237-52572-9(0) , Evans Brothers, Limited) Evans Publishing Group GBR. *Dist:* Independent Pubs. Group.

Henty, G. A. Under Drake's Flag: A Tale of the Spanish Main. Browne, Gordon, illus. 1998. 298p. (J). lib. bdg. 20.99 (978-1-887159-15-9(0)) Preston-Speed Pubns.

McCaughrean, Geraldine. Daredevils & Desperadoes: 20 Stories from British History. Brassey, Richard, illus. 2002. 128p. pap. 9.99 (978-1-84255-059-5(4)) Orion Children's Bks. GBR. *Dist:* Trafalgar Square Publishing.

Petrie, Kristin. Sir Francis Drake. 2004. (Explorers Ser.). (Illus.). 32p. (J). (gr. k-6). lib. bdg. 22.78 (978-1-59197-601-1(4) , Checkerboard Library) ABDO Publishing Co.

Price-Groff, Claire. Queen Elizabeth I. 2000. (Importance of Ser.). (Illus.). 112p. (J). (gr. 7-10). 28.70 (978-1-56006-700-9(4) , Lucent Bks.) Thomson Gale.

Rose, Russell. Tudors. 2003. (Know it All! Ser.). (Illus.). 16p. (J). pap. 6.99 (978-0-7498-5817-9(6)) Egmont Bks., Ltd. GBR. *Dist:* Independent Pubs. Group.

Ross, Stewart. Beware the King. 2007. (Flashbacks Ser.). (Illus.). 64p. (J). (gr. 4-7). pap. 8.95 (***978-0-237-53151-5(8)*** , Evans Brothers, Limited) Evans Publishing Group GBR. *Dist:* Independent Pubs. Group.

Shephard, Colin & Lomas, Tim. Re-Discovering the Making of the UK: Britain 1500-1750. 2001. (Illus.). 120p. pap., stu. ed. 32.50 (***978-0-7195-8544-9(9)*** , Hodder Murray) Hodder Education GBR. *Dist:* Trans-Atlantic Pubns., Inc.

Worth, Richard. King Henry VIII & the Reformation in World History. 2001. (In World History Ser.). (Illus.). 112p. (J). (gr. 5-12). lib. bdg. 26.60 (978-0-7660-1615-6(3)) Enslow Pubs., Inc.

GREAT BRITAIN—HISTORY—TUDORS, 1485-1603—FICTION

Cadnum, Michael. Ship of Fire. 2003. 208p. (J). (gr. 7). 16.99 (978-0-670-89907-4(0) , Viking Juvenile) Penguin Group (USA) Inc.

Cheaney, J. B. The True Prince. 2004. (gr. 5-8). lib. bdg. 14.15 (978-0-613-89784-6(6)) Tandem Library Bks.

Deary, Terry. The Actor, the Rebel, & the Wrinkled Queen. Flook, Helen, illus. 2005. (Read-It! Chapter Bks.). 64p. (J). (ps-k). lib. bdg. 19.95 (978-1-4048-1297-0(0)) Picture Window Bks.

—The Maid, the Witch, & the Cruel Queen. Flook, Helen, illus. 2005. (Read-It! Chapter Bks.). 60p. (J). (ps-k). lib. bdg. 19.95 (978-1-4048-1299-4(7)) Picture Window Bks.

—The Prince, the Cook, & the Cunning King. Flook, Helen, illus. 2005. (Read-It! Chapter Bks.). 60p. (J). (ps-k). lib. bdg. 19.95 (978-1-4048-1298-7(9)) Picture Window Bks.

—The Thief, the Fool, & the Big Fat King. Flook, Helen, illus. 2005. (Read-It! Chapter Bks.). 61p. (J). (ps-k). lib. bdg. 19.95 (978-1-4048-1300-7(4)) Picture Window Bks.

Finney, Patricia & Cavendish, Grace. Assasin, No. 1. 2004. (Lady Grace Mysteries, from the Daybookes of Lady Grace Cavendish Ser.). 208p. (J). (gr. 3-7). lib. bdg. 12.99 (978-0-385-90189-5(5) , Delacorte Bks. for Young Readers) Random Hse. Children's Bks.

—Assassin, No. 1. 2004. (Lady Grace Mysteries, from the Daybookes of Lady Grace Cavendish Ser.). 208p. (J). (gr. 3-7). 9.95 (978-0-385-73151-5(5) , Delacorte Bks. for Young Readers) Random Hse. Children's Bks.

—Feud. 2006. (Lady Grace Mysteries, from the Daybookes of Lady Grace Cavendish Ser.). 192p. (J). (gr. 3-7). 7.95 (978-0-385-73323-6(2)); lib. bdg. 9.99 (978-0-385-90342-4(1)) Random Hse. Children's Bks. (Delacorte Bks. for Young Readers).

Hannah, Martha. The Ghost of Hampton Court. Dowell, Larry, illus. 2006. 32p. (J). 17.95 (978-0-9779808-0-2(4)) CicadaSun.

Meyer, Carolyn. Doomed Queen Anne. 2002. (Young Royals Ser.). (Illus.). 240p. (YA). (gr. 7 up). 17.00 (978-0-15-216523-9(1) , Gulliver Bks.) Harcourt Children's Bks.

—Patience, Princess Catherine. 2004. (Young Royals Ser.). (Illus.). 208p. (YA). 17.00 (978-0-15-216544-4(4) , Gulliver Bks.) Harcourt Children's Bks.

Pennington, Kate. Tread Softly. 2003. (YA). 16.99 (978-0-340-87862-0(2) , Hodder & Stoughton) Hodder General Publishing Division GBR. *Dist:* Trafalgar Square Publishing.

Scholastic, Inc. Staff. Elizabeth I: Red Rose of the House of Tudor, England 1544. 2000. (Royal Diaries Ser.). (J). lthr. 9.95 (978-0-439-26654-3(8)) Scholastic, Inc.

Thomas, Jane Resh. The Counterfeit Princess. 2005. 197p. (J). (978-0-618-93780-6(3) , Clarion Bks.) Houghton Mifflin Co. Trade & Reference Div.

GREAT BRITAIN—HISTORY—17TH CENTURY

see Great Britain—History—Stuarts, 1603-1714

GREAT BRITAIN—HISTORY—STUARTS, 1603-1714

Aronson, Marc. John Winthrop, Oliver Cromwell, & the Land of Promise. 2004. (Illus.). 224p. (J). (gr. 5-9). tchr. ed. 20.00 (978-0-618-18177-3(6) , Clarion Bks.) Houghton Mifflin Co. Trade & Reference Div.

Ashworth, Leon. Guy Fawkes. 2004. (British History Makers Ser.). (Illus.). 32p. (YA). pap. 11.99 (978-1-84234-302-9(5) , Cherrytree Books) Evans Publishing Group GBR. *Dist:* Independent Pubs. Group.

Guy, John. Tudor & Stuart Life. 2004. (Illus.). 32p. (J). (gr. 4-7). pap. 6.95 (978-1-86007-003-7(5)) Ticktock Media Ltd. GBR. *Dist:* Consortium Bk. Sales & Distribution.

Robson, Pam. The Great Plague. 2003. (Illus.). 48p. (J). pap. (978-0-7500-1934-7(4) , Hodder Wayland) Hodder Children's Division.

Shephard, Colin & Lomas, Tim. Re-Discovering the Making of the UK: Britain 1500-1750. 2001. (Illus.). 120p. pap., stu. ed. 32.50 (***978-0-7195-8544-9(9)*** , Hodder Murray) Hodder Education GBR. *Dist:* Trans-Atlantic Pubns., Inc.

GREAT BRITAIN—HISTORY—STUARTS, 1603-1714—FICTION

Forrester, Sandra. Wheel of the Moon. 2000. (Illus.). 176p. (J). (gr. 5-9). 15.95 (978-0-688-17149-0(4)) HarperCollins Pubs.

Hooper, Mary. Newes from the Dead: Being a True Story of Anne Green, Hanged for Infanticide at Oxford Assizes in 1650, Restored to the World & Died Again 1665. 2008. 256p. (YA). 15.95 (***978-1-59643-355-7(8)***) Roaring Brook Pr.

MacDonald, George. St. George & St. Michael. 2006. 68.99 (***978-1-4280-1075-8(0) ;*** pap. 61.99 (***978-1-4280-1052-9(1)***) IndyPublish.com.

Sturtevant, Katherine. A True & Faithful Narrative. l.t. ed. 2006. 289p. (YA). 21.95 (978-0-7862-9081-9(1)) Thorndike Pr.

Woodruff, Elvira. Fearless. 2008. 240p. (J). 16.99 (978-0-439-67703-5(3) , Scholastic Pr.) Scholastic, Inc.

GREAT BRITAIN—HISTORY—PURITAN REVOLUTION, 1642-1660

Aronson, Marc. John Winthrop, Oliver Cromwell, & the Land of Promise. 2004. (Illus.). 224p. (J). (gr. 5-9). tchr. ed. 20.00 (978-0-618-18177-3(6) , Clarion Bks.) Houghton Mifflin Co. Trade & Reference Div.

Ashworth, Leon. Oliver Cromwell. (Illus.). 32p. (978-0-7451-5287-5(2)); pap. (978-1-7540-9010-6(8)) Evans Publishing Group. (Cherrytree Books).

—Oliver Cromwell. 2004. (British History Makers Ser.). (Illus.). 32p. (YA). pap. 11.99 (978-1-84234-281-7(9) , Cherrytree Books) Evans Publishing Group GBR. *Dist:* Independent Pubs. Group.

Farman, John. Roundhead & Cavaliers. 2003. (Illus.). 63p. (J). pap. 3.99 (978-0-330-37646-4(2) , Macmillan Children's Bks.) Pan Macmillan GBR. *Dist:* Trafalgar Square Publishing.

Wellman, Sam. John Bunyan: Author of The Pilgrim's Progress. 1999. (Heroes of the Faith Ser.). (Illus.). 208p. (YA). (gr. 4-7). 14.95 (978-0-7910-5035-4(1) , Chelsea Hse.) Facts On File, Inc.

GREAT BRITAIN—HISTORY—PURITAN REVOLUTION, 1642-1660—FICTION

Cavendish, Grace. Conspiracy. 2005. (Lady Grace Mysteries, from the Daybookes of Lady Grace Cavendish Ser.). 208p. (J). (gr. 3-7). 6.95 (978-0-385-73153-9(1) , Delacorte Bks. for Young Readers) Random Hse. Children's Bks.

Henty, G. A. Friends Though Divided: A Tale of the Civil War. 2004. reprint ed. pap. 15.95 (978-1-4191-2099-2(9)); pap. 1.99 (978-1-4192-2099-9(3)) Kessinger Publishing, LLC.

GREAT BRITAIN—HISTORY—18TH CENTURY—FICTION

Garfield, Leon. Smith. 2000. (J). (978-0-606-21674-6(X)); (gr. 7-12). lib. bdg. 15.25 (978-0-613-30742-0(9)) Tandem Library Bks.

Gavin, Jamila. Coram Boy. 336p. (YA). 2001. (Illus.). (gr. 7-9). 19.00 (978-0-374-31544-3(2) , Farrar, Straus & Giroux (BYR)); 2005. reprint ed. pap. 7.95 (978-0-374-41374-3(6) , Sunburst) Farrar, Straus & Giroux.

Holmes, Victoria. Rider in the Dark: An Epic Horse Story. 2004. (Illus.). 320p. (J). (gr. 5 up). 15.99 (978-0-06-052025-0(6)); lib. bdg. 16.89 (978-0-06-052026-7(4)) HarperCollins Pubs.

Morgan, Nicola. The Highwayman's Footsteps. 2007. (Illus.). 368p. (YA). (gr. 7). 16.99 (***978-0-7636-3472-8(7)***) Candlewick Pr.

GREAT BRITAIN—HISTORY—1714-1837

Clare, John D. Britain 1750-1900. 2003. (Illus.). 96p. pap. 29.50 (***978-0-340-86909-3(7) ;*** pap. 29.50 (***978-0-340-86910-9(0)***) Hodder Education GBR. (Hodder Murray). *Dist:* Trans-Atlantic Pubns., Inc.

Costain, Meredith & Antram, David. You Wouldn't Want to Be an 18th-Century British Convict! 2006. (Illus.). 32p. (YA). (gr. 2-5). pap. 9.95 (978-0-531-16998-8(7) , Watts, Franklin) Scholastic Library Publishing.

Ingram, Scott. King George III. 2003. (Triangle History of the American Revolution Ser.). (Illus.). 104p. (J). 28.70 (978-1-56711-779-0(1) , Blackbirch Pr., Inc.) Thomson Gale.

Kamm, Antony. The Jacobites. Steel, Ewan, illus. 1999. (Scottie Bks.). 40p. (J). (gr. 3-7). pap. 6.95 (978-0-11-495250-1(7)) Stationery Office, The GBR. *Dist:* Balogh International, Inc.

Nardo, Don. Weapons of War. 2002. (American War Library). (Illus.). 112p. (J). 29.95 (978-1-59018-226-0(X) , Lucent Bks.) Thomson Gale.

Schanzer, Rosalyn. George vs. George: The American Revolution As Seen from Both Sides. 2007. (Illus.). 64p. (J). (gr. 4-9). pap. 6.95 (978-1-4263-0042-4(5) , National Geographic Children's Bks.) National Geographic Society.

—George vs. George: The Revolutionary War as Seen by Both Sides. 2004. (Illus.). 64p. (J). (gr. 4-9). 25.90 (978-0-7922-6999-1(3) , National Geographic Children's Bks.) National Geographic Society.

GREAT BRITAIN—HISTORY—1714-1837—FICTION

Bajoria, Paul. The Printer's Devil. 2007. 400p. (J). (gr. 4-8). pap. 6.99 (978-0-316-10678-8(X)) Little Brown & Co.

Olds, Barbara Anne. Haven House. Amatrula, Michele, illus. 2007. 141p. (J). pap. 8.95 (978-0-9744446-0-4(X)) All About Kids Publishing.

GREAT BRITAIN—HISTORY—19TH CENTURY

Clare, John D. Britain 1750-1900. 2003. (Illus.). 96p. pap. 29.50 (***978-0-340-86909-3(7) ;*** pap. 29.50 (***978-0-340-86910-9(0)***) Hodder Education GBR. (Hodder Murray). *Dist:* Trans-Atlantic Pubns., Inc.

Dickens, Charles. Martin Chuzzlewit. 2000. (gr. 7-12). lib. bdg. 19.90 (978-0-613-70856-2(3)) Tandem Library Bks.

Dowswell, Paul. Victorians. (Illus.). 32p. pap. 9.99 (978-0-7502-2613-4(7) , Hodder & Stoughton) Hodder General Publishing Division GBR. *Dist:* Trafalgar Square Publishing.

Greenhaven Staff. Industrial Revolution. 2002. (gr. 7-12). lib. bdg. 33.25 (978-0-613-73852-1(7)) Tandem Library Bks.

Guy, John. Victorian Life. 2004. (Illus.). 32p. (J). (gr. 4-7). pap. (978-1-86007-005-1(1)) Ticktock Media Ltd.

Hepplewhite, Peter & Campbell, Mairi. The Industrial Revolution. 2003. (Illus.). 48p. pap. (978-0-7502-3911-0(5) , Hodder Wayland) Hodder Children's Division.

Lee, Stephen J. Gladstone & Disraeli. 2005. (Questions & Analysis in History Ser.). (Illus.). 208p. 90.00 (978-0-415-32356-7(8)) Routledge.

Maccoby, S. English Radicalism Vol. 5: 1886-1914, 6 vols. 2001. (Routledge Library of British Political History). 650p. (gr. 13). 215.00 (978-0-415-26575-1(4)) Routledge.

Macdonald, Fiona & Antram, David. You Wouldn't Want to Be a Victorian Servant! 2006. (Illus.). 32p. (YA). (gr. 2-5). pap. 9.95 (978-0-531-16997-1(9) , Watts, Franklin) Scholastic Library Publishing.

Malam, John. You wouldn't/be 19th century coal Miner. 2006. (Illus.). 32p. (J). (gr. 2-5). 28.50 (***978-0-531-14971-3(4)***) Scholastic Library Publishing.

Pierce, Alan. The Industrial Revolution. 2005. (American Moments Ser.). (Illus.). 48p. (J). (gr. 4-8). lib. bdg. 25.65 (978-1-59197-933-3(1)) ABDO Publishing Co.

Price-Groff, Claire. Queen Victoria & Nineteenth-Century England. 2003. (Rulers & Their Times Ser.). (Illus.). 96p. (YA). (gr. 8-12). 29.93 (978-0-7614-1488-9(6) , Benchmark Bks.) Cavendish, Marshall Corp.

Sharman, Margaret. Victorians. 2001. (Illus.). 32p. (YA). pap. 9.99 (978-0-237-52573-6(9) , Evans Brothers, Limited) Evans Publishing Group GBR. *Dist:* Independent Pubs. Group.

Steele, Philip. Clothes & Crafts in Victorian Times. 2000. (Clothes & Crafts in History Ser.). (Illus.). 32p. (J). (gr. 4 up). lib. bdg. 24.67 (978-0-8368-2738-5(4)) Stevens, Gareth Inc.

Wooten, Sara McIntosh. The Industrial Revolution. 2003. (People at the Center of Ser.). (Illus.). 48p. (J). 24.95 (978-1-56711-766-0(X) , Blackbirch Pr., Inc.) Thomson Gale.

GREAT BRITAIN—HISTORY—19TH CENTURY—FICTION

Austen, Jane. Love & Friendship A Collection of Juve. 2006. pap. 11.99 ***(978-1-4280-2736-7(X))*** IndyPublish.com.

Avi. The Traitors' Gate. Raude, Karina, illus. 2007. 368p. (J). (gr. 6-9). 17.99 (978-0-689-85335-7(1) , Atheneum/ Richard Jackson Bks.) Simon & Schuster Children's Publishing.

Brontë, Charlotte & Larkin, Rochelle. Jane Eyre. Marcos, Pablo, illus. 2005. (Great Illustrated Classics Ser.). 240p. (J). (gr. 3-8). 21.35 (978-1-59679-243-2(4) , ABDO & Daughters) ABDO Publishing Co.

Burgess, Melvin. The Copper Treasure. Williams, Richard, illus. rev. ed. 2000. 112p. (YA). (gr. 4-7). 15.95 (978-0-8050-6381-3(1) , Holt, Henry & Co. Bks. For Young Readers) Holt, Henry & Co.

Burnett, Frances Hodgson. Little Lord Fauntleroy. (J). 21.95 (978-0-8488-0792-4(8)) Amereon LTD.

—Little Lord Fauntleroy. 2005. 104p. per. 4.95 (978-1-4209-2556-2(3)) Digireads.com.

—Little Lord Fauntleroy. 2006. 164p. (YA). 18.95 ***(978-1-934169-22-3(6))***; pap. 6.95 ***(978-1-934169-23-0(4))*** Norilana Bks.

—Little Lord Fauntleroy. 2005. (Twelve-Point Ser.). lib. bdg. 24.00 (978-1-58287-319-0(4)) North Bks.

—Little Lord Fauntleroy. Rust, Graham, illus. (J). pap. 21.95 (978-0-590-74607-6(3)) Scholastic, Inc.

—Little Lord Fauntleroy. Howell, Troy, illus. 2008. (Classic Starts Ser.). 160p. (J). 5.95 ***(978-1-4027-4578-2(8))*** Sterling Publishing Co., Inc.

—Little Lord Fauntleroy. Birch, Reginald, illus. 2004. reprint ed. pap. 27.95 (978-1-4179-4302-9(5)) Kessinger Publishing, LLC.

—Little Lord Fauntleroy. 2004. reprint ed. pap. 1.99 (978-1-4192-3078-3(6)) Kessinger Publishing, LLC.

—Little Lord Fauntleroy. l.t. ed. 2005. (Large Print Ser.). lib. bdg. 25.00 (978-1-58287-813-3(7)) North Bks.

—Sara Crewe. l.t. ed. 2006. 92p. pap. (978-1-84637-263-6(1)) Echo Library.

Cooper, Susan. Victory. 2007. 224p. (J). pap. 6.99 ***(978-1-4169-1478-5(1)*** , Aladdin) Simon & Schuster Children's Publishing.

Dickens, Charles. Charles Dickens/A Christmas Carol. Lo Famia, Jon, illus. 2005. 48p. (gr. 5-8). 25.50 (978-0-7910-9108-1(2)) Facts On File, Inc.

—Oliver Twist: With a Discussion of Honesty. 2003. (Values in Action Illustrated Classics Ser.). (J). (978-1-59203-051-4(3)) Learning Challenge, Inc.

Dowswell, Paul. Prison Ship: Adventures of a Youn Sailor. 2006. 306p. 16.95 ***(978-1-58237-674-5(3))*** Creative Thinkers, Inc.

—Prison Ship: Adventures of a Young Sailor. 2007. 320p. (YA). pap. 7.95 ***(978-1-59990-156-5(0)*** , Bloomsbury Children) Bloomsbury Publishing.

Dunkle, Clare B. The Hollow Kingdom. 2003. (Hollow Kingdom Trilogy Ser.). (Illus.). 240p. (YA). (gr. 7). 16.95 (978-0-8050-7390-4(6) , Holt, Henry & Co. Bks. For Young Readers) Holt, Henry & Co.

—The Hollow Kingdom, Vol. 5. l.t. ed. 2004. 360p. 21.95 (978-0-7862-6769-9(0) , Large Print Pr.) Thorndike Pr.

Ewing, Juliana Horatia. Mrs. Overtheway's Remembrances. 2006. 41.99 ***(978-1-4280-1444-2(6))***; pap. 35.99 ***(978-1-4280-1422-0(5))*** IndyPublish.com.

Imbernon, Maite & Dickens, Charles. Oliver Twist. 2003. (Timeless Classics Ser.). (SPA., Illus.). 92p. (J). pap. 10.95 (978-84-204-5750-5(7)) Santillana USA Publishing Co., Inc.

Le Feuvre, Amy. Harebell's Friend. 2004. (Golden Inheritance Ser.: Vol. 8). (Illus.). 140p. (J). pap. (978-0-921100-84-3(1)) Inheritance Pubns.

Mack, Tracy & Citrin, Michael. The Fall of the Amazing Zalindas. 2006. (Illus.). 259p. (J). ***(978-1-4287-0951-5(7)*** , Orchard Bks.) Scholastic, Inc.

Michael, Livi. The Whispering Road. 2005. 272p. (YA). (gr. 4). 17.99 (978-0-399-24357-8(7) , Putnam Juvenile) Penguin Group (USA) Inc.

Nesbit, E. Story of the Treasure Seekers. 2006. pap. ***(978-1-4068-3507-6(2))*** Echo Library.

Nesbit, E. The Story of the Treasure Seekers: Being the Adventures of the Bastable Children in Search of A Fortune. l.t. ed. 2005. 288p. pap. (978-1-84637-207-0(0)) Echo Library.

Pullman, Philip. The Ruby in the Smoke. 2002. (Sally Lockhart Trilogy: Bk. 1). 22.00 (978-0-8446-7230-4(0)) Smith, Peter Pub., Inc.

Stretton, Hesba. Cassy. Hymper, W. & Stacey, W. S., illus. 2006. (Golden Inheritance Ser.: Vol. 9). 117p. (J). pap. (978-0-921100-94-2(9)) Inheritance Pubns.

—Lost Gip. 2003. (Golden Inheritance Ser.: Vol. 7). (Illus.). 121p. (J). (978-0-921100-93-5(0)) Inheritance Pubns.

Styles, Showell. Midshipman Quinn Collection. 1999. (gr. 7-12). lib. bdg. 30.35 (978-0-613-80204-8(7)) Tandem Library Bks.

Thoene, Jake & Thoene, Luke. The Mystery of the Yellow Hands. 2006. (Baker Street Detectives Ser.). 144p. (J). 9.99 (978-1-4143-0370-3(X)) Tyndale Hse. Pubs.

GREAT BRITAIN—HISTORY—20TH CENTURY

Adams, Simon. Winston Churchill. 2003. (20th Century History Makers Ser.). (Illus.). 112p. (J). lib. bdg. 32.85 (978-0-7398-5254-5(X)) Raintree.

Lee, Stephen J. Gladstone & Disraeli. 2005. (Questions & Analysis in History Ser.). (Illus.). 208p. 90.00 (978-0-415-32356-7(8)) Routledge.

Ross, Stewart. Britain since 1930. 2003. (Britain Through the Ages Ser.). (Illus.). 32p. pap. 9.99 (978-0-237-52574-3(7) , Evans Brothers, Limited) Evans Publishing Group GBR. *Dist:* Independent Pubs. Group.

Stephens, Chris S. A Wartime Scrapbook. 2004. (Illus.). 32p. pap. 14.95 (978-1-84323-285-8(5)) Beekman Bks., Inc.

GREAT BRITAIN—KINGS AND RULERS

Abbott, Jacob. History of William the Conqueror. 2003. 291p. 89.00 (978-0-7950-4508-0(5)) New Library Press-.Net.

Ashworth, Leon. King Henry VIII. (Illus.). 32p. (978-0-7451-5289-9(9)); pap. (978-0-7540-9012-0(4)); 2001. (978-1-84234-082-0(4)) Evans Publishing Group. (Cherrytree Books).

—King Henry VIII. 2004. (British History Makers Ser.). (Illus.). 32p. (YA). pap. 9.99 (978-1-84234-283-1(5) , Cherrytree Books) Evans Publishing Group GBR. *Dist:* Independent Pubs. Group.

—Queen Victoria. 1999. (British History Makers Ser.). (Illus.). 32p. pap. 11.99 (978-0-7540-9014-4(0) , Cherrytree Books) Evans Publishing Group GBR. *Dist:* Independent Pubs. Group.

Bailey, Jacqui. Royal London. Lilly, Matthew, illus. 2002. 48p. pap. 8.95 (978-0-7136-6261-0(1)) A & C Black GBR. *Dist:* Consortium Bk. Sales & Distribution.

Banham, Dale & Dawson, Ian. King John: A Key Stage 3 Investigation into Medieval Monarchy. 2000. (Illus.). 72p. pap., stu. ed. 26.00 ***(978-0-7195-8539-5(2)*** , Hodder Murray) Hodder Education GBR. *Dist:* Trans-Atlantic Pubns., Inc.

Barnes-Murphy, Rowan. Kings & Queens of Britain. 2003. (Illus.). 40p. (YA). (978-1-84365-027-0(4)) Chrysalis Children's Bks.

Bodleian Library & Collins. The Chapter of Kings. 2005. (Illus.). 37p. 9.99 (978-1-85124-320-4(8)) Bodleian Library GBR. *Dist:* Chicago Distribution Ctr.

Browning, Oscar. True Stories from English History from T. 2006. pap. 33.95 ***(978-1-4254-9960-0(0))*** Kessinger Publishing, LLC.

Can't You Make Them Behave, King George? 2002. (978-1-56137-402-1(4)) Novel Units, Inc.

Can't You Make Them Behave, King George? 2004. 24.95 incl. audio (978-1-56008-171-5(6)); 29.95 incl. cd-rom (978-1-55592-378-5(X)); (J). pap. 14.95 incl. audio (978-1-56008-172-2(4)); (J). pap. 18.95 incl. audio compact disk (978-1-55592-377-8(1)); (J). pap. 18.95 incl. audio compact disk (978-1-55592-380-8(1)); (J). pap. 38.75 incl. audio compact disk (978-1-55592-379-2(8)); (J). pap. 38.75 incl. audio compact disk (978-1-55592-381-5(X)); (J). pap. 32.75 incl. audio (978-1-55592-350-1(X)) Weston Woods Studios, Inc.

Ford, Nick. Henry VIII: The King, His Six Wives & His Court. 2004. (Leaders of the Middle Ages Ser.). (Illus.). 112p. (YA). lib. bdg. 31.95 (978-1-4042-0163-7(7)) Rosen Publishing Group, Inc., The.

Fowke, Bob. The Secret Life of Elizabeth I. 2005. (Illus.). (YA). pap. 9.99 (978-0-340-88422-5(3) , Hodder & Stoughton) Hodder General Publishing Division GBR. *Dist:* Trafalgar Square Publishing.

—The Secret Life of Henry VIII. 2005. (Illus.). (YA). pap. 9.99 (978-0-340-88421-8(5) , Hodder & Stoughton) Hodder General Publishing Division GBR. *Dist:* Trafalgar Square Publishing.

—The Secret Life of Queen Victoria. 2005. (Illus.). (YA). pap. 9.99 (978-0-340-88423-2(1) , Hodder & Stoughton) Hodder General Publishing Division GBR. *Dist:* Trafalgar Square Publishing.

Graves, Michael A. R. Henry VIII. 2003. (Profiles in Power Ser.). 232p. (C). pap. 20.60 (978-0-582-38110-0(X)) Longman Publishing.

Green, John. Kings & Queens of England. 2005. (Illus.). 32p. (J). (gr. 3). pap. 3.95 (978-0-486-44666-0(2)) Dover Pubns., Inc.

Hilliam, Paul. William the Conqueror: First Norman King of England. 2004. (Leaders of the Middle Ages Ser.). (Illus.). 112p. (J). lib. bdg. 31.95 (978-1-4042-0166-8(1)) Rosen Publishing Group, Inc., The.

Imperato, Anthony. Henry VII. 1999. (Pathfinder History Ser.). (Illus.). 64p. (YA). (gr. 11 up). pap. 15.95 (978-0-7487-4308-7(1)) Nelson Thornes Ltd. GBR. *Dist:* Trans-Atlantic Pubns., Inc.

Krohn, Katherine E. Princess Diana. 1999. (Biography Ser.). (Illus.). 112p. (YA). (gr. 6-12). pap. (978-0-8225-9683-7(0) , Lerner Pubns.) Lerner Publishing Group.

Ladybird Books Staff. Kings & Queens of England: Book One (Great Rulers), Bk. 1. rev. ed. (History Ser.: No. 561-24 & 25). (Illus.). 52p. (YA). (gr. 5 up). pap. (978-0-7214-0560-5(6) , Dutton Juvenile) Penguin Group (USA) Inc.

—Kings & Queens of England: Book Two (Great Rulers), Bk. 2. rev. ed. (History Ser.: No. 561-24 & 25). (Illus.). 52p. (YA). (gr. 5 up). pap. (978-0-7214-0561-2(4) , Dutton Juvenile) Penguin Group (USA) Inc.

Marilyn Tower Oliver. Henry VIII. 2004. (Importance of Ser.). (Illus.). 112p. (J). 32.45 (978-1-59018-424-0(6)) Thomson Gale.

McGowen, Tom. William the Conqueror: Last Invader of England. 2007. (Rulers of the Middle Ages Ser.). (Illus.). 160p. (YA). (gr. 7-9). lib. bdg. 34.60 (978-0-7660-2713-8(9)) Enslow Pubs., Inc.

Pryor, Francis. Britain Ad: A Quest for Authur, England & the Anglo-Saxon. movie tie-in ed. 2006. (Illus.). 268p. 35.00 ***(978-0-00-718186-5(8))*** HarperCollins Pubs. Ltd. GBR. *Dist:* Independent Pubs. Group.

Ross, Stewart. Beware the King. 2007. (Flashbacks Ser.). (Illus.). 64p. (J). (gr. 4-7). pap. 8.95 ***(978-0-237-53151-5(8)*** , Evans Brothers, Limited) Evans Publishing Group GBR. *Dist:* Independent Pubs. Group.

—Down with the Romans. 2007. (Flashbacks Ser.). (Illus.). 64p. (J). (gr. 4-7). pap. 8.95 ***(978-0-237-53150-8(X)*** , Evans Brothers, Limited) Evans Publishing Group GBR. *Dist:* Independent Pubs. Group.

Schanzer, Rosalyn. George vs. George: The American Revolution As Seen from Both Sides. 2007. (Illus.). 64p. (J). (gr. 4-9). pap. 6.95 (978-1-4263-0042-4(5) , National Geographic Children's Bks.) National Geographic Society.

—George vs. George: The Revolutionary War as Seen by Both Sides. 2004. (Illus.). 64p. (J). (gr. 4-9). 25.90 (978-0-7922-6999-1(3) , National Geographic Children's Bks.) National Geographic Society.

Streissguth, Thomas. Richard the Lionheart: Crusader King of England. 2007. (Rulers of the Middle Ages Ser.). (Illus.). 160p. (YA). (gr. 7-9). lib. bdg. 34.60 (978-0-7660-2714-5(7)) Enslow Pubs., Inc.

West, David & Gaff, Jackie. Richard the Lionheart: The Life of a King & Crusader. 2005. (Graphic Nonfiction Ser.). (Illus.). 48p. (J). lib. bdg. 26.50 (978-1-4042-0241-2(2)) Rosen Publishing Group, Inc., The.

Wyly, Michael J. King Arthur. 2001. (Mystery Library). (Illus.). 112p. (YA). (gr. 4-12). 27.45 (978-1-56006-771-9(3) , Lucent Bks.) Thomson Gale.

GREAT BRITAIN—NOBILITY

Britton, Tamara L. Prince William. 1999. (Young Profiles Ser.). (Illus.). 32p. (J). (gr. k-6). lib. bdg. 22.78 (978-1-57765-324-0(6) , Checkerboard Library) ABDO Publishing Co.

Lasky, Kathryn. Elizabeth I: Red Rose of the House of Tudor, England 1544. 1999. (Royal Diaries Ser.). (Illus.). 240p. (J). (gr. 4-8). 10.95 (978-0-590-68484-2(1) , Scholastic Pr.) Scholastic, Inc.

GREAT BRITAIN—POLITICS AND GOVERNMENT—FICTION

Chandler, Paul. Mouse of Commons - Mouse of Lords. 2006. 186p. pap. 14.99 (978-1-4116-8447-8(8)) Lulu-.com.

Willard, Barbara. If All the Swords in England. Sax, Robert M., illus. 2000. (Living History Library). x, 181p. (J). (gr. 8-12). reprint ed. pap. 12.95 (978-1-883937-49-2(3) , 49-3) Bethlehem Bks.

GREAT BRITAIN—SOCIAL LIFE AND CUSTOMS

Ashby, Ruth. Elizabethan England. 1998. (Cultures of the Past Ser.). (Illus.). 80p. (J). (gr. 5 up). lib. bdg. 29.93 (978-0-7614-0269-5(1) , Benchmark Bks.) Cavendish, Marshall Corp.

Banting, Erinn. England — The Land. 2004. (Lands, Peoples, & Cultures Ser.). (Illus.). 32p. (J). (978-0-7787-9322-9(2)) Crabtree Publishing Co.

—England — The People. 2004. (Lands, Peoples, & Cultures Ser.). (Illus.). 32p. (J). pap. (978-0-7787-9690-9(6)) Crabtree Publishing Co.

Bowden, Rob. United Kingdom. 2006. (Destination Detectives Ser.). (Illus.). 48p. (J). pap. (978-1-4109-2343-1(6)); lib. bdg. (978-1-4109-2332-5(0)) Steck-Vaughn.

Childs, Alan. Tudor Theatre. (Illus.). 32p. pap. (978-0-7502-3738-3(4) , Hodder Wayland) Hodder Children's Division.

Chrisp, Peter. Welcome to the Globe! The Story of Shakespeare's Theater. 2000. (Eyewitness Readers Ser.). (J). (978-0-606-20130-8(0)) Tandem Library Bks.

Collie, Joanne & Martin, Alex. What's It Like? Life & Culture in Britain Today. 2000. (Illus.). 96p. pap., stu. ed. 19.00 (978-0-521-58662-7(3)) Cambridge Univ. Pr.

Dowswell, Paul. Victorians. (Illus.). 32p. pap. 9.99 (978-0-7502-2613-4(7) , Hodder & Stoughton) Hodder General Publishing Division GBR. *Dist:* Trafalgar Square Publishing.

Foreman, Michael. After the War was Over. 2007. (Illus.). 96p. (J). pap. 16.99 ***(978-1-84365-088-1(6))*** Anova Bks. GBR. *Dist:* Independent Pubs. Group.

Greig, Charlotte. The British Isles. 2002. (Cultures & Costumes Ser.). (Illus.). 64p. (J). (gr. 7-12). lib. bdg. (978-1-59084-431-1(9)) Mason Crest Pubs.

Guy, John. Elizabeth I & the Armada. 2004. (Illus.). 32p. (J). (gr. 4-7). pap. (978-1-86007-029-7(9)) Ticktock Media Ltd.

Hill, Barbara W. Cooking the English Way. 2nd rev. ed. 2003. (Easy Menu Ethnic Cookbooks). (Illus.). 72p. (J). (gr. 5-12). 25.26 (978-0-8225-4105-9(X)) Lerner Publishing Group.

Hunter, Rebecca. Growing up in the Forties. 2003. (Illus.). 32p. pap. (978-0-7502-3434-4(2) , Hodder Wayland) Hodder Children's Division.

—Growing up in the Thirties. 2003. (Illus.). 32p. pap. (978-0-7502-3433-7(4) , Hodder Wayland) Hodder Children's Division.

Jackson, Ellen B. Turn of the Century. Ellis, Jan Davey, illus. 1998. 32p. (J). (gr. 2-7). 17.95 (978-0-88106-369-1(X)) Charlesbridge Publishing, Inc.

Jarvie, Frances. Festivals in Scotland. Galloway, Fhiona, illus. 1999. (Scottie Bks.). 40p. (J). (gr. 3-7). pap. 6.95 (978-0-11-495271-6(X)) Stationery Office, The GBR. *Dist:* Balogh International, Inc.

Johnson, Emma. Medieval Town & Country Life. (Illus.). 32p. 18.95 (978-1-932889-28-4(0)) Sea-To-Sea Pubns.

Macdonald, Fiona. You wouldn't/be victorian Servant. 2006. (Illus.). 32p. (J). (gr. 2-5). 28.50 ***(978-0-531-14972-0(2))*** Scholastic Library Publishing.

Malam, John. You wouldn't/be 19th century coal Miner. 2006. (Illus.). 32p. (J). (gr. 2-5). 28.50 ***(978-0-531-14971-3(4))*** Scholastic Library Publishing.

Price-Groff, Claire. Queen Victoria & Nineteenth-Century England. 2003. (Rulers & Their Times Ser.). (Illus.). 96p. (YA). (gr. 8-12). 29.93 (978-0-7614-1488-9(6) , Benchmark Bks.) Cavendish, Marshall Corp.

Ross, Michael Elsohn. Children of Northern Ireland. Rigau, Felix, photos by. 2000. (World's Children Ser.). (Illus.). 48p. (J). (gr. 3-6). (978-1-57505-433-9(7) , Carolrhoda Bks.) Lerner Publishing Group.

Shuter, Jane. Shakespeare's Birthplace. 2003. (Visiting the Past Ser.). (Illus.). 32p. (J). (gr. 5-7). lib. bdg. 25.64 (978-1-58810-708-4(6)) Heinemann Library.

Stewart, Gail B. Life in Elizabethan London. 2002. (Lucent Library of Historical Eras. Elizabethan England Library). (Illus.). 112p. (J). 28.70 (978-1-59018-100-3(X) , Lucent Bks.) Thomson Gale.

Stott, Colin. Victorian Transport. (Illus.). 32p. pap. (978-0-7502-3752-9(X) , Hodder Wayland) Hodder Children's Division.

Williams, Brian. The Story Behind Charles Dickens' Oliver Twist. 2006. (History in Literature Ser.). (Illus.). 56p. (J). lib. bdg. (978-1-4034-8209-9(8)) Heinemann Library.

Willingham, Elizabeth. Teens in England. 2007. lib. bdg. ***(978-0-7565-2061-8(4))*** Compass Point Bks.

GREAT LAKES

see also Erie, Lake; Huron, Lake (Mich. and Ont.); Michigan, Lake; Ontario, Lake (N.Y. and Ont.); Superior, Lake

Beckett, Harry. Lake Superior. 1999. (Great Lakes of North America Ser.). (Illus.). 32p. (J). (gr. 3-6). lib. bdg. 26.60 (978-0-86593-528-0(9)) Rourke Publishing, LLC.

—Waterways to the Great Lakes. 1999. (Great Lakes of North America Ser.). (Illus.). 32p. (J). (gr. 3-6). lib. bdg. 26.60 (978-0-86593-529-7(7)) Rourke Publishing, LLC.

Blocksma, Mary. What's on the Beach? A Great Lakes Treasure Hunt. 2003. (Illus.). 48p. (YA). pap. 10.95 (978-0-9708575-2-1(7)) Beaver Island Arts.

—What's on the Beach? A Great Lakes Treasure Hunt. Blocksma, Mary, illus. 2003. (Great Lakes Treasure Hunts Ser.: No. 1). (Illus.). 48p. (J). pap. 9.95 (978-0-9708575-1-4(9)) Beaver Island Arts.

Harcourt School Publishers Staff. America's Great Lakes. 3rd ed. 2002. (Horizons Ser.). (Illus.). (J). pap. 5.50 (978-0-15-333413-9(4)) Harcourt Schl. Pubs.

Katz, Sharon. The Great Lakes. 1999. (Ecosystems of North America Ser.). (Illus.). 64p. (YA). (gr. 6 up). lib. bdg. 28.50 (978-0-7614-0898-7(3) , Benchmark Bks.) Cavendish, Marshall Corp.

Kummer, Patricia K. The Great Lakes. 2008. (J). ***(978-0-7614-2853-4(4))*** Cavendish, Marshall Bks., Ltd.

Mitchell, John C. Prehistoric Great Lakes. Woodruff, Thomas R., illus. 1999. 48p. (J). (gr. 2-7). 16.95 (978-0-9621466-3-3(3)) Suttons Bay Pubns.

Stonehouse, Frederick. Final Passage: True Shipwreck Adventures. Meyer, Susan Alby, illus. 2002. (J). 17.95 (978-1-892384-16-4(7)) Avery Color Studios, Inc.

Thompson, Linda. Los Grandes Lagos. 2006. (Expansion de America II Ser.). (SPA.). 48p. (gr. 4-8). pap. 7.95 (978-1-59515-705-8(0)) Rourke Publishing, LLC.

—Great Lakes. 2005. 48p. pap. 7.45 (978-1-59515-826-0(X)) Rourke Publishing, LLC.

Valzania, Kim. Great Lakes. 2004. (Rookie Read-About Geography Ser.). (Illus.). 31p. (J). 20.50 (978-0-516-22758-0(0) , Children's Pr.) Scholastic Library Publishing.

Valzania, Kimberly. Great Lakes. 2004. (Rookie Read-About Geography Ser.). 32p. (J). (gr. 1-2). pap. 5.95 (978-0-516-24648-2(8) , Children's Pr.) Scholastic Library Publishing.

Westfield, Patricia & Soper, Nan. Exploring the Great Lakes: A Logbook of Adventures. 2003. (Illus.). 64p. (J). spiral bd. 27.95 incl. cd-rom (978-0-938682-73-8(3)) River Road Pubns., Inc.

GREAT LAKES—FICTION

Barker, Charles Ferguson. The Day the Great Lakes Drained Away. 2005. (ENG., Illus.). (J). (ps). 18.95 (978-0-9749145-2-7(5)) Mackinac Island Pr., Inc.

Johnson, Rand. Great Lakes Ghost Ship. 2005. (Michigan Chillers: No. 11). 208p. pap. (978-1-893699-84-7(6)) AudioCraft Publishing, Inc.

Maurer, Tracy. Storm Codes. Rodriguez, Christina, illus. 2007. 40p. (J). pap. 8.95 ***(978-0-89317-064-6(X)*** , WW-064X); (gr. 1-7). lib. bdg. 17.95 ***(978-0-89317-063-9(1)*** , WW-0631) Finney Co., Inc. (Windward Publishing).

Yaroslavskaya, Lyudmila. The Great Lakes Legends & Fairy Tales. 2006. (ENG & RUS., Illus.). (J). per. ***(978-0-9791248-0-8(8))*** Yaroslavskaya, Lyudmila.

GREAT LAKES—HISTORY

O'Hara, Megan. Lighthouse: Living in a Great Lakes Lighthouse, 1910 to 1940. 1998. 32p. (J). pap. 21.00 (978-0-516-21252-4(4) , Children's Pr.) Scholastic Library Publishing.

St. Antoine, Sara. The Great Lakes. 2005. (Stories from Where We Live Ser.). (Illus.). 264p. (J). pap. 10.95 (978-1-57131-654-7(X)) Milkweed Editions.

Thompson, Linda. Los Grandes Lagos. 2005. (ENG & SPA., Illus.). 48p. (J). (978-1-59515-661-7(5)) Rourke Publishing, LLC.

—The Great Lakes. 2006. (Expansion of America II Ser.). (Illus.). 48p. (gr. 4-8). 20.95 (978-1-59515-512-2(0)) Rourke Publishing, LLC.

GREAT PLAINS

Collier, Christopher & Collier, James Lincoln. Indians, Cowboys & Farmers: 1865-1910. 2000. (Drama of American History Ser.). (Illus.). 96p. (J). (gr. 5-9). lib. bdg. 31.36 (978-0-7614-1052-2(X) , Benchmark Bks.) Cavendish, Marshall Corp.

Connell, Kate. Dust Bowl Days: Hard Times for Farmers. 2004. (Illus.). 40p. (J). pap. (978-0-7922-4557-5(1)) National Geographic Society.

—Hoping for Rain: The Dust Bowl Adventures of Patty & Earl Buckler. 2004. (I Am American Ser.). (Illus.). 40p. (J). (gr. 3-7). pap. 6.99 (978-0-7922-6903-8(9) , National Geographic Children's Bks.) National Geographic Society.

Coombs, Karen Mueller. Children of the Dust Days. 2005. (Picture the American Past Ser.). (Illus.). 48p. (gr. 2-5). lib. bdg. 22.60 (978-1-57505-360-8(8)) Lerner Publishing Group.

DeAngelis, Therese & DeAngelis, Gina. The Dust Bowl. 2001. (Great Disasters, Reforms & Ramifications Ser.). (Illus.). 112p. (J). 30.00 (978-0-7910-6323-1(2) , Chelsea Hse.) Facts On File, Inc.

E F G

Fowler, Allan. Living on the Plains. 2000. (Rookie Read-About Geography Ser.). (Illus.). 32p. (J). (gr. 1-2). pap. 5.95 (978-0-516-27054-8(0) , Children's Pr.) Scholastic Library Publishing.

—Living on the Plains. 2000. (gr. k-3). lib. bdg. 14.10 (978-0-613-54738-3(1)) Tandem Library Bks.

Harcourt School Publishers Staff. At Play on the Plains On Level. 3rd ed. 2002. (Trophies Reading Program Ser.). (Illus.). pap. 5.10 (978-0-15-323356-2(7)) Harcourt Schl. Pubs.

Heinrichs, Ann. The Dust Bowl. 2004. (We the People Ser.). (Illus.). 48p. (J). 22.60 (978-0-7565-0837-1(1)) Compass Point Bks.

Isaacs, Sally Senzell. The Great Land Rush. 2003. (Illus.). 32p. (J). pap. 7.50 (978-1-4034-4771-5(3)); lib. bdg. 25.64 (978-1-4034-2505-8(1)) Heinemann Library.

—Life in the Dust Bowl. (Picture the Past Ser.). (Illus.). 32p. (J). 2002. (gr. k-3). 7.50 (978-1-58810-413-7(3) , 91186); 2001. (gr. 2-4). lib. bdg. (978-1-58810-248-5(3)) Heinemann Library.

—Life in the Dust Bowl. 2002. (gr. k-3). lib. bdg. 15.90 (978-0-613-84255-6(3)) Tandem Library Bks.

Johnson, Michael. Native Tribes of the Plains & Prairie. 2004. (Native Tribes of North America Ser.). (Illus.). 64p. (J). (gr. 5 up). lib. bdg. 32.67 (978-0-8368-5613-2(9) , World Almanac Library) Stevens, Gareth Inc.

Kalman, Bobbie. Nations of the Plains. 2001. (Native Nations of North America Ser.). (Illus.). 32p. (J). (gr. 5). pap. (978-0-7787-0460-7(2)); (978-0-7787-0368-6(1)) Crabtree Publishing Co.

—Nations of the Plains. 2001. (gr. 3-6). lib. bdg. 16.40 (978-0-613-43479-9(X)) Tandem Library Bks.

Kundiger, Marion S. & Garretson, Jerri. Izzie: Growing up on the Plains in the 1880s. Kundiger, Marion S. & Garretson, Jerri, illus. 1998. (Illus.). 48p. (J). (ps-4). pap. 5.95 (978-0-9659712-1-8(X)) Ravenstone Pr.

McArthur, Debra. The Dust Bowl & the Depression in American History. 2002. (In American History Ser.). (Illus.). 128p. (J). (gr. 5-12). lib. bdg. 26.60 (978-0-7660-1838-9(5)) Enslow Pubs., Inc.

Price, Sean. The Dirty Thirties: Documenting the Dust Bowl. 2006. (American History Through Primary Sources Ser.). (Illus.). 32p. (J). (978-1-4109-2416-2(5)); pap. (978-1-4109-2427-8(0)) Steck-Vaughn.

Quigley, Mary. Prairie Explorer. 2004. (Habitat Explorer Ser.). (Illus.). 32p. (J). (ps-ps). lib. bdg. 25.70 (978-1-4109-0513-0(6)) Raintree.

St. Antoine, Sara, ed. The Great North American Prairie. Mirocha, Paul & Nicholson, Trudy, illus. 2004. (Stories from Where We Live Ser.). 208p. pap. 10.95 (978-1-57131-645-5(0)) Milkweed Editions.

Stone, Lynn M. Bison. 2003. (Animals in U.S. History Ser.). (Illus.). 24p. (J). 25.64 (978-1-58952-698-3(8)) Rourke Publishing, LLC.

Wilkerson, J. L. Scribe of the Great Plains: Mari Sandoz. 1999. (Great Heartlanders Ser.). (Illus.). 131p. (YA). (gr. 4-12). pap. 8.95 (978-0-9664470-0-2(X)) Acorn Bks.

Yancey, Diane. Life During the Dust Bowl. 2004. (Way People Live Ser.). (J). 29.95 (978-1-59018-265-9(0) , Lucent Bks.) Thomson Gale.

GREAT SMOKY MOUNTAINS (N.C. AND TENN.)

Graf, Mike. Great Smoky Mountains National Park. 2002. (National Parks Ser.). (Illus.). 24p. (J). (gr. 2-3). lib. bdg. 18.60 (978-0-7368-1376-1(4) , Bridgestone Bks.) Capstone Pr., Inc.

Hamilton, John. Great Smoky Mountains National Park. 2005. (National Parks Ser.). (Illus.). 32p. (J). (gr. 3-8). lib. bdg. 24.21 (978-1-59197-943-2(9)) ABDO Publishing Co.

Horstman, Lisa. Smoky Mountain Wee Ones. Kemp, Steve, ed. Horstman, Lisa, illus. 2003. (Illus.). 16p. (J). bds. 6.99 (978-0-937207-41-3(1)) Great Smoky Mountains Natural History Assn.

Pancella, Peggy. Great Smoky Mountains National Park. 2006. (Symbols of Freedom Ser.). (Illus.). 32p. (J). (978-1-4034-7796-5(5)) Heinemann Library.

GREAT SMOKY MOUNTAINS (N.C. AND TENN.)—FICTION

O'Connor, Barbara. Greetings from Nowhere. 2008. 208p. (J). 16.00 (***978-0-374-39937-5(9)***) Farrar, Straus & Giroux.

White, Alana J. Come Next Spring. 2002. 180p. (J). pap. 13.95 (978-0-595-22698-6(1) , Backinprint.com) iUniverse, Inc.

Youmans, Marly. The Curse of the Raven Mocker. 2003. 288p. (J). 18.00 (978-0-374-31667-9(8) , Farrar, Straus & Giroux (BYR)) Farrar, Straus & Giroux.

—The Curse of the Raven Mocker. 2006. 288p. (YA). (gr. 7). pap. 7.99 (978-0-14-240696-0(1) , Puffin) Penguin Group (USA) Inc.

GREECE

Adare, Sierra. Greece - The Culture. 1998. (Lands, Peoples & Cultures Ser.). (Illus.). 32p. (J). (gr. 4-5). (978-0-86505-228-4(X)); pap. (978-0-86505-308-3(1)) Crabtree Publishing Co.

—Greece - The Land. 1998. (Lands, Peoples & Cultures Ser.). (Illus.). 32p. (J). (gr. 4-5). (978-0-86505-226-0(3)); pap. (978-0-86505-306-9(5)) Crabtree Publishing Co.

—Greece - The People. 1998. (Lands, Peoples & Cultures Ser.). (Illus.). 32p. (J). (gr. 4-5). pap. (978-0-86505-307-6(3)) Crabtree Publishing Co.

—Greece the Culture. 1999. (gr. 3-6). lib. bdg. 16.40 (978-0-613-12321-1(2)) Tandem Library Bks.

Augustin, Byron & Augustin, Rebecca. Greece. 2006. 40p. (J). (gr. 2-4). pap. 6.95 (978-0-516-24953-7(3) , Children's Pr.) Scholastic Library Publishing.

Brooks, Susie. Greece. 2006. (Our Lives, Our World Ser.). (J). (978-1-59389-287-6(X)) Chrysalis Education.

Claybourne, Anna. Ancient Greece. 2007. (Illus.). 64p. (J). (***978-1-4109-2733-0(4)***); (***978-1-4109-2726-2(1)***) Steck-Vaughn.

Costain, Meredith & Collins, Paul. Welcome to Greece. 2001. (Countries of the World Ser.). (Illus.). 32p. (J). (gr. 4 up). 28.00 (978-0-7910-6545-7(6) , 010204, Chelsea Hse.) Facts On File, Inc.

DeAngelis, Gina. Greece. 2003. (Many Cultures, One World Ser.). (Illus.). 32p. (J). (gr. 2-3). lib. bdg. 23.93 (978-0-7368-2167-4(8) , Bridgestone Bks.) Capstone Pr., Inc.

DuBois, Jill, et al. Greece. 2nd ed. 2003. (Cultures of the World Ser.). (Illus.). 144p. (gr. 5 up). lib. bdg. 37.07 (978-0-7614-1499-5(1) , Cavendish, Marshall Reference Bks.) Cavendish, Marshall Corp.

Etingoff, Kim. Greece. 2006. (European Union Ser.). (Illus.). 88p. (J). (gr. 5 up). lib. bdg. (978-1-4222-0049-0(3)) Mason Crest Pubs.

Frank, Nicole & Yeoh, Hong Nam. Welcome to Greece. 2000. (Welcome to My Country Ser.). (Illus.). 48p. (J). (gr. 2 up). lib. bdg. 26.00 (978-0-8368-2509-1(8)) Stevens, Gareth Inc.

Harvey, Miles. Look What Came from Greece. 1999. (Look What Came from Ser.). (Illus.). 32p. (J). (gr. 2-4). pap. 6.95 (978-0-531-15974-3(4) , Watts, Franklin) Scholastic Library Publishing.

Heinrichs, Ann. Greece. 2002. (Enchantment of the World, Second Ser.). (Illus.). 144p. (YA). (gr. 5-9). pap. 36.00 (978-0-516-22271-4(6) , Children's Pr.) Scholastic Library Publishing.

Kalman, Bobbie. Greece: The People. 1999. (Lands, Peoples, & Cultures Ser.). (Illus.). (J). (978-0-606-18058-0(3)) Tandem Library Bks.

Kaplan, Leslie C. A Primary Source Guide to Greece. 2005. (Countries of the World, a Primary Source Journey Ser.). (Illus.). 24p. (J). 19.95 (978-1-4042-2753-8(9) , PowerKids Pr.) Rosen Publishing Group, Inc., The.

Majoli, Alex. Leros: An Island in the Heart of the Aegean. 2002. (Illus.). 112p. 19.95 (978-0-9542079-2-2(0)) Trolley GBR. *Dist:* D.A.P./Distributed Art Pubs.

Martell, Hazel Mary. Myths & Civilization of the Ancient Greeks. Stalio, Ivan & D'Ottavi, Francesca, illus. 2000. (Myths & Civilization Ser.). 48p. (J). (gr. 3 up). 16.95 (978-0-87226-283-6(9) , 62839B, Bedrick, Peter Bks.) School Specialty Publishing.

Minnis. You Are in Ancient Greece. 2004. (Illus.). 32p. (J). pap. 7.50 (978-1-4109-1009-7(1)) Harcourt Schl. Pubs.

Morgan, Nicola. Ancient Greece. 2000. (People Who Made History Ser.). (Illus.). 48p. (J). (gr. 4-6). lib. bdg. 27.12 (978-0-7398-2747-5(2)) Raintree.

Nardo, Don. The Parthenon of Ancient Greece. 1998. (Building History Ser.). (Illus.). 96p. (YA). (gr. 6-9). 27.45 (978-1-56006-431-2(5) , Lucent Bks.) Thomson Gale.

Nobleman, Marc Tyler. Greece. 2003. (Countries & Cultures Ser.). (Illus.). 64p. (J). (gr. 3-4). lib. bdg. 23.95 (978-0-7368-1547-5(3) , Bridgestone Bks.) Capstone Pr., Inc.

Osler, Tamsin. Greece. 2003. (Changing Face Of... Ser.). (Illus.). 48p. (J). lib. bdg. 28.56 (978-0-7398-6039-7(9)) Raintree.

Pavlovic, Zoran. Greece. 2006. (Modern World Nations Ser.). (Illus.). 104-112p. (J). (gr. 6-12). 30.00 (978-0-7910-8797-8(2) , Chelsea Hse.) Facts On File, Inc.

Pearson, Anne. La Grecia Antigua. 2005. (Dk eyewitness Bks.). 72p. (J). 15.99 (978-0-7566-1485-0(6)); lib. bdg. 19.99 (978-0-7566-1491-1(0)) Dorling Kindersley Publishing, Inc.

Petersen, Christine & Petersen, David. Greece. 2002. (True Bks.). (Illus.). 48p. (J). (gr. 3-5). pap. 6.95 (978-0-516-27359-4(0) , Children's Pr.) Scholastic Library Publishing.

Petersen, David. Greece. 2001. (gr. 3-6). lib. bdg. 15.25 (978-0-613-54418-4(8)) Tandem Library Bks.

Petersen, David & Petersen, Christine. Greece. 2001. (True Geography Bks.). (Illus.). 48p. (J). (gr. 3-5). 25.00 (978-0-516-22255-4(4) , Children's Pr.) Scholastic Library Publishing.

Riehecky, Janet. Greece. 2000. (Countries of the World Ser.). (Illus.). 126p. (J). (gr. 2-3). 18.60 (978-0-7368-0628-2(8) , Bridgestone Bks.) Capstone Pr., Inc.

Roop, Peter. Greece. 1998. (Visit to Ser.). (Illus.). 32p. (J). lib. bdg. 21.36 (978-1-57572-709-7(9)) Heinemann Library.

Routte, Jane & Barnell, Ann Greenman. Greece. 2004. (Teacher Created Materials Ser.: Vol. 3719). (Illus.). 176p. (J). pap. 16.99 (978-0-7439-3719-1(8)) Teacher Created Materials, Inc.

Ryan, Patrick. Greece. 2003. (Countries: Faces & Places Ser.). (Illus.). 32p. (J). (gr. 1-5). 25.64 (978-1-56766-908-4(5)) Child's World, Inc.

Shuter, Jane. Builders, Traders & Craftsmen. 1999. (Ancient Greece Ser.). 32p. (J). (gr. 3-5). lib. bdg. 22.79 (978-1-57572-736-3(6)) Heinemann Library.

—Farmers & Fighters. 1999. (Ancient Greece Ser.). (Illus.). 32p. (J). (gr. 3-5). lib. bdg. 22.79 (978-1-57572-737-0(4)) Heinemann Library.

Sioras, Efstathia. Greece. 1998. (Festivals of the World Ser.). (Illus.). 32p. (J). (gr. 3 up). lib. bdg. 24.67 (978-0-8368-2014-0(2)) Stevens, Gareth Inc.

Spengler, Kremena. Greece: A Question & Answer Book. 2007. (J). (***978-0-7368-6769-6(4)***) Capstone Pr., Inc.

Whiting, Jim. The Volcanic Eruption on Santorini, 1500 BCE. 2007. (Natural Disasters Ser.). (J). lib. bdg. 25.70 (***978-1-58415-568-3(X)***) Mitchell Lane Pubs., Inc.

Yeoh, Hong Nam. Greece. 1999. (Countries of the World Ser.). (Illus.). 96p. (J). (gr. 6 up). lib. bdg. 30.00 (978-0-8368-2309-7(5)) Stevens, Gareth Inc.

GREECE—ANTIQUITIES

Armentrout, David & Armentrout, Patricia. Treasures from Greece. 2000. (Treasures from the Past Ser.). (Illus.). 48p. (J). (gr. 4-8). lib. bdg. 29.93 (978-1-55916-291-3(0)) Rourke Publishing, LLC.

Briers, Audrey. True Stories about Greek Coins. (Illus.). 48p. pap. 6.95 (978-0-907849-56-8(3)) Ashmolean Museum GBR. *Dist:* Weatherhill, Inc.

Halfmann, Janet. Greek Temples. 1999. (Designing the Future Ser.). (Illus.). 32p. (J). (gr. 4-7). lib. bdg. 21.30 (978-0-88682-654-3(3) , Creative Education) Creative Co., The.

Hart, Avery & Mantell, Paul. Ancient Greece! 40 Hands-On Activities to Experience This Wonderous Age. 1999. (Kaleidoscope Kids Bks.). (Illus.). 104p. (J). (gr. 2-8). pap. 12.95 (978-1-885593-25-2(2) , Williamson Bks.) Ideals Pubns.

Hatt, Christine. Ancient Greece. 2004. (Excavating the Past Ser.). (J). pap. 8.50 (978-1-4034-5457-7(4)); lib. bdg. 29.93 (978-1-4034-4837-8(X)) Heinemann Library.

MacDonald, Fiona. The Traveler's Guide to Ancient Greece. Foster, Mike S., illus. 1998. (J). (978-0-590-11762-3(9)) Scholastic, Inc.

Malam, John. Ancient Greece. 2004. (Picturing the Past Ser.). (Illus.). 32p. (J). 15.95 (978-1-59270-022-6(5)) Enchanted Lion Bks., LLC.

—The Ancient Greeks. 1999. (History Starts Here Ser.). (Illus.). 32p. (J). (ps-3). lib. bdg. 25.69 (978-0-7398-1350-8(1)) Raintree.

—The Ancient Greeks. 2000. (History Starts Here Ser.). (Illus.). 32p. (J). (ps-3). pap. 8.95 (978-0-7398-1823-7(6)) Steck-Vaughn.

—Exploring Ancient Greece. 1999. (Remains to Be Seen Ser.). (Illus.). 47p. (YA). (gr. 5-8). (978-0-237-51994-0(1) , Evans Brothers, Limited) Evans Publishing Group.

Nardo, Don. The Parthenon of Ancient Greece. 1998. (Building History Ser.). (Illus.). 96p. (YA). (gr. 6-9). 27.45 (978-1-56006-431-2(5) , Lucent Bks.) Thomson Gale.

Rees, Rosemary. The Ancient Greeks. 2002. (Understanding People in the Past Ser.). (Illus.). 64p. (J). (gr. 4-6). pap. 8.95 (978-1-58810-315-4(3) , 91070) Heinemann Library.

Scarre, Chris & Stefoff, Rebecca. The Palace of Minos at Knossos. 2003. (Digging for the Past Ser.). (Illus.). 48p. (YA). 22.95 (978-0-19-514272-3(1)) Oxford Univ. Pr., Inc.

Sheehan, Sean. Illustrated Encyclopedia of Ancient Greece. 2002. (Books for Young Readers Ser.). (Illus.). 164p. (gr. 4 up). 19.95 (978-0-89236-667-5(2)) Oxford Univ. Pr., Inc.

GREECE—BIOGRAPHY

Behnke, Alison. The Conquests of Alexander the Great. 2007. (Pivotal Moments in History Ser.). 160p. (YA). (gr. 9-12). lib. bdg. 38.60 (978-0-8225-5920-7(X) , Twenty-First Century Bks.) Lerner Publishing Group.

Burgan, Michael. Alexander the Great: World Conqueror. 2006. (J). (978-0-7565-1872-1(5)) Compass Point Bks.

Contopoulos, Catherine K. The Boy, a Kitchen, & His Cave: The Tale of Saint Euphrosynos the Cook. Greene-Gross, Chrissanth, illus. 2002. 32p. (J). 17.00 (978-0-88141-241-3(4)) St. Vladimir's Seminary Pr.

Doak, Robin S. Thucydides: Ancient Greek Historian. 2006. (J). (978-0-7565-1875-2(X)) Compass Point Bks.

Haaren, John H. & Poland, A. Famous Men of Greece (Yesterday's Classics) 2006. (Illus.). 252p. (J). per. 11.95 (978-1-59915-045-1(X)) Yesterday's Classics.

Harkins, Susan and William. The Life & Times of Pythagoras. 2007. (Biography from Ancient Civilizations Ser.). (Illus.). 48p. (J). lib. bdg. 29.95 (***978-1-58415-545-4(0)***) Mitchell Lane Pubs., Inc.

King, Perry Scott. Pericles. 2002. (World Leaders - Past & Present Ser.). E-Book 5.99 (978-1-59155-587-2(6)) ipicturebooks, LLC.

Nardo, Don. Influential Figures of Ancient Greece. 2004. (History Makers Ser.). (J). (gr. 7-10). 29.95 (978-1-59018-524-7(2) , Lucent Bks.) Thomson Gale.

Ross, Stewart. Athens Is Saved. 2007. (Flashbacks Ser.). (Illus.). 64p. (J). (gr. 4-7). pap. 8.95 (***978-0-237-53152-2(6)***, Evans Brothers, Limited) Evans Publishing Group GBR. *Dist:* Independent Pubs. Group.

Shecter, Vicky Alvear. Alexander the Great Rocks the World. Naughton, Terry, illus. 2006. 128p. (J). (gr. 6 up). 18.95 (978-1-58196-045-7(X)) Darby Creek Publishing.

White, John S. The Boys' & Girls' Plutarch. 2004. reprint ed. pap. 28.95 (978-1-4191-5511-6(3)); pap. 1.99 (978-1-4192-5511-3(8)) Kessinger Publishing, LLC.

GREECE—CIVILIZATION

see Civilization, Greek

GREECE—FICTION

Aesop & Pirotta, Saviour. Aesop's Fables. Johnson, Richard, illus. 2005. 80p. (J). (gr. 3-5). 12.95 (978-0-7534-5919-5(1) , Kingfisher) Houghton Mifflin Co. Trade & Reference Div.

Alexander, Lloyd. The Xanadu Adventure. 2005. (Vesper Holly Ser.). (Illus.). 160p. (J). (gr. 5-8). 16.99 (978-0-525-47371-8(8) , Dutton Juvenile) Penguin Group (USA) Inc.

Block, Francesca Lia. Psyche in a Dress. 2006. 128p. (J). (gr. 9 up). 15.99 (978-0-06-076372-5(8)); lib. bdg. 16.89 (978-0-06-076373-2(6)) HarperCollins Pubs. (Cotler, Joanna Books).

Brown, Elizabeth. Aristotle: the Firefly's Message. Schuna, Ramona, illus. 2007. 40p. pap. 19.95 (***978-1-59800-557-8(X)***) Outskirts Press, Inc.

Bunting, Eve. I Have an Olive Tree. Barbour, Karen, photos by. 1999. (Joanna Cotler Bks.). (Illus.). 32p. (J). (ps-3). 15.89 (978-0-06-027574-7(X) , Cotler, Joanna Books) HarperCollins Pubs.

Cadnum, Michael. Nightsong: The Legend of Orpheus & Eurydice. 2006. (Nightsong Ser.). 144p. (J). (gr. 4-7). pap. 16.99 (978-0-439-54535-8(8) , Orchard Bks.) Scholastic, Inc.

Cann, Kate. Grecian Holiday: Or, How I Turned down the Best Possible Thing Only to Have The. 2002. (gr. 7-12). lib. bdg. 14.15 (978-0-613-71506-5(3)) Tandem Library Bks.

—Grecian Holiday: Or, How I Turned down the Best Possible Thing Only to Have the Time of My Life. 2002. 352p. (J). (gr. 8 up). pap. 5.99 (978-0-06-447302-6(3)) HarperCollins Pubs.

Cargill, Linda. Jason & Medea. 2001. 157p. (YA). (gr. 7 up). 9.99 (978-0-88092-548-8(5) , 5485) Royal Fireworks Publishing Co.

Case, Cassandra. Run with Me, Nike! The Olympics in 420, B.C. Brown, Dan, illus. 1999. (Smithsonian Odyssey Ser.: No. 12). 32p. (J). (gr. 2-5). 14.95 (978-1-56899-604-2(7) , B6012); pap. 5.95 (978-1-56899-605-9(5)) Soundprints.

—Run with Me, Nike! The Olympics in Four Hundred Twenty. 1999. (gr. 3-6). lib. bdg. 14.10 (978-0-613-51585-6(4)) Tandem Library Bks.

Catran, Ken. Voyage with Jason. 2006. 208p. (J). 16.95 (978-1-894965-43-9(4)) Simply Read Bks. CAN. *Dist:* Perseus Distribution.

Citra, Becky. Jeremy & the Enchanted Theater. Milne, Jessica, illus. 2004. (Orca Echoes Ser.). 64p. (J). (gr. 2-3). pap. 4.99 (978-1-55143-322-6(2)) Orca Bk. Pubs. USA.

Climo, Shirley. Atlanta's Race: A Greek Myth. 2000. (J). 13.75 (978-0-606-19360-3(X)) Tandem Library Bks.

Cook, Jennifer. Ariadne: The Maiden & the Minotaur. 2005. 208p. (Orig.). pap. (978-0-7344-0637-8(1) , Lothian Bks.) Hachette Livre Australia.

Coville, Bruce. William Shakespeare's A Midsummer Night's Dream. Nolan, Dennis, illus. 2003. 48p. (J). (gr. 2). pap. 7.99 (978-0-14-250168-9(9) , Puffin) Penguin Group (USA) Inc.

Delton, Judy. Angel Spreads Her Wings. Weber, Jill, illus. 2002. 160p. (J). (gr. 2-5). pap. 4.95 (978-0-618-21617-8(0)) Houghton Mifflin Co. Trade & Reference Div.

—Angel Spreads Her Wings. 2002. (gr. 3-6). lib. bdg. 12.95 (978-0-613-90475-9(3)) Tandem Library Bks.

Dostis, Isaac & Haddad Ikonomopoulos, Marcia. Ten Gold Medals: Glory or Freedom. 2005. (Illus.). ii, 72p. (J). (978-0-8197-0770-3(8)) Bloch Publishing Co.

Euripides. Euripides' Hippolytos. Roy, Indrapramit, illus. 2006. (Getty Trust Publications: J. Paul Getty Museum Ser.). 28p. 19.95 (978-0-89236-864-8(0)) Getty Pubns.

Foster, Hal & Murphy, John Cullen. Queen of the Amazons, Vol. 47. 2003. (Prince Valiant Ser.: Vol. 47). 48p. pap. 16.95 (978-1-56097-527-4(X)) Fantagraphics Bks.

Gabrielson, Ernest & Gabrielson, Brian. Home in Ithaca: A novel of Ancient Greece & Troy. 2004. 120p. (YA). pap. 10.95 (978-0-595-30889-7(9)) iUniverse, Inc.

Galloway, Priscilla. Aleta y la Reina: Una Historia de la Antigua Grecia.Tr. of Aleta & the Queen: A Tale of Ancient Greece. (SPA.). (YA). (gr. 5-8). pap. (978-968-6582-27-7(4)) Samara, Ediciones, S. A. de C. V.

Geras, Adele. Ithaka. 2007. (Illus.). 368p. (YA). (gr. 9 up). pap. 6.95 (978-0-15-206104-3(5) , Harcourt Paperbacks) Harcourt Children's Bks.

Geras, Adèle. Ithaka. 2006. 368p. (YA). 17.00 (978-0-15-205603-2(3)) Harcourt Children's Bks.

Guner, Kagan. The Children of Atlantis. 2002. (Illus.). 32p. 7.95 (978-1-84059-325-9(3)) Milet Publishing.

—Icarus. 2002. (Illus.). 32p. 7.95 (978-1-84059-326-6(1)) Milet Publishing.

Halam, Ann. Snakehead. 2008. 272p. (YA). (gr. 7). 16.99 (***978-0-375-84108-6(3)***); lib. bdg. 19.99 (***978-0-375-94108-5(8)***) Random Hse. Children's Bks. (Lamb, Wendy).

Harcourt School Publishers Staff. A Blast from the Past: Take-Home Book. 2001. (Collections Ser.). (Illus.). (J). pap. 1.90 (978-0-15-319556-3(8)) Harcourt Schl. Pubs.

—A Blast from the Past Below Level. 3rd ed. 2002. (Trophies Reading Program Ser.). (Illus.). pap. 5.10 (978-0-15-323414-9(8)) Harcourt Schl. Pubs.

—Phaeton & the Sun Chariot: Take-Home Book. 1999. (Collections Ser.). (Illus.). (J). pap. 1.90 (978-0-15-317304-2(1)) Harcourt Schl. Pubs.

Hemyng, Bracebridge. Jack Harkaway & His Son's Escape from the Brigand's of Greece. 2006. 342p. pap. 14.99 (978-1-4264-2290-4(3)); 386p. pap. 20.99 (978-1-4264-2325-3(X)) BiblioBazaar.

—Jack Harkaway & His Son's Escape from the Brigands of Greece. 2004. reprint ed. pap. 37.95 (978-1-4191-2705-2(5)); pap. 1.99 (978-1-4192-2705-9(X)) Kessinger Publishing, LLC.

Iliad. 1999. (YA). 9.95 (978-1-56137-752-7(X)) Novel Units, Inc.

Ioannides, Mara W. Cohen. A Shout in the Sunshine. 2007. 120p. (J). pap. 12.95 (***978-0-8276-0838-2(1)***) Jewish Pubn. Society.

Johnson, Vargie. Alexander the Great the All-Powerful: What Made Them Famous? 2006. 156p. (J). per. 15.00 (978-1-931195-93-5(5)) KiwE Publishing, Ltd.

Jones, Allan Frewin. Blood Stone, Vol. 6. 2003. 176p. (J). mass mkt. (978-0-330-37476-7(1) , Pan) Pan Macmillan.

Kanaan, Hanan S. The Curse of the Slaves. 2003. (Illus.). 96p. per. 11.95 (978-1-59405-013-8(9)) New Age World Publishing.

Kerisel, Francoise. Diogenes' Lantern. Mansot, Frederick, tr. from FRE. Mansot, Frederick, illus. 2004. (Books for Young Readers Ser.). 22p. 5.95 (978-0-89236-738-2(5)) Oxford Univ. Pr., Inc.

Kindl, Patrice. Lost in the Labyrinth: A Novel. 2002. 208p. (YA). (gr. 5-9). tchr. ed. 16.00 (978-0-618-16684-8(X)) Houghton Mifflin Co. Trade & Reference Div.

Kingsley, Charles. Heroes EasyRead Comfort Edition. 2006. pap. (***978-1-4250-0760-7(0)***) Assistedreadingbooks.com Inc.

—Heroes EasyRead Edition. 2006. pap. (***978-1-4250-0203-9(X)***) Assistedreadingbooks.com Inc.

—Heroes EasyRead Large Edition. 2006. pap. (***978-1-4250-1265-6(5)***) Assistedreadingbooks.com Inc.

—Heroes, the; or, Greek Fairy Tales for M. 2006. pap. (***978-1-4250-0629-7(9)***) Assistedreadingbooks.com Inc.

Lang, Andrew. Tales of Troy & Greece. 2002. (Children's Classics). (ENG., Illus.). 256p. (J). (gr. 3-6). pap. (978-1-85326-172-5(6)) Wordsworth Editions, Ltd.

Lattimore, San Souci. Child of Atlantis. (J). 15.95 (978-0-8118-4089-7(1)) Chronicle Bks. LLC.

Lawrence, Caroline. The Colossus of Rhodes. 2006. (Roman Mysteries Ser.). (Illus.). 208p. (J). 16.95 (978-1-59643-082-2(6)) Roaring Brook Pr.

McLaren, Clemence. Waiting for Odysseus. 2004. (Illus.). 160p. (YA). mass mkt. 5.99 (978-0-689-86705-7(0) , Simon Pulse) Simon & Schuster Children's Publishing.

—Waiting for Odysseus. 2004. (gr. 7-12). lib. bdg. 14.15 (978-0-613-73418-9(1)) Tandem Library Bks.

Norfolk. In the Shape of a Boar. 2002. 336p. pap. 13.00 (978-0-8021-3967-2(1)) Grove/Atlantic, Inc.

Oh, Cirro. Greek & Roman Mythology, Vol. 3. Chun, C. S., illus. 2005. 160p. (J). pap. 12.95 (978-981-05-2766-2(7)) Youngjin (Singapore) Pte Ltd. SGP. *Dist:* Independent Pubs. Group.

O'Malley, Kevin. Mount Olympus Basketball. O'Malley, Kevin, illus. (Illus.). 32p. (J). 2005. (gr. 1-4). pap., pap. 6.95 (978-0-8027-7728-7(7)); 2004. (gr. 2-6). 15.95 (978-0-8027-8844-3(0)) Walker & Co.

—Mount Olympus Basketball. 2004. (Illus.). 32p. (J). (gr. 2-6). 16.85 (978-0-8027-8845-0(9)) Walker & Co.

Oppenheim, Shulamith Levey. Yanni Rubbish. Chayka, Doug, illus. 32p. (J). 2004. pap. 8.95 (978-1-59078-327-6(1)); 2003. 15.95 (978-1-56397-668-1(4)) Boyds Mills Pr.

Orgel, Doris. Ariadne, Awake! Moser, Barry, illus. 1999. 74p. (J). (gr. 6-11). reprint ed. 16.00 (978-0-7881-6477-4(5)) DIANE Publishing Co.

Osborne, Mary Pope. Hour of the Olympics. unabr. ed. 2004. (Magic Tree House Ser. : No. 16). 70p. (J). (gr. k-3). pap. 17.00 incl. audio (978-0-8072-0785-7(3) , LFTR 244 SP, Listening Library) Random Hse. Audio Publishing Group.

—Hour of the Olympics. Murdocca, Sal, illus. 1998. (Magic Tree House Ser.: No. 16). 96p. (J). (gr. k-3). lib. bdg. 11.99 (978-0-679-99062-8(3)) ; mass mkt. 3.99 (978-0-679-89062-1(9)) Random Hse. Children's Bks. (Random Hse. Bks. for Young Readers).

Perkins, Lucy Fitch. Spartan Twins. 2006. 62.99 (***978-1-4280-3561-4(3)***); pap. 55.99 (***978-1-4280-3576-8(1)***) IndyPublish.com.

Plante, Raymond. Le Monde de Xéros. Delezenne, Christine, illus. 2004. (Roman Jeunesse Ser.). (FRE.). 96p. (J). (gr. 4-7). pap. (978-2-89021-615-0(2)) Diffusion du livre Mirabel.

Plato's Journey: Evaluation Guide. 2006. (J). (978-1-55942-421-9(4)) Marsh Media.

Richards, Jean. The First Olympic Games: A Gruesome Greek Myth with a Happy Ending. Thacker, Kat, illus. 2004. 32p. pap. 10.95 (978-0-7613-2443-0(7) , Millbrook Pr.) Lerner Publishing Group.

Richards, Jean & Thacker, Kat, illus. The First Olympic Games: A Gruesome Greek Myth with a Happy Ending. 2000. 40p. (gr. k-3). lib. bdg. 23.90 (978-0-7613-1311-3(7) , Millbrook Pr.) Lerner Publishing Group.

Roberts, Katherine. I Am the Great Horse. 2006. (Illus.). 416p. (YA). pap. 16.99 (978-0-439-82163-6(0) , Chicken Hse., The) Scholastic, Inc.

Russon, Penni. Breathe. 2007. (Illus.). 368p. (J). (gr. 9 up). 16.99 (978-0-06-079393-7(7)) ; lib. bdg. 17.89 (978-0-06-079394-4(5)) HarperCollins Pubs.

Sanderson, Jeannette. The Odyssey: A Greek Myth. 2006. 42.00 (***978-1-4108-6177-1(5)***) Benchmark Education Co.

Shipton, Paul. The Pig Scrolls. 2005. 288p. (J). (gr. 5-9). 15.99 (978-0-7636-2702-7(X)) Candlewick Pr.

Shipton, Paul. The Pig Who Saved the World. 2007. (Illus.). 272p. (J). (gr. 5-9). 15.99 (***978-0-7636-3446-9(8)***) Candlewick Pr.

Spinner, Stephanie. Quicksilver. 2006. 240p. (YA). (gr. 7-11). mass mkt. 5.99 (978-0-440-23845-4(5) , Laurel Leaf) Random Hse. Children's Bks.

Steig, Jeanne. A Gift from Zeus: Sixteen Favorite Myths. Steig, William, illus. 2001. 176p. (gr. 9 up). 18.99 (978-0-06-028405-3(6) , Cotler, Joanna Books) HarperCollins Pubs.

Steig, William. The Greek Project. 2000. (J). pap. 5.95 (978-0-06-443576-5(8)) HarperCollins Pubs.

Warner, Rex. Men & Gods: Myths & Legends of the Ancient Greeks. Gorey, Ward, illus. 2008. 296p. (J). 16.95 (***978-1-59017-263-6(9)*** , NYR Children's Collection) New York Review of Bks., Inc., The.

Wilding, Valerie. Secret Diaries 5 - Greek. 2008. (Illus.). 144p. (J). pap. 7.95 (***978-1-4052-2547-2(5)***) Egmont Bks., Ltd. GBR. *Dist:* Independent Pubs. Group.

Yolen, Jane. Odysseus in the Serpent Maze. 2002. (gr. 3-6). lib. bdg. 14.15 (978-0-613-58609-2(3)) Tandem Library Bks.

Yolen, Jane & Harris, Robert J. Odysseus in the Serpent Maze. 2002. (Young Heroes Ser.). 256p. (J). (gr. 7 up). pap. 5.99 (978-0-06-440847-9(7)) HarperCollins Pubs.

GREECE—HISTORY

Ackroyd, Peter. Ancient Greece. 2006. (Voyages Through Time Ser.). 144p. (J). pap. 9.99 (978-0-7566-2167-4(4)) Dorling Kindersley Publishing, Inc.

Adare, Sierra. Greece the Land. 1999. (gr. 3-6). lib. bdg. 16.40 (978-0-613-11601-5(1)) Tandem Library Bks.

Ancient Greece DBA. 2003. spiral bd. 16.95 (978-1-56004-152-8(8)) Social Studies Schl. Service.

Apel, Melanie Ann. Economy & Industry in Ancient Greece. 2004. (Primary Sources of Ancient Civilizations Ser.). (Illus.). 24p. (J). lib. bdg. (978-0-8239-8942-3(9)) ; lib. bdg. 19.95 (978-0-8239-6774-2(3)) Rosen Publishing Group, Inc., The. (PowerKids Pr.).

—Politics & Government in Ancient Greece. 2004. (Primary Sources of Ancient Civilizations Ser.). (Illus.). 24p. (J). lib. bdg. (978-0-8239-8939-3(9)) ; lib. bdg. 19.95 (978-0-8239-6771-1(9)) Rosen Publishing Group, Inc., The. (PowerKids Pr.).

Augustin, Byron & Augustin, Rebecca. Greece. 2005. (to Z Ser.). (Illus.). 40p. (J). (ps-ps). 24.50 (978-0-516-23664-3(4) , Children's Pr.) Scholastic Library Publishing.

Bankston, John. The Life & Times of Alexander the Great. 2004. (Biography of Ancient Civilizations Ser.). (Illus.). 48p. (J). lib. bdg. (978-1-58415-235-4(4)) Mitchell Lane Pubs., Inc.

Behnke, Alison. The Conquests of Alexander the Great. 2007. (Pivotal Moments in History Ser.). 160p. (YA). (gr. 9-12). lib. bdg. 38.60 (978-0-8225-5920-7(X) , Twenty-First Century Bks.) Lerner Publishing Group.

Benchmark Education Staff. Greece Long Ago. 2005. 2.00 (***978-1-4108-4675-4(X)***) Benchmark Education Co.

Bingham, Jane. Classical Myth: A Treasury of Greek & Roman Legends, Art, & History. 2007. (World of Mythology Ser.). (Illus.). 96p. (YA). (gr. 6 up). 35.95 (***978-0-7656-8104-1(8)***) Sharpe, M.E. Inc.

Boardman, John, et al, eds. The Oxford History of Greece & the Hellenistic World. 2001. (Illus.). 528p. (Orig.). 18.95 (978-0-19-280137-1(6)) Oxford Univ. Pr., Inc.

Bradley, Pamela. Ancient Greece. 2000. (Cambridge Junior History Ser.). 48p. pap. 8.00 (978-0-521-77652-3(X)) Cambridge Univ. Pr.

Brannon, Barbara. Discover Ancient Greece. 2005. 39.00 (***978-1-4108-5163-5(X)***) Benchmark Education Co.

Britton, Tamara L. Greece. 2000. (Countries Ser.). (Illus.). 40p. (J). (gr. k-6). lib. bdg. 22.78 (978-1-57765-385-1(8) , Checkerboard Library) ABDO Publishing Co.

Burgan, Michael. Alexander the Great: World Conqueror. 2006. (J). (978-0-7565-1872-1(5)) Compass Point Bks.

Caper, William. Ancient Greece. 2005. (Navigators Ser.). (J). pap. 44.00 (***978-1-4108-5114-7(1)***) Benchmark Education Co.

Charman, Andrew. Life & Times in Ancient Greece. 2007. (Life & Times Ser.). (Illus.). 32p. (J). pap. 9.95 (***978-0-7534-6150-1(1)*** , Kingfisher) Houghton Mifflin Co. Trade & Reference Div.

Chrisp, Peter. Ancient Greece. 2006. (Google E Guides). (Illus.). 96p. (J). 17.99 (978-0-7566-1956-5(4)) ; (***978-1-4053-1345-2(5)***) Dorling Kindersley Publishing, Inc.

—Ancient Greece. rev. ed. 2004. (Come & Discover My World Ser.). (Illus.). 32p. (gr. 2-5). (J). pap. 7.95 (978-1-58728-066-5(3)) ; 14.95 (978-1-58728-060-3(4)) T&N Children's Publishing. (Two Can Publishing).

Claybourne, Anna. Ancient Greece. 2003. (Illus.). 48p. pap. (978-0-7502-3909-7(3) , Hodder Wayland) Hodder Children's Division.

Cobbold, G. B. Hellas: A Short History of Classical Greek Civilization & Its Predecessors. 1999. (Illus.). 216p. (YA). (gr. 9-12). pap. 13.34 (978-1-877653-64-3(0)) Wayside Publishing.

Colum, Padraic. The Story of the Golden Fleece. Pogany, Willy, illus. unabr. ed. 2005. 256p. (J). (gr. 4). pap. 5.95 (978-0-486-44366-9(3)) Dover Pubns., Inc.

Conley, Kate A. Ancient Greece. 2005. (Life in Ancient Days: Greece Ser.). (J). (978-1-59197-863-3(7)) ABDO Publishing Co.

Crompton, Samuel Willard. Alexander the Great. 2003. (Ancient World Leaders Ser.). (Illus.). 112p. (gr. 6-12). (J). 30.00 (978-0-7910-7219-6(3)) ; pap. 30.00 (978-0-7910-7493-0(5)) Facts On File, Inc. (Chelsea Hse.).

Cumming, David. Greece. Nikiteas, Yiorgos, photos by. 2005. (Letters from Around the World Ser.). (Illus.). 32p. (J). (gr. 3-7). lib. bdg. (978-1-84234-353-1(X) , Cherrytree Books) Evans Publishing Group.

Day, Nancy. Your Travel Guide to Ancient Greece. 2005. (Passport to History Ser.). (Illus.). 96p. (gr. 5-8). lib. bdg. 26.50 (978-0-8225-3076-3(7)) Lerner Publishing Group.

DK Publishing. Ancient Greece. 2008. (DK Eyewitness Bks.). 48p. (J). (gr. 2-8). pap. 9.99 (***978-0-7566-3782-8(1)***) Dorling Kindersley Publishing, Inc.

Doak, Robin S. Thucydides: Ancient Greek Historian. 2006. (J). (978-0-7565-1875-2(X)) Compass Point Bks.

Ganeri, Anita. Alexander the Great: The Life of a King & Conqueror. 2005. (Graphic Nonfiction Ser.). (Illus.). 48p. (J). lib. bdg. 26.50 (978-1-4042-0238-2(2) , 1241094) Rosen Publishing Group, Inc., The.

—Legacies from Ancient Greece. 1999. (Legacies Ser.). (Illus.). 32p. (J). (gr. 4-7). lib. bdg. 16.95 (978-1-929298-49-5(8)) Chrysalis Education.

Gilbert, Adrian. Going to War in Ancient Greece. Bergin, Mark, illus. 2001. (Armies of the Past Ser.). 32p. (J). (gr. 3-6). pap. 6.95 (978-0-531-16351-1(2) , Watts, Franklin) Scholastic Library Publishing.

—Going to War in Ancient Greece. 2001. (gr. 3-6). lib. bdg. 15.25 (978-0-613-54518-1(4)) Tandem Library Bks.

The Golden Age of Greece (NCHS) (YA). (gr. 6-9). spiral bd., tchr.'s planning gde. ed. 15.00 (978-0-382-40950-9(7)) Cobblestone Publishing Co.

Granstrom, Brita. Greek Hero. Manning, Mick, illus. 2008. (Fly on the Wall Ser.). 40p. (J). 16.95 (***978-1-84507-683-2(4)***) Lincoln, Frances Ltd. GBR. *Dist:* Perseus Distribution.

Greene, Jacqueline Dembar. Slavery in Ancient Greece & Rome. 2000. (History of Slavery Library). (Illus.). 64p. (J). (gr. 5-7). 25.50 (978-0-531-11693-7(X) , Watts, Franklin) Scholastic Library Publishing.

—Slavery in Ancient Greece & Rome. 2000. (gr. 3-6). lib. bdg. 17.60 (978-0-613-34473-9(1)) Tandem Library Bks.

Gunther, John. Sterling Point Books: Alexander the Great. 2007. (Sterling Point Bks.). (Illus.). 176p. (J). 12.95 (978-1-4027-4519-5(2)) ; pap. 6.95 (978-1-4027-4139-5(1)) Sterling Publishing Co., Inc.

Gunzi, Christiane. Ancient Greece. 2001. (Collectafact Ser.: Vol. 12). (Illus.). 48p. (J). (gr. 1-5). 4.95 (978-1-58728-760-2(9) , Two Can Publishing) T&N Children's Publishing.

Hardwick, Susan. Greece: World-Wise Kids Guides. 2004. 96p. (978-1-59258-092-7(0)) Hylas Publishing.

Hart, Avery & Mantell, Paul. Ancient Greece! 40 Hands-on Activites to Experience This Wondrous Age. 1999. (Illus.). 103p. (J). (ps-7). lib. bdg. 19.90 (978-0-613-16318-7(4)) Tandem Library Bks.

—Ancient Greece! 40 Hands-On Activities to Experience This Wonderous Age. 1999. (Kaleidoscope Kids Bks.). (Illus.). 104p. (J). (gr. 2-8). pap. 12.95 (978-1-885593-25-2(2) , Williamson Bks.) Ideals Pubns.

Hicks, Peter. Ancient Greece. 1999. (History Beneath Your Feet Ser.). (Illus.). 48p. (J). (gr. 3-7). lib. bdg. 27.12 (978-0-8172-5750-7(0)) Raintree.

Hirsch, E. D., ed. Ancient Greece. 2003. (J). stu. ed. 49.95 (978-0-7690-2952-8(3)) Pearson Learning.

Hollingsworth, Patricia L., et al. Classical Greece. 1998. (Sails - Students' Active Interdisciplinary Learning Ser.: Vol. 1). (Illus.). (YA). (gr. 3-12). pap. 20.00 (978-1-893413-00-9(4)) Univ. Schl. at the Univ. of Tulsa.

Hull, Robert. Trade & Warfare. 2006. (World of Ancient Greece Ser.). (Illus.). 32p. (J). (978-1-59771-062-6(8)) Sea-To-Sea Pubns.

Hull, Robert E. Religion & the Gods. 2000. (World of Ancient Greece Ser.). (Illus.). 32p. (J). (gr. 4-8). 24.00 (978-0-531-14539-5(5) , Watts, Franklin) Scholastic Library Publishing.

—Trade & Warfare. 2000. (World of Ancient Greece Ser.). (Illus.). 32p. (J). pap. 6.95 (978-0-531-15384-0(3)) ; (gr. 4-8). 24.00 (978-0-531-14540-1(9)) Scholastic Library Publishing. (Watts, Franklin).

Hunt, Norman Bancroft. Living in Ancient Greece. 2007. (Living in the Ancient World Ser.). 96p. (gr. 6-12). 35.00 (978-0-8160-6339-0(7)) Facts On File, Inc.

King, Perry Scott. Pericles. 2002. (World Leaders - Past & Present Ser.). E-Book 5.99 (978-1-59155-587-2(6)) ipicturebooks, LLC.

MacDonald, Fiona. I Wonder Why Greeks Built Temples & Other Questions about Ancient Greece. 2006. (I Wonder Why Ser.). 32p. (J). (gr. k-3). pap. 6.95 (978-0-7534-5961-4(2) , Kingfisher) Houghton Mifflin Co. Trade & Reference Div.

—In the Daily Life of the Ancient Greeks. 2002. (Gods & Goddesses Ser.). (Illus.). 48p. (J). (gr. 4 up). 18.95 (978-0-87226-636-0(2) , Bedrick, Peter Bks.) School Specialty Publishing.

—You Wouldn't Want to Be a Slave in Ancient Greece! 2000. (gr. 3-6). lib. bdg. 18.75 (978-0-613-44278-7(4)) Tandem Library Bks.

—You Wouldn't Want to Be a Slave in Ancient Greece! A Life You'd Rather Not Have. Antram, David, illus. 2001. (You Wouldn't Want to Ser.). 32p. (J). (gr. 2-5). 28.50 (978-0-531-14600-2(6)) ; pap. 9.95 (978-0-531-16203-3(6)) Scholastic Library Publishing. (Watts, Franklin).

Malam, John. The Ancient Greeks. 1999. (History Starts Here Ser.). (Illus.). 32p. (J). (ps-3). lib. bdg. 25.69 (978-0-7398-1350-8(1)) Raintree.

—Greek Town. 2000. (Metropolis Ser.). (Illus.). 48p. (J). (gr. 5-7). pap. 8.95 (978-0-531-15379-6(7) , Watts, Franklin) Scholastic Library Publishing.

Malam, John & Bergin, Mark. An Ancient Greek Temple. 2001. (Magnifications Ser.). (Illus.). 48p. (J). (gr. 3-8). 18.95 (978-0-87226-652-0(4) , Bedrick, Peter Bks.) School Specialty Publishing.

Martin, W. Eric & Bordessa, Kris. Tools of the Ancient Greeks: A Kid's Guide to the History & Science of Life in Ancient Greece. 2006. (Tools of Discovery Ser.). (Illus.). 160p. (J). pap. 16.95 (978-0-9749344-6-4(1)) Nomad Pr.

McGee, Marni & Walsh, Kieran. Ancient Greece: Archaeology Unlocks the Secrets of Greece's Past. 2006. (National Geographic Investigates Ser.). (Illus.). 64p. (J). (gr. 3-7). 17.95 (978-0-7922-7826-9(7)) ; lib. bdg. 27.90 (978-0-7922-7872-6(0)) National Geographic Society. (National Geographic Children's Bks.).

McGowen, Tom. Alexander the Great: Conqueror of the Ancient World. 2006. (Rulers of the Ancient World Ser.). (Illus.). 160p. (J). lib. bdg. 27.93 (978-0-7660-2560-8(8)) Enslow Pubs., Inc.

Middleton, Haydn. Ancient Greek Homes. 2002. (People in the Past Ser.). (Illus.). 48p. (J). (gr. 4-6). lib. bdg. 27.07 (978-1-58810-636-0(5)) Heinemann Library.

—Ancient Greek Jobs. 2002. (People in the Past Ser.). (Illus.). 48p. (J). (gr. 4-6). lib. bdg. 27.07 (978-1-58810-638-4(1)) Heinemann Library.

—Ancient Greek War & Weapons. 2002. (People in the Past Ser.). (Illus.). 48p. (J). (gr. 4-6). lib. bdg. 27.07 (978-1-58810-635-3(7)) Heinemann Library.

—Ancient Greek War & Weapons. 2002. (gr. 3-6). lib. bdg. 17.05 (978-0-613-87483-0(8)) Tandem Library Bks.

—Ancient Greek Women. 2002. (People in the Past Ser.). (Illus.). 48p. (J). (gr. 4-6). lib. bdg. 27.07 (978-1-58810-637-7(3)) Heinemann Library.

Middleton, Haydn & Tames, Richard. Ancient Greek Children. 2002. (People in the Past Ser.). 64p. (J). (gr. 4-7). pap. 8.50 (978-1-4034-0131-1(4) , 91636) Heinemann Library.

—Ancient Greek Homes. 2002. (People in the Past Ser.). 64p. (J). (gr. 4-7). pap. 8.50 (978-1-4034-0132-8(2) , 91637) Heinemann Library.

—Ancient Greek War & Weapons. 2002. (People in the Past Ser.). 64p. (J). (gr. 4-7). pap. 8.50 (978-1-4034-0134-2(9) , 91639) Heinemann Library.

—Ancient Greek Women. 2002. (People in the Past Ser.). 64p. (J). (gr. 4-7). pap. 8.50 (978-1-4034-0135-9(7) , 91640) Heinemann Library.

—Greece, 5 bks., Set 1. 2002. (People in the Past Ser.). (J). (gr. 4-6). lib. bdg. 135.35 (978-1-58810-577-6(6)) Heinemann Library.

Miles, Lisa. Encyclopedia of Ancient Greece. 2000. (Usborne Encyclopedia Ser.). (Illus.). 160p. (YA). (gr. 4 up). lib. bdg. 27.95 (978-1-58086-259-2(4)) EDC Publishing.

Miles, Lisa & Reid, Struan. Encyclopedia of Ancient Greece - Internet Linked. rev. ed. 2007. (History Encyclopedias Ser.). 144p. (J). 16.99 (***978-0-7945-1800-4(1)*** , Usborne) EDC Publishing.

Miles, Lisa & Reid, Struan, eds. Encyclopedia of Ancient Greece. 2000. (Usborne Encyclopedia Ser.). (Illus.). 160p. (YA). (gr. 4 up). 19.95 (978-0-7460-3403-3(2)) EDC Publishing.

Minnis. You Are in Ancient Greece, 6 Packs. 2004. (Illus.). pap. 40.50 (978-1-4109-1014-1(8)) Harcourt Schl. Pubs.

Mole, Gavin. Sing It & Say - Ancient Greece. (Illus.). 156p. (J). 10.95 incl. audio (978-1-85909-389-4(2) , Warner Bros. Pubns.) Alfred Publishing Co., Inc.

Morley, Jacqueline. How to Be an Ancient Greek Athlete. 2005. (How to Be Ser.). (Illus.). 32p. (J). (gr. 3-7). 21.90 (978-0-7922-7495-7(4) , National Geographic Children's Bks.) National Geographic Society.

Nardo, Don. Ancient Greece. (Greenhaven Encyclopedia of Ser.). (Illus.). 2006. 324p. (YA). (gr. 9 up). 77.45 (978-0-7377-3388-4(8) , Greenhaven Pr., Inc.); 2002. 112p. (J). 27.45 (978-1-59018-004-4(6) , Lucent Bks.) Thomson Gale.

—Greek Temples. 2002. (Watts Library). (J). (gr. 5-7). 63p. pap. 8.95 (978-0-531-16225-5(7)) ; (Illus.). 64p. 25.50 (978-0-531-12035-4(X)) Scholastic Library Publishing. (Watts, Franklin).

—A History of the Ancient Greeks. 2004. (Lucent Library of Historical Eras). (J). (gr. 7-10). 32.45 (978-1-59018-525-4(0) , Lucent Bks.) Thomson Gale.

—Influential Figures of Ancient Greece. 2004. (History Makers Ser.). (J). (gr. 7-10). 29.95 (978-1-59018-524-7(2) , Lucent Bks.) Thomson Gale.

—Leisure Life of the Ancient Greeks. 2004. (Lucent Library of Historical Eras). (Illus.). 112p. (J). (gr. 7-10). 32.45 (978-1-59018-528-5(5) , Lucent Bks.) Thomson Gale.

—Pericles: Great Leader of Ancient Athens. 2006. (Rulers of the Ancient World Ser.). (Illus.). 160p. (J). lib. bdg. 27.93 (978-0-7660-2561-5(6)) Enslow Pubs., Inc.

—Philip II & Alexander the Great Unify Greece in World History. 2000. (In World History Ser.). (Illus.). 112p. (J). (gr. 5-12). lib. bdg. 26.60 (978-0-7660-1399-5(5)) Enslow Pubs., Inc.

—Warriors of Ancient Greece. 2005. (History Makers Ser.). (J). (978-1-59018-561-2(7) , Lucent Bks.) Thomson Gale.

Nardo, Don, et al. Leaders of Ancient Greece. 1999. (History Makers Ser.). (Illus.). 128p. (YA). (gr. 7-10). 27.45 (978-1-56006-543-2(5) , Lucent Bks.) Thomson Gale.

Nicholson, Robert. Ancient Greece. 2004. (Interfact Ser.). (SPA., Illus.). 48p. (J). (gr. 3-6). 14.95 incl. cd-rom (978-1-58728-455-7(3) , Two Can Publishing) T&N Children's Publishing.

Osborne, Mary Pope & Boyce, Natalie Pope. Ancient Greece & the Olympics: A Nonfiction Companion to Hour of the Olympics. Murdocca, Sal, tr. Murdocca, Sal, illus. 2004. (Magic Tree House Research Guide Ser.: No. 10). 128p. (J). (gr. k-3). pap. 4.99 (978-0-375-82378-7(6)) ; lib. bdg. 11.99 (978-0-375-92378-4(0)) Random Hse. Children's Bks. (Random Hse. Bks. for Young Readers).

Pancella, Peggy. Alexander the Great. 2003. (Historical Biographies Ser.). (Illus.). 32p. (J). pap. 7.50 (978-1-4034-3707-5(6)) ; lib. bdg. 22.79 (978-1-4034-3699-3(1)) Heinemann Library.

Papaloizos, Theodore C. Workbook for a Trip to Greece. 2001. (GRE & ENG.). 106p. (YA). pap. (978-0-932416-24-7(1)) Papaloizos Pubns., Inc.

Pearson, Anne. Ancient Greece. (Dk Eyewitness Books Ser.). (J). pap. 8.95 (978-0-7894-5751-6(2)) ; 2007. 72p. (gr. 3-8). 15.99 incl. cd rom (978-0-7566-3002-7(9)) Dorling Kindersley Publishing, Inc.

—La Antigua Grecia. (Coleccion Biblioteca Visual).Tr. of Ancient Greece. (SPA., Illus.). 64p. (YA). (gr. 5-8). (978-84-372-3771-8(8)) Altea, Ediciones, S.A. - Grupo Santillana.

Pearson, Anne & Dorling Kindersley Publishing Staff. Ancient Greece. 2004. (Eyewitness Books). (Illus.). 72p. (J). lib. bdg. 19.99 (978-0-7566-0648-0(9)) Dorling Kindersley Publishing, Inc.

Powell, Anton. Ancient Greece. 3rd rev. ed. 2007. (Cultural Atlas for Young People Ser.). (Illus.). 96p. (YA). (gr. 5-8). 35.00 (***978-0-8160-6821-0(6)*** , Chelsea Hse.) Facts On File, Inc.

Powell, Anton & Sheehan, Sean. Ancient Greece. 2nd rev. ed. 2003. (Cultural Atlas for Young People Ser.). (Illus.). 96p. (J). (gr. 4-9). 35.00 (978-0-8160-5146-5(1)) Facts On File, Inc.

Powell, Anton, et al. The Greek New. Powell, Anton & Steele, Philip, illus. 1999. (History News Ser.). 32p. (J). (gr. 4-9). pap. 6.99 (978-0-7636-0340-3(6)) Candlewick Pr.

Quennell, Marjorie & Quennell, C. H. Everyday Things in Archaic Greece. 1999. 146p. (YA). pap. 20.00 (978-0-8196-0395-1(3)) Biblo & Tannen Booksellers & Pubs., Inc.

—Everyday Things in Homeric Greece. 1999. 140p. (YA). pap. 20.00 (978-0-8196-0396-8(1)) Biblo & Tannen Booksellers & Pubs., Inc.

Rees, Rosemary. The Ancient Greeks. 2006. (Illus.). 64p. (J). (***978-1-4034-8747-6(2)***) Heinemann Library.

Ross, Stewart. Ancient Greece. 2002. (History in Stone Ser.). 64p. (J). (gr. 3-7). 16.95 (978-1-57145-554-3(X) , Silver Dolphin Bks.) Advantage Pubs. Group.

—Ancient Greece. 2004. (Tales of the Dead Ser.). (Illus.). 32p. (J). 14.99 (978-0-7566-0554-4(7)) Dorling Kindersley Publishing, Inc.

Ryall, Michael. Greece Long Ago. 2005. 39.00 (*978-1-4108-4627-3(X)) Benchmark Education Co.

Sanderson, Caroline. Pick Your Brains about Greece. Williams, Caspar, illus. 2005. (Pick Your Brains Ser.). 128p. pap. 9.95 (978-1-86011-220-1(X)) Cadogan Guides GBR. *Dist:* Globe Pequot Pr., The.

Saunders, Nicholas. The Life of Alexander the Great. 2006. (Stories from History Ser.). 48p. (J). 14.95 (978-0-7696-4713-5(8)) School Specialty Publishing.

Schomp, Virginia. The Ancient Greeks. 2007. (Myths of the World Ser.). 96p. (J). lib. bdg. 32.79 (*978-0-7614-2547-2(0) , Benchmark Bks.) Cavendish, Marshall Corp.

Shecter, Vicky Alvear. Alexander the Great Rocks the World. Naughton, Terry, illus. 2006. 128p. (J). (gr. 6 up). 18.95 (978-1-58196-045-7(X)) Darby Creek Publishing.

Shuter, Jane. Life in a Greek Temple. 2005. (Picture the Past Ser.). (Illus.). 32p. (J). (ps-ps). lib. bdg. 26.79 (978-1-4034-6442-2(1)); pap. (978-1-4034-6449-1(9)) Heinemann Library.

—Life in a Greek Trading Port. 2005. (Picture the Past Ser.). (Illus.). 32p. (J). 25.64 (978-1-4034-6444-6(8)); pap. (978-1-4034-6451-4(0)) Heinemann Library.

Steele, Philip. Clothes & Crafts in Ancient Greece. 2000. (Clothes & Crafts in History Ser.). (Illus.). 32p. (J). (gr. 4 up). lib. bdg. 24.67 (978-0-8368-2734-7(1)) Stevens, Gareth Inc.

—Gods & Gladiators: Everyday Life. 2004. (Illus.). 128p. pap. 17.99 (978-1-84476-032-9(4) , Southwater) Anness Publishing GBR. *Dist:* National Bk. Network.

Sylvester, Diane. Ancient Greece. VanBlaricum, Pam, ed. Hillam, Corbin & Ciccarelli, Gary, illus. 2006. (Museum Ser.). 64p. pap. 13.99 (978-0-88160-387-3(2) , LW441, Learning Works, The) Creative Teaching Pr., Inc.

Tames, Richard. Ancient Greece. 2002. (Find Out about-...Ser.). (Illus.). 64p. (gr. 3-7). pap. 7.95 (978-1-84215-619-3(5) , Southwater) Anness Publishing GBR. *Dist:* National Bk. Network.

—Ancient Greece. 1999. (Step into Ser.). (Illus.). 64p. (gr. 3-7). 12.95 (978-1-85967-916-6(1) , Lorenz Bks.) Anness Publishing, Inc.

—Ancient Greek Children. 2002. (People in the Past Ser.). (Illus.). 48p. (J). (gr. 4-6). lib. bdg. 27.07 (978-1-58810-639-1(X)) Heinemann Library.

Turnbull, Stephanie. Ancient Greeks Internet Referenced. King, Colin, illus. 2004. 32p. (J). (gr. 1 up). pap. 4.95 (978-0-7945-0772-5(7) , Usborne) EDC Publishing.

Wheatley, A. Greeks. 2004. (Illustrated World History Ser.). 96p. (J). lib. bdg. 20.95 (978-1-58086-631-6(X) , Usborne); (Illus.). pap. 12.99 (978-0-7945-0428-1(0)) EDC Publishing.

White, John S., ed. & tr. The Boys' & Girls' Herodotus: Being Parts of the History of Herodotus. White, John S., tr. 1998. (Illus.). 328p. (YA). (gr. 8-12). per. 22.00 (978-0-9667067-0-3(6)) American Home-School Publishing, LLC.

Whiting, Jim. Herodotus. 2006. (Biography from Ancient Civilizations Ser.). (Illus.). 48p. (J). lib. bdg. 20.95 (978-1-58415-509-6(4)) Mitchell Lane Pubs., Inc.

—The Life & Times of Pericles. 2005. (Biography from Ancient Civilizations Ser.). (Illus.). 48p. (J). (ps-7). lib. bdg. 29.95 (978-1-58415-339-9(3)) Mitchell Lane Pubs., Inc.

Williams, Jean Kinney. Empire of Ancient Greece. 2005. (Great Empires of the Past Ser.). (Illus.). 128p. (J). (gr. 6-12). 35.00 (978-0-8160-5561-6(0)) Facts On File, Inc.

GREECE—SOCIAL LIFE AND CUSTOMS

Adare, Sierra. Greece the People. 1999. (gr. 3-6). lib. bdg. 16.40 (978-0-613-11602-2(X)) Tandem Library Bks.

Apel, Melanie Ann. Home Life in Ancient Greece. 2004. (Primary Sources of Ancient Civilizations Ser.). (Illus.). 24p. (J). lib. bdg. (978-0-8239-8940-9(2)); lib. bdg. 19.95 (978-0-8239-6772-8(7)) Rosen Publishing Group, Inc., The. (PowerKids Pr.).

Benduhn, Tea. Ancient Greece. 2006. (Illus.). 24p. (J). pap. (*978-0-8368-7787-8(X)); (gr. 1-3). lib. bdg. 19.93 (*978-0-8368-7782-3(9)) Stevens, Gareth Inc. (Weekly Reader Early Learning Library).

Carlson, Laurie M. Classical Kids: An Activity Guide to Life in Ancient Greece & Rome. 2003. (Kid's Guide Ser.). (Illus.). 200p. (J). (gr. k-7). pap. 14.95 (978-1-55652-290-1(8)) Chicago Review Pr., Inc.

Church, Alfred John. Greek Life & Story. 1998. 320p. (YA). (gr. 6-12). reprint ed. pap. 20.00 (978-0-8196-2056-9(4)) Biblo & Tannen Booksellers & Pubs., Inc.

Claybourne, Anna. Ancient Greece. 2003. (Illus.). 48p. pap. (978-0-7502-3909-7(3) , Hodder Wayland) Hodder Children's Division.

Day, Nancy. Your Travel Guide to Ancient Greece. 2005. (Passport to History Ser.). (Illus.). 96p. (gr. 5-8). lib. bdg. 26.50 (978-0-8225-3076-3(7)) Lerner Publishing Group.

Gioanni, Alain. Thanassis: A Child of Greece. 2005. (Children of the World Ser.). (Illus.). 24p. (J). (gr. k-3). 22.45 (978-1-4103-0284-7(9) , Blackbirch Pr., Inc.) Thomson Gale.

Granstrom, Brita. Greek Hero. Manning, Mick, illus. 2008. (Fly on the Wall Ser.). 40p. (J). 16.95 (*978-1-84507-683-2(4)) Lincoln, Frances Ltd. GBR. *Dist:* Perseus Distribution.

Hammond, Paula. Greece & Turkey. 2002. (Cultures & Costumes Ser.). (Illus.). 64p. (J). (gr. 7 up). lib. bdg. (978-1-59084-437-3(8)) Mason Crest Pubs.

Harcourt School Publishers Staff. Living in Athens. 3rd ed. 2002. (Horizons Ser.). (Illus.). (J). pap. 3.70 (978-0-15-333196-1(8)) Harcourt Schl. Pubs.

Hull, Robert E. Everyday Life. 2000. (World of Ancient Greece Ser.). (Illus.). 32p. (J). (gr. 4-8). pap. 6.95 (978-0-531-15382-6(7) , Watts, Franklin) Scholastic Library Publishing.

MacDonald, Fiona. The Greeks. 2003. (Strange Histories Ser.). (Illus.). 32p. (J). lib. bdg. 25.70 (978-0-7398-6441-8(6)) Raintree.

—The Traveler's Guide to Ancient Greece. Foster, Mike S., illus. 1998. (J). (978-0-590-11762-3(9)) Scholastic, Inc.

Middleton, Haydn & Tames, Richard. Ancient Greek Children. 2002. (People in the Past Ser.). 64p. (J). (gr. 4-7). pap. 8.50 (978-1-4034-0131-1(4) , 91636) Heinemann Library.

Morris, Ting. Ancient Egypt. Young, E., illus. 2006. 32p. (J). (978-1-58340-911-4(4)) Smart Apple Media.

Nardo, Don. The Ancient Greeks at Home & Work. 2004. (Lucent Library of Historical Eras). (Illus.). 112p. (J). (gr. 7-10). 32.45 (978-1-59018-526-1(9) , Lucent Bks.) Thomson Gale.

—Life in Ancient Greece. 2003. (Life During the Great Civilizations Ser.). (Illus.). 48p. (J). (gr. 3-5). 24.95 (978-1-56711-741-7(4) , Blackbirch Pr., Inc.) Thomson Gale.

Owens, Greg. History & Activities of Ancient Greece. 2006. (Hands-On Ancient History Ser.). (Illus.). 32p. (J). (978-1-4034-7920-4(8)); pap. (978-1-4034-7928-0(3)) Heinemann Library.

Parker, Victoria. Greece. 2005. (Illus.). 32p. (J). (ps-7). lib. bdg. 24.21 (978-1-4034-5784-4(0)) Heinemann.

—We're from Greece. 2005. (Illus.). 32p. (J). pap. 7.25 (978-1-4034-5791-2(3)) Heinemann.

Pearson, Anne. Everyday Life in Ancient Greece. 2005. (Clues to the Past Ser.). (Illus.). 32p. (J). (gr. 4-7). lib. bdg. 27.10 (978-1-932889-77-2(9)) Sea-To-Sea Pubns.

Phillips, Dee. Sunken Treasure. 2003. (History Hunters Ser.). (Illus.). 32p. (J). (gr. 3 up). lib. bdg. 24.67 (978-0-8368-3743-8(6)) Stevens, Gareth Inc.

Ross, Stewart. Ancient Greece Daily Life. Hook, Adam, illus. 2006. (Changing Times Ser.). 32p. (J). (gr. 5-7). 27.93 (978-0-7565-2085-4(1)) Compass Point Bks.

—Ancient Greece Entertainment. Hook, Adam, illus. 2006. (Changing Times Ser.). 32p. (J). (gr. 5-6). 27.93 (978-0-7565-2086-1(X)) Compass Point Bks.

Sanderson, Caroline. Pick Your Brains about Greece. Williams, Caspar, illus. 2005. (Pick Your Brains Ser.). 128p. pap. 9.95 (978-1-86011-220-1(X)) Cadogan Guides GBR. *Dist:* Globe Pequot Pr., The.

Senker, Cath. Everyday Life in Ancient Greece. 2003. (Uncovering History Ser.). 46p. (J). lib. bdg. 28.50 (978-1-58340-248-1(9)) Smart Apple Media.

Shuter, Jane. Life in a Greek Trading Port. 2005. (Picture the Past Ser.). (Illus.). 32p. (J). 25.64 (978-1-4034-6444-6(8)); pap. (978-1-4034-6451-4(0)) Heinemann Library.

Sioras, Efstathia. Greece. 1998. (Festivals of the World Ser.). (Illus.). 32p. (J). (gr. 3 up). lib. bdg. 24.67 (978-0-8368-2014-0(2)) Stevens, Gareth Inc.

Tames, Richard. Ancient Greek Children. 2002. (People in the Past Ser.). (Illus.). 48p. (J). (gr. 4-6). lib. bdg. 27.07 (978-1-58810-639-1(X)) Heinemann Library.

Villios, Lynne W. Cooking the Greek Way. 2003. (Easy Menu Ethnic Cookbooks). (Illus.). 72p. pap. 7.95 (978-0-8225-0533-4(9)) Lerner Publishing Group.

—Cooking the Greek Way. Wolfe, Robert L. & Wolfe, Diane, illus. Wolfe, Robert L. & Wolfe, Diane, photos by. 2nd rev. expurg. ed. 2002. (Easy Menu Ethnic Cookbooks). 72p. (J). (gr. 5-12). lib. bdg. 25.26 (978-0-8225-4131-8(9)) Lerner Publishing Group.

Waryncia, Lou, et al. If I Were a Kid in Ancient Greece. 2007. (Children of the Ancient World Ser.). (Illus.). 32p. (J). 17.95 (978-0-8126-7929-8(6)) Cricket Bks.

GREECE, MODERN—HISTORY

Adare, Sierra. Greece the Land. 1999. (gr. 3-6). lib. bdg. 16.40 (978-0-613-11601-5(1)) Tandem Library Bks.

GREED

Berry, Joy Wilt. A Book about Being Greedy. 2005. (Illus.). (J). (978-0-7172-8598-3(7)) Scholastic, Inc.

Leigh, Susan K. God, I Need to Talk to You about Greed. Clark, Bill, illus. 2005. (ENG.). 16p. (J). pap. 0.99 (978-0-7586-0795-9(4)) Concordia Publishing Hse.

GREED—FICTION

Arena, Umberto J. The Angel & the Greedy Kid. 2006. 25p. (J). pap. 7.95 (978-0-533-15387-9(5)) Vantage Pr., Inc.

Bolliger, Max. The Happy Troll. Ignatowicz, Nina, tr. from GER. Sis, Peter, illus. 2005. 32p. (J). reprint ed. 16.95 (978-0-8050-6982-2(8) , Holt, Henry & Co. Bks. For Young Readers) Holt, Henry & Co.

Cox, Judy. One Is a Feast for Mouse. Ebbeler, Jeffrey, illus. 2008. (J). (*978-0-8234-1977-7(0)) Holiday Hse., Inc.

Cox, Phil Roxbee. Don't Be Greedy, Graham. 2006. 24p. (J). pap. 7.99 (978-0-7945-1361-0(1) , Usborne) EDC Publishing.

Delessert, Etienne. Big & Bad. 2008. 32p. (J). (gr. 3-5). 17.00 (*978-0-618-88934-1(5)) Houghton Mifflin Co.

Donnelly, Jennifer & Gammell, Stephen. Humble Pie. 2002. (Illus.). 32p. (J). (gr. k-2). 16.95 (978-0-689-84435-5(2) , Atheneum/Richard Jackson Bks.) Simon & Schuster Children's Publishing.

Edwards, Pamela Duncan. The Leprechaun's Gold. Cole, Henry, illus. 2004. 32p. (J). (ps-2). 15.99 (978-0-06-623974-3(5)); lib. bdg. 16.89 (978-0-06-623975-0(3)) HarperCollins Pubs.

Elya, Susan Middleton. Cowboy Jose. Raglin, Tim, illus. 2005. 32p. (J). 15.99 (978-0-399-23570-2(1) , Putnam Juvenile) Penguin Group (USA) Inc.

Entara Ltd. Staff, photos by. Piggley Makes a Pie. 2006. (Ready-To-Read Ser.). (Illus.). 24p. (J). pap. 3.99 (978-0-689-87613-4(0) , Simon Spotlight) Simon & Schuster Children's Publishing.

Great White Man Eating Shark. 2004. (J). pap. 14.95 incl. audio (978-0-7882-0690-0(7)) Weston Woods Studios, Inc.

The Greedy Crows, 6 vols. (Multicultural Programs Ser.). 16p. (gr. 1-6). 42.50 (978-0-7802-1482-8(X)) Wright Group, The.

Gregory, Kristiana. Seeds of Hope: The Gold Rush Diary of Susanna Fairchild, 1849. 2001. (Dear America Ser.). (Illus.). 176p. (J). (gr. 5-8). pap. 10.95 (978-0-590-51157-5(2)) Scholastic, Inc.

Grimm, Jacob W., et al. The Fisherman & His Wife. 2001. (Illus.). 32p. (gr. 6). 17.95 (978-1-56846-140-3(2)) Creative Co., The.

Harcourt School Publishers Staff. The Dog & His Shadow On Level. 3rd ed. 2002. (Trophies Reading Program Ser.). (Illus.). pap. 5.10 (978-0-15-323074-5(6)) Harcourt Schl. Pubs.

Harrington, Sean P. Patterson & the Great Green Greedy Galumpus. 2000. (Illus.). 20p. (J). (gr. k-4). pap. 10.95 (978-0-9672290-2-7(2)) Harrington, Denis J. Pub.

Hernandez, Norberto, tr. The Goose with the Golden Eggs: A Fable by Aesop. Leonard, Card, illus. 2000. Tr. of Ganso con los Huevos de Oro: Una Fabula de Esopo. (ENG & SPA.). (J). (gr. 1-4). pap. 12.95 incl. audio (978-0-9678821-0-9(9)) Libie Alone Pubns.

Hoving, Isabel. The Dream Merchant. Velmans, Hester, tr. from DUT. 2005. 640p. (YA). (gr. 7 up). 19.99 (978-0-7636-2880-2(8)) Candlewick Pr.

Howells, William Dean. Christmas Every Day. (J). lib. bdg. 16.95 (978-0-8488-1866-1(0)) Amereon LTD.

—Christmas Every Day. 2002. (Illus.). 32p. 12.95 (978-0-8249-5444-4(0)) Ideals Pubns.

Isadora, Rachel. The Fisherman & His Wife. Isadora, Rachel, illus. 2008. 32p. (J). (ps). 16.99 (*978-0-399-24771-2(8) , Putnam Juvenile) Penguin Group (USA) Inc.

Kalz, Jill. Henry Shortbull Swallows the Sun. Erkocak, Sahin, illus. 2007. (Pfeffernut County Ser.). 32p. (J). (gr. k-2). lib. bdg. 23.93 (*978-1-4048-3695-2(0)) Picture Window Bks.

Maccarone, Grace & Burns, Marilyn. It Was Halloween Night: A Scary Math Story - with Tangrams! Straub, Matthew, illus. 2001. (Hello Reader! Math Ser.). (J). (978-0-439-30471-9(7)) Scholastic, Inc.

Madonna. Lotsa de Casha. Paes, Rui, illus. 2005. 48p. (J). 19.95 (978-0-670-05888-4(2)) Callaway Editions, Inc.

Mayo, Frank, illus. King Midas & the Golden Touch: A Tale about Greed. 2006. (J). 6.99 (978-1-59939-022-2(1) , Reader's Digest Young Families, Inc.) Reader's Digest Children's Publishing, Inc.

Myers, Bill. My Life as a Walrus Whoopee Cushion, Vol. 16. 1999. (Incredible Worlds of Wally McDoogle Ser.: No. 16). 128p. (J). (gr. 3-7). pap. 6.99 (978-0-8499-4025-5(7)) Nelson, Thomas Inc.

—Phantom of the Haunted Church. 1998. (Bloodhounds, Inc. Ser.: Vol. 3). (Illus.). 128p. (J). (gr. 3-8). pap. 5.99 (978-1-55661-892-5(1)) Bethany Hse. Pubs.

Schlessinger, Laura. But I Waaannt It! McFeeley, Daniel, illus. 2000. 40p. (J). (ps-2). 15.89 (978-0-06-028958-4(9)); 15.95 (978-0-06-028775-7(6)) HarperCollins Pubs.

Schmidt, Gary D. Straw into Gold. 2001. (Illus.). 176p. (J). (gr. 4-6). tchr. ed. 15.00 (978-0-618-05601-9(7) , Clarion Bks.) Houghton Mifflin Co. Trade & Reference Div.

Simon, Charnan. A Greedy Little Pig. Ramsey, Marcy Dunn, illus. 2006. (Magic Door to Learning Ser.). 24p. (J). (gr. 1-3). 21.36 (978-1-59296-622-6(5)) Child's World, Inc.

Stanley, Diane. Rumpelstiltskin's Daughter. 2002. (gr. k-3). lib. bdg. 15.25 (978-0-613-46097-2(9)) Tandem Library Bks.

Steinbeck, John. Perla. 2000. (SPA.). (gr. 7-12). lib. bdg. 15.25 (978-0-613-62435-0(1)) Tandem Library Bks.

Stevens, Janet & Crummel, Susan Stevens. The Great Fuzz Frenzy. 2005. (Illus.). 56p. (J). (ps-ps). 17.00 (978-0-15-204626-2(7) , Harcourt Children's Bks) Harcourt Children's Bks.

—The Great Fuzz Frenzy. unabr. ed. 2006. (J). (gr. k-3). 27.99 incl. audio (*978-0-8045-6940-8(1) , SAC6941); 29.95 incl. audio compact disk (*978-0-8045-4154-1(X) , SACD4155) Spoken Arts, Inc.

Stine, R.L. Rich Girl. 2005. 132p. (J). lib. bdg. 13.00 (*978-1-4242-0999-6(4)) Fitzgerald Bks.

Tolstoy, Leo. How Much Land Does a Man Need? Abesinova, Elena, illus. 2001. (RUS & ENG.). 32p. (J). (gr. k-4). 15.95 (978-1-56656-407-6(7)) Interlink Publishing Group, Inc.

Tompert, Ann & Chwast, Jacqueline. The Hungry Black Bag. 1999. (Illus.). 32p. (J). (gr. k-3), tchr. ed. 15.00 (978-0-395-89418-7(2) , Walter Lorraine) Houghton Mifflin Co. Trade & Reference Div.

Willard, Nancy. The Flying Bed. Thompson, John, illus. 2007. 48p. (J). (ps-3). pap. 16.99 (978-0-590-25610-0(6) , Blue Sky Pr., The) Scholastic, Inc.

Winterson, Jeanette. The King of Capri. Ray, Jane, illus. 2003. 32p. (J). 16.95 (978-1-58234-830-8(8) , Bloomsbury Children) Bloomsbury Publishing.

Witte, Anna. El Loro Tico Tango. Witte, Anna, illus. 2005. (SPA., Illus.). 24p. (J). pap. 6.99 (978-1-84148-971-1(9)) Barefoot Bks., Inc.

—The Parrot Tico Tango. Witte, Anna, illus. (Illus.). 24p. (J). (gr. k-3). 2005. 15.99 (978-1-84148-243-9(9)); 2004. pap. 6.99 (978-1-905236-11-4(5)) Barefoot Bks., Inc.

GREEK ANTIQUITIES

see Classical Antiquities

GREEK ART

see Art, Greek

GREEK CIVILIZATION

see Civilization, Greek

GREEK LANGUAGE, MODERN—CONVERSATION AND PHRASE BOOKS

Papaloizos, Theodore. Level Two - the Kids of the Neighborhood. 2006. (J). pap. (978-0-932416-99-5(3)) Papaloizos Pubns., Inc.

GREEK LANGUAGE, MODERN—GRAMMAR

Nannas, Anastasia. Let's Learn Greek. Un-Choi, Nicole, illus. 2002. (GRE.). 104p. (J). (gr. k-12). pap., tchr. ed. 17.00 (978-0-918618-85-6(1)) Pella Publishing Co., Inc.

GREEK LITERATURE

Nardo, Don, ed. Readings on "Antigone" 1999. (Literary Companion to American Literature Ser.). (Illus.). 127p. pap. (978-1-56510-968-1(6) , Greenhaven Pr., Inc.) Thomson Gale.

GREEK LITERATURE—HISTORY AND CRITICISM

Novel Units, Inc. Staff. Iliad. 1999. (YA). 11.95 (978-1-56137-753-4(8)) Novel Units, Inc.

GREEK MYTHOLOGY

see Mythology, Classical

GREEKS—FICTION

Barker, M. A. R. A Death of Kings. 2nd ed. 2002. (Illus.). 210p. pap. 19.95 (978-0-9725880-4-1(3)) Zottola Publishing, Inc.

DiTocco, Robyn & DiTocco, Tony. The Hero Perseus: A Mad Myth Mystery. 2004. 220p. (gr. 3-12). 19.95 (978-0-9723429-0-2(7)); pap. 11.95 (978-0-9723429-1-9(5)) Brainstorm Pubns., Inc.

Evans, C & Millard, A. Greek & Norse Legends. 2004. (Myths & Legends Ser.). 112p. (J). lib. bdg. 20.95 (978-1-58086-603-3(4)) EDC Publishing.

Geringer & Czernecki, Stefan. Silverpoint. 1999. 160p. (J). (gr. 5 up). pap. (978-0-06-440432-7(3) , Harper Trophy) HarperCollins Pubs.

Harcourt School Publishers Staff. Phaeton & the Sun Chariot Below Level. 3rd ed. 2002. (Trophies Reading Program Ser.). (Illus.). pap. 5.10 (978-0-15-323147-6(5)) Harcourt Schl. Pubs.

Howard, Annabelle. Three Greek Myths: Pandora, Icarus & Midas. 2005. 40.00 (*978-1-4108-4226-8(6)) Benchmark Education Co.

McLaren, Clemence. Inside the Walls of Troy: A Novel of the Women Who Lived the Trojan War. 2004. 199p. (YA). (gr. 6-10). reprint ed. 18.00 (978-0-7567-7986-3(3)) DIANE Publishing Co.

—Inside the Walls of Troy: A Novel of the Women Who Lived the Trojan War. 2004. 208p. (YA). pap. 5.99 (978-0-689-87397-3(2) , Simon Pulse) Simon & Schuster Children's Publishing.

—Inside the Walls of Troy: A Novel of the Women Who Lived the Trojan War. 1998. (J). 12.15 (978-0-606-13519-1(7)) Tandem Library Bks.

Napoli, Donna Jo. The Great God Pan. 2003. 160p. (YA). (gr. 5). lib. bdg. 17.99 (978-0-385-90120-8(8) , Lamb, Wendy) Random Hse. Children's Bks.

Osterbach, Batya Kirshenbaum. Pini the Pitcher: A Story for Hanukkah. Eisby, Lizzy, illus. 2005. 32p. (J). (gr. 1-4). 16.95 (978-1-932687-50-7(5) , Devora Publishing) Pitspopany Pr.

Schrecengost, Maity. Tasso of Tarpon Springs. Stock, Rose, illus. 1998. 118p. (J). (gr. 3-6). pap. 5.95 (978-0-929895-24-6(X) , Hoot Owl Bks.) Maupin Hse. Publishing.

Spinner, Stephanie. Quicksilver. 2005. (Illus.). 240p. (gr. 7). (J). lib. bdg. 17.99 (978-0-375-92638-9(0)); (YA). 15.95 (978-0-375-82638-2(6)) Random Hse. Children's Bks. (Knopf Bks. for Young Readers).

Tomlinson, Theresa. Voyage of the Snake Lady. 2007. 400p. (J). lib. bdg. 18.89 (*978-0-06-084740-1(9)); (YA). (gr. 7 up). 17.99 (*978-0-06-084739-5(5)) HarperCollins Pubs. (Eos).

GREEKS—UNITED STATES

Frank, Sarah. Greeks in America. 2006. (J). lib. bdg. (978-0-8225-2686-5(7) , Lerner Pubns.) Lerner Publishing Group.

Greene, Meg. Greek Americans. 2003. (Immigrants in America Ser.). (Illus.). 112p. (J). 29.95 (978-1-59018-077-8(1) , Lucent Bks.) Thomson Gale.

Klingel, Cynthia Fitterer. Greek Americans. 2003. (Spirit of America). (Illus.). 32p. (J). (gr. 2-6). 27.07 (978-1-59296-014-9(6)) Child's World, Inc.

Monos, Dimitris. The Greek Americans. Stotsky, Sandra, ed. 1999. (Immigrant Experience Ser.). (Illus.). 128p. (YA). (gr. 5). pap. 9.95 (978-0-7910-3378-4(3) , Chelsea Hse.) Facts On File, Inc.

GREEN TURTLE

Becker, John E. Green Sea Turtles. 2003. (Returning Wildlife Ser.). (Illus.). 48p. (J). 26.20 (978-0-7377-1831-7(5) , Greenhaven Pr., Inc.) Thomson Gale.

Blomquist, Christopher. Green Sea Turtles. 2004. (Library of Turtles & Tortoises). (Illus.). 24p. (J). lib. bdg. 18.75 (978-0-8239-6738-4(7) , PowerKids Pr.) Rosen Publishing Group, Inc., The.

Fletcher, Marty & Scherer, Glenn. The Green Sea Turtle: Help Save This Endangered Species! 2006. (Saving Endangered Species Ser.). (Illus.). 128p. (J). lib. bdg. 33.27 (978-1-59845-033-0(6) , MyReportLinks.com Bks.) Enslow Pubs., Inc.

Gareth Stevens Publishing Staff, contrib. by. Turtles. 2004. (All about Wild Animals Ser.). (Illus.). 32p. (J). (gr. 2 up). lib. bdg. 23.33 (978-0-8368-4123-7(9)) Stevens, Gareth Inc.

Nichols, Wallace J. & Snodgrass, Robert E. Chelonia - Return of the Sea Turtle. Navarro, Dawn E., illus. 2001. 36p. (J). (gr. 1-7). 16.95 (978-0-930118-31-0(6)) Sea Challengers, Inc.

Salariya, Savid. The Journey of a Turtle. Sorace, Carolyn, photos by. 2000. (Lifecycles Ser.). (Illus.). 32p. (J). (gr. k-2). 25.50 (978-0-531-14520-3(4) , Watts, Franklin) Scholastic Library Publishing.

Stille, Darlene. I Am a Sea Turtle: The Life of a Green Sea Turtle. Ouren, Todd, illus. 2004. (I Live in the Ocean Ser.). 24p. (C). (gr. k-2). 22.60 (978-1-4048-0597-2(4)) Picture Window Bks.

GREEN BAY PACKERS (FOOTBALL TEAM)

Dougherty, Terri. Brett Favre. 1999. (Jam Session Ser.). (Illus.). 32p. (J). (gr. 3-8). lib. bdg. 24.21 (978-1-57765-036-2(0) , ABDO & Daughters) ABDO Publishing Co.

Frisch, Aaron. Green Bay Packers. 2005. (Super Bowl Champions Ser.). (Illus.). 24p. (gr. 1-4). 16.95 (978-1-58341-384-5(7) , Creative Education) Creative Co., The.

Gutman, Bill. Brett, Favre: Leader of the Pack. 1998. (Millbrook Sports World Ser.). (Illus.). 48p. (gr. 3-6). lib. bdg. 22.90 (978-0-7613-0310-7(3) , Millbrook Pr.) Lerner Publishing Group.

Molzahn, Arlene Bourgeois. The Green Bay Packers Football Team. 1999. (Great Sports Teams Ser.). (Illus.). 48p. (YA). (gr. 4-10). lib. bdg. 18.95 (978-0-7660-1100-7(3)) Enslow Pubs., Inc.

Nelson, Sharlene P. & Nelson, Ted. Brett Favre. 2000. (Sports Heroes Ser.). (Illus.). 48p. (J). (gr. 3-4). lib. bdg. 21.26 (978-0-7368-0576-6(1) , Capstone High-Interest Bks.) Capstone Pr., Inc.

Potts, Steve. Green Bay Packers. 2001. (Championship Teams Ser.). (Illus.). (J). (978-1-58340-090-6(7)) Smart Apple Media.

Rekela, George R. Brett Favre: Star Quarterback. 2000. (Sports Reports). (Illus.). 104p. (YA). (gr. 4-10). lib. bdg. 26.60 (978-0-7660-1332-2(4)) Enslow Pubs., Inc.

Stewart, Mark & Aikens, Jason. The Green Bay Packers. 2008. (J). (***978-1-59953-131-1(3)***) Norwood Hse. Pr.

Stotts, Stuart. Curly Lambeau: Building the Green Bay Packers. 2007. (Badger Biographies Ser.). 128p. (J). pap. 12.95 (***978-0-87020-389-3(4)***) Wisconsin Historical Society.

GREENBACKS

see Paper Money

GREENE, NATHANAEL, 1742-1786

Bodie, Idella. Quaker Commander. 2001. (Illus.). 89p. (J). 6.95 (978-0-87844-160-0(3)) Sandlapper Publishing Co., Inc.

—The Secret Message. 1998. (Heroes & Heroines of the American Revolution Ser.: Vol. 2). (Illus.). 45p. (J). (ps-3). pap. 5.95 (978-0-87844-145-7(X)) Sandlapper Publishing Co., Inc.

Greene, Meg. Nathanael Greene. 2000. (Revolutionary War Leaders Ser.). (Illus.). 80p. (J). (gr. 4-7). pap. 27.50 (978-0-7910-6135-0(3)); (gr. 8-12). 27.50 (978-0-7910-5977-7(4)) Facts On File, Inc. (Chelsea Hse.).

—Nathanael Greene: Military Leader. 2001. (gr. 5-8). lib. bdg. 17.60 (978-0-613-32866-1(3)) Tandem Library Bks.

Mierka, Gregg A. Nathanael Greene: The General Who Saved the Revolution. 2006. (J). pap. (978-1-59556-017-9(3)); (Illus.). 88p. (gr. 5-11). lib. bdg. 23.95 (978-1-59556-012-4(2)) OTTN Publishing.

GREENHOUSES

Kemper, Bitsy. Out & about at the Greenhouse. Trover, Zachary, illus. 2006. (Field Trips Ser.). 24p. (J). (gr. 2-4). lib. bdg. 25.26 (978-1-4048-2279-5(8)) Picture Window Bks.

GREENLAND

Blashfield, Jean F. Greenland. 2005. (Enchantment of the World, Second Ser.). (Illus.). 144p. (YA). (gr. 5-9). 36.00 (978-0-516-23678-0(4) , Children's Pr.) Scholastic Library Publishing.

Buell, Janet. Greenland Mummies. 1998. (Time Travelers Ser.: 8). (Illus.). 64p. (gr. 5-8). lib. bdg. 25.90 (978-0-7613-3004-2(6) , Twenty-First Century Bks.) Lerner Publishing Group.

Dupre, Kelly. The Raven's Gift: A True Story from Greenland. Dupre, Kelly, illus. 2001. (Illus.). 32p. (J). (gr. k-3). tchr. ed. 15.00 (978-0-618-01171-1(4)) Houghton Mifflin Co. Trade & Reference Div.

Greenland: Individual Title Six-Packs. (On Deck Ser.). 24p. (gr. 4-5). 35.00 (978-0-7578-1081-7(0)) Rigby Education.

Groenlandia: Individual Title Six-Packs. (On Deck en Espanol Ser.).Tr. of Greenland. (SPA.). 24p. (gr. 4-5). 35.00 (978-0-7578-6452-0(X)) Rigby Education.

Mattern, Joanne. Greenland: World's Largest Island. 2002. (Reading Power Ser.). (Illus.). 24p. (J). (gr. 2). lib. bdg. 17.25 (978-0-8239-6018-7(8) , PowerKids Pr.) Rosen Publishing Group, Inc., The.

—Groenlandia. 2004. (Natures Greatest Hits Ser.). (SPA.). 24p. (J). (gr. 3-6). lib. bdg. 17.25 (978-0-8239-6876-3(6) , Buenas Letra) Rosen Publishing Group, Inc., The.

GREENLAND—FICTION

Castle, Caroline. The Big Fuzzy. 2007. (J). lib. bdg. 16.95 (***978-1-59566-368-9(1)***) QEB Publishing Inc.

Davis, Mike. Land of the Lost Mammoths: A Science Adventure. 2003. (Illus.). 174p. (J). 15.95 (978-0-9747078-0-8(5)) Perceval Pr.

Stead, Rebecca. First Light. 2007. 336p. (J). (gr. 4-7). 15.99 (***978-0-375-84017-3(6)***); lib. bdg. 18.99 (***978-0-375-94017-0(0)***) Random Hse. Children's Bks. (Lamb, Wendy).

GREETING CARDS

AG Publishers Editors. Sparkle Card Kit: Everything You Need to Create More than 20 Glittery Greetings! 2003. (American Girl Library). (Illus.). 64p. (J). 19.95 (978-1-58485-707-5(2)) American Girl Publishing, Inc.

Blanchette, Peg & Thibault, Terri. Make Your Own Cool Cards: 40 Awesome Notes & Invitations! 2004. (Quick Starts for Kids! Ser.). (Illus.). 64p. (J). 8.95 (978-1-885593-96-2(1) , Williamson Bks.) Ideals Pubns.

Boase, Petra. Fun at Christmas. 2000. (Fun with... Ser.). (Illus.). 96p. (gr. 3-7). 12.95 (978-1-84215-333-8(1) , Southwater) Anness Publishing GBR. *Dist:* National Bk. Network.

Bond, Felicia. Make Your Own Valentines! 1999. (Illus.). 32p. (J). (ps-2). 9.95 (978-0-694-01259-6(9)) HarperCollins Pubs.

Carter, Tasmin. Handmade Cards. 2002. (Step-by-Step Children's Crafts Ser.). (Illus.). 32p. pap. 7.95 (978-0-85532-981-5(5) , 9815) Search Pr., Ltd. GBR. *Dist:* Independent Pubs. Group.

Chan, Mari. Dark Horse Deluxe Stationery Exotique: Mari-Chan Super Fun Kids. 2003. 4.99 (978-1-56971-922-0(5)) Dark Horse Comics.

Conlon, Mara. Made by Me! Cards & Crafts for Mom & for Dad. 2006. (Pretty Simple Stuff Ser.). 32p. (J). (gr. 2-5). pap. 6.99 (978-0-8431-1850-6(4) , Price Stern Sloan) Penguin Group (USA) Inc.

Detweiler, Molly, ed. Love Bears V: Warm Fuzzies for Your Heart. 2001. (Illus.). 128p. (J). pap. 5.99 (978-0-310-98101-5(8)) Zondervan.

Greathead, Helen. Cards. 2006. (Illus.). 32p. (978-1-58340-955-8(6)) Smart Apple Media.

Hal Leonard Corp., creator. Holy Christmas Carols Coloring Book. 2000. 24p. pap. 6.95 (978-1-57560-368-1(3) , 1575603683) Cherry Lane Music Co.

Hirschmann, Kris. Hello Kitty Stationery. 2001. (Hello Kitty & Her Friends Crafts Club Ser.). (Illus.). 44p. (J). act. bk. ed. (978-0-439-32837-1(3)) Scholastic, Inc.

Hufford, Deborah. Greeting Card Making: Send Your Personal Message. 2005. (Illus.). 32p. (J). (978-0-7368-4385-0(X)) Capstone Pr., Inc.

Humphrey, Paul. How to Make a Card. 2007. (***978-1-59771-100-5(4)***) Sea-To-Sea Pubns.

Im, Angela, ed. Glitter Art. 2005. (Fun Pack Ser.). (Illus.). 48p. (J). lthr. 7.99 (978-0-439-67617-5(7) , Tangerine Pr.) Scholastic, Inc.

LaFosse, Michael. Making Origami Cards Step by Step. 2004. (Kid's Guide to Origami Ser.). (Illus.). 24p. (J). lib. bdg. 21.25 (978-0-8239-6701-8(8) , PowerKids Pr.) Rosen Publishing Group, Inc., The.

Love Bears Heart to Heart Postcard Daybreak. 2000. (Illus.). 106p. (J). spiral bd. 9.99 (978-0-310-98110-7(7)) Zondervan.

MacGregor, Cynthia. Thanks, Aunt Zelda! Thank-You Cards for Kids to Craft. Bell, Anouk Pérusse, illus. 2002. 48p. (J). (gr. k-6). 9.95 (978-1-894222-66-2(0)) Lobster Pr. CAN. *Dist:* Univ. of Toronto Pr.

McLendon, Charles H., Jr. Santa's Stories for Children & Adults, Vol. I. collector's ed. 2002. (Illus.). 12p. (J). (ps-6). pap. 19.95 (978-0-9723225-0-8(7)) Christmas City Distribution, Inc.

Mouse Works Staff. Disney's Make Your Own Christmas Cards. 2000. 40p. (J). 7.99 (978-0-7364-1015-1(5)) Disney Pr.

Otten, Jack. Watch Me Make a Birthday Card. 2002. (Welcome Books). (Illus.). 24p. (J). (ps-2). 18.00 (978-0-516-23948-4(1)); pap. 4.95 (978-0-516-23498-4(6)) Scholastic Library Publishing. (Children's Pr.).

Rau, Dana Meachen. Handmade Cards for Fun! 2007. lib. bdg. (***978-0-7565-3279-6(5)***) Compass Point Bks.

Tamsin, Carter. Handmade Crafts. 2003. (Step-by-Step Ser.). (Illus.). 32p. (J). (gr. 3-5). lib. bdg. 25.64 (978-1-4034-0698-9(7)) Heinemann Library.

Things to Make & Do for Christmas Kid Kit. (Illus.). 32p. (YA). (ps up). 13.95 (978-1-58086-440-4(6)) EDC Publishing.

Watt, Fiona. Christmas decorations & Cards. 2005. 34p. (J). pap. 8.95 (978-0-7945-0795-4(6) , Usborne) EDC Publishing.

—Christmas Stencil Cards. 2007. (Christmas Stencil Cards Ser.). 16p. (J). 9.99 (***978-0-7945-1896-7(6)*** , Usborne) EDC Publishing.

Watt, Fiona. Making Cards. Figg, Non Et Al, illus. 2007. 64p. (J). pap. 14.99 (978-0-7945-1356-6(5) , Usborne) EDC Publishing.

Wild, Anne S. Wildlife Pop-Ups: A Collection of 3 D Greetings Cards on Wildlife Themes to Cut Out & Make. 2004. (Illus.). 36p. (J). 12.00 (978-1-899618-48-4(1)) Tarquin Pubns. GBR. *Dist:* Parkwest Pubns., Inc.

GREETING CARDS—FICTION

Rau, Dana Meachen. I'll Make You a Card, Level C. Bryan-Hunt, Jan, illus. 2002. (Compass Point Early Reader Ser.). 32p. (J). (gr. k up). lib. bdg. 18.60 (978-0-7565-0172-3(5)) Compass Point Bks.

Su, Lucy. Make Cards. Su, Lucy, illus. 2003. (Kitten & Baby Kitten Ser.). (Illus.). 32p. (YA). (978-1-85602-446-4(6)) Chrysalis Children's Bks.

Umansky, Kaye. Sophie & the Mother's Day Card. Currey, Anna, illus. 2005. 30p. (J). 3.95 (978-1-56148-481-2(4)); 9.95 (978-1-56148-479-9(2)) Good Bks.

GRENFELL, WILFRED THOMASON, SIR, 1865-1940

Benge, Janet & Benge, Geoff. Wilfred Grenfell: Fisher of Men. 2003. (Christian Heroes, Then & Now Ser.). (Illus.). 191p. pap. 8.99 (978-1-57658-292-3(2)) YWAM Publishing.

GRIEF

Bender, Janet. Getting Yourself Together When Your Family Comes Apart: Coping with Family Changes. 2004. (Illus.). 50p. (J). per. 19.95 (978-1-931636-28-5(1)) National Center For Youth Issues.

Britain, Lory. My Grandma Died: A Child's Story about Grief & Loss. Deach, Carol, illus. 2002. 32p. (J). 16.95 (978-1-884734-27-4(8)); pap. 6.95 (978-1-884734-26-7(X)) Parenting Pr., Inc.

Chepokas, Rebecca & Chepokas, Rebecca. Good-bye, Mitch: Sorrow, Grief, Inspiration, 2004. per. 14.95 (978-0-9743717-4-0(2)) Amber Woods Publishing.

Coping with Death. 2003. 160p. (J). (ps-7). lib. bdg. 33.25 (978-0-613-73881-1(0)) Tandem Library Bks.

Coping with the Loss of a Loved One: An Inspiring New Book about Appreciating Human Life & Death. 2003. 60p. per. 10.00 net. (978-0-9620180-3-9(1)) Black, Clinton L.

Cunningham, Alexis. A Child's Simple Guide Through Grief. 2000. 48p. (J). (ps-3). pap. 9.95 (978-1-880396-88-9(2)) Jalmar Pr.

Davidson, Judy. Grief Skills for Life: A Personal Journal about Loss for Adolescents. rev. ed. 2002. (Illus.). 112p. (YA). (gr. 7-12). pap. 11.95 (978-0-9719569-1-9(X)) RENEW: Ctr. for Personal Recovery, Inc.

—My Own Grief Journal: A Personal Journal About Loss for the Young Child. rev. ed. 2002. (Illus.). 48p. (J). (gr. 1-5). pap. 11.95 (978-0-9719569-2-6(8)) RENEW: Ctr. for Personal Recovery, Inc.

—My Own Grief Journal: A Personal Journal for Children Ages 7-11 about Loss. rev. ed. 2002. (Illus.). 32p. (J). (gr. 4-5). pap. 11.95 (978-0-9719569-9-5(5)) RENEW: Ctr. for Personal Recovery, Inc.

Dennison, Amy, et al, as told by. After You Lose Someone You Love: Advice & Insight from the Diaries of Three Kids Who've Been There. 2005. (Illus.). 128p. (YA). (ps up). pap. 9.95 (978-1-57542-169-8(0)) Free Spirit Publishing, Inc.

—Our Dad Died: The True Story of Three Kids Whose Lives Changed. 2004. (Illus.). 112p. (J). pap. 9.95 (978-1-57542-135-3(6)) Free Spirit Publishing, Inc.

Dokas, Dara. Remembering Mama. Chostner, Angela L., illus. 2002. 32p. 15.99 (978-0-8066-4352-6(8) , Augsburg Bks.) Augsburg Fortress, Pubs.

Edwards, Dianna. Meet Patou. 2006. (J). pap. 29.95 (978-0-9767756-0-7(3)) Patou Bks., LLC.

—My Journal & Drawings. 2004. (J). spiral bd. (978-0-9767756-4-5(6)) Patou Bks., LLC.

—Why Can't Everything Just Stay the Same? Book Three. 2004. (J). (978-0-9767756-3-8(8)) Patou Bks., LLC.

Fitzgerald, Helen. The Grieving Teen: A Guide for Teenagers & Their Friends. 2000. 224p. (J). pap. 13.00 (978-0-684-86804-2(0) , Fireside) Simon & Schuster.

—The Grieving Teen: A Guide for Teenagers & Their Friends. 2000. 18.65 (978-0-606-20685-3(X)) Tandem Library Bks.

Gaughen, Shasta. Coping with Death. 2003. (Contemporary Issues Companion Ser.). (YA). 176p. pap. 24.95 (978-0-7377-1521-7(9)); 160p. lib. bdg. 36.20 (978-0-7377-1520-0(0)) Thomson Gale. (Greenhaven Pr., Inc.).

Giddens, Sandra & Giddens, Owen. Coping with Grieving & Loss. 2003. (Coping Ser.). 124p. (YA). (gr. 7-12). lib. bdg. 26.50 (978-0-8239-3758-5(5)) Rosen Publishing Group, Inc., The.

Glendinning, Margaret. From Shadow into Light. 2002. 40p. 5.00 (978-0-9714649-6-4(0)) MPG Pr.

Gootman, Marilyn E. When a Friend Dies: A Book for Teens about Grieving & Healing. 2005. (Illus.). 128p. (YA). (gr. 6 up). pap. 9.95 (978-1-57542-170-4(4)) Free Spirit Publishing, Inc.

Grebin, Margaret. Baseball Forever! A Boy's Book on Grief, Loss, & Healing. 2004. (J). per. 10.95 (978-1-59094-076-1(8)) Jawbone Publishing Corp.

Harper, Kimberly. Stepping Stones Through Grief: A Children's Workbook on Death, Grief & Loss. Stratton, David, ed. Carroll, Michelle, illus. 2000. (J). spiral bd., wbk. ed. 5.00 (978-0-9703035-1-6(3)) United Medical Ctr.

Hughes, Lynne. You Are Not Alone: Teens Talk about Life after the Loss of a Parent. 2005. (You Are Not Alone Ser.). (Illus.). 208p. (J). pap. 16.99 (978-0-439-58590-3(2) , Scholastic Pr.) Scholastic, Inc.

Joseph, Judith C. I Hate Strawberry Jam. Spitzer, Hillary, illus. 2002. 120p. (YA). (gr. 3 up). pap. 14.95 (978-0-9715420-0-6(7)) JCJoseph, Ltd.

Kaleidoscope of Grief: When Children Experience Death. 2000. (J). pap. 4.95 (978-0-9717266-0-4(4)) MISS Foundation Publishing.

Kane, Darlene. Missing Hannah: Based on a True Story O. 2006. pap. 26.49 (***978-1-4259-0136-3(0)***) AuthorHouse.

Knox, Jean M. Death & Dying. 2000. (Twenty-First Century Health & Wellness Ser.). (Illus.). 103p. (J). (gr. 7-12). 24.95 (978-0-7910-5986-9(3) , Chelsea Hse.) Facts On File, Inc.

Kuehn, Eileen. After Suicide: Living with the Questions. 2000. (Grief & Loss Ser.). (Illus.). 64p. (J). (gr. 4-6). lib. bdg. 23.93 (978-0-7368-0748-7(9) , LifeMatters Bks.) Capstone Pr., Inc.

—Death: Coping with the Pain. 2001. (Grief & Loss Ser.). (Illus.). 64p. (J). (gr. 4-6). lib. bdg. 23.93 (978-0-7368-0745-6(4) , LifeMatters Bks.) Capstone Pr., Inc.

—Grief & Loss, 4 bks. Incl. After Suicide : Living with the Questions. 2000. lib. bdg. 23.93 (978-0-7368-0748-7(9)); Death : Coping with the Pain. 2001. lib. bdg. 23.93 (978-0-7368-0745-6(4)); Divorce : Finding a Place. 2001. lib. bdg. 23.93 (978-0-7368-0747-0(0)); Loss : Understanding the Emptiness. 2001. lib. bdg. 23.93 (978-0-7368-0746-3(2)); 64p. (J). (gr. 4-6). (Illus.). Set lib. bdg. 95.72 (978-0-7368-0753-1(5) , LifeMatters Bks.) Capstone Pr., Inc.

—Loss: Understanding the Emptiness. 2001. (Grief & Loss Ser.). (Illus.). 64p. (J). (gr. 4-6). lib. bdg. 23.93 (978-0-7368-0746-3(2) , LifeMatters Bks.) Capstone Pr., Inc.

Larabie, Gayle. Is My Dad Still My Dad? 2005. (Illus.). 32p. (J). (978-1-55306-873-0(4)) Essence Publishing.

Latta, Sara L. Dealing with the Loss of a Loved One: Focus on Family Matters. 2002. (Focus on Family Matters Ser.). (Illus.). 64p. (J). 25.00 (978-0-7910-6955-4(9)) Facts On File, Inc.

Liss-Levinson, Nechama & Baskette, Molly Phinney. Remembering My Grandparent: A Kid's Own Grief Workbook in the Christian Tradition. 2006. (Illus.). 48p. (J). wbk. ed. 16.99 (978-1-59473-212-6(4)) SkyLight Paths Publishing.

Marcucci, Lauren Grace. My Daddy & Me: A Book about Grief, for Kids, from a Kid. 2002. (gr. 3-6). lib. bdg. 24.55 (978-0-613-79642-2(X)) Tandem Library Bks.

McClendon, Kristi, illus. A Forever Angel. 2001. 30p. 8.95 (978-1-56123-137-9(1) , FOAC) Centering Corp.

Munoz-Kiehnel, Marisol. Since My Brother Died - Desde Que Murio Mi Hermano. Dietrich, Glanda, illus. 2000. (SPA & ENG.). 20p. (J). (gr. k-4). pap. 5.95 (978-1-56123-135-5(5)) Centering Corp.

My Life Changed: A Journal for Coping with Loss & Grief. 2004. 96p. pap. 4.95 (978-1-57542-139-1(9)) Free Spirit Publishing, Inc.

Peacock, Carol Antoinette. Death & Dying. (Life Balance Ser.). (Illus.). 80p. (J). 2005. (gr. 5-8). pap. 6.95 (978-0-531-16728-1(3)); 2004. 20.50 (978-0-531-12370-6(7)) Scholastic Library Publishing. (Watts, Franklin).

Ruiz, Ruth Anne. Coping with the Death of a Brother or Sister. 2005. (Coping Ser.). (Illus.). 192p. (J). (gr. 7-12). lib. bdg. 26.50 (978-0-8239-2851-4(9)) Rosen Publishing Group, Inc., The.

Ryan, Victoria. When Your Grandparent Dies: A Child's Guide to Good Grief. Alley, Robert W., illus. 2002. 32p. per. 6.95 (978-0-87029-364-1(8) , 20077) Abbey Pr.

Sabin, Ellen. The Healing Book: Facing the Death, & Celebrating the Life, of Someone You Love. 2006. (Illus.). 64p. (J). 16.95 (978-0-9759868-3-7(X)) Watering Can.

Schmidt, Sheila & Markham, Blake, illus. I Cried Too: Grief Recovery Book for Children. l.t. ed. 2001. 35p. lib. bdg. 12.99 (978-0-9716689-1-1(4)) Golden Faith Pubng.

Shavatt, Donna. My Grieving Journey Book. 2002. (Illus.). 48p. 9.95 (978-0-8091-6695-4(X) , 6695-x) Paulist Pr.

Shavatt, Donna & Shavatt, Eve. My Grieving Journey Book. 1999. 32p. (J). (gr. k-12). 14.95 (978-0-9678630-0-9(7)) Shavatt Enterprises.

Stenson, Lila & Stenson, Anna. Daddy, up & Down: Sisters Grieve the Loss of Their Daddy. Ferre', Heidi, ed. Biddix, Cheryl L., illus. 2002. 32p. (J). per. 16.95 (978-0-9658061-1-4(1)) Peaceful Village Publishing.

Stillwell, Elaine. Sweet Memories: For Children & Adults - To Create Healing & Loving Memories for Holidays & Other Special Events. Olsen, Catherine, illus. 1998. (J). 3.95 (978-1-56123-121-8(5)) Centering Corp.

Stone, Penny. How to Help Someone Who Is Grieving. 2005. (New Line of Grief Guides(R) Ser.). 9.95 (978-1-891400-38-4(X)) Champion Pr., Ltd.

Sunderland, Margot & Hancock, Nicky. Helping Children with Loss: A Guidebook. Armstrong, Nicky, tr. (Illus.). 88p. spiral bd. (978-0-86388-467-2(9) , 002-5154) Speechmark Publishing Ltd.

Thomas, Pat. I Miss You: A First Look at Death. Harker, Leslie, illus. 2001. (First Look at Bks.). 32p. (ps-2). pap. 6.99 (978-0-7641-1764-0(5)) Barron's Educational Series, Inc.

—I Miss You: First Look at Death. 2001. (gr. k-3). lib. bdg. 15.25 (978-0-613-81901-5(2)) Tandem Library Bks.

Trampler, Eleisa & Hernandez, Mary L., eds. Tears Are Wept, Memories Are Kept. 2001. (Illus.). 200p. (YA). (gr. 1-12). pap. 14.00 (978-1-59134-004-1(7)) Maval Publishing, Inc.

Wagner, Heather Lehr. Dealing with Terminal Illness in the Family. Rosen, Marvin, ed. 2002. (Focus on Family Matters Ser.). (Illus.). 64p. (YA). (gr. 5 up). 25.00 (978-0-7910-6692-8(4) , Chelsea Hse.) Facts On File, Inc.

Wheeler, Karla. Heart-Shaped Pickles. Wheeler, Jenny Lee, illus. l.t. ed. 2003. 36p. (J). 4.95 (978-0-9675532-2-1(9)) Quality of Life Publishing Co.

Wilson, Antoine. You & a Death in Your Family. 2005. (Family Matters Ser.). (Illus.). 48p. (YA). (gr. 5-8). lib. bdg. 23.95 (978-0-8239-3355-6(5)) Rosen Publishing Group, Inc., The.

Wolfelt, Alan. Healing Your Grieving Heart: 100 Practical Ideas for Kids. (Healing Your Grieving Heart Ser.). 128p. (gr. 1-7). 2001. pap. 11.95 (978-1-879651-27-2(0)); 2000. (J). pap. 9.95 (978-1-879651-19-7(X)) Companion Pr.

—Healing Your Grieving Heart for Teens: 100 Practical Ideas. 2001. (Healing Your Grieving Heart Ser.). 128p. (gr. 8 up). pap. 11.95 (978-1-879651-23-4(8)) Companion Pr.

Wolfelt, Alan D. The Healing Your Grieving Heart Journal for Teens. 2002. (Healing Your Grieving Heart Series Ser.). 128p. pap. 11.95 (978-1-879651-33-3(5)) Companion Pr.

GRIEF—FICTION

Acampora, Paul. Defining Dulcie. 176p. (gr. 7). 2008. (YA). pap. 6.99 (***978-0-14-241183-4(3)*** , Puffin); 2006. (J). 16.99 (978-0-8037-3046-5(2) , Dial) Penguin Group (USA) Inc.

Aitken, Susan. Anna's Scrapbook: Journal of a Sister's Love. Aitken, Sarah, illus. 2000. (J). (978-1-56123-134-8(7)) Centering Corp.

Al-Chokhachy, Elissa. How Can I Help, Papa? A Child's Journey Through Loss & Healing. Graf, Ulrike, illus. 2002. 32p. (J). (ps-7). 15.95 (978-0-9712481-0-6(9)) Works of Hope Publishing.

Angle, Kimberly Greene. Hummingbird. 2008. 256p. (J). 16.95 (***978-0-374-33376-8(9)***) Farrar, Straus & Giroux.

Anthony, Joseph. Innerworld. 2002. 114p. (YA). pap. 9.95 (978-1-55517-574-0(0) , Bonneville Bks.) Cedar Fort, Inc./CFI Distribution.

—Innerworld. 2002. (gr. 7-12). lib. bdg. 18.75 (978-0-613-89648-1(3)) Tandem Library Bks.

Arenella, Betsy Bottino. Isabelle's Dream: A Story & Activity Book for a Child's Grief Journey. Henderson, Dana, illus. 2007. 48p. (J). per. 7.95 (***978-0-9675532-9-0(6)***) Quality of Life Publishing Co.

EFG

Averett, Edward. The Rhyming Season. 2005. 224p. (YA). (gr. 7-7). 16.00 (978-0-618-46948-2(6) , Clarion Bks.) Houghton Mifflin Co. Trade & Reference Div.

Bahr, Mary. If Nathan Were Here. Jerome, Karen A., illus. 2004. 32p. (J). (gr. 1-7). 16.00 (978-0-8028-5187-1(8)); (ps-4). pap. 8.00 (978-0-8028-5235-9(1)) Eerdmans, William B. Publishing Co.

—If Nathan Were Here. 2002. (gr. k-3). lib. bdg. 16.45 (978-0-613-75337-1(2)) Tandem Library Bks.

Banting, Celia. I only said I couldn't Cope. 2006. 240p. (YA). per. 14.99 (*978-0-9786648-2-4(5)) Wighita Pr.

Barron, T. A. Where is Grandpa? 2000. (978-0-606-22527-4(7)) Tandem Library Bks.

—Where Is Grandpa? Soentpiet, Chris K., illus. 2000. 1p. (J). (ps-3). 16.99 (978-0-399-23037-0(8) , Philomel) Penguin Group (USA) Inc.

Belton, Sandra. Store-Bought Baby. 2006. 256p. (J). 15.99 (978-0-06-085086-9(8)); lib. bdg. 16.89 (978-0-06-085087-6(6)) HarperCollins Pubs.

Blackman, Malorie. Knife Edge. 2007. 368p. (YA). (gr. 9 up). 16.99 (978-1-4169-0018-4(7) , Simon & Schuster Children's Publishing) Simon & Schuster Children's Publishing.

Boase, Susan. Lucky Boy. 2002. (Illus.). 32p. (J). (gr. k-3). 15.00 (978-0-618-13175-4(2)) Houghton Mifflin Co. Trade & Reference Div.

Borden, Louise. Across the Blue Pacific: A World War II Story. Parker, Robert Andrew, illus. 2006. 48p. (J). (gr. k-3). 17.00 (978-0-618-33922-8(1)) Houghton Mifflin Co.

Bostrom, Kathleen Long. The Day Scooter Died: A Book about the Death of a Pet. Bladholm, Cheri, illus. 2005. (Helping Kids Heal Ser.). 32p. (J). 9.99 (978-0-310-70902-2(4)) Zonderkidz.

—Papa's Gift: An Inspirational Story of Love & Loss. Porfirio, Guy, illus. ed. 2004. 32p. (J). pap. 6.99 (978-0-310-70923-7(7)) Zonderkidz.

Bradley, Kimberly Brubaker. Halfway to the Sky. 2002. 176p. (gr. 3-7). 15.95 (978-0-385-72960-4(X) , Delacorte Bks. for Young Readers) Random Hse. Children's Bks.

Brisson, Pat. I Remember Miss Perry. Jorisch, Stephane, illus. 2006. 32p. (J). (ps). 16.99 (978-0-8037-2981-0(2) , Dial) Penguin Group (USA) Inc.

Brooks, Bruce. All That Remains. 2002. 176p. (YA). (gr. 7 up). pap. 6.99 (978-0-689-83442-4(X) , Simon Pulse) Simon & Schuster Children's Publishing.

Bryant, Jennifer. Pieces of Georgia. 176p. (J). 2007. (gr. 5-9). 5.99 (*978-0-440-42055-2(5) , Yearling); 2006. (gr. 6-9). 15.95 (978-0-375-83259-8(9) , Knopf Bks. for Young Readers); 2006. (gr. 6-9). lib. bdg. 17.99 (978-0-375-93259-5(3) , Knopf Bks. for Young Readers) Random Hse. Children's Bks.

Bunting, Eve. The Memory String. Rand, Ted, illus. 2000. 40p. (J). (gr. k-3). tchr. ed. 16.00 (978-0-395-86146-2(2) , Clarion Bks.) Houghton Mifflin Co. Trade & Reference Div.

Butcher, Kristin. Hemingway Tradition. 2002. (gr. 7-12). lib. bdg. 16.40 (978-0-613-62955-3(8)) Tandem Library Bks.

—The Hemingway Tradition. 2002. (Orca Soundings Ser.). 96p. (J). (gr. 7-12). pap. 7.95 (978-1-55143-242-7(0)) Orca Bk. Pubs. USA.

Call, Brian D., tr. & illus. Sarah's Cloud. Call, Brian D., illus. 2003. (J). 15.95 (978-1-57008-955-8(8)) Deseret Bk. Co.

Carmi, Daniella. Samir & Yonatan. Lotan, Yael, tr. from HEB. 2002. 192p. (J). (gr. 3-7). pap. 4.99 (978-0-439-13523-8(0) , Scholastic Paperbacks) Scholastic, Inc.

—Samir & Yonatan. 2000. (gr. 3-6). lib. bdg. 13.00 (978-0-613-45824-5(9)) Tandem Library Bks.

—Samir & Yonatan. 2000. (Illus.). 192p. (J). (gr. 3-7). pap. 15.95 (978-0-439-13504-7(4) , Levine, Arthur A. Bks.) Scholastic, Inc.

Carney, Karen L. Together, We'll Get Through This! Learning to Cope with Loss & Transition. Carney, Karen L., illus. 1999. (Barklay & Eve Ser.: Bk. 1). (Illus.). (J). pap. 6.95 (978-0-9667820-0-4(3)) Dragonfly Publishing.

Chalifour, Francis. Le Fils du Pendu. 2006. (FRE.). 168p. (J). (gr. 7). pap. 7.95 (978-0-88776-795-1(8) , Livres Toundra) Tundra Bks., Inc./Livres Toundra, Inc. CAN. *Dist:* Random Hse., Inc.

Chapman, Cynthia. Dog Gone. 2008. 224p. (J). 16.95 (*978-0-312-37123-4(3)) Feiwel & Friends.

Charlton-Trujillo, E. E. Feels Like Home. 2007. 224p. (YA). (gr. 7 up). 15.99 (978-0-385-73332-8(1)); lib. bdg. 18.99 (978-0-385-90349-3(9)) Random Hse. Children's Bks. (Delacorte Bks. for Young Readers).

Cheripko, Jan. Sun Moon Stars Rain. 2006. (Illus.). 160p. (YA). 16.95 (978-1-932425-53-6(5) , Lemniscaat) Boyds Mills Pr.

Clark, Sandra. Goldie Is Upside Down. 2005. (Illus.). 54p. (J). per. (978-0-9755145-3-5(9) , Gibson Bks.) Glory Days Group Publishing.

Collins, Chris. A Mary Little Christmas. Brimer, Molly, illus. l.t. ed. 2002. 32p. (J). lib. bdg. (978-0-9722799-0-1(3)) Words of Grace, Inc.

Cotten, Cynthia. Fair Has Nothing to Do with It. 2007. 160p. (J). (gr. 4-7). 16.00 (978-0-374-39935-1(2)) Farrar, Straus & Giroux.

Couloumbis, Audrey. Getting near to Baby. 2002. (Illus.). (J). 13.19 (978-0-7587-6515-4(0)) Book Wholesalers, Inc.

—Getting near to Baby. 224p. (J). (gr. 5-9). 2001. pap. 5.99 (978-0-698-11892-8(8)); 1999. 17.99 (978-0-399-23389-0(X)) Penguin Group (USA) Inc. (Putnam Juvenile).

—Getting near to Baby. unabr. ed. 2004. 211p. (J). (gr. 5-9). pap. 36.00 incl. audio (978-0-8072-8876-4(4) , LYA 287 SP, Listening Library) Random Hse. Audio Publishing Group.

—Getting near to Baby. 2001. (J). 12.64 (978-0-606-21210-6(8)); (gr. 5-8). lib. bdg. 14.15 (978-0-613-44208-4(3)) Tandem Library Bks.

—Getting near to Baby. l.t. ed. 2000. (Juvenile Ser.). (Illus.). 215p. (J). (gr. 4-7). 22.95 (978-0-7862-2705-1(2)) Thorndike Pr.

Crowe, Carole. Turtle Girl. Postier, Jim, illus. 2007. (J). (*978-1-59078-262-0(3)) Boyds Mills Pr.

Crowe, Carole. Waiting for Dolphins. 2003. 144p. (YA). (gr. 4-6). pap. 9.95 (978-1-59078-073-2(6)); (Illus.). pap. 16.95 (978-1-56397-847-0(4)) Boyds Mills Pr.

—Waiting for Dolphins. 2003. (gr. 3-6). lib. bdg. 18.75 (978-0-613-59368-7(5)) Tandem Library Bks.

Crowley, James. The Magic Hour. 2003. (Illus.). 280p. (J). pap. 17.95 (978-1-55517-713-3(1) , 77131) Cedar Fort, Inc./CFI Distribution.

Cullen, Lynn. Diary of Nelly Vandorn. (gr. 3 up). Date not set. 128p. mass mkt. 4.99 (978-0-06-440926-1(0)); 2002. 192p. (J). 15.95 (978-0-06-029133-4(8)) HarperCollins Pubs.

Davis, Jennifer. Before You Were Big. Cornell, Laura, illus. 2003. 36p. (J). 11.95 (978-0-7611-2732-1(1) , 12732) Workman Publishing Co., Inc.

Dawson, Joy. Maggie, the Color-Blind Cow: A loving heart—that didn't see Color. 2006. (ENG., Illus.). 36p. (J). per. 12.95 (*978-1-59800-892-0(7)) Outskirts Press, Inc.

Deans, Sis Boulos. Every Day & All the Time, Vol. 5. l.t. ed. 2004. 304p. 21.95 (978-0-7862-6386-8(5)) Thorndike Pr.

Dearen, Patrick. On the Pecos Trail. 2001. (gr. 3-6). lib. bdg. 17.60 (978-0-613-83166-6(7)) Tandem Library Bks.

—On the Pecos Trail. 2001. (Lone Star Heroes Ser.). 128p. (gr. 4-7). pap. 8.95 (978-1-55622-830-8(9) , Republic of Texas Pr.) Wordware Publishing, Inc.

Delaney, Mark. Pepperland. 2007. 224p. pap. 7.95 (*978-1-56145-402-0(8) , Peachtree Junior); 2004. 160p. (J). 14.95 (978-1-56145-317-7(X)) Peachtree Pubs., Ltd.

Deriso, Christine Hurley. Do-Over. 2006. 192p. (J). (gr. 4-7). 15.95 (978-0-385-73333-5(X)); lib. bdg. 17.99 (978-0-385-90350-9(2)) Random Hse. Children's Bks. (Delacorte Bks. for Young Readers).

Deriso, Christine Hurley. Do-over. 2007. 160p. (J). (gr. 4-7). 5.99 (*978-0-440-42119-1(5) , Yearling) Random Hse. Children's Bks.

Dessen, Sarah. The Truth about Forever. 2006. 400p. (YA). (gr. 7). reprint ed. pap. 7.99 (978-0-14-240625-0(2) , Puffin) Penguin Group (USA) Inc.

DiCamillo, Kate. The Tiger Rising. 2002. 128p. (YA). (gr. 5-12). pap. 5.99 (978-0-7636-1898-6(5)) Candlewick Pr.

DiSalvo-Ryan, DyAnne. A Dog Like Jack. unabr. ed. 2005. (Illus.). (J). (ps-2). pap. 16.95 incl. audio (978-0-87499-758-3(5)) BBC Audiobooks America.

—A Dog Like Jack. DiSalvo-Ryan, DyAnne, illus. 1999. (Illus.). 32p. (J). (gr. k-3). tchr. ed. 16.95 (978-0-8234-1369-0(1)); pap. 6.95 (978-0-8234-1680-6(1)) Holiday Hse., Inc.

—A Dog Like Jack. 2005. (Live Oak Readalong Ser.). (J). pap. 18.95 incl. audio compact disk (978-1-59519-298-1(0)) Live Oak Media.

—A Dog Like Jack. DiSalvo-Ryan, DyAnne, illus. 2001. (Illus.). pap. 25.95 incl. audio (978-0-87499-759-0(3)); pap. 37.95 incl. audio (978-0-87499-760-6(7)) Live Oak Media.

Dow, Unity. Far & Beyon' 2002. 208p. (YA). (gr. 7 up). pap. 11.95 (978-1-879960-64-0(8)) Aunt Lute Bks.

Drvenkar, Zoran. Tell Me What You See. 2008. 304p. (J). pap. 6.99 (*978-0-439-72453-1(8) , Scholastic Paperbacks) Scholastic, Inc.

Duckworth, Liz. Ragtail Remembers. Barnes, Jeff, illus. 2002. (J). (978-1-56123-163-8(0)) Centering Corp.

Durant, Alan. Always & Forever. Gliori, Debi, tr. Gliori, Debi, illus. 2004. 32p. (J). 16.00 (978-0-15-216636-6(X)) Harcourt Children's Bks.

Easton, Kelly. Aftershock. 176p. (YA). 2007. pap. 6.99 (*978-1-4169-0053-5(5) , Simon Pulse); 2006. (gr. 7 up). 16.95 (978-1-4169-0052-8(7) , McElderry, Margaret K.) Simon & Schuster Children's Publishing.

Eenie Meanie Me & the Very Sad Day. 2005. (J). (978-0-9772878-0-2(7)) Bishop, Susan Lynn.

Elmer, Robert. Candy Bombers. 2006. (Wall Ser.: Bk. 1). 160p. (J). pap. 6.99 (978-0-310-70943-5(1)) Zonderkidz.

Ephron, Delia. Frannie in Pieces. 2007. 384p. (YA). (gr. 7 up). 16.99 (*978-0-06-074716-9(1) , HarperTeen) HarperCollins Pubs.

—Frannie in Pieces. Beckerman, Chad, illus. 2007. 384p. (YA). (gr. 7 up). lib. bdg. 17.89 (*978-0-06-074717-6(X) , HarperTeen) HarperCollins Pubs.

Ewart, Claire. The Giant. Ewart, Claire, illus. 2003. (Illus.). 32p. (J). (ps-3). 16.95 (978-0-8027-8835-1(1)) Walker & Co.

Ewart, Franzeska G. Shadowflight. 2001. (Illus.). 81p. (J). pap. 7.50 (978-0-7497-4380-2(8)) Egmont Bks., Ltd. GBR. *Dist:* Independent Pubs. Group.

Farnes, Catherine. The Way of Escape. 2000. (J). 166p. (gr. 8-12). pap. 6.49 (978-1-57924-453-8(X)); (Illus.). 157p. (gr. 9 up). 6.49 (978-1-57924-454-5(8) , 126599) Jones, Bob Univ. Pr.

Fast, Natalie. The Secret Apartment. 2007. 192p. (gr. 4-7). 5.99 (978-0-553-48794-7(9) , Yearling) Random Hse. Children's Bks.

Ferber, Brenda A. Julia's Kitchen. 2006. (Illus.). 160p. (J). 16.00 (978-0-374-39932-0(8)) Farrar, Straus & Giroux.

Frank, E. R. Wrecked. 256p. (YA). (gr. 7 up). 2007. pap. 8.99 (978-0-689-87384-3(0) , Simon Pulse); 2005. (Illus.). 16.99 (978-0-689-87383-6(2) , Atheneum) Simon & Schuster Children's Publishing.

Fried, Amelie. Is Grandpa Wearing a Suit? Gleich, Jacky, illus. 2007. 32p. (J). (gr. 4-7). 16.95 (*978-0-9787550-4-1(9)) Heryin Publishing Corp.

Friedman, D. Dina. Playing Dad's Song. 2006. 144p. (YA). 16.00 (978-0-374-37173-9(3)) Farrar, Straus & Giroux.

Friend, Natasha. Perfect. 2004. 232p. (J). 16.95 (978-1-57131-652-3(3)); pap. 6.95 (978-1-57131-651-6(5)) Milkweed Editions.

Going, K. L. The Garden of Eve. 2007. (Illus.). 240p. (J). (gr. 3-7). 17.00 (*978-0-15-205986-6(5)) Harcourt Children's Bks.

Golding, Theresa Martin. Kat's Surrender. 2002. (gr. 3-6). lib. bdg. 18.75 (978-0-613-53826-8(9)) Tandem Library Bks.

Gray, Dianne E. Together Apart. 2002. 208p. (J). (gr. 5-9). tchr. ed. 16.00 (978-0-618-18721-8(9)) Houghton Mifflin Co. Trade & Reference Div.

Gregory, Nan. Wild Girl & Gran. ed. 2004. (Illus.). (J). (gr. k-3). spiral bd. (978-0-616-11112-3(6)) Canadian National Institute for the Blind/Institut National Canadien pour les Aveugles.

—Wild Girl & Gran. Lightburn, Ron, illus. 2004. (Northern Lights Books for Children Ser.). 32p. (J). (ps-3). pap. 16.95 (978-0-88995-221-8(3)) Red Deer Pr. CAN. *Dist:* Fitzhenry & Whiteside, Ltd.

Griffin, Adele. The Other Shepards. 1999. (978-0-606-17144-1(4)) Tandem Library Bks.

—The Other Shepards. l.t. ed. 2000. (Illus.). 209p. (J). (gr. 4-7). 20.95 (978-0-7862-2914-7(4)) Thorndike Pr.

—Rainy Season. 1998. (978-0-606-13726-3(2)) Tandem Library Bks.

Haas, Jessie. Unbroken. 2001. 208p. (J). (gr. 5 up). pap. 6.99 (978-0-380-73313-2(7) , Harper Trophy) HarperCollins Pubs.

—Unbroken. 2001. (J). (978-0-606-20962-5(X)); (gr. 5-8). lib. bdg. 14.10 (978-0-613-33735-9(2)) Tandem Library Bks.

—Unbroken. l.t. ed. 2000. (Juvenile Ser.). 248p. (J). (gr. 4-7). 21.95 (978-0-7862-2769-3(9)) Thorndike Pr.

Hacker, Randi. Life As I Knew It. 2006. 240p. (J). pap. 6.99 (978-1-4169-0995-8(8) , Simon Pulse) Simon & Schuster Children's Publishing.

Hafer, Todd. Full Court Press. 2004. (Spirit of the Game, Sports Fiction Ser.). 144p. (J). (gr. 3-6). pap. 4.99 (978-0-310-70668-7(8)) Zonderkidz.

—Goal-Line Stand. Lucado, Max, ed. 2004. (Spirit of the Game, Sports Fiction Ser.). 144p. (J). (gr. 3-6). pap. 4.99 (978-0-310-70669-4(6)) Zonderkidz.

Harding, Sandy Bacon. A Stick, a Stone & a Bone. Mickelson, Brenda, illus. 1999. (Farm Adventures Ser.: Vol. 2). 79p. (J). (gr. 1-6). pap. 6.95 (978-1-890609-08-5(0) , Lion's Paw Bks.) Coronet Bks. & Pubns.

Hawes, Louise. Rosey in the Present Tense. 1999. (Illus.). (J). (978-0-606-20488-0(1)) Tandem Library Bks.

—Rosey in the Present Tense. l.t. ed. 2002. 186p. (J). 22.95 (978-0-7862-4418-8(6)) Thorndike Pr.

—Rosey in the Present Tense. 1999. 176p. (YA). (gr. 7). 16.95 (978-0-8027-8685-2(5)) Walker & Co.

Hemery, Kathleen Maresh. The Healing Tree. Teis, Kyra, illus. 2001. (J). (978-1-56123-153-9(3) , HTRC) Centering Corp.

—Sunflower Promise. Bordelois, Augusto, illus. 2005. (J). (978-1-56123-188-1(6)) Centering Corp.

Henkes, Kevin. Sun & Spoon. 2007. 144p. (J). pap. 5.99 (*978-0-06-128875-3(6) , Harper Trophy) HarperCollins Pubs.

Hershey, Mary. My Big Sister Is So Bossy She Says You Can't Read This Book. 2006. 176p. (gr. 4-7). 5.50 (978-0-553-48797-8(3) , Yearling) Random Hse. Children's Bks.

Hicks, Betty. Out of Order. 2005. 176p. (J). (ps-7). 16.95 (978-1-59643-061-7(3)) Roaring Brook Pr.

—Out of Order. 2007. 176p. (J). pap. 6.99 (*978-0-312-37355-9(4)) Square Fish.

Hill, Frances. The Bug Cemetery. Rosenberry, Vera, illus. rev. ed. 2002. 32p. (J). (gr. k-2). 16.95 (978-0-8050-6370-7(6) , Holt, Henry & Co. Bks. For Young Readers) Holt, Henry & Co.

Hill, Janet Muirhead. Danny's Dragon: A Story of Wartime Loss. Lehmkuhl, Pat & Ore, Peter, illus. 2006. 192p. (J). per. 10.00 (978-0-9772525-0-3(7)) Raven Publishing Inc. of Montana.

Himler, Ronald. Six Is So Much Less Than Seven. Himler, Ronald, illus. 2002. (Illus.). 40p. (J). 16.95 (978-1-887734-91-2(0)) Star Bright Bks., Inc.

Hite, Sid. A Hole in the World. 208p. (J). 2001. (Illus.). pap. 16.95 (978-0-439-09830-4(0)); 2004. (gr. 5 up). reprint ed. pap. 5.99 (978-0-439-09831-1(9) , Scholastic Pr.) Scholastic, Inc.

Hoffman, Alice. Green Angel. 128p. (J). 2003. (gr. 6 up). pap. 16.95 (978-0-439-44384-5(9) , Scholastic Pr.); 2004. reprint ed. pap. 5.99 (978-0-439-44385-2(7) , Scholastic Paperbacks) Scholastic, Inc.

Holt, Kimberly Willis. Keeper of the Night. rev. ed. 2003. (Illus.). 180p. (YA). (gr. 5-8). 16.95 (978-0-8050-6361-5(7) , Holt, Henry & Co. Bks. For Young Readers) Holt, Henry & Co.

—Keeper of the Night. 2005. 309p. (YA). (gr. 7-12). lib. bdg. 13.55 (978-0-606-33249-1(9)) Tandem Library Bks.

Holubitsky, Katherine. Alone at Ninety Foot. 2001. (gr. 7-12). lib. bdg. 15.25 (978-0-613-23678-2(5)); 1999. (J). 13.60 (978-0-606-21583-1(2)) Tandem Library Bks.

Horvath, Polly. The Corps of the Bare-Boned Plane. 2007. 272p. (J). (gr. 7 up). 17.00 (*978-0-374-31553-5(1) , Farrar, Straus & Giroux (BYR)) Farrar, Straus & Giroux.

Hurwin, Davida Lewis. The Farther You Run. 2005. 224p. (YA). (gr. 7). pap. 6.99 (978-0-14-240294-8(X) , Puffin) Penguin Group (USA) Inc.

Hurwin, Davida Wills. The Farther You Run. 2005. 217p. (YA). (gr. 9-12). per. 14.04 (978-0-606-33126-5(3)) Tandem Library Bks.

Jacobs, Deborah Lynn. Choices. 2007. 208p. (YA). (gr. 7 up). 16.95 (*978-1-59643-217-8(9)) Roaring Brook Pr.

Jennings, Richard W. Scribble: A Dog Story, a Ghost Story, a Love Story. 2004. 160p. (YA). (gr. 5-9). tchr. ed. 15.00 (978-0-618-43367-4(8) , Walter Lorraine) Houghton Mifflin Co. Trade & Reference Div.

Johnson, Angela. Looking for Red. 128p. (YA). 2003. (Illus.). pap. 8.95 (978-0-689-86388-2(8) , Simon Pulse); 2002. (gr. 7 up). 15.95 (978-0-689-83253-6(2)) Simon & Schuster Children's Publishing.

—Looking for Red. 2003. (gr. 7-12). lib. bdg. 13.00 (978-0-613-73436-3(X)) Tandem Library Bks.

—Looking for Red. l.t. ed. 2003. 117p. (J). 24.95 (978-0-7862-5603-7(6)) Thorndike Pr.

Johnson, Emily Rhoads. Write Me If You Dare! 2000. (Illus.). 176p. (J). (gr. 3-6). 15.95 (978-0-8126-2944-6(2)) Cricket Bks.

Johnson, Maureen G. The Key to the Golden Firebird. 2005. 304p. (YA). reprint ed. pap. 7.99 (978-0-06-054140-8(7) , Harper Trophy) HarperCollins Pubs.

Johnston, Tony. That Summer. Moser, Barry, illus. 2007. 32p. (J). (gr. 1-4). pap. 6.00 (978-0-15-205856-2(7) , Voyager Bks./Libros Viajeros) Harcourt Children's Bks.

Kadono, Eiko. Grandpa's Soup. Ichikawa, Satomi, illus. 2004. 32p. (J). (ps-3). 16.00 (978-0-8028-5195-6(9)) Eerdmans, William B. Publishing Co.

Kaplow, Julie B. & Pincus, Donna. Samantha Jane's Missing Smile: A Story about Coping with the Loss of a Parent. Spiegel, Beth, illus. 2007. 32p. (J). (ps-3). 14.95 (*978-1-59147-808-9(1)); pap. 8.95 (*978-1-59147-809-6(X)) American Psychological Assn. (Magination Pr.).

Katz, Welwyn W. Out of the Dark. 2001. 185p. (J). (gr. 4). pap. 5.95 (978-0-88899-262-8(9)) Groundwood Bks. CAN. *Dist:* Perseus Distribution.

Keckler, Ben. Incredibly Lonely, That's Me. Davis, Dick, illus. 2007. (J). (gr. 2-7). lib. bdg. 17.95 (*978-0-9769093-2-3(4)) Eagle Creek Pubns., LLC.

Keehn, Sally M. The First Horse I See. 2000. (Illus.). 224p. (YA). (gr. 5-9). pap. 6.99 (978-0-698-11867-6(7) , Putnam Juvenile) Penguin Group (USA) Inc.

—The First Horse I See. 2000. (J). 12.64 (978-0-606-19067-1(8)) Tandem Library Bks.

—First Horse I See. 2000. (gr. 3-6). lib. bdg. 14.15 (978-0-613-29957-2(4)) Tandem Library Bks.

Kelly, Tom. Finn's Going. 2007. 288p. (J). (gr. 5-9). 16.99 (*978-0-06-121453-0(1)); lib. bdg. 17.89 (*978-0-06-121454-7(X)) HarperCollins Pubs. (Greenwillow Bks.).

Kemp, Kristen. Breakfast at Bloomingdales. 2007. 304p. (J). pap. 16.99 (*978-0-439-80987-0(8) , Scholastic Pr.) Scholastic, Inc.

Kemper, Bebe. Seeing Zach. 1999. (Illus.). 32p. (J). 14.95 (978-0-9674363-0-2(3) , Rainy Day Bks.) Purple Chickie Pr.

Kennedy, Marlane. Me & the Pumpkin Queen. 2007. 192p. (J). (gr. 3-7). 15.99 (978-0-06-114022-8(8)); lib. bdg. 16.89 (978-0-06-114023-5(6)) HarperCollins Pubs.

Kennedy, Pamela. Granny's Cozy Quilt of Memories. Wummer, Amy, illus. 2006. 32p. (J). (gr. 4-6). 8.95 (978-0-8249-5538-0(2) , Guideposts) Ideals Pubns.

Kiplinger Pandy, Lori, illus. Flying Hugs & Kisses. l.t. ed. 2006. 32p. (J). 15.95 (978-1-59879-119-8(2)) Lifevest Publishing, Inc.

Koertge, Ron. Strays. 2006. 176p. (YA). (gr. 9 up). 16.99 (978-0-7636-2705-8(4)) Candlewick Pr.

Koller, Jackie French. The Promise. Rogers, Jacqueline, illus. 2001. 80p. (gr. 5-8). 4.99 (978-0-440-41658-6(2) , Yearling) Random Hse. Children's Bks.

Kornblatt, Marc. Understanding Buddy. l.t. ed. 2002. 100p. (J). 21.95 (978-0-7862-3712-8(0)) Thomson Gale.

Kroll, Jeri. Mickey's Little Book of Letters. 2005. 160p. pap. (978-0-7344-0686-6(X) , Lothian Bks.) Hachette Livre Australia.

Landalf, Helen & McConnell, Mary. Getting Used to Candy. 2000. (Illus.). (J). (gr. k-5). 6.95 (978-1-56123-139-3(8)) Centering Corp.

Levithan, David. Marly's Ghost. Selznick, Brian, illus. 176p. 2007. (YA). (gr. 7). 6.99 (*978-0-14-240912-1(X) , Puffin); 2005. (J). 14.99 (978-0-8037-3063-2(2) , Dial) Penguin Group (USA) Inc.

Lewis, Beverly. Shadows Beyond the Gate. 2000. (Summerhill Secrets Ser.: Vol. 10). 144p. (J). (gr. 6-9). pap. 6.99 (978-1-55661-876-5(X)) Bethany Hse. Pubs.

Lion, Melissa. Upstream. 160p. (YA). (gr. 7). 2006. pap. 8.95 (978-0-375-83954-2(2)); 2005. 15.95 (978-0-385-74643-4(1)) Random Hse. Children's Bks. (Lamb, Wendy).

Mackall, Dandi Daley. Eva Underground. 2006. (Illus.). 256p. (YA). 17.00 (978-0-15-205462-5(6)) Harcourt Trade Pubs.

MacLachlan, Patricia. Two Novels: Baby/Journey. 2007. 224p. (J). (gr. 4-7). 16.99 (978-0-385-73423-3(9)); lib. bdg. 19.99 (978-0-385-90436-0(3)) Random Hse. Children's Bks. (Delacorte Bks. for Young Readers).

Mangum, Kay Lynn. A Love Like Lilly. 2006. 336p. (YA). pap. 15.95 (978-1-59038-580-7(2)) Deseret Bk. Co.

Mangum, Kay Lynn. When the Bough Breaks. 2007. 352p. (YA). pap. 15.95 (*978-1-59038-748-1(1)) Deseret Bk. Co.

Marcucci, Lauren Grace. My Daddy & Me: A Book about Grief, for Kids, from a Kid. 2002. 64p. (J). pap. 14.95 (978-1-58597-164-0(2)) Leathers Publishing.

Martin, Ann M. Sunny: Diary Three. 1999. (California Diaries: Bk. 12). 160p. (YA). (gr. 6-8). pap. 4.50 (978-0-590-02390-0(X)) Scholastic, Inc.

—Sunny: Diary Three. 1999. (California Diaries: Bk. 12). (Illus.). (YA). (gr. 6-8). (978-0-606-18523-3(2)) Tandem Library Bks.

Martin, Cheryl. I Love You, Son. 2004. pap. 7.95 (978-0-533-14673-4(9)) Vantage Pr., Inc.

Martino, Carmela. Rosa, Sola. 2005. 256p. (J). (gr. 4-7). 15.99 (978-0-7636-2395-1(4)) Candlewick Pr.

Matthews, Kezi. Flying Lessons. 2002. 160p. (J). (gr. 5-9). 16.95 (978-0-8126-2671-1(0)) Cricket Bks.
—Scorpio's Child. 2001. 160p. (YA). (gr. 6-8). 16.95 (978-0-8126-2890-6(X)) Cricket Bks.
Mazer, Norma Fox. Girlhearts. 2002. (gr. 7-12). lib. bdg. 15.30 (978-0-613-58571-2(2)) Tandem Library Bks.
McCallum, C. Dawn. The Caretaker of Tree Palace. Doxey, Morgan, illus. l.t. ed. 2006. 120p. (J). lib. bdg. 16.95 (978-0-9764026-3-3(7) , 3300) Longhorn Creek Pr.
McCombie, Karen. Indie Kidd: Are We Having Fun Yet? (Hmmm?) Monks, Lydia, illus. 2008. (J). (***978-0-440-42201-3(9)***); 160p. (gr. 2-5). lib. bdg. 9.99 (***978-0-440-42202-0(7)***) Random Hse. Children's Bks. (Yearling).
McDaniel, Lurlene. The Girl Death Left Behind. 1999. (gr. 7-12). lib. bdg. 13.00 (978-0-613-16116-9(5)) Tandem Library Bks.
—Holly's Story. 2005. (Angels in Pink Ser.). 224p. (gr. 7). (YA). 10.95 (978-0-385-73158-4(2)); (J). lib. bdg. 12.99 (978-0-385-90195-6(X)) Random Hse. Children's Bks. (Delacorte Bks. for Young Readers).
—Letting Go of Lisa. (YA). (gr. 7). 2007. 176p. mass mkt. 6.50 (***978-0-440-23868-3(4)*** , Laurel Leaf); 2006. 192p. 10.95 (978-0-385-73159-1(0) , Delacorte Bks. for Young Readers); 2006. 192p. lib. bdg. 12.99 (978-0-385-90196-3(8) , Delacorte Bks. for Young Readers) Random Hse. Children's Bks.
McDaniel, Lurlene. Raina's Story. 2006. (Angels in Pink Ser.). 208p. (YA). (gr. 7). pap. 6.50 (978-0-440-23866-9(8) , Laurel Leaf) Random Hse. Children's Bks.
McDonald, Joyce. Swallowing Stones. 1999. 272p. (YA). (gr. 7-12). mass mkt. 6.99 (978-0-440-22672-7(4) , Laurel Leaf) Random Hse. Children's Bks.
—Swallowing Stones. 1999. 245p. lib. bdg. 13.55 (978-0-606-16721-5(8)); (gr. 7-12). lib. bdg. 13.55 (978-0-613-19465-5(9)) Tandem Library Bks.
McGhee, Alison. All Rivers Flow to the Sea. 176p. (YA). (gr. 9 up). 2007. (Illus.). pap. 7.99 (***978-0-7636-3372-1(0)***); 2005. 15.99 (978-0-7636-2591-7(4)) Candlewick Pr.
McGhee, Alison. Snap! 2004. 144p. (J). (gr. 4-7). 15.99 (978-0-7636-2002-8(5)) Candlewick Pr.
McLaughlin, Kirsten. The Memory Box. Rudolph, Adrienne, illus. 2000. (J). 5.95 (978-1-56123-136-2(3) , MEBC) Centering Corp.
McLean, Jacqueline. Grace from China. 2003. 179p. (J). 16.00 (978-0-9638472-8-7(7)) Yeong & Yeong Bk. Co.
McNish, Cliff. Breathe: A Ghost Story. 2006. 264p. (J). 15.95 (978-0-8225-6443-0(2) , Carolrhoda Bks.) Lerner Publishing Group.
Messer, Celeste M. Three Miracles. 2004. (Adventures of Andi O'Malley Ser.). (Illus.). 82-92p. (J). (gr. 4-7). 4.95 (978-0-9702171-4-1(5)) AshleyAlan Enterprises.
Miracles, Max. Los Milagros de Max. Rubio, Gabriela, illus. (SPA.). 84p. (J). (978-84-392-8700-1(3)) Gaviota Ediciones ESP. *Dist:* Lectorum Pubns., Inc.
Monroe Donovan, Jane. Winter's Gift. Monroe Donovan, Jane, illus. 2004. (Illus.). 32p. (J). 15.95 (978-1-58536-231-8(X)) Sleeping Bear Pr.
Montoya, Louis R. Camilla. 2007. (J). pap. 8.00 (***978-0-8059-7424-9(5)***) Dorrance Publishing Co., Inc.
Murphy, Barbara. Life! How I Love You! Baca, Elena, illus. 2004. (Museo Kids Ser.). 1p. 16.95 (978-0-89013-468-9(5)) Museum of New Mexico Pr.
Myers, Edward. Ice. 2005. 222p. (J). per. 12.95 net. (978-0-9674477-9-7(8)) Montemayor Pr.
Newman, Leslea. The Best Cat in the World. Himler, Ronald, illus. 2004. 32p. (J). (gr. 1-4). 16.00 (978-0-8028-5252-6(1)) Eerdmans, William B. Publishing Co.
Noel, Alyson. Saving Zoe: A Novel. 2007. 240p. (YA). (gr. 8 up). pap. 8.95 (***978-0-312-35510-4(6)*** , St. Martin's Griffin) St. Martin's Pr.
Opperman, Jennifer N. Silent Cry: Katy's Story. 2004. 124p. (YA). pap. 12.95 (978-1-58736-264-4(3) , Starbound Bks.) Wheatmark.
Pavlicin, Karen. Perch, Mrs. Sackets, & Crow's Nest. 2007. (J). 160p. 16.95 (***978-1-934617-00-7(8)***); pap. (***978-1-934617-01-4(6)***) Elva Resa Publishing, LLC. (Alma Little).
Perez, Amada Irma. Nana's Big Surprise/¡Nana, Que Sorpresa! Gonzalez, Maya Christina, tr. Gonzalez, Maya Christina, illus. 2007. (ENG & SPA.). 32p. (J). (gr. 1-2). 16.95 (978-0-89239-190-5(1)) Children's Bk. Pr.
Philbrick, Rodman. The Young Man & the Sea. 2004. 192p. (J). pap. 16.95 (978-0-439-36829-2(4) , Blue Sky Pr., The) Scholastic, Inc.
—The Young Man & the Sea. 2005. 192p. (J). (ps-7). per. 12.64 (978-0-606-33810-3(1)) Tandem Library Bks.
Pollet, Alison. The Pity Party: 8th Grade in the Life of Me, Cass. (Pity Party Ser.). 160p. (J). 2006. pap. 5.99 (978-0-439-68195-7(2) , Scholastic Paperbacks); 2005. (gr. 5-8). pap. 15.95 (978-0-439-68194-0(4) , Orchard Bks.) Scholastic, Inc.
Prestine, Joan Singleton. Someone Special Died. Kylberg, Virginia, illus. 2002. 32p. (J). pap. 6.95 (978-1-57768-655-2(1)) School Specialty Publishing.
Price, Reynolds. A Perfect Friend. 2002. 176p. pap. 11.00 (978-0-7432-2521-2(X) , Scribner) Simon & Schuster.
—A Perfect Friend. l.t. ed. 2001. 150p. (J). (gr. 4-7). 21.95 (978-0-7862-3589-6(6)) Thorndike Pr.
Prose, Francine. Bullyville. 2007. 272p. (J). (gr. 5-8). 16.99 (***978-0-06-057497-0(6)***); lib. bdg. 17.89 (***978-0-06-057498-7(4)***) HarperCollins Pubs. (HarperTeen).
Qualey, Marsha. Just Like That. 240p. (YA). (gr. 7). 2007. pap. 6.99 (978-0-14-240830-8(1) , Puffin); 2005. 16.99 (978-0-8037-2840-0(9) , Dial) Penguin Group (USA) Inc.
Rabin, Staton. Black Powder. 2005. 256p. (J). (gr. 6-9). 16.95 (978-0-689-86876-4(6) , McElderry, Margaret K.) Simon & Schuster Children's Publishing.
Ransom, Candice F. Finding Day's Bottom. 2006. 168p. (J). (gr. 4-6). 15.95 (978-1-57505-933-4(9) , Carolrhoda Bks.) Lerner Publishing Group.
Rapp, Adam. Under the Wolf, under the Dog. 320p. (YA). (gr. 9). 2007. pap. 8.99 (978-0-7636-3365-3(8)); 2004. 16.99 (978-0-7636-1818-6(7)) Candlewick Pr.
Ray, Delia. Ghost Girl: A Blue Ridge Mountain Story. 2006. 236p. (YA). 22.95 (978-0-7862-8876-2(0)) Thorndike Pr.
Roberts, Kristi. My Thirteenth Season. rev. ed. 2005. (Illus.). 160p. (J). 15.95 (978-0-8050-7495-6(3) , Holt, Henry & Co. Bks. For Young Readers) Holt, Henry & Co.
Roberts, Willo Davis. Blood on His Hands. 192p. (J). 2005. mass mkt. 5.99 (978-0-689-85082-0(4) , Simon Pulse); 2004. (Illus.). 16.95 (978-0-689-85074-5(3) , Atheneum/Richard Jackson Bks.) Simon & Schuster Children's Publishing.
—The One Left Behind. (J). 2007. 139p. (gr. 3-7). per. 5.99 (978-0-689-85083-7(2)); 2006. (Illus.). 144p. 16.95 (978-0-689-85075-2(1) , Atheneum) Simon & Schuster Children's Publishing.
Rothman, Juliet Cassuto. A Birthday Present for Daniel: A Child's Story of Loss. Gish, Louise, illus. 2004. 41p. (gr. 3-7). pap. 12.00 (978-1-57392-946-2(8) , Pyr Bks.) Prometheus Bks., Pubs.
Rottman, S. L. Rough Waters. 2000. (Illus.). 224p. (J). (gr. 7-12). pap. 6.99 (978-0-14-130703-9(X) , Puffin) Penguin Group (USA) Inc.
—Rough Waters. 2000. (978-0-606-17869-3(4)); (gr. 7-12). lib. bdg. 15.30 (978-0-613-28627-5(8)) Tandem Library Bks.
Rubright, Lynn. Mama's Window. Smith, Duane, illus. 2005. 89p. (J). 16.95 (978-1-57480-160-6(0)) Lee & Low Bks., Inc.
Rylant, Cynthia. Missing May. unabr. ed. 2004. 89p. (J). (gr. 5-9). pap. 29.00 incl. audio (978-0-8072-8701-9(6) , YA240SP, Listening Library) Random Hse. Audio Publishing Group.
—Missing May. 2004. 112p. (J). pap. 5.99 (978-0-439-61383-5(3) , Scholastic Paperbacks) Scholastic, Inc.
Saenz, Benjamin Alire. Sammy & Juliana in Hollywood. 2006. 368p. (J). pap. 7.99 (978-0-06-084374-8(8)) HarperCollins Pubs.
Salonen, Roxane Beauclair. First Salmon. 2005. (Illus.). 29p. (J). (gr. 3-7). 15.95 (978-1-59078-171-5(6)) Boyds Mills Pr.
Sample, Jewel. Flying Hugs & Kisses Activity Book. 2007. (J). per. 10.99 (***978-1-59879-377-2(2)***) Lifevest Publishing, Inc.
Savage, Deborah. Kotuku. 2002. 304p. (YA). (gr. 7 up). 16.00 (978-0-618-04756-7(5)) Houghton Mifflin Co. Trade & Reference Div.
Schick, Eleanor. Mama. 2000. (Accelerated Reader Bks.). (Illus.). 32p. (J). (gr. k-3). 15.95 (978-0-7614-5060-3(2) , Cavendish Children's Bks.) Cavendish, Marshall Corp.
Scholastic, Inc. Staff & Brooke, Lauren. A Winter's Gift. 3rd rev. ed. 2007. (Heartland Special Edition Ser.). 192p. (J). pap. 5.99 (***978-0-439-92561-7(4)*** , Scholastic Paperbacks) Scholastic, Inc.
Schwiebert, Pat. We Were Gonna Have a Baby, but We Had an Angel Instead. Bills, Taylor, illus. 2004. 24p. pap. 7.95 (978-0-9724241-1-0(3) , 717) Perinatal Loss.
Shands, Linda I. Wild Fire. 2001. (Wakara of Eagle Lodge Ser.: Vol. 1). (Illus.). 176p. (J). (gr. 7-9). pap. 5.99 (978-0-8007-5746-5(7)) Revell.
Simoen, Jan. What about Anna? Nieuwenhuizen, John, tr. from DUT. 2002. (Illus.). 264p. (YA). (gr. 7 up). 16.95 (978-0-8027-8808-5(4)) Walker & Co.
Smith, Cynthia Leitich. Rain Is Not My Indian Name. Earley, Lori, illus. 2001. 144p. (J). (gr. 5-9). 16.99 (978-0-688-17397-5(7)) HarperCollins Pubs.
Smith, Stephen & Caldewell, Lise. Full Court Pressure. 2006. (Game on for Girls Ser.). 128p. (J). pap. 5.99 (978-0-7847-1730-1(3) , 42147) Standard Publishing.
Snyder, Zilpha Keatley. Spyhole Secrets. 2005. 192p. (J). (gr. 3-7). pap. 5.99 (978-0-440-41708-8(2) , Yearling) Random Hse. Children's Bks.
—Spyhole Secrets. 2002. (gr. 3-6). lib. bdg. 13.00 (978-0-613-88326 9(8)) Tandem Library Bks.
Sones, Sonya. One of Those Hideous Books Where the Mother Dies. 272p. (YA). 2004. (Illus.). 16.95 (978-0-689-85820-8(5)); 2005. (gr. 7-12). reprint ed. pap. 6.99 (978-1-4169-0788-6(2) , Simon Pulse) Simon & Schuster Children's Publishing.
Springer, Nancy. Blood Trail. 164p. (YA). (gr. 7 up). pap. 6.95 (***978-0-8234-2063-6(9)***) Holiday Hse., Inc.
Stahler, David, Jr. Gathering of Shades. 2006. pap. (978-0-06-052296-4(8)) HarperCollins Canada, Ltd.
—A Gathering of Shades. 2005. 304p. (J). 15.99 (978-0-06-052294-0(1)); lib. bdg. 16.89 (978-0-06-052295-7(X)) HarperCollins Pubs. (HarperTeen).
Stein, Tammar. Light Years. 272p. (YA). (gr. 9). 2008. mass mkt. 6.99 (***978-0-440-23902-4(8)*** , Laurel Leaf); 2005. 15.95 (978-0-375-83023-5(5) , Knopf Bks. for Young Readers) Random Hse. Children's Bks.
Stein, Tammar. Light Years: A Novel. 2005. 272p. (J). (gr. 9). lib. bdg. 17.99 (978-0-375-93023-2(X) , Knopf Bks. for Young Readers) Random Hse. Children's Bks.
Stroud, Jonathan. The Leap. 2004. 240p. (gr. 5-17). pap. 6.95 (978-0-7868-5195-9(3)) Miramax Bks.
Supplee, Suzanne. When Irish Guys Are Smiling. 2008. (S. A. S. S. (Students Across the Seven Seas) Ser.). 224p. (YA). (gr. 7). pap. 6.99 (***978-0-14-241016-5(0)*** , Puffin) Penguin Group (USA) Inc.
Thong, Roseanne. The Wishing Tree. McLennan, Connie, illus. 2004. 32p. (J). 16.95 (978-1-885008-26-8(0)) Shen's Bks.
Tomey, Ingrid. Grandfather's Day. McKay, Robert A., illus. 2003. 64p. (YA). (gr. 4-6). pap. 9.95 (978-1-56397-947-7(0)) Boyds Mills Pr.
Trueman, Terry. No Right Turn. 2006. 176p. (J). 16.99 (978-0-06-057491-8(7)); lib. bdg. 16.89 (978-0-06-057492-5(5)) HarperCollins Pubs. (HarperTeen).
Turner, Ann. Hard Hit. l.t. ed. 2006. (YA). 21.95 (978-0-7862-8745-1(4)) Thorndike Pr.
Turner, Ann Warren. Hard Hit. 2006. 128p. (J). (gr. 7 up). pap. 16.99 (978-0-439-29680-9(3)) Scholastic, Inc.
Waite, Judy. Shopaholic. 224p. (YA). 2003. (Illus.). 16.95 (978-0-689-85138-4(3) , Atheneum); 2004. reprint ed. pap. 6.99 (978-0-689-85139-1(1) , Simon Pulse) Simon & Schuster Children's Publishing.
Wallace, Bill. No Dogs Allowed! 2004. 214p. (J). (gr. 4-6). tchr. ed. 16.95 (978-0-8234-1818-3(9)) Holiday Hse., Inc.
Wallace-Brodeur, Ruth. Blue Eyes Better. 2003. (Illus.). 112p. (J). (gr. 4-7). pap. 5.99 (978-0-14-250086-6(0) , Puffin) Penguin Group (USA) Inc.
—Blue Eyes Better. 2003. (gr. 5-8). lib. bdg. 14.15 (978-0-613-67139-2(2)) Tandem Library Bks.
Warner, Sally. This Isn't about the Money. 2002. 224p. (J). (gr. 3-6). 15.99 (978-0-670-03574-8(2) , Viking Juvenile) Penguin Group (USA) Inc.
Weigelt, Udo. Bear's Last Journey. Kazeroid, Sibylle, tr. from GER. Kadmon, Cristina, illus. 2003. 32p. (J). (gr. k-3). 15.95 (978-0-7358-1799-9(5)) North-South Bks., Inc.
Weigelt, Udo. Bears Last Journey. Kadmon, Christina, illus. 2007. 0032p. pap. 6.95 (***978-0-7358-2155-2(0)***) North-South Bks., Inc.
Welch, Sheila Kelly. The Shadowed Unicorn. 2000. 192p. (J). (gr. 5-9). 15.95 (978-0-8126-2895-1(0)) Cricket Bks.
Wheeler, Karla. Timmy's Christmas Surprise. Wheeler, Jenny Lee, illus. l.t. ed. 2001. 24p. 4.95 (978-0-9675532-0-7(2)) Quality of Life Publishing Co.
Whelan, Gloria. Time to Keep Silent. 2003. (gr. 5-8). lib. bdg. 16.45 (978-0-613-75511-5(1)) Tandem Library Bks.
Wiles, Deborah. Each Little Bird That Sings. (Illus.). (J). 2005. 272p. 16.00 (978-0-15-205113-6(9)); 2006. 276p. reprint ed. pap. 5.95 (978-0-15-205657-5(2) , Harcourt Paperbacks) Harcourt Children's Bks.
Williams, Maiya. The Golden Hour. 2006. 288p. (J). (gr. 5-10). pap. 5.95 (978-0-8109-9216-0(7)) Abrams, Harry N. , Inc.
Wilson, Jacqueline. Vicky Angel. l.t. ed. 2001. (Illus.). 232p. (J). 16.95 (978-0-7540-6165-6(5) , Galaxy Children's Large Print) BBC Audiobooks America.
—Vicky Angel. 2003. (Illus.). 176p. (gr. 3-7). reprint ed. 5.50 (978-0-440-41808-5(9) , Yearling) Random Hse. Children's Bks.
—Vicky Angel. 2003. (gr. 3-6). lib. bdg. 13.00 (978-0-613-88328-3(4)) Tandem Library Bks.
Wittlinger, Ellen. Blind Faith. (YA). 2007. 304p. pap. 8.99 (***978-1-4169-4906-0(2)*** , Simon Pulse); 2006. 288p. (gr. 7 up). 16.99 (978-1-4169-0273-7(2) , Simon & Schuster Children's Publishing) Simon & Schuster Children's Publishing.
Wood, Debra. Just A Little Child. Blake, Joshua Aaron, illus. l.t. ed. 2006. 33p. (J). per. 12.95 (978-1-59879-087-0(0)) Lifevest Publishing, Inc.
Wood, June Rae. Turtle on a Fence Post. 2001. 272p. (J). pap. 6.99 (978-0-698-11783-9(2) , Putnam Juvenile) Penguin Group (USA) Inc.
Woodson, Jacqueline. Behind You. 128p. (YA). 2006. (gr. 7). pap. 5.99 (978-0-14-240390-7(3) , Puffin); 2004. (gr. 5-12). 15.99 (978-0-399-23988-5(X) , Putnam Juvenile) Penguin Group (USA) Inc.
Yeomans, Ellen. Rubber Houses. 2007. 160p. (J). (gr. 7-17). 15.99 (978-0-316-10647-4(X)) Little Brown & Co.
Yumoto, Kazumi. The Letters. 2003. 176p. (YA). (gr. 7). pap. 5.50 (978-0-440-23822-5(6) , Laurel Leaf) Random Hse. Children's Bks.

GRIEG, EDVARD, 1843-1907

Finck, Henry Theophilus. Edvard Grieg. 2001. 180p. (YA). reprint ed. 88.00 (978-0-7222-6307 5(4)) Library Reprints, Inc.
—Grieg & His Music. 2001. 317p. (YA). reprint ed. 98.00 (978-0-7222-5423-3(7)) Library Reprints, Inc.

GRIFFEY, KEN, JR., 1969-

Dougherty, Terri. Ken Griffey, Jr. 2001. (Jam Session Ser.). (Illus.). 32p. (J). (gr. 3-8). lib. bdg. 24.21 (978-1-57765-472-8(2) , ABDO & Daughters) ABDO Publishing Co.
Gutman, Bill. Ken Griffey, Jr. A Biography. 1998. (J). (978-0-606-13550-4(2)) Tandem Library Bks.
—Ken Griffey, Jr. Baseball's Best. 1998. (Millbrook Sports World Ser.). (Illus.). 48p. (gr. 3-6). lib. bdg. 22.90 (978-0-7613-0415-9(0) , Millbrook Pr.) Lerner Publishing Group.
Rolfe, John, et al. Ken Griffey, Jr. 2000. 112p. (J). pap. 3.99 (978-1-930623-07-1(0)) Sports Illustrated For Kids.
—Ken Griffey, Jr: Superstar Centerfielder. 2005. (Sports Illustrated for Kids Bks.). (Illus.). 176p. (YA). (gr. 7-12). lib. bdg. 30.50 (978-0-8239-3687-8(2)) Rosen Publishing Group, Inc., The.
Rolte, John & Ross, Dalton. Ken Griffey, Jr. 1999. (Sports Illustrated for Kids Bks.). 112p. (J). (gr. 4-6). pap. 3.99 (978-1-886749-58-0(2)) Sports Illustrated For Kids.
Savage, Jeff. Sports Great Ken Griffey, Jr. 2000. (Sports Great Bks.). (Illus.). 64p. (YA). (gr. 4-10). lib. bdg. 22.60 (978-0-7660-1266-0(2)) Enslow Pubs., Inc.
Schaefer, A. R. Ken Griffey, Jr. 2002. (Sports Heroes Ser.). (Illus.). 48p. (J). (gr. 3-4). lib. bdg. 21.26 (978-0-7368-1294-8(6) , Capstone High-Interest Bks.) Capstone Pr., Inc.
Stewart, Mark. Ken Griffey, Jr. 1999. (gr. 3-6). lib. bdg. 14.10 (978-0-613-90736-1(1)) Tandem Library Bks.
Stone, Larry. Ken Griffey, Jr. The Home Run Kid. Rains, Rob, ed. 2003. (Superstar Ser.). (Illus.). 96p. (J). (gr. 4-7). pap. 4.95 (978-1-58261-041-2(X)) Sports Publishing, LLC.

GRIFFINS—FICTION

Jones, Diana Wynne. Year of the Griffin. (J). 2001. 400p. (gr. 7 up). pap. 7.99 (978-0-06-447335-4(X) , Harper Trophy); 2000. 272p. (gr. 5 up). 15.89 (978-0-06-029158-7(3)) HarperCollins Pubs.
—Year of the Griffin. 2001. (gr. 5-8). lib. bdg. 15.30 (978-0-613-44275-6(X)) Tandem Library Bks.
Nitz, Kristin Wolden. Saving the Griffin. Jaeggi, Yoshiko, illus. 2007. 192p. (J). (gr. 3-6). 14.95 (978-1-56145-380-1(3) , Peachtree Junior) Peachtree Pubs., Ltd.
Panagopoulos, Janie Lynn. Calling the Griffin. (YA). pap. (978-0-938682-64-6(4)) River Road Pubns., Inc.
Rodda, Emily. The Flower Fairies. Vitale, Raoul, illus. 2003. (Fairy Realm Ser.: No. 2). 128p. (J). 8.99 (978-0-06-009586-4(5)); lib. bdg. 15.89 (978-0-06-009587-1(3)) HarperCollins Pubs.
Stockton, Frank Richard. The Griffin & the Minor Canon. Sendak, Maurice, illus. 2005. (Sendak Reissues Ser.). 56p. 15.95 (978-0-06-029731-2(X)) HarperCollins Pubs.

GRIMKE, SARAH MOORE, 1792-1873 AND ANGELINA EMILY, 1805-1809

Todras, Ellen H. Angelina Grimke: Voice of Abolition. 1999. (Illus.). xi, 178p. (YA). (gr. 7-12). 25.00 (978-0-208-02485-5(9) , Linnet Bks.) Shoe String Pr., Inc.

GRINCH (FICTITIOUS CHARACTER)—FICTION

Grinch Plush with Book (English) 2000. (J). (978-1-58805-009-0(2)) DS-Max USA, Inc.
Seuss, Dr. The Grinch Meets His Max. 1998. (J). (ps-3). lib. bdg. 11.99 (978-0-679-98836-6(X) , Random Hse. Bks. for Young Readers) Random Hse. Children's Bks.
—How the Grinch Stole Christmas! 1999. (J). 12.99 (978-0-679-89270-0(2) , Random Hse. Bks. for Young Readers) Random Hse. Children's Bks.
—Quomodo Invidiosulus Nomine Grinchus Christi Natalem Abrogaverit: How the Grinch Stole Christmas. Tunberg, Jennifer Morrish & Tunberg, Terence O., trs. from ENG. 1998. (LAT., Illus.). 64p. (ps-3). (J). 25.00 (978-0-86516-419-2(3)); (YA). 19.00 (978-0-86516-420-8(7)) Bolchazy-Carducci Pubs.
Washington, LaVonne & LaShawn. How the Grinch Hare Became A Christian. 2005. 37p. 11.95 (978-1-4116-2322-4(3)) Lulu.com.

GROCERIES

Galko, Francine. Earth Friends at the Grocery Store. 2004. (Heinemann First Library). (Illus.). 32p. (J). pap. (978-1-4034-4903-0(1)) Heinemann Library.
—Ecology at the Grocery Store. 2004. (Heinemann First Library). (Illus.). 32p. (J). lib. bdg. 22.79 (978-1-4034-4898-9(1)) Heinemann Library.
Hoena, B. A. A Visit to the Supermarket. 2004. (Pebble Plus, Let's Visit Ser.). (Illus.). 24p. (J). 13.95 (978-0-7368-2393-7(X) , Pebble Bks.) Capstone Pr., Inc.
Minden, Cecilia. Grocery Shopping by the Numbers. 2008. (J). lib. bdg. 25.26 (***978-1-60279-006-3(X)***) Cherry Lake Publishing.

GROCERY TRADE

see also Supermarkets

Firestone, Mary. Supermarket Managers. 2003. (Community Helpers Ser.). (Illus.). 24p. (J). (gr. 1-2). lib. bdg. (978-0-7368-1614-4(3) , Bridgestone Bks.) Capstone Pr., Inc.
Gillis, Jennifer B. Time to Open! 2006. (Reader's Clubhouse Set B Ser.). (Illus.). 24p. (J). pap. 3.99 (978-0-7641-3301-5(2)) Barron's Educational Series, Inc.
The Letter Nn: At the Grocery Store, 6 vols. (gr. k-2). 17.50 (978-0-7368-4113-9(X)) Red Brick Learning.
Sarver, Amy. Science at the Grocery. 2004. (National Geographic Reading Expeditions Ser.). (Illus.). 24p. (J). pap. (978-0-7922-4567-4(9)) National Geographic Society.
Weber, Valerie & Crawford, Beverly. Shopping in Grandma's Day. Lafford, Stuart, illus. 1999. (In Grandma's Day Ser.). 32p. (J). (ps-3). lib. bdg. 21.27 (978-1-57505-324-0(1) , Carolrhoda Bks.) Lerner Publishing Group.

GROMIT (FICTITIOUS CHARACTER)—FICTION

see Wallace and Gromit (Fictitious Characters)—Fiction

GROOMING, PERSONAL

see Beauty, Personal; Grooming for Men

GROOMING FOR MEN

Sharpman.com Editors. The Young Sharpman's Guide to Grooming: A How-to Book for Sharpmen Ages 13 & Up. 2002. (gr. 7-12). lib. bdg. 22.20 (978-0-613-77826-8(X)) Tandem Library Bks.

GROOMING FOR WOMEN

see Beauty, Personal

GROTTOES

see Caves

GROUND EFFECT MACHINES

see also Helicopters

Bullard, Lisa. Hovercraft. 2007. (Pull Ahead Books-Mighty Movers Ser.). (J). 22.60 (978-0-8225-6421-8(1) , Lerner Pubns.) Lerner Publishing Group.
Hanson, Anders. Let's Go by Hovercraft. 2007. (Let's Go! Ser.). (ENG., Illus.). 24p. (J). (ps-3). lib. bdg. 19.93 (***978-1-59928-900-7(8)*** , SandCastle) ABDO Publishing Co.
Hovercraft. 2007. (Illus.). 32p. (J). pap. 5.95 (***978-0-8225-6427-0(0)*** , First Avenue Editions) Lerner Publishing Group.
Parker, Steve. The LCAC Military Hovercraft. 2008. (J). (***978-1-4296-0095-8(0)***) Capstone Pr., Inc.

E F G

Sautter, Aaron. Hovercrafts. 2007. (Blazers—Horsepower Ser.). (Illus.). 32p. (J). (978-0-7368-6782-5(1) , 1264928) Capstone Pr., Inc.

GROUND PROXIMITY MACHINES

see Ground Effect Machines

GROUND SQUIRRELS

Lynch, Wayne, photos by. Baby Ground Squirrel. (Nature Babies Ser.). (Illus.). (J). (gr. k-3). 36p. pap. (978-1-55041-799-9(1)); 2003. 32p. (978-1-55041-797-5(5)) Fitzhenry & Whiteside, Ltd.

GROUNDHOG

see Woodchuck

GROUP LIVING

see Collective Settlements

GROUSE—FICTION

Beckhorn, Susan Williams. Moose Eggs or, Why Moose Has Flat Antlers. Stevens, Helen, illus. 2007. 32p. (gr. k-3). 15.95 (***978-0-89272-689-9(X)***) Down East Bks.

GROWTH

see also Children—Growth; Growth (Plants)

Aliki. I'm Growing! 2001. (gr. k-3). lib. bdg. 12.95 (978-0-7857-0916-9(9)) Tandem Library Bks.

Balkwill, Fran. SuperCell. Rolph, Mic, illus. 2002. (Making Sense of Science Ser.). 32p. (J). pap. (978-1-85578-093-4(3)) Portland Pr., Ltd.

Bowden, Rob. Globalization. 2004. (21st Century Debates Ser.). (Illus.). 64p. (J). lib. bdg. 28.56 (978-0-7398-6466-1(1)) Raintree.

Burton, Margie, et al. Growing Older. Adams, Alison, ed. 1999. (Early Connections Ser.). 16p. (J). (gr. k-2). pap. 4.50 (978-1-58344-064-3(X)) Benchmark Education Co.

Captain, Tamira. When Do You Grow? Thorne, Sean, illus. 2003. (J). pap. 6.95 (978-0-9742288-0-8(X)) Stories From Four Publishing Co.

Corbett, Pie. Growing Up. 2005. (Building Blocks Ser.). (Illus.). 24p. (J). (gr. 1 up). lib. bdg. 22.80 (978-1-59389-208-1(X)) Chrysalis Education.

Driscoll, Laura. Apples: And How They Grow. Smith, Tammy, illus. 2003. (All Aboard Science Reader Ser.). 32p. (J). (ps-2). pap. 3.99 (978-0-448-43275-5(7) , Grosset & Dunlap) Penguin Group (USA) Inc.

Favor, Lesli J. Everything You Need to Know about Growth Spurts & Delayed Growth. 2005. (Need to Know Library). (Illus.). 64p. (YA). (gr. 4-6). lib. bdg. 25.25 (978-0-8239-3549-9(3)) Rosen Publishing Group, Inc., The.

Fiscus, James. Coping with Growth Spurts & Delayed Growth. 2005. (Coping Ser.). (Illus.). 192p. (YA). (gr. 7-12). lib. bdg. 26.50 (978-0-8239-3508-6(6)) Rosen Publishing Group, Inc., The.

Gaff, Jackie. Looking at Growing Up: How Do People Change? 2008. (Looking at Science: How Things Change Ser.). 32p. (J). (gr. 1-3). lib. bdg. 22.60 (***978-0-7660-3090-9(3)***) Enslow Pubs., Inc.

Glover, David. Living & Growing. 2001. (Experiments in Science Ser.). (Illus.). (J). (978-0-7894-7470-4(0)) Dorling Kindersley Publishing, Inc.

Glover, David & Glover, Penny. Growing. 2005. (Illus.). 30p. (J). (gr. 3-7). lib. bdg. 27.10 (978-1-58340-690-8(5)) Smart Apple Media.

Graver, Jane. How You Are Changing. 1998. (Learning about Sex Ser.: Vol. 3). 64p. (J). (gr. 3-6). 10.99 (978-0-570-03564-0(3)) Concordia Publishing Hse.

Growing: First Grade Newcomer Books. (On Our Way to English Ser.). (gr. 1 up). 23.50 (978-0-7578-7203-7(4)) Rigby Education.

Growing: Individual Title Six-Packs. (Story Steps Ser.). (gr. k-2). 29.00 (978-0-7635-9582-1(9)); (gr. 1-2). 22.00 (978-0-7578-5422-4(2)) Rigby Education.

Harcourt School Publishers Staff. Human Growth & Reproduction. 99th ed. 1998. (Your Health Ser.). (Illus.). (gr. 4-6). pap. 33.30 (978-0-15-311355-0(3)) Harcourt Schl. Pubs.

—Watch Me Grow: Theme Book. 1999. (Collections Ser.). (Illus.). (J). pap. 3.00 (978-0-15-314021-1(6)) Harcourt Schl. Pubs.

Hewitt, Sally. Growing Up. 1999. (It's Science! Ser.). (Illus.). 32p. (J). (gr. k-3). 23.50 (978-0-516-21180-0(3) , Children's Pr.) Scholastic Library Publishing.

—Growing Up. 1999. (gr. k-3). lib. bdg. 15.25 (978-0-613-37374-6(X)) Tandem Library Bks.

Hickman, Pamela. A New Frog: The Life Cycle of an Amphibian. Collins, Heather, illus. unabr. ed. 1999. (My First Look at Nature Ser.). 20p. (J). (gr. k-3). (978-1-55074-615-0(4)) Kids Can Pr., Ltd.

Hickman, Pamela & Collins, Heather. A New Duck: My First Look at the Life Cycle of a Bird. 1999. (My First Look at Nature Ser.). (Illus.). 20p. (J). (gr. k-3). (978-1-55074-613-6(8)) Kids Can Pr., Ltd.

How Does It Grow?, 6 Packs. (gr. k-1). 23.00 (978-0-7635-9037-6(1)) Rigby Education.

James, Diana. Growing Up. 2000. (ps-2). lib. bdg. 12.95 (978-0-613-43324-2(6)) Tandem Library Bks.

James, Diane. Growing Up. Lynn, Sara, illus. rev. ed. 2000. (Play & Discover Ser.). (J). (ps). 32p. pap. 4.95 (978-1-58728-048-1(5)); 9.95 (978-1-58728-044-3(2)) T&N Children's Publishing. (Two Can Publishing).

Lee, Frances. Who Is the Tallest? 1999. (ps-2). lib. bdg. 11.80 (978-0-613-19492-1(6)) Tandem Library Bks.

Llewellyn, Claire. Asi Nace una Mariposa. Giraldo, Maria Cristina, tr. Mendez, Simon, illus. (Coleccion Asi Nace... Ser.). (SPA.). 24p. (J). (gr. k-6). pap. 8.95 (978-1-59437-788-4(X)) Santillana USA Publishing Co., Inc.

—Butterfly: Starting Life Butterly. Mendez, Simon, illus. 2003. (Starting Life Ser.). 24p. (ps-3). 16.95 (978-1-55971-868-4(4) , NorthWord Bks. for Young Readers) T&N Children's Publishing.

—How Animals Grow. 2006. (Illus.). 24p. (J). (978-1-59771-022-0(9)) Sea-To-Sea Pubns.

Lorenz Books Staff. Growing. 2002. (Let's Look at...Ser.). (Illus.). 20p. 5.99 (978-0-7548-1049-0(6) , Lorenz Bks.) Anness Publishing GBR. *Dist:* National Bk. Network.

Losang, Rato K. & Singer, Marilyn. Make Me Over: Eleven Original Stories about Transforming Ourselves. Campbell, Joseph, ed. 2005. 272p. (YA). (gr. 6-12). 17.99 (978-0-525-47480-7(3) , Dutton Adult) Penguin Group (USA) Inc.

Macnair, Patricia Ann. Life Cycle. 2004. (Bodyscope Ser.). (Illus.). 40p. (J). (gr. 3-5). 9.95 (978-0-7534-5780-1(6) , Kingfisher) Houghton Mifflin Co. Trade & Reference Div.

Madaras, Lynda. Ready, Set, Grow! A What's Happening to My Body? Book for Younger Girls. Davick, Linda, tr. Davick, Linda, illus. 2003. 128p. (YA). (gr. 3 up). 22.00 (978-1-55704-587-4(9) , Newmarket Shooting Scripts) Newmarket Pr.

Madaras, Lynda & Madaras, Area. The What's Happening to My Body Book for Boys. 3rd ed. 2007. (Illus.). 272p. (YA). 24.95 (***978-1-55704-769-4(3));*** pap. 12.95 (***978-1-55704-765-6(0))*** Newmarket Pr.

—The What's Happening to My Body Book for Girls. 3rd rev. ed. 2007. (Illus.). 304p. (YA). 24.95 (***978-1-55704-768-7(5));*** pap. 12.95 (***978-1-55704-764-9(2))*** Newmarket Pr.

McLeod, Beatrice. Growing Up. 2000. (Nature Undercover Ser.). (Illus.). 40p. (J). (gr. 5-8). 23.70 (978-1-56711-501-7(2) , Blackbirch Pr., Inc.) Thomson Gale.

Miller, Sara Swan. Learn & Grow. Lacome, Susie, illus. 1999. 8p. (J). (ps-1). bds. 15.99 (978-1-57584-348-3(X) , Reader's Digest Young Families, Inc.) Reader's Digest Children's Publishing, Inc.

National Geographic Society Staff. Incredible Voyage: Exploring the Human Body. 1998. (Illus.). 352p. (YA). (gr. 7 up). 35.00 (978-0-7922-7148-2(3) , National Geographic) National Geographic Society.

Parker, Steve. The Reproductive System. (Body Focus Ser.). (Illus.). 48p. (J). 2003. (gr. 6-8). lib. bdg. 27.07 (978-1-4034-0199-1(3)); 2002. pap. 8.50 (978-1-4034-0455-8(0)) Heinemann Library.

Peak, Lizabeth. Growth Disorders. 2007. (Diseases & Disorders Ser.). 128p. (J). (gr. 7-10). 32.45 (***978-1-59018-673-2(7)*** , Lucent Bks.) Thomson Gale.

Pipe, Jim. Growth & Life Cycles: Tadpole to Frog. 2005. (Illus.). 32p. (J). (gr. 1-4). lib. bdg. 27.10 (978-1-59604-024-3(6)) Stargazer Bks.

Riley, Barbara. Grow, Grow, Grow. Guggenheim, Jaenet, illus. l.t. ed. 2003. 40p. (J). 19.95 (978-1-929115-08-2(3)) Azro Pr., Inc.

Rockwell, Anne F. Growing Like Me. Keller, Holly, illus. 2001. 24p. (J). (ps-k). 15.00 (978-0-15-202202-0(3) , Silver Whistle) Harcourt Trade Pubs.

Royston. Growing. 2004. (My Amazing Body Ser.). (Illus.). pap. 7.50 (978-1-4109-0950-3(6)) Raintree.

—Growing 6-Pack. 2004. (My Amazing Body Ser.). (Illus.). pap. 40.50 (978-1-4109-0957-2(3)) Raintree.

Royston, Angela. Growing. 2004. (My Amazing Body Ser.). (Illus.). 32p. 25.70 (978-1-4109-0481-2(4)) Raintree.

—Human Growth. 2003. (My World of Science Ser.). (Illus.). 32p. (J). (gr. k-2). lib. bdg. 22.79 (978-1-4034-0989-8(7)); pap. 6.50 (978-1-4034-3196-7(5)) Heinemann Library.

Saunders-Smith, Gail. Children. 1998. (J). pap. 13.25 (978-0-516-21238-8(9) , Children's Pr.) Scholastic Library Publishing.

Savage, Candace. Get Growing! Clement, Gary, illus. (J). pap. 6.95 (978-1-55054-203-5(6)) Douglas & McIntyre, Ltd. CAN. *Dist:* Transition Vendor.

Silverstein, Alvin, et al. Growth & Development. 2007. (Science Concepts, Second Ser.). (Illus.). 112p. (YA). (gr. 6-8). lib. bdg. 31.93 (***978-0-8225-6057-9(7)*** , Twenty-First Century Bks.) Lerner Publishing Group.

Spence, Simone. A Children's Book about Growing Up. 2000. (Help Me Succeed Ser.). (Illus.). 230p. (J). (gr. 4-7). pap. 29.95 (978-0-9670647-1-0(6)) EggShell Pr.

—A Children's Book about Growing Up. Friedman, Staci, illus. deluxe ed. 2000. (Help Me Grow Ser.: Vol. 3). 240p. (J). (ps-5). pap. 49.95 incl. audio compact disk (978-0-9670647-2-7(4)) EggShell Pr.

Tuxworth, Nicola. A First Book about Growing. 1999. (Look & Learn Ser.). (Illus.). 24p. (J). (gr. 1 up). lib. bdg. 22.00 (978-0-8368-2370-7(2)) Stevens, Gareth Inc.

Weber, Rebecca. The Cycle of Your Life. 2004. (Spyglass Books). (Illus.). 24p. (J). (gr. 1 up). lib. bdg. 18.60 (978-0-7565-0625-4(5)) Compass Point Bks.

GROWTH—FICTION

Anderson, Rachel & Harter, Debbie. Hello Peanut! 2003. (Illus.). (J). mass mkt. 8.99 (978-0-340-85248-4(8) , Hodder & Stoughton) Hodder General Publishing Division GBR. *Dist:* Trafalgar Square Publishing.

Angelou, Maya. Cedric of Jamaica. Rockwell, Lizzy, illus. 2005. (Random House Pictureback Book Ser.). (J). (978-0-375-83269-7(6)); lib. bdg. (978-0-375-93269-4(0)) Random Hse., Inc.

Baer, Julie. Love Me Later. 2005. (Illus.). 28p. (J). (ps-ps). 16.99 (978-1-932188-03-5(7)) Bollix Bks.

Baer, Julie, illus. & text. I Only Like What I Like. Baer, Julie, text. 2003. 32p. (J). 15.99 (978-1-932188-00-4(2)) Bollix Bks.

Bergstein, Rita. Your Own Big Bed. Hartung, Susan Kathleen, illus. 2008. 32p. (J). (ps). 15.99 (***978-0-670-06079-5(8)*** , Viking Juvenile) Penguin Group (USA) Inc.

Best, Cari & Davenier, Christine. Sally Jean, the Bicycle Queen. 2006. (Illus.). 32p. (J). (gr. k-2). 16.00 (978-0-374-36386-4(2) , Nelanie Kroupa Bks.) Farrar, Straus & Giroux.

Bluthenthal, Diana Cain, illus. I'm a Kid. You're a Baby. 2007. (J). (978-0-689-85470-5(6)) Simon & Schuster Children's Publishing.

Bridges, Margaret Park. Am I Big or Little? Dockray, Tracy, illus. 2002. 32p. (J). (ps-2). pap. 5.95 (978-1-58717-147-5(3) , SeaStar Bks.) Chronicle Bks. LLC.

—Am I Big or Little? 2002. (gr. k-3). lib. bdg. 14.10 (978-0-613-87929-3(5)) Tandem Library Bks.

Bridges, Margaret Park & Dockray, Tracy. Am I Big or Little? 2000. (Illus.). 32p. (J). (ps-3). 16.50 (978-1-58717-020-1(5) , SeaStar Bks.) Chronicle Bks. LLC.

Brimner, Larry Dane. Baby Bear. Date not set. 32p. (J). (ps-3). pap. 5.99 (978-0-06-443703-5(5)) HarperCollins Pubs.

Bunting, Eve. Baby Can. Chambliss, Maxie, illus. 2007. 32p. (J). 15.95 (978-1-59078-322-1(0)) Boyds Mills Pr.

—Little Bear's Little Boat. Carpenter, Nancy, illus. 2003. 32p. (J). (gr. k-ps). tchr. ed. 12.00 (978-0-395-97462-9(3) , Clarion Bks.) Houghton Mifflin Co. Trade & Reference Div.

—My Big Boy Bed. Smith, Maggie, illus. 2003. 32p. (J). (gr. k-ps). 15.00 (978-0-618-17742-4(6) , Clarion Bks.) Houghton Mifflin Co. Trade & Reference Div.

Carlson, Nancy. It's Going to Be Perfect. 2000. (J). (978-0-606-18933-0(5)) Tandem Library Bks.

Carter, Candace. Sid's Surprise. Un Kim, Joung, illus. 2005. 32p. (J). lib. bdg. 10.00 (***978-1-4242-0185-3(3))*** Fitzgerald Bks.

—Sid's Surprise. Kim, Joung Un, illus. 2005. (Green Light Readers Level 1 Ser.). 32p. (J). 12.95 (978-0-15-205183-9(X)); pap. 3.95 (978-0-15-205182-2(1)) Harcourt Children's Bks. (Green Light Readers).

Christophe, Le Masne. Tom Tiene Pesadillas. Bawin, Marie-Aline, illus. 2002. (Tom Ser.). (SPA & ENG.). 24p. (ps-k). 9.95 (978-84-7864-345-5(1)) Combel Editorial, S.A. ESP. *Dist:* Independent Pubs. Group.

—Tom Va a la Escuela. Bawin, Marie-Aline, illus. 2002. (Tom Ser.). (SPA & ENG.). 24p. (ps-k). 9.95 (978-84-7864-316-5(8)) Combel Editorial, S.A. ESP. *Dist:* Independent Pubs. Group.

Clarke, Jane. Only Tadpoles Have Tails. Gray, Jane, illus. 2004. (Flying Foxes Ser.). (J). 46p. (978-0-7787-1484-2(5)); 48p. pap. (978-0-7787-1530-6(2)) Crabtree Publishing Co.

Cohn, Arlen. Firsts: Reflections of a 7-Year Old. Vasconsellos, Daniel, tr. Vasconsellos, Daniel, illus. gif. ed. 2004. 28p. bds. 9.99 (978-1-57939-168-3(0)) Accord Publishing, Ltd.

Cosgrove, Stephen. Minikin. 2000. (gr. k-3). lib. bdg. 13.00 (978-0-613-33659-8(3)) Tandem Library Bks.

Curtis, Jamie Lee. It's Hard to Be Five: Learning How to Work My Control Panel. Cornell, Laura, illus. 2004. 40p. (J). (ps-3). 16.99 (978-0-06-008095-2(7)); lib. bdg. 17.89 (978-0-06-008096-9(5)) HarperCollins Pubs. (Cotler, Joanna Books).

—When I Was Little: A Four-Year-Old's Memoir of Her Youth. braille ed. 2004. (Illus.). (J). (gr. k-3). spiral bd. (978-0-616-01625-1(5)); spiral bd. (978-0-616-01626-8(3)) Canadian National Institute for the Blind/Institut National Canadien pour les Aveugles.

—When I Was Little: A Four-Year-Old's Memoir of Her Youth. Cornell, Laura, illus. 1999. (Joanna Cotler Bks.). 32p. (J). (ps-k). 7.99 (978-0-694-01216-9(5) , Harper Festival) HarperCollins Pubs.

Cyrus, Kurt. Tadpole Rex. 2008. (J). (***978-0-15-205990-3(3))*** Harcourt Trade Pubs.

Danzig, Marsha. The Tiniest Acorn: A Story to Grow By. 1999. (Illus.). 32p. 12.95 (978-0-88391-001-6(2)) Fell, Frederick Pubs., Inc.

Dunbar. Tell Me What Its Like to Be Big. 2001. (Illus.). (J). 16.00 (978-0-15-204741-2(7)) Harcourt Trade Pubs.

Dunbar, Joyce. Tell Me What It's Like to Be Big. Gliori, Debi, illus. 32p. (J). (ps-2). 2001. 16.00 (978-0-15-202564-9(2)); 2005. reprint ed. pap. 6.00 (978-0-15-205247-8(X) , Voyager Bks./Libros Viajeros) Harcourt Children's Bks.

Ferri, Giuliano. Little Tad Grows Up. Ferri, Giuliano, illus. 2007. (Illus.). 32p. (J). (ps-1). 16.99 (***978-0-698-40060-3(7)*** , Minedition) Penguin Group (USA) Inc.

Fidler, Mark. The Call of Sagarmatha. 2002. 142p. pap. 11.95 (978-0-595-25281-7(8) , Writers Club Pr.) iUniverse, Inc.

Franco, Betsy. Mi Dedo Menique. Lucas, Margeaux, illus. (Rookie Reader Espanol Ser.). (SPA.). (J). (gr. k-2). 2002. 24p. pap. 4.95 (978-0-516-26318-2(8)); 2001. 32p. 19.50 (978-0-516-22359-9(3)) Scholastic Library Publishing. (Children's Pr.).

—My Pinkie Finger. Lucas, Margeaux, illus. 2001. (Rookie Reader Espanol Ser.). 32p. (J). (gr. k-2). pap. 4.95 (978-0-516-27295-5(0)); (gr. 1-2). 19.50 (978-0-516-22221-9(X)) Scholastic Library Publishing. (Children's Pr.).

—My Pinkie Finger. 2001. (gr. k-3). lib. bdg. 12.95 (978-0-613-54620-1(2)) Tandem Library Bks.

Frazier, Daniele. The Tiny Brown Seed. Frazier, Craig, illus. 2003. 24p. (J). (ps-1). 14.95 (978-1-932026-11-5(8)) Graphis, U.S., Inc.

Gallen, Tim. Love, Loss, & Algebra Equations. 2001. 244p. pap. 14.95 (978-0-595-17973-2(8) , Writers Club Pr.) iUniverse, Inc.

Gilchrist, Jan Spivey. Indigo & Moonlight Gold. 2000. (gr. k-3). lib. bdg. 15.25 (978-0-613-27899-7(2)) Tandem Library Bks.

Golden Books Staff. Growing up, up, Up! 2008. (Illus.). 48p. (J). (ps-2). pap. 3.99 (978-0-375-83716-6(7) , Golden Bks.) Random Hse. Children's Bks.

Gomi, Taro. My Friends. 2006. (ENG & SPA., Illus.). 40p. (J). pap. 6.95 (978-0-8118-5204-3(0)) Chronicle Bks. LLC.

Goodhart, Pippa. Hoppy Birthday, Jo-Jo! Birkett, Georgie, illus. 2005. (Green Bananas Ser.). 48p. (J). (978-0-7787-1025-7(4)) Crabtree Publishing Co.

—Hoppy Birthday, Jo-Jo! 2005. (Green Bananas Ser.). (Illus.). 48p. (J). (ps). pap. (978-0-7787-1041-7(6)) Crabtree Publishing Co.

Harcourt School Publishers Staff. The Fish's Wish: Take-Home Book. rev. ed. 2001. (Collections Ser.: Bk. 11). (Illus.). (J). pap. 1.90 (978-0-15-319069-8(8)) Harcourt Schl. Pubs.

—I Am Six. 99th ed. 1999. (Signatures Ser.). (Illus.). pap. 14.30 (978-0-15-310846-4(0)) Harcourt Schl. Pubs.

—The Seed Surprise Below Level. 3rd ed. 2002. (Trophies Reading Program Ser.). (Illus.). pap. 5.10 (978-0-15-323052-3(5)) Harcourt Schl. Pubs.

Hassett, John & Hassett, Ann. Can't Catch Me. Hassett, John & Hassett, Ann, illus. 2006. (Illus.). 32p. (J). (gr. k-3). 16.00 (978-0-618-70490-3(6)) Houghton Mifflin Co.

Higgins, Richard P. Basketballs & Babysteps. 2001. 192p. (YA). pap. 13.95 (978-0-595-20051-1(6) , Authors Choice Pr.) iUniverse, Inc.

Hodes, Loren. Too Big, Too Little. . . Just Right! Hodes, Loren, illus. 2002. (Illus.). (J). 9.95 (978-1-880582-72-5(4) , TTTH) Judaica Pr., Inc., The.

Hoffman, Don. Billy Is a Big Boy. Dakins, Todd, illus. 2000. 32p. (J). (ps). 16.95 (978-0-9702518-0-0(7)) Printstar Bks.

—Billy Is a Big Boy Are You a Big Boy Too? Dakins, Todd, illus. 2003. (Are You Big Too? Ser.). 24p. (J). pap. 2.99 (978-1-4037-0196-1(2)) Dalmatian Pr.

Holwitz, Peter. Stick Kid. Holwitz, Peter, illus. 2004. (Illus.). 40p. (J). 13.99 (978-0-399-24163-5(9) , Philomel) Penguin Group (USA) Inc.

Hurwitz, Johanna. Rip-Roaring Russell. Tilley, Debbie, illus. 2001. (Riverside Kids Ser.). 112p. (J). (gr. 1-4). pap. 4.99 (978-0-06-442155-3(4) , Harper Trophy) HarperCollins Pubs.

—Rip-Roaring Russell. 1999. (Beech Tree Chapter Bks.). (Illus.). 96p. (gr. k-4). mass mkt. 4.95 (978-0-688-16664-9(4)) HarperCollins Pubs.

—Rip-Roaring Russell. Tilley, Debbie, illus. 2001. 110p. (J). (ps-ps). per. 12.10 (978-0-613-34915-4(6)) Tandem Library Bks.

Jasin, Janie. The Littlest Christmas Tree: A Tale of Growing & Becoming. Kurtz, Pam, illus. 1998. 32p. (J). (ps-3). 19.95 incl. audio compact disk (978-0-916773-82-3(5)) Book Peddlers.

Johnson, Marion. Caillou: New Shoes. rev. ed. 2008. (Playtime Ser.). (Illus.). 24p. (J). pap. 4.95 (***978-2-89450-634-9(1))*** Chouette Publishing CAN. *Dist:* Independent Pubs. Group.

Jordan, Apple. Big Enough for a Bed. Barrett, John E., photos by. 2002. (Illus.). 12p. (J). (gr. k-ps). bds. 4.99 (978-0-375-82270-4(4) , Random Hse. Bks. for Young Readers) Random Hse. Children's Bks.

Joslin, Mary. The Shore Beyond. Jay, Alison, illus. 2000. 28p. (J). (ps-3). 16.00 (978-1-56148-316-7(8)) Good Bks.

Joyce, William. Big Time Olie. Joyce, William, illus. 2002. (Rolie Polie Olie Ser.). (Illus.). 40p. (J). (ps-3). 15.99 (978-0-06-008810-1(9) , Geringer, Laura Book) HarperCollins Pubs.

—Big Time Olie. Joyce, William, illus. 2006. (Rolie Polie Olie Ser.). 40p. (J). pap. 6.99 (978-0-06-008812-5(5) , Harper Trophy) HarperCollins Pubs.

Karon, Jan. The Trellis & the Seed: A Book of Encouragement for All Ages. Steele, Robert Gantt, illus. 32p. (J). 2005. pap. 5.99 (978-0-14-240317-4(2) , Puffin); 2003. 15.95 (978-0-670-89289-1(0) , Viking Juvenile) Penguin Group (USA) Inc.

Keller, Holly. Farfallina & Marcel. Keller, Holly, illus. (Illus.). 32p. (J). 2002. 16.99 (978-0-06-623932-3(X)); 2005. reprint ed. pap. 6.99 (978-0-06-443872-8(4) , Harper Trophy) HarperCollins Pubs.

—Farfallina & Marcel. 2004. (Illus.). 26p. (J). (ps-ps). lib. bdg. 12.79 (978-0-606-32617-9(0)) Tandem Library Bks.

Ker Conway, Jill. Felipe the Flamingo. 2006. (Illus.). 32p. (J). 12.95 (978-1-55591-547-6(7) , 800.992.2908) Fulcrum Publishing.

Kimble, Maggie T. Peep Learns to Sing. 2004. 21p. pap. 14.95 (978-1-4137-2005-1(6)) PublishAmerica, Inc.

Kirk, Daniel. Bigger. 2000. (Illus.). (J). (978-0-606-18390-1(6)) Tandem Library Bks.

Kittinger, Jo S. Cuando Sea Grande. Lucas, Margeaux, illus. 2005. (Rookie Reader Espanol Ser.). (SPA & ESP.). 23p. (J). (gr. k-2). pap. 4.95 (978-0-516-24692-5(5) , Children's Pr.) Scholastic Library Publishing.

Kroll, Virginia L. On the Way to Kindergarten. Schlossberg, Elisabeth, illus. 2006. 32p. (J). (ps). 15.99 (978-0-399-24168-0(X) , Putnam Juvenile) Penguin Group (USA) Inc.

Laden, Nina. Grow Up. 2003. (Illus.). 26p. (J). bds. 6.95 (978-0-8118-3761-3(0)) Chronicle Bks. LLC.

Le Masne, Christophe. El Abuelo de Tom Ha Muerto. 2002. (Tom Ser.). (SPA & ENG., Illus.). 24p. 9.95 (978-84-7864-500-8(4)) Combel Editorial, S.A. ESP. *Dist:* Independent Pubs. Group.

—Tom Se Pierde. 2002. (Tom Ser.). (SPA & ENG., Illus.). 24p. 9.95 (978-84-7864-499-5(7)) Combel Editorial, S.A. ESP. *Dist:* Independent Pubs. Group.

Lisa, Bruce. Fran's Flower. 1999. 32p. (J). (ps-2). pap. 4.95 (978-0-06-443610-6(1)) HarperCollins Pubs.

Lucado, Max. The Oak Inside the Acorn. Angelini, George, illus. 2006. 48p. (J). 16.99 (978-1-4003-0601-5(9)) Nelson, Thomas Inc.

MacDonald, George. The History of Gutta-Percha Willie. 2006. pap. (***978-1-4250-0933-5(6))*** Assistedreading-books.com Inc.

Mahr, Juli. Mama Tiger, Baba Tiger. 2001. (Illus.). (J). (978-0-606-21314-1(7)) Tandem Library Bks.

Mayer, Mercer. Just Big Enough. Mayer, Mercer, illus. 2004. (Little Critter Ser.). (Illus.). 40p. (J). (ps-2). 6.99 (978-0-06-053963-4(1) , Harper Festival) HarperCollins Pubs.

—When I Grow Up. 2003. (Illus.). 24p. (J). (ps-2). pap. 3.25 (978-0-375-82632-0(7) , Random Hse. Bks. for Young Readers) Random Hse. Children's Bks.

—When I Grow Up. 2003. (ps-2). lib. bdg. 10.95 (978-0-613-82737-9(6)) Tandem Library Bks.

McAllister, Angela. Trust Me, Mom! Collins, Ross, illus. 2005. 32p. (J). (ps-2). 16.95 (978-1-58234-955-8(X)) Bloomsbury Publishing.

McBratney, Sam. When I'm Big. Jeram, Anita, illus. 2007. (Guess How Much I Love You Ser.). 24p. (J). (gr. k-ps). bds. 7.99 (***978-0-7636-3546-6(4)***) Candlewick Pr.

McCarty, Peter. Baby Steps. rev. ed. 2000. (Illus.). 32p. (J). (ps up). 16.00 (978-0-8050-5953-3(9) , Holt, Henry & Co. Bks. For Young Readers) Holt, Henry & Co.

McElmurry, Jill. I'm Not a Baby! 2005. (J). 15.95 (978-0-689-87008-8(6) , Atheneum) Simon & Schuster Children's Publishing.

—I'm Not a Baby. McElmurry, Jill, illus. 2006. (Illus.). 40p. (J). (ps-3). 16.95 (978-0-375-83614-5(4) , Schwartz & Wade Bks.) Random Hse. Children's Bks.

McGhee, Alison. Good-Bye, Crib. MacDonald, Ross, illus. 2008. 32p. (J). 16.99 (978-1-4169-1621-5(0) , Simon & Schuster Children's Publishing) Simon & Schuster Children's Publishing.

McNaughton, Colin. When I Grow Up. McNaughton, Colin, illus. 2005. (Illus.). 40p. (J). (ps-1). 12.99 (978-0-7636-2675-4(9)) Candlewick Pr.

Minshull, Evelyn. Eaglet's World. Gabriel, Andrea, illus. 2002. 32p. (J). (ps-3). 16.95 (978-0-8075-8929-8(2)) Whitman, Albert & Co.

Mitchell, Rita Phillips. Hue Boy. Binch, Caroline, illus. 1999. 32p. (J). (gr. k-3). pap. 11.95 (978-0-14-056354-2(7)) Penguin Bks., Ltd. GBR. *Dist:* Trafalgar Square Publishing.

Moss, Thylias. I Want to Be. 1998. (978-0-606-13511-5(1)) Tandem Library Bks.

Oppel, Kenneth. Silverwing. braille ed. 2003. (J). (gr. 2). spiral bd. (978-0-616-15274-4(4)) Canadian National Institute for the Blind/Institut National Canadien pour les Aveugles.

—Silverwing. 2007. 224p. (J). pap. 6.99 (***978-1-4169-4998-5(4)*** , Aladdin) Simon & Schuster Children's Publishing.

—Silverwing. 1999. (978-0-606-16312-5(3)); (gr. 3-6). lib. bdg. 13.00 (978-0-613-15978-4(0)) Tandem Library Bks.

Patz, Nancy & Roth, Susan L. Babies Can't Eat Kimchee! Patz, Nancy & Roth, Susan L., illus. 2006. (Illus.). 32p. (J). (ps-2). 16.95 (978-1-59990-017-9(3)) Bloomsbury Publishing.

Pinkham, Mark Amaru. Love Me Later. 2005. 202p. 14.95 (978-1-932188-02-8(9)) Adventures Unlimited Pr.

Pitino, Donna Marie. Too-Tall Tina. Woodruff, Liza, illus. 2005. 32p. (J). lib. bdg. 13.00 (***978-1-4242-1076-3(3)***) Fitzgerald Bks.

—Too-Tall Tina. Woodruff, Liza, illus. 2005. (Math Matters Ser.). 32p. (J). pap. 4.95 (978-1-57565-150-7(5)) Kane Pr., The.

Pittar, Gill. Milly, Molly & Jimmy's Seeds. 2004. (Illus.). 28p. (978-1-86972-000-1(8)) Milly Molly Bks.

Radabaugh, Melinda Beth. First Time ABC. 2003. (First Time Ser.). (Illus.). 24p. (J). pap. 5.25 (978-1-4034-3883-6(8)); lib. bdg. 18.50 (978-1-4034-3868-3(4)) Heinemann Library.

Rau, Dana Meachen. I Am in Charge of Me. 2004. (Compass Point Early Reader Ser.). (J). (978-0-7565-0572-1(0)) Compass Point Bks.

—I Am in Charge of Me. Beckes, Shirley, illus. 2004. (Read-It! Readers Ser.). 32p. (C). (gr. k-3). 18.60 (978-1-4048-0646-7(6)) Picture Window Bks.

Rey, H. A. & Rey, Margret. Curious George Plants a Seed. 2007. (Illus.). 24p. (J). (ps-k). 3.99 (***978-0-618-77710-5(5)***) Houghton Mifflin Co. Trade & Reference Div.

—Curious George Tadpole Trouble. 2007. (Illus.). 24p. (J). (ps-k). 3.99 (***978-0-618-77712-9(1)***) Houghton Mifflin Co. Trade & Reference Div.

Riise, Torben. Emily & the Arabic Letter. 2001. 164p. (YA). pap. 11.95 (978-0-595-17399-0(3) , Writers Club Pr.) iUniverse, Inc.

Rosen, Michael J. Three Feet Small. Gorbachev, Valeri, illus. 2005. 32p. (J). 16.00 (978-0-15-204938-6(X) , Gulliver Bks.) Harcourt Children's Bks.

Rovetch, Lissa. TLC Grow with Me! McLeod, Chum, illus. 2005. (J). (978-1-58987-114-4(6)) Kindermusik International.

Rowen, Amy & Rowen, Tyla Marie. Waggin' Tails. 2003. 182p. 23.95 (978-0-595-65740-7(0)); pap. 13.95 (978-0-595-28171-8(0)) iUniverse, Inc.

Sarda, Rosa. I Like Acting Grown-up. 2002. (gr. k-3). lib. bdg. 12.95 (978-0-613-50534-5(4)) Tandem Library Bks.

—I Like Growing Up: Me Gusta Ser Mayor. 2002. (gr. k-3). lib. bdg. 12.95 (978-0-613-50536-9(0)) Tandem Library Bks.

Sarda, Rosa & Curto, Rosa Maria. I Like Acting Grown-Up (Me Gusta Hacer Como Mayores) 2002. (SPA & ENG., Illus.). 22p. (J). pap. 4.95 (978-1-930332-33-1(5)) Lectorum Pubns., Inc.

—I Like Growing Up (Me Gusta Ser Mayor) 2002. (ENG & SPA., Illus.). 22p. (J). 4.95 (978-1-930332-31-7(9)) Lectorum Pubns., Inc.

Schafer, Milton. I'm Big! Lew-Vriethoff, Joanne, illus. 2006. (J). (***978-1-4156-8150-3(3)*** , Dial) Penguin Group (USA) Inc.

Schlessinger, Laura. Dr Laura Schlessinger's Growing up Is Hard. 2003. (gr. k-3). lib. bdg. 14.15 (978-0-613-67188-0(0)) Tandem Library Bks.

—Growing up Is Hard. McFeeley, Daniel, illus. 2003. 40p. (J). (ps-2). pap. 5.99 (978-0-06-052623-8(8) , Harper Trophy) HarperCollins Pubs.

Schlessinger, Laura & McFeeley, Daniel. Growing up Is Hard. 2001. (Illus.). 40p. (J). (ps-2). 15.89 (978-0-06-029201-0(6)) HarperCollins Pubs.

Schultz, Agnes Szenozicska. The Little Tree. 2007. 32p. (J). 14.00 (***978-0-8059-7211-5(0)***) Dorrance Publishing Co., Inc.

Shavick, Andrea. You'll Grow Soon, Alex. Ayto, Russell, illus. 2000. 32p. (J). (ps-3). 15.95 (978-0-8027-8736-1(3)) Walker & Co.

Slater, Dashka & Chien, Catia. The Sea Serpent & Me. Slater, Dashka & Chien, Catia, illus. 2008. 40p. (J). (gr. 3-5). 17.00 (***978-0-618-72394-2(3)***) Houghton Mifflin Co.

Steed, Alice. I Am Three - I Am Four. Trapani, Iza, illus. 2000. 16p. (J). (ps-k). bds. 5.95 (978-1-58089-068-7(7)) Charlesbridge Publishing, Inc.

Stewart, Amber. I'm Big Enough. Marlow, Layn, illus. 2007. 32p. (J). 12.99 (978-0-439-90666-1(0) , Orchard Bks.) Scholastic, Inc.

Stewart, Pauline & Maland, Nick. Sunshine Showers & Four O'Clock Flowers. 2000. (Illus.). 32p. (J). 19.99 (978-0-370-32459-3(5) , Vintage) Random Hse. GBR. *Dist:* Trafalgar Square Publishing.

Stinson, Kathy. Big or Little? Lewis, Robin Baird, illus. 2003. (Toddler Ser.). 32p. (J). (ps-1). pap. 5.95 (978-0-920236-32-1(4)) Annick Pr., Ltd. CAN. *Dist:* Firefly Bks., Ltd.

—Parfois Grand, Parfoit Petit. Homel, David, tr. from ENG. Lewis, Robin Baird, illus. 2006. (FRE.). 23p. (J). (ps-2). reprint ed. pap. 5.00 (978-1-4223-5663-0(9)) DIANE Publishing Co.

Sudduth, Brent H. Buster. Spengler, Kenneth J., illus. (J). 2003. 32p. 15.95 (978-1-59034-478-1(2)); 2002. pap. (978-1-59034-477-4(4)) Mondo Publishing.

Thermes, Jennifer. Sam Bennett's New Shoes. 2006. (Illus.). (J). 15.95 (978-1-57505-822-1(7) , Carolrhoda Bks.) Lerner Publishing Group.

Tildes, Phyllis L. Billy's Big-Boy Bed. 2002. (Illus.). (J). (ps). 15.95 (978-1-57091-475-1(3)) Charlesbridge Publishing, Inc.

—Billy's Big-Boy Bed. 2003. (gr. k-3). lib. bdg. 15.25 (978-0-613-70803-6(2)) Tandem Library Bks.

Tunnell, Michael O. The Wishing Moon. 2004. 272p. (J). (gr. 7). 17.99 (978-0-525-47193-6(6) , Dutton Juvenile) Penguin Group (USA) Inc.

van Genechten, Guido. Kangaroo Christine. van Genechten, Guido, illus. 2006. (Illus.). 32p. (J). 6.95 (978-1-58925-396-4(5) , tiger tales) ME Media LLC.

Waring, Geoff. Oscar & the Frog: A Book about Growing. Waring, Geoff, illus. 2007. (Illus.). 32p. (J). (ps). 11.99 (***978-0-7636-3558-9(8)***) Candlewick Pr.

Williamson, Stafford. Puppyfish. 2005. 48p. (J). pap. 18.49 (978-1-4116-3836-5(0)) Lulu.com.

Wolf, Erica. I Love You Just the Same. Wolf, Erica, illus. rev. ed. 2003. (Illus.). 32p. (J). 16.95 (978-0-8050-7128-3(8) , Holt, Henry & Co. Bks. For Young Readers) Holt, Henry & Co.

Yolen, Jane. Baby Bear's Big Dreams. Sweet, Melissa, illus. 2007. 40p. (J). (ps-k). 16.00 (978-0-15-205291-1(7)) Harcourt Trade Pubs.

GROWTH (PLANTS)

Blackaby, Susan. Plant Packages: A Book about Seeds. DeLage, Charlene, illus. 2004. (Growing Things Ser.). 24p. (C). (gr. k-2). 22.60 (978-1-4048-0108-0(1)) Picture Window Bks.

Branigan, Carrie & Dunne, Richard. How Plants Grow. 2005. (World of Plants Ser.). (Illus.). 30p. (J). (gr. 2-5). lib. bdg. 27.10 (978-1-58340-611-3(5)) Smart Apple Media.

Brynie, Faith Hickman. What Helps Plants Grow? The Nitrogen Cycle Case. 2003. (J). pap. (978-1-58417-156-0(1)) Lake Street Pubs.

Cash, Megan Montague. What Makes the Seasons? Cash, Megan Montague, illus. 2003. (Illus.). 40p. (J). (ps-3). 15.99 (978-0-670-03598-4(X) , Viking Juvenile) Penguin Group (USA) Inc.

Edwards, Nicola. Flowers. 2007. (J). lib. bdg. (978-1-4042-3699-8(6)) Rosen Publishing Group, Inc., The.

Frank, Marjorie Slavick, et al. Science Instant Readers Bk. 1: How Does a Plant Grow? 1999. (Harcourt Science Ser.). (gr. 2 up). pap. 15.50 (978-0-15-316211-4(2)) Harcourt Schl. Pubs.

Growing a Plant: a Journal: Individual Title Six-Packs. (Discovery World Ser.). 16p. (gr. 1-2). 28.00 (978-0-7635-8462-7(2)) Rigby Education.

Hammersmith, Craig. Watch It Grow. 2002. (Spyglass Books). (Illus.). 24p. (J). (gr. 1 up). lib. bdg. 18.60 (978-0-7565-0246-1(2)) Compass Point Bks.

Harcourt School Publishers Staff. How Does a Plant Grow: Science Reader. 1999. (SPA., Illus.). (J). (gr. 2). pap. 3.70 (978-0-15-316116-2(7)) Harcourt Schl. Pubs.

Helbrough, Emma. How Flowers Grow (Level 1) - Internet Referenced. 2007. (Beginners Nature Ser.). 32p. (J). 4.99 (***978-0-7945-1340-5(9)*** , Usborne) EDC Publishing.

Hopkins, William. Plant Development. 2006. (Green World Ser.). (Illus.). 160p. (J). (gr. 6-12). 37.50 (978-0-7910-8562-2(7) , Chelsea Hse.) Facts On File, Inc.

Kravetz, Jonathan. Learning about Plant Growth with Graphic Organizers. 2007. (Graphic Organizers in Science Ser.). (Illus.). 24p. (J). (978-1-4042-2398-1(3)); pap. (978-1-4042-2208-3(1)) Rosen Publishing Group, Inc., The. (PowerKids Pr.).

Leigh, Autumn. It Grows in Spring: Learning the GR Sound. 2002. (PowerPhonics Ser.). (Illus.) (J). 23p. lib. bdg. (978-0-8239-8286-8(6)); 24p. (gr. 1). lib. bdg. 18.50 (978-0-8239-5941-9(4)) Rosen Publishing Group, Inc., The. (PowerKids Pr.).

Lilly, Melinda. Make It Grow. Thompson, Scott M., illus. 2003. (Rourke Discovery Library). 24p. (J). 20.64 (978-1-58952-637-2(6)) Rourke Publishing, LLC.

Llewellyn, Claire. How Plants Grow. 2006. (Illus.). 24p. (J). (978-1-59771-021-3(0)) Sea-To-Sea Pubns.

Mattern, Joanne. How Peas Grows. 2006. (ENG & SPA., Illus.). 24p. (J). 19.33 (978-0-8368-6463-2(8)) Stevens, Gareth Inc.

Morris, Ting & Morris, Neil. Growing Things. Levy, Ruth, illus. 2006. (J). (978-1-59771-026-8(1)) Sea-To-Sea Pubns.

Nadeau, Isaac. Plant Development & Growth. 2006. (Life Science Library). (Illus.). 24p. (J). 21.25 (978-1-4042-2820-7(9) , PowerKids Pr.) Rosen Publishing Group, Inc., The.

Orme, Helen. Why Do Plants Grow in Spring? 2003. (What? Where? Why? Ser.). (Illus.). 24p. (J). (gr. 1 up). lib. bdg. 20.67 (978-0-8368-3790-2(8)) Stevens, Gareth Inc.

Pipe, Jim. Growing Plants. 2007. (J). (***978-1-59604-140-0(4)***) Stargazer Bks.

Rigby Education Staff. Discovery World Org Growing Plant. (Discovery World Ser.). (Illus.). 12p. (gr. 1-2). 27.00 (978-0-7635-2701-3(7)) Rigby Education.

Royston, Angela. Life Cycle of a... Series: An In-Depth Look at Some Familiar Plants & Animals, 4 bks., Set 3. 2000. (Illus.). 32p. (J). (gr. k-2). lib. bdg. 85.44 (978-1-57572-407-2(3)) Heinemann Library.

Science & Technology for Children BOOKS: Plant Growth & Development Set. 2007. (J). 127.60 (***978-1-933008-43-1(1)***) National Science Resources Ctr.

Scrace, Carolyn & Theophylactou, Diana. Growing Things. Scrace, Carolyn, illus. 2002. (Cycles of Life Ser.). (Illus.). 32p. (J). (gr. k-3). pap. 6.95 (978-0-531-14841-9(6) , Watts, Franklin) Scholastic Library Publishing.

Spilsbury, Louise & Spilsbury, Richard. How Do Plants Grow? 2005. (World of Plants Ser.). (Illus.). 32p. (J). pap. (978-1-4034-7365-3(X)) Heinemann.

—Plant Growth. 2003. (Life of Plants Ser.). (Illus.). 48p. (J). (gr. 3-5). lib. bdg. 25.64 (978-1-4034-0294-3(9)); pap. 8.50 (978-1-4034-0502-9(6)) Heinemann Library.

Spilsbury, Richard & Spilsbury, Louise. How Do Plants Grow? 2005. (World of Plants Ser.). (Illus.). 32p. (J). (gr. k-3). lib. bdg. 25.36 (978-1-4034-7360-8(9)) Heinemann.

Stewart, David. How a Seed Grows into a Sunflower. (Amaze Ser.). 32p. (J). 2008. pap. 8.95 (***978-0-531-20453-5(7));*** 2007. spiral bd. 26.00 (***978-0-531-20442-9(1)***) Scholastic Library Publishing. (Children's Pr.).

Stewart, Melissa. How Do Plants Grow? 2006. (Tell Me Why, Tell Me How Ser.). (Illus.). 32p. (J). lib. bdg. 28.50 (978-0-7614-2111-5(4) , Benchmark Bks.) Cavendish, Marshall Corp.

Top That Publishing Staff, ed. Make it Grow. 2004. (Fun Kits Ser.). (Illus.). 48p. (J). (978-1-84510-132-9(4)) Top That! Publishing PLC.

GUADALCANAL, BATTLE OF, SOLOMON ISLANDS, 1942-1943

Hama, Larry. The Battle of Guadalcanal: Land & Sea Warfare in the South Pacific. 2007. (Graphic Battles of World War II Ser.). (Illus.). 48p. (J). (gr. 5-8). lib. bdg. 29.25 (***978-1-4042-0784-4(8)); (978-1-4042-7427-3(8));*** pap. (***978-1-4042-7426-6(X)***) Rosen Publishing Group, Inc., The.

Hama, Larry. Fight to the Death: Battle of Guadalcanal. Elson, Richard & Williams, Anthony, illus. 2007. (Graphic History Ser.). 48p. (J). (gr. 3). pap. 9.95 (978-1-84603-060-4(9)) Osprey Publishing, Ltd. GBR. *Dist:* Random Hse., Inc.

GUAM

Cunningham, Lawrence J. & Beatty, Janice J. Guam: A Natural History. 2001. (Illus.). 208p. (gr. 3-4). (J). pap. 73.27 (978-1-57306-067-7(4)); (YA). pap. 66.60 (978-1-57306-046-2(1)) Bess Pr., Inc.

—A History of Guam. 2001. (Illus.). 344p. (YA). (gr. 4 up). pap. 66.60 (978-1-57306-047-9(X)) Bess Pr., Inc.

Cunningham, Lawrence J., et al. A History of Guam. 2001. (Illus.). 344p. (J). (gr. 4-5). 73.27 (978-1-57306-068-4(2)) Bess Pr., Inc.

GUAM—FICTION

Holt, Kimberly Willis. Keeper of the Night. rev. ed. 2003. (Illus.). 180p. (YA). (gr. 5-8). 16.95 (978-0-8050-6361-5(7) , Holt, Henry & Co. Bks. For Young Readers) Holt, Henry & Co.

—Keeper of the Night. 2005. 336p. (YA). (gr. 7). reprint ed. mass mkt. 6.50 (978-0-553-49441-9(4) , Laurel Leaf) Random Hse. Children's Bks.

—Keeper of the Night. 2005. 309p. (YA). (gr. 7-12). lib. bdg. 13.55 (978-0-606-33249-1(9)) Tandem Library Bks.

—Keeper of the Night. l.t. ed. 2004. 336p. (J). 23.95 (978-0-7862-6431-5(4)) Thorndike Pr.

GUATEMALA

Aboff, Marcie. Guatemala ABCs: A Book about the People & Places of Guatemala. Trover, Zachary, illus. 2006. (Country ABCs Ser.). 32p. (J). (gr. k-5). 23.93 (978-1-4048-1570-4(8)) Picture Window Bks.

Anonimo. Popol Vuh.Tr. of Book of the common People. (SPA.). 232p. 8.50 (978-958-30-0129-1(5)) Panamericana Editorial COL. *Dist:* AIMS International Bks., Inc.

Dendinger, Roger. Guatemala. 2003. (Modern World Nations Ser.). (Illus.). 150p. (gr. 6-12). 30.00 (978-0-7910-7477-0(3) , Chelsea Hse.) Facts On File, Inc.

Englar, Mary. Guatemala: A Question & Answer Book. 2006. (Fact Finders Ser.). (Illus.). 32p. (J). (978-0-7368-4356-0(6) , Fact Finders) Capstone Pr., Inc.

Guatamala. (Countries of the World Ser.). 24p. (J). 6.95 (978-0-7368-8373-3(8)) Capstone Pr., Inc.

Haynes, Tricia. Guatemala. 1999. (Major World Nations Ser.). (Illus.). 144p. (YA). (gr. 4-7). 29.95 (978-0-7910-4974-7(4) , Chelsea Hse.) Facts On File, Inc.

Markel, Rita J. Guatemala in Pictures. 2nd rev. expurg. ed. 2004. (Visual Geography Ser.). (Illus.). 80p. (J). (gr. 5-12). 27.93 (978-0-8225-1998-0(4)) Lerner Publishing Group.

Morrison, Marion. Guatemala. 2005. (Enchantment of the World, Second Ser.: Vol. 2). (Illus.). 144p. (YA). (gr. 5-9). 36.00 (978-0-516-23674-2(1) , Children's Pr.) Scholastic Library Publishing.

Schemenauer, Elma. Welcome to Japan. 2007. (Welcome to the World Ser.). 32p. (J). (gr. 1-5). 27.07 (***978-1-59296-913-5(5)***) Child's World, Inc.

Sheehan, Sean. Guatemala. 1998. (Cultures of the World Ser.). (Illus.). 128p. (gr. 5-12). lib. bdg. 37.07 (978-0-7614-0812-3(6) , Benchmark Bks.) Cavendish, Marshall Corp.

Shields, Charles J. Guatemala. 2002. (Let's Discover Central America Ser.). (Illus.). 63p. (YA). (gr. 5 up). lib. bdg. (978-1-59084-095-5(X)) Mason Crest Pubs.

Silverstone, Michael. Rigoberta Menchu: Defending Human Rights in Guatemala. 1998. (Women Changing the World Ser.). (Illus.). 112p. (gr. 4-7). 19.95 (978-1-55861-198-6(3)) Feminist Pr. at The City Univ. of New York.

Solbiati, Romano. Mayan Tikal. Ripamonti, Aldo, illus. 2001. (Journey to the Past Ser.). 56p. (J). (gr. 6-8). lib. bdg. 27.12 (978-0-7398-1955-5(0)) Raintree.

GUATEMALA—FICTION

Bogunya, Angels. El Maiz Amargo. 2004. (SPA.). 144p. (J). (978-84-263-5237-8(5)) Vives, Luis Editorial (Edelvives) ESP. *Dist:* Lectorum Pubns., Inc.

Cameron, Ann. Colibri. 2003. 240p. (J). (gr. 5-8). 17.00 (978-0-374-31519-1(1) , 53501559, Farrar, Straus & Giroux (BYR)) Farrar, Straus & Giroux.

—Colibri. 2005. 256p. (YA). (gr. 7). pap. 5.99 (978-0-440-42052-1(0) , Laurel Leaf) Random Hse. Children's Bks.

—Colibri. Rioja, Alberto Jimenez, tr. from ENG. 2005. (SPA., Illus.). 256p. (J). (gr. 6-9). pap. 14.99 (978-0-439-68314-2(9) , Scholastic en Espanol) Scholastic, Inc.

—El Lugar Mas Bonito del Mundo. 2000. (SPA., Illus.). 72p. (J). (ps-3). 15.95 (978-84-204-4449-9(9)) Aguilar, S. A. de Ediciones-Grupo Santillana ESP. *Dist:* Santillana USA Publishing Co., Inc.

—El Lugar Mas Bonito del Mundo. Alonso, Juan Ramon, illus. 2003. (SPA.). 70p. (J). (gr. 3-5). pap. 10.95 (978-968-19-0402-9(8)) Santillana USA Publishing Co., Inc.

Carling, Amelia Lau. Mama & Papa Have a Store. 1998. (Illus.). 32p. (J). (ps-3). 16.99 (978-0-8037-2044-2(0) , Dial) Penguin Group (USA) Inc.

—La Tienda de Mama y Papa. Carling, Amelia Lau, illus. 2003. (Illus.). 32p. (J). (ps-3). (SPA & ENG.). 16.95 (978-0-88899-538-4(5) , Libros Tigrillo); (ENG & SPA., pap. 6.95 (978-0-88899-547-6(4)) Groundwood Bks. CAN. *Dist:* Perseus Distribution.

Ichikawa, Satomi. My Pig Amarillo: A Tale from Guatemala. Ichikawa, Satomi, illus. 2003. (Illus.). 32p. (J). (ps-3). 16.99 (978-0-399-23768-3(2) , Philomel) Penguin Group (USA) Inc.

Mikaelsen, Ben. Red Midnight. 2003. 224p. (J). (gr. 5 up). pap. 5.99 (978-0-380-80561-7(8)) HarperCollins Pubs.

—Red Midnight. 2003. (gr. 5-8). lib. bdg. 14.15 (978-0-613-57776-2(0)) Tandem Library Bks.

—Tree Girl. 2005. 240p. (J). pap. 7.99 (978-0-06-009006-7(5) , HarperTeen) HarperCollins Pubs.

Newman, Leslea. Felicia's Favorite Story. Romo, Adriana, illus. 2003. 24p. (J). pap. 9.95 (978-0-9674468-5-1(6)) Two Lives Publishing.

GUERRILLA WARFARE

see also World War, 1939-1945—Underground Movements

Savage, Douglas J. Rangers, Jayhawkers, & Bushwackers in the Civil War. 2000. (Untold History of the Civil War Ser.). (Illus.). 64p. (J). (gr. 3 up). 25.00 (978-0-7910-5430-7(6) , Chelsea Hse.) Facts On File, Inc.

GUEVARA, ERNESTO, 1928-1967

Downing, David. Che Guevara. 2003. (Leading Lives Ser.). (Illus.). 64p. (J). pap. 8.95 (978-1-4034-3493-7(X)) Heinemann Library.

—Ernesto "Che" Guevara. 2003. (Leading Lives Ser.). (Illus.). 64p. (J). lib. bdg. 28.50 (978-1-4034-0832-7(7)) Heinemann Library.

Miller, Calvin Craig. Che Guevara: In Search of Revolution. 2006. (World Leaders Ser.). (Illus.). 160p. (J). (gr. 6 up). lib. bdg. 26.95 (978-1-931798-93-8(1)) Reynolds, Morgan Inc.

Uschan, Michael B. Che Guevara, Firebrand Revolutionary. 2006. (Twentieth Century's Most Influential Hispanics Ser.). (Illus.). 112p. (J). (gr. 7-10). 32.45 (978-1-59018-970-2(1) , Lucent Bks.) Thomson Gale.

GUIDANCE

see Counseling; Educational Counseling; Vocational Guidance

GUIDE DOGS

Brussee, Warren. LAOCH (Lay-ock) the Guide Dog Puppy. 2006. 24p. pap. 11.95 (***978-1-60145-102-6(4)***) Booklocker.com, Inc.

Ereth, Mary. Meet CJ, the Guide Dog Puppy. 1999. 39p. (J). (978-0-9672071-0-0(X)) Southeastern Guide Dogs, Inc.

George, Linda & George, Charles. Guide Dogs. 1998. (Riverfront Dogs at Work Ser.). 48p. (J). lib. bdg. 19.00 (978-0-531-11555-8(0) , Watts, Franklin) Scholastic Library Publishing.

Hall, Becky. Morris & Buddy: The Story of the First Seeing Eye Dog. Doris, Ettlinger, illus. 2007. 40p. (J). 15.95 (***978-0-8075-5284-1(4)***) Whitman, Albert & Co.

Harcourt School Publishers Staff. Friends in Need: Take-Home Book. 2001. (Collections Ser.). (Illus.). (J). pap. 1.90 (978-0-15-319521-1(5)) Harcourt Schl. Pubs.

E F G

—Friends in Need Below Level. 3rd ed. 2002. (Trophies Reading Program Ser.). (Illus.). pap. 5.10 (978-0-15-323319-7(2)) Harcourt Schl. Pubs.

Kent, Deborah. Animal Helpers for the Disabled. 2003. (Watts Library). (Illus.). 64p. (J). 25.50 (978-0-531-12017-0(1) , Watts, Franklin) Scholastic Library Publishing.

Kovatch, Sarah. Special Helpers. 2005. (Illus.). 16p. (J). (978-0-7367-2854-6(6)) Zaner-Bloser, Inc.

Lawrenson, Diana. Guide Dogs: From Puppies to Partners. 2002. (Illus.). 32p. (J). (gr. 4-6). pap. 7.95 (978-1-86508-246-2(5)) Allen & Unwin AUS. *Dist:* Independent Pubs. Group.

LeTourneau, Anthony Alex, illus. Hanni & Beth: Safe & Sound. 2007. (J). (*978-0-9792918-0-7(1)) Blue Marlin Pubns.

McDaniel, Melissa. Guide Dogs. 2005. (Dog Heroes Ser.). (Illus.). 32p. (J). lib. bdg. 25.27 (978-1-59716-013-1(X)) Bearport Publishing Co., Inc.

McGinty, Alice B. Guide Dogs: Seeing for People Who Can't. 1999. (Dogs Helping People Ser.). 24p. (J). (gr. k-4). lib. bdg. 18.75 (978-0-8239-5215-1(0) , PowerKids Pr.) Rosen Publishing Group, Inc., The.

Miller, Marie-Therese. Helping Dogs. 2007. (Dog Tales: True Stories about Amazing Dogs Ser.). (Illus.). 80p. (J). 28.00 (978-0-7910-9035-0(3) , Chelsea Hse.) Facts On File, Inc.

Moore, Eva. Buddy, the First Seeing Eye Dog. Bolognese, Don, illus. 2004. 48p. (J). lib. bdg. 15.00 (978-1-59054-536-2(2)) Fitzgerald Bks.

Patent, Dorothy Hinshaw. Right Dog for the Job: Ira's Path from Service Dog to Guide Dog. 2004. (Illus.). 32p. (J). 17.85 (978-0-8027-8915-0(3)); 16.95 (978-0-8027-8914-3(5)) Walker & Co.

Presnall, Judith Janda. Canine Companions. 2003. (Animals with Jobs Ser.). (Illus.). 48p. (J). 26.20 (978-0-7377-2050-1(6) , Greenhaven Pr., Inc.) Thomson Gale.

GUIDE DOGS—FICTION

Aardvark, E. Gartner Jake. 2005. Orig. Title: Jake, the Gardener. (DAN.). 18.95 (978-0-9766859-6-8(5)) Macaronic Pr.

—Giacco il Giardiniere. 2005. Orig. Title: Jake, the Gardener. (ITA.). 18.95 (978-0-9766859-3-7(0)) Macaronic Pr.

—Jakke, den Traedgaardaren. 2005. (SWE.). 18.95 (978-0-9766859-7-5(3)) Macaronic Pr.

Aardvark, E. S. Jacques, le Jardinier: Chien D'Aveugle Trouve des Tresors. Zimmer, Dirk, illus. 2006. Orig. Title: Jake, the Gardener. (FRE.). 32p. 14.95 (978-0-9766859-1-3(4)) Macaronic Pr.

—Jake, der Gaertner. Zimmer, Dirk, illus. 2006. Orig. Title: Jake, the Gardener. (GER.). 32p. 14.95 (978-0-9766859-2-0(2)) Macaronic Pr.

—Jake, the Gardener: Guide Dog Digs Treasure. Zimmer, Dirk, illus. 2006. (Many Tongue Tales Ser.). Orig. Title: Jake, the Gardener. 14.95 (978-0-9766859-0-6(6)) Macaronic Pr.

—Jakke Puutarhurina. 2005. (FIN.). 18.95 (978-0-9766859-8-2(1)) Macaronic Pr.

—Joao o Jardineiro. 2005. (POR.). 18.95 (978-0-9766859-5-1(7)) Macaronic Pr.

—Juan el Jardinero: El Perro Guia Excavador del Tesoro. 2005. (SPA.). 32p. 18.85 (978-0-9766859-4-4(9)) Macaronic Pr.

Aardvark, Esperanza. Jaap de Tuinman. Zimmer, Dirk, illus. 2006. (DUT.). 14.95 (978-0-9766859-9-9(X)) Macaronic Pr.

Anderson, Laurie Halse. Teacher's Pet. 2003. (Wild at Heart Ser.). (Illus.). 132p. (J). (gr. 4 up). lib. bdg. 23.33 (978-0-8368-3261-7(2)) Stevens, Gareth Inc.

—Teacher's Pet. 2001. (American Girl Wild at Heart Ser.: Bk. 7). (Illus.). (YA). (978-0-606-21529-9(8)) Tandem Library Bks.

Bauer Mueller, Pamela. Hello, Goodbye, I Love You: The Story of Aloha, a Guide Dog for the Blind. 2003. 160p. (J). pap. 8.99 (*978-0-9685097-3-9(8)) Pinata Publishing.

Lewis, Beverly. The Midnight Mystery. 2007. (Cul-de-Sac Kids Ser.: Vol. 24). (Illus.). 80p. (J). (gr. 2-5). pap. 3.99 (978-0-7642-2129-3(9)) Bethany Hse. Pubs.

Little, Jean. Rescue Pup. 2004. (Orca Young Readers Ser.). (Illus.). 144p. (J). (gr. 3-6). pap. 4.99 (978-1-55143-299-1(4)) Orca Bk. Pubs. USA.

GUIDE POSTS

see Signs and Signboards

GUIDED MISSILES

Byers, Ann. American Star Wars Program. 2004. (Library of Weapons of Mass Destruction). (Illus.). 64p. (J). lib. bdg. 26.50 (978-1-4042-0287-0(0)) Rosen Publishing Group, Inc., The.

Green, Michael & Green, Gladys. Remotely Piloted Aircraft: The Predators. 2004. (War Machines Ser.). (Illus.). 32p. (J). 16.95 (978-0-7368-2417-0(0)) Capstone Pr., Inc.

Pitt, Matthew. The Tomahawk Cruise Missile. 2000. (High Interest Bks.). (Illus.). 48p. (YA). (gr. 7-12). pap. 6.95 (978-0-516-23543-1(5) , Children's Pr.) Scholastic Library Publishing.

White Steve. Modern Bombs. 2006. (High-Tech Military Weapons Ser.). (Illus.). 48p. (J). (978-0-531-12093-4(7) , Children's Pr.) Scholastic Library Publishing.

White, Steve. Modern Bombs. 2007. (Illus.). 48p. (J). pap. (978-0-531-18709-8(8)) Children's Pr., Ltd.

GUILDS

see also Labor and Laboring Classes; Labor Unions

Jovinelly, Joann. The Crafts & Culture of a Medieval Guild. 2006. (Illus.). 48p. (J). lib. bdg. (978-1-4042-0757-8(0)) Rosen Publishing Group, Inc., The.

GUILDS—FICTION

Hardinge, Frances. Fly by Night. 2008. 512p. (J). pap. 7.99 (*978-0-06-087630-2(1) , Harper Trophy) HarperCollins Pubs.

Lamprey, L. Masters of the Guild. l.t. ed. 2006. 168p. pap. 14.99 (978-1-4264-2076-4(5)) BiblioBazaar.

GUINEA PIGS

Alderton, David. Guinea Pig. 2003. (Looking after My Pet Ser.). (Illus.). 24p. (gr. k-4). 7.99 (978-0-7548-1156-5(5)) Anness Publishing GBR. *Dist:* National Bk. Network.

Barnes, Julia. Pet Guinea Pigs. 2006. (Pet Pals Ser.). (Illus.). 32p. (J). (gr. 2-5). lib. bdg. 23.93 (978-0-8368-6779-4(3)) Stevens, Gareth Inc.

Barnes, Julia, et al. 101 Facts about Guinea Pigs. 2001. (One Hundred One Facts about Pets Ser.). (Illus.). 32p. (J). (gr. 3 up). lib. bdg. 23.33 (978-0-8368-2887-0(9)) Stevens, Gareth Inc.

Behrend, Katrin. The Guinea Pig. 1999. (Family Pet Ser.). (Illus.). 180p. pap. 10.99 (978-0-7641-1448-9(4)) Barron's Educational Series, Inc.

Binns, Tristan Boyer. Guinea Pigs. 2006. (Keeping Pets Ser.). (Illus.). 48p. (J). (978-1-4034-7701-9(9)) Heinemann Library.

Birmelin, Immanuel & Linke-Grun, Gabriele. My Guinea Pig & Me. Holzner, Renate, illus. Wegler, Monika, photos by. 2001. (For the Love of Animals Ser.). 64p. (J). pap. 6.99 (978-0-7641-1806-7(4)) Barron's Educational Series, Inc.

Blackaby, Susan. A Guinea Pig for You: Caring for Your Guinea Pig. DeLage, Charlene, illus. 2004. (Pet Care Ser.). 24p. (C). (gr. k-3). 22.60 (978-1-4048-0119-6(7)) Picture Window Bks.

Bozzo, Linda. My First Guinea Pig & Other Small Pets. 2007. (My First Pet Library from the American Humane Association Ser.). (Illus.). 32p. (J). (gr. 1-2). lib. bdg. 22.60 (978-0-7660-2752-7(X) , Enslow Elementary) Enslow Pubs., Inc.

Coppendale, Jean. Guinea Pig. 2004. (QEB Animal Lives Ser.). (Illus.). 32p. (J). lib. bdg. 18.95 (978-1-59566-052-7(6)) QEB Publishing Inc.

Curran, Wanda L. Your Guinea Pig: A Kid's Guide to Raising & Showing. 2003. (Illus.). 151p. (J). (gr. 4-7). pap. 14.95 (978-0-88266-889-5(7) , 66889) Storey Publishing, LLC.

Evans, Mark. Guinea Pigs. 2001. (Illus.). (978-0-606-22084-2(4)) Tandem Library Bks.

Foran, Jill. Caring for Your Guinea Pig. 2004. (Caring for Your Pet Ser.). (J). pap. 7.95 (978-1-59036-151-1(2)); (Illus.). 32p. lib. bdg. 18.20 (978-1-59036-116-0(4)) Weigl Pubs., Inc.

Ganeri, Anita. Guinea Pig. 2003. (Heinemann First Library). (Illus.). 32p. (J). pap. (978-1-4034-4272-7(X)) Heinemann Library.

—Guinea Pig. 2003. (gr. k-3). lib. bdg. 15.25 (978-0-613-87670-4(9)) Tandem Library Bks.

—A Pet's Life: Guinea Pigs. 2003. (Heinemann First Library). (Illus.). 32p. (J). lib. bdg. 22.79 (978-1-4034-3996-3(6)) Heinemann Library.

A Guinea Pig for You. (Pet Care Ser.). 24p. (J). 7.95 (978-1-4048-0394-7(7)) Picture Window Bks.

Guinea Pigs. 2002. (Illus.). 21.95 (978-1-57572-476-8(6)) Heinemann Library.

Guinea Pigs, 6 vols. (gr. k-2). 28.95 (978-0-7368-9240-7(0)) Red Brick Learning.

Head, Honor. Guinea Pig. Burton, Jane, photos by. 2000. (My Pet Ser.). (Illus.). 32p. (J). (gr. 3-5). lib. bdg. 25.69 (978-0-7398-2888-5(6)) Raintree.

—Guinea Pig. 2000. (My Pet Ser.). (Illus.). 32p. (J). (gr. 3-5). pap. 8.95 (978-0-7398-3009-3(0)) Steck-Vaughn.

Hibbert, Clare. Life of a Guinea Pig. 2004. (Raintree Perspectives Ser.). (Illus.). 32p. (J). lib. bdg. 25.70 (978-1-4109-0538-3(1)) Raintree.

—The Life of a Guinea Pig. 2004. (Illus.). pap. 7.50 (978-1-4109-0926-8(3)); Pack. pap. 40.50 (978-1-4109-0933-6(6)) Raintree.

Holub, Joan. Why Do Rabbits Hop? A & Other Questions about Rabbits, Guinea Pigs, Hamsters. 2003. (gr. k-3). lib. bdg. 11.80 (978-0-613-61671-3(5)) Tandem Library Bks.

—Why Do Rabbits Hop? And Other Questions about Rabbits, Guinea Pigs, Hamsters & Gerbils. DiVito, Anna, illus. 2003. (Easy-to-Read Ser.). 48p. (J). (gr. 1-3). pap. 3.99 (978-0-14-230120-3(5) , Puffin) Penguin Group (USA) Inc.

Howell, Laura. Guinea Pigs. 2005. 32p. (J). (gr. 1 up). pap. 5.95 (978-0-7945-1115-9(5) , Usborne) EDC Publishing.

Hughes, Sarah. My Guinea Pig. 2001. (My Pets Ser.). (Illus.). 24p. (J). (ps-2). 17.00 (978-0-516-23186-0(3) , Children's Pr.) Scholastic Library Publishing.

—My Guinea Pig. 2001. (gr. k-3). lib. bdg. 12.95 (978-0-613-58866-9(5)) Tandem Library Bks.

Kalman, Bobbie & MacAulay, Kelley. Los Cobayos. 2005. (SPA., Illus.). 32p. (J). (978-0-7787-8457-9(6)) Crabtree Publishing Co.

—Los Cobayos: Guinea Pigs. 2006. (SPA., Illus.). 32p. pap. (978-0-7787-8479-1(7)) Crabtree Publishing Co.

—Guinea Pigs. Crabtree, Marc, illus. Crabtree, Marc, photos by. 2004. (Pet Care Ser.). 32p. (J). pap. (978-0-7787-1787-4(9)); (978-0-7787-1755-3(0)) Crabtree Publishing Co.

King-Smith, Dick. I Love Guinea Pigs. Jeram, Anita, illus. 2nd ed. 2001. (Read & Wonder Ser.). 32p. (J). (ps-3). pap. 6.99 (978-0-7636-1435-5(1)) Candlewick Pr.

—I Love Guinea Pigs. 2001. (ps-2). lib. bdg. 14.15 (978-0-613-44218-3(0)) Tandem Library Bks.

Knutson, Barbara. Love & Roast Chicken: A Trickster Tale from the Andes Mountains. 2004. (Carolrhoda Picture Books Ser.). (Illus.). 40p. (J). (ps-3). 16.95 (978-1-57505-657-9(7)) Lerner Publishing Group.

Lewis, David, contrib. by. Guinea Pigs. 1999. (Junior Pet Care Ser.). (Illus.). 48p. (gr. 4-7). 18.65 (978-0-7910-4908-2(6) , Chelsea Hse.) Facts On File, Inc.

Loves, June. Guinea Pigs & Rabbits. 2003. (Pets Ser.). (Illus.). 32p. (gr. 2-4). 23.00 (978-0-7910-7552-4(4) , Chelsea Hse.) Facts On File, Inc.

Macken, JoAnn Early. Guinea Pigs. 2003. (Let's Read about Pets Ser.). (Illus.). 24p. (J). (ps up). lib. bdg. 19.33 (978-0-8368-3798-8(3)); pap. 7.93 (978-0-8368-3845-9(9)) Stevens, Gareth Inc. (Weekly Reader Early Learning Library).

Miller, M. Guinea Pigs. 2002. (Pets Ser.). (Illus.). 24p. (J). (gr. k-3). pap. 6.50 (978-1-57572-480-5(4) , 90469) Heinemann Library.

Nelson, Robin. Pet Guinea Pig. (First Step Nonfiction). (J). (gr. k-2). 2003. (Illus.). 24p. lib. bdg. 18.60 (978-0-8225-1268-4(8)); 2002. pap. 3.95 (978-0-8225-1299-8(8)) Lerner Publishing Group.

Page, Gill. Getting to Know Your Guinea Pig. 48p. (J). pap. 7.95 (978-0-7938-1203-5(8)) TFH Pubns., Inc.

Petty, Kate. Guinea Pig. 2005. (Illus.). 24p. (J). (gr. 2-5). lib. bdg. 22.80 (978-1-59604-029-8(7)) Stargazer Bks.

Pickett, Robert & Pickett, Justine, illus. Guinea Pig. Pickett, Robert & Pickett, Justine, photos by. 2004. 32p. (J). lib. bdg. (978-1-58340-434-8(1)) Smart Apple Media.

Randolph, Joanne. Guinea Pigs. 2007. (Classroom Pets Ser.). (Illus.). 24p. (J). (gr. k-5). lib. bdg. 21.25 (978-1-4042-3676-9(7) , PowerKids Pr.) Rosen Publishing Group, Inc., The.

Rayner, Matthew. Guinea Pig. 2007. (I Am Your Pet Ser.). 32p. (J). (gr. 2-4). lib. bdg. 23.93 (*978-0-8368-8385-5(3)) Stevens, Gareth Inc.

Ross, Veronica. Guinea Pig. 2002. (My First Ser.). (Illus.). 32p. (J). lib. bdg. 24.25 (978-1-930643-74-1(8)) Chrysalis Education.

Royer, Anne. Little Guinea Pigs. 2006. (Born to Be Wild Ser.). (Illus.). 23p. (J). lib. bdg. 22.00 (978-0-8368-6166-2(3)) Stevens, Gareth Inc.

Royston, Angela. Guinea Pig. 2002. (Life Cycle of a... Ser.). (Illus.). 32p. (J). (gr. k-2). pap. 6.95 (978-1-58810-330-7(7) , 91061) Heinemann Library.

Rustad, Martha E. H. Guinea Pigs. 2001. (All about Pets Ser.). (Illus.). 24p. (J). (gr. k-1). lib. bdg. 15.93 (978-0-7368-0975-7(9) , Pebble Bks.) Capstone Pr., Inc.

Salzmann, Mary Elizabeth. Goofy Guinea Pigs. Nobens, C. A., illus. 2007. (Perfect Pets Ser.). 24p. (J). (gr. k-3). lib. bdg. 19.93 (*978-1-59928-749-2(8) , SandCastle) ABDO Publishing Co.

Silkies & Other Guinea Pigs. 2007. (World Book's Animals of the World Ser.). (Illus.). 64p. (J). (978-0-7166-1334-3(4)) World Bk., Inc.

Souris. 1999. (Pocket Pals Ser.). (FRE.). (J). (ps-1). pap. 1.99 (978-0-85953-735-3(8)) Child's Play-International.

Spengler, Kremena. Caring for Your Guinea Pig. 2008. (J). (*978-1-4296-1255-5(X)) Capstone Pr., Inc.

Viner, Bradley. Guinea Pig. 1999. (All about Your Pet Ser.). (Illus.). 32p. pap. 4.99 (978-0-7641-1013-9(6)) Barron's Educational Series, Inc.

Waters, Jo. The Wild Side of Pet Guinea Pigs. 2004. (Raintree Perspectives Ser.). (Illus.). 32p. (J). 26.36 (978-1-4109-1021-9(0)); pap. 7.50 (978-1-4109-1161-2(6)) Harcourt Schl. Pubs.

GUINEA PIGS—FICTION

Bateson, Catherine. Being Bee. 2007. 136p. (J). (gr. 3-7). 16.95 (*978-0-8234-2104-6(X)) Holiday Hse., Inc.

Berenzy, Alix. Sammy: The Classroom Guinea Pig. 2008. (Illus.). 32p. (J). pap. 6.99 (*978-0-312-37964-3(1)) Square Fish.

Blumenthal, Deborah. Charlie Hits It Big. 2008. (Illus.). 32p. (J). 16.99 (*978-0-06-056353-0(2)); lib. bdg. 17.89 (*978-0-06-056354-7(0)) HarperCollins Pubs.

Cochrane, Gillian. A Week at Aunty Betty's. 2004. 44p. (J). per. 11.41 (978-1-4116-0957-0(3)) Lulu.com.

Cousins, Lucy. Maisy Se Va al Parque. 2000. Tr. of Maisy Goes to the Playground. (Illus.). 16p. (J). (ps-k). (CAT.). 16.95 (978-84-88061-45-5(X)); (SPA., 16.95 (978-84-88061-46-1(3) , RR7147) Serres, Ediciones, S. L. ESP. *Dist:* Lectorum Pubns., Inc.

Daniels, Lucy & Baglio, Ben M. Guinea Pig Gang. Howard, Paul, illus. 1999. (Animal Ark Pets Ser.: No. 8). 112p. (J). (gr. 3-6). pap. 3.99 (978-0-439-05165-1(7)) Scholastic, Inc.

Frederick, Heather Vogel. For Your Paws Only. Comport, Sally Wern, illus. 2005. (Spy Mice Ser.). 272p. (J). (gr. 4-6). 9.95 (978-1-4169-0573-8(1)) Simon & Schuster Children's Publishing.

Freysinger, Karen. Adventures of Countess Pigula Her Royal Imagination. Freysinger, Karen, illus. 2006. (J). 15.95 (978-0-9786729-0-4(9)) Aha! Elora Danan Productions.

Garvey, Linda K. Doug's Twelve Days of Christmas. 1998. (Doug Ser.). (Illus.). 32p. (J). (ps-2). 8.95 (978-0-7868-3197-5(9)) Disney Pr.

Herrick, Steven. Do-Wrong Ron. Magerl, Caroline, illus. 2005. 132p. (J). pap. 6.95 (978-1-86508-661-3(4)) Allen & Unwin AUS. *Dist:* Independent Pubs. Group.

Hudson, Iris. Mac & the Messmaker. Smath, Jerry, illus. 2005. 32p. (J). lib. bdg. 20.00 (*978-1-4242-1107-4(7)) Fitzgerald Bks.

—Mac & the Messmaker. Smath, Jerry, illus. 2005. (Social Studies Connects). 32p. (J). pap. 4.99 (978-1-57565-158-3(0)) Kane Pr., The.

Hurwitz, Johanna. Lexi's Tale. Brewster, Patience, illus. 2002. (Park Pals Adventure Ser.). 112p. (J). (gr. 2-5). pap. 4.95 (978-1-58717-160-4(0) , SeaStar Bks.) Chronicle Bks. LLC.

—Lexi's Tale. 2002. (gr. 3-6). lib. bdg. 11.80 (978-0-613-54420-7(X)) Tandem Library Bks.

—Pee-Wee's Tale. Brewster, Patience, illus. 2000. (J). 104p. pap. 14.95 (978-1-58717-028-7(0)); 96p. (gr. 2-5). 14.95 (978-1-58717-027-0(2)) Chronicle Bks. LLC. (SeaStar Bks.).

—Pee-Wee's Tale. Brewster, Patience, illus. 2001. 104p. (J). (ps-3). per. 11.80 (978-0-613-54426-9(9)) Tandem Library Bks.

Hurwitz, Johanna & Brewster, Patience. Pee-Wee's Tale. 2001. (Park Pals Adventure Ser.). (Illus.). 112p. (J). (gr. 2-5). pap. 4.95 (978-1-58717-111-6(2) , SeaStar Bks.) Chronicle Bks. LLC.

Jennings, Sharon. Priscilla's Paw de Deux. Hendry, Linda, illus. 2002. 36p. (J). (ps-2). (978-1-55041-718-0(5)) Fitzhenry & Whiteside, Ltd.

Kelly, Katy. Lucy Rose: Here's the Thing about Me. Rex, Adam, illus. (J). (gr. 3-7). 2004. 144p. 12.95 (978-0-385-73203-1(1) , Delacorte Bks. for Young Readers); 2004. 144p. lib. bdg. 14.99 (978-0-385-90234-2(4) , Delacorte Bks. for Young Readers); 2006. 160p. reprint ed. 5.99 (978-0-440-42026-2(1) , Yearling) Random Hse. Children's Bks.

Kroll, Steven. Patches Lost & Found. Gott, Barry, illus. 2005. 32p. (J). pap. 5.95 (978-0-7614-5217-1(6)) Cavendish, Marshall Corp.

—Patches Lost & Found. Gott, Barry, illus. 2001. 40p. (J). (gr. k-3). 15.95 (978-1-890817-53-4(8)) Winslow Pr.

—Patches Lost & Found. Gott, Barry, illus. 2005. 32p. (J). (gr. k-4). lib. bdg. 13.15 (978-0-606-33744-1(X)) Tandem Library Bks.

McMullan, Kate. Fluffy & the Firefighters. Smith, Mavis, illus. 2004. 40p. (J). lib. bdg. 15.00 (978-1-59054-430-3(7)) Fitzgerald Bks.

—Fluffy & the Firefighters, Level 3. Smith, Mavis, illus. 2001. (Hello Reader! Ser.). 40p. (J). (gr. 1-3). pap. 3.99 (978-0-439-12917-6(6) , Cartwheel Bks.) Scholastic, Inc.

—Fluffy & the Firefighters. 1999. (gr. k-3). lib. bdg. 11.80 (978-0-613-35510-0(5)) Tandem Library Bks.

—Fluffy Goes Apple Picking. Smith, Mavis, illus. 2002. (Hello Reader! Ser.). 40p. (J). 3.99 (978-0-439-31420-6(8)) Scholastic, Inc.

—Fluffy Goes to School. Smith, Mavis, illus. 1999. (Hello Reader! Ser.: Level 3). 40p. (J). (gr. 1-3). pap. 3.99 (978-0-590-37213-8(0) , Cartwheel Bks.) Scholastic, Inc.

—Fluffy Goes to Washington. Smith, Mavis, illus. 2002. (Hello Reader! Level 3 Ser.). (J). 3.99 (978-0-439-31943-0(9)) Scholastic, Inc.

—Fluffy Learns to Swim. Smith, Mavis, illus. 2002. (Hello Reader! Ser.). (J). pap. 3.99 (978-0-439-31946-1(3)) Scholastic, Inc.

—Fluffy Meets the Dinosaurs. Smith, Mavis, illus. 2004. 40p. (J). lib. bdg. 15.00 (978-1-59054-459-4(5)) Fitzgerald Bks.

—Fluffy Meets the Dinosaurs. 2000. (Hello Reader! Ser.). (Illus.). (J). 10.79 (978-0-606-18545-5(3)) Tandem Library Bks.

—Fluffy Meets the Groundhog. 2001. 10.79 (978-0-606-22246-4(4)) Tandem Library Bks.

—Fluffy Meets the Tooth Fairy. Smith, Mavis, illus. 2003. (Fluffy the Classroom Guinea Pig Ser.). 40p. (J). (gr. 1-3). 3.99 (978-0-439-12918-3(4)) Scholastic, Inc.

—Fluffy Meets the Tooth Fairy. 2000. (gr. k-3). lib. bdg. 11.80 (978-0-613-58150-9(4)) Tandem Library Bks.

—Fluffy Saves Christmas. Smith, Mavis, illus. 2004. 40p. (J). lib. bdg. 15.00 (978-1-59054-462-4(5)) Fitzgerald Bks.

—Fluffy Saves Christmas, Level 3. Smith, Mavis, illus. 1999. (Hello Reader! Ser.). 40p. (J). (gr. 1-3). pap. 3.99 (978-0-590-52308-0(2) , Cartwheel Bks.) Scholastic, Inc.

—Fluffy, the Secret Santa. Smith, Mavis, illus. 2001. (Hello Reader! Ser.). (J). pap. 3.99 (978-0-439-31942-3(0)) Scholastic, Inc.

—Fluffy's 100th Day at School. 2000. (Hello Reader! Ser.). (J). 10.79 (978-0-606-19562-1(9)) Tandem Library Bks.

—Fluffy's Funny Field Trip. Smith, Mavis, illus. 2004. 40p. (J). lib. bdg. 15.00 (978-1-59054-463-1(3)) Fitzgerald Bks.

—Fluffy's Funny Field Trip, Level 3. Smith, Mavis, illus. 2001. (Hello Reader! Ser.). 40p. (J). (gr. 1-3). pap. 3.99 (978-0-439-20673-0(1)) Scholastic, Inc.

—Fluffy's Funny Field Trip. 2001. (Hello Reader! Ser.). (Illus.). (J). 10.79 (978-0-606-21192-5(6)) Tandem Library Bks.

—Fluffy's Happy Halloween. Smith, Mavis, illus. 2004. 40p. (J). lib. bdg. 15.00 (978-1-59054-464-8(1)) Fitzgerald Bks.

—Fluffy's School Bus Adventure. Smith, Mavis, illus. 2004. 40p. (J). lib. bdg. 15.00 (978-1-59054-466-2(8)) Fitzgerald Bks.

—Fluffy's School Bus Adventure. Smith, Mavis, illus. 2001. (Hello Reader! Ser.). 40p. (J). (gr. 1-3). pap. 3.99 (978-0-439-20671-6(5) , Cartwheel Bks.) Scholastic, Inc.

—Fluffy's School Bus Adventure. Smith, Mavis, illus. 2001. (J). (ps-ps). lib. bdg. 11.80 (978-0-613-35512-4(1)) Tandem Library Bks.

—Fluffy's School Bus Adventure. 2001. (Hello Reader! Ser.). (Illus.). (J). 10.79 (978-0-606-21193-2(4)) Tandem Library Bks.

—Fluffy's Silly Summer. 2000. (Hello Reader! Ser.). (Illus.). (J). 10.79 (978-0-606-18873-9(8)) Tandem Library Bks.

—Fluffy's Spring Vacation. Smith, Mavis, illus. 2004. 40p. (J). lib. bdg. 15.00 (978-1-59054-468-6(4)) Fitzgerald Bks.

—Fluffy's Spring Vacation. 2001. (Hello Reader! Ser.). (Illus.). (J). 10.79 (978-0-606-20661-7(2)) Tandem Library Bks.

—Fluffy's Thanksgiving. Smith, Mavis, illus. 2000. (Fluffy the Classroom Guinea Pig Ser.). 40p. (J). (ps-3). pap. 3.99 (978-0-590-37215-2(7)) Scholastic, Inc.

—Fluffy's Trick-or-Treat. Smith, Mavis, illus. 2001. (Hello Reader! Ser.). (J). pap. 3.99 (978-0-439-31941-6(2)) Scholastic, Inc.

—Fluffy's Valentine's Day. Smith, Mavis, illus. 2004. 40p. (J). lib. bdg. 15.00 (978-1-59054-470-9(6)) Fitzgerald Bks.

—Fluffy's Valentine's Day, Level 3. Smith, Mavis, illus. 2000. (Hello Reader! Ser.). 40p. (J). (gr. 1-3). pap. 3.99 (978-0-590-37216-9(5)) Scholastic, Inc.

Meade, Holly. John Willy & Freddy McGee. 2007. 24p. (J). (ps-3). bds. 6.99 (***978-0-7614-5363-5(6)***) Cavendish, Marshall Corp.

—John Willy & Freddy McGee. Meade, Holly, illus. 2005. (Illus.). 32p. (J). (gr. k-3). pap. 5.95 (978-0-7614-5143-3(9)) Cavendish, Marshall Corp.

—John Willy & Freddy Mcgee. 1998. (Accelerated Reader Bks.). (Illus.). 32p. (J). (ps-3). 15.95 (978-0-7614-5033-7(5) , Cavendish Children's Bks.) Cavendish, Marshall Corp.

Myers, Laurie. Guinea Pigs Don't Talk. Taylor, Cheryl, illus. 1998. 80p. (J). (gr. 4-6). pap. 5.95 (978-0-395-92865-3(6) , Clarion Bks.) Houghton Mifflin Co. Trade & Reference Div.

—Guniea Pigs Don't Talk. 1998. (gr. 3-6). lib. bdg. 14.10 (978-0-613-71946-9(8)) Tandem Library Bks.

Nakagawa, Rieko. Guri & Gura's Special Gift. Howlett, Peter & McNamara, Richard B., trs. from JPN. Yamawaki, Yuriko, illus. gif. ed. 2002. (Guri & Gura Ser.). 32p. (ps-3). 10.95 (978-0-8048-3357-8(5)) Tuttle Publishing.

Ohi, Ruth. Clara & the Bossy. Ohi, Ruth, illus. 2006. (Ruth Ohi Picture Book Ser.). (Illus.). 32p. (J). (ps-1). pap. 5.95 (978-1-55037-942-6(9)); lib. bdg. 19.95 (978-1-55037-943-3(7)) Annick Pr., Ltd. CAN. *Dist:* Firefly Bks., Ltd.

Proimos, James & Rheingold, Andy. When Guinea Pigs Fly. 2005. (When Guinea Pigs Fly Ser.). (Illus.). 112p. (J). pap. 3.99 (978-0-439-51902-1(0)); pap. 14.95 (978-0-439-51899-4(7)) Scholastic, Inc.

Rose, Gill. William & the Guinea-Pig: A Book about Responsibility. Archbold, Tim, illus. 2004. (Making Good Choices Ser.). 24p. (C). (gr. k-3). 22.60 (978-1-4048-0664-1(4)) Picture Window Bks.

Roth, Susan L. Great Big Guinea Pigs. 2006. (Illus.). 32p. (J). 17.95 (978-1-58234-724-0(7) , Bloomsbury Children) Bloomsbury Publishing.

Rylant, Cynthia. Little Whistle. Bowers, Tim, illus. 2007. 32p. (J). 24.21 (***978-1-59961-253-9(4)***) Spotlight.

—Little Whistle's Christmas. Bowers, Tim, illus. 2003. (Little Whistle Ser.). 32p. (J). 16.00 (978-0-15-204590-6(2)) Harcourt Children's Bks.

—Little Whistle's Christmas. Bowers, Tim, illus. 2007. 32p. (J). 24.21 (***978-1-59961-254-6(2)***) Spotlight.

—Little Whistle's Dinner Party. Bowers, Tim, illus. 2004. 32p. (J). pap. 6.00 (978-0-15-205062-7(0) , Voyager Bks./Libros Viajeros) Harcourt Children's Bks.

—Little Whistle's Dinner Party. Bowers, Tim, illus. 2007. 32p. (J). 24.21 (***978-1-59961-255-3(0)***) Spotlight.

—Little Whistle's Medicine. Bowers, Tim, illus. (Little Whistle Ser.). 32p. (J). 2005. pap. 6.00 (978-0-15-205244-7(5) , Voyager Bks./Libros Viajeros); 2002. 15.00 (978-0-15-201086-7(6)) Harcourt Children's Bks.

—Little Whistle's Medicine. Bowers, Tim, illus. 2007. 32p. (J). 24.21 (***978-1-59961-256-0(9)***) Spotlight.

Schwartz, Roslyn. The Mole Sisters & the Piece of Moss. Schwartz, Roslyn, illus. 2001. (Mole Sisters Ser.). (Illus.). 32p. (J). (ps-k). lib. bdg. 14.95 (978-1-55037-583-1(0)) Annick Pr., Ltd. CAN. *Dist:* Firefly Bks., Ltd.

Scuderi, Lucia. Dos Ratones en la Luna. 2004. Tr. of Two Mice on the Moon. (SPA., Illus.). (J). 20.99 (978-84-261-3273-4(1)) Juventud, Editorial ESP. *Dist:* Lectorum Pubns., Inc.

Shannon, Margaret. Gullible's Troubles. (Illus.). 32p. (J). (gr. k-3). 2000. pap. 5.95 (978-0-618-07033-6(8)); 1998. tchr. ed. 15.00 (978-0-395-83933-1(5)) Houghton Mifflin Co. Trade & Reference Div.

—Gullible's Troubles. 2000. (J). (978-0-606-19424-2(X)) Tandem Library Bks.

Spelman, Cornelia Maude. When I Feel Good about Myself. Parkinson, Kathy, illus. 2003. (Way I Feel Ser.). 24p. (J). (ps-1). 15.95 (978-0-8075-8887-1(3)) Whitman, Albert & Co.

—When I Feel Sad. Parkinson, Kathy, illus. 2002. (Way I Feel Ser.). 24p. (J). (ps-1). 15.95 (978-0-8075-8891-8(1)); pap. 6.95 (978-0-8075-8899-4(7)) Whitman, Albert & Co.

Wells, Rosemary. Felix & the Worrier. Wells, Rosemary, illus. 2003. (Illus.). 40p. (J). (ps up). 12.99 (978-0-7636-1405-8(X)) Candlewick Pr.

—Felix Feels Better. Wells, Rosemary, illus. 2000. (Illus.). 32p. (J). (ps-k). 12.99 (978-0-7636-0639-8(1)) Candlewick Pr.

Wesley, Valerie Wilson. Willimena, Bk. 2. 2002. 368p. (J). 12.99 (978-0-7868-0466-5(1)) Hyperion Bks. for Children.

—Willimena Rules! Bk. 1: How to Lose Your Class Pet. Roos, Maryn, illus. 2003. 96p. (gr. 2-5). pap. 3.99 (978-0-7868-1322-3(9) , Jump at the Sun) Hyperion Bks. for Children.

GUITAR

America. America: Discovery to Revolution, the American Revolution. 1999. (Guitar Anthology Ser.). (YA). (gr. 7 up). 21.95 (978-0-7692-6757-9(2) , Warner Bros. Pubns.) Alfred Publishing Co., Inc.

Aranjo, Karl W. Guitar Buddy: The Fast Fun & Easy Way to Learn Great Sounding Guitar. 2002. (YA). spiral bd. 17.50 (978-0-9770667-0-4(3)) Aranjo, Karl.

—Guitar Tab: Blank Manuscript Papaer for Guitar Teachers, Students & Songwriters. 2003. (YA). spiral bd. 6.00 (978-0-9770667-2-8(X)) Aranjo, Karl.

Arnold, Bruce E. 1st Steps for a Beginning Guitarist: Chords & Chord Progressions. l.t. ed. 2001. (ENG.). 52p. (J). spiral bd. 23.99 (978-1-890944-90-2(4)) Muse Eek Publishing Co.

—1st Steps for a Beginning Guitarist: Chords & Chord Progressions for Guitar. 2001. 52p. per. 14.99 (978-1-890944-93-3(9)) Muse Eek Publishing Co.

Blues Guitar Legends (German Version) 2004. (GER.). (YA). cd-rom (978-1-891155-19-2(9)) EMedia Corp.

Bozung, Dick. A Beginning Guitar Simplified Method for Everyone: The Guitar Barre Method. 1998. (Illus.). 38p. (YA). (gr. 3 up). spiral bd. 10.00 (978-0-9622341-2-5(5)) Seven Arrows Publishing.

Brown, Buck. Jazz Chops for Guitar: Technique Exercises for the Aspiring Guitarist. 2001. 80p. (YA). pap. 19.95 incl. audio compact disk (978-1-929395-35-4(3)) Workshop Arts, Inc.

Carroll, Quincy. Play Guitar, Vol. 12. 2005. (Illus.). 72p. per. 19.95 incl. DVD (978-0-9760487-2-5(8)) iPlayMusic, Inc.

Casey, Bert. Acoustic Guitar, Vol. 2, l.t. ed. 2003. (Watch & Learn Ser.). (Illus.). 80p. pap. 14.95 (978-1-893907-43-0(0) , 256-535) Watch & Learn, Inc.

—Guitar Primer Spanish Voiceover. 2003. (Watch & Learn Ser.). (SPA.). 14.95 (978-1-893907-21-8(X) , 256-506) Watch & Learn, Inc.

Ciravolo, Tish. Girls Guitar Course 2: Everything a girl needs to know abut playing Guitar!, Vol. 2. 2003. 48p. pap. 14.95 incl. cd-rom (978-0-7390-3175-9(9) , 21971) Alfred Publishing Co., Inc.

Clayton, Stuart. Xtreme Bass. 2005. (Illus.). 80p. audio compact disk 14.95 (978-1-84492-022-8(4)) Sanctuary Publishing, Ltd. GBR. *Dist:* Warner Bros. Pubns.

Fink, Cathy & Marxer, Marcy. Russ Barenberg Teaches 20 Bluegrass Guitar Solos: Repertoire Tunes for Intermediate Players. 1998. (Homespun Ser.). 32p. (gr. 7). pap. 19.95 incl. audio compact disk (978-0-7935-8335-5(7) , 0793583357) Homespun Video.

The Fundamental Guitar Method Book 1: An Introduction to the Guitar & the Fundamentals of Music. 2003. (YA). spiral bd. (978-0-9771357-0-7(5)) Sound Craft Designs.

The Fundamental Guitar Method Book 2: The Science of Harmony. 2004. (YA). spiral bd. (978-0-9771357-1-4(3)) Sound Craft Designs.

Gourse, Leslie. Fancy Fretwork: The Great Jazz Guitarists. 2000. (Art of Jazz Ser.). (Illus.). 144p. (YA). (gr. 8-12). pap. 8.95 (978-0-531-16404-4(7) , Watts, Franklin) Scholastic Library Publishing.

Green, Andrew. Jazz Guitar Structures: Boosting Your Solo Power. 2002. 136p. (C). per. 24.95 (978-0-9700576-0-0(1)) Microphonic Pr.

Griggs, John R. Learning to Play Guitar. 2004. Orig. Title: American Guitar Method. (YA). 7.95 (978-0-9753385-0-6(1)) Griggs Music Co.

Guitar. 2003. (Quick Kiss Guides Ser.). 160p. (YA). pap. 10.00 (978-0-7894-9311-8(X)) Dorling Kindersley Publishing, Inc.

Gunod, Nathaniel. Guitar Theory Made Easy. 2001. (Made Easy). 64p. pap. (978-1-929395-27-9(2)) Workshop Arts, Inc.

Hargett, Paul R. Me & My Bass Guitar: The Life & Music of Victor Lemonte Wooten. unabr. ed. 2004. (Illus.). 336p. per. 18.50 (978-0-9754636-0-4(8)) Amberock Pubns.

Harnsberger, Link. Kids Guitar Course COMPL. 2006. 160p. 24.95 (978-0-7390-4169-7(X)) Alfred Publishing Co., Inc.

Jamie, Humphries. Xtreme Electric Guitar. 2005. (Illus.). 80p. audio compact disk 14.95 (978-1-84492-016-7(X)) Sanctuary Publishing, Ltd. GBR. *Dist:* Warner Bros. Pubns.

Klingel, Cynthia Fitterer & Noyed, Robert B. Guitars. 2002. (Wonder Books Level 1: Musical Instuments Ser.). (Illus.). 24p. (J). (ps-3). 22.79 (978-1-56766-947-3(6)) Child's World, Inc.

Laufer, Peter & Roth, Susan L. Made in Mexico. Roth, Susan L., illus. 2000. (Illus.). 32p. (J). (gr. 3-7). 16.95 (978-0-7922-7118-5(1) , National Geographic Children's Bks.) National Geographic Society.

Manus, Ron & Harnsberger, L. C. Kids Guitar Course 1: The easiest guitar method Ever!, Vol. 1. Shelly, Jeff, illus. 2003. 48p. pap. 14.95 incl. cd-rom (978-0-88284-989-8(1) , 18451) Alfred Publishing Co., Inc.

—Kids Guitar Course 2: The easiest guitar method Ever!, Vol. 2. Shelly, Jeff, illus. 2005. 48p. pap. 14.95 incl. cd-rom (978-0-88284-987-4(5)) Alfred Publishing Co., Inc.

Marks, Anthony. Easy Guitar Tunes Internet Referenced. Abel, Simone, illus. 2004. 32p. (J). pap. 8.95 (978-0-7945-0775-6(1) , Usborne) EDC Publishing.

McCabe, Larry. Easiest Country Guitar for Children. 2007. 32p. 14.95 incl. audio compact disk (***978-0-7866-7563-0(2)***) Mel Bay Pubns., Inc.

—Easiest Fingerpicking Guitar for Children. 2007. 32p. 14.95 incl. audio compact disk (***978-0-7866-7562-3(4)***) Mel Bay Pubns., Inc.

Play Guitar with... Bob Dylan. 2004. (Illus.). 48p. audio compact disk 21.95 (978-0-7119-8217-8(1) , AM955944) Music Sales Corp.

Quick Star Guitar: Symbols, Shapes & Patterns. 2003. (978-0-9746011-0-6(1)) Karma Valley Music.

Scharfglass, Matt. Starting Guitar: The Number One Method for Young Guitarists. 2006. (Illus.). 48p. (J). (ps-7). pap. 9.95 incl. audio compact disk (978-0-7119-6750-2(4) , Amsco Music) Music Sales Corp.

Smith, Douglas W. Classical Guitar for Young Children, Ages 5-12: For Development of Technique, Musicianship, & Memory, Rote Book 1. 2003. (J). 24.95 (978-0-9729879-0-5(8)) Musictech College Pr.

Smith, Matt. Matt Smith's Chop Shop for Guitar: Shortcuts, Tips & Tricks of the Trade. 2001. 96p. (YA). pap. 20.95 incl. audio compact disk (978-1-929395-32-3(9)) Workshop Arts, Inc.

Spilsbury, Richard. Should I Play the Guitar? 2006. (Learning Musical Instruments Ser.). (Illus.). 32p. (J). (gr. 3-5). lib. bdg. 28.21 (978-1-4034-8188-7(1)) Heinemann Library.

Step One: Teach Yourself Guitar. 2004. (Illus.). 32p. pap. 15.00 incl. DVD (978-0-8256-1890-1(8) , AM971311, Schirmer Trade Bks.) Music Sales Corp.

Sternal, Mark John. Bass Guitar Total Scales Techniques & Applications: Lessons for Beginner through Professional. Sternal, Mark John, ed. 2005. per. 24.95 (978-0-9762917-5-6(4)) MJS Music Pubns.

—GUITAR Total Scales Techniques & Applications: Lessons for Beginner Through Professional. 2005. (Illus.). 176p. per. 24.95 (978-0-9762917-0-1(3)) MJS Music Pubns.

—GUITARRA Escalas, Técnicas y Aplicaciones Totales: Lecciones para Principiantes y Profesionales. Hale, Beto, tr. from ENG. 2005. (SPA., Illus.). 176p. per. 14.95 (978-0-9762917-1-8(1)) MJS Music Pubns.

Teach Yourself Bass. 2004. (Step One Teach Yourself Ser.). (Illus.). 32p. VHS, audio compact disk 19.95 (978-0-8256-1879-6(7) , AM970299) Music Sales Corp.

Tomaselli, Anthony. Play Guitar 1. 2003. cd-rom (978-0-9714299-5-6(2)) I Save A Tree.

Turner, Gary. Progressive's Young Beginner Guitar Giant Coloring Book. 2003. (Illus.). 36p. (J). pap. 23.95 incl. audio compact disk (978-1-86469-096-5(8)) Learntoplaymusic.com AUS. *Dist:* Bookworld Trade, Inc.

GUITAR—FICTION

Brammer, Ethriam Cash. My Tata's Guitar / la guitarra de mi Tata. Lechon, Daniel, illus. (ENG & SPA.). 32p. (J). 15.95 (978-1-55885-369-0(3) , Piñata Books) Arte Publico Pr.

Delaney, Mark. Pepperland. 2007. 224p. pap. 7.95 (***978-1-56145-402-0(8)*** , Peachtree Junior); 2004. 160p. (J). 14.95 (978-1-56145-317-7(X)) Peachtree Pubs., Ltd.

Dumas Lachtman, Ofelia. Looking for la Unica. 2004. (ENG & SPA., Illus.). 190p. (J). pap. 9.95 (978-1-55885-412-3(6) , Piñata Books) Arte Publico Pr.

Reisfeld, Randi, ed. Star Struck. 2006. (Teenick Ser.: Bk. 3). (Illus.). 120p. (J). pap. 4.99 (978-0-439-83157-4(1)) Scholastic, Inc.

Seims, Anne R. The Little Guitar. 2005. pap. 7.95 (978-0-533-15104-2(X)) Vantage Pr., Inc.

Shipton, Paul. Ghost in the Guitar. 2000. (Illus.). 48p. (C). pap. 9.00 (978-0-582-31913-4(7)) Longman Publishing Group.

Sonnenblick, Jordan. Notes from the Midnight Driver. 2007. 288p. (J). pap. 6.99 (***978-0-439-75781-2(9)*** , Scholastic Paperbacks); 2006. 272p. (YA). pap. 16.99 (978-0-439-75779-9(7) , Scholastic Pr.) Scholastic, Inc.

Valenzuela, Roger. Paulie Pick Finds Studioland. Valenzuela, Raquel, tr. from ENG. Valenzuela, Roger, illus. 2003. Tr. of Paulie Pick encuentra Estudiolandia. (SPA., Illus.). 32p. 20.00 (978-0-944551-69-1(6)) Book Pubs. of El Paso.

GULF STATES

Here are entered works on the states of the United States that border on the Gulf of Mexico.

Gallagher, Michael. Gulf States. 2005. (Illus.). 44p. (J). (gr. 6-9). lib. bdg. 29.95 (978-1-58340-608-3(5)) Smart Apple Media.

GULF STREAM

Heiligman, Deborah. Mysterious Ocean Highway. 1999. (Illus.). (J). pap. (978-0-7398-0013-3(2)) Steck-Vaughn.

—The Mysterious Ocean Highway: Benjamin Franklin & the Gulf Stream. 1999. (Turnstone Ocean Pilot Bks.). (Illus.). 48p. (J). (gr. 3-7). pap. 7.95 (978-0-7398-1227-3(0)) Steck-Vaughn.

GULLS—FICTION

Cosgrove, Stephen. Jake O'Shawnasey. 2002. (gr. k-3). lib. bdg. 13.00 (978-0-613-64531-7(6)) Tandem Library Bks.

Fietzek, Petra. Sophie & the Seagull. Ginsbach, Julia, illus. 2002. 32p. (J). (ps up). lib. bdg. 24.67 (978-0-8368-3174-0(8)) Stevens, Gareth Inc.

Finale, Frank. A Gull's Story, Part 2: Counting at the Shore. Moore, Margie, illus. 2007. (J). 22.00 (978-0-9777077-0-6(9)) Jersey Shore Pubns.

Finale, Frank. A Gull's Story, Part 3: Colors at the Shore. Moore, Margie, illus. 2007. (J). 22.00 (***978-0-9777077-2-0(5)***) Jersey Shore Pubns.

Huntington, Amy, illus. Seagull Sam. 2007. 32p. (ps-2). 15.95 (***978-0-89272-715-5(2)***) Down East Bks.

Kittinger, Jo S. Feeding the Gulls. Lucas, Margeaux, tr. Lucas, Margeaux, illus. 2004. (Rookie Reader Ser.). 31p. (J). 19.50 (978-0-516-24407-5(8) , Children's Pr.) Scholastic Library Publishing.

Lines, Patricia. Cyril the Seagull. LaFave, Kim, illus. unabr. ed. 34p. (J). (978-0-88971-048-1(1)) Harbour Publishing Co., Ltd.

Luke, Deanna. Marky & the Seagull. Chambers, Lynne, illus. 2001. (Marky Ser.: Vol. 6). 48p. (J). (gr. 2-6). 8.95 (978-1-928777-12-0(0) , BOW Bks.) Blessing Our World, Inc.

—Marky & the Seagull: Story Book. 2001. (Marky Ser.: Vol. 6). (J). cd-rom 5.95 (978-1-928777-33-5(3) , BOW Bks.) Blessing Our World, Inc.

Sargent, Dave & Sargent, David, Jr. Sandy Sea Gull: Making Friends, 20, 16. Lenoir, Jane, illus. 2nd ed. 2003. (Feather Tales Ser.: 16). 42p. (J). lib. bdg. 19.95 (978-1-56763-749-6(3)) Ozark Publishing.

Sepulveda, Luis. The Story of a Seagull & the Cat Who Taught Her to Fly. Peden, Margaret Sayers, tr. from SPA. Sheban, Chris, illus. Tr. of Historia de una Gaviota y del Gato Que le Enseano a Volar. 128p. (J). 2003. (gr. 3-6). pap. 15.95 (978-0-439-40186-9(0)); 2006. reprint ed. pap. 5.99 (978-0-439-40187-6(9)) Scholastic, Inc. (Levine, Arthur A. Bks.).

Seymour's Soaring Red Sox: A Bird's-Eye View of the 2004 World Series. 2005. (J). kivar 19.95 (978-0-9761820-1-6(7)) Cassiopeia Pr.

Wallace, Karen. A Day at Seagull Beach. 1999. (Eyewitness Readers). (Illus.). 32p. (J). (gr. 5-1). pap. 3.99 (978-0-7894-4002-0(4)) Dorling Kindersley Publishing, Inc.

—A Day at Seagull Beach. 1999. (J). 10.75 (978-0-606-18989-7(0)) Tandem Library Bks.

—Day at Seagull Beach. 1999. (gr. k-3). lib. bdg. 11.80 (978-0-613-17163-2(2)) Tandem Library Bks.

Wallace, Karen & Dorling Kindersley Publishing Staff. A Day at Seagull Beach. 1999. (Eyewitness Readers). (Illus.). 32p. (J). (ps-4). 14.99 (978-0-7894-4003-7(2)) Dorling Kindersley Publishing, Inc.

Walsh, Ellen Stoll. Hamsters to the Rescue. 2005. (Illus.). 40p. (J). (ps-1). 16.00 (978-0-15-205202-7(X)) Harcourt Trade Pubs.

GUMBY (FICTITIOUS CHARACTER)—FICTION

Clokeys Staff. Gumby. ed. 2007. (Illus.). 32p. pap. 8.95 (978-0-7624-2183-1(5)) Running Pr. Bk. Pubs.

Harman, Holly. Gumby Fold & Mail Stationery. 2000. (Illus.). 40p. 8.95 (978-0-8118-2738-6(0)) Chronicle Bks. LLC.

—Gumby's Circus. 2000. (Illus.). 22p. (J). (ps). reprint ed. 15.00 (978-0-7567-5737-3(1)) DIANE Publishing Co.

GUN CONTROL

Here are entered general and non-legal works on the control of guns. Works on the legal aspects of gun control are entered under Firearms—Law and Legislation.

Beth Rosenthal. Gun Control. 2006. (Illus.). 244p. (YA). (gr. 7-10). 33.70 (978-0-7377-3597-0(X) , Greenhaven Pr., Inc.) Thomson Gale.

Croft, Jennifer. Everything You Need to Know about Guns in Your Home. 2005. (Need to Know Library). (Illus.). 64p. (YA). (gr. 7-12). lib. bdg. 25.25 (978-0-8239-3162-0(5) , NTGUHO) Rosen Publishing Group, Inc., The.

Currie-McGhee, Leanne K. Gun Control. 2003. (Lucent Overview Ser.). (Illus.). 112p. (J). 29.95 (978-1-56006-658-3(X) , Lucent Bks.) Thomson Gale.

Gonzales, Doreen. A Look at the Second Amendment: To Keep & Bear Arms. 2007. (Constitution of the United States Ser.). (Illus.). 128p. (J). (gr. 5). lib. bdg. 33.27 (978-1-59845-061-3(1) , MyReportLinks.com Bks.) Enslow Pubs., Inc.

Long, Barbara. Gun Control & the Right to Bear Arms: A Pro/Con Issue. 2002. (Hot Pro/Con Issues Ser.). (Illus.). 64p. (YA). (gr. 6-12). lib. bdg. 27.93 (978-0-7660-1819-8(9)) Enslow Pubs., Inc.

Lunger, Norman L. Big Bang: The Loud Debate over Gun Control. 2002. (Worlds Beyond Ser.). (Illus.). 160p. (gr. 7 up). lib. bdg. 25.90 (978-0-7613-2260-3(4) , Twenty-First Century Bks.) Lerner Publishing Group.

Magoon, Kekla. Gun Control. 2007. (Essential Viewpoints Ser.). (Illus.). 112p. (YA). (gr. 7-9). lib. bdg. 32.79 (***978-1-59928-860-4(5)*** , Essential Library) ABDO Publishing Co.

Roleff, Tamara L. Guns & Crime. 2000. (At Issue Ser.). (Illus.). 106p. (J). (gr. 9-12). lib. bdg. 26.20 (978-0-7377-0153-1(6) , Greenhaven Pr., Inc.) Thomson Gale.

Schulson, Rachel. Guns: What You Should Know. 1999. (Illus.). (J). (978-0-606-18774-9(X)) Tandem Library Bks.

—Guns: What You Should Know. Jones, Mary, illus. 2004. (Concept Book Ser.). 24p. (J). (gr. k-5). pap. 5.95 (978-0-8075-3094-8(8)) Whitman, Albert & Co.

Schwarz, Ted. Kids & Guns. 1999. (978-0-606-17536-4(9)); (gr. 7-12). lib. bdg. 18.75 (978-0-613-21854-2(X)) Tandem Library Bks.

Sommers, Michael A. The Right to Bear Arms. 2001. (Individual Rights & Civic Responsibility Ser.). (Illus.). 64p. (YA). (gr. 7-12). lib. bdg. 26.50 (978-0-8239-3232-0(X)) Rosen Publishing Group, Inc., The.

Streissguth, Thomas. Gun Control: The Pros & Cons. 2001. (Issues in Focus Ser.). (Illus.). 128p. (J). (gr. 6-12). lib. bdg. 26.60 (978-0-7660-1673-6(0)) Enslow Pubs., Inc.

Valdez, Angela. Gun Control. 2003. (Point/Counterpoint Ser.). (Illus.). 112p. (gr. 9-13). 32.95 (978-0-7910-7371-1(8)); pap. 15.95 (978-0-7910-7507-4(9)) Facts On File, Inc. (Chelsea Hse.).

—Gun Control. 2003. (gr. 7-12). lib. bdg. 21.05 (978-0-613-85627-0(9)) Tandem Library Bks.

GUNNING

see Hunting; Shooting

GUNPOWDER PLOT, 1605

Ashworth, Leon. Guy Fawkes. (Illus.). 32p. (978-0-7451-5288-2(0) , Cherrytree Books) Evans Publishing Group.

—Guy Fawkes. (British History Makers Ser.). (Illus.). 32p. 2004. (YA). pap. 11.99 (978-1-84234-302-9(5)); 2001. 22.99 (978-1-84234-080-6(8)); 1999. pap. 11.99 (978-0-7540-9011-3(6)) Evans Publishing Group GBR. (Cherrytree Books). *Dist:* Independent Pubs. Group.

GUNS

see Firearms; Ordnance; Rifles

GUTENBERG, JOHANN, 1397-1468

Beckham, Robert. Who in the World Was the Secretive Printer? The Story of Johannes Gutenberg. Mickle, Jed, illus. 2005. 40p. (J). (gr. 2 up). pap. 9.50 (978-0-9728603-6-9(3) , BIO-GUT) Peace Hill Pr.

Childress, Diana. Johannes Gutenberg & the Printing Press. 2008. (YA). lib. bdg. (***978-0-8225-7520-7(5)***) Twenty First Century Bks.

Feinstein, Stephen. Johannes Gutenberg: The Printer Who Gave Words to the World. 2008. (Inventors Who Changed the World Ser.). 128p. (J). (gr. 6 up). lib. bdg. 33.27 (***978-1-59845-077-4(8)*** , MyReportLinks.com Bks.) Enslow Pubs., Inc.

Koscielniak, Bruce. Johann Gutenberg & the Amazing Printing Press. 2003. (Illus.). 40p. (J). (gr. k-3). 16.00 (978-0-618-26351-6(9)) Houghton Mifflin Co. Trade & Reference Div.

Krensky, Stephen. Breaking into Print: Before & after the Invention of the Printing Press. Christensen, Bonnie, illus. 2003. 30p. (J). (gr. 3-8). reprint ed. 18.00 (978-0-7567-6843-0(8)) DIANE Publishing Co.

Olson, Kay. Johann Gutenburg & the Printing Press. 2007. (Graphic Library). (Illus.). 32p. (J). (***978-0-7368-9644-3(9)***) Capstone Pr., Inc.

Olson, Kay Melchisedech. Johann Gutenberg & the Printing Press. Smith, Tod, illus. 2007. (Graphic Library). 32p. (J). 25.26 (978-0-7368-6482-4(2)) Capstone Pr., Inc.

Pollard, Michael. Johann Gutenberg: Master of Modern Printing. 2001. (Giants of Science Ser.). (Illus.). 64p. (J). (gr. 5-8). 27.44 (978-1-56711-335-8(4) , Blackbirch Pr., Inc.) Thomson Gale.

Rees, Fran. Johannes Gutenberg: Inventor of the Printing Press. 2005. (Signature Lives Ser.). (Illus.). 112p. (J). (gr. 5-7). (978-0-7565-0989-7(0)) Compass Point Bks.

GUTHRIE, WOODY, 1912-1967

Christensen, Bonnie. Woody Guthrie: Poet of the People. 2001. (Illus.). 32p. (J). (gr. k-12). 16.95 (978-0-375-81113-5(3) , Knopf Bks. for Young Readers) Random Hse. Children's Bks.

Coombs, Karen Mueller. Woody Guthrie: America's Folksinger. (Illus.). 120p. (J). 2003. pap. 8.95 (978-0-8225-3750-2(8)); 2001. (gr. 4-7). lib. bdg. 27.93 (978-1-57505-464-3(7) , Carolrhoda Bks.) Lerner Publishing Group.

Neimark, Anne E. There Ain't Nobody That Can Sing Like Me. 2002. (Illus.). 128p. (J). (gr. 5-9). 17.95 (978-0-689-83369-4(5) , Atheneum) Simon & Schuster Children's Publishing.

Partridge, Elizabeth. This Land Was Made for You & Me: The Life & Songs of Woody Guthrie. 2002. (Illus.). 224p. (J). (gr. 6-12). 21.99 (978-0-670-03535-9(1) , Viking Juvenile) Penguin Group (USA) Inc.

GUYANA

Jermyn, Leslie. Guyana. 2000. (Cultures of the World Ser.). (Illus.). 128p. (J). (gr. 5-12). lib. bdg. 37.07 (978-0-7614-0994-6(7) , Benchmark Bks.) Cavendish, Marshall Corp.

Morrison, Marion. Guyana. 2003. (Enchantment of the World, Second Ser.). (Illus.). 144p. (J). (gr. 5-9). 36.00 (978-0-516-22377-3(1) , Children's Pr.) Scholastic Library Publishing.

Temple, Bob. Guyana. 2003. (Discovering South America Ser.). (Illus.). 64p. (J). (gr. 5 up). lib. bdg. (978-1-59084-300-0(2)) Mason Crest Pubs.

Woodward, John. Into Wild Guyana. 2004. (Jeff Corwin Experience Ser.). (Illus.). 48p. (J). 11.20 (978-1-4103-0232-8(6)); (gr. 4-7). 24.95 (978-1-4103-0231-1(8)) Thomson Gale. (Blackbirch Pr., Inc.).

GYMNASTICS

see also Physical Education and Training

Bailer, Darice. Solid Gold Gymnastics Stars. 2000. (Step into Reading Ser.). (J). (978-0-606-19519-5(X)) Tandem Library Bks.

Blackall, Bernie. Gymnastics. 1999. (Top Sport Ser.). (Illus.). 32p. (J). (gr. 4-6). lib. bdg. 21.36 (978-1-57572-704-2(8)) Heinemann Library.

Bragg, Linda Wallenberg. Gymnastics. King, Andy, photos by. 2005. (Play-By-Play Ser.). (Illus.). 80p. (gr. 4-8). pap., lib. bdg. 23.93 (978-0-8225-9877-0(9)) Lerner Publishing Group.

Bray-Moffatt, Naia. I Love Gymnastics. Handley, David, photos by. 2005. (Illus.). 48p. (J). (gr. 5). 12.99 (978-0-7566-1011-1(7)) Dorling Kindersley Publishing, Inc.

Bundey, Nikki. In the Gym. Gray, Virginia, illus. 1999. (First Sports Science Ser.). 32p. (J). (gr. 2-4). lib. bdg. 21.27 (978-1-57505-358-5(6) , Carolrhoda Bks.) Lerner Publishing Group.

Compass Point Books, contrib. by. Gymnastics for Fun! (For Fun Ser.). 48p. (YA). pap. 8.95 (978-0-7565-1156-2(9)) Compass Point Bks.

Crossingham, John. Gymnastics in Action. 2002. (Sports in Action Ser.). (Illus.). 32p. (J). (gr. 4). (978-0-7787-0330-3(4)); pap. (978-0-7787-0350-1(9)) Crabtree Publishing Co.

—Gymnastics in Action. 2003. (gr. 3-6). lib. bdg. 15.25 (978-0-613-52846-7(8)) Tandem Library Bks.

Ditchfield, Christin. Gymnastics. 2000. (True Bks.). (Illus.). 48p. (J). (gr. 3-5). 25.00 (978-0-516-21063-6(7) , Children's Pr.) Scholastic Library Publishing.

—Gymnastics. 2000. (gr. 3-6). lib. bdg. 15.25 (978-0-613-51648-8(6)) Tandem Library Bks.

Durrett, Deanne. Dominique Moceanu. 1999. (People in the News Ser.). (Illus.). 112p. (YA). (gr. 6-9). 32.45 (978-1-56006-099-4(9) , Lucent Bks.) Thomson Gale.

Feldman, Jane. I Love Gymnastics! 2000. (Illus.). (J). (978-0-606-18497-7(X)) Tandem Library Bks.

Ganeri, Anita. First Day at Gymnastics, Level 1. 2002. (DK Readers Ser.). (Illus.). 32p. (J). pap. 3.99 (978-0-7894-8513-7(3)) Dorling Kindersley Publishing, Inc.

—First Day of Gymnastics. 2002. (gr. k-3). lib. bdg. 11.80 (978-0-613-55711-5(5)) Tandem Library Bks.

Ganeri, Anita & Dorling Kindersley Publishing Staff. First Day at Gymnastics, Level 1. 2002. (Readers Ser.). (Illus.). 32p. (J). (ps). 12.99 (978-0-7894-8512-0(5)) Dorling Kindersley Publishing, Inc.

Gibbs, Lynne. A Word about Gymnastics. McNicholas, Shelagh, illus. 2005. (Word About Ser.). 24p. (J). (ps-3). pap., pap. 3.95 (978-0-7696-3385-5(4) , Brighter Child) School Specialty Publishing.

Grips-Gymnastik: Gedaechtnis und Denkvermoegen Fix Trainiert. (Pocket-Quizspiel Ser.). (Illus.). 56p. bds. (978-3-411-09401-1(X)) Bibliographisches Institut & F. A. Brockhaus AG DEU. *Dist:* i.b.d., Ltd.

Gruber, Beth. Gymnastics for Fun! 2003. (Sports for Fun! Ser.). (Illus.). 48p. (J). (gr. 3 up). 21.26 (978-0-7565-0487-8(2)) Compass Point Bks.

Gutman, Dan. Gymnastics: The Trials, the Triumphs, the Truth. 1998. (Illus.). 208p. (J). (gr. 4-7). pap. 6.99 (978-0-14-130130-3(9) , Puffin) Penguin Group (USA) Inc.

—Gymnastics: The Trials, the Triumphs, the Truth. 1998. (J). (978-0-606-13454-5(9)) Tandem Library Bks.

Henderson, Lyndsey. Tumble (Gymnastics Fun) 2001. (Teacher's Pet Ser.). 48p. (J). 4.95 (978-0-439-17345-2(0)) Scholastic, Inc.

Herran, Joe & Thomas, Ron. Gymnastics. 2003. (Action Sports Ser.). (Illus.). 32p. (gr. 4-8). 28.00 (978-0-7910-7534-0(6) , Chelsea Hse.) Facts On File, Inc.

Hofstetter, Adam B. Olympic Gymnastics. 2007. (Great Moments in Olympic History Ser.). (Illus.). 48p. (J). (gr. 5-8). lib. bdg. 26.50 (978-1-4042-0968-8(9) , Rosen Central) Rosen Publishing Group, Inc., The.

Holmes, James. The Gymnastics Almanac. 1998. (Illus.). 128p. (J). (gr. 3-6). pap. 6.95 (978-1-56565-966-7(X) , 0966XW); (gr. 4-7). 12.95 (978-1-56565-967-4(8) , 09678W) Lowell Hse. (Roxbury Park).

Housel, Debra J. Gymnastics: Easy Olympic Sports Reader. 2004. (U. S. Olympic Committee Easy Olympic Sports Readers Ser.). 16p. (J). pap. 2.99 (978-1-58000-112-0(2)) Griffin Publishing Group.

Huff, Richard M. The Composite Guide to Gymnastics. 2000. (Composite Guides Ser.). (Illus.). 64p. (J). (gr. 8-12). 18.65 (978-0-7910-5865-7(4) , Chelsea Hse.) Facts On File, Inc.

Hughes, Morgan. Gymnastics. 2005. (Junior Sports Ser.). (Illus.). 32p. (gr. 2-4). 19.95 (978-1-59515-191-9(5)) Rourke Publishing, LLC.

Jones, Jen. Gymnastics Competitions: On Your Way to Victory. 2007. (Gymnastics Ser.). (Illus.). 32p. (J). (gr. 2-6). lib. bdg. 25.26 (978-0-7368-6467-1(9)) Capstone Pr., Inc.

—Gymnastics Essentials: Safety & Equipment. 2007. (Gymnastics Ser.). (Illus.). 32p. (J). (gr. 2-6). lib. bdg. 25.26 (978-0-7368-6468-8(7)) Capstone Pr., Inc.

—Gymnastics Events: Floor, Vault, Bars, & Beam. 2007. (Snap Books). (Illus.). 32p. (J). 25.26 (978-0-7368-6469-5(5)) Capstone Pr., Inc.

—Gymnastics Skills: Beginning Tumbling. 2007. (Gymnastics Ser.). (Illus.). 32p. (J). (gr. 2-6). lib. bdg. 25.26 (978-0-7368-6470-1(9)) Capstone Pr., Inc.

—Gymnastics Training & Fitness: Being Your Best. 2007. (Snap Books). (Illus.). 32p. (J). 25.26 (978-0-7368-6471-8(7)) Capstone Pr., Inc.

Lindner, Heidi, ed. Animals, Animals, Animals. 2004. (Let's Move Ser.). (Illus.). 96p. pap. 12.95 (978-1-84126-065-5(7)) Meyer & Meyer Sport, Ltd. GBR. *Dist:* Lewis International, Inc.

—Great Games: For Small Children, Vol. 1. 2004. (Let's Move Ser.). (Illus.). 96p. pap. 12.95 (978-1-84126-064-8(9)) Meyer & Meyer Sport, Ltd. GBR. *Dist:* Lewis International, Inc.

—Off We Go Outside! 2004. (Let's Move Ser.). (Illus.). 96p. pap. 12.95 (978-1-84126-066-2(5)) Meyer & Meyer Sport, Ltd. GBR. *Dist:* Lewis International, Inc.

Lobosco, Teresa. A Winning Attitude vol. 4554: The Olympic Sport of Gymnastics, Samoiloff, Sheri, ed. Allsport Staff, photos by. 2002. (Illus.). 16p. (J). (gr. 3-6). pap. 3.49 (978-1-57471-925-3(4)) Creative Teaching Pr., Inc.

Lovitt, Chip. American Gymnasts: Gold Medal Dreams. 2000. (gr. 5-8). lib. bdg. 13.00 (978-0-613-73123-2(9)) Tandem Library Bks.

Macken, JoAnn Early. Gymnastics. 2005. (Illus.). 24p. (J). pap. (978-0-8368-4520-4(X)); (YA). lib. bdg. 19.33 (978-0-8368-4513-6(7)) Stevens, Gareth Inc.

Mattern, Joanne. Balance Beam & Floor Exercises. 1999. (Compete Like a Champion Gymnastics Ser.). (Illus.). 48p. (J). (gr. 4-8). lib. bdg. 27.93 (978-0-86593-567-9(X)) Rourke Publishing, LLC.

—Parallel Bars & Horizontal Bars. 1999. (Compete Like a Champion Ser.). (Illus.). 48p. (J). (gr. 4-8). lib. bdg. 27.93 (978-0-86593-570-9(X)) Rourke Publishing, LLC.

—Pommel Horse & the Rings. 1999. (Compete Like a Champion Gymnastics Ser.). (Illus.). 48p. (J). (gr. 4-8). lib. bdg. 27.93 (978-0-86593-568-6(8)) Rourke Publishing, LLC.

—Training & Fitness. 1999. (Compete Like a Champion Gymnastics Ser.). (Illus.). 48p. (J). (gr. 4-8). lib. bdg. 27.93 (978-0-86593-571-6(8)) Rourke Publishing, LLC.

—Uneven Parallel Bars. 1999. (Compete Like a Champion Gymnastics Ser.). (Illus.). 48p. (J). (gr. 4-8). lib. bdg. 27.93 (978-0-86593-569-3(6)) Rourke Publishing, LLC.

—The Vault. 1999. (Compete Like a Champion Gymnastics Ser.). (Illus.). (J). (gr. 4-8). lib. bdg. 27.93 (978-0-86593-566-2(1)) Rourke Publishing, LLC.

McNab, Chris. Gymnastics. 2003. (Sports Injuries Ser.). (Illus.). 64p. (J). lib. bdg. (978-1-59084-633-9(8)) Mason Crest Pubs.

Morley, Christine. The Best Book of Gymnastics. 2003. (Best Book of... Ser.). (Illus.). 32p. (J). (gr. k-3). tchr. ed. 12.95 (978-0-7534-5605-7(2) , Kingfisher) Houghton Mifflin Co. Trade & Reference Div.

Page, Jason. Gymnastics: The Balance Beam, Floor, Rings, Team Events & Lots, Lots More. Alston, John, illus. 2000. (Zeke's Olympic Pocket Guide Ser.). 32p. (J). pap. 3.95 (978-0-8225-5052-5(0) , LernerSports) Lerner Publishing Group.

Pakizer, Debi & Sears, Mary A. Vaulting: The Art of Gymnastics on Horseback. Anderson, Julia & Barnette, Jackie, eds. Sears, Mary A., illus. (Illus.). 24p. (Orig.). (J). (gr. k-6). pap. 5.00 (978-0-9639785-6-1(X)) Sears, M.A.

Porter, David. Winning Gymnastics for Girls. 2004. (Winning Sports for Girls Ser.). (Illus.). 176p. (J). (gr. 9-12). pap. 16.95 (978-0-8160-5230-1(1) , Checkmark Bks.); (gr. 6-12). 35.00 (978-0-8160-5229-5(8)) Facts On File, Inc.

Readhead, Lloyd. Gymnastics. 1998. (Olympic Library). (Illus.). (J). pap. (978-1-57572-036-4(1)) Heinemann Library.

—A World-Class Gymnast. 2004. (Making of a Champion Ser.). (Illus.). 48p. (J). pap. 8.50 (978-1-4034-5533-8(3)); lib. bdg. 27.07 (978-1-4034-4672-5(5)) Heinemann Library.

Rutledge, Rachel. The Best of the Best in Gymnastics. 1999. (Women of Sports Ser.). (Illus.). 64p. (gr. 5 up). lib. bdg. 24.90 (978-0-7613-1321-2(4)); pap. 7.95 (978-0-7613-0784-6(2)) Lerner Publishing Group. (Twenty-First Century Bks.).

—The Best of the Best in Gymnastics. 1999. (Women of Sports Ser.). (978-0-606-17031-4(6)) Tandem Library Bks.

Schlegel, Elfi. Gymnastics Book: The Young Performer's Guide to Gymnastics. 2001. (gr. 5-8). lib. bdg. 25.70 (978-0-613-78536-5(3)) Tandem Library Bks.

Schlegel, Elfi & Dunn, Claire Ross. The Gymnastics Book: A Young Person's Guide to Gymnastics. 2000. (Illus.). 124p. (J). (gr. 3-9). pap. 19.95 (978-1-55263-284-0(9)) Key Porter Bks. CAN. *Dist:* Firefly Bks., Ltd.

—The Gymnastics Book: The Young Performer's Guide to Gymnastics. 2001. (Young Performer's Guide Ser.). (Illus.). 128p. (J). (gr. 3-9). pap. 16.95 (978-1-55209-416-7(2)) Firefly Bks., Ltd.

Simkins, Kate. I Want to Be a Gymnast. 2006. (Dk Readers Ser.). (Illus.). 32p. (J). 14.99 (978-0-7566-2012-7(0)); (gr. 5). pap. 3.99 (978-0-7566-2011-0(2)) Dorling Kindersley Publishing, Inc.

Sports Illustrated for Kids Books. 2005. (Illus.). 176p. (gr. 7-12). lib. bdg. 388.65 (978-0-8239-3925-1(1)) Rosen Publishing Group, Inc., The.

Worsley, Arlene. For the Love of Gymnastics. 2006. (For the Love of Sports Ser.). (J). (978-1-59036-386-7(8)); (978-1-59036-387-4(6)) Weigl Pubs., Inc.

GYMNASTICS—FICTION

Berg, R. J. Jenny Martin & the Unexpected Gift. 2004. (Illus.). 139p. (YA). per. 9.95 (978-0-9666104-2-0(3)) Ziert, Paul Assocs., Inc.

Burnett, Eric. Gymnastics Jenny Stands on Her Own. 2003. 108p. pap. 9.95 (978-0-595-27919-7(8)) iUniverse, Inc.

Christopher, Matt. Dive Right In. ed. 2005. (Sports Classics IV Ser.). 133p. (J). lib. bdg. 15.00 (978-1-59054-753-3(5)) Fitzgerald Bks.

Daniels, Teri. The Feet in the Gym. Foster, Travis, illus. 2001. 40p. (J). (ps-3). pap. 5.95 (978-1-58837-023-5(2)) Winslow Pr.

Denham, Larry Allen. Pioneers. 2007. 392p. per. 21.95 (***978-0-595-41965-4(8)***) iUniverse, Inc.

Hoban, Lillian. Arthur's Birthday Party. Hoban, Lillian, illus. 1999. (I Can Read Bks.). (Illus.). 64p. (J). (gr. k-4). 14.89 (978-0-06-027799-4(8)); 14.95 (978-0-06-027798-7(X)) HarperCollins Pubs.

Holabird, Katharine. Angelina & Alice. 2006. (Angelina Ballerina Ser.). 32p. (J). (ps). 12.99 (978-0-670-06125-9(5) , Viking Juvenile) Penguin Group (USA) Inc.

Kalkipsakis, Thalia. The Worst Gymnast. Oswald, Ash, illus. 2007. (Go Girl! Ser.: Bk. 2). 96p. (Orig.). (J). (gr. 2 up). pap. 3.99 (***978-0-312-34642-3(5)***) Feiwel & Friends.

Lewis, Beverly. Better Than Best. 2000. (Girls Only (Go!) Ser.: Vol. 6). (Illus.). 128p. (J). (gr. 3-8). pap. 6.99 (978-1-55661-641-9(4)) Bethany Hse. Pubs.

Olsen, Ashley. Dream Team. 2002. (gr. k-3). lib. bdg. 12.40 (978-0-613-64707-6(6)) Tandem Library Bks.

Peters, Alison. Tomorrow's Olympian. Islip, Coralie, illus. 2006. (Read-It! Chapter Books). 64p. (J). (gr. 2-4). 19.95 (978-1-4048-1665-7(8)) Picture Window Bks.

Schade, Susan & Buller, Jon. Cat on the Mat. 1998. (Step into Reading Ser.: Vol. 2). (Illus.). 32p. (J). (ps-1). pap. 3.99 (978-0-307-26207-3(3) , Random Hse. Bks. for Young Readers) Random Hse. Children's Bks.

—Cat on the Mat. 1998. (Illus.). 32p. (J). (ps-ps). lib. bdg. 11.80 (978-0-613-16623-2(X)) Tandem Library Bks.

Sparks, Beatrice. Kim: Empty Inside. 2002. (gr. 7-12). lib. bdg. 14.15 (978-0-613-56919-4(9)) Tandem Library Bks.

Sparks, Beatrice, ed. Kim: Empty Inside: The Diary of an Anonymous Teenager. 2002. 176p. (YA). (gr. 7 up). pap. 5.99 (978-0-380-81460-2(9)) HarperCollins Pubs.

Tang, Charles, illus. The Gymnastics Mystery, Vol. 73. 2004. (Boxcar Children Ser.: No. 73). 128p. (gr. 2-5). mass mkt. 4.50 (978-0-8075-3101-3(4)) Whitman, Albert & Co.

Taylor, Sean. Boing! Ingman, Bruce, illus. 2004. 56p. (J). (gr. k-3). 16.99 (978-0-7636-2475-0(6)) Candlewick Pr.

Warner, Gertrude Chandler. The Gymnastics Mystery. 1999. (Boxcar Children Ser.: No. 73). (J). (gr. 2-5). 10.60 (978-0-606-18766-4(9)) Tandem Library Bks.

Wilson, J. M. & Zolkowski, Cathy A. Blue: Adventures of a Gymnast. 2004. 150p. (YA). per. 11.95 (978-0-9667037-5-7(8)) Verona (Bk.) Publishing, Inc.

GYPSIES

Sharp, Anne Wallace. The Gypsies. 2002. (Indigenous Peoples of the World Ser.). (Illus.). 112p. (J). 27.45 (978-1-59018-239-0(1) , Lucent Bks.) Thomson Gale.

Sirimarco, Elizabeth. Gypsies. 1999. (Endangered Cultures Ser.). (Illus.). 32p. (J). (gr. 4-7). lib. bdg. 16.95 (978-1-887068-91-8(0)) Smart Apple Media.

GYPSIES—FICTION

Alexander, Lloyd. Gypsy Rizka. 2000. (Illus.). 208p. (J). (gr. 3-7). pap. 5.99 (978-0-14-130980-4(6) , Puffin) Penguin Group (USA) Inc.

—Gypsy Rizka. unabr. ed. 2000. (YA). pap. 58.99 incl. audio (978-0-7887-3954-5(9) , 41059X4) Recorded Bks., LLC.

—Gypsy Rizka. 2000. (gr. 3-6). lib. bdg. 14.15 (978-0-613-30458-0(6)) Tandem Library Bks.

Bemelmans, Ludwig. Madeline & the Gypsies. 2000. (gr. k-3). lib. bdg. 15.30 (978-0-8085-2352-9(X)) Tandem Library Bks.

—Madeline & the Gypsies. Bemelmans, Ludwig, illus. 2000. (Madeline Ser.). (Illus.). (J). (ps-3). (978-0-606-18428-1(7)) Tandem Library Bks.

Brooks, Kevin. The Road of the Dead. 2006. 352p. (J). (gr. 7 up). pap. 16.99 (978-0-439-78623-2(1) , Chicken Hse., The) Scholastic, Inc.

Brooks, Kevin. Road of the Dead. rev. l.t. ed. 2007. 353p. (YA). 22.95 (***978-0-7862-9550-0(3)***) Thorndike Pr.

Duey, Kathleen. The Sunset Gates. Rayyan, Omar, illus. ed. 2005. 76p. (J). lib. bdg. 15.00 (978-1-59054-918-6(X)) Fitzgerald Bks.

—True Heart. Rayyan, Omar, illus. ed. 2005. 76p. (J). lib. bdg. 15.00 (978-1-59054-920-9(1)) Fitzgerald Bks.

Gypsy Kids: The Adventures of Colby Myers & Mark Howard. 2003. 21.95 (978-1-932277-00-5(5)) Crystal Ball Publishing, LLC.

Hicyilmaz, Gaye. Pictures from the Fire. (J). pap. 11.95 (978-1-85881-896-2(6)) Dolphin Paperbacks GBR. *Dist:* Trafalgar Square Publishing.

Patterson, Geoffrey. The Lion & the Gypsy. 2004. (Illus.). 32p. (J). pap. 7.95 (978-1-84507-140-0(9)) Lincoln, Frances Ltd. GBR. *Dist:* Perseus Distribution.

Phelps, Stuart Eliza. Gypsy's Cousin Joy. 2006. 41.99 (***978-1-4280-4051-9(X)***); pap. 34.99 (***978-1-4280-4064-9(1)***) IndyPublish.com.

Phelps, Stuart Elizabe. Gypsy Breynton. 2006. 94.99 (***978-1-4280-4003-8(X)***); pap. 88.99 (***978-1-4280-3994-0(5)***) IndyPublish.com.

Roderman, Anna Marie. Two Tales of Courage. 2004. 116p. (YA). pap. 7.95 (978-0-87714-318-5(8)) Denlingers Pubs., Ltd.

Roos, Stephen. The Gypsies Never Came. 2001. (Illus.). 128p. (J). (gr. 3-7). 15.00 (978-0-689-83147-8(1)) Simon & Schuster Children's Publishing.

Snyder, Zilpha Keatley. The Gypsy Game. 1998. 240p. (J). (gr. 5-7). pap. 5.99 (978-0-440-41258-8(7) , Yearling) Random Hse. Children's Bks.

—The Gypsy Game. 1998. (J). 12.64 (978-0-606-13104-9(3)) Tandem Library Bks.

Surace, Joan. The Story of Lucia. Rockford, Nancy, illus. 2006. (YA). pap. 8.00 (***978-0-8059-7062-3(2)***) Dorrance Publishing Co., Inc.

H

HABITATIONS, HUMAN

see Architecture, Domestic; Houses; Housing

HABITATIONS OF WILD ANIMALS

see Animals—Habitations

HABITS OF ANIMALS

see Animals—Habits and Behavior

HAIKU

Donegan, Patricia. Haiku. 2004. (Asian Arts & Crafts for Creative Kids Ser.). (Illus.). 64p. (gr. 2-7). 12.95 (978-0-8048-3501-5(2)) Tuttle Publishing.

Grimes, Nikki. A Pocketful of Poems. Steptoe, Javaka, illus. 2001. (J). 15.00. 32p. tchr. ed. 15.00 (978-0-395-93868-3(6)) Houghton Mifflin Co. Trade & Reference Div. (Clarion Bks.).

Lewis, J. Patrick & Janeczko, Paul B. Wing Nuts: Screwy Haiku. Tusa, Tricia, illus. 2006. 32p. (J). (ps-3). 15.99 (978-0-316-60731-5(2)) Little Brown & Co.

Mannis, Celeste Davidson & Hartung, Susan Kathleen. One Leaf Rides the Wind: Counting in a Japanese Garden. Mannis, Celeste Davidson, illus. 2002. (Illus.). 40p. (J). (gr. k-3). 15.99 (978-0-670-03525-0(4) , Viking Juvenile) Penguin Group (USA) Inc.

Nishimoto, Keisuke, ed. Haiku Picturebook for Children. Shimizu, Kozo, illus. 2006. 32p. (gr. 3 up). bds. 14.95 (978-0-89346-916-0(5)) Stone Bridge Pr.

Prelutsky, Jack. If Not for the Cat. Rand, Ted, illus. 2004. 40p. (J). 16.99 (978-0-06-059677-4(5)); lib. bdg. 17.89 (978-0-06-059678-1(3)) HarperCollins Pubs.

Wolf, Alan. Haiku Stickies: 100 Haiku to Write & Leave Behind. 2007. (Illus.). 208p. (J). pap. 4.95 (978-1-60059-075-7(6)) Lark Bks.

HAIL

Burby, Liza N. Hail. 1999. (Extreme Weather Ser.). 24p. (J). (gr. k-4). lib. bdg. 18.75 (978-0-8239-5293-9(2) , PowerKids Pr.) Rosen Publishing Group, Inc., The.

Mezzanotte, Jim. Granizadas. 2006. (ENG & SPA.). (J). lib. bdg. (***978-0-8368-8070-0(6)***); (Illus.). 24p. (gr. 2). pap. (***978-0-8368-8077-9(3)***) Stevens, Gareth Inc. (Weekly Reader Early Learning Library).

—Hail Storms. 2006. (J). pap. (***978-0-8368-7919-3(8)***); lib. bdg. (***978-0-8368-7912-4(0)***) Stevens, Gareth Inc. (Weekly Reader Early Learning Library).

Rain, Snow, & Hail: Individual Title Six-Packs. (Discovery World Ser.). 16p. (gr. 1-2). 28.00 (978-0-7635-8466-5(5)) Rigby Education.

HAIR

Badt, Karin Luisa. Hair There & Everywhere. 2006. (Illus.). 32p. (J). (gr. k-4). reprint ed. 17.00 (978-0-7567-9930-4(9)) DIANE Publishing Co.

Behnke, Alison. Barbers. 2006. (Pull Ahead Books). (Illus.). 32p. (J). (gr. 3-7). 22.60 (978-0-8225-2799-2(5) , Lerner Pubns.) Lerner Publishing Group.

Birch. Head Lice up Close 6 Pack. 2004. pap. 40.50 (978-1-4109-1154-4(3)) Harcourt Schl. Pubs.

Birch, Robin. Head Lice Up Close. 2004. (J). pap. 7.50 (978-1-4109-1147-6(0)); (Illus.). 32p. (J). (gr. 3-5). 26.36 (978-1-4109-1140-7(3)) Harcourt Schl. Pubs.

Bozzo, Linda. Amazing Animal Skin. 2008. (J). lib. bdg. (***978-1-4042-4168-8(X)*** , PowerKids Pr.) Rosen Publishing Group, Inc., The.

Bullis, Janis & Jannsen-Fleischman, Mary Beth. Braids, Bows & Bands. 2000. (Funtastic Kits Ser.). (Illus.). 48p. (J). 12.98 (978-0-7853-3978-6(7)) Publications International, Ltd.

DeGezelle, Terri. Taking Care of My Hair. 2006. (Keeping Healthy Ser.). (Illus.). 24p. (J). (ps-2). 19.93 (978-0-7368-4261-7(6)) Capstone Pr., Inc.

Derkazarian, Susan. You Have Head Lice! 2005. (Rookie Read-About Health Ser.). (Illus.). 32p. (J). (gr. k-2). 20.50 (978-0-516-25879-9(6) , Children's Pr.) Scholastic Library Publishing.

Dorling Kindersley Publishing Staff & Neuman, Maria. Fabulous Hair. Coppola, Angela, photos by. 2006. (Illus.). 96p. pap. 8.99 (978-0-7566-1589-5(5)) Dorling Kindersley Publishing, Inc.

Eddy's Hair: Individual Title Six-Packs. (Sails Literacy Ser.). (gr. 1-2). 36.00 (978-0-7578-6723-1(5)) Rigby Education.

Ehrlich, Fred. Does a Yak Get a Haircut? Bolam, Emily, illus. 2003. (Early Experiences Ser.). 32p. (ps-k). 10.95 (978-1-59354-016-6(7)) Blue Apple Bks.

Ferrell, Pamela. Kids Talk Hair: An Introduction Book for Grown-Ups & Kids. Holcomb, Sabrina, ed. 1999. (Illus.). 120p. (J). pap. 19.95 (978-0-939183-03-6(X)) Cornrows & Co.

Fisher, Leonard Everett. The Wigmakers. 1999. (Colonial Craftsmen Ser.). (Illus.). 48p. (J). (gr. 4-8). lib. bdg. 24.21 (978-0-7614-0933-5(5) , Benchmark Bks.) Cavendish, Marshall Corp.

Fox, Susan. Rainbow Hairstyles: Simple Styles with a Touch of Color. Klutz Press Staff, ed. 2004. (Illus.). 56p. (J). spiral bd. 14.95 (978-1-59174-269-2(2)) Klutz.

Friendship & Hair Braiding. 2003. 32p. 12.98 (978-1-4054-1639-9(4)) Parragon, Inc.

Giblin. Curl It, Braid It, Shave It. (J). Date not set. mass mkt. 4.99 (978-0-06-446210-5(2)); 2002. 160p. 14.95 (978-0-06-028151-9(0)); 2002. lib. bdg. 14.89 (978-0-06-028152-6(9)) HarperCollins Pubs.

Golomb, Ruth Goldfinger & Vavrichek, Sherri Mansfield. The Hair Pulling Habit & You: How to Solve the Trichotillomania Puzzle. Yokel, Uri & Condon-Douglas, Emily, illus. rev. ed. 2000. 147p. (gr. 5-12). pap. 28.95 (978-0-9673050-2-8(0)) Writers' Cooperative of Greater Washington.

Goode, Katherine. Skin & Hair. 2000. (Bodyworks Ser.). (Illus.). 32p. (J). (gr. 3-6). 23.70 (978-1-56711-497-3(0) , Blackbirch Pr., Inc.) Thomson Gale.

Green, Jen. Skin, Hair & Hygiene. 2005. (Illus.). 32p. (J). (gr. 3-7). lib. bdg. 27.10 (978-1-59604-053-3(X)) Stargazer Bks.

Harrison, Emma. From Head to Toe: The Girls' Life Guide to Taking Care of You. Montagna, Frank, illus. 2004. 124p. (J). (978-0-439-44983-0(9)) Scholastic, Inc.

Hartley, Karen. Head Louse. 2000. (gr. k-3). lib. bdg. 14.75 (978-0-613-44361-6(6)) Tandem Library Bks.

Hartley, Karen, et al, contrib. by. Head Louse. 2000. (Bug Books Ser.). (Illus.). 32p. (J). (gr. k-2). lib. bdg. 21.36 (978-1-57572-549-9(5)) Heinemann Library.

Johnson, Anne Akers. Hair Wraps. 1998. (Illus.). 32p. (J). (gr. 4-7). spiral bd. 14.95 (978-1-57054-163-6(9)) Klutz.

Jordan, Jim. Hair: Styling Tips & Tricks for Girls. 2000. (American Girl Library). (Illus.). 64p. (J). (gr. 3 up). pap. 8.95 (978-1-58485-038-0(8) , 51820567) American Girl Publishing, Inc.

—Hair: Styling Tips & Tricks for Girls. 2000. (gr. 3-6). lib. bdg. 17.60 (978-0-613-31274-5(0)) Tandem Library Bks.

Klingel, Cynthia Fitterer & Noyed, Robert B. Hair. Andersen, Gregg, photos by. 2002. (Weekly Reader Early Learning Library). (Illus.). 24p. (J). (ps up). pap. 5.95 (978-0-8368-3154-2(3) , Weekly Reader Early Learning Library) Stevens, Gareth Inc.

—Hair/Pelo. Acosta, Tatiana & Gutiérrez, Guillermo, trs. Andersen, Gregg, photos by. 2002. (Weekly Reader Early Learning Library). (Illus.). 24p. (J). (ps up). pap. (978-0-8368-3323-2(6)); (ENG & SPA., lib. bdg. 19.33 (978-0-8368-3074-3(1)) Stevens, Gareth Inc. (Weekly Reader Early Learning Library).

Krul Araujo, Paige, ed. Fun Pack Make You Own Hair Wraps. 2006. (J). 7.99 (978-0-439-79048-2(4) , Tangerine Pr.) Scholastic, Inc.

Lawrenson, Diana. It's True! Your Hair Is Dead. Hobbs, Leigh, illus. 2006. (It's True! Ser.). 88p. (J). (gr. 5-8). 19.95 (978-1-55451-024-5(4)); pap. 5.95 (978-1-55451-023-8(6)) Annick Pr., Ltd. CAN. *Dist:* Firefly Bks., Ltd.

Levy, Janey. Alopecia Areata. 2006. (Genetic Diseases Ser.). (Illus.). 64p. (J). lib. bdg. (978-1-4042-0693-9(0)) Rosen Publishing Group, Inc., The.

Llewellyn, Claire. Your Hair. 2007. (J). (***978-1-59771-097-8(0)***) Sea-To-Sea Pubns.

Mayer, Cassie. Fur. 2006. (Illus.). 24p. (J). (978-1-4034-8371-3(X)); pap. (978-1-4034-8377-5(9)) Heinemann Library.

Noyed, Robert B. Hair. Klingel, Cynthia Fitterer & Andersen, Gregg, photos by. 2002. (Let's Read about Our Bodies Ser.). (Illus.). 24p. (J). (ps up). lib. bdg. 19.33 (978-0-8368-3065-1(2) , Weekly Reader Early Learning Library) Stevens, Gareth Inc.

Petty Kate. Hair (World Show-and-Tell) 2006. (Illus.). 32p. (J). 8.95 (978-1-58728-532-5(0) , Two Can Publishing) T&N Children's Publishing.

Radabaugh, Melinda Beth. Getting a Haircut. 2003. (First Time Ser.). (Illus.). 24p. (ps-1). (J). lib. bdg. 18.50 (978-1-4034-0225-7(6)); pap. 5.25 (978-1-4034-0464-0(X)) Heinemann Library.

—Me Corto el Cabello. 2003. (La Primera Vez (First Time) Ser.).Tr. of Getting a Haircut. (SPA.). 24p. (J). (ps-1). lib. bdg. 18.50 (978-1-4034-0233-2(7)) Heinemann Library.

Rainis, Kenneth G. Hair, Clothing, & Tire Track Evidence: Crime-Solving Science Experiments. 2006. (Forensic Science Projects Ser.). (Illus.). 128p. (J). (gr. 5 up). lib. bdg. 31.93 (978-0-7660-2729-9(5)) Enslow Pubs., Inc.

Ribble, Karen. Braid Your Own Hair. Ribble, Karen, illus. 2002. (Illus.). 20p. 6.00 (978-0-9725170-0-3(6) , Braided Image Hair Briading) Braided Image.

Royston, Angela. Head Lice. 2001. (It's Catching Ser.). (Illus.). 32p. (J). (gr. k-2). lib. bdg. 21.36 (978-1-58810-229-4(7)) Heinemann Library.

—Healthy Hair. 2003. (Illus.). 32p. (J). pap. 6.95 (978-1-4034-4454-7(4)); lib. bdg. 22.79 (978-1-4034-4445-5(5)) Heinemann Library.

Schaefer, Lola M. El Cabello. 2003. (Es Mi Cuerpo (It's My Body) Ser.).Tr. of Hair. (SPA & ENG., Illus.). 24p. (J). lib. bdg. 18.50 (978-1-4034-0929-4(3)) Heinemann Library.

—Hair. 2003. (It's My Body Ser.). (Illus.). 24p. (J). (ps-1). lib. bdg. 18.50 (978-1-4034-0893-8(9)); pap. 5.25 (978-1-4034-3480-7(8)) Heinemann.

Southwater Staff. Outrageously Cool Hair Braids & Beads. 2002. (Illus.). 96p. (gr. 3-7). pap. 9.95 (978-1-84215-611-7(X) , Southwater) Anness Publishing GBR. *Dist:* National Bk. Network.

Souza, D.M. Look What Whiskers Can Do. 2007. (Look What Animals Can Do Ser.). (Illus.). 48p. (J). 22.60 (978-0-7613-9459-4(1) , Lerner Pubns.) Lerner Publishing Group.

Spilsbury, Louise. Why Should I Wash My Hair? And Other Questions about Healthy Skin & Hair. 2003. (Body Matters Ser.). (Illus.). 32p. (J). lib. bdg. 16.95 (978-1-4034-4685-5(7)) Heinemann Library.

Steck-Vaughn Staff. Early Reader Program Level C: All about Hair, 6 Pack. 2004. (Illus.). pap. 33.00 (978-0-7398-8313-6(5)) Steck-Vaughn.

Swain, Ruth Freeman. Hairdo: What We Do & Did to Our Hair. Smith, Cat Bowman, illus. 2002. 32p. (J). (gr. k-3). tchr. ed. 16.95 (978-0-8234-1522-9(8)) Holiday Hse., Inc.

Vogel, Elizabeth. El Cuidado de Tu Cabello. 2004. (Limpieza y Salud Todo el Dia Ser.). (SPA & ENG., Illus.). 24p. (J). lib. bdg. 16.00 (978-0-8239-6611-0(9)); (gr. 1-2). lib. bdg. 16.00 (978-0-8239-6610-3(0)) Rosen Publishing Group, Inc., The. (Buenas Letra).

Vogel, Elizabeth, et al, contrib. by. Taking Care of My Hair. 2001. (PowerKids Readers Ser.). (Illus.). 24p. (J). (gr. 1). lib. bdg. 16.00 (978-0-8239-5685-2(7) , PKCAHA, PowerKids Pr.) Rosen Publishing Group, Inc., The.

Warrick, Leanne. Hair Trix for Cool Chix: The Real Girl's Guide to Great Hair. 2004. (Cool Chix Ser.). (Illus.). 96p. (J). pap. 9.95 (978-0-8230-2179-6(3)) Watson-Guptill Pubns., Inc.

Whittaker, Nicola. Hair. 2002. (Creature Features Ser.). (Illus.). 32p. (J). (ps up). lib. bdg. 23.33 (978-0-8368-3164-1(0)) Stevens, Gareth Inc.

Wingate, Philippa. The Usborne Book of Hair. rev. ed. 2000. (Usborne Fashion Guides Ser.). (Illus.). 32p. (J). (gr. 4-7). lib. bdg. 15.95 (978-1-58086-225-7(X)) EDC Publishing.

Wingate, Philippa, ed. Hair. rev. ed. 2000. (Fashion Guides Ser.). (Illus.). 32p. (YA). (gr. 4-7). pap. 7.95 (978-0-7460-3383-8(4)) Usborne Publishing, Ltd. GBR. *Dist:* EDC Publishing.

Worthington, Charles. Complete Book of Hairstyling. 2002. (gr. 7-12). lib. bdg. 30.35 (978-0-613-60541-0(1)) Tandem Library Bks.

HAIR—FICTION

Addie's Bad Day. 2003. 22.95 (978-0-673-75904-7(0)) Celebration Pr.

Anholt, Laurence. Picasso & the Girl with a Ponytail. 2007. (Anholt's Artists Books for Children Ser.). 32p. (J). (ps-3). pap. 7.99 (***978-0-7641-3853-9(7)***) Barron's Educational Series, Inc.

Arai, Kiyoko. Beauty Pop, Vol. 6. 2007. (Beauty Pop Ser.). 200p. (YA). pap. 8.99 (***978-1-4215-1323-2(4)***) Viz Media.

Asay, Colleen. What Happened to Grandpa's Hair? 2005. (J). per. 11.95 (978-0-9767658-0-6(2)) Calico Connection, Inc., The.

Azore, Barbara. Wanda & the Wild Hair. Graham, Georgia, illus. 2005. 32p. (J). (ps-1). 15.95 (978-0-88776-717-3(6)) Tundra Bks., Inc./Livres Toundra, Inc. CAN. *Dist:* Random Hse., Inc.

Balukoff, Constance. Mooky's Bad Hair Day. 2004. 21p. pap. 14.95 (978-1-4137-1480-7(3)) PublishAmerica, Inc.

Beserra, Donna. Twirly Shirley In Hurricane Shirley. 2005. 22p. (J). 8.00 (978-0-9729484-4-9(9)) Seventh Street Pr.

Braids for Naya, 6, Pack. (ps-2). 27.00 (978-0-7635-9439-8(3)) Rigby Education.

Bray, Jeannine D. Superfro. Kenyatta, Imani, ed. Mitchell, Denise B., illus. 1998. 72p. (J). (gr. k-6). 14.95 (978-1-886580-10-7(3)) Pinnacle-Syatt Pubns.

Brisson, Pat. Melissa Parkington's Beautiful, Beautiful Hair. Bloom, Suzanne, illus. 2006. (J). 15.95 (978-1-59078-409-9(X)) Boyds Mills Pr.

Cisneros, Sandra. Hairs. ed. 2004. Orig. Title: Pelitos. (SPA., Illus.). (J). (gr. k-3). spiral bd. (978-0-616-01616-9(6)) Canadian National Institute for the Blind/Institut National Canadien pour les Aveugles.

Clarke, Jane. Scratching's Catching! Kingfisher Editors, ed. Lewis, Jan, illus. 2007. (I Am Reading Ser.). 48p. (J). (gr. k-3). pap. 3.95 (978-0-7534-5958-4(2) , Kingfisher) Houghton Mifflin Co. Trade & Reference Div.

Claverie, Jean & Chapouton, Anne Marie. Julian. 2003. (Illus.). 28p. (978-84-85334-71-1(X)) Loguez Ediciones ESP. *Dist:* Lectorum Pubns., Inc.

Cole, Babette. The Hairy Book. 2003. (Illus.). 32p. (J). (gr. k-3). pap. 9.99 (978-0-09-943425-2(3) , Red Fox) Random Hse. Children's Bks. GBR. *Dist:* Trafalgar Square Publishing.

Cole, Kenneth. No Bad News. Ruebartsch, John, photos by. 2001. (Illus.). 40p. (J). (gr. 2-6). pap. 7.95 (978-0-8075-5693-1(9)) Whitman, Albert & Co.

Daniel, Alan. Aaron's Hair. 2002. (ps-2). lib. bdg. 11.80 (978-0-613-49706-0(6)) Tandem Library Bks.

Davi. El Senor Simplon. 2003. (SPA.). (978-968-494-088-8(2) , CI30723) Centro de Informacion y Desarrollo de la Comunicacion y la Literatura MEX. *Dist:* Lectorum Pubns., Inc.

Davis, Jack E. & Palatini, Margie. Bedhead. 2003. (Illus.). 40p. (J). pap. 6.99 (978-0-689-86002-7(1) , Aladdin) Simon & Schuster Children's Publishing.

Doyle, Malachy. Hair Scare. Allen, Jonathan, illus. 2005. 24p. (J). lib. bdg. 22.65 (***978-1-59646-724-8(X)***) Dingles & Co.

Duncan, Lois. The Longest Hair in the World. 2001. (Illus.). (J). (978-0-606-20771-3(6)) Tandem Library Bks.

Ehrlich, Fred. Does a Yak Get a Haircut? 2006. (Illus.). 28p. pap. 5.95 (978-1-59354-158-3(9)) Blue Apple Bks.

Elin Hirschman, Jessica & Bright, Bonnie. The Tangle Tower. 2006. (Illus.). 32p. (J). 14.95 (978-0-9701155-6-0(3)) Cookie Bear Pr., Inc.

Eubank, Patti Reeder, illus. The Princess & the Snarls. 2006. 32p. (J). (ps). 16.95 (978-0-8249-5536-6(6) , Ideals Children's Bks.) Ideals Pubns.

Fernandes, Kim & Fernandes, Eugenie. Little Toby & the Big Hair. Fernandes, Kim & Fernandes, Eugenie, illus. 1998. (Illus.). 32p. (J). (gr. k-2). pap. 5.95 (978-1-55209-257-6(7)) Firefly Bks., Ltd.

Figueras, Nuria. Las Trenzas del Abuelo. Olmos, Roger, illus. 2003. (Libros para Soñar Ser.). (SPA.). 32p. (978-84-8464-180-3(5)) Kalandraka Editora, S.L. ESP. *Dist:* Lectorum Pubns., Inc.

Fitzgerald, F. Scott. Bernice Bobs Her Hair & Other Stories. Date not set. (Nelson Readers Ser.). (Illus.). 86p. (J). pap. (978-0-17-557051-5(5)) Addison-Wesley Longman, Inc.

Ford, Juwanda G. Shop Talk. Hoston, Jim, illus. 2004. 32p. (J). lib. bdg. 15.00 (***978-1-4242-0236-2(1)***) Fitzgerald Bks.

Foster, Bill. The Boy Who Wouldn't Comb His Hair. Kilgore, Jeannette Vrlin, illus. 2002. 32p. (J). (gr. k-6). 14.95 (978-1-931650-15-1(2)) Coastal Publishing Carolina, Inc.

Francis-Harris, Annabel. The Other Side of the Forest. 2006. pap. 19.95 (***978-1-59526-458-9(2)***) Media Creations, Inc.

Fufu Hair Dos. 2001. 65p. (J). 14.95 (978-0-9709119-7-1(1)) Limpid Butterfly Productions, The.

Glatzer, Jenna. Hattie, Get a Haircut! Kendall, Monica, illus. 2005. 32p. 19.95 (978-0-9724853-0-2(9) , Moo Pr.) Keene Publishing.

Graves, Keith. The Unexpectedly Bad Hair of Barcelona Smith. Graves, Keith, illus. 2006. (Illus.). 32p. (J). (ps). 16.99 (978-0-399-24273-1(2) , Philomel) Penguin Group (USA) Inc.

Grimes, Nikki. Wild, Wild Hair. Ford, George, illus. 2002. (J). 11.91 (978-0-7587-1855-6(1)) Book Wholesalers, Inc.

Gurule, Jennifer. Look at Aunt Clare's Hair. Gurule, Jennifer, illus. ed. 2005. (Daddy's Collection). (J). pap. 11.50 (978-1-59134-033-1(0)) Maval Publishing, Inc.

Haddix, Margaret Peterson. Because of Anya. 2002. (Illus.). 128p. (J). (gr. 3-6). 16.95 (978-0-689-83298-7(2)) Simon & Schuster Children's Publishing.

Haircuts for Bella & Rosie. 2004. (J). (978-1-932570-18-2(7)) Literacy Footprints Inc.

Hawkins-Rodgers, Donzella. No Bulley Destroy's Chloe's Hairdo. Hewins, Shirley, illus. 2003. 32p. (J). (gr. 3 up). lib. bdg. 16.95 (978-1-884242-56-4(1)) Multicultural Pubns.

Herron, Carolivia. Nappy Hair. 1998. (Dragonfly Books Ser.). (Illus.). 32p. (J). (gr. k-3). pap. 6.99 (978-0-679-89445-2(4) , Dragonfly Bks.) Random Hse. Children's Bks.

—Nappy Hair. 1999. (J). (978-0-606-16082-7(5)) Tandem Library Bks.

Hinman, Bobbie. The Knot Fairy. 2007. 32p. 15.95 (***978-0-9786791-0-1(5)***) Hinman, Bobbie E. Inc.

Hood, Susan. A Bad Hair Day. Allen, Joy, illus. 1999. (All Aboard Reading Ser.). 32p. (J). (ps-1). pap. 3.99 (978-0-448-41996-1(3) , Grosset & Dunlap) Penguin Group (USA) Inc.

—Bad Hair Day. 1999. (gr. k-3). lib. bdg. 11.80 (978-0-613-21160-4(X)) Tandem Library Bks.

Impey, Martin, illus. Rapunzel. 2007. (First Fairy Tales Ser.). 31p. (J). (***978-1-59771-076-3(8)***) Sea-To-Sea Pubns.

Jablonsky, Alice. Mane Event. 2002. (gr. k-3). lib. bdg. 11.25 (978-0-613-50466-9(6)) Tandem Library Bks.

Jensen, Lisa. If My Hair Were Like Spagetti. Jensen, Lisa, illus. Date not set. (Illus.). (J). (ps-3). mass mkt. 15.95 (978-0-9666973-0-8(8)) Jensen, Lissa.

Jinkins, Jim. Pinky Dinky Doo: Back to School Is Cool! 2005. (Step into Reading Ser.). (Illus.). 48p. (J). (gr. 1-3). pap. 3.99 (978-0-375-83237-6(8) , Random Hse. Bks. for Young Readers) Random Hse. Children's Bks.

—Pinky Dinky Doo: Think Pink! 2006. (Step into Reading Ser.). (Illus.). 48p. (J). (gr. 1-3). pap. 3.99 (978-0-375-83573-5(3)); lib. bdg. 11.99 (978-0-375-93573-2(8)) Random Hse. Children's Bks. (Random Hse. Bks. for Young Readers).

—Pinky Dinky Doo: Back to School Is Cool! 2005. (Step into Reading Ser.). (Illus.). 48p. (J). (gr. 1-3). lib. bdg. 11.99 (978-0-375-93237-3(2) , Random Hse. Bks. for Young Readers) Random Hse. Children's Bks.

Johnson, Helen. Angela's Bad Hair Day. 2004. pap. 7.95 (978-0-533-14788-5(3)) Vantage Pr., Inc.

Johnson, Kelly & Johnson, Dinah. Hair Dance. 2007. (Illus.). 32p. (J). (ps-4). 16.95 (978-0-8050-6523-7(5) , Holt, Henry & Co. Bks. For Young Readers) Holt, Henry & Co.

Johnson, Vincent L. Of Corn Silk & Black Braids. Crockett, Linda, illus. 2005. 32p. (J). (gr. k-3). 17.95 (978-0-9657033-2-1(0)) Marzetta Bks.

Kenji's Haircut: Individual Title Six-Pack Pouch - Level D. (Lighthouse Ser.). 12p. (gr. k-1). 24.00 (978-0-7578-0831-9(X)) Rigby Education.

Kindya, Kimberly. Blossom's Bad Hair Day. 2002. (Powerpuff Girls Plus You Club Ser.). (Illus.). 64p. (J). (978-0-439-33263-7(X)) Scholastic, Inc.

Klein, Adria F. Max Goes to the Barber. Gallagher-Cole, Mernie, illus. 2005. (Read-It! Readers Ser.). 24p. (J). (ps). lib. bdg. 18.60 (978-1-4048-1180-5(X)) Picture Window Bks.

Kompaneyets, Marc. The Squishiness of Things. 2005. (Illus.). 40p. (J). (gr. k-3). 15.95 (978-0-375-82750-1(1) , Knopf Bks. for Young Readers) Random Hse. Children's Bks.

Koren, Edward. Very Hairy Harry. Koren, Edward, illus. 2003. (Illus.). (978-0-06-057744-5(4)); (J). (978-0-06-056868-9(2)) HarperCollins Pubs.

—Very Hairy Harry. 2003. (Illus.). 40p. (J). (ps-3). 15.99 (978-0-06-050907-1(4) , Cotler, Joanna Books) HarperCollins Pubs.

Krosoczka, Jarrett J. Baghead. Krosoczka, Jarrett J., illus. (Illus.). 40p. (J). (ps-2). 2002. 15.95 (978-0-375-81566-9(X) , Knopf Bks. for Young Readers); 2004. reprint ed. pap. 6.99 (978-0-553-11172-9(8) , Dragonfly Bks.) Random Hse. Children's Bks.

Lambert, Janet. For Each Other: A Campbell Story. 2002. (J). per. 9.95 (978-1-930009-57-8(7)) Image Cascade Publishing.

Lubner, Susan Emple. Ruthie Bon Bair: Do Not Go to Bed with Wringing Wet Hair! Whatley, Bruce, illus. 2006. 32p. (J). (ps-3). 15.95 (978-0-8109-5470-0(2)) Abrams, Harry N. , Inc.

Lynne, Rustyna. Hair Texture. Lynne, Rustyna, illus. 2002. (Illus.). 14p. (J). (gr. k-2). spiral bd. 12.95 (978-0-9722829-2-5(0)) Red Carpet Publishing.

—Janel's Shampoo: Special Needs Version. Lynne, Rustyna, illus. 2002. (Illus.). 17p. (J). spiral bd. 12.95 (978-0-9722829-1-8(2)) Red Carpet Publishing.

—Tatiana's Shampoo. Lynne, Rustyna, illus. l.t. ed. 2002. (Illus.). 12p. (J). (gr. k-2). spiral bd. 10.95 (978-0-9719657-2-0(2)) Red Carpet Publishing.

—Tatiana's Shampoo: Special Needs Version. Lynne, Rustyna, illus. l.t. ed. 2002. (Illus.). 14p. (YA). (gr. 3-8). spiral bd. 10.95 (978-0-9719657-3-7(0)) Red Carpet Publishing.

Madrigal, Antonio Hernandez. Erandi's Braids. Peskin, Joy, ed. de Paola, Tomie, illus. 2001. 1p. (J). (ps-3). pap. 6.99 (978-0-698-11885-0(5) , Putnam Juvenile) Penguin Group (USA) Inc.

—Erandi's Braids. de Paola, Tomie, illus. 1999. 32p. (J). (ps-3). 15.99 (978-0-399-23212-1(5) , Putnam Juvenile) Penguin Group (USA) Inc.

Many, Paul. Dad's Bald Head. O'Malley, Kevin, illus. 2007. 32p. (J). (ps-2). 15.95 (***978-0-8027-9579-3(X)***) Walker & Co.

Many, Paul & O'Malley, Kevin. Dad's Bald Head. O'Malley, Kevin, illus. 2007. (Illus.). 32p. (J). (ps-2). 16.85 (***978-0-8027-9580-9(3)***) Walker & Co.

Marek, Catherine. Luke's 1st Haircut. Wilson, Colleen, ed. Mitchell, Hazel, illus. 2006. 30p. (J). per. 8.95 (978-0-9748251-5-1(8) , Pen of A Ready Writer) Zoe Life Publishing.

—Sara's 1st Haircut, Sabrina, Adams, ed. Mitchell, Hazel, illus. l.t. ed. 2005. 30p. (J). per. 9.95 (978-0-9748251-3-7(1)) Zoe Life Publishing.

Marsh, Carole. The Case of the Hunchback Hairdresser. 2006. 64p. (gr. 1-3). 14.95 (***978-0-635-06202-4(X)***) Gallopade International.

McGraw-Hill Staff. Rapunzel. 2001. (gr. k-3). lib. bdg. 11.80 (978-0-613-87941-5(4)) Tandem Library Bks.

Meidell, Sherry. The Devil with the Three Golden Hairs: The Classic Brothers Grimm Folktale. 2006. (Illus.). 32p. (J). 16.95 (978-1-933317-50-2(7)) Silverleaf Pr.

Morton, Elizabeth. Anne's Red Hair. 2001. 32p. (J). (ps-3). pap. 3.99 (978-0-06-442158-4(9) , Avon) HarperCollins Pubs.

Munsch, Robert. Aaron's Hair. Daniel, Alan & Daniel, Lea, illus. 2000. 32p. (J). (ps-1). pap. 11.95 (978-0-439-19258-3(7)) Scholastic, Inc.

—Aaron's Hair. Daniel, Alan, illus. 1998. 32p. (J). (ps-2). 4.99 (978-0-590-21103-1(X)) Scholastic, Inc.

Munsch, Robert, et al. Aaron's Hair. Daniel, Alan & Daniel, Lea, illus. 2002. 32p. (J). pap. 4.99 (978-0-439-38848-1(1) , Cartwheel Bks.) Scholastic, Inc.

Munsch, Robert N. Stephanie's Ponytail. Martchenko, Michael, illus. 2007. (Annikins Ser.). 24p. (J). (ps-2). pap. 1.50 (***978-1-55451-114-3(3)***) Annick Pr., Ltd. CAN. *Dist:* Firefly Bks., Ltd.

Murphy, Jill. The Worst Witch Saves the Day. Murphy, Jill, illus. 2007. (Worst Witch Ser.). (Illus.). 160p. (J). (gr. 3). 13.99 (***978-0-7636-3319-6(4)***) Candlewick Pr.

Napoli, Donna Jo & Furrow, Eva. Bobby the Bold. Hoyt, Ard, illus. 2006. 32p. (J). (ps-12). 16.99 (978-0-8037-2990-2(1) , Dial) Penguin Group (USA) Inc.

Nesbit, E. Melisande. 1999. (J). (978-0-606-16399-6(9)) Tandem Library Bks.

O'Connor, Joe. Where Did Daddy's Hair Go? Payne, Henry, illus. 2006. 40p. (J). (gr. k-3). 14.95 (978-0-375-83571-1(7)); lib. bdg. 16.99 (978-0-375-93571-8(1)) Random Hse. Children's Bks. (Random Hse. Bks. for Young Readers).

Orlev, Uri. Hairy Tuesday. Gleich, Jacky, illus. 1999. 32p. (J). (gr. 1-5). 15.95 (978-1-57255-651-5(X)) Mondo Publishing.

Palatini, Margie. Bedhead. Davis, Jack E., illus. 2nd ed. 2005. (Stories to Go! Ser.). (J). 40p. 4.99 (978-1-4169-0832-6(3)); (***978-1-4156-2894-2(7)***) Simon & Schuster Children's Publishing. (Aladdin).

—Bedhead. 2000. lib. bdg. 15.30 (978-0-613-66481-3(7)) Tandem Library Bks.

Palatini, Margie & Davis, Jack E. Bedhead. 2000. (Illus.). 40p. (J). (ps-3). 16.00 (978-0-689-82397-8(5)) Simon & Schuster Children's Publishing.

Park, Barbara. Junie B. Jones Is a Beauty Shop Guy. unabr. ed. 2004. (Junie B. Jones Ser.: No. 11). 67p. (J). (gr. k-3). pap. 17.00 incl. audio (978-0-8072-0532-7(X) , Listening Library) Random Hse. Audio Publishing Group.

—Junie B. Jones Is a Beauty Shop Guy. Brunkus, Denise, illus. 2006. (Junie B. Jones Ser.: No. 11). (SPA.). 80p. (J). (gr. k-3). pap. 3.99 (978-0-439-66124-9(2) , Scholastic en Espanol) Scholastic, Inc.

Parr, Todd. This Is My Hair. 2004. (Illus.). 24p. (J). (ps-ps). bds. 6.99 (978-0-316-90811-5(8)) Little, Brown Bks. for Young Readers.

Petrosino, Tamara, illus. No Plain Hair. 2006. (I'm Going to Read Ser.). 32p. (J). pap. 3.95 (978-1-4027-3083-2(7)) Sterling Publishing Co., Inc.

Pliszka, Jodi. Bella & Gizmo's Adventures: The Hairless Sphynx Cats. 2005. (Illus.). 25p. (J). per. 18.95 (978-1-933449-03-6(9)) Nightengale Pr.

—Bella & Gizmo's Adventures — the Hairless Sphynx Cats. 2005. (Illus.). 30p. (J). per. 18.95 (978-1-933449-27-2(6)) Nightengale Pr.

Reader's Digest Staff & Katschke, Judy. Barbie Pretty Hairstyle Revised. 2006. (Style Bks.). 12p. (J). bds. 12.99 (978-0-7944-1009-4(X)) Reader's Digest Assn., Inc., The.

Ritchie, Alison. Horrible Haircut. Newsham, Ian, illus. 2001. (Blue Bananas Ser.). 48p. (J). (gr. 1-2). (978-0-7787-0844-5(6)); pap. (978-0-7787-0890-2(X)) Crabtree Publishing Co.

—Horrible Haircut. 2002. (gr. k-3). lib. bdg. 12.95 (978-0-613-52856-6(5)) Tandem Library Bks.

Rose, Gerald. Horrible Melena. (SPA.). (J). 8.95 (978-958-04-7343-5(9)) Norma S.A. COL. *Dist:* Distribuidora Norma, Inc.

Saltzberg, Barney. Crazy Hair Day. Saltzberg, Barney, illus. 2003. (Illus.). 32p. (J). (gr. k-3). 15.99 (978-0-7636-1954-1(X)) Candlewick Pr.

Santa Gets A Haircut. 2005. (J). 5.95 (978-0-9769321-3-0(X)) Steingart, Nathan Publishing.

Sargent, Dave M., Jr. Buffy's Haircut, 9. Huff, Jeane Lirley, illus. 2004. (Doggie Tails Ser.: 9). (J). pap. 9.95 (978-1-56763-860-8(0)) Ozark Publishing.

Sargent, David M., Jr. Buffy's Haircut, 9. Huff, Jeane Lirley, illus. 2004. (Doggie Tails Ser.: 9). (J). lib. bdg. 19.95 (978-1-56763-859-2(7)) Ozark Publishing.

Scholastic, Inc. Staff & Ford, Juwanda G. Shop Talk. Hoston, Jim, illus. 2004. (Just for You! Ser.). 32p. (gr. k-3). pap. 3.99 (978-0-439-56873-9(0) , Teaching Resources) Scholastic, Inc.

Sitare Ltd. Staff. The Save Your Hair Wiz. MacLean, Alistair, ed. Milton, illus. l.t. ed. 2000. 100p. (YA). 10.00 (978-0-940178-66-3(4)) Sitare, Ltd.

Smith Dinbergs, Holly. Hair Scare. Stewart, Chantal, illus. 2005. (Girlz Rock! Ser.). (J). pap. (978-1-59336-702-2(3)) Mondo Publishing.

Spruill, Ed & Spruill, Sonya. Jordan's Hair. Peringer, Stephen Mercer, illus. 2005. 16p. (J). 8.00 (978-0-8170-1484-1(5)) Judson Pr.

Stewart, Dawn. Harriet's Horrible Hair Day. White, Michael, illus. 2000. 32p. (J). (ps-3). 15.95 (978-1-56145-165-4(7)) Peachtree Pubs., Ltd.

Strickland, Michael R. Haircuts at Sleepy Sam's. Holliday, Keaf, illus. 2003. 32p. (J). (gr. 2-4). 15.95 (978-1-56397-562-2(9)) Boyds Mills Pr.

Tarpley, Natasha Anastasia. I Love My Hair! Lewis, E. B., illus. 1998. 32p. (J). (ps-3). 16.99 (978-0-316-52275-5(9)) Little Brown & Co.

—I Love My Hair! Lewis, E. B., illus. (J). (ps-k). 2003. 11p. bds. 6.99 (978-0-316-52558-9(8)); 2001. 32p. pap. 6.99 (978-0-316-52375-2(5)) Little, Brown Bks. for Young Readers.

Tarpley, Natasha Anastasia, ed. & illus. I Love My Hair! Tarpley, Natasha Anastasia, illus. 2001. 12.75 (978-0-606-22561-8(7)) Tandem Library Bks.

Teague, Mark. Moog-Moog Space Barber. 2005. (Illus.). 32p. (J). (ps-ps). pap. 5.99 (978-0-439-78122-0(1) , Scholastic Paperbacks) Scholastic, Inc.

Tiller, Steve. Tangle Fairies. Cremeans, Robert, illus. 2001. 28p. (J). (ps-4). per. 6.95 (978-0-9704597-0-1(X)); 13.95 (978-0-9704597-1-8(8)) MichaelsMind LLC.

Tinkham, Kelly. Hair for Mama. Bates, Amy June, illus. 2007. 32p. (J). (ps-3). 16.99 (978-0-8037-2955-1(3) , Dial) Penguin Group (USA) Inc.

Umansky, Kaye & Chamberlain, Margaret. Need a Trim, Jim. 1999. (Illus.). 32p. (J). 11.99 (978-0-370-32328-2(9)) Random Hse. GBR. *Dist:* Independent Pubs. Group.

Victoria, Lisa, illus. Clara's Gift from the Heart. 2006. (J). 17.95 (978-0-9674602-9-1(8)) Blue Marlin Pubns.

Ward, Barbara Briggs. The Really REALLY Hairy Flight of Snarly Sally. (Illus.). 32p. (ps-3). 14.95 (978-1-890621-23-0(4)) Landauer Corp.

Wax, Wendy. Renoir & the Boy with the Long Hair. Lane, Nancy, illus. 2007. 32p. (J). (ps-3). 14.99 ***(978-0-7641-6041-7(9))*** Barron's Educational Series, Inc.

Wilhelm, Hans. Don't Cut My Hair. 2004. 32p. (J). lib. bdg. 15.00 (978-1-59054-351-1(3)) Fitzgerald Bks.

Wilkerson, L. Kobie, 3rd, reader. Fred & Mary. 2008. (Illus.). 32p. (J). 24.95 incl. DVD, audio compact disk ***(978-0-9796679-0-9(9))*** Gye Nyame Pr.

Wood, Maryrose. Why I Let My Hair Grow Out. 2007. 272p. (J). pap. 9.99 (978-0-425-21380-3(3) , Berkley Trade) Penguin Group (USA) Inc.

Ziefert, Harriet. There Was a Little Girl, She Had a Little Curl. 2006. (Illus.). 36p. (J). 15.95 (978-1-59354-161-3(9)) Blue Apple Bks.

HAITI

Blashfield, Jean F. Haiti. 2007. 144p. (J). 37.00 ***(978-0-516-25949-9(0)*** , Children's Pr.) Scholastic Library Publishing.

Callaway, Julie. My Haiti, My Homeland. 2004. (Illus.). 32p. (J). 12.50 (978-1-58432-181-1(4)) Educa Vision.

Dell'Oro, Suzanne Paul. Haiti. 2001. (Countries of the World Ser.). (Illus.). 126p. (J). (gr. 2-3). 18.60 (978-0-7368-0942-9(2) , Bridgestone Bks.) Capstone Pr., Inc.

Furlong, Kate A. Haiti. 2003. (Countries Ser.). (Illus.). 40p. (J). (gr. k-6). lib. bdg. 22.78 (978-1-57765-841-2(8)) ABDO Publishing Co.

Gaines, Jena. Haitian Immigration. 2003. (Changing Face of North America Ser.). (Illus.). 112p. (J). lib. bdg. (978-1-59084-691-9(5)) Mason Crest Pubs.

Graves, Kerry A. Haiti. 2002. (Countries & Cultures Ser.). (Illus.). 64p. (J). (gr. 3-4). lib. bdg. 23.93 (978-0-7368-1078-4(1) , Bridgestone Bks.) Capstone Pr., Inc.

Grolier Educational Staff, contrib. by. Haiti. 2003. (Illus.). 32p. (J). (978-0-7172-5792-8(4) , Grolier) Scholastic Library Publishing.

Jackson, Kim, ed. Lavi ti Moun: Life of a Child. DeTellis, George, Jr., photos by. 1998. (Illus.). 50p. pap. 10.00 (978-0-9653234-2-0(0)) New Missions, Inc.

Mara, Wil. Haiti. 2006. (Discovering Cultures Ser.). 48p. (J). lib. bdg. 28.50 (978-0-7614-1987-7(X) , Benchmark Bks.) Cavendish, Marshall Corp.

NgCheong-Lum, Roseline. Haiti. 1999. (Festivals of the World Ser.). (Illus.). 32p. (J). (gr. 3 up). lib. bdg. 24.67 (978-0-8368-2015-7(0)) Stevens, Gareth Inc.

Ngcheong-Lum, Roseline & Jermyn, Leslie. Haiti. 2nd ed. 2005. (Cultures of the World Ser.). (Illus.). 144p. (J). (gr. 6-10). lib. bdg. (978-0-7614-1968-6(3) , Benchmark Bks.) Cavendish, Marshall Corp.

Preszler, June. Haiti: A Question & Answer Book. 2007. (Fact Finders Ser.). (Illus.). 32p. (J). ***(978-0-7368-6770-2(8)*** , 1264916) Capstone Pr., Inc.

Rockwell, Anne. Open the Door to Liberty! A Biography of Toussaint L'Ouverture. Christie, Gregory, illus. 2008. (J). ***(978-0-618-60570-5(3))*** Houghton Mifflin Co.

Temple, Bob. Haiti. 2003. (Discovering Latin America Ser.). (Illus.). 64p. (J). (gr. 5 up). lib. bdg. (978-1-59084-302-4(9)) Mason Crest Pubs.

Turck, Mary C. Haiti: Land of Inequality. 1999. (World in Conflict Ser.). (Illus.). 104p. (YA). (gr. 7-12). 25.26 (978-0-8225-3554-6(8) , Lerner Pubns.) Lerner Publishing Group.

Victor, Archimede J. In the Name of Liberty: A History of Haiti (Pre-1492-1806). 1000. 2004. (Illus.). 300p. (YA). per. 30.00 net. (978-0-9720954-1-9(1)) Linive Kreyol Publishing.

Vilsaint, Fequiere. Writing about the History of Haiti. Date not set. 36p. (J). (gr. 3-6). wbk. ed. 5.50 (978-1-881839-58-3(3)) Educa Vision.

Wagner, Michele. Haiti. 2002. (Countries of the World Ser.). (Illus.). 96p. (J). (gr. 6 up). lib. bdg. 30.00 (978-0-8368-2351-6(6)) Stevens, Gareth Inc.

Wagner, Michele & Brown, Katharine. Welcome to Haiti. 2003. (Welcome to My Country Ser.). (Illus.). 48p. (J). (gr. 2 up). lib. bdg. 26.00 (978-0-8368-2551-0(9)) Stevens, Gareth Inc.

Will, Emily. Haiti. 2000. (Modern Nations of the World Ser.). (Illus.). 128p. (J). (gr. 7-10). 29.95 (978-1-56006-761-0(6) , Lucent Bks.) Thomson Gale.

HAITI—FICTION

Conde, Maryse. Reves Amers. pap. 17.95 (978-2-7470-0350-6(7)) Bayard Editions FRA. *Dist:* Distribooks, Inc.

Danticat, Edwidge. Anacaona: Golden Flower, Haiti 1490. 2005. (Royal Diaries). (Illus.). 192p. (J). pap. 10.95 (978-0-439-49906-4(2)) Scholastic, Inc.

Elvgren, Jennifer Riesmeyer. Josias, Hold the Book. Tadgell, Nicole, illus. 2006. 32p. (J). 15.95 (978-1-59078-318-4(2)) Boyds Mills Pr.

Heurtelou, Maude. Sandra: Cinderalla in Haiti. 2004. (CRP., Illus.). 24p. (J). 8.50 (978-1-58432-176-7(8)) Educa Vision.

Lambert, Janet. Five's a Crowd: A Campbell Story. 2002. (J). per. 9.95 (978-1-930009-59-2(3)) Image Cascade Publishing.

Landowne, Youme, illus. Selavi, That Is Life: A Haitian Story of Hope. 2004. 40p. (J). 17.95 (978-0-938317-84-5(9)) Cinco Puntos Pr.

Montero, Mayra. In the Palm of Darkness: A Novel. 1998. 192p. pap. 13.95 (978-0-06-092906-0(5)) HarperCollins Pubs.

Moore, Robin. The Man with the Silver Oar. 2002. 192p. (J). (gr. 5 up). 15.89 (978-0-06-000048-6(1)) HarperCollins Pubs.

Turnbull, Elizabeth. Bel Peyi Mwen: My Beautiful Country - A Children's Coloring Book of Haiti. Battles, Kristopher, illus. 4th ed. 2000. 32p. (J). 5.95 (978-0-9679937-4-4(1)) Light Messages.

Williams, Karen L. Painted Dreams. Stock, Catherine, illus. 1998. 40p. (J). (gr. k-3). 17.99 (978-0-688-13901-8(9)); 15.89 (978-0-688-13902-5(7)) HarperCollins Pubs.

Williams, Karen Lynn. Circles of Hope. Saport, Linda, illus. 2005. 32p. (J). 16.00 (978-0-8028-5276-2(9)) Eerdmans, William B. Publishing Co.

HALE, NATHAN, 1755-1776

Devillier, Christy. Nathan Hale. 2004. (First Biographies Set Iv Ser.). (Illus.). 32p. (J). (gr. k-4). lib. bdg. 22.78 (978-1-59197-513-7(1)) ABDO Publishing Co.

Koestler-Grack, Rachel A. Nathan Hale: Courageous Spy. 2005. (Leaders of the American Revolution Ser.). (Illus.). 124p. (J). (gr. 4-8). lib. bdg. 30.00 (978-0-7910-8623-0(2) , Chelsea Hse.) Facts On File, Inc.

Libertson, Jody. Nathan Hale: Hero of the American Revolution. 2003. (Famous People in American History Ser.). (Illus.). 32p. (YA). pap. (978-0-8239-4189-6(2)) Rosen Publishing Group, Inc., The.

Lough, Loree. Nathan Hale. 1999. (Revolutionary War Leaders Ser.). (Illus.). 80p. (gr. 3 up). (J). 31.00 (978-0-7910-5361-4(X)); (YA). pap. 27.50 (978-0-7910-5704-9(6)) Facts On File, Inc. (Chelsea Hse.).

—Nathan Hale: Revolutionary Hero. 2000. (Illus.). 80p. (J). (gr. 3-17). lib. bdg. 17.60 (978-0-613-43357-0(2)) Tandem Library Bks.

Olson, Nathan. Nathan Hale: Revolutionary Spy. Martin, Cynthia & Schoonover, Brent, illus. 2005. (Graphic Library). 32p. (J). (gr. 3-7). lib. bdg. 25.26 (978-0-7368-4968-5(8)) Capstone Pr., Inc.

Tracy, Kathleen. Nathan Hale. 2006. (Profiles in American History Ser.). (Illus.). 48p. (J). (gr. 4-8). lib. bdg. 20.95 (978-1-58415-447-1(0)) Mitchell Lane Pubs., Inc.

Zemlicka, Shannon. Nathan Hale. 2002. (gr. 3-6). lib. bdg. 14.10 (978-0-613-52450-6(0)) Tandem Library Bks.

—Nathan Hale: Patriot Spy. 2002. (On My Own Biographies Ser.). (Illus.). 48p. (J). lib. bdg. 23.93 (978-0-87614-597-5(7) , Carolrhoda Bks.) Lerner Publishing Group.

HALE, SARAH JOSEPHA (BUELL), 1788-1879

Anderson, Laurie Halse. Thank You, Sarah: The Woman Who Saved Thanksgiving. Faulkner, Matt, illus. 40p. (J). 2005. 6.99 (978-0-689-85143-8(X) , Aladdin); 2002. 16.95 (978-0-689-84787-5(4)) Simon & Schuster Children's Publishing.

Dubois, Muriel L. To My Countrywomen: The Life of Sarah Josepha Hale. 2006. ***(978-0-9723410-1-1(3))*** Apprentice Shop Bks., LLC.

HALLOWEEN

Adam, Winky. Little Halloween Sticker Activity Book. 2001. (Illus.). 4p. (J). (ps-3). 1.50 (978-0-486-41676-2(3)) Dover Pubns., Inc.

American Girl Editorial Staff. Have a Molly Halloween. 2004. (Illus.). 56p. (J). 15.95 (978-1-58485-889-8(3)) American Girl Publishing, Inc.

Barbaresi, Nina. Glow-in-the-Dark Halloween Stickers. 2006. (Dover Little Activity Bks.). 2p. (J). pap. 1.50 (978-0-486-44922-7(X)) Dover Pubns., Inc.

Barnett, Michelle Noble, et al. Theme Pockets - October: Halloween; Night Creatures; Healthy & Happy. Evans, Marilyn, ed. Larsen, Jo, illus. 1999. (Making Books with Pockets). 96p. (J). pap., tchr. ed. 12.99 (978-1-55799-707-4(1) , EMC 593) Evan-Moor Educational Pubs.

Barth, Edna. Witches, Pumpkins, & Grinning Ghosts: The Story of the Halloween Symbols. Arndt, Ursula, illus. 2000. 96p. (J). (gr. 4-6). pap. 7.95 (978-0-618-06782-4(5) , Clarion Bks.) Houghton Mifflin Co. Trade & Reference Div.

—Witches, Pumpkins, & Grinning Ghosts: The Story of the Halloween Symbols. 2000. (gr. 3-6). lib. bdg. 16.40 (978-0-613-30195-4(1)); (Illus.). (J). (978-0-606-20996-0(4)) Tandem Library Bks.

Beaton, Clare. Halloween Fun. 2004. (Fun Activity Ser.). (Illus.). 24p. (J). pap., act. bk. ed. 4.95 (978-0-7641-2750-2(0)) Barron's Educational Series, Inc.

Beylon, Cathy. Halloween Stained Glass Coloring Book. 2007. 16p. (J). pap. 5.95 ***(978-0-486-45677-5(3))*** Dover Pubns., Inc.

BHB International Staff. Witches & Whatnot. 1999. 131p. (J). (gr. 1-4). pap. (978-2-215-06260-8(6)) Editions Heritage, Inc.

Bickico Enterprises, concept. BabyKids: Halloween Book. 2005. 16p. (J). pap. 2.95 (978-0-9746508-6-9(2)) Bickico Enterprises, Inc.

Blair, Beth & Ericsson, Jennifer. The Everything Kids' Halloween Puzzle. 2005. (Illus.). 144p. (J). pap., act. bk. ed. 6.95 (978-1-58062-959-1(8)) Adams Media Corp.

Bodden, Valerie. Halloween. 2005. (My First Look at Holidays Ser.). (Illus.). 24p. (J). (gr. k-3). 15.95 (978-1-58341-368-5(5) , Creative Education) Creative Co., The.

Bolby, Karen. Spooks' Surprise. 2004. (Young Puzzle Adventures Ser.). (Illus.). 32p. (J). (gr. 2 up). lib. bdg. 12.95 (978-1-58086-492-3(9)) EDC Publishing.

Bond, Felicia. The Halloween Play. Bond, Felicia, illus. 2003. Orig. Title: The Halloween Performance. (Illus.). 32p. (J). (ps up). bds. 6.99 (978-0-06-054443-0(0)) HarperCollins Pubs.

Borten, Helen. Halloween. 48p. (J). (gr. 2-5). 1999. lib. bdg. 14.89 (978-0-06-023583-3(7)); 1998. 15.00 (978-0-06-023582-6(9)) HarperCollins Pubs.

Boyds Mills Press, creator. Fun-to-Make Crafts for Halloween. 2005. (Illus.). 64p. (J). (ps-ps). 15.95 (978-1-59078-343-6(3)) Boyds Mills Pr.

Boyds Mills Press Staff. Fun-to-Make Crafts for Halloween. 2005. (Illus.). 63p. (J). (ps-ps). pap. 7.95 (978-1-59078-368-9(9)) Boyds Mills Pr.

Brighter Vision Publishing Staff. Halloween & Thanksgiving. 2000. (Make It Now Crafts Ser.). (Illus.). (J). (ps-3). pap. 3.95 (978-1-55254-178-4(9)) Brighter Vision Pubns.

—Wipe Away Halloween-Numbers. 2000. (Illus.). (J). (ps-3). pap. 2.95 (978-1-55254-182-1(7)) Brighter Vision Pubns.

Brown, Marc. Scared Silly! A Book for the Brave. 2000. (gr. k-3). lib. bdg. 16.15 (978-0-613-30117-6(X)) Tandem Library Bks.

Bull, Jane. Halloween. 2005. (Sticker activity Bks.). 16p. (J). pap. 6.99 (978-0-7566-1224-5(1)) Dorling Kindersley Publishing, Inc.

Carrier, Lark. On Halloween. 1999. (Illus.). 40p. (J). (gr. k-3). 7.95 (978-0-694-01292-3(0) , Harper Festival) HarperCollins Pubs.

Chambers, Catherine. All Saints, All Souls & Halloween. 1999. (World of Holidays Ser.). (Illus.). 32p. (J). (gr. 2-5). pap. 6.95 (978-0-7398-1383-6(8)) Steck-Vaughn.

—All Saints, All Souls & Halloween. 2000. (Illus.). (J). (978-0-606-18476-2(7)) Tandem Library Bks.

Christensen, Jo-Anne. Haunted Halloween Stories Vol. 1: A Collection of Ghost Stories. rev. ed. 2003. (Ghost Stories Ser.). (Illus.). 208p. (J). (gr. 4). pap. (978-1-894877-34-3(9)) Lone Pine Publishing.

Chronicle Books Staff, contrib. by. Homemade Halloween: Fun-To-Make Crafts & Treats. 2003. (Illus.). 32p. (J). pap. 9.95 (978-0-8118-4016-3(6)) Chronicle Bks. LLC.

Court, Rob. How to Draw Halloween Things. 2007. (Doodle Bks.). 32p. (J). 21.36 ***(978-1-59296-808-4(2))*** Child's World, Inc.

Crozon, Alain & Lanchais, A. Halloween! 1999. (What Am I? Ser.). (Illus.). 7p. (J). (ps). 7.95 (978-0-8118-2612-9(0)) Chronicle Bks. LLC.

Dalmatian Press Staff. It's Halloween Shaped Photo Real Sticker BTC. 2004. 32p. pap. 2.99 (978-1-4037-0839-7(8)) Dalmatian Pr.

D'Andrea, Deborah, concept. Picture Me Happy Halloween. 2001. (Picture Me Ser.). 10p. (J). (ps up). bds. 4.99 (978-1-57151-593-3(3)) Playhouse Publishing.

Deschamps, Nicola, ed. Halloween. Shott, Stephen & Crawford, Andy, illus. 2001. (Scratch & Sniff Ser.). 12p. (J). bds. 6.99 (978-0-7894-7858-0(7)) Dorling Kindersley Publishing, Inc.

DK Publishing. Halloween Hide & Seek. 2008. 16p. (J). (ps-k). 4.99 ***(978-0-7566-3816-0(X))*** Dorling Kindersley Publishing, Inc.

DK Publishing Staff. Halloween Surprise. 2007. 10p. (J). (ps-1). 4.99 (978-0-7566-2929-8(2)) Dorling Kindersley Publishing, Inc.

Doinet, Mymi. Halloween: Creepy Crawly, Hairy Scary Things to Do. Chaud, Benjamin, illus. 2002. 32p. (J). pap., act. bk. ed. 5.95 (978-0-8118-3279-3(1)) Chronicle Bks. LLC.

Dorling Kindersley Publishing Staff. Halloween. 2001. (Ultimate Sticker Bks.). (Illus.). 16p. (J). (gr. k-3). pap. 6.99 (978-0-7894-6502-3(7)) Dorling Kindersley Publishing, Inc.

—Sparkly Witch & Wizard. 2005. (Illus.). 12p. (J). bds. 5.99 (978-0-7566-1135-4(0)) Dorling Kindersley Publishing, Inc.

Dorling Kindersley Publishing Staff, contrib. by. My First Halloween. 2nd rev. ed. 2004. (Illus.). 36p. (J). bds. 5.99 (978-0-7566-0505-6(9)) Dorling Kindersley Publishing, Inc.

Dorling Kindersley Publishing Staff & Bull, Jane. The Halloween Book: 50 Creepy Crafts for a Hair-Raising Halloween. Crawford, Andy, photos by. 2000. (Illus.). 48p. (J). (gr. 4-7). 12.95 (978-0-7894-6655-6(4)) Dorling Kindersley Publishing, Inc.

Dorling Kindersley Publishing Staff & Millard, Anne. Halloween. 2002. (Jumbo Shaped Board Bks.). (Illus.). 12p. (J). bds. 6.99 (978-0-7894-8589-2(3)) Dorling Kindersley Publishing, Inc.

Douglas, Bettye. Safari Oklahoma Presents: The Magic of Christmas Around the World. Douglas, Bettye, ed. Douglas, Punchye, illus. (Multicultural). 16p. (J). (gr. k-6). 5.00 (978-0-9703183-4-3(0)) Douglas, Bettye Forum, Inc., The.

Douglas, Punchye, illus. Safari Oklahoma Presents Operation Safe 2000: Halloween Coloring Book. (Safari Oklahoma Presents). 16p. (J). (gr. k-6). 5.00 (978-0-9703183-2-9(4)) Douglas, Bettye Forum, Inc., The.

Ellis, Rowland-Grey & Kentor, Teddy. The Scariest Alphabet Book. 2002. (Illus.). 152p. 6.95 (978-1-57168-717-3(3)) Eakin Pr.

Filipowich, Bob & Ikids. Trick or Treat. 2004. (Illus.). 6p. (J). (ps-ps). 9.99 (978-1-58476-285-0(3)) Innovative Kids.

Flanagan, Alice K. Halloween. Girouard, Patrick, illus. 2001. (Holidays & Festivals Ser.). 32p. (J). (gr. 3 up). lib. bdg. 22.60 (978-0-7565-0086-3(9)) Compass Point Bks.

Fowler, Richard. Lights Out! Shadow Pop-up & Play. 2006. (Illus.). 10p. (J). 9.99 (978-0-7641-6002-8(8)) Barron's Educational Series, Inc.

Fremont, Victoria & Stewart, Pat. Invisible Witches Magic Picture Book. 1998. (Illus.). 16p. (J). pap. 1.00 (978-0-486-40529-2(X)) Dover Pubns., Inc.

Friedman, Pamela. Activites d'Halloween. (FRE.). 16p. pap. (978-0-439-00533-3(7)) Scholastic Canada, Ltd.

Ghigna, Charles & McCauley, Adam. Halloween Night: Twenty-One Spooktacular Poems. rev. ed. 2003. (Illus.). 32p. (gr. k-3). 15.95 (978-0-7624-1552-6(5) , Running Pr. Kids) Running Pr. Bk. Pubs.

Gibbons, Gail. Halloween Is.... (Illus.). 32p. (J). (gr. k-3). pap. 6.95 (978-0-8234-1797-1(2)) Holiday Hse., Inc.

—Halloween Is.... Gibbons, Gail, illus. (Illus.). 32p. (gr. k-3). tchr. ed. 17.95 (978-0-8234-1758-2(1)) Holiday Hse., Inc.

Gillis, Jennifer Blizin. Halloween. 2003. (Holiday Histories Ser.). (Illus.). 32p. (J). pap. 6.50 (978-1-4034-3691-7(6)); lib. bdg. 22.79 (978-1-4034-3506-4(5)) Heinemann Library.

Greene, Carol. The Story of Halloween. Bronson, Linda, illus. 40p. (J). 2005. pap. 6.99 (978-0-06-443774-5(4) , Harper Trophy); 2004. 15.99 (978-0-06-027946-2(X)); 2004. lib. bdg. 16.89 (978-0-06-029560-8(0)) HarperCollins Pubs.

Halloween. 2002. (Big Steps Ser.). (SPA.). 40p. (J). 17.95 (978-980-6437-34-0(9)) Playco Editores, C.A.

Halloween Hunt. 64p. (YA). (gr. 6-12). pap. (978-0-8224-2334-8(0)) Globe Fearon Educational Publishing.

Happy Halloween, 4 bks., Set. 2002. (Illus.). (J). (ps). bds. 7.99 (978-1-57759-876-3(8)) Dalmatian Pr.

Haugen, Brenda. Halloween. Boyd, Sheree, illus. 2004. (Holidays & Celebrations Ser.). 24p. (gr. k-3). 22.60 (978-1-4048-0195-0(2)) Picture Window Bks.

Heinrichs, Ann. Halloween. Weidner, Teri, illus. 2006. (Holidays, Festivals, & Celebrations Ser.). 32p. (J). (gr. k-4). 22.79 (978-1-59296-576-2(8)) Child's World, Inc.

Higgs, Liz Curtis. The Pumpkin Patch Parable. 2006. 32p. (J). 7.99 (978-1-4003-0846-0(1)) Nelson, Thomas Inc.

—The Pumpkin Patch Parable: The Parable Series. 2005. 32p. (J). pap. 3.99 (978-1-4003-0668-8(X)) Nelson, Thomas Inc.

Hopkins, Lee Bennett. Halloween Howls: Holiday Poetry. Schuett, Stacey, illus. 2005. (I Can Read Bks.). 32p. (J). (gr. k-3). lib. bdg. 16.89 (978-0-06-008061-7(2)) HarperCollins Pubs.

Hubbell, Patricia. Boo! Halloween Poems & Limericks. Spackman, Jeff, illus. 40p. 2005. (YA). pap. 5.95 (978-0-7614-5151-8(X)); 1998. (J). 15.95 (978-0-7614-5023-8(8) , Cavendish Children's Bks.) Cavendish, Marshall Corp.

Kawasaki, Shauna Mooney. Ghostly Frights for Halloween Nights. 2002. (Illus.). 96p. pap. 6.95 (978-1-4027-0118-4(7)) Sterling Publishing Co., Inc.

—Ghostly Frights for Halloween Nights. 2002. (gr. 3-6). lib. bdg. 15.25 (978-0-613-81805-6(9)) Tandem Library Bks.

Kessel, Joyce K. Halloween. Carlson, Nancy, illus. 2007. (Yo Solo Festividades (On My Own Holidays) Ser.). (SPA.). 48p. (J). (gr. 2-4). lib. bdg. 25.26 (***978-0-8225-7790-4(9)*** , Ediciones Lerner) Lerner Publishing Group.

Kessel Joyce K. Halloween. Carlson, Nancy, illus. 2007. (Yo solo Festividades (on My Own Holidays) Ser.). (J). pap. 6.95 (****978-0-8225-7793-5(3)*** , Ediciones Lerner) Lerner Publishing Group.

King, Penny & Roundhill, Clare. Spooky Things. 1998. (Making Pictures Ser.). (J). 21.36 (978-1-57572-195-8(3)) Rigby Education.

Klingel, Cynthia Fitterer & Noyed, Robert B. Halloween. 2002. (Wonder Books Level 2: Holidays Ser.). (Illus.). 24p. (J). (ps-3). 22.79 (978-1-56766-955-8(7)) Child's World, Inc.

Knudsen, Michelle. Happy Halloween. Fletcher, Rusty, illus. 2001. (Sparkle 'n' Shimmer Book Ser.). 14p. (J). 5.99 (978-0-689-84401-0(8) , Little Simon) Simon & Schuster Children's Publishing.

Kubish, Shelagh & Craig, Lee, eds. Pumpkin Carving, Vol. 1. rev. ed. 2003. (Illus.). 48p. (gr. 4). pap. (978-1-894877-26-8(8)) Lone Pine Publishing.

Let's Shine Jesus' Light on Halloween. 2006. 16p. (J). pap. 1.99 (978-0-7847-1531-4(9) , 04360) Standard Publishing.

Lowery, Linda. Trick or Treat, It's Halloween! 2000. (gr. k-3). lib. bdg. 10.95 (978-0-613-27266-7(8)) Tandem Library Bks.

MacKall, Dandi Daley. It Must Be Halloween. 2003. (ps-2). lib. bdg. 13.00 (978-0-613-90192-5(4)) Tandem Library Bks.

Margaret, Amy. Halloween. 2002. (Library of the Holidays Ser.). (Illus.). 24p. (J). lib. bdg. 18.75 (978-0-8239-5782-8(9) , PowerKids Pr.) Rosen Publishing Group, Inc., The.

Marx, David F. Halloween. 2000. (Rookie Read-About Holidays Ser.). (Illus.). 32p. (J). (gr. 1-2). 19.50 (978-0-516-22206-6(6)); pap. 5.95 (978-0-516-27154-5(7)) Scholastic Library Publishing. (Children's Pr.).

Marzollo, Jean. I Spy Spooky Night. Wick, Walter, illus. 2005. (I Spy Ser.). 20p. (J). pap. 18.95 (978-0-439-68429-3(3)) Scholastic, Inc.

Mass, Wendy. Celebrate Halloween. 2006. (Celebrate Holidays Ser.). (Illus.). 104p. (J). lib. bdg. 31.93 (978-0-7660-2491-5(1)) Enslow Pubs., Inc.

McCabe, Dennis, illus. Haunted Halloween: Color & Create with Spooky Stickers. 2004. 10p. (J). (ps up). bds. 4.99 (978-1-57151-730-2(8)) Playhouse Publishing.

Mead, Brian. The Spooky Halloween Cut & Color Activity Book. 2003. 48p. (J). (ps-3). pap. 3.99 (978-0-9717509-1-3(2)) Mead, Brian Publishing.

Moffatt, Judith. Trick-or-Treat Faces: A Glowing Book You Can Read in the Dark! Moffatt, Judith, illus. 2000. (Illus.). 12p. (J). (ps-k). 6.95 (978-0-439-18299-7(9) , Cartwheel Bks.) Scholastic, Inc.

Moler, Robert E. If I Were a Halloween Monster: A Mirror-Mask Book with Pop-Up Surprises. Moler, Robert E., illus. 2000. (Illus.). 16p. (J). (gr. 2-5). 13.95 (978-0-316-57778-6(2)) Little, Brown Bks. for Young Readers.

Murray, Julie. Halloween. 2005. (Holidays Ser.). (Illus.). 24p. (J). (gr. k-4). lib. bdg. 21.35 (978-1-57765-952-5(X)) ABDO Publishing Co.

Myers, Janet Nuzum. Spooky Creature Riddles. Ostrom, Bob, illus. 2005. 96p. (J). (ps-ps). pap. 4.95 (978-1-4027-1872-4(1)) Sterling Publishing Co., Inc.

Nudelman, Edwar, ed. A Halloween Reader. 2004. (Illus.). 12p. 8.95 (978-1-58980-260-5(8)) Pelican Publishing Co., Inc.

O'Brien, Joan. Halloween Picture Sticker Activity Book. 2004. (Illus.). 4p. (J). (ps-3). act. bk. ed. 1.50 (978-0-486-43310-3(2)) Dover Pubns., Inc.

O'Hare, Jeffrey A. Halloween Book of Fun: Puzzles, Games, Jokes, Ideas, & More. 2003. (Illus.). 64p. (YA). (gr. 2-7). pap. 7.95 (978-1-56397-959-0(4)) Boyds Mills Pr.

Old, Wendie C. The Halloween Book of Facts & Fun. Billin-Frye, Paige, illus. 2007. 40p. (J). (gr. 3-6). 15.95 (****978-0-8075-3133-4(2)***) Whitman, Albert & Co.

Potts, Steve. Halloween. 2001. (Holiday Ser.). (Illus.). 24p. (J). 21.35 (978-1-58340-120-0(2)) Smart Apple Media.

Random House Disney Staff & Angelilli, Chris. Don't Go Bump in the Night! Halloween Safety. Cash, Megan & Emslie, Peter, illus. 2005. 16p. (J). (ps-k). 6.99 (978-0-7364-2232-1(3) , RH/Disney) Random Hse. Children's Bks.

Rau, Dana. Halloween. 2001. (gr. 3-6). lib. bdg. 15.25 (978-0-613-51649-5(4)) Tandem Library Bks.

Rau, Dana Meachen. Halloween. 2001. (True Holiday Bks.). (Illus.). 48p. (J). (gr. 3-5). 25.00 (978-0-516-22245-5(7) , Children's Pr.) Scholastic Library Publishing.

Rhodes, Vicki. Pumpkin Decorating. 2002. (gr. 3-6). lib. bdg. 15.25 (978-0-613-75551-1(0)) Tandem Library Bks.

Robinson, Fay. Halloween: Disfraces y Golosinas en la Vispera de Todos los Santos. 2005. (Días Festivos Ser.). (SPA., Illus.). 48p. (J). (ps-ps). lib. bdg. 23.93 (978-0-7660-2614-8(0) , Enslow Elementary) Enslow Pubs., Inc.

—Halloween - Costumes & Treats on All Hallows' Eve. 2001. (Finding Out about Holidays Ser.). (Illus.). 48p. (J). (gr. 1-4). lib. bdg. 23.93 (978-0-7660-1632-3(3)) Enslow Pubs., Inc.

—Halloween Crafts. 2004. (Fun Holiday Crafts Kids Can Do Ser.). (Illus.). 32p. (J). lib. bdg. 22.60 (978-0-7660-2236-2(6)) Enslow Pubs., Inc.

Rosinsky, Natalie M. Halloween. 2002. (Let's See Library). (Illus.). 24p. (J). (gr. 1 up). lib. bdg. 19.93 (978-0-7565-0392-5(2)) Compass Point Bks.

Ross, Dave. The Not-so-Scary Monster Handbook: Halloween. Ross, Dave, illus. 2003. (Illus.). (J). 135.44 (978-0-06-055492-7(4)) HarperCollins Pubs.

Ross, Kathy. All New Crafts for Halloween. Leonard, Barbara, illus. 2003. (All New Holiday Crafts for Kids Ser.). 48p. lib. bdg. 23.90 (978-0-7613-2554-3(9)); (J). pap. 7.95 (978-0-7613-1577-3(2)) Lerner Publishing Group. (Millbrook Pr.).

—All New Crafts for Halloween. 2003. (gr. k-3). lib. bdg. 16.40 (978-0-613-88977-3(0)) Tandem Library Bks.

Sacks, Janet. Halloween Party. Rinaldo, Luana, illus. ed. 2005. (Magic Color Bks.). 10p. (J). 3.95 (978-1-4027-2619-4(8) , Sterling/Pinwheel) Sterling Publishing Co., Inc.

—Witch's Night Out. Rinaldo, Luana, illus. 2005. (Magic Color Bks.). 10p. (J). 3.95 (978-1-4027-2620-0(1) , Sterling/Pinwheel) Sterling Publishing Co., Inc.

Savage, Christine Lyseng, et al. Halloween Recipes & Crafts, Vol. 1. rev. ed. 2003. (Ghost Stories Ser.). (Illus.). 160p. (gr. 4). pap. (978-1-894877-10-7(1)) Lone Pine Publishing.

Schaefer, Lola M. Jack-o-Lanterns. Saunders-Smith, Gail, ed. 1998. (Fall Fun Ser.). (Illus.). 24p. (J). (gr. k-1). lib. bdg. 15.93 (978-0-7368-0105-8(7) , Pebble Bks.) Capstone Pr., Inc.

Scholastic, Inc. Staff. It's Halloween! Neusner, Dena, ed. 2003. (Barney Ser.). (Illus.). 64p. (J). 2.99 (978-0-439-52452-0(0)) Scholastic, Inc.

School Zone Publishing Company Staff. You Can't Scare Me: A Book of Numbers. 2000. (Illus.). 18p. (J). bds. 4.99 (978-0-88743-604-8(8) , 06605) School Zone Publishing Co.

Schuh, Mari C. Halloween. Saunders-Smith, Gail, ed. 2001. (Holidays & Celebrations Ser.). (Illus.). 24p. (J). (gr. k-1). lib. bdg. 15.93 (978-0-7368-0980-1(5) , Pebble Bks.) Capstone Pr., Inc.

Simon, Mary Manz. The Pumpkin Gospel: A Story of a New Start with God! 2005. (Illus.). 12p. (J). (ps). per. 8.99 (978-0-7847-1758-5(3) , 04722) Standard Publishing.

Trueit, Trudi Strain. Halloween. 2006. (Rookie Read-About Holidays Ser.). (Illus.). 31p. (J). (978-0-531-12456-7(8)) Children's Pr., Ltd.

—Halloween. rev. ed. 2006. (Rookie Read-About Holidays Ser.). (Illus.). 32p. (J). (gr. 1-2). pap. 5.95 (978-0-531-11837-5(1) , Children's Pr.) Scholastic Library Publishing.

Trumbauer, Lisa. Computer Fun Halloween. 1999. (J). (978-0-606-19150-0(X)) Tandem Library Bks.

Venturi-Pickett, Stacy. The Halloween. (Illus.). 24p. (J). pap., act. bk. ed. 4.95 (978-0-8249-5303-4(7)) Ideals Pubns.

Vidrine, Beverly Barras. Halloween Alphabet. Lyne, Alison Davis, illus. 2004. 32p. (J). pap. 7.95 (978-1-58980-242-1(X)) Pelican Publishing Co., Inc.

Waldron, Jan L. John Pig's Halloween Masks. 1998. (Illus.). (978-0-525-46105-0(1) , Dutton Juvenile) Penguin Group (USA) Inc.

Watson, Wendy. Boo! It's Halloween. Watson, Wendy, illus. 2001. (Illus.). 32p. (J). (gr. k-3). 5.95 (978-0-618-13057-3(8) , Clarion Bks.) Houghton Mifflin Co. Trade & Reference Div.

—Boo! It's Halloween. 2001. (gr. k-3). lib. bdg. 14.10 (978-0-613-35491-2(5)) Tandem Library Bks.

Watt, F. Halloween Activities. 2004. (Illus.). 32p. (J). pap., act. bk. ed. 6.95 (978-0-7945-0337 6(3)) EDC Publishing.

White, Linda. Haunting on a Halloween: Frightful Activities for Kids. Lee, Fran, illus. 2002. 64p. (YA). pap. 9.95 (978-1-58685-112-5(8)) Gibbs Smith, Publisher.

—Haunting on a Halloween: Frightful Activities for Kids. Lee, Fran, illus. 2002. 63p. (J). (ps-ps). lib. bdg. 18.75 (978-0-613-52568-8(X)) Tandem Library Bks.

Wilhelm, Hans. I'm Not Scared! 2005. (Illus.). 30p. (J). (ps-3). lib. bdg. 11.19 (978-0-606-33830-1(6)) Tandem Library Bks.

Williams, Colleen Madonna Flood. My Adventure on Halloween. 2006. 44p. (J). 8.99 (978-1-59092-549-2(1) , Orchard Academy Pr.) Windstorm Creative.

Willis, Abigail & Spenceley, Annabel. Halloween Fun: Great Things to Make & Do. 2003. (Holiday Fun Ser.). (Illus.). 32p. (J). (gr. 3-5). pap. 4.95 (978-0-7534-5683-5(4) , Kingfisher) Houghton Mifflin Co. Trade & Reference Div.

Ziefert, Harriet & Doughty, Rebecca. Halloween Has Boo! 2002. (Illus.). 8p. bds. 6.95 (978-1-929766-67-3(X)) Blue Apple Bks.

Zocchi, Judy. On Halloween Night. Wallis, Rebecca, illus. 2005. (Holiday Happenings Ser.). (J). 32p. pap. 9.95 (978-1-59646-220-5(5)); (ENG.). 32p. lib. bdg. 20.65 (978-1-891997-77-8(7)); per. 9.95 (978-1-59646-221-2(3)) Dingles & Co.

—On Halloween Night/la noche de Halloween. Wallis, Rebecca, illus. 2005. (Holiday Happenings Ser.).Tr. of noche de Halloween. 32p. (J). pap. 9.95 (978-1-59646-222-9(1)); (ENG & SPA.). per. 9.95 (978-1-59646-223-6(X)) Dingles & Co.

—On Halloween Night/La Noche de Halloween. Wallis, Rebecca, illus. 2005. (Holiday Happenings Ser.). (ENG & SPA.). 32p. (J). lib. bdg. 20.65 (978-1-891997-76-1(9)) Dingles & Co.

HALLOWEEN—FICTION

Aboff, Marcie & Funke, Cornelia. Shrek: Classic Shrek Halloween. 2006. (Shrek Ser.). (Illus.). 16p. (J). pap. 5.99 (978-0-439-82817-8(1) , Scholastic) Scholastic, Inc.

Adams, Georgie. The Three Little Witches Storybook. Bolam, Emily, illus. 2002. 96p. (ps-3). 15.99 (978-0-7868-0824-3(1)) Hyperion Bks. for Children.

Adams, Michelle Medlock. What Is Halloween? Wummer, Amy, illus. 2007. 26p. (J). (ps-k). bds. 6.99 (****978-0-8249-6712-3(7)*** , Candy Cane Pr.) Ideals Pubns.

Agran, Rick. Pumpkin Shivaree. Anderson, Sara, illus. 2003. 40p. (J). (gr. k-2). 15.95 (978-1-59354-006-7(X)) Handprint Bks.

Alexander, Heather. Allie Gator's Halloween Hayride. 2006. (Illus.). 24p. (J). pap. 3.95 (978-0-7624-2658-4(6)) Running Pr. Bk. Pubs.

Alley, R. W., illus. A Know-Nothing Halloween. 2002. (Know-Nothings Ser.). (J). 12.30 (978-0-7587-6905-3(9)) Book Wholesalers, Inc.

Anderson, Erin. Boo! Harpster, Steve, illus. 2007. (Scribble & Sing Ser.). 80p. (J). 4.99 (****978-1-4169-3805-7(2)*** , Simon Scribbles) Simon & Schuster Children's Publishing.

Appleton-Smith, Laura. It Is Halloween! Neel, Preston, illus. 1999. (Book to Remember Ser.). (J). (ps-3). pap. 8.95 (978-0-9658246-4-4(0) , Books To Remember) Flyleaf Publishing.

Arena, Felice & Kettle, Phil. Halloween Gotcha! Gordon, Gus, illus. 2004. (J). pap. (978-1-59336-373-4(7)) Mondo Publishing.

Artists, S. I., illus. Baby Strawberry's First Halloween. 2007. (Strawberry Shortcake Baby Ser.). 10p. (J). (ps-ps). bds. 4.99 (978-0-448-44553-3(0) , Grosset & Dunlap) Penguin Group (USA) Inc.

Atwell, Debby. The Warthog's Tail. 2005. (Illus.). 32p. (J). (gr. k-3). 16.00 (978-0-618-50781-8(7) , Walter Lorraine) Houghton Mifflin Co. Trade & Reference Div.

Auch, Mary Jane. Poultrygeist. Jane, Mary & Auch, Herm, illus. 32p. (J). (gr. k-3). reprint ed. 6.95 (978-0-8234-1876-3(6)) Holiday Hse., Inc.

Auzary-Luton, Sylvie. Going Batty! Pottie, Marjolein, illus. 2005. 32p. 15.95 (978-1-59687-186-1(5) , Milk & Cookies) ibooks, Inc.

Averill, Esther. Jenny's Moonlight Adventure. 32p. (J). pap. 12.95 (978-0-553-15145-9(2)) Bantam Bks.

—Jenny's Moonlight Adventure. Averill, Esther, illus. 2005. (New York Review Children's Collection). (Illus.). 32p. (J). (ps-ps). pap. 12.95 (978-1-59017-160-8(8) , NYR Children's Collection) New York Review of Bks., Inc., The.

Axelrod, Amy. Pigs Go to Market: Fun with Math & Shopping. McGinley-Nally, Sharon, illus. 1999. 40p. (J). (ps-3). 6.99 (978-0-689-82553-8(6) , 076714005990, Aladdin) Simon & Schuster Children's Publishing.

—Pigs Go to Market: Halloween Fun with Math & Shopping. 1999. (978-0-606-16330-9(1)); lib. bdg. 14.15 (978-0-613-19419-8(5)) Tandem Library Bks.

B Small Publishing Staff. Crafty Halloween Pumpkins. 1999. (Illus.). 16p. (J). (gr. 4-7). (978-1-874735-58-8(1)) B Small Publishing.

Baby Looney Tunes Visit a Haunted House. 2005. (Baby Looney Tunes Ser.). (Illus.). 14p. (J). (ps-3). bds. 9.95 (978-0-8249-6609-6(0)) Ideals Pubns.

Baglio, Ben M. Beagle in a Backpack. Baum, Ann, illus. 2005. 142p. (J). pap. (****978-0-439-77521-2(3)***) Scholastic, Inc.

Balducci, Rita. Scarecrow Mix: Halloween Pigs/Happy Scarecrow. 1999. (Illus.). (J). (ps-3). pap. 4.50 (978-1-55254-089-3(8)) Brighter Vision Pubns.

Banks, Steven. The Big Halloween Scare. Martinez, Heather, illus. 2005. (Ready-to-Read Ser. Level 2: 1). 32p. (J). lib. bdg. 15.00 (978-1-59054-987-2(2)) Fitzgerald Bks.

—The Big Halloween Scare. Martinez, Heather, illus. 2003. (SpongeBob SquarePants Ready-To-Read Ser.: Vol. 1). 32p. (J). (gr. k-2). pap. 3.99 (978-0-689-84196-5(5) , Simon Spotlight/Nickelodeon) Simon & Schuster Children's Publishing.

—The Big Halloween Scare. Martinez, Heather, illus. 2003. 32p. (J). (gr. k-2). lib. bdg. 11.80 (978-0-613-73339-7(8)) Tandem Library Bks.

Banks, Steven & Vosough, Gene. A Fairly Odd Halloween: A Spooky Pop-up Book. Miller, Victoria, illus. 2005. (Fairly OddParents Ser.). 16p. (J). pap. 6.99 (978-0-689-87676-9(9) , Simon Spotlight/Nickelodeon) Simon & Schuster Children's Publishing.

Bauer, Marion Dane. I'm Not Afraid of Halloween! Fletcher, Rusty, illus. 2006. 16p. (J). 7.99 (978-0-689-85050-9(6) , Little Simon) Simon & Schuster Children's Publishing.

Beall, Pamela Conn & Nipp, Susan Hagen. Who's There on Halloween? Reasoner, Charles, illus. 2003. 18p. (J). bds. 4.99 (978-0-8431-0495-0(3)); bds. 4.99 (978-0-8431-0510-0(0)) Penguin Group (USA) Inc. (Price Stern Sloan).

Bedell, Jane. Mischief & Eve: A Halloween Beginning. Bedell, Jim, illus. 1998. 22p. (J). (gr. 2-4). pap. 3.99 (978-0-9665837-0-0(1)) Bedell, Jane M.

Beechen, Adam. Chuckie's Ghost. Artful Doodlers Limited Staff, illus. 2005. (Ready-To-Read Ser.). 32p. (J). (ps-ps). pap. 3.99 (978-0-689-87723-0(4) , Simon Spotlight/Nickelodeon) Simon & Schuster Children's Publishing.

Bergen, Lara. Attack of the Monster House. 2006. (Monster House Ser.). 24p. (J). pap. 5.99 (978-1-4169-1821-9(3) , Simon Spotlight) Simon & Schuster Children's Publishing.

Bianchi, John. Trick or Treat? Bianchi, John, illus. 2002. (Illus.). 14p. (J). bds. 4.99 (978-0-448-42819-2(9) , Grosset & Dunlap) Penguin Group (USA) Inc.

Big Night in Booville. 2002. (Booville Ser.). (Illus.). 24p. (J). (gr. k-4). 2.99 (978-1-57759-834-3(2)) Dalmatian Pr.

Blackburn, Winfrey P. Putney-a little pumpkin with BIG Ideas. 2007. 48p. (J). 14.95 (****978-0-9790025-5-7(9)***) Acclaim Pr., Inc.

Blissman, Rodger J. Spookster the Halloween Cat. 2004. 85p. (J). (gr. 3-7). pap. 5.99 (978-0-9745895-0-3(0)) Oxfordshire Publishing Co.

Bodel, Garrett. Trick or Treat! Bodel, Garrett, photos by. 2002. (Doll's Life Story Ser.: Vol. 7). (Illus.). 32p. (J). (gr. 2-4). pap. 7.90 (978-0-9720072-3-8(7)) Doll's Life.

Bollinger, Peter. Algernon Graeves Is Scary Enough. Bollinger, Peter, illus. 2005. (Illus.). 32p. (J). (ps-3). lib. bdg. 15.89 (978-0-06-052269-8(0) , Geringer, Laura Book) HarperCollins Pubs.

Borsky, Mary. Benny Bensky & the Giant Pumpkin Heist. Hendry, Linda, illus. 2002. 128p. (J). (gr. 3-7). pap. 7.95 (978-0-88776-607-7(2)) Tundra Bks., Inc./Livres Toundra, Inc. CAN. *Dist:* Random Hse., Inc.

Botts, Mary L., illus. Taylor's Halloween. l.t. ed. 1999. 16p. (J). (gr. k-6). pap. 3.99 (978-0-9668891-1-6(8)) Teach My Children Pubns.

Bourgeois, Paulette. Franklin's Halloween. Clark, Brenda, illus. 2002. (Franklin Ser.). 12.40 (978-1-4046-0326-4(3)) Book Wholesalers, Inc.

Bourgeois, Paulette, et al. Franklin y el Día de Halloween. Clark, Brenda, illus. 1999. (SPA.). (J). pap. (978-1-880507-45-2(5)) Lectorum Pubns., Inc.

Bowman, Andy. Pokey's Garden. Travis, Stephanie, illus. 26p. (J). (gr. k-5). pap. 6.95 (978-1-931650-08-3(X)); lib. bdg. 14.95 (978-1-931650-09-0(8)) Coastal Publishing Carolina, Inc.

Bradbury, Ray. The Halloween Tree. (J). 20.95 (978-0-8488-0432-9(5)) Amereon LTD.

—The Halloween Tree. Mugnaini, Joseph, illus. 1999. 160p. (J). (gr. 5-9). pap. 5.50 (978-0-375-80301-7(7) , Yearling) Random Hse. Children's Bks.

—The Halloween Tree. Mugnaini, Joseph, illus. 1999. 145p. (J). (ps-7). lib. bdg. 11.64 (978-0-606-17231-8(9)) Tandem Library Bks.

Braybrooks, Ann. Pooh's Happy Halloween. 2003. (Illus.). 24p. (J). (gr. k-3). 3.99 (978-0-7364-1329-9(4) , RH/Disney) Random Hse. Children's Bks.

Bridwell, Norman. Clifford's First Halloween. 2006. (Illus.). 32p. (J). pap. 7.99 (978-0-439-82303-6(X) , Cartwheel Bks.) Scholastic, Inc.

—Clifford's Glow-in-the-Dark Halloween. 2001. (Clifford, the Big Red Dog Ser.). (Illus.). 12p. (J). (ps-k). pap. 6.95 (978-0-439-30566-2(7) , Cartwheel Bks.) Scholastic, Inc.

Bridwell, Norman & Fry, Sonali. Clifford's Scary Halloween. Durk, Jim, illus. 2002. (Clifford, the Big Red Dog Ser.). 16p. (J). pap. 4.99 (978-0-439-39453-6(8)) Scholastic, Inc.

Brown, Janet Allison. Happy Halloween. Chaffey, Samantha, illus. 2005. (Holidays In 3D Ser.). 8p. (J). bds. 4.99 (978-0-7641-5831-5(7)) Barron's Educational Series, Inc.

Brown, Marc. Arthur's Halloween. Brown, Marc, illus. 2002. (Arthur Adventure Ser.). (Illus.). (J). 13.15 (978-0-7587-1983-6(3)) Book Wholesalers, Inc.

—Arthur's Halloween. movie tie-in ed. Date not set. (Arthur Adventure Ser.). (J). 16.95 (978-0-316-11855-2(9)) Little Brown & Co.

—Arthur's Lost Puppy. Brown, Marc, illus. 2000. (Arthur Ser.). (Illus.). 24p. (J). (gr. k-3). pap. 3.99 (978-0-679-88466-8(1) , Random Hse. Bks. for Young Readers) Random Hse. Children's Bks.

Brown, Margaret Wise. The Fierce Yellow Pumpkin. Egielski, Richard, illus. 2003. 32p. (J). (ps-1). 15.99 (978-0-06-024479-8(8)); lib. bdg. 16.89 (978-0-06-024481-1(X)) HarperCollins Pubs.

—The Little Scarecrow Boy. Diaz, David, illus. 2005. 40p. (J). (ps-2). reprint ed. pap. 6.99 (978-0-06-077891-0(1) , Harper Trophy) HarperCollins Pubs.

Brown, Rick, illus. Halloween Party. 2007. (I'm Going to Read Ser.). 32p. (J). (gr. 1-2). pap. 3.95 (****978-1-4027-4298-9(3)***) Sterling Publishing Co., Inc.

Broyles, Anne. Shy Mama's Halloween. 2000. (gr. k-3). lib. bdg. 16.40 (978-0-613-53311-9(9)) Tandem Library Bks.

—Shy Mama's Halloween. Morin, Leane, illus. 40p. (J). 2005. (gr. 3-6). 7.95 (978-0-88448-245-1(6)); 2000. (ps-3). 16.95 (978-0-88448-218-5(9)) Tilbury Hse. Pubs.

Bullard, Lisa. Trick-or-Treat on Milton Street. Oeltjenbruns, Joni, illus. (Carolrhoda Picture Books Ser.). 32p. (J). (ps-3). 2004. pap. 6.95 (978-1-57505-793-4(X)); 2003. 15.95 (978-1-57505-158-1(3) , Carolrhoda Bks.) Lerner Publishing Group.

Bunting, Eve. The Bones of Fred McFee. Cyrus, Kurt, illus. 32p. (J). (ps-ps). 2005. pap. 6.00 (978-0-15-205423-6(5) , Voyager Bks./Libros Viajeros); 2002. 16.00 (978-0-15-202004-0(7)) Harcourt Children's Bks.

—Scary, Scary Halloween. 2002. (Illus.). (J). 13.79 (978-0-7587-3578-2(2)) Book Wholesalers, Inc.

Butler, Leah & Peters, Trudy. Owen's Choice: The Night of the Halloween Vandals. 2005. (Illus.). 64p. (J). 18.95 (978-0-9771666-0-2(0)) Spencer's Mill Pr.

By the Light of the Halloween Moon. 2004. pap. 18.95 incl. audio compact disk (978-1-55592-800-1(5)); (J). pap. 38.75 incl. audio compact disk (978-1-55592-817-9(X)); (J). pap. 32.75 incl. audio (978-1-55592-198-9(1)) Weston Woods Studios, Inc.

Campoy, F. Isabel & Ada, Alma Flor. Celebrate Halloween & the Day of the Dead with Cristina & Her Blue Bunny. Martinez, Ivanova, illus. 2006. 31p. (J). (978-1-59820-132-1(8)) Santillana USA Publishing Co., Inc.

H I

Candido, Jeane Heimberger. Levi: The Smartest Boy in the World. 2nd rev. ed. 2007. 44p. (J). 10.99 (978-1-59092-222-4(0)) Windstorm Creative.

Capucilli, Alyssa Satin. Biscuit's Pet & Play Halloween. Andreasen, Dan, illus. 2007. (Biscuit Ser.). 12p. (J). (ps-1). pap. 6.99 ***(978-0-06-112833-2(3)*** , Harper Festival) HarperCollins Pubs.

Capucilli, Alyssa Satin. Happy Halloween, Biscuit! Schories, Pat, illus. 1999. (Biscuit Ser.). 20p. (J). (ps-1). pap. 6.99 (978-0-694-01220-6(3) , Harper Festival) HarperCollins Pubs.

Carlson, Nancy. Harriet's Halloween Candy. (Illus.). 32p. (gr. k-2). anniv. ed. 2003. (J). pap. 6.95 (978-0-87614-926-3(3) , Carolrhoda Bks.); 20th anniv. ed. 2005. 15.95 (978-0-87614-913-3(1)) Lerner Publishing Group.

—Harriet's Halloween Candy. Carlson, Nancy, illus. unabr. ed. (Illus.). (J). pap., tchr. ed. 31.95 incl. audio (978-0-941078-52-8(3)); 24.95 incl. audio (978-0-941078-53-5(1)); pap. 15.95 incl. audio (978-0-941078-51-1(5)) Live Oak Media.

—Harriet's Halloween Candy. 2002. (gr. k-3). lib. bdg. 15.25 (978-0-613-77204-4(0)) Tandem Library Bks.

Carrier, Lark. Five Little Goblins. 2001. (Illus.). 18p. (J). (ps-1). 6.95 (978-0-694-01576-4(8) , Harper Festival) HarperCollins Pubs.

Carrier, Lark, et al. Boo! A Halloween Peek-a-Boo! Book. Carrier, Lark, illus. 2003. (Illus.). 28p. (J). pap. 5.95 (978-0-439-38222-9(X) , Cartwheel Bks.) Scholastic, Inc.

Carter, David A. Halloween Bugs: A Trick or Treat. Carter, David A., illus. 2003. (Illus.). 14p. (J). 10.95 (978-0-689-85916-8(3) , Little Simon) Simon & Schuster Children's Publishing.

Cazet, Denys. Minnie & Moo: The Night of the Living Bed. Cazet, Denys, illus. (I Can Read Bks.). 48p. (J). (gr. k-3). 2004. pap. 3.99 (978-0-06-000505-4(X) , Harper Trophy); 2003. (Illus.). 16.99 (978-0-06-000503-0(3)); 2003. (Illus.). lib. bdg. 16.89 (978-0-06-000504-7(1)) HarperCollins Pubs.

—Never Poke a Squid. Cazet, Denys, illus. 2000. (Illus.). 32p. (J). (ps-2). 17.99 (978-0-531-33279-5(9) , Watts, Franklin) Scholastic Library Publishing.

—Never Poke a Squid. Cazet, Denys, illus. 2000. (Illus.). 32p. (J). (ps-2). pap. 16.95 (978-0-531-30279-8(2) , Orchard Bks.) Scholastic, Inc.

—The Night of the Living Bed. Cazet, Denys, illus. unabr. ed. 2005. (Minnie & Moo Ser.). (J). (gr. k-4). (Illus.). 25.95 incl. audio (978-1-59519-389-6(8)); (Illus.). 28.95 incl. audio compact disk (978-1-59519-393-3(6)); (Illus.). pap. 16.95 incl. audio (978-1-59519-388-9(X)); (Illus.). pap. 18.95 incl. audio compact disk (978-1-59519-392-6(8)); Set. pap. 31.95 incl. audio compact disk (978-1-59519-394-0(4)); Set. (Illus.). pap. 29.95 incl. audio (978-1-59519-390-2(1)) Live Oak Media.

—The Perfect Pumpkin Pie. Cazet, Denys, illus. 2005. (Illus.). 32p. (J). (gr. k-3). 16.99 (978-0-689-86467-4(1) , Atheneum/Richard Jackson Bks.) Simon & Schuster Children's Publishing.

Chanda, J-P. Ghoul Hunters. Spaziante, Patrick, illus. 2005. (Teenage Mutant Ninja Turtles Ser.). 32p. (J). (ps). pap. 3.99 (978-1-4169-0075-7(6) , Simon Spotlight) Simon & Schuster Children's Publishing.

Chetkowski, Emily. Pumpkin Smile. Peterson, Dawn, illus. 2001. 32p. (J). (gr. k-3). 16.95 (978-0-9700974-2-2(5)); (gr. 1-3). pap. 11.95 (978-0-9700974-3-9(3)) Seven Coin Pr.

Chetwin, Grace. On All Hallows' Eve. Chetwin, Grace, illus. 1999. (Illus.). 127p. (J). (ps-3). pap. 20.00 (978-0-9649349-9-3(X) , Rivet Bks.) Feral Pr., Inc.

Choi, Yangsook. Behind the Mask. 2006. (Illus.). 40p. (J). 16.00 (978-0-374-30522-2(6) , Frances Foster Bks.) Farrar, Straus & Giroux.

Christopher, Matt. Day of the Dragon. 2nd ed. 2004. (Extreme Team Ser.: Vol. 2). (Illus.). 64p. (J). (gr. 2-4). pap. 4.99 (978-0-316-73753-1(4)) Little, Brown Bks. for Young Readers.

Chronicle Books LLC Staff. Halloween Takealong Bb. 2008. (J). bds. 6.95 (978-0-8118-5170-1(2)) Chronicle Bks. LLC.

Ciminera, Siobhan. The Spookiest Jack-o'-Lantern Ever! Petrosino, Tamara, illus. 2006. 16p. (J). (ps-2). pap. 4.99 (978-0-8431-2014-1(2) , Price Stern Sloan) Penguin Group (USA) Inc.

Cocca-Leffler, Maryann. Jungle Halloween. Cocca-Leffler, Maryann, illus. 2000. (Illus.). 32p. (J). (ps-1). pap. 6.95 (978-0-8075-4057-2(9)) Whitman, Albert & Co.

Cofer, Amadeus. Mystery of the Golden Pearls: A Halloween Adventure in Clarkesville. 1. l.t. ed. 2004. (Illus.). 36p. (J). 14.00 (978-1-932957-02-0(2)) Legacy Pubs.

Cole, Joanna. Gator Halloween. 2000. pap. 5.95 (978-0-688-17725-6(5)) HarperCollins Pubs.

Collins, Terry. Scary Odd Parents: A FairLy Odd HaLLoween. Schigiel, Gregg, illus. 2004. 24p. (J). lib. bdg. 18.46 ***(*978-1-4242-0969-9(2))*** Fitzgerald Bks.

Collins, Terry. Scary OddParents: A Fairly Odd Halloween. Schigiel, Gregg, illus. 2004. (Fairly OddParents Ser.). 16p. (J). pap. 5.99 (978-0-689-86897-9(9) , Simon Spotlight/Nickelodeon) Simon & Schuster Children's Publishing.

Copeland, Mindy. Halloween Spanish for Young Children. 2005. 12p. 13.52 (978-1-4116-4872-2(2)) Lulu.com.

Costello, David. Here They Come! 2004. (Illus.). 32p. (J). 15.00 (978-0-374-33051-4(4) , Farrar, Straus & Giroux (BYR)) Farrar, Straus & Giroux.

Coulton, Mia. Halloween Danny. Coulton, Mia, photos by. 2001. 12p. (J). 4.95 (978-0-9713518-4-4(8)) Maryruth Bks., Inc.

Cousins, Lucy. Maisy's Halloween. Cousins, Lucy, illus. 2004. (Maisy Ser.). (Illus.). 14p. (J). (gr. k-k). bds. 5.99 (978-0-7636-2579-5(5)) Candlewick Pr.

Coville, Bruce. The Monster's Ring. 2002. lib. bdg. 20.00 incl. audio (978-1-932076-10-3(7) , 02009) Full Cast Audio.

—The Monster's Ring. Coville, Katherine, illus. anniv. exp. ed. 2002. (Magic Shop Bks.). 128p. (YA). (gr. 3-7). 16.00 (978-0-15-204618-7(6)) Harcourt Children's Bks.

Craig, Helen, illus. Angelina's Halloween. 2007. 32p. (J). ***(*978-0-670-91162-2(3)*** , Viking Juvenile) Penguin Group (USA) Inc.

Crimi, Carolyn. Boris & Bella. Grimly, Gris, illus. 32p. (J). 2004. 15.00 (978-0-15-202528-1(6)); 2006. reprint ed. pap. 6.00 (978-0-15-205900-2(8) , Voyager Bks./Libros Viajeros) Harcourt Children's Bks.

Croteau, Marie-Danielle. Fred's Halloween Adventure. Cummins, Sarah, tr. from FRE. St. Aubin, Bruno, illus. 2002. (First Novel Ser.). 64p. ***(*978-0-88780-577-6(9));*** (gr. 1-5). 4.95 (978-0-88780-576-9(0)) Formac Publishing Co., Ltd. CAN. *Dist:* Casemate Pubs. & Bk. Distributors, LLC.

Cushman, Doug. Aunt Eater's Mystery Halloween. Cushman, Doug, illus. 2002. (Aunt Eater Mysteries Ser.). (Illus.). (J). 11.91 (978-0-7587-5992-4(4)) Book Wholesalers, Inc.

—Aunt Eater's Mystery Halloween. Cushman, Doug, illus. 1999. (I Can Read Bks.). (Illus.). 64p. (J). (gr. k-3). pap. 3.99 (978-0-06-444266-4(7) , Harper Trophy) HarperCollins Pubs.

—Aunt Eater's Mystery Halloween. 1998. (I Can Read Bks.). (Illus.). (J). (gr. k-3). 64p. 14.95 (978-0-06-027803-8(X)); 40p. 14.89 (978-0-06-027804-5(8)) HarperCollins Pubs.

—Aunt Eater's Mystery Halloween. Cushman, Doug, illus. 1999. (I Can Read Bks.). (Illus.). 64p. lib. bdg. 10.79 (978-0-606-17301-8(3)) Tandem Library Bks.

—Aunt Eater's Mystery Halloween. 1999. (gr. k-3). lib. bdg. 11.80 (978-0-613-22814-5(6)) Tandem Library Bks.

Cuyler, Margery. The Bumpy Little Pumpkin. Hillenbrand, Will, illus. 2005. 32p. (J). pap. 15.95 (978-0-439-52835-1(6) , Scholastic Pr.) Scholastic, Inc.

—Skeleton Hiccups. Schindler, S. D., illus. 2005. 32p. (J). reprint ed. 6.99 (978-1-4169-0276-8(7) , Aladdin) Simon & Schuster Children's Publishing.

Dadey, Debbie & Jones, Marcia Thornton. Mrs. Jeepers' Scariest Halloween Ever. Gurney, John Steven, illus. 2005. 103p. (J). (978-1-4156-2066-3(0)) Scholastic, Inc.

Dale, Jenny. Trick or Treat? Reid, Mick, illus. 2003. 107p. (J). (978-0-439-54362-0(2)) Scholastic, Inc.

Dalmatian Press Staff. A Big Night in Booville. 2005. (Illus.). 12p. (J). bds. 4.99 (978-1-4037-1495-4(9)) Dalmatian Pr.

—Strawberry Shortcake: Halloween Dress Up. 2005. (Illus.). 48p. (J). pap. 2.99 (978-1-4037-1489-3(4)) Dalmatian Pr.

Dalmatian Press Staff, ed. Halloween Treats. 2006. 48p. pap. 2.99 (978-1-4037-2471-7(7)) Dalmatian Pr.

Danziger, Paula. Orange You Glad It's Halloween, Amber Brown. 2007. (Easy-to-Read, Puffin Ser.). 48p. (J). (gr. k-3). pap. 3.99 (978-0-14-240809-4(3) , Puffin) Penguin Group (USA) Inc.

Davis, Chip, concept. Mannheim Steamroller Halloween - the World Between, Davis, Chip, . 2004. (Illus.). 216p. (YA). per. 19.95 (978-0-9754149-0-3(9)) Mannheim Steamroller, LLC.

deGroat, Diane. Lola's Trick or Treat. deGroat, Diane, illus. 2004. (Illus.). 16p. (J). pap. 6.99 (978-0-06-058389-7(4) , Harper Festival) HarperCollins Pubs.

—Trick or Treat, Smell My Feet. deGroat, Diane, illus. 1999. (Illus.). 32p. (J). (ps-3). pap. 6.99 (978-0-688-17061-5(7) , Harper Trophy) HarperCollins Pubs.

deGroat, Diane & deGroat, Diane, illus. Trick or Treat, Smell My Feet. 1998. 32p. (J). (ps-3). 14.89 (978-0-688-15767-8(X)) HarperCollins Pubs.

—Trick or Treat, Smell My Feet. 1999. (978-0-606-17241-7(6)) Tandem Library Bks.

dePaola, Tomie. My First Halloween. 2008. 14p. (J). (ps-k). bds. 5.99 ***(*978-0-448-44858-9(0)*** , Grosset & Dunlap) Penguin Group (USA) Inc.

Desimini, Lisa. Trick-or-Treat, Smell My Feet! Desimini, Lisa, illus. 2005. (Illus.). 40p. (J). pap. 16.95 (978-0-439-23323-1(2) , Blue Sky Pr., The) Scholastic, Inc.

Devlin, Wende & Devlin, Harry. Cranberry Halloween. unabr. ed. 2001. (J). (gr. k-3). pap. 16.95 incl. audio (978-0-8045-6657-5(7) , 6552-A) Spoken Arts, Inc.

DiCamillo, Kate & Van Dusen, Chris. Princess in Disguise. Van Dusen, Chris, illus. 2007. (Mercy Watson Ser.). (Illus.). 80p. (J). (gr. 1-3). 12.99 ***(*978-0-7636-3014-0(4))*** Candlewick Pr.

Dickinson, Rebecca. Over in the Hollow. Britt, Stephanie, illus. 2008. (J). 15.95 (978-0-8118-5035-3(8)) Chronicle Bks. LLC.

Dickinson, Rebecca, tr. & illus. Over in the Hollow. Dickinson, Rebecca, illus. 2002. (J). (978-0-385-74620-5(2) , Doubleday Bks. for Young Readers) Random Hse. Children's Bks.

Diviny, Sean. Halloween Motel. Rocco, Joe, illus. 32p. (J). (ps-3). Date not set. 5.25 hd 5.99 (978-0-06-443651-9(9)); 2000. 15.95 (978-0-06-028815-0(9) , Cotler, Joanna Books) HarperCollins Pubs.

Dixon, Ann. Trick or Treat. DiFiori, Larry, illus. 1998. (Read with Me Paperback Ser.). 32p. (J). (ps-3). pap. 2.99 (978-0-590-28161-4(5)) Scholastic, Inc.

—Trick or Treat. 1998. (Read with Me Ser.). (J). (978-0-606-13868-0(4)) Tandem Library Bks.

Dolphin Halloween & Elsie's Scrapbook. l.t. ed. 2004. (Illus.). 32p. (J). mass mkt. 4.99 (978-0-9760868-0-2(8)) Pluegl Bks.

Donnell, Frances. Goblins Will Be Seen: When it's time for Halloween. Hebert, Catherine, ed. Merchant, Donna, illus. 2005. 38p. (J). per. 16.95 incl. audio compact disk (978-0-9770893-0-7(4)) 2 Donn Bks.

Dorling Kindersley Publishing Staff. Halloween. 2001. (Touch & Feel Ser.). (Illus.). 12p. (J). (ps-k). bds. 6.99 (978-0-7894-6511-5(6)) Dorling Kindersley Publishing, Inc.

Dower, Laura. Powerpuff Girls Save Halloween. 2002. (gr. k-3). lib. bdg. 14.15 (978-0-613-50497-3(6)) Tandem Library Bks.

Driscoll, Laura. Halloween Treats. Arma, Tom, photos by. 2000. (Touch & Feel Ser.). (Illus.). 12p. (J). (ps). bds. 6.99 (978-0-448-41899-5(1) , Grosset & Dunlap) Penguin Group (USA) Inc.

Druce, Arden. Halloween Night. Wenzel, David W., illus. 2001. 32p. (J). (ps-k). 6.95 (978-0-87358-762-4(6) , Rising Moon Bks. for Young Readers) Northland Publishing.

Dubarle-Bossy, Philippe & Shulman, Mark. Batty Bat. Jennings, Patti, illus. 2004. 8p. (J). bds. 7.95 (978-1-4027-1591-4(9) , Sterling/Pinwheel) Sterling Publishing Co., Inc.

—Spooky Spider. Jennings, Patti, illus. 2004. 8p. (J). bds. 7.95 (978-1-4027-1590-7(0) , Sterling/Pinwheel) Sterling Publishing Co., Inc.

Dunrea, Olivier, illus. Goslings on the Prowl! 2005. (J). (978-0-618-53241-4(2)) Houghton Mifflin Co.

Duval, Kathy. The Three Bears' Halloween. Meisel, Paul, illus. 2007. 32p. (J). (ps-1). 16.95 (978-0-8234-2032-2(9)) Holiday Hse., Inc.

Edwards, Gerry. Candy Klaus Trick or Treat. 2004. 56p. per. 10.95 (978-1-59453-394-5(6) , 1074) Airleaf Publishing & Bookselling.

Egan, Tim. The Experiments of Doctor Vermin. Egan, Tim, illus. 2002. (Illus.). 32p. (J). (gr. k-3). tchr. ed. 15.00 (978-0-618-13224-9(4)) Houghton Mifflin Co. Trade & Reference Div.

Engelbreit, Mary. Queen of Halloween. 2008. 32p. (J). 16.99 ***(*978-0-06-008190-4(2));*** lib. bdg. 17.89 ***(*978-0-06-008191-1(0))*** HarperCollins Pubs.

Engleman, Dennis. Holloween Town. 2004. 37p. (J). (gr. 1-4). pap. 16.95 (978-1-928653-18-9(9)) Regina Orthodox Pr.

Erickson, John R. The Case of the Halloween Ghost. Holmes, Gerald L., illus. 1998. (Hank the Cowdog Ser.: No. 9). 144p. (J). (gr. 2-5). 14.99 (978-0-670-88416-2(2) , Viking Juvenile); No. 9. pap. 4.99 (978-0-14-130385-7(9) , Puffin) Penguin Group (USA) Inc.

Eubank, Patti Reeder, tr. ABCs of Halloween. 2003. (Illus.). 40p. (J). (ps-k). 8.95 (978-0-8249-5467-3(X)) Ideals Pubns.

Faine, Edward Allan. Little Ned Stories. Waites, Joan C., illus. 1999. 128p. (J). (gr. k-3). pap. 9.99 (978-0-9654651-5-1(2)) IM Pr.

Feehan-Vileria, Elaine. The Legend of Old Mr. Clarke. 2004. 58p. per. 17.95 (978-1-4116-1523-6(9)) Lulu.com.

Fernandes, Lindsay. Spooky Scooby Doo! Fernandes, Lindsay, ed. 2004. (Ultimate Sticker Bks.). (Illus.). 16p. (J). pap. 6.99 (978-0-7566-0301-4(3)) Dorling Kindersley Publishing, Inc.

Fernandez, Alberto. A Halloween Story: A frightfully delightful tale by a 5-year-old, for other little monsters Everywhere. de la Fuente, Pilar, illus. 2007. Tr. of Historia de Halloween. 48p. (J). ***(*978-0-9796465-0-8(2))*** Maroma Bks.

Fiorello, Frank. Mom, When Will It Be Halloween? Fiorello, Frank, illus. 1999. (Illus.). 36p. (J). (ps-6). pap. 7.95 (978-0-9646300-4-8(4)); lib. bdg. 11.95 (978-0-9646300-5-5(2)) Pumpkin Patch Publishing.

Fleming, Denise. Pumpkin Eye. rev. ed. 2005. (Illus.). 32p. (J). reprint ed. pap. 6.95 (978-0-8050-7635-6(2) , Owlet Paperbacks for Young Readers) Holt, Henry & Co.

Fontes, Justine. Hocus-Pocus Halloween. Regan, Dana, illus. 2003. (Magical Color Bks.). 10p. (J). 5.95 (978-1-4027-0992-0(7) , Sterling/Pinwheel) Sterling Publishing Co., Inc.

Fowler, Richard. Spooky Shadows. 2007. 10p. (J). (gr. k up). 9.99 ***(*978-0-7641-6082-0(6))*** Barron's Educational Series, Inc.

Franklin TV Staff, ed. Franklin's Halloween Fun. 2005. (Franklin Sticker & Activity Bks.). (Illus.). 16p. (J). (ps-3). (978-1-55337-670-5(6)) Kids Can Pr., Ltd.

Frank's 1st Pumpkin. 2002. (Booville Ser.). (Illus.). 24p. (J). (gr. k-4). 2.99 (978-1-57759-833-6(4)) Dalmatian Pr.

Freeman, Don. Corduroy's Best Halloween Ever. McCue, Lisa, illus. 2001. (Reading Railroad Bks.). 32p. (J). (gr. k-1). 3.99 (978-0-448-42499-6(1) , Grosset & Dunlap) Penguin Group (USA) Inc.

—Corduroy's Best Halloween Ever. 2001. (gr. k-3). lib. bdg. 11.25 (978-0-613-72457-9(7)); (Illus.). (J). 10.29 (978-0-606-21123-9(3)) Tandem Library Bks.

—Corduroy's Trick-or-Treat. McCue, Lisa, illus. 2002. 12p. (J). bds. 5.99 (978-0-670-03562-5(9) , Viking Juvenile) Penguin Group (USA) Inc.

Freeman, Martha. Who Stole Halloween? 224p. (J). (ps-7). 16.95 (978-0-8234-1962-3(2)) Holiday Hse., Inc.

Fry, Sonali. Dora's Spooky Halloween. Style Guide Staff, illus. 2006. (Dora the Explorer Ser.). 16p. (J). bds. 5.99 (978-1-4169-2482-1(5) , Simon Spotlight/Nickelodeon) Simon & Schuster Children's Publishing.

Gaines, Isabel. Pooh's Halloween Parade. 2001. (Winnie the Pooh First Readers Ser.). (Illus.). (J). (978-0-606-21656-2(1)) Tandem Library Bks.

Galbraith, Kathryn Osebold. One Shy Bunny, One Dark Night. Mack, Jeff, illus. 2008. (J). ***(*978-0-15-216246-7(1))*** Harcourt Trade Pubs.

Garfield, Valerie. Sergeant Sniff's Halloween Mystery Treat. 2000. (Sergeant Sniff Scratch-and-Sniff Mystery Ser.). (Illus.). 16p. (J). (ps-k). 6.95 (978-0-694-01513-9(X) , Harper Festival) HarperCollins Pubs.

Gaskin, Jack. The Ghostman's Halloween. Cassidy, Christina, illus. 1998. 12p. (J). (gr. k-4). pap. 5.95 (978-0-9668560-0-2(7)) Equity Research Corp.

Gilbert, Jeff. Trick or Shriek. 2006. 72p. pap. 5.97 (978-0-9646781-1-8(X)) Hairball Pr.

Gilson, Kristin. A Baby-Sitter's Nightmare: Tales Too Scary to Be True. 1998. (Illus.). 112p. (J). (gr. 3-7). pap. 4.95 (978-0-06-440700-7(4)) HarperCollins Pubs.

Golden Books Staff. Trick or Treat. Borlasca, Hector, illus. 2006. 12p. (J). (gr. k-1). bds. 3.99 (978-0-375-87490-1(9) , Golden Bks.) Random Hse. Children's Bks.

—Winnie The Boo! Paint Box. 2000. (Illus.). 32p. (ps-3). pap. 3.99 (978-0-307-09237-3(2) , Golden Bks.) Random Hse. Children's Bks.

Goon, Geraldine. Grandma Tells Dozens of Stories. 2002. (Illus.). 61p. per. (978-1-930493-85-8(1)) Athena Pr.

Gosselin, Kim. Trick or Treat for Diabetes: A Halloween Story for Kids Living with Diabetes. Ditto, Laura, ed. Dineen, Tom, illus. 1999. 28p. (J). (gr. k-6). pap. 11.95 (978-1-891383-07-6(8)) JayJo Bks., LLC.

Gott, Barry & MacKall, Dandi Daley. It Must Be Halloween. 2003. (Illus.). 16p. (J). pap. 4.99 (978-0-689-85024-0(7) , Little Simon) Simon & Schuster Children's Publishing.

Graham-Barber, Lynda. Say Boo. Lehman, Barbara, illus. 2002. 16p. (J). (ps-k). bds. 4.99 (978-0-7636-1890-2(X)) Candlewick Pr.

Grambling, Lois G. T. Rex Trick-or-Treats. Davis, Jack E., illus. 2005. 32p. (J). 12.99 (978-0-06-050252-2(5) , Tegen, Katherine Bks) HarperCollins Pubs.

—T-Rex Trick-or-Treats. Davis, Jack E., illus. 2005. 32p. (J). lib. bdg. 13.89 (978-0-06-050253-9(3) , Tegen, Katherine Bks) HarperCollins Pubs.

Graziani, Maria. A Black Cat on Halloween: Un Gato Negro en Dia de Brujas. Elejalde, Eliana, illus. l.t. ed. 2004. (SPA.). 23p. (J). 7.00 (978-0-9762361-1-5(7)) Ed. Acespanish S.A.C.- Lima, Peru.

Gregory, Valiska. The Mystery of the Grindlecat. 2003. (Illus.). 32p. (J). 18.99 (978-1-57860-142-4(8)); pap. 9.99 (978-1-57860-141-7(X)) Emmis Bks.

Gritton, Steve. The Kandy Witch. 2007. (J). 18.95 ***(*978-0-9795361-0-6(3))*** Bad Frog Art/SMG Bks.

Groening, Matt. The Simpson's Treehouse of Horror Heebie-Jeebie Hullabaloo. 1999. (Treehouse of Horror Ser.). (gr. 5-8). lib. bdg. 25.70 (978-0-613-53669-1(X)) Tandem Library Bks.

Gruber, Michael. The Legend of the Brog. Gruber, Michael & Graves, Linda, illus. 2005. (J). per. 9.95 (978-0-9770413-0-5(1)) Gruber Enterprises.

Guardo, Attilio. Halloween at Clear Creek. 2005. 208p. pap. 19.95 (978-1-4137-8325-4(2)) PublishAmerica, Inc.

Gutman, Dan. Mrs. Patty Is Batty! Paillot, Jim, illus. 2006. (My Weird School Ser.: No. 13). 112p. (J). pap. 3.99 (978-0-06-085380-8(8) , Harper Trophy); lib. bdg. 15.89 (978-0-06-085381-5(6)) HarperCollins Pubs.

Halfmann, Janet. Bewitching the Chickadees. 2007. 88p. (J). pap. 14.99 (978-1-59092-573-7(4) , Orchard Academy Pr.) Windstorm Creative.

Hall, Kirsten. I'm a Princess. DeRosa, Dee, illus. 2003. (My First Reader Ser.). 32p. (J). 18.50 (978-0-516-22928-7(1) , Children's Pr.) Scholastic Library Publishing.

Hall, Zoe. It's Pumpkin Time! Halpern, Shari, illus. 2002. (J). 13.83 (978-0-7587-2878-4(6)) Book Wholesalers, Inc.

—It's Pumpkin Time! Halpern, Shari, illus. 1999. 40p. (J). (ps-2). pap. 5.99 (978-0-590-55849-5(8)) Scholastic, Inc.

—It's Pumpkin Time! 1999. (ps-2). lib. bdg. 14.15 (978-0-613-22878-7(2)) Tandem Library Bks.

—It's Pumpkin Time. 1999. (J). 12.79 (978-0-606-17270-7(X)) Tandem Library Bks.

Hallinan, P. K. Today Is Halloween! (J). (ps-k). 5.95 (978-0-8249-5306-5(1)) Ideals Pubns.

The Halloween Caper. 2007. (J). ***(*978-1-932570-63-2(2))*** Literacy Footprints Inc.

Happy Halloween! 2008. (Max & Ruby Ser.). 24p. (J). (ps-1). 3.99 ***(*978-0-448-44863-3(7)*** , Grosset & Dunlap) Penguin Group (USA) Inc.

Harman, Chuck. Trick or Treat. 2000. (Adventures of Artie the Airplane & His Friends Ser.). (Illus.). 32p. (J). (ps-6). pap. 6.95 (978-1-891736-09-4(4)) Studio Five/Fourteen.

HarperCollins Staff, et al. An I Can Read Halloween Treat, Set. Zimmer, Dirk, illus. 2004. (I Can Read Bks.). (J). (gr. k-3). pap. 11.99 (978-0-06-054237-5(3) , Harper Trophy) HarperCollins Pubs.

Harris, Annmarie. The Countdown to Halloween. Lucas, Margeaux, illus. 2003. 24p. (J). (ps-4). pap. 3.99 (978-0-8431-0462-2(7) , Price Stern Sloan) Penguin Group (USA) Inc.

Harris, Joe. Halloween Ball. 2008. (J). ***(*978-0-375-84975-6(0)); (*978-0-375-84373-0(6));*** lib. bdg. ***(*978-0-375-94975-3(5))*** Random Hse., Inc.

Hatch, Elizabeth. Halloween Night. Pickering, Jimmy, illus. 2005. 32p. (J). (ps-1). 15.95 (978-0-385-74622-9(9)); lib. bdg. 17.99 (978-0-385-90887-0(3)) Random Hse. Children's Bks. (Doubleday Bks. for Young Readers).

The Haunted Halloween, 6 vols. (Woodland Mysteriestm Ser.). 133p. (gr. 3-7). 42.50 (978-0-7802-7924-7(7)) Wright Group, The.

Hendra, Sue. Scary Party. 1998. (J). (978-0-7636-0445-5(3)) Candlewick Pr.

Henkes, Kevin. Julius's Candy Corn. Henkes, Kevin, illus. 2003. (Illus.). 24p. (J). 6.99 (978-0-06-053789-0(2)) HarperCollins Pubs.

Herman, Gail. The Haunted Halloween Party. 2007. (Scooby-Doo! Reader Ser.: No. 20). 32p. (J). pap. 3.99 ***(*978-0-439-78811-3(0))*** Scholastic, Inc.

Herman, Gail. Spike at Halloween. 2002. (ps-2). lib. bdg. 11.80 (978-0-613-64113-5(2)) Tandem Library Bks.

Herman, R. A. The Littlest Pumpkin. Ogden, Betina, illus. 2001. 32p. (J). (ps-2). 3.99 (978-0-439-29544-4(0)) Scholastic, Inc.

—Littlest Pumpkin. 2001. (ps-2). lib. bdg. 11.25 (978-0-613-86020-8(9)) Tandem Library Bks.

—Littlest Pumpkin - Library. 2006. (J). 18.95 (978-0-439-89837-9(4)) Scholastic, Inc.

—Littlest Pumpkin Read Along. 2006. (J). 9.95 (978-0-439-89555-2(3)) Scholastic, Inc.

Higashi/Glaser Design Inc. Staff. Hello Kitty, Hello Halloween! 2005. (Illus.). 24p. (J). (ps-3). bds. 6.95 (978-0-8109-5753-4(1) , Abrams Bks. for Young Readers) Abrams, Harry N. , Inc.

Hill, Eric. Spot's Halloween. Hill, Eric, illus. 2003. (Spot Ser.). (Illus.). 10p. (J). (ps-1). bds. 5.99 (978-0-399-24185-7(X) , Putnam Juvenile) Penguin Group (USA) Inc.

Hill, Eric. Spot's Halloween Party. Hill, Eric, illus. 2007. 6p. (J). (ps-ps). pap. 7.99 (***978-0-399-24778-1(5)*** , Putnam Juvenile) Penguin Group (USA) Inc.

Hillert, Margaret. It's Halloween, Dear Dragon. Kock, Carl, illus. rev. exp. ed. 2007. (Beginning to Read Ser.). 32p. (J). lib. bdg. (978-1-59953-041-3(4)) Norwood Hse. Pr.

Hoban, Lillian. Arthur's Halloween Costume. Hoban, Lillian, illus. 2002. (Arthur the Chimpanzee Ser.). (Illus.). (J). 12.30 (978-0-7587-5553-7(8)) Book Wholesalers, Inc.

Hoffman, Alice & Martin, Wolfe. Moondog. Heo, Yumi, illus. 2004. (J). pap. (978-0-439-09862-5(9)); 32p. pap. 16.95 (978-0-439-09861-8(0)) Scholastic, Inc.

Hoffman, Mary & Riddell, Chris. Dracula's Daughter. 2006. (Yellow Bananas Ser.). (Illus.). (J). 48p. pap. (978-0-7787-1000-4(9)); 43p. (978-0-7787-0954-1(X)) Crabtree Publishing Co.

Holabird, Katharine. Angelina's Halloween. Craig, Helen, illus. 2006. (Angelina Ballerina Ser.). 32p. (J). (ps). pap. 5.99 (978-0-14-240621-2(X) , Puffin) Penguin Group (USA) Inc.

Holub, Joan. The Halloween Queen. Smythe, Theresa, illus. 2004. 32p. (J). (gr. k-3). 15.95 (978-0-8075-3138-9(3)) Whitman, Albert & Co.

—Scaredy-Pants: A Halloween Story. Terry, Will, illus. 2007. (Ant Hill Ser.). 24p. (J). lib. bdg. 13.89 (***978-1-4169-2561-3(9)*** , Aladdin) Simon & Schuster Children's Publishing.

—Scaredy-Pants! A Halloween Story. Terry, Will, illus. 2007. (Ant Hill Ser.). 24p. (J). pap. 3.99 (***978-1-4169-0956-9(7)*** , Aladdin) Simon & Schuster Children's Publishing.

Horowitz, Dave. The Ugly Pumpkin: A Thanksgiving Story. Horowitz, Dave, illus. 2005. (Illus.). 40p. (J). (ps-2). 16.99 (978-0-399-24267-0(8) , Putnam Juvenile) Penguin Group (USA) Inc.

Horton, Joan. Halloween Hoots & Howls. rev. ed. 1999. (Illus.). 32p. (J). (ps-3). 15.95 (978-0-8050-5805-5(2) , Holt, Henry & Co. Bks. For Young Readers) Holt, Henry & Co.

House on Haunted Hill. 2002. (Booville Ser.). (Illus.). 32p. (J). (gr. k-4). 2.99 (978-1-57759-831-2(8)) Dalmatian Pr.

Howe, James. Scared Silly. Morrill, Leslie H., illus. 1998. (Bunnicula & Friends Ser.). 48p. (J). (gr. k-3). pap. 4.95 (978-0-688-16322-8(X)) HarperCollins Pubs.

—Scared Silly. Mack, Jeff, illus. (Bunnicula & Friends Ser.). (J). 2006. 40p. pap. 3.99 (978-0-689-85751-5(9) , Aladdin); 2005. 48p. 14.95 (978-0-689-85726-3(8) , Atheneum) Simon & Schuster Children's Publishing.

Hubbard, Patricia. Trick or Treat Countdown. Letzig, Michael, illus. 1999. 32p. (J). (gr. k-3). tchr. ed. 16.95 (978-0-8234-1367-6(5)) Holiday Hse., Inc.

Hubbell, William. Pumpkin Jack. 2003. (gr. k-3). lib. bdg. 15.25 (978-0-613-75725-6(4)) Tandem Library Bks.

—Pumpkin Jack. Hubbell, William, illus. 2000. (Illus.). 32p. (J). (gr. k-3). pap. 6.95 (978-0-8075-6666-4(7)) Whitman, Albert & Co.

Huck, Charlotte S. A Creepy Countdown. Smith, Jos. A., illus. 2002. (J). 14.43 (978-0-7587-4599-6(0)) Book Wholesalers, Inc.

—A Creepy Countdown. Smith, Jos. A., illus. 2000. 24p. (J). (ps-2). pap. 5.95 (978-0-688-17717-1(4) , Harper Trophy) HarperCollins Pubs.

Hughes, Tom, adapted by. Monster House Movie Novelization. 2006. (Monster House Ser.). 128p. (J). pap. 4.99 (978-1-4169-1817-2(5) , Simon Spotlight) Simon & Schuster Children's Publishing.

Hulme, Joy N. Eerie Feary Feeling: A Hairy Scary Pop-Up Book. Fly, Paul, illus. 1998. 12p. (J). (ps-2). pap. 13.95 (978-0-531-30086-2(2) , Orchard Bks.) Scholastic, Inc.

—Eerie Feary Feeling: A Hairy Scary Pop-up Book. Ely, Paul & Dudley, Dick, illus. 2006. 12p. (J). (gr. k-4). reprint ed. 14.00 (978-1-4223-5171-0(8)) DIANE Publishing Co.

Jacobson, Jennifer Richard. Andy Shane & the Pumpkin Trick. Carter, Abby, illus. 64p. (J). (gr. k-3). 2007. pap. 4.99 (***978-0-7636-3306-6(2));*** 2006. 13.99 (978-0-7636-2605-1(8)) Candlewick Pr.

Jenkins, Jerry B. & Fabry, Chris. Hollywood Holdup. 2006. (Red Rock Mysteries Ser.). 224p. (J). pap. 5.99 (978-1-4143-0151-8(0)) Tyndale Hse. Pubs.

Johnson, Kathleen Jeffrie. A Fast & Brutal Wing. unabr. ed. 2005. (YA). 46.70 incl. audio (978-1-4193-3247-0(3) , 42029) Recorded Bks., LLC.

—A Fast & Brutal Wing. rev. ed. 2004. 192p. (YA). 16.95 (978-1-59643-013-6(3)) Roaring Brook Pr.

Johnson, Lisa. All Hallows' Eve: The Story of the Halloween Fairy. Johnson, Tucker, illus. l.t. ed. 2005. 32p. (J). 12.95 (978-0-9773096-0-3(6)) Positive Spin Pr.

Johnson, Lisa Sferlazza. All Hallows Eve: The Story of the Halloween Fairy. Johnson, Tucker, illus. 2006. 32p. (J). 15.95 (978-0-9773096-1-0(4)) Positive Spin Pr.

Johnson, Sandi, et al. Haunted Doghouse II: Halloween Night, 3 vols. Brundige, Britt, ed. Stargeon, Bobbi, illus. l.t. ed. 2005. 15p. (J). (gr. k-5). spiral bd. 6.99 (978-1-929063-27-7(X) , 351) Moons & Stars Publishing For Children.

Jones, Brien. The Scariest Pumpkin of All. 2003. (Illus.). 63p. (J). (ps-7). per. 9.95 (978-1-59453-014-2(9) , 1670) Airleaf Publishing & Bookselling.

Jones, Marcia Thornton & Dadey, Debbie. Mrs. Jeepers' Scariest Halloween Ever. 2005. (Adventures of the Bailey School Kids Ser.: Bk. 7). (Illus.). 112p. mass mkt. 3.99 (978-0-439-77527-4(2) , Scholastic Paperbacks) Scholastic, Inc.

Jougla, Frederic. Tricked on Halloween: Rina & Jax's Stories. Jougla, Karina, illus. l.t. ed. 2004. 36p. (J). bds. 14.99 (978-0-9754287-0-2(5)) Imagery Pr.

Keeler, Kathleen. I Double Dare You! More Stories to Scare You! Doucet, Bob, illus. 2002. (Hello Reader! Ser.). 40p. (J). pap. 3.99 (978-0-439-32255-3(3) , Cartwheel Bks.) Scholastic, Inc.

Keene, Carolyn. The Halloween Hoax. Pamintuan, Macky, illus. 2007. (Nancy Drew & the Clue Crew Ser.: No. 9). 96p. (J). pap. 3.99 (***978-1-4169-3664-0(5)*** , Aladdin) Simon & Schuster Children's Publishing.

Kelman, Marcy. Halloween Surprise. 2007. 24p. (J). (ps-k). pap. 4.99 (***978-1-4231-0208-3(8))*** Disney Pr.

Kennedy, Marge. The Book of Boo! 2002. (Illus.). 32p. (ps-1). 5.99 (978-0-7868-3364-1(5)) Disney Pr.

Kessel, Joyce K. Halloween. Carlson, Nancy, illus. rev. ed. 2004. (On My Own Holidays Ser.). 48p. (J). (gr. 2-4). lib. bdg. 25.26 (978-0-87614-933-1(6)) Lerner Publishing Group.

Kimball, Linda Hoffman. Come with Me on Halloween. Reed, Mike, illus. 2005. 32p. (J). (ps-1). 16.95 (978-0-8075-3132-7(4)) Whitman, Albert & Co.

Kingfisher Editors, creator. My Halloween Sound Book. 2004. (First Holiday Bks.). (Illus.). 12p. (J). (gr. k-3). bds. 7.95 (978-0-7534-5730-6(X) , Kingfisher) Houghton Mifflin Co. Trade & Reference Div.

Klein, Abby. Halloween Fraidy-Cat. McKinley, John, illus. 2006. (Ready, Freddy! Ser.: No. 8). 96p. (J). pap. 3.99 (978-0-439-78457-3(3) , Blue Sky Pr., The) Scholastic, Inc.

Klein, Abby. The Pumpkin Elf Mystery. McKinley, John, illus. 2007. (Ready, Freddy! Ser.: No. 11). 96p. (J). pap. 3.99 (***978-0-439-89591-0(X)*** , Blue Sky Pr., The) Scholastic, Inc.

Kline, Suzy. Horrible Harry at Halloween. Remkiewicz, Frank, illus. (Horrible Harry Ser.). 64p. (J). 2002. pap. 3.99 (978-0-14-130675-9(0) , Puffin); 2000. (gr. 2-6). 13.99 (978-0-670-88864-1(8) , Viking Juvenile) Penguin Group (USA) Inc.

—Horrible Harry at Halloween. 2002. (gr. 3-6). lib. bdg. 11.80 (978-0-613-45277-9(1)) Tandem Library Bks.

Kneen, Maggie. Halloween Kittens. Kneen, Maggie, illus. 2004. (Illus.). 20p. (J). 15.95 (978-0-8118-4228-0(2)) Chronicle Bks. LLC.

Korman, Justine. It's the Great Pumpkin, Charlie Brown. 2001. (ps-2). lib. bdg. 14.15 (978-0-613-57419-8(2)) Tandem Library Bks.

Kovalski, Maryann. Omar's Halloween. 2007. (Illus.). 32p. (J). (ps-3). per. (***978-1-55455-049-4(1))*** Fitzhenry & Whiteside, Ltd.

Kreib. We're off to Find the Witch's House. Alley, R. W., illus. 2007. 32p. (J). (gr. k). pap. 5.99 (978-0-14-240854-4(9) , Puffin) Penguin Group (USA) Inc.

—We're off to Find the Witch's House. Alley, Robert W., illus. 2005. 32p. (J). (ps-ps). 14.99 (978-0-525-47003-8(4) , Dutton Juvenile) Penguin Group (USA) Inc.

Kroll, Steven. Biggest Pumpkin Ever. Bassett, Jeni, illus. 2007. 32p. (J). pap. 4.99 (***978-0-439-92946-2(6))*** Scholastic, Inc.

Krosoczka, Jarrett J. Annie Was Warned. 2003. (Illus.). 30p. (J). (ps-3). 15.95 (978-0-375-81567-6(8)); lib. bdg. 17.99 (978-0-375-91567-3(2)) Random Hse. Children's Bks. (Knopf Bks. for Young Readers).

Krull, Kathleen. How to Trick or Treat in Outer Space. Brewer, Paul, illus. 2004. 32p. (J). (gr. k-3). tchr. ed. 16.95 (978-0-8234-1844-2(8)) Holiday Hse., Inc.

Labatt, Mary. One Terrible Halloween. Hill-Jackson, Troy, illus. 2002. (Sam Ser.). 120p. (J). (gr. 4-6). (978-1-55337-139-7(9)); (978-1-55337-138-0(0)) Kids Can Pr., Ltd.

—One Terrible Halloween. 2002. (gr. 3-6). lib. bdg. 12.95 (978-0-613-62815-0(2)) Tandem Library Bks.

—Sam's First Halloween. Sarrazin, Marisol, illus. 2004. (Kids Can Read! Ser.). 32p. (J). (gr. k-3). (978-1-55337-355-1(3)) Kids Can Pr., Ltd.

—Sam's First Halloween. 2003. (gr. k-3). lib. bdg. 11.80 (978-0-613-82322-7(2)) Tandem Library Bks.

Labatt, Mary & Sarrazin, Marisol. Sam's First Halloween. 2004. (Kids Can Read! Ser.). (Illus.). 32p. (J). (gr. k-3). (978-1-55337-356-8(1)) Kids Can Pr., Ltd.

Lagonegro, Melissa. Happy Halloween! 2003. (Teenie Halloweenies Ser.). (Illus.). 24p. (J). (gr. k-3). 3.25 (978-0-375-82532-3(0) , Golden Bks.) Random Hse. Children's Bks.

—Happy Halloween! 2003. (gr. k-3). lib. bdg. 10.95 (978-0-613-71930-8(1)) Tandem Library Bks.

Landolf, Diane Wright. Hooray for Halloween! Wolcott, Karen, illus. 2004. (Barbie Ser.). 24p. (J). (ps-2). 3.99 (978-0-375-82757-0(9) , Golden Bks.) Random Hse. Children's Bks.

Lansing, Richard D., Jr. The Black Catskill Cat. Lansing, Randy, illus. 2000. 48p. (J). per. 6.00 (978-0-9661844-7-1(5)) Purple Gorilla, LLC, The.

Laterra, Joann. Halloween Crossing. 2004. 127p. (YA). pap. 14.95 (978-0-7414-2101-2(1)) Infinity Publishing.

Layman, Richard. The Halloween Mouse. Clark, Alan M., illus. 2001. 36p. 25.00 (978-1-58767-047-3(X)) Cemetery Dance Pubns.

Lazo, Jeanne Rae. If Looks Could Kill. 2005. 160p. (J). lib. bdg. 14.95 (978-0-9713756-4-2(X)) Stargazer Publishing Co.

Lee, Quinlan B. Trick or Treat. Johnson, Jay, illus. 2004. (Care Bears Ser.). 24p. (J). pap. 3.50 (978-0-439-66398-4(9)) Scholastic, Inc.

Leon McCann, Jesse. Haunted Halloween: Sticker Storybook. del Sur, Duendes, illus. 2004. (Scooby-Doo Ser.). 24p. (J). pap. 5.99 (978-0-439-60699-8(3) , Scholastic Paperbacks) Scholastic, Inc.

—Scooby-Doo & the Trick-or-Treat Thief. del Sur, Duendes, illus. 2002. (Scooby Doo Ser.). 32p. (J). pap. 5.99 (978-0-439-44294-7(X)) Scholastic, Inc.

Leonard, Rebecca JoAnne. Adirondack Halloween: A Spooky Tale in the North Country. 2006. 48p. (J). pap. 7.95 (***978-1-4327-0139-0(8))*** Outskirts Press, Inc.

Leuck, Laura. One Witch. Schindler, S. D., illus. 32p. (J). 2005. pap. 6.95 (978-0-8027-7729-4(5)); 2004. 15.95 (978-0-8027-8860-3(2)) Walker & Co.

Levack, Joseph, photos by. Picture Me Having Trick or Treat Fun. 1998. (Picture Me Ser.). (Illus.). 10p. (J). (ps up). bds. 4.99 (978-1-57151-548-3(8)) Playhouse Publishing.

Lewis, Kevin. The Runaway Pumpkin. Schindler, S. D., illus. 2003. 32p. (J). (gr. k-2). pap. 15.95 (978-0-439-43974-9(4) , Orchard Bks.) Scholastic, Inc.

Lewis, Kevin & Reeves, Howard. There Was an Old Witch Paperback. Catrow, David, illus. abr. ed. 2000. 32p. (ps-3). pap. 5.99 (978-0-7868-1492-3(6)) Disney Pr.

Litter Bug's Halloween. 2006. (J). 8.95 (***978-0-9788536-4-8(4))*** G Publishing LLC.

The Littles & the Great Halloween Scare. 2002. (Littles Ser.). (Illus.). (J). 12.17 (978-0-7587-8434-6(1)) Book Wholesalers, Inc.

London, Jonathan. Froggy's Halloween. Remkiewicz, Frank, illus. 1999. (Froggy Ser.). 32p. (J). (ps-1). 15.99 (978-0-670-88449-0(9) , Viking Juvenile) Penguin Group (USA) Inc.

—Froggy's Halloween. 2002. (gr. k-3). lib. bdg. 14.15 (978-0-613-45266-3(6)) Tandem Library Bks.

London, Jonathan & Remkiewicz, Frank. Froggy's Halloween. rev. ed. 2001. (Illus.). 1p. (J). pap. 5.99 (978-0-14-230068-8(3) , Puffin) Penguin Group (USA) Inc.

Lowery, Linda. Trick Or Treat, Halloween. 2000. (Pictureback Ser.). (978-0-606-18505-9(4)) Tandem Library Bks.

Maccarone, Grace. Magic Matt & the Jack O'Lantern, Level 1. Bridwell, Norman, illus. 2003. (Reader Ser.). 32p. (J). pap. 3.99 (978-0-439-43992-3(2) , Cartwheel Bks.) Scholastic, Inc.

Maccarone, Grace & Burns, Marilyn. It Was Halloween Night: A Scary Math Story - with Tangrams! Straub, Matthew, illus. 2001. (Hello Reader! Math Ser.). (J). (978-0-439-30471-9(7)) Scholastic, Inc.

MacDonald, Maryann. The Costume Copycat. Wilsdorf, Anne, illus. 2006. 32p. (J). (ps). 10.99 (978-0-8037-2929-2(4) , Dial) Penguin Group (USA) Inc.

Man-Kong, Mary. The Spooky Smells of Halloween. Garofoli, Viviana, illus. 2005. 32p. (J). (ps-2). 8.99 (978-0-375-83285-7(8) , Golden Bks.) Random Hse. Children's Bks.

Martin, Bill, Jr. & Sampson, Michael. Trick or Treat? Meisel, Paul, illus. 2005. 32p. (J). reprint ed. 6.99 (978-1-4169-0262-1(7) , Aladdin) Simon & Schuster Children's Publishing.

Martone, Eric. Jack O' Lantern: A Halloween Tale. 2003. (gr. 3-6). lib. bdg. 17.60 (978-0-613-87781-7(0)) Tandem Library Bks.

Mason, Eva. Halloween Play. Huxtable, John, illus. 2005. (Strawberry Shortcake Ser.). 32p. (J). (ps-2). pap. 3.99 (978-0-448-43910-5(7) , Grosset & Dunlap) Penguin Group (USA) Inc.

Masurel, Claire. Happy Halloween Emily! Calitri, Susan, illus. 2002. (Reading Railroad Bks.). 32p. (J). pap. 3.99 (978-0-448-42691-4(9) , Grosset & Dunlap) Penguin Group (USA) Inc.

—Happy Halloween, Emily! 2002. (gr. k-3). lib. bdg. 11.25 (978-0-613-72492-0(5)) Tandem Library Bks.

Mayer, Mercer. Happy Halloween, Little Critter! Mayer, Mercer, illus. 2004. (Little Critter Ser.). 16p. (J). pap. 6.99 (978-0-06-053971-9(2) , Harper Festival) HarperCollins Pubs.

McCann, Jesse Leon. Haunted Halloween Mask. 2003. (gr. k-3). lib. bdg. 14.15 (978-0-613-72207-0(8)) Tandem Library Bks.

—Scooby Doo & the Halloween Hotel Haunt. 1999. (gr. k-3). lib. bdg. 14.15 (978-0-613-29739-4(3)) Tandem Library Bks.

—Scooby-Doo & the Halloween Hotel Haunt: A Glow in the Dark Mystery! del Sur, Duendes, illus. 1999. (Scooby-Doo Ser.). 24p. (J). (ps-3). pap. 5.99 (978-0-439-11768-5(2)) Scholastic, Inc.

McCann, Jesse Leon, et al. Haunted Halloween Mask. del Sur, Duendes, illus. 2003. (Scooby-Doo Ser.). 24p. (J). pap. 5.99 (978-0-439-44937-3(5) , Scholastic Paperbacks) Scholastic, Inc.

McCourt, Lisa. Happy Halloween, Stinky Face. Moore, Cyd, illus. 2007. 32p. (J). (ps-3). pap. 15.99 (978-0-439-77977-7(4)) Scholastic, Inc.

McCully, Emily Arnold. Grandmas Trick-or-Treat. McCully, Emily Arnold, illus. 2002. (Illus.). 12.34 (978-1-4046-1307-2(2)) Book Wholesalers, Inc.

—Grandmas Trick-or-Treat. McCully, Emily Arnold, illus. (I Can Read Bks.). (Illus.). 48p. (J). (ps-1). 2002. pap. 3.99 (978-0-06-444277-0(2)); 2001. 14.95 (978-0-06-028730-6(6)) HarperCollins Pubs.

McGee, Warner, illus. Monster Halloween Party. 2007. (Backyardigans Ser.). 14p. (J). bds. 6.99 (***978-1-4169-3435-6(9)*** , Simon Spotlight/Nickelodeon) Simon & Schuster Children's Publishing.

McGeorge Endres. Boomer's Halloween. (J). 14.95 (978-0-8118-4229-7(0)) Chronicle Bks. LLC.

McGhee, Alison. A Very Brave Witch. Bliss, Harry, illus. 2006. 32p. (J). (ps-3). 12.95 (978-0-689-86730-9(1) , Simon & Schuster Children's Publishing) Simon & Schuster Children's Publishing.

McGrath, Barbara Barbieri. The M & M's' Brand Halloween Treat Book. 2004. (Illus.). 14p. (J). (ps-3). bds. 6.95 (978-1-57091-420-1(6)) Charlesbridge Publishing, Inc.

McGuirk, Leslie. Tucker's Spooky Halloween. McGuirk, Leslie, illus. 2007. (Illus.). 28p. (J). (ps-k). bds. 7.99 (***978-0-7636-3181-9(7))*** Candlewick Pr.

McMahon, P. J. The Mystery of the Diappearing Dinosaurs. 2005. (Illus.). 120p. (J). (***978-1-4156-0778-7(8)*** , Aladdin) Simon & Schuster Children's Publishing.

—Mystery of the Disappearing Dinosaurs. Manders, John, illus. 2005. 120p. (J). lib. bdg. 15.38 (***978-1-4242-0405-2(4))*** Fitzgerald Bks.

McMullan, Kate. Fluffy's Happy Halloween. Smith, Mavis, illus. 2004. 40p. (J). lib. bdg. 15.00 (978-1-59054-464-8(1)) Fitzgerald Bks.

—Fluffy's Trick-or-Treat. Smith, Mavis, illus. 2001. (Hello Reader! Ser.). (J). pap. 3.99 (978-0-439-31941-6(2)) Scholastic, Inc.

McNamara, Margaret. Snow Day. Gordon, Mike, illus. 2007. (Robin Hill School Ser.). 32p. (J). lib. bdg. 13.89 (***978-1-4169-3492-9(8));*** pap. 3.99 (***978-1-4169-3493-6(6))*** Simon & Schuster Children's Publishing. (Aladdin).

Meister, Cari. Luther's Halloween. Petrone, Valeria, illus. 2004. 32p. (J). (ps-1). 15.99 (978-0-670-03555-7(6) , Viking Juvenile) Penguin Group (USA) Inc.

Melmed, Laura Krauss. Fright Night Flight. Cole, Henry, illus. 2002. 32p. (J). (ps-3). 15.99 (978-0-06-029701-5(8)) HarperCollins Pubs.

Metzger, Steve. It's Halloween! Wilhelm, Hans, illus. 1999. (Dinofours Ser.: No. 13). (J). (ps-1). (978-0-439-06326-5(4)) Scholastic, Inc.

—It's Pumpkin Day! Wilhelm, Hans, illus. 2001. (Dinofours Ser.). (J). (ps-1). pap. 3.25 (978-0-439-29569-7(6)) Scholastic, Inc.

Miller, Jayna. Too Much Trick or Treat. Thatch, Nancy, ed. Miller, Jayna, illus. 2005. (Illus.). 29p. (J). per. 19.95 (978-0-933849-83-9(4)) Landmark Editions, Inc.

Miller, Margaret. Peekaboo Baby. Miller, Margaret, illus. 2001. (Look Baby! Bks.). (Illus.). 14p. (J). bds. 6.99 (978-0-689-84433-1(6) , Little Simon) Simon & Schuster Children's Publishing.

Mills, Claudia. Gus & Grandpa & the Halloween Costume. Stock, Catherine, illus. 2002. (Gus & Grandpa Ser.). 48p. (J). (gr. 1-3). 15.00 (978-0-374-32816-0(1) , Farrar, Straus & Giroux (BYR)) Farrar, Straus & Giroux.

Milnes, Ellen. Trick or Treat, Pooh! 2000. (Learn & Grow Ser.). (Illus.). 14p. (J). (ps up). 5.99 (978-0-7364-0104-3(0)) Mouse Works.

Minor, Wendell. Pumpkin Heads! 2007. 32p. (J). (ps-3). pap. 6.99 (***978-0-590-52138-3(1))*** Scholastic, Inc.

Miranda, Anne. Who Said Boo? 2003. (Illus.). 24p. (ps-k). 12.99 (978-0-7868-0811-3(X)) Hyperion Bks. for Children.

Modesitt, Jeanne. Mouse's Halloween Party. Spowart, Robin, illus. 2004. 32p. (J). (ps up). 13.95 (978-1-56397-950-7(0)) Boyds Mills Pr.

Montes, Marisa. Los Gatos Black on Halloween. Morales, Yuyi, illus. rev. ed. 2006. 32p. (J). 16.95 (978-0-8050-7429-1(5) , Holt, Henry & Co. Bks. For Young Readers) Holt, Henry & Co.

Moulton, Mark Kimball. Miss Fiona's Stupendous Pumpkin Pies. Crouch, Karen Hillard, illus. 2004. 28p. (J). 14.95 (978-0-8249-5489-5(0)) Ideals Pubns.

—Miss Fiona's Stupendous Pumpkin Pies. Crouch, Karen Hillard, illus. 2001. 21p. (J). (gr. k-3). 18.00 (978-0-7412-0865-1(2)) Lang Graphics, Ltd.

—Twisted Sistahs. 2003. (Illus.). 32p. (J). (gr. 3-6). 18.00 (978-0-7412-1600-7(0)) Lang Graphics, Ltd.

Mouse Works Staff. Happy Halloween! 1998. (Giant Lift-the-Flap Ser.). (Illus.). 10p. (J). 8.99 (978-1-57082-749-5(4)) Mouse Works.

Munoz-Furlong, Anne. Alexander Goes Trick-or-Treating. Furlong, Mariel Christine, illus. 1999. 24p. (J). (gr. k-6). pap. 5.00 (978-1-882541-13-3(8)) Food Allergy & Anaphylaxis Network.

Munsch, Robert. Boo! Mart Chenko, Michael, illus. 2004. 32p. (J). pap. 3.99 (978-0-439-62331-5(6) , Cartwheel Bks.) Scholastic, Inc.

Murphy, Chuck. Halloween. Murphy, Chuck, illus. 2000. (Razzle Dazzle Book Ser.). (Illus.). 12p. (J). (ps-k). bds. 5.99 (978-0-689-83827-9(1) , Little Simon) Simon & Schuster Children's Publishing.

Myra, Harold. Halloween, Is It for Real? Kurisu, Jane, illus. 2005. 18p. (J). (ps-ps). bds. 6.99 (978-1-4003-0630-5(2)) Nelson, Thomas Inc.

Natti, Susanna, illus. Lionel in the Fall. 2002. (Lionel Ser.). (J). 11.49 (978-0-7587-1390-2(8)) Book Wholesalers, Inc.

Naylor, Phyllis Reynolds. The Girls Get Even. 2002. (gr. 3-6). lib. bdg. 13.00 (978-0-613-37145-2(3)) Tandem Library Bks.

Neitzel, Shirley. Who Will I Be? A Halloween Rebus Story. Parker, Nancy Winslow, illus. 2005. 32p. (J). 12.99 (978-0-06-056067-6(3)); lib. bdg. 13.89 (978-0-06-056068-3(1)) HarperCollins Pubs.

Nicholas, J. B. The Waving Girl. Waites, Joan C., illus. 2004. 32p. (J). pap. 7.95 (978-1-58980-185-1(7)) Pelican Publishing Co., Inc.

Nikola-Lisa, W. Shake D'em Halloween Bones. 2000. (978-0-606-22080-4(1)) Tandem Library Bks.

—Shake Dem Halloween Bones. Reed, Mike, illus. 2000. 32p. (J). (gr. k-3). 6.95 (978-0-618-07034-3(6)) Houghton Mifflin Co. Trade & Reference Div.

H I

Novak, Matt. No Zombies Allowed. Novak, Matt, illus. 2002. (Illus.). 32p. (J). (gr. k-2). 16.95 (978-0-689-84130-9(2) , Atheneum/Richard Jackson Bks.) Simon & Schuster Children's Publishing.

—On Halloween Street. Novak, Matt, illus. 2001. (Illus.). 20p. (J). 7.99 (978-0-689-84514-7(6) , Little Simon) Simon & Schuster Children's Publishing.

O'Brien, Sarah. Jacks O'Lantern. 2007. (Illus.). 32p. pap. 6.95 (*978-0-7624-3095-6(8) , Running Pr. Minature Editions) Running Pr. Bk. Pubs.

Osborne, Mary Pope. Haunted Castle on Hallows Eve. Murdocca, Sal, illus. 2003. (Magic Tree House Ser.: No. 30). 128p. (J). (gr. k-3). 11.95 (978-0-375-82521-7(5)); lib. bdg. 13.99 (978-0-375-92521-4(X)) Random Hse. Children's Bks. (Random Hse. Bks. for Young Readers).

Ostrow, Kim. Makeup Mayhem. Durk, Jim, illus. 2006. (Ready-To-Read Ser.: Vol. 2). 32p. (J). pap. 3.99 (978-0-689-87724-7(2) , Simon Spotlight) Simon & Schuster Children's Publishing.

Parent, Nancy. Pooh Says Boo. 1998. (Pooh Ser.). (Illus.). 10p. (J). (ps). 4.99 (978-1-57082-752-5(4)) Mouse Works.

Parish, Herman. Happy Haunting, Amelia Bedelia. Sweat, Lynn, illus. (I Can Read Bks.). 64p. (J). 2006. pap. 3.99 (978-0-06-051895-0(2) , Harper Trophy); 2004. 15.99 (978-0-06-051893-6(6)); 2004. lib. bdg. 16.89 (978-0-06-051894-3(4)) HarperCollins Pubs.

Park, Barbara. Junie B. , First Grader Boo... & I Mean It! Brunkus, Denise, illus. 2004. 86p. (J). lib. bdg. 18.46 (*978-1-4242-0359-8(7)) Fitzgerald Bks.

Park, Barbara. Junie B., First Grader: Boo... & I Mean It! Brunkus, Denise, illus. (Junie B. Jones Ser.: No. 24). 96p. (J). (gr. k-3). 2005. pap. 3.99 (978-0-375-82807-2(9)); 2004. 11.95 (978-0-375-82806-5(0)); 2004. lib. bdg. 13.99 (978-0-375-92806-2(5)) Random Hse. Children's Bks. (Random Hse. Bks. for Young Readers).

—Junie B., First Grader: Boo... & I Mean It! Brunkus, Denise, illus. 2005. (Junie B. Jones Ser.: No. 24). 86p. (J). (gr. k-3). lib. bdg. 11.04 (978-0-606-33718-2(0)) Tandem Library Bks.

Parker, Toni Trent. Sweets & Treats. Anderson, Earl, illus. 2002. 16p. (J). pap. 6.95 (978-0-439-33871-4(9) , Cartwheel Bks.) Scholastic, Inc.

Pasillo, Susan. The Perfect Pumpkin. 2006. (J). lib. bdg. 20.95 (*978-1-933732-14-5(8) , Bear Hug Bks.) MidAmerica Publishing Co.

Passen, Lisa. Attack of the 50-Foot Teacher. 2005. (Illus.). 28p. (J). (gr. k-4). reprint ed. 16.00 (978-0-7567-9665-5(2)) DIANE Publishing Co.

—Attack of the 50-Foot Teacher. 2003. (gr. k-3). lib. bdg. 15.25 (978-0-613-75618-1(5)) Tandem Library Bks.

—The Attack of the 50-Foot Teacher. Passen, Lisa, illus. rev. ed. (Illus.). 32p. (J). 2003. (gr. 1-3). pap. 6.95 (978-0-8050-7260-0(8)); 2000. (gr. k-3). 16.00 (978-0-8050-6100-0(2)) Holt, Henry & Co. (Holt, Henry & Co. Bks. For Young Readers).

Patschke, Steve. Halloween Mix: Happy Halloween/Don't Look at It! Don't Touch It! 1999. (Illus.). (J). (ps-3). pap. 4.50 (978-1-55254-090-9(1)) Brighter Vision Pubns.

Pavlovsky, Marsha. I Am Not Scared of Halloween. 2004. 24p. pap. 14.95 (978-1-4137-2368-7(3)) PublishAmerica, Inc.

Pearl, Alyson J. Josie & Friends. 2007. (J). per. 9.99 (*978-1-60247-115-3(0)) Tate Publishing & Enterprises, L.L.C.

Pendleton, Sherry. 'Twas the Night Before Halloween. 2003. (J). per. 13.95 (978-1-932303-35-3(9) , Llumina Pr.) Media Creations, Inc.

Pilkey, Dav. The Hallo-Wiener. 1999. (gr. k-3). lib. bdg. 14.15 (978-0-613-22864-0(2)) Tandem Library Bks.

Pollack, Pam & Belviso, Meg. Halloween Night on Shivermore Street. DuBurke, Randy, illus. 2004. 32p. (J). 15.95 (978-0-8118-3946-4(X)) Chronicle Bks. LLC.

Posner, Fran. Halloween Makes Me Batty! 2007. (Illus.). 12p. (J). (gr. k-k). bds. 3.99 (*978-0-7364-2458-5(X) , Golden Bks.) Random Hse. Children's Bks.

Potter, Beatrix. Peter Rabbit's Halloween. 2003. (Illus.). 10p. (J). (ps-ps). bds. 4.99 (978-0-7232-4900-9(8) , Warne) Penguin Group (USA) Inc.

Pottie, Marjolein & Auzary-Luton, Sylvie. Going Batty! Special Glow-in-the-Dark Surprise Pictures. Auzary-Luton, Sylvie, illus. 2005. (Illus.). 32p. (J). 15.95 (978-0-689-04635-3(9) , Milk & Cookies) ibooks, Inc.

Poydar, Nancy. The Perfectly Horrible Halloween. Poydar, Nancy, illus. 2005. (Illus.). 32p. (J). (gr. k-3). pap. 6.95 (978-0-8234-1769-8(7)) Holiday Hse., Inc.

Preller, James. Case of the Mummy Mystery. 1999. (gr. 3-6). lib. bdg. 11.80 (978-0-613-17901-0(3)) Tandem Library Bks.

Prelutsky, Jack. Halloween Countdown. Yaccarino, Dan, illus. 2002. 24p. (J). (ps-1). 6.99 (978-0-06-000512-2(2)) HarperCollins Pubs.

Priddy, Roger. Funny Faces Halloween Jack. 2007. 24p. (J). bds. 9.95 (*978-0-312-50007-8(6) , Priddy Bks.) St. Martin's Pr.

—Let's Decorate Halloween Stickers. 2007. 24p. (J). 5.95 (*978-0-312-50010-8(6) , Priddy Bks.) St. Martin's Pr.

Rabe, Tish. Spooky Night! Sexton, Brenda, illus. 2006. (Nose Knows Ser.). 10p. (J). (ps-17). bds. 9.99 (978-1-58476-483-0(X) , IKIDS) Innovative Kids.

Random House Disney Staff. Sweet & Spooky Halloween. Marrucchi, Elisa, illus. 2007. 24p. (J). (ps-2). pap. 3.99 (*978-0-7364-2453-0(9) , RH/Disney) Random Hse. Children's Bks.

Reasoner, Charles. Funny Bones. Reasoner, Charles, illus. 2000. (Halloween Ser.). (Illus.). 14p. (J). (ps-k). bds. 4.99 (978-0-8431-7607-0(5) , Price Stern Sloan) Penguin Group (USA) Inc.

—Jack-O-Lantern. 1999. (Halloween Ser.). (Illus.). 14p. (J). bds. 4.99 (978-0-8431-7515-8(X) , Price Stern Sloan) Penguin Group (USA) Inc.

Rees, Celia. A Is for Apparition. (Haunts Ser.: Vol. 2). 122p. (J). pap. (978-0-340-71488-1(3) , Hodder & Stoughton) Hodder General Publishing Division.

Reeves, Howard. There Was an Old Witch. 2000. (gr. k-3). lib. bdg. 14.15 (978-0-613-31797-9(1)) Tandem Library Bks.

Remkiewicz, Frank, illus. Froggy's Halloween. 2002. (J). 13.19 (978-0-7587-5112-6(5)) Book Wholesalers, Inc.

Rex, Michael. Brooms Are for Flying. Rex, Michael, illus. rev. ed. 2000. (Illus.). 32p. (J). (ps-2). 16.00 (978-0-8050-6410-0(9) , Holt, Henry & Co. Bks. For Young Readers) Holt, Henry & Co.

Rey, Margret. Curious George Goes to a Costume Party. Vipah Interactive Staff, illus. 2001. (Curious George Ser.). 24p. (J). (gr. k-3). tchr. ed. 12.95 (978-0-618-06564-6(4)) Houghton Mifflin Co. Trade & Reference Div.

Rey, Margret, et al. Curious George Goes to a Costume Party. Weston, Martha, illus. 2001. (Curious George Ser.). 24p. (J). (gr. k-3). pap. 3.95 (978-0-618-06569-1(5)) Houghton Mifflin Co. Trade & Reference Div.

Ricci, Christine. Dora's Costume Party! Saunders, Zina, illus. 2005. 24p. (J). lib. bdg. 9.00 (*978-1-4242-0978-1(1)) Fitzgerald Bks.

—Dora's Costume Party. 2006. (J). (ps-2). 21.35 (978-1-59961-071-9(X)) Spotlight.

—The Halloween Cat. Saunders, Zina, illus. 2004. (Dora the Explorer Ser.). 24p. (J). pap. 3.99 (978-0-689-86799-6(9) , Simon Spotlight/Nickelodeon) Simon & Schuster Children's Publishing.

Ritchie, Joseph R. Peek-a-Boo! Halverson, Lydia, illus. 2004. 14p. (J). bds. 7.95 (978-0-8249-6550-1(7)) Ideals Pubns.

Roberts, Chris. A Mcspooky Halloween. 2006. (J). pap. 9.00 (*978-0-8059-7196-5(3)) Dorrance Publishing Co., Inc.

Robinson, Barbara. The Best Halloween Ever. (J). (gr. 3 up). 2006. 144p. pap. 5.99 (978-0-06-076601-6(8) , Harper Trophy); 2004. 128p. 14.99 (978-0-06-027862-5(5) , Cotler, Joanna Books); 2004. 128p. lib. bdg. 15.89 (978-0-06-027863-2(3)) HarperCollins Pubs.

Rockwell, Anne F. Apples & Pumpkins. Rockwell, Lizzy, illus. 2nd ed. 2005. (Stories to Go! Ser.). 24p. (J). 4.99 (978-1-4169-0831-9(5) , Aladdin) Simon & Schuster Children's Publishing.

—Halloween Day. 1999. Orig. Title: Halloween. (Illus.). 40p. (J). (ps-k). pap. 5.95 (978-0-06-443589-5(X) , Harper Trophy) HarperCollins Pubs.

Rockwell, Anne F. & Rockwell, Lizzy, illus. Apples & Pumpkins. 2nd ed. 2005. (Stories to Go! Ser.). (J). (*978-1-4156-2884-3(X) , Aladdin) Simon & Schuster Children's Publishing.

Root, Phyllis. Who Said Boo? A Lift-the-Flap Book. Martín Larrañaga, Ana, illus. 2005. 14p. (J). bds. 5.99 (978-0-689-85408-8(0) , Little Simon) Simon & Schuster Children's Publishing.

Ross, Eileen. The Halloween Showdown. Reed, Lynn R., illus. 1999. 32p. (J). (gr. k-3). tchr. ed. 15.95 (978-0-8234-1395-9(0)) Holiday Hse., Inc.

Ruelle, Karen Gray. Spookier Than a Ghost. Ruelle, Karen Gray, illus. 2001. (Illus.). 32p. (J). (gr. k-3). tchr. ed. 14.95 (978-0-8234-1667-7(4)) Holiday Hse., Inc.

—Spookier Than a Ghost. (Holiday House Readers Ser.). (Illus.). 32p. (J). (gr. k-3). pap. 4.95 (978-0-8234-1801-5(4)) Holiday Hse., Inc.

Running Press. Jack O'Lantern's Trick or Treat. 2006. (Illus.). 10p. 4.95 (978-0-7624-2663-8(2)) Running Pr. Bk. Pubs.

Rylant, Cynthia. Moonlight: The Halloween Cat. Sweet, Melissa, illus. 2003. 32p. (J). (ps-k). 14.99 (978-0-06-029711-4(5)); lib. bdg. 16.89 (978-0-06-029712-1(3)) HarperCollins Pubs.

Salzmann, Mary Elizabeth. Robin Hoods. Haberstroh, Anne, illus. 2007. (Fact & Fiction Ser.). 24p. (J). pap. (978-1-59928-467-5(7)); 21.35 (978-1-59928-466-8(9)) ABDO Publishing Co.

Scarry, Richard. Best Halloween Masquerade Ever! 1999. (J). (978-0-606-17198-4(3)) Tandem Library Bks.

The Scary Sounds of Halloween. 2005. (Illus.). 20p. (J). (ps-k). bds. 10.95 (978-0-8249-6623-2(6)) Ideals Pubns.

Schade, Susan & Buller, Jon. Space Dog Jack & the Haunted Spaceship. 2002. (Hello Reader! Ser.). (Illus.). 32p. (J). pap. 3.99 (978-0-439-32315-4(0) , Cartwheel Bks.) Scholastic, Inc.

Scholastic, Inc. Staff. Clifford's Scary Halloween. 2002. (ps-2). lib. bdg. 13.00 (978-0-613-72080-9(6)) Tandem Library Bks.

Scholastic, Inc. Staff. The Great Big Pumpkin. 2007. (Care Bears Ser.). (J). bds. 5.99 (*978-0-439-91888-6(X)) Scholastic, Inc.

School Zone Publishing Company Staff. Pumpkins! A Book of Opposites. 2000. (Illus.). 16p. (J). bds. 4.99 (978-0-88743-607-9(2) , 06608) School Zone Publishing Co.

Schoop, Bernice F. The Legend of Moon-Goblin Town. 2003. pap. 8.95 (978-0-533-14342-9(X)) Vantage Pr., Inc.

Schulman, Janet. 10 Trick-Or-Treaters: A Halloween Counting Book. Davick, Linda, illus. 2005. 32p. (J). (ps-3). 8.95 (978-0-375-83225-3(4)); lib. bdg. 10.99 (978-0-375-93225-0(9)) Random Hse. Children's Bks. (Knopf Bks. for Young Readers).

Schulz, Charles M. It's the Great Pumpkin, Charlie Brown. 2002. 24p. mass mkt. 5.99 (978-0-689-85946-5(5) , Little Simon) Simon & Schuster Children's Publishing.

—It's the Great Pumpkin, Charlie Brown. 2007. (Illus.). 10p. (J). (ps-3). bds. 7.95 (*978-0-7624-3171-7(7)) Running Pr. Bk. Pubs.

Schulz, Charles M. It's the Great Pumpkin, Charlie Brown. ed. 2004. (Illus.). 128p. 4.95 (978-0-7624-2033-9(2) , Running Pr. Minature Editions) Running Pr. Bk. Pubs.

Scooby Doo's Halloween Tricks & Treats. 2006. (Illus.). 128p. 4.95 (978-0-7624-2827-4(9)) Running Pr. Bk. Pubs.

Scroggs, Kirk Brandon. Dracula vs. Grampa at the Monster Truck Spectacular. 2006. (Wiley & Grampa's Creature Features Ser.: No. 1). (Illus.). 112p. (J). (gr. 3-7). pap. 2.99 (978-0-316-05941-1(2)) Little Brown & Co.

Seinfeld, Jerry. Halloween. Bennett, James, illus. 2002. 32p. (J). (ps-17). 12.95 (978-0-316-70625-4(6)) Little, Brown Bks. for Young Readers.

Selznick, Brian. Boy of a Thousand Faces. 2000. (gr. 3-6). lib. bdg. 15.30 (978-0-613-44191-9(5)) Tandem Library Bks.

Serafin, Jordan. Bella: The Crooked Hat Witch. Rubino, Alisa A., illus. 2004. (J). (978-0-932991-57-7(2)) Place In The Woods, The.

Seuling, Barbara. Robert & the Back-to-School Special. Brewer, Paul, illus. 2002. (Robert Bks.). 120p. (J). 15.95 (978-0-8126-2662-9(1)) Cricket Bks.

Shaw, Nancy. Sheep Trick or Treat. 2000. (J). (978-0-606-19428-0(2)) Tandem Library Bks.

Shaw, Nancy E. Sheep Trick or Treat. Apple, Margot, illus. 2000. 32p. (J). (gr. k-3). pap. 5.95 (978-0-618-07035-0(4)) Houghton Mifflin Co. Trade & Reference Div.

Shelby, Patty. Trick or Treat at the House of the Man That Gave Away Fifty-Cent Pieces. l.t. ed. 2004. (Illus.). 16p. per. 19.95 (978-1-59453-496-6(9) , 2591) Airleaf Publishing & Bookselling.

Shinju, Mariko. A Pumpkin Story. Shinju, Mariko, illus. 1998. (Illus.). 32p. (J). (ps-4). 16.95 (978-1-880851-36-4(9)) Greene Bark Pr., Inc.

Shulman, Mark. Haunted Halloween House. Ostrom, Bob, illus. 2006. (Storytime Stickers Ser.). 16p. (J). pap. 4.95 (978-1-4027-3584-4(7)) Sterling Publishing Co., Inc.

Shulman, Mark & Less, Emma. Halloween Fun. Harpster, Steve, illus. 2005. (Little Scribbles Ser.). 12p. bds. 5.95 (978-1-4027-2253-0(2)) Sterling Publishing Co., Inc.

Sierra, Judy. The House That Drac Built. Hillenbrand, Will, illus. 1998. (J). (ps-ps). lib. bdg. 14.15 (978-0-613-09949-3(4)) Tandem Library Bks.

Silverhardt, Lauryn. SpongeBob SpookyPants. Style Guide Staff, illus. 2004. (Spongebob Squarepants Ser.). 16p. (J). bds. 5.99 (978-0-689-87320-1(4) , Simon Spotlight/Nickelodeon) Simon & Schuster Children's Publishing.

Silverman, Erica. The Halloween House. Agee, Jon, illus. 2008. 32p. (J). pap. 6.99 (*978-0-312-38013-7(5)) Square Fish.

Silverman, Erica. Halloween House. 1999. (J). (978-0-606-17220-2(3)) Tandem Library Bks.

Simont, Marc, illus. Nate the Great & the Halloween Hunt. 2002. (Nate the Great Ser.). (J). 12.87 (978-0-7587-0697-3(9)) Book Wholesalers, Inc.

Simpson, Fiona, ed. Teenick Vol. 7: Zoey 101. 2006. (Zoey 101 Ser.). 112p. (J). pap. 4.99 (978-0-439-88259-0(1) , Scholastic) Scholastic, Inc.

Skarmeas, Nancy J. My Jack-o'-Lantern. Levy, Pamela R., illus. 2001. 26p. (J). (ps-k). 6.95 (978-0-8249-4117-8(9)) Ideals Pubns.

Smith, Audrey. The Halloween Misfits. 2004. 23p. (J). pap. 14.95 incl. audio compact disk (978-0-9722673-4-2(4)) Audrey Productions.

Speirs, John. The Best Halloween Hunt Ever. Speirs, John, illus. 2000. (Read with Me Paperback Ser.). (Illus.). 32p. (J). (ps-3). pap. 3.50 (978-0-439-19259-0(5) , Cartwheel Bks.) Scholastic, Inc.

—Best Halloween Hunt Ever. 2000. (gr. k-3). lib. bdg. 10.95 (978-0-613-24343-8(9)) Tandem Library Bks.

Spirn, Michele Sobel. A Know-Nothing Halloween. Alley, R. W., illus. 2000. (I Can Read Bks.). 48p. (J). (gr. k-3). 14.95 (978-0-06-028185-4(5)) HarperCollins Pubs.

—A Know-Nothing Halloween. 2001. (978-0-606-22290-7(1)) Tandem Library Bks.

Spohn, Kate. Turtle & Snake's Spooky Halloween. Spohn, Kate, illus. 2003. (Easy-to-Read Ser.). (Illus.). 32p. (J). (gr. k-1). pap. 3.99 (978-0-14-250078-1(X) , Puffin) Penguin Group (USA) Inc.

—Turtle & Snake's Spooky Halloween. 2002. (Viking Easy-to-Read Ser.). (Illus.). 32p. (J). 13.99 (978-0-670-03560-1(2) , Viking Juvenile) Penguin Group (USA) Inc.

Spurr, Elizabeth. Halloween Sky Ride. Long, Ethan, illus. 32p. (J). 6.95 (978-0-8234-2041-4(8)); 16.95 (978-0-8234-1870-1(7)) Holiday Hse., Inc.

—Pumpkin Hill. Martin, Whitney, illus. 32p. (J). 16.95 (978-0-8234-1869-5(3)) Holiday Hse., Inc.

Staake, Bob. This Is NOT a Pumpkin. Staake, Bob, illus. 2007. 32p. (J). (ps). bds. 6.99 (*978-1-4169-3353-3(0) , Little Simon) Simon & Schuster Children's Publishing.

Stamper, Judith Bauer. Five Haunted Houses. Raglin, Tim, illus. 2001. (Hello Reader! Ser.). 48p. (J). (gr. 2-4). pap. 3.99 (978-0-439-20546-7(8) , Cartwheel Bks.) Scholastic, Inc.

Steer, Dugald. Snappy Little Halloween. Matthews, Derek, illus. 2004. 20p. (J). (gr. k-4). reprint ed. 13.00 (978-0-7567-7403-5(9)) DIANE Publishing Co.

Stierle, Cynthia & Artful Doodlers Limited Staff. Halloween Rescue! 2007. (Go, Diego, Go! Ser.). 16p. (J). pap. 5.99 (*978-1-4169-3351-9(4) , Simon Spotlight/Nickelodeon) Simon & Schuster Children's Publishing.

Stilton, Geronimo. It's Halloween, You 'Fraidy Mouse! Wolf, Matt, illus. 2004. 113p. (J). lib. bdg. 10.00 (*978-1-4242-0280-5(9)) Fitzgerald Bks.

—It's Halloween, You 'Fraidy Mouse! 2004. (Geronimo Stilton Ser.: No. 11). (Illus.). 128p. (J). (gr. 2-3). pap. 5.99 (978-0-439-55973-7(1) , Scholastic Paperbacks) Scholastic, Inc.

—It's Halloween, You 'Fraidy Mouse! 2004. (Geronimo Stilton Ser.: No. 11). (Illus.). 113p. (J). (gr. 2-5). lib. bdg. 13.94 (978-0-606-33274-3(X)) Tandem Library Bks.

Stine, R. L. Attack of the Jack-o'-Lanterns. rev. ed. 2005. (Goosebumps Ser.). 144p. (ps-7). mass mkt. 4.99 (978-0-439-72405-0(8)) Scholastic, Inc.

—Haunted Mask. 2003. (Goosebumps Ser.). 144p. (J). pap. 4.99 (978-0-439-56833-3(1) , 53655427, Scholastic Paperbacks) Scholastic, Inc.

—Haunted Mask. 2003. (gr. 5-8). lib. bdg. 13.00 (978-0-613-70775-6(3)) Tandem Library Bks.

—The Haunted Mask II. rev. ed. 2004. (Goosebumps Ser.). 144p. (J). (gr. 4-7). 4.99 (978-0-439-67113-2(2) , Scholastic Paperbacks) Scholastic, Inc.

—Trick or...Trapped! 1999. (Give Yourself Goosebumps: No. 7). 144p. (Orig.). (J). (gr. 3-7). pap. 3.99 (978-0-590-99393-7(3)) Scholastic, Inc.

Stutson, Caroline. By the Light of the Halloween Moon. Hawkes, Kevin, illus. unabr. ed. 1998. (J). (ps-3). 24.95 incl. audio (978-0-7882-0680-1(X) , HRA370); pap. 14.95 incl. audio (978-0-7882-0667-2(2) , PRA370) Weston Woods Studios, Inc.

Sweeney, Jacqueline. Who Said Boo? Hart, G. K. & Empey, Mark, illus. 2000. (We Can Read! Ser.). 32p. (J). (gr. 1-2). lib. bdg. 21.36 (978-0-7614-0924-3(6) , Benchmark Bks.) Cavendish, Marshall Corp.

Swobud, I. K. Don't Go up Haunted Hill... or Else! Random House Staff, illus. 1999. (Storybook Ser.). 24p. (J). (gr. k-ps). pap. 3.99 (978-0-307-13309-0(5) , Golden Bks.) Random Hse. Children's Bks.

Tagg, Christine. Who Will You Meet on Scary Street? Nine Pop-up Nightmares! Fuge, Charles, illus. 2004. 20p. (J). reprint ed. 15.00 (978-0-7567-8003-6(9)) DIANE Publishing Co.

Tallarico, Tony, illus. Halloween: Ultimate Hidden Pictures. 2003. 48p. (J). (ps-4). pap. 3.99 (978-0-8431-0264-2(0) , Price Stern Sloan) Penguin Group (USA) Inc.

Tanner, Suzy-Jane. The Spooky Halloween Surprise. Tanner, Suzy-Jane, illus. 1998. (Lift-the-Flap Bk.). (Illus.). 20p. (J). (ps up). 6.95 (978-0-694-01123-0(1) , Harper Festival) HarperCollins Pubs.

Teague, Mark. One Halloween Night. Teague, Mark, illus. 2005. (Illus.). 32p. (J). (ps-ps). reprint ed. pap. 5.99 (978-0-439-75538-2(7) , Scholastic Paperbacks) Scholastic, Inc.

Tegen, Katherine. Dracula & Frankenstein Are Friends. Cushman, Doug, illus. 2003. 32p. (J). (ps-3). 15.99 (978-0-06-000115-5(1)) HarperCollins Pubs.

Thaler, Mike. The Halloween Party from the Black Lagoon. Lee, Jared D., illus. 2004. (Little Apple Ser.). 64p. (J). pap. (978-0-439-68075-2(1)) Scholastic, Inc.

Thiesing, Lisa. A Dark & Noisy Night. Chassman, Neil A. & Murdock, Robert, eds. Thiesing, Lisa, illus. 2005. (Illus.). 32p. (J). (gr. 1-3). 13.99 (978-0-525-47388-6(2) , Dutton Juvenile) Penguin Group (USA) Inc.

Thiesing, Lisa. A Dark & Noisy Night: A Silly Thriller with Peggy the Pig. 2005. (Dutton Easy Reader Ser.). (Illus.). 32p. (J). (*978-1-4156-1784-7(8) , Dutton Juvenile) Penguin Group (USA) Inc.

Thompson, Jill. Scary Godmother. 2005. (Illus.). 48p. pap. 9.95 (978-1-57989-070-4(9)) Sirius Entertainment, Inc.

—Scary Godmother: Ghoul's Out for Summer. 2002. (Illus.). 128p. pap. 14.95 (978-1-57989-052-0(0)) Sirius Entertainment, Inc.

—Scary Godmother: The Revenge of Jimmy. 2006. (Illus.). 48p. pap. 9.95 (978-1-57989-071-1(7)) Sirius Entertainment, Inc.

—Scary Godmother Vol. 4: The Boo Flu. 2000. (Illus.). 48p. 19.95 (978-1-57989-038-4(5)) Sirius Entertainment, Inc.

Thompson, Jill, creator. Scary Godmother: The Mystery Date. 2004. (Illus.). 48p. pap. 9.95 (978-1-57989-072-8(5)) Sirius Entertainment, Inc.

Thompson, Lauren. Mouse's First Halloween. Erdogan, Buket, illus. 2000. 32p. (J). (ps-3). 12.95 (978-0-689-83176-8(5)) Simon & Schuster Children's Publishing.

—Mouse's First Halloween. Erdogan, Buket, illus. 2003. (Classic Board Bks.). 34p. (J). 7.99 (978-0-689-85584-9(2) , Little Simon) Simon & Schuster Children's Publishing.

Tomos, Angharad. Mali Meipen. 2005. (WEL., Illus.). 48p. pap. (978-0-86243-104-4(2)) Y Lolfa.

Trasler, Janee. Ghost Eats It All: Little Boo Books. 2006. (Illus.). 24p. (J). (ps-1). 5.99 (978-0-316-01844-9(9)) Little Brown & Co.

Troiano, Joe. Little Scribbles: Halloween Fun with Spookley the Square Pumpkin. Banta, Susan, illus. 2006. (Little Scribbles Ser.). 12p. (J). bds. 5.95 (978-1-4027-4017-6(4)) Sterling Publishing Co., Inc.

—Storytime Stickers: It's Halloween with Spookley the Square Pumpkin. Banta, Susan, illus. 2006. (Storytime Stickers Ser.). 16p. (J). pap. 4.95 (978-1-4027-4018-3(2)) Sterling Publishing Co., Inc.

Tucker, Jennifer Herrick. Little Pumpkin. l.t. ed. 2001. 65p. (J). per. 9.95 (978-0-9715198-0-0(3)) PJN & Assocs.

Tudor, Tasha. Pumpkin Moonshine. 1998. (Illus.). 46p. (J). 6.95 (978-0-446-91246-4(8)) Grand Central Publishing.

—Pumpkin Moonshine. Tudor, Tasha, illus. 2000. (Illus.). 40p. (J). (ps-3). 13.95 (978-0-689-82846-1(2)) Simon & Schuster Children's Publishing.

Tunnell, Michael O. Halloween Pie. Highlights Staff, ed. Omalley, Kevin, illus. 2004. 32p. (J). (gr. k-2). pap. 9.95 (978-1-59078-250-7(X)) Boyds Mills Pr.

Turnowski, Lauren. The Great Halloween Costume Contest. Pierce, Mindy, illus. 2003. (Sticker Stories Ser.). 24p. (J). (ps-2). pap. 4.99 (978-0-448-43115-4(7) , Grosset & Dunlap) Penguin Group (USA) Inc.

Vail, Rachel & Bjorkman, Steve. Halloween Knight. 2004. (Illus.). (J). (ps-2). lib. bdg. 12.19 (978-0-606-29858-2(4)) Tandem Library Bks.

Van Draanen, Wendelin. Sammy Keyes & the Skeleton Man. VanDraanen, Wendelin, illus. 2000. (Sammy Keyes Ser.: Bk. 2). pap. 39.95 incl. audio compact disk (978-0-87499-884-9(0)) Live Oak Media.

—Sammy Keyes & the Skeleton Man. 1999. (Sammy Keyes Ser.: Bk. 2). (gr. 5-8). lib. bdg. 13.00 (978-0-613-16187-9(4)) Tandem Library Bks.

Van Rynbach, Iris. Five Little Pumpkins. 2003. (Illus.). 24p. (J). (ps up). pap. 8.95 (978-1-59078-087-9(6)) Boyds Mills Pr.

—Five Little Pumpkins. 2003. (ps-2). lib. bdg. 17.60 (978-0-613-79889-1(9)) Tandem Library Bks.

Vande Velde, Vivian. All Hallow's Eve: 13 Stories. 2006. (Illus.). 240p. (YA). 17.00 (978-0-15-205576-9(2)) Harcourt Children's Bks.

Vaughan, Marcia. We're Going on a Ghost Hunt. Schweninger, Ann, illus. 2001. 32p. (J). (gr. k-2). 15.00 (978-0-15-202353-9(4)) Harcourt Children's Bks.

Waldron, Jan L. John Pig's Halloween. McPhail, David M., illus. 2001. 32p. (J). pap. 6.99 (978-0-14-056836-3(0) , Puffin) Penguin Group (USA) Inc.

—John Pig's Halloween. McPhail, David M., illus. 1998. 18p. (J). pap. 14.98 (978-1-58048-045-1(4)) Sandvik Publishing.

—John Pig's Halloween. 2001. (gr. 3-6). lib. bdg. 15.30 (978-0-613-58416-6(3)) Tandem Library Bks.

Walters, Jennie. Lauren's Spooky Sleepover. 2003. (Illus.). 128p. (J). pap. 7.99 (978-0-340-79591-0(3) , Hodder & Stoughton) Hodder General Publishing Division GBR. *Dist:* Trafalgar Square Publishing.

Walton, Rick. Mrs. McMurphy's Pumpkin. Bettoli, Delana, illus. 2004. 32p. (J). 8.99 (978-0-06-053409-7(5) , Harper Festival) HarperCollins Pubs.

—What Do We Do with the Baby? 2008. (Illus.). 32p. (J). lib. bdg. 17.89 (978-0-06-008420-2(0)) HarperCollins Pubs.

Weber, Ken. Five-Minute Halloween Mysteries. 2007. (Illus.). 128p. 4.95 (*978-0-7624-3076-5(1) , Running Pr. Minature Editions) Running Pr. Bk. Pubs.

Weiss, Bobbi J. G. & Weiss, David Cody. Trouble on Oak Street. Spaziante, Patrick, illus. 2006. (Monster House Ser.). 32p. (J). pap. 3.99 (978-1-4169-1822-6(1) , Simon Spotlight) Simon & Schuster Children's Publishing.

Welling, Peter J. Darlene Halloween & the Great Chicago Fire. Welling, Peter J., illus. 2007. 32p. (J). (gr. k-3). 15.95 (*978-1-58980-479-1(1)) Pelican Publishing Co., Inc.

Wells, Rosemary. The Halloween Parade. Wheeler, Jody, illus. 2001. (Yoko & Friends School Days Ser.: No. 3). 32p. (gr. k-2). 9.99 (978-0-7868-0723-9(7) , Volo) Hyperion Bks. for Children.

—The Halloween Parade. 2001. (J). 10.79 (978-0-606-22548-9(X)); lib. bdg. 11.80 (978-0-613-53195-5(7)) Tandem Library Bks.

—Max's Halloween. 2004. (Board Books). (Illus.). 16p. (J). (ps-ps). bds. 5.99 (978-0-670-05899-0(8) , Viking Juvenile) Penguin Group (USA) Inc.

West, Kipling. A Rattle of Bones: A Halloween Book of Collective Nouns. West, Kipling, illus. 1999. (Illus.). 32p. (J). (ps-1). pap. 15.95 (978-0-531-30196-8(6) , Orchard Bks.) Scholastic, Inc.

West, Tracey. The Halloween Goblin. 2006. (Pixie Tricks Ser.: No. 4). (Illus.). 96p. (J). (gr. 1-4). 3.99 (978-0-439-17980-5(7) , Scholastic Paperbacks) Scholastic, Inc.

—The Halloween Goblin. 2000. (gr. 3-6). lib. bdg. 11.80 (978-0-613-25435-9(X)) Tandem Library Bks.

Weston, Martha. Tuck's Haunted House. Weston, Martha, illus. 2002. (Illus.). 32p. (J). (gr. k-3). tchr. ed. 14.00 (978-0-618-15966-6(5) , Clarion Bks.) Houghton Mifflin Co. Trade & Reference Div.

Whalen, Erin T. Charlie Gets Spooked, 3 vols. 2004. (Illus.). 32p. (J). (gr. k-3). 16.95 (978-1-929265-04-6(2)); pap. 8.95 (978-1-929265-05-3(0)) Lily & Co. Publishing.

Wheeler, Lisa. When Pigs Fly. Ansley, Frank, illus. 2005. (Fitch & Chip Ser.). 48p. (J). pap. 3.99 (978-0-689-84956-5(7) , Aladdin) Simon & Schuster Children's Publishing.

White, Linda. Too Many Pumpkins. Lloyd, Megan, illus. 32p. (J). (gr. k-3). reprint ed. 6.95 (978-0-8234-1320-1(9)) Holiday Hse., Inc.

Williams, Jacklyn. Happy Halloween, Gus! Cushman, Doug, illus. 2005. (Read-It! Readers Ser.). 32p. (J). (gr. k-3). 18.60 (978-1-4048-0960-4(0)) Picture Window Bks.

Williams, Sam. Teddy Bears' Trick-or-Treat. McQuade, Jacqueline, illus. 2001. 12p. (J). (ps-1). pap. 14.95 (978-0-439-20403-3(8) , Cartwheel Bks.) Scholastic, Inc.

Willson, Sarah. Dora's Halloween Adventure. Savitsky, Steven, illus. 2003. (Dora the Explorer Ser.). 14p. (J). bds. 5.99 (978-0-689-85844-4(2) , Simon Spotlight/ Nickelodeon) Simon & Schuster Children's Publishing.

—Tricked for Treats! A Rugrats Halloween. 1999. (gr. k-3). lib. bdg. 14.15 (978-0-613-22524-3(4)) Tandem Library Bks.

Wing, Natasha. The Night Before Halloween. Fisher, Cynthia, illus. 1999. (All Aboard Bks.). 32p. (J). (ps-3). pap. 3.99 (978-0-448-41965-7(3) , Grosset & Dunlap) Penguin Group (USA) Inc.

—The Night Before Halloween. 1999. (gr. k-3). lib. bdg. 11.25 (978-0-613-22092-7(7)) Tandem Library Bks.

Winkler, Henry & Oliver, Lin. My Dog's a Scaredy-Cat: A Halloween Tail. Watson, Jesse Joshua, illus. 2006. (Hank Zipzer Ser.: No. 10). 160p. (J). 13.99 (978-0-448-43879-5(8) , Grosset & Dunlap) Penguin Group (USA) Inc.

—My Dog's a Scaredy-Cat: A Halloween Tail. Heyer, Carol & Watson, Jesse Joshua, illus. 2006. (Hank Zipzer Ser.: No. 10). 160p. (J). (gr. 3-7). pap. 4.99 (978-0-448-43878-8(X) , Grosset & Dunlap) Penguin Group (USA) Inc.

Winters, Kay. Teeny Tiny Ghost. 1999. (gr. k-3). lib. bdg. 14.10 (978-0-613-22943-2(6)) Tandem Library Bks.

Wojciechowski, Susan. The Best Halloween of All. Meddaugh, Susan, illus. 2000. 32p. (J). (ps-3). pap. 4.99 (978-0-7636-1241-2(3)) Candlewick Pr.

—The Best Halloween of All. Meddaugh, Susan, illus. 2000. (J). (ps-ps). lib. bdg. 13.00 (978-0-613-31973-7(7)) Tandem Library Bks.

Wolf, Jackie. My Sparkle Pumpkin. 2003. (Picture Me Ser.). (Illus.). 10p. (J). (ps up). bds. 6.99 (978-1-57151-721-0(9)) Playhouse Publishing.

—Picture Me Peek-a-Boo! 2004. (Illus.). 10p. (J). (ps up). bds. 4.99 (978-1-57151-570-4(4)) Playhouse Publishing.

Wood, Phyllis. Pass Me a Pine Cone, Please. 2006. pap. 12.50 (*978-1-4259-7445-9(7)) AuthorHouse.

Yaccarino, Dan, illus. Five Little Pumpkins. 1998. 16p. (J). bds. 5.99 (978-0-694-01177-3(0) , Harper Festival) HarperCollins Pubs.

Yolen, Jane. Beneath the Ghost Moon. 1998. (978-0-606-13189-6(2)) Tandem Library Bks.

Yoon, Salina. Halloween. 2004. (Illus.). 12p. (J). (ps-1). bds. 5.99 (978-0-8431-1078-4(3) , Price Stern Sloan) Penguin Group (USA) Inc.

—Halloween Party. 2007. (Salina Yoon Bks.). 10p. (J). (ps-k). bds. 5.99 (978-0-8431-2485-9(7) , Price Stern Sloan) Penguin Group (USA) Inc.

—Monsters. 2004. (Illus.). 12p. (J). (ps-1). bds. 5.99 (978-0-8431-1079-1(1) , Price Stern Sloan) Penguin Group (USA) Inc.

—A Spooktacular Halloween. 2006. (Illus.). 10p. (J). (ps-k). bds. 5.99 (978-0-8431-2018-9(5) , Price Stern Sloan) Penguin Group (USA) Inc.

—Spooky Pumpkin. Yoon, Salina, illus. 2004. (Illus.). 10p. (J). bds. 5.99 (978-0-689-85392-0(0) , Little Simon) Simon & Schuster Children's Publishing.

—Spooky's First Halloween. 2007. (Salina Yoon Bks.). 10p. (J). (ps-k). bds. 5.99 (978-0-8431-2486-6(5) , Price Stern Sloan) Penguin Group (USA) Inc.

Zack's Halloween Costume. 2001. (978-1-58453-161-6(4)) Pioneer Valley Educational Pr., Inc.

Ziefert, Harriet. Ding-Dong, Trick or Treat! Demarest, Chris L., illus. 2004. 22p. (J). (ps-3). reprint ed. pap. 12.00 (978-0-7567-8258-0(9)) DIANE Publishing Co.

—On Halloween Night. Andriani, Renee W., illus. 2001. 24p. (J). (ps-2). pap. 5.99 (978-0-14-056820-2(4) , Puffin) Penguin Group (USA) Inc.

Ziefert, Harriet. Two Little Witches 8x8 Stkr Bk. Taback, Simms, illus. 2007. 20p. (J). (gr. k-k). pap. 3.99 (*978-0-7636-3309-7(7)) Candlewick Pr.

Zuravicky, Orli. Dear Diary: Monster House. 2006. (Illus.). 32p. (J). lib. bdg. 15.00 (*978-1-4242-1561-4(7)) Fitzgerald Bks.

Zuravicky, Orli & Redbank, Tennant. Dear Diary, co. Spaziante, Patrick, illus. 2006. (Monster House Ser.). 32p. (J). pap. 3.99 (978-1-4169-1820-2(5) , Simon Spotlight) Simon & Schuster Children's Publishing.

HALLUCINOGENIC DRUGS

Cefrey, Holly. Hallucinogens & Your Neurons: The Incredibly Disgusting Story. 2005. (Illus.). 48p. (J). (gr. k-3). lib. bdg. 25.25 (978-1-4042-0633-5(7) , Rosen Central) Rosen Publishing Group, Inc., The.

Drew-Edwards, Suzanna. LSD & Other Hallucinogens. 2005. (What's the Deal? Ser.). (Illus.). 56p. (J). (978-1-4034-7029-4(4)) Heinemann Library.

Hurwitz, Ann Ricki & Hurwitz, Sue. Hallucinogens. rev. ed. 1999. (Drug Abuse Prevention Library). (Illus.). 64p. (J). (gr. 7-12). lib. bdg. 25.25 (978-0-8239-3006-7(8) , DRHALL) Rosen Publishing Group, Inc., The.

Jaffe, Steven L., ed. LSD, PCP & Other Hallucinogens. 1999. (Junior Drug Awareness Ser.). (Illus.). 80p. (J). (gr. 4-8). 32.00 (978-0-7910-5183-2(8) , Chelsea Hse.) Facts On File, Inc.

McCage, Crystal. Hallucinogens. 2007. (YA). lib. bdg. (*978-1-60152-014-2(X)) ReferencePoint Pr., Inc.

Mehling, Randi. Hallucinogens. 2003. (Drugs, the Straight Facts Ser.). (Illus.). 112p. (gr. 9-13). 30.00 (978-0-7910-7261-5(4) , Chelsea Hse.) Facts On File, Inc.

Monroe, Judy. LSD, PCP & Hallucinogen Drug Dangers. 2001. (Drug Dangers Ser.). (Illus.). 64p. (YA). (gr. 4-10). pap. 13.26 (978-0-7660-1965-2(9)) Enslow Pubs., Inc.

Nelson, Sheila. Hallucinogens: Unreal Visions. 2008. (*978-1-4222-0155-8(4)) Mason Crest Pubs.

Raczek, Linda Theresa. Teen Addiction. 2003. (Illus.). 112p. (J). 29.95 (978-1-56006-779-5(9) , Lucent Bks.) Thomson Gale.

Robbins, Paul R. Hallucinogens. 2001. (Drug Library). (Illus.). 112p. (YA). (gr. 6-12). pap. 13.26 (978-0-7660-1921-8(7)) Enslow Pubs., Inc.

Ross-Flanigan, Nancy. Peyote. 2001. (Drug Library). (Illus.). 112p. (YA). (gr. 6-12). pap. 13.26 (978-0-7660-1928-7(4)) Enslow Pubs., Inc.

Ruschmann, Paul. Legalizing Marijuana/By Paul Ruschmann. 2003. (Point/Counterpoint Ser.). (Illus.). 112p. (gr. 9-13). 32.95 (978-0-7910-7483-1(8) , Chelsea Hse.) Facts On File, Inc.

HAMER, FANNIE LOU, 1918-1977

Donovan, Sandy. Fannie Lou Hamer. 2003. (Illus.). 64p. (J). pap. 8.95 (978-1-4109-0316-7(8)); lib. bdg. 28.56 (978-0-7398-7030-3(0)) Raintree.

Fiorelli, June Estep. Fannie Lou Hamer: A Voice for Freedom. 2004. (Avisson Young Adult Ser.). (Illus.). 117p. (J). pap. 19.95 (978-1-888105-62-9(3)) Avisson Pr., Inc.

Litwin, Laura Baskes. Fannie Lou Hamer: Fighting for the Right to Vote. 2002. (African-American Biographies Ser.). (Illus.). 128p. (J). (gr. 6-12). lib. bdg. 26.60 (978-0-7660-1772-6(9)) Enslow Pubs., Inc.

HAMILTON, ALEXANDER, 1757-1804

Burton, Alma Holman. Four American Patriots: Patrick Henry, Alexander Hamilton, Andrew Jackson, Ulysses S. Grant: A Book for Young Americans. 2000. (Illus.). (J). (978-0-89526-204-2(5)) Regnery Publishing, Inc., An Eagle Publishing Co.

Collier, James Lincoln. Alexander Hamilton You Never. 2004. (You Never Knew Ser.). (J). (gr. 4-6). pap. 6.95 (978-0-516-25834-8(6) , Children's Pr.) Scholastic Library Publishing.

—The Alexander Hamilton You Never Knew. 2003. (You Never Knew Ser.). (Illus.). 80p. (J). 25.50 (978-0-516-24345-0(4) , Children's Pr.) Scholastic Library Publishing.

DeCarolis, Lisa. Alexander Hamilton: Federalist & Founding Father. 2005. (Library of American Lives & Times). (Illus.). 112p. (J). (gr. 4-8). lib. bdg. 31.95 (978-0-8239-5735-4(7)) Rosen Publishing Group, Inc., The.

DeGraw, Aleine. Alexander Hamilton: American Statesman. 2003. (Famous People in American History Ser.). (Illus.). 32p. (J). lib. bdg. (978-0-8239-4173-5(6)) Rosen Publishing Group, Inc., The.

Haugen, Brenda & Santella, Andrew. Alexander Hamilton: Founding Father & Statesman. 2004. (Signature Lives Ser.). (Illus.). 112p. (J). 30.60 (978-0-7565-0827-2(4) , 1240126) Compass Point Bks.

Jones, Veda Boyd. Alexander Hamilton. 1999. (Revolutionary War Leaders Ser.). (Illus.). 80p. (gr. 3 up). (J). 31.00 (978-0-7910-5354-6(7)); (YA). pap. (978-0-7910-5697-4(X)) Facts On File, Inc. (Chelsea Hse.).

—Alexander Hamilton: First U. S. Secretary of the Treasury. 2000. (gr. 5-8). lib. bdg. 17.60 (978-0-613-43292-4(4)) Tandem Library Bks.

Kallen, Stuart A. Alexander Hamilton. 2001. (Founding Fathers Ser.). (Illus.). 64p. (J). (gr. 3-8). lib. bdg. 25.65 (978-1-57765-006-5(9) , ABDO & Daughters) ABDO Publishing Co.

Kent, Zachary. Alexander Hamilton: Creating a Nation. 2004. (America's Founding Fathers Ser.). (Illus.). 128p. (J). lib. bdg. 26.60 (978-0-7660-2181-5(5)) Enslow Pubs., Inc.

McLeese, Don. Alexander Hamilton. (Heroes of the American Revolution Ser.). 32p. 2005. (Illus.). (gr. 2-5). 19.95 (978-1-59515-219-0(9)); 2004. pap. 5.95 (978-1-59515-317-3(9)) Rourke Publishing, LLC.

McNeese, Tim. Alexander Hamilton: Framer of the Constitution. 2005. (Leaders of the American Revolution Ser.). (Illus.). 152p. (J). (gr. 4-8). lib. bdg. 30.00 (978-0-7910-8616-2(X) , Chelsea Hse.) Facts On File, Inc.

Miller, Chuck. Alexander Hamilton. 2003. (America's Founders Ser.). (J). pap. (978-1-58417-081-5(6)); lib. bdg. (978-1-58417-018-1(2)) Lake Street Pubs.

Perrin, Pat. The Mystery of the Deadly Duel. 2004. (Illus.). 64p. (J). pap. (*978-0-7891-5996-0(1)) Perfection Learning Corp.

Roberts, Russell. Alexander Hamilton. 2006. (Profiles in American History Ser.). (Illus.). 48p. (J). (gr. 4-8). lib. bdg. 20.95 (978-1-58415-436-5(5)) Mitchell Lane Pubs., Inc.

Rosenberg, Pam. Alexander Hamilton: Soldier & Statesman. 2004. (Our People Ser.). (Illus.). 32p. (J). (gr. 2-6). 27.07 (978-1-59296-172-6(X)) Child's World, Inc.

Rosenburg, John M. Alexander Hamilton: America's Bold Lion. 2000. (Single Titles Ser.: up). (Illus.). 192p. (gr. 7-12). lib. bdg. 26.90 (978-0-7613-1617-6(5) , Millbrook Pr.) Lerner Publishing Group.

Whitelaw, Nancy. More Perfect Union: The Story of Alexander Hamilton. 2nd rev. exp. ed. 2004. (Notable Americans Ser.). (Illus.). 128p. (YA). (gr. 6-12). 23.95 (978-1-931798-03-7(6)) Reynolds, Morgan Inc.

HAMSTERS

Alderton, David. Hamster: Looking after My Pet. 2002. (Illus.). 24p. 7.99 (978-0-7548-1088-9(7) , Lorenz Bks.) Anness Publishing GBR. *Dist:* National Bk. Network.

Barnes, Julia, et al. 101 Facts about Hamsters. 2002. (One Hundred One Facts about Pets Ser.). (Illus.). 32p. (J). (gr. 3 up). lib. bdg. 23.33 (978-0-8368-3018-7(0)) Stevens, Gareth Inc.

Bodden, Valerie. Hamsters. 2006. (My First Look at: Pets Ser.). (Illus.). 24p. 15.95 (*978-1-58341-459-0(2) , Creative Education) Creative Co., The.

Coppendale, Jean. Gerbils & Hamsters. 2004. (QEB You & Your Pet Ser.). (Illus.). 32p. (J). lib. bdg. 18.95 (978-1-59566-055-8(0)) QEB Publishing Inc.

Foran, Jill. Caring for Your Hamster. Marshall, Diana & Nault, Jennifer, eds. 2003. (Caring for Your Pet Ser.). (Illus.). 32p. (J). pap. 7.95 (978-1-59036-066-8(4)) Weigl Pubs., Inc.

Foran, Jill, told to. Caring for Your Hamster. 2002. (Caring for Your Pet Ser.). (Illus.). 32p. (J). lib. bdg. 18.20 (978-1-59036-036-1(2)) Weigl Pubs., Inc.

Frost, Helen. Hamsters. 2000. (All about Pets Ser.). (Illus.). 24p. (J). (gr. k-1). lib. bdg. 15.93 (978-0-7368-0658-9(X) , Pebble Bks.) Capstone Pr., Inc.

Ganeri, Anita. Hamsters. 2003. (Heinemann First Library). (Illus.). 32p. (J). pap. (978-1-4034-4273-4(8)) Heinemann Library.

—Hamsters. 2003. (gr. k-3). lib. bdg. 15.25 (978-0-613-89653-5(X)) Tandem Library Bks.

—A Pet's Life: Hamsters. 2003. (Heinemann First Library). (Illus.). 32p. (J). lib. bdg. 22.79 (978-1-4034-3997-0(4)) Heinemann Library.

Hamsters. (All about Pets Ser.). 24p. (J). 5.95 (978-0-7368-8786-1(5)) Capstone Pr., Inc.

Hamsters. 2007. (Illus.). (J). cd-rom 9.99 (*978-0-9795190-3-1(9)) Color & Learn.

Hamsters, 6 vols. (gr. k-2). 28.95 (978-0-7368-9238-4(9)) Red Brick Learning.

Head, Honor. Hamsters & Gerbils. Burton, Jane, photos by. 2000. (My Pet Ser.). (Illus.). 32p. (J). (gr. 3-5). lib. bdg. 25.69 (978-0-7398-2886-1(X)) Raintree.

—Hamsters & Gerbils. 2000. (My Pet Ser.). (Illus.). 32p. (J). (gr. 3-5). pap. 8.95 (978-0-7398-3010-9(4)) Steck-Vaughn.

Hibbert, Clare. Hamster. 2004. (Illus.). 32p. (J). lib. bdg. 27.10 (978-1-58340-433-1(3)) Smart Apple Media.

Hinds, Kathryn. Hamsters & Gerbils. 2000. (Perfect Pets Ser.). (Illus.). 32p. (J). (gr. 3-5). lib. bdg. 25.64 (978-0-7614-1104-8(6) , Benchmark Bks.) Cavendish, Marshall Corp.

Hollimann, Peter & Linke-Grun, Gabriele. My Hamster & Me. Holzner, Renate, illus. Wegler, Monika, photos by. 2001. (For the Love of Animals Ser.). 64p. pap. 6.99 (978-0-7641-1805-0(6)) Barron's Educational Series, Inc.

Holub, Joan. Why Do Rabbits Hop? A & Other Questions about Rabbits, Guinea Pigs, Hamsters. 2003. (gr. k-3). lib. bdg. 11.80 (978-0-613-61671-3(5)) Tandem Library Bks.

Landau, Elaine. Your Pet Hamster. rev. ed. 2006. (True Book Ser.). (Illus.). 47p. (J). (978-0-531-16798-4(4)) Children's Pr., Ltd.

—Your Pet Hamster. 1998. (True Bks.). (Illus.). 48p. (J). (gr. 3-5). pap. 6.95 (978-0-516-26265-9(3) , Children's Pr.) Scholastic Library Publishing.

Lewis, David, contrib. by. Hamsters. 1999. (Junior Pet Care Ser.). (Illus.). 48p. (YA). (gr. 4-7). 18.65 (978-0-7910-4907-5(8) , Chelsea Hse.) Facts On File, Inc.

Marshall, Diana. Caring for Your Hamster. 2003. (gr. 3-6). lib. bdg. 16.40 (978-0-613-79820-4(1)) Tandem Library Bks.

Meredith, Susan. Hamsters. rev. ed. 2004. (First Pets Ser.). 32p. (J). (gr. 1 up). pap. 5.95 (978-0-7945-0796-1(4) , Usborne) EDC Publishing.

Meredith, Susan, ed. Hamsters. 1999. (First Pets Ser.). (Illus.). 32p. (YA). (gr. k-3). lib. bdg. 12.95 (978-1-58086-167-0(9)) EDC Publishing.

Meredith, Susan, et al. Hamsters. Fox, Christyan, illus. 2004. 30p. (J). (978-0-439-78698-0(3)) Scholastic, Inc.

Miller, M. Hamsters. 2002. (Pets Ser.). (Illus.). 24p. (J). (gr. k-3). pap. 6.50 (978-1-57572-481-2(2) , 90470) Heinemann Library.

Miller, Michaela. Hamsters. 1998. (Pets Ser.). (Illus.). 24p. (J). (gr. 1-3). lib. bdg. 21.36 (978-1-57572-576-5(2)) Heinemann Library.

Murray, Julie. Hamsters. 2002. (Buddy Book Ser.). (Illus.). 24p. (J). (gr. k-4). lib. bdg. 21.35 (978-1-57765-725-5(X)) ABDO Publishing Co.

Nelson, Robin. Pet Hamster. (First Step Nonfiction). (J). (gr. k-2). 2003. (Illus.). 24p. lib. bdg. 18.60 (978-0-8225-1269-1(6)); 2002. pap. 3.95 (978-0-8225-1313-1(7)) Lerner Publishing Group.

Page, Gill. Getting to Know Your Hamster. 48p. (J). pap. 7.95 (978-0-7938-1202-8(X)) TFH Pubns., Inc.

Petty, Kate. Hamster. 2005. (Illus.). 24p. (J). (gr. 2-5). lib. bdg. 22.80 (978-1-59604-028-1(9)) Stargazer Bks.

Rayner, Matthew & BVetMed MRCVS Staff. Hamster. Greenaway, Frank & Burton, Jane, photos by. 2004. (I Am Your Pet Ser.). (Illus.). 32p. (J). (gr. 2 up). lib. bdg. 23.33 (978-0-8368-4104-6(2)) Stevens, Gareth Inc.

Richardson, Adele. Caring for Your Hamster. 2007. (First Facts Ser.). (Illus.). 24p. (J). (gr. k-3). lib. bdg. 21.26 (978-0-7368-6387-2(7)) Capstone Pr., Inc.

Rockwell, Anne F. My Pet Hamster. Lum, Bernice, illus. 2002. (Let's-Read-and-Find-Out Science Ser.). 40p. (J). (ps-1). 15.99 (978-0-06-028564-7(8)); 17.89 (978-0-06-028565-4(6)); pap. 4.99 (978-0-06-445205-2(0)) HarperCollins Pubs.

—My Pet Hamster. 2002. (gr. k-3). lib. bdg. 13.00 (978-0-613-56071-9(X)) Tandem Library Bks.

Ross, Veronica. Hamster. 2002. (My First Ser.). (Illus.). 32p. (J). lib. bdg. 24.25 (978-1-930643-75-8(6)) Chrysalis Education.

Sjonger, Rebecca & Kalman, Bobbie. Hamsters. Crabtree, Marc, illus. Crabtree, Marc, photos by. 2004. (Pet Care Ser.). 32p. (J). pap. (978-0-7787-1785-0(2)); (978-0-7787-1753-9(4)) Crabtree Publishing Co.

—Los Hamsters. 2005. (ENG & SPA., Illus.). 32p. (J). (978-0-7787-8456-2(8)) Crabtree Publishing Co.

—Los Hamsters: Hamsters. 2006. (SPA & ENG., Illus.). 32p. pap. (978-0-7787-8478-4(9)) Crabtree Publishing Co.

Spilsbury, Louise & Spilsbury, Richard. Hamsters. 2006. (Keeping Pets Ser.). (Illus.). 48p. (J). (978-1-4034-7702-6(7)) Heinemann Library.

Starosta, Paul. Face-to-Face with the Hamster. 2004. (Illus.). 25p. (J). 9.95 (978-1-57091-456-0(7)) Charlesbridge Publishing, Inc.

Thomas, Lyn. My Pet Hamster. Kurisu, Jane, illus. 2002. 24p. (J). (gr. k-3). (978-1-55337-099-4(6)) Kids Can Pr., Ltd.

—My Pet Hamster. 2002. (gr. k-3). lib. bdg. 12.95 (978-0-613-87664-3(4)) Tandem Library Bks.

Viner, Bradley. Hamster. 1999. (All about Your Pet Ser.). (Illus.). 32p. pap. 4.99 (978-0-7641-1014-6(4)) Barron's Educational Series, Inc.

Wild Side of Hamsters,the Sb 6. 2004. pap. (978-1-4109-1420-0(8)) Harcourt Schl. Pubs.

Wood, Selina. Hamster. 2006. (Owning a Pet Ser.). (J). (978-1-59771-054-1(7)) Sea-To-Sea Pubns.

HAMSTERS—FICTION

All Aboard! Softi's Adventures. 2003. (J). mass mkt. (978-1-932233-36-0(9)) Aurora Libris Corp.

Banks, Lynne Reid. I, Houdini: The Amazing Story of an Escape-Artist Hamster. 2003. (gr. 3-6). lib. bdg. 13.00 (978-0-613-70811-1(3)) Tandem Library Bks.

Bateman, Teresa. Hamster Camp: How Harry Got Fit. Cote, Nancy, illus. 2005. 32p. (J). (gr. k-4). 15.95 (978-0-8075-3139-6(1)) Whitman, Albert & Co.

Birney, Betty G. Friendship According to Humphrey. (J). (gr. 2-4). 2006. 176p. pap. 5.99 (978-0-14-240633-5(3) , Puffin); 2005. 160p. 14.99 (978-0-399-24264-9(3) , Putnam Juvenile) Penguin Group (USA) Inc.

—Surprises According to Humphrey. 2008. 192p. (J). (gr. 3). 14.99 (*978-0-399-24730-9(0) , Putnam Juvenile) Penguin Group (USA) Inc.

—Trouble According to Humphrey. (J). 2008. 192p. (gr. 3-4). 5.99 (*978-0-14-241089-9(6) , Puffin); 2007. 176p. (gr. 2-4). 14.99 (978-0-399-24505-3(7)) Penguin Group (USA) Inc.

H
I

Birney, Betty G. The World According to Humphrey. 144p. (J). (gr. 2-4). 2005. pap. 5.99 (978-0-14-240352-5(0) , Puffin); 2004. 14.99 (978-0-399-24198-7(1) , Putnam Juvenile) Penguin Group (USA) Inc.

Blacker, Terence & Unwin, Pippa. Houdini the Disappearing Hamster. 1999. (Illus.). 32p. (J). (gr. k-3). pap. 8.99 (978-0-86264-907-4(2)) Andersen GBR. *Dist:* Independent Pubs. Group.

Burkett, Larry. A Home for the Hamsters. 2000. (Great Smoky Mountain Storybook Ser.). (Illus.). 32p. (J). (ps-3). 7.99 (978-0-8024-0982-9(2)) Moody Pubs.

The Busy Hamster. 2003. (J). per. (978-1-57657-889-6(5)) Paradise Pr., Inc.

Daniels, Lucy & Baglio, Ben M. Hamster Hotel. Howard, Paul, illus. 1999. (Animal Ark Pets Ser.: No. 4). 128p. (J). (gr. 3-6). pap. 3.99 (978-0-439-05161-3(4)) Scholastic, Inc.

Delittle, Cathy. Hamster Cheeks. Milicevic, Adam, illus. 2007. 32p. (J). 14.95 (***978-1-892633-14-9(0)***) Delittle Storyteller Co.

Donald, Margaret. Tipsy: The Hurricane Hero. 2007. 26p. (J). 14.95 (***978-81-8386-050-5(8)***) India Research Pr. IND. *Dist:* Independent Pubs. Group.

Field, Ellen, et al. Jingle's Journey. Brower, Howard, illus. 2003. (Hamtaro Ser.). 32p. (J). 3.99 (978-0-439-54239-5(1) , Scholastic Paperbacks) Scholastic, Inc.

Frederick, Heather Vogel. For Your Paws Only. Comport, Sally Wern, illus. 2005. (Spy Mice Ser.). 272p. (J). (gr. 4-6). 9.95 (978-1-4169-0573-8(1)) Simon & Schuster Children's Publishing.

Gregory, Valiska. A Valentine for Norman Noggs. Winborn, Marsha, illus. 1999. 32p. (J). (gr. k-3). 14.95 (978-0-06-027656-0(8)); 15.89 (978-0-06-027657-7(6)) HarperCollins Pubs.

—Valentine for Norman Noggs. 1999. (978-0-606-18726-8(X)) Tandem Library Bks.

Harcourt School Publishers Staff. Trofeos Below Level: Frida/Ventrnrio. 3rd ed. 2002. (SPA., Illus.). (gr. 1). pap. 5.50 (978-0-15-323873-4(9)) Harcourt Schl. Pubs.

Hawkins, Elizabeth. Monster of a Hamster. (Illus.). 96p. (J). 7.95 (978-0-14-038124-5(4)) Penguin Bks., Ltd. GBR. *Dist:* Trafalgar Square Publishing.

Hiebert, Elfrieda H. & Juel, Connie. My Hamster, Van. (Little Book Practice Reader Ser.). (J). (978-0-8136-0790-0(6)) Modern Curriculum Pr.

Inkpen, Deborah. Harriet. 1998. (Illus.). 24p. (J). (ps-2). 12.95 (978-0-7641-5080-7(4)); pap. 6.99 (978-0-7641-0575-3(2)) Barron's Educational Series, Inc.

Jammin' and Jones. Hamster on My Hip. 2006. (ENG.). 44p. per. 24.49 (***978-1-4259-0578-1(1)***) AuthorHouse.

Jenkins, Jane John. The Adventures of Harry the Hamster. Grenda, Janet W., illus. 2001. (J). (978-0-9674867-2-7(6)) Campbell Hse. Museum.

Jennings, Sharon. Priscilla's Paw de Deux. Hendry, Linda, illus. 2002. 36p. (J). (ps-2). (978-1-55041-718-0(5)) Fitzhenry & Whiteside, Ltd.

Johnson, Sandi. Harold the Hopping Hamster. Johnson, Britt, ed. Sturgeon, Bobbi, illus. l.t. ed. 2003. 34p. (J). (gr. k-5). spiral bd. 8.99 (978-1-929063-91-8(1) , 322) Moons & Stars Publishing For Children.

Kawai, Ritsuko. Balloon Adventure. Kawai, Ritsuko, illus. 2003. (Hamtaro Ser.). (Illus.). 16p. (YA). pap. 7.95 (978-1-56931-815-7(8)) Viz Media.

—Hamtaro Gets Lost & Other Stories Vol. 2. Kawai, Ritsuko, illus. 2003. (Adventures of Hamtaro Ser.). (Illus.). 92p. (YA). (gr. 1-3). 9.95 (978-1-56931-817-1(4)) Viz Media.

—Hamtaro, Let's Play! Vol. 4: A Playground for Ham-Ham. Kawai, Ritsuko, illus. 2003. (Hamtaro Ser.). 16p. (YA). (gr. 1-3). pap. 7.95 (978-1-56931-821-8(2)) Viz Media.

—A Home for Hamtaro & Other Stories, Vol. 1. Kawai, Ritsuko, illus. 2003. (Adventures of Hamtaro Ser.: Vol. 1). (Illus.). 78p. (YA). 9.95 (978-1-56931-782-2(8)) Viz Media.

—The Little Lost Caterpillar, Vol. 3. Kawai, Ritsuko, illus. 2003. (Hamtaro Ser.). (Illus.). 16p. (YA). pap. 7.95 (978-1-56931-816-4(6)) Viz Media.

Kenah, Katharine. The Best Seat in Second Grade. Carter, Abby, illus. (I Can Read Bks.). 48p. (J). 2006. pap. 3.99 (978-0-06-000736-2(2) , Harper Trophy); 2005. 16.99 (978-0-06-000734-8(6)); 2005. lib. bdg. 17.89 (978-0-06-000735-5(4)) HarperCollins Pubs.

Kimmel, Eric A. The Great Texas Hamster Drive: An Original Tall Tale. Whatley, Bruce, illus. 2007. 40p. (J). (ps-2). 16.99 (***978-0-7614-5357-4(1)***) Cavendish, Marshall Corp.

Klein, Abby. Stop That Hamster! McKinley, John, illus. 2007. (Ready, Freddy! Ser.). 96p. (J). pap. 3.99 (***978-0-439-89592-7(8)*** , Blue Sky Pr., The) Scholastic, Inc.

Krailing, Tessa. Where's Iggy? Lewis, Jan & Eastwood, John, illus. 1999. (Petsitters Club Ser.: No. 8). 96p. (J). (gr. 1-4). pap. 3.95 (978-0-7641-0693-4(7)) Barron's Educational Series, Inc.

Ladd, Frances Ann, et al. Bijou's Big Adventure. 2003. (Hamtaro Ser.: No. 2). 24p. (J). pap. 3.50 (978-0-439-54235-7(9) , Scholastic Paperbacks) Scholastic, Inc.

Lakin, Patricia. Max & Mo Go Apple Picking. Floca, Brian, illus. 2007. (Ready-to-Reads Ser.). 32p. (J). pap. 3.99 (***978-1-4169-2535-4(X)***); lib. bdg. 13.89 (***978-1-4169-2536-1(8)***) Simon & Schuster Children's Publishing. (Aladdin).

—Max & Mo Make a Snowman. Floca, Brian, illus. 2007. (Ready-to-Reads Ser.). 32p. (J). lib. bdg. 13.89 (***978-1-4169-2538-5(4)***); pap. 3.99 (***978-1-4169-2537-8(6)***) Simon & Schuster Children's Publishing. (Aladdin).

—Max & Mo's First Day at School. Floca, Brian, illus. 2007. (Ready-to-Reads Ser.). 32p. (J). (ps-1). pap. 3.99 (***978-1-4169-2533-0(3)***); lib. bdg. 13.89 (***978-1-4169-2534-7(1)***) Simon & Schuster Children's Publishing. (Aladdin).

Little Hamster & the Great Flood. 2001. (Illus.). 10p. (J). (ps-k). 10.99 (978-0-8254-7228-2(8)) Kregel Pubns.

McAllister, Angela. Monster Pet! Middleton, Charlotte, illus. 2005. 32p. (J). 15.95 (978-1-4169-0371-0(2) , McElderry, Margaret K.) Simon & Schuster Children's Publishing.

McMahon, P. J. The Case of the Psychic Hamster. 2005. (Freaky Joe Club Ser.: No. 4). (Illus.). 153p. (J). (978-1-4155-7725-7(0) , Aladdin) Simon & Schuster Children's Publishing.

McMahon, P. J. Case of the Psychic Hamster. Manders, John, illus. 2005. 153p. (J). lib. bdg. 15.38 (***978-1-4242-0404-5(6)***) Fitzgerald Bks.

McNamara, Margaret. Groundhog Day. Gordon, Mike, illus. 2006. 32p. (J). lib. bdg. 15.00 (***978-1-4242-0954-5(4)***) Fitzgerald Bks.

McNamara, Margaret & Gordon, Mike. Groundhog Day. 2005. (Robin Hill School Ser.). (Illus.). 32p. (J). pap. 3.99 (978-1-4169-0507-3(3) , Aladdin) Simon & Schuster Children's Publishing.

Morgan, Michaela. Silly Sausage & the Little Visitor. Shulman, Dee, illus. 2006. (Read-It! Chapter Books). (J). 21.26 (978-1-4048-2735-6(8)) Picture Window Bks.

Murschetz, Luis. El Hamster Pedal. 2001. (SPA., Illus.). 32p. (J). (gr. k-2). (978-84-204-4587-8(8) , AF3027) Alfaguara, Ediciones, S.A.- Grupo Santillana ESP. *Dist:* Lectorum Pubns., Inc.

Nakagawa, Rieko. Guri & Gura's Special Gift. Howlett, Peter & McNamara, Richard B., trs. from JPN. Yamawaki, Yuriko, illus. gif. ed. 2002. (Guri & Gura Ser.). 32p. (ps-3). 10.95 (978-0-8048-3357-8(5)) Tuttle Publishing.

Norac, Carl. La Isla de los Mimos. 2003. Tr. of I Love to Cuddle. (SPA., Illus.). 32p. (J). (978-84-95150-66-0(2) , COR3070) Corimbo, Editorial S.L. ESP. *Dist:* Lectorum Pubns., Inc.

Preller, James. The Case of Hermie the Missing Hamster. Alley, R. W., illus. 2001. (Jigsaw Jones Mystery Ser.: No. 1). 80p. (J). (gr. 1-4). pap. 3.99 (978-0-590-69125-3(2)) Scholastic, Inc.

Rathmann, Peggy. Faltan 10 Minutos Para Dormir. 2003. (SPA.). (gr. k-3). lib. bdg. 15.25 (978-0-613-81125-5(9)) Tandem Library Bks.

—10 Minutes till Bedtime. Rathmann, Peggy, illus. 1998. (Illus.). 48p. (J). (ps-1). 16.99 (978-0-399-23103-2(X) , Putnam Juvenile) Penguin Group (USA) Inc.

—10 Minutes Till Bedtime. Rathmann, Peggy, illus. 2002. (Illus.). (J). 23.64 (978-0-7587-1888-4(8)) Book Wholesalers, Inc.

Reiche, Deitlof. Book Two in the Golden Hamster Saga. Cepeda, Joe, illus. 2006. 208p. (J). pap. 4.99 (978-0-439-53156-6(X) , Scholastic Paperbacks) Scholastic, Inc.

Reiche, Dietlof. Freddy in Peril. Brownjohn, John & Cepeda, Joe, trs. from GER. Cepeda, Joe, illus. 2004. (Golden Hamster Saga: Bk. 2). 208p. (J). pap. 16.95 (978-0-439-53155-9(1)) Scholastic, Inc.

—Freddy to the Rescue. Cepeda, Joe, illus. 2006. (Golden Hamster Saga Ser.: Bk. 3). 240p. (J). pap. 4.99 (978-0-439-53158-0(6) , Scholastic Paperbacks) Scholastic, Inc.

—Freddy to the Rescue. Brownjohn, John, tr. from GER. Cepeda, Joe, illus. 2005. (Golden Hamster Saga: Bk. 3). 240p. (J). pap. 16.95 (978-0-439-53157-3(8)) Scholastic, Inc.

—Freddy's Final Quest Book Five in Golden Hamster. 2008. 208p. pap. 5.99 (***978-0-439-87415-1(7)*** , Scholastic Paperbacks) Scholastic, Inc.

—The Golden Hamster Saga, Bk. 1. Brownjohn, John, tr. from GER. Cepeda, Joe, illus. 2005. (I, Freddy Ser.). 208p. (J). reprint ed. pap. 4.99 (978-0-439-28357-1(4) , Scholastic Paperbacks) Scholastic, Inc.

—The Haunting of Freddy. 2007. (Golden Hamster Saga Ser.: Bk. 4). 320p. (J). pap. 5.99 (978-0-439-53160-3(8) , Scholastic Paperbacks) Scholastic, Inc.

—I, Freddy, Vol. 1. Brownjohn, John, tr. from GER. Cepeda, Joe, illus. 2003. (Golden Hamster Saga: Bk. 1). 208p. (J). pap. 15.95 (978-0-439-28356-4(6)) Scholastic, Inc.

Reiche, Dietlof & Brownjohn, John. Freddy in Peril: Book Two in the Golden Hamster Saga. Cepeda, Joe, illus. 2004. 202p. (J). pap. (978-0-439-64984-1(6)) Scholastic, Inc.

—Freddy's Final Quest. Cepeda, Joe, illus. 2007. (Golden Hamster Saga Ser.: Bk. 5). 304p. (J). pap. 16.99 (978-0-439-87414-4(9) , Scholastic Pr.) Scholastic, Inc.

—The Haunting of Freddy. Cepeda, Joe, illus. 2006. (Golden Hamster Saga Ser.: Bk. 4). 320p. (J). pap. 16.99 (978-0-439-53159-7(4) , Scholastic Pr.) Scholastic, Inc.

Rone, Trenton. Once upon a Hamster, 2003. (YA). spiral bd. 14.95 (978-0-9744437-3-7(5)) Imagination Workshop, The.

Rovetch, L. Bob. Hot Dog & Bob & the Dangerously Dizzy Attack of the Alien Hypno Hamsters. Whamond, Dave, illus. 2007. 96p. (J). pap. 4.95 (978-0-8118-5602-7(X)) Chronicle Bks. LLC.

Rovetch, Lissa. Hot Dog & Bob Adventure. Whamond, Dave, illus. 2007. 96p. (J). 15.50 (978-0-8118-5601-0(1)) Chronicle Bks. LLC.

Schwartz, Roslyn. The Mole Sisters & the Piece of Moss. Schwartz, Roslyn, illus. 2001. (Mole Sisters Ser.). (Illus.). 32p. (J). (ps-k). lib. bdg. 14.95 (978-1-55037-583-1(0)) Annick Pr., Ltd. CAN. *Dist:* Firefly Bks., Ltd.

Stanek, Gerald R. Sarah 'n' Dippity. Stanek, Joyce Huntington, illus. 2004. 28p. (J). 14.95 (978-0-9747417-0-3(1)) Shiver Hill Bks.

Steele, Michael Anthony & Kawai, Ritsuko. Calling All Ham-Hams! 2003. (Hamtaro Ser.: Bk. 1). (Illus.). 48p. (J). pap. 3.99 (978-0-439-54236-4(7) , Scholastic Paperbacks) Scholastic, Inc.

Suen, Anastasia. Hamster Chase. 2002. (gr. k-3). lib. bdg. 11.80 (978-0-613-71579-9(9)) Tandem Library Bks.

—The Hamster Chase. Eitzen, Allan, illus. 2002. (Easy-to-Read Ser.). 32p. (J). pap. 3.99 (978-0-14-230134-0(5) , Puffin) Penguin Group (USA) Inc.

Thomson, Pat. The Badcat Gang. Phillips, Mike, illus. 2006. 48p. (J). lib. bdg. (***978-1-4048-3112-4(6)***) Picture Window Bks.

Wallace, Carol. One Nosy Pup. Bjorkman, Steve, illus. 40p. (J). 15.95 (978-0-8234-1917-3(7)) Holiday Hse., Inc.

Walsh, Ellen Stoll. Hamsters to the Rescue. 2005. (Illus.). 40p. (J). (ps-1). 16.00 (978-0-15-205202-7(X)) Harcourt Trade Pubs.

Weiss, Ellen. I Don't Want to Go to School! A Fold-Out Surprise Book. Bennett, Andy, illus. 2006. (PBS Kids(R) Ser.). 18p. (J). 6.95 (***978-1-57791-313-9(2)***) Brighter Minds Children's Publishing.

Wiebe, Trina. Hamsters Don't Glow in the Dark. Pavanel, Jane, ed. Sarrazin, Marisol, illus. 2004. (Abby & Tess Pet-Sitters Ser.: Vol. 4). 96p. (J). (gr. 2-4). pap. 5.95 (978-1-894222-15-0(6)) Lobster Pr. CAN. *Dist:* Univ. of Toronto Pr.

—Hamsters Don't Glow in the Dark. 2000. (gr. 3-6). lib. bdg. 14.10 (978-0-613-62556-2(0)) Tandem Library Bks.

HANCOCK, JOHN, 1737-1793

Adler, David A. & Adler, Michael S. A Picture Book of John Hancock. Himler, Ronald, illus. 2007. 32p. (J). (ps-3). 16.95 (***978-0-8234-2005-6(1)***) Holiday Hse., Inc.

Fritz, Jean. Will You Sign Here, John Hancock? Hyman, Trina Schart, illus. (J). (gr. 2-7). 2005. 29.95 incl. audio compact disk (978-0-439-76750-7(4) , WHCD480); 2004. 24.95 incl. audio (978-1-56008-217-0(8) , WHBC480) Weston Woods Studios, Inc.

Gaines, Ann Graham. John Hancock: President of the Continental Congress. 2000. (Revolutionary War Leaders Ser.). (Illus.). 80p. (J). (gr. 4-7). pap. 8.95 (978-0-7910-6133-6(7)); (gr. 8-12). 27.50 (978-0-7910-5975-3(8)) Facts On File, Inc. (Chelsea Hse.).

Kallen, Stuart A. John Hancock. 2001. (Founding Fathers Ser.). (Illus.). 64p. (J). (gr. 3-8). lib. bdg. 25.65 (978-1-57765-010-2(7) , ABDO & Daughters) ABDO Publishing Co.

Kjelle, Marylou Morano. John Hancock. 2006. (Profiles in American History Ser.). (Illus.). 48p. (J). (gr. 4-8). lib. bdg. 20.95 (978-1-58415-443-3(8)) Mitchell Lane Pubs., Inc.

Ransom, Candice F. John Hancock. 2005. (History Maker Bios Ser.). (Illus.). 48p. (J). (gr. 3-4). 26.60 (978-0-8225-1547-0(4) , Lerner Pubns.) Lerner Publishing Group.

Sign Here, John Hancock. 2004. pap. 32.75 incl. audio (978-1-55592-360-0(7)) Weston Woods Studios, Inc.

Sisson, Kathryn Cleven. John Hancock: Independent Boy. Underdown, Harold, ed. Morrison, Cathy, illus. 2005. (Young Patriots Ser.: 9). 120p. (J). 15.95 (978-1-882859-45-0(6)); pap. 9.95 (978-1-882859-46-7(4)) Patria Pr., Inc.

Somervill, Barbara A. John Hancock: Signer for Independence. 2004. (Signature Lives Ser.). (Illus.). 112p. (J). 30.60 (978-0-7565-0828-9(2) , 1240133) Compass Point Bks.

Will You Sign Here, John Hancock? 2004. pap. 14.95 incl. audio (978-1-56008-224-8(0)) Weston Woods Studios, Inc.

HAND

Agassi, Martine. Hands Are Not for Hitting. Heinlen, Marieka, illus. (Best Behavior Ser.). (J). 2006. 24p. 7.95 (978-1-57542-200-8(X)); 2002. 24p. bds. 7.95 (978-1-57542-112-4(7)); 2000. 40p. pap. 11.95 (978-1-57542-077-6(5)) Free Spirit Publishing, Inc.

Aliki. My Hands. Aliki, illus. rev. ed. 2000. (Let's-Read-and-Find-Out Science Ser.). (Illus.). 32p. (J). (ps-1). 15.89 (978-0-690-04880-3(7)) HarperCollins Pubs.

—My Hands. 2000. (Let's-Read-and-Find-Out Ser.). (Illus.). (J). (978-0-613-21843-6(2)) Tandem Library Bks.

Brown, Janet Allison. Left Hand, Right Hand: A Hands-on Book about Left & Right. Endersby, Frank, illus. 2006. 16p. (J). bds. 5.99 (978-0-7641-5924-4(0)) Barron's Educational Series, Inc.

—Mano izquierda, Mano Derecha: Left Hand, Right Hand (Spanish Edition) Endersby, Frank, illus. 2006. (SPA.). 16p. (J). bds. 5.99 (978-0-7641-5925-1(9)) Barron's Educational Series, Inc.

Degezelle, Terri. Taking Care of My Hands & Feet. 2005. (Pebble Plus Ser.). (Illus.). 24p. (J). (ps-7). lib. bdg. 19.93 (978-0-7368-4262-4(4)) Capstone Pr., Inc.

Douglas, Lloyd G. My Hands. 2004. (Wel-My Body Ser.). (Illus.). 24p. (J). 18.00 (978-0-516-24059-6(5)); pap. 4.95 (978-0-516-22128-1(0)) Scholastic Library Publishing. (Children's Pr.).

Fernandez, A. & Fernandez, Q. Hooray for My Hands. (Hooray for My Senses Ser.). (Illus.). (J). 19.27 (978-1-58952-377-7(6)) Rourke Publishing, LLC.

Hands: Big Book: Level B. 8p. 20.95 (978-0-322-00360-6(1)) Wright Group, The.

Hansen, Rosanna. Bones! All Kinds of Hands, All Kinds of Feet. 2001. (Hello Reader! Science Ser.). (Illus.). (J). (978-0-439-31707-8(X)) Scholastic, Inc.

Hunt, Connie. Hooray for Hands! Melmon, Deborah, illus. 2008. (J). (***978-1-58728-700-8(5)*** , Two Can Publishing) T&N Children's Publishing.

Klingel, Cynthia Fitterer & Noyed, Robert B. Hands. Andersen, Gregg, photos by. 2002. (Weekly Reader Early Learning Library). (Illus.). 24p. (J). (ps up). pap. 5.95 (978-0-8368-3155-9(1)); lib. bdg. 19.33 (978-0-8368-3066-8(0)) Stevens, Gareth Inc. (Weekly Reader Early Learning Library).

—Hands/Manos. Acosta, Tatiana & Gutiérrez, Guillermo, trs. Andersen, Gregg, photos by. 2002. (Weekly Reader Early Learning Library). (Illus.). 24p. (J). (ps up). (SPA & ENG.). pap. (978-0-8368-3324-9(4)); (ENG & SPA., lib. bdg. 19.33 (978-0-8368-3075-0(X)) Stevens, Gareth Inc. (Weekly Reader Early Learning Library).

Kroll, Virginia L. Hands! Falwell, Cathryn, illus. 2003. 32p. (J). (ps up). 9.95 (978-1-56397-051-1(1)) Boyds Mills Pr.

Paratore, Coleen. 26 Big Things Small Hands Do. Reed, Mike, illus. 2004. 32p. (J). (ps up). 16.95 (978-1-57542-166-7(6)) Free Spirit Publishing, Inc.

Perkins, Al. Hand, Hand, Fingers, Thumb. Perkins, Al, illus. 2002. (Illus.). (J). 16.70 (978-0-7587-1238-7(3)) Book Wholesalers, Inc.

Schaefer, Lola M. Arms, Elbows, Hands, & Fingers. 2003. (It's My Body Ser.). (Illus.). 24p. (J). (ps-1). lib. bdg. 18.50 (978-1-4034-0889-1(0)); pap. 5.75 (978-1-4034-3478-4(6)) Heinemann Library.

—Brazos, Codos, Manos y Dedos. (Es Mi Cuerpo (It's My Body) Ser.).Tr. of Arms, Elbows, Hands & Fingers. 24p. pap. 5.25 (978-1-4034-3380-0(1)) Heinemann Library.

Sideri, Simona. Hands. Noble, Sheilagh, tr. Noble, Sheilagh, illus. 2004. (J). lib. bdg. (978-1-58340-493-5(7)) Smart Apple Media.

HANDEL, GEORGE FRIDERIC, 1685-1759

Cencetti, Greta. Handel. 2002. (Classic Composers Ser.). (Illus.). 40p. (J). incl. audio compact disk (978-1-59069-096-3(6) , T2106) Studio Mouse LLC.

—Handel: Getting to Know Your Classical Composers. 2002. (Classic Composers Ser.). (Illus.). 32p. (978-1-59069-029-1(X) , T2006) Studio Mouse LLC.

Flower, Newman. George Frideric Handel, His Personality & His Times. 2001. 378p. (YA). reprint ed. 98.00 (978-0-7222-5427-1(X)) Library Reprints, Inc.

Getzinger, Donna & Felsenfeld, Daniel. George Frideric Handel & Music for Voices. 2004. (Classical Composers Ser.). (Illus.). 144p. (YA). (gr. 6-12). 26.95 (978-1-931798-23-5(0)) Reynolds, Morgan Inc.

Marshall, Julian. Handel. 2001. 136p. (YA). reprint ed. 88.00 (978-0-7222-5197-3(1)) Library Reprints, Inc.

Ramsay, Edward B. Lectures on the Genius of Handel, & the Distinctive Character of His Sacred Compositions. 2001. 124p. (YA). reprint ed. 88.00 (978-0-7222-5428-8(8)) Library Reprints, Inc.

Robinson, Percy. Handel & His Orbit. 2001. 223p. (YA). reprint ed. 98.00 (978-0-7222-5429-5(6)) Library Reprints, Inc.

Rockstro, William Smyth. The Life of George Frederick Handel. 2001. 452p. (YA). reprint ed. 98.00 (978-0-7222-5430-1(X)) Library Reprints, Inc.

Wheeler, Opal. Handel at the Court of Kings. 2006. (Illus.). 168p. (J). per. 12.95 (978-1-933573-03-8(1) , 4481) Zeezok Publishing.

Wilcox, Judy. Handel at the Court of Kings Study Guide. 2006. (Illus.). 32p. (J). 4.95 (978-1-933573-04-5(X) , 4482) Zeezok Publishing.

Williams, Charles F. A. Handel. 2001. 267p. (YA). reprint ed. 98.00 (978-0-7222-6311-2(2)); 98.00 (978-0-7222-5435-6(0)) Library Reprints, Inc.

HANDICAPPED

see People with Disabilities

HANDICRAFT

see also Basket Making; Beadwork; Bookbinding; Decoration and Ornament; Design, Decorative; Glass Painting and Staining; Hobbies; Jewelry; Leatherwork; Metalwork; Modeling; Needlework; Puppet Making; Stencil Work; Weaving

Aboff, Marcie. Sugar & Spice. Cutting, David A., illus. 2006. (Holly Hobbie & Friends Ser.). 48p. (J). act. bk. ed. 3.99 (978-1-4169-4105-7(3) , Simon Scribbles) Simon & Schuster Children's Publishing.

Aboff, Marcie, et al. Dream BIG! Cutting, David A. & Riley, Kellee, illus. 2007. (Holly Hobbie & Friends Ser.). 400p. (J). 5.99 (***978-1-4169-3550-6(9)*** , Simon Scribbles) Simon & Schuster Children's Publishing.

Abramson, Jordan. The Hanukkah Candle Kit: Everything You Need to Make Eight Nights of Lights. 2003. (Running Press Kids Kits Ser.). (Illus.). 48p. pap. 19.95 (978-0-7624-1561-8(4) , Running Pr. Kids) Running Pr. Bk. Pubs.

AG Publishers Editors. Sparkle Card Kit: Everything You Need to Create More than 20 Glittery Greetings! 2003. (American Girl Library). (Illus.). 64p. (J). 19.95 (978-1-58485-707-5(2)) American Girl Publishing, Inc.

Ages 1-2 Activity Fall 2002. 2002. pap. 6.99 (978-1-59185-000-7(2)) CharismaLife Pubs.

Ages 1-2 Activity Winter 2002-2003. 2002. pap. 6.99 (978-1-59185-087-8(8)) CharismaLife Pubs.

Ages 2-3 Activity Fall 2002. 2002. pap. 3.29 (978-1-59185-004-5(5)) CharismaLife Pubs.

Ages 2-3 Activity Winter 2002-2003. 2002. pap. 3.29 (978-1-59185-091-5(6)) CharismaLife Pubs.

Ages 4-5 Activity Fall 2002. 2002. pap. 3.29 (978-1-59185-015-1(0)) CharismaLife Pubs.

Ages 4-5 Activity Winter 2002-2003. 2002. pap. 3.29 (978-1-59185-102-8(5)) CharismaLife Pubs.

Agranoff, Tracey. Kids Love Jewish Holiday Crafts. Horton, Mike & Marshall, Geoffrey, photos by. 2001. (Illus.). 144p. (gr. k-5). 16.95 (978-1-930143-11-1(7)) Pitspopany Pr.

—Kids Love Jewish Holiday Crafts. 2000. (Kids Love Ser.). (Illus.). 144p. (J). (gr. k-5). 21.95 (978-1-930143-06-7(0)) Pitspopany Pr.

Albregts, Lisa & Cape, Elizabeth. Best Friends: Tons of Crazy, Cool Things to Do with Your Girlfriends. 1998. (Illus.). 152p. (J). (gr. 3-7). pap. 12.95 (978-1-55652-326-7(2)) Chicago Review Pr., Inc.

All New Crafts for Mother's Day & Father's Day. 2007. 48p. (J). (gr. k-4). pap. 7.95 (***978-0-8225-6368-6(1)*** , First Avenue Editions) Lerner Publishing Group.

Amado, Elisa. Un Barrilete: Para el Dia de los Muertos. 1999. 13.75 (978-0-606-17570-8(9)) Tandem Library Bks.

Anderson, Maxine. Amazing Leonardo da Vinci: Inventions You Can Build Yourself. 2006. (Build It Yourself Ser.). (Illus.). 128p. (J). pap. 14.95 (978-0-9749344-2-6(9)) Nomad Pr.

—Great Civil War Projects You Can Build Yourself. 2005. (Build It Yourself Ser.). (Illus.). 144p. (J). (ps-17). pap. 14.95 (978-0-9749344-1-9(0)) Nomad Pr.

Andrews-Goebel, Nancy. La Vasija Que Juan Fabrico. Cortes, Eunice, tr. Diaz, David, illus. 2004. (SPA.). (J). 16.95 (978-1-58430-229-2(1)) Lee & Low Bks., Inc.

Apache Helicopter. 2004. (Press-Out & Build Ser.). (Illus.). 24p. (J). per. (978-1-84229-723-0(6)) Top That! Publishing PLC.

Apperley, Dawn. The Mermaid's Manual. 2004. (Illus.). 20p. (J). 16.95 (978-1-58234-888-9(X) , Bloomsbury Children) Bloomsbury Publishing.

Araujo, Paige Krul, ed. How to Make Scoubidous, Boondoggles, & Lanyards Too! 2006. (Illus.). 32p. (J). 5.99 (978-0-439-84316-4(2) , Tangerine Pr.) Scholastic, Inc.

Arima, Elaine. The Kids 'n' Clay Ceramics Book: Handbuilding & Wheel-Throwing Projects from the Kids 'n' Clay Pottery Studio. Arima, Curtis, illus. 2004. 128p. (J). (gr. k up). 16.95 (978-1-883672-89-8(9) , Tricycle Pr.) Ten Speed Pr.

Armstrong, Nancy. Mini Snowman in a Box Scholastic Ed. 2004. 32p. pap. (978-0-7624-2332-3(3)) Running Pr. Bk. Pubs.

Arts & Crafts. Date not set. (Get Crafty Ser.). (Illus.). 48p. (J). pap. 4.98 (978-0-7525-8408-9(1)) Parragon, Inc.

Arty Facts, 12 bks. Incl. Animals & Art Activities. Sacks, Janet. 2002. lib. bdg. (978-0-7787-1108-7(0)); Communication & Art Activities. Stringer, John. 2002. lib. bdg. (978-0-7787-1119-3(6)); Insects, Bugs, & Art Activities. Parker, Steve & Goodman, Polly. 2002. lib. bdg. (978-0-7787-1109-4(9)); Light, Color & Art Activities. Taylor, Barbara, text. 2002. lib. bdg. (978-0-7787-1114-8(5)); Machines, Transportation & Art Activities. Stringer, John. 2003. lib. bdg. (978-0-7787-1116-2(1)); Oceans & Art Activities. Sacks, Janet & Goodman, Polly, texts. 2002. lib. bdg. (978-0-7787-1115-5(3)); Our Bodies & Art Activities. McCormick, Rosie. 2002. lib. bdg. (978-0-7787-1117-9(X)); Planet Earth & Art Activities. Cooper, John. 2002. lib. bdg. (978-0-7787-1111-7(0)); Plants & Art Activities. McCormick, Rosie. 2002. lib. bdg. (978-0-7787-1110-0(2)); Space & Art Activities. Goodman, Polly. 2002. lib. bdg. (978-0-7787-1112-4(9)); Structures, Materials, & Art Activities. Taylor, Barbara. 2002. lib. bdg. (978-0-7787-1113-1(7)); Weather & Art Activities. Sacks, Janet. 2002. lib. bdg. (978-0-7787-1118-6(8)); 48p. (J). (gr. 3-4). (Illus.). 2002. (978-0-7787-1107-0(2)); Set pap. (978-0-7787-1135-3(8)) Crabtree Publishing Co.

Ashman, Iain. Wizard's Castle. 2004. (Cut-Out Models Ser.). (Illus.). 32p. (J). (gr. 4 up). pap. 9.95 (978-0-7945-0016-0(1) , Usborne) EDC Publishing.

Ayres, Mary. Jumbo Book of Kids Crafts. 2002. 88p. per. 12.99 (978-1-59612-030-3(4)) Grace Pubns., LLC.

Bailey, Gerry. Great Inventors. (Crafty Inventions Ser.). (Illus.). 48p. (J). (ps-3). 12.95 (978-1-904668-77-0(1)) Mercury Bks. Ltd. GBR. *Dist:* International Publishers Marketing.

—High-Tech Inventions. (Crafty Inventions Ser.). (Illus.). 48p. (J). (ps-3). 12.95 (978-1-904668-78-7(X)) Mercury Bks. Ltd. GBR. *Dist:* International Publishers Marketing.

—Outer Space. (Crafty Inventions Ser.). (Illus.). 48p. (J). (ps-3). 12.95 (978-1-904668-76-3(3)) Mercury Bks. Ltd. GBR. *Dist:* International Publishers Marketing.

—Underwater Machines. (Crafty Inventions Ser.). (Illus.). 48p. (J). (ps-3). 12.95 (978-1-904668-79-4(8)) Mercury Bks. Ltd. GBR. *Dist:* International Publishers Marketing.

Baker, Diane. Make Your Own Hairwear: Beaded Barrettes, Clips, Dangles & Headbands. Michaels, Alexandra, illus. 2001. (Quick Starts for Kids! Ser.). 64p. (J). (gr. 3 up). pap. 8.95 (978-1-885593-63-4(5) , Williamson Bks.) Ideals Pubns.

Balchin, Judy. Collage. 2003. (Step-by-Step Ser.). (Illus.). 32p. (J). (gr. 3-5). lib. bdg. 25.64 (978-1-4034-0697-2(9)) Heinemann Library.

—Creative Lettering. (Step-by-Step Ser.). (Illus.). 32p. (J). 2003. pap. 7.95 (978-1-4034-0709-2(6)); 2001. lib. bdg. 24.22 (978-1-57572-331-0(X)) Heinemann Library.

—Creative Lettering. 2002. (gr. 3-6). lib. bdg. 16.40 (978-0-613-85900-4(6)) Tandem Library Bks.

—Decorative Painting. (Step-by-Step Ser.). (Illus.). 32p. 2003. pap. 7.95 (978-1-4034-0708-5(8)); 2001. (J). (gr. 3-5). lib. bdg. 24.22 (978-1-57572-330-3(1)) Heinemann Library.

—Decorative Painting. 2002. (gr. 3-6). lib. bdg. 16.40 (978-0-613-86422-0(0)) Tandem Library Bks.

—Paper Mache. 2000. (Step-by-Step Ser.). (Illus.). 32p. (J). (gr. 3-5). lib. bdg. 24.22 (978-1-57572-328-0(X)) Heinemann Library.

—Papier Mache. 2003. (Step-by-Step Ser.). (Illus.). 32p. pap. 7.95 (978-1-4034-0706-1(1)) Heinemann Library.

—Papier Mache. 2001. (Step-by-Step Children's Crafts Ser.). (Illus.). 32p. pap. 7.95 (978-0-85532-912-9(2) , 9122) Search Pr., Ltd. GBR. *Dist:* Independent Pubs. Group.

—Papier Mache. 2002. (gr. 3-6). lib. bdg. 16.40 (978-0-613-88909-4(6)) Tandem Library Bks.

Balchin, Judy, et al. Crafty Activities: Over 50 Fun & Easy Things to Make. 2007. (Illus.). 160p. (J). (gr. 2 up). pap. 19.95 (***978-1-84448-250-4(2)***) Search Pr., Ltd. GBR. *Dist:* Independent Pubs. Group.

Balchin, Judy, et al. Step-by-Step: Exciting Arts & Crafts Projects. 2001. (Illus.). (J). (gr. 5-7). lib. bdg. 193.76 (978-1-58810-015-3(4)); Set 1. (gr. 3-5). lib. bdg. 96.88 (978-1-57572-334-1(4)); Set 2. (gr. 5-7). lib. bdg. 96.88 (978-1-57572-433-1(2)) Heinemann Library.

Balkwill, Richard. Clothes & Crafts in Ancient Egypt. 2000. (Clothes & Crafts in History Ser.). (Illus.). 32p. (J). (gr. 4-6). lib. bdg. 24.67 (978-0-8368-2733-0(3)) Stevens, Gareth Inc.

Banner, Shawn. Room for You: Find Your Style & Make Your Room Say You! 2001. (gr. 3-6). lib. bdg. 16.40 (978-0-613-83324-0(4)) Tandem Library Bks.

Banner, Shawn, illus. Room for You: Find Your Style & Make Your Room Say You! 2001. (American Girl Library). 80p. (J). (gr. 3 up). pap. 7.95 (978-1-58485-369-5(7)) American Girl Publishing, Inc.

Barbara, Diane & Donnier, Christine. Mom & Me: A Special Book for You & Your Mom to Fill in Together & Share with Each Other. 2004. (Illus.). 48p. (J). (ps-3). 16.95 (978-0-8109-4820-4(6)) Abrams, Harry N. , Inc.

Barchers, Suzanne I. & Rauen, Peter J. Holiday Storybook Stew: Cooking Through the Year with Books Kids Love. 1998. (Illus.). 128p. (gr. k-6). pap. 15.95 (978-1-55591-972-6(3)) Fulcrum Publishing.

Barker, Cicely Mary. Flower Fairies Art Activity Book. 2007. 72p. (J). (ps). pap. 9.99 (978-0-7232-5915-2(1) , Warne) Penguin Group (USA) Inc.

Bartholomew, Alan. Electric Gadgets & Gizmos: Battery-Powered Buildable Gadgets That Go! annual Bartholomew, Lynn, illus. 1998. (Kids Can Do It Ser.). 156p. (J). (gr. 4-6). (978-1-55074-439-2(9)) Kids Can Pr., Ltd.

—Electric Gadgets & Gizmos: Battery-Powered Buildable Gadgets That Go! Bartholomew, Lynn, illus. 1998. 47p. (J). (ps-7). lib. bdg. 14.10 (978-0-613-16348-4(6)) Tandem Library Bks.

Bassachs, Anna G., et al. Tiny Hands: Winter. 1998. (Tiny Hands Ser.). (Illus.). 48p. (J). (ps-k). pap. 7.95 (978-0-7641-0741-2(0)) Barron's Educational Series, Inc.

Beak, Nick Huckleberry. Crafty Kids, 8 bks. Freeman, John, photos by. Incl. Crafty Badges. Boase, Petra. 2000. lib. bdg. 26.00 (978-0-8368-2500-8(4)); Crafty Detectives. Boase, Petra. 2000. lib. bdg. 26.00 (978-0-8368-2501-5(2)); Crafty Juggling. Boase, Petra. 2000. lib. bdg. 26.00 (978-0-8368-2502-2(0)); Crafty Magic. Boase, Petra. 1999. lib. bdg. 25.26 (978-0-8368-2481-0(4)); Crafty Masks. 1999. lib. bdg. 26.00 (978-0-8368-2482-7(2)); Crafty Puppets. Boase, Petra. 1999. lib. bdg. 26.00 (978-0-8368-2480-3(6)); Crafty Stamping. Boase, Petra. 2000. lib. bdg. 26.00 (978-0-8368-2503-9(9)); Crafty T-Shirts. Boase, Petra. 1999. lib. bdg. 26.00 (978-0-8368-2483-4(0)); 64p. (J). (gr. 3 up). (Illus.). Set lib. bdg. 156.00 (978-0-8368-2739-2(2)) Stevens, Gareth Inc.

—Now Try This! Over 100 Really Brilliant Things to Do by Yourself & with Friends. 2002. (Illus.). 256p. pap. 19.99 (978-1-84215-713-8(2) , Southwater) Anness Publishing GBR. *Dist:* National Bk. Network.

Beard, Daniel Carter. The American Boy's Handy Book: Turn-of-the-Century Classic of Crafts & Activities. 2003. (Dover Value Editions Ser.). (Illus.). 464p. (J). pap. 9.95 (978-0-486-43138-3(X)) Dover Pubns., Inc.

—The American Boy's Handy Book: What to Do & How to Do It. 2001. (Illus.). 408p. pap. 11.95 (978-1-58667-065-8(4)) Derrydale Pr., The.

Beaton, Clare. Make Your Own Noah's Ark. Beaton, Clare, illus. 2007. (Illus.). (J). (gr. k-3). 9.95 (***978-0-8198-4862-8(X)***) Pauline Bks. & Media.

Bell, Alison. Let's Party! Chung, Kun-Sung, illus. 2005. 64p. (J). pap. 14.95 (978-1-894222-99-0(7)) Lobster Pr. CAN. *Dist:* Univ. of Toronto Pr.

Bell-Rehwoldt, Sheri. Amazing Maya Inventions You Can Build Yourself. 2007. (Build It Yourself Ser.). (Illus.). 128p. (J). pap. 14.95 (978-0-9771294-6-1(2)) Nomad Pr.

Berger, Thomas & Berger, Petra. Crafts Through the Year. Lawson, Polly, tr. from DUT. 2000. (Illus.). 118p. 19.95 (978-0-86315-322-8(4)) Floris Bks. GBR. *Dist:* Gryphon Hse., Inc., SteinerBooks, Inc.

—The Gnome Craft Book. 2001. (Illus.). 80p. pap. 15.95 (978-0-86315-300-6(3)) Floris Bks. GBR. *Dist:* Gryphon Hse., Inc., SteinerBooks, Inc.

Best of Bible Crafts. 2004. 12.99 (978-1-56417-988-3(5)) School Specialty Publishing.

The Best of Bridal Ideas. 2003. 11.99 (978-0-930184-00-1(9)) Clapper Publishing Co.

The Best of Clay Pots II. 2003. 11.99 (978-0-930184-03-2(3)) Clapper Publishing Co.

Better Homes and Gardens Books Staff, contrib. by. Big Book of Kids' Crafts: 301 Projects for Kids 4 to 12. 2004. (Illus.). 304p. (J). (978-0-696-22540-6(9)) Meredith Bks.

Beylon, Cathy. Freddy, the Fireman: With 28 Sticker Costumes. 1999. (Stickers Ser.). (Illus.). 4p. (J). (gr. k-5). pap. 1.50 (978-0-486-40754-8(3)) Dover Pubns., Inc.

Bhatt, Sonal. Totally Beads. 2002. (Illus.). 80p. (gr. 3-7). pap. 9.95 (978-0-8069-8399-8(X)) Sterling Publishing Co., Inc.

—Totally Beads. 2002. (gr. 3-6). lib. bdg. 18.75 (978-0-613-75654-9(1)) Tandem Library Bks.

Blakey, Nancy. Lotions, Potions, & Slime: Mudpies & More! Watts, Melissah, illus. 2004. 120p. (J). (ps-7). 9.95 (978-1-883672-21-8(X) , Tricycle Pr.) Ten Speed Pr.

Blanchette, Peg & Thibault, Terri. Make Your Own Cool Cards: 40 Awesome Notes & Invitations! 2004. (Quick Starts for Kids! Ser.). (Illus.). 64p. (J). 8.95 (978-1-885593-96-2(1) , Williamson Bks.) Ideals Pubns.

Bledsoe, Karen E. Chinese New Year Crafts. 2005. (Fun Holiday Crafts Kids Can Do Ser.). (Illus.). 32p. (J). lib. bdg. 22.60 (978-0-7660-2347-5(8) , Enslow Elementary) Enslow Pubs., Inc.

—Hanukkah Crafts. 2004. (Fun Holiday Crafts Kids Can Do Ser.). (Illus.). 32p. (J). lib. bdg. 22.60 (978-0-7660-2238-6(2)) Enslow Pubs., Inc.

Bliss, Helen. Paper. 1998. (Craft Workshop Ser.). (Illus.). 32p. (J). (gr. 3). pap. (978-0-86505-791-3(5)); lib. bdg. (978-0-86505-781-4(8)) Crabtree Publishing Co.

Bliss, Helen & Thomson, Ruth. Models. 1998. (Craft Workshop Ser.). (Illus.). 32p. (J). (gr. 3). pap. (978-0-86505-788-3(5)) Crabtree Publishing Co.

Blocher, Wendy. Happy Birthday, Grades K-3. Yuh, Catherine, illus. 1999. (Primary Theme Ser.). 32p. pap., tchr. ed. 7.99 (978-1-57471-629-0(8) , 2457) Creative Teaching Pr., Inc.

Blue Lantern Studio Staff, ed. Make It Yourself. 2007. (Illus.). 17.95 (***978-1-59583-188-0(6)*** , Green Tiger Pr.) Laughing Elephant.

Boase, Petra. Badge Factory. 2001. (Illus.). 64p. (gr. 3-7). pap. 6.95 (978-1-84215-478-6(8) , Southwater) Anness Publishing GBR. *Dist:* National Bk. Network.

—Fun at Christmas. 2000. (Fun with... Ser.). (Illus.). 96p. (gr. 3-7). 12.95 (978-1-84215-333-8(1) , Southwater) Anness Publishing GBR. *Dist:* National Bk. Network.

—Stamp Factory. 2003. (Fun Factory Ser.). (Illus.). 64p. (gr. k-2). pap. 9.99 (978-1-84215-827-2(9) , Southwater) Anness Publishing GBR. *Dist:* National Bk. Network.

Boase, Petra & Beak, Nick Huckleberry. Crafty Badges. Freeman, John, photos by. 2000. (Crafty Kids Ser.). (Illus.). 64p. (J). (gr. 3 up). lib. bdg. 26.00 (978-0-8368-2500-8(4)) Stevens, Gareth Inc.

—Crafty Stamping. Freeman, John, photos by. 2000. (Crafty Kids Ser.). (Illus.). 64p. (J). (gr. 3 up). lib. bdg. 26.00 (978-0-8368-2503-9(9)) Stevens, Gareth Inc.

—Crafty T-Shirts. Freeman, John, photos by. 1999. (Crafty Kids Ser.). 64p. (J). (gr. 3 up). lib. bdg. 26.00 (978-0-8368-2483-4(0)) Stevens, Gareth Inc.

Boase, Petra & Smith, Thomasina. Dough Craft. 2004. (Fun Factory Ser.). (Illus.). 64p. pap. 9.99 (978-1-84215-926-2(7) , Southwater) Anness Publishing GBR. *Dist:* National Bk. Network.

Bond, Felicia. Make Your Own Valentines! 1999. (Illus.). 32p. (J). (ps-2). 9.95 (978-0-694-01259-6(9)) HarperCollins Pubs.

Bonnell, Jennifer. D i Y: Do It Yourself Girl. 2003. (gr. 7-12). lib. bdg. 22.25 (978-0-613-67449-2(9)) Tandem Library Bks.

Boonyadhistarn, Thiranut. Fingernail Art: Dazzling Fingers & Terrific Toes. 2007. (Snap Books Craft Ser.). (Illus.). 32p. (J). (gr. 4-8). lib. bdg. 25.26 (978-0-7368-6474-9(1)) Capstone Pr., Inc.

—Valentines: Cards & Crafts from the Heart. 2007. (Snap Books). (Illus.). 32p. (J). 25.26 (978-0-7368-6475-6(X)) Capstone Pr., Inc.

Borg, Janet. My Favorite Nature Book: Stars & Planets: Includes an Activity Kit with Posters, Stickers & Glow-in-the-Dark Stars. Weiss, Anne & Estellon, Pascale, illus. 2006. 24p. 9.95 (978-1-57990-923-9(X)) Lark Bks.

Borst, Donna & Mitchell, Judy, eds. The Best of Holidays & Seasonal Celebrations: Arts & Crafts. 2001. (Illus.). 128p. (J). (ps-3). pap. 13.95 (978-1-57310-280-3(6)) Teaching & Learning Co.

Bose, Terri. Craft Adventures. 2003. (gr. 3-6). lib. bdg. 22.25 (978-0-613-71018-3(5)) Tandem Library Bks.

Botermans, Jack & Bookman International B.V. Staff. Fantastic Paper Airplanes. 2004. (Illus.). 96p. (J). pap. 7.95 (978-1-4027-1149-7(2)) Sterling Publishing Co., Inc.

Bourgeois, Paulette. Franklin & Me: A Book about Me, Written & Drawn by Me (with a Little Help from Franklin) Clark, Brenda, illus. unabr. ed. 1998. 32p. (J). (gr. k-3). (978-1-55074-442-2(9)) Kids Can Pr., Ltd.

Boursin, Didier. Easy Origami: 24 Simple, Easy-to-follow Projects for Beginners to the Art of Origami. 2005. (Illus.). 64p. (J). (gr. 2-7). pap. 9.95 (978-1-55297-939-6(3)) Firefly Bks., Ltd.

Boxes of Fun: Individual Title Six-Packs. (Story Steps Ser.). (gr. k-2). 29.00 (978-0-7635-9594-4(2)) Rigby Education.

Boyd, Heidi. Fairy Crafts. 2003. (Illus.). 96p. pap. 14.99 (978-1-58180-430-0(X) , North Light Bks.) F & W Pubns., Inc.

Boyds Mills Press. Easy-to-Do Holiday Crafts: From Everyday Household Items! 2004. (Illus.). 384p. (YA). spiral bd. 19.95 (978-1-59078-316-0(6)) Boyds Mills Pr.

—Fun-to-Make Crafts for Every Day. 2004. (Illus.). 64p. (J). 15.95 (978-1-59078-341-2(7)); pap. 7.95 (978-1-59078-366-5(2)) Boyds Mills Pr.

Boyds Mills Press, creator. Fun-to-Make Crafts for Christmas. 2005. (Illus.). 63p. (J). (ps-ps). per. 15.95 (978-1-59078-342-9(5)) Boyds Mills Pr.

—Fun-to-Make Crafts for Halloween. 2005. (Illus.). 64p. (J). (ps-ps). 15.95 (978-1-59078-343-6(3)) Boyds Mills Pr.

Boyds Mills Press Staff. Fun-to-Make Crafts for Halloween. 2005. (Illus.). 63p. (J). (ps-ps). pap. 7.95 (978-1-59078-368-9(9)) Boyds Mills Pr.

Braham, Clare B. & Esche, Maria Bonfanti. Kids Celebrate! Activities for Special Days Throughout the Year. Jones, Mary, illus. 1998. 304p. (J). (ps). pap. 17.95 (978-1-55652-292-5(4)) Chicago Review Pr.

Braithwaite, Jill. From Tree to Table. (Start to Finish Ser.). (J). 2004. (Illus.). 24p. 18.60 (978-0-8225-0947-9(4)); 2002. pap. 4.95 (978-0-8225-0751-2(X)) Lerner Publishing Group. (Lerner Pubns.).

Braman, Arlette. Kids Around the World Create! the Best Crafts & Activities from Many Lands. 1999. (gr. 3-6). lib. bdg. 22.20 (978-0-613-16520-4(9)) Tandem Library Bks.

Braman, Arlette N. Secrets of Ancient Cultures: The Maya-Activities & Crafts from a Mysterious Land. Nidenoff, Michele, illus. 2003. 118p. pap. 12.95 (978-0-471-21981-1(9) , Wiley) Wiley, John & Sons, Inc.

Brend, Dawn. Jazzy Jewelry: Recycle Materials to Make Cool Stuff. 2007. (EcoCrafts Ser.). (Illus.). 48p. (J). pap. 7.95 (***978-0-7534-5969-0(8)*** , Kingfisher) Houghton Mifflin Co. Trade & Reference Div.

Brighter Vision Publishing Staff. Everyday Crafts to Make. 2000. (Make It Now Crafts Ser.). (Illus.). (J). (ps-3). pap. 3.95 (978-1-55254-176-0(2)) Brighter Vision Pubns.

—Halloween & Thanksgiving. 2000. (Make It Now Crafts Ser.). (Illus.). (J). (ps-3). pap. 3.95 (978-1-55254-178-4(9)) Brighter Vision Pubns.

—Summertime Crafts to Make. 2000. (Make It Now Crafts Ser.). (Illus.). (J). (ps-3). pap. 3.95 (978-1-55254-177-7(0)) Brighter Vision Pubns.

Brown, Robin C. The Crafts of Florida's First People. 2003. (Illus.). 64p. (J). pap. 9.95 (978-1-56164-282-3(7)) Pineapple Pr., Inc.

Browning, Marie. Totally Cool Polymer Clay Projects. (Illus.). 96p. 2005. (J). pap. 12.95 (978-1-4027-2789-4(5)); 2004. 19.95 (978-1-4027-0642-4(1)) Sterling Publishing Co., Inc.

Bruder, Mikyla. Button Girl: More Than 20 Cute-as-as-Button Projects. Nobles, Scott, photos by. 2005. (Illus.). 64p. (J). 12.95 (978-0-8118-4553-3(2)) Chronicle Bks. LLC.

—The Star Wars Party Book: Recipes & Ideas for Galactic Occasions. Frankeny, Frankie, illus. Frankeny, Frankie, photos by. 2002. (Star Wars Ser.). 60p. (J). (gr. 3-5). 17.95 (978-0-8118-3491-9(3)) Chronicle Bks. LLC.

Buckingham, Linda. Projection Art for Kids: Murals & Painting Projects for Kids of All Ages. 2002. (Illus.). 128p. pap. 14.95 (978-0-88179-197-6(0)) Hartley & Marks Publishers, Inc. CAN. *Dist:* Perseus Distribution.

Build Your Own Classic Sports Cars: A Complete, Easy-to-Assemble Model. 2002. 16p. (J). 3.98 (978-0-7525-7655-8(0)) Parragon, Inc.

Build Your Own Farmyard: A Complete, Easty-to-Assemble Model. 2002. 16p. (J). 3.98 (978-0-7525-7656-5(9)) Parragon, Inc.

Build Your Own Human Skeleton: A Complete Easy-to-Assemble Model. 2002. 16p. (J). 3.98 (978-0-7525-7657-2(7)) Parragon, Inc.

Build Your Own Planes That Fly: A Complete, Easy-to-Assemble Model. 2002. 16p. (J). 3.98 (978-0-7525-7659-6(3)) Parragon, Inc.

Build Your Own Steam Locomotive: A Complete, Easy-to-Assemble Model. 2002. 16p. (J). 3.98 (978-0-7525-7660-2(7)) Parragon, Inc.

Bull, Jane. The Best Craft Book Ever. 2006. (Illus.). 192p. (J). pap. 14.99 (978-0-7566-2236-7(0)) Dorling Kindersley Publishing, Inc.

—Make It! 2008. 128p. (J). (gr. 2-6). 16.99 (***978-0-7566-3837-5(2)***) Dorling Kindersley Publishing, Inc.

Bull, Jane. The Vacation Activity Book. 2007. 48p. (J). (gr. 1-3). 12.99 (978-0-7566-2942-7(X)) Dorling Kindersley Publishing, Inc.

Bullis, Janis & Jannsen-Fleischman, Mary Beth. Braids, Bows & Bands. 2000. (Funtastic Kits Ser.). (Illus.). 48p. (J). 12.98 (978-0-7853-3978-6(7)) Publications International, Ltd.

Bulloch, Ivan. I Wish I Were a Fairy. 1999. (ps-2). lib. bdg. 15.25 (978-0-613-43331-0(9)) Tandem Library Bks.

—Make Toys. James, Diane, illus. rev. ed. 2000. (Let's Ser.). 24p. (J). (ps-1). 9.95 (978-1-58728-028-3(0)); pap. 5.95 (978-1-58728-032-0(9)) T&N Children's Publishing. (Two Can Publishing).

Bulloch, Ivan & James, Diane. Juguemos Con Papel. 2004. (Juguemos Con Ser.). (SPA., Illus.). 24p. (ps-3). (J). pap. 5.95 (978-1-58728-505-9(3)); 9.95 (978-1-58728-503-5(7)) T&N Children's Publishing. (Two Can Publishing).

—Juguemos Con Pintura. 2004. (Juguemos Con Ser.). (SPA., Illus.). 24p. (ps-3). (J). pap. 5.95 (978-1-58728-504-2(5)); 9.95 (978-1-58728-502-8(9)) T&N Children's Publishing. (Two Can Publishing).

Burgess, Rachel, ed. Medical Marvels. (Crafty Inventions Ser.). (Illus.). 48p. (J). (ps). 12.95 (978-1-904668-75-6(5)) Mercury Bks. Ltd. GBR. *Dist:* International Publishers Marketing.

—Weapons of War. (Crafty Inventions Ser.). (Illus.). 48p. (J). (ps). 12.95 (978-1-904668-74-9(7)) Mercury Bks. Ltd. GBR. *Dist:* International Publishers Marketing.

Candle Making for Kids With Other. 1999. mass mkt. 168.60 (978-0-590-63241-6(8)) Scholastic, Inc.

Canizares, Susan, et al. Clay Art with Gloria Elliott. 1999. (Learning Center Emergent Readers Ser.). (Illus.). (J). 2.50 (978-0-439-04595-7(9)) Scholastic, Inc.

Cano-Murillo, Kathy. The Crafty Diva's D.I.Y. Stylebook: A Grrrl's [sic] Guide to Cool Creations You Can Make, Show Off, & Share. Wheeler, Carrie, illus. Samora, John, photos by. 2004. 144p. pap. 12.95 (978-0-8230-6993-4(1)) Watson-Guptill Pubns., Inc.

—The Crafty Diva's Lifestyle Makeover: Awesome Ideas to Spice up Your Life! Wheeler, Carrie, illus. 2005. 144p. (YA). pap. 12.95 (978-0-8230-1008-0(2)) Watson-Guptill Pubns., Inc.

Capozzi, Suzy. Forever Friends. Cutting, David A., illus. 2006. (Holly Hobbie & Friends Ser.). 32p. (J). act. bk. ed. 4.99 (978-1-4169-4106-4(1) , Simon Scribbles) Simon & Schuster Children's Publishing.

Carlson, Bruce. Halloween Fun Stuff. 1999. (Illus.). 140p. (J). spiral bd. 9.95 (978-1-57166-105-0(0)) Hearts 'N Tummies Cookbook Co.

Carlson, Laurie M. Colonial Kids: An Activity Guide to Life in the New World. 2003. (Kid's Guide Ser.). (Illus.). 160p. (J). (gr. k-7). pap. 14.95 (978-1-55652-322-9(X)) Chicago Review Pr., Inc.

—Days of Knights & Damsels: An Activity Guide. 2003. (Kid's Guide Ser.). (Illus.). 184p. (J). (gr. k-7). pap. 14.95 (978-1-55652-291-8(6)) Chicago Review Pr., Inc.

—Green Thumbs: A Kid's Activity Guide to Indoor & Outdoor Gardening. 2003. (Kid's Guide Ser.). (Illus.). 144p. (J). (gr. k-7). pap. 12.95 (978-1-55652-238-3(X)) Chicago Review Pr., Inc.

—Kids Create! Trezzo-Braren, Loretta, illus. 1999. (Williamson Kids Can! Ser.). 160p. (J). (gr. 3 up). lib. bdg. 25.26 (978-0-8368-2232-8(3)) Stevens, Gareth Inc.

Carole Marsh. Patriotic Projects. 2004. (Patriotic Favorites Ser.). 32p. pap. 5.95 (978-0-635-02386-5(5)) Gallopade International.

H I

Carson-Dellosa Classroom Creations: 119 Uses for Decorative Materials. 2001. 64p. pap. 9.99 (978-0-88724-657-9(5), CD-0053) Carson-Dellosa Publishing Co., Inc.

Carter, Tamsin. Handmade Cards. 2003. (gr. 3-6). lib. bdg. 16.40 (978-0-613-88510-2(4)) Tandem Library Bks.

Casagranda, Brigitte. Salt Dough Fun. 2005. (I Made It Myself! Ser.). (Illus.). 24p. (J). (ps-17). lib. bdg. 22.00 (978-0-8368-5967-6(7)) Stevens, Gareth Inc.

Castaldo, Nancy F. Rainy Day Play: Explore, Create, Discover, Pretend. 2005. (Illus.). 144p. (J). pap. 12.95 (978-1-55652-563-6(X)) Chicago Review Pr., Inc.

—Winter Day Play! Activities, Crafts, & Games for Indoors & Out. 2001. (Illus.). 176p. (J). pap. 13.95 (978-1-55652-381-6(5)) Chicago Review Pr., Inc.

Chantilly, Lili. Lili Chantilly: All My Fabulous Friends Address Book. 2004. (Illus.). 96p. (J). 7.95 (978-0-7611-3408-4(5), 13408) Workman Publishing Co., Inc.

—Lili Chantilly: All My Fabulous Friends Memory Book. 2004. (Illus.). 96p. (J). 9.95 (978-0-7611-3406-0(9), 13406) Workman Publishing Co., Inc.

—Lili Chantilly: My Amazing Life Journal. 2004. (Illus.). 96p. (J). 9.95 (978-0-7611-3404-6(2), 13404) Workman Publishing Co., Inc.

—Lili Chantilly: My Totally Best Days Ever Scrapbook. 2004. (Illus.). 96p. (J). 9.95 (978-0-7611-3405-3(0), 13405) Workman Publishing Co., Inc.

Chapman, Gillian. Art from Fabric. 2007. (J). lib. bdg. (*978-1-4042-3722-3(4), PowerKids Pr.) Rosen Publishing Group, Inc., The.

—Aztec Crafts from the Past. 2000. (Crafts from the Past Ser.). (Illus.). 37p. (J). (gr. 4-7). pap. 9.95 (978-0-688-17748-5(4)) HarperCollins Pubs.

—Bible Make & Do, Vol. 4. 32p. (J). 7.99 (978-0-7586-0582-5(X)) Concordia Publishing Hse.

Chapman, Gillian & Robson, Pam. Art from Rocks & Shells. 2007. (J). lib. bdg. (*978-1-4042-3727-8(5), PowerKids Pr.) Rosen Publishing Group, Inc., The.

Check, Laura. Almost-Instant Scrapbooks. Day, Betsy, tr. Day, Betsy, illus. 2004. (Quick Starts for Kids! Ser.). 64p. (J). pap. 8.95 (978-1-885593-90-0(2), Williamson Bks.) Ideals Pubns.

—Paper Plate Crafts: Creative Art Fun for 3- to 7-Year-Olds. Martin Jourdenais, Norma Jean, illus. 2000. (Little Hands Bks.). 144p. (J). (ps-2). pap. 12.95 (978-1-885593-43-6(0), Williamson Bks.) Ideals Pubns.

Cherkerzian, Diane. Merry Things to Make: Christmas Fun & Crafts. 2003. (gr. 3-6). lib. bdg. 16.40 (978-0-613-78902-8(4)) Tandem Library Bks.

Cherry, Winky. My First Embroidery Book Level 2: A Name Sampler. Palmer, Pati, ed. Cherry, Winky, illus. 2003. (My First Sewing Book Ser.). (Illus.). 40p. (J). (ps-6). pap. 14.95 (978-0-935278-31-6(1)) Palmer-Pletsch Assocs.

Chessen, Betsey & Chanko, Pamela. Crafts. 1999. (Social Studies Emergent Readers). (J). 2.50 (978-0-439-04568-1(1)) Scholastic, Inc.

—Crafts. 1999. (ps-2). lib. bdg. 10.10 (978-0-613-21381-3(5)) Tandem Library Bks.

Childcraft Supplements. 2000. (J). (gr. k-6). (978-0-7166-0664-2(X)); (Illus.). 1784p. 119.00 (978-0-7166-0665-9(8)) World Bk., Inc.

Chronicle Books Staff, contrib. by. Homemade Halloween: Fun-To-Make Crafts & Treats. 2003. (Illus.). 32p. (J). pap. 9.95 (978-0-8118-4016-3(6)) Chronicle Bks. LLC.

Church, Jayne, illus. Curious Camel. 1999. (Waggy Tales Ser.). 10p. (ps up). 6.99 (978-0-7847-1116-3(X), 03524, Bean Sprouts) Standard Publishing.

Cisneros, Kathy. Bottle Cap Activities: Recycled Crafts for All Ages. 1998. (Illus.). 208p. lib. bdg. 26.95 (978-0-89334-282-1(3)); (gr. 4-8). 26.95 (978-0-89334-288-3(2)) Humanics Publishing Group.

Civardi, Anne & King, Penny. Festival Decorations. 1998. (Craft Workshop Ser.). (Illus.). 32p. (J). (gr. 3). pap. (978-0-86505-790-6(7)); lib. bdg. (978-0-86505-780-7(X)) Crabtree Publishing Co.

Clark, Sondra. Craft Fun with Sondra. 1999. (gr. 3-6). lib. bdg. 14.10 (978-0-613-21380-6(7)) Tandem Library Bks.

Clark, Sondra & Clark, Silvana. Craft Fun with Sondra: Over 55 Arts & Crafts Projects. Clark, Sondra, illus. 1999. (Illus.). 128p. (J). (ps-3). pap. 5.95 (978-0-689-83069-3(6)) Meadowbrook Pr.

Clothes & Crafts in History, 6 bks. Incl. Clothes & Crafts in Ancient Egypt. Balkwill, Richard. lib. bdg. 24.67 (978-0-8368-2733-0(3)); Clothes & Crafts in Ancient Greece. Steele, Philip. lib. bdg. 24.67 (978-0-8368-2734-7(1)); Clothes & Crafts in Aztec Times. Dawson, Imogene. lib. bdg. 24.67 (978-0-8368-2735-4(X)); Clothes & Crafts in Roman Times. Steele, Philip. lib. bdg. 24.67 (978-0-8368-2737-8(6)); Clothes & Crafts in the Middle Ages. Dawson, Imogene. lib. bdg. 24.67 (978-0-8368-2736-1(8)); Clothes & Crafts in Victorian Times. Steele, Philip. lib. bdg. 24.67 (978-0-8368-2738-5(4)); 32p. (J). (gr. 4 up). 2000. (Illus.). 2000. Set lib. bdg. 148.02 (978-0-8368-2732-3(5)) Stevens, Gareth Inc.

Cobb, Mary. A Sampler View of Colonial Life: With Projects Kids Can Make. Ellis, Jan Davey, illus. 1998. 64p. (gr. 2-4). lib. bdg. 24.90 (978-0-7613-0372-5(3), Millbrook Pr.) Lerner Publishing Group.

—Sampler View of Colonial Life: With Projects Kids Can Make. 1999. (gr. 3-6). lib. bdg. 17.60 (978-0-613-26821-9(0)) Tandem Library Bks.

Cohen, Cambria, et al. 150 Nifty Super Crafts. 2000. (Illus.). 256p. (J). (gr. 3-7). pap. 9.95 (978-0-7373-0514-2(2)) Lowell Hse. Juvenile.

Collay, Ryan & Dubrow, Joanne. Stuartship. Roark, Sydney, illus. 1998. 40p. (J). (gr. k-3). pap. 9.95 (978-0-9667394-0-4(X)) Flowerpress Bks. & Creative Hands.

Collins, Carolyn Strom & Eriksson, Christina Wyss. My Little House Crafts Book: 18 Projects from Laura Ingalls Wilder's. Collier, Mary, illus. 1998. (Little House Ser.). 64p. (J). (gr. 3 up). pap. 12.99 (978-0-06-446204-4(8), Harper Trophy) HarperCollins Pubs.

Conlon, Mara. Made by Me! Cards & Crafts for Mom & for Dad. 2006. (Pretty Simple Stuff Ser.). 32p. (J). (gr. 2-5). pap. 6.99 (978-0-8431-1850-6(4), Price Stern Sloan) Penguin Group (USA) Inc.

Conner, Wendy Simpson. The Children's Beading Book: Techniques for Little Beadlovers. 2002. (Beading Bks.: Vol. 8). (Illus.). 52p. (J). 11.95 (978-0-9645957-6-7(1)) Interstellar Publishing Co.

Cook Communications Staff. Spur of the Moment Crafts: Instant Crafts to Fit Your Class Needs. 2004. (Creative Bible Activities for Children Ser.). 96p. (J). (gr. 6-11). pap., pap. 16.99 (978-0-7814-4121-6(8), 0781441218) Cook, David C. Publishing Co.

Cook, Deanna F. Family Fun Craft. 2001. 256p. (J). 14.99 (978-0-7868-5323-6(9)) Disney Pr.

—Kids' Pumpkin Projects: Planting & Harvesting Fun. 2000. (Good Times Bks.: Vol. 20). (Illus.). 98p. (J). (gr. k-5). pap. 8.95 (978-1-885593-21-4(X), Williamson Bks.) Ideals Pubns.

Cool Stuff Teach Me to Quilt. 2005. 52p. 10.95 (978-1-57486-635-3(4)) Leisure Arts, Inc.

Coon, Cyndi, illus. Art That Pops! How to Make Wacky 3-D Creations That Jump, Spin, & Spring! 2006. 48p. (J). pap. (*978-0-439-81337-2(9)) Scholastic, Inc.

Cooper, Ilene. Jewish Holidays All Year Round: A Family Treasury. Savadier, Elivia, illus. 2002. 80p. (J). 19.95 (978-0-8109-0550-4(7)) Abrams, Harry N., Inc.

Cooper, John. Planet Earth & Art Activities. 2002. (Arty Facts Ser.). (Illus.). 48p. (J). (gr. 3-4). pap. (978-0-7787-1139-1(0)); lib. bdg. (978-0-7787-1111-7(0)) Crabtree Publishing Co.

Corba, Anna. Travel: Ready-to-Use Scrapbook Pages. 2005. (Instant Memories Ser.). (Illus.). 128p. pap. 14.95 incl. audio compact disk (978-1-4027-2643-9(0), Chapelle) Sterling Publishing Co., Inc.

Cordray, Laurie. Bible Crafts for All Seasons. 2005. (Godprints Bible Funstuff Ser.). (Illus.). 112p. (J). pap., pap. 16.99 (978-0-7814-4205-3(2), 0781442052) Cook, David C. Publishing Co.

Corwin, Judith Hoffman. Native American Crafts of California, the Great Basin, & the Southwest. 2002. (gr. 3-6). lib. bdg. 16.40 (978-0-613-59523-0(8)) Tandem Library Bks.

—Native American Crafts of the Northeast & Southeast. Corwin, Judith Hoffman, illus. 2003. (Native American Crafts Ser.). (Illus.). 48p. (J). (gr. 3-6). pap. 7.95 (978-0-531-15593-6(5), Watts, Franklin) Scholastic Library Publishing.

—Native American Crafts of the Northeast & Southeast. 2002. (gr. 3-6). lib. bdg. 16.40 (978-0-613-59524-7(6)) Tandem Library Bks.

—Native American Crafts of the Northwest Coast, the Arctic, & the Subarctic. 2002. (gr. 3-6). lib. bdg. 16.40 (978-0-613-59525-4(4)) Tandem Library Bks.

—Native American Crafts of the Plains & Plateau. 2002. (gr. 3-6). lib. bdg. 16.40 (978-0-613-59526-1(2)) Tandem Library Bks.

Craft Workshop, 4 bks. Incl. Fabric. Stoppleman, Monica & Crowe, Carol. lib. bdg. (978-0-86505-779-1(6)); Festival Decorations. Civardi, Anne & King, Penny. lib. bdg. (978-0-86505-780-7(X)); Models. Bliss, Helen & Thomson, Ruth. lib. bdg. (978-0-86505-778-4(8)); Paper. Bliss, Helen. lib. bdg. (978-0-86505-781-4(8)); 32p. (J). (gr. 3). (Illus.). 1998. (978-0-86505-776-0(1)); Set pap. (978-0-86505-786-9(9)) Crabtree Publishing Co.

Crafts. (Butterfly Bks.). (ARA., Illus.). 15p. (J). 11.95 (978-0-86685-616-4(1), LDL6161) International Bk. Ctr., Inc.

Craig, Rebecca. Dream Bedroom: Use Recycled Materials to Make Cool Crafts. 2007. (EcoCrafts Ser.). (Illus.). 48p. (J). (gr. 3-5). pap. 7.95 (*978-0-7534-5966-9(3), Kingfisher) Houghton Mifflin Co. Trade & Reference Div.

—EcoCrafts. 2007. (Illus.). 48p. (J). (*978-1-4287-3452-4(X), Kingfisher) Houghton Mifflin Co. Trade & Reference Div.

—Gorgeous Gifts. 2007. (EcoCrafts Ser.). (Illus.). 48p. (J). (gr. 3-5). pap. 7.95 (*978-0-7534-5967-6(1), Kingfisher) Houghton Mifflin Co. Trade & Reference Div.

Crea con Plastilina. (Coleccion Manualidades Divertidas).Tr. of Making Things with Plasticine. (SPA.). (J). (gr. k-3). 10.00 (978-84-342-1459-0(8)) Parramon Ediciones S.A. ESP. *Dist:* Distribuidora Norma, Inc., Lectorum Pubns., Inc.

Crea y Recicla.Tr. of Creating & Recycling. (SPA.). (J). (gr. k-3). 10.00 (978-84-342-1992-2(1)) Parramon Ediciones S.A. ESP. *Dist:* Distribuidora Norma, Inc., Lectorum Pubns., Inc.

Create a Critter. 48p. (gr. 2-3). 6.99 (978-0-7682-0152-9(7), FS83108) Schaffer, Frank Pubns.

Creative Bracelets. 2004. (Formula Fun Ser.). (Illus.). 48p. (J). (978-1-84229-877-0(1)) Top That! Publishing PLC.

Creative Crafts for Kids. 2006. 48p. pap. 3.99 (978-0-7666-2273-9(8)) Modern Publishing.

Creative Kids: Arts, Crafts, & More. 2004. pap. 15.99 (978-0-7439-3200-4(5)) Teacher Created Materials, Inc.

Cressy, Judith. What Can You Do with a Paper Bag? Hats, Wigs, Masks, Crowns, Helmets, & Headdresses Inspired by Works of Art from the Metropolitan Museum of Art. 2001. (gr. 3-6). lib. bdg. 24.55 (978-0-613-51097-4(6)) Tandem Library Bks.

Crexells, Cristina & Llimos Plomer, Anna. Plants & Seeds. 2003. (Let's Create! Ser.). (Illus.). 32p. (J). (gr. 2 up). lib. bdg. 23.33 (978-0-8368-3748-3(7)) Stevens, Gareth Inc.

Dakota, Heather. Tote-Ally You: Design Your Own Purse. 2005. (Illus.). 47p. (978-0-439-73671-8(4)) Scholastic, Inc.

Dalkin, Monika & Hollis, Mignonne. The Other Rope Book. 30p. (J). (gr. 2-6). 10.95 (978-0-9644524-0-4(5)) Jolly Geranium, Inc.

Dall, Mary Doerfler. Little Hands Create! Art & Activities for Kids Ages 3 to 6. Rakitin, Sarah, illus. 2004. (Williamson's Little Hands Book Ser.). (J). 20p. pap. 12.95 (978-0-8249-8664-3(4)); pap. 12.95 (978-1-885593-65-8(1)) Ideals Pubns. (Williamson Bks.).

Daning, Tom, ed. Fun-to-Make Crafts for Easter. 2004. (Illus.). 64p. (J). 15.95 (978-1-59078-340-5(9)); 7.95 (978-1-59078-365-8(4)) Boyds Mills Pr.

Danks, Fiona & Schofield, Jo. Nature's Playground: Activities, Crafts, & Games to Encourage Children to Get Outdoors. 2007. 192p. (J). (gr. 2-4). pap. 16.95 (*978-1-55652-723-4(3)) Chicago Review Pr., Inc.

Dann, Penny. My Big Rainy Day Activity Book. Smee, Nicola, illus. 2004. 96p. (J). act. bk. ed. 7.99 (978-1-85854-554-7(4)) Brimax Books Ltd. GBR. *Dist:* Byeway Bks.

David C. Cook. Noah's Park Children's Church Craft Book: Green Edition. 2002. (Children's Church Kits Ser.). (Illus.). 112p. (J). 14.99 (978-0-7814-3843-8(8), 0781438438) Cook, David C. Publishing Co.

Davis, Jane. Crochet: Fantastic Jewelry, Hats, Purses, Pillows & More. 2005. (Kids' Crafts Ser.). (Illus.). 112p. 19.95 (978-1-57990-477-7(7)) Lark Bks.

Dawson, Imogene. Clothes & Crafts in Aztec Times. 2000. (Clothes & Crafts in History Ser.). (Illus.). 32p. (J). (gr. 4 up). lib. bdg. 24.67 (978-0-8368-2735-4(X)) Stevens, Gareth Inc.

—Clothes & Crafts in the Middle Ages. 2000. (Clothes & Crafts in History Ser.). (Illus.). 32p. (J). (gr. 4 up). lib. bdg. 24.67 (978-0-8368-2736-1(8)) Stevens, Gareth Inc.

Day, Eileen. I'm Good at Building. 2003. (Heinemann Read & Learn Ser.). (Illus.). 24p. (J). pap. 5.25 (978-1-4034-3443-2(3)); lib. bdg. 18.50 (978-1-4034-0899-0(8)) Heinemann Library.

—I'm Good at Building. 2003. (gr. k-3). lib. bdg. 13.30 (978-0-613-70654-4(4)) Tandem Library Bks.

—I'm Good at Making Art. 2003. (Heinemann Read & Learn Ser.). (Illus.). 24p. (J). pap. 5.25 (978-1-4034-3446-3(8)); lib. bdg. 18.50 (978-1-4034-0898-3(X)) Heinemann Library.

—I'm Good at Making Art. 2003. (gr. k-3). lib. bdg. 13.30 (978-0-613-70657-5(9)) Tandem Library Bks.

Decora con Moviles. (Coleccion Manualidades Divertidas).Tr. of Decorating with Mobiles. (SPA.). (J). (gr. k-3). 10.00 (978-84-342-1846-8(1)) Parramon Ediciones S.A. ESP. *Dist:* Distribuidora Norma, Inc., Lectorum Pubns., Inc.

Denega, Danielle. Patchwork Crafts. Style Guide Staff, illus. 2006. (Raggedy Ann Ser.). 48p. (J). 3.99 (978-1-4169-1750-2(0), Simon Scribbles) Simon & Schuster Children's Publishing.

Dennen, Sue. Make Your Own Calendar 2001. Dennen, Sue, illus. 2000. (Illus.). 24p. (J). (gr. 1-5). pap. 6.95 (978-0-316-19210-1(4)) Little Brown & Co.

Desmoulins, Virginie. Girls' Best Book of Knitting, Sewing, & Embroidery. 2007. (Illus.). 112p. (J). (gr. 2-9). 19.95 (*978-1-58479-600-8(6)) Stewart, Tabori & Chang.

Dickinson, Gill. Crafts for Kids: Birthdays*Easter*Halloween*Christmas*Mother's Day*Thanksgiving*and More. 2006. (Illus.). 144p. (J). pap. 12.95 (978-0-600-61506-4(5), Hamlyn) Octopus Publishing Group GBR. *Dist:* Sterling Publishing Co., Inc.

—Festive Crafts for Kids: Fun, Easy-to-Follow Projects for 2 to 6 Year Olds. 2003. (Illus.). 144p. (J). 19.95 (978-0-600-60692-5(9), Hamlyn) Octopus Publishing Group GBR. *Dist:* Sterling Publishing Co., Inc.

DiSalle, Rachel & Warwick, Ellen. Junk Drawer Jewelry. Kurisu, Jane, illus. 2006. 40p. (978-1-55337-966-9(7)); (978-1-55337-965-2(9)) Kids Can Pr., Ltd.

Disfruta con Papel Mache. (Coleccion Manualidades Divertidas). (SPA.). (J). (gr. 10-13). 10.00 (978-84-342-1993-9(X)) Parramon Ediciones S.A. ESP. *Dist:* Distribuidora Norma, Inc., Lectorum Pubns., Inc.

Divierte Haciendo Titeres. (SPA.). (J). (gr. k-3). 10.00 (978-84-342-1461-3(X)) Parramon Ediciones S.A. ESP. *Dist:* Distribuidora Norma, Inc., Lectorum Pubns., Inc.

Dixon, Louisa. What Did I Do Today? 42p. (J). (gr. k-3). pap. 12.95 (978-0-9635811-0-5(4)) Rosemont, Ltd.

Dixon, Louisa & Boshers, Martha. What Did I Do Today? For Young Writers. 42p. (J). (gr. 3-7). pap. 12.95 (978-0-9635811-2-2(2)) Rosemont, Ltd.

Doherty, Patricia. Petal Perfect. 2007. 32p. (J). 17.95 (*978-1-59369-185-1(8), Pleasant Co.) American Girl Publishing, Inc.

Doinet, Mymi. Halloween: Creepy Crawly, Hairy Scary Things to Do. Chaud, Benjamin, illus. 2002. 32p. (J). pap., act. bk. ed. 5.95 (978-0-8118-3279-3(1)) Chronicle Bks. LLC.

Doney, Meryl. Crafts from Many Cultures, 6 bks. Incl. Festivals. lib. bdg. 23.33 (978-0-8368-4043-8(7)); Masks. lib. bdg. 23.33 (978-0-8368-4044-5(5)); Musical Instruments. lib. bdg. 23.33 (978-0-8368-4045-2(3)); Paper Crafts. lib. bdg. 23.33 (978-0-8368-4046-9(1)); Puppets. lib. bdg. 23.33 (978-0-8368-4047-6(X)); Toys. lib. bdg. 23.33 (978-0-8368-4048-3(8)); 32p. (J). (gr. 3 up). (Illus.). 2004. Set lib. bdg. 139.98 (978-0-8368-4042-1(9)) Stevens, Gareth Inc.

—Paper Crafts. 2004. (Crafts from Many Cultures Ser.). (Illus.). 32p. (J). (gr. 3 up). lib. bdg. 23.33 (978-0-8368-4046-9(1)) Stevens, Gareth Inc.

Don't Prick Me, You Little Stick! Your Personal Needles-at-a-Glance Case. 2001. 14p. 9.95 (978-0-9709866-1-0(0)) Leihuna Enterprises.

Dorling Kindersley Publishing Staff & Bull, Jane. The Crafty Art Book. 2004. (Dk Eyewitness Books Ser.). (Illus.). 48p. (J). 12.99 (978-0-7566-0550-6(4)) Dorling Kindersley Publishing, Inc.

—First Craft Activity Book. 2006. (Illus.). 48p. (J). 9.99 (978-0-7566-2579-5(3)) Dorling Kindersley Publishing, Inc.

—The Halloween Book: 50 Creepy Crafts for a Hair-Raising Halloween. Crawford, Andy, photos by. 2000. (Illus.). 48p. (J). (gr. 4-7). 12.95 (978-0-7894-6655-6(4)) Dorling Kindersley Publishing, Inc.

Douglas, Vincent & School Specialty Publishing Staff. Holiday & Everyday Projects. 2003. (Crafty Kids Ser.). (Illus.). 48p. (J). (gr. k-3). 12.95 (978-1-57768-528-9(8), Waterbird Bks.) School Specialty Publishing.

—Holiday & Everyday Projects. Crafty Kids, ed. 2003. (Crafty Kids Ser.). (Illus.). 48p. (J). (gr. k-3). 6.95 (978-0-7696-3153-0(3), Waterbird Bks.) School Specialty Publishing.

—Music Makers & Toys. 2003. (Crafty Kids Ser.). (Illus.). 48p. (J). (gr. k-3). 12.95 (978-1-57768-518-0(0), Waterbird Bks.) School Specialty Publishing.

—Music Makers & Toys. Crafty Kids, ed. 2003. (Crafty Kids Ser.). (Illus.). 48p. (J). (gr. k-3). 6.95 (978-0-7696-3151-6(7), Waterbird Bks.) School Specialty Publishing.

—Nature's Treasures Craft Kit. 2004. (Craft Kits Ser.). (Illus.). 52p. (J). pap. 16.95 (978-1-58845-628-1(5), Brighter Child) School Specialty Publishing.

—Paper & Paint. 2003. (Crafty Kids Ser.). (Illus.). 48p. (J). (gr. k-3). 12.95 (978-1-57768-527-2(X), Waterbird Bks.) School Specialty Publishing.

—Sculpting & Drama. 2003. (Crafty Kids Ser.). (Illus.). 48p. (J). (gr. k-3). 12.95 (978-1-57768-517-3(2), Waterbird Bks.) School Specialty Publishing.

—Sculpting & Drama. Crafty Kids, ed. 2003. (Crafty Kids Ser.). (Illus.). 48p. (J). (gr. k-3). pap. 6.95 (978-0-7696-3150-9(9), Waterbird Bks.) School Specialty Publishing.

Dower, Laura. Starring Me & You Diary. Sundberg and Associates Staff, illus. 2001. 64p. (J). (gr. 3-6). pap. 9.95 (978-0-439-26217-0(8)) Scholastic, Inc.

Downs, Dorothy. Patchwork: Seminole & Miccosukee Art & Activities. 2005. (Illus.). 55p. (J). (gr. 3-7). pap. 9.95 (978-1-56164-332-5(7)) Pineapple Pr., Inc.

Doyle, Richard. Twelve Fairyland Bookmarks. 2004. (Dover Little Activity Bks.). (Illus.). 6p. (J). (gr. k). pap. 1.50 (978-0-486-43021-8(9)) Dover Pubns., Inc.

Drake, David. Crickets Activities & Crafts. 2002. (Cricket of Dew Drop Dell Ser.). (Illus.). 36p. (J). 3.49 (978-1-885631-64-0(2), Family Of Man Pr., The) Hutchison, G.F. Pr.

Drinkard, Lawson. Hiding in a Fort. 1999. (J). (978-0-606-17088-8(X)) Tandem Library Bks.

Eckold, David. Robot Challenge Kit. 2002. (Illus.). 1p. (J). 29.99 (978-0-7894-8888-6(4)) Dorling Kindersley Publishing, Inc.

Eder, Enelle. Create & Take Bible Crafts: Exploring Nature. 2004. (Create & Take Bible Crafts). 96p. (J). (gr. k-6). pap. 11.95 (978-1-58411-005-7(8)) Rainbow Pubs. & Legacy Pr.

—Create & Take Bible Crafts: Old Testament Heroes. 2004. 96p. (J). (gr. k-6). pap. 11.95 (978-1-58411-006-4(6)) Rainbow Pubs. & Legacy Pr.

—Create & Take Bible Crafts: Special Days. 2004. 96p. (J). (gr. k-6). pap. 11.95 (978-1-58411-008-8(2)) Rainbow Pubs. & Legacy Pr.

Edwards, Diane. Norwegian Rosemaling for Young People. 2003. (Illus.). 40p. 10.95 (978-0-9674583-4-2(X), 1) Rosemaling & Crafts.

Eggleton, Jill. Kids Say: Individual Title, 6 Packs. Storey, Jim, illus. (Sails Literacy Ser.). 16p. (gr. 2-3). 27.00 (978-0-7578-0704-6(6)) Rigby Education.

Elliot, Marion. 100 Fantastic Things to Do. 2004. (Illus.). 192p. pap. 24.99 (978-1-84476-016-9(2), Southwater) Anness Publishing GBR. *Dist:* National Bk. Network.

Elton, Candice & Elton, Richard. Every Kid Needs Secret Jewelry. 2005. (Illus.). 48p. (J). spiral bd. 19.95 (978-1-58685-707-3(X)) Gibbs Smith, Publisher.

Elton, Richard & Elton, Candice. Every Kid Needs a Rubber Band Launcher. 2007. (J). (*978-1-4236-0268-2(4)) Gibbs Smith, Publisher.

Equipo Staff. Crea con Huevos. (Coleccion Manualidades Divertidas).Tr. of Making Things with Eggs. (SPA.). 76p. (J). (gr. k-3). 10.00 (978-84-342-1899-4(2)) Parramon Ediciones S.A. ESP. *Dist:* Distribuidora Norma, Inc., Lectorum Pubns., Inc.

Eriksson, Christina Wyss & Collins, Carolyn Strom. Inside the Secret Garden: A Treasury of Crafts, Recipes, & Activities. Collier, Mary & Tudor, Tasha, illus. 2002. 136p. (J). (gr. 3 up). 24.99 (978-0-06-027922-6(2)) HarperCollins Pubs.

Erlbach, Arlene & Erlbach, Herbert. Mother's Day Crafts. 2005. (Fun Holiday Crafts Kids Can Do Ser.). (Illus.). 32p. (J). lib. bdg. 22.60 (978-0-7660-2348-2(6), Enslow Elementary) Enslow Pubs., Inc.

—Thanksgiving Day Crafts. 2005. (Fun Holiday Crafts Kids Can Do Ser.). 32p. (J). lib. bdg. 22.60 (978-0-7660-2345-1(1), Enslow Elementary) Enslow Pubs., Inc.

—Valentine's Day Crafts. 2004. (Fun Holiday Crafts Kids Can Do Ser.). (Illus.). 32p. (J). lib. bdg. 22.60 (978-0-7660-2237-9(4)) Enslow Pubs., Inc.

Evans, Joy & Moore, Jo Ellen. Paper Tube Zoo. Evans, Joy, illus. 2000. (Craft Book Ser.). (Illus.). 80p. (J). (gr. k-3). pap., tchr. ed. 9.99 (978-1-55799-780-7(2), EMC 771) Evan-Moor Educational Pubs.

Evertson, Sandra. Babies: Ready-to-Use Scrapbook Pages. 2005. (Instant Memories Ser.). (Illus.). 128p. pap. 14.95 incl. audio compact disk (978-1-4027-2379-7(2), Chapelle) Sterling Publishing Co., Inc.

Fab Fingers. 2004. (Formula Fun Ser.). (Illus.). 48p. (J). (978-1-84229-581-6(0)) Top That! Publishing PLC.

Farm Fun Crafts for Kids. 16.99 (978-0-8307-2990-6(9), Gospel Light) Gospel Light Pubns.

Faughn, Jackie. More Fun Around the World. 1998. 48p. (ps). pap. 6.99 (978-1-56309-260-2(3) , N987103) New Hope Pubs.

Fiano, Kim Sullivan, compiled by. Kingdom Crafts for Kids: Includes Projects for Children from Preschool to Sixth Grade: Colorful Projects with a Royal Castle Theme, Reproducible Awards & Certificates, Bible Memory Verse Coloring Posters. 1999. pap. 17.00 (978-0-8307-2184-9(3)) Gospel Light Pubns.

Filian, Cathie & Piacenza, Steve. Creative Juice (DIY) 50 Re-Crafting Projects to Make with Recycled Stuff. 2007. (Illus.). 128p. pap. 14.95 (***978-1-60059-148-8(5)***) Lark Bks.

Fisscher, Tiny. The Four Princesses. de Wolf, Barbara, illus. 2001. 64p. (J). (gr. k-7). 18.95 (978-1-929132-19-5(0)) Kane/Miller Bk. Pubs., Inc.

Fittes, Francine. Craft Lacing Madness. 2006. (Illus.). 48p. pap. 6.99 (978-0-7153-2480-6(2)) F & W Pubns., Inc.

Flanagan, Jennifer. Fun with Gel Markers. 2002. (Illus.). 32p. (J). (978-0-439-33624-6(4)) Scholastic, Inc.

Flanders, Aaron. Balloon Animals. 2003. 128p. pap. 8.95 (978-0-07-143742-4(8)) McGraw-Hill Cos., The.

—Balloon Cartoons & Other Favorites. 2003. 128p. pap. 8.95 (978-0-07-143744-8(4)) McGraw-Hill Cos., The.

—Balloon Hats & Accessories. 2003. 128p. pap. 8.95 (978-0-07-143745-5(2)) McGraw-Hill Cos., The.

Flynn, Nancy. Jeaneology: Crafty Ways to Reinvent Your Old Blues. Baer-Block, Roxy, illus. 2007. 120p. (J). spiral bd. 14.95 (***978-0-9772660-3-6(6)*** , Zest Bks.) Orange Avenue Publishing.

For Fun!, 21 vols. 2006. 48p. (YA). (gr. 3-5). 474.60 (978-0-7565-1867-7(9)) Compass Point Bks.

Forte, Imogene. Arts & Crafts. 2004. (Fun Things to Make & Do Ser.). (Illus.). 80p. (J). per. 9.95 (978-0-86530-613-4(3)) Incentive Pubns., Inc.

Foster, Juliana. The Girls' Book: How to Be the Best at Everything. Enright, Amanda, illus. 2007. (Girls' Book Ser.). 128p. (J). (gr. 4-7). 9.99 (***978-0-545-01629-2(0)*** , Scholastic Pr.) Scholastic, Inc.

Fox, Susan & Phillips, Karen. Dial with Style: Decorate Your Cell Phone. 2005. (Illus.). 38p. (J). (gr. 6 up). 12.95 (978-1-57054-875-8(7)) Klutz.

Francis, Suzanne. How to Make an Egg Swim, Grow Mold, Eat "Ants," & Other Ways to Play with Your Food. 2004. (How to Survive Anything Club Ser.). (Illus.). 80p. (J). (978-0-439-57909-4(0)) Scholastic, Inc.

Freixenet, A. Adorna con Mosaico. (Coleccion Manualidades Divertidas).Tr. of Decorate with Mosaics. (SPA.). 88p. (J). (gr. k-3). 10.00 (978-84-342-1901-4(8)) Parramon Ediciones S.A. ESP. *Dist:* Distribuidora Norma, Inc., Lectorum Pubns., Inc.

Freixenet, Anna. Creating with Mosaics. 2000. (Crafts for All Seasons Ser.). (Illus.). 32p. (J). (gr. 3-8). lib. bdg. 23.70 (978-1-56711-440-9(7) , Blackbirch Pr., Inc.) Thomson Gale.

French, Cathy. Haz un movil de animales & Make an Animal Mobile. 2005. spiral bd. 66.00 (***978-1-4108-5619-7(4)***) Benchmark Education Co.

Friedman, Debra & Kurisu, Jane. Picture This: Fun Photography & Crafts. 2004. (Kids Can Do It Ser.). (Illus.). 40p. (J). (gr. 4-6). (978-1-55337-047-5(3)); (978-1-55337-046-8(5)) Kids Can Pr., Ltd.

Fun for Little Hands Series, 7 bks., Set. 2003. (Illus.). (J). 21.33 (978-0-929371-92-4(5)) Kar-Ben Publishing.

Fun Projects for Kids. Date not set. (Get Crafty Ser.). (Illus.). 48p. (J). pap. 4.98 (978-0-7525-8409-6(X)) Parragon, Inc.

Fun Things to Make & Do: Individual Title Six-Packs. (Discovery World Ser.). 16p. (gr. 1-2). 28.00 (978-0-7635-8458-0(4)) Rigby Education.

Fun with Plaster: Individual Title Six-Packs. (Rigby Focus Ser.). 16p. (gr. 1 up). 28.00 (978-0-7578-5324-1(2)); 30.00 (978-0-7578-5556-6(3)) Rigby Education.

Furstinger, Nancy. Creative Crafts for Critters. Béha, Philippe, illus. 2001. 48p. (J). (gr. 2-7). pap. 8.95 (978-0-7737-6135-3(7)) Stoddart Kids CAN. *Dist:* Fitzhenry & Whiteside, Ltd.

—Creative Crafts for Critters. 2001. (Hello Reader! Ser.). (Illus.). (J). (978-0-606-21128-4(4)) Tandem Library Bks.

Gabriel, Faith K. Nifty Thrifty Animal Crafts. 2007. (Nifty Thrifty Crafts for Kids Ser.). (Illus.). 32p. (J). lib. bdg. 22.60 (978-0-7660-2779-4(1) , Enslow Elementary) Enslow Pubs., Inc.

Gakken Co. Ltd. Editors & Time-Life Books Editors. Things to Do. 1999. (Illus.). 88p. (J). (gr. 1-4). 14.95 (978-0-8094-4897-5(1)) Time-Life, Inc.

Gallivan, Marion F. Fun for Kids: An Index to Children's Craft Books, Vol. III. 2002. (Illus.). 320p. 54.50 (978-0-8108-4256-4(4)) Scarecrow Pr., Inc.

Galvani, Anouchka. Craft Lacing Mania. 2006. (Illus.). 48p. pap. 6.99 (978-0-7153-2479-0(9)) F & W Pubns., Inc.

Galvin, Jennifer. My Catholic Lent & Easter. 2003. 32p. act. bk. ed. 6.95 (978-0-8091-6706-7(9) , 6706-9) Paulist Pr.

Gamache, Dale & Gamache, Robin. La Clase Divertida (The FUN Class) Cuaderno de Actividades, Level 1. 1999. (ENG & SPA., Illus.). (J). (gr. k-6). pap., wbk. ed. 15.00 (978-0-9710190-1-0(0)) La Clase Divertida, Inc.

Ganeri, Anita & Wright, France. 2005. (Illus.). 32p. (J). (978-1-932889-91-8(4)) Sea-To-Sea Pubns.

—Mexico. 2005. (Illus.). 32p. (J). (gr. 4-7). lib. bdg. 27.10 (978-1-932889-94-9(9)) Sea-To-Sea Pubns.

Gessat, Audrey. Crafts from Salt Dough. 2002. (Step by Step Ser.). (Illus.). 32p. (J). (gr. 2-3). lib. bdg. 22.60 (978-0-7368-1475-1(2) , Bridgestone Bks.) Capstone Pr., Inc.

Gibbons, Gail. From Sheep to Sweater. 2005. (J). (978-0-8234-1885-5(5)) Holiday Hse., Inc.

Gibson, R. Papier Mache. 2000. (Kid Kits Ser.). (Illus.). 23p. (J). (gr. 3-7). 14.95 (978-1-58086-280-6(2)) EDC Publishing.

—Recortar y Pegar. 2004. Tr. of I Can Cut & Stick. (SPA., Illus.). 32p. (J). lib. bdg. 12.95 (978-1-58086-361-2(2)) EDC Publishing.

—What Shall I Make? 2004. (What Shall I Do Today? Ser.). 32p. (J). pap. 7.95 (978-0-7945-0376-5(4)); lib. bdg. 15.95 (978-1-58086-565-4(8)) EDC Publishing.

Gibson, R. & Watt, F. Summer Activities. 2004. (Illus.). 32p. (J). pap., act. bk. ed: 6.95 (978-0-7945-0398-7(5)) EDC Publishing.

Gibson, Ray. Big Book of Things to Do: Combined Volume. Stitt, Sue, illus. 2004. (What Shall I Do Today? Ser.). 192p. (J). pap. 18.95 (978-0-7945-0442-7(6) , Usborne) EDC Publishing.

—Ideas para Navidad. 2004. Tr. of Christmas Activities. (ENG & SPA., Illus.). 34p. (J). (ps-3). pap. 8.95 (978-0-7460-3899-4(2)) EDC Publishing.

—Recortar y Pegar. 2004. Tr. of I Can Cut & Stick. (SPA., Illus.). 32p. (J). pap. 4.95 (978-0-7460-4536-7(0)) EDC Publishing.

—What Shall I Do Today: Combined Volume. Barlow, Amanda, illus. rev. ed. 2004. (What Shall I Do Today? Ser.). 96p. (J). pap. 11.95 (978-0-7945-0706-0(9) , Usborne) EDC Publishing.

Gilbert, LaBritta. 50 Great Make-It, Take-It Projects. 2002. 80p. (J). (gr. k-5). pap. 18.95 (978-1-57950-070-2(6) , Upstart Bks.) Highsmith Inc.

Gilpin, R. Fairy Things to Make & Do. 2004. (Illus.). 32p. (J). pap., act. bk. ed. 6.95 (978-0-7945-0576-9(7)) EDC Publishing.

Gilpin, Rebecca. Monster Things to Make & Do. Harrison, Erica Et Al, illus. 2006. 32p. (J). pap. 6.99 (978-0-7945-1354-2(9) , Usborne) EDC Publishing.

—Things to Make for Dads. MEREDITH SAMANTHA ET AL, illus. 2006. 32p. (J). pap. 8.99 (978-0-7945-1272-9(0) , Usborne) EDC Publishing.

Gilpin, Rebecca. Valentine Things to Make & Do. 2006. (Usborne Activities Ser.). (Illus.). 31p. (J). (***978-0-439-78705-5(X)***) Scholastic, Inc.

Girlfriends' Get-Together Craft Book. 2007. 48p. (J). (gr. 2-6). pap. 7.95 (***978-0-7613-9465-5(6)*** , First Avenue Editions) Lerner Publishing Group.

Gnojewski, Carol. African-American Crafts Kids Can Do! 2006. (Multicultural Crafts Kids Can Do! Ser.). (Illus.). 32p. (J). lib. bdg. 22.60 (978-0-7660-2457-1(1) , Enslow Elementary) Enslow Pubs., Inc.

—American Indian Crafts Kids Can Do! 2006. (Multicultural Crafts Kids Can Do! Ser.). (Illus.). 32p. (J). lib. bdg. 22.60 (978-0-7660-2458-8(X) , Enslow Elementary) Enslow Pubs., Inc.

—Cinco de Mayo Crafts. 2005. (Fun Holiday Crafts Kids Can Do Ser.). (Illus.). 32p. (J). lib. bdg. 22.60 (978-0-7660-2344-4(3) , Enslow Elementary) Enslow Pubs., Inc.

—Earth Day Crafts. 2005. (Fun Holiday Crafts Kids Can Do Ser.). (Illus.). 32p. (J). lib. bdg. 22.60 (978-0-7660-2346-8(X) , Enslow Elementary) Enslow Pubs., Inc.

—Kwanzaa Crafts. 2004. (Fun Holiday Crafts Kids Can Do Ser.). (Illus.). 32p. (J). lib. bdg. 22.60 (978-0-7660-2203-4(X)) Enslow Pubs., Inc.

—St. Patrick's Day Crafts. 2004. (Fun Holiday Crafts Kids Can Do Ser.). (Illus.). 32p. (J). lib. bdg. 22.60 (978-0-7660-2256-0(0)) Enslow Pubs., Inc.

Golden Books Staff. Toy Story 2 - Woody's Challenge: Paint Box Book. 1999. (Disney Ser.). (Illus.). 32p. (J). (ps-3). pap. 3.99 (978-0-307-09239-7(9) , Golden Bks.) Random Hse. Children's Bks.

Goldie, Sonia. My Favorite Nature Book: Animals in Their Homes: Includes an Activity Kit with Posters, Stickers & Puzzles. Weiss, Anne & Estellon, Pascale, illus. 2006. 24p. 9.95 (978-1-57990-920-8(5)) Lark Bks.

Golosi, Rosanne. Best Friends Forever! Martini, Angela, illus. 2005. 64p. (J). (***978-0-439-80072-3(2)***) Scholastic, Inc.

Goodings, Christina. Look What I Made! 2001. (Illus.). 48p. (J). 16.99 (978-0-7459-4473-9(6) , Lion) Lion Hudson plc GBR. *Dist:* Independent Pubs. Group.

—Whizzy Bizzy Christmas. 2004. (Illus.). 32p. (J). pap. 5.50 (978-0-7459-4888-1(X)) Lion Hudson plc GBR. *Dist:* Independent Pubs. Group.

Goodman, Polly. Space & Art Activities. 2002. (Arty Facts Ser.). (Illus.). 48p. (J). (gr. 3-4). pap. (978-0-7787-1140-7(4)); lib. bdg. (978-0-7787-1112-4(9)) Crabtree Publishing Co.

—Space & Art Activities. 2002. (ps-2). lib. bdg. 17.60 (978-0-613-57136-4(3)) Tandem Library Bks.

Gordon. 52 Series: Creative Craft Projects. 2006. (Illus.). 6.95 (978-0-8118-5103-9(6)) Chronicle Bks. LLC.

Gordon, Lynn. The Super Duper Art & Craft Book Activity Book. Johnson, Karen & Synarski, Susan, illus. 2005. 112p. (J). 12.95 (978-0-8118-5007-0(2)) Chronicle Bks. LLC.

—52 Fun after School Activities. Johnson, Karen, illus. 2002. (gr. 4-7). 6.95 (978-0-8118-3232-8(5)) Chronicle Bks. LLC.

Gould, Roberta. The Kid's Book of Incredibly Fun Crafts. Martin Jourdenais, Norma Jean, illus. 2004. (Williamson's Kids Can! Ser.). 128p. (J). pap. 14.95 (978-1-885593-85-6(6) , Williamson Bks.) Ideals Pubns.

—The Kids' Multicultural Craft Book: 50 Creative Activities from 30 Countries. Jourdenais, Norma Jean, illus. 2004. (Williamson Multicultural Kids Can! Book Ser.). 128p. (J). pap. 12.95 (978-1-885593-91-7(0) , Williamson Bks.) Ideals Pubns.

—Kidtopia: 'Round the Country & Back Through Time in 60 Projects. 2000. (gr. 3-6). lib. bdg. 23.40 (978-0-613-85262-3(1)) Tandem Library Bks.

—Kidtopia: 'Round the Country & Back Through Time in 60 Projects. 2004. (Illus.). 160p. (gr. 1-7). 13.95 (978-1-58246-026-0(4) , Tricycle Pr.) Ten Speed Pr.

Grafton, Carol Belanger, ed. Victorian Roses Stickers. 2004. (Illus.). 4p. pap. 5.95 (978-0-486-43382-0(X)) Dover Pubns., Inc.

Green, Marilyn. Beaded Bobby Pins. 1999. (Illus.). 48p. (YA). (gr. 4-7). 14.95 (978-1-57054-401-9(8)) Klutz.

Green, Marilyn & Hutnick, Theresa, eds. Picture Tags. 2004. (Illus.). 18p. (J). 14.95 (978-1-57054-855-0(2)) Klutz.

Grolier Educational Staff, contrib. by. Crafts for Kids, 16 vols. 2003. (Illus.). (J). (978-0-7172-5760-7(6) , Grolier) Scholastic Library Publishing.

Group Publishing Staff. I Can Make It Myself: Bible Story Crafts for Preschoolers. 2004. (Illus.). 95p. pap. 17.99 (978-0-7644-2225-6(1) , Flagship Church Resources) Group Publishing, Inc.

Grover, Jill Williams. Tween Friends: Ideas & Projects for Room Decorating. 2006. (Illus.). 128p. (J). pap. (978-1-4027-2364-3(4)) Sterling Publishing Co., Inc.

Gryski, Camilla. Camilla Gryski's Cat's Cradle: A Book of String Games. Sankey, Tom, illus. 2001. (String Games Ser.). 32p. (J). (gr. 4-6). (978-1-55337-090-1(2)) Kids Can Pr., Ltd.

Guhin, Paula. Can We Eat the Art? Incredible Edibles & Art You Can't Eat. Schimmell, David, illus. 2001. 80p. (J). (gr. k-8). pap. 9.95 (978-0-86530-471-0(8) , IP #280-0) Incentive Pubns., Inc.

Haab, Rachel. Fairies: Petal People You Make Yourself. 2001. (Illus.). 40p. (J). spiral bd. 16.95 (978-1-57054-649-5(5)) Klutz.

—Hadas. Esteve, Laura, tr. Esparza, Bob, photos by. 2005. (SPA., Illus.). 38p. (J). spiral bd. 20.95 (978-987-1078-27-1(7)) Klutz Latino MEX. *Dist:* Independent Pubs. Group.

Haab, Sherri. Unas Divertidas. 2005. (SPA., Illus.). 58p. (J). (gr. 4-7). spiral bd. 23.95 (978-968-5528-12-2(8)) Klutz Latino MEX. *Dist:* Independent Pubs. Group.

—Hip Handbag Bk. Edwards, Nina, illus. 2004. 96p. (YA). (gr. 5-8). pap. 9.95 (978-0-8230-2263-2(3)) Watson-Guptill Pubns., Inc.

Haab, Sherri & Haab, Michelle. Dangles & Bangles: 25 Funky Accessories to Make & Wear. Pollak, Barbara, illus. 2005. 96p. (J). pap. 9.95 (978-0-8230-0064-7(8)) Watson-Guptill Pubns., Inc.

Haab, Sherri & Klutz Press Staff. The Shrinky Dinks Book. 1999. (Illus.). 38p. (J). (gr. 4-7). 12.95 (978-1-57054-407-1(7) , 51456384) Klutz.

Haab, Sherri & Torres, Laura. Wire-O-Mania. 2000. (Illus.). 60p. (J). (gr. 4-7). spiral bd. 12.95 (978-1-57054-522-1(7)) Klutz.

Haab, Sherri, et al. Capsters. 2005. (Illus.). 24p. (J). spiral bd. 14.95 (978-1-57054-205-3(8)) Klutz.

Haglund, Jill. Scrapbooking for Kids, Vol. 1. Arquette, Kerry, ed. Boshell, Kristine, illus. Booth, Herb, photos by. lt. ed. 1999. 128p. (J). (gr. 1-5). pap. 19.95 (978-1-891898-01-3(9)) Tweety Jill Pubns.

Haley, Amanda, illus. Doodle Studio: More Than 100 Easy-to-Draw Doodles to Decorate Stickers, Shrink Film, Magnets & More! 2002. (American Girl Library). 96p. 14.95 (978-1-58485-507-1(X)) American Girl Publishing, Inc.

Haley, Gail E., illus. Costumes for Plays & Playing. 2002. 134p. (J). 19.95 (978-1-887905-62-6(6)) Parkway Pubs., Inc.

Halls, Kelly Milner. Look What You Can Make with Craft Sticks. 2001. (gr. 3-6). lib. bdg. 14.10 (978-0-613-59324-3(3)) Tandem Library Bks.

—Look What You Can Make with Craft Sticks: Over 80 Pictured Crafts & Dozens of Other Ideas. Schneider, Hank, photos by. 2003. (Illus.). 48p. (YA). (ps-7). pap. 5.95 (978-1-56397-997-2(7)) Boyds Mills Pr.

—Look What You Can Make with Plastic-Foam Trays. 2003. (gr. 3-6). lib. bdg. 14.10 (978-0-613-59329-8(4)) Tandem Library Bks.

Halls, Kelly Milner, ed. Look What You Can Make with Plastic-Foam Trays: Over 90 Pictured Crafts & Dozens of More Ideas. 2003. (Illus.). 48p. (J). pap. 5.95 (978-1-59078-078-7(7)) Boyds Mills Pr.

Hampton, Ronald E. Mini-Lathe Magic: Big Projects from a Small Lathe. 2002. (Schiffer Book for Woodworkers Ser.). (Illus.). 64p. (gr. 10-13). pap. 14.95 (978-0-7643-1614-2(1)) Schiffer Publishing, Ltd.

Hands on Crafts for Kids Staff. 20-Minute Crafts. 2002. (Illus.). 128p. (gr. 2-7). pap. 12.95 (978-1-4027-0068-2(7)) Sterling Publishing Co., Inc.

Hankin, Rosie. Crafty Kids: Fun Projects for You & Your Toddler. 2006. (Illus.). 64p. (J). pap. 8.99 (978-0-7641-3542-2(2)) Barron's Educational Series, Inc.

Hannah, Sue. Crafty Concoctions: 101 Craft Supply Recipes. 2003. (Illus.). xi, 140p. (J). 7.95 (978-0-88166-462-1(6)) Meadowbrook Pr.

Hantman, Clea. Hey, Day! 2001. 74.75 (978-0-06-000169-8(0)) HarperCollins Pubs.

—I Wanna Make Gifts. Houshyar, Azadeh, illus. 2006. 144p. (J). pap. 9.99 (978-0-689-87464-2(2) , Aladdin) Simon & Schuster Children's Publishing.

—I Wanna Re-Do My Room. Houshyar, Azadeh, illus. 2006. 144p. (J). pap. 9.99 (978-0-689-87463-5(4) , Aladdin) Simon & Schuster Children's Publishing.

Hantman, Clea & Houshyar, Azadeh. I Wanna Make Jewels, Shoes, & More! 2007. (J). pap. 9.99 (978-0-689-87465-9(0) , Aladdin) Simon & Schuster Children's Publishing.

Harry, Cindy Groom. Looney Lanyard Lace. 2000. (Funtastic Kits Ser.). (Illus.). 48p. (J). 12.98 (978-0-7853-3979-3(5)) Publications International, Ltd.

Hart, Marj. Christian Crafts: Simple Paper Projects. Armbrust, Janet, illus. 2001. 64p. (J). (ps-4). pap. 8.99 (978-0-7647-0588-5(1)) School Specialty Publishing.

Hartman, Sarah. Asian-American Crafts Kids Can Do! 2006. (Multicultural Crafts Kids Can Do! Ser.). (Illus.). 32p. (J). lib. bdg. 22.60 (978-0-7660-2455-7(5) , Enslow Elementary) Enslow Pubs., Inc.

—Middle Eastern Crafts Kids Can Do! 2006. (Multicultural Crafts Kids Can Do! Ser.). (Illus.). 32p. (J). lib. bdg. 22.60 (978-0-7660-2456-4(3) , Enslow Elementary) Enslow Pubs., Inc.

Haslam, Andrew. Arctic Peoples: The Hands-on Approach to History. 2001. (gr. 3-6). lib. bdg. 16.40 (978-0-613-43299-3(1)) Tandem Library Bks.

Hauser, Elizabeth Ingrid. Princess Crafts. Perrett, Lisa, illus. 2005. 96p. pap. 9.95 (978-1-4027-2225-7(7)) Sterling Publishing Co., Inc.

Hauser, Jill Frankel. Easy Art Fun! Do-It-Yourself Crafts for Beginning Readers. Hauser, Savlan, illus. 2001. (Little Hands Read-and-Do Book Ser.). 112p. (J). (ps-3). pap. 12.95 (978-1-885593-62-7(7) , Williamson Bks.) Ideals Pubns.

—Gizmos & Gadgets: Creating Science Contraptions That Work (And Knowing Why) Kline, Michael P., illus. 1999. (Kids Can Bks.). 144p. (J). (gr. 2-9). pap. 12.95 (978-1-885593-26-9(0) , Williamson Bks.) Ideals Pubns.

—Little Hands Celebrate America! Learning about the U.S.A Through Crafts & Activities. 2004. (Williamson's Little Hands Book Ser.). (Illus.). 128p. (J). 12.95 (978-1-885593-93-1(7) , Williamson Bks.) Ideals Pubns.

Hayden, Kate. Les Indiens des Plaines. 2000. (Come & Discover My World Ser.). (FRE., Illus.). 32p. (J). pap. 7.95 (978-1-58728-194-5(5) , Two Can Publishing) T&N Children's Publishing.

Healton, Sarah H. & Whiteside, Kay H. Look What I Made! Creative Crafts. Date not set. (J). (gr. 1-3). 16.95 (978-0-07-027701-4(X) , Teach Yourself) McGraw-Hill Trade.

Hedderwick, Mairi. Katie Morag's Rainy Day Book. 2000. (Illus.). 32p. (J). (gr. k-2). 17.95 (978-0-370-32550-7(8)) Random Hse. GBR. *Dist:* Trafalgar Square Publishing.

Heller, D. M. Let's Make a Fish with Everyday Materials. 2006. (Illus.). 24p. (J). lib. bdg. (978-1-4042-3062-0(9)) Rosen Publishing Group, Inc., The.

—Let's Make a Lion with Everyday Materials. 2006. (Illus.). 24p. (J). (978-1-4042-3060-6(2)) Rosen Publishing Group, Inc., The.

—Let's Make a Monkey with Everyday Materials. 2006. (Illus.). 24p. (J). (978-1-4042-3061-3(0)) Rosen Publishing Group, Inc., The.

—Let's Make an Owl with Everyday Materials. 2006. (Illus.). 24p. (J). lib. bdg. (978-1-4042-3063-7(7)) Rosen Publishing Group, Inc., The.

Hendry, Linda. Cat Crafts. Hendry, Linda, illus. unabr. ed. 2004. (Kids Can Do It Ser.). (Illus.). 134p. (J). (gr. 4-6). (978-1-55074-921-2(8)) Kids Can Pr., Ltd.

—Cat Crafts. unabr. ed. 2004. (Kids Can Do It Ser.). (Illus.). 330p. (J). (gr. 4-6). (978-1-55074-964-9(1)) Kids Can Pr., Ltd.

—Dog Crafts. Hendry, Linda, illus. 2004. (Kids Can Do It Ser.). (Illus.). 40p. (J). (gr. 4-6). (978-1-55074-960-1(9)); (978-1-55074-962-5(5)) Kids Can Pr., Ltd.

—Making Gift Bags. 1999. (gr. 3-6). lib. bdg. 14.10 (978-0-613-21953-2(8)) Tandem Library Bks.

—Making Gift Boxes. 1999. (Kids Can Do It Ser.). (Illus.). 136p. (J). (gr. 4-6). (978-1-55074-503-0(4)) Kids Can Pr., Ltd.

—Making Picture Frames. 1999. (gr. 3-6). lib. bdg. 14.10 (978-0-613-16384-2(2)) Tandem Library Bks.

Hendry, Linda, illus. Horse crafts. 2006. 40p. 6.95 (978-1-55337-647-7(1)) Kids Can Pr., Ltd. CAN. *Dist:* Wybel Marketing Group.

Henley, Karyn. Arts & Crafts, Volume 1: Bible Story Activities for ages 2 To 5, Vol. 1. 2004. (J). per. 19.99 (978-1-933803-00-5(2)) Child Sensitive Communication, LLC.

—Arts & Crafts, Volume 2: Bible Story Activities for ages 2 To 5, Vol. 2. 2004. (J). per. 19.99 (978-1-933803-01-2(0) , AC2) Child Sensitive Communication, LLC.

Higham, Cindy. Snowflakes for All Seasons. 2nd rev. ed. 1998. Orig. Title: Snowflakes Made Easy & Fun. (Illus.). 72p. (Orig.). (J). pap. 8.95 (978-0-9664524-0-2(2)) All Season Snowflakes.

—Snowflakes for All Seasons. 2004. Orig. Title: Snowflakes Made Easy & Fun. (Illus.). 80p. (Orig.). pap. 9.95 (978-1-58685-528-4(X)) Gibbs Smith, Publisher.

Highlights for Children Editorial Staff. Look What You Can Make with Paper Plates. 2003. (Illus.). 48p. (YA). (ps). pap., stu. ed. 5.95 (978-1-56397-643-8(9)) Boyds Mills Pr.

Hill, Paige. Family: Ready-to-Use Scrapbook Pages. 2005. (Instant Memories Ser.). (Illus.). 128p. pap. 14.95 incl. audio compact disk (978-1-4027-2380-3(6) , Chapelle) Sterling Publishing Co., Inc.

Holabird, Katharine. My First Activity Book. Craig, Helen, illus. 2007. 32p. (J). 9.99 (978-0-448-44550-2(6) , Grosset & Dunlap) Penguin Group (USA) Inc.

—Tip-Top Christmas Crafts. Craig, Helen, illus. 2006. (Angelina Ballerina Ser.). 40p. (J). (ps-3). pap. 5.99 (978-0-448-44387-4(2) , Grosset & Dunlap) Penguin Group (USA) Inc.

Hollow, Michele C. Nifty Thrifty Math Crafts. 2007. (Nifty Thrifty Crafts for Kids Ser.). (Illus.). 32p. (J). lib. bdg. 22.60 (978-0-7660-2781-7(3) , 1264782, Enslow Elementary) Enslow Pubs., Inc.

—Nifty Thrifty Sports Crafts. 2007. (Nifty Thrifty Crafts for Kids Ser.). (Illus.). 32p. (J). (gr. 3-4). lib. bdg. 22.60 (978-0-7660-2782-4(1) , Enslow Elementary) Enslow Pubs., Inc.

Holub, Joan. Dinosaurs. 2003. (ps-2). lib. bdg. 14.15 (978-0-613-84475-8(0)) Tandem Library Bks.

Horne, Richard & Szirtes, Helen. 101 Things to Do Before You're Old & Boring. 2006. (Illus.). 224p. (YA). (gr. 7 up). pap. 9.95 (978-0-8027-7745-4(7)) Walker & Co.

How to Make a Sun Hat. (ps-2). 23.00 (978-0-7635-9011-6(8)) Rigby Education.

Hufford, Deborah. Book Making & Paper Making: Be Your Own Publisher. 2005. (Snap Books Craft Ser.). (Illus.). 32p. (J). (gr. 3-5). lib. bdg. 22.60 (978-0-7368-4382-9(5)) Capstone Pr., Inc.

—Crafts. 2005. (Illus.). (J). (gr. 3-4). lib. bdg. 151.56 (978-0-7368-4432-1(5)) Capstone Pr., Inc.

—Fashion Crafts: Create Your Own Style. 2005. (Snap Books Craft Ser.). (Illus.). 32p. (J). (gr. 3-5). lib. bdg. 22.60 (978-0-7368-4384-3(1)) Capstone Pr., Inc.

—Room Decorating: Make Your Space Unique. 2005. (Snap Books Craft Ser.). (Illus.). 32p. (J). (gr. 3-5). 22.60 (978-0-7368-4386-7(8)) Capstone Pr., Inc.

Humphrey, Paul. How to Make a Present. 2007. (J). ***978-1-59771-103-6(9))** Sea-To-Sea Pubns.

Hunt, Sara, ed. Card Making Kit. 2005. (American Girl Today Ser.). (Illus.). 24p. (J). pap. 9.95 (978-1-58485-974-1(1), American Girl) American Girl Publishing, Inc.

—Room Crafts: Add Some Simple Style to Your Space. 2004. (American Girl Library(R) Ser.). (Illus.). 64p. spiral bd. 9.95 (978-1-58485-911-6(3)) American Girl Publishing, Inc.

Hunter, Dette. 38 Ways to Entertain Your Babysitter. MacEachern, Stephen, illus. 2003. 48p. (J). (ps-4). pap., act. bk. ed. 9.95 (978-1-55037-794-1(9)); lib. bdg., act. bk. ed. 19.95 (978-1-55037-795-8(7)) Annick Pr., Ltd. CAN. *Dist:* Firefly Bks., Ltd.

—38 Ways to Entertain Your Grandparents. Betteridge, Deirdre, illus. 2002. 48p. (J). (ps-4). pap., act. bk. ed. 9.95 (978-1-55037-748-4(5)); lib. bdg., act. bk. ed. 19.95 (978-1-55037-749-1(3)) Annick Pr., Ltd. CAN. *Dist:* Firefly Bks., Ltd.

—38 Ways to Entertain Your Parents on Summer Vacation. Macaulay, Kitty, illus. 2005. 48p. (J). (ps-4). pap., act. bk. ed. 9.95 (978-1-55037-886-3(4)); lib. bdg., act. bk. ed. 19.95 (978-1-55037-887-0(2)) Annick Pr., Ltd. CAN. *Dist:* Firefly Bks., Ltd.

Hutnick, Theresa & Phillips, Karen. Insectos Insolitos. Fox, Peter, photos by. 2005. (SPA., Illus.). 38p. (J). spiral bd. 17.95 (978-987-1078-43-1(9)) Klutz Latino MEX. *Dist:* Independent Pubs. Group.

Hutnick, Theresa & Smith, Megan. Ribbon Purses. 2006. (Illus.). 50p. (J). spiral bd. 14.95 (978-1-57054-240-4(6)) Klutz.

I Made It Myself: Kids Craft Projects. 88.00 (978-0-8368-5963-8(4)) Stevens, Gareth Inc.

I'm an Artist: Individual Title Six-Packs. (Literatura 2000 Ser.). (gr. 2-3). 33.00 (978-0-7635-0202-7(2)) Rigby Education.

Im, Angela, ed. How to Make Balloon Animals. 2005. (J). lthr. 8.99 (978-0-439-68024-0(7) , Tangerine Pr.) Scholastic, Inc.

Instructional Fair Staff. New Testament Bible Story Crafts: Bible Based Activities That Every Christian Educator Will Treasure. 1999. 63p. (C). pap. 6.99 (978-1-56822-327-8(7)) Schaffer, Frank Pubns.

Irvin, Christine M. Cardboard Tube Mania. 2002. (Craft Mania Ser.). (Illus.). 32p. (J). (gr. 2-4). pap. 23.50 (978-0-516-21674-4(0) , Children's Pr.) Scholastic Library Publishing.

—Cardboard Tube Mania. 2002. (gr. 3-6). lib. bdg. 15.25 (978-0-613-59456-1(8)) Tandem Library Bks.

—Craft Mania: 36 Fun Crafts for Kids! 2004. (Illus.). 96p. (J). pap. 8.99 (978-0-517-22338-3(4) , Gramercy) Random Hse. Value Publishing.

—Craft Stick Mania. 2002. (Craft Mania Ser.). (Illus.). 32p. (J). (gr. 2-4). pap. 23.50 (978-0-516-21676-8(7) , Children's Pr.) Scholastic Library Publishing.

—Craft Stick Mania. 2002. (gr. 3-6). lib. bdg. 15.25 (978-0-613-59463-9(0)) Tandem Library Bks.

—Egg Carton Mania. 2002. (Craft Mania Ser.). (Illus.). 32p. (J). (gr. 2-4). pap. 23.50 (978-0-516-22277-6(5) , Children's Pr.) Scholastic Library Publishing.

—Egg Carton Mania. 2002. (gr. 3-6). lib. bdg. 15.25 (978-0-613-59467-7(3)) Tandem Library Bks.

—Milk Carton Mania. 2002. (gr. 3-6). lib. bdg. 15.25 (978-0-613-59520-9(3)) Tandem Library Bks.

—Paper Cup Mania. 2002. (Craft Mania Ser.). (Illus.). 32p. (J). (gr. 2-4). pap. 23.50 (978-0-516-22278-3(3) , Children's Pr.) Scholastic Library Publishing.

—Pie Pan Mania. (Craft Mania Ser.). (Illus.). 32p. (J). (gr. 2-4). 2003. pap. 6.95 (978-0-516-27762-2(6)); 2002. pap. 23.50 (978-0-516-22280-6(5)) Scholastic Library Publishing. (Children's Pr.).

—Pie Pan Mania. 2002. (gr. 3-6). lib. bdg. 15.25 (978-0-613-59540-7(8)) Tandem Library Bks.

—Pipe Cleaner Mania. 2002. (Craft Mania Ser.). (Illus.). 32p. (J). (gr. 2-4). pap. 23.50 (978-0-516-22279-0(1) , Children's Pr.) Scholastic Library Publishing.

—Pipe Cleaner Mania. 2002. (gr. 3-6). lib. bdg. 15.25 (978-0-613-59541-4(6)) Tandem Library Bks.

Jackson, Paul & A'Court, Angela. Best Ever Book of Paper Fun & Origami. 2000. (Illus.). 256p. (gr. 4-7). pap. 24.95 (978-0-7548-0244-0(2) , Lorenz Bks.) Anness Publishing GBR. *Dist:* National Bk. Network.

Jacobs, Daniel. Patterns. 2005. (Yellow Umbrella Books for Early Readers). (Illus.). 17p. (J). (978-0-7368-5281-4(6)); (978-0-7368-5317-0(0)) Capstone Pr., Inc.

Jalali, Yassaman. Celebrating Norouz (Persian New Year) Zamanian, Marjan, illus. 2003. 28p. (J). (ps-6). pap. 12.99 (978-0-9728020-0-0(2)) Saman Publishing.

James, Diane. Fun to Make & Do. 2004. (Crafty Ideas Ser.). (Illus.). 124p. (gr. 3-6). 24.95 (978-1-58728-111-2(2) , Two Can Publishing) T&N Children's Publishing.

—Junk. 2001. (Crafty Ideas Ser.). (J). (gr. 2-7). 9.95 (978-1-58728-262-1(3)); pap. 5.95 (978-1-58728-122-8(8)) T&N Children's Publishing. (Two Can Publishing).

—Models. 2004. (Crafty Ideas Ser.). (SPA., Illus.). 32p. (J). (gr. 2-5). pap. 5.95 (978-1-58728-124-2(4) , Two Can Publishing) T&N Children's Publishing.

—Models. Barnes, Jon, photos by. 2004. (Crafty Ideas Ser.). (SPA., Illus.). 30p. (gr. 2-5). 9.95 (978-1-58728-265-2(8) , Two Can Publishing) T&N Children's Publishing.

—Paint. 2004. (Crafty Ideas Ser.). (SPA., Illus.). (gr. 2-5). 32p. (J). pap. 5.95 (978-1-58728-125-9(2)); 30p. 9.95 (978-1-58728-263-8(1)) T&N Children's Publishing. (Two Can Publishing).

—Papel Mache. 2004. (Crafty Ideas Ser.).Tr. of Papier Mache. (SPA., Illus.). 32p. (J). (ps-3). 9.95 (978-1-58728-486-1(3)); pap. 5.95 (978-1-58728-487-8(1)) T&N Children's Publishing. (Two Can Publishing).

—Print. 2004. (Crafty Ideas Ser.). (SPA., Illus.). 32p. (gr. 2-5). (J). pap. 5.95 (978-1-58728-128-0(7)); 9.95 (978-1-58728-266-9(6)) T&N Children's Publishing. (Two Can Publishing).

Jaskiel, Stan. Make Your Own Birdhouses & Feeders. 2001. (gr. 3-6). lib. bdg. 16.40 (978-0-613-57609-3(8)) Tandem Library Bks.

Jayne, Caroline F. String Figures & How to Make Them. 1999. (Illus.). 407p. (gr. 7 up). pap. 11.95 (978-0-486-20152-8(X)) Dover Pubns., Inc.

Jennings, Terry. Wood. 2006. (Illus.). 32p. (YA). (gr. 1 up). lib. bdg. 27.10 (978-1-932333-00-8(2)) Chrysalis Education.

Johnson, Anne Akers. Hair Wraps. 1998. (Illus.). 32p. (J). (gr. 4-7). spiral bd. 14.95 (978-1-57054-163-6(9)) Klutz.

—Hemp Bracelets. 1998. (Illus.). 32p. (J). (gr. 4-7). stu. ed. 14.95 (978-1-57054-187-2(6)) Klutz.

—Juegos con una Cuerda. 2004. Orig. Title: Cat's Cradle: A Book of String Figures. (SPA., Illus.). 36p. (J). spiral bd. 11.95 (978-968-5528-14-6(4)) Klutz Latino MEX. *Dist:* Independent Pubs. Group.

—Trenzas Locas. 2005. (SPA., Illus.). 32p. (J). spiral bd. 17.95 (978-968-5528-06-1(3)) Klutz Latino MEX. *Dist:* Independent Pubs. Group.

Johnson, Anne Akers & Paddock, Kate. Room Lanterns: A Punch-Out Book of Party Lights, Shades & Ideas. 2005. (Illus.). 36p. (YA). (gr. 4-7). spiral bd. 19.95 (978-1-57054-219-0(8)) Klutz.

Johnson, Ginger. Make Your Own Christmas Ornaments. Martin Jourdenais, Norma Jean, illus. 2002. (Quick Starts for Kids! Ser.). 64p. (YA). (gr. 3 up). pap. 8.95 (978-1-885593-79-5(1) , Williamson Bks.) Ideals Pubns.

—Paper-Folding Fun! 50 Awesome Crafts to Weave, Twist, & Curl. Day, Betsy, illus. 2002. (Williamson Kids Can!(R) Ser.). 128p. (J). (gr. 3 up). pap. 12.95 (978-1-885593-67-2(8) , Williamson Bks.) Ideals Pubns.

Johnson, Joni. 98 Activities - Fast Fun for Tiny Hands: Creative Craft Ideas for Preschoolers. 1999. 40p. (J). (ps-2). pap. 3.95 (978-1-880710-39-5(0)) Monterey Pacific Pubs.

Johnson, Susan & Johnson, Wil. Making Collages. 2003. (Illus.). 32p. (J). pap. 6.00 (978-1-59034-183-4(X)) Mondo Publishing.

Jordan, Apple. Fashion Seasons. Style Guide Staff & Riley, Kellee, illus. 2006. (Holly Hobbie & Friends Ser.). 48p. (J). act. bk. ed. 3.99 (978-1-4169-1851-6(5) , Simon Scribbles) Simon & Schuster Children's Publishing.

Jovinelly, Joann. The Crafts & Culture of a Medieval Guild. 2006. (Illus.). 48p. (J). lib. bdg. (978-1-4042-0757-8(0)) Rosen Publishing Group, Inc., The.

Jovinelly, Joann & Netelkos, Jason. The Crafts & Culture of a Medieval Castle. 2006. (Illus.). 47p. (J). (978-1-4042-0760-8(0)) Rosen Publishing Group, Inc., The.

—The Crafts & Culture of a Medieval Cathedral. 2006. (Illus.). 28p. (J). lib. bdg. (978-1-4042-0758-5(9)) Rosen Publishing Group, Inc., The.

—The Crafts & Culture of a Medieval Manor. 2006. (Illus.). 48p. (J). lib. bdg. (978-1-4042-0756-1(2)) Rosen Publishing Group, Inc., The.

—The Crafts & Culture of a Medieval Monastery. 2006. (Crafts & Culture of the Middle Ages Ser.). (Illus.). 48p. (J). (gr. 4-8). lib. bdg. 29.25 (978-1-4042-0759-2(7)) Rosen Publishing Group, Inc., The.

—The Crafts & Culture of a Medieval Town. 2006. (Crafts & Culture of the Middle Ages Ser.). (Illus.). 48p. (J). (gr. 4-8). lib. bdg. 29.25 (978-1-4042-0761-5(9)) Rosen Publishing Group, Inc., The.

—The Crafts & Culture of the Ancient Hebrews. 2002. (Crafts of the Ancient World Ser.). (Illus.). 48p. (YA). (gr. 5-8). lib. bdg. 29.25 (978-0-8239-3511-6(6) , Rosen Central) Rosen Publishing Group, Inc., The.

—The Crafts & Culture of the Aztecs. 2002. (Crafts of the Ancient World Ser.). (Illus.). 48p. (YA). (gr. 5-8). lib. bdg. 29.25 (978-0-8239-3512-3(4) , Rosen Central) Rosen Publishing Group, Inc., The.

—The Crafts & Culture of the Romans. 2002. (Crafts of the Ancient World Ser.). (Illus.). 48p. (YA). (gr. 5-8). lib. bdg. 29.25 (978-0-8239-3513-0(2) , Rosen Central) Rosen Publishing Group, Inc., The.

—The Crafts & Culture of the Vikings. 2002. (Crafts of the Ancient World Ser.). (Illus.). 48p. (YA). (gr. 5-8). lib. bdg. 29.25 (978-0-8239-3514-7(0) , Rosen Central) Rosen Publishing Group, Inc., The.

—Crafts of the Ancient World, 6 bks. Incl. Crafts & Culture of the Ancient Egyptians. lib. bdg. 29.25 (978-0-8239-3509-3(4)); Crafts & Culture of the Ancient Greeks. lib. bdg. 29.25 (978-0-8239-3510-9(8)); Crafts & Culture of the Ancient Hebrews. lib. bdg. 29.25 (978-0-8239-3511-6(6)); Crafts & Culture of the Aztecs. lib. bdg. 29.25 (978-0-8239-3512-3(4)); Crafts & Culture of the Romans. lib. bdg. 29.25 (978-0-8239-3513-0(2)); Crafts & Culture of the Vikings. lib. bdg. 29.25 (978-0-8239-3514-7(0)); 48p. (YA). (gr. 5-8). (Illus.). 2002. Set lib. bdg. 175.50 (978-0-8239-9690-2(5) , Rosen Central) Rosen Publishing Group, Inc., The.

Kane, Barbara. Making Mini Books. 2002. (Illus.). 58p. (J). 16.95 (978-1-57054-977-9(X)) Klutz.

—Potholders & Other Loopy Projects. 2003. (Illus.). 40p. (J). (gr. 1 up). spiral bd. 16.95 (978-1-57054-963-2(X)) Klutz.

—Quilting: Design & Make Your Own Patchwork Projects. 2005. (Illus.). 64p. (YA). (gr. 5-9). spiral bd. 21.95 (978-1-57054-215-2(5)) Klutz.

—Velvet Art: Create Fabulous Fuzzy Masterpieces. 2003. (Illus.). 10p. (J). pap. 19.95 (978-1-59174-259-3(5) , 53643125) Klutz.

Kane, Barbara & Haab, Sherri. Making Mini Books. 2002. (Illus.). 71p. (J). (gr. 1 up). spiral bd. 19.95 (978-1-57054-760-7(2)) Klutz.

Kate, Maggie. Old-Time Circus Stickers. 1999. (Illus.). (J). pap. 1.00 (978-0-486-40602-2(4)) Dover Pubns., Inc.

Kawasaki, Shauna Mooney. Ghostly Frights for Halloween Nights. 2002. (gr. 3-6). lib. bdg. 15.25 (978-0-613-81805-6(9)) Tandem Library Bks.

Kaye, Teri, ed. Christmas Crafts on a Budget: Over 100 Project Ideas. 2005. 19.99 (978-0-9759638-2-1(1)) Gizmo Enterprises, Inc.

Kennedy, Marge. Disney's Christmas Crafts for Kids: More Than 75 Festive Ideas for Making Decorations, Wrapping & Gifts. 1998. (Illus.). (J). 18.95 (978-0-7868-3196-8(0)) Disney Pr.

Kidz Chat Fall 2002. 2002. pap. 14.99 (978-1-59185-027-4(4)) CharismaLife Pubs.

Kidz Chat Winter 2002-03. 2002. pap. 14.99 (978-1-59185-114-1(9)) CharismaLife Pubs.

Kilby, Janice Eaton, et al. The Book of Wizard Craft: In Which the Apprentice Finds Spells, Potions, Fantastic Tales & 50 Enchanting Things to Make. Burnett, Lindy, illus. deluxe ed. 2001. 144p. (J). (gr. 4-6). 7.95 (978-1-57990-206-3(5)) Lark Bks.

King, David C. Projects about the Ancient Aztecs. 2006. (Hands-On History Ser.). (Illus.). 48p. (J). lib. bdg. 29.93 (978-0-7614-2256-3(0) , Benchmark Bks.) Cavendish, Marshall Corp.

King, Nancy Jo. Get Crafty: 60 Cool Holiday Crafts for Year-Round Fun. 2001. (Get Crafty: Vol. 1). 96p. pap. 7.95 (978-0-9678285-3-4(8)) Lunchbox Pr.

King, Penny & Roundhill, Clare. Amazing Animals. 1998. (Making Pictures Ser.). (J). 21.36 (978-1-57572-192-7(9)) Heinemann Library.

—Secrets of the Sea. 1998. (Making Pictures Ser.). (J). 21.36 (978-1-57572-194-1(5)) Heinemann Library.

—Spooky Things. 1998. (Making Pictures Ser.). (J). 21.36 (978-1-57572-195-8(3)) Rigby Education.

Kinmont, Ritchie. Every Kid Needs Things That Fly. Casey, Robert, photos by. 2005. (Illus.). 136p. (J). 14.95 (978-1-58685-509-3(3) , 1241179) Gibbs Smith, Publisher.

Kirby, Huguette. Crafts from Felt. 2002. (Step by Step Ser.). (Illus.). 32p. (J). (gr. 2-3). lib. bdg. 22.60 (978-0-7368-1474-4(4) , Bridgestone Bks.) Capstone Pr., Inc.

—Crafts from Modeling Clay. 2002. (Step by Step Ser.). (Illus.). 32p. (J). (gr. 2-3). lib. bdg. 22.60 (978-0-7368-1477-5(9) , Bridgestone Bks.) Capstone Pr., Inc.

Klutz Blossom Bracelets Kit. 8.95 (978-1-57054-750-8(5)) Klutz.

Klutz Boondoggle 24-pack. (J). (978-1-878257-78-9(1)) Klutz.

Klutz Boondoggle 6 Cp W/display. (Illus.). 46p. (J). (978-1-878257-77-2(3)) Klutz.

Klutz Buck Book 24-pack. (J). (978-1-878257-56-7(0)) Klutz.

Klutz Editors. Amazing Lacing. 2005. (Chicken Socks Ser.). (Illus.). 22p. (J). (ps-7). 9.95 (978-1-59174-356-9(7)) Klutz.

—Klutz Design Your Own Charm Watch. 2005. (Illus.). 28p. (J). 21.95 (978-1-57054-212-1(0)) Klutz.

—Super Scissors Book. 2006. (Illus.). 44p. (YA). 12.95 (978-1-59174-203-6(X)) Klutz.

Klutz Press Staff. The Adventures of Brenda Bender: Bendable Wire Heroine. 1999. (Bender Family Ser.). (Illus.). 32p. (YA). (ps-3). 9.95 (978-1-57054-470-5(0)) Klutz.

—The Adventures of Fender Bender: Bendable Wire Bow-Wow. 1999. (Bender Family Ser.). (Illus.). 32p. (YA). (ps-3). 9.95 (978-1-57054-464-4(6)) Klutz.

—The Adventures of Joe Bender: Bendable Wire Hero. 1999. (Bender Family Ser.). (Illus.). 32p. (YA). (ps-3). 9.95 (978-1-57054-467-5(0)) Klutz.

—Arte en Ventanas. 2004. (SPA., Illus.). 62p. (J). spiral bd. 23.95 (978-968-5528-16-0(0)) Klutz Latino MEX. *Dist:* Independent Pubs. Group.

—The Body Crayon Book. 1999. (Illus.). 42p. (YA). (ps-3). 14.95 (978-1-57054-403-3(4)) Klutz.

—Book of Artrageous Projects. 2000. (Illus.). 66p. (J). (gr. 4-7). 19.95 (978-1-57054-185-8(X)) Klutz.

—Itty Bitty Ballerinas 6 Copy Pack. 2005. (Illus.). 32p. (J). (gr. 3 up). 9.95 (978-1-59174-276-0(5)) Klutz.

—Make Your Own Itty-Bitty Angels. 2005. (Illus.). 32p. (J). (gr. 3 up). spiral bd. 9.95 (978-1-59174-275-3(7)) Klutz.

—Make Your Own Itty-Bitty Mixpack (18-disp) (J). 179.10 (978-1-57054-888-8(9)) Klutz.

—Make Your Own Itty-Bitty Princesses. 2005. (Illus.). 32p. (J). (gr. 3 up). 9.95 (978-1-59174-277-7(3)) Klutz.

—My Fabulous Life in Pictures. 2002. (Illus.). 40p. (J). (gr. 4-7). spiral bd. 19.95 (978-1-57054-916-8(8)) Klutz.

—Painted Rocks. 2000. (Illus.). 64p. (J). (gr. 4-7). 14.95 (978-1-57054-529-0(4)) Klutz.

Klutz Press Staff, contrib. by. Squashing Flowers, Squeezing Leaves: A Nature Press & Book. 2001. (Illus.). 48p. (J). (gr. 4-7). spiral bd. 19.95 (978-1-57054-591-7(X)) Klutz.

Klutz Press Staff, creator. How to Make Pompom Animals. 2005. (Illus.). 22p. (J). spiral bd. 9.95 (978-1-59174-095-7(9)) Klutz.

Klutz Press Staff, ed. T-Shirt Art: Make Your Own Iron-on Designs. 2004. (Illus.). 60p. (J). spiral bd. 19.95 (978-1-57054-850-5(1)) Klutz.

—Totally Tape. 2005. (Chicken Socks). (Illus.). 44p. (J). 9.95 (978-1-59174-368-2(0)) Klutz.

Klutz Slappies Cat Minnow Animal Bracelet. (J). 4.95 (978-1-57054-624-2(X)) Klutz.

Klutz Slappies Koala Button Animal Bracelet. (J). 4.95 (978-1-57054-700-3(9)) Klutz.

Klutz Slappies Leopard Dash Animal Bracelet. (J). 4.95 (978-1-57054-616-7(9)) Klutz.

Klutz Slappies Lion Ruff Animal Bracelet. (J). 4.95 (978-1-57054-627-3(4)) Klutz.

Klutz Slappies Lizard Jinx Animal Bracelet. 4.95 (978-1-57054-625-9(8)) Klutz.

Klutz Slappies Monkey Scooter Animal Bracelet. 4.95 (978-1-57054-702-7(5)) Klutz.

Klutz Slappies Mouse Tickle Animal Bracelet. (J). 4.95 (978-1-57054-621-1(5)) Klutz.

Klutz Slappies Spotted Dog Pepper Anim Bracelet. (J). 4.95 (978-1-57054-629-7(0)) Klutz.

Klutz Slappies Tiger Squeak Animal Bracelet. 4.95 (978-1-57054-611-2(8)) Klutz.

Klutz Slappies Unicorn Twink Animal Bracelet. (J). 4.95 (978-1-57054-713-3(0)) Klutz.

Klutz Slappies Zebra Pinkie Animal Bracelet. (J). 4.95 (978-1-57054-619-8(3)) Klutz.

Knowlton, Laurie. Bible Crafts for Christian Kid. 2001. 80p. (J). pap. 10.99 (978-0-7647-0543-4(1)) School Specialty Publishing.

Knox, Joy, compiled by. Croppin' Dictum: Big, Strong Titles. 2004. (YA). spiral bd. (978-0-9754972-1-0(9)) JoyRox, LLC.

—Croppin' Dictum: Travel & Holiday. 2004. (YA). spiral bd. (978-0-9754972-2-7(7)) JoyRox, LLC.

Kohl, MaryAnn F. Mudworks: Creative Clay, Dough, & Modeling Experiences. Kerr, Kathleen, illus. 2003. (Bright Ideas for Learning Ser.: Vol. 2). 152p. (J). (ps-6). pap. 18.95 (978-0-935607-02-4(1)) Bright Ring Publishing, Inc.

Kohl, MaryAnn F. & Gainer, Cindy. Good Earth Art: Environmental Art for Kids. Gainer, Cindy, illus. 2003. (Bright Ideas for Learning Ser.: Vol. 3). (Illus.). 244p. (Orig.). (J). (ps-6). pap. 18.95 (978-0-935607-01-7(3)) Bright Ring Publishing, Inc.

Kohl, MaryAnn F. & Solga, Kim. Discovering Great Artists: Hands-on Art for Children in the Styles of the Great Masters. Van Slyke, Rebecca, illus. 2003. (Bright Ideas for Learning Ser.: Vol. 6). 144p. (Orig.). (J). (ps-12). pap. 18.95 (978-0-935607-09-3(9)) Bright Ring Publishing, Inc.

Kranz, Linda. Let's Rock! 2003. (Craft Ser.). (Illus.). 64p. (YA). (gr. 1-6). pap. 11.95 (978-1-55971-870-7(6) , NorthWord Bks. for Young Readers) T&N Children's Publishing.

Krul, Paige, ed. Stencil Art. 2001. (Illus.). 42p. (J). (gr. 4-7). lthr. 13.95 (978-0-439-24958-4(9) , Tangerine Pr.) Scholastic, Inc.

Kubish, Shelagh & Craig, Lee, eds. Pumpkin Carving, Vol. 1. rev. ed. 2003. (Illus.). 48p. (gr. 4). pap. (978-1-894877-26-8(8)) Lone Pine Publishing.

Kuhn, Jean. Build Your Own Kaleidoscope. Cook, Corinda, illus. 2006. 32p. (YA). (gr. 6-10). pap. 9.00 (978-0-7881-9908-0(0)) DIANE Publishing Co.

Kuhn, Jean & Vrato, Elizabeth. Build Your Own Kaleidoscope. 2003. (Mega Mini Kitstm Ser.). (Illus.). 32p. 8.95 (978-0-7624-1607-3(6) , Running Pr. Miniature Editions) Running Pr. Bk. Pubs.

Kumon Publishing North America, creator. My Book of Easy Crafts. 2005. (Illus.). 80p. per. 6.95 (978-1-933241-03-6(9)) Kumon Publishing North America, Inc.

Kuroi, Ken, illus. Goldilocks & the Three Bears. 2004. (Heian's Origami Fairy Tales Ser.). 16p. (gr. k-3). pap. 7.95 (978-0-89346-914-6(9)) Heian International Publishing, Inc.

Kyle, Carolyn. Let There Be Light. 2004. (Illus.). 40p. (YA). 19.95 (978-1-932327-10-6(X) , 2032710X) CKE Pubns.

Ladizinsky, Eric, et al. 150 Nifty Super Rainy-Day Activities. 2000. (Illus.). 240p. (J). (gr. 3-7). pap. 9.95 (978-0-7373-0515-9(0)) Lowell Hse. Juvenile.

LaFosse, Michael. Making Origami Animals Step by Step. 2002. (Kid's Guide to Origami Ser.). (Illus.). 24p. (J). lib. bdg. 21.25 (978-0-8239-5877-1(9) , PowerKids Pr.) Rosen Publishing Group, Inc., The.

—Making Origami Cards Step by Step. 2004. (Kid's Guide to Origami Ser.). (Illus.). 24p. (J). lib. bdg. 21.25 (978-0-8239-6701-8(8) , PowerKids Pr.) Rosen Publishing Group, Inc., The.

—Making Origami Masks Step by Step. 2004. (Kid's Guide to Origami Ser.). (Illus.). 24p. (J). lib. bdg. 21.25 (978-0-8239-6703-2(4) , PowerKids Pr.) Rosen Publishing Group, Inc., The.

—Making Origami Paper Airplanes Step by Step. 2004. (Kid's Guide to Origami Ser.). (Illus.). 24p. (J). lib. bdg. 21.25 (978-0-8239-6700-1(X) , PowerKids Pr.) Rosen Publishing Group, Inc., The.

—Making Origami Puzzles Step by Step. 2004. (Kid's Guide to Origami Ser.). (Illus.). 24p. (J). lib. bdg. 21.25 (978-0-8239-6704-9(2) , PowerKids Pr.) Rosen Publishing Group, Inc., The.

Lamerand, Violaine. Crafts from Junk. 2002. (Step by Step Ser.). (Illus.). 32p. (J). (gr. 2-3). lib. bdg. 22.60 (978-0-7368-1479-9(5) , Bridgestone Bks.) Capstone Pr., Inc.

—Crafts from Papier-Mache. 2002. (Step by Step Ser.). (Illus.). 32p. (J). (gr. 2-3). lib. bdg. 22.60 (978-0-7368-1478-2(7) , Bridgestone Bks.) Capstone Pr., Inc.

—Making Masks. 2002. (Step by Step Ser.). (Illus.). 32p. (J). (gr. 2-3). lib. bdg. 22.60 (978-0-7368-1476-8(0) , Bridgestone Bks.) Capstone Pr., Inc.

Lane, Nickel. Book Making for Everyone. 2004. 33p. (J). pap. 9.77 (978-1-4116-1729-2(0)) Lulu.com.

Lapin, Gloria. Fun Times: Little Books to Make & Read with Other. 1999. (J). (ps-3). pap. 2.95 (978-1-55254-019-0(7)) Brighter Vision Pubns.

Larousse Kingfisher Chambers Staff. Holiday Fun. 2000. (Illus.). (J). (978-0-606-19825-7(3)) Tandem Library Bks.

Lee, Jacqueline, ed. Decorate Your Locker: So It's Completely & Totally Your Own (at Least for a Year) 2004. (Klutz Ser.). (Illus.). 24p. (J). 9.95 (978-1-59174-270-8(6)) Klutz.

Lee, Quinlan B. The Art of Silliness. 2006. (VeggieTales Ser.). 96p. (J). 2.99 (978-1-4169-1787-8(X) , Simon Scribbles) Simon & Schuster Children's Publishing.

Leedy, Loreen. Look at My Book: How Kids Can Write & Illustrate Terrific Books. 2005. (Illus.). 32p. (J). 6.95 (978-0-8234-1959-3(2)) Holiday Hse., Inc.

Lehne, Judith Logan. The Busy Mom's Book of Quick Crafts for Kids. Wood, Tracey, illus. 2005. 144p. (J). pap. 6.95 (978-1-4027-1952-3(3)) Sterling Publishing Co., Inc.

Lerner, Linda, et al. 101 Holiday Crafts for Year-Round Fun. 2003. (Illus.). 72p. (J). (978-0-7853-8909-5(1)) Publications International, Ltd.

Let's Create!, 8 bks. Incl. Clay. Llimos Plomer, Anna. 2003. lib. bdg. 23.33 (978-0-8368-3746-9(0)); Metal. Parramon's Editorial Team Staff. Parramon's Editorial Team Staff, photos by. 2004. lib. bdg. 23.33 (978-0-8368-4016-2(X)); Paper. Llimos Plomer, Anna. 2003. lib. bdg. 23.33 (978-0-8368-3747-6(9)); Papier Mache. Parramon's Editorial Team Staff. Parramon's Editorial Team Staff, photos by. 2004. lib. bdg. 23.33 (978-0-8368-4017-9(8)); Plants & Seeds. Crexells, Cristina & Llimos Plomer, Anna. 2003. lib. bdg. 23.33 (978-0-8368-3748-3(7)); Recyclables. Parramon's Editorial Team Staff. Parramon's Editorial Team Staff, photos by. 2004. lib. bdg. 23.33 (978-0-8368-4018-6(6)); Stones & "Stuff" Parramon's Editorial Team Staff. Parramon's Editorial Team Staff, photos by. 2004. lib. bdg. 23.33 (978-0-8368-4019-3(4)); Wood & Cork. Llimos Plomer, Anna. 2003. lib. bdg. 23.33 (978-0-8368-3749-0(5)); 32p. (J). (gr. 2 up). (Illus.). 2003. Set lib. bdg. 186.64 (978-0-8368-4168-8(9)) Stevens, Gareth Inc.

Let's Create! Clay; Paper; Plants & Seeds; Wood & Cork, 4 bks. 2003. (Illus.). (J). (gr. 2 up). lib. bdg. 90.40 (978-0-8368-3745-2(2)) Stevens, Gareth Inc.

Let's Do Arts & Crafts. (Illus.). (J). (gr. k-1). 103.50 (978-1-4042-3290-7(7) , Powerstart Pr.) Rosen Publishing Group, Inc., The.

Levine, Gail Carson. Ella Enchanted Scrapbook. movie tie-in ed. 2004. (Illus.). 48p. (gr. 3-6). pap. 5.99 (978-0-7868-1802-0(6)) Hyperion Bks. for Children.

Lewis, Amanda. Making Memory Books. Melo, Esperanca, illus. 1999. 40p. (J). (ps-7). lib. bdg. 15.25 (978-0-613-21954-9(6)) Tandem Library Bks.

Lewis, Amanda & Melo, Esperanca. Making Memory Books. 1999. (Kids Can Do It Ser.). (Illus.). 136p. (J). (gr. 4-6). (978-1-55074-567-2(0)) Kids Can Pr., Ltd.

Lewis, Sue. Month-by-Month Crafts: Over 70 Simple, Seasonal Craft Ideas. Dobelmann, Collene, ed. 2005. (Illus.). 112p. (J). pap. (978-1-59198-130-5(1) , 2495) Creative Teaching Pr., Inc.

Lieurance, Suzanne, et al. School Projects for Pennies. Ulrich, George, illus. 2001. 240p. (J). lib. bdg. 24.95 (978-1-56674-311-2(7)) Forest Hse. Publishing Co., Inc.

Lincoln, Margarette. The Pirate's Handbook: How to Become a Rogue of the High Seas. (Illus.). (J). pap. 15.99 (978-0-590-24558-6(9)) Scholastic, Inc.

—The Pirate's Handbook: How to Become a Rogue of the High Seas. 1998. (Puffin Book Ser.). (978-0-606-13711-9(4)) Tandem Library Bks.

Lingo, Susan L. Collect-n-Make Crafts for Kids. Stoker, Bruce, ed. Carter, Paula Becker, illus. 2006. 112p. (YA). (gr. 1-7). 15.99 (978-0-7847-1198-9(4) , 02432) Standard Publishing.

—Power-Packed Crafts. 2004. 112p. (J). 15.99 (978-0-7847-7212-6(6) , 09447) Standard Publishing.

Lipsey Edwards, Jennifer. My Very Favorite Art Book: I Love to Collage! 2006. (My Very Favorite Art Book Ser.). (Illus.). 48p. (J). 9.95 (978-1-57990-770-9(9)) Lark Bks.

Little Kid Crafts for All Seasons: Kid Tested Crafts That Parents Love Too! 2003. (Illus.). per. 29.95 (978-0-9741210-4-8(5)) Christine, Yates.

Lively, Kate. 200 Amazing Things to Make, Do & Play! 2005. (Illus.). 512p. 29.99 (978-0-7548-1392-7(4) , Lorenz Bks.) Anness Publishing GBR. *Dist:* National Bk. Network.

Llimos, Anna & Sadurni, Laia. Crea Motivos de Navidad. (Coleccion Manualidades Divertidas).Tr. of Create Christmas Decorations. (SPA.). 32p. (J). (gr. k-3). 10.00 (978-84-342-2080-5(6)) Parramon Ediciones S.A. ESP. *Dist:* Distribuidora Norma, Inc., Lectorum Pubns., Inc.

—Creating by Recycling. 2000. (Crafts for All Seasons Ser.). (Illus.). 32p. (J). (gr. 3-8). lib. bdg. 23.70 (978-1-56711-436-2(9) , Blackbirch Pr., Inc.) Thomson Gale.

—Creating with Salt Dough. 2000. (Crafts for All Seasons Ser.). (Illus.). 32p. (J). (gr. 3-8). lib. bdg. 23.70 (978-1-56711-435-5(0) , Blackbirch Pr., Inc.) Thomson Gale.

Llimos Plomer, Anna. Barro. Casanova, Jose Maria, illus. 2000. (Let's Create Ser.). (SPA.). 32p. (J). 12.00 (978-84-342-2428-5(3)) Parramon Ediciones S.A. ESP. *Dist:* Lectorum Pubns., Inc.

—Clay. 2003. (Let's Create! Ser.). (Illus.). 32p. (J). (gr. 2 up). lib. bdg. 23.33 (978-0-8368-3746-9(0)) Stevens, Gareth Inc.

Llimos Plomer, Anna. Easy Earth-Friendly Crafts in 5 Steps. 2008. (Easy Crafts in 5 Steps Ser.). 32p. (J). (gr. 3-4). lib. bdg. 22.60 (***978-0-7660-3086-2(5)***) Enslow Pubs., Inc.

Llimos Plomer, Anna. Materiales de Reciclaje. Casanova, Jose Maria, illus. 2000. (Let's Create Ser.). (SPA.). 32p. (J). 12.00 (978-84-342-2433-9(X)) Parramon Ediciones S.A. ESP. *Dist:* Lectorum Pubns., Inc.

—Paper. 2003. (Let's Create! Ser.). (Illus.). 32p. (J). (gr. 2 up). lib. bdg. 23.33 (978-0-8368-3747-6(9)) Stevens, Gareth Inc.

—Wood & Cork. 2003. (Let's Create! Ser.). (Illus.). 32p. (J). (gr. 2 up). lib. bdg. 23.33 (978-0-8368-3749-0(5)) Stevens, Gareth Inc.

Lomas Garza, Carmen. Magic Windows (Ventanas Magicas) Lomas Garza, Carmen, illus. 1999. (ENG & SPA., Illus.). 32p. (J). (gr. 1-4). 15.95 (978-0-89239-157-8(X)) Children's Bk. Pr.

—Making Magic Windows (Creating Papel Picado) Cut Paper Art with Carmen Lomas Garza. Lomas Garza, Carmen, illus. 1999. (ENG & SPA., Illus.). 64p. (J). (gr. 4-7). pap. 9.95 (978-0-89239-159-2(6)) Children's Bk. Pr.

Look What I Found at Grandma's! 2004. (J). 11.99 (978-0-930184-10-0(6)) Clapper Publishing Co.

Look What You Can Make! Individual Title Six-Packs. (Story Steps Ser.). (gr. k-2). 29.00 (978-0-7635-9600-2(0)) Rigby Education.

Lorenz Books Staff. Amazing Activities & Things to Do: All Kinds of Fun Projects to Keep You Busy! 2000. (Amazing Clever Crafts & Tricks Ser.). (Illus.). 96p. (J). (gr. 3-7). 9.95 (978-0-7548-0358-4(9) , Lorenz Bks.) Anness Publishing, Inc.

—Amazing Clever Crafts: Lots of Really Crafty Things to Make! 2000. (Amazing Clever Crafts & Tricks Ser.). (Illus.). 96p. (J). (gr. 3-7). pap. 9.95 (978-0-7548-0237-2(X) , Lorenz Bks.) Anness Publishing, Inc.

—The Best Ever Book of 100 Incredible Things to Make, Do & Play. 2000. (Illus.). 192p. (J). (gr. 3-7). pap. 17.00 (978-1-85967-728-5(2)) Anness Publishing, Inc.

Lou, Weber. Crafty Paper Projects. 2005. (Illus.). 240p. (J). 12.98 (978-1-4127-1036-7(7) , 7233900) Publications International, Ltd.

Lupton, Ellen & Lupton, Julia Reinhard. D.I.Y. Kids. 2007. (Illus.). 144p. pap. 14.95 (***978-1-56898-707-1(2)***) Princeton Architectural Pr.

MacDonald, Fiona. Science, Crafts & Technology. 2001. (Through the Ages Ser.). (Illus.). 64p. (gr. 3-7). 12.95 (978-0-7548-0850-3(5)) Anness Publishing GBR. *Dist:* National Bk. Network.

MacGregor, Cynthia. Thanks, Aunt Zelda! Thank-You Cards for Kids to Craft. Bell, Anouk Pérusse, illus. 2002. 48p. (J). (gr. k-6). 9.95 (978-1-894222-66-2(0)) Lobster Pr. CAN. *Dist:* Univ. of Toronto Pr.

MacKinnon, Debbie. Post-it Kids' Parties: Create Funny Hats, Groovy Gifts & Crazy Cards with Post-it Notes. 2005. (Illus.). 32p. pap. 7.95 (978-0-7432-8433-2(X) , Fireside) Simon & Schuster.

MacLeod, Elizabeth. Bake It & Build It. Walker, Tracy, illus. (Kids Can Do It Ser.). (J). (gr. 4-6). 2004. 40p. (978-1-55337-754-2(0)); 1998. 134p. (978-1-55074-427-9(5)) Kids Can Pr., Ltd.

The Magic of Snowflakes II. 2001. 15.95 (978-0-9719384-2-7(3)) Light in Glass Publishing.

Mains, Barbara, ed. I Touched the Moon! Stories & Crafts for Kids. Lewis, Robin Baird et al, illus. Chevrier, Tim, photos by. 2001. 48p. (J). (ps-k). pap. 12.95 (978-1-55037-674-6(8)); lib. bdg. 19.95 (978-1-55037-675-3(6)) Annick Pr., Ltd. CAN. *Dist:* Firefly Bks., Ltd.

Major, John & Belanus, Betty J. Caravan to America: Living Arts of the Silk Road. 2002. (Illus.). 144p. (J). (gr. 3-6). pap. 15.95 (978-0-8126-2677-3(X)); (gr. 4-6). 24.95 (978-0-8126-2666-7(4)) Cricket Bks.

Make a Rainbow, 6 Pk. (Story Steps Ser.). (gr. k-2). 23.00 (978-0-7635-9812-9(7)) Rigby Education.

Make Your Own KC the Carrot & Art the Amoeba Craft Kit. 2001. 5.95 (978-1-930514-22-5(0) , KCKIT) Diana Waring Presents.

Make Your Own Little Golden Book & Backpack. 2000. (Little Golden Bks.). (Illus.). (J). 16.99 (978-0-307-19595-1(3) , Golden Bks.) Random Hse. Children's Bks.

Make Your Own Pompom Pals. 2006. (Creative Studio Ser.). (Illus.). 48p. (YA). (978-1-905359-87-5(X)) Top That! Publishing PLC.

Making Amazing Art: 40 Activities Using the 7 Elements of Art Design. 2007. (Illus.). 128p. (J). (gr. 2-8). 16.99 (***978-0-8249-6794-9(1)***); pap. 12.99 (***978-0-8249-6795-6(X)***) Ideals Pubns. (Williamson Bks.).

Makosz, Rory. Latino Arts & Their Influence on the United States: Songs, Dreams, & Dances. 2005. (Illus.). 112p. (J). (ps-7). lib. bdg. (978-1-59084-938-5(8) , 1234500) Mason Crest Pubs.

Man-Kong, Mary. Party Time! Create It All with Play-Doh Colors & Stencil. 2003. (Play-Doh Ser.). (Illus.). 10p. (J). 9.95 (978-0-7624-1563-2(0) , Running Pr. Kids) Running Pr. Bk. Pubs.

Manning, Mick & Granstrom, Brita. Dinomania: Things to Do with Dinosaurs. 2002. (Illus.). 32p. (J). (gr. k-3). 16.95 (978-0-8234-1641-7(0)) Holiday Hse., Inc.

Maring, Therese, ed. Scrapbook Studio: Everything You Need To Make A Fresh & Funky Scrapbook— In A Flash. Lukatz, Casey, illus. 2005. (American Girl Library). 40p. (YA). 17.95 (978-1-58485-731-0(5) , American Girl) American Girl Publishing, Inc.

Marsh, Carole. Quilt Our African American. 2002. 36p. (gr. 3-8). pap. 7.95 (978-0-635-01577-8(3)) Gallopade International.

—Wyoming People Projects: 30 Cool, Activities, Crafts, Experiments & More for Kids to Do to Learn about Your State! 2003. (Wyoming Experience Ser.). 32p. (gr. k-5). pap. 5.95 (978-0-635-02019-2(X) , Marsh, Carole Bks.) Gallopade International.

Martin, Laura C. Recycled Crafts Box: Sock Puppets, Cardboard Castles, Bottle Bugs & 37 More Earth-Friendly Projects & Activities You Can Create. 2004. (Illus.). 96p. (J). pap. 10.95 (978-1-58017-522-7(8) , 67522); tchr. ed. 19.95 (978-1-58017-523-4(6) , 67523) Storey Publishing, LLC. (Storey Kids).

Martin, Laura C. & Cain, David. Nature's Art Box: From T-Shirts to Twig Baskets, 65 Cool Projects for Crafty Kids to Make with Natural Materials You Can Find Anywhere. 2003. (Illus.). (gr. 3-7). 224p. tchr. ed. 23.95 (978-1-58017-503-6(1) , 67503); 192p. (J). pap. 16.95 (978-1-58017-490-9(6) , 67490) Storey Publishing, LLC. (Storey Kids).

Marxhausen, Kim. Paper Paint & Print. 2004. 80p. (ps-3). 9.99 (978-0-7586-0054-7(2)) Concordia Publishing Hse.

Masessa, Ed. The Wandmaker's Guidebook. Araujo, Paige Krul, ed. Jankowski, Dan, illus. 2006. 18p. (J). 22.99 (978-0-439-86265-3(5) , Tangerine Pr.) Scholastic, Inc.

Matsudaira, Lori. Year Round Crafts & Activities for Children. 1998. (Illus.). 175p. (J). (ps-8). 14.95 (978-1-887188-04-3(5)) Silesia Companies, Inc.

May, Darcy. Christmas Gift Labels. 2005. (Illus.). 4p. pap. 1.50 (978-0-486-44128-3(8)) Dover Pubns., Inc.

McAllister, Buff. Sewing with Felt: Learn Basic Stitches to Create More Than 60 Colorful Projects. Schneider, Hank, photos by. 2003. (Illus.). 88p. (YA). spiral bd. 19.95 (978-1-56397-999-6(3)) Boyds Mills Pr.

McArthur, Alex & Shepard, Tristram. Textiles Technology for Key Stage 3. 2000. (Design & Make It Ser.). (Illus.). 144p. (J). (gr. 6-9). pap., stu. ed. 22.50 (978-0-7487-4431-2(2)) Nelson Thornes Ltd. GBR. *Dist:* Trans-Atlantic Pubns., Inc.

McCallum, Graham. 4000 Animal, Bird & Fish Motifs: A Sourcebook. 2005. (Illus.). 384p. pap. 17.95 (978-0-7134-8939-2(1) , Batsford, B. T. Ltd.) Anova Bks. GBR. *Dist:* Sterling Publishing Co., Inc.

McClendon, Kristi, illus. A Forever Angel. 2001. 30p. 8.95 (978-1-56123-137-9(1) , FOAC) Centering Corp.

McCormick, Rosie. Our Bodies & Art Activities. 2002. (Arty Facts Ser.). (Illus.). 48p. (J). (gr. 3-4). pap. (978-0-7787-1145-2(5)); lib. bdg. (978-0-7787-1117-9(X)) Crabtree Publishing Co.

—Our Bodies & Art Activities. 2002. (gr. 3-6). lib. bdg. 17.60 (978-0-613-52891-7(3)) Tandem Library Bks.

—Plants & Art Activities. 2002. (Arty Facts Ser.). (Illus.). 48p. (J). (gr. 3-4). pap. (978-0-7787-1138-4(2)); lib. bdg. (978-0-7787-1110-0(2)) Crabtree Publishing Co.

—Plants & Art Activities. 2002. (gr. 3-6). lib. bdg. 17.60 (978-0-613-82416-3(4)) Tandem Library Bks.

McGraw-Hill Staff. Holiday & Everyday Projects. 2003. (gr. k-3). lib. bdg. 15.25 (978-0-613-88630-7(5)) Tandem Library Bks.

McGraw, Mary. Stamp Your Stuff! Make Your Own Stamps & Decorate Your Room, Clothes & Favorite Things. 2003. (Illus.). 64p. pap. 12.99 (978-1-58180-386-0(9) , North Light Bks.) F & W Pubns., Inc.

McNamara, Beth Branigan, et al. Big Book of Ideas for Children's Faith Formation. 2001. (Illus.). 352p. pap. 24.95 (978-0-87973-018-5(8)) Our Sunday Visitor, Publishing Div.

McOmber, Rachel B., ed. McOmber Phonics Storybooks: You Can Make It. rev. ed. (Illus.). (J). (978-0-944991-51-0(3)) Swift Learning Resources.

McPhail, David M. Fix-It. McPhail, David M., illus. 2002. (Illus.). 12p. (J). bds. 6.99 (978-0-525-46849-3(8) , Dutton Juvenile) Penguin Group (USA) Inc.

Mead, Brian. The Spooky Halloween Cut & Color Activity Book. 2003. 48p. (J). (ps-3). pap. 3.99 (978-0-9717509-1-3(2)) Mead, Brian Publishing.

Medina, Sarah. Having Fun with Paint. 2007. (J). (***978-1-4042-3718-6(6)*** , PowerKids Pr.) Rosen Publishing Group, Inc., The.

—Having Fun with Printing. 2007. (J). lib. bdg. (***978-1-4042-3719-3(4)*** , PowerKids Pr.) Rosen Publishing Group, Inc., The.

—Having Fun with Sculpture. 2007. (J). lib. bdg. (978-1-4042-3720-9(8) , PowerKids Pr.) Rosen Publishing Group, Inc., The.

—Having Fun with Textiles. 2007. (J). lib. bdg. (978-1-4042-3717-9(8) , PowerKids Pr.) Rosen Publishing Group, Inc., The.

Merrill, Yvonne Y. Hands-on America Vol. 2: Art Activities about Colonial America, African-Americans, & Southeast Indians. 2006. (Hands-on Ser.). 71p. (J). pap. 20.00 (978-0-9778797-0-4(4)) KITS Publishing.

—Hands-on Ancient People: Art Activities about Mesopotamia, Egypt, & Islam. 2003. (gr. 3-6). lib. bdg. 30.40 (978-0-613-77802-2(2)) Tandem Library Bks.

Miller, Heather. Nifty Thrifty Art Crafts. 2007. (Nifty Thrifty Crafts for Kids Ser.). (Illus.). 32p. (J). (gr. 3-4). lib. bdg. 22.60 (978-0-7660-2780-0(5) , Enslow Elementary) Enslow Pubs., Inc.

Milne, A. A. Disney's Pooh's Treasury of Special Days. Case, Cassandra, ed. 2000. (Illus.). 85p. (J). (978-0-7172-6413-1(0) , Grolier) Scholastic Library Publishing.

Mitchell, Mari Rutz. Creating Clever Castles & Cars (from Boxes & Other Stuff) Kids Ages 3-8 Make Their Own Pretend Play Spaces. Kline, Michael P., illus. 2006. (Williamson Little Hands Book Ser.). 128p. (J). 14.95 (978-0-8249-6783-3(6) , 1256115); pap. 12.95 (978-0-8249-6782-6(8) , 1256115) Ideals Pubns. (Williamson Bks.).

Modela con Pasta de Sal. (SPA.). (J). (gr. k-3). 10.00 (978-84-342-1991-5(3)) Parramon Ediciones S.A. ESP. *Dist:* Distribuidora Norma, Inc., Lectorum Pubns., Inc.

Modelos. (One Hundred One Things to Do Ser.).Tr. of Models. (SPA.). (J). (gr. 3-5). pap. 4.76 (978-950-724-206-9(6)) Lumen ARG. *Dist:* Lectorum Pubns., Inc.

Moffatt, Judith. Bugs: A Read & Do Book. 2001. (Hello Reader! Ser.). (Illus.). (J). (978-0-606-21088-1(1)) Tandem Library Bks.

—Snow Shapes: A Read & Do Book. Moffatt, Judith, illus. 2000. (Hello Reader! Ser.). (Illus.). 32p. (J). (gr. k-2). pap. 3.99 (978-0-439-09858-0(0)) Scholastic, Inc.

—Snow Shapes: A Read-and-Do Book. 2000. (Hello Reader! Ser.). (Illus.). (J). (978-0-606-19614-7(5)) Tandem Library Bks.

—Valentines: A Read-and-Do Book. 1999. (gr. k-3). lib. bdg. 11.80 (978-0-613-64822-6(6)) Tandem Library Bks.

Monaghan, Kimberly. Organic Crafts: 75 Earth-Friendly Art Activities. 2007. (Illus.). 160p. (J). (gr. 2-5). pap. 14.95 (978-1-55652-640-4(7)) Chicago Review Pr., Inc.

Monster Stickers. 2004. (Art Rom Create Your Own... Ser.). (Illus.). 24p. (J). pap. incl. audio compact disk (978-1-84229-734-6(1)) Top That! Publishing PLC.

Moody, Ben. Just Tooling Around. 2001. (Illus.). 28p. pap. (978-1-892214-89-8(X) , 6008-10) Tandy Leather Co.

Moran, Erin. Colorful Spring. Pickett, Danny, illus. 2005. 32p. (J). mass mkt. 15.95 (978-0-9763778-0-1(2)) Seal Rock Publishing, LLC.

Morgan, Sally. Old Clothes. 2007. (***978-1-59920-011-8(2)***) Smart Apple Media.

Morris, Ting. Ancient China. 2006. (Arts & Crafts of Ser.). (Illus.). 32p. (J). (978-1-58340-914-5(9) , 1262690) Smart Apple Media.

—Ancient Egypt. Young, E., illus. 2006. 32p. (J). (978-1-58340-911-4(4)) Smart Apple Media.

—Ancient Greece. 2006. (Arts & Crafts of Ser.). (Illus.). 32p. (J). (978-1-58340-912-1(2) , 1262692) Smart Apple Media.

—Ancient Rome. 2006. (Arts & Crafts of Ser.). (Illus.). 32p. (J). (978-1-58340-913-8(0) , 1262693) Smart Apple Media.

—Animals. 2006. (Illus.). 32p. (J). (978-1-59771-025-1(3)) Sea-To-Sea Pubns.

—Native Americans. Young, E., illus. 2006. 32p. (J). (978-1-58340-916-9(5)) Smart Apple Media.

Morris, Ting & Morris, Neil. Dinosaurs. Levy, Ruth & Cowne, Joanne, illus. 2007. 32p. (J). (***978-1-59771-029-9(6)***) Sea-To-Sea Pubns.

—Music. Levy, Ruth, illus. 2006. 32p. (J). (978-1-59771-027-5(X)) Sea-To-Sea Pubns.

—Rainforest. Hulse, Gillian, illus. 2006. 32p. (J). (978-1-59771-028-2(8)) Sea-To-Sea Pubns.

Morris, Ting & Young, E. Aztecs & Maya. 2006. (Illus.). 32p. (J). (978-1-58340-915-2(7) , 1262694) Smart Apple Media.

Mouse Works Staff. Make Your Own Finger Puppets. 2000. (Illus.). 40p. (J). (gr. 1-5). 7.99 (978-0-7364-1017-5(1)) Mouse Works.

Moyer, Bernadette A. Bee an Artist & Bee Creative: Sketch Book. 1999. (Illus.). 50p. (J). (gr. k-12). spiral bd. 12.95 (978-0-9666183-6-5(X)) Two Bee-A-TwinBee Publishing, LLC.

Mulanax, Carol. How to Make a Towel Monkey & other Cruise Ship Favorites. 2006. spiral bd. 14.95 (978-0-9787477-0-1(4)) Tiny Tortoise Publishing, LLC.

Mulcahy, Lisa, et al. Bye Bye Boredom! The Girl's Life Big Book of Fun. 2003. (Illus.). 124p. (J). (978-0-439-44976-2(6)) Scholastic, Inc.

Muldrow, Diane. Dream Vacation. Cuddy, Robbin, illus. 2007. (Groovy Girls Ser.). 96p. (J). 2.99 (***978-1-4169-3508-7(8)*** , Simon Scribbles) Simon & Schuster Children's Publishing.

My Book of Pasting. 2005. (J). per. 6.95 (978-1-933241-02-9(0)) Kumon Publishing North America, Inc.

My First Book of Cutting. 2004. (Illus.). 80p. (J). per. 6.95 (978-4-7743-0708-4(4)) Kumon Publishing North America, Inc.

Mystery Crafts for Kids. 2004. pap. 14.99 (978-0-570-05270-8(X)) Concordia Publishing Hse.

Nathan, Emma. Artesanias. 2002. (Abre los Ojos y Aprende Serie).Tr. of Eyeopeners: Crafts. (SPA.). 24p. (J). (-3). 22.45 (978-1-4103-0025-6(0) , Blackbirch Pr., Inc.) Thomson Gale.

—Arts & Crafts. 2002. (Eyeopeners Ser.). (Illus.). 24p. (J). 22.45 (978-1-56711-598-7(5) , Blackbirch Pr., Inc.) Thomson Gale.

Navidad. 2002. (Big Steps Ser.). (SPA.). 40p. (J). 17.95 (978-980-6437-35-7(7)) Playco Editores, C.A.

Nayer, Judy. Projects for Preschoolers Arts & Crafts. 1999. (Projects for Preschoolers Ser.). (Illus.). 48p. (J). (ps-1). mass mkt. 4.99 (978-0-7681-0080-8(1) , 67305, McClanahan Bk.) Learning Horizons, Inc.

Newcomb, Rain. Girls' World Book of Jewelry: 50 Cool Designs to Make. 2004. (Illus.). 128p. pap. 14.95 (978-1-57990-473-9(4)) Lark Bks.

Newcomb, Rain & Gaines, Thom. Digital Photo Madness! 50 Weird & Wacky Things to Do with Your Digital Camera. 2006. (Illus.). 128p. (J). pap. 9.95 (978-1-57990-624-5(9)) Lark Bks.

Nicholson, Libby. Creating with Fimo. 1999. (gr. k-3). lib. bdg. 14.10 (978-0-613-81240-5(9)) Tandem Library Bks.

Nickelodeon Staff. Nick Jr. I Made It Myself! Christmas: 38 Festive Crafts & Recipes. 2004. (Illus.). 24p. (J). spiral bd. 12.95 (978-0-8118-4420-8(X)) Chronicle Bks. LLC.

Niven, Felicia Lowenstein. Nifty Thrifty Music Crafts. 2007. (Nifty Thrifty Crafts for Kids Ser.). (Illus.). 32p. (J). (gr. 3-4). lib. bdg. 22.60 (978-0-7660-2784-8(8) , 1264783, Enslow Elementary) Enslow Pubs., Inc.

Northwestern Publishing House Staff. Good News Daily Craft Book. 2001. (Vacation Bible Study Ser.). (J). pap. (978-0-8100-1317-9(7)) Northwestern Publishing Hse.

Norton, Frances Maree. The Victorian Tea Spirit: A Girl's Guide to Her Secret Self, 1. 100th ed. 2003. (Illus.). 230p. (YA). per. 19.95 (978-0-9632938-1-7(8)) Norton, Frances M.

O'Brien, Joan. Decorating Easter Eggs. 2001. (Illus.). 4p. (J). pap. 1.50 (978-0-486-41841-4(3)) Dover Pubns., Inc.

Ochester, Betsy. Look What You Can Make with Egg Cartons. 2000. (gr. 3-6). lib. bdg. 14.10 (978-0-613-59326-7(X)) Tandem Library Bks.

Ochester, Betsy, ed. Look What You Can Make with Egg Cartons: Over 90 Pictured Crafts & Dozens of Other Ideas. Schneider, Hank, photos by. 2003. (Illus.). 48p. (YA). (gr. 3-5). pap. 5.95 (978-1-56397-906-4(3)) Boyds Mills Pr.

H I

Oficios: Actividades Creativas para la Educacion Infantil. (Manitas Creativas Ser.). (SPA., Illus.). (J). (ps-k). 14.00 (978-84-342-2262-5(0)) Parramon Ediciones S.A. ESP. *Dist:* Distribuidora Norma, Inc., Lectorum Pubns., Inc.

Olexiewicz, Charlene. Super More Friendship Crafts. 2000. (Fifty Nifty Ser.). (Illus.). 80p. (J). (gr. 3-7). pap. 6.95 (978-0-7373-0501-2(0)) Lowell Hse. Juvenile.

O'Sullivan, Joanne. The Girls' World Book of Friendship Crafts: Cool Stuff to Make with Your Best Friends. 2005. (Illus.). 144p. pap. 14.95 (978-1-57990-471-5(8)) Lark Bks.

Oswald, Diane. Christian Crafts from Plastic Containers. Skiles, Janet, illus. 2005. (J). pap. 8.99 (978-0-7647-0589-2(X)) School Specialty Publishing.

Otten, Jack. Making Things, 6 Vols. 2004. (Illus.). 24p. (J). (ps-2). 87.00 (978-0-516-29693-7(0) , Children's Pr.) Scholastic Library Publishing.

—Watch Me Build a Sandcastle. 2002. (Welcome Books). (Illus.). 24p. (J). (ps-k). 18.00 (978-0-516-23946-0(5)); pap. 4.95 (978-0-516-23496-0(X)) Scholastic Library Publishing. (Children's Pr.).

—Watch Me Build a Sandcastle. 2002. (gr. k-3). lib. bdg. 12.95 (978-0-613-58809-6(6)) Tandem Library Bks.

—Watch Me Make a Bird Feeder. 2002. (Welcome Bks.). (Illus.). 24p. (J). (ps-2). pap. 4.95 (978-0-516-23497-7(8) , Children's Pr.) Scholastic Library Publishing.

—Watch Me Make a Bird Feeder. 2002. (gr. k-3). lib. bdg. 12.95 (978-0-613-58810-2(X)) Tandem Library Bks.

—Watch Me Make a Birthday Card. 2002. (Welcome Books). (Illus.). 24p. (J). (ps-2). 18.00 (978-0-516-23948-4(1)); pap. 4.95 (978-0-516-23498-4(6)) Scholastic Library Publishing. (Children's Pr.).

Oxlade, Chris. Writing & Printing. (Illus.). 32p. (YA). (gr. 3 up). lib. bdg. 27.10 (978-1-932889-08-6(6)) Sea-To-Sea Pubns.

Oxlade, Chris, et al. 300 Science & History Projects. 2006. (Illus.). 512p. pap. 19.99 (978-1-84476-310-8(2) , Southwater) Anness Publishing GBR. *Dist:* National Bk. Network.

Panchyk, Richard & Ketchum, William C., Jr. American Folk Art for Kids: With 21 Activities. 2004. (For Kids Ser.). (Illus.). 128p. (J). pap. 16.95 (978-1-55652-499-8(4)) Chicago Review Pr., Inc.

Panik, Alison Saeger. Ginger Snap's Cookie Book: A Sugar & Spice Adventure. 2005. (Illus.). 39p. (J). (978-0-439-70467-0(7)) Scholastic, Inc.

Parker, Steve. Insects, Bugs, & Art Activities. 2002. (gr. 3-6). lib. bdg. 17.60 (978-0-613-82415-6(6)) Tandem Library Bks.

Parker, Steve & Goodman, Polly. Insects, Bugs, & Art Activities. 2002. (Arty Facts Ser.). (Illus.). 48p. (J). (gr. 3-4). pap. (978-0-7787-1137-7(4)); lib. bdg. (978-0-7787-1109-4(9)) Crabtree Publishing Co.

Parramon's Editorial Team Staff. Papier Mache. Parramon's Editorial Team Staff, photos by. 2004. (Let's Create! Ser.). (Illus.). 32p. (J). (gr. 2 up). lib. bdg. 23.33 (978-0-8368-4017-9(8)) Stevens, Gareth Inc.

—Recyclables. Parramon's Editorial Team Staff, photos by. 2004. (Let's Create! Ser.). (Illus.). 32p. (J). (gr. 2 up). lib. bdg. 23.33 (978-0-8368-4018-6(6)) Stevens, Gareth Inc.

—Stones & "Stuff" Parramon's Editorial Team Staff, photos by. 2004. (Let's Create! Ser.). (Illus.). 32p. (J). (gr. 2 up). lib. bdg. 23.33 (978-0-8368-4019-3(4)) Stevens, Gareth Inc.

Parrish, Maisie. Funstation Dough Craft, 5 vols., Set. 1998. (Funstations Ser.). (Illus.). 48p. (J). (gr. 3-7). 17.95 (978-1-57145-351-8(2) , Silver Dolphin Bks.) Advantage Pubs. Group.

Parsons, Susan. Funtastic Kid Crafts. 2002. (Bible Funstuff Series! Ser.). 112p. pap., pap. 16.99 (978-0-7814-3838-4(1) , 0781438381) Cook, David C. Publishing Co.

Patten, Dennis. The Matchstick Fun Book. 1999. (Illus.). 48p. (J). (gr. 6-12). pap. 9.95 (978-0-7641-1215-7(5)) Barron's Educational Series, Inc.

Pensiero, Janet. Totally Cool Journals, Notebooks & Diaries. 2005. (Illus.). 96p. (J). pap. 9.95 (978-1-4027-2241-7(9)) Sterling Publishing Co., Inc.

Peter Pig & his Food. 2004. (Play Pals Ser.). (Illus.). 12p. (J). bds. (978-1-84229-646-2(9)) Top That! Publishing PLC.

Phillips, Matt. Make Your Own Fun Frames! Jaskiel, Stan, illus. 2001. (Quick Starts for Kids! Ser.). 64p. (YA). (gr. 3 up). pap. 8.95 (978-1-885593-64-1(3) , Williamson Bks.) Ideals Pubns.

Piece of Cake, 6 Packs. (gr. k-1). 23.00 (978-0-7635-9051-2(7)) Rigby Education.

Pinol, Roser. Creating with Paper. 2000. (Crafts for All Seasons Ser.). (Illus.). 32p. (J). (gr. 3-8). lib. bdg. 23.70 (978-1-56711-434-8(2) , Blackbirch Pr., Inc.) Thomson Gale.

Pleasant Company Staff. Fantastic Sticker Art. 2004. (American Girl Library(R) Ser.). (Illus.). 42p. (J). 19.95 (978-1-58485-910-9(5)) American Girl Publishing, Inc.

Plomer, Anna Olimos & Parramon Studios Staff. Let's Create! Plastic, Cardboard, Fabrics, Clay. 2001. (Illus.). 128p. (J). (gr. k up). pap. 14.95 (978-0-7641-1819-7(6)) Barron's Educational Series, Inc.

Pomaska, Anna. Sun, Moon & Stars Armband Tattoos. 2003. (Dover Little Activity Bks.). (Illus.). 2p. (J). pap. 1.50 (978-0-486-42642-6(4)) Dover Pubns., Inc.

Pomeroy, Diana. One Potato: A Counting Book of Potato Prints. 2000. (Illus.). 28p. (J). (ps-3). pap. 6.00 (978-0-15-202330-0(5) , Harcourt Paperbacks) Harcourt Children's Bks.

—One Potato: A Counting Book of Potato Prints. 2000. (978-0-606-18807-4(X)) Tandem Library Bks.

Ponte, June. Fun & Simple Mid-Atlantic State Crafts: New York, New Jersey, Pennsylvania, Delaware, Maryland, & Washington, D. C. 2008. (Fun & Simple State Crafts Ser.). (Illus.). 48p. (J). (gr. 3-4). lib. bdg. 23.93 (*978-0-7660-2933-0(6)* , Enslow Elementary) Enslow Pubs., Inc.

—Fun & Simple New England State Crafts: Maine, New Hampshire, Vermont, Massachusetts, Rhode Island, & Connecticut. 2008. (Fun & Simple State Crafts Ser.). (Illus.). 48p. (J). (gr. 3-4). lib. bdg. 23.93 (*978-0-7660-2934-7(4)* , Enslow Elementary) Enslow Pubs., Inc.

—Fun & Simple Southeastern State Crafts: West Virginia, Virginia, North Carolina, South Carolina, Georgia, & Florida. 2008. (J). (*978-0-7660-2935-4(2)*) Enslow Pubs., Inc.

—Fun & Simple Southern State Crafts: Kentucky, Tennessee, Alabama, Mississippi, Louisiana, & Arkansas. 2008. (J). (*978-0-7660-2936-1(0)*) Enslow Pubs., Inc.

Pope, Terri A. Look What I Made! Easy Holiday Crafts for Young Children. Weaver-Spencer, Jennifer, ed. Ling, George, illus. 1998. 96p. (ps-1). pap. 11.99 (978-0-88724-470-4(X) , CD-0060) Carson-Dellosa Publishing Co., Inc.

Popular Mechanics Press Editors. The Boy Mechanic: 200 Classic Things to Build. 2006. (Illus.). 272p. 9.95 (978-1-58816-509-1(4)) Sterling Publishing Co., Inc.

—How to Make Cool Gadgets for Your Room. Rodrigues, Teco, illus. 2001. (Popular Mechanics for Kids Ser.). 64p. (J). (gr. 4-7). pap. 8.95 (978-0-688-17727-0(1) , Harper Trophy) HarperCollins Pubs.

Popular Mechanics Staff. The Boy Mechanic: Best Projects from the Classic Popular Mechanics Series. 2006. 144p. pap. 7.95 (978-0-486-45227-2(1)) Dover Pubns., Inc.

Powell, Michelle. Mosaics. (Step-by-Step Ser.). (Illus.). 32p. 2003. (YA). pap. 7.95 (978-1-4034-0710-8(X)); 2001. (J). (gr. 3-5). lib. bdg. 24.22 (978-1-57572-332-7(8)) Heinemann Library.

—Mosaics. 2001. (gr. k-3). lib. bdg. 17.60 (978-0-613-76977-8(5)) Tandem Library Bks.

—Printing. 2000. (Step-by-Step Ser.). (Illus.). 32p. (J). (gr. 3-5). lib. bdg. 24.22 (978-1-57572-329-7(8)) Heinemann Library.

—Printing. 2000. (Step-by-Step Children's Crafts Ser.). (Illus.). 32p. (ps-3). pap. 7.95 (978-0-85532-911-2(4) , 9114) Search Pr., Ltd. GBR. *Dist:* Independent Pubs. Group.

Pratt, Leonie. Knights & Castles Things to Make & Do. Thompson, Josephine Et Al, illus. 2006. 32p. (J). pap. 6.99 (978-0-7945-1355-9(7) , Usborne) EDC Publishing.

—Sparkly Things to Make & Do. 2005. (Illus.). 32p. (J). pap. 6.95 (978-0-7945-0834-0(0) , Usborne) EDC Publishing.

Press, Judy. All Around Town! Exploring Your Community Through Craft Fun. 2002. (Williamson's Little Hands Book Ser.). (Illus.). 128p. (J). (ps-3). pap. 12.95 (978-1-885593-68-9(6) , Williamson Bks.) Ideals Pubns.

—Around-the-World Art & Activities: Visiting the 7 Continents Through Craft Fun. 2000. (Little Hands Bks.). (Illus.). 144p. (J). (ps-3). pap. 12.95 (978-1-885593-45-0(7) , Williamson Bks.) Ideals Pubns.

—ArtStarts for Little Hands! 2000. (gr. k-3). lib. bdg. 22.20 (978-0-613-27715-0(5)) Tandem Library Bks.

—At the Zoo! Explore the Animal World with Craft Fun. Campbell, Jenny, illus. 2001. (Little Hands Bks.). 128p. (J). (ps-2). pap. 12.95 (978-1-885593-61-0(9) , Williamson Bks.) Ideals Pubns.

Press, Judy. Big Fun Christmas Crafts & Activities. 2006. (Illus.). 128p. (J). pap. 12.95 (978-0-8249-6786-4(0) , Williamson Bks.) Ideals Pubns.

Press, Judy. Big Fun Christmas Crafts & Activities. 2006. (Illus.). 128p. (J). 16.95 (978-0-8249-6787-1(9) , Williamson Bks.) Ideals Pubns.

—Little Hands Sea Life Art & Activities: Creative Learning Experiences for 3- to 7-Year Olds. 2004. (Williamson's Little Hands Book Ser.). (Illus.). 128p. (J). 12.95 (978-1-885593-94-8(5) , Williamson Bks.) Ideals Pubns.

Price, Karen. Scrapbooking for Kids. Blauberg, Alyssa, illus. 1999. 24p. (J). ring bd. 9.95 (978-1-58295-013-6(X) , Beehive Bk.) Pace Products, Inc.

Price, Pam. Cool Rubber Stamp Art. 2005. (Cool Crafts Ser.). (J). (gr. k-6). lib. bdg. 22.78 (978-1-59197-743-8(6) , Checkerboard Library) ABDO Publishing Co.

Priddy, Roger. Sticker Activity Fun Pirate. 2007. 48p. (J). bds. 3.95 (978-0-312-49920-4(5) , Priddy Bks.) St. Martin's Pr.

—Sticker Activity Fun Princess. 2007. 48p. (J). bds. 3.95 (978-0-312-49919-8(1) , Priddy Bks.) St. Martin's Pr.

—Wipe Clean Activity Atlas. 2007. 42p. (J). bds. 14.95 (978-0-312-49736-1(9) , Priddy Bks.) St. Martin's Pr.

Priddy, Roger & Priddy Books Staff. Sticker Activity Fun on the Farm: Play & Learn. rev. ed. 2006. 48p. (J). bds. 3.47 (978-0-312-49798-9(9) , Priddy Bks.) St. Martin's Pr.

—Sticker Activity Fun Teddy Bears: Play & Learn. rev. ed. 2006. 48p. (J). bds. 3.47 (978-0-312-49799-6(7) , Priddy Bks.) St. Martin's Pr.

Prime, D. Hacen un Album de Recortes. (Serie Sara y Pablo - Sarah & Paul Ser.: No. 4). Tr. of Make a Scrapbook. (SPA.). (J). 2.99 (978-0-7899-0498-0(5) , 498898) Editorial Unilit.

Prins, M. D. Paper Galaxy: Out-of-This-World Projects to Cut, Fold & Paste. 2007. (Illus.). 128p. pap. 12.95 (978-1-4027-4716-8(0)) Sterling Publishing Co., Inc.

Provo Craft Designers Staff. Cheery Holiday Greetings. 1999. (Illus.). 16p. (J). (978-1-58050-068-5(4) , 40-6200) Provo Craft.

Pugliano-Martin, Carol. Artesanías del mundo & Making Crafts from Around the World. 2005. spiral bd. 77.00 (*978-1-4108-5674-6(7)*) Benchmark Education Co.

Pugliano-Martin, Carol. Making Crafts from Around the World. 2004. (Navigators Ser.). (J). pap. 38.00 (978-1-4108-0410-5(0)) Benchmark Education Co.

Quasha, Jennifer. The Birth & Growth of a Nation: Hands-On Projects about Symbols of American Liberty. 2001. (Great Social Studies Projects Ser.). (Illus.). 24p. (J). (gr. 3). lib. bdg. 19.95 (978-0-8239-5703-3(9) , PowerKids Pr.) Rosen Publishing Group, Inc., The.

—Gold Rush: Hands-On Projects about Mining the Riches of California. 2001. (Great Social Studies Projects Ser.). (Illus.). 24p. (J). (gr. 3). lib. bdg. 19.95 (978-0-8239-5705-7(5) , PowerKids Pr.) Rosen Publishing Group, Inc., The.

—Jamestown: Hands-On Projects about One of America's First Communities. 2001. (Great Social Studies Projects Ser.). (Illus.). 24p. (J). (gr. 3). lib. bdg. 19.95 (978-0-8239-5701-9(2) , PowerKids Pr.) Rosen Publishing Group, Inc., The.

—The Pony Express: Hands-On Projects about Early Communication. 2001. (Great Social Studies Projects Ser.). (Illus.). 24p. (J). (gr. 3). lib. bdg. 19.95 (978-0-8239-5702-6(0) , PowerKids Pr.) Rosen Publishing Group, Inc., The.

Quick to Create Snowmen, Vol. I. 2003. 11.99 (978-0-930184-04-9(1)) Clapper Publishing Co.

Quick to Create Snowmen 2, Vol. II. 2003. 11.99 (978-0-930184-05-6(X)) Clapper Publishing Co.

Raintree Steck-Vaughn Staff. Art from Paper. 2000. (Salvaged Ser.). (Illus.). (J). (ps-3). 24.26 (978-0-8172-5275-5(4)) Raintree.

Rainy Day Projects. Date not set. (Get Crafty Ser.). (Illus.). 48p. (J). pap. 4.98 (978-0-7525-8410-2(3)) Parragon, Inc.

Reid, Barbara. Fun with Modeling Clay. Reid, Barbara, illus. 1998. (Kids Can Do It Ser.). (Illus.). 134p. (J). (gr. 4-6). (978-1-55074-510-8(7)) Kids Can Pr., Ltd.

Reid, Struan. The Science & History Project Book. 2004. (Illus.). 512p. 45.00 (978-0-7548-1445-0(9) , Lorenz Bks.) Anness Publishing GBR. *Dist:* National Bk. Network.

Reiser, Lynn W. Cherry Pies & Lullabies. 1998. (Illus.). 40p. (J). (ps-3). 16.89 (978-0-688-13392-4(4)) HarperCollins Pubs.

Reitzes, Fretta & Teitelman, Beth. Wonderplay, Too: Games, Crafts, & Creative Activities for 3- to 6-year Olds. 2007. (Illus.). 112p. pap. 12.95 (*978-0-7624-2863-2(5)* , Running Pr.) Running Pr. Bk. Pubs.

Revoir, Katherine Q. Create! A Sketchbook & Journal. Carluccio, Maria, illus. 2001. 96p. (gr. 4-7). 14.95 (978-0-8118-2784-3(4)) Chronicle Bks. LLC.

Rhatigan, Joe. In Print! 40 Cool Publishing Projects for Kids. 2004. (Illus.). 128p. (YA). 20.00 (978-0-7567-8235-1(X)) DIANE Publishing Co.

—Soapmaking: 50 Fun & Fabulous Soaps to Melt & Pour. 2005. (Illus.). 112p. (J). pap. 9.95 (978-1-57990-674-0(5)) Lark Bks.

Rhatigan, Joe & Newcomb, Rain. Stamp It! 50 Amazing Projects to Make. 2005. (Illus.). 112p. (J). (ps-9). pap. 9.95 (978-1-57990-756-3(3)) Lark Bks.

Rhatigan, Joe, et al. Craft It! 50 Fun Stamp, Paper & Polymer Clay Projects. 2005. (Illus.). 176p. (J). (978-0-7607-9514-9(2)) Barnes & Noble, Inc.

Ribble, Karen. Beginning Hair Braiding Taught. 2005. (Illus.). 22p. 7.00 (978-0-9725170-6-5(5)) Braided Image.

Richmond, Margie Hayes, ed. Look What You Can Make with Tubes: Over 90 Pictured Crafts & Dozens of More Ideas. 2003. (Illus.). 48p. (YA). (gr. k-7). pap., stu. ed. 5.95 (978-1-56397-677-3(3)) Boyds Mills Pr.

Rigby Education Staff. Discovery World Org Fun Things. (Discovery World Ser.). (Illus.). 12p. (gr. 1-2). 27.00 (978-0-7635-2700-6(9)) Rigby Education.

Riley, Karen. Landfill Lunch Box. (Illus.). 32p. (J). pap. 11.95 (978-0-9708135-0-3(3)) S.C.R.A.P. Gallery.

Ritchey, Kate. Creepy Crafts for Boys & Ghouls. Guy-Christiansen, Debbie, illus. 2006. (Pretty Simple Stuff Ser.). 32p. (J). (gr. 2-5). pap. 6.99 (978-0-8431-2023-3(1) , Price Stern Sloan) Penguin Group (USA) Inc.

Rivera, Diego. Diego Rivera Tattoos. 2004. (Art Tattoos Ser.). (Illus.). 2p. pap. 1.50 (978-0-486-43523-7(7)) Dover Pubns., Inc.

Robertson, Linda. Kwanzaa Fun: Great Things to Make & Do. 2003. (Holiday Fun Ser.). 32p. (J). (gr. 3-5). pap. 4.95 (978-0-7534-5685-9(0) , Kingfisher) Houghton Mifflin Co. Trade & Reference Div.

Robins, Deri & Perry, Kate. Mixed Media. 2006. (Illus.). 32p. (J). 9.95 (978-1-58728-545-5(2) , Two Can Publishing) T&N Children's Publishing.

Robinson, Fay. Christmas Crafts. 2004. (Fun Holiday Crafts Kids Can Do Ser.). (Illus.). 32p. (J). lib. bdg. 22.60 (978-0-7660-2257-7(9)) Enslow Pubs., Inc.

—Father's Day Crafts. 2005. (Fun Holiday Crafts Kids Can Do Ser.). (Illus.). 32p. (J). lib. bdg. 22.60 (978-0-7660-2343-7(5) , Enslow Elementary) Enslow Pubs., Inc.

—Halloween Crafts. 2004. (Fun Holiday Crafts Kids Can Do Ser.). (Illus.). 32p. (J). lib. bdg. 22.60 (978-0-7660-2236-2(6)) Enslow Pubs., Inc.

—Hispanic-American Crafts Kids Can Do! 2006. (Multicultural Crafts Kids Can Do! Ser.). (Illus.). 32p. (J). lib. bdg. 22.60 (978-0-7660-2459-5(8) , Enslow Elementary) Enslow Pubs., Inc.

Roche, Denis. Oodles to Do with Loo-Loo & Boo: The Collected Art Adventures. Roche, Denis, illus. 2001. (Illus.). 64p. (J). (gr. k-3). pap. 9.95 (978-0-618-15423-4(X)) Houghton Mifflin Co. Trade & Reference Div.

Rock. Easter: Fun & Festive Things To Make. 1999. (Illus.). 24p. (J). pap. 4.95 (978-0-7459-4050-2(1) , Lion) Lion Hudson plc GBR. *Dist:* Trafalgar Square Publishing.

Rock, Lois. Christmas: Crafts, Stories, Carols. 1999. (Illus.). 48p. (J). (gr. k-3). 16.99 (978-0-7459-3907-0(4) , Lion) Lion Hudson plc GBR. *Dist:* Independent Pubs. Group.

—Easter: Crafts, Stories, Facts. 2003. (Illus.). 48p. (J). pap. 11.99 (978-0-7459-4653-5(4) , Lion) Lion Hudson plc GBR. *Dist:* Independent Pubs. Group.

—Festivals of the Christian Year. 2002. (Illus.). 48p. (J). pap. 11.99 (978-0-7459-4636-8(4) , Lion) Lion Hudson plc GBR. *Dist:* Independent Pubs. Group.

—First Festivals - Easter: Crafts, Stories, Facts. (Illus.). 48p. (J). 16.95 (978-0-7459-3906-3(6) , Lion) Lion Hudson plc GBR. *Dist:* Trafalgar Square Publishing.

—The Time of Jesus: Crafts that Recreate Everyday Life. 2003. (Illus.). 64p. (J). pap. 19.99 (978-0-7459-3881-3(7) , Lion) Lion Hudson plc GBR. *Dist:* Independent Pubs. Group.

Ros, Jordina & Estadella, Pere. Fun Crafts with 2D & 3D Figures. 2006. (Arts & Crafts Fun Ser.). (Illus.). 48p. (J). (gr. 3-7). lib. bdg. 23.93 (978-0-7660-2652-0(3) , Enslow Elementary) Enslow Pubs., Inc.

—Fun Crafts with Colors. 2006. (Arts & Crafts Fun Ser.). (Illus.). 48p. (J). (gr. 3-7). lib. bdg. 23.93 (978-0-7660-2655-1(8) , Enslow Elementary) Enslow Pubs., Inc.

—Fun Crafts with Dots & Lines. 2006. (Arts & Crafts Fun Ser.). (Illus.). 48p. (J). (gr. 3-7). lib. bdg. 23.93 (978-0-7660-2656-8(6) , Enslow Elementary) Enslow Pubs., Inc.

—Fun Crafts with Shapes. 2006. (Arts & Crafts Fun Ser.). (Illus.). 48p. (J). (gr. 3-7). lib. bdg. 23.93 (978-0-7660-2657-5(4) , Enslow Elementary) Enslow Pubs., Inc.

—Fun Crafts with Sizes & Spaces. 2006. (Arts & Crafts Fun Ser.). (Illus.). 48p. (J). (gr. 3-7). lib. bdg. 23.93 (978-0-7660-2653-7(1) , Enslow Elementary) Enslow Pubs., Inc.

—Fun Crafts with Textures. 2006. (Arts & Crafts Fun Ser.). (Illus.). 48p. (J). (gr. 3-7). lib. bdg. 23.93 (978-0-7660-2654-4(X) , Enslow Elementary) Enslow Pubs., Inc.

Rosin, Nancy. Love: Ready-to-Use Scrapbook Pages. 2005. (Instant Memories Ser.). (Illus.). 128p. pap. 14.95 incl. audio compact disk (978-1-4027-2642-2(2) , Chapelle) Sterling Publishing Co., Inc.

Ross, Kathy. All-Girl Crafts. 2005. (Illus.). 48p. (J). (ps-7). lib. bdg. 25.26 (978-0-7613-2776-9(2) , Millbrook Pr.) Lerner Publishing Group.

—All-Girl Crafts. Garvin, Elaine, illus. 2005. 48p. (J). (gr. 3-6). pap., lib. bdg. 7.95 (978-0-7613-2391-4(0) , First Avenue Editions) Lerner Publishing Group.

—All New Crafts for Earth Day. 2006. (Illus.). (J). pap. 7.95 (978-0-8225-5976-4(5) , First Avenue Editions) Lerner Publishing Group.

—All New Crafts for Earth Day. Holm, Sharon Lane, illus. 2006. 47p. (J). 25.26 (978-0-7613-3400-2(9) , Millbrook Pr.) Lerner Publishing Group.

—All New Crafts for Easter. Holm, Sharon Lane, tr. Holm, Sharon Lane, illus. 2004. (All New Holiday Crafts for Kids Ser.). 48p. lib. bdg. 25.26 (978-0-7613-2921-3(8) , Millbrook Pr.) Lerner Publishing Group.

—All New Crafts for Halloween. Leonard, Barbara, illus. 2003. (All New Holiday Crafts for Kids Ser.). 48p. lib. bdg. 23.90 (978-0-7613-2554-3(9)); (J). pap. 7.95 (978-0-7613-1577-3(2)) Lerner Publishing Group. (Millbrook Pr.).

—All New Crafts for Halloween. 2003. (gr. k-3). lib. bdg. 16.40 (978-0-613-88977-3(0)) Tandem Library Bks.

—All New Crafts for Kwanzaa. Holm, Sharon Lane, illus. 2006. 48p. (J). pap. 7.95 (978-0-8225-3435-8(5) , First Avenue Editions) Lerner Publishing Group.

—All New Crafts for Mother's Day & Father's Day. Holm, Sharon Lane, illus. 2007. (All New Holiday Crafts for Kids Ser.). 48p. (J). (gr. k-3). lib. bdg. 25.26 (978-0-8225-6367-9(3) , Millbrook Pr.) Lerner Publishing Group.

—All New Crafts for Thanksgiving. Holm, Sharon Lane, illus. (J). (gr. k-2). 2005. 48p. pap. 7.95 (978-0-7613-2394-5(5) , First Avenue Editions); 2004. lib. bdg. 25.26 (978-0-7613-2922-0(6) , Millbrook Pr.) Lerner Publishing Group.

—All New Crafts for Valentines. Leonard, Barbara, illus. 2002. (All New Holiday Crafts for Kids Ser.). 48p. (gr. k-3). lib. bdg. 23.90 (978-0-7613-2553-6(0) , Millbrook Pr.) Lerner Publishing Group.

—All New Crafts for Valentine's Day. Leonard, Barbara, illus. 2002. (All-New Holiday Crafts for Kids Ser.: Bk. 3). 48p. (J). (gr. k-3). pap. 7.95 (978-0-7613-1576-6(4) , Millbrook Pr.) Lerner Publishing Group.

—All-New Crafts for Valentine's Day. 2002. (gr. k-3). lib. bdg. 16.40 (978-0-613-91018-7(4)) Tandem Library Bks.

—The Best Birthday Parties Ever! A Kid's Do-It-Yourself Guide. 1999. (Illus.). 80p. (J). (gr. 3-6). pap. 9.95 (978-0-7613-0989-5(6) , Millbrook Pr.) Lerner Publishing Group.

—The Best Birthday Parties Ever! A Kid's Do-it-Yourself Guide. Holm, Sharon Lane, illus. 1999. (Crafts from Kathy Ross Ser.). 80p. (gr. 3-6). lib. bdg. 24.90 (978-0-7613-1410-3(5) , Millbrook Pr.) Lerner Publishing Group.

—Best Birthday Parties Ever! A Kid's Do-It-Yourself Guide. Holm, Sharon Lane, illus. 1999. 78p. (J). (ps-7). lib. bdg. 18.75 (978-0-613-16597-6(7)) Tandem Library Bks.

—Christmas Tree Ornaments Kids Can Make. Holm, Sharon Lane, illus. 1998. 64p. (gr. k-3). pap. 9.95 (978-0-7613-0337-4(5) , Millbrook Pr.) Lerner Publishing Group.

—Crafts for Kids Who are Learning about Farm Animals. Barger, Jan, illus. 2007. (Crafts for Kids Who Are Learning about Ser.). 48p. (J). (gr. k-3). lib. bdg. 25.26 (*978-0-8225-6366-2(5)* , Millbrook Pr.) Lerner Publishing Group.

—Crafts for Kids Who are Learning about Insects. Barger, Jan, illus. 2008. (J). lib. bdg. (*978-0-8225-7591-7(4)* , Millbrook Pr.) Lerner Publishing Group.

—Crafts for Kids Who Are Learning about Transportation. Barger, Jan, illus. 2006. 48p. (J). lib. bdg. 25.26 (978-0-7613-9464-8(8) , Millbrook Pr.) Lerner Publishing Group.

—Crafts for Kids Who Are Wild about the Wild. Holm, Sharon Lane, illus. 1998. (Crafts from Kathy Ross Ser.). 176p. (J). (gr. 3-6). spiral bd. 18.95 (978-0-7613-0440-1(1)) Lerner Publishing Group.

—Crafts for St. Patrick's Day. Holm, Sharon Lane, illus. (Holiday Crafts for Kids Ser.). 48p. (gr. k-3). 2000. (J). pap. 7.95 (978-0-7613-0447-0(9)); 1999. lib. bdg. 24.90 (978-0-7613-1306-9(0)) Lerner Publishing Group. (Millbrook Pr.).

—Crafts from Your Favorite Bible Stories. 2000. (gr. k-3). lib. bdg. 16.40 (978-0-613-24728-3(0)) Tandem Library Bks.

—Crafts from Your Favorite Children's Songs. Enright, Vicky, illus. 2001. (Crafts from Kathy Ross Ser.). 48p. (gr. k-3). lib. bdg. (978-0-7613-1912-2(3)); pap. 8.95 (978-0-7613-1438-7(5)) Lerner Publishing Group. (Millbrook Pr.).

—Crafts from Your Favorite Children's Stories. Garvin, Elaine, illus. 2001. (Crafts from Kathy Ross Ser.). 48p. (gr. k-3). lib. bdg. 24.90 (978-0-7613-1772-2(4) , Millbrook Pr.) Lerner Publishing Group.

—Crafts from Your Favorite Children's Stories. 2001. (Illus.). (J). (978-0-606-22373-7(8)) Tandem Library Bks.

—Crafts from Your Favorite Childrens Stories. 2001. (gr. k-3). lib. bdg. 17.60 (978-0-613-45174-1(0)) Tandem Library Bks.

—Crafts from Your Favorite Fairy Tales. Enright, Vicky, illus. 2001. 51p. 20.00 (978-0-7881-9963-9(3)) DIANE Publishing Co.

—Crafts from Your Favorite Fairy Tales. 1998. 3. (Illus.). 48p. (J). (gr. k-4). pap. 8.95 (978-0-7613-0342-8(1) , Millbrook Pr.) Lerner Publishing Group.

—Crafts from Your Favorite Nursery Rhymes. Garvin, Elaine, illus. 2002. 48p. (gr. k-3). (J). pap. 8.95 (978-0-7613-1589-6(6)); lib. bdg. 24.90 (978-0-7613-2523-9(9)) Lerner Publishing Group. (Millbrook Pr.).

—Crafts from Your Favorite Nursery Rhymes. 2002. (gr. k-3). lib. bdg. 17.60 (978-0-613-90448-3(6)) Tandem Library Bks.

—Crafts That Celebrate Black History. Stow, Jenny, illus. 2002. 48p. (J). (ps-3). pap. 8.95 (978-0-7613-1681-7(7) , First Avenue Editions) Lerner Publishing Group.

—Crafts to Make in the Fall. Enright, Vicky, illus. 1998. (Crafts for All Seasons Ser.). 64p. (J). (gr. k-3). pap. 9.95 (978-0-7613-0335-0(9) , First Avenue Editions) Lerner Publishing Group.

—Crafts to Make in the Fall. 1998. (gr. k-3). lib. bdg. 18.75 (978-0-613-90452-0(4)) Tandem Library Bks.

—Crafts to Make in the Winter. Enright, Vicky, illus. 1999. (Crafts for All Seasons Ser.: 3). 64p. (J). (gr. k-3). pap. 9.95 (978-0-7613-0336-7(7) , First Avenue Editions) Lerner Publishing Group.

—Fairies. Bosch, Nicole in den, illus. 2008. (Girl Crafts Ser.). (J). lib. bdg. 25.26 (***978-0-8225-7509-2(4)*** , Millbrook Pr.) Lerner Publishing Group.

—Girlfriends' Get-Together Craft Book. Bosch, Nicole in den, illus. 2007. (Girl Crafts Ser.). 48p. (J). (gr. 2-5). lib. bdg. 25.26 (978-0-7613-3408-8(4) , Millbrook Pr.) Lerner Publishing Group.

—The Jewish Holiday Craft Book. Levine, Melinda, illus. 2001. 95p. (J). (gr. 5-7). pap. 13.00 (978-0-7567-5122-7(5)) DIANE Publishing Co.

—Kathy Ross Crafts Colors. Barger, Jan, illus. 2003. (Crafts from Kathy Ross Ser.). 48p. (J). lib. bdg. 23.93 (978-0-7613-2651-9(0) , Millbrook Pr.) Lerner Publishing Group.

—Kathy Ross Crafts Letter Shapes. Barger, Jan, illus. 2002. (Crafts from Kathy Ross Ser.). 64p. (ps-1). lib. bdg. 24.90 (978-0-7613-2103-3(9) , Millbrook Pr.) Lerner Publishing Group.

—Kathy Ross Crafts Letter Sounds. Barger, Jan, illus. 2002. (Crafts from Kathy Ross Ser.). 64p. (ps-1). lib. bdg. 24.90 (978-0-7613-2102-6(0) , Millbrook Pr.) Lerner Publishing Group.

—Kathy Ross Crafts Numbers. Barger, Jan, illus. 2003. 48p. (J). lib. bdg. 23.90 (978-0-7613-2105-7(5) , Millbrook Pr.) Lerner Publishing Group.

—Kathy Ross Crafts Numbers. Barger, Jan, illus. 2003. 47p. (J). (ps 3). lib. bdg. 16.40 (978-0-613-38981-9(5)) Tandem Library Bks.

—Kathy Ross Crafts Triangles, Rectangles, Circles, & Squares. Barger, Jan, illus. 2002. (Crafts from Kathy Ross Ser.). 48p. (ps-1). lib. bdg. 23.90 (978-0-7613-2104-0(7) , Millbrook Pr.) Lerner Publishing Group.

—Kathy Ross Crafts Triangles, Rectangles, Circles, & Squares! 2002. (gr. k-3). lib. bdg. 16.40 (978-0-613-88975-9(4)) Tandem Library Bks.

—Kathy Ross Crafts Triangles, Rectangles, Circles & Squares. Barger, Jan, illus. 2002. (Crafts from Kathy Ross Ser.). 48p. (J). (gr. k-2). pap. 7.95 (978-0-7613-1696-1(5) , Millbrook Pr.) Lerner Publishing Group.

—Letter Shapes. Barger, Jan, illus. 2002. (Crafts from Kathy Ross Ser.). 64p. (J). (gr. k-2). pap. 8.95 (978-0-7613-1490-5(3) , Millbrook Pr.) Lerner Publishing Group.

—Letter Sounds. Barger, Jan, illus. 2002. (Crafts from Kathy Ross Ser.). 64p. (J). (gr. k-2). pap. 8.95 (978-0-7613-1491-2(1) , Millbrook Pr.) Lerner Publishing Group.

—Look What You Can Make with Plastic Bottles & Tubs: Over 80 Pictured Crafts & Dozens of Other Ideas. Schneider, Hank, photos by. 2003. (Illus.). 48p. (YA). (ps-7). pap. 5.95 (978-1-56397-567-7(X)) Boyds Mills Pr.

—More of the Best Holiday Crafts Ever! Holm, Sharon Lane, illus. 2005. 160p. (J). (gr. k-4). bds. 19.95 (978-0-7613-2345-7(7)) Lerner Publishing Group.

—Star-Spangled Crafts. 2003. (gr. k-3). lib. bdg. 16.40 (978-0-613-59022-8(8)) Tandem Library Bks.

—Step-by-Step Crafts for Fall. Emery, Jennifer, illus. 2006. 48p. (J). 15.95 (978-1-59078-448-8(0)); pap. 6.95 (978-1-59078-357-3(3)) Boyds Mills Pr.

—Step-By-Step Crafts for Spring. Emery, Jennifer, illus. 2007. 48p. (J). pap. (978-1-59078-476-1(6)); (978-1-59078-359-7(X)) Boyds Mills Pr.

—Step-By-Step Crafts for Summer. Emery, Jennifer, illus. 2007. 48p. (J). pap. (978-1-59078-477-8(4)) Boyds Mills Pr.

—Step-by-Step Crafts for Summer. Emery, Jennifer, illus. 2007. 48p. (J). (gr. 3-4). 15.95 (978-1-59078-360-3(3)) Boyds Mills Pr.

—Step-by-Step Crafts for Winter. Emery, Jennifer, illus. 2006. 48p. (J). 15.95 (978-1-59078-449-5(9)); pap. 6.95 (978-1-59078-358-0(1)) Boyds Mills Pr.

—Things to Make for Your Doll. Garvin, Elaine, illus. 2003. 48p. (J). (gr. k-2). lib. bdg. (978-0-7613-2861-2(0) , Millbrook Pr.); pap. 7.95 (978-0-7613-1781-4(3) , First Avenue Editions) Lerner Publishing Group.

Ross, Kathy. Things to Make for Your Room. Bosch, Nicole in den, illus. 2008. (J). lib. bdg. (***978-0-8225-7593-1(0)*** , Millbrook Pr.) Lerner Publishing Group.

Ross, Kathy, ed. Look What You Can Make with Dozens of Household Items! Over 500 Pictured Crafts & Dozens of More Ideas! Schneider, Hank, photos by. 2003. (Illus.). 384p. (YA). (gr. k-7). spiral bd. 24.99 (978-1-59078-058-9(2)) Boyds Mills Pr.

—Look What You Can Make with Newspapers, Magazines, & Greeting Cards: Over 80 Pictured Crafts & Dozens of Other Ideas. Schneider, Hank, photos by. 2003. (Illus.). 48p. (YA). (ps-7). pap. 5.95 (978-1-56397-566-0(1)) Boyds Mills Pr.

Ross, Kathy, illus. Community Workers. 2006. (Crafts for Kids Who Are Learning about Ser.). 48p. (J). (gr. k-2). lib. bdg. 25.26 (978-0-7613-2743-1(6)) Lerner Publishing Group.

Ross, Kathy & Connelly, Gwen, illus. Crafts from Your Favorite Bible Stories. 2000. (Crafts from Kathy Ross Ser.: 3). 64p. (J). (gr. k-3). pap. 7.95 (978-0-7613-1295-6(1) , First Avenue Editions) Lerner Publishing Group.

Ross, Kathy & Garvey, Elaine. Crafts from Your Favorite Children's Stories. 2001. (Single Titles Ser.: 3). (Illus.). 48p. (J). pap. 8.95 (978-0-7613-1492-9(X) , Millbrook Pr.) Lerner Publishing Group.

Ross, Kathy & Holm, Sharon Lane. Crafts for Kids Who Are Learning about Insects & Other Creepy Crawlies. 2008. (Crafts for Kids Who Are Learning about... Ser.). (J). lib. bdg. 25.26 (***978-0-8225-6809-4(8)*** , Millbrook Pr.) Lerner Publishing Group.

Rusackas, Francesca. Friendship Crafts. Olexiewicz, Charlene, illus. 1999. (Girls Wanna Have Fun! Ser.). 64p. (J). (gr. 2-7). pap. 9.95 (978-0-7373-0161-8(9) , 01619W) McGraw-Hill/Contemporary.

—60 Super Simple Friendship Crafts, Guianan, Eve, illus. 1999. (Sixty Super Simple Ser.). 80p. (J). (gr. 3-7). pap. 6.95 (978-0-7373-0062-8(0) , 00620W) McGraw-Hill/Contemporary.

Sabbeth, Carol. Kids' Computer Creations: Using Your Computer for Art & Craft Fun. 1999. (Kids Can Bks.: No. 14). (Illus.). 160p. (J). (ps-5). pap. 12.95 (978-0-913589-92-2(6) , Williamson Bks.) Ideals Pubns.

Sacks, Janet. Oceans & Art Activities. 2002. (gr. 3-6). lib. bdg. 17.60 (978-0-613-52889-4(1)) Tandem Library Bks.

—Weather & Art Activities. 2002. (Arty Facts Ser.). (Illus.). 48p. (J). (gr. 3-4). pap. (978-0-7787-1146-9(3)); lib. bdg. (978-0-7787-1118-6(8)) Crabtree Publishing Co.

—Weather & Art Activities. 2002. (gr. 3-6). lib. bdg. 17.60 (978-0-613-52928-0(6)) Tandem Library Bks.

Sacks, Janet & Goodman, Polly, texts. Oceans & Art Activities. 2002. (Arty Facts Ser.). (Illus.). 48p. (J). (gr. 3-4). pap. (978-0-7787-1143-8(9)); lib. bdg. (978-0-7787-1115-5(3)) Crabtree Publishing Co.

Sacks, Janet, et al. Animals & Art Activities. 2002. (Arty Facts Ser.). (Illus.). 48p. (J). (gr. 3-4). pap. (978-0-7787-1136-0(6)); lib. bdg. (978-0-7787-1108-7(0)) Crabtree Publishing Co.

Sadler, Judy Ann. Beading: Bracelets, Earrings, Necklaces & More. Walker, Tracy, illus. unabr. ed. 1998. (Kids Can Do It Ser.). 134p. (J). (gr. 4-6). (978-1-55074-338-8(4)) Kids Can Pr., Ltd.

—Beads.Tr. of Perles. (FRE., Illus.). (J). pap. 7.99 (978-0-590-24194-6(X)) Scholastic, Inc.

—Christmas Crafts from Around the World. Bradford, June, illus. 2004. (Kids Can Do It Ser.). 40p. (J). (gr. 4-6). (978-1-55337-428-2(2)); (978-1-55337-427-5(4)) Kids Can Pr., Ltd.

—Christmas Crafts from Around the World. 2003. (gr. 3-6). lib. bdg. 15.25 (978-0-613-84415-4(7)) Tandem Library Bks.

—Corking. Hendry, Linda, illus. 1998. (Kids Can Do It Ser.). 32p. (J). (gr. 4-6). (978-1-55074-265-7(5)) Kids Can Pr., Ltd.

—The Kids Can Press Jumbo Book of Crafts. Price, Caroline, illus. 1998. (Jumbo Bks.). 208p. (J). (gr. 4-6). (978-1-55074-375-3(9)) Kids Can Pr., Ltd.

—Kids Can Press Jumbo Book of Easy Crafts. Price, Caroline, illus. 2001. (Jumbo Bks.). 208p. (J). (gr. 4-6). (978-1-55074-811-6(4)) Kids Can Pr., Ltd.

—Making Fleece Crafts. Bradford, June, illus. 2000. (Kids Can Do It Ser.). 40p. (J). (gr. 4-6). (978-1-55074-847-5(5)) Kids Can Pr., Ltd.

—Making Fleece Crafts. 2000. (gr. 3-6). lib. bdg. 14.10 (978-0-613-30590-7(6)) Tandem Library Bks.

Sadler, Judy Ann & Bradford, June. Beanbag Buddies: And Other Stuffed Toys. 1999. (Kids Can Do It Ser.). (Illus.). 134p. (J). (gr. 4-6). (978-1-55074-590-0(5)) Kids Can Pr., Ltd.

—Making Fleece Crafts. 2000. (Kids Can Do It Ser.). (Illus.). 40p. (J). (gr. 4-6). (978-1-55074-739-3(8)) Kids Can Pr., Ltd.

Sander, Sonia. Jingle Bells, VeggieTales! Cutting, David A., illus. 2006. (VeggieTales Ser.). 32p. (J). act. bk. ed. 4.99 (978-1-4169-3984-9(9) , Simon Scribbles) Simon & Schuster Children's Publishing.

—The Kooky Carry-along Coloring Kit. 2008. (Wow! Wow! Wubbzy! Ser.). 80p. (J). 5.99 (***978-1-4169-4794-3(9)*** , Simon Scribbles) Simon & Schuster Children's Publishing.

—Master of Disguise. 2008. (Wow! Wow! Wubbzy! Ser.). 48p. (J). 3.99 (***978-1-4169-4791-2(4)*** , Simon Scribbles) Simon & Schuster Children's Publishing.

Savage, Christine Lyseng, et al. Halloween Recipes & Crafts, Vol. 1. rev. ed. 2003. (Ghost Stories Ser.). (Illus.). 160p. (gr. 4). pap. (978-1-894877-10-7(1)) Lone Pine Publishing.

Schaefer, Lola M. Jack o Lanterns. (Fall Fun Ser.). 24p. (J). pap. 5.95 (978-0-7368-8106-7(9)) Capstone Pr., Inc.

Schecter, Deborah. Colorful Crayon Art. 2001. (Illus.). 32p. (J). (978-0-439-33618-5(X)) Scholastic, Inc.

—Creating with Collage. 2002. (Illus.). 32p. (J). (978-0-439-33619-2(8)) Scholastic, Inc.

—Hello Kitty Felt. 2002. (Hello Kitty & Her Friends Crafts Club Ser.). (Illus.). 44p. (J). act. bk. ed. (978-0-439-32842-5(X)) Scholastic, Inc.

—Mix It up with Crayons & Paint. 2002. (Illus.). 32p. (J). (978-0-439-33622-2(8)) Scholastic, Inc.

—Shape, Sculpt, & Roll: [with Crayola Model Magic]. 2001. (Illus.). 32p. (J). (978-0-439-33617-8(1)) Scholastic, Inc.

Scheunemann, Pam. Cool Clay Projects. 2005. (Cool Crafts Ser.). (Illus.). 32p. (J). (gr. k-6). lib. bdg. 22.78 (978-1-59197-740-7(1) , Checkerboard Library) ABDO Publishing Co.

Schneider, Hank, photos by. Look What You Can Make with Plastic Bottles & Tubs: Over 80 Pictured Crafts & Dozens of Other Ideas. 2002. (Illus.). 48p. (J). (ps-ps). lib. bdg. 14.10 (978-0-613-59328-1(6)) Tandem Library Bks.

Scholastic, Inc. Staff. Month-by-Month Thematic Stationery. 1999. pap. 9.95 (978-0-439-04392-2(1)) Scholastic, Inc.

School Specialty Publishing. Big Book of Bible Crafts. 2001. 160p. (J). pap. 14.99 (978-0-7647-0504-5(0)) School Specialty Publishing.

Schuh, Debby & Stephani, Julie. Kids Scrapbooking: Easy As 1-2-3. 2002. (gr. 3-6). lib. bdg. 18.75 (978-0-613-77108-5(7)) Tandem Library Bks.

Schulz, Charles M. The Peanuts Guide to the Seasons: A Jumbo Activity Book. Bennett, Elizabeth, illus. 2003. (Peanuts Club with Charlie Brown & Friends Ser.). 144p. (J). (978-0-439-46826-8(4)) Scholastic, Inc.

Schulz, Charles M. & Bennett, Elizabeth. The Peanuts Guide to Sports: A Jumbo Activity Book. 2003. (Peanuts Club with Charlie Brown & Friends Ser.). (Illus.). 144p. (J). (978-0-439-46824-4(8)) Scholastic, Inc.

Schuman, Jo Miles. Art from Many Hands: Multicultural Art Projects. rev. ed. 2003. (ENG., Illus.). 304p. (J). pap. 29.95 (978-0-87192-593-0(1)) Davis Pubns., Inc.

Schwarz, Renee. Funky Junk: Cool Stuff to Make with Hardware. 2004. (Kids Can Do It Ser.). (Illus.). 40p. (J). (gr. 4-6). (978-1-55337-388-9(X)); (978-1-55337-387-2(1)) Kids Can Pr., Ltd.

Schwarz, Renée. Wind Chimes & Whirligigs. Schwarz, Renée, illus. 2007. (Kids Can Do It Ser.). (Illus.). 40p. (YA). (gr. 3 up). (***978-1-55337-868-6(7)***); (***978-1-55337-870-9(9)***) Kids Can Pr., Ltd.

Scouting Crafts. 2004. (J). 11.99 (978-0-930184-08-7(4)) Clapper Publishing Co.

Seix, Victoria. Crafts from Nature. 2000. (Crafts for All Seasons Ser.). (Illus.). 32p. (J). (gr. 3-8). lib. bdg. 23.70 (978-1-56711-433-1(4) , Blackbirch Pr., Inc.) Thomson Gale.

Senisi, Ellen B. Berry Smudges & Leaf Prints: Finding & Making Colors from Nature. Senisi, Ellen B., photos by. 2005. (Illus.). 40p. (J). (gr. 4-8). reprint ed. 17.00 (978-0-7567-9707-2(1)) DIANE Publishing Co.

Sevaly, Karen. Nothing But... Patterns! Reproducible Patterns for All Occasions! Sevaly, Karen, illus. 1999. (Illus.). 80p. (J). pap. 9.95 (978-1-57882-021-4(9) , TF-1653) Teacher's Friend Pubns., Inc.

Shepherd, Nellie. Puppets. 2003. (My Art Class Ser.). (Illus.). 48p. (J). 12.99 (978-0-7894-9856-4(1)) Dorling Kindersley Publishing, Inc.

Sherman, Michael. Klutz Wax Strings: Make Things with String That Clings. 2003. (Illus.). 46p. (J). spiral bd. 12.95 (978-1-59174-262-3(5) , 53643126) Klutz.

—Suction Cup Critters: Make Your Own Window Grabbers. 2005. (Illus.). 20p. (J). (gr. 1 up). 14.95 (978-1-57054-267-1(8)) Klutz.

Shouting in the Hush Arbor Arts & Crafts Leader. 7.00 (978-0-687-32642-6(7)) Abingdon Pr.

Shouting in the Hush Arbor Director's Manual. 14.00 (978-0-687-32582-5(X)) Abingdon Pr.

Shouting in the Hush Arbor Outreach Follow-up Leader. 7.00 (978-0-687-32572-6(2)) Abingdon Pr.

Sibbett, Ed, Jr. Children's Bookplates. 1998. 181p. pap. 3.50 (978-0-486-26642-8(7)) Dover Pubns., Inc.

Simpson, Sam. Christian Crafts Paper Plate Animals. 2001. 64p. (J). (ps). pap. 7.95 (978-0-86653-732-2(5) , SS2854, In Celebration) Schaffer, Frank Pubns.

Sing, Dick. Turning Ornaments & Eggs. 2002. (Illus.). 64p. (gr. 10-13). pap. 14.95 (978-0-7643-1463-6(7)) Schiffer Publishing, Ltd.

Siomades, Lorianne. Look What You Can Make with Boxes: Over 90 Pictured Crafts & Dozens of Other Ideas. 2003. (Illus.). 48p. (YA). (gr. k-7). pap. 5.95 (978-1-56397-704-6(4)) Boyds Mills Pr.

Small, B. Crafty Birthday Balloons. 1999. (Illus.). 16p. (978-1-874735-57-1(3)) B Small Publishing.

—Crafty Hearts. 1999. (Illus.). 16p. (978-1-874735-62-5(X)) B Small Publishing.

Smolinski, Jill. Holiday Origami. Fraser, Mary Ann, illus. 2nd rev. ed. 1999. (Origami Ser.). 48p. (gr. 3-7). pap. 8.95 (978-0-7373-0094-9(9) , 9780737300949) McGraw-Hill Cos., The.

—Holiday Origami. 1999. (gr. 3-6). lib. bdg. 17.60 (978-0-613-73742-5(3)) Tandem Library Bks.

Souter, Gillian. Beads 'n' Badges. Watson, Clare, illus. Martin, Andre, photos by. 2001. (Handy Crafts Ser.). 48p. (J). (gr. 2 up). lib. bdg. 24.67 (978-0-8368-2819-1(4)) Stevens, Gareth Inc.

—Great Gifts. Watson, Clare, illus. Martin, Andre, photos by. 2001. (Handy Crafts Ser.). 48p. (J). (gr. 2 up). lib. bdg. 24.67 (978-0-8368-2820-7(8)) Stevens, Gareth Inc.

—Handy Crafts, 8 bks. Watson, Clare, illus. Martin, Andre, photos by. Incl. Beads 'n' Badges. 2001. lib. bdg. 24.67 (978-0-8368-2819-1(4)); Great Gifts. 2001. lib. bdg. 24.67 (978-0-8368-2820-7(8)); Holiday Handiwork. 2002. lib. bdg. 24.67 (978-0-8368-3050-7(4)); Odds 'n' Ends Art. 2002. lib. bdg. 24.67 (978-0-8368-3051-4(2)); Paints Plus. 2001. lib. bdg. 24.67 (978-0-8368-2821-4(6)); Perfect Parties. 2001. lib. bdg. 24.67 (978-0-8368-2822-1(4)); Rainy Day Fun. 2002. lib. bdg. 24.67 (978-0-8368-3052-1(0)); Terrific Toys. 2002. lib. bdg. 24.67 (978-0-8368-3053-8(9)); 48p. (J). (gr. 2 up). (Illus.). 2002. Set lib. bdg. 197.36 (978-0-8368-3140-5(3)) Stevens, Gareth Inc.

—Holiday Handiwork. Watson, Clare, illus. Martin, Andre, photos by. 2002. (Handy Crafts Ser.). 48p. (J). (gr. 2 up). lib. bdg. 24.67 (978-0-8368-3050-7(4)) Stevens, Gareth Inc.

—Odds 'n' Ends Art. Watson, Clare, illus. Martin, Andre, photos by. 2002. (Handy Crafts Ser.). 48p. (J). (gr. 2 up). lib. bdg. 24.67 (978-0-8368-3051-4(2)) Stevens, Gareth Inc.

—Paints Plus. Watson, Clare, illus. Martin, Andre, photos by. 2001. (Handy Crafts Ser.). 48p. (J). (gr. 2 up). lib. bdg. 24.67 (978-0-8368-2821-4(6)) Stevens, Gareth Inc.

—Perfect Parties. Watson, Clare, illus. Martin, Andre, photos by. 2001. (Handy Crafts Ser.). 48p. (J). (gr. 2 up). lib. bdg. 24.67 (978-0-8368-2822-1(4)) Stevens, Gareth Inc.

—Rainy Day Fun. Watson, Clare, illus. Martin, Andre, photos by. 2002. (Handy Crafts Ser.). 48p. (J). (gr. 2 up). lib. bdg. 24.67 (978-0-8368-3052-1(0)) Stevens, Gareth Inc.

South, Lianne & Robins, Deri. Creative Bracelets. Hall, Mary, illus. 2000. 24p. (J). (978-0-439-24962-1(7)) Scholastic, Inc.

Southwater Staff. Fun with Face Painting. 2001. (Fun with... Ser.). (Illus.). 96p. 12.95 (978-1-84215-446-5(X) , Southwater) Anness Publishing GBR. *Dist:* National Bk. Network.

—Outrageously Amazing Crafty Things to Do. 2002. (Illus.). 96p. (gr. 3-7). pap. 9.95 (978-1-84215-612-4(8) , Southwater) Anness Publishing GBR. *Dist:* National Bk. Network.

—Outrageously Fun Things to Do Activity Book. 2002. (Illus.). 96p. pap. 9.95 (978-1-84215-610-0(1)) Anness Publishing GBR. *Dist:* National Bk. Network.

Spann, Mary Beth. Month-by-Month Collaborative Books for Young Learners: Easy Patterns & How-to's for Creating 20 Adorable Rhyming Books for Young Children to Make & Share. 2000. (Month-by-Month Ser.). (Illus.). 72p. pap. 10.95 (978-0-439-04882-8(6)) Scholastic, Inc.

Sparkle Fun. 2002. (Illus.). 10p. (J). 16.95 (978-1-74047-141-1(5)) Book Co. Publishing Pty, Ltd., The AUS. *Dist:* Leonard, Hal Corp.

Spooky Stickers. 2004. (Art Rom Create Your Own... Ser.). (Illus.). 24p. (J). pap. incl. audio compact disk (978-1-84229-738-4(4)) Top That! Publishing PLC.

Stacy, Lori & Jacobowski, Jeanne. Hello Kitty Pipe Cleaners. 2001. (Hello Kitty & Her Friends Crafts Club Ser.). (Illus.). 44p. (J). act. bk. ed. (978-0-439-32838-8(1)) Scholastic, Inc.

Stapleton, Dorothy. Kids Can Quilt: Fun & Easy Projects for Your Small Quilter. 2004. (Illus.). 128p. (J). pap. 16.95 (978-0-7641-2770-0(5)) Barron's Educational Series, Inc.

Steck-Vaughn Staff. Art/How To: Story Sticks/Lion. 1998. (Illus.). (J). pap. (978-0-8172-8640-8(3)) Steck-Vaughn.

Steele, Philip. Clothes & Crafts in Ancient Greece. 2000. (Clothes & Crafts in History Ser.). (Illus.). 32p. (J). (gr. 4 up). lib. bdg. 24.67 (978-0-8368-2734-7(1)) Stevens, Gareth Inc.

—Clothes & Crafts in Roman Times. 2000. (Clothes & Crafts in History Ser.). (Illus.). 32p. (J). (gr. 4 up). lib. bdg. 24.67 (978-0-8368-2737-8(6)) Stevens, Gareth Inc.

—Clothes & Crafts in Victorian Times. 2000. (Clothes & Crafts in History Ser.). (Illus.). 32p. (J). (gr. 4 up). lib. bdg. 24.67 (978-0-8368-2738-5(4)) Stevens, Gareth Inc.

Step by Step, 6 bks. Incl. Crafts from Felt. Kirby, Huguette. lib. bdg. 22.60 (978-0-7368-1474-4(4)); Crafts from Junk. Lamerand, Violaine. lib. bdg. 22.60 (978-0-7368-1479-9(5)); Crafts from Modeling Clay. Kirby, Huguette. lib. bdg. 22.60 (978-0-7368-1477-5(9)); Crafts from Papier-Mache. Lamerand, Violaine. lib. bdg. 22.60 (978-0-7368-1478-2(7)); Crafts from Salt Dough. Gessat, Audrey. lib. bdg. 22.60 (978-0-7368-1475-1(2)); Making Masks. Lamerand, Violaine. lib. bdg. 22.60 (978-0-7368-1476-8(0)); 32p. (J). (gr. 2-3). 2002. (Illus.). 2002. Set lib. bdg. 135.60 (978-0-7368-1480-5(9) , Bridgestone Bks.) Capstone Pr., Inc.

Step-by-Step Crafts for Children. 2000. (J). pap. (978-0-7534-5039-0(9) , Kingfisher) Houghton Mifflin Co. Trade & Reference Div.

Sterling Publishing Company Staff, ed. Make a Doll's Shop: Press Out & Play. 2000. (Press Out & Play Bks.). (Illus.). 16p. (gr. k-2). pap. 5.95 (978-0-8069-2669-8(4)) Sterling Publishing Co., Inc.

Stevens, Clive. Paperfolding. (Step-by-Step Ser.). (Illus.). 32p. (J). 2003. pap. 7.95 (978-1-4034-0711-5(8)); 2001. (gr. 3-5). lib. bdg. 24.22 (978-1-57572-333-4(6)) Heinemann Library.

Stevens, Denise. Busy Hands: Art & Crafts for Children Ages 2-7. Stevens, Tim, ed. 1999. (Illus.). vi, 60p. spiral bd. 6.95 (978-1-928981-00-8(3)) Tabletop Productions.

Stewart, Jennifer, ed. Christmas Fun: Sticker Book. Kolding, Richard Max, illus. 1999. 28p. (J). (ps-2). act. bk. ed. 3.29 (978-0-7847-1095-1(3) , 22079, Bean Sprouts) Standard Publishing.

Stillinger, Doug. Aviones de Papel. 2005. (SPA., Illus.). 56p. (J). spiral bd. 19.95 (978-987-1078-44-8(7)) Klutz Latino MEX. *Dist:* Independent Pubs. Group.

—Baterias en Accion. 2005. (SPA., Illus.). 62p. (J). spiral bd. 23.95 (978-987-1078-28-8(5)) Klutz Latino MEX. *Dist:* Independent Pubs. Group.

—Klutz Building Cards - How to Build Pirate Ships. 2006. (Illus.). 30p. (YA). spiral bd. 12.95 (978-1-57054-228-2(7)) Klutz.

Stillwell, Elaine. Sweet Memories: For Children & Adults - To Create Healing & Loving Memories for Holidays & Other Special Events. Olsen, Catherine, illus. 1998. (J). 3.95 (978-1-56123-121-8(5)) Centering Corp.

Stohs, Anita Reith. Praise God with Paper Cups: 45 Easy Bible Crafts. 2005. (ENG., Illus.). 64p. (J). 9.99 (978-0-7586-0842-0(X)) Concordia Publishing Hse.

Stoppleman, Monica & Crowe, Carol. Fabric. 1998. (Craft Workshop Ser.). (Illus.). 32p. (J). (gr. 3). lib. bdg. (978-0-86505-779-1(6)) Crabtree Publishing Co.

Stoppleman, Monica, et al. Fabric. 1998. (Craft Workshop Ser.). (Illus.). 32p. (J). (gr. 3). pap. (978-0-86505-789-0(3)) Crabtree Publishing Co.

Storms, Biz. Quilting. Bradford, June, illus. 2004. (Kids Can Do It Ser.). 40p. (J). (gr. 4-6). (978-1-55074-805-5(X)); (978-1-55074-967-0(6)) Kids Can Pr., Ltd.

—Quilting. Bradford, June, illus. 2003. 40p. (J). (ps-7). lib. bdg. 14.10 (978-0-613-50827-8(0)) Tandem Library Bks.

Strang Communications Company Staff, ed. Ages 1-2 Activities: Summer 2002. 2002. (J). pap., act. bk. ed. 6.99 (978-1-57405-952-6(1)) CharismaLife Pubs.

—Ages 2-3 Activities: Summer 2002. 2002. (J). pap., act. bk. ed. 3.29 (978-1-57405-956-4(4)) CharismaLife Pubs.

Stringer, John. Communication & Art Activities. 2002. (Arty Facts Ser.). (Illus.). 48p. (J). (gr. 3-4). pap. (978-0-7787-1147-6(1)); lib. bdg. (978-0-7787-1119-3(6)) Crabtree Publishing Co.

—Communication & Art Activities. 2002. (gr. 3-6). lib. bdg. 17.60 (978-0-613-52824-5(7)) Tandem Library Bks.

—Machines, Transportation & Art Activities. (Arty Facts Ser.). (Illus.). 48p. (J). (gr. 3-4). 2003. lib. bdg. (978-0-7787-1116-2(1)); 2002. pap. (978-0-7787-1144-5(7)) Crabtree Publishing Co.

—Machines, Transportation & Art Activities. 2002. (gr. 3-6). lib. bdg. 17.60 (978-0-613-52874-0(3)) Tandem Library Bks.

Strom Collins, Carolyn. My Little House Crafts Book: 18 Projects from Laura Ingalls Wilder's Little House Stories. 1998. (Little House Ser.). (978-0-606-13635-8(5)) Tandem Library Bks.

Stull, Katherine & McGuffee, Julie, eds. Hands-On Crafts for Kids: Crafting Together. Gregg, Pam, illus. 1999. 114p. (J). (gr. 2-6). pap. 15.95 (978-1-891514-02-9(4)) Hands On Crafts For Kids.

Sturgill, Ruthy. Christmas Tree Advent Calendar: A Country Quilted & Appliquéd Project. 2006. 96p. pap. 24.95 (978-1-59800-539-4(1)) Outskirts Press, Inc.

Sunderlage, Barb, ed. The Best of Angels: Joyful Angels for All Occasions. 2002. 52p. pap. 14.99 (978-0-9652041-6-3(2) , Pack-O-Fun, Inc.) Clapper Publishing Co.

—The Best of Snow Friends. 2002. 32p. pap. 11.99 (978-0-9652041-7-0(0) , Pack-O-Fun, Inc.) Clapper Publishing Co.

Takagi, Satoshi. Origami for Playtime. 2004. (Illus.). 158p. pap. 12.95 (978-4-88996-131-7(3)) Japan Pubn. Trading Co. JPN. *Dist:* Oxford Univ. Pr., Inc.

Tamsin, Carter. Handmade Crafts. 2003. (Step-by-Step Ser.). (Illus.). 32p. (J). (gr. 3-5). lib. bdg. 25.64 (978-1-4034-0698-9(7)) Heinemann Library.

Tandy, Rachel, ed. The Foam Book. 2005. (Chicken Socks). (Illus.). 24p. (J). 9.95 (978-1-59174-350-7(8)) Klutz.

—Make Your Own Twinkly Tiaras. 2005. (Chicken Socks). (Illus.). 20p. (J). spiral bd. 12.95 (978-1-59174-371-2(0)) Klutz.

—Melty Beads. 2005. (Chicken Socks). (Illus.). 22p. (J). 12.95 (978-1-59174-362-0(1)) Klutz.

Taylor, Barbara. Light, Color & Art Activities. 2002. (gr. 3-6). lib. bdg. 17.60 (978-0-613-52871-9(9)) Tandem Library Bks.

—Structures, Materials, & Art Activities. (Arty Facts Ser.). (Illus.). 48p. (J). (gr. 3-4). 2011. pap. (978-0-7787-1141-4(2)); 2002. lib. bdg. (978-0-7787-1113-1(7)) Crabtree Publishing Co.

—Structures, Materials & Art Activities. 2002. (ps-2). lib. bdg. 17.60 (978-0-613-57140-1(1)) Tandem Library Bks.

Taylor, Barbara, text. Light, Color & Art Activities. 2002. (Arty Facts Ser.). (Illus.). 48p. (J). (gr. 3-4). pap. (978-0-7787-1142-1(0)); lib. bdg. (978-0-7787-1114-8(5)) Crabtree Publishing Co.

Temko, Florence. Cut & Color My Fun Furniture. 2006. 32p. (J). pap. 3.95 (978-0-486-45293-7(X)) Dover Pubns., Inc.

—Traditional Crafts from China. Gooch, Randall, illus. 2005. (Culture Crafts Ser.). 64p. (gr. 3-8). 23.93 (978-0-8225-2939-2(4)) Lerner Publishing Group.

—Traditional Crafts from Japan. Gooch, Randall, illus. 2005. (Culture Crafts Ser.). (gr. 3-8). 23.93 (978-0-8225-2938-5(6)) Lerner Publishing Group.

—Traditional Crafts from the Caribbean. 2005. (Culture Crafts Ser.). (Illus.). 64p. (gr. 3-8). 23.93 (978-0-8225-2937-8(8)) Lerner Publishing Group.

Terzian, Alexandra M. The Kids' Multicultural Art Book. 1999. (Williamson Kids Can! Ser.). (Illus.). 160p. (J). (gr. 3 up). lib. bdg. 25.26 (978-0-8368-2233-5(1)) Stevens, Gareth Inc.

Terzian, Alexandra M. The Kids Multicultural Art Book. Terzian, Alexandria M., illus. 2007. 160p. (gr. 1-2). pap. 12.99 ***(978-0-8249-6808-3(5));*** (Illus.). 16.99 ***(978-0-8249-6807-6(7))*** Ideals Pubns. (Williamson Bks.).

Things to Make & Do. (J). Date not set. 64p. 5.98 (978-1-4054-0412-9(4)); Date not set. 48p. pap. 4.98 (978-0-7525-8411-9(1)); 2003. (Illus.). 64p. 12.98 (978-1-4054-1220-9(8)) Parragon, Inc.

Things to Make & Do for Christmas. 2002. (Activity Books). 32p. (J). pap. (978-0-7945-0055-9(2) , Usborne) EDC Publishing.

Things to Make & Do for Christmas Kid Kit. (Illus.). 32p. (YA). (ps up). 13.95 (978-1-58086-440-4(6)) EDC Publishing.

Thoenig, Donald. Double Image Magic Artwork & Cards: Christmas. 2003. pap. 16.95 (978-0-9729546-0-0(0)) SMC Publishing.

Thomas, John. The Ultimate Book of Kid Concoctions 2. 2006. (Illus.). 80p. (J). pap. 14.99 (978-0-8054-4444-5(0)) B&H Publishing Grp.

Thomas, John & Thomas, Danita. Kid Concoctions & Contraptions: A New Wacky & Zany Collection of Concoctions & Contraptions. 2006. (Illus.). 80p. (J). pap. 14.99 (978-0-8054-4446-9(7)) B&H Publishing Grp.

—Kid Concoctions of Biblical Proportions. 2007. (Illus.). 80p. (J). pap. 14.99 (978-0-8054-4447-6(5)) B&H Publishing Grp.

—The Ultimate Book of All Occasion Kid Concoctions: More Than 50 Wacky, Wild & Crazy Concoctions for All Occasions. 2006. (Illus.). 80p. (J). pap. 14.99 (978-0-8054-4445-2(9)) B&H Publishing Grp.

—The Ultimate Book of Kid Concoctions. 2006. (Illus.). 80p. (J). pap. 14.99 (978-0-8054-4443-8(2)) B&H Publishing Grp.

Thomas, John E. & Pagel, Danita. The Ultimate Book of Kid Concoctions Vol. 1: More Than 65 Wacky, Wild & Crazy Concoctions. 4 vols. Durr, Robb, illus. Dragga, Bill, photos by. 1998. 80p. (J). (ps-9). per. 14.95 (978-0-9661088-0-4(9)) Kid Concoctions Co.

Thomas, John E. & Thomas, Danita. Kid Concoctions & Contraptions Vol. 4: A New Wacky & Zany Collection of Concoctions & Contraptions. Durr, Robb, illus. 4th ed. 2002. 80p. (J). per. 14.95 (978-0-9661088-8-0(4)) Kid Concoctions Co.

—The Ultimate Book of Kid Concoctions Vol. 2: More Than 65 New Wacky, Wild & Crazy Concoctions, 4 vols. Briller, Margaret, ed. Durr, Robb, illus. 2000. 80p. (J). (ps-9). per. 14.95 (978-0-9661088-1-1(7)) Kid Concoctions Co.

Thompson, Ruth. What Are Textiles? 2005. (Illus.). 30p. (J). (gr. 3-7). lib. bdg. 27.10 (978-1-932889-90-1(6)) Sea-To-Sea Pubns.

Thompson, Sharon & Booth, Vanessa. Christian Crafts for Gift-Giving. Seltzer, Erin, ed. 2004. (Illus.). 64p. (J). per. 8.99 (978-1-59441-008-6(9) , CD-204002) Carson-Dellosa Publishing Co., Inc.

Tiede, Karen. Carve Smart. 2004. 189p. (YA). pap. 19.95 (978-0-7414-2093-0(7)) Infinity Publishing.

Tierney, Tom. Mary Queen of Scots Paper Dolls. 2007. 16p. (J). 5.95 ***(978-0-486-46195-3(5))*** Dover Pubns., Inc.

—Soap Opera Divas Paper Dolls. 2007. 32p. 6.95 ***(978-0-486-46222-6(6))*** Dover Pubns., Inc.

Tin Treasures: Six-Pack. (Greetings Ser.: Vol. 3). 24p. (gr. 2-3). 31.00 (978-0-7635-9419-0(9)) Rigby Education.

Tofts, Hannah. Collage. 2004. (Crafty Ideas Ser.). (SPA., Illus.). 32p. (gr. 2-5). (J). pap. 5.95 (978-1-58728-121-1(X)); 9.95 (978-1-58728-260-7(7)) T&N Children's Publishing. (Two Can Publishing).

—Collage. 2001. (gr. 3-6). lib. bdg. 14.10 (978-0-613-83314-1(7)) Tandem Library Bks.

Top That Publishing Editors, ed. Fiendish Faces. Dahl, Roald, illus. 2005. 24p. (J). pap. (978-1-905359-53-0(5)) Top That! Publishing PLC.

—Stupendous Stampers. Dahl, Roald, illus. 2005. 24p. (J). pap. (978-1-905359-50-9(0)) Top That! Publishing PLC.

Top That! Team Staff, contrib. by. I [Love] Dogs & Puppies. 2002. (Art Rom Ser.). (Illus.). 48p. (J). (978-0-439-53072-9(5)) Scholastic, Inc.

Torres, Laura. Best Friends Forever! 199 Projects to Make & Share. 2004. (Illus.). 160p. (YA). pap. 13.95 (978-0-7611-3274-5(0) , 13274) Workman Publishing Co., Inc.

—The Fantastic Foam Book. 1998. (Illus.). 20p. (J). (gr. 4-7). spiral bd. 14.95 (978-1-57054-144-5(2)) Klutz.

—Formas Fantasticas. 2004. (SPA., Illus.). 40p. (J). spiral bd. 17.95 (978-968-5528-04-7(7)) Klutz Latino MEX. *Dist:* Independent Pubs. Group.

Traig, Jennifer & Balmain, Julianne. Crafty Girl: Cool Stuff. 2001. (Illus.). 120p. (gr. 7 up). pap. 12.95 (978-0-8118-2945-8(6)) Chronicle Bks. LLC.

Trottier, Maxine. Native Crafts: Inspired by North America's First People. Melo, Esperanca, illus. unabr. ed. 2000. (Kids Can Do It Ser.). (J). (gr. 4-6). 132p. (978-1-55074-549-8(2)); 40p. (978-1-55074-854-3(8)) Kids Can Pr., Ltd.

—Native Crafts: Inspired by North America's First People. 2000. (Illus.). (J). (978-0-606-18228-7(4)) Tandem Library Bks.

Trulock, Alison. Build Your Own Snow Globe. 2003. (Mega Mini Kitstm Ser.). (Illus.). 32p. pap. 8.95 (978-0-7624-1620-2(3) , Running Pr. Minature Editions) Running Pr. Bk. Pubs.

Tubb, Kristin O'Donnell. Craft Corner Art Studio. Riley, Kellee, illus. 2007. (Holly Hobbie & Friends Ser.). 48p. (J). 9.99 ***(978-1-4169-3423-3(5)*** , Simon Scribbles) Simon & Schuster Children's Publishing.

Tull, Mary, et al. Northern Asia: Understanding Geography & History Through Art. 1999. (Artisans Around the World Ser.). (Illus.). 48p. (J). (gr. 4-8). lib. bdg. 27.12 (978-0-7398-0119-2(8)) Raintree.

Turck, Mary C. Mexico & Central America: A Fiesta of Cultures, Crafts, & Activities for Ages 8-12. 2004. (Illus.). 160p. (J). pap. 16.95 (978-1-55652-525-4(7)) Chicago Review Pr., Inc.

The Ultimate Guide to the Perfect Card: A Cardmaker's Best Friend. 2004. (Illus.). 180p. per. 17.15 (978-0-9745339-5-7(5)) Bluegrass Publishing Inc.

Umnik, Sharon D. 175 Easy-to-Do Christmas Crafts. 2003. (gr. 3-6). lib. bdg. 15.25 (978-0-613-78846-5(X)) Tandem Library Bks.

—175 Easy-to-Do Valentine Crafts. 2002. (gr. k-3). lib. bdg. 16.40 (978-0-613-78827-4(3)) Tandem Library Bks.

Umnik, Sharon D., ed. 175 Easy-to-Do Valentine Crafts. 2003. (Illus.). (J). (gr. k-5). pap. 7.95 (978-1-56397-672-8(2)) Boyds Mills Pr.

Urton, Andrea. Animals. 2001. (Illus.). 48p. (J). (gr. 3-7). pap. 8.95 (978-0-7373-0536-4(3)) Lowell Hse. Juvenile.

—Bugs. 2001. (Illus.). 48p. (J). (gr. 4-7). pap. 8.95 (978-0-7373-0537-1(1)) Lowell Hse. Juvenile.

Van Vleet, Carmella. Great Ancient Egypt Projects You Can Build Yourself. 2006. (Build It Yourself Ser.). (Illus.). 128p. (J). (gr. 4-6). pap. 14.95 (978-0-9771294-5-4(4)) Nomad Pr.

VBS-Fiesta-Cactus Crafts & Missions: Leader Manual (Group's Fiesta! Where Kids Are Fired Up about Jesus. 2006. 64p. pap. 9.99 (978-0-7644-2954-5(X)) Group Publishing, Inc.

Veigele, William J. Sea Bag of Memories: Images, Poems, Thoughts, & Crafts of the small Ship Sailors of World War II. 2003. 320p. (YA). (gr. 10 up). 39.95 (978-0-9645867-4-1(6)) Astral Publishing Co.

Wagner, Lisa. Cool Painted Stuff. 2005. (Cool Crafts Ser.). (Illus.). 32p. (J). (gr. k-6). lib. bdg. 22.78 (978-1-59197-742-1(8) , Checkerboard Library) ABDO Publishing Co.

Walker, Lester. Housebuilding for Children 2nd Ed. 2007. 192p. pap. 16.95 ***(978-1-58567-906-5(2))*** Penguin Group (USA) Inc.

Wallace, Mary. I Can Make That! Fantastic Crafts for Kids. 2005. (Illus.). 160p. (J). (ps). 16.95 (978-1-897066-33-1(3)) Maple Tree Pr. CAN. *Dist:* Perseus Distribution.

Walpole, Brenda. Funstation Let's Grow It!, 5 vols., Set. 1998. (Funstations Ser.). (Illus.). 48p. (J). (gr. 3-7). 17.95 (978-1-57145-348-8(2) , Silver Dolphin Bks.) Advantage Pubs. Group.

Walsh, Danny, et al. The Cardboard Box Book: 25 Things to Make & Do with & Empty Box. Halloran, Josh, illus. Norris, Martin, photos by. 2006. 112p. (J). (gr. 3-5). pap. 12.95 (978-0-8230-0610-6(7)) Watson-Guptill Pubns., Inc.

Walsh-Kezele, Mary. Hello Kitty Craft Sticks Activity Book. 2002. (Hello Kitty & Her Friends Crafts Club Ser.). (Illus.). 44p. (J). (978-0-439-32839-5(X)) Scholastic, Inc.

Walton, Sally. I Can Make Things: How-to-Make Craft Projects for the Very Young. 2000. (Show Me How Ser.). (Illus.). 48p. (ps-2). pap. 7.95 (978-0-7548-0222-8(1) , Lorenz Bks.) Anness Publishing GBR. *Dist:* National Bk. Network.

Walton, Stewart & Walton, Sally. Stamp Decorating: A Step-by-Step Guidebook & Inspirational Sourcebook, with over 80 Projects & Techniques. (Illus.). 256p. (J). pap. (978-0-681-64292-8(0)) Anness Publishing.

Ward, Fred. Opals. Ward, Charlotte, ed. 2nd ed. 2000. (Fred Ward Gem Book Ser.). (Illus.). 64p. per. 14.95 (978-1-887651-04-2(7)) Gem Bk. Pubs.

Warrick, Leanne. Chillin Trix for Cool Chix. 2005. (Cool Chix Ser.). (Illus.). 96p. (J). (gr. 5-12). pap. 9.95 (978-0-8230-4501-3(3)) Watson-Guptill Pubns., Inc.

Warwick, Ellen. Stuff for Your Space. Lum, Bernice, tr. Lum, Bernice, illus. 2004. (Kids Can Do It Ser.). 40p. (J). (gr. 4-6). (978-1-55337-399-5(5)); (978-1-55337-398-8(7)) Kids Can Pr., Ltd.

Watson, David. Papermaking. 2000. (Step-by-Step Ser.). (Illus.). 32p. (J). (gr. 3-5). lib. bdg. 24.22 (978-1-57572-327-3(1)) Heinemann Library.

—Papermaking. 1999. (Step-by-Step Children's Crafts Ser.). (Illus.). 32p. pap. 7.95 (978-0-85532-913-6(0) , 9130) Search Pr., Ltd. GBR. *Dist:* Independent Pubs. Group.

Watt, Et Al, Fiona. Fabulous Sparkly Activity Books. 2007. 32p. (J). pap. 29.99 (978-0-7945-1412-9(X) , Usborne) EDC Publishing.

Watt, Fiona. Big Bk of Vacation Things to Make & Do. 2006. (Illus.). 96p. (J). 14.99 (978-0-7945-1317-7(4) , Usborne) EDC Publishing.

—Fairy Things to Stitch & Sew. Fearn, Katrina, illus. 2006. 32p. (J). pap. 6.99 (978-0-7945-1235-4(6) , Usborne) EDC Publishing.

—Wizard, Pirate & Princess Things to Make & Do (Combined Volume) 2006. 96p. (J). 14.99 (978-0-7945-1415-0(4) , Usborne) EDC Publishing.

Watt, Fiona & Gilpin, Rebecca. Big Bk of Fairy Things to Make & Do. 2006. 96p. (J). pap. 14.99 (978-0-7945-1437-2(5) , Usborne) EDC Publishing.

Watt, Fiona & Gilpin, Rebecca. The Usborne Big Book of Christmas Things to Make & Do. Fearn, Katrina, illus. 2005. 99p. (J). ***(978-0-439-81506-2(1))*** Scholastic, Inc.

WATT FIONA ET AL. 50 Fairy Things to Make & Do. 2006. 50p. (J). 9.99 (978-0-7945-1318-4(2) , Usborne) EDC Publishing.

Weber, Kriss. Flower Pot Zoo: Terra-Cotta Treasures. 2002. 9.95 (978-0-9753192-0-8(5)) KD Duet Publishing.

Wellford, Lin. Painting on Rocks for Kids. 2002. (Illus.). 64p. (J). (gr. 1-7). pap. 12.99 (978-1-58180-255-9(2) , North Light Bks.) F & W Pubns., Inc.

—Painting on Rocks for Kids. 2002. (gr. k-3). lib. bdg. 22.25 (978-0-613-87127-3(8)) Tandem Library Bks.

What a Great Idea!, 6 Packs. (gr. k-1). 23.00 (978-0-7635-9072-7(X)) Rigby Education.

Wilkens, Drew. Gecko's Vol. 2: More Bead Animals. Wilkens, Kelley, ed. Wilkens, Drew, illus. 2nd ed. 1998. (Illus.). 74p. pap. 7.95 (978-0-9663591-1-4(9)) Bead Man Pr.

Williams, Beckie. Born Free Animal Friends. Morton, Robert, illus. 2005. 16p. (J). (ps-ps). (978-1-84510-758-1(6)) Top That! Publishing PLC.

Williams, Jack S. Craftsmen & Craftswomen. 2004. (People of the California Missions Ser.). (Illus.). 64p. (J). lib. bdg. 25.50 (978-0-8239-6280-8(6) , PowerKids Pr.) Rosen Publishing Group, Inc., The.

Willis, Abigail & Spenceley, Annabel. Halloween Fun: Great Things to Make & Do. 2003. (Holiday Fun Ser.). (Illus.). 32p. (J). (gr. 3-5). pap. 4.95 (978-0-7534-5683-5(4) , Kingfisher) Houghton Mifflin Co. Trade & Reference Div.

Wilson, Mary Ann & Cooley, Brian. Make-A-Saurus: My Life with Raptors & Other Dinosaurs. 2000. (Illus.). 58p. (J). (ps-6). lib. bdg. 24.55 (978-0-613-78401-6(4)) Tandem Library Bks.

Wilson, Sule Greg C. African-American Quilting: The Warmth of Tradition. 1999. (Library of African American Arts & Culture). (Illus.). 64p. (YA). (gr. 7-12). lib. bdg. 26.50 (978-0-8239-1854-6(8) , AAQUCR) Rosen Publishing Group, Inc., The.

Wirtzfeld, Beverly. Bear's Designs Unlimited, Vol. I. 60p. (J). (gr. 4-10). ring bd. 4.95 (978-0-9638473-0-0(9)) Bear's Designs Unlimited.

Woggon, Bill & Lucas, John. Katy Keene Movie Premiere Paper Dolls: Featuring Movie Star Errol Swoon. 1999. (Illus.). 24p. (J). pap. 5.95 (978-0-87588-468-4(7)) Hobby Hse. Pr., Inc.

Wolf, Gita & Ravishankar, Anushka. Masks & Performance. 2003. (Illus.). 144p. 10.99 (978-81-86211-47-2(0)) Penguin Group (USA) Inc.

Woodcock, Victoria. Making Stuff for Kids. 2007. (Illus.). 144p. pap. 24.95 ***(978-1-906155-00-1(3))*** Black Dog Publishing Ltd. GBR. *Dist:* Perseus Distribution.

Woram, Catherine. Crafting with Kids: Creative Fun for Children Aged 3-10. Davies, Vanessa, photos by. 2006. (Illus.). 128p. (J). pap. (978-1-84597-252-3(X)) Ryland Peters & Small.

Wright, Rachel. The Egyptians. (Illus.). 32p. (YA). (gr. 3 up). lib. bdg. 27.10 (978-1-932889-00-0(0)) Sea-To-Sea Pubns.

Year-Round Crafts for Kids. 2005. (Illus.). 136p. (978-0-7853-8840-1(0) , 3468500) Publications International, Ltd.

Zakarin, Debra Mostow. Happening Hanukkah: Creative Ways to Celebrate. Haley, Amanda, illus. 2002. 64p. (J). (gr. 3-6). pap. 5.99 (978-0-448-42869-7(5) , Grosset & Dunlap) Penguin Group (USA) Inc.

Zalben, Jane Breskin. Pearl's Passover: A Family Celebration Through Stories, Recipes, Crafts, & Songs. Zalben, Jane Breskin, illus. 2002. (Illus.). 48p. (J). (gr. k-3). 16.00 (978-0-689-81487-7(9)) Simon & Schuster Children's Publishing.

HANDWRITING

see Writing

HANGING

see Capital Punishment

HANNIBAL, 247-183 B.C.

Abbott, Jacob. Hannibal. 2005. reprint ed. pap. 28.95 (978-0-7661-9515-8(5)) Kessinger Publishing, LLC.

Warrick, Karen Clemens. Hannibal: Great General of the Ancient World. 2006. (Rulers of the Ancient World Ser.). (Illus.). 160p. (J). lib. bdg. 27.93 (978-0-7660-2564-6(0)) Enslow Pubs., Inc.

HANNIBAL, 247-183 B.C.—FICTION

Henty, G. A. The Young Carthaginian: A Tale of the Times of Hannibal. 2004. reprint ed. pap. 27.95 (978-1-4191-8911-1(5)); pap. 1.99 (978-1-4192-8911-8(X)) Kessinger Publishing, LLC.

—The Young Carthaginian: A Tale of the Times of Hannibal. 2004. pap. 8.95 (978-1-57646-874-6(7)) Quiet Vision Publishing.

HANUKKAH

Adler, David A. The Kids' Catalog of Hanukkah. 2004. (New Children's Titles Ser.). (Illus.). 160p. pap. 16.95 (978-0-8276-0805-4(5)) Jewish Pubn. Society.

Bastyra, Judy & Ward, Catherine. Hanukkah Fun: Great Things to Make & Do. 2003. (Holiday Fun Ser.). (Illus.). 32p. (J). (gr. 3-5). pap. 4.95 (978-0-7534-5684-2(2) , Kingfisher) Houghton Mifflin Co. Trade & Reference Div.

Bearman, Jane. Eight Nights: A Chanukah Counting Book. 1999. (Illus.). (J). (ps-3). pap. 6.00 (978-0-8074-0025-8(4)) URJ Pr.

Ben-Zvi, Rebecca Tova. Four Sides, Eight Nights: A New Spin on Hanukkah. Natti, Susanna, illus. 48p. (J). 2006. pap. 7.95 (978-1-59643-181-2(4)); 2005. 16.95 (978-1-59643-059-4(1)) Roaring Brook Pr.

Bledsoe, Karen E. Hanukkah Crafts. 2004. (Fun Holiday Crafts Kids Can Do Ser.). (Illus.). 32p. (J). lib. bdg. 22.60 (978-0-7660-2238-6(2)) Enslow Pubs., Inc.

Bodden, Valerie. Hanukkah. 2005. (My First Look at Holidays Ser.). (Illus.). 24p. (gr. k-3). 15.95 (978-1-58341-369-2(3) , Creative Education) Creative Co., The.

Charette, Beverly. The Story of Chanukah for Children. Keller, Dick, illus. 2001. (J). (ps-3). pap. 3.95 (978-0-8249-5382-9(7) , Ideals Children's Bks.) Ideals Pubns.

Chiel, Kinneret. Complete Book of Hanukah. (Illus.). (J). (gr. 6-8). pap. 6.95 (978-0-87068-367-1(5)) Ktav Publishing Hse., Inc.

Clark, Anne, et al. Hanukkah. 1998. (World of Holidays Ser.). (Illus.). 32p. (gr. 2-5). lib. bdg. 25.70 (978-0-8172-4614-3(2)) Raintree.

Cohen, Santiago. It's Hanukkah! 2003. (Illus.). 16p. 8.95 (978-1-59354-021-0(3)) Blue Apple Bks.

Cohn, Janice. The Christmas Menorahs: How a Town Fought Hate. 2000. (J). 13.75 (978-0-606-19688-8(9)) Tandem Library Bks.

Davis, Kate. Hanukkah's Here! Filipowich, Bob, illus. ed. 2001. (Mini Soft Shapes Ser.). 8p. (J). (ps-ps). 6.99 (978-1-58476-081-8(8)) Innovative Kids.

Donahue, Shari Faden. Celebrate Hanukkah with Me. 1998. 32p. (J). 15.95 (978-0-9634287-2-1(1)) Arimax, Inc.

Dorling Kindersley Publishing Staff. My First Hanukkah. 2nd ed. 2005. (My First Word Books). (Illus.). 36p. (J). (ps-ps). per., bds. 5.99 (978-0-7566-1105-7(9)) Dorling Kindersley Publishing, Inc.

Dorling Kindersley Publishing Staff, ed. Hanukkah. 2004. (Ultimate Sticker Bks.). 16p. (J). pap. 6.99 (978-0-7566-0546-9(6)) Dorling Kindersley Publishing, Inc.

Erlbach, Arlene. Hanukkah Celebrating the Holiday of Lights. 2002. (Finding Out about Holidays Ser.). (Illus.). 48p. (J). (gr. 1-4). lib. bdg. 23.93 (978-0-7660-1577-7(7)) Enslow Pubs., Inc.

Fishman, Cathy Goldberg. Hanukkah. Young, Mary O'Keefe, illus. (On My Own Holidays Ser.). 48p. (J). 2004. (gr. 2-4). lib. bdg. 25.26 (978-1-57505-195-6(8)); 2003. (gr. k-3). pap. 5.95 (978-1-57505-583-1(X)) Lerner Publishing Group.

—On Hanukkah. Hall, Melanie W., illus. 2005. 27p. (J). (gr. k-4). reprint ed. 16.00 (978-0-7567-9289-3(4)) DIANE Publishing Co.

—On Hanukkah. 2001. (gr. k-3). lib. bdg. 15.30 (978-0-613-73378-6(9)) Tandem Library Bks.

Fishman, Cathy Goldberg & Hall, Melanie. On Hanukkah. Hall, Melanie W., illus. 2001. 40p. (J). pap. 6.99 (978-0-689-84579-6(0), Aladdin) Simon & Schuster Children's Publishing.

Foran, Jill. Hanukkah. 2003. (Celebrating Cultures Ser.). (Illus.). 24p. (J). lib. bdg. 15.95 (978-1-59036-092-7(3)) Weigl Pubs., Inc.

Freedland, Sara. Hanukkah! A Three-Dimensional Celebration. Clarke, Sue, illus. 2nd ed. 1999. 18p. (J). (gr. 3-7). 18.99 (978-0-7636-0890-3(4)) Candlewick Pr.

Ganeri, Anita. The Hanukkah Story. Phillips, Rachael, illus. 2004. (Holiday Stories Ser.). (J). lib. bdg. (978-1-58340-490-4(2)) Smart Apple Media.

Gillis, Jennifer Blizin. Hanukkah. 2002. (Candle Time Ser.). (Illus.). 24p. (J). (ps-1). lib. bdg. 18.50 (978-1-58810-530-1(X)) Heinemann Library.

Gillis, Jennifer Blizin & Jordan, Denise M. Hanukkah. 2002. (Fiestas Con Velas (Candle Time) Ser.). 24p. (J). (ps-1). (SPA.). lib. bdg. 18.50 (978-1-58810-785-5(X)); (SPA., Illus.). pap. 5.25 (978-1-58810-832-6(5) , 91590); (Illus.). pap. 5.25 (978-1-58810-739-8(6) , 91386) Heinemann Library.

Goodman, L. J. & Silverhardt, Lauryn. Oh Chanukah. Conrad, Liz, illus. 2003. 12p. (J). bds. 5.99 (978-0-8431-0508-7(9) , Price Stern Sloan) Penguin Group (USA) Inc.

Groner, Judyth Saypol & Wikler, Madeline. All about Hanukkah. Kreiswirth, Kinny, illus. 32p. (J). (gr. k-5). 2003. pap. 5.95 (978-1-58013-051-6(8)); 1999. 12.95 incl. audio (978-1-58013-057-8(7)) Kar-Ben Publishing.

Hanukkah, Vol. 2. 2005. (One World, Many Cultures Ser.). (YA). (gr. k-3). (978-0-7368-9434-0(9) , Pebble Bks.) Capstone Pr., Inc.

Hanukkah Books. 2nd ed. 2001. 20.85 (978-0-06-001358-5(3)) HarperCollins Pubs.

Heiligman, Deborah. Celebrate Hanukkah: With Light, Latkes, & Dreidels. 2006. (Holidays Around the World Ser.). (Illus.). 32p. (J). (gr. 1-4). 15.95 (978-0-7922-5924-4(6) , National Geographic Children's Bks.) National Geographic Society.

—Celebrate Hanukkah:With Light, Latkes, & Dreidels. 2006. (Holidays Around the World Ser.). (Illus.). 32p. (gr. 1-4). 23.90 (978-0-7922-5925-1(4) , National Geographic Children's Bks.) National Geographic Society.

Heller, Daryl. Hannukah. 2004. (My Library of Holidays). (Illus.). 24p. (J). lib. bdg. 16.00 (978-1-4042-2525-1(0) , PowerKids Pr.) Rosen Publishing Group, Inc., The.

Hughes, Monica. My Hanukkah. 2003. (Festivals Ser.). (Illus.). 24p. (J). pap. 5.50 (978-1-4109-0664-9(7)); lib. bdg. 18.56 (978-1-4109-0638-0(8)) Raintree.

—My Hanukkah. 2003. (ps-2). lib. bdg. 13.55 (978-0-613-78202-9(X)) Tandem Library Bks.

Johnston, M. C. Hanukkah. 2002. (Wonder Books Level 2: Holidays Ser.). (Illus.). 24p. (J). (ps-3). 22.79 (978-1-56766-024-1(X)) Child's World, Inc.

Kaiser, Cecily. On the First Night of Chanukah. 2007. 24p. (J). pap. 3.99 (***978-0-439-75802-4(5)** , Cartwheel Bks.) Scholastic, Inc.

Koffsky, Ann D. The Hanukkah Herald: Activity Book: Games, Activities, Songs. 1998. (Illus.). 16p. (J). (gr. 3-5). pap. 3.99 (978-0-914080-13-8(X)) Shulsinger Sales, Inc.

Lakeshore Learning Materials Staff, contrib. by. Hanukkah Celebration Kit. 2000. (J). pap. 29.95 (978-1-929255-88-7(8)) Lakeshore Learning Materials.

Levy, Barbara Soloff. Learning about Chanukah. 2001. (Illus.). 16p. (J). (ps-5). pap. 1.50 (978-0-486-41645-8(3)) Dover Pubns., Inc.

Marsh, Carole. Hanukkah: Activities, Crafts, Recipes & More! 2003. 32p. (J). (gr. 1-6). pap. 6.95 (978-0-635-02174-8(9)) Gallopade International.

Martinez, Debbie. Celebrating Chanukah: Eight Nights. 1999. (ps-2). lib. bdg. 10.65 (978-0-613-34115-8(5)) Tandem Library Bks.

—Celebrating Chanukah No. 4532: Eight Nights. Kupperstein, Joel, ed. Bynum, Janie, illus. 1999. 16p. (J). (ps-2). pap. 2.99 (978-1-57471-577-4(1)) Creative Teaching Pr., Inc.

Marx, David F. Chanukah. 2000. (Rookie Read-About Holidays Ser.). (Illus.). 32p. (J). (gr. 1-2). 19.50 (978-0-516-22204-2(X)); pap. 5.95 (978-0-516-27152-1(0)) Scholastic Library Publishing. (Children's Pr.).

Mazo, Chaim. The Energizing Hanukkah Story for Children. Channen, Don, illus. rev. ed. 1998. 48p. (J). (gr. 2-7). pap. 7.95 (978-0-943706-27-6(0) , Devora Publishing) Pitspopany Pr.

Modesitt, Jeanne. It's Hanukkah! Spowart, Robin, illus. 1999. 32p. (J). (gr. k-3). tchr. ed. 15.95 (978-0-8234-1451-2(5)) Holiday Hse., Inc.

Murray, Julie. Hanukkah. 2005. (Holidays Ser.). (Illus.). 24p. (J). (gr. k-4). lib. bdg. 21.35 (978-1-57765-953-2(8)) ABDO Publishing Co.

Newman, Leslea. The Eight Nights of Chanukah. Savadier, Elivia, illus. 2005. 24p. (J). (ps-3). 12.95 (978-0-8109-5785-5(X) , Abrams Bks. for Young Readers) Abrams, Harry N. , Inc.

O'Hare, Jeff, ed. Hanukkah: Festival of Lights. Friedman, Arthur & Rhinelander, Mary F., illus. 2001. 64p. (J). pap. 7.95 (978-1-56397-907-1(1)) Boyds Mills Pr.

O'Hare, Jeffrey A. Hanukkah: Festival of Lights. 2003. (gr. 3-6). lib. bdg. 16.40 (978-0-613-78913-4(X)) Tandem Library Bks.

Potts, Steve. Hanukkah. 2001. (Holiday Ser.). (Illus.). 24p. (J). 21.35 (978-1-58340-116-3(4)) Smart Apple Media.

Powell, Jillian. Hanukkah. 2006. (J). (978-1-58340-944-2(0)) Smart Apple Media.

Raabe, Emily. A Hanukkah Holiday Cookbook. 2002. (Festive Foods for the Holidays Ser.). (Illus.). 24p. (J). (gr. 2-5). lib. bdg. 19.95 (978-0-8239-5626-5(1) , PowerKids Pr.) Rosen Publishing Group, Inc., The.

Rau, Dana Meachen. Chanukah. 2000. (gr. 3-6). lib. bdg. 15.25 (978-0-613-51624-2(9)) Tandem Library Bks.

Rose, David, et al. Hanukkah. 1998. (World of Holidays Ser.). (Illus.). 32p. (J). (gr. 2-5). pap. 7.95 (978-0-8172-8105-2(3)) Steck-Vaughn.

Rosinsky, Natalie M. Hanukkah. 2002. (Let's See Library). (Illus.). 24p. (J). (gr. 1 up). lib. bdg. 19.93 (978-0-7565-0390-1(6)) Compass Point Bks.

Roth, Susan L. Hanukkah, Oh Hanukkah. 2004. (Illus.). 24p. (J). (ps). 10.99 (978-0-8037-2843-1(3) , Dial) Penguin Group (USA) Inc.

Rubin, Ellen. Hanakkah Puzzle Book. 2005. (Illus.). 4p. (J). bds. 12.95 (978-1-930143-87-6(7) , Devora Publishing) Pitspopany Pr.

Schaefer, Lola M. Hanukkah. Saunders-Smith, Gail, ed. 2000. (Holidays & Celebrations Ser.). (Illus.). 24p. (J). (gr. k-1). lib. bdg. 15.93 (978-0-7368-0662-6(8) , Pebble Bks.) Capstone Pr., Inc.

Schotter, Roni. Hanukkah! Hafner, Marylin, illus. 2003. 22p. (J). (ps-ps). bds. 6.99 (978-0-316-77623-3(8)) Little Brown & Co.

Schram, Peninnah. The Chanukah Blessing. Allon, Jeffrey, illus. 2004. (J). (ps-3). 13.95 (978-0-8074-0733-2(X) , 101973) URJ Pr.

Sievert, Terri. Hanukkah. 2006. (First Facts Ser.). (Illus.). 24p. (J). (978-0-7368-5389-7(8)) Capstone Pr., Inc.

Silverman, Maida. Festival of Lights: The Story of Hanukkah. Ewing, Carolyn, illus. 1999. (Festival of Lights Ser.). 32p. (J). (gr. k-3). pap. 5.99 (978-0-689-83083-9(1) , Aladdin) Simon & Schuster Children's Publishing.

—Festival of Lights: The Story of Hanukkah. 1999. (gr. k-3). lib. bdg. 14.15 (978-0-613-21532-9(X)); (Illus.). (J). (978-0-606-17919-5(4)) Tandem Library Bks.

Smith, Dian G. Hanukkah Lights. Kitchel, JoAnn, illus. 2001. 16p. (J). (ps-2). 14.95 (978-0-8118-3257-1(0)) Chronicle Bks. LLC.

Sokoloff, David. My Chanukah. Sokoloff, David, illus. 1998. (Illus.). 24p. (Orig.). (J). (ps-5). pap. 1.00 (978-1-889655-06-2(6)) Jewish Educational Toys.

Sokoloff, David, illus. Chanukah. 1998. 12p. (J). (ps-1). bds. 5.00 (978-1-889655-13-0(9)) Jewish Educational Toys.

Sper, Emily. Hanukkah: A Counting Book in English - Hebrew - Yiddish. Sper, Emily, illus. 2003. (Hanukkah Ser.). (ENG, HEB & YID.). 28p. (J). pap. 5.99 (978-0-439-56704-6(1) , Cartwheel Bks.) Scholastic, Inc.

—Hanukkah: A Counting Book in English, Hebrew, & Yiddish. 2001. (HEB, YID & ENG., Illus.). 32p. (J). (ps-1). pap. 6.95 (978-0-439-28291-8(8) , Cartwheel Bks.) Scholastic, Inc.

Stone, Tanya Lee. D Is for Dreidel: A Hanukkah Alphabet Book. Apperley, Dawn, illus. 2002. 24p. (J). (gr. k-2). pap. 4.99 (978-0-8431-4576-2(5) , Price Stern Sloan) Penguin Group (USA) Inc.

The Story of Chanukah. 2002. (Illus.). 24p. (J). 6.95 (978-0-8249-4225-0(6)) Ideals Pubns.

Trueit, Trudi Strain. Chanukah. 2006. (Rookie Read-About Holidays Ser.). (Illus.). (J). 31p. 20.50 (978-0-531-12452-9(5)); 32p. (gr. 1-2). pap. 5.95 (978-0-531-11833-7(9)) Scholastic Library Publishing. (Children's Pr.).

Trueit, Trudi Strain. Hanukkah. 2007. (Holidays, Festivals, & Celebrations Ser.). 32p. (J). (gr. k-4). 22.79 (***978-1-59296-813-8(9)**) Child's World, Inc.

Wengrov, Charles & Dick, Judy. Your Hanukkah Book: Color the Pictures & Learn the Story. 1998. (Illus.). 28p. (J). (gr. 2-5). pap. 3.99 (978-0-914080-15-2(6)) Shulsinger Sales, Inc.

Winne, Joanne. Let's Get Ready for Hanukkah. 2001. (Celebrations Ser.). (Illus.). (J). (ps-2). 24p. 17.00 (978-0-516-23174-7(X)); lib. bdg. (978-0-516-23277-5(0)) Scholastic Library Publishing. (Children's Pr.).

—Let's Get Ready for Hanukkah. 2001. (ps-2). lib. bdg. 12.95 (978-0-613-51084-4(4)) Tandem Library Bks.

Zakarin, Debra Mostow. Happening Hanukkah: Creative Ways to Celebrate. Haley, Amanda, illus. 2002. 64p. (J). (gr. 3-6). pap. 5.99 (978-0-448-42869-7(5) , Grosset & Dunlap) Penguin Group (USA) Inc.

Zalben, Jane Breskin. Pearl's Eight Days of Chanukah. Zalben, Jane Breskin, illus. 2003. (Illus.). 40p. (J). (ps-3). lib. bdg. 15.30 (978-0-613-88073-2(0)) Tandem Library Bks.

Zocchi, Judy. On Hanukkah. Wallis, Rebecca, illus. 2005. (Holiday Happenings Ser.). 32p. (J). pap. 9.95 (978-1-59646-196-3(9)); lib. bdg. 20.65 (978-1-891997-45-7(9)); per. 9.95 (978-1-59646-197-0(7)) Dingles & Co.

—On Hanukkah/la Hanukkah. Wallis, Rebecca, illus. 2005. (Holiday Happenings Ser.).Tr. of Hanukkah. (ENG & SPA.). 32p. (J). pap. 9.95 (978-1-59646-198-7(5)); lib. bdg. 20.65 (978-1-891997-46-4(7)); per. 9.95 (978-1-59646-199-4(3)) Dingles & Co.

Zorn, Steven. The Little Book of Hanukkah. 2000. (Miniature Edition Ser.). (Illus.). 128p. (J). (gr. 4-7). 4.95 (978-0-7624-0790-3(5) , Running Pr. Minature Editions) Running Pr. Bk. Pubs.

Zucker, Jonny. Eight Candles for Light: A Chanukah Story. Cohen, Jan Barger, illus. 2002. (Festival Time! Ser.). 24p. (J). pap. 6.95 (978-0-7641-2266-8(5)) Barron's Educational Series, Inc.

HANUKKAH—FICTION

Ada, Alma Flor. Celebrate Hannukah with Bubbe's Tales. Epelbaum, Mariano, illus. 2006. 31p. (J). (978-1-59820-134-5(4)) Santillana USA Publishing Co., Inc.

Adler, David A. One Yellow Daffodil: A Hanukkah Story. Bloom, Lloyd, illus. 1999. 32p. (J). (gr. 1-5). pap. 7.00 (978-0-15-202094-1(2) , Harcourt Paperbacks) Harcourt Children's Bks.

—One Yellow Daffodil: A Hanukkah Story. 1999. (gr. 3-6). lib. bdg. 14.15 (978-0-613-22137-5(0)) Tandem Library Bks.

Benderly, Beryl Lieff. Jason's Miracle: A Hanukkah Story. 2004. 114p. (J). (gr. 4-8). reprint ed. (978-0-7567-7792-0(5)) DIANE Publishing Co.

—Jason's Miracle: A Hanukkah Story. 2000. (Illus.). 120p. (J). (gr. 4-8). 14.95 (978-0-8075-3781-7(0)) Whitman, Albert & Co.

Bietz, Barbara. Like a Maccabee. White, Anita, illus. l.t. ed. 2006. 136p. (J). (978-1-59287-136-0(4) , 59287-1364) Yaldah Publishing.

Bloom, Daniel. Bubbie & Zadie Come to My House. 2006. 32p. (J). 16.95 (978-0-7570-0298-4(6)) Square One Publishers.

Brian Cleary Staff. Eight Wild Nights. 2006. (J). pap. 7.95 (978-1-58013-229-9(4)) Kar-Ben Publishing.

Bunting, Eve. One Candle. Popp, K. Wendy, illus. (J). (ps-3). 2004. 40p. pap. 6.99 (978-0-06-008560-5(6) , Harper Trophy); 2002. 32p. 15.99 (978-0-06-028115-1(4) , Cotler, Joanna Books); 2002. 32p. lib. bdg. 17.89 (978-0-06-028116-8(2) , Cotler, Joanna Books) HarperCollins Pubs.

Burstein, Chaya M. Hanukkah Cat. Henn, Judy Hanks, illus. 2003. 32p. (J). (ps-3). pap. 6.95 (978-1-58013-029-5(1)) Kar-Ben Publishing.

Capucilli, Alyssa Satin. Biscuit's Hanukkah. Schories, Pat, illus. 2005. (Biscuit Ser.). 16p. (J). 4.99 (978-0-06-009469-0(9) , Harper Festival) HarperCollins Pubs.

Carter, David A. Chanukah Bugs: A Pop-up Celebration. Carter, David A., illus. 2002. (Illus.). 16p. (J). (ps-2). 10.95 (978-0-689-81860-8(2) , Little Simon) Simon & Schuster Children's Publishing.

Chwast, Seymour. The Miracle of Hanukkah. 2006. (Illus.). 28p. 14.95 (978-1-59354-157-6(0)) Blue Apple Bks.

Cleary, Brian P. Eight Wild Nights: A Family Hanukkah Tale. Udovic, David, illus. 2006. 24p. (J). 16.95 (978-1-58013-152-0(2)) Kar-Ben Publishing.

Codell, Esmé Raji. Hanukkah, Shmanukkah! Pham, LeUyen, illus. 2005. 64p. (ps-2). 16.99 (978-0-7868-5179-9(1)) Hyperion Pr.

Cooper, Ilene. Sam I Am. 256p. (J). 2006. pap. 5.99 (978-0-439-43968-8(X)); 2004. (gr. 4-7). pap. 15.95 (978-0-439-43967-1(1) , Scholastic Pr.) Scholastic, Inc.

da Costa, Deborah. Hanukkah Moon. Mocz, Gosia, illus. 2007. (Hanukkah Ser.). (J). (gr. 1-5). 17.95 (***978-1-58013-244-2(8)**) Kar Ben Publishing.

—Hanukkah Moon. Mosz, Gosia, illus. 2007. (Hanukkah Ser.). (J). (gr. 1-5). pap. 7.95 (***978-1-58013-245-9(6)**) Kar-Ben Publishing.

Edwards, Michelle. Papa's Latkes. Gustavson, Adam & Schuett, Stacey, illus. 2004. 32p. (J). (gr. k-2). 15.99 (978-0-7636-0779-1(7)) Candlewick Pr.

Edwards, Michelle. Papa's Latkes. Schuett, Stacey, illus. 2007. 32p. (J). (gr. k-2). pap. 6.99 (***978-0-7636-3563-3(4)**) Candlewick Pr.

Fish, Dorothy & Cohen, Betty. Manny the Happy Hanukkah Menorah: Count the Nights of Hanukkah. Fish, Dorothy & Cohen, Betty, illus. 2000. (Illus.). 24p. (J). (ps-3). pap. 5.50 (978-0-914080-42-8(3)) Shulsinger Sales, Inc.

Fuchs, Menucha. A Chanukah Surprise & Other Chanukah Stories. Greenberg, Chana, illus. 2000. (Children's Learning Ser.: Vol. 4). 48p. (J). (gr. 1-4). pap. 4.95 (978-1-880582-52-7(X)) Judaica Pr., Inc., The.

Glaser, Linda. The Borrowed Hanukkah Latkes. Cote, Nancy, illus. 2004. 32p. (J). (gr. 1-4). pap. 6.95 (978-0-8075-0842-8(X)) Whitman, Albert & Co.

—Borrowed Hanukkah Latkes. 2001. (gr. k-3). lib. bdg. 15.25 (978-0-613-75607-5(X)) Tandem Library Bks.

—Mrs. Greenberg's Messy Hanukkah. Cote, Nancy, illus. 32p. (J). (gr. 1-3). 2006. 6.95 (978-0-8075-5298-8(4)); 2004. 15.95 (978-0-8075-5297-1(6)) Whitman, Albert & Co.

Goldin, Barbara Diamond. The Best Hanukkah Ever. Katz, Avi, illus. 2007. 32p. (J). (gr. k-3). 16.99 (***978-0-7614-5355-0(5)**) Cavendish, Marshall Corp.

Goldin, Barbara Diamond. While the Candles Burn: Eight Stories for Hanukkah. 1999. (978-0-606-17434-3(6)) Tandem Library Bks.

Hartt-Snowbell, Sarah. Yesterday's Santa & the Chanukah Miracle. Gallinger, Patty, illus. 2004. 32p. (J). (gr. 1-4). pap. 10.95 (978-0-929141-14-5(8)) Napoleon Publishing/Rendezvous Pr. CAN. *Dist:* AtlasBooks Distribution.

Holland, Cheri. Maccabee Jamboree: A Hanukkah Countdown. Schanzer, Rosalyn, illus. 1998. 24p. (J). (ps-1). pap. 4.95 (978-1-58013-019-6(4)) Kar-Ben Publishing.

Howland, Naomi. Latkes, Latkes, Good to Eat: A Chanukah Story. 2004. (Illus.). 32p. (J). (ps-3). pap. 5.95 (978-0-618-49295-4(X) , Clarion Bks.) Houghton Mifflin Co. Trade & Reference Div.

—Latkes, Latkes, Good to Eat: A Chanukah Story. Howland, Naomi, illus. 1999. (Illus.). 32p. (J). (gr. k-3). tchr. ed. 16.00 (978-0-395-89903-8(6) , Clarion Bks.) Houghton Mifflin Co. Trade & Reference Div.

Hubner, Carol Korb. The Twisted Menora: And Other Devora Doresh Mysteries. Morganroth, G. A., illus. 3rd ed. 2000. (Judaica Youth Ser.). 123p. (J). (gr. 3-8). pap. 9.95 (978-1-880582-48-0(1)) Judaica Pr., Inc., The.

Hyman, Trina Schart, illus. Herschel & the Hanukkah Goblins. (Caldecott Honor Book Ser.). 32p. (gr. k-3). 6.95 (978-0-8234-1131-3(1)) Holiday Hse., Inc.

Jacqueline Jules Staff. The Ziz & the Hanukkah Miracle. 2006. (J). pap. 7.95 (978-1-58013-164-3(6)) Kar-Ben Publishing.

Jules, Jacqueline. The Ziz And the Hanukkah Miracle. Kahn, Katherine, illus. 2006. 32p. (J). 17.95 (978-1-58013-160-5(3)) Kar-Ben Publishing.

Katz, Karen. Where Is Baby's Dreidel? A Lift-the-Flap Book. Katz, Karen, illus. 2007. (Illus.). 14p. (J). (ps). bds., bds. 6.99 (***978-1-4169-3623-7(8)** , Little Simon) Simon & Schuster Children's Publishing.

Kimmel, Eric A. The Chanukkah Guest. Carmi, Giora, illus. 32p. (J). (gr. k-3). 6.95 (978-0-8234-0978-5(3)); tchr. ed. 17.95 (978-0-8234-0788-0(8)) Holiday Hse., Inc.

—Herschel & the Hanukkah Goblins. Hyman, Trina Schart, illus. (Caldecott Honor Book Ser.). 32p. (gr. k-3). pap., tchr. ed. 17.95 (978-0-8234-0769-9(1)) Holiday Hse., Inc.

—When Mindy Saved Hanukkah. McClintock, Barbara, illus. 32p. (J). (ps-3). 2005. pap. 5.99 (978-0-439-76990-7(6) , Scholastic Paperbacks); 1998. pap. 15.95 (978-0-590-37136-0(3)) Scholastic, Inc.

—Zigazak! A Magical Hanukkah Night. Goodell, Jon, illus. 2001. 32p. (J). (ps-3). 15.95 (978-0-385-32652-0(1)); lib. bdg. 17.99 (978-0-385-90004-1(X)) Random Hse. Children's Bks. (Doubleday Bks. for Young Readers).

Kimmelman, Leslie. The Runaway Latkes. Yalowitz, Paul, illus. 2000. 32p. (J). (ps-2). 15.95 (978-0-8075-7176-7(8)) Whitman, Albert & Co.

Koons, Jon. A Confused Hanukkah: An Original Story of Chelm. Schindler, S. D., illus. 2004. 40p. (J). (gr. k). 16.99 (978-0-525-46969-8(9) , Dutton Juvenile) Penguin Group (USA) Inc.

Koss, Amy Goldman. How I Saved Hanukkah. 2000. (J). 11.64 (978-0-606-20239-8(0)) Tandem Library Bks.

Krensky, Stephen. Hanukkah at Valley Forge. Harlin, Greg, illus. 2006. 32p. (J). (gr. k). 17.99 (978-0-525-47738-9(1) , Dutton Juvenile) Penguin Group (USA) Inc.

Kropf, Latifa Berry & Cohen, Tod. It's Hanukkah Time! 2004. (Illus.). 24p. (J). (ps-1). (978-1-58013-120-9(4)) Kar-Ben Publishing.

Krulik, Nancy E. Is It Hanukkah Yet? DiSalvo-Ryan, Dyanne, illus. 2000. 32p. (J). (gr. k-3). lib. bdg. 11.80 (978-0-613-25736-7(7)) Tandem Library Bks.

Kushner, Ellen. The Golden Dreydl. Winn-Lederer, Ilene, illus. 2007. 128p. (J). (gr. 3-6). 15.95 (978-1-58089-135-6(7)) Charlesbridge Publishing, Inc.

Lamstein, Sarah. Letter on the Wind: A Chanukah Tale. Waldman, Neil, illus. 2007. (J). (ps-3). 16.95 (***978-1-932425-74-1(8)**) Boyds Mills Pr.

Lehman-Wilzig, Tami. Keeping the Promise: A Torah's Journey. Orback, Craig, illus. 2004. (J). 16.95 (978-0-929371-79-5(8)) Kar-Ben Publishing.

Levine, Abby. This Is the Dreidel. Billin-Frye, Paige, tr. Billin-Frye, Paige, illus. 2003. 24p. (J). (ps-1). 15.95 (978-0-8075-7884-1(3)) Whitman, Albert & Co.

Lissy, Jessica. A Blue's Clues Chanukah. Kanemoto, Dan & Oxley, Jennifer, illus. 2003. (Blue's Clues Ser.). 24p. (J). (ps-2). pap. 3.99 (978-0-689-85840-6(X) , Simon Spotlight/Nickelodeon) Simon & Schuster Children's Publishing.

Manushkin, Fran. Hannukah Story. 2007. (Latkes & Applesauce Ser.). 32p. (J). pap. 6.99 (***978-0-439-93048-2(0)** , Scholastic Paperbacks) Scholastic, Inc.

McKissack, Patricia C. Messy Bessey's Holidays. 1999. (gr. k-3). lib. bdg. 12.95 (978-0-613-37457-6(5)) Tandem Library Bks.

McKissack, Patricia C. & McKissack, Fredrick L. Messy Bessey's Holidays. Regan, Dana, illus. 1999. (Rookie Readers Ser.). 32p. (J). (gr. 1-2). 19.50 (978-0-516-20829-9(2) , Children's Pr.) Scholastic Library Publishing.

Medearis, Angela Shelf. Too Many Holidays? Papp, Robert, illus. 2003. 149p. (J). (978-0-439-52327-1(3)) Scholastic, Inc.

Melmed, Laura Krauss. Moishe's Miracle: A Hanukkah Story. Slonim, David, illus. 2005. 32p. (J). (ps-3). pap. 6.95 (978-0-8118-5234-0(2)) Chronicle Bks. LLC.

—Moishe's Miracle: A Hanukkah Story. Slonim, David, illus. 2000. 32p. (J). (ps up). 15.95 (978-0-688-14682-5(1)); lib. bdg. 15.89 (978-0-688-14683-2(X)) HarperCollins Pubs.

Metzger, Steve. Dinofours, Our Holiday Show! Wilhelm, Hans, illus. 2002. (J). 3.50 (978-0-439-38218-2(1)) Scholastic, Inc.

Moorman, Margaret. Light the Lights! A Story about Celebrating Hanukkah & Christmas. Moorman, Margaret, illus. 1999. (Illus.). 32p. (J). (gr. k-2). pap. 6.99 (978-0-590-48383-4(8) , Cartwheel Bks.) Scholastic, Inc.

H I

—Light the Lights: A Story about Celebrating Hanukkah & Christmas. 1999. (gr. k-3). lib. bdg. 14.15 (978-0-613-86971-3(0)) Tandem Library Bks.

Moss, Marissa. The Ugly Menorah. 2000. (978-0-606-20400-2(8)); (J). (978-0-606-20137-7(8)) Tandem Library Bks.

Motoyama, Keiko & MacKall, Dandi Daley. Who'll Light the Chanukah Candles? 2003. (Illus.). 16p. (J). pap. 4.99 (978-0-689-85025-7(5) , Little Simon) Simon & Schuster Children's Publishing.

Newman, Leslea. Runaway Dreidel! Brooker, Krysten, illus. 2007. 32p. (J). pap. 6.99 (*978-0-312-37142-5(X)) Square Fish.

Osterbach, Batya. Pini the Pitcher: A Story for Hanukkah. Elsby, Lizzy, illus. 2005. 32p. (J). (gr. 1-4). pap. 9.95 (978-1-932687-51-4(3) , Devora Publishing) Pitspopany Pr.

Polacco, Patricia. The Trees of the Dancing Goats. Polacco, Patricia, illus. 2002. (Illus.). (J). 25.11 (978-0-7587-3858-5(7)) Book Wholesalers, Inc.

—The Trees of the Dancing Goats. Polacco, Patricia, illus. 2000. (Illus.). 32p. (J). (gr. k-3). 7.99 (978-0-689-83857-6(3) , Aladdin) Simon & Schuster Children's Publishing.

—The Trees of the Dancing Goats. 2000. (J). (978-0-606-20094-3(0)) Tandem Library Bks.

—Trees of the Dancing Goats. 2000. (gr. k-3). lib. bdg. 15.30 (978-0-613-30164-0(1)) Tandem Library Bks.

Randall, Ronne. The Hanukkah Mice. Kneen, Maggie, illus. 2002. 20p. (J). (ps-1). 15.95 (978-0-8118-3623-4(1)) Chronicle Bks. LLC.

Rappaport, Doreen. The Year of the Paper Menorahs. Alcorn, Stephen, illus. 2000. 32p. (J). 15.99 (978-0-7868-0400-9(9)) Hyperion Bks. for Children.

Rau, Dana Meachen. Holiday Time. 2004. (Compass Point Early Reader Ser.). (J). 18.60 (978-0-7565-0571-4(2)) Compass Point Bks.

Rauchwerger, Diane Levin. Dinosaur on Hanukkah. Wolff, Jason, illus. 2005. 24p. (J). (ps-k). pap. 6.95 (978-1-58013-143-8(3)); 15.95 (978-1-58013-145-2(X)) Kar-Ben Publishing.

Rocklin, Joanne. The Very Best Hanukkah Gift. 2001. (978-0-606-22400-0(9)) Tandem Library Bks.

—Very Best Hanukkah Gift. 2001. (gr. 3-6). lib. bdg. 12.40 (978-0-613-85709-3(7)) Tandem Library Bks.

Rosen, Michael J. Chanukah Lights Everywhere. Iwai, Melissa, illus. 2006. 32p. (J). pap. 6.00 (978-0-15-205675-9(0) , Voyager Bks./Libros Viajeros) Harcourt Children's Bks.

—Chanukah Lights Everywhere. Iwai, Melissa, illus. 2000. (J). (978-0-15-201810-8(7)) Harcourt Trade Pubs.

Roth, Susan L. Hanukkah, Oh Hanukkah. Roth, Susan L., illus. 2006. 24p. (J). (ps). pap. 5.99 (978-0-14-240701-1(1) , Puffin) Penguin Group (USA) Inc.

Rouss, Sylvia A. Sammy Spider's Hanukkah Fun Book. Kahn, Katherine Janus, illus. 2003. 24p. (J). (ps-3). pap. 4.95 (978-1-58013-032-5(1)) Kar-Ben Publishing.

Schuman, Burt E. Chanukah on the Prairie. Kaye, Rosalind Charney, illus. 2004. (gr. k-3). 13.95 (978-0-8074-0814-8(X) , 381780) URJ Pr.

Shostak, Myra. Rainbow Candles: A Hanukkah Counting Book. Springer, Sally, illus. 2003. 12p. (J). (ps up). bds. (978-1-58013-031-8(3)) Kar-Ben Publishing.

Spinner, Stephanie. It's a Miracle! A Hanukkah Storybook. 2007. (Illus.). 40p. (J). (ps-3). 6.99 (*978-1-4169-5001-1(X) , Aladdin) Simon & Schuster Children's Publishing.

Spinner, Stephanie & McElmurry, Jill. It's a Miracle! A Hanukkah Storybook. 2003. (Illus.). 48p. (J). (gr. k-3). 16.95 (978-0-689-84493-5(X) , Atheneum/Anne Schwartz Bks.) Simon & Schuster Children's Publishing.

Stillerman, Marci. Nine Spoons: A Chanukah Story. Rosenfeld, D. L., ed. Gerber, Perren, illus. 1998. 32p. (J). (gr. k-3). 11.95 (978-0-922613-84-7(2)) Hachai Publishing.

Tanner, Suzy-Jane. The Great Hanukkah Party. 1998. (Lift-the-Flap Book Ser.). (Illus.). 20p. (J). (ps up). pap. 6.95 (978-0-694-01121-6(5)) HarperCollins Pubs.

Van Syckle, A. & Schwartz, Josh. The OC: 'twas the Night Before Chrismukkah. 2005. 206p. (YA). (978-1-4156-3915-3(9)) Scholastic, Inc.

Winnie the Pooh & the Hanukkah Dreidel. 1998. (Winnie the Pooh Ser.). (Illus.). 8p. (J). (ps-1). pap. 2.99 (978-1-57082-994-9(2)) Mouse Works.

Yorinks, Arthur. The Flying Latke. Steig, William & Colin, Paul, illus. 2002. 32p. (J). pap. 6.99 (978-0-689-85348-7(3) , Aladdin) Simon & Schuster Children's Publishing.

—Flying Latke. 2002. (gr. k-3). lib. bdg. 15.30 (978-0-613-90793-4(0)) Tandem Library Bks.

—The Flying Latke. ed. 2004. (Illus.). (J). (gr. k-3). spiral bd. (978-0-616-03066-0(5)) Canadian National Institute for the Blind/Institut National Canadien pour les Aveugles.

Zalben, Jane Breskin. The Magic Menorah: A Modern Chanukah Tale. Diamond, Donna, illus. 2001. 64p. (J). (gr. 3-5). 15.00 (978-0-689-82606-1(0)) Simon & Schuster Children's Publishing.

HAPPINESS

Bingham, Jane & Turner, Helen. Happy. 2006. (QEB Everybody Feels Ser.). (Illus.). 24p. (J). lib. bdg. 17.95 (978-1-59566-213-2(8)) QEB Publishing Inc.

Cabrera, Jane, illus. If You're Happy & You Know It! 2005. 32p. (J). 16.95 (978-0-8234-1881-7(2)) Holiday Hse., Inc.

DK Publishing Staff. Happy Baby. 2007. (Let's Play Ser.). 16p. (J). ring bd. 9.99 (978-0-7566-2599-3(8)) Dorling Kindersley Publishing, Inc.

Doudna, Kelly. I Feel Happy. l.t. ed. 1999. (How Do You Feel? Ser.). (Illus.). 24p. (J). (ps-3). lib. bdg. 19.93 (978-1-57765-188-8(X) , SandCastle) ABDO Publishing Co.

Dyer, Wayne W. & Tracy, Kristina. Incredible You! 10 Ways to Let Your Greatness Shine Through. Siegel, Melanie, illus. 2005. 32p. (ps-3). 14.95 (978-1-4019-0782-2(2)) Hay Hse., Inc.

Francis, Snip & Gilbert, Melanie. Happy Stories (Football Cover) 12 True Stories for Happy Living. 2002. (Illus.). 112p. (J). 14.95 (978-1-890616-24-3(9)) Salamander Group, Inc., The.

—Happy Stories (Raining Cover) 12 True Stories for Happy Living. 2002. (Illus.). 112p. (J). 14.95 (978-1-890616-25-0(7)) Salamander Group, Inc., The.

—Happy Stories (Swimming Cover) 12 True Stories for Happy Living. 2002. (Illus.). 112p. (J). 14.95 (978-1-890616-26-7(5)) Salamander Group, Inc., The.

Franzen, Lenore. Happiness. 2004. (My Feelings Ser.). (Illus.). 24p. (J). lib. bdg. 15.95 (978-1-58341-320-3(0) , Creative Education) Creative Co., The.

Frost, Helen. Feeling Happy. Saunders-Smith, Gail, ed. 2000. (Emotions Ser.). (Illus.). 24p. (J). (gr. k-1). lib. bdg. 15.93 (978-0-7368-0669-5(5) , Pebble Bks.) Capstone Pr., Inc.

Happiness Is Being Thankful for... A Child's Journal. 1999. (Illus.). 22p. (J). (ps-6). pap. 9.95 (978-0-9676761-0-4(X)) Zeek, Jeanie A.

Knapp, Stephen. The Key to Real Happiness. 2002. 95p. pap. 6.95 (978-1-930627-04-8(1)) World Relief Network, The.

Knudsen, Sherilyn. The Smart Way to Be. Bodily, Michael, illus. 2005. 32p. (J). per. 9.95 (978-0-9768451-0-2(5)) HPN Publishing.

Lazear, Jonathon. Come On, Get Happy. 2004. (Illus.). 384p. (978-0-00-717532-1(9) , HarperElement) HarperCollins Pubs. Ltd.

Leonard, Marcia. Happy. Bartholomew, illus. 2001. (How I Feel Ser.). 24p. (J). lib. bdg. 13.45 (978-1-56674-286-3(2)) Forest Hse. Publishing Co., Inc.

—I Feel Happy. Bartholomew, illus. 2003. 24p. (J). bds. 2.95 (978-0-8249-6523-5(X)) Ideals Pubns.

Mandino, Og. Og Mandino's Great Trilogy: The Greatest Salesman in the World, the Greatest Secret in the World & the Greatest Miracle in the World. 2008. 420p. (J). (978-0-8119-0428-5(8)) Lifetime Bks.

McCloud, Carol. Have You Filled a Bucket Today? A Guide to Daily Happiness for Kids. Messing, Dave, illus. 2006. (J). pap. 9.95 (978-0-9785075-1-0(7) , Ferne Pr.) Nelson Publishing & Marketing.

Medina, Sarah. Happy. 2007. (J). 24p. (978-1-4034-9299-9(9)); (978-1-4034-9292-0(1)) Heinemann Library.

Milet Limited Publishing Staff & Swain, Gwenyth. Smiling. 2000. (Small World Ser.). (Illus.). 24p. (J). (CHI & ENG.). pap. 9.95 (978-1-84059-116-3(1)); (GUJ & ENG., pap. 9.95 (978-1-84059-117-0(X)); (PAN & ENG., pap. 9.95 (978-1-84059-118-7(8)); (TUR & ENG., pap. 9.95 (978-1-84059-119-4(6)); (URD & ENG., pap. 9.95 (978-1-84059-120-0(X)); (VIE & ENG., pap. 9.95 (978-1-84059-121-7(8)) Milet Publishing.

—Smiling. Datta, Kanai, tr. from ENG. 2000. (Small World Ser.). (BEN & ENG., Illus.). 24p. (J). pap. 9.95 (978-1-84059-115-6(3)) Milet Publishing.

Murphy, Patricia J. Staying Happy. (Pull Ahead Bks.). (Illus.). 32p. (J). (ps-7). 2006. 22.60 (978-0-8225-2796-1(0)); 2005. pap. 5.95 (978-0-8225-2774-9(X)) Lerner Publishing Group. (Lerner Pubns.).

Nelson, Robin. Happy. 2003. (First Step Nonfiction Ser.). (Illus.). 8p. (J). pap. 3.95 (978-0-8225-3888-2(1) , Lerner Pubns.) Lerner Publishing Group.

Warhola, James. If You're Happy & You Know It: Jungle Edition. Geist, Ken, ed. 2007. 32p. (J). (ps-k). pap. 14.99 (978-0-439-72766-2(9) , Orchard Bks.) Scholastic, Inc.

HARBORS

see also Docks; Pilots and Pilotage

Evans, Fred. Maritime & Port Security. 2003. (Securing the Nation Ser.). (Illus.). 112p. (J). (gr. 9-13). 30.00 (978-0-7910-7614-9(8) , Chelsea Hse.) Facts On File, Inc.

Lassieur, Allison. Pirate Hideouts: Secret Spots & Shelters. 2007. (Edge Books, the Real World of Pirates). (Illus.). 32p. (J). 23.93 (978-0-7368-6426-8(1)) Capstone Pr., Inc.

Millard, Anne & Garrett, Leslie. A Port Through Time. Noon, Steve, illus. 2006. 32p. (J). 19.99 (978-0-7566-2221-3(2)) Dorling Kindersley Publishing, Inc.

El Puerto (The Harbour) (Coleccion Aqui Se Trabaja). (SPA., Illus.). (J). 10.95 (978-84-207-3625-9(2) , ANY764) Grupo Anaya, S.A. ESP. *Dist:* Continental Bk. Co., Inc.

Shuter, Jane. Life in a Greek Trading Port. 2005. (Picture the Past Ser.). (Illus.). 32p. (J). 25.64 (978-1-4034-6444-6(8)); pap. (978-1-4034-6451-4(0)) Heinemann Library.

Snyder, Margaret. Day at the Harbor. deluxe ed. 1999. (Talking Pages Ser.). (Illus.). (ps-3). 12.95 (978-1-58224-013-8(2)) Futech Interactive Products, Inc.

HARBORS—FICTION

Cortez, Jess S. My Trip to the Harbor. Cortez, Jess S., illus. ed. 2005. (Illus.). 16p. (J). (978-0-9776291-0-7(4)) Enlil, LLC.

Italia, John. The Birds of the Harbor. 2007. 32p. 15.95 (*978-0-9726614-7-8(6)) Shenanigan Bks.

Massey, Rachel. The Perfect Harbor. 2007. (J). 16.95 (*978-1-933660-40-0(6) , Tadpole Pr. 4 Kids) Smooth Sailing Pr.

HARDING, WARREN G. (WARREN GAMALIEL), 1865-1923

Joseph, Paul. Warren G. Harding. 1999. (United States Presidents Ser.). (Illus.). 32p. (J). (gr. k-6). lib. bdg. 22.78 (978-1-57765-234-2(7) , Checkerboard Library) ABDO Publishing Co.

Kent, Deborah. Warren G. Harding. 2004. (Encyclopedia of Presidents Ser.). (Illus.). 110p. (J). 34.00 (978-0-516-22965-2(6) , Children's Pr.) Scholastic Library Publishing.

Landau, Elaine. Warren G. Harding. 2005. (Presidential Leaders Ser.). (Illus.). 120p. (J). 29.27 (978-0-8225-0850-2(8) , Lerner Pubns.) Lerner Publishing Group.

Marsh, Carole. Warren G. Harding: An Ohio Experience Reader. 2001. (J). (gr. k-5). pap. 1.95 (978-0-635-00448-2(8)) Gallopade International.

Parker, Lewis K. How to Draw the Life & Times of Warren G. Harding. 2007. (Kid's Guide to Drawing the Presidents of the United States of America Ser.). (Illus.). 32p. (J). 25.25 (978-1-4042-3005-7(X) , PowerKids Pr.) Rosen Publishing Group, Inc., The.

Schultz, Randy. Warren G. Harding: A MyReportLinks. Com Book. 2003. (Presidents Ser.). (Illus.). 48p. (J). (gr. 4-10). lib. bdg. 25.26 (978-0-7660-5103-4(X) , MyReportLinks.com Bks.) Enslow Pubs., Inc.

Somervill, Barbara A. Warren G. Harding. 2003. (Profiles of the Presidents Ser.). (Illus.). 64p. (J). (gr. 4 up). lib. bdg. 23.93 (978-0-7565-0275-1(6)) Compass Point Bks.

Souter, Gerry & Souter, Janet. Warren G. Harding: Our Twenty-Ninth President. 2001. (Spirit of America: Our Presidents Ser.). (Illus.). 48p. (J). (gr. 2-6). 28.50 (978-1-56766-839-1(9)) Child's World, Inc.

Venezia, Mike, illus. Warren G. Harding. 2006. 32p. (J). (978-0-516-22633-0(9)) Children's Pr., Ltd.

HARDY BOYS (FICTITIOUS CHARACTERS)—FICTION

Dixon, Franklin W. All Eyes on First Prize. 1999. (Hardy Boys Are: No. 14). (J). (gr. 2-4). (978-0-606-19046-6(5)) Tandem Library Bks.

—The Apeman's Secret. 2005. (Hardy Boys Ser.: No. 62). (Illus.). 192p. (J). (gr. 3-8). 5.99 (978-0-448-43699-9(X) , Grosset & Dunlap) Penguin Group (USA) Inc.

—Bayport Buccaneers. 2007. (Hardy Boys (All New) Undercover Brothers Ser.). 176p. (J). pap. 4.99 (*978-1-4169-3403-5(0) , Aladdin) Simon & Schuster Children's Publishing.

—Blown Away. 2006. (Illus.). (J). (Hardy Boys (All New) Undercover Brothers Ser.: No. 10). 160p. pap. 4.99 (978-1-4169-1173-9(1)); 147p. (978-1-4156-7590-8(2)) Simon & Schuster Children's Publishing. (Aladdin).

—Boardwalk Bust. 2005. 164p. (J). lib. bdg. 16.92 (*978-1-4242-0385-7(6)) Fitzgerald Bks.

—Burned. 2005. 154p. (J). lib. bdg. 16.92 (*978-1-4242-0391-8(0)) Fitzgerald Bks.

—The Caribbean Cruise Caper. 1999. (Hardy Boys Mystery Stories Ser.: No. 154). 160p. (J). (gr. 3-6). pap. 4.99 (978-0-671-02549-6(X) , Aladdin) Simon & Schuster Children's Publishing.

—The Caribbean Cruise Caper. 1999. (gr. 5-8). lib. bdg. 13.00 (978-0-613-17130-4(6)); (Hardy Boys Mystery Stories Ser.: No. 154). (J). (gr. 3-6). (978-0-606-17130-4(4)) Tandem Library Bks.

—The Castle Conundrum. 2001. (Hardy Boys Mystery Stories Ser.: No. 168). (Illus.). 160p. (J). (gr. 3-6). pap. 9.95 (978-0-7434-0683-3(4) , Aladdin) Simon & Schuster Children's Publishing.

—The Castle Conundrum. 2002. (gr. 5-8). lib. bdg. 13.00 (978-0-613-63268-3(0)) Tandem Library Bks.

—The Dangerous Transmission. ed. 2005. (Hardy Boys II Ser.: No. 184). 147p. (J). lib. bdg. 15.00 (978-1-59054-850-9(7)) Fitzgerald Bks.

—Daredevils. l.t. ed. 2003. (Hardy Boys Mystery Ser.). 139p. (J). 21.95 (978-0-7862-5309-8(6)) Thorndike Pr.

—Death & Diamonds. 2007. (Hardy Boys (All New) Undercover Brothers Ser.: No. 15). 176p. (J). pap. 4.99 (978-1-4169-3402-8(2) , Aladdin) Simon & Schuster Children's Publishing.

—Disappearing Floor, No. 19. 2006. (Hardy Boys (Hardcover) Ser.). 228p. (J). (ps-3). 17.95 (978-1-55709-287-8(7)) Applewood Bks.

—Double Jeopardy. ed. 2005. (Hardy Boys II Ser.: No. 181). 150p. (J). lib. bdg. 15.00 (978-1-59054-838-7(8)) Fitzgerald Bks.

—Double Jeopardy. 2003. (Hardy Boys Ser.: No. 181). 160p. (J). pap. 4.99 (978-0-689-85780-5(2) , Aladdin) Simon & Schuster Children's Publishing.

—Double Jeopardy. 2003. 150p. (J). (gr. 3-7). per. 13.00 (978-0-613-89000-7(0)) Tandem Library Bks.

—The End of the Trail. 2000. (Hardy Boys Mystery Stories Ser.: No. 162). 144p. (J). (gr. 3-6). pap. 4.99 (978-0-671-04759-7(0) , Aladdin) Simon & Schuster Children's Publishing.

—The End of the Trail. 2000. (gr. 5-8). lib. bdg. 13.00 (978-0-613-27806-5(2)) Tandem Library Bks.

—Extreme Danger. 2005. 165p. (J). lib. bdg. 16.92 (*978-1-4242-0383-3(X)) Fitzgerald Bks.

—Extreme Danger. 2005. (Hardy Boys Ser.). 172p. pap. 4.99 (978-1-4169-0002-3(0)); (Illus.). 165p. (J). (*978-1-4156-0379-6(0)) Simon & Schuster Children's Publishing. (Aladdin).

—Farming Fear. ed. 2005. (Hardy Boys II Ser.: No. 188). 154p. (J). lib. bdg. 15.00 (978-1-59054-839-4(6)) Fitzgerald Bks.

—Farming Fear. 2004. (Hardy Boys Ser.: No. 188). 160p. (J). pap. 4.99 (978-0-689-86739-2(5) , Aladdin) Simon & Schuster Children's Publishing.

—Feeding Frenzy. 2008. (Hardy Boys (All New) Undercover Brothers Ser.). 160p. (J). pap. 4.99 (*978-1-4169-5499-6(6) , Aladdin) Simon & Schuster Children's Publishing.

—Footprints under the Window. Gretta, J. Clemens, illus. 2001. (Hardy Boys Mystery Stories Ser.: No. 12). 218p. (J). (gr. 4-7). per. 14.95 (978-1-55709-270-0(2)) Applewood Bks.

—Foul Play. 2007. (Hardy Boys (All New) Undercover Brothers Ser.: No. 19). 192p. (J). pap. 4.99 (*978-1-4169-4977-0(1) , Aladdin) Simon & Schuster Children's Publishing.

—A Game Called Chaos. 2000. (Hardy Boys Ser.: No. 160). 160p. (J). (gr. 3-6). pap. 9.95 (978-0-671-03870-0(2) , Aladdin) Simon & Schuster Children's Publishing.

—A Game Called Chaos. 2000. (gr. 5-8). lib. bdg. 13.00 (978-0-613-27846-1(1)) Tandem Library Bks.

—The Great Airport Mystery. 2004. (Hardy Boys Mystery Stories Ser.: No. 9). 228p. (J). (gr. 4-7). 14.95 (978-1-55709-267-0(2)) Applewood Bks.

—The Hardy Boys, Vols. 1-6. 1998. (J). 22.98 (978-0-448-41671-7(9) , Grosset & Dunlap) Penguin Group (USA) Inc.

—The Hardy Boys. 75th collector's anniv. ed. 2002. (Hardy Boys Ser.). (Illus.). 464p. (J). pap. 7.99 (978-0-689-85620-4(2) , Aladdin) Simon & Schuster Children's Publishing.

—Hardy Boys Starter Set. 2007. (Hardy Boys Ser.). 128p. (J). lthr. 25.98 (*978-0-448-44820-6(3) , Grosset & Dunlap) Penguin Group (USA) Inc.

—Hazed. 2007. (Hardy Boys (All New) Undercover Brothers Ser.: No. 14). 160p. (J). pap. 4.99 (978-1-4169-1803-5(5) , Aladdin) Simon & Schuster Children's Publishing.

—The Hidden Harbor Mystery. Gretter, J. Clemens, illus. 2003. (Hardy Boys Mystery Stories Ser.). 219p. (J). (gr. 4-7). per. 14.95 (978-1-55709-272-4(9)) Applewood Bks.

—Hidden Mountain. ed. 2005. (Hardy Boys II Ser.: No. 186). 154p. (J). lib. bdg. 15.00 (978-1-59054-841-7(8)) Fitzgerald Bks.

—Hide & Sneak. 2002. (Hardy Boys Ser.: Vol. 174). 144p. (J). pap. 4.99 (978-0-7434-3758-5(6) , Aladdin) Simon & Schuster Children's Publishing.

—Hide & Sneak. 2002. (gr. 5-8). lib. bdg. 13.00 (978-0-613-45059-1(0)) Tandem Library Bks.

—Hunting for Hidden Gold. Rogers, Walter S., illus. 2004. (Hardy Boys Mystery Stories Ser.: No. 5). 210p. (J). (gr. 4-7). 17.95 (978-1-55709-148-2(X)) Applewood Bks.

—In Plane Sight. ed. 2005. (Hardy Boys I Ser.: No. 176). 148p. (J). lib. bdg. 15.00 (978-1-59054-842-4(6)) Fitzgerald Bks.

—In Plane Sight. 2002. 148p. (gr. 5-8). lib. bdg. 13.00 (978-0-613-63303-1(2)) Tandem Library Bks.

—Kickoff to Danger. ed. 2005. (Hardy Boys I Ser.: No. 170). 149p. (J). lib. bdg. 15.00 (978-1-59054-843-1(4)) Fitzgerald Bks.

—Kidnapped at the Casino. 2007. (Hardy Boys Undercover Brothers: Super Mystery Ser.). 240p. (J). pap. 5.99 (978-1-4169-3923-8(7) , Aladdin) Simon & Schuster Children's Publishing.

—Line of Fire. (Illus.). (J). mass mkt. 2.95 (978-0-671-70492-6(3) , Simon Pulse) Simon & Schuster Children's Publishing.

—The London Deception. 1999. (Hardy Boys Mystery Stories Ser.: No. 158). (J). (gr. 3-6). (978-0-606-19052-7(X)) Tandem Library Bks.

—Martial Law. 2006. 152p. (J). lib. bdg. 16.92 (*978-1-4242-0389-5(9)) Fitzgerald Bks.

—Martial Law. 2006. (Illus.). (J). (Hardy Boys Ser.: No. 9). 160p. pap. 4.99 (978-1-4169-0398-7(4)); 152p. (978-1-4156-6852-8(3)) Simon & Schuster Children's Publishing. (Aladdin).

—The Missing Chums, No. 4. Rogers, Walter S., illus. 2004. (Hardy Boys Mystery Stories Ser.: No. 4). 210p. (J). (gr. 4-7). reprint ed. 17.95 (978-1-55709-147-5(1)) Applewood Bks.

—Motocross Madness. ed. 2005. (Hardy Boys II Ser.: No. 190). 154p. (J). lib. bdg. 15.00 (978-1-59054-844-8(2)) Fitzgerald Bks.

—Murder at the Mall. 2007. (Hardy Boys (All New) Undercover Brothers Ser.). 176p. (J). pap. 4.99 (*978-1-4169-3930-6(X) , Aladdin) Simon & Schuster Children's Publishing.

—Mystery of Smugglers Cove. 2005. (Hardy Boys Ser.: No. 64). (Illus.). 192p. (J). (gr. 3-8). 6.99 (978-0-448-43701-9(5) , Grosset & Dunlap) Penguin Group (USA) Inc.

—The Mystery of the Black Rhino. ed. 2005. (Hardy Boys I Ser.: No. 178). 151p. (J). lib. bdg. 15.00 (978-1-59054-851-6(5)) Fitzgerald Bks.

—The Mystery of the Black Rhino. 2003. (gr. 5-8). lib. bdg. 13.00 (978-0-613-61646-1(4)) Tandem Library Bks.

—Mystery of the Samurai Sword. 2005. (Hardy Boys Ser.: Vol. 60). (Illus.). 196p. (J). (gr. 3-8). pap. 5.99 (978-0-448-43697-5(3) , Grosset & Dunlap) Penguin Group (USA) Inc.

—The Mystery of the Silver Star, No. 86. 1999. pap. (978-0-671-70995-2(X) , Aladdin) Simon & Schuster Children's Publishing.

—Night of the Werewolf. 2005. (Hardy Boys Ser.: No. 59). (Illus.). 196p. (J). (gr. 3-8). pap. 5.99 (978-0-448-43696-8(5) , Grosset & Dunlap) Penguin Group (USA) Inc.

—No Way Out. ed. 2005. (Hardy Boys II Ser.: No. 187). 149p. (J). lib. bdg. 15.00 (978-1-59054-845-5(0)) Fitzgerald Bks.

—One False Step. ed. 2005. (Hardy Boys II Ser.: No. 189). 150p. (J). lib. bdg. 15.00 (978-1-59054-846-2(9)) Fitzgerald Bks.

—One False Step. 2005. 150p. (J). (978-1-4155-7722-6(6) , Aladdin) Simon & Schuster Children's Publishing.

—Passport to Danger. 2005. (Hardy Boys I Ser.: No. 179). 147p. (J). lib. bdg. 15.00 (978-1-59054-847-9(7)) Fitzgerald Bks.

—Passport to Danger. 2003. (gr. 5-8). lib. bdg. 13.00 (978-0-613-66466-0(3)) Tandem Library Bks.

—The Pentagon Spy. 2005. (Hardy Boys Ser.: No. 61). (Illus.). 192p. (J). (gr. 3-8). 5.99 (978-0-448-43698-2(1), Grosset & Dunlap) Penguin Group (USA) Inc.

—Pirates Ahoy! 1999. (Hardy Boys Are: No. 13). (J). (gr. 2-4). (978-0-606-17731-3(0)) Tandem Library Bks.

—Pushed. 2007. (Hardy Boys (All New) Undercover Brothers Ser.). 154p. (J). (gr. 3-7). per. 4.99 (***978-1-4169-4802-5(3)***, Aladdin) Simon & Schuster Children's Publishing.

—Revenge of the Desert Phantom. (Hardy Boys Mystery Stories Ser.: No. 84). (J). (gr. 3-6). (978-0-671-49730-9(8), Simon & Schuster Children's Publishing) Simon & Schuster Children's Publishing.

—Running on Fumes. 2005. 150p. (J). lib. bdg. 16.92 (***978-1-4242-0384-0(8)***) Fitzgerald Bks.

—Running on Fumes. 2005. (Illus.). 150p. (J). (***978-1-4156-0714-5(1)***, Aladdin) Simon & Schuster Children's Publishing.

—The Secret of the Caves, No. 7. Rogers, Walter S., illus. 2004. (Hardy Boys Mystery Stories Ser.: No. 7). 228p. (J). (gr. 4-7). reprint ed. 14.95 (978-1-55709-150-5(1)) Applewood Bks.

—The Secret of the Soldier's Gold. ed. 2005. (Hardy Boys II Ser.: No. 182). 147p. (J). lib. bdg. 15.00 (978-1-59054-852-3(3)) Fitzgerald Bks.

—Sheer Terror. 2001. (Hardy Boys Casefiles Ser.: No. 81). (Illus.). 160p. (YA). (gr. 6 up). mass mkt. 3.99 (978-0-7434-0431-0(9), Simon & Schuster Children's Publishing) Simon & Schuster Children's Publishing.

—The Sinister Signpost, Vol. 15. 2004. (Hardy Boys(R) Mystery Ser.). 228p. (J). (gr. 4-7). 17.95 (978-1-55709-273-1(7)) Applewood Bks.

—Skin & Bones. ed. 2005. (Hardy Boys I Ser.: No. 164). 148p. (J). lib. bdg. 15.00 (978-1-59054-848-6(5)) Fitzgerald Bks.

—Slip, Slide & Slap Shot. 1999. (Hardy Boys Are: No. 15). (J). (gr. 2-4). (978-0-606-19063-3(5)) Tandem Library Bks.

—Speed Times Five. ed. 2005. (Hardy Boys I Ser.: No. 173). 150p. (J). lib. bdg. 15.00 (978-1-59054-849-3(3)) Fitzgerald Bks.

—The Stone Idol. 2005. (Hardy Boys Ser.: No. 65). (Illus.). 196p. (J). (gr. 3-8). pap. 6.99 (978-0-448-43702-6(3), Grosset & Dunlap) Penguin Group (USA) Inc.

—The Test Case. l.t. ed. 2002. 169p. (J). 21.95 (978-0-7862-4657-1(X)) Thorndike Pr.

—Thrill Ride. 2005. 154p. (J). lib. bdg. 16.92 (***978-1-4242-0386-4(4)***) Fitzgerald Bks.

—Thrill Ride. 2005. (Illus.). 154p. (J). (978-1-4156-0585-1(8), Aladdin) Simon & Schuster Children's Publishing.

—Top Ten Ways to Die. 2006. 169p. (J). lib. bdg. 16.92 (***978-1-4242-0390-1(2)***) Fitzgerald Bks.

—Top Ten Ways to Die. 2006. (Hardy Boys Ser.: No. 8). (Illus.). 160p. (J). pap. 4.99 (978-1-4169-0846-3(3), Aladdin) Simon & Schuster Children's Publishing.

—Training for Trouble. ed. 2005. (Hardy Boys I Ser.: No. 161). 147p. (J). lib. bdg. 15.00 (978-1-59054-853-0(1)) Fitzgerald Bks.

—Training for Trouble. 2000. (Hardy Boys Mystery Stories Ser.: No. 161). 160p. (J). (gr. 3-6). pap. 4.99 (978-0-671-04758-0(2), Aladdin) Simon & Schuster Children's Publishing.

—Training for Trouble. 2000. (gr. 5-8). lib. bdg. 13.00 (978-0-613-28109-6(8)) Tandem Library Bks.

—Trick-or-Trouble. ed. 2005. (Hardy Boys I Ser.: No. 175). 154p. (J). lib. bdg. 15.00 (978-1-59054-854-7(X)) Fitzgerald Bks.

—Trouble in Paradise. 2006. (Hardy Boys (All New) Undercover Brothers Ser.: No. 12). 176p. (J). pap. 4.99 (978-1-4169-1178-4(2), Aladdin) Simon & Schuster Children's Publishing.

—Trouble in Warp Space. ed. 2005. (Hardy Boys I Ser.: No. 172). 154p. (J). lib. bdg. 15.00 (978-1-59054-855-4(8)) Fitzgerald Bks.

—Trouble in Warp Space. 2002. (gr. 3-6). lib. bdg. 13.00 (978-0-613-45115-4(5)) Tandem Library Bks.

—Trouble in Warp Space. l.t. ed. 2002. 181p. (J). 21.95 (978-0-7862-4658-8(8)) Thorndike Pr.

—Typhoon Island. ed. 2005. (Hardy Boys II Ser.: No. 180). 148p. (J). lib. bdg. 15.00 (978-1-59054-857-8(4)) Fitzgerald Bks.

—Typhoon Island. 2003. (gr. 5-8). lib. bdg. 13.00 (978-0-613-66472-1(8)) Tandem Library Bks.

—The Vanishing Thieves. 2005. (Hardy Boys Ser.). (Illus.). 196p. (J). (gr. 3-8). pap. 6.99 (978-0-448-43703-3(1), Grosset & Dunlap) Penguin Group (USA) Inc.

—Wanted. 2006. (Hardy Boys Undercover Brothers Ser.: No.1). 192p. (J). pap. 5.99 (978-1-4169-1258-3(4), Aladdin) Simon & Schuster Children's Publishing.

—Warehouse Rumble. ed. 2005. (Hardy Boys II Ser.: No. 183). 152p. (J). lib. bdg. 15.00 (978-1-59054-858-5(2)) Fitzgerald Bks.

—What Happened at Midnight, No. 10. 2000. (Hardy Boys Mystery Stories Ser.: No. 10). (Illus.). 228p. (J). (gr. 4-7). 17.95 (978-1-55709-268-7(0)) Applewood Bks.

—While the Clock Ticked. Gretta, J. Cleme, illus. 2000. (Hardy Boys Mystery Stories Ser.: No. 11). 213p. (J). (gr. 4-7). per. 14.95 (978-1-55709-269-4(9)) Applewood Bks.

—A Will to Survive. 1999. (Hardy Boys Mystery Stories Ser.: No. 156). (J). (gr. 3-6). (978-0-606-19051-0(1)) Tandem Library Bks.

—Wreck & Roll. ed. 2005. (Hardy Boys II Ser.: No. 185). 153p. (J). lib. bdg. 15.00 (978-1-59054-859-2(0)) Fitzgerald Bks.

Dixon, Franklin W. & Walker, Jeff. The Mystery of the Black Rhino. 2003. (Hardy Boys Ser.). (Illus.). 160p. (J). pap. 4.99 (978-0-689-85598-6(2), Aladdin) Simon & Schuster Children's Publishing.

—Passport to Danger, Vol. 179. 2003. (Hardy Boys Ser.). 160p. (J). pap. 4.99 (978-0-689-85779-9(9), Aladdin) Simon & Schuster Children's Publishing.

Hardy Boys. 2006. (J). (gr. 3-8). 72.63 (978-1-59961-060-3(4)) Spotlight.

Keene, Carolyn. Operation Titanic. 1998. (Nancy Drew & Hardy Boys Super Mystery Ser.: No. 35). (YA). (gr. 6 up). (978-0-606-13650-1(9)) Tandem Library Bks.

Keene, Carolyn & Dixon, Franklin W. Terror on Tour. 2007. (Nancy Drew & the Hardy Boys Ser.: No. 1). 224p. (J). pap. 5.99 (***978-1-4169-2726-6(3)***, Aladdin) Simon & Schuster Children's Publishing.

Lobdell, Scott. The Hardy Boys #8: Board to Death. Henrique, Paulo, illus. 8th rev. ed. 2007. (Hardy Boys: Undercover Brothers Ser.). 112p. (J). 12.95 (978-1-59707-054-6(8)); pap. 7.95 (978-1-59707-053-9(X)) Papercutz.

—The Hardy Boys #9: to Die or Not to Die. Henrique, Paulo, illus. 9th rev. ed. 2007. (Hardy Boys: Undercover Brothers Ser.). 112p. (J). 12.95 (***978-1-59707-063-8(7)***); pap. 7.95 (***978-1-59707-062-1(9)***) Papercutz.

—Identity Theft. 2006. (J). (gr. 3-8). 24.21 (978-1-59961-062-7(0)) Spotlight.

—Mad House. 2006. (J). (gr. 3-8). 24.21 (978-1-59961-063-4(9)) Spotlight.

—Malled. Rendon, Daniel, illus. 4th rev. ed. 2006. (Hardy Boys Graphic Novel Ser.: No. 4). 96p. (J). 12.95 (978-1-59707-015-7(7)); pap. 7.95 (978-1-59707-014-0(9)) Papercutz.

—Ocean of Osyria. 2006. (J). (gr. 3-8). 24.21 (978-1-59961-061-0(2)) Spotlight.

—The Opposite Numbers. Rendon, Daniel, illus. 7th rev. ed. 2006. (Hardy Boys Ser.: No. 7). 96p. (J). pap. 7.95 (978-1-59707-034-8(3)) Papercutz.

—The Oppsite Numbers. Rendon, Daniel, illus. 7th rev. ed. 2006. (Hardy Boys Ser.: No. 7). 96p. (J). 12.95 (978-1-59707-035-5(1)) Papercutz.

Lobdell, Scott & Rendon, Daniel. Hyde & Shriek. 6th rev. ed. 2006. (Hardy Boys Ser.: No. 6). (Illus.). 96p. (J). pap. 7.95 (978-1-59707-028-7(9)) Papercutz.

—Identity Theft. 2nd rev. ed. 2005. (Hardy Boys Graphic Novel Ser.: No. 2). (Illus.). 96p. (J). (gr. 3-9). 12.95 (978-1-59707-007-2(6)); pap., pap. 7.95 (978-1-59707-003-4(3)) Papercutz.

—Mad House. 3rd rev. ed. 2005. (Hardy Boys Graphic Novel Ser.: No. 3). (Illus.). 96p. (J). (gr. 3-7). pap., pap. 7.95 (978-1-59707-010-2(6)) Papercutz.

Rendon, Daniel & Lobdell, Scott. Mad House. 3rd rev. ed. 2005. (Hardy Boys Graphic Novel Ser.: No. 3). (Illus.). 96p. (J). (gr. 3-7). 12.95 (978-1-59707-011-9(4)) Papercutz.

Walker, Jeff & Dixon, Franklin W. In Plane Sight. 2002. (Hardy Boys Ser.). (Illus.). 160p. (J). pap. 4.99 (978-0-7434-3760-8(8), Aladdin) Simon & Schuster Children's Publishing.

HARES

see Rabbits

HARLEM (NEW YORK, N.Y.)

Gaines, Ann Graham. The Harlem Renaissance in American History. 2002. (In American History Ser.). (Illus.). 112p. (J). (gr. 5-12). lib. bdg. 26.60 (978-0-7660-1458-9(4)) Enslow Pubs., Inc.

Hill, Laban Carrick. Harlem Stomp! A Cultural History of the Harlem Renaissance. Myers, Christopher, illus. 2004. 160p. (J). (gr. 7-17). 18.99 (978-0-316-81411-9(3)) Little Brown & Co.

Kallen, Stuart A. The Harlem Renaissance. 2001. (Black History Ser.). (Illus.). 48p. (J). (gr. 3-8). lib. bdg. 25.65 (978-1-57765-468-1(4), ABDO & Daughters) ABDO Publishing Co.

McKissack, Lisa Beringer. Women of the Harlem Renaissance. 2006. 48p. (J). (978-0-7565-2034-2(7)) Compass Point Bks.

Price, Sean. Rebirth of a People: Harlem Renaissance. 2006. (American History Through Primary Sources Ser.). (Illus.). 32p. (J). (978-1-4109-2415-5(7)) Raintree.

—Rebirth of a People: Harlem Renaissance. 2006. (American History Through Primary Sources Ser.). (Illus.). 32p. (J). pap. (978-1-4109-2426-1(2)) Steck-Vaughn.

HARLEM (NEW YORK, N.Y.)—FICTION

Blumenthal, Scott & Hodus, Brett. Hoop City. 2002. 138p. 9.95 (978-0-9708992-1-7(1)) Scobre Pr. Corp.

Campbell, Terry. Harlem & Momma: A Short Children Story. 2005. 42p. (J). pap. 10.00 (978-0-9761560-0-0(8)) Sweet T. C. Campbell.

Childress, Alice. A Hero Ain't Nothin' but a Sandwich. 2000. 128p. (J). (gr. 7-12). pap. 5.99 (978-0-698-11854-6(5), Putnam Juvenile) Penguin Group (USA) Inc.

—A Hero Ain't Nothin' but a Sandwich. 2000. 12.64 (978-0-606-17821-1(X)) Tandem Library Bks.

Coleman, Evelyn. Mystery of the Dark Tower. 2000. (History Mysteries Ser.). (978-0-606-18356-7(6)) Tandem Library Bks.

Collier, Bryan. Uptown. rev. ed. (Illus.). 32p. (J). 2004. pap. 7.95 (978-0-8050-7399-7(X)); 2000. 17.95 (978-0-8050-5721-8(8)) Holt, Henry & Co. (Holt, Henry & Co. Bks. For Young Readers).

—Uptown. 2004. (gr. k-3). lib. bdg. 15.25 (978-0-613-75623-5(1)) Tandem Library Bks.

Creary, Eve M. A Silent Witness in Harlem. O'Loughlin, Marianne, illus. 2002. (Mysteries in Time Ser.: Vol. 10). 96p. (J). (gr. 3-8). lib. bdg. 14.95 (978-1-893110-27-4(3)) Silver Moon Pr.

Grimes, Nikki. Jazmin's Notebook. 2002. (Illus.). (J). 12.34 (978-0-7587-0368-2(6)) Book Wholesalers, Inc.

—Jazmin's Notebook. 112p. (J). 1998. (gr. 8-12). 15.99 (978-0-8037-2224-8(9), Dial); 2000. (gr. 5-9). reprint ed. pap. 5.99 (978-0-14-130702-2(1), Puffin) Penguin Group (USA) Inc.

—Jazmin's Notebook. 2000. (gr. 7-12). lib. bdg. 14.15 (978-0-613-23623-2(8)); (Illus.). (J). 12.64 (978-0-606-18414-4(7)) Tandem Library Bks.

Levine, Gail Carson. Dave at Night. 2001. 304p. (J). (gr. 3-7). reprint ed. pap. 6.99 (978-0-06-440747-2(0), Harper Trophy) HarperCollins Pubs.

—Dave at Night. unabr. ed. 2004. 278p. (J). (gr. 4-7). pap. 38.00 incl. audio (978-0-8072-8379-0(7), YA174SP, Listening Library) Random Hse. Audio Publishing Group.

—Dave at Night. 1999. (YA). pap., stu. ed. 69.95 incl. audio (978-0-7887-3794-7(5), 41038) Recorded Bks., LLC.

Littlesugar, Amy. Tree of Hope. 2001. (gr. k-3). lib. bdg. 15.30 (978-0-613-44423-1(X)) Tandem Library Bks.

McDonald, Janet. Brother Hood. 2004. 176p. (YA). 16.00 (978-0-374-30995-4(7), Frances Foster Bks.) Farrar, Straus & Giroux.

—Brother Hood. l.t. ed. 2005. 179p. 20.95 (978-0-7862-7334-8(8), Large Print Pr.) Thorndike Pr.

McKissack, Patricia C. A Song for Harlem. James, Gordon C., illus. 2007. (Scraps of Time Ser.: No. 3). 96p. (J). (gr. 3-4). 14.99 (978-0-670-06209-6(X), Viking Juvenile) Penguin Group (USA) Inc.

Michelson, Richard. Happy Feet: The Savoy Ballroom Lindy Hoppers & Me. Lewis, E. B., illus. 2005. 32p. (J). (ps-ps). 16.00 (978-0-15-205057-3(4)) Harcourt Children's Bks.

Myers, Walter Dean. The Beast. 2005. 192p. (YA). (gr. 7-12). 6.99 (978-0-439-36842-1(1), Scholastic Paperbacks) Scholastic, Inc.

—The Dream Bearer. 2003. 192p. (J). (gr. 5 up). 15.99 (978-0-06-029521-9(X), Amistad) HarperCollins Pubs.

—The Dream Bearer. l.t. ed. 2003. 207p. (J). 25.95 (978-0-7862-5923-6(X)) Thorndike Pr.

—Los Escorpiones. (SPA.). (YA). (gr. 5-8). pap. (978-958-04-4381-0(5), NR8278) Norma S.A. COL. *Dist:* Lectorum Pubns., Inc.

—Game. 2008. 240p. (J). 16.99 (***978-0-06-058294-4(4)***); lib. bdg. 17.89 (***978-0-06-058295-1(2)***) HarperCollins Pubs. (HarperTeen).

—Handbook for Boys: A Novel. (Amistad Ser.). (J). (gr. 5 up). 2003. 224p. pap. 6.99 (978-0-06-440930-8(9)); 2002. (Illus.). 192p. 16.99 (978-0-06-029146-4(X)) HarperCollins Pubs.

—Handbook for Boys: A Novel. 2003. (gr. 5-8). lib. bdg. 14.15 (978-0-613-65786-0(1)) Tandem Library Bks.

—Harlem Summer. (Illus.). (J). 2008. 304p. 17.99 (***978-0-439-91624-0(0)***); 2007. 176p. (gr. 7 up). pap. 16.99 (978-0-439-36843-8(X)) Scholastic, Inc. (Scholastic Pr.).

—Motown & Didi: A Love Story. 2002. (Illus.). (J). 13.40 (978-0-7587-0384-2(8)) Book Wholesalers, Inc.

—The Mouse Rap. 3rd ed. (J). pap. 3.95 (978-0-13-800087-5(5)) Prentice Hall (Schl. Div.).

—Street Love. (J). 2007. 160p. pap. 7.99 (***978-0-06-440732-8(2)***); 2006. 144p. 15.99 (978-0-06-028079-6(4)); 2006. 144p. (gr. 8 up). lib. bdg. 16.89 (978-0-06-028080-2(8)) HarperCollins Pubs. (Amistad).

—145th Street: Short Stories. 160p. (YA). (gr. 7 up). 2001. pap. 5.99 (978-0-440-22916-2(2), Laurel Leaf); 2000. 15.99 (978-0-385-32137-2(6), Delacorte Bks. for Young Readers) Random Hse. Children's Bks.

—145th Street: Short Stories. 2001. (978-0-606-22414-7(9)) Tandem Library Bks.

Myers, Walter Dean. 145th Street: Short Stories. 2007. 160p. (YA). (gr. 7). lib. bdg. 18.99 (***978-0-385-90538-1(6)***, Delacorte Bks. for Young Readers) Random Hse. Children's Bks.

Myers, Walter Dean & Myers, Walter Dean. 145th Street: Short Stories. 2001. 151p. (YA). (gr. 7-12). per. 13.55 (978-0-613-36855-1(X)) Tandem Library Bks.

Nishiyama, Nuriko. Harlem Beat No.03. 2003. (gr. 7-12). lib. bdg. 18.75 (978-0-613-82608-2(5)) Tandem Library Bks.

Ramsey, R. M. The Browser Bunch: The Browser Files Presents... the Big Lie. 2006. (J). pap. 8.00 (***978-0-8059-7172-9(6)***) Dorrance Publishing Co., Inc.

Ringgold, Faith. Tar Beach. Ringgold, Faith, illus. 2002. (Illus.). (J). 14.79 (978-0-7587-5352-6(7)) Book Wholesalers, Inc.

Robinson, Sharon. Slam Dunk! 2007. 160p. (J). (gr. 4-7). pap. 16.99 (***978-0-439-67199-6(X)***, Scholastic Pr.) Scholastic, Inc.

Smalls, Irene. Don't Say Ain't. Bootman, Colin, illus. 32p. (J). (gr. k-3). 2004. pap. 6.95 (978-1-57091-382-2(X)); 2003. 15.95 (978-1-57091-381-5(1)) Charlesbridge Publishing, Inc.

—Don't Say Ain't. 2004. (gr. k-3). lib. bdg. 15.25 (978-0-613-70806-7(7)) Tandem Library Bks.

—Irene & the Big, Fine Nickel. Geter, Tyrone, illus. 2nd ed. 2003. 32p. (J). (ps-3). pap. 5.99 (978-0-316-69832-0(6)) Little, Brown Bks. for Young Readers.

—Irene & the Big, Fine Nickel. 2003. (gr. k-3). lib. bdg. 7.20 (978-0-613-71768-7(6)) Tandem Library Bks.

Taylor, Debbie. Sweet Music in Harlem. Morrison, Frank, tr. Morrison, Frank, illus. 2004. 32p. (J). 16.95 (978-1-58430-165-3(1)) Lee & Low Bks., Inc.

Volponi, Paul. Rucker Park Setup. 2007. 208p. (J). 15.99 (978-0-670-06130-3(1), Viking Juvenile) Penguin Group (USA) Inc.

Weisleder, Stanley. Wings of the Panther. 2004. 224p. 15.00 (978-0-936783-38-3(9)) Merril Pr.

HARLEM (NEW YORK, N.Y.)—SOCIAL CONDITIONS

Brown, Claude. Manchild in the Promised Land. 1999. (gr. 7-12). lib. bdg. 22.25 (978-0-613-37158-2(5)) Tandem Library Bks.

Higginsen, V. & Johnson, H. A Harlem Century. 2000. (J). 20.00 (978-0-517-70949-8(X)); lib. bdg. 21.99 (978-0-517-70950-4(3)) Random Hse. Children's Bks. (Random Hse. Bks. for Young Readers).

Kallen, Stuart A. A Travel Guide to Harlem Renaissance. 2003. (J). 29.95 (978-1-59018-358-8(4), Lucent Bks.) Thomson Gale.

Slovey, Christine. Harlem Renaissance. 2000. (Illus.). xxix, 293p. (J). (gr. 4-7). 67.00 (978-0-7876-4836-7(1), GML00502-114880, UXL) Thomson Gale.

Wood, Michele, illus. I See the Rhythm. 1998. (J). (gr. 2-4). pap. 21.27 (978-0-516-21191-6(9), Children's Pr.) Scholastic Library Publishing.

Worth, Richard. Harlem Renaissance: An Explosion of African-American Culture. 2008. (J). (***978-0-7660-2907-1(7)***) Enslow Pubs., Inc.

HARMONICA

How to Play the Harmonica. 2002. 64p. (J). pap. 9.98 (978-0-7525-4261-4(3)) Parragon, Inc.

Maxwell, Stuart. Starting Blues Harmonica. 2006. 32p. pap. 9.95 (978-0-8256-3442-0(3), Amsco Music) Music Sales Corp.

HARMONICA—FICTION

Guest, Elissa Haden. Iris & Walter, Lost & Found. Davenier, Christine, illus. (Iris & Walter Ser.). 44p. (J). 2006. pap. 5.95 (978-0-15-205662-9(9), Harcourt Paperbacks); 2004. 15.00 (978-0-15-216701-1(3), Gulliver Bks.) Harcourt Children's Bks.

Johnston, Tony. The Harmonica. Mazellan, Ron, illus. 2004. 32p. (J). 15.95 (978-1-57091-547-5(4)) Charlesbridge Publishing, Inc.

McCloskey, Robert. Lentil. 2000. (J). pap. 3.95 (978-0-590-04411-0(7)) Scholastic, Inc.

HAROLD (FICTITIOUS CHARACTER : JOHNSON)—FICTION

Crockett, Johns. Harold et le crayon Rose. pap. 13.95 (978-2-266-09592-1(7)) Presses Pocket FRA. *Dist:* Distribooks, Inc.

Johnson, Crockett. Harold at the North Pole. 2004. (Illus.). 48p. (J). (ps-3). pap. 5.99 (978-0-06-058628-7(1), Harper Trophy) HarperCollins Pubs.

—Harold at the North Pole. Johnson, Crockett, illus. 1998. (Harold & the Purple Crayon Ser.). (Illus.). 48p. (J). (ps-3). 14.89 (978-0-06-028074-1(3)) HarperCollins Pubs.

—Harold's ABC. Johnson, Crockett, illus. 2002. (Illus.). (J). 14.43 (978-0-7587-2696-4(1)) Book Wholesalers, Inc.

—Harold's Circus. Johnson, Crockett, illus. 2002. (Illus.). (J). 14.47 (978-0-7587-2697-1(X)) Book Wholesalers, Inc.

—Harold's Trip to the Sky. Johnson, Crockett, illus. 2002. (Illus.). (J). 15.53 (978-0-7587-2698-8(8)) Book Wholesalers, Inc.

—A Picture for Harold's Room. Johnson, Crockett, illus. 2002. (Illus.). (J). 12.30 (978-0-7587-6236-8(4)) Book Wholesalers, Inc.

Murawski, Kevin, illus. Harold & the Purple Crayon: Race Car. 2004. 32p. (J). (ps-ps). lib. bdg. 10.79 (978-0-606-29918-3(1)) Tandem Library Bks.

—Harold & the Purple Crayon: Under the Sea. 2004. 32p. (J). (ps-ps). lib. bdg. 10.79 (978-0-606-29924-4(6)) Tandem Library Bks.

HARRIET THE SPY (FICTITIOUS CHARACTER)—FICTION

Ericson, Helen & Fitzhugh, Louise. Harriet Spies Again. 2002. 240p. (gr. 5 up). 15.95 (978-0-385-32786-2(2), Delacorte Bks. for Young Readers) Random Hse. Children's Bks.

Fitzhugh, Louise. Harriet the Spy. 298p. (J). (gr. 3-5). pap. 5.95 (978-0-8072-1535-7(X)); 1999. pap. 38.00 incl. audio (978-0-8072-8069-0(0), YA993SP) Random Hse. Audio Publishing Group. (Listening Library).

—Harriet the Spy. (Illus.). (gr. 5-7). 2001. 320p. pap. 6.50 (978-0-440-41679-1(5), Yearling); 2000. 304p. (J). 15.95 (978-0-385-32783-1(8), Delacorte Bks. for Young Readers) Random Hse. Children's Bks.

—Harriet the Spy. 2001. (gr. 3-6). lib. bdg. 14.15 (978-0-613-33759-5(X)); (Illus.). (J). 12.64 (978-0-606-21226-7(4)) Tandem Library Bks.

—The Long Secret. 2001. (Illus.). 288p. (J). (gr. 5 up). 15.95 (978-0-385-32784-8(6), Delacorte Bks. for Young Readers) Random Hse. Children's Bks.

HARRISON, BENJAMIN, 1833-1901

Adelson, Bruce. Benjamin Harrison. 2007. (Presidential Leaders Ser.). (Illus.). 111p. (J). 29.27 (978-0-8225-1497-8(4), Lerner Pubns.) Lerner Publishing Group.

Francis, Sandra. Benjamin Harrison: Our Twenty-Third President. 2001. (Spirit of America: Our Presidents Ser.). (Illus.). 48p. (J). (gr. 2-6). 28.50 (978-1-56766-860-5(7)) Child's World, Inc.

Green, Robert. Benjamin Harrison. 2003. (Profiles of the Presidents Ser.). (Illus.). 64p. (J). (gr. 4 up). lib. bdg. 23.93 (978-0-7565-0270-6(5)) Compass Point Bks.

Joseph, Paul. Benjamin Harrison. 2000. (United States Presidents Ser.). (Illus.). 32p. (J). (gr. k-6). lib. bdg. 22.78 (978-1-57765-243-4(6), Checkerboard Library) ABDO Publishing Co.

Marsh, Carole. Benjamin Harrison: An Ohio Experience Reader. 2001. (J). (gr. k-5). pap. 1.95 (978-0-635-00445-1(3)) Gallopade International.

Mis, Melody S. How to Draw the Life & Times of Benjamin Harrison. 2007. (Kid's Guide to Drawing the Presidents of the United States of America Ser.). (Illus.). 32p. (J). 25.25 (978-1-4042-3000-2(9), PowerKids Pr.) Rosen Publishing Group, Inc., The.

Venezia, Mike. Benjamin Harrison. 2006. (Illus.). 32p. (YA). (gr. 3-4). pap. 7.95 (978-0-516-25400-5(6), Children's Pr.) Scholastic Library Publishing.

Venezia, Mike, illus. Benjamin Harrison. 2006. (Getting to Know the U. S. Presidents Ser.). 32p. (J). (gr. 3-4). 27.00 (978-0-516-22628-6(2) , Children's Pr.) Scholastic Library Publishing.

Williams, Jean Kinney. Benjamin Harrison. 2004. (Encyclopedia of Presidents Ser.). (Illus.). 110p. (J). 34.00 (978-0-516-22959-1(1) , Children's Pr.) Scholastic Library Publishing.

Young, Jeff C. Benjamin Harrison: A MyReportLinks.com Book. 2002. (Presidents Ser.). (Illus.). 48p. (J). (gr. 4-10). lib. bdg. 25.26 (978-0-7660-5075-4(0) , MyReportLinks.com Bks.) Enslow Pubs., Inc.

HARRISON, WILLIAM HENRY, 1773-1841

Billman, Hilary Barton. How to Draw the Life & Times of William Henry Harrison. 2006. (Kid's Guide to Drawing the Presidents of the United States of America Ser.). (Illus.). 32p. (J). 25.25 (978-1-4042-2986-0(8) , PowerKids Pr.) Rosen Publishing Group, Inc., The.

Doak, Robin S. William Henry Harrison. 2003. (Profiles of the Presidents Ser.). (Illus.). 64p. (J). (gr. 4 up). lib. bdg. 23.93 (978-0-7565-0257-7(8)) Compass Point Bks.

Gaines, Ann Graham. William Henry Harrison: Our Ninth President. 2001. (Spirit of America: Our Presidents Ser.). (Illus.). 48p. (J). (gr. 2-6). 28.50 (978-1-56766-848-3(8)) Child's World, Inc.

Greene, Meg. William Henry Harrison. 2007. (Presidential Leaders Ser.). 112p. (J). (gr. 6-12). 29.27 (978-0-8225-1511-1(3) , Twenty-First Century Bks.) Lerner Publishing Group.

Joseph, Paul. William H. Harrison. 1999. (United States Presidents Ser.). (Illus.). 32p. (J). (gr. k-6). lib. bdg. 22.78 (978-1-57765-232-8(0) , Checkerboard Library) ABDO Publishing Co.

Lillard, David. William Henry Harrison: A MyReportLinks. Com Book. 2003. (Presidents Ser.). (Illus.). 48p. (J). lib. bdg. 25.26 (978-0-7660-5150-8(1) , MyReportLinks.com Bks.) Enslow Pubs., Inc.

Otfinoski, Steven. William Henry Harrison. 2003. (Encyclopedia of Presidents Ser.). (Illus.). 110p. (J). 34.00 (978-0-516-22761-0(0) , Children's Pr.) Scholastic Library Publishing.

Peckham, Howard. William Henry Harrison Young Tippecanoe. 2001. (gr. 3-6). lib. bdg. 18.75 (978-0-613-80223-9(3)) Tandem Library Bks.

—William Henry Harrison, Young Tippecanoe. Underdown, Harold, ed. Morrison, Cathy, illus. 2nd ed. 2001. (Young Patriots Ser.: Vol. 2). 112p. (J). (gr. 3 up). pap. 9.95 (978-1-882859-07-8(3)) Patria Pr., Inc.

Venezia, Mike. William Henry Harrison: Ninth President 1841. Venezia, Mike, illus. 2005. (Getting to Know the U. S. Presidents Ser.). (Illus.). 32p. (J). (gr. 3-4). pap. 7.95 (978-0-516-27483-6(X) , Children's Pr.) Scholastic Library Publishing.

Venezia, Mike, illus. William Henry Harrison. 2005. (Getting to Know the U. S. Presidents Ser.). 32p. (J). (gr. 3-4). 26.00 (978-0-516-22614-9(2) , Children's Pr.) Scholastic Library Publishing.

HARVEY, WILLIAM, 1578-1657

Elford, Jole Shack. William Harvey & the Mechanics of the Heart. 2005. (Illus.). 141p. (YA). (gr. 6-10). reprint ed. 28.00 (978-0-7567-9712-6(8)) DIANE Publishing Co.

Yount, Lisa. William Harvey: Discoverer of How Blood Circulates. 2008. (Great Minds of Science Ser.). 128p. (J). (gr. 5 up). lib. bdg. 31.93 (***978-0-7660-3010-7(5)***) Enslow Pubs., Inc.

HASIDISM

Touger, Malka, adapted by. Please Tell Me What the Rebbe Said: Torah Insights Adapted from the Works of the Lubavitcher Rebbe, 3 vols., Vol. 3. 2002. (Illus.). 132p. (J). bds. 15.00 (978-1-881400-69-1(7)) S.I.E.

HASTINGS, BATTLE OF, 1066

Crompton, Samuel Willard. Hastings. (Battles That Changed the World Ser.). (J). pap. 30.00 (978-0-7910-7164-9(2)); 2002. (Illus.). 112p. (gr. 7-10). 30.00 (978-0-7910-6680-5(0)) Facts On File, Inc. (Chelsea Hse.).

HATS

Carlson, Laurie M. Boss of the Plains: The Hat that Won the West. 2000. (gr. 3-6). lib. bdg. 16.45 (978-0-613-28427-1(5)) Tandem Library Bks.

Carlson, Laurie M. & Dorling Kindersley Publishing Staff. Boss of the Plains: The Hat That Won the West. 2000. (Illus.). 32p. (J). (ps-5). pap. 7.99 (978-0-7894-2657-4(9)) Dorling Kindersley Publishing, Inc.

Cooper, Sharon Katz. Whose Hat Is This? A Look at Hats Workers Wear—Hard, Tall, & Shiny. Muehlenhardt, Amy Bailey, illus. 2006. (Whose Is It? Ser.). 24p. (J). (ps-2). 22.60 (978-1-4048-1600-8(3)) Picture Window Bks.

Corbett, Sara. Hats off to Hats! 2006. (Illus.). 32p. (J). (gr. k-4). reprint ed. 17.00 (978-0-7567-9929-8(5)) DIANE Publishing Co.

Fisher, Leonard Everett. The Hatters. 2000. (Colonial Craftsmen Ser.). (Illus.). 48p. (J). (gr. 4-8). lib. bdg. 21.36 (978-0-7614-1146-8(1) , Benchmark Bks.) Cavendish, Marshall Corp.

Fleming, Sarah. Make a Paper Hat. 2000. (Cambridge Reading Ser.). (Illus.). 10p. pap. 5.00 (978-0-521-77458-1(6)) Cambridge Univ. Pr.

Hats: Big Book: Level B. 8p. 20.95 (978-0-322-00359-0(8)) Wright Group, The.

Hats: Level B. 8p. 24.95 (978-0-7802-8919-2(6)) Wright Group, The.

Hats: Level G, 6 vols. (Wonder Worldtm Ser.). 16p. 29.95 (978-0-7802-4579-2(2)) Wright Group, The.

Hats Hats Hats. 2002. (Illus.). (J). pap. 3.74 (978-0-7398-5848-6(3)) Steck-Vaughn.

McDonald, Fiona. Hats & Headdresses Through History. 2006. (Why Do We Wear? Ser.). (Illus.). 32p. (J). lib. bdg. (978-0-8368-6854-8(4)) Stevens, Gareth Inc.

Reynolds, Helen. Hats & Hairstyles. 2003. (Fashionable History of Costume Ser.). (Illus.). 32p. (J). lib. bdg. 25.70 (978-1-4109-0030-2(4)) Raintree.

Seto, Alex. Whose Hat? 2006. 14p. pap. 7.95 (978-0-9734496-5-5(9)) ADVAN Pr., Inc. CAN. *Dist:* Biblio Distribution.

HATS—FICTION

Adams, Pam. Mrs. Honey's Hat Lap Book. 1999. (Illus.). 32p. (J). (ps-3). 26.99 (978-0-85953-814-5(1)) Child's Play-International.

Asch, Frank. Happy Birthday, Moon. 2005. (Stories to Go! Ser.). (Illus.). (J). (***978-1-4156-0411-3(8)*** , Aladdin) Simon & Schuster Children's Publishing.

Bandsuh, Jim. Helmet Hank. 2007. (J). per. 15.99 (***978-1-933156-19-4(8)*** , Visikid Bks.) GSVQ Publishing.

Blackaby, Susan. Rembrandt's Hat. DePalma, Mary Newell, illus. 2002. 32p. (J). (gr. k-3). 15.00 (978-0-618-11452-8(1)) Houghton Mifflin Co. Trade & Reference Div.

Bolam, Emily, illus. Father's Day Is Coming. 2007. (I'm Going to Read Ser.: No. 2). 32p. (J). pap. 3.95 (978-1-4027-4247-7(9)) Sterling Publishing Co., Inc.

Brett, Jan. The Hat. 1999. (Illus.). (J). (ps-k). 32p. pap. 17.99 (978-0-399-23463-7(2)) ; 28p. bds. 7.99 (978-0-399-23461-3(6)) Penguin Group (USA) Inc. (Putnam Juvenile).

Bridwell, Norman. The Cat & the Bird in the Hat. Bridwell, Norman, illus. 2000. (Hello Reader! Ser.). (Illus.). 32p. (J). (ps-3). pap. 3.99 (978-0-439-15433-8(2)) Scholastic, Inc.

—The Cat & the Bird in the Hat. 2000. (Hello Reader! Ser.). (Illus.). (J). (978-0-606-18531-8(3)) Tandem Library Bks.

Brumbeau, Jeff. Miss Hunnicutt's Hat. de Marcken, Gail, illus. 2003. 48p. (J). (gr. k-3). pap. 16.95 (978-0-439-31895-2(5) , Orchard Bks.) Scholastic, Inc.

Butler, M. Christina. One Snowy Night. Macnaughton, Tina, illus. 2007. 26p. (J). (ps). bds. 8.95 (***978-1-56148-591-8(8)***) Good Bks.

Chaconas, Dori. Virginnie's Hat. Meade, Holly, illus. 2007. 32p. (J). (ps-1). 16.99 (978-0-7636-2397-5(0)) Candlewick Pr.

Charnan, Simon. I've Lost My Hat. 2006. (Rookie Reader Skill Set Ser.). (Illus.). 32p. (J). (gr. k-2). 19.50 (978-0-531-12088-0(0) , Children's Pr.) Scholastic Library Publishing.

Cinar, Lisa. The Day It All Blew Away. 2007. (Illus.). 52p. (J). (gr. 2 up). 16.95 (***978-1-894965-71-2(X)***) Simply Read Bks. CAN. *Dist:* Perseus Distribution.

Claus, Nancy. Santa's Hat. Ferchaud, Steve, illus. 2006. (J). (***978-0-9746747-6-6(1)***) Cypress Bay Publishing.

Courtney, Richard, illus. The Special Delivery. 2002. (Jellybean Bks.). 24p. (J). (gr. k-2). pap. 3.25 (978-0-375-81494-5(9) , Random Hse. Bks. for Young Readers) Random Hse. Children's Bks.

D'Amico, Carmela & D'Amico, Steven. Ella the Elegant Elephant. 2004. (Illus.). (J). (ps-3). 56p. pap. 16.95 (978-0-439-62792-4(3)); (978-0-439-62793-1(1)) Scholastic, Inc. (Levine, Arthur A. Bks.).

Dunrea, Olivier. Peedie. (Illus.). 32p. (J). (ps-k). 2008. bds. 6.95 (***978-0-618-75506-6(3)***); 2004. tchr. ed. 9.95 (978-0-618-35652-2(5)) Houghton Mifflin Co. Trade & Reference Div.

Eisenberg Sasso, Sandy. Butterflies Under Our Hats. 2006. (Illus.). 32p. (J). 16.95 (978-1-55725-474-0(5)) Paraclete Pr., Inc.

Engelbreit, Mary. Queen of Easter. Engelbreit, Mary, illus. 2006. (Ann Estelle Stories Ser.). (Illus.). 32p. (J). 15.99 (978-0-06-008184-3(8)); lib. bdg. 16.89 (978-0-06-008185-0(6)) HarperCollins Pubs.

Evans, Nate & Numeroff, Laura Nate. Sherman Crunchley. Bowers, Tim, illus. 2005. 32p. (J). pap. 5.99 (978-0-14-240385-3(7) , Puffin) Penguin Group (USA) Inc.

Failing, Barbara Larmon. Lasso Lou & Cowboy Mccoy. Arnold, Tedd, illus. 2003. 40p. (J). (gr. k-3). 16.99 (978-0-8037-2578-2(7) , Dial) Penguin Group (USA) Inc.

The Flat Hat: KinderReaders Individual Title Six-Packs. (Kinderstarters Ser.). 8p. (ps-1). 21.00 (978-0-7635-8662-1(5)) Rigby Education.

Fox, Mem. The Magic Hat. Tusa, Tricia, illus. 2006. 32p. (J). reprint ed. pap. 7.00 (978-0-15-205715-2(3) , Voyager Bks./Libros Viajeros) Harcourt Children's Bks.

Gelman, Rita Golden. Hello, Cat, You Need a Hat. 1999. (Hello Reader! Ser.). (Illus.). (J). (978-0-606-18557-8(7)) Tandem Library Bks.

Gill, Janice. Hats. 1998. (ps-3). pap. 4.95 (978-0-89868-407-0(2)); lib. bdg. 10.95 (978-0-89868-348-6(3)) ARO Publishing Co.

Goldberg, Jacqueline. Una Senora Con Sombrero. (SPA.). (J). pap. (978-980-01-0478-1(X)) Monte Avila Editores Latinoamericana CA VEN. *Dist:* Lectorum Pubns., Inc.

Gorbachev, Valeri. Whose Hat Is It? 2004. 30p. (J). lib. bdg. 13.85 (***978-1-4242-0713-8(4)***) Fitzgerald Bks.

—Whose Hat Is It? Gorbachev, Valeri, illus. (My First I Can Read Bks.). (Illus.). 32p. (J). (ps up). 2005. pap. 3.99 (978-0-06-053436-3(2) , Harper Trophy); 2004. 14.99 (978-0-06-053434-9(6)); 2004. lib. bdg. 15.89 (978-0-06-053435-6(4)) HarperCollins Pubs.

Gruetzke, Mary, ed. Maya & Miguel: The Magic Easter Hat. 2006. (Scholastic Reader Ser.). (Illus.). 32p. (J). pap. 3.99 (978-0-439-80902-3(9)) Scholastic, Inc.

Hanson, Warren, illus. Kiki's Hats. 2007. (J). (***978-0-931674-94-5(8)***) Waldman Hse. Pr., Inc.

Harcourt School Publishers Staff. A Hat for Sam Advanced Level. 3rd ed. 2002. (Trophies Reading Program Ser.). (Illus.). (J). (gr. 1). pap. 3.70 (978-0-15-323007-3(X)) Harcourt Schl. Pubs.

—Rainbow Hats. 3rd ed. 2002. (Trophies English Language Learners Ser.). (Illus.). (J). pap. 3.20 (978-0-15-327578-4(2)) Harcourt Schl. Pubs.

Hassett, Ann. The Finest Christmas Tree. Hassett, John, illus. 2005. 32p. (J). (gr. k-3). 16.00 (978-0-618-50901-0(1) , Walter Lorraine) Houghton Mifflin Co. Trade & Reference Div.

The Hat. (Little Book Practice Reader). (J). (978-0-8136-5339-6(8)) Modern Curriculum Pr.

Hats. Date not set. 5.95 (978-0-89868-349-3(1)) ARO Publishing Co.

Hats: Individual Title Six-Packs. (Sails Literacy Ser.). 16p. (gr. k up). 27.00 (978-0-7635-4443-0(4)) Rigby Education.

Hofmeister, Alan, et al. The Hat. (Reading for All Learners Ser.). (Illus.). (J). pap. (978-1-56861-105-1(6)) Swift Learning Resources.

—Mat in the Hat. (Reading for All Learners Ser.). (Illus.). (J). pap. (978-1-56861-106-8(4)) Swift Learning Resources.

Holm, Sharon Lane. Zoe's Hats: A Book of Colors & Patterns. Holm, Sharon Lane, illus. 2003. (Illus.). 32p. (J). (ps up). 13.95 (978-1-59078-042-8(6)) Boyds Mills Pr.

Howard, Elizabeth Fitzgerald. Aunt Flossie's Hats (and Crab Cakes Later) Ransome, James E., illus. 10th anniv. ed. 2001. 40p. (J). (gr. k-3). tchr. ed. 16.00 (978-0-618-12038-3(6) , Clarion Bks.) Houghton Mifflin Co. Trade & Reference Div.

Karon, Jan. Miss Fannie's Hat. Goffe, Toni, illus. 2003. 32p. (ps-2). cd-rom 17.99 (978-0-8066-4585-8(7) , Augsburg Bks.) Augsburg Fortress, Pubs.

—Miss Fannie's Hat. Goffe, Toni, illus. 2001. (Picture Puffin Ser.). 32p. (J). (ps-3). pap. 6.99 (978-0-14-056812-7(3) , Puffin) Penguin Group (USA) Inc.

—Miss Fannie's Hat. 2001. (gr. 3-6). lib. bdg. 15.30 (978-0-613-31483-1(2)); (Illus.). (J). (978-0-606-20802-4(X)) Tandem Library Bks.

Katz, Karen. Twelve Hats for Lena: A Book of Months. Katz, Karen, illus. 2002. (Illus.). 34p. (J). (ps-3). 17.99 (978-0-689-84873-5(0) , McElderry, Margaret K.) Simon & Schuster Children's Publishing.

Keats, Ezra Jack. Jennie's Hat. Keats, Ezra Jack, illus. 2003. (Illus.). 40p. (J). pap. 6.99 (978-0-14-250035-4(6) , Puffin) Penguin Group (USA) Inc.

—Jennie's Hat. 2003. (Illus.). 40p. (J). (gr. k-3). 15.99 (978-0-670-03625-7(0) , Viking Juvenile) Penguin Group (USA) Inc.

—Jennie's Hat. 2003. (gr. k-3). lib. bdg. 15.30 (978-0-613-61710-9(X)) Tandem Library Bks.

Keller, Holly. The Hat. 2005. (Green Light Readers Level 1 Ser.). (Illus.). 24p. (J). 12.95 (978-0-15-205179-2(1)); pap. 3.95 (978-0-15-205178-5(3)) Harcourt Children's Bks. (Green Light Readers).

—What a Hat! Keller, Holly, illus. 2003. (Illus.). 24p. (J). 15.99 (978-0-06-051479-2(5)) HarperCollins Pubs.

Kimmel, Eric A. Stormy's Hat. U'Ren, Andrea, illus. 2008. 32p. (J). 16.95 (978-0-374-37262-0(4)) Farrar, Straus & Giroux.

Kirk, Ruth Lynn. Charlie Ate My Hat! 2004. 32p. pap. 7.99 (978-0-9675410-2-0(6)) Shamrock Pr.

Klise, Kate. Shall I Knit You A Hat? A Christmas Yarn. Klise, M. Sarah, illus. 2007. 32p. (J). pap. 6.99 (***978-0-312-37139-5(X)***) Square Fish.

Klise, Kate. Shall I Knit You a Hat? A Christmas Yarn. Klise, M. Sarah, illus. rev. ed. 2004. 32p. (J). 16.95 (978-0-8050-7318-8(3) , Holt, Henry & Co. Bks. For Young Readers) Holt, Henry & Co.

Kuskin, Karla. Under My Hood I Have a Hat. Kosaka, Fumi, illus. 2004. 32p. (J). (ps-2). 14.99 (978-0-06-057242-6(6) , Geringer, Laura Book) HarperCollins Pubs.

Ladd, Debbie. Nurse Robin's Hats. Nakasone, Shaun, illus. 2006. 52p. (J). 16.95 (978-0-9727615-3-6(5)) Deb on Air Bks.

Lakeshore Learning Materials Staff, contrib. by. Caps for Sale Packet. 2000. (J). pap. 19.95 (978-1-929255-39-9(X)) Lakeshore Learning Materials.

Lamb, Albert. Woolly Winter Hat. McPhail, David, illus. 2006. 32p. (J). pap. 6.99 (978-0-439-79304-9(1)) Scholastic, Inc.

Landstrom, Olof & Landstrom, Lena. Will's New Cap. Fishe, Richard E., tr. from SWE. Landstrom, Olof & Landstrom, Lena, illus. 2000. (Illus.). 28p. (J). (ps-k). reprint ed. pap. 4.95 (978-91-29-64877-5(7)) R & S Bks. SWE. *Dist:* Macmillan.

Langford, Jane. An Old Red Hat. Axworthy, Anni, illus. 2004. 24p. (J). lib. bdg. 22.65 (***978-1-59646-676-0(6)***) Dingles & Co.

LeapFrog Staff, compiled by. Casey Cat Has a Hat. 2001. (J). (ps-2). spiral bd. 10.95 (978-1-58605-032-0(X)) LeapFrog Enterprises, Inc.

Low, Alice. Aunt Lucy Went to Buy a Hat. Huliska-Beith, Laura, illus. 2004. 32p. (J). (ps-3). lib. bdg. 16.89 (978-0-06-008972-6(5)) HarperCollins Pubs.

—Aunt Lucy Went to Buy a Hat. Huliska-Beith, Laura, tr. Huliska-Beith, Laura, illus. 2004. 32p. (J). (ps-3). 15.99 (978-0-06-008971-9(7)) HarperCollins Pubs.

Lucado, Max. A Hat for Ivan. Wenzel, David, illus. 2005. 32p. 15.99 (978-1-58134-414-1(7)); 28p. bds. 6.99 (978-1-58134-656-5(5)) Crossway Bks. (Crossway Bibles).

Luthardt, Kevin. Hats! Luthardt, Kevin, illus. 2004. (Illus.). 32p. (J). (gr. k-3). 16.95 (978-0-8075-3171-6(5)) Whitman, Albert & Co.

Madison, Ron. Ned's Hat: A Lesson about Safety. Cololo, David, illus. l.t. ed. 2002. (Health & Safety Ser.). 20p. (ps-2). 4.95 (978-1-887206-21-1(3)) Ned's Head Productions.

McCann, Jesse Leon. The Cat in the Hat. 2003. (Illus.). 24p. (J). (gr. k-k). 0.33 (978-0-375-82780-8(3) , Golden Bks.) Random Hse. Children's Bks.

Meddaugh, Susan. Leopold's Hat. 2002. (J). 15.00 (978-0-618-15278-0(4) , Walter Lorraine) Houghton Mifflin Co. Trade & Reference Div.

Mlawer, Teresa, tr. Se Venden Gorras. unabr. ed. 1999. (SPA., Illus.). (J). (gr. k-3). pap., tchr. ed. 37.95 incl. audio (978-0-87499-514-5(0)) Live Oak Media.

—Se Venden Gorras. Slobodkina, Esphyr, illus. unabr. ed. 1999. (SPA.). (J). (gr. k-3). 25.95 incl. audio (978-0-87499-513-8(2)); pap. 16.95 incl. audio (978-0-87499-512-1(4) , LK3259) Live Oak Media.

Mom Likes Hats. 2003. (J). (978-1-58453-253-8(X)) Pioneer Valley Educational Pr., Inc.

Moncure, Jane Belk. Word Bird's Hats. 2002. (New Word Bird Library). (Illus.). 32p. (J). (ps-3). 22.79 (978-1-56766-997-8(2)) Child's World, Inc.

Moore, Lilian. While You Were Chasing a Hat. Litzinger, Rosanne, illus. 2001. (Growing Tree Ser.). 24p. (J). (gr. k-3). 9.95 (978-0-694-01342-5(0) , Harper Festival) HarperCollins Pubs.

Morgan, Richard. The Rat-a-Tat-Hat Book. 2000. (Illus.). 10p. (J). 9.99 (978-0-370-32502-6(8)) Random Hse. GBR. *Dist:* Independent Pubs. Group.

Mortensen, Lyn. Effie May & Her Outrageous Hats. Mortensen, Lyn, illus. 2006. (J). per. (978-0-9767570-1-6(X)) Whitegate Bks.

Nash, Margaret. Hetty's New Hat. Impey, Martin, illus. 2005. (Reading Corner Ser.). 24p. (J). (gr. k-3). lib. bdg. 22.80 (978-1-59771-007-7(5)) Sea-To-Sea Pubns.

O'Malley, Kevin. My Lucky Hat. O'Malley, Kevin, illus. 1999. (Illus.). 32p. (J). (gr. k-4). 15.95 (978-1-57255-710-9(9)) Mondo Publishing.

Opheim, Sandra. Whose Hat Is That? Horton, Lori, illus. 2004. (J). 5.95 (978-0-9758958-0-1(X)) Better Than One Publishing.

The Peddler's Caps: Individual Title Six-Packs. 16p. (gr. 2 up). 35.00 (978-0-7635-9231-8(5)) Rigby Education.

Pittar, Gill. Milly, Molly & the Sunhat (book W/dolls) 2006. 28p. pap. (978-1-86972-102-2(0)) Milly Molly Bks.

Powell, Jillian. The Naughty Puppy. Durantz, Summer, illus. 2004. (Read-It! Readers Ser.). 32p. (C). (gr. k-3). 18.60 (978-1-4048-0067-0(0)) Picture Window Bks.

Powell, Richard. Whose Hat Is That? Martín Larrañaga, Ana, illus. 2004. (Ana's Mini Movers Ser.). 12p. (J). 5.95 (978-1-58925-740-5(5) , tiger tales) ME Media LLC.

Pratt, Pierre. Leon sans Son Chapeau - Follow That Hat! ed. 2004. (J). (gr. k-3). spiral bd. (978-0-616-03076-9(2)) Canadian National Institute for the Blind/Institut National Canadien pour les Aveugles.

Rabe, Tish. Harry's Magic Hat. Watson, Richard, illus. 2007. 24p. (J). (ps-1). pap. 6.99 (***978-1-58476-610-0(7)*** , IKIDS) Innovative Kids.

Rau, Dana Meachen. Hats!, Level B. Harvey, Paul, illus. 2001. (Early Reader Ser.). 32p. (J). (gr. k up). lib. bdg. 18.60 (978-0-7565-0073-3(7)) Compass Point Bks.

Rex, Michael. Scarecrow. Rex, Michael, illus. 2003. (Word-by-Word First Reader Ser.). (Illus.). 32p. (J). pap. 3.99 (978-0-439-49311-6(0) , Cartwheel Bks.) Scholastic, Inc.

Riemer, Bernice. The Old Straw Hat. 2006. (ENG., Illus.). 40p. (J). per. 15.95 (***978-1-59800-844-9(7)***) Outskirts Press, Inc.

Rigby Education Staff. Animal Advertisements. (Sails Literacy Ser.). (Illus.). 16p. (gr. 2-3). 27.00 (978-0-7635-9944-7(1) , 699441C99) Rigby Education.

Ross, Dev. Old Blue Hat. 2002. (gr. k-3). lib. bdg. 11.80 (978-0-613-84225-9(1)) Tandem Library Bks.

—We Both Read-the Old Blue Hat. Johnson, Meredith, illus. 2002. (We Both Read Ser.). 44p. (J). (gr. 1 up). 7.99 (978-1-891327-37-7(2)); pap. 3.99 (978-1-891327-38-4(0)) Treasure Bay, Inc.

Rumford, James. Don't Touch My Hat. 2007. (Illus.). 40p. (J). (ps-3). lib. bdg. 18.99 (978-0-375-93782-8(X) , Knopf Bks. for Young Readers) Random Hse. Children's Bks.

—Don't Touch My Hat! 2007. (Illus.). 40p. (J). (ps-3). 16.99 (978-0-375-83782-1(5) , Knopf Bks. for Young Readers) Random Hse. Children's Bks.

Ryan. Queens Birthday Hat. (Illus.). 32p. (J). pap. 7.95 (978-0-14-038709-4(9)) Penguin Bks., Ltd. GBR. *Dist:* Trafalgar Square Publishing.

Saez, Juanjo. Dentro del Sombrero. 2001. (SPA., Illus.). (J). (gr. k-2). 12.76 (978-84-88342-28-7(4) , KK30072) S.A. Kokinos ESP. *Dist:* Lectorum Pubns., Inc.

Salerno, Steven, illus. Coco the Carrot. 2005. 40p. (J). 16.95 (978-0-7614-5191-4(9)) Cavendish, Marshall Corp.

—Coco the Carrot. 2002. 40p. (J). 15.95 (978-1-890817-87-9(2)) Winslow Hse. Bks.

Santa's Hat. 2003. (J). per. (978-1-57657-927-5(1)) Paradise Pr., Inc.

Savoie, Jacques & Zekina, Daniela. Un Chapeau Qui Tournait Autour de la Terre. 2003. (Illus.). 24p. (J). pap. (978-2-89021-295-4(5)) Diffusion du livre Mirabel.

School Zone Publishing Company Staff & Hoffman, Joan. Mia's Sun Hat. 2000. (Start to Read Board Bks.). (Illus.). 10p. (J). (ps-k). bds. 4.99 (978-0-88743-811-0(3) , 06813) School Zone Publishing Co.

Schraff, Anne. Bajo Mi Sombrero. de la Vega, Eida, tr. Zemke, Deborah, illus. 2001. (Books for Young Learners).Tr. of Under My Sombrero. (SPA.). 12p. (J). (gr. k-2). pap. 5.00 (978-1-57274-435-6(9) , 2827) Owen, Richard C. Pubs., Inc.

Seuss, Dr. The Cat in the Hat Book & CD. 2005. (Illus.). 64p. (J). (gr. k-3). pap. 9.95 incl. audio compact disk (978-0-375-83492-9(3) , Random Hse. Bks. for Young Readers) Random Hse. Children's Bks.

—The Cat in the Hat Comes Back. 2006. (Illus.). 64p. (J). (gr. k-3). 9.95 (978-0-375-87538-0(7) , Random Hse. Bks. for Young Readers) Random Hse. Children's Bks.

—Los Quinientos Sombreros de Bartolome Cubbins. de la Vega, Eida, tr. from ENG. Seuss, Dr., illus. 1998. (SPA., Illus.). 48p. (J). (ps-3). lib. bdg. 14.95 (978-1-880507-47-6(1) , LC8260) Lectorum Pubns., Inc.

H I

Simon, Charnan. I've Lost My Hat. 2007. (Rookie Reader Ser.). (Illus.). 31p. (J). pap. (***978-0-531-12490-1(8)***) Children's Pr., Ltd.

Slingsby, Janet. Hetty's 100 Hats. Dodd, Emma, illus. 2005. 40p. (J). (ps-ps). 16.00 (978-1-56148-456-0(3)) Good Bks.

Slobodkina, Esphyr. Caps for Sale. 2000. (J). pap. 19.97 incl. audio (978-0-7366-9218-2(5)) Books on Tape, Inc.

—Caps for Sale. Slobodkina, Esphyr, illus. (Illus.). (J). (gr. k-3). 2005. pap. 16.95 incl. audio (978-0-87499-058-4(0)); 2000. 25.95 incl. audio (978-0-87499-059-1(9)) Live Oak Media.

—Caps for Sale, 2 bks. Mlawer, Teresa, tr. Slobodkina, Esphyr, illus. unabr. ed. 1999. (ENG & SPA., Illus.). (J). (gr. k-3). pap. 33.95 incl. audio (978-0-87499-562-6(0)) Live Oak Media.

—Caps for Sale. 2004. (J). 24.95 incl. audio (978-0-89719-863-9(8) , HRA012) Weston Woods Studios, Inc.

—Caps for Sale: A Tale of a Peddler, Some Monkeys, & Their Monkey Business. 2000. (978-0-606-20342-5(7)) Tandem Library Bks.

—Caps for Sale Board Book: A Tale of a Peddler, Some Monkeys & Their Monkey Business. Slobodkina, Esphyr, illus. 2008. 32p. (J). 8.99 (***978-0-06-147453-8(3)*** , Harper Festival) HarperCollins Pubs.

—Circus Caps for Sale. Slobodkina, Esphyr, illus. 2004. (Illus.). 40p. (J). (ps-2). reprint ed. 17.00 (978-0-7567-8345-7(3)) DIANE Publishing Co.

—Circus Caps for Sale. Slobodkina, Esphyr, illus. (Illus.). 48p. (J). (ps-2). 2002. 16.99 (978-0-06-029655-1(0)); 2004. reprint ed. pap. 6.99 (978-0-06-443793-6(0) , Harper Trophy) HarperCollins Pubs.

—Se Venden Gorras. Slobodkina, Esphyr, illus. 1999. (Illus.). 28.95 incl. audio compact disk (978-1-59519-195-3(X)); pap. 39.95 incl. audio compact disk (978-1-59519-194-6(1)); (SPA., (J). pap. 18.95 incl. audio compact disk (978-1-59519-193-9(3)) Live Oak Media.

El Sombrero de Juan/Harry's Hat. 2005. (Libros en Espanol Para Ninos Ser.). (SPA.). (YA). (ps-1). 11.97 (978-0-8215-0993-7(4)); 15.75 (978-0-8215-1203-6(X)) Sadlier, William H. Inc.

Son, John. Finding My Hat. 2005. (First Person Fiction Ser.). 192p. (J). reprint ed. pap. 6.99 (978-0-439-43539-0(0) , Scholastic Paperbacks) Scholastic, Inc.

Staton, Debbie. Twiggle. Patzelt, Kasie, illus. l.t. ed. 2006. 26p. (J). per. 12.99 (***978-1-59879-199-0(0)***) Lifevest Publishing, Inc.

Stephens, Monique Z. The Easter Bonnet Parade: All Aboard Reading Station Stop 1. S. I. Artists Staff, illus. 2004. (All Aboard Reading Ser.). 32p. (J). (ps-2). mass mkt. 3.99 (978-0-448-43486-5(5) , Grosset & Dunlap) Penguin Group (USA) Inc.

Stewaart, Toni D., illus. The Man, the Hat, & the Cat. 1999. 13p. (Orig.). (J). (gr. k-2). pap. 2.50 (978-1-889658-02-5(2)) New Canaan Publishing Co. LLC.

Stoeke, Janet Morgan. A Hat for Minerva Louise. Stoeke, Janet Morgan, illus. 2002. (Minerva Louise Ser.). (Illus.). (J). 13.19 (978-0-7587-2701-5(1)) Book Wholesalers, Inc.

—A Hat for Minerva Louise. 2nd ed. 2002. (Illus.). (978-0-525-46875-2(7) , Dutton Juvenile) Penguin Group (USA) Inc.

Tétro, Marc. My New Hat. 2005. (Illus.). (978-1-55278-543-0(2)) McArthur & Co. CAN. *Dist:* National Bk. Network.

Thompson, Kay & McClatchy, Lisa. Eloise's New Bonnet. Lyon, Tammie, illus. 2007. (Eloise Ser.). 32p. (J). pap. 3.99 (978-0-689-87452-9(9) , Aladdin) Simon & Schuster Children's Publishing.

Tompert, Ann. Harry's Hats. Elizalde, Marcelo, illus. (Rookie Reader Skill Set Ser.). (J). (gr. k-2). 2005. 32p. pap. 4.95 (978-0-516-24647-5(X)); 2004. 31p. 19.50 (978-0-516-23613-1(X)) Scholastic Library Publishing. (Children's Pr.).

Turner-Denstaedt, Melanie. Grandma's Good Hat. Morrison, Frank, illus. 2008. (J). (978-0-374-32794-1(7)) Farrar, Straus & Giroux.

Ungerer, Tomi. El Sombrero.Tr. of Hat. (SPA.). 40p. (J). (gr. 2-3). 8.50 (978-84-204-3026-3(9)) Alfaguara, Ediciones, S.A.- Grupo Santillana ESP. *Dist:* Lectorum Pubns., Inc.

Venn, Cecilia. That Is Not My Hat. Handelman, Dorothy, photos by. 1998. (Real Kids Readers Ser.: 3). (Illus.). 32p. (J). (gr. 2-4). pap. 4.99 (978-0-7613-2033-3(4) , Millbrook Pr.) Lerner Publishing Group.

We Like Hats. 2004. (J). (978-1-932570-16-8(0)) Literacy Footprints Inc.

Weeks, Sarah. Who's under That Hat? A Lift-the-Flap Pop-Up Adventure. Carter, David A., illus. 2005. 14p. (J). (ps). 6.98 (978-0-15-205467-0(7) , Red Wagon Bks.) Harcourt Children's Bks.

—Who's under That Hat? A Lift-the-Flap Pop-up Adventure. Carter, David A., illus. 2006. 14p. (J). (ps-2). 14.00 (978-1-4223-5440-7(7)) DIANE Publishing Co.

Weiss, Ellen, et al. Hello Kitty's Easter Bonnet Surprise. Hirashima, Jean, illus. 2004. 22p. (J). (ps-3). 12.95 (978-0-8109-4819-8(2)) Abrams, Harry N. , Inc.

Weninger, Brigitte. Elf's Hat. 2002. (gr. k-3). lib. bdg. 15.25 (978-0-613-84073-6(9)) Tandem Library Bks.

Yoxen, Jackie. Hannah's Sunday Hats. Francis, Lauren, illus. l.t. ed. 2006. 32p. (J). 19.95 (***978-1-59879-184-6(2)***) Lifevest Publishing, Inc.

HATSHEPSUT, QUEEN OF EGYPT

Galford, Ellen. Hatshepsut: The Princess Who Became King. 2005. (World History Biographies Ser.). (Illus.). 64p. (J). (gr. 3-7). 17.95 (978-0-7922-3645-0(9) , National Geographic Children's Bks.) National Geographic Society.

—Hatshepsut: The Princess Who Became King. 2005. (World History Biographies Ser.). (Illus.). 64p. (J). (gr. 3-7). 27.90 (978-0-7922-3646-7(7) , National Geographic Children's Bks.) National Geographic Society.

Galford, Ellen. World History Biographies: Hatshepsut: The Princess Who Became King. 2007. (NG World History Biographies Ser.). (Illus.). 64p. (J). (gr. 3-7). pap. 6.95 (***978-1-4263-0133-9(2)*** , National Geographic Children's Bks.) National Geographic Society.

Greenblatt, Miriam. Hatshepsut & Ancient Egypt. 1999. (Rulers & Their Times Ser.). (Illus.). 80p. (YA). (gr. 6 up). lib. bdg. 29.93 (978-0-7614-0911-3(4) , Benchmark Bks.) Cavendish, Marshall Corp.

Ross, Stewart. The Finest Pharaoh of All! Princess Hatshepsut Takes over Egypt. Shields, Susan, illus. 1999. (Coming Alive Ser.). 62p. (J). pap. 8.99 (978-0-237-51960-5(7) , Evans Brothers, Limited) Evans Publishing Group GBR. *Dist:* Independent Pubs. Group.

Thomas, Susanna. Hatsheput: The First Woman Pharaoh. 2003. (Leaders of Ancient Egypt Ser.). (Illus.). 112p. (J). (gr. 5-8). lib. bdg. 31.95 (978-0-8239-3594-9(9) , Rosen Central) Rosen Publishing Group, Inc., The.

HAUNTED HOUSES

see also Ghosts

Brucken, Kelli M. Haunted Houses. 2006. (Encounters with Ser.). (Illus.). 48p. (gr. 4-8). 26.20 (978-0-7377-3475-1(2) , Greenhaven Pr., Inc.) Thomson Gale.

Brzycki, M. L. & Krueger, S. L. It Came from the Freezer ... or Was it the Drapes? l.t. ed. 2004. (Illus.). 110p. (YA). per. 13.00 (978-0-9747581-0-7(8)) StrangeDays Publishing.

Claybourne, Anna, ed. Ghosts & Hauntings. 2000. (Ghosts & Hauntings Ser.). (Illus.). 96p. (YA). (gr. 3-7). pap. 13.95 (978-0-7460-3716-4(3)) EDC Publishing.

Everett, Lawrence. Ghosts & Legends of Southeastern Ohio & Beyond: Tales of Legends, Hauntings & the Unexplained, 2. 2003. 124p. (YA). pap. 11.95 (978-0-7414-1760-2(X)) Infinity Publishing.

Floyd, E. Randall. In the Realm of Ghosts & Hauntings. 2002. 190p. pap. 16.95 (978-1-891799-06-8(1)) Harbor Hse.

Halton, Melanie. The Ultimated Haunted House Glow in the Dark Sticker Book. Halton, Melanie, ed. Kavanagh, Peter, illus. 2002. (Ultimate Sticker Bks.). 16p. (J). pap. 6.99 (978-0-7894-8857-2(4)) Dorling Kindersley Publishing, Inc.

Hamilton, John. Haunted Places. 2007. (ENG., Illus.). 32p. (J). lib. bdg. 24.21 (***978-1-59928-768-3(4)*** , ABDO & Daughters) ABDO Publishing Co.

Holub, Joan. Haunted States of America. 2001. 11.64 (978-0-606-22106-1(9)) Tandem Library Bks.

Kallen, Stuart A. Haunted Houses. 2007. (J). lib. bdg. (***978-1-60152-026-5(3)***) ReferencePoint Pr., Inc.

Krohn, Katherine E. Haunted Houses. 2006. (Edge Books, the Unexplained). 32p. (J). (978-0-7368-5450-4(9)) Capstone Pr., Inc.

Marts, Michael. Ghosts in Amityville: The Haunted House. 2007. (Graphic Mysteries Ser.). (Illus.). 24p. (J). (978-1-4042-2345-5(2)); pap. (978-1-4042-2155-0(7)); (gr. 2-6). lib. bdg. 21.25 (978-1-4042-3402-4(0)) Rosen Publishing Group, Inc., The. (PowerKids Pr.).

Netzley, Patricia D. Haunted Houses. 2000. (Mystery Library). (Illus.). 96p. (J). (gr. 4-12). 29.95 (978-1-56006-685-9(7) , Lucent Bks.) Thomson Gale.

Oester, Dave. My Adventure in a Haunted House. 2006. 44p. (J). 8.99 (978-1-59092-418-1(5) , Orchard Academy Pr.) Windstorm Creative.

Oxlade, Chris. The Mystery of Haunted Houses. 2006. (Can Science Solve? Ser.). (Illus.). 32p. (J). 29.29 (978-1-4034-8334-8(5)); 2nd ed. pap. 7.85 (978-1-4034-8343-0(4)) Heinemann Library.

Red Bird Press Staff. Secret Spex Haunted House. 2004. (Secret Picture Search Ser.). 18p. (J). pap. 5.95 (978-1-902626-67-3(2)) Red Bird Publishing GBR. *Dist:* Weatherhill, Inc.

Smith, Barbara. Horribly Haunted Houses, Vol. 1. rev. ed. 2004. (Haunted Kids Ser.). (Illus.). 144p. (J). (gr. 4-6). pap. (978-1-894877-54-1(3)) Lone Pine Publishing.

Thay, Edrick. Haunted Houses, Vol. 1. rev. ed. 2003. (Ghost Stories Ser.). (Illus.). 256p. (J). (gr. 4). pap. (978-1-894877-30-5(6)) Lone Pine Publishing.

Watkins, Graham. Ghosts & Poltergeists. 2005. (Unsolved Mysteries Ser.). (Illus.). 48p. (YA). (gr. 5-8). lib. bdg. 25.25 (978-0-8239-3563-5(9)) Rosen Publishing Group, Inc., The.

Wlodarski, Robert James & Nathan-Wlodarski, Anne. The Haunted Whaley House, Old Town, San Diego, California: A History & Guide to the Most Haunted House in America. 2nd ed. 2004. (Illus.). xxii, 196p. (J). (978-0-9649088-7-1(5)) G-Host Publishing.

Xlade, Chris. The Mystery of Haunted Houses, Set 1. 2002. (Can Science Solve? Ser.). (Illus.). 32p. (J). (gr. 4-7). pap. 7.50 (978-1-58810-456-4(7) , 91157) Heinemann Library.

HAUTZIG, ESTHER RUDOMIN

Holt, Rinehart and Winston Staff. The Endless Steppe. 3rd ed. 2002. pap., stu. ed. 13.20 (978-0-03-067528-7(6)) Holt, Rinehart & Winston.

—The Endless Steppe: With Connections. 3rd ed. 2002. 14.64 (978-0-03-067527-0(8)) Holt, Rinehart & Winston.

HAWAII

Adams, Colleen. Hawaii: The Aloha State. 2003. (Reading Room Collection). (Illus.). 24p. (J). lib. bdg. 18.75 (978-0-8239-3713-4(5)) Rosen Publishing Group, Inc., The.

Arita Vera. All Around the Islands. Moen Cabanting Ruth, illus. 2005. 24p. 12.95 (978-1-933067-09-4(8)) Mutual Publishing LLC.

Baunach, Ecomae. Island of Oahu. 2000. (Travel Book for Kids Ser.: No. 1). (Illus.). 32p. (J). (ps-3). pap. 8.95 (978-0-9651202-9-6(5)) Park Publishing.

—Islands of Kauai & Niiha. Baunach, Ecomae, illus. 2000. (Travel Book for Kids Ser.: No. 2). (Illus.). 28p. (J). (ps-3). pap. 8.95 (978-0-9651202-8-9(7)) Park Publishing.

—Maui & Hawaii Islands. Baunach, Ecomae, illus. 2000. (Travel Book for Kids Ser.: No. 3). (Illus.). 32p. (J). (ps-3). pap. 8.95 (978-0-9651202-7-2(9)) Park Publishing.

Bellamy, Fannie Lillian Miles. Fanning Island. 2006. (Illus.). 40p. (J). pap. 14.95 (***978-1-59663-509-8(6)*** , Castle Keep Pr.) Rock, James A. & Co. Pubs.

Bradley, Barbara. Hawaiian Kids Cook & Color Book. pap. 5.95 (978-0-930492-43-4(9)) Hawaiian Service, Inc.

Burnham, Brad. Kazumura Cave: The World's Longest Lava Tube. 2003. (Famous Caves of the World Ser.). (Illus.). 24p. (J). lib. bdg. 18.75 (978-0-8239-6261-7(X) , PowerKids Pr.) Rosen Publishing Group, Inc., The.

Doak, Robin S. Hawaii: The Aloha State. 2003. (World Almanac Library of the States). (Illus.). 48p. (J). (gr. 5 up). pap. 14.95 (978-0-8368-5320-9(2)); lib. bdg. 30.00 (978-0-8368-5149-6(8)) Stevens, Gareth Inc. (World Almanac Library).

Eyre, David L. By Wind, By Wave: An Introduction to Hawaii's Natural History. Boynton, David, photos by. 2000. (Illus.). 192p. (YA). (gr. 7-13). pap. 22.46 (978-1-57306-112-4(3)) Bess Pr., Inc.

Feinstein, Stephen. The Pacific States. 2006. (Regions of the USA Ser.). (Illus.). 56p. (J). (978-1-4109-2310-3(X)); pap. (978-1-4109-2318-9(5)) Steck-Vaughn.

Foran, Jill. A Guide to Hawaii. 2000. (American States Ser.). (Illus.). 32p. (J). (gr. 3-7). lib. bdg. 16.95 (978-1-930954-50-2(6)) Weigl Pubs., Inc.

Gaines, Ann. Hawaii. 2006. (It's My State! Ser.). (Illus.). 80p. (J). (gr. 3-6). lib. bdg. 29.93 (978-0-7614-1926-6(8) , Benchmark Bks.) Cavendish, Marshall Corp.

Gill, Shelley. Hawaii. Goto, Scott, illus. 2006. (J). pap. 6.95 (978-0-88106-297-7(9)); 32p. 16.95 (978-0-88106-296-0(0)) Charlesbridge Publishing, Inc.

Goh, Geok Yian. Uniquely Hawaii. 2004. (Heinemann State Studies). (Illus.). 48p. (J). pap. 8.50 (978-1-4034-4714-2(4)); lib. bdg. 27.07 (978-1-4034-4645-9(8)) Heinemann Library.

Goldberg, Jake. Hawaii. 1998. (Celebrate the States Ser.). (Illus.). 144p. (J). (gr. 4-8). lib. bdg. 37.07 (978-0-7614-0203-9(9) , Benchmark Bks.) Cavendish, Marshall Corp.

Goldberg, Jake & Hart, Joyce. Hawaii. 2nd ed. 2007. (Celebrate the States Ser.). (J). lib. bdg. 39.93 (978-0-7614-2349-2(4) , Benchmark Bks.) Cavendish, Marshall Corp.

Goldsberry, U'ilani. A Is for Aloha: A Hawaii Alphabet. Yee, Tammy, illus. 2005. (Discover America State by State Ser.). 40p. (J). (gr. k-5). 17.95 (978-1-58536-146-5(1)) Sleeping Bear Pr.

Green, Yuko. Story of Hawaii Coloring Book. 1998. (Illus.). 48p. (J). pap. 3.95 (978-0-486-40565-0(6)) Dover Pubns., Inc.

Guide to Hawaiian Style Origami for Keiki. 2001. (J). 7.99 (978-0-89610-331-3(5)) Island Heritage Publishing.

Hawaii. 2000. (Switched on Schoolhouse Ser.). (Illus.). (YA). (gr. 7-12). pap. 24.95 incl. cd-rom (978-0-7403-0263-3(9) , SOSHI) Alpha Omega Pubns., Inc.

Heinrichs, Ann. Hawaii. 2005. (Welcome to the USA Ser.). 40p. (J). (gr. 1-5). 27.07 (978-1-59296-374-4(9)) Child's World, Inc.

—Hawaii. 2003. (This Land Is Your Land Ser.). (Illus.). 48p. (J). (gr. 3 up). lib. bdg. 22.60 (978-0-7565-0346-8(9)) Compass Point Bks.

Hide & Seek in Hawaii 2. 2000. (Illus.). 32p. (J). bds. 9.95 (978-1-56647-345-3(4)) Booklines Hawaii, Ltd.

Hirschi, Ron. Swimming with Humuhumu: A Young Snorkeler's First Guide to Hawaiian Sea Life. Yee, Tammy, illus. 32p. (J). 14.99 (978-0-931548-67-3(5) , 25098-000) Island Heritage Publishing.

Ho'omaka'ika'i Staff. Explorations! Ho'omaka'ika'i. 2000. 165p. (J). pap. 15.93 (978-0-87336 053 1(2)) Kamehameha Schools Pr.

Ho'omaka'ika'i Staff of Kamehameha Schools. Explorations! Ho'Omaka'Ika'I. 3rd ed. 2003. (Illus.). 168p. (J). pap. 11.95 (978-0-87336-074-6(5)) Kamehameha Schools Pr.

Jansen, Marilyn. Amaryllis of Hawaii: Imaginations, Poetry, & Story. Jansen, Marilyn, illus. 5000th l.t. ed. 2004. (Illus.). 92p. (YA). 15.95 (978-0-9761070-0-2(7)) Jansen, Marilyn.

Johnston, Joyce. Hawaii. 2nd exp. rev. ed. (Hello U. S. A. Ser.). (Illus.). 84p. (J). (gr. 3-6). 2002. lib. bdg. 25.26 (978-0-8225-4056-4(8)); 2003. pap. 6.95 (978-0-8225-4152-3(1)) Lerner Publishing Group.

—Hawaii. 2001. (Illus.). 84p. (J). (ps-7). lib. bdg. 15.25 (978-0-613-89184-4(8)) Tandem Library Bks.

Juvik, James O., et al. Puke Palapala Aina o Hawaii na ka Haumana. Kawai'eaia, Keiki et al, trs. 2000. Orig. Title: Student Atlas of Hawai'i. (HAW., Illus.). 48p. 10.95 (978-1-57306-115-5(8)) Bess Pr., Inc.

—Student Atlas of Hawaii. 2000. (Illus.). 48p. (gr. 4-13). 9.95 (978-1-57306-049-3(6)) Bess Pr., Inc.

Keiki Calabash Coloring & Activity. 2002. (J). 4.99 (978-0-89610-332-0(3)) Island Heritage Publishing.

Keiki Discovery Hawaii: Color & Activity Book. 2001. (J). 4.99 (978-0-89610-458-7(3)); 5.99 (978-0-89610-345-0(5)) Island Heritage Publishing.

Keiki Discovery Kauai: Color & Activity Book. 2001. (J). 4.99 (978-0-89610-455-6(9)) Island Heritage Publishing.

Keiki Discovery Maui: Color & Activity Book. 2001. (J). 4.99 (978-0-89610-457-0(5)) Island Heritage Publishing.

Keiki Discovery Maui Color & Activity with Crayons. 2001. (Illus.). (J). 5.99 (978-0-89610-335-1(8)) Island Heritage Publishing.

Keiki Discovery Oahu: Color & Activity Book. 2001. (J). 4.99 (978-0-89610-456-3(7)); 5.99 (978-0-89610-338-2(2)) Island Heritage Publishing.

Kent, Deborah. Hawaii. 2007. (America the Beautiful, Third Ser.). 144p. (J). spiral bd. 38.00 (***978-0-531-18573-5(7)*** , Children's Pr.) Scholastic Library Publishing.

Kent, Deborah. Hawaii's Road to Statehood. 2004. (Cornerstones of Freedom Ser.). (Illus.). 48p. (J). 26.00 (978-0-516-24241-5(5) , Children's Pr.) Scholastic Library Publishing.

Knapp, Ron. Hawaii: A MyReportLinks.com Book. 2002. (States Ser.). (Illus.). 48p. (J). (gr. 4-10). lib. bdg. 25.26 (978-0-7660-5020-4(3) , MyReportLinks.com Bks.) Enslow Pubs., Inc.

Kummer, Patricia K. Hawaii. rev. ed. 2002. (One Nation Ser.). (Illus.). 48p. (J). (gr. 3-4). lib. bdg. 22.60 (978-0-7368-1235-1(0) , Bridgestone Bks.) Capstone Pr., Inc.

Lopes, Marilyn/Jansen. Amaryllis of Hawaii Big Coloring Book: Drawings of Hawaii to Color. 2007. (ENG & HAW.). (YA). pap. 5.00 (***978-0-9761070-5-7(8)*** Jansen, Marilyn.

—Amaryllis of Hawaii Pocket Coloring Book: Drawings of Hawaii to Color. 2007. (ENG & HAW.). (J). pap. 3.00 (***978-0-9761070-7-1(4)*** Jansen, Marilyn.

Markrich, Mike & Bourke, Bob. Hanauma Bay. Kanae, Billy, illus. (J). pap. 5.95 (978-0-9643421-0-1(3)) Ecology Comics.

Marsh, Carole. The Big Hawaii Reproducible Activity Book. 2001. (Carole Marsh Hawaii Bks.). (Illus.). 96p. (J). (gr. 2-6). pap., act. bk. ed. 9.95 (978-0-7933-9939-0(4)) Gallopade International.

—Hawaii Classic Christmas Trivia. 2002. (Carole Marsh Hawaii Bks.). (Illus.). 32p. (J). pap. 6.95 (978-0-635-01389-7(4) , 13894); lib. bdg. 21.95 (978-0-635-01390-3(8) , 13908) Gallopade International. (Marsh, Carole Bks.).

—Hawaii Current Events Projects: 30 Cool, Activities, Crafts, Experiments & More for Kids to Do to Learn about Your State! 2003. (Hawaii Experience Ser.). 32p. (gr. k-5). pap. 5.95 (978-0-635-02030-7(0) , Marsh, Carole Bks.) Gallopade International.

—The Hawaii Experience Pocket Guide. 2001. (Carole Marsh Hawaii Bks.). (Illus.). 96p. (J). (gr. 3-8). pap. 6.95 (978-0-7933-9910-9(6)) Gallopade International.

—Hawaii Geography Projects: 30 Cool, Activities, Crafts, Experiments & More for Kids to Do to Learn about Your State! 2003. (Hawaii Experience Ser.). 32p. (gr. k-5). pap. 5.95 (978-0-635-01830-4(6) , Marsh, Carole Bks.) Gallopade International.

—Hawaii Government Projects: 30 Cool, Activities, Crafts, Experiments & More for Kids to Do to Learn about Your State! 2003. (Hawaii Experience Ser.). 32p. (gr. k-5). pap. 5.95 (978-0-635-01930-1(2) , Marsh, Carole Bks.) Gallopade International.

—Hawaii Jeopardy. 2001. (Carole Marsh Hawaii Bks.). (Illus.). 32p. (J). (gr. 3-8). pap. 7.95 (978-0-7933-9794-5(4)) Gallopade International.

—Hawaii "Jography" A Fun Run Thru Our State! 2001. (Illus.). 32p. (J). (gr. 3-8). pap. 7.95 (978-0-7933-9823-2(1)) Gallopade International.

—Hawaii Millionaire: Game Book. 2001. (Carole Marsh Hawaii Bks.). (Illus.). 32p. (J). (gr. 3-8). pap., act. bk. ed. 9.95 (978-0-635-00038-5(5)) Gallopade International.

—Hawaii People Projects: 30 Cool, Activities, Crafts, Experiments & More for Kids to Do to Learn about Your State! 2003. (Hawaii Experience Ser.). 32p. (gr. k-5). pap. 5.95 (978-0-635-01980-6(9) , Marsh, Carole Bks.) Gallopade International.

—Hawaii Survivor: Game Book. 2001. (Carole Marsh Hawaii Bks.). (Illus.). 32p. (J). (gr. 3-8). pap., act. bk. ed. 9.95 (978-0-635-00532-8(8)) Gallopade International.

—Hawaii Symbols & Facts Projects: 30 Cool, Activities, Crafts, Experiments & More for Kids to Do to Learn about Your State! 2003. (Hawaii Experience Ser.). 32p. (gr. k-5). pap. 5.95 (978-0-635-01880-9(2) , Marsh, Carole Bks.) Gallopade International.

—My First Book about Hawaii. 2001. (Carole Marsh Hawaii Bks.). (Illus.). 32p. (J). (gr. k-4). pap. 7.95 (978-0-7933-9881-2(9)) Gallopade International.

—Who Wants to Be a Millionaire? 2001. (Carole Marsh Hawaii Bks.). lib. bdg. 29.95 (978-0-635-00039-2(3)) Gallopade International.

Mattern, Joanne. Mauna Loa. 2004. (Natures Greatest Hits Ser.). (SPA.). 24p. (J). (gr. 3-6). lib. bdg. 17.25 (978-0-8239-6877-0(4) , Buenas Letra) Rosen Publishing Group, Inc., The.

—Mauna Loa: World's Largest Active Volcano. 2002. (Reading Power Ser.). (Illus.). 24p. (J). (gr. 2). lib. bdg. 17.25 (978-0-8239-6014-9(5) , PowerKids Pr.) Rosen Publishing Group, Inc., The.

Mauna Loa: Individual Title Six-Packs. (On Deck en Espanol Ser.). (SPA.). 24p. (gr. 4-5). 35.00 (978-0-7578-6447-6(3)) Rigby Education.

McAuliffe, Emily. Hawaii: Facts & Symbols. 1999. (States & Their Symbols Ser.). (Illus.). 24p. (J). (gr. k-3). pap. 15.00 (978-0-531-12001-9(5) , Watts, Franklin) Scholastic Library Publishing.

—Hawaii Facts & Symbols. (States & Their Symbols Ser.). 24p. (J). 2000. (Illus.). (gr. 2-3). lib. bdg. 13.95 (978-0-7368-0375-5(0) , Bridgestone Bks.); 2003. lib. bdg. 19.93 (978-0-7368-2241-1(0)) Capstone Pr., Inc.

Moen Cabanting, Ruth, illus. 1-2-3 Waikiki Trolley. 2005. 20p. 4.75 (978-1-933067-06-3(3)) Beachhouse Publishing, LLC.

Murray, Julie. Hawaii. 2006. (Illus.). 32p. (J). (gr. 2-4). lib. bdg. 22.78 (978-1-59197-670-7(7) , Buddy Bks.) ABDO Publishing Co.

Nelson, Sharlene P. & Nelson, Ted W. Hawaii Volcanoes National Park. 1998. (True Bks.). (Illus.). 48p. (J). (gr. 3-5). 25.00 (978-0-516-20623-3(0) , Children's Pr.) Scholastic Library Publishing.

H
I

Neri, Penelope J. Hawaii. 2003. (From Sea to Shining Sea Ser.: 2). (Illus.). 80p. (J). (gr. 3-5). 30.50 (978-0-516-22383-4(6) , Children's Pr.) Scholastic Library Publishing.

Noland, Karen L. Friends of the Menehune. (J). 9.95 (978-0-9643674-0-1(8)) Kaukini Ranch Pr.

Petersen, David. Haleakala National Park. 2001. (National Parks Ser.). (Illus.). 48p. (J). (gr. 3-5). 25.00 (978-0-516-21666-9(X) , Children's Pr.) Scholastic Library Publishing.

—Haleakala National Park. 2001. (gr. 3-6). lib. bdg. 15.25 (978-0-613-54529-7(X)) Tandem Library Bks.

Rumford, James. Kahalaopuna: Ka U'i o Manoa. Rumford, James, illus. 2001. (HAW., Illus.). 32p. (J). (gr. 2-7). 12.95 (978-1-891839-03-0(9)) Manoa Pr.

—Kahalaopuna: The Beauty of Manoa. Rumford, James, illus. 2001. (Illus.). 32p. (J). (gr. 2-7). 12.95 (978-1-891839-02-3(0)) Manoa Pr.

Shofner, Shawndra. Hawaii. 2008. (J). ***978-1-58341-636-5(6)** , Creative Education) Creative Co., The.

Staub, Frank. Children of Hawaii. 1998. (World's Children Ser.). (Illus.). 40p. (J). (gr. 3-6). lib. bdg. 23.93 (978-1-57505-253-3(9) , Carolrhoda Bks.) Lerner Publishing Group.

Sullivan, Jody. Hawaii. 2003. (Land of Liberty Ser.). (Illus.). 64p. (J). (gr. 3-4). lib. bdg. 23.93 (978-0-7368-1579-6(1) , Bridgestone Bks.) Capstone Pr., Inc.

Taylor-Butler, Christine. Hawaii. 2007. (Rookie Read-about' Geography: States Ser.). 32p. (J). pap. 5.95 (***978-0-531-16812-7(3));** (Illus.). (gr. 1-2). 20.50 (978-0-531-12571-7(8)) Scholastic Library Publishing. (Children's Pr.).

Thomas, William. Hawaii. 2006. (Portraits of the States Ser.). (J). pap. (978-0-8368-4716-1(4)); lib. bdg. (978-0-8368-4699-7(0)) Stevens, Gareth Inc.

Voyagers. 2005. 160p. 29.95 (978-0-943357-04-1(7)) Kawainui Pr.

Webster, Christine. Mauna Loa. (Natural Wonders of the U. S. A. Ser.). (Illus.). 32p. (J). 2004. pap. 7.95 (978-1-59036-162-7(8)); 2003. lib. bdg. 18.20 (978-1-59036-040-8(0)) Weigl Pubs., Inc.

Yee, T. Keiki Discovery Land of Aloha: Color & Activity Book. 2001. (J). pap. 5.99 (978-0-89610-433-4(8)) Island Heritage Publishing.

—Keiki Discovery Land of Aloha Color & Activity Book. 2002. (J). pap. 5.99 (978-0-89610-430-3(3)) Island Heritage Publishing.

HAWAII—FICTION

Advantage Publishers Group & Saidens, Amy. Surfer Girl Sticker Book. 2007. (Illus.). 24p. (J). 14.95 (978-1-59223-632-9(4) , Silver Dolphin Bks.) Advantage Pubs. Group.

Aloha Bear - Footprint Detective. 2002. (J). pap. 8.99 (978-0-89610-290-3(4)) Island Heritage Publishing.

Aloha Potter! Evaluation Guide: Evaluation Guide. 2006. (J). (978-1-55942-397-7(8)) Marsh Media.

Asato, Dennis. A Dolphin Day in Hawaii. 2001. (Illus.). 50p. (J). (ps-1). pap. 9.95 (978-0-9702618-2-3(9)) Anoai Pr.

—A Dolphin Day in Hawaii. Asato, Dennis, illus. l.t. ed. 1999. (Illus.). 50p. (J). (ps-1). 12.00 (978-0-9653971-8-6(1)) Anoai Pr.

Ay, Joy Mitsu. Paniolo Pete & the Wild Pua'a. Pratt, Christine Joy, illus. 2001. (J). 8.99 (978-0-89610-348-1(X)) Island Heritage Publishing.

Bair, Katie, et al. NHS Hawaii Pocket Manga, Vol. 1. 2006. 144p. (YA). pap. 12.95 (978-0-9768043-1-4(X)) Antarctic Pr., Inc.

Bates, Gale. The Jewel in the Forest. Hinds McCarty, Carole, illus. 2000. (J). 10.99 (978-0-89610-440-2(0)) Island Heritage Publishing.

Beamer, Winona Desha & Beamer-Trapp, Kaliko. Pua Polu: The Pretty Blue Hawaiian Flower. Loebel-Fried, Caren Keala, illus. 2005. (HAW & ENG.). 36p. (J). audio compact disk 14.95 (978-1-58178-041-3(9)) Bishop Museum Pr.

Berardy, Lloyd, 1st. A Tropical Bear in Hawaii Goes Underwater. 2006. (J). 12.95 (978-1-4276-0212-1(3)) Aardvark Global Publishing.

Bikle, Edie. Kapono & the Turtle. Hennings-Chilton, Connie, illus. 2001. (J). 10.99 (978-0-89610-199-9(1)) Island Heritage Publishing.

Blake-Brekke, Carri. Billy Bully Bug: Learns a Lesson in Hawaii. Melton, Jodi, illus. 2003. (Mrs. B's Story Time... With a Twist! Ser.). 20p. (J). pap. 11.95 incl. audio compact disk (978-0-9720549-2-8(8)) Mom's Pride Enterprises.

Bowen, Lance, illus. Keiki's First Word Book. 2004. (HAW & ENG.). 32p. (J). pap. 10.95 (978-0-9729905-5-4(0)) Beachhouse Publishing, LLC.

Bridgman, C. A. Santa's Hawaiian Vacation. (J). 14.95 (978-0-681-32827-3(4)) Booklines Hawaii, Ltd.

Brouwer, Sigmund. The Volcano of Doom. 2002. (Accidental Detectives). 144p. (J). pap. 5.99 (978-0-7642-2564-2(2)) Bethany Hse. Pubs.

—Volcano of Doom. 2002. (gr. 3-6). lib. bdg. 14.15 (978-0-613-87242-3(8)) Tandem Library Bks.

Carolan. Goodnight Hawaiian Moon. 2006. 32p. 17.95 (***978-0-9715333-2-5(6))** Banana Patch Pr.

Carolan, Joanna F., illus. Ten Days in Hawaii: A Counting Book. l.t. ed. 2002. 32p. (J). 16.95 (978-0-9715333-4-9(2)) Banana Patch Pr.

Chanànie, Gloria. Fearful Frannie & Her Fateful Trip to Maui. 2003. 57p. 9.95 (978-1-4137-0162-3(0)) PublishAmerica, Inc.

Ching, Tokie. Girl's Day in Hawaii with Yuki Chan. 2006. 40p. (J). 12.95 (***978-1-56647-820-5(0))** Mutual Publishing LLC.

Collins Malia. Pele & Poliahu. Peterson Kathleen, illus. 2005. 24p. 14.95 (978-1-933067-13-1(6)) Mutual Publishing LLC.

Culbertson, Jan E. The Legend of the Lost Tiki. 2006. 95p. (YA). pap. 13.95 (978-1-58909-315-7(1)) Bookstand Publishing.

Dilz, Ric. My Grandma Could do Anything in Hawaii. 2006. (J). 7.95 (***978-0-9758704-2-6(4))** Rein Designs, Inc.

Disney Press Staff. Lilo & Stitch. 2nd rev. ed. 2006. (Illus.). 48p. (gr. 1-4). pap. 3.99 (978-1-4231-0141-3(3)) Disney Pr.

Donivee, Martin. Snow White & the Seven Menehune. 2004. (Illus.). 44p. 9.95 (978-1-57306-235-0(9)) Bess Pr., Inc.

Duckett, Brenda. The Giggling Purple Dragon. 2006. 84p. pap. 9.99 (978-1-4116-3826-6(3)) Lulu.com.

Ebie, Mora. Going to the Zoo in Hawaii. 2006. (Illus.). 28p. (J). 10.95 (978-1-56647-790-1(5)) Mutual Publishing LLC.

Endicott, Jodi. I Had a Dollar in Hawaii: A Story of One Dollar That Traveled Hawaii. Loffel, Hans & Nehmad, Debbie, illus. 1999. 32p. (J). (ps-3). 8.95 (978-0-9621280-7-3(4)) Words & Pictures Publishing, Inc.

Entz, Susan & Galarza, Sheri. Menehune Mischief. Hale, Bruce, illus. 1999. (Hawaiian Values Ser.: Vol. 5). 24p. (J). (ps-2). 5.95 (978-1-57306-091-2(7)) Bess Pr., Inc.

—The Mystery of the Shark & the Poi. Hale, Bruce, illus. 1999. (Hawaiian Values Ser.: Vol. 1). 24p. (J). (ps-2). 5.95 (978-1-57306-087-5(9)) Bess Pr., Inc.

Farley, Terri. The Shining Stallion. 2007. (Phantom Stallion: Wild Horse Island Ser.: No. 2). 224p. (J). (gr. 5 up). pap. 4.99 (***978-0-06-081543-1(4)** , Harper Trophy) HarperCollins Pubs.

Gamble, Adam. Good Night Hawaii. Veno, Joe, illus. 2007. (Good Night Our World Ser.). 20p. (J). bds. 9.95 (***978-1-60219-007-8(0))** Our World of Books.

George, Jean Craighead. Dear Katie, the Volcano Is a Girl. 32p. (J). pap. (978-0-7868-1178-6(1)) Hyperion Bks. for Children.

Gillespie, Jane. S Went Surfing: An ABC Book for Keiki. Cabanting, Ruth, illus. 2004. 32p. (J). 12.95 (978-1-933067-00-1(4)) Beachhouse Publishing, LLC.

Gleasner, Diana C. Popoki's Incredible Adventure at the Volcano. Winton, Andrea E., illus. 1999. (J). (978-0-9651185-5-2(X)) Gleasner, Bill & Diana Inc.

Goldsberry, U'i. The Shark Man of Hana. Chang, Roy, illus. 2004. (HAW.). 32p. (J). 14.95 (978-1-933067-01-8(2)) Beachhouse Publishing, LLC.

Golembe, Carla. The Story of Hula. 2004. (Illus.). 32p. (J). 16.95 incl. audio compact disk (978-1-57306-185-8(9)) Bess Pr., Inc.

Gunn, Robin Jones. Island Dreamer. rev. ed. 1999. (Christy Miller Ser.: Bk. 5). 176p. (J). (gr. 7-12). pap. 6.99 (978-1-56179-718-9(9)) Bethany Hse. Pubs.

—Whispers. 2004. (Glenbrooke Ser.: Bk. 2). 288p. pap. 12.99 (978-1-59052-192-2(7) , Multnomah) WaterBrook Pr.

Gutman, Dan. The Million Dollar Putt. 2006. 176p. (gr. 3-7). 15.99 (978-0-7868-3641-3(5)) Hyperion Bks. for Children.

Gutman, Dan. Million Dollar Putt. 2007. 176p. (gr. 3-7). pap. 5.99 (***978-0-7868-3642-0(3))** Hyperion Pr.

Hale, Chaika P. Mama Is Hapai. Asato, Dennis, illus. l.t. ed. 1998. 32p. (J). (gr. 1-6). 14.00 (978-0-9653971-2-4(2)) Anoai Pr.

Hamilton, Bethany & Bundschuh, Rick. Clash. 2007. (Soul Surfer#8482; Ser.). (Illus.). 144p. (J). pap. 6.99 (978-0-310-71222-0(X)) Zonderkidz.

Hamilton, Elizabeth L. Date with Responsibility. 2004. (Character-in-Action Ser.: No. 2). (Illus.). 384p. (YA). per. 19.95 (978-0-9713749-0-4(2) , Character-in-Action) Quiet Impact, Inc.

Han, C. C. Ponopono. 2002. pap. 8.99 (978-0-89610-151-7(7)) Island Heritage Publishing.

Harcourt School Publishers Staff. The World under the Water: Take-Home Book. 1999. (Collections Ser.). (Illus.). (J). pap. 1.90 (978-0-15-317235-9(5)) Harcourt Schl. Pubs.

Harlow, Joan Hiatt. Thunder from the Sea. 2005. 243p. (J). (gr. 3-7). per. 12.04 (978-0-606-33897-4(7)) Tandem Library Bks.

Hayashi, Leslie Ann. Fables from the Sea. Bishop, Kathleen Wong, illus. 2000. (Kolowalu Bks.). 40p. (ps-5). 14.95 (978-0-8248-2224-8(2) , Kolowalu Bk.) Univ. of Hawaii Pr.

Holub, Joan. Lydia & the Island Kingdom: A Story Based on the Real Life of Princess Liliuokalani of Hawaii. Aleshina, Nonna, illus. 2007. (Young Princesses Around the World Ser.). 48p. (J). pap. 3.99 (***978-0-689-87199-3(6)** , Aladdin) Simon & Schuster Children's Publishing.

Hopkins, Jane. Diving for Colors in Hawaii: A Color Identification Book for Keiki. Bosgra, Johann, illus. 2003. 18p. (J). bds. 6.95 (978-0-9729905-1-6(8)) Beachhouse Publishing, LLC.

—Diving for Numbers in Hawaii. Bosgra, Johann, illus. 2003. 20p. (J). bds. 6.95 (978-0-9729905-0-9(X)) Beachhouse Publishing, LLC.

Hossack, Sylvie A. Green Mango Magic. 1998. (Avon Camelot Bks.). 128p. (J). (gr. 3-7). 14.00 (978-0-380-97613-3(7)) HarperCollins Pubs.

Hula Girl. 2000. (YA). 3.49 (978-0-89610-391-7(9)) Island Heritage Publishing.

Ide, Laurie Shimizu. Okazu at the Zoo. Kanekuni, Daniel, illus. 2006. (J). (978-1-56647-776-5(X)) Mutual Publishing LLC.

Kapono, Henry. A Beautiful Hawaiian Day. Szabo, Susan, illus. 2000. 32p. (J). bds. 9.95 (978-1-56647-346-0(2)) Booklines Hawaii, LLC.

Keene, Carolyn. Mystery on Maui. 1998. (Nancy Drew Mystery Stories: No. 143). (J). (gr. 3-6). (978-0-606-13645-7(2)) Tandem Library Bks.

Keene, Carolyn. Trade Wind Danger. 2005. 148p. (J). lib. bdg. 15.00 (***978-1-4242-0243-0(4))** Fitzgerald Bks.

Kelly, Jack. Keoni's Dream. 1999. (J). 17.95 (978-0-9662777-1-5(6)) Pleiades Publishing.

Keoni the Good Menehune. 2005. (Illus.). 28p. (J). (gr. 1-2). 14.95 (978-0-9764474-0-5(1)) Kaimanu Prodns., Ltd.

Kono, Erin Eitter. Hula Lullaby. 2005. (Illus.). 32p. (J). (ps-1). 15.99 (978-0-316-73591-9(4)) Little Brown & Co.

Kulling, Monica. Go, Stitch, Go! Shimabukuro, Denise & Disney Storybook Artists Staff, illus. 2002. (Step into Reading Ser.). 32p. (J). (ps-1). pap. 3.99 (978-0-7364-1350-3(2) , RH/Disney) Random Hse. Children's Bks.

—Go, Stitch, Go. 2002. (ps-2). lib. bdg. 11.80 (978-0-613-50612-0(X)) Tandem Library Bks.

Lantz, Frances L. Hawaii Five-Go! 2003. (gr. 3-6). lib. bdg. 13.00 (978-0-613-81422-5(3)) Tandem Library Bks.

Levitin, Sonia. Strange Relations. 2007. 304p. (gr. 7). (J). 15.99 (978-0-375-83751-7(5)); (YA). lib. bdg. 18.99 (978-0-375-93751-4(X)) Random Hse. Children's Bks. (Knopf Bks. for Young Readers).

Lin, Grace. Olvina Swims. rev. ed. 2007. (Illus.). 32p. (J). (ps-2). 16.95 (978-0-8050-7661-5(1)) Holt, Henry & Co.

The Little Hawaiian Rainbow. 2000. (J). 8.99 (978-0-89610-353-5(6)) Island Heritage Publishing.

Lorimer, Janet. Tug-of-War: Set 2. 2002. 32p. (YA). 2.95 (978-1-56254-423-2(3) , SP 4233) Saddleback Educational Publishing.

Matsuura, Richard & Matsuura, Ruth. Ali'i Kai. Chao, Linus, illus. (J). 7.95 (978-1-887916-05-9(9)) Orchid Isle Publishing Co.

—Hawaiian Christmas Story. Chao, Linus, illus. (J). 8.95 (978-1-887916-01-1(6)) Orchid Isle Publishing Co.

Mazer, Harry. A Boy at War: A Novel of Pearl Harbor. 2002. (gr. 3-6). lib. bdg. 13.00 (978-0-613-65106-6(5)) Tandem Library Bks.

McCann, Jesse Leon. Scooby-Doo & the Tiki's Curse. 2004. (Scooby-Doo Ser.). (Illus.). 24p. (J). 3.50 (978-0-439-54604-1(4) , Scholastic Paperbacks) Scholastic, Inc.

McDermott, Gerald. Pig-Boy: A Trickster Tale from Hawaii. 2008. (J). (***978-0-15-216590-1(8))** Harcourt Trade Pubs.

McGrath, E. J. The Magic of Believing. 2002. pap. 5.99 (978-0-89610-200-2(9)) Island Heritage Publishing.

McLaren, Clemence. Dance for the Aina. 2003. 160p. 9.95 (978-1-57306-151-3(4)) Bess Pr., Inc.

Momi Tropical Water Hide & Seek. 2002. (J). 8.99 (978-0-89610-349-8(8)) Island Heritage Publishing.

Moran, Edna Cabcabin, illus. & retold by. The Sleeping Giant: A Tale from Kauai. Moran, Edna Cabcabin, retold by. 2006. (J). (978-1-933067-20-9(9)) Beachhouse Publishing, LLC.

Murakami, Jon & Yeh, Phil. The Winged Tiger & the Dragons of Hawaii. 2005. 48p. pap. 11.95 (978-0-9755635-0-2(5)) Eastland Studios.

Myers, Tim & Arakaki, Daryl. Let's Call Him Lau-Wiliwili-Humuhumu-Nukunuku-Nukunuku-Apua'a-'Oi'Oi. 2005. (Illus.). 24p. (J). 16.95 incl. cd-rom (978-1-57306-252-7(9)) Bess Pr., Inc.

Nunes, Shiho S. The Power of the Stone. Kane, Herb Kawainui, illus. 2002. mass mkt. 4.99 (978-0-89610-283-5(1)) Island Heritage Publishing.

Omoto, Gail. Kai Gets the Point. 2006. (J). 16.95 (978-1-933835-05-1(2)) Partners in Development.

Osborne, Mary Pope. High Tide in Hawaii. Murdocca, Sal, illus. 2003. (Magic Tree House Ser.: No. 28). 96p. (J). (gr. k-3). lib. bdg. 11.99 (978-0-375-90616-9(9)); (gr. 1-4). pap. 3.99 (978-0-375-80616-2(4)) Random Hse. Children's Bks. (Random Hse. Bks. for Young Readers).

—High Tide in Hawaii. 2003. (Magic Tree House Ser.: No. 28). (J). (gr. k-3). lib. bdg. 11.80 (978-0-613-62386-5(X)) Tandem Library Bks.

Park, Barbara. Junie B., First Grader: Aloha-Ha-Ha! Brunkus, Denise, illus. 2007. (Junie B. Jones Ser.: No. 26). 128p. (J). (gr. 1-4). 4.99 (978-0-375-83404-2(4) , Random Hse. Bks. for Young Readers) Random Hse. Children's Bks.

—Junie B., First Grader: Aloha-Ha-Ha! 2006. (Junie B. Jones Ser.: No. 26). (Illus.). 128p. (J). (gr. k-3). lib. bdg. 13.95 (978-0-375-93403-2(0)); (gr. 2-5). 11.95 (978-0-375-83403-5(6)) Random Hse. Children's Bks. (Random Hse. Bks. for Young Readers).

Pike, Christopher, pseud. Bury Me Deep. 2001. (gr. 7-12). lib. bdg. 14.15 (978-0-613-74176-7(5)); (J). 12.64 (978-0-606-21093-5(8)) Tandem Library Bks.

Random House Books for Young Readers Staff, ed. Hawaiian Shirt. 1998. (J). pap. 3.25 (978-0-679-89413-1(6) , Random Hse. Bks. for Young Readers) Random Hse. Children's Bks.

Richardson, Faith. Angel Walker. 2003. Orig. Title: The Sea, the Song & the Trumpetfish. (Illus.). 172p. (J). 19.95 (978-0-9744989-2-8(0)); pap. 12.95 (978-0-9744989-3-5(9)) Fox Song Bks.

Riley, Judi. When I Am Quiet on Maui. 2005. 40p. 12.95 (***978-0-9740582-1-4(1))** Tiki Tales.

Riley, Judi. When I Am Quiet on Oahu. 2006. 40p. (gr. 1-2). 12.95 (978-0-9740582-2-1(X)) Tiki Tales.

Robinson, Don Leonard, illus. G Is for Gecko: An Alphabet Adventure in Hawaii. 2006. (J). (***978-1-933067-18-6(7))** Beachhouse Publishing, LLC.

Robison, Dan, Jr. Kimo's Escape: The Story of a Hawaiian Boy Who Learns to Believe in Himself. 2005. 100p. (J). per. 19.95 (978-0-922993-28-4(9)) Marquette Bks., LLC.

The Royal Waker Upper. 2003. (J). 10.99 (978-0-89610-992-6(5)) Island Heritage Publishing.

Rumford, James. Dog-of-the-Sea-Waves. 2004. (ENG & HAW., Illus.). 48p. (J). (gr. k-3). tchr. ed. 16.00 (978-0-618-35611-9(8)) Houghton Mifflin Co. Trade & Reference Div.

Salisbury, Graham. House of the Red Fish. 2006. 304p. (gr. 7). (J). 16.95 (978-0-385-73121-8(3)); (YA). lib. bdg. 18.99 (978-0-385-90145-1(3)) Random Hse. Children's Bks. (Lamb, Wendy).

—Island Boyz: Short Stories. 2003. (gr. 5-8). lib. bdg. 14.15 (978-0-613-72335-0(X)) Tandem Library Bks.

—Jungle Dogs. unabr. ed. 2000. (YA). (gr. 5 up). pap., stu. ed. 59.95 incl. audio (978-0-7887-4336-8(8) , 41131) Recorded Bks., LLC.

—Jungle Dogs. 1999. 11.64 (978-0-606-17837-2(6)) Tandem Library Bks.

—Lord of the Deep. braille ed. 2003. (J). (gr. 2). spiral bd. (978-0-616-15872-2(6)) Canadian National Institute for the Blind/Institut National Canadien pour les Aveugles.

—Lord of the Deep. 2003. 192p. (J). (gr. 5). pap. 5.99 (978-0-440-22911-7(1) , Laurel Leaf) Random Hse. Children's Bks.

—Lord of the Deep. 2003. (gr. 5-8). lib. bdg. 13.55 (978-0-613-61296-8(5)) Tandem Library Bks.

—Lord of the Deep: A Novel. 2006. 182p. (J). (gr. 6-10). reprint ed. 16.00 (***978-1-4223-5841-2(0))** DIANE Publishing Co.

—Shark Bait. 1999. (978-0-606-16449-8(9)) Tandem Library Bks.

—Under the Blood-Red Sun. 2005. 272p. (YA). (gr. 7-10). pap. 6.50 (978-0-553-49487-7(2) , Laurel Leaf) Random Hse. Children's Bks.

Samantha's Hawaii Adventure. 1998. (Illus.). 2p. (J). (ps-1). 15.00 (978-1-888074-87-1(6)) Pockets of Learning.

Samuels, Barbara & Dorling Kindersley Publishing Staff. Aloha, Dolores. 2000. (Melanie Kroupa Bks.). (Illus.). 32p. (J). (ps-2). 15.95 (978-0-7894-2508-9(4)) Dorling Kindersley Publishing, Inc.

Seashore Touch & See Hi? 2004. (J). 8.99 (978-0-89610-999-5(2)) Island Heritage Publishing.

Skurzynski, Gloria & Ferguson, Alane. Rage of Fire. (J). (gr. 3-7). 2001. (Mysteries in Our National Parks Ser.). 160p. pap. 5.95 (978-0-7922-7653-1(1)); 1999. (National Parks Mysteries Ser.: No. 2). (Illus.). 164p. 15.95 (978-0-7922-7035-5(5)) National Geographic Society. (National Geographic Children's Bks.).

Spradlin, Michael P. Spy Goddess, Book Two: to Hawaii, with Love. 2008. (Spy Goddess Ser.). 288p. (J). pap. 6.99 (***978-0-06-059412-1(8)** , HarperTeen) HarperCollins Pubs.

Spradlin, Michael P. To Hawaii, with Love. 2006. (Spy Goddess Ser.). (Illus.). 208p. (J). lib. bdg. 16.89 (978-0-06-059411-4(X)); (YA). 15.99 (978-0-06-059410-7(1)) HarperCollins Pubs.

Steele, Margaret. Wuz Da Nite Befo: A Pidgin Christmas Story in Hawaii. Chang, Roy, illus. 2005. 24p. 10.95 (978-1-56647-750-5(6)) Mutual Publishing LLC.

Stuefloten, Helen. There's A Giant in the Garden. Janguay, Patricia, illus. l.t. ed. 2006. 35p. (J). per. 11.99 (978-1-59879-161-7(3)) Lifevest Publishing, Inc.

Suzuki, Genevieve A. The Original Poi Cats on Oahu. 2005. 40p. 13.95 (978-1-56647-718-5(2)) Mutual Publishing LLC.

Sweeney, Jacqueline. Aloha! 2002. (We Can Read! Ser.). (Illus.). 32p. (J). 21.36 (978-0-7614-1510-7(6) , Benchmark Bks.) Cavendish, Marshall Corp.

—Lava. Hart, G. K. & Hart, Vikki, illus. Hart, G. K. & Hart, Vikki, photos by. 2002. (We Can Read! Ser.). 32p. (J). 21.36 (978-0-7614-1511-4(4) , Benchmark Bks.) Cavendish, Marshall Corp.

—Little Honu. Hart, G. K. & Hart, Vikki, illus. Hart, G. K. & Hart, Vikki, photos by. 2002. (We Can Read! Ser.). 32p. (J). 21.36 (978-0-7614-1512-1(2) , Benchmark Bks.) Cavendish, Marshall Corp.

Swish Swish Hawaiian Fish. 2002. per. 6.99 (978-0-89610-145-6(2)) Island Heritage Publishing.

Tackett, Mike. Holoholo I Hawaii. 2007. 24p. (J). pap. 5.95 (978-1-56647-791-8(3)) Mutual Publishing LLC.

Talley, Linda. Aloha Potter! - hardcover Book. Chase, Andra, illus. 2004. 30p. (J). (978-1-55942-200-0(9)) Marsh Media.

Thorpe, Kiki. Lilo & Stitch: The Junior Novelization. 2002. (ps-2). lib. bdg. 13.00 (978-0-613-50630-4(8)) Tandem Library Bks.

Toki, Wilfred. Grandpa, What's a Humuhumu? Toki, Wilfred, illus. Hoover, John, photos by. 2004. (Illus.). 64p. (J). pap. 8.95 (978-0-9729905-9-2(3)) Beachhouse Publishing, LLC.

—Moku & the Heoe of Waimea. Toki, Wilfred, illus. 2004. (Illus.). 32p. (J). 12.95 (978-0-9729905-7-8(7)) Beachhouse Publishing, LLC.

Tokyopop Staff, creator. Contents under Pressure, Vol. 3. 2005. (Lilo & Stitch Ser.). (Illus.). 89p. (gr. 3-7). pap., pap. 7.99 (978-1-59532-069-8(5) , Tokyopop Kids) TOKYOPOP, Inc.

Tutu Nene - Hawaiian Mother Goose Rhymes. 2004. (J). audio compact disk 14.99 (978-0-931548-60-4(8)) Island Heritage Publishing.

Vigil-Pion, Evangelina. Marina's Muumuu/ el muumuu de Marina. Torrecilla, Pablo, illus. 2001. Tr. of Muumuu de Marina. (ENG & SPA.). 32p. (J). (ps-3). 14.95 (978-1-55885-350-8(2) , Piñata Books) Arte Publico Pr.

Villanueva, Leonard. Kaipo & the Mighty Ahi. Villanueva, Leonard, illus. 2004. (Illus.). (J). 14.95 (978-0-9729905-6-1(9)) Beachhouse Publishing, LLC.

Wallace, Bill. Aloha Summer. 2000. (J). 10.64 (978-0-606-19487-7(8)) Tandem Library Bks.

Westerman, Rob. The Legend of Kalikimaka: Alohalani, Kalikimaka Auntie. Tahleh, Eleykaa, illus. 2003. 32p. (J). 12.95 (978-0-9761992-0-5(3)) Gold Boy Music/Pubn.

Williams, Laura E. Torch Fishing with the Sun. Broeck, Fabricio Vanden, illus. 2003. 32p. (J). (gr. 4-6). 15.95 (978-1-56397-685-8(4)) Boyds Mills Pr.

Winkler, Henry & Oliver, Lin. Summer School! What Genius Thought That Up? 2006. (Hank Zipzer Ser.: No. 8). (J). (gr. 3-8). 24.21 (978-1-59961-107-5(4)) Spotlight.

—Summer School! What Genius Thought That Up? 2005. (Hank Zipzer Ser.: No. 8). (Illus.). 157p. (J). (ps-7). per. 11.64 (978-0-606-33097-8(6)) Tandem Library Bks.

Yamanaka, Lois-Ann. The Heart's Language. Jasinski, Aaron, illus. 2005. 32p. (ps-3). 15.99 (978-0-7868-1848-8(4)) Hyperion Bks. for Children.

—Name Me Nobody. 2000. 240p. (gr. 8-17). pap. 5.99 (978-0-7868-1466-4(7)) Disney Pr.

—Name Me Nobody. 2000. (gr. 7-12). lib. bdg. 14.15 (978-0-613-31521-0(9)) Tandem Library Bks.

Yee, T. Leilani's Hula. 2002. (J). pap. 3.99 (978-0-89610-379-5(X)) Island Heritage Publishing.

Yeh, Julie. Poppie's Adventures: Serpents in Paradise. Hsu, Jack, illus. 2003. 48p. (J). per. (978-0-9742386-0-9(0)) Way Out Comics.

HAWAII—HISTORY

Crouch, Howard E. Brother Dutton of Molokai. 2000. (Illus.). 160p. (J). 10.95 (978-0-9606330-6-7(5)) Damien-Dutton Society for Leprosy Aid, Inc.

El estado de Hawai 21: Leveled Books. 2001. (McGraw-Hill. Lectura Ser.). (ENG & SPA.). (gr. 1 up). (978-0-02-187998-4(2)) Macmillan/McGraw-Hill Schl. Div.

Hazlett, Richard W. Puuhonua o Honaunau: A Place of Refuge. Hazlett, Richard W., illus. 2nd ed. 1998. (Illus.). 74p. (J). (gr. 3-8). reprint ed. pap. 3.95 (978-0-940295-17-9(2)) Hawaii Natural History Assn.

Holm, Barbara. A Visit to Hawaii. Ingram, Anne, illus. 2005. 32p. (J). pap. 5.95 (978-0-9772200-0-7(1)) Visit to Hawaii, A.

Linnea, Sharon. Princess Ka'iulani: Hope of a Nation, Heart of a People. 1999. (Women of Spirit Ser.). (Illus.). 242p. (J). (gr. 5-9). 18.00 (978-0-8028-5145-1(2)) Eerdmans, William B. Publishing Co.

Marsh, Carole. Hawaii History Projects: 30 Cool, Activities, Crafts, Experiments & More for Kids to Do to Learn about Your State! 2003. (Hawaii Experience Ser.). 32p. (gr. k-5). pap. 5.95 (978-0-635-01780-2(6) , Marsh, Carole Bks.) Gallopade International.

—My First Pocket Guide Hawaii. 2000. (Hawaii Experience! Ser.). (Illus.). 96p. (J). (gr. 3-8). 12.95 (978-0-635-01301-9(0) , 13010) Gallopade International.

McDonnell, Peter. The Last Princess. 2005. (Illus.). 16p. ***978-0-7367-2910-9(0)*** Zaner-Bloser, Inc.

Obregon, Jose M. Hawaii/Hawai. 2005. (Bilingual Library of the United States of America: Set 1). (ENG & SPA., Illus.). 32p. (J). (ps-k). lib. bdg. 22.50 (978-1-4042-3076-7(9) , Buenas Letra) Rosen Publishing Group, Inc., The.

Quasha, Jennifer. How to Draw Hawaiis Sights & Symbols. 2002. (Kids Guide to Drawing America Ser.). 32p. (J). lib. bdg. 25.25 (978-0-8239-6067-5(6) , PowerKids Pr.) Rosen Publishing Group, Inc., The.

Rayson, Ann. Modern History of Hawai'i. 2004. (Illus.). 304p. lib. bdg. (978-1-57306-209-1(X)) Bess Pr., Inc.

Sherman, Josepha. Queen Lydia Liliuokalani, Last Ruler of Hawaii. 2004. (On My Own Biography Ser.). (J). lib. bdg. 22.60 (978-1-57505-650-0(X) , Carolrhoda Bks.) Lerner Publishing Group, Inc.

Wade, Mary Dodson. Tsunami: Monster Waves. 2002. (American Disasters Ser.). (Illus.). 64p. (J). (ps-10). lib. bdg. 23.93 (978-0-7660-1786-3(9)) Enslow Pubs., Inc.

HAWAII—HISTORY—FICTION

Frederick, Heather Vogel. The Education of Patience Goodspeed. 2006. (Illus.). 320p. (J). reprint ed. pap. 5.99 (978-1-4169-1394-8(7) , Aladdin) Simon & Schuster Children's Publishing.

Fredericks, Anthony D. The Tsunami Quilt: Grandfather's Story. Yee, Tammy, illus. rev. ed. 2007. 40p. (J). 17.95 ***(978-1-58536-313-1(8))*** Sleeping Bear Pr.

Hostetter, Joyce. Healing Water. 2008. (YA). ***(978-1-59078-514-0(2)*** , Calkins Creek) Boyds Mills Pr.

Robison, Dan. Death Chant: Kimo's Battle with the Shamanic Forces. 2006. 194p. (J). pap. (978-0-922993-52-9(1)) Marquette Bks., LLC.

Robison, Dan. Kimo's Legacy: The Battle to Unite Hawaii. 2007. 220p. (J). per. 22.95 ***(978-0-922993-78-9(5))*** Marquette Bks., LLC.

Rumford, James. Dog-of-the-Sea-Waves. 2004. (ENG & HAW., Illus.). 48p. (J). (gr. k-3). tchr. ed. 16.00 (978-0-618-35611-9(8)) Houghton Mifflin Co. Trade & Reference Div.

—When Silver Needles Swam: The Story of Tutu's Quilt. 1998. (ENG & HAW., Illus.). 30p. (J). (gr. 1-6). 10.95 (978-1-891839-00-9(4)) Manoa Pr.

Salisbury, Graham. House of the Red Fish. 2008. 304p. (YA). (gr. 7). mass mkt. 6.50 ***(978-0-440-23838-6(2)*** , Laurel Leaf) Random Hse. Children's Bks.

—Night of the Howling Dogs. 2007. 208p. (J). (gr. 3-7). 16.99 ***(978-0-385-73122-5(1));*** lib. bdg. 19.99 ***(978-0-385-90146-8(1))*** Random Hse. Children's Bks. (Lamb, Wendy).

HAWAIIAN LANGUAGE

Andrews, Lilinoe. Hiki I Na 'Elala Ke Kokua Ia 'Oe. Parker, Brook, illus. 1999. (HAW.). 40p. (J). (gr. k-2). pap. 5.95 incl. audio (978-1-58191-056-8(8)) Aha Punana Leo.

—I Mea Aha Ke Kai? Parker, Brook, illus. 1999. (HAW.). 28p. (J). pap. 6.95 incl. audio (978-1-58191-080-3(0)) Aha Punana Leo.

—Ka 'Ekake Li'ili'i O Mekiko. Andrews, Lilinoe, illus. 1999. (Illus.). 36p. (J). (gr. 2-3). pap. 5.95 incl. audio (978-1-58191-086-5(X)) Aha Punana Leo.

—Ka Nohona Kua'aina. Andrews, Lilinoe, illus. 1999. (HAW., Illus.). 44p. (J). (gr. 2-3). pap. 5.95 incl. audio (978-1-58191-053-7(3)) Aha Punana Leo.

—Ke Kanaka Mahi'ai Pomaika'i. Parker, Brook, illus. 1999. (HAW.). 16p. (J). pap. 6.95 incl. audio (978-1-58191-076-6(2)) Aha Punana Leo.

—'O Kelekolio Ka Manini Li'ili'i. Ka'ai, Maile, illus. 1999. (HAW.). 36p. (J). pap. 6.95 incl. audio (978-1-58191-070-4(3)) Aha Punana Leo.

Burgess, Kawika. Jonah Kuhio Kalaniana'ole: He Keiki Ali'i Hope Loa o Hawai'i Nei. NeSmith, Keao, ed. 1999. (Illus.). 37p. (YA). (gr. 10-12). pap. (978-0-9665331-1-8(9)) Hale Kuamo'o Hawaiian Language Ctr. at UHH.

Cleeland, Hokulani. He Leka Na Kahilina. Parker, Brook, illus. 1999. (HAW.). 20p. (J). (gr. 1-3). pap. 5.95 incl. audio (978-1-58191-051-3(7)) Aha Punana Leo.

—He Lumi Hou Ko Ka Hale. Parker, Brook, illus. 1999. (HAW.). 24p. (J). (gr. 1-2). pap. 5.95 incl. audio (978-1-58191-052-0(5)) Aha Punana Leo.

—Hele 'O Kawika Laua 'O Kamuela I Ka Pule. Parker, Brook, illus. 1999. (HAW.). 20p. (J). (gr. k-1). pap. 5.95 incl. audio (978-1-58191-055-1(X)) Aha Punana Leo.

—Na Hana a Ka La'i. Parker, Brook, illus. 1999. (HAW.). 20p. (J). pap. 5.95 incl. audio (978-1-58191-050-6(9)) Aha Punana Leo.

Gaison, Na'ilima. Ka'u Papa Hula. Ka'ai, Maile, illus. 1999. (HAW.). 24p. (J). pap. 6.95 incl. audio (978-1-58191-066-7(5)) Aha Punana Leo.

—'O Ni'i Ka Polewao. Parker, Brook, illus. 1999. (HAW.). 20p. (J). pap. 6.95 incl. audio (978-1-58191-024-7(X)) Aha Punana Leo.

Hawaiian Kids Coloring Book. No. 1. pap. 4.95 (978-0-930492-41-0(2)); No. 2. pap. 4.95 (978-0-930492-42-7(0)) Hawaiian Service, Inc.

Higashi, Ku'ulei. Iosepa Kaho'oluhi Nawahiokalani'opu'u. 1999. (HAW., Illus.). 24p. (J). (gr. 2-3). pap. 5.95 incl. audio (978-1-58191-081-0(9)) Aha Punana Leo.

—Luka Ke'elikolani. 1999. (HAW., Illus.). 24p. (J). (gr. 2). pap. 5.95 incl. audio (978-1-58191-065-0(7)) Aha Punana Leo.

Kahalio'umi, Umi, illus. Kumu'ulu. 2000. 32p. (J). (gr. 3-5). pap. 7.95 (978-0-9665331-4-9(3)) Hale Kuamo'o Hawaiian Language Ctr. at UHH.

Kai, Mahele Kumuwaiwai. Malama I Na Kahawai. Burgess, Kawika & NeSmith, Keao, eds. Kuamoyo-Kikowaena, Hale, photos by. 1999. (Illus.). (YA). (gr. 7 up). (978-0-9665331-0-1(0)) Hale Kuamo'o Hawaiian Language Ctr. at UHH.

Ka'ilianu, Robert. Kumu Kou. Bernardino, Haunani, ed. McPherson, Mele, illus. 1999. 39p. (YA). (gr. 5-8). pap. 6.95 (978-0-9665331-3-2(5)) Hale Kuamo'o Hawaiian Language Ctr. at UHH.

Kawai'ae'a, Keiki C. Na Moku Kaulana. Kahalio'umi, Umi, illus. 1999. (HAW.). 24p. (J). pap. 5.95 incl. audio (978-1-58191-078-0(9)) Aha Punana Leo.

Lenci, Kaleimakana, et al. Mo'olelo Polenesia. Pe'a, Kalani, illus. 2000. 80p. (YA). (gr. 7-8). pap. 11.95 (978-0-9665331-8-7(6)) Hale Kuamo'o Hawaiian Language Ctr. at UHH.

Motta, Hau'oli & Wilson, William H. He Mau Hana Ka'u E Hana Ai. Parker, Brook, illus. 1999. (HAW.). 24p. (J). pap. 6.95 incl. audio (978-1-58191-079-7(7)) Aha Punana Leo.

Napoleon, Kawika. 'O Lepeamoa. Parker, Brook, illus. 1999. (HAW.). 32p. (J). (gr. 2-3). pap. 5.95 incl. audio (978-1-58191-057-5(6)) Aha Punana Leo.

Napoleon, Kawika & Wilson, William H. No Ma'ikoha A Me Ka Wauke. Parker, Brook, illus. 1999. (HAW.). 32p. (J). (gr. 1-3). pap. 5.95 incl. audio (978-1-58191-062-9(2)) Aha Punana Leo.

Omoto, Garrett, illus. Tutu Books- A set of three Books w/ CD. 2006. (ENG & HAW.). (YA). (978-1-933835-04-4(4)) Partners in Development.

Prel. Satawalese Alphabet. 2006. (Illus.). 64p. (J). bds. 4.95 (978-1-57306-261-9(8)) Bess Pr., Inc.

Roback, Kekoa. 'O Pa'ao. Parker, Brook, illus. 1999. (HAW.). 28p. (J). (gr. 3-4). pap. 5.95 incl. audio (978-1-58191-064-3(9)) Aha Punana Leo.

Tinkham, Tom. Island English for Micronesia. Miranda, Roland, illus. 2001. 256p. 19.95 (978-1-57306-131-5(X)) Bess Pr., Inc.

Wilson, William H. 'A'ohe Inoa Komo 'Ole O Ka 'Ai. Parker, Brook, illus. 1999. (HAW.). 24p. (J). (gr. 2-4). pap. 5.95 incl. audio (978-1-58191-058-2(4)) Aha Punana Leo.

—He Lahui Kanaka 'Oiwi Anei Ko Hawai'i Nei? Parker, Brook, illus. 1999. (HAW.). 24p. (J). (gr. 4). pap. 5.95 incl. audio (978-1-58191-054-4(1)) Aha Punana Leo.

—Na Koko O Keia Keiki Hawai'i. Parker, Brook, illus. 1999. (HAW.). 20p. (J). (gr. k-2). pap. 5.95 incl. audio (978-1-58191-060-5(6)) Aha Punana Leo.

—No Haunui Laua 'O Hauiki. Parker, Brook, illus. 1999. (HAW.). 20p. (J). (gr. 1-3). pap. 5.95 incl. audio (978-1-58191-063-6(0)) Aha Punana Leo.

—No Punia Me Ka Lua Ula. Parker, Brook, illus. 1999. (HAW.). 40p. (J). (gr. 1-3). pap. 5.95 incl. audio (978-1-58191-061-2(4)) Aha Punana Leo.

—'O Haloa, Ka Hawai'i Mua Loa. Parker, Brook, illus. 1999. (HAW.). 28p. (J). pap. 5.95 incl. audio (978-1-58191-084-1(3)) Aha Punana Leo.

Wilson, William H., et al. E Ho'opili Mai. 1999. (HAW., Illus.). 24p. (J). (gr. k-2). pap. 6.95 incl. audio (978-1-58191-077-3(0)) Aha Punana Leo.

Wong, Laiana. He Pepe Wale No Au. Andrade, Maile, illus. 1999. (HAW.). 24p. (J). pap. 5.95 incl. audio (978-1-58191-071-1(1)) Aha Punana Leo.

—I Ka'u Moe'uhane. Andrade, Pelika & Andrade, Makali'i, illus. 1999. (HAW.). 12p. (J). (gr. 1-3). pap. 5.95 incl. audio (978-1-58191-072-8(X)) Aha Punana Leo.

—Ka 'Omole Kupaianaha O Ka Lua. Morales, Kaipo, illus. 1999. (HAW.). 20p. (J). (gr. 1-2). pap. 5.95 incl. audio (978-1-58191-074-2(6)) Aha Punana Leo.

—Ka 'O'o 'A'a O Alaka'i. Jones, 'Oiwi, illus. 1999. (HAW.). 24p. (J). (gr. 2-3). pap. 5.95 incl. audio (978-1-58191-073-5(8)) Aha Punana Leo.

—Ka Ua Poko. Neff, Craig, illus. 1999. (HAW.). 40p. (J). (gr. 3-4). pap. 5.95 incl. audio (978-1-58191-075-9(4)) Aha Punana Leo.

HAWKS

Deady, Kathleen W. Hawks. 2002. (Predators in the Wild Ser.). (Illus.). 32p. (J). (gr. 3-4). lib. bdg. 21.26 (978-0-7368-1064-7(1) , Capstone High-Interest Bks.) Capstone Pr., Inc.

Dingwall, Laima & Switzer, Merebeth. Walrus. 1999. (Getting to Know ... Nature's Children Ser.). (Illus.). 47p. (J). (978-0-7172-8838-0(2) , Grolier) Scholastic Library Publishing.

Harvey, Bev. The Hawk Family. 2003. (Animal Families Ser.). (Illus.). 32p. (gr. 2-4). 23.00 (978-0-7910-7544-9(3) , Chelsea Hse.) Facts On File, Inc.

Kops, Deborah. Hawks. 2000. (Wild Birds of Prey! Ser.). (Illus.). 24p. (J). (gr. 3-6). 22.45 (978-1-56711-271-9(4) , Blackbirch Pr., Inc.) Thomson Gale.

McCarthy, Meghan. City Hawk: The Story of Pale Male. McCarthy, Meghan, illus. 2007. 40p. (J). (ps-3). 15.99 ***(978-1-4169-3359-5(X))*** Simon & Schuster Children's Publishing.

McQuay, Peri Phillips. A Wing in the Door: Life with a Red-Tailed Hawk. 2001. (World As Home Ser.). (Illus.). 206p. pap. 15.95 (978-1-57131-239-6(0)) Milkweed Editions.

Schaefer, Lola M. The Red-Tailed Hawk. Taylor, Stephen, illus. 1999. (Books for Young Learners). 16p. (J). (gr. k-2). pap. 5.00 (978-1-57274-134-8(1) , 2864) Owen, Richard C. Pubs., Inc.

Schulman, Janet. Pale Male: Citizen Hawk of New York City. So, Meilo, illus. 2008. (J). ***(978-0-375-84558-1(5));*** lib. bdg. ***(978-0-375-94558-8(X))*** Knopf, Alfred A. Inc.

Sharth, Sharon. The Georgia Colony. 2006. (New Naturebooks). (Illus.). 32p. (J). (gr. 1-5). 27.07 (978-1-59296-640-0(3)) Child's World, Inc.

Sharth, Sharon & Davis, Marc. The Georgia Colony. 2003. (Spirit of America: Our Colonies Ser.). (Illus.). 40p. (J). (gr. 2-6). 28.50 (978-1-56766-612-0(4)) Child's World, Inc.

Warhol, Tom. Hawks. 2005. (Animalways Ser.). (Illus.). 112p. (J). (gr. 4-7). lib. bdg. (978-0-7614-1744-6(3) , Benchmark Bks.) Cavendish, Marshall Corp.

Wechsler, Doug. Red-Tailed Hawks. 2001. (Really Wild Life of Birds of Prey Ser.). (Illus.). 24p. (J). lib. bdg. 18.75 (978-0-8239-5596-1(6) , PowerKids Pr.) Rosen Publishing Group, Inc., The.

HAWKS—FICTION

Houk, Randy. Rico's Hawk. Lane, Nancy, illus. 1998. 32p. (J). 12.95 (978-1-58021-029-4(5)); pap. 5.95 (978-1-58021-030-0(9)); (gr. 1-4). pap. 9.95 incl. audio (978-1-58021-033-1(3)); (gr. 1-4). pap. 19.95 incl. audio (978-1-58021-031-7(7)) Benefactory, Inc., The.

—Rico's Hawk: Includes Plush Toy Animal. Lane, Nancy, illus. 1998. 32p. (J). 29.95 (978-1-58021-038-6(4)); pap. 14.95 (978-1-58021-032-4(5)) Benefactory, Inc., The.

—Rico's Hawk: Includes Tape & Plush Toy Animal. Lane, Nancy, illus. 1998. 32p. (J). 34.95 incl. audio (978-1-58021-037-9(6)) Benefactory, Inc., The.

Lasky, Kathryn. Robin Hood: The Boy Who Became a Legend. 1999. (J). (978-0-590-25933-0(4) , Blue Sky Pr., The) Scholastic, Inc.

Le Sueur, Meridel. Sparrow Hawk. DesJarlait, Robert, illus. 2004. 176p. (gr. 7 up). reprint ed. 13.95 (978-0-930100-22-3(0)) Holy Cow! Pr.

Lee, Prema. Maki's Journey Begins. 2004. (Illus.). (J). per. 11.95 (978-0-9754116-0-5(8)) Magic Wordweaver Pr.

Lispi, Robert. Buddy Hawk: Story of Buddy Hawk. 2005. (J). pap. 8.00 (978-0-8059-6602-2(1)) Dorrance Publishing Co., Inc.

Livingston, Timothy J. & Livingston, Mary A. FireStorm in the Forest: When A Forest Burns. Livingston, Timothy J., illus. 2006. (Illus.). 32p. (J). 20.95 ***(978-0-9635757-1-5(6))*** Red Tail Publishing.

Mollel, Tololwa M. Kitoto the Mighty. Frost, Kristi, illus. 1998. 28p. (J). (gr. k-3). 14.95 (978-0-7737-3019-9(2)) Stoddart Kids CAN. *Dist:* Fitzhenry & Whiteside, Ltd.

Price, Joan. Hawk in the Wind. 1999. 124p. (YA). (gr. 7-9). 9.99 (978-0-88092-446-7(2) , 4462) Royal Fireworks Publishing Co.

Schaefer, Lola M. Arrowhawk. Swiatkowska, Gabi, illus. rev. ed. 2004. 32p. (J). 17.95 (978-0-8050-6371-4(4) , Holt, Henry & Co. Bks. For Young Readers) Holt, Henry & Co.

HAWTHORNE, NATHANIEL, 1804-1864

Bloom, Harold, ed. Young Goodman Brown. 2005. (Bloom's Modern Critical Interpretations Ser.). (Illus.). 144-176p. (gr. 9-13). 45.00 (978-0-7910-8124-2(9) , Chelsea Hse.) Facts On File, Inc.

Diorio, Mary Ann L. A Student's Guide to Nathaniel Hawthorne. 2004. (Understanding Literature Ser.). (Illus.). 160p. (YA). lib. bdg. 27.93 (978-0-7660-2283-6(8)) Enslow Pubs., Inc.

Roberts, Russell. Nathaniel Hawthorne. 2006. (Classic Storytellers Ser.). (Illus.). 48p. (J). lib. bdg. 20.95 (978-1-58415-454-9(3) , 1259541) Mitchell Lane Pubs., Inc.

Sterling, Laurie A. Bloom's How to Write about Nathaniel Hawthorne. 2007. (Bloom's How to Write about Literature Ser.). 256p. (YA). (gr. 9 up). 45.00 ***(978-0-7910-9481-5(2)*** , Chelsea Hse.) Facts On File, Inc.

HAYDN, JOSEPH, 1732-1809

Hadden, James C. Haydn. 2001. 231p. (YA). reprint ed. 98.00 (978-0-7222-6310-5(4)) Library Reprints, Inc.

Norton, James R. Haydn's World. 2007. (J). ***(978-1-4042-0727-1(9))*** Rosen Publishing Group, Inc., The.

Summerer, Eric Michael. Franz Joseph Haydn. 2006. (Primary Source Library of Famous Composers). (Illus.). 32p. (J). 21.95 (978-1-4042-2767-5(9) , PowerKids Pr.) Rosen Publishing Group, Inc., The.

Townsend, Pauline D. Joseph Haydn. 2001. 124p. (YA). reprint ed. 88.00 (978-0-7222-5201-7(3)) Library Reprints, Inc.

Wheeler, Opal & Deucher, Sybil. Joseph Haydn, the Merry Little Peasant. Greenwalt, Mary, illus. 2005. 120p. (J). per. 10.95 (978-1-933573-00-7(7)) Zeezok Publishing.

Wilcox, Judy. Joseph Haydn, the Merry Little Peasant. 2006. (J). stu. ed. 4.95 (978-1-933573-01-4(5)) Zeezok Publishing.

HAYDN, JOSEPH, 1732-1809—FICTION

Celenza, Anna Harwell. The Farewell Symphony. Kitchel, JoAnn E., illus. 2005. 32p. (J). pap. 7.95 (978-1-57091-407-2(9)) Charlesbridge Publishing, Inc.

—The Farewell Symphony. 2000. (Illus.). 32p. (J). (ps-3). 19.95 (978-1-57091-406-5(0)) Charlesbridge Publishing, Inc.

HAYES, RUTHERFORD BIRCHARD, 1822-1893

Francis, Sandra. Rutherford B. Hayes: Our Nineteenth President. 2001. (Spirit of America: Our Presidents Ser.). (Illus.). 48p. (J). (gr. 2-6). 28.50 (978-1-56766-856-8(9)) Child's World, Inc.

Knapp, Ron. Rutherford B. Hayes: A MyReportLinks.com Book. 2002. (Presidents Ser.). (Illus.). 48p. (J). (gr. 4-10). lib. bdg. 25.26 (978-0-7660-5010-5(6) , MyReportLinks.com Bks.) Enslow Pubs., Inc.

Levy, Debbie. Rutherford B. Hayes. 2007. (Presidential Leaders Ser.). (Illus.). 112p. (J). 29.27 (978-0-8225-1493-0(1) , Lerner Pubns.) Lerner Publishing Group.

Marsh, Carole. Rutherford B. Hayes: An Ohio Experience Reader. 2001. (J). (gr. k-5). pap. 1.95 (978-0-635-00443-7(7)) Gallopade International.

Otfinoski, Steven. Rutherford B. Hayes. 2004. (Encyclopedia of Presidents Ser.). (Illus.). 110p. (J). 34.00 (978-0-516-22866-2(8) , Children's Pr.) Scholastic Library Publishing.

Santella, Andrew. Rutherford B. Hayes. 2003. (Profiles of the Presidents Ser.). (Illus.). 64p. (J). (gr. 4 up). lib. bdg. 23.93 (978-0-7565-0266-9(7)) Compass Point Bks.

Schlesinger, Arthur M., Sr., et al, eds. The Election of 1876 & the Administration of Rutherford B. Hayes. 2003. (Major Presidential Elections & the Administrations That Followed Ser.). (Illus.). 154p. (YA). (gr. 7). lib. bdg. (978-1-59084-356-7(8)) Mason Crest Pubs.

Venezia, Mike. Rutherford B. Hayes. 2006. (Illus.). 32p. (YA). (gr. 3-4). pap. 7.95 (978-0-516-25404-3(9) , Children's Pr.) Scholastic Library Publishing.

Venezia, Mike, illus. Rutherford B. Hayes. 2006. (Getting to Know the U. S. Presidents Ser.). 32p. (J). (gr. 3-4). 27.00 (978-0-516-22624-8(X) , Children's Pr.) Scholastic Library Publishing.

Welsbacher, Anne. Rutherford B. Hayes. 2001. (United States Presidents Ser.). (Illus.). 32p. (J). (gr. k-6). lib. bdg. 22.78 (978-1-57765-248-9(7) , Checkerboard Library) ABDO Publishing Co.

HAZARDOUS WASTES

see also Pollution

Bryan, Nichol. Love Canal: Pollution Crisis. 2003. (Environmental Disasters Ser.). (Illus.). 48p. (J). (gr. 5 up). pap. 11.95 (978-0-8368-5515-9(9) , World Almanac Library) Stevens, Gareth Inc.

Cothran, Helen, ed. Garbage & Recycling. 2002. (Opposing Viewpoints Ser.). (Illus.). 200p. (J). (gr. 10-12). pap. 24.95 (978-0-7377-1229-2(5) , Greenhaven Pr., Inc.) Thomson Gale.

Greeley, August. Toxic Waste: Chemical Spills in Our World. 2003. (Man-Made Disasters Ser.). (Illus.). 24p. (J). lib. bdg. 17.25 (978-0-8239-6483-3(3) , PowerKids Pr.) Rosen Publishing Group, Inc., The.

McGowan, Keith. Hazardous Waste. 2nd rev. ed. 2000. (Overview Ser.). (Illus.). 112p. (J). (gr. 6-9). lib. bdg. 29.95 (978-1-56006-699-6(7) , LML00902-178051, Lucent Bks.) Thomson Gale.

Parks, Peggy J. Toxic Waste. 2006. (Our Environment Ser.). (Illus.). 48p. (J). (gr. 4-8). 26.20 (978-0-7377-1823-2(4) , Kidhaven) Thomson Gale.

Reed, Jennifer Bond. Love Canal. 2002. (Great Disasters, Reforms & Ramifications Ser.). (Illus.). 112p. (J). 30.00 (978-0-7910-6742-0(4) , Chelsea Hse.) Facts On File, Inc.

Sherrow, Victoria. Love Canal: Toxic Waste Tragedy. 2001. (American Disasters Ser.). (Illus.). 48p. (J). (gr. 4-10). lib. bdg. 23.93 (978-0-7660-1553-1(X)) Enslow Pubs., Inc.

Toxic Waste: Chemical Spills in Our World: Individual Title Six-Packs. (On Deck Ser.: Vol. 2). 24p. (gr. 4-5). 35.00 (978-0-7578-5834-5(1)) Rigby Education.

HAZARDOUS WASTES—FICTION

Dunphy, Catherine. Caitlin. 2006. (Degrassi Junior High Ser.). 184p. (YA). (gr. 5-10). 7.95 (978-1-55028-923-7(3)) Lorimer, James & Co., Ltd., Pubs. CAN. *Dist:* Casemate Pubs. & Bk. Distributors, LLC.

HEALTH

see also Children—Health and Hygiene; Grooming for Men; Physical Education and Training; Sanitation; Sleep

The Adventures of MolarMan Oral Health Educational Package: MolarMan DVD in English/Spanish/ASL & Bilingual Coloring Workbook in English/Spanish. 2006. (ENG & SPA.). (J). DVD ***(978-0-9791794-2-6(4))*** Johnson, Gary.

Afrika, Llaila. African Holistic Health. 7th ed. 2004. 584p. pap. 18.95 (978-1-881316-82-4(3)) A & B Distributors & Pubs. Group.

Allergies, Asthma & Exercise: The Science of Health. 1999. (Science @ Work Ser.). (Illus.). 48p. (J). (gr. 4-6). pap. 27.12 (978-0-7398-0140-6(6)) Raintree.

H I

Amos, Janine. Is Helen Pregnant? 2003. (Body Matters Ser.). (Illus.). 32p. (YA). 19.99 (978-1-84234-107-0(3) , Cherrytree Books) Evans Publishing Group GBR. *Dist:* Independent Pubs. Group.

Anderson, Judith. Me & My Body. 2007. (J). ***(978-1-59771-086-2(5))*** Sea-To-Sea Pubns.

Anthony, Mark, et al. Gut Instinct: Diet's Missing Link. 2003. (Illus.). 216p. per. 19.95 (978-0-9743664-0-1(4)) Leap Forward Pubns.

Apel, Melanie Ann. Let's Talk about Living with a Parent with Multiple Sclerosis. 2001. (Let's Talk Library). (Illus.). 24p. (J). (gr. 3). lib. bdg. 18.75 (978-0-8239-5621-0(0) , PowerKids Pr.) Rosen Publishing Group, Inc., The.

April, Elyse. We Like to Eat Well. Agrell, Lewis, illus. 2007. 32p. (J). pap. 9.95 ***(978-1-890772-69-7(0))*** Hohm Pr.

Ayer, Eleanor H. La Paternidad Adolescente. 2002. (Todo lo Que Necesitas Saber Ser.). (SPA & ENG., Illus.). 64p. (YA). lib. bdg. 26.50 (978-0-8239-3585-7(X) , Buenas Letra) Rosen Publishing Group, Inc., The.

Bagley, Katie. Keep Clean: A Look at Hygiene. 2001. (Your Health Ser.). (Illus.). 24p. (J). (gr. 1-2). lib. bdg. 18.60 (978-0-7368-0974-0(0) , Bridgestone Bks.) Capstone Pr., Inc.

Baker, Sue. Oh Baby!. Stockham, Jess, illus. 2006. (Blanket Babies Ser.). 12p. (J). 6.99 (978-1-904550-87-7(8)) Child's Play-International.

Barnett, Michelle Noble, et al. Theme Pockets - October: Halloween; Night Creatures; Healthy & Happy. Evans, Marilyn, ed. Larsen, Jo, illus. 1999. (Making Books with Pockets). 96p. (J). pap., tchr. ed. 12.99 (978-1-55799-707-4(1) , EMC 593) Evan-Moor Educational Pubs.

Bartone, John C., Sr. Bioterrorism Potential of Hantaan Virus with Index & Medical Analysis of New Information for Reference & Research: Index & Ana. 2003. 185p. 57.50 (978-0-7883-3152-7(3) , 0-7883-31523) ABBE Pubs. Assn. of Washington, D.C.

Bell, Alison. Your Beauty, Your Health, Yourself. 2000. (Your Body, Your Self Bks.). (Illus.). 144p. (J). (gr. 4-8). pap. 8.95 (978-0-7373-0350-6(6) , 03506W) Lowell Hse. Juvenile.

Benchmark Education Staff, compiled by. Good for You! & Personal Health. 2005. spiral bd. 75.00 ***(978-1-4108-5808-5(1))*** Benchmark Education Co.

—Health & Human Body. 2006. spiral bd. 179.00 ***(978-1-4108-7108-4(8))*** Benchmark Education Co.

Berry, Joy Wilt. A Book about Being Messy. 2005. (Illus.). (J). (978-0-7172-8577-8(4)) Scholastic, Inc.

—Teach Me about Bathtime: A Special Times Book. Fitzpatrick, Roey, illus. rev. ed. 1999. (Teach Me about Ser. : Vol. 2). 32p. (J). (ps). bds. 5.95 (978-1-58634-001-8(8) , 01-0101-02) Goldstar Publishing, Inc.

Berry, Ron. Everybody Takes a Bath. Sharp, Chris, illus. 2006. 10p. (J). (ps). 8.95 (978-0-8249-6681-2(3) , Ideals Children's Bks.) Ideals Pubns.

Booth. Health Care Science Technology: Career Foundations: Student Motivation. 2004. (gr. 6-12). 208.00 (978-0-07-829742-7(7)) Glencoe/McGraw-Hill.

Botvin, Gilbert J. Life Skills Training: Promoting Health & Personal Development. 1998. (Illus.). 48p. (J). (gr. 6-9). pap., stu. ed., wbk. ed. 4.00 (978-0-933665-05-7(9)) Princeton Health Pr.

A Boy's Guide to Growing up - Booklet, 10 per packet. 2005. (Illus.). (J). 63.95 (978-1-55942-211-6(4)) Marsh Media.

Brenner, Barbara, et al. Ou est Ce Poisson? (FRE., Illus.). (J). pap. 6.99 (978-0-590-24226-4(1)) Scholastic, Inc.

Brush Well. (Your Health Ser.). 24p. (J). 6.95 (978-0-7368-4453-6(8)) Capstone Pr., Inc.

Bull, Dave. What Every Girl Should Know: An A to Z of Health - From Allergies to Zits. 1999. (Illus.). 160p. (YA). (gr. 4 up). pap. 5.95 (978-1-902618-18-0(1)) Element Children's Bks.

Burke, Tracy W. Just the Fats Part II: Nutrition for Every Body. 2002. 108p. pap. 10.95 (978-0-595-22102-8(5) , Writers Club Pr.) iUniverse, Inc.

Burstein, John. Avoiding Injuries. 2006. (Illus.). 32p. (J). lib. bdg. ***(978-0-8368-7739-7(X))*** Stevens, Gareth Inc.

—Keeping Clean. 2006. (Illus.). 32p. (J). lib. bdg. ***(978-0-8368-7742-7(X))*** Stevens, Gareth Inc.

Burton, Margie, et al. Cleaning My Room. Adams, Alison, ed. 1999. (Early Connections Ser.). 16p. (J). (gr. k-2). pap. 4.50 (978-1-58344-056-8(9)) Benchmark Education Co.

Busse, Gregory. Morphine. 2006. (Drugs Ser.). (Illus.). 104p. (J). (gr. 9-12). 30.00 (978-0-7910-8551-6(1) , Chelsea Hse.) Facts On File, Inc.

Byrd, Sandra. The Inside-Out Beauty Book: Tips & Tools for Girls Like You. 2002. (Girls Like You Ser.; Vol. 2). (Illus.). 128p. (gr. 4-7). pap. 7.99 (978-0-7642-2493-5(X)) Bethany Hse. Pubs.

Can Buildings Make You Sick? 2004. (Nova Ser.). (gr. 7 up). 19.95 (978-1-57807-915-5(2) , WG2217) WGBH Boston Video.

Carter, Stephanie & Lederman, JoAnn. Meditapes Three - Thinking Thin & Healthy. 1998. (YA). (gr. 7 up). pap. 24.95 incl. audio (978-1-893868-02-1(8)) Meditapes.

Cassidy, Albert, Jr. & Bennedetti, Eric. The Amazing Adventures of Dr. Snappy & Sam: Dr. Snappy vs. Subluxor. Romanchick, Jennifer, ed. Cassidy, Albert, Jr., illus. 2005. (Illus.). 16p. (J). 9.99 (978-0-9770527-0-7(2)) All Health Chiropractic Ctrs. Inc.

Cherry Lake Publishing, compiled by. Heathly for Life. 2008. lib. bdg. ***(978-1-60279-105-3(8))*** Cherry Lake Publishing.

—Real World Math: Health & Wellness. 2008. lib. bdg. ***(978-1-60279-103-9(1))*** Cherry Lake Publishing.

Christopher, Garrett. Your Amazing Senses: A Content Area Reader-health. 2005. (Emergent (Prek-2) Health Package Ser.). 12p. (YA). (ps-2). 25.20 (978-0-8215-7827-8(8)) Sadlier, William H. Inc.

Clarke, Liam. Health & Social Care for Foundation GNVQ. 2nd ed. 2000. (Illus.). 368p. (J). pap. 42.50 (978-0-7487-3509-9(7)) Nelson Thornes Ltd. GBR. *Dist:* Trans-Atlantic Pubns., Inc.

—Health & Social Care for Intermediate GNVQ. 2nd ed. 2000. (Illus.). 224p. (J). pap. 42.50 (978-0-7487-3508-2(9)) Nelson Thornes Ltd. GBR. *Dist:* Trans-Atlantic Pubns., Inc.

Clarke, Liam, et al. Health & Social Care for Advanced GNVQ. 3rd ed. 2000. (Illus.). 344p. (J). pap. 59.50 (978-0-7487-3510-5(0)) Nelson Thornes Ltd. GBR. *Dist:* Trans-Atlantic Pubns., Inc.

Clean & Healthy All Day Long, 6 bks. Incl. Brushing My Teeth. Vogel, Elizabeth. lib. bdg. 16.00 (978-0-8239-5683-8(0) , PKBRTE); Eating Right. Vogel, Elizabeth. lib. bdg. 16.00 (978-0-8239-5686-9(5) , PKEATI); Let's Exercise. Vogel, Elizabeth. lib. bdg. 16.00 (978-0-8239-5687-6(3) , PKEXER); Taking Care of My Hair. Vogel, Elizabeth, contrib. by. lib. bdg. 16.00 (978-0-8239-5685-2(7) , PKCAHA); Taking My Bath. Vogel, Elizabeth, contrib. by. lib. bdg. 16.00 (978-0-8239-5682-1(2) , PKTABA); Washing My Hands. Vogel, Elizabeth. lib. bdg. 16.00 (978-0-8239-5684-5(9) , PKWAHA); 24p. (J). (gr. 1). (Illus.). 2001. Set lib. bdg. 88.50 (978-0-8239-7073-5(6) , PKCLHE, PowerKids Pr.) Rosen Publishing Group, Inc., The.

Coder, Kelly, ed. Investigating Science - Taking Care of Me. 2003. 48p. 9.95 (978-1-56234-570-9(2) , Mailbox Bks., The) Education Ctr., Inc.

Compact Guides to Health & Fitness, 17 vols., Set. 2002. (Illus.). 36,52p. (YA). (gr. 8 up). lib. bdg. (978-1-59084-245-4(6)) Mason Crest Pubs.

Compton, Leanne, et al. Jump Start 7 & 8: Health & Physical Education. 2007. pap. 41.00 incl. cd-rom ***(978-0-521-70156-3(2))*** Cambridge Univ. Pr.

Conrad, David. Burps, Boogers, & Bad Breath. 2002. (Spyglass Books). (Illus.). 24p. (J). (gr. 1 up). lib. bdg. 18.60 (978-0-7565-0228-7(4)) Compass Point Bks.

Cook, David Fuller, compiled by. A Balanced Approach to Long Life & Vitality, Signature Edition: As Used in Fitness, Wellness, Clinical Weight Loss, & Cardiac Rehabilitation Programs. 2003. (Illus.). 80p. spiral bd. 31.95 (978-0-9741629-0-4(6)) Cook, David.

Cook, David Fuller, ed. A Balanced Approach to Long Life & Vitality for Christians: As Used in Fitness, Wellness, Clinical Weight Loss, & Cardiac Rehabilitation Programs. 2003. (Illus.). 105p. spiral bd. 33.95 (978-0-9741629-4-2(9)) Cook, David.

Cooper, Evan. Um, Like... OM: A Girl Goddess's Guide to Yoga. 2005. (Illus.). 192p. (J). (gr. 7-17). pap. 9.99 (978-0-316-98001-2(3)) Little Brown & Co.

Coping: Health & Well-Being, 7 bks. Incl. Coping with Allergies. Schwartz, Robert H. & Deane, Peter M. G. 128-192p. 1999. lib. bdg. 26.50 (978-0-8239-2511-7(0) , COALLE); Coping with Anxiety & Panic Attacks. Lee, Jordan. 128p. 2000. lib. bdg. 26.50 (978-0-8239-3202-3(8) , COANPA); Coping with Diabetes. Kelly, Pat. 192p. 2000. lib. bdg. 25.25 (978-0-8239-3203-0(6) , CODIAB); Coping with Hereditary Diseases. Jacobs, Marian B. 152p. 1999. lib. bdg. 26.50 (978-0-8239-2823-1(3) , COHEDI); Coping with Melanoma & Other Skin Cancers. Long, Wendy. 128-192p. 1999. lib. bdg. 26.50 (978-0-8239-2852-1(7) , COMELA); Coping with Migraines & Other Headaches. Votava, Andrea. 162p. 2000. lib. bdg. 26.50 (978-0-8239-3197-2(8)); Coping with Teen Suicide. Murphy, James M. 128-192p. 1999. lib. bdg. 26.50 (978-0-8239-2824-8(1) , COTESU); (YA). (gr. 7-12). (Illus.). 1999. Set lib. bdg. 159.00 (978-0-8239-9296-6(9)) Rosen Publishing Group, Inc., The.

Costello, Patricia. Legend's of Health & Fitness, 10 vols., Set. 2000. (Illus.). 960p. (gr. 6-10). lib. bdg. 257.00 (978-1-58415-062-6(9)) Mitchell Lane Pubs., Inc.

Cox, Judith. The Wellness Tree. Rogers, Denny, illus. 2003. 32p. (J). (gr. k-4). pap. 2.95 (978-1-878044-35-8(4)) Mayhaven Publishing.

Crump, Marguerite. Don't Sweat It! Everybody's Answers to Questions You Don't Want to Ask: A Guide for Young People. 2004. (Laugh & Learn Ser.). (Illus.). 128p. (YA). (gr. 4-8). pap. 12.95 (978-1-57542-114-8(3)) Free Spirit Publishing, Inc.

Dahl, Michael. Cold, Colder, Coldest: Animals That Adapt to Cold Weather. Jensen, Brian, illus. 2005. (Animal Extremes Ser.). 24p. (J). (ps). lib. bdg. 22.60 (978-1-4048-1014-3(5)) Picture Window Bks.

Daisy Duck & her Bath. 2004. (Play Pals Ser.). (Illus.). 12p. (J). bds. (978-1-84229-643-1(4)) Top That! Publishing PLC.

Dann, Penny, illus. Josh B'Gosh & the Doctor. 1998. 10p. (J). 5.99 (978-1-929174-09-6(8)) Oshkosh B'Gosh, Inc.

Dawson, Susan H. & Norton, Susan R. Pyramid Pal - Fruits: Eating Should Always Be Fun for Kid. O'Hare, Mark, illus. 2000. (Adventures in Eating with the Nutrition Champion of Kids Ser.). 16p. (J). pap. 3.00 (978-1-58000-066-6(5)) Griffin Publishing Group.

—Pyramid Pal - Grains: Eating Should Always Be Fun for a Kid. O'Hare, Mark, illus. 2000. (Adventures in Eating with the Nutrition Champion of Kids Ser.). 24p. (J). pap. 3.50 (978-1-58000-064-2(9)) Griffin Publishing Group.

—Pyramid Pal - Meat, Poultry, Fish: Eating Should Always Be Fun for a Kid. O'Hare, Mark, illus. 2000. (Adventures in Eating with the Nutrition Champion of Kids Ser.). 32p. (J). pap. 4.00 (978-1-58000-068-0(1)) Griffin Publishing Group.

—Pyramid Pal - Milk: Eating Should Always Be Fun for a Kid. O'Hare, Mark, illus. 2000. (Adventures in Eating with the Nutrition Champion of Kids Ser.). 16p. (J). pap. 3.00 (978-1-58000-067-3(3)) Griffin Publishing Group.

—Pyramid Pal - Sweets: Eating Should Always Be Fun for a Kid. O'Hare, Mark, illus. 2000. (Adventures in Eating with the Nutrition Champion of Kids Ser.). 16p. (J). pap. 3.00 (978-1-58000-069-7(X)) Griffin Publishing Group.

—Pyramid Pal - The Begining: Eating Should Always Be Fun for a Kid. O'Hare, Mark, illus. 2000. (Adventures in Eating with the Nutrition Champion of Kids Ser.). 16p. (J). pap. 3.00 (978-1-58000-063-5(0)) Griffin Publishing Group.

—Pyramid Pal - Vegetables: Eating Should Always Be Fun for a Kid. O'Hare, Mark, illus. 2000. (Adventures in Eating with the Nutrition Champion of Kids Ser.). 16p. (J). pap. 3.00 (978-1-58000-065-9(7)) Griffin Publishing Group.

Degrassi Health: Educational Set. 2004. (Degrassi Junior High Ser.). (gr. 7 up). 99.95 (978-1-57807-221-7(2) , WG675K) WGBH Boston Video.

Derkazarian, Susan. You Have Head Lice! 2005. (Rookie Read-about Health Ser.). (Illus.). (J). (gr. k-2). 31p. pap. 5.95 (978-0-516-27920-6(3)); 32p. 20.50 (978-0-516-25879-9(6)) Scholastic Library Publishing. (Children's Pr.).

DK Publishing Staff. Brushing My Teeth. 2007. 12p. (J). (ps-1). bds. 6.99 (978-0-7566-3021-8(5)) Dorling Kindersley Publishing, Inc.

—Doctor's Office. 2007. (Illus.). 12p. (J). 6.99 (978-0-7566-2585-6(8)) Dorling Kindersley Publishing, Inc.

The Doctor's Office. 2005. (Transportation Ser.). (YA). (gr. k-3). (978-1-56065-836-8(3) , Pebble Bks.) Capstone Pr., Inc.

Doernberg, Steven L. Clown of Natural Health Vol. 2: Work Is Play, Play Is Learning. 1999. 15p. (YA). (gr. 2-11). mass mkt. 3.50 (978-0-9648663-3-1(1)) Clown of Natural Health.

Dorling Kindersley Publishing Staff. Bathtime. 2003. (DK Touch & Feel Ser.). (Illus.). 12p. (J). bds. 6.99 (978-0-7894-9839-7(1)) Dorling Kindersley Publishing, Inc.

Douglas, Ann & Douglas, Julie. Body Talk: The Straight Facts on Fitness, Nutrition, & Feeling Great about Yourself! Davila, Claudia, illus. 2nd ed. 2006. (Girl Zone Ser.). 64p. (J). 19.95 (978-1-897066-62-1(7)); pap. 9.95 (978-1-897066-61-4(9)) Maple Tree Pr. CAN. *Dist:* Perseus Distribution.

Duckworth, Katie. Health. 2004. (Children's Rights Ser.). (J). lib. bdg. 27.10 (978-1-58340-420-1(1)) Smart Apple Media.

Dumas, Glenda F. Respect You Draw & Color Book Bk. 3: Cleanliness. 1999. 36p. (J). (ps-2). mass mkt. 9.99 (978-1-930457-04-1(9)) Glenda's Place.

—Respeto Tu Libro para Dibujar y Colorear Libro 3: Limpieza. 1999. Tr. of Respect You Draw & Color Book. (SPA.). 36p. (J). (ps-2). mass mkt. 9.99 (978-1-930457-05-8(7)) Glenda's Place.

Durant, Penny Raife & Dorling Kindersley Publishing Staff. Sniffles, Sneezes, Hiccups, & Coughs. 2005. (Dk Readers Ser.). (Illus.). 32p. (J). (ps-ps). 12.99 (978-0-7566-1107-1(5)); pap. 3.99 (978-0-7566-1106-4(7)) Dorling Kindersley Publishing, Inc.

Early Health Package. 2005. (Emergent (Prek-2) Health Package Ser.). (YA). (ps-2). 126.00 (978-0-8215-7864-3(2)) Sadlier, William H. Inc.

Ehrlich, Fred. Does an Elephant Take a Bath? Bolam, Emily, illus. 2005. (Early Experiences Ser.). (J). ***(978-1-4156-3337-3(1))*** Handprint Bks.

Elgin, Kathy. Health & Disease. 2005. (Changing Times Ser.). (YA). (978-0-7565-0889-0(4)) Compass Point Bks.

Emergent Health Package. 2005. (YA). (ps-2). 243.00 (978-0-8215-7889-6(8)); 135.00 (978-0-8215-7879-7(0)) Sadlier, William H. Inc.

Emmer, Rick. Virus Hunter. 2005. (Weird Careers in Science Ser.). (Illus.). 84p. (J). (gr. 4-8). lib. bdg. 25.00 (978-0-7910-8705-3(0) , Chelsea Hse.) Facts On File, Inc.

Eshom, Dan. Top of Your Game: A Guy's Guide to Looking & Feeling Good. 2000. (Guys' Guides Ser.). (Illus.). 48p. (YA). (gr. 5-8). lib. bdg. 17.95 (978-0-8239-3083-8(1) , GUTOGA, Rosen Central) Rosen Publishing Group, Inc., The.

Farnsworth, Vesta J. The House We Live in or the Making of the Body. 2004. reprint ed. pap. 24.95 (978-1-4179-2036-5(X)) Kessinger Publishing, LLC.

Federer, Jessica Joy. Bobby Bacteria & Friends: Inside UR Body Books Presents. l.t. ed. 2005. (Illus.). 80p. (J). bds. 9.99 (978-0-9753455-3-5(2)) Amerisearch, Inc.

Ferraro, Bonita. Rules All Around: A Content Area Reader-health. 2005. (Emergent (Prek-2) Health Package Ser.). 12p. (YA). (ps-2). 25.20 (978-0-8215-7829-2(4)) Sadlier, William H. Inc.

Fettig, Jamie. The Creator's Manual for Your Body. 2004. per. 14.95 (978-0-9761555-0-8(8) , 1-773-665-4005) Bazuji Publishing LLC.

Fisher, Enid Broderick. Food & Health. 1998. (Good Health Guides). (Illus.). 32p. (J). (gr. 4 up). lib. bdg. 22.60 (978-0-8368-2178-9(5)) Stevens, Gareth Inc.

Forte, Imogene & Frank, Marjorie. Human Body & Health. 2002. (Basic Not Boring Ser.). tchr. ed., per. 7.95 (978-0-86530-552-6(8)) Incentive Pubns., Inc.

Fraser, K. & Tatchell, Judy. Fitness & Health. 1999. (Introductions Ser.). (Illus.). 48p. (YA). (gr. 6 up). lib. bdg. 15.95 (978-0-88110-234-5(2)) EDC Publishing.

Freese, Joan. Tables & Graphs of Healthy Things. 2007. (J). pap. ***(978-0-8368-8480-7(9))*** ; 24p. (gr. 1-3). lib. bdg. 19.93 ***(978-0-8368-8471-5(X))*** Stevens, Gareth Inc. (Weekly Reader Early Learning Library).

From Head to Toes. 2005. (Emergent (Prek-2) Health Package Ser.). 12p. (YA). (ps-2). 25.20 (978-0-8215-7846-9(4)) Sadlier, William H. Inc.

Fromm, Jim, prod. Human Health Cd Mac Labpak. (YA). cd-rom 322.50 (978-0-7365-4366-8(X)) Films Media Group.

Frost, Helen. Eating Right. Saunders-Smith, Gail, ed. 2000. (Food Guide Pyramid Ser.). (Illus.). 24p. (J). (gr. k-1). lib. bdg. 15.93 (978-0-7368-0535-3(4) , Pebble Bks.) Capstone Pr., Inc.

Furgang, Kathy. Tener habitos sanos & Having Healthful Habits. 2005. spiral bd. 84.00 ***(978-1-4108-5710-1(7))*** Benchmark Education Co.

Gaff, Jackie. Why Must I... Exercise? Fairclough, Chris, photos by. 2005. (Illus.). 32p. (J). (gr. 2-5). lib. bdg. (978-1-84234-348-7(3) , Cherrytree Books) Evans Publishing Group.

—Why Must I Wash My Hands? Fairclough, Chris, photos by. 2005. (Illus.). 32p. (J). (gr. 2-5). lib. bdg. (978-1-84234-350-0(5) , Cherrytree Books) Evans Publishing Group.

Gareth Stevens Publishing Staff, contrib. by. Health. 2002. (Discovery Channel School Science Ser.). (Illus.). 32p. (J). (gr. 5 up). lib. bdg. 24.67 (978-0-8368-3213-6(2)) Stevens, Gareth Inc.

Gibbons, Charlie, et al. Big Books. 99th ed. 1999. (Your Health Ser.). (gr. 1 up). pap. 104.00 (978-0-15-311350-5(2)); (gr. 2 up). pap. 104.00 (978-0-15-311351-2(0)) Harcourt Schl. Pubs.

Girls Know Best, 7 bks. l.t. ed. Incl. Boys Know It All : Wise Thoughts & Wacky Ideas from Guys Like You. Roehm, Michelle, compiled by. 167p. 1999. lib. bdg. 23.33 (978-0-8368-2455-1(5)); Girls Know Best Vol. 2 : Tips on Life & Fun Stuff to Do. Monson-Burton, Marianne, compiled by. 1999. lib. bdg. 23.33 (978-0-8368-2453-7(9)); Girls Know Best Vol. 3 : Your Words, Your World. Monson-Burton, Marianne, compiled by. 153p. 2000. lib. bdg. 23.33 (978-0-8368-2672-2(8)); Girls Knows Best : Advice for Girls from Girls on Just about Everything. Roehm, Michelle, compiled by. 160p. 1999. lib. bdg. 23.33 (978-0-8368-2452-0(0)); Girls Who Rocked the World : Heroines from Sacagawea to Sheryl Swoopes. Welden, Amelie. McCann, Jerry, illus. 117p. 1999. lib. bdg. 23.33 (978-0-8368-2454-4(7)); Girls Who Rocked the World Vol. 2 : Heroines from Harriet Tubman to Mia Hamm. Roehm, Michelle, compiled by. 152p. 2000. lib. bdg. 23.33 (978-0-8368-2673-9(6)); Throw Like a Girl : Discovering the Body, Mind & Spirit of the Athlete in You! Frost, Shelley & Troussieux, Ann. 128p. 2000. lib. bdg. 23.33 (978-0-8368-2674-6(4)); (J). (gr. 3 up). (Illus.). Set lib. bdg. 163.31 (978-0-8368-2741-5(4)) Stevens, Gareth Inc.

Glencoe McGraw-Hill Staff. Glencoe Health, Human Sexuality. 9th ed. 2003. (C). (gr. 6-12). stu. ed. 13.96 (978-0-07-830945-8(X) , 9780078309458) Glencoe/McGraw-Hill.

Glencoe McGraw-Hill Staff, et al. Glencoe Health, 3 vols. 9th ed. 2003. 884p. (C). (gr. 9-12). stu. ed. 80.64 (978-0-07-826326-2(3) , 9780078263262) Glencoe/McGraw-Hill.

Glibbery, Caroline. Join the Total Fitness Gang. 1998. (Good Health Guides). (Illus.). 32p. (J). (gr. 4 up). lib. bdg. 22.60 (978-0-8368-2181-9(5)) Stevens, Gareth Inc.

Glover, David & Glover, Penny. Staying Healthy. 2005. (Illus.). 30p. (J). (gr. 3-7). lib. bdg. 27.10 (978-1-58340-693-9(X)) Smart Apple Media.

Goodacre, Sonia, et al. A Global Perspective on Health & Human Development: VCE Units 3 & 4. 2003. 400p. pap. 25.90 (978-0-521-53840-4(8)) Cambridge Univ. Pr.

Gordon, James S. Stress Management. 2000. (Twenty-First Century Health & Wellness Ser.). 112p. (J). (gr. 7-12). 36.00 (978-0-7910-5987-6(1) , Chelsea Hse.) Facts On File, Inc.

Gordon, Melanie Apel. Let's Talk about Head Lice. 1999. (Let's Talk Library). 24p. (YA). (gr. 3 up). pap. 13.95 (978-1-56838-276-0(6)) Hazelden Publishing & Educational Services.

—Let's Talk about Head Lice. 1999. (Let's Talk Library). (Illus.). 24p. (J). (gr. 3). lib. bdg. 18.75 (978-0-8239-5200-7(2) , PowerKids Pr.) Rosen Publishing Group, Inc., The.

Gordon, Sharon. Keeping Clean. (Rookie Read-About Health Ser.). (Illus.). 32p. (J). (gr. k-2). 2003. pap. 5.95 (978-0-516-26951-1(8)); 2002. pap. 20.50 (978-0-516-22572-2(3)) Scholastic Library Publishing. (Children's Pr.).

—Keeping Clean. 2002. (gr. k-3). lib. bdg. 14.10 (978-0-613-59652-7(8)) Tandem Library Bks.

Gottlieb, Jeff & Gottlieb, Martha. Spriggles - Motivational Books for Children: Spriggles: Health & Nutrition. Gottlieb, Alexander, illus. 2002. 32p. (J). (ps-5). per. 8.95 (978-1-930439-01-6(6)) Mountain Watch Pr.

Goulding, Sylvia. Healthy Eating. 2005. (Healthy Kids Ser.). (Illus.). 32p. (gr. 3-6). 19.95 (978-1-59515-204-6(0)) Rourke Publishing, LLC.

—Taking Care of Your Body. 2005. (Healthy Kids Ser.). (Illus.). 32p. (gr. 3-6). 19.95 (978-1-59515-202-2(4)) Rourke Publishing, LLC.

Gray, Shirley W. Cleanliness for Good Health. 2003. (Living Well). (Illus.). 32p. (J). (gr. 2-6). 27.07 (978-1-59296-084-2(7)) Child's World, Inc.

—Exercising for Good Health. 2003. (Living Well). (Illus.). 32p. (J). (gr. 2-6). 27.07 (978-1-59296-081-1(2)) Child's World, Inc.

—Prevention & Good Health. 2003. (Living Well). (Illus.). 32p. (J). (gr. 2-6). 27.07 (978-1-59296-083-5(9)) Child's World, Inc.

Gregson, Susan R. Healthy Eating. 2000. (Perspectives on Physical Health Ser.). (Illus.). 64p. (J). (gr. 4-6). lib. bdg. 23.93 (978-0-7368-0420-2(X) , LifeMatters Bks.) Capstone Pr., Inc.

Grogan, Marijo. My Journal: A Place to Begin. Skardarasy, Doreen, ed. 1999. (YA). 72p. (YA). (gr. 5-8). 9.95 (978-0-9678801-2-9(2)) Acorn Publishing.

Grolier Educational Staff, contrib. by. Addiction: Tobacco, Alcohol, & Other Drugs, 8 vols., Vol. 1. 2002. (Illus.). (J). (978-0-7172-5576-4(X) , Grolier) Scholastic Library Publishing.

—Diseases & Disabling Conditions, 8 vols., Vol. 8. 2002. (Illus.). (J). (978-0-7172-5583-2(2) , Grolier) Scholastic Library Publishing.

—Environmental Poisoning, 8 vols., Vol. 6. 2002. (Illus.). (J). (978-0-7172-5581-8(6) , Grolier) Scholastic Library Publishing.

—Health Matters!, 8 vols., Set. Incl. Vol. 1. Addiction : Tobacco, Alcohol, & Other Drugs. (978-0-7172-5576-4(X)); Vol. 2. Mental Health, Depression, Suicide, & Other Issues. (978-0-7172-5577-1(8)); Vol. 3. Sexuality & Pregnancy. (978-0-7172-5578-8(6)); Vol. 4. Physical Activity, Weight, & Eating Disorders. (978-0-7172-5579-5(4)); Vol. 5. Injuries & Violence. (978-0-7172-5580-1(8)); Vol. 6. Environmental Poisoning. (978-0-7172-5581-8(6)); Vol. 7. HIV Infections, AIDS, & STDs. (978-0-7172-5582-5(4)); Vol. 8. Diseases & Disabling Conditions. (978-0-7172-5583-2(2)); (J). (Illus.). 2002. 459.00 (978-0-7172-5575-7(1) , Grolier) Scholastic Library Publishing.

—HIV Infections, AIDS, & STDs, 8 vols., Vol. 7. 2002. (Illus.). (J). (978-0-7172-5582-5(4) , Grolier) Scholastic Library Publishing.

—Injuries & Violence, 8 vols., Vol. 5. 2002. (Illus.). (J). (978-0-7172-5580-1(8) , Grolier) Scholastic Library Publishing.

—Mental Health, Depression, Suicide, & Other Issues, 8 vols., Vol. 2. 2002. (Illus.). (J). (978-0-7172-5577-1(8) , Grolier) Scholastic Library Publishing.

—Physical Activity, Weight, & Eating Disorders, 8 vols., Vol. 4. 2002. (Illus.). (J). (978-0-7172-5579-5(4) , Grolier) Scholastic Library Publishing.

—Sexuality & Pregnancy, 8 vols., Vol. 3. 2002. (Illus.). (J). (978-0-7172-5578-8(6) , Grolier) Scholastic Library Publishing.

Grover, Jan. Healthcare. 2007. (Current Controversies Ser.). 240p. (J). (gr. 10-12). 36.20 ***(978-0-7377-3427-0(2));*** pap. 24.95 ***(978-0-7377-3428-7(0))*** Thomson Gale. (Greenhaven Pr., Inc.).

Grow up Healthy. (J). (ps-2). 23.99 (978-0-8136-4246-8(9)) Modern Curriculum Pr.

Guys' Guides. 2005. (Illus.). 48p. (gr. 5-8). lib. bdg. 95.80 (978-0-8239-4094-3(2)) Rosen Publishing Group, Inc., The.

Guys' Guides, 6 bks. Incl. Chillin' A Guy's Guide to Friendship. Sommers, Michael A. (YA). 2005. lib. bdg. 23.95 (978-0-8239-3160-6(9) , GUCHIL); Dating & Relating : A Guy's Guide to Girls. McCarthy, Tara. (YA). 1999. lib. bdg. 17.95 (978-0-8239-3110-1(2) , GUDARE, Rosen Central); Real Deal : A Guy's Guide to Being a Guy. Roberts, Jeremy. (YA). 2005. lib. bdg. 23.95 (978-0-8239-3104-0(8) , GUREDE); Stay Cool : A Guy's Guide to Handling Conflict. Hayhurst, Chris. (YA). 2005. lib. bdg. 23.95 (978-0-8239-3159-0(5) , GUSTCO); Top of Your Game : A Guy's Guide to Looking & Feeling Good. Eshom, Dan. (YA). 2000. lib. bdg. 17.95 (978-0-8239-3083-8(1) , GUTOGA, Rosen Central); You Ought to Know : A Guy's Guide to Sex. Kelly, Bill. (J). 2005. lib. bdg. 23.95 (978-0-8239-3084-5(X) , GUYOSH); 48p. (gr. 5-8). (Illus.). Set lib. bdg. 107.70 o.p. (978-0-8239-9088-7(5) , GUGUID, Rosen Central) Rosen Publishing Group, Inc., The.

H Is for Hygiene: H Is for Hope Book Series. 2007. (Illus.). (J). 8.00 ***(978-0-9794377-0-0(9))*** Turngroup Technologies, LLC.

Happy, Healthy Me! 2000. (Learning Fun for Little Ones Ser.). (Illus.). 64p. (ps-1). pap. 8.99 (978-0-88724-584-8(6) , CD-6411) Carson-Dellosa Publishing Co., Inc.

Harcourt School Publishers Staff. Be Active! Program: Health & Fitness. 4th ed. 2004. (Illus.). (J). (gr. k-2). 311.60 (978-0-15-341407-7(3)); (gr. 3-6). 314.90 (978-0-15-341408-4(1)) Harcourt Schl. Pubs.

—Elements of Safety & Health: Intermediate Level. 3rd ed. 2003. 43.40 (978-0-15-339905-3(8)) Harcourt Schl. Pubs.

—Elements of Safety & Health: Primary Level. 3rd ed. 2003. 43.40 (978-0-15-339904-6(X)) Harcourt Schl. Pubs.

—Harcourt Science: Health Activity Book. 2nd ed. 2002. (Harcourt Science Ser.). (Illus.). (gr. 1 up). pap., pupil's gde. ed. 20.80 (978-0-15-325764-3(4)); (gr. 2 up). pap., pupil's gde. ed. 20.80 (978-0-15-325765-0(2)); (gr. 3 up). pap., pupil's gde. ed. 25.90 (978-0-15-325766-7(0)); (gr. 4 up). pap., pupil's gde. ed. 25.90 (978-0-15-325767-4(9)); (gr. 5 up). pap., pupil's gde. ed. 25.90 (978-0-15-325768-1(7)); (gr. 6 up). pap., pupil's gde. ed. 25.90 (978-0-15-325769-8(5)) Harcourt Schl. Pubs.

—Health & Fitness: Activity Book. 4th ed. 2003. (ps). pap., act. bk. ed. 4.80 (978-0-15-341170-0(8)) Harcourt Schl. Pubs.

—Health & Fitness: Resources for Spanish Speakers. 4th ed. 2004. (SPA.). (gr. 1). pap. 20.00 (978-0-15-341180-9(5)); (gr. 2). pap. 20.00 (978-0-15-341181-6(3)); (gr. 3). pap. 25.40 (978-0-15-341182-3(1)); (gr. 4). pap. 25.40 (978-0-15-341183-0(X)); (gr. 5). pap. 25.40 (978-0-15-341184-7(8)); (gr. 6). pap. 25.40 (978-0-15-341185-4(6)) Harcourt Schl. Pubs.

—Health & Fitness 2006 - Grade 1. 2nd ed. 2002. tchr. ed. 150.90 (978-0-15-337533-0(7)); stu. ed. 39.80 (978-0-15-337524-8(8)) Harcourt Schl. Pubs.

—Health & Fitness 2006 - Grade 2. 2nd ed. 2002. tchr. ed. 153.10 (978-0-15-337534-7(5)); stu. ed. 39.80 (978-0-15-337525-5(6)) Harcourt Schl. Pubs.

—Health & Fitness 2006 - Grade 3. 2nd ed. 2002. 168.60 (978-0-15-337535-4(3)); stu. ed. 46.70 (978-0-15-337526-2(4)) Harcourt Schl. Pubs.

—Health & Fitness 2006 - Grade 4. 2nd ed. 2002. 50.10 (978-0-15-337527-9(2)); tchr. ed. 171.50 (978-0-15-337536-1(1)) Harcourt Schl. Pubs.

—Health & Fitness 2006 - Grade 5. 2nd ed. 2002. 53.10 (978-0-15-337529-3(9)); tchr. ed. 177.80 (978-0-15-337537-8(X)) Harcourt Schl. Pubs.

—Health & Fitness 2006 - Grade 6. 2nd ed. 2002. 56.20 (978-0-15-337530-9(2)); tchr. ed. 182.70 (978-0-15-337538-5(8)) Harcourt Schl. Pubs.

—Health & Fitness 2006 - Grade K. 2nd ed. 2002. tchr. ed. 137.40 (978-0-15-337531-6(0)) Harcourt Schl. Pubs.

—Health & Fitness 5-Pack: Activity Book. 4th ed. 2003. (ps). act. bk. ed. 23.70 (978-0-15-341171-7(6)) Harcourt Schl. Pubs.

—Health & Fitness, Grade 3-6. 4th ed. 2003. pap., tchr. ed. 88.20 (978-0-15-341101-4(5)) Harcourt Schl. Pubs.

—Health & Fitness, Grade K-2. 4th ed. 2003. pap., tchr. ed. 84.80 (978-0-15-341100-7(7)) Harcourt Schl. Pubs.

—A Visit to the Doctor. 3rd ed. 2002. (Illus.). pap. 5.10 (978-0-15-327703-0(3)) Harcourt Schl. Pubs.

—Your Health. 2002. 2nd ed. (ps). pap., act. bk. ed. 5.00 (978-0-15-338353-4(3)); 3rd ed. (Illus.). (gr. 1 up). pap. 99.10 (978-0-15-334698-9(1)) Harcourt Schl. Pubs.

—Your Health Big Book. 3rd ed. 2002. (Your Health Ser.). (Illus.). (gr. 2 up). pap. 99.10 (978-0-15-334699-6(X)) Harcourt Schl. Pubs.

—Your Health Big Book, Grade 1. 3rd ed. 2002. (Your Health Ser.). (gr. 1 up). pap., tchr. ed. 43.50 (978-0-15-334700-9(7)) Harcourt Schl. Pubs.

—Your Health Big Book, Grade 2. 3rd ed. 2002. (Your Health Ser.). (gr. 2 up). pap., tchr. ed. 43.50 (978-0-15-334701-6(5)) Harcourt Schl. Pubs.

—Your Health, Pre-K. 2nd ed. 2002. tchr. ed. 86.40 (978-0-15-338352-6(6)) Harcourt Schl. Pubs.

Harris, H. Robie. Its Perfectly Normal: Changing Bodies, Growing up, Sex, & Sexual Health. Emberley, Michael, illus. 10th anniv. ed. 2004. 96p. (J). (gr. 5 up). 22.99 (978-0-7636-2610-5(4)) Candlewick Pr.

Harris, Robie H. Its Perfectly Normal: A Book about Changing Bodies, Growing Up, Sex, & Sexual Health. Emberley, Michael, illus. 10th anniv. ed. 2004. 96p. (gr. 5 up). pap. 10.99 (978-0-7636-2433-0(0)) Candlewick Pr.

Hayes, Marilyn. Jumbo Health Yearbook: Grade 3. (Jumbo Health Ser.). 96p. (J). (gr. 3). 15.95 (978-0-8209-0063-6(X) , B JHY 3) ESP, Inc.

—Jumbo Health Yearbook: Grade 4. (Jumbo Health Ser.). 96p. (J). (gr. 4). 15.95 (978-0-8209-0064-3(8) , B JHY 4) ESP, Inc.

Health. 2000. (McGraw-Hill Health Ser.). (gr. 1 up). (978-0-02-277384-7(3)); (gr. 2 up). (978-0-02-277386-1(X)); Vol. 2. (gr. 2 up). (978-0-02-277387-8(8)) Macmillan/McGraw-Hill Schl. Div.

Health Activity Pad. 1999. (McGraw-Hill Health Ser.). (gr. 3 up). (978-0-02-276868-3(8)); (gr. 4 up). (978-0-02-276869-0(6)); (gr. 5 up). (978-0-02-276871-3(8)); (gr. 6 up). (978-0-02-276872-0(6)) Macmillan/McGraw-Hill Schl. Div.

Health Alert, 5 bks., Group 2. Incl. Allergies. Hicks, Terry Allan. (Illus.). 64p. (978-0-7614-1918-1(7)); Common Cold. Hicks, Terry Allan. (Illus.). 64p. (978-0-7614-1913-6(6)); Eating Disorders. Bjorklund, Ruth. (Illus.). 64p. (978-0-7614-1914-3(4)); Food Borne Illnesses. Bjorklund, Ruth. (Illus.). 64p. (978-0-7614-1917-4(9)); Leukemia. Klosterman, Lorrie. (978-0-7614-1916-7(0)); Mononucleosis. Hoffmann, Gretchen. (Illus.). 64p. (978-0-7614-1915-0(2)); (J). 2005. 2005. (978-0-7614-1912-9(8) , Benchmark Bks.) Cavendish, Marshall Corp.

Health & Fitness, 4 bks., Set. 2000. (Illus.). (J). pap. (978-0-7398-4275-1(7)) Raintree.

Health & Fitness, 4 bks., Set. Incl. Adolescence. Bryan, Jenny. 1999. lib. bdg. 27.12 (978-0-7398-1346-1(3)); Diet & Nutrition. Westcott, Patsy. 2000. lib. bdg. 27.12 (978-0-7398-1344-7(7)); Drinking, Smoking & Other Drugs. Haughton, Emma & Haughton, Emma. 1999. lib. bdg. 27.12 (978-0-7398-1345-4(5)); Exercise. Sadgrove, Judy. 1999. lib. bdg. 27.12 (978-0-7398-1347-8(1)); (Illus.). 48p. (J). (gr. 4-6). 1999. Set lib. bdg. 108.48 (978-0-7398-1348-5(X)) Raintree.

Health & the Human Body Classroom Library. (gr. k-2). lib. bdg. 81.95 (978-0-7368-7134-1(9)) Red Brick Learning.

Health & the Human Body Complete Unit. (gr. k-2). 468.95 (978-0-7368-7144-0(6)) Red Brick Learning.

Health & the Human Body II Classroom Library. (gr. k-2). lib. bdg. 63.95 (978-0-7368-8825-7(X)) Red Brick Learning.

Health & the Human Body II Complete Unit. (gr. k-2). 363.95 (978-0-7368-9068-7(8)) Red Brick Learning.

Health Big Book. 2000. (McGraw-Hill Health Ser.). (gr. k up). (978-0-02-277382-3(7)); Vol. 2. (gr. 1 up). (978-0-02-277385-4(1)) Macmillan/McGraw-Hill Schl. Div.

Health Issues New Titles: Incl. Asthma/Cancer/Diabetes/Dyslexia, 4 bks. 2002. (Illus.). (YA). (gr. 6-8). lib. bdg. 114.16 (978-0-7398-5270-5(1)) Raintree.

Health Issues Series, 12 bks., Set. Incl. AIDS. Whelan. (YA). 2001. lib. bdg. 28.54 (978-0-7398-4771-8(6)); Alcohol. Lamb, Kirsten. (YA). 2002. lib. bdg. 28.54 (978-0-7398-4772-5(4)); Asthma. Lennard-Brown, Sarah. (J). 2002. lib. bdg. 28.54 (978-0-7398-5218-7(3)); Cancer. Lamb, Kirsten. (J). 2002. lib. bdg. 28.54 (978-0-7398-5219-4(1)); Diabetes. Whelan, Jo. (J). 2002. lib. bdg. 28.54 (978-0-7398-5220-0(5)); Drugs. Lennard-Brown, Sarah. (YA). 2002. lib. bdg. 28.54 (978-0-7398-4773-2(2)); Dyslexia. Wiltshire, Paula. (J). 2002. lib. bdg. 28.54 (978-0-7398-5221-7(3)); Eating Disorders. Whelan, Jo. (YA). 2001. lib. bdg. 28.54 (978-0-7398-4421-2(0)); Pregnancy. Lamb, Kirsten. (YA). 2001. lib. bdg. 28.54 (978-0-7398-4418-2(0)); Sexually Transmitted Diseases. Whelan, Jo. (YA). 2001. lib. bdg. 28.54 (978-0-7398-4420-5(2)); Smoking. Morgan, Sally. (YA). 2002. lib. bdg. 28.54 (978-0-7398-4774-9(0)); Stress & Depression. Lennard-Brown, Sarah. (YA). 2001. lib. bdg. 28.54 (978-0-7398-4419-9(9)); 64p. (gr. 6-8). (Illus.). 2002. Set lib. bdg. 342.72 (978-0-7398-5271-2(X)) Raintree.

Health Matters Field Trip Series, 3 cass.; set. 2004. (NOVA Classroom Field Trips Ser.). (gr. 7 up). tchr. ed. 49.95 (978-1-57807-639-0(0) , WG1156) WGBH Boston Video.

Health Matters Series. 2003. (J). (gr. 3-5). lib. bdg. 145.32 (978-1-58810-849-4(X)) Heinemann Library.

Health Quest, Set. 2004. (Illus.). 360p. (ps-2). 35.95 (978-1-58095-929-2(6) , ES9615, Lifepac) Alpha Omega Pubns., Inc.

Health Quest II, 5 vols., Set. 2004. (Illus.). (YA). (gr. 9-12). tchr. ed., stu. ed. 33.95 (978-0-7403-0182-7(9) , ES9715, Lifepac) Alpha Omega Pubns., Inc.

Health Syllabus & Tests. 1999. 10p. (J). ring bd. 2.50 (978-1-57896-065-1(7) , 2317, Hewitt Homeschooling Resources) Hewitt Research Foundation, Inc.

Healthy Eating New Food Guide Pyramid. 2006. (Illus.). 24p. (J). (gr. k-2). 18.50 ***(978-0-531-17852-2(8))*** Scholastic Library Publishing.

Heart E Heart & Friends Storybook for Children Ages 3 to 5 Years Old: A Children's Way to a Healthy Lifestyle. 2005. (J). per. 7.95 (978-0-9762703-3-1(1)) Gilliam, T. & Associates, LLC.

Heart E Heart & Friends Storybook for Children Ages 5 to 8 Years Old: A Children's Way to a Healthy Lifestyle. 2005. (J). per. 6.95 (978-0-9762703-4-8(X)) Gilliam, T. & Associates, LLC.

Heinlen, Marieka, illus. Germs Are Not for Sharing. 2006. (Best Behavior Ser.). 40p. (J). (ps-2). pap. 11.95 (978-1-57542-197-1(6)) Free Spirit Publishing, Inc.

—Germs Are Not for Sharing Board Book. 2006. (Best Behavior Ser.). 24p. (J). (ps). 7.95 (978-1-57542-196-4(8)) Free Spirit Publishing, Inc.

Hewitt, Sally. Health & Diet: Looking after Myself. 2005. (Science Starters Ser.). (Illus.). 32p. (J). (gr. 3-7). lib. bdg. 27.10 (978-1-59604-011-3(4)) Stargazer Bks.

Hibbert, Adam. Puberty: It's Your Health. 2005. (Illus.). 48p. (YA). (gr. 6 up). lib. bdg. 29.95 (978-1-58340-592-5(5)) Smart Apple Media.

Holt, Rinehart and Winston Staff. Decisions for Health: Blue Edition. 4th ed. Date not set. (YA). 62.20 (978-0-03-066817-3(4)) Holt, Rinehart & Winston.

—Decisions for Health Blue. 4th ed. 2004. (SPA.). 62.20 (978-0-03-068149-3(9)) Holt, Rinehart & Winston.

—Decisions for Health Blue: Chapter Resource Introduction Booklet. 4th ed. Date not set. pap. 4.20 (978-0-03-068934-5(1)) Holt, Rinehart & Winston.

—Decisions for Health Blue: Decision-Making. 4th ed. Date not set. pap., wbk. ed. 7.20 (978-0-03-068356-5(4)) Holt, Rinehart & Winston.

—Decisions for Health Blue, Chptr. 21: Health & Environment. 4th ed. 2004. pap. 11.20 (978-0-03-068057-1(3)) Holt, Rinehart & Winston.

—Decisions for Health Green. 4th ed. 2004. (SPA.). 53.60 (978-0-03-068147-9(2)); pap., stu. ed. 11.13 (978-0-03-068348-0(3)) Holt, Rinehart & Winston.

—Decisions for Health Green: Chapter Resource Introduction Booklet. 4th ed. Date not set. (YA). pap. 4.20 (978-0-03-068932-1(5)) Holt, Rinehart & Winston.

—Decisions for Health Green: Decision-Making Workbook. 4th ed. 2004. pap., wbk. ed. 5.60 (978-0-03-068346-6(7)) Holt, Rinehart & Winston.

—Decisions for Health Red. 4th ed. 2004. (SPA.). 59.00 (978-0-03-068148-6(0)) Holt, Rinehart & Winston.

—Decisions for Health Red: Chapter Resource Introduction Booklet. 4th ed. Date not set. pap. 4.20 (978-0-03-068933-8(3)) Holt, Rinehart & Winston.

—Decisions for Health Red: Decision-Making. 4th ed. 2004. pap., wbk. ed. 7.00 (978-0-03-068351-0(3)) Holt, Rinehart & Winston.

—Decisions for Health Green Chptr. 15: Health & Safety. 4th ed. 2004. pap. 11.20 (978-0-03-068037-3(9)) Holt, Rinehart & Winston.

—Environmental Science Chptr. 20: Environment & Human Health. 4th ed. Date not set. pap. 11.20 (978-0-03-068082-3(4)) Holt, Rinehart & Winston.

—Healthcare Blue, Chptr. 20: Consumer Health. 4th ed. 2004. pap. 11.20 (978-0-03-068056-4(5)) Holt, Rinehart & Winston.

—Holt Science & Technology Chapter 28: Life Science: Staying Healthy. 5th ed. 2004. (Illus.). pap. 12.86 (978-0-03-030261-9(7)) Holt, Rinehart & Winston.

—A Lifetime of Health: Chapter Resource File Introduction Booklet. 4th ed. Date not set. pap. 4.20 (978-0-03-068931-4(7)) Holt, Rinehart & Winston.

—A Lifetime of Health: Life Skills. 4th ed. Date not set. pap., wbk. ed. 11.20 (978-0-03-068117-2(0)) Holt, Rinehart & Winston.

—A Lifetime of Health Chptr. 16: Adolesence & Adulthood. 4th ed. Date not set. pap. 11.20 (978-0-03-068109-7(X)) Holt, Rinehart & Winston.

—A Lifetime of Health Chptr. 19: Building Relationships. 4th ed. Date not set. pap. 11.20 (978-0-03-068113-4(8)) Holt, Rinehart & Winston.

—Reading Guide Program Lifehealth Sexual Resource. 4th ed. 2003. cd-rom 59.33 (978-0-03-066618-6(X)) Holt, Rinehart & Winston.

Honeyman-Lowe, Gina & Lowe, John C. Your Guide to Metabolic Health. 2003. (Illus.). 384p. (YA). per. 24.95 (978-0-9741238-0-6(3)) McDowell Health-Science Bks., LLC.

Houston, Jack. Jumbo Health Yearbook: Grade 5. (Jumbo Health Ser.). 96p. (J). (gr. 5). 15.95 (978-0-8209-0065-0(6) , B JHY 5) ESP, Inc.

—Jumbo Health Yearbook: Grade 6. (Jumbo Health Ser.). 96p. (J). (gr. 6). 15.95 (978-0-8209-0066-7(4) , B JHY 6) ESP, Inc.

—Jumbo Health Yearbook: Grade 7. (Jumbo Health Ser.). 96p. (J). (gr. 7). 15.95 (978-0-8209-0067-4(2) , B JHY 7) ESP, Inc.

—Jumbo Health Yearbook: Grade 8. (Jumbo Health Ser.). 96p. (YA). (gr. 8). 15.95 (978-0-8209-0068-1(0) , B JHY 8) ESP, Inc.

Hungry Kids, Healthy Kids. 2005. (Illus.). 32p. per. 3.95 (978-0-9747133-8-0(4)) Thomas, Frederic Inc.

It's Time to Wash. 2002. 12p. (J). bds. 7.95 (978-1-84250-493-2(2)) Parragon, Inc.

Ivey, Catherine. Totally Amazing Careers in Health Sciences. 2006. (J). 7.80 (978-0-9753920-9-6(3)) Sally Ride Science.

Izenberg, Neil, ed. Human Diseases & Conditions, 3 vols., Set. 1999. (Illus.). 912p. (J). 355.00 (978-0-684-80543-6(X) , GML00502-167276, Charles Scribner's Sons) Thomson Gale.

—Human Diseases & Disorders, 3 vols. 1999. (Illus.). (J). Vol. 1. 125.00 (978-0-684-80541-2(3)); Vol. 2. vii, 311p. 125.00 (978-0-684-80542-9(1)) Simon & Schuster.

Jesse, Janeen. The Nail Book: Professional Secrets of Personal Nail Care. l.t. ed. 2004. (Illus.). 120p. (YA). cd-rom 24.95 (978-0-9748796-1-1(4) , EB030915CD) Pro-NailTech.com.

Johnson, Gary M., illus. The Adventures of MolarMan: Oral Health Bilingual (English/Spanish) Coloring Workbook. 2006. (ENG & SPA.). (J). ***(978-0-9791794-1-9(6))*** Johnson, Gary.

Johnson, Kandy & Kids for Health Staff. Health Education Adventure Video Series, Kids for Health: Fifth Grade Facilitator's Manual. 2nd ed. 2006. (Illus.). (J). spiral bd. 175.00 (978-1-933847-12-2(3)) Kids For Health, Inc.

—Health Education Adventure Video Series, Kids for Health: Fifth Grade Facilitator's Manual/DVD Set. 2nd ed. 2006. (Illus.). spiral bd. 400.00 incl. DVD (978-1-933847-33-7(6)) Kids For Health, Inc.

—Health Education Adventure Video Series, Kids for Health: Fifth Grade Facilitator's Manual/VHS Set, VHS. 2nd ed. 2006. (Illus.). spiral bd. 400.00 incl. VHS (978-1-933847-05-4(0)) Kids For Health, Inc.

—Health Education Adventure Video Series, Kids for Health: First Grade Facilitator's Manual. 2nd ed. 2006. (Illus.). spiral bd. 210.00 (978-1-933847-08-5(5)) Kids For Health, Inc.

—Health Education Adventure Video Series, Kids for Health: First Grade Facilitator's Manual/DVD Set. 2nd ed. 2006. (Illus.). spiral bd. 475.00 incl. DVD (978-1-933847-29-0(8)) Kids For Health, Inc.

—Health Education Adventure Video Series, Kids for Health: First Grade Facilitator's Manual/VHS Set, VHS. 2nd ed. 2006. (Illus.). spiral bd. 475.00 incl. VHS (978-1-933847-01-6(8)) Kids For Health, Inc.

—Health Education Adventure Video Series, Kids for Health: Fourth Grade Facilitator's Manual. 2nd ed. 2006. (Illus.). spiral bd. 175.00 (978-1-933847-11-5(5)) Kids For Health, Inc.

—Health Education Adventure Video Series, Kids for Health: Fourth Grade Facilitator's Manual/DVD, DVD. 2nd ed. 2006. (Illus.). spiral bd. 400.00 incl. DVD (978-1-933847-32-0(8)) Kids For Health, Inc.

—Health Education Adventure Video Series, Kids for Health: Fourth Grade Facilitator's Manual/VHS Set, VHS. 2nd ed. 2006. (Illus.). spiral bd. 400.00 incl. VHS (978-1-933847-04-7(2)) Kids For Health, Inc.

—Health Education Adventure Video Series, Kids for Health: Kindergarten Facilitator's Manual. 2nd ed. 2006. (Illus.). spiral bd. 210.00 (978-1-933847-07-8(7)) Kids For Health, Inc.

—Health Education Adventure Video Series, Kids for Health: Kindergarten Facilitator's Manual/DVD Set. 2nd ed. 2006. (Illus.). spiral bd. 475.00 incl. DVD (978-1-933847-28-3(X)) Kids For Health, Inc.

—Health Education Adventure Video Series, Kids for Health: Second Grade Facilitator's Manual. 2nd ed. 2006. (Illus.). spiral bd. 210.00 (978-1-933847-09-2(3)) Kids For Health, Inc.

—Health Education Adventure Video Series, Kids for Health: Second Grade Facilitator's Manual/DVD Set. 2nd ed. 2006. (Illus.). spiral bd. 475.00 incl. DVD (978-1-933847-30-6(1)) Kids For Health, Inc.

—Health Education Adventure Video Series, Kids for Health: Second Grade Facilitator's Manual/VHS Set, VHS. 2nd ed. 2006. (Illus.). spiral bd. 475.00 incl. VHS (978-1-933847-02-3(6)) Kids For Health, Inc.

—Health Education Adventure Video Series, Kids for Health: Sixth Grade Facilitator's Manual. 2nd ed. 2006. (Illus.). spiral bd. 175.00 (978-1-933847-13-9(1)) Kids For Health, Inc.

—Health Education Adventure Video Series, Kids for Health: Sixth Grade Facilitator's Manual/DVD Set. 2nd ed. 2006. (Illus.). spiral bd. 400.00 incl. DVD (978-1-933847-34-4(4)) Kids For Health, Inc.

—Health Education Adventure Video Series, Kids for Health: Sixth Grade Facilitator's Manual/VHS Set, VHS. 2nd ed. 2006. (Illus.). spiral bd. 400.00 incl. VHS (978-1-933847-06-1(9)) Kids For Health, Inc.

—Health Education Adventure Video Series, Kids for Health: Third Grade Facilitator's Manual. 2nd ed. 2006. (Illus.). spiral bd. 210.00 (978-1-933847-10-8(7)) Kids For Health, Inc.

—Health Education Adventure Video Series, Kids for Health: Third Grade Facilitator's Manual/DVD Set. 2nd ed. 2006. (Illus.). spiral bd. 475.00 incl. DVD (978-1-933847-31-3(X)) Kids For Health, Inc.

—Health Education Adventure Video Series, Kids for Health: Third Grade Facilitator's Manual/VHS Set, VHS. 2nd ed. 2006. (Illus.). spiral bd. 475.00 incl. VHS (978-1-933847-03-0(4)) Kids For Health, Inc.

Kalbacken, Joan. Food Safety. De Capua, Sarah E., ed. 1998. (Illus.). 48p. (J). (ps-ps). lib. bdg. 13.75 (978-0-606-22896-1(9)) Tandem Library Bks.

Keep Books at The Ohio State University Staff. Health & Safety 1. ed. 2006. (Illus.). 8p. (J). pap. (978-1-893986-26-8(8)) Keep Bks.

—Health & Safety 2, Set. 2006. (J). pap. (978-1-893986-27-5(6)) Keep Bks.

Keep Clean. (Your Health Ser.). 24p. (J). 6.95 (978-0-7368-4448-2(1)) Capstone Pr., Inc.

Keeping Clean: Early Level Satellite Individual Title Six-Packs. (Sails Literacy Ser.). 16p. (gr. 1-2). 27.00 (978-0-7578-6517-6(8)) Rigby Education.

Keeping Healthy. 2005. (Pebble Plus Ser.). (Illus.). (J). (gr. k-1). lib. bdg. 95.58 (978-0-7368-4406-2(6)) Capstone Pr., Inc.

Keeping Water Clean, 6 vols. (gr. k-2). 28.95 (978-0-7368-8639-0(7)) Red Brick Learning.

Kellogg, John Harvey. The House We Live In: Based on First Book in Physiology & Hygiene. Brazille, Leonard et al, eds. 3rd rev. ed. 1998. (Illus.). 80p. (J). (gr. 3-8). reprint ed. pap. 7.95 (978-0-9665786-0-7(0)) L.M.N. Publishing International, Inc.

Ketch, Susan & Scraper, Katherine. It's Snack Time! Futrell, Ashley, ed. 2005. 128p. (J). per. 11.99 (978-1-59441-043-7(7) , CD-104043) Carson-Dellosa Publishing Co., Inc.

KIDs: Healthy Water, Healthy People. 2001. 16p. (J). pap. 0.60 (978-1-888631-08-1(2)) Watercourse, The.

Kids for Health Staff & Johnson, Kandy. Health Education Adventure Video Series, Kids for Heatlh: Kindergarten Facilitator's Manual/VHS Set, VHS. 2nd ed. 2006. (Illus.). spiral bd. 475.00 incl. VHS (978-1-933847-00-9(X)) Kids For Health, Inc.

Kleinberg, Naomi. Grover's Guide to Good Eating. Leigh, Tom & Yee, Josie, illus. 2007. (Happy Healthy Monsters Ser.). 32p. (J). (ps-ps). 6.99 (*978-0-375-84063-0(X) , Random Hse. Bks. for Young Readers) Random Hse. Children's Bks.

Kleinmintz, Neala. A Healthy You. Grimm, Gary, ed. Schwab, Vanessa, illus. 1999. 32p. (YA). (gr. 1 up). 12.95 (978-1-56490-124-8(6)) Grim, Gary & Assocs.

Koellhoffer, Tara. Health & Medicine. 2006. (Illus.). 64p. (J). 30.00 (978-0-7910-9122-7(8) , Chelsea Clubhouse) Facts On File, Inc.

Kray, Peter. The Monster. 2003. 91p. per. 12.95 (978-0-9715715-1-8(1)) Greenleaf Book Group.

Lassieur, Allison. Head Lice. 2000. (My Health Ser.). (Illus.). 48p. (YA). (gr. 3-5). pap. 6.95 (978-0-531-16450-1(0) , Watts, Franklin) Scholastic Library Publishing.

Lasslett, Sally, et al. Jump Start 9 & 10: Health & Physical Education. 2007. pap. 41.00 incl. cd-rom (*978-0-521-70167-9(8)) Cambridge Univ. Pr.

Learning Works Staff & Schwartz, Linda. Squeaky Clean Hygiene. Clark Editorial and Design Staff, ed. Armstrong, Beverly, illus. 1999. (Learning Works Health Ser.). 56p. (J). (gr. 1-3). pap. 9.99 (978-0-88160-308-8(2) , LW-377, Learning Works, The) Creative Teaching Pr., Inc.

Leeds, Elke, contrib. by. Toolbox of Hope: For When Your Body Doesn't Feel Good. l.t. ed. 2001. (Illus.). 132p. spiral bd. 24.95 (978-0-9716673-0-3(6)) Healing Heart Communications, Inc.

Levchuck, Caroline M. & Drohan, Michele Ingber. Healthy Living, 3 vols. 2000. (J). (978-0-7876-3921-1(4)) Thomson Gale.

—Healthy Living: Exercise, Nutrition & Other Healthy Habits, 3 vols., Set. 2000. (Illus.). 650p. (J). (gr. 5-8). lib. bdg. 181.00 (978-0-7876-3918-1(4) , GML00502-113715, UXL) Thomson Gale.

Levchuck, Caroline M. & Drohan, Michele Ingber, contrib. by. Healthy Living, 3 vols. 2000. (J). (978-0-7876-3919-8(2) , UXL); (978-0-7876-3920-4(6)) Thomson Gale.

Lewellen, Judie. The Teen Body Book: A Guide to Your Changing Body. 1999. (Your Body, Your Self Bks.). (Illus.). 144p. (YA). (gr. 4-9). pap. 11.95 (978-0-7373-0165-6(1) , 01651W) McGraw-Hill/Contemporary.

Lewis, Carole. New First Place Favorites. 2004. 19.99 (978-0-8307-3231-9(4) , Gospel Light) Gospel Light Pubns.

Libal, Autumn. Fats, Sugars, & Empty Calories: The Fast Food Habit. 2004. (Obesity Ser.). (Illus.). 104p. (J). (ps-7). lib. bdg. 23.95 (978-1-59084-943-9(4)) Mason Crest Pubs.

Library of Health & Living Set. 2005. (Library of Health & Living Ser.). (gr. 9). 304p. 3130.00 (978-0-8160-6536-3(5)); 304-1120p. 3055.00 (978-0-8160-6334-5(6)); 304-1120p. 2496.00 (978-0-8160-6123-5(8)) Facts On File, Inc.

Lieberman, E. James & Troccoli, Karen L. Like It Is: A Teen Sex Guide. 1998. (Illus.). 216p. (C). (gr. 6 up). pap. 29.95 (978-0-7864-0526-8(0)) McFarland & Co., Inc. Pubs.

Lilly, Melinda. Dirty & Clean. Thompson, Scott M., illus. 2003. 24p. (J). 20.64 (978-1-58952-636-5(8)) Rourke Publishing, LLC.

Limpieza y Salud Todo el Dia Series. 2003. (Limpieza y Salud Todo el Dia Ser.). (Illus.). (J). 96.00 (978-0-8239-6908-1(8)); Set. (SPA., lib. bdg. 96.00 (978-0-8239-6907-4(X)) Rosen Publishing Group, Inc., The. (Buenas Letra).

Llewellyn, Claire. Around Town. Gordon, Mike, illus. 2006. (Watch Out! Bks.). 32p. (J). (gr. k-2). pap. 5.99 (978-0-7641-3326-8(8)) Barron's Educational Series, Inc.

—Como Nacen los Bebes? Aprender Sobre Sexualidad. Gordon, Mike, illus. (SPA.). (J). (gr. k-2). pap. (978-950-24-0944-3(2)) Albatros ARG. *Dist:* Lectorum Pubns., Inc.

—Health & Growth. 2005. (Illus.). 24p. (J). (gr. 1-4). lib. bdg. (978-1-84234-336-4(X) , Cherrytree Books) Evans Publishing Group.

—How to Stay Healthy. 2006. (Illus.). 24p. (J). (978-1-59771-024-4(5)) Sea-To-Sea Pubns.

—Me Hace Bien o Mal? Aprender Sobre Medicamentos, Drogas y Salud. Gordon, Mike, illus. (SPA.). (J). (gr. k-2). pap. (978-950-24-0946-7(9)) Albatros ARG. *Dist:* Lectorum Pubns., Inc.

—Why Should I Eat Well? Gordon, Mike, illus. 2005. (Why Should I? Bks.). 32p. (J). pap. 6.99 (978-0-7641-3217-9(2)) Barron's Educational Series, Inc.

—Why Wash? 1999. (gr. k-3). lib. bdg. 14.45 (978-0-613-30877-9(8)) Tandem Library Bks.

Llewellyn, Claire. Your Body. 2007. (J). (*978-1-59771-096-1(2)) Sea-To-Sea Pubns.

Llewelyn, Clair. Keep Healthy! 2006. (Illus.). 24p. (J). lib. bdg. 16.95 (978-1-59566-194-4(8)) QEB Publishing Inc.

Lombardo, Michelle. The Healthy Heart Challenge Activity Book. Herron, Mark, illus. 2000. 32p. (J). (gr. 2-4). pap., wbk. ed. 4.95 (978-0-9648438-8-2(9)) Wellness, Inc.

—The Organ Wise Guys - the Healthy Heart Challenge. Herron, Mark, illus. 2000. (OrganWise Guys: 3). 32p. (J). (gr. 2-4). mass mkt. 14.95 (978-0-9648438-7-5(0)) Wellness, Inc.

Mackenzie, Catherine. The Deep Black Pond at No 12 12: Tammy & Jake Learn about Health & Sickness. (Illus.). 160p. (J). mass mkt. 5.99 (978-1-85792-733-7(8) , Christian Focus) Christian Focus Pubns. GBR. *Dist:* Riverside.

Mahony, Mary. There's an "S" on My Back, "S" Is for Scoliosis. 1999. (Illus.). 196p. (YA). (gr. 5-8). pap. 14.95 (978-0-9658879-1-5(X)) Redding Pr.

Manfredini, Becky. Get up & Move! A Content Area Reader-health. 2005. (Emergent (Prek-2) Health Package Ser.). 16p. (YA). (ps-2). 25.20 (978-0-8215-7826-1(X)) Sadlier, William H. Inc.

Martin, Mildred A. Prudence & Your Health: Workbook for Prudence & the Millers. Martin, Don L., ed. 2002. (Miller Family Ser.). (Illus.). 84p. (J). (gr. 3-6). pap., wbk. ed. 4.50 (978-1-884377-07-5(6)) Green Pastures Pr.

McCaslin, Donna B. My Medical Assistant. 2003. spiral bd. 14.95 (978-0-9718851-2-7(5)) Leigh, Kimbra Inc.

McCauley, John. Harley Teaches. McCauley, John, illus. 1998. (Illus.). 34p. (J). (gr. k-6). 12.95 (978-0-9664005-7-1(7)) American Health Pr.

McCoy, Kathy & Wibbelsman, Charles. The Teenage Body Book. rev. ed. 1999. (Illus.). 1p. (J). (gr. 7-12). pap. 18.95 (978-0-399-52535-3(1) , Perigee Trade) Penguin Group (USA) Inc.

McEwen, Rebecca. Healthy Habits. 2004. (Spyglass Books). (Illus.). 24p. (J). (gr. 1 up). lib. bdg. 18.60 (978-0-7565-0627-8(1)) Compass Point Bks.

McGraw-Hill Staff. Glencoe Health. 10th ed. 2004. (C). stu. ed. 83.32 (978-0-07-861211-4(X) , 9780078612114) Glencoe/McGraw-Hill.

—Glencoe Health, Spanish Student Edition. 10th ed. 2004. (SPA.). (C). 83.32 (978-0-07-862021-8(X) , 9780078620218) Glencoe/McGraw-Hill.

—A Guide to Wellness. (Glencoe Health Ser.). 6th ed. 1998. stu. ed. 89.32 (978-0-02-651562-7(8) , 9780026515627); 8th ed. 2002. (C). stu. ed. 84.64 (978-0-07-823864-2(1) , 9780078238642) Glencoe/McGraw-Hill.

—A Guide to Wellness, Modules, Abstinence. 6th ed. 1998. 13.96 (978-0-02-651588-7(1) , 9780026515887) Glencoe/McGraw-Hill.

—A Guide to Wellness, Modules, HIV/AIDS & Society. 6th ed. 1998. (C). 13.32 (978-0-02-651580-1(6) , 9780026515801) Glencoe/McGraw-Hill.

—A Guide to Wellness, Modules, the Reality of Drugs. 6th ed. 1998. 13.32 (978-0-02-651586-3(5) , 9780026515863) Glencoe/McGraw-Hill.

—Health: Making Life Choices. 2nd ed. 2001. stu. ed. 82.64 (978-0-658-01118-4(9) , 9780658011184) Glencoe/McGraw-Hill.

—Teen Health Course 1. 5th ed. 2002. (Three-Level Middle School Health Ser.). (gr. 6 up). pap., stu. ed., wbk. ed. 11.32 (978-0-07-826117-6(1) , 9780078261176); (C). stu. ed. 60.64 (978-0-07-823935-9(4) , 9780078239359) Glencoe/McGraw-Hill.

—Teen Health, Course 1. 6th ed. 2004. stu. ed. 63.96 (978-0-07-861095-0(8) , 9780078610950) Glencoe/McGraw-Hill.

—Teen Health Course 1, Adolescence: Growing & Changing. 5th ed. 2002. (Three-Level Middle School Health Ser.). (gr. 6 up). 15.32 (978-0-07-826143-5(0) , 9780078261435) Glencoe/McGraw-Hill.

—Teen Health Course 1, Building Character. 5th ed. 2002. (Three-Level Middle School Health Ser.). (gr. 6 up). 15.32 (978-0-07-826145-9(7) , 9780078261459) Glencoe/McGraw-Hill.

—Teen Health Course 1, Conflict Resolution. 5th ed. 2002. (Three-Level Middle School Health Ser.). (gr. 6 up). 15.32 (978-0-07-826147-3(3) , 9780078261473) Glencoe/McGraw-Hill.

—Teen Health Course 1, Spanish Student Edition. 4th ed. 2004. (SPA.). 63.96 (978-0-07-861898-7(3) , 9780078618987) Glencoe/McGraw-Hill.

—Teen Health Course 2. 5th ed. 2002. (Three-Level Middle School Health Ser.). (gr. 7 up). stu. ed. 65.96 (978-0-07-823937-3(0) , 9780078239373) Glencoe/McGraw-Hill.

—Teen Health, Course 2. 6th ed. 2004. stu. ed. 67.32 (978-0-07-861097-4(4) , 9780078610974) Glencoe/McGraw-Hill.

—Teen Health Course 2, Modules, Abstinence. 5th ed. 2002. (Three-Level Middle School Health Ser.). (gr. 7 up). 15.32 (978-0-07-826179-4(1) , 9780078261794) Glencoe/McGraw-Hill.

—Teen Health Course 2, Modules, Safety & Injury Prevention. 5th ed. 2002. (Three-Level Middle School Health Ser.). (C). (gr. 7 up). 15.32 (978-0-07-826181-7(3) , 9780078261817) Glencoe/McGraw-Hill.

—Teen Health Course 2, Modules, Tobacco, Alcohol, & Other Drugs. 5th ed. 2002. (Three-Level Middle School Health Ser.). (C). (gr. 7 up). 15.32 (978-0-07-826183-1(X) , 9780078261831) Glencoe/McGraw-Hill.

—Teen Health Course 2, Spanish Student Edition. 3rd ed. 2004. (SPA.). (C). 67.32 (978-0-07-861899-4(1) , 9780078618994) Glencoe/McGraw-Hill.

—Teen Health Course 3. 5th ed. 2002. (Three-Level Middle School Health Ser.). (gr. 8 up). stu. ed. 69.32 (978-0-07-823939-7(7) , 9780078239397) Glencoe/McGraw-Hill.

—Teen Health, Course 3. 6th ed. 2004. stu. ed. 71.32 (978-0-07-861099-8(0) , 9780078610998) Glencoe/McGraw-Hill.

—Teen Health Course 3, Modules, Healthy Relationships & Sexuality. 5th ed. 2002. (Three-Level Middle School Health Ser.). (C). (gr. 8 up). 15.32 (978-0-07-826211-1(9) , 9780078262111) Glencoe/McGraw-Hill.

McKay, Sindy. We Both Read-Happy & Healthy. 2003. 44p. (J). (gr. 1-2). 7.99 (978-1-891327-47-6(X)) Treasure Bay, Inc.

McMahon, Kara. Squeaky Clean (All about Hygiene) Goldberg, Barry, illus. 2006. 32p. (J). (ps-k). 6.99 (978-0-375-83508-7(3) , Random Hse. Bks. for Young Readers) Random Hse. Children's Bks.

McNulty, John. I Am Your Health. 2006. (Illus.). 32p. (J). (*978-0-9769580-6-2(6)) I Am Your Playground LLC.

Miller, Connie Colwell. Disgusting Places. 2007. (J). (978-0-7368-6801-3(1)) Capstone Pr., Inc.

Miller, Edward. The Monster Health Book: A Guide to Eating Healthy, Being Active, & Feeling Great for Monsters & Kids! Miller, Edward, illus. 2006. (Illus.). 40p. (J). (gr. k-5). 16.95 (978-0-8234-1956-2(8)) Holiday Hse., Inc.

Minden, Cecilia. Exercise by the Numbers. 2008. (J). lib. bdg. 25.26 (*978-1-60279-010-0(8)) Cherry Lake Publishing.

Mitchell, Melanie. Killing Germs. 2005. (Illus.). 32p. (J). pap. 5.95 (978-0-8225-2772-5(3) , Lerner Pubns.) Lerner Publishing Group.

—Mantenerse Limpio. 2005. (Libros para Avanzar (Pull Ahead Bks.)). (SPA., Illus.). 32p. (J). (gr. 3-7). lib. bdg. 22.60 (978-0-8225-3168-5(2) , Ediciones Lerner) Lerner Publishing Group.

Monson-Burton, Marianne. Girls Know Best Vol. 3: Your Words, Your World. 1999. (gr. 3-6). lib. bdg. 17.60 (978-0-613-33368-9(3)) Tandem Library Bks.

Monson-Burton, Marianne, compiled by. Girls Know Best Vol. 3: Your Words, Your World. l.t. ed. 2000. (Girls Know Best Ser.). (Illus.). 153p. (J). (gr. 3 up). lib. bdg. 23.33 (978-0-8368-2672-2(8)) Stevens, Gareth Inc.

Moores, Jeff. The Body Book: An Owner's Guide to Fueling, Fixing, & Running the Most Important Machine You Own. 2002. (Read 180 Ser.). (Illus.). 69p. (YA). (978-0-439-12349-5(6)) Scholastic, Inc.

Morcos, Ann Conti & Pembo, Anthony J., Jr., eds. Health. 2000. (Illus.). (YA). (gr. 6-9). pap. 4.95 (978-1-55708-685-3(0) , MCR754) McDonald Publishing Co.

Mullican, Judy. Healthy Me. Metzger, Jeanne, illus. 2000. (CB Ser.). 7p. (J). (ps-1). pap. 10.95 (978-1-57332-158-7(3)) HighReach Learning, Inc.

Murphy, Frank & Rovin-Murphy, Deborah. Fresh & Fun: Health & Safety:Dozens of Instant & Irresistible Ideas & Activities from Creative Teachers Across the Coun. 2002. 32p. pap. 8.95 (978-0-439-28848-4(7)) Scholastic, Inc.

Murphy, Stuart J. Mighty Maddie. Lum, Bernice, illus. 2004. (MathStart Ser.). 40p. (J). 15.99 (978-0-06-053159-1(2)); pap. 5.99 (978-0-06-053161-4(4)) HarperCollins Pubs.

My Health, 2. 2004. 384.00 (978-0-531-14702-3(9)) Scholastic Library Publishing.

Naik, Anita. My Body, Myself: The Ultimate Health Book for Girls. 2nd rev. ed. 2003. 9999p. (J). pap. 8.99 (978-0-330-34333-6(5) , Macmillan Children's Bks.) Pan Macmillan GBR. *Dist:* Trafalgar Square Publishing.

Nance, Christopher. Choices. 2003. 80p. (J). pap. 6.00 (978-0-9648363-4-1(3)) CPI Pubs.

Nelson, Robin. Staying Clean. 2006. (Illus.). 32p. (J). (gr. 2). pap. 5.95 (978-0-8225-2773-2(1) , Lerner Pubns.) Lerner Publishing Group.

Newton, David E., ed. Sick! Diseases & Disorders, Injuries & Infections, 4 vols., Set. 2000. (Illus.). 814p. (J). (gr. 6 up). lib. bdg. 235.00 (978-0-7876-3922-8(2) , GML00502-1137193719, UXL) Thomson Gale.

—Sick! Diseases & Disorders, Injuries & Infections, 4 vols. 2000. (Illus.). (J). (978-0-7876-3923-5(0)); (978-0-7876-3924-2(9)); (978-0-7876-3925-9(7)); (978-0-7876-3926-6(5)) Thomson Gale. (UXL).

Nuevo Investiguemos 1: Ciencias Naturales y de la Salud. (SPA.). (J). (gr. 1). (978-958-02-1575-2(8)) Editorial Voluntad S.A. COL. *Dist:* Distribuidora Norma, Inc.

Nuevo Investiguemos 2: Ciencias Naturales y de la Salud. (SPA.). (J). (gr. 2). (978-958-02-1576-9(6)) Editorial Voluntad S.A. COL. *Dist:* Distribuidora Norma, Inc.

Nuevo Investiguemos 3: Ciencias Naturales y de la Salud. (SPA.). (J). (gr. 3). (978-958-02-1577-6(4)) Editorial Voluntad S.A. COL. *Dist:* Distribuidora Norma, Inc.

Nuevo Investiguemos 4: Ciencias Naturales y de la Salud. (SPA.). (J). (gr. 4). (978-958-02-1578-3(2)) Editorial Voluntad S.A. COL. *Dist:* Distribuidora Norma, Inc.

Nuevo Investiguemos 5: Ciencias Naturales y de la Salud. (SPA.). (J). (gr. 5). (978-958-02-1579-0(0)) Editorial Voluntad S.A. COL. *Dist:* Distribuidora Norma, Inc.

Nuevo Investiguemos 6: Ciencias Naturales y de la Salud. (SPA.). (978-958-02-1534-9(0)) Editorial Voluntad S.A. COL. *Dist:* Distribuidora Norma, Inc.

Nuevo Investiguemos 7: Ciencias Naturales y de la Salud. (SPA.). (YA). (gr. 7). (978-958-02-1535-6(9)) Editorial Voluntad S.A. COL. *Dist:* Distribuidora Norma, Inc.

Nygard, Bonnie, et al. Wow! Ruby Learns about the World of Wellness: Student Book - Orange Level. 2005. (World of Wellness Health Education Ser.). (Illus.). 88p. pap. 12.00 (978-0-7360-5756-1(0)) Human Kinetics Pubs.

Nygard, Bonnie K., et al. Wow! Cody Investigates the World of Wellness: Student Book - Green Level. 2005. (World of Wellness Health Education Ser.). (Illus.). 88p. pap. 12.00 (978-0-7360-5578-9(9)) Human Kinetics Pubs.

—Wow! Ruby Discovers the World of Wellness: Big Book - Red Level. 2005. (World of Wellness Health Education Ser.). (Illus.). 40p. 79.00 (978-0-7360-5759-2(5)) Human Kinetics Pubs.

—WOW! Ruby Explores the World of Wellness: Student Book - Yellow Level. 5th rev. ed. 2005. (World of Wellness Health Education Ser.). (Illus.). 88p. pap. 12.00 (978-0-7360-5577-2(0)) Human Kinetics Pubs.

—Wow! T. J. 's Adventures in the World of Wellness: Student Book - Blue Level. 2005. (World of Wellness Health Education Ser.). (Illus.). 88p. pap. 12.00 (978-0-7360-5579-6(7)) Human Kinetics Pubs.

Obesity: Modern-Day Epidemic, 10 vols., Set. Incl. America's Unhealthy Lifestyle : Supersize It! Sanna, Ellyn. 2004. (978-1-59084-942-2(6)); Clothing, Cosmetic, & Self-Esteem Tips : Making the Most of the Body You Have. Esherick, Joan. 2005. (978-1-59084-951-4(5)); Diet & Your Emotions : The Comfort Food Falsehood. Esherick, Joan. 2004. lib. bdg. 23.95 (978-1-59084-950-7(7)); Diseases & Disabilities Caused by Weight Problems : The Overloaded Body. Ford, Jean. 2005. (978-1-59084-944-6(2)); Fats, Sugars, & Empty Calories : The Fast Food Habit. Libal, Autumn. 2004. lib. bdg. 23.95 (978-1-59084-943-9(4)); How Genetics & Environment Shape Us : The Destined Body. Hunter, William. 2005. lib. bdg. 23.95 (978-1-59084-948-4(5)); Importance of Physical Activity & Exercise : The Fitness Factor. Libal, Autumn. 2005. lib. bdg. 23.95 (978-1-59084-945-3(0)); Medications & Surgeries for Weight Loss : When Dieting Isn't Enough. Hunter, William. 2005. (978-1-59084-947-7(7)); Social Discrimination & Body Size : Too Big to Fit? Libal, Autumn. 2005. lib. bdg. 23.95 (978-1-59084-949-1(3)); Truth about Diets : The Pros & Cons. Ford, Jean & Libal, Autumn. 2005. lib. bdg. 23.95 (978-1-59084-946-0(9)); (J). (ps-7). (Illus.). 104p. 2005. Set lib. bdg. 239.50 (978-1-59084-941-5(8)) Mason Crest Pubs.

O'Brien-Palmer, Michelle. Healthy Me: Fun Ways to Develop Good Health & Safety Habits. Lee, Fran, illus. 1999. 160p. (J). (gr. k-3). pap. 12.95 (978-1-55652-359-5(9)) Chicago Review Pr., Inc.

Oetting, Judy. Germs. Herr, Tad, illus. 2006. (Rookie Reader Skill Set Ser.). 32p. (J). (gr. k-2). 19.50 (978-0-516-24980-3(0) , Children's Pr.) Scholastic Library Publishing.

Oetting, Judy & Herr, Tad. Germs. 2006. (Illus.). 32p. (YA). pap. 4.95 (978-0-516-24995-7(9) , Children's Pr.) Scholastic Library Publishing.

Olson, Karen W. Eat, Run & Live Healthy. Hamelin, Marie-Micheline, illus. 2006. 20p. (J). pap. 10.95 (978-1-894778-32-9(4)) Theytus Bks., Ltd. CAN. *Dist:* Orca Bk. Pubs. USA.

—Healthy Choices, Healthy Lives. Hamelin, Marie-Micheline, illus. 2006. 20p. (J). pap. 10.95 (978-1-894778-31-2(6)) Theytus Bks., Ltd. CAN. *Dist:* Orca Bk. Pubs. USA.

Penner, Lucille Recht. Clean-Sweep Campers. Billin-Frye, Paige, illus. 2000. (Math Matters Ser.). 32p. (J). (gr. 1-3). pap. 4.95 (978-1-57565-096-8(7)) Kane Pr., The.

Platkin, Charles. Lighten Up. 2005. 224p. (YA). (gr. 7-12). pap. 7.99 (978-1-59514-065-4(4) , Razorbill) Penguin Group (USA) Inc.

Play it Safe! 2005. (Emergent (Prek-2) Health Package Ser.). 12p. (YA). (ps-2). 25.20 (978-0-8215-7848-3(0)) Sadlier, William H. Inc.

Posters. (McGraw-Hill Health Ser.). 2000. (gr. k up). (978-0-02-276893-5(9)); 2000. (gr. 1 up). (978-0-02-276894-2(7)); 2000. (gr. 2 up). (978-0-02-276895-9(5)); 1999. (gr. 3-4). (978-0-02-276896-6(3)); 1999. (gr. 5-6). (978-0-02-276897-3(1)) Macmillan/McGraw-Hill Schl. Div.

Rabe, Tish. Oh the Things You Can Do That Are Good for You. Ruiz, Aristides, illus. 2001. (Cat in the Hat's Learning Library). 48p. (J). (gr. k-3). lib. bdg. 11.99 (978-0-375-91098-2(0) , Random Hse. Bks. for Young Readers) Random Hse. Children's Bks.

—Oh the Things You Can Do That Are Good for You! All About Staying Healthy. Ruiz, Aristides, illus. 2001. (Cat in the Hat's Learning Library). 48p. (J). (gr. k-3). 8.99 (978-0-375-81098-5(6) , Random Hse. Bks. for Young Readers) Random Hse. Children's Bks.

Raintree Steck-Vaughn Staff. Trb Decisions for Health. 2000. pap. (978-0-7398-4549-3(7)) Steck-Vaughn.

Ramos, Pilar. La Invitacion. (SPA.). 32p. (J). 10.00 (978-84-342-2516-9(6)) Parramon Ediciones S.A. ESP. *Dist:* Distribuidora Norma, Inc.

Reybold, Laura. Everything You Need to Know about the Dangers of Tattooing & Body Piercing. rev. ed. 2001. (Need to Know Library). (Illus.). 64p. (YA). (gr. 4-6). lib. bdg. 25.25 (978-0-8239-3469-0(1)) Rosen Publishing Group, Inc., The.

Reznick, Jenny. Eating Right: A Content Area Reader. 2005. (Emergent (Prek-2) Health Package Ser.). 20p. (YA). (ps-2). 25.20 (978-0-8215-7828-5(6)) Sadlier, William H. Inc.

Rigby Education Staff. Living Together. (Sails Literacy Ser.). (Illus.). 16p. (gr. 1-2). 27.00 (978-0-7635-9898-3(4) , 698984C99) Rigby Education.

Riley, Peter D. Health. Moller, Ray, photos by. 2003. (Everyday Science Ser.). (Illus.). 32p. (J). (gr. 1 up). lib. bdg. 23.33 (978-0-8368-3715-5(0)) Stevens, Gareth Inc.

Roberts, Jeremy. Drugs & Dieting. 2005. (Drug Abuse Prevention Library). (Illus.). 64p. (YA). (gr. 7-12). lib. bdg. 25.25 (978-0-8239-3357-0(1)) Rosen Publishing Group, Inc., The.

Roehm, Michelle, ed. Girls Know Best: Advice for Girls on Just about Everything. Roth, Marci Doane, illus. 1999. 160p. (J). (gr. 4-7). 6.98 (978-1-56731-313-0(2) , MJF Bks.) Fine Communications.

Romain, Trevor. Stress Can Really Get on Your Nerves! 2000. (gr. 7-12). lib. bdg. 18.75 (978-0-613-87644-5(X)) Tandem Library Bks.

Rookie Read-About Health, 4 bks., Set. 2005. (Illus.). (J). 78.00 (978-0-516-25212-4(7) , Children's Pr.) Scholastic Library Publishing.

Ross, Veronica. Fit & Well. 2002. (My Healthy Body Ser.). (Illus.). 32p. (J). lib. bdg. 24.25 (978-1-930643-82-6(9)) Chrysalis Education.

Rotsky, Leslie A. Mi Cuerpo Sano. 2007. (Sesame Street Ser.). (SPA & ENG.). 48p. (J). pap., wbk. ed. 5.99 ***978-1-59545-078-4(5))** Learning Horizons, Inc.

Royston. Staying Health 6-Pack. 2004. (My Amazing Body Ser.). (Illus.). pap. 40.50 (978-1-4109-0960-2(3)) Raintree.

Royston, Angela. Get Some Rest! 2003. (Illus.). 32p. (J). pap. (978-1-4034-4451-6(X)) Heinemann Library.

—Keep Healthy! 2003. (Illus.). 32p. pap. 6.95 (978-1-4034-4450-9(1)); (J). lib. bdg. (978-1-4034-4441-7(2)) Heinemann Library.

—Staying Healthy. 2004. (My Amazing Body Ser.). (Illus.). 32p. (J). (gr. 2-4). pap. 7.50 (978-1-4109-0953-4(0)) Raintree.

—Why Does My Body Smell? 2003. (Body Matters Ser.). (Illus.). 32p. pap. 7.50 (978-1-4034-0463-3(1)) Heinemann Library.

—Why Does My Body Smell? And Other Questions about Hygiene. 2003. (Body Matters Ser.). (Illus.). 32p. (J). (gr. 3-5). lib. bdg. 24.22 (978-1-4034-0208-0(6)) Heinemann Library.

Royston, Angela, contrib. by. Clean & Healthy. 1999. 32p. (J). (gr. k-2). lib. bdg. 21.36 (978-1-57572-981-7(4)) Heinemann Library.

Sakelaris, Page. Giggle Belly. Torrey, Richard L., illus. 2000. (Rookie Reader Skill Set Ser.). 32p. (J). (gr. k-2). pap. 4.95 (978-0-516-27047-0(8) , Children's Pr.) Scholastic Library Publishing.

—Giggle Belly. 2000. (gr. k-3). lib. bdg. 12.95 (978-0-613-54509-9(5)) Tandem Library Bks.

Schnapp, William David, et al. Medically Clueless: A Health Guide for Young People. 2002. (YA). (gr. 9-12). per. 8.95 (978-0-9719337-1-2(5)) Elma Colletes & Sons.

Scholastic, Inc. Staff & Wilson-Max, Ken. Bathtime: This Is Way We Take a Bath. 2004. 10p. (J). bds. 7.95 (978-0-439-57787-8(X) , Cartwheel Bks.) Scholastic, Inc.

Scholastic Library Publishing Staff, ed. Rookie Read-About Health. 2004. 342.00 (978-0-516-24705-2(0)) Scholastic Library Publishing.

Sesame Street Health & Safety. 2006. (J). spiral bd. 5.99 ***978-1-58610-982-0(0))** Learning Horizons, Inc.

Sesame Street My Healthy Body. 2005. (J). spiral bd. 4.99 ***978-1-58610-939-4(1))** Learning Horizons, Inc.

Sesame's: A Giant Coloring Book that teaches Healthy Eating Habits. 2006. (J). 6.99 (978-1-59949-499-9(X)) Food Marketing Consultants, Inc.

Sexuality & Relationships Student Edition. 1999. (McGraw-Hill Health Ser.). (gr. 5-6). (978-0-02-276899-7(8)) Macmillan/McGraw-Hill Schl. Div.

Sfakianos, Jeffrey N. Avian Flu. 2006. (Deadly Diseases & Epidemics Ser.). (Illus.). 88p. (J). (gr. 9-12). 31.95 (978-0-7910-8675-9(5) , Chelsea Hse.) Facts On File, Inc.

Smith, Carrie Myers. Fitastic Kids: A Complete Guide to Health & Wellness for Children of All Ages. 2005. 200p. wbk. ed. 18.95 (978-1-891400-51-3(7)) Champion Pr., Ltd.

Smith, Liz. A Girl's Guide to Growing up - Booklet, 10 per packet. Perry, Gala, illus. 2005. (J). 63.95 (978-1-55942-207-9(6)) Marsh Media.

Solway, Andrew. What's Living in Your Bedroom? 2004. (Hidden Life Ser.). (Illus.). 32p. (J). pap. 7.50 (978-1-4034-5484-3(1)); lib. bdg. 25.64 (978-1-4034-4845-3(0)) Heinemann Library.

Spilsbury, Louise. Why Should I Eat This Carrot? And Other Questions about Healthy Eating. 2003. (Body Matters Ser.). (Illus.). 32p. (J). lib. bdg. (978-1-4034-4680-0(6)) Heinemann Library.

—Why Should I Get off the Couch? And Other Questions about Health & Exercise. 2003. (Body Matters Ser.). (Illus.). 32p. (J). lib. bdg. 16.95 (978-1-4034-4681-7(4)) Heinemann Library.

—Why Should I Go to Bed Now? And Other Questions about a Healthy Mind. 2003. (Body Matters Ser.). (Illus.). 32p. (J). lib. bdg. (978-1-4034-4682-4(2)) Heinemann Library.

—Why Should I Wash My Body? And Other Questions about Keeping Clean & Healthy. 2003. (Body Matters Ser.). (Illus.). 32p. (J). lib. bdg. 16.95 (978-1-4034-4684-8(9)) Heinemann Library.

Splish Splash. 2002. (Baby Faces Ser.). (Illus.). (J). bds. (978-0-439-33947-6(2)) Scholastic, Inc.

Sprung, Barbara. Stress. 1998. (Preteen Pressures Ser.). (Illus.). 48p. (J). (gr. 4-8). lib. bdg. 25.69 (978-0-8172-5033-1(6)) Raintree.

Steck-Vaughn Staff. Health. 2000. (Illus.). (J). (gr. 1). pap. (978-0-7398-2703-1(0)); (gr. 2). pap. 6.95 (978-0-7398-2704-8(9)); (gr. 3). pap. (978-0-7398-2705-5(7)); (gr. 4). pap. (978-0-7398-2706-2(5)); (gr. 5). pap. 6.95 (978-0-7398-2707-9(3)); (gr. 6). pap. (978-0-7398-2854-0(1)) Steck-Vaughn.

StepFast Resource Guide. 2001. cd-rom 14.99 (978-0-9710965-3-0(8)) Potomac Conference of Seventh-Day Adventists.

Stewart, Alex. Keeping Clean. 1999. (Everyday History Ser.). (J). (978-0-606-19404-4(5)); (gr. 3-6). lib. bdg. 15.25 (978-0-613-54597-6(4)) Tandem Library Bks.

Stop Germs. 2005. (Emergent (Prek-2) Health Package Ser.). 12p. (YA). (ps-2). 25.20 (978-0-8215-7850-6(2)) Sadlier, William H. Inc.

Student Edition. (McGraw-Hill Health Ser.). 2000. (gr. 1 up). (978-0-02-277367-0(3)); 2000. (gr. 2 up). (978-0-02-277368-7(1)); 1999. (gr. 3 up). (978-0-02-276417-3(8)); 1999. (gr. 4 up). (978-0-02-276418-0(6)); 1999. (gr. 5 up). (978-0-02-276419-7(4)); 1999. (gr. 6 up). (978-0-02-276420-3(8)) Macmillan/McGraw-Hill Schl. Div.

Swain, Gwenyth. Wash Up! 2003. (Illus.). 24p. (J). (ps-2). pap. 6.95 (978-1-57505-161-1(3)) Lerner Publishing Group.

—Wash Up! 2002. (gr. k-3). lib. bdg. 15.25 (978-0-613-46114-6(2)) Tandem Library Bks.

Take Care of Your Ears! With Annie Funelli & the Funsters. 2002. (Lessons for a Healthy Childhood Ser.). (J). (gr. k-3). instr.'s gde. ed. 69.95 (978-1-55942-188-1(6) , 9234V9) Marsh Media.

Take Care of Your Eyes! With Annie Funelli & the Funsters. 2002. (Lessons for a Healthy Childhood Ser.). (J). (gr. k-3). instr.'s gde. ed. 69.95 (978-1-55942-189-8(4) , 9235V9) Marsh Media.

Tiller, Jerome. Sammy's Day at the Fair: The Digestive System Featuring Gut Feelings & Reactions. 2004. 48p. (J). lib. bdg. 15.95 (978-1-59298-046-8(5)) Beaver's Pond Pr., Inc.

Turnbull, Stephanie. Why Do We Eat? (Level 2) - Internet Referenced. 2006. (Illus.). 32p. (J). 4.99 (978-0-7945-1333-7(6) , Usborne) EDC Publishing.

Varcoe, Marilyn J. & Burnett, Patricia. Toxic Stress: 7 Steps to Recovery. 2004. (Illus.). 200p. 24.95 (978-1-930842-02-1(3)) Edwards, J.W. Inc.

Vedral, Joyce L. Toning for Teens: The 20-Minute Workout That Makes You Look Good & Feel Great! 2002. (Illus.). 192p. pap. 15.95 (978-0-446-67815-5(5)) Grand Central Publishing.

Vogel, Elizabeth. Brushing My Teeth. 2001. (PowerKids Readers Ser.). (Illus.). 24p. (J). (gr. 1). lib. bdg. 16.00 (978-0-8239-5683-8(0) , PKBRTE, PowerKids Pr.) Rosen Publishing Group, Inc., The.

—A Comer Sanamente! 2004. (Limpieza y Salud Todo el Dia Ser.). (SPA & ENG., Illus.). 24p. (J). (gr. 1-2). lib. bdg. 16.00 (978-0-8239-6612-7(7) , Buenas Letra) Rosen Publishing Group, Inc., The.

—El Cuidado de Tu Cabello. 2004. (Limpieza y Salud Todo el Dia Ser.). (SPA & ENG., Illus.). 24p. (J). lib. bdg. 16.00 (978-0-8239-6611-0(9) , Buenas Letra) Rosen Publishing Group, Inc., The.

—A Hacer Ejercicio! 2004. (Limpieza y Salud Todo el Dia Ser.). (SPA & ENG., Illus.). 24p. (J). (gr. 1-2). lib. bdg. 16.00 (978-0-8239-6614-1(3) , Buenas Letra) Rosen Publishing Group, Inc., The.

—A Lavarse Las Manos! 2004. (Limpieza y Salud Todo el Dia Ser.). (SPA & ENG., Illus.). 24p. (J). lib. bdg. 16.00 (978-0-8239-6619-6(4)); (gr. 1-2). lib. bdg. 16.00 (978-0-8239-6618-9(6)) Rosen Publishing Group, Inc., The. (Buenas Letra).

—A Lavarse Los Dientes! 2004. (Limpieza y Salud Todo el Dia Ser.). (SPA & ENG., Illus.). 24p. (J). (gr. 1-2). lib. bdg. 16.00 (978-0-8239-6620-2(8) , Buenas Letra) Rosen Publishing Group, Inc., The.

—Washing My Hands. 2001. (PowerKids Readers Ser.). (Illus.). 24p. (J). (gr. 1). lib. bdg. 16.00 (978-0-8239-5684-5(9) , PKWAHA, PowerKids Pr.) Rosen Publishing Group, Inc., The.

Wainwright, Tabitha. You & an Illness in Your Family. 2005. (Family Matters Ser.). (Illus.). 48p. (YA). (gr. 5-8). lib. bdg. 23.95 (978-0-8239-3352-5(0)) Rosen Publishing Group, Inc., The.

Wallerstein, Claire, et al. Just the Facts, 20 bks. 2003. (Illus.). (YA). Set 1-3. (gr. 6-8). lib. bdg. 512.80 (978-1-4034-0823-5(8)); Set 3. lib. bdg. 153.84 (978-1-4034-0822-8(X)) Heinemann Library.

Wandberg, Robert. Creative Problem Solving: What's a Better Way? (Life Skills-Contemporary Issues Ser.). 48p. pap. 8.95 (978-0-7368-8835-6(7) , LifeMatters Bks.) Capstone Pr., Inc.

Wash Your Hands. 2000. (Li'l Learners Club Ser.: Vol. 2). (Illus.). (J). (ps-k). (978-1-930560-73-4(7)) International Masters Pubs., Inc.

Watson, Mary Ann, et al. Balancing Act: For People with Dizziness & Balance Disorders. 2nd ed. 2001. per. 15.00 (978-0-9632611-5-1(0)) Vestibular Disorders Assn.

Webber, Diane. The Skin You're In: Staying healthy inside & Out. 2007. (Scholastic Choices Ser.). 112p. (J). spiral bd. 27.00 ***978-0-531-13869-4(0)** , Children's Pr.) Scholastic Library Publishing.

Wenkman, Leeann. Body Buddies Say.... "Wash Your Hands!" Pettersen, Shawn, illus. 1999. (J). (ps-k). 32p. 7.95 (978-0-9670790-1-1(2)); 26p. pap. 4.95 (978-0-9670790-0-4(4)) Sunrise Pubns.

West, Dorothy F. Nutrition & Fitness: Lifestyle Choices for Wellness. 2000. (Illus.). 496p. (YA). (gr. 9-12). 50.00 (978-1-56637-510-8(X)) Goodheart-Willcox Pub.

—Nutrition, Food, & Fitness: The Science of Wellness. 2006. (Illus.). 510p. (gr. 9-12). 42.75 (978-1-59070-527-8(0)) Goodheart-Willcox Pub.

Whatsa Hygiene? 1999. (Health & Human Development Resource Library). (J). (gr. 4-6). tchr. ed. 69.95 (978-1-55942-113-3(4) , 9221V9) Marsh Media.

White, Ellen G. The Ministry of Healing. 2005. reprint ed. pap. 42.95 (978-1-4191-4425-7(1)) Kessinger Publishing, LLC.

White, Lee. Teenage Human Body Operator's Manual. 1998. (gr. 7-12). lib. bdg. 18.75 (978-0-613-80274-1(8)) Tandem Library Bks.

White, Nancy. The President's Challenge: A Content Area Reader-health. 2005. (Emergent (Prek-2) Health Package Ser.). 16p. (YA). (ps-2). 25.20 (978-0-8215-7830-8(8)) Sadlier, William H. Inc.

Wilkinson, Jody. Health 4 Life. 2004. 240p. pap. 14.99 (978-0-8307-3051-3(6) , Gospel Light) Gospel Light Pubns.

Williams, Carmelita K. & Johns, Jerry L. Take-Home Books, Blakline Masters: Content Area Readers-health. 2002. (J). pap. (978-0-8215-7859-9(6) , Sadlier-Oxford) Sadlier, William H. Inc.

Williams, Kara. Frequently Asked Questions about My Pyramid: Eating Right. 2006. (FAQ Ser.). (Illus.). 64p. (J). (gr. 7-12). lib. bdg. 27.95 ***978-1-4042-1974-8(9))** Rosen Publishing Group, Inc., The.

Winchester, Bob. Excercise & Eating Right Are Okay, I Guess, 8 vols., Vol. 2. 2002. (Illus.). (J). per. (978-1-932062-09-0(2)) Hability Solution Services, Inc.

Winkler, Peter. Keeping Fit. 2003. (Human Body Ser.). (Illus.). 32p. (J). pap. (978-0-7922-8863-3(7)) National Geographic Society.

Wunderink, Steve. Work Out! Active Devotions for Teens. 2000. (Devotions Ser.). (Illus.). 131p. 8.25 (978-1-56212-541-7(9) , 160475, Faith Alive Christian Resources) CRC Pubns.

Yagyu, Geniehiro. All about Scabs. Stinchecum, Amanda M., tr. from JPN. Yagyu, Geniehiro, illus. 2004. (My Body Science Ser.). (Illus.). 28p. (J). (ps-3). 12.95 (978-0-916291-82-2(0)) Kane/Miller Bk. Pubs., Inc.

Youngs, Jennifer Leigh. Feeling Great, Looking Hot, & Loving Yourself! Health Fitness & Beauty for Teen. 2000. (gr. 7-12). lib. bdg. 24.55 (978-0-613-90258-8(0)) Tandem Library Bks.

Your Health, 6 bks. Incl. Brush Well : A Look at Dental Care. Bagley, Katie. 24p. lib. bdg. 18.60 (978-0-7368-0969-6(4)); Eat Right : Tips for Good Nutrition. Bagley, Katie. 32p. 18.60 (978-0-7368-0971-9(6)); Feel Good : Understand Your Emotions. Feeney, Kathy. 24p. lib. bdg. 18.60 (978-0-7368-0972-6(4)); Get Moving : Tips on Exercise. Feeney, Kathy. 24p. lib. bdg. 18.60 (978-0-7368-0973-3(2)); Keep Clean : A Look at Hygiene. Bagley, Katie. 24p. lib. bdg. 18.60 (978-0-7368-0974-0(0)); Sleep Well : You Need to Rest. Feeney, Kathy. 24p. lib. bdg. 18.60 (978-0-7368-0970-2(8)); (J). (gr. 1-2). 2001. (Illus.). Set lib. bdg. 111.60 (978-0-7368-1013-5(7) , Bridgestone Bks.) Capstone Pr., Inc.

HEALTH—FICTION

Allen, Constance. Come Play with Elmo! 2006. (Sesame Street). (Illus.). 10p. (J). bds. 12.99 (978-0-7944-0778-0(1)) Reader's Digest Assn., Inc., The.

Auxier, Bryan. Where Have All the Dragons Gone? Daniels, Regina, illus. l.t. ed. 2002. 32p. (J). (gr. 3-7). pap. 7.95 (978-0-9719144-0-7(0)) Where? Pr., Inc.

Berry, Ron. Everybody Takes a Bath. Sharp, Chris, illus. 2006. 10p. (J). (ps). 8.95 (978-0-8249-6681-2(3) , Ideals Children's Bks.) Ideals Pubns.

Bonilla, Daniel. My Magnificent Horse: An Inspirational. 2005. 76p. pap. 14.95 (978-1-4137-8617-0(0)) PublishAmerica, Inc.

Brennan, Eileen. Dirtball Pete. 2008. (J). (978-0-375-83425-7(7)); lib. bdg. (978-0-375-93425-4(1)) Random Hse., Inc.

Cepeda, Joe. The Swing. 2006. (Illus.). (J). ***978-1-4287-0187-8(7)** , Levine, Arthur A. Bks.) Scholastic, Inc.

Colbert, Don. The Toxic Detective. 2004. 24p. (J). (gr. k-3). pap. 9.99 (978-1-59185-205-6(6) , Charisma Kids) Strang Communications Co.

Cole, Joanna. My Friend the Doctor. Chambliss, Maxie, illus. 2005. 32p. (J). (ps up). 6.99 (978-0-06-050500-4(1)) HarperCollins Pubs.

Davidow, Shelley. Spirit of the Mountain. 2003. 144p. (YA). pap. 10.00 (978-0-86315-427-0(1)) Floris Bks. GBR. *Dist:* SteinerBooks, Inc.

Deem, Saitofi Anne. Myrtle Learns about Hygiene. 1998. (Teachable Moments Ser.). (Illus.). 8p. (J). (ps-3). pap. 7.95 (978-1-930694-09-5(1)) Myrtle Learns.

—Myrtle Learns How You Catch an Illness. 1998. (Teachable Moments Ser.). (Illus.). 8p. (J). (ps-3). pap. 7.95 (978-1-930694-10-1(5)) Myrtle Learns.

—Myrtle Learns to Get Along. 1998. (Teachable Moments Ser.). (Illus.). 8p. (J). (ps-3). pap. 7.95 (978-1-930694-08-8(3)) Myrtle Learns.

—Myrtle Learns to Take Care of Boo Boos. 1998. (Teachable Moments Ser.). (Illus.). 12p. (J). (ps-3). pap. 7.95 (978-1-930694-01-9(6)) Myrtle Learns.

—Myrtle Learns Why Exercise Is Important. 1998. (Teachable Moments Ser.). (Illus.). 8p. (J). pap. 7.95 (978-1-930694-06-4(7)) Myrtle Learns.

—Myrtle Teachable Moments Series, 16 vols. Incl. Myrtle Learns about Asthma. 8p. pap. 7.95 (978-1-930694-00-2(8)); Myrtle Learns about Dangerous Situations. 8p. pap. 7.95 (978-1-930694-03-3(2)); Myrtle Learns about Diabetes. 12p. pap. 7.95 (978-1-930694-04-0(0)); Myrtle Learns about Hygiene. 8p. pap. 7.95 (978-1-930694-09-5(1)); Myrtle Learns about Lice. 12p. pap. 7.95 (978-1-930694-11-8(3)); Myrtle Learns about Medicine. 8p. pap. 7.95 (978-1-930694-12-5(1)); Myrtle Learns about Safety. 8p. pap. 7.95 (978-1-930694-13-2(X)); Myrtle Learns about Seizures. 8p. pap. 7.95 (978-1-930694-14-9(8)); Myrtle Learns How You Catch an Illness. 8p. pap. 7.95 (978-1-930694-10-1(5)); Myrtle Learns to Eat Well. 12p. pap. 7.95 (978-1-930694-05-7(9)); Myrtle Learns to Get Along. 8p. pap. 7.95 (978-1-930694-08-8(3)); Myrtle Learns to Make Friends. 8p. pap. 7.95 (978-1-930694-07-1(5)); Myrtle Learns to Take Care of Boo Boos. 12p. pap. 7.95 (978-1-930694-01-9(6)); Myrtle Learns Why Exercise Is Important. 8p. pap. 7.95 (978-1-930694-06-4(7)); Myrtle Makes a Choice. 8p. pap. 7.95 (978-1-930694-02-6(4)); Myrtle's Friend Is Very Sick. 8p. pap. 7.95 (978-1-930694-15-6(6)); (J). (ps-3). 1998. (Illus.). Set pap. 114.48 (978-1-930694-16-3(4)) Myrtle Learns.

Devine, Jennifer. Scardust. Fry, Akiko K., illus. 2005. (ENG.). 28p. (J). per. 23.25 (978-1-4208-6461-8(0)) AuthorHouse.

Driscoll, Laura & Artifact Group. Welcome to LazyTown! A Foldout Book with Flaps! 2006. (LazyTown Ser.). (Illus.). 14p. (J). 7.99 (978-1-4169-0058-0(6) , Simon Spotlight/Nickelodeon) Simon & Schuster Children's Publishing.

Dufresne, Didier. Solamente un Poco de Gripe. Vinent, Julia, tr. Modere, Armelle, illus. 2004. (SPA.). 32p. (J). 14.99 (978-84-8470-123-1(9)) Corimbo, Editorial S.L. ESP. *Dist:* Lectorum Pubns., Inc.

Ehrlich, Fred. You Can't Take Your Body to a Repair Shop. 2004. (Illus.). 40p. 15.95 (978-1-59354-057-9(4)) Handprint Bks.

Evans, Jan. Repetitive Rhonda. 2007. (Illus.). 29p. (J). 18.95 ***978-0-9720176-7-1(4))** Breath & Shadows Productions.

Fapojuwo, Moyo Bukola. Kemi Shows You How to Be A Healthy Kid. 2006. (SPA.). (J). lib. bdg. 5.95 (978-1-59971-225-3(3)) Aardvark Global Publishing.

Franklin, Shawna. Catching Achoo. 2006. (ENG.). 28p. per. 11.95 ***978-1-59800-492-2(1))** Outskirts Press, Inc.

Goodrow, Carol. The Treasure of Health & Happiness. 2006. 96p. 14.00 (978-1-891369-60-5(1)) Consortium Bk. Sales & Distribution.

Hamsa, Bobbie. Dirty Larry. Catanese, Donna, illus. rev. ed. 2003. (Rookie Reader Espanol Ser.). 24p. (J). (gr. k-2). pap. 4.95 (978-0-516-27493-5(7) , Children's Pr.) Scholastic Library Publishing.

—Dirty Larry. rev. ed. 2002. (Rookie Readers Ser.). (J). lib. bdg. 16.00 (978-0-516-22561-6(8) , Children's Pr.) Scholastic Library Publishing.

—Dirty Larry. Catanese, Donna, illus. rev. ed. 2002. (Rookie Readers Ser.). 23p. (J). (gr. k-1). 19.50 (978-0-516-22668-2(1) , Children's Pr.) Scholastic Library Publishing.

—Dirty Larry. 2002. (ps-2). lib. bdg. 12.95 (978-0-613-59125-6(9)) Tandem Library Bks.

Harcourt School Publishers Staff. Keep Well Day Advanced Level. 3rd ed. 2002. (Trophies Reading Program Ser.). (Illus.). pap. 5.10 (978-0-15-323030-1(4)) Harcourt Schl. Pubs.

Jocelyn, Marthe. Would You? 2008. (YA). ***978-0-375-83703-6(5));** lib. bdg. ***978-0-375-93703-3(X))** Dell Publishing. (Delacorte Pr.).

Korman Fontes, Justine. Clean up, Grumpy Bunny! 2007. (Scholastic Reader Level 1 Ser.). 32p. (J). pap. 3.99 (978-0-439-87381-9(9) , Cartwheel Bks.) Scholastic, Inc.

Krumrey, Melanie. Bagels, Buddy, & Me: A Story about Gluten Intolerance & Celiac Disease. 2007. (Illus.). 40p. (YA). per. 14.95 ***978-0-9797703-0-2(0))** Mustard Seed Pr.

Lowry, Lois. Messenger. 2004. 176p. (YA). (gr. 7 up). tchr. ed. 16.00 (978-0-618-40441-4(4) , Walter Lorraine) Houghton Mifflin Co. Trade & Reference Div.

—Messenger. l.t. ed. 2004. 184p. 23.95 (978-0-7862-6686-9(4) , Large Print Pr.) Thorndike Pr.

Lydon, Jeff. Donald Dent. Behles, Liza, illus. 2003. 34p. (J). per. 10.00 (978-0-9724922-0-1(8)) Authors & Artists Publishers of New York, Inc.

Mattern, Joanne. Batter Up! 2005. 40.00 ***978-1-4108-4193-3(6))** Benchmark Education Co.

McDaniel, Lurlene. The Angels Trilogy. 2002. (Angels Trilogy). 560p. (YA). (gr. 7). mass mkt. 7.50 (978-0-553-57098-4(6) , Laurel Leaf) Random Hse. Children's Bks.

—A Rose for Melinda. 2002. (Illus.). 208p. (YA). (gr. 7 up). mass mkt. 5.50 (978-0-553-57090-8(0) , Laurel Leaf) Random Hse. Children's Bks.

McPhate, Paul. The Puggles: The Adventures of Carly & Vinigin. 2006. (ENG.). 48p. per. 12.95 ***978-1-4241-4481-5(7))** PublishAmerica, Inc.

Mercer, Adrienne. Rebound. 2002. (gr. 3-6). lib. bdg. 13.55 (978-0-613-78322-4(0)) Tandem Library Bks.

Montgomery Gibson, Jane. Oh Forsooth! I've Lost a Tooth! Montgomery Gibson, Jane, illus. 2005. (J). bds. 8.99 (978-1-4183-0021-0(7)) Christ Inspired, Inc.

Mullican, Judy. Going to the Health Club. 2006. (J). pap. (978-1-57332-397-0(7)) HighReach Learning, Inc.

Muncy, Brenda. Truly Lucky. 2006. (ENG.). 32p. per. 16.49 ***978-1-4259-6289-0(0))** AuthorHouse.

North, Merry. Squeaky Clean. 2005. 9p. ***978-1-57151-752-4(9))** Playhouse Publishing.

Palatini, Margie. Gorgonzola. Bowers, Tim, illus. 2008. 32p. (J). 16.99 (978-0-06-073897-6(9)); lib. bdg. 17.89 (978-0-06-073898-3(7)) HarperCollins Pubs.

Poth, Karen. Larryboy in Tip Top Cape Shape. Big Idea, Inc. Staff, illus. 2006. (Big Idea Books / LarryBoy#8482; Ser.). 14p. (J). 6.99 (978-0-310-71154-4(1)) Zonderkidz.

Ritchey, Melissa. The Kabeezles. 2006. (Illus.). 16p. (J). lib. bdg. 18.95 (978-0-9761128-5-3(X)) Hafabanana Pr.

Robbins, Sandra. Ring Around a Rainbow: A Health & Safety Adventure. rev. ed. 2001. 32p. (J). (gr. k-5). pap. 11.95 incl. audio (978-1-882601-31-8(9)); pap. 6.95 (978-1-882601-32-5(7)) See-More's Workshop.

—Ring Around a Rainbow: A Healthy & Safety Story. 2001. (See-More's Stories Ser.). 32p. (J). pap. 16.95 incl. audio compact disk (978-1-882601-42-4(4)) See-More's Workshop.

Santillo, LuAnn. Toad. Santillo, LuAnn, ed. 2003. (Half-Pint Kids Readers Ser.). (Illus.). 7p. (ps-1). pap. (978-1-59256-107-0(1)) Half-Pint Kids, Inc.

Schaefer, Lola M. Loose Tooth. Wickstrom, Sylvie Kantorovitz, illus. 2005. (My First I Can Read Bks.). 32p. (J). (ps-ps). pap. 3.99 (978-0-06-052778-5(1)) HarperCollins Pubs.

Schertle, Alice & Parkins, Schertle. The Adventures of Old Bo Bear. 2006. (Illus.). 32p. (J). 16.95 (978-0-8118-3476-6(X)) Chronicle Bks. LLC.

Schiavi, Sherry. Chelsea's Healthy Secrets. Huffmaster, Elizabeth, illus. 2004. (J). per. 14.95 (978-0-9746378-0-8(7)) Celltrition.

Seglie, Susan & Schiefelbein, Janis. JR Gets Rady for School: A Visit to the Health Clinic. Papish, Adam, illus. 2001. (J). 4.95 (978-0-9747243-0-0(0)) Seglie, Susan M.

Thompson, Tolya LaShawn. Worry Wart Wes. Perez, Juan R., illus. 2002. (Smarties Ser.: Vol. 2). (J). (gr. 2-4). lib. bdg. 16.00 (978-0-9708296-1-0(2)) Savor Publishing Hse., Inc.

Thomson, Linda. Harry the Hypno-potamus: Metaphorical Tales for the Treatment of Children. 2005. (Illus.). 176p. (978-1-904424-57-4(0), 4570) Crown Hse. Publishing.

Viorst, Judith. Super-Completely & Totally the Messiest! Glasser, Robin Preiss, illus. 2006. 32p. (J). 15.99 (978-1-4169-4200-9(9), Atheneum) Simon & Schuster Children's Publishing.

Wallace, Nancy Elizabeth. Count down to Clean Up! 2001. (Illus.). 32p. (J). (gr. k-3). tchr. ed. 14.00 (978-0-618-10130-6(6)) Houghton Mifflin Co. Trade & Reference Div.

Wells, Rosemary. The Germ Busters. 2002. (ps-2). lib. bdg. 11.80 (978-0-613-53188-7(4)) Tandem Library Bks.

Weyn, Suzanne. A Spa Day with Mom. Mingus, Cathi, illus. 2006. 16p. (J). 9.99 (978-1-4169-0974-3(5), Little Simon) Simon & Schuster Children's Publishing.

Willson, Sarah. Brand-New Daddy. 2001. lib. bdg. 14.15 (978-0-613-43921-3(X)) Tandem Library Bks.

Young, Eugene Randolph, illus. & des. The Food Convention. Young, Eugene Randolph, des. l.t. ed. 2006. 32p. (J). 16.95 ***(978-0-9792000-0-7(8))** Les Lurn Pubs.

HEALTH, MENTAL

see Mental Health

HEALTH, PUBLIC

see Public Health

HEALTH EDUCATION

Gibbons, Charlie, et al. Graph Links Activity Package for Health. 2003. (Your Health Ser.). (gr. 3-6). 71.90 (978-0-15-306441-8(2)) Harcourt Schl. Pubs.

—Graph Links Activity Package for Health: Macintosh. 2003. (Your Health Ser.). (gr. 3-6). (978-0-15-306928-4(7)) Harcourt Schl. Pubs.

—Pupil's Editions. 99th ed. 1998. (Your Health Ser.). (gr. 1 up). pap., pupil's gde. ed. 44.70 (978-0-15-310139-7(3)); (gr. 2 up). pap., pupil's gde. ed. 44.70 (978-0-15-310140-3(7)); (gr. 3 up). pupil's gde. ed. 52.50 (978-0-15-310141-0(5)); (gr. 4 up). pupil's gde. ed. 56.20 (978-0-15-310142-7(3)); (gr. 5 up). pupil's gde. ed. 58.90 (978-0-15-310143-4(1)); (gr. 6 up). pupil's gde. ed. 62.50 (978-0-15-310144-1(X)) Harcourt Schl. Pubs.

—Teacher's Editions. 99th ed. (Your Health Ser.). 2003. (gr. 2 up). tchr. ed. 131.60 (978-0-15-310146-5(6)); 2003. (gr. 1 up). tchr. ed. 131.60 (978-0-15-310145-8(8)); 1999. (gr. 3 up). tchr. ed. 146.20 (978-0-15-310147-2(4)); 1999. (gr. 4 up). tchr. ed. 159.50 (978-0-15-310148-9(2)); 1999. (gr. 5 up). tchr. ed. 166.20 (978-0-15-310149-6(0)); 1999. (gr. 6 up). tchr. ed. 176.10 (978-0-15-310150-2(4)) Harcourt Schl. Pubs.

Goodrow, Carol. Happy Feet, Healthy Food: Your Child's First Journal of Exercise & Healthy Eating. Goodrow, Carol, illus. 2004. (Illus.). 112p. 14.00 (978-1-891369-46-9(6)) Breakaway Bks.

Harcourt School Publishers Staff. Your Health. (Your Health Ser.). (Illus.). 3rd ed. 2003. (gr. 2 up). pupil's gde. ed. 40.60 (978-0-15-334301-8(X)); 3rd ed. 2003. act. bk. ed. 5.70 (978-0-15-334670-5(1)); 3rd ed. 2002. (gr. 3 up). pupil's gde. ed. 47.60 (978-0-15-334302-5(8)); 3rd ed. 2002. (gr. 1 up). pupil's gde. ed. 40.60 (978-0-15-334300-1(1)); 3rd ed. 2002. (gr. 4 up). pupil's gde. ed. 51.40 (978-0-15-334303-2(6)); 3rd ed. 2002. (gr. 5 up). pupil's gde. ed. 54.70 (978-0-15-334304-9(4)); 3rd ed. 2002. (gr. 6 up). pupil's gde. ed. 57.70 (978-0-15-334305-6(2)); 3rd ed. 2002. (gr. 1 up). pap., act. bk. ed. 7.10 (978-0-15-334671-2(X)); 3rd ed. 2002. (gr. 2 up). pap., act. bk. ed. 7.10 (978-0-15-334672-9(8)); 3rd ed. 2002. (gr. 3 up). pap., act. bk. ed. 7.10 (978-0-15-334673-6(6)); 3rd ed. 2002. (gr. 4 up). pap., act. bk. ed. 7.10 (978-0-15-334674-3(4)); 3rd ed. 2002. (gr. 5 up). pap., act. bk. ed. 7.10 (978-0-15-334675-0(2)); 3rd ed. 2002. (gr. 6 up). pap., act. bk. ed. 7.10 (978-0-15-334676-7(0)); 99th ed. 1999. pap., act. bk. ed. 6.10 (978-0-15-311336-9(7)); 99th ed. 1998. (gr. 1 up). pap., act. bk. ed. 7.10 (978-0-15-311337-6(5)); 99th ed. 1998. (gr. 2 up). pap., act. bk. ed. 7.10 (978-0-15-311338-3(3)); 99th ed. 1998. (gr. 3 up). pap., act. bk. ed. 7.10 (978-0-15-311339-0(1)); 99th ed. 1998. (gr. 4 up). pap., act. bk. ed. 7.10 (978-0-15-311340-6(5)); 99th ed. 1998. (gr. 5 up). pap., act. bk. ed. 7.10 (978-0-15-311341-3(3)); 99th ed. 1998. (gr. 6 up). pap., act. bk. ed. 7.10 (978-0-15-311342-0(1)) Harcourt Schl. Pubs.

—Your Health: Growth, Development & Reproduction. 3rd ed. 2002. (Your Health Ser.). (Illus.). (gr. 3-6). pap. 58.20 (978-0-15-334691-0(4)) Harcourt Schl. Pubs.

—Your Health, Grade 1. 3rd ed. 2002. (Your Health Ser.). (gr. 1 up). tchr. ed. 152.40 (978-0-15-334307-0(9)) Harcourt Schl. Pubs.

—Your Health, Grade 2. 3rd ed. 2002. (Your Health Ser.). (gr. 2 up). tchr. ed. 154.60 (978-0-15-334308-7(7)) Harcourt Schl. Pubs.

—Your Health, Grade 3. 3rd ed. 2002. (Your Health Ser.). (gr. 3 up). tchr. ed. 170.30 (978-0-15-334309-4(5)) Harcourt Schl. Pubs.

—Your Health, Grade 4. 3rd ed. 2002. (Your Health Ser.). (gr. 4 up). tchr. ed. 173.30 (978-0-15-334310-0(9)) Harcourt Schl. Pubs.

—Your Health, Grade 5. 3rd ed. 2002. (Your Health Ser.). (gr. 5 up). tchr. ed. 179.60 (978-0-15-334311-7(7)) Harcourt Schl. Pubs.

—Your Health, Grade 6. 3rd ed. 2002. (Your Health Ser.). (gr. 6 up). tchr. ed. 184.60 (978-0-15-334312-4(5)) Harcourt Schl. Pubs.

Illinois State University, Center for Mathematics, Science and Technology Staff. Integrated Mathematics, Science & Technology: Wellness Module. 1999. (Illus.). (YA). (gr. 6-12). stu. ed. 5.99 (978-0-02-647838-0(2)) Glencoe/McGraw-Hill.

Jukes, Mavis. Guy Book. 2002. (gr. 7-12). lib. bdg. 22.20 (978-0-613-60561-8(6)) Tandem Library Bks.

Lombardo, Michelle. The OrganWise Guys - Basic Training for Better Health Vol. 2, 2 vols. Herron, Mark, illus. 1998. 35p. (J). (gr. 2-5). (978-0-9648438-3-7(8)) Wellness, Inc.

Mayo Clinic Health Information, 11 bks., Set. (Illus.). (gr. 8 up). lib. bdg. 329.45 (978-1-59084-545-5(5)) Mason Crest Pubs.

McTavish, Sandra. Life Skills: 225 Ready-to-Use Health Activities for Success & Well-Being (Grades 6-12) 2003. (Illus.). 288p. pap. 29.95 (978-0-7879-6959-2(1)) Wiley, John & Sons, Inc.

Medical & Health Issues for Teens. (Illus.). (YA). (978-0-7613-3300-5(2), Twenty-First Century Bks.) Lerner Publishing Group.

Michener, Dorothy. Health & Success: Active Learning Strategies to Promote Student Wellness. Harvey, Gayle S., illus. 1999. (Kids' Stuff Ser.). 96p. (J). (gr. 4-8). pap. 10.95 (978-0-86530-412-3(2), IP 412-2) Incentive Pubns., Inc.

Nygard, Bonnie, et al. Wow! Cody Investigates the World of Wellness. 2005. (World of Wellness Health Education Ser.). (Illus.). 88p. 19.00 (978-0-7360-6230-5(0)) Human Kinetics Pubs.

—Wow! Ruby Explores the World of Wellness. 2005. (World of Wellness Health Education Ser.). (Illus.). 88p. 19.00 (978-0-7360-6229-9(7)) Human Kinetics Pubs.

—Wow! Ruby Learns about the World of Wellness. 2005. (World of Wellness Health Education Ser.). (Illus.). 88p. 19.00 (978-0-7360-6228-2(9)) Human Kinetics Pubs.

—Wow! Sydney Travels Through the World of Wellness. 2005. (World of Wellness Health Education Ser.). (Illus.). 88p. 19.00 (978-0-7360-6232-9(7)) Human Kinetics Pubs.

—Wow! T.J.'s Adventures in the World of Wellness. 2005. (World of Wellness Health Education Ser.). (Illus.). 88p. 19.00 (978-0-7360-6231-2(9)) Human Kinetics Pubs.

Nygard, Bonnie K., et al. Wow! Ruby Learns about the World of Wellness: Big Book - Orange Level. 2005. (World of Wellness Health Education Ser.). (Illus.). 40p. 79.00 (978-0-7360-5757-8(9)) Human Kinetics Pubs.

—Wow! Sydney Travels Through the World of Wellness: Student Book - Purple Level. 2005. (World of Wellness Health Education Ser.). (Illus.). 88p. pap. 12.00 (978-0-7360-5580-2(0)) Human Kinetics Pubs.

Paonessa, Mary. Growth & Development with Friends, 8 vols. 3rd rev. ed. 2003. (Human Growth & Development Ser.). (Illus.). 41p. (J). (gr. 5 up). pap. 9.00 (978-0-9711721-0-4(2), 388) Paon Pubns.

—Growth & Development with Friends & Family, 8 vols. 3rd rev. ed. 2003. (Human Growth & Development Ser.). (Illus.). 64p. (J). (gr. 6 up). pap. 11.00 (978-0-9711721-2-8(9), 390) Paon Pubns.

—Growth & Development with Friends & School, 8 vols. 3rd ed. 2003. (Human Growth & Development Ser.). (Illus.). (J). (gr. 7 up). 112p. pap., tchr. ed. 15.00 (978-0-9711721-5-9(3), 393); 91p. pap. (978-0-9711721-4-2(5), 392) Paon Pubns.

Santillo, LuAnn. The Doctor. Santillo, LuAnn, ed. 2003. (Half-Pint Kids Readers Ser.). (Illus.). 7p. (J). (ps-1). pap. (978-1-59256-121-6(7)) Half-Pint Kids, Inc.

Silverthorne, Sandy. Surviving Zits: How to Cope with Your Changing Self. Silverthorne, Sandy, illus. 2006. (Illus.). 96p. (YA). (gr. 3-6). pap. 5.99 (978-0-7847-1435-5(5), 42177) Standard Publishing.

Weinberg, Hedy, et al. My Mom Has Hepatitis C. Chen, Joy, illus. 2000. 32p. (J). (gr. k-7). 15.95 (978-1-57826-075-1(2), Hatherleigh Pr.) Hatherleigh Co., Ltd., The.

HEALTH OF CHILDREN

see Children—Health and Hygiene

HEARING

see also Ear

Arnold, Caroline. Did You Hear That? 2001. (gr. 3-6). lib. bdg. 15.25 (978-0-613-51242-8(1)) Tandem Library Bks.

—Did You Hear That? Animals with Super Hearing. Trachok, Cathy, illus. 2001. (J). pap. 6.95 (978-1-57091-405-8(2)); 32p. 16.95 (978-1-57091-404-1(4)) Charlesbridge Publishing, Inc.

—Did You Hear That? Animals with Super Hearing. 2001. (978-0-606-22634-9(6)) Tandem Library Bks.

Ballard, Carol. Ears. 2003. (Body Focus Ser.). (Illus.). 48p. (J). lib. bdg. 27.07 (978-1-4034-0749-8(5)); pap. (978-1-4034-3297-1(X)) Heinemann Library.

Barraclough, Sue. What Can I Hear? (What Can I? Ser.). (Illus.). 24p. (J). 2006. lib. bdg. 20.64 (978-1-4109-2163-5(8)); 2005. pap. 5.75 (978-1-4109-2169-7(7)) Raintree.

—What Can I Hear? 2005. (J). (978-1-4034-7078-2(2)); pap. (978-1-4034-7084-3(7)) Steck-Vaughn.

Beaumont, S. Baby Senses Hearing. 2005. 12p. bds. (978-1-905051-46-5(8)) Make Believe Ideas.

Cobb, Vicki. Perk up Your Ears: Discover Your Sense of Hearing. 2003. (Five Senses Ser.). 32p. pap. 7.95 (978-0-7613-1981-8(6), Millbrook Pr.) Lerner Publishing Group.

Douglas, Lloyd G. My Ears. 2004. (Wel-My Body Ser.). (J). 18.00 (978-0-516-24062-6(5)); 24p. pap. 4.95 (978-0-516-22126-7(4)) Scholastic Library Publishing. (Children's Pr.).

Dubovoy, Silvia. Orejas. 2002. (SPA.). (gr. k-3). lib. bdg. 15.25 (978-0-613-64569-0(3)) Tandem Library Bks.

Furgang, Kathy, et al, contrib. by. My Ears. 2001. (My Body Ser.). (Illus.). 24p. (J). lib. bdg. 19.95 (978-0-8239-5572-5(9), PowerKids Pr.) Rosen Publishing Group, Inc., The.

Gordon, Sharon. Hearing. 2002. (Rookie Read-About Health Ser.). (Illus.). 32p. (J). (gr. k-2). pap. 5.95 (978-0-516-25989-5(X), Children's Pr.) Scholastic Library Publishing.

—Hearing. 2001. (gr. k-3). lib. bdg. 14.10 (978-0-613-50700-4(2)) Tandem Library Bks.

Granowsky, Alvin. Sounds. 2001. (ps-2). lib. bdg. 13.00 (978-0-613-45225-0(9)) Tandem Library Bks.

Hall, Kirsten. Animal Hearing. 2005. (Illus.). 24p. (J). pap. (978-0-8368-4808-3(X)); lib. bdg. 19.33 (978-0-8368-4802-1(0)) Stevens, Gareth Inc.

—Animal Hearing: El Oído en Los Animales. 2005. (ENG & SPA., Illus.). 24p. (J). pap. (978-0-8368-4820-5(9)); lib. bdg. 19.33 (978-0-8368-4814-4(4)) Stevens, Gareth Inc.

Hearing, 6 vols. (gr. k-2). 28.95 (978-0-7368-8583-6(8)) Red Brick Learning.

Hidalgo, Maria. Hearing. 2003. 24p. (J). lib. bdg. 21.35 (978-1-58340-304-4(3)) Smart Apple Media.

Jordan, Denise. We Can Listen. 2003. (Heinemann Read & Learn Ser.). (Illus.). 24p. (J). pap. 5.25 (978-1-4034-4414-1(5)); lib. bdg. 18.50 (978-1-4034-4408-0(0)) Heinemann Library.

Klingel, Cynthia Fitterer & Noyed, Robert B. Ears. Andersen, Gregg, photos by. 2002. (Weekly Reader Early Learning Library). (Illus.). 24p. (J). (ps up). pap. 5.95 (978-0-8368-3151-1(9)); lib. bdg. 19.33 (978-0-8368-3062-0(8)) Stevens, Gareth Inc. (Weekly Reader Early Learning Library).

—Ears/Orejas. Acosta, Tatiana & Gutiérrez, Guillermo, trs. Andersen, Gregg, photos by. 2002. (Weekly Reader Early Learning Library). (Illus.). 24p. (J). (ps up). (SPA & ENG.). pap. (978-0-8368-3320-1(1)); (ENG & SPA., lib. bdg. 19.33 (978-0-8368-3071-2(7)) Stevens, Gareth Inc. (Weekly Reader Early Learning Library).

Libra, Anna. Why Does Loud Music Hurt My Ears? An Inside Look at the Ear. 2003. (J). pap. (978-1-58417-072-3(7)); lib. bdg. (978-1-58417-009-9(3)) Lake Street Pubs.

Llewellyn, Claire. Hearing. 2005. (Illus.). 24p. (J). (gr. 1-4). lib. bdg. 22.80 (978-1-932889-47-5(7)) Sea-To-Sea Pubns.

—Sound & Hearing. 2005. (Illus.). 24p. (J). (gr. 1-4). lib. bdg. (978-1-84234-332-6(7), Cherrytree Books) Evans Publishing Group.

Mackill, Mary. Hearing. 2006. (Heinemann Read & Learn Ser.). (Illus.). 24p. (J). (978-1-4034-7375-2(7)); pap. (978-1-4034-7382-0(X)) Steck-Vaughn.

Mayo Clinic Staff, contrib. by. 10 Tips for Better Hearing. 2002. (Compact Guides to Fitness & Health Ser.). (Illus.). 36,52p. lib. bdg. (978-1-59084-265-2(0)) Mason Crest Pubs.

Mokhemar, Mary Ann. Just for Kids Interactive Auditory Processing Pictures Manual. 2006. (J). 0.00 (978-0-7606-0665-0(X)) LinguiSystems, Inc.

Molter, Carey. Sense of Hearing. l.t. ed. 2001. (Senses Ser.). (Illus.). 24p. (J). (ps-3). lib. bdg. 19.93 (978-1-57765-627-2(X), SandCastle) ABDO Publishing Co.

Murphy, Patricia J. Hearing. 2003. (True Bks.). (gr. 3-5). pap. 6.95 (978-0-516-26970-2(4), Children's Pr.) Scholastic Library Publishing.

—Hearing. 2003. (gr. 3-6). lib. bdg. 15.25 (978-0-613-67968-8(7)) Tandem Library Bks.

Murray, Julie. Sound & Hearing. 2007. (First Science Ser.). (Illus.). 24p. (J). 21.35 (978-1-59679-831-1(9), Buddy Bks.) ABDO Publishing Co.

Nelson, Robin. Hearing. 2005. (First Step Nonfiction Ser.). (Illus.). 24p. (gr. k-2). lib. bdg. 17.27 (978-0-8225-1264-6(5)) Lerner Publishing Group.

El Oído (Hearing) (J). 2007. pap. 4.25 (978-0-8225-6548-2(X)); 2006. (SPA.). 18.60 (978-0-8225-6221-4(9)) Lerner Publishing Group. (Ediciones Lerner).

Olien, Rebecca. Hearing. 2005. (Illus.). 24p. (J). (ps-7). lib. bdg. 21.26 (978-0-7368-4301-0(9)) Capstone Pr., Inc.

Pringle, Laurence P. Hearing. 2000. (Explore Your Senses Ser.). (Illus.). 32p. (J). (gr. 4-8). lib. bdg. 25.64 (978-0-7614-0735-5(9), Benchmark Bks.) Cavendish, Marshall Corp.

Pryor, Kimberley Jane. Hearing. 2003. (Senses Ser.). (Illus.). 32p. (gr. 2-4). 23.00 (978-0-7910-7554-8(0), Chelsea Hse.) Facts On File, Inc.

Rau, Dana Meachen. Shhhh...listen! A Book about Your Sense of Hearing. Peterson, Rick, illus. 2005. (Amazing Body Ser.). 24p. (C). (gr. k-3). 22.60 (978-1-4048-1018-1(8)) Picture Window Bks.

Royston, Angela. Hearing. 2005. (Illus.). 32p. (J). (gr. 1 up). lib. bdg. 27.10 (978-1-59389-205-0(5)) Chrysalis Education.

—Sound & Hearing. (Illus.). 32p. (J). (gr. k-2). 2002. pap. 6.95 (978-1-4034-0045-1(8), 91489); 2001. lib. bdg. 21.36 (978-1-58810-246-1(7)) Heinemann Library.

—Sound & Hearing. 2002. (gr. k-3). lib. bdg. 15.25 (978-0-613-90102-4(9)) Tandem Library Bks.

Schaefer, Lola M. The Way Things Move Series, 6 bks., Set. 1999. (Illus.). (J). (ps-2). pap. 79.50 (978-0-516-29665-4(5), Children's Pr.) Scholastic Library Publishing.

Schuh, Mari. The Sense of Hearing. 2007. (Illus.). 24p. (J). lib. bdg. 19.95 (978-1-60014-070-9(X)) Bellwether Media.

Sherman, Josepha. The Ear: Learning How We Hear. 2002. (3-D Library of the Human Body). (Illus.). 48p. (YA). (gr. 5-8). lib. bdg. 26.50 (978-0-8239-3529-1(9), Rosen Central) Rosen Publishing Group, Inc., The.

Sian Revision Vision & Hearing. 2004. (J). (978-1-59242-079-7(6)) Delta Education, LLC.

Silverstein, Alvin. Earaches. 2002. (gr. 3-6). lib. bdg. 15.25 (978-0-613-54181-7(2)) Tandem Library Bks.

Silverstein, Alvin, et al. Earaches. 2002. (My Health Ser.). (Illus.). 48p. (J). (gr. 3-5). pap. 6.95 (978-0-531-15562-2(5), Watts, Franklin) Scholastic Library Publishing.

—Hearing. 2001. (Senses & Sensors Ser.). (Illus.). 64p. (gr. 5-8). lib. bdg. 25.90 (978-0-7613-1666-4(3), Millbrook Pr.) Lerner Publishing Group.

Spilsbury, Louise. Why Should I Turn down the Volume? And Other Questions about Healthy Ears & Eyes. 2003. (Body Matters Ser.). (Illus.). 32p. (J). lib. bdg. 16.95 (978-1-4034-4683-1(0)) Heinemann Library.

Trumbauer, Lisa. Animal Ears. 2000. (Yellow Umbrella Books). (Illus.). 16p. (J). (gr. 1). lib. bdg. 14.60 (978-0-7368-0723-4(3), Pebble Bks.) Capstone Pr., Inc.

Woodward, Kay. Hearing. 2005. (Illus.). 24p. (J). lib. bdg. 22.00 (978-0-8368-4406-1(8)) Stevens, Gareth Inc.

HEART

see also Blood—Circulation

Angliss, Sarah. The Power Pack: Cardiovascular System. 1999. 32p. (J). lib. bdg. 16.95 (978-1-929298-19-8(6)) Chrysalis Education.

El Aparato Circulatorio (the Circulatory System) 2007. (J). pap. 7.95 (978-0-8225-6653-3(2), Ediciones Lerner) Lerner Publishing Group.

El Aparato Circulatorio (The Circulatory System) 2006. (Libros Sobre el Cuerpo Humano para Madrugadores Ser.). (SPA.). 48p. (J). 25.26 (978-0-8225-6252-8(9), Ediciones Lerner) Lerner Publishing Group.

Ballard, Carol. The Heart & Circulation. 2005. (Exploring the Human Body Ser.). (Illus.). 32p. (J). (gr. 4-8). lib. bdg. 24.95 (978-0-7377-3019-7(6), Greenhaven Pr., Inc.) Thomson Gale.

Bankston, John. Christiaan Barnard & the Story of the First Heart Transplant. l.t. ed. 2002. (Unlocking the Secrets of Science Ser.). (Illus.). 56p. (gr. 4-10). lib. bdg. 25.70 (978-1-58415-120-3(X)) Mitchell Lane Pubs., Inc.

—Robert Jarvik & the First Artificial Heart. l.t. ed. 2002. (Unlocking the Secrets of Science Ser.). (Illus.). 56p. (gr. 4-10). lib. bdg. 25.70 (978-1-58415-116-6(1)) Mitchell Lane Pubs., Inc.

Berger, Melvin & Berger, Gilda. Your Heart. 2005. (Illus.). pap. (978-0-439-77369-0(5)) Scholastic, Inc.

Cassan, Adolfo. The Heart & Lungs. 2005. (Inside the Human Body Ser.). (Illus.). 32p. (J). (gr. 4-8). 28.00 (978-0-7910-9012-1(4), Chelsea Clubhouse) Facts On File, Inc.

Curry, Don L. How Does Your Heart Work? 2004. (Rookie Read-About Health Ser.). 31p. (J). (gr. k-2). pap. 5.95 (978-0-516-27855-1(X), Children's Pr.) Scholastic Library Publishing.

DeGezelle, Terri. Your Heart. 2002. (Bridgestone Science Library). (Illus.). 24p. (J). (gr. 1-2). lib. bdg. 18.60 (978-0-7368-1148-4(6), Bridgestone Bks.) Capstone Pr., Inc.

Fitzpatrick, Anne. The Heart. 2003. (Illus.). 24p. (J). lib. bdg. 21.35 (978-1-58340-308-2(6)) Smart Apple Media.

Freeman, J. A., et al. Red's True Heart. 2001. (J). (978-0-929895-96-3(7)) Maupin Hse. Publishing.

Furgang, Kathy. My Heart. 2001. (My Body Ser.). (Illus.). 24p. (J). lib. bdg. 19.95 (978-0-8239-5574-9(5), PowerKids Pr.) Rosen Publishing Group, Inc., The.

Gray, Susan H. The Heart. 2005. (Human Body Ser.). (Illus.). 32p. (J). (gr. 2-6). 27.07 (978-1-59296-427-7(3)) Child's World, Inc.

Gray, Susan Heinrichs. The Circulatory System. 2003. (Body Systems Ser.). (Illus.). 32p. (J). (gr. 2-6). 27.07 (978-1-59296-036-1(7)) Child's World, Inc.

Heart. 2001. (Human Anatomy Ser.). (J). (gr. k-12). vinyl bd. 4.95 (978-1-58845-080-7(5)) School Specialty Publishing.

Hoffman, Nancy. Heart Transplants. 2003. (Great Medical Discoveries Ser.). (Illus.). 128p. (J). 29.95 (978-1-56006-929-4(5), Lucent Bks.) Thomson Gale.

Houghton, Gillian. Blood: The Circulatory System. 2007. (Body Works). (Illus.). 24p. (J). (gr. 2-4). lib. bdg. 21.25 (978-1-4042-3472-7(1), PowerKids Pr.) Rosen Publishing Group, Inc., The.

—The Circulatory System. 2007. (How Your Body Works). (Illus.). 24p. (J). pap. (978-1-4042-2181-9(6), PowerKids Pr.) Rosen Publishing Group, Inc., The.

Johnson, Rebecca L. Respiration & Circulation. 2004. (National Geographic Reading Expeditions Ser.). (Illus.). 32p. (J). pap. (978-0-7922-4586-5(5)) National Geographic Society.

LeVert, Suzanne. The Heart. 2001. (Kaleidoscope Ser.). (Illus.). 48p. (J). (gr. 3 up). lib. bdg. 25.64 (978-0-7614-1306-6(5), Benchmark Bks.) Cavendish, Marshall Corp.

Libra, Anna. How Do My Cuts Heal? An Inside Look at the Circulatory System. 2003. (J). (978-1-58417-003-7(4)); pap. (978-1-58417-066-2(2)) Lake Street Pubs.

Lindeen, Carol. My Heart Inside & Out. 2007. 24p. (J). (978-0-7368-6691-0(4), Pebble Bks.) Capstone Pr., Inc.

Nettleton, Pamela Hill. Thump-Thump: Learning about Your Heart. Shipe, Becky, illus. 2004. (Amazing Body Ser.). 24p. (C). (gr. k-3). 22.60 (978-1-4048-0255-1(X)) Picture Window Bks.

Parker, Steve. Heart, Blood, & Lungs. 2004. (Understanding the Human Body Ser.). (Illus.). 32p. (J). lib. bdg. 24.67 (978-0-8368-4206-7(5)) Stevens, Gareth Inc.

Petrie, Kristin. The Circulatory System. 2007. (Checkerboard Science Library). (Illus.). 32p. (J). 22.78 (978-1-59679-709-3(6)) ABDO Publishing Co.

Ross, Veronica. The Heart. 2004. (J). lib. bdg. 27.10 (978-1-59389-164-0(4)) Chrysalis Education.

School Specialty Publishing. The Heart. 2004. (On-File Ser.). 4p. (J). (gr. 4-6). ring bd. 4.99 (978-0-7424-2905-5(9), Instructional Fair) Schaffer, Frank Pubns.

Showers, Paul. Hear Your Heart. Keller, Holly, illus. rev. ed. (Let's-Read-and-Find-Out Science Ser.). 40p. (J). (gr. k-4). 2001. 15.95 (978-0-06-025410-0(6)); 2001. pap. 5.99 (978-0-06-445139-0(9) , Harper Trophy); 2000. 15.89 (978-0-06-025411-7(4)) HarperCollins Pubs.

—Hear Your Heart. 2001. (gr. k-3). lib. bdg. 13.00 (978-0-613-31300-1(3)); (Illus.). (J). 11.79 (978-0-606-20694-5(9)) Tandem Library Bks.

Simon, Seymour. The Heart: Our Circulatory System. (J). 2006. 32p. 16.99 (978-0-06-087720-0(0)); 2006. (Illus.). 32p. pap. 6.99 (978-0-06-087721-7(9)); 1999. (Illus.). pap. 6.99 (978-0-688-17059-2(5) , Harper Trophy) HarperCollins Pubs.

Superlibro de el cuerpo humano: corazon y Pulmones: Unit 6: el cuerpo humano: corazon y pulmones (Human Body: Heart & Lungs) 2000. (McGraw-Hill Ciencias Ser.). (ENG & SPA.). (gr. 2 up). (978-0-02-277176-8(X)) Macmillan/McGraw-Hill Schl. Div.

Taylor-Butler, Christine. The Circulatory System. 2007. (True Booktrade;: Health & the Human Body Ser.). 48p. (J). spiral bd. 26.00 (***978-0-531-16856-1(5)*** , Children's Pr.) Scholastic Library Publishing.

Thump-Thump. (Amazing Body Ser.). 24p. (J). 7.95 (978-1-4048-0506-4(0)) Picture Window Bks.

Viegas, Jennifer. The Heart: Learning How Our Blood Circulates. 2002. (3-D Library of the Human Body). (Illus.). 48p. (YA). (gr. 5-8). lib. bdg. 26.50 (978-0-8239-3532-1(9) , Rosen Central) Rosen Publishing Group, Inc., The.

Walker, Richard. The Heart in Action. 2004. (Body Science Ser.). (J). lib. bdg. 27.10 (978-1-58340-457-7(0)) Smart Apple Media.

Walton, Karen A. How Will They Get That Heart down Your Throat? A Child's View of Transplants. Peterson, Allison P., illus. 2nd ed. 1999. 56p. (J). (gr. k-6). pap. 17.50 (978-1-880664-98-8(4)) E. M. Productions.

World Book, Inc Staff, contrib. by. The Circulatory System. 2006. (World Book's Human Body Works). (Illus.). 48p. (J). (978-0-7166-4427-9(4)) World Bk., Inc.

Your Heart. (Your Body Ser.). 24p. (J). 6.95 (978-0-7368-3352-3(8)) Capstone Pr., Inc.

HEART—DISEASES

Angliss, Sarah. The Power Pack: Cardiovascular System. 1999. 32p. (J). lib. bdg. 16.95 (978-1-929298-19-8(6)) Chrysalis Education.

Cut to the Heart. 2004. (NOVA Ser.). (gr. 7 up). 19.95 (978-1-57807-051-0(1) , WG2409) WGBH Boston Video.

Gold, John Coopersmith. Heart Disease. rev. ed. 2000. (Health Watch Ser.). (Illus.). 48p. (YA). (gr. 4-10). lib. bdg. 23.93 (978-0-7660-1653-8(6)) Enslow Pubs., Inc.

Gregson, Susan R. Heart Disease. 2001. (Perspectives on Disease & Illness Ser.). (Illus.). 64p. (J). (gr. 4-6). lib. bdg. 23.93 (978-0-7368-0749-4(7) , LifeMatters Bks.) Capstone Pr., Inc.

Haney, Johannah. Heart Disease. 2004. (Illus.). 63p. (J). 28.50 (978-0-7614-1801-6(6) , Benchmark Bks.) Cavendish, Marshall Corp.

Johansson, Philip. Heart Disease. 1998. (Diseases & People Ser.). (Illus.). 128p. (YA). (gr. 6-12). lib. bdg. 20.95 (978-0-7660-1051-2(1)) Enslow Pubs., Inc.

Olien, Rebecca. The Circulatory System. 2006. (J). (978-0-7368-5408-5(8)) Capstone Pr., Inc.

Sheen, Barbara. Heart Disease. 2004. (Illus.). 93p. (J). (gr. 7-10). 32.45 (978-1-59018-347-2(9) , Lucent Bks.) Thomson Gale.

Silverstein, Alvin, et al. Heart Disease. 2006. (Twenty-First Century Medical Library). (Illus.). 96p. (J). (gr. 8 up). 27.93 (978-0-7613-3420-0(3) , Twenty-First Century Bks.) Lerner Publishing Group.

Stillman, Deborah L. & Levin, Sidney L. The Heart That Attacked My Family: How Life Changes When Someone You Love Has Heart Disease. Stillman, Deborah L. & Levin, Sidney L., illus. (Illus.). 40p. (J). (gr. 2-6). 2000. 16.95 (978-0-9637795-5-7(9)); 1998. pap. 10.95 (978-0-9637795-6-4(7)) MinervaPress.

Taylor, Robert. Strokes. 2006. (Illus.). 112p. (J). (gr. 7-10). 32.45 (978-1-59018-967-2(1) , 1256798, Lucent Bks.) Thomson Gale.

Vander Hook, Sue. Heart Disease. 2000. (Understanding Illness Ser.). (Illus.). 32p. (J). lib. bdg. 16.95 (978-1-58340-026-5(5)) Smart Apple Media.

Werther, Scott P. Ecstasy & Your Heart: The Incredibly Disgusting Story. 2005. (Incredibly Disgusting Drugs Ser.). (Illus.). 48p. (YA). (gr. 5-8). lib. bdg. 25.25 (978-0-8239-3390-7(3)) Rosen Publishing Group, Inc., The.

HEAT

see also Fire; Temperature; Thermodynamics; Thermometers and Thermometry

Ballard, Carol. Heating & Cooling. 2007. (J). (***978-1-4034-9925-7(X)***); pap. (***978-1-4034-9933-2(0)***) Heinemann Library.

Bratton, Catherine. Physics: Heat Transfer. 2002. (Illus.). 2p. (J). pap. 2.00 (978-0-9719268-0-6(8)) davishooligans.

Bryant-Mole, Karen & Ansary, Mir Tamim. Hot & Cold. 2002. (Illus.). 24p. (J). (gr. 1-3). pap. 6.50 (978-1-4034-0051-2(2) , 91495) Heinemann Library.

Burke, Jennifer S. Hot Days. 2000. (gr. k-3). lib. bdg. 12.95 (978-0-613-62206-6(5)) Tandem Library Bks.

Burton, Margie, et al. Heat. Adams, Alison, ed. 1999. (Early Connections Ser.). 16p. (J). (gr. k-2). pap. 4.50 (978-1-58344-065-0(8)) Benchmark Education Co.

Challen, Paul C. Drought & Heat Wave Alert! 2004. (Disaster Alert! Ser.). (Illus.). 32p. (J). (978-0-7787-1578-8(7)); pap. (978-0-7787-1610-5(4)) Crabtree Publishing Co.

Chambers, Catherine. Heat Wave. 2007. (Wild Weather Ser.). (Illus.). 32p. (J). (gr. 2-4). lib. bdg. 25.36 (***978-1-4034-9578-5(5)***) Heinemann Library.

Cole, Joanna. El Autobus Magico en el Artico: Un Libro Sobre el Calor. 1998. (Coleccion El Autobus Magico). (SPA., Illus.). (J). (gr. k-4). pap. 3.50 (978-0-590-38664-7(6) , SO8203, Scholastic en Espanol) Scholastic, Inc.

—El Autobus Magico en el Artico: Un Libro Sobre el Calor. 1999. (Magic School Bus Ser.). (Illus.). (J). (gr. 1-4). (978-0-606-15520-5(1)) Tandem Library Bks.

Cole, Joanna & Schreiber, Anne. The Magic School Bus in the Arctic: A Book about Heat. Degan, Bruce & Ruiz, Art, illus. 1998. (Magic School Bus Ser.). 32p. (J). (gr. 1-4). pap. 3.99 (978-0-590-18724-4(4)) Scholastic, Inc.

Dahl, Michael. Hot, Hotter, Hottest: Animals That Adapt to Great Heat. Jensen, Brian, illus. 2005. (Animal Extremes Ser.). 24p. (C). (gr. k-2). 22.60 (978-1-4048-1017-4(X)) Picture Window Bks.

Ellse, Mark, et al. Electricity & Thermal Physics. 2nd rev. ed. 2004. (Nelson Advanced Science Ser.). (Illus.). 146p. (YA). pap. 39.50 (978-0-7487-7663-4(X)) Nelson Thornes Ltd. GBR. *Dist:* Trans-Atlantic Pubns., Inc.

Fandel, Jennifer. Heat. 2002. (Illus.). 23p. (J). lib. bdg. 21.35 (978-1-58340-152-1(0)) Smart Apple Media.

Fiedler, Julie. Learning about Heat & Temperature with Graphic Organizers. 2007. (Graphic Organizers in Science Ser.). (Illus.). 24p. (J). lib. bdg. (978-1-4042-3408-6(X) , PowerKids Pr.) Rosen Publishing Group, Inc., The.

Frank, Marjorie Slavick, et al. Science Instant Readers Bk. 10: Heat Changes Things. 1999. (Harcourt Science Ser.). (gr. 1 up). pap. 15.50 (978-0-15-316208-4(2)) Harcourt Schl. Pubs.

Gardner, Robert. Sizzling Science Projects with Heat & Energy. 2006. (Fantastic Physical Science Experiments Ser.). (Illus.). 48p. (J). lib. bdg. 23.93 (978-0-7660-2586-8(1) , Enslow Elementary) Enslow Pubs., Inc.

Gareth Stevens Publishing Staff, contrib. by. Heat. 2003. (Discovery Channel School Science Ser.). (Illus.). 32p. (J). (gr. 5 up). lib. bdg. 24.67 (978-0-8368-3358-4(9)) Stevens, Gareth Inc.

Gish, Melissa. Temperature. 2005. (My First Look at Science Ser.). (Illus.). 24p. (gr. k-3). 15.95 (978-1-58341-375-3(8) , Creative Education) Creative Co., The.

Granowsky, Alvin. Hot & Cold. 2001. 11.79 (978-0-606-22435-2(1)) Tandem Library Bks.

Group/McGraw-Hill, Wright. Heat: Level F, 6 vols. (Take Twostm Ser.). 16p. 29.95 (978-0-322-08953-2(0)) Wright Group, The.

Harcourt School Publishers Staff. Harcourt Science: Heat Changes Things Reader. 1999. (Illus.). pap. 3.10 (978-0-15-314860-6(8)) Harcourt Schl. Pubs.

Heat. 2001. (Physical Science Ser.). (J). (gr. k-12). vinyl bd. 4.95 (978-1-58845-116-3(X)) School Specialty Publishing.

Hewitt, Sally. Heat. 2006. (Science Starters Ser.). (Illus.). 32p. (J). (978-1-59604-080-9(7)) Stargazer Bks.

Hidalgo, Maria. Heat. 2006. (My First Look at Weather Ser.). (Illus.). 24p. 15.95 (978-1-58341-449-1(5) , Creative Education) Creative Co., The.

Holland, Gini. Hot & Cold. 2007. (J). pap. (***978-0-8368-8299-5(7)***); 24p. lib. bdg. 17.27 (***978-0-8368-8294-0(6)***) Stevens, Gareth Inc. (Weekly Reader Early Learning Library).

—Hot & Cold: Caliente y Frío. 2007. (SPA & ENG.). (J). pap. (***978-0-8368-8309-1(8)*** , Weekly Reader Early Learning Library) Stevens, Gareth Inc.

—Hot & Cold/Caliente y Frio. 2007. (I Know Opposites/ Conceptos Contrarios Ser.). (SPA & ENG.). 24p. (J). (gr. k-2). lib. bdg. 17.27 (***978-0-8368-8304-6(7)*** , Weekly Reader Early Learning Library) Stevens, Gareth Inc.

Holt, Rinehart and Winston Staff. Holt Science & Technology Chapter 10: Physical Science: Heat & Heat Technology. 5th ed. 2004. (Illus.). pap. 12.86 (978-0-03-030401-9(6)) Holt, Rinehart & Winston.

—Holt Science & Technology Chptr. 13: Heat & Technology: Chapter Resources - Tennessee Edition. 3rd ed. 2003. (J). pap. 11.40 (978-0-03-069121-8(4)) Holt, Rinehart & Winston.

Hunter, Rebecca M. Hot & Cold. 2000. (Discovering Science Ser.). (Illus.). 32p. (J). (gr. 3-5). lib. bdg. 25.69 (978-0-7398-2972-1(6)) Raintree.

—Hot & Cold. 2000. (Discovering Science Ser.). (Illus.). 32p. (J). (gr. 3-5). pap. 8.95 (978-0-7398-3016-1(3)) Steck-Vaughn.

Keeping Warm. 2006. (Yellow Umbrella Science Ser.). 8,16p. (J). 6.50 (978-0-7368-1711-0(5)) Red Brick Learning.

Kids Publishing Science Staff. Transforming Energy: All about Heat, Work & Energy. 1999. (J). pap. 6.95 (978-1-891418-17-4(3)) Science Kids.

Mahaney, Ian F. Heat. 2007. 24p. (J). pap. (978-1-4042-2186-4(7)); (Illus.). (gr. 4-6). lib. bdg. 21.25 (978-1-4042-3477-2(2)) Rosen Publishing Group, Inc., The. (PowerKids Pr.).

Martin, Elena. Hot or Cold? 2003. (Yellow Umbrella Books). (Illus.). 16p. (J). (gr. 1). lib. bdg. 14.60 (978-0-7368-2012-7(4) , Pebble Bks.) Capstone Pr., Inc.

—Hot or Cold? 2003. (Math Ser.). (J). (978-0-7368-1698-4(4)) Yellow Umbrella Pr.

Moran, Jeffrey B. How Do We Know the Laws of Thermodynamics? 2001. (Great Scientific Questions & the Scientists Who Answered Them Ser.). (Illus.). 112p. (YA). (gr. 4-6). lib. bdg. 26.50 (978-0-8239-3384-6(9)) Rosen Publishing Group, Inc., The.

Murray, Julie & Abdo Publishing Staff. Hot & Cold. 2007. (Illus.). 24p. (J). 21.35 (978-1-59679-825-0(4)) ABDO Publishing Co.

Parker, Steve. Heat & Energy. 2004. (Science View Ser.). (Illus.). 32p. (J). (gr. 4-8). 28.00 (978-0-7910-8207-2(5) , Chelsea Hse.) Facts On File, Inc.

Prentice-Hall Staff. Heat Energy. 2nd ed. (J). tchr. ed. 18.97 (978-0-13-400706-9(9)); pap., act. bk. ed. (978-0-13-400722-9(0)) Prentice Hall (Schl. Div.).

Rau, Dana Meachen. Hot & Bright: A Book about the Sun. Shea, Denise, illus. 2005. (Amazing Science Ser.). 24p. (J). (ps-k). lib. bdg. 22.60 (978-1-4048-1135-5(4)) Picture Window Bks.

Riley, Peter D. Keeping Warm. 2007. (J). (***978-1-59920-027-9(9)***) Smart Apple Media.

Royston, Angela. Conductors & Insulators. 2003. (My World of Science Ser.). (Illus.). 32p. pap. 6.95 (978-1-4034-3164-6(7)); (J). lib. bdg. 22.79 (978-1-4034-0851-8(3)) Heinemann Library.

—Hot & Cold. (My World of Science Ser.). (Illus.). 32p. (J). (gr. k-2). 2002. pap. 6.95 (978-1-4034-0040-6(7) , 91484); 2001. lib. bdg. 21.36 (978-1-58810-241-6(6)) Heinemann Library.

—Hot & Cold. 2002. (gr. k-3). lib. bdg. 14.75 (978-0-613-86991-1(5)) Tandem Library Bks.

Rubin, Alan. Keeping Warm. 2003. (Yellow Umbrella Books). (Illus.). 16p. (J). (gr. 1). lib. bdg. 14.60 (978-0-7368-2019-6(1) , Pebble Bks.) Capstone Pr., Inc.

Sadler, Wendy. Hot & Cold: Feel It! 2005. (Raintree Perspectives Ser.). (Illus.). 32p. (J). pap. (978-1-4109-1562-7(X)); lib. bdg. (978-1-4109-1554-2(9)) Steck-Vaughn.

Schmauss, Judy Kentor. Too, Too Hot. 2006. (Reader's Clubhouse Set A Ser.). (Illus.). 24p. (J). pap. 3.99 (978-0-7641-3285-8(7)) Barron's Educational Series, Inc.

Searle, Bobbi. Heat & Energy. 2001. (978-0-606-22380-5(0)) Tandem Library Bks.

Sheehan, Thomas F. Keeping Warm, Keeping Cool. 2006. (City Science Ser.). (Illus.). 24p. (gr. k-3). 14.95 (978-1-59515-413-2(2)) Rourke Publishing, LLC.

—Para Calentarse, para Refrescarse (Keeping Warm, Keeping Cool) Sarfatti, Esther, tr. from ENG. 2005. (Ciencia Citadina Ser.). (ENG & SPA., Illus.). 24p. (J). (gr. 3-7). lib. bdg. 21.36 (978-1-59515-666-2(6)) Rourke Publishing, LLC.

Stille, Darlene R. Temperature: Heating Up & Cooling Down. Boyd, Sheree, illus. 2004. (Amazing Science Ser.). 24p. (C). (gr. k-4). 22.60 (978-1-4048-0247-6(9)) Picture Window Bks.

Sullivan, Navin. Temperature. 2006. (Measure Up! Ser.). (Illus.). 48p. (J). (gr. 4-7). lib. bdg. 29.93 (978-0-7614-2322-5(2) , Benchmark Bks.) Cavendish, Marshall Corp.

Tanaka, Shelley. The Heat Is On. Beinicke, Steve, illus. (J). pap. 4.99 (978-1-55054-200-4(1)) Douglas & McIntyre, Ltd. CAN. *Dist:* Transition Vendor.

Taylor, Kim. Heat. (Illus.). 32p. (YA). (gr. 3 up). lib. bdg. 27.10 (978-1-931983-77-8(1)) Chrysalis Education.

Thomas, Rick. Sizzle! A Book about Heat Waves. Shea, Denise, illus. 2005. (Amazing Science Ser.). 24p. (C). (gr. k-3). 22.60 (978-1-4048-0927-7(9)) Picture Window Bks.

Trumbauer, Lisa. All about Heat. 2004. (Rookie Read-About Science Ser.). 32p. (J). (gr. 1-2). pap. 4.95 (978-0-516-25846-1(X) , Children's Pr.) Scholastic Library Publishing.

—Caliente o Frio? 2005. Tr. of Hot or Cold. (SPA., Illus.). 16p. (J). (gr. k-1). lib. bdg. 15.93 (978-0-7368-4129-0(6)) Capstone Pr., Inc.

Wadsworth, Pamela. Golwg Gyntaf Ar Egni. 2005. (WEL., Illus.). 24p. pap. (978-1-85596-257-6(8)) Dref Wen.

Waiakea High Writer's Group. Hot Lava, Cool Rain. 2001. (gr. 7-12). lib. bdg. 25.20 (978-0-613-74532-1(9)) Tandem Library Bks.

Walker, Sally M. El Calor (Heat) 2007. (Libros de Energía para madrugadores (Early Bird Energy) Ser.). (SPA.). 48p. (J). (gr. 2-5). lib. bdg. 26.60 (***978-0-8225-7718-8(6)*** , Ediciones Lerner) Lerner Publishing Group.

Walker, Sally M. Heat. 2006. (Early Bird Energy Ser.). (Illus.). 48p. (J). (ps-7). 25.26 (978-0-8225-2459-5(7) , Lerner Pubns.) Lerner Publishing Group.

Whyman, Kathryn. Energy & Heat. 2004. (J). lib. bdg. (978-1-932799-22-4(2)) Stargazer Bks.

Winholtz, Wallie, et al. Thermodynamic Thrills. Hixson, Bryce, illus. 2002. (J). per. 14.95 (978-0-9660965-2-1(5)) Loose In The Lab.

Wood, Robert W. Heat Fundamentals. 1999. (Funtastic Science Activities for Kids Ser.). (Illus.). 160p. (YA). (gr. 4-7). lib. bdg. 25.25 (978-0-7910-4842-9(X) , Chelsea Hse.) Facts On File, Inc.

HEAT—EXPERIMENTS

Ardley, Neil. The Science Book of Hot & Cold. 1998. (Illus.). (978-0-8172-9801-2(0)) Steck-Vaughn.

Bryant-Mole, Karen & Ansary, Mir Tamim. Hot & Cold. 2002. (Illus.). 24p. (J). (gr. 1-3). pap. 6.50 (978-1-4034-0051-2(2) , 91495) Heinemann Library.

Gardner, Robert. Really Hot Science Projects with Temperature: How Hot Is It? How Cold Is It? 2003. (Sensational Science Experiments Ser.). (Illus.). 48p. (J). lib. bdg. 23.93 (978-0-7660-2015-3(0)) Enslow Pubs., Inc.

Gould, Alan. Convection: A Current Event. Klofkorn, Lisa, illus. Hoyt, Richard, photos by. rev. ed. 2005. (Great Explorations in Math & Science Ser.). 60p. (J). reprint ed. pap. 10.50 (978-1-931542-05-0(8) , GEMS) Univ. of California, Berkeley, Lawrence Hall of Science.

Heating. 2004. (Illus.). 24p. (J). (ps-ps). pap. 5.75 (978-1-4034-5103-3(6)) Heinemann Library.

Lauw, Darlene. Heat. 2002. (gr. 3-6). lib. bdg. 16.40 (978-0-613-52851-1(4)) Tandem Library Bks.

Lauw, Darlene & Puay, Lim Cheng. Heat. 2002. (Science Alive! Ser.). (Illus.). 32p. (J). (gr. 4-5). pap. (978-0-7787-0605-2(2)); lib. bdg. (978-0-7787-0559-8(5)) Crabtree Publishing Co.

Stille, Darlene R. Hot & Cold. 2001. (Simply Science Ser.). (Illus.). 32p. (J). (gr. 3 up). lib. bdg. 19.93 (978-0-7565-0090-0(7)) Compass Point Bks.

Whitehouse, Patricia, tr. Heating. 2004. (J). lib. bdg. (978-1-4034-5098-2(6)) Heinemann Library.

HEAT—FICTION

Albee, Sarah. Fun in the Sun. Williams, Sue, illus. 2006. (Step-By-Step Readers Ser.). (J). pap. (978-1-59939-058-1(2) , Reader's Digest Young Families, Inc.) Reader's Digest Children's Publishing, Inc.

Barclay, Jane. How Hot Was It? Cole, Kathryn, ed. Donato, Janice, illus. 24p. (J). 14.95 (978-1-894222-70-9(9)) Lobster Pr. CAN. *Dist:* Univ. of Toronto Pr.

Best, Cari. When Catherine the Great & I Were Eight! Potter, Giselle, illus. 2003. 32p. (J). (gr. k-3). 16.00 (978-0-374-39954-2(9) , Farrar, Straus & Giroux (BYR)) Farrar, Straus & Giroux.

Broach, Elise. Wet Dog! Catrow, David, illus. 32p. (J). (gr. k). 2007. pap. 5.99 (978-0-14-240855-1(7) , Puffin); 2005. 16.99 (978-0-8037-2809-7(3) , Dial) Penguin Group (USA) Inc.

Cook, Sherry & Johnson, Terri. Hallie Heat, 26 vols. Kuhn, Jesse, illus. l.t. ed. 2006. (Quirkles—Exploring Phonics through Science Ser.: 8). 32p. (J). 7.99 (978-1-933815-07-7(8) , Quirkles, The) Creative 3, LLC.

Frazier, Craig. Stanley Goes for a Drive. 2004. (Illus.). 40p. (J). 15.95 (978-0-8118-4429-1(3)) Chronicle Bks. LLC.

Layton, Neal. Hot Hot Hot. Layton, Neal, illus. 2004. (Illus.). 32p. (J). (ps-3). 15.99 (978-0-7636-2148-3(X)) Candlewick Pr.

Now It's Hot! Individual Title Six-Packs. (Rigby Focus Ser.). 16p. (gr. k up). 26.00 (978-0-7578-5295-4(5)); 28.00 (978-0-7578-5529-0(6)) Rigby Education.

Spinelli, Eileen. Heat Wave. Lewin, Betsy, illus. 2007. 32p. (J). (gr. k-3). 16.00 (978-0-15-216779-0(X)) Harcourt Trade Pubs.

Van Leeuwen, Jean. Amanda Pig & the Really Hot Day. Schweninger, Ann, illus. 2007. 48p. (J). pap. 3.99 (978-0-14-240775-2(5) , Puffin) Penguin Group (USA) Inc.

Van Leeuwen, Jean & Van Leeuwen, Jean. Amanda Pig & the Really Hot Day. Schweninger, Ann, illus. 2005. (Easy-to-Read, Dial Ser.). 48p. (J). (ps-ps). 14.99 (978-0-8037-2887-5(5) , Dial) Penguin Group (USA) Inc.

HEATHCLIFF (FICTITIOUS CHARACTER)—FICTION

Brontë, Emily. Wuthering Heights. abr. ed. (Classics Illustrated Ser.). (Illus.). 52p. (YA). pap. 4.95 (978-1-57209-011-8(1)) Classics International Entertainment, Inc.

—Wuthering Heights: Abridged for Children. 1998. (Illus.). 48p. (YA). (gr. 4-7). pap. 6.95 (978-0-8114-6847-3(X)) Steck-Vaughn.

HEATING

Clinton, Susan. Heating & Air Conditioning Servicer. (Careers Without College Ser.). pap. 6.95 (978-0-7368-8545-4(5) , LifeMatters Bks.) Capstone Pr., Inc.

Plumbing, Heating, Air Conditioning & Refrigeration Student Activity. 2004. (YA). cd-rom (978-1-57078-954-0(1) , CEV60033) C E V Multimedia, Ltd.

HEAVEN

see also Heaven

Alcorn, Randy. Tell Me about Heaven. Dicianni, Ron, illus. 2007. 48p. (J). pap. 19.99 (***978-1-58134-853-8(3)***) Crossway Bks.

Alcorn, Randy C. & Washington, Linda M. Heaven for Kids. 2006. (Illus.). 224p. (J). pap. 13.99 (978-1-4143-1040-4(4)) Tyndale Hse. Pubs.

Anderson, Carolyn B. Heaven Is a Real Place. 2007. 73p. per. 8.95 (***978-1-59824-512-7(0)***) E-BookTime LLC.

Anderson, Debby. Let's Talk about Heaven. 2003. (Illus.). 32p. (J). (ps-2). 12.99 (978-0-7814-3077-7(1) , 0781430771) Cook, David C. Publishing Co.

Andreae, Giles. Heaven Is Having You. Cabban, Vanessa, illus. 2002. 32p. (J). tchr. ed. 15.95 (978-1-58925-016-1(8) , tiger tales) ME Media LLC.

Berkley, Deborah Hall. They All Come. 2001. (Illus.). 32p. 19.95 (978-1-890306-33-5(9)) Warwick Hse. Publishing.

Bohlmann, Katherine. Grandpa, Is There a Heaven? Erickson, David, illus. 2001. 32p. (J). (ps-2). 14.99 (978-0-570-07136-5(4)) Concordia Publishing Hse.

Bostrom, Kathleen & Kucharik, Elena. What about Heaven? 2000. (Little Blessings Ser.). (Illus.). 80p. (J). 9.99 (978-0-8423-7353-1(5)) Tyndale Hse. Pubs.

Dent, Jenny. Where Is Heaven? (Spiritual Teachings for Children Ser.). (Illus.). 32p. (J). (gr. k-9). 17.95 (978-0-85487-052-3(0)) White Eagle Publishing Trust GBR. *Dist:* DeVorss & Co.

Dlugos, Pamela J. Messages from Heaven: Be a Shining Star. Dlugos, Pamela J., illus. Date not set. (Illus.). 64p. (J). (gr. 4-6). pap. 10.95 (978-0-9661564-0-9(4)) Rejoyce Pubns.

Enns, Aiden S. & Meinders, Miriam. Where Is Heaven? Gospel of Matthew. 1999. (Generation Why Ser.: Vol. 4.6). 44p. (YA). (gr. 9-12). pap. 14.95 (978-0-87303-286-5(1)) Faith & Life Pr.

Freed, Shirley Ann & Moon, Louise. In Heaven I Will. Morelan, Bill, ed. Harrell, Rob, illus. l.t. ed. 2002. 16p. (J). (gr. 1-2). pap. 3.99 (978-1-58938-025-7(8)) Concerned Communications.

Ganeri, Anita. The Children's Illustrated Encyclopedia of Heaven. 2002. (Illus.). 159p. (J). (gr. 2-6). reprint ed. 20.00 (978-0-7567-5704-5(5)) DIANE Publishing Co.

—The Children's Illustrated Encyclopedia of Heaven. 1999. (Illus.). 160p. (J). 19.95 (978-1-902618-12-8(2)) Element Children's Bks.

Let's Talk about Heaven, No. 3. 1999. 32p. (J). (978-0-7814-0195-1(X)) Cook, David C. Publishing Co.

Libby, Larry. Someday Heaven. McLoughlin, Wayne, illus. 2001. 40p. (J). 12.99 (978-0-310-70105-7(8)) Zonderkidz.

Noel, N. A. & Sisson, John W. On Earth As It Is in Heaven. Noel, N. A., illus. 1999. (Illus.). 32p. (J). (gr. k-8). 19.95 (978-0-9652531-3-0(9)) Noel Studio, Inc.

Wilkinson, Bruce & Thomas, Mack. A Life God Rewards: Guys Only. ltd. ed. 2006. 96p. bds. 9.99 (978-1-60142-002-2(1) , Multnomah Kidz) WaterBrook Pr.

H I

HEAVEN—FICTION

Anderson, Andrea Patrice. Heaven's Diary: Our Gift from God. 2006. 37.00 (***978-0-8059-8845-1(9)***) Dorrance Publishing Co., Inc.

Andreae, Giles. Heaven Is Having You. Cabban, Vanessa, illus. 2007. 24p. (J). (ps-k). bds. 7.95 (***978-1-58925-820-4(7)*** , tiger tales) ME Media LLC.

Carter, Don. Heaven's All-Star Jazz Band. Carter, Don, illus. 2002. (Illus.). 40p. (J). (gr. k-3). 15.95 (978-0-375-81571-3(6) , Knopf Bks. for Young Readers) Random Hse. Children's Bks.

Coleman, Pansy J. & Coleman, Jason A. The Wings of an Angel. 2004. 259p. pap. 21.95 (978-1-4137-2232-1(6)) PublishAmerica, Inc.

Crosse, Joanna. A Child's Book of Angels. Whelan, Olwyn, illus. 2000. 64p. (J). (gr. 1-4). 19.99 (978-1-84148-082-4(7)) Barefoot Bks., Inc.

Hale, Joyce P. Does Heaven Have a Refrigerator? Rawlings, Stacey, illus. 2002. 40p. per. 15.95 (978-0-9715926-1-2(6)) Passage Publishing.

Ivey, Janet Clowes. Tell Me about Heaven...I Think I'm Forgetting. McLaughlin, Catherine R., illus. 2002. 32p. (gr. k-3). 9.95 (978-1-59093-071-7(1)) Warehousing & Fulfillment Specialists, LLC (WFS, LLC).

Kroll-Smith, Steve. When I Dream of Heaven: Angelina's Story. 2000. (gr. 5-8). lib. bdg. 14.95 (978-0-613-36900-8(9)) Tandem Library Bks.

Kubler-Ross, Elisabeth. Remember the Secret. 2004. (Illus.). 32p. (ps-3). pap. 9.95 (978-1-883672-79-9(1) , Tricycle Pr.) Ten Speed Pr.

Lester, Julius. Why Heaven Is Far Away. Cepeda, Joe, illus. 2002. 40p. (J). (gr. 1-3). pap. 16.95 (978-0-439-17871-6(1) , Scholastic Pr.) Scholastic, Inc.

Lewis, Beverly. What is Heaven Like? 2006. (Illus.). 32p. (J). 14.99 (978-0-7642-0184-4(0)) Bethany Hse. Pubs.

Lindsay, Linda. People Heaven. l.t. ed. 2005. (Illus.). (J). 36p. 16.99 (978-1-59879-020-7(X)); 26p. per. 11.99 (978-1-59879-005-4(6)) Lifevest Publishing, Inc.

Madonna, Ritchie. Yakov & the Seven Thieves. Madonna, Ritchie, ed. Spirin, Gennady, illus. 2004. 48p. (J). (gr. k-3). 19.95 (978-0-670-05887-7(4)) Callaway Editions, Inc.

Orndorff, John C. Princess Mary & the Prophet. 2002. (J). per. 6.95 (978-1-893213-02-9(1)) Pensive Bks.

Pelz, Ramona. My Name Is Mae. Trousdale, Taryn, illus. 2003. (J). per. 9.95 (978-1-58597-190-9(1)) Leathers Publishing.

Raphaelo. Willowick: A New Dawn Series: Book One. 2005. 132p. pap. 19.95 (978-1-4137-7963-9(8)) PublishAmerica, Inc.

Rouss, Sylvia. Littlest Tree. Binus, Ari, illus. 2005. 32p. (J). pap. 9.95 (978-1-932687-26-2(2) , Devora Publishing) Pitspopany Pr.

Rylant, Cynthia. The Heavenly Village: A Novel. 1999. 96p. (J). (gr. 5-9). pap. 15.95 (978-0-439-04096-9(5) , Blue Sky Pr., The) Scholastic, Inc.

—The Heavenly Village: A Novel. 2000. (gr. 5-8). lib. bdg. 13.00 (978-0-613-53819-0(6)) Tandem Library Bks.

Tazewell, Charles. The Littlest Uninvited One. Tribble, Gail, illus. 2001. (J). (ps-3). 16.95 (978-0-8249-5404-8(1) , Ideals Children's Bks.) Ideals Pubns.

—Make Me a Miracle. Sofo, Frank, illus. 2000. 240p. 22.95 (978-1-58029-108-8(2) , Celebrity Bks.) Warehousing & Fulfillment Specialists, LLC (WFS, LLC).

Tucker Goes to Heaven. 2006. pap. 13.95 (***978-1-59526-457-2(4)***) Media Creations, Inc.

van Ommen, Sylvia. Jellybeans. 2006. (Illus.). 56p. (J). pap. 8.95 (978-1-55643-632-1(7)) North Atlantic Bks.

Wallace-Lang, Maxine Lois. Sheldon's Adventures in Heaven. Porfirio, Guy, illus. 2003. 48p. (J). 12.99 (978-0-8280-1508-0(2)) Review & Herald Publishing Assn.

HEBREW LANGUAGE

Agnon, Shmuel Yosef. Agnon's Alef Bet: Poems. Friend, Robert, tr. from HEB. Zeldich, Arieh, illus. 1998. 72p. 19.95 (978-0-8276-0599-2(4)) Jewish Pubn. Society.

Amery, H. First Thousand Words. rev. ed. 2004. (HEB.). 64p. (J). 12.99 (978-0-7945-0029-0(3)) EDC Publishing.

Amery, Heather, et al. The First 1000 Words in Hebrew. (Illus.). 47p. (J). (ps-7). lib. bdg. 20.95 (978-0-88110-573-5(2)) EDC Publishing.

Baum, Roberta Osser. Back-to-School Hebrew Reading Refresher. 1999. (ENG & HEB., Illus.). 32p. (J). (978-0-87441-679-4(5)) Behrman Hse., Inc.

Berlitz Editors. Hebrew Phrase Book. 4th rev. ed. 1999. (Phrase Bks.). (HEB & ENG., Illus.). 224p. pap. 8.95 (978-2-8315-6927-7(3) , 569273) Berlitz Publishing.

Blitz, Shmuel. Megilat Ester: The ArtScroll Children's Megillah. Katz, Tova, illus. 2003. (ArtScroll Ser.). (ENG & HEB.). 79p. (J). 16.99 (978-1-57819-708-8(2) , MCHH); pap. 10.99 (978-1-57819-709-5(0) , MCHP) Mesorah Pubns., Ltd.

Bluedorn, Johannah. Little Bitty Baby Learns Hebrew. Bluedorn, Johannah, illus. 2005. (Illus.). 26p. (J). bds. 12.00 (978-1-933228-00-6(8)) Trivium Pursuit.

Burke, David. BEAUTY & the BEAST (English to Hebrew - Level 3) Learn HEBREW Through Fairy Tales. 2007. (ENG & HEB.). (J). per. 14.95 incl. audio compact disk (***978-1-891888-94-6(3)***) Slangman Publishing.

—CINDERELLA (English to Hebrew - Level 1) Learn HEBREW Through Fairy Tales. 2007. (ENG & HEB.). (J). per. 14.95 incl. audio compact disk (***978-1-891888-92-2(7)***) Slangman Publishing.

—GOLDILOCKS (English to Hebrew - Level 2) Learn HEBREW Through Fairy Tales. 2007. (ENG & HEB.). (J). per. 14.95 incl. audio compact disk (***978-1-891888-93-9(5)***) Slangman Publishing.

Castberg, C. & Adler, Lillian W. The New Reading Hebrew: A Guided Instruction Course. 2004. (Illus.). 126p. (J). 9.98 (978-0-87441-728-9(7)) Behrman Hse., Inc.

Gold, Shalom. The Dik Duk Buk. 1998. (Illus.). 54p. (gr. 9-12). pap. 9.95 (978-1-56062-322-9(5)) CIS Communications, Inc.

Goldstein, Rose B. Songs to Share. Schloss, E., illus. (ENG & HEB.). 64p. (J). (ps-5). 2.95 (978-0-8381-0720-1(6) , 10-720) United Synagogue of America Bk. Service.

Goodman, Marlene. Let's Learn Hebrew Picture Dictionary. 2003. (ENG & HEB., Illus.). 80p. 11.95 (978-0-07-140825-7(8) , 9780071408257) McGraw-Hill Cos., The.

Hazan, Maurice, creator. Hebrew Dialogues Game Level 1. 2005. (HEB.). (J). 126.00 (978-1-933209-66-1(6)) Symtalk, Inc.

—Hebrew Dialogues Game Level 2. 2005. (HEB.). (J). 126.00 (978-1-933209-67-8(4)) Symtalk, Inc.

Hernandez, Robert. Hebrew Made Easy: Learn How to Pronounce, Read & Understand Hebrew! 2000. (Illus.). 86p. (J). spiral bd., wbk. ed. 12.95 (978-0-615-11335-7(4)) SonRise Pubns.

Hewbrew Penmanship. 2006. (C). 10.00 (978-0-9677313-9-1(9)) Friedman, Yuda.

Hippocrene Books, ed. Hebrew Children's Picture Dictionary: English-Hebrew/Hebrew-English. 2006. (Illus.). 114p. pap. 14.95 (978-0-7818-1163-7(5)) Hippocrene Bks., Inc.

Kaye, Terry, et al. Hebrew Through Prayer, Bk. 1. Siegel, Adam, ed. Ben-Moshe, Jana, illus. 96p. (J). (gr. 4-5). pap. 6.95 (978-0-87441-563-6(2)) Behrman Hse., Inc.

Let's Learn Aleph-Beis. (Yoni Gold Board Book Ser.). (J). bds. 4.95 (978-1-58330-149-4(6)) Feldheim Pubs.

Mahoney, Judy. Teach Me... Hebrew W/Cassette: A Musical Journey Through the Day. 2004. (Teach Me...Ser.). (ENG & HEB., Illus.). 20p. (J). (ps-7). pap. 13.95 (978-0-934633-54-3(1)) Teach Me Tapes, Inc.

Marzel, Pepi, illus. My First Hebrew Word Book. 2005. 32p. (J). (ps-2). lib. bdg. 17.95 (978-1-58013-126-1(3)) Kar-Ben Publishing.

Musleah, Rahel & Jarrett, Judy. Apples & Pomegranates: A Rosh Ha-Shanah Seder. 2004. (ENG & HEB., Illus.). 64p. (J). pap. 7.95 (978-1-58013-123-0(9)) Kar-Ben Publishing.

Passport Books Staff, ed. Let's Learn Hebrew. Goodman, Marlene, illus. 2003. (Let's Learn... Picture Dictionary Ser.). (HEB.). 72p. (J). (gr. 4-7). 11.95 (978-0-8442-8490-3(4) , 84904, Passport Bks.) McGraw-Hill Trade.

Resnikoff, Irene, et al. OG Returns: OG's Further Adventures in Prayerbook Hebrew. Goldstien, Jessica, ed. Jokelson, Paul, illus. 1998. (OG the Terrible Ser.: Vol. 2). (HEB.). 24p. (J). (gr. 1-6). pap. 4.50 (978-0-939144-27-3(1)) EKS Publishing Co.

The Rosetta Stone Language Library: Hebrew Level 1. 2005. (J). (gr. 1 up). cd-rom 209.00 (978-1-883972-76-9(0)) Fairfield Language Technologies.

Tarnor, Pearl, et al. Shalom U-Verakhah: The New Hebrew Primer. 1999. (ENG & HEB., Illus.). 160p. (J). (978-0-87441-654-1(X)); (978-0-87441-677-0(9)) Behrman Hse., Inc.

Vocabulary Pt. 2: Sifreinu. Date not set. (Orig.). (J). (gr. 3 up). pap. 1.00 (978-0-8266-0206-0(1)) Kehot Pubn. Society.

Yacobi, Diana, et al. Sarah, David & YOU Read Hebrew: Book 1. 2005. (***978-0-9761648-1-4(7)***) Sarah & David LLC.

HEBREW LITERATURE

see also Bible; Jewish Literature

Reudor. Hebrew Letters Tell Their Story. 1999. (Illus.). 48p. (J). (ps-3). pap. 9.95 (978-0-943706-23-8(8)) Pitspopany Pr.

Reudor Staff. The Hebrew Letters Tell Their Story. 1999. (Doodle Family Ser.). (Illus.). 48p. (J). (ps-3). 16.95 (978-0-943706-24-5(6)) Pitspopany Pr.

HEBREWS

see Jews

HEDGEHOGS

Leach, Michael. Hedgehog. 2006. (Illus.). (J). (ps). pap. 11.99 (978-0-7502-4772-6(X) , Hodder & Stoughton) Hodder General Publishing Division GBR. *Dist:* Trafalgar Square Publishing.

Miller, Sara Swan. Moles & Hedgehogs: What They Have in Common. 2001. (Animals in Order Ser.). (Illus.). 48p. (J). (gr. 4-6). pap. 6.95 (978-0-531-13957-8(3) , Watts, Franklin) Scholastic Library Publishing.

—Moles & Hedgehogs: What They Have in Common. 2001. (Illus.). 48p. (J). (gr. 4-7). lib. bdg. 15.25 (978-0-613-37463-7(0)) Tandem Library Bks.

Mulder, Nancy. Caring for Your Hedgehog. 2006. (J). pap. (978-1-59036-471-0(6)); lib. bdg. (978-1-59036-470-3(8)) Weigl Pubs., Inc.

Otfinoski, Steven. Hedgehogs & Other Insectivores, Vol. 4. World Book, Inc. Staff, ed. 2002. (World Book's Animals of the World Ser.: Set 1). 64p. (J). (978-0-7166-1241-4(0)) World Bk., Inc.

HEDGEHOGS—FICTION

Anderson, Lena. Hedgehog, Pig, & the Sweet Little Friend. Sandin, Joan, tr. from SWE. 2007. (Illus.). 32p. (J). (ps-1). 16.00 (***978-91-29-66742-4(9)***) R & S Bks. SWE. *Dist:* Macmillan.

Berg, Brook. What Happened to Marion's Book? Alberg, Nathan, illus. 2003. 48p. (J). (ps-2). per. 16.95 (978-1-932146-05-9(9) , Upstart Bks.) Highsmith Inc.

Brett, Jan. The Hat. Brett, Jan, illus. 2002. (Illus.). (J). 23.64 (978-0-7587-2700-8(3)) Book Wholesalers, Inc.

—The Hat. unabr. ed. 2001. (J). 27.95 incl. audio (978-0-8045-6855-5(3) , 6855) Spoken Arts, Inc.

—Hedgie Blasts Off! Brett, Jan, illus. 2006. (Illus.). 32p. (J). (ps-3). 16.99 (978-0-399-24621-0(5) , Putnam Juvenile) Penguin Group (USA) Inc.

—El Sombrero. (Buenas Noches Coleccion).Tr. of Hat. (SPA.). (J). 7.95 (978-958-04-4169-4(3)) Norma S.A. COL. *Dist:* Distribuidora Norma, Inc., Lectorum Pubns., Inc.

Butler, M. Christina. One Snowy Night. Macnaughton, Tina, illus. 26p. (J). (ps). 2007. bds. 8.95 (***978-1-56148-591-8(8)***); 2005. 16.00 (978-1-56148-452-2(0)) Good Bks.

Butler, M. Christina. One Winter's Day. Macnaughton, Tina, illus. 2006. 28p. (J). 16.00 (978-1-56148-532-1(2)) Good Bks.

Castan, Javier Saez. The Three Hedgehogs. 2004. (Illus.). 32p. (J). 15.95 (978-0-88899-595-7(4)) Groundwood Bks. CAN. *Dist:* Perseus Distribution.

Daniels, Lucy. Hedgehogs in the Hall. l.t. ed. 2000. (Illus.). 214p. (J). pap. (978-0-7540-6109-0(4) , CLP 303) BBC Audio.

Davies, Caroline & Martin, Sharon. Cotiau Newydd. 2005. (WEL., Illus.). 12p. (978-1-86101-081-0(8)) Acen Limited.

Dennard, Deborah. Hedgehog Haven: A Story of a British Hedgerow Community. 2005. (Soundprints' Wild Habitats Ser.). (Illus.). 32p. (J). (gr. 1-4). 8.95 incl. audio (978-1-59249-108-7(1) , SC7020) Soundprints.

—Hedgehog Haven: The Story of an English Hedgerow Community. Hynes, Robert, illus. (Wild Habitats Ser.). (J). (gr. 1-4). 2005. 32p. 15.95 (978-1-56899-987-6(9) , B7020); 2005. 32p. 19.95 incl. audio (978-1-56899-989-0(5) , BC7020); 2005. 32p. pap. 6.95 (978-1-56899-988-3(7) , S7020); 2001. 36p. 26.95 (978-1-56899-991-3(7)) Soundprints.

Dennard, Deborah, text. Hurry up, Hedgehog! 2005. (Amazing Animal Adventures Ser.). (Illus.). 32p. (J). (ps-1). pap. 3.95 (978-1-59249-149-0(9) , S2012) Soundprints.

Fox, CiCi. Hodgepodge the Hedgehog. 2006. pap. 7.95 (978-0-533-15238-4(0)) Vantage Pr., Inc.

French, El & French, Vivian. Hedgehogs & the Big Bag. 1998. (Illus.). 64p. (J). 7.95 (978-0-14-036874-1(4)) Penguin Bks., Ltd. GBR. *Dist:* Trafalgar Square Publishing.

Fullerton, Charlotte. Aqua Planet. 2006. (Sonic X Ser.). (Illus.). 48p. (J). (gr. 1-3). pap. 4.99 (978-0-448-44254-9(X) , Grosset & Dunlap) Penguin Group (USA) Inc.

Gallagher, Mike. Sonic the Hedgehog Archives, Vol. 1. 2006. 112p. pap. 7.49 (978-1-879794-20-7(9)) Archie Comic Pubns., Inc.

Gallagher, Mike & DeCesare, Angelo. Sonic the Hedgehog Archives, Vol. 2. 2006. 112p. pap. 7.49 (978-1-879794-21-4(7)) Archie Comic Pubns., Inc.

Hedgehogs: Individual Title Six-Packs. (Sails Literacy Ser.). (gr. 1-2). 36.00 (978-0-7578-6728-6(6)) Rigby Education.

Karu, Tim, et al. Henry & the White Wolf. Karu, Tyler, illus. 2000. (Illus.). 32p. (J). (ps-3). 12.95 (978-0-7611-2135-0(8) , 12135) Workman Publishing Co., Inc.

Lawhead, Stephen R. The Tale of Anabelle Hedgehog. 2003. (Illus.). 112p. pap. 6.99 (978-0-7459-4677-1(1) , Lion) Lion Hudson plc GBR. *Dist:* Trafalgar Square Publishing.

Lucas, Celia. Madoc's Prickly Problem. 2000. (Illus.). 132p. pap. 11.95 (978-1-85902-777-6(6)) Beekman Bks., Inc.

Pfister, Marcus. The Happy Hedgehog. 2003. (Illus.). 32p. (J). pap. 6.95 (978-0-7358-1816-3(9)) North-South Bks., Inc.

Potter, Beatrix. The Tale of Mrs. Tiggy-Winkle. Potter, Beatrix, illus. 2002. (Illus.). (J). 15.23 (978-0-7587-3749-6(1)) Book Wholesalers, Inc.

—The Tale of Mrs. Tiggy-Winkle, Vol. 6. 2002. (Illus.). 64p. (J). 6.99 (978-0-7232-4775-3(7) , Warne) Penguin Group (USA) Inc.

Rowe, John A. I Want a Hug. 2007. (Illus.). 32p. (J). (ps-3). 16.99 (***978-0-698-40064-1(X)*** , Minedition) Penguin Group (USA) Inc.

Scamell, Ragnhild. Ouch! Terry, Michael, illus. 2006. 26p. (J). 16.00 (978-1-56148-511-6(X)) Good Bks.

Slaughter, Hope. Buckley & Wilberta, Forever Friends. Torrence, Susan, illus. l.t. ed. 1998. 64p. (J). (gr. 1-3). lib. bdg. 14.95 (978-0-931093-16-6(3)) Red Hen Pr.

Stewart, Paul. A Little Bit of Winter. Riddell, Chris, illus. 1999. 32p. (J). (ps-2). 14.95 (978-0-06-028278-3(9)) HarperCollins Pubs.

—Rabbit's Wish. Riddell, Chris, illus. 2001. 32p. (J). (ps-2). 12.95 (978-0-06-029518-9(X)) HarperCollins Pubs.

—Un Regalo de Cumpleanos. Riddell, Chris, illus. (SPA.). 30p. (J). (gr. k-2). (978-84-348-6840-3(7) , SM30935) SM Ediciones ESP. *Dist:* Lectorum Pubns., Inc.

Symes, Ruth. Harriet Dancing. Church, Caroline, illus. 2008. 32p. (J). 16.99 (***978-0-545-03204-9(0)*** , Chicken Hse., The) Scholastic, Inc.

Ward, Nick. Farmer George & the Hedgehogs. 2001. (Illus.). 32p. (YA). (gr. k up). pap. 14.95 (978-1-86205-441-7(X) , Pavilion Bks., Ltd.) Anova Bks. GBR. *Dist:* Trafalgar Square Publishing.

Wheeler, Lisa. Hokey Pokey: Another Prickly Love Story. Bynum, Janie, illus. 2006. 32p. (J). (ps-1). 15.99 (978-0-316-00090-1(6)) Little Brown & Co.

Wilhelm, Hans. Hello, Sun! Wilhelm, Hans, illus. 2005. (Illus.). 32p. (gr. k-2). 15.25 (978-1-57505-348-6(9)) Lerner Publishing Group.

Williams, Jacklyn. Happy Birthday, Gus! Cushman, Doug, illus. 2005. (Read-It! Readers Ser.). 32p. (J). (gr. k-3). 18.60 (978-1-4048-0957-4(0)) Picture Window Bks.

—Happy Easter, Gus! Cushman, Doug, illus. 2005. (Read-It! Readers Ser.). 32p. (J). (gr. k-3). 18.60 (978-1-4048-0959-8(7)) Picture Window Bks.

—Happy Halloween, Gus! Cushman, Doug, illus. 2005. (Read-It! Readers Ser.). 32p. (J). (gr. k-3). 18.60 (978-1-4048-0960-4(0)) Picture Window Bks.

—Happy Thanksgiving, Gus! Cushman, Doug, illus. 2005. (Read-It! Readers Ser.). 32p. (J). (gr. k-3). 18.60 (978-1-4048-0961-1(9)) Picture Window Bks.

—Happy Valentine's Day, Gus! Cushman, Doug, illus. 2005. (Read-It! Readers Ser.). 32p. (J). (gr. k-3). 18.60 (978-1-4048-0962-8(7)) Picture Window Bks.

—Let's Go Fishing, Gus! Cushman, Doug, illus. 2006. (Read-It! Readers Ser.). (J). 19.93 (978-1-4048-2713-4(7)) Picture Window Bks.

—Make a New Friend, Gus! Cushman, Doug, illus. 2006. (Read-It! Readers Ser.). (J). 19.93 (978-1-4048-2711-0(0)) Picture Window Bks.

—Merry Christmas Gus! Cushman, Doug, illus. 2005. (Read-It! Readers Ser.). 32p. (J). (gr. k-3). 18.60 (978-1-4048-0958-1(9)) Picture Window Bks.

—Pick a Pet, Gus! Cushman, Doug, illus. 2006. (Read-It! Readers Ser.). (J). 19.93 (978-1-4048-2712-7(9)) Picture Window Bks.

—Welcome to Third Grade, Gus! Cushman, Doug, illus. 2006. (Read-It! Readers Ser.). (J). 19.93 (978-1-4048-2714-1(5)) Picture Window Bks.

HELICOPTERS

Apache Helicopter. 2004. (Press-Out & Build Ser.). (Illus.). 24p. (J). per. (978-1-84229-723-0(6)) Top That! Publishing PLC.

Baysura, Kelly. Helicopters. 2001. (Flying Machines Ser.). (Illus.). 24p. (J). (gr. 1-4). lib. bdg. 20.64 (978-1-58952-004-2(1)) Rourke Publishing, LLC.

Bender, Lionel. Airplanes & Helicopters. 2006. (J). (978-1-59389-261-6(6)) Chrysalis Education.

Biesty, Stephen. Stephen Biesty's Incredible Pop-up Cross-Sections. Biesty, Stephen, illus. 2004. (Illus.). 6p. (gr. 4-8). reprint ed. 17.00 (978-0-7567-7292-5(3)) DIANE Publishing Co.

Bitetto, Marco A. V. Helicopters. 2000. (Theme Stream Ser.: Vol. 2). 10p. (Illus.). (YA). (gr. 12 up). (978-1-58578-111-9(8)); (YA). (gr. 7). (978-1-58578-113-3(4)); (Illus.). (J). (978-1-58578-110-2(X)); (Illus.). (YA). (gr. 9). (978-1-58578-112-6(6)) Institute of Cybernetics Research, Inc.

Bledsoe, Glen & Bledsoe, Karen. The World's Fastest Helicopters. 2002. (Built for Speed Ser.). (Illus.). 48p. (J). (gr. 3-4). lib. bdg. 21.26 (978-0-7368-1059-3(5) , Capstone High-Interest Bks.) Capstone Pr., Inc.

Bledsoe, Karen & Bledsoe, Glen. Helicopters: High-Flying Heroes. 2006. (Mighty Military Machines Ser.). (Illus.). 48p. (J). (gr. 4-10). lib. bdg. 23.93 (978-0-7660-2663-6(9)) Enslow Pubs., Inc.

Braulick, Carrie A. U.S. Army Helicopters. 2006. (Blazers—Military Vehicles Ser.). (Illus.). 32p. (J). (978-0-7368-5468-9(1)) Capstone Pr., Inc.

Built for Speed: World's Fastest Boats; Cars; Helicopters; Military Airplanes; Superbikes; Trains; Trucks; Wildest Roller Coasters, 8 bks. (Illus.). (J). (gr. 3-4). lib. bdg. 170.08 (978-0-7368-1081-4(1) , Capstone High-Interest Bks.) Capstone Pr., Inc.

Castor, Hariet. Planes & Helicopters. rev. ed. 2005. 32p. (J). pap. 6.95 (978-0-7945-0841-8(3) , Usborne) EDC Publishing.

Dartford, Mark. Helicopters. 2004. (Military Hardware in Action Ser.). (Illus.). 48p. (J). (gr. 4-9). lib. bdg. 25.26 (978-0-8225-4707-5(4)) Lerner Publishing Group.

David, Jack. Apache Helicopters. 2007. (Illus.). 24p. (J). lib. bdg. 19.95 (978-1-60014-102-7(1)) Bellwether Media.

—Apache Helicopters. 2007. (Torque: Military Machines Ser.). (Illus.). 24p. (J). (gr. 3-7). lib. bdg. 20.00 (***978-0-531-18498-1(6)*** , Children's Pr.) Scholastic Library Publishing.

David West. Helicopter. 2006. (Illus.). 32p. (J). pap. (978-1-4109-2565-7(X)) Steck-Vaughn.

Doeden, Matt. Helicopteros Militares. 2006. (ENG & SPA.). (J). (978-0-7368-5874-8(1)) Capstone Pr., Inc.

—Military Helicopters. 2005. (Pebble Plus: Mighty Machines Ser.). (Illus.). 24p. (J). 19.93 (978-0-7368-3658-6(6)) Capstone Pr., Inc.

Eden, Paul E. Helicopters. 2006. (Aircraft of the World Ser.). (Illus.). 62p. (J). lib. bdg. (978-0-8368-6904-0(4)) Stevens, Gareth Inc.

Ellis, Catherine. Helicopters. 2007. (Mega Military Machines Ser.). (Illus.). 24p. (J). (gr. k-5). lib. bdg. 21.25 (978-1-4042-3666-0(X)) Rosen Publishing Group, Inc., The.

Ethan, Eric. Helicopters. Ethan, Eric, photos by. 2002. (Emergency Vehicles Ser.). (Illus.). 24p. (YA). (gr. 1 up). lib. bdg. 20.67 (978-0-8368-3046-0(6)) Stevens, Gareth Inc.

Goldberg, Jan. The C-130 Hercules. 2005. (U. S. Warplanes Ser.). (Illus.). 48p. (YA). (gr. 5-8). lib. bdg. 26.50 (978-0-8239-3873-5(5)) Rosen Publishing Group, Inc., The.

Goodman, Susan E. Choppers! Doolittle, Michael, photos by. 2004. (Step into Reading Ser.: Vol. 4). (Illus.). 48p. (J). (gr. 2-4). pap. 3.99 (978-0-375-82517-0(7) , Random Hse. Bks. for Young Readers) Random Hse. Children's Bks.

Green, Michael & Green, Gladys. Super Cobra Attack Helicopters: the AH-1W. 2005. (War Machines Ser.). (Illus.). 32p. (J). (ps-ps). lib. bdg. 22.60 (978-0-7368-3779-8(5)) Capstone Pr., Inc.

—Weapons Carrier Helicopters: The UH-60 Black Hawks. 2005. (War Machines Ser.). (Illus.). 32p. (J). (ps-ps). lib. bdg. 22.60 (978-0-7368-3780-4(9)) Capstone Pr., Inc.

Hansen, Ole Steen. The AH-64 Apache Helicopter. 2006. (Illus.). 32p. (J). (978-0-7368-5250-0(6) , 1244012) Capstone Pr., Inc.

—Helicopters. 2003. (Story of Flight Ser.). (Illus.). 32p. (J). (gr. 4). pap. (978-0-7787-1224-4(9)); lib. bdg. (978-0-7787-1208-4(7)) Crabtree Publishing Co.

Hanson, Anders. Let's Go by Helicopter. 2007. (Let's Go! Ser.). (ENG., Illus.). 24p. (J). (ps-3). lib. bdg. 19.93 (***978-1-59928-898-7(2)*** , SandCastle) ABDO Publishing Co.

Helicopters. 2004. (Mega MacHines Ser.). (Illus.). 16p. (J). (978-2-7643-0201-9(0)) Phidal Publishing, Inc./Editions Phidal, Inc.

Holden, Henry M. Black Hawk Helicopter. 2002. (Aircraft Ser.). (Illus.). 48p. (J). (gr. 4-10). lib. bdg. 23.93 (978-0-7660-1568-5(8)) Enslow Pubs., Inc.

Lindeen, Mary. Helicopters. 2007. (Illus.). 24p. (J). lib. bdg. 19.95 (978-1-60014-119-5(6)) Bellwether Media.

Loves, June. Helicopters. 2001. (Flight Ser.). (Illus.). 32p. (J). (gr. 5 up). 22.95 (978-0-7910-6562-4(6) , 010304, Chelsea Hse.) Facts On File, Inc.

Military Helicopters. (Mighty MacHines Ser.). 24p. (J). 6.95 (978-0-7368-5140-4(2)) Capstone Pr., Inc.

Millican, Judy. The Helicopter Ride. Gray, Stacy A., illus. 2003. 8p. (J). (ps-1). bds. 10.95 (978-1-57332-252-2(0)) HighReach Learning, Inc.

Mullican, Judy. The Helicopter Ride: Big Book. Gray, Stacy A., illus. 2003. 8p. (J). (ps-1). bds. 10.95 (978-1-57332-245-4(8)) HighReach Learning, Inc.

Otfinoski, Steven. Whirling Around: Helicopters Then & Now. 1998. (Here We Go! Ser.). (Illus.). 32p. (J). (gr. 1-12). lib. bdg. 22.79 (978-0-7614-0610-5(7) , Benchmark Bks.) Cavendish, Marshall Corp.

Parsont, Meg. Helicopter. Curti, Anna, illus. 1999. (Go Bks.). 12p. (J). (ps-k). 5.95 (978-0-7892-0544-5(0) , Abbeville Kids) Abbeville Pr., Inc.

Pitt, Matthew. Apache Helicopter: The AH-64. 2000. (gr. 7-12). lib. bdg. 15.25 (978-0-613-58687-0(5)) Tandem Library Bks.

Randolph, Joanne. Emergency Helicopters. 2008. (J). lib. bdg. (***978-1-4042-4151-0(5)*** , PowerKids Pr.) Rosen Publishing Group, Inc., The.

Richardson, Adele D. Transport Helicopters. 2000. (Transportation Library). (Illus.). 24p. (J). (gr. 1-2). lib. bdg. 18.60 (978-0-7368-0608-4(3) , Bridgestone Bks.) Capstone Pr., Inc.

Roberts, Cynthia. Rescue Helicopters. 2007. (Machines at Work Ser.). 24p. (J). (gr. 2-4). 22.79 (978-1-59296-835-0(X)) Child's World, Inc.

Rustad, Martha E. H. Helicopters. 2008. (J). (***978-1-4296-0828-2(5)***) Capstone Publishing.

Stille, Darlene R. Helicopters. 2004. (Illus.). 32p. (J). (gr. 1 up). 21.26 (978-0-7565-0606-3(9)) Compass Point Bks.

Sweetman, Bill. Attack Helicopters: The AH-64 Apaches. 2001. (War Planes Ser.). (Illus.). 32p. (J). (gr. 3-4). lib. bdg. 17.08 (978-0-7368-0789-0(6) , Capstone High-Interest Bks.) Capstone Pr., Inc.

—Combat Rescue Helicopters: The MH-53 Pave Lows. 2002. (War Planes Ser.). (Illus.). 32p. (J). (gr. 3-4). lib. bdg. 21.26 (978-0-7368-1067-8(6) , Capstone High-Interest Bks.) Capstone Pr., Inc.

West, David. Why Things Don't Work. 2006. (Illus.). 32p. (J). (978-1-4109-2558-9(7)) Steck-Vaughn.

Zuehlke, Jeffrey. Helicopters. 2005. (Pull Ahead Bks.). (Illus.). 32p. (J). (gr. k-2). lib. bdg. 22.60 (978-0-8225-1540-1(7)) Lerner Publishing Group.

HELICOPTERS—FICTION

Book Company Staff. Happy Helicopters. 2003. (Button Bks.). (Illus.). (J). bds. 12.95 (978-1-74047-302-6(7)) Book Co. Publishing Pty, Ltd., The AUS. *Dist:* Penton Overseas, Inc.

Fensham, Elizabeth. Helicopter Man. 2005. (Illus.). 144p. (J). (ps-7). 15.95 (978-1-58234-981-7(9) , Bloomsbury Children) Bloomsbury Publishing.

Glass, Andrew. The Wondrous Whirligig: The Wright Brothers¿ First Flying Machine. Glass, Andrew, illus. 2007. (Illus.). 30p. (J). reprint ed. 17.00 (***978-1-4223-6765-0(7)***) DIANE Publishing Co.

Hayler, Kate. Helicoptero Al Rescate. 2003. (Tough Stuff Ser.). (SPA.). 10p. (ps-17). 8.99 (978-0-7868-1978-2(2)) Hyperion Bks. for Children.

Rogers, Christopher M., illus. Homer the Helicopter Grand Canyon Adventures: N/a. 2007. Tr. of N/a. 72p. (J). 18.95 (***978-0-9786352-3-7(X)***) Buscher, Julie W.

HELPFULNESS

Amos, Janine. Being Helpful. Spenceley, Annabel, illus. 2002. (Courteous Kids Ser.). 32p. (J). (ps up). lib. bdg. 23.33 (978-0-8368-3169-6(1)) Stevens, Gareth Inc.

Ancona, George. Mis Quehaceres. 32p. (J). 2006. (SPA.). (gr. 1-3). pap. 8.95 (978-0-516-25499-9(5)); 2005. (ENG & SPA., Illus.). 21.00 (978-0-516-25291-9(7)) Scholastic Library Publishing. (Children's Pr.).

Bower, Gary. Tessa's Treasures: Cherishing Others. Bower, Jan, illus. 2000. (Thinking of Others: Vol. 1). 32p. (J). (ps-3). lib. bdg. 16.95 (978-0-9704621-0-7(7)) Storybook Meadow Publishing.

Chessen, Betsey & Chanko, Pamela. Thank You! 1999. (Social Studies Emergent Readers). (J). 2.50 (978-0-439-04558-2(4)) Scholastic, Inc.

—Thank You! 1999. (ps-2). lib. bdg. 10.10 (978-0-613-22481-9(7)) Tandem Library Bks.

Clark, Sondra. You Can Change Your World! Creative Ways to Volunteer & Make a Difference. 2003. (gr. 7-12). lib. bdg. 17.60 (978-0-613-75303-6(8)) Tandem Library Bks.

Day, Eileen. I'm Good at Helping. 2003. (Heinemann Read & Learn Ser.). (Illus.). 24p. (J). pap. 5.25 (978-1-4034-3445-6(X)); lib. bdg. 18.50 (978-1-4034-0897-6(1)) Heinemann Library.

—I'm Good at Helping. 2003. (gr. k-3). lib. bdg. 13.30 (978-0-613-70656-8(0)) Tandem Library Bks.

Jordan, Denise. Let's Do It Together. 2003. (You & Me Ser.). (Illus.). 24p. (J). (ps-1). lib. bdg. 18.50 (978-1-4034-4406-6(4)) Heinemann Library.

Jordan, Denise M. Let's Do It Together. 2004. (Heinemann Read & Learn Ser.). (Illus.). 24p. (J). (ps-1). pap. 5.25 (978-1-4034-4412-7(9)) Heinemann Library.

King, Alyson L. Chores Around the House. 2007. (Illus.). 24p. pap. (***978-1-59515-963-2(0)***) Rourke Publishing, LLC.

—Quehaceres en el Hogar. 2007. (SPA & ENG., Illus.). 24p. (J). (***978-1-60044-297-1(8)***) Rourke Publishing, LLC.

LeapFrog Staff, compiled by. Helping Others: (Blue Book) 2002. (J). (ps-2). 19.95 (978-1-58605-688-9(3)) LeapFrog Enterprises, Inc.

—Helping Others: (Green Book) 2002. (J). (ps-2). 19.95 (978-1-58605-686-5(7)) LeapFrog Enterprises, Inc.

—Helping Others: (Orange Book) 2002. (J). (ps-2). 19.95 (978-1-58605-687-2(5)) LeapFrog Enterprises, Inc.

—Helping Others: (Purple Book) 2002. (J). (ps-2). 19.95 (978-1-58605-685-8(9)) LeapFrog Enterprises, Inc.

Leeper, Angela. I Care. 2005. (You & Me Ser.). (Illus.). 24p. (J). lib. bdg. (978-1-4034-6074-5(4)) Heinemann Library.

The Letter Jj: Helping at School, 6 vols. (gr. k-2). 17.50 (978-0-7368-4109-2(1)) Red Brick Learning.

The Letter Mm: People Who Help Us, 6 vols. (gr. k-2). 17.50 (978-0-7368-4112-2(1)) Red Brick Learning.

Mattern, Joanne. Do You Help Others? 2007. (Are You a Good Friend? Ser.). 24p. (J). (gr. k-2). pap. 5.95 (***978-0-8368-8278-0(4)***); lib. bdg. 19.93 (***978-0-8368-8273-5(3)***) Stevens, Gareth Inc. (Weekly Reader Early Learning Library).

—Do You Help Others?/¿Ayudas a los Demas? 2007. (Are You a Good Friend?/Buenos Amigos Ser.). (SPA & ENG.). 24p. (J). (gr. k-2). pap. 5.95 (***978-0-8368-8288-9(1)***); lib. bdg. 19.93 (***978-0-8368-8283-4(0)***) Stevens, Gareth Inc. (Weekly Reader Early Learning Library).

Maurer, Tracy. A to Z of Helping Hands. 2002. (A to Z Ser.). (Illus.). 48p. (J). (gr. k-2). 20.95 (978-1-58952-061-5(0)) Rourke Publishing, LLC.

Mayer, Cassie. Being Helpful. 2007. (J). (***978-1-4034-9485-6(1)***); pap. (***978-1-4034-9493-1(2)***) Heinemann Library.

Medina, Sarah. Caring. 2007. (Illus.). 24p. (J). (978-1-4034-9302-6(2)); (978-1-4034-9295-1(6)) Heinemann Library.

Meiners, Cheri J. Respect & Take Care of Things. Johnson, Meredith, illus. 2004. (Learning to Get Along Ser.). 40p. (J). (ps-3). pap. 10.95 (978-1-57542-160-5(7)) Free Spirit Publishing, Inc.

Meiners, Cheryl J. Reach Out & Give. 2006. (Learning to Get Along Ser.). (Illus.). 40p. (J). (ps-3). pap. 10.95 (978-1-57542-204-6(2)) Free Spirit Publishing, Inc.

Parry, Alan. Rabbit Helps Out. Parry, Linda, illus. 2004. (ps-3). 5.00 (978-0-687-09713-5(4)) Abingdon Pr.

Schab, Lisa & Gardner, Richard. The Helping, Caring, & Sharing. Schader, Karen, ed. Barr, Steve, illus. 2003. (J). per., wbk. ed. 19.95 (978-1-58815-058-5(5) , 67238) Childswork/Childsplay.

Shore, Hennie & Gardner, Richard. Helping, Caring, & Sharing Scriptbook. Schader, Karen, ed. 2003. (J). spiral bd. 24.95 (978-1-58815-059-2(3) , 67239) Childswork/Childsplay.

Siegel, Danny & Eisenberger, Naomi. Mitzvah Magic: Kids Can Do Mitzvahs. 2002. (Illus.). 64p. (J). (gr. 2 up). pap. 8.95 (978-1-58013-034-9(8)) Kar-Ben Publishing.

Steck-Vaughn Staff. Help Is on the Way. 2000. pap. (978-0-7398-4492-2(X)) Steck-Vaughn.

Thomas, Shelley Moore. Somewhere Today: A Book of Peace. Futran, Eric, illus. 1998. (J). (ps-2). pap. 13.95 (978-0-8075-7546-8(1)) Whitman, Albert & Co.

—Somewhere Today: A Story of Peace. 2001. (gr. k-3). lib. bdg. 15.25 (978-0-613-70963-7(2)) Tandem Library Bks.

World Book, Inc. Staff, contrib. by. Heroes & Helpers: A Supplement to Childcraft: The How & Why Library. 2003. (Illus.). 208p. (J). pap. (978-0-7166-0606-2(2)) World Bk., Inc.

HELPFULNESS—FICTION

Albee, Sarah. Max Can Fix That. Schick, Joel, illus. 2006. (Step-By-Step Readers Ser.). (J). pap. (978-1-59939-055-0(8) , Reader's Digest Young Families, Inc.) Reader's Digest Children's Publishing, Inc.

Asch, Frank. Monsieur Saguette & His Baguette. Asch, Frank, illus. 2004. (Illus.). 32p. (J). (gr. k-3). (978-1-55337-461-9(4)) Kids Can Pr., Ltd.

Bennett, Leonie. Locket Out. Adams, Arlene, illus. 2004. 24p. (J). lib. bdg. 22.65 (***978-1-59646-688-3(X)***) Dingles & Co.

Berenstain, Stan & Berenstain, Jan. The Berenstain Bears Lend a Helping Hand. 1998. (Berenstain Bears First Time Bks.). (Illus.). 32p. (J). (gr. k-3). pap. 3.99 (978-0-679-88956-4(6) , Random Hse. Bks. for Young Readers) Random Hse. Children's Bks.

BigIdeas Staff, et al. Bob te da una Mano. 2004. 12p. (J). 5.99 (978-0-8297-4301-2(4)) Vida Pubs.

Blackaby, Susan. Dan Gets Set. Haugen, Ryan, illus. 2005. (Read-It! Readers Ser.). 32p. (J). (gr. k-3). 18.60 (978-1-4048-1011-2(0)) Picture Window Bks.

Blackaby, Susan, et al. Dan Pone la Mesa. Haugen, Ryan, illus. 2006. (Read-It! Readers Ser.). (ENG & SPA.). 32p. (J). (ps-3). 19.95 (978-1-4048-1682-4(8)) Picture Window Bks.

Blyton, Enid. Mister Meddle's Muddles. (Illus.). 111p. (J). pap. 6.95 (978-0-7475-3860-8(3)) Bloomsbury Publishing Plc GBR. *Dist:* Trafalgar Square Publishing.

—Mr Pink-Whistle Interferes. (Illus.). 112p. (J). pap. 7.99 (978-0-7475-3859-2(X)) Bloomsbury Publishing Plc GBR. *Dist:* Trafalgar Square Publishing.

Bowdish, Lynea. How to Be Nice— & Other Lessons I Didn't Learn. Gray, Leslie, illus. 2006. 47p. (J). pap. (978-1-59336-726-8(0)) Mondo Publishing.

Braybrooks, Ann. Just Be Nice... & Help a Friend! 2000. (Disney Ser.). (Illus.). 24p. (J). (ps-k). pap. 3.29 (978-0-307-13312-0(5) , 13312, Golden Bks.) Random Hse. Children's Bks.

Bryant, Megan E. Berry Thankful! Strawberry Shortcake. 2004. (Strawberry Shortcake Ser.). (Illus.). 32p. (J). (gr. k-1). mass mkt. 3.99 (978-0-448-43517-6(9) , Grosset & Dunlap) Penguin Group (USA) Inc.

Burns, Joanne. Ollie Oyster's Ouch. 2005. 21p. 8.99 (978-1-4116-5337-5(8)) Lulu.com.

Clarizio, Laura. If i Had a Magic Carpet. 2005. 48p. pap. 12.95 (978-1-4137-8557-9(3)) PublishAmerica, Inc.

Clark, Brenda, illus. Franklin Helps Out. 2002. (Franklin Ser.). 12.40 (978-1-4046-0314-1(X)) Book Wholesalers, Inc.

Clark, Laura Shipp & Shipp, Dave. The Donut Repair Club Helps Out. Caldwell, Lise, ed. Burris, Priscilla, illus. 1999. (Happy Day Bks.). 24p. (J). (ps-2). pap. 2.49 (978-0-7847-1089-0(9) , 04285, Bean Sprouts) Standard Publishing.

Costello, David. I Can Help. 2007. (J). (978-0-374-33526-7(5)) Farrar, Straus & Giroux.

Currey, Anna. Truffle Goes to Town. Currey, Anna, illus. 2003. (Illus.). 32p. (YA). (978-1-85602-429-7(6)) Chrysalis Children's Bks.

de Beer, Hans. Little Polar Bear, Take Me Home! 2001. (ps-2). lib. bdg. 15.25 (978-0-613-44363-0(2)) Tandem Library Bks.

De Groat, Diane. Mother, You're the Best! (but Sister, You're a Pest!) 2008. 32p. (J). 16.99 (***978-0-06-123899-4(6)***); lib. bdg. 17.89 (***978-0-06-123900-7(3)***) HarperCollins Pubs.

DiPucchio, Kelly. Mrs. Mcbloom, Clean up Your Classroom! Francis, Guy, illus. 2005. 32p. (gr. k-3). 15.99 (978-0-7868-0932-5(9)) Hyperion Bks. for Children.

Eddy, Ron. What's up with King George? A Story about Helping. Eddy, Ron & Vann, Robert, illus. 2006. (VeggieTales Ser.). 16p. (J). 5.99 (978-1-4169-4062-3(6) , Little Simon Inspirations) Simon & Schuster Children's Publishing.

Edwards, Pamela Duncan. The Leprechaun's Gold. Cole, Henry, illus. 2000. 40p. (J). reprint ed. pap. 6.99 (978-0-06-443878-0(3)) HarperCollins Pubs.

Falwell, Cathryn. Los Dibujos de David. de la Vega, Eida, tr. Falwell, Cathryn, illus. 2005. (Illus.). 32p. (J). (ps-k). pap. 7.95 (978-1-58430-258-2(5)) Lee & Low Bks., Inc.

Firth, Barbara, illus. Good Job, Little Bear. 2002. (Little Bear Picture Bks.). (J). 23.40 (978-0-7587-2616-2(3)) Book Wholesalers, Inc.

—You & Me, Little Bear. 2002. (Little Bear Picture Bks.). (J). 14.79 (978-0-7587-4058-8(1)) Book Wholesalers, Inc.

Forman, Lillian. Help Is on the Way. Neely, Keith, illus. 2002. 16p. (J). (978-0-439-35175-1(8)) Scholastic, Inc.

Fusco, Kimberly Newton. Tending to Grace. 2004. 176p. (gr. 7). (J). lib. bdg. 16.99 (978-0-375-92862-8(6)); (YA). 14.95 (978-0-375-82862-1(1)) Random Hse. Children's Bks. (Knopf Bks. for Young Readers).

Givner, Joan. Ellen Fremedon, Volunteer. 2007. 192p. (gr. 3-7). 17.95 (978-0-88899-743-2(4)) Groundwood Bks. CAN. *Dist:* Perseus Distribution.

Gonick, Larry. Attack of the Smart Pies. 2005. (Illus.). 192p. (J). 15.95 (978-0-8126-2740-4(7)) Cricket Bks.

Graham, Christine. Three Little Robbers. Boase, Susan, illus. 2007. 64p. (J). (gr. 2-5). 16.95 (***978-0-8050-8094-0(5)***) Holt, Henry & Co.

Granowsky, Alvin. Can I Help? 2001. 11.79 (978-0-606-22430-7(0)) Tandem Library Bks.

Grant, Nancy. Maggie & the Backyard Helpers. 2006. (ENG.). 60p. per. 12.95 (***978-1-4241-4373-3(X)***) PublishAmerica, Inc.

Graves, Sue. A Busy Week. Sharp, Melanie, illus. 2005. (Reading Corner Ser.). 24p. (J). (gr. k-3). lib. bdg. 22.80 (978-1-59771-005-3(9)) Sea-To-Sea Pubns.

Greenwald, Sandra. The Basket of Plenty. 2000. 32p. (J). pap. 8.00 (978-0-8059-5008-3(7)) Dorrance Publishing Co., Inc.

Griffin, Lydia. BeBa & the Curious Creature Catchers. Lostimolo, Stephanie, illus. l.t. ed. 2006. 32p. (J). 16.95 (978-0-9770516-0-1(9)) Laffin Minor Pr.

Halbert, John E. I Could If I Wanted To. Zeigler, Sandy, illus. 1998. 48p. (J). 17.95 (978-0-9630968-4-5(2)) Impact Seminars, Inc.

Hall, Frostie. Dread Champions for the King, Book 2: For the King! 2006. 112p. per. (978-1-55452-044-2(4)) Essence Publishing.

Hall, Frostie. The Humble Beginning. 2004. (ENG.). 95p. pap. (***978-1-55306-838-9(6)***) Essence Publishing.

Hallinan, P. K. Let's Be Helpful. 2004. (Illus.). 26p. (J). bds. 7.95 (978-0-8249-6563-1(9)) Ideals Pubns.

Harcourt School Publishers Staff. I Can Help. 3rd ed. 2002. (Trophies English Language Learners Ser.). (Illus.). (J). pap. 3.20 (978-0-15-327565-4(0)) Harcourt Schl. Pubs.

—No Problem: Take-Home Book. 1999. (Signatures Ser.). (Illus.). (J). pap. 1.90 (978-0-15-313903-1(X)) Harcourt Schl. Pubs.

—Trofeos Below Level: En el Parque. 3rd ed. 2002. (SPA., Illus.). (J). pap. 3.50 (978-0-15-323863-5(1)) Harcourt Schl. Pubs.

Hargreaves, Roger. Little Miss Helpful. 1999. (ps-2). lib. bdg. 10.65 (978-0-613-21913-6(9)) Tandem Library Bks.

Help for Santa. 2006. (J). (***978-1-932570-76-2(4)***) Literacy Footprints Inc.

Hensley, Sarah M. Helping in My Town. Middleton, Mikell, illus. l.t. ed. 2003. (Hrl Big Book Ser.). 8p. (J). (ps-1). pap. 10.95 (978-1-57332-274-4(1)); pap. 10.95 (978-1-57332-275-1(X)) HighReach Learning, Inc.

—I Can Be a Friend. 2006. (J). pap., tchr. ed. (978-1-57332-436-6(1)); pap. (978-1-57332-437-3(X)) HighReach Learning, Inc.

Hobbs, Leigh. Old Tom, Man of Mystery. 2005. (Illus.). 32p. (J). (gr. k-2). per. 16.95 (978-1-56145-346-7(3)) Peachtree Pubs., Ltd.

Hockerman, Dennis, illus. The Lion & the Mouse: A Tale about Being Helpful. 2006. (J). 6.99 (978-1-59939-007-9(8)) Reader's Digest Young Families, Inc.

Hodgson, Mona Gansberg. Desert Detectives. Sharp, Chris, illus. 1999. (Desert Critter Friends Ser.: Vol. 5). 48p. (J). (ps-2). 4.99 (978-0-570-05083-4(9) , 56-1907GJ) Concordia Publishing Hse.

—Desert Detectives. 1998. (ps-2). lib. bdg. 13.00 (978-0-613-72810-2(6)) Tandem Library Bks.

Hoffman, Eric. La Senora Juguetona. 1999. (SPA.). (gr. k-3). lib. bdg. 19.90 (978-0-613-80187-4(3)) Tandem Library Bks.

Janovitz, Marilyn. Can I Help? 1998. (Illus.). 32p. (J). (ps-3). pap. 5.95 (978-1-55858-904-9(X)) North-South Bks., Inc.

Jenkins, Jane J. The Little Fir Tree. 2005. (Illus.). 32p. (J). per. 7.95 (978-1-59453-184-2(6) , Airleaf Publishing) Airleaf Publishing & Bookselling.

Jennings, Patti. El Abuelo Oso lo Arregla Todo. 2003. (Busy Bears Ser.).Tr. of Grandpa Bear Fixes It. (ENG & SPA., Illus.). 10p. 14.95 (978-84-7864-704-0(X)) Combel Editorial, S.A. ESP. *Dist:* Independent Pubs. Group.

—El Desayuno de los Osos. 2003. (Busy Bears Ser.). (SPA & ENG., Illus.). 10p. 14.95 (978-84-7864-703-3(1)) Combel Editorial, S.A. ESP. *Dist:* Independent Pubs. Group.

Jennings, Sharon, et al. Franklin Makes a Deal. Southern, Shelley et al, illus. 2004. (Franklin TV StoryBks.). 32p. (J). (gr. k-3). (978-1-55337-469-5(X)) Kids Can Pr., Ltd.

Judge, Lita. One Thousand Tracings: Healing the Wounds of World War II. Judge, Lita, illus. 2007. 40p. (gr. k-4). 15.99 (***978-1-4231-0008-9(5)***) Hyperion Pr.

Keilbart, L. S. One. Benson, Barbara, illus. 2007. 76p. (J). pap. 10.95 (***978-1-85756-610-9(6)***) Janus Publishing Co. GBR. *Dist:* Independent Pubs. Group.

King-Smith, Dick. Mysterious Miss Slade. Kronheimer, Ann, illus. 2002. 128p. (gr. 3-5). 4.99 (978-0-440-41674-6(4) , Yearling) Random Hse. Children's Bks.

—Mysterious Miss Slade. 2002. (gr. 3-6). lib. bdg. 13.00 (978-0-613-88331-3(4)) Tandem Library Bks.

Kirk, David. Bedtime Story/David Kirk. 2006. (Illus.). 32p. (J). (***978-1-4156-8869-4(9)***); (***978-0-448-44514-4(X)***) Penguin Group (USA) Inc.

Klett, David E. Rachel & the Wizard of Lake Lure: The Lake Lure Chronicles - Book 2. 2006. (J). lib. bdg. 17.95 (***978-0-9779325-1-1(6)***) Five Oaks Pr.

Kroll, Virginia L. Makayla Cares about Others. Cote, Nancy, illus. 2007. (Way I ACT Books). 24p. (J). 15.95 (978-0-8075-4945-2(2)) Whitman, Albert & Co.

Krosoczka, Jarrett J. Giddy up Cowgirl. 2006. (Illus.). 40p. (J). 15.99 (978-0-670-06050-4(X) , Viking Juvenile) Penguin Group (USA) Inc.

Lehman, Barbara. Train Stop. 2008. 32p. (J). (ps-k). 16.00 (***978-0-618-75640-7(X)***) Houghton Mifflin Co.

Mahoney, Daniel J. A Really Good Snowman. 2005. (Illus.). 32p. (J). (gr. k-3). 15.00 (978-0-618-47554-4(0) , Clarion Bks.) Houghton Mifflin Co. Trade & Reference Div.

Maizel, Karen, illus. Jake Helps Out. 2007. (I Can Read!). 32p. (J). pap. 3.99 (***978-0-310-71457-6(5)***) Zonderkidz.

Manzano, Sonia. A Box Full of Kittens. Phelan, Matt, illus. 2007. 40p. (J). (ps-2). 16.99 (978-0-689-83089-1(0) , Atheneum) Simon & Schuster Children's Publishing.

Mark, Jan. Useful Idiots. 2004. 416p. (YA). (gr. 7). 17.99 (978-0-385-75023-3(4) , Fickling, David Bks.) Random Hse. Children's Bks.

Martenz, Arden. Glenda: A Story about Cooperation & Caring. Garafano, Marie, illus. 2001. 16p. (J). (gr. 1-4). pap. 6.95 (978-1-57543-088-1(6)) MAR*CO Products, Inc.

Mayer, Mercer. Helping Mom, Vol. 3. 2002. (Little Critter First Readers Ser.). (Illus.). 24p. (J). (gr. 1-2). pap. 3.95 (978-1-57768-816-7(3)) School Specialty Publishing.

—Helping Mom. 2000. (gr. k-3). lib. bdg. 11.80 (978-0-613-67629-8(7)) Tandem Library Bks.

McCafferty, Catherine. Picture Me as Dad's Little Helper. Rasmussen, Wendy, illus. 2001. (Picture Me Ser.). 10p. (J). (ps up). bds. 4.99 (978-1-57151-588-9(7)) Playhouse Publishing.

—Picture Me as Mom's Little Helper. Rasmussen, Wendy, illus. 2001. (Picture Me Ser.). 10p. (J). (ps up). bds. 4.99 (978-1-57151-587-2(9)) Playhouse Publishing.

McGovern, Ann. The Lady in the Box. Backer, Marni, illus. 1999. 40p. (J). (ps up). pap. 9.95 (978-1-890515-15-7(9)) Turtle Bks.

McKissack, Patricia C. & McKissack, Fredrick L. Messy Bessey & the Birthday Overnight. Regan, Dana, illus. 1998. (Rookie Readers Ser.). 32p. (J). (gr. 1-2). 19.50 (978-0-516-20828-2(4) , Children's Pr.) Scholastic Library Publishing.

Moser, Lisa. Sticky Burr: Adventures in Burrwood Forest. Gorbachev, Valeri, illus. 2007. (J). (***978-0-7636-3567-1(7)***) Candlewick Pr.

Mullican, Judy. Patty Helps Out. Coates, Jennifer, illus. l.t. ed. 1999. (Cuddle Bks.). 8p. (J). (ps-k). pap. 10.95 (978-1-57332-140-2(0)); pap. 10.95 (978-1-57332-141-9(9)) HighReach Learning, Inc.

—You Can Help! 2006. (J). (978-1-57332-418-2(3)) HighReach Learning, Inc.

Murray, Mary, et al. Bob Lends a Helping ... Hand? 2003. (Illus.). 12p. 4.99 (978-0-310-70538-3(X)) Zondervan.

Muth, Jon J. Zen Ties. 2008. (J). pap. (***978-0-439-63425-0(3)*** , Scholastic Pr.) Scholastic, Inc.

Myers, Anna. Hoggee. 2007. 192p. (J). pap. 6.95 (***978-0-8027-9683-7(4)***) Walker & Co.

Nakagawa, Rieko. Guri y Gura Aprenden a Nadar. Yamawaki, Yuriko, illus. 2001. (SPA.). (J). pap. (978-980-257-256-4(X) , EK6378) Ekare, Ediciones.

Nanny & I Meet Odie. 2006. (J). lib. bdg. 18.99 (978-0-9724394-1-2(1)) Sylables.

O'Connor, Barbara. Taking Care of Moses. 2004. 144p. (J). 16.00 (978-0-374-38038-0(4) , Frances Foster Bks.) Farrar, Straus & Giroux.

Papineau, Lucie & Homel, David. Little Gil. Beshwaty, Steve, illus. 2001. 32p. (J). (ps up). pap. (978-1-894363-77-8(9)) Dominique & Friends.

Parker, Jean Black. Amanda's Helping Hands. 2006. 17.00 (978-0-8059-9156-7(5)) Dorrance Publishing Co., Inc.

Pennix, Ladaro, II & Washington-Pennix, Loretha. Granny¿s Helpers. 2006. (Illus.). 22p. (J). per. 10.95 (978-1-59453-974-9(X) , 3186, Airleaf Publishing) Airleaf Publishing & Bookselling.

Phoenix, Woodrow & Price, Robin. Count Milkula: A Tale of Milk & Monsters! 2007. 32p. (J). 19.95 (*978-0-9546576-5-9(9)) Mogzilla GBR. *Dist:* Independent Pubs. Group.

Pittar, Gill. Milly, Molly & Sock Heaven. 2004. 28p. (978-1-86972-015-5(6)) Milly Molly Bks.

—Milly, Molly & Sock Heaven (book W/dolls) 2006. 28p. pap. (978-1-86972-098-8(9)) Milly Molly Bks.

Prentiss, Timothy. A Good Pick. 2006. (Early Explorers Ser.). (J). 34.00 (*978-1-4108-6111-5(2)) Benchmark Education Co.

Punnett, Dick. Help Jumbo Escape: A Talk-along Book. Dunnington, Tom, illus. 2nd ed. 2005. (Talk-Along Bks.). 32p. (J). pap. 6.99 (978-0-9657211-2-7(4)) Tomoka Pr.

Rau, Dana Meachen. In the Yard, Level A. 2001. (Early Reader Ser.). (Illus.). 24p. (J). (gr. k up). lib. bdg. 18.60 (978-0-7565-0116-7(4)) Compass Point Bks.

Rich Man's Song. 2005. (Illus.). 48p. (J). 12.95 (978-0-9745264-2-3(8)) Marquise Publishing.

Rudisill, J. J., et al, illus. No More Chores. 1999. (Wimzie's House Bks.). 24p. (J). pap. 3.99 (978-0-88724-542-8(0) , CD-4848) Carson-Dellosa Publishing Co., Inc.

Rylant, Cynthia. Annie & Snowball & the Prettiest House: The Second Book of Their Adventures. Stevenson, Sucie, illus. 2007. (Annie & Snowball Ser.). 40p. (J). (gr. k-2). 15.99 (*978-1-4169-0939-2(7) , Simon & Schuster Children's Publishing) Simon & Schuster Children's Publishing.

Santillo, LuAnn. Running Fox. Santillo, LuAnn, ed. 2003. (Half-Pint Kids Readers Ser.). (Illus.). 7p. (J). (ps-1). pap. (978-1-59256-079-0(2)) Half-Pint Kids, Inc.

Schadler, Cherie D. & Jones, Ann Biedenharn. When the Rain Came Down in Bayou Town! 2000. (Illus.). 32p. (J). (ps-3). 15.95 (978-1-56554-680-6(6)) Pelican Publishing Co., Inc.

Shannon, George. Wise Acres. Zemke, Deborah, illus. 2004. 40p. (J). 15.95 (978-1-59354-041-8(8)) Handprint Bks.

Sherlock, Patti. Letters from Wolfie. 2004. 256p. (J). (gr. 3-7). 16.99 (978-0-670-03694-3(3) , Viking Juvenile) Penguin Group (USA) Inc.

Sierra, Judy. Preschool to the Rescue. Hillenbrand, Will, illus. 2001. 32p. (J). (ps-2). 16.00 (978-0-15-202035-4(7) , Gulliver Bks.) Harcourt Children's Bks.

Smith, Alexander McCall. The Perfect Hamburger & Other Delicious Stories. Rankin, Laura, illus. 2007. 288p. (J). (gr. 2-4). 15.95 (*978-1-59990-134-3(X)); pap. 7.95 (*978-1-59990-157-2(9)) Bloomsbury Publishing. (Bloomsbury Children).

Smith, Todd Aaron. Riley O'Smiley. 2006. (Illus.). 32p. (J). 12.99 (978-1-4003-0818-7(6)) Nelson, Thomas Inc.

Superstar Charlie. 2006. 16p. (J). pap. 1.99 (978-0-7847-1707-3(9) , 04168) Standard Publishing.

Tidd, Louise Vitellaro. Let Me Help! Handelman, Dorothy, photos by. 1999. (Real Kids Readers Ser.). (Illus.). 32p. (gr. k-2). lib. bdg. 18.90 (978-0-7613-2067-8(9) , Millbrook Pr.) Lerner Publishing Group.

—Let Me Help! 1999. (J). (978-0-606-19157-9(7)); lib. bdg. 11.80 (978-0-613-18159-4(X)) Tandem Library Bks.

Tidd, Louise Vitellaro & Handelman, Dorothy. Let Me Help! 1999. (Real Kids Readers Ser.: 2). (Illus.). 32p. (J). (gr. k-2). pap. 4.99 (978-0-7613-2092-0(X) , Millbrook Pr.) Lerner Publishing Group.

Tierno, Susan F. I Did My Best. Ramirez, Michael, illus. 1998. (Think-Kids Book Collection). 16p. (J). (gr. 1-4). pap. 2.95 (978-1-58237-011-8(7)) Creative Thinkers, Inc.

—Lo Hice Bien! Alvarado, Ana María, tr. Ramirez, Michael, illus. 2000. (Think-Kids Book Collection).Tr. of I Did My Best Ser.. (SPA.). 16p. (J). pap. 2.95 (978-1-58237-040-8(0)) Creative Thinkers, Inc.

Timbers, James. Salmon & Fuzz in Helping a Friend. 2004. 30p. pap. 14.95 (978-1-4137-2602-2(X)) PublishAmerica, Inc.

Torrisi, Cathy. Who Will Help Ms. A? Moehl, Crista K., illus. 2002. (Read-To-Me Ser.). 24p. (J). (978-0-7665-1201-6(0)) Abrams, Harry N. , Inc.

Tregebov, Rhea. What-If Sara. Franson, Leanne, illus. 2000. 12p. (J). (ps-3). 10.95 (978-1-896764-22-1(3)); pap. 4.95 (978-1-896764-20-7(7)) Second Story Pr. CAN. *Dist:* Orca Bk. Pubs. USA.

Waber, Bernard. Betty's Day Off. Date not set. (J). (978-0-618-46875-1(7)) Houghton Mifflin Co.

Waddell, Martin. Charlie's Tasks. Postgate, Daniel, illus. 2006. 32p. (J). lib. bdg. (*978-1-4048-3137-7(1)) Picture Window Bks.

Waddell, Martin. You & Me, Little Bear. ed. 2004. (Illus.). (J). (ps-2). spiral bd. (978-0-616-01802-6(9)); spiral bd. (978-0-616-01803-3(7)) Canadian National Institute for the Blind/Institut National Canadien pour les Aveugles.

Wallace, Carol. Turkeys Together. Rogers, Jaqueline, illus. 40p. (J). (ps). 15.95 (978-0-8234-1895-4(2)) Holiday Hse., Inc.

Weigelt, U. & Kadmon, C. Hide, Easter Bunny, Hide! 2006. (Illus.). 32p. (J). 16.95 (978-0-7358-2054-8(6)) North-South Bks., Inc.

Wenger, Brahm & Green, Alan. Dewey Doo-It Builds a House: A Children's Story about Habitat for Humanity. 2006. (Illus.). 32p. 17.95 (978-0-9745143-2-1(2)) RandallFraser Publishing.

Wheeler, Lisa. Old Cricket. Goembel, Ponder, illus. 2006. 32p. (J). reprint ed. pap. 6.99 (978-1-4169-1855-4(8) , Aladdin) Simon & Schuster Children's Publishing.

Wheeler, Lisa & Goembel, Ponder. Old Cricket. 2003. (Illus.). 32p. (J). (ps-2). 17.99 (978-0-689-84510-9(3) , Atheneum/Richard Jackson Bks.) Simon & Schuster Children's Publishing.

HELPING BEHAVIOR

see Helpfulness

HEMINGWAY, ERNEST, 1899-1961

Bloom, Harold, intro. Nick Adams. 2004. (Bloom's Major Literary Characters Ser.). (Illus.). 180p. (gr. 9-13). 40.00 (978-0-7910-7885-3(X) , Chelsea Hse.) Facts On File, Inc.

Boon, Kevin A. Ernest Hemingway: The Sun Also Rises & Other Works. 2007. (Writers & Their Works). 160p. (YA). (gr. 9 up). lib. bdg. 39.93 (978-0-7614-2590-8(X) , Benchmark Bks.) Cavendish, Marshall Corp.

Hemingway, Ernest. The Old Man & the Sea. Bloom, Harold, ed. 1999. (Modern Critical Interpretations Ser.). 150p. (YA). 45.00 (978-0-7910-4778-1(4) , Chelsea Hse.) Facts On File, Inc.

Kimbrel, William. Bloom's How to Write about Ernest Hemingway. 2007. 256p. (gr. 9). 45.00 (*978-0-7910-9485-3(5) , Chelsea Hse.) Facts On File, Inc.

Marsh, Carole. Ernest Hemingway. 2002. (One Thousand Readers Ser.). (Illus.). 12p. (J). (gr. k-4). 2.95 (978-0-635-01510-5(2) , 15102) Gallopade International.

Pingelton, Timothy J. A Student's Guide to Ernest Hemingway. 2005. (Understanding Literature Ser.). (Illus.). 160p. (YA). (gr. 7-13). lib. bdg. 27.93 (978-0-7660-2431-1(8)) Enslow Pubs., Inc.

Riggs, Kate. Ernest Hemingway. 2008. (*978-1-58341-661-7(7) , Creative Education) Creative Co., The.

Whiting, Jim. Ernest Hemingway. 2005. (Classic Storytellers Ser.). (Illus.). 48p. (J). (gr. 6-8). lib. bdg. 29.95 (978-1-58415-376-4(8)) Mitchell Lane Pubs., Inc.

Yannuzzi, Della A. Ernest Hemingway: Writer & Adventurer. 1998. (People to Know Ser.). (Illus.). 112p. (YA). (gr. 6-12). lib. bdg. 26.60 (978-0-89490-979-5(7)) Enslow Pubs., Inc.

HENRY IV, KING OF ENGLAND, 1367-1413

Murphy. Henry the Fourth: Ordinals Big Book. 2002. (Illus.). pap. (978-0-7398-6781-5(4)) Steck-Vaughn.

Shakespeare, William. Henry V. Gill, Roma, ed. 2004. (Oxford School Shakespeare Ser.). (Illus.). 184p. 8.95 (978-0-19-832058-6(2)) Oxford Univ. Pr., Inc.

HENRY VII, KING OF ENGLAND, 1457-1509

Imperato, Anthony. Henry VII. 1999. (Pathfinder History Ser.). (Illus.). 64p. (YA). (gr. 11 up). pap. 15.95 (978-0-7487-4308-7(1)) Nelson Thornes Ltd. GBR. *Dist:* Trans-Atlantic Pubns., Inc.

HENRY VIII, KING OF ENGLAND, 1491-1547

Ashworth, Leon. King Henry VIII. (Illus.). 32p. (978-0-7451-5289-9(9)); pap. (978-0-7540-9012-0(4)); 2001. (978-1-84234-082-0(4)) Evans Publishing Group. (Cherrytree Books).

—King Henry VIII. 2004. (British History Makers Ser.). (Illus.). 32p. (YA). pap. 9.99 (978-1-84234-283-1(5) , Cherrytree Books) Evans Publishing Group GBR. *Dist:* Independent Pubs. Group.

Brassey, Richard. Henry VIII. (Illus.). 24p. (J). pap. 8.99 (978-1-84255-216-2(3)) Dolphin Paperbacks GBR. *Dist:* Trafalgar Square Publishing.

Crompton, Samuel Willard. Thomas More: And His Struggles of Conscience. 2005. (Makers of the Middle Ages & Renaissance Ser.). (Illus.). 140p. (J). (gr. 4-8). lib. bdg. 30.00 (978-0-7910-8636-0(4) , Chelsea Hse.) Facts On File, Inc.

Ford, Nick. Henry VIII: The King, His Six Wives & His Court. 2004. (Leaders of the Middle Ages Ser.). (Illus.). 112p. (YA). lib. bdg. 31.95 (978-1-4042-0163-7(7)) Rosen Publishing Group, Inc., The.

Graves, Michael A. R. Henry VIII. 2003. (Profiles in Power Ser.). 232p. (C). pap. 20.60 (978-0-582-38110-0(X)) Longman Publishing.

Green, Robert. King Henry VIII. 1998. (First Bks.). 64p. (J). 23.00 (978-0-531-20305-7(0) , Watts, Franklin) Scholastic Library Publishing.

Guy, John. Henry VIII & His Six Wives. 2004. (Illus.). 32p. (J). (gr. 4-7). pap. (978-1-86007-030-3(2)) Ticktock Media Ltd.

MacDonald, Alan. Henry the VIII & His Chopping Block. Reeve, Philip, illus. 2000. (Famous Dead People Ser.). 192p. (J). (gr. 4-7). pap. 4.50 (978-0-439-21125-3(5)) Scholastic, Inc.

—Henry VIII & His Chopping Block. 2000. (Famous Dead People Ser.). (J). 11.15 (978-0-606-19566-9(1)) Tandem Library Bks.

Ross, Stewart. Beware the King. 2007. (Flashbacks Ser.). (Illus.). 64p. (J). (gr. 4-7). pap. 8.95 (*978-0-237-53151-5(8) , Evans Brothers, Limited) Evans Publishing Group GBR. *Dist:* Independent Pubs. Group.

Worth, Richard. King Henry VIII & the Reformation in World History. 2001. (In World History Ser.). (Illus.). 112p. (J). (gr. 5-12). lib. bdg. 26.60 (978-0-7660-1615-6(3)) Enslow Pubs., Inc.

HENRY VIII, KING OF ENGLAND, 1491-1547—FICTION

Deary, Terry. The Thief, the Fool, & the Big Fat King. Flook, Helen, illus. 2005. (Read-It! Chapter Bks.). 61p. (J). (ps-k). lib. bdg. 19.95 (978-1-4048-1300-7(4)) Picture Window Bks.

Gould, Janet Hardy, et al. Henry VIII & His Six Wives, Level 2. 2000. (Bookworms Ser.). (Illus.). 6.50 (978-0-19-422975-3(0)) Oxford Univ. Pr., Inc.

Hannah, Martha. The Ghost of Hampton Court. Dowell, Larry, illus. 2006. 32p. (J). 17.95 (978-0-9779808-0-2(4)) CicadaSun.

HENRY THE NAVIGATOR, PRINCE OF PORTUGAL, 1394-1460

Hurwicz, Claude. Henry the Navigator. 2001. (Famous Explorers Ser.). (Illus.). 24p. (J). (gr. 3). lib. bdg. 18.75 (978-0-8239-5560-2(5) , PowerKids Pr.) Rosen Publishing Group, Inc., The.

HENRY, PATRICK, 1736-1799

Adler, David A. A Picture Book of Patrick Henry. Wallner, John et al, illus. 2005. 32p. (J). (gr. k-3). pap. 6.95 (978-0-8234-1678-3(X)) Holiday Hse., Inc.

Burton, Alma Holman. Four American Patriots: Patrick Henry, Alexander Hamilton, Andrew Jackson, Ulysses S. Grant: A Book for Young Americans. 2000. (Illus.). (J). (978-0-89526-204-2(5)) Regnery Publishing, Inc., An Eagle Publishing Co.

Espinosa, Rod. Patrick Henry. 2007. (Bio-Graphics Ser.). (Illus.). 32p. (J). (gr. 3-6). lib. bdg. 27.07 (*978-1-60270-070-3(2) , Graphic Planet) Magic Wagon.

Gillis, Jennifer Blizin. Patrick Henry. 2004. (Illus.). 32p. (J). pap. 7.50 (978-1-4034-5968-8(1)); lib. bdg. 24.22 (978-1-4034-5960-2(6)) Heinemann Library.

Glaser, Jason. Patrick Henry: Liberty or Death. McDonnell, Peter, illus. 2005. (Graphic Library). 32p. (J). (gr. 3-7). lib. bdg. 25.26 (978-0-7368-4970-8(X)) Capstone Pr., Inc.

Glaser, Jason & McDonnell, Peter. Patrick Henry: Muerte o Libertad. McDonnell, Peter, illus. 2007. (Graphic Library). (ENG & SPA.). (J). 25.26 (978-0-7368-6608-8(6)) Capstone Pr., Inc.

Grote, JoAnn A. Patrick Henry. 1999. (Revolutionary War Leaders Ser.). (Illus.). 80p. (J). (gr. 3 up). 31.00 (978-0-7910-5357-7(1)); pap. 8.95 (978-0-7910-5700-1(3)) Facts On File, Inc. (Chelsea Hse.).

Harkins, Susan & Harkins, William H. The Life & Times of Patrick Henry. 2006. (Profiles in American History Ser.). (Illus.). 48p. (J). (gr. 4-8). lib. bdg. 29.95 (978-1-58415-438-9(1)) Mitchell Lane Pubs., Inc.

Heinrichs, Ann. Patrick Henry: Orator & Patriot. 2004. (Our People Ser.). (Illus.). 32p. (J). (gr. 2-6). 27.07 (978-1-59296-176-4(2)) Child's World, Inc.

Jarnow, Jesse. Patrick Henry's Liberty or Death Speech: A Primary Source Investigation. 2004. (Great Historic Debates & Speeches Ser.). (Illus.). 64p. (J). lib. bdg. 29.25 (978-1-4042-0152-1(1)) Rosen Publishing Group, Inc., The.

Kallen, Stuart A. Patrick Henry. 2001. (Founding Fathers Ser.). (Illus.). 64p. (J). (gr. 3-8). lib. bdg. 25.65 (978-1-57765-012-6(3) , ABDO & Daughters) ABDO Publishing Co.

Kukla, Amy & Kukla, Jon. Patrick Henry: Voice of the Revolution. 2002. (Library of American Lives & Times). (Illus.). 112p. (J). lib. bdg. 31.95 (978-0-8239-5725-5(X) , PowerKids Pr.) Rosen Publishing Group, Inc., The.

Lerner Publishing Group Staff. Liberty or Death: A Story about Patrick Henry. 2003. (gr. 3-6). lib. bdg. 14.10 (978-0-613-77205-1(9)) Tandem Library Bks.

Marsh, Carole. Patrick Henry. 2002. (One Thousand Readers Ser.). (Illus.). 12p. (J). (gr. k-4). 2.95 (978-0-635-01544-0(7) , 15447) Gallopade International.

—The Virginia Reader: Patrick Henry. 2001. (Virginia Experience! Ser.). 12p. (J). (gr. k-4). pap. 2.95 (978-0-635-00368-3(6)) Gallopade International.

McPherson, Stephanie Sammartino. Liberty or Death: A Story about Patrick Henry. Debon, Nicolas, illus. 2003. (Creative Minds Biography Ser.). 64p. (J). pap. 6.95 (978-0-87614-930-0(1)); 22.60 (978-1-57505-178-9(8)) Lerner Publishing Group. (Carolrhoda Bks.).

Welch, Catherine A. Patrick Henry. 2006. (History Maker Bios Ser.). (Illus.). 48p. (J). 26.60 (978-0-8225-5941-2(2) , Lerner Pubns.) Lerner Publishing Group.

Where Was Patrick Henry on the 29Th of May? 2004. 24.95 incl. audio (978-1-56008-215-6(1)) Weston Woods Studios, Inc.

Where Was Patrick Henry on the 29th of May? 2004. 29.95 incl. cd-rom (978-1-55592-484-3(0)); pap. 14.95 incl. audio (978-1-56008-222-4(4)); pap. 18.95 incl. audio compact disk (978-1-55592-483-6(2)); pap. 18.95 incl. audio compact disk (978-1-55592-486-7(7)); pap. 32.75 incl. audio (978-1-55592-356-3(9)); pap. 32.75 incl. audio (978-1-55592-348-8(8)); pap. 32.75 incl. audio (978-1-55592-487-4(5)) Weston Woods Studios, Inc.

HENRY, PATRICK, 1736-1799—FICTION

Olasky, Susan. Annie Henry: Adventures in the American Revolution. 2005. (Illus.). 528p. (J). pap. 16.99 (978-1-58134-521-6(6) , Crossway Bibles) Crossway Bks.

—Annie Henry & the Mysterious Stranger. 2003. (Adventures of the American Revolution Ser.: Vol. 3). 144p. (YA). (gr. 3-7). pap. 5.99 (978-0-89107-907-1(6)) Crossway Bks.

Rinaldi, Ann. Or Give Me Death: A Novel of Patrick Henry's Family. (Great Episodes Ser.). 240p. (YA). 2004. pap. 6.95 (978-0-15-205076-4(0)); 2003. 17.00 (978-0-15-216687-8(4)) Harcourt Children's Bks. (Gulliver Bks.).

HENSON, MATTHEW ALEXANDER, 1866-1955

Armentrout, David & Armentrout, Patricia. Matthew Henson. 2004. (Discover the Life of an American Legend Ser.). (Illus.). 24p. (gr. 2-5). 20.64 (978-1-58952-658-7(9)) Rourke Publishing, LLC.

Bedesky, Baron. Peary & Henson: The Race to the North Pole. 2006. (In the Footsteps of Explorers Ser.). (Illus.). 32p. (J). (gr. 3-9). (978-0-7787-2426-1(3)) Crabtree Publishing Co.

Harcourt School Publishers Staff. To the Top of the World. 3rd ed. 2002. (Trophies English Language Learners Ser.). (Illus.). pap. 5.10 (978-0-15-327878-5(1)) Harcourt Schl. Pubs.

Hoena, B. A. Matthew Henson. 2005. (Illus.). 24p. (J). (ps-7). lib. bdg. 15.93 (978-0-7368-5249-4(2) , Pebble Bks.) Capstone Pr., Inc.

—Matthew Henson: Arctic Adventurer. Miller, Phil & Barnett, Charles, III, illus. 2005. (Graphic Library). 32p. (J). (gr. 3-7). lib. bdg. 25.26 (978-0-7368-4634-9(4)) Capstone Pr., Inc.

Johnson, Dolores. Onward: A Photobiography of African-American Polar Explorer Matthew Henson. 2005. (National Geographic Photographer Ser.). (Illus.). 64p. (J). (gr. k-3). 17.95 (978-0-7922-7914-3(X)); 27.90 (978-0-7922-7915-0(8)) National Geographic Society. (National Geographic Children's Bks.).

Kramer, Candice. Matthew Henson at the North Pole. 2004. (Reader's Theater Ser.). (J). pap. 22.00 (978-1-4108-0798-4(3)) Benchmark Education Co.

Litwin, Laura Baskes. Matthew Henson: Co-Discoverer of the North Pole. 2001. (African-American Biographies Ser.). (Illus.). 128p. (J). (gr. 6-12). lib. bdg. 26.60 (978-0-7660-1546-3(7)) Enslow Pubs., Inc.

Weatherford, Carole Boston. I, Matthew Henson. Velasquez, Eric, illus. 2007. 32p. (J). 16.95 (*978-0-8027-9688-2(5)); 17.85 (*978-0-8027-9689-9(3)) Walker & Co.

Weidt, Maryann N. Matthew Henson. (History Maker Bios Ser.). (Illus.). 48p. (J). 2003. (gr. 2-4). 26.60 (978-0-8225-0397-2(2)); 2002. pap. 6.95 (978-0-8225-1565-4(2)) Lerner Publishing Group. (Lerner Pubns.).

HERACLES (GREEK MYTHOLOGY)

see also Hercules (Roman Mythology)

Ford, James. The Twelve Labors of Hercules. Rutherford, Peter, illus. 2004. (Ancient Myths Ser.). 32p. (gr. 3-5). 23.93 (978-1-4048-0904-8(X)) Picture Window Bks.

Ford, James Evelyn. The Twelve Labours of Hercules. Rutherford, Peter, illus. 2004. (Ancient Myths Ser.). (J). (978-0-7565-0666-7(2)) Compass Point Bks.

Harris, John. Strong Stuff: Herakles & His Labors. Baseman, Gary, illus. 2005. (Getty Trust Publications). 32p. (gr. 3 up). 16.95 (978-0-89236-784-9(9) , J. Paul Getty Museum) Getty Pubns.

McCaughrean, Geraldine. Hercules. 2005. (Heroes Ser.). 152p. (J). 15.95 (978-0-8126-2737-4(7)) Cricket Bks.

Storrie, Paul D. Hercules. Kurth, Steve, illus. 2007. (Graphic Myths & Legends Ser.). 48p. (YA). (gr. 4-9). pap. 8.95 (*978-0-8225-6485-0(8)); (J). 26.60 (978-0-8225-3084-8(8)) Lerner Publishing Group.

Storrie Paul D. Hércules (Hercules) Los doce trabajos (the Twelve Labors) Kurth, Steve, illus. 2007. (Mitos y leyendas en viñetas (Graphic Myths & Legends) Ser.). (J). pap. 8.95 (*978-0-8225-7967-0(7) , Ediciones Lerner) Lerner Publishing Group.

Whiting, Jim. Hercules. 2007. (Profiles in Greek & Roman Mythology Ser.). (Illus.). 48p. (J). (gr. 4-9). lib. bdg. 29.95 (*978-1-58415-553-9(1)) Mitchell Lane Pubs., Inc.

HERALDRY

see also Chivalry; Decorations of Honor; Flags; Knights and Knighthood

Clack, Barbra. The Pledge of Allegiance. Clack, Barbra, illus. 2005. (Illus.). 32p. (J). (gr. 2-5). 14.95 (978-1-931721-48-6(3)) Bright Sky Pr.

Cooper, Jason. Flores/Flowers. 2003. (La Guia De Rourke Para Los Simbolos De Los Estados). (ENG & SPA., Illus.). 64p. (gr. 3-8). 20.95 (978-1-58952-398-2(9)) Rourke Publishing, LLC.

DeStefano, Susan. Symbols of America. 2005. (Illus.). 16p. (J). (978-0-7608-9258-9(X)) Sundance/Newbridge Educational Publishing.

Scholastic, Inc. Staff & Keenan, Sheila. O, Say Can You See? America's Symbols, Landmarks, & Important Words. 2007. 64p. (J). pap. 5.99 (*978-0-439-59360-1(3) , Scholastic Nonfiction) Scholastic, Inc.

Stanley, Robert E., Sr. Northwest Native Arts: Creative Colors 1, 2 vols. 2003. (Northwest Native Arts Ser.). (Illus.). 32p. (gr. 3 up). pap. 5.95 (978-0-88839-532-0(9)) Hancock Hse. Pubs.

—Northwest Native Arts: Creative Colors 2, 2 vols., Vol. 3. 2003. (North West Native Arts Ser.). (Illus.). 24p. pap. 4.95 (978-0-88839-533-7(7)) Hancock Hse. Pubs.

West, Delno C. & West, Jean M. Uncle Sam & Old Glory. Manson, Christopher, illus. 2000. 40p. (J). (gr. 2-5). 17.99 (978-0-689-82043-4(7) , Atheneum) Simon & Schuster Children's Publishing.

HERBAGE

see Grasses

HERBALS

see Botany; Herbs; Materia Medica

HERBS

Ayers, Patricia. A Kids Guide to How Herbs Grow. 2000. (Digging in the Dirt Ser.). 24p. (J). (gr. k-4). lib. bdg. 18.75 (978-0-8239-5464-3(1) , PowerKids Pr.) Rosen Publishing Group, Inc., The.

Cass, Hyla. User's Guide to Ginkgo Biloba. 2002. (Basic Health Publications User's Guide). 96p. pap. 5.95 (978-1-59120-019-2(9)) Basic Health Pubns., Inc.

Fell, Derek. Herbs. 2000. (Let's Investigate Ser.). (Illus.). 32p. (YA). (gr. 4 up). pap. (978-1-58341-002-8(3) , Creative Education) Creative Co., The.

Gleason, Carrie. The Biography of Tobacco. 2006. (How Did That Get Here? Ser.). (Illus.). 32p. (J). (978-0-7787-2489-6(1) , 1259497) Crabtree Publishing Co.

Gunderson, Jessica. Friends & Flowers. Doerrfeld, Cori, illus. 2007. (J). lib. bdg. (*978-1-4048-2291-7(7)) Picture Window Bks.

Hopman, Ellen Evert. Walking the World in Wonder: A Children's Herbal. 2000. (Illus.). 160p. (gr. k-5). 19.95 (978-0-89281-878-5(6) , Healing Arts Pr.) Inner Traditions International, Ltd.

Ichikawa, Satomi. Rosy's Garden. (Illus.). (J). (978-0-399-22388-4(6) , Philomel) Penguin Group (USA) Inc.

Maurer, Tracy. Growing Herbs. 2000. (Green Thumb Guides Ser.). (Illus.). 24p. (J). (gr. 2-6). lib. bdg. 23.93 (978-1-55916-253-1(8)) Rourke Publishing, LLC.

Monroe, Judy. Herbal Drug Dangers. (Drug Dangers Ser.). (Illus.). 64p. (YA). (gr. 4-10). 2001. pap. 13.26 (978-0-7660-1964-5(0)); 2000. lib. bdg. 27.93 (978-0-7660-1319-3(7)) Enslow Pubs., Inc.

HERBS, MEDICAL

see Botany, Medical

HERCULES (ROMAN MYTHOLOGY)

see also Heracles (Greek Mythology)

Burleigh, Robert. Hercules. 1999. (Illus.). 32p. (J). (ps-3). 16.98 (978-0-7398-1482-6(6)) Raintree.

Ford, James Evelyn. The Twelve Labours of Hercules. Rutherford, Peter, illus. 2004. (Ancient Myths Ser.). (J). (978-0-7565-0666-7(2)) Compass Point Bks.

Loewen, Nancy. Hercules. 1999. (Greek & Roman Mythology Ser.). (Illus.). 48p. (J). (gr. 3-4). lib. bdg. 22.60 (978-0-7368-0049-5(2) , Bridgestone Bks.) Capstone Pr., Inc.

Saunders, Nick. The Twelve Labours of Hercules. 2006. (J). pap. (***978-0-8368-8151-6(6)***); lib. bdg. (***978-0-8368-7751-9(9)***) Stevens, Gareth Inc. (World Almanac Library).

HERCULES (ROMAN MYTHOLOGY)—FICTION

Cartwright, Stephen, illus. Hercules. 2004. (Young Reading Series Two Ser.). 64p. (J). (gr. 2 up). pap. 5.95 (978-0-7945-0453-3(1) , Usborne) EDC Publishing.

Nelson, Ray, et al. Hercules' Spring Book. Siegel, Joseph & Habecker, Mary Beth, eds. Peeples, Aaron et al, illus. 2000. 32p. (J). (gr. 1-3). pap. 12.00 (978-1-883772-23-9(0)) Flying Rhinoceros, Inc.

Stamper, Judith Bauer & Keenan. Hercules & the Maze of the Minotaur. 1998. (Disney's First Readers Ser.: Vol. 3). 40p. (J). (gr. 2-4). pap. 3.50 (978-0-7868-4171-4(0)) Disney Pr.

Stamper, Judith Bauer & Sol Studios Staff. Hercules & the Maze of the Minotaur. 1999. (Illus.). (J). (978-0-590-39387-4(1)) Scholastic, Inc.

HEREDITY

Benchmark Education Staff. Heredity. 2005. 2.00 (***978-1-4108-4650-1(4)***) Benchmark Education Co.

Brannon, Barbara. Discover Heredity. 2005. 39.00 (***978-1-4108-5136-9(2)***) Benchmark Education Co.

Christie, Lee. Basic Heredity. 2006. (Navigators Ser.). (J). pap. 44.00 (***978-1-4108-6238-9(0)***) Benchmark Education Co.

Freedman, Jeri. How Do We Know about Genetics & Heredity? 2005. (Great Scientific Questions & the Scientists Who Answered Them Ser.). (Illus.). 112p. (J). (gr. 7-12). lib. bdg. 26.50 (978-1-4042-0074-6(6)) Rosen Publishing Group, Inc., The.

Fullick, Ann. Adaptation & Competition. 2005. (Life Science In-Depth Ser.). (J). pap. (978-1-4034-7526-8(1)); (Illus.). 64p. (978-1-4034-7518-3(0)) Heinemann Library.

—Inheritance & Selection. 2005. (Life Science In-Depth Ser.). (Illus.). 64p. (J). pap. (978-1-4034-7531-2(8)); lib. bdg. (978-1-4034-7523-7(7)) Heinemann Library.

Gallant, Roy A. The Treasure of Inheritance. 2002. (Story of Science Ser.). (Illus.). 78p. (J). 29.93 (978-0-7614-1426-1(6) , Benchmark Bks.) Cavendish, Marshall Corp.

Gardner, Robert. Health Science Projects about Heredity. 2001. (Science Projects Ser.). (Illus.). 128p. (YA). (gr. 6-12). lib. bdg. 26.60 (978-0-7660-1438-1(X)) Enslow Pubs., Inc.

Hil, Mcgraw. Gr 6 Heredity & Chg Sci. 2000. (McGraw-Hill Science Ser.). (gr. 6 up). (978-0-02-278236-8(2)) Macmillan/McGraw-Hill Schl. Div.

—Sciasmtbk Heredity & Chan. 2000. (McGraw-Hill Science Ser.). (gr. 6 up). (978-0-02-277776-0(8)) Macmillan/McGraw-Hill Schl. Div.

—Trfpaswak Heredity & Chan. 2000. (McGraw-Hill Science Ser.). (gr. 6 up). (978-0-02-277657-2(5)) Macmillan/McGraw-Hill Schl. Div.

Holt, Rinehart and Winston Staff. Holt Science & Technology Chapter 5: Life Science: Heredity. 5th ed. 2004. (Illus.). pap. 12.86 (978-0-03-030181-0(5)) Holt, Rinehart & Winston.

—Holt Science & Technology Chptr. 2: Heredity: Chapter Resources - Tennessee Edition. 3rd ed. 2003. (YA). pap. 11.40 (978-0-03-069159-1(1)) Holt, Rinehart & Winston.

Morgan, Sally. From Mendel's Peas to Genetic Fingerprinting: Discovering Inheritance. 2006. (Chain Reactions Ser.). (Illus.). 64p. (YA). (gr. 6-9). lib. bdg. 34.29 (978-1-4034-8837-4(1)) Heinemann Library.

Parsons, Michelle Hyde. Heredity. 2005. 39.00 (***978-1-4108-4602-0(4)***) Benchmark Education Co.

Stille, Darlene R. Heredity. 2007. (J). pap. (***978-0-8368-8448-7(5)***); 48p. (gr. 5-8). lib. bdg. 26.60 (***978-0-8368-8439-5(6)***) Stevens, Gareth Inc.

HERMETIC ART AND PHILOSOPHY

see Astrology; Occultism

HERMITS—FICTION

Alger, Horatio. Mark Manning's Mission: The Story of a Shoe Factory Boy. unabr. ed. 2002. (Polyglot Press Alger Ser.). (Illus.). (J). pap. 17.95 (978-1-4115-0022-8(9)) Polyglot Pr., Inc.

Ballantyne, Michael. Blown to Bits or the Lonely Man of Rakat. 2006. 36.99 (***978-1-4280-4221-6(0)***); pap. 30.99 (***978-1-4280-4226-1(1)***) IndyPublish.com.

Ballantyne, R. M. Blown to Bits; or, the Lonely Man of Rak. 2006. pap. (***978-1-4065-0515-3(3)***) Dodo Pr.

Barry, Jack. The Hermit's Handbook. Leue, Mary, ed. Leue, Mary, illus. Leue, Mary, photos by. 2004. (Philaterra Ser.). 208p. pap. 12.95 (978-1-878115-14-0(6)) Down-To-Earth-Bks.

Bauer, Joan. Backwater. 2005. 185p. (YA). (gr. 7-12). pap. 7.99 (978-0-14-240434-8(9) , Puffin) Penguin Group (USA) Inc.

—Backwater. 2000. (978-0-606-20077-6(0)) Tandem Library Bks.

Clarke, Jane. Sherman Swaps Shells. Parker, Ant, illus. (Flying Foxes Ser.). 48p. (J). 2004. pap. (978-0-7787-1531-3(0)); 2003. (978-0-7787-1485-9(3)) Crabtree Publishing Co.

Gaetz, Dayle. Crossbow. 2007. (Orca Currents Ser.). 112p. (YA). (gr. 5 up). pap. (***978-1-55143-841-2(0)***); lib. bdg. (***978-1-55143-843-6(7)***) Orca Bk. Pubs.

Hanh, Thich Nhat. The Hermit & the Well. Mai, Vo-Dinh, illus. 2004. 36p. (J). 15.00 (978-1-888375-31-2(0)) Parallax Pr.

Nervelle, Rosemarie. The Witch of Beaver Creek Mine. 2007. 160p. (gr. 5-9). 14.95 (***978-0-89272-741-4(1)***) Down East Bks.

Sordo, Maria Luisa Rodriguez. El Senor de Alfoz. 1998. (SPA.). (gr. 7-12). lib. bdg. 14.10 (978-0-613-80663-3(8)) Tandem Library Bks.

HEROES

see also Courage; Explorers; Mythology; Saints

Albee, Jo. American Heroes. 2003. (Compass Point Phonics Readers Ser.). (Illus.). 16p. (J). (gr. 1 up). 13.26 (978-0-7565-0502-8(X)) Compass Point Bks.

Allberti, Frances C. Finding Rover. Gremillion, Barry, illus. 2006. (J). per. (978-0-9785937-1-1(5)) Open Pages Publishing.

American Heroes, 6 bks., Set. Incl. Abraham Lincoln : A Courageous Leader. Collard, Sneed B. (gr. 3-5). lib. bdg. 28.50 (978-0-7614-2162-7(9)); Benjamin Franklin : The Man Who Could Do Just about Anything. Collard, Sneed B., III. (gr. 3-5). lib. bdg. 28.50 (***978-0-7614-2161-0(0)***); David Crockett : Fearless Frontiersman. Collard, Sneed B., III. lib. bdg. 28.50 (978-0-7614-2160-3(2)); John Adams : Our Second President. Collard, Sneed B., III. lib. bdg. 28.50 (***978-0-7614-2159-7(9)***); Rosa Parks : The Courage to Make a Difference. Collard, Sneed B., III. (gr. 3-5). lib. bdg. 28.50 (978-0-7614-2163-4(7)); Sacagawea : Brave Shoshone Girl. Collard, Sneed B., III. (gr. 3-5). lib. bdg. 28.50 (978-0-7614-2166-5(1)); (Illus.). 48p. (J). 2006. 2006. Set lib. bdg. 171.00 (***978-0-7614-2158-0(0)***, Benchmark Bks.) Cavendish, Marshall Corp.

Barnes, Dana R. & DeRemer, Leigh Ann. Contemporary Heroes & Heroines. 2000. (Illus.). 628p. (J). 110.00 (978-0-7876-3262-5(7) , GML12001-112883) Thomson Gale.

Barron, T. A. The Hero's Trail: A Guide for a Heroic Life. 2007. 144p. (J). (gr. 3 up). pap. 6.99 (978-0-14-240760-8(7) , Puffin) Penguin Group (USA) Inc.

—The Hero's Trail: A Hiking Guide for a Heroic Life. 2002. (Illus.). 160p. (J). (gr. 3). 15.99 (978-0-399-23860-4(3) , Philomel) Penguin Group (USA) Inc.

Bledsoe, Karen & Bledsoe, Glen. Helicopters: High-Flying Heroes. 2006. (Mighty Military Machines Ser.). (Illus.). 48p. (J). (gr. 4-10). lib. bdg. 23.93 (978-0-7660-2663-6(9)) Enslow Pubs., Inc.

Bodie, Idella. Heroes & Heroines of the American Revolution. 2004. (J). pap., instr.'s gde. ed. (978-0-87844-173-0(5)) Sandlapper Publishing Co., Inc.

—Heroines of the American Revolution. 2003. (Illus.). 99p. (J). pap. 6.95 (978-0-87844-170-9(0)) Sandlapper Publishing Co., Inc.

Bolden, Tonya. Portraits of African-American Heroes. Pitcairn, Ansel, illus. 2003. 88p. (J). (gr. 2). 18.99 (978-0-525-47043-4(3) , Dutton Juvenile) Penguin Group (USA) Inc.

Bruning, John Robert, Jr. Elusive Glory: African-American Heroes of World War II. 2001. (Illus.). 144p. (J). (gr. 6-12). pap. 19.95 (978-1-888105-48-3(8)) Avisson Pr., Inc.

Buckley, Annie. Hero Girls. 2006. (Girls Rock! Ser.). (Illus.). 32p. (J). (gr. 1-5). 24.21 (978-1-59296-744-5(2)) Child's World, Inc.

Carroll, Colleen. How Artists See Heroes: Myth History War Everyday. 2003. (How Artists See Ser.). (Illus.). 48p. (gr. 3-6). 12.95 (978-0-7892-0773-9(7)) Abbeville Pr., Inc.

Casad, Dede W. Texans of Valor: Military Heroes of the Twentieth Century. 1998. (Illus.). 152p. pap. 17.95 (978-1-57168-113-3(2)) Eakin Pr.

Chelsea House Publishing Staff. Heroes of the Faith. 1998. (J). 179.50 (978-0-7910-5050-7(5) , Chelsea Hse.) Facts On File, Inc.

Chin-Lee, Cynthia. Akira to Zoltan: Twenty-Six Men Who Changed the World. Halsey, Megan & Addy, Sean, illus. 2006. 32p. (J). 15.95 (978-1-57091-579-6(2)) Charlesbridge Publishing, Inc.

Defalco, Tom. The Amazing Spider-Man: The Ultimate Guide. 2007. 184p. (J). 24.99 (978-0-7566-2675-4(7)) Dorling Kindersley Publishing, Inc.

Denenberg, Dennis. 50 American Heroes Every Kid Should Meet. Roscoe, Lorraine, illus. 2002. 112p. (gr. 4 up). pap. (978-0-7613-1645-9(0) , Twenty-First Century Bks.) Lerner Publishing Group.

Denenberg, Dennis & Roscoe, Lorraine. 50 American Heroes Every Kid Should Meet. 2001. (Inspiring People Ser.). (Illus.). 128p. (J). (gr. 4 up). lib. bdg. 29.90 (978-0-7613-1612-1(4) , Twenty-First Century Bks.) Lerner Publishing Group.

—50 American Heroes Every Kid Should Meet! rev. ed. 2005. (Illus.). 128p. (J). (gr. 3-7). pap. 14.95 (978-0-7613-9548-5(2) , First Avenue Editions) Lerner Publishing Group.

Desouza, Lar, illus. Boys Who Rocked the World: From King Tut to Tiger Woods. 2001. 64p. (gr. 3-7). pap. (978-1-58270-045-8(1)) Beyond Words Publishing, Inc.

Gale Research Staff. Contemporary Heroes & Heroines, Bk. III. 1998. (Illus.). 699p. (J). 110.00 (978-0-7876-2215-2(X) , GML14099-111730) Thomson Gale.

Garrison, Mary. Slaves Who Dared: The Stories of Ten African-American Heroes. 2002. (Illus.). 150p. (J). (gr. 4-6). lib. bdg. 19.95 (978-1-57249-272-1(4) , White Mane Kids) White Mane Publishing Co., Inc.

Gray, Peter C. How to Draw Manga Heroes & Villains. 2006. (Kid's Guide to Drawing Ser.). (Illus.). 32p. (J). 25.25 (978-1-4042-3330-0(X) , PowerKids Pr.) Rosen Publishing Group, Inc., The.

—How to Draw Manga Male Action Figures. 2006. (Kid's Guide to Drawing Ser.). (Illus.). 32p. (J). lib. bdg. (978-1-4042-3328-7(8) , PowerKids Pr.) Rosen Publishing Group, Inc., The.

Hamilton, John. Knights & Heroes. 2005. (Illus.). 32p. (J). (gr. 4-8). lib. bdg. 24.21 (978-1-59679-336-1(8) , ABDO & Daughters) ABDO Publishing Co.

Hazell, Rebecca. Heroes: Great Men Through the Ages. Hazell, Rebecca, illus. 2000. (Illus.). 80p. (YA). (gr. 6-7). reprint ed. 20.00 (978-0-7881-9099-5(7)) DIANE Publishing Co.

Heroes for Young Readers Activity Guide Package Special for Books 13-16. 2006. pap. 35.99 (***978-1-57658-378-4(3)***) YWAM Publishing.

Hirschhorn, Vera. America's Young Heroes: A Journal for You: Learn about Yourself, Learn the Lessons of the Civil War. 2nd rev. ed. 2002. 117p. (YA). (gr. 5-10). pap. 24.95 (978-0-9718197-0-2(X)) America's Young Heroes Pubns.

Hoffman, Eric. Heroines & Heroes (Heroinas y Heroes) de la Vega, Eida, tr. Rosen, Judi, illus. 2004. (Anti-Bias Books for Kids). (ENG & SPA.). 32p. (J). (ps-3). pap. 11.95 (978-1-884834-68-4(X) , 709101) Redleaf Pr.

Jael, tr. & illus. Superheroes: [includes Drawing & Tracing Paper]. Jael, illus. 2002. (Ready, Set, Draw Ser.). (J). (978-1-58865-073-3(1)) Kidsbooks, Inc.

James, Lesley. Women Who Made a Scene: Heroines, Villainesses, Eccentrics. 2002. (Remarkable Women). (Illus.). 80p. (YA). (gr. 6-9). lib. bdg. 32.85 (978-0-8172-5735-4(7)) Raintree.

Kingsley, Charles. Heroes of Greek Mythology. 2006. (Illus.). 240p. pap. 8.95 (978-0-486-44854-1(1)) Dover Pubns., Inc.

Lee, Meredith Chan. First Heroes: A 5-Generation Quest. 2002. (Illus.). 160p. (YA). 19.95 (978-0-9715417-0-2(1) , 2106) A/P Pr.

Louis, Nancy. Heroes of the Day. 2002. (War on Terrorism Ser.). (Illus.). 64p. (J). (gr. 4-8). lib. bdg. 25.65 (978-1-57765-658-6(X) , ABDO & Daughters) ABDO Publishing Co.

Mabie, H. W., ed. Heroes Every Child Should Know (Yesterday's Classics) 2006. 396p. (J). per. 13.95 (978-1-59915-097-0(2)) Yesterday's Classics.

Mabie, Hamilton Wright. Heroes Every Child Should Know. 2005. 31.95 (978-1-4218-0941-0(9) , 1st World Library - Literary Society) 1st World Publishing, Inc.

Mabie, Hamilton Wright. Heroines That Every Child Should Know: T. 2006. (Illus.). pap. 28.95 (***978-1-4286-0305-9(0)***) Kessinger Publishing, LLC.

Mattern, Joanne. Life Stories of 100 American Heroes. 2001. (Values in Action Ser.). (Illus.). 573p. (J). (978-1-56156-978-6(X)) Kidsbooks, Inc.

Meloche, Renee. Corrie Ten Boom: A Hero for Young Readers. Pollard, Bryan, illus. 2002. (Heroes for Young Readers Ser.). 32p. 8.99 (978-1-57658-231-2(0)) YWAM Publishing.

—Eric Liddell: A Hero for Young Readers. Pollard, Bryan, illus. 2002. (Heroes for Young Readers Ser.). 32p. 8.99 (978-1-57658-230-5(2)) YWAM Publishing.

—George Muller: A Hero for Young Readers. Pollard, Bryan, illus. 2002. (Heroes for Young Readers Ser.). 32p. 8.99 (978-1-57658-232-9(9)) YWAM Publishing.

—Nate Saint: On a Wing & a Prayer. Pollard, Bryan, illus. 2002. (Heroes for Young Readers Ser.). 32p. 8.99 (978-1-57658-229-9(9)) YWAM Publishing.

Molan, Chris, illus. Heroic Stories. 2004. (Red Hot Reads Ser.). 256p. (J). (gr. 4-8). pap. 6.95 (978-0-7534-5720-7(2) , Kingfisher) Houghton Mifflin Co. Trade & Reference Div.

Morris, Deborah. Real Kids, Real Adventures in Texas. 2002. 102p. pap. 8.95 (978-1-55622-933-6(X) , Republic of Texas Pr.) Wordware Publishing, Inc.

—Real Kids Real Adventures in Texas: Blanco River Rescue. 2002. (gr. k-3). lib. bdg. 17.60 (978-0-613-87965-1(1)) Tandem Library Bks.

Murray, Kirsty. What Kids Are Made Of: True Stores of Young Rescuers, Rulers & Rebels. 2000. (gr. 3-6). lib. bdg. 16.40 (978-0-613-56688-9(2)) Tandem Library Bks.

—What Kids Are Made Of: True Stories of Young Rescuers, Rulers & Rebels. 2000. (Illus.). 160p. (J). (gr. 1-6). pap. 7.95 (978-1-55652-414-1(5)) Chicago Review Pr., Inc.

My Hero. 2002. (Benchmark Bks.). (J). pap. 3.74 (978-0-7398-5846-2(7)) Steck-Vaughn.

Osborn. Born to Fly. 2003. (gr. 5-8). lib. bdg. 13.55 (978-0-613-84567-0(6)) Tandem Library Bks.

Osborn, Shane & McConnell, Malcolm. Born to Fly: The Heroic Story of Downed U. S. Navy Pilot Lt. Shane Osborn. 2003. 192p. (gr. 5). 5.99 (978-0-440-23796-9(3) , Yearling) Random Hse. Children's Bks.

—Born to Fly: The Heroic Story of Downed U. S. Navy Pilot Lt. Shane Osborn. l.t. ed. 2002. 403p. 29.45 (978-0-7862-4101-9(2)) Thomson Gale.

O'Shei, Tim. The World's Most Amazing Survival Stories. 2007. (Edge Books, the World's Top Ten). (Illus.). 32p. (J). 23.93 (978-0-7368-6437-4(7) , 1258961) Capstone Pr., Inc.

Ovations, 12 bks. rev. ed. 2000. (J). lib. bdg. 255.60 (978-0-88682-937-7(2) , Creative Education) Creative Co., The.

Parham, Jerrill. Boundary Breakers: Remarkable People. 2007. (Shockwave: History & Politics Ser.). (Illus.). 36p. (J). (gr. 4-6). 25.00 (***978-0-531-17752-5(1)***, Children's Pr.) Scholastic Library Publishing.

Rava, Giuseppe & Alex, Ben. Heroes Who Changed the World. 2000. (Illus.). 480p. 29.95 (978-87-7247-065-8(8)) Scandinavia Publishing Hse. DNK. *Dist:* National Bk. Network.

Roche, George, et al. The Book of Heroes: Great Men & Women in American History. 1998. (Illus.). 256p. (gr. 7 up). (978-0-89526-381-0(5)) Regnery Publishing, Inc., An Eagle Publishing Co.

Roehm, Michelle. Girls Who Rocked the World, Vol. 2. 2000. (YA). (978-0-606-19486-0(X)) Tandem Library Bks.

Roehm, Michelle, compiled by. Girls Who Rocked the World Vol. 2: Heroines from Harriet Tubman to Mia Hamm. 2000. (Girls Know Best Ser.). (Illus.). 152p. (J). (gr. 3 up). lib. bdg. 23.33 (978-0-8368-2673-9(6)) Stevens, Gareth Inc.

Ross, Margie Dover. Emma Sansom: Confederate Heroine. 2001. (Alabama Roots Biography Ser.). (Illus.). 104p. (J). (978-1-878561-83-1(9)) Seacoast Publishing, Inc.

San Souci, Robert D. Larger Than Life: The Adventures of American Legendary Heroes. Colon, Raul, illus. 2000. (978-0-15-200398-2(3)) Harcourt Trade Pubs.

Sautter, Aaron. How to Draw Comic Heroes. Martin, Cynthia, illus. 2008. (J). (***978-1-4296-0074-3(8)***) Capstone Pr., Inc.

—How to Draw Manga Warriors. Martin, Cynthia, illus. 2008. (J). (***978-1-4296-0078-1(0)***) Capstone Pr., Inc.

Schiffman, Jessica, illus. Sybil Ludington: Freedom's Brave Rider. 2005. 32p. (J). pap. (***978-0-7367-2931-4(3)***) Zaner-Bloser, Inc.

Smallwood, James. Oklahoma & Its Heroes. 2001. (Illus.). 104p. 15.95 (978-1-57168-581-0(2)) Eakin Pr.

Sowash, Rick. Heroes of Ohio: 23 True Tales of Courage & Character. 2003. (J). 19.95 (978-0-9762412-5-6(0)); pap. 11.95 (978-0-9762412-4-9(2)) Sowash, Rick Publishing Co.

Stephens, Jay. Heroes! Draw Your Own Superheroes, Gadget Geeks & Other Do-Gooders. 2007. (Illus.). 64p. (J). pap. 5.95 (***978-1-60059-179-2(5)***); (gr. 4-6). 12.95 (978-1-57990-934-5(5)) Lark Bks.

Trudel, Sylvain. Des Heros Comme Vous et Moi. 2000. (Premier Roman Ser.). (FRE.). 192p. (J). (gr. 2-5). pap. (978-2-89021-386-9(2)) Diffusion du livre Mirabel.

Walder, Chaim. Our Heroes. 1998. 200p. 21.99 (978-0-87306-866-6(1)) Feldheim Pubs.

Wallace, Archer. Men Who Played the Game. 2003. 127p. 89.00 (978-0-7950-5139-5(5)) New Library Press.Net.

Waters, Fiona. Great Irish Heroes. 2004. (Illus.). 64p. (J). 21.00 (978-0-7171-3793-0(7)) Gill & MacMillan, Ltd. IRL. *Dist:* Irish Bks. & Media, Inc.

Watts, Claire. Super Heroes. 2000. (gr. 3-6). lib. bdg. 11.80 (978-0-613-46106-1(1)) Tandem Library Bks.

Watts, Claire & Nicholson, Robert. Super Heroes. 2000. (Info Adventure Ser.). (Illus.). 32p. (J). (gr. 3-6). pap. 3.95 (978-1-58728-105-1(8) , Two Can Publishing) T&N Children's Publishing.

Weil, Ann. Great Heroes. 2006. (Atomic Ser.). (Illus.). 32p. (J). (gr. 4-6). lib. bdg. 28.21 (978-1-4109-2483-4(1)) Raintree.

—Great Heroes. 2006. (Illus.). 32p. (J). pap. (978-1-4109-2488-9(2)) Steck-Vaughn.

Welden, Amelie. Girls Who Rocked the World: Heroines from Sacagawea to Sheryl Swoopes. McCann, Jerry, illus. l.t. ed. 1999. (Girls Know Best Ser.). 117p. (J). (gr. 3 up). lib. bdg. 23.33 (978-0-8368-2454-4(7)) Stevens, Gareth Inc.

World Book, Inc. Staff, contrib. by. Heroes & Helpers: A Supplement to Childcraft: The How & Why Library. 2003. (Illus.). 208p. (J). pap. (978-0-7166-0606-2(2)) World Bk., Inc.

Zalben, Jane. Paths to Peace: People Who Changed the World. 2006. (Illus.). 48p. (J). (gr. 3). 18.99 (978-0-525-47734-1(9) , Dutton Juvenile) Penguin Group (USA) Inc.

Zondervan. Todays Heroes: Ben Carson; David Robinson; Dave Dravecky; & Chuck Colson Pack —Prison Fellowship: Ben Carson; David Robinson; Dave Dravecky; & Chuck Colson Pack —Prison Fellowship. 2001. (J). pap. 19.96 (978-0-310-70366-2(2)) Zonderkidz.

HEROES—FICTION

Adpot-a-Hulk. 2003. (J). per. (978-1-57657-819-3(4)) Paradise Pr., Inc.

Alex de Campi & Edo Fuijkschot. Agent Boo, Vol. 1. 2006. (Illus.). 96p. pap. 4.99 (978-1-59816-802-0(9) , Tokyopop Kids) TOKYOPOP, Inc.

Alexander, Lloyd. The Illyrian Adventure. 2000. (Vesper Holly Ser.). (Illus.). 144p. (J). (gr. 5-9). pap. 5.99 (978-0-14-130313-0(1) , Puffin) Penguin Group (USA) Inc.

—The Illyrian Adventure. 1999. (Vesper Holly Ser.). (YA). (gr. 7 up). 12.64 (978-0-606-16832-8(X)) Tandem Library Bks.

Alger, Horatio. Facing the World. 2006. pap. (***978-1-4250-2212-9(X)***) Assistedreadingbooks.com Inc.

—Facing the World. 2006. pap. (***978-1-4065-0704-1(0)***) Dodo Pr.

Allende, Isabel & Vega, Diego. Young Zorro: The Iron Brand. 2007. 240p. (J). pap. 6.99 (978-0-06-083947-5(3) , Rayo) HarperCollins Pubs.

Alston, Emerson. Moccasins. 2000. 128p. (gr. 7-12). 11.95 (978-1-56315-220-7(7)) SterlingHouse Pubs., Inc.

—Moccasins. 2000. (gr. 7-12). lib. bdg. 16.40 (978-0-613-88171-5(0)) Tandem Library Bks.

Alter, Judy. Sam Houston Is My Hero. 2003. (Chaparral Book for Young Readers Ser.). 140p. (J). pap. 15.95 (978-0-87565-277-1(8)) Texas Christian Univ. Pr.

Amma, Jill. The Indaba Tree Odyssey: An African Tale. 2006. 360p. pap. 18.95 (978-0-7414-3172-1(6)) Infinity Publishing.

Andersen, D. R. The Matter Marvels. 2005. 40.00 (****978-1-4108-4216-9(9)***) Benchmark Education Co.

Anderson, John David. Standard Hero Behavior. 2007. 288p. (J). (gr. 5-9). 16.00 (****978-0-618-75920-0(4)*** , Clarion Bks.) Houghton Mifflin Co. Trade & Reference Div.

Anderson, M. T. The Clue of the Linoleum Lederhosen: M. T. Anderson's Thrilling Tales. Cyrus, Kurt, illus. 2007. (M. T. Anderson's Thrilling Tales Ser.). 272p. (J). pap. 5.95 (978-0-15-205407-6(3) , Harcourt Paperbacks) Harcourt Children's Bks.

Archie, 6 bks., Set. 2007. (J). 145.26 (****978-1-59961-257-7(7)***) Spotlight.

Artful Doodlers. TMNT: Intense Action. 2008. (Teenage Mutant Ninja Turtles Ser.). 224p. (J). 4.99 (****978-1-4169-5102-5(4)*** , Simon Scribbles) Simon & Schuster Children's Publishing.

Bagley, Mark, illus. Ultimate Spider-Man: Double Trouble. 2002. (Ultimate Spider-Man Ser.). 27.19 (978-1-4046-2382-8(5)) Book Wholesalers, Inc.

—Ultimate Spider-Man: Learning Curve. 2002. 21.09 (978-1-4046-2220-3(9)) Book Wholesalers, Inc.

—Ultimate Spider-Man: Legacy. 2002. (Ultimate Spider-Man Ser.). 20.83 (978-1-4046-2353-8(1)) Book Wholesalers, Inc.

—Ultimate Spider-Man: Power & Responsibility. 2002. (YA). 23.04 (978-1-4046-0900-6(8)) Book Wholesalers, Inc.

Bailey, Len. Clabbernappers. 2005. (Illus.). 224p. (J). 17.95 (978-0-7653-0981-5(5) , Tor Bks.) Doherty, Tom Assocs., LLC.

Bailey, Sian, illus. Grandfather Mountain: Stories of Gods & Heroes from Many Cultures. 2004. 80p. (J). (gr. 3-6). 19.99 (978-1-84148-789-2(9)) Barefoot Bks., Inc.

Balaban, Bob. Beware of Dog. 2002. (gr. 3-6). lib. bdg. 13.00 (978-0-613-72091-5(1)) Tandem Library Bks.

Ballard, Curt. A Child of the Veil. 2001. 126p. (J). pap. 7.99 (978-1-889893-64-8(1)) Emerald Hse. Group, Inc.

Barracca, Debra. Maxi, the Hero. Buehner, Mark, illus. 2002. (J). 14.04 (978-0-7587-3112-8(4)) Book Wholesalers, Inc.

Beard, George & Hutchins, Harold. The Adventures of Super Diaper Baby. Beard, George, illus. 2002. (Captain Underpants Ser.). (Illus.). 128p. (gr. 2-5). mass mkt. 4.99 (978-0-439-37606-8(8) , Blue Sky Pr., The) Scholastic, Inc.

Bell, Hilari. Rise of a Hero. 2006. (Farsala Trilogy Ser.: No. 2). 592p. (YA). pap. 6.99 (978-0-689-85417-0(X) , Simon Pulse) Simon & Schuster Children's Publishing.

Belton, Sandra. The Tallest Tree: The Paul Robeson Story. 2008. 160p. (J). lib. bdg. 17.89 (****978-0-06-052750-1(1)*** , Amistad) HarperCollins Pubs.

Bendis, Brian Michael. Avengers Disassembled HC. 2007. (Illus.). 184p. 24.99 (978-0-7851-2294-4(X)) Marvel Enterprises, Inc.

Bendis, Brian Michael & Straczynski, J. Michael. The Road to Civil War. 2007. (Civil War Ser.). (Illus.). 160p. (J). pap. 14.99 (978-0-7851-1974-6(4)) Marvel Enterprises, Inc.

Benton, Jim. Howard Hubbins Half Hour Hero. 2008. (J). pap. (****978-0-06-059774-0(7)***) HarperCollins Pubs.

Berry, Connie Lee. The Criminal in the Caymans. 2007. (Incredible Journey Bks.). 85p. (J). pap. 3.95 (****978-0-9772848-0-1(8)***) Kid's Fun Pr.

Big Guy Books Staff & Duey, Kathleen. Parche, Vol. 3. Gould, Robert, photos by. 2003. (Soldados en el Tiempo: Vol. 3). (SPA.). 48p. (J). pap. 8.95 (978-1-929945-37-5(X)) Big Guy Bks., Inc.

Blackman, Malorie. Sinclair, Wonder Bear. Allwright, Deborah, illus. 2005. (Blue Go Bananas Ser.). 43p. (J). (978-0-7787-2631-9(2)) Crabtree Publishing Co.

Boniface, William. The Extraordinary Adventures of Ordinary Boy, Book 1: the Hero Revealed. Gilpin, Stephen, illus. 2008. (Extraordinary Adventures of Ordinary Boy Ser.). 320p. (J). pap. 6.99 (****978-0-06-077466-0(5)*** , Harper Trophy) HarperCollins Pubs.

—The Hero Revealed. Gilpin, Stephen, illus. 2006. (Extraordinary Adventures of Ordinary Boy Ser.). 304p. (J). 15.99 (978-0-06-077464-6(9)); lib. bdg. 16.89 (978-0-06-077465-3(7)) HarperCollins Pubs.

—The Return of Meteor Boy? Gilpin, Stephen, illus. 2007. (Extraordinary Adventures of Ordinary Boy Ser.). 352p. (J). (gr. 3-7). lib. bdg. 17.89 (978-0-06-077468-4(1)); 16.99 (978-0-06-077467-7(3)) HarperCollins Pubs.

Bourgeois, Paulette. Franklin & the Hero. Clark, Brenda, illus. 2000. (Franklin TV-Tie In Ser.). 32p. (J). (ps-3). pap. 4.50 (978-0-439-20380-7(5)) Scholastic, Inc.

Breen, Steve. Violet the Pilot. 2008. 32p. (J). (ps). 16.99 (****978-0-8037-3125-7(6)*** , Dial) Penguin Group (USA) Inc.

Bridwell, Norman. Clifford to the Rescue. Bridwell, Norman, illus. 2002. (Clifford, the Big Red Dog Ser.). (Illus.). (J). 11.45 (978-0-7587-5005-1(6)) Book Wholesalers, Inc.

—Clifford to the Rescue. Bridwell, Norman, illus. 2000. (Clifford, the Big Red Dog Ser.). (Illus.). 32p. (J). (gr. k-2). pap. 3.99 (978-0-439-14038-6(2) , Cartwheel Bks.) Scholastic, Inc.

—Clifford to the Rescue. 2000. (ps-2). lib. bdg. 11.25 (978-0-613-24611-8(X)); (Illus.). (J). 10.30 (978-0-606-18535-6(6)) Tandem Library Bks.

Brouwer, Sigmund. Sewer Rats. 2006. 112p. (gr. 5-10). lib. bdg. 14.95 (978-1-55143-527-5(6)); (J). pap. 7.95 (978-1-55143-488-9(1)) Orca Bk. Pubs. USA.

Brown, Marc. Buster's Sugartime. 2006. (Postcards from Buster Ser.). 32p. (J). (gr. 1-4). 14.99 (978-0-316-15915-9(8)) Little Brown & Co.

Brownlow, Mike. Mickey Moonbeam. Brownlow, Mike, illus. 2006. (Illus.). 32p. (J). 16.95 (978-1-58234-704-2(2) , Bloomsbury Children) Bloomsbury Publishing.

Brubaker, Ed. Fantastic Four: Books of Doom TPB: Books of Doom TPB. 2007. (Illus.). 144p. pap. 14.99 (978-0-7851-1704-9(0)) Marvel Enterprises, Inc.

Bruchac, Joseph. Heroes & Heroines, Monsters & Magic: Native American Legends & Folktales. Burgevin, Daniel, illus. 2004. 200p. (gr. 3-7). reprint ed. pap. 12.95 (978-0-89594-995-0(4) , Crossing Pr., Inc.) Ten Speed Pr.

Buckley, James, Jr. Spider-Man's Amazing Powers. 2001. (Readers Ser.). (Illus.). 48p. (gr. 3-12). pap. 3.99 (978-0-7894-7923-5(0)) Dorling Kindersley Publishing, Inc.

Buehner, Caralyn. Superdog: The Heart of a Hero. Buehner, Mark, illus. 2004. 32p. (J). (ps-3). 16.99 (978-0-06-623620-9(7)); lib. bdg. 17.89 (978-0-06-623621-6(5)) HarperCollins Pubs.

Busiek, Kurt. The Liberty Project. 2003. 232p. (YA). pap. 11.95 (978-0-9716338-2-7(7)) About Comics.

Busiek, Kurt, et al. Avengers Assemble HC, Vol. 3. 2006. (Illus.). 424p. 34.99 (978-0-7851-2130-5(7)) Marvel Enterprises, Inc.

Cabot, Meg. All-am. 2008. 256p. (J). pap. 7.99 (****978-0-06-147989-2(6)*** , HarperTeen) HarperCollins Pubs.

—All American Girl. 2003. 416p. (YA). (gr. 7 up). pap. 6.99 (978-0-06-447277-7(9)) HarperCollins Pubs.

—All American Girl. 2002. (gr. 7-12). lib. bdg. 15.30 (978-0-613-62192-2(1)) Tandem Library Bks.

—All American Girl. l.t. ed. 2003. 354p. (J). 25.95 (978-0-7862-6102-4(1) , Large Print Pr.) Thorndike Pr.

—Ready or Not. 2nd ed. 2005. 256p. (J). (gr. 7 up). lib. bdg. 16.89 (978-0-06-072451-1(X)) HarperCollins Pubs.

Carroll, Michael. Gathering. 2008. (Quantum Prophecy Ser.). 224p. (YA). (gr. 5). 16.99 (****978-0-399-24726-2(2)*** , Philomel) Penguin Group (USA) Inc.

Catran, Ken. Voyage with Jason. 2006. 208p. (J). 16.95 (978-1-894965-43-9(4)) Simply Read Bks. CAN. *Dist:* Perseus Distribution.

Cazet, Denys. Minnie & Moo: Minnie & Moo & the Musk of Zorro. Cazet, Denys, illus. 2002. (Live Oak Readalong Ser.). (Illus.). (J). pap. 18.95 incl. audio compact disk (978-1-59112-388-0(7)) Live Oak Media.

—Minnie & Moo & the Musk of Zorro. Cazet, Denys, illus. 2002. (Minnie & Moo Ser.). (Illus.). (J). 11.49 (978-0-7587-6205-4(4)) Book Wholesalers, Inc.

—Minnie & Moo & the Musk of Zorro. Cazet, Denys, illus. 2002. (Live Oak Readalong Ser.). (Illus.). (ps-3). (J). pap. 16.95 incl. audio (978-0-87499-918-1(9)); 28.95 incl. audio compact disk (978-1-59112-589-1(8)); pap. 31.95 incl. audio compact disk (978-1-59112-588-4(X)) Live Oak Media.

—Minnie & Moo & the Musk of Zorro. 2000. (ps-2). lib. bdg. 11.80 (978-0-613-32838-8(8)); (Illus.). (J). (978-0-606-22032-3(1)) Tandem Library Bks.

Cazet, Denys & Dorling Kindersley Publishing Staff. Minnie & Moo & the Musk of Zorro. 2000. (Illus.). 48p. (J). (gr. 1-3). pap. 3.99 (978-0-7894-2653-6(6)); (gr. 5-3). 12.99 (978-0-7894-2652-9(8)) Dorling Kindersley Publishing, Inc.

Cerasini, Marc. Meet Casey Jones. 2004. (gr. k-3). lib. bdg. 11.80 (978-0-613-83490-2(9)) Tandem Library Bks.

Chapman, Andrew. Heroic Feats. 2005. (Thrillogy Ser.). (Illus.). 48p. (gr. 4-8). 17.50 (978-0-7910-8889-0(8)) Facts On File, Inc.

Children School Staff, School, illus. Kara Finds Sunshine on a Rainy Day. 2002. 37p. (J). per. 11.95 (978-0-9717790-2-0(3)) Unchained Spirit Enterprises.

Ciencin, Scott. Green Gotham. Burchett, Rick, illus. 2005. (Scholastic Reader Ser.). 40p. (J). (ps-k). pap. 3.99 (978-0-439-47102-2(8) , Cartwheel Bks.) Scholastic, Inc.

Ciencin, Scott, et al. Masters of Mayhem. 2005. (Illus.). 79p. (J). (****978-1-4156-3054-9(2)***) Disney Pr.

Citra, Becky. Jeremy & the Enchanted Theater. Milne, Jessica, illus. 2004. 64p. (J). lib. bdg. 20.00 (****978-1-4242-1258-3(8)***) Fitzgerald Bks.

Clack, Cynthia. Doodles the American Hero. 2007. (J). lib. bdg. 21.95 (****978-0-9787533-0-6(5)***) Tiger Tale Publishing Co.

Claremont, Chris. Excalibur Classic : Cross-Time Caper Book 1 TPB, Vol. 3. 2007. (Illus.). 216p. pap. 24.99 (978-0-7851-2202-9(8)) Marvel Enterprises, Inc.

—Wolverine by Claremont & Miller Premiere HC. 2007. (Illus.). 144p. 19.99 (978-0-7851-2329-3(6)) Marvel Enterprises, Inc.

Claremont, Chris & Lee. X-Men: Mutant Genesis TPB: Mutant Genesis TPB. 2nd ed. 2006. (Illus.). 184p. pap. 19.99 (978-0-7851-2212-8(5)) Marvel Enterprises, Inc.

Clark, Brenda, illus. Franklin & the Hero. 2002. (Franklin Ser.). 12.40 (978-1-4046-0309-7(3)) Book Wholesalers, Inc.

Clevenger, Lee. IncrediBoy: Be Careful What You Wish. 2004. 267p. (J). pap. 12.95 (978-0-9764052-0-7(2)) Thomas Max Publishing.

Cobot, Meg. All-American Girl. 2004. 416p. (J). (gr. 7 up). pap. 44.00 incl. audio (978-0-8072-2281-2(X) , Listening Library) Random Hse. Audio Publishing Group.

Cole, Bob. Power Reading: Chapter/Sci-Fi/Superhero. Ford, David, illus. 2004. 25p. (J). (gr. 3-4). vinyl bd. 39.95 (978-1-883186-62-3(5) , PPSF2) National Reading Styles Institute, Inc.

—Power Reading: Comic Book/Superhero. Ford, David, illus. 2005. 34p. (J). (gr. 2-4). vinyl bd. 29.95 (978-1-883186-79-1(X) , PPSFC2) National Reading Styles Institute, Inc.

Colon, Suzan. Runaway. 2003. (gr. 7-12). lib. bdg. 14.15 (978-0-613-71775-5(9)) Tandem Library Bks.

—Smallville No.9: Temptation Book. 2004. (gr. 7-12). lib. bdg. 14.15 (978-0-613-71778-6(3)) Tandem Library Bks.

Cormier, Robert. Heroes. 2006. (York Notes Ser.). 112p. pap. (978-1-4058-3559-6(1)) Pearson Education, Ltd.

—Heroes. 2000. 144p. (YA). (gr. 7-12). pap. 5.99 (978-0-440-22769-4(0) , Laurel Leaf) Random Hse. Children's Bks.

—Heroes. 2000. 135p. (YA). (gr. 7-12). lib. bdg. 13.55 (978-0-613-23622-5(X)); per. 12.15 (978-0-606-17836-5(8)) Tandem Library Bks.

—Heroes. l.t. ed. 2000. 147p. (YA). (gr. 8-12). 21.95 (978-0-7862-2909-3(8)) Thorndike Pr.

Curry, Don, ed. Spider-Man 3: Deluxe Sound Storybook. 2007. 22p. (J). 15.95 (978-0-696-23409-5(2)) Meredith Bks.

Dale, Jenny. Husky Hero. Reid, Mick, illus. 2003. 108p. (J). (978-0-439-54361-3(4)) Scholastic, Inc.

Dalmatian Press Staff. Power Rangers: Transforming Time. 2007. 24p. pap. 3.50 (****978-1-4037-3704-5(5)***) Dalmatian Pr.

—Power Rangers Carry-along Stories: 6 Storybooks in a Box! Spanish Edition. rev. ed. 2007. 144p. pap. 9.99 (****978-1-4037-3273-6(6)***) Dalmatian Pr.

D'Andrea, Deborah & Borlasca, Hector. Pretend & Play Superhero. 2005. (Illus.). (J). (****978-1-57151-751-7(0)***) Playhouse Publishing.

Danko, Dan & Mason, Tom. Sidekicks, Vol. 3. 2004. (Illus.). 112p. (J). 13.95 (978-0-316-73426-4(8)) Little Brown & Co.

—Sidekicks 6: Invasion of the Evil Teachers from Planet Buttface. 2005. 128p. (J). pap. 4.99 (978-0-316-15896-1(8)) Little Brown & Co.

David, Lawrence. The Cupcaked Crusader. Gott, Barry, illus. 2002. (Horace Splattly Ser.: Vol. 1). 144p. (J). pap. 4.99 (978-0-14-230021-3(7) , Puffin) Penguin Group (USA) Inc.

—Horace Splattly: The Cupcaked Crusader. (gr. 3-6). 2003. lib. bdg. 13.00 (978-0-613-61708-6(8)); 2002. lib. bdg. 13.00 (978-0-613-45274-8(7)); 2002. lib. bdg. 13.00 (978-0-613-45275-5(5)) Tandem Library Bks.

—To Catch a Clownosaurus. Gott, Barry, tr. Gott, Barry, illus. 2003. (Horace Splattly Ser.). 160p. (J). pap. 4.99 (978-0-14-250135-1(2) , Puffin) Penguin Group (USA) Inc.

David, Peter. Wolverine Classic, Vol. 3. 2006. (Illus.). 144p. (YA). pap. 14.99 (978-0-7851-2053-7(X)) Marvel Enterprises, Inc.

Davis, Alan, et al, illus. Excalibur Classic Vol. 2: Two-Edged Sword. 2006. 200p. pap. 24.99 (978-0-7851-2201-2(X)) Marvel Enterprises, Inc.

De Bie, Erik Scott. Ghostwalker. 2005. (Fighters Ser.). 318p. (978-1-4156-3838-5(1)) Wizards of the Coast.

DeFalco, Tom & Reader's Digest Staff. Marvel Heroes the Battle Unfolds Fold-Out Flap Book. 2007. 10p. (J). 12.99 (****978-0-7944-1306-4(4)***) Reader's Digest Assn., Inc., The.

Denton, Terry. The Wooden Cow. Denton, Terry, illus. 2003. (Storymaze Ser.: Vol. 3). (Illus.). 120p. (J). (gr. 3-5). pap. 6.95 (978-1-86508-783-2(1)) Allen & Unwin AUS. *Dist:* Independent Pubs. Group.

DiTocco, Robyn & DiTocco, Tony. The Hero Perseus: A Mad Myth Mystery. 2004. 220p. (gr. 3-12). 19.95 (978-0-9723429-0-2(7)); pap. 11.95 (978-0-9723429-1-9(5)) Brainstorm Pubns., Inc.

DK Publishing. Marvel Heroes Amazing Powers. 2008. (Dk Readers Ser.). 48p. (J). 14.99 (****978-0-7566-3495-7(4)***) Dorling Kindersley Publishing, Inc.

—Marvel Heroes Greatest Battles. 2008. (Dk Readers Ser.). 48p. (J). 14.99 (****978-0-7566-3497-1(0)***); pap. 3.99 (****978-0-7566-3496-4(2)***) Dorling Kindersley Publishing, Inc.

Dorling Kindersley Publishing Staff. Glow-in-the-Dark Marvel Heroes. 2006. (Ultimate Sticker Bks.). 16p. (J). pap. 6.99 (978-0-7566-2002-8(3)) Dorling Kindersley Publishing, Inc.

—Marvel Heroes. 2006. (Ultimate Sticker Bks.). 16p. (J). pap. 6.99 (978-0-7566-2000-4(7)) Dorling Kindersley Publishing, Inc.

Dorling Kindersley Publishing Staff & Sauders, Catherine. Marvel Heroes Amazing Powers. 2008. (Dk Readers Ser.). 48p. (J). pap. 3.99 (****978-0-7566-3494-0(6)***) Dorling Kindersley Publishing, Inc.

Dorling Kindersley Publishing Staff & Thomas, Roy. Conan: The Ultimate Guide to the World's Most Savage Barbarian. 2006. (Illus.). 160p. 24.99 (978-0-7566-2095-0(3)) Dorling Kindersley Publishing, Inc.

Douzou, Olivier & Derrien, Philippe. Super H. Douzou, Olivier, illus. 2002. (Illus.). 36p. (J). 11.95 (978-1-84059-333-4(4)) Milet Publishing.

Dower, Laura. Beat Your Greens. 2001. (gr. k-3). lib. bdg. 11.25 (978-0-613-43796-7(9)) Tandem Library Bks.

Driscoll, Laura. Real Heroes Don't Wear Capes. Wummer, Amy, illus. 2007. (Social Studies Connects). 32p. (J). (gr. k-2). pap. 4.99 (****978-1-57565-245-0(5)***) Kane Pr., The.

Eaton, Maxwell. Superheroes. 2007. (Adventures of Max & Pinky Ser.). 32p. (J). (gr. k-3). lib. bdg. 15.99 (****978-0-375-93805-4(2)*** , Knopf Bks. for Young Readers) Random Hse. Children's Bks.

Ebon Research Systems Staff. Dare to Be: Roberto Clemente. l.t. ed. 2003. Tr. of Atrevete a Ser un Heroe. . . Roberto Clemente. (ENG & SPA., Illus.). 22p. 3.99 (978-0-9648313-5-3(X)) Ebon Research Systems Publishing, LLC.

—Dare to Be Vol. 2: Lessons in the Life of Esperanza. l.t. ed. 2003. Tr. of Atrevete Ser... Un Heroe. (ENG & SPA., Illus.). 16p. (J). 3.99 (978-0-9648313-4-6(1)) Ebon Research Systems Publishing, LLC.

Egan, Kate. Spider-Man 2: Hands off, Doc Ock! Mones, Isidre et al, illus. 2004. (Spider-Man Ser.). 24p. (J). (ps-2). pap. 3.99 (978-0-06-057138-2(1) , Harper Festival) HarperCollins Pubs.

Faerber, Jay, et al. Captain Universe Universal Heroes. 2006. (Illus.). 136p. (YA). pap. 13.99 (978-0-7851-1857-2(8)) Marvel Enterprises, Inc.

Farshtey, Greg. Downfall. 2008. (Bionicle Legends Ser.: No. 8). 128p. (J). pap. 4.99 (****978-0-439-89037-3(3)*** Scholastic, Inc.

—Prisoners of the Pit. 2007. (Bionicle Legends Ser.: No. 7). 144p. (J). pap. 4.99 (****978-0-439-89034-2(9)***) Scholastic, Inc.

—Shadows in the Sky. 2008. (Bionicle Legends Ser.). 128p. (J). 4.99 (****978-0-439-91641-7(0)*** , Scholastic) Scholastic, Inc.

—Time Trap. 2005. 137p. (J). (****978-1-4156-3150-8(6)***) Scholastic, Inc.

Farshtey, Greg. Web of Shadows. 2005. 139p. (J). (978-1-4156-0699-5(4)) Scholastic, Inc.

Federation of Children's Book Groups, contrib. by. Heroes & Villains. 2002. (Illus.). 208p. pap. 8.99 (978-0-340-85398-6(0) , Hodder & Stoughton) Hodder General Publishing Division GBR. *Dist:* Trafalgar Square Publishing.

Fisch, Sholly. No Place Like Home. 2000. (gr. k-3). lib. bdg. 10.95 (978-0-613-32901-9(5)) Tandem Library Bks.

Flanagan, John. The Burning Bridge. 2007. (Ranger's Apprentice Ser.: Bk. 2). 288p. (J). (gr. 5 up). pap. 7.99 (978-0-14-240842-1(5) , Puffin) Penguin Group (USA) Inc.

—The Icebound Land. (Ranger's Apprentice Ser.: Bk. 3). (J). (gr. 5). 2008. 288p. 7.99 (****978-0-14-241075-2(6)*** , Puffin); 2007. 260p. 16.99 (978-0-399-24456-8(5) , Philomel) Penguin Group (USA) Inc.

Flanagan, John. The Ruins of Gorlan. 2006. (Ranger's Apprentice Ser.: Bk. 1). 272p. (J). (gr. 5). pap. 6.99 (978-0-14-240663-2(5) , Puffin) Penguin Group (USA) Inc.

Fogg, K. L. Serpent Tide. 2006. 16.95 (978-1-59156-861-2(7)) Covenant Communications, Inc.

Fox, Gardner. The Atom - Archives, Vol. 2. rev. ed. 2003. (Illus.). 216p. 49.95 (978-1-4012-0014-5(1)) DC Comics.

Friesen, Ray. Lookit! A Cheese Related Mishap Vol. 1: And Other Stories. 2006. 96p. pap. 8.95 (978-0-9728177-6-9(X)) Don't Eat Any Bugs Prodns.

Fuqua, Jonathon Scott. Willoughby Spit Wonder. 2004. (Illus.). 160p. (J). (gr. 5-8). 15.99 (978-0-7636-1776-9(8)) Candlewick Pr.

Gaffney, Sean. Larryboy & the Emperor of Envy. 2002. (Big Idea Books). (Illus.). 96p. pap. 4.99 (978-0-310-70467-6(7)) Zonderkidz.

Gaiman, Neil. Marvel 1602 TPB (Quill Award Edition) 2006. (Illus.). 248p. (YA). pap. 19.99 (978-0-7851-2311-8(3)) Marvel Enterprises, Inc.

Garza, Xavier. Lucha Libre: The Man in the Silver Mask. Garza, Xavier, illus. 2007. (SPA.). 40p. (J). pap. 8.95 (****978-1-933693-10-1(X)***) Cinco Puntos Pr.

—Lucha Libre: The Man in the Silver Mask. Crosthwaite, Luis Humberto, tr. 2005. (ENG & SPA., Illus.). 40p. (gr. 2-5). 17.95 (978-0-938317-92-0(X)) Cinco Puntos Pr.

Gerber, Steve, et al. Omega: The Unknown Classic. 2005. (Illus.). 224p. (YA). pap. 29.99 (978-0-7851-2009-4(2)) Marvel Enterprises, Inc.

Gerver, Jane E. The Santa Snatcher. Spaziante, Patrick, illus. 2004. 32p. (J). lib. bdg. 15.00 (****978-1-4242-0959-0(5)***) Fitzgerald Bks.

—The Santa Snatcher. 2004. (Ready-to-Read Ser.). 32p. (J). pap. 3.99 (978-0-689-87018-7(3) , Simon Spotlight) Simon & Schuster Children's Publishing.

Godwin, Jane. Falling from Grace. 2007. 204p. (YA). (gr. 6 up). 16.95 (****978-0-8234-2105-3(8)***) Holiday Hse., Inc.

Golden Books Staff. The Christmas Hero. 2007. 16p. (J). pap. 0.38 (****978-0-375-84432-4(5)*** , Golden Bks.) Random Hse., Inc.

Graham, Bob. Max. 2002. (gr. k-3). lib. bdg. 14.15 (978-0-613-56517-2(7)) Tandem Library Bks.

Gray, Margaret. The Lovesick Salesman. Cecil, Randy, illus. rev. ed. 2004. 192p. (J). 16.95 (978-0-8050-7558-8(5) , Holt, Henry & Co. Bks. For Young Readers) Holt, Henry & Co.

Greco, Francesca. Gideon. 2002. (Illus.). 40p. (J). 16.95 (978-1-932065-02-2(4)) Star Bright Bks., Inc.

Greene, Daryl C. Benjamin's Dog Joseph: A Three Legged Hero. Akers-Bell, Mary, illus. 2003. 48p. (J). (gr. 2-4). pap. 9.95 (978-0-9700827-4-9(6)); lib. bdg. 17.95 (978-0-9700827-5-6(4)) Densmore-Reid Pubns.

Gruenwald, Mark, et al. Squadron Supreme: Death of a Universe. 2006. (Illus.). 240p. (YA). pap. 24.99 (978-0-7851-2091-9(2)) Marvel Enterprises, Inc.

Gutman, Dan. Funny Boy Meets the Airsick Alien from Andromeda. Dykes, John, illus. 3rd rev. ed. 1999. (L.A.F. Ser.: No. 3). 128p. (gr. 2-6). pap. 3.99 (978-0-7868-1330-8(X)) Hyperion Pr.

—Funny Boy Meets the Airsick Alien from Andromeda. 1999. (gr. 3-6). lib. bdg. 11.80 (978-0-613-21571-8(0)) Tandem Library Bks.

—Funny Boy Takes on the Chit-Chatting Cheese from Chattanooga. 2001. (L.A.F. Bks.). (Illus.). 128p. (gr. 2-6). pap. 4.99 (978-0-7868-1445-9(4)) Disney Pr.

—Funny Boy Takes on the Chit-Chatting Cheese from Chattanooga. 2000. (gr. 3-6). lib. bdg. 13.00 (978-0-613-31228-8(7)) Tandem Library Bks.

Hale, Bruce. Pirates of Underwhere. Hillman, Shane, illus. 2008. (Underwhere Ser.). 160p. (J). 15.99 (****978-0-06-085127-9(9)***); lib. bdg. 16.89 (****978-0-06-085128-6(7)***) HarperCollins Pubs.

—Prince of Underwhere. Hillman, Shane, illus. 2008. (Underwhere Ser.). 176p. (J). lib. bdg. 16.89 (****978-0-06-085125-5(2)***); (gr. 3-7). 15.99 (****978-0-06-085124-8(4)***) HarperCollins Pubs.

Hamilton, John. Defending the Nation, 8 vols., Set. Incl. Army. lib. bdg. 22.78 (978-1-59679-754-3(1)); CIA. lib. bdg. 22.78 (978-1-59679-756-7(8)); Coast Guard.

lib. bdg. 22.78 (978-1-59679-755-0(X)); FBI. lib. bdg. 22.78 (978-1-59679-757-4(6) , Checkerboard Library); Marine Corps. lib. bdg. 22.78 (978-1-59679-758-1(4) , Checkerboard Library); Navy. lib. bdg. 22.78 (978-1-59679-760-4(6) , Checkerboard Library); Special Forces. lib. bdg. 22.78 (978-1-59679-759-8(2) , Checkerboard Library); (Illus.). 32p. (J). (gr. 3-5). 2007. Set lib. bdg. 182.24 (*978-1-59679-752-9(5) , Checkerboard Library) ABDO Publishing Co.

Hands, Cynthia. Townsville's Super Trio. 2001. 32p. (J). (ps-2). pap. 3.99 (978-0-307-10495-3(8) , Golden Bks.) Random Hse. Children's Bks.

Hannan, Peter. Attack of the 50-Foot Alien Creep-Oids! Hannan, Peter, illus. 2007. (Super Goofballs Ser.: Bk. 4). 144p. (J). (gr. 2-6). pap. 4.99 (*978-0-06-085217-7(8) , Harper Trophy) HarperCollins Pubs.

—Goofballs in Paradise. Hannan, Peter, illus. 2007. (Super Goofballs Ser.: Bk. 2). (Illus.). 128p. (J). (gr. 2-6). pap. 4.99 (978-0-06-085213-9(5) , Harper Trophy) HarperCollins Pubs.

—Super Goofballs, Book 5: Doomed in Dreamland. Hannan, Peter, illus. 2008. (Super Goofballs Ser.). 144p. (J). pap. 4.99 (*978-0-06-085219-1(4) , Harper Trophy) HarperCollins Pubs.

—Super Underwear... & Beyond! Hannan, Peter, illus. 2007. (Super Goofballs Ser.). 160p. (J). pap. 4.99 (*978-0-06-085215-3(1) , Harper Trophy) HarperCollins Pubs.

Hannan, Peter. That Stinking Feeling. Hannan, Peter, illus. 2007. (Super Goofballs Ser.: Bk.1). (Illus.). 160p. (J). (gr. 2-6). pap. 4.99 (978-0-06-085211-5(9) , Harper Trophy) HarperCollins Pubs.

Hapka, Cathy, adapted by. Fantastic 4: The Movie Storybook. 2005. (Illus.). 48p. (J). (*978-1-4156-0389-5(8)) HarperCollins Pubs.

Harper, Benjamin. Battling the Bad Guys: Storybook & Dvd. 2006. (Marvel Heroes Ser.). (Illus.). 32p. (J). bds. 17.99 (978-0-7944-1136-7(3)) Reader's Digest Assn., Inc., The.

Harper, Benjamin. TMNT Underground Art Studio. 2007. (Teenage Mutant Ninja Turtles Ser.). (Illus.). 48p. (J). (ps-3). 9.99 (*978-1-4169-3856-9(7) , Simon Scribbles) Simon & Schuster Children's Publishing.

Harper, Charise Mericle. Fashion Kitty. 2005. (Illus.). 96p. (gr. 3-7). pap. 8.99 (978-0-7868-5134-8(1)) Hyperion Pr.

Heide, Iris van der. A Strange Day. Cate, Marijke Ten, illus. 2007. 32p. (J). 16.95 (*978-1-932425-94-9(2) , Lemniscaat) Boyds Mills Pr.

Heinberg, Allan. Family Matters. 2006. (Young Avengers Ser.: Vol. 2). (Illus.). 184p. (YA). 22.99 (978-0-7851-2021-6(1)) Marvel Enterprises, Inc.

Hero in My Eyes. 2006. (J). bds. 21.95 (*978-0-9745191-2-8(X)) Lynn Tyner Mitchum & James Rogers.

Heroes. ldr.'s ed. 1998. (Cross Training Ser.: Vol. 4). 72p. (YA). (gr. 7-9). pap. 15.00 incl. VHS (978-1-57405-029-5(X)) CharismaLife Pubs.

Heroes in Training. 2003. (J). per. (978-1-57657-823-0(2)) Paradise Pr., Inc.

Herrera, Juan Felipe. Super Cilantro Girl / La Supernina del Cilantro. Robledo Tapia, Honorio, illus. 2003. (ENG & SPA.). 32p. (J). 16.95 (978-0-89239-187-5(1)) Children's Bk. Pr.

Hinkes, Enid. Police Cat. Rasmussen, Wendy, illus. 2005. 32p. (J). (gr. k-3). 15.95 (978-0-8075-5758-7(7)) Whitman, Albert & Co.

Holm, Jennifer L. & Holm, Matthew. Our Hero. 2005. (Babymouse Ser.). (Illus.). 96p. (J). (gr. 2-5). pap. 5.95 (978-0-375-83230-7(0)); lib. bdg. 12.99 (978-0-375-93230-4(5)) Random Hse. Children's Bks. (Random Hse. Bks. for Young Readers).

Howe, James. The Odorous Adventures of Stinky Dog. Helquist, Brett, illus. 2003. (Tales from the House of Bunnicula Ser.). 112p. (J). bds. 9.95 (978-0-689-85633-4(4) , Atheneum) Simon & Schuster Children's Publishing.

Howe, Norma. The Adventures of Blue Avenger. 2000. 229p. (YA). (gr. 7-12). lib. bdg. 15.30 (978-0-613-29862-9(4)); 1999. (J). 13.64 (978-0-606-20028-8(2)) Tandem Library Bks.

Hulk the Hero. 2003. (J). per. (978-1-57657-821-6(6)) Paradise Pr., Inc.

Hulk's Big Mess. 2003. (J). per. (978-1-57657-822-3(4)) Paradise Pr., Inc.

Iliad. 1999. (YA). 9.95 (978-1-56137-752-7(X)) Novel Units, Inc.

Jacques, Brian. The Angel's Command. Elliot, David, illus. 2003. (Castaways of the Flying Dutchman Ser.: No. 2). 384p. (J). (gr. 5-6). 23.99 (978-0-399-23999-1(5) , Philomel) Penguin Group (USA) Inc.

—Castaways of the Flying Dutchman. Schoenherr, Ian, illus. 2001. (Castaways of the Flying Dutchman Ser.: No. 1). 1p. (J). (gr. 4-7). 23.99 (978-0-399-23601-3(5) , Philomel) Penguin Group (USA) Inc.

James, B. J., et al. Supertwins Meet the Dangerous Dino-Robots, No. 3. Demarest, Chris L., illus. 2003. (Scholastic Reader Ser.). 32p. (J). pap. 3.99 (978-0-439-46625-7(3) , Cartwheel Bks.) Scholastic, Inc.

Jeremiatt, Omani. Paper Boy. Rollins, Bernic, illus. 2003. 40p. (J). (gr. 6-8). pap. 10.00 (978-1-929188-09-3(9)) Morton Bks.

Jolley, Dan. Iron Man: The Movie Storybook. 2008. (Iron Man Ser.). 256p. (J). 6.99 (*978-0-06-082198-2(1) , Harper Entertainment) HarperCollins Pubs.

Jones, Brian and Brad. The Righteous Heroes. 2005. 36p. pap. 13.99 (978-1-4116-5423-5(4)) Lulu.com.

Jones, Bruce. Captain America Legends: What Price Glory. Rude, Steve, illus. 2003. (Captain America Ser.). 96p. (YA). pap. 9.99 (978-0-7851-1227-3(8)) Marvel Enterprises, Inc.

Katula, Bob. Larryboy & the Awful Ear Wacks Attacks. Kenney, Cindy, ed. 2002. (Big Idea Bks.). (Illus.). 96p. pap. 4.99 (978-0-310-70468-3(5)) Zonderkidz.

Kavanagh, Terry. Batman: Tell-A-Riddle Telephone Book. Doescher, Erik et al, illus. 2002. (J). (978-0-7853-6402-3(1)) Publications International, Ltd.

Kelly, Kc. Action Adventures: Magnetic Book & Playset. 2006. (Marvel Heroes Ser.). (Illus.). 16p. (J). bds. 14.99 (978-0-7944-1134-3(7)) Reader's Digest Assn., Inc., The.

Kirby, Jack. Black Panther by Jack Kirby Volume 2 TPB, Vol. 2. 2006. (Illus.). 112p. pap. 19.99 (978-0-7851-2069-8(6)) Marvel Enterprises, Inc.

Kirk, David. Captain Sunny Patch. 2006. (Illus.). 32p. (J). (*978-1-4156-8868-7(0)); (*978-0-448-44515-1(8)) Callaway Editions, Inc.

Kirkman, Robert. Marvel Zombies HC (Spider-Man Cover) 2006. (Illus.). 136p. 19.99 (*978-0-7851-2608-9(2)) Marvel Enterprises, Inc.

Kliebenstein, Shane & McCracken, Craig. The Powerpuff Girls Telephone Book. 2002. (Illus.). (J). (978-0-7853-6400-9(5)) Publications International, Ltd.

Knife & Packer. Captain Fact: Space Adventure. 2004. (Illus.). 103p. (J). (*978-1-4156-0561-5(0)) Hyperion Bks. for Children.

Kroll, Virginia L. Especially Heroes. Ladwig, Tim, illus. 2004. 32p. (J). 16.00 (978-0-8028-5221-2(1)) Eerdmans, William B. Publishing Co.

Kurumada, Masami. Knights of the Zodiac, Vol. 17. 2006. (Knights of the Zodiac Ser.). 208p. (YA). pap. 7.95 (978-1-4215-0660-9(2)) Viz Media.

Lee, Ingrid. The True Story of George. Denis, Stephane, illus. 2004. 62p. (J). lib. bdg. 20.00 (*978-1-4242-1262-0(6)) Fitzgerald Bks.

Lee, Stan. Superhero Christmas. Jessell, Tim, illus. 2004. 32p. (J). (ps-2). 16.89 (978-0-06-056560-2(8)) HarperCollins Pubs.

Lee, Stan, et al. John Buscema. 2007. (Marvel Visionaries Ser.). (Illus.). 368p. 34.99 (978-0-7851-2161-9(7)) Marvel Enterprises, Inc.

Lennon, Joan. Questors. 2007. 368p. (J). (gr. 5-9). 16.99 (*978-1-4169-3658-9(0) , McElderry, Margaret K.) Simon & Schuster Children's Publishing.

Lethcoe, Jason. Amazing Adventures from Zoom's Academy: The Capture of the Crimson Cape. 2006. (Illus.). 144p. (J). pap. 12.95 (978-0-345-48356-0(1) , Ballantine Bks.) Random House Publishing Group.

—Zoom's Academy. 2006. (Illus.). 304p. (J). pap. 14.95 (978-0-345-49641-6(8) , Ballantine Bks.) Random House Publishing Group.

Linhart, Sandra Miller. What Does a Hero Look Like? 2007. 44p. (J). pap. 16.99 (978-1-59092-576-8(9) , Little Blue Works) Windstorm Creative.

Lovhaug, Lewis J. Angel Armor: Just a Boy. 2003. 224p. (YA). pap. 15.95 (978-0-595-28475-7(2)) iUniverse, Inc.

Mabie, Hamilton Wright. Heroes Every Child Should Know. 2005. 368p. pap. 15.95 (978-1-59540-641-5(7) , 1st World Library - Literary Society) 1st World Publishing, Inc.

—Heroes Every Child Should Know. 2006. 268p. pap. 13.99 (978-1-4264-1392-6(0)); 258p. pap. 16.99 (978-1-4264-1445-9(5)) BiblioBazaar.

—Heroes Every Child Should Know. 2004. reprint ed. pap. 26.95 (978-1-4191-2360-3(2)); pap. 1.99 (978-1-4192-2360-0(7)) Kessinger Publishing, LLC.

MacDonald, Ross. Another Perfect Day. MacDonald, Ross, illus. rev. ed. 2002. (Illus.). 32p. (J). (ps-3). 15.95 (978-0-7613-1595-7(0)) Roaring Brook Pr.

—Bad Baby. MacDonald, Ross, illus. 2005. (Illus.). 32p. (J). 16.95 (978-1-59643-064-8(8)) Roaring Brook Pr.

MacPhail, Catherine. Dark Waters. 2005. 176p. (YA). pap. 6.95 (978-1-58234-986-2(X)); 2003. 177p. (J). (gr. 5 up). 15.95 (978-1-58234-846-9(4)) Bloomsbury Publishing. (Bloomsbury Children).

Mantlo, Bill, et al. Champions Classic, Vol. 2. 2007. (Illus.). 216p. pap. 19.99 (978-0-7851-2098-8(X)) Marvel Enterprises, Inc.

Mason, Tom & Danko, Dan. The Ultimate Pocket Guide. 2007. (Avatar Ser.). 48p. (J). pap. 3.99 (*978-1-4169-4736-3(1) , Simon Spotlight) Simon & Schuster Children's Publishing.

Mazer, Harry. Heroes Don't Run: A Novel of the Pacific War. 2007. 128p. (J). pap. 5.99 (978-1-4169-3394-6(8) , Aladdin) Simon & Schuster Children's Publishing.

McAvennie, Mike. Batmobile Owner's Manual. Chasemore, Richard & Su, E. J., illus. 2008. 32p. (J). (gr. 5-12). 24.99 (*978-0-7566-3839-9(9)) Dorling Kindersley Publishing, Inc.

McCaughrean, Geraldine, retold by. Odysseus. 2004. (Heroes Ser.). (Illus.). 128p. (J). 15.95 (978-0-8126-2721-3(0)) Cricket Bks.

McClements, George. Baron Von Baddie Wins. 2008. (J). (*978-0-15-206138-8(X)) Harcourt Trade Pubs.

McCorkle, Mark & Schooley, Bob. Grudge Match. 2005. (Illus.). 80p. (J). (978-1-4155-9100-0(8)) Disney Pr.

McLeod, Bob. SuperHero ABC. McLeod, Bob, illus. 2006. (Illus.). 40p. (J). (ps-1). 16.99 (978-0-06-074514-1(2)); lib. bdg. 16.89 (978-0-06-074515-8(0)) HarperCollins Pubs.

McMullan, Kate & Lemaitre, Pascal. Supercat. 2002. (Illus.). 32p. (J). (ps). bds. 6.95 (978-0-7611-2644-7(9) , 12644) Workman Publishing Co., Inc.

Meredith, Randy. Marvel Puzzle Peril. 2007. (Illus.). 10p. (J). (gr. 1-5). ring bd. 9.95 (*978-1-57791-377-1(9)) Brighter Minds Children's Publishing.

—My First Marvel Super Hero Factbook. 2006. (Marvel Ser.). 5p. (J). bds. 8.95 (*978-1-57791-298-9(5)) Brighter Minds Children's Publishing.

Millar, Mark. Ultimate X-Men: The Tomorrow People. 2002. (gr. 5-8). lib. bdg. 24.55 (978-0-613-53690-5(8)) Tandem Library Bks.

Miller, William. Joe Louis, My Champion. Pate, Rodney, tr. Pate, Rodney, illus. 2004. 32p. (J). 16.95 (978-1-58430-161-5(9)) Lee & Low Bks., Inc.

Montoya, Martha, creator. Mi heroe Favorito: Take-Home. 2005. (Los Kitos Ser.). (SPA.). (YA). (gr. 1-3). 15.00 (978-0-8215-8811-6(7)) Sadlier, William H. Inc.

Morpurgo, Michael. Jo-Jo the Melon Donkey. Kerins, Tony, illus. 2002. (Yellow Bananas Ser.). 48p. (J). (gr. 3-4). pap. (978-0-7787-0988-6(4)); lib. bdg. (978-0-7787-0942-8(6)) Crabtree Publishing Co.

Morris, Deborah. Teens 911: Snowbound. 2002. (Illus.). 250p. (YA). pap. 12.95 (978-0-7573-0039-4(1) , HCI Teens) Health Communications, Inc.

Murphy, Stephen, et al. The Secret. S. I. International Staff & Ostrom, Bob, illus. 2004. (Teenage Mutant Ninja Turtles Ser.). 32p. (J). pap. 3.99 (978-0-689-86965-5(7) , Simon Spotlight) Simon & Schuster Children's Publishing.

Murphy, Steve. Look Out! It's Turtle Titan! Spaziante, Patrick, illus. 2004. (Teenage Mutant Ninja Turtles Ser.). 24p. (J). pap. 3.99 (978-0-689-86900-6(2) , Simon Spotlight) Simon & Schuster Children's Publishing.

—Look Out! It's Turtle Titan! 2004. (gr. k-3). lib. bdg. 11.80 (978-0-613-83491-9(7)) Tandem Library Bks.

Nakagawa, Hirotaka. Sumo Boy. Hasegawa, Yoshifumi, illus. 2006. 40p. (J). (ps-k). 15.99 (978-0-7868-3635-2(0)) Hyperion Pr.

O'Connor, Ilett. He Man. Kahn, Alisha, illus. Wells, Wadell, photos by. 2002. 24p. (J). pap. 10.00 (978-0-9717003-3-8(8)) O'Connor, Ilett K.

Oeming, Michael Avon. Thor: Blood Oath HC: Blood Oath HC. 2006. (Illus.). 144p. 19.99 (978-0-7851-2274-6(5)) Marvel Enterprises, Inc.

O'Malley, Kevin. Captain Raptor & the Moon Mystery. O'Brien, Patrick, illus. 2005. 32p. (J). 17.85 (978-0-8027-8936-5(6)); 16.95 (978-0-8027-8935-8(8)) Walker & Co.

Ostrom, Bob, illus. Spider-Man 2: Hurry up, Spider-Man! 2004. (Spider-Man Ser.). 24p. (J). (ps-2). pap. 3.99 (978-0-06-057137-5(3) , Harper Festival) HarperCollins Pubs.

O'Toole, Katherine. A Time for Heroes. Wise, Noreen, ed. Favazza, Keith, illus. 2001. (Lemonade Collection). 208p. (YA). (gr. 5 up). pap. 15.50 (978-1-58584-275-9(3)) Huckleberry Pr.

Owens, Vivian W. How Oswa Came to Own All Music: The Legend of Oswa. Owens, April U., ed. Owens, John D., III, illus. 2000. 84p. (YA). 16.95 (978-0-9623839-9-1(6)) Eschar Pubns.

Parker, Jeff. Come Out & Fight Like a (Molecule) Man. 2007. (Fantastic Four Set II Ser.). 24p. (J). (gr. 2-6). 21.35 (*978-1-59961-388-8(3)) Spotlight.

—Doom, Where's My Car?! 2007. (Fantastic Four Set II Ser.). 24p. (J). (gr. 2-6). 21.35 (*978-1-59961-389-5(1)) Spotlight.

—Finding Zemo. 2007. (Avengers Ser.). 24p. (J). (gr. 2-6). 21.35 (*978-1-59961-383-3(2)) Spotlight.

—Law of the Jungle. 2007. (Fantastic Four Set II Ser.). 24p. (J). (gr. 2-6). 21.35 (*978-1-59961-390-1(5)) Spotlight.

Pass, Erica. Big SuperHero Wish! Goldberg, Barry, illus. ed. 2005. (Fairly Odd Parents Ser.: 6). 24p. (J). lib. bdg. 15.00 (978-1-59054-801-1(9)) Fitzgerald Bks.

Pattou, Edith. Hero's Song: The First Song of the Eirren. 1998. 12.65 (978-0-606-13479-8(4)) Tandem Library Bks.

Paulsen, Gary. The White Fox Chronicles. 2002. (gr. 5-8). lib. bdg. 13.55 (978-0-613-67131-6(7)) Tandem Library Bks.

Peek-a-Boo, Hulk. 2003. (J). per. (978-1-57657-816-2(X)) Paradise Pr., Inc.

Peterson, Doug. LarryBoy & the Mudslingers. Big Idea Design Staff, illus. 2006. (Big Idea Books). 32p. (J). 9.99 (978-0-310-71149-0(5)) Zonderkidz.

—Larryboy Versus the Volcano. 2004. (Illus.). 96p. pap. 4.99 (978-0-310-70728-8(5)) Zonderkidz.

Peterson, Scott. Batman Beyond: Hear No Evil. Delaney, John, illus. 2002. (Pictureback(R) Ser.). 24p. (J). (ps-3). 3.99 (978-0-375-80654-4(7) , Random Hse. Bks. for Young Readers) Random Hse. Children's Bks.

—New Hero in Town. 2000. (gr. k-3). lib. bdg. 10.95 (978-0-613-32879-1(5)) Tandem Library Bks.

Pilkey, Dav. The Adventures of Captain Underpants. An Epic Novel. 2004. (Captain Underpants Ser.: No. 1). (J). lib. bdg. 19.95 (978-0-439-68434-7(X) , Scholastic, Inc.) Scholastic, Inc.

—The Adventures of Super Diaper Baby. 2004. (J). lib. bdg. 19.95 (978-0-439-68435-4(8) , Scholastic, Inc.) Scholastic, Inc.

—The Adventures of Super Diaper Baby. Pilkey, Dav, illus. 2002. (Captain Underpants Ser.). (Illus.). 128p. (J). (gr. 2-5). pap. 16.95 (978-0-439-37605-1(X) , Blue Sky Pr., The) Scholastic, Inc.

—Las Aventuras del Capitan Calzoncillos. 2001. (Captain Underpants Ser.: No. 1). (SPA.). (gr. 3-6). lib. bdg. 13.00 (978-0-613-54408-5(0)) Tandem Library Bks.

—El Capitan Calzoncillos la Ridicula Historia De. 2008. 176p. (J). pap. 4.99 (*978-0-545-02583-6(4) , Scholastic en Espanol) Scholastic, Inc.

—El Capitan Calzoncillos y la Furia de la Supermujer Macroelastica. 2003. (Captain Underpants Ser.). (SPA., Illus.). 176p. (J). (gr. 2-5). pap. 4.99 (978-0-439-53820-6(3) , Scholastic en Espanol) Scholastic, Inc.

—Captain Underpants & the Attack of the Talking Toilets. (Captain Underpants Ser.: No. 2). (J). 2004. lib. bdg. 19.95 (978-0-439-68436-1(6) , Scholastic, Inc.); 1999. (Illus.). 144p. (gr. 2-5). pap. 16.95 (978-0-590-63136-5(5) , Blue Sky Pr., The) Scholastic, Inc.

—Captain Underpants & the Attack of the Talking Toilets. Pilkey, Dav, illus. 1999. (Captain Underpants Ser.: No. 2). (Illus.). 144p. (J). (gr. 2-5). pap. 4.99 (978-0-590-63427-4(5)) Scholastic, Inc.

—Captain Underpants & the Attack of the Talking Toilets. collector's ed. 2007. 144p. (J). pap. 9.99 (*978-0-545-02727-4(6)) Scholastic, Inc.

—Captain Underpants & the Attack of the Talking Toilets. 1999. (Captain Underpants Ser.: No. 2). (Illus.). (J). (gr. 2-5). 11.64 (978-0-606-15830-5(8)); (gr. 3-6). lib. bdg. 13.00 (978-0-613-11382-3(9)) Tandem Library Bks.

—Captain Underpants & the Big, Bad Battle of the Bionic Booger Boy Pt. 1: The Night of the Nasty Nostril Nuggets. 2004. (Captain Underpants Ser.: Bk. 6). (J). lib. bdg. 19.95 (978-0-439-68438-5(2) , Scholastic, Inc.) Scholastic, Inc.

—Captain Underpants & the Big, Bad Battle of the Bionic Booger Boy Pt. 1: The Night of the Nasty Nostril Nuggets. Pilkey, Dav, illus. 2003. (Captain Underpants Ser.: Bk. 6). (Illus.). 176p. (J). 4.99 (978-0-439-37610-5(6) , Blue Sky Pr., The) Scholastic, Inc.

—Captain Underpants & the Big, Bad Battle of the Bionic Booger Boy Pt. 1: The Night of the Nasty Nostril Nuggets. 2003. (Captain Underpants Ser.: Bk. 6). (gr. 3-6). lib. bdg. 13.00 (978-0-613-68836-9(8)) Tandem Library Bks.

—Captain Underpants & the Big, Bad Battle of the Bionic Booger Boy Pt. 2: The Revenge of the Ridiculous Robo-Boogers. 2004. (Captain Underpants Ser.: Bk. 7). (J). lib. bdg. 19.95 (978-0-439-68437-8(4) , Scholastic, Inc.) Scholastic, Inc.

—Captain Underpants & the Big, Bad Battle of the Bionic Booger Boy Pt. 2: The Revenge of the Ridiculous Robo-Boogers. Pilkey, Dav, illus. 2003. (Captain Underpants Ser.). (Illus.). 176p. (J). (gr. 3-6). 4.99 (978-0-439-37612-9(2)); pap. 16.95 (978-0-439-37611-2(4)) Scholastic, Inc. (Blue Sky Pr., The).

—Captain Underpants & the Big, Bad Battle of the Bionic Booger Boy Pt. 2: The Revenge of the Ridiculous Robo-Boogers. 2003. (Captain Underpants Ser.: Bk. 7). lib. bdg. 13.00 (978-0-613-68837-6(6)) Tandem Library Bks.

—Captain Underpants & the Invasion of the Incredibly Naughty Cafeteria Ladies from Outer Space: And the Subsequent Assault of the Equally Evil Lunchroom Zombie Nerds. 2004. (Captain Underpants Ser.: No. 3). (J). lib. bdg. 19.95 (978-0-439-68439-2(0) , Scholastic, Inc.) Scholastic, Inc.

—Captain Underpants & the Invasion of the Incredibly Naughty Cafeteria Ladies from Outer Space: And the Subsequent Assault of the Equally Evil Lunchroom Zombie Nerds. Pilkey, Dav, illus. 1999. (Captain Underpants Ser.: No. 3). (Illus.). 144p. (J). (gr. 2-5). 4.99 (978-0-439-04996-2(2) , Blue Sky Pr., The) Scholastic, Inc.

—Captain Underpants & the Invasion of the Incredibly Naughty Cafeteria Ladies from Outer Space: And the Subsequent Assault of the Equally Evil Lunchroom Zombie Nerds. 1999. (Captain Underpants Ser.: No. 3). (Illus.). 134p. (J). (gr. 2-5). pap. 16.95 (978-0-439-04995-5(4) , Blue Sky Pr., The) Scholastic, Inc.

—Captain Underpants & the Invasion of the Incredibly Naughty Cafeteria Ladies from Outer Space: And the Subsequent Assault of the Equally Evil Lunchroom Zombie Nerds. 1999. (Captain Underpants Ser.: No. 3). (gr. 3-6). lib. bdg. 13.00 (978-0-613-17900-3(5)) Tandem Library Bks.

—Captain Underpants & the Perilous Plot of Professor Poopypants. 2004. (Captain Underpants Ser.: No. 4). (J). lib. bdg. 19.95 (978-0-439-68440-8(4) , Scholastic, Inc.) Scholastic, Inc.

—Captain Underpants & the Perilous Plot of Professor Poopypants. Pilkey, Dav, illus. 2000. (Captain Underpants Ser.: No. 4). (Illus.). 160p. (J). (gr. 2-5). pap. 4.99 (978-0-439-04998-6(9)); pap. 16.95 (978-0-439-04997-9(0)) Scholastic, Inc. (Blue Sky Pr., The).

—Captain Underpants & the Perilous Plot of Professor Poopypants. 2000. (Captain Underpants Ser.: No. 4). (gr. 3-6). lib. bdg. 13.00 (978-0-613-21289-2(4)); (Illus.). (J). (gr. 2-5). 11.64 (978-0-606-18526-4(7)) Tandem Library Bks.

—Captain Underpants & the Preposterous Plight of the Purple Potty People. 2006. 176p. (J). 19.99 (978-0-439-90381-3(5) , Blue Sky Pr., The) Scholastic, Inc.

—Captain Underpants Books 1-4 Boxset. 2007. (J). pap. 19.96 (*978-0-545-02287-3(8) , Blue Sky Pr., The) Scholastic, Inc.

—The First Captain Underpants Collection: Captain Underpants & the Perilous Plot of Professor Poopypants; Captain Underpants & the Invasion of the Incredibly Naughty Cafeteria Ladies from Outer Space; Captain Underpants & the Attack of the Talking Toilets; The Adventures of Captain Underpants. 2004. (Captain Underpants Ser.). (Illus.). (J). 19.96 (978-0-439-69862-7(6)) Scholastic, Inc.

—Mighty Robot vs. the Uranium Unicorns from Uranus. Ontiveros, Martin, illus. 2005. (Ricky Ricotta Ser.: Bk. 7). 128p. (J). pap. 16.99 (978-0-439-37646-4(7) , Blue Sky Pr., The) Scholastic, Inc.

—Ricky Ricotta Y el Poderoso Robot Contra Los Mecamonos de Marte. 2007. (Ricky Ricotta Ser.: No. 4). 144p. (J). pap. 3.99 (978-0-439-85105-3(X) , Scholastic en Espanol) Scholastic, Inc.

—Ricky Ricotta Y el Poderoso Robot Contra Los Mecamonos de Marte. Ontiveros, Martin, illus. 2002. (Ricky Ricotta Ser.: No. 4). 144p. (gr. 2-4). pap. 3.99 (978-0-439-25296-6(2)); (J). (ps-3). pap. 16.95 (978-0-439-25295-9(4)) Scholastic, Inc. (Blue Sky Pr., The).

—Ricky Ricotta's Giant Robot vs. the Voodoo Vultures from Venus. Ontiveros, Martin, illus. 2001. (Ricky Ricotta Ser.: No. 3). 128p. (J). (ps-3). pap. 16.95 (978-0-439-23624-9(X)) Scholastic, Inc.

—Ricky Ricotta's Mighty Robot vs. the Stupid Stinkbugs from Saturn. Ontiveros, Martin, illus. 2003. (Ricky Ricotta Ser.: No. 6). 128p. (J). pap. 16.95 (978-0-439-37644-0(0) , Blue Sky Pr., The) Scholastic, Inc.

H I

Pilkey, Dav, illus. Captain Underpants & the Big, Bad Battle of the Bionic Booger Boy Pt. 1: The Night of the Nasty Nostril Nuggets. 2003. (Captain Underpants Ser.: Bk. 6). 176p. (J). pap. 16.95 (978-0-439-37609-9(2) , Blue Sky Pr., The) Scholastic, Inc.

Pinkney, Brian. Adventures of Sparrow Boy. 2000. (J). 13.79 (978-0-606-19246-0(8)) Tandem Library Bks.

—The Adventures of Sparrowboy. Pinkney, Brian, illus. 2002. (Illus.). (J). 14.47 (978-0-7587-1906-5(X)) Book Wholesalers, Inc.

—The Adventures of Sparrowboy. Pinkney, Brian, illus. 2000. (Illus.). 40p. (J). (ps-3). 7.99 (978-0-689-83534-6(5) , Aladdin) Simon & Schuster Children's Publishing.

—Adventures of Sparrowboy. 2000. (gr. k-3). lib. bdg. 14.15 (978-0-613-28396-0(1)) Tandem Library Bks.

Power Range Time Force: Time to Save the World. 2007. 24p. pap. 3.50 (*978-1-4037-3568-3(9)) Dalmatian Pr.

Power Ranger Wild Force: Red Lion Roar. 2007. 24p. pap. 3.50 (*978-1-4037-3567-6(0)) Dalmatian Pr.

Power Rangers: Super Legends. 2007. 224p. (J). mass mkt. 4.99 (*978-1-4037-3897-4(1)) Dalmatian Pr.

Prentiss, Elizabeth. Aunt Jane's Hero. 1999. (J). (ps up). pap. 7.95 (978-1-881545-63-7(6)) A B Publishing.

Priest, Christopher. Black Panther: The Client. 2001. (gr. 5-8). lib. bdg. 24.55 (978-0-613-53671-4(1)) Tandem Library Bks.

Puckett, Kelley. Batman's Dark Secret. Muth, Jon J., illus. 2000. (Hello Reader! Ser.). 32p. (J). (gr. 1-3). pap. 3.99 (978-0-439-09551-8(4)) Scholastic, Inc.

—Batman's Dark Secret. 2000. (Hello Reader! Ser.). (Illus.). (J). 10.79 (978-0-606-18517-2(8)) Tandem Library Bks.

Quinn, Zoe. Cabin Fever. 2007. (Caped Sixth Grader Ser.). 144p. (J). (gr. 4-7). 5.50 (978-0-440-42082-8(2)); (Illus.). lib. bdg. 11.99 (978-0-385-90307-3(3)) Random Hse. Children's Bks. (Yearling).

—The Caped 6th Grader: Happy Birthday, Hero! 2006. (Illus.). 144p. (J). (gr. 4-7). pap. 4.99 (978-0-440-42079-8(2) , Yearling) Random Hse. Children's Bks.

—The Caped 6th Grader: Happy Birthday, Hero! Spangler, Brie, illus. 2006. 144p. (J). (gr. 4-7). lib. bdg. 11.99 (978-0-385-90304-2(9) , Yearling) Random Hse. Children's Bks.

—The Caped 6th Grader: Totally Toxic. 2006. 160p. (gr. 4-7). lib. bdg. 11.99 (978-0-385-90305-9(7) , Yearling) Random Hse. Children's Bks.

Recorvits, Helen. Where Heroes Hide. 2002. (Illus.). 144p. (J). (gr. 4-6). 16.00 (978-0-374-33057-6(3) , Farrar, Straus & Giroux (BYR)) Farrar, Straus & Giroux.

Redondo, Jesus, illus. Turtle Rescue! 2004. (Ready-to-Read Ser.). 32p. (J). pap. 3.99 (978-0-689-87007-1(8) , Simon Spotlight) Simon & Schuster Children's Publishing.

Reed, Brian. Ms. Marvel TPB, Vol. 1. 2007. (Illus.). 136p. pap. 14.99 (978-0-7851-1996-8(5)) Marvel Enterprises, Inc.

Richards, Zackary. Frostie the Deadman. 2004. 222p. (J). pap. 14.95 (978-0-9713069-8-1(2)) Burns, Nicholas K. Publishing.

Rodda, Emily. Rowan & the Ice Creepers. 2003. (Rowan of Rin Ser.). 272p. (J). (gr. 3 up). 15.99 (978-0-06-029780-0(8)) HarperCollins Pubs.

—Rowan & the Ice Creepers. 2004. 262p. (J). (gr. 3-7). lib. bdg. 13.04 (978-0-606-32643-8(X)) Tandem Library Bks.

—Rowan & the Keeper of the Crystal. (Rowan of Rin Ser.). 2004. 224p. (gr. 3 up). pap. 5.99 (978-0-06-056073-7(8)); 2002. 208p. (J). (gr. 2 up). pap. 5.99 (978-0-06-441025-0(0)); 2002. 208p. (J). (gr. 2 up). 15.99 (978-0-06-029776-3(X)); 2002. (Illus.). 208p. (J). (gr. 2 up). lib. bdg. 16.89 (978-0-06-029777-0(8)) HarperCollins Pubs.

—Rowan & the Travelers. (Rowan of Rin Ser.). 2004. 192p. (gr. 3 up). pap. 5.99 (978-0-06-056072-0(X)); 2002. 176p. (J). (gr. 2 up). pap. 5.95 (978-0-06-441026-7(9) , Harper Trophy) HarperCollins Pubs.

—Rowan & the Zebak. (Rowan of Rin Ser.). (J). 2004. 224p. (gr. 3 up). pap. 5.99 (978-0-06-056074-4(6)); 2003. (Illus.). 208p. (gr. 2 up). pap. 5.99 (978-0-06-441024-3(2) , Harper Trophy); 2002. 208p. (gr. 2 up). 15.99 (978-0-06-029778-7(6)) HarperCollins Pubs.

—Rowan of Rin. (Rowan of Rin Ser.). (J). 2004. (Illus.). 176p. (gr. 3 up). pap. 5.99 (978-0-06-056071-3(1)); 2002. (gr. 2 up). pap. 5.95 (978-0-06-441019-9(6) , Harper Trophy) HarperCollins Pubs.

—The Valley of the Lost. 2001. (gr. 5-8). lib. bdg. 13.00 (978-0-613-43903-9(1)) Tandem Library Bks.

Rogers, Gregory. Midsummer Knight. Rogers, Gregory, illus. 2007. (Illus.). 32p. (J). (gr. 1-4). 16.95 (*978-1-59643-183-6(0)) Roaring Brook Pr.

Salvatore, R. A. & Dabb, Andrew. Demonwars, Vol. 1. 2007. (Illus.). 144p. (YA). pap. 18.99 (*978-1-932796-89-6(4)) Devil's Due Publishing, Inc.

Sander, Sonia. Sports Heroes. Franchesco! & Hardin, Greg, illus. 2007. (VeggieTales Ser.). 96p. (J). 2.99 (978-1-4169-3512-4(6) , Simon Scribbles) Simon & Schuster Children's Publishing.

Sargent, Dave & Sargent, Pat. Ben. Lenoir, Jane, illus. 2001. (Saddle Up Ser.). 36p. (J). pap. 6.95 (978-1-56763-644-4(6)) Ozark Publishing.

—Ben: (Bay Sabino) Help Others, 30. Lenoir, Jane, illus. 2001. (Saddle Up Ser.: 2). 36p. (J). lib. bdg. 22.60 (978-1-56763-643-7(8)) Ozark Publishing.

—Bubba No. 6: (Bay) Speed Is Not Everything, 30, vol. 6. Lenoir, Jane, illus. 2001. (Saddle Up Ser.: 6). 36p. (J). lib. bdg. 22.60 (978-1-56763-599-7(7)) Ozark Publishing.

—Chalky No. 12: (Chalky Grullo) I'm Forgetful, 25, 12. Lenoir, Jane, illus. 2001. (Saddle Up Ser.: 12). 36p. (J). pap. 6.95 (978-1-56763-604-8(7)); lib. bdg. 22.60 (978-1-56763-603-1(9)) Ozark Publishing.

—Comanche: (Red Bay) Perseverance, 25, 19. Lenoir, Jane, illus. 2001. (Saddle Up Ser.: 19). 36p. (J). pap. 6.95 (978-1-56763-648-2(9)); lib. bdg. 22.60 (978-1-56763-647-5(0)) Ozark Publishing.

—Flash: Speed Counts. Lenoir, Jane, illus. 2001. (Saddle Up Ser.). 36p. (J). pap. 6.95 (978-1-56763-614-7(4)); lib. bdg. 22.60 (978-1-56763-613-0(6)) Ozark Publishing.

—Hank: (Black Sabino) Be Responsible, 25, 33. Lenoir, Jane, illus. 2001. (Saddle Up Ser.). 36p. (J). pap. 6.95 (978-1-56763-656-7(X)); lib. bdg. 22.60 (978-1-56763-655-0(1)) Ozark Publishing.

Satterwhite, William. Stealth,, Vol. 1. 2005. 44p. (YA). pap. 5.75 (978-1-4116-2395-8(9)) Lulu.com.

Scholastic Editorial Staff. Exo-force Sticker Book. Schutz, Samantha, ed. 2006. (Lego Ser.). 16p. (J). pap. 4.99 (978-0-439-82810-9(4)) Scholastic, Inc.

Scholastic, Inc. Staff. Meet the Rescue Heroes. 2002. (gr. k-3). lib. bdg. 11.80 (978-0-613-72122-6(5)) Tandem Library Bks.

—Rescue Heroes No. 2: Movie Reader. 2004. (Rescue Heroes Ser.). 32p. (J). pap. 3.99 (978-0-439-62511-1(4)) Scholastic, Inc.

Scholastic, Inc. Staff. Snow Fun. 2007. (Care Bears Ser.). 24p. (J). pap. 3.99 (*978-0-545-01310-9(0)) Scholastic, Inc.

Schutz, Samantha, ed. LEGO: Escape from Sentai Mountain. 2006. (LEGO Exo-Force Ser.: Vol. 1). (Illus.). 64p. (J). pap. 3.99 (978-0-439-82808-6(2)) Scholastic, Inc.

Schwarz, Viviane. Timothy & the Strong Pajamas. 2008. 40p. (J). pap. 16.99 (*978-0-545-03329-9(2) , Levine, Arthur A. Bks.) Scholastic, Inc.

Shalant, Phyllis. The Great Cape Rescue. 2007. (Society of Super Secret Heroes Ser.: Bk. 1). 128p. (J). (gr. 2-4). 15.99 (978-0-525-47404-3(8) , Dutton Juvenile) Penguin Group (USA) Inc.

Sheldon, Dyan. Confessions of a Hollywood Star. 2006. 208p. (YA). (gr. 7). 15.99 (978-0-7636-3075-1(6)) Candlewick Pr.

Siefken, Paul. Not Another Buttercup. Cook, Christopher, illus. 2002. (Powerpuff Girls Plus You Club Ser.). 64p. (J). (978-0-439-33267-5(2)) Scholastic, Inc.

Spaziante, Patrick, illus. Meet Casey Jones. 2004. (Teenage Mutant Ninja Turtles Ser.). 24p. (J). pap. 3.99 (978-0-689-86899-3(5) , Simon Spotlight) Simon & Schuster Children's Publishing.

Speregen, Devra Newberger, et al. Hero for a Day. 1999. (Brother's Keeper Ser.: No. 1). 112p. (J). (gr. 3-6). pap. 3.99 (978-0-671-03547-1(9) , Aladdin) Simon & Schuster Children's Publishing.

Springer, Nancy. Rowan Hood: Outlaw Girl of Sherwood Forest. 2002. (Tales of Rowan Hood Ser.: No. 1). 192p. (J). (ps-7). pap. 5.99 (978-0-698-11972-7(X) , Putnam Juvenile) Penguin Group (USA) Inc.

Stamper, Judith Bauer & Keenan. Hercules & the Maze of the Minotaur. 1998. (Disney's First Readers Ser.: Vol. 3). 40p. (J). (gr. 2-4). pap. 3.50 (978-0-7868-4171-4(0)) Disney Pr.

Stamper, Judith Bauer & Sol Studios Staff. Hercules & the Maze of the Minotaur. 1999. (Illus.). (J). (978-0-590-39387-4(1)) Scholastic, Inc.

Starlin, Jim. Infinity War. 2006. (Illus.). 400p. (YA). pap. 29.99 (978-0-7851-2105-3(6)) Marvel Enterprises, Inc.

Starlin, Jim & Edelman, Scott. Silver Surfer Rebirth of Thanos. 2006. (Illus.). 224p. pap. (978-0-7851-2046-9(7)) Diamond Bks.

Straczynski, J. Amazing Spiderman: Coming Home. 2001. (gr. 5-8). lib. bdg. 25.70 (978-0-613-60526-7(8)) Tandem Library Bks.

Straczynski, J. M. Hyperion. 2006. (Illus.). 120p. pap. 14.99 (978-0-7851-1895-4(0)) Marvel Enterprises, Inc.

Strickland, Brad. Be a Wolf! Lt. ed. 1999. (Adventures of Wishbone Ser.: No. 1). (Illus.). 144p. (J). (gr. 4 up). lib. bdg. 22.60 (978-0-8368-2297-7(8)) Stevens, Gareth Inc.

Strohm, Keith Francis. Bladesinger. 2006. (Fighters Ser.). (Illus.). 312p. (978-1-4156-6627-2(X)) Wizards of the Coast.

Sullivan, Stephen D. Iron Man: The Junior Novel. 2008. (Iron Man Ser.). 144p. (J). pap. 4.99 (*978-0-06-082197-5(3) , Harper Entertainment) HarperCollins Pubs.

Takeuchi, Naoko. Sailor Moon, 11 vols. (Illus.). 184p. (gr. 7-12). Vol. 2. 2nd rev. ed. 1998. (Sailor Moon Ser.: Vol. 2). pap. 9.99 (978-1-892213-05-1(2)); Vol. 3. 3rd rev. ed. 1999. pap. 9.99 (978-1-892213-06-8(0)) TOKYOPOP, Inc.

—Sailor Moon Supers, Vol. 3. 3rd rev. ed. 2000. (Illus.). 160p. (gr. 7-12). pap. 9.99 (978-1-892213-26-6(5)) TOKYOPOP, Inc.

Tauss, Marc. Superhero. Tauss, Marc, illus. 2005. (Illus.). 40p. (J). (gr. k-3). pap. 16.99 (978-0-439-62734-4(6) , Scholastic Pr.) Scholastic, Inc.

Teitelbaum, Michael. Cine en casa: Heroes de Cine: Movie Theater: Marvel Heroes. 2007. (Cine en casa Disney Ser.). (Illus.). 46p. (J). 24.95 (*978-970-718-535-7(X) , Silver Dolphin en Español) Advanced Marketing, S. de R. L. de C. V. MEX. *Dist:* Perseus Distribution.

—Marvel Heroes Mix & Match. 2007. 12p. (J). bds. 14.99 (978-0-7944-1229-6(7)) Reader's Digest Assn., Inc., The.

—Marvel Heroes Puzzle Master. 2006. (Marvel Heroes Ser.). 32p. (J). bds. 9.99 (978-0-7944-1137-4(1)) Reader's Digest Assn., Inc., The.

—Marvel Heroes Storybook & Movie Projector. 2006. (Movie Theater Storybooks Ser.). (Illus.). 48p. (J). bds. 24.99 (978-0-7944-1135-0(5)) Reader's Digest Assn., Inc., The.

—The Story of Spider-Man, Vol. 4. O'Neill, Cynthia, ed. 2001. (Readers Ser.). (Illus.). 48p. (J). (gr. 3-12). pap. 3.99 (978-0-7894-7921-1(4)) Dorling Kindersley Publishing, Inc.

Teitelbaum, Michael & Dorling Kindersley Publishing Staff. The Story of Spider-Man. 2001. (Dk Readers Ser.). (Illus.). 48p. (J). (gr. 3-12). 12.99 (978-0-7894-7920-4(6)) Dorling Kindersley Publishing, Inc.

Teitelbaum, Michael, et al. Spider-Man: Amazing Powers. 2001. (Dorling Kindersley Readers Ser.). (Illus.). 48p. (J). (gr. 3-12). 12.99 (978-0-7894-7922-8(2)) Dorling Kindersley Publishing, Inc.

Thomas, Jim. Super Slam Turtles! Spaziante, Patrick, illus. 2005. 22p. (J). lib. bdg. 15.00 (*978-1-4242-0971-2(4)) Fitzgerald Bks.

Thomas, Roy. Roy Thomas. 2006. (Marvel Visionaries Ser.). (Illus.). 352p. (YA). 34.99 (978-0-7851-2088-9(2)) Marvel Enterprises, Inc.

Top That Publishing Staff, ed. Halfpipe Heroes. 2004. (Wicked Tattoos Ser.). (Illus.). 16p. (J). pap. (978-1-84510-111-4(1)) Top That! Publishing PLC.

Trine, Greg. The Curse of the Bologna Sandwich. Montijo, Rhode, illus. 2006. (Melvin Beederman, Superhero Ser.). 144p. (J). 15.95 (978-0-8050-7928-9(9)); pap. 5.99 (978-0-8050-7836-7(3)) Holt, Henry & Co.

—The Fake Cape Caper. Montijo, Rhode, illus. 5th rev. ed. 2007. (Melvin Beederman, Superhero Ser.). 144p. (J). pap. 5.99 (*978-0-8050-8159-6(3)); (gr. 2 up). 16.95 (*978-0-8050-8158-9(5)) Holt, Henry & Co. (Holt, Henry & Co. Bks. For Young Readers).

—The Grateful Fred. Montijo, Rhode, illus. 3rd rev. ed. 2006. (Melvin Beederman, Superhero Ser.). 144p. (J). 15.95 (978-0-8050-7921-0(1)) Holt, Henry & Co.

—The Grateful Fred. Montijo, Rhode, illus. 3rd rev. ed. 2006. (Melvin Beederman, Superhero Ser.). 144p. (J). pap. 5.99 (978-0-8050-7922-7(X)) Holt, Henry & Co.

—The Revenge of the McNasty Brothers. Montijo, Rhode, illus. 2nd rev. ed. 2006. (Melvin Beederman, Superhero Ser.). 144p. (J). 15.95 (978-0-8050-7929-6(7)); pap. 5.99 (978-0-8050-7837-4(1)) Holt, Henry & Co.

—Terror in Tights. Montijo, Rhode, illus. 4th rev. ed. 2007. (Melvin Beederman, Superhero Ser.). 144p. (J). (gr. 2-4). 16.95 (978-0-8050-7923-4(8)); pap. 5.99 (978-0-8050-7924-1(6)) Holt, Henry & Co.

Van Draanen, Wendelin. Attack of the Tagger. Biggs, Brian, illus. unabr. ed. 2006. (Shredderman Ser.: Bk. 2). (J). (gr. 3-6). pap. 24.95 incl. audio (*978-1-59519-758-0(3)); pap. 28.95 incl. audio compact disk (*978-1-59519-759-7(1)) Live Oak Media.

—Attack of the Tagger. 2006. (Shredderman Ser.: Bk. 2). (Illus.). 176p. (gr. 2-5). 5.50 (978-0-440-41913-6(1) , Yearling) Random Hse. Children's Bks.

—Enemy Spy. 2006. (Shredderman Ser.: Bk. 4). 192p. (J). (gr. 2-5). 5.50 (978-0-440-41915-0(8) , Yearling) Random Hse. Children's Bks.

—Meet the Gecko. 2006. (Shredderman Ser.: Bk. 3). 176p. (J). (gr. 2-5). 5.50 (978-0-440-41914-3(X) , Yearling) Random Hse. Children's Bks.

—Secret Identity. Biggs, Brian, illus. unabr. ed. 2006. (Shredderman Ser.: Bk. 1). (J). (gr. 2-4). pap. 24.95 incl. audio (*978-1-59519-762-7(1)); pap. 28.95 incl. audio compact disk (*978-1-59519-763-4(X)) Live Oak Media.

—Secret Identity. Biggs, Brian, illus. (Shredderman Ser.: Bk. 1). 144p. (J). (gr. 2-5). 2004. 12.95 (978-0-375-82351-0(4) , Knopf Bks. for Young Readers); 2004. lib. bdg. 14.99 (978-0-375-92351-7(9) , Knopf Bks. for Young Readers); 2006. reprint ed. 5.50 (978-0-440-41912-9(3) , Yearling) Random Hse. Children's Bks.

Vaughan, Brian K. Escape to New York. 2006. (Runaways Ser.: Vol. 5). (Illus.). 144p. pap. 7.99 (978-0-7851-1901-2(9)) Marvel Enterprises, Inc.

Vega, Diego & Adkins, Jan. Young Zorro (Spanish Edition) El joven Zorro: la marca de Hierro. 2007. (SPA.). 256p. (J). pap. 6.99 (*978-0-06-115378-5(8) , Rayo) HarperCollins Pubs.

Verne, Jules. Michael Strogoff. 2002. (gr. 3-6). lib. bdg. 31.55 (978-0-613-83365-3(1)) Tandem Library Bks.

Voigt, Cynthia. Jackaroo: A Novel of the Kingdom. 2003. (Kingdom Ser.). (Illus.). 368p. (YA). mass mkt. 6.99 (978-0-689-86435-3(3) , Simon Pulse) Simon & Schuster Children's Publishing.

Waid, Mark. Fantastic Four, Vol. 3. 2005. (Illus.). 256p. (YA). 29.99 (978-0-7851-2011-7(4)) Marvel Enterprises, Inc.

—Supreme Justice. 2001. lib. bdg. 28.00 (978-0-613-92134-3(8)) Tandem Library Bks.

Walsh, Sheila. Will, God's Mighty Warrior. 2006. (Will, God's Mighty Warrior Ser.). (Illus.). 32p. (J). 12.99 (978-1-4003-0805-7(4)) Nelson, Thomas Inc.

Walt Disney Productions Staff. Little Town Heroes. Walt Disney Productions Staff, illus. 2005. (Illus.). 64p. (J). (ps-2). pap. 3.99 (978-0-7364-2332-8(X) , Golden/Disney) Random Hse. Children's Bks.

Waters, Zack C. Blood Moon Rider. 2006. 126p. (J). 13.95 (978-1-56164-350-9(5)) Pineapple Pr., Inc.

Watson, Andi. Quest. Iwahara, Yuji, illus. 2004. (Marvel Heroes Ser.). 120p. (YA). pap. 13.99 (978-0-7851-1298-3(7)) Marvel Enterprises, Inc.

Wax, Wendy. Meet Leatherhead. Spaziante, Patrick, illus. 2005. 22p. (J). lib. bdg. 15.00 (*978-1-4242-0972-9(2)) Fitzgerald Bks.

Weigel, Jeff. Atomic Ace: (He's Just My Dad) Weigel, Jeff, illus. 2004. (Illus.). 32p. (J). (gr. 1-4). pap. 6.95 (978-0-8075-3217-1(7)) Whitman, Albert & Co.

Weigel, Jeff, illus. Atomic Ace & the Robot Rampage. 2006. 32p. (J). 15.95 (978-0-8075-0484-0(X)); pap. 6.95 (978-0-8075-0485-7(8)) Whitman, Albert & Co.

Weigelt, Udo. Super Guinea Pig to the Rescue. Spranger, Nina, illus. 2007. 32p. (J). 17.85 (*978-0-8027-9706-3(7)); 16.95 (*978-0-8027-9705-6(9)) Walker & Co.

Weinberger, Kimberly & West, Tracey. Changing Places, No. 2. 2001. (Cardcaptors Ser.). (Illus.). 24p. (J). (ps-3). pap. 3.50 (978-0-439-25368-0(3)) Scholastic, Inc.

West, Tracey. Blossom & the Haunted House. Alger, Bill, illus. 2002. (Pick a Powerpuff Path Ser.). 64p. (J). (978-0-439-33264-4(8)) Scholastic, Inc.

West, Tracey, adapted by. Jack in! MegaMan! 2006. 59p. (J). (*978-0-439-76837-5(3)) Scholastic, Inc.

Whatley, Bruce & Smith, Rosie. Captain Pajamas. 2000. (Illus.). 32p. (J). (ps-3). 15.89 (978-0-06-026614-1(7)) HarperCollins Pubs.

Wildsmith, Brian. The Little Wood Duck. Wildsmith, Brian, illus. 2006. (Illus.). 32p. (J). 16.95 (978-1-59572-042-9(1)); pap. 6.95 (978-1-59572-049-8(9)) Star Bright Bks., Inc.

Wisler, G. Clifton. The Drummer Boy of Vicksburg. 1999. (J). 12.64 (978-0-606-16768-0(4)) Tandem Library Bks.

Wisniewski, David. Sumo Mouse. Wisniewski, David, illus. 2002. (Illus.). 32p. (J). (ps-3). 16.95 (978-0-8118-3492-6(1)) Chronicle Bks. LLC.

—Sumo Mouse. Wisniewski, David, illus. 2004. (Illus.). 26p. (J). (gr. k-4). reprint ed. 17.00 (978-0-7567-8506-2(5)) DIANE Publishing Co.

Woodward, Simon. Brave Dave: The Makings of a Hero. 2006. pap. 12.49 (*978-1-4259-5996-8(2)) AuthorHouse.

X-Men. 2003. (J). (978-1-57657-859-9(3)) Paradise Pr., Inc.

Yolen, Jane. Atalanta & the Arcadian Beast. 2004. (gr. 3-6). lib. bdg. 14.15 (978-0-613-83009-6(1)) Tandem Library Bks.

Yolen, Jane & Harris, Robert J. Atalanta & the Arcadian Beast. 2003. (Young Heroes Ser.: Bk. 3). 256p. (J). 15.99 (978-0-06-029454-0(X)) HarperCollins Pubs.

Yonge, M. Charlotte. A Book of Golden Deeds. 2006. 64.99 (*978-1-4219-9676-9(6)); pap. 58.99 (*978-1-4219-9678-3(2)) IndyPublish.com.

Yourgrau, Barry. Another NASTYbook: The Curse of the Tweeties. DeJesus, Robert, illus. 2006. 176p. (J). 11.99 (978-0-06-057981-4(1)); lib. bdg. 13.89 (978-0-06-057982-1(X)) HarperCollins Pubs. (Cotler, Joanna Books).

—Nasty Book. 2005. 192p. (J). (gr. k-9). 11.99 (978-0-06-057978-4(1) , Cotler, Joanna Books) HarperCollins Pubs.

—Nasty Book, No. 3. Swaab, Neil, illus. 2007. 160p. (J). 12.99 (*978-0-06-077676-3(5) , Cotler, Joanna Books) HarperCollins Pubs.

—NASTYbook. 2007. 192p. (J). pap. 5.99 (*978-0-06-057980-7(3) , Harper Trophy) HarperCollins Pubs.

Zusak, Markus. I Am the Messenger. 368p. (YA). 2005. (gr. 9). 16.95 (978-0-375-83099-0(5)); 2005. (gr. 9). lib. bdg. 18.99 (978-0-375-93099-7(X)); 2006. (gr. 7). reprint ed. pap. 8.95 (978-0-375-83667-1(5)) Random Hse. Children's Bks. (Knopf Bks. for Young Readers).

HEROINES

see Heroes; Women in the Bible

HEROISM

see Courage; Heroes

HERONS

Carney, Margaret. Where Does a Tiger-Heron Spend the Night? Watt, Melanie, illus. unabr. ed. 2002. 32p. (J). (gr. k-3). (978-1-55337-022-2(8)) Kids Can Pr., Ltd.

Hall, Margaret. Herons. Saunders-Smith, Gail, ed. 2004. (Wetland Animals Ser.). (Illus.). 24p. (J). (gr. k-1). lib. bdg. 15.93 (978-0-7368-2064-6(7) , Pebble Bks.) Capstone Pr., Inc.

HERONS—FICTION

Gorbachev, Valeri. Heron & Turtle. Gorbachev, Valeri, illus. 2006. (Illus.). 40p. (J). (gr. k). 15.99 (978-0-399-24321-9(6) , Philomel) Penguin Group (USA) Inc.

Harms, John. Saving of Valiant Blue Heron. 2001. (gr. 3-6). lib. bdg. 15.25 (978-0-613-77815-2(4)) Tandem Library Bks.

Jewett, Sarah Orne. A White Heron. Alvord, Douglas, illus. 2005. 32p. (J). pap. 10.95 (978-1-56792-287-5(2)) Godine, David R. Pub.

McGaw, Wayne T. T-Boy of the Bayou. Crespo, George, illus. 2003. 32p. (J). (ps-3). 15.95 (978-0-87614-648-4(5) , Carolrhoda Bks.) Lerner Publishing Group.

Myers, Anna. Flying Blind. 2003. 192p. (YA). 16.95 (978-0-8027-8879-5(3)) Walker & Co.

Quigley, Mary. Granddad's Fishing Buddy. Jorisch, Stephane, illus. 2007. 32p. (J). (ps-3). 16.99 (978-0-8037-2942-1(1) , Dial) Penguin Group (USA) Inc.

Ramirez, Antonio. Napí. Domi, illus. 2004. 32p. (J). 15.95 (978-0-88899-610-7(1)) Groundwood Bks. CAN. *Dist:* Perseus Distribution.

Ramirez, Antonio & Domi. Napí. 2004. (SPA., Illus.). 32p. (J). 15.95 (978-0-88899-611-4(X)) Groundwood Bks. CAN. *Dist:* Perseus Distribution.

Van Leeuwen, Jean. Oliver the Mighty Pig, Level 2. Schweninger, Ann, illus. 2004. (Easy-to-Read Ser.). 48p. (J). (gr. k-3). 14.99 (978-0-8037-2886-8(7) , Dial) Penguin Group (USA) Inc.

HERPETOLOGISTS

Boekhoff, P. M. & Kallen, Stuart A. Steve Irwin. 2003. (Famous People Ser.). (Illus.). 48p. (J). 26.20 (978-0-7377-1890-4(0) , Greenhaven Pr., Inc.) Thomson Gale.

Eding, June. Steve Irwin: Wildlife Warrior: An Unauthorized Biography. 2007. 32p. (J). 7.99 (*978-0-8431-2679-2(5) , Price Stern Sloan) Penguin Group (USA) Inc.

Matthews, Sheelagh. Steve Irwin. 2007. (J). (*978-1-59036-649-3(2)); (*978-1-59036-650-9(6)) Weigl Pubs., Inc.

McNeil, Niki, et al. HOCPP 1107 Steve Irwin. 2006. spiral bd. 21.00 (*978-1-60308-107-8(0)) In the Hands of a Child.

Ritchey, Richard I. True Adventures of the Reptileman. 2007. 60p. per. 10.95 (*978-0-595-45020-6(2)) iUniverse, Inc.

HERSCHEL, CAROLINE LUCRETIA, 1750-1848

Robinson, Ella M. Stars in her Heart. 2005. 127p. per. 10.95 (978-1-57258-318-4(5)) TEACH Services, Inc.

HERSCHEL, WILLIAM, SIR, 1738-1822

Robinson, Ella M. Stars in her Heart. 2005. 127p. per. 10.95 (978-1-57258-318-4(5)) TEACH Services, Inc.

HERSHEY, MILTON SNAVELY, 1857-1945

Gillis, Jennifer Blizin. Milton Hershey: The Founder of Hershey's Chocolate. 2005. (Illus.). 32p. (J). lib. bdg. (978-1-4034-6345-6(X)) Heinemann Library.

—Milton Hershey: The Man with the Chocolate Dream. 2005. (Illus.). 32p. (J). pap. (978-1-4034-6359-3(X)) Heinemann Library.

Simon, Charnan. Milton Hershey: Chocolate King, Town Builder. De Capua, Sarah, ed. 1998. (Community Builders Ser.). (Illus.). 48p. (J). (gr. 3-5). pap. 6.95 (978-0-516-26330-4(7), Children's Pr.) Scholastic Library Publishing.

Sutcliffe, Jane. Milton Hershey. Parlin, Tim, illus. 2004. (History Maker Bios Ser.). 48p. (J). 26.60 (978-0-8225-0247-0(X), Lerner Pubns.) Lerner Publishing Group.

HESSE, HERMANN, 1877-1962

Hesse, Hermann. Bajo la Rueda. 2003. (SPA.). bds. 6.98 (978-968-6769-57-9(9)) Epoca, Editorial, S.A. de C.V. MEX. *Dist:* Giron Bks.

HIAWATHA, 15TH CENT.

Longfellow, Henry Wadsworth. The Song of Hiawatha. 2003. (Illus.). 32p. (J). 16.95 (978-1-59354-002-9(7)) Handprint Bks.

Marsh, Carole. Hiawatha: An Ohio Experience Reader. 2001. (J). (gr. k-5). pap. 1.95 (978-0-635-00426-0(7)) Gallopade International.

Taylor, C. J. Peace Walker: The Legend of Hiawatha & Tekanawita. 2004. (Illus.). 48p. (J). (gr. 3). 15.95 (978-0-88776-547-6(5)) Tundra Bks., Inc./Livres Toundra, Inc. CAN. *Dist:* Random Hse., Inc.

HIBERNATION

see Animals—Hibernation

HICCUPS—FICTION

Albee, Sarah. Hic! Brannon, Tom, illus. 2006. (Step-By-Step Readers Ser.). (J). pap. (978-1-59939-061-1(2), Reader's Digest Young Families, Inc.) Reader's Digest Children's Publishing, Inc.

Brown, Marc. Arthur's Hiccups. 2001. (Arthur Ser.). (Illus.). (J). (ps-3). lib. bdg. (978-0-375-90699-2(1), Random Hse. Bks. for Young Readers) Random Hse. Children's Bks.

—Arthur's Hiccups. 2001. (Arthur Ser.). (gr. k-3). lib. bdg. 11.80 (978-0-613-85128-2(5)); 10.79 (978-0-606-22767-4(9)) Tandem Library Bks.

Brown, Marc & Schulman, Janet. Arthur's Hiccups. Brown, Marc, illus. 2001. (Arthur Ser.). (Illus.). 24p. (J). (gr. k-3). lib. bdg. 11.99 (978-0-375-90698-5(3), Random Hse. Bks. for Young Readers) Random Hse. Children's Bks.

Feely, Jenny. Sebastian Gets the Hiccups. 2000. (gr. k-3). lib. bdg. 11.80 (978-0-613-29741-7(5)) Tandem Library Bks.

Hannah's Hiccups: Individual Title Six-Packs. (gr. k-1). 23.00 (978-0-7635-8831-1(8)) Rigby Education.

Higgins, Kitty. Wild Bill Hiccups. 2005. 40.00 (*978-1-4108-4213-8(4)) Benchmark Education Co.

Hofmeyr, Dianne. Hic... Hic... Hiccups! Moyo, Sihambile, tr. 1999. (Cambridge African Language Library Ser.). (NDE., Illus.). 16p. pap. 3.70 (978-0-521-65808-9(X)) Cambridge Univ. Pr.

Holabird, Katharine. Angelina Has the Hiccups! Craig, Helen, illus. 2006. (Angelina Ballerina Ser.). 32p. (J). (ps-1). pap. 3.99 (978-0-448-44389-8(9), Grosset & Dunlap) Penguin Group (USA) Inc.

Jennings, Sharon. Franklin Has the Hiccups. Gagnon, Celeste et al, illus. 2006. 32p. (J). lib. bdg. 15.38 (*978-1-4242-1178-4(6)) Fitzgerald Bks.

Jennings, Sharon, et al. Franklin Has the Hiccups. Lei, John, illus. 32p. (978-1-55337-802-0(4)) Kids Can Pr., Ltd.

—Franklin Has the Hiccups. Lei, John, illus. 2006. 32p. 3.95 (978-1-55337-803-7(2)) Kids Can Pr., Ltd. CAN. *Dist:* Wybel Marketing Group.

Mei Ling's Hiccups. 2004. (CHI & ENG., Illus.). (J). (978-1-85269-703-7(2)) Mantra Publishing, Ltd.

Meng, Cece. The Wonderful Thing about Hiccups. Pedersen, Janet, illus. 2007. 32p. (J). (gr. k-3). 16.00 (978-0-618-59544-0(9), Clarion Bks.) Houghton Mifflin Co. Trade & Reference Div.

Mills, David & Brazell, Derek, illus. Mei Ling's Hiccups: Higgadii Mii Linig. 2004. (TAM, CZE, VIE, SPA & GUJ.). 23p. (J). (978-1-85269-564-4(1)) Mantra Publishing, Ltd.

Preller, James. Hiccups for Elephants. Wilhelm, Hans, illus. 2004. 32p. (J). lib. bdg. 15.00 (978-1-59054-396-2(3)) Fitzgerald Bks.

Watson-Dubisch, Carolyn. Bug-a-boo, 1. l.t. ed. 2006. (Illus.). 32p. (J). per. 9.95 (978-0-9779295-1-5(5)) Medusa Road Pr.

Weare, Tim. Hide-and-Seek with Leo. 2001. (Hand Puppet Board Bks.). (Illus.). 10p. (J). (ps). pap., bds. 14.95 (978-0-439-29719-6(2), Cartwheel Bks.) Scholastic, Inc.

HICKOK, WILD BILL, 1837-1876

Marsh, Carole. "Wild Bill" Hickok. 2002. (One Thousand Readers Ser.). (Illus.). 12p. (J). (gr. k-4). 2.95 (978-0-635-01518-1(8), 15188) Gallopade International.

Phillips, Larissa. Wild Bill Hickok: Legend of the American Wild West. 2003. (Primary Sources of Famous People in American History Ser.). (Illus.). 32p. (J). pap. (978-0-8239-4194-0(9)) Rosen Publishing Group, Inc., The.

Rosa, Joseph G. Wild Bill Hickok: Sharpshooter & U.S. Marshal of the Wild West. 2005. (Library of American Lives & Times). (Illus.). 112p. (gr. 4-8). lib. bdg. 31.95 (978-0-8239-6632-5(1)) Rosen Publishing Group, Inc., The.

HIEROGLYPHICS

Coulter, Lavrie. Secrets in Stone: All about Maya Hieroglyphs. English, Sarah Jane, illus. 2003. 48p. (gr. 4-8). 18.00 (978-0-7567-9000-4(X)) DIANE Publishing Co.

Fine, Jil. Mayan Writing in Mesoamerica. 2003. (Writing in the Ancient World Ser.). (Illus.). 24p. (J). lib. bdg. 17.25 (978-0-8239-6511-3(2), PowerKids Pr.) Rosen Publishing Group, Inc., The.

Harper, Ellen. Fun with Egyptian Symbols Stencils. 2003. (Dover Little Activity Bks.). (Illus.). 6p. (J). (gr. k-5). pap. 1.50 (978-0-486-43109-3(6)) Dover Pubns., Inc.

Milton, Joyce. Hieroglyphs. Micucci, Charles, illus. 2000. 32p. (J). (gr. 2-6). pap. 6.99 (978-0-448-41976-3(9), Grosset & Dunlap) Penguin Group (USA) Inc.

Platt, Richard. Hieroglyphics Vol. 9: The Secrets of Ancient Egyptian Writing to Unlock & Discover. 2003. (Treasure Chest Ser.). (Illus.). 32p. (J). pap. 22.95 (978-0-7624-1593-9(2), Running Pr. Kids) Running Pr. Bk. Pubs.

Rumford, James. Seeker of Knowledge: The Man Who Deciphered Egyptian Hieroglyphs. (Illus.). 32p. (J). (gr. k-3). 2003. pap. 6.95 (978-0-618-33345-5(2)); 2000. tchr. ed. 16.00 (978-0-395-97934-1(X)) Houghton Mifflin Co. Trade & Reference Div.

—Seeker of Knowledge: The Man Who Deciphered Egyptian Hieroglyphs. 2000. (gr. k-3). lib. bdg. 15.25 (978-0-613-60835-0(6)) Tandem Library Bks.

HIGH SCHOOL EDUCATION

see Education, Secondary

HIGH SCHOOLS

Anonymous. Diary of a Junior Year. (Real Teens Ser.: Vol. 4). (YA). (gr. 7 up). 2000. 196p. pap. 4.99 (978-0-439-08411-6(3), Scholastic Paperbacks); 1999. pap. 59.88 (978-0-439-13483-5(8)); 1999. mass mkt. 59.88 (978-0-439-11746-3(1)); 1999. mass mkt. 59.88 (978-0-439-09275-3(2)) Scholastic, Inc.

—Diary of a Junior Year. 1999. (Real Teens Ser.: Vol. 1). (YA). (gr. 7 up). 11.64 (978-0-606-17278-3(5)); (978-0-606-17547-0(4)) Tandem Library Bks.

Beat the Stuyvesant High School Exam (SSHSAT) l.t. ed. 2001. per. 30.00 (978-0-9706484-0-2(5), Beat The Test) Trademark Universal, Inc.

Bluestein, Jane & Katz, Eric. High School's Not Forever. 2005. (Illus.). 250p. (YA). (gr. 8-12). pap. 12.95 (978-0-7573-0256-5(4)) Health Communications, Inc.

Creating Your High School Portfolio: An Interactive Guide for Documenting & Planning Your Education, Career, & Life. 2003. 160p. 8.95 (978-1-56370-906-7(6), J9066) JIST Publishing.

Diary of a Junior Year. 2000. (Real Teens Ser.: Vol. 6). 160p. (YA). (gr. 7 up). pap. 4.99 (978-0-439-08413-0(X)) Scholastic, Inc.

Farrell, Juliana. High School: The Real Deal. 2001. (gr. 7-12). lib. bdg. 16.40 (978-0-613-81954-1(3)) Tandem Library Bks.

Gottesman, Gregg & Baer, Daniel, eds. High School Survival. 1999. (Illus.). 256p. (YA). (gr. 8-12). pap. 10.95 (978-0-02-863250-6(8)) Peterson's.

Howe, Randy. 101 Ways to Adjust to High School: Randy Howe. 2007. (G - Reference,Information & Interdisciplinary Subjects Ser.). 224p. pap. 9.95 (978-1-4195-4177-3(3)) Kaplan Publishing.

Messina, Noreen E. TeenWork: Four Teens Tell All: A Guide for Finding Jobs. 2006. (Illus.). 126p. (gr. 6-12). pap. 12.75 (978-1-59070-598-8(X)) Goodheart-Willcox Pub.

Miller, Mara. School Desegregation & the Story of the Little Rock Nine. 2008. (From Many Cultures, One History Ser.). (Illus.). 128p. (J). (gr. 5 up). lib. bdg. 31.93 (*978-0-7660-2835-7(6)) Enslow Pubs., Inc.

Nuwer, Hank. High School Hazing: When Rites Become Wrongs. 2000. (Single Titles Ser.). (Illus.). 144p. (YA). (gr. 8-12). 24.00 (978-0-531-11682-1(4), Watts, Franklin) Scholastic Library Publishing.

Shostak, Jerome & Peters, Max. SSAT/ISEE: How to Prepare for the High School Entrance Examinations. 9th ed. 2001. (Illus.). viii, 626p. (YA). mass mkt. 14.95 (978-0-7641-1380-2(1)) Barron's Educational Series, Inc.

Zweiback, Adam J. COOP/HSPT - How to Prepare for the Catholic High School Entrance Examinations. 3rd ed. 2001. (Illus.). viii, 693p. (J). pap. 14.95 (978-0-7641-1377-2(1)) Barron's Educational Series, Inc.

HIGH SPEED AERODYNAMICS

see Aerodynamics, Supersonic

HIGH SPEED AERONAUTICS

see also Aerodynamics, Supersonic; Rockets (Aeronautics)

Harkins, Susan Sales. Breaking the Sound Barrier: The Story of Chuck Yeager. 2005. (Monumental Milestones Ser.). (Illus.). 48p. (YA). (ps-7). lib. bdg. 29.95 (978-1-58415-398-6(9), 1244924) Mitchell Lane Pubs., Inc.

HIGHER EDUCATION

see Education, Higher

HIGHWAY ACCIDENTS

see Traffic Accidents

HIGHWAY CONSTRUCTION

see Roads

HIGHWAY TRANSPORTATION

see Transportation, Automotive

HIGHWAYMEN

see Robbers and Outlaws

HIGHWAYS

see Roads; Streets

HIJACKING OF AIRCRAFT

Beyer, Mark. Sky Marshals. 2003. (High Interest Bks.). (Illus.). 48p. (J). 23.00 (978-0-516-24314-6(4)); (YA). (gr. 7-12). pap. 6.95 (978-0-516-24377-1(2)) Scholastic Library Publishing. (Children's Pr.).

Buell, Tonya. The Crash of United Flight 93 on September 11, 2001. 2005. (Terrorist Attacks Ser.). (Illus.). 64p. (YA). (gr. 7-12). lib. bdg. 26.50 (978-0-8239-3857-5(3)) Rosen Publishing Group, Inc., The.

Grow, Mary L. Attack on America: The Day the Twin Towers Collapsed. 2002. (American Disasters Ser.). 64p. (YA). (gr. 4-10). lib. bdg. 23.93 (978-0-7660-2118-1(1)) Enslow Pubs., Inc.

Wright, John. The U. S. Transportation Security Administration. 2003. (Rescue & Prevention Ser.). (Illus.). 96p. (J). (gr. 7 up). lib. bdg. (978-1-59084-412-0(2)) Mason Crest Pubs.

HIJACKING OF AIRCRAFT—FICTION

Peretti, Frank E. Trapped at the Bottom of the Sea. 144p. 2004. (Cooper Kids Adventures Ser.: No. 4). (gr. 4-7). 5.99 (978-0-89107-594-3(1)); Vol. 4. 2005. (Cooper Kids Adventure Ser.: Vol. 4). (gr. 3-6). pap. 5.99 (978-1-58134-621-3(2), Crossway Bibles) Crossway Bks.

HIKING

see also Walking

Andryszewski, Tricia. Step by Step along the Appalachian Trail. 1998. (Step by Step Ser.). (Illus.). 80p. (gr. 4-7). lib. bdg. 24.90 (978-0-7613-0273-5(5), Millbrook Pr.) Lerner Publishing Group.

—Step by Step along the Pacific Crest Trail. 1998. (Step by Step Ser.). (Illus.). 80p. (gr. 4-7). lib. bdg. 24.90 (978-0-7613-0274-2(3), Twenty-First Century Bks.) Lerner Publishing Group.

Bradley, Kimberly Brubaker. Halfway to the Sky. 2002. 176p. (gr. 3-7). 15.95 (978-0-385-72960-4(X), Delacorte Bks. for Young Readers) Random Hse. Children's Bks.

Brown, John. Journey into the Desert. 2002. (Illus.). 48p. (YA). 19.95 (978-0-19-515777-2(X)) Oxford Univ. Pr., Inc.

Cefrey, Holly. Let's Take a Hike! Converting Fractions to Decimals. 2004. (PowerMath Ser.). (Illus.). 24p. (J). lib. bdg. (978-0-8239-8928-7(3)); lib. bdg. 21.25 (978-0-8239-8979-9(8)) Rosen Publishing Group, Inc., The. (PowerKids Pr.).

DeForge, Lauretta. Take a Hike in Lane County. DeForge, Lauretta, illus. 2000. (Illus.). 44p. (YA). pap. 5.95 (978-0-9677846-1-8(1)) DeForge Communincations.

Dinio-Durkin, Cecilia. Hit the Trail! The Camping Kit for Kids. 1998. (J). pap. 16.95 (978-0-8362-5450-1(3)) Andrews McMeel Publishing.

Dorling Kindersley Publishing Staff & McManners, Hugh. Hiking. 2004. (101 Essential Tips Ser.). (Illus.). 72p. (gr. 12). pap. 5.00 (978-0-7566-0614-5(4)) Dorling Kindersley Publishing, Inc.

Eckart, Edana. I Can Go Hiking. 2003. (Wel-Sports Ser.). (Illus.). 24p. (J). 18.00 (978-0-516-24276-7(8)); pap. 4.95 (978-0-516-24368-9(3)) Scholastic Library Publishing. (Children's Pr.).

—I Can Go Hiking. 2003. (gr. k-3). lib. bdg. 12.95 (978-0-613-59636-7(6)) Tandem Library Bks.

Hanna, Dawn. Best Hikes & Walks of Southwestern British Columbia, Vol. 1. 2nd rev. ed. 2006. (Illus.). 360p. (J). (gr. 4). pap. (978-1-55105-455-1(8)) Lone Pine Publishing.

The Hiking & Camping Coloring Book. 2004. (J). mass mkt. (978-0-9745863-8-0(2)) Cypress Knees Publishing.

Hiking Together: Fourth Grade Guided Comprehension Level K. (On Our Way to English Ser.). (gr. 4 up). 34.50 (978-0-7578-7145-0(3)) Rigby Education.

Hooks, Kristine. Essential Hiking for Teens. 2000. (High Interest Bks.). (Illus.). 48p. (J). (gr. 7-12). 23.00 (978-0-516-23357-4(2), Children's Pr.) Scholastic Library Publishing.

Keller, Kristin Thoennes. Hiking. 2001. (Great Outdoors Ser.). (Illus.). 48p. (J). (gr. 3-4). lib. bdg. 21.26 (978-0-7368-0916-0(3), Capstone High-Interest Bks.) Capstone Pr., Inc.

Kids Can Press Staff, Press Can, ed. This Is Daniel Cook on A Hike. 2006. (Illus.). 28p. (J). (978-1-55453-080-9(6)); (978-1-55453-079-3(2)) Kids Can Pr., Ltd.

Lone Riders: Coral Pink Sand Dunes. 1998. (Illus.). 40p. pap. 9.95 (978-1-878261-50-2(9)) OutbackUSA, LLC.

Loy, Jessica. Follow the Trail: A Young Person's Guide to the Great Outdoors. rev. ed. 2003. (Illus.). 48p. (J). (gr. 2-7). 18.95 (978-0-8050-6195-6(9), Holt, Henry & Co. Bks. For Young Readers) Holt, Henry & Co.

Mason, Paul. Hiking & Camping. 2007. (J). (*978-1-59920-129-0(1)) Smart Apple Media.

Morina, Barbara. Hiking: A Hikers Journal. Morina, Barbara, ed. 2002. (Write It down Ser.). (Illus.). 202p. (YA). (gr. 2 up). 19.95 (978-1-892033-29-1(1)) Journals Unlimited, Inc.

Pastel, JoAnne & Fitzsimmons, Kakie. Anna Goes Hiking: Learn about Hiking & Nature. VanDeWeghe, Lindsay & Bohnet, Christopher, illus. l.t. ed. 2007. 40p. (J). lib. bdg. 14.95 (*978-0-9777121-7-5(6)) Interface Publishing.

Rae, Cheri. Hiking. 2008. (J). pap. 7.95 (*978-1-60279-086-5(8)) Cherry Lake Publishing.

Rich, D. The Denver Hiking Guide: 45 Hikes Within 45 Minutes of Denver. 2nd rev. ed. 1999. (Illus.). 104p. (Orig.). (J). pap. 12.95 (978-1-889593-58-6(3)) 3D Pr., Inc.

Richardson, Gillian. Hiking. 2007. (J). (*978-1-59036-659-2(X)); (*978-1-59036-660-8(3)) Weigl Pubs., Inc.

Slade, Suzanne. Let's Go Hiking. 2007. (Adventures Outdoors Ser.). (Illus.). 32p. (J). (gr. 4-6). lib. bdg. 23.95 (978-1-4042-3651-6(1), PowerKids Pr.) Rosen Publishing Group, Inc., The.

Thoennes Keller, Kristin. Hiking. 2008. (*978-1-4296-0821-3(8)) Capstone Pr., Inc.

White, Linda. Trekking on a Trail: Hiking Adventures for Kids. Lee, Fran, illus. 2000. 64p. (YA). (gr. 1 up). reprint ed. pap. 9.95 (978-0-87905-941-5(9)) Gibbs Smith, Publisher.

—Trekking on a Trail: Hiking Adventures for Kids. 2000. (gr. 3-6). lib. bdg. 18.75 (978-0-613-52636-4(8)) Tandem Library Bks.

Wilson, Jef. Hiking for Fun! 2006. (For Fun! Ser.). (Illus.). 48p. (J). (gr. 3-5). 22.60 (978-0-7565-1686-4(2)) Compass Point Bks.

Young, Joan H. North Country Cache: Adventures on a National Scenic Trail. 2005. (Illus.). 402p. (YA). per. 24.95 (978-0-9765432-1-3(4)) Bks. Leaving Footprints.

The 4000-Footers of the White Mountains: A Guide & History. 2001. 336p. per. 19.95 (978-1-931271-01-1(1)) Bondcliff Bks.

HILLARY, EDMUND, SIR, 1919-

Brennan, Kristine. Sir Edmund Hillary: Modern Day Explorer. 2001. (Explorers of the New World Ser.). (Illus.). 63p. (J). (gr. 4-7). pap. 25.00 (978-0-7910-6163-3(9), Chelsea Hse.) Facts On File, Inc.

—Sir Edmund Hillary: Modern Day Explorer. 2001. (gr. 3-6). lib. bdg. 17.60 (978-0-613-33056-5(0)) Tandem Library Bks.

—Sir Edmund Hillary: Modern-Day Explorer. 2000. (Explorers of the New World Ser.). (Illus.). 64p. (J). (gr. 8-12). 25.00 (978-0-7910-5953-1(7), Chelsea Hse.) Facts On File, Inc.

Coburn, Broughton. My Triumph on Everest: A Photobiography of Sir Edmund Hillary. 2000. (Illus.). 64p. (J). (gr. 3-7). 17.95 (978-0-7922-7114-7(9), National Geographic Children's Bks.) National Geographic Society.

—Triumph on Everest. 2003. (gr. 3-6). lib. bdg. 16.40 (978-0-613-62453-4(X)) Tandem Library Bks.

—Triumph on Everest: A Photobiography of Sir Edmund Hillary. 2003. (Illus.). 64p. (J). (gr. 5). 7.95 (978-0-7922-7932-7(8), National Geographic Children's Bks.) National Geographic Society.

Elish, Dan. Edmund Hillary: First to the Top. 2007. (Great Explorations Ser.). (Illus.). 80p. (YA). (gr. 5-9). lib. bdg. 32.79 (*978-0-7614-2224-2(2), Benchmark Bks.) Cavendish, Marshall Corp.

Jones, Brenn. Learning about Teamwork from the Lives of Sir Edmund Hillary & Tenzig Norgay. 2002. (Character Building Book Ser.). (Illus.). 24p. (J). (gr. 3). lib. bdg. 18.75 (978-0-8239-5778-1(0), PowerKids Pr.) Rosen Publishing Group, Inc., The.

Kerr, James. Hillary & Norgay's Mount Everest Adventure. 2007. (J). (*978-1-4034-9755-0(9)) Heinemann Library.

Whipple, Heather. Hillary & Norgay: To the Top of Mount Everest. 2007. (Illus.). 32p. (J). (gr. 3-9). (*978-0-7787-2418-6(2)); pap. (*978-0-7787-2454-4(9)) Crabtree Publishing Co.

HIMALAYA MOUNTAINS

Chapman, Simon. In the Himalayas. Chapman, Simon, illus. 2005. (Illus.). 103p. (J). lib. bdg. 20.00 (*978-1-4242-0626-1(X)) Fitzgerald Bks.

Currie, Stephen. The Himalayas. 2004. (Illus.). 112p. (J). (gr. 7-10). 29.95 (978-1-59018-497-4(1), Lucent Bks.) Thomson Gale.

Harcourt School Publishers Staff. The Himalayan Mountains. 3rd ed. 2002. (Horizons Ser.). (Illus.). (J). pap. 3.70 (978-0-15-333208-1(5)) Harcourt Schl. Pubs.

Maynard, Charles W. The Himalayas. 2004. (Great Mountain Ranges of the World Ser.). (Illus.). 24p. (J). lib. bdg. 21.25 (978-0-8239-6694-3(1), PowerKids Pr.) Rosen Publishing Group, Inc., The.

Nagda, Ann Whitehead. World above the Clouds: A Story of a Himalayan Ecosystem. Kratter, Paul, illus. 2005. (Wild Habitats Ser.: Vol. 18). (J). (gr. 1-4). 36p. 15.95 (978-1-56899-878-7(3), B7017), 32p. pap. 6.95 (978-1-56899-879-4(1), S7017) Soundprints.

—World above the Clouds: A Story of a Himalayan Ecosystem Including 9" Toy. Kratter, Paul, illus. (Wild Habitats Ser.: Vol. 18). 36p. (J). (gr. 1-4). 2005. 17.95 (978-1-56899-883-1(X), PS7017); 2000. 26.95 (978-1-56899-882-4(1), PB7017) Soundprints.

Reynolds, Jan. Himalaya: Vanishing Cultures. 2007. 32p. (J). (*978-1-60060-129-3(4)); (*978-1-60060-144-6(8)) Lee & Low Bks., Inc.

Somervill, Barbara A. The Magnificent Himalayas. 2004. (Geography of the World Ser.). (Illus.). 32p. (J). (gr. 2-6). 27.07 (978-1-59296-332-4(3)) Child's World, Inc.

HIMALAYA MOUNTAINS—FICTION

Delgado, Josep Francesc. Nima, El Sherpa. 2003. (SPA.). 168p. (978-84-8453-060-2(4), PT31196) Ediciones del Bronce ESP. *Dist:* Lectorum Pubns., Inc.

Gelsey, James. Chill-Out Scooby-Doo. 2007. (Scooby-Doo Video Tie-In Novelization Ser.). 64p. (J). pap. 3.99 (*978-0-439-91595-3(3)) Scholastic, Inc.

Gelsey, James, et al. Chill-Out Scooby-Doo. 2007. (Scooby-Doo 8x8 Video Tie-In Ser.). 24p. (J). pap. 3.99 (*978-0-439-91597-7(X)) Scholastic, Inc.

Gross, Philip. The Lastling. 2006. 256p. (YA). (gr. 7). 16.00 (978-0-618-65998-2(6), Clarion Bks.) Houghton Mifflin Co. Trade & Reference Div.

Gustaveson, Dave. The Himalayan Rescue. 2000. (Reel Kids Adventures Ser.: Bk. 10). 168p. (gr. 5-7). pap. 6.99 (978-1-57658-027-1(X)) YWAM Publishing.

Lama, Nurbu Tenzing. Himalaya. Tanaka, Shelley, tr. from FRE. Lama, Nurbu Tenzing, illus. 2002. (Illus.). 40p. (J). 16.95 (978-0-88899-480-6(X)) Groundwood Bks. CAN. *Dist:* Perseus Distribution.

H
I

Mills, J. C. Carew. rev. ed. 2007. (Illus.). 248p. pap. 7.95 (*978-1-55263-788-3(3)*) Key Porter Bks. CAN. *Dist:* Perseus Distribution.

Munnik, Hema. Bhole: Adventures of a Young Yogi. 2006. 352p. pap. 18.95 (978-81-88157-37-2(6)) Lotus Pr.

Naga, Ann Whitehead. World above the Clouds: A Story of a Himalayan Ecosystem. 2005. (Soundprints' Wild Habitats Ser.). (Illus.). 36p. (J). (gr. 1-4). 8.95 incl. audio (978-1-59249-105-6(7) , SC7017) Soundprints.

Nagda, Ann Whitehead. World above the Clouds: A Story of A Himalayan Ecosystem. 2000. (gr. 3-6). lib. bdg. 14.10 (978-0-613-56876-0(1)) Tandem Library Bks.

Neale, Jonathan. Himalaya. 2004. 160p. (J). (gr. 5-9). tchr. ed. 16.00 (978-0-618-41200-6(X)) Houghton Mifflin Co. Trade & Reference Div.

Stryer, Andrea Stenn. Kami & the Yaks. Dodson, Bert, illus. 2007. 48p. (J). (gr. k-3). 16.95 (*978-0-9778961-0-3(2)*); pap. 9.95 (*978-0-9778961-1-0(0)*) Bay Otter Pr.

Thompson, Kate. Only Human. 2006. (Missing Link Trilogy Ser.: Bk. 2). 320p. (YA). 16.95 (978-1-58234-651-9(8) , Bloomsbury Children) Bloomsbury Publishing.

Thorpe, Kiki. Snowbound. 2000. (gr. k-3). lib. bdg. 11.80 (978-0-613-31727-6(0)) Tandem Library Bks.

Vandersteen, Willy. Sagarmatha. Geerts, Paul, illus. 1998. (Greatest Adventures of Spike & Suzy Ser.: Vol. 1). 56p. (J). (gr. 2-9). 11.95 (978-0-9533178-0-6(3)) Intes International (UK) Ltd. GBR. *Dist:* Diamond Comic Distributors, Inc.

HINDUISM

see also Yoga

Chopra, Deepak. Fire in the Heart: A Spiritual Guide for Teens. 208p. (YA). 2006. pap. 9.95 (978-0-689-86217-5(2) , Simon Pulse); 2004. (Illus.). 14.95 (978-0-689-86216-8(4)) Simon & Schuster Children's Publishing.

Das, Rasamandala. Hinduism. 2005. (Illus.). 48p. (J). pap. (978-0-8368-5873-0(5)); lib. bdg. 30.00 (978-0-8368-5867-9(0)) Stevens, Gareth Inc. (World Almanac Library).

Ganeri, Anita. Hindu. (Illus.). 32p. (YA). (gr. 3 up). lib. bdg. 27.10 (978-1-932889-13-0(2)) Sea-To-Sea Pubns.

—Hindu Festivals Through the Year. 2003. (Year of Festivals Ser.). 30p. (J). lib. bdg. 24.25 (978-1-58340-372-3(8)) Smart Apple Media.

—Hindu Mandirs. 2005. (Let's Find Out about Ser.). (Illus.). 32p. (J). 25.36 (978-1-4034-7033-1(2)) Steck-Vaughn.

—Hinduism: Babu's Story. 2006. (This Is My Faith Bks.). (Illus.). 32p. (J). (gr. 1-4). 11.99 (978-0-7641-5965-7(8)); pap. 4.99 (978-0-7641-3474-6(4)) Barron's Educational Series, Inc.

—My Hindu Faith. 2006. (World Faiths Ser.). (Illus.). 32p. (J). (978-1-84234-392-0(0) , Cherrytree Books) Evans Publishing Group.

—My Hindu Faith. 1998. (My Faith Ser.). (Illus.). 32p. 9.99 (978-0-237-51896-7(1) , Evans Brothers, Limited) Evans Publishing Group GBR. *Dist:* Independent Pubs. Group.

—The Ramayana & Other Hindu Texts. 2003. 30p. (J). lib. bdg. 24.25 (978-1-58340-242-9(X)) Smart Apple Media.

George, Charles. Hindu. 2004. (What Makes Me A—? Ser.). (Illus.). 48p. (J). 26.20 (978-0-7377-2267-3(3) , Greenhaven Pr., Inc.) Thomson Gale.

Gibson, Lynne. Hinduism. 2003. (Living Religions Ser.). (Illus.). 62p. (J). 28.56 (978-0-7398-6384-8(3)) Raintree.

Gillis, Jennifer Blizin & Jordan, Denise M. Diwali. 2002. (Fiestas Con Velas (Candle Time) Ser.). (SPA.). 24p. (J). (ps-1). lib. bdg. 18.50 (978-1-58810-782-4(5)); (Illus.). pap. 5.25 (978-1-58810-829-6(5) , 91588) Heinemann Library.

Hartney, Chris, et al. Livewire Investigates Hinduism. 2004. (Livewires Ser.). (Illus.). 32p. pap. 4.10 (978-0-521-60111-5(8)) Cambridge Univ. Pr.

Hinduism. 2004. (Exploring World Beliefs Ser.). (Illus.). 48p. 7.99 (978-0-7439-3681-1(7)) Teacher Created Materials, Inc.

Hughes, Monica. My Divali. 2003. (Festivals Ser.). (Illus.). 24p. (J). pap. 5.50 (978-1-4109-0663-2(9)); lib. bdg. 18.56 (978-1-4109-0637-3(X)) Raintree.

Jani, Mahendra & Jani, Vandana. What You Will See Inside a Hindu Temple. Bhargava, Neirah & Dave, Vijay, photos by. 2005. (What You Will See Inside- Ser.). (Illus.). 32p. (J). pap. 17.99 (978-1-59473-116-7(0)) SkyLight Paths Publishing.

Jendresen, Erik & Greene, Joshua M. Hanuman: Based on Valmiki's Ramayana. Ming, Li, illus. 2003. 40p. (YA). (ps-3). 15.95 (978-1-883672-78-2(3) , Tricycle Pr.) Ten Speed Pr.

Johari, Harish & Sperling, Vatsala. How Parvati Won the Heart of Shiva. Weltevrede, Pieter, illus. 2004. (Classic Indian Stories for Children Ser.). 32p. (J). 15.95 (978-1-59143-042-1(9) , Bear Cub Bks.) Bear & Co.

Jones, Constance & Ryan, James. Encyclopedia of Hinduism. 2008. (Encyclopedia of World Religions Ser.). 528p. (gr. 9). pap. 21.95 (*978-0-8160-7336-8(8)* , Checkmark Bks.) Facts On File, Inc.

Jordan, Denise M. Diwali. 2002. (Candle Time Ser.). (Illus.). 24p. (J). (ps-1). pap. 5.25 (978-1-58810-736-7(1) , 91385); lib. bdg. 18.50 (978-1-58810-527-1(X)) Heinemann Library.

Krishnaswami, Uma. The Broken Tusk: Stories of the Hindu God Ganesha. Selven, Maniam, illus. 2006. 128p. pap. 16.95 (978-0-87483-806-0(1)) August Hse. Pubs., Inc.

Marchant, Kerena. Hindu Cookbook. Mukhida, Zul, illus. 2001. (Holiday Cookbooks from Around the World). 32p. (J). (gr. 4-7). lib. bdg. 25.69 (978-0-7398-3264-6(6)) Raintree.

—Hindu Festivals. 2001. (Festival Tales Ser.). (Illus.). 32p. (J). (gr. 4-7). lib. bdg. 25.69 (978-0-7398-2734-5(0)) Raintree.

—Krishna & Hinduism. 2002. (Great Religious Leaders Ser.). (Illus.). 48p. (J). lib. bdg. 28.50 (978-1-58340-218-4(7)) Smart Apple Media.

Mead, Jean & Nason, Ruth. Visiting a Mandir. 2005. (Start up Religion Ser.). (Illus.). 24p. (J). (gr. 1-4). lib. bdg. (978-1-84234-346-3(7) , Cherrytree Books) Evans Publishing Group.

Parker. The Ganges. 2003. pap. 35.10 (978-1-4109-0240-5(4)); (Illus.). 32p. (J). pap. 6.95 (978-1-4109-0051-7(7)) Raintree.

Parker-Rock, Michelle. Diwali: The Hindu Festival of Lights, Feasts, & Family. 2004. (Finding Out about Holidays Ser.). (Illus.). 48p. (J). lib. bdg. 23.93 (978-0-7660-2235-5(8)) Enslow Pubs., Inc.

Parker, Victoria. The Ganges. 2003. (Holy Places Ser.). (Illus.). 32p. (J). 24.28 (978-0-7398-6078-6(X)) Raintree.

Penney, Sue. Hinduism. 2000. (World Beliefs & Cultures Ser.). (Illus.). 48p. (J). lib. bdg. 25.64 (978-1-57572-356-3(5)) Heinemann Library.

Prasad, Ramananda, tr. from SAN. The Bhagavad-Gita: The Sacred Song. 4th ed. 2004. 384p. 24.95 (978-0-9621099-2-8(4)) American Gita Society.

Prime, Ranchor. Hinduism. (Illus.). 64p. (YA). (gr. 4 up). lib. bdg. 29.95 (978-1-59389-129-9(6)) Chrysalis Education.

—Hinduism. 2005. (World Religions Ser.). (Illus.). 58p. (J). (gr. 4-12). pap. 12.95 (978-1-55285-655-0(0) , Walrus Bks.) Whitecap Bks., Ltd. CAN. *Dist:* Firefly Bks., Ltd.

Rajan, Gayatri. The Story of Santoshi Devi. (Illus.). 40p. (Orig.). (J). (gr. k-6). pap. (978-0-9644226-0-5(3)) Buddhi Pubns.

Ramen, Fred. Hindian Mythology. 2006. (Mythology Around the World Ser.). (J). (978-1-4042-0735-6(X)) Rosen Publishing Group, Inc., The.

Rasamandala Das. Hinduism Around the World. 2007. (J). (*978-1-59920-057-6(0)*) Smart Apple Media.

Rasamandala Das & Ganeri, Anita. Hindu Prayer & Worship. 2007. (*978-1-59771-093-0(8)*) Sea-To-Sea Pubns.

Ries, Julien. Man & the Divine in Hinduism. 2002. (Religions of Mankind Ser.). (Illus.). 32p. (YA). (gr. 5 up). 21.95 (978-0-7910-6625-6(8) , Chelsea Hse.) Facts On File, Inc.

Robinson, James B. Hinduism. 2004. (Religions of the World Ser.). (Illus.). (gr. 9-13). 150p. 35.00 (978-0-7910-7858-7(2)); 120p. pap. 15.95 (978-0-7910-8013-9(7)) Facts On File, Inc. (Chelsea Hse.).

Rossi, Ann. India. 2004. (National Geographic Reading Expeditions Ser.). (Illus.). 24p. (J). pap. (978-0-7922-4537-7(7)) National Geographic Society.

Scudder, John. Dr. Scudder's Tales for Little Readers. 2006. 32.99 (*978-1-4280-0818-2(7)*); pap. 25.99 (*978-1-4280-0810-6(1)*) IndyPublish.com.

See & Paint: Gods & Goddesses. 18p. (J). (ps-5). 2.95 (978-81-7120-245-4(4)) Sri Ramakrishna Math IND. *Dist:* Vedanta Pr.

Senker, Cath. My Hindu Year. 2007. (J). lib. bdg. (*978-1-4042-3731-5(3)* , PowerKids Pr.) Rosen Publishing Group, Inc., The.

Shakti, Ananta. Vaishnava Saints. 2002. 124p. (J). pap. (978-1-887089-39-5(X)) Torchlight Publishing.

Spilsbury, Louise & Spilsbury, Richard. Living on the Ganges River. 2007. (J). (*978-1-4109-2820-7(9)*); (*978-1-4109-2829-0(2)*) Steck-Vaughn.

Teece, Geoff. Hinduism. 2004. (Religion in Focus Ser.). (J). lib. bdg. (978-1-58340-466-9(X)) Smart Apple Media.

Vaalmaiki. The Story of Divaali. Mistry, Nilesh, illus. 2002. 40p. (J). (gr. 2-4). 16.99 (978-1-84148-936-0(0)) Barefoot Bks., Inc.

Valmiki, Sri. The Ramayana for Young Readers. Acharya, Milly, illus. 1998. 62p. (J). 12.50 (978-81-7223-285-6(3)) HarperCollins Pubs.

Vyas, Neera. Hinduism Pupil Book. Taylor, Ina, ed. 2006. (Illus.). 64p. (YA). pap. 21.00 (978-0-7487-9673-1(8)) Nelson Thornes Ltd. GBR. *Dist:* Trans-Atlantic Pubns., Inc.

Wangu, Madhu Bazaz. Hinduism. 2nd rev. ed. 2001. (World Religions Ser.). (Illus.). 128p. (J). (gr. 4-9). 30.00 (978-0-8160-4400-9(7)) Facts On File, Inc.

Wood, Angela. Hindu Mandir. 1999. (Places of Worship Ser.). (Illus.). 32p. (J). (gr. 2 up). lib. bdg. 23.33 (978-0-8368-2607-4(8)) Stevens, Gareth Inc.

Young, Serinity. Hinduism. 2006. (World Religions Ser.). (Illus.). 144p. (J). (gr. 8 up). lib. bdg. 39.93 (978-0-7614-2116-0(5) , Benchmark Bks.) Cavendish, Marshall Corp.

HIP-HOP MUSIC

see Rap (Music)

HIPPIES—FICTION

Fietzek, Petra. Trommeln, Trommeln. 2002. (GER.). 128p. pap. 15.00 (978-1-4000-3958-6(4) , New Media German Language) Random House Foreign Language Publishing.

Gutman, Dan. Mr. Louie Is Screwy! Paillot, Jim, illus. 2007. (My Weird School Ser.: No. 20). 112p. (J). lib. bdg. 15.89 (*978-0-06-123480-4(X)*); pap. 3.99 (*978-0-06-123479-8(6)* , Harper Trophy) HarperCollins Pubs.

Lindbergh, Reeve. My Hippie Grandmother. Carter, Abby, illus. 2003. 24p. (J). (ps). 15.99 (978-0-7636-0671-8(5)) Candlewick Pr.

HIPPOCRATES

Whiting, Jim. Hippocrates. 2006. (Biography from Ancient Civilizations Ser.). (Illus.). 48p. (J). lib. bdg. 20.95 (978-1-58415-512-6(4) , 1259600) Mitchell Lane Pubs., Inc.

HIPPOPOTAMUS

Barbe-Julian, Colette. Little Hippopotamuses. 2005. (Born to Be Wild Ser.). (Illus.). 24p. (J). (ps). lib. bdg. 22.00 (978-0-8368-4736-9(9)) Stevens, Gareth Inc.

Bebe Hipopotamo: Individual Title Six-Packs. (Coleccion Pm Ser.).Tr. of Baby hippo. (SPA.). 16p. (gr. 1 up). 26.00 (978-0-7578-2982-6(1)) Rigby Education.

Edwards, Roberta. Best Friends: The True Story of Owen & Mzee. Schwartz, Carol, illus. 2007. (All Aboard Science Reader Ser.). 32p. (J). pap. 3.99 (978-0-448-44567-0(0) , Grosset & Dunlap) Penguin Group (USA) Inc.

Evento, Susan. The Mighty Hippopotamus. 2003. (Illus.). 32p. (J). pap. 6.00 (978-1-59034-493-4(6)) Mondo Publishing.

Gareth Stevens Publishing Staff, contrib. by. Hippos. 2004. (All about Wild Animals Ser.). (Illus.). 32p. (J). (gr. 2 up). lib. bdg. 23.33 (978-0-8368-4118-3(2)) Stevens, Gareth Inc.

Hatkoff, Craig & Hatkoff, Isabella. Owen & Mzee: A Day Together. 2008. (Fairy House Ser.). 112p. (J). bds. 6.99 (*978-0-545-03766-2(2)*) Scholastic, Inc.

Hatkoff, Craig, et al. Owen & Mzee: The Language of Friendship. Greste, Peter, photos by. 2007. (Illus.). 40p. (J). (ps-3). pap. 16.99 (978-0-439-89959-8(1) , Scholastic Pr.) Scholastic, Inc.

—Owen & Mzee: The True Story of a Remarkable Friendship. Greste, Peter, illus. 2006. 40p. (J). (ps-3). pap. 16.99 (978-0-439-82973-1(9) , Scholastic Pr.) Scholastic, Inc.

Hippos. 2003. (J). per. (978-1-57657-944-2(1)) Paradise Pr., Inc.

Hippos: Individual Title Six-Packs. (Story Steps Ser.). (gr. k-2). 32.00 (978-0-7635-9618-7(3)); (gr. 1-2). 36.00 (978-0-7578-6771-2(5)) Rigby Education.

Jango-Cohen, Judith. Hippopotamuses. 2006. (Animals Animals Ser.). (Illus.). 48p. (J). lib. bdg. 28.50 (978-0-7614-2238-9(2) , Benchmark Bks.) Cavendish, Marshall Corp.

Kendell, Patricia. Hippos. 2003. (In the Wild Ser.). (Illus.). 32p. (J). lib. bdg. 25.70 (978-0-7398-6635-1(4)) Raintree.

Leach, Michael. Hippopotamus: Habitats, Life Cycles, Food Chains, Threats. 2001. (Natural World Ser.). (Illus.). 48p. (J). (gr. 3-7). lib. bdg. 27.12 (978-0-7398-2769-7(3)) Raintree.

Macken, JoAnn Early. Hippos. 2002. (Weekly Reader Early Learning Library). (Illus.). 24p. (J). (ps up). pap. 5.95 (978-0-8368-3283-9(3)); lib. bdg. 19.33 (978-0-8368-3270-9(1)) Stevens, Gareth Inc. (Weekly Reader Early Learning Library).

Pingry, Patricia A. Baby Hippopotamus. Sharp, Chris, illus. 2004. (San Diego Zoo Animal Library: Vol. 5). 26p. (J). bds. 6.95 (978-0-8249-6554-9(X)) Ideals Pubns.

Ring, Susan. Project Hippopotamus. Kissock, Heather & Marshall, Diana, eds. 2003. (Zoo Life Ser.). (Illus.). 24p. (J). pap. 6.95 (978-1-59036-057-6(5)) Weigl Pubs., Inc.

—Project Hippopotomus. 2002. (Zoo Babies Ser.). (Illus.). 24p. (J). lib. bdg. 15.15 (978-1-59036-013-2(3)) Weigl Pubs., Inc.

Stewart, Melissa. Hippopotamuses. 2002. (True Book Ser.). (Illus.). 48p. (J). (gr. 3-5). 25.00 (978-0-516-22200-4(7) , Children's Pr.) Scholastic Library Publishing.

Stone, Tanya Lee. Hippos. 2003. (Wild Wild World Ser.). 24p. (YA). 24.94 (978-1-56711-815-5(1) , Blackbirch Pr., Inc.) Thomson Gale.

Storad, Conrad J. Hippos. 2006. (Early Bird Nature Books). (Illus.). 48p. (J). (gr. 3-7). 25.26 (978-0-8225-2869-2(X) , Lerner Pubns.) Lerner Publishing Group.

Suen, Anastasia. A Hippopotamus Grows Up. Denman, Michael L. & Huiett, William J., illus. 2005. (Wild Animals Ser.). 24p. (J). (ps). lib. bdg. 23.93 (978-1-4048-0988-8(0)) Picture Window Bks.

Twinn, Michael. Pocket Hippo. Adams, Pam, illus. 2000. 12p. (J). bds. 1.99 (978-0-85953-880-0(X)) Child's Play-International.

Walker, Sally M. Hippos. 2008. (Nature Watch Ser.). (J). lib. bdg. 26.60 (*978-0-8225-7512-2(4)* , Lerner Pubns.) Lerner Publishing Group.

Ward, Rebecca. Hippo. 1999. (J). (978-1-84100-211-8(9)) Quadrillion Publishing.

Whitehouse, Patricia. El Hipopotamo. 2003. (Animales Del Zoologico Ser.). (SPA., Illus.). 24p. pap. 5.25 (978-1-4034-0654-5(5)) Heinemann Library.

—El Hipopotamo. 2003. (Animales del Zoologico (Zoo Animals) Ser.). (SPA.). 24p. (J). (ps-1). lib. bdg. 17.08 (978-1-4034-0406-0(2)) Heinemann Library.

—Hippopotamus. 2003. (Zoo Animals Ser.). (Illus.). 24p. (ps-1). (J). lib. bdg. 17.08 (978-1-58810-899-9(6)); pap. 5.25 (978-1-4034-0645-3(6)) Heinemann Library.

Wildlife Education, Ltd. Staff & Brust, Beth W. Hippos. Francis, John, illus. (Zoobooks Ser.). (J). 2001. 24p. 15.95 (978-0-937934-79-1(8)); 1998. 18p. pap. 2.95 (978-0-937934-54-8(2)) Wildlife Education, Ltd.

Wilsdon, Christina. Hippopotamus. 2006. (J). (978-1-59939-077-2(9) , Reader's Digest Young Families, Inc.) Reader's Digest Children's Publishing, Inc.

Winter, Jeanette. Mama: A True Story, in Which a Baby Hippo Loses His Mama During a Tsunami, but Finds a New Home, & a New Mama. 2006. (Illus.). 32p. (J). 16.00 (978-0-15-205495-3(2)) Harcourt Children's Bks.

Zumbusch, Amelie von. Hippos. 2007. (Safari Animals Ser.). (Illus.). 24p. (J). (gr. k-3). lib. bdg. 21.25 (978-1-4042-3617-2(1) , PowerKids Pr.) Rosen Publishing Group, Inc., The.

HIPPOPOTAMUS—FICTION

Bauer, Marion Dane. A Mama for Owen. Butler, John, illus. 2007. 32p. (J). 15.99 (978-0-689-85787-4(X) , Simon & Schuster Children's Publishing) Simon & Schuster Children's Publishing.

Big Hippo & Little Hippo: Individual Title Six-Packs. (Sails Literacy Ser.). (gr. 1-2). 36.00 (978-0-7578-4008-1(6)) Rigby Education.

Bigosinski, Jeremi. Harry Hippo's Flight: Adventures in Hippoville. Bigosinski, Jeremi, illus. l.t. ed. 2002. (Illus.). 24p. (J). 9.95 (978-0-9722265-0-9(8)) Hippoville Publishing, LLC.

Bloom, Becky. Leo & Lester. Biet, Pascal, illus. 2003. (J). 32p. 15.95 (978-1-59034-582-5(7)); 33p. pap. (978-1-59034-583-2(5)) Mondo Publishing.

Boynton, Sandra. But Not the Hippopotamus. 2001. (Illus.). (J). bds. 4.99 (978-0-689-83626-8(0) , Simon & Schuster Children's Publishing) Simon & Schuster Children's Publishing.

—Hippos Go Berserk. Boynton, Sandra, illus. 2000. (Illus.). 16p. (J). (ps-3). bds. 7.99 (978-0-689-83434-9(9) , Little Simon) Simon & Schuster Children's Publishing.

—Hippos Go Berserk! 2000. (Illus.). 32p. (J). per. 7.99 (978-0-689-83499-8(3) , Simon & Schuster Children's Publishing) Simon & Schuster Children's Publishing.

—Your Personal Penguin. 2006. (Illus.). 24p. (J). bds. 6.95 (978-0-7611-4372-7(6)) Workman Publishing Co., Inc.

Brez, Lisa. Hickerdoodle Meets a Chigger. l.t. ed. 2004. (Illus.). 40p. (J). per. 6.99 (978-0-9743758-5-4(3)) Red Engine Pr.

Canetti, Yanitzia. Completamente Diferente. Peinador, Angeles, tr. Peinador, Angeles, illus. (SPA.). 32p. (J). (gr. 1-2). 7.20 (978-84-241-8068-3(2) , EV31696) Everest de Ediciones y Distribucion, S.L. ESP. *Dist:* Lectorum Pubns., Inc.

—Completamente Diferente. Peinador, Angeles, illus. 2002. (SPA.). 32p. (J). (gr. k-2). 13.99 (978-84-241-7973-1(0) , EV2817) Everest de Ediciones y Distribucion, S.L. ESP. *Dist:* Lectorum Pubns., Inc.

Castle, Caroline. Funny! 2005. (Illus.). 32p. (J). pap. 11.95 (978-0-09-943302-6(8) , Red Fox) Random Hse. Children's Bks. GBR. *Dist:* Trafalgar Square Publishing.

Coplans, Peta & Camp, Lindsay. Hippo's River Cafe. 1998. (Illus.). 26p. (J). 19.99 (978-0-86264-804-6(1)) Andersen GBR. *Dist:* Independent Pubs. Group.

Delaney, Michael. Birdbrain Amos: Mr. Fun. 2006. (Illus.). 160p. (J). (gr. 3). 15.99 (978-0-399-24278-6(3) , Philomel) Penguin Group (USA) Inc.

Delval, Marie He. Hippopo va se Baigner. 12.95 (978-2-227-75604-5(7)) Bayard Editions FRA. *Dist:* Distribooks, Inc.

Durber, Matt & Brooks, Felicity. Muddy Hippo. 2007. (Play Bks). 10p. (J). bds. 10.99 (*978-0-7945-1688-8(2)* , Usborne) EDC Publishing.

Duvoisin, Roger. Veronica. 2006. 40p. (J). (ps-3). 15.95 (978-0-375-83566-7(0)); lib. bdg. 17.99 (978-0-375-93566-4(5)) Random Hse. Children's Bks. (Knopf Bks. for Young Readers).

Duvoisin, Roger. Veronica on Petunia's Farm. 2008. 40p. (J). (gr. k-3). 16.99 (*978-0-375-85211-4(5)* , Knopf Bks. for Young Readers) Random Hse. Children's Bks.

Faulkner, Keith. The Hiccuping Hippo. 2004. (Illus.). 16p. (J). (ps). 12.99 (978-0-8037-2963-6(4) , Dial) Penguin Group (USA) Inc.

Fox, Mary Virginia. The Hippo Hungry. Chapin, Patrick, illus. 2002. (Two Can Read Ser.). 16p. (J). 2.99 (978-1-56472-652-0(5)) Edupress, Inc.

French, Vivian. Mrs. Hippo's Pizza Parlor. Scruton, Clive, illus. 2004. (I Am Reading Ser.). 48p. (J). (gr. k-3). pap. 3.95 (978-0-7534-5823-5(3) , Kingfisher) Houghton Mifflin Co. Trade & Reference Div.

Goldsmith, Howard. The Twiddle Twins' Amusement Park Mystery. Jordan, Charles, illus. 1998. (Mondo Ser.). 40p. (J). (gr. 1-5). pap. 4.50 (978-1-57255-618-8(8)) Mondo Publishing.

—The Twiddle Twins' Single Footprint Mystery. Jordan, Charles, illus. 1998. (Mondo Ser.). 40p. (J). (gr. 1-5). pap. 4.50 (978-1-57255-619-5(6)) Mondo Publishing.

Grambling, Lois G. This Whole Tooth Fairy Thing's Nothing but a Big Rip-off! Payne, Thomas, illus. 2002. 32p. (J). (gr. k-3). 15.95 (978-0-7614-5104-4(8) , Cavendish Children's Bks.) Cavendish, Marshall Corp.

Gregory, Valiska. Shirley's Wonderful Baby. Degen, Bruce, illus. 1999. 32p. pap. 5.95 (978-0-06-443513-0(X)) HarperCollins Pubs.

Hartman, Bob. Time to Go, Hippo! Simpson, Kate, illus. 2002. 32p. (ps-3). 8.99 (978-0-8066-4365-6(X) , Augsburg Bks.) Augsburg Fortress, Pubs.

—Time to Go, Hippo! Simpson, Kate, illus. 2000. 32p. (J). pap. 9.99 (978-0-7459-4454-8(X) , Lion) Lion Hudson plc GBR. *Dist:* Independent Pubs. Group.

Hatkoff, Craig & Hatkoff, Isabella. Best Friends. 2007. (Owen & Mzee Ser.). 12p. (J). bds. 6.99 (978-0-439-92782-4(9) , Scholastic Pr.) Scholastic, Inc.

Henry Hippo. 2002. 12p. bds. 2.50 (978-1-56021-400-7(7)) W.J. Fantasy, Inc.

El Hipopotamo. 2002. Tr. of Hippo. (SPA., Illus.). 22p. (J). 6.50 (978-84-246-1734-9(7)) La Galera, S.A. Editorial ESP. *Dist:* AIMS International Bks., Inc.

A Hippo in June's Tub, Vol. 2. 2005. (Early Library). (YA). (ps-3). 23.94 (978-0-8215-8958-8(X)) Sadlier, William H. Inc.

Hippo Pot & Hippo Tot, Set. A,6 Packs. (gr. k-3). 29.00 (978-0-7635-0532-5(3)) Rigby Education.

Horowitz, Dave. A Monkey among Us. Horowitz, Dave, illus. 2004. (Illus.). 40p. (J). (ps-1). 14.99 (978-0-06-054335-8(3) , Harper Festival) HarperCollins Pubs.

Horton, Joan. Hippopotamus Stew & Other Silly Animal Poems. Adinolfi, JoAnn, illus. rev. ed. 2006. 32p. (J). 16.95 (978-0-8050-7350-8(7) , Holt, Henry & Co. Bks. For Young Readers) Holt, Henry & Co.

Jenkins, Emily. Hug, Hug, Hug! A Bea & Haha Book. Bogacki, Tomek, illus. 2006. (Bea & Haha Board Bks.). 14p. (J). 5.95 (978-0-374-30581-9(1)) Farrar, Straus & Giroux.

—Num, Num, Num! A Bea & Haha Book. Bogacki, Tomek, illus. 2006. (Bea & Haha Board Bks.). 14p. (J). 5.95 (978-0-374-30583-3(8)) Farrar, Straus & Giroux.

Jeyaveeran, Ruth. The Spectacular Adventures of Sophie & Sebastian. Jeyaveeran, Ruth, illus. 2005. (Illus.). 32p. (J). (gr. k-3). 16.00 (978-0-618-50756-6(6)) Houghton Mifflin Co. Trade & Reference Div.

Jones, Shelley V. & Sprick, Marilyn. Turtle in the Tuba: Read Well Level K Unit 8 Storybook. McDonnell, Kevin, illus. 2004. (Read Well Level K Ser.). 20p. (978-1-57035-672-8(6)) Sopris West Educational Services.

Landstrom, Lena. A Hippo's Tale. Sandin, Joan, tr. from SWE. 2007. (Illus.). 32p. (J). (ps-1). 15.00 (***978-91-29-66603-8(1)***) R & S Bks. SWE. *Dist:* Macmillan.

Law, Felicia. Rumble Meets Harry Hippo. Pak, Yoon Mi, illus. 2006. (Read-It! Readers Ser.). 32p. (J). (gr. 2-4). 18.60 (978-1-4048-1338-0(1)) Picture Window Bks.

Lee, Hector Viveros. I Had a Hippopotamus. Lee, Hector Viveros, illus. (Illus.). 32p. (J). (gr. k-1). 1999. bds. 6.95 (978-1-880000-96-0(2)); 1998. 6.95 (978-1-880000-62-5(8)) Lee & Low Bks., Inc.

—Yo Tenia un Hipopotamo. Lee, Hector Viveros, illus. 1999. (SPA., Illus.). 34p. (J). (ps-1). bds. 5.56 net. (978-1-880000-97-7(0) , LW5519) Lee & Low Bks., Inc.

Lester, Helen. Hurty Feelings. Munsinger, Lynn M., illus. 32p. (J). (gr. k-3). 2007. 6.95 (***978-0-618-84062-5(1));*** 2004. tchr. ed. 16.00 (978-0-618-41082-8(1)) Houghton Mifflin Co. Trade & Reference Div. (Walter Lorraine).

London, Jonathan. Zack at the Dentist. Medoff, Jack, illus. 2004. 32p. (J). pap. 3.50 (978-0-439-53776-6(2) , Cartwheel Bks.) Scholastic, Inc.

Long, Olivia. Hortense, the Happy Hippo. Long, Olivia, illus. Date not set. (Kaleidoscope Ser.). (Illus.). 32p. (J). (ps-4). (978-1-880042-03-8(7)) Shelf-Life Bks.

Magorian, James. The Hippopotamus. Cowman, Amy H., illus. 1998. 19p. (J). (gr. 2-5). pap. 6.00 (978-0-930674-49-6(9)) Black Oak Pr.

Marshall, James. George & Martha. Marshall, James, illus. 2002. (George & Martha Ser.). (Illus.). (J). 14.74 (978-0-7587-2568-4(X)) Book Wholesalers, Inc.

—George & Martha. 2007. (Illus.). 24p. (J). (ps-3). 15.00 (***978-0-618-96331-7(6)***) Houghton Mifflin Co. Trade & Reference Div.

—George & Martha Back in Town. Marshall, James, illus. 2002. (George & Martha Ser.). (Illus.). (J). 14.74 (978-0-7587-2569-1(8)) Book Wholesalers, Inc.

—George & Martha Encore. Marshall, James, illus. 2002. (George & Martha Ser.). (Illus.). (J). 14.74 (978-0-7587-2570-7(1)) Book Wholesalers, Inc.

—George & Martha One Fine Day. Marshall, James, illus. 2002. (George & Martha Ser.). (Illus.). (J). 14.74 (978-0-7587-2571-4(X)) Book Wholesalers, Inc.

—George & Martha Rise & Shine. Marshall, James, illus. 2002. (George & Martha Ser.). (Illus.). (J). 14.74 (978-0-7587-2572-1(8)) Book Wholesalers, Inc.

—George & Martha Round & Round. Marshall, James, illus. 2002. (George & Martha Ser.). (Illus.). (J). 14.74 (978-0-7587-2573-8(6)) Book Wholesalers, Inc.

—George & Martha Tons of Fun. Marshall, James, illus. 2002. (George & Martha Ser.). (Illus.). (J). 14.74 (978-0-7587-2574-5(4)) Book Wholesalers, Inc.

—Jorge y Marta. 2000. (SPA., Illus.). 48p. (J). (gr. k-3). 16.00 (978-0-618-05075-8(2) , HM4632); pap. 6.95 (978-0-618-05076-5(0) , HM0196) Houghton Mifflin Co. Trade & Reference Div.

—Jorge y Marta. 2000. (SPA.). (ps-2). lib. bdg. 15.25 (978-0-613-27917-8(4)); (Illus.). (J). 13.75 (978-0-606-18210-2(1)) Tandem Library Bks.

Marshall, James. Two Great Friends. 2007. (George & Martha Ser.). (Illus.). 24p. (J). (ps-3). 15.00 (***978-0-618-96178-8(X)***) Houghton Mifflin Co. Trade & Reference Div.

Marten, Bos & Bos, Claire. Maurice the Hippo. 1998. (Illus.). 20p. (J). (ps-k). pap. 8.95 (978-0-531-30098-5(6) , Orchard Bks.) Scholastic, Inc.

Maxwell, Malcolm. The Hippo Club. 2002. 32p. pap. 14.00 (978-0-8059-5892-8(4)) Dorrance Publishing Co., Inc.

May, Tessa. Bella Wishes. Rodriguez, Dave, illus. 2004. 35p. pap. 13.95 incl. audio compact disk (978-0-9759325-0-6(0)) CarLou Interactive Media & Publishing.

McKay, Sharon E. Harley's Blue Day. 2001. (Hippo Tub Co. Ser.). (Illus.). 40p. (J). pap. 6.95 (978-1-894454-18-6(9)) Balmur Entertainment, Ltd. CAN. *Dist:* General Distribution Services, Inc.

MCP Staff. Where Can a Hippo Hide?, Level 4, Bk. 36. (J). (ps-3). 24.50 (978-0-8136-1966-8(1)) Modern Curriculum Pr.

Medearis, Angela Shelf. On the Way to the Pond. Cauley, Lorinda Bryan, illus. 2006. (Green Light Readers Level 2 Ser.). 32p. (J). 12.95 (978-0-15-205599-8(1)); pap. 3.95 (978-0-15-205623-0(8)) Harcourt Trade Pubs.

Meng, Cece. The Wonderful Thing about Hiccups. Pedersen, Janet, illus. 2007. 32p. (J). (gr. k-3). 16.00 (978-0-618-59544-0(9) , Clarion Bks.) Houghton Mifflin Co. Trade & Reference Div.

Morris, Clarine. Sam, the Hippo No One Wanted. Bamford, Daneen, illus. 2000. (J). (ps-7). pap. 3.00 (978-0-9650312-9-5(2)) Cosmo Starr Bks.

Neugebauer, Charise. Real Winner. Nascimbeni, Barbara, illus. 2000. 32p. (J). (gr. k-3). 16.50 (978-0-7358-1253-6(5) , Michael Neugebauer Bks.) North-South Bks., Inc.

Noel, Delia & Galloway, Ruth. Yawn Like a Hippo. 2002. 12p. (J). (ps). bds. 4.95 (978-0-7641-5479-9(6)) Barron's Educational Series, Inc.

Nussbaum, Ben. Toko Hippo. Wenzel, Gregory, illus. 2006. 36p. (J). pap. 6.95 (978-1-59249-578-8(8)) Soundprints.

—Toko Hippo Micro Ppb. Wenzel, Gregory, illus. 2006. 32p. (J). pap. 2.95 (978-1-59249-579-5(6)) Soundprints.

—Toko the Hippo. Wenzel, Gregory, illus. 2006. (African Wildlife Foundation Kids Ser.). 27p. (J). pap. 8.95 incl. audio compact disk (978-1-59249-580-1(X)) Soundprints.

Payne, Tony & Payne, Jan. The Hippo-Not-Amus. Parker-Rees, Guy, illus. 2004. 32p. (J). pap. 16.95 (978-0-439-56418-2(2) , Orchard Bks.) Scholastic, Inc.

Reitze, Glenn Logan. Ernie the Easter Hippopotamus: A Comic Adventure for Anytime. Reitze, Glenn Logan, illus. 2007. (Illus.). 50p. (J). lib. bdg. 19.95 (***978-0-88265-040-1(8)*** , Fine Art Editions) North American International.

Reitze, Glenn Logan, illus. & text. Ernie the Easter Hippotamus: A Comic Adventure for Anytime. Reitze, Glenn Logan, text. 2007. (J). pap. (***978-0-88265-041-8(6)***) North American International.

Rogers, Alan. Higher & Higher. 2004. (Little Giants Ser.). (Illus.). 16p. (J). (ps-k). 5.95 (978-1-58728-153-2(8)); pap. 3.95 (978-1-58728-396-3(4)) T&N Children's Publishing. (Two Can Publishing).

—El Hipopotamo Amarillo. 2004. (Pequenos Gigantes Ser.).Tr. of Yellow Hippo. (SPA., Illus.). 16p. (ps-k). (J). pap. 3.95 (978-1-58728-956-9(3)); 5.95 (978-1-58728-142-6(2)) T&N Children's Publishing. (Two Can Publishing).

—El Hipopotamo Amarillo. Rogers, Alan, illus. 2000. (Pequenos Gigantes Ser.).Tr. of Yellow Hippo. (SPA., Illus.). 15p. (J). (ps-ps). lib. bdg. 10.75 (978-0-606-20704-1(X)) Tandem Library Bks.

—Hippo Jaune. 2003. (Little Giants Ser.). (FRE., Illus.). (ps-k). 5.95 (978-1-58728-178-5(3) , Two Can Publishing) T&N Children's Publishing.

—Salta y Sube. 2004. (Pequenos Gigantes Ser.).Tr. of Higher & Higher. (SPA., Illus.). 16p. (ps-k). (J). pap. 3.95 (978-1-58728-961-3(X)); 5.95 (978-1-58728-296-6(8)) T&N Children's Publishing. (Two Can Publishing).

—Toujours Plus Haut! 2003. (Little Giants Ser.). (FRE., Illus.). 16p. (ps-k). 5.95 (978-1-58728-181-5(3) , Two Can Publishing) T&N Children's Publishing.

—Yellow Hippo. 2004. (Little Giants Ser.). (Illus.). 16p. (ps-k). (J). pap. 3.95 (978-1-58728-160-0(0)); 5.95 (978-1-58728-157-0(0)) T&N Children's Publishing. (Two Can Publishing).

Rossacci, Jacob. Harold the Hippo Learns to Sing. 2003. (J). 8.95 (978-1-932205-74-9(8)) Word Association Pubs.

Rox, John. I Want a Hippopotamus for Christmas. Whatley, Bruce, illus. 2005. 32p. (J). 16.99 (978-0-06-052942-0(3)) HarperCollins Pubs.

Safari Press Staff, ed. Book Buddy - Hippo with Story Book. (Illus.). 10p. (J). (ps-3). pap. (978-1-881469-86-5(7)) Safari, Ltd.

Sargent, Dave & Sargent, Pat. Hippy Hippo: Cleanliness, 56 vols., 47. Lenoir, Jane, illus. 2001. (Animal Pride Ser.: Vol. 47). 36p. (J). lib. bdg. 19.95 (978-1-56763-535-5(0)) Ozark Publishing.

Sargent, Dave, et al. Hippy Hippo: Cleanliness, 17, 47. 2000. (Animal Pride Ser.). (Illus.). 42p. (J). pap. 6.95 (978-1-56763-536-2(9)) Ozark Publishing.

Saylor, Shelle, illus. Harvey: The Ugly Little Hippopotamus. 2001. (J). 10.95 (978-1-58930-049-1(1)) Selah Publishing Group, LLC.

Scheer, Ruth. Hippopotamus, My Friend. 1999. (Grandmother Ruth Stories Ser.). (J). pap. 9.95 (978-0-9671761-0-9(7)) Scheer Delight Publishing.

School Specialty Publishing. My Very Best Coloring & Activity Book: Hippo Dance. 2002. 120p. (J). (gr. k-3). pap. 1.99 (978-0-7696-2789-2(7) , American Education Publishing) School Specialty Publishing.

Sundberg, Angela M., et al. The Pottamus Family & the Unhappy Pottamus. Sundberg, Angela M. et al, illus. 2007. (J). pap. 16.00 (***978-0-8059-7478-2(4)***) Dorrance Publishing Co., Inc.

Tidd, Louise Vitellaro. Can a Hippo Nop? Brown, Kevin, illus. 2004. 20p. (J). (gr. k-2). pap. 4.95 (978-1-57874-043-7(6)) Kaeden Corp.

Towle, Barbara. How Timbo & Trevor Got Together. Spellman, Susan, illus. 2007. (J). 19.95 (978-1-933002-21-7(2)) PublishingWorks.

Waber, Bernard. Evie & Margie. Waber, Bernard, illus. 2003. (Illus.). 32p. (J). (gr. k-3). 15.00 (978-0-618-34124-5(2) , Walter Lorraine) Houghton Mifflin Co. Trade & Reference Div.

Wax, Wendy. Hippo Rules: A Tale of Good Manners. Terry, Michael, illus. 2007. 12p. (J). 12.99 (***978-0-7944-1289-0(0)***) Reader's Digest Assn., Inc., The.

Wax, Wendy. Valentine for Tommy. 2003. (gr. k-3). lib. bdg. 11.80 (978-0-613-57563-8(6)) Tandem Library Bks.

Weare, Tim, illus. I'm a Little Giraffe: A Finger-Puppet Pal. 2002. (I'm A Little Ser.). 12p. (J). (ps-k). bds. 6.95 (978-0-439-40641-3(2) , Cartwheel Bks.) Scholastic, Inc.

Wild, Margaret. Kiss, Kiss! Strevens-Marzo, Bridget, illus. 2003. 24p. (J). 12.95 (978-0-689-86279-3(2)) Simon & Schuster Children's Publishing.

—Kiss Kiss! Strevens-Marzo, Bridget, illus. ed. 2006. 24p. (J). 6.99 (978-1-4169-3440-0(5)) Simon & Schuster Children's Publishing.

Wilson, Karma & Watts, Suzanne. Hilda Must Be Dancing. 2004. (Illus.). 32p. (J). 16.99 (978-0-689-84788-2(2) , McElderry, Margaret K.) Simon & Schuster Children's Publishing.

Ziefert, Harriet & Boon, Emilie. Little Hippo's New Friend. 1998. (Little Hippo Ser.). (Illus.). (J). (ps). (978-0-7894-3105-9(X)) Dorling Kindersley Publishing, Inc.

—Little Hippo's New School. Ziefert, Harriet & Boon, Emilie, illus. 1998. (Little Hippo Ser.). (Illus.). (J). (ps). (978-0-7894-3106-6(8)) Dorling Kindersley Publishing, Inc.

HIROSHIMA-SHI (JAPAN)

The Atomic Bomb. 2004. (Historical Reader Ser.). (Illus.). 224p. (J). (gr. 6-12). 13.32 (978-0-395-98665-3(6) , 2-99909) McDougal Littell Inc.

Bodden, Valerie. The Bombing of Hiroshima & Nagasaki. 2007. (J). (978-1-58341-545-0(9) , Creative Education) Creative Co., The.

Coerr, Eleanor. Sadako. Young, Ed, illus. 2002. (J). 24.55 (978-0-7587-3544-7(8)) Book Wholesalers, Inc.

—Sadako & the Thousand Paper Cranes. Himler, Ronald, illus. 2004. 80p. (gr. 8). pap. 5.99 (978-0-14-240113-2(7) , Puffin) Penguin Group (USA) Inc.

—Sadako & the Thousand Paper Cranes. Himler, Ronald, illus. 1999. 79p. (J). (ps-ps). lib. bdg. 13.00 (978-0-613-23029-2(9)) Tandem Library Bks.

—Sadako & the Thousand Paper Cranes. 1999. (978-0-606-17425-1(7)) Tandem Library Bks.

Harris, Nathaniel. Hiroshima. 2004. (Illus.). 56p. (J). 27.07 (978-1-4034-4872-9(8)); pap. (978-1-4034-6259-6(3)) Heinemann Library.

Himler, Ronald, illus. Sadako & the Thousand Paper Cranes. 2005. 80p. (J). pap. 3.99 (978-0-14-240440-9(3) , Puffin) Penguin Group (USA) Inc.

Hook, Jason. Hiroshima. 2002. (Days That Shook the World Ser.). 48p. (J). lib. bdg. 27.12 (978-0-7398-5234-7(5)) Raintree.

Langley, Andrew. Hiroshima & Nagasaki: Fire from the Sky. 2006. (Snapshots in History Ser.). (Illus.). 96p. (J). (gr. 5-7). 30.60 (978-0-7565-1621-5(8)) Compass Point Bks.

Lawton, Clive A. Hiroshima. 60th anniv. ed. 2004. (Illus.). 48p. (J). (gr. 5 up). 18.99 (978-0-7636-2271-8(0)) Candlewick Pr.

Orr, Tamra. The Atom Bomb: Creating & Exploding the First Nuclear Weapon. 2004. (Library of Weapons of Mass Destruction). (Illus.). 64p. (J). lib. bdg. 26.50 (978-1-4042-0292-4(7)) Rosen Publishing Group, Inc., The.

Richard Tames. Hiroshima. 2nd ed. 2006. (Illus.). 32p. (J). pap. (***978-1-4034-9149-7(6)***) Heinemann Library.

Sadako & the Thousand Paper Cranes. 1999. (J). 9.95 (978-1-56137-178-5(5)); 11.95 (978-1-56137-631-5(0)) Novel Units, Inc.

Tames, Richard. Hiroshima: The Shadow of the Bomb. (Point of Impact Ser.). (Illus.). 32p. 2006. (YA). (gr. 5-8). lib. bdg. 29.29 (***978-1-4034-9140-4(2));*** 2002. (J). (gr. 5-7). pap. 7.50 (978-1-58810-353-6(6) , 91113); 2000. (J). lib. bdg. 24.22 (978-1-57572-414-0(6)) Heinemann Library.

—Hiroshima: The Shadow of the Bomb. 2001. (Illus.). (J). 32p. (gr. 4-7). lib. bdg. 15.25 (978-0-613-36102-6(4)); 12.75 (978-0-606-22000-2(3)) Tandem Library Bks.

HIROSHIMA-SHI (JAPAN)—FICTION

Nilsson, Troy, 2nd. Hiroshima Stones: The Shadow Stones of Hiroshima - a Story of Love & War. Nilsson, Troy, 2nd, illus. collector's aut. ed. 2003. Orig. Title: Hiroshima Stones. (Illus.). 248p. (YA). 24.95 (978-0-9724771-1-6(X) , Nilsson, Troy) Nilsson Media.

HISPANIC AMERICANS

Here are entered works on United States citizens of Latin American descent. Works on citizens of Latin American countries are entered under Latin Americans. Works on citizens of Latin American countries in the United States are entered under Latin Americans—United States.

Abrams, Lea. Freddie Prinze Jr. 2001. (Latinos in the Limelight Ser.). (Illus.). 64p. (J). (gr. 4-7). 27.50 (978-0-7910-6479-5(4) , Chelsea Hse.) Facts On File, Inc.

Alegre, Cesar. Extraordinary Hispanic Americans. 2006. (Extraordinary People Ser.). (Illus.). 288p. (J). (978-0-516-25343-5(3)) Children's Pr., Ltd.

Allison, Amy. John Leguizamo. 2001. (Latinos in the Limelight Ser.). (Illus.). 64p. (J). (gr. 6-9). 27.50 (978-0-7910-6477-1(8) , Chelsea Hse.) Facts On File, Inc.

Alter, Judy. Great Women of the Old West. 2001. (We the People Ser.). (Illus.). 48p. (J). (gr. 4 up). lib. bdg. 22.60 (978-0-7565-0099-3(0)) Compass Point Bks.

Amigos de la A a la Z: Un Alfabeto del Mundo Hispanico. 2002. (SPA.). 32p. (J). pap. 13.95 (978-1-58105-813-0(6)) Santillana USA Publishing Co., Inc.

Ancona, George. Barrio: El Barrio de Jose. Ancona, George, photos by. 1998. Tr. of Barrio: Jose's Neighborhood. (SPA., Illus.). 48p. (J). (gr. 2-7). pap. 9.00 (978-0-15-201808-5(5) , Harcourt Paperbacks) Harcourt Children's Bks.

—Mi Escuela: My School. (Somos Latinos (We Are Latinos) Ser.). 2005. (SPA., Illus.). 32p. (J). (gr. 1-3). pap. 8.95 (978-0-516-25066-3(3) , Children's Pr.); 2004. 20.00 (978-0-516-23686-5(5) , Watts, Franklin) Scholastic Library Publishing.

—Mis Quehaceres. 32p. (J). 2006. (SPA.). (gr. 1-3). pap. 8.95 (978-0-516-25499-9(5)); 2005. (ENG & SPA., Illus.). 21.00 (978-0-516-25291-9(7)) Scholastic Library Publishing. (Children's Pr.).

Aykroyd, Clarissa. Julia Alvarez. 2007. (Twentieth Century Most Influential Hispanics Ser.). (Illus.). 128p. (gr. 7-10). 31.20 (***978-1-4205-0022-6(8)*** , Lucent Bks.) Thomson Gale.

Benson, Sonia, et al, eds. UXL Hispanic American Almanac. 2nd ed. 2002. (Illus.). xvii, 247p. (J). 67.00 (978-0-7876-6598-2(3) , UXL) Thomson Gale.

—UXL Hispanic American Chronology. 2nd ed. 2002. 200p. (J). 67.00 (978-0-7876-6600-2(9) , UXL) Thomson Gale.

Benson, Sonia & Straub, Deborah Gillan, eds. UXL Hispanic American Voices. 2nd ed. 2002. (Illus.). xxi, 294p. (J). 67.00 (978-0-7876-6603-3(3) , UXL) Thomson Gale.

Brackett, Virginia R. Jeff Bezos. (Latinos in the Limelight Ser.). (Illus.). 64p. (J). 2001. (gr. 3 up). 27.50 (978-0-7910-6104-6(3)); 2000. pap. (978-0-7910-6105-3(1)) Facts On File, Inc. (Chelsea Hse.).

Brown, Monica. My Name Is Celia: The Life of Celia Cruz. Lopez, Rafael, illus. 2004. Tr. of Me Llamo Celia; la Vida de Celia Cruz. (ENG & SPA.). 32p. (gr. 2-4). 15.95 (978-0-87358-872-0(X) , Luna Rising) Northland Publishing.

Buckley, Annie. Ellen Ochoa. 2008. (J). lib. bdg. 26.00 (***978-1-60279-075-9(2)***) Cherry Lake Publishing.

Cabat, Robert & Cabat, Louis. Momentos Hispanos. 2nd ed. 1999. (SPA & ENG.). 195p. (YA). (gr. 11). pap. (978-0-87720-520-3(5) , R664P) AMSCO Schl. Pubns., Inc.

Cardona, Rodolfo & Cockcroft, James D., eds. Hispanics of Achievement. 1999. (Illus.). 128p. (J). (gr. 5-12). 99.50 (978-0-7910-3762-1(2) , Chelsea Hse.) Facts On File, Inc.

Chelsea House Publishing Staff. Latinos in the Limelight, 8 vols., Set. 2001. (Illus.). 64p. (YA). (gr. 3 up). 143.60 (978-0-7910-6096-4(9) , Chelsea Hse.) Facts On File, Inc.

Cockcroft, James D. Latinos in Beisbol. 2004. (Illus.). 207p. (J). (gr. 4-9). reprint ed. pap. 10.00 (978-0-7567-7347-2(4)) DIANE Publishing Co.

Courtot, Marilyn, ed. Hispanic Peoples of North, Central, South America & the Caribbean. 1998. (Illus.). 44p. (Orig.). (J). pap. 14.99 (978-1-890920-08-1(8)) Children's Literature.

Cruz, Barbara. Triumphs & Struggles for Latino Civil Rights. 2008. (From Many Cultures, One History Ser.). (Illus.). 128p. (J). (gr. 5 up). lib. bdg. 31.93 (***978-0-7660-2804-3(6)***) Enslow Pubs., Inc.

Davies, Gill. Hispanic America 1490s - the Present. Aronson, Marc, ed. 2005. (National Geographic Timelines Ser.). (Illus.). 64p. (J). 27.90 (978-0-7922-7077-5(0)) National Geographic Society.

—Hispanic America 1490s- the Present. Aronson, Marc, ed. 2005. (National Geographic Timelines Ser.). (Illus.). 64p. (J). 17.95 (978-0-7922-6455-2(X)) National Geographic Society.

Doak, Robin. Struggling to Become American: 1899-1940. 2006. (Latino-American History Ser.). (Illus.). 112p. (YA). (gr. 5-8). 35.00 (978-0-8160-6443-4(1) , Chelsea Hse.) Facts On File, Inc.

Downs, Cynthia. Celebrating Hispanic Culture. 2005. 80p. (J). per. 10.99 (978-0-88724-921-1(3) , CD-104040) Carson-Dellosa Publishing Co., Inc.

Ellen Ochoa: Reaching for the Stars. 2005. (Book Treks Ser.). (J). (gr. 3 up). stu. ed. 34.95 (978-0-673-62081-1(6)) Celebration Pr.

Ellen Ochoa 6-Pack. 2005. (Hispanic-American Biographies Ser.). (Illus.). pap. 51.30 (978-1-4109-1314-2(7)); pap. 51.30 (978-1-4109-1315-9(5)) Raintree.

Escamilla, Kathy, intro. Famous People of Hispanic Heritage. 1998. (Illus.). 96p. (J). (gr. 5). 129.50 (978-1-883845-89-6(0) , Chelsea Hse.) Facts On File, Inc.

—Famous People of Hispanic Heritage: Isabel Allende, Oscar de la Hoya, Mary Joe Fernandez, Jimmy Smits, Vol. 8. (Contemporary American Success Stories Ser.: Vol. VIII). (Illus.). 96p. (gr. 4-10). lib. bdg. 12.95 (978-1-883845-41-4(6)) Mitchell Lane Pubs., Inc.

—Famous People of Hispanic Heritage: Pedro Jose Greer, Jr., Nancy Lopez, Rafael Palmeiro, Hilda Perera, Vol. 6. (Contemporary American Success Stories Ser.: Vol. 6). (Illus.). 96p. (gr. 4-10). lib. bdg. 21.95 (978-1-883845-34-6(3)) Mitchell Lane Pubs., Inc.

—Famous People of Hispanic Heritage: Rebecca Lobo, Bill Richardson, Linda Chavez Thompson, Carlos Mencia, Vol. 10. (Contemporary American Success Stories Ser.: Vol. X). (Illus.). 96p. (gr. 4-10). lib. bdg. 12.95 (978-1-883845-67-4(X)) Mitchell Lane Pubs., Inc.

—Famous People of Hispanic Heritage Vol. 6: Pedro Jose Greer, Jr., Nancy Lopez, Rafael Palmeiro, Hilda Perera. (Contemporary American Success Stories Ser.: Vol. 6). (Illus.). 96p. (gr. 4-10). lib. bdg. 12.95 (978-1-883845-33-9(5)) Mitchell Lane Pubs., Inc.

—Famous People of Hispanic Heritage Vol. 9: Raul Julia, Mariah Carey, Andres Galarraga, Jackie Guerra. (Contemporary American Success Stories Ser.: Vol. IX). (Illus.). 96p. (gr. 4-10). lib. bdg. 12.95 (978-1-883845-43-8(2)) Mitchell Lane Pubs., Inc.

—Famous People of Hispanic Heritage Vol. 10: Rebecca Lobo, Bill Richardson, Linda Chavez Thompson, Carlos Mencia. (Contemporary American Success Stories Ser.: Vol. X). (Illus.). 96p. (gr. 4-10). lib. bdg. 21.95 (978-1-883845-68-1(8)) Mitchell Lane Pubs., Inc.

Feder, Chris Welles. Brain Quest Hispanic America. 2005. (Illus.). (J). 10.95 (978-0-7611-3997-3(4) , 13997) Workman Publishing Co., Inc.

Franchino, Vicky. Spanish Americans. 2004. (Our Cultural Heritage Ser.). 32p. (J). (gr. 2-6). 27.07 (978-1-59296-183-2(5)) Child's World, Inc.

Francisco Dallmeier, 6 Packs. 2005. (Hispanic-American Biographies Ser.). (Illus.). pap. 51.30 (978-1-4109-1316-6(3)) Raintree.

Friends from A to Z: A Glossary of the Hispanic World. 2002. (Gateways to the Sun). 32p. (J). (gr. k-6). pap. 13.95 (978-1-58105-971-7(X)) Santillana USA Publishing Co., Inc.

Furman, Leah. Jennifer Lopez. (Latinos in the Limelight Ser.). (Illus.). 64p. (J). 2002. pap. (978-0-7910-6111-4(6)); 2001. (gr. 3 up). 27.50 (978-0-7910-6110-7(8)) Facts On File, Inc. (Chelsea Hse.).

Garza, Carmen Lomas. In My Family. 2000. Tr. of En Mi Familia. (SPA.). (gr. 3-6). lib. bdg. 16.40 (978-0-613-28536-0(0)) Tandem Library Bks.

Glencoe McGraw-Hill Staff. Glencoe Hispanic American Literature. 2001. 329p. 31.96 (978-0-07-822927-5(8) , 9780078229275) Glencoe/McGraw-Hill.

Granados, Christine & Garcia, Kimberly. Careers in Technology. 2001. (Latinos at Work Ser.). (Illus.). 96p. (gr. 5-12). lib. bdg. 32.75 (978-1-58415-087-9(4)) Mitchell Lane Pubs., Inc.

Gravenhorst, Edna Campos. Ay, Mijo! Why Do You Want to Be an Engineer? 2007. 155p. (***978-0-9745346-3-3(3)***) Big River Distribution.

The Great Hispanic Heritage. (Illus.). (gr. 6-12). lib. bdg. (978-0-7910-8049-8(8) , Chelsea Hse.) Facts On File, Inc.

Grolier Publishing Company Staff, contrib. by. Hispanic American Biographies, 8 vols. 2006. (Illus.). (J). (978-0-7172-6125-3(5)); (978-0-7172-6126-0(3)); (978-0-7172-6127-7(1)); (978-0-7172-6128-4(X)); (978-0-7172-6129-1(8)); (978-0-7172-6130-7(1)); (978-0-7172-6131-4(X)); (978-0-7172-6132-1(8)); Set. (gr. 6 up). (978-0-7172-6124-6(7)) Grolier, Ltd.

Guzman, Lila & Guzman, Rick. George Lopez: Comedian & TV Star. 2006. (Famous Latinos Ser.). (Illus.). 32p. (J). lib. bdg. 22.60 (978-0-7660-2644-5(2) , Enslow Elementary) Enslow Pubs., Inc.

Guzman, Lila & Guzman, Rick. George Lopez: Comediante y estrella de TV. 2007. (Latinos Famosos Ser.). (Illus.). 32p. (J). (gr. 3-4). lib. bdg. 22.60 (***978-0-7660-2680-3(9)*** , Enslow Elementary) Enslow Pubs., Inc.

Hansen-Krening, Nancy, et al, eds. Kaleidoscope: A Multicultural Booklist for Grades K-8. 4th ed. 2003. (NCTE Bibliography Ser.). (Illus.). 118p. (J). pap. 30.95 (978-0-8141-2539-7(5) , 25395) National Council of Teachers of English.

Hill, Christine M. Ten Hispanic American Authors. 2002. (Collective Biographies Ser.). (Illus.). 112p. (J). (gr. 6-12). lib. bdg. 26.60 (978-0-7660-1541-8(6)) Enslow Pubs., Inc.

Hispanic-American Biographies, 6 bks., Set 2. 2004. 188.14 (978-1-4109-1301-2(5)) Raintree.

Hispanic-American Biographies, 10 bks., Sets. Incl. Adriana Ocampo. Guidici, Cynthia. (gr. 6-9). 2005. lib. bdg. 32.86 (978-1-4109-1297-8(3)); Cesar Chavez. Olmstead, Mary. (gr. 4-6). 2004. 32.86 (978-1-4109-0710-3(4)); Ellen Ochoa. Iverson, Teresa. (gr. 4-6). 2004. 32.86 (978-1-4109-1299-2(X)); Francisco Dallmeier. Kloepfer, Deanne & Abarca, Patricia. (gr. 4-6). 2004. 32.86 (978-1-4109-1300-5(7)); Judy Baca. Olmstead, Mary. (gr. 4-6). 2004. 32.86 (978-1-4109-0709-7(0)); Luis Alvarez. Randall, Tina. (gr. 4-6). 2004. 32.86 (978-1-4109-1295-4(7)); Mario Molina. Guidici, Cynthia. (gr. 4-6). 2004. 32.86 (978-1-4109-1296-1(5)); Roberto Clemente. Olmstead, Mary. (gr. 4-6). 2004. 32.86 (978-1-4109-0711-0(2)); Severo Ochoa. Garretson, Gregory. (gr. 4-6). 2004. 32.86 (978-1-4109-1298-5(1)); Tito Puente. Olmstead, Mary. (gr. 4-6). 2004. 32.86 (978-1-4109-0713-4(9)); (Illus.). 64p. (J). 2004. 328.57 (978-1-4109-1302-9(3)) Raintree.

Hispanica. 2002. (SPA.). (YA). (gr. 7 up). cd-rom 179.00 (978-1-56409-039-3(6) , 40502) World Bk., Inc.

Hoyt-Goldsmith, Diane. Las Posadas: An Hispanic Christmas Celebration. 2000. (Illus.). 32p. (J). (ps-7). pap. 6.95 (978-0-8234-1635-6(6)) Holiday Hse., Inc.

Hunter, Miranda. Latino Americans & Immigration Laws: Crossing the Border. 2005. (Illus.). 112p. (J). (ps-7). lib. bdg. (978-1-59084-939-2(6)) Mason Crest Pubs.

—Story Of Latino Civil Rights: Fighting for Justice. 2005. (Illus.). 112p. (J). lib. bdg. (978-1-59084-934-7(5)) Mason Crest Pubs.

Hurst, Heidi. Jennifer Lopez. 2003. (People in the News Ser.). (Illus.). 112p. (J). 32.45 (978-1-59018-325-0(8) , Lucent Bks.) Thomson Gale.

Isaacs, Sally Senzell. Life in St. Augustine. (Picture the Past Ser.). (Illus.). 32p. (J). 2003. lib. bdg. (978-1-58810-694-0(2)); 2002. (gr. 1-3). pap. 7.50 (978-1-4034-0526-5(3)) Heinemann Library.

Iverson, Teresa. Ellen Ochoa. 2006. (Biografías de Hispanoamericanos Ser.). (ENG & SPA.). (J). 32.86 (978-1-4109-2128-4(X)); pap. 9.90 (978-1-4109-2135-2(2)) Steck-Vaughn.

Jaffe, Elizabeth Dana. Ellen Ochoa. 2004. (Rookie Biography Ser.). (Illus.). 31p. 20.50 (978-0-516-21721-5(6) , Children's Pr.) Scholastic Library Publishing.

Johnston, Lissa Jones. Ellen Ochoa: Pioneering Astronaut. 2006. (Fact Finders Ser.). (Illus.). 32p. (J). (978-0-7368-5438-2(X)) Capstone Pr., Inc.

Kennedy, Mike & Stewart, Mark. Latino Baseball's Finest Fielders/Las Mejores Estrellas del Beisbol Latino. Kalmanovitz, Manuel, tr. 2002. (En Fuego Ser.). (SPA & ENG., Illus.). 64p. (gr. 5 up). lib. bdg. 26.90 (978-0-7613-2566-6(2) , Twenty-First Century Bks.) Lerner Publishing Group.

—Latino Baseball's Hottest Hitters/Los Mejores Bateadores del Beisbol Latino. Kalmanovitz, Manuel, tr. 2002. (En Fuego Ser.). (ENG & SPA., Illus.). 64p. (gr. 5 up). lib. bdg. 26.90 (978-0-7613-2567-3(0) , Twenty-First Century Bks.) Lerner Publishing Group.

King, David C. Projects about the Spanish West. 2005. (Hands-On History Ser.). (Illus.). 47p. (J). (978-0-7614-1982-2(9) , Benchmark Bks.) Cavendish, Marshall Corp.

Korman, Susan. Christina Aguilera. (Latinos in the Limelight Ser.). (Illus.). 64p. (J). 2002. pap. 27.50 (978-0-7910-6107-7(8)); 2001. (gr. 3 up). 31.00 (978-0-7910-6106-0(X) , Chelsea Hse.) Facts On File, Inc.

Laezman, Rick. 100 Hispanic Americans Who Changed History. 2005. (People Who Changed History Ser.). (Illus.). 112p. (J). lib. bdg. 30.00 (978-0-8368-5769-6(0) , World Almanac Library) Stevens, Gareth Inc.

—100 Hispanic-Americans Who Shaped American History. 2001. (gr. 7-12). lib. bdg. 16.40 (978-0-613-67509-3(6)) Tandem Library Bks.

Latino American Biographies. (YA). (gr. 6-12). pap. 14.50 (978-0-8359-0849-8(6)) Globe Fearon Educational Publishing.

Latinos at Work: Career Role Models for Young Adults, 10 vols., Set. 2002. (Illus.). (YA). (gr. 5-12). lib. bdg. 229.50 (978-1-58415-090-9(4)) Mitchell Lane Pubs., Inc.

Latinos in Baseball: Sammy Sosa; Roberto Alomar; Tino Martinez; Moises Alou; Pedro Martinez; Bobby Bonilla; Alex Rodriguez; Bernie Williams; Manny Ramirez; Vinny Castilla; Ivan Rodriguez; Ramon Martinez, 12 vols. 2000. (Illus.). 768p. (YA). (gr. 5 up). lib. bdg. 227.40 (978-1-58415-053-4(X)) Mitchell Lane Pubs., Inc.

Layden, Joe. Heroe del Jonron: La Historia de Sammy Sosa, 1 vol. 1998. (SPA., Illus.). 58p. (J). (gr. 2-9). pap. 3.99 (978-0-439-07758-3(3)) Scholastic, Inc.

Libal, Autumn. Women in the Hispanic World. 2005. (Women's Issues, Global Trends Ser.). (Illus.). 112p. (J). lib. bdg. (978-1-59084-858-6(6)) Mason Crest Pubs.

Lomas Garza, Carmen. In My Family. 2000. Tr. of En Mi Familia. (Illus.). (J). 14.75 (978-0-606-18039-9(7)) Tandem Library Bks.

—In My Family (En Mi Familia) Lomas Garza, Carmen, illus. 2000. (ENG & SPA., Illus.). 32p. (J). (gr. 1-4). pap. 7.95 (978-0-89239-163-9(4)) Children's Bk. Pr.

Luis Alvarez 6-Pack. 2005. (Hispanic-American Biographies Ser.). (Illus.). pap. 51.30 (978-1-4109-1311-1(2)) Raintree.

Mario Molina, 6 Pack. 2005. (Hispanic-American Biographies Ser.). (Illus.). pap. 51.30 (978-1-4109-1312-8(0)) Raintree.

Marquez, Heron. Latin Sensations. (Biography Ser.). (Illus.). 112p. (gr. 6-12). 2005. lib. bdg. 27.93 (978-0-8225-4993-2(X)); 2003. (YA). pap. 7.95 (978-0-8225-9695-0(4) , Lerner Pubns.) Lerner Publishing Group.

Marsh, Carole. The Best Book of Hispanic Biographies. 2003. (Fiesta! Siesta! And All the Rest-a! Ser.). 32p. (J). (gr. 3-8). pap. 7.95 (978-0-635-02116-8(1)) Gallopade International.

—The BIG Book of Hispanic Activities. 2003. (Fiesta! Siesta! And All the Rest-a! Ser.). 48p. (J). (gr. 2-6). pap. 9.95 (978-0-635-02115-1(3)) Gallopade International.

—Celebrating Hispanic Heritage: 20 Days of Activities, Reading, Recipes, Parties, Plays & More. 2003. (Fiesta! Siesta! And All the Rest-a! Ser.). 24p. (J). (gr. 1-8). pap. 5.95 (978-0-635-02119-9(6)) Gallopade International.

—Hispanic Trivia: The Hispanic Experience A to Z! 2003. (Fiesta! Siesta! And All the Rest-a! Ser.). 32p. (J). (gr. 3-8). pap. 7.95 (978-0-635-02118-2(8)) Gallopade International.

Maruis, Barbara, intro. Famous People of Hispanic Heritage. 1998. (Contemporary American Success Stories Ser.). (Illus.). 960p. (YA). (gr. 4-10). 219.50 (978-1-883845-90-2(4) , Chelsea Hse.) Facts On File, Inc.

McElroy, Lisa Tucker. Alberto Gonzales: Attorney General. 2006. (Gateway Biographies Ser.). (Illus.). 48p. (J). 23.93 (978-0-8225-3418-1(5)) Lerner Publishing Group.

McIntosh, Kenneth. The Latino Religious Experience: People of Faith & Vision. 2005. (Illus.). 112p. (J). (ps-7). lib. bdg. (978-1-59084-933-0(7)) Mason Crest Pubs.

—Latinos Today: Facts & Figures. 2005. (Illus.). 112p. (J). (ps-7). lib. bdg. (978-1-59084-940-8(X)) Mason Crest Pubs.

Media Projects, Inc., Staff. Almanac of Hispanic American History, 2 vols. 2003. (Illus.). 144p. (gr. 6-8). stu. ed. 86.95 (978-0-313-32605-9(3) , MS2605, Greenwood Pr.) Greenwood Publishing Group, Inc.

Media Projects, Inc., Staff, contrib. by. Student Almanac of Hispanic American History, 2 vols. 2003. (Illus.). (J). (978-0-313-32606-6(1)); 80.00 (978-0-313-32607-3(X)) Greenwood Publishing Group, Inc. (Greenwood Pr.).

Mintzer, Richard. Latino Americans in Sports, Film, Music & Government: Trailblazers. 2005. (Illus.). 112p. (J). (ps-7). lib. bdg. (978-1-59084-936-1(1)) Mason Crest Pubs.

Morris, Ann. Grandma Francisca Remembers: A Hispanic-American Family Story. 2002. (Illus.). 32p. (J). (gr. 5 up). pap. 7.95 (978-0-7613-1733-3(3) , Millbrook Pr.) Lerner Publishing Group.

—Grandma Francisca Remembers: A Hispanic-American Family Story. Linenthal, Peter, photos by. 2001. (What Was It Like, Grandma? Ser.). (Illus.). 32p. (gr. k-3). lib. bdg. 22.90 (978-0-7613-2315-0(5) , Millbrook Pr.) Lerner Publishing Group.

Nagel, Carol DeKane. UXL Hispanic American Reference Library Cumulative Index. 2nd ed. 2002. 50p. (J). 5.00 (978-0-7876-6601-9(7) , UXL) Thomson Gale.

Nagel Rob. UXL Hispanic American Biography. Benson, Sonia & Rose, Sharon, eds. 2nd ed. 2002. (UXL Hispanic American Reference Library). (Illus.). viii, 321p. (J). 67.00 (978-0-7876-6599-9(1) , UXL) Thomson Gale.

Nava, Yolanda. It's All in the Frijoles: 100 Famous Latinos Share Real-Life Stories, Time-Tested Dichos, Favorite Folk Tales & Inspiring Words of Wisdom. 2000. (Illus.). (J). 21.65 (978-0-606-18894-4(0)) Tandem Library Bks.

Nickles, Greg. The Hispanics. 2000. (We Came to North America Ser.). (Illus.). 32p. (J). (gr. 4). (978-0-7787-0186-6(7)); pap. (978-0-7787-0200-9(6)) Crabtree Publishing Co.

—The Hispanics. 2000. (We Came to North America Ser.). (J). 15.75 (978-0-606-20109-4(2)) Tandem Library Bks.

—Hispanics. 2001. (gr. 3-6). lib. bdg. 17.60 (978-0-613-32641-4(5)) Tandem Library Bks.

Nickle's, Greg. The Hispanics: We Came to North America. 2006. (Illus.). 32p. (J). (gr. 4-8). reprint ed. 19.00 (978-0-7567-9903-8(1)) DIANE Publishing Co.

Ochoa, George & New York Public Library Staff. The New York Public Library Amazing Hispanic American History: A Book of Answers for Kids. 1998. (New York Public Library Books for Kids: Vol. 7). (Illus.). 192p. (gr. 5-9). pap. 12.95 (978-0-471-19204-6(X) , Wiley-Interscience) Wiley, John & Sons, Inc.

Oleksy, Walter. Hispanic-American Scientists. 1998. (American Profiles Ser.). (Illus.). 160p. (YA). (gr. 5-12). 25.00 (978-0-8160-3704-9(3)) Facts On File, Inc.

Olmstead. Antonio Novello 6-Pack. 2004. (Hispanic-American Biographies Ser.). (Illus.). pap. 51.30 (978-1-4109-1194-0(2)) Raintree.

—Cesar Chavez. 2005. (Biografías Hispanoamericanas Ser.). (SPA.). (J). 32.86 (978-1-4109-1590-0(5)) Raintree.

—Cleto Rodriguez. 2004. (Hispanic-American Biographies Ser.). (Illus.). 28.56 (978-1-4109-0714-1(7)) Raintree.

—Hispanic-American Biographies Series, 5 vols., Set 1. 2004. (Illus.). 125.43 (978-1-4109-0715-8(5)) Harcourt Schl. Pubs.

—Judy Baca. (Hispanic-American Biographies Ser.). 2005. pap. 9.50 (978-1-4109-1594-8(8)); 2005. pap. 34.20 (978-1-4109-1599-3(9)); 2004. (Illus.). pap. 51.30 (978-1-4109-1191-9(8)) Harcourt Schl. Pubs.

—Roberto Clemente. 2005. (Hispanic-American Biographies Ser.). pap. 9.50 (978-1-4109-1596-2(4)); Pack. pap. 34.20 (978-1-4109-1601-3(4)) Harcourt Schl. Pubs.

—Roberto Clemente. 2005. (Biografías Hispanoamericanas Ser.). (SPA.). (J). 32.86 (978-1-4109-1591-7(3)) Raintree.

—Roberto Clemente 6-Pack. 2004. (Hispanic-American Biographies Ser.). (Illus.). pap. 51.30 (978-1-4109-1193-3(4)) Harcourt Schl. Pubs.

—Tito Puente. 2005. (Hispanic-American Biographies Ser.). pap. 9.50 (978-1-4109-1597-9(2)) Harcourt Schl. Pubs.

—Tito Puente. 2005. (Biografías Hispanoamericanas Ser.). (SPA.). (J). 32.86 (978-1-4109-1592-4(1)) Raintree.

—Tito Puente 6-Pack. (Hispanic-American Biographies Ser.). 2005. pap. 34.20 (978-1-4109-1602-0(2)); 2004. (Illus.). pap. 51.30 (978-1-4109-1195-7(0)) Harcourt Schl. Pubs.

Olmstead, Mary. Antonia Novella. 2004. (J). pap. 9.50 (978-1-4109-0918-3(2)); (Illus.). lib. bdg. 28.56 (978-1-4109-0712-7(0)) Raintree.

—Judy Baca. Pomenta, Allison, tr. 2005. (Biografías Hispanoamericanas Ser.). (SPA., Illus.). 64p. (J). (ps-7). lib. bdg. 32.86 (978-1-4109-1589-4(1)) Raintree.

—Tito Puente. 2004. (Hispanic-American Biographies Ser.). (Illus.). 64p. (J). pap. 9.50 (978-1-4109-0919-0(0)) Harcourt Schl. Pubs.

—Tito Puente. 2004. (Hispanic-American Biographies Ser.). (Illus.). 64p. (J). (gr. 4-6). 32.86 (978-1-4109-0713-4(9)) Raintree.

Ortiz Cofer, Judith, ed. Riding Low Through Streets of Gold: Latino Literature for Young Adults. 192p. (YA). pap. 14.95 (978-1-55885-380-5(4) , Piñata Books) Arte Publico Pr.

O'Shea, Tim. Scott Gomez. 2001. (Latinos in the Limelight Ser.). (Illus.). 64p. (J). (gr. 4-7). 27.50 (978-0-7910-6475-7(1) , Chelsea Hse.) Facts On File, Inc.

Richter, Glenda. The Stories of Juana Briones: Alta California Pioneer. Heywood, Della, illus. 2002. 64p. (J). (gr. 3-6). 14.95 (978-0-9700379-0-9(2)); pap. 7.95 (978-0-9700379-1-6(0)) Bookhandler Pr.

Rodriguez, Alex. Hit a Grand Slam. 1998. 40p. 14.95 (978-0-87833-997-6(3)) Taylor Trade Publishing.

Rodriguez, Art. Forgotten Memories: (Sequel to East Side Dreams) 2002. 166p. (gr. 7-12). pap. 12.95 (978-0-9671555-2-4(5)) Dream House Pr.

Rosinsky, Natalie M. California Ranchos. 2006. (We the People Ser.). (Illus.). 48p. (J). (gr. 4-6). 23.93 (978-0-7565-1633-8(1)) Compass Point Bks.

Scott, Kieran. Cameron Diaz. (Latinos in the Limelight Ser.). (Illus.). 64p. (J). 2002. pap. 27.50 (978-0-7910-6109-1(4)); 2001. (gr. 3 up). 19.75 (978-0-7910-6108-4(6) , Chelsea Hse.) Facts On File, Inc.

Seidman, David. Creating a New Future. 2007. (Latino-American History Ser.). (Illus.). 112p. (J). (gr. 5-8). 35.00 (978-0-8160-6445-8(8) , Chelsea Hse.) Facts On File, Inc.

Severo Ochoa 6-Pack. 2005. (Hispanic-American Biographies Ser.). (Illus.). pap. 51.30 (978-1-4109-1313-5(9)) Raintree.

Silverstone, Michael. Latino Legends: Hispanics in Major League Baseball. 2003. (High Five Reading Ser.). (Illus.). (J). 64p. lib. bdg. 22.60 (978-0-7368-2791-1(9)); 48p. pap. 23.93 (978-0-7368-2832-1(X)) Capstone Pr., Inc.

Sosa, Carlos. Celebrations. 2007. (Familia Banderas Ser.). (Illus.). 48p. (J). (gr. 3-7). per. 9.95 (***978-1-933669-11-3(X))*** Literary Architects, LLC.

—Cultures. 2007. (Familia Banderas Ser.). (Illus.). 48p. (J). (gr. 3-7). per. 9.95 (***978-1-933669-12-0(8))*** Literary Architects, LLC.

Sosa, Carlos & Castaneda, Patricia. Celebrations: La Familia Banderas. 2006. (Illus.). 48p. (J). pap. 9.95 (978-1-933669-03-8(9)) Literary Architects, LLC.

—Cultures: La Familia Banderas. 2006. (Illus.). 48p. (J). pap. 9.95 (978-1-933669-04-5(7)) Literary Architects, LLC.

Steele, Christy. Hispanic Culture. 2006. (Discovering the Arts Ser.). (Illus.). 48p. (gr. 4-8). 20.95 (978-1-59515-520-7(1)) Rourke Publishing, LLC.

Steele, Christy, et al. Fighting for American Values. 2007. (Latino-American History Ser.). 112p. (J). (gr. 5-8). 35.00 (978-0-8160-6444-1(X) , Chelsea Hse.) Facts On File, Inc.

Stewart, Mark. Alex Rodriguez: Gunning for Greatness. 1999. (New Wave Ser.). (Illus.). 48p. (gr. 4 up). lib. bdg. 22.90 (978-0-7613-1515-5(2) , Millbrook Pr.) Lerner Publishing Group.

—Scott Gomez: Open up the Ice. 2001. (New Wave Ser.). (Illus.). 48p. (gr. 4 up). lib. bdg. 22.90 (978-0-7613-2268-9(X) , Millbrook Pr.) Lerner Publishing Group.

Stewart, Mark & Kennedy, Mike. Latino Baseball's Finest Fielders/Las Mas Destacados Guantes del Beisbol Latino. Kalmanovitz, Manuel, tr. 2003. (En Fuego Ser.). (ENG & SPA., Illus.). 48p. (J). (gr. 5 up). pap. 9.95 (978-0-7613-1749-4(X) , Twenty-First Century Bks.) Lerner Publishing Group.

—Latino Baseball's Hottest Hitters. Kalmanovitz, Manuel, tr. 2003. (En Fuego Ser.). (SPA & ENG., Illus.). 48p. (J). (gr. 5 up). pap. 9.95 (978-0-7613-1775-3(9) , Twenty-First Century Bks.) Lerner Publishing Group.

Torres, John Albert. Bobby Bonilla. 1999. (Latinos in Baseball Ser.). (Illus.). 64p. (YA). (gr. 4-7). lib. bdg. 18.95 (978-1-883845-83-4(1)) Mitchell Lane Pubs., Inc.

—Tino Martinez. 1999. (Latinos in Baseball Ser.). (Illus.). 72p. (gr. 4-10). lib. bdg. 18.95 (978-1-883845-82-7(3)) Mitchell Lane Pubs., Inc.

Urrea, Luis Alberto. Vatos. 2000. (gr. 7-12). lib. bdg. 30.35 (978-0-613-45158-1(9)) Tandem Library Bks.

Watson, Marilyn Myrick. Raul Castro: Arizona's First Hispanic Governor. 2007. (J). (***978-0-9790826-5-8(X)); (*978-0-9790826-6-5(8))*** Acacia Publishing, Inc.

Wheeler, Jill C. Jennifer Lopez. 2003. (Star Tracks Ser.). (Illus.). 64p. (J). (gr. 3-8). lib. bdg. 25.65 (978-1-57765-770-5(5)) ABDO Publishing Co.

Wilson, Wayne. Freddie Prinze, Jr. 2000. (Real-Life Reader Biography Ser.). (Illus.). 32p. (J). (gr. 3-8). lib. bdg. 15.95 (978-1-58415-063-3(7)) Mitchell Lane Pubs., Inc.

Winter, Jonah. Beisbol! Latino Baseball Pioneers & Legends. 2001. (SPA., Illus.). 32p. (J). (gr. 1 up). pap. 13.56 (978-1-58430-012-0(4)) Lee & Low Bks., Inc.

Zymet, Cathy Alter. Enrique Iglesias. 2001. (Latinos in the Limelight Ser.). (Illus.). 64p. (J). (gr. 4-7). 27.50 (978-0-7910-6478-8(6) , Chelsea Hse.) Facts On File, Inc.

—Ricky Martin. 2001. (Latinos in the Limelight Ser.). (Illus.). 64p. (J). (gr. 4-7). 27.50 (978-0-7910-6100-8(0) , Chelsea Hse.) Facts On File, Inc.

HISPANIC AMERICANS—FICTION

Ada, Alma Flor & Campoy, F. Isabel. Celebrate Christmas & Three Kings' Day with Pablo & Carlitos. Torres, Walter, illus. 2006. (J). (978-1-59820-136-9(0)) Santillana USA Publishing Co., Inc.

Altman, Linda Jacobs. El Camino de Amelia. ed. 2004. (SPA., Illus.). (J). (gr. k-3). spiral bd. (978-0-616-14603-3(5)) Canadian National Institute for the Blind/Institut National Canadien pour les Aveugles.

Alvarez, Julia. Antes de Ser Libre. Valenzuela, Liliana, tr. 2004. (SPA.). 192p. (YA). (gr. 7). lib. bdg. 17.99 (978-0-375-91545-1(1) , Knopf Bks. for Young Readers) Random Hse. Children's Bks.

—Un Regalo de Gracias: La Leyenda de la Altagracia. Valenzuela, Liliana, tr. Vidal, Beatriz, illus. 2005. (SPA.). 40p. (J). (gr. k-3). pap. 7.99 (978-0-553-11343-3(7) , Dragonfly Bks.) Random Hse. Children's Bks.

Anaya, Rudolfo. Curse of the ChupaCabra. 2006. 174p. (YA). 24.95 (978-0-8263-4114-3(4)) Univ. of New Mexico Pr.

Bang, Molly Garrett. Tiger's Fall. 2003. (gr. 3-6). lib. bdg. 13.00 (978-0-613-65098-4(0)) Tandem Library Bks.

Bencastro, Mario. A Promise to Keep. Giersbach-Rascon, Susan, tr. from SPA. 2005. 134p. (J). (gr. 3-7). pap. 9.95 (978-1-55885-457-4(6) , Piñata Books) Arte Publico Pr.

Blackaby, Susan. Allie's Bike. Tenney, Shawna, illus. 2006. (Read-It! Readers Ser.). (J). 19.93 (978-1-4048-2403-4(0)) Picture Window Bks.

Campoy, F. Isabel & Ada, Alma Flor. Celebrate Chinese New Year with the Fong Family. Castro, Mima, illus. 2006. (Stories to Celebrate Ser.). 31p. (J). (978-1-59820-126-0(3)) Santillana USA Publishing Co., Inc.

Campoy, F. Isabel, et al. Celebra el Ano Nuevo Chino con la Familia Fong. Castro, Mima, illus. 2006. (J). (978-1-59820-114-7(X) , Alfaguara) Santillana USA Publishing Co., Inc.

Carlson, Lori M. Voices in First Person: Reflections on Latino Identity. 2008. 96p. (J). (***978-1-4169-0635-3(5))*** Simon & Schuster Children's Publishing.

Carlson, Lori Marie. Vivan los Reyes Magos! Martinez, Ed, illus. 2000. (SPA.). (J). (gr. 1-3). lib. bdg. 16.00 (978-1-880507-74-2(9) , LC0104) Lectorum Pubns., Inc.

Carson, Diana Pastora. All the Muchos in the World: A Special Story about Love. Pruitt, Ginny, illus. 2006. 32p. (J). pap. 8.95 (978-0-8198-0779-3(6)) Pauline Bks. & Media.

Castilla, Julia Mercedes. Emilio. 1999. 160p. (YA). (gr. 4-7). pap. 9.95 (978-1-55885-271-6(9) , Piñata Books) Arte Publico Pr.

—Emilio. (SPA.). (YA). (gr. 5-8). 8.95 (978-958-04-4149-6(9) , NR3970) Norma S.A. COL. *Dist:* Distribuidora Norma, Inc., Lectorum Pubns., Inc.

Colato Lainez, Rene. Waiting for Papa/Esperando a Papa. Accardo, Anthony, illus. Tr. of Esperando a Papa. (ENG & SPA.). 32p. (gr. 1-3). 15.95 (978-1-55885-403-1(7) , Piñata Books) Arte Publico Pr.

De Anda, Diane. Dancing Miranda. Castilla, Julia Mercedes, tr. from ENG. Alvarez, Lamberto, illus. 2001. Tr. of Baila, Miranda, Baila. (SPA & ENG.). 32p. (J). (ps-3). 14.95 (978-1-55885-323-2(5) , Piñata Books) Arte Publico Pr.

de Paola, Tomie. Adelita: A Mexican Cinderella Story. 2004. (SPA., Illus.). 40p. (J). (gr. k-3). pap. 6.99 (978-0-14-240187-3(0) , Puffin) Penguin Group (USA) Inc.

—Marcus Counts: One, Two, Three. 2003. (SPA., Illus.). 14p. (J). (ps-1). bds. 5.99 (978-0-399-24011-9(X) , Putnam Juvenile) Penguin Group (USA) Inc.

—A New Barker in the House. (Illus.). 32p. (J). (ps up). 2004. pap. 5.99 (978-0-14-240141-5(2) , Puffin); 2002. (SPA., 13.99 (978-0-399-23865-9(4) , Putnam Juvenile) Penguin Group (USA) Inc.

deRubertis, Barbara. Count on Pablo. Thornburgh, Rebecca McKillip, illus. 1999. (Math Matters Ser.). 32p. (gr. k-2). pap. 4.95 (978-1-57565-090-6(8)) Kane Pr., The.

—Count on Pablo. 1999. (Math Matters Ser.). (Illus.). (J). 11.75 (978-0-606-18217-1(9)) Tandem Library Bks.

Dominguez, Kelli Kyle. The Perfect Pinata: La Pinata Perfecta. Mlawer, Teresa, tr. Paterson, Diane, illus. 2002. (ENG & SPA.). 32p. (J). (gr. k-3). 15.95 (978-0-8075-6495-0(8)) Whitman, Albert & Co.

Donahue, Jill L. Rudy Helps Out. Previn, Stacey, illus. 2006. (Read-It! Readers Ser.). (J). 19.93 (978-1-4048-2420-1(0)) Picture Window Bks.

Dorros, Arthur. Abuela. Kleven, Elisa, illus. 2002. (J). 14.04 (978-0-7587-1901-0(9)) Book Wholesalers, Inc.

Dorros, Arthur. Papa & Me. Gutierrez, Rudy, illus. 2008. 32p. (J). 16.99 ***978-0-06-058156-5(5)***); lib. bdg. 17.89 ***(978-0-06-058157-2(3))*** HarperCollins Pubs.

Dougherty, Terri. The Camping Scare. Thompson, Jeffrey, illus. 2006. (Read-It! Readers Ser.). (J). 19.93 (978-1-4048-2405-8(7)) Picture Window Bks.

Drake, Isabelle. La Cancion de Gabriela: Como Me Adapto a un Lugar Nuevo. Burris, Priscilla Garcia, illus. 2007. (SPA.). 32p. (J). (ps-3). 12.99 ***(978-0-06-114102-7(X)*** , Rayo) HarperCollins Pubs.

Draper, Sharon M. Romiette & Julio. 2009. 320p. (YA). pap. 8.99 ***(978-1-4169-5514-6(3)*** , Simon Pulse) Simon & Schuster Children's Publishing.

—Romiette & Julio. Lowenbein, Adam, illus. (YA). (gr. 7-12). 2001. 336p. mass mkt. 6.99 (978-0-689-84209-2(0) , Simon Pulse); 1999. 240p. 18.99 (978-0-689-82180-6(8) , Atheneum) Simon & Schuster Children's Publishing.

Elya, Susan Middleton. Tooth on the Loose. Mattheson, Jenny, illus. 2008. (SPA & ENG.). 32p. (J). (ps-k). 16.99 ***(978-0-399-24459-9(X)*** , Putnam Juvenile) Penguin Group (USA) Inc.

Encinas, Carlos. The New Engine: La Maquina Nueva. 2001. (Illus.). (J). 15.95 (978-1-885772-24-4(6)) Kiva Publishing, Inc.

English, Karen. Speak English for Us, Marisol! Sanchez, Enrique O., illus. 2000. (Concept Book Ser.). 32p. (J). (gr. 1-4). 15.95 (978-0-8075-7554-3(2)) Whitman, Albert & Co.

Ewing, Lynne. Party Girl. 1999. 128p. (YA). (gr. 9-11). pap. 5.50 (978-0-375-80210-2(X) , Laurel Leaf) Random Hse. Children's Bks.

—Party Girl. 1999. (978-0-606-17373-5(0)); (gr. 7-12). lib. bdg. 13.00 (978-0-613-23023-0(X)) Tandem Library Bks.

Fernandez, Giselle. Gigi & the Birthday Ring. Petersen, Sheli, illus. 2005. (J). (978-1-56492-358-5(4)) Laredo Publishing Co., Inc.

Ficklin, Jonene H. The Garden Gate. 2005. (YA). 14.95 (978-0-9761188-2-4(3)) Victor's Crown Publishing.

French, Jackie. Alicia's Happy Day (English/Spanish Bilingual) Van Wright, Cornelius & Hu, Ying-Hwa, illus. 2007. 36p. (J). pap. 5.95 ***(978-1-59572-116-7(9))*** Star Bright Bks., Inc.

Fry, Sonali. Dora the Detective. Fruchter, Jason, illus. 2004. (Dora the Explorer Ser.). 10p. (J). bds. 8.99 (978-0-689-86531-2(7) , Simon Spotlight/Nickelodeon) Simon & Schuster Children's Publishing.

Gershator, David. Bread Is for Eating. 1998. Tr. of Spanish). 13.75 (978-0-606-13225-1(2)) Tandem Library Bks.

Gershator, David & Gershator, Phillis. Bread Is for Eating. Shaw-Smith, Emma, illus. 2003. Tr. of Spanish). (ENG & SPA.). 25p. (J). (gr. k-4). reprint ed. 16.00 (978-0-7567-9033-2(6)) DIANE Publishing Co.

Gonzalez, Rigoberto. Soledad Sigh-Sighs / Soledad Suspiros. Ibarra, Rosa, illus. 2003. Tr. of Soledad Suspiros. (ENG & SPA.). 32p. (J). 16.95 (978-0-89239-180-6(4)) Children's Bk. Pr.

Griessman, Annette. The Fire. Gore, Leonid, illus. 2005. 32p. (J). (ps-3). 16.99 (978-0-399-24019-5(5) , Putnam Juvenile) Penguin Group (USA) Inc.

Griffin, Peni R. The Music Thief. rev. ed. 2002. 160p. (YA). (gr. 5-8). 16.95 (978-0-8050-7055-2(9) , Holt, Henry & Co. Bks. For Young Readers) Holt, Henry & Co.

—The Music Thief. l.t. ed. 2003. 190p. (J). 21.95 (978-0-7862-5606-8(0)) Thorndike Pr.

Grimes, Nikki. Oh, Brother! Benny, Mike, illus. 2008. 32p. (J). 17.89 (978-0-688-17295-4(4)); 16.99 (978-0-688-17294-7(6)) HarperCollins Pubs.

H. Kraus, Joanna & Luisa, Anna. A Night of Tamales & Roses. 2007. 32p. (J). 15.95 ***(978-0-9726614-4-7(1))*** Shenanigan Bks.

Harcourt School Publishers Staff. Meet My Family. 3rd ed. 2002. (Trophies English Language Learners Ser.). (Illus.). (J). pap. 4.10 (978-0-15-327583-8(9)) Harcourt Schl. Pubs.

Haugaard, Kay. No Place. Peterson-Albandoz, Michelle, illus. 1999. 175p. (J). (gr. 3-8). 15.95 (978-1-57131-616-5(7)) Milkweed Editions.

—No Place. 2nd ed. 2007. (Illus.). 140p. pap. 6.95 ***(978-1-57131-675-2(2))*** Milkweed Editions.

—No Place. 1999. (J). (978-0-606-19034-3(1)) Tandem Library Bks.

Hernandez, David. Suckerpunch. 2008. 224p. (J). 16.99 ***(978-0-06-117330-1(4)***); lib. bdg. 17.89 ***(978-0-06-117331-8(2))*** HarperCollins Pubs. (HarperTeen).

Ibarra, Maria Teresa Ornelas. Penny & Me. 2006. (J). ***(978-0-9774306-6-6(9))*** Acacia Publishing, Inc.

Jiménez, Francisco. Breaking Through. 2002. 208p. (J). (gr. 7). pap. 6.95 (978-0-618-34248-8(6)) Houghton Mifflin Co. Trade & Reference Div.

Keats, Ezra Jack. Dreams. Keats, Ezra Jack, illus. 2000. (Illus.). 40p. (J). (ps-3). pap. 7.99 (978-0-14-056744-1(5) , Puffin) Penguin Group (USA) Inc.

—Dreams. 2000. 13.79 (978-0-606-20356-2(7)); (J). (978-0-606-20232-9(3)); lib. bdg. 15.30 (978-0-613-29937-4(X)) Tandem Library Bks.

—My Dog Is Lost! Keats, Ezra Jack, illus. 2002. (Illus.). (J). 14.04 (978-0-7587-4531-6(1)) Book Wholesalers, Inc.

Keats, Ezra Jack & Shaw, Tucker. Dreams. 2000. (Illus.). 40p. (J). (ps-2). 15.99 (978-0-670-89225-9(4) , Viking Juvenile) Penguin Group (USA) Inc.

Klein, Adria F. Max & Buddy Go to the Vet. Gallagher-Cole, Mernie, illus. 2007. (J). lib. bdg. ***(978-1-4048-3679-2(9))*** Picture Window Bks.

—Max & the Adoption Day Party. 2007. (Read-It! Readers Ser.). 24p. (J). ***(978-1-4048-3283-1(1)*** , 1265792) Picture Window Bks.

—Max & the Adoption Day Party. Gallagher-Cole, Mernie, illus. 2006. (Read-It! Readers Ser.). 24p. (J). (gr. k-2). lib. bdg. 19.93 ***(978-1-4048-3145-2(2)*** , 1265792) Picture Window Bks.

—Max Celebrates Chinese New Year. 2007. (Read-It! Readers Ser.). (Illus.). 24p. (J). ***(978-1-4048-3287-9(4)*** , 1265794) Picture Window Bks.

—Max Celebrates Chinese New Year. Gallagher-Cole, Mernie, illus. 2006. (Read-It! Readers Ser.). 24p. (J). (gr. k-2). lib. bdg. 19.93 ***(978-1-4048-3147-6(9)*** , 1265794) Picture Window Bks.

—Max Goes to a Cookout. 2007. (Read-It! Readers Ser.). (Illus.). 24p. (J). ***(978-1-4048-3290-9(4)*** , 1265793) Picture Window Bks.

—Max Goes to a Cookout. Gallagher-Cole, Mernie, illus. 2006. (Read-It! Readers Ser.). 24p. (J). ***(978-1-4048-3146-9(0)*** , 1265793) Picture Window Bks.

—Max Goes to the Barber. Gallagher-Cole, Mernie, illus. 2005. (Read-It! Readers Ser.). 24p. (J). (ps). lib. bdg. 18.60 (978-1-4048-1180-5(X)) Picture Window Bks.

—Max Goes to the Dentist. Gallagher-Cole, Mernie, illus. 2005. (Read-It! Readers Ser.). 24p. (J). (ps). lib. bdg. 18.60 (978-1-4048-1181-2(8)) Picture Window Bks.

—Max Goes to the Doctor. Gallagher-Cole, Mernie, illus. 2007. (J). lib. bdg. ***(978-1-4048-3680-8(2))*** Picture Window Bks.

—Max Goes to the Farm. Gallagher-Cole, Mernie, illus. 2007. (J). lib. bdg. ***(978-1-4048-3678-5(0))*** Picture Window Bks.

—Max Goes to the Grocery Store. Gallagher-Cole, Mernie, illus. 2007. (J). lib. bdg. ***(978-1-4048-3682-2(9))*** Picture Window Bks.

—Max Goes to the Library. Gallagher-Cole, Mernie, illus. 2005. (Read-It! Readers Ser.). 24p. (J). (ps). lib. bdg. 18.60 (978-1-4048-1182-9(6)) Picture Window Bks.

—Max Goes to the Playground. Gallagher-Cole, Mernie, illus. 2007. (J). lib. bdg. ***(978-1-4048-3681-5(0))*** Picture Window Bks.

—Max Goes to the Zoo. Gallagher-Cole, Mernie, illus. 2007. (J). lib. bdg. ***(978-1-4048-3677-8(2))*** Picture Window Bks.

—Max Learns Sign Language. 2007. (Read-It! Readers Ser.). (Illus.). 24p. (J). ***(978-1-4048-3545-0(8)*** , 1265795) Picture Window Bks.

—Max Learns Sign Language. Gallagher-Cole, Mernie, illus. 2006. (Read-It! Readers Ser.). 24p. (J). (gr. k-2). lib. bdg. 19.93 ***(978-1-4048-3148-3(7)*** , 1265795) Picture Window Bks.

—Max Stays Overnight. 2007. (Read-It! Readers Ser.). (Illus.). 24p. (J). ***(978-1-4048-3547-4(4)*** , 1265796) Picture Window Bks.

—Max Stays Overnight. Gallagher-Cole, Mernie, illus. 2006. (Read-It! Readers Ser.). 24p. (J). ***(978-1-4048-3149-0(5)*** , 1265796) Picture Window Bks.

—Max Va De Compras. Lozano, Clara, tr. Gallagher-Cole, Mernie, illus. 2006. (SPA.). 24p. 19.99 ***(978-1-4048-2669-4(6))*** Picture Window Bks.

—Max's Fun Day. 2007. (Read-It! Readers Ser.). (Illus.). 24p. (J). ***(978-1-4048-3549-8(0)*** , 1265797) Picture Window Bks.

—Max's Fun Day. Gallagher-Cole, Mernie, illus. 2006. (Read-It! Readers Ser.). 24p. (J). ***(978-1-4048-3150-6(9)*** , 1265797) Picture Window Bks.

Lachtman, Ofelia Dumas. The Trouble with Tessa. 122p. (J). (ps-7). pap. 9.95 (978-1-55885-448-2(7) , Piñata Books) Arte Publico Pr.

Lachtman, Ofelia Dumas, et al. Pepita Takes Time (Pepita, Siempre Tarde) 2000. (SPA & ENG., Illus.). 32p. (J). (ps-2). 14.95 (978-1-55885-304-1(9) , Piñata Books) Arte Publico Pr.

Manzano, Sonia. A Box Full of Kittens. Phelan, Matt, illus. 2007. 40p. (J). (ps-2). 16.99 (978-0-689-83089-1(0) , Atheneum) Simon & Schuster Children's Publishing.

Marcantonio, Patricia Santos, et al. Red Ridin' in the Hood: And Other Cuentos. Alarcao, Renato, illus. 2005. 192p. (J). 16.00 (978-0-374-36241-6(6) , Farrar, Straus & Giroux (BYR)) Farrar, Straus & Giroux.

Martelli, Dawn. Like Me. Wharton, Jennifer Heyd, illus. 2004. (J). (978-1-893516-01-4(6)) Our Child Pr.

Martin, Ann M. Amalia: Diary Three. 2000. (California Diaries: Bk. 14). (Illus.). 144p. (YA). (gr. 6-8). pap. 4.99 (978-0-439-09548-8(4)) Scholastic, Inc.

—Amalia: Diary Three. 1999. (California Diaries: Bk. 14). (Illus.). (YA). (gr. 6-8). (978-0-606-18525-7(9)) Tandem Library Bks.

McConnie Zapater, Beatriz. Fiesta. Ortega, Jose, illus. 2005. (Multicultural Celebrations Ser.). 32p. (J). 4.95 (978-1-59373-009-3(8)) Bunker Hill Publishing, Inc.

Miller-Lachmann, Lyn. Once upon a Cuento. 2003. 228p. pap. 15.95 (978-1-880684-99-3(3)) Curbstone Pr.

Montes, Marisa. A Crazy Mixed-Up Spanglish Day. Cepeda, Joe, illus. 2003. (Get Ready for Gabi Ser.). 128p. (J). pap. 12.95 (978-0-439-51710-2(9) , Scholastic Paperbacks); pap. 3.99 (978-0-439-47519-8(8)) Scholastic, Inc.

—No More Spanish! Cepeda, Joe, illus. 2004. (Get Ready for Gabi Ser.). 128p. (J). pap. 3.99 (978-0-439-47522-8(8) , Scholastic Paperbacks) Scholastic, Inc.

—Please Don't Go. Cepeda, Joe, illus. 2004. (Get Ready for Gabi Ser.: No. 4). 128p. (J). pap. 3.99 (978-0-439-47523-5(6) , Scholastic Paperbacks) Scholastic, Inc.

—Who's That Girl. Cepeda, Joe, illus. 2003. (Get Ready for Gabi Ser.). 112p. (J). pap. 12.95 (978-0-439-51711-9(7) , Scholastic Pr.) Scholastic, Inc.

Mora, Pat. Let's Eat! A Comer! Suarez, Maribel, illus. 2008. (My Family: Mi Familia Ser.). (SPA & ENG.). 24p. (J). 12.99 ***(978-0-06-085038-8(8)***); lib. bdg. 14.89 ***(978-0-06-085039-5(6))*** HarperCollins Pubs. (Rayo).

Namm, Diane. Pick a Pet. Suarez, Maribel, tr. Suarez, Maribel, illus. 2004. (My First Reader Ser.). 31p. (J). 18.50 (978-0-516-24417-4(5) , Children's Pr.) Scholastic Library Publishing.

Nikola-Lisa, W. My Teacher Can Teach—Anyone! Galindo, Felipe, illus. 2004. 32p. (J). (ps-2). 16.95 (978-1-58430-163-9(5)) Lee & Low Bks., Inc.

Orozco, Jose-Luis. Fiestas: A Year of Latin-American Songs & Celebrations. Kleven, Elisa, illus. 2004. (SPA.). 48p. (J). (gr. k). pap. 7.99 (978-0-14-240199-6(4) , Puffin) Penguin Group (USA) Inc.

Ozeta, Valerie. Legend of the Red Wolf. 2nd ed. 1999. (Illus.). 34p. (J). (gr. 3-7). pap. 5.95 (978-0-9661687-1-6(2)) Red Wolf Publishing.

Ricci, Christine. Dora's Book of Manners. Hall, Susan T., illus. 2004. (Dora the Explorer Ser.). 24p. (J). pap. 3.50 (978-0-689-86533-6(3) , Simon Spotlight/Nickelodeon) Simon & Schuster Children's Publishing.

—Dora's Book of Manners. 2004. (ps-2). lib. bdg. 11.25 (978-0-613-73450-9(5)) Tandem Library Bks.

—Say Cheese! Savitsky, Steven, illus. 2004. (Dora the Explorer Ser.). 24p. (J). pap. 3.99 (978-0-689-86496-4(5) , Simon Spotlight/Nickelodeon) Simon & Schuster Children's Publishing.

Rice, David. Crazy Loco. Clayton, Christian, illus. 2003. 144p. (YA). (gr. 6-11). pap. 5.99 (978-0-14-250056-9(9) , Puffin) Penguin Group (USA) Inc.

Rodriguez, Luis. It Doesn't Have to Be This Way. Galvez, Daniel, illus. 1999. 32p. (J). pap. 21.27 (978-0-516-21698-0(8) , Children's Pr.) Scholastic Library Publishing.

Rodriguez, Luis J. It Doesn't Have to Be This Way: No Tiene que ser as #0237;: Una Historia del Barrio. Galvez, Daniel, illus. 2004. 32p. (J). pap. 7.95 (978-0-89239-203-2(7)) Children's Bk. Pr.

Roper, Robert, illus. Dora Goes to School. 2004. (Dora the Explorer Ser.). 24p. (J). pap. 3.99 (978-0-689-86494-0(9) , Simon Spotlight/Nickelodeon) Simon & Schuster Children's Publishing.

Soto, Gary. Accidental Love. 2008. 192p. (YA). pap. 6.95 ***(978-0-15-206113-5(4)*** , Harcourt Paperbacks) Harcourt Children's Bks.

Starr, Meg. Alicia's Happy Day. Van Wright, Cornelius & Hu, Ying-Hwa, illus. 2003. 36p. (J). pap. 5.95 (978-1-932065-06-0(7)) Star Bright Bks., Inc.

—Alicia's Happy Day. Hu, Ying-Hwa & Van Wright, Cornelius, illus. 2003. 36p. (J). (ps-3). 15.95 (978-1-887734-85-1(6)) Star Bright Bks., Inc.

Starr, Meg. Alicia's Happy Day (English/Spanish Bilingual) Van Wright, Cornelius & Hu, Ying-Hwa, illus. 2007. 36p. (J). 15.95 ***(978-1-59572-115-0(0))*** Star Bright Bks., Inc.

Style Guide Staff, illus. Boots's Backpack Book. 2002. (Dora the Explorer Ser.). 16p. (J). bds. 6.99 (978-0-689-85156-8(1) , Simon Spotlight/Nickelodeon) Simon & Schuster Children's Publishing.

Torres, Leyla. El Festival de Cometas. Torres, Leyla, illus. 2004. (SPA., Illus.). 32p. (J). 16.00 (978-0-374-32299-1(6) , Frances Foster Bks.) Farrar, Straus & Giroux.

—The Kite Festival. Torres, Leyla, illus. 2004. (Illus.). 32p. (J). 16.00 (978-0-374-38054-0(6) , Farrar, Straus & Giroux (BYR)) Farrar, Straus & Giroux.

Valdes, Leslie. Dora's Christmas Parade. Aikins, Dave, illus. 2003. (Dora the Explorer Ser.). 32p. (J). 5.99 (978-0-689-85843-7(4) , Simon Spotlight/Nickelodeon) Simon & Schuster Children's Publishing.

—Dora's Christmas Parade. 2003. (gr. k-3). lib. bdg. 14.15 (978-0-613-73391-5(6)) Tandem Library Bks.

—Happy Mother's Day, Mami! Fruchter, Jason, illus. 2003. (Dora the Explorer Ser.: Vol. 3). 24p. (J). pap. 3.99 (978-0-689-85233-6(9) , Simon Spotlight/Nickelodeon) Simon & Schuster Children's Publishing.

—Happy Mother's Day, Mami! 2003. (ps-2). lib. bdg. 11.80 (978-0-613-73353-3(3)) Tandem Library Bks.

Weller, Frances Ward. The Day the Animals Came: A Story of Saint Francis Day. Long, Loren, illus. 2006. 35p. (J). (gr. k-4). reprint ed. 17.00 (978-1-4223-5396-7(6)) DIANE Publishing Co.

Willson, Sarah. Dora's Halloween Adventure. Savitsky, Steven, illus. 2003. (Dora the Explorer Ser.). 14p. (J). bds. 5.99 (978-0-689-85844-4(2) , Simon Spotlight/Nickelodeon) Simon & Schuster Children's Publishing.

HISPANO-AMERICAN WAR, 1898

see Spanish-American War, 1898

HISTOCHEMISTRY

see Biochemistry

HISTOLOGY

see Anatomy; Anatomy, Comparative; Cells

HISTORIANS

see also Archaeologists

Doak, Robin S. Thucydides: Ancient Greek Historian. 2006. (J). (978-0-7565-1875-2(X)) Compass Point Bks.

Durden, Robert F. Carter G. Woodson: Father of African-American History. 1998. (African-American Biographies Ser.). (Illus.). 128p. (YA). (gr. 6-12). lib. bdg. 26.60 (978-0-89490-946-7(0)) Enslow Pubs., Inc.

Florescano, Enrique. La Historia y el Historiador. 2000. 11.80 (978-0-606-17684-2(5)) Tandem Library Bks.

Gillis, Jennifer Blizin. Mercy Otis Warren: Author & Historian. 2005. (Signature Lives Ser.). (Illus.). 112p. (J). (gr. 5-7). (978-0-7565-0982-8(3)) Compass Point Bks.

Gonzales Bertrand, Diane. Ricardo's Race: La Carrera de Ricardo. (SPA.). (J). 15.95 ***(978-1-55885-481-9(9))*** Arte Publico Pr.

Levene, Rebecca. Captain Cook. 2005. (Illus.). 64p. (J). 8.95 (978-0-7945-1051-0(5) , Usborne) EDC Publishing.

Meltzer, Milton. Milton Meltzer: Writing Matters. 2004. (Single Title - Bios Ser.). (Illus.). 160p. (J). 29.00 (978-0-531-12257-0(3) , Watts, Franklin) Scholastic Library Publishing.

Shirley, David. Alex Haley: Author. 2005. (Black Americans of Achievement Ser.). (Illus.). 112p. (J). (gr. 6-12). 30.00 (978-0-7910-8249-2(0)); pap. 13.25 (978-0-7910-8369-7(1)) Facts On File, Inc. (Chelsea Hse.).

HISTORIC BUILDINGS

Foreman, Stephen. Hylands: The Story on an Essex Country House & Its Owner. Henry, Ian, ed. 2nd unabr. ed. 1999. (Illus.). 128p. (gr. 4-12). pap. 15.00 (978-0-86025-492-8(5)) Henry, Ian Pubns. GBR. *Dist:* Empire Publishing Service.

Shuter, Jane. Carisbrooke Castle. 1999. (Visiting the Past Ser.). 32p. (J). (gr. 5-7). lib. bdg. 24.22 (978-1-57572-857-5(5)) Heinemann Library.

Steele, Philip. Wonders of the World. 2007. (Kingfisher Knowledge Ser.). (Illus.). 64p. (J). (gr. 3-5). 12.95 (978-0-7534-5979-9(5) , Kingfisher) Houghton Mifflin Co. Trade & Reference Div.

Tung, Anthony M. Wonders of Civilization Fandex. 2007. (Illus.). 50p. (J). 9.95 ***(978-0-7611-4355-0(6))*** Workman Publishing Co., Inc.

HISTORIC SITES

see also Historic Buildings; Monuments

Armentrout, David & Armentrout, Patricia. Historic Sites & Monuments. 2002. (Guides to State Symbols). (Illus.). 48p. (gr. 3-8). 20.95 (978-1-58952-085-1(8)) Rourke Publishing, LLC.

Bateman, Helen & Denshire, Jayne. Asia. 2006. (Illus.). 32p. (J). (978-1-58340-800-1(2) , 1262715) Smart Apple Media.

—Europe. 2006. (Illus.). 32p. (J). (978-1-58340-803-2(7)) Smart Apple Media.

—North America. 2006. (Illus.). 32p. (J). (978-1-58340-802-5(9)) Smart Apple Media.

—South America. 2006. (Illus.). 32p. (J). (978-1-58340-801-8(0) , 1262719) Smart Apple Media.

Bial, Raymond. The Forts: Building America. 2001. (Building America Ser.). (Illus.). 56p. (J). (gr. 4 up). lib. bdg. 27.07 (978-0-7614-1334-9(0) , Benchmark Bks.) Cavendish, Marshall Corp.

DK Publishing Staff. Great Wonders of the Natural World. 2007. 64p. (J). (gr. 3-6). 19.99 (978-0-7566-2980-9(2)) Dorling Kindersley Publishing, Inc.

Gillis, Jennifer Blizin. Battlefields. 2008. (J). ***(978-1-60044-559-0(4))*** Rourke Publishing, LLC.

—Restored Villages. 2008. (J). ***(978-1-60044-563-7(2))*** Rourke Publishing, LLC.

Hurd, Owen. Chicago History for Kids: Triumphs & Tragedies of the Windy City Includes 21 Activities. 2007. (For Kids Ser.). (Illus.). 192p. (YA). (gr. 4-9). pap. 14.95 ***(978-1-55652-654-1(7))*** Chicago Review Pr., Inc.

Nash, Gary B. Landmarks of the American Revolution. 2003. (American Landmarks Ser.). (Illus.). 160p. (YA). 32.00 (978-0-19-512849-9(4)) Oxford Univ. Pr., Inc.

Nathan, Emma. Lugares Conocidos. 2002. (Abre los Ojos y Aprende Serie).Tr. of Eyeopeners: Landmarks. (SPA.). 24p. (J). (-3). 24.94 (978-1-4103-0026-3(9) , Blackbirch Pr., Inc.) Thomson Gale.

National Landmarks, 4 bks. Incl. Lincoln Memorial. Deady, Kathleen W. lib. bdg. 18.60 (978-0-7368-1114-9(1)); Statue of Liberty. Deady, Kathleen W. lib. bdg. 18.60 (978-0-7368-1115-6(X)); Vietnam Veterans Memorial. Dubois, Muriel L. lib. bdg. 18.60 (978-0-7368-1116-3(8)); Washington Monument. Dubois, Muriel L. lib. bdg. 18.60 (978-0-7368-1117-0(6)); 24p. (J). (gr. 2-3). 2002. (Illus.). Set lib. bdg. 74.40 (978-0-7368-1158-3(3) , Bridgestone Bks.) Capstone Pr., Inc.

Park, Ted. Canada. 1999. (Taking Your Camera to Ser.). (Illus.). 32p. (J). (gr. 4-7). lib. bdg. 22.83 (978-0-7398-1803-9(1)) Raintree.

Passport to North Carolina Historic Sites. 1998. (Guides to State Historic Sites). (Illus.). 52p. (YA). (gr. 8-12). pap. 5.00 (978-0-86526-281-2(0)) North Carolina Office of Archives & History.

Places In History. 180.00 (978-0-8368-5809-9(3)) Stevens, Gareth Inc.

Putnam, Jeff. National Monuments: Events & Times. 2004. (Illus.). iii, 75p. (J). pap. ***(978-0-7367-1787-8(0))*** Zaner-Bloser, Inc.

Scholastic, Inc. Staff & Keenan, Sheila. O, Say Can You See? America's Symbols, Landmarks, & Important Words. 2007. 64p. (J). pap. 5.99 ***(978-0-439-59360-1(3)*** , Scholastic Nonfiction) Scholastic, Inc.

Silber, Nina. Landmarks of the Civil War. 2003. (American Landmarks Ser.). (Illus.). 144p. (YA). 30.00 (978-0-19-512920-5(2)) Oxford Univ. Pr., Inc.

Steele, Philip. Wonders of the World. 2007. (Kingfisher Knowledge Ser.). (Illus.). 64p. (J). (gr. 3-5). 12.95 (978-0-7534-5979-9(5) , Kingfisher) Houghton Mifflin Co. Trade & Reference Div.

Stone, Lynn M. America's Monuments. 2003. (Land of Liberty Ser.). (Illus.). 24p. (gr. 2-5). 17.95 (978-1-58952-312-8(1)) Rourke Publishing, LLC.

Torpie, Kate. Our National Treasures. 2002. (Illus.). 32p. (J). pap. 6.00 (978-1-59034-042-4(6)); (gr. 1-5). 15.95 (978-1-59034-191-9(0)) Mondo Publishing.

U. S. History Little Books: Famous Places. 2002. 144p. (J). (gr. k-3). 14.99 (978-0-7439-3259-2(5) , 3259) Teacher Created Materials, Inc.

Whiting, Jim. Threat to Ancient Egyptian Treasures. 2007. (On the Verge of Extinction Ser.). (Illus.). 32p. (J). (gr. 1-4). lib. bdg. 25.70 ***(978-1-58415-588-1(4))*** Mitchell Lane Pubs., Inc.

H
I

HISTORIC SITES—FICTION

Andrews, Jane. Ten Boys Who Lived on the Road from Long Ago to Now (Yesterday's Classics) 2006. (J). 9.95 (***978-1-59915-064-2(6)***) Yesterday's Classics.

HISTORICAL ATLASES

see Historical Geography—Maps

HISTORICAL CHRONOLOGY

see Chronology, Historical

HISTORICAL DICTIONARIES

see History—Dictionaries

HISTORICAL GEOGRAPHY

Boehm, Richard G., et al. Daily Geography: Early United States. 1999. (Harcourt Brace Social Studies). (gr. k-7). pap. 41.00 (978-0-15-310429-9(5)) Harcourt Schl. Pubs.

Diagram Group, contrib. by. Before Life. 2004. (Life on Earth Ser.). (Illus.). 112p. (J). (gr. 4-9). 35.00 (978-0-8160-5045-1(7)) Facts On File, Inc.

McNeese, Tim. Masada. 2003. (Sieges That Changed the World Ser.). (Illus.). 112p. (gr. 6-12). 30.00 (978-0-7910-7103-8(0) , Chelsea Hse.) Facts On File, Inc.

Nathan, Emma. Landmarks. 2002. (Illus.). 23p. (J). 22.45 (978-1-4103-0028-7(5) , Blackbirch Pr., Inc.) Thomson Gale.

Spickert, Diane Nelson. Earth Steps: A Rock's Journey Through Time. Wallace, Marianne D., illus. 2004. 32p. (J). (gr. 4-6). 17.95 (978-1-55591-986-3(3)) Fulcrum Publishing.

Watson, Susan. Valuing World Heritage. 2003. 32p. (J). lib. bdg. 24.25 (978-1-58340-401-0(5)) Smart Apple Media.

HISTORICAL GEOGRAPHY—MAPS

Atlas Historico (Historical Atlas) 1999. (ENG & SPA.). 160p. (YA). (gr. 8-12). 35.95 (978-84-348-4115-4(0)) SM Ediciones ESP. *Dist:* Distribooks, Inc.

Due, Andrea. The Atlas of the Bible Lands. Ravalgia, Paola & Chesi, Matteo, illus. 2001. (Atlas Ser.). 64p. (J). (gr. 5 up). 19.95 (978-0-87226-559-2(5) , 65595B, Bedrick, Peter Bks.) School Specialty Publishing.

Facts on File, Inc. Staff. Historical Maps on File. 3rd rev. ed. 2005. (Illus.). 608p. (gr. 6-12). 350.00 (978-0-8160-5897-6(0)) Facts On File, Inc.

Hammon, Inc. Staff, ed. Historical Atlas of the World. 5th rev. ed. 2003. (Atlas Ser.). (Illus.). 72p. (YA). (gr. 9-12). pap. 11.95 (978-0-8437-1391-6(7) , 713917) Hammond World Atlas Corp.

Hammond World Atlas Corporation Staff. Historical World Atlas. 5th ed. 2003. (Atlas Ser.). (Illus.). 76p. (gr. 9-12). tchr. ed. 16.95 (978-0-8437-1390-9(9) , 713909) Langenscheidt Pubs Inc.

Haywood, John. The Age of Discovery Vol. 3: 1492 to 1815. 2000. (World Atlas of the Past Ser.). (Illus.). 64p. (YA). 25.00 (978-0-19-521691-2(1)) Oxford Univ. Pr., Inc.

—The Medieval World Vol. 2: A. D. 1 to 1492. 2000. (World Atlas of the Past Ser.). (Illus.). 64p. (YA). 25.00 (978-0-19-521690-5(3)) Oxford Univ. Pr., Inc.

National Geographic, creator. National Geographic World Atlas for Young Explorers. 3rd ed. 2007. (Illus.). 191p. (J). (gr. 3-7). 24.95 (***978-1-4263-0088-2(3)*** , National Geographic Children's Bks.) National Geographic Society.

World Historical Atlases Series, 5 Bks, Set. 2004. (J). 135.35 (978-0-7614-1638-8(2)) Cavendish, Marshall Corp.

HISTORIOGRAPHY

see also Historians

Japanese-American National Museum Staff. Regenerations Oral History Project Vol. 3: Rebuilding Japanese American Families, Communities & Civil Rights in the Resettlement Era. unabr. ed. 2000. (Illus.). 505p. (YA). (gr. 9-12). (978-1-881161-08-0(0)) Japanese American National Museum.

Japanese-American National Museum Staff & Chicago Japanese American Historical Society Staff. Regenerations Oral History Project Vol. 3: Rebuilding Japanese American Families, Communities & Civil Rights in the Resettlement Era. unabr. ed. 2000. (Illus.). 708p. (YA). (gr. 9-12). (978-1-881161-07-3(2)) Japanese American National Museum.

Japanese-American National Museum Staff & Japanese American Historical Society of San Diego Staff. Regenerations Oral History Project Vol. 3: Rebuilding Japanese American Families, Communities & Civil Rights in the Resettlement Era. unabr. ed. 2000. 386p. (YA). (gr. 9-12). (978-1-881161-09-7(9)) Japanese American National Museum.

Japanese-American National Museum Staff & Japanese American Resource Center-Museum Staff. Regenerations Oral History Project Vol. 3: Rebuilding Japanese American Families, Communities & Civil Rights in the Resettlement Era. unabr. ed. 2000. 727p. (YA). (gr. 9-12). (978-1-881161-10-3(2)) Japanese American National Museum.

Japanese-American National Museum Staff, et al. Regenerations Oral History Project Vol. 3: Rebuilding Japanese American Families, Communities & Civil Rights in the Resettlement Era. unabr. ed. 2000. (Illus.). 2326p. (YA). (gr. 9-12). (978-1-881161-06-6(4)) Japanese American National Museum.

Lorenz Books Staff. Exploring History: A Journey Through Time, from Prehistory to the Modern World. 2001. (Illus.). 512p. (gr. 3-7). 45.00 (978-0-7548-0647-9(2)) Anness Publishing GBR. *Dist:* National Bk. Network.

McClaine, L. S. History Activities for Fun & Learning. 1998. 40p. (J). (gr. k-8). pap. 3.95 (978-1-890537-04-3(7)) Nutmeg Pubns.

Meltzer, Milton. Milton Meltzer: Writing Matters. 2004. (Single Title - Bios Ser.). (Illus.). 160p. (J). 29.00 (978-0-531-12257-0(3) , Watts, Franklin) Scholastic Library Publishing.

Schrecengost, Maity. Researching Events. 1998. (Illus.). (gr. 5-9). 20p. tchr. ed., spiral bd. 7.95 (978-1-57950-022-1(6) , P32-34985); 32p. (J). pap. 8.95 (978-1-57950-018-4(8)) Highsmith Inc. (Upstart Bks.).

Wills, Adele. Texts Through History. 2004. (Routledge a Level English Guides Ser.). (Illus.). 96p. 19.95 (978-0-415-31910-2(2)); 71.95 (978-0-415-31909-6(9)) Routledge.

HISTORY, ANCIENT

see also Archaeology; Bible; Civilization

Ackroyd, Peter. Cities of Blood. 2004. (Voyages Through Time Ser.). (Illus.). 144p. (J). 19.99 (978-0-7566-0729-6(9)) Dorling Kindersley Publishing, Inc.

The Ancient World. 2002. (Questions & Answers Ser.). 32p. (J). 7.95 (978-0-7525-7241-3(5)) Parragon, Inc.

Ancient World History: Patterns of Interaction. 2003. (gr. 6-12). stu. ed. (978-0-618-18393-7(0) , 2-01388) McDougal Littell Inc.

Ancient World History: Patterns of Interaction. 2005. (gr. 6-12). tchr. ed. (978-0-618-37681-0(X) , 2-00462) McDougal Littell Inc.

Ancient World History: Patterns of Interaction: EEdition. (gr. 6-12). 2005. cd-rom (978-0-618-43267-7(1) , 2-00805); 2003. cd-rom (978-0-618-28480-1(X) , 2-90159) McDougal Littell Inc.

Ancient World History: Patterns of Interaction: EEdition Plus Online. (gr. 6-12). 2005. (978-0-618-42268-5(4) , 2-00681); 2003. (978-0-618-19413-1(4) , 2-70055) McDougal Littell Inc.

Ancient World History: Patterns of Interaction: EEdition Plus Online with purchase of print Pupil's Edition- 3 Year. 2003. (gr. 6-12). (978-0-618-25835-2(3) , 2-10026) McDougal Littell Inc.

Ancient World History: Patterns of Interaction: EEdition Plus Online with purchase of print Pupil's Edition- 4 Year. 2003. (gr. 6-12). (978-0-618-25836-9(1) , 2-10027) McDougal Littell Inc.

Ancient World History: Patterns of Interaction: EEdition Plus Online with purchase of print Pupil's Edition- 5 Year. 2003. (gr. 6-12). (978-0-618-25837-6(X) , 2-10028) McDougal Littell Inc.

Ancient World History: Patterns of Interaction: EEdition Plus Online with purchase of print Pupil's Edition-1 Year. 2005. (gr. 6-12). (978-0-618-42278-4(1) , 2-00683) McDougal Littell Inc.

Ancient World History: Patterns of Interaction: EEdition Plus Online with purchase of print Pupil's Edition-2 Year. 2005. (gr. 6-12). (978-0-618-42279-1(X) , 2-00684) McDougal Littell Inc.

Ancient World History: Patterns of Interaction: EEdition Plus Online with purchase of print Pupil's Edition-3 Year. 2005. (gr. 6-12). (978-0-618-42280-7(3) , 2-00685) McDougal Littell Inc.

Ancient World History: Patterns of Interaction: EEdition Plus Online with purchase of print Pupil's Edition-4 Year. 2005. (gr. 6-12). (978-0-618-42281-4(1) , 2-00686) McDougal Littell Inc.

Ancient World History: Patterns of Interaction: EEdition Plus Online with purchase of print Pupil's Edition-5 Year. 2005. (gr. 6-12). (978-0-618-42282-1(X) , 2-00687) McDougal Littell Inc.

Ancient World History: Patterns of Interaction: EEdition Plus Online with purchase of print Pupil's Edition-6 Year. 2005. (gr. 6-12). (978-0-618-42283-8(8) , 2-00688) McDougal Littell Inc.

Battle. (Dk Eyewitness Books Ser.). (J). pap. 8.95 (978-0-7894-6033-2(5)) Dorling Kindersley Publishing, Inc.

Bauer, Susan Wise. The Story of the World: Ancient Times: from the Earliest Nomads to the Last Roman Emperor. 3rd ed. 2006. 300p. pap., act. bk. ed. 34.95 incl. cd-rom (978-1-933339-05-4(5)) Peace Hill Pr.

—The Story of the World: History for the Classical Child: Volume 1: Ancient Times: from the Earliest Nomads to the Last Roman Emperor, Revised Edition. 2nd ed. 2006. (Illus.). 350p. 24.95 (978-1-933339-01-6(2)) Peace Hill Pr.

Beautiful Feet Ancient History Syllabus. 1999. 8p. (J). ring bd. 1.00 (978-1-57896-063-7(0) , 2417, Hewitt Homeschooling Resources) Hewitt Research Foundation, Inc.

Beck, Roger B. Ancient World History: Patterns of Interaction: Pupil's Edition. l.t. ed. 2005. (YA). (gr. 9-12). 83.76 (978-0-618-37679-7(8) , 2-00460) McDougal Littell Inc.

Benchmark Education Staff, compiled by. Early River Civilizations. 2006. spiral bd. 330.00 (***978-1-4108-7011-7(1));*** 2006. spiral bd. 169.00 (***978-1-4108-7139-8(8));*** 2005. (J). spiral bd. 265.00 (***978-1-4108-5773-6(5)***) Benchmark Education Co.

—Social Studies Theme: Early River Civilizations. 2005. spiral bd. 115.00 (***978-1-4108-5325-7(X)***) Benchmark Education Co.

Bingham, Jane. Ency of the Ancient World (Reduced Format) 2007. 400p. (J). pap. 19.99 (978-0-7945-1141-8(4) , Usborne) EDC Publishing.

—Encyclopedia of Ancient World. 2004. (History Encyclopedias Ser.). (Illus.). 400p. (J). 39.95 (978-0-7945-0364-2(0) , Usborne) EDC Publishing.

Bluedorn, Harvey & Bluedorn, Laurie. Ancient History from Primary Sources: A Literary Timeline. 2003. (Illus.). 223p. pap. 59.00 (978-0-9743616-4-2(X)) Trivium Pursuit.

Bogarad, Carley Rees & Schmidt, Jan Zlotnik. Legacies. 2nd ed. 2001. 1440p. (C). pap. 79.95 (978-0-15-506953-4(5)) Thomson Heinle.

Bowman, John S. Exploration in the World of the Ancients, 10 vols. 2004. (Discovery & Exploration Ser.). (Illus.). 160p. (YA). (gr. 6-12). 40.00 (978-0-8160-5257-8(3)) Facts On File, Inc.

Brewer, Paul. Warfare in the Ancient World. 1999. (History of Warfare Ser.). (Illus.). 80p. (YA). (gr. 7-12). lib. bdg. 29.97 (978-0-8172-5442-1(0)) Raintree.

Bush, Jane. If Rocks Could Talk. 2001. (gr. k-3). lib. bdg. 21.05 (978-0-613-88555-3(4)) Tandem Library Bks.

Camibucci, Patricia. Ancient & World History: Over 15 Complete Printable Unit Studies with Interactive Links. 2002. 160p. (gr. k-12). cd-rom 15.95 (978-1-891400-91-9(6)) Champion Pr., Ltd.

Casterline, Linda & Gleason, Katherine. Ancient World: A Chapter Book. 2003. (True Tales Ser.). (Illus.). 48p. (J). 22.50 (978-0-516-22916-4(8) , Children's Pr.) Scholastic Library Publishing.

Chandler, Fiona & McCaffrey, Susie. The Usborne Internet-Linked Ancient World. 2005. (Illus.). 96p. (***978-0-439-78503-7(0)***) Scholastic, Inc.

Cox, Phil Roxbee & Reid, S. Who Were the First People? rev. ed. 2004. (Starting Point History Ser.). (Illus.). 32p. (J). lib. bdg. 12.95 (978-1-58086-499-2(6)) EDC Publishing.

Cox, Phil Roxbee & Reid, Struan. Who Were the First People? 2004. (Starting Point History Ser.). (Illus.). 32p. (J). pap. 4.95 (978-0-7945-0339-0(X) , Usborne) EDC Publishing.

De Angelis, Therese. Wonders of the Ancient World. 1998. (Costume, Tradition & Culture). (Illus.). 64p. (YA). (gr. 5 up). 19.75 (978-0-7910-5170-2(6) , Chelsea Hse.) Facts On File, Inc.

Denver Museum of Natural History Staff. Prehistoric Coloring Book. Leggitt, Marjorie C., illus. 1998. 32p. pap. 4.95 (978-1-57098-216-3(3)) Rinehart, Roberts Pubs.

Forbes, Claire. Ancient Peoples. 2000. (J). (978-0-606-20291-6(9)) Tandem Library Bks.

Gleason, Katherine. Ancient World. 2004. (True Tales Ser.). (J). (gr. 2-4). pap. 4.95 (978-0-516-24600-0(3) , Children's Pr.) Scholastic Library Publishing.

Harcourt School Publishers Staff. Clues to Long Ago. 3rd ed. 2002. (Horizons Ser.). (Illus.). (J). pap. 3.70 (978-0-15-333127-5(5)) Harcourt Schl. Pubs.

Harding, Alexandra Hanson. Ancient Rome: A Complete Resource Packed with Background Information, Plays, Writing & World Study Activities. 2000. (Illus.). 80p. pap. 12.95 (978-0-439-05920-6(8)) Scholastic, Inc.

Harness, Cheryl. Ghosts of the Nile. Harness, Cheryl, illus. 2004. 32p. (J). 16.95 (978-0-689-83478-3(0)) Simon & Schuster Children's Publishing.

Harris, Nicholas. The Ancient World. 2006. 32p. (gr. 2-4). 23.70 (978-1-4103-0352-3(7) , Blackbirch Pr., Inc.) Thomson Gale.

Harrison, James. A Magic Skeleton Book: Discovering Ancient Egypt. Smith, Jan & Bull, Peter, illus. 2004. (Magic Color Bks.). 12p. (J). 9.95 (978-1-4027-1596-9(X) , Sterling/Pinwheel) Sterling Publishing Co., Inc.

Hart, Avery & Gallagher, Sandra. Ancient Rome! Exploring the Culture, People & Ideas of This Powerful Empire. Kline, Michael P., illus. 2001. (Kaleidoscope Kids Bks.). 96p. (J). (gr. 3-9). pap. 12.95 (978-1-885593-60-3(0) , Williamson Bks.) Ideals Pubns.

Harvey, Gill & Reid, Struan. Encyclopedia of Ancient Egypt. 2004. (History Encyclopedias Ser.). (Illus.). 144p. (J). 19.95 (978-0-7945-0118-1(4) , Usborne); (gr. 4 up). lib. bdg. 27.95 (978-1-58086-387-2(6)) EDC Publishing.

Haslam, Andrew. Hommes de l'Age de Pierre. 2000. (Make It Work! History Ser.). (FRE., Illus.). 64p. (J). pap. 7.95 (978-1-58728-188-4(0) , Two Can Publishing) T&N Children's Publishing.

Haywood, John. Everyday Life in the Ancient World. 2003. (Illustrated History Encyclopedia Ser.). (Illus.). 264p. pap. 19.99 (978-0-7548-1224-1(3)) Anness Publishing GBR. *Dist:* National Bk. Network.

—The War for Power & Knowledge. 2003. (Illus.). 264p. pap. 19.99 (978-0-7548-1201-2(4)) Anness Publishing GBR. *Dist:* National Bk. Network.

Hindley, Judy, et al. Time Traveler: Visit Medieval Times, the Viking Age, the Roman World & Ancient Egypt. rev. ed. 2004. (Time Travelers Bks.). (Illus.). 130p. (J). (gr. 3-6). 22.95 (978-0-7460-3365-4(6)) EDC Publishing.

The History Student's Toolkit. (C). stu. ed. 2.66 (978-0-669-39797-0(0)) Houghton Mifflin College Div.

Holmes & Thom. The First Vertebrates. 2008. (Prehistoric Earth Ser.). 208p. (gr. 6-12). 35.00 (***978-0-8160-5958-4(6)*** , Chelsea Hse.) Facts On File, Inc.

Holt, Rinehart and Winston Staff. The Ancient World. 3rd ed. 2001. (J). (gr. 6). 18.40 (978-0-03-065033-8(X)) Holt, Rinehart & Winston.

—The Human Journey: Ancient. 3rd ed. 2001. 75.40 (978-0-03-065506-7(4)) Holt, Rinehart & Winston.

—The Human Journey: The Ancient World: Online Edition. 3rd ed. 2003. 75.93 (978-0-03-072543-2(7)) Holt, Rinehart & Winston.

Howitt, Carolyn. The British Museum Quiz Book. 2004. (Illus.). 80p. (J). pap. 9.95 (978-0-7141-3035-4(4)) British Museum Pr.

Howitt, Carolyn. 500 Things to Know about the Ancient World. 2007. 144p. (J). (gr. 5 up). pap. 9.99 (***978-0-7641-3863-8(4)***) Barron's Educational Series, Inc.

Hunt, Norman Bancroft. Living in the Ancient World. 2007. (Living in the Ancient World Ser.). 576p. (gr. 6-12). 210.00 (978-0-8160-6336-9(2)) Facts On File, Inc.

Hurdman, Charlotte, et al. Ancient World: How People Lived in the Stone Age, Ancient Egypt, Ancient Greec & the Roman Empire. 2003. (Illustrated History Encyclopedia Ser.). (Illus.). 264p. (gr. 3-7). pap. 19.99 (978-0-7548-1199-2(9) , Lorenz Bks.) Anness Publishing GBR. *Dist:* National Bk. Network.

Johnson, Terri, compiled by. What Really Happened in Ancient Times: A Collection of Historical Biographies, 4. 2006. (Illus.). 240p. (J). per. 15.95 (***978-1-932786-21-7(X)***) Knowledge Quest.

Journey to the Past, 6 bks., Set. Incl. Ancient Egypt. Solbiati, Romano. lib. bdg. 27.12 (978-0-7398-1954-8(2)); Classical Athens. Denti, Mario. lib. bdg. 27.12 (978-0-7398-1953-1(4)); Florence in the 1440s. Zelasco, Marco & Zelasco, Pierangelo. Ripamonti, Aldo, illus. lib. bdg. 27.12 (978-0-7398-1957-9(7)); Imperial Rome. Denti, Mario. lib. bdg. 27.12 (978-0-7398-1952-4(6)); Mayan Tikal. Solbiati, Romano. Ripamonti, Aldo, illus. lib. bdg. 27.12 (978-0-7398-1955-5(0)); Medieval Paris. Tartaglino, Anna Cazzini & Torcellan, Nanda. lib. bdg. 27.12 (978-0-7398-1956-2(9)); 56p. (J). (gr. 6-8). (Illus.). 2001. Set lib. bdg. 162.72 (978-0-7398-1958-6(5)) Raintree.

Little, Frances Delanoy. Ancient Stories from the Dardanelles 1924. 2004. reprint ed. pap. 30.95 (978-1-4179-7641-6(1)) Kessinger Publishing, LLC.

Loon, Willem Van Hen. Ancient Man or the Beginning of Civiliza. 2006. 24.99 (***978-1-4280-3308-5(4));*** pap. 18.99 (***978-1-4280-3299-6(1)***) IndyPublish.com.

Lorenz Books Staff. The Encyclopedia of Ancient History. 2000. (Illus.). 512p. (ps-3). 40.00 (978-0-7548-0592-2(1)) Anness Publishing GBR. *Dist:* National Bk. Network.

MacDonald, Fiona. Women in Ancient Rome. 2000. (Other Half of History Ser.). (Illus.). 48p. (J). (gr. 3 up). 17.95 (978-0-87226-570-7(6) , 65706B, Bedrick, Peter Bks.) School Specialty Publishing.

Maier, Kimberly. History Odyssey, Ancients - Level Three. 2006. (YA). ring bd. 38.00 (***978-0-9766057-6-8(7)***) Pandia Pr.

McGraw-Hill Staff. Journey Across Time: Early Ages, Course 1. 2004. stu. ed. 71.96 (978-0-07-860309-9(9) , 9780078603099) Glencoe/McGraw-Hill.

Merrill, Yvonne. Ancient People: Art Activities about Minoans, Mycenaeans, Trojans, Ancient Greeks, Etruscans, & Romans. 2nd ed. 2004. (Hands-on Ser.). (Illus.). 88p. pap. 20.00 (978-0-9643177-9-6(6)) KITS Publishing.

Millard, A. & Sims, L. Ancient Egypt, Ancient Greece, Ancient Rome. 2004. (Time Tours Ser.). (Illus.). 192p. (J). pap. 17.95 (978-0-7945-0461-8(2)) EDC Publishing.

Morris, Neil. Ancient World. 2003. (Knowledge Masters Ser.). (Illus.). 32p. (YA). pap. incl. cd-rom (978-1-903954-49-2(5)) Chrysalis Children's Bks.

Patent, Dorothy Hinshaw. Mystery of the Lascaux Cave. 1998. (Frozen in Time Ser.). (Illus.). 64p. (J). (gr. 5-9). lib. bdg. 28.50 (978-0-7614-0784-3(7)) Cavendish, Marshall Corp.

—Secrets of the Ice Man. 1999. (Frozen in Time Ser.). (Illus.). 72p. (J). (gr. 5-9). lib. bdg. 28.50 (978-0-7614-0782-9(0) , Benchmark Bks.) Cavendish, Marshall Corp.

Putnam, James. Momias. 2005. (Dk eyewitness Bks.). 72p. (J). 15.99 (978-0-7566-1482-9(1)); lib. bdg. 19.99 (978-0-7566-1488-1(0)) Dorling Kindersley Publishing, Inc.

Quadrillion Media Staff. Seven Wonders of the Ancient World (Die Sieben Weltwunder), Vol. 3. 1998. (Start Me Up Ser.: Vol. 3). 48p. (J). (gr. 3-8). mass mkt. 12.95 (978-1-58185-002-4(6) , Tessloff Publishing) Quadrillion Media LLC.

Rees, Rosemary. The Ancient Greeks. 2002. (Understanding People in the Past Ser.). (Illus.). 64p. (J). (gr. 4-6). pap. 8.95 (978-1-58810-315-4(3) , 91070) Heinemann Library.

Reid, S. & Chisholm, J. Who Built the Pyramids? rev. ed. 2004. (Starting Point History Ser.). (Illus.). 32p. (J). pap. 4.95 (978-0-7945-0343-7(8) , Usborne) EDC Publishing.

Rojas, Emilio. La Simple Historia de un Cualquiera: No Siempre Es Cualquier Historia. 2003. (SPA.). 205p. (YA). 15.95 (978-968-6966-02-2(1)) EDITER'S Publishing Hse. MEX. *Dist:* EDITER'S Publishing Hse.

Service, Pamela F. 300 B.C. (Around the World) 2001. (Around the World Ser.). (Illus.). 96p. (J). 29.93 (978-0-7614-1080-5(5) , Benchmark Bks.) Cavendish, Marshall Corp.

Shoreline Publishing Group Staff. Great Empires of the Past Set. 2005. (Great Empires of the Past Ser.). 128-128p. (gr. 6-12). 280.00 (978-0-8160-6318-5(4)) Facts On File, Inc.

Steele, Philip. Ancient China. 2002. (Illus.). 64p. pap. 7.95 (978-1-84215-616-2(0)) Anness Publishing GBR. *Dist:* National Bk. Network.

Stefoff, Rebecca. The Ancient Mediterranean World. 2004. (World Historical Atlases Ser.). (Illus.). 48p. (J). 27.07 (978-0-7614-1641-8(2) , Benchmark Bks.) Cavendish, Marshall Corp.

Synge, M. B. On the Shores of the Great Sea (Yesterday's Classics) Synge, E. M., illus. l.t. ed. 2006. 240p. (J). per. 11.95 (978-1-59915-013-0(1)) Yesterday's Classics.

Van Loon, Hendrik Willem. Ancient Man. 2004. reprint ed. pap. 15.95 (978-1-4191-0682-8(1)); pap. 1.99 (978-1-4192-0682-5(6)) Kessinger Publishing, LLC.

Whitfield, Cathy. History Odyssey, Ancients (level One) 2007. ring bd. 31.00 (***978-0-9766057-8-2(3)***) Pandia Pr.

HISTORY, ANCIENT—FICTION

Banks, Lynne Reid. Moses in Egypt: A Novel Inspired by The Prince of Egypt & The Book of Exodus. 1998. (Prince of Egypt Ser.). (Illus.). 128p. (J). (gr. 5-9). pap. 4.99 (978-0-8499-5898-4(9)) Nelson, Thomas Inc.

Denenburg, Barry. Pandora of Athens,399 B. C. 2004. (Life & Times Ser.). 176p. (J). (gr. 4-7). pap. 10.95 (978-0-439-64982-7(X)) Scholastic, Inc.

Frantz, Jennifer. Sid & the Mini-Sloths. 2006. (Ice Age 2 Ser.). (Illus.). 24p. (J). pap. 3.99 (978-0-06-083967-3(8)) HarperCollins Pubs.

Harcourt School Publishers Staff. A Blast from the Past: Take-Home Book. 2001. (Collections Ser.). (Illus.). (J). pap. 1.90 (978-0-15-319556-3(8)) Harcourt Schl. Pubs.

—A Blast from the Past Below Level. 3rd ed. 2002. (Trophies Reading Program Ser.). (Illus.). pap. 5.10 (978-0-15-323414-9(8)) Harcourt Schl. Pubs.

Holmes, Victoria. Rider in the Dark: An Epic Horse Story. 2006. 320p. (J). pap. 6.99 (978-0-06-052027-4(2)) HarperCollins Pubs.

Morris, Charles. Historic Tales the Romance of Reality Spanish America. 2006. (Illus.). (YA). cd-rom (978-1-892824-26-4(4)) AFCHRON.

Mracek, Ann. Friendship Flies the Sun: The Ancient Egyptian Legend of Scarab Beetle. l.t. ed. 2005. (DAN., Illus.). 32p. (J). per. 15.99 (978-0-9766488-0-2(6)) Mracek, Ann.

Reformation & Enlightenment. 2004. (Stories in History Ser.). (gr. 6-12). (978-0-618-14223-1(1) , 2-00243) McDougal Littell Inc.

Seguin, Marilyn Weymouth. Vision Quest: Searching for a Passage to the Pacific with Lewis & Clark. unabr. ed. 2002. 30p. (J). pap. incl. audio compact disk (978-1-58472-346-2(7) , In Audio) Sound Room Pubs., Inc.

Seigelson, Kim. Trembling Earth. 2004. 160p. (YA). (gr. 5). 17.99 (978-0-399-24021-8(7) , Philomel) Penguin Group (USA) Inc.

Wagner, Edward. The Second People: The Beginning. 2000. (Second People Ser.). 396p. (YA). mass mkt. 14.00 (978-0-9679422-0-9(9)) Wagner Publishing.

Wetterer, Margaret K., et al. Historical Fiction Series. Young, Mary O. et al, illus. 2000. pap. 51.95 incl. audio compact disk (978-1-59112-859-5(5)) Live Oak Media.

Zeman, Ludmila & Boileau, Michele. Le Roi Gilgamesh. 2000. (Gilgamesh Trilogy Ser.). (FRE & SPA., Illus.). 24p. (J). (gr. 3). pap. 9.95 (978-0-88776-526-1(2) , Livres Toundra) Tundra Bks., Inc./Livres Toundra, Inc. CAN. *Dist:* Random Hse., Inc.

HISTORY—ATLASES

see Historical Geography—Maps

HISTORY, BIBLICAL

see Bible—History of Biblical Events

HISTORY—CHRONOLOGY

see Chronology, Historical

HISTORY, CHURCH

see Church History

HISTORY—CRITICISM

see Historiography

HISTORY—DICTIONARIES

Cantor, Norman F. A Pimlico Encyclopedia of the Middle Ages. (Illus.). (J). pap. (978-0-14-028927-5(5) , Puffin) Penguin Group (USA) Inc.

Chandler, F. First Encyclopedia of History. 2004. (First Encyclopedias Ser.). (Illus.). 64p. (J). lib. bdg. 17.99 (978-1-58086-518-0(6)) EDC Publishing.

Chandler, Fiona. First Encyclopedia of History. 2004. (First Encyclopedias Ser.). (Illus.). 64p. (J). pap. 9.99 (978-0-7945-0386-4(1) , Usborne) EDC Publishing.

Chandler, Fiona, et al. The Usborne First Encyclopedia of History. Hancock, David, illus. 2005. 64p. (J). (978-0-439-78717-8(3)) Scholastic, Inc.

Gall, Timothy L. & Gall, Susan B. Junior Worldmark Encyclopedia of the Nations, 10 vols., Set. 5th rev. ed. 2007. 520.00 (978-1-4144-1095-1(6) , UXL) Thomson Gale.

—Junior Worldmark Encyclopedia of the Nations, 9 vols. 3rd ed. Incl. Junior Worldmark Encyclopedia of the Nations Vol. 1 : Afghanistan to Brunei Darussalam. (978-0-7876-5367-5(5)); Junior Worldmark Encyclopedia of the Nations Vol. 2 : Bulgaria to Czech Republic. (978-0-7876-5368-2(3)); Junior Worldmark Encyclopedia of the Nations Vol. 3 : Denmark to Guyana. (978-0-7876-5369-9(1)); Junior Worldmark Encyclopedia of the Nations Vol. 4 : Haiti to Kyrgyzstan. (978-0-7876-5370-5(5)); Junior Worldmark Encyclopedia of the Nations Vol. 5 : Laos to Myanmar. (978-0-7876-5371-2(3)); Junior Worldmark Encyclopedia of the Nations Vol. 6 : Nambia to Portugal. (978-0-7876-5372-9(1)); Junior Worldmark Encyclopedia of the Nations Vol. 7 : Qatar to South Africa. (978-0-7876-5373-6(X)); Junior Worldmark Encyclopedia of the Nations Vol. 8 : Spain to Tuvalu. (978-0-7876-5374-3(8)); Junior Worldmark Encyclopedia of the Nations Vol. 9 : Uganda to Zimbabwe. (978-0-7876-5375-0(6)); (J). (Illus.). 2200p. 2001. lib. bdg. (978-0-7876-5366-8(7) , GML00502-173512, UXL) Thomson Gale.

—Junior Worldmark Encyclopedia of the Nations Vol. 1: Afghanistan to Brunei Darussalam, 9 vols. 3rd ed. 2001. (Illus.). (J). (978-0-7876-5367-5(5) , UXL) Thomson Gale.

—Junior Worldmark Encyclopedia of the Nations Vol. 2: Bulgaria to Czech Republic, 9 vols. 3rd ed. 2001. (Illus.). (J). (978-0-7876-5368-2(3) , UXL) Thomson Gale.

—Junior Worldmark Encyclopedia of the Nations Vol. 3: Denmark to Guyana, 9 vols. 3rd ed. 2001. (Illus.). (J). (978-0-7876-5369-9(1) , UXL) Thomson Gale.

—Junior Worldmark Encyclopedia of the Nations Vol. 4: Haiti to Kyrgyzstan, 9 vols. 3rd ed. 2001. (Illus.). (J). (978-0-7876-5370-5(5) , UXL) Thomson Gale.

—Junior Worldmark Encyclopedia of the Nations Vol. 5: Laos to Myanmar, 9 vols. 3rd ed. 2001. (Illus.). (J). (978-0-7876-5371-2(3) , UXL) Thomson Gale.

—Junior Worldmark Encyclopedia of the Nations Vol. 6: Nambia to Portugal, 9 vols. 3rd ed. 2001. (Illus.). (J). (978-0-7876-5372-9(1) , UXL) Thomson Gale.

—Junior Worldmark Encyclopedia of the Nations Vol. 7: Qatar to South Africa, 9 vols. 3rd ed. 2001. (Illus.). (J). (978-0-7876-5373-6(X) , UXL) Thomson Gale.

—Junior Worldmark Encyclopedia of the Nations Vol. 8: Spain to Tuvalu, 9 vols. 3rd ed. 2001. (Illus.). (J). (978-0-7876-5374-3(8) , UXL) Thomson Gale.

—Junior Worldmark Encyclopedia of the Nations Vol. 9: Uganda to Zimbabwe, 9 vols. 3rd ed. 2001. (Illus.). (J). (978-0-7876-5375-0(6) , UXL) Thomson Gale.

Gall, Timothy L. & Gall, Susan B. Junior Worldmark Encyclopedia of the Nations/[edited By] Timothy L. Gall & Susan Bevan Gall. 5th ed. 2007. ***(978-1-4144-1096-8(4)); (*978-1-4144-1097-5(2)); (*978-1-4144-1098-2(0)); (*978-1-4144-1099-9(9)); (*978-1-4144-1100-2(6)); (*978-1-4144-1101-9(4)); (*978-1-4144-1102-6(2)); (*978-1-4144-1103-3(0)); (*978-1-4144-1104-0(9)); (*978-1-4144-1105-7(7))*** Thomson Gale.

Isaacs, Alan. Oxford Dictionary of World History. 2000. (gr. 7-12). lib. bdg. 26.85 (978-0-613-64758-8(0)) Tandem Library Bks.

Lemberg, David S. & Canby, Courtlandt. Encyclopedia of Historic Places, 3 vols. 2nd rev. ed. 2007. (Illus.). 1776p. (YA). (gr. 9-12). 300.00 (978-0-8160-5344-5(8)) Facts On File, Inc.

Mi Primera Enciclopedia de Historia - Internet Linked. 2006. 64p. (J). pap. 9.99 (978-0-7460-7080-2(2) , Usborne) EDC Publishing.

Palmer, Joy. The Questions Dictionary of History. (Illus.). 1p. ***(978-1-84190-034-6(6))*** Continuum International Publishing Group, Ltd.

Ward, Brian. The History Encyclopedia. 2005. (Illus.). 256p. 24.99 (978-0-7548-1505-1(6) , Lorenz Bks.) Anness Publishing GBR. *Dist:* National Bk. Network.

Wilkinson, Philip, et al. The Illustrated History Encyclopedia: Civilizations, Exploration & Conquest. 2001. (Illus.). 256p. pap. 19.95 (978-1-84215-527-1(X) , Southwater) Anness Publishing GBR. *Dist:* National Bk. Network.

HISTORY—HISTORIOGRAPHY

see Historiography

HISTORY, MILITARY

see Military History

HISTORY—MISCELLANEA

Ash, Russell. Fantastic Millennium Facts. 1999. (Illus.). 128p. (J). (gr. 3-8). lib. bdg. (978-1-55209-441-9(3)) Firefly Bks., Ltd.

Banks, Cameron. History Undercover: Top Secret. 2003. (History Channel Presents...Ser.). (Illus.). 80p. (J). (gr. 3-7). pap. 4.99 (978-0-439-40148-7(8) , Scholastic Paperbacks) Scholastic, Inc.

—History Undercover: Top Secret. 2003. (gr. 3-6). lib. bdg. 13.00 (978-0-613-72085-4(7)) Tandem Library Bks.

—History's Mysteries: Bizarre Beings. 2002. (History Channel Presents...Ser.). (Illus.). 80p. (J). pap. 4.99 (978-0-439-40149-4(6) , Scholastic Paperbacks) Scholastic, Inc.

Blackwood, Gary L. Enigmatic Events. 2005. (Unsolved History Ser.). (Illus.). 72p. (J). (gr. 3-7). lib. bdg. (978-0-7614-1889-4(X) , Benchmark Bks.) Cavendish, Marshall Corp.

Haslam, Andrew. Living History. 2004. (Make It Work! History Ser.). (Illus.). 192p. (gr. 3-6). 29.95 (978-1-58728-381-9(6) , Two Can Publishing) T&N Children's Publishing.

History Songs. 2001. (Illus.). 24p. pap., tchr. ed., wbk. ed. 15.95 incl. audio compact disk Audio Memory Publishing.

Llewellyn, Claire. Great Discoveries & Amazing Adventures: The Stories of Hidden Marvels & Lost Treasures. 2004. (Illus.). 80p. (J). (gr. 4-6). 18.95 (978-0-7534-5783-2(0) , Kingfisher) Houghton Mifflin Co. Trade & Reference Div.

Patent, Dorothy Hinshaw. Frozen in Time - Group 2, 3 bks., Set. Incl. Incredible Story of China's Buried Warriors. lib. bdg. 27.07 (978-0-7614-0783-6(9)); Lost City of Pompeii. lib. bdg. 27.07 (978-0-7614-0785-0(5)); Treasures of the Spanish Main. lib. bdg. 28.50 (978-0-7614-0786-7(3)); (J). (gr. 5-9). (Illus.). 2000. Set lib. bdg. 81.21 (978-0-7614-0799-7(5) , Benchmark Bks.) Cavendish, Marshall Corp.

Saari, Peggy. Great Misadventures. 1998. (J). 99.00 (978-0-7876-2799-7(2)); 99.00 (978-0-7876-2800-0(X)); 99.00 (978-0-7876-2801-7(8)); 99.00 (978-0-7876-2802-4(6)) Thomson Gale. (UXL).

—Great Misadventures: Bad Ideas That Led to Big Disasters, 4 vols. Betz, Des Chenes, ed. 1998. (Illus.). 729p. (J). (gr. 4-7). lib. bdg. 235.00 (978-0-7876-2798-0(4) , GML00502-112339, UXL) Thomson Gale.

Simmons, Alex. Mysteries of the Past: A Chapter Book. 48p. (J). 2006. (gr. 2-4). pap. 4.95 (978-0-516-25451-7(0)); 2005. (Illus.). (ps-ps). 22.50 (978-0-516-25184-4(8)) Scholastic Library Publishing. (Children's Pr.).

Storm, Rachel. 120 Great History Projects: Fun Craft & Cooking Activities Re-Create the Skills of the Past. 2002. (Illus.). 256p. (gr. 3-7). 29.95 (978-0-7548-0807-7(6) , Lorenz Bks.) Anness Publishing GBR. *Dist:* National Bk. Network.

HISTORY, MODERN

Here are entered works covering the period after 1453.

see also Civilization, Modern; Reformation; Renaissance

Bailey, Viola & Wise, Ella. Victorian Times. Date not set. (Focus on History Ser.). (Illus.). 64p. (J). pap. 129.15 (978-0-582-18240-0(9)) Addison-Wesley Longman, Ltd. GBR. *Dist:* Trans-Atlantic Pubns., Inc.

Barnes, Teresa Woods. The Discovery: A Meeting Between the Old World & the New World. 2000. 43p. (YA). spiral bd. 12.00 (978-0-932776-25-9(6)) Adonis Pr.

Beller, Susan Provost. The History Puzzle: How We Know What We Know about the Past. 2006. (Illus.). 128p. (J). 26.60 (978-0-7613-2877-3(7) , Millbrook Pr.) Lerner Publishing Group.

Berger, Samantha. Then & Now. 1999. (J). pap. 3.25 (978-0-439-04602-2(5)) Scholastic, Inc.

Bingham, Marjorie. An Age of Empires, 1200-1750. 2006. 32.95 (978-0-19-522268-5(7)) Oxford Univ. Pr., Inc.

Bingham, Marjorie Wall. An Age of Empires, 1200-1750. 2005. (Medieval & Early Modern World Ser.). (Illus.). 160p. (YA). 32.95 (978-0-19-517839-5(4)) Oxford Univ. Pr., Inc.

Chapman, Victoria L. & Lindroth, David. The 20th Century, Vol. 4. 2nd ed. 2004. (World History on File Ser.). (Illus.). 232p. (J). (gr. 9-12). ring bd. 140.00 (978-0-8160-5765-8(6)) Facts On File, Inc.

Chrisp, Peter. Invaders. 1998. (Fact Finders Ser.). (Illus.). 1p. (J). (gr. 3-7). pap. (978-0-563-37626-2(0)) BBC Worldwide.

Clare, John D. A World Study after 1900. 2003. (Illus.). 96p. pap. 29.50 ***(978-0-340-86912-3(7)*** , Hodder Murray) Hodder Education GBR. *Dist:* Trans-Atlantic Pubns., Inc.

DeMarco, Neil. A World Study after 1900. 2003. (Illus.). 96p. pap. 29.50 ***(978-0-340-86913-0(5)*** , Hodder Murray) Hodder Education GBR. *Dist:* Trans-Atlantic Pubns., Inc.

Desmarais, Kathleen. History Odyssey, Early Modern (level Two) 2007. ring bd. 38.00 ***(978-0-9766057-9-9(1))*** Pandia Pr.

Dorling Kindersley Publishing Staff. Children's History of the 20th Century. 1999. (Millennium Ser.). (Illus.). 352p. (J). (gr. 3-7). 29.95 (978-0-7894-4722-7(3)) Dorling Kindersley Publishing, Inc.

Douglas, Vincent & School Specialty Publishing Staff. Modern History. 2001. (History of the World Ser.). (Illus.). 48p. (J). 18.95 (978-1-57768-955-3(0) , Bedrick, Peter Bks.) School Specialty Publishing.

Essential Facts. 2004. (I-Quest Ser.). (J). (978-1-84229-753-7(8)) Top That! Publishing PLC.

Frasier, Debra. El Dia en Que Tu Naciste. Ada, Alma Flor & Campoy, F. Isabel, trs. 1998. (SPA., Illus.). 32p. (J). (gr. k-2). pap. 7.00 (978-0-15-201709-5(7) , HB7090, Red Wagon Bks.) Harcourt Children's Bks.

Gay, Kathlyn & Gay, Martin. Voices from the Past, 6 vols. 2004. (History & Social Studies Ser.). (Illus.). 64p. (YA). (gr. 5 up). (978-0-7613-1146-1(7) , Twenty-First Century Bks.) Lerner Publishing Group.

Gray, Margie. When the Brook & River Meet: A Literature Based Unit Study on the Victorian Era. Bowan, Julie, ed. 1999. 200p. (YA). (gr. 7-12). pap. 30.00 (978-0-9652511-1-2(X)) Cadron Creek Curriculum.

Group/McGraw-Hill, Wright. Castle Life in the Middle Ages, 6 vols. (Book2WebTM Ser.). (gr. 4-8). 36.50 (978-0-322-04449-4(9)) Wright Group, The.

Hanes, Sharon M., et al. Cold War: Biographies, 2 vols. 2003. (Cold War Reference Library). (Illus.). (J). 400p. 120.00 (978-0-7876-7663-6(2)); xxxv, 473p. (978-0-7876-7664-3(0)); xxxv, 473p. (978-0-7876-7665-0(9)) Thomson Gale. (UXL).

Haslam, Andrew. Living History. 2004. (Make It Work! History Ser.). (Illus.). 192p. (gr. 3-6). 29.95 (978-1-58728-381-9(6) , Two Can Publishing) T&N Children's Publishing.

History: Student Testing Kit. 2004. (Illus.). (J). (gr. 1-8). stu. ed. 5.00 (978-0-7403-0043-1(1) , HD001); (YA). (gr. 7-12). stu. ed. 5.00 (978-0-7403-0044-8(X) , HD002) Alpha Omega Pubns., Inc.

Holt, Rinehart and Winston Staff. The Human Journey: Modern. 3rd ed. 2001. 75.40 (978-0-03-065507-4(2)) Holt, Rinehart & Winston.

Huff, Toby E. An Age of Science & Revolutions, 1600-1800. (Illus.). 2006. 173p. (J). 32.95 (978-0-19-522269-2(5)); 2005. 176p. (YA). (gr. 7 up). 32.95 (978-0-19-517724-4(X)) Oxford Univ. Pr., Inc.

Hughes, Morgan. The Sprints. 1999. (Illus.). 48p. (J). (gr. 4-8). lib. bdg. 27.93 (978-1-57103-291-1(6)) Rourke Publishing, LLC.

—The Throws. 1999. (Illus.). 48p. (J). (gr. 4-8). lib. bdg. 27.93 (978-1-57103-292-8(4)) Rourke Publishing, LLC.

Hughes, Shirley. A Brush with the Past 1900-1950: The Years That Changed Our Lives. 2005. (Illus.). 112p. 24.99 ***(978-0-370-32839-3(6))*** Transworld Publishers Ltd. GBR. *Dist:* Independent Pubs. Group.

Jennings, Peter & Brewster, Todd. The Century for Young People. Armstrong, Jennifer, ed. 2004. (Illus.). 245p. (YA). (gr. 6-10). reprint ed. 30.00 (978-0-7567-8181-1(7)) DIANE Publishing Co.

Jones, Charlotte Foltz. Accidents May Happen. 1998. (Illus.). 96p. (J). (gr. 3-7). reprint ed. pap. 11.95 (978-0-385-32240-9(2) , Delacorte Bks. for Young Readers) Random Hse. Children's Bks.

—Accidents May Happen: 50 Inventions Discovered by Mistake. 1998. (J). 18.60 (978-0-606-13109-4(4)) Tandem Library Bks.

Karecki, Jason, illus. The Adventures of Drake Montana Vol. 1: The Great Migration. 1998. 24p. (J). (gr. k-5). (978-1-890716-07-3(3)) K&M International.

Kovacs, Charles. The Age of Revolution. 2003. 240p. (YA). pap. 19.95 (978-0-86315-395-2(X)) Floris Bks. GBR. *Dist:* SteinerBooks, Inc.

Levy, Patricia. From Punk Rock to Perestroika: The Mid 1970s to the Mid 1980s. 2005. (Modern Eras Uncovered Ser.). (Illus.). 56p. (J). 32.86 (978-1-4109-1789-8(4)) Raintree.

—From Punk Rock to Perestroika: The Mid 1970s to the Mid 1980s. 2005. (Modern Eras Uncovered Ser.). (Illus.). 56p. (J). pap. (978-1-4109-1798-0(3)) Steck-Vaughn.

—From Speakeasies to Stalinism: The 1920s to the Mid-1930s. 2005. (Modern Eras Uncovered Ser.). (Illus.). 56p. (J). (978-1-4109-1785-0(1)); pap. (978-1-4109-1794-2(0)) Steck-Vaughn.

—Modern Eras Uncovered: From Beatlemania to Watergate. 2005. (Modern Eras Uncovered Ser.). (Illus.). 56p. (J). (978-1-84443-965-2(8)); (978-1-84443-955-3(0)) Steck-Vaughn.

—Modern Eras Uncovered: From Compact Discs to the Gulf War. 2005. (Modern Eras Uncovered Ser.). (Illus.). 56p. (J). (978-1-84443-967-6(4)); (978-1-84443-957-7(7)) Steck-Vaughn.

—Modern Eras Uncovered: From Punk Rock to Perestroika. 2005. (Modern Eras Uncovered Ser.). (Illus.). 56p. (J). (978-1-84443-966-9(6)); (978-1-84443-956-0(9)) Steck-Vaughn.

—Modern Eras Uncovered: From the World Wide Web to September 11. 2005. (Modern Eras Uncovered Ser.). (Illus.). 56p. (J). (978-1-84443-968-3(2)) Steck-Vaughn.

Levy, Patricia & Sheehan, Sean. Modern Eras Uncovered: From the World Wide Web to September 11. 2005. (Modern Eras Uncovered Ser.). (Illus.). 56p. (J). (978-1-84443-958-4(5)) Steck-Vaughn.

Levy, Patricia & Sheehan, Sean. From Compact Discs to the Gulf War: The Mid 1980s to the Early 1990s. 2005. (Modern Eras Uncovered Ser.). (Illus.). 56p. (J). 32.86 (978-1-4109-1790-4(8)) Raintree.

—From Compact Discs to the Gulf War: The Mid 1980s to the Early 1990s. 2005. (Modern Eras Uncovered Ser.). (Illus.). 56p. (J). pap. (978-1-4109-1799-7(1)) Steck-Vaughn.

—From the World Wide Web to September 11: The Early 1990s to 2001. 2005. (Modern Eras Uncovered Ser.). (Illus.). 56p. (J). 32.86 (978-1-4109-1791-1(6)) Raintree.

—From the World Wide Web to September 11: The Early 1990s to 2001. 2005. (Modern Eras Uncovered Ser.). (Illus.). 56p. (J). pap. (978-1-4109-1800-0(9)) Steck-Vaughn.

MacDonald, Fiona, et al. Warfare in the 20th Century: The Age of Global Conflict. 2004. (Battle Zones Ser.). (Illus.). 48p. (J). (gr. 5-8). 18.95 (978-1-57768-594-4(6) , Bedrick, Peter Bks.) School Specialty Publishing.

Marx, Trish. One Boy from Kosovo. 2000. (Illus.). (YA). (gr. 2-5). 24p. 15.95 (978-0-688-17732-4(8)); 32p. 15.89 (978-0-688-17733-1(6)) HarperCollins Pubs.

Matas, Carol. More Minds. 1998. 10p. (J). pap. 4.50 (978-0-590-39469-7(X)) Scholastic, Inc.

—Of Two Minds. 1998. 208p. (J). pap. 4.50 (978-0-590-39468-0(1)) Scholastic, Inc.

Maynard, Christopher. Revolution. 2001. (History News Ser.). (Illus.). 32p. (J). (gr. 3 up). lib. bdg. 24.67 (978-0-8368-2878-8(X)) Stevens, Gareth Inc.

Mellett, Peter & Gifford, Clive. 1000 Years of Famous People. 2002. (Illus.). 260p. (J). (gr. 5-9). tchr. ed. 24.95 (978-0-7534-5540-1(4) , Kingfisher) Houghton Mifflin Co. Trade & Reference Div.

Mochizuki, Ken. Pasaje a la Libertad: La Historia de Chiune Sugihara. 1999. (978-0-606-17081-9(2)) Tandem Library Bks.

Monumental Milestones: Great Events of Modern Times. 2007. (Monumental Milestones Ser.). (YA). lib. bdg. ***(978-1-58415-543-0(4))*** Mitchell Lane Pubs., Inc.

Morris, Neil. Modern World Leaders. (Illus.). 48p. (YA). (gr. 5 up). lib. bdg. 29.95 (978-1-932333-79-4(7)) Chrysalis Education.

Our Century, 7 bks. Incl. Our Century : 1900-1910. Greene, Janice. lib. bdg. 27.33 (978-0-8368-1032-5(5)); Our Century : 1910-1920. Liberatore, Karen. lib. bdg. 27.33 (978-0-8368-1033-2(3)); Our Century : 1930-1940. Owen, Marna. lib. bdg. 27.33 (978-0-8368-1035-6(X)); Our Century : 1940-1950. Hill, Prescott. lib. bdg. 27.33 (978-0-8368-1036-3(8)); Our Century : 1950-1960. Jones, S. D. lib. bdg. 27.33 (978-0-8368-1037-0(6)); Our Century : 1970-1980. Hill, Prescott. lib. bdg. 27.33 (978-0-8368-1039-4(2)); Our Century : 1980-1990. Suter, Joanne. lib. bdg. 27.33 (978-0-8368-1040-0(6)); 64p. (J). (gr. 4 up). 1993. (Illus.). Set lib. bdg. 191.31 (978-0-8368-1031-8(7)) Stevens, Gareth Inc.

Quadrillion Media Staff. History No. III. 1999. (J). pap. 3.95 (978-1-58185-100-7(6)) Quadrillion Media LLC.

Raintree Steck-Vaughn Staff. New Perspectives, 8 bks., Set. 1998. (New Perspectives Ser.). (YA). (gr. 5-12). 228.40 (978-0-8172-5022-5(0)) Raintree.

Ross, Stewart. 1990s. 2000. (Take Ten Years Ser.). (Illus.). 48p. 24.99 (978-0-237-51958-2(5) , Evans Brothers, Limited) Evans Publishing Group GBR. *Dist:* Independent Pubs. Group.

Ryan, James G. & Schlup, Leonard C., eds. Historical Dictionary of the 1940s. 2006. (Illus.). 648p. 159.00 (978-0-7656-0440-8(X) , Sharpe Reference) Sharpe, M.E. Inc.

Scott, Janine. The Two Great Wars. 2007. (Shockwave: History & Politics Ser.). (Illus.). 36p. (J). (gr. 4-6). lib. bdg. 25.00 (***978-0-531-17756-3(4)*** , Children's Pr.) Scholastic Library Publishing.

Sheehan, Sean. From Beatlemania to Watergate. 2005. (Modern Eras Uncovered Ser.). (Illus.). 56p. (J). (ps-1). lib. bdg. 32.86 (978-1-4109-1788-1(6)) Steck-Vaughn.

—From Beatlemania to Watergate: The Early 1960s to the Mid 1970s. 2005. (Modern Eras Uncovered Ser.). (Illus.). 56p. (J). pap. (978-1-4109-1797-3(5)) Steck-Vaughn.

—From Jessie Owens to Hiroshima: The Mid 1930s to 1945. 2005. (Modern Eras Uncovered Ser.). (Illus.). 56p. (J). (978-1-4109-1786-7(X)); pap. (978-1-4109-1795-9(9)) Steck-Vaughn.

—From Television to the Berlin Wall: The Mid-1940s to the Early 1960s. 2005. (Modern Eras Uncovered Ser.). (Illus.). 56p. (J). (978-1-4109-1787-4(8)); pap. (978-1-4109-1796-6(7)) Steck-Vaughn.

—From the Wright Brothers to the Treaty of Versailles: The 1900s to 1918. 2005. (Modern Eras Uncovered Ser.). (Illus.). 56p. (J). (978-1-4109-1784-3(3)); pap. (978-1-4109-1793-5(2)) Steck-Vaughn.

—Modern Eras Uncovered: From Jesse Owens to Hiroshima. 2005. (Modern Eras Uncovered Ser.). (Illus.). 56p. (J). (978-1-84443-962-1(3)); (978-1-84443-952-2(6)) Steck-Vaughn.

—Modern Eras Uncovered: From Speakeasies to Stalinism. 2005. (Modern Eras Uncovered Ser.). (Illus.). 56p. (J). (978-1-84443-961-4(5)) Steck-Vaughn.

—Modern Eras Uncovered: From Television to the Berlin Wall. 2005. (Modern Eras Uncovered Ser.). (Illus.). 56p. (J). (978-1-84443-963-8(1)) Steck-Vaughn.

—Modern Eras Uncovered: From the Wright Brothers to the Treaty of Versailles. 2005. (Modern Eras Uncovered Ser.). (Illus.). 56p. (J). (978-1-84443-960-7(7)); (978-1-84443-950-8(X)) Steck-Vaughn.

Sheehan, Sean & Levy, Pat. Modern Eras Uncovered: From Speakeasies to Stalinism. 2005. (Modern Eras Uncovered Ser.). (Illus.). 56p. (J). (978-1-84443-951-5(8)) Steck-Vaughn.

—Modern Eras Uncovered: From Television to the Berlin Wall. 2005. (Modern Eras Uncovered Ser.). (Illus.). 56p. (J). pap. (978-1-84443-953-9(4)) Steck-Vaughn.

Shephard, Colin & Shephard, Keith. Re-Discovering the Twentieth Century World: A World Study After 1900. 2001. (Illus.). 136p. pap., stu. ed. 32.50 (*978-0-7195-8548-7(1) , Hodder Murray) Hodder Education GBR. *Dist:* Trans-Atlantic Pubns., Inc.

Smith, Bonnie G., ed. The Medieval & Early Modern World, 7 vols., Set. 2005. (Medieval & Early Modern World Ser.). (Illus.). 1232p. (YA). 230.00 (978-0-19-522157-2(5)) Oxford Univ. Pr., Inc.

Smith, Bonnie G. & Kelley, Donald R. The Medieval & Early Modern World: Primary Sources & Reference Volume. 2006. 32.95 (978-0-19-522300-2(4)) Oxford Univ. Pr., Inc.

—Primary Sources & Reference Volume. 2005. (Medieval & Early Modern World Ser.). (Illus.). 176p. (YA). 32.95 (978-0-19-517848-7(3)); (978-0-19-523081-9(7)) Oxford Univ. Pr., Inc.

Stich, Paul & Kime, Sue Ann. Global History: STAReview. Garnsey, Wayne, ed. Fairbanks, Eugene B., illus. 2000. (N & N Social Studies Ser.). (ENG.). 320p. (YA). (gr. 9-10). per. 15.95 (978-0-935487-70-1(0) , STAReviews) N&N Publishing Co., Inc.

Tames, Richard. 1900-1919. 2005. (Illus.). 48p. (YA). (gr. 6 up). lib. bdg. 29.95 (978-1-932889-69-7(8)) Sea-To-Sea Pubns.

—1920s. 2005. (Illus.). 48p. (YA). (gr. 6 up). lib. bdg. 29.95 (978-1-932889-70-3(1)) Sea-To-Sea Pubns.

Walsh, Ben. Essential Modern World History. 2002. (Illus.). 240p. pap., stu. ed. 42.00 (*978-0-7195-7715-4(2) , Hodder Murray) Hodder Education GBR. *Dist:* Trans-Atlantic Pubns., Inc.

Waugh, Steven. Essential Modern World History. 2001. (Illus.). 640p. (YA). (gr. 9-11). pap. 47.50 (978-0-7487-6006-0(7)) Nelson Thornes Ltd. GBR. *Dist:* Trans-Atlantic Pubns., Inc.

Weinberger, Kimberly A. Journey to a New Land: An Oral History. Meers, Tony, illus. 2000. 32p. (J). (gr. 2-5). 15.95 (978-1-57255-811-3(3)) Mondo Publishing.

Weisner-Hanks, Merry E. Teaching Guide to an Age of Voyages, 1450-1600. 2005. (Medieval & Early Modern World Ser.). 122p. (YA). 19.95 (978-0-19-522344-6(6)) Oxford Univ. Pr., Inc.

Whitfield, Cathy. History Odyssey, Early Modern - Level One. 2006. (J). ring bd. 31.00 (*978-0-9766057-5-1(9)) Pandia Pr.

Wiesner-Hanks, Merry E. An Age of Voyages, 1350-1600. 2005. (Medieval & Early Modern World Ser.). (Illus.). 192p. (YA). (gr. 7 up). 32.95 (978-0-19-517672-8(3)) Oxford Univ. Pr., Inc.

Wiesner, Merry E. An Age of Voyages, 1450-1600. 2006. (Illus.). 189p. 32.95 (978-0-19-522264-7(4)) Oxford Univ. Pr., Inc.

1000 Things You Should Know about Modern History. (Illus.). 64p. (YA). (gr. 5 up). lib. bdg. (978-1-59084-468-7(8)) Mason Crest Pubs.

HISTORY, NATURAL

see Natural History

HISTORY, NAVAL

see Naval History

see names of countries with the subdivision History, Naval e. g. United States—History, Naval

HISTORY—SOURCES

Raintree Steck-Vaughn Staff, ed. History Beneath Your Feet, 4 bks., Set. 2000. (J). pap. 108.48 (978-0-8172-5754-5(3)) Raintree.

Tait, Leia. Primary Sources. 2007. (*978-1-59036-764-3(2)); lib. bdg. (*978-1-59036-763-6(4)) Weigl Pubs., Inc.

HISTORY, UNIVERSAL

see World History

HISTORY—YEARBOOKS

Gall, Timothy L. & Gall, Susan B., eds. Junior Worldmark Encyclopedia of the Nations, 9 vols. 2nd ed. 1999. (Illus.). (J). (978-0-7876-3804-7(8)); (978-0-7876-3805-4(6)) Thomson Gale.

Seibert, Patricia. We Were Here: A Short History of Time Capsules. 2002. (Illus.). 48p. (J). (gr. 3-6). lib. bdg. 22.90 (978-0-7613-0423-4(1) , Millbrook Pr.) Lerner Publishing Group.

HISTRIONICS

see Acting; Theater

HITCHHIKING

see Walking

HITLER, ADOLF, 1889-1945

Altman, Linda Jacobs. Adolf Hitler: Evil MasterMind of the Holocaust. 2005. (Holocaust Heroes & Nazi Criminals Ser.). (Illus.). 160p. (YA). (gr. 7-13). lib. bdg. 27.93 (978-0-7660-2533-2(0)) Enslow Pubs., Inc.

—Hitler's Rise to Power & the Holocaust. 2003. (Holocaust in History Ser.). (Illus.). 128p. (J). (gr. 5-12). lib. bdg. 26.60 (978-0-7660-1991-1(8)) Enslow Pubs., Inc.

—The Holocaust, Hitler & Nazi Germany. 1999. (Holocaust Remembered Ser.). (Illus.). 112p. (YA). (gr. 6-12). lib. bdg. 26.60 (978-0-7660-1230-1(1)) Enslow Pubs., Inc.

Bartoletti, Susan Campbell. Hitler Youth: Growing up in Hitler's Shadow. 2005. (Illus.). 176p. (J). pap. 19.95 (978-0-439-35379-3(3)) Scholastic, Inc.

Beyer, Mark. Heinrich Muller: Gestapo Chief. 2005. (Holocaust Biographies Ser.). (Illus.). 112p. (YA). (gr. 7-12). lib. bdg. 26.50 (978-0-8239-3376-1(8)) Rosen Publishing Group, Inc., The.

Daynes, Katie. Adolf Hitler. Tomlins, Karen, illus. 2006. 64p. (J). 8.99 (978-0-7945-1261-3(5) , Usborne) EDC Publishing.

Dolan, Terrance. Adolf Hitler: A Study in Hate. 2005. (Holocaust Biographies Ser.). (Illus.). 112p. (YA). (gr. 7-12). lib. bdg. 26.50 (978-0-8239-3317-4(2) , HBHITL) Rosen Publishing Group, Inc., The.

Dufner, Annette. The Rise of Adolf Hitler. 2003. (Illus.). 144p. (YA). pap. 23.70 (978-0-7377-1519-4(7)); lib. bdg. 33.70 (978-0-7377-1518-7(9)) Thomson Gale. (Greenhaven Pr., Inc.).

—Rise of Adolf Hitler. 2003. (gr. 7-12). lib. bdg. 30.35 (978-0-613-73875-0(6)) Tandem Library Bks.

Freeman, Charles. The Rise of the Nazis. 1998. (New Perspectives Ser.). (Illus.). 80p. (J). (gr. 4-7). 28.54 (978-0-8172-5015-7(8)) Raintree.

—The Rise of the Nazis. 2005. (How Did It Happen? Ser.). (Illus.). 48p. (J). (gr. 7-10). lib. bdg. 29.95 (978-1-59018-608-4(7) , Lucent Bks.) Thomson Gale.

Gogerly, Liz. Adolf Hitler. 2003. (Twentieth Century History Makers Ser.). (Illus.). 112p. (J). lib. bdg. 32.85 (978-0-7398-5256-9(6)) Raintree.

Gottfried, Ted. Children of the Slaughter: Young People of the Holocaust. Alcorn, Stephen, illus. (Holocaust History Ser.). 112p. (YA). (gr. 7-12). 22.95 (978-1-58013-202-2(2)) Kar-Ben Publishing.

—Children of the Slaughter: Young People of the Holocaust. 2001. (Holocaust Ser.: up). (Illus.). 112p. (J). (gr. 7 up). lib. bdg. (978-0-7613-1716-6(3) , Twenty-First Century Bks.) Lerner Publishing Group.

—Nazi Germany: The Face of Tyranny. Alcorn, Stephen, illus. (Holocaust History Ser.). 112p. (YA). (gr. 7-12). 22.95 (978-1-58013-203-9(0)) Kar-Ben Publishing.

—Nazi Germany: The Face of Tyranny. 2000. (Holocaust Ser.: up). (Illus.). 128p. (gr. 7 up). lib. bdg. (978-0-7613-1714-2(7) , Twenty-First Century Bks.) Lerner Publishing Group.

Gutsche, Henry. Hitler's Willing Warrior. 190p. (YA). (gr. 7 up). 9.99 (978-0-88092-520-4(5)) Royal Fireworks Publishing Co.

Harris, Nathaniel. The Rise of Hitler. 2004. (Illus.). 56p. (J). pap. 8.95 (978-1-4034-5526-0(0)); lib. bdg. 27.07 (978-1-4034-4866-8(3)) Heinemann Library.

Haugen, Brenda. Adolf Hitler: Dictator of Nazi Germany. 2006. (Signature Lives Ser.). (Illus.). 112p. (J). (gr. 5-7). 30.60 (978-0-7565-1589-8(0)) Compass Point Bks.

Lace, William W. Hitler & the Nazis. 1999. (American War Library). (Illus.). 112p. (YA). (gr. 4-12). 27.45 (978-1-56006-372-8(6) , LML00902-177757, Lucent Bks.) Thomson Gale.

Malam, John. Hitler Invades Poland: 1 September 1939. 2002. (Dates with History Ser.). (Illus.). 31p. (J). lib. bdg. 24.25 (978-1-58340-212-2(8)) Smart Apple Media.

Rice, Earle, Jr. Adolf Hitler & Nazi Germany. 2005. (World Leaders Ser.). (Illus.). 176p. (J). (gr. 3-7). lib. bdg. 26.95 (978-1-931798-78-5(8)) Reynolds, Morgan Inc.

Rice, Earle, Jr. Blitzkrieg! Hitler's Lightning War. 2007. (Monumental Milestones Ser.).Tr. of 48. (Illus.). (YA). lib. bdg. 29.95 (*978-1-58415-542-3(6)) Mitchell Lane Pubs., Inc.

Shuter, Jane. Life & Death in Hitler's Europe. 2003. (Holocaust Ser.). 56p. (Illus.). (J). lib. bdg. 28.50 (978-1-4034-0811-2(4)); pap. 8.95 (978-1-4034-3203-2(1)) Heinemann Library.

—Life & Death in Hitler's Europe. 2003. (gr. 5-8). lib. bdg. 17.60 (978-0-613-60969-2(7)) Tandem Library Bks.

Stalcup, Brenda. Adolf Hitler. (People Who Made History Ser.). (Illus.). 202p. (YA). (gr. 9-12). 2000. lib. bdg. 32.45 (978-0-7377-0223-1(0)); 1999. 21.20 (978-0-7377-0222-4(2)) Thomson Gale. (Greenhaven Pr., Inc.).

Tames, Richard. Adolf Hitler. 1998. (Profiles Ser.). (Illus.). 56p. (J). lib. bdg. 24.22 (978-1-57572-689-2(0)) Heinemann Library.

Taylor, David. Adolf Hitler. 2001. (Leading Lives Ser.). (Illus.). 64p. (J). (gr. 5-7). lib. bdg. 27.86 (978-1-58810-162-4(2)) Heinemann Library.

Wilson, Mike. Adolf Hitler, 6 vols. 1999. (Livewire Real Lives Ser.). (Illus.). 16p. pap. (978-0-340-67983-8(2) , Hodder Arnold) Hodder Education.

Woolf, Alex. The Rise of Nazi Germany. 2004. (Questioning History Ser.). (J). lib. bdg. 28.50 (978-1-58340-442-3(2)) Smart Apple Media.

Wukovits, John F. World War II in Europe. 2004. (World History Ser.). (Illus.). 112p. (gr. 7-10). 32.45 (978-1-59018-185-0(9) , Lucent Bks.) Thomson Gale.

Zdrok, Jodie L. 1880-1900 (Events That Changed the World) 2004. (gr. 10-12). 22.45 (978-0-7377-2038-9(7) , Greenhaven Pr., Inc.) Thomson Gale.

HOAXES

see Impostors and Imposture

HOBBIES

see also Collectors and Collecting; Handicraft

Cobb, Mary. A Sampler View of Colonial Life: With Projects Kids Can Make. 1999. (J). (978-0-606-20197-1(1)) Tandem Library Bks.

Eckold, David. Ultimate Spy Kit. 2003. (J). 29.99 (978-0-7894-9868-7(5)) Dorling Kindersley Publishing, Inc.

Gilpin, Rebecca. Fairy Things to Make & Do Kid Kit. McCafferty, Jan, illus. 2004. (Kid Kits Ser.). 32p. (J). 15.99 (978-1-58086-727-6(8)); 15.99 (978-1-58086-731-3(6)) EDC Publishing. (Usborne).

Harcourt School Publishers Staff. What Do You Like: Library Edition. 1999. (Illus.). (J). 4.70 (978-0-15-314303-8(7)) Harcourt Schl. Pubs.

—What Do You Like: Take-Home Book. 1999. (Signatures Ser.). (Illus.). (J). (gr. 1). pap. 1.70 (978-0-15-313817-1(3)) Harcourt Schl. Pubs.

Hubley, Dan & Hubley, Mary. Kids Collect: Amazing Collections for Fun, Crafts, & Science Fair Projects. Hubley, Mary, illus. 2002. (Illus.). 176p. (J). per. 13.95 (978-0-9707267-1-1(6)) Bluefish Bay Publishing.

Lorenz Books Staff. The Best Ever Book of 100 Incredible Things to Make, Do & Play. 2000. (Illus.). 192p. (J). (gr. 3-7). pap. 17.00 (978-1-85967-728-5(2)) Anness Publishing, Inc.

My Cool Hobbies. (Girls' World Ser.). 16p. (J). (978-2-7643-0144-9(8)) Phidal Publishing, Inc./Editions Phidal, Inc.

My Hobby, 6 Packs. (Rigby Focus Ser.). 16p. (gr. 1 up). 30.00 (978-0-7578-5544-3(X)) Rigby Education.

My Hobby: Individual Title Six-Packs. (Rigby Focus Ser.). 16p. (gr. 1 up). 28.00 (978-0-7578-5312-8(9)) Rigby Education.

Rue, Nancy N. The Fun-Finder Book: It's a God Thing! 2003. (YWOF Library). 112p. (J). pap. 7.99 (978-0-310-70258-0(5)) Zondervan.

Scholastic, Inc. Staff. Trendy Toes. Im, Angela, ed. 2003. (Fun Pack Ser.). 48p. (J). pap. 7.99 (978-0-439-40005-3(8) , Tangerine Pr.) Scholastic, Inc.

Sordu, John R. & Dean, Robert. Big Battles for Little Hands: Wargaming Source Book for Children. Palmer, Chris, photos by. 2002. (Illus.). 141p. (YA). 25.00 (978-1-889584-10-2(X) , 071102) LMW Works.

Wilkes, Angela. Mini Activities for All Year Round. 2004. (Activities for All Year Round Ser.). 96p. (J). 7.95 (978-0-7945-0770-1(0) , Usborne) EDC Publishing.

HOBBIES—FICTION

Cook, Samantha & Saad. Best Little Knitter in the West: The Bin Saad, Sermsah. 2000. (Illus.). 32p. (J). pap. 12.95 (978-1-875641-52-9(1)) Magabala Bks. AUS. *Dist:* International Specialized Bk. Services.

Jennings, Sharon. Franklin's Trading Cards. Jeffrey, Sean et al, illus. 2003. 32p. (J). (978-0-439-41816-4(X)) Scholastic, Inc.

Jennings, Sharon, et al. Franklin's Trading Cards. Southern, Shelley & Jeffrey, Sean, illus. 2004. (Kids Can Read Ser.). 32p. (J). (gr. k-3). (978-1-55337-464-0(9)); (978-1-55337-463-3(0)) Kids Can Pr., Ltd.

Polacco, Patricia. Rotten Richie & the Ultimate Dare. Polacco, Patricia, illus. 2006. (Illus.). 48p. (J). (gr. k). 16.99 (978-0-399-24531-2(6) , Philomel) Penguin Group (USA) Inc.

Van Wert, Faye. Empty Pockets. Van Wert, Faye, illus. 2000. (J). (ps-1). 16.95 (978-1-880851-61-6(X)) Greene Bark Pr., Inc.

Watterson, Bill. Die Welt der Wunder. Bartoszko, Alexandra, tr. from ENG. (Calvin & Hobbes Ser.: Vol. 16). (GER., Illus.). 64p. (J). pap. (978-3-8105-0365-7(7)) Kruger, Wolfgang Verlag, GmbH DEU. *Dist:* International Bk. Import Service, Inc.

HOCKEY

Adelson, Bruce. The Composite Guide to Field Hockey. 2000. (Composite Guide Ser.). (Illus.). 64p. (YA). (gr. 4 up). pap. 5.95 (978-0-7910-5872-5(7) , Chelsea Hse.) Facts On File, Inc.

—Hat Trick Trivia. Pulver, Harry, illus. 1998. (Sports Trivia Ser.). 64p. (J). (gr. 5-9). pap. (978-0-8225-9806-0(X)); lib. bdg. 23.93 (978-0-8225-3315-3(4)) Lerner Publishing Group. (Lerner Pubns.).

Aretha, David. The Montreal Canadiens Hockey Team. 1998. (Great Sports Teams Ser.). (Illus.). 48p. (YA). (gr. 4-10). lib. bdg. 23.93 (978-0-7660-1022-2(8)) Enslow Pubs., Inc.

Ayers, Tom. The Illustrated Rules of Ice Hockey. Hoyt, Eleanor, illus. 2001. 32p. (J). (ps-3). pap. 5.95 (978-0-8249-5420-8(3) , Ideals Children's Bks.) Ideals Pubns.

—Illustrated Rules of Ice Hockey. 2001. (gr. k-3). lib. bdg. 14.10 (978-0-613-76751-4(9)) Tandem Library Bks.

Barth, Katrin & Nordmann, Lutz. Learning... Field Hockey. 2007. (Illus.). 152p. (J). pap. 14.95 (978-1-84126-210-9(2)) Meyer & Meyer Sport, Ltd. GBR. *Dist:* Perseus Distribution.

Brill, Marlene Targ. Ice Hockey. 2001. (Winning Women in Sports Ser.). (Illus.). 104p. (YA). (gr. 4 up). lib. bdg. 14.95 (978-1-56674-308-2(7)) Forest Hse. Publishing Co., Inc.

—Winning Women in Ice Hockey. 1999. (Sport Success Ser.). 90p. (YA). (gr. 5 up). pap. 6.95 (978-0-7641-1115-0(9)) Barron's Educational Series, Inc.

Brown, Jonatha A. Hockey. 2004. (Illus.). 24p. (J). pap. (978-0-8368-4347-7(9)); lib. bdg. 19.33 (978-0-8368-4340-8(1)) Stevens, Gareth Inc.

Buckley, James, Jr. Great Moments in Hockey. 2002. (Great Moments in Sports Ser.). (Illus.). 48p. (J). (gr. 5 up). pap. 14.60 (978-0-8368-5361-2(X)); lib. bdg. 30.00 (978-0-8368-5347-6(4)) Stevens, Gareth Inc. (World Almanac Library).

Bylsma, Dan & Bylsma, Jay M. So You Want to Play in the NHL: A Guide for Young Players. 2000. (Illus.). 208p. pap. 14.95 (978-0-8092-9952-2(6) , 9780809299522) McGraw-Hill Cos., The.

Carty, Michelle. Give It Your All Vol. 4559: The Olympic Sport of Ice Hockey, Samoiloff, Sheri, ed. Allsport Staff, photos by. 2002. (Illus.). 16p. (J). (gr. 3-6). pap. 3.49 (978-1-57471-930-7(0)) Creative Teaching Pr., Inc.

Compete Like a Champion - Hockey, 5 bks., Set. (Illus.). (J). (gr. 4-8). lib. bdg. 167.60 (978-1-57103-218-8(5)) Rourke Publishing, LLC.

Danakas, John & Brignall, Richard. Small Town Glory. 2006. (Recordbooks Ser.). (Illus.). 120p. (J). (gr. 7-12). (*978-1-55028-961-9(6)) Lorimer, James & Co., Ltd., Pubs. CAN. *Dist:* Casemate Pubs. & Bk. Distributors, LLC.

—Small Town Glory: The story of the Kenora Thistles' remarkable quest for the Stanley Cup. 2006. (Recordbooks Ser.). (Illus.). 120p. (J). (gr. 7-12). 8.95 (*978-1-55028-943-5(8)) Lorimer, James & Co., Ltd., Pubs. CAN. *Dist:* Casemate Pubs. & Bk. Distributors, LLC.

Ditchfield, Christin. Ice Hockey. 2003. (True Books Ser.). (Illus.). 48p. (J). 25.00 (978-0-516-22588-3(X) , Children's Pr.) Scholastic Library Publishing.

—Ice Hockey. 2003. (gr. 3-6). lib. bdg. 15.25 (978-0-613-67969-5(5)) Tandem Library Bks.

Dunn, Joeming W. Miracle on Ice. Dunn, Ben, illus. 2007. (Graphic History Ser.). 32p. (J). (gr. 3-6). lib. bdg. 27.07 (*978-1-60270-077-2(X) , Graphic Planet) Magic Wagon.

Duplacey, James. History's Hottest Wingers. 1999. (gr. 3-6). lib. bdg. 12.95 (978-0-613-21706-4(3)) Tandem Library Bks.

—Hockey's Hottest Goalies. 1999. (gr. 3-6). lib. bdg. 12.95 (978-0-613-21711-8(X)) Tandem Library Bks.

—Wingers. 1999. (Hockey's Hottest Ser.). (Illus.). 118p. (J). (gr. 2-5). (978-1-55074-596-2(4)) Kids Can Pr., Ltd.

Egan, Tracie. Field Hockey. 2005. (Sports from Coast to Coast Ser.). (Illus.). 48p. (J). (gr. 5-8). lib. bdg. 26.50 (978-1-4042-0182-8(3)) Rosen Publishing Group, Inc., The.

Fast & Furious: Individual Title, 6 packs. (Rigby Infoquest Ser.). 32p. (gr. 4 up). 37.00 (978-0-7578-5725-6(6)) Rigby Education.

Fauchald, Nick. Face Off! You Can Play Hockey. Rooney, Ronnie, illus. 2005. (Game Day Ser.). 24p. (J). (ps). lib. bdg. 22.60 (978-1-4048-1154-6(0)) Picture Window Bks.

Feldman, Heather. Wayne Gretzky: Individual Title Six-Packs. (On Deck Ser.). 24p. (gr. 4-5). 35.00 (978-0-7578-1002-2(0)) Rigby Education.

Foley, Mike. Hockey. King, Andy, photos by. 2005. (Play-by-Play Ser.). (Illus.). 80p. (J). (gr. 4-8). pap., lib. bdg. 23.93 (978-0-8225-9878-7(7)) Lerner Publishing Group.

—Play by Play: By Mike Foley. 2000. (gr. 3-6). lib. bdg. 16.40 (978-0-613-85028-5(9)) Tandem Library Bks.

Fried, Mark. Great Teams In..., 6 vols., Set 1. 2005. 166.74 (978-1-4109-1489-7(5)); pap. 45.90 (978-1-4109-1496-5(8)) Raintree.

—Great Teams in Hockey. 2005. (Great Teams Ser.). (Illus.). 48p. (J). 29.29 (978-1-4109-1486-6(0)); pap. 8.50 (978-1-4109-1493-4(3)) Raintree.

—Great Teams in Hockey 6-Pack. 2005. pap. 51.00 (978-1-4109-1500-9(X)) Raintree.

Frisch, Aaron. New York Islanders. 2004. (Stanley Cup Champions Ser.). (Illus.). 32p. (J). lib. bdg. (978-1-58341-276-3(X) , Creative Education) Creative Co., The.

George, Charles & George, Linda. Roller Hockey. 1998. (Sports Alive! Ser.). (Illus.). 48p. (J). (gr. 3-4). lib. bdg. 21.26 (978-0-7368-0053-2(0) , Capstone High-Interest Bks.) Capstone Pr., Inc.

Goodman, Michael E. Detroit Red Wings. 2004. (Stanley Cup Champions Ser.). (Illus.). 32p. (J). lib. bdg. (978-1-58341-278-7(6) , Creative Education) Creative Co., The.

—Montreal Canadiens. 2004. (Stanley Cup Champions Ser.). (Illus.). 32p. (J). lib. bdg. (978-1-58341-273-2(5) , Creative Education) Creative Co., The.

Goodman, Michael E. The Story of the Montreal Canadiens. 2008. (J). (*978-1-58341-618-1(8) , Creative Education) Creative Co., The.

Helmer, Diana Star & Owens, Thomas. The History of Hockey. 2000. (Sports Throughout History Ser.). 24p. (J). (gr. k-4). lib. bdg. 18.75 (978-0-8239-5468-1(4) , PowerKids Pr.) Rosen Publishing Group, Inc., The.

La Historia del Hockey, 6 Packs. (On Deck en Espanol Ser.).Tr. of Story of Hockey. (SPA.). 24p. (gr. 4-5). 35.00 (978-0-7578-6398-1(1)) Rigby Education.

Hockey for Fun! (For Fun Ser.). 48p. (YA). 8.95 (978-0-7565-1157-9(7)) Compass Point Bks.

Hockey sobre Hielo: Individual Title Six-Packs. (On Deck en Espanol Ser.).Tr. of Ice Hockey. (SPA.). 24p. (gr. 4-5). 35.00 (978-0-7578-6392-9(2)) Rigby Education.

Ice Hockey: Individual Title, 6 Packs. (On Deck Ser.). 24p. (gr. 4-5). 35.00 (978-0-7578-1009-1(8)) Rigby Education.

Johnstone, Robb. For the Love of Hockey. Craats, Rennay, ed. 2001. (For the Love of Sports Ser.). (Illus.). 24p. (J). (gr. 1-3). lib. bdg. 15.95 (978-1-930954-15-1(8)) Weigl Pubs., Inc.

Kalman, Bobbie. Hockey in Action. 2000. (gr. 3-6). lib. bdg. 14.10 (978-0-613-21710-1(1)) Tandem Library Bks.

Kennedy, Mike. Ice Hockey. 2003. (Watts Library). (Illus.). 64p. (J). 25.50 (978-0-531-12273-0(5) , Watts, Franklin) Scholastic Library Publishing.

—Roller Hockey. 2002. (Illus.). 63p. (J). (gr. 4-7). lib. bdg. 17.60 (978-0-613-51670-9(2)) Tandem Library Bks.

Kings of the Ice: A History of World Hockey. 2002. (YA). (gr. 6 up). cd-rom (978-1-55375-005-5(5)) NDE Publishing.

Leonetti, Mike. The Greatest Goal. Thompson, Sean, illus. 2002. (Hockey Heroes Ser.). 32p. (J). (ps-3). 15.95 (978-1-55192-318-5(1)) Raincoast Bk. Distribution CAN. *Dist:* Perseus Distribution.

Litke, Ronald. Ice Hockey. 1998. (Successful Sports Ser.). 32p. (J). lib. bdg. 21.36 (978-1-57572-074-6(4)) Heinemann Library.

Macnow, Glen. The Philadelphia Flyers Hockey Team. 2000. (Great Sports Teams Ser.). (Illus.). 48p. (YA). (gr. 4-10). lib. bdg. 23.93 (978-0-7660-1279-0(4)) Enslow Pubs., Inc.

Mayo, Terry. The Illustrated Rules of In-Line Hockey. 2001. (Illus.). (YA). lib. bdg. 14.10 (978-0-613-76752-1(7)) Tandem Library Bks.

McAuliffe, Bill. The Story of the Colorado Avalanche. 2008. (J). (*978-1-58341-616-7(1) , Creative Education) Creative Co., The.

—The Story of the Toronto Maple Leafs. 2008. (J). (*978-1-58341-621-1(8) , Creative Education) Creative Co., The.

McFarlane, Brian. Real Stories from the Rink. Nease, Steve, illus. 2002. 96p. (J). (gr. 5 up). pap. 14.95 (978-0-88776-604-6(8)) Tundra Bks., Inc./Livres Toundra, Inc. CAN. *Dist:* Random Hse., Inc.

McKinley, Michael. Ice Time: The Story of Hockey. 2006. (Illus.). 80p. (YA). (gr. 5-8). 18.95 (978-0-88776-762-3(1)) Tundra Bks., Inc./Livres Toundra, Inc. CAN. *Dist:* Random Hse., Inc.

Miller, Raymond H. Jaromir Jagr. 2003. (Stars of Sports Ser.). (Illus.). 48p. (J). 26.20 (978-0-7377-1539-2(1) , Greenhaven Pr., Inc.) Thomson Gale.

Muskat, Carrie. Ice Hockey. 1999. (Composite Guide Ser.). (Illus.). 64p. (YA). (gr. 4-7). 28.00 (978-0-7910-4727-9(X) , Chelsea Hse.) Facts On File, Inc.

Napier, Matt. Hat Tricks Count. rev. ed. 2007. (Board Ser.). 32p. bds. 7.99 (***978-1-58536-346-9(4)***) Sleeping Bear Pr.

—Hat Tricks Count. Rose, Melanie, illus. rev. ed. 2005. (Sports Alphabet Ser.). 40p. (J). (gr. k-5). 16.95 (978-1-58536-163-2(1)) Sleeping Bear Pr.

—Z Is for Zamboni: A Hockey Alphabet. Rose, Melanie, illus. rev. ed. 2002. 40p. (J). (ps). 19.95 (978-1-58536-065-9(1)) Sleeping Bear Pr.

Newby, John. Heart of the Game. 2005. (J). pap. 12.95 (978-1-55278-531-7(9)) McArthur & Co. CAN. *Dist:* National Bk. Network.

—Heart of the Game: Minor Hockey Moments. 2004. (Illus.). 32p. 16.95 (978-1-55278-395-5(2)) McArthur & Co. CAN. *Dist:* National Bk. Network.

Nichols, John. Boston Bruins. 2004. (Stanley Cup Champions Ser.). (Illus.). 32p. (J). lib. bdg. (978-1-58341-275-6(1) , Creative Education) Creative Co., The.

—Dallas Stars. 2004. (Stanley Cup Champions Ser.). (Illus.). 32p. (J). lib. bdg. (978-1-58341-280-0(8) , Creative Education) Creative Co., The.

—The History of the Colorado Avalanche. 2004. (Stanley Cup Champions Ser.). (Illus.). 32p. (J). lib. bdg. (978-1-58341-277-0(8) , Creative Education) Creative Co., The.

—Philadelphia Flyers. 2004. (Stanley Cup Champions Ser.). (Illus.). 32p. (J). lib. bdg. (978-1-58341-279-4(4) , Creative Education) Creative Co., The.

—Toronto Maple Leafs. 2004. (Stanley Cup Champions Ser.). (Illus.). 32p. (J). lib. bdg. (978-1-58341-274-9(3) , Creative Education) Creative Co., The.

Nicholson, Lorna Schultz. Pink Power: The First Women's Hockey World Champions. 2007. (Recordbooks Ser.). (Illus.). 128p. (YA). (gr. 7-12). 8.95 (***978-1-55028-987-9(X)***) Lorimer, James & Co., Ltd., Pubs. CAN. *Dist:* Casemate Pubs. & Bk. Distributors, LLC.

O'Shei, Tim. The Detroit Red Wings Hockey Team. 2000. (Great Sports Teams Ser.). (Illus.). 48p. (YA). (gr. 4-10). lib. bdg. 23.93 (978-0-7660-1282-0(4)) Enslow Pubs., Inc.

Otten, Jack. Hockey Sobre Hielo. 2004. (Entrenamiento Deportivo Ser.). (SPA & ENG., Illus.). 24p. (J). lib. bdg. 17.25 (978-0-8239-6847-3(2) , Buenas Letra) Rosen Publishing Group, Inc., The.

—Ice Hockey. 2002. (Reading Power Ser.). (Illus.). 24p. (J). (gr. 1). lib. bdg. 17.25 (978-0-8239-5976-1(7) , PowerKids Pr.) Rosen Publishing Group, Inc., The.

Owens, Tom & Helmer, Diana Star. Hockey. 1999. (Game Plan Ser.). (Illus.). 64p. (gr. 5-8). lib. bdg. 26.90 (978-0-7613-3236-7(7) , Twenty-First Century Bks.) Lerner Publishing Group.

Romanuk, Paul. Hockey Superstars 1999-2000: Today's Hottest Names in the Game! 1999. (Hockey Superstars Ser.). (Illus.). 48p. (J). (gr. 4-7). pap. 4.99 (978-1-55209-399-3(9)) Firefly Bks., Ltd.

Ross, Dalton. The Top Teams Ever: Football, Baseball, Basketball & Hockey Winners. 2005. (Sports Illustrated for Kids Bks.). (Illus.). 176p. (YA). (gr. 7-12). lib. bdg. 27.95 (978-0-8239-3693-9(7)) Rosen Publishing Group, Inc., The.

Ross, Jesse. All-Star Sports Puzzles: Hockey: Games, Trivia, Puzzles & More! 2007. 64p. pap. 7.95 (***978-1-55192-810-4(8)***) Raincoast Bk. Distribution CAN. *Dist:* Perseus Distribution.

Rossiter, Sean & Carson, Paul. The Basics. 2nd rev. ed. 2006. (Hockey the NHL Way Ser.). (Illus.). 96p. pap. 12.95 (978-1-55365-212-0(6) , Greystone Bks.) Douglas & McIntyre, Ltd. CAN. *Dist:* Transition Vendor.

—Skating for Power & Speed. 2003. (Hockey the NHL Way Ser.). (Illus.). 64p. (J). (gr. 3-7). pap. 9.95 (978-1-55054-916-4(2)) Douglas & McIntyre, Ltd. CAN. *Dist:* Transition Vendor.

—Tips from the Pros. 2003. (Hockey the NHL Way Ser.). (Illus.). 64p. (J). pap. 9.95 (978-1-55054-864-8(6)) Douglas & McIntyre, Ltd. CAN. *Dist:* Transition Vendor.

Rossiter, Sean, et al. Power Plays & Penalty Killing. 2003. (Hockey the NHL Way Ser.). (Illus.). 64p. (J). pap. 9.95 (978-1-55054-791-7(7)) Douglas & McIntyre, Ltd. CAN. *Dist:* Transition Vendor.

Sandler, Michael. Hockey: Miracle on Ice. 2006. (Upsets & Comebacks Ser.). (Illus.). 32p. (J). lib. bdg. 25.27 (978-1-59716-168-8(3)) Bearport Publishing Co., Inc.

Sias, John. Kids' Book of Hockey: Skills, Strategies, Equipment & the Rules of the Game. 2000. (Illus.). 1p. (gr. 1-11). pap. 9.95 (978-0-8065-1921-0(5) , Citadel Pr.) Kensington Publishing Corp.

Siemiatycki, Jack & Slodovnick, Avi. The Hockey Card. Barrette, Doris, illus. 32p. (J). pap. 6.95 (978-1-894222-80-8(6)) Lobster Pr. CAN. *Dist:* Univ. of Toronto Pr.

Skog, Jason. The Story of the Chicago Blackhawks. 2008. (J). (***978-1-58341-615-0(3)*** , Creative Education) Creative Co., The.

Slodovnick, Avi, et al. La Carte de Hockey. Barrette, Doris, illus. (FRE.). 32p. (J). pap. 6.95 (978-1-894222-64-8(4)) Lobster Pr. CAN. *Dist:* Univ. of Toronto Pr.

Stewart, Mark. The Stanley Cup. Kennedy, Mike, ed. 2003. (Watts History of Sports Ser.). (Illus.). 160p. (J). 34.50 (978-0-531-11956-3(4) , Watts, Franklin) Scholastic Library Publishing.

Stewart, Mark Alan. Hockey: A History of the Fastest Game on Ice. 1998. (History of Sports Ser.). (Illus.). 128p. (YA). (gr. 5-8). 34.50 (978-0-531-11494-0(5) , Watts, Franklin) Scholastic Library Publishing.

The Story of Hockey: Individual Title Six-Packs. (On Deck Ser.). 24p. (gr. 4-5). 35.00 (978-0-7578-1015-2(2)) Rigby Education.

Stubbs, Dave. Our Game: The History of Hockey in Canada. Portnoy, Neal, illus. 2006. 48p. (J). (gr. 3-7). (978-1-897073-27-8(5)) Lobster Pr.

—Our Game: The History of Hockey in Canada. Portnoy, Neal, illus. 2006. 48p. (J). (gr. 3-7). pap. (978-1-897073-46-9(1)) Lobster Pr.

Suen, Anastasia. The Story of Hockey. 2002. (Reading Power Ser.). (Illus.). 24p. (J). (gr. 2). lib. bdg. 17.25 (978-0-8239-5997-6(X) , PowerKids Pr.) Rosen Publishing Group, Inc., The.

Sullivan, Michael J. The New York Rangers Hockey Team. 1998. (Great Sports Teams Ser.). (Illus.). 48p. (YA). (gr. 4-10). lib. bdg. 23.93 (978-0-7660-1023-9(6)) Enslow Pubs., Inc.

Thomas, Keltie. How Hockey Works: Includes the Latest NHL Rules. 2nd ed. 2006. (How Sports Work Ser.). (Illus.). 64p. 21.95 (978-1-897066-64-5(3)) Maple Tree Pr. CAN. *Dist:* Perseus Distribution.

—How Hockey Works: Includes the Latest NHL Rules. Hall, Greg, illus. 2nd ed. 2006. (How Sports Work Ser.). 64p. pap. 9.95 (978-1-897066-65-2(1)) Maple Tree Pr. CAN. *Dist:* Perseus Distribution.

—How Hockey Works: The Science of Hockey. 2002. (gr. 3-6). lib. bdg. 18.75 (978-0-613-51113-1(1)) Tandem Library Bks.

Thomas, Ron & Herran, Joe. Getting into Hockey. 2005. (Getting Into Ser.). (Illus.). 32p. (J). (ps-8). lib. bdg. 28.00 (978-0-7910-8810-4(3) , Chelsea Clubhouse) Facts On File, Inc.

Tinkham, J. K. Life Lessons on Ice. 2002. 112p. pap. 9.95 (978-0-595-21685-7(4) , Writers Club Pr.) iUniverse, Inc.

U. S. Olympic Committee. A Basic Guide to Ice Hockey. 2002. (Olympic Guides). (Illus.). 160p. (J). (gr. 6 up). lib. bdg. 23.33 (978-0-8368-3103-0(9)) Stevens, Gareth Inc.

Walker, Niki. Hockey in Action. 1999. (Sports in Action Ser.). (Illus.). (J). 12.75 (978-0-606-18059-7(1)) Tandem Library Bks.

Walker, Niki & Dann, Sarah. Le Hockey. 2006. (FRE., Illus.). 32p. (gr. 3-4). pap. (978-2-89579-090-7(6)) Crabtree Publishing Co.

—Hockey in Action. 1999. (Sports in Action Ser.). (Illus.). 32p. (J). (gr. 3-4). (978-0-7787-0160-6(3)) ; pap. (978-0-7787-0172-9(7)) Crabtree Publishing Co.

Weekes, Don. Rockin' Hockey Trivia: Games - Puzzles - Quizzes. 2003. 128p. (gr. 3-7). pap. 6.95 (978-1-55054-799-3(2) , SPO02000) Douglas & McIntyre, Ltd. CAN. *Dist:* Transition Vendor.

—Shootout Hockey Trivia: Games & Quizzes. 2006. 128p. pap. 8.95 (978-1-55365-203-8(7) , Greystone Bks.) Douglas & McIntyre, Ltd. CAN. *Dist:* Transition Vendor.

Will, Sandra. Hockey for Fun! 2003. (Sports for Fun! Ser.). (Illus.). 48p. (J). (gr. 3 up). 21.26 (978-0-7565-0488-5(0)) Compass Point Bks.

Wilson, Stacy. The Hockey Book for Girls. Slavin, Bill, illus. Wilson, Stacy, photos by. 2000. (Books for Girls Ser.). 40p. (J). (gr. 4-6). (978-1-55074-719-5(3)) Kids Can Pr., Ltd.

—Hockey Book for Girls. 2000. (gr. 3-6). lib. bdg. 15.25 (978-0-613-30473-3(X)) Tandem Library Bks.

Wright, John. Hockey. 2003. (Sports Injuries Ser.). (Illus.). 64p. (J). lib. bdg. (978-1-59084-634-6(6)) Mason Crest Pubs.

Wukovits, John F. Hockey. 2000. (History of Sports Ser.). (Illus.). 96p. (YA). (gr. 6-9). 29.95 (978-1-56006-745-0(4) , Lucent Bks.) Thomson Gale.

Zweig, Eric. Long Shot: The Team from Winnipeg That Won the First-Ever Olympic Hockey Gold. 2007. (Recordbooks Ser.). (Illus.). 112p. (gr. 7-12). (J). 8.95 (***978-1-55028-974-9(8)***); (YA). (***978-1-55028-975-6(6)***) Lorimer, James & Co., Ltd., Pubs. CAN. *Dist:* Casemate Pubs. & Bk. Distributors, LLC.

HOCKEY—BIOGRAPHY

Banks, Kerry. Pavel Bure. 2003. (Hockey Heroes Ser.). (Illus.). 48p. (J). (gr. 3-6). pap. 7.95 (978-1-55054-920-1(0)) Douglas & McIntyre, Ltd. CAN. *Dist:* Transition Vendor.

—Teemu Selanne. 2003. (Hockey Heroes Ser.). (Illus.). pap. 7.95 (978-1-55054-678-1(3)) Sterling Publishing Co., Inc.

Benson, Michael. Wayne Gretzky, Hockey Player. 2004. (Ferguson Career Biographies Ser.). (Illus.). 128p. (J). (gr. 6-12). 25.00 (978-0-8160-5545-6(9) , Ferguson Publishing Co.) Facts On File, Inc.

Bonner, Mike. Paul Kariya. 1999. (Ice Hockey Legends Ser.). (Illus.). 64p. (YA). (gr. 2-5). lib. bdg. 18.65 (978-0-7910-5015-6(7) , Chelsea Hse.) Facts On File, Inc.

Brehm, Mike & Russo, Michael. Rising Stars: The 10 Best Young Players in the NHL. 2005. (Sports Illustrated for Kids Bks.). (Illus.). 176p. (YA). (gr. 7-12). lib. bdg. 32.00 (978-0-8239-3575-8(2)) Rosen Publishing Group, Inc., The.

Brehm, Mike & Russo, Mike. Rising Stars: The 10 Best Young Players in the NHL. 2000. (Illus.). 96p. (J). (gr. 2-8). pap. 3.99 (978-1-930623-11-8(9)) Sports Illustrated For Kids.

Burgan, Michael. Dominik Hasek. 1999. (Ice Hockey Legends Ser.). (Illus.). 64p. (YA). (gr. 2-5). 12.95 (978-0-7910-5014-9(9) , Chelsea Hse.) Facts On File, Inc.

Dater, Adrian. The Colorado Avalanche. 2003. (Illus.). 112p. (J). 29.95 (978-1-59018-305-2(3) , Lucent Bks.) Thomson Gale.

Doeden, Matt. Wayne Gretzky. 2007. (J). lib. bdg. (***978-0-8225-7165-0(X)***) Twenty First Century Bks.

Duplacey, James. Centers. 1999. (Hockey's Hottest Ser.). (Illus.). 120p. (J). (gr. 2-5). (978-1-55074-681-5(2)) Kids Can Pr., Ltd.

—Defensemen. 1999. (Hockey's Hottest Ser.). (Illus.). 32p. (J). (gr. 2-5). (978-1-55074-683-9(9)) Kids Can Pr., Ltd.

—Defensemen. unabr. ed. 1999. (Hockey's Hottest Ser.). (Illus.). 32p. (J). (gr. 1-4). pap. 4.95 (978-1-55074-594-8(8)) Kids Can Pr., Ltd. CAN. *Dist:* General Distribution Services, Inc.

Feldman, Heather. Wayne Gretzky: Estrella del Hockey. 2002. (Hockey Star Ser.). (SPA., Illus.). 24p. (J). lib. bdg. 17.25 (978-0-8239-6121-4(4) , PowerKids Pr.) Rosen Publishing Group, Inc., The.

—Wayne Gretzky: Hockey Star. 2001. (Reading Power Ser.). (Illus.). 24p. (J). (gr. 1). lib. bdg. 17.25 (978-0-8239-5715-6(2) , PKGRET, PowerKids Pr.) Rosen Publishing Group, Inc., The.

—Wayne Gretzky, Estrella del Hockey. 2002. (Coleccion Power Kids). (SPA & ENG., Illus.). 24p. (J). (gr. k-2). lib. bdg. 17.25 (978-0-8239-6139-9(7) , RN31308) Rosen Publishing Group, Inc., The.

Frisch, Aaron. Eric Lindros. 1999. (Ovations Ser.). (Illus.). 32p. (YA). (gr. 4-7). pap. (978-0-88682-998-8(4) , Creative Education) Creative Co., The.

Grabowski, John F. Detroit Redwings. 2003. (Illus.). 112p. (J). 29.95 (978-1-59018-269-7(3) , Lucent Bks.) Thomson Gale.

Greene, Meg. Peter Forsberg. 1999. (Ice Hockey Legends Ser.). (Illus.). 64p. (YA). (gr. 2-5). lib. bdg. 18.65 (978-0-7910-5013-2(0) , Chelsea Hse.) Facts On File, Inc.

Harling, Michael. Jaromir Jagr. 2003. (Hockey Heroes Ser.). (Illus.). 48p. (J). (gr. 3-6). pap. 7.95 (978-1-55054-836-5(0)) Douglas & McIntyre, Ltd. CAN. *Dist:* Transition Vendor.

—Peter Forsberg. 2003. (Hockey Heroes Ser.). (Illus.). 48p. (J). pap. 7.95 (978-1-55054-793-1(3)) Douglas & McIntyre, Ltd. CAN. *Dist:* Transition Vendor.

Harris, Paul. Brendan Shanahan: Power Forward. 2000. (Sport Snaps Ser.). (Illus.). 56p. (YA). pap. 12.95 (978-1-892920-05-8(0)) GHB Publishers, LLC.

Johnson, Tami. Girls' Ice Hockey. 2008. (J). (***978-1-4296-0133-7(7)***) Capstone Pr., Inc.

Kirkpatrick, Rob, et al, contrib. by. Wayne Gretzky, Hockey All-Star. 2001. (Great Record Breakers in Sports Ser.). (Illus.). 24p. (J). lib. bdg. 18.75 (978-0-8239-5631-9(8) , PowerKids Pr.) Rosen Publishing Group, Inc., The.

Kramer, Sydelle A. Great Gretzky. 2000. (All Aboard Reading Ser.). (Illus.). (J). 10.79 (978-0-606-18467-0(8)) Tandem Library Bks.

Labrecque, Ellen. Ice Kings. 2007. (World's Greatest Athletes Ser.). 32p. (J). (gr. 1-5). 27.07 (978-1-59296-789-6(2)) Child's World, Inc.

Loverro, Thom. Cammi Granato: Hockey Pioneer. 2000. (Sports Achievers Biographies Ser.). (SPA., Illus.). 64p. (YA). (gr. 4-9). lib. bdg. (978-0-8225-3682-6(X)); pap. (978-0-8225-9862-6(0)) Lerner Publishing Group. (LernerSports).

Luecking, Dave. Hockey's Scorers & Goalies: The NHL's Biggest Stars. Gramling, Scott, ed. 1999. 32p. (J). (gr. 1-9). pap. 3.99 (978-1-886749-55-9(8)) Sports Illustrated For Kids.

Murdico, Suzanne J. Mario Lemieux. 1998. (Overcoming the Odds Ser.). (Illus.). 48p..(J). (gr. 3-8). (978-0-8172-4126-1(4)) Raintree.

—Mario Lemieux. 1998. (Overcoming the Odds Ser.). (Illus.). 48p. (J). (gr. 4-7). pap. 7.95 (978-0-8172-8004-8(9)) Steck-Vaughn.

O'Ree, Willie. Story of Willie O'Ree. 2000. (978-0-606-18473-1(2)) Tandem Library Bks.

O'Shea, Tim. Scott Gomez. 2001. (Latinos in the Limelight Ser.). (Illus.). 64p. (J). (gr. 4-7). 27.50 (978-0-7910-6475-7(1) , Chelsea Hse.) Facts On File, Inc.

O'Shei, Tim. Mario Lemieux. 2001. (Overcoming Adversity Ser.). (Illus.). 112p. (J). 30.00 (978-0-7910-6307-1(0) , Chelsea Hse.) Facts On File, Inc.

Powell, Phelan. John LeClair. 1999. (Ice Hockey Legends Ser.). (Illus.). 64p. (YA). (gr. 2-5). lib. bdg. 18.65 (978-0-7910-5016-3(5) , Chelsea Hse.) Facts On File, Inc.

Raber, Thomas R. Wayne Gretzky: Hockey Great. rev. exp. ed. 1999. (Sports Achievers Biographies Ser.). (Illus.). 80p. (YA). (gr. 4-9). lib. bdg. (978-0-8225-3677-2(3) , LernerSports) Lerner Publishing Group.

Rappoport, Ken. Mario Lemieux: Star Center. 1998. (Sports Reports). (Illus.). 112p. (YA). (gr. 4-10). lib. bdg. 26.60 (978-0-89490-932-0(0)) Enslow Pubs., Inc.

Romanuk, Paul. Le Hockey Ses Supervedettes 2004-2005. annual 2004. (FRE., Illus.). (J). pap. (978-0-439-96134-9(3)) Scholastic Canada, Ltd.

—Hockey Superstars 2004-2005. annual 2004. (Illus.). (J). pap. (978-0-439-96133-2(5)) Scholastic Canada, Ltd.

Rossiter, Sean. Dominik Hasek. 2003. (Hockey Heroes Ser.). (Illus.). 44p. (gr. 5-9). 6.95 (978-1-55054-679-8(1)) Douglas & McIntyre, Ltd. CAN. *Dist:* Transition Vendor.

—Mario Lemieux. 2003. (Hockey Heroes Ser.). (Illus.). 64p. pap. 12.95 (978-1-55054-870-9(0)) Douglas & McIntyre, Ltd. CAN. *Dist:* Transition Vendor.

Santella, Andrew. Wayne Gretzky: The Great One. 1999. (Book Report Biographies Ser.). (Illus.). 112p. (YA). pap. 6.95 (978-0-531-15954-5(X) , Watts, Franklin) Scholastic Library Publishing.

Schnaber, Dean. Sergei Fedorov. 1999. (Ice Hockey Legends Ser.). (Illus.). 64p. (YA). (gr. 2-5). lib. bdg. 18.65 (978-0-7910-5012-5(2) , Chelsea Hse.) Facts On File, Inc.

Schnakenberg, Robert E. Martin Brodeur. 1999. (Ice Hockey Legends Ser.). (Illus.). 64p. (YA). (gr. 2-5). lib. bdg. 18.65 (978-0-7910-5011-8(4) , Chelsea Hse.) Facts On File, Inc.

Shea, Therese. Hockey Stars. 2007. (Sports Stars Ser.). (Illus.). 48p. (J). pap. (978-0-531-18704-3(7)) Children's Pr., Ltd.

—Hockey Stars. 2006. (Sports Stars Ser.). (Illus.). 48p. (J). (978-0-531-12587-8(4) , Children's Pr.) Scholastic Library Publishing.

Spiros, Dean. Top 10 Hockey Goalies. 1998. (Sports Top 10 Ser.). (Illus.). 48p. (YA). (gr. 4-10). lib. bdg. 23.93 (978-0-7660-1010-9(4)) Enslow Pubs., Inc.

Stewart, Mark. Mario Lemieux: Own the Ice. 2002. (gr. 3-6). lib. bdg. 17.60 (978-0-613-90446-9(X)) Tandem Library Bks.

—Scott Gomez: Open up the Ice. 2001. (New Wave Ser.). (Illus.). 48p. (gr. 4 up). lib. bdg. 22.90 (978-0-7613-2268-9(X) , Millbrook Pr.) Lerner Publishing Group.

Stewart, Mark Alan. Mario Lemieux: Own the Ice. 2002. 64p. (gr. 4-12). (J). pap. 8.95 (978-0-7613-1687-9(6)); (Illus.). lib. bdg. 24.90 (978-0-7613-2555-0(7)) Lerner Publishing Group. (Millbrook Pr.).

Wayne Gretzky: Individual Title Six-Packs. (On Deck en Espanol Ser.). (SPA.). 24p. (gr. 4-5). 35.00 (978-0-7578-6385-1(X)) Rigby Education.

Wilner, Barry. Mark Messier. 1999. (Ice Hockey Legends Ser.). (Illus.). 64p. (YA). (gr. 4-7). 12.95 (978-0-7910-4559-6(5) , Chelsea Hse.) Facts On File, Inc.

HOCKEY—FICTION

Aryal, Aimee. Let's Go, Red Wings! 2007. (YA). 14.95 (***978-1-932888-75-1(6)***) Mascot Bks., Inc.

Atkins, Ben. The Breakaway Kid. 2005. 30p. 14.99 (978-1-4116-2792-5(X)) Lulu.com.

—The Breakaway Kid. Woods, Vanessa, illus. 2nd rev. ed. 2005. (ENG.). 32p. (J). per. 8.00 (978-0-9768653-0-8(0)) Summer Day Publishing, LLC.

Beveridge, Cathy. Offside. 2005. 336p. mass mkt. 7.95 (978-1-894345-25-5(8)) Thistledown Pr., Ltd. CAN. *Dist:* Literary Pr. Group of Canada.

—One on One. 2005. 224p. pap. 7.95 (978-1-894345-80-4(0)) Thistledown Pr., Ltd. CAN. *Dist:* Literary Pr. Group of Canada.

Bossley, Michele Martin. Goon Squad. 2003. (Sports Stories Ser.). 104p. (J). (gr. 4-8). 7.95 (978-1-55028-808-7(3)); (***978-1-55028-809-4(1)***) Lorimer, James & Co., Ltd., Pubs. CAN. *Dist:* Casemate Pubs. & Bk. Distributors, LLC.

—Power Play. 2001. (Sports Stories Ser.). 128p. (gr. 3-8). (J). (***978-1-55028-747-9(8)***); 7.95 (978-1-55028-746-2(X)) Lorimer, James & Co., Ltd., Pubs. CAN. *Dist:* Casemate Pubs. & Bk. Distributors, LLC.

Bouchard, David. That's Hockey. Griffiths, Dean, illus. 2004. 32p. (J). (ps-2). 7.95 (978-1-55143-348-6(6)) Orca Bk. Pubs. USA.

Bradfield, Roger. The Flying Hockey Stick. Bradfield, Roger, illus. 2006. (J). 18.95 (978-1-930900-31-8(7)) Purple Hse. Pr.

Brewster, Jim. Wild League on Ice. 1998. (J). pap. 5.95 (978-0-9683303-4-0(7)) Tumbleweed Pr.

Brooks, Bruce. Dooby. 1998. (Wolfbay Wings Ser.: No. 8). (Illus.). (J). 128p. (gr. 5 up). pap. 4.50 (978-0-06-440708-3(X)); 32p. (ps-1). 14.89 (978-0-06-027898-4(6)) HarperCollins Pubs.

—Prince. 1998. (Wolfbay Wings Ser.: No. 5). (Illus.). 144p. (J). (gr. 4-7). pap. 4.50 (978-0-06-440600-0(8)) HarperCollins Pubs.

—Prince. 1998. (Wolfbay Wings Ser.: No. 5). (J). (gr. 4-7). (978-0-606-13925-0(7)) Tandem Library Bks.

—Reed. 1998. (Wolfbay Wings Ser.: No. 9). (Illus.). 96p. (J). (gr. 5 up). 14.89 (978-0-06-028055-0(7)) HarperCollins Pubs.

—Shark. 1998. (Wolfbay Wings Ser.: No. 6). (Illus.). (J). 144p. (gr. 4 up). pap. 4.50 (978-0-06-440681-9(4)); 32p. (ps-3). 14.89 (978-0-06-027570-9(7)) HarperCollins Pubs.

—Shark. 1998. (Wolfbay Wings Ser.: No. 6). (J). (gr. 4-7). (978-0-606-13926-7(5)) Tandem Library Bks.

—Subtle. 1999. (Wolfbay Wings Ser.: No. 10). (J). (gr. 4-7). (978-0-606-17770-2(1)) Tandem Library Bks.

Brouwer, Sigmund. Blazer Drive. 2007. (Orca Sports Ser.). 176p. (YA). (gr. 5 up). pap. (***978-1-55143-717-0(1)***) Orca Bk. Pubs.

—Hitmen Triumph. 2007. (Orca Sports Ser.). 176p. (YA). (gr. 5 up). pap. (***978-1-55143-873-3(9)***) Orca Bk. Pubs.

—Rebel Glory. 2006. (Illus.). 144p. (J). pap. 8.95 (978-1-55143-631-9(0)) Orca Bk. Pubs. USA.

—Tiger Threat. 2006. 144p. (J). pap. 8.95 (978-1-55143-639-5(6)) Orca Bk. Pubs. USA.

—Timberwolf Chase. 2006. (Illus.). 64p. (J). pap. 4.99 (978-1-55143-548-0(9)) Orca Bk. Pubs. USA.

—Timberwolf Hunt. Griffiths, Dean, illus. 2007. (Orca Echoes Ser.). 64p. (J). (gr. 2-4). pap. (***978-1-55143-726-2(0)***) Orca Bk. Pubs.

—Timberwolf Revenge. 2006. (Illus.). 64p. (J). pap. 4.99 (978-1-55143-544-2(6)) Orca Bk. Pubs. USA.

—Timberwolf Trap. Griffiths, Dean, illus. 2007. (Orca Echoes Ser.). 64p. (J). (gr. 2-4). pap. (***978-1-55143-722-4(8)***) Orca Bk. Pubs.

—Winter Hawk Star. 2007. (Orca Sports Ser.). 176p. (YA). (gr. 5 up). pap. (***978-1-55143-869-6(0)***) Orca Bk. Pubs.

Brown, Marc. Arthur & the Goalie Ghost. Brown, Marc, illus. 5th ed. 2001. (Arthur Good Sports Ser.: Bk. 5). (Illus.). 64p. (J). (gr. 2-4). 14.95 (978-0-316-12042-5(1)); pap. 3.95 (978-0-316-12146-0(0)) Little, Brown Bks. for Young Readers.

Brownridge, William Roy. The Final Game: The Further Adventures of the Moccasin Goalie. Brownridge, William Roy, illus. 2001. (Illus.). 32p. (J). (ps-2). 7.95 (978-1-55143-102-4(5)) Orca Bk. Pubs. USA.

—The Moccasin Goalie. Brownridge, William Roy, illus. 2001. (Illus.). 32p. (J). (ps-2). 7.95 (978-1-55143-054-6(1)) Orca Bk. Pubs. USA.

H I

Carter, Anne Laurel. The F Team. Cowles, Rose, illus. 2003. 32p. (J). (ps-2). 16.95 (978-1-55143-241-0(2)) Orca Bk. Pubs. USA.

—In the Clear. 2001. 176p. (J). (gr. 3-7). pap. 6.95 (978-1-55143-192-5(0)) Orca Bk. Pubs. USA.

Christopher, Matt. Body Check. 2003. (gr. 3-6). lib. bdg. 12.40 (978-0-613-70808-1(3)) Tandem Library Bks.

—Body Check. 2003. (Matt Christopher Sports Ser.). 144p. (J). (gr. 3-7). pap. 4.99 (978-0-316-13405-7(8)) Little Brown & Co.

—Cool as Ice. 2001. 160p. (J). (gr. 3-7). pap. 4.99 (978-0-316-13520-7(8)) Little Brown & Co.

—Cool as Ice. 2001. (J). 11.15 (978-0-606-21121-5(7)); (gr. 3-6). lib. bdg. 12.40 (978-0-613-35635-0(7)) Tandem Library Bks.

—Face-Off. ed. 2005. (Sports Classics III Ser.). 119p. (J). lib. bdg. 15.00 (978-1-59054-755-7(1)) Fitzgerald Bks.

—Ice Magic. 2007. (J). lib. bdg. (*978-1-59953-112-0(7)) Norwood Hse. Pr.

—Inline Skater. ed. 2005. (Sports Classics IV Ser.). 153p. (J). lib. bdg. 15.00 (978-1-59054-759-5(4)) Fitzgerald Bks.

—Roller Hockey Radicals. ed. 2005. (Sports Classics III Ser.). 157p. (J). lib. bdg. 15.00 (978-1-59054-767-0(5)) Fitzgerald Bks.

—Roller Hockey Radicals. 1998. 160p. (J). (gr. 3-7). 15.95 (978-0-316-13739-3(1)) Little Brown & Co.

—Roller Hockey Radicals, 58. 1998. (Matt Christopher Sports Classics Ser.). (978-0-606-13747-8(5)) Tandem Library Bks.

Christopher, Matt & Mantell, Paul. Cool as Ice. 2001. 160p. (J). (gr. 4-7). 15.95 (978-0-316-13489-7(9)) Little Brown & Co.

Conrad, Peter C. Other Choices: A Novel. 2002. 164p. (YA). pap. 12.95 (978-0-595-22728-0(7) , Writers Club Pr.) iUniverse, Inc.

Dadey, Debbie & Jones, Marcia Thornton. Frankenstein Doesn't Slam Hockey Pucks. Gurney, John Steven, illus. 1999. (Adventures of the Bailey School Kids Ser.: No. 34). 80p. (J). (gr. 2-4). pap. 3.99 (978-0-590-18984-2(0)) Scholastic, Inc.

Danakas, John. Brothers on Ice. 2001. (Sports Stories Ser.). 102p. (J). (gr. 3-8). (*978-1-55028-680-9(3)); 7.95 (978-1-55028-679-3(X)) Lorimer, James & Co., Ltd., Pubs. CAN. *Dist:* Casemate Pubs. & Bk. Distributors, LLC.

Fidler, Mark. Pond Puckster. 2nd ed. 2003. 148p. (J). (gr. 4-8). reprint ed. pap. 11.95 (978-0-9721839-0-1(6)) BLR Bks.

—Two Faced Forward. 2005. 145p. (J). (gr. 4-8). pap. 11.95 (978-0-9721839-3-2(0)) BLR Bks.

FitzGerald, Dawn. Getting in the Game. 2007. 160p. (J). pap. 6.99 (*978-0-312-37753-3(3)) Square Fish.

Fitzgerald, Dawn. Getting in the Game. rev. ed. 2005. 144p. (J). 15.95 (978-1-59643-044-0(3)) Roaring Brook Pr.

Flanagan, Katie. Polar Bears on Ice. 2001. (Hello Reader! Ser.). (Illus.). (J). pap. (978-0-439-32360-4(6)) Scholastic, Inc.

Forsyth, C. A. Hockey Heat Wave. 1999. (gr. 7-12). lib. bdg. 13.55 (978-0-613-18219-5(7)) Tandem Library Bks.

Forsyth, Christine. Two on One. 2005. (Sports Stories Ser.). 112p. (J). (gr. 3-8). (*978-1-55028-901-5(2)); 7.95 (978-1-55028-900-8(4)) Lorimer, James & Co., Ltd., Pubs. CAN. *Dist:* Casemate Pubs. & Bk. Distributors, LLC.

Gregerson, Jonathan, illus. Minerva's Dream. 1999. (J). 30.00 (978-0-8172-7282-1(8)) Steck-Vaughn.

Guest, Jacqueline. Goal in Sight. 2003. (gr. 3-6). lib. bdg. 13.55 (978-0-613-78325-5(5)) Tandem Library Bks.

Gutman, Dan. The Million Dollar Goal. 2nd ed. 2006. 176p. (J). (gr. 3-7). pap. 5.99 (978-1-4231-0083-6(2)) Hyperion Pr.

Holohan, Maureen. Ice Cold. 1999. (Broadway Ballplayers Ser.: No. 6). (Illus.). 164p. (J). (gr. 4-8). (978-0-9659091-5-0(8)) Broadway Ballplayers, Inc.

Hughes, Pat. Open Ice. 288p. (YA). (gr. 9). 2007. mass mkt. 6.50 (*978-0-553-49444-0(9) , Laurel Leaf); 2005. 15.95 (978-0-385-74675-5(X) , Lamb, Wendy) Random Hse. Children's Bks.

Jennings, Sharon. Franklin Plays Hockey. Koren, Mark et al, illus. ed. 2005. (Franklin Picture Books I). 30p. (J). lib. bdg. 15.00 (978-1-59054-709-0(8)) Fitzgerald Bks.

Jennings, Sharon, et al. Franklin Plays Hockey. Koren, Mark & Lei, John, illus. 2002. (Franklin TV Storybook Ser.). 32p. (J). (ps-3). (978-1-55337-056-7(2)) Kids Can Pr., Ltd.

Klein, Abby. Don't Sit on My Lunch! McKinley, John, illus. 2005. 96p. (J). (ps-3). lib. bdg. 11.19 (978-0-606-34119-6(6)) Tandem Library Bks.

—Don't Sit on My Lunch. Mckinley, John, illus. 2005. (Ready, Freddy! Ser.: No. 4). 96p. (J). pap. 15.95 (978-0-439-55601-9(5)); 4th ed. pap. 3.99 (978-0-439-55602-6(3)) Scholastic, Inc. (Blue Sky Pr., The).

Kline, Suzy. Molly Gets Mad. Bluthenthal, Diana Cain, illus. 2001. 1p. (J). (gr. 1-4). 14.99 (978-0-399-23408-8(X) , Putnam Juvenile) Penguin Group (USA) Inc.

Korman, Gordon. All-Mars All-Stars, Vol. 2. 1999. (Slapshots Ser.: Vol. 2). (Illus.). 144p. (J). (gr. 4-7). pap. 4.50 (978-0-590-70620-9(9) , Scholastic Paperbacks) Scholastic, Inc.

—The Chicken Doesn't Skate. 1998. 192p. (J). (gr. 4-8). pap. 4.50 (978-0-590-85301-9(5)) Scholastic, Inc.

—The Face-off Phony, Vol. 3. 2000. (Slapshots Ser.: Vol. 3). 144p. (J). (gr. 3-6). pap. 4.50 (978-0-590-70629-2(2)) Scholastic, Inc.

—The Stars from Mars. 1999. (Slapshots Ser.: Vol. 1). (Illus.). 144p. (gr. 1-4). pap. 4.50 (978-0-590-70619-3(5)) Scholastic, Inc.

LaSalle, Peter. Hockey Sur Glace: Stories. 1998. 224p. reprint ed. pap. 13.00 (978-1-891369-00-1(8)) Breakaway Bks.

Leonetti. The Greatest Goal. Thompson, Sean, illus. 2004. (Hockey Heroes Ser.). 32p. pap. 6.95 (978-1-55192-574-5(5)) Raincoast Bk. Distribution CAN. *Dist:* Perseus Distribution.

Leonetti, Mike. The Goalie Mask. Letain, Shayne, illus. 2006. (Hockey Heroes Ser.). 32p. pap. 6.95 (978-1-55192-929-3(5)) Raincoast Bk. Distribution CAN. *Dist:* Perseus Distribution.

—Gretzky's Game. Banning, Greg, illus. 32p. (J). (ps-3). 2007. pap. 7.95 (*978-1-55192-889-0(2)); 2006. 15.95 (978-1-55192-851-7(5)) Raincoast Bk. Distribution CAN. *Dist:* Perseus Distribution.

—My Leafs Sweater. ed. 2004. (Illus.). (J). (gr. k-5). spiral bd. (978-0-616-01700-5(6)) Canadian National Institute for the Blind/Institut National Canadien pour les Aveugles.

—My Leafs Sweater. Thompson, Sean, illus. 2002. (Hockey Heroes Ser.). 32p. (J). (gr. k-5). pap. 6.95 (978-1-55192-306-2(8)) Raincoast Bk. Distribution CAN. *Dist:* Perseus Distribution.

—Number Four, Bobby Orr! Letain, Shayne, illus. (Hockey Heroes Ser.). 32p. (J). 2006. pap. 6.95 (978-1-55192-671-1(7)); 2003. 15.95 (978-1-55192-551-6(6)) Raincoast Bk. Distribution CAN. *Dist:* Perseus Distribution.

Letain, Shayne, illus. The Goalie Mask. 2004. (Hockey Heroes Ser.). 32p. (J). 15.95 (978-1-55192-703-9(9)) Raincoast Bk. Distribution CAN. *Dist:* Perseus Distribution.

Lewis, Maggie. Morgy Coast to Coast. Chesworth, Michael, illus. 2005. 144p. (J). (gr. 3-5). 15.00 (978-0-618-44896-8(9)) Houghton Mifflin Co. Trade & Reference Div.

MacGregor, Roy. The Complete Screech Owls, Vol. 1. 2005. 488p. (J). pap. 15.95 (978-0-7710-5484-6(X) , Screech Owls) McClelland & Stewart CAN. *Dist:* Random Hse., Inc.

—Danger in Dinosaur Valley. Banning, Gregory C., illus. 1999. (Screech Owls Ser.: No. 10). 128p. (J). (gr. 4-7). mass mkt. 4.95 (978-0-7710-5620-8(6) , Screech Owls) McClelland & Stewart CAN. *Dist:* Random Hse., Inc.

—Death down Under. 2001. (Screech Owls Ser.: No. 15). (Illus.). 128p. (J). (gr. 4-7). mass mkt. 4.95 (978-0-7710-5644-4(3) , Screech Owls) McClelland & Stewart CAN. *Dist:* Random Hse., Inc.

—Forever: The Annual Hockey Classic. Deines, Brian, illus. 2005. 64p. (J). 22.95 (978-0-88995-306-2(6)) Red Deer Pr. CAN. *Dist:* Fitzhenry & Whiteside, Ltd.

—The Ghost of the Stanley Cup. Banning, Gregory C., illus. 1999. (Screech Owls Ser.: No. 11). 128p. (J). (gr. 4-7). mass mkt. 4.95 (978-0-7710-5622-2(2) , Screech Owls) McClelland & Stewart CAN. *Dist:* Random Hse., Inc.

—Horror on River Road. 2000. (Screech Owls Ser.: No. 14). (Illus.). 128p. (J). (gr. 4-7). mass mkt. 4.95 (978-0-7710-5643-7(5) , Screech Owls) McClelland & Stewart CAN. *Dist:* Random Hse., Inc.

—Nightmare in Nagano. Banning, Gregory C., illus. 1998. (Screech Owls Ser.: No. 9). 120p. (J). (gr. 4-7). mass mkt. 3.95 (978-0-7710-5619-2(2) , Screech Owls) McClelland & Stewart CAN. *Dist:* Random Hse., Inc.

—The Quebec City Crisis. Banning, Gregory C., illus. 1998. (Screech Owls Ser.: No. 7). 120p. (J). (gr. 4-7). mass mkt. 4.95 (978-0-7710-5617-8(6) , Screech Owls) McClelland & Stewart CAN. *Dist:* Random Hse., Inc.

—The Screech Owls's Home Loss. Banning, Gregory C., illus. 1998. (Screech Owls Ser.: No. 8). 128p. (J). (gr. 4-7). mass mkt. 4.95 (978-0-7710-5618-5(4) , Screech Owls) McClelland & Stewart CAN. *Dist:* Random Hse., Inc.

—The Secret of the Deep Woods. 2003. 128p. (J). (gr. 4 up). mass mkt. 4.95 (978-0-7710-5646-8(X) , Screech Owls) McClelland & Stewart CAN. *Dist:* Random Hse. of Canada, Ltd., Random Hse., Inc.

—Sudden Death in New York City. 2000. (Screech Owls Ser.: No. 13). (Illus.). 128p. (J). (gr. 4-7). mass mkt. 3.95 (978-0-7710-5642-0(7) , Screech Owls) McClelland & Stewart CAN. *Dist:* Random Hse., Inc.

—The West Coast Murders. Banning, Gregory C., illus. 2000. (Screech Owls Ser.: No. 12). 128p. (J). (gr. 4-7). mass mkt. 4.95 (978-0-7710-5623-9(0) , Screech Owls) McClelland & Stewart CAN. *Dist:* Random Hse., Inc.

Mahony, Mary. Stand Tall, Harry. Pasternack, Susan, ed. Larkin, Catherine, illus. 2002. 200p. (J). (gr. 4). pap. 14.95 (978-0-9658879-2-2(8)) Redding Pr.

Maloney, Peter. The Magic Hockey Stick. Zekauskas, Felicia, illus. 2001. 40p. (J). pap. 5.99 (978-0-14-230015-2(2) , Puffin) Penguin Group (USA) Inc.

—The Magic Hockey Stick. 2001. (978-0-606-22510-6(2)) Tandem Library Bks.

—Magic Hockey Stick. 2001. (gr. k-3). lib. bdg. 14.15 (978-0-613-44400-2(0)) Tandem Library Bks.

—The Magic Hockey Stick. ed. 2001. (J). (gr. 1). spiral bd. (978-0-616-07240-0(6)); (gr. 2). spiral bd. (978-0-616-07241-7(4)) Canadian National Institute for the Blind/Institut National Canadien pour les Aveugles.

Maloney, Peter & Zekauskas, Felicia. The Magic Hockey Stick. Arico, Diane, ed. 1999. (Illus.). 40p. (J). (ps-3). 16.99 (978-0-8037-2476-1(4) , Dial) Penguin Group (USA) Inc.

Mantell, Paul, text. Cool As Ice: Cool As Ice: the #1 Sports Series for Kids. ed. 2005. (Sports Classics III Ser.). 148p. (J). lib. bdg. 15.00 (978-1-59054-751-9(9)) Fitzgerald Bks.

Marzollo, Jean. Hockey Hero. 1999. (Hello Reader! Ser.). (Illus.). (J). (978-0-606-18560-8(7)) Tandem Library Bks.

Marzollo, Jean & Marzollo, Dave. Hockey Hero. Kelley, True, illus. 1999. (Hello Reader! Ser.: Level 3). 32p. (J). (gr. 1-3). pap. 3.99 (978-0-590-38397-4(3) , Cartwheel Bks.) Scholastic, Inc.

McFarlane, Brian. Kapuskasing Kids. 12th ed. 2008. 200p. pap. 6.95 (*978-1-55168-285-3(0)) Key Porter Bks. CAN. *Dist:* Perseus Distribution.

—On the Hockey Highway, Vol. 2. 2nd ed. 2007. (Mitchell Brothers Ser.). 220p. pap. 6.95 (*978-1-55168-245-7(1)) Key Porter Bks. CAN. *Dist:* Perseus Distribution.

—The Season of Surprises. 9th ed. 2008. 184p. pap. 6.95 (*978-1-55168-300-3(8)) Key Porter Bks. CAN. *Dist:* Perseus Distribution.

—The Stanley Cup Dream. 6th ed. 2007. 200p. (J). (gr. 3-7). pap. 6.95 (*978-1-55168-259-4(1)) Key Porter Bks. CAN. *Dist:* Perseus Distribution.

McFarlane, Leslie. Leslie Mcfarlane's Hockey Stories, 2 vols. 2006. (Illus.). 176p. (J). 13.95 (*978-1-55263-848-4(0)) Key Porter Bks. CAN. *Dist:* Perseus Distribution.

—McGonigle Scores! 2006. 256p. (J). pap. 9.95 (*978-1-55263-834-7(0)) Key Porter Bks. CAN. *Dist:* Perseus Distribution.

McGugan, Jim. Bridge 6. ed. 2004. (Illus.). (J). (gr. k-3). spiral bd. (978-0-616-01721-0(9)) Canadian National Institute for the Blind/Institut National Canadien pour les Aveugles.

—Bridge 6. Mills, Judith Christine, illus. 1999. 15p. (J). (ps-3). 16.95 (978-0-7737-3137-0(7)) Stoddart Kids CAN. *Dist:* Fitzhenry & Whiteside, Ltd.

McMahon, Patricia. The Mystery of the Morphing Hockey Stick. Manders, John, illus. 2004. 138p. (J). lib. bdg. 15.38 (*978-1-4242-0403-8(8)) Fitzgerald Bks.

Mizzoni, Chris, illus. Clancy with the Puck. 2007. 32p. (J). (ps up). 16.95 (*978-1-55192-804-3(3)) Raincoast Bk. Distribution CAN. *Dist:* Perseus Distribution.

Moore-Malinos, Jennifer & Roca, Nuria. Ganar no es Todo! Winning Isn't Everything (Spanish Edition) Fabrega, Marta, illus. 2007. (Vive y Aprende Ser.). (SPA.). 32p. (J). (ps-2). pap. 6.99 (*978-0-7641-3792-1(1)) Barron's Educational Series, Inc.

—Winning Isn't Everything! Fabrega, Marta, illus. 2007. (Live & Learn Ser.). 32p. (J). (ps-2). pap. 6.99 (*978-0-7641-3791-4(3)) Barron's Educational Series, Inc.

Myers, Bill. My Life as a Human Hockey Puck. Mangiat, Jeff, illus. 2005. (Incredible Worlds of Wally McDoogle Ser.: Vol. 7). 128p. (J). (ps-7). 9.99 (978-1-4003-0639-8(6)) Nelson, Thomas Inc.

Paulsen, Gary. Dancing Carl. 2001. (YA). 21.25 (978-0-8446-7183-3(5)) Smith, Peter Pub., Inc.

Richmond, Sandra. Shoot to Score. 1999. (gr. 7-12). lib. bdg. 13.55 (978-0-613-23480-1(4)) Tandem Library Bks.

Salata, Estelle. Blue Ice. (YA). 2001. 128p. (gr. 5-9). pap. (978-1-55041-546-9(8)); 2000. 124p. (gr. 7 up). (978-1-55041-653-4(7)) Fitzhenry & Whiteside, Ltd.

—Blue Ice. 2001. (gr. 3-6). lib. bdg. 16.40 (978-0-613-53594-6(4)) Tandem Library Bks.

Scholastic, Inc. Staff. Franklin's Big Hockey Game. 2002. (gr. k-3). lib. bdg. 14.15 (978-0-613-72043-4(1)) Tandem Library Bks.

Schultz Nicholson, Lorna. Against the Boards. 2005. (Sports Stories Ser.). 112p. (J). (gr. 3-8). (*978-1-55028-865-0(2)); 7.95 (978-1-55028-864-3(4)) Lorimer, James & Co., Ltd., Pubs. CAN. *Dist:* Casemate Pubs. & Bk. Distributors, LLC.

—Delaying the Game. 2005. (Sports Stories Ser.). 112p. (J). (gr. 3-8). (*978-1-55028-895-7(4)); 7.95 (978-1-55028-894-0(6)) Lorimer, James & Co., Ltd., Pubs. CAN. *Dist:* Casemate Pubs. & Bk. Distributors, LLC.

—Northern Star. 2006. (Sports Stories Ser.). 112p. (J). (gr. 3-8). (*978-1-55028-911-4(X)); 7.95 (978-1-55028-910-7(1)) Lorimer, James & Co., Ltd., Pubs. CAN. *Dist:* Casemate Pubs. & Bk. Distributors, LLC.

—Roughing. 2004. (Sports Stories Ser.). 112p. (J). (gr. 4-8). (*978-1-55028-859-9(8)); 7.95 (978-1-55028-858-2(X)) Lorimer, James & Co., Ltd., Pubs. CAN. *Dist:* Casemate Pubs. & Bk. Distributors, LLC.

—Too Many Men. 2006. (Sports Stories Ser.). 128p. (J). (gr. 3-8). (*978-1-55028-949-7(7)); 7.95 (*978-1-55028-948-0(9)) Lorimer, James & Co., Ltd., Pubs. CAN. *Dist:* Casemate Pubs. & Bk. Distributors, LLC.

Schwartz, Ellen. Yossi's Goal. 2006. (Illus.). 144p. (J). pap. 5.95 (978-1-55143-492-6(X)) Orca Bk. Pubs. USA.

Scudamore, Beverly. Misconduct. 2004. (Sports Stories Ser.). 112p. (J). (gr. 4-8). (*978-1-55028-855-1(5)); 7.95 (978-1-55028-854-4(7)) Lorimer, James & Co., Ltd., Pubs. CAN. *Dist:* Casemate Pubs. & Bk. Distributors, LLC.

Shaw, Mary. Brady Brady & the B Team, 12 vols. Temple, Chuck, illus. l.t. ed. 2006. 32p. (J). per. (*978-1-897169-09-4(4)) Brady Brady, Inc.

—Brady Brady & the Big Mistake, 11vols. Temple, Chuck, illus. l.t. ed. 2004. 32p. (J). per. (978-0-9735557-4-5(2)) Brady Brady, Inc.

—Brady Brady & the Big Mistake. Temple, Chuck, illus. 2002. 32p. (ps-3). 4.95 (978-0-7737-6304-3(X)) Stoddart Kids CAN. *Dist:* Fitzhenry & Whiteside, Ltd.

—Brady Brady & the Great Exchange, 11 vols. Temple, Chuck, illus. l.t. ed. 2003. 32p. (J). per. (978-0-9735557-5-2(0)) Brady Brady, Inc.

—Brady Brady & the Great Exchange. Temple, Chuck, illus. 2002. 32p. (gr. k-3). 4.95 (978-0-7737-6303-6(1)) Stoddart Kids CAN. *Dist:* Fitzhenry & Whiteside, Ltd.

—Brady Brady & the Great Exchange. 2003. (gr. k-3). lib. bdg. 12.95 (978-0-613-81881-0(4)) Tandem Library Bks.

—Brady Brady & the Great Rink, 11 vols. Temple, Chuck, illus. l.t. ed. 2004. 32p. (J). per. (978-0-9735557-0-7(X)) Brady Brady, Inc.

—Brady Brady & the Great Rink. Temple, Chuck, illus. 2002. (Brady Brady Ser.). 32p. (ps-3). 4.95 (978-0-7737-6224-4(8)) Stoddart Kids CAN. *Dist:* Fitzhenry & Whiteside, Ltd.

—Brady Brady & the MVP, 11 vols. Temple, Chuck, illus. l.t. ed. 2004. 32p. (J). per. (978-0-9735557-7-6(7)) Brady Brady, Inc.

—Brady Brady & the MVP. Temple, Chuck, illus. 2004. 32p. (J). (gr. k-3). (978-1-55005-094-3(X)) Fitzhenry & Whiteside, Ltd.

—Brady Brady & the Puck on the Pond, 11 vols. Temple, Chuck, illus. l.t. ed. 2005. 32p. (J). per. (978-1-897169-07-0(8)) Brady Brady, Inc.

—Brady Brady & the Runaway Goalie, 11 vols. Temple, Chuck, illus. l.t. ed. 2004. 32p. (J). per. (978-0-9735557-1-4(8)) Brady Brady, Inc.

—Brady Brady & the Runaway Goalie. Temple, Chuck, illus. 2002. (Brady Brady Ser.). 32p. (ps-3). 4.95 (978-0-7737-6225-1(6)) Stoddart Kids CAN. *Dist:* Fitzhenry & Whiteside, Ltd.

—Brady Brady & the Singing Tree, 11 vols. Temple, Chuck, illus. l.t. ed. 2004. 32p. (J). per. (978-0-9735557-3-8(4)) Brady Brady, Inc.

—Brady Brady & the Singing Tree. Temple, Chuck, illus. 2002. 32p. 4.95 (978-0-7737-6272-5(8)) Stoddart Kids CAN. *Dist:* Fitzhenry & Whiteside, Ltd.

—Brady Brady & the Twirlin' Torpedo, 11 vols. Temple, Chuck, illus. l.t. ed. 2004. 32p. (J). per. (978-0-9735557-2-1(6)) Brady Brady, Inc.

—Brady Brady & the Twirlin' Torpedo. Temple, Chuck, illus. 2002. 32p. (ps-3). 4.95 (978-0-7737-6271-8(X)) Stoddart Kids CAN. *Dist:* Fitzhenry & Whiteside, Ltd.

Skuy, David. Off the Crossbar. 2005. 182p. (YA). pap. 13.50 (978-1-59411-105-1(7)) Writers' Collective, The.

Slodovnick, Avi & Siemiatycki, Jack. The Hockey Card. Barrette, Doris, illus. 2002. 32p. (J). (gr. 1-5). (978-1-894222-65-5(2)) Lobster Pr.

Stevenson, James. Sam the Zamboni Man. Stevenson, Harvey, illus. 2000. 30p. (YA). (gr. 9-11). reprint ed. 15.00 (978-0-7881-6924-3(6)) DIANE Publishing Co.

Swan, Bill. Deflection. 2004. (Sports Stories Ser.). 112p. (J). (gr. 4-8). (*978-1-55028-853-7(9)); 7.95 (978-1-55028-852-0(0)) Lorimer, James & Co., Ltd., Pubs. CAN. *Dist:* Casemate Pubs. & Bk. Distributors, LLC.

Teamwork Time. 2006. 16p. (J). pap. 1.99 (978-0-7847-1708-0(7) , 04169) Standard Publishing.

Tibo, Gilles. Alex & Sarah. Germain, Philippe, illus. 2005. (Read-It! Readers Ser.). 32p. (J). (ps). lib. bdg. 18.60 (978-1-4048-1352-6(7)) Picture Window Bks.

—Alex & the Game of the Century. Germain, Philippe, illus. 2005. (Read-It! Readers Ser.). 32p. (J). (gr. k-3). 18.60 (978-1-4048-1079-2(X)) Picture Window Bks.

—Alex & the New Equipment Level 3. Germain, Philippe, illus. 2000. 32p. (J). (gr. 1-4). pap. (978-1-894363-09-9(4)) Dominique & Friends.

—Alex & the Team Jersey. Germain, Philippe, illus. 2005. (Read-It! Readers Ser.). 32p. (J). (gr. k-3). 18.60 (978-1-4048-1024-2(2)) Picture Window Bks.

—Alex & the Team Sweater Level Three. Germain, Philippe, illus. 2000. 32p. (J). (gr. 1-4). pap. (978-1-894363-00-6(0)) Dominique & Friends.

—Alex & Toolie. Germain, Philippe, illus. 2005. (Read-It! Readers Ser.). 32p. (C). (gr. k-3). 18.60 (978-1-4048-1027-3(7)) Picture Window Bks.

Tibo, Gilles, et al. Alex & Hockey-Playing Dog. 2000. (Illus.). (J). (gr. 1-4). pap. (978-1-894363-43-3(4)) Dominique & Friends.

Vandervelde, Beatrice. Home Ice. 2004. (Sports Stories Ser.). 104p. (J). (gr. 4-8). (*978-1-55028-863-6(6)); 7.95 (978-1-55028-862-9(8)) Lorimer, James & Co., Ltd., Pubs. CAN. *Dist:* Casemate Pubs. & Bk. Distributors, LLC.

Walsh, Ann. Shabash! 2006. 120p. (J). (gr. 3-8). pap., tchr. ed. 5.95 (978-0-88878-355-4(8) , Sandcastle Bks.) Dundurn Group, The CAN. *Dist:* Univ. of Toronto Pr.

Walters, T. E. Power Play. 2000. (gr. 7-12). lib. bdg. 18.75 (978-0-613-88312-2(8)) Tandem Library Bks.

—Power Play. 2000. 116p. (gr. 7-12). pap. 9.95 (978-0-595-09876-7(2) , Writers Club Pr.) iUniverse, Inc.

Warner, Gertrude Chandler. Hockey Mystery. 2001. (gr. 3-6). lib. bdg. 11.80 (978-0-613-30474-0(8)) Tandem Library Bks.

Wendel, Tim. My Man Stan. 2006. (J). 15.95 (978-0-9766104-7-2(7)) Arbutus Pr.

Wheeler, Lisa. Dino-Hockey. Gott, Barry, illus. 2007. (Carolrhoda Picture Bks.). 32p. (J). (gr. k-4). 16.95 (*978-0-8225-6191-0(3) , Carolrhoda Bks.) Lerner Publishing Group.

Zamboni Brez. 2003. 183p. (J). (gr. 4-8). pap. 11.95 (978-0-9721839-1-8(4)) BLR Bks.

HOGS

see Pigs

HOGWARTS SCHOOL OF WITCHCRAFT AND WIZARDRY (IMAGINARY PLACE)—FICTION

Harry Potter & the Chamber of Secrets. 2002. (Harry Potter Ser.). (Illus.). (J). 15.23 (978-0-7587-4426-5(9)) Book Wholesalers, Inc.

Harry Potter & the Sorcerer's Stone. 2002. (Harry Potter Ser.). (Illus.). (J). 15.23 (978-0-7587-0016-2(4)) Book Wholesalers, Inc.

Magical Movie Scenes from Harry Potter & the Sorcerer's Stone: A Poster Book. movie tie-in ed. 2001. (Illus.). 32p. (YA). (gr. 1 up). mass mkt. 6.99 (978-0-439-34256-8(2)) Scholastic, Inc.

Rowling, J. K. Harry Potter & the Chamber of Secrets. braille ed. 1999. (Harry Potter Ser.: Year 2). 520p. (YA). (gr. 3 up). pap. 17.99 (978-0-939173-35-8(2)) National Braille Pr.

—Harry Potter & the Chamber of Secrets. 2003. 203p. 23.95 (978-7-02-003344-7(X) , HAP02) People's Literature Publishing Hse. CHN. *Dist:* China Bks. & Periodicals, Inc.

—Harry Potter & the Chamber of Secrets. unabr. ed. 2004. (Harry Potter Ser.: Year 2). 352p. (J). (gr. 3 up). pap. 46.00 incl. audio (978-0-8072-8207-6(3) , S YA 137 SP, Listening Library) Random Hse. Audio Publishing Group.

—Harry Potter & the Chamber of Secrets. (RUS., Illus.). 28.95 (978-5-8451-0947-7(7)) Rosmen-Izdat RUS. *Dist:* Distribooks, Inc.

—Harry Potter & the Chamber of Secrets. 2003. (Harry Potter Ser.: Year 2). 352p. (J). 24.95 (978-0-439-55489-3(6) , Levine, Arthur A. Bks.) Scholastic, Inc.

—Harry Potter & the Chamber of Secrets. GrandPré, Mary, illus. (Harry Potter Ser.: Year 2). (J). 2002. 448p. mass mkt. 6.99 (978-0-439-42010-5(5) , Levine, Arthur A. Bks.); 2000. 352p. (gr. 3 up). mass mkt. 8.99 (978-0-439-06487-3(2)) Scholastic, Inc.

—Harry Potter & the Chamber of Secrets. Mark, Mona, illus. 2000. (Harry Potter Ser.: Year 2). 16p. (YA). (gr. 3 up). pap. 5.95 (978-0-439-21114-7(X)) Scholastic, Inc.

—Harry Potter & the Chamber of Secrets. GrandPré, Mary, illus. (Harry Potter Ser.: Year 2). 352p. (J). 1999. (gr. 3 up). 22.99 (978-0-439-06486-6(4)); 2002. 75.00 (978-0-439-20353-1(8)) Scholastic, Inc. (Levine, Arthur A. Bks.).

—Harry Potter & the Chamber of Secrets. 2000. (Harry Potter Ser.: Year 2). (YA). (gr. 3 up). 13.64 (978-0-606-19181-4(X)) Tandem Library Bks.

—Harry Potter & the Chamber of Secrets. l.t. ed. 2003. 464p. 13.95 (978-1-59413-001-4(9)) Thorndike Pr.

—Harry Potter & the Chamber of Secrets. GrandPré, Mary, illus. l.t. ed. 2000. (Harry Potter Ser.: Year 2). 464p. (gr. 3 up). 24.95 (978-0-7862-2273-5(5) , Large Print Pr.) Thorndike Pr.

—Harry Potter & the Deathly Hallows. braille ed. 2007. (Harry Potter Ser.: Year 7). 34.99 (***978-0-939173-57-0(3)***) National Braille Pr.

—Harry Potter & the Deathly Hallows. GrandPré, Mary, illus. 2007. (Harry Potter Ser.: Year 7). 784p. (J). (gr. 4-7). 34.99 (***978-0-545-01022-1(5)***); 784p. (YA). (gr. 6 up). 39.99 (***978-0-545-02936-0(8)***); 816p. (J). 65.00 (***978-0-545-02937-7(6)***) Scholastic, Inc. (Levine, Arthur A. Bks.).

—Harry Potter & the Deathly Hallows. l.t. ed. 2007. (Harry Potter Ser.: Year 7). (YA). 34.95 (***978-0-7862-9665-1(8)***) Thorndike Pr.

—Harry Potter & the Goblet of Fire. braille ed. 2000. (Harry Potter Ser.: Year 4). 650p. (YA). (gr. 3 up). pap. 25.95 (978-0-939173-37-2(9)) National Braille Pr.

—Harry Potter & the Goblet of Fire. 2003. (Harry Potter Ser.: Year 4). 752p. (J). 30.95 (978-0-439-55490-9(X) , Levine, Arthur A. Bks.) Scholastic, Inc.

—Harry Potter & the Goblet of Fire. GrandPré, Mary, illus. 2002. (Harry Potter Ser.: Year 4). 752p. (J). (gr. 3 up). mass mkt. 9.99 (978-0-439-13960-1(0) , Levine, Arthur A. Bks.) Scholastic, Inc.

—Harry Potter & the Goblet of Fire. 2000. (Harry Potter Ser.: Year 4). (Illus.). 16p. (YA). (gr. 3 up). pap. 5.95 (978-0-439-23194-7(9)) Scholastic, Inc.

—Harry Potter & the Goblet of Fire. GrandPré, Mary, illus. 2000. (Harry Potter Ser.: Year 4). 752p. (J). (gr. 3 up). 29.99 (978-0-439-13959-5(7) , Levine, Arthur A. Bks.) Scholastic, Inc.

—Harry Potter & the Goblet of Fire. 2002. (gr. 3-6). lib. bdg. 17.60 (978-0-613-49674-2(4)) Tandem Library Bks.

—Harry Potter & the Goblet of Fire. l.t. ed. 2003. 936p. 14.95 (978-1-59413-003-8(5)) Thorndike Pr.

—Harry Potter & the Goblet of Fire. GrandPré, Mary, illus. l.t. ed. 2000. (Harry Potter Ser.: Year 4). 936p. (gr. 3 up). 25.95 (978-0-7862-2927-7(6) , Large Print Pr.) Thorndike Pr.

—Harry Potter & the Half-Blood Prince, 9 vols. braille ed. 2005. (Harry Potter Ser.: 6). (YA). 29.99 (978-0-939173-39-6(5) , HALF) National Braille Pr.

—Harry Potter & the Half-Blood Prince. 2003. (Harry Potter Ser.). 496p. 24.95 (***978-7-02-005323-0(8)*** , HAP06) People's Literature Publishing Hse. CHN. *Dist:* China Bks. & Periodicals, Inc.

—Harry Potter & the Half-Blood Prince. GrandPré, Mary, illus. (J). 2005. (Harry Potter Ser.: Year 6). 672p. 34.99 (978-0-439-78677-5(0)); 2005. (Harry Potter Ser.: Year 6). 672p. 29.99 (978-0-439-78454-2(9)); 2005. (Harry Potter Ser.: Year 6). 704p. 60.00 (978-0-439-79132-8(4)); 2006. 672p. reprint ed. pap. 9.99 (978-0-439-78596-9(0)) Scholastic, Inc. (Levine, Arthur A. Bks.).

—Harry Potter & the Half-Blood Prince. l.t. ed. 2005. (Harry Potter Ser.: Year 6). 832p. 29.95 (978-0-7862-7745-2(9) , Large Print Pr.) Thorndike Pr.

—Harry Potter & the Order of the Phoenix, 13 vols. braille ed. 2003. (Harry Potter Ser.: Year 5). (YA). 29.99 (978-0-939173-38-9(7)) National Braille Pr.

—Harry Potter & the Order of the Phoenix. GrandPré, Mary, illus. 2003. (Harry Potter Ser.: Year 5). (J). (gr. 3-6). 896p. 34.99 (978-0-439-56761-9(0)); 870p. 29.99 (978-0-439-35806-4(X)); 896p. 60.00 (978-0-439-56762-6(9)) Scholastic, Inc.

—Harry Potter & the Order of the Phoenix. l.t. ed. 2003. (Harry Potter Ser.: Year 5). 1093p. 29.95 (978-0-7862-5778-2(4) , Large Print Pr.) Thorndike Pr.

—Harry Potter & the Prisoner of Azkaban. 2002. (Harry Potter Ser.). (Illus.). (YA). 16.26 (978-0-7587-5662-6(3)) Book Wholesalers, Inc.

—Harry Potter & the Prisoner of Azkaban. braille ed. 1999. (Harry Potter Ser.: Year 3). (YA). (gr. 3 up). pap. 19.95 (978-0-939173-36-5(0)) National Braille Pr.

—Harry Potter & the Prisoner of Azkaban. 2000. (J). tchr. ed. 9.95 (978-1-58130-656-9(3)); stu. ed. 11.95 (978-1-58130-657-6(1)) Novel Units, Inc.

—Harry Potter & the Prisoner of Azkaban. 2004. (Harry Potter Ser.: Year 3). 560p. mass mkt. 7.99 (978-0-439-65548-4(X) , Scholastic Paperbacks) Scholastic, Inc.

—Harry Potter & the Prisoner of Azkaban. GrandPré, Mary, illus. (Harry Potter Ser.: Year 3). 448p. (gr. 3 up). 2001. (YA). mass mkt. 8.99 (978-0-439-13636-5(9) , Levine, Arthur A. Bks.); 1999. (J). 22.99 (978-0-439-13635-8(0)) Scholastic, Inc.

—Harry Potter & the Prisoner of Azkaban. 2001. (gr. 3-6). lib. bdg. 16.45 (978-0-613-37106-3(2)) Tandem Library Bks.

—Harry Potter & the Prisoner of Azkaban. l.t. ed. 2003. 592p. 13.95 (978-1-59413-002-1(7)) Thorndike Pr.

—Harry Potter & the Prisoner of Azkaban. GrandPré, Mary, illus. l.t. ed. 2000. (Harry Potter Ser.: Year 3). 592p. (gr. 3 up). 24.95 (978-0-7862-2274-2(3) , Large Print Pr.) Thorndike Pr.

—Harry Potter & the Sorcerer's Stone. unabr. ed. (Harry Potter Ser.: Year 1). 320p. (gr. 3 up). (YA). pap. 62.00 incl. audio (978-0-8072-1547-0(3)); 2004. (J). pap. 46.00 incl. audio (978-0-8072-8119-2(0) , S YA 108 SP) Random Hse. Audio Publishing Group. (Listening Library).

—Harry Potter & the Sorcerer's Stone. GrandPré, Mary, illus. 2001. (Harry Potter Ser.: Year 1). 400p. (J). (gr. 3 up). mass mkt. 6.99 (978-0-439-36213-9(X)) Scholastic, Inc.

—Harry Potter & the Sorcerer's Stone. 2000. (Harry Potter Ser.: Year 1). (Illus.). 16p. (YA). (gr. 3 up). pap. 5.95 (978-0-439-21116-1(6)) Scholastic, Inc.

—Harry Potter & the Sorcerer's Stone. GrandPré, Mary, illus. (Harry Potter Ser.: Year 1). 320p. (gr. 3 up). 1999. (YA). mass mkt. 8.99 (978-0-590-35342-7(X)); 1998. (J). pap. 22.99 (978-0-590-35340-3(3) , Levine, Arthur A. Bks.) Scholastic, Inc.

—Harry Potter & the Sorcerer's Stone. collector's ed. 2000. (Harry Potter Ser.: Year 1). 320p. (YA). (gr. 3 up). 75.00 (978-0-439-20352-4(X)) Scholastic, Inc.

—Harry Potter & the Sorcerer's Stone. l.t. ed. 2003. 423p. 13.95 (978-1-59413-000-7(0)) Thorndike Pr.

—Harry Potter & the Sorcerer's Stone. GrandPré, Mary, illus. l.t. ed. 1999. (Harry Potter Ser.: Year 1). 422p. (gr. 3 up). 24.95 (978-0-7862-2272-8(7) , Large Print Pr.) Thorndike Pr.

—Harry Potter Boxed Set, Bks. 1-7. 2007. (Harry Potter Ser.: Years 1-7). (J). 195.00 (***978-0-545-04425-7(1)*** , Levine, Arthur A. Bks.) Scholastic, Inc.

—Harry Potter Boxed Set: Harry Potter & the Sorcerer's Stone; Harry Potter & the Chamber of Secrets; Harry Potter & the Prisoner of Azkaban, 3 vols. GrandPré, Mary, illus. (Harry Potter Ser.: Years 1-3). (YA). 2002. pap. 21.97 (978-0-439-32466-3(1)); 1999. (gr. 3 up). 55.85 (978-0-439-13316-6(5)) Scholastic, Inc. (Levine, Arthur A. Bks.).

—Harry Potter Boxed Set: Harry Potter & the Sorcerer's Stone; Harry Potter & the Chamber of Secrets; Harry Potter & the Prisoner of Azkaban; Harry Potter & the Goblet of Fire, 4 vols. GrandPré, Mary, illus. 2000. (Harry Potter Ser.: Years 1-4). (YA). (gr. 3 up). 85.80 (978-0-641-06631-3(7) , Levine, Arthur A. Bks.) Scholastic, Inc.

—Harry Potter Coffret: Harry Potter a l'Ecole des Sorciers; Harry Potter et la Chambre des Secrets; Harry Potter et le Prisonnier d'Azkaban. 1999. (Harry Potter Ser.: Years 1-3). Tr. of Harry Potter Boxed Set: Harry Potter & the Chamber of Secrets; Harry Potter & the Sorcerer's Stone; Harry Potter & the Prisoner of Azkaban. (FRE.). (YA). (gr. 3 up). pap. 43.95 (978-2-07-052929-2(0)) Gallimard, Editions FRA. *Dist:* Distribooks, Inc.

—Harry Potter Coffret: Harry Potter a l'Ecole des Sorciers; Harry Potter et la Chambre des Secrets; Harry Potter et le Prisonnier d'Azkaban; Harry Potter et la Coupe de Feu. 1999. (Harry Potter Ser.: Years 1-3). Tr. of Harry Potter Boxed Set: Harry Potter & the Chamber of Secrets; Harry Potter & the Sorcerer's Stone; Harry Potter & the Prisoner of Azkaban; Harry Potter et la COupe de Feu. (FRE.). 1400p. (YA). (gr. 3 up). pap. 34.95 (978-0-320-03843-3(2)) French & European Pubns., Inc.

—Harry Potter e a Camara Secreta. (POR.). pap. 28.95 (978-85-325-1166-9(X)) Rocco, Editora, Ltda BRA. *Dist:* Distribooks, Inc.

—Harry Potter e a Pedra Filosofal. (POR.). pap. 28.95 (978-85-325-1101-0(5)) Rocco, Editora, Ltda BRA. *Dist:* Distribooks, Inc.

—Harry Potter e a Prisioneiro de Azkaban. (POR.). pap. 29.95 (978-85-325-1206-2(2)) Rocco, Editora, Ltda BRA. *Dist:* Distribooks, Inc.

—Harry Potter e o Calice de Fogo. (POR.). pap. 38.95 (978-85-325-1252-9(6)) Rocco, Editora, Ltda BRA. *Dist:* Distribooks, Inc.

—Harry Potter et la Chambre des Secrets. 1999. (Harry Potter Ser.: Year 2). Tr. of Harry Potter & the Chamber of Secrets. (FRE.). (YA). (gr. 3 up). pap. 13.95 (978-0-320-03778-8(9)) French & European Pubns., Inc.

—Harry Potter et la Chambre des Secrets. 1999. (Harry Potter Ser.: Year 2). Tr. of Harry Potter & the Chamber of Secrets. (FRE., Illus.). 358p. (YA). (gr. 3 up). pap. 16.95 (978-2-07-052455-6(8)) Gallimard, Editions FRA. *Dist:* Distribooks, Inc.

—Harry Potter et la Coupe de Feu. 2001. (Harry Potter Ser.: Year 4). Tr. of Harry Potter & the Goblet of Fire. (FRE.). (YA). (gr. 3 up). pap. 34.95 (978-0-320-03932-4(3)) French & European Pubns., Inc.

—Harry Potter et la Coupe de Feu.Tr. of Harry Potter & the Goblet of Fire. (FRE., Illus.). 766p. pap. 19.95 (978-2-07-054351-9(X)) Gallimard, Editions FRA. *Dist:* Distribooks, Inc.

—Harry Potter et le Prisonnier d'Azkaban. 1999. (Harry Potter Ser.: Year 3). Tr. of Harry Potter & the Prisoner of Azkaban. (FRE.). 465p. (YA). (gr. 3 up). pap. 16.95 (978-2-07-052818-9(9)) Gallimard, Editions FRA. *Dist:* Distribooks, Inc.

—Harry Potter et l'Ecole des Sorciers. 3rd ed. 1998. (Harry Potter Ser.: Year 1). Tr. of Harry Potter & the Sorcerer's Stone. (FRE., Illus.). (YA). (gr. 3 up). pap. 14.95 (978-2-07-050142-7(6)) Distribooks, Inc.

—Harry Potter et l'Ecole des Sorciers. 1999. (Harry Potter Ser.: Year 1). Tr. of Harry Potter & the Sorcerer's Stone. (FRE.). (YA). (gr. 3 up). pap. 16.95 (978-0-320-03780-1(0)) French & European Pubns., Inc.

—Harry Potter et l'Ecole des Sorciers.Tr. of Harry Potter & the Sorcerer's Stone. 2007. 311p. pap. 14.95 (***978-2-07-061236-9(8)***); 2000. (FRE.). (J). pap. 14.95 (978-2-07-051426-7(9)) Gallimard, Editions FRA. *Dist:* Distribooks, Inc.

—Harry Potter und der Gefangene von Azkaban. 1999. (Harry Potter Ser.: Year 3). Tr. of Harry Potter & the Prisoner of Azkaban. (GER.). (YA). (gr. 3 up). pap. 34.95 (978-3-551-55169-6(3)) Carlsen Verlag DEU. *Dist:* Distribooks, Inc.

—Harry Potter und der Stein der Weisen. 1999. (Harry Potter Ser.: Year 1). (GER.). 335p. (YA). (gr. 3 up). pap. 34.95 (978-3-551-55167-2(7)) Carlsen Verlag DEU. *Dist:* Distribooks, Inc.

—Harry Potter und die Kammer des Schreckens. 1999. (Harry Potter Ser.: Year 2). Tr. of Harry Potter & the Chamber of Secrets. (GER.). (YA). (gr. 3 up). pap. 36.95 (978-3-551-55168-9(5)) Carlsen Verlag DEU. *Dist:* Distribooks, Inc.

—Harry Potter y el Prisionero de Azkaban. 2000. (Harry Potter Ser.: Year 3). (SPA.). 359p. (YA). (gr. 3 up). 16.95 (978-84-7888-568-8(4)) Baker & Taylor Bks.

—Harry Potter y el Prisionero de Azkaban. 2004. (Harry Potter Ser.: Year 3). (SPA., Illus.). 360p. (gr. 3 up). 17.95 (978-84-7888-519-0(6) , SAL1889) Emece Editores ESP. *Dist:* Lectorum Pubns., Inc.

—Harry Potter y el Prisionero de Azkaban. 2000. (Harry Potter Ser.: Year 3). (SPA.). (YA). (gr. 3 up). 16.95 (978-0-320-03783-2(5)) French & European Pubns., Inc.

—Harry Potter y el Prisionero de Azkaban. 2001. (Harry Potter Ser.: Year 3). (SPA.). (YA). (gr. 3 up). (978-0-606-88519-5(6)) Tandem Library Bks.

—Harry Potter y la Camara Secreta. 2004. (Harry Potter Ser.: Year 2). (SPA., Illus.). 288p. (YA). (gr. 3 up). 15.95 (978-84-7888-495-7(5) , SAL4595) Emece Editores ESP. *Dist:* Lectorum Pubns., Inc.

—Harry Potter y la Camara Secreta. 1999. (Harry Potter Ser.: Year 2). (SPA.). (YA). (gr. 3 up). 14.95 (978-0-320-03781-8(9)) French & European Pubns., Inc.

—Harry Potter y la Camara Secreta. 2001. (Harry Potter Ser.: Year 2). (SPA.). (YA). (gr. 3 up). (978-0-606-88495-2(5)) Tandem Library Bks.

—Harry Potter y la Piedra Filosofal. 2004. (Harry Potter Ser.: Bk. 1). (SPA., Illus.). 256p. (YA). (gr. 7 up). 15.95 (978-84-7888-445-2(9) , SAL2819) Emece Editores ESP. *Dist:* Lectorum Pubns., Inc.

—Harry Potter y la Piedra Filosofal. 1999. (Harry Potter Ser.: Year 1). (SPA.). (YA). (gr. 3 up). 14.95 (978-0-320-03782-5(7)) French & European Pubns., Inc.

—Harry Potter y la Piedra Filosofal. 2001. (Harry Potter Ser.: Year 1). (SPA.). (YA). (gr. 3 up). (978-0-606-88445-7(9)) Tandem Library Bks.

Rowling, J. K. & Dale, Jim. Harry Potter & the Goblet of Fire. unabr. ed. 2004. (Harry Potter Ser.). 752p. (J). pap. 65.00 incl. audio (978-0-8072-1196-0(6) , S YA 270 SP, Listening Library) Random Hse. Audio Publishing Group.

Scholastic, Inc. Staff. Prisoner of Azkaban Movie Lenticular Poster Book. Reisfeld, Randi, ed. 2004. (Harry Potter Ser.). 16p. (J). pap. 9.99 (978-0-439-62562-3(9) , Scholastic Paperbacks) Scholastic, Inc.

HOISTING MACHINERY

see also Cranes, Derricks, etc.; Elevators

Whitehouse, Patricia. Maquinas Que Se Mueven. 2007. (SPA & ENG., Illus.). 24p. (J). (***978-1-60044-277-3(3)***) Rourke Publishing, LLC.

HOLIDAY COOKERY

see also Christmas Cookery

Barchers, Suzanne I. & Rauen, Peter J. Holiday Storybook Stew: Cooking Through the Year with Books Kids Love. 1998. (Illus.). 128p. (gr. k-6). pap. 15.95 (978-1-55591-972-6(3)) Fulcrum Publishing.

Bastyra, Judy & Ward, Catherine. Hanukkah Fun: Great Things to Make & Do. 2003. (Holiday Fun Ser.). (Illus.). 32p. (J). (gr. 3-5). pap. 4.95 (978-0-7534-5684-2(2) , Kingfisher) Houghton Mifflin Co. Trade & Reference Div.

Chronicle Books Staff, contrib. by. Homemade Halloween: Fun-To-Make Crafts & Treats. 2003. (Illus.). 32p. (J). pap. 9.95 (978-0-8118-4016-3(6)) Chronicle Bks. LLC.

Cornell, Kari A., ed. Holiday Cooking Around the World. Wolfe, Robert L. & Wolfe, Diane, illus. Wolfe, Robert L. & Wolfe, Diane, photos by. 2nd rev. exp. ed. 2003. (Easy Menu Ethnic Cookbooks). 72p. (J). (gr. 5-12). pap. 7.95 (978-0-8225-4159-2(9)) Lerner Publishing Group.

Holiday Appetizers. (Illus.). 94p. (978-0-7853-5603-5(7)) Publications International, Ltd.

Larousse Kingfisher Chambers Staff. Holiday Fun. 2000. (Illus.). (J). (978-0-606-19825-7(3)) Tandem Library Bks.

Raabe, Emily. An Easter Holiday Cookbook. 2002. (Festive Foods for the Holidays Ser.). (Illus.). 24p. (J). (gr. 2-5). lib. bdg. 19.50 (978-0-8239-5624-1(5) , PowerKids Pr.) Rosen Publishing Group, Inc., The.

—A Hanukkah Holiday Cookbook. 2002. (Festive Foods for the Holidays Ser.). (Illus.). 24p. (J). (gr. 2-5). lib. bdg. 19.95 (978-0-8239-5626-5(1) , PowerKids Pr.) Rosen Publishing Group, Inc., The.

—A Passover Holiday Cookbook. 2002. (Festive Foods for the Holidays Ser.). (Illus.). 24p. (J). (gr. 2-5). lib. bdg. 19.95 (978-0-8239-5625-8(3) , PowerKids Pr.) Rosen Publishing Group, Inc., The.

—A Thanksgiving Holiday Cookbook. 2002. (Festive Foods for the Holidays Ser.). (Illus.). 24p. (J). lib. bdg. 19.95 (978-0-8239-5628-9(8) , PowerKids Pr.) Rosen Publishing Group, Inc., The.

Rauchwerger, Lisa. Chocolate Chip Challah: And Other Twists on the Jewish Holiday Table. Rauchwerger, Lisa, illus. 2004. (Illus.). 127p. (gr. k-3). pap. 17.95 (978-0-8074-0700-4(3) , 510606) URJ Pr.

Stull. Festival Foods Around-the-World. 1999. (Illus.). (J). pap. (978-0-7398-2405-4(8)) Steck-Vaughn.

Tabs, Judy & Steinberg, Barbara. Matzah Meals: A Passover Cookbook for Kids. Hauser, Bill, illus. 2004. (Passover Ser.). 64p. (J). (gr. k up). pap. 7.95 (978-1-58013-086-8(0)) Kar-Ben Publishing.

Thompson, Stuart, et al. Chinese Cookbook. 2001. (Holiday Cookbooks from Around the World). (Illus.). 32p. (J). lib. bdg. 25.69 (978-0-7398-3262-2(X)) Raintree.

White, Linda. Haunting on a Halloween: Frightful Activities for Kids. Lee, Fran, illus. 2002. 64p. (YA). pap. 9.95 (978-1-58685-112-5(8)) Gibbs Smith, Publisher.

—Haunting on a Halloween: Frightful Activities for Kids. Lee, Fran, illus. 2002. 63p. (J). (ps-ps). lib. bdg. 18.75 (978-0-613-52568-8(X)) Tandem Library Bks.

Willis, Abigail & Spenceley, Annabel. Halloween Fun: Great Things to Make & Do. 2003. (Holiday Fun Ser.). (Illus.). 32p. (J). (gr. 3-5). pap. 4.95 (978-0-7534-5683-5(4) , Kingfisher) Houghton Mifflin Co. Trade & Reference Div.

Wolfe, Robert L. & Wolfe, Diane, illus. Holiday Cooking Around the World. Wolfe, Robert L. & Wolfe, Diane, photos by. 2nd rev. exp. ed. 2002. (Easy Menu Ethnic Cookbooks). 72p. (J). (gr. 5-12). 25.26 (978-0-8225-4128-8(9) , Lerner Pubns.) Lerner Publishing Group.

HOLIDAY DECORATIONS

All New Crafts for Mother's Day & Father's Day. 2007. 48p. (J). (gr. k-4). pap. 7.95 (***978-0-8225-6368-6(1)*** , First Avenue Editions) Lerner Publishing Group.

American Girl Editorial Staff. Have a Molly Halloween. 2004. (Illus.). 56p. (J). 15.95 (978-1-58485-889-8(3)) American Girl Publishing, Inc.

Beaton, Clare. Halloween Fun. 2004. (Fun Activity Ser.). (Illus.). 24p. (J). pap., act. bk. ed. 4.95 (978-0-7641-2750-2(0)) Barron's Educational Series, Inc.

Bledsoe, Karen E. Chinese New Year Crafts. 2005. (Fun Holiday Crafts Kids Can Do Ser.). (Illus.). 32p. (J). lib. bdg. 22.60 (978-0-7660-2347-5(8) , Enslow Elementary) Enslow Pubs., Inc.

Chronicle Books Staff, contrib. by. Homemade Halloween: Fun-To-Make Crafts & Treats. 2003. (Illus.). 32p. (J). pap. 9.95 (978-0-8118-4016-3(6)) Chronicle Bks. LLC.

Civardi, Anne & King, Penny. Festival Decorations. 1998. (Craft Workshop Ser.). (Illus.). 32p. (J). (gr. 3). pap. (978-0-86505-790-6(7)); lib. bdg. (978-0-86505-780-7(X)) Crabtree Publishing Co.

Corwin, Judith Hoffman. Kwanzaa Crafts: A Holiday Craft Book. 2004. (Illus.). 48p. (J). (gr. k-4). reprint ed. pap. 6.00 (978-0-7567-7711-1(9)) DIANE Publishing Co.

Draw 50 Holiday Decorations. 2002. (Draw 50 Ser.). (Illus.). (J). 17.60 (978-0-7587-4703-7(9)) Book Wholesalers, Inc.

Erlbach, Arlene & Erlbach, Herbert. Mother's Day Crafts. 2005. (Fun Holiday Crafts Kids Can Do Ser.). (Illus.). 32p. (J). lib. bdg. 22.60 (978-0-7660-2348-2(6) , Enslow Elementary) Enslow Pubs., Inc.

Fun for Little Hands Series, 7 bks., Set. 2003. (Illus.). (J). 21.33 (978-0-929371-92-4(5)) Kar-Ben Publishing.

Gnojewski, Carol. Cinco de Mayo Crafts. 2005. (Fun Holiday Crafts Kids Can Do Ser.). (Illus.). 32p. (J). lib. bdg. 22.60 (978-0-7660-2344-4(3) , Enslow Elementary) Enslow Pubs., Inc.

—Earth Day Crafts. 2005. (Fun Holiday Crafts Kids Can Do Ser.). (Illus.). 32p. (J). lib. bdg. 22.60 (978-0-7660-2346-8(X) , Enslow Elementary) Enslow Pubs., Inc.

Gordon, Lynn. 52 Activities for Jewish Holidays. 2004. (Illus.). 52p. 6.95 (978-0-8118-4124-5(3)) Chronicle Bks. LLC.

Holabird, Katharine. Tip-Top Christmas Crafts. Craig, Helen, illus. 2006. (Angelina Ballerina Ser.). 40p. (J). (ps-3). pap. 5.99 (978-0-448-44387-4(2) , Grosset & Dunlap) Penguin Group (USA) Inc.

Irvine, Joan. How to Make Holiday Pop-Ups. Hendry, Linda, illus. 2004. 64p. (J). (gr. 4-8). reprint ed. pap. 7.00 (978-0-7567-7507-0(8)) DIANE Publishing Co.

Kawasaki, Shauna Mooney. Ghostly Frights for Halloween Nights. 2002. (Illus.). 96p. pap. 6.95 (978-1-4027-0118-4(7)) Sterling Publishing Co., Inc.

King, Penny & Roundhill, Clare. Spooky Things. 1998. (Making Pictures Ser.). (J). 21.36 (978-1-57572-195-8(3)) Rigby Education.

Lerner, Linda, et al. 101 Holiday Crafts for Year-Round Fun. 2003. (Illus.). 72p. (J). (978-0-7853-8909-5(1)) Publications International, Ltd.

McGee, Randel. Paper Crafts for Chinese New Year. 2008. (Paper Craft Fun for Holidays Ser.). (Illus.). 48p. (J). (gr. 3-4). lib. bdg. 23.93 (***978-0-7660-2950-7(6)*** , Enslow Elementary) Enslow Pubs., Inc.

—Paper Crafts for Day of the Dead. 2008. (Paper Craft Fun for Holidays Ser.). (Illus.). 48p. (J). (gr. 3-4). lib. bdg. 23.93 (***978-0-7660-2951-4(4)*** , Enslow Elementary) Enslow Pubs., Inc.

Numeroff, Laura Joffe. Easter Egg Designs. Date not set. (J). 7.99 (978-0-694-01419-4(2)) HarperCollins Pubs.

O'Brien, Joan. Decorating Easter Eggs. 2001. (Illus.). 4p. (J). pap. 1.50 (978-0-486-41841-4(3)) Dover Pubns., Inc.

Robinson, Fay. Father's Day Crafts. 2005. (Fun Holiday Crafts Kids Can Do Ser.). (Illus.). 32p. (J). lib. bdg. 22.60 (978-0-7660-2343-7(5) , Enslow Elementary) Enslow Pubs., Inc.

—Halloween Crafts. 2004. (Fun Holiday Crafts Kids Can Do Ser.). (Illus.). 32p. (J). lib. bdg. 22.60 (978-0-7660-2236-2(6)) Enslow Pubs., Inc.

Ross, Kathy. All New Crafts for Halloween. Leonard, Barbara, illus. 2003. (All New Holiday Crafts for Kids Ser.). 48p. lib. bdg. 23.90 (978-0-7613-2554-3(9)); (J). pap. 7.95 (978-0-7613-1577-3(2)) Lerner Publishing Group. (Millbrook Pr.).

—All New Crafts for Halloween. 2003. (gr. k-3). lib. bdg. 16.40 (978-0-613-88977-3(0)) Tandem Library Bks.

HI

—All New Crafts for Thanksgiving. Holm, Sharon Lane, illus. (J). (gr. k-2). 2005. 48p. pap. 7.95 (978-0-7613-2394-5(5) , First Avenue Editions); 2004. lib. bdg. 25.26 (978-0-7613-2922-0(6) , Millbrook Pr.) Lerner Publishing Group.

—More of the Best Holiday Crafts Ever! Holm, Sharon Lane, illus. 2005. 160p. (J). (gr. k-4). bds. 19.95 (978-0-7613-2345-7(7)) Lerner Publishing Group.

—Star-Spangled Crafts. 2003. (gr. k-3). lib. bdg. 16.40 (978-0-613-59022-8(8)) Tandem Library Bks.

Schaefer, Lola M. Jack-o-Lanterns. Saunders-Smith, Gail, ed. 1998. (Fall Fun Ser.). (Illus.). 24p. (J). (gr. k-1). lib. bdg. 15.93 (978-0-7368-0105-8(7) , Pebble Bks.) Capstone Pr., Inc.

Small, B. Crafty Easter Eggs. 1999. (Illus.). 16p. (978-1-874735-63-2(8)) B Small Publishing.

Smolinski, Jill. Holiday Origami. Fraser, Mary Ann, illus. 2nd rev. ed. 1999. (Origami Ser.). 48p. (gr. 3-7). pap. 8.95 (978-0-7373-0094-9(9) , 9780737300949) McGraw-Hill Cos., The.

—Holiday Origami. 1999. (gr. 3-6). lib. bdg. 17.60 (978-0-613-73742-5(3)) Tandem Library Bks.

Souter, Gillian. Holiday Handiwork. Watson, Clare, illus. Martin, Andre, photos by. 2002. (Handy Crafts Ser.). 48p. (J). (gr. 2 up). lib. bdg. 24.67 (978-0-8368-3050-7(4)) Stevens, Gareth Inc.

Visca, Curt & Visca, Kelley. How to Draw Cartoon Holiday Symbols. 2004. (Kid's Guide to Drawing Ser.). (Illus.). 24p. (J). lib. bdg. 21.25 (978-0-8239-6726-1(3) , PowerKids Pr.) Rosen Publishing Group, Inc., The.

White, Linda. Haunting on a Halloween: Frightful Activities for Kids. Lee, Fran, illus. 2002. 64p. (YA). pap. 9.95 (978-1-58685-112-5(8)) Gibbs Smith, Publisher.

—Haunting on a Halloween: Frightful Activities for Kids. Lee, Fran, illus. 2002. 63p. (J). (ps-ps). lib. bdg. 18.75 (978-0-613-52568-8(X)) Tandem Library Bks.

Willis, Abigail & Spenceley, Annabel. Halloween Fun: Great Things to Make & Do. 2003. (Holiday Fun Ser.). (Illus.). 32p. (J). (gr. 3-5). pap. 4.95 (978-0-7534-5683-5(4) , Kingfisher) Houghton Mifflin Co. Trade & Reference Div.

HOLIDAYS

see also Fasts and Feasts

also names of holidays, e.g. Fourth of July

American Holidays. 2004. (Illus.). lib. bdg. 7.95 (978-0-8225-4780-8(5)) Lerner Publishing Group.

Aminah, Ibrahim Ali. The Three Muslim Festivals. Ghazi, A., ed. Hadzic, Aldin, illus. l.t. ed. 1998. 68p. (J). (gr. 4-7). 9.00 (978-1-56316-308-1(X)) IQRA International Educational Foundation.

Ancona, George. Mis Fiestas. 32p. (J). 2006. (SPA.). (gr. 1-3). pap. 8.95 (978-0-516-25497-5(9)); 2005. (ENG & SPA.). 21.00 (978-0-516-25290-2(9)) Scholastic Library Publishing. (Children's Pr.).

Andrade, Mary J. The Vigil of Little Angels, Day of the Dead in Mexico. Murguia, Jose, illus. 2001. 36p. (J). (gr. 1-6). 19.95 (978-0-9665876-3-0(4)) La Oferta Publishing Co.

Ansary, Mir Tamim. Arbor Day. 2006. (Holiday Histories Ser.). (Illus.). 32p. (J). (***978-1-4034-8882-4(7)***) Heinemann Library.

—Columbus Day. 2006. (Illus.). 32p. (J). (***978-1-4034-8883-1(5)***) Heinemann Library.

—El Día de Accion de Gracias. 2003. (SPA.). 32p. (J). pap. 6.95 (978-1-4034-3030-4(6)) Heinemann Library.

—El Día de los Caídos. 2003. Tr. of Flag Day. (SPA.). 32p. (J). pap. 6.95 (978-1-4034-3028-1(4)) Heinemann Library.

—El Día de los Caidos. 2003. (Historias de Fiestas Ser.).Tr. of Flag Day. (SPA., Illus.). 32p. (J). lib. bdg. 22.79 (978-1-4034-3005-2(5)) Heinemann Library.

—El Día de los Caidos. 2003. Tr. of Flag Day. (SPA.). (gr. k-3). lib. bdg. 14.75 (978-0-613-86893-8(5)) Tandem Library Bks.

—El Día de Martin Luther King, Jr. 2003. Tr. of Martin Luther King, Jr. Day. (SPA.). 32p. (J). pap. 6.95 (978-1-4034-3027-4(6)) Heinemann Library.

—El Día de Martin Luther King, Jr. 2003. Tr. of Martin Luther King, Jr. Day. (SPA.). (gr. k-3). lib. bdg. 14.75 (978-0-613-86892-1(7)) Tandem Library Bks.

—Earth Day. (Holiday Histories Ser.). (Illus.). 32p. (J). 2006. (***978-1-4034-8884-8(3)***); 2001. lib. bdg. 21.36 (978-1-58810-220-1(3)) Heinemann Library.

—Earth Day. 2001. 13.75 (978-0-606-22384-3(3)) Tandem Library Bks.

—Election Day. (Holiday Histories Ser.). (Illus.). 32p. (J). (gr. k-2). 2001. lib. bdg. 21.36 (978-1-58810-221-8(1)); 2nd ed. 2006. (***978-1-4034-8885-5(1)***) Heinemann Library.

—Flag Day. (Heinemann First Library). (Illus.). (J). (gr. k-2). 2001. 32p. lib. bdg. 21.36 (978-1-58810-222-5(X)); 2nd ed. 2006. 31p. (***978-1-4034-8886-2(X)***) Heinemann Library.

—Flag Day. 2001. (Holiday Histories Ser.). 13.75 (978-0-606-22382-9(7)) Tandem Library Bks.

—Independence Day. 2006. (Illus.). 32p. (J). (***978-1-4034-8887-9(8)***) Heinemann Library.

—Martin Luther King, Jr. Day. (Illus.). 32p. (J). 2006. (***978-1-4034-8889-3(4)***); 2002. pap. 6.95 (978-1-58810-432-8(X) , 91160); 1999. lib. bdg. 21.36 (978-1-57572-873-5(7)) Heinemann Library.

—Martin Luther King Jr. Day. 2002. (Illus.). 32p. (J). (gr. k-3). lib. bdg. 14.75 (978-0-613-36108-8(3)) Tandem Library Bks.

—Memorial Day. 32p. (J). 2006. (Illus.). (***978-1-4034-8890-9(8)***); 2002. (Illus.). pap. 6.95 (978-1-58810-433-5(8) , 91161); 1999. lib. bdg. 21.36 (978-1-57572-874-2(5)) Heinemann Library.

—President's Day. (Holiday Histories Ser.). 32p. (J). (gr. k-2). 2002. (Illus.). pap. 6.95 (978-1-58810-434-2(6) , 91162); 1999. lib. bdg. 21.36 (978-1-57572-875-9(3)) Heinemann Library.

—Presidents' Day. 2006. (Illus.). 32p. (J). (***978-1-4034-8891-6(6)***) Heinemann Library.

—Thanksgiving Day. 2001. (Holiday Histories Ser.). (Illus.). 32p. (J). (gr. k-2). lib. bdg. 21.36 (978-1-58810-224-9(6)) Heinemann Library.

—Veteran's Day. (Holiday Histories Ser.). 32p. (J). (gr. k-2). 2002. (Illus.). pap. 6.95 (978-1-58810-435-9(4) , 91163); 1999. lib. bdg. (978-1-57572-876-6(1)) Heinemann Library.

Ansary, Mir Tamim. Veterans Day. 2006. (Holiday Histories Ser.). (Illus.). 32p. (J). (***978-1-4034-8893-0(2)***) Heinemann Library.

Ansary, Tamim. Earth Day. 2002. (Holiday Histories Ser.). (Illus.). 32p. (J). (gr. k-2). pap. 6.95 (978-1-58810-570-7(9) , 91685) Heinemann Library.

Barchers, Suzanne I. & Rauen, Peter J. Holiday Storybook Stew: Cooking Through the Year with Books Kids Love. 1998. (Illus.). 128p. (gr. k-6). pap. 15.95 (978-1-55591-972-6(3)) Fulcrum Publishing.

Barth, Edna. Lilies, Rabbits, & Painted Eggs: The Story of the Easter Symbols. Arndt, Ursula, illus. 2001. 64p. (gr. 4-6). (J). tchr. ed. 16.00 (978-0-618-09646-6(9)); (YA). pap. 7.95 (978-0-618-09648-0(5)) Houghton Mifflin Co. Trade & Reference Div. (Clarion Bks.).

—Shamrocks, Harps, & Shillelaghs: The Story of the St. Patrick's Day Symbols. 2001. (J). (978-0-606-20909-0(3)); (gr. 3-6). lib. bdg. 16.40 (978-0-613-35567-4(9)) Tandem Library Bks.

Batchlor, Larry G. Juneteenth Story Activity & Coloring Book: From African Slaves to African Americans. Goings, Kenneth & La Rue, Linda, eds. Walker, Felix C., illus. l.t. ed. 2000. 60p. (J). (gr. 4-7). pap. 10.00 (978-0-9701357-0-4(X)) Jubilee Day/Juneteenth Celebration.

Becker, Michelle Aki. Groundhog Day. 2003. (Rookie Read-About Holidays Ser.). (Illus.). (J). 32p. 20.50 (978-0-516-25883-6(4)); 31p. (gr. 1-2). pap. 5.95 (978-0-516-27924-4(6)) Scholastic Library Publishing. (Children's Pr.).

—Groundhog Day. 2003. (gr. k-3). lib. bdg. 14.10 (978-0-613-63599-8(X)) Tandem Library Bks.

Berg, Elizabeth. Ethiopia. 1999. (Festivals of the World Ser.). (Illus.). 32p. (J). (gr. 3 up). lib. bdg. 24.67 (978-0-8368-2032-4(0)) Stevens, Gareth Inc.

—USA (Festivals of the World) 1999. (Festivals of the World Ser.). (Illus.). 32p. (J). (gr. 3 up). lib. bdg. 24.67 (978-0-8368-2028-7(2)) Stevens, Gareth Inc.

Berger, Gilda. Celebrate! Stories of the Jewish Holidays. Catalanotto, Peter, illus. 2002. 128p. (J). (gr. k-3). pap. 8.99 (978-0-439-43052-4(6) , Scholastic Paperbacks) Scholastic, Inc.

—Celebrate! Stories of the Jewish Holidays. 2002. (gr. 5-8). lib. bdg. 17.60 (978-0-613-50189-7(6)) Tandem Library Bks.

Berger, Samantha & Daniel, Moreton. Celebrations. 1999. (ps-2). lib. bdg. 10.10 (978-0-613-21314-1(9)) Tandem Library Bks.

Berger, Samantha & Moreton, Daniel. Celebrations. 1999. (Social Studies Emergent Readers). (J). 2.50 (978-0-439-04557-5(6)) Scholastic, Inc.

Best Holiday Books, 17 bks., Set. (Illus.). (J). (gr. 1-4). lib. bdg. 322.15 (978-0-89490-337-3(3)) Enslow Pubs., Inc.

Big Book Holidays. 2004. (ps-2). pap. 11.99 (978-0-7647-0971-5(2)) School Specialty Publishing.

Bijan, Nancy N. Let's Celebrate! Bijan, Nancy N., illus. l.t. ed. 1998. (Second Ser.). (Illus.). 22p. (J). (ps-6). pap. 6.95 (978-1-880710-19-7(6)) Monterey Pacific Pubs.

Birenbaum, Barbara. Groundhog Willie's Shadow. 2001. (Story Within a Story Ser.). (Illus.). iii, 29p. (J). (gr. 3-5). 19.95 (978-0-935343-74-8(1)) Peartree.

Bodden, Valerie. Thanksgiving. 2005. (My First Look at Holidays Ser.). (Illus.). 24p. (gr. k-3). 15.95 (978-1-58341-370-8(7) , Creative Education) Creative Co., The.

Boothroyd, Jennifer. Holidays. 2006. (First Step Nonfiction Ser.). (Illus.). 8p. (J). pap. (978-0-8225-5728-9(2) , Lerner Pubns.) Lerner Publishing Group.

Borst, Donna & Mitchell, Judy, eds. The Best of Holidays & Seasonal Celebrations: Arts & Crafts. 2001. (Illus.). 128p. (J). (ps-3). pap. 13.95 (978-1-57310-280-3(6)) Teaching & Learning Co.

—The Best of Holidays & Seasonal Celebrations, PreK-K, Issues 5-8. 2000. (Illus.). 320p. (J). pap., tchr. ed. 24.95 (978-1-57310-235-3(0)) Teaching & Learning Co.

Braham, Clare B. & Esche, Maria Bonfanti. Kids Celebrate! Activities for Special Days Throughout the Year. Jones, Mary, illus. 1998. 304p. (J). (ps). pap. 17.95 (978-1-55652-292-5(4)) Chicago Review Pr., Inc.

Bredeson, Carmen. Purim. 2003. (Rookie Read. . . Holidays Ser.). (Illus.). 32p. (J). 20.50 (978-0-516-25880-5(X) , Children's Pr.) Scholastic Library Publishing.

—St. Patrick's Day. 2003. (Rookie Read-About Holidays Ser.). (Illus.). 32p. (J). 20.50 (978-0-516-25857-7(5) , Children's Pr.) Scholastic Library Publishing.

Brill, Marlene Targ. Veterans Day. Wang, Qi Z., illus. 2005. (On My Own Holidays Ser.). 48p. (J). (gr. k-3). pap. 5.95 (978-1-57505-766-8(2)) Lerner Publishing Group.

Brode, Robyn. April. 2003. (Weekly Reader Early Learning Library). (Illus.). 24p. (J). (ps-2). pap. 7.93 (978-0-8368-3615-8(4)); lib. bdg. 19.33 (978-0-8368-3579-3(4)) Stevens, Gareth Inc. (Weekly Reader Early Learning Library).

—December. 2003. (Illus.). 24p. (J). pap. (978-0-8368-3623-3(5)); lib. bdg. 19.33 (978-0-8368-3587-8(5) , Weekly Reader Early Learning Library) Stevens, Gareth Inc.

—February. 2003. (Weekly Reader Early Learning Library). (Illus.). 24p. (J). (ps-2). pap. 7.93 (978-0-8368-3613-4(8)); lib. bdg. 19.33 (978-0-8368-3577-9(8)) Stevens, Gareth Inc. (Weekly Reader Early Learning Library).

—January. 2003. (Weekly Reader Early Learning Library). (Illus.). 24p. (J). (ps-2). pap. 7.93 (978-0-8368-3612-7(X)); lib. bdg. 19.33 (978-0-8368-3576-2(X)) Stevens, Gareth Inc. (Weekly Reader Early Learning Library).

—July. 2003. (Weekly Reader Early Learning Library). (Illus.). 24p. (J). (ps-2). pap. 7.93 (978-0-8368-3618-9(9)); lib. bdg. 19.33 (978-0-8368-3582-3(4)) Stevens, Gareth Inc. (Weekly Reader Early Learning Library).

—June. 2003. (Weekly Reader Early Learning Library). (Illus.). 24p. (J). (ps-2). pap. 7.93 (978-0-8368-3617-2(0)); lib. bdg. 19.33 (978-0-8368-3581-6(6)) Stevens, Gareth Inc. (Weekly Reader Early Learning Library).

—March. (Months of the Year Ser.). (Illus.). 24p. (J). (ps up). lib. bdg. 19.33 (978-0-8368-3578-6(6)); 2003. pap. 7.93 (978-0-8368-3614-1(6)) Stevens, Gareth Inc. (Weekly Reader Early Learning Library).

—May. 2003. (Weekly Reader Early Learning Library). (Illus.). 24p. (J). (ps-2). pap. 7.93 (978-0-8368-3616-5(2)); lib. bdg. 19.33 (978-0-8368-3580-9(8)) Stevens, Gareth Inc. (Weekly Reader Early Learning Library).

—November. 2003. (Illus.). 24p. (J). pap. (978-0-8368-3622-6(7)); lib. bdg. 19.33 (978-0-8368-3586-1(7) , Weekly Reader Early Learning Library) Stevens, Gareth Inc.

—October. 2003. (Illus.). 24p. (J). pap. (978-0-8368-3621-9(9)); lib. bdg. 19.33 (978-0-8368-3585-4(9) , Weekly Reader Early Learning Library) Stevens, Gareth Inc.

—September. 2003. (Illus.). 24p. (J). pap. (978-0-8368-3620-2(0)); lib. bdg. 19.33 (978-0-8368-3584-7(0) , Weekly Reader Early Learning Library) Stevens, Gareth Inc.

Bulla, Clyde Robert. The Story of Valentine's Day. 1999. (gr. 3-6). lib. bdg. 14.10 (978-0-613-22450-5(7)) Tandem Library Bks.

Button, Beth & Mitchell, Judy, eds. The Best of Holidays & Seasonal Celebrations: Kid Space - School Yard Learning Adventures. 2000. (Illus.). 128p. (J). (ps-3). pap., tchr. ed. 13.95 (978-1-57310-261-2(X)) Teaching & Learning Co.

Cabot, Meg. Holiday Princess. McLaren, Chesley, illus. 2005. (Princess Diaries). 144p. (J). 12.99 (978-0-06-075434-1(6)) HarperCollins Pubs.

Ceremonies & Celebrations, 6 bks., Set. Incl. Births. Dineen, Jacqueline. lib. bdg. 25.69 (978-0-7398-3267-7(0)); Feasts & Fasting. Marchant, Kerena. Sloan, Frank, ed. lib. bdg. 25.69 (978-0-7398-3268-4(9)); Growing Up. Behar, Susan. Sloan, Frank, ed. lib. bdg. 25.69 (978-0-7398-3269-1(7)); Life's End. Broadbent, Lynne & Chaplin, Denise. Sloan, Frank, ed. lib. bdg. 25.69 (978-0-7398-3270-7(0)); Pilgrimages & Journeys. Kendall, Sue. Sloan, Frank, ed. lib. bdg. 25.69 (978-0-7398-3271-4(9)); Weddings. Sonntag, Linda. lib. bdg. 25.69 (978-0-7398-3272-1(7)); 32p. (J). (ps-3). 2001. (Illus.). 2001. Set lib. bdg. 154.14 (978-0-7398-3273-8(5)) Raintree.

Chambers, Catherine. All Saints, All Souls & Halloween. 1999. (World of Holidays Ser.). (Illus.). 32p. (J). (gr. 2-5). pap. 6.95 (978-0-7398-1383-6(8)) Steck-Vaughn.

—All Saints, All Souls & Halloween. 2000. (Illus.). (J). (978-0-606-18476-2(7)) Tandem Library Bks.

—Carnival. 1998. (World of Holidays Ser.). (Illus.). 32p. (J). (gr. 2-5). lib. bdg. 25.69 (978-0-8172-4613-6(4)) Raintree.

Chan, Arlene. Awakening the Dragon: The Dragon Boat Festival. Zhang, Song Nan, illus. 2004. 24p. (J). (gr. 1-4). 15.95 (978-0-88776-656-5(0)) Tundra Bks., Inc./Livres Toundra, Inc. CAN. *Dist:* Random Hse., Inc.

Chan, Hingman. Celebrating Chinese New Year. Yoon, Selina, ed. 2004. (Illus.). 32p. (J). pap., act. bk. ed. 7.95 (978-1-932457-04-9(6) , Asia for Kids) Infini Pr., LLC.

Chancellor, Deborah. Holiday! Celebration Days Around the World. 2000. (Eyewitness Readers Ser.: 2). (J). 10.79 (978-0-606-20122-3(X)) Tandem Library Bks.

—Holiday! Celebration Days Around the World. 2000. (gr. k-3). lib. bdg. 11.80 (978-0-613-32645-2(8)) Tandem Library Bks.

Chancellor, Deborah & Dorling Kindersley Publishing Staff. Holiday! Celebration Days Around the World. 2000. (Readers Ser.). (Illus.). 32p. (J). (gr. 1-3). pap. 3.99 (978-0-7894-5711-0(3)); (ps-3). 12.95 (978-0-7894-5710-3(5)) Dorling Kindersley Publishing, Inc.

Chin, Steven A. Dragon Parade: A Chinese New Year Story. 2000. (J). 12.80 (978-0-606-19075-6(9)) Tandem Library Bks.

Christian Bulletin Board Idea Book: Holidays & Seasons. 2006. 144p. (J). (gr. 1-6). 15.99 (978-1-4206-7070-7(0)) Teacher Created Resources, Inc.

Cipriano, Jeri S. Celebraciones. 2005. (ENG & SPA.). (J). 15.93 (978-0-7368-4173-3(3)) Yellow Umbrella Pr.

—Celebrations. 2003. (Illus.). 17p. (J). 15.93 (978-0-7368-2925-0(3)); pap. (978-0-7368-2884-0(2)) Yellow Umbrella Pr.

Clark, Anne, et al. Hanukkah. 1998. (World of Holidays Ser.). (Illus.). 32p. (gr. 2-5). lib. bdg. 25.70 (978-0-8172-4614-3(2)) Raintree.

Collins, Stanley H., et al. Holidays & Celebrations. Schneider, Jane & Kifer, Kathy, illus. 1999. (Beginning Sign Language Ser.). 32p. (J). pap. 6.95 (978-0-931993-10-7(5)) Garlic Pr.

Colon Garcia, Aurora. Cinco de Mayo. 2003. (Holiday Histories Ser.). (Illus.). 32p. (J). pap. 6.50 (978-1-4034-3686-3(X)); lib. bdg. (978-1-4034-3501-9(4)) Heinemann Library.

Cooper, Jason. Earth Day. 2002. (Rourke Discovery Library). (Illus.). 24p. (J). lib. bdg. 20.64 (978-1-58952-218-3(4)) Rourke Publishing, LLC.

—Flag Day. 2002. 24p. (J). lib. bdg. 20.64 (978-1-58952-219-0(2)) Rourke Publishing, LLC.

—Kwanzaa. 2002. (Illus.). 24p. (J). lib. bdg. 20.64 (978-1-58952-220-6(6)) Rourke Publishing, LLC.

Cooper, Walsh. Holiday Celebrations. 2002. (Holidays & Festivals Ser.). 165.14 (978-1-58952-216-9(8)) Rourke Publishing, LLC.

Coppendale, Jean. Special Holidays. 2006. (Illus.). 32p. (YA). (gr. 1 up). lib. bdg. 27.10 (978-1-931983-98-3(4)) Chrysalis Education.

Cotton, Jacqueline S. Memorial Day. 2002. (Rookie Read-About Holidays Ser.). (Illus.). 32p. (J). (gr. 1-2). pap. 5.95 (978-0-516-27369-3(8) , Children's Pr.) Scholastic Library Publishing.

—Memorial Day. 2002. (Illus.). 31p. (J). (ps-3). lib. bdg. 14.10 (978-0-613-54017-9(4)) Tandem Library Bks.

—Veterans Day. 2002. (Rookie Read-About Holidays Ser.). (Illus.). 32p. (J). (gr. 1-2). pap. 20.50 (978-0-516-22672-9(X)); pap. 5.95 (978-0-516-27499-7(6)) Scholastic Library Publishing. (Children's Pr.).

—Veterans Day. 2002. (gr. k-3). lib. bdg. 14.10 (978-0-613-54376-7(9)) Tandem Library Bks.

Cretin, Nadine. Livre des Fetes. 2000. Tr. of Book of Holidays. (FRE.). (J). 17.95 (978-2-07-059364-4(9)) Gallimard, Editions FRA. *Dist:* AIMS International Bks., Inc.

de Jongh, Tim & Vandyck, William. How to Have the Best Holiday Ever. Rowe, Alan, illus. 96p. pap. 7.99 (978-0-340-66730-9(3) , Coronet) Hodder General Publishing Division GBR. *Dist:* Trafalgar Square Publishing.

Dean, Sheri. Memorial Day. 2006. (Illus.). 24p. (J). pap. 5.95 (978-0-8368-6514-1(6)); (ENG & SPA., pap. 5.95 (978-0-8368-6528-8(6)); lib. bdg. 19.33 (978-0-8368-6507-3(3)); (ENG & SPA., lib. bdg. 19.33 (978-0-8368-6521-9(9)) Stevens, Gareth Inc.

Demi. Kites: Magic Wishes That Fly up to the Sky. 2000. (gr. k-3). lib. bdg. 15.30 (978-0-613-28339-7(2)) Tandem Library Bks.

DeSpain, Pleasant. Tales of Holidays, Vol. 5. Bell, Don, illus. 2002. (Books of Nine Lives: Vol. 5). 80p. (gr. 4-7). 14.95 (978-0-87483-667-7(0)) August Hse. Pubs., Inc.

Dillon, Susan, et al. Scholastic Big Book of Holidays Around the Year. 2003. 128p. pap. 14.95 (978-0-439-48809-9(5) , Teaching Resources) Scholastic, Inc.

Disney Press Staff. Celebrate the Year with Winnie. 1999. 208p. (J). 19.99 (978-0-7868-3262-0(2)) Disney Pr.

Ditchfield, Christin. Memorial Day. 2003. (True Book Ser.). (Illus.). 48p. (J). 25.00 (978-0-516-22783-2(1) , Children's Pr.) Scholastic Library Publishing.

DK Publishing. Celebrations Around the World. 2008. 16p. (J). pap. 2.49 (***978-0-7566-3316-5(8)***) Dorling Kindersley Publishing, Inc.

Douglas, Lloyd G. Let's Get Ready for Earth Day. 2003. (gr. k-3). lib. bdg. 12.95 (978-0-613-59660-2(9)) Tandem Library Bks.

—Let's Get Ready for Martin Luther King, Jr. Day. 2003. (Wel-Celebrations Ser.). (Illus.). 24p. (J). 17.00 (978-0-516-24259-0(8)); pap. 4.95 (978-0-516-24351-1(9)) Scholastic Library Publishing. (Children's Pr.).

—Let's Get Ready for Memorial Day. 2003. (Welcome Books Celebrations). (Illus.). 24p. (J). (ps-2). 17.00 (978-0-516-24263-7(6)); pap. 4.95 (978-0-516-24355-9(1)) Scholastic Library Publishing. (Children's Pr.).

Douglas, Susan. Ramadan. 2004. (gr. k-3). lib. bdg. 14.10 (978-0-613-79242-4(4)) Tandem Library Bks.

Douglas, Vincent & School Specialty Publishing Staff. Fun for Special Days Kit. 2005. (Book Notes Ser.). (Illus.). 64p. (J). pap. 17.95 (978-0-7696-3887-4(2) , American Education Publishing) School Specialty Publishing.

Douglass, Susan L. Ramadan. Reeves, Jeni, illus. 2004. (On My Own Holidays Ser.). 48p. (J). (gr. 2-4). lib. bdg. 25.26 (978-0-87614-932-4(8)) Lerner Publishing Group.

Douglass, Susan L & Reeves. Ramadan. 2003. (On My Own Holidays Ser.). (Illus.). 48p. (J). (gr. k-3). 5.95 (978-1-57505-584-8(8)) Lerner Publishing Group.

Drew, Rosa & Phillips, Heather. Celebrating Chinese New Year No. 4524: Nick's New Year. Kupperstein, Joel, ed. Noll, Cheryl Kirk, illus. 1999. 16p. (J). (ps-2). pap. 2.99 (978-1-57471-569-9(0)) Creative Teaching Pr., Inc.

Eriback, Arlene. Happy New Year, Everywhere! 2001. (J). (978-0-606-22056-9(9)) Tandem Library Bks.

Erlbach, Arlene. Christmas - Celebrating Life, Giving & Kindness. 2001. (Finding Out about Holidays Ser.). (Illus.). 48p. (J). (gr. 1-4). lib. bdg. 23.93 (978-0-7660-1576-0(9)) Enslow Pubs., Inc.

Erlbach, Arlene & Holm, Sharon Lane. Happy New Year Everywhere! 2001. (Single Titles Ser.). (Illus.), 48p. (gr. k-3). pap. 8.95 (978-0-7613-1488-2(1) , Millbrook Pr.) Lerner Publishing Group.

Fairview Press Staff, ed. Holiday Hope: Remembering Loved Ones During Special Times of the Year. 1998. (Illus.). 160p. pap. 10.95 (978-1-57749-074-6(6)) Fairview Pr.

Ferro, Jennifer. Brazilian Foods & Culture. 1999. (Festive Foods & Celebrations Ser.). (Illus.). 48p. (J). (gr. 3-6). lib. bdg. 27.93 (978-1-57103-301-7(7)) Rourke Publishing, LLC.

—Italian Foods & Culture. 1999. (Festive Foods & Celebrations Ser.). (Illus.). 48p. (J). (gr. 3-6). lib. bdg. 27.93 (978-1-57103-302-4(5)) Rourke Publishing, LLC.

—Moroccan Foods & Culture. 1999. (Festive Foods & Celebrations Ser.). (Illus.). 48p. (J). (gr. 3-6). lib. bdg. 27.93 (978-1-57103-304-8(1)) Rourke Publishing, LLC.

—Russian Foods & Culture. 1999. (Festive Foods & Celebrations Ser.). (Illus.). 48p. (J). (gr. 3-5). lib. bdg. 20.95 (978-1-57103-305-5(X)) Rourke Publishing, LLC.

—Vietnamese Foods & Culture. 1999. (Festive Foods & Celebrations Ser.). (Illus.). 48p. (J). (gr. 3-6). lib. bdg. 27.93 (978-1-57103-306-2(8)) Rourke Publishing, LLC.

Festival Tales, 4 bks., Set. Incl. Christian Festivals. Pirotta, Saviour & Cann, Helen. lib. bdg. 25.69 (978-0-7398-2732-1(4)); Hindu Festivals. Marchant, Kerena. lib. bdg. 25.69 (978-0-7398-2734-5(0)); Jewish Festivals. Pirotta, Saviour & Kelly, Anne M. lib. bdg. 25.69 (978-0-7398-2733-8(2)); Muslim Festivals. Marchant, Kerena. Barber, Tina, illus. lib. bdg. 25.69 (978-0-7398-2735-2(9)); 32p. (J). (gr. 4-7). 2001. Set lib. bdg. 102.76 (978-0-7398-2736-9(7)) Raintree.

Fishman, Cathy Goldberg. Hanukkah. Young, Mary O'Keefe, illus. 2004. (On My Own Holidays Ser.). 48p. (J). (gr. 2-4). lib. bdg. 25.26 (978-1-57505-195-6(8)) Lerner Publishing Group.

—On Rosh Hashanah & Yom Kippur. 2000. (J). (978-0-606-19250-7(6)) Tandem Library Bks.

—On Sukkot & Simchat Torah. Hall, Melanie W., illus. (J). (ps-4). 2006. 32p. lib. bdg. 17.95 (978-1-58013-165-0(4)); 2005. pap. (978-1-58013-166-7(2)) Kar-Ben Publishing.

—Passover. Marshall, Ann, illus. 2006. (On My Own Holidays Ser.). (J). 48p. 25.26 (978-1-57505-656-2(9)); pap. 5.95 (978-1-57505-695-1(X) , First Avenue Editions) Lerner Publishing Group.

Flanagan, Alice K. Chinese New Year. Zhurkina, Svetlana, illus. 2003. (Holidays & Festivals Ser.). 32p. (J). (gr. 3 up). lib. bdg. 22.60 (978-0-7565-0479-3(1)) Compass Point Bks.

—Cinco de Mayo. Girouard, Patrick, illus. 2003. (Holidays & Festivals Ser.). 32p. (J). (gr. 3 up). lib. bdg. 22.60 (978-0-7565-0480-9(5)) Compass Point Bks.

—Holidays & Festivals, 8 bks. Incl. Carnival. Collier-Morales, Roberta, illus. 2003. lib. bdg. 22.60 (978-0-7565-0478-6(3)); Chinese New Year. Zhurkina, Svetlana, illus. 2003. lib. bdg. 22.60 (978-0-7565-0479-3(1)); Christmas. Woodworth, Viki, illus. 2001. lib. bdg. 22.60 (978-0-7565-0085-6(0)); Cinco de Mayo. Girouard, Patrick, illus. 2003. lib. bdg. 22.60 (978-0-7565-0480-9(5)); Halloween. Girouard, Patrick, illus. 2001. lib. bdg. 22.60 (978-0-7565-0086-3(9)); Passover. Koffsky, Ann D., illus. 2003. lib. bdg. 22.60 (978-0-7565-0481-6(3)); Thanksgiving. Kelleher, Kathie, illus. 2001. lib. bdg. 22.60 (978-0-7565-0087-0(7)); Valentine's Day. Dieterichs, Shelley, illus. 2001. lib. bdg. 22.60 (978-0-7565-0088-7(5)); 32p. (J). (gr. 3 up). Set lib. bdg. 180.80 (978-0-7565-0497-7(X)) Compass Point Bks.

Foran, Jill. Christmas. 2003. (Celebrating Cultures Ser.). (Illus.). 24p. (J). lib. bdg. 15.95 (978-1-59036-091-0(5)) Weigl Pubs., Inc.

—Hanukkah. 2003. (Celebrating Cultures Ser.). (Illus.). 24p. (J). lib. bdg. 15.95 (978-1-59036-092-7(3)) Weigl Pubs., Inc.

—Martin Luther King Jr. Day. 2004. (American Holidays Ser.). (Illus.). 24p. (J). pap. 6.95 (978-1-59036-167-2(9)); lib. bdg. 17.10 (978-1-59036-107-8(5)) Weigl Pubs., Inc.

Frost, Helen. Independence Day. (National Holidays Ser.). 24p. (J). pap. 5.95 (978-0-7368-8726-7(1)) Capstone Pr., Inc.

—Martin Luther King, Jr Day. (National Holidays Ser.). 24p. (J). pap. 5.95 (978-0-7368-8727-4(X)) Capstone Pr., Inc.

—Memorial Day. (National Holidays Ser.). 24p. (J). pap. 5.95 (978-0-7368-8728-1(8)) Capstone Pr., Inc.

—Memorial Day. Saunders-Smith, Gail, ed. 2000. (National Holidays Ser.). (Illus.). 24p. (J). (gr. k-1). lib. bdg. 15.93 (978-0-7368-0544-5(3) , Pebble Bks.) Capstone Pr., Inc.

—National Holidays: Independence Day; Martin Luther King, Jr. Day; Memorial Day; President's Day, 4 bks. Saunders-Smith, Gail, ed. 2000. (Illus.). (J). (gr. k-1). lib. bdg. 58.40 (978-0-7368-0562-9(1) , Pebble Bks.) Capstone Pr., Inc.

—Presidents' Day. (National Holidays Ser.). 24p. (J). pap. 5.95 (978-0-7368-8729-8(6)) Capstone Pr., Inc.

Ganeri, Anita. The Hanukkah Story. Phillips, Rachael, illus. 2004. (Holiday Stories Ser.). (J). lib. bdg. (978-1-58340-490-4(2)) Smart Apple Media.

—The Passover Story. Phillips, Rachael, illus. 2004. (Holiday Stories Ser.). (J). lib. bdg. 22.80 (978-1-58340-491-1(0)) Smart Apple Media.

Ganz, Yaffa. Lag Ba'omer & Tu Bishvat with Bina, Benny, & Chaggai Hayonah. 1999. 27p. 9.99 (978-1-57819-155-0(6) , YTUB) Mesorah Pubns., Ltd.

Garcia, James. Cinco de Mayo. 2003. (Proud Heritage-The Hispanic Library). (Illus.). 40p. (J). (gr. 3-7). 28.50 (978-1-56766-174-3(2)) Child's World, Inc.

Garcia, Yolanda P. Celebremos. 2001. Tr. of Let's Celebrate. (SPA., Illus.). (J). (gr. 1-6). pap. 10.95 (978-0-935303-03-2(0)) Victory Publishing.

Gibbons, Gail. Groundhog Day. Gibbons, Gail, illus. 2007. (Illus.). 32p. (J). (ps-3). pap. 6.95 (***978-0-8234-2116-9(3)***) Holiday Hse., Inc.

—Groundhog Day! Gibbons, Gail, illus. (Illus.). 32p. (J). 16.95 (978-0-8234-2003-2(5)) Holiday Hse., Inc.

—Thanksgiving Is... (Illus.). 32p. (J). tchr. ed. 17.95 (978-0-8234-1849-7(9)) Holiday Hse., Inc.

Gilchrist, Cherry. A Calendar of Festivals. Cann, Helen, illus. 2006. 79p. (J). (gr. 4-8). reprint ed. pap. 10.00 (978-1-4223-5551-0(9)) DIANE Publishing Co.

—Sun-day, Moon-day: How the Week was Made. Hall, Amanda, illus. 1998. 80p. (J). (gr. 3-7). 18.95 (978-1-901223-63-7(9)) Barefoot Bks., Inc.

Gillis, Jennifer Blizin. Candle Time 123. 2002. (Candle Time Ser.). (Illus.). 24p. (J). (ps-1). pap. 5.25 (978-1-58810-742-8(6) , 91382); lib. bdg. 18.50 (978-1-58810-533-2(4)) Heinemann Library.

—Candle Time ABC. 2002. (Candle Time Ser.). (Illus.). 24p. (J). (ps-1). lib. bdg. 18.50 (978-1-58810-532-5(6)) Heinemann Library.

—Christmas. 2002. (Candle Time Ser.). (Illus.). 24p. (J). (ps-1). lib. bdg. 18.50 (978-1-58810-529-5(6)) Heinemann Library.

—Halloween. 2003. (Holiday Histories Ser.). (Illus.). 32p. (J). pap. 6.50 (978-1-4034-3691-7(6)); lib. bdg. 22.79 (978-1-4034-3506-4(5)) Heinemann Library.

—Hanukkah. 2002. (Candle Time Ser.). (Illus.). 24p. (J). (ps-1). lib. bdg. 18.50 (978-1-58810-530-1(X)) Heinemann Library.

—St. Patrick's Day. 2003. (Holiday Histories Ser.). (Illus.). 32p. (J). pap. 6.50 (978-1-4034-3689-4(4)); lib. bdg. 22.79 (978-1-4034-3504-0(9)) Heinemann Library.

Gillis, Jennifer Blizin & Jordan, Denise M. Candle Time ABC. 2002. (Candle Time Ser.). (Illus.). 24p. (J). (ps-1). pap. 5.25 (978-1-58810-741-1(8) , 91383) Heinemann Library.

—Christmas. 2002. (Candle Time Ser.). (Illus.). 24p. (J). (ps-1). pap. 5.25 (978-1-58810-738-1(8) , 91384) Heinemann Library.

—Las Posadas. 2002. (Fiestas Con Velas (Candle Time) Ser.). 24p. (J). (ps-1). (SPA.). lib. bdg. 18.50 (978-1-58810-786-2(8)); (SPA., Illus.). pap. 5.25 (978-1-58810-833-3(3) , 91592); (Illus.). pap. 5.25 (978-1-58810-740-4(X) , 91389) Heinemann Library.

Glazer, Devorah. A Touch of the High Holidays: A Touch & Feel Book. Seva, illus. 2006. 16p. (J). bds. 7.95 (978-0-8266-0020-2(4)) Merkos L'Inyonei Chinuch.

Gnojewski, Carol. Cinco de Mayo: Celebrating Hispanic Pride. 2002. (Finding Out about Holidays Ser.). (Illus.). 48p. (J). (gr. 1-4). lib. bdg. 23.93 (978-0-7660-1575-3(0)) Enslow Pubs., Inc.

—Day of the Dead: A Latino Celebration of Family & Life. 2005. (Finding Out about Holidays Ser.). (Illus.). 48p. (J). lib. bdg. 23.93 (978-0-7660-1780-1(X) , Enslow Elementary) Enslow Pubs., Inc.

—Kwanzaa: Seven Days of African-American Pride. 2004. (Finding Out about Holidays Ser.). (Illus.). 48p. (J). lib. bdg. 23.93 (978-0-7660-2209-6(9)) Enslow Pubs., Inc.

—Martin Luther King, Jr. , Day: Honoring a Man of Peace. 2002. (Finding Out about Holidays Ser.). (Illus.). 48p. (J). (gr. 1-4). lib. bdg. 23.93 (978-0-7660-1574-6(2)) Enslow Pubs., Inc.

—Ramadan: A Muslim Time of Fasting, Prayer, & Celebration. 2004. (Finding Out about Holidays Ser.). (Illus.). 48p. (J). (gr. 2-5). lib. bdg. 23.93 (978-0-7660-2275-1(7)) Enslow Pubs., Inc.

Golden Books Staff. Holidays at the Homestead. Brannon, Tom, illus. 2005. 32p. (J). (ps-2). pap. 3.99 (978-0-375-83226-0(2) , Golden Bks.) Random Hse. Children's Bks.

Greenfield Educational Center Staff. A Fun Vacation. 2000. (I Can Read Ser.: Bk. 12). (CHI & ENG., Illus.). 8p. (J). pap. 2.99 (978-962-563-105-9(4)) Greenfield Enterprises, Ltd. HKG. *Dist:* Cheng & Tsui Co.

Griffin, Robert H. & Shurgin, Ann H. Buddha's Birthday, Carnival, Christmas, Vol. 1. 2000. (Illus.). (J). (978-0-7876-3928-0(1) , UXL) Thomson Gale.

—Easter, Halloween & Festivals of the Dead, Vol. 2. 2000. (Illus.). (J). (978-0-7876-3929-7(X) , UXL) Thomson Gale.

—Hanukkah, Independence Day, Kwanzaa, Vol. 3. 2000. (Illus.). (J). (978-0-7876-3930-3(3) , UXL) Thomson Gale.

Grolier Educational Staff, contrib. by. Argentina. 2003. (Illus.). 32p. (J). (978-0-7172-5789-8(4)); (978-0-7172-5788-1(6)) Scholastic Library Publishing. (Grolier).

—Hungary. 2003. (Illus.). 32p. (J). (978-0-7172-5793-5(2) , Grolier) Scholastic Library Publishing.

—Kenya. 2003. (Illus.). 32p. (J). (978-0-7172-5795-9(9) , Grolier) Scholastic Library Publishing.

—Thailand. 2003. (Illus.). 32p. (J). (978-0-7172-5803-1(3) , Grolier) Scholastic Library Publishing.

—Tunisia. 2003. (Illus.). 32p. (J). (978-0-7172-5804-8(1) , Grolier) Scholastic Library Publishing.

Hall, Dorothy & Daniel, Marie. Guess the Covered Word for Seasons & Holidays. 2003. 48p. (J). per. 25.99 (978-0-88724-125-3(5)) Carson-Dellosa Publishing Co., Inc.

Hallinan, P. K. Holidays & Special Feelings, 8 bks. (Illus.). (J). lib. bdg. 108.60 (978-1-56674-909-1(3)) Forest Hse. Publishing Co., Inc.

Halpern, Chaiky, illus. The Hamentash That Ran Away. (J). (ps-4). 2.95 (978-0-87306-250-3(7)) Feldheim Pubs.

Hamilton, Lynn. Memorial Day. 2004. (American Holidays Ser.). (Illus.). 24p. (J). pap. 6.95 (978-1-59036-168-9(7)); lib. bdg. 17.10 (978-1-59036-105-4(9)) Weigl Pubs., Inc.

—Presidents Day. 2004. (American Holidays Ser.). (Illus.). 24p. (J). lib. bdg. 17.10 (978-1-59036-108-5(3)) Weigl Pubs., Inc.

—Presidents' Day. 2004. (American Holidays Ser.). (Illus.). 24p. (J). pap. 6.95 (978-1-59036-169-6(5)) Weigl Pubs., Inc.

Harcourt School Publishers Staff. Celebration. 3rd ed. 2002. (Illus.). pap. 5.10 (978-0-15-327695-8(9)) Harcourt Schl. Pubs.

—Holidays, Family, & Fun. 3rd ed. 2002. (Trophies English Language Learners Ser.). (Illus.). pap. 5.10 (978-0-15-327830-3(7)) Harcourt Schl. Pubs.

—Our Holidays. 3rd ed. 2002. (Horizons Ser.). (Illus.). (J). pap. 3.70 (978-0-15-333129-9(1)) Harcourt Schl. Pubs.

—School Holidays. 3rd ed. 2002. (Trophies English Language Learners Ser.). (Illus.). pap. 5.10 (978-0-15-327752-8(1)) Harcourt Schl. Pubs.

Haugen, Brenda. Christmas. Ouren, Todd, illus. 2004. (Holidays & Celebrations Ser.). 24p. (gr. k-3). 22.60 (978-1-4048-0192-9(8)) Picture Window Bks.

—Easter. Boyd, Sheree, illus. 2004. (Holidays & Celebrations Ser.). 24p. (gr. k-3). 22.60 (978-1-4048-0194-3(4)) Picture Window Bks.

—Halloween. Boyd, Sheree, illus. 2004. (Holidays & Celebrations Ser.). 24p. (gr. k-3). 22.60 (978-1-4048-0195-0(2)) Picture Window Bks.

—Holidays & Celebrations, 8 bks. Incl. Birthdays. Ouren, Todd, illus. (C). 22.60 (978-1-4048-0198-1(7)); Christmas. Ouren, Todd, illus. 22.60 (978-1-4048-0192-9(8)); Easter. Boyd, Sheree, illus. 22.60 (978-1-4048-0194-3(4)); Halloween. Boyd, Sheree, illus. 22.60 (978-1-4048-0195-0(2)); St. Patrick's Day. Boyd, Sheree, illus. 22.60 (978-1-4048-0197-4(9)); Thanksgiving. Ouren, Todd, illus. 22.60 (978-1-4048-0191-2(X)); Valentine's Day. Ouren, Todd, illus. 22.60 (978-1-4048-0193-6(6)); 100th Day of School. Boyd, Sheree, illus. (C). 22.60 (978-1-4048-0196-7(0)); 24p. (gr. k-3). 2004. 2003. 170.08 (978-1-4048-0190-5(1)) Picture Window Bks.

—St. Patrick's Day. Boyd, Sheree, illus. 2004. (Holidays & Celebrations Ser.). 24p. (gr. k-3). 22.60 (978-1-4048-0197-4(9)) Picture Window Bks.

—Thanksgiving. Ouren, Todd, illus. 2004. (Holidays & Celebrations Ser.). 24p. (gr. k-3). 22.60 (978-1-4048-0191-2(X)) Picture Window Bks.

—Valentine's Day. Ouren, Todd, illus. 2004. (Holidays & Celebrations Ser.). 24p. (gr. k-3). 22.60 (978-1-4048-0193-6(6)) Picture Window Bks.

Heiligman, Deborah. Celebrate Independence Day: With Parades, Picnics, & Fireworks. 2007. (Holidays Around the World Ser.). (Illus.). 32p. (J). (gr. 2-5). 15.95 (978-1-4263-0074-5(3)); lib. bdg. 23.90 (978-1-4263-0075-2(1)) National Geographic Society. (National Geographic Children's Bks.).

Heiligman, Deborah. Celebrate Rosh Hashanah & Yom Kippur: With Honey, Prayers, & the Shofar. 2007. (Holidays Around the World Ser.). (Illus.). 32p. (J). (gr. 2-5). 15.95 (***978-1-4263-0076-9(X)***); lib. bdg. 23.90 (***978-1-4263-0077-6(8)***) National Geographic Society. (National Geographic Children's Bks.).

Hildebrandt, Ziporah. This Is Our Seder. Roraback, Robin, illus. 1999. 32p. (J). (gr. k-3). tchr. ed. 15.95 (978-0-8234-1436-9(1)) Holiday Hse., Inc.

Hill, Sandi. Celebrating Cinco de Mayo No. 4527: Fiesta Time! Kupperstein, Joel, ed. Martirot, Claude, illus. 1999. 16p. (J). (ps-2). pap. 2.99 (978-1-57471-572-9(0)) Creative Teaching Pr., Inc.

Hintz, Martin & Hintz, Kate. Celebrate!, 4 bks. Incl. Christmas : Why We Celebrate It the Way We Do. 22.60 (978-1-56065-327-1(2)); Halloween : Why We Celebrate It the Way We Do. 22.60 (978-1-56065-326-4(4)); Kwanzaa : Why We Celebrate It the Way We Do. lib. bdg. 22.60 (978-1-56065-329-5(9)); Thanksgiving : Why We Celebrate It the Way We Do. lib. bdg. 22.60 (978-1-56065-328-8(0)); 48p. (J). (gr. 3-4). 1996. (Illus.). Set lib. bdg. 90.40 (978-1-56065-638-8(7) , Bridgestone Bks.) Capstone Pr., Inc.

Hitz, Demi. Happy, Happy Chinese New Year! 2003. (Illus.). 24p. (J). (ps-3). 8.95 (978-0-375-82642-9(4) , Crown Books For Young Readers) Random Hse. Children's Bks.

Ho Siow Yen & Rabe, Monica. South Korea. 1998. (Festivals of the World Ser.). (Illus.). 32p. (J). (gr. 3 up). lib. bdg. 24.67 (978-0-8368-2019-5(3)) Stevens, Gareth Inc.

Holiday Celebrations, 8 vols. 2000. (Illus.). 24p. 103.60 (978-1-58209-554-7(X)) Books Are Fun, Ltd.

Holiday Histories, 4 bks. , Set. 2002. 80.00 (978-1-58810-130-3(4)); 289.50 (978-1-58810-131-0(2)) Heinemann Library.

Holidays. 2005. (J). (gr. k-4). lib. bdg. 128.10 (978-1-59197-584-7(0)) ABDO Publishing Co.

Holidays & Celebrations, 8 bks. Incl. Chinese New Year. Schaefer, Lola M. Saunders-Smith, Gail, ed. 2001. lib. bdg. 15.93 (978-0-7368-0660-2(1)); Christmas. Schuh, Mari C. Saunders-Smith, Gail, ed. 2001. lib. bdg. 15.93 (978-0-7368-0979-5(1)); Cinco de Mayo. Schaefer, Lola M. Saunders-Smith, Gail, ed. 2000. lib. bdg. 15.95 (978-0-7368-0661-9(X)); Easter. Schuh, Mari C. 2002. lib. bdg. 15.93 (978-0-7368-1445-4(0)); Halloween. Schuh, Mari C. Saunders-Smith, Gail, ed. 2001. lib. bdg. 15.93 (978-0-7368-0980-1(5)); Hanukkah. Schaefer, Lola M. Saunders-Smith, Gail, ed. 2000. lib. bdg. 15.93 (978-0-7368-0662-6(8)); Kwanzaa. Schaefer, Lola M. Saunders-Smith, Gail, ed. 2000. lib. bdg. 15.93 (978-0-7368-0663-3(6)); New Year's Day. Schuh, Mari C. 2002. lib. bdg. 15.93 (978-0-7368-1446-1(9)); Passover. Schuh, Mari C. 2002. lib. bdg. 15.93 (978-0-7368-1447-8(7)); St. Patrick's Day. Schuh, Mari C. 2002. lib. bdg. 15.93 (978-0-7368-1448-5(5)); Thanksgiving. Schuh, Mari C. Saunders-Smith, Gail, ed. 2001. lib. bdg. 15.93 (978-0-7368-0981-8(3)); Valentine's Day. Schuh, Mari C. Saunders-Smith, Gail, ed. 2001. lib. bdg. 15.93 (978-0-7368-0982-5(1)); 24p. (J). (gr. k-1). (Illus.). 2001. Set lib. bdg. 191.16 (978-0-7368-1449-2(3) , Pebble Bks.) Capstone Pr., Inc.

Holidays Around the World. (Illus.). 32p. (J). pap. 2.25 (978-1-55254-196-8(7) , BV24016) Brighter Vision Pubns.

Holidays Classroom Library. (gr. k-2). lib. bdg. 54.95 (978-0-7368-7143-3(8)) Red Brick Learning.

Holidays Complete Unit. (gr. k-2). 311.95 (978-0-7368-7153-2(5)) Red Brick Learning.

Holidays of the Church Year. (Imagine That! Activity Bks.). (Illus.). 48p. (J). pap. 5.95 (978-0-87162-836-7(8) , E2302) Warner Pr. Pubs.

Hoyt-Goldsmith, Diane. Celebrating Chinese New Year. Migdale, Lawrence, photos by. (Illus.). 32p. (gr. 4-6). (J). pap. 6.95 (978-0-8234-1520-5(1)); (YA). tchr. ed. 17.95 (978-0-8234-1393-5(4)) Holiday Hse., Inc.

—Celebrating Kwanzaa. Migdale, Lawrence, photos by. (Illus.). 32p. (J). (ps-7). pap. 6.95 (978-0-8234-1130-6(3)) Holiday Hse., Inc.

—Cinco de Mayo: Celebrating Mexican-American Traditions. Migdale, Lawrence, illus. Migdale, Lawrence, photos by. 2008. (J). (***978-0-8234-2107-7(4)***) Holiday Hse., Inc.

Hoyt-Goldsmith, Diane. Three Kings Day: A Celebration at Christmastime. Migdale, Lawrence, illus. 32p. (J). (gr. 4-6). tchr. ed. 16.95 (978-0-8234-1839-8(1)) Holiday Hse., Inc.

Hughes, Monica. My Christmas. 2003. (Festivals Ser.). (Illus.). 24p. (J). pap. 5.50 (978-1-4109-0665-6(5)); lib. bdg. 18.56 (978-1-4109-0639-7(6)) Raintree.

—My Divali. 2003. (Festivals Ser.). (Illus.). 24p. (J). pap. 5.50 (978-1-4109-0663-2(9)); lib. bdg. 18.56 (978-1-4109-0637-3(X)) Raintree.

—My Hanukkah. 2003. (Festivals Ser.). (Illus.). 24p. (J). pap. 5.50 (978-1-4109-0664-9(7)); lib. bdg. 18.56 (978-1-4109-0638-0(8)) Raintree.

—My Hanukkah. 2003. (ps-2). lib. bdg. 13.55 (978-0-613-78202-9(X)) Tandem Library Bks.

—My Id-Ul-Fitr. 2003. (Festivals Ser.). (Illus.). 24p. (J). pap. 5.50 (978-1-4109-0666-3(3)) Raintree.

—My Id-ul-Fitr. 2003. (Festivals Ser.). (Illus.). 24p. (J). lib. bdg. 18.56 (978-1-4109-0640-3(X)) Raintree.

—My Rosh Hashanah. 2003. (Festivals Ser.). (Illus.). 24p. (J). pap. 5.50 (978-1-4109-0667-0(1)); lib. bdg. 18.56 (978-1-4109-0641-0(8)) Raintree.

—My Rosh Hashanah. 2003. (ps-2). lib. bdg. 13.55 (978-0-613-78203-6(8)) Tandem Library Bks.

Imler, Kathryn A. Valentine's Day. 2003. (Holiday Histories Ser.). (Illus.). 32p. (J). lib. bdg. 22.79 (978-1-4034-3502-6(2)) Heinemann Library.

Ishii, Minako. Girls' Day / Boys' Day. 2007. 64p. 16.95 (***978-1-57306-274-9(X)***) Bess Pr., Inc.

Israel, Elaine. Celebrate Winter Holidays. 2001. pap. 12.95 (978-0-439-07345-5(6)) Scholastic, Inc.

Jackson, Ellen B. The Spring Equinox: Celebrating the Greening of the Earth. Ellis, Jan Davey, illus. 2002. (Traditions of the Seasons Ser.). 32p. (gr. 2-4). lib. bdg. 24.90 (978-0-7613-1955-9(7) , Millbrook Pr.) Lerner Publishing Group.

—Spring Equinox: The Greening of the Earth. 2003. (gr. k-3). lib. bdg. 16.40 (978-0-613-90690-6(X)) Tandem Library Bks.

—The Summer Solstice. 2003. (Illus.). 32p. (J). (gr. 3-6). pap. 7.95 (978-0-7613-1985-6(9) , Millbrook Pr.) Lerner Publishing Group.

—The Summer Solstice. Ellis, Jan Davey, illus. 2001. 4. 32p. (gr. 4-7). 14.95 (978-0-7613-1283-3(8) , Millbrook Pr.) Lerner Publishing Group.

—Summer Solstice. Ellis, Jan Davey, illus. 2001. (Traditions of the Seasons Ser.). 32p. (gr. 2-4). lib. bdg. (978-0-7613-1623-7(X) , Millbrook Pr.) Lerner Publishing Group.

Jackson, Garnet N. First Thanksgiving. 2000. (gr. k-3). lib. bdg. 11.80 (978-0-613-35508-7(3)) Tandem Library Bks.

Jango-Cohen, Judith. Chinese New Year. Chin, Jason, illus. 2005. (On My Own Holidays Ser.). 48p. (J). (gr. k-3). 5.95 (978-1-57505-763-7(8)) Lerner Publishing Group.

Jones, Lynda. Kids Around the World Celebrate! the Best Feasts & Festivals from Many Lands. 2000. (gr. 3-6). lib. bdg. 22.20 (978-0-613-25878-4(9)) Tandem Library Bks.

Jordan, Denise M. Juneteenth. 2003. (Holiday Histories Ser.). 32p. pap. 6.95 (978-1-4034-3690-0(8)) Heinemann Library.

Julie Murray. Holidays. 2005. (J). (gr. k-4). lib. bdg. 128.10 (978-1-57765-950-1(3) , Buddy Bks.) ABDO Publishing Co.

Just for Journaling: Holidays & Seasons. 2004. 128p. (J). per. 11.99 (978-1-59441-004-8(6) , DJ-604000) Carson-Dellosa Publishing Co., Inc.

Kain, Kathleen. All about Holidays. Mahan, Ben, illus. 2004. (Treasure Tree Ser.). 32p. (J). (978-0-7166-1644-3(0)) World Bk., Inc.

—All about Holidays: With Inspector McQ. Mahan, Ben, illus. 2004. (Early Literacy Library). 32p. (gr. 2-5). 219.00 (978-0-7166-1647-4(5)) World Bk., Inc.

Kaplan, Leslie C. Chinese New Year. 2004. (Library of Holidays). (Illus.). 24p. (J). lib. bdg. 18.75 (978-0-8239-6658-5(5) , PowerKids Pr.) Rosen Publishing Group, Inc., The.

—Flag Day. 2004. (Library of Holidays). (Illus.). 24p. (J). lib. bdg. 18.75 (978-0-8239-6659-2(3) , PowerKids Pr.) Rosen Publishing Group, Inc., The.

—Martin Luther King Jr. Day. 2004. (Library of Holidays). (Illus.). 24p. (J). lib. bdg. 18.75 (978-0-8239-6661-5(5) , PowerKids Pr.) Rosen Publishing Group, Inc., The.

Keely, Jack. Holiday Mood Swings. Keely, Jack, illus. 2002. (Illus.). 64p. (J). 7.99 (978-0-8431-4963-0(9) , Price Stern Sloan) Penguin Group (USA) Inc.

Kimmel, Eric A. Wonders & Miracles: A Passover Companion. 2004. (Wonders & Miracles Ser.). (Illus.). 144p. (J). pap. 18.95 (978-0-439-07175-8(5)) Scholastic, Inc.

Kindersley, Barnabas & Kindersley, Anabel, photos by. Celebraciones. 2005. Tr. of Celebrations. (SPA., Illus.). (J). (gr. 1-4). 18.95 (978-0-9628720-5-1(9)) Iaconi, Mariuccia Bk. Imports.

Klebanow, Barbara & Fischer, Sara. American Holidays: Exploring Traditions, Customs, & Backgrounds. 2005. pap. 16.50 (978-0-86647-196-1(0)) Pro Lingua Assocs., Inc.

Knudsen Shannon. La Pascua en todo el mundo (Easter around the World) Erickson, David L., illus. 2007. (Yo solo Festividades (on My Own Holidays) Ser.). (J). pap. 6.95 (***978-0-8225-7794-2(1)*** , Ediciones Lerner) Lerner Publishing Group.

Knudsen, Shannon. La Pascua en Todo el Mundo (Easter Around the World) Erickson, David L., illus. 2007. (Yo Solo Festividades (On My Own Holidays) Ser.). (SPA.). 48p. (J). (gr. 2-4). lib. bdg. 25.26 (***978-0-8225-7791-1(7)*** , Ediciones Lerner) Lerner Publishing Group.

Kropf, Latifa Berry. It's Sukkah Time. Cohen, Tod, illus. Cohen, Tod, photos by. 2003. (Sukkot & Simchat Torah Ser.). 24p. (J). (ps-1). (978-1-58013-084-4(4)) Kar-Ben Publishing.

Kupperstein, Joel. Celebrating Patriotic Holidays: Honoring America. 1999. (ps-2). lib. bdg. 10.65 (978-0-613-34123-3(6)) Tandem Library Bks.

Lakeshore Learning Materials Staff, contrib. by. Cinco de Mayo Celebration Kit. 2000. (J). pap. 29.95 (978-1-929255-86-3(1)) Lakeshore Learning Materials.

Landau, Elaine. Easter: Parades, Chocolates, & Celebration. 2004. (Finding Out about Holidays Ser.). (Illus.). 48p. (J). lib. bdg. 23.93 (978-0-7660-2172-3(6)) Enslow Pubs., Inc.

H
I

—St. Patrick's Day: Parades, Shamrocks & Leprechauns. 2002. (Finding Out about Holidays Ser.). (Illus.). 48p. (J). (gr. 1-4). lib. bdg. 23.93 (978-0-7660-1777-1(X)) Enslow Pubs., Inc.

—Thanksgiving Day: A Time to Be Thankful. 2001. (Finding Out about Holidays Ser.). (Illus.). 48p. (J). (gr. 1-4). lib. bdg. 23.93 (978-0-7660-1572-2(6)) Enslow Pubs., Inc.

—Veterans Day: Remembering Our War Heroes. 2002. (Finding Out about Holidays Ser.). (Illus.). 48p. (J). (gr. 1-4). lib. bdg. 23.93 (978-0-7660-1775-7(3)) Enslow Pubs., Inc.

Larousse Kingfisher Chambers Staff. Holiday Fun. 2000. (Illus.). (J). (978-0-606-19825-7(3)) Tandem Library Bks.

Lee, Uk-Bae. Sori's Harvest Moon Day: A Story of Korea - Including Doll. Lee, Uk-Bae, illus. 1999. Orig. Title: Sori's Chu-Suk. (Illus.). 32p. (J). (gr. k-3). 25.95 (978-1-56899-690-5(X)) Soundprints.

Lerner Publishing Group Staff. On My Own Holidays: Classroom Set. 2005. (Illus.). (J). (gr. 2-4). 70.95 (978-0-8225-2768-8(5)) Lerner Publishing Group.

Let's See Library-Holidays Complete Set. (Let's See Library-Holidays Ser.). (gr. 1-3). 358.74 (978-0-7565-0726-8(X)) Compass Point Bks.

Levy, Barbara Soloff. How to Draw Holiday Pictures. 2007. 32p. (J). pap. 2.95 (***978-0-486-45662-1(5)***) Dover Pubns., Inc.

Levy, Janice. Celebrate! It's Cinco de Mayo!/¡Celebremos! ¡Es el Cinco de Mayo! Arisa, Miguel, tr. Lopez, Loretta, illus. 2007. (ENG & SPA.). 32p. (J). (ps-2). 16.95 (***978-0-8075-1176-3(5)***); pap. 6.95 (***978-0-8075-1177-0(3)***) Whitman, Albert & Co.

Lilly, Melinda. Pilgrims in America. 2002. (Rourke Discovery Library). (Illus.). 24p. (J). lib. bdg. 20.64 (978-1-58952-360-9(1)) Rourke Publishing, LLC.

Lowery, Linda. Cinco de Mayo. Knutson, Barbara, illus. 2005. (On My Own Holidays Ser.). 48p. (J). (gr. k-3). pap. 5.95 (978-1-57505-764-4(6)); (gr. 2-4). 25.26 (978-1-57505-654-8(2)) Lerner Publishing Group.

—El Cinco de Mayo. Knutson, Barbara, illus. 2005. (Yo Solo - Festividades (on My Own - Holidays) Ser.).Tr. of Cinco de Mayo. (SPA.). 48p. (J). (ps-ps). pap. 5.95 (978-0-8225-3119-7(4)); lib. bdg. 25.26 (978-0-8225-3118-0(6), Ediciones Lerner) Lerner Publishing Group.

—Day of the Dead. Knutson, Barbara, illus. 2004. (On My Own Holidays Ser.). 48p. (J). (gr. 2-4). lib. bdg. 25.26 (978-0-87614-914-0(X)) Lerner Publishing Group.

—Day of the Dead. 2004. (gr. k-3). lib. bdg. 14.10 (978-0-613-79241-7(6)) Tandem Library Bks.

—Earth Day. Bergherr, Mary, illus. rev. ed. 2004. (On My Own Holidays Ser.). 48p. (J). (gr. 2-4). lib. bdg. 25.26 (978-1-57505-700-2(X)) Lerner Publishing Group.

—Martin Luther King Jr Day. 2004. (gr. k-3). lib. bdg. 14.10 (978-0-613-79212-7(2)) Tandem Library Bks.

Lowery, Linda & Knutson, Barbara. Day of the Dead. 2003. (On My Own Holidays Ser.). (Illus.). 48p. (J). (gr. k-3). 5.95 (978-1-57505-581-7(3)) Lerner Publishing Group.

—El Día de los Muertos. Knutson, Barbara, illus. 2005. (Yo Solo Festividades (On My Own Holidays) Ser.). (SPA & ENG., Illus.). 48p. (J). (gr. 2-4). lib. bdg. 25.26 (978-0-8225-3122-7(4), Ediciones Lerner) Lerner Publishing Group.

Mackall, Dandi Daley. Off to Plymouth Rock. 2006. 26p. (J). bds. 9.99 (978-1-4003-0822-4(4)) Nelson, Thomas Inc.

Marchant, Kerena. Id-Ul-Fitr. 1998. (Festivals Ser.). (Illus.). 32p. (gr. 2-4). lib. bdg. 22.90 (978-0-7613-0963-5(2), Millbrook Pr.) Lerner Publishing Group.

Margaret, Amy. Memorial Day. 2002. (Library of Holidays). (Illus.). 24p. (J). lib. bdg. 18.75 (978-0-8239-5784-2(5), PowerKids Pr.) Rosen Publishing Group, Inc., The.

—Presidents' Day. 2002. (Library of Holidays). (Illus.). 24p. (J). lib. bdg. 18.75 (978-0-8239-5786-6(1), PowerKids Pr.) Rosen Publishing Group, Inc., The.

—St. Patrick's Day. 2002. (Library of Holidays). (Illus.). 24p. (J). lib. bdg. 18.75 (978-0-8239-5783-5(7), PowerKids Pr.) Rosen Publishing Group, Inc., The.

Margaret, Amy & Randolph, Joanne. Groundhog Day. 2002. (Library of Holidays). (Illus.). 24p. (J). lib. bdg. 18.75 (978-0-8239-5785-9(3), PowerKids Pr.) Rosen Publishing Group, Inc., The.

Markham, Lois. Harvest. 1998. (World Celebrations & Ceremonies Ser.). (Illus.). 24p. (J). (gr. 3-5). 22.45 (978-1-56711-275-7(7), Blackbirch Pr., Inc.) Thomson Gale.

Marsh, Carole. Alaska Classic Christmas Trivia. 2002. (Carole Marsh Alaska Bks.). (Illus.). 32p. pap. 6.95 (978-0-635-01371-2(1), 13711, Marsh, Carole Bks.); lib. bdg. 21.95 (978-0-635-01372-9(X), 1372X) Gallopade International.

—Arizona Classic Christmas Trivia. 2002. (Carole Marsh Arizona Bks.). (Illus.). 32p. pap. 6.95 (978-0-635-01373-6(8), 13738, Marsh, Carole Bks.); lib. bdg. 21.95 (978-0-635-01374-3(6), 13746) Gallopade International.

—Arkansas Classic Christmas Trivia. 2002. (Carole Marsh Arkansas Bks.). (Illus.). 32p. pap. 6.95 (978-0-635-01375-0(4), 13754); lib. bdg. 21.95 (978-0-635-01376-7(2), 13762) Gallopade International. (Marsh, Carole Bks.).

—California Classic Christmas Trivia. 2002. (Carole Marsh California Bks.). (Illus.). 32p. pap. 6.95 (978-0-635-01377-4(0), 13770); lib. bdg. 21.95 (978-0-635-01378-1(9), 13789) Gallopade International. (Marsh, Carole Bks.).

—Colorado Classic Christmas Trivia. 2002. (Carole Marsh Colorado Bks.). (Illus.). 32p. pap. 6.95 (978-0-635-01379-8(7), 13797); lib. bdg. 21.95 (978-0-635-01380-4(0), 13800) Gallopade International. (Marsh, Carole Bks.).

—Connecticut Classic Christmas Trivia. 2002. (Carole Marsh Connecticut Bks.). (Illus.). 32p. pap. 6.95 (978-0-635-01381-1(9), 13819); lib. bdg. 21.95 (978-0-635-01382-8(7), 13827) Gallopade International. (Marsh, Carole Bks.).

—Delaware Classic Christmas Trivia. 2002. (Carole Marsh Delaware Bks.). (Illus.). 32p. pap. 6.95 (978-0-635-01383-5(5), 13835); lib. bdg. 21.95 (978-0-635-01384-2(3), 13843) Gallopade International. (Marsh, Carole Bks.).

—Florida Classic Christmas Trivia. 2002. (Carole Marsh Florida Bks.). (Illus.). 32p. pap. 6.95 (978-0-635-01385-9(1), 13851, Marsh, Carole Bks.); lib. bdg. 21.95 (978-0-635-01386-6(X), 1386X) Gallopade International.

—Georgia Classic Christmas Trivia. 2002. (Carole Marsh Georgia Bks.). (Illus.). 32p. pap. 6.95 (978-0-635-01387-3(8)); lib. bdg. 21.95 (978-0-635-01388-0(6), 13886) Gallopade International. (Marsh, Carole Bks.).

—Hawaii Classic Christmas Trivia. 2002. (Carole Marsh Hawaii Bks.). (Illus.). 32p. (J). pap. 6.95 (978-0-635-01389-7(4), 13894); lib. bdg. 21.95 (978-0-635-01390-3(8), 13908) Gallopade International. (Marsh, Carole Bks.).

—Idaho Classic Christmas Trivia. 2002. (Carole Marsh Idaho Bks.). (Illus.). 32p. pap. 6.95 (978-0-635-01391-0(6), 13916); lib. bdg. 14.95 (978-0-635-01392-7(4), 13924) Gallopade International. (Marsh, Carole Bks.).

—Illinois Classic Christmas Trivia. 2002. (Carole Marsh Illinois Bks.). (Illus.). 32p. pap. 6.95 (978-0-635-01393-4(2), 13932); lib. bdg. 21.95 (978-0-635-01394-1(0), 13940) Gallopade International.

—Indiana Classic Christmas Trivia. 2002. (Carole Marsh Indiana Bks.). (Illus.). 32p. pap. 6.95 (978-0-635-01395-8(9), 13959); lib. bdg. 21.95 (978-0-635-01396-5(7), 13967) Gallopade International. (Marsh, Carole Bks.).

—Iowa Classic Christmas Trivia. 2002. (Carole Marsh Iowa Bks.). (Illus.). 32p. pap. 6.95 (978-0-635-01397-2(5), 13975, Marsh, Carole Bks.); lib. bdg. 21.95 (978-0-635-01398-9(3)) Gallopade International.

—Kansas Classic Christmas Trivia. 2002. (Carole Marsh Kansas Bks.). (Illus.). 32p. pap. 14.95 (978-0-635-01399-6(1), 13991, Marsh, Carole Bks.); lib. bdg. 21.95 (978-0-635-01400-9(9), 14009) Gallopade International.

—Kentucky Classic Christmas Trivia. 2002. (Carole Marsh Kentucky Bks.). (Illus.). 32p. pap. 6.95 (978-0-635-01401-6(7), 14017); lib. bdg. 21.95 (978-0-635-01402-3(5), 14025) Gallopade International. (Marsh, Carole Bks.).

—Louisiana Classic Christmas Trivia. 2002. (Carole Marsh Louisiana Bks.). (Illus.). 32p. pap. 6.95 (978-0-635-01403-0(3), 14033, Marsh, Carole Bks.); lib. bdg. 21.95 (978-0-635-01404-7(1), 14041) Gallopade International.

—Maine Classic Christmas Trivia. 2002. (Carole Marsh Maine Bks.). (Illus.). 32p. pap. 6.95 (978-0-635-01405-4(X), 1405X); lib. bdg. 21.95 (978-0-635-01406-1(8), 14068, Marsh, Carole Bks.) Gallopade International.

—Maryland Classic Christmas Trivia. 2002. (Carole Marsh Maryland Bks.). (Illus.). 32p. pap. 6.95 (978-0-635-01407-8(6), 14076); lib. bdg. 21.95 (978-0-635-01408-5(4), 14084) Gallopade International. (Marsh, Carole Bks.).

—Massachusetts Classic Christmas Trivia. 2002. (Carole Marsh Massachusetts Bks.). (Illus.). 32p. pap. 6.95 (978-0-635-01409-2(2), 14092); lib. bdg. 21.95 (978-0-635-01410-8(6), 14106) Gallopade International. (Marsh, Carole Bks.).

—Michigan Classic Christmas Trivia. 2002. (Carole Marsh Michigan Bks.). (Illus.). 32p. pap. 6.95 (978-0-635-01411-5(4), 14114); lib. bdg. 21.95 (978-0-635-01412-2(2), 14122) Gallopade International. (Marsh, Carole Bks.).

—Minnesota Classic Christmas Trivia. 2002. (Carole Marsh Minnesota Bks.). (Illus.). 32p. pap. 14.95 (978-0-635-01413-9(0), 14130); lib. bdg. 21.95 (978-0-635-01414-6(9), 14149) Gallopade International. (Marsh, Carole Bks.).

—Mississippi Classic Christmas Trivia. 2002. (Carole Marsh Mississippi Bks.). (Illus.). 32p. pap. 6.95 (978-0-635-01415-3(7), 14157); lib. bdg. 21.95 (978-0-635-01416-0(5), 14165) Gallopade International. (Marsh, Carole Bks.).

—Missouri Classic Christmas Trivia. 2002. (Carole Marsh Missouri Bks.). (Illus.). 32p. pap. 6.95 (978-0-635-01417-7(3), 14173); lib. bdg. 21.95 (978-0-635-01418-4(1), 14181) Gallopade International. (Marsh, Carole Bks.).

—Montana Classic Christmas Trivia. 2002. (Carole Marsh Montana Bks.). (Illus.). 32p. pap. 6.95 (978-0-635-01419-1(X), 1419X); lib. bdg. 21.95 (978-0-635-01420-7(3), 14203, Marsh, Carole Bks.) Gallopade International.

—Nebraska Classic Christmas Trivia. 2002. (Carole Marsh Nebraska Bks.). (Illus.). 32p. pap. 6.95 (978-0-635-01421-4(1), 14211, Marsh, Carole Bks.); lib. bdg. 21.95 (978-0-635-01422-1(X), 1422X) Gallopade International.

—Nevada Classic Christmas Trivia. 2002. (Carole Marsh Nevada Bks.). (Illus.). 32p. pap. 6.95 (978-0-635-01423-8(8), 14238); lib. bdg. 21.95 (978-0-635-01424-5(6), 14246) Gallopade International. (Marsh, Carole Bks.).

—New Hampshire Classic Christmas Trivia. 2002. (Carole Marsh New Hampshire Bks.). (Illus.). 32p. pap. 6.95 (978-0-635-01425-2(4), 14254); lib. bdg. 21.95 (978-0-635-01426-9(2), 14262, Marsh, Carole Bks.) Gallopade International.

—New Jersey Classic Christmas Trivia. 2002. (Carole Marsh New Jersey Bks.). (Illus.). 32p. pap. 6.95 (978-0-635-01427-6(0), 14270); lib. bdg. 21.95 (978-0-635-01428-3(9), 14289) Gallopade International. (Marsh, Carole Bks.).

—New Mexico Classic Christmas Trivia. 2002. (Carole Marsh New Mexico Bks.). (Illus.). 32p. pap. 6.95 (978-0-635-01429-0(7), 14297); lib. bdg. 21.95 (978-0-635-01430-6(0), 14300) Gallopade International. (Marsh, Carole Bks.).

—New York Classic Christmas Trivia. 2002. (Carole Marsh New York Bks.). (Illus.). 32p. pap. 6.95 (978-0-635-01431-3(9), 14319); lib. bdg. 21.95 (978-0-635-01432-0(7), 14327) Gallopade International. (Marsh, Carole Bks.).

—North Carolina Classic Christmas Trivia. 2002. (Carole Marsh North Carolina Bks.). (Illus.). 32p. pap. 6.95 (978-0-635-01433-7(5), 14335); lib. bdg. 21.95 (978-0-635-01434-4(3), 14343) Gallopade International. (Marsh, Carole Bks.).

—North Dakota Classic Christmas Trivia. 2002. (Carole Marsh North Dakota Bks.). (Illus.). 32p. pap. 6.95 (978-0-635-01435-1(1), 14351, Marsh, Carole Bks.); lib. bdg. 21.95 (978-0-635-01436-8(X), 01436X) Gallopade International.

—Oklahoma Classic Christmas Trivia. 2002. (Carole Marsh Oklahoma Bks.). (Illus.). 32p. (J). pap. 6.95 (978-0-635-01437-5(8), 14378); lib. bdg. 21.95 (978-0-635-01438-2(6), 14386) Gallopade International. (Marsh, Carole Bks.).

—Oregon Classic Christmas Trivia. 2002. (Carole Marsh Oregon Bks.). (Illus.). 32p. pap. 14.95 (978-0-635-01439-9(4), 14394); lib. bdg. 21.95 (978-0-635-01440-5(8), 14408, Marsh, Carole Bks.) Gallopade International.

—Pennsylvania Classic Christmas Trivia. 2002. (Carole Marsh Pennsylvania Bks.). (Illus.). 32p. pap. 6.95 (978-0-635-01441-2(6), 14416); lib. bdg. 21.95 (978-0-635-01442-9(4), 14424) Gallopade International. (Marsh, Carole Bks.).

—Rhode Island Classic Christmas Trivia. 2002. (Carole Marsh Rhode Island Bks.). (Illus.). 32p. pap. 14.95 (978-0-635-01443-6(2), 14432); lib. bdg. 21.95 (978-0-635-01444-3(0), 14440) Gallopade International. (Marsh, Carole Bks.).

—South Carolina Classic Christmas Trivia. 2002. (Carole Marsh South Carolina Bks.). (Illus.). 32p. pap. 6.95 (978-0-635-01445-0(9), 14459); lib. bdg. 21.95 (978-0-635-01446-7(7), 14467) Gallopade International. (Marsh, Carole Bks.).

—South Dakota Classic Christmas Trivia. 2002. (Carole Marsh South Dakota Bks.). (Illus.). 32p. pap. 14.95 (978-0-635-01447-4(5), 14475); lib. bdg. 21.95 (978-0-635-01448-1(3), 14483) Gallopade International. (Marsh, Carole Bks.).

—Tennessee Classic Christmas Trivia. 2002. (Carole Marsh Tennessee Bks.). (Illus.). 32p. pap. 6.95 (978-0-635-01449-8(1), 14491); lib. bdg. 21.95 (978-0-635-01450-4(5), 14505) Gallopade International. (Marsh, Carole Bks.).

—Texas Classic Christmas Trivia. 2002. (Carole Marsh Texas Bks.). (Illus.). 32p. pap. 6.95 (978-0-635-01451-1(3), 14513); lib. bdg. 21.95 (978-0-635-01452-8(1), 14521) Gallopade International. (Marsh, Carole Bks.).

—Utah Classic Christmas Trivia. 2002. (Carole Marsh Utah Bks.). (Illus.). 32p. pap. 6.95 (978-0-635-01453-5(X), 1453X); lib. bdg. 21.95 (978-0-635-01454-2(8), 14548, Marsh, Carole Bks.) Gallopade International.

—Vermont Classic Christmas Trivia. 2002. (Carole Marsh Vermont Bks.). (Illus.). 32p. pap. 14.95 (978-0-635-01455-9(6), 14556); lib. bdg. 21.95 (978-0-635-01456-6(4), 14564) Gallopade International. (Marsh, Carole Bks.).

—Virginia Classic Christmas Trivia. 2002. (Carole Marsh Virginia Bks.). (Illus.). 32p. pap. 6.95 (978-0-635-01457-3(2), 14572); lib. bdg. 21.95 (978-0-635-01458-0(0), 14580) Gallopade International. (Marsh, Carole Bks.).

—Washington Classic Christmas Trivia. 2002. (Carole Marsh Washington Bks.). (Illus.). 32p. pap. 6.95 (978-0-635-01459-7(9), 14599, Marsh, Carole Bks.) Gallopade International.

Martin Luther King, Jr. Day. 2001. (Illus.). (J). pap. 21.95 (978-1-58810-028-3(6)) Heinemann Library.

Marx, David F. Chinese New Year. 2002. (Rookie Read-About Holidays Ser.). (Illus.). 32p. (J). (gr. 1-2). pap. 5.95 (978-0-516-27375-4(2), Children's Pr.) Scholastic Library Publishing.

—Chinese New Year. 2002. (gr. k-3). lib. bdg. 14.10 (978-0-613-54125-1(1)) Tandem Library Bks.

—Easter. 2001. (Rookie Read-About Holidays Ser.). (Illus.). 32p. (gr. 1-2). pap. 5.95 (978-0-516-27175-0(X), Children's Pr.) Scholastic Library Publishing.

—Easter. 2001. (gr. k-3). lib. bdg. 14.10 (978-0-613-54186-2(3)) Tandem Library Bks.

—Martin Luther King, Jr. Day. 2001. (Rookie Read-About Holidays Ser.). (Illus.). 32p. (J). (gr. 1-2). pap. 5.95 (978-0-516-27177-4(6), Children's Pr.) Scholastic Library Publishing.

—Passover. 2001. (Rookie Read-About Holidays Ser.). (Illus.). 32p. (J). (gr. 1-2). pap. 5.95 (978-0-516-27178-1(4), Children's Pr.) Scholastic Library Publishing.

—Presidents' Day. 2002. (Rookie Read-About Holidays Ser.). (Illus.). 32p. (J). (gr. 1-2). 20.50 (978-0-516-22268-4(6)); pap. 5.95 (978-0-516-27376-1(0)) Scholastic Library Publishing. (Children's Pr.).

Mattern, Joanne. Celebrate Cinco de Mayo. 2006. (Celebrate Holidays Ser.). (Illus.). 104p. (J). lib. bdg. 31.93 (978-0-7660-2579-0(9)) Enslow Pubs., Inc.

McKay, Susan. Switzerland. 1999. (Festivals of the World Ser.). (Illus.). 32p. (J). (gr. 3 up). lib. bdg. 24.67 (978-0-8368-2027-0(4)) Stevens, Gareth Inc.

Miller, Marilyn. Thanksgiving. 1998. (World of Holidays Ser.). (Illus.). 32p. (J). (gr. 2-5). lib. bdg. 25.69 (978-0-8172-4612-9(6)) Raintree.

Mir Tamim Ansary. Columbus Day. 2nd ed. 2006. (Illus.). 32p. (J). pap. (***978-1-4034-8896-1(7)***) Heinemann Library.

—Earth Day. 2nd ed. 2006. (Holiday Histories Ser.). (Illus.). 32p. (J). pap. (***978-1-4034-8897-8(5)***) Heinemann Library.

—Independence Day. 2nd ed. 2006. (Illus.). 32p. (J). pap. (***978-1-4034-8900-5(9)***) Heinemann Library.

—Martin Luther King Jr. Day. 2nd ed. 2006. (Illus.). 32p. (J). pap. (***978-1-4034-8902-9(5)***) Heinemann Library.

—Memorial Day. 2nd ed. 2006. (Illus.). 32p. (J). pap. (***978-1-4034-8903-6(3)***) Heinemann Library.

—Presidents' Day. 2nd ed. 2006. (Illus.). 32p. (J). pap. (***978-1-4034-8904-3(1)***) Heinemann Library.

Mishler, Donna. Celebrate America. Hughes, Jack, illus. 2002. 32p. (J). (ps-5). pap. 5.95 (978-1-893709-06-5(X)) Suthernsky.

Mitchell, Judy. Holidays. Rojas, Mary Galan, illus. 2001. (Pictures to Color Ser.). 32p. (J). (ps-k). pap. 4.95 (978-1-57310-265-0(2)) Teaching & Learning Co.

Mitchell, Judy & Borst, Donna, eds. The Best of Holidays & Seasonal Celebrations. 2001. 320p. (J). Issues 9-13. (Illus.). (ps-k). pap. 24.95 (978-1-57310-298-8(9)); Issues 22-26. (gr. 1-3). pap. 24.95 (978-1-57310-299-5(7)) Teaching & Learning Co.

—The Best of Holidays & Seasonal Celebrations, Grades 1-3, Issues 18-21. 2000. (Illus.). 320p. (J). pap., tchr. ed. 24.95 (978-1-57310-228-5(8)) Teaching & Learning Co.

Moehn, Heather. World Holidays: A Watts Guide for Children. 2000. (Watts Reference Ser.). (Illus.). 124p. (YA). (gr. 4 up). pap. 19.95 (978-0-531-16490-7(X), Watts, Franklin) Scholastic Library Publishing.

—World Holidays: A Watts Guide for Children. 2000. (gr. 3-6). lib. bdg. 30.35 (978-0-613-72663-4(4)) Tandem Library Bks.

Most, Bernard. Happy Holidaysaurus! Most, Bernard, illus. 2002. (Illus.). (J). 22.34 (978-0-7587-2695-7(3)) Book Wholesalers, Inc.

Murphy, Bryan. Celebrations & Festivals. 2001. (gr. 3-6). lib. bdg. 15.25 (978-0-613-87125-9(1)) Tandem Library Bks.

Murphy, Patricia J. Canada Day. 2002. (Rookie Read-About Holidays Ser.). (Illus.). 32p. (J). (gr. 1-2). pap. 20.50 (978-0-516-22662-0(2)); pap. 5.95 (978-0-516-27487-4(2)) Scholastic Library Publishing. (Children's Pr.).

—Canada Day. 2002. (Illus.). 31p. (J). (ps-3). lib. bdg. 14.10 (978-0-613-53983-8(4)) Tandem Library Bks.

—Our National Holidays. 2002. (Let's See Library). (Illus.). 24p. (J). (gr. 1 up). lib. bdg. 19.93 (978-0-7565-0194-5(6)) Compass Point Bks.

Murray, Julie. Chinese New Year. 2005. (Buddy Book Ser.). (Illus.). 24p. (J). (gr. k-4). lib. bdg. 21.35 (978-1-59197-585-4(9)) ABDO Publishing Co.

—Cinco de Mayo. 2005. (Buddy Book Ser.). (Illus.). 24p. (J). (gr. k-4). lib. bdg. 21.35 (978-1-59197-586-1(7)) ABDO Publishing Co.

—Independence Day. 2005. (Buddy Book Ser.). (Illus.). 24p. (J). (gr. k-4). lib. bdg. 21.35 (978-1-59197-588-5(3)) ABDO Publishing Co.

—Martin Luther King, Jr. Day. 2005. (Buddy Book Ser.). (Illus.). 24p. (J). (gr. k-4). lib. bdg. 21.35 (978-1-59197-589-2(1)) ABDO Publishing Co.

—President's Day. 2005. (Buddy Book Ser.). (Illus.). 24p. (J). (gr. k-4). lib. bdg. 21.35 (978-1-59197-590-8(5)) ABDO Publishing Co.

Musleah, Rahel & Jarrett, Judy. Apples & Pomegranates: A Rosh Ha-Shanah Seder. 2004. (ENG & HEB., Illus.). 64p. (J). pap. 7.95 (978-1-58013-123-0(9)) Kar-Ben Publishing.

National Holidays, 4 bks. Incl. Flag Day. Schuh, Mari C. 2003. lib. bdg. 15.93 (978-0-7368-1652-6(6)); Independence Day. Frost, Helen. Saunders-Smith, Gail, ed. 2000. lib. bdg. 15.93 (978-0-7368-0542-1(7)); Labor Day. Schuh, Mari C. 2003. lib. bdg. 15.93 (978-0-7368-1653-3(4)); Martin Luther King, Jr. Day. Frost, Helen. Saunders-Smith, Gail, ed. 2000. lib. bdg. 15.93 (978-0-7368-0543-8(5)); Memorial Day. Frost, Helen. Saunders-Smith, Gail, ed. 2000. lib. bdg. 15.93 (978-0-7368-0544-5(3)); Presidents' Day. Frost, Helen. Saunders-Smith, Gail, ed. 2000. lib. bdg. 15.93 (978-0-7368-0545-2(1)); Thanksgiving Day. Schuh, Mari C. 2003. lib. bdg. 15.93 (978-0-7368-1654-0(2)); Veterans Day. Schuh, Mari C. 2003. lib. bdg. 15.93 (978-0-7368-1655-7(0)); 24p. (J). (gr. k-1). (Illus.). 1999. Set lib. bdg. 127.44 (978-0-7368-1671-7(2), Pebble Bks.) Capstone Pr., Inc.

National Holidays Set. (gr. k-2). 114.95 (978-0-7368-9056-4(4)) Red Brick Learning.

Nelson, Robin. Earth Day. 2003. (First Step Nonfiction Ser.). (Illus.). 24p. (J). (gr. k-2). lib. bdg. 18.60 (978-0-8225-1283-7(1)) Lerner Publishing Group.

—Martin Luther King, Jr. Day. 2003. (First Step Nonfiction Ser.). (Illus.). 24p. (J). (gr. k-2). lib. bdg. 18.60 (978-0-8225-1282-0(3)) Lerner Publishing Group.

—Memorial Day. 2003. (First Step Nonfiction Ser.). (Illus.). 24p. (J). (gr. k-2). lib. bdg. 18.60 (978-0-8225-1273-8(4)) Lerner Publishing Group.

—Veterans Day. (First Step Nonfiction Ser.). (Illus.). 23p. (J). (ps-7). 2006. 18.60 (978-0-8225-2617-9(4)); 2004. pap. (978-0-8225-5379-3(1)) Lerner Publishing Group. (Lerner Pubns.).

NgCheong-Lum, Roseline. Haiti. 1999. (Festivals of the World Ser.). (Illus.). 32p. (J). (gr. 3 up). lib. bdg. 24.67 (978-0-8368-2015-7(0)) Stevens, Gareth Inc.

Nicholas, St. Our Holidays (Their Meaning & Spirit) 2006. 94.99 (***978-1-4280-0657-7(5)***); pap. 88.99 (***978-1-4280-0678-2(8)***) IndyPublish.com.

H
I

Un Nino Dios. 2002. Tr. of One Baby Jesus. (SPA.). 24p. (J). 6.95 (978-0-8249-4234-2(5)) Ideals Pubns.

Noble, Marty. Invisible Nutcracker Magic Picture Book. 1999. (Dover Little Activity Bks.). (Illus.). 16p. (J). (ps-5). pap. 1.50 (978-0-486-40531-5(1)) Dover Pubns., Inc.

Nobleman, Marc Tyler. Earth Day. 2004. (Let's See Ser.). 24p. (J). (gr. 1 up). lib. bdg. 19.93 (978-0-7565-0645-2(X)) Compass Point Bks.

—Groundhog Day. 2004. (Let's See Ser.). (Illus.). 24p. (J). (gr. 1 up). lib. bdg. 19.93 (978-0-7565-0648-3(4)) Compass Point Bks.

—Kwanzaa. 2004. (Let's See Ser.). (Illus.). 24p. (J). (gr. 1 up). lib. bdg. 19.93 (978-0-7565-0647-6(6)) Compass Point Bks.

—Martin Luther King, Jr. Day. 2004. (Let's See Ser.). (Illus.). 24p. (J). (gr. 1-3). lib. bdg. 19.93 (978-0-7565-0646-9(8)) Compass Point Bks.

—Memorial Day. 2004. (Let's See Ser.). (Illus.). 24p. (J). (gr. 1 up). lib. bdg. 19.93 (978-0-7565-0771-8(5)) Compass Point Bks.

O'Brien, Joan. Holidays Around the World. 2006. 32p. (J). pap. 3.95 (978-0-486-45161-9(5)) Dover Pubns., Inc.

O'Shea, Maria. Turkey. 1999. (Festivals of the World Ser.). (Illus.). 32p. (J). (gr. 3 up). lib. bdg. 24.67 (978-0-8368-2037-9(1)) Stevens, Gareth Inc.

Outcalt, Todd. Holidays, Holy Days, & Other Big Days for Youth. 2004. 112p. 13.00 (978-0-687-08204-9(8)) Abingdon Pr.

Parker-Rock, Michelle. Diwali: The Hindu Festival of Lights, Feasts, & Family. 2004. (Finding Out about Holidays Ser.). (Illus.). 48p. (J). lib. bdg. 23.93 (978-0-7660-2235-5(8)) Enslow Pubs., Inc.

Pickels, Dwayne E. Ancient & Annual Customs. 1999. (Looking Into the Past Ser.). (Illus.). 64p. (YA). (gr. 5 up). 14.00 (978-0-7910-4682-1(6) , Chelsea Hse.) Facts On File, Inc.

Picture Window Books, contrib. by. St Patrick's Day. (Holidays & Celebrations Ser.). 24p. (J). pap. 7.95 (978-1-4048-0493-7(5)) Picture Window Bks.

Pingry, Patricia A. The Easter Story. 2006. (Illus.). 32p. pap. 3.95 (978-0-8249-5531-1(5) , Ideals Children's Bks.) Ideals Pubns.

—The Easter Story. Utt, Mary Ann, illus. 2003. 26p. (J). bds. 6.95 (978-0-8249-4231-1(0)) Ideals Pubns.

—The Story of Easter. Wells, Lorraine Schreiner, illus. (J). 2002. (ENG & SPA.). 32p. 3.95 (978-0-8249-4204-5(3)); 1998. 26p. bds. 6.95 (978-0-8249-4090-4(3)) Ideals Pubns.

—The Story of Saint Patrick's Day. Levy, Pamela R., illus. 2001. 26p. (J). bds. 6.95 (978-0-8249-4145-1(4)) Ideals Pubns.

Pomaska, Anna. Easter. 2002. (Illus.). 64p. (J). pap., act. bk. ed. 1.50 (978-0-486-28329-6(1)) Dover Pubns., Inc.

Pratt, Susan, et al. Celebrate Holidays. Howard, Joan, ed. Filipov, Alex & Wyand, Glenn, illus. 1999. 48p. (J). (gr. k-3). pap. 14.95 incl. audio (978-1-894262-23-1(9) , JMP119K) Jordan Music Productions, Inc.

Presidents' Day. 2001. (Illus.). (J). pap. 21.95 (978-1-58810-027-6(8)) Heinemann Library.

Primm III, E. Russell & Petelinsek, Kathleen. Holidays & Celebrations. 2006. (Talking Hands Ser.).Tr. of Días de Fiesta y Celebraciones. (ENG & SPA.). 24p. (J). (ps). 21.36 (978-1-59296-453-6(2)) Child's World, Inc.

Raintree Steck-Vaughn Staff. Holidays Peschool Skills. 1999. pap. (978-0-7398-2917-2(3)) Steck-Vaughn.

—A World of Holidays, 13 bks., Set. 1998. (World of Holidays Ser.). (Illus.). (J). lib. bdg. 333.97 (978-0-8172-4618-1(5)) Raintree.

Rau, Dana. Kwanzaa. 2000. (gr. 3-6). lib. bdg. 15.25 (978-0-613-51658-7(3)) Tandem Library Bks.

Rau, Dana Meachen. Chanukah. 2000. (gr. 3-6). lib. bdg. 15.25 (978-0-613-51624-2(9)) Tandem Library Bks.

—Martin Luther King, Jr. Day. 2001. (gr. 3-6). lib. bdg. 15.25 (978-0-613-51661-7(3)) Tandem Library Bks.

Reynolds, Jan. Celebrate! Connections among Cultures. 2006. (Illus.). 32p. (J). (gr. k-3). 16.95 (978-1-58430-253-7(4)) Lee & Low Bks., Inc.

Richards, Jon. On Holidays. 2005. (Illus.). 32p. (J). (gr. 3 up). lib. bdg. 27.10 (978-1-59389-197-8(0)) Chrysalis Education.

Roberts, Russell. Holidays & Celebrations in Colonial America. 2006. (Building America Ser.). (Illus.). 48p. (J). (gr. 4-8). lib. bdg. 20.95 (978-1-58415-467-9(5)) Mitchell Lane Pubs., Inc.

Robinson, Fay. Chinese New Year - A Time for Parades, Family & Friends. 2001. (Finding Out about Holidays Ser.). (Illus.). 48p. (J). (gr. 1-4). lib. bdg. 23.93 (978-0-7660-1631-6(5)) Enslow Pubs., Inc.

Robson, Pam & Brown, Alan. How I Celebrate: A Young Person's Guide to Celebrations of the World. Gower, Teri, illus. 2001. 64p. (gr. 3-6). lib. bdg. 22.90 (978-0-7613-1952-8(2) , Millbrook Pr.) Lerner Publishing Group.

Roop, Peter & Roop, Connie. Let's Celebrate Earth Day. Connelly, Gwen, illus. 2001. 32p. pap. 6.95 (978-0-7613-1690-9(6) , Millbrook Pr.) Lerner Publishing Group.

—Let's Celebrate Presidents' Day. Connelly, Gwen, illus. 2001. (Let's Celebrate Ser.). 32p. (J). (gr. k-3). lib. bdg. 22.90 (978-0-7613-1813-2(5) , Millbrook Pr.) Lerner Publishing Group.

—Let's Celebrate St. Patrick's Day. Connelly, Gwen, illus. 2003. 32p. (J). (gr. 3-6). pap. 6.95 (978-0-7613-1782-1(1)); lib. bdg. 22.90 (978-0-7613-2505-5(0)) Lerner Publishing Group. (Millbrook Pr.).

Roraff, Susan. Chile. 1998. (Festivals of the World Ser.). (Illus.). 32p. (J). (gr. 3 up). lib. bdg. 24.67 (978-0-8368-2012-6(6)) Stevens, Gareth Inc.

Rosinsky, Natalie M. Christmas. 2002. (Let's See Library). (Illus.). 24p. (J). (gr. 1 up). lib. bdg. 19.93 (978-0-7565-0389-5(2)) Compass Point Bks.

—Halloween. 2002. (Let's See Library). (Illus.). 24p. (J). (gr. 1 up). lib. bdg. 19.93 (978-0-7565-0392-5(2)) Compass Point Bks.

—Hanukkah. 2002. (Let's See Library). (Illus.). 24p. (J). (gr. 1 up). lib. bdg. 19.93 (978-0-7565-0390-1(6)) Compass Point Bks.

—Juneteenth. 2004. (Let's See Ser.). (Illus.). 24p. (J). (gr. 1). lib. bdg. 19.93 (978-0-7565-0770-1(7)) Compass Point Bks.

—Let's See Library - Holidays, 6 bks. Incl. Christmas. lib. bdg. 19.93 (978-0-7565-0389-5(2)); Halloween. lib. bdg. 19.93 (978-0-7565-0392-5(2)); Hanukkah. lib. bdg. 19.93 (978-0-7565-0390-1(6)); St. Patrick's Day. lib. bdg. 19.93 (978-0-7565-0394-9(9)); Thanksgiving. lib. bdg. 19.93 (978-0-7565-0391-8(4)); Valentine's Day. lib. bdg. 19.93 (978-0-7565-0393-2(0)); 24p. (J). (gr. 1 up). 2002. (Illus.). 2003. Set lib. bdg. 119.60 (978-0-7565-0403-8(1)) Compass Point Bks.

—St. Patrick's Day. 2002. (Let's See Library). (Illus.). 24p. (J). (gr. 1 up). lib. bdg. 19.93 (978-0-7565-0394-9(9)) Compass Point Bks.

—Thanksgiving. 2002. (Let's See Library). (Illus.). 24p. (J). (gr. 1 up). lib. bdg. 19.93 (978-0-7565-0391-8(4)) Compass Point Bks.

Rue, Nancy N. The Year 'Round Holiday Book: It's a God Thing! 2002. (Ywof Library). (Illus.). 112p. (J). pap. 7.99 (978-0-310-70256-6(9)) Zonderkidz.

San Vicente, Luis. The Festival of Bones, el Festival de las Calaveras: The Little-Bitty Book for the Day of the Dead. Byrd, John Williams & Byrd, Bobby, trs. San Vicente, Luis, illus. 2002. (SPA & ENG., Illus.). 32p. (J). (gr. k-5). 14.95 (978-0-938317-67-8(9)) Cinco Puntos Pr.

Sanders, Nancy I. Earth Day. 2003. (True Book Ser.). (Illus.). 48p. (J). 25.00 (978-0-516-22762-7(9) , Children's Pr.) Scholastic Library Publishing.

—Earth Day, April 22. 2003. (gr. 3-6). lib. bdg. 15.25 (978-0-613-89013-7(2)) Tandem Library Bks.

—Independence Day. 2003. (Illus.). 47p. (J). (gr. 3-5). lib. bdg. 15.25 (978-0-613-89015-1(9)) Tandem Library Bks.

Sanna, Ellyn. Folk Festivals. 2002. (North American Folklore Ser.). (Illus.). 112p. (YA). (gr. 7 up). lib. bdg. (978-1-59084-340-6(1)) Mason Crest Pubs.

Santella, Andrew. The First Thanksgiving. 2003. (Cornerstones of Freedom). (Illus.). 48p. (J). (gr. 4-6). 26.00 (978-0-516-24204-0(0) , Children's Pr.) Scholastic Library Publishing.

Schaefer, Lola M. Chinese New Year. Saunders-Smith, Gail, ed. 2001. (Holidays & Celebrations Ser.). (Illus.). 24p. (J). (gr. k-1). lib. bdg. 15.93 (978-0-7368-0660-2(1) , Pebble Bks.) Capstone Pr., Inc.

—Cinco de Mayo. Saunders-Smith, Gail, ed. 2000. (Holidays & Celebrations Ser.). (Illus.). 24p. (J). (gr. k-1). lib. bdg. 15.95 (978-0-7368-0661-9(X) , Pebble Bks.) Capstone Pr., Inc.

—Cinco de Mayo, Vol. 2. 2005. (One World, Many Cultures Ser.). 24p. (YA). (gr. k-3). pap. (978-0-7368-9430-2(6) , Pebble Bks.) Capstone Pr., Inc.

Schaun, George & Schaun, Virginia. American Holidays & Special Days. Wisniewski, David, illus. 3rd ed. 2002. 256p. (J). 20.00 (978-0-917882-54-8(7)) Maryland Historical Pr.

Scholastic, Inc. Staff. Happy Holidays. 1999. (J). pap. 3.95 (978-0-439-07234-2(4)) Scholastic, Inc.

—Seasons & Holidays. 2004. (Biggie Patterns Ser.). 48p. pap. 10.99 (978-0-439-46840-4(X)) Scholastic, Inc.

Scholastic Library Publishing Staff. Rookie Read-About Holidays. 2004. 532.00 (978-0-516-24706-9(9)) Scholastic Library Publishing.

Schuh, Mari C. Easter. (Holidays & Celebrations Ser.). (Illus.). 24p. (gr. k-1). 2002. (J). lib. bdg. 15.93 (978-0-7368-1445-4(0)); Vol. 2. 2005. (YA). (978-0-7368-9398-5(9)) Capstone Pr., Inc. (Pebble Bks.).

—Labor Day. 2003. (National Holidays Ser.). (Illus.). 24p. (J). (gr. k-1). lib. bdg. 15.93 (978-0-7368-1653-3(4) , Pebble Bks.) Capstone Pr., Inc.

—Passover. 2002. (Holidays & Celebrations Ser.). (Illus.). 24p. (J). (gr. k-1). lib. bdg. 15.93 (978-0-7368-1447-8(7) , Pebble Bks.) Capstone Pr., Inc.

—Veterans Day. 2003. (National Holidays Ser.). (Illus.). 24p. (J). (gr. k-1). lib. bdg. 15.93 (978-0-7368-1655-7(0) , Pebble Bks.) Capstone Pr., Inc.

A Second Birthday: 6 Small Books. (Greetings Ser.: Vol. 2). 24p. (gr. 2-3). 31.00 (978-0-7635-9414-5(8)) Rigby Education.

A Second Birthday: Big Book. (Greetings Ser.: Vol. 2). 24p. (gr. 2-3). 31.00 (978-0-7635-5698-3(X)) Rigby Education.

Sesame Street Countdown to the Holiday. 2006. (J). 3.99 (***978-1-59545-117-0(X)***) Learning Horizons, Inc.

Sesame Street Merry Monsters Holiday Wipe Off. 2006. (J). 3.99 (***978-1-59545-116-3(1)***) Learning Horizons, Inc.

Shaw, Brenda Sanderson. Telling Kids the Truth about Holidays: Is Santa Real? 2005. 60p. pap. 19.95 (978-1-59800-040-5(3)) Outskirts Press, Inc.

Shea, Pegi Deitz & Weill, Cynthia. Ten Mice for Tet. Trang, Ngoc, illus. 2003. 36p. (J). 15.95 (978-0-8118-3496-4(4)) Chronicle Bks. LLC.

Shinju, Mariko. A Pumpkin Story. Shinju, Mariko, illus. 1998. (Illus.). 32p. (J). (ps-4). 16.95 (978-1-880851-36-4(9)) Greene Bark Pr., Inc.

Simonds, Nina, et al. Moonbeams, Dumplings & Dragon Boats: A Treasury of Chinese Holiday Tales, Activities & Recipes. So, Meilo, illus. 2002. 80p. (J). (gr. 4-7). 21.00 (978-0-15-201983-9(9)) Harcourt Children's Bks.

Sioras, Efstathia. Greece. 1998. (Festivals of the World Ser.). (Illus.). 32p. (J). (gr. 3 up). lib. bdg. 24.67 (978-0-8368-2014-0(2)) Stevens, Gareth Inc.

Sosa, Carlos. Celebrations. 2007. (Familia Banderas Ser.). (Illus.). 48p. (J). (gr. 3-7). per. 9.95 (***978-1-933669-11-3(X)***) Literary Architects, LLC.

Sosa, Carlos & Castaneda, Patricia. Celebrations: La Familia Banderas. 2006. (Illus.). 48p. (J). pap. 9.95 (978-1-933669-03-8(9)) Literary Architects, LLC.

St Patrick's Day, Vol. 2. 2005. (One World, Many Cultures Ser.). (YA). (gr. k-3). (978-0-7368-9404-3(7) , Pebble Bks.) Capstone Pr., Inc.

The Story of Chanukah. 2002. (Illus.). 24p. (J). 6.95 (978-0-8249-4225-0(6)) Ideals Pubns.

Sullivan, Erin Ash. Holidays Around the World. 2006. (Navigators Ser.). (J). pap. 38.00 (***978-1-4108-6244-0(5)***) Benchmark Education Co.

Sussman, Ellen. Cooking with Kids. Mitchell, Judy, ed. 2000. (Illus.). 128p. (J). (ps-3). pap., tchr. ed. 13.95 (978-1-57310-260-5(1)) Teaching & Learning Co.

Sussman, Ellen & Mitchell, Judy, eds. Songs, Action Rhymes & Fingerplays. 2000. (Illus.). 128p. (J). (ps-3). pap., tchr. ed. 13.95 (978-1-57310-236-0(9)) Teaching & Learning Co.

Swain, Gwenyth. Celebrating. 1999. (Small World Ser.). (Illus.). 24p. (J). (ps-2). lib. bdg. 19.93 (978-1-57505-258-8(X) , Carolrhoda Bks.) Lerner Publishing Group.

Sweeney, Alyse. Nonfiction Read & Write Booklets: Holidays: 10 Interactive Reproducible Booklets That Help Students Build Content Knowledge & Reading Comprehension Skills. 2007. 48p. pap. 10.99 (978-0-439-56758-9(0) , Teaching Resources) Scholastic, Inc.

Tait, Leia. Cinco de Mayo. 2006. (J). (978-1-59036-460-4(0)); (978-1-59036-463-5(5)) Weigl Pubs., Inc.

Taylor, Charles A. Juneteenth: A Celebration of Freedom. Taylor, Charles A., Jr., illus. 2002. 32p. (YA). (gr. 5-8). trans. 19.95 (978-0-940880-68-9(7)) Open Hand Publishing, LLC.

Thoennes, Kristin. Christmas in France. 1998. (Christmas Around the World Ser.). (Illus.). 24p. (J). (gr. 2-3). 18.60 (978-0-7368-0088-4(3) , Bridgestone Bks.) Capstone Pr., Inc.

—Christmas in Germany. 1998. (Christmas Around the World Ser.). (Illus.). 24p. (J). (gr. 2-3). lib. bdg. 19.93 (978-0-7368-0089-1(1) , Bridgestone Bks.) Capstone Pr., Inc.

—Christmas in Italy. 1998. (Christmas Around the World Ser.). (Illus.). 24p. (J). (gr. 2-3). 18.60 (978-0-7368-0090-7(5) , Bridgestone Bks.) Capstone Pr., Inc.

—Christmas in Norway. 1998. (Christmas Around the World Ser.). (Illus.). 24p. (J). (gr. 2-3). 18.60 (978-0-7368-0091-4(3) , Bridgestone Bks.) Capstone Pr., Inc.

Thomas, John E. & Thomas, Danita. The Ultimate Book of Holiday Kid Concoctions Vol. 3: More Than 50 Wacky, Wild & Crazy Holiday Concoctions, 4 vols., Vol. 3. Durr, Robb & Durr, Zachariah, illus. 2001. 83p. (J). (ps-9). per. 14.95 (978-0-9661088-3-5(3) , 50,000) Kid Concoctions Co.

Totally Lent! A Child's Journey to Easter 2007. 2006. (J). 5.95 (978-1-933178-46-2(9)) Pflaum Publishing Group.

Totally Lent! A Child's Journey to Easter 2008. 2007. (J). 5.95 (***978-1-933178-70-7(1)***) Pflaum Publishing Group.

Totally Lent! A Kid's Journey to Easter 2007. 2006. (J). 5.95 (978-1-933178-45-5(0)) Pflaum Publishing Group.

Totally Lent! A Kid's Journey to Easter 2008. 2007. (J). 5.95 (***978-1-933178-71-4(X)***) Pflaum Publishing Group.

Totally Lent! A Teen's Journey to Easter 2007. 2006. (J). 5.95 (978-1-933178-44-8(2)) Pflaum Publishing Group.

Totally Lent! A Teen's Journey to Easter 2008. 2007. (YA). 5.95 (***978-1-933178-72-1(8)***) Pflaum Publishing Group.

Tran, Kim-Lan & Millar, Louise. Tet: The New Year. Vo-Dinh, Mai, illus. 2005. (Multicultural Celebrations Ser.). 32p. (J). 4.95 (978-1-59373-012-3(8)) Bunker Hill Publishing, Inc.

Trueit, Trudi Strain. Diwali. 2006. (Rookie Read-About Holidays Ser.). (Illus.). 31p. (J). (978-0-531-12454-3(1)) Children's Pr., Ltd.

—Diwali. rev. ed. 2006. 32p. (YA). (gr. 1-2). pap. 5.95 (978-0-531-11835-1(5) , Children's Pr.) Scholastic Library Publishing.

—Earth Day. rev. ed. 2006. 32p. (YA). (gr. 1-2). pap. 5.95 (978-0-531-11836-8(3) , Children's Pr.) Scholastic Library Publishing.

—Memorial Day. 2007. (Holidays, Festivals, & Celebrations Ser.). 32p. (J). (gr. k-4). 22.79 (***978-1-59296-815-2(5)***) Child's World, Inc.

—President's Day. 2007. (Holidays, Festivals, & Celebrations Ser.). 32p. (J). (gr. k-4). 22.79 (***978-1-59296-816-9(3)***) Child's World, Inc.

Urrutia, Maria C., et al. Cinco de Mayo: Yesterday & Today. 2002. (SPA., Illus.). 32p. (J). (gr. 5 up). pap. 6.95 (978-0-88899-484-4(2)) Groundwood Bks. CAN. *Dist:* Perseus Distribution.

Urrutia, Maria Cristina & Orozco, Rebeca. Cinco de Mayo: Yesterday & Today. 2006. (SPA., Illus.). 29p. (J). (gr. 4-8). reprint ed. 16.00 (978-1-4223-5464-3(4)) DIANE Publishing Co.

Van Fenema, Joyce. Netherlands. 1998. (Festivals of the World Ser.). (Illus.). 32p. (J). (gr. 3 up). lib. bdg. 24.67 (978-0-8368-2016-4(9)) Stevens, Gareth Inc.

Vasquez, Sarah. Cinco de Mayo. 1999. (World of Holidays Ser.). (Illus.). 32p. (J). (gr. 2-5). lib. bdg. 25.70 (978-0-8172-5562-6(1)) Raintree.

Vazquez, Sarah. Cinco de Mayo. 1999. (World of Holidays Ser.). (Illus.). 32p. (J). (gr. 2-5). pap. 8.95 (978-0-8172-4205-3(8)) Steck-Vaughn.

Venter, Sahm. Youth Day: June 16. 2007. (Exploring our National Days Ser.). 72p. pap. 20.00 (***978-1-77009-235-8(8)***) Jacana Media ZAF. *Dist:* Independent Pubs. Group.

Veteran's Day. 2001. (Illus.). (J). pap. 21.95 (978-1-58810-026-9(X)) Heinemann Library.

Viesti, Joseph F. & Hall, Diane. Celebrate! in South Asia. 2000. (Illus.). 30p. (YA). (gr. 6-7). reprint ed. 16.00 (978-0-7881-9296-8(5)) DIANE Publishing Co.

Wade, Mary Dodson. Cinco de Mayo. 2003. (Rookie Read-About Holidays Ser.). (Illus.). 32p. (J). (gr. 1-2). pap. 5.95 (978-0-516-27489-8(9) , Children's Pr.) Scholastic Library Publishing.

—Cinco de Mayo. 2003. (gr. k-3). lib. bdg. 14.10 (978-0-613-59594-0(7)) Tandem Library Bks.

—El Dia de los Muertos. 2002. (Rookie Read-About Holidays Ser.).Tr. of Day of the Dead. (Illus.). 32p. (J). (gr. 1-2). pap. 20.50 (978-0-516-22493-0(X) , Children's Pr.) Scholastic Library Publishing.

—El Dia de Los Muertos. 2002. (SPA.). lib. bdg. 14.10 (978-0-613-54193-0(6)) Tandem Library Bks.

—Presidents' Day: Honoring the Birthdays of Washington & Lincoln. 2004. (Finding Out about Holidays Ser.). (Illus.). 48p. (J). lib. bdg. 23.93 (978-0-7660-2234-8(X)) Enslow Pubs., Inc.

Wallace, Paula S. The World of Holidays. 2003. (Life Around the World Ser.). (Illus.). 48p. (J). (gr. 2 up). lib. bdg. 24.67 (978-0-8368-3661-5(8)) Stevens, Gareth Inc.

Walsh, Kieran. Chinese New Year. 2002. (Illus.). 24p. (J). lib. bdg. 20.64 (978-1-58952-215-2(X)) Rourke Publishing, LLC.

Watson, Yolanda. Which Holiday Is It? 2003. (Compass Point Phonics Readers Ser.). (Illus.). 16p. (J). (gr. 1 up). 13.26 (978-0-7565-0533-2(X)) Compass Point Bks.

Which Holiday Is It? Set B, 6 vols. (Phonics Readers Ser.). (gr. k-2). 17.50 (978-0-7368-3210-6(6)) Red Brick Learning.

Williams, Colleen Madonna Flood. The Festivals of Mexico. 2002. (Encyclopedia of Mexico Ser.). (Illus.). 64,80p. (YA). (gr. 5 up). lib. bdg. (978-1-59084-078-8(X)) Mason Crest Pubs.

—My Adventure on Father's Day. 2007. 44p. (J). 8.99 (978-1-59092-547-8(5) , Orchard Academy Pr.) Windstorm Creative.

—My Adventure on Groundhog Day. 2007. 44p. (J). 8.99 (978-1-59092-548-5(3) , Orchard Academy Pr.) Windstorm Creative.

—My Adventure on Martin Luther King Jr. Day. 2007. 44p. (J). 8.99 (978-1-59092-551-5(3) , Orchard Academy Pr.) Windstorm Creative.

—My Adventure on President's Day. 2007. 44p. (J). 8.99 (978-1-59092-555-3(6) , Orchard Academy Pr.) Windstorm Creative.

—My Adventure on St. Patrick's Day. 2007. 44p. (J). 8.99 (978-1-59092-556-0(4) , Orchard Academy Pr.) Windstorm Creative.

—My Adventure on Veteran's Day. 2006. 44p. (J). 8.99 (978-1-59092-559-1(9) , Orchard Academy Pr.) Windstorm Creative.

Willoughby, Robert. Three Easter Journeys. 2004. (Illus.). 24p. (ps-3). pap. 5.00 (978-0-687-04851-9(6)) Abingdon Pr.

Wilson, Sule Greg C. Kwanzaa! Africa Lives in a New World Festival. 1999. (Library of African American Arts & Culture). (Illus.). 64p. (YA). (gr. 7-12). lib. bdg. 26.50 (978-0-8239-1857-7(2) , AAKWAN) Rosen Publishing Group, Inc., The.

Winchester, Faith. African American Holidays. 1999. (Ethnic Holidays Ser.). (Illus.). 24p. (J). (gr. 2-3). lib. bdg. 18.60 (978-1-56065-456-8(2) , Bridgestone Bks.) Capstone Pr., Inc.

—Ethnic Holidays, 4 bks. Incl. African American Holidays. 1999. lib. bdg. 18.60 (978-1-56065-456-8(2)); Asian Holidays. 1996. lib. bdg. 18.60 (978-1-56065-458-2(9)); Hispanic Holidays. 1996. lib. bdg. 18.60 (978-1-56065-457-5(0)); Muslim Holidays. 1999. lib. bdg. 18.60 (978-1-56065-459-9(7)); 24p. (J). (gr. 2-3). (Illus.). Set lib. bdg. 74.40 (978-1-56065-631-9(X) , Bridgestone Bks.) Capstone Pr., Inc.

—Muslim Holidays. 1999. (Ethnic Holidays Ser.). (Illus.). 24p. (J). (gr. 2-3). lib. bdg. 18.60 (978-1-56065-459-9(7) , Bridgestone Bks.) Capstone Pr., Inc.

Winne, Joanne. Celebrations, 6 bks., Set. 2004. (Illus.). 24p (J). (ps-2). 174.00 (978-0-516-22995-9(8) , Children's Pr.) Scholastic Library Publishing.

Winter, Jeanette. Calavera Abecedario: A Day of the Dead Alphabet Book. 2004. (Illus.). 48p. (J). 16.00 (978-0-15-205110-5(4)) Harcourt Children's Bks.

World Book, Inc. Staff, contrib. by. Harvest Celebrations. 2002. (World Book's Celebrations & Rituals Around the World Ser.). (Illus.). 44p. (J). (978-0-7166-5007-2(X)) World Bk., Inc.

—National Celebrations. 2002. (World Book's Celebrations & Rituals Around the World Ser.). (Illus.). 44p. (J). (978-0-7166-5009-6(6)) World Bk., Inc.

—Spring Celebrations. 2002. (World Book's Celebrations & Rituals Around the World Ser.). (Illus.). 44p. (J). (978-0-7166-5008-9(8)) World Bk., Inc.

—Winter Celebrations. 2003. (World Book's Celebrations & Rituals Around the World Ser.). (Illus.). 46p. (J). (978-0-7166-5013-3(4)) World Bk., Inc.

World of Holidays Series, 13 bks., Set. 2000. (World of Holidays Ser.). (Illus.). pap. 333.97 (978-0-7398-4199-0(8)) Steck-Vaughn.

Worth, Bonnie. Hurray for Today: All About Holidays. Ruiz, Aristides, tr. Ruiz, Aristides & Mathieu, Joe, illus. 2004. (Cat in the Hat's Learning Library). 48p. (J). (gr. k-3). 8.99 (978-0-375-82275-9(5) , Random Hse. Bks. for Young Readers) Random Hse. Children's Bks.

—Hurray for Today: All about Holidays. Ruiz, Aristides, tr. Ruiz, Aristides, illus. 2004. (Cat in the Hat's Learning Library Ser.). 48p. (J). (gr. k-3). lib. bdg. 11.99 (978-0-375-92275-6(X) , Random Hse. Bks. for Young Readers) Random Hse. Children's Bks.

Yolen, Jane & Christiana, David. The Book of Fairy Holidays. 1998. (J). (978-0-590-60356-0(6) , Blue Sky Pr., The) Scholastic, Inc.

Yu, Ling. Cooking the Chinese Way. 2nd exp. rev. ed. (Easy Menu Ethnic Cookbooks). (Illus.). 72p. (J). (gr. 5-12). 2002. lib. bdg. 25.26 (978-0-8225-4104-2(1)); 2003. pap. 7.95 (978-0-8225-4160-8(2)) Lerner Publishing Group.

—Cooking the Chinese Way. 2001. (Illus.). 72p. (J). (gr. 4-7). lib. bdg. 16.40 (978-0-613-59145-4(3)) Tandem Library Bks.

Zemlicka, Shannon. Easter Around the World. Erickson, David, illus. 2005. (On My Own Holidays Ser.). 48p. (J). (gr. k-3). 5.95 (978-1-57505-765-1(4)); (gr. 2-4). 25.26 (978-1-57505-655-5(0)) Lerner Publishing Group.

Zocchi, Judy. On Chinese New Year. Wallis, Rebecca, illus. 2005. (Holiday Happenings Ser.). 32p. (J). pap. 9.95 (978-1-59646-188-8(8)); lib. bdg. 20.65 (978-1-891997-55-6(6)) Dingles & Co.

—On Chinese New Year/el Año Nuevo Chino. Wallis, Rebecca, illus. 2005. (Holiday Happenings Ser.).Tr. of Año Nuevo Chino. (ENG & SPA.). 32p. (J). pap. 9.95 (978-1-59646-190-1(X)); lib. bdg. 20.65 (978-1-891997-56-3(4)) Dingles & Co.

—On Christmas Eve. Wallis, Rebecca, illus. 2005. (Holiday Happenings Ser.). 32p. (J). lib. bdg. 20.65 (978-1-891997-47-1(5)) Dingles & Co.

—On Easter Morning. Wallis, Rebecca, illus. 2005. (Holiday Happenings Ser.). (ENM.). 32p. (J). lib. bdg. 20.65 (978-1-891997-41-9(6)) Dingles & Co.

—On Halloween Night. Wallis, Rebecca, illus. 2005. (Holiday Happenings Ser.). (ENG.). 32p. (J). lib. bdg. 20.65 (978-1-891997-77-8(7)) Dingles & Co.

—On Independence Day. Wallis, Rebecca, illus. 2005. (Holiday Happenings Ser.). 32p. (J). per. 9.95 (978-1-59646-209-0(4)) Dingles & Co.

—On Independence Day/el día de la Independencia. Wallis, Rebecca, illus. 2005. (Holiday Happenings Ser.).Tr. of día de la Independencia. (ENG & SPA.). 32p. (J). per. 9.95 (978-1-59646-211-3(6)) Dingles & Co.

—On Saint Patrick's Day. Wallis, Rebecca, illus. 2005. (Holiday Happenings Ser.). (ENG.). 32p. (J). lib. bdg. 20.65 (978-1-891997-39-6(4)) Dingles & Co.

—On Thanksgiving Day. Wallis, Rebecca, illus. 2004. (Holiday Happenings Ser.). (ENM.). 32p. (J). lib. bdg. 20.65 (978-1-891997-74-7(2)) Dingles & Co.

—On Three Kings Day. Wallis, Rebecca, illus. 2005. (Holiday Happenings Ser.). 32p. (J). pap. 9.95 (978-1-59646-204-5(3)); lib. bdg. 20.65 (978-1-891997-53-2(X)); per. 9.95 (978-1-59646-205-2(1)) Dingles & Co.

—On Three Kings Day/el día de los tres Reyes Magos. Wallis, Rebecca, illus. 2005. (Holiday Happenings Ser.).Tr. of día de los tres Reyes Magos. (ENG & SPA.). 32p. (J). pap. 9.95 (978-1-59646-206-9(X)); lib. bdg. 20.65 (978-1-891997-54-9(8)); per. 9.95 (978-1-59646-207-6(8)) Dingles & Co.

—On Valentine's Day. Wallis, Rebecca, illus. 2005. (Holiday Happenings Ser.). 32p. (J). lib. bdg. 20.65 (978-1-891997-79-2(3)) Dingles & Co.

Zucker, Jonny. Lanterns & Firecrackers: A Chinese New Year Story. Cohen, Jan Barger, illus. 2004. (Festival Time! Ser.). 24p. (J). pap. 6.95 (978-0-7641-2668-0(7)) Barron's Educational Series, Inc.

Zwierzynska-Coldicott, Aldona M. Poland. 1998. (Festivals of the World Ser.). (Illus.). 32p. (J). (gr. 3 up). lib. bdg. 24.67 (978-0-8368-2018-8(5)) Stevens, Gareth Inc.

The 100th Day of School. (Holidays & Celebrations Ser.). 24p. (J). 7.95 (978-1-4048-0492-0(7)) Picture Window Bks.

HOLIDAYS—DRAMA

Halligan, Terry. Funny Skits & Sketches. Behr, Joyce, illus. unabr. ed. 2003. 128p. (YA). (gr. 4-12). pap. 15.00 (978-0-88734-688-0(X)) Players Pr., Inc.

HOLIDAYS—FICTION

Ada, Alma Flor. Le Hamaca de la Vaca: O un Amigo Mas. 2000. Tr. of In the Cow's Backyard. (SPA.). (gr. k-3). lib. bdg. 17.60 (978-0-613-79370-4(6)) Tandem Library Bks.

Ahlstrom, Leonard. Christmas Shoes for Children. 2004. pap. 7.99 (978-0-9714147-1-6(8)) Point To Point Publishing.

Allon, Jeffrey, illus. Ten Holiday Jewish Children's Stories. 2000. (Storyteller Ser.). 48p. (J). (ps-3). 16.95 (978-0-943706-47-4(5)); pap. 9.95 (978-0-943706-48-1(3)) Pitspopany Pr.

Amado, Elisa. Barrilete: A Kite for the Day of the Dead. 1999. (SPA., Illus.). (J). (ps-3). pap. 6.95 (978-0-88899-381-6(1) , Libros Tigrillo) Groundwood Bks. CAN. *Dist:* Transition Vendor.

American Girl Editorial Staff, creator. The American Girls Holiday Treasury. 2005. (American Girls Collection). (Illus.). 429p. (J). (gr. 3-7). 34.95 incl. audio compact disk (978-1-59369-060-1(6) , American Girl) American Girl Publishing, Inc.

Anderson, Laurie Halse. No Time for Mother's Day. 2001. (978-0-606-21356-1(2)); 1999. lib. bdg. 15.25 (978-0-613-37020-2(1)) Tandem Library Bks.

—Thank You, Sarah: The Woman Who Saved Thanksgiving. 2003. mass mkt. 6.99 (978-0-689-84902-2(8) , Aladdin) Simon & Schuster Children's Publishing.

Awdry, Wilbert V. Thomas's Christmas Delivery. Stubbs, Tommy, illus. 2004. (Thomas & Friends Ser.). 32p. (J). (ps-2). 8.99 (978-0-375-82877-5(X) , Random Hse. Bks. for Young Readers) Random Hse. Children's Bks.

Baglio, Ben M. Kitten in the Cold. McNicholas, Shelagh, illus. 1999. (Animal Ark Ser.). 144p. (J). (gr. 3-5). pap. 3.99 (978-0-439-09698-0(7)) Scholastic, Inc.

Bell, Frank & Bowler, Colin. Panda Patrol Go on Holiday. Seaman, Paul, illus. 2004. 24p. pap. 7.00 (978-1-84161-083-2(6)) Ravette Publishing, Ltd. GBR. *Dist:* Parkwest Pubns., Inc.

Bentley, Dawn. Gingerbread Man. 2005. (Holiday Sparkler Bks.). (Illus.). 10p. (J). 4.95 (978-1-58117-163-1(3) , Intervisual/Piggy Toes) Dalmatian Pr.

Berenstain, Stan & Berenstain, Jan. The Berenstain Bears & the Mama's Day Surprise. 2004. (Berenstain Bears First Time Bks.). (Illus.). 32p. (J). (gr. k-3). pap. 3.99 (978-0-375-81132-6(X)); lib. bdg. 10.99 (978-0-375-91132-3(4)) Random Hse. Children's Bks. (Random Hse. Bks. for Young Readers).

Bick, Janice. Belinda Lee. 2006. 17.00 (***978-0-8059-8850-5(5)***) Dorrance Publishing Co., Inc.

Bickel, Karla. Easter Lights. Bickel, Karla, illus. l.t. ed. 2004. (Illus.). 16p. (J). (ps-6). pap. 5.00 (978-1-891452-14-7(2) , 7) Heart Arbor Bks.

Blake, Jon & Roberts, David. Holiday Mania at the House of Fun. 2007. (Illus.). 128p. pap. 6.95 (***978-0-340-93129-5(9)***) Hodder Children's Division GBR. *Dist:* Independent Pubs. Group.

Blumberg, Margie. Avram's Gift. McGaw, Laurie, illus. 48p. 2005. (YA). pap. 7.95 (978-0-9624166-3-7(0)); 2003. (J). (gr. 3 up). (978-0-9624166-2-0(2)) MB Publishing, LLC.

Boniface, William. Five Little Turkeys. Adams, Lynn, illus. 2003. 12p. (J). (ps). 5.99 (978-0-8431-0464-6(3) , Price Stern Sloan) Penguin Group (USA) Inc.

Book Company Staff. Teddy Mini Box Set. 2002. (Pop-up Books Mini Ser.). 14p. (J). 15.95 (978-1-74047-209-8(8)) Book Co. Publishing Pty, Ltd., The AUS. *Dist:* Penton Overseas, Inc.

Bourgeois, Paulette. Franklin's Holiday Treasury. Clark, Brenda, illus. 2002. (Franklin Treasuries Ser.). 128p. (J). (gr. k-3). (978-1-55337-045-1(7)) Kids Can Pr., Ltd.

Bracegirdle, Paul. Comet Can't Wait for Christmas. Mitchell, Susan, illus. 2007. 16p. (J). (ps-1). pap. 5.99 (***978-0-689-87139-9(2)*** , Little Simon) Simon & Schuster Children's Publishing.

Bridwell, Norman. Clifford Celebrates the Year. 2002. (Clifford Ser.). (Illus.). 256p. (J). pap. 10.99 (978-0-439-46770-4(5)) Scholastic, Inc.

Brimner, Larry Dane. A Flag for All. Tripp, Christine, illus. 2003. (Rookie Choices Ser.). 32p. (J). (gr. 1-2). pap. 5.95 (978-0-516-27792-9(8) , Children's Pr.) Scholastic Library Publishing.

—Flag for All. 2002. (gr. k-3). lib. bdg. 14.10 (978-0-613-59479-0(7)) Tandem Library Bks.

Brownlow, Brooke. The Magic of Old Oak Hill. 2005. 48p. pap. 12.95 (978-1-4241-0223-5(5)) PublishAmerica, Inc.

Bryant, Megan E. The Berry Blossom Festival. MJ Illustrations Staff, illus. 2007. (Strawberry Shortcake Ser.). 1p. (J). (gr. k-2). bds. 9.99 (978-0-448-44555-7(7) , Grosset & Dunlap) Penguin Group (USA) Inc.

Budgell, Gill. A Week in the Holidays. 2000. (Cambridge Reading Ser.). (Illus.). 14p. pap. 5.00 (978-0-521-77449-9(7)) Cambridge Univ. Pr.

Bunting, Eve. A Perfect Father's Day. 2002. (Illus.). (J). 13.79 (978-0-7587-3390-0(9)) Book Wholesalers, Inc.

Cambridge Young Writers Staff. I'm Telling You!, 6 vols., Pack. 2001. (Cambridge Reading Ser.). (Illus.). 80p. pap. 46.00 (978-0-521-01353-6(4)) Cambridge Univ. Pr.

Cann, Kate. Mediterranean Holiday. 2007. 336p. (J). pap. 5.99 (***978-0-06-115216-0(1)*** , HarperTeen) HarperCollins Pubs.

Capalija, Ann Marie. Rose Blossom's First Christmas. LoRaso, Carlo, illus. 2005. (My Little Pony Ser.). 24p. (J). (ps-2). pap. 4.99 (978-0-06-076182-0(2) , Harper Festival) HarperCollins Pubs.

Capstone Press Staff. Celebrate! Series, 3 bks. 1999. (gr. 3-7). pap. (978-0-516-29999-0(9) , Children's Pr.) Scholastic Library Publishing.

Capucilli, Alyssa Satin. Biscuit Loves Father's Day. Schories, Pat, illus. 2004. 20p. (J). 6.99 (978-0-06-009463-8(X) , Harper Festival) HarperCollins Pubs.

—Biscuit Loves Mother's Day. Schories, Pat & Young, Mary O'Keefe, illus. 2004. 20p. (J). pap. 6.99 (978-0-06-009462-1(1) , Harper Festival) HarperCollins Pubs.

Carr, Roe Annie. Nan Sherwood's Winter Holidays or Rescui. 2006. 78.99 (***978-1-4219-9942-5(0)***); pap. 72.99 (***978-1-4219-9946-3(3)***) IndyPublish.com.

Chapman, Brenda. Hiding in Hawk's Creek. 2006. 134p. (J). pap. 8.95 (978-1-894917-24-7(3)) Napoleon Publishing/Rendezvous Pr. CAN. *Dist:* AtlasBooks Distribution.

Ching, Tokie. Girl's Day in Hawaii with Yuki Chan. 2006. 40p. (J). 12.95 (***978-1-56647-820-5(0)***) Mutual Publishing LLC.

Clark, Emma Chichester. Merry Christmas to You, Blue Kangaroo! Clark, Emma Chichester, illus. 2004. (Illus.). 32p. (J). (gr. k-k). lib. bdg. 17.99 (978-0-385-90918-1(7) , Doubleday Bks. for Young Readers) Random Hse. Children's Bks.

Clugston-Major, Chynna. Inbetween Days, 3 vols. 2003. (Blue Monday Ser.: Vol. 3). (Illus.). 96p. (YA). pap. 9.95 (978-1-929998-66-1(X)) Oni Pr., Inc.

Collins, Terry. Scary Odd Parents: A FairLy Odd HaLLoween. Schigiel, Gregg, illus. 2004. 24p. (J). lib. bdg. 18.46 (***978-1-4242-0969-9(2)***) Fitzgerald Bks.

Collins, Terry. Scary OddParents: A Fairly Odd Halloween. Schigiel, Gregg, illus. 2004. (Fairly OddParents Ser.). 16p. (J). pap. 5.99 (978-0-689-86897-9(9) , Simon Spotlight/Nickelodeon) Simon & Schuster Children's Publishing.

Cooper, Alexandra. Spin the Dreidel! Gévry, Claudine, illus. 2004. 14p. (J). 7.99 (978-0-689-86430-8(2) , Little Simon) Simon & Schuster Children's Publishing.

Cousins, Lucy. With Love from Maisy. 2004. (Maisy Ser.). (Illus.). 16p. (J). (gr. k-k). 13.99 (978-0-7636-2513-9(2)) Candlewick Pr.

Cox, Judy. Go to Sleep, Groundhog. Meisel, Paul, illus. 32p. (gr. k-3). tchr. ed. 17.95 (978-0-8234-1645-5(3)) Holiday Hse., Inc.

Crocitto, Frank. A Child's Christmas in Brooklyn. Horrigan, Jeremiah, ed. Horrigan, Grady Kane, illus. 2001. 96p. (YA). (gr. 4 up). 10.95 (978-0-9677558-2-3(4) , CHBO1) Candlepower, Inc.

DaColl, Ivar. El Dia de Muertos. 2004. Tr. of Day of the Dead. (SPA., Illus.). (J). 14.95 (978-1-930332-44-7(0)) Lectorum Pubns., Inc.

Davies, Hunter. Flossie Teacake's Holiday. 2000. (Illus.). 176p. (J). pap. 8.99 (978-0-09-940372-2(2)) Random Hse. GBR. *Dist:* Independent Pubs. Group.

DeJong, Meindert. Una Gata Casi Blanca. (SPA.). (YA). (gr. 5-8). pap. (978-84-279-3385-9(1) , NG3487) Noguer y Caralt Editores, S. A. ESP. *Dist:* Lectorum Pubns., Inc.

Demi, Hitz. Happy New Year! / Kung-Hsi Fa-Ts'Ai! 1999. (Illus.). 40p. (J). (gr. k-3). pap. 6.99 (978-0-517-88592-5(1) , Dragonfly Bks.) Random Hse. Children's Bks.

Deshpande, Shashi. 3 Novels. 2006. 379p. (***978-0-14-333511-5(1)*** , Puffin) Penguin Group (USA) Inc.

Dia de Fiesta 10: Leveled Books. 2001. (McGraw-Hill. Lectura Ser.). (ENG & SPA.). (gr. 1 up). (978-0-02-187939-7(7)) Macmillan/McGraw-Hill Schl. Div.

Dickens, Charles. A Christmas Carol. 2004. (Aladdin Classics Ser.). 128p. (J). pap. 3.99 (978-0-689-87180-1(5) , Aladdin) Simon & Schuster Children's Publishing.

Edwards, Gerry. Candy Claus: From Claus to Claus. 2004. 91p. per. 10.95 (978-1-59453-393-8(8) , 1075) Airleaf Publishing & Bookselling.

Ellis, Rolant. Castell Marwolaeth Boenus Ac Erchyll. 2005. (WEL., Illus.). 75p. pap. (978-0-86243-377-2(0)) Y Lolfa.

Feldman, Thea & Auerbach, Annie. The Snow Family: A Winter's Tale. Alderson, Lisa, illus. 2005. 12p. (J). 13.00 (978-0-7567-9460-6(9)) DIANE Publishing Co.

Flanders, Elizabeth Phyllis. The Ringmaster. Owens, Kimberley, photos by. 2000. (Holidays & Celebrations Ser.). (Illus.). 20p. (J). (ps-7). pap. 7.95 (978-1-931006-10-1(5)) SteppingStones BookCard Pubns., LLC.

Fleming, Sheila G. A Very Berra Holiday. 2002. 108p. pap. 9.95 (978-0-595-25600-6(7) , Weekly Reader Teacher's Pr) iUniverse, Inc.

Ford, Juwanda G. Together for Kwanzaa. Hehenberger, Shelly, illus. 2000. 24p. (J). (gr. k-3). pap. 3.99 (978-0-375-80329-1(7) , Random Hse. Bks. for Young Readers) Random Hse. Children's Bks.

—Together for Kwanzaa. 2000. (gr. k-3). lib. bdg. 10.95 (978-0-613-27277-3(3)) Tandem Library Bks.

Francis, Dorothy Brenner. Cody Smith & the Holiday Mysteries. Ersland, William, illus. 2001. (Cover-to-Cover Novel Ser.). 76p. (J). pap. (978-0-7891-5382-1(3)); (gr. 2-5). lib. bdg. 13.95 (978-0-7807-9743-7(4)) Perfection Learning Corp.

Gaetz, Dayle Campbell. Spoiled Rotten. 2005. (Orca Currents Ser.). 112p. (J). (gr. 4-10). pap. 7.95 (978-1-55143-474-2(1)) Orca Bk. Pubs. USA.

Garland, Michael. King Puck. Garland, Michael, illus. 2007. (Illus.). 32p. (J). (gr. k-3). 16.99 (978-0-06-084809-5(X)); lib. bdg. 17.89 (978-0-06-084810-1(3)) HarperCollins Pubs.

Gatehouse, John. Eric's Elephant on Holiday. (Illus.). 32p. (J). pap. 7.95 (978-0-14-038612-7(2)) Penguin Bks., Ltd. GBR. *Dist:* Trafalgar Square Publishing.

Golden Books Staff. Very Best Friends. 1999. (Disney Ser.). 24p. (J). (ps-3). pap. 3.29 (978-0-307-13142-3(4) , Golden Bks.) Random Hse. Children's Bks.

Golding, Theresa Martin & Boyds Mills Press Staff. Memorial Day Surprise. 2004. (Illus.). 32p. (J). (gr. k-2). 15.95 (978-1-59078-048-0(5)) Boyds Mills Pr.

Gonzales, David. Mijos: The Fiesta Face-Off. Gonzales, David, illus. 2005. (Mijos Ser.: No. 1). (Illus.). 96p. (J). pap. 4.99 (978-0-439-56234-8(1) , Scholastic Paperbacks) Scholastic, Inc.

Greenburg, Kay. Josh & Alisha Celebrate Chanukah. Correll, Cory, illus. l.t. ed. 1999. 40p. (J). (ps-6). 13.95 (978-0-9666903-0-9(3)) Stop & Smell the Roses, L.L.C.

Greene, Stephanie. Rugrats' First Kawanza. 2001. (gr. k-3). lib. bdg. 14.15 (978-0-613-43954-1(6)) Tandem Library Bks.

Hall. Here Comes Zelda Claus: And Other Holiday Disasters. 2001. (J). pap. (978-0-15-216468-3(5)) Harcourt Trade Pubs.

Hapka, Cathy. Picture Me Christmas Princess. Hill, Heather C. & Roush, April, illus. 2003. (Picture Me Holiday Ser.). 10p. (J). (ps up). bds. 6.99 (978-1-57151-571-1(2)) Playhouse Publishing.

Harcourt School Publishers Staff. The Happy Day: Library Edition. 1999. (Collections Ser.). (Illus.). (J). 5.30 (978-0-15-314305-2(3)) Harcourt Schl. Pubs.

Henry, Henther French. Life, Liberty & the Pursuit of Jellybeans: A Fourth of July Story. Henry, Henther French, illus. 2004. (Claire's Holiday Adventures Ser.). (Illus.). 32p. (gr. k-4). 15.95 (978-0-9706341-6-0(1)) Cubbie Blue Publishing.

—Life, Liberty & the Pursuit of Jellybeans: An Independence Day Story. Henry, Henther French, illus. 2004. (Claire's Holiday Adventures Ser.). (Illus.). 32p. (gr. k-4). 16.95 (978-0-9706341-5-3(3)) Cubbie Blue Publishing.

Herrington, Chris. Harry & Hannah: The Christmas Adventure. 2003. 72p. 15.00 (978-0-9722343-2-0(2)) Herrington Teddy Bears.

Higgins, Mayer Emily. Holidays at the Grange or A Weeks Deligh. 2006. 42.99 (***978-1-4280-4884-3(7)***) IndyPublish.com.

Hillert, Margaret. Fun Days. (J). 4.95 (978-0-87895-678-4(6)) Modern Curriculum Pr.

Holub, Joan. Dragon Dance: A Chinese New Year Lift-the-Flap Book. Huang, Benrei, illus. 2003. (Lift-the-Flap, Puffin Ser.). 16p. (J). (gr. k-1). pap. 6.99 (978-0-14-240000-5(9) , Puffin) Penguin Group (USA) Inc.

—Hooray for St. Patrick's Day! Meisel, Paul, illus. 2002. (Lift-the-Flap Bks.). 16p. (J). pap. 6.99 (978-0-14-230061-9(6) , Puffin) Penguin Group (USA) Inc.

Hungry Holidays for Bella & Rosie. 2005. (J). (978-1-932570-52-6(7)) Literacy Footprints Inc.

Johnston, Tony. Day of the Dead. 2000. 12.80 (978-0-606-20323-4(0)) Tandem Library Bks.

Johnston, Tony & Johnston, Tony. Day of the Dead. Winter, Jeannette, illus. 2000. (J). (ps-17). lib. bdg. 14.15 (978-0-613-29921-3(3)) Tandem Library Bks.

Karpinski, David. Sarah's Christmas Presence. 2006. 58p. pap. 8.95 (978-0-7414-3411-1(3)) Infinity Publishing.

Katz, Karen. Counting Christmas. Katz, Karen, illus. 2007. (Classic Board Bks.). (Illus.). 30p. (J). (ps-1). bds. 7.99 (***978-1-4169-3624-4(6)*** , Little Simon) Simon & Schuster Children's Publishing.

—Grandpa & Me. Katz, Karen, illus. 2004. (Illus.). 14p. (J). 6.99 (978-0-689-86644-9(5) , Little Simon) Simon & Schuster Children's Publishing.

—My First Chinese New Year. rev. ed. 2005. (Illus.). 32p. (J). 14.95 (978-0-8050-7076-7(1) , Holt, Henry & Co. Bks. For Young Readers) Holt, Henry & Co.

Keep, Richard Cleminson, illus. Clatter Bash! A Day of the Dead Celebration. 2004. 32p. (J). (ps-3). 15.95 (978-1-56145-322-1(6)) Peachtree Pubs., Ltd.

Kemp, Gene. The Hairy Hands. unabr. ed. 2000. (Read-Along Ser.). 168p. (J). pap. 24.95 incl. audio (978-0-7540-6223-3(6) , RA024, Chivers Children's Audio Bks.) BBC Audiobooks America.

Kimmel, Eric A. When Mindy Saved Hanukkah. McClintock, Barbara, illus. 2005. 32p. (J). pap. 5.99 (978-0-439-76990-7(6) , Scholastic Paperbacks) Scholastic, Inc.

Kirk, David. Happy Heartwood Day. 2005. (Miss Spider Ser.). (Illus.). 24p. (J). (ps-2). pap. 3.99 (978-0-448-43975-4(1) , Grosset & Dunlap) Penguin Group (USA) Inc.

Klein, Adria F. Max Celebrates Chinese New Year. 2007. (Read-It! Readers Ser.). (Illus.). 24p. (J). (***978-1-4048-3287-9(4)*** , 1265794) Picture Window Bks.

Kleinberg, Naomi. Have Yourself a Furry Little Christmas. Womble, Louis, illus. 2007. 12p. (J). (gr. k-ps). bds. 4.99 (***978-0-375-84133-0(4)*** , Random Hse. Bks. for Young Readers) Random Hse. Children's Bks.

Kline, Suzy. Horrible Harry & the Holidaze. Remkiewicz, Frank, illus. 2004. (Horrible Harry Ser.). 80p. (J). pap. 3.99 (978-0-14-240205-4(2) , Puffin) Penguin Group (USA) Inc.

—Horrible Harry & the Holidaze. Remkiewicz, Frank, illus. 2004. 67p. (J). (gr. 2-5). per. 11.19 (978-0-606-32710-7(X)) Tandem Library Bks.

Kline, Suzy & Kline, Suzy. Horrible Harry & the Holidaze. Remkiewicz, Frank, illus. 2003. (Horrible Harry Ser.). 64p. (J). (gr. 2-k). 13.99 (978-0-670-03642-4(0) , Viking Juvenile) Penguin Group (USA) Inc.

Kling, M. Terry & Ryan, Patricia K. The Holiday Miracle. Starbrook, Dirk, illus. l.t. ed. 2000. 73p. (J). (ps-5). 15.95 (978-0-9701849-0-0(5)) Citadel Entertainment Group.

Koffsky, Ann D. I Can! Koffsky, Ann D., illus. 1999. (J). (ps-k). spiral bd. 5.99 (978-0-914080-31-2(8)) Shulsinger Sales, Inc.

Krapp, JoAnn Vergona & Zaner, Gene. Holiday Time: An Anthology of Children's Holiday Stories. Matregrano, Theresa, illus. rev. ed. 2002. 140p. pap. 14.50 (978-0-9722576-0-2(8)) JoAnn Vergona Krapp & Gene Zaner.

Krulik, Nancy E. Love Stinks!, No. 15. John and Wendy Staff, illus. 2004. (Katie Kazoo, Switcheroo Ser.: No. 15). 80p. (J). (gr. 2-5). mass mkt. 3.99 (978-0-448-43640-1(X) , Grosset & Dunlap) Penguin Group (USA) Inc.

Kubler, Annie. Wheels on the Bus. 2005. (Illus.). 16p. (J). (ENG & ARA.). bds. 9.95 (978-1-84444-970-5(X)); (ENG & BEN., bds. 9.95 (978-1-84444-971-2(8)); (ENG & CHI., bds. 9.95 (978-1-84444-972-9(6)); (ENG & CHI., bds. 9.95 (978-1-84444-973-6(4)); (ENG & FRE., bds. 9.95 (978-1-84444-974-3(2)); (ENG & GUJ., bds. 9.95 (978-1-84444-975-0(0)); (ENG & PAN., bds. 9.95 (978-1-84444-976-7(9)); (POR & ENG., bds. 9.95 (978-1-84444-977-4(7)); (ENG & SOM., bds. 9.95 (978-1-84444-978-1(5)); (ENG & SPA., bds. 9.95 (978-1-84444-979-8(3)); (ENG & TUR., bds. 9.95 (978-1-84444-980-4(7)); (ENG & URD., bds. 9.95 (978-1-84444-981-1(5)) Mantra Lingua GBR. *Dist:* Mantra Publishing, Ltd.

—Wheels on the Bus. 2001. (gr. k-3). lib. bdg. 15.30 (978-0-613-77000-2(5)) Tandem Library Bks.

Kuester, David Allen. A Holiday Dream: An Interactive Play. 1999. 28p. (J). pap. 4.00 (978-0-88680-550-0(3)) Clark, I. E. Pubns.

Lagonegro, Melissa. The Fairest of the Fall. Emslie, Peter, illus. 2003. (Disney Princess Ser.). 24p. (J). (gr. k-3). pap. 3.25 (978-0-7364-2148-5(3) , RH/Disney) Random Hse. Children's Bks.

Lang, George. Pixy's Holiday Journey. 2006. 33.99 (***978-1-4280-4243-8(1)***); pap. 26.99 (***978-1-4280-4261-2(X)***) IndyPublish.com.

Lanton, Sandy. Lots of Latkes: A Hanukkah Story. Redenbaugh, Vicki J., illus. 2003. 32p. (J). (ps-3). 14.95 (978-1-58013-091-2(7)) Kar-Ben Publishing.

Laterra, Joann. Halloween Crossing. 2004. 127p. (YA). pap. 14.95 (978-0-7414-2101-2(1)) Infinity Publishing.

Lau, Barbara & Nesbitt, Kris. Sokita Celebrates the New Year: A Cambodian American Holiday. Chatterley, Cedric N., photos by. 2004. 32p. (J). per. 9.95 (978-0-9747456-0-2(X)) Greensboro Historical Museum, Inc.

Levack, Joseph, photos by. Picture Me Christmas Cutie. 2001. (Picture Me Ser.). (Illus.). 10p. (J). (ps up). bds. 6.99 (978-1-57151-594-0(1)) Playhouse Publishing.

Llorente, Pilar Molina. El Largo Verano de Eugenia Mestre. (SPA.). 128p. (YA). (gr. 5-8). (978-84-207-2790-5(3) , GS5805) Grupo Anaya, S.A. ESP. *Dist:* Lectorum Pubns., Inc.

Lowes, Tom, illus. Casey's Four Holiday Celebrations. l.t. ed. 2003. 38p. (J). 16.95 (978-0-9722099-9-1(9) , C4HC) Caseys World Bks.

Luenn, Nancy. A Gift for Abuelita: Celebrating the Day of the Dead. Chapman, Robert, illus. 1998. Tr. of Un Regalo para Abuelita: En Celebration del Dia de los Muertos. (ENG & SPA.). 32p. (gr. k-3). 15.95 (978-0-87358-688-7(3)) , Rising Moon Bks. for Young Readers) Northland Publishing.

May, Robert L. Rudolph the Red-Nosed Reindeer. Wenzel, David, illus. 2004. 22p. (J). (ps). bds. 5.99 (978-0-448-43642-5(6) , Grosset & Dunlap) Penguin Group (USA) Inc.

May, Scott & Reetz, Kurt. The Yuggs: An Ohf-Ful Holiday. 2000. mass mkt. 8.95 (978-1-931179-44-7(1)) Long Hill Productions, Inc.

—The Yuggs: An Ohff-Ful Holiday. 2000. mass mkt. 4.50 (978-1-931179-13-3(1)) Long Hill Productions, Inc.

Mayer, Mercer. Happy Father's Day. Mayer, Mercer, illus. 2007. (Little Critter Ser.: Bk. 2). (Illus.). 20p. (J). pap. 6.99 (***978-0-06-053965-8(8)*** , Harper Festival) HarperCollins Pubs.

—It's Earth Day, No. 5. 2008. (Little Critter Ser.). (Illus.). 24p. (J). pap. 3.99 (***978-0-06-053959-7(3)*** , Harper Festival) HarperCollins Pubs.

McDonald, Megan. The Holly Joliday. Reynolds, Peter H., illus. 2007. (Judy Moody Ser.). 96p. (J). (gr. k-3). 14.99 (***978-0-7636-3237-3(6))*** Candlewick Pr.

McKissack, Patricia C. & McKissack, Fredrick L. Messy Bessey's Holidays. Regan, Dana, illus. 1999. (Rookie Reader Skill Set Ser.). 32p. (J). (gr. k-2). pap. 4.95 (978-0-516-26476-9(1) , Children's Pr.) Scholastic Library Publishing.

McNamara, Margaret. Martin Luther King Jr. Day. Gordon, Mike, illus. 2007. (Robin Hill School Ser.). 32p. (J). pap. 3.99 (***978-1-4169-3494-3(4));*** lib. bdg. 13.89 (***978-1-4169-3495-0(2))*** Simon & Schuster Children's Publishing. (Aladdin).

McOmber, Rachel B., ed. Bags... Bags (Holidays) rev. ed. (Illus.). (J). (978-0-944991-98-5(X)) Swift Learning Resources.

—McOmber Phonics Storybooks: Boyer's Toy Store. rev. ed. (Illus.). (J). (978-0-944991-69-5(6)) Swift Learning Resources.

Meacham, Edie M. Roodey's Junk Food Summer. 2004. 50p. pap. 12.95 (978-1-4137-3286-3(0)) PublishAmerica, Inc.

Medearis, Angela Shelf. Too Many Holidays? Papp, Robert, illus. 2003. 149p. (J). (978-0-439-52327-1(3)) Scholastic, Inc.

Milne, A. A. Disney's Pooh's Treasury of Special Days. Case, Cassandra, ed. 2000. (Illus.). 85p. (J). (978-0-7172-6413-1(0) , Grolier) Scholastic Library Publishing.

Montgomery, L. M. Christmas with Anne & Other Holiday Stories. Wilmshurst, Rea, ed. 2001. (Illus.). 224p. (YA). (gr. 5 up). pap. 4.99 (978-0-553-57100-4(1) , Starfire) Random Hse. Children's Bks.

Mouse Works Staff. Honey of a Day. 1998. (Tiny Pops Ser.). 9p. (J). (ps). 3.98 (978-1-57082-791-4(5)) Mouse Works.

Muldrow, Diane. On the Back Burner, No. 6. Pollak, Barbara, illus. 2007. (Dish Ser.). 160p. (J). pap. 4.99 (978-0-448-44531-1(X) , Grosset & Dunlap) Penguin Group (USA) Inc.

—On the Back Burner with Other. 2003. (gr. 3-6). lib. bdg. 13.00 (978-0-613-72488-3(7)) Tandem Library Bks.

Multicultural Staff. Ravi's Diwali Surprise Story P. (J). 48.95 (978-0-8136-2338-2(3)) Modern Curriculum Pr.

Murphy, Chuck. Easter Egg Hunt. Murphy, Chuck, illus. 1999. (Razzle Dazzle Book Ser.). (Illus.). 12p. (J). (ps-k). 5.99 (978-0-689-82259-9(6) , Little Simon) Simon & Schuster Children's Publishing.

My Holiday Dress. 2003. (J). per. (978-1-57657-929-9(8)) Paradise Pr., Inc.

Napoli, Donna Jo. Happy Holidays. 2000. (Angelwings Ser.: No. 14). (Illus.). (J). 10.79 (978-0-606-21613-5(8)) Tandem Library Bks.

Nielsen, Laura F. Mrs. Muddle's Holidays. Yezerski, Thomas, illus. 2008. 32p. (J). 16.95 (***978-0-374-35094-9(9))*** Farrar, Straus & Giroux.

Olcott, Frances Jenkins. Good Stories for Great Holidays. l.t. ed. 2006. 324p. pap. 19.99 (978-1-4264-1125-0(1)) BiblioBazaar.

—Good Stories for Holidays. 2004. reprint ed. pap. 27.95 (978-1-4191-2211-8(8)); pap. 1.99 (978-1-4192-2211-5(2)) Kessinger Publishing, LLC.

Olsen, Mary-Kate & Olsen, Ashley. Mary-Kate & Ashley Sweet 16 No.12: Dream Holiday. 2003. (gr. 3-6). lib. bdg. 13.00 (978-0-613-71958-2(1)) Tandem Library Bks.

—Two of a Kind No. 32: Santa Girls. 2003. (gr. 3-6). lib. bdg. 13.00 (978-0-613-85153-4(6)) Tandem Library Bks.

Orozco, Jose-Luis. Fiestas: A Year of Latin-American Songs & Celebrations. Kleven, Elisa, illus. 2004. (SPA.). 48p. (J). (gr. k). pap. 7.99 (978-0-14-240199-6(4) , Puffin) Penguin Group (USA) Inc.

Osborne, Mary Pope. Rocking Horse Christmas. Bittinger, Ned, illus. 2004. (Bookshelf Ser.). 32p. (J). (gr. k-ps). pap. 5.99 (978-0-439-66938-2(3) , Scholastic Paperbacks) Scholastic, Inc.

Pascual, Emilio. Dias de Reyes Magos. Serrano, Javier U., illus. 4th ed. 2003. (SPA.). 158p. (978-84-207-9079-4(6) , GS4140) Grupo Anaya, S.A. ESP. *Dist:* Lectorum Pubns., Inc.

Pass, Erica. Christmas Every Day. Saunders, Zina, illus. 2004. 16p. (J). lib. bdg. 12.00 (***978-1-4242-0970-5(6))*** Fitzgerald Bks.

Penrose, Margaret. Dorothy Dale's Queer Holidays. 2006. 78.99 (***978-1-4280-4790-7(5));*** pap. 72.99 (***978-1-4280-4799-0(9))*** IndyPublish.com.

Pfeffer, Z. My Yom Tov Album. 2004. (Illus.). 105p. (J). 16.95 (978-1-931681-58-2(9)) Israel Bk. Shop.

Pilkey, Dav. Dumb Bunnies' Easter (Bkshelf) 2008. 32p. pap. 6.99 (***978-0-545-00880-8(8)*** , Scholastic Paperbacks) Scholastic, Inc.

Pinkwater, Daniel M. Big Bob & the Winter Holiday Potato. Pinkwater, Jill, illus. 2001. (Hello Reader! Ser.). 32p. (J). (gr. 1-3). pap. 3.99 (978-0-439-04243-7(7) , Cartwheel Bks.) Scholastic, Inc.

—Big Bob & the Winter Holiday Potato. 1999. (gr. k-3). lib. bdg. 11.80 (978-0-613-17985-0(4)) Tandem Library Bks.

Random House Disney Staff & Lagonegro, Melissa. Sweethearts in the Snow. Emslie, Peter & Marrucchi, Elisa, illus. 2003. (Disney Princess Ser.). 24p. (J). (ps-2). pap. 3.25 (978-0-7364-2170-6(X) , RH/Disney) Random Hse. Children's Bks.

Rau, Dana Meachen. Holiday Time. 2004. (Compass Point Early Reader Ser.). (J). 18.60 (978-0-7565-0571-4(2)) Compass Point Bks.

—I'll Make You a Card, Level C. Bryan-Hunt, Jan, illus. 2002. (Compass Point Early Reader Ser.). 32p. (J). (gr. k up). lib. bdg. 18.60 (978-0-7565-0172-3(5)) Compass Point Bks.

Reed, Patrick. Happy Everything! 1998. (Illus.). 40p. (J). pap. 12.00 (978-1-891989-01-8(4)) Fundbuilder$, U.S.A.

Regan, Dana, illus. Messy Bessey's Holidays. 2002. (Messy Bessey Ser.). (J). 12.83 (978-0-7587-7188-9(6)) Book Wholesalers, Inc.

Reiss, Mike. Santa Claustrophobia. Catrow, David, illus. 2002. 32p. (J). (gr. 2-5). 10.99 (978-0-8431-7756-5(X) , Price Stern Sloan) Penguin Group (USA) Inc.

—Santa Claustrophobia. Catrow, David, illus. 2006. 32p. (J). (ps). pap. 5.99 (978-0-14-240376-1(8) , Puffin) Penguin Group (USA) Inc.

Rigby Education Staff. Dad's Pasta. (Sails Literacy Ser.). (Illus.). 16p. (gr. 2-3). 27.00 (978-0-7635-9951-5(4) , 699514C99) Rigby Education.

Rinaldi, Ann. Come Juneteenth. 2007. (Great Episodes Ser.). (Illus.). 256p. (YA). 17.00 (978-0-15-205947-7(4)) Harcourt Children's Bks.

Roberts, Bethany. Fourth of July Mice ! 2004. (Illus.). 32p. (J). (ps-1). tchr. ed. 13.00 (978-0-618-31367-9(2) , Clarion Bks.) Houghton Mifflin Co. Trade & Reference Div.

Robinson, Angela. Ho Ho Ho: A Jolly Holiday Sticker Book. Cressy, Mike, illus. 2004. 16p. (J). pap. 4.99 (978-0-439-63584-4(5)) Scholastic, Inc.

Santomero, Angela C. A Blue's Clues Holiday. 2004. (Blue's Clues Ser.). 24p. (J). pap. 3.99 (978-0-689-86797-2(2) , Simon Spotlight/Nickelodeon) Simon & Schuster Children's Publishing.

Schoberle, Cecile. Reptar's Surprise Visit. Haefele, Steve, illus. 1999. 24p. (J). (gr. k-3). per. 3.50 (978-0-671-02881-7(2) , Simon & Schuster Children's Publishing) Simon & Schuster Children's Publishing.

—Reptar's Surprise Visit. 1999. (gr. k-3). lib. bdg. 11.25 (978-0-613-15954-8(3)) Tandem Library Bks.

Schultz, Charles M. Be My Valentine, Charlie Brown. 2007. (Illus.). 10p. (J). pap. 7.95 (***978-0-7624-3173-1(3)*** , Running Pr. Kids) Running Pr. Bk. Pubs.

Schulz, Charles M. It's the Great Pumpkin, Charlie Brown. 2007. (Illus.). 10p. (J). (ps-3). bds. 7.95 (***978-0-7624-3171-7(7))*** Running Pr. Bk. Pubs.

Schwartz, Howard. Day the Rabbi Disappeared: Jewish Holiday Tales of Magic. 2003. (gr. 3-6). lib. bdg. 18.75 (978-0-613-89176-9(7)) Tandem Library Bks.

Sedgwick, Patricia Louise. Santa's Key. deluxe ed. 2004. (Illus.). 12.95 incl. audio compact disk (978-0-9688190-1-2(X)) F. D. & D. Corp. CAN. *Dist:* Hushion Hse. Publishing, Ltd.

Shih, Bernadette. Good Friends: Diversity in America. Litster, Marie, illus. 2001. 48p. (J). lib. bdg. 15.95 (978-0-9700209-9-4(6) , Phaelos Bks.) Phaelos Publishing.

Shragg, Karen. A Solstice Tree for Jenny. Schwabacher, Heidi, illus. 2004. (Young Readers Ser.). 50p. (gr. k up). 12.00 (978-1-57392-930-1(1) , Pyr Bks.) Prometheus Bks., Pubs.

Silverhardt, Lauryn. Una Fiesta de Sorpresa. Lee, Josie, illus. 2004. (Dora the Explorer Ser.). (SPA.). 22p. (J). bds. 4.99 (978-0-689-87392-8(1) , Libros Para Ninos) Simon & Schuster Children's Publishing.

—SpongeBob SpookyPants. Style Guide Staff, illus. 2004. (Spongebob Squarepants Ser.). 16p. (J). bds. 5.99 (978-0-689-87320-1(4) , Simon Spotlight/Nickelodeon) Simon & Schuster Children's Publishing.

Skinner, Daphne. Palapalooza. Smath, Jerry, illus. 2006. 32p. (J). lib. bdg. 20.00 (***978-1-4242-1113-5(1))*** Fitzgerald Bks.

—Palapalooza. Smath, Jerry, illus. 2006. (Social Studies Connects). 32p. (J). pap. 4.99 (978-1-57565-163-7(7)) Kane Pr., The.

Smith, Emily. Annie & the Aliens. Parks, Paul, illus. 2002. (Young Corgi Ser.). 80p. 8.99 (978-0-552-54829-8(4) , Corgi) Transworld Publishers Ltd. GBR. *Dist:* Independent Pubs. Group.

Spelvin, Justin. Blue's Big Parade! Chernichaw, Ian, illus. 2005. (Blue's Clues Ser.). 24p. (J). pap. 3.99 (978-0-689-87673-8(4) , Simon Spotlight/Nickelodeon) Simon & Schuster Children's Publishing.

Spohn, Kate. Turtle & Snake's Happy-Spooky Halloween. 2003. (gr. k-3). lib. bdg. 11.80 (978-0-613-87830-2(2)) Tandem Library Bks.

Stanley, Diane. Thanksgiving on Plymouth Plantation. Berry, Holly, illus. 2004. (Time-Traveling Twins Ser.). 48p. (J). (gr. k-5). 15.99 (978-0-06-027069-8(1)); lib. bdg. 16.89 (978-0-06-027076-6(4)) HarperCollins Pubs. (Cotler, Joanna Books).

Stern, Ricki. Mission Impossible. Date not set. (Beryl E. Bean Ser.: Vol. 3). (Illus.). (J). lib. bdg. 15.89 (978-0-06-028773-3(X) , Harper Trophy) HarperCollins Pubs.

Stern, Ricki & Worcester, Heidi P. Beryl E. Bean: Mission Impossible Friendship. Bates, Amy June, illus. 2002. (J). pap. 5.99 (978-0-06-442122-5(8) , Harper Trophy) HarperCollins Pubs.

Stone, Indigo. The Last Pumpkin. Hower, Jack T., Jr., photos by. 2000. (Holidays & Celebrations Ser.). (Illus.). 20p. (J). pap. 7.95 (978-1-931006-11-8(3)) SteppingStones BookCard Pubns., LLC.

Swallow, Pamela C. Groundhog Gets a Say. Bunkus, Denise, illus. 2007. 40p. (J). (ps). pap. 6.99 (***978-0-14-240896-4(4)*** , Puffin) Penguin Group (USA) Inc.

Syckle, A. Van & Hruby, Andes. 'Twas the Night Before Chrismukkah. novel ed. 2005. (O. C. Ser.: No. 7). 264p. (J). (gr. 7-12). pap. 6.99 (978-0-439-74571-0(3) , Scholastic Paperbacks) Scholastic, Inc.

Thompson, Jill. Scary Godmother Vol. 4: The Boo Flu. 2000. (Illus.). 48p. 19.95 (978-1-57989-038-4(5)) Sirius Entertainment, Inc.

Thompson, Kay & Knight, Hilary. Eloise at Christmastime. 1999. (Illus.). 56p. (J). (ps-3). 17.95 (978-0-689-83039-6(4)) Simon & Schuster Children's Publishing.

Vail, Rachel. The (Almost) Perfect Mother's Day. Bjorkman, Steve, illus. 2003. (Mama Rex & T Ser.: No. 8). 32p. (J). pap. 14.95 (978-0-439-40718-2(4) , Orchard Bks.) Scholastic, Inc.

Valdes, Leslie. Happy Mother's Day, Mami! Fruchter, Jason, illus. 2003. (Dora the Explorer Ser.: Vol. 3). 24p. (J). pap. 3.99 (978-0-689-85233-6(9) , Simon Spotlight/ Nickelodeon) Simon & Schuster Children's Publishing.

—Happy Mother's Day, Mami! 2003. (ps-2). lib. bdg. 11.80 (978-0-613-73353-3(3)) Tandem Library Bks.

Van Allsburg, Chris. The Polar Express. 20th anniv. ed. 2005. (Illus.). 32p. (J). 35.00 (978-0-618-61169-0(X)) Houghton Mifflin Co. Trade & Reference Div.

Van Syckle, A. & Schwartz, Josh. The OC: 'twas the Night Before Chrismukkah. 2005. 206p. (YA). (978-1-4156-3915-3(9)) Scholastic, Inc.

Wade, Mary Dodson. El Dia de los Muertos. 2002. (Rookie Read-About Holidays Ser.).Tr. of Day of the Dead. (Illus.). 32p. (J). (gr. 1-2). pap. 5.95 (978-0-516-27354-9(X) , Children's Pr.) Scholastic Library Publishing.

Waters, George T. The Perfect Little Pumpkin. Duquet, Guy J., illus. l.t. ed. 2006. 34p. (J). per. 14.95 (***978-1-59879-286-7(5))*** Lifevest Publishing, Inc.

Waters, Tony. Cinnamon's Busy Year. Guevara, Linda L. & Merrill, Libby, eds. Waters, Tony, illus. 2003. (Illus.). 32p. (J). (ps-3). pap. 5.95 (978-0-9710278-2-4(X)) All About Kids Publishing.

Wells, Carolyn. Two Little Women on a Holiday. 2004. reprint ed. pap. 22.95 (978-1-4191-9150-3(0)) Kessinger Publishing, LLC.

—Two Little Women on A Holiday. 2004. reprint ed. pap. 1.99 (978-1-4192-9150-0(5)) Kessinger Publishing, LLC.

Wells, Rosemary. Morris's Disappearing Bag. 2001. (Illus.). (J). (ps-ps). lib. bdg. 15.30 (978-0-613-44236-7(9)) Tandem Library Bks.

What Do You Want? 2000. (Illus.). (J). (978-0-8431-4652-3(4) , Price Stern Sloan) Penguin Group (USA) Inc.

Wheeler, Lisa & Floca, Brian. Uncles & Antlers. 2004. (Illus.). 40p. (J). 15.95 (978-0-689-86469-8(8) , Atheneum/Richard Jackson Bks.) Simon & Schuster Children's Publishing.

Winnie the Pooh & the Hanukkah Dreidel. 1998. (Winnie the Pooh Ser.). (Illus.). 8p. (J). (ps-1). pap. 2.99 (978-1-57082-994-9(2)) Mouse Works.

Wong, Janet S. This Next New Year. Choi, Yangsook, illus. 2000. 32p. (J). (ps-3). 16.00 (978-0-374-35503-6(7) , Farrar, Straus & Giroux (BYR)) Farrar, Straus & Giroux.

Yoon, Salina. Spooky Pumpkin. Yoon, Salina, illus. 2004. (Illus.). 10p. (J). bds. 5.99 (978-0-689-85392-0(0) , Little Simon) Simon & Schuster Children's Publishing.

Zalben, Jane Breskin. Beni's Family Treasury: Stories for the Jewish Holidays. Zalben, Jane Breskin, illus. rev. ed. 1998. (Illus.). 120p. (J). (ps-4). 18.95 (978-0-8050-5889-5(3) , Holt, Henry & Co. Bks. For Young Readers) Holt, Henry & Co.

Ziefert, Harriet. This Is Thanksgiving. Zemke, Deborah, illus. 2004. 40p. (J). 8.95 (978-1-59354-065-4(5)) Blue Apple Bks.

Zucker, Jonny. Fasting & Dates: A Ramadan & Eid-ul-Fitr Story. Cohen, Jan Barger, illus. 2004. (Festival Time! Ser.). 24p. (J). pap. 6.95 (978-0-7641-2671-0(7)) Barron's Educational Series, Inc.

—Lighting a Lamp: A Diwali Story. Cohen, Jan Barger, illus. 2004. (Festival Time! Ser.). 24p. (J). pap. 6.95 (978-0-7641-2670-3(9)) Barron's Educational Series, Inc.

Zusman, Evelyn. The Passover Parrot. Kahn, Katherine Janus, illus. 2000. 32p. (J). (ps-3). pap. 6.95 (978-1-58013-024-0(0)) Kar-Ben Publishing.

HOLIDAYS—POETRY

Dixon, Peter. Peter Dixon's Grand Prix of Poetry. Thomas, David, illus. 2003. 62p. (J). pap. 6.99 (978-0-330-35544-5(9) , Pan) Pan Macmillan GBR. *Dist:* Trafalgar Square Publishing.

Duggan, Paul. Deux Squelettes au Téléphone. Sylvestre, Daniel, illus. 2004. (Picture Bks.). (FRE.). 32p. (J). (gr. 4). (978-2-89021-677-8(2)) Diffusion du livre Mirabel.

Hall, Melanie, illus. Hanukkah Lights: Holiday Poetry. 2004. 32p. (J). lib. bdg. 13.85 (***978-1-4242-1153-1(0))*** Fitzgerald Bks.

Jules, Jacqueline. Clap & Count! Action Rhymes for the Jewish Year. Springer, Sally, illus. 2000. 56p. (J). (ps-1). 17.95 (978-1-58013-067-7(4)) Kar-Ben Publishing.

Koontz, Dean. Every Day's a Holiday: Amusing Rhymes for Happy Times. Parks, Phil, illus. 2003. 144p. (J). 18.89 (978-0-06-008585-8(1)); (gr. 3 up). 17.99 (978-0-06-008584-1(3)) HarperCollins Pubs.

Pilkey, Dav. 'Twas the Night Before Thanksgiving. 2004. (Bookshelf Ser.). 32p. (J). (gr. k-ps). pap. 6.99 (978-0-439-66937-5(5) , Scholastic Paperbacks) Scholastic, Inc.

Scholastic, Inc. Staff. Spiders, Bats, & Pumpkin Eaters. Maccarone, Grace, ed. Smath, Jerry, illus. 2004. 5p. (J). bds. 5.95 (978-0-439-62333-9(2) , Cartwheel Bks.) Scholastic, Inc.

Whitehead, Jenny. Holiday Stew: A Kid's Portion of Holiday & Seasonal Poems. Whitehead, Jenny, illus. rev. ed. 2007. (Illus.). 64p. (J). 17.95 (978-0-8050-7715-5(4)) Holt, Henry & Co.

Yaccarino, Dan, illus. Five Little Pumpkins. 1998. 16p. (J). bds. 5.99 (978-0-694-01177-3(0) , Harper Festival) HarperCollins Pubs.

HOLLAND (MICH.)—FICTION

Bowman, Crystal. Windmills & Woodenshoes. Tanis, Joel E., illus. 1999. 40p. (J). (gr. 2-6). 15.00 (978-0-9636050-2-3(X)) Cygnet Publishing Co.

HOLLYWOOD (LOS ANGELES, CALIF.)

Moving up to Hollywoodland: True Stories of Hollywood - 1920 To 1932. 2001. per. 14.95 net. (978-0-9746689-0-1(7)) Arnold Publishing Co.

HOLLYWOOD (LOS ANGELES, CALIF.)—FICTION

Belshe, Judy. The Fry Family Goes to Hollywood. 2007. (Illus.). 50p. (J). spiral bd. 10.00 (***978-0-9655530-4-9(3))*** Belshe, Judy.

Blumenthal, Deborah. Charlie Hits It Big. 2008. (Illus.). 32p. (J). 16.99 (***978-0-06-056353-0(2));*** lib. bdg. 17.89 (***978-0-06-056354-7(0))*** HarperCollins Pubs.

Bonin, Liane. Pretty on the Outside: Fame Unlimited. 2007. 288p. (YA). pap. 9.99 (***978-0-451-22122-3(2)*** , N A L Trade) Penguin Group (USA) Inc.

Burns, Laura J. Go West, Darcy! 2006. (Darcy's Wild Life Ser.: Bk. 6). 160p. (J). (***978-1-4156-8867-0(2)*** , Grosset & Dunlap) Penguin Group (USA) Inc.

Burr, Daniela. Murder in Hollywood Hills. 2007. (Nancy Drew Movie Ser.). 128p. (J). pap. 5.99 (978-1-4169-3899-6(0) , Simon Spotlight) Simon & Schuster Children's Publishing.

Calonita, Jen. Secrets of My Hollywood Life. 2006. 256p. (J). (gr. 7-17). 16.99 (978-0-316-15442-0(3)) Little Brown & Co.

—Secrets of My Hollywood Life. 2007. 256p. (J). (gr. 7 up). pap. 7.99 (***978-0-316-15443-7(1)*** , Poppy) Little, Brown Bks. for Young Readers.

—Secrets of My Hollywood Life: On Location. 2nd ed. 2007. 240p. (J). (gr. 7 up). 16.99 (***978-0-316-15439-0(3))*** Little, Brown Bks. for Young Readers.

Collins, Yvonne & Rideout, Sandy. The New & Improved Vivien Leigh Reid: Diva in Control. 2007. 240p. (gr. 7-10). pap. 9.95 (978-0-312-35828-0(8) , St. Martin's Griffin); 231p. (YA). (***978-1-4287-1928-6(8))*** St. Martin's Pr.

Dean, Zoey. A-List, the: the Second Collection. 2007. (J). (gr. 10-17). pap. 29.99 (***978-0-316-06691-4(5)*** , Poppy) Little, Brown Bks. for Young Readers.

—Beautiful Stranger. 2007. (A-List Ser.: No. 9). 304p. (J). (gr. 9-17). pap. 9.99 (***978-0-316-11352-6(2)*** , Poppy) Little, Brown Bks. for Young Readers.

Douglas, Lola. True Confessions of a Hollywood Starlet. 2005. 272p. (YA). (gr. 7-12). 16.99 (978-1-59514-035-7(2) , Razorbill) Penguin Group (USA) Inc.

Frees, Jessie Lynch. Jackie Winquackey & Her 43 Cats Go to Hollywood. Gebr, Jaroslav, illus. 2005. 32p. (J). 14.99 (978-0-9760553-0-3(9)) Tizbit Books, LLC.

Greenburg, Dan. Weird Planet: Lights, Camera... Liftoff! Pamintuan, Macky, illus. 2007. (Weird Planet Ser.: No. 5). 96p. (J). (gr. 2-5). pap. 3.99 (***978-0-375-84336-5(1)*** , Random Hse. Bks. for Young Readers) Random Hse. Children's Bks.

—Weird Planet No. 5: Lights, Camera... Liftoff! Pamintuan, Macky, illus. 2007. (Stepping Stone Bks.). 96p. (J). (gr. 2-5). lib. bdg. 11.99 (***978-0-375-94336-2(6)*** , Random Hse. Bks. for Young Readers) Random Hse. Children's Bks.

Handford, Martin. Where's Waldo? in Hollywood. Handford, Martin, illus. 2007. (Waldo Ser.). (Illus.). 32p. (J). (gr. k-7). pap. 7.99 (***978-0-7636-3501-5(4))*** Candlewick Pr.

Hare, Mimi & Naylor, Clare. The First Assistant: A Continuing Tale from Behind the Hollywood Curtain. 2007. 288p. pap. 14.00 (978-0-452-28836-2(3) , Plume) Penguin Group (USA) Inc.

Hirshfield, Lynn & Fishbein, Dena. Sassafras Goes to Hollywood. 2007. 32p. (J). 15.99 (978-0-8431-2191-9(2) , Price Stern Sloan) Penguin Group (USA) Inc.

Hogan, Mary. Susanna Hits Hollywood. 2008. (YA). (***978-0-385-73514-8(6));*** 256p. lib. bdg. (***978-0-385-90503-9(3))*** Dell Publishing. (Delacorte Pr.).

Kennedy, Mary. Tales of a Hollywood Gossip Queen. 2006. 256p. (YA). (gr. 12). pap. 9.99 (978-0-425-20993-6(8) , Berkley Trade) Penguin Group (USA) Inc.

Kerston, Caroline. Hollywood Harry. 2005. 28.00 (978-0-8059-9458-2(0)) Dorrance Publishing Co., Inc.

Leonard, Elmore. A Coyote's in the House. 2004. (Illus.). 160p. 15.95 (978-0-06-054404-1(X) , Harper Entertainment) HarperCollins Pubs.

Margolis, Leslie. Price of Admission. 2007. 224p. (YA). pap. 8.99 (978-1-4169-2455-5(8) , Simon Pulse) Simon & Schuster Children's Publishing.

Morgan, Allen. Matthew & the Midnight Movie. Martchenko, Michael, illus. 2002. (Matthew's Midnight Adventures Ser.). 32p. (YA). 6.99 (978-0-7737-6273-2(6)) Stoddart Kids CAN. *Dist:* Fitzhenry & Whiteside, Ltd.

Paterson, Aileen. Maisie Goes to Hollywood. Paterson, Aileen, illus. 2001. (Illus.). 32p. (J). (ps-3). pap. (978-1-871512-40-3(9)) Glowworm Bks., Ltd.

Perez, Lana. Bella Goes Hollywood. 2006. (Star Sisterz Ser.: Bk. 8). 144p. (YA). pap. 4.99 (978-0-7869-4030-1(1) , Mirrorstone) Wizards of the Coast.

HI

Pfeffer, Susan Beth. Revenge of the Aztecs. 2004. 118p. (J). lib. bdg. 16.92 (***978-1-4242-0763-3(0)***) Fitzgerald Bks.

Pfeffer, Susan Beth. Revenge of the Aztecs: A Story of 1920s Hollywood. 2001. (American Portraits Ser.). (Illus.). 114p. (J). (gr. 5-8). 15.32 (978-0-8092-0586-8(6) , 9780809205868) Jamestown.

—Revenge of the Aztecs: A Story of 1920s Hollywood. 2004. (Jamestown's American Portraits Ser.). (Illus.). 120p. (J). (gr. 5-7). pap. 4.95 (978-0-7696-3431-9(1) , Waterbird Bks.) School Specialty Publishing.

—Revenge of the Aztecs: A Story of 1920s Hollywood. 2000. (978-0-606-21875-7(0)); (gr. 5-8). lib. bdg. 14.95 (978-0-613-36866-7(5)) Tandem Library Bks.

Pfeffer, Susan Beth & McGraw-Hill Staff. Revenge of the Aztecs: A Story of 1920s Hollywood. 2001. (Jamestown Classics Ser.). (Illus.). 114p. (J). (gr. 5-8). pap. 10.00 (978-0-8092-0627-8(7) , 9780809206278) Jamestown.

Roter, Jordan. Girl in Development. 2008. 320p. (YA). (gr. 7). pap. 7.99 (***978-0-14-240822-3(0)*** , Puffin) Penguin Group (USA) Inc.

Roter, Jordan. Girl of Development (Splashproof Ed) 2007. 1p. (YA). (gr. 7). pap. 7.99 (978-0-14-240838-4(7) , Puffin) Penguin Group (USA) Inc.

Savage, Derek. Cool Cat Goes to Hollywood. Bustamante, Denny, illus. 2001. (Cool Cat Ser.: Vol. 2). 32p. (J). pap. 9.95 (978-0-9673000-4-7(5)) Savage Bks.

Sharmat, Marjorie Weinman. Dog-Gone Hollywood. 2000. (Illus.). (J). (978-0-606-18853-1(3)) Tandem Library Bks.

Sheldon, Dyan. Confessions of a Hollywood Star. 2006. 208p. (YA). (gr. 7). 15.99 (978-0-7636-3075-1(6)) Candlewick Pr.

Van Draanen, Wendelin. Sammy Keyes & the Hollywood Mummy. VanDraanen, Wendelin, illus. 2001. (Sammy Keyes Ser.: Bk. 6). pap. 36.95 incl. audio (978-0-87499-800-9(X)); pap. 54.95 incl. audio compact disk (978-0-87499-868-9(9)) Live Oak Media.

—Sammy Keyes & the Hollywood Mummy. 2002. (Sammy Keyes Ser.: Bk. 6). (gr. 5-8). lib. bdg. 13.00 (978-0-613-50639-7(1)) Tandem Library Bks.

Van Etten, David. Likely Story (Book 1) 2008. (Likely Story Ser.). 208p. (J). (gr. 7). 15.99 (***978-0-375-84676-2(X)***); lib. bdg. 18.99 (***978-0-375-94676-9(4)***) Random Hse. Children's Bks. (Knopf Bks. for Young Readers).

Vaughan, Christina. Artie Goes to Hollywood. (J). 2007. 32p. cd-rom (***978-0-9798242-0-3(6)***); 2000. (Artie Stories Ser.: Vol. 2). (Illus.). 34p. (gr. 1-5). spiral bd. 18.95 (978-0-9641697-6-0(2) , You-Draw-It Bks.) Castlebrook Pubns.

Wallace, Karen. Alice Goes to Hollywood. Dewar, Bob, illus. 2006. (Read-It! Chapter Books). 48p. (J). (gr. 2-4). 19.95 (978-1-4048-1678-7(X)) Picture Window Bks.

Wilcox, Mary. Caught on Tape. 2007. (Hollywood Sisters Ser.). 208p. (J). (gr. 5). 7.99 (***978-0-385-73356-4(9)***); lib. bdg. 10.99 (***978-0-385-90371-4(5)***) Random Hse. Children's Bks. (Delacorte Bks. for Young Readers).

—The Hollywood Sisters: Star Quality. 2008. (J). (***978-0-385-90513-8(0)***); pap. (***978-0-385-73527-8(8)***) Dell Publishing. (Delacorte Pr.).

—The Hollywood Sisters: Backstage Pass. 2006. 256p. (J). (gr. 5). 7.95 (978-0-385-73354-0(2)); lib. bdg. 9.99 (978-0-385-90369-1(3)) Random Hse. Children's Bks. (Delacorte Bks. for Young Readers).

—On Location. 2007. (Hollywood Sisters Ser.). 240p. (J). (gr. 5). 7.99 (978-0-385-73355-7(0) , Delacorte Bks. for Young Readers) Random Hse. Children's Bks.

HOLMES, OLIVER WENDELL, 1841-1935

Littlefield, Sophie W. & Wiecek, William. Oliver Wendell Holmes Jr: The Supreme Court & American Legal Thought. 2005. (Library of American Lives & Times). (Illus.). 112p. (J). (gr. 5-8). lib. bdg. 31.95 (978-1-4042-2652-4(4) , PowerKids Pr.) Rosen Publishing Group, Inc., The.

HOLMES, SHERLOCK (FICTITIOUS CHARACTER)—FICTION

Brook, H. & Doyle, Arthur Conan. The Hound of the Baskervilles. 2004. (Paperback Classics Ser.). 144p. (J). lib. bdg. 12.95 (978-1-58086-605-7(0)) EDC Publishing.

Bullimore, Tom. Sherlock Holmes' Mini-Mysteries. 2005. (Illus.). 112p. pap. 6.95 (978-1-4027-2653-8(8)) Sterling Publishing Co., Inc.

Doyle, Arthur Conan. The Adventure of the Speckled Band. Stemach, Jerry, ed. Letwenko, Michael, illus. 2000. 65.00 incl. audio, cd-rom (978-1-58702-338-5(5)); 2002. 104p. 150.00 (978-1-58702-041-4(6)); 2000. 104p. 50.00 (978-1-58702-496-2(9)) Johnston, Don Inc.

—The Adventures & Memoirs of Sherlock Holmes. 2001. (gr. 7-12). lib. bdg. 22.25 (978-0-613-64240-8(6)) Tandem Library Bks.

—The Adventures & the Memoirs of Sherlock Holmes. McKowen, Scott, illus. 2004. (Unabridged Classics Ser.). 576p. 9.95 (978-1-4027-1453-5(X)) Sterling Publishing Co., Inc.

—Adventures of Sherlock Holmes. 1998. (Wordsworth Classics Ser.). (YA). (gr. 6-12). 5.27 (978-0-89061-033-6(9) , R0339WW) Jamestown.

—Adventures of Sherlock Holmes. 2004. (Illus.). 336p. (J). (gr. 4-8). pap. 3.99 (978-0-439-57428-0(5) , Scholastic Paperbacks) Scholastic, Inc.

—Las Aventuras de Sherlock Holmes. 2000. (SPA., Illus.). 339p. (978-84-206-3692-4(4)) Alianza Editorial, S. A.

—Favorite Sherlock Holmes Detective Stories. unabr. ed. 2000. (Dover Juvenile Classics Ser.). (Illus.). 208p. (J). (gr. 4-7). pap. 2.50 (978-0-486-41242-9(3)) Dover Pubns., Inc.

—The Hound of the Baskervilles. 2004. (Fast Track Classics Ser.). (Illus.). 48p. (J). pap. 8.99 (978-0-237-52402-9(3) , Evans Brothers, Limited) Evans Publishing Group GBR. *Dist:* Independent Pubs. Group.

—The Hound of the Baskervilles: Another Adventure of Sherlock Holmes, Level 4. abr. ed. 2000. (Bookworms Ser.). (Illus.). 6.50 (978-0-19-423035-3(X)) Oxford Univ. Pr., Inc.

—The Hound of the Baskervilles: Another Adventure of Sherlock Holmes. 2004. (Whole Story Ser.). (Illus.). 192p. (J). 17.99 (978-0-670-03654-7(4) , Viking Juvenile) Penguin Group (USA) Inc.

—The Hound of the Baskervilles: Another Adventure of Sherlock Holmes. 2000. (Aladdin Classics Ser.). 256p. (J). (gr. 4-11). pap. 5.99 (978-0-689-83571-1(X) , Aladdin) Simon & Schuster Children's Publishing.

—The Hound of the Baskervilles: Another Adventure of Sherlock Holmes. 2001. (gr. 7-12). lib. bdg. 16.45 (978-0-613-64290-3(2)); 2001. (gr. 7-12). lib. bdg. 12.95 (978-0-613-37148-3(8)); 2001. (Illus.). (J). 13.75 (978-0-606-21554-1(9)); 2000. (gr. 3-6). lib. bdg. 11.80 (978-0-613-63203-4(6)) Tandem Library Bks.

—The Hounds of the Baskervilles. abr. ed. 2001. (gr. 7-12). lib. bdg. 15.25 (978-0-613-43833-9(7)) Tandem Library Bks.

—The Return of Sherlock Holmes. l.t. ed. 1998. (Large Print Heritage Ser.). 278p. (YA). (gr. 7-12). lib. bdg. 29.95 (978-1-58118-038-1(1)) LRS.

—El Sabueso de los Baskerville. 2nd ed. 2002. (Clover Ser.). (SPA., Illus.). 256p. (YA). (978-84-392-8024-8(6) , EV5542) Gaviota Ediciones ESP. *Dist:* Lectorum Pubns., Inc.

—Sherlock Holmes & the Case of the Hound of the Baskervilles. Vogel, Malvina G., ed. Marcos, Pablo, illus. 2006. 237p. (YA). (gr. 4-8). 10.00 (978-0-7567-9834-5(5)) DIANE Publishing Co.

—The Sign of Four. 2001. (gr. 7-12). lib. bdg. 15.30 (978-0-613-64324-5(0)) Tandem Library Bks.

—A Study in Scarlet. 2001. (gr. 7-12). lib. bdg. 15.30 (978-0-613-64328-3(3)) Tandem Library Bks.

Doyle, Arthur Conan, ed. Adventures of Sherlock Holmes. Lynch, Brendan, illus. 2002. (Great Illustrated Classics Ser.). 240p. (J). (gr. 3-8). 21.35 (978-1-57765-678-4(4) , ABDO & Daughters) ABDO Publishing Co.

Doyle, Sir Arthur Canon. The Great Adventures of Sherlock Holmes. 2006. (Illus.). 61p. (J). lib. bdg. 30.77 (***978-1-4242-1327-6(4)***) Fitzgerald Bks.

Harvey, Bob, illus. The Hound of the Baskervilles. 2004. (Paperback Classics Ser.). 144p. (J). pap. 4.95 (978-0-7945-0574-5(0) , Usborne) EDC Publishing.

The Hound of Baskervilles Study Guide. 2000. (Illus.). 48p. (YA). per. 17.95 (978-1-56254-290-0(7) , SP2907) Saddleback Educational Publishing.

King, Laurie R. The Beekeeper's Apprentice. 2002. (Mary Russell Mystery Ser.: Vol. 1). (gr. 7-12). lib. bdg. 21.05 (978-0-613-57620-8(9)) Tandem Library Bks.

Mack, Tracy & Citrin, Michael. The Fall of the Amazing Zalindas. 2006. (Illus.). 259p. (J). (***978-1-4287-0951-5(7)*** , Orchard Bks.) Scholastic, Inc.

Peacock, Shane. Death in the Air: His Second Case. 2008. 260p. 19.95 (***978-0-88776-851-4(2)***) Tundra Bks., Inc./Livres Toundra, Inc. CAN. *Dist:* Random Hse. of Canada, Ltd.

—Eye of the Crow: The Boy Sherlock Holmes, His First Case. 2007. (Boy Sherlock Holmes Ser.). 260p. (J). (gr. 5-9). 19.95 (***978-0-88776-850-7(4)***) Tundra Bks., Inc./Livres Toundra, Inc. CAN. *Dist:* Random Hse. of Canada, Ltd.

Townsend, John Rowe. The Hound of the Baskervilles. 2007. (Oxford Children's Classics). (Illus.). 320p. (YA). 9.95 (***978-0-19-272004-7(X)***) Oxford Univ. Pr., Inc.

Vanneman, Alan. Sherlock Holmes & the Giant Rat of Sumatra. (Otto Penzler Bks.). 304p. 2002. pap. 14.00 (978-0-7867-1125-3(6)); 2001. (Illus.). 24.00 (978-0-7867-0956-4(1)) Avalon Publishing Group.

HOLOCAUST, JEWISH (1939-1945)

Abells, Chana Byers. The Children We Remember. 2002. (gr. 3-6). lib. bdg. 15.25 (978-0-613-53801-5(3)) Tandem Library Bks.

Abramson, Ann. Who Was Anne Frank? Harrison, Nancy, illus. 2007. (Who Was... ? Ser.). 112p. (J). pap. 4.99 (978-0-448-44482-6(8) , Grosset & Dunlap) Penguin Group (USA) Inc.

Adler, David A. A Hero & the Holocaust: The Story of Janusz Korczak & His Children. Farnsworth, Bill, illus. 2002. 32p. (J). (gr. 4-6). tchr. ed. 16.95 (978-0-8234-1548-9(1)) Holiday Hse., Inc.

Alagna, Magdalena. Anne Frank: Young Voice of the Holocaust. 2005. (Holocaust Biographies Ser.). (Illus.). 112p. (YA). (gr. 7-12). lib. bdg. 26.50 (978-0-8239-3373-0(3)) Rosen Publishing Group, Inc., The.

Altman, Linda Jacobs. Adolf Hitler: Evil MasterMind of the Holocaust. 2005. (Holocaust Heroes & Nazi Criminals Ser.). (Illus.). 160p. (YA). (gr. 7-13). lib. bdg. 27.93 (978-0-7660-2533-2(0)) Enslow Pubs., Inc.

—Crimes & Criminals of the Holocaust. 2004. (Holocaust in History Ser.). (Illus.). 104p. (J). lib. bdg. 26.60 (978-0-7660-1995-9(0)) Enslow Pubs., Inc.

—The Forgotten Victims of the Holocaust. 2003. (Holocaust in History Ser.). (Illus.). 128p. (YA). (gr. 5-12). lib. bdg. 26.60 (978-0-7660-1993-5(4)) Enslow Pubs., Inc.

—Hitler's Rise to Power & the Holocaust. 2003. (Holocaust in History Ser.). (Illus.). 128p. (J). (gr. 5-12). lib. bdg. 26.60 (978-0-7660-1991-1(8)) Enslow Pubs., Inc.

—The Holocaust Ghettos. 1998. (Holocaust Remembered Ser.). (Illus.). 112p. (YA). (gr. 6-12). lib. bdg. 26.60 (978-0-89490-994-8(0)) Enslow Pubs., Inc.

—The Holocaust, Hitler & Nazi Germany. 1999. (Holocaust Remembered Ser.). (Illus.). 112p. (YA). (gr. 6-12). lib. bdg. 26.60 (978-0-7660-1230-1(1)) Enslow Pubs., Inc.

—Impact of the Holocaust. 2004. (Holocaust in History Ser.). (Illus.). 104p. (J). lib. bdg. 26.60 (978-0-7660-1996-6(9)) Enslow Pubs., Inc.

—The Jewish Victims of the Holocaust. 2003. (Holocaust in History Ser.). (Illus.). 128p. (J). (gr. 5-12). lib. bdg. 26.60 (978-0-7660-1992-8(6)) Enslow Pubs., Inc.

—Resisters & Rescuers: Standing up Against the Holocaust. 2003. (Holocaust in History Ser.). (Illus.). 104p. (J). (gr. 5-12). lib. bdg. 26.60 (978-0-7660-1994-2(2)) Enslow Pubs., Inc.

Ashby, Ruth. Anne Frank: Young Diarist. 2005. 186p. (J). lib. bdg. 18.46 (***978-1-4242-2208-7(7)***) Fitzgerald Bks.

Auerbacher, Inge. I Am a Star: Child of the Holocaust. unabr. ed. 2000. (YA). pap. 33.24 incl. audio (978-0-7887-3847-0(X) , 41045X4) Recorded Bks., LLC.

Axelrod, Toby. Hans & Sophie Scholl: German Resisters of the White Rose. 2005. (Holocaust Biographies Ser.). (Illus.). 112p. (YA). (gr. 7-12). lib. bdg. 26.50 (978-0-8239-3316-7(4) , HBHOBI) Rosen Publishing Group, Inc., The.

—Rescuers Defying the Nazis: Non-Jewish Teens Who Rescued Jews. 1999. (Teen Witnesses to the Holocaust Ser.). (Illus.). 64p. (YA). (gr. 7-12). lib. bdg. 26.50 (978-0-8239-2848-4(9) , TWRESC) Rosen Publishing Group, Inc., The.

Ayer, Eleanor H. Parallel Journeys. 2000. (gr. 7-12). lib. bdg. 14.15 (978-0-613-28600-8(6)) Tandem Library Bks.

Bard, Mitchell G. The Holocaust. 2001. (Complete History of Ser.). (Illus.). 567p. (YA). (gr. 7-10). lib. bdg. 123.75 (978-0-7377-0373-3(3) , Greenhaven Pr., Inc.) Thomson Gale.

Bartel, Judy. The Holocaust: A Primary Source History. 2005. (Illus.). 48p. lib. bdg. 26.00 (978-0-8368-5979-9(0)) Stevens, Gareth Inc.

Bartoletti, Susan Campbell. Hitler Youth: Growing up in Hitler's Shadow. 2005. (Illus.). 176p. (J). pap. 19.95 (978-0-439-35379-3(3)) Scholastic, Inc.

Bauer, Yehuda. History of the Holocaust. 2001. (gr. 7-12). lib. bdg. 28.00 (978-0-613-50117-0(9)) Tandem Library Bks.

—A History of the Holocaust. rev. ed. 2002. (Single Titles-Adult Ser.). (YA). (gr. 9-12). pap. 17.95 (978-0-531-15576-9(5) , Watts, Franklin) Scholastic Library Publishing.

Bauer, Yehuda & Keren, Nili. A History of the Holocaust. rev. ed. 2001. (Single Titles Social Studies Ser.). (Illus.). 432p. (YA). (gr. 9-12). 37.50 (978-0-531-11884-9(3) , Watts, Franklin) Scholastic Library Publishing.

Bayer, Linda N. Elie Wiesel: Spokesman for Remembrance. 2005. (Holocaust Biographies Ser.). (Illus.). 112p. (J). (gr. 7-12). lib. bdg. 26.50 (978-0-8239-3306-8(7) , HBWIES) Rosen Publishing Group, Inc., The.

—Elie Wiesel: Spokesman for Remembrance. 1999. (Illus.). 112p. (YA). per. 10.95 (978-1-56254-456-0(X) , SP456X) Saddleback Educational Publishing.

Beyer, Mark. Emmanuel Ringelblum: Historian of the Warsaw Ghetto. 2005. (Holocaust Biographies Ser.). (Illus.). 112p. (YA). (gr. 7-12). lib. bdg. 26.50 (978-0-8239-3375-4(X)) Rosen Publishing Group, Inc., The.

—Heinrich Muller: Gestapo Chief. 2005. (Holocaust Biographies Ser.). (Illus.). 112p. (YA). (gr. 7-12). lib. bdg. 26.50 (978-0-8239-3376-1(8)) Rosen Publishing Group, Inc., The.

Bitton-Jackson, Livia. I Have Lived a Thousand Years: Growing up in the Holocaust. 1999. 224p. (YA). (gr. 7-12). pap. 5.99 (978-0-689-82395-4(9) , Simon Pulse) Simon & Schuster Children's Publishing.

—I Have Lived a Thousand Years: Growing up in the Holocaust. 1999. (J). 11.64 (978-0-606-15948-7(7)); (gr. 7-12). lib. bdg. 13.00 (978-0-613-17811-2(4)) Tandem Library Bks.

Bloom, Harold, ed. & tr. Literature of the Holocaust. Bloom, Harold, tr. 2003. (Bloom's Period Studies Ser.). (Illus.). 350p. (gr. 9-13). 45.00 (978-0-7910-7677-4(6) , Chelsea Hse.) Facts On File, Inc.

Bodden, Valerie. The Holocaust. 2007. (978-1-58341-547-4(5) , Creative Education) Creative Co., The.

Brooks, Philip. Viewing the Holocaust Today. 2003. (Holocaust Ser.). 56p. (Illus.). (J). (gr. 6-8). lib. bdg. 28.50 (978-1-4034-0815-0(7)); pap. 8.95 (978-1-4034-3207-0(4)) Heinemann Library.

Brown, Jonatha A. Anne Frank. 2004. (People to Know Ser.). (J). pap. (978-0-8368-4316-3(9)); (Illus.). 24p. (J). pap. (978-0-8368-4358-3(4)); (Illus.). 24p. (YA). lib. bdg. 19.33 (978-0-8368-4309-5(6)) Stevens, Gareth Inc.

—Anne Frank. Acosta, Tatiana & Gutierrez, Guillermo, trs. 2004. (Gente Que Hay Que Conocer Ser.). (SPA., Illus.). 24p. (J). lib. bdg. 19.33 (978-0-8368-4351-4(7)) Stevens, Gareth Inc.

—Anne Frank. 2003. (Trailblazers of the Modern World Ser.). (Illus.). 48p. (J). (gr. 5 up). lib. bdg. 30.00 (978-0-8368-5090-1(4)); pap. 10.95 (978-0-8368-5250-9(8)) Stevens, Gareth Inc. (World Almanac Library).

Byers, Ann. The Holocaust Camps. 1998. (Holocaust Remembered Ser.). (Illus.). 128p. (YA). (gr. 6-12). lib. bdg. 26.60 (978-0-89490-995-5(9)) Enslow Pubs., Inc.

—Holocaust Overview. 1998. (Holocaust Remembered Ser.). (Illus.). 128p. (YA). (gr. 6-12). lib. bdg. 26.60 (978-0-7660-1062-8(7)) Enslow Pubs., Inc.

—Oskar Schindler: Saving Jews from the Holocaust. 2005. (Holocaust Heroes & Nazi Criminals Ser.). (Illus.). 160p. (J). (gr. 6-12). lib. bdg. 27.93 (978-0-7660-2534-9(9)) Enslow Pubs., Inc.

Callahan, Kerry P. Mordechai Anielewicz: Hero of the Warsaw Ghetto Uprising. 2005. (Holocaust Biographies Ser.). (Illus.). 112p. (YA). (gr. 7-12). lib. bdg. 26.50 (978-0-8239-3377-8(6)) Rosen Publishing Group, Inc., The.

Cooper, Jason. U. S. Holocaust Memorial Museum. 2000. (Historic Landmarks Ser.). (Illus.). 24p. (J). (gr. 1-4). lib. bdg. 20.64 (978-1-55916-330-9(5)) Rourke Publishing, LLC.

Crispin, M. Holocaust: A QandA Guide to Help Young Adults Really Understand the Holocaust. 2006. (Illus.). 230p. pap. 32.95 (978-0-7618-3542-4(3)) Univ. Pr. of America, Inc.

DeMarco, Neil. The Holocaust. 2001. (Illus.). 32p. pap. 21.00 (***978-0-340-79979-6(X)*** , Hodder Murray) Hodder Education GBR. *Dist:* Trans-Atlantic Pubns., Inc.

Denenberg, Barry. Portrait of Anne Frank & Her Family. 2005. (Shadow Life Ser.). (Illus.). 240p. (J). pap. 16.95 (978-0-439-41678-8(7)) Scholastic, Inc.

Dolan, Sean. Adolf Eichmann: Engineer of Death. 2005. (Holocaust Biographies Ser.). (Illus.). 112p. (J). (gr. 7-12). lib. bdg. 26.50 (978-0-8239-3308-2(3) , HBEICH) Rosen Publishing Group, Inc., The.

Dolan, Terrance. Adolf Hitler: A Study in Hate. 2005. (Holocaust Biographies Ser.). (Illus.). 112p. (YA). (gr. 7-12). lib. bdg. 26.50 (978-0-8239-3317-4(2) , HBHITL) Rosen Publishing Group, Inc., The.

Downing, David. Aftermath & Remembrance. 2005. (World Almanac Library of the Holocaust). (Illus.). 48p. pap. (978-0-8368-5955-3(3)); (YA). (gr. 5 up). lib. bdg. 30.00 (978-0-8368-5948-5(0)) Stevens, Gareth Inc. (World Almanac Library).

—Fighting Back. 2005. (World Almanac Library of the Holocaust). (Illus.). 48p. pap. (978-0-8368-5953-9(7)); (YA). (gr. 10-12). lib. bdg. 30.00 (978-0-8368-5946-1(4)) Stevens, Gareth Inc. (World Almanac Library).

—Nazi Death Camps. 2005. (World Almanac Library of the Holocaust). (Illus.). 48p. pap. (978-0-8368-5954-6(5)); (YA). (gr. 5 up). lib. bdg. 30.00 (978-0-8368-5947-8(2)) Stevens, Gareth Inc. (World Almanac Library).

—The Origins of the Holocaust. 2005. (World Almanac Library of the Holocaust). (Illus.). 48p. (J). (978-0-8368-5950-8(2) , World Almanac Library) Stevens, Gareth Inc.

—Origins of the Holocaust. 2006. (World Almanac Library of the Holocaust). (Illus.). 48p. (YA). (gr. 7-10). lib. bdg. 30.00 (978-0-8368-5943-0(X) , World Almanac Library) Stevens, Gareth Inc.

—Persecution & Emigration. 2005. (World Almanac Library of the Holocaust). (Illus.). 48p. pap. (978-0-8368-5951-5(0)); (YA). (gr. 5 up). lib. bdg. 30.00 (978-0-8368-5944-7(8)) Stevens, Gareth Inc. (World Almanac Library).

—Toward Genocide. 2005. (World Almanac Library of the Holocaust). (Illus.). 48p. pap. (978-0-8368-5952-2(9)); (YA). (gr. 10-12). lib. bdg. 30.00 (978-0-8368-5945-4(6)) Stevens, Gareth Inc. (World Almanac Library).

—World Almanac Library of the Holocaust, 6 vols., Set. Incl. Aftermath & Remembrance. (gr. 5 up). 2005. lib. bdg. 30.00 (978-0-8368-5948-5(0)); Fighting Back. (gr. 10-12). 2005. lib. bdg. 30.00 (978-0-8368-5946-1(4)); Nazi Death Camps. (gr. 5 up). 2005. lib. bdg. 30.00 (978-0-8368-5947-8(2)); Origins of the Holocaust. (gr. 7-10). 2006. lib. bdg. 30.00 (978-0-8368-5943-0(X)); Persecution & Emigration. (gr. 5 up). 2005. lib. bdg. 30.00 (978-0-8368-5944-7(8)); Toward Genocide. (gr. 10-12). 2005. lib. bdg. 30.00 (978-0-8368-5945-4(6)); (Illus.). 48p. (YA). , World Almanac Library Set lib. bdg. 180.00 (978-0-8368-5942-3(1)) Stevens, Gareth Inc.

Draper, Allison Stark. Pastor Andre Trocme: Spiritual Leader of the French Village, Le Chambon. 2005. (Holocaust Biographies Ser.). (Illus.). 112p. (YA). (gr. 7-12). lib. bdg. 26.50 (978-0-8239-3378-5(4)) Rosen Publishing Group, Inc., The.

Epstein, Rachel S. Anne Frank. 1998. (First Bks.). (Illus.). 64p. (J). (gr. 5-7). pap. 6.95 (978-0-531-15883-8(7) , Watts, Franklin) Scholastic Library Publishing.

Finkelstein, Norman H. Remember Not to Forget: A Memory of the Holocaust. Hokanson, Lois & Hokanson, Lars, illus. 2004. 32p. pap. 9.95 (978-0-8276-0770-5(9)) Jewish Pubn. Society.

Forest, James H. Silent As a Stone: Mother Maria of Paris & the Trash Can Rescue. Pancheshnaya, Dasha, illus. 2007. (J). 18.00 (***978-0-88141-314-4(3)***) St. Vladimir's Seminary Pr.

Fox, Anne L. & Abraham-Podietz, Eva. Ten Thousand Children: True Stories Told by Children Who Escaped the Holocaust on the Kindertransport. 1998. (Illus.). 128p. (J). (gr. 4-7). pap. 12.95 (978-0-87441-648-0(5)) Behrman Hse., Inc.

Frank, Anne. Anne Frank: The Diary of a Young Girl. adapted ed. pap., tchr. ed. 4.95 (978-0-8359-0138-3(6)) Globe Fearon Educational Publishing.

—Anne Frank: The Diary of a Young Girl. 241p. (J). (gr. 4-6). pap. 4.99 (978-0-8072-1363-6(2) , Listening Library) Random Hse. Audio Publishing Group.

Fremon, David K. Holocaust Heroes. 1998. (Holocaust Remembered Ser.). (Illus.). 128p. (YA). (gr. 6-12). lib. bdg. 26.60 (978-0-7660-1046-8(5)) Enslow Pubs., Inc.

Galens, Judy. Experiencing Eras & Events: Experiencing the Holocaust, 2 vols. Grunow, Elizabeth Shaw, ed. 2002. (Experiencing Eras & Events Ser.). (Illus.). 400p. (J). lib. bdg. 120.00 (978-0-7876-5414-6(0) , GML00502-173636, UXL) Thomson Gale.

Giddens, Sandra. Escape: Teens Who Escaped the Holocaust to Freedom. 1999. (Teen Witnesses to the Holocaust Ser.). (Illus.). 64p. (YA). (gr. 7-12). lib. bdg. 26.50 (978-0-8239-2843-9(8) , TWESCA) Rosen Publishing Group, Inc., The.

Goff, Elizabeth Hudson & Brown, Jonatha A. Anne Frank. 2006. (Graphic Biographies (World Almanac Library (Firm))). (Illus.). (J). pap. (978-0-8368-6248-5(1)); 32p. lib. bdg. 26.00 (978-0-8368-6196-9(5)) Stevens, Gareth Inc. (World Almanac Library).

Gold, Alison Leslie. A Special Fate: Chiune Sugihara: Hero of the Holocaust. 2000. (Illus.). 176p. (YA). (gr. 4-9). pap. 15.95 (978-0-590-39525-0(4) , Scholastic Reference) Scholastic, Inc.

Gottfried, Ted. Children of the Slaughter: Young People of the Holocaust. Alcorn, Stephen, illus. (Holocaust History Ser.). 112p. (YA). (gr. 7-12). 22.95 (978-1-58013-202-2(2)) Kar-Ben Publishing.

—Children of the Slaughter: Young People of the Holocaust. 2001. (Holocaust Ser.: up). (Illus.). 112p. (J). (gr. 7 up). lib. bdg. (978-0-7613-1716-6(3) , Twenty-First Century Bks.) Lerner Publishing Group.

—Deniers of the Holocaust: Who They Are, What They Do, Why They Do It. Alcorn, Stephen, illus. (Holocaust History Ser.). 112p. (YA). (gr. 7-12). 22.95 (978-1-58013-200-8(6)) Kar-Ben Publishing.

—Deniers of the Holocaust: Who They Are, What They Do, Why They Do It. Alcorn, Stephen, illus. 2001. (Holocaust Ser.). 112p. (gr. 7 up). lib. bdg. 29.90 (978-0-7613-1950-4(6) , Twenty-First Century Bks.) Lerner Publishing Group.

—Heroes of the Holocaust. Alcorn, Stephen, illus. (Holocaust History Ser.). 112p. (YA). (gr. 7-12). 22.95 (978-1-58013-222-0(7)) Kar-Ben Publishing.

—Heroes of the Holocaust. Alcorn, Stephen, illus. 2001. (Holocaust Ser.: up). 112p. (J). (gr. 7 up). lib. bdg. 29.90 (978-0-7613-1717-3(1) , Twenty-First Century Bks.) Lerner Publishing Group.

—The Holocaust, 5 vols. Alcorn, Stephen, illus. 2004. (History & Social Studies Ser.). (YA). (gr. 7 up). (978-0-7613-3148-3(4) , Twenty-First Century Bks.) Lerner Publishing Group.

—Martyrs to Madness: The Victims of the Nazis. Alcorn, Stephen, illus. 2000. (Holocaust Ser.: up). 128p. (gr. 7). lib. bdg. (978-0-7613-1715-9(5) , Twenty-First Century Bks.) Lerner Publishing Group.

—Nazi Germany: The Face of Tyranny. Alcorn, Stephen, illus. (Holocaust History Ser.). 112p. (YA). (gr. 7-12). 22.95 (978-1-58013-203-9(0)) Kar-Ben Publishing.

—Nazi Germany: The Face of Tyranny. 2000. (Holocaust Ser.: up). (Illus.). 128p. (gr. 7 up). lib. bdg. (978-0-7613-1714-2(7) , Twenty-First Century Bks.) Lerner Publishing Group.

Grant, R. G. The Holocaust. 1998. (New Perspectives Ser.). (Illus.). 64p. (J). (gr. 4-7). 19.98 (978-0-8172-5016-4(6)) Raintree.

Greenfeld, Howard. A Promise Fulfilled: Theodor Herzl, Chaim Weizmann, David Ben-Gurion, & the Creation of the State of Israel. 2005. (Illus.). 144p. (J). (gr. 7 up). 18.99 (978-0-06-051504-1(X)); 19.89 (978-0-06-051505-8(8)) HarperCollins Pubs.

Griscom, Laura, illus. The Boy Named 27091: A Teenager's Struggle for Survival during the Holocaust. 2007. (J). lib. bdg. 6.95 ***978-0-9633705-4-9(5))** Share Publishing.

Hasday, Judy L. The Holocaust. 2001. (Great Disasters, Reforms & Ramifications Ser.). (Illus.). 112p. (J). 30.00 (978-0-7910-5790-2(9) , Chelsea Hse.) Facts On File, Inc.

Heims, Neil. Reading the Diary of Anne Frank. 2005. (Engaged Reader Ser.). (Illus.). 81p. (J). (gr. 4-8). lib. bdg. 25.00 (978-0-7910-8829-6(4) , Chelsea Hse.) Facts On File, Inc.

Hermann, Spring. Anne Frank: Hope in the Shadows of the Holocaust. 2005. (Holocaust Heroes & Nazi Criminals Ser.). (Illus.). 160p. (J). (gr. 6-12). lib. bdg. 27.93 (978-0-7660-2531-8(4)) Enslow Pubs., Inc.

Hillman, Laura. I Will Plant You a Lilac Tree: A Memoir of a Schindler's List Survivor. 2005. (Illus.). 256p. (YA). 16.95 (978-0-689-86980-8(0) , Atheneum) Simon & Schuster Children's Publishing.

Hodgson, Julie. Polly Mae. 2006. 115p. 20.00 (978-1-4116-6340-4(3)) Lulu.com.

Hoestlandt, Jo. Star of Fear, Star of Hope. 2000. Tr. of Grande Peur sous les Etoiles. (J). (978-0-606-20411-8(3)) Tandem Library Bks.

The Holocaust, 4 bks., Set. Incl. After the Holocaust. Sheehan, Sean. (YA). (gr. 6-8). lib. bdg. 28.54 (978-0-7398-3259-2(X)); Death Camps. Sheehan, Sean. (J). (gr. 5-8). lib. bdg. 28.54 (978-0-7398-3258-5(1)); Holocaust Causes. Levy, Patricia. (J). (gr. 6-8). lib. bdg. 28.54 (978-0-7398-3257-8(3)); Survival & Resistance. Sheehan, Sean. (YA). (gr. 6-8). lib. bdg. 28.54 (978-0-7398-3260-8(3)); 64p. (Illus.). 2001. 114.16 (978-0-7398-3261-5(1)) Raintree.

Holocaust Biographies. 2005. (Illus.). 112p. (gr. 7-12). lib. bdg. 319.20 (978-0-8239-3912-1(X)) Rosen Publishing Group, Inc., The.

Holocaust Biographies, 8 bks., Set 1. Incl. Adolf Eichmann : Engineer of Death. Dolan, Sean. (J). lib. bdg. 26.50 (978-0-8239-3308-2(3) , HBEICH); Adolf Hitler : A Study in Hate. Dolan, Terrance. (YA). lib. bdg. 26.50 (978-0-8239-3317-4(2) , HBHITL); Elie Wiesel : Spokesman for Remembrance. Bayer, Linda N. (J). lib. bdg. 26.50 (978-0-8239-3306-8(7) , HBWIES); Hans & Sophie Scholl : German Resisters of the White Rose. Axelrod, Toby. (YA). lib. bdg. 26.50 (978-0-8239-3316-7(4) , HBHOBI); Hermann Goering : Hitler's Second in Command. Ramen, Fred. (YA). lib. bdg. 26.50 (978-0-8239-3307-5(5) , HBGORI); Joseph Goebbels : Nazi Propaganda Minister. Roberts, Jeremy. (J). lib. bdg. 26.50 (978-0-8239-3309-9(1) , HBGOEB); Oskar Schindler : Righteous Gentile. Roberts, Jeremy. (J). lib. bdg. 26.50 (978-0-8239-3310-5(5) , HBSCHI); Raoul Wallenberg : Swedish Diplomat & Humanitarian. Streissguth, Thomas. (J). lib. bdg. 26.50 (978-0-8239-3318-1(0) , HBRAWA); 112p. (gr. 7-12). (Illus.). 2005. Set lib. bdg. 212.00 (978-0-8239-9121-1(0) , HBHOBI); Set lib. bdg. 212.00 (978-0-8239-9424-3(4)) Rosen Publishing Group, Inc., The.

Holocaust DBA. 2001. spiral bd. 16.95 (978-1-56004-115-3(3)) Social Studies Schl. Service.

Houghton, Sarah. Elie Wiesel: A Holocaust Survivor Cries Out for Peace. 2003. (High Five Reading Ser.). (Illus.). (J). 64p. lib. bdg. 22.60 (978-0-7368-2792-8(7)); 48p. pap. 8.75 (978-0-7368-2833-8(8)) Capstone Pr., Inc.

—Elie Wiesel: A Holocaust Survivor Cries Out for Peace, 6 vols. (gr. 4 up). 49.95 (978-0-7368-2843-7(5) , High Five) Red Brick Learning.

Jacobsen, Ruth. Rescued Images: Memories of a Childhood in Hiding. 2001. (Illus.). 96p. (YA). (gr. 7). 19.95 (978-1-931414-00-5(9)) Mikaya Pr.

Jaegermann, Judith. My Childhood in the Holocaust. 2004. (Illus.). 59p. (YA). per. (978-965-90462-2-5(7)) Mazo Pubs.

Johnson, Stephen, ed. From the Holocaust to Healing the World. 2003. per. 7.95 (978-0-9659781-1-8(7)) Holocaust Museum Houston.

Koestler-Grack, Rachel A. The Story of Anne Frank. 2003. (Breakthrough Biographies Ser.). (Illus.). 32p. (gr. 3-5). 23.00 (978-0-7910-7311-7(4) , Chelsea Hse.) Facts On File, Inc.

Kustanowitz, Esther. The Hidden Children of the Holocaust: Teens Who Hid from the Nazis. 1999. (Teen Witnesses to the Holocaust Ser.). (Illus.). 64p. (YA). (gr. 7-12). lib. bdg. 26.50 (978-0-8239-2562-9(5) , TWHICH) Rosen Publishing Group, Inc., The.

Lace, William W. Hitler & the Nazis. 1999. (American War Library). (Illus.). 112p. (YA). (gr. 4-12). 27.45 (978-1-56006-372-8(6) , LML00902-177757, Lucent Bks.) Thomson Gale.

Landau, Ronnie S. Studying the Holocaust: Issues, Readings, & Documents. 1998. (Illus.). 208p. 36.95 (978-0-415-16144-2(4)); 130.00 (978-0-415-16143-5(6)) Routledge.

Lawton, Clive A. The Story of the Holocaust. 2000. (Single Titles Social Studies Ser.). (Illus.). 48p. (gr. 4-7). pap. 9.95 (978-0-531-15376-5(2) , Watts, Franklin) Scholastic Library Publishing.

—The Story of the Holocaust. 2000. (J). (978-0-606-19795-3(8)) Tandem Library Bks.

Lee, Carol Ann. Anne Frank & the Children of the Holocaust. 256p. (gr. 4). 2008. (J). 6.99 ***978-0-14-241069-1(1)** , Puffin); 2006. (YA). 16.99 (978-0-670-06107-5(7) , Viking Juvenile) Penguin Group (USA) Inc.

Lee, George. Holocaust. 1998. (Illus.). 80p. (J). pap. 9.95 (978-1-58037-070-7(5)) Twain, Mark Media, Inc. Pubs.

Levine, Ellen. Darkness over Denmark: The Danish Resistance & the Rescue of the Jews. 2005. (Illus.). 178p. (YA). (gr. 7 up). pap. 14.95 (978-0-8234-1755-1(7)) Holiday Hse., Inc.

Levine, Karen. Hana's Suitcase. 120p. (gr. 5-8). 2007. (YA). pap. 9.95 ***978-0-8075-3147-1(2));** 2003. (Illus.). (J). 15.95 incl. audio compact disk (978-0-8075-3148-8(0)) Whitman, Albert & Co.

Levine, Karen. Hana's Suitcase: A True Story. 2005. (Holocaust Remembrance Ser.: Vol. 3). (Illus.). 112p. (YA). (gr. 3-6). pap. 14.95 (978-1-896764-55-9(X)); 104p. (gr. 4 up). 19.95 (978-1-896764-61-0(4)) Second Story Pr. CAN. *Dist:* Orca Bk. Pubs. USA, Univ. of Toronto Pr., Orca Bk. Pubs. USA.

—Hana's Suitcase: A True Story. 2003. (Illus.). 120p. (J). (gr. 5-8). 24.95 (978-0-8075-3149-5(9)) Whitman, Albert & Co.

Levy, Patricia. The Holocaust. 2003. (Questioning History Ser.). (J). lib. bdg. 28.50 (978-1-58340-267-2(5)) Smart Apple Media.

—The Holocaust Causes. 2001. (Holocaust Ser.). (Illus.). 64p. (J). (gr. 6-8). lib. bdg. 28.54 (978-0-7398-3257-8(3)) Raintree.

Lobel, Anita. No Pretty Pictures: A Child of War. 2000. (Illus.). 208p. (J). (gr. 5 up). pap. 6.99 (978-0-380-73285-2(8)) HarperCollins Pubs.

—No Pretty Pictures: A Child of War. 2000. (978-0-606-17979-9(8)); (gr. 5-8). lib. bdg. 14.15 (978-0-613-28590-2(5)) Tandem Library Bks.

Maarsen, Jacqueline Van. A Friend Called Anne: One Girl's Story of War, Peace & a Unique Friendship with Anne Frank. 2005. (Illus.). 176p. (J). (gr. 3). 15.99 (978-0-670-05958-4(7) , Viking Juvenile) Penguin Group (USA) Inc.

Macmillan Reference Library Staff & Smelser, Ronald. Learning about the Holocaust, 4 vols., Set. 2000. (Illus.). 867p. (YA). (gr. 7 up). stu. ed. 460.00 (978-0-02-865536-9(2) , GML00502-171700, Macmillan Reference USA) Thomson Gale.

Mara, Wil. Anne Frank. 2006. (Illus.). 31p. (978-0-516-29841-2(0)) Children's Pr., Ltd.

McArthur, Debra. Raoul Wallenberg: Rescuing Thousands from the Nazis' Grasp. 2005. (Holocaust Heroes & Nazi Criminals Ser.). (Illus.). 160p. (J). (gr. 6-12). lib. bdg. 27.93 (978-0-7660-2530-1(6)) Enslow Pubs., Inc.

Metzger, Lois. Yours, Anne: The Life of Anne Frank. 2004. (Illus.). 97p. (J). (978-0-439-59099-0(X)) Scholastic, Inc.

Millman, Isaac. Hidden Child. Millman, Isaac, illus. 2005. (Illus.). 80p. (J). (gr. 4-9). 18.00 (978-0-374-33071-2(9) , Farrar, Straus & Giroux (BYR)) Farrar, Straus & Giroux.

Mochizuki, Ken. Pasaje a la Libertad: La Historia de Chiune Sugihara. Sarfati, Esther, tr. Lee, Dom, illus. 1999. (SPA.). 32p. (J). (gr. 3-5). 12.76 net. (978-1-880000-81-6(4) , LW8823) Lee & Low Bks., Inc.

—Pasajea la Libertad. ed. 2004. (SPA., Illus.). (J). (gr. k-4). spiral bd. (978-0-616-03091-2(6)) Canadian National Institute for the Blind/Institut National Canadien pour les Aveugles.

—Passage to Freedom: The Sugihara Story. Lee, Dom, illus. 32p. (J). 2003. 6.95 (978-1-58430-157-8(0)); 1999. (gr. 1 up). 15.95 (978-1-880000-49-6(0)) Lee & Low Bks., Inc.

—Passage to Freedom: The Sugihara Story. Lee, Dom, illus. 2002. (J). pap. 18.95 incl. audio compact disk (978-1-59112-334-7(8)); 2000. pap. 35.95 incl. audio compact disk (978-1-59112-544-0(8)); 2000. (J). (gr. 1-6). 24.95 incl. audio (978-0-87499-631-9(7)) Live Oak Media.

Moore, Ann & Culpin, Christopher. The Holocaust. 2003. (Illus.). 64p. pap. 26.00 ***978-0-7195-7709-3(8));** pap., tchr. ed. 62.50 ***978-0-7195-7710-9(1))** Hodder Education GBR. (Hodder Murray). *Dist:* Trans-Atlantic Pubns., Inc.

Moore, Lisa. Elie Wiesel: Surviving the Holocaust, Speaking Out Against Genocide. 2005. (Holocaust Heroes & Nazi Criminals Ser.). (Illus.). 160p. (YA). (gr. 7-13). lib. bdg. 27.93 (978-0-7660-2576-9(4)) Enslow Pubs., Inc.

Morris, Ann. Grandma Esther Remembers: A Jewish-American Family Story. 2002. (Illus.). 32p. (J). (gr. 5 up). pap. 7.95 (978-0-7613-1731-9(7) , Millbrook Pr.) Lerner Publishing Group.

Nasser, Stephen. My Brother's Voice: How a Young Hungarian Boy Survived the Holocaust: A True Story. Rosenthal, Sherry, ed. 2004. 232p. (YA). 19.95 (978-1-932173-09-3(9)) Stephens Pr. LLC.

Nicholson, Dorinda Makanaonalani Stagner. Remember World War II: Kids Who Survived Tell Their Stories. 2005. (Remember Ser.). (Illus.). 64p. (J). (gr. 5). 27.90 (978-0-7922-7191-8(2) , National Geographic Children's Bks.) National Geographic Society.

Nieuwsma, Milton J. Kinderlager: An Oral History of Young Holocaust Survivors. 1998. (Illus.). 192p. (YA). (gr. 4-7). tchr. ed. 18.95 (978-0-8234-1358-4(6)) Holiday Hse., Inc.

Nir, Yehuda. The Lost Childhood: A World War II Memoir. 2000. (Illus.). 304p. (J). (gr. 7 up). pap. 4.99 (978-0-439-16390-3(0) , Scholastic Pr.) Scholastic, Inc.

Opdyke, Irene Gut. In My Hands: Memories of a Holocaust Rescuer. (Illus.). (YA). (gr. 9-8). 2004. 304p. mass mkt. 6.99 (978-0-553-49411-2(2) , Laurel Leaf); 1999. 288p. pap. 18.00 (978-0-679-89181-9(1) , Knopf Bks. for Young Readers) Random Hse. Children's Bks.

—In My Hands: Memories of A Holocaust Rescuer. 2001. (gr. 7-12). lib. bdg. 21.10 (978-0-613-49500-4(4)) Tandem Library Bks.

Opdyke, Irene Gut & Armstrong, Jennifer. In My Hands: Memories of a Holocaust Rescuer. unabr. ed. 2004. 248p. (J). (gr. 5 up). pap. 42.00 incl. audio (978-0-8072-0867-0(1) , LYA 150 SP, Listening Library) Random Hse. Audio Publishing Group.

Patz, Nancy. Who Was the Woman Who Wore the Hat? 2003. (Illus.). 48p. (J). (gr. 2 up). 14.99 (978-0-525-46999-5(0) , Dutton Juvenile) Penguin Group (USA) Inc.

Perl, Lila. Four Perfect Pebbles: A Holocaust Story. 1999. (Illus.). 144p. (J). (gr. 3 up). pap. 5.99 (978-0-380-73188-6(6) , Harper Trophy) HarperCollins Pubs.

—Four Perfect Pebbles: A Holocaust Story. 1999. (Illus.). (J). 12.64 (978-0-606-17971-3(2)) Tandem Library Bks.

Poole, Josephine. Anne Frank. Barrett, Angela, illus. 2005. 40p. (J). (gr. 5). lib. bdg. 19.99 (978-0-375-93242-7(9)); 17.95 (978-0-375-83242-0(4)) Random Hse. Children's Bks. (Knopf Bks. for Young Readers).

Pressler, Mirjam. Anne Frank: A Hidden Life. Bell, Anthea, tr. 2001. (Illus.). 176p. (J). (ps-7). lib. bdg. 16.45 (978-0-613-44185-8(0)) Tandem Library Bks.

—Anne Frank: A Hidden Life. 2001. (Illus.). (J). 14.64 (978-0-606-21038-6(5)) Tandem Library Bks.

Price, Sean. Varian Fry: A Hero of the Holocaust. 2007. (J). ***978-1-4109-2696-8(6));** pap. ***978-1-4109-2707-1(5))** Steck-Vaughn.

Rabinovici, Schoschana. Thanks to My Mother. 2000. (978-0-606-18455-7(4)) Tandem Library Bks.

—Thanks to My Mother: An Unforgettable True Story. Skofield, James, tr. 2000. (Illus.). 246p. (YA). (gr. 7-12). lib. bdg. 17.60 (978-0-613-28670-1(7)) Tandem Library Bks.

Ramen, Fred. Hermann Goering: Hitler's Second in Command. 2005. (Holocaust Biographies Ser.). (Illus.). 112p. (YA). (gr. 7-12). lib. bdg. 26.50 (978-0-8239-3307-5(5) , HBGORI) Rosen Publishing Group, Inc., The.

Roberts, Jeremy. Joseph Goebbels: Nazi Propaganda Minister. 2005. (Holocaust Biographies Ser.). (Illus.). 112p. (J). (gr. 7-12). lib. bdg. 26.50 (978-0-8239-3309-9(1) , HBGOEB) Rosen Publishing Group, Inc., The.

—Oskar Schindler: Righteous Gentile. 2005. (Holocaust Biographies Ser.). (Illus.). 112p. (J). (gr. 7-12). lib. bdg. 26.50 (978-0-8239-3310-5(5) , HBSCHI) Rosen Publishing Group, Inc., The.

Rochman, Hazel. Bearing Witness: Stories of the Holocaust. 1999. (Illus.). 144p. (YA). (gr. 7 up). pap. 8.95 (978-0-531-07115-1(4) , Orchard Bks.) Scholastic, Inc.

—Bearing Witness: Stories of the Holocaust. 1999. (J). (978-0-606-17246-2(7)) Tandem Library Bks.

Rogasky, Barbara. Smoke & Ashes: The Story of the Holocaust. exp. rev. ed. 2002. (Illus.). (J). (gr. 7 up). 276p. tchr. ed. 27.50 (978-0-8234-1612-7(7)); 272p. pap. 14.95 (978-0-8234-1677-6(1)) Holiday Hse., Inc.

Rosenberg, Maxine B. Hiding to Survive: Stories of Jewish Children Rescued from the Holocaust. 1998. 16.50 (978-0-606-13481-1(6)) Tandem Library Bks.

Rubin, Susan Goldman. Fireflies in the Dark: The Story of Freidl Dicker-Brandeis & the Children of Terezin. (Illus.). 48p. (J). (gr. 4-6). 2005. pap. 8.95 (978-0-8234-1681-3(X)); 2000. tchr. ed. 18.95 (978-0-8234-1461-1(2)) Holiday Hse., Inc.

Rubin, Susan Goldman & Weissberger, Ela. The Cat with the Yellow Star: Coming of Age in Terezin. 2006. (Illus.). 40p. (J). (gr. 3-7). 16.95 (978-0-8234-1831-2(6)) Holiday Hse., Inc.

Ruelle, Karen Gray & DeSaix, Deborah Durland. Hidden on the Mountain: Stories of Children Sheltered from the Nazis in Le Chambon. 2006. (Illus.). 272p. (J). (gr. 5 up). 24.95 (978-0-8234-1928-9(2)) Holiday Hse., Inc.

Russo, Marisabina. Always Remember Me: How One Family Survived World War II. Russo, Marisabina, illus. 2005. (Illus.). 48p. (J). (gr. 1-5). 17.99 (978-0-689-86920-4(7) , Atheneum) Simon & Schuster Children's Publishing.

Saunders, Nicholas. The Life of Anne Frank. 2006. (Stories from History Ser.). 48p. (J). 14.95 (978-0-7696-4714-2(6)); pap. 6.95 (978-0-7696-4695-4(6)) School Specialty Publishing.

Schmittroth, Linda. People of the Holocaust. 1998. (J). 49.00 (978-0-7876-1744-8(X)); pap. 49.00 (978-0-7876-1745-5(8)) Thomson Gale. (UXL).

Schroeder, Peter W. & Schroeder-Hildebrand, Dagmar. Six Million Paper Clips: The Making of a Children's Holocaust Memorial. (Illus.). (J). (gr. 3-7). 2005. 48p. 17.95 (978-1-58013-169-8(7)); 2004. 64p. pap. 7.95 (978-1-58013-176-6(X)) Kar-Ben Publishing.

Schur, Maxine Rose. Hannah Szenes: A Song of Light. rev. ed. 1998. 106p. pap. 9.95 (978-0-8276-0628-9(1)) Jewish Pubn. Society.

Senker, Cath. Anne Frank: Voice of Hope. 2001. (Famous Lives Ser.). (Illus.). 48p. (J). (gr. 3-7). lib. bdg. 27.12 (978-0-8172-5719-4(5)) Raintree.

—Fs: On the Frontline Surviving the Holocaust. 2005. (Illus.). 48p. (J). (978-1-84443-694-1(2)); pap. (978-1-84443-701-6(9)) Steck-Vaughn.

—Surviving the Holocaust. 2006. (On the Front Line Ser.). (Illus.). 48p. (978-1-4109-2197-0(2)); pap. (978-1-4109-2204-5(9)) Steck-Vaughn.

Sheehan, Sean. After the Holocaust. 2001. (Holocaust Ser.). (Illus.). 64p. (YA). (gr. 6-8). lib. bdg. 28.54 (978-0-7398-3259-2(X)) Raintree.

—The Death Camps. 2001. (Holocaust Ser.). (Illus.). 64p. (J). (gr. 5-8). lib. bdg. 28.54 (978-0-7398-3258-5(1)) Raintree.

—The Holocaust. 2007. (J). ***978-1-84193-727-4(4))** Smart Apple Media.

—The Holocaust. 2005. (How Did It Happen? Ser.). (Illus.). 48p. (J). (gr. 7-10). lib. bdg. 29.95 (978-1-59018-607-7(9) , Lucent Bks.) Thomson Gale.

—Survival & Resistance. 2001. (Holocaust Ser.). (Illus.). 64p. (YA). (gr. 6-8). lib. bdg. 28.54 (978-0-7398-3260-8(3)) Raintree.

Shuter, Jane. Aftermath of the Holocaust. 2003. (Holocaust Ser.). 56p. (Illus.). (J). (gr. 6-8). lib. bdg. 28.50 (978-1-4034-0807-5(6)); pap. 8.95 (978-1-4034-3199-8(X)) Heinemann Library.

—Aftermath of the Holocaust. 2003. (Illus.). 56p. (J). (gr. 4-7). lib. bdg. 17.60 (978-0-613-60949-4(2)) Tandem Library Bks.

—Auschwitz. (Visiting the Past Ser.). 32p. (J). (gr. 5-7). 2002. (Illus.). pap. 6.95 (978-1-58810-408-3(7) , 91179); 1999. lib. bdg. 24.22 (978-1-57572-856-8(7)) Heinemann Library.

—Auschwitz. 2001. (978-0-606-22578-6(1)) Tandem Library Bks.

—The Camp System. 2003. (Holocaust Ser.). 56p. (Illus.). (YA). lib. bdg. 28.50 (978-1-4034-0809-9(2)); pap. 8.95 (978-1-4034-3201-8(5)) Heinemann Library.

—Life & Death in Hitler's Europe. 2003. (Holocaust Ser.). 56p. (Illus.). (J). lib. bdg. 28.50 (978-1-4034-0811-2(4)); pap. 8.95 (978-1-4034-3203-2(1)) Heinemann Library.

—Life & Death in Hitler's Europe. 2003. (gr. 5-8). lib. bdg. 17.60 (978-0-613-60969-2(7)) Tandem Library Bks.

—Life & Death in the Camps. 2003. (Holocaust Ser.). (Illus.). 56p. (J). lib. bdg. 28.50 (978-1-4034-0812-9(2)); pap. 8.95 (978-1-4034-3204-9(X)) Heinemann Library.

—Prelude to the Holocaust. 2003. (Holocaust Ser.). (Illus.). 56p. (J). lib. bdg. 28.50 (978-1-4034-0813-6(0)); pap. 8.95 (978-1-4034-3205-6(8)) Heinemann Library.

—Resistance to the Nazis. 2003. (Holocaust Ser.). (Illus.). 56p. (J). lib. bdg. 28.50 (978-1-4034-0814-3(9)); pap. 8.95 (978-1-4034-3206-3(6)) Heinemann Library.

—Survivors of the Holocaust. 2003. (Holocaust Ser.). 56p. (Illus.). (J). (gr. 6-8). lib. bdg. 28.50 (978-1-4034-0810-5(6)); pap. 8.95 (978-1-4034-3202-5(3)) Heinemann Library.

—Survivors of the Holocaust. 2003. (gr. 5-8). lib. bdg. 17.60 (978-0-613-60989-0(1)) Tandem Library Bks.

Shuter, Jane, et al. The Holocaust, 9 bks., Set. 2003. (Illus.). (YA). (gr. 6-8). lib. bdg. 256.50 (978-1-4034-0694-1(4)) Heinemann Library.

Siegal, Aranka. Upon the Head of the Goat: A Childhood in Hungary, 1939-1944. 2003. (gr. 5-8). lib. bdg. 14.10 (978-0-613-59754-8(0)) Tandem Library Bks.

Singer, Flora M. Flora - I Was but A Child. 2007. (J). pap. 15.95 ***978-0-9760739-8-7(6))** Holocaust Survivors' Memoirs Project.

Smith, Frank Dabba. Elsie's War: A Story of Courage in Nazi Germany. (Illus.). 32p. (978-0-7112-1861-1(7)) Lincoln, Frances Ltd. GBR. *Dist:* Transition Vendor.

—My Secret Camera: Life in the Lodz Ghetto. 2000. (Illus.). 40p. (J). (gr. 4-7). lib. bdg. 27.12 (978-0-7398-2198-5(9)) Raintree.

Somervill, Barbara A. The Holocaust Museum. 2007. (J). lib. bdg. ***978-0-7565-3357-1(0))** Compass Point Bks.

Soumerai, Eve Nussbaum & Schulz, Carol D. A Voice from the Holocaust. 2003. (Voices of the Twentieth Century Conflict Ser.). (Illus.). 160p. 39.95 (978-0-313-32358-4(5) , GR2358, Greenwood Pr.) Greenwood Publishing Group, Inc.

Spielman, Gloria. Janusz Korczak's Children. 2007. (Kar-Ben for Older Readers Ser.). (Illus.). (J). (gr. 2-5). 17.95 (978-1-58013-255-8(3)) Kar-Ben Publishing.

—Janusz Korczak's Children. Archambault, Matthew, illus. 2007. (Kar-Ben for Older Readers Ser.). (J). (gr. 2-5). pap. 7.95 ***978-0-8225-7050-9(5))** Kar-Ben Publishing.

Stalcup, Brenda. Adolf Hitler. (People Who Made History Ser.). (Illus.). 202p. (YA). (gr. 9-12). 2000. lib. bdg. 32.45 (978-0-7377-0223-1(0)); 1999. 21.20 (978-0-7377-0222-4(2)) Thomson Gale. (Greenhaven Pr., Inc.).

Steele, D. Kelley. Would You Salute? One Child's Story of the Holocaust. Rickenbaker, Becky Hyatt, illus. 2006. 48p. (J). (gr. 4-6). 22.95 (978-0-9711534-2-4(6)) Hidden Path Pubn., Inc.

Stillman, Lorry. The Spirit That Moves Us Vol. 3: Using Literature, Art, & Music to Teach About The Holocaust At The Secondary & College Level, Vol. 3. 3rd ed. 2005. 220p. pap. 19.95 (978-0-88448-230-7(8)) Tilbury Hse. Pubs.

H I

Streissguth, Thomas. Raoul Wallenberg: Swedish Diplomat & Humanitarian. 2005. (Holocaust Biographies Ser.). (Illus.). 112p. (J). (gr. 7-12). lib. bdg. 26.50 (978-0-8239-3318-1(0) , HBRAWA) Rosen Publishing Group, Inc., The.

Streissguth, Thomas & Streissguth, Tom. Adolf Eichmann: Executing the Final Solution. 2005. (Holocaust Heroes & Nazi Criminals Ser.). (Illus.). 160p. (YA). (gr. 7-13). lib. bdg. 27.93 (978-0-7660-2575-2(6)) Enslow Pubs., Inc.

Taylor, Peter Lane & Nicola, Christos. The Secret of Priest's Grotto: A Holocaust Survival Story. 2007. 64p. (gr. 5 up). (YA). pap. 8.95 (*978-1-58013-261-9(8)); (J). 18.95 (978-1-58013-260-2(X)) Kar-Ben Publishing.

Tito, E. Tina. Liberation: Teens in the Concentration Camps & the Teen Soldiers Who Liberated Them. 1999. (Teen Witnesses to the Holocaust Ser.). (Illus.). 64p. (YA). (gr. 7-12). lib. bdg. 26.50 (978-0-8239-2846-0(2) , TWLIBE) Rosen Publishing Group, Inc., The.

Toll, Nelly. Behind the Secret Window: A Memoir of a Hidden Childhood During World War II. 2003. 176p. (J). (gr. 3-6). pap. 5.99 (978-0-14-230241-5(4) , Puffin) Penguin Group (USA) Inc.

Topek, Susan R. Ten Good Rules. Schanzer, Rosalyn, illus. 2004. (General Jewish Interest Ser.). 24p. (J). (ps-1). pap. 6.95 (978-0-929371-30-6(5)) Kar-Ben Publishing.

Tryszynska-Frederick, Luba. Luba: The Angel of Bergen-Belsen. Marshall, Ann, illus. 2004. 48p. (J). 16.95 (978-1-58246-098-7(1) , Tricycle Pr.) Ten Speed Pr.

Ungerer, Tomi. Tomi: A Childhood under the Nazis. 1998. (Illus.). 175p. (YA). (gr. 6 up). 29.95 (978-1-57098-163-0(9) , Rinehart, Roberts International) Rinehart, Roberts Pubs.

Uschan, Michael V. The Holocaust. 2005. (World History Ser.). (Illus.). 112p. (YA). (gr. 7-10). lib. bdg. 32.45 (978-1-59018-252-9(9) , Lucent Bks.) Thomson Gale.

—Women of the Holocaust. 2006. (J). (978-1-59018-570-4(6) , Lucent Bks.) Thomson Gale.

van Maarsen, Jacqueline & Lee, Carol Ann. A Friend Called Anne. 2007. 176p. (J). (gr. 3). pap. 6.99 (978-0-14-240719-6(4) , Puffin) Penguin Group (USA) Inc.

Vander Zee, Ruth. Erika's Story. Innocenti, Roberto, illus. 2003. 32p. (YA). (gr. 3 up). 15.95 (978-1-56846-176-2(3)) Creative Co., The.

Wagner, Heather Lehr. Elie Wiesel: Messenger for Peace. 2007. (Modern Peacemakers Ser.). (Illus.). 120p. (YA). (gr. 9 up). 30.00 (978-0-7910-9220-0(8) , Chelsea Hse.) Facts On File, Inc.

Warren, Andrea. Surviving Hitler: A Boy in the Nazi Death Camps. 160p. (J). (gr. 5 up). 2002. pap. 6.99 (978-0-06-000767-6(2) , Harper Trophy); 2001. (Illus.). 17.99 (978-0-688-17497-2(3)); 2001. (Illus.). lib. bdg. 17.89 (978-0-06-029218-8(0)) HarperCollins Pubs.

—Surviving Hitler: A Boy in the Nazi Death Camps. 2002. (gr. 3-6). lib. bdg. 15.30 (978-0-613-56635-3(1)) Tandem Library Bks.

Watts, Irene N. & Boraks-Nemetz, Lillian, compiled by. Tapestry of Hope: Holocaust Writings for Young People. 2003. (Illus.). 256p. (J). (gr. 6 up). 18.95 (978-0-88776-638-1(2)) Tundra Bks., Inc./Livres Toundra, Inc. CAN. *Dist:* Random Hse., Inc.

Whiteley, Suzanne Mehler. Appel Is Forever: A Child's Memoir. 1999. (Illus.). 184p. (J). 39.95 (978-0-8143-2821-7(0)) Wayne State Univ. Pr.

Whiting, Jim. Anne Frank. 2007. (What's So Great About... ? Ser.). (J). lib. bdg. 25.70 (*978-1-58415-581-2(7)) Mitchell Lane Pubs., Inc.

Whiting, Jim. The Story of the Holocaust. 2005. (Monumental Milestones Ser.). (Illus.). 48p. (YA). lib. bdg. (978-1-58415-400-6(4)) Mitchell Lane Pubs., Inc.

Wieviorka, Annette. Auschwitz Explained to My Child. Brumer, Leah R., tr. from FRE. 2002. (Explained to My Child Ser.). (Illus.). 96p. pap. 7.95 (978-1-56924-552-1(5)); (J). 14.95 (978-1-56924-516-3(9)) Da Capo Pr., Inc.

Willoughby, Susan. Art, Music, & Writings from the Holocaust. 2003. (Illus.). 56p. pap. 8.95 (978-1-4034-3200-1(7)) Heinemann Library.

—Art, Music, & Writings of the Holocaust. 2003. (Holocaust Ser.). (Illus.). 56p. (J). (gr. 6-8). lib. bdg. 28.50 (978-1-4034-0808-2(4)) Heinemann Library.

—The Holocaust. (20th Century Perspectives Ser.). (Illus.). 48p. (J). (gr. 5-7). 2001. lib. bdg. 25.64 (978-1-57572-436-2(7)); Set 1. 2002. pap. 7.95 (978-1-58810-375-8(7) , 91127) Heinemann Library.

—The Holocaust. 2001. 15.30 (978-0-606-22493-2(9)) Tandem Library Bks.

Wood, Angela Gluck & Stone, Dan G. Holocaust: The Events & Their Impact on Real People. 2007. 192p. (J). (gr. 5-12). 29.99 (978-0-7566-2535-1(1)) Dorling Kindersley Publishing, Inc.

Woog, Adam. Anne Frank. 2004. (Heroes & Villains Ser.). (Illus.). 112p. (J). 29.95 (978-1-59018-349-6(5) , Lucent Bks.) Thomson Gale.

Worth, Richard. Heinrich Himmler: Murderous Architect of the Holocaust. 2005. (Holocaust Heroes & Nazi Criminals Ser.). (Illus.). 160p. (YA). (gr. 7-13). lib. bdg. 27.93 (978-0-7660-2532-5(2)) Enslow Pubs., Inc.

Wukovits, John F. Anne Frank. 1998. (Importance of Ser.). (Illus.). 96p. (YA). (gr. 7-10). 32.45 (978-1-56006-353-7(X) , Lucent Bks.) Thomson Gale.

Yeatts, Tabitha. The Holocaust Survivors. 1998. (Holocaust Remembered Ser.). (Illus.). 128p. (YA). (gr. 6-12). lib. bdg. 26.60 (978-0-89490-993-1(2)) Enslow Pubs., Inc.

Ziemian, Joseph. The Cigarette Sellers of Three Crosses Square. 2005. (Library of Holocaust Testimonies). (Illus.). 168p. pap. 17.50 (978-0-85303-686-9(1)) Vallentine Mitchell Pubs. GBR. *Dist:* International Specialized Bk. Services.

Zimering, Sabina. Hiding in the Open: A Holocaust Memoir. 2001. 230p. pap. 14.95 (978-0-87839-171-4(1)) North Star Pr. of St. Cloud.

HOLOCAUST, JEWISH (1939-1945)—FICTION

Adler, David A. Hiding from the Nazis. Ritz, Karen, illus. 2000. 32p. (J). (ps-3). pap. 6.95 (978-0-8234-1666-0(6)) Holiday Hse., Inc.

—One Yellow Daffodil: A Hanukkah Story. Bloom, Lloyd, illus. 1999. 32p. (J). (gr. 1-5). pap. 7.00 (978-0-15-202094-1(2) , Harcourt Paperbacks) Harcourt Children's Bks.

Bennett, Cherie & Gottesfeld, Jeff. Anne Frank & Me. 2002. 291p. (YA). pap. 6.99 (978-0-698-11973-4(8) , Putnam Juvenile) Penguin Group (USA) Inc.

Boyne, John. The Boy in the Striped Pajamas. 2006. 224p. (YA). (gr. 7). 15.95 (978-0-385-75106-3(0)); lib. bdg. 17.99 (978-0-385-75107-0(9)) Random Hse. Children's Bks. (Fickling, David Bks.).

Codell, Esmé Raji. Vive la Paris! 2006. 224p. (J). (gr. 3-7). 15.99 (978-0-7868-5124-9(4)) Hyperion Pr.

Deedy, Carmen Agra. The Yellow Star: The Legend of King Christian X of Denmark. Sorensen, Henri, illus. 2000. 32p. (J). (gr. 3-7). 16.95 (978-1-56145-208-8(4) , Q24691) Peachtree Pubs., Ltd.

Denenberg, Barry. One Eye Laughing, the Other Weeping: The Diary of Julie Weiss, Vienna, Austria to New York, 1938. 2000. (Dear America Ser.). (Illus.). 256p. (J). (gr. 4-9). pap. 12.95 (978-0-439-09518-1(2)) Scholastic, Inc.

Dostis, Isaac & Haddad Ikonomopoulos, Marcia. Ten Gold Medals: Glory or Freedom. 2005. (Illus.). ii, 72p. (J). (978-0-8197-0770-3(8)) Bloch Publishing Co.

Dunlop, Ed. Escape to Liechtenstein. 2003. 152p. (J). (gr. 4-7). 7.49 (978-1-59166-013-2(0)) Jones, Bob Univ. Pr.

—The Incredible Rescues. Halverson, Tom, illus. 2003. 166p. (J). (gr. 4-7). 7.49 (978-1-59166-012-5(2)) Jones, Bob Univ. Pr.

Fleischman, Sid. The Entertainer & the Dybbuk. 2007. 192p. (J). (gr. 4-9). 16.99 (*978-0-06-134445-9(1)); lib. bdg. 17.89 (*978-0-06-134446-6(X)) HarperCollins Pubs. (Greenwillow Bks.).

Friedman, D. Dina. Escaping into the Night. 2006. (Illus.). 208p. (J). 16.99 (978-1-4169-0258-4(9) , Simon & Schuster Children's Publishing) Simon & Schuster Children's Publishing.

Goldman, Alex J. I Am a Holocaust Torah. Berger, Susanne, illus. Abfier, Mel, photos by. 2000. 40p. (J). (gr. 4-7). 12.95 (978-965-229-236-0(2)) Gefen Publishing Hse., Ltd ISR. *Dist:* Gefen Bks.

—I Am a Holocaust Torah. 1999. (Illus.). (gr. 4-7). 14.95 (978-965-229-154-7(4)) Gefen Publishing Hse., Ltd ISR. *Dist:* Gefen Bks.

Greif, Jean-Jacques. The Fighter. 2006. 288p. (YA). (gr. 9 up). 16.95 (978-1-58234-891-9(X) , Bloomsbury Children) Bloomsbury Publishing.

Hausfater, Rachel. The Little Boy Star: An Allegory of the Holocaust. Latyk, Olivier, illus. 2006. 32p. (978-1-59687-172-4(5)) ibooks, Inc.

Hoestlandt, Jo. Star of Fear, Star of Hope. 1998. Tr. of Grande Peur sous les Etoiles. (J). pap. 3.95 (978-0-439-04457-8(X)) Scholastic, Inc.

—Star of Fear, Star of Hope. 2000. Tr. of Grande Peur sous les Etoiles. (J). (978-0-606-20296-1(X)); (gr. 3-6). lib. bdg. 17.60 (978-0-613-29518-5(8)) Tandem Library Bks.

Johnston, Tony. The Harmonica. Mazellan, Ron, illus. 2004. 32p. (J). 15.95 (978-1-57091-547-5(4)) Charlesbridge Publishing, Inc.

Kacer, Kathy. Clara's War. 2005. (Holocaust Remembrance Ser.). (Illus.). 196p. (YA). (gr. 5 up). pap. 5.95 (978-1-896764-42-9(8)) Second Story Pr. CAN. *Dist:* Orca Bk. Pubs. USA, Univ. of Toronto Pr., Univ. of Toronto Pr.

—Clara's War. 2001. (gr. 5-8). lib. bdg. 14.10 (978-0-613-51538-2(2)) Tandem Library Bks.

—Secret of Gabi's Dresser. 1999. (gr. 3-6). lib. bdg. 12.95 (978-0-613-29338-9(X)) Tandem Library Bks.

Katies Choice. 2005. (YA). per. (978-1-59872-217-8(4)) Instantpublisher.com.

Kerr, Judith. When Hitler Stole Pink Rabbit.Tr. of Cuando Hitler Robo el Conejo Rosa. (SPA.). 172p. (J). 11.95 (978-84-204-3201-4(6)) Santillana USA Publishing Co., Inc.

Kositsky, Lynne. The Thought of High Windows. 176p. (J). 2005. (gr. 7-12). (978-1-55337-622-4(6)); 2004. (gr. 13 up). (978-1-55337-621-7(8)) Kids Can Pr., Ltd.

Lawton, Wendy. Shadow of His Hand: A Story Based on the Life of Holocaust Survivor Anita Dittman. 2004. (Daughters of the Faith Ser.). 160p. (J). pap. 6.99 (978-0-8024-4074-7(6)) Moody Pubs.

Littlesugar, Amy. Willy & Max: A Holocaust Story. Low, William, illus. 2006. 40p. (J). (ps). 15.99 (978-0-399-23483-5(7) , Philomel) Penguin Group (USA) Inc.

Lowenstein, Sallie Claire. Waiting for Eugene. 2006. (Illus.). 201p. (J). (*978-1-4156-6166-6(9)) Book Wholesalers, Inc.

Matas, Carol & Matas, Carol. Greater Than Angels. 1999. 177p. lib. bdg. 11.64 (978-0-606-17196-0(7)) Tandem Library Bks.

Mazer, Norma Fox. Good Night, Maman. Mazer, Norma Fox, illus. 2001. (Harper Trophy Bks.). 192p. (J). (gr. 5 up). pap. 6.99 (978-0-06-440923-0(6) , Harper Trophy) HarperCollins Pubs.

—Good Night, Maman. 2001. (Illus.). (J). 12.64 (978-0-606-21217-5(5)) Tandem Library Bks.

—Good Night Maman: A Novel. 2006. 185p. (J). (gr. k-4). reprint ed. 16.00 (*978-1-4223-5862-7(3)) DIANE Publishing Co.

Mazer, Norma Fox. GoodNight, Maman. 1999. (C). 16.00 net. (978-0-15-202677-6(0)) Harcourt College Pubs.

Melnikoff, Pamela. Prisoner in Time. 2001. 144p. (gr. 5-8). pap. 9.95 (978-0-8276-0735-4(0)) Jewish Pubn. Society.

Moskin, Marietta D. I Am Rosemarie. 1999. 258p. (J). pap. 12.95 (978-0-7351-0226-2(0)); lib. bdg. 24.95 (978-0-7351-0225-5(2)) Replica Bks.

—I Am Rosemarie. 2000. (J). pap. 1.95 (978-0-590-04278-9(5)) Scholastic, Inc.

Newbery, Linda. Sisterland. 2004. 384p. (J). (gr. 7). 15.95 (978-0-385-75026-4(9) , Fickling, David Bks.) Random Hse. Children's Bks.

Orlev, Uri. Run Boy, Run. Halkin, Hillel, tr. from HEB. 2003. 192p. (YA). (gr. 5 up). tchr. ed. 15.00 (978-0-618-16465-3(0) , Walter Lorraine) Houghton Mifflin Co. Trade & Reference Div.

Orlev, Uri. Run, Boy, Run. Halkin, Hillel, tr. 10th ed. 2007. 192p. (J). (gr. 5 up). 6.95 (*978-0-618-95706-4(5)) Houghton Mifflin Co. Trade & Reference Div.

Pausewang, Gudrun. Final Journey. Crampton, Patricia, tr. 1998. 160p. (J). (gr. 7-12). pap. 6.99 (978-0-14-130104-4(X) , Puffin) Penguin Group (USA) Inc.

Pressler, Mirjam. Malka. Murdoch, Brian, tr. from GER. 2003. 288p. (YA). (gr. 5-12). 18.99 (978-0-399-23984-7(7) , Philomel) Penguin Group (USA) Inc.

Propp, Vera W. When the Soldiers Were Gone. 2001. (Illus.). (J). (978-0-606-20989-2(1)) Tandem Library Bks.

Radin, Ruth Y. Escape to the Forest: Based on a True Story of the Holocaust. Hamlin, Janet, illus. 96p. (J). (gr. 4 up). 2001. pap. 4.25 (978-0-06-440822-6(1)); 2000. 13.89 (978-0-06-028521-0(4)) HarperCollins Pubs.

Rappaport, Doreen. The Secret Seder. McCully, Emily Arnold, illus. 2005. 40p. (gr. k-4). 16.99 (978-0-7868-0777-2(6)) Hyperion Bks. for Children.

Roseman, Kenneth D. Escape from the Holocaust. 1998. (gr. 3-6). lib. bdg. 17.60 (978-0-613-88955-1(X)) Tandem Library Bks.

Roy, Jennifer Rozines. Yellow Star. 2006. 256p. (YA). (gr. 5-9). 16.95 (978-0-7614-5277-5(X)) Cavendish, Marshall Corp.

Sachs, Marilyn. Lost in America. rev. ed. 2005. 160p. (J). 16.95 (978-1-59643-040-2(0)) Roaring Brook Pr.

Sasson, Jean. Ester's Child. 2003. (gr. 7-12). lib. bdg. 22.20 (978-0-613-70913-2(6)) Tandem Library Bks.

Schmidt, Gary. Mara's Stories: Glimmers in the Darkness. 2008. 128p. (J). pap. 6.99 (*978-0-312-37388-7(0)) Square Fish.

Schwartz, Ellen. Jesse's Star. 2000. (Young Reader Ser.). (Illus.). 96p. (J). (gr. 3-6). pap. 4.99 (978-1-55143-143-7(2)) Orca Bk. Pubs. USA.

—Jesse's Star. 2000. (Illus.). 108p. (J). (gr. 2-6). lib. bdg. 13.00 (978-0-613-33651-2(8)) Tandem Library Bks.

Spinelli, Jerry. Milkweed. 2003. (Illus.). 224p. (J). (gr. 5). 15.95 (978-0-375-81374-0(8)); lib. bdg. 17.99 (978-0-375-91374-7(2)) Random Hse. Children's Bks. (Knopf Bks. for Young Readers).

—Milkweed. l.t. ed. 2003. 279p. (YA). 23.95 (978-0-7862-6146-8(3) , Large Print Pr.) Thorndike Pr.

Suzuki, Etsuo. Anne Frank. 2006. (Illus.). 160p. pap. 9.95 (978-1-56970-974-0(2)) Digital Manga Publishing.

Taylor, Marilyn. Faraway Home. 2003. 224p. (J). (gr. 5 up). pap. 7.95 (978-0-86278-643-4(6)) O'Brien Pr., Ltd., The IRL. *Dist:* Independent Pubs. Group.

Vander Zee, Ruth & Sneider, Marian. Eli Remembers. Farnsworth, Bill, illus. 2007. 32p. (J). (gr. 3-7). 18.00 (*978-0-8028-5309-7(9) , Eerdmans Bks For Young Readers) Eerdmans, William B. Publishing Co.

Williams, Laura E. Behind the Bedroom Wall. Goldstein, A. Nancy, illus. 2005. (Historical Fiction for Young Readers Ser.). 184p. (J). (ps-7). pap. 6.95 (978-1-57131-658-5(2)) Milkweed Editions.

Wiseman, Eva. Kanada. 2006. (Illus.). 264p. (J). (gr. 5). pap. 9.95 (978-0-88776-729-6(X)) Tundra Bks., Inc./Livres Toundra, Inc. CAN. *Dist:* Random Hse., Inc.

—My Canary Yellow Star. 2002. (gr. 5-8). lib. bdg. 15.25 (978-0-613-62688-0(5)) Tandem Library Bks.

—My Canary Yellow Star. 2001. (Illus.). 240p. (J). (gr. 3-7). pap. 6.95 (978-0-88776-533-9(5)) Tundra Bks., Inc./Livres Toundra, Inc. CAN. *Dist:* Random Hse., Inc.

Yolen, Jane. The Devil's Arithmetic. 2002. (J). 13.19 (978-0-7587-9594-6(7)) Book Wholesalers, Inc.

—The Devil's Arithmetic. 2004. (Puffin Modern Classics Ser.). 176p. (gr. 3). pap. 6.99 (978-0-14-240109-5(9) , Puffin) Penguin Group (USA) Inc.

HOLOCAUST SURVIVORS

Here are entered works on persons who survived the Jewish Holocaust of 1939-1945, with emphasis on their lives since 1945.

Appelbaum, Barbara G. & Lovenheim, Barbara, eds. Perilous Journeys: Personal Stories of German & Austrian Jews Who Escaped the Holocaust, 2001. (Illus.). 106p. (YA). pap. 22.95 (978-0-9710686-0-5(7)) Jewish Community Federation of Rochester, NY, Inc.

Ayer, Eleanor H. In the Ghettos: Teens Who Survived the Ghettos of the Holocaust. 1999. (Teen Witnesses to the Holocaust Ser.). (Illus.). 64p. (YA). (gr. 7-12). lib. bdg. 26.50 (978-0-8239-2845-3(4) , TWGHET) Rosen Publishing Group, Inc., The.

—Parallel Journeys. 2000. (gr. 7-12). lib. bdg. 14.15 (978-0-613-28600-8(6)) Tandem Library Bks.

Bayer, Linda N. Elie Wiesel: Spokesman for Remembrance. 2005. (Holocaust Biographies Ser.). (Illus.). 112p. (J). (gr. 7-12). lib. bdg. 26.50 (978-0-8239-3306-8(7) , HBWIES) Rosen Publishing Group, Inc., The.

—Elie Wiesel: Spokesman for Remembrance. 1999. (Illus.). 112p. (YA). pet. 10.95 (978-1-56254-456-0(X) , SP456X) Saddleback Educational Publishing.

Bitton-Jackson, Livia. My Bridges of Hope. 2002. (gr. 7-12). lib. bdg. 13.00 (978-0-613-73376-2(2)) Tandem Library Bks.

—My Bridges of Hope: Searching for Life & Love after Auschwitz. 2002. 384p. (YA). reprint ed. pap. 5.99 (978-0-689-84898-8(6) , Simon Pulse) Simon & Schuster Children's Publishing.

—My Bridges of Hope: Searching for Life & Love after Auschwitz. 2001. (YA). (978-0-606-20815-4(1)) Tandem Library Bks.

Currie, Stephen. Escapes from Nazi Persecution. 2003. (Great Escapes Ser.). (Illus.). 112p. (J). 29.95 (978-1-59018-279-6(0) , Lucent Bks.) Thomson Gale.

Downing, David. Aftermath & Remembrance. 2005. (World Almanac Library of the Holocaust). (Illus.). 48p. pap. (978-0-8368-5955-3(3)); (YA). (gr. 5 up). lib. bdg. 30.00 (978-0-8368-5948-5(0)) Stevens, Gareth Inc. (World Almanac Library).

Fox, Anne. Ten Thousand Children. 1999. (gr. 3-6). lib. bdg. 17.05 (978-0-613-50376-1(7)) Tandem Library Bks.

Gertner, Sheina Sachar. The Tree Stood Still. 2006. 96p. per. 9.95 (*978-1-58939-886-3(6)) Virtualbookworm.com Publishing, Inc.

Gottfried, Ted. Children of the Slaughter: Young People of the Holocaust. Alcorn, Stephen, illus. (Holocaust History Ser.). 112p. (YA). (gr. 7-12). 22.95 (978-1-58013-202-2(2)) Kar-Ben Publishing.

—Children of the Slaughter: Young People of the Holocaust. 2001. (Holocaust Ser.: up). (Illus.). 112p. (J). (gr. 7 up). lib. bdg. (978-0-7613-1716-6(3) , Twenty-First Century Bks.) Lerner Publishing Group.

—Displaced Persons: Growing up American after the Holocaust. 2001. (Holocaust Ser.). (Illus.). 112p. (gr. 7 up). lib. bdg. 29.90 (978-0-7613-1924-5(7) , Twenty-First Century Bks.) Lerner Publishing Group.

Harris, Samuel R. Sammy Child Survivor of the Holocaust. 2005. (Illus.). 128p. pap. 14.95 (978-0-9759253-0-0(X)) Harris, Samuel.

Houghton, Sarah. Elie Wiesel: A Holocaust Survivor Cries Out for Peace. 2003. (High Five Reading Ser.). (Illus.). (J). 64p. lib. bdg. 22.60 (978-0-7368-2792-8(7)); 48p. pap. 8.75 (978-0-7368-2833-8(8)) Capstone Pr., Inc.

—Elie Wiesel: A Holocaust Survivor Cries Out for Peace, 6 vols. (gr. 4 up). 49.95 (978-0-7368-2843-7(5) , High Five) Red Brick Learning.

Jacobsen, Ruth. Rescued Images: Memories of a Childhood in Hiding. 2001. (Illus.). 96p. (YA). (gr. 7). 19.95 (978-1-931414-00-5(9)) Mikaya Pr.

Johnson, Stephen, ed. From the Holocaust to Healing the World. 2003. per. 7.95 (978-0-9659781-1-8(7)) Holocaust Museum Houston.

Kemeny, Esther. On the Shores of Darkness: The Memoir of Esther Kemeny, Haller, Heather, ed. 2003. (Illus.). 144p. per. (978-0-9743961-7-0(6)) Haller Company, The.

Krinitz, Esther Nisenthal & Steinhardt, Bernice. Memories of Survival. Krinitz, Esther Nisenthal, illus. 2005. (Illus.). 64p. (gr. k-4). 15.99 (978-0-7868-5126-3(0)) Hyperion Pr.

Moore, Lisa. Elie Wiesel: Surviving the Holocaust, Speaking Out Against Genocide. 2005. (Holocaust Heroes & Nazi Criminals Ser.). (Illus.). 160p. (YA). (gr. 7-13). lib. bdg. 27.93 (978-0-7660-2576-9(4)) Enslow Pubs., Inc.

Morris, Ann. Grandma Esther Remembers: A Jewish-American Family Story. Linenthal, Peter, illus. 2002. (What Was It Like, Grandma? Ser.). 32p. (gr. k-3). lib. bdg. 22.90 (978-0-7613-2318-1(X) , Millbrook Pr.) Lerner Publishing Group.

Nasser, Stephen & Rosenthal, Sherry. My Brother's Voice: How a Young Hungarian Boy Survived the Holocaust: A True Story. 2003. 232p. (YA). pap. 14.95 (978-1-932173-10-9(2)) Stephens Pr. LLC.

Opdyke, Irene Gut. In My Hands: Memories of a Holocaust Rescuer. 1999. (Illus.). 288p. (YA). (gr. 9-8). pap. 18.00 (978-0-679-89181-9(1) , Knopf Bks. for Young Readers) Random Hse. Children's Bks.

Opdyke, Irene Gut & Armstrong, Jennifer. In My Hands: Memories of a Holocaust Rescuer. unabr. ed. 2004. 248p. (J). (gr. 5 up). pap. 42.00 incl. audio (978-0-8072-0867-0(1) , LYA 150 SP, Listening Library) Random Hse. Audio Publishing Group.

Perl, Lila. Four Perfect Pebbles. 1999. (gr. 5-8). lib. bdg. 14.15 (978-0-7857-1852-9(4)) Tandem Library Bks.

Sheehan, Sean. After the Holocaust. 2001. (Holocaust Ser.). (Illus.). 64p. (YA). (gr. 6-8). lib. bdg. 28.54 (978-0-7398-3259-2(X)) Raintree.

—Survival & Resistance. 2001. (Holocaust Ser.). (Illus.). 64p. (YA). (gr. 6-8). lib. bdg. 28.54 (978-0-7398-3260-8(3)) Raintree.

Shuter, Jane. Aftermath of the Holocaust. 2003. (Holocaust Ser.). 56p. (Illus.). (J). (gr. 6-8). lib. bdg. 28.50 (978-1-4034-0807-5(6)); pap. 8.95 (978-1-4034-3199-8(X)) Heinemann Library.

—Aftermath of the Holocaust. 2003. (Illus.). 56p. (J). (gr. 4-7). lib. bdg. 17.60 (978-0-613-60949-4(2)) Tandem Library Bks.

—Survivors of the Holocaust. 2003. (Holocaust Ser.). 56p. (Illus.). (J). (gr. 6-8). lib. bdg. 28.50 (978-1-4034-0810-5(6)); pap. 8.95 (978-1-4034-3202-5(3)) Heinemann Library.

—Survivors of the Holocaust. 2003. (gr. 5-8). lib. bdg. 17.60 (978-0-613-60989-0(1)) Tandem Library Bks.

Siegal, Aranka. Grace in the Wilderness: After the Liberation, 1945-1948. 2003. (gr. 5-8). lib. bdg. 14.10 (978-0-613-59626-8(9)) Tandem Library Bks.

—Grace in the Wilderness: After the Liberation 1945-1948. unabr. ed. 1998. (YA). Class Set. 124.70 incl. audio (978-0-7887-2539-5(4) , 46709); Homework Set. (gr. 7). 58.24 incl. audio (978-0-7887-2234-9(4) , 40718) Recorded Bks., LLC.

Singer, Flora M. Flora - I Was but A Child. 2007. (J). pap. 15.95 (*978-0-9760739-8-7(6)) Holocaust Survivors' Memoirs Project.

Stinson, Kathy. Cornelia Oberlander: The Art of the Possible. 2008. 96p. 22.95 (*978-0-88776-804-0(0)) Tundra Bks., Inc./Livres Toundra, Inc. CAN. *Dist:* Random Hse. of Canada, Ltd.

Surviving the Holocaust 6-Pack. 2004. (Illus.). pap. 48.35 (978-1-4109-1478-1(X)) Raintree.

Vander Zee, Ruth. Erika's Story. Innocenti, Roberto, illus. 2003. 32p. (YA). (gr. 3 up). 15.95 (978-1-56846-176-2(3)) Creative Co., The.

Wagner, Heather Lehr. Elie Wiesel: Messenger for Peace. 2007. (Modern Peacemakers Ser.). (Illus.). 120p. (YA). (gr. 9 up). 30.00 (978-0-7910-9220-0(8) , Chelsea Hse.) Facts On File, Inc.

Warren, Andrea. Surviving Hitler: A Boy in the Nazi Death Camps. 2002. (gr. 3-6). lib. bdg. 15.30 (978-0-613-56635-3(1)) Tandem Library Bks.

Yeatts, Tabitha. The Holocaust Survivors. 1998. (Holocaust Remembered Ser.). (Illus.). 128p. (YA). (gr. 6-12). lib. bdg. 26.60 (978-0-89490-993-1(2)) Enslow Pubs., Inc.

Zullo, Allan. True Stories of Children in the Holocaust. 2005. (Survivors Ser.). (Illus.). 208p. (J). pap. 4.99 (978-0-439-66996-2(0) , Scholastic Paperbacks) Scholastic, Inc.

HOLOCAUST SURVIVORS—FICTION

Adler, David A. One Yellow Daffodil: A Hanukkah Story. 1999. (gr. 3-6). lib. bdg. 14.15 (978-0-613-22137-5(0)) Tandem Library Bks.

Bat-Ami, Miriam. Two Suns in the Sky. 1999. 208p. (YA). (gr. 7-12). 17.95 (978-0-8126-2900-2(0)) Cricket Bks.

—Two Suns in the Sky. 2001. 208p. (J). pap. 6.99 (978-0-14-230036-7(5) , Puffin) Penguin Group (USA) Inc.

—Two Suns in the Sky. 2001. (gr. 7-12). lib. bdg. 15.30 (978-0-613-44425-5(6)) Tandem Library Bks.

Fried, Leah. Where Is Shimmele? Ruppaport, Aviva, tr. from HEB. 2003. (Illus.). 318p. (YA). (gr. 6-8). 20.00 (978-1-885220-31-8(6)) Moznaim Publishing Corp.

Lakin, Patricia. Don't Forget. Rand, Ted, illus. 2000. 32p. (YA). (gr. k-3). pap. 5.95 (978-0-688-17522-1(8)) HarperCollins Pubs.

Mamet, David. Bar Mitzvah. Sultan, Donald, illus. 1999. 45p. (YA). reprint ed. 27.00 (978-0-7567-6490-6(4)) DIANE Publishing Co.

—Bar Mitzvah. 1999. (Illus.). 48p. (gr. 8). 26.95 (978-0-8212-2546-2(4)) Little Brown & Co.

Mazer, Norma Fox. Good Night, Maman. Mazer, Norma Fox, illus. 2001. (Harper Trophy Bks.). 192p. (J). (gr. 5 up). pap. 6.99 (978-0-06-440923-0(6) , Harper Trophy) HarperCollins Pubs.

Mazer, Norma Fox. Good Night Maman: A Novel. 2006. 185p. (J). (gr. k-4). reprint ed. 16.00 (*978-1-4223-5862-7(3)) DIANE Publishing Co.

McMillan, Frank. Cezanne Is Missing. 2006. 323p. (YA). pap. 14.95 (978-0-9711359-4-9(0)) Cambridge Hse. Publishing Co., LLC.

Semel, Nava & Silveira, Carlos. Clases de Vuelo. Silveira, Carlos, tr. 2002. (Joven Coleccion Ser.). (SPA., Illus.). 206p. (978-84-89804-06-7(0)) Loguez Ediciones ESP. *Dist:* Lectorum Pubns., Inc.

Watts, Irene N. Goodbye Marianne. 1998. 48p. pap. 6.95 (978-1-896239-03-3(X)) Shillingford, J. Gordon Publishing CAN. *Dist:* Univ. of Toronto Pr.

HOLOGRAPHY

Kasper, Joseph E. & Feller, Steven A. The Complete Book of Holograms: How They Work & How to Make Them. l.t. ed. 2001. (Illus.). 224p. pap. 11.95 (978-0-486-41580-2(5)) Dover Pubns., Inc.

HOLY GRAIL

see Grail

HOLY ROMAN EMPIRE

Bhote, Themina. Charlemagne: Life & Times of an Early Medieval Emperor. 2004. (Medieval Leaders Ser.). (Illus.). 112p. (J). lib. bdg. 31.95 (978-1-4042-0161-3(0)) Rosen Publishing Group, Inc., The.

Gelfand, Dale Evva. Charlemagne. 2003. (Ancient World Leaders Ser.). (Illus.). 112p. (gr. 6-12). 30.00 (978-0-7910-7224-0(X) , Chelsea Hse.) Facts On File, Inc.

Scheuerman, Richard D. & Ellis, Arthur K., eds. Eleanor of Aquitaine & the Crusade of the Kings: A Medieval Journey of Discovery Travelogue. LeGette, James, illus. unabr. ed. 2000. 494p. (YA). (gr. 5-8). ring bd. 69.95 (978-1-885360-19-9(3)) Demco, Inc.

Schlesinger, Arthur M., Jr., intro. Ancient World Leaders. (Illus.). (gr. 6-12). lib. bdg. (978-0-7910-8056-6(0) , Chelsea Hse.) Facts On File, Inc.

Whiting, Jim. The Life & Times of Charlemagne. 2005. (Biography from Ancient Civilizations Ser.). (Illus.). 48p. (J). (gr. 4-8). lib. bdg. 29.95 (978-1-58415-346-7(6)) Mitchell Lane Pubs., Inc.

HOLY SCRIPTURES

see Bible

HOLY SEE

see Catholic Church; Popes

HOME

see also Home Economics; Marriage

Beaton, Clare, illus. At Home: A la Casa. 2001. (Bilingual First Bks.). (SPA & ENG.). 24p. (J). (ps-k). pap. 4.99 (978-0-7641-1692-6(4)) Barron's Educational Series, Inc.

Burton, Margie, et al. Homes for People. Evento, Susan, ed. 1998. (Early Connections Ser.). 16p. (J). (gr. k-2). pap. 4.25 (978-1-892393-44-9(1)) Benchmark Education Co.

Canizares, Susan & Berger, Samantha. At Home. 2000. (Scholastic Placebook Ser.). (Illus.). (J). (978-0-439-15367-6(0)) Scholastic, Inc.

Chapman, Cindy. Where Is Your Home? 2003. (Compass Point Phonics Readers Ser.). (Illus.). 16p. (J). (gr. 1 up). 13.26 (978-0-7565-0532-5(1)) Compass Point Bks.

Hill, Lee Sullivan. Homes Keep Us Warm. 2000. (Building Block Bks.). (Illus.). 32p. (J). (gr. k-3). lib. bdg. (978-1-57505-430-8(2) , Carolrhoda Bks.) Lerner Publishing Group.

LeapFrog Staff, compiled by. Home: (Blue Book) 2002. (J). (ps-2). 19.95 (978-1-58605-680-3(8)) LeapFrog Enterprises, Inc.

—Home: (Green Book) 2002. (J). (ps-2). 19.95 (978-1-58605-678-0(6)) LeapFrog Enterprises, Inc.

—Home: (Orange Book) 2002. (J). (ps-2). 19.95 (978-1-58605-679-7(4)) LeapFrog Enterprises, Inc.

—Home: (Purple Book) 2002. (J). (ps-2). 19.95 (978-1-58605-677-3(8)) LeapFrog Enterprises, Inc.

—Home Days. 2002. (J). (ps-1). 14.95 (978-1-58605-755-8(3)) LeapFrog Enterprises, Inc.

The Letter Hh: Homes, 6 vols. (gr. k-2). 17.50 (978-0-7368-4107-8(5)) Red Brick Learning.

Michels, Dia L. Look What I See! Where Can I Be?, 3 vols. 2001. (Look What I See! Where Can I Be? Ser.). (Illus.). (J). 39.95 (978-1-930775-37-4(7)) Platypus Media, L.L.C.

Nelson, Robin. Home. 2003. (First Step Nonfiction Ser.). (Illus.). 24p. (J). (gr. k-2). lib. bdg. 18.60 (978-0-8225-4642-9(6)) Lerner Publishing Group.

Parramon, José María. Mi Calle. Borday, Irene, illus. (Coleccion Estoy En...).Tr. of My Street. (SPA.). 32p. (J). (gr. k-3). 6.36 (978-84-342-1003-5(7)) Parramon Ediciones S.A. ESP. *Dist:* Lectorum Pubns., Inc.

—Mi Casa. Borday, Irene, illus. (Coleccion Estoy En...).Tr. of My House. (SPA.). 32p. (J). (gr. k-3). 6.36 (978-84-342-1002-8(9)) Parramon Ediciones S.A. ESP. *Dist:* Lectorum Pubns., Inc.

—Mi Jardin. Borday, Irene, illus. (Coleccion Estoy En...).Tr. of My Garden. (SPA.). 32p. (J). (gr. k-3). 6.36 (978-84-342-1005-9(3)) Parramon Ediciones S.A. ESP. *Dist:* Lectorum Pubns., Inc.

Parramon, José María & Bordoy, Irene. Mi Calle.Tr. of My Street. (SPA., Illus.). (J). (ps-1). 6.95 (978-958-04-1277-9(4)) Norma S.A. COL. *Dist:* Distribuidora Norma, Inc.

Primm & Petelinsek, Kathleen. Home. 2004. (Talking Hands, Listening Eyes Ser.).Tr. of Casa. (ENG & SPA., Illus.). 24p. (J). (ps-3). 21.36 (978-1-59296-021-7(9)) Child's World, Inc.

Richardson, Adele. Manners at Home. 2006. (First Facts Ser.). (J). (978-0-7368-4293-8(4)) Capstone Pr., Inc.

Roop, Peter & Roop, Connie. A Home Album. 1998. (Long Ago & Today Ser.). (Illus.). 24p. (J). (gr. 1-3). lib. bdg. 19.92 (978-1-57572-602-1(5)) Heinemann Library.

Rylant, Cynthia & Halperin, Wendy Anderson. Let's Go Home: The Wonderful Things about a House. 2002. (Illus.). 32p. (J). reprint ed. 16.95 (978-0-689-82326-8(6)) Simon & Schuster Children's Publishing.

Schaefer, Lola M. Mobile Home. 2003. (Heinemann Read & Learn Ser.). (Illus.). 24p. (J). pap. 5.25 (978-1-4034-0486-2(0)) Heinemann Library.

School Specialty Publishing. Learn about Home. 2005. (Learn about Coloring Bks.). 32p. (J). (ps-3). pap. 1.99 (978-0-7696-4161-4(X) , Brighter Child) School Specialty Publishing.

Tuxworth, Nicola. My Home. 2002. (Let's Look at...Ser.). (Illus.). 20p. 5.99 (978-0-7548-1050-6(X) , Lorenz Bks.) Anness Publishing GBR. *Dist:* National Bk. Network.

Weitzman, Elizabeth. Staying in a Shelter. 2004. (Lets Talk Library). (Illus.). 24p. (J). lib. bdg. 18.75 (978-0-8239-6812-1(X) , PowerKids Pr.) Rosen Publishing Group, Inc., The.

HOME—FICTION

A la Maison. 2000. (Collection des Mots pour Lire). (FRE.). 28p. (J). 15.95 (978-2-03-653001-0(X)) Librairie Larousse FRA. *Dist:* Distribooks, Inc.

Ashman, Linda. Castles, Caves, & Honeycombs. Stringer, Lauren, illus. 2001. 32p. (J). (ps-k). 17.00 (978-0-15-202211-2(2)) Harcourt Children's Bks.

Avery, Terry. Moon Rabbit Builds a Fine House. l.t. ed. 2000. (Illus.). 32p. (J). (ps-3). 17.95 (978-1-929115-00-6(8)) Azro Pr., Inc.

Baglio, Ben M. Kittens in the Kitchen. McNicholas, Shelagh, illus. 1998. (Animal Ark Ser.: No. 1). (J). (gr. 3-5). (978-0-606-13129-2(9)) Tandem Library Bks.

—Pony on the Porch. McNicholas, Shelagh, illus. 1998. (Animal Ark Ser.: No. 2). (J). (gr. 3-5). (978-0-606-13130-8(2)) Tandem Library Bks.

Baker, Jeannie. Home. Baker, Jeannie, illus. 2004. 32p. (J). 16.99 (978-0-06-623935-4(4)) HarperCollins Pubs.

Banks, Kate. The Cat Who Walked Across France. Hallensleben, Georg, illus. 2004. 40p. (J). 16.00 (978-0-374-39968-9(9) , Farrar, Straus & Giroux (BYR)) Farrar, Straus & Giroux.

Benton, Imogene. Yaassit. Berlin, James, tr. Strum, Beth & Brunk, Cara, illus. l.t. ed. 2001. 8p. (J). pap. 17.00 (978-1-58084-179-5(1)) Lower Kuskokwim Schl. District.

—Yaassit. Kiokun, Dorothy & Berlin, James, trs. Strum, Beth & Brunk, Cara, illus. l.t. ed. 2001. 12p. (J). pap. 17.00 (978-1-58084-180-1(5)) Lower Kuskokwim Schl. District.

Blackstone, Stella. Oso en Casa. 2003. (SPA.). (gr. k-3). lib. bdg. 14.15 (978-0-613-65706-8(3)) Tandem Library Bks.

Bode, N. E. The Anybodies. Ferguson, Peter, illus. 288p. (J). 2004. 16.99 (978-0-06-055735-5(4)); 2004. lib. bdg. 17.89 (978-0-06-055736-2(2)); 2005. reprint ed. pap. 6.99 (978-0-06-055737-9(0)) HarperCollins Pubs.

Bonniol, Magali. El Ogro De Mariuchi. 2003. (SPA.). 40p. (978-84-8470-112-5(3)) Corimbo, Editorial S.L.

Brown, Margaret Wise. Home for a Bunny. Williams, Garth, illus. 2003. (Big Little Golden Bks.). 32p. (J). (gr. k-k). reprint ed. 8.99 (978-0-307-10546-2(6) , Golden Bks.) Random Hse. Children's Bks.

—Home for a Bunny. 1999. (978-0-606-22796-4(2)) Tandem Library Bks.

Brown, Tony. Water's Edge. 2006. 180p. per. (*978-1-84685-163-6(7) , Exposure Publishing) Meadow Bks.

Carey, Elizabeth Doyle. The Callahan Cousins #2: Home Sweet Home. 2nd ed. 208p. (J). pap. 7.99 (978-0-316-73732-6(1)) Little Brown & Co.

—Home Sweet Home No. 2. 2nd ed. 2005. (Callahan Cousins Ser.: No. 2). (Illus.). 206p. (J). (gr. 3-7). 10.99 (978-0-316-73692-3(9)) Little Brown & Co.

Cherrington, Janelle. There's No Nest Like Home. 2000. (gr. k-3). lib. bdg. 11.25 (978-0-613-31798-6(X)) Tandem Library Bks.

Clements, Andrew. Slippers at Home. Bynum, Janie, illus. 2005. 32p. (J). (ps-2). 12.99 (978-0-525-47138-7(3) , Dutton Juvenile) Penguin Group (USA) Inc.

Cogan, Karen. Pancho Finds A Home. Davidson, Blanche, illus. 2007. 32p. (J). 19.95 (*978-1-929115-16-7(4)) Azro Pr., Inc.

Cole, Joanna & Van Horn, William. Ca C'est Chez Moi.Tr. of This is the Place for Me. (FRE.). (J). 6.99 (978-0-590-71919-3(X)) Scholastic, Inc.

CourseCrafters Staff, des. Interactive Storybooks - This Is My House. 2003. (J). spiral bd. 14.95 (978-1-58605-964-4(5)) LeapFrog Enterprises, Inc.

Derksen, Barbara Ann. Scruffles Finds a Home. 2007. per. (*978-1-59872-935-1(7)) Instantpublisher.com.

DiYeso, William. Almost Home. 2004. 222p. pap. 19.95 (978-1-4137-4729-4(9)) PublishAmerica, Inc.

Dowell, Frances O'Roark. Where I'd Like to Be. 240p. (J). 2003. (Illus.). (gr. 5-9). 15.95 (978-0-689-84420-1(4) , Atheneum); 2004. reprint ed. pap. 5.99 (978-0-689-87067-5(1) , Aladdin) Simon & Schuster Children's Publishing.

—Where I'd Like to Be. 2004. 232p. (J). (gr. k-9). lib. bdg. 11.64 (978-0-606-32673-5(1)) Tandem Library Bks.

—Where I'd Like to Be. l.t. ed. 2003. 162p. (J). 22.95 (978-0-7862-5741-6(5)) Thorndike Pr.

Duey, Kathleen. The Journey Home. Rayyan, Omar, illus. 2003. (Unicorn's Secret Ser.). 80p. (J). pap. 3.99 (978-0-689-85374-6(2) , Aladdin) Simon & Schuster Children's Publishing.

Edwards, Julie Andrews. Mandy. Westerman, Johanna, illus. 2nd ed. 2006. (Julie Andrews Collection). 320p. (J). 16.99 (978-0-06-113162-2(8)) ; pap. 6.99 (978-0-06-120707-5(1)) HarperCollins Pubs. (Julie Andrews Collection).

Edwards, Pamela Duncan. The Old House. Cole, Henry, illus. 2007. 32p. (J). (ps). 16.99 (*978-0-525-47796-9(9) , Dutton Juvenile) Penguin Group (USA) Inc.

Emmett, Jonathan. No Place Like Home. Cabban, Venessa, illus. 2005. 32p. (J). (ps-1). 15.99 (978-0-7636-2554-2(X)) Candlewick Pr.

Faulkner, Keith. Who's Home? McEwan, Joseph, illus. 12p. (J). (ps). pap. 4.99 (978-1-881445-33-3(X)) Sandvik Publishing.

Fitzgerald, Joanne. This Is Me & Where I Am. Fitzgerald, Joanne, illus. 2004. (Illus.). 32p. (J). (gr. k-1). (978-1-55041-819-4(X)) Fitzhenry & Whiteside, Ltd.

Florence, Leigh Anne. Woody, the Kentucky Wiener: The Adoption. Asher, James, illus. 2003. 32p. (J). (gr. 1-3). pap. 12.95 (978-0-9741417-0-1(4)) HotDiggetyDog Pr.

Fowler. Ladybird Moves Home. 2000. (Illus.). 32p. (J). 10.95 (978-0-385-40382-5(8)) Transworld Publishers Ltd. GBR. *Dist:* Trafalgar Square Publishing.

Fraser, Lynne. Henry's New Home. Fraser, Jess, illus. 2007. (J). cd-rom 9.99 (*978-0-9795190-9-3(8)) Color & Learn.

French & Currey. Squeaky Cleaners: In a Tip. 1999. (Illus.). 61p. (J). pap. 7.99 (978-0-340-72664-8(4) , Hodder & Stoughton) Hodder General Publishing Division GBR. *Dist:* Trafalgar Square Publishing.

Frost, Helen. Keesha's House. 2003. (Illus.). 128p. (YA). 16.00 (978-0-374-34064-3(1) , Farrar, Straus & Giroux (BYR)) Farrar, Straus & Giroux.

Giles, S. A. A Home for All: How a Little Puppy Finds a Home. 2006. 20.00 (978-0-8059-9076-8(3)) Dorrance Publishing Co., Inc.

Granowsky, Alvin. My Home. 2001. (gr. k-3). lib. bdg. 13.00 (978-0-613-45206-9(2)) Tandem Library Bks.

Harcourt School Publishers Staff. The Best Home: Take-Home Book. rev. ed. 2001. (Collections Ser.: Bk. 10). (Illus.). (J). pap. 1.90 (978-0-15-319068-1(X)) Harcourt Schl. Pubs.

—A Bug Needs a Home: Independent Reader. 3rd ed. 2002. (Trophies Reading Program Ser.). (Illus.). (J). pap. 2.90 (978-0-15-325487-1(4)) Harcourt Schl. Pubs.

—Going Home: Take-Home Book. 1999. (Signatures Ser.). (Illus.). (J). pap. 1.90 (978-0-15-313879-9(3)) Harcourt Schl. Pubs.

—The Town Bird & the Country Bird: On Level. 3rd ed. 2002. (Trophies Reading Program Ser.). (Illus.). (J). (gr. 1). pap. 4.10 (978-0-15-322992-3(6)) Harcourt Schl. Pubs.

—The Tree House Below Level. 3rd ed. 2002. (Trophies Reading Program Ser.). (Illus.). pap. 5.10 (978-0-15-323050-9(9)) Harcourt Schl. Pubs.

Hensley, Terri Anne. Henry's new Home. 2007. (J). per. 6.95 (*978-0-9789057-1-2(7)) Huntington Ludlow Media Group.

Jackson, Tyrone. Save Our Home. 2006. (ENG.). 88p. per. 14.95 (*978-1-4241-0875-6(6)) PublishAmerica, Inc.

Johnson, Edward L. The Music of Home. Johnson, Edward L., illus. 1999. (Illus.). 134p. (YA). pap. 9.75 (978-0-7392-0197-8(2) , PO3189) Morris Publishing.

Kline, Trish & Donev, Mary. Coming Home: KA Reader 8. 2007. (Illus.). 32p. (J). per. 20.00 (*978-1-934307-01-4(7)) Ghost Hunter Productions.

Knoll, Anne. The Secret Life of Thomas Bradford. 1998. 155p. (J). 9.99 (978-0-88092-421-4(7) , 4217) Royal Fireworks Publishing Co.

Lin, Grace. Robert's Snow. 2004. (Illus.). 40p. (J). (ps). 15.99 (978-0-670-05911-9(0) , Viking Juvenile) Penguin Group (USA) Inc.

Lindbergh, Reeve. Our Nest. McElmurry, Jill, illus. 2004. 32p. (J). (ps-1). 15.99 (978-0-7636-1286-3(3)) Candlewick Pr.

Little People at Home. 1998. (Fisher-Price Little People Toddler Skills Workbooks Ser.: Vol. 4). (Illus.). (J). pap. (978-0-7666-0185-7(4) , Honey Bear Bks.) Modern Publishing.

Mala, Rich. The Family Tree. Tasselmyer, Daniel, illus. 2002. 20p. (J). (ps-5). mass mkt. 4.95 (978-0-9704307-2-4(8)) Mala Vision.

Manushkin, Fran. The Shivers in the Fridge. Zelinsky, Paul O., illus. 2006. 32p. (J). (ps-3). 16.99 (978-0-525-46943-8(5) , Dutton Juvenile) Penguin Group (USA) Inc.

Maris, Ron. Pwy Sy 'na? 2005. (WEL., Illus.). 17p. (978-0-900439-79-7(3)) Gwasg Carreg Gwalch.

Matthew's House. 2001. (Gospel Road Story Bks.). (Illus.). 12p. (J). (ps-k). 0.99 (978-0-8254-7222-0(9)) Kregel Pubns.

McCarty, Peter. Little Bunny on the Move. McCarty, Peter, illus. rev. ed. 1999. (Illus.). 32p. (J). (ps-3). 15.95 (978-0-8050-4620-5(8) , Holt, Henry & Co. Bks. For Young Readers) Holt, Henry & Co.

McNicholas, Shelagh, illus. Puppies in the Pantry. 1998. (Animal Ark Ser.: No. 3). (J). (gr. 3-5). (978-0-606-13131-5(0)) Tandem Library Bks.

Michels, Dia L. Look What I See! Where Can I Be? at Home. Bowles, Michael J. N., photos by. 2002. 32p. 16.95 (978-1-930775-06-0(7)) Platypus Media, L.L.C.

Miles, Ellen. Scout. 2007. (Puppy Place Ser.: No. 7). 80p. (J). pap. 3.99 (*978-0-439-87412-0(2) , Scholastic Paperbacks) Scholastic, Inc.

Miller, Elizabeth I. Just Like Home. Reisberg, Mira, illus. 2004. Tr. of Como en Mi Tierra. (ENG & SPA.). 32p. (J). (gr. 1-3). 15.95 (978-0-8075-4068-8(4)) Whitman, Albert & Co.

—Just Like Home: Como en Mi Tierra. Reisberg, Mira, illus. 2004. 32p. (J). (gr. 1-3). pap. 6.95 (978-0-8075-4069-5(2)) Whitman, Albert & Co.

Moon, Nicola. My Most Favorite Thing. 2nd ed. 2002. (Illus.). 15.99 (978-0-525-46874-5(9) , Dutton Juvenile) Penguin Group (USA) Inc.

Munsch, Robert. Jonathan Cleaned up - Then He Heard a Sound: Or Blackberry Subway Jam. Martchenko, Michael, illus. 2003. (Annikins Ser.: Vol. 1). 32p. (J). (ps-2). pap. 1.25 (978-0-920236-21-5(9)) Annick Pr., Ltd. CAN. *Dist:* Firefly Bks., Ltd.

Octopus Finds a Home. 2002. (Oceanic Mini Bks.). (Illus.). 32p. (J). (978-1-59069-003-1(6) , H1004) Studio Mouse LLC.

Ogg, Debby F. A Home Within. 1998. (Illus.). 32p. (J). (ps-5). pap. (978-1-892039-05-7(2)) Bienestar, Inc.

Olson, Meredith B. Willis's Windowslats. Olson, Meredith B., illus. 1999. (Illus.). 64p. (J). (gr. 3-4). 15.95 (978-0-9657061-6-2(8)) Glenhaven Pubns.

Ormerod, Jan. Sunshine. 2004. (Illus.). 32p. (J). 15.95 (978-1-84507-048-9(8)) Lincoln, Frances Ltd. GBR. *Dist:* Perseus Distribution.

Payne, Essie Kathryn Scott. Mama & the Hills of Home: My Spiritual Pillars. 2002. 15.95 (978-0-9760089-0-3(4)) Azure Venture Publishing Co.

Pollak, Dale. Velocity. 2008. 144p. pap. 22.95 (*978-0-9760095-7-3(9)) New Year Publishing.

Price, Mathew. Knock! Knock! Claverie, Jean, illus. 2003. (Peekaboo Board Bks.). 10p. (J). bds. 4.99 (978-0-7696-3158-5(4) , Gingham Dog Pr.) School Specialty Publishing.

—Who Lives Here? Morozumi, Atsuko, illus. 2003. (Tommy Board Bks.). 10p. (J). bds., bds. 4.99 (978-0-7696-2982-7(2)) School Specialty Publishing.

Reynolds, Marilynn. Goodbye to Griffith Street. Benoit, Renne, illus. 2004. 32p. (J). (ps-2). 16.95 (978-1-55143-285-4(4)) Orca Bk. Pubs. USA.

Rigby Education Staff. Animals That Build. (Sails Literacy Ser.). (Illus.). 16p. (gr. 1-2). 27.00 (978-0-7635-9897-6(6) , 698976C99) Rigby Education.

Roll, Claudia M. A Home for Nathan. Rizer, Finn, illus. 1999. 48p. (J). (ps-2). pap. 6.95 (978-0-9674058-0-3(7)) Snyder, William Foundation for Animals, The.

Romanelli, David. What's in the Attic? Bolzicco, Leonardo, illus. 2000. (J). (ps-3). (978-0-7696-1845-6(6) , American Education Publishing) School Specialty Publishing.

Rowen, Amy & Rowen, Tyla Marie. Waggin' Tales. 2003. 182p. (YA). 23.95 (978-0-595-66087-2(8)); pap. 13.95 (978-0-595-29955-3(5)) iUniverse, Inc.

Rue, Nancy N. Lily the Rebel. 2001. (gr. 3-6). lib. bdg. 13.00 (978-0-613-71721-2(X)) Tandem Library Bks.

Rylant, Cynthia. Bunny Bungalow. Hayashi, Nancy, illus. 2002. 32p. (J). (ps-k). pap. 6.00 (978-0-15-216316-7(6) , Voyager Bks./Libros Viajeros) Harcourt Children's Bks.

—Bunny Bungalow. Hayashi, Nancy, illus. 2002. (J). (ps-3). lib. bdg. 14.15 (978-0-613-53798-8(X)) Tandem Library Bks.

Sendak, Maurice. The Sign on Rosie's Door. Sendak, Maurice, illus. 2002. (Sendak Reissues Ser.). (Illus.). 48p. (ps-3). reprint ed. 15.95 (978-0-06-028795-5(0)) HarperCollins Pubs.

Shreeve, Elizabeth. Hector Springs Loose. Levy, Pamela R., illus. 2004. (Ready-for-Chapters Ser.). 80p. (J). pap. 3.99 (978-0-689-86414-8(0) , Aladdin) Simon & Schuster Children's Publishing.

Smith, Linda. The Inside Tree. Brown, Kathryn, illus. Date not set. 32p. (J). (ps-3). 5.99 (978-0-06-443542-0(3)) HarperCollins Pubs.

—The Inside Tree. 2002. 32p. (J). (ps-3). 14.95 (978-0-06-028241-7(X)) HarperCollins Pubs.

Snyder, Lavinia Branca. Going Home: The Little Stories of Manoosh & Baloosh. 2003. (Illus.). 24p. (J). mass mkt. (978-1-932233-01-8(6)) Aurora Libris Corp.

Spinelli, Eileen. A Safe Place Called Home. Hale, Christy, illus. 2001. 32p. (J). (gr. k-3). 15.95 (978-0-7614-5085-6(8) , Cavendish Children's Bks.) Cavendish, Marshall Corp.

Valliere, Connie. Billy the Builder Bear Builds a House. Quick, Bob, illus. 1998. 32p. (J). (gr. k-6). pap. 6.95 (978-1-890394-22-6(X) , Sage Creek Pr.) Rhodes & Easton.

H I

Weiss, Ellen. Welcome to the Big Blue House! Ewers, Joe, illus. 1999. (Bear in the Big Blue House Ser.). 12p. (J). (ps-k). bds. 5.99 (978-0-689-82386-2(X) , 076714004993, Simon Spotlight) Simon & Schuster Children's Publishing.

Widner, Rose. Limbo & the Talking Umbrella. 1998. (Illus.). 16p. (J). (gr. k-3). pap. 6.00 (978-0-8059-4338-2(2)) Dorrance Publishing Co., Inc.

Wong, Janet S. Homegrown House. Lewis, Earl B, illus. 2008. (J). (*978-0-689-84718-9(1) , McElderry, Margaret K.) Simon & Schuster Children's Publishing.

HOME AND SCHOOL

Berry, Ron & Norris, Annette. I Hate Homework! Organizer. 2000. (Nerds' Secrets Ser.). (Illus.). 40p. (YA). 12.99 (978-1-891100-73-4(4)) Smart Kids Publishing.

Bradford-Vernon, Jennifer R. How to Be Your Child's First Teacher: Insights for Parent Involvement. 2003. (Illus.). 176p. (gr. k-1). 14.99 (978-1-56822-998-0(4) , IF27018) School Specialty Publishing.

Fienberg, Anna & Fienberg, Barbara. The Big Big Big Book of Tashi. Gamble, Kim, illus. 2002. (Tashi Ser.). 448p. (J). (gr. 1-5). pap. 15.95 (978-1-86508-563-0(4)) Allen & Unwin AUS. *Dist:* Independent Pubs. Group.

The I Hate Homework Handbook. 2000. (Nerds' Secrets Ser.). (Illus.). 40p. (J). 9.99 (978-1-891100-70-3(X)) Smart Kids Publishing.

Marsh, Carole. Heroes & Helpers Resource Book for Teachers & Parents. 2004. 48p. (gr. 2-8). pap. 12.95 (978-0-635-01101-5(8)) Gallopade International.

Scholastic, Inc. Staff. A Note from Your Teacher. 1999. (Orig.). (J). pap. 3.95 (978-0-439-07233-5(6)) Scholastic, Inc.

HOME DECORATION

see Interior Decoration

HOME ECONOMICS

see also Consumer Education; Cookery; Dairying; Entertaining; Food; Fuel; Furniture; Heating; House Cleaning; Interior Decoration; Sewing; Shopping

Beco, Alice. People Who Love Houses. 2006. (Cool Careers Without College Ser.). (Illus.). 144p. (J). (gr. 5-8). lib. bdg. 33.25 (978-1-4042-0753-0(8)) Rosen Publishing Group, Inc., The.

Beylon, Cathy. My Play Kitchen Sticker Activity Book. 2000. (Dover Little Activity Bks.). 4p. (J). pap. 1.50 (978-0-486-40981-8(3)) Dover Pubns., Inc.

Brent, Lynnette R. At Home. 2003. (Times Change Ser.). (Illus.). 32p. (J). (978-1-4034-4537-7(0)) Heinemann Library.

—At Home: Long Ago & Today. 2003. (Times Change Ser.). (Illus.). 32p. (J). lib. bdg. 24.22 (978-1-4034-4531-5(1)) Heinemann Library.

Brighter Vision Publishing Staff. Teaching House: A Parent's Guide to Early Learning Activities Around the House. 1999. (Learning Everywhere Ser.). (Illus.). 32p. (J). pap. 3.99 (978-1-55254-139-5(8) , BV15010) Brighter Vision Pubns.

Buck, Patricia R. Mommy & Me in the Kitchen: Mixes, Recipes, Gifts & Ideas for Each Month of the Year! Johnson, Sheryl Lynn, illus. 1999. 70p. (J). pap. 9.95 (978-0-615-11330-2(3)) Sheryl Lynn's.

Coats, Lynda. Far above Rubies. Gleaton, Terry, ed. 4th exp. ed. 2001. 632p. (YA). ring bd. 59.95 (978-1-930165-00-7(5)) Small Ventures.

Foundations for Living, Set. 2004. 47.95 (978-0-7403-0371-5(6) , Lifepac) Alpha Omega Pubns., Inc.

Gross, Pati Myers. Home Safety. Marger, Carol, ed. Gibson, Tom, illus. 1999. (Adventures in the Roo World - Young Roo Ser.: Vol. 4). 24p. (J). (ps-2). pap. 4.95 (978-0-9652579-4-7(0)) Roo Pubns.

Home Economics, 11 vols., Set. 2004. (Illus.). (YA). (gr. 9-12). tchr. ed., stu. ed. 51.95 (978-0-7403-0162-9(4) , ES9815, Lifepac) Alpha Omega Pubns., Inc.

Lawson, Julia & Browne, Naima. Early Birds Tidy up. Millard, Peter, photos by. l.t. ed. 2005. (Stepping Stones Ser.). (Illus.). 24p. (J). (ps). pap. 9.95 (978-0-237-52918-5(1) , Evans Brothers, Limited) Evans Publishing Group GBR. *Dist:* Independent Pubs. Group.

Our Homes. 2007. (J). (*978-1-933834-15-3(3)) Brown Bear Books.

Pollock, Sudie. Will the Dollars Stretch? Teen Parents Living on Their Own. rev. ed. 2001. (Teen Pregnancy & Parenting Ser.). 112p. (J). (gr. 7 up). pap. 8.95 (978-1-885356-78-9(1)) Morning Glory Pr., Inc.

Richards, Jon. In the Home. 2005. (Illus.). 32p. (J). (gr. 3 up). lib. bdg. 27.10 (978-1-59389-198-5(9)) Chrysalis Education.

Robinson, Sharon, et al. Home Economics. 2007. (Illus.). 96p. pap. 29.50 (*978-0-340-92711-3(9) , Hodder Murray) Hodder Education GBR. *Dist:* Trans-Atlantic Pubns., Inc.

Schaefer, Lola M. La Casa Rodante. 2003. (Hogar Para Mi (A Home for Me) Ser.). (SPA.). 24p. (J). (ps-1). lib. bdg. 18.50 (978-1-4034-0270-7(1)) Heinemann Library.

Shields, Charles J. Martha Stewart. 2001. (Women of Achievement Ser.). (Illus.). 112p. (J). pap. 30.00 (978-0-7910-6319-4(4)); 30.00 (978-0-7910-6318-7(6)) Facts On File, Inc. (Chelsea Hse.).

Solis, Lisa. Classroom Cupboard: Lessons, Activities & Culinary Concoctions for Kids. 2003. (Illus.). 160p. pap. 27.00 (978-1-56308-957-2(2) , LU9572) Libraries Unlimited, Inc.

Stone, Lynn M. Harvest to Home. 2002. (Harvest to Home Ser.). (gr. 2-5). 59.80 (978-1-58952-125-4(0)) Rourke Publishing, LLC.

The Book Company, ed. Home. (Sparkle Bks.). (J). bds. 4.99 (978-1-74047-330-9(2)) Book Co. Publishing Pty, Ltd., The AUS. *Dist:* Penton Overseas, Inc.

Wooten, Sarah M. Martha Stewart: America's Lifestyle Expert. 1998. (Library of Famous Women). (Illus.). 64p. (J). (gr. 4-8). 24.95 (978-1-56711-254-2(4) , Blackbirch Pr., Inc.) Thomson Gale.

HOME ECONOMICS—EQUIPMENT AND SUPPLIES

see also Household Equipment and Supplies

Irvin, Christine M. Pie Pan Mania. 2002. (Craft Mania Ser.). (Illus.). 32p. (J). (gr. 2-4). pap. 23.50 (978-0-516-22280-6(5) , Children's Pr.) Scholastic Library Publishing.

HOME ECONOMICS—VOCATIONAL GUIDANCE

Greenberger, Robert. People Who Love to Organize, Manage, & Plan. 2006. (Cool Careers Without College Ser.). (Illus.). 144p. (YA). (gr. 5-8). lib. bdg. 33.25 (978-1-4042-0752-3(X)) Rosen Publishing Group, Inc., The.

HOME EDUCATION

see Self-Culture

HOME MISSIONS

see Missions

HOME STUDY COURSES

see Self-Culture

HOMELESS PERSONS

see also Homelessness

Stearman, Kaye. Homelessness. 1999. (Talking Points Ser.). (Illus.). 64p. (YA). (gr. 4-7). lib. bdg. 27.12 (978-0-8172-5312-7(2)) Raintree.

—Why Do People Live on the Streets? 2001. (Exploring Tough Issues Ser.). (Illus.). 48p. (J). (gr. 4-7). lib. bdg. 25.69 (978-0-7398-3232-5(8)) Raintree.

Vescia, Monique & Sachar, Louis. A Reading Guide to Holes by Louis Sachar. 2003. (Bookfiles Ser.). 64p. (J). pap. 4.99 (978-0-439-46336-2(X) , Scholastic Reference) Scholastic, Inc.

HOMELESS PERSONS—FICTION

Ballard, John H. SoulMates: A Novel to End World Hunger, 2 bks. in 1. Ellen, Joan, ed. Litzenger, Roseanne, illus. 1998. (Soul to Soul Adventure Ser.). 524p. (YA). (gr. 7 up). 19.95 (978-0-932279-06-4(6)); (gr. 4-7). pap. 14.95 (978-0-932279-05-7(8)) World Citizens.

Barclift, Betty. Gypsy Summer: A Novel. 2003. 160p. (J). pap. 6.99 (978-0-8254-2038-2(5)) Kregel Pubns.

Blank, Jessica. Almost Home. rev. ed. 2007. 256p. (YA). (gr. 7 up). 15.99 (*978-1-4231-0642-5(3)) Hyperion Pr.

Booth, Coe. Tyrell. 2006. 320p. (J). pap. 16.99 (978-0-439-83879-5(7) , PUSH) Scholastic, Inc.

Bowsher, Melodie. My Lost & Found Life. (YA). 2007. 320p. pap. 7.95 (*978-1-59990-155-8(2)); 2006. 350p. 16.95 (978-1-58234-736-3(0)) Bloomsbury Publishing. (Bloomsbury Children).

Carey, Janet Lee. The Double Life of Zoe Flynn. 2004. (Illus.). 240p. (J). 16.95 (978-0-689-85604-4(0) , Atheneum) Simon & Schuster Children's Publishing.

Cassidy. Street Life. 1999. 98p. (J). pap. 11.99 (978-0-7043-4968-1(X)) Women's Pr., Ltd., The GBR. *Dist:* Independent Pubs. Group.

Chitty, Joan E. Charlie Macaffee: Search for the Genie's Body. 2005. 267p. pap. 21.95 (978-1-4241-0007-1(0)) PublishAmerica, Inc.

Clements, Andrew. Room One: A Mystery or Two. Blair, Chris, illus. 2006. 176p. (J). (gr. 3-7). 15.95 (978-0-689-86686-9(0)) Simon & Schuster Children's Publishing.

Cole, Brock. Good Enough to Eat. 2007. (Illus.). 32p. (J). (gr. k). 16.00 (*978-0-374-32737-8(8) , Farrar, Straus & Giroux (BYR)) Farrar, Straus & Giroux.

Cooley, Beth. Shelter. 2006. 224p. (YA). (gr. 7). 15.95 (978-0-385-73330-4(5)); lib. bdg. 17.99 (978-0-385-90347-9(2)) Random Hse. Children's Bks. (Delacorte Bks. for Young Readers).

Creel, Ann Howard. A Ceiling of Stars. 2000. (Illus.). (J). (978-0-606-18354-3(X)) Tandem Library Bks.

De Palma, Toni. Under the Banyan Tree. 2007. 192p. (YA). (gr. 7 up). 16.95 (978-0-8234-1965-4(7)) Holiday Hse., Inc.

Estes, Max. Coffee & Donuts. 2006. (Illus.). 128p. pap. 10.00 (978-1-891830-80-8(5)) Top Shelf Productions.

Fenner, Carol. The King of Dragons. 2000. (J). (978-0-606-19716-8(8)); (gr. 3-6). lib. bdg. 13.00 (978-0-613-28547-6(6)) Tandem Library Bks.

Fogelin, Adrian. Anna Casey's Place in the World. 2003. 224p. (J). (gr. 3-6). pap. 6.95 (978-1-56145-295-8(5) , Q32694) Peachtree Pubs., Ltd.

—Anna Casey's Place in the World. Schultz, Suzy, illus. 2001. 224p. (J). (gr. 3-7). 14.95 (978-1-56145-249-1(1) , Q32694) Peachtree Pubs., Ltd.

Fuchshuber, Annegert. Carly. Howe, Florence & Kirk, Heidi, trs. from ENG. 2004. (Illus.). 28p. (ps-3). 16.95 (978-1-55861-177-1(0)) Feminist Pr. at The City Univ. of New York.

Garcia, Angela Irene. His Name Is Joe. Davis, Ami, illus. 2002. 12.99 (978-0-9726313-0-3(5)) From The Heart Bks.

Grantner, Anne M. & Haggart, Gary. Without a Home. Hannon, Kenneth, photos by. 2003. (Illus.). 35p. (YA). (gr. 5 up). pap. 12.95 (978-0-9740929-0-4(8)) Shelter of Flint, Inc.

Greene, Janice. No Exit: Set 3. 2002. 32p. (YA). 2.95 (978-1-56254-429-4(2) , SP 4292) Saddleback Educational Publishing.

Gunning, Monica. A Shelter in Our Car. Pedlar, Elaine, tr. Pedlar, Elaine, illus. 2004. 32p. (J). 16.95 (978-0-89239-189-9(8)) Children's Bk. Pr.

Hodson, Christopher. Little Library Literacy: Lizo's Song Ndebele. Pulles, Elizabeth, illus. 2007. pap. (*978-0-521-70282-9(8)) Cambridge Univ. Pr.

—Little Library Literacy: Lizo's Song Siswati. Pulles, Elizabeth, illus. 2007. pap. (*978-0-521-70286-7(0)) Cambridge Univ. Pr.

—Little Library Literacy: Lizo's Song Xhosa. Pulles, Elizabeth, illus. 2007. pap. (*978-0-521-70283-6(6)) Cambridge Univ. Pr.

Howe, James. Dew Drop Dead. 2000. (Sebastian Barth Mysteries Ser.). 160p. (J). (gr. 3-7). pap. 5.99 (978-0-689-80760-2(0) , Aladdin) Simon & Schuster Children's Publishing.

—Dew Drop Dead. 2000. (gr. 5-8). lib. bdg. 13.00 (978-0-613-22838-1(3)) Tandem Library Bks.

—Dew Drop Dead: A Sebastian Barth Mystery. 2000. (J). 11.64 (978-0-606-17314-8(5)) Tandem Library Bks.

Howie. Have You Seen Christmas? 2006. (Illus.). 32p. 18.00 (978-0-687-49678-5(0)) Abingdon Pr.

Hyde, Catherine Ryan. Becoming Chloe. 2006. 224p. (YA). (gr. 9). 15.95 (978-0-375-83258-1(0)); lib. bdg. 17.99 (978-0-375-93258-8(5)) Random Hse. Children's Bks. (Knopf Bks. for Young Readers).

Koja, Kathe. The Blue Mirror. 2004. 128p. (YA). 16.00 (978-0-374-30849-0(7) , Farrar, Straus & Giroux (BYR)) Farrar, Straus & Giroux.

—The Blue Mirror. 2006. 128p. (YA). (gr. 8). pap. 6.99 (978-0-14-240693-9(7) , Puffin) Penguin Group (USA) Inc.

—The Blue Mirror. l.t. ed. 2004. 134p. 21.95 (978-0-7862-6960-0(X) , Large Print Pr.) Thorndike Pr.

Landowne, Youme, illus. Selavi, That Is Life: A Haitian Story of Hope. 2004. 40p. (J). 17.95 (978-0-938317-84-5(9)) Cinco Puntos Pr.

Lowry, Lois. Stay! Keeper's Story. 1999. (gr. 3-6). lib. bdg. 13.00 (978-0-613-17863-1(7)) Tandem Library Bks.

McGovern, Ann. The Lady in the Box. Backer, Marni, illus. 1999. 40p. (J). (ps up). pap. 9.95 (978-1-890515-15-7(9)) Turtle Bks.

—La Senora de la Caja de Carton. Peluffo, Ana Luisa, tr. Backer, Marni, illus. 1999. (SPA.). 40p. (J). (gr. 3-5). pap. 8.95 (978-1-890515-16-4(7) , TK1337) Turtle Bks.

Mills, Charles. The Great Sleepy-Time Stew Rescue. 2004. (Honors Club Story Ser.: Vol. 4). (Illus.). 127p. (J). (978-0-8163-2009-7(8)) Pacific Pr. Publishing Assn.

Myers, Christopher A. Fly! Myers, Christopher A., illus. 2001. (Illus.). 32p. (ps-17). 16.49 (978-0-7868-2373-4(9) , Jump at the Sun) Hyperion Bks. for Children.

Nunez, Ralph. Cooper's Tale. Madeline, Simon, illus. 2000. (J). per. 5.95 (978-0-9641784-7-2(8)) Homes for the Homeless, Inc.

Nunez, Ralph da Costa & Kwok, Karina. Saily's Journey. Madeline, Gerstein-Simon, illus. 2002. per. (978-0-9641784-9-6(4)) Homes for the Homeless, Inc.

O'Connor, Barbara. How to Steal a Dog. 2007. 176p. (J). (gr. 3-7). 16.00 (978-0-374-33497-0(8)) Farrar, Straus & Giroux.

Polacco, Patricia. I Can Hear the Sun. Polacco, Patricia, illus. 1999. (Illus.). 40p. (J). (ps-3). pap. 5.99 (978-0-698-11857-7(X) , Putnam Juvenile) Penguin Group (USA) Inc.

—I Can Hear the Sun. 1999. (J). (978-0-606-17412-1(5)); lib. bdg. 14.15 (978-0-613-22873-2(1)) Tandem Library Bks.

Rapp, Adam. 33 Snowfish. Ering, Timothy Basil, illus. 2006. 192p. (YA). (gr. 10). pap. 6.99 (978-0-7636-2917-5(0)) Candlewick Pr.

Rushton, Rosie. Sophie. 2000. (gr. 5-8). lib. bdg. 13.00 (978-0-613-31732-0(7)) Tandem Library Bks.

Sachar, Louis. Buracos. pap. 29.95 (978-85-336-1280-8(X)) Livraria Martins Editora BRA. *Dist:* Distribooks, Inc.

—Holes. 1998. 240p. (J). (gr. 4-7). 17.00 (978-0-374-33265-5(7) , Farrar, Straus & Giroux (BYR)) Farrar, Straus & Giroux.

—Holes. 240p. (J). (gr. 4-6). pap. 5.99 (978-0-8072-8073-7(9) , Listening Library) Random Hse. Audio Publishing Group.

—Holes. 2000. (Newbery Ser.). (Illus.). 240p. (J). (gr. 5-6). reprint ed. pap. 6.50 (978-0-440-41480-3(6) , Yearling) Random Hse. Children's Bks.

—Holes. l.t. ed. 2003. 288p. pap. 10.95 (978-0-7862-6190-1(0)) Thorndike Pr.

Scholastic, Inc. Staff & Martin, Cory. O. C. , the Novelization. 2004. (O. C. Novelization Ser.: No. 1). 264p. (J). pap. 6.99 (978-0-439-66059-4(9)) Scholastic, Inc.

Seskin Steve & Shamblin Allen. Chance to Shine. 2006. (Illus.). 32p. 16.95 incl. audio compact disk (978-1-58246-167-0(8) , Tricycle Pr.) Ten Speed Pr.

Sweeney, Matthew. Fox. 2002. (Illus.). 176p. (J). pap. 12.95 (978-0-7475-6040-1(4)) Bloomsbury Publishing Plc GBR. *Dist:* Independent Pubs. Group.

Tetzner, Lisa. The Black Brothers. Binder, Hannes, illus. 2004. 146p. (YA). 16.95 (978-1-932425-04-8(7) , Lemniscaat) Boyds Mills Pr.

Van Draanen, Wendelin. Runaway. 256p. 2008. (YA). (gr. 3-7). mass mkt. 6.50 (*978-0-440-42109-2(8) , Laurel Leaf); 2006. (J). (gr. 5). 15.95 (978-0-375-83522-3(9) , Knopf Bks. for Young Readers); 2006. (J). (gr. 5). lib. bdg. 17.99 (978-0-375-93522-0(3) , Knopf Bks. for Young Readers) Random Hse. Children's Bks.

Van Draanen, Wendelin. Sammy Keyes & the Sisters of Mercy. VanDraanen, Wendelin, illus. 2001. (Sammy Keyes Ser.: Bk. 3). pap. 49.95 incl. audio compact disk (978-0-87499-838-2(7)) Live Oak Media.

—Sammy Keyes & the Sisters of Mercy. 1999. (Sammy Keyes Ser.: Bk. 3). (Illus.). 240p. (J). (gr. 5-8). pap. 5.99 (978-0-375-80183-9(9) , Yearling) Random Hse. Children's Bks.

—Sammy Keyes & the Sisters of Mercy. 1999. (Sammy Keyes Ser.: Bk. 3). (gr. 5-8). lib. bdg. 13.00 (978-0-613-22298-3(9)) Tandem Library Bks.

Wahl, Jan. This Christmas Present. McCurdy, Michael, illus. 1999. 64p. (gr. 5-9). 18.00 (978-1-56846-165-6(8) , Creative Editions) Creative Co., The.

Wallace, Barbara Brooks. Secret in St. Something. 2003. (Illus.). 160p. (J). (ps-7). pap. 9.95 (978-0-689-85601-3(6) , Aladdin) Simon & Schuster Children's Publishing.

Walters, Eric. Sketches. 2008. 232p. (YA). (gr. 6). 15.99 (*978-0-670-06294-2(4) , Viking Juvenile) Penguin Group (USA) Inc.

Wittlinger, Ellen. Gracie's Girl. 2002. (Illus.). 192p. (J). (gr. 4-7). pap. 4.99 (978-0-689-84960-2(5) , Aladdin) Simon & Schuster Children's Publishing.

—Gracie's Girl. Hamlin, Janet, illus. 2000. 192p. (J). (gr. 3-7). 16.95 (978-0-689-82249-0(9)) Simon & Schuster Children's Publishing.

—Gracie's Girl. 2002. (gr. 3-6). lib. bdg. 13.00 (978-0-613-53441-3(7)) Tandem Library Bks.

Wyss, Thelma Hatch. Ten Miles from Winnemucca. 2002. 144p. (J). (gr. 7 up). 15.95 (978-0-06-029783-1(2)) HarperCollins Pubs.

HOMELESSNESS

see also Homeless Persons

Gerdes, Louise. The Homless. 2007. (Opposing Viewpoints Ser.). 240p. (J). (gr. 10-12). 36.20 (*978-0-7377-3654-0(2)); pap. 24.95 (*978-0-7377-3655-7(0)) Thomson Gale. (Greenhaven Pr., Inc.).

Gottfried, Ted. Homelessness: Whose Problem Is It? 1999. (Issue & Debate Ser.: up). 128p. (gr. 7-12). lib. bdg. 25.90 (978-0-7613-0953-6(5) , Twenty-First Century Bks.) Lerner Publishing Group.

Harrison, Jean. Home. 2004. (Children's Rights Ser.). (J). lib. bdg. 27.10 (978-1-58340-418-8(X)) Smart Apple Media.

Haughton, Emma & Clarke, Penny. Rights in the Home. 2005. (What Do We Mean by Human Rights? Ser.). (Illus.). 46p. (J). (gr. 5-9). lib. bdg. 29.95 (978-1-932889-65-9(5)) Sea-To-Sea Pubns.

Kaye, Cathryn Berger. A Kids' Guide to Hunger & Homelessness: How to Take Action. 2007. (Illus.). 48p. (J). pap. (*978-1-57542-240-4(9)) Free Spirit Publishing, Inc.

Stearman, Kaye. Why Do People Live on the Streets? 2001. (Exploring Tough Issues Ser.). (Illus.). 48p. (J). (gr. 4-7). lib. bdg. 25.69 (978-0-7398-3232-5(8)) Raintree.

Walker, Ida. Homelessness. 2007. (Introducing Issues with Opposing Viewpoints Ser.). (Illus.). 144p. (gr. 7-10). 33.70 (*978-0-7377-3851-3(0) , Greenhaven Pr., Inc.) Thomson Gale.

HOMELESSNESS—FICTION

Arterburn, Stephen & Hunt, Angela Elwell. Paige. 2004. (Young Believer on Tour Ser.). (J). pap. 3.99 (978-0-8423-8338-7(7)) Tyndale Hse. Pubs.

Cole, Stephen. The Adventures of Mr. Bean. 2002. (Illus.). 64p. (J). pap. 6.99 (978-1-84222-659-9(2)) Carlton Bks., Ltd. GBR. *Dist:* Independent Pubs. Group.

Creel, Ann Howard. A Ceiling of Stars. 1999. (gr. 5-8). lib. bdg. 14.10 (978-0-613-24514-2(8)) Tandem Library Bks.

Falk, Karen. Tacianna & the Endless Ball of String. 2006. 83p. pap. 14.95 (978-1-4241-3287-4(8)) PublishAmerica, Inc.

Goodwin, Catherine. Seeking Shelter. 2006. 154p. (J). pap. (*978-1-55380-033-0(8)) Ronsdale Pr.

Haverfield, Mary. Harriett the Homeless Raccoon. Haverfield, Mary, illus. 2005. (Illus.). 32p. (J). (ps-3). 17.95 (978-1-931721-60-8(2)) Bright Sky Pr.

Hill, Kirkpatrick. Do Not Pass Go. 2007. 240p. (J). 15.99 (978-1-4169-1400-6(5) , McElderry, Margaret K.) Simon & Schuster Children's Publishing.

Holtwijk, Inele. Asphalt Angels. Boeke, Wanda, tr. 2004. 184p. (YA). pap. 7.95 (978-1-886910-43-0(X) , Lemniscaat) Boyds Mills Pr.

Johnson, Lindsay Lee. Soul Moon Soup. 1998. 134p. (J). (gr. 5 up). 15.95 (978-1-886910-87-4(1) , Lemniscaat) Boyds Mills Pr.

King, Stephen Michael. Mutt Dog! 2005. (Illus.). 32p. (J). (ps-ps). 16.00 (978-0-15-205561-5(4)) Harcourt Children's Bks.

—Mutt Dog! King, Stephen Michael, illus. 2005. (Illus.). 32p. (J). (978-1-86504-636-5(1) , Scholastic Pr.) Scholastic, Inc.

—Mutt Dog! 2005. (Illus.). 32p. (J). pap. (978-1-86504-637-2(X) , Scholastic Pr.) Scholastic, Inc.

Lachenmeyer, Nathaniel. Broken Beaks. Ingpen, Robert R., illus. 2005. 32p. (J). 15.95 (978-0-85572-335-4(1)) Warwick Publishing CAN. *Dist:* Perseus Distribution.

Lawton, Wendy. Changing Faces: Real TV, Take 1. 2004. (Real Tv - Real Transformations Series (Take 1) Ser.). 224p. (J). pap. 10.99 (978-0-8024-5413-3(5)) Moody Pubs.

Nunez, Ralph da Costa & Ellison, Jesse Andrews. Voyage to Shelter Cove. Simon, Madeline Gerstein, illus. 2005. (J). pap. 5.00 (978-0-9724425-3-4(7)) Homes for the Homeless, Inc.

Silvey, Diane. Raven's Flight. 2001. (gr. 7-12). lib. bdg. 15.25 (978-0-613-78635-5(1)) Tandem Library Bks.

Sweet, Melissa, illus. Tupelo Rides the Rails. 2008. (J). (*978-0-618-71714-9(5)) Houghton Mifflin Co.

Voyage to Shelter Cove. 2006. (Illus.). (J). pap., act. bk. ed. 2.00 (978-0-9724425-5-8(3) , White Tiger Pr.) Homes for the Homeless, Inc.

HOMER—ADAPTATIONS

McCarty, Nick. The Iliad. Ambrus, Victor G., illus. 2000. (Myths & Legends Ser.). 96p. (J). (gr. 5-9). pap. 15.95 (978-0-7534-5321-6(5) , Kingfisher) Houghton Mifflin Co. Trade & Reference Div.

Redmond, Diane. The Odyssey, Vol. 4. Smith, Barry, illus. unabr. ed. 2003. (Curtain up! Ser.: Vol. 4). 48p. (J). (gr. 1-4). pap. 15.00 (978-0-7136-4628-3(4)) A & C Black GBR. *Dist:* Players Pr., Inc.

HOMER, WINSLOW, 1836-1910

Homer, Winslow. Winslow Homer. Venezia, Mike, tr. Venezia, Mike, illus. 2004. (Getting to Know World Artists Ser.). 32p. (J). 27.00 (978-0-516-22579-1(0) , Children's Pr.) Scholastic Library Publishing.

Venezia, Mike. Winslow Homer. Venezia, Mike, illus. 2004. (Getting. . Know Artists Pb Ser.). (Illus.). 32p. (J). (gr. 3-4). pap. 6.95 (978-0-516-26979-5(8) , Children's Pr.) Scholastic Library Publishing.

HOMES

see Houses

HOMESTEAD LAW

Landau, Elaine. The Homestead Act. 2006. (True Book - Westward Expansion Ser.). (Illus.). 48p. (J). (gr. 3-5). 25.00 (978-0-516-25870-6(2) , Children's Pr.) Scholastic Library Publishing.

Porterfield, Jason. The Homestead ACT of 1862. 2005. (Illus.). 64p. (J). (gr. 5-8). lib. bdg. 29.25 (978-1-4042-0178-1(5)) Rosen Publishing Group, Inc., The.

HOMOSEXUALITY

Andryszewski, Tricia. Gay Rights. 2000. (Single Titles Ser.: up). (Illus.). 112p. (gr. 7 up). lib. bdg. (978-0-7613-1568-1(3) , Twenty-First Century Bks.) Lerner Publishing Group.

Butt, Sheila K. Does God Love Michael's Two Daddies. Perkins, Ken, illus. 2007. 16p. (J). 7.95 ***(978-0-932859-94-5(1))*** Apologetics Pr., Inc.

Carlson-Berne, Emma. Homosexuality. 2007. (Introducing Issues with Opposing Viewpoints Ser.). (Illus.). 144p. (gr. 7-10). 33.70 ***(978-0-7377-3852-0(9)*** , Greenhaven Pr., Inc.) Thomson Gale.

Combs, Bobbie. ABC a Family Alphabet Book. Keane, Desiree & Rappa, Brian, illus. 2001. 32p. (J). pap. 8.95 (978-0-9674468-1-3(3)) Two Lives Publishing.

Connors, Paul. Homosexuality. 2007. (Current Controversies Ser.). (Illus.). 224p. (gr. 10-12). 34.95 ***(978-0-7377-3721-9(2)***); pap. 23.70 ***(978-0-7377-3722-6(0))*** Thomson Gale. (Greenhaven Pr., Inc.).

Ford, Michael T. Outspoken: Role Models from the Lesbian & Gay Community. 1998. 240p. (J). (gr. 7-12). 16.00 (978-0-688-14896-6(4)) HarperCollins Pubs.

Garden, Nancy. Hear Us Out! Lesbian & Gay Stories of Struggle, Progress, & Hope, 1950 to the Present. 2007. (Illus.). 240p. (YA). (gr. 7 up). 18.00 (978-0-374-31759-1(3)) Farrar, Straus & Giroux.

Goldenberg, Linda. We're Here: A History of Lesbian & Gay Pride in the United States. 1998. (Lesbian & Gay Experience Ser.). (YA). pap. (978-0-531-11358-5(2) , Watts, Franklin) Scholastic Library Publishing.

Hudson, David L. Gay Rights. 2004. (Point/Counterpoint Ser.). (Illus.). 112p. (J). (gr. 9-13). 32.95 (978-0-7910-8094-8(3) , Chelsea Hse.) Facts On File, Inc.

Huegel, Kelly. GLBTQ: The Survival Guide for Queer & Questioning Teens. 2003. (gr. 7-12). lib. bdg. 25.70 (978-0-613-67411-9(1)) Tandem Library Bks.

—GLBTQ* The Survival Guide for Queer & Questioning Teens (*Gay, Lesbian, Bisexual, Transgender, Questioning) 2004. (Illus.). 240p. (YA). (gr. 8 up). pap. 15.95 (978-1-57542-126-1(7)) Free Spirit Publishing, Inc.

Jimmy, Creech. Rise above the Law: The Appeal to the Jury: the United Methodist's Trial of Jimmy Creech. 2001. 60p. 60.00 (978-0-9704958-0-8(3)) Swing Bridge Pr., The.

Kafka, Tina. Gay Rights. 2006. (Overview Ser.). 112p. (J). (gr. 7-10). 32.45 (978-1-59018-637-4(0) , Lucent Bks.) Thomson Gale.

Kaster, Jeffrey. What Catholic Teens Should Know about Homosexuality. Larking, Jean K., ed. 2004. (What Catholic Teens Should Know Ser.). (Illus.). 8p. (YA). 7.95 (978-0-89837-236-6(4) , 441010) Pflaum Publishing Group.

Levithan, David & Merrell, Billy. The Full Spectrum: A New Generation of Writing about Gay, Lesbian, Bisexual, Transgender, Questioning, & Other Identities. 2006. (Illus.). 288p. (YA). (gr. 7). pap. 9.95 (978-0-375-83290-1(4) , Knopf Bks. for Young Readers) Random Hse. Children's Bks.

Marcovitz, Hal. Teens & Gay Issues. 2005. (Gallup Youth Survey, Major Issues & Trends Ser.). (Illus.). 112,128p. (J). (gr. 7-9). lib. bdg. 22.95 (978-1-59084-873-9(X)) Mason Crest Pubs.

Mastoon, Adam. Shared Heart: Portraits & Stories Celebrating Lesbian, Gay & Bisexual Young People. 2001. (YA). (978-0-606-21430-8(5)) Tandem Library Bks.

—The Shared Heart: Portraits & Stories Celebrating Lesbian, Gay, & Bisexual Young People. 2001. 192p. (YA). (gr. 8 up). 15.89 (978-0-06-029556-1(2)); (Illus.). (gr. 7 up). reprint ed. pap. (978-0-06-447304-0(X) , HarperTeen) HarperCollins Pubs.

Mayo, Jeanne. Uncensored: Dating, Relationship, & Sex. 2007. 224p. pap. 14.99 (978-1-57794-821-6(1)) Harrison Hse., Inc.

Murray, Stephen O. Heterogender Homosexuality in Honduras. 2002. 222p. pap. 16.95 (978-0-595-22681-8(7) , Writers Club Pr.) iUniverse, Inc.

Oliver, Marilyn Tower. Gay & Lesbian Rights: A Struggle. 1998. (Illus.). 128p. (YA). (gr. 6-12). lib. bdg. 26.60 (978-0-89490-958-0(4)) Enslow Pubs., Inc.

Rashid, Norrina. Girl2girl. 2001. (gr. 7-12). lib. bdg. 24.55 (978-0-613-80036-5(2)) Tandem Library Bks.

Smith, Jennifer. Gay Rights Movement. 2003. (gr. 7-12). lib. bdg. 33.25 (978-0-613-73615-2(X)) Tandem Library Bks.

Snow, Judith E. How It Feels to Have a Gay or Lesbian Parent: A Book by Kids for Kids of All Ages. 2004. (Illus.). (J). 1p. pap. 12.95 (978-1-56023-420-3(2)); 123p. 19.95 (978-1-56023-419-7(9)) Haworth Pr., Inc., The. (Harrington Park Pr.).

HOMOSEXUALITY—FICTION

Abel, Kathleen. Smile So Big. 2008. (J). 16.00 (978-0-15-200671-6(0)) Harcourt Trade Pubs.

Alyson Publications Staff & Valentine, Johnny. The Daddy Machine. 2nd ed. 2004. (Illus.). 16.95 (978-1-55583-887-4(1)) Alyson Pubns.

Balkovec, Lisa. Setting It Straight. 2006. (YA). per. 13.95 (978-1-932172-24-9(6)) McKenna Publishing Group.

Bildner, Phil. Playing the Field. 2006. (Illus.). 192p. (YA). 15.95 (978-1-4169-0284-3(8)) Simon & Schuster Children's Publishing.

Brannen, Sarah S. Uncle Bobby's Wedding. Brannen, Sarah S., illus. 2008. 32p. (J). (ps). 15.99 ***(978-0-399-24712-5(2)*** , Putnam Juvenile) Penguin Group (USA) Inc.

Carlson, Melody. Bright Purple. 2006. 224p. (YA). pap. 12.99 (978-1-57683-950-8(8) , Th1nk Bks.) NavPress Publishing Group.

Chambers, Aidan. Postcards from No Man's Land. 2004. 320p. (J). (gr. 9 up). reprint ed. pap. 7.99 (978-0-14-240145-3(5) , Puffin) Penguin Group (USA) Inc.

Cohn, Rachel & Levithan, David. Nick & Norah's Infinite Playlist. 2006. 192p. (YA). (gr. 9). 16.95 (978-0-375-83531-5(8)); lib. bdg. 18.99 (978-0-375-93531-2(2)) Random Hse. Children's Bks. (Knopf Bks. for Young Readers).

Donovan, Stacey. Who I Am Keeps Happening. 2004. (YA). (978-0-7636-1988-6(4)) Candlewick Pr.

Freymann-Weyr, Garret. My Heartbeat. 2002. 160p. (YA). (gr. 7-12). 15.00 (978-0-618-14181-4(2)) Houghton Mifflin Co. Trade & Reference Div.

Garden, Nancy. Annie on My Mind. 2007. (Illus.). 272p. (YA). pap. 8.00 (978-0-374-40011-8(3) , Farrar, Straus & Giroux (BYR)) Farrar, Straus & Giroux.

—Holly's Secret. 2000. 144p. (YA). (gr. 3-7). 16.00 (978-0-374-33273-0(8) , Farrar, Straus & Giroux (BYR)) Farrar, Straus & Giroux.

—The Year They Burned the Books. 1999. 256p. (YA). (gr. 7-12). 17.00 (978-0-374-38667-2(6) , Farrar, Straus & Giroux (BYR)) Farrar, Straus & Giroux.

Gonzalez, Rigoberto & Alvarez, Cecilia Concepcion. Antonio's Card. 2005. (ENG & SPA., Illus.). 32p. (J). 16.95 (978-0-89239-204-9(5)) Children's Bk. Pr.

Haan, Linda de & Nijland, Stern. King & King. 2004. (Illus.). 32p. 14.95 (978-1-58246-061-1(2) , Tricycle Pr.) Ten Speed Pr.

—King & King & Family. 2004. (Illus.). 32p. (J). 14.95 (978-1-58246-113-7(9) , Tricycle Pr.) Ten Speed Pr.

Hall, John. Is He or Isn't He? 2006. 304p. (J). pap. 8.99 (978-0-06-078747-9(3)) HarperCollins Pubs.

Harmon, Michael B. The Last Exit to Normal. 2008. (YA). ***(978-0-375-84098-2(2)***); lib. bdg. ***(978-0-375-94098-9(7))*** Knopf, Alfred A. Inc.

Hartinger, Brent. Geography Club. 240p. (J). 2003. 17.99 (978-0-06-001221-2(8)); 2004. reprint ed. pap. 7.99 (978-0-06-001223-6(4) , HarperTeen) HarperCollins Pubs.

—Geography Club. 2004. (gr. 7-12). lib. bdg. 15.30 (978-0-613-71366-5(4)) Tandem Library Bks.

—The Order of the Poison Oak. 2006. 240p. (J). reprint ed. pap. 6.99 (978-0-06-056732-5(5) , HarperTeen) HarperCollins Pubs.

—Split Screen: Attack of the Soul-Sucking Brain Zombies/ Bride of the Soul-Sucking Brain Zombies. 2007. 304p. (J). (gr. 9 up). 16.99 (978-0-06-082408-2(5)); lib. bdg. 17.89 (978-0-06-082409-9(3)) HarperCollins Pubs. (HarperTeen).

Hoffman, Eric. Best Colors (Los Mejores Colores) de la Vega, Eida, tr. Henriquez, Celeste, illus. 2004. (Anti-Bias Books for Kids). (ENG & SPA.). 32p. (J). (ps-3). pap. 11.95 (978-1-884834-69-1(8) , 709201) Redleaf Pr.

Howe, James. Totally Joe. 2007. 208p. (J). (gr. 4-8). pap. 5.99 ***(978-0-689-83958-0(8))*** Kaplan Bks.

Jacobson, Jennifer Richard. Stained. 208p. (YA). (gr. 8 up). 2005. (Illus.). 16.95 (978-0-689-86745-3(X) , Atheneum); 2006. reprint ed. pap. 6.99 (978-1-4169-1337-5(8) , Simon Pulse) Simon & Schuster Children's Publishing.

Jenkins, A. M. Breaking Boxes. 2000. (978-0-606-17834-1(1)) Tandem Library Bks.

Johnson, Maureen. The Bermudez Triangle. 2005. 384p. (YA). (gr. 9-12). reprint ed. pap. 7.99 (978-1-59514-033-3(6) , Razorbill) Penguin Group (USA) Inc.

Jones, Carrie. Tips on Having a Gay (ex) Boyfriend. (J). 2008. 264p. pap. 9.95 ***(978-0-7387-1341-0(4)*** , Flux); 2007. (Illus.). 288p. (gr. 7 up). 16.95 (978-0-7387-1050-1(4)) Llewellyn Pubns.

Juby, Susan. Another Kind of Cowboy. 2007. 352p. (J). lib. bdg. 17.89 ***(978-0-06-076518-7(6)***); (YA). lib. bdg. ***(978-0-06-076521-7(6)***); 352p. (YA). (gr. 9 up). 16.99 ***(978-0-06-076517-0(8))*** HarperCollins Pubs. (HarperTeen).

Koertge, Ron. Boy Girl Boy. 2007. (Illus.). 180p. (YA). (gr. 9 up). pap. 6.95 (978-0-15-205865-4(6) , Harcourt Paperbacks) Harcourt Children's Bks.

Koertge, Ronald. Boy Girl Boy. 2005. 176p. (YA). (gr. 9-17). 16.00 (978-0-15-205325-3(5)) Harcourt Children's Bks.

Koja, Kathe. Talk. 2005. 144p. (YA). 16.00 (978-0-374-37382-5(5) , Farrar, Straus & Giroux (BYR)) Farrar, Straus & Giroux.

—Talk. 2008. 160p. (YA). pap. 6.99 ***(978-0-312-37605-5(7))*** Square Fish.

—Talk. l.t. ed. 2006. 183p. (YA). 21.95 (978-0-7862-8811-3(6)) Thorndike Pr.

LaRochelle, David. Absolutely, Positively Not. 2005. 219p. (YA). (978-0-439-59110-2(4)); 224p. (J). (gr. 7-12). pap. 16.95 (978-0-439-59109-6(0)) Scholastic, Inc. (Levine, Arthur A. Bks.).

Lecesne, James. Absolute Brightness. 2008. 480p. (J). 17.99 ***(978-0-06-125627-1(7)***); lib. bdg. 18.89 ***(978-0-06-125628-8(5))*** HarperCollins Pubs. (HarperTeen).

Levithan, David. Wide Awake. 2006. 240p. (YA). (gr. 9). 16.95 (978-0-375-83466-0(4)); lib. bdg. 18.99 (978-0-375-93466-7(9)) Random Hse. Children's Bks. (Knopf Bks. for Young Readers).

Levithan, David & Cohn, Rachel. Naomi & Ely's No Kiss List. 2007. (YA). (gr. 9 up). 240p. 16.99 ***(978-0-375-84440-9(6)***); 192p. lib. bdg. 19.99 ***(978-0-375-94440-6(0))*** Random Hse. Children's Bks. (Knopf Bks. for Young Readers).

Limb, Sue. Girl, (Nearly) 16: Absolute Torture. 2008. (Girl, 15 Ser.). 224p. (YA). (gr. 5-11). mass mkt. 6.50 ***(978-0-440-23897-3(8)*** , Laurel Leaf) Random Hse. Children's Bks.

Lyon, George Ella. Sonny's House of Spies. 2004. (Illus.). 304p. (J). 16.95 (978-0-689-85168-1(5) , Atheneum/ Richard Jackson Bks.) Simon & Schuster Children's Publishing.

Manning, Sarra. Pretty Things (Splashproof Ed.) 2007. 1p. (YA). (gr. 7). pap. 6.99 (978-0-14-240859-9(X) , Puffin) Penguin Group (USA) Inc.

Myracle, Lauren. Kissing Kate. 2007. 208p. (YA). (gr. 7). pap. 7.99 (978-0-14-240869-8(7) , Puffin) Penguin Group (USA) Inc.

Newbery, Linda. The Shell House. 2004. 352p. (YA). (gr. 7-11). reprint ed. mass mkt. 6.50 (978-0-440-23786-0(6) , Laurel Leaf) Random Hse. Children's Bks.

Papademetriou, Lisa & Tebbetts, Christopher. M or F? 2006. 320p. (YA). (gr. 7-12). reprint ed. pap. 6.99 (978-1-59514-091-3(3) , Razorbill) Penguin Group (USA) Inc.

Peters, Julie Anne. Between Mom & Jo. 2006. 240p. (J). (gr. 7-17). 16.99 (978-0-316-73906-1(5)) Little Brown & Co.

Peters, Julie Anne. Far from Xanadu. 2007. 288p. (YA). (gr. 7 up). pap. 7.99 ***(978-0-316-15971-5(9))*** Little, Brown Bks. for Young Readers.

Plum-Ucci, Carol. What Happened to Lani Garver. (YA). 2002. 328p. (gr. 9 up). 17.00 (978-0-15-216813-1(3)); 2004. 336p. reprint ed. pap. 6.95 (978-0-15-205088-7(4) , Harcourt Paperbacks) Harcourt Children's Bks.

Reardon, Robin. A Secret Edge. 2007. 304p. pap. 15.00 ***(978-0-7582-1927-5(X))*** Kensington Publishing Corp.

Reynolds, Marilyn. Love Rules. (True-to-Life Series from Hamilton High). 224p. (J). (gr. 8 up). 2003. 18.95 (978-1-885356-75-8(7)); 2001. pap. 9.95 (978-1-885356-76-5(5)) Morning Glory Pr., Inc.

Richardson, Justin & Parnell, Peter. And Tango Makes Three. Cole, Henry, illus. 2005. 32p. (J). 15.99 (978-0-689-87845-9(1)) Simon & Schuster Children's Publishing.

Ryan, Patrick. Saints of Augustine. 2007. 320p. (J). lib. bdg. 17.89 ***(978-0-06-085811-7(7)***); (gr. 7 up). 16.99 ***(978-0-06-085810-0(9))*** HarperCollins Pubs. (HarperTeen).

Ryan, Sara. Empress of the World. 224p. (YA). (gr. 7). 2003. pap. 7.99 (978-0-14-250059-0(3) , Puffin); 2001. 15.99 (978-0-670-89688-2(8) , Viking Juvenile) Penguin Group (USA) Inc.

Sanchez, Alex. Getting It. 2006. 224p. (YA). 16.95 (978-1-4169-0896-8(X)) Simon & Schuster Children's Publishing.

—The God Box. 2007. 272p. (YA). (gr. 7 up). 16.99 ***(978-1-4169-0899-9(4)*** , Simon & Schuster Children's Publishing) Simon & Schuster Children's Publishing.

—Rainbow Boys. (YA). 2003. 272p. 8.99 (978-0-689-85770-6(5) , Simon Pulse); 2001. 256p. (gr. 9 up). 17.00 (978-0-689-84100-2(0)) Simon & Schuster Children's Publishing.

—Rainbow Boys. 2003. (gr. 7-12). lib. bdg. 16.45 (978-0-613-66434-9(5)) Tandem Library Bks.

—Rainbow High. 272p. (YA). 2003. (Illus.). 16.95 (978-0-689-85477-4(3)); 2005. reprint ed. 8.99 (978-0-689-85478-1(1) , Simon Pulse) Simon & Schuster Children's Publishing.

—Rainbow Road. 2007. 272p. (YA). pap. 8.99 (978-1-4169-1191-3(X) , Simon Pulse) Simon & Schuster Children's Publishing.

—So Hard to Say. 240p. 2004. (J). 15.95 (978-0-689-86564-0(3)); 2006. (Illus.). (YA). reprint ed. pap. 7.99 (978-1-4169-1189-0(8) , Aladdin) Simon & Schuster Children's Publishing.

Sanchez, Alex & Frost, Michael. Getting It. 2007. 240p. (YA). pap. 8.99 ***(978-1-4169-0898-2(6)*** , Simon Pulse) Simon & Schuster Children's Publishing.

Sanchez, Alex & Louth, Jack. Rainbow Road. 2005. 256p. (J). 16.95 (978-0-689-86565-7(1)) Simon & Schuster Children's Publishing.

Scoppettone, Sandra. Happy Endings Are All Alike. 2004. (Alyson Classics Library). 208p. (gr. 8-12). reprint ed. pap. 10.00 (978-1-55583-511-8(2)) Alyson Pubns.

Selvadurai, Shyam. Swimming in the Monsoon Sea. 2005. 280p. (J). 18.95 (978-0-88776-735-7(4)) Tundra Bks., Inc./Livres Toundra, Inc. CAN. *Dist:* Random Hse., Inc.

Setterington, Ken. Mom & Mum Are Getting Married. Priestley, Alice, illus. 2005. 24p. (J). 11.95 (978-1-896764-84-9(3)) Second Story Pr. CAN. *Dist:* Orca Bk. Pubs. USA.

Shaw, Tucker. The Hookup Artist. 2007. 208p. (J). pap. 7.99 (978-0-06-075622-2(5) , HarperTeen) HarperCollins Pubs.

Shyer, Marlene Fanta. The Rainbow Kite. 2002. 208p. (YA). (gr. 7-10). 15.95 (978-0-7614-5122-8(6)) Cavendish, Marshall Corp.

Sloan, Brian. A Really Nice Prom Mess. 2005. 272p. (YA). (gr. 7 up). 14.95 (978-0-689-87438-3(3) , Simon & Schuster Children's Publishing) Simon & Schuster Children's Publishing.

—Tale of Two Summers. 2006. 256p. (YA). 15.95 (978-0-689-87439-0(1) , Simon & Schuster Children's Publishing) Simon & Schuster Children's Publishing.

Sones, Sonya. One of Those Hideous Books Where the Mother Dies. 272p. (YA). 2004. (Illus.). 16.95 (978-0-689-85820-8(5)); 2005. (gr. 7-12). reprint ed. pap. 6.99 (978-1-4169-0788-6(2) , Simon Pulse) Simon & Schuster Children's Publishing.

Steinhofel, Andreas. The Center of the World. 2007. 480p. (YA). (gr. 9). pap. 7.99 (978-0-440-22932-2(4) , Laurel Leaf) Random Hse. Children's Bks.

Stevens, Tracey. Chalice of the Goddess. Snowden, Susan, ed. Stevens, Tracey, illus. 2004. (Illus.). 313p. (YA). per. 17.95 (978-0-9719628-4-2(7)) Amazing Dreams Publishing.

Summer, Jane, ed. Not the Only One: Lesbian & Gay Fiction for Teens. 2004. 224p. pap. 13.95 (978-1-55583-834-8(0)) Alyson Pubns.

Taylor, William. The Blue Lawn. 1999. 128p. (gr. 7-12). pap. 10.95 (978-1-55583-493-7(0)) Alyson Pubns.

—The Blue Lawn. 1999. (J). 17.75 (978-0-606-19431-0(2)) Tandem Library Bks.

Trueman, Terry. 7 Days at the Hot Corner, No. 2. 2007. 160p. (J). (gr. 7 up). 15.99 (978-0-06-057494-9(1)); lib. bdg. 16.89 (978-0-06-057495-6(X)) HarperCollins Pubs. (HarperTeen).

Valentine, Johnny. The Daddy Machine. Schmidt, Lynette, illus. 2nd ed. 2004. 32p. (Orig.). pap. 10.95 (978-1-55583-846-1(4)) Alyson Pubns.

—The Duke Who Outlawed Jelly Beans: And Other Stories. Schmidt, Lynette, illus. 2nd ed. 2004. 32p. pap. 10.95 (978-1-55583-847-8(2)) Alyson Pubns.

—One Dad, Two Dads, Brown Dad, Blue Dads. Sarecky, Melody, illus. 2004. 32p. (J). pap. 10.95 (978-1-55583-848-5(0)) Alyson Pubns.

Walker, Kate. Peter. 2001. 240p. (YA). (gr. 7). pap. 5.95 (978-0-618-11130-5(1)) Houghton Mifflin Co. Trade & Reference Div.

—Peter. 2001. (gr. 7-12). lib. bdg. 14.10 (978-0-613-63640-7(6)); (Illus.). (J). (978-0-606-21380-6(5)) Tandem Library Bks.

Wallace, Kim. Erik & Isabelle Junior Year at Foresthill High. 2006. (YA). per. 12.00 (978-0-9755848-2-8(0)) Foglight Pr.

Weyr, Garret. My Heartbeat. 2003. 176p. (YA). pap. 7.99 (978-0-14-240066-1(1) , Puffin) Penguin Group (USA) Inc.

—My Heartbeat. 2003. (gr. 7-12). lib. bdg. 16.45 (978-0-613-81700-4(1)) Tandem Library Bks.

Winick, Judd. Pedro & Me: Friendship, Loss & What I Learned. 2001. (Illus.). (J). (978-0-606-20504-7(7)) Tandem Library Bks.

Wittlinger, Ellen. Love & Lies: Marisol's Story. 2008. 256p. (YA). ***(978-1-4169-1623-9(7)*** , Simon & Schuster Children's Publishing) Simon & Schuster Children's Publishing.

Woodson, Jacqueline. The Dear One. 2004. 144p. (YA). pap. 6.99 (978-0-14-250190-0(5) , Puffin) Penguin Group (USA) Inc.

—From the Notebooks of Melanin Sun. 2003. 160p. (J). (gr. 7 up). pap. 5.99 (978-0-590-45881-8(7) , Scholastic Paperbacks) Scholastic, Inc.

—The House You Pass on the Way. 2003. 112p. (YA). reprint ed. pap. 5.99 (978-0-14-250191-7(3) , Puffin); (gr. 5). 16.99 (978-0-399-23969-4(3) , Putnam Juvenile) Penguin Group (USA) Inc.

—The House You Pass on the Way. 1999. (J). (978-0-606-16085-8(X)) Tandem Library Bks.

—The House You Pass on the Way. l.t. ed. 2004. 109p. (J). 22.95 (978-0-7862-6428-5(4)) Thorndike Pr.

HONDURAS

Dendinger, Roger E. Honduras. 2007. (Modern World Nations Ser.). 136p. (J). (gr. 6-12). 30.00 ***(978-0-7910-9510-2(X)*** , Chelsea Hse.) Facts On File, Inc.

Haynes, Tricia. Honduras. 1999. (Major World Nations Ser.). (Illus.). 144p. (YA). (gr. 4-7). 29.95 (978-0-7910-4975-4(2) , Chelsea Hse.) Facts On File, Inc.

Kras, Sara Louise. Honduras. 2006. (Enchantment of the World, Second Ser.). (Illus.). 144p. (J). 36.00 (978-0-516-24871-4(5) , Children's Pr) Scholastic Library Publishing.

McGaffey, L. Honduras. 1999. (Cultures of the World Ser.). (Illus.). 128p. (gr. 5-12). lib. bdg. 37.07 (978-0-7614-0955-7(6) , Benchmark Bks.) Cavendish, Marshall Corp.

Shields, Charles J. Honduras. 2002. (Let's Discover Central America Ser.). (Illus.). 63p. (YA). (gr. 5 up). lib. bdg. (978-1-59084-096-2(8)) Mason Crest Pubs.

HONESTY

see also Truthfulness and Falsehood

Amos, Janine. Admitting Mistakes. Spenceley, Annabel, illus. 2002. (Courteous Kids Ser.). 32p. (J). (ps up). lib. bdg. 23.33 (978-0-8368-3168-9(3)) Stevens, Gareth Inc.

Amos, Janine. Liar. 2007. (Good & Bad Ser.). (Illus.). 32p. (J). (ps-2). pap. 9.95 ***(978-1-84234-395-1(5)*** , Evans Brothers, Limited) Evans Publishing Group GBR. *Dist:* Independent Pubs. Group.

Berry, Joy Wilt. A Book about Cheating. 2005. (Illus.). (J). (978-0-7172-8583-9(9)) Scholastic, Inc.

—A Book about Lying. 2005. (Illus.). (J). (978-0-7172-8576-1(6)) Scholastic, Inc.

Burch, Regina G. I Can Tell the Truth. Motoyama, Keiko, illus. 2004. 16p. (J). lib. bdg. 19.33 (978-0-8368-4249-4(9)) Stevens, Gareth Inc.

—Telling the Truth Vol. 3125: Learning about Honesty, Integrity, & Trustworthiness K-3. Hamaguchi, Carla, ed. Motoyama, Keiko, illus. 2002. (Character Education Readers). 16p. (J). (ps-3). pap. 1.99 (978-1-57471-826-3(6)) Creative Teaching Pr., Inc.

Character Ed Says Honesty Counts. 2006. (J). 4.95 (978-1-55548-057-8(8) , 678) Human Relations Media.

Currie, Stephen. Cheating. 2007. (J). ***(978-1-60217-011-7(8))*** Erickson Pr.

H I

Donahue, Jill L. Being Honest. Previn, Stacey, illus. 2007. (J). lib. bdg. (***978-1-4048-3775-1(2)***) Picture Window Bks.

Doudna, Kelly. Honestly! 2007. (Character Concepts Ser.). (Illus.). 24p. (J). (gr. k-3). lib. bdg. 19.93 (***978-1-59928-735-5(8)***) ABDO Publishing Co.

Finn, Carrie. Kids Talk about Honesty. Muehlenhardt, Amy Bailey, illus. 2006. (Kids Talk Junior Ser.). (J). 23.93 (978-1-4048-2317-4(4)) Picture Window Bks.

Gordon, Sharon. Decimos la Verdad. 2006. (Bookworms Ser.). (SPA & ENG., Illus.). 24p. (J). lib. bdg. 22.79 (978-0-7614-2362-1(1) , Benchmark Bks.) Cavendish, Marshall Corp.

—We Tell the Truth. 2005. (Bookworms Ser.). (ENG & SPA., Illus.). 24p. (J). (gr. 3-7). lib. bdg. (978-0-7614-1996-9(9) , Benchmark Bks.) Cavendish, Marshall Corp.

—We Tell the Truth (Decimos la Verdad) 2006. (Bookworms Ser.). (ENG & SPA., Illus.). 24p. (J). lib. bdg. 22.79 (978-0-7614-2442-0(3)) Cavendish, Marshall Corp.

Leeper, Angela. I Am Honest. 2004. (You & Me Ser.). (Illus.). 24p. (J). pap. (978-1-4034-6080-6(9)); lib. bdg. 20.64 (978-1-4034-6072-1(8)) Heinemann Library.

Mead, David. Little Abe Lincoln Learns a Lesson in Honesty: Honesty. Sharp, Chris, illus. 2003. (American Virtues for Kids Ser.). (J). bds. 6.95 (978-0-9746440-0-4(5)) Ideals Pubns.

Meiners, Cheri J. Be Honest & Tell the Truth. Johnson, Meredith, illus. 2007. 40p. (J). (ps-3). pap. 10.95 (***978-1-57542-258-9(1)***) Free Spirit Publishing, Inc.

Nettleton, Pamela Hill. Is That True? Kids Talk about Honesty. Muehlenhardt, Amy Bailey, illus. 2004. (Kids Talk Ser.). 32p. (C). (gr. 2-5). 23.93 (978-1-4048-0619-1(9)) Picture Window Bks.

PowerXpress Living God's Word - Honesty. 99.00 (978-0-687-00099-9(8)) Abingdon Pr.

PowerXpress Living God's Word Honesty. 9.95 incl. audio compact disk (978-0-687-05661-3(6)) Abingdon Pr.

Roberts, Cynthia. Honesty. 2007. (Learn about Values Ser.). 24p. (J). 21.36 (978-1-59296-671-4(3)) Child's World, Inc.

—Patience. 2007. (Learn about Values Ser.). 24p. (J). 21.36 (978-1-59296-673-8(X)) Child's World, Inc.

Rondina, Catherine. Lying: Straight Up. Workman, Dan, illus. 2006. (Deal with It Ser.). 32p. (J). (gr. 4-8). pap. 12.95 (978-1-55028-906-0(3)) Lorimer, James & Co., Ltd., Pubs. CAN. *Dist:* Casemate Pubs. & Bk. Distributors, LLC.

Salzmann, Mary Elizabeth. Honesty Counts. 2003. (Character Counts Ser.). (Illus.). 32p. (J). (gr. k-6). lib. bdg. 22.78 (978-1-57765-872-6(8)) ABDO Publishing Co.

—I Am Honest. 2003. (Building Character Ser.). (Illus.). 24p. (J). (ps-3). lib. bdg. 19.93 (978-1-57765-828-3(0)) ABDO Publishing Co.

Schuette, Sarah L. I Am Honest. Saunders-Smith, Gail, ed. 2002. (Character Values Ser.). (Illus.). 24p. (J). (gr. k-1). lib. bdg. 14.60 (978-0-7368-1440-9(X) , Pebble Bks.) Capstone Pr., Inc.

—Soy Honrado (I Am Honest) 2003. (Character Values Bilingual Ser.). (SPA., Illus.). 24p. (J). lib. bdg. 15.93 (978-0-7368-2303-6(4)) Capstone Pr., Inc.

Simon, Mary Manz. What Did Jesus Do? Stories about Honesty & Forgiveness. Kennedy, Anne, illus. 1998. (What Did Jesus Do? Ser.). (J). (ps-3). 7.99 (978-0-8499-5857-1(1)) Nelson, Thomas Inc.

Snyder, Margaret. Honesty. 1999. (Doing the Right Thing Ser.). (Illus.). 32p. (J). (gr. k-3). lib. bdg. 26.60 (978-1-55916-232-6(5)) Rourke Publishing, LLC.

Thoennes Keller, Kristin. Honesty. 2005. (Illus.). 24p. (J). 21.26 (978-0-7368-3681-4(0)) Capstone Pr., Inc.

Thomas, Pat. I'm Telling the Truth: A First Look at Honesty. Harker, Lesley, illus. 2006. (First Look At... Ser.). 32p. (J). pap. 6.99 (978-0-7641-3214-8(8)) Barron's Educational Series, Inc.

Wan, Guofang. Virtually True: Questioning Online Media. 2007. (Fact Finders Ser.). (Illus.). 32p. (J). (***978-0-7368-7863-0(7)*** , 1264914) Capstone Pr., Inc.

Wilmore, Kathy. Muhammad Ali: With a Discussion of Honesty. 2003. (Values in Action Ser.). (J). (978-1-59203-065-1(3)) Learning Challenge, Inc.

HONESTY—FICTION

Abercrombie, Barbara. The Show-and-Tell Lion. Cravath, Lynne Avril, illus. 2006. 32p. (J). (ps-2). 16.95 (978-0-689-86408-7(6) , McElderry, Margaret K.) Simon & Schuster Children's Publishing.

Alger, Horatio. $500: Or, Jacob Marlowe's Secret. unabr. ed. 2002. (Polyglot Press Alger Ser.). (Illus.). (J). pap. 17.95 (978-1-931927-97-0(9)) Polyglot Pr., Inc.

Amato, Mary. The Naked Mole Rat Letters. 208p. (J). (Illus.). 16.95 (978-0-8234-1927-2(4)); 2007. (gr. 3-7). pap. 6.95 (***978-0-8234-2098-8(1)***) Holiday Hse., Inc.

Amesse, Susan. Kissing Brendan Callahan. 2005. 160p. (J). (gr. 5-8). 15.95 (978-1-59643-015-0(X)) Roaring Brook Pr.

Andersen, Hans Christian. The Emperor's New Clothes: Honesty. Neidigh, Sherry, illus. 2005. (J). pap. (978-1-4127-3759-3(1)) Publications International, Ltd.

Bourgeois, Paulette. Franklin Miente. Clark, Brenda, illus. 2000. (Franklin Ser.). (SPA.). (J). (ps-3). pap. 5.95 (978-1-880507-69-8(2) , LC4551) Lectorum Pubns., Inc.

—Franklin Miente. 2000. (Franklin Ser.). (SPA., Illus.). (J). (ps-3). 12.75 (978-0-606-18243-0(8)) Tandem Library Bks.

Bowen, Fred. Winners Take All. Casale, Paul, illus. 2000. (All-Star Sport Story Ser.). 104p. (J). (gr. 3-7). pap. 4.95 (978-1-56145-229-3(7) , Q26776) Peachtree Pubs., Ltd.

—Winners Take All. 2000. (J). (978-0-606-19863-9(6)); (gr. 3-6). lib. bdg. 12.95 (978-0-613-36750-9(2)) Tandem Library Bks.

Breathed, Berkeley. Edward Fudwupper Fibbed Big. 2000. (Illus.). 48p. (J). (ps-17). 15.99 (978-0-316-10675-7(5)) Little Brown & Co.

—Edward Fudwupper Fibbed Big. Breathed, Berkeley, illus. 2003. (Illus.). 40p. (J). (gr. 1-4). pap. 6.99 (978-0-316-14425-4(8)) Little, Brown Bks. for Young Readers.

—Edward Fudwupper Fibbed Big. 2003. (gr. k-3). lib. bdg. 15.30 (978-0-613-71786-1(4)) Tandem Library Bks.

Bridwell, Norman, et al. T-Bone Tells the Truth. Binder, Eric & Lloyd, Gita, illus. 2002. (Clifford's Big Red Ideas Ser.). 7p. (J). bds. 4.99 (978-0-439-39450-5(3)) Scholastic, Inc.

Brightwood, Laura, illus. The Woodsman & His Ax. Brightwood, Laura, . 2007. (J). DVD (***978-1-934409-07-7(3)***) 3-C Institute for Social Development.

Brimner, Larry Dane. Money Trouble. Tripp, Christine, illus. 2002. (Rookie Choices Ser.). 32p. (J). (gr. 1-2). pap. 5.95 (978-0-516-25976-5(8) , Children's Pr.) Scholastic Library Publishing.

—Money Trouble. 2001. (gr. k-3). lib. bdg. 14.10 (978-0-613-54441-2(2)) Tandem Library Bks.

—The Noodle Game. Tripp, Christine, illus. (Rookie Choices Ser.). 32p. (J). (gr. 1-2). 2002. pap. 5.95 (978-0-516-25977-2(6)); 2001. 19.50 (978-0-516-22157-1(4)) Scholastic Library Publishing. (Children's Pr.).

—The Sparkle Thing. 2001. (gr. k-3). lib. bdg. 14.10 (978-0-613-54360-6(2)) Tandem Library Bks.

Brisson, Pat. The Summer My Father Was Ten. 2003. (Illus.). 32p. (J). (gr. k-2). 15.95 (978-1-56397-435-9(5)) Boyds Mills Pr.

—The Summer My Father Was Ten. Shine, Andrea, illus. 2003. 32p. (J). (gr. k-2). pap. 9.95 (978-1-56397-829-6(6)) Boyds Mills Pr.

—The Summer My Father Was Ten. Shine, Andrea, illus. 1999. (J). (ps-ps). lib. bdg. 17.60 (978-0-613-23818-2(4)) Tandem Library Bks.

—The Summer My Father Was Ten. 1999. (978-0-606-18015-3(X)) Tandem Library Bks.

Brouwer, Sigmund. Long Shot. 2002. (Watch Out for Joel Ser.). (Illus.). 32p. (J). (gr. 1-3). pap. 3.99 (978-0-7642-2581-9(2)) Bethany Hse. Pubs.

—Long Shot. 2002. (gr. k-3). lib. bdg. 11.80 (978-0-613-87751-0(9)) Tandem Library Bks.

—Mystery Pennies. 2003. (Watch Out for Joel Ser.). (Illus.). 32p. (J). pap. 3.99 (978-0-7642-2584-0(7)) Bethany Hse. Pubs.

Brown, Marc. Arthur in a Pickle. 1999. (Arthur Ser.). (Illus.). 24p. (J). (gr. k-3). lib. bdg. 11.99 (978-0-679-98469-6(0) , Random Hse. Bks. for Young Readers) Random Hse. Children's Bks.

—Arthur in a Pickle. 1999. (Arthur Ser.). lib. bdg. 11.80 (978-0-613-65119-6(7)) Tandem Library Bks.

—Arthur's Classroom Fib. 2007. (Illus.). 24p. (J). (gr. 1-3). pap. 3.99 (978-0-375-82975-8(X)); lib. bdg. 11.99 (978-0-375-92975-5(4)) Random Hse. Children's Bks. (Random Hse. Bks. for Young Readers).

—Arthur's Science Fair Trouble. Brown, Marc, illus. 2003. (Arthur Ser.). (Illus.). 24p. (J). (gr. k-3). pap. 3.99 (978-0-375-81003-9(X)); lib. bdg. 11.99 (978-0-375-91003-6(4)) Random Hse. Children's Bks. (Random Hse. Bks. for Young Readers).

—Arthur's Science Fair Trouble. 2003. (Arthur Ser.). (gr. k-3). lib. bdg. 11.80 (978-0-613-70564-6(5)) Tandem Library Bks.

Bulion, Leslie. Uncharted Waters. 2006. 155p. (J). 14.95 (978-1-56145-365-8(X) , Peachtree Junior) Peachtree Pubs., Ltd.

Bunting, Eve. A Day's Work. 2002. (Illus.). (J). 13.79 (978-0-7587-2361-1(X)) Book Wholesalers, Inc.

Cabot, Meg. Pants on Fire. 2007. 272p. (gr. 7-10). (J). lib. bdg. 17.89 (978-0-06-088016-3(3)); (YA). 16.99 (978-0-06-088015-6(5)) HarperCollins Pubs. (HarperTeen).

Cadnum, Michael. Rundown. Moore, Lisa, ed. 2001. 176p. (YA). pap. 6.99 (978-0-14-131087-9(1) , Puffin) Penguin Group (USA) Inc.

—Rundown. 2001. (J). (978-0-606-20894-9(1)); 168p. (YA). (gr. 8-12). per. 15.30 (978-0-613-33725-0(5)) Tandem Library Bks.

Cappo, Nan Willard. Cheating Lessons. 2002. 240p. (J). (gr. 6-10). 16.00 (978-0-689-84378-5(X) , Atheneum) Simon & Schuster Children's Publishing.

Carlson, Nancy L., tr. & illus. Harriet & the Garden. Carlson, Nancy L., illus. 2nd rev. ed. (Nancy Carlson's Neighborhood Ser.). 32p. (gr. k-2). 2005. 15.95 (978-1-57505-710-1(7)); 2004. (J). pap. (978-1-57505-612-8(7)) Lerner Publishing Group.

Carlson, Nathan, et al. The Great Train Set Robbery. 2001. (Little Dogs on the Prairie Ser.). (Illus.). 64p. (J). (gr. 1-4). 4.99 (978-0-8499-7649-0(9)) Nelson, Thomas Inc.

Child, Lauren. Whoops! but It Wasn't Me. 2006. (Charlie & Lola Ser.). (Illus.). 32p. (J). (ps-2). pap. 5.99 (978-0-448-44413-0(5) , Grosset & Dunlap) Penguin Group (USA) Inc.

Choldenko, Gennifer. Notes from a Liar & Her Dog. (J). (gr. 5-7). 2003. 224p. pap. 6.99 (978-0-14-250068-2(2) , Puffin); 2001. (Illus.). 1p. 16.99 (978-0-399-23591-7(4) , Putnam Juvenile) Penguin Group (USA) Inc.

—Notes from a Liar & Her Dog. 2004. 224p. (J). (gr. 4-7). pap. 38.00 incl. audio (978-0-8072-2097-9(3) , Listening Library) Random Hse. Audio Publishing Group.

—Notes from a Liar & Her Dog. 2001. lib. bdg. 14.15 (978-0-613-67468-3(5)) Tandem Library Bks.

Collodi, Carlo. Pinocchio: A Classic Story about Honesty. 2003. (Illus.). 32p. per. 3.95 (978-0-9747133-2-8(5) , Values to Live By Classic Stories) Thomas, Frederic Inc.

Cosby, Bill. My Big Lie. Honeywood, Varnette P., illus. 1999. (Little Bill Books for Beginning Readers Ser.). 40p. (J). (gr. k-3). pap. 15.95 (978-0-590-52160-4(8)); (gr. 1-5). pap. 3.99 (978-0-590-52161-1(6)) Scholastic, Inc.

—My Big Lie. 1999. (gr. k-3). lib. bdg. 11.80 (978-0-613-16979-0(4)); (J). (978-0-606-16631-7(9)) Tandem Library Bks.

Cosgrove, Stephen. Flynn "Flea" Flicker: Sticking to the Truth. Arroyo, Fian, illus. 2004. (J). (978-1-58804-353-5(3)) PCI Educational Publishing.

Coville, Bruce. The Skull of Truth. 1999. (gr. 3-6). lib. bdg. 13.00 (978-0-613-17061-1(X)) Tandem Library Bks.

—The Skull of Truth: A Magic Shop Book. Lippincott, Gary A., illus. 2007. (Magic Shop Book Ser.). 208p. (J). pap. 5.95 (978-0-15-206084-8(7) , Magic Carpet Bks.) Harcourt Children's Bks.

Cox, Judy. Butterfly Buddies. Sims, Blanche, illus. 2001. 96p. (J). (gr. 4-6). tchr. ed. 15.95 (978-0-8234-1654-7(2)) Holiday Hse., Inc.

Cummings, Priscilla. What Mr. Mattero Did. 2007. 224p. (J). (gr. 3). pap. 6.99 (978-0-14-240856-8(5) , Puffin) Penguin Group (USA) Inc.

Day, Lauren. What Kind of Friend Are You? 1999. (Rockett's World Ser.: No. 2). (Illus.). 128p. (J). (gr. 4-7). pap. 3.99 (978-0-439-06312-8(4)) Scholastic, Inc.

—What Kind of Friend Are You? 1999. (Rockett's World Ser.: No. 2). (J). (gr. 4-7). (978-0-606-17050-5(2)) Tandem Library Bks.

Defosse, Rosana Curiel. Santiago & the Fox of Hatsune. Barradas, Leticia, illus. (SPA.). 32p. (J). (gr. 3-5). pap. 7.95 (978-970-29-0134-1(0)) Santillana USA Publishing Co., Inc.

deGroat, Diane. Liar, Liar, Pants on Fire. deGroat, Diane, illus. 2006. (Illus.). 27p. (J). (gr. k-4). reprint ed. 16.00 (978-0-7567-9987-8(2)) DIANE Publishing Co.

DeLuise, Dom. King Bob's New Clothes. 1999. (J). (978-0-606-18949-1(1)) Tandem Library Bks.

Demi. The Empty Pot. 2007. (Illus.). 32p. (J). pap. 23.95 (***978-0-8050-8227-2(1)*** , Holt, Henry & Co. Bks. For Young Readers) Holt, Henry & Co.

Dickens, Charles. Oliver Twist: With a Discussion of Honesty. 2003. (Values in Action Illustrated Classics Ser.). (J). (978-1-59203-051-4(3)) Learning Challenge, Inc.

Doyle, Dennis M. & Doyle, Patrick J. Rumors at School. 2001. (Illus.). 88p. (J). (gr. 4-9). 7.95 (978-0-8091-6686-2(0) , 6700-x) Paulist Pr.

Fletcher, Ralph. Spider Boy. 1998. 183p. (J). (ps-7). per. 13.00 (978-0-613-08798-8(4)) Tandem Library Bks.

Foreman, Michael. Norman's Ark. Foreman, Michael, illus. 2006. (Illus.). 32p. (J). pap. 6.95 (978-1-58925-401-5(5) , tiger tales) ME Media LLC.

Friedman, Laurie B. Honestly, Mallory! Pollak, Barbara, illus. 2007. (Mallory Ser.). 160p. (J). (gr. 2-6). 15.95 (***978-0-8225-6193-4(X)*** , Carolrhoda Bks.) Lerner Publishing Group.

Gaard, Betty. The Theft. 2000. 190p. (YA). (gr. 7 up). pap. 6.49 (978-1-57924-375-3(4) , 124487) Jones, Bob Univ. Pr.

Gemmen, Heather. But It's True. Lagares, Luciano, illus. 2004. (Tough Stuff for Kids Ser.). 36p. (J). (gr. 4-7). pap., pap. 5.99 (978-0-7814-4033-2(5) , 0781440335) Cook, David C. Publishing Co.

Goldman, Leslie. Truth Hurts. 2003. (gr. 3-6). lib. bdg. 13.00 (978-0-613-66471-4(X)) Tandem Library Bks.

Greene, Stephanie. Owen Foote, Super Spy. Weston, Martha, illus. 2005. 96p. (J). (gr. k-3). pap. 5.95 (978-0-618-55159-0(X) , Clarion Bks.) Houghton Mifflin Co. Trade & Reference Div.

Grindley, Sally. Will You Forgive Me? Dann, Penny, illus. 2001. 32p. (J). (ps-k). tchr. ed. 15.95 (978-0-7534-5295-0(2) , Kingfisher) Houghton Mifflin Co. Trade & Reference Div.

Gutman, Anne. Lisa in the Jungle. Hallensleben, Georg, illus. 2003. (Misadventures of Gaspard & Lisa Ser.). 32p. (J). (ps-3). 9.95 (978-0-375-82254-4(2) , Knopf Bks. for Young Readers) Random Hse. Children's Bks.

Hall, Kirsten. Little Lies: All about Math. Luedecke, Bev, illus. 2003. (Beastieville Ser.). 32p. (J). 19.50 (978-0-516-22896-9(X) , Children's Pr.) Scholastic Library Publishing.

Hallinan, P. K. Let's Be Honest. 2003. (Illus.). 24p. (J). bds. 7.95 (978-0-8249-5478-9(5)) Ideals Pubns.

Hamilton, Elizabeth L. Jeremy Rabbit's Honesty Pie. 2003. (Character Critters Ser.: No. 2). (Illus.). 32p. (J). (ps-3). per. 5.95 (978-0-9713749-5-9(3) , Character-in-Action) Quiet Impact, Inc.

Harcourt School Publishers Staff. Honest Neighbors On Level. 3rd ed. 2002. (Trophies Reading Program Ser.). (Illus.). pap. 5.10 (978-0-15-323256-5(0)) Harcourt Schl. Pubs.

Hershey, Mary. My Big Sister Is So Bossy She Says You Can't Read This Book. 2006. 176p. (gr. 4-7). 5.50 (978-0-553-48797-8(3) , Yearling) Random Hse. Children's Bks.

Howell, Trisha Adelena. The Adventures of Melon & Turnip. Lopez, Paul, illus. 2004. 32p. 15.95 (978-1-931210-04-1(7)) Howell Canyon Pr.

Johnson, Barbara. The Tasty Taffy Tale & Super-Stretching the Truth: A Book about Honesty. Frazier, Victoria Ponikvar, illus. 1999. (Geranium Lady Ser.: Vol. 4). 32p. (J). (ps-2). 4.97 (978-0-8499-5951-6(9)) Nelson, Thomas Inc.

Katschke, Judy. If I Were President. 1999. (gr. 3-6). lib. bdg. 11.80 (978-0-613-21748-4(9)) Tandem Library Bks.

Keller, Holly. That's Mine, Horace. Keller, Holly, illus. 2000. (Illus.). 24p. (J). (ps up). 16.99 (978-0-688-17159-9(1)) HarperCollins Pubs.

Kent, Renee Holmes. Tell the Truth, Cassie, Vol. 6. 2004. (Adventures in Misty Falls Ser.: Vol. 6). (Illus.). 100p. (J). (gr. 4-7). pap. 4.99 (978-1-56309-452-1(5) , N007110) New Hope Pubs.

Kline, Suzy. Horrible Harry & the Mud Gremlins. Remkiewicz, Frank, illus. 2003. 64p. (J). (gr. 2-6). 13.99 (978-0-670-03617-2(X) , Viking Juvenile) Penguin Group (USA) Inc.

Korman, Gordon. Liar, Liar, Pants on Fire. 1999. (gr. 3-6). lib. bdg. 11.80 (978-0-613-11773-9(5)) Tandem Library Bks.

Koss, Amy Goldman. Smoke Screen. 2000. (978-0-606-21791-0(6)) Tandem Library Bks.

Kroll, Virginia L. Honest Ashley. Cote, Nancy, illus. 2006. (Way I ACT Ser.). 24p. (J). 15.95 (978-0-8075-3371-0(8)) Whitman, Albert & Co.

Leaney, Cindy. Lost & Found: Honesty. Wilks, Peter, tr. Wilks, Peter, illus. 2003. 32p. (J). 28.50 (978-1-58952-736-2(4)) Rourke Publishing, LLC.

Leigh, Tom, illus. Pinocchio: A Tale of Honesty. 2006. (J). 6.99 (978-1-59939-005-5(1) , Reader's Digest Young Families, Inc.) Reader's Digest Children's Publishing, Inc.

Lewis, Beverly. Sealed with a Kiss. rev. ed. 2002. (Holly's Heart Ser.: Bk. 3). 160p. (YA). pap. 6.99 (978-0-7642-2502-4(2)) Bethany Hse. Pubs.

Lucado, Max. Flo the Lyin' Fly. 2004. (Max Lucado's Hermie & Friends Ser.). (Illus.). 48p. (J). 12.99 (978-1-4003-0286-4(2)) Nelson, Thomas Inc.

Lucado, Max, creator. Flo, the Lyin' Fly. 2006. 38p. (J). bds. 12.99 (978-1-4003-0889-7(5)) Nelson, Thomas Inc.

Luper, Eric. Big Slick. 2007. 240p. (YA). (gr. 9 up). 16.00 (***978-0-374-30799-8(7)***) Farrar, Straus & Giroux.

MacKall, Dandi Daley. Horse of a Different Color, Vol. 4. 2000. (Horsefeathers Ser.: Vol. 4). 192p. (YA). (gr. 7-11). 5.99 (978-0-570-07009-2(0)) Concordia Publishing Hse.

McClintock, Norah. Snitch. 2005. (Orca Soundings Ser.). 112p. (J). (gr. 7-12). pap. 7.95 (978-1-55143-484-1(9)) Orca Bk. Pubs. USA.

McDonald, Joyce. Shades of Simon Gray. (YA). (gr. 7). 2003. 272p. pap. 6.50 (978-0-440-22804-2(2) , Laurel Leaf); 2001. 256p. lib. bdg. 17.99 (978-0-385-90026-3(0) , Delacorte Bks. for Young Readers) Random Hse. Children's Bks.

—Shades of Simon Gray. 2003. (gr. 7-12). lib. bdg. 13.55 (978-0-613-60396-6(6)) Tandem Library Bks.

McKissack, Patricia C. The Honest-to-Goodness Truth. 2002. (Illus.). (J). 25.11 (978-0-7587-2741-1(0)) Book Wholesalers, Inc.

—The Honest-to-Goodness Truth. Potter, Giselle, illus. 2000. 40p. (J). (ps-3). 16.00 (978-0-689-82668-9(0) , Atheneum/Anne Schwartz Bks.) Simon & Schuster Children's Publishing.

—The Honest-to-Goodness Truth. 2003. (gr. k-3). lib. bdg. 15.30 (978-0-613-61627-0(8)) Tandem Library Bks.

McKissack, Patricia C. & Potter, Giselle. The Honest-to-Goodness Truth. 2003. (Illus.). 40p. (J). (ps-3). pap. 7.99 (978-0-689-85395-1(5) , Aladdin) Simon & Schuster Children's Publishing.

Messer, Celeste M. The Boy Who Cried Wolf. Hoeffner, Deb, illus. 2004. 82-92p. 4.95 (978-0-9702171-9-6(6)) AshleyAlan Enterprises.

Metzger, Steve. My Seeds Won't Grow! Wilhelm, Hans, illus. 2000. (Dinofours Ser.: No. 18). (J). (ps-1). (978-0-439-06329-6(9)) Scholastic, Inc.

Moorehead, Michael. The Student from Zombie Island: Conquering the Rumor Monster. Parks, Kathy, illus. 2007. 40p. (J). bds. 15.95 net. (***978-1-58985-072-9(6)***) Five Star Pubns., Inc.

Morgan, Melissa J. Reality Bites, No. 15. 2007. (Camp Confidential Ser.). 160p. (J). pap. 4.99 (978-0-448-44539-7(5) , Grosset & Dunlap) Penguin Group (USA) Inc.

Morris, Gilbert. Too Smart Jones & the Pool Party Thief: A Gilbert Morris Mystery. 1999. (Gilbert Morris Mysteries Ser.: Vol. 1). (Illus.). 115p. (J). (gr. 2-7). pap. 5.99 (978-0-8024-4025-9(8)) Moody Pubs.

Myers, Bill. My Life As a Prickly Porcupine from the Planet Pluto. 2004. (Incredible Worlds of Wally McDoogle Ser.). 128p. (J). pap. 6.99 (978-0-8499-5994-3(2)) Nelson, Thomas Inc.

—My Life as Dinosaur Dental Floss. Mangiat, Jeff, illus. 2005. (Incredible Worlds of Wally McDoogle Ser.). 128p. (J). 9.99 (978-1-4003-0614-5(0)) Nelson, Thomas Inc.

Napoli, Donna Jo. Give & Take. Ben-Ami, Doren & Klementz-Harte, Lauren, illus. 2000. (Angelwings Ser.: No. 5). 96p. (J). (gr. 2-5). pap. 7.95 (978-0-689-83205-5(2) , Aladdin) Simon & Schuster Children's Publishing.

—Give & Take. 2000. (Angelwings Ser.: No. 5). (Illus.). (J). 10.79 (978-0-606-17908-9(9)) Tandem Library Bks.

—Know-It-All. Klementz-Harte, Lauren, illus. 2000. (Angelwings Ser.: No. 11). 96p. (J). (gr. 4-7). pap. 7.95 (978-0-689-83572-8(8) , Aladdin) Simon & Schuster Children's Publishing.

—Know-It-All. 2000. (Angelwings Ser.: No. 11). (Illus.). (J). (978-0-606-20385-2(0)) Tandem Library Bks.

—Lies & Lemons. 2000. (Angelwings Ser.: No. 9). 96p. (J). (gr. 4-7). pap. 7.95 (978-0-689-83209-3(5) , Aladdin) Simon & Schuster Children's Publishing.

—Lies & Lemons. 2000. (Angelwings Ser.: No. 9). (Illus.). (J). (978-0-606-20387-6(7)) Tandem Library Bks.

Nolan, Peggy. The Spy Who Came in from the Sea. 144p. (J). 2001. pap. 8.95 (978-1-56164-245-8(2)); 2000. (gr. 5-9). 14.95 (978-1-56164-186-4(3)) Pineapple Pr., Inc.

Pearson, Mary E. Scribbler of Dreams. 2002. 240p. (YA). (gr. 7 up). pap. 5.95 (978-0-15-204569-2(4) , Harcourt Paperbacks) Harcourt Children's Bks.

—Scribbler of Dreams. (gr. 7-12). 2005. 223p. (YA). per. 12.60 (978-0-606-25453-3(6)); 2001. lib. bdg. 14.10 (978-0-613-69084-3(2)) Tandem Library Bks.

Pennypacker, Sara. Pierre in Love. Mathers, Petra, illus. 2007. 40p. (J). pap. 16.99 (978-0-439-51740-9(0) , Orchard Bks.) Scholastic, Inc.

Peterson, Doug. The Mess Detectives: The Big Sleepover. 2004. (Mess Detectives Ser.). (Illus.). 40p. 6.99 (978-0-310-70736-3(6)) Zonderkidz.

Plato's Journey: Evaluation Guide. 2006. (J). (978-1-55942-421-9(4)) Marsh Media.

Poydar, Nancy. Zip, Zip—Homework! 2008. (J). (***978-0-8234-2090-2(6)***) Holiday Hse., Inc.

Principals New Cloth. 1998. (J). pap. 3.95 (978-0-439-04435-6(9)) Scholastic, Inc.

Random House Disney Staff. Honesty. 2007. (Pictureback(R) Ser.). 24p. (J). (ps-2). pap. 3.99 (***978-0-7364-2503-2(9)*** , RH/Disney) Random Hse. Children's Bks.

Rankin, Laura. Ruthie & the (Not So) Teeny Tiny Lie. Rankin, Laura, illus. 2007. (Illus.). 32p. (J). (ps-2). 15.95 (978-1-59990-010-0(6)) Bloomsbury Publishing.

Richards, Kitty. Bird Who Cried Wolf. 2000. (gr. k-3). lib. bdg. 11.80 (978-0-613-24367-4(6)) Tandem Library Bks.

—Prilla & the Butterfly Lie. Shimabukuro, Denise, illus. 2007. (Stepping Stone Bks.). 128p. (J). (gr. 1-5). 5.99 (978-0-7364-2419-6(9) , RH/Disney) Random Hse. Children's Bks.

—Prilla & the Butterfly Lie. Shimabukuro, Denise, illus. 2007. (Disney Fairies Ser.). 113p. (J). (***978-1-4287-2536-2(9)***) Random Hse., Inc.

Robberecht, Thierry. Sam Tells Stories. Goossens, Philippe, illus. 2007. 32p. (J). (gr. k-3). 12.00 (978-0-618-73280-7(2) , Clarion Bks.) Houghton Mifflin Co. Trade & Reference Div.

Robberecht, Thierry. Sarah's Little Ghosts. Goossens, Philippe, illus. 2007. 32p. (J). (ps-3). 16.00 (***978-0-618-89210-5(9)*** , Clarion Bks.) Houghton Mifflin Co. Trade & Reference Div.

Rue, Nancy N. The Discovery. 2001. (Christian Heritage Ser.). (Illus.). 192p. (J). (gr. 3-7). pap. (978-1-56179-862-9(2)) Focus on the Family Publishing.

Rushton, Rosie. Friends, Enemies. 2004. 240p. (gr. 5-17). 15.99 (978-0-7868-5177-5(5)) Hyperion Paperbacks for Children.

—Friends, Enemies. 2006. 240p. (gr. 5-17). pap. 5.99 (978-0-7868-5178-2(3)) Hyperion Pr.

Sargent, Dave. Blackie. Lenoir, Jane, illus. 2000. (J). (978-1-56763-447-1(8)); lib. bdg. 19.95 (978-1-56763-448-8(6)) Ozark Publishing.

Schooley, Bob & McCorkle, Mark. Liar of Kudzu. 2007. 192p. (J). 15.99 (978-1-4169-1488-4(9)) Simon & Schuster Children's Publishing.

Schumacher, Julie. The Book of One Hundred Truths. 192p. (gr. 4-7). 2008. 5.99 (***978-0-440-42085-9(7)*** , Yearling); 2006. (J). 15.95 (978-0-385-73290-1(2) , Delacorte Bks. for Young Readers); 2006. (J). lib. bdg. 17.99 (978-0-385-90311-0(1) , Delacorte Bks. for Young Readers) Random Hse. Children's Bks.

Seidler, Tor. Terpin. 2002. (Illus.). 112p. (J). 14.89 (978-0-06-623608-7(8) , Geringer, Laura Book) HarperCollins Pubs.

—Terpin. 2004. (gr. 3-6). lib. bdg. 14.15 (978-0-613-81688-5(9)) Tandem Library Bks.

Shinn, Sharon. The Truth-Teller's Tale. 2007. (Firebird Ser.). 304p. (YA). pap. 7.99 (978-0-14-240784-4(4) , Puffin) Penguin Group (USA) Inc.

Shreve, Susan. Jonah, the Whale. 1999. 110p. (J). (ps-7). per. 13.00 (978-0-613-06739-3(8)) Tandem Library Bks.

Spirn, Michele & Strong, Jeremy. Missing. O'Connor, Niamh, illus. 2007. 112p. (J). (***978-1-59889-278-9(9)***) Stone Arch Bks.

Stevens, Janet & Crummel, Susan Stevens. Jackalope. Stevens, Janet, illus. 2003. (Illus.). 56p. (J). (gr. k-3). 17.00 (978-0-15-216736-3(6)) Harcourt Children's Bks.

Tayleur, Karen. Liar! David Mortimore Baxter. Garvey, Brann, illus. 2007. 71p. (J). pap. (***978-1-59889-206-2(1)***) Stone Arch Bks.

Thomas, Jeana. Why Was Blueberry Orange? Honesty. Triefenbach, Lisa, illus. 2001. (Camp of Champs Ser.: Vol. 1). 24p. (J). (ps-3). pap. 6.95 (978-0-9701118-3-8(5) , 050-001) Charm Pubns., Inc.

Tomey, Ingrid. Nobody Else Has to Know. 2000. 240p. (YA). (gr. 7-12). pap. 5.50 (978-0-440-22782-3(8) , Laurel Leaf) Random Hse. Children's Bks.

—Nobody Else Has to Know. 2000. 231p. (YA). (gr. 8-12). lib. bdg. 13.00 (978-0-613-28372-4(4)); 1999. (J). (978-0-606-19744-1(3)) Tandem Library Bks.

Twain, Mark. The Spelling Bee. Bates, Amy, illus. 2007. (Adventures of Tom Sawyer Ser.: Bk. 4). 32p. (J). pap. 3.95 (978-1-4027-4269-9(X)) Sterling Publishing Co., Inc.

Wallace, Patrick. Jared: Boy from the Bottom. Boller, David, illus. 2003. 153p. (J). per. (978-0-9740753-0-3(2)) Heritage Youth, Inc.

Weston, Martha & Greene, Stephanie. Owen Foote, Super Spy. Weston, Martha, illus. 2001. (Illus.). 96p. (J). (gr. 4-6). tchr. ed. 15.00 (978-0-618-11752-9(0) , Clarion Bks.) Houghton Mifflin Co. Trade & Reference Div.

Wilhelm, Hans. Tyrone the Double Dirty Rotten Cheater. (FRE.). (J). pap. 6.99 (978-0-590-74141-5(1)) Scholastic, Inc.

Wilson, Budge & LaFave, Kim. Duff's Monkey Business. 2000. (New First Novels Ser.). (Illus.). 63p. (gr. 1-5). 4.95 (978-0-88780-498-4(5)); (978-0-88780-499-1(3)) Formac Publishing Co., Ltd. CAN. *Dist:* Casemate Pubs. & Bk. Distributors, LLC.

Wittlinger, Ellen. Love & Lies: Marisol's Story. 2008. 256p. (YA). (***978-1-4169-1623-9(7)*** , Simon & Schuster Children's Publishing) Simon & Schuster Children's Publishing.

Woods, Ron. The Hero. 2003. 224p. (J). (gr. 4-7). pap. 5.50 (978-0-440-22978-0(2) , Yearling) Random Hse. Children's Bks.

HONEY

see also Bees

Fujiwara, Yumiko. Honey: A Gift from Nature. Ise, Hideko, illus. 2006. 28p. (J). pap. 7.95 (978-1-929132-94-2(8)) Kane/Miller Bk. Pubs., Inc.

Ghione, Yvette. This Is Daniel Cook Making Honey. Gagnon, Céleste, illus. 2007. (This Is Daniel Cook Ser.). 24p. (J). (ps-1). (***978-1-55453-086-1(5)); (*978-1-55453-085-4(7)***) Kids Can Pr., Ltd.

Gibbons, Gail. The Honey Makers. 2000. (Illus.). (J). (978-0-606-18694-0(8)) Tandem Library Bks.

Haag, Ruth. Honeybees Make Honey. 2002. Tr. of Abejas de Miel Producen la Miel. (SPA.). 22p. pap. 6.00 (978-0-9665497-5-1(9)) Haag Pr.

Honey Bees & Honey, 6 vols. (gr. k-2). 28.95 (978-0-7368-8244-6(8)) Red Brick Learning.

Jones, Carol. Honey. 2002. (From Farm to You Ser.). (Illus.). 32p. (gr. 4-8). 28.00 (978-0-7910-7009-3(3) , Chelsea Hse.) Facts On File, Inc.

Milton, Joyce. Honeybees. Mueller, Peter, illus. 2003. (All Aboard Science Reader Station Stop Ser.). 48p. (J). (gr. 1-3). pap. 3.99 (978-0-448-42846-8(6) , Grosset & Dunlap) Penguin Group (USA) Inc.

—Honeybees, Vol. 2. Mueller, Pete, illus. 2003. (All Aboard Science Reader Station Stop Ser.: No. 2). 48p. (J). (gr. 1-3). 13.89 (978-0-448-43142-0(4) , Grosset & Dunlap) Penguin Group (USA) Inc.

—Honeybees. 2003. (gr. k-3). lib. bdg. 11.80 (978-0-613-64410-5(7)) Tandem Library Bks.

Murray, Julie. Flower to Honey. 2007. (Beginning to End Ser.). (Illus.). 24p. (J). (gr. k-3). lib. bdg. 21.35 (978-1-59679-836-6(X) , Buddy Bks.) ABDO Publishing Co.

Nelson, Robin. From Flower to Honey. (From Start to Finish Ser.). (J). (gr. k-2). 2003. (Illus.). 24p. lib. bdg. 18.60 (978-0-8225-0717-8(X)); 2002. pap. 4.95 (978-0-8225-0667-6(X)) Lerner Publishing Group.

Pattrick, Steve. Bees & Honey: KinderFacts Individual Title Six-Packs. (Kinderstarters Ser.). 8p. (ps-1). 21.00 (978-0-7635-8740-6(0)) Rigby Education.

Robson, Pam. Honey. Robson, Paul, ed. 1998. (What's for Lunch? Ser.). (Illus.). 32p. (J). (gr. k-2). pap., stu. ed. 6.95 (978-0-516-26220-8(3) , Children's Pr.) Scholastic Library Publishing.

Rockwell, Anne. Honey in a Hive. Schindler, S. D., illus. 2005. (Let's-Read-and-Find-Out Science Ser.). 40p. (J). (ps-ps). 15.99 (978-0-06-028566-1(4)) HarperCollins Pubs.

Rockwell, Anne F. Honey in a Hive. Schindler, S. D., illus. 2005. (Let's-Read-and-Find-Out Science Ser.). 40p. (J). (gr. k-4). pap. 5.99 (978-0-06-445204-5(2)); lib. bdg. 16.89 (978-0-06-028567-8(2)) HarperCollins Pubs.

Schaefer, Lola M. Honey Bees & Honey, Vol. 4. 2005. (Bugs, Bugs, Bugs Ser.). 24p. (YA). (gr. k-3). pap. (978-0-7368-8204-0(9) , Pebble Bks.) Capstone Pr., Inc.

Spilsbury, Louise. Honey. 2001. (Food in Focus Ser.). (Illus.). 32p. (J). (gr. k-2). lib. bdg. 21.36 (978-1-58810-146-4(0)) Heinemann Library.

Stewart, Melissa. How Do Bees Make Honey? 2008. (J). (***978-0-7614-2923-4(9)***) Cavendish, Marshall Bks., Ltd.

HONG KONG (CHINA)

Barber, Nicola. Hong Kong. 2004. (Great Cities of the World Ser.). (Illus.). 48p. (J). pap. 11.95 (978-0-8368-5198-4(6)); (YA). lib. bdg. 30.00 (978-0-8368-5038-3(6)) Stevens, Gareth Inc. (World Almanac Library).

Lyle, Garry. Hong Kong. 1999. (Major World Nations Ser.). (Illus.). 144p. (YA). (gr. 4-7). lib. bdg. 21.95 (978-0-7910-4990-7(6) , Chelsea Hse.) Facts On File, Inc.

Meissner, David. Living in Hong Kong. 2003. (Early Connections Ser.). (J). pap. 33.00 (978-1-4108-1075-5(5)) Benchmark Education Co.

Sasek, Miroslav. This Is Hong Kong. 2007. (This Is ... Ser.). (Illus.). 64p. (J). (gr. 3-5). 17.95 (978-0-7893-1560-1(2)) Universe Publishing.

Stein, R. Conrad. Hong Kong. Downing, Joan, ed. 1998. (Cities of the World Ser.). (Illus.). 64p. (J). (gr. 4-9). pap. 9.95 (978-0-516-26327-4(7) , Children's Pr.) Scholastic Library Publishing.

Stone, Lynn M. Hong Kong. 2000. (China Ser.). (Illus.). 24p. (J). (gr. 1-4). lib. bdg. 19.27 (978-1-55916-317-0(8)) Rourke Publishing, LLC.

Zurlo, Tony. Life in Hong Kong. 2001. (Way People Live Ser.). (Illus.). 112p. (YA). (gr. 7-10). 28.70 (978-1-56006-384-1(X) , LML00902-177768, Lucent Bks.) Thomson Gale.

HONG KONG (CHINA)—FICTION

Barrett, Dean. The Boat Girl & the Magic Fish. 2nd ed. 2002. 32p. 6.95 (978-0-9661899-5-7(7)) Village East Bks.

Berkeley, Jon. Chopsticks. 2005. (Illus.). 32p. (J). (ps-3). 16.95 (978-0-375-83309-0(9) , Random Hse. Bks. for Young Readers) Random Hse. Children's Bks.

Crotty, Martha. Hong Kong Kitty. Thurn, Gwen & Thurn, David Ryan, illus. 2005. (J). per. 14.00 (978-0-9766017-0-8(2)) Ironcreek Pr.

McOmber, Rachel B., ed. McOmber Phonics Storybooks: A Package from Hong Kong. rev. ed. (Illus.). (J). (978-0-944991-61-9(0)) Swift Learning Resources.

Uncle Markie. Piglette & Bobo in the New Territories. 2003. (YA). ring bd. 9.95 (978-1-933129-06-8(9)) Studio 403.

—Piglette & BoBo See Hong Kong. l.t. ed. 2002. 46p. ring bd. 9.95 (978-0-9633943-8-5(X)) Studio 403.

HOOVER, HERBERT, 1874-1964

Chang, David A. Y. O. Herbert Hoover: A MyReportLinks.com Book. 2002. (Presidents Ser.). (Illus.). 48p. (J). (gr. 4-10). lib. bdg. 25.26 (978-0-7660-5006-8(8) , MyReportLinks.com Bks.) Enslow Pubs., Inc.

Holford, David M. Herbert Hoover. 1999. (United States Presidents Ser.). (Illus.). 128p. (YA). (gr. 5-12). lib. bdg. 26.60 (978-0-7660-1035-2(X)) Enslow Pubs., Inc.

Joseph, Paul. Herbert Hoover. 2001. (United States Presidents Ser.). (Illus.). 32p. (J). (gr. k-6). lib. bdg. 22.78 (978-1-57765-301-1(7) , Checkerboard Library) ABDO Publishing Co.

Kendall, Martha E. Herbert Hoover. 2004. (Encyclopedia of Presidents Ser.). (Illus.). 110p. (J). 34.00 (978-0-516-22963-8(X) , Children's Pr.) Scholastic Library Publishing.

Ruth, Amy. Herbert Hoover. 2004. (Presidential Leaders Ser.). (Illus.). 112p. (J). (gr. 6-12). lib. bdg. 29.27 (978-0-8225-0821-2(4)) Lerner Publishing Group.

Souter, Gerry & Souter, Janet. Herbert Hoover: Our Thirty-First President. 2001. (Spirit of America: Our Presidents Ser.). (Illus.). 48p. (J). (gr. 2-6). 28.50 (978-1-56766-865-0(8)) Child's World, Inc.

Teitelbaum, Michael. Herbert Hoover. 2002. (Profiles of the Presidents Ser.). (Illus.). 64p. (J). (gr. 4 up). lib. bdg. 23.93 (978-0-7565-0277-5(2)) Compass Point Bks.

Wilson, Natashya. How to Draw the Life & Times of Herbert Hoover. 2007. (Kid's Guide to Drawing the Presidents of the United States of America Ser.). (Illus.). 32p. (J). 25.25 (978-1-4042-3007-1(6) , PowerKids Pr.) Rosen Publishing Group, Inc., The.

HOOVER, J. EDGAR (JOHN EDGAR), 1895-1972

Cunningham, Kevin. J. Edgar Hoover: Controversial FBI Director. 2005. (Signature Lives Ser.). (Illus.). 112p. (J). (gr. 5-7). (978-0-7565-0997-2(1)) Compass Point Bks.

Streissguth, Thomas. J. Edgar Hoover: Powerful FBI Director. 2002. (Historical American Biographies Ser.). (Illus.). 128p. (YA). (gr. 6-12). lib. bdg. 26.60 (978-0-7660-1623-1(4)) Enslow Pubs., Inc.

HOOVER DAM (ARIZ. AND NEV.)

DuTemple, Lesley A. The Hoover Dam. 2003. (Great Building Feats Ser.). (Illus.). 96p. (J). (gr. 5-9). 27.93 (978-0-8225-4691-7(4)) Lerner Publishing Group.

Lusted, Marcia Amidon. Hoover Dam. 2003. (Building History Ser.). (Illus.). 112p. (J). 32.45 (978-1-59018-296-3(0) , Lucent Bks.) Thomson Gale.

Mann, Elizabeth. The Hoover Dam: The Story of Hard Times, Tough People & the Taming of a Wild River. Witschonke, Alan, illus. (Wonders of the World Book Ser.). 48p. (J). (gr. 4-8). 2006. pap. 9.95 (978-1-931414-13-5(0)); 2001. 19.95 (978-1-931414-02-9(5)) Mikaya Pr.

Murray, Julie. Hoover Dam. 2005. (All Aboard America Ser.). (Illus.). 24p. (J). (gr. k-4). lib. bdg. 21.35 (978-1-59197-506-9(9)) ABDO Publishing Co.

Roza, Greg. The Hoover Dam: Applying Problem-Solving Strategies. 2006. (Math for the Real World Ser.). (Illus.). 32p. (J). pap. (978-1-4042-6065-8(X)); lib. bdg. (978-1-4042-3356-0(3)) Rosen Publishing Group, Inc., The.

HORMONES

Kim, Melissa L. The Endocrine & Reproductive Systems. 2003. (Human Body Library Ser.). (Illus.). 48p. (YA). (gr. 4-10). lib. bdg. 23.93 (978-0-7660-2020-7(7)) Enslow Pubs., Inc.

HORN (MUSICAL INSTRUMENT)

Feldstein, Sandy & Clark, Larry. Barbara Allen - Horn in F Solo with Piano Acc. W/CD. 2005. (YA). pap. 9.95 (978-1-932895-62-9(0)) PlayinTime Productions, Inc.

Froseth, James O. Horn in F Home Helper First Lessons at School & at Home. 2005. 20p. 7.95 (978-1-57999-502-7(0) , M577) GIA Pubns., Inc.

Gourse, Leslie. Blowing on the Changes: The Art of the Jazz Horn Players. 1998. (Art of Jazz Ser.). (Illus.). 144p. (J). (gr. 8-12). pap. 8.95 (978-0-531-15880-7(2) , Watts, Franklin) Scholastic Library Publishing.

HORNADAY, WILLIAM TEMPLE, 1854-1937

Caper, William. American Bison: A Scary Prediction. 2008. (America's Animal Comebacks Ser.). (J). lib. bdg. 25.27 (***978-1-59716-504-4(2)***) Bearport Publishing Co., Inc.

HORNETS

Markle, Sandra. Hornets: Incredible Insect Architects. 2008. (Insect World Ser.). (J). lib. bdg. 27.93 (***978-0-8225-7297-8(4)*** , Lerner Pubns.) Lerner Publishing Group.

HOROLOGY

see Clocks and Watches; Sundials

HOROSCOPES

see Astrology

HORROR STORIES

Ada, Alma Flor. El Susto de los Fantasmas. (Cuentos para Todo el Ano Ser.). (SPA., Illus.). 16p. (J). (gr. k-3). pap. 8.95 (978-1-58105-170-4(0)) Santillana USA Publishing Co., Inc.

—El Susto de los Fantasmas. 1999. (SPA.). (gr. k-3). lib. bdg. 17.60 (978-0-613-79447-3(8)) Tandem Library Bks.

Ahlberg, Allan. The Improbable Cat. Bailey, Peter, illus. 2004. 128p. (gr. 5). 9.95 (978-0-385-73186-7(8) , Delacorte Bks. for Young Readers) Random Hse. Children's Bks.

Ahlberg, Allan & Ahlberg, Janet. It Was a Dark & Stormy Night. (Illus.). 80p. (J). pap. 8.95 (978-0-14-130027-6(2)) Penguin Bks., Ltd. GBR. *Dist:* Trafalgar Square Publishing.

Aikawa, Yu. Dark Edge, Vol. 6. 2006. (Illus.). 200p. (YA). pap. 9.95 (978-1-59796-026-7(8)) DrMaster Pubns. Inc.

Akino, Matsuri. Pet Shop of Horrors, 10 vols., Vol. 4. Iwo, Tomoharu & Masumoto, Bryan, trs. from JPN. Akino, Matsuri, illus. rev. ed. 2004. (Teen Ser.). (Illus.). 210p. (YA). pap. 9.99 (978-1-59182-501-2(6) , Tokyopop Adult) TOKYOPOP, Inc.

—Pet Shop of Horrors, 10 vols. rev. ed. 2004. (Teen Ser.). (Illus.). 192p. (YA). (gr. 11 up). Vol. 5. pap. 9.99 (978-1-59182-502-9(4)); Vol. 6. pap. 9.99 (978-1-59182-503-6(2)) TOKYOPOP, Inc. (Tokyopop Adult).

—Pet Shop of Horrors, 10 vols., Vol. 7. Bourque, Jeremiah, tr. from JPN. rev. ed. 2004. (Teen Ser.). (Illus.). 192p. (YA). (gr. 11 up). pap. 9.99 (978-1-59182-504-3(0) , Tokyopop Adult) TOKYOPOP, Inc.

Almond, David. Clay. 2006. 256p. (J). (gr. 7). 15.95 (978-0-385-73171-3(X)); lib. bdg. 17.99 (978-0-385-90208-3(5)) Random Hse. Children's Bks. (Delacorte Bks. for Young Readers).

Anderson, M. T. Thirsty. 256p. (YA). (gr. 9 up). 2005. pap. 5.99 (978-0-7636-2750-8(X)); 2003. (Illus.). pap. 7.99 (978-0-7636-2014-1(9)) Candlewick Pr.

Andrews, V. C. Rain. 2000. (gr. 7-12). lib. bdg. 16.45 (978-0-613-28031-0(8)) Tandem Library Bks.

Applegate, Katherine. Im Dienste des Drachen. 2002. (Ever-World Ser.: No. 5). (GER.). 160p. pap. 15.00 (978-1-4000-3978-4(9) , New Media German Language) Random House Foreign Language Publishing.

Aragones, Sergio. Boogeyman. 1999. 112p. (YA). (gr. 7 up). pap. 9.95 (978-1-56971-374-7(X)) Dark Horse Comics.

Archer, Chris. Aftershock. 1998. (Mindwarp Ser.: No. 6). (Illus.). 144p. (YA). (gr. 6-8). pap. 3.99 (978-0-671-01487-2(0) , Simon Pulse) Simon & Schuster Children's Publishing.

—Aftershock. 1998. (gr. 3-6). lib. bdg. 11.80 (978-0-613-73103-4(4)) Tandem Library Bks.

—Fright Club No. 1: Bad Bear Day. 2001. 160p. (J). (gr. 4-7). mass mkt. 3.99 (978-1-931497-23-7(0)) 17th Street Productions, An Alloy Online Inc. Co.

—Fright Club No. 2: Open Wide. 2001. 160p. (J). (gr. 4-7). mass mkt. 3.99 (978-1-931497-24-4(9)) 17th Street Productions, An Alloy Online Inc. Co.

—Fright Club No. 3: Poodlesaurus. 2001. 176p. mass mkt. 3.99 (978-1-931497-25-1(7)) 17th Street Productions, An Alloy Online Inc. Co.

—Fright Club No. 4: I Know What You Flushed Last Summer. 2001. 176p. (J). (gr. 4-7). pap. 3.99 (978-1-931497-26-8(5)) 17th Street Productions, An Alloy Online Inc. Co.

—Fright Club No. 5: Live Bait. 2001. 160p. (J). (gr. 4-7). pap. 3.99 (978-1-931497-27-5(3)) 17th Street Productions, An Alloy Online Inc. Co.

—Fright Club No. 7: Revenge of the Claw. 2001. 160p. (J). (gr. 4-7). pap. 3.99 (978-1-931497-29-9(X)) 17th Street Productions, An Alloy Online Inc. Co.

Arnold, Nick. Blood, Bones & Body Bits. 1998. (Horrible Science Ser.). (J). (gr. 5-9). pap. 3.99 (978-0-590-13859-8(6) , Scholastic Paperbacks) Scholastic, Inc.

—Chemical Chaos. 1998. (Horrible Science Ser.). (J). (gr. 5-9). pap. 3.99 (978-0-590-10885-0(9)) Scholastic, Inc.

—Disgusting Digestion. 1999. (Horrible Science Ser.). (Illus.). 160p. (gr. 7-12). pap. 3.99 (978-0-439-04362-5(X)) Scholastic, Inc.

—Disgusting Digestion. 1999. (Horrible Science Ser.). (J). (978-0-606-16592-1(4)) Tandem Library Bks.

—Fatal Forces. 1999. (Horrible Science Ser.). 160p. (gr. 7-12). pap. 3.99 (978-0-439-04363-2(8)) Scholastic, Inc.

—Nasty Nature. 1998. (Horrible Science Ser.). (Illus.). 159p. (YA). (gr. 5-9). pap. 3.99 (978-0-590-21687-6(2)) Scholastic, Inc.

Asfar, Dan. Dylan Mcbryde. 2005. 240p. (gr. 4). (978-1-894877-62-6(4)) Lone Pine Publishing.

Athkins, D. Secret Santa. 2001. (gr. 7-12). lib. bdg. 13.00 (978-0-613-58133-2(4)) Tandem Library Bks.

Atwater-Rhodes, Amelia. 666: The Number of the Beast. 2007. (666 Ser.). 336p. (J). (gr. 7 up). pap. 14.99 (***978-0-545-02117-3(0)***) Scholastic, Inc.

Austad, Julie. Uncle's Trunk. 2001. (gr. 7-12). lib. bdg. 31.55 (978-0-613-73988-7(4)) Tandem Library Bks.

Baglio, Ben M. Horse in the House. 2001. (gr. 3-6). lib. bdg. 11.80 (978-0-613-62776-4(8)) Tandem Library Bks.

Bailey, Peter, illus. The Kingfisher Book of Scary Stories. 2002. (Story Collections). 80p. (J). (gr. 3-5). pap. 10.95 (978-0-7534-5389-6(4) , Kingfisher) Houghton Mifflin Co. Trade & Reference Div.

Balawajder, Thomas, et al. The Ultimate Homework Survival Guide: A Reality Horror Production. Wise, Noreen, ed. 2nd ed. 2003. (Illus.). 64p. (J). per. 6.95 (978-1-58584-559-0(0)) Huckleberry Pr.

Barker, Clive. The Thief of Always. 2002. 224p. (J). (gr. 5 up). reprint ed. pap. 5.99 (978-0-06-440994-0(5) , Harper Trophy) HarperCollins Pubs.

Barnes, Creighton D. The Ghost Who Was Afraid of the Dark: The Ghost & the Flag. 2000. 148p. (gr. 4-7). pap. 8.95 (978-1-893652-92-7(0) , Writers Club Pr.) iUniverse, Inc.

Bates, Penny. A Murder of Crows. 2004. (Shades Ser.). 60p. (J). pap. 7.99 (978-0-237-52648-1(4) , Evans Brothers, Limited) Evans Publishing Group GBR. *Dist:* Independent Pubs. Group.

Baudet, Stephanie. New Library of Horror: Dracula. 128p. (J). pap. 7.95 (978-0-233-99578-6(1)) Andre Deutsch GBR. *Dist:* Trans-Atlantic Pubns., Inc.

Be Afraid! Tales of Horror. 2000. (gr. 7-12). lib. bdg. 15.25 (978-0-613-77316-4(0)) Tandem Library Bks.

Be Very Afraid! More Tales of Horror. 2002. (gr. 5-8). lib. bdg. 16.40 (978-0-613-77261-7(X)) Tandem Library Bks.

Becker, Tom. Darkside Book 1 Don't Turn Out the Light. 2008. 304p. (J). pap. 16.99 (***978-0-545-03739-6(5)*** , Orchard Bks.) Scholastic, Inc.

Bedard, Tony. Route 666 Traveler: Highway of Horror. Moline, Karl et al, illus. 2004. (Route 666 Traveler Ser.). 160p. (YA). pap. 9.95 (978-1-59314-041-0(X)) CrossGeneration Comics, Inc.

Beere, Peter. At Gehenna's Door. l.t. ed. 2000. (Illus.). 304p. 18.99 (978-0-7089-9500-6(4)) Ulverscroft Large Print Bks. GBR. *Dist:* Ulverscroft Large Print Bks., Ltd.

Bellairs, John. The Spell of the Sorcerer's Skull. 2002. (J). (gr. 3 up). 21.50 (978-0-8446-7206-9(8)) Smith, Peter Pub., Inc.

Benjamin, David. Secrets from Beyond. Rawlings, Steve, illus. 2000. (Sixth Sense Ser.: Vol. 1). 160p. (gr. 4-7). pap. 4.99 (978-0-439-20270-1(1)) Scholastic, Inc.

Benson, E. F. The Confession of Charles Linkworth. 2004. reprint ed. pap. 15.95 (978-1-4191-5738-7(8)); pap. 1.99 (978-1-4192-5738-4(2)) Kessinger Publishing, LLC.

Berenstain, Stan & Berenstain, Jan. The Berenstain Bear Scouts & the Evil Eye. 1998. (Berenstain Bear Scouts Ser.). (J). (gr. 3-6). pap. 3.99 (978-0-590-94488-5(6) , Scholastic Paperbacks) Scholastic, Inc.

—The Berenstain Bears Go on a Ghost Walk. 2005. (Berenstain Bears Ser.). (Illus.). 32p. (J). (ps-2). 8.99 (978-0-06-057399-7(6)); pap. 3.99 (978-0-06-057383-6(X)) HarperCollins Pubs. (Harper Festival).

Bichoman Vuelve de la Tumba. (Fantasmas de Fear Street Coleccion). (SPA.). (YA). (gr. 5-8). pap. 7.95 (978-950-04-1718-1(9) , EM9292) Emecé Editores S.A. ARG. *Dist:* Lectorum Pubns., Inc., Planeta Publishing Corp.

Black, Theodor, illus. Ghosts & Golems: Haunting Tales of the Supernatural. 2003. (Jps Young Adult Story Collections). 128p. pap. 9.95 (978-0-8276-0763-7(6)) Jewish Pubn. Society.

Blacker, Terence. Ms. Wiz Loves Dracula. 2003. (Illus.). 57p. (J). pap. 6.99 (978-0-330-34873-7(6) , Pan) Pan Macmillan GBR. *Dist:* Trafalgar Square Publishing.

Blackmoor, Brandon & Blackmoor, Susan. Dwellers in Darkness. 2000. 150p. (YA). (gr. 10 up). pap. 15.00 (978-0-9641722-5-8(9)) Black Gate Publishing.

Blair, Cynthia. Curse. 2000. 192p. (J). pap. 1.99 (978-0-06-106261-2(8)) HarperCollins Pubs.

Bledsoe, Glen. Creepy Classics III. 1999. (Roxbury Park Bks.). (Illus.). viii, 120p. (J). (gr. 3-7). pap. 5.95 (978-0-7373-0122-9(8) , 01228W) McGraw-Hill/Contemporary.

Bledsoe, Glen & Bledsoe, Karen, compiled by. Classic Sea Stories. 1999. (Roxbury Park Bks.). (Illus.). 123p. (J). (gr. 3-7). pap. 5.95 (978-0-7373-0041-3(8) , 00418W) McGraw-Hill/Contemporary.

Bradman, Tony. Deadly Game. Chatterton, Martin, illus. 2004. (Tales of Terror Ser.). 105p. (J). (gr. 4-7). pap. 7.50 (978-1-4052-1127-7(X)) Egmont Bks., Ltd. GBR. *Dist:* Independent Pubs. Group.

—Incredibly Creepy Stories. 2000. (Illus.). 170p. (J). 16.95 (978-0-385-40676-5(2)) Transworld Publishers Ltd. GBR. *Dist:* Trafalgar Square Publishing.

Bradman, Tony & Chatterton, Martin. Final Cut. 2004. (Illus.). 85p. (J). pap. 7.50 (978-1-4052-1125-3(3)) Egmont Bks., Ltd. GBR. *Dist:* Independent Pubs. Group.

—Voodoo Child. 2004. (Illus.). 88p. (J). pap. 7.50 (978-1-4052-1126-0(1)) Egmont Bks., Ltd. GBR. *Dist:* Independent Pubs. Group.

Brereton, Dan. The Dust Waltz. 1998. (Buffy the Vampire Slayer Ser.). (Illus.). 80p. (YA). (gr. 7 up). pap. 9.95 (978-1-56971-342-6(1)) Dark Horse Comics.

Brewer, Heather. The Chronicles of Vladimir Tod: Eighth Grade Bites. 2008. 288p. (J). (gr. 4-6). pap. 7.99 (****978-0-14-241187-2(6)*** , Puffin) Penguin Group (USA) Inc.

Brin, Susannah. Ghost in the Desert. rev. ed. 1999. (Take Ten Ser.). 64p. (YA). (gr. 4-12). pap. 3.95 (978-1-58659-052-9(9)) Artesian Pr.

—Ghost in the Desert. 2000. (gr. 5-8). lib. bdg. 11.80 (978-0-613-51212-1(X)) Tandem Library Bks.

—Haunted Beach House. 2000. (gr. 5-8). lib. bdg. 11.80 (978-0-613-51214-5(6)) Tandem Library Bks.

—The Haunted Beach House. rev. ed. 1999. (Take Ten Ser.). 63p. (YA). (gr. 4-12). pap. 3.95 (978-1-58659-053-6(7)) Artesian Pr.

—Trapped in the Sixties. rev. ed. 1999. (Take Ten Ser.). 64p. (YA). (gr. 4-12). pap. 3.95 (978-1-58659-054-3(5)) Artesian Pr.

Bruchac, James & Bruchac, Joseph. When the Chenoo Howls: Native American Tales of Terror. Sauts, William, illus. 1999. 136p. (J). (gr. 3-7). 16.95 (978-0-8027-8638-8(3)); pap. 10.95 (978-0-8027-7576-4(4)) Walker & Co.

Bruchac, Joseph. Bearwalker. Comport, Sally Wern, illus. 2007. 224p. (J). (gr. 5-8). 15.99 (****978-0-06-112309-2(9));*** lib. bdg. 16.89 (****978-0-06-112311-5(0))*** HarperCollins Pubs.

—Skeleton Man. Comport, Sally Wern, illus. 2003. 128p. (gr. 5 up). pap. 4.99 (978-0-06-440888-2(4)) HarperCollins Pubs.

—Skeleton Man. 2001. 128p. (J). (gr. 5 up). 16.99 (978-0-06-029075-7(7)) HarperCollins Pubs.

—Skeleton Man. 2003. (gr. 5-8). lib. bdg. 13.00 (978-0-613-66605-3(4)) Tandem Library Bks.

—Whisper in the Dark. Comport, Sally Wern, illus. 2005. 192p. (J). (gr. 5 up). 15.99 (978-0-06-058087-2(9)); lib. bdg. 16.89 (978-0-06-058088-9(7)) HarperCollins Pubs.

Brush Creations & Holmes, A. M. X. Robbie Virtual vs. Vlad the Vampire: Book 1. 2007. 56p. pap. 9.95 (****978-0-7414-3621-4(3))*** Infinity Publishing.

Buchanan, Paul. Dances with Werewolves, Vol. 8. 2000. (Heebie Jeebies Ser.: Vol. 6). 128p. (J). (gr. 3-7). pap. 5.99 (978-0-8054-1982-5(9)) B&H Publishing Grp.

—Return to Terror Cove. 2001. (Heebie Jeebies Ser.: Vol. 10). 138p. (J). (gr. 3-7). pap. 5.99 (978-0-8054-2333-4(8)) B&H Publishing Grp.

Buffie, Margaret. The Dark Garden. 2001. (Margaret Buffie Ser.). 240p. (YA). (gr. 13 up). (978-1-55337-091-8(0)) Kids Can Pr., Ltd.

Bunting, Eve. The Lambkins. Keegan, Jonathan, illus. 2005. 192p. (J). (gr. 5 up). 15.99 (978-0-06-059906-5(5)); lib. bdg. 16.89 (978-0-06-059907-2(3)) HarperCollins Pubs. (Cotler, Joanna Books).

—Night of the Gargoyles. 2002. (Illus.). (J). 15.70 (978-0-7587-2849-4(2)) Book Wholesalers, Inc.

—Night of the Gargoyles. Wiesner, David, illus. 1999. 32p. (J). (gr. k-3). pap. 7.95 (978-0-395-96887-1(9) , Clarion Bks.) Houghton Mifflin Co. Trade & Reference Div.

—Night of the Gargoyles. Wiesner, David, illus. 1999. (J). (ps-ps). lib. bdg. 16.40 (978-0-613-22907-4(X)) Tandem Library Bks.

Burchett, Janet & Vogler, Sara. Knight Frights. 2nd ed. (Illus.). 96p. (J). pap. 6.99 (978-0-330-36813-1(3) , Pan) Pan Macmillan GBR. *Dist:* Trafalgar Square Publishing.

Burke, Janine. The Deadly Doll. Tan, Shaun, illus. 2008. 80p. (J). pap. (****978-1-59889-914-6(7));*** (YA). (gr. 5-9). lib. bdg. 16.95 (****978-1-59889-858-3(2))*** Stone Arch Bks.

Burke, Morgan. After Hours. 2005. (Party Room Ser.: No. 2). 256p. (YA). (gr. 11 up). mass mkt. 5.99 (978-0-689-87226-6(7) , Simon Pulse) Simon & Schuster Children's Publishing.

Burke, Morgan & Blattberg, Julie. Last Call. 2005. (Party Room Ser.: No. 3). 272p. (YA). (gr. 11 up). pap. 5.99 (978-0-689-87227-3(5) , Simon Pulse) Simon & Schuster Children's Publishing.

Burt, Steve. Even Odder: More Stories to Chill the Heart. Hagerman, Jessica, illus. 2003. 144p. pap. 14.95 (978-0-9741407-0-4(8)) Burt Creations.

—Oddest Yet: Even More Stories to Chill the Heart. Hagerman, Jessica, illus. 2004. 144p. (gr. 5 up). pap. 14.95 (978-0-9741407-1-1(6)) Burt Creations.

Burton, Tim. Sleepy Hollow: Including the Classic Story by Washington Irving. 1999. (gr. 7-12). lib. bdg. 14.15 (978-0-613-73091-4(7)) Tandem Library Bks.

Byars, Betsy. The Two-Thousand-Pound Goldfish. 2000. (Illus.). 160p. (J). (gr. 3 up). pap. 4.95 (978-0-06-440855-4(8) , Harper Trophy) HarperCollins Pubs.

—The Two-Thousand-Pound Goldfish. 2000. (978-0-606-18725-1(1)) Tandem Library Bks.

Cabot, Meg. Haunted. 2004. (Mediator Ser.: Bk. 5). 288p. (J). (gr. 7 up). pap. 6.99 (978-0-06-447278-4(7) , Harper Trophy) HarperCollins Pubs.

Cabot, Meg, et al. Prom Nights from Hell. 2007. (YA). (gr. 9 up). 320p. 16.99 (****978-0-06-125310-2(3));*** 240p. pap. 9.99 (****978-0-06-125309-6(X))*** HarperCollins Pubs. (HarperTeen).

Calchman, J. B. Vampire Heart. (Illus.). 288p. (J). 9.95 (978-0-14-038627-1(0)) Penguin Bks., Ltd. GBR. *Dist:* Trafalgar Square Publishing.

Carnevale, Michael. The Hotel Coolidge. 2007. 91p. pap. 10.95 (****978-0-7414-3752-5(X))*** Infinity Publishing.

Carpenter, Michelle D. More No Fear here Six Scary Stories to Thrill You & the Kids + Extras. 2004. 61p. per. 9.99 (978-1-4116-1706-3(1)) Lulu.com.

—No Fear Here Five Scary Stories to Thrill You & the Kids. 2004. 85p. per. 6.54 (978-1-4116-1579-3(4)) Lulu.com.

Carrol, Jacqueline. Strongest Evil. 2003. (gr. 3-6). lib. bdg. 13.00 (978-0-613-72477-7(1)) Tandem Library Bks.

Carroll, Rick, ed. Hawaii's Best Spooky Tales Vol. 2: More True Local Spine-Tinglers. 2000. (Illus.). 152p. 12.95 (978-1-57306-040-0(2)) Bess Pr., Inc.

—Hawaii's Best Spooky Tales Vol. 3: More True Local Spine-Tinglers. 1999. (Illus.). 160p. 12.95 (978-1-57306-100-1(X)) Bess Pr., Inc.

Carter, Dean Vincent. The Hand of the Devil. 2006. 288p. (YA). (gr. 9). pap. 7.95 (978-0-385-73371-7(2)); lib. bdg. 9.99 (978-0-385-90386-8(3)) Random Hse. Children's Bks. (Delacorte Bks. for Young Readers).

Carver, Peter, ed. The Horrors! Ghastly Stories for Teen Readers. 2005. 184p. (YA). (gr. 8-12). pap. 9.95 (978-0-88995-313-0(9)) Red Deer Pr. CAN. *Dist:* Fitzhenry & Whiteside, Ltd.

Cary, Kate. Bloodline. 2006. 352p. (YA). (gr. 7-12). pap. 8.99 (978-1-59514-078-4(6) , Razorbill) Penguin Group (USA) Inc.

—Reckoning. 2007. (Bloodline Ser.: Bk. 2). 320p. (YA). (gr. 9 up). 16.99 (978-1-59514-013-5(1) , Razorbill) Penguin Group (USA) Inc.

La Casa de los Alaridos. (Fantasmas de Fear Street Coleccion). (SPA.). (YA). (gr. 5-8). pap. 7.95 (978-950-04-1870-6(3) , EM10013) Emecé Editores S.A. ARG. *Dist:* Lectorum Pubns., Inc., Planeta Publishing Corp.

Cast, P. C. & Cast, Kristin. Marked: A House of Night Novel. 2007. (House of Night Novels Ser.). 320p. (YA). (gr. 9 up). pap. 8.95 (****978-0-312-36026-9(6)*** , St. Martin's Griffin) St. Martin's Pr.

Caswell, Brian. Double Exposure. 2005. 240p. (YA). pap. 18.95 (978-0-7022-3533-7(4)) Univ. of Queensland Pr. AUS. *Dist:* International Specialized Bk. Services.

Chandler, Elizabeth. The Deep End of Fear. 2003. (Dark Secrets Ser.). 320p. (YA). mass mkt. 5.99 (978-0-689-85259-6(2) , Simon Pulse) Simon & Schuster Children's Publishing.

—Legacy of Lies. 2004. 182p. (YA). (gr. 7-12). per. 11.64 (978-0-606-29817-9(7)) Tandem Library Bks.

Charles, Veronika Martenova. Don't Go in There! Parkins, David, illus. 2007. (Easy-to-Read Spooky Tales Ser.). 56p. (J). (gr. k-2). pap. 5.95 (978-0-88776-781-4(8) , Delacorte Bks. for Young Readers) Random Hse. Children's Bks.

—Don't Go into the Forest! Parkins, David, illus. 2007. (Easy-to-Read Spooky Tales Ser.). 56p. (J). (gr. k-2). pap. 5.95 (978-0-88776-778-4(8) , Delacorte Bks. for Young Readers) Random Hse. Children's Bks.

—Don't Go into the Forest! Franson, Leanne, illus. 2001. (Easy to Read Spooky Tales Ser.: No. 2). 56p. (J). (gr. 1-4). pap. (978-0-7737-6190-2(X)) Stoddart Kids.

—Don't Go Near the Water! Franson, Leanne, illus. 2002. 56p. (J). (gr. 1-4). pap. (978-0-7737-6231-2(0)) Stoddart Kids.

—Don't Go near the Water! Parkins, David, illus. 2007. (Easy-to-Read Spooky Tales Ser.). 56p. (J). (gr. k-2). pap. 5.95 (978-0-88776-780-7(X) , Delacorte Bks. for Young Readers) Random Hse. Children's Bks.

—Don't Open the Door! Parkins, David, illus. 2007. (Easy-to-Read Spooky Tales Ser.). 56p. (J). (gr. k-2). pap. 5.95 (978-0-88776-779-1(6) , Delacorte Bks. for Young Readers) Random Hse. Children's Bks.

—Don't Walk Alone at Night! Parkins, David, illus. 2007. (Easy-to-Read Spooky Tales Ser.). 56p. (J). (gr. k-2). pap. 5.95 (978-0-88776-782-1(6) , Delacorte Bks. for Young Readers) Random Hse. Children's Bks.

Chase, Mary. The Wicked, Wicked Ladies in the Haunted House. Sis, Peter, illus. 2005. 144p. (J). (gr. 3-7). 5.99 (978-0-440-41956-3(5) , Yearling) Random Hse. Children's Bks.

Chris Wooding. The Haunting of Alaizabel Cray. l.t. ed. 2006. 463p. (YA). 22.95 (978-0-7862-8739-0(X)) Thorndike Pr.

Christopher, John. The White Mountains: The Tripods Trilogy. l.t. ed. 2000. 168p. (J). 25.95 (978-0-7838-9170-5(9)) Thorndike Pr.

Clamp. Fugue. Olsen, Lillian, tr. 2002. (X/1999 Ser.: Vol. 10). (Illus.). 180p. (YA). pap. 9.95 (978-1-56931-896-6(4)) Viz Media.

Clare, Cassandra. City of Bones. 2007. (Mortal Instruments Ser.). (YA). 496p. (gr. 9 up). 17.99 (978-1-4169-1428-0(5)); 485p. (****978-1-4287-3999-4(8))*** Simon & Schuster Children's Publishing. (McElderry, Margaret K.).

Clark, Mary Higgins. Ghost Ship: A Cape Cod Story. Minor, Wendell, illus. 2007. 40p. (J). (gr. 1-5). 17.99 (978-1-4169-3514-8(2) , Simon & Schuster/Paula Wiseman Bks.) Simon & Schuster Children's Publishing.

Clasicos de Terror, Vol. I. (Clasicos Juveniles Coleccion). (SPA.). (YA). (gr. 5-8). pap. (978-950-11-1282-5(9) , SG4721) Sigmar ARG. *Dist:* Lectorum Pubns., Inc.

Clasicos de Terror III. (Coleccion Clasicos Juveniles). (SPA.). (YA). (gr. 5-8). (978-950-11-1617-5(4)) Sigmar ARG. *Dist:* Lectorum Pubns., Inc.

Clement-Moore, Rosemary. Hell Week. 2008. 336p. (YA). 16.99 (****978-0-385-73414-1(X));*** lib. bdg. 19.99 (****978-0-385-90429-2(0))*** Dell Publishing. (Delacorte Pr.).

—Prom Dates from Hell. 2008. 304p. (YA). pap. 8.99 (****978-0-385-73413-4(1)*** , Delacorte Bks. for Young Readers) Random Hse. Children's Bks.

Climer, Steven Lee. Young of Heart. 2006. (YA). pap. (****978-0-9790649-5-1(3))*** Mardi Gras Publishing, LLC.

Coffin, Bill & Siembieda, Kevin. Systems Failure. Marciniszyn, Alex et al, eds. Wilson, Michael et al, illus. 1999. 144p. (YA). (gr. 8 up). pap. 12.95 (978-1-57457-038-0(2)) Palladium Bks., Inc.

Cohen, Daniel. Ghostly Warnings. 1999. (Illus.). 48p. (J). pap. 5.99 (978-0-14-038693-6(9) , Puffin) Penguin Group (USA) Inc.

Cohen, Sheldon, illus. La Chasse-Galerie. 2004. (FRE.). 24p. (J). (gr. 3-7). 15.95 (978-0-88776-635-0(8)) Tundra Bks., Inc./Livres Toundra, Inc. CAN. *Dist:* Random Hse., Inc.

Colandro, Lucille. There Was an Old Lady Who Swallowed a Bat! Lee, Jared D., illus. 2005. 32p. (J). (ps-ps). pap. 5.99 (978-0-439-73766-1(4) , Cartwheel Bks.) Scholastic, Inc.

Colby, C. B., et al. Scary Stories for Halloween Nights. 2005. (Illus.). 96p. (J). (gr. k-17). pap. 5.95 (978-1-4027-2181-6(1)) Sterling Publishing Co., Inc.

—Scary Stories for Sleepovers. 2006. (Illus.). 96p. pap. 5.95 (978-1-4027-2182-3(X)) Sterling Publishing Co., Inc.

Cole, Stephen. Resurrection, No. 3. 2005. (Wereling Ser.). 272p. (YA). (gr. 7-12). mass mkt. 5.99 (978-1-59514-043-2(3) , Razorbill) Penguin Group (USA) Inc.

—Wounded, Vol. 1. 2005. (Wereling Ser.). 272p. (YA). (gr. 7-12). mass mkt. 6.99 (978-1-59514-041-8(7) , Razorbill) Penguin Group (USA) Inc.

Cooper, Louise. Short & Scary! A Book of Very Short Scary Stories. 2002. (Illus.). 96p. (978-0-19-278190-1(1)) Oxford Univ. Pr., Inc.

Cormier, Robert. El Sindrome de la Ternura. Palmer, Magdalena, tr. 2005. (Escritura desatada Ser.). (SPA.). 208p. (YA). pap. 11.95 (978-84-666-0160-3(0)) Ediciones B ESP. *Dist:* Independent Pubs. Group.

Cormier, Shawn P. NiDemon. 2005. (YA). per. 12.95 (978-0-9740151-1-8(3)) Pine View Pr.

Cosgrove, Stephen. Creole. James, Robin, illus. 2001. (Serendipity Bks.). 32p. (J). (ps-3). pap. 4.99 (978-0-8431-7631-5(8) , Price Stern Sloan) Penguin Group (USA) Inc.

—Creole. 2000. (gr. k-3). lib. bdg. 13.00 (978-0-613-33656-7(9)) Tandem Library Bks.

Cote, Denis. Aux Portes de L'Horreur. Sylvestre, Daniel, illus. 2002. (Roman Plus Ser.). (FRE.). 160p. (YA). (gr. 8 up). pap. (978-2-89021-228-2(9)) Diffusion du livre Mirabel.

Coville, Bruce. Odds Are Good: An Oddly Enough & Odder Than Ever Omnibus. 2006. (Illus.). 352p. (J). pap. 6.95 (978-0-15-205716-9(1) , Magic Carpet Bks.) Harcourt Children's Bks.

Cowley, Joy. Nicketty-Nacketty, Noo-Noo-Noo. Moroney, Tracey, illus. 1999. 32p. (J). (ps-2). pap. 4.95 (978-1-57255-558-7(0)) Mondo Publishing.

Cox, Phil Roxbee. Mystery Mansion. 2005. (Young Reading Series 2 Ser.). 64p. (J). (gr. 2 up). pap. 5.99 (978-0-7945-0928-6(2) , Usborne) EDC Publishing.

Crew, Gary. The End of the Line. Rogers, Gregory, illus. 2008. 80p. (J). pap. (****978-1-59889-915-3(5));*** (YA). (gr. 5-9). lib. bdg. 16.95 (****978-1-59889-859-0(0))*** Stone Arch Bks.

Cross, Gillian. Tightrope. 2001. (YA). (978-0-606-21489-6(5)) Tandem Library Bks.

Crossley-Holland, Kevin. Enchantment: Fairy Tales, Ghost Stories & Tales of Wonder. Clark, Emma Chichester, illus. 2003. 128p. (YA). reprint ed. 22.00 (978-0-7567-6961-1(2)) DIANE Publishing Co.

Crowell, Peter Thomas. Haunted Mountain: The Tales of True Adventure, Book Two. 2006. (J). 19.95 (****978-0-9740290-8-5(4))*** Crowell, Peter T. Pubns.

Culture Shock. 1998. (Eyewitness Fun Fax Inserts Ser.). (Illus.). (J). (gr. 4-8). pap. 2.95 (978-0-7894-3011-3(8)) Dorling Kindersley Publishing, Inc.

Cursed Creatures. 2006. (Ghost Stories Ser.). (Illus.). 128p. (J). lib. bdg. (978-0-8368-6821-0(8)) Stevens, Gareth Inc.

Cusick, Richie Tankersley. The House Next Door. 2002. (gr. 7-12). lib. bdg. 13.00 (978-0-613-74151-4(X)) Tandem Library Bks.

—The Unseen 2 Rest in Peace. 2005. 304p. (YA). (gr. 7). pap. 6.99 (978-0-14-240464-5(0) , Puffin) Penguin Group (USA) Inc.

—The Unseen II. 2004. 288p. (YA). pap. (****978-0-439-96799-0(6))*** Scholastic, Inc.

—The Unseen III. 2005. 272p. (YA). pap. (****978-0-439-96344-2(3)*** , Scholastic) Scholastic, Inc.

Cusick, Richie Tankersley. The Unseen IV. 2005. (Point Horror Ser.). 400p. pap. (978-0-439-96345-9(1)) Scholastic, Inc.

Dadey, Debbie & Jones, Marcia Thornton. Dracula Doesn't Rock & Roll. Gurney, John Steven, illus. 2000. (Adventures of the Bailey School Kids Ser.: No. 39). 80p. (J). (gr. 2-4). mass mkt. 3.99 (978-0-439-04399-1(9) , Scholastic Paperbacks) Scholastic, Inc.

—Dracula Doesn't Rock & Roll. 2000. (Adventures of the Bailey School Kids Ser.: No. 39). (Illus.). (J). (gr. 2-4). 10.79 (978-0-606-18537-0(2)); 1999. (gr. 3-6). lib. bdg. 11.80 (978-0-613-21464-3(1)) Tandem Library Bks.

—Ghouls Don't Scoop Ice Cream. 1998. (Adventures of the Bailey School Kids Ser.: No. 31). (J). (gr. 2-4). 10.79 (978-0-606-13426-2(3)) Tandem Library Bks.

—Mrs. Jeepers' Scariest Halloween Ever. Gurney, John Steven, illus. 2005. 103p. (J). (978-1-4156-2066-3(0)) Scholastic, Inc.

—Sea Monsters Don't Ride Motorcycles. Gurney, John Steven, illus. 2000. (Adventures of the Bailey School Kids Ser.: No. 40). 80p. (J). (gr. 2-4). pap. 3.99 (978-0-439-04401-1(4) , Scholastic Paperbacks) Scholastic, Inc.

—Sea Monsters Don't Ride Motorcycles. 2000. (Adventures of the Bailey School Kids Ser.: No. 40). (J). (gr. 2-4). (978-0-606-18601-8(8)) Tandem Library Bks.

—Wolfmen Don't Hula Dance. 1999. (Adventures of the Bailey School Kids Ser.: No. 36). (J). (gr. 2-4). (978-0-606-16938-7(5)) Tandem Library Bks.

Dalmatian Press Staff. Boo! Glow in the Dark SBTC. 2004. 46p. pap. 2.99 (978-1-57759-829-9(6)) Dalmatian Pr.

Dalmatian Press Staff, adapted by. Dr. Jekyll & Mr. Hyde. 2002. (YA). (gr. 9-12). stu. ed. (978-1-58130-785-6(3)) Novel Units, Inc.

—The Strange Case of Dr. Jekyll & Mr. Hyde. 2002. (Spot the Classics Ser.). (Illus.). 171p. (J). (gr. k-5). 4.99 (978-1-57759-552-6(1)) Dalmatian Pr.

Dalmatian Press Staff, ed. Scary Fun. 2006. 400p. 5.99 (978-1-4037-2430-4(X)) Dalmatian Pr.

Dark Horse Comics Staff, et al. Darth Maul. (Star Wars Ser.). (Illus.). 96p. (YA). (gr. 7 up). pap. 12.95 (978-1-56971-542-0(4)) Dark Horse Comics.

D'Ath, Justin. Terrors of Nature. 2005. (Thrillogy Ser.). (Illus.). 48p. (gr. 4-8). 17.50 (978-0-7910-8892-0(8)) Facts On File, Inc.

—Terrors of Nature. 2000. (gr. 7-12). lib. bdg. 10.95 (978-0-613-29095-1(X)) Tandem Library Bks.

Davie, Jan. Stairway to the Stars. 2005. 76p. pap. (****978-1-84401-569-6(6))*** Athena Pr.

Davis, Dan, illus. Scooby-Doo & the Samurai Ghost. 2005. (Scooby-Doo Ser.). 24p. (J). 3.99 (978-0-439-69644-9(5)) Scholastic, Inc.

Deary, Terry. True Horror Stories. Wyatt, David, illus. l.t. ed. 2000. 264p. (J). pap. (978-0-7540-6092-5(6) , CLP 290) BBC Audio.

—True Horror Stories. Wyatt, David, illus. unabr. l.t. ed. 2000. (Read-Along Ser.). 208p. (J). pap. 29.95 incl. audio (978-0-7540-6226-4(0) , RA027, Chivers Children's Audio Bks.) BBC Audiobooks America.

Debrandt, Don. Shakedown. 2000. (Angel Ser.: No. 5). 320p. (YA). (gr. 7 up). pap. 5.99 (978-0-7434-0696-3(6) , Simon Pulse) Simon & Schuster Children's Publishing.

—Shakedown. 2000. (gr. 7-12). lib. bdg. 14.15 (978-0-613-63231-7(1)) Tandem Library Bks.

DeCandido, Keith R. A. The Deathless. 2007. (Buffy the Vampire Slayer Ser.). 224p. (YA). pap. 6.99 (978-1-4169-3630-5(0) , Simon Spotlight Entertainment) Simon & Schuster.

Deitz, Luke D. W. Haunting in the Graveyard. Deitz, George & Deitz, Kristine, eds. Deitz, Luke D. W., illus. 1999. (Illus.). 20p. (J). (gr. 1-4). 1.25 (978-0-938985-21-1(3)) Quarrier Pr.

Delbanco, Andrew, ed. Edgar Allan Poe. DuBois, Gerard, illus. 2006. (Stories for Young People Ser.). 48p. (J). (gr. 6 up). 14.95 (978-1-4027-1515-0(3)) Sterling Publishing Co., Inc.

Diggins, Matthew. Andrew & the Secret Gallery. Diggins, Matthew, illus. 2007. 32p. (J). (gr. 1-5). 15.95 (****978-1-60108-016-5(6))*** Red Cygnet Pr.

Disney Press Staff, ed. Haunted Mansion. 2007. 96p. (gr. 8-17). pap. 9.99 (****978-1-4231-0393-6(9))*** Disney Pr.

Dodds, Robert. Nightland. 2002. 144p. (YA). pap. 8.99 (978-1-84270-081-5(2)) Carlton Bks., Ltd. GBR. *Dist:* Independent Pubs. Group.

Dokey, Cameron & Burge, Constance M. Picture Perfect. 2005. (Charmed Ser.). 208p. (YA). pap. 5.99 (978-1-4169-0025-2(X) , Simon Spotlight Entertainment) Simon & Schuster.

The Doomed & the Dead. 2006. (Ghost Stories Ser.). (Illus.). 128p. (J). (gr. 7-9). lib. bdg. 25.27 (978-0-8368-6822-7(6)) Stevens, Gareth Inc.

Dorling Kindersley Publishing Staff, ed. Skeleton. 2004. (Dk Eyewitness Books Ser.). (Illus.). 72p. (J). 15.99 (978-0-7566-0727-2(2)) Dorling Kindersley Publishing, Inc.

Dowswell, P. & Allan, Tony. True Ghost Stories. 2004. (True Adventure Stories Ser.). 144p. (J). pap. 4.95 (978-0-7945-0274-4(1)); lib. bdg. 12.95 (978-1-58086-601-9(8)) EDC Publishing.

Doyle, Arthur Conan. Tales of Mystery & Terror. l.t. ed. 1999. (Large Print Heritage Ser.). 340p. (gr. 7-12). lib. bdg. 33.95 (978-1-58118-047-3(0) , 22516) LRS.

Dracula. (J). 9.95 (978-1-56156-373-9(0)) Kidsbooks, Inc.

Dresden, Sean, ed. Campfire Tales Vol. 1: The Most Terrifying Tales Ever Told, 2 vols. 2000. (Roxbury Park Bks.). (Illus.). 96p. (J). (gr. 3-7). pap. 4.95 (978-0-7373-0437-4(5) , 04375W, Roxbury Park Juvenile) Lowell Hse. Juvenile.

—Campfire Tales Vol. 2: The Most Terrifying Tales Ever Told. 2000. (Roxbury Park Bks.). (Illus.). 96p. (J). (gr. 3-7). pap. 4.95 (978-0-7373-0436-7(7) , 04367W, Roxbury Park Juvenile) Lowell Hse. Juvenile.

Duey, Kathleen. Beware the Alien Invasion! 2000. (Alone in the Dark Ser.). (Illus.). 32p. (J). pap. 3.95 (978-1-891100-15-4(7)) Smart Kids Publishing.

—Boogeyman in the Basement! 2000. (Alone in the Dark Ser.). (Illus.). 32p. (J). pap. 3.95 (978-1-891100-12-3(2)) Smart Kids Publishing.

—Nowhere to Run, Nowhere to Hide! 2000. (Alone in the Dark Ser.). (Illus.). 32p. (J). pap. 3.95 (978-1-891100-14-7(9)) Smart Kids Publishing.

—Stay Out of the Graveyard! 2000. (Alone in the Dark Ser.). (Illus.). 32p. (J). pap. 3.95 (978-1-891100-13-0(0)) Smart Kids Publishing.

Duncan, Lois. Locked in Time. 2002. (Illus.). (J). 13.38 (978-0-7587-4791-4(8)) Book Wholesalers, Inc.

Dunne, Colin. Werewolf. 128p. (J). pap. 7.95 (978-0-233-99580-9(3)) Andre Deutsch GBR. *Dist:* Trans-Atlantic Pubns., Inc.

Durgin, Doranna. Impressions. 2003. (gr. 7-12). lib. bdg. 14.15 (978-0-613-61777-2(0)) Tandem Library Bks.

Dussling, Jennifer. Creep Show. Spackman, Jeff, illus. 1999. (Eek! Stories to Make You Shriek Ser.). (J). (978-0-606-19883-7(0)) Tandem Library Bks.

Duval, Alex. Initiation. 2006. (Vampire Beach Ser.: Vol. 2). 192p. (YA). mass mkt. 5.99 (978-1-4169-1167-8(7) , Simon Pulse) Simon & Schuster Children's Publishing.

—Legacy. 2007. (Vampire Beach Ser.). 240p. (YA). mass mkt. 5.99 (****978-1-4169-1169-2(3)*** , Simon Pulse) Simon & Schuster Children's Publishing.

Duval, Alex. Ritual. 2007. (Vampire Beach Ser.). 208p. (YA). mass mkt. 5.99 (978-1-4169-1168-5(5) , Simon Pulse) Simon & Schuster Children's Publishing.

Fangorn. Little Horrors. 2004. (Illus.). 32p. (J). (ps-3). pap. 9.99 (978-1-86007-130-0(9)) Ticktock Media Ltd. GBR. *Dist:* Consortium Bk. Sales & Distribution.

Fast & Horr. Night Games. 2001. 32p. (YA). (gr. 6-12). pap. (978-0-8224-3768-0(6)) Globe Fearon Educational Publishing.

—Tomb of Horror. 2001. 32p. (YA). (gr. 6-12). pap. (978-0-8224-3777-2(5)) Globe Fearon Educational Publishing.

Ferguson, Dwayne. Ghost Ranch: The Legend of Mad Jake, 2004. (Kid Caramel: Bk. 4). (J). pap. 4.50 (978-0-940975-17-0(3) , Sankofa Bks.) Just Us Bks., Inc.

—The Werewolf of PS 40, Vol. 2. 1998. (Kid Caramel: Vol. 2). 72p. (J). (gr. 4-7). pap. 4.50 (978-0-940975-82-8(3) , Sankofa Bks.) Just Us Bks., Inc.

Fienberg, Anna & Fienberg, Barbara. Tashi & the Haunted House. Gamble, Kim, illus. (Tashi Ser.). 64p. (Orig.). (J). (gr. k-2). 2007. pap. 5.95 (****978-1-74114-953-1(3));*** 2003. pap. 5.95 (978-1-86508-840-2(4)) Allen & Unwin AUS. *Dist:* Independent Pubs. Group.

Fischman, Sheila, tr. from FRE. The Flying Canoe. Oberman, Sheldon & Cohen, Sheldon, illus. 2004. 24p. (J). (gr. 3-7). 15.95 (978-0-88776-636-7(6)) Tundra Bks., Inc./Livres Toundra, Inc. CAN. *Dist:* Random Hse., Inc.

Fleischman, Paul. A Fate Totally Worse Than Death. 2003. (gr. 7-12). lib. bdg. 14.15 (978-0-613-74822-3(0)) Tandem Library Bks.

Ford, Mike. Switching Channels. 1998. (Eerie Indiana Ser.: No. 13). 176p. (J). (gr. 3-7). pap. 4.50 (978-0-380-80103-9(5)) HarperCollins Pubs.

—They Say You Should Follow. 1998. (Eerie Indiana Ser.: No. 12). 144p. (J). (gr. 3-7). pap. 3.99 (978-0-380-79788-2(7)) HarperCollins Pubs.

Fort, Gloria. Patarana. 2000. (Dulces Suenos Collection). (SPA., Illus.). 10p. (J). 7.95 (978-84-348-6261-6(1)) SM Ediciones ESP. *Dist.* Distribooks, Inc.

From the Grave. 2007. (Ghost Stories Ser.). 128p. (YA). (gr. 7-9). lib. bdg. 25.27 (978-0-8368-6823-4(4)) Stevens, Gareth Inc.

Funke, Cornelia. Ghosthunters & the Totally Moldy Baroness! 2007. (Ghosthunters Ser.). 144p. (J). pap. 4.99 (978-0-439-86267-7(1)); (Illus.). (gr. 2-5). pap. 16.99 (978-0-439-86266-0(3)) Scholastic, Inc. (Chicken Hse., The).

Furie, Peter. Cyber Screams: Numchuks' Curse. 2005. 189p. (J). per. 12.95 (978-0-9772927-0-7(3)) Bangzoom Pubs.

Gaiman, Neil. Coraline. McKean, Dave, illus. 3rd ed. 2003. (SPA.). 160p. (978-84-7888-579-4(X) , 1952) Emece Editores.

—Coraline. 2006. (P. S. Ser.). 192p. pap. 12.95 (978-0-06-113937-6(8)) HarperCollins Pubs.

—Coraline. McKean, Dave, illus. (J). 2004. 208p. (gr. 7 up). pap. 6.99 (978-0-06-057591-5(3)); 2003. 176p. (gr. 3 up). pap. 6.99 (978-0-380-80734-5(3)) HarperCollins Pubs. (Harper Trophy).

—Coraline. 2002. (gr. 5-8). lib. bdg. 14.15 (978-0-613-67322-8(0)) Tandem Library Bks.

Galdone, Paul, retold by. King of the Cats. unabr. ed. 2001. (J). (gr. k-4). pap. 16.90 incl. audio (978-0-8045-6517-2(1) , 6517) Spoken Arts, Inc.

Gallagher, Diana G. Bad Bargain. 2006. (Buffy the Vampire Slayer Ser.). 208p. (YA). pap. 6.99 (978-1-4169-1919-3(8) , Simon Spotlight Entertainment) Simon & Schuster.

—Doomsday Deck. 2000. (gr. 7-12). lib. bdg. 14.15 (978-0-613-63278-2(8)) Tandem Library Bks.

—Mist & Stone. 2003. (gr. 7-12). lib. bdg. 14.15 (978-0-613-66520-9(1)) Tandem Library Bks.

—Prime Evil. 2000. (Buffy the Vampire Slayer Ser.: No. 10). 272p. (YA). pap. 5.99 (978-0-671-03930-1(X) , Simon Pulse) Simon & Schuster Children's Publishing.

—Prime Evil. 2000. (gr. 7-12). lib. bdg. 14.15 (978-0-613-63335-2(0)) Tandem Library Bks.

Gammell, Stephen, illus. More Scary Stories to Tell in the Dark. 80p. (J). (gr. 4-6). pap. 4.95 (978-0-8072-1424-4(8) , Listening Library) Random Hse. Audio Publishing Group.

Gantos, Jack. The Love Curse of the Rumbaughs. 2006. 192p. (YA). (gr. 7 up). 17.00 (978-0-374-33690-5(3) , Farrar, Straus & Giroux (BYR)) Farrar, Straus & Giroux.

—The Love Curse of the Rumbaughs. 2008. 208p. (YA). pap. 7.99 (****978-0-312-38052-6(6))*** Square Fish.

Garfield, Henry. My Father the Werewolf. 2005. (Illus.). 240p. (J). (gr. 8-12). 17.95 (978-0-689-85180-3(4) , Atheneum) Simon & Schuster Children's Publishing.

Garmon, Larry Mike. Bride of Frankenstein: Vow of Vengence. 2002. (gr. 5-8). lib. bdg. 12.40 (978-0-613-72087-8(3)) Tandem Library Bks.

Garton, Ray. Resurrecting Ravana. 2000. (gr. 7-12). lib. bdg. 14.15 (978-0-613-22261-7(X)); 1999. (Buffy the Vampire Slayer Ser.: No. 9). (Illus.). (J). (978-0-606-18366-6(3)) Tandem Library Bks.

Gauthier, Bertrand. Les Tenebres Piegees, Vol. RJ 65. Jorisch, Stephane, illus. 2003. (Roman Jeunesse Ser.). (FRE.). 96p. (YA). (gr. 4-7). pap. (978-2-89021-292-3(0)) Diffusion du livre Mirabel.

Gelsey, James. Scooby-Doo & the Groovy Ghost. 8th ed. 2000. (Scooby-Doo Mysteries Ser.: No. 8). (Illus.). 64p. (J). (ps-3). pap. 3.99 (978-0-439-11347-2(4) , Scholastic Paperbacks) Scholastic, Inc.

—Scooby-Doo & the Groovy Ghost. 2000. (gr. 3-6). lib. bdg. 11.80 (978-0-613-22338-6(1)) Tandem Library Bks.

—Scooby-Doo & the Haunted Castle. 1998. (Scooby-Doo Mysteries Ser.: No. 1). (Illus.). 64p. (ps-3). pap. 3.99 (978-0-590-81909-1(7)) Scholastic, Inc.

—Scooby-Doo & the Mummy's Curse. 1998. (Scooby-Doo Mysteries Ser.: No. 2). (Illus.). 64p. (ps-3). 3.99 (978-0-590-81910-7(0)) Scholastic, Inc.

—Scooby-Doo & the Spooky Strikeout. 2000. (gr. 3-6). lib. bdg. 11.80 (978-0-613-26854-7(7)) Tandem Library Bks.

—Scooby-Doo! & the Spooky Strikeout. del Sur, Duendes, illus. 2000. (Scooby-Doo Mysteries Ser.: No. 10). 64p. (J). (ps-3). 3.99 (978-0-439-11349-6(0)) Scholastic, Inc.

—Scooby-Doo & the Vampire's Revenge. 1999. (Scooby-Doo Mysteries Ser.: No. 6). (Illus.). 64p. (J). (ps-3). mass mkt. 3.99 (978-0-439-08278-5(1)) Scholastic, Inc.

—Scooby-Doo & the Vampire's Revenge. 1999. (gr. 3-6). lib. bdg. 11.80 (978-0-613-17940-9(4)) Tandem Library Bks.

Gilbert, Jeff. Trick or Shriek. 2006. 72p. pap. 5.97 (978-0-9646781-1-8(X)) Hairball Pr.

Gilman, Laura Anne. Deep Water. 2000. (Buffy the Vampire Slayer Ser.: No. 14). (Illus.). (YA). (gr. 7 up). (978-0-606-18365-9(5)) Tandem Library Bks.

Gilson, Kristin. A Baby-Sitter's Nightmare: Tales Too Scary to Be True. 1998. (Illus.). 112p. (J). (gr. 3-7). pap. 4.95 (978-0-06-440700-7(4)) HarperCollins Pubs.

Glencoe McGraw-Hill Staff. Classic Horror Stories. 2001. stu. ed. 32.64 (978-0-8442-8098-1(4) , 9780844280981); pap., stu. ed. 25.32 (978-0-8442-8099-8(2) , 9780844280998) Glencoe/McGraw-Hill.

Golden, Christopher. Ghost Roads. 1999. (gr. 7-12). lib. bdg. 15.30 (978-0-613-73059-4(3)) Tandem Library Bks.

—Immortal. 2000. (gr. 7-12). lib. bdg. 14.15 (978-0-613-63302-4(4)) Tandem Library Bks.

—Lost Slayer Bind Up. 2003. lib. bdg. 15.30 (978-0-613-61792-5(4)) Tandem Library Bks.

—Monster Book. 2000. (gr. 7-12). lib. bdg. 26.85 (978-0-613-63322-2(9)) Tandem Library Bks.

—Spike & Dru: Pretty Maids All in a Row. 2001. (Buffy the Vampire Slayer Ser.: Vol. 2). 368p. (YA). (gr. 8-12). reprint ed. pap. 6.99 (978-0-7434-1892-8(1) , Simon Pulse) Simon & Schuster Children's Publishing.

—Spike & Dru: Pretty Maids All in a Row. 2001. (gr. 7-12). lib. bdg. 15.30 (978-0-613-74152-1(8)) Tandem Library Bks.

Golden, Christopher & Holder, Nancy. Ghost Roads, 3 vols. 1999. (Buffy the Vampire Slayer Ser.: No. 2). 384p. (YA). pap. 6.99 (978-0-671-02749-0(2) , Simon Pulse) Simon & Schuster Children's Publishing.

—The Watchers Guide Buffy the Vampire Slayer, Vol. 1. rev. ed. 1998. (Buffy the Vampire Slayer Ser.). (Illus.). 304p. (YA). pap. 17.95 (978-0-671-02433-8(7) , Simon Pulse) Simon & Schuster Children's Publishing.

Golden, Christopher, et al. The Blood of Carthage. 2001. (Buffy the Vampire Slayer Ser.). 128p. (YA). pap. 12.95 (978-1-56971-534-5(3)) Dark Horse Comics.

—The Origin. 1999. (Buffy the Vampire Slayer Ser.). 80p. (YA). (gr. 7 up). pap. 9.95 (978-1-56971-429-4(0)) Dark Horse Comics.

Gollub, Matthew. Tio Culebra. Martinez, Leovigildo, illus. 2002. Tr. of Uncle Snake. (SPA.). 32p. pap. 6.95 (978-1-889910-24-6(4)) Tortuga Pr.

—Tio Culebra. Guzman, Martin Luis, tr. Martinez, Leovigildo, illus. 2002. Tr. of Uncle Snake. (SPA.). 32p. 15.95 (978-1-889910-23-9(6)) Tortuga Pr.

Gordon, Lawrence. Haunted High: The Ghost Chronicles. 2000. (gr. 7-12). lib. bdg. 21.05 (978-0-613-87684-1(9)) Tandem Library Bks.

Gorey, Edward. The Haunted Looking Glass: Ghost Stories. 2001. (gr. 3-6). lib. bdg. 22.20 (978-0-613-56413-7(8)) Tandem Library Bks.

Gorog, Judith. When Nobody's Home: Fifteen Baby-Sitting Tales of Terror. 1998. (Point Paperback Ser.). (gr. 7-12). pap. 3.99 (978-0-590-46874-9(X)) Scholastic, Inc.

Grant, John & Stocks, Mike. Classic Horror. 2004. 432p. (J). 12.95 (978-0-7945-0616-2(X) , Usborne) EDC Publishing.

Grant, Steven, et al. Ghost Rider Team-up TPB. 2007. (Illus.). 144p. pap. 15.99 (978-0-7851-2257-9(5)) Marvel Enterprises, Inc.

Graves, Damien. Cat Lady. 2007. (Midnight Library: No. 4). 176p. (J). pap. 5.99 (978-0-439-89391-6(7)) Scholastic, Inc.

—End Game. 2006. (Midnight Library: No. 3). 192p. (J). pap. 5.99 (978-0-439-87188-4(3) , Scholastic Paperbacks) Scholastic, Inc.

Gray, Keith. Creepers. 2004. 192p. (J). pap. 8.99 (****978-0-09-947564-4(2))*** Transworld Publishers Ltd. GBR. *Dist:* Independent Pubs. Group.

Greene, Janice. The House on the Hill, Set 2. 2002. 32p. (YA). 2.95 (978-1-56254-419-5(5) , SP 4195) Saddleback Educational Publishing.

Greenwood, Kerry. Alien Invasions. 2005. (Thrillogy Ser.). (Illus.). 48p. (gr. 4-8). 17.50 (978-0-7910-8865-4(0)) Facts On File, Inc.

Gross, Philip. Point Horror: Facetaker. l.t. ed. 2005. 176p. (J). pap. (978-0-7540-6130-4(2) , CLP 323) BBC Audio.

—Point Horror Unleashed: Transformer. l.t. ed. 1999. 292p. (J). pap. (978-0-7540-6057-4(8) , CLP 265) BBC Audio.

Gutman, Dan. The Million Dollar Strike. 2006. 224p. (gr. 3-7). pap. 5.99 (978-0-7868-3751-9(9)) Hyperion Pr.

Gutman, Dan. Million Dollar Strike. 2004. 176p. (J). lib. bdg. 18.46 (****978-1-4242-2107-3(2))*** Fitzgerald Bks.

Hagerty, Carol, ed. Dr. Jekyll & Mr. Hyde. 1998. (Classics Ser.: Set II). (Illus.). 80p. (YA). (gr. 5-12). per. 7.95 (978-1-56254-260-3(5) , SP2605) Saddleback Educational Publishing.

—Dracula. 1998. (Classics Ser.: Set II). (Illus.). 80p. (YA). (gr. 5-12). pap. 7.95 (978-1-56254-262-7(1) , SP2621) Saddleback Educational Publishing.

Hall, Traci. Rhiannon, Goddess in Training. 2006. 350p. (YA). pap. (978-1-932815-58-0(9) , Bronze Medallion) Medallion Pr., Inc.

Hamilton, Martha. Scared Witless: Thirteen Eerie Tales to Tell. 2006. (Illus.). 64p. (J). 15.95 (978-0-87483-796-4(0)) August Hse. Pubs., Inc.

Hansen, Lynne. The Change: Heritage of Horror Series. 2004. (Heritage of Horror Ser.: 2). 108p. (YA). pap. 9.00 (978-0-7599-4491-6(1)) Hard Shell Word Factory.

—The Return. 2002. (Heritage of Horror Ser.: 1). 104p. (YA). pap. 9.00 (978-0-7599-0522-1(3)) Hard Shell Word Factory.

Hardcastle, Nick, illus. Vampire Stories. 2004. (Red Hot Reads Ser.). 224p. (J). (gr. k-3). pap. 6.95 (978-0-7534-5735-1(0) , Kingfisher) Houghton Mifflin Co. Trade & Reference Div.

Harlen, Jonathan. The Plague. Jellett, Tom, illus. 2008. (J). lib. bdg. (****978-1-59889-861-3(2));*** 80p. pap. (****978-1-59889-917-7(1))*** Stone Arch Bks.

Harper, Meg. My Mum & Other Horror Stories. l.t. ed. 2005. (J). pap. (978-1-4056-6012-9(0) , CLP 496) BBC Audio.

—My Mum & Other Horror Stories. 2005. (Illus.). pap. 29.95 incl. audio (978-0-7540-6291-2(0) , Chivers Children's Audio Bks.) BBC Audiobooks America.

—My Mum & Other Horror Stories. 2003. (My Mum Ser.). 160p. (J). pap. 9.99 (978-0-7459-4830-0(8) , Lion) Lion Hudson plc GBR. *Dist:* Independent Pubs. Group.

Harris, Mark. Dario Figg & the Phantom of Murk. 2001. 192p. pap. 13.95 (978-0-595-18933-5(4) , Writers Club Pr.) iUniverse, Inc.

Harrison, Emma. Something Wiccan This Way Comes. 2003. (gr. 7-12). lib. bdg. 14.15 (978-0-613-61818-2(1)) Tandem Library Bks.

Hart, J. J. Zombie Monkey Monster Jamboree. Meugniot, Will, illus. 2006. 141p. (J). 12.95 (978-1-933925-07-3(8) , Actionopolis) Komikwerks, LLC.

Hartzell, Andy. Fox Bunny Funny. 2007. 104p. pap. 10.00 (****978-1-891830-97-6(X))*** Top Shelf Productions.

Heiligman, Deborah. Too Perfect. 1999. (Eek! Stories to Make You Shriek Ser.). (J). (978-0-606-19884-4(9)) Tandem Library Bks.

Henderson, Alice. Portal Through Time. 2006. (Buffy the Vampire Slayer Ser.). 352p. (YA). pap. 6.99 (978-1-4169-1918-6(X) , Simon Spotlight Entertainment) Simon & Schuster.

Herbert, James. The Fog. 2003. (Illus.). vi, 345p. (J). pap. 13.99 (978-0-330-37615-0(2) , Pan) Pan Macmillan GBR. *Dist:* Trafalgar Square Publishing.

—The Magic Cottage. 1999. 394p. 32.50 (978-0-333-76129-8(4)) Macmillan Publishers Ltd. GBR. *Dist:* Independent Pubs. Group.

—The Rats. 2003. 197p. (J). 32.50 (978-0-333-76118-2(9)) Macmillan Publishers Ltd. GBR. *Dist:* Trafalgar Square Publishing.

—The Rats. (Illus.). 197p. (J). pap. 13.99 (978-0-330-37614-3(4) , Pan) Pan Macmillan GBR. *Dist:* Trafalgar Square Publishing.

Herbert, James. The Secret of Crickley Hall. 2006. 400p. 39.95 (****978-1-4050-0520-3(3))*** Pan Macmillan GBR. *Dist:* Trans-Atlantic Pubns., Inc.

Herman, Gail. Scooby-Doo on Zombie Island. 1998. (Scooby-Doo Movie Storybooks). (Illus.). 32p. (J). (ps-3). pap. 3.50 (978-0-590-38652-4(2)) Scholastic, Inc.

Hill, David. Ghosts & Ghoulies. 2005. (Thrillogy Ser.). (Illus.). 48p. (gr. 4-8). 17.50 (978-0-7910-8888-3(X)) Facts On File, Inc.

—Ghosts & Ghoulies. 2000. (gr. 7-12). lib. bdg. 12.10 (978-0-613-28851-4(3)) Tandem Library Bks.

Hill, Susan. The Woman in Black. Lawrence, John, illus. 2002. 144p. (J). pap. 15.95 (978-1-56792-189-2(2)) Godine, David R. Pub.

—The Woman in Black. 2001. (gr. 7-12). lib. bdg. 25.70 (978-0-613-78975-2(X)) Tandem Library Bks.

Ho, Jason, illus. Frankenstein. 2007. (Graphic Horror Ser.). 32p. (YA). (gr. 5-8). lib. bdg. 27.07 (****978-1-60270-059-8(1)*** , Graphic Planet) Magic Wagon.

Hobbs, William. Howling Hill. Kastner, Jill, illus. 1998. 32p. (J). (gr. k-3). 17.99 (978-0-688-15429-5(8)); 15.89 (978-0-688-15430-1(1)) HarperCollins Pubs.

Hodgson, William Hope. The Sea Horses. 2004. reprint ed. pap. 1.99 (978-1-4192-8166-2(6)) Kessinger Publishing, LLC.

Hoh, Diane. The Train. 2000. 176p. (gr. 7-12). pap. 11.95 (978-0-595-09381-6(7) , Backinprint.com) iUniverse, Inc.

—Train. 2000. (gr. 7-12). lib. bdg. 21.05 (978-0-613-84104-7(2)) Tandem Library Bks.

Holder, Nancy. The Angel Chronicles. (Buffy the Vampire Slayer Ser.: No. 6). (Illus.). (YA). (gr. 7 up). Vol. 1. 1998. 224p. pap. 5.99 (978-0-671-02133-7(8)); Vol. 3. 1999. 192p. pap. 5.99 (978-0-671-02631-8(3)) Simon & Schuster Children's Publishing. (Simon Pulse).

—Blood & Fog. 2003. (Buffy the Vampire Slayer Ser.: Vol. 16). 304p. (YA). mass mkt. 6.99 (978-0-7434-0039-8(9) , Simon Pulse) Simon & Schuster Children's Publishing.

—The Evil That Men Do. 2000. (Buffy the Vampire Slayer Ser.: No. 6). 352p. (YA). pap. 6.99 (978-0-671-02635-6(6) , Simon Pulse) Simon & Schuster Children's Publishing.

—Journals of Rupert Giles. 2002. (gr. 7-12). lib. bdg. 14.15 (978-0-613-63306-2(7)) Tandem Library Bks.

—Not Forgotten. 2000. (Angel Ser.: No. 2). 256p. (YA). (gr. 7 up). pap. 5.99 (978-0-671-04145-8(2) , Simon Pulse) Simon & Schuster Children's Publishing.

—Not Forgotten. 2000. (gr. 7-12). lib. bdg. 14.15 (978-0-613-28001-3(6)) Tandem Library Bks.

—Smallville: Hauntings. 2003. (gr. 7-12). lib. bdg. 14.15 (978-0-613-72304-6(X)) Tandem Library Bks.

Holder, Nancy & Matsuda, Jeff. Keep Me in Mind. 2005. (Buffy the Vampire Slayer Ser.). 256p. (YA). pap. 6.99 (978-0-689-86956-3(8) , Simon Spotlight Entertainment) Simon & Schuster.

Horowitz, Anthony. The Complete Horowitz Horror. 2008. 448p. (J). (gr. 4-6). pap. 7.99 (****978-0-14-241162-9(0)*** , Puffin) Penguin Group (USA) Inc.

—Groosham Grange. l.t. ed. 2005. 208p. (J). pap. (978-0-7540-7819-7(1) , CLP 409) BBC Audio.

—Horowitz Horror: Stories You'll Wish You Never Read. 2006. 208p. (J). (gr. 4). 11.99 (978-0-399-24489-6(1) , Philomel) Penguin Group (USA) Inc.

—More Horowitz Horror: More Stories You'll Wish You'd Never Read. 2007. 208p. (YA). (gr. 4 up). 11.99 (978-0-399-24519-0(7) , Philomel) Penguin Group (USA) Inc.

Horror, 10 vols. 2005. (Double Fastback Ser.). (J). (gr. 6-12). 64p. pap. 54.95 (978-0-13-024469-7(4)); 32p. pap. 54.95 (978-0-13-024451-2(1)) Globe Fearon Educational Publishing.

Hotel Horror. (Fantasmas de Fear Street Coleccion). (SPA.). (YA). (gr. 5-8). Vol. 1. pap. 7.95 (978-950-04-2091-4(0) , EM11732); Vol. 2. pap. 7.95 (978-950-04-2092-1(9) , EM11736) Emecé Editores S.A. ARG. *Dist:* Lectorum Pubns., Inc., Planeta Publishing Corp.

Howe, James. The Fright Before Christmas. 1999. (Bunnicula & Friends Ser.). (J). (gr. k-3). (978-0-606-17244-8(0)) Tandem Library Bks.

—Scared Silly. Morrill, Leslie H., illus. 1998. (Bunnicula & Friends Ser.). 48p. (J). (gr. k-3). pap. 4.95 (978-0-688-16322-8(X)) HarperCollins Pubs.

Hughes, Dawn Marie. Deadwood: Haunted Stories. 2006. 94p. pap. 14.95 (978-1-4241-2600-2(2)) PublishAmerica, Inc.

Hunter, Michele. Scary Stories for Stormy Nights, Vol. 8. 1999. 96p. (J). (gr. 3-6). pap. 5.95 (978-0-7373-0045-1(0) , Roxbury Park) Lowell Hse.

—Scary Stories for Stormy Nights. Angeloch, Eric, illus. 1998. (Scary Stories for Stormy Nights Ser.: Vol. 6). 96p. (J). (gr. 3-7). pap. 5.95 (978-1-56565-901-8(5) , 09015W, Roxbury Park Juvenile) Lowell Hse. Juvenile.

Hurston, Zora Neale. The Skull Talks Back: And Other Haunting Tales. Jenkins, Leonard, illus. 2004. 64p. (J). (gr. 5 up). 15.99 (978-0-06-000631-0(5)) HarperCollins Pubs.

Hurston, Zora Neale & Thomas, Joyce Carol. The Skull Talks Back: And Other Haunting Tales. Jenkins, Leonard, illus. 2004. 64p. (J). (gr. 5 up). lib. bdg. 16.89 (978-0-06-000634-1(X)) HarperCollins Pubs.

I Know What You Did Last Summer. 1999. (YA). 9.95 (978-1-56137-229-4(3)) Novel Units, Inc.

Ingelvie, Bodie. Dudleytown Curse. 2007. 320p. pap. 14.99 (****978-1-59554-321-9(X))*** Nelson, Thomas Inc.

Invisible Man. (ARA., Illus.). 100p. (YA). pap. 5.95 (978-0-86685-741-3(9) , LDL934) Librairie du Liban Pubns. FRA. *Dist:* International Bk. Ctr., Inc.

Ireland, Kenneth. The Ghost Train. 2004. 126p. (J). 5.00 (978-1-84161-032-0(1)) Ravette Publishing, Ltd. GBR. *Dist:* Parkwest Pubns., Inc.

—Sleep Well. 2004. 126p. (J). 5.00 (978-1-84161-030-6(5)) Ravette Publishing, Ltd. GBR. *Dist:* Parkwest Pubns., Inc.

—The Werewolf Mask. 2004. 126p. (J). 5.00 (978-1-84161-033-7(X)) Ravette Publishing, Ltd. GBR. *Dist:* Parkwest Pubns., Inc.

Jackson, R. Eugene. Ghoul School: A 2-Act Comedy. 1998. (Illus.). 64p. (YA). pap. 4.00 (978-0-88680-454-1(X) , C454X) Clark, I. E. Pubns.

Jackson, Steve. House of Hell. 2006. (Fighting Fantasy Gamebooks Ser.). 320p. mass mkt. 6.99 (978-0-7434-9297-3(8)) Simon & Schuster, Inc.

Jacques, Brian. The Ribbajack & Other Curious Yarns. (J). 2006. 176p. (gr. 3). pap. 6.99 (978-0-14-240378-5(4) , Puffin); 2004. 128p. (gr. 4). 16.99 (978-0-399-24220-5(1) , Philomel) Penguin Group (USA) Inc.

James, Robert. Bring Me a Dream. 1998. (Eerie Indiana Ser.: No. 9). 128p. (J). (gr. 3-7). pap. 3.99 (978-0-380-79785-1(2)) HarperCollins Pubs.

James, Robert & Ford, Mike. Who Framed Alice Prophet? 1998. (Eerie Indiana Ser.: No. 8). (J). (gr. 3-7). pap. 3.99 (978-0-380-79784-4(4)) HarperCollins Pubs.

Jennings, Sharon, et al. Franklin's Library Book. Gagnon, Celeste, illus. 2005. (Kids Can Read Ser.). 32p. (J). (gr. 1-2). (978-1-55337-713-9(3)); (978-1-55337-712-2(5)) Kids Can Pr., Ltd.

Jinks, Catherine. Eloise: A Ghost Story. 2007. (Allie's Ghost Hunters Ser.). 180p. (J). (gr. 4-7). pap. 7.95 (****978-1-74114-659-2(3)***) Allen & Unwin AUS. *Dist:* Independent Pubs. Group.

—Eustace: A Ghost Story. 2007. (Allie's Ghost Hunters Ser.). 168p. (J). (gr. 4-7). pap. 7.95 (****978-1-74114-660-8(7)***) Allen & Unwin AUS. *Dist:* Independent Pubs. Group.

Johnson, Liliane & Dufton, Jo S. Children's Chillers & Thrillers. Bruhn, Joan Z., illus. 136p. (Orig.). (J). pap. 10.00 (978-0-930069-04-9(8)) Jasmine Pr.

Johnston, Tony. Very Scary. 1999. (978-0-606-17226-4(2)) Tandem Library Bks.

Jones, Allan F. The Plague Pit. 2003. 128p. (J). mass mkt. 6.99 (978-0-330-36807-0(9) , Pan) Pan Macmillan GBR. *Dist:* Trafalgar Square Publishing.

Jones, Allan Frewin. The Monk's Curse, Vol. 7. 2003. 176p. (J). mass mkt. 6.99 (978-0-330-37477-4(X) , Pan) Pan Macmillan GBR. *Dist:* Trafalgar Square Publishing.

—The Wreckers. 2003. 163p. (J). mass mkt. (978-0-330-36810-0(9) , Pan) Pan Macmillan.

Jones, Kelley. Kelley Jone's the Hammer. Lewis, Dana & Smith, Toren, trs. 2001. 120p. pap. 12.95 (978-1-56971-340-2(5)) Dark Horse Comics.

Jones, Marcia Thornton & Dadey, Debbie. Beware of the Blabbermouth! Francis, Guy, illus. 2005. 81p. (J). (gr. 2-5). lib. bdg. 11.19 (978-0-606-33813-4(6)) Tandem Library Bks.

—Howling at the Hauntlys' Gurney, John Steven, illus. 1998. (Bailey City Monsters Ser.: No.2). (J). (gr. 2-4). pap. 3.99 (978-0-590-10845-4(X)) Scholastic, Inc.

—Vampire Trouble. 1998. (Bailey City Monsters Ser.: No. 3). (Illus.). 80p. (J). (gr. 2-4). pap. 3.99 (978-0-590-10846-1(8)) Scholastic, Inc.

Kane, Christy. Tales of the Sisters Kane. 2006. (Illus.). 96p. (YA). 20.00 (978-0-9778949-4-9(0)) Baby Tattoo Bks.

Karnowski, Anthony. Cameron & the Grim. 2006. 176p. pap. 13.95 (978-1-59113-919-5(8)) Booklocker.com, Inc.

Katschke, Judy, et al. Help! There's a Ghost in My Room! 2003. (Full House Ser.: No. 1). (Illus.). 96p. mass mkt. 4.99 (978-0-06-054083-8(4) , 53751756, Harper Entertainment) HarperCollins Pubs.

Kaye, Amy. Focus on This! 2003. (Real Deal Ser.). (YA). mass mkt. 5.99 (978-0-8439-5252-0(0)) Dorchester Publishing Co., Inc.

Kaye, Michael. Summer Camp Race of Horror. 2002. 108p. pap. 9.95 (978-0-595-23726-5(6) , Writers Club Pr.) iUniverse, Inc.

Keating, T. P. Bleeding Hearts: the Diary of a Country Vampire. 2005. 272p. (YA). pap. 12.48 (978-1-4116-4815-9(3)) Lulu.com.

Keeler, Kathleen. I Dare You: Stories to Scare You. Doucet, Bob, illus. 2000. (Hello Reader! Ser.: Level 4). Orig. Title: Are You a Scaredy Cat. 40p. (J). (gr. 1-3). pap. 3.99 (978-0-439-09855-7(6)) Scholastic, Inc.

—I Dare You: Stories to Scare You. 2000. Orig. Title: Are You a Scaredy Cat. (Illus.). (J). 10.79 (978-0-606-18878-4(9)) Tandem Library Bks.

—I Double Dare You! More Stories to Scare You! Doucet, Bob, illus. 2002. (Hello Reader! Ser.). 40p. (J). pap. 3.99 (978-0-439-32255-3(3) , Cartwheel Bks.) Scholastic, Inc.

Kehl, Mark. Scary Stories for Stormy Nights. 1998. (Scary Stories for Stormy Nights Ser.: Vol. 7). (Illus.). 95p. (J). (gr. 3-7). pap. 5.95 (978-1-56565-965-0(1) , 09651W, Roxbury Park) Lowell Hse.

Kehret, Peg. Backstage Fright. unabr. ed. 1998. (J). (gr. 4). Class Set. 79.70 incl. audio (978-0-7887-2543-2(2) , 46713); Homework Set. (Frightmares Ser.: Vol. 8). 30.24 incl. audio (978-0-7887-2238-7(7) , 40722) Recorded Bks., LLC.

—Earthquake Terror. 1998. (Puffin Novel Ser.). 144p. (J). (gr. 3-7). pap. 5.99 (978-0-14-038343-0(3) , Puffin) Penguin Group (USA) Inc.

—Earthquake Terror. 1998. (Puffin Novel Ser.). (J). 11.64 (978-0-606-13073-8(X)) Tandem Library Bks.

Kelley, Amy. Spooky Campfire Stories. 2000. (Spooky Ser.). (Illus.). 116p. (J). pap. 7.95 (978-1-56044-867-9(9) , Falcon) Globe Pequot Pr., The.

Kenner, Julie. Good Ghouls Do. 2007. 320p. (YA). (gr. 12 up). pap. 9.99 (****978-0-425-21703-0(5)*** , Berkley Trade) Penguin Group (USA) Inc.

King, Kirsty. My New Friends. 2005. 52p. pap. (****978-1-84401-576-4(9)***) Athena Pr.

King, Stephen. Dreamcatcher. 2001. (gr. 7-12). lib. bdg. 16.45 (978-0-613-50299-3(X)) Tandem Library Bks.

Kingfisher Editors, ed. Seriously Spooky Stories. 2007. (Super Shorts Ser.). 160p. (J). (gr. k-3). pap. 6.95 (978-0-7534-6074-0(2) , Kingfisher) Houghton Mifflin Co. Trade & Reference Div.

Kipling, Rudyard. The Room in the Tower & Other Stories: Penguin Reading Lab, Level 2. 2001. 48p. pap. 7.66 (978-0-582-41667-3(1)) Longman Publishing Group.

Klause, Annette Curtis. Blood & Chocolate. 2007. (J). 288p. pap. 8.99 (****978-0-385-73421-9(2));*** 272p. lib. bdg. 11.99 (****978-0-385-90434-6(7)***) Random Hse. Children's Bks. (Delacorte Bks. for Young Readers).

Kline, Suzy. Horrible Harry & the Ant Invasion. 1998. (Horrible Harry Ser.: No. 2). (Illus.). 64p. (J). (gr. 2-4). pap. 3.99 (978-0-14-130082-5(5) , Puffin) Penguin Group (USA) Inc.

Knudsen, Michelle. Case of Vampire Vivian. 2003. (gr. k-3). lib. bdg. 13.00 (978-0-613-79275-2(0)) Tandem Library Bks.

Koehler, Karen. The Maiden No. 1: Out of the Ashes. 2003. 248p. (gr. 4-12). pap. 15.00 (978-0-9679220-3-4(8) , Black Death Bks.) KHP Industries.

Koontz, Dean. Intensity. 2000. (gr. 7-12). lib. bdg. 16.45 (978-0-613-39476-5(3)) Tandem Library Bks.

—Ticktock. 2000. (gr. 7-12). lib. bdg. 16.45 (978-0-613-49461-8(X)) Tandem Library Bks.

—Watchers. 2003. (gr. 7-12). lib. bdg. 16.45 (978-0-613-57487-7(7)) Tandem Library Bks.

La Fevers, Robin. Werewolf Rising. 2006. 176p. (J). (gr. 5). 16.99 (978-0-525-47665-8(2) , Dutton Juvenile) Penguin Group (USA) Inc.

L'Allier, Peter. Rotten Robbie & the Legend of Wanibinoo. 2006. (Illus.). (YA). 18.95 (978-0-9724022-8-6(4)) Dr. Todd, LLC.

Lanagan, Margo. Red Spikes. 2007. 176p. (gr. 9). (J). 16.99 (****978-0-375-84320-4(5));*** (YA). lib. bdg. 19.99 (****978-0-375-94577-9(6)***) Random Hse. Children's Bks. (Knopf Bks. for Young Readers).

Lancaster, Susan. The Caves & the Skull. 2004. 160p. pap. 12.95 (978-0-9730350-1-8(3)) Snosrap Publishing CAN. *Dist:* Hushion Hse. Publishing, Ltd.

Landy, Derek. Landy Mid Grade: Raising Cain. 2006. (Skulduggery Pleasant Ser.). 384p. (J). pap. 7.99 (978-0-06-124090-4(7) , Harper Trophy) HarperCollins Pubs.

Lasky, Kathryn. Blood Secret. 2004. (Illus.). 256p. (J). (gr. 7 up). 15.99 (978-0-06-000066-0(X)) HarperCollins Pubs.

Laurence, James. Faith Trials. 2001. (gr. 7-12). lib. bdg. 14.15 (978-0-613-63284-3(2)) Tandem Library Bks.

Le Fanu, J. Sheridan. Madam Crowl's Ghost & the Dead Sexton. 2004. reprint ed. pap. 15.95 (978-1-4191-3188-2(5)); pap. 1.99 (978-1-4192-3188-9(X)) Kessinger Publishing, LLC.

Le Guin, Ursula K. Catwings. Schindler, S. D., illus. 2002. (Catwings Ser.: No. 1). 12.17 (978-0-7587-9240-2(9)) Book Wholesalers, Inc.

—Catwings. 2003. (Catwings Ser.: No. 1). 48p. (J). pap. 3.99 (978-0-439-55189-2(7)) Scholastic, Inc.

Lectorum Publications Staff, contrib. by. Comodin Embrujado. 2000. (Fantasmas de Fear Street Coleccion). (SPA.). (YA). (gr. 5-8). pap. 7.95 (978-950-04-1892-8(4) , EM4471) Emecé Editores S.A. ARG. *Dist:* Lectorum Pubns., Inc., Planeta Publishing Corp.

Lee, Stan & Byrne, John. Villainy of Doctor Doom. Kirby, Jack, illus. 1999. 176p. reprint ed. pap. 17.95 (978-0-7851-0732-3(0) , From the Hse. of Ideas) Marvel Enterprises, Inc.

Leiber, Fritz. Gonna Roll the Bones. Wiesner, David, illus. 2004. 32p. (J). 16.95 (978-0-689-03591-3(8)); (978-0-689-03637-8(X)) ibooks, Inc. (Milk & Cookies).

Leroux, Gaston. The Phantom of the Opera. Howell, Troy, illus. 2008. (Classic Starts Ser.). 160p. (J). 5.95 (****978-1-4027-4580-5(X)***) Sterling Publishing Co., Inc.

Leroux, Gaston. The Phantom of the Opera. l.t. ed. 1999. (Large Print Heritage Ser.). 420p. (J). (gr. 7-12). lib. bdg. 35.95 (978-1-58118-043-5(8) , 22512) LRS.

Leroux, Gaston & Larkin, Rochelle. The Phantom of the Opera. Schoolcraft, Robert, illus. 2005. (Great Illustrated Classics Ser.). 240p. (J). (gr. 3-8). 21.35 (978-1-59679-248-7(5) , ABDO & Daughters) ABDO Publishing Co.

Levithan, David. The Mummy, Level 2. 2001. 48p. (C). pap. 9.00 (978-0-582-45193-3(0)) Longman Publishing Group.

Lobdell, Scott & Nicieza, Fabian. Slayer, Interrupted. 2003. (Angel/Buffy the Vampire Slayer Ser.). 104p. (YA). pap. 12.95 (978-1-59307-011-3(X)) Dark Horse Comics.

Loeb, Jeph. The Witching Hour. rev. ed. 2003. (Illus.). 160p. pap. 19.95 (978-1-56389-945-4(0)) DC Comics.

Lorey, Dean. Nightmare Academy. Wyatt, David, illus. 2007. (Nightmare Academy Ser.). 320p. (J). (gr. 5 up). 16.99 (****978-0-06-134042-0(1)***) HarperCollins Pubs.

Lubar, David. The Curse of the Campfire Weenies: And Other Warped & Creepy Tales. rev. ed. 2007. 207p. (J). (gr. 5 up). 15.95 (****978-0-7653-1807-7(5)*** , Starscape) Doherty, Tom Assocs., LLC.

Lubar, David. Invasion of the Road Weenies: And Other Warped & Creepy Tales. 192p. (J). 2006. 5.99 (978-0-7653-5325-2(3)); 2005. 16.95 (978-0-7653-1447-5(9)) Doherty, Tom Assocs., LLC. (Starscape).

Lupton, Hugh. Freaky Tales from Far & Wide. Berkshire, Lisa, illus. 2000. 48p. (J). (ps-3). 15.95 (978-1-902283-16-6(3)) Barefoot Bks., Inc.

Lutzen, Hanna. Vlad the Undead. 2001. (gr. 7-12). lib. bdg. 14.10 (978-0-613-88930-8(4)) Tandem Library Bks.

Madame M's Creepy. l.t. ed. 2002. (Illus.). 60p. (J). per., act. bk. ed. 5.95 (978-0-9704159-2-9(3)) Creepy Little Productions.

Mahy, Margaret. Don't Read This! And Other Tales of the Unnatural. 2004. (Illus.). 208p. (J). reprint ed. pap. 7.95 (978-1-932425-25-3(X) , Lemniscaat) Boyds Mills Pr.

Maneru, Maria, et al. Mis Primeros Relatos de Miedo. Jos, Luis Telleria, illus. 2004. 312p. (J). (978-968-13-3782-7(4)) Editorial Diana, S.A. MEX. *Dist:* Lectorum Pubns., Inc.

Mariotte, Jeff. Close to the Ground. 2000. (Angel Ser.: No. 4). 320p. (YA). (gr. 7 up). pap. 5.99 (978-0-671-04147-2(9) , Simon Pulse) Simon & Schuster Children's Publishing.

—Close to the Ground. 2002. (gr. 7-12). lib. bdg. 14.15 (978-0-613-63187-7(0)) Tandem Library Bks.

—Fall. 2004. (Witch Season Ser.). 320p. (YA). mass mkt. 5.99 (978-0-689-86724-8(7) , Simon Pulse) Simon & Schuster Children's Publishing.

—Summer. Frost, Michael, photos by. 2004. (Witch Season Ser.). 320p. (YA). mass mkt. 5.99 (978-0-689-86665-4(8) , Simon Pulse) Simon & Schuster Children's Publishing.

Martin, Les & Poe, Edgar Allan. Tales of Terror. 2007. (Stepping Stone Bks.). 96p. (J). (gr. 2-5). pap. 3.99 (978-0-375-84055-5(9) , Random Hse. Bks. for Young Readers) Random Hse. Children's Bks.

Matthews, Andrew. Point Horror: Darker. l.t. ed. 2000. 224p. (J). pap. (978-0-7540-6111-3(6) , CLP 305) BBC Audio.

Mayer, Mercer. Critters of the Night Glow-in-the-Dark. 1998. (J). 9.99 (978-0-679-88707-2(5) , Random Hse. Bks. for Young Readers) Random Hse. Children's Bks.

McBay, Bruce. Waiting for Sarah. 2003. (gr. 7-12). lib. bdg. 16.40 (978-0-613-83712-5(6)) Tandem Library Bks.

McCann, Jesse Leon. The Mystery Mall. 1998. (Scooby-Doo 3-D Storybooks: No. 2). (Illus.). 16p. (J). (ps-3). pap. 5.99 (978-0-590-38656-2(5)) Scholastic, Inc.

—Scooby-Doo & the Weird Water Park. 2000. (Scooby-Doo Original Titles Ser.: No. 3). (Illus.). 32p. (J). (ps-3). 3.50 (978-0-439-17253-0(5)) Scholastic, Inc.

—Scooby-Doo!TM & the Fantastic Puppet Factory. 2000. (Scooby-Doo Original Titles Ser.: No. 4). (Illus.). 32p. (J). (ps-3). 3.50 (978-0-439-17254-7(3)) Scholastic, Inc.

McCormick, Maggie. Dead Good Read: Classic Tales of Mystery & Horror. 1999. (978-1-84100-265-1(8)) Quadrillion Publishing.

McEown, Pat. Homecoming. 2000. (Illus.). 64p. pap. 7.95 (978-1-56971-405-8(3)) Dark Horse Comics.

McFarlane, Todd & Harmon, Paul. All Beasts Will Show Their Teeth. 2006. (Illus.). 128p. (YA). pap. 12.99 (978-1-58240-588-9(3)) Image Comics.

McKay, Sindy. We Both Read-Ben & Becky in the Haunted House. Johnson, Meredith, illus. 1999. (We Both Read Ser.). 44p. (J). (gr. 2 up). 7.99 (978-1-891327-14-8(3)); pap. 3.99 (978-1-891327-18-6(6)) Treasure Bay, Inc.

McKissack, Patricia C. The Dark-Thirty. Pinkney, Brian, illus. 2001. 176p. (J). (gr. 5). 6.50 (978-0-679-89006-5(8) , Yearling) Random Hse. Children's Bks.

—The Dark-Thirty: Southern Tales of the Supernatural. Pinkney, Brian, illus. 2004. 122p. (J). (gr. 5-8). reprint ed. pap. 17.00 (978-0-7567-7601-5(5)) DIANE Publishing Co.

—Dark-Thirty Southern Tales of the Supernatural. 2001. (gr. 5-8). lib. bdg. 13.55 (978-0-613-33690-1(9)) Tandem Library Bks.

Metz, Melinda & Burns, Laura J. Colony. 2005. (Buffy the Vampire Slayer Ser.). 256p. (YA). pap. 6.99 (978-1-4169-0057-3(8) , Simon Spotlight Entertainment) Simon & Schuster.

Mind Grabber. 64p. (YA). (gr. 6-12). pap. (978-0-8224-2335-5(9)) Globe Fearon Educational Publishing.

Moro, Robin, et al, illus. Read Aloud Spooky Stories. 320p. 15.98 (978-0-7853-6338-5(6) , 7159100) Publications International, Ltd.

Morris, Tony, illus. The Kingfisher Treasury of Ghost Stories. 2005. (Kingfisher Treasury of Stories Ser.). 160p. (gr. k-3). pap. 5.95 (978-0-7534-5890-7(X) , Kingfisher) Houghton Mifflin Co. Trade & Reference Div.

Moser, Barry, illus. Scary Stories. 2006. 96p. (J). (gr. 6-9). 16.95 (978-0-8118-5414-6(0) , SeaStar Bks.) Chronicle Bks. LLC.

Mullins, Denvil. Soapy-Dope: The Monster Who Lived in a Chuckhole. 2001. 32p. (J). (ps-3). 9.95 (978-1-57072-163-2(7)) Overmountain Pr.

Mutis, Alvaro. La Mansion de Araucaima: Diario de Lecumberri. (SPA.). (J). 8.00 (978-958-04-6975-9(X)) Norma S.A. COL. *Dist:* Distribuidora Norma, Inc.

Myers, Bill. The Undead. 2002. (Forbidden Doors Ser.: Vol. 8). (Illus.). 192p. (J). mass mkt. 4.99 (978-0-8423-5740-1(8)) Tyndale Hse. Pubs.

Myers, Bill & Riordan, James. The Wiccan. 2003. (Forbidden Doors Ser.: Vol. 11). 160p. (J). mass mkt. 5.99 (978-0-8423-7203-9(2) , 75 7203-2) Tyndale Hse. Pubs.

Nagler, Michelle H. Surf Scare. 2003. (gr. k-3). lib. bdg. 11.80 (978-0-613-72204-9(3)) Tandem Library Bks.

Naifeh, Ted. Courtney Crumrin & the Night Things. Jones, James Lucas, ed. 2005. (Illus.). 120p. lib. bdg. 19.00 (978-0-606-33365-8(7)) Tandem Library Bks.

Nance, Andrew. Daemon Hall. Polhemus, Coleman, illus. 2007. 272p. (YA). 16.95 (****978-0-8050-8171-8(2)***) Holt, Henry & Co.

Navarro, Yvonne. Paleo. 2000. (Buffy the Vampire Slayer Ser.: No. 11). 272p. (YA). pap. 6.99 (978-0-7434-0034-3(8) , Simon Pulse) Simon & Schuster Children's Publishing.

—Paleo. 2000. (gr. 7-12). lib. bdg. 15.30 (978-0-613-63329-1(6)) Tandem Library Bks.

—Shattered Twilight: Wicked Willow Two. 2004. (Buffy the Vampire Slayer Ser.). 272p. (YA). mass mkt. 13.95 (978-0-689-86953-2(3) , Simon Spotlight Entertainment) Simon & Schuster.

Naylor, Phyllis Reynolds. Jade Green: A Ghost Story. 2001. (gr. 5-8). lib. bdg. 13.00 (978-0-613-36438-6(4)); (Illus.). (J). 11.64 (978-0-606-20732-4(5)) Tandem Library Bks.

Neri, Filippo. Steam Park. Piero, Ruggeri, illus. 2006. 44p. 16.95 (978-1-894965-63-7(9)) Simply Read Bks. CAN. *Dist:* Perseus Distribution.

Night of the Living Dummy II. 2004. 120p. (J). (gr. 4-7). lib. bdg. 12.04 (978-0-606-30596-9(3)) Tandem Library Bks.

Nixon, Joan Lowery. The Haunting. 2000. (gr. 7-12). lib. bdg. 13.00 (978-0-613-28370-0(8)) Tandem Library Bks.

—Whispers from the Dead, unabr. ed. 2000. (YA). pap., stu. ed. 49.75 incl. audio (978-0-7887-3858-6(5) , 41058X4) Recorded Bks., LLC.

Norman, Tony. Terror World. Savage, Paul, illus. 2006. (Pathway Books). 33p. (J). 21.26 (978-1-59889-008-2(5)) Stone Arch Bks.

Noyes, Deborah. Gothic! Ten Original Dark Tales. 2006. 256p. (YA). (gr. 9). pap. 7.99 (978-0-7636-2737-9(2)) Candlewick Pr.

Noyes, Deborah, ed. Gothic! Ten Original Dark Tales. 2004. (Illus.). 256p. (YA). (gr. 9 up). 15.99 (978-0-7636-2243-5(5)) Candlewick Pr.

Noyes, Deborah, ed. The Restless Dead: Ten Original Stories of the Supernatural. 2007. (Illus.). 256p. (YA). (gr. 7). 16.99 (****978-0-7636-2906-9(5)***) Candlewick Pr.

Nye, Alex. Chill. 2006. 176p. (YA). 11.95 (978-0-86315-546-8(4)) Floris Bks. GBR. *Dist:* SteinerBooks, Inc.

Odom, Mel. Redemption. 2000. (gr. 7-12). lib. bdg. 14.15 (978-0-613-28038-9(5)) Tandem Library Bks.

—Revenant. 2001. (Buffy the Vampire Slayer Ser.: No. 12). 400p. (YA). pap. 6.99 (978-0-7434-0035-0(6) , Simon Pulse) Simon & Schuster Children's Publishing.

—Revenant. 2001. (gr. 7-12). lib. bdg. 15.30 (978-0-613-63340-6(7)) Tandem Library Bks.

—Tales of the Slayer. 2001. (gr. 7-12). lib. bdg. 17.65 (978-0-613-63351-2(2)) Tandem Library Bks.

Olin, Sean. Killing Britney. 2005. 240p. (YA). (gr. 9 up). pap. 8.99 (978-0-689-87778-0(1) , Simon Pulse) Simon & Schuster Children's Publishing.

Olliver, Jane. Kingfisher Treasury of Spooky Stories. 2003. (gr. k-3). lib. bdg. 14.10 (978-0-613-90575-6(X)) Tandem Library Bks.

Olson, Arielle North. Ask the Bones: Scary Stories from Around the World. 2002. (gr. 5-8). lib. bdg. 14.15 (978-0-613-56203-4(8)) Tandem Library Bks.

Olson, Arielle North & Schwartz, Howard. Ask the Bones: Scary Stories from Around the World. Linn, David, illus. 1999. 160p. (J). (gr. 3-7). 16.99 (978-0-670-87581-8(3) , Viking Juvenile) Penguin Group (USA) Inc.

Olson, Arielle North & Schwartz, Howard. More Bones. 2008. 176p. (J). (gr. 3). 15.99 (****978-0-670-06339-0(8)*** , Viking Juvenile) Penguin Group (USA) Inc.

Orme, David. Something Evil. Savage, Paul, illus. 2006. 40p. (J). (gr. 2-3). lib. bdg. (978-1-59889-017-4(4)) Stone Arch Bks.

Osborne, Mary Pope. The Land of the Dead. Howell, Troy, illus. 2nd rev. ed. 2003. (Odyssey Ser.: No. 2). 112p. (gr. 3-6). pap. 4.99 (978-0-7868-0929-5(9)) Hyperion Bks. for Children.

Paiba, Helen, compiled by. Scary Stories for Nine Year Olds. (Illus.). 280p. (J). (gr. 4). pap. 8.99 (978-0-330-37492-7(3) , Pan) Pan Macmillan GBR. *Dist:* Trafalgar Square Publishing.

Papineau, Lucie, et al. Baby Vampire, Gulp! Constantin, Pascale, illus. 1999. (Monster Country Ser.). 32p. (J). pap. (978-1-894363-21-1(3)) Dominique & Friends.

Paradine, Mike. King of Toys. 2006. 83p. pap. 14.95 (978-1-4241-2694-1(0)) PublishAmerica, Inc.

Parry, Glyn. Last Gasp. 2005. (Thrillogy Ser.). (Illus.). 48p. (gr. 4-8). 17.50 (978-0-7910-8890-6(1)) Facts On File, Inc.

Patrick, David. Nero Demare & the Legend of the Vampires. 2007. 284p. (YA). per. 17.95 (****978-0-595-42014-8(1)***) iUniverse, Inc.

Patschke, Steve. The Spooky Book. McElligott, Matthew, illus. 2001. (J). (gr. k-3). 26.90 incl. audio (978-0-8045-6871-5(5) , 6871) Spoken Arts, Inc.

Peel, John. Book of Nightmares. 1998. (Diadem Ser.: No. 6). (J). pap. 3.99 (978-0-590-14966-2(0) , Scholastic Paperbacks) Scholastic, Inc.

—Book of Nightmares. 1998. (Diadem Ser.). (978-0-606-13329-6(1)) Tandem Library Bks.

Pepper, Dennis. New Young Oxford Book of Ghost Stories. 2000. (gr. 7-12). lib. bdg. 22.20 (978-0-613-58672-6(7)) Tandem Library Bks.

Perkins, T J. On Forbidden Ground: Sequel to Mystery of the Attic. 2006. (Illus.). 112p. (YA). 10.99 (978-0-9777538-7-1(5)) GumShoe Press.

Perro Monstruoso. (Fantasmas de Fear Street Coleccion). (SPA.). (YA). (gr. 5-8). pap. 7.95 (978-950-04-1930-7(0) , EM0316) Emecé Editores S.A. ARG. *Dist:* Lectorum Pubns., Inc., Planeta Publishing Corp.

Perry, Glyn & Parry, Glyn. Invisible Girl. 2003. 160p. (YA). pap. 15.25 (978-1-920731-48-9(2)) Fremantle Pr. AUS. *Dist:* International Specialized Bk. Services.

Perry, Janet & Gentle, Victor. Mad Scientists. 1999. (Imagination Library). (Illus.). 24p. (J). (gr. 2 up). lib. bdg. 22.00 (978-0-8368-2438-4(5)) Stevens, Gareth Inc.

—Vampires. 1999. (Imagination Library). (Illus.). 24p. (J). (gr. 2 up). lib. bdg. 22.00 (978-0-8368-2442-1(3)) Stevens, Gareth Inc.

—Zombies. 1999. (Imagination Library). (Illus.). 24p. (J). (gr. 2 up). lib. bdg. 22.00 (978-0-8368-2443-8(1)) Stevens, Gareth Inc.

Peterson, Brandon & Brereton, Dan. Giant Killer. 2006. (Illus.). 128p. (YA). pap. 14.99 (978-1-58240-539-1(5)) Image Comics.

Petrucha, Stefan. Lurker. 2007. (Wicked Dead Ser.: No. 1). 224p. (J). (gr. 7 up). pap. 7.99 (****978-0-06-113849-2(5)*** , HarperTeen) HarperCollins Pubs.

—Snared. 2008. (Wicked Dead Ser.: No.3). 224p. (J). pap. 7.99 (****978-0-06-113851-5(7)*** , HarperTeen) HarperCollins Pubs.

Petrucha, Stefan & Pendleton, Thomas. Crush. 2008. (Wicked Dead Ser.). 224p. (J). pap. 7.99 (****978-0-06-113852-2(5)*** , HarperTeen) HarperCollins Pubs.

—Teacher's Pet. 2008. (YA). (****978-0-06-113853-9(3)*** , HarperTeen) HarperCollins Pubs.

—Torn. 2007. (Wicked Dead Ser.: No. 2). 224p. (YA). (gr. 7 up). pap. 7.99 (****978-0-06-113850-8(9)*** , HarperTeen) HarperCollins Pubs.

Philbrick, Rodman & Harnett, Lynn. Le Dernier Cauchemar Bk. 3: The Final Nightmare.Tr. of Maison de la Rue du Cerisier: Le Dernier Cauchemar. (FRE.). (YA). pap. 5.99 (978-0-590-24676-7(3)) Scholastic, Inc.

—L' Ensorcellement Bk. 1: The Haunting.Tr. of Maison de la Rue du Cerisier: L'Ensorcellement. (FRE.). (YA). pap. 5.99 (978-0-590-24674-3(7)) Scholastic, Inc.

—La Terreur Bk. 2: The Horror.Tr. of Maison de la Rue du Cerisier: La Terreur. (FRE.). (YA). pap. 5.99 (978-0-590-24675-0(5)) Scholastic, Inc.

Pienkowski, Jan. Haunted House. Pienkowski, Jan, illus. 2005. (Illus.). 12p. (J). (ps up). 14.99 (978-0-7636-2818-5(2)) Candlewick Pr.

Pierce, Meredith A. Gathering of Gargoyles, Vol. 2. 1998. (Darkangel Trilogy Ser.). 12.65 (978-0-606-13415-6(8)) Tandem Library Bks.

Pijoan, Teresa. Stories from a Dark & Evil World. Sharon, Franco, tr. Kosharek, Daniel, illus. 1999. (Bilingual Ser.).Tr. of Cuentos del Mundo Malevolo. (SPA.). 200p. (gr. 8-12). pap. 14.95 (978-1-878610-71-3(6)) Red Crane Bks., Inc.

Pike, Christopher, pseud. Bury Me Deep. 2001. 224p. (YA). reprint ed. mass mkt. 5.99 (978-0-7434-2424-0(7) , Simon Pulse) Simon & Schuster Children's Publishing.

—Christopher Pike's Tales of Terror. 4th ed. (Illus.). (YA). (978-0-671-55085-1(3) , Simon & Schuster Children's Publishing) Simon & Schuster Children's Publishing.

—Christopher Pike's Tales of Terror, No. 2. 1998. 11.15 (978-0-606-13275-6(9)) Tandem Library Bks.

—The Grave: A Novel. 1999. (Illus.). (YA). 12.64 (978-0-606-17950-8(X)) Tandem Library Bks.

—The Hollow Skull. (Illus.). (J). 14.00 (978-0-671-55060-8(8) , Simon & Schuster Children's Publishing) Simon & Schuster Children's Publishing.

—The Hollow Skull. 1998. 12.64 (978-0-606-12965-7(0)) Tandem Library Bks.

—The Living Dead. 1998. (Spooksville Ser.: No. 21). (J). (gr. 4-6). (978-0-606-13797-3(1)) Tandem Library Bks.

—Phone Fear. 1998. (Spooksville Ser.). (J). (gr. 4-6). (978-0-606-13799-7(8)) Tandem Library Bks.

—Remember Me. ed. 2001. (Remember Me Ser.: No. 1). 240p. (YA). (gr. 8 up). reprint ed. mass mkt. 5.99 (978-0-7434-2801-9(3) , Simon Pulse) Simon & Schuster Children's Publishing.

—Remember Me. 2002. (Remember Me Ser.: No. 1). (gr. 7-12). lib. bdg. 14.15 (978-0-613-52993-8(6)) Tandem Library Bks.

—Road to Nowhere. ed. 2002. 224p. (YA). mass mkt. 5.99 (978-0-7434-2428-8(X) , Simon Pulse) Simon & Schuster Children's Publishing.

—Road to Nowhere. 2002. (gr. 7-12). lib. bdg. 14.15 (978-0-613-74177-4(3)) Tandem Library Bks.

Pilkey, Dav. God Bless the Gargoyles. 1999. (Illus.). 36p. (J). (ps-3). pap. 7.00 (978-0-15-202104-7(3) , Harcourt Paperbacks) Harcourt Children's Bks.

—God Bless the Gargoyles. 1999. (J). (978-0-606-17359-9(5)); lib. bdg. 14.15 (978-0-613-21606-7(7)) Tandem Library Bks.

Piven, Hanoch. The Scary Show of Mo & Jo. Piven, Hanoch, illus. 2005. (Illus.). 32p. (J). (ps-3). 18.95 (978-0-7624-2097-1(9) , Running Pr. Kids) Running Pr. Bk. Pubs.

Plum-Ucci, Carol. The She. 2005. (Illus.). 372p. (YA). (gr. 9-17). reprint ed. pap. 6.95 (978-0-15-205453-3(7) , Harcourt Paperbacks) Harcourt Children's Bks.

Poe, Edgar Allan. The Cask of Amontillado. Kisner, Don, ed. rev. ed. 1998. 44p. (YA). (gr. 7 up). ring bd. 38.00 incl. audio (978-1-878298-15-7(1)) Balance Publishing Co.

—Edgar Allan Poe. McConnell, James, illus. 2004. (Great American Short Stories Ser.). 73p. (J). lib. bdg. 23.33 (978-0-8368-4254-8(5)) Stevens, Gareth Inc.

—El Escarabajo de Oro: El Diablo en el Capanario, Corazon Traidor, El Gato Negro, Silencio. 2000. (Coleccion "Clasicos Juveniles" Ser.). (SPA.). 108p. (gr. 4-7). pap. 8.95 (978-1-58348-835-5(9)) iUniverse, Inc.

—The Raven & Other Writings. 2003. (Aladdin Classics Ser.). 448p. pap. 4.99 (978-0-689-86352-3(7) , Aladdin) Simon & Schuster Children's Publishing.

—Tales of Mystery & Imagination. Jones, Barry, illus. 2004. (Paperback Classics Ser.). 144p. (J). pap. 4.95 (978-0-7945-0186-0(9) , Usborne) EDC Publishing.

—Tales of Mystery & Madness. Grimly, Gris, illus. 2004. 144p. (J). 17.95 (978-0-689-84837-7(4) , Atheneum) Simon & Schuster Children's Publishing.

—Tales of Mystery & Terror. Pablo Marcos Studio Staff, illus. 2002. (Great Illustrated Classics Ser.). 240p. (J). (gr. 3-8). 21.35 (978-1-57765-815-3(9) , ABDO & Daughters) ABDO Publishing Co.

—Tales of Terror from Edgar Allan Poe. McCurdy, Michael, illus. 2005. 96p. (J). (gr. 5-7). 15.95 (978-0-375-83305-2(6)); lib. bdg. 17.99 (978-0-375-93305-9(0)) Random Hse. Children's Bks. (Knopf Bks. for Young Readers).

Poe, Edgar Allan & Allan, T. Tales of Mystery & Imagination. 144p. (J). lib. bdg. 12.95 (978-1-58086-677-4(8) , Usborne) EDC Publishing.

Poe, Edgar Allan & Bierce, Ambrose. Tales of Mystery & Horror. 2005. 160p. (J). per. 6.99 (978-1-58049-362-8(9) , PWH3629) Prestwick Hse., Inc.

Poe, Edgar Allan & Coleman, Wim. Retold Edgar Allan Poe. Aspengren, Michael A., illus. 2000. (Retold Classics Anthologies Ser.). 128p. (J). (978-0-7891-5123-0(5)) Perfection Learning Corp.

Poe, Edgar Allan & Delbanco, Andrew. Edgar Allan Poe. Dubois, Gérard, illus. 2006. (Stories for Young People Ser.). 80p. (J). (*978-1-4027-4233-0(9)) Sterling Publishing Co., Inc.

Poe, Edgar Allan & Naudi, Margaret. Tales of Mystery & Imagination, Level 3. 2nd ed. 2000. (Bookworms Ser.). (Illus.). 80p. 6.50 (978-0-19-423017-9(1)) Oxford Univ. Pr., Inc.

Poe, Edgar Allan, et al. The Fall of the House of Usher. (Classics Illustrated Ser.). (Illus.). 52p. (YA). pap. 4.95 (978-1-57209-014-9(6)) Classics International Entertainment, Inc.

Pond Sharon Johnson. Tales from Beach Cottage. 2006. 124p. pap. 14.95 (978-1-933251-24-0(7)) Parkway Pubs., Inc.

Powell, Jillian. Roller Coaster. Savage, Paul, illus. 2008. (Keystone Books). (J). pap. (*978-1-59889-902-3(3)); 33p. (YA). (gr. 5-9). lib. bdg. 21.26 (*978-1-59889-850-7(7)) Stone Arch Bks.

Price, Susan. Horror Stories. 2003. (gr. 5-8). lib. bdg. 15.25 (978-0-613-67414-0(6)) Tandem Library Bks.

—Olly Spellmaker & the Sulky Smudge. l.t. ed. 2005. (J). pap. (978-0-7540-7936-1(8) , CLP 485) BBC Audio.

Price, Susan, selected by. The Dark Side: Truly Terrifying Tales. 2007. 272p. (J). (gr. 4-7). pap. 6.95 (*978-0-7534-6143-3(9) , Kingfisher) Houghton Mifflin Co. Trade & Reference Div.

Priestley, Chris. Uncle Montague's Tales of Terror. Roberts, David, illus. 2007. 192p. (J). (gr. 3-7). 12.95 (*978-1-59990-118-3(8) , Bloomsbury Children) Bloomsbury Publishing.

Pullman, Philip. The Subtle Knife. (His Dark Materials Ser.: Bk. 2). (YA). (gr. 7-12). 2003. lib. bdg. 15.30 (978-0-613-72255-1(8)); 2002. lib. bdg. 21.05 (978-0-613-71929-2(8)) Tandem Library Bks.

Punter, Russell. Monsters, Stories Of. 2004. (Young Reading Series One Ser.). 48p. (J). (gr. 2 up). pap. 5.95 (978-0-7945-0757-2(3) , Usborne) EDC Publishing.

Rand, Johnathan. Aliens Attack Alpena. 1999. (Michigan Chillers: Vol. 4). 208p. (YA). pap. 5.99 (978-1-893699-09-0(9)) AudioCraft Publishing, Inc.

—Gargoyles of Gaylord. 2000. (Michigan Chillers: Vol. 5). 204p. (YA). pap. 5.99 (978-1-893699-10-6(2)) AudioCraft Publishing, Inc.

—Mackinaw City Mummies. 2001. (Michigan Chillers: Vol. 10). (YA). pap. 5.99 (978-1-893699-18-2(8)) AudioCraft Publishing, Inc.

—Michigan Mega-Monsters. 2001. (American Chillers: Vol. 1). 208p. (YA). pap. 5.99 (978-1-893699-19-9(6)) AudioCraft Publishing, Inc.

—Poltergeists of Petoskey. 1999. (Michigan Chillers: Vol. 3). 224p. (J). pap. 5.99 (978-1-893699-08-3(0)) AudioCraft Publishing, Inc.

—Strange Spirits of St. Ignace. 2000. (Michigan Chillers: Vol. 6). 208p. (YA). pap. 5.99 (978-1-893699-11-3(0)) AudioCraft Publishing, Inc.

—Terror Stalks Traverse City. 1999. (Michigan Chillers: Vol. 2). 208p. (J). pap. 5.99 (978-1-893699-07-6(2)) AudioCraft Publishing, Inc.

Rand, Jonathan. Sinister Spiders or Saginaw. 2001. (Michigan Chillers: Vol. 9). 265p. (YA). pap. 5.99 (978-1-893699-15-1(3)) AudioCraft Publishing, Inc.

Randall, Rod. Along Came a Spider. 2000. (Heebie Jeebies Ser.: Vol. 7). 138p. (J). (gr. 3-7). pap. 5.99 (978-0-8054-1981-8(0)) B&H Publishing Grp.

Randau, Rod. Piranha Picnic. 2001. (Heebie Jeebies Ser.: Vol. 9). 138p. (J). (gr. 3-7). pap. 5.99 (978-0-8054-2332-7(X)) B&H Publishing Grp.

Random House Disney Staff. Haunted Mansion: The Junior Novelization. 2003. (gr. 3-6). lib. bdg. 13.00 (978-0-613-73704-3(0)) Tandem Library Bks.

Ratnett, Michael & Smyth, Iain. Monster Train. Goulding, June, illus. 2000. 12p. (J). (ps-1). pap. 15.95 (978-0-531-30293-4(8) , Orchard Bks.) Scholastic, Inc.

Rees, Celia. Host Rides Out. 2002. (gr. 3-6). lib. bdg. 16.40 (978-0-613-71842-4(9)) Tandem Library Bks.

Reiche, Dietlof. The Haunting of Freddy. 2007. (Golden Hamster Saga Ser.: Bk. 4). 320p. (J). pap. 5.99 (978-0-439-53160-3(8) , Scholastic Paperbacks) Scholastic, Inc.

Reiss, Kathryn. Pale Phoenix. 2003. (gr. 7-12). lib. bdg. 14.10 (978-0-613-67837-7(0)) Tandem Library Bks.

Ren Wright, Betty & Wright, Betty Ren. The Moonlight Man. 2005. 192p. (J). (ps-7). pap. 4.99 (978-0-590-25238-6(0) , Scholastic Paperbacks) Scholastic, Inc.

Richards, Justin. The Invisible Detective: Double Life. 2005. 160p. (J). (gr. 4). 10.99 (978-0-399-24313-4(5) , Putnam Juvenile) Penguin Group (USA) Inc.

—The Invisible Detective: Ghost Soldiers. 2006. 160p. (J). (gr. 4). 11.99 (978-0-399-24500-8(6) , Putnam Juvenile) Penguin Group (USA) Inc.

—The Invisible Detective: Shadow Beast. 2005. 160p. (YA). (gr. 4). 10.99 (978-0-399-24314-1(3) , Putnam Juvenile) Penguin Group (USA) Inc.

Richards, Zackary. Frostie the Deadman. 2004. 222p. (J). pap. 14.95 (978-0-9713069-8-1(2)) Burns, Nicholas K. Publishing.

Richardson, E. E. Devil's Footsteps. 192p. 2006. (YA). (gr. 9). mass mkt. 5.99 (978-0-440-23916-1(8) , Laurel Leaf); 2005. (J). (gr. 7 up). lib. bdg. 17.99 (978-0-385-90279-3(4) , Delacorte Bks. for Young Readers); 2005. (YA). (gr. 7 up). 15.95 (978-0-385-73263-5(5) , Delacorte Bks. for Young Readers) Random Hse. Children's Bks.

—The Intruders. 2006. 208p. (J). (gr. 7). 15.95 (978-0-385-73264-2(3) , Delacorte Bks. for Young Readers) Random Hse. Children's Bks.

Riddle, Waide. The Chocolate Man: A Children's Horror Tale. 2003. 24p. (J). 9.95 (978-0-9724619-1-7(4)) Passage Publishing.

Ridley, R. W. Dèlon City: Book Two of the Oz Chronicles. 2006. (YA). per. 14.99 (*978-0-9792067-0-2(7)) Middleburry Hse. Publishing.

Robertson, M. P., retold by. The Moon in Swampland. 2004. (Illus.). 32p. (J). 15.95 (978-1-84507-095-3(X)) Lincoln, Frances Ltd. GBR. *Dist:* Perseus Distribution.

Rocklin, Joanne. This Book Is Haunted. Adinolfi, JoAnn, illus. (I Can Read Bks.). 48p. (J). (gr. k-3). 2003. pap. 3.99 (978-0-06-444261-9(6)); 2002. 17.89 (978-0-06-028457-2(9)) HarperCollins Pubs.

—This Book Is Haunted. 2001. (gr. k-3). lib. bdg. 11.80 (978-0-613-68388-3(9)) Tandem Library Bks.

Rodríguez, Pedro, illus. The Big Book of Horror: 21 Tales to Make You Tremble. 2006. 112p. (J). (gr. 4-6). 12.95 (978-1-4027-3860-9(9)) Sterling Publishing Co., Inc.

Ross, Harriet, ed. Great Horror Stories. 2000. (Illus.). 160p. (J). (gr. 3-9). pap. 6.95 (978-0-87460-188-6(6)) Lion Bks.

Ross, Tony, illus. Scary Stories for 8 Year 0lds. 221p. (J). (gr. 3). pap. 8.99 (978-0-330-34944-4(9) , Pan) Pan Macmillan GBR. *Dist:* Trafalgar Square Publishing.

Roxbury Park Staff. Scary Classics: Stories from the Greatest Horror Writers of All Time. 2000. (Illus.). viii, 246p. (J). pap. 9.95 (978-0-7373-0438-1(3) , Roxbury Park) Lowell Hse.

Rushby, Pamela. Haunted Houses: Footsteps, Shadows in the Garden, the Midnight Children. 2005. (Triple Play-Yellow Ser.). (Illus.). 48p. (gr. 4-8). 41.85 (978-0-7910-9078-7(7)) Facts On File, Inc.

San Souci, Daniel. Haunting of Pomo Point. 1999. (J). (978-0-385-32146-4(5) , Dell Books for Young Readers) Random Hse. Children's Bks.

San Souci, Robert D. Dare to Be Scared: Thirteen Stories to Chill & Thrill. Ouimet, David, illus. 2003. (Dare to Be Scared Ser.). 144p. (J). (gr. 3-7). 16.95 (978-0-8126-2688-9(5)) Cricket Bks.

—More Short & Shivery. Coville, Katherine, illus. 2002. 176p. (J). (gr. 5). pap. 5.50 (978-0-440-41857-3(7) , Yearling) Random Hse. Children's Bks.

—More Short & Shivery. 2002. (gr. 5-8). lib. bdg. 15.30 (978-0-613-86685-9(1)) Tandem Library Bks.

—Triple-Dare to Be Scared: Thirteen Further Freaky Tales. Ouimet, David, illus. 2007. (Dare to Be Scared Ser.). 240p. (J). (gr. 6-9). 16.95 (978-0-8126-2749-7(0)) Cricket Bks.

Santillana U. S. A. Publishing Co, Inc. Staff. Los Mejores Relatos de Terror. 2000. (SPA., Illus.). 175p. (J). (gr. 8-12). pap. 11.95 (978-84-204-4491-8(X)) Santillana USA Publishing Co., Inc.

Schade, Susan. Baseball Camp on the Planet of the Eyeballs. Buller, Jon, illus. 1998. (Step into Reading Step 3 Bks.). (J). (gr. 2-3). (978-0-606-13950-2(8)) Tandem Library Bks.

Schkolnik, Saul. Cuentos de Terror, de Magia y de Otras Cosas Extranas. (SPA.). (YA). (gr. 5-8). pap. (978-956-13-1319-4(7) , AB0160) Bello, Andres CHL. *Dist:* Lectorum Pubns., Inc.

Schreiber, Ellen. Kissing Coffins. 2005. (Vampire Kisses Ser.: Bk. 2). (gr. 7 up). 176p. (J). lib. bdg. 16.89 (978-0-06-077623-7(4)); 2nd ed. 165p. 16.99 (978-0-06-077622-0(6)) HarperCollins Pubs. (Tegen, Katherine Bks).

Schroeder, Lisa. I Heart You, You Haunt Me. 2008. 240p. (YA). pap. 7.99 (*978-1-4169-5520-7(8) , Simon Pulse) Simon & Schuster Children's Publishing.

Schultz, Mark. Predator: Hell & Hot Water. 1998. (gr. 7-12). lib. bdg. 18.75 (978-0-613-78998-1(9)) Tandem Library Bks.

Schwartz, Alvin. Historias de Miedo 2: Relatos Espeluznantes para No Dejarte Dormir. Irving, George S., illus. 2004. (Historias de Miedo Scary Stories to Tell in the Dark Ser.).Tr. of More Scary Stories to Tell in the Dark. (SPA.). (YA). pap. 9.99 (978-84-241-8663-0(X)) Everest de Ediciones y Distribucion, S.L. ESP. *Dist:* Lectorum Pubns., Inc.

—Historias de Miedo 3: Relatos Aterradores para Helarte la Sangre. Irving, George S., illus. 2004. (Historias de Miedo Scary Stories to Tell in the Dark Ser.).Tr. of Scary Stories 3: More Tales to Chill Your Bones. (SPA.). (YA). pap. 9.99 (978-84-241-8664-7(8)) Everest de Ediciones y Distribucion, S.L. ESP. *Dist:* Lectorum Pubns., Inc.

—In a Dark, Dark Room & Other Scary Stories. 2002. (Illus.). (J). 11.91 (978-0-7587-6149-1(X)) Book Wholesalers, Inc.

—Scary Stories. 2002. (J). 14.47 (978-0-7587-6726-4(9)) Book Wholesalers, Inc.

—Scary Stories 3: More Tales to Chill Your Bones. 2002. (Illus.). (J). 14.47 (978-0-7587-6725-7(0)) Book Wholesalers, Inc.

—Scary Stories 3: More Tales to Chill Your Bones. Gammell, Stephen, illus. 2001. (Scary Stories Ser.). 128p. (J). (gr. 4 up). 16.99 (978-0-06-021794-5(4)) HarperCollins Pubs.

—Scary Stories Box Set: Scary Stories 3: More Tales to Chill Your Bones; More Scary Storiess: To Tell in the Dark; Scary Stories: To Tell in the Dark. Gammell, Stephen, illus. 2001. (Trophy Bk.). 208p. (J). (gr. 4 up). pap. 17.97 (978-0-06-440465-5(X) , Harper Trophy) HarperCollins Pubs.

Scott, James. Frankenstein: Activity Pack. 2002. 136p. (YA). (gr. 7-12). pap. 34.95 (978-1-58049-609-4(1) , PA0106) Prestwick Hse., Inc.

Scott, Stefanie. Meet the Stars of Buffy the Vampire Slayer. 1998. (Illus.). 128p. (J). (gr. 6-8). pap. 4.99 (978-0-590-51477-4(6)) Scholastic, Inc.

Seabrooke, Brenda. The Vampire in My Bathtub. 1999. 160p. (J). (gr. 4-6). tchr. ed. 16.95 (978-0-8234-1505-2(8)) Holiday Hse., Inc.

SeaStar Publishing Staff, ed. Scary Stories: To Read When It's Dark. 2000. (Reading Rainbow Ser.). (Illus.). 64p. (J). (gr. 1-3). pap. 3.99 (978-1-58717-035-5(3) , SeaStar Bks.) Chronicle Bks. LLC.

Sedgwick, Marcus. The Book of Dead Days. 2006. pap. 5.50 (978-0-440-41909-9(3)); 288p. (J). (gr. 5). reprint ed. pap. 7.95 (978-0-385-74704-2(7) , Lamb, Wendy) Random Hse. Children's Bks.

Sedgwick, Marcus. The Dark Flight Down. 240p. 2008. (YA). (gr. 7). pap. 7.99 (*978-0-553-48784-8(1)); 2005. (J). (gr. 5-7). 15.95 (978-0-385-74645-8(8)) Random Hse. Children's Bks. (Lamb, Wendy).

Selznick, Brian. The Boy of a Thousand Faces. Selznick, Brian, illus. 2000. (Illus.). 48p. (J). (gr. 3 up). lib. bdg. 14.89 (978-0-06-026266-2(4) , Geringer, Laura Book) HarperCollins Pubs.

Seymour, Lee. Monster Lake. 2005. 212p. (J). pap. 12.00 (978-1-889186-56-6(2) , Little Devil Books) Necro Pubns.

Shadow, Nick & Graves, Damien. Voices. 2006. (Apple Ser.: Vol. 1). (Illus.). 176p. (J). pap. 5.99 (978-0-439-86356-8(2)) Scholastic, Inc.

Shahan, Sherry. Wait until Dark: Seven Scary Sleepover Stories. 2000. (gr. 3-6). lib. bdg. 18.75 (978-0-613-81927-5(6)) Tandem Library Bks.

Shan, Darren, pseud. Allies of the Night. (Cirque du Freak: Bk. 8). (J). (gr. 5-17). 2006. 224p. mass mkt. 6.99 (978-0-316-10653-5(4)); 2005. 256p. pap. 7.99 (978-0-316-11437-0(5)) Little Brown & Co.

—Allies of the Night. 2004. (Cirque du Freak: Bk. 8). (Illus.). 192p. (J). (gr. 5-17). 15.99 (978-0-316-15570-0(5)) Little, Brown Bks. for Young Readers.

—Bec. 2007. (Demonata Ser.: No. 4). 256p. (J). (gr. 7 up). 16.99 (978-0-316-01389-5(7)) Little Brown & Co.

—Blood Beast. 2007. (Demonata Ser.: No. 5). 240p. (YA). (gr. 10-17). 16.99 (*978-0-316-00377-3(8)) Little, Brown Bks. for Young Readers.

—Cirque du Freak: Book 1, 2, 3. 2007. 736p. pap. 7.95 (*978-0-316-02304-7(3)) Little, Brown Bks. for Young Readers.

—Cirque du Freak: Trials of Death; the Vampire Prince; Hunters of the Dusk; Allies of the Night. 2006. (Cirque du Freak: No. 2). (J). (gr. 7-17). pap. 27.99 (978-0-316-01684-1(5)) Little Brown & Co.

—Cirque du Freak Boxed Set: Killers of the Dawn; The Lake of Souls; Lord of the Shadows; Sons of Destiny, 3. 2007. (Cirque du Freak: Bks. 9-12). (J). (gr. 7-17). pap. 27.99 (*978-0-316-06697-6(4)) Little, Brown Bks. for Young Readers.

—Demon Thief. 2006. (Demonata Ser.: No. 2). 256p. (J). (gr. 10-17). 15.99 (978-0-316-01237-9(8)) Little Brown & Co.

—Demon Thief. 2007. (Demonata Ser.: No. 2). 256p. (J). (gr. 10-17). pap. 8.99 (*978-0-316-01238-6(6)) Little, Brown Bks. for Young Readers.

—The Demonata. 2007. (YA). (gr. 10-12). pap., per. 26.99 (*978-0-316-02141-8(5)) Little, Brown Bks. for Young Readers.

—Hunters of the Dusk. 2005. (Cirque du Freak: Bk. 7). (J). (gr. 5-17). 256p. mass mkt. 6.99 (978-0-316-00098-7(1)); (Illus.). 224p. pap. 7.99 (978-0-316-60211-2(6)) Little Brown & Co.

—Hunters of the Dusk. 2004. (Cirque du Freak: Bk. 7). (Illus.). 224p. (J). (gr. 5-17). 15.95 (978-0-316-60596-0(4)) Little, Brown Bks. for Young Readers.

—Killers of the Dawn. (Cirque du Freak: Bk. 9). 224p. (J). (gr. 5-17). 2006. mass mkt. 6.99 (978-0-316-01666-7(7)); 2006. pap. 7.99 (978-0-316-10654-2(2)); 2005. 15.99 (978-0-316-15626-4(4)) Little Brown & Co.

—The Lake of Souls. (Cirque du Freak: Bk. 10). (J). (gr. 5-17). 2006. 272p. pap. 7.99 (978-0-316-01665-0(9)); 2005. (Illus.). 302p. 16.99 (978-0-316-15627-1(2)) Little Brown & Co.

—The Lake of Souls. 2007. (Cirque du Freak: Bk. 10). 288p. (J). (gr. 5-17). mass mkt. 6.99 (978-0-316-15437-6(7)) Little, Brown Bks. for Young Readers.

—A Living Nightmare. 2001. (Cirque du Freak: Bk. 1). (J). 272p. (gr. k-3). 15.95 (978-0-316-60340-9(6)); (Illus.). viii, 279p. (gr. 3-6). pap. (978-0-316-64852-3(3)) Little, Brown Bks. for Young Readers.

—Lord Loss. (Demonata Ser.: No. 1). 240p. (J). 2006. (gr. 10-17). pap. 8.99 (978-0-316-01233-1(5)); 2005. (gr. 7-17). 15.99 (978-0-316-11499-8(5)) Little Brown & Co.

—Lord of the Shadows. 2006. (Cirque du Freak: Bk. 11). (Illus.). 240p. (J). (gr. 3-7). 16.99 (978-0-316-15628-8(0)) Little Brown & Co.

—Lord of the Shadows. 2007. (Cirque du Freak: Bk. 11). (J). (gr. 3-7). 208p. mass mkt. 6.99 (*978-0-316-01662-9(4)); 256p. pap. 7.99 (*978-0-316-01661-2(6)) Little, Brown Bks. for Young Readers.

—Slawter. 2006. (Demonata Ser.: No. 3). 240p. (J). (gr. 10-17). 16.99 (978-0-316-01387-1(0)) Little Brown & Co.

—Slawter. 2007. (Demonata Ser.: No. 3). 240p. (J). (gr. 10-17). pap. 8.99 (*978-0-316-01388-8(9)) Little, Brown Bks. for Young Readers.

—Sons of Destiny. 2006. (Cirque du Freak: Bk. 12). 256p. (J). (gr. 3-7). 16.99 (978-0-316-15629-5(9)) Little Brown & Co.

—Sons of Destiny. 2007. (Cirque du Freak: Bk. 12). 272p. (J). (gr. 3-7). mass mkt. 6.99 (*978-0-316-01664-3(0)); (gr. 7-17). pap. 7.99 (*978-0-316-01663-6(2)) Little, Brown Bks. for Young Readers.

—Trials of Death. (Cirque du Freak: Bk. 5). 224p. (J). (gr. 5-17). 2005. mass mkt. 6.99 (978-0-316-00095-6(7)); 2004. pap. 7.99 (978-0-316-60395-9(3)); 2003. (Illus.). 16.99 (978-0-316-60367-6(8)) Little, Brown Bks. for Young Readers.

—Tunnels of Blood. 2004. (Cirque du Freak: Bk. 3). (Illus.). 240p. (J). (gr. 3-7). mass mkt. 6.99 (978-0-316-90573-2(9)) Little, Brown Bks. for Young Readers.

—Vampire Mountain. (Cirque du Freak: Bk. 4). (J). 2004. 208p. (gr. 3-7). mass mkt. 6.99 (978-0-316-90574-9(7)); 2003. (Illus.). 208p. (gr. 5-8). pap. 7.99 (978-0-316-60542-7(5)); 2003. (Illus.). 240p. (gr. 5-8). pap. 7.99 (978-0-316-60608-0(1)); 2002. (Illus.). 208p. (gr. 5-17). 15.95 (978-0-316-60806-0(8)); 2002. 240p. (gr. 5-17). 16.99 (978-0-316-60763-6(0)) Little, Brown Bks. for Young Readers.

—Vampire Mountain. 2003. (Cirque du Freak: Bk. 4). (gr. 5-8). lib. bdg. 14.75 (978-0-613-71781-6(3)); (J). (gr. 3-6). lib. bdg. 15.30 (978-0-613-71782-3(1)) Tandem Library Bks.

Shelley, Mary Wollstonecraft. Frankenstein. Pablo Marcos Studio Staff, illus. 2002. (Great Illustrated Classics Ser.). 240p. (J). (gr. 3-8). 21.35 (978-1-57765-686-9(5) , ABDO & Daughters) ABDO Publishing Co.

—Frankenstein. Stevens, David, ed. 1998. (Illus.). 286p. pap. 13.00 (978-0-521-58702-0(6)) Cambridge Univ. Pr.

—Frankenstein. 2001. (Fast Track Classics Ser.). (Illus.). 46p. pap. 9.99 (978-0-237-52280-3(2) , Evans Brothers, Limited) Evans Publishing Group GBR. *Dist:* Independent Pubs. Group.

—Frankenstein. Cruz, Nardo, illus. 2005. 48p. (gr. 5-8). 25.50 (978-0-7910-9100-5(7)) Facts On File, Inc.

—Frankenstein. (J). 9.95 (978-1-56156-309-8(9)) Kidsbooks, Inc.

—Frankenstein. Barr, Ken, illus. 2005. (Stepping Stone Bks.). 96p. (J). (gr. 3-5). pap. 3.99 (978-0-394-84827-3(6) , Random Hse. Bks. for Young Readers) Random Hse. Children's Bks.

—Frankenstein. Munteanu, Anca, ed. 2001. (Illus.). 240p. pap., stu. ed. 9.99 (978-0-7645-8726-9(9) , Cliff Notes) Wiley, John & Sons, Inc.

—Frankenstein. Hegarty, Carol, ed. 1998. (Classics Ser.: Set I). (Illus.). 80p. (YA). (gr. 5-12). 6.95 (978-1-56254-264-1(8) , SP2648) Saddleback Educational Publishing.

—Frankenstein. Akib, Jamel, illus. 2006. (Classic Starts Ser.). 160p. (J). 4.95 (978-1-4027-2666-8(X)) Sterling Publishing Co., Inc.

—Frankenstein: Or the Modern Prometheus. Joseph, M. K., ed. 1998. (Oxford World's Classics Ser.). 260p. (gr. 7 up). 7.95 (978-0-19-283487-4(8)) Oxford Univ. Pr., Inc.

—Frankenstein: With a Discussion of Tolerance. Clift, Eva, tr. Clift, Eva, illus. 2003. (Values in Action Illustrated Classics Ser.). (J). (978-1-59203-048-4(3)) Learning Challenge, Inc.

Shelley, Mary Wollstonecraft & Grant, J. Frankenstein. 144p. (J). lib. bdg. 12.95 (978-1-58086-667-5(0) , Usborne) EDC Publishing.

Shusterman, Neal. Darkness Creeping: Twenty Twisted Tales. 2007. 304p. (YA). (gr. 5 up). pap. 7.99 (978-0-14-240721-9(6) , Puffin) Penguin Group (USA) Inc.

—Full Tilt. 208p. (YA). 2004. mass mkt. 5.99 (978-0-689-87325-6(5) , Simon Pulse); 2003. (Illus.). 16.95 (978-0-689-80374-1(5)) Simon & Schuster Children's Publishing.

—Full Tilt. l.t. ed. 2003. 243p. (J). 22.95 (978-0-7862-5886-4(1)) Thorndike Pr.

—The Schwa Was Here. 2004. 240p. (J). (gr. 6). 16.99 (978-0-525-47182-0(0) , Dutton Juvenile) Penguin Group (USA) Inc.

Siembieda, Kevin. Heros Unlimited G. M. Guide. Marciniszyn, Alex et al, eds. Zeleznik, John et al, illus. 1999. (Heroes Unlimited Ser.). 224p. (YA). (gr. 8 up). pap. 20.95 (978-1-57457-035-9(8)) Palladium Bks., Inc.

—Rifter, No. 8. Smith, Wayne & Osten, James, eds. Brom, Gerald et al, illus. 1999. (Rifter Ser.: Vol. 8). 112p. (YA). (gr. 8 up). pap. 7.95 (978-1-57457-036-6(6)) Palladium Bks., Inc.

Siembieda, Kevin & Thompson, Eric. Rifts Canada. Marciniszyn, Alex et al, eds. Perez, Ramon et al, illus. 1999. (Rifts Worldbook Ser.: Vol. 20). 192p. (YA). (gr. 8 up). pap. 20.95 (978-1-57457-025-0(0)) Palladium Bks., Inc.

—Rifts Xiticix Invasion. Marciniszyn, Alex et al, eds. Perez, Ramon et al, illus. 1999. (Rifts Worldbook Ser.: Vol. 23). 160p. (YA). (gr. 8 up). pap. 16.95 (978-1-57457-031-1(5)) Palladium Bks., Inc.

Sierra, Judy. The House That Dracula Built. 1998. (978-0-606-13492-7(1)) Tandem Library Bks.

Simon, Seymour. The Halloween Horror & Other Cases, Bk. 2. Schindler, S. D., illus. 1998. (Einstein Anderson, Science Detective Ser.). (J). (gr. 3-6). pap. 3.99 (978-0-380-72656-1(4)) HarperCollins Pubs.

Simpson, Sandra. Mina Fox Meets the Lady of the Library. 2007. (YA). per. 10.99 ***978-1-59886-968-2(X))** Tate Publishing & Enterprises, L.L.C.

Skeleton. 2001. (Human Anatomy Ser.). (J). (gr. k-12). vinyl bd. 4.95 (978-1-58845-086-9(4)) School Specialty Publishing.

Skillchecks for Horror. 2005. (Double Fastback Ser.). (J). (gr. 6-12). 64p. pap. 5.95 (978-0-13-024476-5(7)); 32p. pap. 5.95 (978-0-13-024459-8(7)) Globe Fearon Educational Publishing.

Slade, Arthur G. Ghost Hotel, Vol. 2. 2004. (Canadian Chills Ser.: Vol. 2). (Illus.). 144p. (J). (gr. 4-8). pap. 6.95 (978-1-55050-306-7(5)) Coteau Bks. CAN. *Dist:* Fitzhenry & Whiteside, Ltd.

Sleator, William. The Boy Who Couldn't Die. 2005. 184p. (YA). (gr. 7-17). pap. 6.95 (978-0-8109-8790-6(2)) Abrams, Harry N. , Inc.

Small, Mary. Catastrophe Cat. Stewart, Chantal, illus. 2004. 73p. (J). pap. 13.50 (978-1-920694-37-1(4)) Univ. of Western Australia Pr. AUS. *Dist:* International Specialized Bk. Services.

Snyder, Zilpha Keatley. The Unseen. 2005. 208p. 5.99 (978-0-440-41930-3(1) , Yearling) Random Hse. Children's Bks.

Sommers, Stephen. The Mummy. novel ed. 1999. (Illus.). 172p. (J). pap. 3.99 (978-0-439-05015-9(4)) Scholastic, Inc.

Souhami, Jessica. In the Dark, Dark Wood. 2007. (Illus.). 24p. (J). 7.95 ***978-1-84507-755-6(5))** Lincoln, Frances Ltd. GBR. *Dist:* Perseus Distribution.

Spenceley, Annabel, illus. The Kingfisher Treasury of Spooky Stories. 2003. (Kingfisher Treasury of Stories Ser.). 160p. (J). (gr. k-3). pap. 5.95 (978-0-7534-5634-7(6) , Kingfisher) Houghton Mifflin Co. Trade & Reference Div.

The Spirits Within: A Millersburg Novel. 2006. (YA). per. 7.99 (978-0-9765478-2-2(1)) Stone Acres Publishing Co.

Stafford, Nikki. Bite Me! An Unofficial Guide to the World of Buffy the Vampire Slayer. 1998. (Illus.). 250p. pap. 19.95 (978-1-55022-361-3(5)) ECW Pr. CAN. *Dist:* Independent Pubs. Group.

Stanescu, Gabriel. The Man Who Tried to Cheat Death: Romanian Scary Stories Anthology. Ricketts, Mac L., ed. Ricketts, Mac L., tr. 2000. (Illus.). 65p. (J). lib. bdg. 10.00 (978-1-887304-12-2(6)) Criterion Publishing Co., Inc.

Stark, Kirt. Campfire Chills: 13 Haunting Ghost Tales. Luther, Maridee D., illus. 2000. 57p. (YA). (gr. 8 up). pap. 6.95 (978-0-9665002-2-6(9)) Dark Woods Publishing.

Starks, R. The Fish Gut Experiment. Jellett, Tom, illus. 2008. (J). lib. bdg. ***978-1-59889-862-0(0));** 80p. pap. ***978-1-59889-918-4(X))** Stone Arch Bks.

Staub, Wendy Corsi. Voodoo Moon. 2000. (gr. 7-12). lib. bdg. 14.15 (978-0-613-73080-8(1)) Tandem Library Bks.

Steiber, Ellen. Haunted. 1998. (X-Files Young Adult Ser.: No. 15). 144p. (J). (gr. 4-7). pap. 4.50 (978-0-06-447191-6(8)) HarperCollins Pubs.

Stein, R. How I Got My Shrunken Head. 2003. (gr. 5-8). lib. bdg. 13.00 (978-0-613-70977-4(2)) Tandem Library Bks.

Stevens, Tim, illus. More Ghost Stories. 2004. (Red Hot Reads Ser.). 224p. (J). (gr. k-3). pap. 6.95 (978-0-7534-5736-8(9) , Kingfisher) Houghton Mifflin Co. Trade & Reference Div.

Stevenson, Robert Louis. Dr. Jekyll & Mr. Hyde. (Classics Illustrated Ser.). (Illus.). 52p. (YA). pap. 4.95 (978-1-57209-008-1(1)) Classics International Entertainment, Inc.

—Dr. Jekyll & Mr. Hyde. (YA). (gr. 5-12). pap. 6.50 (978-0-8224-9255-9(5)) Globe Fearon Educational Publishing.

—Dr Jekyll & Mr Hyde. abr. ed. 1999. (gr. 7-12). lib. bdg. 15.25 (978-0-613-32488-5(9)) Tandem Library Bks.

—Dr. Jekyll & Mr. Hyde. Redondo, Nestor, illus. 2nd ed. 1998. (Illustrated Classic Book Ser.). 61p. (J). (gr. 3 up). reprint ed. pap. 4.95 (978-1-56767-237-4(X)) Educational Insights, Inc.

—Dr. Jekyll & Mr. Hyde: And Other Stories of the Supernatural. 2006. (Scholastic Classics Ser.). iv, 143p. (J). (gr. 9-12). 25.00 (978-0-531-16985-8(5) , Watts, Franklin) Scholastic Library Publishing.

—The Strange Case of Dr. Jekyll & Mr. Hyde. 2002. (Great Illustrated Classics Ser.). (Illus.). 240p. (J). (gr. 3-8). 21.35 (978-1-57765-800-9(0) , ABDO & Daughters) ABDO Publishing Co.

—The Strange Case of Dr. Jekyll & Mr. Hyde. (Young Collector's Illustrated Classics Ser.). (Illus.). 192p. (J). (gr. 3-7). 9.95 (978-1-56156-460-6(5)) Kidsbooks, Inc.

—The Strange Case of Dr. Jekyll & Mr. Hyde. Akib, Jamel, illus. 2006. (Classic Starts Ser.). 160p. 4.95 (978-1-4027-2667-5(8) , 1252057) Sterling Publishing Co., Inc.

—The Strange Case of Dr. Jekyll & Mr. Hyde: With a Discussion of Moderation. Clift, Eva, tr. Clift, Eva, illus. 2003. (Values in Action Illustrated Classics Ser.). (J). (978-1-59203-053-8(X)) Learning Challenge, Inc.

Stewart, Paul. Wakening. 2000. (Yearling Book Ser.). (Illus.). 197p. (J). pap. 8.99 (978-0-440-86347-2(3)) Transworld Publishers Ltd. GBR. *Dist:* Trafalgar Square Publishing.

Stine, R. L. All-Day Nightmare. 2000. (Give Yourself Goosebumps Ser.: No. 42). (Illus.). 144p. (J). (gr. 3-7). pap. 3.99 (978-0-439-13530-6(3) , Scholastic Paperbacks) Scholastic, Inc.

—Alone in Snakebite Canyon. 1998. (Give Yourself Goosebumps Ser.: No. 26). 10p. (J). (gr. 3-7). pap. 3.99 (978-0-590-39997-5(7) , Scholastic Paperbacks) Scholastic, Inc.

—Are You Terrified Yet? 1998. (Goosebumps Series 2000: No. 9). 144p. (J). (gr. 3-7). pap. 3.99 (978-0-590-39996-8(9)) Scholastic, Inc.

—Attack of the Jack-o'-Lanterns. rev. ed. 2005. (Goosebumps Ser.). 144p. (ps-7). mass mkt. 4.99 (978-0-439-72405-0(8)) Scholastic, Inc.

—Beware! 2004. (Illus.). 224p. (J). (gr. 3 up). pap. 5.99 (978-0-06-055547-4(5)) HarperCollins Pubs.

—Beware, the Snowman. rev. ed. 2006. (Goosebumps Ser.). 144p. (J). pap. 4.99 (978-0-439-86393-3(7) , Scholastic Paperbacks) Scholastic, Inc.

—Bienvenidos a la Casa de la Muerte. 2004. (Escalofrios Ser.). Orig. Title: Welcome to Dead House. (SPA.). 128p. (J). (gr. 4-7). pap. 4.99 (978-0-439-62627-9(7) , Scholastic en Espanol) Scholastic, Inc.

—Bound Galley - Haunted Mask Lives! Date not set. (J). pap. (978-0-06-449214-0(1) , Harper Trophy) HarperCollins Pubs.

—Brain Juice. 1998. (Goosebumps Series 2000: No. 12). 121p. (J). (gr. 3-7). pap. 3.99 (978-0-590-76784-2(4)) Scholastic, Inc.

—Bride of the Living Dummy. 1998. (Goosebumps Series 2000: No. 2). 122p. (J). (gr. 3-7). pap. 3.99 (978-0-590-39990-6(X)) Scholastic, Inc.

—Bride of the Living Dummy. 1998. (Goosebumps Series 2000: No. 2). (J). (gr. 3-7). (978-0-606-12950-3(2)) Tandem Library Bks.

STINE, R. L. Calling All Creeps. 2007. (Goosebumps Ser.). 144p. (J). pap. 4.99 ***978-0-439-92221-0(6))** Scholastic, Inc.

Stine, R. L. Camp Nowhere. 2001. (Nightmare Room Ser.). (Illus.). (J). 10.64 (978-0-606-21352-3(X)) Tandem Library Bks.

—Checkout Time at the Dead-End Hotel. 1998. (Give Yourself Goosebumps Ser.: No. 27). 10p. (J). (gr. 3-7). pap. 3.99 (978-0-590-39998-2(5) , Scholastic Paperbacks) Scholastic, Inc.

—Checkout Time at the Dead-End Hotel. 1998. (Give Yourself Goosebumps Ser.: No. 27). (J). (gr. 3-7). (978-0-606-13266-4(X)) Tandem Library Bks.

—The Confession. 2005. (Fear Street Ser.). 160p. (YA). pap. 5.99 (978-1-4169-0322-2(4) , Simon Pulse) Simon & Schuster Children's Publishing.

—Creature Teacher. 1998. (Goosebumps Series 2000: No. 3). 125p. (J). (gr. 3-7). pap. 3.99 (978-0-590-39989-0(6) , Scholastic Paperbacks) Scholastic, Inc.

—Creature Teacher. 1998. (Goosebumps Series 2000: No. 3). (J). (gr. 3-7). (978-0-606-13440-8(9)) Tandem Library Bks.

—The Curse of the Cave Creatures. 1999. (Give Yourself Goosebumps: No. 5). 144p. (J). (gr. 3-7). pap. 3.99 (978-0-590-18734-3(1) , Scholastic Paperbacks) Scholastic, Inc.

—Danger Time. 41st ed. 2000. (Give Yourself Goosebumps Ser.: No. 41). 144p. (J). (gr. 3-7). pap. 3.99 (978-0-439-12186-6(8) , Scholastic Paperbacks) Scholastic, Inc.

—Darkest Dawn. 2005. 182p. (YA). (978-1-4156-1459-4(8) , Simon Pulse) Simon & Schuster Children's Publishing.

—Dear Diary, I'm Dead. 2001. (Nightmare Room Ser.: Vol. 5). (J). 10.64 (978-0-606-20068-4(1)) Tandem Library Bks.

—Deep Trouble. 2003. (Goosebumps Ser.). 144p. pap. 4.99 (978-0-439-56828-9(5) , 53655422, Scholastic Paperbacks) Scholastic, Inc.

—Deep Trouble. 2003. (gr. 5-8). lib. bdg. 13.00 (978-0-613-70776-3(1)) Tandem Library Bks.

—Deep Trouble II, Vol. 2. rev. ed. 2006. (Goosebumps Ser.). 144p. (J). pap. 4.99 (978-0-439-83780-4(4) , Scholastic Paperbacks) Scholastic, Inc.

—Un Dia en Horrorland. 1998. (Escalofrios Ser.: No. 16). (SPA., Illus.). 32p. (J). pap. 3.99 (978-0-590-53816-9(0) , SO7530, Scholastic Paperbacks) Scholastic, Inc.

—Un Dia en Horrorland. 1998. (Escalofrios Ser.: No. 16). (978-0-606-13369-2(0)) Tandem Library Bks.

—Don't Close Your Eyes! 2006. 144p. (J). (gr. 2-5). 8.99 (978-0-385-90933-4(0)); (Mostly Ghostly Ser.: No. 8). 6.95 (978-0-385-74695-3(4)) Random Hse. Children's Bks. (Delacorte Bks. for Young Readers).

—Don't Go to Sleep! 2005. (Goosebumps Ser.). 144p. (J). pap. 1.99 (978-0-439-79626-2(1) , Scholastic Paperbacks) Scholastic, Inc.

—Elevator to Nowhere. 1999. (Give Yourself Goosebumps Ser.: No. 34). (Illus.). 144p. (gr. 3-7). pap. 3.99 (978-0-590-51670-9(1)) Scholastic, Inc.

—Escape from Horror House. 1999. (Give Yourself Goosebumps Ser.: No. 37). 137p. (J). (gr. 3-7). pap. 3.99 (978-0-590-51682-2(5)) Scholastic, Inc.

—Fear Games. 2001. (Nightmare Room Ser.). (Illus.). (J). 10.64 (978-0-606-21353-0(8)) Tandem Library Bks.

—Fear Street Boxed Set. (Fear Street Ser.). (YA). (gr. 7 up). mass mkt. (978-0-671-01508-4(7)); mass mkt. (978-0-671-01509-1(5)) Simon & Schuster Children's Publishing. (Simon Pulse).

—Al Final de la Noche. Alonso, Victoria, tr. 2005. (Escritura desatada Ser.). (SPA.). 216p. (YA). 17.95 (978-84-666-0772-8(2)) Ediciones B ESP. *Dist:* Independent Pubs. Group.

—Freaks & Shrieks. 2005. 144p. (J). (gr. 2-5). lib. bdg. 8.99 (978-0-385-90932-7(2)); (Mostly Ghostly Ser.: Vol. 7). 6.95 (978-0-385-74694-6(6)) Random Hse. Children's Bks. (Delacorte Bks. for Young Readers).

—Fright Camp. 1998. (Goosebumps Series 2000: No. 8). 122p. (J). (gr. 3-7). pap. 3.99 (978-0-590-39995-1(0) , Scholastic Paperbacks) Scholastic, Inc.

—Fright Camp. 1998. (Goosebumps Series 2000: No. 8). (J). (gr. 3-7). (978-0-606-13444-6(1)) Tandem Library Bks.

—Full Moon Fever. 1999. (Goosebumps Series 2000: No. 22). 144p. (gr. 3-7). pap. 3.99 (978-0-590-68530-6(9)) Scholastic, Inc.

—Ghost Beach. 2003. (Goosebumps Ser.). 144p. mass mkt. 4.99 (978-0-439-56830-2(7) , 53655424, Scholastic Paperbacks) Scholastic, Inc.

—Ghost Beach. 2003. (gr. 5-8). lib. bdg. 13.00 (978-0-613-70848-7(2)) Tandem Library Bks.

—Ghost Camp. 2003. (Goosebumps Ser.). 144p. mass mkt. 4.99 (978-0-439-56831-9(5) , 53655425, Scholastic Paperbacks) Scholastic, Inc.

—Ghost Camp. 2003. (gr. 5-8). lib. bdg. 13.00 (978-0-613-70725-1(7)) Tandem Library Bks.

—Ghost in the Mirror. 2000. (Goosebumps Series 2000: No. 25). (Illus.). 144p. (J). (gr. 3-7). pap. 3.99 (978-0-439-13535-1(4) , Scholastic Paperbacks) Scholastic, Inc.

—Ghouls Gone Wild. 2005. 144p. (J). (gr. 2-5). lib. bdg. 8.99 (978-0-385-90930-3(6)); (Mostly Ghostly Ser.: Bk. 5). 6.95 (978-0-385-74692-2(X)) Random Hse. Children's Bks. (Delacorte Bks. for Young Readers).

—The Girl Who Cried Monster. 2005. 137p. (J). (ps-7). 12.04 (978-0-606-33299-6(5)) Tandem Library Bks.

—Goosebumps: Be Careful What You Wish For. 2005. (Goosebumps Ser.). 144p. (J). pap. 4.99 (978-0-439-66990-0(1) , Scholastic Paperbacks) Scholastic, Inc.

—Goosebumps: The Beast from the East. 2005. (Goosebumps Ser.). 144p. 4.99 (978-0-439-72403-6(1)) Scholastic, Inc.

—Goosebumps: The Curse of Camp Cold Lake. 2005. (Goosebumps Ser.). 144p. pap. 4.99 (978-0-439-72404-3(X)) Scholastic, Inc.

—Goosebumps: The Girl Who Cried Monster. 2005. (Goosebumps Ser.). 144p. pap. 4.99 (978-0-439-69353-0(5) , Scholastic Paperbacks) Scholastic, Inc.

—Goosebumps: Why I'm Afraid of Bees. 2005. (Goosebumps Ser.). 144p. (J). 4.99 (978-0-439-69354-7(3) , Scholastic Paperbacks) Scholastic, Inc.

—Goosebumps Boxed Set: Attack of the Mutant; My Hairiest Adventure; A Night in Terror Tower; The Cuckoo Clock of Doom, No. 7. 1998. (Goosebumps Ser.: Nos. 25-28). (J). (gr. 3-7). 14.00 (978-0-590-22370-6(4)) Scholastic, Inc.

—Goosebumps Gold, (Goosebumps Gold Ser.: No. 10). (J). (gr. 3-7). Date not set. pap. (978-0-06-440920-9(1)); Date not set. pap. (978-0-06-440921-6(X)); Date not set. pap. (978-0-06-440922-3(8)); Date not set. pap. (978-0-06-440918-6(X)); Date not set. pap. (978-0-06-440919-3(8)); 2001. pap. (978-0-06-440917-9(1)); 2001. pap. (978-0-06-440916-2(3)); 2001. pap. (978-0-06-440915-5(5)); 2001. pap. (978-0-06-440914-8(7)) HarperCollins Pubs. (Harper Trophy).

—Goosebumps Series 2000 Boxed Set: Are You Terrified Yet?; Headless Halloween; Attack of the Graveyard Ghouls; Brain Juice, 4 bks., Bk. 3. 1998. (Goosebumps Series 2000: Nos. 9-12). (J). (gr. 3-7). 15.96 (978-0-590-88002-2(0)) Scholastic, Inc.

—Goosebumps Series 2000 Boxed Set: Cry of the Cat; Bride of the Living Dummy; Creature Teacher; Invasion of the Body Squeezers Part 1, 4 bks., Bk. 1. 1998. (Goosebumps Series 2000: Nos. 1-4). (J). (gr. 3-7). 15.96 (978-0-590-35822-4(7)) Scholastic, Inc.

—Goosebumps Series 2000 Boxed Set: The Werewolf in the Living Room; Horrors of the Black Ring; Return to Ghost Camp; Be Afraid, Be Very Afraid, 4 bks., Bk. 5. 1999. (Goosebumps Series 2000: Nos. 17-20). (J). (gr. 3-7). 15.96 (978-0-439-07160-4(7)) Scholastic, Inc.

—Goosebumps Triple Header, Bk. 2. 1998. 159p. (J). pap. 4.50 (978-0-590-76252-6(4) , Scholastic Paperbacks) Scholastic, Inc.

—Goosebumps Triple Header, Bk. 2. 1998. (978-0-606-13446-0(8)) Tandem Library Bks.

—Gritos en el Campo de Juego. 2000. (Fantasmas de Fear Street Coleccion). (SPA.). (YA). (gr. 5-8). pap. 7.95 (978-950-04-1903-1(3) , EM4473) Emecé Editores S.A. ARG. *Dist:* Lectorum Pubns., Inc., Planeta Publishing Corp.

—Happy Holidays from Dead House. 2000. (Goosebumps Gold Ser.: No. 2). (J). (gr. 3-7). pap. (978-0-06-440912-4(0) , Harper Trophy) HarperCollins Pubs.

—The Haunted Car. 1999. (Goosebumps Series 2000: No. 21). (Illus.). (J). (gr. 3-7). (978-0-606-18552-3(6)) Tandem Library Bks.

—Haunted Mask. 2003. (Goosebumps Ser.). 144p. (J). pap. 4.99 (978-0-439-56833-3(1) , 53655427, Scholastic Paperbacks) Scholastic, Inc.

—Haunted Mask. 2003. (gr. 5-8). lib. bdg. 13.00 (978-0-613-70775-6(3)) Tandem Library Bks.

—The Haunted Mask II. rev. ed. 2004. (Goosebumps Ser.). 144p. (J). (gr. 4-7). 4.99 (978-0-439-67113-2(2) , Scholastic Paperbacks) Scholastic, Inc.

—The Haunted Mask Lives! 2000. (Goosebumps Gold Ser.: No. 1). (J). (gr. 3-7). pap. 3.99 (978-0-06-440911-7(2)) HarperCollins Pubs.

—The Haunting Hour: Chills in the Dead of Night. (Illus.). 160p. (J). (gr. 3 up). 2002. pap. 5.99 (978-0-06-441045-8(5)); 2001. 15.99 (978-0-06-623604-9(5)); 2001. 14.89 (978-0-06-623605-6(3)) HarperCollins Pubs.

—Haunting Hour: Chills in the Dead of Night. 2002. (gr. 3-6). lib. bdg. 13.00 (978-0-613-54437-5(4)) Tandem Library Bks.

—Headless Ghost. rev. ed. 2004. (Goosebumps Ser.). 134p. (J). (gr. 4-7). pap. 4.99 (978-0-439-66987-0(1) , Scholastic Paperbacks) Scholastic, Inc.

—Headless Halloween. 1998. (Goosebumps Series 2000: No. 10). 114p. (J). (gr. 3-7). pap. 3.99 (978-0-590-76781-1(X)) Scholastic, Inc.

—Hocus-Pocus Horror. 1999. (Give Yourself Goosebumps Ser.: No. 35). 137p. (J). (gr. 3-7). pap. 3.99 (978-0-590-51673-0(6)) Scholastic, Inc.

—Horrors of the Black Ring. 1999. (Goosebumps Series 2000: No. 18). (Illus.). 144p. (gr. 3-7). pap. 3.99 (978-0-590-68522-1(8)) Scholastic, Inc.

—How I Got My Shrunken Head. 2003. (Goosebumps Ser.). 144p. mass mkt. 4.99 (978-0-439-56835-7(8) , 53655429, Scholastic Paperbacks) Scholastic, Inc.

—How to Kill a Monster. 2003. (gr. 3-6). lib. bdg. 13.00 (978-0-613-72283-4(3)) Tandem Library Bks.

—How to Kill A Monster. 2003. (Goosebumps Ser.). 144p. mass mkt. 4.99 (978-0-439-56836-4(6) , 53655430, Scholastic Paperbacks) Scholastic, Inc.

—The Howler. 2001. (Nightmare Room Ser.). (Illus.). (J). (978-0-606-21350-9(3)) Tandem Library Bks.

—I Am Your Evil Twin. 1998. (Goosebumps Series 2000: No. 6). 126p. (J). (gr. 3-7). pap. 3.99 (978-0-590-39993-7(4) , Scholastic Paperbacks) Scholastic, Inc.

—Into the Jaws of Doom. 1998. (Give Yourself Goosebumps: No. 1). 10p. (J). (gr. 3-7). pap. 3.99 (978-0-590-39777-3(X)) Scholastic, Inc.

—Into the Jaws of Doom. 1998. (Give Yourself Goosebumps: No. 1). (J). (gr. 3-7). (978-0-606-13059-2(4)) Tandem Library Bks.

—Into the Twister of Terror. 1999. (Give Yourself Goosebumps Ser.: No. 38). 144p. (gr. 3-7). pap. 3.99 (978-0-590-51706-5(6)) Scholastic, Inc.

—Invaders from the Big Screen. 1998. (Give Yourself Goosebumps Ser.: No. 29). 137p. (J). (gr. 3-7). pap. 3.99 (978-0-590-40289-7(7) , Scholastic Paperbacks) Scholastic, Inc.

—Invaders from the Big Screen. 1998. (Give Yourself Goosebumps Ser.: No. 29). (J). (gr. 3-7). (978-0-606-13525-2(1)) Tandem Library Bks.

—Invasion of the Body Squeezers. 1998. (Goosebumps Series 2000: No. 4). (J). (gr. 3-7). Vol. 1. 120p. pap. 3.99 (978-0-590-39991-3(8)); Vol. 2. 10p. pap. 3.99 (978-0-590-39992-0(6)) Scholastic, Inc. (Scholastic Paperbacks).

—Invasion of the Body Squeezers. 1998. (Goosebumps Series 2000: No. 4). (J). (gr. 3-7). Vol. 1. (978-0-606-13441-5(7)); Pt. 2. (978-0-606-13442-2(5)) Tandem Library Bks.

—It Came from Beneath the Sink. 2003. (Goosebumps Ser.). 144p. mass mkt. 4.99 (978-0-439-56837-1(4) , 53655431, Scholastic Paperbacks) Scholastic, Inc.

—It Came from Beneath the Sink. 2003. (gr. 3-6). lib. bdg. 13.00 (978-0-613-72284-1(1)) Tandem Library Bks.

—It Came from the Internet. 1999. (Give Yourself Goosebumps Ser.: No. 33). 144p. (gr. 3-7). pap. 3.99 (978-0-590-51665-5(5)) Scholastic, Inc.

—It's Only a Nightmare! 1998. (Give Yourself Goosebumps Ser.: No. 32). 144p. (J). (gr. 3-7). pap. 3.99 (978-0-590-76785-9(2)) Scholastic, Inc.

—Jekyll & Heidi. 1999. (Goosebumps Series 2000: No. 14). 144p. (J). (gr. 3-7). pap. 3.99 (978-0-590-68517-7(1)) Scholastic, Inc.

—Killer's Kiss. 2005. (Fear Street Ser.). 160p. (YA). pap. 5.99 (978-1-4169-0320-8(8) , Simon Pulse) Simon & Schuster Children's Publishing.

—Let's Get This Party Haunted! 2005. 144p. (J). (gr. 2-5). lib. bdg. 8.99 (978-0-385-90931-0(4)); (Mostly Ghostly Ser.: No. 6). 6.95 (978-0-385-74693-9(8)) Random Hse. Children's Bks. (Delacorte Bks. for Young Readers).

—Liar Liar. 2000. (Nightmare Room Ser.: No. 4). 160p. (J). (gr. 5 up). pap. 3.99 (978-0-06-440902-5(3) , Avon) HarperCollins Pubs.

—Liar Liar. 2000. (gr. 5-8). lib. bdg. 11.80 (978-0-613-31416-9(6)) Tandem Library Bks.

—La Mascara Maldita. 1998. (Escalofrios Ser.: No. 11). Tr. of Haunted Mask. (SPA.). (J). pap. 3.99 (978-0-590-14927-3(X) , Scholastic Paperbacks) Scholastic, Inc.

—La Mascara Maldita. 1998. (Escalofrios Ser.: No. 11). Tr. of Haunted Mask. (978-0-606-13554-2(5)) Tandem Library Bks.

—Midnight Games. 2005. (Fear Street Nights Ser.). 160p. (YA). pap. 5.99 (978-0-689-87865-7(6) , Simon Pulse) Simon & Schuster Children's Publishing.

—Monster Blood. 2003. (Goosebumps Ser.). 144p. (J). pap. 4.99 (978-0-439-56839-5(0) , 53655433, Scholastic Paperbacks) Scholastic, Inc.

—Monster Blood. 2003. (gr. 3-6). lib. bdg. 13.00 (978-0-613-67466-9(9)) Tandem Library Bks.

—Monster Blood II. rev. ed. 2004. (Goosebumps Ser.). 144p. (J). (gr. 4-7). 4.99 (978-0-439-66988-7(X) , Scholastic Paperbacks) Scholastic, Inc.

—Monster Blood II. 2004. 121p. (J). (ps-7). lib. bdg. 11.64 (978-0-606-32488-5(7)) Tandem Library Bks.

—Monster Blood III. 2007. (Goosebumps Ser.). 144p. (J). pap. 4.99 (978-0-439-89112-7(4)) Scholastic, Inc.

—Moonlight Secrets. 2005. (Fear Street Nights Ser.). 160p. (YA). pap. 5.99 (978-0-689-87864-0(8) , Simon Pulse) Simon & Schuster Children's Publishing.

—Mutacion Fatal. 2003. (SPA.). pap. (978-0-590-01798-5(5)) Scholastic GBR. *Dist:* Lectorum Pubns., Inc.

—My Hairiest Adventure. 2006. (Goosebumps Ser.). 144p. (J). pap. 4.99 (978-0-439-86394-0(5) , Scholastic Paperbacks) Scholastic, Inc.

—The New Girl. 2006. (Fear Street Ser.). 176p. (YA). pap. 5.99 (978-1-4169-1810-3(8) , Simon Pulse) Simon & Schuster Children's Publishing.

—Night of a Thousand Claws. 1998. (Give Yourself Goosebumps Ser.: No. 28). 137p. (J). (gr. 3-7). pap. 3.99 (978-0-590-40034-3(7) , Scholastic Paperbacks) Scholastic, Inc.

—Night of a Thousand Claws. 1998. (Give Yourself Goosebumps Ser.: No. 28). (J). (gr. 3-7). (978-0-606-13661-7(4)) Tandem Library Bks.

—Night of the Living Dummy 2. 2004. (Goosebumps Ser.). 144p. (J). 4.99 (978-0-439-57374-0(2)) Scholastic, Inc.

—Nightmare Hour. 2000. (Illus.). 160p. (J). (gr. 5 up). pap. 5.99 (978-0-06-440842-4(6) , Avon) HarperCollins Pubs.

—Nightmare Hour: Time for Terror. 1999. (Illus.). 160p. (J). (gr. 3 up). 16.99 (978-0-06-028688-0(1)) HarperCollins Pubs.

—Nightmare Hour: Time for Terror. 2000. (gr. 5-8). lib. bdg. 14.15 (978-0-613-71481-5(4)) Tandem Library Bks.

—La Noche del Muneco Viviente II. 1999. (Escalofrios/Goosebumps Ser.: Vol. 31). (SPA.). 110p. (J). (gr. 3-7). pap. 3.99 (978-0-439-06627-3(1) , SO31217) Scholastic, Inc.

—La Noche del Muneco Viviente II. 1999. (SPA., Illus.). (J). (978-0-606-16955-4(5)) Tandem Library Bks.

—One Day at Horrorland. (Goosebumps Ser.). 144p. 2005. (J). pap. 1.99 (978-0-439-79630-9(X)); 2003. mass mkt. 4.99 (978-0-439-56841-8(2) , 53655435) Scholastic, Inc. (Scholastic Paperbacks).

—One Day at HorrorLand. 2003. (gr. 5-8). lib. bdg. 13.00 (978-0-613-70771-8(0)) Tandem Library Bks.

—One Night in Doom House. 2005. (Mostly Ghostly Ser.). 144p. (gr. 2-5). lib. bdg. 8.99 (978-0-385-90915-0(2)); Vol. 3. (J). 6.95 (978-0-385-74665-6(2)) Random Hse. Children's Bks. (Delacorte Bks. for Young Readers).

—One Night in Payne House. 1998. (Give Yourself Goosebumps: No. 4). 144p. (J). (gr. 3-7). pap. 3.99 (978-0-590-43378-5(4)) Scholastic, Inc.

—Padres de Otra Dimension. (Fantasmas de Fear Street Coleccion). (SPA.). (YA). (gr. 5-8). pap. 7.95 (978-950-04-1963-5(7) , EM10792) Emecé Editores S.A. ARG. *Dist:* Lectorum Pubns., Inc., Planeta Publishing Corp.

—The Perfect Date. 2005. (Fear Street Ser.). 160p. (YA). pap. 5.99 (978-1-4169-0323-9(2) , Simon Pulse) Simon & Schuster Children's Publishing.

—Return of the Mummy. rev. ed. 2006. (Goosebumps Ser.). 144p. (J). pap. 4.99 (978-0-439-83778-1(2) , Scholastic Paperbacks) Scholastic, Inc.

—Return to Ghost Camp. 1999. (Goosebumps Series 2000: No. 19). 112p. (gr. 3-7). pap. 3.99 (978-0-590-68523-8(6)) Scholastic, Inc.

—Return to Horrorland. 1999. (Goosebumps Series 2000: No. 13). 120p. (J). (gr. 3-7). pap. 3.99 (978-0-590-18733-6(3)) Scholastic, Inc.

—Return to Terror Tower. 1998. (Give Yourself Goosebumps: No. 2). 135p. (J). (gr. 3-7). pap. 3.99 (978-0-590-39999-9(3) , Scholastic Paperbacks) Scholastic, Inc.

—Return to Terror Tower. 1998. (Give Yourself Goosebumps: No. 2). (J). (gr. 3-7). (978-0-606-13737-9(8)) Tandem Library Bks.

—Revenge of the Body Squeezers. 1999. (Give Yourself Goosebumps: No. 6). (Illus.). 144p. (J). (gr. 3-7). pap. 3.99 (978-0-590-51674-7(4)) Scholastic, Inc.

—Revenge of the Living Dummy. 2008. (Goosebumps Horrorland Ser.). 144p. (J). 5.99 (***978-0-439-91869-5(3)*** , Scholastic Paperbacks) Scholastic, Inc.

—Revenge R Us. 1998. (Goosebumps Series 2000: No. 7). 118p. (J). (gr. 3-7). pap. 3.99 (978-0-590-39994-4(2) , Scholastic Paperbacks) Scholastic, Inc.

—The Rich Girl. 2005. (Fear Street Ser.). 144p. (YA). pap. 5.99 (978-1-4169-0324-6(0) , Simon Pulse) Simon & Schuster Children's Publishing.

—Sangre de Monstruo II. 1998. (Escalofrios/Goosebumps Ser.: No. 18). (SPA.). (J). (gr. 4-7). pap. 3.99 (978-0-590-04873-6(2) , SO4091) Scholastic, Inc.

—Say Cheese & Die! 2003. (gr. 5-8). lib. bdg. 13.00 (978-0-613-70770-1(2)) Tandem Library Bks.

—The Scarecrow Walks at Midnight. 2003. (Goosebumps Ser.). 144p. pap. 4.99 (978-0-439-56843-2(9) , 53657970, Scholastic Paperbacks) Scholastic, Inc.

—Scarecrow Walks at Midnight. 2003. (gr. 3-6). lib. bdg. 13.00 (978-0-613-72285-8(X)) Tandem Library Bks.

—Scary Birthday to You! 1999. (Give Yourself Goosebumps Ser.: No. 39). 144p. (gr. 3-7). pap. 3.99 (978-0-590-99390-6(9)) Scholastic, Inc.

—Scream School. 1999. (Goosebumps Series 2000: No. 15). 117p. (gr. 3-7). pap. 3.99 (978-0-590-68519-1(8)) Scholastic, Inc.

—Secret Admirer. 2005. (Fear Street Ser.). 160p. (YA). pap. 5.99 (978-1-4169-0820-3(X) , Simon Pulse) Simon & Schuster Children's Publishing.

—Shadow Girl. 2001. (Nightmare Room Ser.). (Illus.). (J). (978-0-606-21351-6(1)) Tandem Library Bks.

—Ship of Ghouls. 1999. (Give Yourself Goosebumps Ser.: No. 36). 144p. (gr. 3-7). pap. 3.99 (978-0-590-51723-2(6)) Scholastic, Inc.

—Sitter. 2003. (gr. 7-12). lib. bdg. 22.20 (978-0-613-71731-1(7)) Tandem Library Bks.

—Slappy New Year. 2001. (Goosebumps Gold Ser.: No. 3). (J). (gr. 3-7). pap. 4.95 (978-0-06-440913-1(9) , Harper Trophy) HarperCollins Pubs.

—Stay Out of the Basement. 2003. (Goosebumps Ser.). 144p. (J). pap. 4.99 (978-0-439-56845-6(5) , 53657972, Scholastic Paperbacks) Scholastic, Inc.

—Stay Out of the Basement. 2003. (gr. 5-8). lib. bdg. 13.00 (978-0-613-70767-1(2)) Tandem Library Bks.

—Switched. 2006. (Fear Street Ser.). 160p. (YA). pap. 5.99 (978-1-4169-1375-7(0) , Simon Pulse) Simon & Schuster Children's Publishing.

—They Call Me Creature. 2001. (Nightmare Room Ser.). (Illus.). (J). (978-0-606-20823-9(2)) Tandem Library Bks.

—Trapped in the Circus of Fear. 1998. (Give Yourself Goosebumps: No. 3). 131p. (J). (gr. 3-7). pap. 3.99 (978-0-590-41920-8(X) , Scholastic Paperbacks) Scholastic, Inc.

—Trick or...Trapped! 1999. (Give Yourself Goosebumps: No. 7). 144p. (Orig.). (J). (gr. 3-7). pap. 3.99 (978-0-590-99393-7(3)) Scholastic, Inc.

—The Weekend at Poison Lake. ed. 1999. (Give Yourself Goosebumps Ser.: No. 8). (Illus.). 144p. (Orig.). (J). (gr. 3-7). pap. 3.99 (978-0-590-99652-5(5)) Scholastic, Inc.

—Welcome to Camp Nightmare. 2003. (Goosebumps Ser.). 160p. pap. 4.99 (978-0-439-56846-3(3) , 53657973, Scholastic Paperbacks) Scholastic, Inc.

—Welcome to Camp Nightmare. 2003. (gr. 5-8). lib. bdg. 13.00 (978-0-613-70846-3(6)) Tandem Library Bks.

—Welcome to Dead House. (Goosebumps Ser.: No. 1). 144p. (J). 2007. pap. 2.99 (***978-0-545-01316-1(X));*** 2003. pap. 4.99 (978-0-439-56847-0(1) , 53657974, Scholastic Paperbacks) Scholastic, Inc.

—Welcome to Dead House. 2003. (gr. 3-6). lib. bdg. 13.00 (978-0-613-70766-4(4)) Tandem Library Bks.

—The Werewolf in the Living Room. 1999. (Goosebumps Series 2000: No. 17). 112p. (J). (gr. 3-7). pap. 3.99 (978-0-590-68521-4(X)) Scholastic, Inc.

—The Werewolf of Fever Swamp. 2003. (Goosebumps Ser.). 144p. pap. 4.99 (978-0-439-56848-7(X)) Scholastic, Inc.

—The Werewolf of Fever Swamp. 2003. (gr. 5-8). lib. bdg. 13.00 (978-0-613-68300-5(5)) Tandem Library Bks.

—Werewolf of Twisted Tree Lodge. 1998. (Give Yourself Goosebumps Ser.: No. 31). 137p. (J). (gr. 3-7). pap. 3.99 (978-0-590-46306-5(3)) Scholastic, Inc.

—What Scares You the Most? 2001. (Nightmare Room Ser.). (Illus.). (J). (978-0-606-21354-7(6)) Tandem Library Bks.

—Why I'm Afraid of Bees. 2005. 117p. (J). (gr. 2-5). lib. bdg. 12.04 (978-0-606-33300-9(2)) Tandem Library Bks.

—Yo Fui un Zombi. (Fear Street Ser.). (SPA.). (YA). (gr. 7 up). pap. 7.95 (978-950-04-2027-3(9) , EM10970) Emecé Editores S.A. ARG. *Dist:* Lectorum Pubns., Inc., Planeta Publishing Corp.

—You Can't Scare Me! 2004. (Goosebumps Ser.). 144p. (J). mass mkt. 4.99 (978-0-439-57365-8(3)) Scholastic, Inc.

—You're Plant Food. 1998. (Give Yourself Goosebumps Ser.: No. 30). 144p. (J). (gr. 3-7). pap. 3.99 (978-0-590-41974-1(9) , Scholastic Paperbacks) Scholastic, Inc.

—You're Plant Food. 1998. (Give Yourself Goosebumps Ser.: No. 30). (J). (gr. 3-7). (978-0-606-13933-5(8)) Tandem Library Bks.

—Zapped in Space. 1998. (Give Yourself Goosebumps Ser.: No. 23). (J). (gr. 3-7). (978-0-606-13072-1(1)) Tandem Library Bks.

—Zombie School. 1999. (Give Yourself Goosebumps Ser.: No. 40). 135p. (J). (gr. 3-7). pap. 3.99 (978-0-590-99397-5(6)) Scholastic, Inc.

Stine, R. L., ed. Midnight Games. 2005. 183p. (YA). (978-1-4156-1074-9(6) , Simon Pulse) Simon & Schuster Children's Publishing.

Stine, R. L., et al. Beware! R. L. Stine Picks His Favorite Scary Stories. 2002. (Illus.). 224p. (J). (gr. 3 up). 14.99 (978-0-06-623842-5(0)) HarperCollins Pubs.

Stine, R.L. The Best Friend. 2006. 147p. (J). lib. bdg. 13.00 (***978-1-4242-0993-4(5))*** Fitzgerald Bks.

—Boy Next Door. 2006. 147p. (J). lib. bdg. 13.00 (***978-1-4242-1008-4(9))*** Fitzgerald Bks.

—Creep from the Deep. 2008. (Goosebumps Horrorland Ser.). 160p. (J). 5.99 (***978-0-439-91870-1(7)*** , Scholastic Paperbacks) Scholastic, Inc.

—Darkest Dawn. 2005. 182p. (YA). lib. bdg. 20.00 (***978-1-4242-0994-1(3))*** Fitzgerald Bks.

—Killer's Kiss. 2005. 149p. (J). lib. bdg. 13.00 (***978-1-4242-0997-2(8))*** Fitzgerald Bks.

—Midnight Games. 2005. 183p. (YA). lib. bdg. 20.00 (***978-1-4242-1119-7(0))*** Fitzgerald Bks.

—The Perfect Date. 2005. 147p. (J). lib. bdg. 13.00 (***978-1-4242-0996-5(X))*** Fitzgerald Bks.

—Rich Girl. 2005. 132p. (J). lib. bdg. 13.00 (***978-1-4242-0999-6(4))*** Fitzgerald Bks.

Stocks, Mike. Victorian horror Stories. 2005. 144p. (J). pap. 4.95 (978-0-7945-0237-9(7) , Usborne) EDC Publishing.

Stoker, Bram. Bram Stoker/Dracula. Redondo, Nestor, illus. 2005. 48p. (gr. 5-8). 25.50 (978-0-7910-9109-8(0)) Facts On File, Inc.

—Bram Stoker's Dracula. Needle, Jan, ed. Blythe, Gary, illus. 2004. 336p. (J). (gr. 7 up). 18.99 (978-0-7636-2508-5(6)) Candlewick Pr.

—Dracula. Redondo, Nestor, illus. 1998. (Illustrated Classic Book Ser.). 61p. (J). (gr. 3 up). pap. 4.95 (978-1-56767-261-9(2)) Educational Insights, Inc.

—Dracula. Moser, Barry, illus. 2000. (Books of Wonder). 430p. (J). (gr. 7-12). 21.95 (978-0-688-13921-6(3)) HarperCollins Pubs.

—Dracula. 2002. (ENG.). 368p. 27.99 (***978-1-4043-3654-4(0))*** IndyPublish.com.

—Dracula. 2000. 502p. (gr. 4-7). pap. 4.99 (978-0-439-15411-6(1)) Scholastic, Inc.

—Dracula. Akib, Jamel, illus. 2007. (Classic Starts Ser.). (J). 160p. 4.95 (978-1-4027-3690-2(8)); 151p. (***978-1-4287-4215-4(8))*** Sterling Publishing Co., Inc.

Stoker, Bram & Mucci, Michael. Dracula. Halliar, Bill, illus. 2008. (All-Action Classics Ser.). 128p. (J). pap. 6.95 (978-1-4027-3152-5(3)) Sterling Publishing Co., Inc.

Stoker, Bram, et al. Dracula. Marcos, Pablo, illus. 2005. (Great Illustrated Classics Ser.). 239p. (J). (gr. 3-8). 21.35 (978-1-59679-240-1(X) , ABDO & Daughters) ABDO Publishing Co.

Stolarz, Laurie Faria. Project 17. rev. ed. 2007. 256p. (gr. 7 up). 15.99 (***978-0-7868-3856-1(6))*** Hyperion Bks. for Children.

Stone, Tom B. Aullidos Alrededor del Fogon. 2002. (Graveyard School Ser.). (SPA.). (J). 5.95 (978-950-24-0898-9(5) , AL30677) Albatros ARG. *Dist:* Lectorum Pubns., Inc.

—Colonia de Vacaciones Dracula. 2002. (Graveyard School Ser.). (SPA.). (J). 5.95 (978-950-24-0774-6(1) , AL30659) Albatros ARG. *Dist:* Lectorum Pubns., Inc.

—El Equipo del Terror. 2002. (Graveyard School Ser.). (SPA.). (J). pap. 5.95 (978-950-24-0790-6(3) , AL30665) Albatros ARG. *Dist:* Lectorum Pubns., Inc.

—El Esqueleto del Skate. 2002. (Graveyard School Ser.). (SPA.). (J). pap. 5.95 (978-950-24-0770-8(9) , AL30655) Albatros ARG. *Dist:* Lectorum Pubns., Inc.

—Un Fantasma en el Bano de Varones. 2002. (Graveyard School Ser.). (SPA.). (J). pap. 5.95 (978-950-24-0788-3(1) , AL30663) Albatros ARG. *Dist:* Lectorum Pubns., Inc.

—Jack y los Frijoles Magicos. 2002. (Graveyard School Ser.). (SPA.). (J). pap. 5.95 (978-950-24-0899-6(3) , AL30670) Albatros ARG. *Dist:* Lectorum Pubns., Inc.

—El Lago de Lodo. 2002. (Graveyard School Ser.). (SPA.). (J). pap. 5.95 (978-950-24-0775-3(X) , AL30660) Albatros ARG. *Dist:* Lectorum Pubns., Inc.

—La Maestra Horripilante. 2002. (Graveyard School Ser.). (SPA.). (J). pap. 5.95 (978-950-24-0894-1(2) , AL30673) Albatros ARG. *Dist:* Lectorum Pubns., Inc.

—No le Cuentes a la Momia. 2002. (Graveyard School Ser.). (SPA.). (J). pap. 5.95 (978-950-24-0875-0(6) , AL30669) Albatros ARG. *Dist:* Lectorum Pubns., Inc.

—Pequeno Hombre Lobo. 2002. (Graveyard School Ser.). (SPA.). (J). pap. 5.95 (978-950-24-0772-2(5) , AL30657) Albatros ARG. *Dist:* Lectorum Pubns., Inc.

—Un Susto Mortal! 2002. (Graveyard School Ser.). (SPA.). (J). pap. 5.95 (978-950-24-0776-0(8) , Al30661) Albatros ARG. *Dist:* Lectorum Pubns., Inc.

—Un Susto Navideno. 2002. (Graveyard School Ser.). (SPA.). (J). pap. 5.95 (978-950-24-0874-3(8) , AL30668) Albatros ARG. *Dist:* Lectorum Pubns., Inc.

—Terror en el Campamento. 2002. (Graveyard School Ser.). (SPA.). (J). pap. 5.95 (978-950-24-0872-9(1) , AL30666) Albatros ARG. *Dist:* Lectorum Pubns., Inc.

—La Venganza de los Dinosaurios. 2002. (Graveyard School Ser.). (SPA.). (J). pap. 5.95 (978-950-24-0773-9(3) , AL30658) Albatros ARG. *Dist:* Lectorum Pubns., Inc.

—Le Venganza del Esqueleto. 2002. (Graveyard School Ser.). (SPA.). (J). pap. 5.95 (978-950-24-0895-8(0) , AL30674) Albatros ARG. *Dist:* Lectorum Pubns., Inc.

Stroud, Jonathan. Buried Fire. 2004. 332p. (J). pap. (978-0-7818-5794-9(5)) Hippocrene Bks., Inc.

—Buried Fire. 2004. 336p. (gr. 5-17). pap. 6.95 (978-0-7868-5194-2(5)) Miramax Bks.

Sumimoto, Mark & Siembieda, Kevin. Rifts Splynn Dimensional Market. Marciniszyn, Alex et al, eds. Perez, Ramon et al, illus. 1999. (Rifts Worldbook Ser.: Vol. 21). 192p. (YA). (gr. 8 up). pap. 20.95 (978-1-57457-027-4(7)) Palladium Bks., Inc.

Swindells, Robert. Room 13 & Inside the Worm. 2008. 352p. (YA). pap. 9.95 (***978-0-552-55591-3(6))*** Transworld Publishers Ltd. GBR. *Dist:* Independent Pubs. Group.

Tabori, Lena & Tabori-Fried, Natasha, eds. The Little Big Book of Chills & Thrills. (Illus.). 352p. (J). (ps-7). 24.95 (978-1-932183-85-6(X) , Welcome Bks.) Welcome Enterprises, Inc.

Tagg, Christine. Who Will You Meet on Scary Street? Nine Pop-up Nightmares! Fuge, Charles, illus. 2004. 20p. (J). reprint ed. 15.00 (978-0-7567-8003-6(9)) DIANE Publishing Co.

Takahashi, Rumiko. InuYasha. 2003. (Illus.). 186p. (gr. 3-6). per. 17.60 (978-0-613-89444-9(8)) Tandem Library Bks.

Tamura, Yumi. Chicago Book of Justice, Vol. 2. Tamura, Yumi, illus. 2003. (Chicago Ser.: Vol. 2). (Illus.). 200p. (YA). pap. 15.95 (978-1-56931-829-4(8)) Viz Media.

Tan, Shaun, illus. The Haunted Playground. 2008. (J). lib. bdg. (***978-1-59889-860-6(4));*** 80p. pap. (***978-1-59889-916-0(3))*** Stone Arch Bks.

Taylor, Drew Hayden. The Night Wanderer: A Native Gothic Novel. 2007. 224p. (YA). (gr. 7-12). 21.95 (***978-1-55451-100-6(3));*** pap. 10.95 (***978-1-55451-099-3(6))*** Annick Pr., Ltd. CAN. *Dist:* Firefly Bks., Ltd.

Thaler, Mike. The School Bus Driver from the Black Lagoon. Lee, Jared D., illus. 1999. (Black Lagoon Ser.). 32p. (J). (ps-3). pap. 3.50 (978-0-439-06750-8(2) , Cartwheel Bks.) Scholastic, Inc.

—The School Bus Driver from the Black Lagoon. 1999. (Black Lagoon Ser.). (J). (ps-3). (978-0-606-17548-7(2)) Tandem Library Bks.

Thiele, Colin. The Twilight Ghost: Beware the Terror in the Town of Twilight! 2006. (Chomps Ser.). 108p. (J). pap. 3.95 (978-0-7624-2652-2(7) , Running Pr. Kids) Running Pr. Bk. Pubs.

Thomas, Patrick. The Wildsidhe Chronicles Bk. 1: Welcome to the Wildsidhe. 2002. (J). pap. 7.99 (978-1-890096-12-0(1)) Padwolf Publishing, Inc.

Thompson, B. B. Strangetales: A Book of Beginning. Cuce, Thomas A. & Sutphin, Eric, illus. 2002. (Strangetales Ser.). 172p. pap. 4.95 (978-0-9725614-0-2(4)) Tricorner Publishing.

Thompson, Bart A. Mummy. Miroglio, Brian, illus. 2007. (Graphic Horror Ser.). 32p. (YA). (gr. 5-8). lib. bdg. 27.07 (***978-1-60270-061-1(3)*** , Graphic Planet) Magic Wagon.

Thornhill, Gail. The Secret Life of Truly Jones. 2003. 196p. (J). pap. 12.99 (978-1-58832-081-0(2)) Unlimited Publishing LLC.

Thrillogy. 2006. (Illus.). (gr. 4-8). 77.70 (978-0-7910-9071-8(X)) Facts On File, Inc.

Tolan, Stephanie S. The Face in the Mirror. 1998. 224p. (J). (gr. 5-9). 15.00 (978-0-688-15394-6(1)) HarperCollins Pubs.

Tolson, Scott. Predator Kindred. 1998. (gr. 7-12). lib. bdg. 24.55 (978-0-613-79059-8(6)) Tandem Library Bks.

Townsend, John. Hunter's Moon. 2004. (Shades Ser.). 64p. (J). pap. 7.99 (978-0-237-52647-4(6) , Evans Brothers, Limited) Evans Publishing Group GBR. *Dist:* Independent Pubs. Group.

Tres Deseos Malignos. (Fear Street Ser.). (SPA.). (YA). (gr. 7 up). pap. 7.95 (978-950-04-1891-1(6)) Emecé Editores S.A. ARG. *Dist:* Lectorum Pubns., Inc., Planeta Publishing Corp.

Triple-Decker, 3 vols., Set. pap. 20.00 (978-0-9657367-4-9(1)) Less Pr.

Umezu, Kazuo. Blood. Umezu, Kazuo, illus. 2002. (Orochi Ser.). (Illus.). 224p. (YA). pap. 16.95 (978-1-56931-787-7(9)) Viz Media.

Urrea, Lourdes, et al. Athon Labar. rev. ed. 2006. (Ediciones Castillo Castillo Del Terror Ser.). (SPA.). 136p. (J). (gr. 2-6). pap. 6.95 (978-970-20-0309-0(1)) Castillo, Ediciones, S. A. de C. V. MEX. *Dist:* Macmillan.

—En Busca de Dracu. 2005. (Ediciones Castillo Castillo Del Terror Ser.).Tr. of Looking for Dracu. (SPA.). (J). (gr. 2-6). pap. 7.95 (978-970-20-0339-7(3)) Castillo, Ediciones, S. A. de C. V. MEX. *Dist:* Iaconi, Mariuccia Bk. Imports.

—Piel de Gallilna. 2005. (Ediciones Castillo Castillo Del Terror Ser.).Tr. of Chicken Bumps. (SPA.). (J). (gr. 2-6). pap. 7.95 (978-970-20-0292-5(3)) Castillo, Ediciones, S. A. de C. V. MEX. *Dist:* Iaconi, Mariuccia Bk. Imports.

—El Secreto Gitano. 2005. (Ediciones Castillo Castillo Del Terror Ser.).Tr. of Gypsy Secret. (SPA.). (J). (gr. 2-6). pap. 7.95 (978-970-20-0310-6(5)) Castillo, Ediciones, S. A. de C. V. MEX. *Dist:* Iaconi, Mariuccia Bk. Imports.

Ury, Allen B. Scary Stories for Sleep-Overs. Been, Dwight, illus. 1998. (Scary Stories for Sleep-Overs Ser.: Vol. 9). 96p. (J). (gr. 4-7). pap. 5.95 (978-1-56565-895-0(7) , 08957W) Lowell Hse.

—Scary Stories for Sleep-Overs. 1999. (Scary Stories for Sleep-Overs Ser.: Vol. 10). (Illus.). 96p. (J). (gr. 3-7). pap. 5.95 (978-0-7373-0114-4(7) , 01147W) McGraw-Hill/Contemporary.

—Scary Stories for Sleep-Overs: Tomb of Eternity. 1999. 128p. (J). (gr. 3-7). pap. 5.95 (978-1-56565-604-8(0)) McGraw-Hill/Contemporary.

—Scary Stories for When You're Home Alone. Reese, Eric, illus. 1998. (Scary Stories for When You're Home Alone Ser.: Vol. 4). 96p. (J). (gr. 4-7). pap. 5.95 (978-1-56565-899-8(X)) Lowell Hse. Juvenile.

Van Belkom, Edo, ed. Be Afraid! Tales of Horror. 2000. 184p. (J). (gr. 6-9). pap. 6.95 (978-0-88776-496-7(7)) Tundra Bks., Inc./Livres Toundra, Inc. CAN. *Dist:* Random Hse., Inc.

Van Belkom, Edo, selected by. Be Very Afraid! More Tales of Horror. 2002. 200p. (J). (gr. 6 up). pap. 7.95 (978-0-88776-595-7(5)) Tundra Bks., Inc./Livres Toundra, Inc. CAN. *Dist:* Random Hse., Inc.

Van Draanen, Wendelin. Sammy Keyes & the Skeleton Man. 1999. (Sammy Keyes Ser.: Bk. 2). (Illus.). 176p. (J). (gr. 5-8). pap. 5.99 (978-0-375-80054-2(9) , Yearling) Random Hse. Children's Bks.

Van Helsing, Cornelius & De Wolff, Gustav. Vampyre: The Terrifying Lost Journal of Dr. Cornelius Van Helsing. 2007. 32p. (J). (gr. 5 up). 19.99 (*978-0-06-124780-4(4)) HarperCollins Pubs.

Van Pelt, James. Strangers & Beggars: Stories. 2002. (gr. 7-12). lib. bdg. 28.05 (978-0-613-60619-6(1)) Tandem Library Bks.

Vande Velde, Vivian. All Hallow's Eve: 13 Stories. 2006. (Illus.). 240p. (YA). 17.00 (978-0-15-205576-9(2)) Harcourt Children's Bks.

—Being Dead. 2003. 224p. (YA). pap. 6.95 (978-0-15-204912-6(6) , Magic Carpet Bks.) Harcourt Children's Bks.

—Being Dead: Stories. 2001. (gr. 7-12). lib. bdg. 15.25 (978-0-613-68194-0(0)) Tandem Library Bks.

Vargo, Tim. Unbound: A Tale of Temptation & Terror. 2003. 242p. pap. 12.95 (978-1-930008-04-5(X)) Willowgate Pr.

Vita. Head in the Clouds. 2004. (Illus.). 108p. pap. 44.50 (978-0-9760062-0-6(0)) Magic Woman Pubns.

Viz Media Staff. The Year's Best Articles, 2003. 2003. (Best of Animerica Ser.). (Illus.). 96p. (YA). pap. 12.95 (978-1-56931-899-7(9)) Viz Media.

Walker, Chris, creator. Collision Course Goad by Zombi-enose. 2005. (Illus.). 60p. (YA). 13.95 (978-0-9768670-0-5(1)) Icecat Bks.

Walker, John. The Origin of the Vampire: How It All Started. 1998. 16p. (YA). (gr. 6-12). pap. 6.00 (978-0-8059-4262-0(9)) Dorrance Publishing Co., Inc.

Wallace, Barbara Brooks. Peppermints in the Parlor. unabr. ed. 2004. (Illus.). 208p. (J). (gr. 3-7). pap. 36.00 incl. audio (978-0-8072-8785-9(7) , YA267SP, Listening Library) Random Hse. Audio Publishing Group.

—Peppermints in the Parlor. 2005. 208p. (J). pap. 5.99 (978-0-689-87417-8(0) , Aladdin) Simon & Schuster Children's Publishing.

Watson, Andi, et al. The Remaining Sunlight. 1999. (Buffy the Vampire Slayer Ser.). (Illus.). 88p. (YA). (gr. 7 up). pap. 9.95 (978-1-56971-354-9(5)) Dark Horse Comics.

—Uninvited Guests. 1999. (Buffy the Vampire Slayer Ser.). (Illus.). 96p. (YA). (gr. 7 up). pap. 10.95 (978-1-56971-436-2(3)) Dark Horse Comics.

Webb, Janeen. Tales from Beyond. 2005. (Thrillogy Ser.). (Illus.). 48p. (gr. 4-8). 17.50 (978-0-7910-8891-3(X)) Facts On File, Inc.

Webb, Margot & Chorpash, Marci. My Grandmommy Is Shrinking. 2003. 60p. pap. 8.95 (978-0-595-29143-4(0)) iUniverse, Inc.

Weinberg, Larry. Frankenstein. 2000. (Golden Star Reader Ser.). (Illus.). (J). 10.79 (978-0-606-18854-8(1)) Tandem Library Bks.

Weird & Spooky Tales. Date not set. (Illus.). 192p. (J). (gr. 3-8). pap. 13.95 (978-0-87460-391-0(9)) Lion Bks.

West, Tracey. Abracadanger. 2003. (gr. 3-6). lib. bdg. 13.00 (978-0-613-72531-6(X)) Tandem Library Bks.

—Revenge of the Gargoyle. 2003. (gr. 3-6). lib. bdg. 13.00 (978-0-613-72523-1(9)) Tandem Library Bks.

Westall, Robert. The Scarecrows. 2005. 199p. (J). pap. 9.99 (978-0-09-948234-5(7) , Red Fox) Random Hse. Children's Bks. GBR. *Dist:* Trafalgar Square Publishing.

Westerfeld, Scott. The Last Days. 304p. (YA). (gr. 9-12). 2007. pap. 8.99 (978-1-59514-128-6(6)); 2006. 16.99 (978-1-59514-062-3(X)) Penguin Group (USA) Inc. (Razorbill).

Whedon, Joss & Others. Buffy the Vampire Slayer Omnibus Volume 1. 2007. (Illus.). 296p. (YA). pap. 24.95 (*978-1-59307-784-6(X)) Dark Horse Comics.

Whitethrow, Lord. Cuentos Escalofriantes para Ninos. 1999. (Stories for Children Ser.).Tr. of Scary Stories for Kids. (SPA.). 125p. (J). mass mkt. 7.95 (978-970-643-149-3(7)) Selector, S.A. de C.V. MEX. *Dist:* Libros Sin Fronteras.

Wild, Margaret. Woolvs in the Sitee. Spudvilas, Anne, illus. 2007. 40p. (YA). (gr. 7 up). 17.95 (*978-1-59078-500-3(2) , Front Street) Boyds Mills Pr.

Wilson, Eric G. Vampires of Ottawa. 2001. (Liz Austen Mystery Ser.). (Illus.). 108p. (J). (gr. 3-7). pap. 4.99 (978-1-55143-228-1(5)) Orca Bk. Pubs. USA.

Windsor, Patricia. Nightwood. 2006. 256p. (YA). (gr. 9). pap. 7.95 (978-0-385-73312-0(7)); lib. bdg. 9.99 (978-0-385-90331-8(6)) Random Hse. Children's Bks. (Delacorte Bks. for Young Readers).

Wood, David & Leroux, Gaston. The Phantom Cat of the Opera. Day, Peters, illus. 2001. 40p. (J). (gr. 2-5). 16.95 (978-0-8230-4018-6(6)) Watson-Guptill Pubns., Inc.

Wooding, Chris. The Haunting of Alaizabel Cray. 2004. 304p. (J). pap. 16.95 (978-0-439-54656-0(7)) Scholastic, Inc.

Wright, Terry. The One-Eyed Monster. 2006. 48p. pap. 12.95 (978-1-4241-3696-4(2)) PublishAmerica, Inc.

Yambar, Chris, ed. Edison's Frankenstein 1910. Bihun, Robb, illus. 2003. (YA). mass mkt. 7.95 (978-1-929515-27-1(8)) Comic Library International.

Yeager, Graham. Diablo: The Third Millersburg Novel. 2006. 145p. (YA). per. 7.99 (*978-0-9765478-4-6(8)) Stone Acres Publishing Co.

—Stone Hedge: The Fourth Millersburg Novel. 2006. 142p. (YA). per. 7.99 (*978-0-9765478-6-0(4)) Stone Acres Publishing Co.

Yoon, Salina. Five Spooky Ghosts. Yoon, Salina, illus. 2005. (Illus.). 10p. (J). (ps-1). bds. 5.99 (978-0-8431-1443-0(6) , Price Stern Sloan) Penguin Group (USA) Inc.

Young, Richard. Favorite Scary Stories of American Children. 1999. (J). 11.60 (978-0-606-19258-3(1)) Tandem Library Bks.

Zamani, Qamar. A Dark, Dark Tale. 2002. (URD & ENG., Illus.). 29p. (J). 19.95 (978-1-85269-401-2(7)) Mantra Publishing, Ltd. GBR. *Dist:* AIMS International Bks., Inc.

Zander, R. W. When the Zombies Come Marchin' Home. 2003. 158p. (978-0-439-39868-8(1)) Scholastic, Inc.

—Zombies Don't Date. 2003. 158p. (J). (978-0-439-39869-5(X)) Scholastic, Inc.

Zindel, Paul. The Doom Stone. 2004. 192p. (gr. 6-10). pap. 5.99 (978-0-7868-5151-5(1)) Hyperion Bks. for Children.

—Rats. 2000. (Untitled Zindel #2 Ser.: Vol. 2). 176p. (gr. 5-9). pap. 4.99 (978-0-7868-1225-7(7)) Disney Pr.

—Rats. unabr. ed. 2000. (YA). pap., stu. ed. 59.99 incl. audio (978-0-7887-4346-7(5) , 41140) Recorded Bks., LLC.

—Rats. 2000. (gr. 5-8). lib. bdg. 13.00 (978-0-613-30103-9(X)) Tandem Library Bks.

Zornow, Jeff. Werewolf. Zornow, Jeff, illus. 2007. (Graphic Horror Ser.). (Illus.). 32p. (YA). (gr. 5-8). lib. bdg. 27.07 (*978-1-60270-062-8(1) , Graphic Planet) Magic Wagon.

Zucker, Jonny. Creature Chase. Troiano, Enzo, illus. 2007. 33p. (J). pap. (*978-1-59889-424-0(2)); 40p. (YA). (gr. 5-9). 21.26 (*978-1-59889-336-6(X)) Stone Arch Bks.

—A Deck of Monsters. Williams, Anthony, illus. 2008. (J). pap. (*978-1-59889-898-9(1)); 33p. (YA). (gr. 5-9). lib. bdg. 21.26 (*978-1-59889-846-0(9)) Stone Arch Bks.

Zucker, Jonny. Steel Eyes. Savage, Paul, illus. 2006. (Keystone Books (Stone Arch)). 33p. (J). (978-1-59889-019-8(0)) Stone Arch Bks.

HORSE

see Horses

HORSE RACING

Baker, Kent. Thoroughbred Racing. 2001. (Horse Library). (Illus.). 64p. (J). 25.00 (978-0-7910-6654-6(1) , Chelsea Hse.) Facts On File, Inc.

Broyles, Janell. Barrel Racing. 2005. (World of Rodeo Ser.). (Illus.). 48p. (J). lib. bdg. 26.50 (978-1-4042-0543-7(8)) Rosen Publishing Group, Inc., The.

Curry, Marion. Horse & Pony Competitions. 2006. (Illus.). 32p. (J). lib. bdg. (978-0-8368-6834-0(X)) Stevens, Gareth Inc.

Dubowski, Cathy East & Dubowski, Mark. A Horse Named Seabiscuit. Rowe, Michael Langham, illus. 2003. (All Aboard Reading Ser.). 48p. (J). (gr. 2-6). mass mkt. 3.99 (978-0-448-43342-4(7) , Grosset & Dunlap) Penguin Group (USA) Inc.

Dubowski, Mark. Horse Named Seabiscuit. 2003. (gr. k-3). lib. bdg. 11.80 (978-0-613-70545-5(9)) Tandem Library Bks.

Green, John. Great Race Horses. 2006. 32p. (J). pap. 3.95 (978-0-486-45162-6(3)) Dover Pubns., Inc.

Hillenbrand, Laura. Seabiscuit: An American Legend. 2002. (gr. 7-12). lib. bdg. 25.70 (978-0-613-64787-8(4)) Tandem Library Bks.

Hubbard, Crystal. Jimmy Winkfield: The Last Black King of the Kentucky Derby. Oyler, Tami, illus. 2007. (J). (*978-1-58430-274-2(7)) Lee & Low Bks., Inc.

Kuhn, Betsy. Top 10 Jockeys. 1999. (Sports Top 10 Ser.). (Illus.). 48p. (YA). (gr. 4-10). lib. bdg. 23.93 (978-0-7660-1130-4(5)) Enslow Pubs., Inc.

Lister, T., compiled by. Chemistry at the Races: The Work of the Horseracing Forensic Laboratory. 2002. (Illus.). 45p. pap. 14.95 (978-0-85404-385-9(3) , 0854043853) Royal Society of Chemistry, The GBR. *Dist:* Springer.

Parker, Marjorie Hodgson. Assault: The Crippled Champion, the King Ranch Racehorse. 2004. (Illus.). 80p. 14.95 (978-1-931721-34-9(3)) Bright Sky Pr.

Spoilyourhorse Com Staff. SpoilYourHorse. com Horse Bits: A Study Guide for Beginning Rider & Instructor. 2003. 142p. (YA). pap. 14.95 (978-0-595-27996-8(1)) iUniverse, Inc.

Tate, Nikki. Behind the Scenes at the Racetrack. 2007. 88p. (*978-1-55455-032-6(7)) Fitzhenry & Whiteside, Ltd.

Trollinger, Patsi B. Perfect Timing: How Isaac Murphy Became One of the World's Greatest Jockeys. LaGarrigue, Jerome, illus. 2006. 32p. (J). (gr. 2-5). 15.99 (978-0-670-06083-2(6) , Viking Juvenile) Penguin Group (USA) Inc.

Valentine, Billy, comment & compiled by. Dear Smarty: A Collection of Letters Written to Smarty Jones by Children, Families & Other Animals from Across America. Valentine, Billy, compiled by. 2nd ed. 2005. 152p. (YA). pap. 19.95 (978-0-9763935-0-4(6) , 1214) Braveheart Pr., LLC.

HORSE RACING—FICTION

Allthewaybay. 2004. (YA). per. 7.95 (978-0-9749320-0-2(0)) Bay Horse Creations LLC.

Archer, Colleen Rutherford. Galloping Goldrush: The Journey Begins. Stafford, Susan, ed. 2005. (J). per. 11.95 (978-0-9740841-5-2(8)) K&B Products.

Auerbach, Annie. Horseland #5: Western Riding Winner. 2008. (Horseland Ser.). 96p. (J). pap. 3.99 (*978-0-06-134171-7(1) , Harper Entertainment) HarperCollins Pubs.

Baglio, Ben M. Racehorse in the Rain. 2006. (Animal Ark Hauntings Ser.: No. 40). (Illus.). 160p. (J). pap. 3.99 (978-0-439-68496-5(X)) Scholastic, Inc.

Bates, Michelle. Horse for the Summer. 2003. (gr. 3-6). lib. bdg. 12.95 (978-0-613-67632-8(7)) Tandem Library Bks.

—Racing Vacation. 2003. 100p. (J). pap. 4.99 (978-0-7945-0504-2(X) , Usborne) EDC Publishing.

Campbell, Joanna. A Dangerous Ride. 1999. (Ashleigh Ser.: No. 6). 192p. (gr. 4-7). mass mkt. 4.99 (978-0-06-106559-0(5) , Harper Entertainment) HarperCollins Pubs.

—Derby Day. 1999. (gr. 3-6). lib. bdg. 12.40 (978-0-613-21428-5(5)) Tandem Library Bks.

—Down to the Wire. 1999. (Thoroughbred Ser.: No. 38). 176p. (gr. 4-7). mass mkt. 4.99 (978-0-06-106609-2(5) , Harper Entertainment) HarperCollins Pubs.

—Down to the Wire. 1999. (gr. 3-6). lib. bdg. 12.40 (978-0-613-21462-9(5)) Tandem Library Bks.

—Living Legend. 2000. (Thoroughbred Ser.: No. 39). 192p. (gr. 4-7). mass mkt. 4.50 (978-0-06-106633-7(8) , Harper Entertainment) HarperCollins Pubs.

—Living Legend. 2000. (gr. 3-6). lib. bdg. 12.40 (978-0-613-21919-8(8)) Tandem Library Bks.

Dawson, JoAnn. Willie to the Rescue. 2006. 264p. 15.95 (978-0-9746561-0-6(0)); pap. 8.95 (978-0-9746561-2-0(7)) FT Richards Publishing.

Dorling Kindersley Publishing Staff, ed. Down to the Wire. 2004. (Dk Readers Ser.). (Illus.). 48p. (J). pap. 3.99 (978-0-7566-0838-5(4)) Dorling Kindersley Publishing, Inc.

—Down to the Wire: Baseball's Great Pennant Races. 2004. (Dk Readers Ser.). (Illus.). 48p. (J). (gr. 5). 12.99 (978-0-7566-0837-8(6)) Dorling Kindersley Publishing, Inc.

Farley, Terri. Red Feather Filly. 2004. 201p. (J). lib. bdg. 16.92 (*978-1-4242-0828-9(9)) Fitzgerald Bks.

Farley, Walter. The Black Stallion Challenged. 2003. (Black Stallion Ser.). (Illus.). 240p. (J). (gr. 5-8). pap. 5.99 (978-0-394-84371-1(1) , Random Hse. Bks. for Young Readers) Random Hse. Children's Bks.

—The Black Stallion Challenged. 2003. (gr. 5-8). lib. bdg. 14.15 (978-0-613-81950-3(0)) Tandem Library Bks.

—The Black Stallion's Courage. 2004. (Black Stallion Ser.). (Illus.). 240p. (J). (gr. 5-8). pap. 5.99 (978-0-394-83918-9(8) , Yearling) Random Hse. Children's Bks.

—The Black Stallion's Filly. Rowe, John, illus. 2002. (Black Stallion Ser.). 288p. (J). (gr. 5-8). pap. 5.99 (978-0-394-83916-5(1) , Yearling) Random Hse. Children's Bks.

—The Island Stallion Races. 2003. (Black Stallion Ser.). (Illus.). 256p. (J). (gr. 5-8). pap. 5.99 (978-0-394-84375-9(4) , Yearling) Random Hse. Children's Bks.

Fate of the Stallion! 2000. (Illus.). 166p. per. 14.95 (978-0-9679514-0-9(2) , by title) Pennywood Pr.

Hart, Alison. Gabriel's Horses. 2007. 224p. (J). (gr. 3-7). 14.95 (*978-1-56145-398-6(6) , Peachtree Junior) Peachtree Pubs., Ltd.

—Gabriel's Triumph. 2007. 160p. (J). (gr. 3-7). 14.95 (*978-1-56145-410-5(9) , Peachtree Junior) Peachtree Pubs., Ltd.

Hector, Rachel. Re-Ride. 2003. 149p. (YA). pap. 11.95 (978-0-595-26707-1(6) , Writers Club Pr.) iUniverse, Inc.

Henry, Marguerite. Born to Trot. 2002. (Illus.). 13.40 (978-1-4046-1350-8(1)) Book Wholesalers, Inc.

James, Will. The Dark Horse. (Illus.). 288p. 35.00 (978-0-87842-484-9(9) , 818) Mountain Pr. Publishing Co., Inc.

—The Dark Horse, Vol. 1. James, Will, illus. rev. ed. (Illus.). 288p. (J). (gr. 4). pap. 18.00 (978-0-87842-486-3(5) , 817) Mountain Pr. Publishing Co., Inc.

Jarmes, Jon Jeffery. Jason Post: Magic at the Downs. 2006. (YA). 19.95 (978-0-9770483-0-4(6)) Speech Publishing Hse.

Lawrence, Caroline. The Charioteer of Delphi. 2007. (Roman Mysteries Ser.). (Illus.). 210p. (J). (gr. 6-9). 16.95 (*978-1-59643-085-3(0)) Roaring Brook Pr.

Ransom, Candice. Horses in the Wind: A Tale of Seabiscuit. 2007. 128p. (J). (gr. 1-5). pap. 4.99 (*978-0-7869-4355-5(6) , Mirrorstone) Wizards of the Coast.

Robertson, Barbara. Rosemary & the Mystery Down Under. 2002. (Illus.). 128p. (J). (gr. 4-6). pap. 4.95 (978-1-890817-64-0(3)) Winslow Pr.

Sargent, Dave & Sargent, Pat. Brandy: (Blue Roan) Beauty Is Inside, 30, 5. Lenoir, Jane, illus. 2003. (Saddle Up Ser.: Vol. 5). 42p. (J). lib. bdg. 22.60 (978-1-56763-799-1(X)); mass mkt. 6.95 (978-1-56763-800-4(7)) Ozark Publishing.

Smith, Alexander McCall. Harriet Bean & the League of Cheats. Rankin, Laura, illus. 80p. (J). 2007. pap. 4.95 (978-1-59990-054-4(8)); 2006. 9.95 (978-1-58234-976-3(2)) Bloomsbury Publishing. (Bloomsbury Children).

Stevenson, James. Runaway Horse! A Novel. Date not set. (J). 15.99 (978-0-06-051978-0(9)); 16.89 (978-0-06-051979-7(7)) HarperCollins Pubs.

HORSEBREAKING

see Horses—Training

HORSEMANSHIP

see also Rodeos

Adelman, Beth. The Pony Guide. 2006. (Girls Rock! Ser.). (Illus.). 32p. (J). (gr. 1-5). 24.21 (978-1-59296-749-0(3)) Child's World, Inc.

Barth, Katrin & Sieber, Antonia. Learning Horseback Riding. 2005. (Learning ... Training ... Ser.). (Illus.). 136p. pap. 14.95 (978-1-84126-153-9(X)) Meyer & Meyer Sport, Ltd. GBR. *Dist:* Perseus Distribution.

—Training Horseback Riding. 2005. (Learning ... Training ... Ser.). (Illus.). 152p. pap. 14.95 (978-1-84126-156-0(4)) Meyer & Meyer Sport, Ltd. GBR. *Dist:* Perseus Distribution.

Binns, Tristan Boyer. Horses & Ponies. 2006. (Keeping Pets Ser.). (Illus.). 48p. (J). (978-1-4034-7703-3(5)) Heinemann Library.

Blackledge, Annabel. Let's Go Riding. 2005. (Dk Readers Ser.). (Illus.). 32p. (J). 12.99 (978-0-7566-1693-9(X)); pap. 3.99 (978-0-7566-1694-6(8)) Dorling Kindersley Publishing, Inc.

Bolte, Betty. Dressage. 2001. (Horse Library). (Illus.). 64p. (J). 25.00 (978-0-7910-6656-0(8) , Chelsea Hse.) Facts On File, Inc.

Budd, Jackie. The Best Book of Ponies. 1999. (Best Book of... Ser.). (Illus.). 32p. (J). (gr. k-3). tchr. ed. 12.95 (978-0-7534-5172-4(7) , Kingfisher) Houghton Mifflin Co. Trade & Reference Div.

—Horse & Pony Jumping. 1999. (Complete Guides to Horses & Ponies Ser.). (Illus.). 64p. (J). (gr. 4 up). lib. bdg. 27.33 (978-0-8368-2446-9(6)) Stevens, Gareth Inc.

—Horse & Pony Tack. 1999. (Complete Guides to Horses & Ponies Ser.). (Illus.). 64p. (J). (gr. 4 up). lib. bdg. 27.33 (978-0-8368-2447-6(4)) Stevens, Gareth Inc.

—The World of Horses. 2004. (World Of Ser.). (Illus.). 64p. (J). (gr. 4-6). pap. 8.95 (978-0-7534-5753-5(9) , Kingfisher) Houghton Mifflin Co. Trade & Reference Div.

Calder, Kate. Horseback Riding in Action. 2000. (Sports in Action Ser.). (Illus.). 32p. (J). (gr. 3-4). (978-0-7787-0167-5(0)); pap. (978-0-7787-0179-8(4)) Crabtree Publishing Co.

—Horseback Riding in Action. 2000. (J). 12.75 (978-0-606-22835-0(7)) Tandem Library Bks.

Davis, Caroline. The Young Equestrian: Professional Instruction for Ambitious Riders. 2000. (Illus.). 178p. pap. 19.95 (978-1-55209-484-6(7)); (YA). (gr. 4 up). 29.95 (978-1-55209-495-2(2)) Firefly Bks., Ltd.

Davis, Michele S. & Makris, Alexandra. Magical Mac: The True Story of a Healing Horse. 2002. (Illus.). 35p. (J). pap. (978-0-9715395-0-1(2)) Serendipity Pubns.

Dickins, Rosie & Pratt, Leonie. Horse & Pony Treasury. 2006. 96p. (J). 19.99 (978-0-7945-1431-0(6) , Usborne) EDC Publishing.

Draper, Allison Stark. Trail Riding: Have Fun, Be Smart. 2005. (Explore the Outdoors Ser.). (Illus.). 64p. (YA). (gr. 7-12). lib. bdg. 26.50 (978-0-8239-3170-5(6) , EOTRRI) Rosen Publishing Group, Inc., The.

Draper, Judith. My First Horse & Pony Book. Roberts, Matthew, photos by. 2005. (Illus.). 48p. (J). (gr. k-3). 9.95 (978-0-7534-5878-5(0) , Kingfisher) Houghton Mifflin Co. Trade & Reference Div.

—My First Horse & Pony Show & Games. 2007. (J). (978-0-7534-6038-2(6) , Kingfisher) Houghton Mifflin Co. Trade & Reference Div.

Draper, Judith, et al. My First Horse & Pony Care Book: From Boots & Bedding to Saddles & Stables. Roberts, Matthew, photos by. 2006. (My First Horse & Pony Ser.). (Illus.). 48p. (J). (gr. k-3). 9.95 (978-0-7534-5989-8(2) , Kingfisher) Houghton Mifflin Co. Trade & Reference Div.

Edom, H. & Sims, L. Starting Riding. rev. ed. 2004. (First Skills Ser.). (Illus.). 32p. (J). pap. 4.99 (978-0-7945-0441-0(8)); lthr. 12.99 (978-1-58086-544-9(5)) EDC Publishing.

Edom, Helen. Starting Riding. 2002. (gr. k-3). lib. bdg. 12.95 (978-0-613-90705-7(1)) Tandem Library Bks.

Firefly, Books. Quiero Ser Vaquero. 2003. (SPA.). (ps-2). lib. bdg. 14.15 (978-0-613-78625-6(4)) Tandem Library Bks.

Gaydon, S. Activators Riding. (Illus.). 128p. pap. 8.99 (978-0-340-71517-8(0) , Hodder & Stoughton) Hodder General Publishing Division GBR. *Dist:* Trafalgar Square Publishing.

Gruber, Beth. Horseback Riding for Fun. 2004. (Activities for Fun Ser.). (Illus.). 48p. (J). (gr. 3 up). lib. bdg. 21.26 (978-0-7565-0585-1(2)) Compass Point Bks.

Haas, Jessie. Safe Horse, Safe Rider: A Young Rider's Guide to Responsible Horsekeeping. Haar, Amanda, ed. 2003. (Illus.). 160p. (J). (gr. 4-7). pap. 16.95 (978-0-88266-700-3(9) , 66700) Storey Publishing, LLC.

Harvey, G. & Dickens, R. Little Book of Riding & Pony Care. rev. ed. 2004. (Complete Book of Riding & Pony Care Ser.). (Illus.). 144p. (J). 7.95 (978-0-7945-0611-7(9)) EDC Publishing.

—Riding & Pony Care. 2004. (Complete Book of Riding & Pony Care Ser.). (Illus.). 144p. (J). (gr. 3 up). pap. 15.95 (978-0-7945-0181-5(8) , Usborne); lib. bdg. 23.95 (978-1-58086-422-0(8)) EDC Publishing.

Harvey, Gill. Complete Book of Riding & Pony Care. 2002. (gr. 3-6). lib. bdg. 25.70 (978-0-613-75306-7(2)) Tandem Library Bks.

Hayden, Kate. Horse Show, Vol. 2. 2001. (Readers Ser.). (Illus.). 32p. (J). (gr. 5-3). pap. 3.99 (978-0-7894-7371-4(2)) Dorling Kindersley Publishing, Inc.

—Horse Show. 2001. (gr. k-3). lib. bdg. 11.80 (978-0-613-35146-1(0)); (Illus.). (J). 10.79 (978-0-606-21236-6(1)) Tandem Library Bks.

Hayden, Kate & Dorling Kindersley Publishing Staff. Horse Show. 2001. (Readers Ser.). (Illus.). 32p. (J). (gr. 1-3). 12.99 (978-0-7894-7372-1(0)) Dorling Kindersley Publishing, Inc.

Haywood, Rosie. Dressage. 1999. (Riding School Ser.). (Illus.). 32p. (YA). (gr. 3 up). lib. bdg. 13.95 (978-1-58086-201-1(2)) EDC Publishing.

Haywood, Rosie, ed. Dressage. 1999. (Riding School Ser.). (Illus.). 32p. (YA). (gr. 3 up). pap. 5.95 (978-0-7460-2925-1(X)) EDC Publishing.

Henderson, Carolyn. Learn to Ride. 2005. (Illus.). 48p. (J). 9.99 (978-0-7566-1449-2(X)) Dorling Kindersley Publishing, Inc.

Herran, Joe & Thomas, Ron. Equestrian Sports. 2003. (Action Sports Ser.). (Illus.). 32p. (gr. 4-8). 28.00 (978-0-7910-7533-3(8) , Chelsea Hse.) Facts On File, Inc.

Hill, Cherry. Cherry Hill's Horse Care for Kids: Grooming, Feeding, Behavior, Stable & Pasture, Health Care, Handling & Safety, Enjoying. 2002. (Illus.). 116p. (J). (gr. 3-7). pap. 16.95 (978-1-58017-407-7(8) , 67407, Storey Kids) Storey Publishing, LLC.

—Riding Western. Vincer, Carole, illus. 2002. (Threshold Picture Guides Ser.: Vol. 46). 24p. (YA). pap. 12.95 (978-1-872119-42-7(5)) Half Halt Pr.

—Your Pony, Your Horse: A Kid's Guide to Care & Enjoyment. Balmuth, Deborah, ed. 2003. (Storey's Your Ser.). (Illus.). 161p. (Orig.). (J). (gr. 4-7). pap. 14.95 (978-0-88266-908-3(7) , 66908) Storey Publishing, LLC.

Horseback Riding for Fun! (For Fun Ser.). 48p. (YA). 8.95 (978-0-7565-1158-6(5)) Compass Point Bks.

Hughes, Mary. Western Riding. 2001. (Horse Library). (Illus.). 64p. (J). (gr. 4-8). 25.00 (978-0-7910-6655-3(X) , Chelsea Hse.) Facts On File, Inc.

Jahiel, Jessica. The Horseback Almanac. 1998. (Illus.). 112p. (J). (gr. 2-7). 12.95 (978-1-56565-952-0(X) , 09529W); (gr. 3-7). pap. 6.95 (978-1-56565-897-4(3) , 08973W) Lowell Hse. Juvenile. (Roxbury Park Juvenile).

Jeffrey, Laura S. Horses: How to Choose & Care for a Horse. 2004. (American Humane Pet Care Library). (Illus.). 48p. (J). lib. bdg. 23.93 (978-0-7660-2519-6(5)) Enslow Pubs., Inc.

Kalman, Bobbie. Horseback Riding in Action. 2001. (gr. 3-6). lib. bdg. 14.10 (978-0-613-32651-3(2)) Tandem Library Bks.

Kelley, Brent P. Horse Care & Health. 2001. (Horse Library). (Illus.). 64p. (J). 25.00 (978-0-7910-6653-9(3) , Chelsea Hse.) Facts On File, Inc.

Kidd, Jane. A Young Person's Guide to Dressage. 1999. (Illus.). 144p. (J). 29.99 (978-1-900667-55-5(X)) Compass Equestrian Ltd. GBR. *Dist:* Trafalgar Square Publishing.

Kimball, Cheryl. Horse Showing for Kids: Training, Grooming, Trailering, Apparel, Tack, Competing, Sportsmanship. 2004. (Illus.). 160p. (J). pap. 16.95 (978-1-58017-501-2(5) , 67501); tchr. ed. 26.95 (978-1-58017-573-9(2) , 67573) Storey Publishing, LLC. (Storey Kids).

Kissock, Heather. Horseback Riding. 2007. (J). ***978-1-59036-661-5(1)); (*978-1-59036-662-2(X))** Weigl Pubs., Inc.

Knotts, Bob. Equestrian Events. 2000. (True Bks.). (Illus.). 48p. (J). (gr. 3-5). pap. 6.95 (978-0-516-27025-8(7) , Children's Pr.) Scholastic Library Publishing.

Krementz, Jill. A Very Young Rider. ed. 2007. 124p. 24.95 **(*978-0-9755516-2-2(0))** DreamHouse Publishing, Inc.

Landau, Elaine. Your Pet Pony. 2006. (True Book Ser.). (Illus.). 47p. (J). (978-0-531-16797-7(6)) Children's Pr., Ltd.

Needham, Kate. Pony Guide. 2006. (Illus.). 31p. (J). (978-0-439-78703-1(3)) Scholastic, Inc.

Newhouse, Maxwell. The RCMP Musical Ride. 2004. (Illus.). 24p. (J). 15.95 (978-0-88776-683-1(8)) Tundra Bks., Inc./Livres Toundra, Inc. CAN. *Dist:* Random Hse., Inc.

Nichols, Catherine. Therapy Horses. 2007. (Horse Power Ser.). 32p. (J). lib. bdg. 25.27 (978-1-59716-400-9(3)) Bearport Publishing Co., Inc.

Pakizer, Debi & Sears, Mary A. Vaulting: The Art of Gymnastics on Horseback. Anderson, Julia & Barnette, Jackie, eds. Sears, Mary A., illus. (Illus.). 24p. (Orig.). (J). (gr. k-6). pap. 5.00 (978-0-9639785-6-1(X)) Sears, M.A.

Pinch, Dorothy Henderson. Happy Horsemanship. 1998. (Illus.). 192p. pap. 13.00 (978-0-684-85215-7(2) , Fireside) Simon & Schuster.

Presnall, Judith Janda. Horse Therapists. 2001. (Animals with Jobs Ser.). (Illus.). 48p. (J). (gr. 3-5). 23.70 (978-0-7377-0615-4(5) , LML00902-178553, Kidhaven) Thomson Gale.

Ransford, Sandy. First Riding Lessons. Langrish, Bob, illus. 2004. (Kingfisher Riding Club Ser.). 64p. (J). (gr. 4-8). pap. 8.95 (978-0-7534-5743-6(1) , Kingfisher) Houghton Mifflin Co. Trade & Reference Div.

—First Riding Lessons. Langrish, Bob, photos by. 2002. (Kingfisher Riding Club Ser.). (Illus.). 64p. (J). (gr. 5-9). tchr. ed. 14.95 (978-0-7534-5454-1(8) , Kingfisher) Houghton Mifflin Co. Trade & Reference Div.

—Horse & Pony Factfile: An Essential Guide to the World of Horses & Ponies. Kingfisher Publications, Inc. Staff, ed. 2006. (Illus.). 224p. (J). (gr. 3-5). vinyl bd. 12.95 (978-0-7534-6039-9(4) , Kingfisher) Houghton Mifflin Co. Trade & Reference Div.

—The Kingfisher Illustrated Horse & Pony Encyclopedia. Langrish, Bob, photos by. 2004. (Illus.). 224p. (J). (gr. 5-9). 24.95 (978-0-7534-5781-8(4) , Kingfisher) Houghton Mifflin Co. Trade & Reference Div.

Raynor, Maggie, illus. A Bit More Than a Mouth. 1999. (Pony Guides Ser.: No. 5). 16p. (J). (gr. 1-5). pap. 5.99 (978-1-900667-04-3(5)) Compass Equestrian Ltd. GBR. *Dist:* Trafalgar Square Publishing.

—Bodywork. 1999. (Pony Guides Ser.: No. 3). 16p. (J). (gr. 1-5). pap. 6.99 (978-1-900667-02-9(9)) Compass Equestrian Ltd. GBR. *Dist:* Trafalgar Square Publishing.

—Filling up the Tank. 1999. (Pony Guides Ser.: No. 7). 16p. (J). (gr. 1-5). pap. 6.99 (978-1-900667-06-7(1)) Compass Equestrian Ltd. GBR. *Dist:* Trafalgar Square Publishing.

—Forelegs & Four Feet. 1999. (Pony Guides Ser.: No. 4). 16p. (J). (gr. 1-5). pap. 6.99 (978-1-900667-03-6(7)) Compass Equestrian Ltd. GBR. *Dist:* Trafalgar Square Publishing.

—Head First. 1999. (Pony Guides Ser.: No. 2). 16p. (J). (gr. 1-5). pap. 6.99 (978-1-900667-01-2(0)) Compass Equestrian Ltd. GBR. *Dist:* Trafalgar Square Publishing.

—More Than Just a Pet. 1999. (Pony Guides Ser.: No. 1). 16p. (J). (gr. 1-5). pap. 6.99 (978-1-900667-00-5(2)) Compass Equestrian Ltd. GBR. *Dist:* Trafalgar Square Publishing.

—Top, Tail & Overcoat. 1999. (Pony Guides Ser.: No. 6). 16p. (J). (gr. 1-5). pap. 6.99 (978-1-900667-05-0(3)) Compass Equestrian Ltd. GBR. *Dist:* Trafalgar Square Publishing.

—Why Does He Do That? 1999. (Pony Guides Ser.: No. 8). 16p. (J). (gr. 1-5). pap. 6.99 (978-1-900667-07-4(X)) Compass Equestrian Ltd. GBR. *Dist:* Trafalgar Square Publishing.

Richter, Judy. Judy Richter's Riding for Kids: Stable Care, Equipment, Tack, Clothing, Longeing, Lessons, Jumping, Showing. 2003. (Illus.). 144p. (J). (gr. 2-7). pap. 16.95 (978-1-58017-510-4(4) , 67510, Storey Kids) Storey Publishing, LLC.

—Riding for Kids: Stable Care, Equipment, Tack, Clothing, Longeing, Lessons, Jumping, Showing. 2003. (Illus.). 144p. (J). tchr. ed. 23.95 (978-1-58017-511-1(2) , 67511, Storey Kids) Storey Publishing, LLC.

Riding: Level I, 6 vols. (Wonder Worldtm Ser.). 16p. 29.95 (978-0-7802-2024-9(2)) Wright Group, The.

Saunders, Catherine. Riding School. Handley, David, photos by. 2003. (Pony Club Ser.). (Illus.). 48p. (J). (gr. 3 up). 12.99 (978-0-7894-9294-4(6)) Dorling Kindersley Publishing, Inc.

Smith, Lucy. The Usborne Book of Horses & Ponies. Gray, Miranda & Trotter, Stuart, illus. 2006. 32p. (J). pap. **(*978-0-439-88983-4(9))** Scholastic, Inc.

Stillerman, Robbie. Hannah the Horseback Rider Sticker Paper Doll. 2006. (Dover Little Activity Bks.). 4p. (J). pap. 1.50 (978-0-486-44822-0(3)) Dover Pubns., Inc.

Talbert, Marc. Ahold of the Reins. Date not set. 124p. (J). (gr. 3-7). pap. 6.99 (978-0-06-440950-6(3)) HarperCollins Pubs.

—Holding the Reins: A Ride Through Cowgirl Life. Van Cleve, Barbara, illus. 2003. 112p. (J). (gr. 3-7). lib. bdg. 17.89 (978-0-06-029256-0(3)) HarperCollins Pubs.

—Holding the Reins: A Ride Through Cowgirl Life. Van Cleve, Barbara, photos by. 2003. (Illus.). 112p. (J). (gr. 3-7). 16.99 (978-0-06-029255-3(5)) HarperCollins Pubs.

U. S. Olympic Committee. A Basic Guide to Equestrian. 2001. (Olympic Guides). (Illus.). 160p. (J). (gr. 6 up). lib. bdg. 23.33 (978-0-8368-2797-2(X)) Stevens, Gareth Inc.

Ward, Lesley. Jumping for Kids. 2007. (J). 128p. 26.95 (978-1-58017-671-2(2)); (Illus.). 144p. pap. 16.95 (978-1-58017-672-9(0)) Storey Publishing, LLC.

—Let's Go to a Show! How to Win Ribbons & Have Fun, Too. 2002. (Illus.). 112p. pap. 14.95 (978-1-889540-85-6(4)) BowTie Pr.

Weimken, Simone. You & Your Horse. 2004. (Illus.). 80p. pap. 12.99 (978-0-7153-1731-0(8)) David & Charles Pubs. GBR. *Dist:* F & W Pubns., Inc.

Wright, John. Equestrian Sport. 2003. (Sports Injuries Ser.). (Illus.). 64p. (J). lib. bdg. (978-1-59084-629-2(X)) Mason Crest Pubs.

HORSEMANSHIP—FICTION

Anderson, Laurie Halse. Fear of Falling. 2003. (Wild at Heart Ser.). (Illus.). 105p. (J). (gr. 4 up). lib. bdg. 23.33 (978-0-8368-3255-6(8)) Stevens, Gareth Inc.

Anderson, Peggy Perry. We Go in a Circle. 2004. (Illus.). 32p. (J). (gr. k-3). tchr. ed. 15.00 (978-0-618-44756-5(3) , Walter Lorraine) Houghton Mifflin Co. Trade & Reference Div.

Auerbach, Annie. Back in the Saddle Again. 2007. (Horseland Ser.: Vol. 2). 96p. (J). (gr. 2-5). pap. 3.99 **(*978-0-06-134168-7(1)** , Harper Entertainment) HarperCollins Pubs.

—The Trail Ride Terror. 2007. (Horseland Ser.: Vol. 3). 96p. (J). (gr. 2-5). pap. 3.99 **(*978-0-06-134169-4(X)** , Harper Entertainment) HarperCollins Pubs.

Bang-Campbell, Monika. Little Rat Rides. Bang, Molly, illus. 2006. (Little Rat Ser.). 48p. (J). pap. 5.95 (978-0-15-205598-1(3) , Harcourt Paperbacks) Harcourt Children's Bks.

—Little Rat Rides. Bang, Molly Garrett, tr. Bang, Molly Garrett, illus. 2004. (Little Rat Ser.). 48p. (J). 15.00 (978-0-15-204667-5(4)) Harcourt Children's Bks.

Betancourt, Jeanne. The Unlucky Pony. Bachem, Paul, illus. 2000. (Pony Pals Ser.: No. 24). 96p. (J). (gr. 2-5). pap. 3.99 (978-0-439-06490-3(2) , Scholastic Paperbacks) Scholastic, Inc.

—The Unlucky Pony. 2000. (Pony Pals Ser.: Vol. 24). (J). (gr. 2-5). (978-0-606-19602-4(1)) Tandem Library Bks.

Brooke, Lauren. All or Nothing. 2007. (Chestnut Hill Ser.: No. 6). 184p. (J). lib. bdg. 15.38 **(*978-1-4242-1719-9(9))** Fitzgerald Bks.

—All or Nothing. 2007. (Chestnut Hill Ser.: No. 6). 192p. (J). pap. 4.99 (978-0-439-85999-8(9) , Scholastic Paperbacks) Scholastic, Inc.

—Chestnut Hill. 2006. 208p. (J). pap. 4.99 (978-0-439-73857-6(1) , Scholastic Paperbacks) Scholastic, Inc.

—Sooner or Later. 2003. (Heartland Ser.: No. 12). 160p. (J). pap. 4.99 (978-0-439-33968-1(5) , Scholastic Paperbacks) Scholastic, Inc.

—Sooner or Later. 2003. (gr. 3-6). lib. bdg. 12.40 (978-0-613-72024-3(5)) Tandem Library Bks.

—Tomorrow's Promise. 2002. (Heartland Ser.: No. 10). 176p. (J). pap. 4.99 (978-0-439-31717-7(7)) Scholastic, Inc.

—Tomorrow's Promise. 2002. (gr. 3-6). lib. bdg. 12.40 (978-0-613-62922-5(1)) Tandem Library Bks.

Bryant, Bonnie. Carole: The Inside Story. 1999. (J). (978-0-606-19288-0(3)) Tandem Library Bks.

—Conformation Faults. 1999. (Pine Hollow Ser.: No. 5). (YA). (gr. 7 up). (978-0-606-18958-3(0)) Tandem Library Bks.

—Course of Action. 1999. (Pine Hollow Ser.: No. 8). (YA). (gr. 7 up). (978-0-606-18959-0(9)) Tandem Library Bks.

—Horse Crazy. 2007. (Saddle Club Ser.: No. 1). 144p. (J). (gr. 4-7). lib. bdg. 11.99 (978-0-385-90417-9(7) , Yearling) Random Hse. Children's Bks.

—Horse Play. 2007. (Saddle Club Ser.: No. 7). 144p. (J). (gr. 4-6). lib. bdg. 11.99 **(*978-0-385-90423-0(1)** , Yearling) Random Hse. Children's Bks.

—Horse Power. 2007. (Saddle Club Ser.: No. 4). 144p. (J). (gr. 4-6). lib. bdg. 11.99 (978-0-385-90420-9(7) , Yearling) Random Hse. Children's Bks.

—Horse Sense. 2007. (Saddle Club Ser.: No. 3). 144p. (J). (gr. 4-7). lib. bdg. 11.99 (978-0-385-90419-3(3) , Yearling) Random Hse. Children's Bks.

—Horse Show. 2007. (Saddle Club Ser.: No. 8). 160p. (J). (gr. 4-6). lib. bdg. 11.99 **(*978-0-385-90424-7(X)** , Yearling) Random Hse. Children's Bks.

—Horse Shy. 2007. (Saddle Club Ser.: No. 2). 144p. (J). (gr. 4-6). lib. bdg. 11.99 (978-0-385-90418-6(5) , Yearling) Random Hse. Children's Bks.

—Lisa: The Inside Story. 1999. (J). (978-0-606-19289-7(1)) Tandem Library Bks.

—Penalty Points. 1999. (Pine Hollow Ser.: No. 7). (YA). (gr. 7 up). (978-0-606-18964-4(5)) Tandem Library Bks.

—Riding to Win. 1999. (Pine Hollow Ser.: No. 9). (YA). (gr. 7 up). (978-0-606-19287-3(5)) Tandem Library Bks.

—Shying at Trouble. 1999. (Pine Hollow Ser.: No. 6). (YA). (gr. 7 up). (978-0-606-18967-5(X)) Tandem Library Bks.

—Stevie: The Inside Story. 1999. (978-0-606-17154-0(1)) Tandem Library Bks.

Bryant, Megan E. Strawberry Shortcake's Filly Friends: All Aboard Reading Station Stop 1. 2004. (Strawberry Shortcake Ser.: 1). (Illus.). 32p. (J). (ps-2). mass mkt. 3.99 (978-0-448-43574-9(8) , Grosset & Dunlap) Penguin Group (USA) Inc.

Campbell, Joanna. Derby Fever. 2002. (Thoroughbred Ser.: No.53). 176p. (gr. 3-7). mass mkt. 4.99 (978-0-06-106823-2(3)) HarperCollins Pubs.

—Derby Fever. 2002. (gr. 3-6). lib. bdg. 13.00 (978-0-613-67186-6(4)) Tandem Library Bks.

—Kaitlin's Wild Ride. Innelli, ed. 2004. (Thoroughbred Ser.: No. 68). 176p. mass mkt. 4.99 (978-0-06-073813-6(8) , Harper Entertainment) HarperCollins Pubs.

—The Price of Fame. 2004. (Thoroughbred Ser.: No. 64). (Illus.). 176p. mass mkt. 4.99 (978-0-06-058674-4(5) , Harper Entertainment) HarperCollins Pubs.

—Starstruck. 2004. (Thoroughbred Ser.: No. 63). (Illus.). 176p. mass mkt. 4.99 (978-0-06-058673-7(7) , Harper Entertainment) HarperCollins Pubs.

Challenge of Choice. 2002. (YA). per. 11.95 (978-0-9656307-3-3(0)) Sunrise Selections.

Chu, Jennifer. Breaking the Fall. 2004. (Thoroughbred Ser.: No. 67). 176p. (J). pap. 4.99 (978-0-06-073812-9(X) , Harper Entertainment) HarperCollins Pubs.

Circle of Blue. 2006. (J). (978-1-933343-37-2(0) , PONY) Stabenfeldt Inc.

Clayton, Elaine. Blue Ribbon for Sugar. Clayton, Elaine, illus. 2006. (Illus.). 32p. (J). 16.95 (978-1-59643-157-7(1)) Roaring Brook Pr.

Cole, Cathleen. Four Seasons Stables: A Saddle Seat Rid. 2006. 53p. pap. 12.95 **(*978-1-4241-3430-4(7))** PublishAmerica, Inc.

Edge, Laura Bufano. Wild West Dreams. 2006. (J). pap. (978-0-88092-623-2(6)); lib. bdg. (978-0-88092-622-5(8)) Royal Fireworks Publishing Co.

Felder, Deborah G. Pretty Lady of Saratoga. Rabinowitz, Sandy & Keiffer, Christa, illus. l.t. ed. 1999. (Treasured Horses Collection). 122p. (J). (gr. 4 up). lib. bdg. 23.33 (978-0-8368-2404-9(0)) Stevens, Gareth Inc.

Gaard, Betty. Jericho Ride. 2003. (Illus.). 165p. (J). pap. (978-1-57924-968-7(X)) Jones, Bob Univ. Pr.

Gerrard, Roy. Sir Cedric Rides Again. 1998. (978-0-606-13775-1(0)) Tandem Library Bks.

Haas, Jessie. Birthday Pony. Apple, Margot, illus. 2004. 80p. (J). (gr. 2 up). 15.99 (978-0-06-057359-1(7)); lib. bdg. 16.89 (978-0-06-057360-7(0)) HarperCollins Pubs.

Hallem, J. Horsing Around. Squire, Stan, illus. 2006. (Read-It! Chapter Books). 64p. (J). (gr. 2-4). 19.95 (978-1-4048-1666-4(6)) Picture Window Bks.

Hammerle, Susa & Trapp, K. Let's Try Horseback Riding. 2006. (Illus.). 24p. (J). 12.95 (978-0-7358-2093-7(7)) North-South Bks., Inc.

Higgenson, Hadley. Keeker & the Horse Show Show-Off. Andersen, Maja, illus. 2006. (Sneaky Pony Ser.: Bk. 2). 48p. (J). pap. 3.95 (978-0-8118-5303-3(9)) Chronicle Bks. LLC.

Higgenson, Hadley & Andersen, Maja. Keeker & the Sneaky Pony. Andersen, Maja, illus. 2006. (Sneaky Pony Ser.: Bk. 1). (Illus.). 48p. (J). pap. 3.95 (978-0-8118-5217-3(2)) Chronicle Bks. LLC.

Hill, Janet Muirhead. Starlight's Courage: Revised Edition. Lehmkuhl, Pat, illus. 2nd ed. 2007. 170p. (J). per. 9.00 **(*978-0-9772525-4-1(X))** Raven Publishing Inc. of Montana.

Hubbard, Coleen. The Flying Angels. Rabinowitz, Sandy & Keiffer, Christa, illus. l.t. ed. 1999. (Treasured Horses Collection). 128p. (J). (gr. 4 up). lib. bdg. 23.33 (978-0-8368-2401-8(6)) Stevens, Gareth Inc.

Huws, Emily. Nid Fy Mai I. 2005. (WEL., Illus.). 62p. (978-1-84512-025-2(6)) Cymdeithas Lyfrau Ceredigion.

Juby, Susan. Another Kind of Cowboy. 2007. 352p. (J). lib. bdg. 17.89 **(*978-0-06-076518-7(6));** (YA). lib. bdg. **(*978-0-06-076521-7(6));** 352p. (YA). (gr. 9 up). 16.99 **(*978-0-06-076517-0(8))** HarperCollins Pubs. (Harper-Teen).

Litty, Julie. Chloe & the Magic Baton. Litty, Julie, illus. 2006. 32p. (J). (ps-3). 16.99 (978-0-698-40039-9(9) , Minedition) Penguin Group (USA) Inc.

MacKall, Dandi Daley. Horse of a Different Color, Vol. 4. 2000. (Horsefeathers Ser.: Vol. 4). 192p. (YA). (gr. 7-11). 5.99 (978-0-570-07009-2(0)) Concordia Publishing Hse.

—Horse of a Different Color. 2000. (gr. 7-12). lib. bdg. 14.15 (978-0-613-72832-4(7)) Tandem Library Bks.

McMahon, Kate & Myler, Terry. Timber Twig. 1998. 142p. pap. 10.95 (978-1-901737-01-1(2)) Anvil Bks., Ltd. IRL. *Dist:* Dufour Editions, Inc.

Newhall, Mary. Calamity Jinx. 2005. (Thoroughbred Ser.: Vol. 71). (Illus.). 165p. (J). **(*978-1-4155-9659-3(X)** , Harper Entertainment) HarperCollins Pubs.

Novara, Joseph. Wa-Tonka! Camp Cowboys. Lawson, Robert, illus. 2000. 232p. (J). per. 9.95 (978-0-9671978-9-0(9)) Syncopated Pr.

Patrick, Denise Lewis. The Longest Ride. rev. ed. 1999. (Illus.). 176p. (J). (gr. 4-9). 15.95 (978-0-8050-4715-8(8) , Holt, Henry & Co. Bks. For Young Readers) Holt, Henry & Co.

Reed, Neil, illus. The Midnight Unicorn. 2006. 36p. (J). (gr. k-2). 14.95 (978-1-4027-3218-8(X)) Sterling Publishing Co., Inc.

Saunders, Susan. Riding School Rivals. 1998. (Treasured Horses Ser.: Vol. 4). (J). (gr. 3-9). pap. 3.99 (978-0-590-31656-9(7)) Scholastic, Inc.

—Riding School Rivals, 4. 1998. (Treasured Horses Ser.). (J). (978-0-606-13864-2(1)) Tandem Library Bks.

Taylor, Lori. What to Do When Your Hoof Turns Blue!!! Taylor, Lori, illus. l.t. ed. 2006. (Illus.). 28p. (J). per. 11.99 **(*978-1-59879-220-1(2))** Lifevest Publishing, Inc.

Wedekind, Annie. A Horse of Her Own. 2008. 288p. (J). 16.95 **(*978-0-312-36927-9(1))** Feiwel & Friends.

Whitney, Kim Ablon. The Perfect Distance. 2007. 256p. (YA). (gr. 7). pap. 5.99 (978-0-553-49467-9(8) , Laurel Leaf) Random Hse. Children's Bks.

HORSES

see also Ponies

Alderton, David. Horses. 2nd rev. ed. 2003. (DK Pockets Ser.). (Illus.). 160p. pap. 6.99 (978-0-7894-9588-4(0)) Dorling Kindersley Publishing, Inc.

All about Horses. 2005. 38p. 28.00 (978-0-7910-8685-8(2) , Chelsea Hse.) Facts On File, Inc.

Andrekson, Judy. JB Andrew: Mustang Magic. Parkins, David, illus. 2008. 96p. pap. 7.95 **(*978-0-88776-837-8(7))** Tundra Bks., Inc./Livres Toundra, Inc. CAN. *Dist:* Random Hse. of Canada, Ltd.

—Little Squire: The Jumping Pony. Parkins, David, illus. 2007. (True Horse Stories Ser.). 80p. (J). (gr. 3-6). pap. 7.95 (978-0-88776-770-8(2)) Tundra Bks., Inc./Livres Toundra, Inc. CAN. *Dist:* Random Hse., Inc.

—Miskeen: The Dancing Horse. Parkins, David, illus. 2007. (True Horse Stories Ser.). 96p. (J). (gr. 3-6). pap. 7.95 (978-0-88776-771-5(0)) Tundra Bks., Inc./Livres Toundra, Inc. CAN. *Dist:* Random Hse., Inc.

Apte, Sunita. Police Horses. 2007. (Horse Power Ser.). (J). lib. bdg. 25.27 (978-1-59716-401-6(1)) Bearport Publishing Co., Inc.

Ashe, E. Happy Horse: A Children's Book of Horses. Ashe, E., illus. 2003. (Illus.). 18p. (J). bds. 12.95 (978-0-9727849-0-0(X) , 0-9727849-0-X) Happy Horse Publishing, Ltd.

Barbé-Julien, Colette. Little Horses. 2006. (Born to Be Wild Ser.). (Illus.). 23p. (J). lib. bdg. 22.00 (978-0-8368-6167-9(1)) Stevens, Gareth Inc.

Barbe-Julien, Colette. El Potro. 2005. (Quien eres tu? Ser.). 24p. (J). 7.95 (978-84-7864-233-5(1)) Combel Editorial, S.A. ESP. *Dist:* Independent Pubs. Group.

Barnes, Julia. Horses at Work. 2006. (Illus.). 32p. (J). 23.33 (978-0-8368-6225-6(2)) Stevens, Gareth Inc.

Barnes, Julia, et al. 101 Facts about Horses & Ponies. 2002. (One Hundred One Facts about Pets Ser.). (Illus.). 32p. (J). (gr. 3 up). lib. bdg. 23.33 (978-0-8368-3019-4(9)) Stevens, Gareth Inc.

Bates, Michelle. Midnight Horse Kid Kit. 2005. 112p. (J). 11.99 (978-1-58086-799-3(5)); 11.99 (978-1-58086-759-7(6)) EDC Publishing. (Usborne).

Bell, N. W. The Great American Horse Book: A Childrens Guide to Horse's. l.t. ed. 2003. Tr. of Gran Libro Del Calballo Americano. (SPA., Illus.). 32p. (J). 10.99 (978-0-9729753-0-8(6)) Really Big Coloring Bks., Inc.

Bell, Rachael. Horses. (Farm Animals Ser.). (Illus.). 32p. (J). (gr. k-2). 2001. pap. 6.95 (978-1-58810-365-9(X) , 91089); 2000. lib. bdg. 21.36 (978-1-57572-531-4(2)) Heinemann Library.

Bennett, Kathy. Pony Pointers: How to Safely Care for Your Horse or Pony. Peterson, Carol A., illus. 2004. 48p. (J). per. 7.99 (978-0-9763209-0-6(8)) Trail Trotters Bk. Ranch.

Binns, Tristan Boyer. Horses & Ponies. 2006. (Keeping Pets Ser.). (Illus.). 48p. (J). (978-1-4034-7703-3(5)) Heinemann Library.

Bolam, Emily. Chunky Farm Horse. 2000. (Chunky Farm Bks.). (Illus.). 14p. (J). (ps-k). bds. 5.99 (978-0-7641-5322-8(6)) Barron's Educational Series, Inc.

Bozzo, Linda. My First Horse. 2007. (My First Pet Library from the American Humane Association Ser.). (Illus.). 32p. (J). (gr. 1-2). lib. bdg. 22.60 (978-0-7660-2753-4(8) , Enslow Elementary) Enslow Pubs., Inc.

Brazen Horse. 2006. (J). (978-1-933343-30-3(3) , PONY) Stabenfeldt Inc.

Bright, Michael & Dunstone, Nigel. Wild Horses, 3 vols. 2001. (Nature Watch Ser.). (Illus.). 64p. (J). (gr. 3-7). 14.99 (978-0-7548-0866-4(1)) Anness Publishing GBR. *Dist:* National Bk. Network.

Budd, Jackie. The Complete Guides to Horses & Ponies, 4 bks. Incl. Horse & Pony Care. 1998. lib. bdg. 26.60 (978-0-8368-2047-8(9)); Horse & Pony Jumping. 1999. lib. bdg. 27.33 (978-0-8368-2446-9(6)); Horse & Pony Tack. 1999. lib. bdg. 27.33 (978-0-8368-2447-6(4)); Understanding Horses & Ponies. 1999. lib. bdg. 27.33 (978-0-8368-2448-3(2)); 64p. (J). (gr. 4 up). (Illus.). Set lib. bdg. 81.99 (978-0-8368-2470-4(9)) Stevens, Gareth Inc.

—Understanding Horses & Ponies. 1999. (Complete Guides to Horses & Ponies Ser.). (Illus.). 64p. (J). (gr. 4 up). lib. bdg. 27.33 (978-0-8368-2448-3(2)) Stevens, Gareth Inc.

—The World of Horses. 2004. (World Of Ser.). (Illus.). 64p. (J). (gr. 4-6). pap. 8.95 (978-0-7534-5753-5(9) , Kingfisher) Houghton Mifflin Co. Trade & Reference Div.

Budiansky, Stephen. The World According to Horses: How They Run, See, & Think. rev. ed. 2000. (Illus.). 112p. (J). (gr. 5-9). 17.95 (978-0-8050-6054-6(5) , Holt, Henry & Co. Bks. For Young Readers) Holt, Henry & Co.

Bull, Peter, illus. Horses. 2005. (J). (gr. 3-4). lib. bdg. 226.00 (978-0-7368-4429-1(5)) Capstone Pr., Inc.

—Horses. Date not set. (Old MacDonald Stickers Ser.). 16p. (J). 2.98 (978-0-7525-7060-0(9)) Parragon, Inc.

—Horses, 6 vols. (gr. k-2). 28.95 (978-0-7368-9241-4(9)) Red Brick Learning.

H
I

Butterfield, Moira. Horse. 2000. (Who Am I? Ser.). (Illus.). 32p. (J). (ps-1). lib. bdg. 16.95 (978-1-929298-90-7(0)) Chrysalis Education.

Byrne, Susan K. Sierra Cloud: A True Story About a Horse with Courage. Stockbridge, Joan, ed. Byrne, Susan K., photos by. l.t. ed. 2002. (Illus.). 36p. (J). (gr. 3-7). spiral bd. 14.95 (978-0-9723652-0-8(6)) R&R Pubns.

—Sierra-Cloud - A True Story about a Horse with Courage: The Writing & Drawing Journal. l.t. ed. 2002. 34p. (J). (gr. 3-7). spiral bd. 4.95 (978-0-9723652-1-5(4)) R&R Pubns.

Chapple, Judy. Your Horse: A Step-by-Step Guide to Horse Ownership. 2003. (Illus.). 144p. (YA). (gr. 8 up). pap. 16.95 (978-0-88266-353-1(4) , 66353) Storey Publishing, LLC.

Clutton-Brock, Juliet. Horse. (DK Eyewitness Bks.). 72p. 2008. (J). (gr. 3-8). 15.99 (***978-0-7566-3775-0(9)***); 2004. (Illus.). 15.99 (978-0-7566-0686-2(1)) Dorling Kindersley Publishing, Inc.

Clutton-Brock, Juliet & Dorling Kindersley Publishing Staff. Horse. 2004. (Eyewitness Books). (Illus.). 72p. (J). lib. bdg. 19.99 (978-0-7566-0685-5(3)) Dorling Kindersley Publishing, Inc.

Coleman, Lori. The American Saddlebred Horse. 2006. (Edge Books, Horses). (Illus.). 32p. (J). (978-0-7368-5458-0(4) , 1252814) Capstone Pr., Inc.

—The Friesian Horse. 2006. (Edge Books, Horses). (Illus.). 32p. (J). (978-0-7368-5825-0(3) , 1252819) Capstone Pr., Inc.

—The Tennessee Walking Horse. 2006. (Edge Books, Horses). (Illus.). 32p. (J). (978-0-7368-5461-0(4) , 1252818) Capstone Pr., Inc.

Cooper, Jason. Foal to Horse. 2003. (Illus.). 24p. (J). 20.64 (978-1-58952-694-5(5)) Rourke Publishing, LLC.

Cowley, Joy. Where Horses Run Free: A Dream for the American Mustang. Johnson, Layne, illus. 2003. 32p. (YA). (gr. k-2). pap. 15.95 (978-1-59078-062-6(0)) Boyds Mills Pr.

Criscione, Rachel Damon. The Appaloosa. 2007. (Illus.). 24p. (J). lib. bdg. (978-1-4042-3450-5(0) , PowerKids Pr.) Rosen Publishing Group, Inc., The.

—The Morgan. 2007. (Illus.). 24p. (J). lib. bdg. (***978-1-4042-3451-2(9)*** , PowerKids Pr.) Rosen Publishing Group, Inc., The.

—The Mustangs. 2007. (Illus.). 24p. (J). lib. bdg. (978-1-4042-3452-9(7) , PowerKids Pr.) Rosen Publishing Group, Inc., The.

—The Palomino. 2007. (Illus.). 24p. (J). lib. bdg. (978-1-4042-3449-9(7) , PowerKids Pr.) Rosen Publishing Group, Inc., The.

—The Quarter Horse. 2007. (Illus.). 24p. (J). lib. bdg. (978-1-4042-3448-2(9) , PowerKids Pr.) Rosen Publishing Group, Inc., The.

Crisp, Marty. Everything Horse. 2005. (Kids' FAQs Ser.). (Illus.). 64p. pap. 7.95 (978-1-55971-921-6(4) , NorthWord Bks. for Young Readers) T&N Children's Publishing.

—Everything Horse: What Kids Really Want to Know about Horses. 2005. (Kids' FAQs Ser.). (Illus.). 64p. 10.95 (978-1-55971-920-9(6) , NorthWord Bks. for Young Readers) T&N Children's Publishing.

Curry, Marion. Horse & Pony Basics. 2006. (Illus.). 32p. (J). lib. bdg. (978-0-8368-6831-9(5)) Stevens, Gareth Inc.

—Horse & Pony Breeds. 2006. (Illus.). 32p. (J). lib. bdg. (978-0-8368-6832-6(3)) Stevens, Gareth Inc.

—Horse & Pony Care. 2006. (Illus.). 32p. (J). lib. bdg. (978-0-8368-6833-3(1)) Stevens, Gareth Inc.

Dalgleish, Sharon. Working Horses. 2005. (Farm Animals Ser.). (Illus.). 32p. (J). (gr. 2-4). 23.00 (978-0-7910-8273-7(3) , Chelsea Hse.) Facts On File, Inc.

Davis, Michele S. & Makris, Alexandra. Magical Mac: The True Story of a Healing Horse. 2002. (Illus.). 35p. (J). pap. (978-0-9715395-0-1(2)) Serendipity Pubns.

DeLaCroix, Alice F. Mattie's Whisper. 2001. 136p. (gr. 7-12). pap. 12.95 (978-0-595-15072-4(1) , Backinprint.com) iUniverse, Inc.

Dell, Pamela. Appaloosas. 2007. (Majestic Horses Ser.). 32p. (J). (gr. k-4). 27.07 (978-1-59296-780-3(9)) Child's World, Inc.

—Arabians. 2007. (Majestic Horses Ser.). 32p. (J). (gr. k-4). 27.07 (978-1-59296-781-0(7)) Child's World, Inc.

—Clydesdales. 2007. (Majestic Horses Ser.). 32p. (J). (gr. k-4). 27.07 (978-1-59296-782-7(5)) Child's World, Inc.

—Przewalski's Horses. 2007. (Majestic Horses Ser.). 32p. (J). (gr. k-4). 27.07 (978-1-59296-784-1(1)) Child's World, Inc.

—Thoroughbreds. 2007. (Majestic Horses Ser.). 32p. (J). (gr. k-4). 27.07 (978-1-59296-786-5(8)) Child's World, Inc.

DeMeyer, Patricia. Little Horsey Little Lessons: A Young Girl & Her Special Horse Help Teach Skills for Life. Christie, Terri, illus. 1999. 40p. (J). (gr. 1-6). pap. 9.95 (978-0-9666433-0-5(5)) Saddle Tree Pr.

Denniston, David. The American Paint Horse. 2005. (Horses Ser.). (Illus.). 32p. (J). 22.60 (978-0-7368-3763-7(9)) Capstone Pr., Inc.

Dickins, Rosie & Pratt, Leonie. Horse & Pony Treasury. 2006. 96p. (J). 19.99 (978-0-7945-1431-0(6) , Usborne) EDC Publishing.

Diedrich, John. The Clydesdale Horse. 2005. (Horses Ser.). (Illus.). 32p. (J). 22.60 (978-0-7368-3766-8(3)) Capstone Pr., Inc.

—The Thoroughbred Horse. 2005. (Horses Ser.). (Illus.). 32p. (J). 22.60 (978-0-7368-3768-2(X)) Capstone Pr., Inc.

DK Publishing. Pony. 2007. (See How They Grow Ser.). 24p. (J). pap. 3.99 (***978-0-7566-3374-5(5)***) Dorling Kindersley Publishing, Inc.

Dorling Kindersley Publishing Staff. Horse. (Ultimate sticker Bks.). 16p. (J). 2005. pap. 6.99 (978-0-7566-0975-7(5)); 2003. (Illus.). pap. 3.99 (978-0-7894-9826-7(X)) Dorling Kindersley Publishing, Inc.

—Ponies. 1999. (Touch & Feel Ser.). (Illus.). 12p. (J). (ps-k). bds. 6.99 (978-0-7894-4748-7(7)) Dorling Kindersley Publishing, Inc.

Doudna, Kelly. Foals. l.t. ed. 1999. (Baby Animals Ser.). (Illus.). 24p. (J). (ps-3). lib. bdg. 19.93 (978-1-57765-183-3(9) , SandCastle) ABDO Publishing Co.

Douglas, Vincent & Gibbs, Lynne. A Word about Horses. 2005. (Word About Ser.). (Illus.). 24p. (J). pap. 3.95 (978-0-7696-3387-9(0) , Brighter Child) School Specialty Publishing.

Draper. Book of Horses. 2000. (Illus.). 160p. pap. 14.95 (978-1-84215-202-7(5) , Southwater) Anness Publishing GBR. *Dist:* National Bk. Network.

Draper, Judith, et al. My First Horse & Pony Care Book: From Boots & Bedding to Saddles & Stables. Roberts, Matthew, photos by. 2006. (My First Horse & Pony Ser.). (Illus.). 48p. (J). 9.95 (978-0-7534-5989-8(2) , Kingfisher) Houghton Mifflin Co. Trade & Reference Div.

Draw 50 Horses. 2002. (Illus.). (J). 17.60 (978-0-7587-4165-3(0)) Book Wholesalers, Inc.

Dubowski, Cathy East & Dubowski, Mark. A Horse Named Seabiscuit. Rowe, Michael Langham, illus. 2003. (All Aboard Reading Ser.). 48p. (J). (gr. 2-6). mass mkt. 3.99 (978-0-448-43342-4(7) , Grosset & Dunlap) Penguin Group (USA) Inc.

Einhorn, Kama. Sesame Subjects: My First Book about Horses & Ponies. Moroney, Christopher, illus. 2008. (Sesame Subjects Ser.). 24p. (J). (gr. k-1). 7.99 (***978-0-375-84210-8(1)*** , Random Hse. Bks. for Young Readers) Random Hse. Children's Bks.

Evers, June V. The Wonderful Life of Lola: A Day at the Beach. 2006. (Illus.). 16p. (J). pap. 4.95 (978-0-9638814-8-9(5)) Horse Hollow Pr., Inc.

Evers, June V., ed. The Original Book of Horse Treats: Recipes You Can Make at Home for Your Horse. 2003. (Illus.). 72p. (J). spiral bd. 19.95 (978-0-9638814-1-0(8)) Horse Hollow Pr., Inc.

Felber, Bill. The Horse in War. (Horse Library). (Illus.). 64p. (J). 2005. pap. 200.00 (978-0-7910-6650-8(9)); 2001. 25.00 (978-0-7910-6651-5(7)) Facts On File, Inc. (Chelsea Hse.).

Fetty, Margaret. Show Horses. 2007. (Horse Power Ser.). (J). lib. bdg. 25.27 (978-1-59716-399-6(6)) Bearport Publishing Co., Inc.

Funston, Sylvia. The Kids' Horse Book. 2005. (Illus.). 72p. (J). pap. 6.95 (978-1-897066-37-9(6)) Maple Tree Pr. CAN. *Dist:* Perseus Distribution.

Gaff, Jackie. I Wonder Why Horses Wear Shoes: And Other Questions about Horses. 2006. (I Wonder Why Ser.). (Illus.). 32p. (J). (gr. k-3). pap. 6.95 (978-0-7534-5962-1(0) , Kingfisher) Houghton Mifflin Co. Trade & Reference Div.

—I Wonder Why Horses Wear Shoes & Other Questions about Horses. (Illus.). 32p. (J). 2006. (978-1-4156-8057-5(4)); 2002. tchr. ed. 12.95 (978-0-7534-5447-3(5)) Houghton Mifflin Co. Trade & Reference Div. (Kingfisher).

Gentle, Victor & Perry, Janet. Appaloosas. 1998. (Illus.). 24p. (J). (gr. 1 up). lib. bdg. 19.93 (978-0-8368-2129-1(7)) Stevens, Gareth Inc.

—Chincoteague Ponies. 2001. (Great American Horses Ser.). (Illus.). 24p. (J). (gr. 1 up). lib. bdg. 22.00 (978-0-8368-2935-8(2)) Stevens, Gareth Inc.

—Florida Cracker Horses. 2001. (Great American Horses Ser.). (Illus.). 24p. (J). (gr. 1 up). lib. bdg. 22.00 (978-0-8368-2936-5(0)) Stevens, Gareth Inc.

—Great American Horses, 6 bks. Incl. Chincoteague Ponies. lib. bdg. 22.00 (978-0-8368-2935-8(2)); Florida Cracker Horses. lib. bdg. 22.00 (978-0-8368-2936-5(0)); Miniature Horses. lib. bdg. 22.00 (978-0-8368-2937-2(9)); Saddlebreds. lib. bdg. 22.00 (978-0-8368-2938-9(7)); Standardbreds. lib. bdg. 22.00 (978-0-8368-2939-6(5)); Tennessee Walking Horses. lib. bdg. 22.00 (978-0-8368-2940-2(9)); 24p. (J). (gr. 1 up). (Illus.). 2001. Set lib. bdg. 127.60 (978-0-8368-2983-9(2)) Stevens, Gareth Inc.

—Miniature Horses. 2001. (Great American Horses Ser.). (Illus.). 24p. (J). (gr. 1 up). lib. bdg. 22.00 (978-0-8368-2937-2(9)) Stevens, Gareth Inc.

—Morgans. 1998. (Illus.). 24p. (J). (gr. 1 up). lib. bdg. 19.93 (978-0-8368-2130-7(0)) Stevens, Gareth Inc.

—Mustangs: America's Wild Horse. 1998. (Illus.). 24p. (J). (gr. 1 up). lib. bdg. 19.93 (978-0-8368-2131-4(9)) Stevens, Gareth Inc.

—Paints & Pintos. 1998. (Illus.). 24p. (J). (gr. 1 up). lib. bdg. 19.93 (978-0-8368-2132-1(7)) Stevens, Gareth Inc.

—Palominos. 1998. (Illus.). 24p. (J). (gr. 1 up). lib. bdg. 19.93 (978-0-8368-2133-8(5)) Stevens, Gareth Inc.

—Quarter Horses. 1998. (Illus.). 24p. (J). (gr. 1 up). lib. bdg. 19.93 (978-0-8368-2134-5(3)) Stevens, Gareth Inc.

—Saddlebreds. 2001. (Great American Horses Ser.). (Illus.). 24p. (J). (gr. 1 up). lib. bdg. 22.00 (978-0-8368-2938-9(7)) Stevens, Gareth Inc.

—Standardbreds. 2001. (Great American Horses Ser.). (Illus.). 24p. (J). (gr. 1 up). lib. bdg. 22.00 (978-0-8368-2939-6(5)) Stevens, Gareth Inc.

—Tennessee Walking Horses. 2001. (Great American Horses Ser.). (Illus.). 24p. (J). (gr. 1 up). lib. bdg. 22.00 (978-0-8368-2940-2(9)) Stevens, Gareth Inc.

Getha, Patricia & Maltseff, Michele. Drawing Horses Kit: A Complete Drawing Kit for Beginners. 2008. (Walter Foster Drawing Kits Ser.). (Illus.). 32p. pap. 19.95 (***978-1-60058-056-7(4)***) Foster, Walter Publishing, Inc.

Gibbons, Gail. Horses! Gibbons, Gail, illus. 2005. (Illus.). 32p. (gr. k-3). (J). 6.95 (978-0-8234-1875-6(8)); tchr. ed. 16.95 (978-0-8234-1703-2(4)) Holiday Hse., Inc.

Gilkerson, Patricia. My Adventure with Wild Horses. 2006. 44p. (J). 8.99 (978-1-59092-312-2(X) , Orchard Academy Pr.) Windstorm Creative.

Gordon, Sharon. Guess Who Runs. 2004. (SPA & ENG., Illus.). 31p. (J). 21.36 (978-0-7614-1763-7(X) , Benchmark Bks.) Cavendish, Marshall Corp.

Gordon, Sharon. Guess Who Runs: Adivina Quién Corre. 2007. (SPA & ENG.). (J). (***978-0-7614-2885-5(2)); (978-0-7614-2868-8(2)***) Cavendish, Marshall Bks., Ltd.

Grant, Sheena. Horses. Morice, Diana, illus. 2005. (Twenty4Sevens Ser.). 48p. (J). pap. (978-0-439-78527-3(8)) Scholastic, Inc.

Green, Emily. Horses. 2007. (Blastoff! Readers Ser.). 24p. (J). (gr. k-2). 18.50 (***978-0-531-17553-8(7)*** , Children's Pr.) Scholastic Library Publishing.

Green, Emily K. Horses. 2007. (Illus.). 24p. (J). lib. bdg. 16.95 (978-1-60014-067-9(X)) Bellwether Media.

Green, Jen & Dunstone, N. Wild Horses. 2004. (Nature Fact File Ser.). (Illus.). 64p. pap. 7.99 (978-1-84215-895-1(3) , Southwater) Anness Publishing GBR. *Dist:* National Bk. Network.

Green, John. Big Book of Horses to Color. 2006. 160p. (J). pap. 7.95 (978-0-486-45178-7(X)) Dover Pubns., Inc.

—Favorite Horses: Coloring Book. 2005. (Illus.). 32p. (J). (ps-ps). pap. 3.95 (978-0-486-44010-1(9)) Dover Pubns., Inc.

—Horse Anatomy: Coloring Book. 2006. 32p. pap. 3.95 (978-0-486-44813-8(4)) Dover Pubns., Inc.

—Horses of the Old West. 2007. 32p. (J). pap. 3.95 (***978-0-486-45675-1(7)***) Dover Pubns., Inc.

—Horses Stickers. 1999. (Illus.). 4p. pap. 5.95 (978-0-486-40596-4(6)) Dover Pubns., Inc.

—Horses Tattoos. 2003. (Dover Little Activity Bks.). (Illus.). 2p. (J). (gr. k-5). pap. 1.50 (978-0-486-43029-4(4)) Dover Pubns., Inc.

—Learning about Ponies. 2004. (Learning about Ser.). (Illus.). 16p. (J). (gr. 3-5). pap. 1.50 (978-0-486-43316-5(1)) Dover Pubns., Inc.

—Wonderful World of Horses Coloring Book. 2005. 32p. (J). (gr. 2). pap. 3.95 (978-0-486-44465-9(1)) Dover Pubns., Inc.

Gruber, Beth. Horse Sense. 2004. (Pet's Point of View Ser.). 32p. (J). (gr. 4 up). lib. bdg. 22.60 (978-0-7565-0702-2(2)) Compass Point Bks.

Haas, Jessie. Safe Horse, Safe Rider: A Young Rider's Guide to Responsible Horsekeeping. Haar, Amanda, ed. 2003. (Illus.). 160p. (J). (gr. 4-7). pap. 16.95 (978-0-88266-700-3(9) , 66700) Storey Publishing, LLC.

Hansard, Peter. Field Full of Horses. Lilly, Kenneth, illus. 2001. (Read & Wonder Ser.). 32p. (J). (ps-3). pap. 6.99 (978-0-7636-1434-8(3)) Candlewick Pr.

—Field Full of Horses. 2001. (ps-2). lib. bdg. 14.15 (978-0-613-44207-7(5)) Tandem Library Bks.

Hansen, Rosanna. Panda: A Guide Horse for Ann. Soderstrom, Neil, photos by. 2005. (Illus.). 48p. (J). (gr. 3-5). 19.95 (978-1-59078-184-5(8)) Boyds Mills Pr.

Hanson, Anders. Handsome Horses. Nobens, C. A., illus. 2007. (Perfect Pets Ser.). 24p. (J). (gr. k-3). lib. bdg. 19.93 (***978-1-59928-750-8(1)*** , SandCastle) ABDO Publishing Co.

Harcourt School Publishers Staff. Black Cowboys & Wild Horses Level D: Readers. 2001. (Collections Ser.). (Illus.). pap. 12.10 (978-0-15-314379-3(7)) Harcourt Schl. Pubs.

—Horsepower: Library Edition. 1999. (Collections Ser.). (Illus.). (J). 4.70 (978-0-15-314333-5(9)) Harcourt Schl. Pubs.

—Horses & Riders: Take-Home Book. 1999. (Signatures Ser.). (Illus.). (J). (gr. 4). pap. 1.90 (978-0-15-313904-8(8)) Harcourt Schl. Pubs.

—The Story of the Horse Advanced Level. 3rd ed. 2002. (Trophies Reading Program Ser.). (Illus.). pap. 5.10 (978-0-15-323485-9(7)) Harcourt Schl. Pubs.

Harper, Don. Horses. 2006. (Illus.). 64p. (J). (gr. 5-8). 26.20 (978-1-4103-0655-5(0) , Blackbirch Pr., Inc.) Thomson Gale.

Harpster, Steve. Horses. 2006. (Pencil, Paper, Draw! Ser.). (Illus.). 64p. (J). pap., pap., spiral bd. 5.95 (978-1-4027-2977-5(4)) Sterling Publishing Co., Inc.

Harvey, Bev. The Horse Family. 2003. (Animal Families Ser.). (Illus.). 32p. (gr. 2-4). 23.00 (978-0-7910-7545-6(1) , Chelsea Hse.) Facts On File, Inc.

Harvey, Gill. Understanding Your Pony. 1998. (Riding School Ser.). (Illus.). 32p. (YA). (gr. 3 up). pap. 5.95 (978-0-7460-2923-7(3)); lib. bdg. 13.95 (978-1-58086-012-3(5)) EDC Publishing.

Head, Honor. Ponies & Horses. 2007. (QEB Know Your Pet Ser.). (Illus.). 32p. (J). lib. bdg. 19.95 (978-1-59566-219-4(7)) QEB Publishing Inc.

Henderson, Carolyn. Horse & Pony Book. 2007. (Illus.). 160p. (J). (gr. 4-7). pap. 10.99 (***978-0-7566-3146-8(7)***) Dorling Kindersley Publishing, Inc.

Henry, Marguerite. Album of Horses. 1999. (Illus.). (J). (gr. 3-6). lib. bdg. 21.10 (978-0-7857-0926-8(6)) Tandem Library Bks.

Hiley, Lisa. The Horse Breeds Poster Book. Langrish, Bob, photos by. 2003. (Illus.). 64p. (J). (gr. 3-6). pap. 9.95 (978-1-58017-507-4(4) , 67507, Storey Kids) Storey Publishing, LLC.

Hill, Cherry. Cherry Hill's Horse Care for Kids: Grooming, Feeding, Behavior, Stable & Pasture, Health Care, Handling & Safety, Enjoying. 2002. (Illus.). (J). (gr. 3-7). 128p. tchr. ed. 23.95 (978-1-58017-476-3(0) , 67476); 116p. pap. 16.95 (978-1-58017-407-7(8) , 67407) Storey Publishing, LLC. (Storey Kids).

—Your Pony, Your Horse: A Kid's Guide to Care & Enjoyment. Balmuth, Deborah, ed. 2003. (Storey's Your Ser.). (Illus.). 161p. (Orig.). (J). (gr. 4-7). pap. 14.95 (978-0-88266-908-3(7) , 66908) Storey Publishing, LLC.

Holub, Joan. Why Do Horses Neigh? DiVito, Anna, illus. 2003. (Easy-to-Read Ser.). 48p. (J). (gr. 1-3). pap. 3.99 (978-0-14-230119-7(1) , Puffin) Penguin Group (USA) Inc.

—Why Do Horses Neigh? 2003. (gr. k-3). lib. bdg. 11.80 (978-0-613-61670-6(7)) Tandem Library Bks.

Hong, Chen Jiang. The Magic Horse of Han Gan. 2006. (Illus.). 38p. (gr. 1-5). 16.95 (978-1-59270-063-9(2)) Enchanted Lion Bks., LLC.

Hood, Karen Jean Matsko. Gaited Horse: A Daily Journal. 2006. (J). 24.95 (978-1-59434-790-0(5)); spiral bd. 19.95 (978-1-59434-792-4(1)); per. 19.95 (978-1-59434-791-7(3)); ring bd. 24.95 (978-1-59434-794-8(8)); spiral bd. 22.95 (978-1-59434-796-2(4)); spiral bd. 22.95 (978-1-59434-795-5(6)) Whispering Pine Pr., Inc.

—Gaited Horse Activity & Coloring Book-English/French/Italian Edition: Braille. 2006. (J). spiral bd. 22.95 (978-1-59649-983-6(4)) Whispering Pine Pr., Inc.

—Gaited Horse Activity & Coloring Book-English/German/Spanish Edition: Braille. 2006. (J). spiral bd. 17.95 (978-1-59649-961-4(3)) Whispering Pine Pr., Inc.

—Icelandic Horse Activity & Coloring Book: Eductional Book Series. 2nd braille ed. 2006. spiral bd. 49.95 (978-1-59649-546-3(4)) Whispering Pine Pr., Inc.

Horsepower: Individual Title Six-Packs. (Rigby Infoquest Ser.). 24p. (gr. 3 up). 34.00 (978-0-7578-5769-0(8)) Rigby Education.

Horses: Individual Title Six-Packs. 16p. (gr. 2 up). 36.00 (978-0-7635-9210-3(2)) Rigby Education.

Horses Have Foals. (Animals & Their Young Ser.). 24p. (J). 7.95 (978-0-7565-1242-2(5)) Compass Point Bks.

Horses on the Farm, 6 vols. (gr. k-2). 28.95 (978-0-7368-9383-1(0)) Red Brick Learning.

Horses Set II. 2006. (J). (gr. k-6). 128.10 (978-1-59679-312-5(0) , Checkerboard Library) ABDO Publishing Co.

Jeffrey, Laura S. Horses: How to Choose & Care for a Horse. 2004. (American Humane Pet Care Library). (Illus.). 48p. (J). lib. bdg. 23.93 (978-0-7660-2519-6(5)) Enslow Pubs., Inc.

Jepperson, Richard. Two Fires in the Night: The Third Part of the Crazy Horse Chronicles. Mundie, Ken, illus. 2003. viii, 56p. (YA). (gr. 7-12). 16.95 (978-0-9672012-2-1(5)) String of Beads Pubns.

Johnston, Marianne. Horses Past & Present. 2000. (Prehistoric Animals & Their Modern-Day Relatives Ser.). 24p. (J). (gr. k-4). lib. bdg. 18.75 (978-0-8239-5207-6(X) , PowerKids Pr.) Rosen Publishing Group, Inc., The.

Kalman, Bobbie. Les Chevaux. 2002. (FRE., Illus.). 32p. pap. (978-2-920660-86-1(1)) Crabtree Publishing Co.

—What Is a Horse? 2001. (gr. 3-6). lib. bdg. 14.10 (978-0-613-43525-3(7)) Tandem Library Bks.

Kalman, Bobbie & Levigne, Heather. Qué Es un Caballo? 2006. (ENG & SPA., Illus.). 32p. (978-0-7787-8766-2(4)) Crabtree Publishing Co.

—Que es un Caballo? 2006. (ENG & SPA.). 32p. (gr. 2-3). pap. (978-0-7787-8812-6(1)) Crabtree Publishing Co.

—What Is a Horse? 2001. (Science of Living Things Ser.). (Illus.). 32p. (J). (gr. 2-3). (978-0-86505-984-9(5)); pap. (978-0-86505-961-0(6)) Crabtree Publishing Co.

Kathrens, Ginger. Cloud: Wild Stallion of the Rockies. 2001. (Illus.). 128p. pap. 24.95 (978-1-889540-70-2(6)) BowTie Pr.

—Cloud's Legacy: The Wild Stallion Returns. 2004. (Illus.). 200p. 24.95 (978-1-931993-12-8(2)) BowTie Pr.

Keaster, Diane. Chickadee-the Traveler, 11. l.t. ed. 2004. (ZC Horses: Vol. 8). (Illus.). 77p. (J). 7.95 (***978-0-9721496-7-9(8)***) ZC Horses Series of Children's Bks.

Keaster, Diane W. Darby-The Cow Dog. l.t. ed. 2005. (ZC Horses: Vol. 9). (Illus.). 65p. (J). 7.95 (***978-0-9721496-9-3(4)***) ZC Horses Series of Children's Bks.

Keaster, Diane Wilmae. Leroy-the Stallion, 25 bks. Page, Deb, illus. l.t. ed. 2003. (ZC Horses: 6). 76p. (J). 5.50 net. (978-0-9721496-5-5(1)) ZC Horses Series of Children's Bks.

Kelley, Brent P. Horse Breeds of the World. 2001. (Horse Library). (Illus.). 64p. (J). (gr. 4-8). 25.00 (978-0-7910-6652-2(5) , Chelsea Hse.) Facts On File, Inc.

—Horse Care & Health. 2001. (Horse Library). (Illus.). 64p. (J). 25.00 (978-0-7910-6653-9(3) , Chelsea Hse.) Facts On File, Inc.

Kimball, Cheryl. Horse Showing for Kids: Training, Grooming, Trailering, Apparel, Tack, Competing, Sportsmanship. 2004. (Illus.). 160p. (J). pap. 16.95 (978-1-58017-501-2(5) , 67501); tchr. ed. 26.95 (978-1-58017-573-9(2) , 67573) Storey Publishing, LLC. (Storey Kids).

Kulling, Monica. Horses. Ogden, Betina, illus. 2001. 24p. (J). (gr. k-1). pap. 3.25 (978-0-375-81217-0(2) , Random Hse. Bks. for Young Readers) Random Hse. Children's Bks.

Langrish, Bob. Horses & Friends Poster Book. 2004. (Illus.). 64p. (J). pap. 9.95 (978-1-58017-580-7(5) , 67580, Storey Kids) Storey Publishing, LLC.

Langrish, Bob, et al, photos by. Dream Horses: A Poster Book. 2004. (Illus.). 64p. (J). pap. 9.95 (978-1-58017-574-6(0) , 67574, Storey Kids) Storey Publishing, LLC.

Langton, Mandy & Pilgrim, Anne. The Pony Puzzle Book, Bk. 2. 2001. (Illus.). 92p. pap. 11.99 (978-0-85131-850-9(9) , Allen, J. A. & Company, Limited) Hale, Robert Ltd. GBR. *Dist:* Independent Pubs. Group.

Lauber, Patricia. True-or-False Book of Horses. Schanzer, Rosalyn, illus. 2000. 32p. (J). (ps-3). 16.99 (978-0-688-16919-0(8)) HarperCollins Pubs.

Learning about Horses, 16 bks. Incl. American Saddlebred Horse. Wilcox, Charlotte. 1996. lib. bdg. 21.26 (978-1-56065-364-6(7)); Appaloosa Horse. Stewart, Gail B. 1995. lib. bdg. 21.26 (978-1-56065-243-4(8)); Arabian Horse. Stewart, Gail B. 1995. lib. bdg. 21.26 (978-1-56065-244-1(6)); Chincoteague Pony. Wilcox, Charlotte. 1996. lib. bdg. 21.26 (978-1-56065-363-9(9)); Lipizzaner Horse. Wilcox, Charlotte. 1997. lib. bdg. 21.26 (978-1-56065-464-3(3)); Miniature Horses. Wilcox, Charlotte. 1997. lib. bdg. 21.26 (978-1-56065-465-0(1)); Morgan Horse. Wilcox, Charlotte. Munoz, William, photos by. 1996. lib. bdg. 21.26 (978-1-56065-362-2(0)); Mustangs & Wild Horses. Stewart, Gail B. 1996. lib. bdg. 21.26 (978-1-56065-301-1(9)); Palomino

Horse. Stewart, Gail B. Munoz, William, photos by. 1995. lib. bdg. 21.26 (978-1-56065-299-1(3)); Pinto Horse. Stewart, Gail B. 1995. lib. bdg. 21.26 (978-1-56065-298-4(5)); Przewalski's Horse. Wilcox, Charlotte. 1997. lib. bdg. 21.26 (978-1-56065-466-7(X)); Quarter Horse. Stewart, Gail B. 1995. lib. bdg. 21.26 (978-1-56065-242-7(X)); Shetland Pony. Stewart, Gail B. 1995. lib. bdg. 21.26 (978-1-56065-300-4(0)); Standardbred Horse. Wilcox, Charlotte. 1997. lib. bdg. 21.26 (978-1-56065-467-4(8)); Tennessee Walking Horse. Wilcox, Charlotte. 1996. lib. bdg. 21.26 (978-1-56065-365-3(5)); Thoroughbred Horse : Born to Run. Stewart, Gail B. 1995. lib. bdg. 21.26 (978-1-56065-245-8(4)); 48p. (J). (gr. 3-4). (Illus.). Set lib. bdg. 340.16 (978-1-56065-648-7(4) , Capstone High-Interest Bks.) Capstone Pr., Inc.

Libby, Barbara M. I Rode the Red Horse: Secretariat's Belmont Race. Libby, Barbara M., illus. 2003. (Illus.). 32p. (J). (ps-3). 16.95 (978-1-58150-096-7(3) , Eclipse Pr.) Blood-Horse, Inc., The.

Lister, T., compiled by. Chemistry at the Races: The Work of the Horseracing Forensic Laboratory. 2002. (Illus.). 45p. pap. 14.95 (978-0-85404-385-9(3) , 0854043853) Royal Society of Chemistry, The GBR. *Dist:* Springer.

Littlefield, Cindy A. Jump! A Horsin' Around Card Game. 2004. (Illus.). 53p. (J). 9.95 (978-1-58017-581-4(3) , 67581, Storey Kids) Storey Publishing, LLC.

—Stampede! A Horsin' Around Card Game. 2004. (Illus.). 53p. (J). 9.95 (978-1-58017-582-1(1) , 67582, Storey Kids) Storey Publishing, LLC.

Littlefield, Cindy A. & Littlefield. Horse Games & Puzzles for Kids: 102 Brainteasers, Word Games, Jokes & Riddles, Picture Puzzlers, Matches & Logic Tests for Horse-Loving Kids. 2004. (Illus.). 144p. (J). pap. 9.95 (978-1-58017-538-8(4) , 67538, Storey Kids) Storey Publishing, LLC.

Lomberg, Michelle. Caring for Your Horse. 2004. (Caring for Your Pet Ser.). (J). pap. 7.95 (978-1-59036-152-8(0)); (Illus.). 32p. lib. bdg. 16.95 (978-1-59036-117-7(2)) Weigl Pubs., Inc.

LoPopolo, Carlos. History of the Western Horse Coloring Book, Vol. 1. LoPopolo, Cindy Rodger, ed. House, Laurie Bolting, illus. 2000. 35p. (J). (gr. 1-8). spiral bd. 14.95 (978-1-58707-003-7(0)) LoPopolo, Carlos.

Maas, Sarah. The Morgan Horse. 2005. (Horses Ser.). 32p. (J). 22.60 (978-0-7368-3767-5(1)) Capstone Pr., Inc.

Maass, Sarah. The Appaloosa Horse. 2006. (Edge Books, Horses). (Illus.). 32p. (J). (978-0-7368-4372-0(8)) Capstone Pr., Inc.

—The Belgian Horse. 2006. (Edge Books, Horses). (J). (978-0-7368-4373-7(6)) Capstone Pr., Inc.

—The Lipizzan Horse. 2006. (Edge Books, Horses). (Illus.). 32p. (J). (978-0-7368-5459-7(2) , 1252816) Capstone Pr., Inc.

—The Percheron Horse. 2006. (Edge Books, Horses). (Illus.). 32p. (J). (978-0-7368-5460-3(6) , 1252817) Capstone Pr., Inc.

Macken, JoAnn Early. Horses: Los Caballos. 2004. (ENG & SPA., Illus.). 24p. (J). pap. (978-0-8368-4295-1(2)); lib. bdg. 19.33 (978-0-8368-4288-3(X)) Stevens, Gareth Inc.

—Horses/JoAnn Early Macken. 2004. (Illus.). 24p. (J). pap. (978-0-8368-4281-4(2)); lib. bdg. 19.33 (978-0-8368-4274-6(X)) Stevens, Gareth Inc.

Mataya, Doris. Shasta Daisy. 2006. (Illus.). 32p. (J). per. 10.95 (***978-1-59453-814-8(X)*** , 2452, Airleaf Publishing) Airleaf Publishing & Bookselling.

Mattern, Joanne. Mounted Police. 2002. (Reading Power Ser.). (Illus.). 24p. (J). (gr. 1). lib. bdg. 17.25 (978-0-8239-5981-5(3) , PowerKids Pr.) Rosen Publishing Group, Inc., The.

Mayne, Don. Drawing Horses (That Look Real) 2002. (Quick Starts for Kids! Ser.). (Illus.). 64p. (J). (gr. 3 up). pap. 8.95 (978-1-885593-74-0(0) , Williamson Bks.) Ideals Pubns.

McKerley, Jennifer Guess. Man O' War: The Best Racehorse Ever. Widener, Terry, illus. 2005. (Step into Reading Ser.). 48p. (J). (gr. 1-3). pap. 3.99 (978-0-375-83164-5(9)); lib. bdg. 11.99 (978-0-375-93164-2(3)) Random Hse. Children's Bks. (Random Hse. Bks. for Young Readers).

McNeil, Niki, et al. HOCPP1036 Horses. 2005. spiral bd. 19.50 (***978-1-60308-036-1(8)***) In the Hands of a Child.

Meadows, Graham. Horses. Meadows, Graham, photos by. 1998. (Animals Are Not Like Us Ser.). (Illus.). 24p. (J). (ps up). lib. bdg. 21.26 (978-0-8368-2253-3(6)) Stevens, Gareth Inc.

Mickle, Shelley Fraser. Barbaro: America's Horse. 2007. 160p. (J). (gr. 3-7). lib. bdg. 16.89 (***978-1-4169-4866-7(X)*** , Aladdin Library); pap. 8.99 (***978-1-4169-4865-0(1)*** , Aladdin) Simon & Schuster Children's Publishing.

Milbourne, Anna. Horses & Ponies (Level 1) - Internet Referenced. 2007. (Illus.). 32p. (J). 4.99 (978-0-7945-1397-9(2) , Usborne) EDC Publishing.

Miller, Heather. My Horses. 2000. (Welcome Bks.). (Illus.). 24p. (J). (ps-2). pap. 4.95 (978-0-516-23033-7(6)); 17.00 (978-0-516-23108-2(1)) Scholastic Library Publishing. (Children's Pr.).

Miller, Sara Swan. Horses & Rhinos: What They Have in Common. 2000. (Animals in Order Ser.). (Illus.). 48p. (J). (gr. 4-6). pap. 6.95 (978-0-531-16401-3(2) , Watts, Franklin) Scholastic Library Publishing.

Moody, Ralph. American Horses. O'Keeffe, Neil, illus. 2004. 185p. 25.00 (978-0-8032-3248-8(9)); 1p. pap. 12.95 (978-0-8032-8301-5(6) , MOOAMX) Univ. of Nebraska Pr. (Bison Bks.).

Moser, Barry, illus. A Horse Named Funny Cide. 2006. 32p. (J). (ps-3). 16.99 (978-0-399-24462-9(X) , Putnam Juvenile) Penguin Group (USA) Inc.

Mounted Police: Individual Title Six-Packs. (On Deck Ser.). 24p. (gr. 4-5). 35.00 (978-0-7578-1027-5(6)) Rigby Education.

Mudpuppy Press Staff. Magic Horses 100-piece Puzzle. 2005. (J). 12.99 (978-0-7353-0512-0(9)) Galison.

Murray, Julie. Arabian Horses. 2002. (Buddy Book Ser.). (Illus.). 24p. (J). (gr. k-4). lib. bdg. 21.35 (978-1-57765-701-9(2)) ABDO Publishing Co.

—Clydesdale Horses. 2005. (Animal Kingdom Set Ii Ser.). (Illus.). 24p. (J). (gr. k-4). lib. bdg. 21.35 (978-1-59197-306-5(6)) ABDO Publishing Co.

—Pinto Horses. 2005. (Animal Kingdom Set Ii Ser.). (Illus.). 24p. (J). (gr. k-4). lib. bdg. 21.35 (978-1-59197-331-7(7)) ABDO Publishing Co.

Nelson, Robin. From Foal to Horse. 2003. (Start to Finish Ser.). (Illus.). 24p. (J). (gr. k-2). lib. bdg. 18.60 (978-0-8225-0941-7(5)) Lerner Publishing Group.

Nichols, Catherine. Therapy Horses. 2007. (Horse Power Ser.). 32p. (J). lib. bdg. 25.27 (978-1-59716-400-9(3)) Bearport Publishing Co., Inc.

Packard, Mary. Working Horses. 2007. (Horse Power Ser.). (J). lib. bdg. 25.27 (978-1-59716-403-0(8)) Bearport Publishing Co., Inc.

Page, Deb, illus. Darby-the Cow Dog, 9 vols. l.t. ed. 2005. (ZC Horses: 9). 76p. (J). pap. 5.00 net. (978-0-9721496-8-6(6)) ZC Horses Series of Children's Bks.

Parise-Peterson, Amanda. The Spanish Mustang. 2006. (Edge Books, Horses). (Illus.). 32p. (J). (978-0-7368-4375-1(2)) Capstone Pr., Inc.

Parker, Helen. Horse & Pony. 2006. (Lift Stick & Learn Ser.). (Illus.). 12p. (J). (ps-k). pap. 4.95 (978-1-84610-283-7(9)) Make Believe Ideas GBR. *Dist:* Ingram Pub. Services.

Parker, Marjorie Hodgson. Assault: The Crippled Champion, the King Ranch Racehorse. 2004. (Illus.). 80p. 14.95 (978-1-931721-34-9(3)) Bright Sky Pr.

Patent, Dorothy Hinshaw. Horses. Munoz, William, photos by. 2001. (Early Bird Nature Bks.). (Illus.). 48p. (J). (gr. 2-4). lib. bdg. 25.26 (978-0-8225-3045-9(7) , Lerner Pubns.) Lerner Publishing Group.

—Mystery of the Lascaux Cave. 1998. (Frozen in Time Ser.). (Illus.). 64p. (J). (gr. 5-9). lib. bdg. 28.50 (978-0-7614-0784-3(7)) Cavendish, Marshall Corp.

Penny, Malcolm. Wild Horses. 2002. (Secret World Of... Ser.). (Illus.). 48p. (J). lib. bdg. 27.12 (978-0-7398-4987-3(5)) Raintree.

Perry, Kate. Horse Heroes: True Stories of Amazing Horses. 1999. (Eyewitness Readers). (Illus.). 48p. (J). (gr. 2-4). pap. 3.99 (978-0-7894-4000-6(8)) Dorling Kindersley Publishing, Inc.

Peterson, Cris. Horsepower. 2001. (J). 16.75 (978-0-606-20710-2(4)) Tandem Library Bks.

—Horsepower: The Wonder of Draft Horses. Upitis, Alvis, photos by. 2001. (Illus.). 32p. (J). (ps-ps). pap. 10.95 (978-1-56397-943-9(8)) Boyds Mills Pr.

—Horsepower: The Wonder of Draft Horses. 2001. (gr. k-3). lib. bdg. 18.75 (978-0-613-42385-4(2)) Tandem Library Bks.

Petty, Kate. Horse Heroes. 1999. (gr. k-3). lib. bdg. 11.80 (978-0-613-17289-9(2)) Tandem Library Bks.

—Horse Heroes: True Stories of Amazing Horses. 1999. (Eyewitness Readers Ser.). (Illus.). 48p. lib. bdg. 10.75 (978-0-606-16986-8(5)) Tandem Library Bks.

Pickeral, Tamsin. The Encyclopedia of Horses & Ponies. 2003. 384p. (YA). pap. 19.95 (978-0-7525-8277-1(1)) Parragon, Inc.

Pipe, Jim. Horses. 2006. (Read & Play Ser.). 24p. (J). (ps-k). lib. bdg. 22.80 (978-1-59604-114-1(5)) Stargazer Bks.

Pleasant Company Staff. Girls & Their Horses: True Tales from American Girls. 2000. (J). 14.75 (978-0-606-20219-0(6)) Tandem Library Bks.

Presnall, Judith Janda. Race Horses. 2004. (Animals with Jobs Ser.). (Illus.). 48p. (J). (gr. 4-7). 26.20 (978-0-7377-2051-8(4) , Greenhaven Pr., Inc.) Thomson Gale.

Price, Roger & Stern, Leonard. My Little Pony Mad Libs Junior. 2005. (Illus.). 48p. (J). (gr. k-3). pap. 3.99 (978-0-8431-1621-2(8) , Price Stern Sloan) Penguin Group (USA) Inc.

Price, Steven D. Kids' Book of the American Quarter Horse. 1999. (gr. 3-6). lib. bdg. 30.35 (978-0-613-90263-2(7)) Tandem Library Bks.

Ransford, Sandy. First Riding Lessons. Langrish, Bob, illus. 2004. (Kingfisher Riding Club Ser.). 64p. (J). (gr. 4-8). pap. 8.95 (978-0-7534-5743-6(1) , Kingfisher) Houghton Mifflin Co. Trade & Reference Div.

—First Riding Lessons. Langrish, Bob, photos by. 2002. (Kingfisher Riding Club Ser.). (Illus.). 64p. (J). (gr. 5-9). tchr. ed. 14.95 (978-0-7534-5454-1(8) , Kingfisher) Houghton Mifflin Co. Trade & Reference Div.

—Horse & Pony Breeds. Langrish, Bob, photos by. (Kingfisher Riding Club Ser.). (Illus.). 64p. (J). 2007. (gr. 3-5). pap. 8.95 (978-0-7534-6075-7(0)); 2003. (gr. 5-9). tchr. ed. 14.95 (978-0-7534-5575-3(7)) Houghton Mifflin Co. Trade & Reference Div. (Kingfisher).

—Horse & Pony Care. Langrish, Bob, illus. 2004. (Kingfisher Riding Club Ser.). 64p. (J). (gr. 4-8). pap. 8.95 (978-0-7534-5744-3(X) , Kingfisher) Houghton Mifflin Co. Trade & Reference Div.

—Horse & Pony Care. Langrish, Bob, photos by. 2002. (Kingfisher Riding Club Ser.). (Illus.). 64p. (J). (gr. 4-6). tchr. ed. 14.95 (978-0-7534-5439-8(4) , Kingfisher) Houghton Mifflin Co. Trade & Reference Div.

—Horse & Pony Factfile: An Essential Guide to the World of Horses & Ponies. Kingfisher Publications, Inc. Staff, ed. 2006. (Illus.). 224p. (J). (gr. 3-5). vinyl bd. 12.95 (978-0-7534-6039-9(4) , Kingfisher) Houghton Mifflin Co. Trade & Reference Div.

—Horses & Ponies. Langrish, Bob, photos by. 2001. (Riding Club Ser.). (Illus.). 96p. (J). (gr. 4-6). tchr. ed. 18.95 (978-0-7534-5343-8(6) , Kingfisher) Houghton Mifflin Co. Trade & Reference Div.

—The Kingfisher Illustrated Horse & Pony Encyclopedia. Langrish, Bob, photos by. 2004. (Illus.). 224p. (J). (gr. 5-9). 24.95 (978-0-7534-5781-8(4) , Kingfisher) Houghton Mifflin Co. Trade & Reference Div.

Regan, Lisa & Williams, Beckie. Born Free How to Draw Wild Horses. Forder, Nicholas, illus. 2005. 48p. (J). pap. (978-1-84510-746-8(2)) Top That! Publishing PLC.

Reid, Struan. Dictionary of horses & ponies - internet Linked. Khan, Aziz, illus. rev. ed. 2004. 128p. (J). pap. 14.95 (978-0-7945-0843-2(X) , Usborne) EDC Publishing.

Roberts, Monty. Shy Boy: The Horse That Came in from the Wild. 2000. (gr. 7-12). lib. bdg. 28.00 (978-0-613-36668-7(9)); (Illus.). (J). (978-0-606-20502-3(0)) Tandem Library Bks.

Royston, Angela. El Cabaelo. 2002. Tr. of Horse. (SPA.). (J). 4.95 (978-84-243-2787-3(X)) Publicaciones Fher, S.A. ESP. *Dist:* AIMS International Bks., Inc.

Rustad, Martha E. H. Horses. 2001. (All about Pets Ser.). (Illus.). 24p. (J). (gr. k-1). lib. bdg. 15.93 (978-0-7368-0976-4(7) , Pebble Bks.) Capstone Pr., Inc.

Ryden, Hope. Wild Horses I Have Known. 1999. (Illus.). 96p. (YA). (gr. 5-9). tchr. ed. 20.00 (978-0-395-77520-2(5) , Clarion Bks.) Houghton Mifflin Co. Trade & Reference Div.

Sandler, Michael. Military Horses. 2007. (Horse Power Ser.). (Illus.), 32p. (J). lib. bdg. 25.27 (978-1-59716-402-3(X)) Bearport Publishing Co., Inc.

—Race Horses. 2007. (Horse Power Ser.). (J). lib. bdg. 25.27 (978-1-59716-398-9(8)) Bearport Publishing Co., Inc.

Sarkisian, Kevin. I Have a Horse: Learning the H Sound. (PowerPhonics Ser.). (Illus.). (J). 2002. 24p. (gr. 1). lib. bdg. 18.50 (978-0-8239-5906-8(6)); 2001. 23p. lib. bdg. 26.40 (978-0-8239-8251-6(3)) Rosen Publishing Group, Inc., The. (PowerKids Pr.).

Schafer, Susan. Horses. 2002. (Perfect Pets Ser.). (Illus.). 32p. (J). 25.64 (978-0-7614-1395-0(2) , Benchmark Bks.) Cavendish, Marshall Corp.

Schuh, Mari C. Horses on the Farm. 2002. (On the Farm Ser.). (Illus.). 24p. (J). (gr. k-1). lib. bdg. 15.93 (978-0-7368-1189-7(3) , Pebble Bks.) Capstone Pr., Inc.

—Horses on the Farm. (On the Farm Ser.). 24p. (J). pap. 5.95 (978-0-7368-9382-4(2)) Capstone Pr., Inc.

Schwartz, David M. El Caballo. Kuhn, Dwight, photos by. 2001. (Springboards into Science Ser.). (SPA., Illus.). 24p. (J). (gr. 1 up). lib. bdg. 20.67 (978-0-8368-2991-4(3) , GHS31410) Stevens, Gareth Inc.

—Horse. Kuhn, Dwight, photos by. 2001. (Springboards into Science Ser.). (Illus.). 24p. (J). (gr. 1 up). lib. bdg. 20.67 (978-0-8368-2974-7(3)) Stevens, Gareth Inc.

Shulman, Mark. Horsing Around. Nethery, Susan, illus. 2005. (Storytime Stickers Ser.). 16p. (J). pap. 4.95 (978-1-4027-1808-3(X)) Sterling Publishing Co., Inc.

Siino, Betsy Sikora. What Your Horse Needs. 2000. (gr. 7-12). lib. bdg. 12.95 (978-0-613-33230-9(X)) Tandem Library Bks.

Simon, Seymour. Horses. Simon, Seymour, illus. (Illus.). (J). (ps-1). Date not set. 32p. pap. 6.99 (978-0-06-446256-3(0)); 2006. 40p. 16.99 (978-0-06-028944-7(9)); 2006. 40p. lib. bdg. 16.89 (978-0-06-028945-4(7)) HarperCollins Pubs.

Sly, Debby. Fun with Ponies & Horses: Training, Riding, Grooming, Games. 2003. (Illus.). 128p. (J). pap. (978-1-59258-018-7(1)) Hylas Publishing.

Smith, L. Horses & Ponies. 32p. (J). lib. bdg. 14.95 (978-1-58086-743-6(X) , Usborne) EDC Publishing.

—The Usborne Book of Horses & Ponies. rev. ed. 2004. (Young Nature Ser.). (Illus.). 32p. (Orig.). (J). pap. 6.95 (978-0-7945-0850-0(2) , Usborne) EDC Publishing.

Smith, Lucy. The Usborne Book of Horses & Ponies. Gray, Miranda & Trotter, Stuart, illus. 2006. 32p. (J). pap. (***978-0-439-88983-4(9)***) Scholastic, Inc.

Spector, Joanna. Horses & Ponies Spotter's Guide. rev. ed. 2004. (Spotter's Guides). (Illus.). 64p. (J). pap. 5.95 (978-0-7945-0738-1(7) , Usborne) EDC Publishing.

—Horses & Ponies Sticker Bk. 2007. 24p. (J). pap. 8.99 (978 0 7945 1585-0(1) , Usborne) EDC Publishing.

Stafford, Susan, ed. Horse Tales for the Soul. (Horse Tales for the Soul Ser.: 4). 160p. Vol. 4. 2002. per. 19.95 (978-0-9740841-0-7(7)); Vol. 5. 2004. per. 19.95 (978-0-9740841-1-4(5)) K&B Products.

Stanley, George Edward. Wild Horses. Rowe, Michael Langham, illus. 2007. 48p. (J). (gr. 2-4). 3.99 (978-0-375-84438-6(4)); lib. bdg. 11.99 (978-0-375-94438-3(9)) Random Hse. Children's Bks. (Random Hse. Bks. for Young Readers).

Staub, Frank J. Running Free: America's Wild Horses. 2006. (Prime Ser.). (Illus.). 48p. (J). lib. bdg. 23.93 (978-0-7660-2670-4(1)) Enslow Pubs., Inc.

Stefoff, Rebecca. Horses. 2000. (Animal Ways Ser.). (Illus.). 112p. (J). (gr. 5 up). lib. bdg. 31.36 (978-0-7614-1139-0(9) , Benchmark Bks.) Cavendish, Marshall Corp.

Sterling & Ward, Adam. We Love Horses Friendship Book. 2001. (Illus.). 64p. (gr. 2-5). 5.95 (978-0-8069-8064-5(8) , Balloon Bks.) Sterling Publishing Co., Inc.

Stockland, Patricia M. In the Horse Stall. Ouren, Todd, illus. 2007. (Barnyard Buddies Ser.). 24p. (J). (ps-2). lib. bdg. 25.65 (***978-1-60270-024-6(9)*** , Looking Glass Library) Magic Wagon.

Stone, Lynn M. Arabian Horses. 2008. (J). (***978-1-60044-581-1(0)***) Rourke Publishing, LLC.

—Horses Have Foals. 2000. (Animals & Their Young Ser.). (Illus.). 24p. (J). (gr. 1 up). lib. bdg. 18.60 (978-0-7565-0002-3(8)) Compass Point Bks.

—Miniature Horses. 2001. (Weird Pets Ser.). (Illus.). 24p. (J). (gr. 1-4). lib. bdg. 20.64 (978-1-58952-039-4(4)) Rourke Publishing, LLC.

—Paint Horses. 2008. (J). (***978-1-60044-582-8(9)***) Rourke Publishing, LLC.

—Thoroughbred Horses. 2008. (J). (***978-1-60044-583-5(7)***) Rourke Publishing, LLC.

—Wild Horses. (J). 2008. (***978-1-60044-584-2(5)***); 1998. (Illus.). 24p. (gr. 2-5). lib. bdg. 23.93 (978-0-86593-513-6(0)) Rourke Publishing, LLC.

Storey Publishing Staff. Horses in Action. 2007. (Illus.). 64p. pap. 9.95 (978-1-58017-666-8(6)) Storey Publishing, LLC.

Stubblefield, Karen. Anna & Chen. 2003. 37p. pap. 14.95 (978-1-4137-0350-4(X)) PublishAmerica, Inc.

The Sunday Horse: Individual Title Six-Packs. (Action Packs Ser.). 120p. (gr. 3-5). 44.00 (978-0-7635-8435-1(5)) Rigby Education.

Swanson, Diane. Welcome to the World of Wild Horses. 2002. (Welcome to the World Ser.). (Illus.). 32p. (J). (ps-2). 9.95 (978-1-55285-321-4(7)); pap. 5.95 (978-1-55285-320-7(9)) Whitecap Bks., Ltd. CAN. *Dist:* Firefly Bks., Ltd.

—Wild Horses. 2004. (Welcome to the World of Animals Ser.). (Illus.). 32p. (J). (gr. 3 up). lib. bdg. 23.33 (978-0-8368-4026-1(7)) Stevens, Gareth Inc.

—Wild Horses. 2002. (gr. k-3). lib. bdg. 14.10 (978-0-613-78515-0(0)) Tandem Library Bks.

Thompson, Cornelia. My Very Own Horse Book. 2006. 70p. pap. 19.95 (978-1-57054-845-1(5)) Klutz.

Top That Publishing Staff, ed. Wacky Pony. 2004. (Wacky Animals Ser.). (Illus.). 10p. (J). pap. (978-1-84510-092-6(1)) Top That! Publishing PLC.

Tracqui, Valerie. Face-to-Face with the Horse: Faster Than the Wind. Delaborde, Gilles, photos by. 2004. (Face to Face Ser.). (Illus.). 28p. (J). (ps-2). 9.95 (978-1-57091-450-8(8)) Charlesbridge Publishing, Inc.

Ulmer, Michael. An Equestrain Alphabet. van Frankenhuyzen, Gijsbert, illus. rev. ed. 2007. 40p. pap. 7.95 (***978-1-58536-334-6(0)***) Sleeping Bear Pr.

Ulmer, Michael. H Is for Horse: An Eqestrian Alphabet. van-Frankenhuyze, Gijsbert, illus. rev. ed. 2004. 40p. (J). 17.95 (978-1-58536-213-4(1)) Sleeping Bear Pr.

Van Cleaf, Kristin. American Paint Horses. 2006. (Illus.). 24p. (J). (gr. k-6). 21.35 (978-1-59679-313-2(9) , Checkerboard Library) ABDO Publishing Co.

—Miniature Horses. 2006. (Checkerboard Animal Library). (Illus.). 24p. (J). (gr. k-6). 21.35 (978-1-59679-315-6(5) , Checkerboard Library) ABDO Publishing Co.

—Mustang Horses. 2006. (Checkerboard Animal Library). (Illus.). 24p. (J). (gr. k-6). 21.35 (978-1-59679-316-3(3) , Checkerboard Library) ABDO Publishing Co.

—Przewalski's Horses. 2006. (Checkerboard Animal Library). (Illus.). 24p. (J). (gr. k-6). 21.35 (978-1-59679-317-0(1) , Checkerboard Library) ABDO Publishing Co.

—Quarter Horses. 2006. (Checkerboard Animal Library). (Illus.). 24p. (J). (gr. k-6). 21.35 (978-1-59679-318-7(X) , Checkerboard Library) ABDO Publishing Co.

Vogel, Julia. Wild Horses. 2004. (Our Wild World Ser.). (Illus.). 48p. (J). (gr. 2-5). ring bd. 10.95 (978-1-55971-881-3(1)); pap. 7.95 (978-1-55971-882-0(X)) T&N Children's Publishing. (NorthWord Bks. for Young Readers).

von Kessel, Carola. Horse Care with Caddie. Guhe, Irmtraud, illus. 2004. 32p. 22.50 (978-3-86127-949-5(5)) Cadmos Verlag GmbH GBR. *Dist:* Trans-Atlantic Pubns., Inc.

—Understanding Horses with Caddie. Guhe, Irmtraud, illus. 2004. 32p. 22.50 (978-3-86127-948-8(7)) Cadmos Verlag GmbH GBR. *Dist:* Trans-Atlantic Pubns., Inc.

Wagner, Kathi & Racine, Sheryl. The Everything Kids' Horses Book. 2006. (Everything Ser.). (Illus.). 144p. (J). pap. 7.95 (978-1-59337-608-6(1)) Adams Media Corp.

Ward, Lesley. Let's Go to a Show! How to Win Ribbons & Have Fun, Too. 2002. (Illus.). 112p. pap. 14.95 (978-1-889540-85-6(4)) BowTie Pr.

Ward, Lesley, ed. Your Healthy & Happy Horse: How to Care for Your Horse & Have Fun, Too! 2003. (Illus.). 112p. pap. 12.95 (978-1-931993-40-1(8)) BowTie Pr.

Weimken, Simone. You & Your Horse. 2004. (Illus.). 80p. pap. 12.99 (978-0-7153-1731-0(8)) David & Charles Pubs. GBR. *Dist:* F & W Pubns., Inc.

Wendorf, Sarah. A Is for Appaloosa! 2005. 24p. (J). 8.13 (978-1-4116-3235-6(4)) Lulu.com.

Wexo, John Bonnett. Wild Horses. 2001. (Zoobooks Ser.). 24p. (J). (gr. 1-7). 15.95 (978-1-888153-00-2(8)) Wildlife Education, Ltd.

Wild Horses: Individual Title Six-Packs. (Action Packs Ser.). 120p. (gr. 3-5). 44.00 (978-0-7635-8434-4(7)) Rigby Education.

Wildlife Education, Ltd. Staff. Wild Horses. Hoopes, Barbara, illus. 2001. (Zoobooks Ser.). 18p. (Orig.). (YA). (gr. 5 up). pap. 2.95 (978-0-937934-08-1(9)) Wildlife Education, Ltd.

Wilsdon, Christina. Horses. 2007. (J). (***978-1-59939-075-8(2)*** , Reader's Digest Young Families, Inc.) Reader's Digest Children's Publishing, Inc.

Wolfman, Judy. Life on a Horse Farm. Winston, David Lorenz, photos by. 2005. (Life on a Farm Ser.). (Illus.). 48p. (gr. 2-5). lib. bdg. 23.93 (978-1-57505-517-6(1)) Lerner Publishing Group.

Wood, Kim Marie. The Magic of Horses: Activity Book. Spatrisano-Graham, Kimberly, illus. 2000. 64p. (gr. 2-12). pap., wbk. ed. 14.95 (978-0-9671978-3-8(X)) Syncopated Pr.

—The Power of Horses. Graham, Kimberly, illus. 1999. 68p. (YA). (gr. 3-12). pap., wbk. ed., act. bk. ed. 14.95 (978-0-9671978-1-4(3)) Syncopated Pr.

World Book, Inc Staff, contrib. by. Arabians & Other Horses. 2007. (World Book's Animals of the World Ser.). (Illus.). 64p. (J). (978-0-7166-1331-2(X)) World Bk., Inc.

Yerxa, Leo. Ancient Thunder. 2006. (Illus.). 32p. 18.95 (978-0-88899-746-3(9)) Groundwood Bks. CAN. *Dist:* Perseus Distribution.

Yorks, Sharon Lene. Finals Bound. 2003. (Cloverleaf Ser.: Bk. 2). (Illus.). 240p. (J). (gr. 6 up). pap. 5.99 (978-0-9720132-2-2(9)) Tumbleweed Publishing.

HORSES—FICTION

Abel, Janice. The Little White Christmas Horse. Gallagher, Denyce, illus. 2006. (J). per. 10.95 (***978-0-9655739-6-2(6)***) Abel Publishing.

Abercrombie, Josephine. Charlie the Horse. 2004. (Illus.). (J). 15.99 (978-0-9769648-0-3(5)) J A Interests, Inc.

Ackerman, Ned. Spirit Horse. 2002. 176p. (J). pap. 4.99 (978-0-590-39720-9(6)) Scholastic, Inc.

Ada, Alma Flor & Campoy, F. Isabel. Singing Horse. (Literature Collection of Gateways to the Sun Ser.). 32p. (J). (gr. k-6). pap. 12.95 (978-1-59437-718-1(9)) Santillana USA Publishing Co., Inc.

Adams, Jean Ekman. Clarence & the Great Surprise. Adams, Jean Ekman, illus. 2001. (Illus.). 32p. (J). (gr. k-2). 15.95 (978-0-87358-795-2(2) , Rising Moon Bks. for Young Readers) Northland Publishing.

—Clarence & the Purple Horse Bounce into Town. Adams, Jean Ekman, illus. 2003. (Illus.). 32p. (ps-3). 15.95 (978-0-87358-826-3(6) , Rising Moon Bks. for Young Readers) Northland Publishing.

—Clarence Goes Out West & Meets a Purple Horse. 2000. (Illus.). 32p. (ps-1). 15.95 (978-0-87358-753-2(7) , Rising Moon Bks. for Young Readers) Northland Publishing.

Addy, Sharon Hart. When Wishes Were Horses. Sneed, Brad, illus. 2002. 32p. (J). (gr. k-3). tchr. ed. 15.00 (978-0-618-13166-2(3)) Houghton Mifflin Co. Trade & Reference Div.

Adler, C. S. One Unhappy Horse. 2001. (Illus.). 160p. (J). (gr. 4-6). tchr. ed. 16.00 (978-0-618-04912-7(6) , Clarion Bks.) Houghton Mifflin Co. Trade & Reference Div.

Aldridge, James. The Marvellous Mongolian. 2003. 144p. (J). (gr. 4-7). pap. (978-1-55041-820-0(3)) Fitzhenry & Whiteside, Ltd.

Alexander, Samantha. Jodie. (Illus.). 136p. mass mkt. 6.99 (978-0-330-36836-0(2) , Pan) Pan Macmillan GBR. *Dist:* Trafalgar Square Publishing.

—Steph, Vol. 3. 3rd ed. 120p. mass mkt. 6.99 (978-0-330-36838-4(9) , Pan) Pan Macmillan GBR. *Dist:* Trafalgar Square Publishing.

Alltheway buy. 2004. (YA). per. 7.95 (978-0-9749320-0-2(0)) Bay Horse Creations LLC.

Ambrus, Victor, illus. Horse & Pony Stories. 2003. (Red Hot Reads Ser.). 256p. (gr. 4-8). pap. 6.95 (978-0-7534-5639-2(7) , Kingfisher) Houghton Mifflin Co. Trade & Reference Div.

Ambrus, Victor G., illus. More Horse & Pony Stories. 2004. (Red Hot Reads Ser.). 224p. (J). (gr. k-3). pap. 6.95 (978-0-7534-5734-4(2) , Kingfisher) Houghton Mifflin Co. Trade & Reference Div.

Amery, Heather. New Pony. Cartwright, Stephen, illus. rev. ed. 2004. (Farmyard Tales Readers Ser.). 16p. (J). pap. 5.95 (978-0-7945-0787-9(5) , Usborne) EDC Publishing.

Anderson, C. W. Blaze & the Forest Fire. 1999. reprint ed. 21.95 (978-1-56849-718-1(0)) Buccaneer Bks., Inc.

—Blaze & the Forest Fire. 1999. (J). (gr. 1-4). 21.75 (978-0-8446-7000-3(6)) Smith, Peter Pub., Inc.

—Blaze & the Gary Spotted Pony. 1999. reprint ed. 21.95 (978-1-56849-717-4(2)) Buccaneer Bks., Inc.

—Blaze & the Gray Spotted Pony. 2001. (J). (gr. 1-4). 21.25 (978-0-8446-7165-9(7)) Smith, Peter Pub., Inc.

—Blaze & the Lost Quarry. 1999. (J). (gr. 1-4). 21.75 (978-0-8446-7001-0(4)) Smith, Peter Pub., Inc.

—Blaze & the Mountain Lion. 1999. (J). (gr. 1-4). 21.75 (978-0-8446-6999-1(7)) Smith, Peter Pub., Inc.

—Blaze & Thunderbolt. (J). (gr. 1-4). 21.50 (978-0-8446-7167-3(3)) Smith, Peter Pub., Inc.

—Blaze Shows the Way. 2001. (gr. 1-4). 22.25 (978-0-8446-7166-6(5)) Smith, Peter Pub., Inc.

Anderson, Laurie Halse. Fear of Falling. 2003. (Wild at Heart Ser.). (Illus.). 105p. (J). (gr. 4 up). lib. bdg. 23.33 (978-0-8368-3255-6(8)) Stevens, Gareth Inc.

—Trickster. 2003. (Wild at Heart Ser.). (Illus.). 124p. (J). (gr. 4). lib. bdg. 23.33 (978-0-8368-3264-8(7)) Stevens, Gareth Inc.

—Trickster. 2000. (American Girl Wild at Heart Ser.: Bk. 3). (YA). (978-0-606-18360-4(4)) Tandem Library Bks.

Anderson, Laurie Halse. The Trickster, No. 3. 2008. (Vet Volunteers Ser.: No. 3). 144p. (J). (gr. 3). 6.99 (***978-0-14-241083-7(7)*** , Puffin) Penguin Group (USA) Inc.

Anderson, Peggy Perry. We Go in a Circle. 2004. (Illus.). 32p. (J). (gr. k-3). tchr. ed. 15.00 (978-0-618-44756-5(3) , Walter Lorraine) Houghton Mifflin Co. Trade & Reference Div.

Andrews, Neva. Wild Horse Summer. 2000. (Illus.). 120p. (gr. 4-7). pap. 9.95 (978-0-595-14766-3(6)) iUniverse, Inc.

Animal I Can Hear s/s - Horse. 2005. (J). bds. (978-1-4194-0059-9(2)) Paradise Pr., Inc.

Arena, Jacqueline. Horsing Around. Maddock, Monika, illus. 2005. (Girlz Rock! Ser.). (J). pap. (978-1-59336-703-9(1)) Mondo Publishing.

Armstrong, Jennifer. Magnus at the Fire. Smith, Owen, illus. 2005. 32p. (J). 15.95 (978-0-689-83922-1(7) , Simon & Schuster Children's Publishing) Simon & Schuster Children's Publishing.

Attema, Martha. Hero. 2003. (Orca Young Readers Ser.). (Illus.). 144p. (J). (gr. 3-6). pap. 5.95 (978-1-55143-251-9(X)) Orca Bk. Pubs. USA.

Auerbach, Annie. Back in the Saddle Again. 2007. (Horseland Ser.: Vol. 2). 96p. (J). (gr. 2-5). pap. 3.99 (***978-0-06-134168-7(1)*** , Harper Entertainment) HarperCollins Pubs.

—Horseland #5: Western Riding Winner. 2008. (Horseland Ser.). 96p. (J). pap. 3.99 (***978-0-06-134171-7(1)*** , Harper Entertainment) HarperCollins Pubs.

—The Trail Ride Terror. 2007. (Horseland Ser.: Vol. 3). 96p. (J). (gr. 2-5). pap. 3.99 (***978-0-06-134169-4(X)*** , Harper Entertainment) HarperCollins Pubs.

—Welcome to Horseland. 2007. (Horseland Ser.: Vol. 1). 96p. (J). (gr. 2-5). pap. 3.99 (***978-0-06-134167-0(3)*** , Harper Entertainment) HarperCollins Pubs.

Baglio, Ben M. Foals in the Field. Gregory, Jenny, illus. 2002. (Animal Ark Ser.: No. 24). 144p. (J). (gr. 3-6). pap. 3.99 (978-0-439-34385-5(2)) Scholastic, Inc.

—Foals in the Field. 2001. (gr. 3-6). lib. bdg. 11.80 (978-0-613-58116-5(4)) Tandem Library Bks.

—Horse in the House. Gregory, Jenny, illus. 2002. (Animal Ark Ser.: No. 26). 176p. (J). 3.99 (978-0-439-34387-9(9)) Scholastic, Inc.

—Horse in the House. 2001. (gr. 3-6). lib. bdg. 11.80 (978-0-613-62776-4(8)) Tandem Library Bks.

—Mare in the Meadow. Baum, Ann, tr. Baum, Ann, illus. 2003. (Animal Ark Hauntings Ser.). 144p. (J). 3.99 (978-0-439-34392-3(5) , Scholastic Paperbacks) Scholastic, Inc.

—Mustang in the Mist. Baum, Ann, illus. 2007. (Animal Ark Hauntings Ser.: No. 48). 160p. (J). pap. 3.99 (978-0-439-77524-3(8)) Scholastic, Inc.

—Pony on the Porch. McNicholas, Shelagh, illus. 1998. (Animal Ark Ser.: No. 2). (J). (gr. 3-5). (978-0-606-13130-8(2)) Tandem Library Bks.

—Racehorse in the Rain. 2006. (Animal Ark Hauntings Ser.: No. 40). (Illus.). 160p. (J). pap. 3.99 (978-0-439-68496-5(X)) Scholastic, Inc.

—Shetland in the Shed. Gregory, Jenny, illus. 2001. (Animal Ark Ser.: No. 20). 144p. (J). (gr. 3-5). 3.99 (978-0-439-23019-3(5)) Scholastic, Inc.

Bagnold, Enid. National Velvet. (Charming Classics). (J). 2002. 320p. (ps-k). 6.99 (978-0-694-01579-5(2)); 1999. 272p. (gr. 3-7). pap. 6.99 (978-0-380-81056-7(5) , Harper Trophy) HarperCollins Pubs.

—National Velvet. 1999. 265p. (J). (gr. 4-7). lib. bdg. 14.15 (978-0-8085-5431-8(X)) Tandem Library Bks.

Bailey, Elinor Peace. Winifred Finds Her Shoes. Bailey, Elinor Peace, illus. 2002. (J). 9.50 (978-0-9716586-1-5(7)) Fairfield Processing Corp.

Baker, Carin Greenberg. Pride of the Green Mountains. 1998. (Treasured Horses Ser.: Vol. 3). (J). (gr. 3-9). pap. 4.50 (978-0-590-31654-5(0)) Scholastic, Inc.

—Pride of the Green Mountains, No. 3. 1998. (Treasured Horses Ser.). (J). (978-0-606-13863-5(3)) Tandem Library Bks.

Bampton, Bob. Animal Friends Little Pony Board Book. 1999. (Illus.). 14p. (J). (ps-3). 7.95 (978-1-58185-222-6(3)) Quadrillion Media LLC.

Bang-Campbell, Monika. Little Rat Rides. Bang, Molly, illus. 2006. (Little Rat Ser.). 48p. (J). pap. 5.95 (978-0-15-205598-1(3) , Harcourt Paperbacks) Harcourt Children's Bks.

—Little Rat Rides. Bang, Molly Garrett, tr. Bang, Molly Garrett, illus. 2004. (Little Rat Ser.). 48p. (J). 15.00 (978-0-15-204667-5(4)) Harcourt Children's Bks.

Barnes, Laura T. Ernest & the Big Itch. Camburn, Carol A., illus. 2002. (Ernest Ser.). 32p. (J). (ps-3). 15.95 (978-0-9674681-4-9(2)) Barnesyard Bks.

—Ernest's Special Christmas. Camburn, Carol A., illus. 2003. (Ernest Ser.). 36p. (J). (gr. k-3). 17.95 (978-0-9674681-3-6(2)) Barnesyard Bks.

—Twist & Ernest. Camburn, Carol A., illus. 2002. (Ernest Ser.: Vol. 1). 32p. (J). (ps-3). 15.95 (978-0-9674681-0-5(8)) Barnesyard Bks.

Bastedo, Jamie. Free as the Wind: Saving the Horses of Sable Island. Tooke, Susan, illus. 2007. 32p. (J). (gr. k-3). 17.95 (***978-0-88995-350-5(3)***) Red Deer Pr. CAN. *Dist:* Fitzhenry & Whiteside, Ltd.

Bates, M. A Horse for the Summer. 2004. (Sandy Lane Stables Ser.). 100p. (J). lib. bdg. 12.95 (978-1-58086-557-9(7)); (Illus.). pap. 4.95 (978-0-7945-0501-1(5) , Usborne) EDC Publishing.

—Horse in Danger. 2004. (Sandy Lane Stables Ser.). (J). 128p. pap. 4.99 (978-0-7945-0502-8(3)); 100p. lib. bdg. 12.95 (978-1-58086-579-1(8)) EDC Publishing.

—The Perfect Pony. 2004. (Sandy Lane Stables Ser.). 100p. (J). lib. bdg. 12.95 (978-1-58086-574-6(7)) EDC Publishing.

—Strangers at the Stables. 2004. (Sandy Lane Stables Ser.). (J). 128p. pap. 4.99 (978-0-7945-0503-5(1)); 100p. lib. bdg. 12.99 (978-1-58086-580-7(1)) EDC Publishing.

Bates, Michelle. Horse in Danger. 1998. (Sandy Lane Stables Ser.). 100p. (J). (gr. 4-7). lib. bdg. 11.95 (978-1-58086-148-9(2)); (Illus.). pap. 3.95 (978-0-7460-3327-2(3)) EDC Publishing.

—Midnight Horse. 2003. 100p. (J). pap. 4.95 (978-0-7945-0506-6(6) , Usborne) EDC Publishing.

—Perfect Pony. 1999. (Sandy Lane Stables Ser.). (Illus.). 100p. (J). (gr. 4-8). pap. 3.95 (978-0-7460-3329-6(X)) EDC Publishing.

—The Perfect Pony. 2004. (Illus.). 112p. (J). (978-0-439-63994-1(8)) Scholastic, Inc.

Battlecry Forever! 2007. (J). (978-1-933343-45-7(1) , PONY) Stabenfeldt Inc.

Baud, Jane Scroggins. The Girl Who Wanted to be a Horse. Darr, Cynthia G., illus. 1st ed. 2001. 32p. (J): (gr. k-6). 17.95 (978-1-929701-04-9(7)) Under the Green Umbrella.

Beekman, Kelley Lee. Sir Eli & the Halloween Dragon: The Legend of the Toasted Marshmallow. 2006. 55p. pap. 12.95 (***978-1-4241-4047-3(1)***) PublishAmerica, Inc.

Belgue, Nancy. Casey Little: Yo-Yo Queen. 2005. (Orca Young Readers Ser.). (Illus.). 144p. (J). (gr. 3-6). pap. 5.95 (978-1-55143-357-8(5)) Orca Bk. Pubs. USA.

Beobi & the Magic Coloring Book at the Horse Stables. 2006. (J). 3.99 (978-0-9743847-5-7(5)) Cohn, Tricia.

Betancourt, Jeanne. Lost & Found Pony. Bachem, Paul, illus. 2001. (Pony Pals Ser.: Vol. 29). 96p. (J). (gr. 2-5). pap. 3.99 (978-0-439-16572-3(5)) Scholastic, Inc.

—The Movie Star Pony. Bachem, Paul, illus. 2000. (Pony Pals Ser.: No. 26). 96p. (J). (gr. 2-5). pap. 3.99 (978-0-439-06492-7(9)) Scholastic, Inc.

—Pony & the Bear. Bachem, Paul, illus. 1999. (Pony Pals Ser.: No. 23). 85p. (J). (gr. 2-5). pap. 3.99 (978-0-439-06489-7(9)) Scholastic, Inc.

—Pony & the Bear. 1999. (Pony Pals Ser.: No. 23). (J). (gr. 2-5). (978-0-606-19601-7(3)) Tandem Library Bks.

—The Pony & the Missing Dog. 2000. (Pony Pals Ser.: Vol. 27). (Illus.). 96p. (J). (gr. 2-5). pap. 3.99 (978-0-439-21639-5(7)) Scholastic, Inc.

—Stolen Ponies. Bachem, Paul, illus. 1999. (Pony Pals Ser.: No. 20). 96p. (J). (gr. 2-5). pap. 3.99 (978-0-590-63401-4(1)) Scholastic, Inc.

—Stolen Ponies. 1999. (Pony Pals Ser.: No. 20). (J). (gr. 2-5). (978-0-606-19598-0(X)) Tandem Library Bks.

—Western Pony. Bachem, Paul, illus. 1999. (Pony Pals Ser.: No. 22). 96p. (J). (gr. 2-5). pap. 3.99 (978-0-439-06488-0(0)) Scholastic, Inc.

—Western Pony. 1999. (Pony Pals Ser.: No. 22). (J). (gr. 2-5). (978-0-606-19600-0(5)) Tandem Library Bks.

—What's Wrong with My Pony? 2001. (Pony Pals Ser.: No. 33). (Illus.). 96p. (J). (gr. 2-5). pap. 3.99 (978-0-439-30642-3(6)) Scholastic, Inc.

—The Winning Pony. 1999. (Pony Pals Ser.: No. 21). (J). (gr. 2-5). (978-0-606-19599-7(8)) Tandem Library Bks.

Biro, Val, illus. & retold by. The Donkey That Sneezed. Biro, Val, retold by. 1998. 32p. (J). (gr. k-3). pap. 4.99 (978-1-887734-47-9(3)) Star Bright Bks., Inc.

The Black Stallion. 2002. (Black Stallion Ser.). 14.45 (978-0-7587-8504-6(6)) Book Wholesalers, Inc.

The Black Stallion: Novel Units. 2000. (J). 9.95 (978-1-56137-094-8(0)) Novel Units, Inc.

The Black Stallion Returns. 2002. (Black Stallion Ser.). (Illus.). (J). 14.45 (978-0-7587-6460-7(X)) Book Wholesalers, Inc.

Blake, Edna L. & Boatwright, Edith. Grandma & her Amazing Colt, Dripper! Allen, Kathy, illus. 2005. 50p. (J). 12.00 (978-0-9668906-3-1(9)) Blake, Edna.

Blanck, Cathy. A Party for Arty. 2004. (Illus.). 32p. (J). pap. (978-0-9753059-0-4(5)) Red Barn Reading Inc.

Blau, Eric & Duey, Kathleen. Katie & the Mustang, 4 vols., Vol. 3. 2004. 144p. (J). (gr. 3). 15.99 (978-0-525-47274-2(6) , Dutton Juvenile) Penguin Group (USA) Inc.

Bograd, Larry & Hubbard, Coleen. Colorado Summer. Rabinowitz, Sandy & Keiffer, Christa, illus. l.t. ed. 1999. (Treasured Horses Collection). 128p. (J). (gr. 4 up). lib. bdg. 23.33 (978-0-8368-2277-9(3)) Stevens, Gareth Inc.

Bolle, Frank, illus. Great Stories about Horses. 2001. 160p. (J). (gr. 3-9). lib. bdg. (978-0-87460-203-6(3)) Lion Bks.

Bonnell, Kris. Mmm, Apples. 2006. (J). 3.95 (***978-1-933727-22-6(5)***) Reading Reading Bks., LLC.

Book Buddy: Horse with Story Book. Orig. Title: Child's Play. (Illus.). 10p. (J). (ps-3). reprint ed. (978-1-881469-75-9(1)) Safari, Ltd.

Bossley, Michele Martin. Jumper. 2006. 144p. (J). pap. 8.95 (978-1-55143-620-3(5)) Orca Bk. Pubs. USA.

Bradley, Kimberly Brubaker. The Perfect Pony. McNicholas, Shelagh, illus. 2007. (J). (***978-1-4287-3296-4(9)*** , Dial) Penguin Group (USA) Inc.

Branson, Terri. Mirror of the Carousel. l.t. ed. 2007. (Illus.). 24p. (J). 9.99 (***978-0-9787421-8-8(4)***) Dragonfly Publishing, Inc.

Branson, Terri & Wilks, Jackie. Mirror of the Carousel. 2006. (Illus.). 24p. (J). lib. bdg. 24.95 (978-0-9765786-9-7(7)); per. 14.99 (978-0-9765786-8-0(9)) Dragonfly Publishing, Inc.

Brooke, Lauren. After the Storm, No. 2. 2000. (Heartland Ser.: No. 2). 176p. (gr. 3-6). mass mkt. 4.99 (978-0-439-13022-6(0)) Scholastic, Inc.

—After the Storm. 2000. (gr. 3-6). lib. bdg. 12.40 (978-0-613-24101-4(0)) Tandem Library Bks.

—All or Nothing. 2007. (Chestnut Hill Ser.: No. 6). 184p. (J). lib. bdg. 15.38 (***978-1-4242-1719-9(9)***) Fitzgerald Bks.

—Always There. 2005. (Heartland Ser.: No. 20). 176p. 4.99 (978-0-439-65368-8(1) , Scholastic Paperbacks) Scholastic, Inc.

—Beyond the Horizon. 2nd rev. ed. 2007. (Heartland Ser.). 208p. (J). pap. 5.99 (978-0-439-91610-3(0) , Scholastic Paperbacks) Scholastic, Inc.

—Breaking Free. 2000. (Heartland Ser.: No. 3). 160p. (J). (gr. 3-6). pap. 4.99 (978-0-439-13024-0(7)) Scholastic, Inc.

—Breaking Free. 2000. (gr. 3-6). lib. bdg. 12.40 (978-0-613-32341-3(6)) Tandem Library Bks.

—Chestnut Hill. 2006. 224p. (J). pap. 4.99 (978-0-439-73856-9(3)) Scholastic, Inc.

—Come What May, No. 5. 2001. (Heartland Ser.: No. 5). 160p. (J). (gr. 3-6). 4.99 (978-0-439-13026-4(3)) Scholastic, Inc.

—Come What May. 2001. (gr. 3-6). lib. bdg. 12.40 (978-0-613-43012-8(3)) Tandem Library Bks.

—Coming Home. 2000. (Heartland Ser.: No. 1). 144p. (J). (gr. 3-6). 4.99 (978-0-439-13020-2(4)) Scholastic, Inc.

—Coming Home. 2000. (gr. 3-6). lib. bdg. 12.40 (978-0-613-24660-6(8)) Tandem Library Bks.

—Darkest Hour. 2003. (Heartland Ser.). 160p. mass mkt. 4.99 (978-0-439-42508-7(5) , Scholastic Paperbacks) Scholastic, Inc.

—Darkest Hour. 2003. (gr. 3-6). lib. bdg. 12.40 (978-0-613-72128-8(4)) Tandem Library Bks.

—Every New Day. 2002. (Heartland Ser.: No. 9). 160p. mass mkt. 4.99 (978-0-439-31716-0(9)) Scholastic, Inc.

—Every New Day. 2002. (gr. 3-6). lib. bdg. 12.40 (978-0-613-62900-3(0)) Tandem Library Bks.

—Everything Changes. 2003. (Heartland Ser.). 176p. mass mkt. 4.99 (978-0-439-42509-4(3) , Scholastic Paperbacks) Scholastic, Inc.

—Everything Changes. 2003. (gr. 3-6). lib. bdg. 13.00 (978-0-613-72129-5(2)) Tandem Library Bks.

—From This Day On. 2005. 171p. (J). (978-1-4155-9728-6(6)) Scholastic, Inc.

—Holding Fast. 2004. (Heartland Ser.: No. 16). 176p. (J). pap. 4.99 (978-0-439-42511-7(5) , Scholastic Paperbacks) Scholastic, Inc.

—Love Is a Gift. 2004. (Heartland Ser.). 176p. mass mkt. 4.99 (978-0-439-42510-0(7) , Scholastic Paperbacks) Scholastic, Inc.

—New Beginnings. 2005. (Heartland Ser.: Vol. 18). 176p. (J). pap. 4.99 (978-0-439-65366-4(5) , Scholastic Paperbacks) Scholastic, Inc.

—The New Class. 2005. (Chestnut Hill Ser.: No. 1). 224p. (J). (ps-7). pap. 4.99 (978-0-439-73854-5(7) , Scholastic Paperbacks) Scholastic, Inc.

—Out of the Darkness. 2002. (Heartland Ser.: No. 7). 160p. (gr. 3-7). mass mkt. 4.99 (978-0-439-31714-6(2)) Scholastic, Inc.

—Out of the Darkness. 2002. (gr. 3-6). lib. bdg. 12.40 (978-0-613-62913-3(2)) Tandem Library Bks.

—A Season of Hope. 2004. (Heartland Ser.: No. 17). 176p. (J). (gr. 4-7). pap. 4.99 (978-0-439-65365-7(7) , Scholastic Paperbacks) Scholastic, Inc.

—Sooner or Later. 2003. (Heartland Ser.: No. 12). 160p. (J). pap. 4.99 (978-0-439-33968-1(5) , Scholastic Paperbacks) Scholastic, Inc.

—Sooner or Later. 2003. (gr. 3-6). lib. bdg. 12.40 (978-0-613-72024-3(5)) Tandem Library Bks.

—Taking Chances, No. 4. 2001. (Heartland Ser.: No. 4). 192p. (gr. 3-6). mass mkt. 4.99 (978-0-439-13025-7(5)) Scholastic, Inc.

—Taking Chances. 2001. (gr. 3-6). lib. bdg. 12.40 (978-0-613-33119-7(2)) Tandem Library Bks.

—Tomorrow's Promise. 2002. (Heartland Ser.: No. 10). 176p. (J). pap. 4.99 (978-0-439-31717-7(7)) Scholastic, Inc.

—Tomorrow's Promise. 2002. (gr. 3-6). lib. bdg. 12.40 (978-0-613-62922-5(1)) Tandem Library Bks.

—True Enough. 2003. (Heartland Ser.: No. 11). 160p. 4.99 (978-0-439-33967-4(7)) Scholastic, Inc.

—True Enough. 2003. (gr. 3-6). lib. bdg. 12.40 (978-0-613-66676-3(3)) Tandem Library Bks.

Brooks, Heather. Running Horse Ridge #1. 2008. (Running Horse Ridge Ser.). 224p. (J). pap. 5.99 (***978-0-06-142980-4(5)*** , Harper Trophy) HarperCollins Pubs.

Brouillet, Chrystine. The Enchanted Horses. Gaboriau, Linda, tr. Gagnon, Nathalie, illus. 1998. (FRE.). 116p. (J). (gr. 3-7). pap. 6.95 (978-0-921556-63-3(2)) Ragweed Pr. CAN. *Dist:* Univ. of Toronto Pr.

Brown, Corinne. Wishful Watoosi: The Horse That Wished He Wasn't. 2006. (Illus.). 32p. (J). 16.95 (978-0-9721057-2-9(7) , 3000) Cowgirl Peg Enterprises LLC.

Brown, Virginia Pounds. Gold Disc of Coosa: A Young Adult Historical Novel. 2003. (gr. 7-12). lib. bdg. 17.60 (978-0-613-79797-9(3)) Tandem Library Bks.

Bryant, Bonnie. Dude Ranch. 2007. (Saddle Club Ser.: No. 6). 144p. (J). (gr. 4-6). lib. bdg. 11.99 (978-0-385-90422-3(3) , Yearling) Random Hse. Children's Bks.

—Hoof Beat. 2008. (Saddle Club(R) Ser.). 144p. (J). (gr. 4-7). lib. bdg. 11.99 (***978-0-385-90536-7(X)*** , Yearling) Random Hse. Children's Bks.

—Lucky Horse. 1999. (Saddle Club Ser.: No. 89). (J). (gr. 4-6). (978-0-606-19639-0(0)) Tandem Library Bks.

—Trail Mates. 2007. (Saddle Club Ser.: No. 5). 144p. (J). (gr. 4-6). lib. bdg. 11.99 (978-0-385-90421-6(5) , Yearling) Random Hse. Children's Bks.

Bryant, Megan E. Strawberry Shortcake's Filly Friends: All Aboard Reading Station Stop 1. 2004. (Strawberry Shortcake Ser.: 1). (Illus.). 32p. (J). (ps-2). mass mkt. 3.99 (978-0-448-43574-9(8) , Grosset & Dunlap) Penguin Group (USA) Inc.

Buchanan, William J. Diablo: The Devil Steer. 2004. 151p. (J). (gr. 6-10). 9.95 (978-0-8263-3139-7(4)) Univ. of New Mexico Pr.

Burks, Brian. Corre con Caballos. Vinos, Maria, tr. Pelaez, Ricardo, illus. 2003. (la Orilla Del Viento Ser.). (SPA.). 93p. (J). pap. 7.50 (978-968-16-7057-3(4) , 168) Fondo de Cultura Economica USA.

Burningham, John. Humbert. 2000. (Illus.). 32p. (J). pap. 8.99 (978-0-09-941322-6(1) , Red Fox) Random Hse. Children's Bks. GBR. *Dist:* Trafalgar Square Publishing.

Butts, Christina. Horse & the Dog A Grand Fairy Tale A. 2006. pap. 15.38 (***978-1-4116-1235-8(3)***) Lulu.com.

Byars, Betsy. Little Horse. McPhail, David M., illus. rev. ed. 2002. (Redfeather Chapter Book Ser.). 64p. (J). (gr. 1-3). 15.95 (978-0-8050-6413-1(3) , Holt, Henry & Co. Bks. For Young Readers) Holt, Henry & Co.

—Little Horse on His Own. McPhail, David M., tr. McPhail, David M., illus. rev. ed. 2004. 48p. (J). 15.95 (978-0-8050-7352-2(3) , Holt, Henry & Co. Bks. For Young Readers) Holt, Henry & Co.

Calvert, J. Oliver. Honey Childrens Series Honey Meets the Prince Book One. 2006. (J). 15.77 (978-0-9771318-1-5(5)) Hope Harvest Publishing.

Campbell-Fells. Blue Ribbon Girls. 2005. 145p. pap. 13.95 (978-0-7414-2593-5(9)) Infinity Publishing.

Campbell, Joanna. Camp Saddlebrook. 1998. (Thoroughbred Ser.: No. 28). 192p. (gr. 4-7). mass mkt. 4.99 (978-0-06-106530-9(7)) HarperCollins Pubs.

—Cassidy's Secret. 1999. (Thoroughbred Ser.: No. 32). 176p. (gr. 4-7). mass mkt. 4.99 (978-0-06-106543-9(9) , Harper Entertainment) HarperCollins Pubs.

—Christina's Courage. 1998. (Thoroughbred Ser.: No. 27). 176p. (gr. 4-7). mass mkt. 4.99 (978-0-06-106529-3(3)) HarperCollins Pubs.

—Cindy's Bold Start. 2001. (Thoroughbred Ser.: No. 48). 176p. (gr. 4-7). mass mkt. 4.99 (978-0-06-106822-5(5) , Harper Entertainment) HarperCollins Pubs.

—Cindy's Bold Start. 2001. (gr. 3-6). lib. bdg. 12.40 (978-0-613-67180-4(5)) Tandem Library Bks.

—Cindy's Desert Adventure. 2001. (Thoroughbred Ser.: No. 47). 176p. (gr. 4-7). mass mkt. 4.99 (978-0-06-106671-9(0) , Harper Entertainment) HarperCollins Pubs.

—Cindy's Desert Adventure. 2001. (gr. 3-6). lib. bdg. 12.40 (978-0-613-67181-1(3)) Tandem Library Bks.

—Cindy's Last Hope. 2002. (Thoroughbred Ser.: No. 54). 176p. (gr. 3-7). mass mkt. 4.99 (978-0-06-009046-3(4)) HarperCollins Pubs.

—Cindy's Last Hope. 2002. (gr. 3-6). lib. bdg. 13.00 (978-0-613-67182-8(1)) Tandem Library Bks.

—Close Call. 2000. (gr. 3-6). lib. bdg. 13.00 (978-0-613-24617-0(9)) Tandem Library Bks.

—A Dangerous Ride. 1999. (Ashleigh Ser.: No. 6). 192p. (gr. 4-7). mass mkt. 4.99 (978-0-06-106559-0(5) , Harper Entertainment) HarperCollins Pubs.

—Dangerous Ride. 1999. (gr. 3-6). lib. bdg. 12.40 (978-0-613-16083-4(5)) Tandem Library Bks.

—Dead Heat. 1999. (Thoroughbred Ser.: No. 35). 176p. (gr. 4-7). mass mkt. 4.99 (978-0-06-106564-4(1)) HarperCollins Pubs.

—Dead Heat. 1999. (gr. 3-6). lib. bdg. 13.00 (978-0-613-16086-5(X)) Tandem Library Bks.

—Derby Dreams. 2001. (Thoroughbred Ser.: No. 10). (Illus.). 176p. (gr. 4-7). mass mkt. 4.99 (978-0-06-106672-6(9) , Harper Entertainment) HarperCollins Pubs.

—Derby Dreams. 2001. (gr. 3-6). lib. bdg. 13.00 (978-0-613-67185-9(6)) Tandem Library Bks.

—Faith in a Long Shot. 2003. (Thoroughbred Ser.: Vol. 57). 176p. mass mkt. 4.99 (978-0-06-009049-4(9) , Harper Entertainment) HarperCollins Pubs.

—Faith in a Long Shot. 2003. (gr. 3-6). lib. bdg. 13.00 (978-0-613-67192-7(9)) Tandem Library Bks.

—Forbidden Stallion. 1999. (gr. 3-6). lib. bdg. 13.00 (978-0-613-16108-4(4)) Tandem Library Bks.

—Good-Bye, Midnight Wanderer. 1999. (gr. 3-6). lib. bdg. 12.40 (978-0-613-15804-6(0)) Tandem Library Bks.

—Great Expectations. 2002. (gr. 3-6). lib. bdg. 13.00 (978-0-613-67198-9(8)) Tandem Library Bks.

—A Home for Melanie. 1998. (Thoroughbred Ser.: No. 31). 176p. (gr. 4-7). mass mkt. 4.99 (978-0-06-106541-5(2) , Harper Entertainment) HarperCollins Pubs.

—Hoofprints in the Snow. 2002. (Thoroughbred Ser.: No. 56). 176p. mass mkt. 4.99 (978-0-06-009048-7(0)) HarperCollins Pubs.

—Hoofprints in the Snow. 2002. (gr. 3-6). lib. bdg. 13.00 (978-0-613-58679-5(4)) Tandem Library Bks.

—Legacy's Gift. 2005. (Thoroughbred Ser.: Vol. 72). 176p. mass mkt. 4.99 (978-0-06-078117-0(3) , Harper Entertainment) HarperCollins Pubs.

—Living Legend. 2000. (Thoroughbred Ser.: No. 39). 192p. (gr. 4-7). mass mkt. 4.50 (978-0-06-106633-7(8) , Harper Entertainment) HarperCollins Pubs.

—Living Legend. 2000. (gr. 3-6). lib. bdg. 12.40 (978-0-613-21919-8(8)) Tandem Library Bks.

—Melanie's Double Jinx. 2005. (Thoroughbred Ser.: No. 69). 176p. mass mkt. 4.99 (978-0-06-075831-8(7) , Harper Entertainment) HarperCollins Pubs.

—Melanie's Last Ride. 1998. (Thoroughbred Ser.: No. 29). 192p. (gr. 4-7). mass mkt. 4.99 (978-0-06-106531-6(5) , Harper Entertainment) HarperCollins Pubs.

—Melanie's Treasure. 1998. (Thoroughbred Ser.: No. 25). 160p. (gr. 4-7). mass mkt. 4.99 (978-0-06-106798-3(9)) HarperCollins Pubs.

—On the Track. 1999. (Thoroughbred Ser.: No. 34). 176p. (gr. 4-7). mass mkt. 4.99 (978-0-06-106563-7(3)) HarperCollins Pubs.

—On the Track. 1999. (gr. 3-6). lib. bdg. 13.00 (978-0-613-16170-1(X)) Tandem Library Bks.

—Parker's Passion. 2003. (Thoroughbred Ser.: No. 61). (Illus.). 176p. mass mkt. 4.99 (978-0-06-054441-6(4) , Harper Entertainment) HarperCollins Pubs.

—Parker's Passion. 2003. (gr. 3-6). lib. bdg. 13.00 (978-0-613-68457-6(5)) Tandem Library Bks.

—Price of Fame. 2004. (gr. 3-6). lib. bdg. 13.00 (978-0-613-71521-8(7)) Tandem Library Bks.

—The Prize. 2002. (Ashleigh Ser.: No. 13). 176p. (gr. 3-7). mass mkt. 4.99 (978-0-06-009144-6(4) , Harper Entertainment) HarperCollins Pubs.

—Prize. 2002. (gr. 3-6). lib. bdg. 13.00 (978-0-613-67218-4(6)) Tandem Library Bks.

—Racing Image. 2001. (Thoroughbred Ser.: No. 46). (Illus.). 176p. (gr. 4-7). mass mkt. 4.50 (978-0-06-106670-2(2)) HarperCollins Pubs.

—Racing Image. 2001. (gr. 3-6). lib. bdg. 12.40 (978-0-613-67219-1(4)) Tandem Library Bks.

—Rising Star. 2001. (Thoroughbred Ser.: No. 49). (Illus.). 176p. mass mkt. 4.99 (978-0-06-106824-9(1) , Harper Entertainment) HarperCollins Pubs.

—Rising Star. 2001. (gr. 3-6). lib. bdg. 12.40 (978-0-613-67222-1(4)) Tandem Library Bks.

—Star of Shadowbrook Farm (0804) 2008. (YA). (*978-1-933343-77-8(X)) Stabenfeldt Inc.

—Stardust's Foal. 2003. (gr. 3-6). lib. bdg. 13.00 (978-0-613-67226-9(7)) Tandem Library Bks.

—Star's Chance. 2001. (Thoroughbred Ser.: No. 45). 176p. (gr. 4-7). mass mkt. 4.99 (978-0-06-106669-6(9) , Harper Entertainment) HarperCollins Pubs.

—Star's Chance. 2001. (gr. 3-6). lib. bdg. 12.40 (978-0-613-67227-6(5)) Tandem Library Bks.

—Star's Inspiration. 2003. (Thoroughbred Ser.: No. 59). (Illus.). 176p. mass mkt. 4.99 (978-0-06-009051-7(0) , Harper Entertainment) HarperCollins Pubs.

—Star's Inspiration. 2003. (gr. 3-6). lib. bdg. 13.00 (978-0-613-66737-1(9)) Tandem Library Bks.

—Starstruck. 2004. (Thoroughbred Ser.: No. 63). (gr. 3-6). lib. bdg. 13.00 (978-0-613-71520-1(9)) Tandem Library Bks.

—Sterling's Second Chance. 1998. (Thoroughbred Ser.: No. 26). 176p. (gr. 4-7). mass mkt. 4.99 (978-0-06-106799-0(7) , Harper Entertainment) HarperCollins Pubs.

—Team Player. 2001. (Thoroughbred Ser.: No.50). 176p. mass mkt. 4.99 (978-0-06-106825-6(X)) HarperCollins Pubs.

—Team Player. 2001. (gr. 3-6). lib. bdg. 12.40 (978-0-613-67228-3(3)) Tandem Library Bks.

—Thoroughbred Box Set, Nos. 1-4. 2003. (Thoroughbred Ser.). (Illus.). pap. 19.96 (978-0-06-055585-6(8) , Harper Entertainment) HarperCollins Pubs.

—Ultimate Risk. 2000. (Thoroughbred Ser.: No. 40). 176p. (gr. 4-7). mass mkt. 4.99 (978-0-06-106634-4(6) , Harper Entertainment) HarperCollins Pubs.

—Ultimate Risk. 2000. (gr. 3-6). lib. bdg. 12.40 (978-0-613-22550-2(3)) Tandem Library Bks.

—Unbridled Fury. 2003. (Thoroughbred Ser.: No. 62). (Illus.). 176p. mass mkt. 4.99 (978-0-06-056634-0(5) , Harper Entertainment) HarperCollins Pubs.

—Unbridled Fury. 2003. (Thoroughbred Ser.: No. 62). (gr. 3-6). lib. bdg. 13.00 (978-0-613-85743-7(7)) Tandem Library Bks.

Carbone, Elisa. Last Dance on Holladay Street. 2006. 208p. (YA). (gr. 7-11). mass mkt. 5.99 (978-0-553-49426-6(0) , Laurel Leaf) Random Hse. Children's Bks.

Carpenter Czerw, Nancy. Itty & Bitty: Friends on the Farm. Berlin, Rose Mary & Bauer, Dana, illus. 2006. (Itty & Bitty Ser.). 32p. (J). 15.95 (978-0-9755618-3-6(9)) McWitty Pr., Inc.

—Itty & Bitty: Two Miniature Horses. Bauer, Dana, illus. 2006. (Itty & Bitty Ser.). 32p. (J). 15.95 (978-0-9755618-2-9(0)) McWitty Pr., Inc.

Casanova, Mary. Stealing Thunder. 2000. 144p. (gr. 3-7). pap. 5.99 (978-0-7868-1480-0(2)) Hyperion Bks. for Children.

—Stealing Thunder. 2000. (J). (978-0-606-20192-6(0)); (gr. 3-6). lib. bdg. 14.15 (978-0-613-30762-8(3)) Tandem Library Bks.

Castlemon, Harry. Sportsmans Club in the Saddle. 2006. pap. 30.95 (*978-1-4286-5231-6(0)) Kessinger Publishing, LLC.

Center for Learning Network Staff. All the Pretty Horses: Curriculum Unit —Novel Series — Grades 9-12. 2001. (Novel Ser.). 60p. (YA). tchr. ed., spiral bd. 19.95 (978-1-56077-667-3(6)) Ctr. for Learning, The.

Cerf, Christopher & Peterson, Paige. Blackie the Horse That Stood Still. (Illus.). 64p. (J). 18.95 (978-1-59962-017-6(0) , Welcome Bks.) Welcome Enterprises, Inc.

Chaconas, Dori. Pennies in a Jar. Lewin, Ted, illus. 2007. 32p. (J). (ps-3). 16.95 (*978-1-56145-422-8(2) , Peachtree Junior) Peachtree Pubs., Ltd.

Chandler, Andrew Robert. Horatio the Half-Hooved Horse. 2003. (J). per. (978-1-59196-438-4(5)) Instantpublisher.com.

Charlotte & the White Horse. 2004. (J). 24.95 incl. audio (978-1-56008-180-7(5)) Weston Woods Studios, Inc.

Charming Horse Library. 2006. (Charming Classics: No. 3). (J). pap. 19.99 (978-0-06-111717-6(X) , Harper Festival) HarperCollins Pubs.

Chester, Laura. Hiding Glory. Lippincott, Gary, illus. 2007. 160p. (J). 18.95 (*978-1-59543-616-0(2)) Willow Creek Pr., Inc.

Chesterfield, Sadie. Horseland. 2008. (Horseland Ser.: No. 4). 96p. (J). pap. 3.99 (*978-0-06-134170-0(3) , Harper Entertainment) HarperCollins Pubs.

Choldenko, Gennifer. Moonstruck: The True Story of the Cow Who Jumped over the Moon. 1999. (978-0-606-17169-4(X)) Tandem Library Bks.

Choukas, Nita & Tyler, Gillian. Bayberry & Beau. 2006. (Illus.). 112p. (J). 15.95 (978-1-933392-35-6(5)) Chelsea Green Publishing.

Christmas Colt. 2006. (J). (978-1-933343-36-5(2) , PONY) Stabenfeldt Inc.

Circle of Blue. 2006. (J). (978-1-933343-37-2(0) , PONY) Stabenfeldt Inc.

Clancy, Kaycee. Sky Painters. 2007. (J). per. 11.95 (*978-0-9776777-8-8(9)) Legacy Publishing Services, Inc.

Clark, Ann Nolan. Bringer of the Mystery Dog. Howe, Oscar, illus. 2000. 48p. (J). (gr. k-5). 6.95 (978-1-885772-20-6(3)) Kiva Publishing, Inc.

Clear the Hurdles, Sara! 2005. (J). (978-1-933343-01-3(X) , PONY) Stabenfeldt Inc.

Clover, Peter. Sheltie & the Runaway, No. 3. 2001. (Sheltie Ser.). (Illus.). (J). (978-0-606-20914-4(X)) Tandem Library Bks.

—Sheltie the Shetland Pony. 2001. (Sheltie Ser.). (Illus.). (J). (978-0-606-20912-0(3)) Tandem Library Bks.

Cocquyt, Kathryn. A Pony for Luke. Parker, Pam, illus. 1998. (J). 14.95 (978-1-56554-277-8(0)) Pelican Publishing Co., Inc.

Cole, Cathleen. Four Seasons Stables: A Saddle Seat Rid. 2006. 53p. pap. 12.95 (*978-1-4241-3430-4(7)) PublishAmerica, Inc.

Coles, Chantel. Valentina: Lisa's Dream Come True. 2005. 50p. pap. 12.95 (978-1-4137-9771-8(7)) PublishAmerica, Inc.

Connor, Elizabeth & Kinzler, Mary. Libby Saves Beauty's Colt. Garrett, Stephen, photos by. ltd. l.t. ed. 1999. (Illus.). 106p. (J). (gr. 2-6). 12.95 (978-0-9658468-1-3(4)) Adbeth Pr.

Cook, Sherry & Johnson, Terri. Hallie Heat, 26 vols. Kuhn, Jesse, illus. l.t. ed. 2006. (Quirkles—Exploring Phonics through Science Ser.: 8). 32p. (J). 7.99 (978-1-933815-07-7(8) , Quirkles, The) Creative 3, LLC.

Coons, Anita. What about Me? 2003. (Illus.). 96p. (J). (gr. k-8). per. 10.95 (978-1-930648-56-2(1)) Goose River Pr.

Cosgrove, Stephen. Nitter Pitter. James, Robin, illus. ed. 2002. (Serendipity Ser.). 32p. (J). reprint ed. pap. 4.99 (978-0-8431-4870-1(5) , Price Stern Sloan) Penguin Group (USA) Inc.

—Nitter Pitter. 2002. (gr. k-3). lib. bdg. 13.00 (978-0-613-57629-1(2)) Tandem Library Bks.

Cotten, Cynthia S. Snow Ponies. Cockcroft, Jason, illus. rev. ed. 2001. 32p. (J). (ps-1). 16.95 (978-0-8050-6063-8(4) , Holt, Henry & Co. Bks. For Young Readers) Holt, Henry & Co.

Crane, Crankey. Horse Book. 2006. 23p. (J). 12.99 (978-1-4116-7116-4(3)) Lulu.com.

Crazy Dream Horse. 2005. 19.95 net. (978-0-9749501-0-5(6)) Inheritance Pr., Inc.

Curry, Kenneth. Star & Peanut. 2007. (Illus.). 22p. (J). 10.95 (*978-0-9798364-9-7(2)) Curry Brothers Publishing.

Dalmatian Press Staff, adapted by. Black Beauty. Date not set. (C). pap. (978-0-7593-9884-9(4) , Thomson Learning) CENGAGE Learning.

Dangerous Summer 3. 2007. (J). (978-1-933343-50-1(8) , PONY) Stabenfeldt Inc.

Daniels, Lucy. Charity at Home. 6th rev. ed. 2003. (Horseshoe Trilogies Ser.: Bk. 6). (Illus.). 128p. (gr. 3-7). pap. 4.99 (978-0-7868-1749-8(6) , Volo) Hyperion Bks. for Children.

—Charity's Gift. 9th rev. ed. 2004. (Horseshoe Trilogies Ser.: No. 9). (Illus.). 144p. (gr. 3-7). pap. 4.99 (978-0-7868-1752-8(6)) Hyperion Bks. for Children.

—The Horseshoe Trilogies: Charity at Home. 2003. (gr. 3-6). lib. bdg. 13.00 (978-0-613-91007-1(9)) Tandem Library Bks.

—The Horseshoe Trilogies: Keeping Faith. 2002. (gr. 3-6). lib. bdg. 13.00 (978-0-613-70895-1(4)) Tandem Library Bks.

—The Horseshoe Trilogies: Sweet Chari. 2002. (gr. 3-6). lib. bdg. 13.00 (978-0-613-70903-3(9)) Tandem Library Bks.

—The Horseshoe Trilogies: Where There's Hope. 2003. (gr. 3-6). lib. bdg. 13.00 (978-0-613-90437-7(0)) Tandem Library Bks.

—Keeping Faith. 2002. (Horshoe Trilogies: Bk. 1). 144p. (gr. 8-17). 9.99 (978-0-7868-1960-7(X)) Hyperion Pr.

—Last Hope. Elwell, Tristan, illus. 2002. (Horshoe Trilogies: Bk. 2). 144p. (gr. 8-17). 9.99 (978-0-7868-1961-4(8)) Hyperion Pr.

—Leap of Faith. Elwell, Tristan, illus. 2004. (Horseshoe Trilogies Ser.: No. 7). 144p. (gr. 3-7). pap. 4.99 (978-0-7868-1750-4(X)) Hyperion Bks. for Children.

Darling, Fiona. The Horse's Curse. 2003. 144p. (J). pap. 7.95 (978-0-86327-904-1(X)) Wolfhound Pr. IRL. *Dist:* Interlink Publishing Group, Inc.

Davis, Eugene. From the Horse's Mouth. 2002. (gr. 5 up). per. 14.99 (978-0-9721438-0-6(7)) Rhoman Bks.

Davis, Joyce E. Fancy the Prancing Horse. 2003. (Illus.). 24p. 10.95 (978-1-58597-180-0(4)) Leathers Publishing.

Davis, Susan Page. Sarah's Long Ride. 2007. 173p. (J). (*978-1-59166-737-7(2)) Jones, Bob Univ. Pr.

Dawson, JoAnn. Lady's Big Surprise. 2007. (Lucky Foot Stable Ser.). 272p. (J). (gr. 3 up). pap. 6.99 (*978-1-4022-0996-3(7) , Sourcebooks Jabberwocky) Sourcebooks, Inc.

—Star of Wonder. 2007. (Lucky Foot Stable Ser.). 192p. (J). (gr. 3 up). pap. 6.99 (*978-1-4022-0997-0(5) , Sourcebooks Jabberwocky) Sourcebooks, Inc.

DeJong, Meindert. La Colina Que Canta. (SPA., Illus.). 120p. (YA). (gr. 5-8). (978-84-279-3434-4(3) , NG3494) Noguer y Caralt Editores, S. A. ESP. *Dist:* Lectorum Pubns., Inc.

Demeritt, Mary Anne. The Twilight Ride of the Pink Fairy. Daniel, Ellen, illus. 2006. (J). 17.95 (*978-1-58597-410-8(2)) Leathers Publishing.

DeMeyer, Patricia. Little Horsey Little Lessons: A Young Girl & Her Special Horse Help Teach Skills for Life. Christie, Terri, illus. 1999. 40p. (J). (gr. 1-6). pap. 9.95 (978-0-9666433-0-5(5)) Saddle Tree Pr.

Denslow, Sharon Phillips. All Their Names Were Courage. 2003. 144p. (J). (gr. 2 up). 15.99 (978-0-06-623810-4(2)) HarperCollins Pubs.

Devine, Pauline. Best Friends Again. 2000. (Illus.). 128p. (J). (gr. 3-7). pap. 9.95 (978-1-901737-14-1(4)) Anvil Bks., Ltd. IRL. *Dist:* Dufour Editions, Inc.

—The Hungry Horse. 2001. 64p. (YA). (gr. 1 up). pap. 8.95 (978-1-901737-33-2(0)) Anvil Bks., Ltd. IRL. *Dist:* Dufour Editions, Inc.

Diablo - A Day Like Any Other. 2007. (J). (978-1-933343-43-3(5) , PONY) Stabenfeldt Inc.

Diablo - Race Against Time. 2006. (J). (978-1-933343-29-7(X) , PONY) Stabenfeldt Inc.

Diablo's Double. 2005. (J). (978-1-933343-02-0(8) , PONY) Stabenfeldt Inc.

Diaz, Katacha. Wild Horse Country. Casale, Paul, illus. 2005. (Wild Reading Adventures! Ser.). (J). (ps-2). 32p. 2.95 (978-1-59249-139-1(1) , S7155); 36p. 9.95 (978-1-59249-140-7(5) , PS7155); 36p. 15.95 (978-1-59249-137-7(5) , B7105); 32p. 8.95 incl. audio (978-1-59249-220-6(7) , SC7105); 36p. pap. 6.95 (978-1-59249-138-4(3) , S7105) Soundprints.

Dickerson, Karle. The Forgotten Filly. 2008. (YA). (*978-1-933343-79-2(6)) Stabenfeldt Inc.

Dickerson, Karle & Campbell, Joanna. The Forgotten Filly. 1998. (Ashleigh's Thoroughbred Collection). 192p. (gr. 3-7). mass mkt. 4.99 (978-0-06-106486-9(6)) HarperCollins Pubs.

Dillon, Eilis. Island of Horses. 2004. (New York Review Children's Collection). 224p. (J). pap. 17.95 (978-1-59017-102-8(0) , NYR Children's Collection) New York Review of Bks., Inc., The.

Disney Storybook Artists Staff, illus. Disney's Home on the Range: A Hero of a Horse. 2004. (Step into Reading Ser.). 32p. (J). (ps-1). pap. 3.99 (978-0-7364-2210-9(2) , RH/Disney) Random Hse. Children's Bks.

Distler, Christine A. Pegasus: The Introduction. 2005. 84p. pap. 11.95 (978-1-59113-763-4(2)) Booklocker.com, Inc.

Dodgson, Y. K. The Day the Horse Was Free. T. W. Zimmerman, illus. 2004. 16p. (J). 11.95 (978-0-9748091-0-6(1)) Alaska Avenue Pr.

—The Day the Horse Was Free. Zimmerman, T. W., illus. rev. ed. 2005. 24p. (J). 11.95 (978-0-9748091-1-3(X)) Alaska Avenue Pr.

Dorsey, Angela. Horse Angel: Silver Dream 0710. 2007. (YA). (*978-1-933343-64-8(8)) Stabenfeldt Inc.

—Horse Angel - Fighting Chance. 2008. (J). (*978-1-933343-78-5(8)) Stabenfeldt Inc.

—Horse Angel Comic. 2008. (J). pap. (*978-1-933343-82-2(6)) Stabenfeldt Inc.

—Horse Angel Comic: Rough Diamond 0711. 2007. (YA). pap. (*978-1-933343-66-2(4)) Stabenfeldt Inc.

Douglas, Vincent. Spirit Coloring & Activity: Young Spirit. 2001. (Illus.). 32p. pap. 1.49 (978-0-7696-2754-0(4)) School Specialty Publishing.

Douthwaite, Wendy. The Orange Pony. 2003. (Illus.). 86p. (J). (gr. 2-7). mass mkt. 6.99 (978-0-330-33631-4(2) , Pan) Pan Macmillan GBR. *Dist:* Trafalgar Square Publishing.

Dow, Jill. Windy Edge: Maggie's Holiday. 2004. (Windy Edge Farm Ser.). (Illus.). 26p. (J). pap. 7.95 (978-1-84507-248-3(0)) Lincoln, Frances Ltd. GBR. *Dist:* Perseus Distribution.

Duey, Kathleen. Castle Avamir. Rayyan, Omar, illus. 2003. (Unicorn's Secret Ser.). 80p. (J). pap. 3.99 (978-0-689-85372-2(6) , Aladdin) Simon & Schuster Children's Publishing.

—Castle Avamir. 2003. (gr. 3-6). lib. bdg. 11.80 (978-0-613-66482-0(5)) Tandem Library Bks.

—Hoofbeats: Lara & the Gray Mare. 2005. (Hoofbeats Ser.: Bk. 1). 144p. (J). (gr. 4). pap. 4.99 (978-0-14-240230-6(3) , Puffin) Penguin Group (USA) Inc.

—Hoofbeats Bk. 3: Lara at Athenry Castle. 2005. 144p. (J). (gr. 4). pap. 4.99 (978-0-14-240220-7(6) , Puffin) Penguin Group (USA) Inc.

—Hoofbeats Bk. 4: Lara & the Silent Place. 2005. 144p. (gr. 4-7). pap. 4.99 (978-0-14-240233-7(8) , Puffin) Penguin Group (USA) Inc.

—HOOFBEATS: Margret & Flynn: 1875: Margret & Flynn: 1875. 2008. 144p. (YA). (gr. 3). 15.99 (*978-0-525-47936-9(8) , Dutton Juvenile) Penguin Group (USA) Inc.

—Hoofbeats Silence & Lily 1773. 2007. 160p. (J). (gr. 5). 15.99 (*978-0-525-47852-2(3) , Dutton Juvenile) Penguin Group (USA) Inc.

—Katie & the Mustang, Bk. 1. 2004. (Hoofbeats Ser.: Bk 1). 128p. pap. 4.99 (978-0-14-240090-6(4) , Puffin) Penguin Group (USA) Inc.

—Katie & the Mustang. 2004. 132p. (J). (ps-k). per. 11.64 (978-0-606-32524-0(7)) Tandem Library Bks.

—Katie & the Mustang Book One, 4 vols. 2004. 144p. (J). (gr. 3). Vol. 2. 15.99 (978-0-525-47273-5(8)); Vol. 4. 15.99 (978-0-525-47275-9(4)) Penguin Group (USA) Inc. (Dutton Juvenile).

—Lara & the Moon-Colored Filly, Vol. 2. 2005. (Hoofbeats Ser.: Bk. 2). 144p. (J). (gr. 4). pap. 4.99 (978-0-14-240231-3(1) , Puffin) Penguin Group (USA) Inc.

—Lara at Athenry Castle, Vol. 3. 2005. (Hoofbeats Ser.: No. 7). 128p. (J). (gr. 3-6). 15.99 (978-0-525-47340-4(8) , Dutton Juvenile) Penguin Group (USA) Inc.

—Margret & Flynn 1875. 2008. 160p. (J). (gr. 3). 5.99 (*978-0-14-241019-6(5) , Puffin) Penguin Group (USA) Inc.

—Mountains of the Moon. 2002. (gr. 3-6). lib. bdg. 11.80 (978-0-613-58375-6(2)) Tandem Library Bks.

—Silence & Lily: 1773. 2007. 176p. (J). (gr. 5). pap. 5.99 (*978-0-14-240909-1(X) , Puffin) Penguin Group (USA) Inc.

Duey, Kathleen. True Heart. Rayyan, Omar, illus. ed. 2005. 76p. (J). lib. bdg. 15.00 (978-1-59054-920-9(1)) Fitzgerald Bks.

—True Heart. Rayyan, Omar, illus. 2003. (Unicorn's Secret Ser.). 80p. (J). pap. 3.99 (978-0-689-85370-8(X) , Aladdin) Simon & Schuster Children's Publishing.

Duffy, Martin. Peg Leg Gus. 2007. (J). pap. (*978-0-9785853-3-4(X)) Ogma Pr.

Dvorak, Denise L. Clarence the Carousel Horse. 2007. pap. 16.99 (*978-1-60247-015-6(4)) Tate Publishing & Enterprises, L.L.C.

Earhart, Kristin. Happy's Holiday. 2007. (Big Apple Barn Ser.). 96p. (J). pap. 3.99 (*978-0-545-01774-9(2) , Scholastic Paperbacks) Scholastic, Inc.

—Patch. 2008. (Stablemates Ser.). 48p. (J). pap. 3.99 (*978-0-439-72240-7(3) , Cartwheel Bks.) Scholastic, Inc.

—Patch. Papp, Lisa, illus. 2006. (Breyer Stablemates Ser.). 48p. (J). pap. 4.99 (978-0-439-72236-0(5) , Cartwheel Bks.) Scholastic, Inc.

—Starlight. Andreasen, Dan, illus. 2006. (Breyer Stablemates Ser.). 48p. (J). pap. 4.99 (978-0-439-72237-7(3) , Cartwheel Bks.) Scholastic, Inc.

Ebers, Georg. The Greylock. 2004. reprint ed. pap. 15.95 (978-1-4191-6506-1(2)); pap. 1.99 (978-1-4192-6506-8(7)) Kessinger Publishing, LLC.

Echo of Hooves. 2005. (J). (978-1-933343-10-5(9) , PONY) Stabenfeldt Inc.

Edge, Laura Bufano. Wild West Dreams. 2006. (J). pap. (978-0-88092-623-2(6)); lib. bdg. (978-0-88092-622-5(8)) Royal Fireworks Publishing Co.

Edwards, Ken & Fletcher, Lyn, illus. My Little Pony: Storybook Collection. 2005. (My Little Pony Ser.). 192p. (J). (ps-1). 10.99 (978-0-06-074447-2(2) , Harper Festival) HarperCollins Pubs.

Egan, Kate. Pony Party. LoRaso, Carlo, illus. 2004. (My Little Pony Ser.). 24p. (J). (ps-1). pap. 3.99 (978-0-06-054950-3(5) , Harper Festival) HarperCollins Pubs.

Egan, Tim. Roasted Peanuts. 2006. (Illus.). 32p. (J). (gr. k-3). 16.00 (978-0-618-33718-7(0)) Houghton Mifflin Co.

H I

Eleanor, Coalson. Simon Says Run. 2006. (Illus.). (J). 8.95 (978-1-56167-944-7(5)) American Literary Pr.

Ellmore, Melba C. U-Shaped Shoes. Roseberry, Susan, illus. 2001. 32p. (J). (ps-3). 14.95 (978-0-8249-5425-3(4) , Ideals Children's Bks.) Ideals Pubns.

Elya, Susan Middleton. Cowboy Jose. Raglin, Tim, illus. 2005. 32p. (J). 15.99 (978-0-399-23570-2(1) , Putnam Juvenile) Penguin Group (USA) Inc.

Emerson, Charlotte. Beth's Snow Dancer. 1999. (Little Women Journals Ser.). (J). (978-0-606-16347-7(6)) Tandem Library Bks.

Emerson, Charlotte & Alcott, Louisa May. Beth's Snow Dancer. Wasden, Kevin, illus. 1999. (Little Women Journals). 128p. (J). (gr. 3-7). pap. 3.99 (978-0-380-79704-2(6)) HarperCollins Pubs.

Emmett, Jonathan. She'll Be Coming 'Round the Mountain. Allwright, Deborah, illus. 2007. 32p. (J). 16.99 (978-1-4169-3652-7(1) , Atheneum) Simon & Schuster Children's Publishing.

Emshwiller, Carol. Mister Boots. 2007. (Firebird Ser.). 192p. (YA). pap. 6.99 (978-0-14-240770-7(4) , Puffin) Penguin Group (USA) Inc.

Evans, Margaret. The Tale of Rainbow's End. 2007. pap. 11.00 (*978-0-8059-8716-4(9)) Dorrance Publishing Co., Inc.

Farley, Steven. The Black Stallion's Shadow. 2000. (Black Stallion Ser.). (Illus.). 192p. (J). (gr. 5-8). pap. 5.99 (978-0-679-89046-1(7) , Random Hse. Bks. for Young Readers) Random Hse. Children's Bks.

—The Black Stallion's Shadow. (J). (ps-7). 2000. 182p. per. 14.15 (978-0-613-24378-0(1)); 1999. 12.64 (978-0-606-22852-7(7)) Tandem Library Bks.

—Hard Lessons. Schwartz, Joanie, illus. 1999. (Young Black Stallion Ser.: No. 6). 144p. (J). (gr. 4-6). lib. bdg. 11.99 (978-0-375-90092-1(6) , Random Hse. Bks. for Young Readers) Random Hse. Children's Bks.

—Hard Lessons. 1999. (Young Black Stallion Ser.: No. 6). (J). (gr. 4-6). (978-0-606-16965-3(2)) Tandem Library Bks.

—The Homecoming. 1999. (Young Black Stallion Ser.: No. 3). (J). (gr. 4-6). (978-0-606-16962-2(8)) Tandem Library Bks.

—South Wind Spring. 2000. (Young Black Stallion Ser.: No. 7). (Illus.). 144p. (J). (gr. 4-6). pap. 3.99 (978-0-375-80139-6(1) , Random Hse. Bks. for Young Readers) Random Hse. Children's Bks.

—Wild Spirit. 1999. (Young Black Stallion Ser.: No. 4). (J). (gr. 4-6). (978-0-606-16963-9(6)) Tandem Library Bks.

—The Yearling. Schwartz, Joanie, illus. 1999. (Young Black Stallion Ser.: No. 5). 144p. (J). (gr. 4-6). lib. bdg. 11.99 (978-0-375-90091-4(8) , Random Hse. Bks. for Young Readers) Random Hse. Children's Bks.

—The Yearling. 1999. (Young Black Stallion Ser.: No. 5). (J). (gr. 4-6). (978-0-606-16964-6(4)) Tandem Library Bks.

Farley, Terri. Blue Wings. 2006. 242p. (J). lib. bdg. 16.92 (*978-1-4242-1035-0(6)) Fitzgerald Bks.

—Blue Wings. 2006. (Phantom Stallion Ser.). (Illus.). 256p. (J). pap. 4.99 (978-0-06-075848-6(1)) HarperCollins Pubs.

—The Challenger, Vol. 6. 2003. (Phantom Stallion Ser.: Vol. 6). 240p. (J). (gr. 5 up). pap. 4.99 (978-0-06-441090-8(0) , Avon) HarperCollins Pubs.

—Dark Sunshine, Vol. 3. 2002. (Phantom Stallion Ser.: Vol. 3). (Illus.). 240p. (gr. 5 up). pap. 4.99 (978-0-06-441087-8(0) , Avon) HarperCollins Pubs.

—Dark Sunshine. 2002. (gr. 5-8). lib. bdg. 13.00 (978-0-613-66699-2(2)) Tandem Library Bks.

—Dawn Runner. 2006. (Phantom Stallion Ser.: No. 21). 224p. (J). pap. 4.99 (978-0-06-081538-7(8)) HarperCollins Pubs.

—Desert Dancer. 2003. (Phantom Stallion Ser.: Vol. 7). (Illus.). 240p. (J). (gr. 5 up). pap. 4.99 (978-0-06-053725-8(6)) HarperCollins Pubs.

—Desert Dancer. 2003. (gr. 5-8). lib. bdg. 13.00 (978-0-613-66959-7(2)) Tandem Library Bks.

—Firefly. 2005. 214p. (J). lib. bdg. 16.92 (*978-1-4242-0835-7(1)) Fitzgerald Bks.

—Firefly. 2005. (Illus.). (J). (Phantom Stallion Ser.: No. 18). 224p. pap. 4.99 (978-0-06-075846-2(5)); 214p. (*978-1-4156-2263-6(9) , Avon Bks.) HarperCollins Pubs.

—Free Again, Vol. 5. 2003. (Phantom Stallion Ser.: No. 5). (Illus.). 224p. (J). (gr. 5 up). pap. 4.99 (978-0-06-441089-2(7) , Avon) HarperCollins Pubs.

—Free Again. 2003. (gr. 5-8). lib. bdg. 13.00 (978-0-613-66706-7(9)) Tandem Library Bks.

—Gift Horse. 2003. (Phantom Stallion Ser.: No. 9). 240p. (J). (gr. 5 up). pap. 4.99 (978-0-06-056157-4(2)) HarperCollins Pubs.

—Golden Ghost. 2003. (Phantom Stallion Ser.: No. 8). (Illus.). 224p. (gr. 5 up). pap. 4.99 (978-0-06-053726-5(4)) HarperCollins Pubs.

—Golden Ghost. 2003. (gr. 5-8). lib. bdg. 13.00 (978-0-613-67623-6(8)) Tandem Library Bks.

—Gypsy Gold. 2006. (Phantom Stallion Ser.). 240p. (J). pap. 4.99 (978-0-06-081540-0(X) , Harper Trophy) HarperCollins Pubs.

—Heartbreak Bronco. 2004. 227p. (J). lib. bdg. 16.92 (*978-1-4242-0830-2(0)) Fitzgerald Bks.

—Heartbreak Bronco. 2004. (Phantom Stallion Ser.). 240p. (J). (gr. 5 up). pap. 4.99 (978-0-06-058314-9(2)) HarperCollins Pubs.

—The Horse Charmer. 2007. (Phantom Stallion Ser.: No. 1). 240p. (J). pap. 4.99 (*978-0-06-081542-4(6) , Harper Trophy) HarperCollins Pubs.

—Moonrise. 2005. 197p. (J). lib. bdg. 16.92 (*978-1-4242-0831-9(9)) Fitzgerald Bks.

—Moonrise, Vol. 14. 2005. (Phantom Stallion Ser.). (Illus.). 208p. (gr. 5 up). pap. 4.99 (978-0-06-058315-6(0)) HarperCollins Pubs.

—Mountain Mare. 2005. 214p. (J). lib. bdg. 16.92 (*978-1-4242-0834-0(3)) Fitzgerald Bks.

—Mountain Mare. 2005. (Phantom Stallion Ser.). 224p. (J). pap. 4.99 (978-0-06-075845-5(7)) HarperCollins Pubs.

—Mustang Moon. 2002. (Phantom Stallion Ser.: No. 2). (Illus.). 240p. (gr. 5 up). pap. 4.99 (978-0-06-441086-1(2) , Avon) HarperCollins Pubs.

—Mustang Moon. 2002. (gr. 5-8). lib. bdg. 13.00 (978-0-613-52711-8(9)) Tandem Library Bks.

—Phantom Stallion. 2008. (Phantom Stallion: Wild Horse Island Ser.: No. 4). 240p. (J). pap. 4.99 (*978-0-06-088617-2(X) , Harper Trophy); 2007. 224p. pap. 1.99 (*978-0-06-133928-8(3)) HarperCollins Pubs.

—Phantom Stallion Box Set: The Wild One; Mustang Moon; Dark Sunshine. Call, Greg, illus. 2004. (Phantom Stallion Ser.). 704p. (J). (gr. 5 up). pap. 14.99 (978-0-06-059504-3(3) , HarperCollins) HarperCollins Pubs.

—Phantom Stallion: Wild Horse Island #5: Fire Maiden. 2008. (Phantom Stallion: Wild Horse Island Ser.). 272p. (J). pap. 4.99 (*978-0-06-088618-9(8) , Harper Trophy) HarperCollins Pubs.

—Rain Dance. 2004. 180p. (J). lib. bdg. 16.92 (*978-1-4242-0829-6(7)) Fitzgerald Bks.

—Rain Dance. 2004. (Phantom Stallion Ser.: No. 12). 192p. (gr. 5 up). pap. 4.99 (978-0-06-058313-2(4)) HarperCollins Pubs.

—Rain Forest Rose. 2007. (Phantom Stallion: Wild Horse Island Ser.). 224p. (J). (gr. 5 up). pap. 4.99 (*978-0-06-088616-5(1) , Harper Trophy) HarperCollins Pubs.

—Red Feather Filly. 2004. 201p. (J). lib. bdg. 16.92 (*978-1-4242-0828-9(9)) Fitzgerald Bks.

—Red Feather Filly. 2004. (Phantom Stallion Ser.: Vol. 10). 208p. (J). (gr. 5 up). pap. 4.99 (978-0-06-056158-1(0)) HarperCollins Pubs.

—The Renegade. 2002. (Phantom Stallion Ser.: No. 4). (Illus.). 240p. (J). (gr. 5 up). pap. 4.99 (978-0-06-441088-5(9)) HarperCollins Pubs.

—Run Away Home. 2006. (Phantom Stallion Ser.). (Illus.). 288p. (J). pap. 4.99 (978-0-06-081541-7(8) , Harper Trophy) HarperCollins Pubs.

—Secret Star. 2006. (Phantom Stallion Ser.). (Illus.). 224p. (J). pap. 4.99 (978-0-06-075847-9(3)) HarperCollins Pubs.

—The Shining Stallion. 2007. (Phantom Stallion: Wild Horse Island Ser.: No. 2). 224p. (J). (gr. 5 up). pap. 4.99 (*978-0-06-081543-1(4) , Harper Trophy) HarperCollins Pubs.

—Untamed, Vol. 11. 2004. (Phantom Stallion Ser.). (Illus.). 224p. (J). (gr. 5 up). pap. 4.99 (978-0-06-056159-8(9)) HarperCollins Pubs.

—Untamed. 2004. (gr. 5-8). lib. bdg. 13.00 (978-0-613-71464-8(4)) Tandem Library Bks.

—Wild Honey. 2006. (Phantom Stallion Ser.: No. 22). (Illus.). 320p. (J). pap. 4.99 (978-0-06-081539-4(6)) HarperCollins Pubs.

—The Wild One. 2002. (Phantom Stallion Ser.: No. 1). 224p. (J). (gr. 5 up). pap. 4.99 (978-0-06-441085-4(4) , Avon) HarperCollins Pubs.

—Wild One. 2002. (gr. 5-8). lib. bdg. 13.00 (978-0-613-52735-4(6)) Tandem Library Bks.

Farley, Walter. Big Black Horse. Schucker, James, illus. 2007. 64p. (J). (ps-4). 14.99 (*978-0-375-84035-7(4)); lib. bdg. 17.99 (*978-0-375-94054-5(5) , Random Hse. Bks. for Young Readers) Random Hse. Children's Bks.

—The Black Stallion. l.t. ed. 2005. 290p. (J). pap. (978-0-7540-6198-4(1) , CLP 390) BBC Audio.

—The Black Stallion & Satan. 2002. (Black Stallion Ser.). 224p. (J). (gr. 5-8). pap. 5.99 (978-0-679-81346-0(2) , Yearling) Random Hse. Children's Bks.

—The Black Stallion Challenged. 2003. (Black Stallion Ser.). (Illus.). 240p. (J). (gr. 5-8). pap. 5.99 (978-0-394-84371-1(1) , Random Hse. Bks. for Young Readers) Random Hse. Children's Bks.

—The Black Stallion Mystery. 2004. (Black Stallion Ser.). 224p. (J). (gr. 5-8). reprint ed. pap. 5.99 (978-0-679-82700-9(5) , Yearling) Random Hse. Children's Bks.

—The Black Stallion Revolts. Rowe, John, illus. 2002. (Black Stallion Ser.). 288p. (J). (gr. 5-8). pap. 5.99 (978-0-394-83613-3(8) , Yearling) Random Hse. Children's Bks.

—The Black Stallion Revolts. 2002. (gr. 5-8). lib. bdg. 14.15 (978-0-613-70885-2(7)) Tandem Library Bks.

—The Black Stallion's Courage. 2004. (Black Stallion Ser.). (Illus.). 240p. (J). (gr. 5-8). pap. 5.99 (978-0-394-83918-9(8) , Yearling) Random Hse. Children's Bks.

—The Black Stallion's Filly. Rowe, John, illus. 2002. (Black Stallion Ser.). 288p. (J). (gr. 5-8). pap. 5.99 (978-0-394-83916-5(1) , Yearling) Random Hse. Children's Bks.

—The Black Stallion's Filly. 2002. (gr. 5-8). lib. bdg. 14.15 (978-0-613-70886-9(5)) Tandem Library Bks.

—The Island Stallion. 2003. (Black Stallion Ser.). (Illus.). 240p. (J). (gr. 5-8). pap. 5.99 (978-0-394-84376-6(2) , Yearling) Random Hse. Children's Bks.

—The Island Stallion Races. 2003. (Black Stallion Ser.). (Illus.). 256p. (J). (gr. 5-8). pap. 5.99 (978-0-394-84375-9(4) , Yearling) Random Hse. Children's Bks.

—The Island Stallion's Fury. 2003. (Black Stallion Ser.). (Illus.). 224p. (J). (gr. 5-8). pap. 5.99 (978-0-394-84373-5(8) , Yearling) Random Hse. Children's Bks.

—The Young Black Stallion. 2002. (Black Stallion Ser.). (YA). 14.45 (978-0-7587-8501-5(1)) Book Wholesalers, Inc.

Feld, Ellen F. Blackjack. 2001. 179p. (J). (gr. 4-7). pap. 7.95 (978-0-9709002-0-3(1)) Willow Bend Publishing.

—Blackjack: Dreaming of a Morgan Horse. (Illus.). (J). 2004. 199p. per. 9.95 (978-0-9709002-3-4(6)); 3rd rev. ed. 2007. 235p. per. 9.95 (*978-0-9709002-8-9(7)) Willow Bend Publishing.

—Rusty: The High-Flying Morgan Horse. 2004. (Illus.). 200p. (J). per. 9.95 (978-0-9709002-4-1(4)) Willow Bend Publishing.

—Shadow: The Curious Morgan Horse. 2006. (Illus.). 32p. (J). 15.95 (978-0-9709002-6-5(0)) Willow Bend Publishing.

Felder, Deborah G. Changing Times. 1998. (Treasured Horses Ser.: Vol. 5). (Illus.). (J). (gr. 3-7). pap. 4.50 (978-0-590-31657-6(5)) Scholastic, Inc.

—Changing Times, 5. 1998. (Treasured Horses Ser.). (J). (978-0-606-13865-9(X)) Tandem Library Bks.

—Pretty Lady of Saratoga. Rabinowitz, Sandy & Keiffer, Christa, illus. l.t. ed. 1999. (Treasured Horses Collection). 122p. (J). (gr. 4 up). lib. bdg. 23.33 (978-0-8368-2404-9(0)) Stevens, Gareth Inc.

Ferrone, John M. Margo & the Trail Ride. Ferrone, John M., photos by. Date not set. (Illus.). 36p. (J). (ps-5). pap. 16.95 (978-1-928811-05-3(1)) Story Stuff, Inc.

Few, Cyndi. Going to Nanna & Poppy's Ranch : for My Grandson-Talon. 2006. (ENG.). 28p. per. 14.00 (*978-1-4259-4179-6(6)) AuthorHouse.

Findlay, Jamieson. The Blue Roan Girl. 2004. (Illus.). 272p. (J). 16.95 (978-0-439-62752-8(4)) Scholastic, Inc.

Fleischman, Sid. The Midnight Horse. Sis, Peter, illus. 2004. 96p. (J). pap. 4.99 (978-0-06-072216-6(9) , Harper Trophy) HarperCollins Pubs.

Flores-Galbis, Enrique. Raining Sardines. 2007. 176p. (J). (gr. 5-9). 16.95 (978-1-59643-166-9(0)) Roaring Brook Pr.

A Foal Is Born. 2007. (J). (978-1-933343-46-4(X) , PONY) Stabenfeldt Inc.

Francis, Dick. Blood Sport. 1999. (gr. 7-12). lib. bdg. 15.30 (978-0-613-12525-3(8)) Tandem Library Bks.

Frantic Flight. 2005. (J). (978-1-933343-07-5(9) , PONY) Stabenfeldt Inc.

Frantz, Jennifer. My Little Pony: The Big Balloon Race. Thompson Brothers Staff & Binder, Eric, illus. 2004. (Festival Reader Ser.). 24p. (J). (ps-1). pap. 3.99 (978-0-06-073268-4(7) , Harper Festival) HarperCollins Pubs.

Freedom's Whisper. 2007. (J). (978-1-933343-52-5(4) , PONY) Stabenfeldt Inc.

Fremont, Walter & Young, Susan W. Rambunctious Rattler. 1999. 138p. (J). (gr. 4-7). pap. 7.49 (978-1-57924-262-6(6) , 121483) Jones, Bob Univ. Pr.

The Frog Who Thought He Was a Horse: Individual Title Six-Packs. (Literatura 2000 Ser.). (gr. 2-3). 33.00 (978-0-7635-0225-6(1)) Rigby Education.

Frosty: The Adventures of a Morgan Horse. (Illus.). (J). 2003. 199p. per. 9.95 (978-0-9709002-2-7(8)); 2nd ed. 2007. 232p. per. 9.95 (*978-0-9709002-7-2(9)) Willow Bend Publishing.

Gaited Horse Activity & Coloring Book-English/German/Spanish Edition. 2006. (ENG, GER & SPA.). (J). spiral bd. 17.95 (978-1-59210-287-7(5)) Whispering Pine Pr., Inc.

Gaited Horse Story Book. 2005. (J). 15.95 (978-1-59649-418-3(2)) Whispering Pine Pr., Inc.

Garcia, Marina. Mateo de Paseo por el Museo. 2003. (SPA., Illus.). 36p. (J). 17.95 (978-84-8488-068-4(0)) Serres, Ediciones, S. L. ESP. *Dist:* Lectorum Pubns., Inc.

Garland, Sherry. Best Horse on the Force. 2006. 112p. (J). pap. 7.95 (978-1-58980-437-1(6)) Pelican Publishing Co., Inc.

Gerver, Jane E. Lucky. Rogers, Jacqueline, illus. 2007. (Stablemates Ser.). 48p. (J). 4.99 (978-0-439-72234-6(9)) Scholastic, Inc.

The Ghost Horse of Meadow Green. 2005. (J). (978-1-933343-03-7(6) , PONY) Stabenfeldt Inc.

Goble. The Girl Who Love Wild Horses. 1998. (J). pap. 5.99 (978-0-87628-362-2(8)) Ctr. for Applied Research in Education, The.

Goble, Paul. The Girl Who Loved Wild Horses. Goble, Paul, illus. 2001. (Illus.). 28.95 incl. audio compact disk (978-1-59112-752-9(1)); pap. 39.95 incl. audio compact disk (978-1-59112-534-1(0)) Live Oak Media.

—The Girl Who Loved Wild Horses. unabr. ed. 2001. (Illus.). (J). (ps-2). pap. 16.95 incl. audio (978-0-87499-762-0(3)) Live Oak Media.

—The Girl Who Loved Wild Horses. 2001. 32p. (J). 17.99 (978-0-689-84504-8(9) , Atheneum/Richard Jackson Bks.) Simon & Schuster Children's Publishing.

Gold Fever. 2005. (J). (978-1-933343-00-6(1) , PONY) Stabenfeldt Inc.

Goodspeed, Judy. Saddle Up. 2007. (Illus.). 24p. (J). 7.98 (*978-0-9794660-7-6(5)); 24.99 (*978-0-9794660-0-7(8)); per. 12.99 (*978-0-9794660-1-4(6)) Dragonfly Publishing, Inc.

Goulet, Charles. The Godmother: First Lady of the West. 2001. 132p. pap. 10.95 (978-0-595-19281-6(5) , Writers Club Pr.) iUniverse, Inc.

Grant, K. M. Blaze of Silver. 2007. 272p. 16.95 (978-0-8027-9625-7(7)) Walker & Co.

—Blood Red Horse. 2006. 288p. (J). pap. 7.95 (978-0-8027-7734-8(1)) Walker & Co.

—Green Jasper. (J). 2007. 272p. pap. 7.95 (978-0-8027-9627-1(3)); 2006. 256p. 16.95 (978-0-8027-8073-7(3)) Walker & Co.

Gray, Rita. The Wild Little Horse. Wolff, Ashley, illus. 2005. 32p. (J). (ps-ps). 15.99 (978-0-525-47455-5(2) , Dutton Juvenile) Penguin Group (USA) Inc.

The Green Horse Summer. 2006. (J). (978-1-933343-28-0(1) , PONY) Stabenfeldt Inc.

Griffith, Helen V. Cougar. 2001. (J). (978-0-606-21124-6(1)) Tandem Library Bks.

Grooms, Molly. We Are Puppies. 2005. 40p. bds. 12.95 (978-90-5843-815-7(5)) YoYo Bks. BEL. *Dist:* National Bk. Network.

Grosgebauer, Clare Ham. Snickerdoodle & the Roller-Skating Horse! Rissing, Karen, illus. 3rd ed. 2005. 36p. (gr. k-3). 12.99 (978-0-9741888-4-3(0)) Small Wonders Enterprises.

Grovet, Heather. Beanie, the Horse That Wasn't a Horse. 2004. 95p. (J). (978-0-8163-2053-0(5)) Pacific Pr. Publishing Assn.

Guest, Elissa Haden. Iris & Walter & the Birthday Party. Davenier, Christine, illus. 2008. (Iris & Walter Ser.). 44p. (J). pap. 5.95 (*978-0-15-205388-8(3) , Harcourt Paperbacks) Harcourt Children's Bks.

—Iris & Walter & the Birthday Party. Davenier, Christine, illus. 2006. (Iris & Walter Ser.). 44p. (J). 15.00 (978-0-15-205015-3(9)) Harcourt Trade Pubs.

Gunter, Frances. Golden Horseshoe, Vol. 1. 2003. (YA). per. 9.95 (978-0-9710389-1-2(0)) Elk River Pr.

—Golden Horseshoe 2, Vol. 2. 2003. (Illus.). 95p. (J). per. 9.95 (978-0-9710389-2-9(9)) Elk River Pr.

Gutierrez, Astrid Romero. Cuentos de Unicornios para Ninos. 1999. (Stories for Children Ser.).Tr. of Unicorn Stories for Kids. (SPA., Illus.). 125p. (J). 7.95 (978-970-643-188-2(8)) Selector, S.A. de C.V. MEX. *Dist:* Libros Sin Fronteras.

Haas, Jessie. Jigsaw Pony. Hu, Ying-Hwa, illus. 2005. 128p. (J). 15.99 (978-0-06-078245-0(5)); (gr. 2-4). lib. bdg. 16.89 (978-0-06-078250-4(1)) HarperCollins Pubs.

—Runaway Pony. Apple, Margot, illus. 2004. 56p. (J). (ps-ps). lib. bdg. 11.05 (978-0-606-32634-6(0)) Tandem Library Bks.

—Scamper & the Horse Show. Apple, Margot, illus. 2004. 32p. (J). 15.99 (978-0-06-001338-7(9)) HarperCollins Pubs.

—Unbroken. 2001. 208p. (J). (gr. 5 up). pap. 6.99 (978-0-380-73313-2(7) , Harper Trophy) HarperCollins Pubs.

—Unbroken. 2001. (J). (978-0-606-20962-5(X)); (gr. 5-8). lib. bdg. 14.10 (978-0-613-33735-9(2)) Tandem Library Bks.

—Unbroken. l.t. ed. 2000. (Juvenile Ser.). 248p. (J). (gr. 4-7). 21.95 (978-0-7862-2769-3(9)) Thorndike Pr.

—Will You, Won't You? 2000. 176p. (J). (gr. 5 up). 15.89 (978-0-06-029197-6(4)) HarperCollins Pubs.

Haffner, Kirstin. Born to Be Free. 2006. 133p. pap. 11.95 (978-1-4116-8471-3(0)) Lulu.com.

Hahn, Cathe. Step Up! Artley, Bob, illus. 2005. 32p. (J). 15.95 (978-1-58980-214-8(4)) Pelican Publishing Co., Inc.

Half Moon Ranch: Rodeo Rocky. 2006. (J). (978-1-933343-40-2(0) , PONY) Stabenfeldt Inc.

Half Moon Ranch: Wild Horses. 2006. (J). (978-1-933343-33-4(8) , PONY) Stabenfeldt Inc.

Harcourt School Publishers Staff. Adopting a Wild Horse Advanced Level. 3rd ed. 2002. (Trophies Reading Program Ser.). (Illus.). pap. 5.10 (978-0-15-323290-9(0)) Harcourt Schl. Pubs.

—The Black Stallion: Reader's Choice Book. 2001. (Collections Ser.). (Illus.). pap. 13.20 (978-0-15-314389-2(4)) Harcourt Schl. Pubs.

—Bronco Buster: Take-Home Book. 2001. (Collections Ser.). (Illus.). (J). (gr. 6). pap. 1.90 (978-0-15-319666-9(1)) Harcourt Schl. Pubs.

—Cheyenne Horses Advanced Level. 3rd ed. 2002. (Trophies Reading Program Ser.). (Illus.). pap. 5.10 (978-0-15-323200-8(5)) Harcourt Schl. Pubs.

—Friendly Hands. 3rd ed. 2002. (Trophies English Language Learners Ser.). (Illus.). pap. 5.10 (978-0-15-327894-5(3)) Harcourt Schl. Pubs.

—My Horse & North: Library Edition. 1999. (Collections Ser.). (Illus.). (J). (gr. 3). 5.30 (978-0-15-314319-9(3)) Harcourt Schl. Pubs.

—The Pig Who Cried Help: Take-Home Book. 1999. (Collections Ser.). (Illus.). (J). pap. 1.90 (978-0-15-317311-0(4)) Harcourt Schl. Pubs.

—The Pony Express & the Rescue: Take-Home Book. 1999. (Collections Ser.). (Illus.). (J). pap. 1.90 (978-0-15-317313-4(0)) Harcourt Schl. Pubs.

—Return of the Wild Horses: Take-Home Book. 1999. (Signatures Ser.). (Illus.). (J). pap. 1.90 (978-0-15-313894-2(7)) Harcourt Schl. Pubs.

—Trofeos Advanced Level: Los Caballos. 3rd ed. 2002. (SPA., Illus.). pap. 6.80 (978-0-15-324111-6(X)) Harcourt Schl. Pubs.

—Vaquero, the Cowboy Advanced level. 3rd ed. 2002. (Trophies Reading Program Ser.). (Illus.). pap. 5.10 (978-0-15-323375-3(3)) Harcourt Schl. Pubs.

Harlow, Joan Hiatt. Midnight Rider. 2006. 384p. (J). pap. 5.99 (978-0-689-87010-1(8) , Aladdin) Simon & Schuster Children's Publishing.

Harlow, Joan Hiatt & Minor, Wendell. Midnight Rider. 2005. (Illus.). 416p. (J). 15.95 (978-0-689-87009-5(4) , McElderry, Margaret K.) Simon & Schuster Children's Publishing.

Hart, Alison. Gabriel's Horses. 2007. 224p. (J). (gr. 3-7). 14.95 (*978-1-56145-398-6(6) , Peachtree Junior) Peachtree Pubs., Ltd.

Hart, Alison. Shadow Horse. 2001. 272p. (J). (gr. 5-8). mass mkt. 4.99 (978-0-375-80263-8(0) , Random Hse. Bks. for Young Readers) Random Hse. Children's Bks.

—Shadow Horse. 2001. (gr. 5-8). lib. bdg. 13.00 (978-0-613-85134-3(X)); (J). (978-0-606-20905-2(0)) Tandem Library Bks.

Hasley, Dennis. Painting A Horse. 2008. (Illus.). 32p. (J). 16.95 (*978-1-59643-238-3(1)) Roaring Brook Pr.

Hassanein, Amany F. Goha & His Donkey. Gorbachev, Valeri, illus. 1999. (Books for Young Learners). 16p. (J). (gr. k-2). pap. 5.95 (978-1-57274-180-5(5)) Owen, Richard C. Pubs., Inc.

Havers, Elinore. Dream Pony. 2001. (Illus.). 127p. pap. 3.00 (978-0-7188-2253-8(6)) Lutherworth Pr., The GBR. *Dist:* Parkwest Pubns., Inc.

—Gay & the Ponies. 2004. (Illus.). 128p. (J). pap. 3.00 (978-0-7188-2254-5(4)) Lutherworth Pr., The GBR. *Dist:* Parkwest Pubns., Inc.

Hawkins, Al. April Is Born: Adventures of a New Quarter Horse Filly. Erickson, Terri, illus. l.t. ed. 2004. 24p. (J). pap. 9.50 (978-0-9640056-5-5(4)) Arrowhead Publishing.

Heaton, Layce D. The Many Tracks of Lap'n Tap, 1. Heaton, Layce D., illus. 2006. (Illus.). 32p. (J). lib. bdg. 18.95 (978-0-9761128-3-9(3)) Hafabanana Pr.

Hector, Rachel Claus. Six Second Slack. 2002. 134p. pap. 10.95 (978-0-595-21513-3(0) , Writers Club Pr.) iUniverse, Inc.

Heinz, Brian. Cheyenne Medicine Hat. Manchess, Gregory, illus. 2006. 32p. (J). 18.95 (978-1-56846-181-6(X)) Creative Co., The.

Henrietta: Not Everybody Wears Horseshoes. 2004. (Illus.). 32p. (J). 6.99 (978-0-9744520-1-2(7)) Glitter Creek, Inc.

Henry, Marguerite. Black Gold. 2002. (YA). 13.40 (978-0-7587-6672-4(6)) Book Wholesalers, Inc.

—Born to Trot. 2002. (Illus.). 13.40 (978-1-4046-1350-8(1)) Book Wholesalers, Inc.

—Brown Sunshine of Sawdust Valley. Shields, Bonnie, illus. 1998. 112p. (gr. 3-7). mass mkt. 5.99 (978-0-689-80779-4(1) , Aladdin) Simon & Schuster Children's Publishing.

—Justin Morgan Had a Horse. 2002. (Illus.). (J). 13.40 (978-0-7587-0280-7(9)) Book Wholesalers, Inc.

—Justin Morgan Had a Horse. 2000. (J). (gr. 3-6). tchr. ed. 99.00 incl. VHS (978-0-89625-730-6(4) , 68E44VL00) Disney Educational Productions.

—Justin Morgan Had a Horse. Dennis, Wesley, illus. 2006. 176p. (J). pap. 5.99 (978-1-4169-2785-3(9) , Aladdin) Simon & Schuster Children's Publishing.

—Justin Morgan Had a Horse. Dennis, illus. 2002. 176p. (J). 17.95 (978-0-689-85279-4(7)) Simon & Schuster Children's Publishing.

—Justin Morgan Had a Horse. 2003. (J). (gr. 3-8). 20.25 (978-0-8446-7245-8(9)) Smith, Peter Pub., Inc.

—King of the Wind. 2002. (Illus.). (J). 13.40 (978-0-7587-0197-8(7)) Book Wholesalers, Inc.

—King of the Wind. Dennis, Wesley, illus. deluxe ed. 2005. 173p. (J). (gr. 2-6). reprint ed. pap. 21.00 (978-0-7567-8753-0(X)) DIANE Publishing Co.

—King of the Wind. unabr. ed. 2004. 173p. (J). (gr. 4-7). pap. 38.00 incl. audio (978-0-8072-8697-5(4) , YA239SP, Listening Library) Random Hse. Audio Publishing Group.

—King of the Wind. l.t. ed. 2001. (Illus.). 216p. (J). (gr. 4-7). 21.95 (978-0-7862-2848-5(2)) Thorndike Pr.

—King of the Wind: The Story of the Godolphin Arabian. Dennis, Wesley, illus. 2006. 176p. (J). pap. 5.99 (978-1-4169-2786-0(7) , Aladdin) Simon & Schuster Children's Publishing.

—Marguerite Henry Treasury of Horses: Misty of Chincoteague, Justin Morgan Had a Horse, King of the Wind. Dennis, Wesley, illus. 2007. 528p. (J). 15.99 (978-1-4169-3954-2(7) , Aladdin) Simon & Schuster Children's Publishing.

—Misty's Twilight. Dennis, Wesley & Grandpré, Karen Haus, illus. 2007. 144p. (J). pap. 5.99 (978-1-4169-2787-7(5) , Aladdin) Simon & Schuster Children's Publishing.

—Misty's Twilight. 2001. (J). (gr. 3-6). 21.75 (978-0-8446-7177-2(0)) Smith, Peter Pub., Inc.

—Mustang: Wild Spirit of the West. 2002. (Illus.). 13.40 (978-1-4046-1358-4(7)) Book Wholesalers, Inc.

—San Domingo: The Medicine Hat Stallion. 2001. (J). (gr. 4-8). 21.75 (978-0-8446-7178-9(9)) Smith, Peter Pub., Inc.

—Stormy: Misty's Foal. 2002. (Illus.). (J). 13.40 (978-0-7587-6608-3(4)) Book Wholesalers, Inc.

Henry, Marguerite & Dennis, Wesley. Stormy, Misty's Foal. 2007. 224p. (J). pap. 5.99 (978-1-4169-2788-4(3) , Aladdin) Simon & Schuster Children's Publishing.

Hickox, Rebecca. Per & the Dala Horse. Gilbert, Yvonne, illus. 2003. 32p. (J). pap. 8.95 (978-1-57534-034-0(8)) Skandisk, Inc.

Higginson, Hadley. Keeker & Pony Camp Catastrophe, Bk. 5. Parrett, Lisa, illus. 2007. 56p. (J). 15.50 (978-0-8118-5596-9(1)) Chronicle Bks. LLC.

—Keeker & the Horse Show Show-Off. Andersen, Maja, illus. 2006. (Sneaky Pony Ser.: Bk. 2). 48p. (J). 15.50 (978-0-8118-5135-0(4)) Chronicle Bks. LLC.

—Keeker & the Pony Camp Catastrophe. Parrett, Lisa, illus. 2007. (Keeker & the Sneaky Pony Ser.: Bk. 5). 56p. (J). (gr. k-3). pap. 3.95 (978-0-8118-5597-6(X)) Chronicle Bks. LLC.

High, Linda Oatman. The Girl on the High-Diving Horse. Lewin, Ted, illus. 2005. 40p. (J). (ps-ps). pap. 6.99 (978-0-14-240278-8(8) , Puffin) Penguin Group (USA) Inc.

Hill, Janet Muirhead. The Many Adventures of Miranda & Starlight: Six Volume Set. Lehmkuhl, Pat, illus. 2007. (J). 49.95 ***(978-0-9772525-7-2(4))*** Raven Publishing Inc. of Montana.

—Miranda & Starlight: (the Starlight Books, 1), 6 vols. Lehmkuhl, Pat, illus. 2nd rev. ed. 2003. (Starlight Bks.: 1). 168p. (J). (gr. 3-7). per. 9.00 (978-0-9714161-4-7(1)) Raven Publishing Inc. of Montana.

—Starlight Comes Home: (the Starlight Books, 6) Lehmkuhl, Pat, illus. 2004. (Starlight Bks.). 236p. (YA). per. 9.00 (978-0-9714161-6-1(8)) Raven Publishing Inc. of Montana.

—Starlight Shines for Miranda: (the Starlight Books, 5) Lehmkuhl, Pat, illus. 2004. (Starlight Bks.). 192p. (J). (gr. 4-8). per. 9.00 (978-0-9714161-5-4(X)) Raven Publishing Inc. of Montana.

—Starlight's Courage: Revised Edition. Lehmkuhl, Pat, illus. 2nd ed. 2007. 170p. (J). per. 9.00 ***(978-0-9772525-4-1(X))*** Raven Publishing Inc. of Montana.

—Starlight's Courage: (the Starlight Books, 2), 6 vols. Lehmkuhl, Pat, illus. 2002. (Starlight Bks.: Bk. 2). 180p. (J). (gr. 4-7). pap. 9.00 (978-0-9714161-1-6(7)) Raven Publishing Inc. of Montana.

—Starlight's Shooting Star: The Starlight Books, 4. Lehmkuhl, Pat, illus. 2003. (Starlight Bks.). 192p. (J). (gr. 3-8). per. 9.00 (978-0-9714161-3-0(3)) Raven Publishing Inc. of Montana.

Hinton, S. E. Taming the Star Runner. 1999. (YA). 22.00 (978-0-8446-7027-0(8)) Smith, Peter Pub., Inc.

Hodgson, Julie. Miniature Horse Tales. 2005. 37p. (J). 15.00 (978-1-4116-4144-0(2)) Lulu.com.

Hoffman, Mary. City of Stars. 2003. (Stravaganza Ser.: Vol. 2). (Illus.). 300p. (J). 17.95 (978-1-58234-839-1(1) , Bloomsbury Children) Bloomsbury Publishing.

Holmes, Victoria. The Horse from the Sea. (J). 2006. (Illus.). 336p. pap. 6.99 (978-0-06-052030-4(2)); 2005. 320p. (gr. 5 up). 15.99 (978-0-06-052028-1(0)) HarperCollins Pubs.

—The Horse from the Sea: An Epic Horse Story. 2005. 320p. (J). (gr. k-9). lib. bdg. 16.89 (978-0-06-052029-8(9)) HarperCollins Pubs.

—Rider in the Dark: An Epic Horse Story. 320p. (J). 2006. pap. 6.99 (978-0-06-052027-4(2)); 2004. (Illus.). (gr. 5 up). 15.99 (978-0-06-052025-0(6)); 2004. (Illus.). (gr. 5 up). lib. bdg. 16.89 (978-0-06-052026-7(4)) HarperCollins Pubs.

Hood, Karen Jean Matsko. Gaited Horse Activity & Coloring Book. 2006. (J). 17.95 (978-1-59649-626-2(6)); cd-rom 13.95 (978-1-59649-625-5(8)); spiral bd. 22.95 (978-1-59649-972-0(9)) Whispering Pine Pr., Inc.

—Gaited Horse Activity & Coloring Book-English/French/Italian Edition. 2006. (J). 19.95 (978-1-59649-714-6(9)); spiral bd. 19.95 (978-1-59649-716-0(5)); cd-rom 13.95 (978-1-59649-717-7(3)) Whispering Pine Pr., Inc.

—Lost Medal. 2006. (J). spiral bd. 22.95 (978-1-59434-757-3(3)); cd-rom 24.95 (978-1-59434-760-3(3)); spiral bd. 22.95 (978-1-59434-756-6(5)) Whispering Pine Pr., Inc.

Hopka, Cathy. Dreamer: Inspired by a True Story. 2005. (Illus.). 136p. (J). (gr. 4-7). pap. 4.99 (978-0-439-77494-9(2)) Scholastic, Inc.

Hopson, Lily J. The Gray Colt & his World. 2005. pap. 7.95 (978-0-533-14895-0(2)) Vantage Pr., Inc.

Horse Angel - Chica's Story. 2007. (J). (978-1-933343-48-8(6) , PONY) Stabenfeldt Inc.

Horse Angel - Ride into Fear. 2005. (J). (978-1-933343-11-2(7) , PONY) Stabenfeldt Inc.

Horse Angel - Run Wild. 2006. (J). (978-1-933343-26-6(5) , PONY) Stabenfeldt Inc.

A Horse Called Trouble. 2006. (J). (978-1-933343-34-1(6) , PONY) Stabenfeldt Inc.

Horse Sense. 2005. 44p. (J). 3.99 (978-0-9763213-2-3(7)) OHC Group LLC.

The Horse with the Skinny Tail. 2002. (J). 14.95 (978-0-915082-28-5(4) , —, Gemini Pr) Project Publishing & Design.

Hubbard, Coleen. Christmas in Silver Lake, Rabinowitz, Sandy & Keiffer, Christa, illus. l.t. ed. 1999. (Treasured Horses Collection). 128p. (J). (gr. 4 up). lib. bdg. 23.33 (978-0-8368-2400-1(8)) Stevens, Gareth Inc.

—The Flying Angels. Rabinowitz, Sandy & Keiffer, Christa, illus. l.t. ed. 1999. (Treasured Horses Collection). 128p. (J). (gr. 4 up). lib. bdg. 23.33 (978-0-8368-2401-8(6)) Stevens, Gareth Inc.

—A Horse for Hannah. Rabinowitz, Sandy & Keiffer, Christa, illus. l.t. ed. 1999. (Treasured Horses Collection). 128p. (J). (gr. 4 up). lib. bdg. 23.33 (978-0-8368-2402-5(4)) Stevens, Gareth Inc.

—Louisiana Blue. Rabinowitz, Sandy & Keiffer, Christa, illus. l.t. ed. 1999. (Treasured Horses Collection). 128p. (J). (gr. 4 up). lib. bdg. 23.33 (978-0-8368-2403-2(2)) Stevens, Gareth Inc.

—Rush for Gold. Rabinowitz, Sandy & Keiffer, Christa, illus. l.t. ed. 1999. (Treasured Horses Collection). 128p. (J). (gr. 4 up). lib. bdg. 23.33 (978-0-8368-2405-6(9)) Stevens, Gareth Inc.

Hubler, Marsha. Skye's Final Test, Vol. 6. 2005. (Keystone Stables Ser.). (Illus.). 112p. (J). pap. 4.99 (978-0-310-70799-8(4)) Zonderkidz.

—Teamwork at Camp Tioga. 2005. (Keystone Stables Ser.). (Illus.). 128p. (J). pap. 4.99 (978-0-310-70575-8(4)) Zonderkidz.

—Trouble Times Two. 2005. (Keystone Stables Ser.). (Illus.). 128p. (J). pap. 4.99 (978-0-310-70574-1(6)) Zondervan.

—The Trouble with Skye. 2004. (Keystone Stables Ser.: No. 1). 144p. (J). pap. 4.99 (978-0-310-70572-7(X)) Zonderkidz.

—A True Test for Skye. 2004. (Keystone Stables Ser.). (Illus.). 144p. (J). pap. 4.99 (978-0-310-70573-4(8)) Zonderkidz.

—The Winning Summer. 2005. (Keystone Stables Ser.: Bk. 5). (Illus.). 144p. (J). pap. 4.99 (978-0-310-70798-1(6)) Zonderkidz.

Hudspeth, Elly Shafter & Peyton, Barbara. Colt Revolt: Memoirs of Three Mischievous, but Adorable Equine Siblings. Wilkins, Rhett, illus. 2007. 140p. pap. 12.95 ***(978-1-60145-223-8(3))*** Booklocker.com, Inc.

Hughes, Jenny. The Horse in the Portrait. 2008. (YA). ***(978-1-933343-72-3(9))*** Stabenfeldt Inc.

Hungry Horse: Individual Title Six-Packs. (Literatura 2000 Ser.). (gr. 1-2). 28.00 (978-0-7635-0057-3(7)) Rigby Education.

Icelandic Horse Adventures in Learning Book. 2005. (J). 15.95 (978-1-59649-224-0(4)) Whispering Pine Pr., Inc.

Icelandic Horse Story Book. 2005. (J). 15.95 (978-1-59649-424-4(7)) Whispering Pine Pr., Inc.

If Wishes Were Horses. 2007. (J). (978-1-933343-53-2(2) , PONY) Stabenfeldt Inc.

Inny. Epiphany Rose-the Message. 2006. pap. 8.99 ***(978-1-60034-097-0(0))*** Xulon Pr., Inc.

Ivey, Jean. Wadduda of the Desert: A Legend of the Arabian War Mare. Dorwin, Judy Frazier, illus. 1998. 230p. (J). (gr. 4-12). pap. 9.95 (978-0-9658891-3-1(0)) Elan Pr.

James, Will. The Dark Horse. (Illus.). 288p. 35.00 (978-0-87842-484-9(9) , 818) Mountain Pr. Publishing Co., Inc.

—The Dark Horse, Vol. 1. James, Will, illus. rev. ed. (Illus.). 288p. (J). (gr. 4). pap. 18.00 (978-0-87842-486-3(5) , 817) Mountain Pr. Publishing Co., Inc.

—In the Saddle with Uncle Bill. rev. ed. 2001. (Illus.). 208p. (J). (gr. 3-4). 26.00 (978-0-87842-427-6(X) , 808); pap. 14.00 (978-0-87842-428-3(8) , 807) Mountain Pr. Publishing Co., Inc.

—My First Horse, Vol. 1. rev. ed. (Illus.). 48p. (J). (gr. 4). 16.00 (978-0-87842-488-7(1) , 819) Mountain Pr. Publishing Co., Inc.

—Scorpion: A Good Bad Horse. 2001. (Illus.). 254p. (YA). 30.00 (978-0-87842-436-8(9) , 810); (gr. 4). pap. 15.00 (978-0-87842-435-1(0) , 809) Mountain Pr. Publishing Co., Inc.

—Smokey: The Cowhorse, Vol. 1. rev. ed. (Tumbleweed Ser.). (Illus.). 260p. (gr. 4-7). pap. 16.00 (978-0-87842-413-9(X) , 804) Mountain Pr. Publishing Co., Inc.

—Smokey Vol. 1: The Cowhorse. rev. ed. (Tumbleweed Ser.). (Illus.). 260p. (J). (gr. 4-7). 36.00 (978-0-87842-414-6(8) , 805) Mountain Pr. Publishing Co., Inc.

—Smoky Cowhorse. 2008. 336p. (J). pap. 6.99 ***(978-1-4169-4941-1(0))*** , Aladdin) Simon & Schuster Children's Publishing.

—Smoky, the Cow Horse. 2003. (J). (gr. 3-8). 20.50 (978-0-8446-7247-2(5)) Smith, Peter Pub., Inc.

—Smoky the Cowhorse. 2005. reprint ed. pap. 30.95 (978-0-7661-9507-3(4)) Kessinger Publishing, LLC.

—Smoky the Cowhorse. 2000. (gr. 3-6). lib. bdg. 25.75 (978-0-613-84454-3(8)) Tandem Library Bks.

—Young Cowboy. (Tumbleweed Ser.). (Illus.). (J). 2000. 72p. (978-0-87842-444-3(X)); 2004. 88p. (gr. 4-7). 15.00 (978-0-87842-419-1(9) , 806) Mountain Pr. Publishing Co., Inc.

Jenner, Caryn. Black Beauty. 2000. (gr. k-3). lib. bdg. 11.80 (978-0-613-24377-3(3)) Tandem Library Bks.

Johnston. Hero of Lesser Causes. 2003. (gr. 7-12). lib. bdg. 18.75 (978-0-613-77314-0(4)) Tandem Library Bks.

Jones, Elisabeth. Moonlight & Shadow. Coplestone, James, illus. 2002. 32p. (J). 15.95 (978-1-929927-42-5(8)) Ragged Bears USA.

Joyce, Jacqueline. Prickly Pete, Cody Coyote & That Bowlegged Horse. DelMar Communication International Staff, tr. 1998. (Illus.). 36p. (Orig.). (J). (ps-4). (SPA.). pap. 7.95 (978-0-9652211-9-1(9) , 11138); pap. 7.95 (978-0-9652211-8-4(0) , 11137) Bear Path, The.

Juby, Susan. Another Kind of Cowboy. 2007. 352p. (J). lib. bdg. 17.89 ***(978-0-06-076518-7(6));*** (YA). lib. bdg. ***(978-0-06-076521-7(6));*** 352p. (YA). (gr. 9 up). 16.99 ***(978-0-06-076517-0(8))*** HarperCollins Pubs. (HarperTeen).

K., Ruepp & U., Heyne. Anna's Prince. 2006. (Illus.). 32p. (J). 15.95 (978-0-7358-2081-4(3)) North-South Bks., Inc.

Kahler, Janet C. 1918 Covered Wagon Adventure. 2006. (Illus.). 94p. (J). per. 10.95 (978-1-57258-444-0(0) , 945-6305) TEACH Services, Inc.

Karr, D. The Adventures of Barrett: The Racehorse. 2005. 63p. pap. 12.95 (978-1-4137-7743-7(0)) PublishAmerica, Inc.

Kasten, Victoria. Mighty Stallion. 2005. 70p. (J). per. 7.95 (978-0-9788850-0-7(7)) Kasten, Victoria.

—Mighty Stallion 2 Fury's Journey. 2006. 72p. (J). per. 7.95 (978-0-9788850-1-4(5)) Kasten, Victoria.

Katschke, Judy. Untamed Spirit. 2006. (Flicka Ser.). 64p. (J). pap. 4.99 (978-0-06-087607-4(7)) HarperCollins Pubs.

Kaya Does It Her Way. 2007. (J). (978-1-933343-47-1(8) , PONY) Stabenfeldt Inc.

Keehn, Sally M. The First Horse I See. 2000. (Illus.). 224p. (YA). (gr. 5-9). pap. 6.99 (978-0-698-11867-6(7) , Putnam Juvenile) Penguin Group (USA) Inc.

—The First Horse I See. 2000. (J). 12.64 (978-0-606-19067-1(8)) Tandem Library Bks.

—First Horse I See. 2000. (gr. 3-6). lib. bdg. 14.15 (978-0-613-29957-2(4)) Tandem Library Bks.

Keene, Carolyn. Riding Club Crime. 2003. (gr. 5-8). lib. bdg. 13.00 (978-0-613-65082-3(4)) Tandem Library Bks.

Keene, Carolyn & Greene, James. The Missing Horse Mystery. 1998. (Nancy Drew Mystery Stories: No. 145). 160p. (J). (gr. 3-6). pap. 4.99 (978-0-671-00754-6(8) , Aladdin) Simon & Schuster Children's Publishing.

Keffer, Lois. Fancy the Filly's Not Selfish or Silly. 1999. (J). 9.99 (978-1-57673-442-1(0)) Zondervan.

Keith, Harold. Chico & Dan. Arbuckle, Scott, illus. 1998. 120p. (gr. 4-7). 16.95 (978-1-57168-216-1(3)) Eakin Pr.

Kennedy, Shannon. Bad Horse Day. 1999. (Horse Country Top-Hands Ser.: Vol. 2). 100p. (J). (gr. 5 up). pap. 5.99 (978-0-9653703-3-2(X)) Copalis Publishing.

Kent, Deborah. Blackwater Creek. Kingfisher Editors, ed. 2005. (Saddles, Stars, & Stripes Ser.). 192p. (J). (gr. 4-6). 8.95 (978-0-7534-5885-3(3) , Kingfisher) Houghton Mifflin Co. Trade & Reference Div.

—Saddles, Stars & Stripes: Chance of a Lifetime. Kingfisher Editors, ed. 2005. (Saddles, Stars, & Stripes Ser.). 192p. (gr. 4-6). 8.95 (978-0-7534-5884-6(5) , Kingfisher) Houghton Mifflin Co. Trade & Reference Div.

Kenworthy, Mary. Tid Bit. 2004. 59p. pap. 12.95 (978-1-4137-5231-1(4)) PublishAmerica, Inc.

Kilgras, Heidi. Horse Show Champ. Wolcott, Karen, illus. 2008. (J). ***(*978-0-375-84701-1(4));*** lib. bdg. ***(*978-0-375-94701-8(9))*** Random Hse., Inc.

Kinsey-Warnock, Natalie. If Wishes Were Horses. Kinsey-Warnock, Natalie, illus. 2002. (Illus.). 144p. (J). pap. 5.99 (978-0-14-230143-2(4) , Puffin) Penguin Group (USA) Inc.

—If Wishes Were Horses. 2002. (gr. 3-6). lib. bdg. 14.15 (978-0-613-45283-0(6)) Tandem Library Bks.

Kirk, Ruth Lynn. Charlie Ate My Hat! 2004. 32p. pap. 7.99 (978-0-9675410-2-0(6)) Shamrock Pr.

Koldofsky, Eleanor. Clip-Clop. Parkins, David, illus. 2005. 24p. (J). (gr. k-2). 15.95 (978-0-88776-681-7(1)) Tundra Bks., Inc./Livres Toundra, Inc. CAN. *Dist:* Random Hse., Inc.

Kondak, Margarida. The Wild Horses of Summer Bay. Kondak, Mary, illus. l.t. ed. 2002. 31p. 9.95 (978-1-890692-06-3(9)) Wizard Works.

Koops, Sheena. Voice of the Valley. 2006. 208p. (J). pap. 8.95 (978-1-55143-514-5(4)) Orca Bk. Pubs. USA.

Krauss, Ruth. Charlotte & the White Horse. Sendak, Maurice, illus. 2001. (Sendak Reissues Ser.). 32p. (J). 12.89 (978-0-06-028641-5(5)); 14.95 (978-0-06-028640-8(7)) HarperCollins Pubs.

Kressley, Carson. You're Different & That's Super. Lee, Jared D., illus. 2005. 64p. (J). 12.95 (978-1-4169-0070-2(5)) Simon & Schuster Children's Publishing.

Kroll, Jeri. Riding the Blues. 2002. (Illus.). 160p. (YA). pap. (978-0-7344-0171-7(X) , Lothian Bks.) Hachette Livre Australia.

—Riding the Blues. 2001. (gr. 7-12). lib. bdg. 22.20 (978-0-613-90915-0(1)) Tandem Library Bks.

Lambert, Janet. Star Dream. 2002. (J). per. 9.95 (978-1-930009-53-0(4) , 800-691-7779) Image Cascade Publishing.

Lammie, Karen J., illus. Neigh! 2005. (On the Farm Ser.). 10p. (J). (ps-ps). bds. 4.95 (978-0-7641-5828-5(7)) Barron's Educational Series, Inc.

Landsey, P. J. Horse Sense: Auction Action. 2007. (YA). per. 14.99 ***(*978-1-59886-934-7(5))*** Tate Publishing & Enterprises, L.L.C.

Lange, Willem. John & Tom. Dodson, Bert, illus. 2001. (Family Heritage Ser.). 36p. (J). (ps-2). 15.95 (978-0-916718-17-6(4)) Vermont Folklife Ctr.

Lardone, Lilia. Caballero Negro. (Torre de Papel Ser.). (SPA.). (J). (gr. 4 up). 7.95 (978-958-04-5052-8(8)) Norma S.A. COL. *Dist:* Distribuidora Norma, Inc.

Lauer, Lucy S. A Horse Named Kat. 2006. 272p. (YA). per. 7.95 (978-0-9713497-3-5(8)) Cave Hollow Pr.

Lawlor, Laurie. Horseback on the Boston Post Road, Seventeen Hundred & Four. 2002. (gr. 3-6). lib. bdg. 13.00 (978-0-613-50323-5(6)) Tandem Library Bks.

Lawrence, Caroline. The Charioteer of Delphi. 2007. (Roman Mysteries Ser.). (Illus.). 210p. (J). (gr. 6-9). 16.95 ***(*978-1-59643-085-3(0))*** Roaring Brook Pr.

Lawson, Robert. Mr. Revere & I. 2003. (J). (gr. 4-8). 22.50 (978-0-8446-7258-8(0)) Smith, Peter Pub., Inc.

Layos, Alexandra. An Almost True Horse Tale. Bauer, Dana, illus. l.t. ed. 2003. 20p. (J). (gr. 1-5). pap. 8.95 (978-0-9655501-3-0(3)) Saddle & Bridle, Inc.

—The Missing Link: Blue Ribbon Days #1. Hoffman, illus. 2002. 152p. (YA). pap. 9.95 (978-0-9655501-2-3(5)) Saddle & Bridle, Inc.

—Timeless: Blue Ribbon Days #2, 2. 2005. (Illus.). 128p. (YA). pap. 10.95 (978-0-9655501-4-7(1)) Saddle & Bridle, Inc.

Lee, Betsy B. Albert, the Apple-Eating Appaloosa: Dolch Sight Word Horse Stories. 2002. (J). pap. 6.49 (978-0-9658853-7-9(2)) Learning Abilities Bks.

—The Buggy That Boogied Away. Lee, Sarah Ann, illus. 2006. 24p. (J). pap. 6.95 (978-0-9720267-7-2(0)) Learning Abilities Bks.

—Whoa, Wiggle-Worm: A Little Lemon Book about an Overly Active Child, 1 bk. Varnedoe, Catharine E., illus. l.t. ed. 2003. 24p. (J). pap. 7.95 (978-0-9720267-3-4(8)) Learning Abilities Bks.

—10,000 White Horses. 2001. 32p. (J). pap. 5.95 (978-0-9658853-6-2(4)) Learning Abilities Bks.

—10,000 White Horses 10,000 Caballos Blancos. Cruz-Torres, Natty, tr. Varnedoe, Catharine E., illus. l.t. ed. 2002. (SPA & ENG.). 24p. (J). pap. 5.95 (978-0-9720267-2-7(X)) Learning Abilities Bks.

Legend of the Island Horse. 2006. (J). (978-1-933343-22-8(2)) Stabenfeldt Inc.

Lehmkuhl, Pat, illus. Starlight, Star Bright: (the Starlight Books, 3), 6 vols. 2003. (Starlight Bks.: Bk. 3). 192p. (J). (gr. 3-7). per. 9.00 (978-0-9714161-2-3(5)) Raven Publishing Inc. of Montana.

Leigh, S. Dream Pony. 2004. (Sandy Lane Stables Ser.). 100p. (J). pap. 4.95 (978-0-7945-0500-4(7)); lib. bdg. 12.95 (978-1-58086-556-2(9)) EDC Publishing.

Leigh, Susannah. Dream Pony. 1998. (Sandy Lane Stables Ser.). 100p. (J). (gr. 4-8). lib. bdg. 11.95 (978-0-88110-997-9(5)) EDC Publishing.

—Dream Pony. 2003. (gr. 3-6). lib. bdg. 12.95 (978-0-613-67613-7(0)) Tandem Library Bks.

Leland, Toni M. Christa Joins A Horse Club: Second in Christa Duncan(UNKNOWN CHARACTER) Series. Leland, Toni M., illus. 2004. Orig. Title: Christa Joins 4-H. (Illus.). (J). pap. 6.95 (978-1-887932-49-3(6) , SmallHorse Pr.) Equine Graphics Publishing Group.

—Christa Meets a Mini. Leland, Toni M., illus. 2002. 68p. (J). pap. (978-1-887932-57-8(7) , SmallHorse Pr.) Equine Graphics Publishing Group.

Lester, Alison. The Snow Pony. 208p. (J). (gr. 5-9). 2006. pap. 5.95 (978-0-618-77125-7(5)); 2003. (Illus.). tchr. ed. 15.00 (978-0-618-25404-0(8)) Houghton Mifflin Co. Trade & Reference Div. (Walter Lorraine).

Lester, Julius. Black Cowboy, Wild Horses. Pinkney, Jerry, illus. 1998. 32p. (J). (gr. k-3). 18.99 (978-0-8037-1787-9(3) , Dial) Penguin Group (USA) Inc.

Lewis, Anthony, illus. The Kingfisher Treasury of Pony Stories. 2003. (Kingfisher Treasury of Stories Ser.). 160p. (J). (gr. k-3). pap. 5.95 (978-0-7534-5666-8(4) , Kingfisher) Houghton Mifflin Co. Trade & Reference Div.

Lewis, C. S. The Horse & His Boy. Baynes, Pauline, illus. 2006. (Narnia Ser.). 240p. (J). 11.99 (978-0-06-112524-9(5)) HarperCollins Pubs.

Lewis, Steve, Sr. The Course of a Horse. 2006. (J). 65.00 (978-1-59971-897-2(9)) Aardvark Global Publishing.

H I

Light, Carol, illus. Oops, a Curious Horse Story Telling Board. 2003. (J). (978-0-9745803-4-0(1)) Little Big Tomes.

Lindgren, Astrid. Do You Know Pippi Longstocking? Dyssegaard, Elisabeth Kallick, tr. Nyman, Ingrid, illus. 2005. 32p. (J). pap. 4.95 (978-91-29-66203-0(6)) R & S Bks. SWE. *Dist:* Macmillan.

—Pippi Calzaslargas. 2003. (SPA., Illus.). 137p. (J). (gr. 3-5). (978-84-261-3192-8(1) , JV30550) Juventud, Editorial ESP. *Dist:* Lectorum Pubns., Inc.

Littleton, Mark. Hoofbeats on the Trail. 2002. (Ally OConnor Adventures Ser.: Vol. 3). 128p. (J). (gr. 4-7). pap. 5.99 (978-0-8010-6427-2(9)) Baker Bks.

—Tracks in the Sand. 2001. (Ally OConnor Adventures Ser.: Vol. 1). 128p. (J). (gr. 4-7). pap. 5.99 (978-0-8010-4490-8(1)) Baker Bks.

Lodge, Jo. Horse. 2006. (Cosy Cuddlers Ser.). (Illus.). 8p. (J). (ps). 7.99 (978-0-333-98753-7(5)) Macmillan Publishers Ltd. GBR. *Dist:* Trafalgar Square Publishing.

London, Jonathan. Little Pinto of Mustang Canyon. San Souci, Daniel, illus. 2007. 40p. (J). (gr. k-3). pap. 4.99 (***978-0-7636-3513-8(8)***) Candlewick Pr.

Long, Olivia. A Horse of a Different Color. Long, Olivia, illus. Date not set. (Kaleidoscope Ser.). (Illus.). 32p. (J). (ps-4). 9.95 (978-1-880042-01-4(0) , SL12451) Shelf-Life Bks.

Lost in the Wilderness. 2006. (J). (978-1-933343-39-6(7) , PONY) Stabenfeldt Inc.

Lottridge, Celia Barker. Ticket to Curlew. 2007. 144p. (J). pap. 7.95 (***978-0-88899-843-9(0)***) Groundwood Bks. CAN. *Dist:* Perseus Distribution.

Lovelace, Maud Hart. Winona's Pony Cart. Neville, Vera, illus. 2000. 128p. (J). (gr. 3 up). 15.89 (978-0-06-028875-4(2)) HarperCollins Pubs.

—Winona's Pony Cart. 2000. (gr. 3-6). lib. bdg. 14.10 (978-0-613-27599-6(3)); (Illus.). (J). (978-0-606-20481-1(4)) Tandem Library Bks.

Lubner, Susan. A Horse's Tale. Moore, Margie, illus. 2008. 32p. (J). 16.95 (***978-0-8109-9490-4(9)*** , Abrams Bks. for Young Readers) Abrams, Harry N. , Inc.

Lyon, Irving W. & O'Connor, Sandra Day. Chico: A True Story from the Childhood of the First Woman Supreme Court Justice. 2005. (Illus.). 32p. (J). (gr. k). 16.99 (978-0-525-47452-4(8) , Dutton Adult) Penguin Group (USA) Inc.

MacDonald, Anne Louise. The Ghost Horse of Meadow Green. 2005. (Illus.). 208p. (YA). (gr. 5-9). (978-1-55337-637-8(4)); (978-1-55337-636-1(6)) Kids Can Pr., Ltd.

MacHado, Ana Maria. Mi Reino Por un Caballo. (SPA.). pap. 11.95 (978-950-07-2222-3(4)) Editorial Sudamericana S.A. ARG. *Dist:* Distribooks, Inc.

MacKall, Dandi Daley. All the King's Horses, Vol. 8. 2001. (Horsefeathers Ser.: Vol. 8). (Illus.). 192p. (J). (gr. 7-11). 5.99 (978-0-570-07129-7(1)) Concordia Publishing Hse.

—Bold Beauty. 2002. (Winnie The Horse Gentler Ser.: Bk. 3). (Illus.). 208p. (J). mass mkt. 5.99 (978-0-8423-5544-5(8)) Tyndale Hse. Pubs.

—Buckskin Bandit. 2004. (Winnie the Horse Gentler Ser.: No. 8). (Illus.). (J). mass mkt. 5.99 (978-0-8423-8724-8(2)) Tyndale Hse. Pubs.

—Eager Star. 2002. (Winnie the Horse Gentler Ser.: Bk. 2). (Illus.). 208p. (J). (gr. 4-7). mass mkt. 5.99 (978-0-8423-5543-8(X)) Tyndale Hse. Pubs.

—Friendly Foal. 2004. (Winnie the Horse Gentler Ser.: No. 7). 224p. (J). mass mkt. 5.99 (978-0-8423-8723-1(4)) Tyndale Hse. Pubs.

—Gift Horse. 2003. (gr. 3-6). lib. bdg. 14.15 (978-0-613-76879-5(5)) Tandem Library Bks.

—Home Is Where Your Horse Is, Vol. 6. 2000. (Horsefeathers Ser.: Vol. 6). (Illus.). 192p. (J). (gr. 7-11). 5.99 (978-0-570-07087-0(2)) Concordia Publishing Hse.

—Home Is Where Your Horse Is. 2000. (gr. 7-12). lib. bdg. 14.15 (978-0-613-72790-7(8)) Tandem Library Bks.

—Horse Angels, Vol. 5. 2000. (Horsefeathers Ser.: Vol. 5). (Illus.). 192p. (J). (gr. 7-11). 5.99 (978-0-570-07086-3(4)) Concordia Publishing Hse.

—Horse Angels. 2000. (gr. 7-12). lib. bdg. 14.15 (978-0-613-72789-1(4)) Tandem Library Bks.

—Horse Cents, Vol. 2. 2000. (Horsefeathers Ser.: Vol. 2). 192p. (J). (gr. 7-11). 5.99 (978-0-570-07007-8(4)) Concordia Publishing Hse.

—Horse Cents. 2000. (gr. 7-12). lib. bdg. 14.15 (978-0-613-72830-0(0)) Tandem Library Bks.

—Horse of a Different Color. 2000. (gr. 7-12). lib. bdg. 14.15 (978-0-613-72832-4(7)) Tandem Library Bks.

—Horsefeathers. 2000. (Horsefeathers Ser.: Vol. 1). (Illus.). 192p. (YA). (gr. 7-11). 5.99 (978-0-570-07006-1(6)) Concordia Publishing Hse.

—Horsefeathers. 2000. (gr. 7-12). lib. bdg. 14.15 (978-0-613-72829-4(7)) Tandem Library Bks.

—Horsefeathers' Mystery. 2001. (gr. 7-12). lib. bdg. 14.15 (978-0-613-72845-4(9)) Tandem Library Bks.

—Horsefeathers Mystery, Vol. 7. 2001. (Horsefeathers Ser.: Vol. 7). (Illus.). 192p. (J). (gr. 7-12). 5.99 (978-0-570-07128-0(3)) Concordia Publishing Hse.

Mackall, Dandi Daley. Merry Creature Christmas. 2006. 24p. (J). bds. 9.99 (978-1-4003-0823-1(2)) Nelson, Thomas Inc.

MacKall, Dandi Daley. Midnight Mystery. 2002. (Winnie The Horse Gentler Ser.: Bk. 4). (Illus.). 208p. (J). mass mkt. 5.99 (978-0-8423-5545-2(6)) Tyndale Hse. Pubs.

—Wild Thing. 2002. (Winnie The Horse Gentler Ser.: 1). (Illus.). 192p. (J). mass mkt. 5.99 (978-0-8423-5542-1(1)) Tyndale Hse. Pubs.

Maclean, Christine. Mary Margaret Meets Her Match. 2007. 176p. (J). (gr. 3-5). 15.99 (978-0-525-47775-4(6) , Dutton Juvenile) Penguin Group (USA) Inc.

Maddern, Eric. The King with Horse's Ears. Hess, Paul, illus. 2004. 32p. (J). pap. 7.95 (978-1-84507-309-1(6)) Lincoln, Frances Ltd. GBR. *Dist:* Perseus Distribution.

The Magical Horses Vol. 2000: A Fairy Tale for the Young & the Young at Heart. l.t. ed. 2005. (Illus.). 127p. (J). per. (978-0-9738625-0-8(5)) Blue Cat Publishing.

Magness, Lee. Silver Dasher. 2003. 164p. pap. 12.95 (978-0-595-29043-7(4)) iUniverse, Inc.

Malcolm, Jahnna N. The Stallion of Box Canyon. Rabinowitz, Sandy & Keiffer, Christa, illus. l.t. ed. 1999. (Treasured Horses Collection). 122p. (J). (gr. 4 up). lib. bdg. 23.33 (978-0-8368-2283-0(8)) Stevens, Gareth Inc.

Man-Kong, Mary. Barbie & the Magic of Pegasus. 2006. (Illus.). 22p. (J). (gr. k-ps). bds. 4.99 (978-0-375-83539-1(3) , Golden Bks.) Random Hse. Children's Bks.

—The Magic of Pegasus Book & CD. 2005. (Illus.). 24p. (J). (ps-2). pap. 9.95 (978-0-375-83402-8(8) , Golden Bks.) Random Hse. Children's Bks.

The Many Tracks of Lap'n Tap. 2007. (J). per. 10.95 (***978-0-9761128-4-6(1)***) Hafabanana Pr.

Marlow, Herb. Sundancer. Newberry, Loretta, illus. 2004. 56p. (J). lib. bdg. 21.95 (978-1-893595-39-2(0)); per. 14.95 (978-1-893595-41-5(2)) Four Seasons Bks., Inc.

Marlow, Susan K. Andrea Carter & the Long Ride Home. 2005. 128p. (J). (ps-7). pap. 7.99 (978-0-8254-3188-3(3)) Kregel Pubns.

Marrs, Christie, creator. The Perfect Gift. l.t. ed. 2004. (Illus.). 57p. (J). mass mkt. 5.99 (978-1-928890-19-5(9)) I.B. Hoofinit Co.

Martin, Jacqueline Briggs. The Finest Horse in Town. Gaber, Susan, illus. 2003. 32p. (J). 17.95 (978-1-930900-27-1(9)) Purple Hse. Pr.

Martinello, Marian L. Ready's Gifts. 2003. (Illus.). 158p. (YA). (gr. 8 up). per. 12.95 (978-0-9724113-0-1(5)) MindCatcher Pr.

Martone, Ginny. The White Stallion. 2006. (ENG.). 60p. per. 12.95 (***978-1-4241-4332-0(2)***) PublishAmerica, Inc.

Matheson, Shirlee Smith. Fastback Beach. 2006. (Orca Soundings Ser.). 112p. (YA). lib. bdg. 14.95 (978-1-55143-580-0(2)) Orca Bk. Pubs. USA.

Matty & the Moonlight Horse. 2005. (J). (978-1-933343-06-8(0) , PONY) Stabenfeldt Inc.

McAdoo, Grami & McAdoo, O'Pa. The Adventures of Sergeants Socks: The Journey Home. McAdoo, Grami, illus. l.t. ed. 2003. (Illus.). 122p. (J). pap. 9.95 (978-0-9714358-3-4(9)) Longhorn Creek Pr.

McCaffrey, Anne. Black Horses for the King. 1998. 224p. mass mkt. 6.99 (978-0-345-42257-6(0) , Del Rey) Random House Publishing Group.

McCament, Janice. 'Ole Paint Rocks. 2007. (J). per. 9.99 (***978-1-59886-925-5(6)***) Tate Publishing & Enterprises, L.L.C.

McCann, Jesse Leon. The Case of the Hollywood Hound. 2001. (Ace Ventura Chapter Bks.: No. 4). (Illus.). (J). 10.79 (978-0-606-20532-0(2)) Tandem Library Bks.

—The Case of the Stolen Stallion. Fantascope Staff, illus. 2001. (Ace Ventura Chapter Book Ser.: No. 2). 64p. (J). (gr. 6). pap. 3.99 (978-0-439-20655-6(3)) Scholastic, Inc.

McCaughrean, Geraldine & Ross. El Caballo de Madera. 2005. (Mythology Series Collection Mitos Ser.). (SPA., Illus.). 50p. (J). (gr. 2-3). 9.95 (978-84-348-6432-0(0)) SM Ediciones ESP. *Dist:* Iaconi, Mariuccia Bk. Imports.

McClean, Will. Go, Bluey Go! Turnmyre, Dustin, illus. 2003. 32p. (J). 14.95 (978-1-57072-252-3(8)) Overmountain Pr.

McCormic, Maxine Griffith. Casey's Hoof Prints. Christensen, D. J., illus. 2006. 72p. (J). pap. 14.95 (978-1-59299-217-1(X)) Inkwater Pr.

McDaniel, Lurlene. A Horse for Mandy. 2004. 80p. (J). (gr. 3-5). pap. 4.99 (978-1-58196-011-2(5)) Darby Creek Publishing.

McDonald, Ann-Eve. I Can't Go to School Today, My Horses Might Escape. 2004. (J). (978-0-9770158-0-1(7)) BeachWalk Bks. Inc.

McGeorge, Constance W. Chestnut. Whyte, Mary, illus. 2004. 32p. (J). 16.95 (978-1-56145-321-4(8)) Peachtree Pubs., Ltd.

McKissack, Patricia. Away West. James, Gordon, illus. 2006. (Scraps of Time Ser.). 128p. (J). (gr. 3). pap. 4.99 (978-0-14-240688-5(0) , Puffin) Penguin Group (USA) Inc.

McMahon, Kate. A Horse of Another Colour. 1998. (Illus.). 96p. (YA). (gr. 3-7). pap. 9.95 (978-1-901737-17-2(9)) Anvil Bks., Ltd. IRL. *Dist:* Dufour Editions, Inc.

Meister, Cari. My Pony Jack at the Horse Show: Viking Easy to Read Level 1. Young, Amy, illus. 2006. (Easy-to-Read,Viking Children's Ser.). 32p. (J). (ps). 13.99 (978-0-670-05919-5(6) , Viking Adult) Penguin Group (USA) Inc.

Micek, Greg & Carter, Lee. The Great White Horse. Springle, Taylor, illus. 1998. (Dad & Me Ser.). 64p. (J). (gr. k-4). pap. 6.95 (978-1-888237-15-3(5)) Baxter Pr.

Mighty Stallion 3 Glory's Legend. 2006. (J). per. 8.95 (978-0-9788850-2-1(3)) Kasten, Victoria.

Mighty Stallion 4 Dancer's Dream. 2007. (J). per. 8.95 (***978-0-9788850-3-8(1)***) Kasten, Victoria.

Mills, Elizabeth. Belle. 2007. (Stablemates Ser.). 48p. (J). pap. 4.99 (***978-0-439-88336-8(9)***) Scholastic, Inc.

Mindgue, Frank. Little Horse. Cripe, B. Lee, illus. 1999. 80p. (YA). (gr. 3-12). pap. 9.95 (978-0-932991-59-1(9) , Different Bks.) Place In The Woods, The.

Mini Cuentos: Relampago, Caballo Salvaje, Pelirrojo y Tania.Tr. of Mini Faiy Tales: Lightning the Wild Horse. (SPA.). (J). (gr. k-4). 4.98 (978-970-607-620-5(4)) Larousse, Ediciones, S. A. de C. V. MEX. *Dist:* Continental Bk. Co., Inc.

Moeri, Louise. The Devil in Ol' Rosie. l.t. ed. 2002. (Juvenile Ser.). 161p. (J). 21.95 (978-0-7862-3808-8(9)) Thomson Gale.

Monroe Donovan, Jane. Winter's Gift. Monroe Donovan, Jane, illus. 2004. (Illus.). 32p. (J). 15.95 (978-1-58536-231-8(X)) Sleeping Bear Pr.

Montgomery Buvens, Norma O'Rene. A Salute for Trixey. Smith, Normareen Buvens, illus. 2001. 40p. 16.95 (978-1-57168-943-6(5)) Eakin Pr.

Montgomery, Rutherford G. Big Red: A Wild Stallion. Crowell, Pers, illus. 2004. (Classic Ser.). 164p. (gr. 4-7). pap. 13.95 (978-0-87004-404-5(4)) Caxton Pr.

—The Capture of the Golden Stallion. (J). 22.95 (978-0-8488-0132-8(6)) Amereon LTD.

—The Golden Stallion's Victory. (J). 20.95 (978-0-8488-0133-5(4)) Amereon LTD.

Moore, Inga, illus. Horse Tales. 2005. 152p. (J). (gr. 4-7). 18.99 (978-0-7636-2657-0(0)) Candlewick Pr.

Moray-Williams, Ursula & Williams, Ursula Moray. The Further Adventures of Gobbolino & the Little Wooden Horse. Howard, Paul, illus. 2002. (Kingfisher Modern Classics Ser.). 240p. (J). (gr. k-3). tchr. ed. 15.95 (978-0-7534-5495-4(5) , Kingfisher) Houghton Mifflin Co. Trade & Reference Div.

Morck, Irene. Old Bird. Wood, Muriel, illus. 2002. 32p. (J). (gr. k-3). (978-1-55041-695-4(2)) Fitzhenry & Whiteside, Ltd.

—Tough Trails. 2003. (Orca Soundings Ser.). 96p. (J). (gr. 7-12). pap. 7.95 (978-1-55143-271-7(4)) Orca Bk. Pubs. USA.

—Tough Trails. 2003. (gr. 7-12). lib. bdg. 16.40 (978-0-613-88501-0(5)) Tandem Library Bks.

Morey, Walt. Year of the Black Pony. 2006. (Living History Library). 172p. (J). pap. 11.95 (***978-1-932350-08-1(X)***) Bethlehem Bks.

Morpurgo, Michael. War Horse. 2007. 176p. (J). (gr. 4-7). 16.99 (978-0-439-79663-7(6) , Scholastic Pr.) Scholastic, Inc.

—The White Horse of Zennor & Other Stories. 2004. 160p. pap. 9.99 (978-0-7497-4695-7(5)) Egmont Bks., Ltd. GBR. *Dist:* Trafalgar Square Publishing.

Mortenson, R. K. Landon Snow & the Auctor's Riddle. 2005. (Landon Now Ser.). (Illus.). 224p. (J). (gr. 4-7). 9.97 (978-1-59310-881-6(8)) Barbour Publishing, Inc.

Mortenson, Randall Kent. Landon Snow & the Island of Arcanum. 2006. 224p. (J). 9.97 (978-1-59789-358-9(7) , Barbour Bks.) Barbour Publishing, Inc.

Mudd, Missy. Candy Bar Caper. 2007. (J). per. 7.99 (***978-1-59886-843-2(8)***) Tate Publishing & Enterprises, L.L.C.

Mudpuppy Press Staff. Magic Horses Seal & Seek Stationery. 2005. (Illus.). (J). 7.99 (978-0-7353-0098-9(4)) Galison.

Mullins, Patricia, illus. One Horse Waiting for Me. 1998. 32p. (J). (ps-2). per. 16.00 (978-0-689-81381-8(3) , 878849, Simon & Schuster Children's Publishing) Simon & Schuster Children's Publishing.

Muncy, Brenda. Truly Lucky. 2006. (ENG.). 32p. per. 16.49 (***978-1-4259-6289-0(0)***) AuthorHouse.

Murray, Anna. Sarah's Page. 1998. (Illus.). 144p. (J). (gr. 4-7). 14.00 (978-1-886947-58-0(9)) Sleeping Bear Pr.

My Horse Glory. 2004. (Illus.). (J). (978-1-59577-013-4(5)) Starfall Education.

My Pony. (Early Intervention Levels Ser.). 23.10 (978-0-7362-0018-9(5)) Hampton-Brown Bks.

Myers, Stacy Erin. Maremaid: A Pony's Tale. Myers, Stacy Erin, illus. 2000. (Illus.). 32p. (J). (ps-3). pap. 15.95 (978-1-929845-11-8(1)) DeFranco Entertainment.

Mystic Tide. 2007. (J). (978-1-933343-44-0(3) , PONY) Stabenfeldt Inc.

Nation, Kay. Jamie Learns to Love. 2006. pap. 10.00 (***978-1-4257-0534-3(0)***) Xlibris Corp.

Neuhaus, Eve. Journey to Mythaca. 2006. 347p. (YA). per. 16.95 (***978-1-59594-101-5(0)*** , Wingspan Pr.) WingSpan Publishing.

Newbery 8-Book Box Set: Island of Blue Dolphins; Johnny Tremain; Belle Prater's Boy; A Wrinkle in Time; Black Cauldron; Black Pearl; The Watsons Go to Birmingham; Lily's Crossing. 2000. (J). pap. 45.96 (978-0-440-79921-4(X) , Yearling) Random Hse. Children's Bks.

Newhall, Mary. Bridal Dreams. 2004. 163p. (J). (gr. 3-7). per. 12.04 (978-0-606-32970-5(6)) Tandem Library Bks.

Newhall, Mary. Calamity Jinx. 2005. (Thoroughbred Ser.: Vol. 71). (Illus.). 165p. (J). (***978-1-4155-9659-3(X)*** , Harper Entertainment) HarperCollins Pubs.

Newhall, Mary & Campbell, Joanna. Calamity Jinx. 2005. (Thoroughbred Ser.: No. 71). (Illus.). 176p. mass mkt. 4.99 (978-0-06-078116-3(5) , Harper Entertainment) HarperCollins Pubs.

Nichols, Michelle Faith. Someday I'm Going to Have Some Horses. Conklin, Dana, illus. 2002. 20p. (J). lib. bdg. 18.95 (978-0-9660271-0-5(8)) Bear Paw's Enterprises.

Nowack, JoAnne Chitwood. A Horse Called Saskatoon. 2001. 128p. (J). pap. (978-0-8280-1562-2(7)) Review & Herald Publishing Assn.

—A Horse Called Tamarindo. 2001. (Horse Called Ser.: Vol. 5). (Illus.). 144p. (J). pap. 7.99 (978-0-8280-1499-1(X)) Review & Herald Publishing Assn.

O'Grady, Standish Hayes. The Pursuit of the Gilla Decair & His Horse. 2004. reprint ed. pap. 15.95 (978-1-4191-7950-1(0)); pap. 1.99 (978-1-4192-7950-8(5)) Kessinger Publishing, LLC.

O'Hara, Mary. My Friend Flicka. 1999. (Illus.). 320p. (YA). (gr. 4-7). reprint ed. 37.95 (978-1-56849-725-9(3)) Buccaneer Bks., Inc.

—My Friend Flicka. 2003. (Charming Classics). (Illus.). 352p. (J). 6.99 (978-0-06-052429-6(4)) HarperCollins Pubs.

—My Friend Flicka Book. 2005. (Charming Classics). 352p. pap. 6.99 (978-0-06-084595-7(3) , Harper Festival) HarperCollins Pubs.

Oldfield, J. Silver Cloud. 2002. (Illus.). 229p. pap. (978-0-340-85108-1(2) , Hodder & Stoughton) Hodder General Publishing Division.

Oldfield, Jenny. Crazy Horse. 2005. (Horses of Half Moon Ranch Ser.). (Illus.). (J). pap. (978-0-340-91067-2(4) , Hodder Children's Books) Hodder Children's Division.

—Danny Boy. 2005. (Horses of Half Moon Ranch Ser.). (Illus.). (J). pap. (978-0-340-91072-6(0) , Hodder Children's Books) Hodder Children's Division.

—Diamond Charm. 2002. (Illus.). (J). mass mkt. 9.99 (978-0-340-84353-6(5) , Hodder & Stoughton) Hodder General Publishing Division GBR. *Dist:* Trafalgar Square Publishing.

—El Dorado. l.t. ed. 2003. (Illus.). 208p. (J). 16.95 (978-0-7540-7840-1(X) , Galaxy Children's Large Print) BBC Audiobooks America.

—Eagle Wing. 2001. (Illus.). mass mkt. 9.99 (978-0-340-79174-5(8) , Coronet) Hodder General Publishing Division GBR. *Dist:* Trafalgar Square Publishing.

—Golden Dawn. 2005. (Horses of Half Moon Ranch Ser.). (Illus.). (J). pap. (978-0-340-91074-0(7) , Hodder Children's Books) Hodder Children's Division.

—Gunsmoke. 2005. (Horses of Half Moon Ranch Ser.). (Illus.). (J). pap. (978-0-340-91073-3(9) , Hodder Children's Books) Hodder Children's Division.

—Half Moon Ranch. 2008. (J). pap. (***978-1-933343-89-1(3)***) Stabenfeldt Inc.

—Half Moon Ranch: Johnny Mohawk. 2008. (YA). (***978-1-933343-74-7(5)***) Stabenfeldt Inc.

—Hollywood Princess. 2005. (Horses of Half Moon Ranch Ser.). (Illus.). (J). pap. (978-0-340-91071-9(2) , Hodder Children's Books) Hodder Children's Division.

—The Horses of Half Moon Ranch. 2001. (Illus.). 152p. pap. 8.99 (978-0-340-77965-1(9) , Hodder & Stoughton) Hodder General Publishing Division GBR. *Dist:* Trafalgar Square Publishing.

—Horses of Half-Moon Ranch: Jethro Junior. (Illus.). 160p. (J). pap. 9.99 (978-0-340-77868-5(7) , Hodder & Stoughton) Hodder General Publishing Division GBR. *Dist:* Trafalgar Square Publishing.

—Johnny Mohawk. 2005. (Horses of Half Moon Ranch Ser.). (Illus.). (J). pap. (978-0-340-91068-9(2) , Hodder Children's Books) Hodder Children's Division.

—Lady Roseanne. (Illus.). mass mkt. 9.99 (978-0-340-79171-4(3) , Coronet) Hodder General Publishing Division GBR. *Dist:* Trafalgar Square Publishing.

—The Midnight Lady. 2005. (Horses of Half Moon Ranch Ser.). (Illus.). (J). pap. (978-0-340-91069-6(0) , Hodder Children's Books) Hodder Children's Division.

—Moondance. 2001. (Illus.). 144p. pap. 8.99 (978-0-340-79170-7(5) , Coronet) Hodder General Publishing Division GBR. *Dist:* Trafalgar Square Publishing.

—Rodeo Rocky. 2005. (Horses of Half Moon Ranch Ser.). (Illus.). (J). pap. (978-0-340-91066-5(6) , Hodder Children's Books) Hodder Children's Division.

—Shining Star. 2007. (My Magical Pony Ser.). (Illus.). 128p. (J). pap. 6.95 (***978-0-340-90323-0(6)***) Hodder Children's Division GBR. *Dist:* Independent Pubs. Group.

—Silver Mist 2. 2007. (Illus.). 144p. pap. 6.95 (***978-0-340-90324-7(4)***) Hodder Children's Division GBR. *Dist:* Independent Pubs. Group.

—Silver Spur. 2001. (Illus.). 144p. (J). pap. 9.99 (978-0-340-79169-1(1)) Macmillan Publishers Ltd. GBR. *Dist:* Trafalgar Square Publishing.

—Skylark. 2001. (Illus.). 160p. (J). pap. 9.99 (978-0-340-79173-8(X) , Hodder & Stoughton) Hodder General Publishing Division GBR. *Dist:* Trafalgar Square Publishing.

—Steamboat Charlie. 2001. (Illus.). 160p. (J). pap. 9.99 (978-0-340-79172-1(1) , Hodder & Stoughton) Hodder General Publishing Division GBR. *Dist:* Independent Pubs. Group.

—Third Time Lucky. 2005. (Horses of Half Moon Ranch Ser.). (Illus.). (J). pap. (978-0-340-91070-2(4) , Hodder Children's Books) Hodder Children's Division.

—Wild Horses. 2005. (Horses of Half Moon Ranch Ser.). (Illus.). (J). pap. (978-0-340-91065-8(8) , Hodder Children's Books) Hodder Children's Division.

Oldfield, Jenny, compiled by. Horse & Pony Stories. 2007. (Illus.). 128p. (J). pap. 9.95 (***978-0-7534-6156-3(0)*** , Kingfisher) Houghton Mifflin Co. Trade & Reference Div.

Oldfield, Jenny, compiled by. The Kingfisher Book of Horse & Pony Stories. 2005. (Kingfisher Book of Ser.). (Illus.). 128p. (J). (gr. 4-6). 17.00 (978-0-7534-5850-1(0) , Kingfisher) Houghton Mifflin Co. Trade & Reference Div.

Ongman, Gudrun Geibel. The Sleep Ponies. 2000. (Illus.). 32p. (J). 16.95 (978-0-9677204-0-1(0)) Mindcastle Bks., Inc.

Oracle of the Horses. 2005. (YA). per. (978-0-615-12836-8(X)) Miller, Don G.

Orme, Helen. Horsing Around. 2008. (Siti's Sisters Ser.). 36p. pap. 7.95 (***978-1-84167-685-2(3)***) Ransom Publishing Ltd. GBR. *Dist:* International Publishers Marketing.

Orndorff, John C. Princess Mary & the Prophet. 2002. (J). per. 6.95 (978-1-893213-02-9(1)) Pensive Bks.

Ortega, James M. The Eight-Legged Horse. 2006. (ENG.). 84p. (J). per. 8.95 (***978-1-59800-861-6(7)***) Outskirts Press, Inc.

Osorio, Marta. El Caballito Que Queria Volar. (SPA., Illus.). 110p. (J). (978-84-392-8111-5(0)) Gaviota Ediciones ESP. *Dist:* Lectorum Pubns., Inc.

—El Caballito Que Queria Volar. (SPA.). 48p. (J). (gr. 3-5). 9.45 (978-84-305-6075-2(0)) Susaeta Ediciones, S.A. ESP. *Dist:* Lectorum Pubns., Inc.

Oswald, Nancy. Nothing Here but Stones: A Jewish Pioneer Story. rev. ed. 2004. (Illus.). 224p. (C). 16.95 (978-0-8050-7465-9(1) , Holt, Henry & Co. Bks. For Young Readers) Holt, Henry & Co.

Otsuka, Yuzo. Suho's White Horse: A Mongolian Legend. Akaba, Suekichi, illus. 2006. 32p. (J). 17.95 incl. audio compact disk (978-1-74126-021-2(3)) R.I.C. Pubns. AUS. *Dist:* SCB Distributors.

Peck, Robert Newton. Horse Thief: A Novel. 2003. (Illus.). 288p. (J). (gr. 7 up). pap. 6.99 (978-0-06-441075-5(7)) HarperCollins Pubs.

—Horse Thief: A Novel. 2003. (gr. 7-12). lib. bdg. 14.15 (978-0-613-65695-5(4)) Tandem Library Bks.

Perez, Marlene. A Rainbow Year (Big Book) ed. 2004. (Shared Connections Ser.). (J). pap., instr.'s gde. ed. 27.00 (978-1-4108-1603-0(6)) Benchmark Education Co.

Perry, Charles. The Legend of Scarface. Perry, Charles, photos by. 2005. (ACE., Illus.). 12p. (J). pap. 5.00 (978-1-57274-752-4(8) , 2764, Bks. for Young Learners) Owen, Richard C. Pubs., Inc.

Peterson, Cris. Wild Horses: Black Hills Sanctuary. Upitis, Alvis, illus. 2003. 32p. (YA). (gr. 4-6). 16.95 (978-1-56397-745-9(1)) Boyds Mills Pr.

Peyton, K. Blind Beauty. 2005. 368p. (YA). (gr. 7-12). pap. 7.99 (978-0-14-240351-8(2) , Puffin) Penguin Group (USA) Inc.

Peyton, K. M. Stealaway. Wyatt, David, illus. 2004. 96p. (J). 12.95 (978-0-8126-2722-0(9)) Cricket Bks.

Pierson, Jan. The Carson Kids & the Mystery of the Cove Point Stallion. 2000. 128p. (Orig.). pap. 9.95 (978-0-595-09073-0(7) , Backinprint.com) iUniverse, Inc.

—The Haunted Horse of Gold Hill (Gold Hill, Nevada) 2006. (Ghostowners Ser.: Vol. 4). (Illus.). 109p. pap. 9.95 (978-0-9721800-3-0(6)) WildWest Publishing.

Pinkwater, Daniel M. Rainy Morning. Pinkwater, Jill, illus. 1999. (Pinkwater Ser.: Vol. 1). 32p. (J). (gr. k-3). 16.00 (978-0-689-81143-2(8) , Atheneum) Simon & Schuster Children's Publishing.

Pinter, Sarah. Electra. 2003. 134p. 21.95 (978-0-595-65843-5(1)); pap. 11.95 (978-0-595-28742-0(5)) iUniverse, Inc.

Pistole, Katy. Flying High. 2003. (Illus.). 126p. (J). 7.99 (978-0-8163-1942-8(1)) Pacific Pr. Pubns.

—The Palomino. 2002. (Sonrise Farm Ser.). (Illus.). 128p. (J). 7.99 (978-0-8163-1863-6(8)) Pacific Pr. Publishing Assn.

—Stolen Gold, Vol. 2. 2002. (Illus.). 127p. (J). pap. 7.99 (978-0-8163-1882-7(4)) Pacific Pr. Publishing Assn.

Platt, Chris. Moon Shadow. 2006. 192p. (J). 14.95 (978-1-56145-382-5(X) , Peachtree Junior) Peachtree Pubs., Ltd.

—Stardust's Foal. 2003. (Ashleigh Ser.). 176p. pap. 4.99 (978-0-06-009146-0(0) , Harper Entertainment) HarperCollins Pubs.

Polacco, Patricia. Mrs. Mack. Polacco, Patricia, illus. 2001. (Illus.). 40p. (J). (ps-3). pap. 6.99 (978-0-698-11887-4(1) , Putnam Juvenile) Penguin Group (USA) Inc.

—Mrs. Mack. 1998. (Illus.). 40p. (J). (gr. 1-5). 16.99 (978-0-399-23167-4(6) , Philomel) Penguin Group (USA) Inc.

—Mrs. Mack. 2001. (J). (978-0-606-20813-0(5)); lib. bdg. 15.30 (978-0-613-33714-4(X)) Tandem Library Bks.

Pony Farm Mystery. 2006. (J). (978-1-933343-25-9(7) , PONY) Stabenfeldt Inc.

The Pony Trek. 2005. (J). (978-1-933343-08-2(7) , PONY) Stabenfeldt Inc.

The Pony Winter. 2007. (J). (978-1-933343-42-6(7) , PONY) Stabenfeldt Inc.

Porte, Barbara Ann. Harry's Pony. Abolafia, Yossi, illus. 2003. (I Can Read Bks.). 64p. (J). 16.89 (978-0-06-050658-2(X)); pap. 4.99 (978-0-06-050659-9(8)) HarperCollins Pubs.

—Harry's Pony. Abolafia, Yossi, illus. 2003. 54p. (J). (ps-ps). lib. bdg. 11.80 (978-0-613-68429-3(X)) Tandem Library Bks.

Porter, Pamela. Sky. Gerber, Mary Jane, illus. 2005. 88p. (J). (gr. 4-7). pap. 5.95 (978-0-88899-607-7(1) , Libros Tigrillo) Groundwood Bks. CAN. *Dist:* Perseus Distribution.

Potter, Author Tina M. The Horse Story. 2005. 36p. (J). pap. 9.65 (978-1-4116-5761-8(6)) Lulu.com.

Powell, Neva. The Long Crossing. Powell, Eugene, illus. 1998. 128p. (YA). (gr. 4-7). pap. 12.95 (978-0-9661072-7(5)) Avocet Pr., Inc.

Pullein-Thompson, Christine. Horse & Pony Stories. 2003. (gr. 5-8). lib. bdg. 15.25 (978-0-613-67415-7(4)) Tandem Library Bks.

Pullein-Thompson, Christine, retold by. Saddle Up: Thoroughbred Horse Stories. 2007. 280p. (J). pap. 6.95 (*978-0-7534-6145-7(5) , Kingfisher) Houghton Mifflin Co. Trade & Reference Div.

Pullein-Thompson, Diana & Puddephatt, Neal. Classic Horse & Pony Stories. 2000. (Read & Listen Ser.). (J). pap. incl. audio compact disk (978-0-7894-6362-3(8)) Dorling Kindersley Publishing, Inc.

Puttock, Simon. Horsey. Julian, Russell, illus. 2004. 32p. (J). 17.99 (978-1-4052-1058-4(3)); pap. 8.99 (978-1-4052-1059-1(1)) Egmont Bks., Ltd. GBR. *Dist:* Independent Pubs. Group.

Pye, Sylvia. Dusty & the Magic Gold Dust. 2004. 108p. pap. 16.95 (978-1-4137-1124-0(3)) PublishAmerica, Inc.

Raine, Bonnie. Islands. MacMenamin, John, illus. 2003. 48p. (J). per. (978-1-931456-74-6(7)) Athena Pr.

Random House Disney Staff. A Horse to Love: an Enchanted Stables Story. 2007. (Pictureback(R) Ser.). 16p. (J). (ps-2). pap. 3.99 (*978-0-7364-2504-9(7) , RH/Disney) Random Hse. Children's Bks.

Ransom, Candice. Rescue on the Outer Banks. Ritz, Karen, illus. 2002. 48p. (J). (gr. 1-3). lib. bdg. 14.10 (978-0-613-46163-4(0)) Tandem Library Bks.

Ransom, Candice F. Rescue on the Outer Banks. Ritz, Karen, illus. 2002. (On My Own History Ser.). 48p. (J). (gr. 1-3). lib. bdg. 23.93 (978-0-87614-460-2(1) , Carolrhoda Bks.) Lerner Publishing Group.

Rattlesnake Rock. 2006. (J). (978-1-933343-16-7(8)) Stabenfeldt Inc.

Ravasio, Tom. Shekinah, Lord of the Horses: Book Two: The Gamble. 2005. 192p. (J). per. (978-1-55306-949-2(8) , Guardian Bks.) Essence Publishing.

Ray, Mary Lyn. My Carousel Horse. Taxali, Gary, illus. 2000. (J). 13.95 (978-0-15-200023-3(2)) Harcourt Trade Pubs.

Red Pony. 1999. (YA). 11.95 (978-1-56137-441-0(5)); (J). 9.95 (978-1-56137-440-3(7)) Novel Units, Inc.

Redmond, Shirley-Raye. The Princess & Her Pony. 2007. (Illus.). 24p. (J). (*978-1-4048-1238-3(5)) Picture Window Bks.

—The Princess & Her Pony. Senturk, Burak, illus. 2006. 24p. (J). (*978-1-4048-3142-1(8)) Picture Window Bks.

Reed, Sharon. Tara: Prairie Horse Series. 2006. pap. 14.00 (*978-0-8059-7091-3(6)) Dorrance Publishing Co., Inc.

Reekie, Jocelyn. The Week of the Horse. 2004. 4p. pap., tchr. ed. (978-1-55192-707-7(1)); 160p. pap. 7.95 (978-1-55192-655-1(5)) Raincoast Bk. Distribution CAN. *Dist:* Transition Vendor, Perseus Distribution.

Reeve, Phyllis Cardoze. One for Sorrow, Two for Joy. 2002. 150p. (YA). (gr. 6-9). pap. 14.95 (978-0-9725590-0-3(0)) Reeve, Phyllis.

Reid, Mayne. WarTrail or the Hunt of the Wild Horse A. 2006. (Illus.). pap. 40.95 (*978-1-4286-5282-8(5)) Kessinger Publishing, LLC.

Rhema, Dan. Bluegrass Breeze. Leonard, Michael, illus. 2004. (J). per. 19.95 (978-0-9729835-1-8(1)) Mesquite Tress Pr., LLC.

Richards, Laura E. The Wooing of Calvin Parks. 2004. reprint ed. pap. 28.95 (978-1-4179-2877-4(8)) Kessinger Publishing, LLC.

Roberts, Katherine. I Am the Great Horse. 2006. (Illus.). 416p. (YA). pap. 16.99 (978-0-439-82163-6(0) , Chicken Hse., The) Scholastic, Inc.

Robertson, Barbara. Rosemary & the Mystery Down Under. 2002. (Illus.). 128p. (J). (gr. 4-6). pap. 4.95 (978-1-890817-64-0(3)) Winslow Pr.

Robin: The Lovable Morgan Horse, 4 vols. 2005. (Illus.). 200p. (J). per. 9.95 (978-0-9709002-5-8(2)) Willow Bend Publishing.

Rocking Horse. 2004. (J). per. (978-1-57657-382-2(6)) Paradise Pr., Inc.

Rodriguez, Elisabeth. Jumping Jack. 2006. pap. 14.99 (*978-1-4259-8197-6(6)) AuthorHouse.

Rodriguez, Lauren. Finding Her Courage. 2005. 170p. pap. 19.95 (978-1-4137-7131-2(9)) PublishAmerica, Inc.

Ross, Tony & Willis, Jeanne. Dozy Mare. 2005. (Illus.). 32p. (J). 17.95 (*978-1-84270-386-1(2)) Transworld Publishers Ltd. GBR. *Dist:* Independent Pubs. Group.

Rottman, S. L. Hero. 2000. (Illus.). 176p. (J). (gr. 7-12). pap. 5.99 (978-0-14-130701-5(3) , Puffin) Penguin Group (USA) Inc.

—Hero. 2000. 12.64 (978-0-606-17860-0(0)); (gr. 7-12). lib. bdg. 14.15 (978-0-613-28520-9(4)) Tandem Library Bks.

Rowdy's Big day: Horses & Ponies. 2002. (Illus.). 24p. (J). (gr. k-5). pap. 2.99 (978-1-57759-377-5(4)) Dalmatian Pr.

Roy, Ron. The Runaway Racehorse. Gurney, John Steven, illus. 2002. (A to Z Mysteries Ser.: No. 18). 96p. (J). (gr. 2-5). 11.99 (978-0-375-91367-9(X)); pap. 3.99 (978-0-375-81367-2(5)) Random Hse. Children's Bks. (Random Hse. Bks. for Young Readers).

—The Runaway Racehorse. Gurney, John Steven, illus. 2002. (A to Z Mysteries Ser.: No. 18). (J). (gr. k-3). lib. bdg. 11.80 (978-0-613-50495-9(X)) Tandem Library Bks.

Ruano, Moises & Ruano, Alfonso. El Caballo Fantastico. 2001. Tr. of Fantastic Horse. (SPA.). 40p. (J). (gr. 3). (978-84-348-1681-7(4)) SM Ediciones.

Rue, Nancy N. Horse Crazy Lily. 2003. (gr. 3-6). lib. bdg. 13.00 (978-0-613-71715-1(5)) Tandem Library Bks.

—Horse Crazy Lily. 2003. (Young Women of Faith Ser.). 128p. (J). pap. 5.99 (978-0-310-70263-4(1)) Zonderkidz.

Rueda, Claudia. La Suerte de Ozu. (Los Primerisimos Ser.). (SPA.). 30p. (J). (978-968-16-7051-1(5)) Fondo de Cultura Economica USA.

Ruepp, Krista. Horses in the Fog. 1999. (Illus.). (J). (978-0-606-18321-5(3)) Tandem Library Bks.

—Runaway Pony. Heyne, Ulrike, illus. 2005. 32p. (J). (ps-ps). 15.95 (978-0-7358-1985-6(8)) North-South Bks., Inc.

—Winter Pony. James, J. Alison, tr. from GER. Heyne, Ulrike, illus. 2002. 32p. (J). 15.95 (978-0-7358-1691-6(3)) North-South Bks., Inc.

Ryan, Pam Muñoz. Paint the Wind. 2007. 336p. (J). (gr. 4-7). pap. 16.99 (*978-0-439-87362-8(2) , Scholastic Pr.) Scholastic, Inc.

Saddle Island 2: Secrets in the Sand. 2007. (J). (978-1-933343-51-8(6) , PONY) Stabenfeldt Inc.

Sanchez, Elaine K. The General's Secret. Hughes, Janee, illus. 2001. 40p. (J). 14.95 (978-0-89802-758-7(6)) Beautiful America Publishing Co.

Sandoz, Maria. Crazy Horse. 2000. 31.95 (978-0-8488-2825-7(9)) Amereon LTD.

Santillo, LuAnn. Trot, Trot. Santillo, LuAnn, ed. 2003. (Half-Pint Kids Readers Ser.). (Illus.). 7p. (J). (ps-1). pap. (978-1-59256-067-7(9)) Half-Pint Kids, Inc.

Saport, Linda, illus. All the Pretty Little Horses. 1999. 32p. (J). (gr. k-ps). tchr. ed. 15.00 (978-0-395-93097-7(9) , Clarion Bks.) Houghton Mifflin Co. Trade & Reference Div.

Sargent, Dave & Denton, Ivan. Misty's Miracle No. 4: Overcome Fear, 6. Denton, Ivan, illus. 2004. (Illus.). 36p. (J). pap. 9.95 (978-1-59381-005-4(9)) Ozark Publishing.

—Misty's Miracle No. 4: Overcoming Fear, 6 vols., Vol. 4. Denton, Ivan, illus. 2004. (Real Cowboy Ser.: 4). (Illus.). 36p. (J). lib. bdg. 22.60 (978-1-59381-004-7(0)) Ozark Publishing.

Sargent, Dave & Sargent, Pat. Bashful: (Dusty Dun) Be Brave. Lenoir, Jane, illus. 2003. (Saddle Up Ser.: Vol. 1). 42p. (J). pap. 6.95 (978-1-56763-684-0(5)); lib. bdg. 22.60 (978-1-56763-683-3(7)) Ozark Publishing.

—Ben. Lenoir, Jane, illus. 2001. (Saddle Up Ser.). 36p. (J). pap. 6.95 (978-1-56763-644-4(6)) Ozark Publishing.

—Ben: (Bay Sabino) Help Others, 30. Lenoir, Jane, illus. 2001. (Saddle Up Ser.: 2). 36p. (J). lib. bdg. 22.60 (978-1-56763-643-7(8)) Ozark Publishing.

—Biscuit: (Skewbald) Follow the Rules, 25, vol. 3. Lenoir, Jane, illus. 2001. (Saddle Up Ser.: 3). 36p. (J). pap. 6.95 (978-1-56763-676-5(4)); lib. bdg. 22.60 (978-1-56763-675-8(6)) Ozark Publishing.

—Bo: (Linebacked Orange Dun) Be Happy, 30, vol. 4. Lenoir, Jane, illus. 2003. (Saddle Up Ser.: Vol. 4). 42p. (J). lib. bdg. 22.60 (978-1-56763-685-7(3)); mass mkt. 6.95 (978-1-56763-686-4(1)) Ozark Publishing.

—Brandy: (Blue Roan) Beauty Is Inside, 30, 5. Lenoir, Jane, illus. 2003. (Saddle Up Ser.: Vol. 5). 42p. (J). lib. bdg. 22.60 (978-1-56763-799-1(X)); mass mkt. 6.95 (978-1-56763-800-4(7)) Ozark Publishing.

—Bubba No. 6: (Bay) Speed Is Not Everything, 30, vol. 6. Lenoir, Jane, illus. 2001. (Saddle Up Ser.: 6). 36p. (J). lib. bdg. 22.60 (978-1-56763-599-7(7)) Ozark Publishing.

—Buck: (Bucksin) Curious, 30, 7. Lenoir, Jane, illus. 2001. (Saddle Up Ser.: 7). 36p. (J). lib. bdg. 22.60 (978-1-56763-601-7(2)) Ozark Publishing.

—Buck: (Buckskin) Curious, 25, 7. Lenoir, Jane, illus. 2001. (Saddle Up Ser.: 7). 36p. (J). pap. 6.95 (978-1-56763-602-4(0)) Ozark Publishing.

—Buckshot: (Blue Eyed Chestnut) Mind Your Manners, 25, 8. Lenoir, Jane, illus. 2001. (Saddle Up Ser.: 8). 36p. (J). pap. 6.95 (978-1-56763-674-1(8)); lib. bdg. 22.60 (978-1-56763-673-4(X)) Ozark Publishing.

—Buttons: (Muddy Dun) Have Courage, 9. Lenoir, Jane, illus. 2003. (Saddle Up Ser.: Vol. 9). 42p. (J). pap. 6.95 (978-1-56763-688-8(8)); lib. bdg. 22.60 (978-1-56763-687-1(X)) Ozark Publishing.

—Cactus: (Smoky Black) Competition Is Good, 25, 10. Lenoir, Jane, illus. 2001. (Saddle Up Ser.: 10). 36p. (J). pap. 6.95 (978-1-56763-672-7(1)); lib. bdg. 22.60 (978-1-56763-671-0(3)) Ozark Publishing.

—Cassidy: (Dark Bucksin) Equal Rights for All, 30, 11. Lenoir, Jane, illus. 2001. (Saddle Up Ser.: 11). 36p. (J). lib. bdg. 22.60 (978-1-56763-669-7(1)) Ozark Publishing.

—Chalky No. 12: (Chalky Grullo) I'm Forgetful, 25, 12. Lenoir, Jane, illus. 2001. (Saddle Up Ser.: 12). 36p. (J). pap. 6.95 (978-1-56763-604-8(7)); lib. bdg. 22.60 (978-1-56763-603-1(9)) Ozark Publishing.

—Charcoal: (Charcoal Grey) Be Decisive, 25, 13. Lenoir, Jane, illus. 2001. (Saddle Up Ser.: 13). 36p. (J). pap. 6.95 (978-1-56763-606-2(3)); lib. bdg. 22.60 (978-1-56763-605-5(5)) Ozark Publishing.

—Charlie: (Appaloosa) Be Brave, 25, 14. Lenoir, Jane, illus. 2001. (Saddle Up Ser.: 14). 36p. (J). pap. 6.95 (978-1-56763-608-6(X)); lib. bdg. 22.60 (978-1-56763-607-9(1)) Ozark Publishing.

—Chet: (Chestnut) Be Optimistic, 25, 15. Lenoir, Jane, illus. 2001. (Saddle Up Ser.: 15). 36p. (J). pap. 6.95 (978-1-56763-610-9(1)); lib. bdg. 22.60 (978-1-56763-609-3(8)) Ozark Publishing.

—Chick: (Chocolate Chestnut) Be Loyal, 30, 16. Lenoir, Jane, illus. 2003. (Saddle Up Ser.: Vol. 16). 42p. (J). pap. 6.95 (978-1-56763-678-9(0)); lib. bdg. 22.60 (978-1-56763-677-2(2)) Ozark Publishing.

—Chub: (Dapple Black) Be Dependable, 30, 17. Lenoir, Jane, illus. 2001. (Saddle Up Ser.: 17). 36p. (J). lib. bdg. 22.60 (978-1-56763-645-1(4)) Ozark Publishing.

—Chub: (Dappled Black) Be Dependable, 25, 17. Lenoir, Jane, illus. 2001. (Saddle Up Ser.: 17). 36p. (J). pap. 6.95 (978-1-56763-646-8(2)) Ozark Publishing.

—Cocoa: (Brown) Dignity, 25, 18. Lenoir, Jane, illus. 2001. (Saddle Up Ser.: 18). 36p. (J). pap. 6.95 (978-1-56763-612-3(8)); lib. bdg. 22.60 (978-1-56763-611-6(X)) Ozark Publishing.

—Comanche: (Red Bay) Perseverance, 25, 19. Lenoir, Jane, illus. 2001. (Saddle Up Ser.: 19). 36p. (J). pap. 6.95 (978-1-56763-648-2(9)); lib. bdg. 22.60 (978-1-56763-647-5(0)) Ozark Publishing.

—Cricket: (Seal Brown) Do Your Best, 30, 20. Lenoir, Jane, illus. 2003. (Saddle Up Ser.: Vol. 20). 42p. (J). pap. 6.95 (978-1-56763-650-5(0)); lib. bdg. 22.60 (978-1-56763-649-9(7)) Ozark Publishing.

—Dan: (Dappled Mahogany Bay) Determination, 25, 21. Lenoir, Jane, illus. 2001. (Saddle Up Ser.: 21). 36p. (J). pap. 6.95 (978-1-56763-652-9(7)); lib. bdg. 22.60 (978-1-56763-651-2(9)) Ozark Publishing.

—Dizzy: (Claybank) Have Courage, 30 vols., Vol. 22. Lenoir, Jane, illus. 2001. (Saddle Up Ser.: 22). 36p. (J). lib. bdg. 22.60 (978-1-56763-679-6(9)) Ozark Publishing.

—Duke: (Dappled Palomino) Good Behavior, 30 vols., Vol. 23. Lenoir, Jane, illus. 2003. (Saddle Up Ser.: Vol. 23). 42p. (J). pap. 6.95 (978-1-56763-682-6(9)); lib. bdg. 22.60 (978-1-56763-681-9(0)) Ozark Publishing.

—Dusty: (Grey Sabino) Be Helpful, 30 vols., Vol. 24. Lenoir, Jane, illus. 2003. (Saddle Up Ser.: Vol. 24). 42p. (J). pap. 6.95 (978-1-56763-808-0(2)); lib. bdg. 22.60 (978-1-56763-807-3(4)) Ozark Publishing.

—Flash: Speed Counts. Lenoir, Jane, illus. 2001. (Saddle Up Ser.). 36p. (J). pap. 6.95 (978-1-56763-614-7(4)); lib. bdg. 22.60 (978-1-56763-613-0(6)) Ozark Publishing.

—Freckles: (Flea-bitten Grey) Be Proud of Old Glory, 30 vols., Vol. 26. Lenoir, Jane, illus. 2003. (Saddle Up Ser.: Vol. 26). 42p. (J). pap. 6.95 (978-1-56763-810-3(4)); lib. bdg. 22.60 (978-1-56763-809-7(0)) Ozark Publishing.

—Ginger: (Lilac Roan) Be Likeable, 30 vols., Vol. 27. Lenoir, Jane, illus. 2003. (Saddle Up Ser.: Vol. 27). 42p. (J). pap. 6.95 (978-1-56763-812-7(0)); lib. bdg. 22.60 (978-1-56763-811-0(2)) Ozark Publishing.

—Gizmo: (Flea-bitten Dun) Don't Be Silly, 25 vols., Vol. 28. Lenoir, Jane, illus. 2001. (Saddle Up Ser.: 28). 36p. (J). pap. 6.95 (978-1-56763-654-3(3)); lib. bdg. 22.60 (978-1-56763-653-6(5)) Ozark Publishing.

—Goober: (Silver Dapple) Appreciate Others, 30 vols., Vol. 29. Lenoir, Jane, illus. 2003. (Saddle Up Ser.: Vol. 29). 42p. (J). lib. bdg. 22.60 (978-1-56763-689-5(6)) Ozark Publishing.

—Goober: (Sliver Dapple) Appreciate Others, 30 vols., Vol. 29. Lenoir, Jane, illus. 2004. (Saddle Up Ser.: Vol. 29). 42p. (J). pap. 6.95 (978-1-56763-690-1(X)) Ozark Publishing.

—Grady: (Dappled Grey) Proud to Be an American, 30 vols., Vol. 30. Lenoir, Jane, illus. 2003. (Saddle Up Ser.: Vol. 30). 42p. (J). lib. bdg. 22.60 (978-1-56763-813-4(9)) Ozark Publishing.

—Grady: Proud to Be an American, 30 vols. Lenoir, Jane, illus. 2003. (Saddle Up Ser.: Vol. 30). 42p. (J). pap. 6.95 (978-1-56763-814-1(7)) Ozark Publishing.

—Gus: (Slate Grullo) Be Thankful, 30, 32. Lenoir, Jane, illus. 2003. (Saddle Up Ser.: Vol. 32). 42p. (J). lib. bdg. 22.60 (978-1-56763-693-2(4)); pap. 6.95 (978-1-56763-694-9(2)) Ozark Publishing.

—Hank: (Black Sabino) Be Responsible, 25, 33. Lenoir, Jane, illus. 2001. (Saddle Up Ser.). 36p. (J). pap. 6.95 (978-1-56763-656-7(X)); lib. bdg. 22.60 (978-1-56763-655-0(1)) Ozark Publishing.

—Hondo: (Silver Dun) Look for Good in Others, 30, 34. Lenoir, Jane, illus. 2003. (Saddle Up Ser.: Vol. 34). 42p. (J). pap. 6.95 (978-1-56763-802-8(3)); lib. bdg. 22.60 (978-1-56763-801-1(5)) Ozark Publishing.

—Hoot: (Grullo) Be Creative, 30, 35. Lenoir, Jane, illus. 2003. (Saddle Up Ser.: Vol. 35). 42p. (J). pap. 6.95 (978-1-56763-696-3(9)); lib. bdg. 22.60 (978-1-56763-695-6(0)) Ozark Publishing.

—Jet: (Jet Black) Good Attitude, 30, 36. Lenoir, Jane, illus. 2001. (Saddle Up Ser.: 36). 36p. (J). lib. bdg. 22.60 (978-1-56763-615-4(2)) Ozark Publishing.

—Kiowa: (Paint) Be Trustworthy, 25, 37. Lenoir, Jane, illus. 2001. (Saddle Up Ser.: 37). 36p. (J). pap. 6.95 (978-1-56763-618-5(7)); lib. bdg. 22.60 (978-1-56763-617-8(9)) Ozark Publishing.

—Lily: (Lilac Dun) A Second Chance, 30, 38. Lenoir, Jane, illus. 2003. (Saddle Up Ser.: Vol. 38). 42p. (J). pap. 6.95 (978-1-56763-698-7(5)); lib. bdg. 22.60 (978-1-56763-697-0(7)) Ozark Publishing.

—Mack: (Medicine Hat Paint) Be a Leader, 30, 39. Lenoir, Jane, illus. 2003. (Saddle Up Ser.: Vol. 39). 42p. (J). pap. 6.95 (978-1-56763-700-7(0)); lib. bdg. 22.60 (978-1-56763-699-4(3)) Ozark Publishing.

—Maggie: (Piebald) Be a Hero, 30, 40. Lenoir, Jane, illus. 2001. (Saddle Up Ser.: 40). 36p. (J). lib. bdg. 22.60 (978-1-56763-619-2(5)); pap. 6.95 (978-1-56763-620-8(9)) Ozark Publishing.

—Monte: (Silver Bucksin) Take Pride in Your Work, 30, 41. Lenoir, Jane, illus. 2001. (Saddle Up Ser.). 36p. (J). lib. bdg. 22.60 (978-1-56763-657-4(8)) Ozark Publishing.

—Monte: (Silver Buckskin) Take Pride in Your Work, 25, 41. Lenoir, Jane, illus. 2001. (Saddle Up Ser.: 41). 36p. (J). pap. 6.95 (978-1-56763-658-1(6)) Ozark Publishing.

—Nick: (Linebacked Claybank Dun) Crime Does Not Pay, 30, 42. Lenoir, Jane, illus. 2003. (Saddle Up Ser.: Vol. 42). 42p. (J). pap. 6.95 (978-1-56763-702-1(7)); lib. bdg. 22.60 (978-1-56763-701-4(9)) Ozark Publishing.

—Nubbin: (Linebacked Apricot Dun) Freedom, 30, 43. Lenoir, Jane, illus. 2003. (Saddle Up Ser.: Vol. 43). 42p. (J). pap. 6.95 (978-1-56763-704-5(3)); lib. bdg. 22.60 (978-1-56763-703-8(5)) Ozark Publishing.

—Pal: (Palomino) Be Friendly, 25, 44. Lenoir, Jane, illus. 2001. (Saddle Up Ser.: 44). 36p. (J). pap. 6.95 (978-1-56763-622-2(5)); lib. bdg. 22.60 (978-1-56763-621-5(7)) Ozark Publishing.

—Patches: (Lobo Dun) Make Responsible Decisions, 30. Lenoir, Jane, illus. (Saddle Up Ser.: Vol. 45). 42p. (J). 2002. pap. 6.95 (978-1-56763-706-9(X)); 45. 2003. lib. bdg. 22.60 (978-1-56763-705-2(1)) Ozark Publishing.

—Pete: (Pink-skinned Palomino) Be a Hero, 30, 46. Lenoir, Jane, illus. 2003. (Saddle Up Ser.: Vol. 46). 42p. (J). lib. bdg. 22.60 (978-1-56763-707-6(8)) Ozark Publishing.

—Pete: Pink-skinned Palomino) Be a Hero, 30, 46. Lenoir, Jane, illus. 2003. (Saddle Up Ser.: Vol. 46). 42p. (J). pap. 6.95 (978-1-56763-708-3(6)) Ozark Publishing.

—Popcorn: (Blue Corn) Work Hard, 30, 47. Lenoir, Jane, illus. 2001. (Saddle Up Ser.). 36p. (J). lib. bdg. 22.60 (978-1-56763-659-8(4)); pap. 6.95 (978-1-56763-660-4(8)) Ozark Publishing.

—Ranger: (Olive Grullo) Be Honest, 30, 48. Lenoir, Jane, illus. 2003. (Saddle Up Ser.: Vol. 48). 42p. (J). pap. 6.95 (978-1-56763-710-6(8)); lib. bdg. 22.60 (978-1-56763-709-0(4)) Ozark Publishing.

—Rascal: (Red Dun) Responsible Leadership, 30, 49. Lenoir, Jane, illus. 2003. (Saddle Up Ser.: Vol. 49). 42p. (J). pap. 6.95 (978-1-56763-712-0(4)) Ozark Publishing.

—Ring: (Silver Grullo) Grace & Pride, 25. Lenoir, Jane, illus. 2001. 36p. (J). (Animal Pride Ser.: 50). pap. 6.95 (978-1-56763-662-8(4)); 50. (Saddle Up Ser.). lib. bdg. 22.60 (978-1-56763-661-1(6)) Ozark Publishing.

—Rocky: (Blue-eyed Palomino) Be Free, 30, 51. Lenoir, Jane, illus. (Saddle Up Ser.: Vol. 51). 42p. (J). 2003. lib. bdg. 22.60 (978-1-56763-713-7(2)); 2002. pap. 6.95 (978-1-56763-714-4(0)) Ozark Publishing.

—Rusty: (Red Roan) Be Strong & Brave, 30, 52. Lenoir, Jane, illus. 2003. (Saddle Up Ser.: Vol. 52). 42p. (J). pap. 6.95 (978-1-56763-804-2(X)); lib. bdg. 22.60 (978-1-56763-803-5(1)) Ozark Publishing.

—Snow: (White) Be Truthful, 25, 53. Lenoir, Jane, illus. 2001. (Saddle Up Ser.: 53). 36p. (J). pap. 6.95 (978-1-56763-624-6(1)); lib. bdg. 22.60 (978-1-56763-623-9(3)) Ozark Publishing.

—Sonny: (Linebacked Yellow Dun) Have Orderly Manners, 30, 54. Lenoir, Jane, illus. 2003. (Saddle Up Ser.: Vol. 54). 42p. (J). lib. bdg. 22.60 (978-1-56763-715-1(9)) Ozark Publishing.

—Sonny: (Linebacked Yllow Dun) Have Orderly Manners, 30, 54. Lenoir, Jane, illus. 2003. (Saddle Up Ser.: Vol. 54). 42p. (J). pap. 6.95 (978-1-56763-716-8(7)) Ozark Publishing.

—Speck: (Black Patterned Leopard) Good Attitude, 25, 55. Lenoir, Jane, illus. 2001. (Saddle Up Ser.). 36p. (J). pap. 6.95 (978-1-56763-664-2(0)); lib. bdg. 22.60 (978-1-56763-663-5(2)) Ozark Publishing.

—Stinky: (Sorrel) Don't Be Mischievous, 25, 56. Lenoir, Jane, illus. 2001. (Saddle Up Ser.: 56). 36p. (J). pap. (978-1-56763-666-6(7)); lib. bdg. 22.60 (978-1-56763-665-9(9)) Ozark Publishing.

—Sugar: (Cream) Curiosity Is Good, 25, 57. Lenoir, Jane, illus. 2001. (Saddle Up Ser.: 57). 36p. (J). pap. 6.95 (978-1-56763-668-0(3)); lib. bdg. 22.60 (978-1-56763-667-3(5)) Ozark Publishing.

—Whiskers: (Roan) Pride & Peace, 30, 59. Lenoir, Jane, illus. (Saddle Up Ser.: Vol. 59). 42p. (J). 2003. pap. 6.95 (978-1-56763-806-6(6)); 2002. lib. bdg. 22.60 (978-1-56763-805-9(8)) Ozark Publishing.

—White Thunder: I'm a Leader, 56 vols., 6. Huff, Jeane, illus. 2nd rev. ed. 2003. (Animal Pride Ser.: 6). 42p. (J). lib. bdg. 19.95 (978-1-56763-769-4(8)) Ozark Publishing.

—Zeb: (Zebra Dun) Be Prepared, 30, 60. Lenoir, Jane, illus. 2003. (Saddle Up Ser.: Vol. 60). 42p. (J). pap. 6.95 (978-1-56763-718-2(3)); lib. bdg. 22.60 (978-1-56763-717-5(5)) Ozark Publishing.

Saunders, Susan. Kate's Secret Plan. 1998. (Treasured Horses Ser.: Vol. 6). (J). (gr. 3-7). pap. 3.99 (978-0-590-31658-3(3)) Scholastic, Inc.

—Kate's Secret Plan. Rabinowitz, Sandy & Keiffer, Christa, illus. l.t. ed. 1999. (Treasured Horses Collection). 128p. (J). (gr. 4 up). lib. bdg. 23.33 (978-0-8368-2278-6(1)) Stevens, Gareth Inc.

—Kate's Secret Plan, 6. 1998. (Treasured Horses Ser.). (J). (978-0-606-13866-6(8)) Tandem Library Bks.

—Lucky Lady. 2000. 128p. (J). (gr. 4-7). 14.95 (978-0-380-97784-0(2)) HarperCollins Pubs.

—Riding School Rivals, 4. 1998. (Treasured Horses Ser.). (J). (978-0-606-13864-2(1)) Tandem Library Bks.

Schindel, John. Busy Horsies. Lark, Casi, photos by. 2007. (Illus.). 20p. (J). pap. 6.95 (*978-1-58246-223-3(2) , Tricycle Pr.) Ten Speed Pr.

Schnetzler, Pattie L. Widdermaker. Sealock, Rick, illus. 2005. 32p. (gr. k-2). 15.95 (978-0-87614-647-7(7)) Lerner Publishing Group.

Scholastic, Inc. Staff & Brooke, Lauren. A Winter's Gift. 3rd rev. ed. 2007. (Heartland Special Edition Ser.). 192p. (J). pap. 5.99 (*978-0-439-92561-7(4) , Scholastic Paperbacks) Scholastic, Inc.

Schultz, Jan Neubert. Horse Sense: The Story of Will Sasse, His Horse Star & the Outlaw Jesse James. 2005. (Adventures in Time Ser.). (Illus.). 180p. (J). (gr. 4-8). 15.95 (978-1-57505-998-3(3)) Lerner Publishing Group.

Scorned. 2005. (J). (978-1-933343-09-9(5) , PONY) Stabenfeldt Inc.

Seeley, Bonnie L. Sun & Ponies, Wind & Sky. Seeley, Douglas A., illus. Lidard, Kelly, photos by. 2004. 32p. (J). lib. bdg. 11.95 (978-0-9728380-1-6(5)) Seelcraft Publishing.

Sequins. 2001. (J). (978-0-9700756-8-0(5)) Pajo Publishing Co.

Sewell, Anna. Black Beauty. 2005. 27.95 (978-1-4218-0905-2(2) , 1st World Library - Literary Society) 1st World Publishing, Inc.

—Black Beauty. 2002. (Great Illustrated Classics Ser.). (Illus.). 240p. (J). (gr. 3-8). 21.35 (978-1-57765-681-4(4) , ABDO & Daughters) ABDO Publishing Co.

—Black Beauty. (J). 21.95 (978-0-88411-065-1(6)) Amereon LTD.

—Black Beauty. Dryhurst, Dinah, illus. 2000. 224p. (J). pap. 8.95 (978-1-86205-240-6(9) , Pavilion Bks., Ltd.) Anova Bks. GBR. *Dist:* Trafalgar Square Publishing.

—Black Beauty. (Great Classics for Children Ser.). (Illus.). 192p. (J). 5.99 (978-1-4037-0592-1(5)); 2005. 5.99 (978-1-4037-1384-1(7)) Dalmatian Pr.

—Black Beauty. 2005. 92p. per. 4.95 (978-1-4209-2539-5(3)) Digireads.com.

—Black Beauty. Ambrus, Victor G., illus. 2005. (READ & LISTEN Bks.). 64p. (J). 9.99 (978-0-7566-1274-0(8)) Dorling Kindersley Publishing, Inc.

—Black Beauty. 1999. (Dover Evergreen Classics Ser.). (Illus.). 208p. (J). (gr. 4-7). pap. 2.50 (978-0-486-40788-3(8)) Dover Pubns., Inc.

—Black Beauty. 2001. (Fast Track Classics Ser.). (Illus.). 48p. pap. 9.99 (978-0-237-52284-1(5) , Evans Brothers, Limited) Evans Publishing Group GBR. *Dist:* Independent Pubs. Group.

—Black Beauty. (Charming Classics). 288p. 2005. 6.99 (978-0-06-084596-4(1) , Harper Festival); 1998. (J). (gr. 3-7). pap. 6.99 (978-0-694-01243-5(2)) HarperCollins Pubs.

—Black Beauty. Andrew, Ian P., illus. 2001. (Kingfisher Classics Ser.). 352p. (J). (gr. 4-6). tchr. ed. 15.95 (978-0-7534-5379-7(7) , Kingfisher) Houghton Mifflin Co. Trade & Reference Div.

—Black Beauty. 2001. (J). (gr. 4-7). 17.95 (978-0-8249-5400-0(9)) Ideals Pubns.

—Black Beauty. Stemach, Jerry, ed. Ham, Jeff, illus. 2000. (J). 65.00 incl. audio, cd-rom (978-1-58702-312-5(1)) Johnston, Don Inc.

—Black Beauty. (Illus.). 192p. (J). 9.95 (978-1-56156-310-4(2)) Kidsbooks, Inc.

—Black Beauty. 2001. (Twelve-Point Ser.). (J). lib. bdg. 24.00 (978-1-58287-132-5(9)) North Bks.

—Black Beauty. Chitouras, Barbara, illus. 2002. (Classics for Young Readers Ser.). 208p. (J). per. 7.99 (978-0-87552-728-4(0)) P & R Publishing.

—Black Beauty. Aldous, Kate, illus. 2003. 288p. (J). 9.98 (978-1-4054-1675-7(0)) Parragon, Inc.

—Black Beauty. (Puffin Classics Ser.). 2008. 288p. (J). (gr. 3). pap. 4.99 (*978-0-14-132103-5(2) , Puffin); 2002. 240p. mass mkt. 4.95 (978-0-451-52865-0(4) , Signet Classics) Penguin Group (USA) Inc.

—Black Beauty. (J). 8.97 (978-0-13-052329-7(1)) Prentice Hall PTR.

—Black Beauty. (Illus.). 226p. (YA). (978-0-681-99550-5(5) , Random House) Random House Publishing Group.

—Black Beauty. 2000. (Illus.). 240p. (gr. 5-7). 5.99 (978-0-440-41645-6(0) , Yearling) Random Hse. Children's Bks.

—Black Beauty. 1998. (Children's Classics Ser.). (Illus.). 240p. (J). 5.99 (978-0-517-18958-0(5) , Children's Classics) Random Hse. Value Publishing.

—Black Beauty. 2006. (Scholastic Classics Ser.). x, 203p. (J). (gr. 9-12). 25.00 (978-0-531-16981-0(2) , Watts, Franklin) Scholastic Library Publishing.

—Black Beauty. 2000. 256p. (J). (gr. 4-7). pap. 4.50 (978-0-590-42354-0(1) , Scholastic Paperbacks) Scholastic, Inc.

—Black Beauty. 2001. (Classics Ser.). (Illus.). 224p. (J). (gr. 4-7). pap. 4.99 (978-0-689-84255-9(4) , Aladdin) Simon & Schuster Children's Publishing.

—Black Beauty. 2006. (J). (gr. 4-8). 24.21 (978-1-59961-113-6(9)) Spotlight.

—Black Beauty. 2005. (Illus.). 176p. (J). (ps-7). per. 17.04 (978-0-606-33757-1(1)); 2001. (gr. 3-6). lib. bdg. 11.80 (978-0-613-63178-5(1)); 2001. (gr. 5-8). lib. bdg. 11.80 (978-0-613-66691-6(7)); 1999. (gr. 3-6). lib. bdg. 10.10 (978-0-613-85409-2(8)) Tandem Library Bks.

—Black Beauty. 1998. (Children's Classics). (ENG.). 208p. (YA). (ps up). pap. (978-1-85326-109-1(2) , 1092WW) Wordsworth Editions, Ltd.

—Black Beauty. 2002. (Spot the Classics Ser.). (Illus.). 178p. (J). (gr. k-5). 4.99 (978-1-57759-544-1(0)) Dalmatian Pr.

—Black Beauty. McKowen, Scott, illus. 2004. (Unabridged Classics Ser.). 208p. 9.95 (978-1-4027-1452-8(1)) Sterling Publishing Co., Inc.

—Black Beauty. Corvino, Lucy, illus. 2005. (Classic Starts Ser.). 160p. 4.95 (978-1-4027-1144-2(1)) Sterling Publishing Co., Inc.

—Black Beauty. Tanner, Jennifer, illus. 2007. (Graphic Revolve Ser.). 63p. (J). 22.60 (978-1-59889-046-4(8)) Stone Arch Bks.

—Black Beauty. unabr. ed. 2004. (Chrysalis Children's Classics Ser.). (Illus.). 208p. (YA). pap. (978-1-84365-062-1(2)) Chrysalis Children's Bks.

—Black Beauty. (J). reprint ed. lib. bdg. 48.00 (978-0-7426-1042-2(X)); 2001. (Illus.). pap. 28.00 (978-0-7426-6042-7(7)) Classic Bks.

—Black Beauty. 2nd ed. 1998. (Illustrated Classic Book Ser.). (Illus.). 61p. (J). (gr. 3 up). reprint ed. pap. 4.95 (978-1-56767-253-4(1)) Educational Insights, Inc.

—Black Beauty. deluxe ed. 2005. (Charming Classics). 288p. (J). 9.99 (978-0-06-075770-0(1) , Harper Festival) HarperCollins Pubs.

—Black Beauty. Stemach, Jerry, ed. Ham, Jeff, illus. l.t. ed. (J). 2002. 150.00 (978-1-58702-023-0(8)); 2000. 50.00 (978-1-58702-508-2(6)) Johnston, Don Inc.

—Black Beauty. 2004. reprint ed. pap. 15.95 (978-1-4191-1018-4(7)); pap. 1.99 (978-1-4192-1018-1(1)) Kessinger Publishing, LLC.

—Black Beauty. l.t. ed. 1999. (Large Print Heritage Ser.). 260p. (YA). (gr. 7-12). lib. bdg. 29.95 (978-1-58118-042-8(X) , 22511) LRS.

—Black Beauty. l.t. ed. 2004. (Large Print Ser.). 268p. 25.00 (978-1-58287-619-1(3)) North Bks.

—Black Beauty. l.t. ed. 2001. 240p. (J). 28.95 (978-0-7838-9522-2(4)) Thorndike Pr.

—Black Beauty, Level 2. 2001. (Illus.). 48p. (C). pap. 9.00 (978-0-582-42121-9(7)) Pearson ESL.

—Black Beauty, 2 vols., Set. l.t. ed. (YA). (gr. 8 up). reprint ed. 10.00 (978-0-89064-017-3(3)) National Assn. for Visually Handicapped.

—Black Beauty, Level 4. 2nd abr. ed. 2000. (Bookworms Ser.). (Illus.). 90p. 6.50 (978-0-19-423028-5(7)) Oxford Univ. Pr., Inc.

—Black Beauty: And a Discussion of Kindness. Martin, Richard, illus. 2003. (Values in Action Illustrated Classics Ser.). 191p. (J). (978-1-59203-028-6(9)) Learning Challenge, Inc.

—Black Beauty: The Autobiography of a Horse. 2000. (gr. 5-8). lib. bdg. 12.40 (978-0-613-28253-6(1)) Tandem Library Bks.

—Black Beauty's Early Days in the Meadow. Donovan, Jane Monroe, illus. rev. ed. 2006. 32p. (J). 15.95 (978-1-58536-296-7(4)) Sleeping Bear Pr.

Sewell, Anna & Dorling Kindersley Publishing Staff. Black Beauty. Ambrus, Victor G., illus. 2000. (Classic Readers Ser.). (J). (gr. 2-4). 32p. 12.99 (978-0-7894-5702-8(4)); Vol. 4. 48p. pap. 3.99 (978-0-7894-5388-4(6)) Dorling Kindersley Publishing, Inc.

Sewell, Anna & Marsh, Laura F. Black Beauty. 2006. (My First Classics Ser.). 112p. (J). pap. 4.99 (978-0-06-079148-3(9) , Harper Festival) HarperCollins Pubs.

Sewell, Anna & Sebag-Montefiore, Mary. Black Beauty. 2006. 64p. (J). 8.99 (978-0-7945-1193-7(7) , Usborne) EDC Publishing.

Sewell, Anna, et al. Black Beauty. 2001. (Young Reader's Classics Ser.). (Illus.). 95p. (J). 16.95 (978-1-55263-322-9(5) , Key Porter kids) Key Porter Bks. CAN. *Dist:* Firefly Bks., Ltd.

Shah, Idries. The Magic Horse. Freeman, Julie, illus. 2001. 34p. (J). 6.99 (978-1-883536-26-8(X) , MAHO2, Hoopoe Bks.) ISHK.

Sharp, Thelma & Laner, Doris. The Saturday Appaloosa. Graham, Georgia, illus. 2004. (Northern Lights Books for Children Ser.). 32p. (J). (ps-1). 16.95 (978-0-88995-213-3(2)) Red Deer Pr. CAN. *Dist:* Fitzhenry & Whiteside, Ltd.

Shaw, Esther. The Winter Mare. 2005. (ENG., Illus.). 198p. pap. (*978-1-84401-447-7(9)) Athena Pr.

Shaw, Janet Beeler. Changes for Kaya. 2002. (gr. 3-6). lib. bdg. 14.10 (978-0-613-46214-3(9)) Tandem Library Bks.

—Changes for Kaya Bk. 6: A Winter Story. Farnsworth, Bill & McAliley, Susan, illus. 2002. (American Girls Collection: Bk. 6). 80p. (gr. 2-7). (J). 12.95 (978-1-58485-434-0(0)); 6.95 (978-1-58485-433-3(2)) American Girl Publishing, Inc.

—Meet Kaya. 2002. (gr. 3-6). lib. bdg. 14.10 (978-0-613-46227-3(0)) Tandem Library Bks.

Shefelman, Janice J. & Shefelman, Tom, illus. Son of Spirit Horse. 2004. 74p. (J). (978-1-57168-833-0(1) , Eakin Pr.) Eakin Pr.

Shepherd, JaiLeen. Anan: Lea's Special Friend—Part II of the Lea Trilogy. 2006. (J). per. 15.95 (978-1-889743-55-4(0)) Robbie Dean Pr.

—Lea's Song: The Life of a Special Little Horse. 2006. (J). per. 13.95 (978-1-889743-54-7(2)) Robbie Dean Pr.

Sherman, Josepha. Magic Hoofbeats: Horse Tales from Many Lands. Wingerter, Linda, illus. 2004. 80p. (J). 19.99 (978-1-84148-091-6(6)) Barefoot Bks., Inc.

Shipman, Todd. Morse the Horse Gets His Chance. 2007. 24p. (J). per. 17.99 (*978-1-59886-819-7(5)) Tate Publishing & Enterprises, L.L.C.

Shortstuff Bucks!!, 3 vols. 2005. (Illus.). 32p. (J). 16.95 (978-0-9721057-4-3(3) , 3000) Cowgirl Peg Enterprises LLC.

Siamon, Sharon. Brave Horse. 2004. (Mustang Mountain Ser.: Vol. 6). (Illus.). 160p. (J). (gr. 3-7). pap. 6.95 (978-1-55285-528-7(7)) Whitecap Bks., Ltd. CAN. *Dist:* Firefly Bks., Ltd.

—Dark Horse. 2005. (Mustang Mountain Ser.). 176p. (J). (gr. 3-7). pap. 6.95 (978-1-55285-720-5(4) , Walrus Bks.) Whitecap Bks., Ltd. CAN. *Dist:* Firefly Bks., Ltd.

—Fire Horse. 2002. (gr. 3-6). lib. bdg. 15.25 (978-0-613-78589-1(4)) Tandem Library Bks.

—Fire Horse. 2002. (Mustang Mountain Ser.). 144p. (J). (gr. 3-7). pap. 6.95 (978-1-55285-457-0(4)) Whitecap Bks., Ltd. CAN. *Dist:* Firefly Bks., Ltd.

—Gallop to the Sea. 2006. (Saddle Island Ser.). 168p. (J). (gr. 3-7). pap. 6.95 (978-1-55285-713-7(1) , Walrus Bks.) Whitecap Bks., Ltd. CAN. *Dist:* Firefly Bks., Ltd.

—Mustang Mountain Vol. 7: Free Horse. 2004. (Mustang Mountain Ser.). 160p. (J). (gr. 3-7). pap. 6.95 (978-1-55285-608-6(9)) Whitecap Bks., Ltd. CAN. *Dist:* Firefly Bks., Ltd.

—Night Horse. 2002. (Mustang Mountain Ser.: No. 3). 144p. (J). (gr. 3-7). pap. 6.95 (978-1-55285-363-4(2)) Whitecap Bks., Ltd. CAN. *Dist:* Firefly Bks., Ltd.

—Race to the Rescue. 2007. (Saddle Island Ser.). 172p. (J). (gr. 3-7). pap. 6.95 (*978-1-55285-855-4(3) , Walrus Bks.) Whitecap Bks., Ltd. CAN. *Dist:* Firefly Bks., Ltd.

—Rodeo Horse. 2003. (Mustang Mountain Ser.). (Illus.). 144p. (J). (gr. 3-7). pap. 6.95 (978-1-55285-467-9(1)) Whitecap Bks., Ltd. CAN. *Dist:* Firefly Bks., Ltd.

—Secrets in the Sand. 2007. (J). (978-1-933343-27-3(3) , PONY) Stabenfeldt Inc.

—Secrets in the Sand. 2006. (Saddle Island Ser.). 208p. (J). (gr. 3-7). pap. 6.95 (978-1-55285-714-4(X) , Walrus Bks.) Whitecap Bks., Ltd. CAN. *Dist:* Firefly Bks., Ltd.

—Sky Horse. 2001. (Mustang Mountain Ser.). 128p. (J). (gr. 3-7). pap. 6.95 (978-1-55285-456-3(6)) Whitecap Bks., Ltd. CAN. *Dist:* Firefly Bks., Ltd.

—Stone Horse. 2006. (Mustang Mountain Ser.). 208p. (J). (gr. 3-7). pap. 6.95 (978-1-55285-798-4(0) , Walrus Bks.) Whitecap Bks., Ltd. CAN. *Dist:* Firefly Bks., Ltd.

—Swift Horse. 2005. (Mustang Mountain Ser.). 176p. (J). (gr. 3-7). pap. 6.95 (978-1-55285-659-8(3) , Walrus Bks.) Whitecap Bks., Ltd. CAN. *Dist:* Firefly Bks., Ltd.

—Wild Horse. 2003. (Mustang Mountain Ser.). 144p. (J). (gr. 3-7). pap. 6.95 (978-1-55285-413-6(2)) Whitecap Bks., Ltd. CAN. *Dist:* Firefly Bks., Ltd.

Silverman, Erica. Cowgirl Kate & Cocoa. Lewin, Betsy, illus. 2006. (Cowgirl Kate & Cocoa Ser.). 44p. (J). pap. 5.95 (978-0-15-205660-5(2) , Harcourt Paperbacks) Harcourt Children's Bks.

—Cowgirl Kate & Cocoa. Lewin, Betsy, illus. 2005. (Cowgirl Kate & Cocoa Ser.). 44p. (J). 15.00 (978-0-15-202124-5(8)) Harcourt Trade Pubs.

—Cowgirl Kate & Cocoa: Rain or Shine. Lewin, Betsy, illus. 2008. 44p. (J). 15.00 (*978-0-15-205384-0(0)) Harcourt Trade Pubs.

—Cowgirl Kate & Cocoa: School Days. Lewin, Betsy, illus. 2007. (Cowgirl Kate & Cocoa Ser.). 48p. (J). 15.00 (978-0-15-205378-9(6)) Harcourt Trade Pubs.

—Cowgirl Kate & Cocoa: School Days. Lewin, Betsy, illus. 2008. (Cowgirl Kate & Cocoa Ser.). 48p. (J). pap. 5.95 (*978-0-15-206130-2(4) , Harcourt Paperbacks) Harcourt Children's Bks.

Silverman, Erica. Partners. Lewin, Betsy, illus. 2007. (Cowgirl Kate & Cocoa Ser.). 44p. (J). pap. 5.95 (978-0-15-206010-7(3) , Harcourt Paperbacks) Harcourt Children's Bks.

Simms, Jory. Scout's Honor #4. 2006. (Darcy's Wild Life Ser.: Vol. 4). 160p. (J). (gr. 2-4). pap. 4.99 (978-0-448-44261-7(2) , Grosset & Dunlap) Penguin Group (USA) Inc.

Sireau, Christine. Theo: The Blue Rider Pigeon. Tannenbaum, Rose, illus. 2005. 20p. (J). (ps-3). pap. 15.00 (978-0-88010-561-3(5)) SteinerBooks, Inc.

Skurzynski, Gloria & Ferguson, Alane. Ghost Horses. 2000. (National Parks Mysteries Ser.: Vol. 6). (Illus.). 160p. (J). (gr. 3-7). 15.95 (978-0-7922-7055-3(X) , National Geographic Children's Bks.) National Geographic Society.

Slade, Arthur. Megiddo's Shadow. 2006. (Illus.). 304p. (J). (gr. 7). 15.95 (978-0-385-74701-1(2) , Lamb, Wendy) Random Hse. Children's Bks.

Smith, Sally. Rosebud Roams Charleston: A Child 's Clippity-Clop Guide to the City. 1999. (Illus.). (J). (978-0-933101-19-7(8)) Legacy Pubns.

Smith, Valerie H. The Spirit Stories: A Series of Short Stories for Children. 2007. 64p. per. 8.95 (*978-1-59824-450-2(7)) E-BookTime LLC.

Sneve, Virginia Driving Hawk. High Elk's Treasure. 2002. (EMC Masterpiece Series Access Editions). (Illus.). xxv, 110p. (J). 9.95 (978-0-8219-2414-3(1) , 35370) EMC/Paradigm Publishing.

Snyder, Zilpha Keatley. Gib & the Gray Ghost. 2001. 230p. (gr. 3-6). lib. bdg. 13.55 (978-0-613-36816-2(9)) Tandem Library Bks.

—Gib Rides Home. 1999. (YA). (gr. 5 up). pap. 59.75 incl. audio (978-0-7887-2993-5(4) , 40875) Recorded Bks., LLC.

—Gib Rides Home. 1999. (J). 11.64 (978-0-606-16723-9(4)) Tandem Library Bks.

—Gib Rides Home. 2002. (Juvenile Ser.). (Illus.). (J). 21.95 (978-0-7862-4856-8(4)) Thorndike Pr.

Speer, Bonnie Stahlman. Miss Little Britches: A Story of Junior Rodeo. 1999. 141p. (J). (gr. 4 up). mass mkt. 11.95 (978-1-889683-12-6(4)) Reliance Pr.

Springer, Nancy. Sky Rider. 2000. 128p. (J). (gr. 7 up). pap. 4.95 (978-0-380-79565-9(5) , Harper Trophy) HarperCollins Pubs.

Stabenfeldt, prod. Starshine Legacy 2: Comic Book 0706. 2007. (YA). pap. (*978-1-933343-56-3(7)) Stabenfeldt Inc.

Stafford, Liliana. A Race Is Run. 2001. (Illus.). 128p. (YA). pap. 12.95 (978-1-876268-52-7(2)) Univ. of Western Australia Pr. AUS. *Dist:* International Specialized Bk. Services.

—Shah. 2004. (Illus.). 137p. (Orig.). (J). pap. 11.95 (978-1-920694-11-1(0)) Univ. of Western Australia Pr. AUS. *Dist:* International Specialized Bk. Services.

—Through the Starting Flags. 2001. (Chiko Ser. : Bk. 1). (Illus.). 171p. (YA). pap. 12.95 (978-1-876268-51-0(4)) Univ. of Western Australia Pr. AUS. *Dist:* International Specialized Bk. Services.

Standish, Burt L. Frank Merriwell's Horse. Rudman, Jack, ed. 2003. (Frank Merriwell Ser.). pap. 9.95 (978-0-8373-9146-5(6)) Merriwell, Frank Inc.

Stanley, George Edward. Ghost Horse. 2000. (gr. 3-6). lib. bdg. 11.80 (978-0-613-27851-5(8)) Tandem Library Bks.

Starshine Legacy 1. 2006. (J). (978-1-933343-38-9(9) , PONY) Stabenfeldt Inc.

Steers, Billy. Tractor Mac Arrives at the Farm. Steers, Billy, illus. 2004. (Illus.). 24p. (J). (ps-ps). pap. 3.29 (978-1-59445-042-6(0)) Dogs in Hats Children's Publishing Co.

Stein, David Ezra. Cowboy Ned & Andy. Stein, David Ezra, illus. 2006. (Illus.). 32p. (J). (ps-1). 14.95 (978-1-4169-0041-2(1) , Simon & Schuster Children's Publishing) Simon & Schuster Children's Publishing.

—Ned's New Friend. Stein, David Ezra, illus. 2007. (Cowboy Ned & Andy Ser.). 32p. (J). (ps-1). 14.99 (978-1-4169-2490-6(6) , Simon & Schuster Children's Publishing) Simon & Schuster Children's Publishing.

Stern, Shirley. Giddy-Up! 2008. (Franny's Feet Ser.). 32p. (J). (ps-1). 3.99 (*978-1-4169-4916-9(X) , Simon Scribbles) Simon & Schuster Children's Publishing.

Stevenson, James. Runaway Horse! A Novel. Date not set. (J). 15.99 (978-0-06-051978-0(9)); 16.89 (978-0-06-051979-7(7)) HarperCollins Pubs.

Street, Jane. Snow Baby. Yandell, Charlene, illus. 2002. 30p. (J). 11.95 (978-1-887905-56-5(1)) Parkway Pubs., Inc.

Strong, Frances Dinkins. Beth's Fella. Payne, Kay, illus. 2006. 112p. (J). pap. 9.95 (978-0-9720267-6-5(2)) Learning Abilities Bks.

—A Lucky Pair. Roscoe, Mattie Dinkins, illus. l.t. ed. 2002. 28p. pap. 6.49 (978-0-9720267-0-3(3)) Learning Abilities Bks.

Sundberg, Peggy. Isabelle Lives a Dream. Wiles, Pat, illus. l.t. ed. 2003. 32p. (J). 15.95 (978-0-9721057-1-2(9)) Cowgirl Peg Enterprises LLC.

—Lonesome the Little Horse: His Mountain Adventure. l.t. ed. 2002. (Illus.). 32p. (J). 15.95 (978-0-9721057-0-5(0)) Cowgirl Peg Enterprises LLC.

Surprise for Horse. 2000. 14p. (J). bds. 7.95 (978-0-7525-4603-2(1)) Parragon, Inc.

Swobud, I. K. The Case of the Blue-Ribbon-Horse. 1998. (New Adventures of Mary-Kate & Ashley Ser.). 86p. (J). (gr. 2-7). pap. 3.99 (978-0-590-29309-9(5)) Scholastic, Inc.

Szymanski, Lois. A Perfect Pony. 2005. (Charming Ponies Ser.). 80p. (Orig.). (J). pap. 4.99 (978-0-06-078144-6(0)) HarperCollins Pubs.

—A Pony Promise. 2005. (Charming Ponies Ser.). (Illus.). 96p. (J). pap. 4.99 (978-0-06-078143-9(2) , Harper Festival) HarperCollins Pubs.

Szymanski, Lois K. Charming Ponies: A Pony Named Patches. 2008. (Charming Ponies Ser.). 96p. (J). pap. 4.99 (*978-0-06-128871-5(3) , Harper Festival) HarperCollins Pubs.

—A First Pony Library. 2007. (Charming Ponies Ser.: No. 1). (J). (gr. 2-5). pap., pap. 14.99 (*978-0-06-143029-9(3) , Harper Festival) HarperCollins Pubs.

—A Pony to the Rescue. 2007. (Charming Ponies Ser.). 96p. (J). (gr. 2-5). pap. 4.99 (*978-0-06-128869-2(1) , Harper Festival) HarperCollins Pubs.

Talbott, Hudson. O'sullivan Stew. 2001. (gr. k-3). lib. bdg. 15.30 (978-0-613-33718-2(2)) Tandem Library Bks.

Taschek, Karen. Horse of Seven Moons. 2005. (Illus.). 192p. (YA). pap. 14.95 (978-0-8263-3215-8(3)) Univ. of New Mexico Pr.

Tate, Nikki. Keeping Secrets at Dark Creek. 2002. (StableMates Ser.: Vol. 7). (Illus.). 154p. (J). (gr. 3-8). pap. 5.95 (978-1-55039-123-7(2)) Sono Nis Pr. CAN. *Dist:* Orca Bk. Pubs. USA.

—Raven's Revenge, Vol. 5. 1999. (Stablemates Ser.: Vol. 5). 154p. (J). (gr. 3-7). pap. 4.50 (978-1-55039-095-7(3)) Sono Nis Pr. CAN. *Dist:* Orca Bk. Pubs. USA.

—Raven's Revenge. 1999. (gr. 3-6). lib. bdg. 12.40 (978-0-613-29726-4(1)) Tandem Library Bks.

—Return to Skoki Lake. 2000. (Stablemates Ser.: Vol. 6). (Illus.). 192p. (J). (gr. 4-7). pap. 4.95 (978-1-55039-102-2(X)) Sono Nis Pr. CAN. *Dist:* Orca Bk. Pubs. USA.

—Return to Skoki Lake. 1999. (gr. 3-6). lib. bdg. 12.95 (978-0-613-29730-1(X)) Tandem Library Bks.

Taylor, Bonnie Highsmith. Kodi's Mare. Marks, Dea, illus. 2000. (Cover-to-Cover Novel Ser.). 82p. (J). pap. (978-0-7891-2929-1(9)); (gr. 2-5). lib. bdg. 13.95 (978-0-7807-8962-3(8)) Perfection Learning Corp.

Taylor, Lori. What to Do When Your Hoof Turns Blue!!! Taylor, Lori, illus. l.t. ed. 2006. (Illus.). 28p. (J). per. 11.99 ***(978-1-59879-220-1(2))*** Lifevest Publishing, Inc.

Tazewell, Charles. The Littlest Red Horse. Sofo, Frank, illus. 2001. (J). (ps-3). 16.95 (978-0-8249-5405-5(X) , Ideals Children's Bks.) Ideals Pubns.

—The Littlest Red Horse. Sofo, Frank, illus. 1999. 32p. (J). (gr. 2-5). 16.95 (978-1-57102-157-1(4)) Warehousing & Fulfillment Specialists, LLC (WFS, LLC).

Thorpe, Kiki. Horsefeathers! 2001. (Woody's Roundup Ser.: No. 6). (Illus.). 64p. (gr. 2-5). pap. 4.99 (978-0-7868-4461-6(2)) Disney Pr.

Tiddle, Deanna Hessedal. Apartment Horse & Friends. 2003. 62p. (J). pap. 9.95 (978-0-7414-1724-4(3)) Infinity Publishing.

Tomlinson, Theresa. Voyage of the Snake Lady. 2007. 400p. (J). lib. bdg. 18.89 ***(978-0-06-084740-1(9));*** (YA). (gr. 7 up). 17.99 ***(978-0-06-084739-5(5))*** HarperCollins Pubs. (Eos).

Toresen, Eli B. Summer with Prince (0711) 2007. (YA). ***(978-1-933343-68-6(0)*** , PONY) Stabenfeldt Inc.

—Yearbook Trouble at the Riding Stable 0711. 2007. (YA). ***(978-1-933343-67-9(2))*** Stabenfeldt Inc.

Torrel, Wendy. Guardian of Dreams: A Bedtime Story. Klingbeil, Kendall, illus. l.t. ed. 2004. 32p. (J). 14.95 (978-0-9746890-0-5(9)); pap. 10.95 (978-0-9746890-1-2(7)) White Tulip Publishing.

Tracey, Diane Eurich. Sensational Sidney the Circus Horse. Kuessner, Pat, ed. Thiel, Caresse C., illus. 2002. 28p. (Orig.). (J). (gr. 2-6). pap. 12.00 (978-0-9701441-5-7(6) , 628548) Bokmal Pr.

Tuminelly, Nancy. Horse Shoes. 2006. (Fact & Fiction Ser.). (Illus.). 24p. (J). 21.35 (978-1-59679-943-1(9) , Sand-Castle) ABDO Publishing Co.

—Horse Shoes. Nobens, C. A., illus. 2006. (Fact & Fiction Ser.). 24p. (J). pap. (978-1-59679-944-8(7)) ABDO Publishing Co.

Turnbull, Ann. El Caballo de Arena. Foreman, Michael, illus. (Barril Sin Fondo Ser.). (SPA.). (J). (gr. 3-5). pap. (978-968-6465-00-6(6)) Casa de Estudios de Literatura y Talleres Artisticos Amaquemecan A.C. MEX. *Dist:* Lectorum Pubns., Inc.

Turnbull, Ann & Foreman, Michael. Sandhorse. 2002. (Illus.). 32p. (J). pap. 11.00 (978-1-84270-099-0(5)) Andersen GBR. *Dist:* Trafalgar Square Publishing.

Tyrrell, Helen. Nora & the Dancing Horse. 2003. 231p. (J). pap. 14.95 (978-0-7414-1349-9(3)) Infinity Publishing.

—Nora & the Summer Horses. 2000. 204p. (J). pap. 13.95 (978-0-7414-0529-6(6)) Infinity Publishing.

Ulrich, Ann Carol. The Mystery at Hickory Hill: Annette Vetter Adventure #1. 2006. (Illus.). 196p. (YA). per. 9.95 (978-0-944851-25-8(8)) Earth Star Pubns.

Valeska, Jon & Fripp, Jean. Thunder & the Pirates. Fripp, Jean, ed. Laroche, Bridget, illus. 2004. 32p. (J). (gr. k-4). 5.99 (978-0-9701008-9-4(2)) Bicast, Inc.

Van Camp, Richard. What's the Most Beautiful Thing You Know about Horses? Littlechild, George, illus. 32p. (J). 2003. pap. 7.95 (978-0-89239-185-1(5)); 1998. (gr. 1 up). 15.95 (978-0-89239-154-7(5)) Children's Bk. Pr.

—What's the Most Beautiful Thing You Know about Horses? 2003. (gr. k-3). lib. bdg. 16.40 (978-0-613-70988-0(8)) Tandem Library Bks.

Vaughan, Christina. The Horse Knows the Way. 2000. (Illus.). (J). (gr. 2-6). spiral bd. 18.95 (978-0-9641697-5-3(4) , You-Draw-It Bks.) Castlebrook Pubns.

Wallace, Bill. Beauty. 2007. 192p. (J). pap. 5.99 ***(978-1-4169-4942-8(9)*** , Aladdin) Simon & Schuster Children's Publishing.

Wallen, Virginia. Sonny & Sammy. 2006. 17.00 (978-0-8059-9809-2(8)) Dorrance Publishing Co., Inc.

Walsh, Ann. Horse Power. 2007. (Orca Currents Ser.). 112p. lib. bdg. ***(978-1-55143-883-2(6));*** (YA). (gr. 5 up). pap. ***(978-1-55143-881-8(X))*** Orca Bk. Pubs.

Warner, Gertrude Chandler. The Mystery of the Wild Ponies. 2000. (Boxcar Children Ser.: Vol. 77). (Illus.). (J). (gr. 2-5). (978-0-606-18908-8(4)) Tandem Library Bks.

—Mystery of the Wild Ponies. 2000. (gr. 3-6). lib. bdg. 11.80 (978-0-613-27993-2(X)) Tandem Library Bks.

Warner, Gertrude Chandler, creator. The Mystery of the Wild Ponies, Vol. 77. 2004. (Boxcar Children Ser.: No. 77). (Illus.). 135p. (J). (gr. 2-5). pap. 3.95 (978-0-8075-5466-1(9)) Whitman, Albert & Co.

Watch Out, Sara! 2006. (J). (978-1-933343-35-8(4) , PONY) Stabenfeldt Inc.

Watson, Sammy, illus. Susie, the Whispering Horse. 2000. 32p. (J). (gr. k-7). 17.95 (978-1-893672-01-7(8)) Johnson, Michael Presentations.

Weale, David. Everything That Shines. McNevin, Dale, illus. 28p. pap. 6.95 (978-0-9698606-8-6(4)) Acorn Pr., The CAN. *Dist:* Goose Lane Editions.

Wedekind, Annie. A Horse of Her Own. 2008. 288p. (J). 16.95 ***(978-0-312-36927-9(1))*** Feiwel & Friends.

Weed, Thurlow R. Camel Fables from the Sailors of the Sudan. 2004. 84p. pap. 15.95 (978-0-7414-2229-3(8)) Infinity Publishing.

Welch, Sheila Kelly. A Horse for All Seasons: Collected Stories. 2003. (Illus.). 160p. (YA). (gr. 4-6). pap. 11.95 (978-1-59078-035-0(3)) Boyds Mills Pr.

West, Tracy. Dreamer: Inspired by a True Story. 2005. (Scholastic Reader Ser.). (Illus.). 32p. (J). (ps-3). pap. 3.99 (978-0-439-77495-6(0)) Scholastic, Inc.

Weyn, Suzanne & Earhart, Kristin. Snowflake. Rogers, Jacqueline, illus. 2006. (Breyer Stablemates Ser.). 48p. (J). pap. 4.99 (978-0-439-84313-3(8) , Cartwheel Bks.) Scholastic, Inc.

Whint, Ana Lee. Espalemit. 2003. (ENG.). 112p. pap. 9.95 ***(978-0-595-26259-5(7)*** , Writers Club Pr.) iUniverse, Inc.

Whitney, Kim Ablon. The Perfect Distance. 2007. 256p. (YA). (gr. 7). pap. 5.99 (978-0-553-49467-9(8) , Laurel Leaf) Random Hse. Children's Bks.

Williams, Susan. Wind Rider. 2006. 320p. (J). 16.99 (978-0-06-087236-6(5)); (YA). lib. bdg. 17.89 (978-0-06-087237-3(3)) HarperCollins Pubs.

Willis, Jeanne & Ross, Tony. Dozy Mare. 2006. (Illus.). 32p. (J). (ps-k). pap. 9.99 (978-1-84270-524-7(5)) Andersen GBR. *Dist:* Independent Pubs. Group.

Wilson, Diane Lee. Firehorse. 2006. 336p. (J). (gr. 7 up). 16.95 (978-1-4169-1551-5(6) , McElderry, Margaret K.) Simon & Schuster Children's Publishing.

—I Rode a Horse of Milk White Jade. 1999. (Illus.). 304p. (J). (gr. 5 up). pap. 7.99 (978-0-06-440773-1(X) , Harper Trophy) HarperCollins Pubs.

—I Rode a Horse of Milk White Jade. 1999. (Illus.). 288p. (J). (gr. k-9). lib. bdg. 15.30 (978-0-613-20158-2(2)) Tandem Library Bks.

—Rode a Horse of Milk White Jade. 1999. 14.64 (978-0-606-17306-3(4)) Tandem Library Bks.

Winfrey, Elizabeth. How to Hide a Horse. 1999. (gr. 3-6). lib. bdg. 11.80 (978-0-613-21732-3(2)) Tandem Library Bks.

Wojciechowska, Maia. A Kingdom in a Horse. 143p. (YA). (gr. 5 up). pap. 4.50 (978-0-8072-1391-9(8) , Listening Library) Random Hse. Audio Publishing Group.

Wolf, Carla. Moving Towards a Dream. 2006. 91p. pap. 14.95 ***(978-1-4241-5444-9(8))*** PublishAmerica, Inc.

Wood, Kim Marie. Forelocks, Fetlocks & Horse Tales. Graham, Kimberly, illus. 1999. 110p. (J). per. 5.95 (978-0-9671978-2-1(1)) Syncopated Pr.

Wyont, Wanda. Sunbeam. Huskins, Suzanne Hallier, illus. 2006. 32p. (J). 12.50 (978-1-933251-07-3(7)) Parkway Pubs., Inc.

Yorks, Sharon Lee. The Twin Who Wins. 2002. (Cloverleaf Ser.: Bk. 1). (Illus.). 224p. (J). (gr. 6 up). mass mkt. 5.99 (978-0-9720132-0-8(2)) Tumbleweed Publishing.

Young, Ed. Donkey Trouble. 1998. (J). (978-0-606-13342-5(9)) Tandem Library Bks.

Young, Ed & Adams, Tracey. The Lost Horse: A Chinese Folktale. 2004. (Illus.). 32p. (J). pap. 6.00 (978-0-15-205023-8(X) , Voyager Bks./Libros Viajeros) Harcourt Children's Bks.

Young, Ella. Tangle-Coated Horse. (Illus.). 186p. (J). pap. 12.95 (978-0-86315-517-8(0) , 971) Floris Bks. GBR. *Dist:* SteinerBooks, Inc.

Zoehfeld, Kathleen Weidner. Flicka: The Movie Novel. 2006. (Flicka Ser.). (Illus.). 144p. (J). pap. 4.99 (978-0-06-087606-7(9)) HarperCollins Pubs.

Zoehfeld, Kathleen Weidner, et al. Flicka: A Friend for Katy. 2006. (I Can Read Bks.). 32p. (J). pap. 3.99 (978-0-06-087609-8(3) , Harper Trophy) HarperCollins Pubs.

HORSES—HISTORY

Eytcheson, Pat & Mitchell, Mark. Let's Ride a Horse. 2000. (Illus.). 50p. (J). 9.95 (978-1-57168-354-0(2)) Eakin Pr.

The Horse, of Course: Individual Title Six Packs. (Action Packs Ser.). 128p. (gr. 3-5). 44.00 (978-0-7635-3308-3(4)) Rigby Education.

MacGregor, Carol. Shoshoni Pony: First Horse in the Northwest. Lee, Dick, illus. 2004. 32p. 15.95 (978-0-87004-431-1(1) , 043110) Caxton Pr.

Oakeshott, R. Ewart. A Knight & His Horse. 2nd rev. ed. 1999. (Illus.). 128p. (gr. 5-12). pap. 13.95 (978-0-8023-1297-6(7)) Dufour Editions, Inc.

Stone, Lynn M. Mustang. 2003. (Animals in U.S. History Ser.). (Illus.). 24p. (J). 25.64 (978-1-58952-700-3(3)) Rourke Publishing, LLC.

HORSES—PICTORIAL WORKS

Amirsadeghi, Hossein, et al, eds. Arabians. van Lent, Rik, Jr., photos by. 2006. (Illus.). 256p. pap. 35.00 (978-0-8118-5401-6(9)) Chronicle Bks. LLC.

Chester, Laura & DeMari, Donna. Heartbeat for Horses. 2007. 176p. 29.95 ***(978-1-59543-443-2(7))*** Willow Creek Pr., Inc.

Langrish, Bob, et al, photos by. Dream Horses: A Poster Book. 2004. (Illus.). 64p. (J). pap. 9.95 (978-1-58017-574-6(0) , 67574, Storey Kids) Storey Publishing, LLC.

Murawski, Laura. How to Draw Horses. 2001. (Kid's Guide to Drawing Ser.). (Illus.). 24p. (J). (gr. 3). lib. bdg. 21.25 (978-0-8239-5552-7(4) , PowerKids Pr.) Rosen Publishing Group, Inc., The.

Roalf, Peggy. Horses: Looking at Paintings. 2004. (Illus.). 48p. (J). (gr. 4-8). reprint ed. 17.00 (978-0-7567-7531-5(0)) DIANE Publishing Co.

Steadman, Barbara. Horse & Stable: Sticker Picture Book. 1998. (Illus.). (J). pap. 5.95 (978-0-486-40380-9(7)) Dover Pubns., Inc.

HORSES—POETRY

Alonzo, Sandra. Gallop-O-Gallop. Murphy, Kelly, illus. 2007. 40p. (J). (ps-4). 16.99 (978-0-8037-2967-4(7) , Dial) Penguin Group (USA) Inc.

Chester, Laura & DeMari, Donna. Heartbeat for Horses. 2007. 176p. 29.95 ***(978-1-59543-443-2(7))*** Willow Creek Pr., Inc.

Schwartz, Betty Ann, ed. My Kingdom for a Horse. Berenzy, Alix, illus. rev. ed. 2001. 48p. (J). (gr. 3-7). 17.95 (978-0-8050-6212-0(2) , Holt, Henry & Co. Bks. For Young Readers) Holt, Henry & Co.

HORSES—TRAINING

Bolte, Betty. Dressage. 2001. (Horse Library). (Illus.). 64p. (J). 25.00 (978-0-7910-6656-0(8) , Chelsea Hse.) Facts On File, Inc.

Dubowski, Cathy East & Dubowski, Mark. A Horse Named Seabiscuit. Rowe, Michael Langham, illus. 2003. (All Aboard Reading Ser.). 48p. (J). (gr. 2-6). mass mkt. 3.99 (978-0-448-43342-4(7) , Grosset & Dunlap) Penguin Group (USA) Inc.

Lineberger Bridges, Emily. Dear Dolly: A How Not to Guide for Working with Horses. Stafford, Susan, ed. Shields, Bonnie, illus. 2002. 167p. per. 19.95 (978-0-9646181-7-6(6)) K&B Products.

Roberts, Monty. Man Who Listens to Horses. 1999. (gr. 7-12). lib. bdg. 16.45 (978-0-613-28941-2(2)) Tandem Library Bks.

—The Man Who Listens to Horses: The Story of a Real Life Horse Whisperer. 1999. (YA). (978-0-606-16370-5(0)) Tandem Library Bks.

Weatherwax, Barbara. Gaited Games: Activities for the Young Gaited Horse Fancier. Weatherwax, Barbara, illus. 2004. (Illus.). 50p. (J). (gr. 1-8). 10.00 (978-0-9740793-2-5(4)) Markwin Pr.

HORSESHOE CRABS

Crenson, Victoria. Horseshoe Crabs & Shorebirds: The Story of a Food Web. Cannon, Annie, illus. 2003. 32p. (J). 16.95 (978-0-7614-5115-0(3)) Cavendish, Marshall Corp.

Schaefer, Lola M. Horseshoe Crabs. 2002. (Musty-Crusty Animals Ser.). 24p. (J). (ps-1). lib. bdg. 17.08 (978-1-58810-515-8(6)); (Illus.). pap. 5.25 (978-1-58810-724-4(8) , 91377) Heinemann Library.

HORTICULTURE

see Gardening

HOSPITALITY

see Entertaining

HOSPITALS

see also Children—Hospitals; Medical Centers; Nurses and Nursing

Amos, Janine. Hospital. Green, Gwen, illus. Hampton, Angela, photos by. 2002. (Separations Ser.). 32p. (J). (gr. 3 up). lib. bdg. 23.33 (978-0-8368-3091-0(1)) Stevens, Gareth Inc.

Attebury, Nancy Garhan. Out & about at the Hospital. Trover, Zachary, illus. 2005. (Field Trips Ser.). 24p. (J). (ps). lib. bdg. 23.93 (978-1-4048-1148-5(6)) Picture Window Bks.

Aylmore, Angela. We Work in a Hospital. 2006. (Where We Work Ser.). (Illus.). 24p. (J). 21.36 (978-1-4109-2246-5(4)) Raintree.

—We Work in a Hospital. 2006. (Where We Work Ser.). (Illus.). 24p. (J). (978-1-4109-2251-9(0)) Steck-Vaughn.

Bailey, Debbie. The Hospital. Huszar, Susan, photos by. 2000. (Talk-about-Bks.: No. 15). (Illus.). 14p. (J). (gr. k-ps). bds. 5.95 (978-1-55037-632-6(2)) Annick Pr., Ltd. CAN. *Dist:* Firefly Bks., Ltd.

—El Hospital. Huszar, Susan, photos by. 2000. (Hablemos Ser.: No. 15). (SPA., Illus.). 14p. (J). (gr. k-ps). bds. 5.95 (978-1-55037-638-8(1)) Annick Pr., Ltd. CAN. *Dist:* Firefly Bks., Ltd.

Beylon, Cathy. At the Hospital. 2003. (Dover Coloring Bks.). (Illus.). 32p. (J). pap. 2.95 (978-0-486-43033-1(2)) Dover Pubns., Inc.

—Hospital Emergency Room Sticker Activity Book. 2001. (Illus.). 4p. (J). pap. 1.50 (978-0-486-41626-7(7)) Dover Pubns., Inc.

Fleming, Sarah. I Broke My Arm. 2000. (Cambridge Reading Ser.). (Illus.). 10p. pap. 5.00 (978-0-521-77462-8(4)) Cambridge Univ. Pr.

Gordon, Sharon. ¿Qué Hay Dentro de un Hospital? 2006. (Bookworms Ser.). (SPA & ENG., Illus.). 32p. (J). lib. bdg. 22.79 (978-0-7614-2394-2(X)) Cavendish, Marshall Corp.

—What's Inside a Hospital? (¿Qué Hay Dentro de un Hospital?) 2006. (Bookworms Ser.). (ENG & SPA., Illus.). 32p. (J). lib. bdg. 22.79 (978-0-7614-2474-1(1)) Cavendish, Marshall Corp.

Hunter, Rebecca. My First Visit to Hospital. Fairclough, Chris, photos by. 2007. (First Times Ser.). (Illus.). 21p. (J). (ps-1). per. 10.95 ***(978-0-237-52694-8(8)*** , Evans Brothers, Limited) Evans Publishing Group GBR. *Dist:* Independent Pubs. Group.

Kalman, Bobbie. Hospital Workers in the Emergency Room. 2004. (My Community & Its Helpers Ser.). (Illus.). 32p. (J). (978-0-7787-2095-9(0)); pap. (978-0-7787-2123-9(X)) Crabtree Publishing Co.

Koll, Hilary, et al. Using Math in the ER. 2006. (Math-works!). (Illus.). 31p. (J). pap. (978-0-8368-6769-5(6)); lib. bdg. (978-0-8368-6762-6(9)) Stevens, Gareth Inc.

Murphy, Patricia. Everything You Need to Know about Staying in the Hospital. 2005. (Need to Know Library). (Illus.). 64p. (YA). (gr. 7-12). 25.25 (978-0-8239-3325-9(3)) Rosen Publishing Group, Inc., The.

Price, Susan. The Elves & the Shoemaker Big Book American English Edition. 2000. (Cambridge Reading Ser.). (Illus.). pap. 28.00 (978-0-521-79889-1(2)) Cambridge Univ. Pr.

Rosenberg, Pam. Ugh! Icky, Sticky, Gross Stuff in the Hospital. 2007. (Icky, Sticky, Gross-Out Bks.). 24p. (J). (gr. 2-6). 22.79 ***(978-1-59296-897-8(X))*** Child's World, Inc.

Rosinsky, Natalie M. A Hospital. 2003. 24p. (J). lib. bdg. 21.35 (978-1-58340-327-3(2)) Smart Apple Media.

Schaefer, Lola M. Hospital. 2000. (Who Works Here? Ser.). (Illus.). 32p. (J). (gr. 1-3). lib. bdg. 21.36 (978-1-57572-519-2(3)) Heinemann Library.

Shea, Kitty. Out & About at the Vet Clinic. Shipe, Becky, illus. 2004. (Field Trips Ser.). 24p. (C). (gr. k-3). 23.93 (978-1-4048-0296-4(7)) Picture Window Bks.

Sloan, Peter. Hospital. 1999. (gr. k-3). lib. bdg. 11.80 (978-0-613-30479-5(9)) Tandem Library Bks.

Thomas, Pat. Do I Have to Go to the Hospital? A First Look at Going to the Hospital. Harker, Lesley, illus. 2006. (First Look At... Ser.). 32p. (J). pap. 6.99 (978-0-7641-3215-5(6)) Barron's Educational Series, Inc.

Townsend, John. Bedpans, Blood & Bandages: A History of Hospitals. (Freestyle Express Ser.). 2006. 56p. (978-1-4109-2539-8(0)); 2006. 48p. pap. (978-1-4109-2544-2(7)); 2005. (Illus.). 56p. (J). lib. bdg. 32.86 (978-1-4109-1334-0(1)) Steck-Vaughn.

Tubbs, Janet. A Trip to the Hospital, 2000. (Illus.). 16p. (J). (ps-4). pap. 19.95 (978-1-881185-24-6(9)) Arcadia Pr.

Wells, Pauline. Going into Hospital. (Talkabouts Ser.: No. 735-12). (Illus.). 48p. (J). (ps). 3.50 (978-0-7214-0849-1(4) , Dutton Juvenile) Penguin Group (USA) Inc.

HOSPITALS—FICTION

Accardo, Reba, told to. Surgery for Me? 2005. (J). pap. 8.00 (978-0-8059-6697-8(8)) Dorrance Publishing Co., Inc.

Adler, David A. The Valentine Baby Mystery. Natti, Susanna, illus. 2006. (Cam Jansen Ser.: No. 25). 80p. (J). (gr. 2). pap. 3.99 (978-0-14-240694-6(5) , Puffin) Penguin Group (USA) Inc.

Baglio, Ben M. Hound at the Hospital. Baum, Ann & Gregory, Jenny, illus. 2004. (Animal Ark Hauntings Ser.). 144p. (J). pap. 3.99 (978-0-439-44891-8(3)) Scholastic, Inc.

Blacker, Terence & Ross, Tony. In Stitches with Ms. Wiz, 4 vols. 2003. (Illus.). 57p. (J). pap. 8.99 (978-0-330-34764-8(0) , Pan) Pan Macmillan GBR. *Dist:* Trafalgar Square Publishing.

Blance, Ellen & Cook. Monster Goes to the Hospital. Date not set. (Illus.). 40p. pap. 129.15 (978-0-582-19305-5(2)) Addison-Wesley Longman, Ltd. GBR. *Dist:* Trans-Atlantic Pubns., Inc.

Bond, Michael & Jankel, Karen. Paddington Bear Goes to the Hospital. Alley, R. W., illus. 2001. (Paddington Ser.). 40p. (J). (ps-3). 12.95 (978-0-694-01563-4(6)) HarperCollins Pubs.

Bourgeois, Paulette. Franklin Goes to the Hospital. ed. 2004. (Illus.). (J). (ps-2). spiral bd. (978-0-616-03024-0(X)); spiral bd. (978-0-616-04547-3(6)) Canadian National Institute for the Blind/Institut National Canadien pour les Aveugles.

—Franklin Goes to the Hospital. Clark, Brenda, illus. 2000. (Franklin Ser.). (J). (ps-3). 30p. (978-1-55074-734-8(7)); 32p. (978-1-55074-732-4(0)) Kids Can Pr., Ltd.

—Franklin Goes to the Hospital. Clark, Brenda, illus. 2000. (Franklin Ser.). 32p. (J). (ps-3). pap. 4.99 (978-0-439-08370-6(2)) Scholastic, Inc.

—Franklin Goes to the Hospital. Clark, Brenda, illus. 2000. (J). (ps-ps). lib. bdg. 12.40 (978-0-613-25254-6(3)) Tandem Library Bks.

—Franklin Goes to the Hospital. 2000. (Franklin Ser.). (Illus.). (J). (ps-3). 11.30 (978-0-606-18547-9(X)) Tandem Library Bks.

—Franklin Va al Hospital. Varela, Alejandra Lopez, tr. Clark, Brenda, illus. (SPA.). (J). (gr. k-2). pap. 5.95 (978-1-930332-26-3(2) , LC1130); rein bd. 10.95 (978-1-930332-27-0(0) , LC1301) Lectorum Pubns., Inc.

—Franklin Va Al Hospital. 2002. (SPA.). (gr. k-3). lib. bdg. 14.10 (978-0-613-64502-7(2)) Tandem Library Bks.

Bridwell, Norman. Clifford Visita el Hospital. Bridwell, Norman, illus. 2000. (Clifford, the Big Red Dog Ser.). (SPA., Illus.). 32p. (J). (ps-k). pap. 3.50 (978-0-439-18897-5(0) , SO4989, Scholastic en Espanol) Scholastic, Inc.

—Clifford Visits the Hospital. Bridwell, Norman, illus. 2002. (Clifford, the Big Red Dog Ser.). (Illus.). (J). 11.45 (978-0-7587-5004-4(8)) Book Wholesalers, Inc.

—Clifford Visits the Hospital. Bridwell, Norman, illus. 2000. (Clifford, the Big Red Dog Ser.). (Illus.). 32p. (J). (ps-k). pap. 3.50 (978-0-439-14096-6(X)) Scholastic, Inc.

—Clifford Visits the Hospital. 2000. (ps-2). lib. bdg. 11.25 (978-0-613-24612-5(8)); (Illus.). (J). 10.30 (978-0-606-18868-5(1)) Tandem Library Bks.

—Clifford Vista el Hospital. 2000. (SPA.). (gr. k-3). lib. bdg. 10.95 (978-0-613-24613-2(6)) Tandem Library Bks.

Brill, Sarah. Glory. 2002. 140p. pap. 10.95 (978-1-876756-25-3(X)) Spinifex Pr. AUS. *Dist:* Independent Pubs. Group.

—Glory. 2002. (gr. 7-12). lib. bdg. 19.90 (978-0-613-85840-3(9)) Tandem Library Bks.

Brooks, Bruce. Vanishing. 2000. (J). pap. 4.95 (978-0-06-440754-0(3)); 1999. 112p. (YA). (gr. 5 up). 14.89 (978-0-06-028237-0(1) , Geringer, Laura Book) HarperCollins Pubs.

Bruna, Dick. Miffy in the Hospital: A Storybook. 1999. (Miffy Ser.). (Illus.). 28p. (J). (ps-k). 4.95 (978-1-56836-297-7(8)) Kodansha America, Inc.

Bucki, Jo Dee & O'Malley, John. Maya Visits a Hospital: Love Is the Best Medicine, 110 vols. Hicks, Mindy, ed. Matthews, Ashley, illus. l.t. ed. 2007. 32p. (J). per. 4.95 (978-0-9769069-0-2(2)) Maya Ventures & Publishing.

Campbell-Fells. Blue Ribbon Girls. 2005. 145p. pap. 13.95 (978-0-7414-2593-5(9)) Infinity Publishing.

Carmi, Daniella. Samir & Yonatan. Lotan, Yael, tr. from HEB. 2002. 192p. (J). (gr. 3-7). pap. 4.99 (978-0-439-13523-8(0) , Scholastic Paperbacks) Scholastic, Inc.

H
I

—Samir & Yonatan. 2000. (gr. 3-6). lib. bdg. 13.00 (978-0-613-45824-5(9)) Tandem Library Bks.

—Samir & Yonatan. 2000. (Illus.). 192p. (J). (gr. 3-7). pap. 15.95 (978-0-439-13504-7(4) , Levine, Arthur A. Bks.) Scholastic, Inc.

Choyce, Lesley. Sudden Impact. 2005. (Orca Currents Ser.). 112p. (J). (gr. 4-10). pap. 7.95 (978-1-55143-476-6(8)) Orca Bk. Pubs. USA.

Civardi, Anne. Going to the Hospital. Cartwright, Stephen, illus. rev. ed. 2005. 16p. (J). pap. 4.99 (978-0-7945-1006-0(X) , Usborne) EDC Publishing.

Coloring Fun Presbyterian Children's Hospital: Coloring/ Activity Book. 2006. (J). (***978-1-933934-30-3(1)***) Educational Adventures.

Cousins, Lucy. Maisy Goes to the Hospital. 2007. (Maisy Ser.). (Illus.). 32p. (J). (ps-k). 12.99 (978-0-7636-3377-6(1)) Candlewick Pr.

Davis, David. Nurse's Night Before Christmas. Rice, James, illus. 2003. 32p. pap. 15.95 (978-1-58980-152-3(0)) Pelican Publishing Co., Inc.

Dyer, K. C. Ms. Zephyr's Notebook. 2007. 206p. (YA). pap. 12.99 (***978-1-55002-691-7(7)*** , Boardwalk Bks.) Dundurn Group, The CAN. *Dist:* Univ. of Toronto Pr.

Fletcher, Christine. Tallulah Falls. 2006. 304p. (YA). 16.95 (978-1-58234-662-5(3) , Bloomsbury Children) Bloomsbury Publishing.

Grovet, Heather. What's Wrong with Rusty. 2004. 144p. (J). pap. 7.99 (978-0-8280-1756-5(5)) Review & Herald Publishing Assn.

Gutman, Anne. Gaspard in the Hospital. Hallensleben, Georg, illus. 2001. (Misadventures of Gaspard & Lisa Ser.). 32p. (J). (ps-3). 9.95 (978-0-375-81116-6(8) , Knopf Bks. for Young Readers) Random Hse. Children's Bks.

Halpern, Julie. Get Well Soon. 2007. 208p. (YA). (gr. 7 up). 16.95 (***978-0-312-36795-4(3)***) Feiwel & Friends.

Hapka, Cathy, et al. Merry Christmas, Curious George. Young, Mary O'Keefe, illus. 2006. 32p. (J). (ps-k). 16.00 (978-0-618-69237-8(1)) Houghton Mifflin Co.

Harcourt School Publishers Staff. Emergency! 3rd ed. 2002. (Trophies English Language Learners Ser.). (Illus.). pap. 5.10 (978-0-15-327886-0(2)) Harcourt Schl. Pubs.

Hoekstra, Molly. Upstream: A Novel. 2001. 221p. (YA). (gr. 6-12). pap. 15.95 (978-0-936389-86-8(9)) Tudor Pubs., Inc.

Holliday, Susan. Riding the Storm. 2000. 128p. (J). (978-1-85902-870-4(5)) Pont Bks.

Hopkins, Ellen. Impulse. 2007. 672p. (YA). (gr. 9 up). 16.99 (978-1-4169-0356-7(9) , McElderry, Margaret K.) Simon & Schuster Children's Publishing.

Hudson, Charlotte & McQuillan, Mary. Get Well Soon. Hudson, Charlotte & McQuillan, Mary, illus. 2007. (Illus.). 32p. (J). pap. 10.95 (***978-0-09-943945-5(X)*** , Red Fox) Random Hse. Children's Bks. GBR. *Dist:* Independent Pubs. Group.

Inns, Christopher. Help! 2006. (Illus.). 32p. pap. 7.95 (978-1-84507-123-3(9)) Lincoln, Frances Ltd. GBR. *Dist:* Perseus Distribution.

Jaworski, Anna M. My Brother Needs an Operation. Ball, Linda, illus. 1998. 57p. (J). (ps-5). 20.00 (978-0-9652508-2-5(2)) Baby Hearts Pr.

Johnson, Lindsay Lee. Worlds Apart. 2005. 176p. (J). (gr. 5). 16.95 (978-1-932425-28-4(4) , Lemniscaat) Boyds Mills Pr.

Karim, Roberta. This Is a Hospital, Not a Zoo! 2002. (gr. k-3). lib. bdg. 14.10 (978-0-613-72912-3(9)) Tandem Library Bks.

Kent, Renee Holmes. Robyn to the Rescue, Vol. 5. 2004. (Adventures in Misty Falls Ser.: Vol. 5). (Illus.). 100p. (J). (gr. 4-7). pap. 4.99 (978-1-56309-451-4(7) , N007109) New Hope Pubs.

Kerr, Judith. Mog Vee Ee Tee. 2005. (Illus.). 32p. (J). (ps). pap. 9.99 (978-0-00-717128-6(5) , HarperCollins Children's Bks.) HarperCollins Pubs. Ltd. GBR. *Dist:* Independent Pubs. Group.

Ladd, Debbie. Nurse Robin's Hats. Nakasone, Shaun, illus. 2006. 52p. (J). 16.95 (978-0-9727615-3-6(5)) Deb on Air Bks.

Leonetti, Mike. Number Four, Bobby Orr! Letain, Shayne, illus. (Hockey Heroes Ser.). 32p. (J). 2006. pap. 6.95 (978-1-55192-671-1(7)); 2003. 15.95 (978-1-55192-551-6(6)) Raincoast Bk. Distribution CAN. *Dist:* Perseus Distribution.

Mayer, Mercer. My Trip to the Hospital, No. 5. Mayer, Mercer, illus. 2005. (Little Critter Ser.). (Illus.). 24p. (J). (ps-2). pap. 3.99 (978-0-06-053949-8(6) , Harper Festival) HarperCollins Pubs.

McDaniel, Lurlene. Angels Watching over Me. 2002. (Angels Trilogy: No. 1). (J). (gr. 7-12). lib. bdg. 15.30 (978-0-613-90626-5(8)) Tandem Library Bks.

Mills, Claudia. Gus & Grandpa at the Hospital. Stock, Catherine, illus. 2001. (Sunburst Bks.). 48p. (J). (gr. 1-3). pap. 4.95 (978-0-374-42812-9(3) , Sunburst) Farrar, Straus & Giroux.

Morgan, Allen. Matthew & the Midnight Hospital. ed. 2004. (Illus.). (J). (gr. k-3). spiral bd. (978-0-616-01529-2(1)) Canadian National Institute for the Blind/Institut National Canadien pour les Aveugles.

Morgan, Allen & Martchenko, Michael. Matthew & the Midnight Hospital. 1999. (Matthew's Midnight Adventures Ser.). (Illus.). 32p. (J). (ps-3). 6.99 (978-0-7737-6014-1(8)) Stoddart Kids CAN. *Dist:* Fitzhenry & Whiteside, Ltd.

My Home Town Has a Hospital. 2000. 20p. (J). 7.95 (978-1-931006-50-7(4)) SteppingStones BookCard Pubns., LLC.

Nabb, Magdalen. Josie Smith in the Hospital. 2000. (Illus.). 126p. (J). pap. 7.99 (978-0-00-674720-8(5)) HarperCollins Pubs. Ltd. GBR. *Dist:* Independent Pubs. Group.

Nickel, Laura. Alexander's Hospital Stay. 2004. 45p. pap. 19.95 (978-1-4137-3060-9(4)) PublishAmerica, Inc.

Orr, Wendy. Peeling the Onion. 1999. (Laurel-Leaf Bks.). 176p. (YA). (gr. 7-12). mass mkt. 5.50 (978-0-440-22773-1(9) , Laurel Leaf) Random Hse. Children's Bks.

—Peeling the Onion: A Gripping Story, Told with Honesty & Biting Humour. 1999. (978-0-606-15918-0(5)); (gr. 7-12). lib. bdg. 13.00 (978-0-613-15339-3(1)) Tandem Library Bks.

Rey, H. A. Curious George Goes to the Hospital. Rey, H. A., illus. 2002. (Curious George Picture Bks.). (J). 13.79 (978-0-7587-2319-2(9)) Book Wholesalers, Inc.

Rose, Malcolm. Blood Brother. 2008. (Traces Ser.). 160p. (J). (gr. 4-9). pap. 5.95 (***978-0-7534-6170-9(6)*** , Kingfisher) Houghton Mifflin Co. Trade & Reference Div.

Ross, Tony. No Quiero Ir al Hospital. 2004. Tr. of I Don't Want to Go to Hospital. (SPA., Illus.). (J). 6.50 (978-84-348-7752-8(X)) SM Ediciones ESP. *Dist:* Lectorum Pubns., Inc.

Skene, Pat. The Whoosh of Gadoosh. Keith, Doug, illus. 2002. 32p. 15.95 (978-0-9701907-0-3(0)) Illumination Arts Publishing Co., Inc.

Slanina, Anne M. The Adventures of Annie Mouse: Baby Brother Goes to the Hospital. Agnew, Alicia, illus. 2007. 28p. (J). 16.99 (***978-0-9793379-1-8(7)***); per. 9.99 (***978-0-9793379-0-1(9)***) Annie Mouse Bks.

Slegers, Liesbet. Kevin Goes to the Hospital. 2002. (On My Way Ser.). (Illus.). 28p. (J). 7.95 (978-1-929132-33-1(6)) Kane/Miller Bk. Pubs., Inc.

Snicket, Lemony, pseud. The Hostile Hospital. Helquist, Brett, illus. 2001. (Series of Unfortunate Events Ser.: Bk. 8). (J). 272p. (gr. 5 up). 12.99 (978-0-06-440866-0(3)); 255p. (gr. 4-7). lib. bdg. (978-0-06-623919-4(2)); 8th ed. 272p. (gr. 5 up). lib. bdg. 15.89 (978-0-06-028891-4(4)) HarperCollins Pubs.

Snow, C. P. Last Things. 2000. 396p. 9.95 (978-1-84232-432-5(2)) House of Stratus, Inc. GBR. *Dist:* Midpoint Trade Bks., Inc.

Stilton, Geronimo. Merry Christmas, Geronimo! Wolf, Matt, illus. 2004. (Geronimo Stilton Ser.: No. 12). 113p. (J). lib. bdg. 10.00 (***978-1-4242-0281-2(7)***) Fitzgerald Bks.

Stock, Catherine, illus. Gus & Grandpa at the Hospital. 2002. (Gus & Grandpa Ser.). (J). 22.19 (978-0-7587-1234-9(0)) Book Wholesalers, Inc.

Thiel, Annie. Dakota's Mom Goes to the Hospital. 2006. (Playdate Kids Ser.). (Illus.). 14.95 (978-1-933721-03-3(0)) Playdate Kids Publishing.

Toten, Teresa. The Game. 2004. (Illus.). 160p. (YA). (gr. 9 up). pap. 7.95 (978-0-88995-232-4(9)) Red Deer Pr. CAN. *Dist:* Fitzhenry & Whiteside, Ltd.

Trembath, Don. Bachelors. 2002. (gr. 3-6). lib. bdg. 15.25 (978-0-613-85895-3(6)) Tandem Library Bks.

Vizzini, Ned. It's Kind of a Funny Story: A Novel. 2006. 448p. (gr. 8 up). 16.95 (978-0-7868-5196-6(1)) Miramax Bks.

Watson, Kim. A Trip to the Hospital. 2001. (Little Bill Books for Beginning Readers Ser.). (Illus.). (J). (978-0-606-21300-4(7)) Tandem Library Bks.

—Trip to the Hospital. 2001. (gr. k-3). lib. bdg. 11.25 (978-0-613-35705-0(1)) Tandem Library Bks.

Wells, Helen. Cherry Ames, Army Nurse. 2005. (YA). pap. (978-0-9771597-2-7(8)) Springer.

—Cherry Ames, Chief Nurse. 2005. (YA). pap. (978-0-9771597-3-4(6)) Springer.

—Cherry Ames, Senior Nurse. 2005. (YA). pap. (978-0-9771597-1-0(X)) Springer.

—Cherry Ames, Student Nurse. 2005. (YA). pap. (978-0-9771597-0-3(1)) Springer.

—Cherry Ames, Veterans' Nurse. 2006. ix, 213p. (J). (978-0-8261-0400-7(2)) Springer.

Whybrow, Ian. Sammy & the Robots. Reynolds, Adrian, illus. 2001. 32p. (J). (ps-1). pap. 15.95 (978-0-531-30327-6(6) , Orchard Bks.) Scholastic, Inc.

Wilkins, Harry. Rachael's Way. 2002. (gr. 7-12). lib. bdg. 18.75 (978-0-613-78043-8(4)) Tandem Library Bks.

HOSPITALS—STAFF

Kalman, Bobbie. Hospital Workers in the Emergency Room. 2004. (My Community & Its Helpers Ser.). (Illus.). 32p. (J). (978-0-7787-2095-9(0)); pap. (978-0-7787-2123-9(X)) Crabtree Publishing Co.

HOSTESSES, AIRLINE

see Flight Attendants

HOT RODS

see Automobile Racing; Automobiles

HOTELS, MOTELS, ETC.

Hotel Owners. 2000. (My Ancestors—My Heroes Ser.: Vol. 48). (J). (gr. 3-4). (978-1-893091-47-4(3)) Parker Publishing Co.

HOTELS, MOTELS, ETC.—FICTION

Alger, Horatio. Joe the Hotel Boy. 2006. pap. (***978-1-4065-0712-6(1)***) Dodo Pr.

Alger, Horatio. Joe the Hotel Boy: Or, Winning Out by Pluck. unabr. ed. 2002. (Polyglot Press Alger Ser.). (Illus.). (J). pap. 17.95 (978-1-4115-0015-0(6)) Polyglot Pr., Inc.

Anderson, M. T. The Clue of the Linoleum Lederhosen: M. T. Anderson's Thrilling Tales. Cyrus, Kurt, illus. 2007. (M. T. Anderson's Thrilling Tales Ser.). 272p. (J). pap. 5.95 (978-0-15-205407-6(3) , Harcourt Paperbacks) Harcourt Children's Bks.

Averill, Esther. The Hotel Cat: A Jenny's Cat Club Book. Averill, Esther, illus. 2005. (New York Review Children's Collection Ser.). (Illus.). 180p. (J). 17.95 (978-1-59017-159-2(4) , NYR Children's Collection) New York Review of Bks., Inc., The.

Carnevale, Michael. The Hotel Coolidge. 2007. 91p. pap. 10.95 (***978-0-7414-3752-5(X)***) Infinity Publishing.

Carr, Richard Wallace. Dolly & Ike at the Willard Hotel: Abraham Lincoln's Slippers. Parrish, Mary, illus. 2005. (J). 15.95 (978-0-933165-08-3(0)) Dicmar Publishing Co.

Evans, Douglas. The Elevator Family. 2001. (Illus.). 96p. (J). (gr. 3-7). pap. 5.50 (978-0-440-41650-0(7) , Yearling) Random Hse. Children's Bks.

Evelyn. Lucy the Elephant & Sami the Mouse: A Bedtime Story. Conforti, John W., tr. Conforti, John W., illus. 2003. (J). (978-0-9740115-0-9(9)) WeBeANS Corp.

—Lucy the Elephant & Sami the Mouse: The Birthday Party. Conforti, John W., illus. 2004. (J). (978-0-9740115-1-6(7)) WeBeANS Corp.

Fevens, Irene. New Time New Place. 2000. 252p. (YA). mass mkt. (978-0-9686720-6-0(0)) Editions Odyssey.

Fine, Anne. The Tulip Touch. l.t. ed. 2000. (Illus.). 228p. (J). pap. (978-0-7540-6091-8(8) , CLP 288) BBC Audio.

—The Tulip Touch. unabr. l.t. ed. 2003. (Read-Along Ser.). 200p. (J). pap. 29.95 incl. audio (978-0-7540-6227-1(9) , RA028, Galaxy Children's Large Print) BBC Audiobooks America.

—The Tulip Touch. 1999. (978-0-606-16711-6(0)) Tandem Library Bks.

Funke, Cornelia. Ghosthunters & the Gruesome Invincible Lightning Ghost. 2006. (Ghosthunters Ser.). 192p. (J). pap. 4.99 (978-0-439-83309-7(4) , Scholastic Paperbacks); (Illus.). pap. 16.99 (978-0-439-84962-3(4) , Chicken Hse., The) Scholastic, Inc.

Gage, Jenny, photos by. Hotel Andromeda: Fiction by Heidi Julavits & Photographs by Jenny Gage. 2004. (Illus.). 90p. (YA). (gr. 13 up). 20.00 (978-1-891273-04-9(3)) Artspace Bks.

Grace, N. B. Double Trouble, Bk. 2. 2nd rev. ed. 2006. (Suite Life of Zack & Cody Ser.: Vol. 2). (Illus.). 80p. (gr. 2-5). pap. 3.99 (978-0-7868-4936-9(3)) Disney Pr.

Graham, Alastair. Full Moon Soup. 2007. (Illus.). 32p. (J). 12.95 (***978-1-905417-54-4(3)***) Boxer Bks., Ltd. GBR. *Dist:* Sterling Publishing Co., Inc.

Graham, Alistair. Full Moon Soup. Graham, Alistair, illus. 2003. (Full Moon Soup & Full Moon Afloat Ser.). (Illus.). 32p. (YA). pap. (978-1-85602-071-8(1)) Chrysalis Children's Bks.

Graham, Denise R. Curse of the Lost Grove. 2005. (Knights of the Silver Dragon Ser.: Bk. 10). (Illus.). 177p. (J). (***978-1-4156-3841-5(1)*** , Mirrorstone) Wizards of the Coast.

Hotel Horror. (Fantasmas de Fear Street Coleccion). (SPA.). (YA). (gr. 5-8). Vol. 1. pap. 7.95 (978-950-04-2091-4(0) , EM11732); Vol. 2. pap. 7.95 (978-950-04-2092-1(9) , EM11736) Emecé Editores S.A. ARG. *Dist:* Lectorum Pubns., Inc., Planeta Publishing Corp.

Hurst, Carol Otis. You Come to Yokum. Life, Kay, illus. 2005. 144p. (YA). (gr. 4-6). 15.00 (978-0-618-55122-4(0) , Walter Lorraine) Houghton Mifflin Co. Trade & Reference Div.

John Philip Duck. 2004. (J). 27.95 incl. audio (978-0-8045-6932-3(0)); 29.95 incl. audio compact disk (978-0-8045-4127-5(2)) Spoken Arts, Inc.

Johnson, Janet L. The Ritz Carlton Cat. l.t. ed. 1999. (Illus.). 12p. pap. 18.95 (978-0-9673389-0-3(5)) Johnson, Janet L.

King, M. C. Room of Doom, Bk. 3. 3rd rev. ed. 2006. (Suite Life of Zack & Cody Ser.: Vol. 3). (Illus.). 80p. (gr. 2-5). pap. 3.99 (978-0-7868-4937-6(1)) Disney Pr.

Kopetz, Mark. Red Herrings at Rock Island: A Door County Mystery. 2005. 15.00 (978-0-940473-42-3(9)) Caxton, Wm Ltd.

Kovacs, Deborah. Catie Copley. Williams, Jared T., illus. 2007. 32p. (J). (gr. k-3). 17.95 (***978-1-56792-332-2(1)***) Godine, David R. Pub.

Law, Felicia. Joey's Day at Rumble's Cave Hotel. Pak, Yoon Mi, illus. 2006. (Read-It! Readers Ser.). 32p. (J). (gr. 2-4). 18.60 (978-1-4048-1339-7(X)) Picture Window Bks.

—Rumble Meets Buddy Beaver. 2005. (Read-It! Readers Ser.). (Illus.). 32p. (J). (ps-k). lib. bdg. 18.60 (978-1-4048-1287-1(3)) Picture Window Bks.

—Rumble Meets Chester the Chef. Pak, Yoon Mi, illus. 2006. (Read-It! Readers Ser.). 32p. (J). (gr. 2-4). 18.60 (978-1-4048-1335-9(7)) Picture Window Bks.

—Rumble Meets Keesha Kangaroo. 2005. (Read-It! Readers Ser.). (Illus.). 32p. (J). (ps-k). lib. bdg. 18.60 (978-1-4048-1290-1(3)) Picture Window Bks.

—Rumble Meets Lucas Lizard. Pak, Yoon Mi, illus. 2006. (Read-It! Readers Ser.). 32p. (J). (gr. 2-4). 18.60 (978-1-4048-1334-2(9)) Picture Window Bks.

—Rumble Meets Milly the Maid. Pak, Yoon Mi, illus. 2007. (Read-It! Readers Ser.). (J). 19.93 (978-1-4048-1341-0(1)) Picture Window Bks.

—Rumble Meets Penny Panther. 2005. (Read-It! Readers Ser.). (Illus.). 32p. (J). (ps-k). lib. bdg. 18.60 (978-1-4048-1331-1(4)) Picture Window Bks.

—Rumble Meets Sylvia & Sally Swan. 2005. (Read-It! Readers Ser.). (Illus.). 32p. (J). (ps-k). lib. bdg. 18.60 (978-1-4048-1541-4(4)) Picture Window Bks.

—Rumble Meets Vikki Viper. Pak, Yoon Mi, illus. 2006. (Read-It! Readers Ser.). 32p. (J). (gr. 2-4). 18.60 (978-1-4048-1342-7(X)) Picture Window Bks.

—Rumble Meets Wally Warthog. 2005. (Read-It! Readers Ser.). (Illus.). 32p. (J). (ps-k). lib. bdg. 18.60 (978-1-4048-1289-5(X)) Picture Window Bks.

—Rumble Meets Wilson Wolf. Pak, Yoon Mi, illus. 2006. (Read-It! Readers: Rumble's Cave Hotel Ser.). 32p. (J). (gr. k-3). (978-1-4048-1288-8(1)) Picture Window Bks.

—Rumble the Dragon's Cave. 2005. (Read-It! Readers Ser.). (Illus.). 32p. (J). (ps-k). lib. bdg. 18.60 (978-1-4048-1353-3(5)) Picture Window Bks.

Liebig, Nelda Johnson. Carrie & the Boarding House. 2005. 128p. (J). pap. 10.95 (978-1-883953-35-5(9)) Midwest Traditions, Inc.

Mason, Jane B. & Hines-Stephens, Sarah. Inn Trouble. Shelley, John, illus. 2005. 69p. (J). (***978-1-4156-0304-8(9)*** , Aladdin) Simon & Schuster Children's Publishing.

Naylor, Phyllis Reynolds. Bernie Magruder & the Bats in the Belfry. 2004. (Bernie Magruder Ser.). (Illus.). 144p. (J). pap. 5.99 (978-0-689-85067-7(0) , Aladdin) Simon & Schuster Children's Publishing.

—Bernie Magruder & the Bats in the Belfry. DiTerlizzi, Tony, illus. 2003. (Bernie Magruder Ser.). 144p. (J). (gr. 4-7). 16.95 (978-0-689-85066-0(2) , Atheneum) Simon & Schuster Children's Publishing.

—Bernie Magruder & the Bats in the Belfry. l.t. ed. 2003. (Bernie Magruder Ser.). 139p. (J). 22.95 (978-0-7862-5739-3(3)) Thorndike Pr.

—Bernie Magruder & the Case of the Big Stink. 2001. 11.64 (978-0-606-22812-1(8)) Tandem Library Bks.

—Bernie Magruder & the Disappearing Bodies. 2001. 11.64 (978-0-606-22813-8(6)); (gr. 3-6). lib. bdg. 13.00 (978-0-613-50182-8(9)) Tandem Library Bks.

—Bernie Magruder & the Disappearing Bodies. l.t. ed. 2001. (Juvenile Ser.). 153p. (J). 20.95 (978-0-7862-3467-7(9)) Thorndike Pr.

—Bernie Magruder & the Haunted Hotel. 2001. 11.64 (978-0-606-22814-5(4)) Tandem Library Bks.

—Bernie Magruder & the Haunted Hotel. l.t. ed. 2001. 127p. (J). 20.95 (978-0-7862-3600-8(0)) Thorndike Pr.

—Bernie Magruder & the Pirate's Treasure. 2001. (978-0-606-22788-9(1)); (gr. 3-6). lib. bdg. 13.00 (978-0-613-22950-0(9)) Tandem Library Bks.

Nixon & Brush. Champagne with a Corpse. (Thumbprint Mysteries Ser.). 32.86 (978-0-8092-0420-5(7)) McGraw-Hill/Contemporary.

O'Connor, Barbara. Greetings from Nowhere. 2008. 208p. (J). 16.00 (***978-0-374-39937-5(9)***) Farrar, Straus & Giroux.

Page, Katherine Hall. Down East. 1998. (Christie & Company Ser.). (YA). (gr. 6-8). reprint ed. pap. 3.99 (978-0-380-78033-4(X)) HarperCollins Pubs.

Paratore, Coleen. The Cupid Chronicles. 2006. (Wedding Planner's Daughter Ser.). 224p. (J). 15.95 (978-1-4169-0867-8(6) , Simon & Schuster Children's Publishing) Simon & Schuster Children's Publishing.

Paratore, Coleen Murtagh. The Cupid Chronicles. 2008. (Wedding Planner's Daughter Ser.). 224p. (J). pap. 5.99 (***978-1-4169-5484-2(8)*** , Aladdin) Simon & Schuster Children's Publishing.

—Willa by Heart. 2008. (Wedding Planner's Daughter Ser.). 240p. (J). 15.99 (***978-1-4169-4076-0(6)***) Simon & Schuster Children's Publishing.

Pearson, Mary E. A Room on Lorelei Street. rev. ed. 2005. 272p. (YA). 16.95 (978-0-8050-7667-7(0)) Holt, Henry & Co.

Pinkwater, Daniel M. At the Hotel Larry. Pinkwater, Jill, illus. 2005. 32p. (J). pap. 5.95 (978-0-7614-5178-5(1)) Cavendish, Marshall Corp.

Polacco, Patricia. John Philip Duck. Polacco, Patricia, illus. 2004. (Illus.). 48p. (J). (ps-5). 16.99 (978-0-399-24262-5(7) , Philomel) Penguin Group (USA) Inc.

Richards, Kitty. Hotel Hangout, Bk. 1. 2006. (Suite Life of Zack & Cody Ser.: Vol. 1). (Illus.). 80p. (gr. 2-5). pap. 3.99 (978-0-7868-4935-2(5)) Disney Pr.

Rigby Education Staff. Bird Hotel. (Sails Literacy Ser.). (Illus.). 16p. (gr. 1-2). 27.00 (978-0-7635-9924-9(7) , 699247C99) Rigby Education.

Roy, Ron. The Haunted Hotel. Gurney, John Steven, illus. 1999. (A to Z Mysteries Ser.: No. 8). (J). (gr. k-3). lib. bdg. 11.80 (978-0-613-16122-0(X)) Tandem Library Bks.

Rylant, Cynthia. Old Town in the Green Groves: Laura Ingalls Wilder's Lost Little House Years. 2007. (Little House Ser.). 192p. (J). pap. 6.99 (978-0-06-088546-5(7) , Harper Trophy) HarperCollins Pubs.

—Old Town in the Green Groves: Laura Ingalls Wilder's Lost Little House Years. LaMarche, Jim, illus. (Little House Ser.). 176p. (J). 2004. pap. 5.99 (978-0-06-440990-2(2) , Harper Trophy); 2002. 15.99 (978-0-06-029561-5(9)) HarperCollins Pubs.

Schwarz, Larry. Ellen's 11-Star Spectacular Super Deluxe Hotel. Denato, Kelly, illus. 2006. 32p. (J). (ps-1). 15.99 (978-0-316-86902-7(3)) Little Brown & Co.

Schwarz, Laurence. Ellen's 11-Star Spectacular Super Deluxe Hotel. Denato, Kelly, illus. 2006. (J). (978-1-4156-8083-4(3)) Little Brown & Co.

Simmie, Lois. El Gato Ya Se Va. Nugent, Cynthia, illus. 2000. (Primeras Lecturas Coleccion). (SPA.). 36p. (J). (gr. 1). pap. 7.50 (978-980-257-250-2(0)) Ekare, Ediciones VEN. *Dist:* Lectorum Pubns., Inc.

Stilton, Geronimo. Surf's up Geronimo. 2005. (Geronimo Stilton Ser.: No. 20). (Illus.). 128p. (J). 5.99 (978-0-439-69143-7(5) , Scholastic Paperbacks) Scholastic, Inc.

—Surf's up, Geronimo! 2005. (Geronimo Stilton Ser.: No. 20). (Illus.). 109p. (J). (978-1-4156-0622-3(6)) Scholastic, Inc.

Stine, R. L. Checkout Time at the Dead-End Hotel. 1998. (Give Yourself Goosebumps Ser.: No. 27). (J). (gr. 3-7). (978-0-606-13266-4(X)) Tandem Library Bks.

Thesman, Jean. The Tree of Bells. 1999. 240p. (J). (gr. 5-9). tchr. ed. 15.00 (978-0-395-90510-4(9)) Houghton Mifflin Co. Trade & Reference Div.

Thompson, Kay. Eloise. Knight, Hilary, illus. 2002. (Eloise Ser.). (SPA.). 64p. (J). (gr. k-3). 17.00 (978-84-264-3735-8(4) , LM30420) Editorial Lumen ESP. *Dist:* Distribooks, Inc., Lectorum Pubns., Inc.

—Eloise. 5th ed. 1998. (Eloise Ser.). (FRE., Illus.). 5p. (J). (ps-3). pap. 13.95 (978-2-07-052125-8(7)) Gallimard, Editions FRA. *Dist:* Distribooks, Inc.

—Eloise. 2001. (Eloise Ser.). (Illus.). 64p. (J). (ps). 22.00 incl. audio compact disk (978-0-689-84311-2(9) , Simon & Schuster Children's Publishing) Simon & Schuster Children's Publishing.

—Eloise: The Absolutely Essential. Knight, Hilary, illus. 50th anniv. ed. 2005. (Eloise Ser.). 80p. (J). (ps-3). 19.95 (978-1-4169-0823-4(4)) Simon & Schuster Children's Publishing.

—Eloise at the Wedding. Lyon, Tammie, illus. 2006. (Eloise Ser.). 32p. (J). (ps-1). pap. 3.99 (978-0-689-87449-9(9) , Aladdin) Simon & Schuster Children's Publishing.

—Eloise Takes a Bawth. Knight, Hilary, illus. ltd. ed. 2002. (Eloise Ser.). 300.00 (978-0-689-84694-6(0) , Simon & Schuster Children's Publishing) Simon & Schuster Children's Publishing.

—Eloise the Absolutely Essential Edition. Knight, Hilary, illus. 1999. 80p. (J). (ps-3). 19.95 (978-0-689-82703-7(2)) Simon & Schuster Children's Publishing.

Thompson, Kay. Eloise's Christmas Trinkles. Knight, Hilary, illus. 2007. (Eloise Ser.). 48p. (J). (ps-3). 9.99 ***978-0-689-87425-3(1))** Simon & Schuster Children's Publishing.

Thompson, Kay & Brenner, Marie. Kay Thompson's Eloise: The Absolutely Essential 50th Anniversary Edition: A Book for Precocious Grown-Ups. Knight, Hilary, illus. 2007. 84p. (J). reprint ed. 20.00 (***978-1-4223-6789-6(4))** DIANE Publishing Co.

Thompson, Kay & Cheshire, Marc. Here Comes Eloise! Bracken, Carolyn, illus. 2004. (Eloise Ser.). 16p. (J). (ps-1). pap. 6.99 (978-0-689-87154-2(6) , Little Simon) Simon & Schuster Children's Publishing.

Thompson, Kay & Crowley, Mart. Eloise Takes a Bawth. Knight, Hilary, illus. 2002. (Eloise Ser.). 80p. (J). (ps-3). 17.95 (978-0-689-84288-7(0)) Simon & Schuster Children's Publishing.

Thompson, Kay & Knight, Hilary. Eloise at Christmastime. 1999. (Illus.). 56p. (J). (ps-3). 17.95 (978-0-689-83039-6(4)) Simon & Schuster Children's Publishing.

—Eloise in Moscow. 40th ed. 2000. (Illus.). 80p. (J). (ps-3). 17.00 (978-0-689-83211-6(7)) Simon & Schuster Children's Publishing.

—Eloise in Paris. 1999. (Eloise Ser.). (Illus.). 72p. (J). (ps-3). 18.00 (978-0-689-82704-4(0)) Simon & Schuster Children's Publishing.

Thompson, Kay & McClatchy, Lisa. Eloise's New Bonnet. Lyon, Tammie, illus. 2007. (Eloise Ser.). 32p. (J). pap. 3.99 (978-0-689-87452-9(9) , Aladdin) Simon & Schuster Children's Publishing.

Trumbauer, Lisa. Mountain Manor Mystery. Hawkes, Kevin, illus. 2006. 96p. (J). pap. (978-1-59034-810-9(9)) Mondo Publishing.

Vail, Emily Blake. The Grey Ghost of the Pharaoh. Barbra K. Mudd, illus. 2004. 176p. (YA). per. 8.99 (978-0-935087-27-7(3)) Wright Publishing, Inc.

Weiss, Ellen. Eloise & the Very Secret Room. Lyon, Tammie, illus. 2006. (Eloise Ser.). 32p. (J). pap. 3.99 (978-0-689-87450-5(2) , Aladdin) Simon & Schuster Children's Publishing.

Wilson, Jacqueline. The Bed & Breakfast Star. Sharratt, Nick, illus. l.t. ed. 2000. 255p. (J). pap. (978-0-7540-6090-1(X) , CLP 292) BBC Audio.

—The Bed & Breakfast Star. Sharratt, Nick, illus. unabr. ed. 2000. (Read-Along Ser.). 242p. (J). pap. 29.95 incl. audio (978-0-7540-6231-8(7) , RA032, Chivers Children's Audio Bks.) BBC Audiobooks America.

—The Bed & Breakfast Star. Sharratt, Nick, illus. 2001. (Yearling Book Ser.). 32p. pap. 9.99 (978-0-440-86324-3(4) , Corgi) Transworld Publishers Ltd. GBR. *Dist:* Trafalgar Square Publishing.

Wyche, Blonnie Bunn. The Anchor: P. Moore, Proprietor. 2003. 224p. 12.00 (978-1-889199-05-4(2)) Banks Channel Bks.

Yee, Wong Herbert. Fireman Small - Fire down Below! 2004. 32p. (J). (gr. k-3). pap. 5.95 (978-0-618-49492-7(8)) Houghton Mifflin Co. Trade & Reference Div.

HOTELS, MOTELS, ETC.—VOCATIONAL GUIDANCE

Rue, Nancy N. Choosing a Career in Hotels, Motels & Resorts. rev. ed. 1999. (World of Work Ser.). (Illus.). 64p. (YA). (gr. 7-12). lib. bdg. 25.25 (978-0-8239-2999-3(X) , WWHOMO) Rosen Publishing Group, Inc., The.

HOUDINI, HARRY, 1874-1926

Cobb, Vicki. Harry Houdini: A Photographic Story of a Life. 2005. (Biography Ser.). (Illus.). 128p. (gr. 8). pap. 4.99 (978-0-7566-1245-0(4)) Dorling Kindersley Publishing, Inc.

Cox, Clinton. Houdini: Master of Illusion. 2001. (Illus.). 208p. (J). (gr. 4-9). pap. 16.95 (978-0-590-94960-6(8)) Scholastic, Inc.

Dorling Kindersley Publishing Staff, ed. Harry Houdini: A Photographic Story of a Life. 2005. (Biography Ser.). (Illus.). 128p. (J). (gr. 8). 14.99 (978-0-7566-1246-7(2)) Dorling Kindersley Publishing, Inc.

Fleischman, Sid. Escape! The Story of the Great Houdini. 2006. (Illus.). 224p. (J). (gr. 4-8). 18.99 (978-0-06-085094-4(9)); lib. bdg. 19.89 (978-0-06-085095-1(7)) HarperCollins Pubs.

Kent, Zachary. Harry Houdini: Escape Artist & Master Magician. 2002. (Historical American Biographies Ser.). (Illus.). 128p. (YA). (gr. 6-12). lib. bdg. 26.60 (978-0-7660-1619-4(6)) Enslow Pubs., Inc.

Krull, Kathleen. Houdini: World's Greatest Mystery Man & Escape King. Velasquez, Eric, illus. 32p. (J). 2007. pap. 6.95 (***978-0-8027-9646-2(X));** 2005. 17.85 (978-0-8027-8954-9(4)); 2005. 16.95 (978-0-8027-8953-2(6)) Walker & Co.

Kulling, Monica. The Great Houdini. 1999. (J). (978-0-606-16897-7(4)) Tandem Library Bks.

—The Great Houdini: World Famous Magician & Escape Artist. Reas, Anne, illus. 2003. (Step into Reading Step 3 Bks.). 48p. (J). (gr. 2-4). pap. 3.99 (978-0-679-88573-3(0) , Random Hse. Bks. for Young Readers) Random Hse. Children's Bks.

Lakin, Patricia. Harry Houdini: Esape Artist. Geary, Rick, illus. 2002. (Ready-to-Read Ser.). 32p. (J). pap. 3.99 (978-0-689-84815-5(3) , Aladdin) Simon & Schuster Children's Publishing.

—Harry Houdini: Young Magician. 2002. (gr. 3-6). lib. bdg. 11.80 (978-0-613-57573-7(3)) Tandem Library Bks.

—Harry Houdini, Escape Artist. Geary, Rick, illus. ed. 2005. 32p. (J). lib. bdg. 15.00 (978-1-59054-944-5(9)) Fitzgerald Bks.

MacLeod, Elizabeth. Harry Houdini: A Magical Life. (Illus.). 32p. (978-1-55337-769-6(9)); 2005. (J). (gr. 3-7). (978-1-55337-770-2(2)) Kids Can Pr., Ltd.

Marsh, Carole. Harry Houdini. 2002. (One Thousand Readers Ser.). (Illus.). 12p. (J). (gr. k-4). 2.95 (978-0-635-01511-2(0) , 15110) Gallopade International.

Mullin, Rita Thievon. Sterling Biographies: Harry Houdini: Death-Defying Showman. 2007. (Sterling Biographies Ser.). (Illus.). 128p. (J). 12.95 (***978-1-4027-4953-7(8));** pap. 5.95 (***978-1-4027-3262-1(7))** Sterling Publishing Co., Inc.

Rau, Dana Meachen. Harry Houdini: Master Magician. 2001. (Book Report Biographies Ser.). (Illus.). 100p. (YA). (gr. 6-8). pap. 6.95 (978-0-531-15551-6(X) , Watts, Franklin) Scholastic Library Publishing.

Sutherland, Tui. Who Was Harry Houdini? 2002. (gr. 3-6). lib. bdg. 13.00 (978-0-613-45331-8(X)) Tandem Library Bks.

Sutherland, Tui & O'Brien, John. Who Was Harry Houdini? Harrison, Nancy, illus. 2002. (Who Was...? Ser.). 112p. (J). pap. 4.99 (978-0-448-42686-0(2) , Grosset & Dunlap) Penguin Group (USA) Inc.

HOUSE BOATS

see Houseboats

HOUSE CLEANING

Burton, Margie, et al. Cleaning My Room. Adams, Alison, ed. 1999. (Early Connections Ser.). 16p. (J). (gr. k-2). pap. 4.50 (978-1-58344-056-8(9)) Benchmark Education Co.

Malam, John. Cleaning the House. 2000. (Everyday History Ser.). (Illus.). 32p. (J). (gr. 3-4). pap. 6.95 (978-0-531-15411-3(4) , Watts, Franklin) Scholastic Library Publishing.

—Cleaning the House. 2000. (Illus.). (J). 32p. (gr. 4-7). lib. bdg. 15.25 (978-0-613-54134-3(0)); (978-0-606-20610-5(8)) Tandem Library Bks.

Swain, Gwenyth. Tidy Up! 2003. (Illus.). 24p. (J). (ps-2). pap. 6.95 (978-1-57505-160-4(5)) Lerner Publishing Group.

—Tidy Up! 2002. (gr. k-3). lib. bdg. 15.25 (978-0-613-46109-2(6)) Tandem Library Bks.

HOUSE DECORATION

see Interior Decoration

HOUSE FLIES

see Flies

HOUSE FURNISHINGS

see Interior Decoration

HOUSE PLANTS

Ayers, Patricia. A Kid's Guide to How Plants Grow. 2000. (Digging in the Dirt Ser.). 24p. (J). (gr. k-4). lib. bdg. 18.75 (978-0-8239-5465-0(X) , PowerKids Pr.) Rosen Publishing Group, Inc., The.

Lawlor, Elizabeth P. Discover Nature Around the House: Things to Know & Things to Do. 2003. (gr. 3-6). lib. bdg. 24.55 (978-0-613-76161-1(8)) Tandem Library Bks.

HOUSEBOATS

Gallagher, Debbie. River & Sea Homes. 2007. (J). (***978-1-59920-152-8(6))** Smart Apple Media.

Schaefer, Lola M. La Casa Flotante. 2002. (SPA.). 24p. (J). pap. 5.25 (978-1-4034-0491-6(7)) Heinemann Library.

—Houseboat. 2003. (Home for Me Ser.). (Illus.). 24p. (J). (ps-1). lib. bdg. 18.50 (978-1-4034-0262-2(0)); pap. 5.25 (978-1-4034-0485-5(2)) Heinemann Library.

HOUSEBOATS—FICTION

Fitzhugh, Keese Perc. Roy Blakeley (His Story) 2006. 95.99 (***978-1-4280-0398-9(3));** pap. 88.99 (***978-1-4280-0390-3(8))** IndyPublish.com.

Hope, Laura Lee. Bobbsey Twins on A Houseboat. 2006. 62.99 (***978-1-4280-2339-0(9))** IndyPublish.com.

Winfield, Arthur M. The Rover Boys on the River or the Search for the Missing. 2006. (ENG.). 272p. per. 27.95 (***978-1-4286-4115-0(7))** Kessinger Publishing, LLC.

HOUSEHOLD APPLIANCES

see Household Equipment and Supplies

HOUSEHOLD APPLIANCES, ELECTRIC

Fabra, Jordi Sierra. Las Fans. 1999. (SPA.). 280p. 9.95 (978-84-239-9060-3(5)) Espasa Calpe, S.A. ESP. *Dist:* Libros Sin Fronteras.

—Las Fans. 1999. (978-0-606-17690-3(X)) Tandem Library Bks.

How things Work: Level Q, 6 vols., Vol. 3. (Explorers Ser.). 32p. (gr. 3-6). 44.95 (978-0-7699-0620-1(6)) Shortland Pubns. (U. S. A.) Inc.

Jan's New Fan: KinderReaders Individual Title, 6 Packs. (Kinderstarters Ser.). 8p. (ps-1). 21.00 (978-0-7635-8666-9(8)) Rigby Education.

Kachur, Matthew. Nuestro mundo eléctrico & Our Current World. 2005. spiral bd. 77.00 (***978-1-4108-5680-7(1))** Benchmark Education Co.

Rigby Education Staff. Fans. (Illus.). 8p. (J). bds. 3.95 (978-0-7635-6492-6(3) , 764923C99) Rigby Education.

Sloan, Peter. Machines in the Home. 1999. (gr. k-3). lib. bdg. 11.80 (978-0-613-30574-7(4)) Tandem Library Bks.

HOUSEHOLD EMPLOYEES—FICTION

Auer, Chris. The Littlest Magi: A Christmas Tale. Eagle, Bruce, illus. 2004. 32p. (J). 15.99 (978-0-310-70663-2(7)) Zonderkidz.

Crisp, Marty. The Most Precious Gift. Cooper, Floyd, illus. 2006. 32p. (J). (gr. k). 16.99 (978-0-399-24296-0(1) , Philomel) Penguin Group (USA) Inc.

Grey, Christopher Peter. Leonardo's Shadow: Or, My Astonishing Life as Leonardo da Vinci's Servant. 2006. 400p. (YA). 16.95 (978-1-4169-0543-1(X) , Atheneum) Simon & Schuster Children's Publishing.

Grindley, Sally. Spilled Water. 2004. 224p. (J). 15.95 (978-1-58234-937-4(1) , Bloomsbury Children) Bloomsbury Publishing.

Harlow, Joan Hiatt. Midnight Rider. 2006. 384p. (J). pap. 5.99 (978-0-689-87010-1(8) , Aladdin) Simon & Schuster Children's Publishing.

Harlow, Joan Hiatt & Minor, Wendell. Midnight Rider. 2005. (Illus.). 416p. (J). 15.95 (978-0-689-87009-5(4) , McElderry, Margaret K.) Simon & Schuster Children's Publishing.

Hooper, Mary. Newes from the Dead: Being a True Story of Anne Green, Hanged for Infanticide at Oxford Assizes in 1650, Restored to the World & Died Again 1665. 2008. 256p. (YA). 15.95 (***978-1-59643-355-7(8))** Roaring Brook Pr.

Levine, Phyllis. Matilda. 2007. 108p. pap. 12.95 (***978-1-60047-079-0(3))** Wasteland Pr.

Lowry, Lois. Anastasia Asusordenes. 2003. Tr. of Anastasia at Your Order. (SPA.). 120p. (J). 9.95 (978-84-239-7073-5(6)) Espasa Calpe, S.A. ESP. *Dist:* Planeta Publishing Corp.

—Anastasia at Your Service. 149p. (J). (gr. 4-6). pap. 3.99 (978-0-8072-1409-1(4) , Listening Library) Random Hse. Audio Publishing Group.

Milord, Susan. The Ghost on the Hearth. Dabcovich, Lydia, illus. 2003. (Family Heritage Ser.). 36p. (J). (gr. 1-5). 15.95 (978-0-916718-18-3(2)) Vermont Folklife Ctr.

Parish, Herman. Amelia Bedelia 4 Mayor. Sweat, Lynn, illus. 2001. (I Can Read Bks.). 64p. (J). (gr. k-2). pap. 3.99 (978-0-06-444309-8(4) , Harper Trophy) HarperCollins Pubs.

—Calling Doctor Amelia Bedelia. Sweat, Lynn, illus. (I Can Read Bks.). 64p. (J). 2004. (gr. k-3). pap. 3.99 (978-0-06-008780-7(3) , Harper Trophy); 2002. (gr. 1-2). 15.99 (978-0-06-001421-6(0)); 2002. (gr. 1-2). lib. bdg. 17.89 (978-0-06-001422-3(9)) HarperCollins Pubs.

Parish, Peggy. Amelia Bedelia. Siebel, Fritz, illus. 1999. (I Can Read Bks.). 64p. (J). (ps-3). 16.99 (978-0-694-01296-1(3) , Harper Festival) HarperCollins Pubs.

—Amelia Bedelia. Thomas, Barbara Siebel & Siebel, Fritz, illus. 2000. (Coleccion Ya Se Leer). (SPA.). (J). (gr. 1-3). 15.95 (978-1-880507-76-6(5) , LC0355); pap. 6.99 (978-1-880507-75-9(7) , LC0360) Lectorum Pubns., Inc.

—Amelia Bedelia. Siebel, Fritz, illus. 1999. (J). (gr. 1-3). 9.95 (978-1-56137-023-8(1)) Novel Units, Inc.

—Amelia Bedelia. 2001. (SPA., Illus.). (J). 13.75 (978-0-606-21546-6(8)) Tandem Library Bks.

—Amelia Bedelia. Siebel, Fritz, illus. 1999. (I Can Read Bks.). (J). (gr. 1-3). 11.50 (978-0-88103-916-0(0)) Tandem Library Bks.

—Amelia Bedelia & the Baby. Sweat, Lynn, illus. 2004. (I Can Read Bks.). 64p. (J). (gr. k-3). pap. 3.99 (978-0-06-051105-0(2) , Harper Trophy) HarperCollins Pubs.

—Amelia Bedelia Goes Camping. Sweat, Lynn, illus. 2003. (I Can Read Bks.). 64p. (J). (ps-ps). pap. 3.99 (978-0-06-051106-7(0) , Harper Trophy) HarperCollins Pubs.

—Amelia Bedelia Goes Camping. 2003. (gr. k-3). lib. bdg. 11.80 (978-0-613-62664-4(8)) Tandem Library Bks.

—Amelia Bedelia's Family Album. Sweat, Lynn, illus. 2003. (I Can Read Bks.). 48p. (J). (gr. k-3). pap. 3.99 (978-0-06-051116-6(8) , Harper Trophy) HarperCollins Pubs.

—Amelia Bedelia's Family Album. 2003. (gr. k-3). lib. bdg. 11.80 (978-0-613-62129-8(8)) Tandem Library Bks.

—Good Work, Amelia Bedelia. Sweat, Lynn, illus. 2003. (I Can Read Bks.). 64p. (J). (gr. k-3). pap. 3.99 (978-0-06-051115-9(X)) HarperCollins Pubs.

—Good Work, Amelia Bedelia. 2003. (gr. k-3). lib. bdg. 11.80 (978-0-613-68343-2(9)) Tandem Library Bks.

—Thank You, Amelia Bedelia. 1999. (I Can Read Bks.). (J). (gr. 1-3). 11.55 (978-0-88103-910-8(1)) Tandem Library Bks.

Qamar, Amjed. Beneath My Mother's Feet. 2008. 208p. (J). (***978-1-4169-4728-8(0))** Simon & Schuster Children's Publishing.

Thank You, Amelia Bedelia. 2002. (Amelia Bedelia Ser.). (J). 12.34 (978-0-7587-6292-4(5)) Book Wholesalers, Inc.

Warburton, Carol. Edge of Night: A Novel. 2004. (Illus.). 278p. pap. 14.95 (978-1-59156-013-5(6)) Covenant Communications, Inc.

Wollman, Jessica. Switched. 2007. 256p. (gr. 7). (J). lib. bdg. 18.99 (978-0-385-90410-0(X)); (YA). 15.99 (978-0-385-73396-0(8)) Random Hse. Children's Bks. (Delacorte Bks. for Young Readers).

HOUSEHOLD EQUIPMENT AND SUPPLIES

see also Household Appliances, Electric

Abrams, Pam. Gadgetology: Kid-Friendly Recipes, Playtime Activities, & Simple Experiments Using 35 Fun Kitchen Gadgets. 2007. 96p. 14.95 (978-1-55832-346-9(5)) Harvard Common Pr.

Bidder, Jane. Inventions We Use at Home. 2006. (Illus.). 32p. (J). lib. bdg. (978-0-8368-6898-2(6)) Stevens, Gareth Inc.

Brownstein, Jerry & Brownstein, Kathy. Beacon Blankets: Make Warm Friends. 2001. (Schiffer Book for Collectors Ser.). (Illus.). 176p. (gr. 10-13). 49.95 (978-0-7643-1359-2(2)) Schiffer Publishing, Ltd.

Dalgleish, Sharon. How Things Work. 1999. (Explorers Ser.). (Illus.). 32p. (J). (978-0-7699-0496-2(3)) Shortland Pubns. (U. S. A.) Inc.

Litchfield, Jo. Home. Litchfield, Jo, illus. 2006. 12p. (J). bds. 7.99 (978-0-7945-1425-9(1) , Usborne) EDC Publishing.

Lunis, Natalie. Household Inventions: From Toilets to Toasters. 2006. (Which Came First? Ser.). (Illus.). 32p. (J). lib. bdg. 25.27 (978-1-59716-131-2(4)) Bearport Publishing Co., Inc.

Our Homes. 2007. (J). (***978-1-933834-15-3(3))** Brown Bear Books.

Rau, Dana Meachen. Chefs. 2007. (Tools We Use Ser.). 32p. (J). lib. bdg. 22.79 (***978-0-7614-2657-8(4)** , Benchmark Bks.) Cavendish, Marshall Corp.

—Los Chefs. 2007. (Instrumentos de Trabajo Ser.). (SPA.). 32p. (J). lib. bdg. 22.79 (***978-0-7614-2798-8(8)** , Benchmark Bks.) Cavendish, Marshall Corp.

—Chefs/Los Chefs. 2007. (Tools We Use/Instrumentos de Trabajo Ser.). (SPA & ENG.). 32p. (J). lib. bdg. 22.79 (***978-0-7614-2822-0(4)** , Benchmark Bks.) Cavendish, Marshall Corp.

Richards, Jon. In the Home. 2005. (Illus.). 32p. (J). (gr. 3 up). lib. bdg. 27.10 (978-1-59389-198-5(9)) Chrysalis Education.

Ridley, Sarah. A Metal Can. 2006. (How It's Made Ser.). (Illus.). 32p. (J). lib. bdg. (978-0-8368-6702-2(5)) Stevens, Gareth Inc.

Romanek, Trudee. Switched on, Flushed down, Tossed Out: Investigating the Hidden Workings of Your Home. MacEachern, Stephen, illus. 2005. 48p. (J). (gr. 3-5). pap. 12.95 (978-1-55037-902-0(X)); lib. bdg. 24.95 (978-1-55037-903-7(8)) Annick Pr., Ltd. CAN. *Dist:* Firefly Bks., Ltd.

Sloan, Peter. Machines in the Home. 1999. (gr. k-3). lib. bdg. 11.80 (978-0-613-30574-7(4)) Tandem Library Bks.

Snyder, Inez. Cooking Tools. 2002. (Welcome Bks.). (Illus.). 24p. (J). (ps-2). pap. 4.95 (978-0-516-24035-0(8) , Children's Pr.) Scholastic Library Publishing.

—Cooking Tools. 2002. (gr. k-3). lib. bdg. 12.95 (978-0-613-58829-4(0)) Tandem Library Bks.

Thomas, John & Thomas, Danita. The Ultimate Book of All Occasion Kid Concoctions: More Than 50 Wacky, Wild & Crazy Concoctions for All Occasions. 2006. (Illus.). 80p. (J). pap. 14.99 (978-0-8054-4445-2(9)) B&H Publishing Grp.

—The Ultimate Book of Kid Concoctions. 2006. (Illus.). 80p. (J). pap. 14.99 (978-0-8054-4443-8(2)) B&H Publishing Grp.

HOUSEHOLD MANAGEMENT

see Home Economics

HOUSEHOLD MOVING

see Moving, Household

HOUSEKEEPING

see Home Economics

HOUSES

Here are entered general works on houses.

see also Apartment Houses; Building; Building—Repair and Reconstruction

Adamson, Heather. Homes in Many Cultures. 2008. (J). (***978-1-4296-0020-0(9)** , Pebble Bks.) Capstone Pr., Inc.

Anderson, Judith. Looking at Settlements. 2007. (J). (***978-1-59920-052-1(X))** Smart Apple Media.

Barber, Nicola. Island Home. 2007. (Homes Around the World Ser.). 32p. (J). (gr. 2-5). pap. (***978-0-7787-3555-7(9))** Crabtree Publishing Co.

—Mobile Home. 2007. (Homes Around the World Ser.). 32p. (J). (gr. 2-5). pap. (***978-0-7787-3556-4(7))** Crabtree Publishing Co.

—Mountain Home. 2007. 32p. (gr. 7-10). pap. (***978-0-7787-3557-1(5))** Crabtree Publishing Co.

—Village Home. 2007. 32p. (gr. 7-10). pap. (***978-0-7787-3558-8(3))** Crabtree Publishing Co.

—Waterside Home. 2007. 32p. (gr. 7-10). pap. (***978-0-7787-3559-5(1))** Crabtree Publishing Co.

Bass, Hester. So Many Houses. Arzoumanian, Alik, illus. 2006. (Rookie Reader Skill Set Ser.). 32p. (J). (gr. k-2). 19.50 (978-0-516-24977-3(0) , Children's Pr.) Scholastic Library Publishing.

Bial, Raymond. The Houses: Building America. 2001. (Building America Ser.). (Illus.). 56p. (J). (gr. 4 up). lib. bdg. 27.07 (978-0-7614-1335-6(9) , Benchmark Bks.) Cavendish, Marshall Corp.

—Longhouses. 2004. (American Community Ser.). (Illus.). 48p. (J). (gr. 2-5). 29.00 (978-0-516-23707-7(1) , Children's Pr.) Scholastic Library Publishing.

Brent, Lynnette R. At Home. 2003. (Times Change Ser.). (Illus.). 32p. (J). (978-1-4034-4537-7(0)) Heinemann Library.

—At Home: Long Ago & Today. 2003. (Times Change Ser.). (Illus.). 32p. (J). lib. bdg. 24.22 (978-1-4034-4531-5(1)) Heinemann Library.

Brooks, F. & Litchfield, J. En Casa. 2004. Tr. of At Home. (SPA., Illus.). 10p. (J). 4.95 (978-0-7460-4825-2(4)) EDC Publishing.

A Buscar Casa: Individual Title, 6 pack. (Coleccion Pm Ser.).Tr. of House hunting. (SPA.). 16p. (gr. 1 up). 26.00 (978-0-7578-3035-8(8)) Rigby Education.

Butterfield, Moira. Switches, Doors, Knobs & Drawers. Lewis, Jan, illus. 1998. (Can You Find? Ser.). (J). (978-0-382-39991-6(9)); pap. (978-0-382-39990-9(0)) Silver Pr. Co.

Carle, Eric. My Very First Book of Animal Homes. Carle, Eric, illus. 2007. 20p. (J). (ps-k). bds. 5.99 (978-0-399-24647-0(9) , Philomel) Penguin Group (USA) Inc.

Dorling Kindersley Publishing Staff. A Home. 2005. (TOUCH & FEEL Ser.). 12p. (J). bds. 6.99 (978-0-7566-1200-9(4)) Dorling Kindersley Publishing, Inc.

—It's Time for Bed! 2006. (Illus.). 12p. (J). bds. 6.99 (978-0-7566-2126-1(7)) Dorling Kindersley Publishing, Inc.

Dorros, Arthur. This Is My House. 1998. Tr. of Esta Es Mi Casa. (J). 19.95 (978-0-590-72811-9(3)) Scholastic, Inc.

H I

Emberley, Rebecca. My Room/Mi Cuarto. 2005. (SPA., Illus.). 10p. (J). (ps-ps). bds. 6.99 (978-0-316-00052-9(3)) Little Brown & Co.

Gallagher, Debbie. Mud, Grass, & Ice Homes. 2007. (J). (***978-1-59920-154-2(2)**) Smart Apple Media.

—River & Sea Homes. 2007. (J). (***978-1-59920-152-8(6)**) Smart Apple Media.

Gillis, Jennifer Blizin. Hogares para Todos. 2007. (SPA & ENG., Illus.). 24p. (J). (***978-1-60044-290-2(0)**) Rourke Publishing, LLC.

Gillis, Jennifer Blizin. Homes for Everyone. 2007. (Illus.). 24p. (J). (978-1-60044-201-8(3)) Rourke Publishing, LLC.

Gordon, Sharon. At Home (Mi Casa), 6 bks., Set. Incl. At Home by the Ocean (Mi Casa Junto Al Mar) (Illus.). 32p. lib. bdg. 22.79 (978-0-7614-2456-7(3)); At Home in the City (Mi Casa en la Ciudad) (Illus.). 32p. lib. bdg. 22.79 (978-0-7614-2452-9(0)); At Home in the Desert (Mi Casa en el Desierto) (Illus.). 32p. lib. bdg. 22.79 (978-0-7614-2453-6(9)); At Home on the Farm (Mi Casa en la Granja) (Illus.). 32p. lib. bdg. 22.79 (978-0-7614-2454-3(7)); At Home on the Mountain (Mi Casa en la Montaña) 32p. lib. bdg. 22.79 (978-0-7614-2455-0(5)); At Home on the Ranch (Mi Casa en el Rancho) (Illus.). 32sp. lib. bdg. 22.79 (978-0-7614-2458-1(X)); (J). 2006. (ENG & SPA.). 2007. Set lib. bdg. 136.71 (***978-0-7614-2451-2(2)**) Cavendish, Marshall Corp.

Grant, Donald. La Casa. (SPA., Illus.). 40p. (J). (978-84-348-3728-7(5) , CA9913) SM Ediciones ESP. *Dist:* Lectorum Pubns., Inc.

Green, Jen. In a House. 2002. (Small Worlds Ser.). (Illus.). 32p. (J). (gr. 3-4). pap. (978-0-7787-0154-5(9)); lib. bdg. (978-0-7787-0140-8(9)) Crabtree Publishing Co.

—In a House. 2002. (gr. 3-6). lib. bdg. 17.60 (978-0-613-52961-7(8)) Tandem Library Bks.

Guin, Valerie. Where We Live. 2005. (Illus.). 30p. (J). (gr. 3-7). lib. bdg. 27.10 (978-1-58340-698-4(0)) Smart Apple Media.

Gustafson, Angela. Imagine a House: A Journey to Fascinating Houses Around the World. 2003. (What a World We Live in Ser.). (Illus.). 32p. (J). (gr. k-6). lib. bdg. 16.95 (978-0-9726849-0-3(5)) Out of the Box.

Hall, Margaret. Homes. (Around the World Ser.). 32p. pap. 6.95 (978-1-4034-4005-1(0)) Heinemann Library.

Hall, Margaret C. Homes. 2001. (Around the World Ser.). (Illus.). 32p. (J). lib. bdg. 21.36 (978-1-58810-103-7(7)) Heinemann Library.

Harcourt School Publishers Staff. A House & a Teepee, 5 Pack, Below Level. 3rd ed. 2002. (Trophies Reading Program Ser.). (Illus.). (gr. 1). pap. 20.10 (978-0-15-326809-0(3)) Harcourt Schl. Pubs.

—A House & a Teepee: Below Level. 3rd ed. 2002. (Trophies Reading Program Ser.). (Illus.). (J). pap. 4.10 (978-0-15-322959-6(4)) Harcourt Schl. Pubs.

—Trofeos Advanced Level: La Casa de Andres. 3rd ed. 2002. (SPA., Illus.). pap. 6.80 (978-0-15-323938-0(7)) Harcourt Schl. Pubs.

—Trofeos Below Level: Una Casa/Tipi. 3rd ed. 2002. (SPA., Illus.). pap. 5.50 (978-0-15-323870-3(4)) Harcourt Schl. Pubs.

Hardy, Caroline. Through the Peephole Dangerous Places (Home Safety) Daykin, Louise, illus. 2006. (Through the Peephole Ser.). 48p. 9.95 (978-1-84560-013-6(4)) Mercury Bks. Ltd. GBR. *Dist:* International Publishers Marketing.

Harper, Kathryn, et al. I-Read Year 1 Anthology: Where I Live. 2007. (I-read Ser.). (Illus.). 40p. pap. (***978-0-521-70476-2(6)**) Cambridge Univ. Pr.

Hemmel, David. Living in the Key West Style Anywhere: A Complete Guide to Planning a Home in the Charming Key West Style. 2004. (Illus.). 144p. per. 22.95 (978-0-9745637-0-1(6)) Duval Publishing.

Home. (Butterfly Bks.). (ARA., Illus.). 15p. (J). 11.95 (978-0-86685-615-7(3) , LDL6153) International Bk. Ctr., Inc.

Home. 32p. 1.99 (978-0-7682-0245-8(0) , FS144007) Schaffer, Frank Pubns.

Homes Around the World: Individual Title Six-Packs. (Rigby Focus Ser.). 16p. (gr. 1 up). 28.00 (978-0-7578-5317-3(X)); 30.00 (978-0-7578-5549-8(0)) Rigby Education.

Houses: Individual Title Six-Packs. (gr. 1-2). 22.00 (978-0-7635-9161-8(0)) Rigby Education.

Houses: KinderFacts Individual Title Six-Packs. (Kinderstarters Ser.). 8p. (ps-1). 21.00 (978-0-7635-8745-1(1)) Rigby Education.

Iverson, Carol. Houses. 2001. (Designing the Future Ser.). (Illus.). 32p. (J). (978-1-58341-187-2(9) , Creative Education) Creative Co., The.

Jensen, Patricia. My House. Becker, Wayne, illus. 2003. (My First Reader Ser.). 32p. (J). 18.50 (978-0-516-22934-8(6) , Children's Pr.) Scholastic Library Publishing.

Kalman, Bobbie. Life in a Longhouse. 2001. (gr. 3-6). lib. bdg. 16.40 (978-0-613-43464-5(1)) Tandem Library Bks.

Kane, Andy. Changing Rooms: Handy Andy's Homework. 2003. (Illus.). 192p. bds. 24.95 (978-0-563-55192-8(5)) BBC Worldwide Americas.

Kane, Barry & Kane, Tracy. Fairy Houses ... Everywhere! 2006. (Fairy Houses Ser.). 56p. (J). 14.95 (978-0-9708104-4-1(X)) Light-Beams Publishing.

Koury, Jen. Scotty Skidsteer Helps Build a House. Hilko, Steve & Linden, Pat, eds. Koury, Jen, illus. 1999. (Johnny Tractor Toybooks Ser.). (Illus.). 10p. (J). (ps-1). (978-1-887327-21-3(5)) Ertl Co., Inc.

Kreger, Claire. Homes: From Start to Finish. Carney, Patrick, illus. Carney, Patrick, photos by. 2003. 32p. (J). 24.95 (978-1-4103-0169-7(9) , Blackbirch Pr., Inc.) Thomson Gale.

Lorenz, Albert. House: Showing How People Have Lived Throughout History with Examples Drawn from the Lives of Legendary Men & Women. Lorenz, Albert & Schleh, Joy, illus. 1998. 48p. (J). (gr. 3-8). reprint ed. 18.00 (978-0-7567-6161-5(8)) DIANE Publishing Co.

MacDonald, Fiona. Homes. (Discovering World Cultures Ser.). (Illus.). 40p. (J). (gr. 4). 2001. pap. (978-0-7787-0247-4(2)); 2000. lib. bdg. (978-0-7787-0237-5(5)) Crabtree Publishing Co.

—Homes. 2001. (gr. 3-6). lib. bdg. 17.60 (978-0-613-32647-6(4)); 2000. (J). (978-0-606-20110-0(6)) Tandem Library Bks.

Malam, John. Ancient Egyptian Homes. 2003. (People in the Past Ser.). (Illus.). 48p. (J). (gr. 4-6). lib. bdg. 27.07 (978-1-4034-0310-0(4)) Heinemann Library.

—Homes. 2002. (People in the Past Ser.). (Illus.). 48p. (J). pap. (978-1-4034-0514-2(X)) Heinemann Library.

Mattern, Joanne. Homes. 2004. (Yesterday & Today Ser.). (Illus.). 32p. (J). 23.70 (978-1-4103-0425-4(6) , Blackbirch Pr., Inc.) Thomson Gale.

—Houses. 2002. (Illus.). 24p. (J). lib. bdg. 21.35 (978-1-58340-147-7(4)) Smart Apple Media.

Mayer, Cassie. Homes. 2007. (J). (***978-1-4034-9399-6(5)**); pap. (***978-1-4034-9408-5(8)**) Heinemann Library.

McCormick, Rosie. Homes. 2003. (Starters Ser.). 24p. (J). lib. bdg. 21.35 (978-1-58340-261-0(6)) Smart Apple Media.

Middleton, Haydn. Ancient Greek Homes. 2002. (People in the Past Ser.). (Illus.). 48p. (J). (gr. 4-6). lib. bdg. 27.07 (978-1-58810-636-0(5)) Heinemann Library.

Middleton, Haydn & Tames, Richard. Ancient Greek Homes. 2002. (People in the Past Ser.). 64p. (J). (gr. 4-7). pap. 8.50 (978-1-4034-0132-8(2) , 91637) Heinemann Library.

Murray, W. Home. 2nd ed. (Talkabouts Ser.: No. 735-2). (Illus.). 48p. (J). (ps). 3.50 (978-0-7214-1097-5(9) , Dutton Juvenile) Penguin Group (USA) Inc.

My Home. (All about Me Ser.).Tr. of Mi casa. 24p. (J). 6.95 (978-1-4048-0161-5(8)) Picture Window Bks.

My House. 2003. (J). per. (978-1-57657-175-0(0)) Paradise Pr., Inc.

Nathan, Emma. Casas. 2002. (Abre los Ojos y Aprende Serie).Tr. of Eyeopeners: Homes. (SPA.). 24p. (J). (-3). 22.45 (978-1-4103-0027-0(7) , Blackbirch Pr., Inc.) Thomson Gale.

—Homes. 2002. (Illus.). 23p. (J). 22.45 (978-1-4103-0029-4(3) , Blackbirch Pr., Inc.) Thomson Gale.

Nelson, Robin. Home. 2003. (First Step Nonfiction Ser.). (Illus.). 24p. (J). (gr. k-2). lib. bdg. 18.60 (978-0-8225-4642-9(6)) Lerner Publishing Group.

—Where Is My Home? (First Step Nonfiction Ser.). (gr. k-2). 2005. (Illus.). 24p. lib. bdg. 17.27 (978-0-8225-0189-3(9)); 2001. (J). pap. 3.95 (978-0-8225-1978-2(X) , Lerner Pubns.) Lerner Publishing Group.

Newhouse, Maxwell. The House That Max Built. 2008. (Illus.). 24p. 18.95 (***978-0-88776-774-6(5)**) Tundra Bks., Inc./Livres Toundra, Inc. CAN. *Dist:* Random Hse. of Canada, Ltd.

Nicodemus, Laura Konger. Grandma's House Had No Electricity, 4 vols. Nicodemus, Laura Konger, illus. 2002. (Illus.). 16p. (J). 3.99 (978-0-9722816-2-7(X)) Grandma's Stories, Inc.

Oliver, Clare. Life in a House. 2002. (Microhabitats Ser.). (Illus.). 31p. (J). lib. bdg. 25.69 (978-0-7398-4333-8(8)) Raintree.

Pancella, Peggy. Home Safety. 2004. (Heinemann First Library). (Illus.). 32p. (J). 6.95 (978-1-4034-4941-2(4)); lib. bdg. 22.79 (978-1-4034-4932-0(5)) Heinemann Library.

Parker, Victoria. Homes. 2006. (Heinemann Read & Learn Ser.). (Illus.). 24p. (J). pap. (978-1-4034-7891-7(0)); lib. bdg. (978-1-4034-7885-6(6)) Steck-Vaughn.

Peterson, Virginia, et al, eds. The Environment: Protecting Our Home. 3rd rev. ed. 1998. (Information Plus Compact Ser.). (Illus.). 88p. (YA). (gr. 6-9). pap. 22.00 (978-1-57302-080-0(X)) Thomson Gale.

Petty, Kate. Homes. 2006. (World Show-and-Tell Ser.). (Illus.). 32p. (ps-1). (J). 8.95 (978-1-58728-548-6(7)); 14.95 (978-1-58728-547-9(9)) T&N Children's Publishing.

Platt, Richard. Pompeii. Cappon, Manuela, illus. 2007. (Through Time Ser.). 48p. (J). (gr. 1-5). 16.95 (***978-0-7534-6044-3(0)** , Kingfisher) Houghton Mifflin Co. Trade & Reference Div.

Prince, Sarah. Grandpa's House. 1999. (ps-2). lib. bdg. 11.55 (978-0-613-30445-0(4)) Tandem Library Bks.

Richmond, Marianne R. Congrats on Your New Home. 2005. (Illus.). 40p. (YA). 7.95 (978-0-9770000-3-6(6)) Marianne Richmond Studios, Inc.

Rigby Education Staff. Let's Sleep. (Sails Literacy Ser.). (Illus.). 16p. (gr. 1-2). 27.00 (978-0-7635-9887-7(9) , 698879C99) Rigby Education.

Ring, Susan. Los Hogares. 2005. Tr. of Homes. (SPA., Illus.). 16p. (J). (gr. 1 up). lib. bdg. 15.93 (978-0-7368-4177-1(6)) Capstone Pr., Inc.

—Places We Live. 2006. (Illus.). 16p. (J). (gr. k-2). 15.93 (978-0-7368-5850-2(4) , Yellow Umbrella Bks.) Capstone Pr., Inc.

Roop, Peter & Roop, Connie. A Home Album. 1998. (Long Ago & Today Ser.). (Illus.). 24p. (J). (gr. 1-3). lib. bdg. 19.92 (978-1-57572-602-1(5)) Heinemann Library.

Rosenberg, Pam. Yecch! Icky, Sticky, Gross Stuff in Your House. 2007. (Icky, Sticky, Gross-Out Bks.). 24p. (J). (gr. 2-6). 22.79 (***978-1-59296-898-5(8)**) Child's World, Inc.

Royston, Angela. Buildings of the Future. 2007. (J). pap. (***978-1-4329-0131-8(1)**); lib. bdg. (***978-1-4329-0126-4(5)**) Heinemann Library.

Royston, Angela. Where People Live. 1998. (Geography Starts Here Ser.). (Illus.). 32p. (J). (gr. 1-4). lib. bdg. 25.69 (978-0-8172-5116-1(2)) Raintree.

Rylant, Cynthia & Halperin, Wendy Anderson. Let's Go Home: The Wonderful Things about a House. 2002. (Illus.). 32p. (J). reprint ed. 16.95 (978-0-689-82326-8(6)) Simon & Schuster Children's Publishing.

Schaefer, A. R. Homes Around the World. 2007. (J). (978-1-59515-967-0(3)) Rourke Publishing, LLC.

Schaefer, Lola M. La Casa. (Un hogar para mi (A Home For Me) Ser.). 24p. pap. 5.25 (978-1-4034-0490-9(9)) Heinemann Library.

—La casa rodante. (Un hogar para mi (A Home For Me) Ser.). 24p. pap. 5.25 (978-1-4034-0492-3(5)) Heinemann Library.

—El departamento. (Un hogar para mi (A Home For Me) Ser.). 24p. pap. 5.25 (978-1-4034-0487-9(9)) Heinemann Library.

—Hogares 1 2 3. (Un hogar para mi (A Home For Me) Ser.). 24p. pap. 5.25 (978-1-4034-0488-6(7)) Heinemann Library.

—Homes 1 2 3. 2003. (Heinemann Read & Learn Ser.). (Illus.). 24p. (J). pap. 5.25 (978-1-4034-0482-4(8)) Heinemann Library.

—Homes A B C. 2003. (Illus.). 24p. pap. 5.25 (978-1-4034-0483-1(6)) Heinemann Library.

—Homes ABC. 2003. (Home for Me Ser.). (Illus.). 24p. (J). (ps-1). lib. bdg. 18.50 (978-1-4034-0260-8(4)) Heinemann Library.

—House. 2003. (Home for Me Ser.). (Illus.). 24p. (J). (ps-1). lib. bdg. 18.50 (978-1-4034-0261-5(2)); pap. 5.25 (978-1-4034-0484-8(4)) Heinemann Library.

—Mobile Home. 2003. (Home for Me Ser.). (Illus.). 24p. (J). (ps-1). lib. bdg. 18.50 (978-1-4034-0263-9(9)) Heinemann Library.

Schuh, Mari C. In My Home. 2006. (Illus.). 24p. (J). (978-0-7368-4238-9(1) , Pebble Bks.) Capstone Pr., Inc.

Skinner, Tina. Log & Timber Frame Homes. 2003. (Schiffer Design Book Ser.). (Illus.). 224p. (gr. 10-13). 44.95 (978-0-7643-1754-5(7)) Schiffer Publishing, Ltd.

Smith, Alastair, ed. Homes & Houses Then & Now. 2004. (Then & Now Flip Flaps Ser.). (SPA., Illus.). 16p. (J). (gr. 2 up). pap. 7.95 (978-0-7460-3100-1(0)) EDC Publishing.

Southwater Staff. My Home: Look & Learn. 2000. (Look & Learn Ser.). (Illus.). 32p. (ps). 7.95 (978-1-84215-169-3(X) , Southwater) Anness Publishing GBR. *Dist:* National Bk. Network.

Stone, Lynn M. Houses. 2001. (How are They Built? Ser.). (Illus.). 48p. (J). (gr. 4-8). lib. bdg. 29.93 (978-1-58952-137-7(4)) Rourke Publishing, LLC.

Walker, Lester. Housebuilding for Children 2nd Ed. 2007. 192p. pap. 16.95 (***978-1-58567-906-5(2)**) Penguin Group (USA) Inc.

Waters, Jennifer. Right at Home. 2002. (Spyglass Books). (Illus.). 24p. (J). (gr. 1 up). lib. bdg. 18.60 (978-0-7565-0380-2(9)) Compass Point Bks.

Watson, Donna. Houses: Past & Present. 2005. (Illus.). 24p. (J). (***978-0-328-13351-2(5)** , Scott Foresman) Addison-Wesley Educational Pubs., Inc.

Wilkinson, Philip & Dorling Kindersley Publishing Staff. Building. 2000. (Eyewitness Bks.). (Illus.). 64p. (J). (gr. 4-7). lib. bdg. 19.99 (978-0-7894-6607-5(4)) Dorling Kindersley Publishing, Inc.

Williams, Brian. Ancient Roman Homes. (People in the Past Ser.). (Illus.). 48p. (J). 2003. (gr. 4-6). lib. bdg. 25.64 (978-1-58810-631-5(4)); 2002. pap. 8.50 (978-1-4034-0519-7(0)) Heinemann Library.

Yates, Vicki. Buildings. 2007. (J). (***978-1-4034-9830-4(X)**); pap. (***978-1-4034-9838-0(5)**) Heinemann Library.

Yolen, Jane. House, House. Stemple, Jason, photos by. 1998. (Accelerated Reader Bks.). (Illus.). 32p. (J). (gr. 2-6). 15.95 (978-0-7614-5013-9(0) , Cavendish Children's Bks.) Cavendish, Marshall Corp.

HOUSES—FICTION

Ables, Troy. Around This Old House. 2004. 20p. pap. 14.95 (978-1-4137-3169-9(4)) PublishAmerica, Inc.

Adams, Pam. This Is the House That Jack Built. 2001. (Illus.). 16p. (J). (ps-1). bds. 5.99 (978-0-85953-468-0(5)) Child's Play-International.

Aigner-Clark, Julie. Baby Einstein: La casa de Violet Violet's House, Spanish-Language Edition. Zaidi, Nadeem, illus. 2005. (Baby Einstein: Libros de Carton Ser.). (SPA.). 10p. (J). bds. 9.95 (978-970-718-305-6(5) , Silver Dolphin en Español) Advanced Marketing, S. de R. L. de C. V. MEX. *Dist:* Perseus Distribution.

—Violet's House: A Giant Touch-and-Feel Book. Zaidi, Nadeem, illus. 2003. 10p. (ps-17). 9.99 (978-0-7868-1872-3(7)) Disney Pr.

Alexander, Marge. Adventures at the Grandparents' House. 2001. 96p. 9.99 (978-1-58169-064-4(9) , Evergreen Pr.) Genesis Communications, Inc.

Avila, Juan Casas. Dos Casos de Casas y Algunas Otras Cosas. Jimenez, Leticia Serrano, illus. rev. ed. 2006. (Castillo de la Lectura Verde Ser.). (SPA.). 72p. (J). pap. 7.95 (978-970-20-0175-1(7)) Castillo, Ediciones, S. A. de C. V. MEX. *Dist:* Macmillan.

Banks, Kate. The Great Blue House. Hallensleben, Georg, illus. 2005. 40p. (J). 16.00 (978-0-374-32769-9(6) , Farrar, Straus & Giroux (BYR)) Farrar, Straus & Giroux.

Baran, Robin. Flight of the Robbins. 2006. pap. 7.95 (978-0-533-15430-2(8)) Vantage Pr., Inc.

The Barnabys' New House, 6 Packs. (Literatura 2000 Ser.). (gr. 1-2). 28.00 (978-0-7635-0458-8(0)) Rigby Education.

Berenstain, Stan & Berenstain, Jan. The Berenstain Bears Clean House. 2005. (Illus.). 30p. (J). lib. bdg. 9.00 (***978-1-4242-0815-9(7)**) Fitzgerald Bks.

Blance, Ellen & Cook. Monster Cleans His House. Date not set. (Illus.). 16p. pap. 129.15 (978-0-582-18590-6(4)) Addison-Wesley Longman, Ltd. GBR. *Dist:* Trans-Atlantic Pubns., Inc.

—Monster Looks for a House. Date not set. (Illus.). 16p. pap. 129.15 (978-0-582-18589-0(0)) Addison-Wesley Longman, Ltd. GBR. *Dist:* Trans-Atlantic Pubns., Inc.

Blazin' Hot: Coloring/Activity Book (English) 2005. (Illus.). (J). (978-0-9770455-0-1(1)) Educational Adventures.

Blazin' Hot: Picture Book (English) 8x8. 2006. (J). (978-1-933934-29-7(8)) Educational Adventures.

Blazin' Hot Picture Book (English) 2005. (Illus.). (J). (978-0-9765953-9-7(7)) Educational Adventures.

Boston, Lucy M. Children of Green Knowe. 2002. (gr. 3-6). lib. bdg. 14.15 (978-0-613-54457-3(9)) Tandem Library Bks.

—The Children of Green Knowe. Boston, Peter, illus. 2002. (Green Knowe Ser.). 192p. (YA). reprint ed. (gr. 3 up). 17.00 (978-0-15-202462-8(X) , Harcourt Young Classics); (gr. 4-7). pap. 6.95 (978-0-15-202468-0(9) , Odyssey Classics) Harcourt Children's Bks.

—An Enemy at Green Knowe. Boston, Peter, illus. 2002. (Green Knowe Ser.). 192p. (YA). (gr. 4-7). reprint ed. pap. 6.00 (978-0-15-202481-9(6) , Odyssey Classics) Harcourt Children's Bks.

—The River at Green Knowe. Boston, Peter, illus. 2002. (Green Knowe Ser.). 176p. (YA). (gr. 4-7). reprint ed. pap. 6.00 (978-0-15-202607-3(X) , Odyssey Classics) Harcourt Children's Bks.

—A Stranger at Green Knowe. Boston, Peter, illus. 2002. (Green Knowe Ser.). 208p. (YA). reprint ed. (gr. 3 up). 17.00 (978-0-15-202583-0(9) , Harcourt Young Classics); (gr. 4-7). pap. 6.95 (978-0-15-202589-2(8) , Odyssey Classics) Harcourt Children's Bks.

—The Treasure of Green Knowe. Boston, Peter, illus. 2002. (Green Knowe Ser.). 224p. (YA). (gr. 4-7). reprint ed. pap. 7.00 (978-0-15-202601-1(0) , Odyssey Classics) Harcourt Children's Bks.

Bratun, Katy. Gingerbread Mouse. Bratun, Katy, illus. 2007. 32p. (J). pap. 6.99 (***978-0-06-009082-1(0)** , Harper Trophy) HarperCollins Pubs.

Brezenoff, Steven. Burning Secrets. Vue, Tou, illus. 2008. (J). pap. (***978-1-59889-920-7(1)**); (YA). (gr. 5-9). lib. bdg. 17.95 (***978-1-59889-854-5(X)**) Stone Arch Bks.

Brightwood, Laura, illus. The House That Talked to Itself. 2006. (J). (978-0-9779290-3-0(5)) 3-C Institute for Social Development.

Brooks, Nigel & Horner, Abigail. Town Mouse House: How We Lived One Hundred Years Ago. 2000. (Illus.). 32p. (J). (gr. k-3). 15.95 (978-0-8027-8732-3(0)) Walker & Co.

Brown, Margaret Wise. Robin's Room. Johnson, Stephen T. & Fancher, Lou, illus. 2002. 40p. (ps-2). 14.99 (978-0-7868-0602-7(8)); 15.49 (978-0-7868-2516-5(2)) Hyperion Bks. for Children.

—The Wonderful House. Miller, J. P., illus. 2003. 48p. (J). (gr. k-k). 12.95 (978-0-307-10326-0(9) , Golden Bks.) Random Hse. Children's Bks.

Burns Knight, Margy. Talking Walls. unabr. ed. 1999. (Illus.). (J). (gr. 1-4). audio 15.95 (978-1-883332-33-4(8)) Tilbury Hse. Pubs.

Burton, Virginia Lee. The Little House. Burton, Virginia Lee, illus. 2002. (Illus.). (J). 13.79 (978-0-7587-0054-4(7)) Book Wholesalers, Inc.

—The Little House. 1998. (Carry-Along Book & Cassette Favorites Ser.). 1p. (J). (gr. k-3). pap. 9.95 incl. audio (978-0-395-89112-4(4)) Houghton Mifflin Co. Trade & Reference Div.

Cappetta, Cynthia. Chairs, Chairs, Chairs! Stromoski, Rick, illus. 1999. (Rookie Reader Skill Set Ser.). 32p. (J). (gr. k-2). pap. 4.95 (978-0-516-26474-5(5) , Children's Pr.) Scholastic Library Publishing.

—Chairs, Chairs, Chairs! 1999. (gr. k-3). lib. bdg. 12.95 (978-0-613-37308-1(1)) Tandem Library Bks.

Cassedy, Sylvia. Behind the Attic Wall. 1998. (gr. 4-7). 22.50 (978-0-8446-6965-6(2)) Smith, Peter Pub., Inc.

Chausse, Sylvie. Los Gatos de Mama Tatin. Crozat, Francois, illus. 2003. (SPA.). 32p. (J). (gr. k-2). (978-84-8418-067-8(0) , ZZ30446) Zendrera Zariquiey, Editorial ESP. *Dist:* Lectorum Pubns., Inc.

Chouette Publishing. Caillou: In My House. Brignaud, Pierre, illus. rev. ed. 2007. (My First Dictionary Ser.). 16p. (J). bds. 12.95 (***978-2-89450-627-1(9)**) Chouette Publishing CAN. *Dist:* Independent Pubs. Group.

Citra, Becky. Ellie's New Home. 1999. (Young Reader Ser.). (Illus.). 82p. (J). (gr. 3-6). pap. 4.99 (978-1-55143-164-2(5)) Orca Bk. Pubs. USA.

—Ellie's New Home. 1999. (gr. 3-6). lib. bdg. 13.00 (978-0-613-29608-3(7)) Tandem Library Bks.

Cleaning House. 2003. (J). per. (978-1-57657-964-0(6)) Paradise Pr., Inc.

Clown Paints His House: Early Level Satellite Individual Title Six-Packs. (Sails Literacy Ser.). 16p. (gr. 1-2). 27.00 (978-0-7578-2920-8(1)) Rigby Education.

Covino, Beth Ann. The Little Green House. Stroud, Jamie, illus. 2000. 16p. (J). pap. 5.95 (978-1-891846-22-9(1)) Business Word, The.

Coxe, Molly. Bookworm. 2000. (J). (978-0-606-18920-0(3)) Tandem Library Bks.

Cutsche, Brigitte. The House on Oak Tree Lane. Vol. 3. Dodge, Chris, illus. 2000. (Holt's Friends Ser.). 120p. (J). (gr. 4-6). 9.99 (978-0-88092-516-7(7)) Royal Fireworks Publishing Co.

Doyon, Stephanie. Buying Time. 1999. (On the Road Ser.: No. 2). (978-0-606-18898-2(3)) Tandem Library Bks.

Duncan, Dave. The Crooked House. 2000. (King's Daggers Ser.: Vol. 2). (Illus.). 256p. (J). (gr. 7 up). pap. 5.99 (978-0-380-80099-5(3)) HarperCollins Pubs.

Durand, Delphine. My House. Adams, Sarah, tr. 2007. (Illus.). 44p. (J). (gr. k-2). 12.95 (***978-1-905341-09-2(1)**) WingedChariot Pr. GBR. *Dist:* Independent Pubs. Group.

Eggleton, Jill. Matilda's Plans, 6 Pks. Webb, Philip, illus. (Sails Literacy Ser.). 16p. (gr. 2-3). 27.00 (978-0-7578-0707-7(0)) Rigby Education.

—The Zacharys' Plans: Individual Title Six-Packs. Hawley, Kelvin, illus. (Sails Literacy Ser.). 16p. (gr. 2-3). 27.00 (978-0-7578-0701-5(1)) Rigby Education.

Fiorentini, Paolo, illus. My House. 2005. (J). 16.95 (978-0-7641-7846-7(6)) Barron's Educational Series, Inc.

Fitch, Sheree. There's a Mouse in My House! braille ed. 2004. (Illus.). (J). (gr. k-3). spiral bd. (978-0-616-07234-9(1)); spiral bd. (978-0-616-07235-6(X)) Canadian National Institute for the Blind/Institut National Canadien pour les Aveugles.

—There's a Mouse in My House! 1999. (ps-2). lib. bdg. 15.25 (978-0-613-27220-9(X)) Tandem Library Bks.

Fleming, Candace. Tippy-Tippy-Tippy, Hide! Karas, G. Brian, illus. 2007. 40p. (J). (ps-3). 16.99 (978-0-689-87479-6(0) , Atheneum) Simon & Schuster Children's Publishing.

Forsting, Sandy. The House at the End of the Street. Lauer, Heidi, illus. 1998. 48p. (J). (ps-3). 19.95 (978-0-9666156-0-9(3)) Keepsake Chronicles.

Fox, Christyan & Fox, Diane. What Shape Is That, Piggy-wiggy? 2002. (Illus.). 10p. (J). (ps-k). bds. 5.95 (978-1-929766-44-4(0)) Handprint Bks.

Fritz, Jean. The Cabin Faced West. 2001. (Illus.). 1p. (J). pap. 5.99 (978-0-698-11936-9(3) , Putnam Juvenile) Penguin Group (USA) Inc.

Gaiman, Neil. Los lobos de la Pared: Wolves in the Walls. 2006. (SPA.). 64p. 22.95 (978-1-59497-222-5(2)) Public Square Bks.

Garland, Michael. Mystery Mansion: A Look Again Book. Garland, Michael, illus. 2001. (Illus.). 32p. (J). 15.99 (978-0-525-46675-8(4) , Dutton Juvenile) Penguin Group (USA) Inc.

Gershator, Phillis. Old House, New House. Potter, Katherine, illus. 2008. (J). (***978-0-7614-5386-4(5)*** Cavendish, Marshall Corp.

Giacomucci, Carol. A New Home. 2006. 23p. pap. 10.95 (978-0-7414-3498-2(9)) Infinity Publishing.

Golden Books Staff. The House that Jack Built. Miller, J. P., illus. 2008. (Little Golden Book Ser.). 24p. (J). 2.99 (978-0-375-83530-8(X) , Golden Bks.) Random Hse. Children's Bks.

Goodhart, Pippa. House that Jack Built. Parker, Andy, illus. 2004. 24p. (J). lib. bdg. 22.65 (***978-1-59646-700-2(2)***) Dingles & Co.

Group/McGraw-Hill, Wright. The New House: Level H, 6 vols. (Take Twostm Ser.). 16p. 29.95 (978-0-322-09000-2(8)) Wright Group, The.

Gwent (Wales), Staff Development Unit Staff & Acen Staff, contrib. by. Croeso I Gartref Llew. 2005. (WEL., Illus.). 8p. (978-1-874049-34-0(3)) Acen Limited.

Harcourt School Publishers Staff. Andy's New Home Advanced Level. 3rd ed. 2002. (Trophies Reading Program Ser.). (Illus.). pap. 5.10 (978-0-15-323027-1(4)) Harcourt Schl. Pubs.

—The Furniture in My House. 3rd ed. 2002. (Trophies English Language Learners Ser.). (Illus.). (J). pap. 4.10 (978-0-15-327593-7(6)) Harcourt Schl. Pubs.

—Take a Tour of My House. 3rd ed. 2002. (Trophies English Language Learners Ser.). (Illus.). (J). pap. 4.10 (978-0-15-327582-1(0)) Harcourt Schl. Pubs.

Hayes, Malcolm. The Dreamcatchers. 2006. 282p. pap. (***978-1-4120-8320-1(6)***) Trafford Publishing.

Hébert, Marie-Francine. Une Maison dans la Baleine. Germain, Philippe, illus. 2003. (Premier Roman Ser.). (FRE.). 64p. (J). (gr. 2-5). pap. (978-2-89021-240-4(8)) Diffusion du livre Mirabel.

Herbert, James. The Magic Cottage. 1999. 394p. 32.50 (978-0-333-76129-8(4)) Macmillan Publishers Ltd. GBR. *Dist:* Independent Pubs. Group.

Hill, Eric. Spot Ayuda en la Casa. (SPA.). pap. 4.95 (978-950-07-1968-1(1)) Editorial Sudamericana S.A. ARG. *Dist:* Distribooks, Inc.

—Spot en Casa. (SPA.). pap. 4.95 (978-950-07-1962-9(2)) Editorial Sudamericana S.A. ARG. *Dist:* Distribooks, Inc.

Hillert, Margaret. A House for Little Red. Oechsli, Kelly, illus. rev. ed. 2006. (Beginning to Read Ser.). 32p. (J). lib. bdg. 18.60 (978-1-59953-029-1(5)) Norwood Hse. Pr.

Hirashima, Jean. Hello Kitty's House & Garden: Reusable Sticker Book. Henry, Allison, illus. 2003. 12p. (J). (ps-3). 13.95 (978-0-8109-4230-1(5)) Abrams, Harry N. , Inc.

Hoberman, Mary Ann. A House Is a House for Me. Betty, Fraser, illus. 2007. 48p. (J). (ps). 7.99 (***978-0-14-240773-8(9)*** , Puffin) Penguin Group (USA) Inc.

Hood, Susan. In My House. 1999. (Lamaze Ser.). (Illus.). 14p. (J). (ps). 8.99 (978-1-56799-894-8(1) , Friedman-Fairfax) Friedman, Michael Publishing Group, Inc.

The House That Jack Built (English) 2000. (J). (978-1-58805-117-2(X)) DS-Max USA, Inc.

Hughes, Carol. Toots & the Upside Down House. 1998. (J). pap. 3.99 (978-0-679-89162-8(5)) Random Hse., Inc.

—Toots & Upside down House. l.t. ed. 1998. (Illus.). 184p. (J). pap. (978-0-7540-6037-6(3) , CLP 241) BBC Audio.

Hutchins, Pat. The House That Sailed Away. 1999. (Plays for Young People Ser.). (Illus.). 104p. (gr. 4-7). pap. 10.95 (978-1-84002-097-7(0)) Theatre Communications Group, Inc.

I Can Say- Around the House. 2005. (J). bds. (978-1-4194-0036-0(3)) Paradise Pr., Inc.

Irwin, Inez Haynes. Maida's Little House. 2004. reprint ed. pap. 27.95 (978-1-4179-4236-7(3)) Kessinger Publishing, LLC.

James, Catherine. The Sad Little House. Collier, Kevin Scott, illus. l.t. ed. 2006. 28p. (J). E-Book 9.95 incl. cd-rom (978-1-933090-18-4(9)) Guardian Angel Publishing, Inc.

Jensen, Patricia. My House. 2004. (My First Reader Ser.). 29p. (J). (gr. k-1). pap. 3.95 (978-0-516-24636-9(4) , Children's Pr.) Scholastic Library Publishing.

Johns, Linda. Hannah West on Millionaire's Row. 2007. (Hannah West Ser.). 160p. (J). (gr. 5). 6.99 (***978-0-14-240824-7(7)*** , Puffin) Penguin Group (USA) Inc.

Johnson, D. B. Henry Builds a Cabin. 2002. (Illus.). 32p. (J). (gr. k-3). 15.00 (978-0-618-13201-0(5)) Houghton Mifflin Co. Trade & Reference Div.

Karon, Jan, et al. Violet Comes to Stay. McCully, Emily Arnold, illus. 2006. (Mitford Ser.). 36p. (J). (gr. k). 15.99 (978-0-670-06073-3(9) , Viking Juvenile) Penguin Group (USA) Inc.

Keller, Holly. What I See. 2003. (Green Light Readers Level 1 Ser.). (Illus.). 24p. (J). 11.95 (978-0-15-204814-3(6)); pap. 3.95 (978-0-15-204854-9(5)) Harcourt Children's Bks. (Green Light Readers).

—What I See. 2000. (gr. k-3). lib. bdg. 11.80 (978-0-613-66389-2(6)) Tandem Library Bks.

Kent, Lorna, illus. In My House. 2004. 8p. (J). bds. 3.99 (978-1-85854-086-3(0)) Brimax Books Ltd. GBR. *Dist:* Byeway Bks.

Kessler, Leonard. Mr. Pine's Purple House. Kessler, Leonard, illus. 64p. 2000. (Illus.). (J). 17.95 (978-1-930900-02-8(3)); 35th ed. 2001. 16.00 (978-1-930900-15-8(5)) Purple Hse. Pr.

King, Kirsty. My New Friends. 2005. 52p. pap. (***978-1-84401-576-4(9)***) Athena Pr.

Kipnis, Itzik. The Little House. Leviant, Curt, tr. from YID. Craft, Dana Duane, illus. 1999. 24p. (J). (ps-3). pap. (978-1-894303-21-7(0)) Raven Rock Publishing.

Krauss, Ruth. A Very Special House. Sendak, Maurice, illus. 2001. (Sendak Reissues Ser.). 32p. (J). 16.95 (978-0-06-028638-5(5)); 14.89 (978-0-06-028639-2(3)) HarperCollins Pubs.

Landa, Norbert. The Secret House of Papa Mouse. Turk, Hanne, illus. 2004. 30p. (J). lib. bdg. 24.67 (978-0-8368-4106-0(9)) Stevens, Gareth Inc.

Lavigne, Guy & Godbout, Real. La Maison du Pendu. 2003. (Roman Jeunesse Ser.). (Illus.). 96p. (YA). (gr. 4-7). pap. (978-2-89021-328-9(5)) Diffusion du livre Mirabel.

Le Sieg, Theodore, tr. & illus. Come over to My House. Le Sieg, Theodore, illus. Date not set. (J). lib. bdg. 11.99 (978-0-679-98255-5(8)); 7.99 (978-0-679-88255-8(3)) Random Hse. Children's Bks. (Random Hse. Bks. for Young Readers).

Lembcke, Marjaleena & Martínez, Eduardo. Tiempo de Secretos. Steffens, Klaus & Martínez, Eduardo, trs. Steffens, Klaus, illus. 2002. (SPA.). 144p. (978-84-89804-58-6(3)) Loguez Ediciones ESP. *Dist:* Lectorum Pubns., Inc.

Leon McCann, Jesse. Haunted Halloween: Sticker Storybook. del Sur, Duendes, illus. 2004. (Scooby-Doo Ser.). 24p. (J). pap. 5.99 (978-0-439-60699-8(3) , Scholastic Paperbacks) Scholastic, Inc.

Leonard, Finley Mary. The Story of the Big Front Door. 2007. (ENG.). 192p. 19.99 (***978-1-4280-7183-4(0)***); per. 13.99 (***978-1-4280-7193-3(8)***) IndyPublish.com.

Lobel, Arnold, illus. Ming Lo Moves the Mountain: Ming Lo Txav Lub Pob Tsuas. 2000. 32p. (J). (ps-3). pap. 6.95 (978-0-9629298-2-3(4) , MCH-2-4) Minnesota Humanities Commission.

Lodico, Cheryl. The Wacky World of Winnie & Willie. 2007. 14.00 (***978-0-8059-8362-3(7)***) Dorrance Publishing Co., Inc.

Lohans, Alison. The Raspberry Room. Newland, Gillian, illus. 2006. 59p. (J). lib. bdg. 20.00 (***978-1-4242-1247-7(2)***) Fitzgerald Bks.

Low, Alice. Blueberry Mouse. Friend, David Michael, tr. Friend, David Michael, illus. 2004. (J). 15.95 (978-1-59336-111-2(4)); pap. (978-1-59336-112-9(2)) Mondo Publishing.

MacDonald, Betty Bard. The Squeaky Door. Date not set. 32p. (J). (ps-1). pap. 4.99 (978-0-06-443566-6(0)) HarperCollins Pubs.

MacDonald, Margaret Read. The Squeaky Door. DePalma, Mary Newell, illus. 2006. 40p. (J). (ps-1). 12.99 (978-0-06 028373 5(4)); lib. bdg. 13.89 (978-0-06-028374-2(2)) HarperCollins Pubs.

Martin, Cathy. Uff Da! Clark, Richard, tr. Clark, Richard, illus. 2004. 32p. (J). 14.95 (978-1-58246-117-5(1) , Tricycle Pr.) Ten Speed Pr.

McDonald, Megan. My House Has Stars. Catalanotto, Peter, illus. 2001. 32p. (J). (gr. k-3). reprint ed. pap. 5.95 (978-0-531-07181-6(2) , Orchard Bks.) Scholastic, Inc.

—My House Has Stars. 2001. (Illus.). (J). (978-0-606-21563-3(8)) Tandem Library Bks.

McMullan, Kate. Baby Goose. Lemaitre, Pascal, illus. 2004. 48p. (ps-ps). 15.99 (978-0-7868-0430-6(0)) Hyperion Bks. for Children.

Medearis, Angela Shelf. We Eat Dinner in the Bathtub. Rogers, Jacqueline, illus. 2004. 32p. (J). lib. bdg. 15.00 (978-1-59054-395-5(5)) Fitzgerald Bks.

Meister, Cari. A New Roof Level A. Lin, Grace, illus. 2002. (Rookie Readers Ser.). 24p. (J). (gr. k-1). 19.50 (978-0-516-22369-8(0) , Children's Pr.) Scholastic Library Publishing.

Molloy, Michael. The House on Falling Star Hill. 2004. (Illus.). 384p. (J). pap. 16.95 (978-0-439-57740-3(3) , Chicken Hse., The) Scholastic, Inc.

Montgomery, L. M. Ana y la Casa de Sus Suenos. (Coleccion "Ana, la de Tejas Verdes"). (SPA.). 256p. (YA). (gr. 5-8). (978-84-7888-637-1(0) , SAL8825) Emece Editores ESP. *Dist:* Lectorum Pubns., Inc.

—Ana y la Casa de Sus Suenos. 2000. (Coleccion "Ana, la de Tejas Verdes" Ser.). (SPA.). 256p. (J). 10.95 (978-84-7888-217-5(0)) Lectorum Pubns., Inc.

Moore, Ulysses. House of Mirrors. 2007. (Ulysses Moore Ser.: No. 3). 256p. (J). pap. 5.99 (***978-0-439-77672-1(4)***) Scholastic, Inc.

Moreland, Marian H. & Moreland, Richard. Wee Three Kings. 1999. (Instant Christmas Pageant Ser.). 48p. (J). (gr. k-6). pap. 24.99 incl. audio compact disk (978-0-7644-2149-5(2)) Group Publishing, Inc.

Morris, Helen. Enemni (My House) Conmy, Bet & Nevak, Caroline, illus. l.t. ed. 1999. (ESK.). 8p. (J). (gr. k-3). pap. 17.00 (978-1-58084-158-0(9)) Lower Kuskokwim Schl. District.

—Enka (My House) Conmy, Bet & Nevak, Caroline, illus. l.t. ed. 1999. (ESK.). 8p. (J). (gr. k-3). pap. 17.00 (978-1-58084-159-7(7)) Lower Kuskokwim Schl. District.

—My House. Conmy, Bet & Nevak, Caroline, illus. l.t. ed. 1999. 8p. (J). (gr. k-3). pap. 17.00 (978-1-58084-157-3(0)) Lower Kuskokwim Schl. District.

My Home: Individual Title-Six Packs. (Chiquilibros Ser.). (gr. k-1). 23.00 (978-0-7635-0447-2(5)) Rigby Education.

My Home: Kindergarten Guided Reading Level B. (On Our Way to English Ser.). (gr. k up). 27.75 (978-0-7578-7014-9(7)) Rigby Education.

My House: Individual Title Six-Packs. (Literatura 2000 Ser.). (gr. 1-2). 28.00 (978-0-7635-0142-6(5)) Rigby Education.

Myers, Bill. The House That Went Ker-Splat! The Parable of the Wise & Foolish Builder. Smith, Andy J., illus. 2008. (J). (***978-0-310-71220-6(3)***) Zonderkidz.

Namey, Laura. The Roof House. Wise, Noreen, ed. Killeen, Dan, illus. 2001. (Lemonade Collection). 64p. (J). (gr. 1-6). pap. 7.50 (978-1-58584-274-2(5)) Huckleberry Pr.

The New House, 6, Pack. (Sails Literacy Ser.). 16p. (gr. k up). 27.00 (978-0-7635-4447-8(7)) Rigby Education.

Nixon, Joan Lowery. The House on Hackman's Hill. 2001. 128p. (J). (gr. 4-7). pap. 4.50 (978-0-590-42370-0(3)) Scholastic, Inc.

—The House on Hackman's Hill. 2001. (J). 11.15 (978-0-606-19923-0(3)) Tandem Library Bks.

Norton, Andre. Octagon Magic. 2005. (Magic Bks.: No. 2). 192p. (J). (gr. 5). 5.99 (978-0-7653-5298-9(2) , Starscape) Doherty, Tom Assocs., LLC.

Onish, Liane. The Alphabet Eurps Build Eurpsville. 1999. (Eurps Concept Bks.). (Illus.). (J). 7.95 (978-1-892522-05-4(5)) Eurpsville USA, Inc.

Owl & Mouse in the House: Individual Title Six-Packs. (Sails Literacy Ser.). (gr. 1-2). 36.00 (978-0-7578-4016-6(7)) Rigby Education.

Page, Jason. Wham Bam Boozle: A Gnastly, Noisy, Stinky Pop-Up Book! Quigley, Sebastian, illus. 2003. 12p. (J). (gr. k-4). reprint ed. 12.00 (978-0-7567-6906-2(X)) DIANE Publishing Co.

Paros, Jennifer. Violet Bing & the Grand House. 2007. 112p. (J). (gr. 1-4). 14.99 (978-0-670-06151-8(4) , Viking Juvenile) Penguin Group (USA) Inc.

Perez, Monica, et al. Curious George Builds a Home. 2006. (Illus.). 24p. (J). (gr. k-3). 3.99 (978-0-618-72395-9(1)) Houghton Mifflin Co.

Petach, Heidi. Wee Three Pigs. Petach, Heidi, illus. 2002. (Reading Railroad Bks.). (Illus.). 32p. (J). (ps-2). pap. 3.49 (978-0-448-42528-3(9) , Grosset & Dunlap) Penguin Group (USA) Inc.

—Wee Three Pigs. 2002. (gr. k-3). lib. bdg. 11.25 (978-0-613-71015-2(0)) Tandem Library Bks.

Puppy's House. Date not set. (Illus.). (J). bds. 4.98 (978-1-4054-0787-8(5)) Parragon, Inc.

Rau, Dana Meachen. My Special Space. 2004. (Rookie Reader Espanol Ser.). (Illus.). 31p. (J). (gr. k-2). pap. 4.95 (978-0-516-27788-2(X) , Children's Pr.) Scholastic Library Publishing.

—My Special Space. Kim, Julie J., illus. 2003. (Rookie Reader - Level C Ser.). 32p. (J). 19.50 (978-0-516-22881-5(1) , Children's Pr.) Scholastic Library Publishing.

Reed, Patrick. Who Lives Here? 1998. (Illus.). 40p. (J). pap. 12.00 (978-1-891989-00-1(6)) Fundbuilder$, U.S.A.

Rigby Education Staff. All Clean. (Sails Literacy Ser.). (Illus.). 16p. (gr. 1-2). 27.00 (978-0-7635-9901-0(8) , 699018C99) Rigby Education.

—House for Mouse. (Sails Literacy Ser.). (Illus.). 16p. (gr. 1-2). 27.00 (978-0-7635-9893-8(3)) Rigby Education.

Robeson, K. S. Chloe & Bia Bk. 2: Tales from Wind Creek. 2003. 96p. per. 8.95 (978-0-9723530-1-4(1)) Falcor Bks.

Root, Phyllis. The House That Jill Built. Durand, Delphine, illus. 2005. 20p. (J). (ps-1). 15.99 (978-0-7636-1008-1(9)) Candlewick Pr.

Root, Phyllis. The House That Jill Built: A Pop-up Book. Durand, Delphine, illus. 2007. 18p. (J). reprint ed. 16.00 (***978-1-4223-6756-8(8)***) DIANE Publishing Co.

Rosen, Michael. This Is Our House. Graham, Bob, illus. 2005. 32p. (J). (ps-1). pap. 5.99 (978-0-7636-2816-1(6)) Candlewick Pr.

—This Is Our House. 1998. (J). (978-0-606-13845-1(5)) Tandem Library Bks.

Rundstrom, T. S. A Herd of Cows Came by My House. Waldron, Drue K. & Stevens, Amber, illus. 2002. 59p. (J). per. 16.00 (978-1-932062-18-2(1)) Hability Solution Services, Inc.

Rushby, Pamela. Haunted Houses: Footsteps, Shadows in the Garden, the Midnight Children. 2005. (Triple Play-Yellow Ser.). (Illus.). 48p. (gr. 4-8). 41.85 (978-0-7910-9078-7(7)) Facts On File, Inc.

Rylant, Cynthia. Let's Go Home: The Wonderful Things about a House. Halperin, Wendy Anderson, illus. 2005. 32p. (J). pap. 7.99 (978-1-4169-0839-5(0) , Aladdin) Simon & Schuster Children's Publishing.

—Mr. Putter & Tabby Paint the Porch. Howard, Arthur, illus. 2001. (Mr. Putter & Tabby Ser.). 44p. (J). (gr. 1-4). pap. 5.95 (978-0-15-202474-1(3) , Harcourt Paperbacks) Harcourt Children's Bks.

—Mr. Putter & Tabby Paint the Porch. 2001. (Mr. Putter & Tabby Ser.). (978-0-606-22609-7(5)); lib. bdg. 14.10 (978-0-613-46257-0(2)) Tandem Library Bks.

Sanchez, Gloria. Chinto y Tom. (SPA.). 80p. (J). (978-84-348-8101-3(2)) SM Ediciones ESP. *Dist:* Lectorum Pubns., Inc.

Scarry, Richard. Mi Casa.Tr. of My Home. (SPA., Illus.). (J). 6.95 (978-950-04-0715-1(9)) Emecé Editores S.A. ARG. *Dist:* Planeta Publishing Corp.

—Mi Casa. 2003. (Richard Scarry Ser.).Tr. of My Home. (SPA., Illus.). (J). pap. (978-970-690-845-2(5)) Planeta Mexicana Editorial S. A. de C. V.

Scholastic, Inc. Staff, ed. Play Kitchen. (Illus.). 8p. (J). pap. 19.99 (978-0-590-24958-4(4)) Scholastic, Inc.

Scholastic, Inc. Staff & Krovatin, Christopher. The Best Ghost Stories Ever. 2004. (Scholastic Classics Ser.). 192p. (J). (gr. 4 up). pap. 3.99 (978-0-439-57426-6(9) , Scholastic Paperbacks) Scholastic, Inc.

Scholastic, Inc. Staff & Martin, Cory. O. C. , the Novelization. 2004. (O. C. Novelization Ser.: No. 1). 264p. (J). pap. 6.99 (978-0-439-66059-4(9)) Scholastic, Inc.

School Zone Publishing Company Staff & Hoenecke, Karen. Mouse Finds a House. 2000. (Start to Read Board Bks.). (Illus.). 10p. (J). (ps-k). bds. 4.99 (978-0-88743-807-3(5) , 06803) School Zone Publishing Co.

Sculthorp, Jeffrey A. Shelly's Home. Wingate, Lynae & Kober, John R., eds. Walter, Lorin, illus. 2000. (Wickleville Woods Ser.). 28p. (J). (ps-2). pap. 4.99 (978-1-889319-75-9(9) , Wickleville Woods) Trend Enterprises, Inc.

Shefelman, Janice J. & Shefelman, Tom, illus. Victoria House. 2002. (J). 16.95 (978-1-57168-705-0(X)); 8.95 (978-1-57168-706-7(8)) Eakin Pr.

Shreeve, Elizabeth. Hector Afloat. Levy, Pamela R., illus. 2004. 71p. (J). lib. bdg. 15.00 (***978-1-4242-0902-6(1)***) Fitzgerald Bks.

Skiff, Andrea. Blueberry & the Victorian House. Peterson, Elizabeth J., ed. 1998. (Illus.). 27p. (J). (gr. k-5). reprint ed. per. 6.95 (978-0-938911-03-6(1)) Individualized Education Systems/Poppy Lane Publishing.

Smith, Stephanie. Ermine's New Home. Hynes, Robert, illus. 2nd ed. 2005. (Soundprints' Read-And-Discover Ser.). (J). (gr. 1-3). 48p. 7.95 (978-1-931465-18-2(5) , B2001); 32p. pap. 3.95 (978-1-931465-17-5(7) , S2001) Soundprints.

Spietz, Heidi A. Natalie's New Home. Henderson, Frances, ed. l.t. ed. 1998. (Illus.). 27p. (J). (gr. 1-2). pap. 5.00 (978-0-929487-12-0(5)) American Montessori Consulting.

Steinbrenner, Jessica. My Messy Room. 2007. (Illus.). 32p. pap. 14.95 (***978-1-59687-854-9(1)*** , Milk & Cookies) ibooks, Inc.

Stine, R. L. Escape from Horror House. 1999. (Give Yourself Goosebumps Ser.: No. 37). 137p. (J). (gr. 3-7). pap. 3.99 (978-0-590-51682-2(5)) Scholastic, Inc.

Strangway, Melissa. 56 Water Street. 2007. 104p. per. 9.95 (***978-0-595-42429-0(5)***) iUniverse, Inc.

Swegles, Maryanne. Digging for Bottles. 2005. (Illus.). 28p. (J). 15.00 (978-0-9768418-0-7(0)) Hydrangea Pr.

Taylor, Dorothy L. Abigail's New Home. Schimmel, Beth, illus. (Valley View Farm Tales Ser.). 20p. (J). (gr. k-3). 7.50 (978-0-9610640-0-6(5)) Taylor, Dorothy Loring.

Teddy Bear-House. 2003. (J). per. (978-1-57657-162-0(9)) Paradise Pr., Inc.

Trimble, Marcia. P. Hermit Claims a Castle. Ulrich, George, illus. 1999. 32p. (J). (ps-3). 15.95 (978-1-891577-44-4(1)) Images Pr.

Trouble at Laura's House. 2005. (J). (978-1-58453-291-0(2)) Pioneer Valley Educational Pr., Inc.

Troulis, Jennifer. Penelope & Priscilla & the Enchanted House of Whispers. 2005. (Illus.). (J). pap. 13.95 (978-0-9768602-0-4(1)) Twin Monkeys Pr.

Tunsel, Darrell. The Little House That No One Wanted. 2004. 41p. pap. 19.95 (978-1-4137-1422-7(6)) PublishAmerica, Inc.

Tusquets, Esther, tr. La Casa Que Jack Construyo. Falconer, Elizabeth, illus. 2nd ed. 1998. (SPA.). 26p. (J). (gr. k-3). 13.56 net. (978-84-264-3659-7(5) , LM4561) Lectorum Pubns., Inc.

Ugon, Gabriela Armand. El Secreto de la Casa Gris. (SPA.). (J). 8.95 (978-958-04-7349-7(8)) Norma S.A. COL. *Dist:* Distribuidora Norma, Inc.

Van Patter, Bruce. Farley Found It. (Illus.). (J). 16.95 (978-1-59078-351-1(4)) Boyds Mills Pr.

Van Stockum, Hilda. The Borrowed House. 2nd ed. 2000. (Young Adult Historical Library). 221p. (YA). (gr. 9-12). reprint ed. pap. 12.95 (978-1-883937-46-1(9)) Bethlehem Bks.

Veit, Barbara. Who Stole My House? Martens, Marianne, tr. from GER. Cantone, Anna Laura, illus. 2007. 32p. (J). (gr. k-2). 15.95 (978-0-7358-2122-4(4)) North-South Bks., Inc.

Volkmer, Todd. Stacey Mcduver's House. 2005. 19p. (J). 12.38 (978-1-4116-6425-8(6)) Lulu.com.

Walsh, Vivian & Seibold, J. Otto. Gluey: A Snail Tale. 2002. (Illus.). 48p. (J). 15.00 (978-0-15-216620-5(3)) Harcourt Children's Bks.

Watson-Dubisch, Carolyn. Night of the Armadillos, 1. Watson-Dubisch, Carolyn, illus. l.t. ed. 2006. (Illus.). 32p. (J). per. 9.95 (978-0-9779295-2-8(3)) Medusa Road Pr.

Weinstein, Anya. Words Like Weeds Bk. 1: Ring Around the Moon. 2003. (gr. 7-12). lib. bdg. 22.20 (978-0-613-89757-0(9)) Tandem Library Bks.

Wells, Rosemary & Wells, Tom. The House in the Mail. 2004. (Illus.). 48p. (J). pap. 6.99 (978-0-14-240061-6(0) , Puffin) Penguin Group (USA) Inc.

—The House in the Mail. Andreasen, Dan, illus. 2002. 32p. (J). (gr. 1-5). 16.99 (978-0-670-03545-8(9) , Viking Juvenile) Penguin Group (USA) Inc.

Wild, Margaret. The Little Crooked House. Bentley, Jonathan, illus. 2006. 40p. 16.95 (978-1-894965-59-0(0)) Simply Read Bks. CAN. *Dist:* Perseus Distribution.

Wilder, Laura Ingalls. Little House in the Big Woods. Williams, Garth, illus. (Charming Classics). 256p. (J). 2005. pap. 6.99 (978-0-06-079750-8(9) , Harper Festival); 2001. 19.95 (978-0-06-029647-6(X)) HarperCollins Pubs.

Wilson-Max, Ken. Max Paints the House. 2000. (Illus.). 32p. (ps-k). 14.99 (978-0-7868-0537-2(4)) Disney Pr.

Wood, Audrey. The Napping House. Wood, Don, illus. 2004. 32p. (J). 17.95 (978-0-15-205080-1(9)) Harcourt Children's Bks.

The Worst House, 6 Packs. (Bookweb Ser.). 32p. (gr. 3 up). 34.00 (978-0-7635-3930-6(9)) Rigby Education.

Yeager, Graham. Stone Hedge: The Fourth Millersburg Novel. 2006. 142p. (YA). per. 7.99 (***978-0-9765478-6-0(4)***) Stone Acres Publishing Co.

HOUSES OF ANIMALS

see Animals—Habitations

HOUSING

see also Apartment Houses; City Planning; Homelessness

Bial, Raymond. Tenement: Immigrant Life on the Lower East Side. Bial, Raymond, illus. 2002. (Illus.). 48p. (J). (gr. 4-6). tchr. ed. 16.00 (978-0-618-13849-4(8)) Houghton Mifflin Co. Trade & Reference Div.

Habitat for Humanity: Individual Title Six-Packs. (On Deck Ser.). 24p. (gr. 4-5). 35.00 (978-0-7578-1037-4(3)) Rigby Education.

Hemminger, Marcia. Habitats Early Learner Photo Fun Activities. Rogers, Kathy, ed. 2001. (Illus.). 8p. (J). (ps-1). pap. 6.95 (978-1-56472-382-6(8)) Edupress, Inc.

Hopkinson, Deborah. Shutting Out the Sky: Life in the Tenements of New York, 1880-1924. 2003. (Illus.). 144p. (J). pap. 17.95 (978-0-439-37590-0(8) , Orchard Bks.) Scholastic, Inc.

McLeish, Ewan. Sustainable Homes. 2006. (Sustainable Futures Ser.). (Illus.). 48p. (J). (978-1-58340-982-4(3) , 1262624) Smart Apple Media.

Miller, Jake. Who's Who in a Public Housing Community. 2005. (Communities at Work Ser.). (Illus.). 24p. (J). 19.95 (978-1-4042-2786-6(5)); pap. (978-1-4042-5026-0(3)) Rosen Publishing Group, Inc., The. (PowerKids Pr.).

Pascal, Janet B. Jacob Riis: Reporter & Reformer. 2005. (Oxford Portraits Ser.). (Illus.). 176p. (YA). 28.00 (978-0-19-514527-4(5)) Oxford Univ. Pr., Inc.

Schuh, Mari C. In My Home. 2006. (Illus.). 24p. (J). (978-0-7368-4238-9(1) , Pebble Bks.) Capstone Pr., Inc.

Solway, Andrew. What's Living in Your Bedroom? 2004. (Hidden Life Ser.). (Illus.). 32p. (J). pap. 7.50 (978-1-4034-5484-3(1)); lib. bdg. 25.64 (978-1-4034-4845-3(0)) Heinemann Library.

Suen, Anastasia. Habitat for Humanity. 2002. (Reading Power Ser.). (Illus.). 24p. (J). (gr. 2). lib. bdg. 17.25 (978-0-8239-6006-4(4) , PowerKids Pr.) Rosen Publishing Group, Inc., The.

—Habitat Para la Humanidad. 2004. (Organizaciones de Ayuda Ser.). (SPA & ENG., Illus.). 24p. (J). (gr. 3-6). lib. bdg. 17.25 (978-0-8239-6857-2(X) , Buenas Letra) Rosen Publishing Group, Inc., The.

Townsend, John. Dreary Dwellings & Frightful Families. 2006. (Illus.). 48p. (J). (978-1-4109-1873-4(4)) Steck-Vaughn.

HOUSING—FICTION

Charles, Norma. Boxcar Kid. 2007. 136p. (YA). pap. 9.99 (***978-1-55002-755-6(7)*** , Sandcastle Bks.) Dundurn Group, The CAN. *Dist:* Univ. of Toronto Pr.

Gage, Wilson & Dewan, Ted. Crispin: The Pig Who Had It All. Dewan, Ted, illus. 2002. (Illus.). 32p. (J). (gr. k-3). pap. 6.99 (978-0-440-41745-3(7) , Dragonfly Bks.) Random Hse. Children's Bks.

Hoberman, Mary Ann. A House Is a House for Me. Fraser, Betty, illus. 2000. (J). pap. 19.97 incl. audio (978-0-7366-9199-4(5)) Books on Tape, Inc.

Ljungkvist, Laura. Follow the Line Through the House. 2007. (Illus.). 32p. (J). (gr. k-3). 16.99 (978-0-670-06225-6(1) , Viking Juvenile) Penguin Group (USA) Inc.

HOUSTON, SAM, 1793-1863

Boraas, Tracey. Sam Houston: Soldier & Statesman. 2002. (Let Freedom Ring Ser.). (Illus.). 48p. (J). (gr. 3-4). lib. bdg. 22.60 (978-0-7368-1350-1(0) , Bridgestone Bks.) Capstone Pr., Inc.

Caravantes, Peggy. American in Texas: The Story of Sam Houston. 2004. (Notable Americans Ser.). (Illus.). 144p. (YA). (gr. 6-12). 23.95 (978-1-931798-19-8(2)) Reynolds, Morgan Inc.

Fritz, Jean. Make Way for Sam Houston. 1998. 112p. (J). (gr. 4-7). pap. 5.99 (978-0-698-11646-7(1) , Putnam Juvenile) Penguin Group (USA) Inc.

Gregson, Susan R. Sam Houston: Texas Hero. 2005. (Signature Lives Ser.). (Illus.). 112p. (J). (gr. 5-7). (978-0-7565-1004-6(X)) Compass Point Bks.

Guzzetti, Paula. An American Hero: Sam Houston. 1998. (YA). (978-0-7614-0791-1(X) , Benchmark Bks.) Cavendish, Marshall Corp.

Harkins, Susan Sales & Harkins, William H. Sam Houston. 2006. (What's So Great About... ? Ser.). (Illus.). 32p. (J). (gr. 1-4). lib. bdg. (978-1-58415-482-2(9)) Mitchell Lane Pubs., Inc.

Kiely Miller, Barbara. Sam Houston. 2007. (J). pap. (***978-0-8368-8323-7(3)*** , Weekly Reader Early Learning Library) Stevens, Gareth Inc.

Marsh, Carole. Sam Houston. 2002. (One Thousand Readers Ser.). (Illus.). 12p. (J). (gr. k-4). 2.95 (978-0-635-01568-6(4) , 15684) Gallopade International.

Miller, Barbara Kiely. Sam Houston. 2007. (Great Americans Ser.). 24p. (J). (gr. 2-4). lib. bdg. 19.93 (***978-0-8368-8316-9(0)*** , Weekly Reader Early Learning Library) Stevens, Gareth Inc.

Sam Houston. (First Biographies Ser.). 24p. (J). 5.95 (978-0-7368-5087-2(2)); 48p. (YA). 7.95 (978-0-7368-4511-3(9)) Capstone Pr., Inc.

Sam Houston, 6 vols. (gr. 2-5). 39.95 (978-0-7368-4594-6(1)) Red Brick Learning.

Woodward, Walter M. Sam Houston: For Texas & the Union. 2005. (Library of American Lives & Times). (Illus.). 112p. (YA). (gr. 4-8). lib. bdg. 31.95 (978-0-8239-5739-2(X)) Rosen Publishing Group, Inc., The.

HOUSTON, SAM, 1793-1863—FICTION

Kutchinski, Marjorie. Liberty, Justice & F'Rall: The Dog Heroes of the Texas Republic. 1998. 152p. (gr. k-5). 15.95 (978-1-57168-217-8(1)) Eakin Pr.

Sargent, Dave & Sargent, Pat. Grady: (Dappled Grey) Proud to Be an American, 30 vols., Vol. 30. Lenoir, Jane, illus. 2003. (Saddle Up Ser.: Vol. 30). 42p. (J). lib. bdg. 22.60 (978-1-56763-813-4(9)) Ozark Publishing.

—Grady: Proud to Be an American, 30 vols. Lenoir, Jane, illus. 2003. (Saddle Up Ser.: Vol. 30). 42p. (J). pap. 6.95 (978-1-56763-814-1(7)) Ozark Publishing.

HOUSTON OILERS (FOOTBALL TEAM)

Frisch, Aaron. The History of the Tennessee Titans. 2004. (NFL Today Ser.). (Illus.). 32p. 18.95 (978-1-58341-316-6(2) , Creative Education) Creative Co., The.

HOVERCRAFT

see Ground Effect Machines

HOWE, GORDIE, 1928-

Leonetti, Mike. A Hero Named Howe. Banning, Greg, illus. 2006. 32p. 15.95 (978-1-55192-931-6(7)) Raincoast Bk. Distribution CAN. *Dist:* Perseus Distribution.

HOWE, JULIA WARD, 1819-1910

Raum, Elizabeth. Julia Ward Howe. 2004. (Illus.). 32p. (J). pap. 6.95 (978-1-4034-5708-0(5)); lib. bdg. (978-1-4034-4995-5(3)) Heinemann Library.

HUDSON, HENRY, D. 1611

Doak, Robin S. Hudson: Henry Hudson Searches for a Passage to Asia. 2003. (Exploring the World Ser.). (Illus.). 48p. (J). (gr. 4 up). lib. bdg. 22.60 (978-0-7565-0422-9(8)) Compass Point Bks.

Edwards, Judith. Henry Hudson & His Voyages of Exploration in World History. 2002. (In World History Ser.). (Illus.). 128p. (YA). (gr. 5-12). lib. bdg. 26.60 (978-0-7660-1885-3(7)) Enslow Pubs., Inc.

Gleason, Carrie. Henry Hudson: Seeking the Northwest Passage. 2005. (In the Footsteps of Explorers Ser.). (Illus.). 32p. (J). (ps-9). (978-0-7787-2408-7(5)); pap. (978-0-7787-2444-5(1)) Crabtree Publishing Co.

Goodman, Joan Elizabeth. Beyond the Sea of Ice: The Voyages of Henry Hudson. Rangel, Fernando, illus. 1999. (Great Explorers Ser.: Vol. 1). 48p. (J). (gr. k-12). 19.95 (978-0-9650493-8-2(8)) Mikaya Pr.

Hurwicz, Claude. Henry Hudson. 2001. (Famous Explorers Ser.). (Illus.). 24p. (J). (gr. 3). lib. bdg. 18.75 (978-0-8239-5561-9(3) , PowerKids Pr.) Rosen Publishing Group, Inc., The.

Kline, Trish. Henry Hudson. (Discover the Life of an Explorer Ser.). 2003. (Illus.). 24p. (gr. 2-5). 14.95 (978-1-58952-296-1(6)); 2002. (SPA.). 19.27 (978-1-58952-430-9(6)) Rourke Publishing, LLC.

Manning, Ruth. Henry Hudson. (Groundbreakers Ser.). 48p. (J). (gr. 5-7). 2002. pap. 8.50 (978-1-58810-342-0(0) , 91093); 2000. (Illus.). lib. bdg. 25.64 (978-1-57572-370-9(0)) Heinemann Library.

—Henry Hudson. 2001. (gr. 5-8). lib. bdg. 17.05 (978-0-613-86815-0(3)) Tandem Library Bks.

Molzahn, Arlene Bourgeois. Henry Hudson: Explorer of the Hudson River. 2003. (Explorers! Ser.). (Illus.). 48p. (J). lib. bdg. 23.93 (978-0-7660-2070-2(3)) Enslow Pubs., Inc.

Otfinoski, Steven. Henry Hudson: In Search of the Northwest Passage. 2007. (Great Explorations Ser.). (Illus.). 80p. (J). lib. bdg. 32.79 (***978-0-7614-2225-9(0)*** , Benchmark Bks.) Cavendish, Marshall Corp.

Petrie, Kristin. Henry Hudson. 2007. (Illus.). 32p. (J). 22.78 (978-1-59679-741-3(X)) ABDO Publishing Co.

Saffer, Barbara. Henry Hudson: Ill-Fated Explorer of North America's Coast. 2001. (Explorers of New Worlds Ser.). (Illus.). (J). 63p. pap. 25.00 (978-0-7910-6437-5(9)); 64p. 25.00 (978-0-7910-6436-8(0)) Facts On File, Inc. (Chelsea Hse.).

—Henry Hudson: Ill-Fated Explorer of North America's Coast. 2002. (gr. 3-6). lib. bdg. 17.60 (978-0-613-65422-7(6)) Tandem Library Bks.

Santella, Andrew. Henry Hudson. 2002. (Watts Library). (Illus.). 64p. (J). (gr. 5-7). pap. 8.95 (978-0-531-16577-5(9) , Watts, Franklin) Scholastic Library Publishing.

—Henry Hudson. 2001. (gr. 3-6). lib. bdg. 17.60 (978-0-613-51651-8(6)) Tandem Library Bks.

Smalley, Carol. Henry Hudson. 2006. (What's So Great About... ? Ser.). (Illus.). 32p. (J). (gr. 1-4). lib. bdg. (978-1-58415-479-2(9)) Mitchell Lane Pubs., Inc.

HUDSON RIVER AND VALLEY

Baron, Robert C. Hudson: The Story of a River. Locker, Thomas, illus. 2004. 32p. (J). 17.95 (978-1-55591-512-4(4)) Fulcrum Publishing.

Childress, Diana. Along the Hudson. 2003. (Rivers of North America Ser.). (J). lib. bdg. (978-0-8225-4697-9(3) , Lerner Pubns.) Lerner Publishing Group.

Harmon, Daniel E. Hudson River. 2004. (Rivers in American Life & Times Ser.). (Illus.). 120p. (gr. 9-13). 30.00 (978-0-7910-7727-6(6) , Chelsea Hse.) Facts On File, Inc.

Lourie, Peter. Hudson River: An Adventure from the Mountains to the Sea. 2003. (River Ser.). (Illus.). 48p. (YA). (gr. 4-6). pap. 10.95 (978-1-56397-703-9(6)) Boyds Mills Pr.

Molzahn, Arlene Bourgeois. Henry Hudson: Explorer of the Hudson River. 2003. (Explorers! Ser.). (Illus.). 48p. (J). lib. bdg. 23.93 (978-0-7660-2070-2(3)) Enslow Pubs., Inc.

Whitcraft, Melissa. The Hudson River. (Watts Library). (Illus.). 64p. (J). (gr. 5-7). 2000. pap. 8.95 (978-0-531-16425-9(X)); 1999. 25.50 (978-0-531-11739-2(1)) Scholastic Library Publishing. (Watts, Franklin).

—Hudson River. 1999. (gr. 3-6). lib. bdg. 17.60 (978-0-613-29447-8(5)) Tandem Library Bks.

Wood, Ian. The Hudson River. 2003. (Rivers of North America Ser.). (Illus.). 32p. (J). (gr. 3 up). lib. bdg. 24.67 (978-0-8368-3755-1(X)) Stevens, Gareth Inc.

HUDSON'S BAY COMPANY

Bailey, Katie. Radisson & Groseilliers: Fur Traders of the North. 2006. (In the Footsteps of Explorers Ser.). (Illus.). 32p. (J). (gr. 3-14). pap. (978-0-7787-2458-2(1) , 1253444); (978-0-7787-2422-3(0) , 1253444) Crabtree Publishing Co.

HUGGINS, HENRY (FICTITIOUS CHARACTER)—FICTION

Cleary, Beverly. Henry & Beezus. 2002. (Illus.). (J). 13.83 (978-0-7587-0018-6(0)) Book Wholesalers, Inc.

—Henry & Beezus. (Henry Huggins Ser.). 192p. (J). (gr. 1-4). pap. 4.99 (978-0-8072-1484-8(1) , Listening Library) Random Hse. Audio Publishing Group.

—Henry & the Clubhouse. 2002. (Illus.). (J). 13.83 (978-0-7587-9142-9(9)) Book Wholesalers, Inc.

—Henry & the Paper Route. unabr. ed. 2000. (Henry Huggins Ser.). (J). (gr. 1-4). pap. 34.24 incl. audio (978-0-7887-3797-8(X) , 41041X4) Recorded Bks., LLC.

—Henry Huggins. Darling, Louis, illus. 2004. (SPA.). 160p. (J). pap. 6.99 (978-0-06-073600-2(3) , Rayo) HarperCollins Pubs.

HUGHES, LANGSTON, 1902-1967

Bryant, Philip. Langston Hughes. 2003. (African-American Biographies Ser.). 64p. pap. 8.95 (978-1-4109-0037-1(1)) Raintree.

Bryant, Philip S. Langston Hughes. 2003. (African-American Biographies Ser.). (Illus.). 64p. (J). lib. bdg. 28.56 (978-0-7398-6871-3(3)) Raintree.

Burleigh, Robert. Langston's Train Ride. Jenkins, Leonard, tr. Jenkins, Leonard, illus. 2004. 32p. (J). (ps-3). pap. 16.95 (978-0-439-35239-0(8) , Orchard Bks.) Scholastic, Inc.

Gibson, Karen Bush. Langston Hughes. 2006. (Poets & Playwrights Ser.). (Illus.). 112p. (YA). (gr. 6-12). lib. bdg. 37.10 (978-1-58415-431-0(4)) Mitchell Lane Pubs., Inc.

Haugen, Brenda. Langston Hughes: The Voice of Harlem. 2005. (Signature Lives Ser.). (Illus.). 112p. (J). (gr. 5-7). 30.60 (978-0-7565-0993-4(9)) Compass Point Bks.

Hoena, B. A. Langston Hughes. 2005. (Fact Finders Ser.). (Illus.). 32p. (J). 22.60 (978-0-7368-3745-3(0)) Capstone Pr., Inc.

Hudson, Katura J. & Hudson, Cheryl Willis. Langston's Legacy: 101 Ways to Celebrate the Life & Work of Langston Hughes. Hudson, Stephan, photos by. 2004. 48p. (J). (gr. 4 up). pap. 7.95 (978-0-940975-99-6(8) , Sankofa Bks.) Just Us Bks., Inc.

Jones, Lynda & Garnett, Ron. Five Famous Writers. 2001. (Great Black Heroes Ser.). (Illus.). 48p. (J). (978-0-590-48035-2(9)) Scholastic, Inc.

McKissack, Patricia C. & McKissack, Fredrick L. Langston Hughes: Great American Poet. rev. ed. 2002. (Great African Americans Ser.). (Illus.). 32p. (J). (gr. 1-4). lib. bdg. 18.60 (978-0-7660-1695-8(1)) Enslow Pubs., Inc.

Perdomo, Willie. Visiting Langston. Collier, Bryan, illus. rev. ed. 2002. 32p. (J). (ps-3). 16.95 (978-0-8050-6744-6(2) , Holt, Henry & Co. Bks. For Young Readers) Holt, Henry & Co.

Raatma, Lucia. Langston Hughes: African-American Author & Poet. 2002. (Journey to Freedom Ser.). (Illus.). 40p. (J). (gr. 3-7). 28.50 (978-1-56766-647-2(7)) Child's World, Inc.

Rhynes, Martha E. I, Too, Sing America: The Story of Langston Hughes. 2004. (World Writers Ser.). (Illus.). 144p. (YA). (gr. 6-12). 23.95 (978-1-883846-89-3(7) , First Biographies) Reynolds, Morgan Inc.

Shull, Jodie A. Langston Hughes: Life Makes Poems. 2006. (African-American Biography Library). (Illus.). 128p. (YA). lib. bdg. 31.93 (978-0-7660-2468-7(7)) Enslow Pubs., Inc.

Walker, Alice. Langston Hughes: American Poet. Deeter, Catherine, illus. 48p. (J). 2006. reprint ed. pap. 7.99 (978-0-06-079889-5(0)); 2002. (gr. 4 up). 16.99 (978-0-06-021518-7(6)) HarperCollins Pubs. (Amistad).

Wallace, Maurice O. Langston Hughes: The Harlem Renaissance. 2007. (Writers & Their Works). 160p. (YA). (gr. 9 up). lib. bdg. 39.93 (***978-0-7614-2591-5(8)*** , Benchmark Bks.) Cavendish, Marshall Corp.

HULL HOUSE (CHICAGO, ILL.)

Alter, Judy & Rosenberg, Pam. Pocahontas: Native American Peacemaker. 2003. (Spirit of America). (Illus.). 32p. (J). (gr. 2-6). 27.07 (978-1-59296-010-1(3)) Child's World, Inc.

HUMAN-ANIMAL RELATIONSHIPS

see also Animals And Civilization

Ajmera, Maya & Fisher, Alex. A Kid's Best Friend. 2004. (It's a Kid's World Ser.). (Illus.). 32p. (J). (ps-2). 15.95 (978-1-57091-513-0(X)); pap. 6.95 (978-1-57091-514-7(8)) Charlesbridge Publishing, Inc.

Boothroyd, Jennifer. People & the Environment. 2008. (First Step Nonfiction - Ecology Ser.). (J). lib. bdg. 18.60 (***978-0-8225-8601-2(0)*** , Lerner Pubns.) Lerner Publishing Group.

Brunke, Dawn Baumann. Awakening to Animal Voices: A Teen Guide to Telepathic Communication with All Life. 2004. (Illus.). 272p. (J). 14.95 (978-0-89281-136-6(6) , Healing Arts Pr.) Inner Traditions International, Ltd.

Burton, Frances. That's Me, Tyler! Thompson, Karmen, illus. 2002. 32p. (J). (ps-3). lib. bdg. 15.95 (978-0-9650769-2-0(X)) Stonehill Publishing.

Byrne, Susan K. Sierra Cloud: A True Story About a Horse with Courage. Stockbridge, Joan, ed. Byrne, Susan K., photos by. l.t. ed. 2002. (Illus.). 36p. (J). (gr. 3-7). spiral bd. 14.95 (978-0-9723652-0-8(6)) R&R Pubns.

—Sierra-Cloud - A True Story about a Horse with Courage: The Writing & Drawing Journal. l.t. ed. 2002. 34p. (J). (gr. 3-7). spiral bd. 4.95 (978-0-9723652-1-5(4)) R&R Pubns.

Collins, Ellen. A Biography: My Life As a Basset Hound (2005. 51p. pap. 12.95 (978-1-4137-8776-4(2)) PublishAmerica, Inc.

Creative Media Applications Staff. Exploring Animal Rights & Animal Welfare, 4 vols. 2002. (Middle School ESL Ser.). (Illus.). 512p. (J). (gr. 5 up). 135.00 (978-0-313-32245-7(7) , MS2245, Greenwood Pr.) Greenwood Publishing Group, Inc.

—Exploring Animal Rights & Animal Welfare Vol. 1: Using Animals for Food, 4 vols. 2002. (Middle School ESL Ser.). (Illus.). 128p. (J). (978-0-313-32246-4(5)) Greenwood Publishing Group, Inc.

—Exploring Animal Rights & Animal Welfare Vol. 2: Using Animals in the Laboratory & Classroom, 4 vols. 2002. (Middle School ESL Ser.). (Illus.). 128p. (J). (978-0-313-32247-1(3)) Greenwood Publishing Group, Inc.

—Exploring Animal Rights & Animal Welfare Vol. 3: Using Animals for Entertainment, 4 vols. 2002. (Middle School ESL Ser.). (Illus.). 128p. (J). (978-0-313-32248-8(1)) Greenwood Publishing Group, Inc.

—Exploring Animal Rights & Animal Welfare Vol. 4: Using Animals for Clothing, 4 vols. 2002. (Middle School ESL Ser.). (Illus.). 128p. (J). (978-0-313-32249-5(X)) Greenwood Publishing Group, Inc.

Davis, Michele S. & Makris, Alexandra. Magical Mac: The True Story of a Healing Horse. 2002. (Illus.). 35p. (J). pap. (978-0-9715395-0-1(2)) Serendipity Pubns.

Dewey, Jennifer Owings. Paisano, the Roadrunner. Meinzer, Wyman, photos by. 2002. (Illus.). 48p. (gr. 3-6). lib. bdg. 23.90 (978-0-7613-1250-5(1) , Millbrook Pr.) Lerner Publishing Group.

Helfer, Ralph. The World's Greatest Elephant. Lewin, Ted, illus. 2006. 48p. (J). (gr. 5). 16.99 (978-0-399-24190-1(6) , Philomel) Penguin Group (USA) Inc.

Hodgkins, Fran. Animals among Us: Living with Suburban Wildlife. 2000. (Illus.). ix, 117p. (J). (gr. 4-7). 19.50 (978-0-208-02478-7(6) , Linnet Bks.) Shoe String Pr., Inc.

Huckleberry, Jim. The Christmas Cat. 2005. (Illus.). 24p. (J). per. 9.95 (978-1-59453-750-9(X) , 3022, Airleaf Publishing) Airleaf Publishing & Bookselling.

Kalman, Bobbie. Swimming with Dolphins. 2003. (gr. 3-6). lib. bdg. 15.25 (978-0-613-52919-8(7)) Tandem Library Bks.

Kathrens, Ginger. Cloud: Wild Stallion of the Rockies. 2001. (Illus.). 128p. pap. 24.95 (978-1-889540-70-2(6)) BowTie Pr.

—Cloud's Legacy: The Wild Stallion Returns. 2004. (Illus.). 200p. 24.95 (978-1-931993-12-8(2)) BowTie Pr.

Katz, Jon. Dog Year: Twelve Months, Four Dogs, & Me. 2003. (gr. 7-12). lib. bdg. 22.20 (978-0-613-58362-6(0)) Tandem Library Bks.

Keenan, Sheila. A History of Pets & People. Waters, Kate, ed. 2007. (Animals in the House Ser.). (Illus.). 112p. (J). (gr. 4-7). pap. 17.99 (978-0-439-69286-1(5)) Scholastic, Inc.

Kent, Deborah. Animal Helpers for the Disabled. 2003. (Watts Library). 64p. (J). (gr. 5-7). pap. 8.95 (978-0-531-16663-5(5) , Watts, Franklin) Scholastic Library Publishing.

Marrin, Albert. Oh, Rats! The Story of Rats & People. Mordan, C. B., illus. 2006. 48p. (J). (gr. 3-6). 16.99 (978-0-525-47762-4(4) , Dutton Juvenile) Penguin Group (USA) Inc.

Mason, Chris. Why Do People Harm Animals? 2002. (Exploring Tough Issues Ser.). (Illus.). 48p. (J). lib. bdg. 25.69 (978-0-7398-4962-0(X)) Raintree.

Mataya, Doris. Shasta Daisy. 2006. (Illus.). 32p. (J). per. 10.95 (***978-1-59453-814-8(X)*** , 2452, Airleaf Publishing) Airleaf Publishing & Bookselling.

Nichols, Catherine. Therapy Horses. 2007. (Horse Power Ser.). 32p. (J). lib. bdg. 25.27 (978-1-59716-400-9(3)) Bearport Publishing Co., Inc.

Richmond, Marianne R. Goodbye, Faithful Friend: Remembering Your Dog with Love. 2005. (Illus.). 40p. (YA). 7.95 (978-0-9770000-1-2(X)) Marianne Richmond Studios, Inc.

—Goodbye, Lovable Friend: Remembering Your Cat with Affection. 2005. (Illus.). 40p. (YA). 7.95 (978-0-9770000-0-5(1)) Marianne Richmond Studios, Inc.

Sayre, April Pulley. If You Should Hear a Honey Guide. 2000. (J). (978-0-606-19425-9(8)) Tandem Library Bks.

Schaefer, Peggy. More Stories of Dogs. 2005. (Illus.). 205p. 12.95 (978-0-8249-4639-5(1)) Ideals Pubns.

Steele, Philip. Animal Matters. 2001. (Life Files Ser.). (Illus.). 62p. 24.99 (978-0-237-52080-9(X)); pap. 15.99 (978-0-237-52081-6(8)) Evans Publishing Group GBR. (Evans Brothers, Limited). *Dist:* Independent Pubs. Group.

Stone, Lynn M. Living with Snakes. 2000. (Eye to Eye with Snakes Ser.). (Illus.). 24p. (J). (gr. 1-4). lib. bdg. 20.64 (978-1-55916-264-7(3)) Rourke Publishing, LLC.

—Wolves & People. 2001. (Wolves Discovery Library). (Illus.). 24p. (J). (gr. 1-4). lib. bdg. 19.27 (978-1-55916-242-5(2)) Rourke Publishing, LLC.

Toor, Atif. Animal Encounters. 2006. (True Tales Ser.). (Illus.). 48p. (J). (gr. 2-4). pap. 4.95 (978-0-516-25455-5(3) , Children's Pr.) Scholastic Library Publishing.

—Animal Encounters: A Chapter Book. 2005. (True Tales Ser.). (Illus.). 48p. (J). (ps-ps). 22.50 (978-0-516-25190-5(2) , Children's Pr.) Scholastic Library Publishing.

Vinocur, Terry. Dogs Helping Kids with Feelings. 1999. (Dogs Helping People Ser.). 24p. (J). (gr. k-4). lib. bdg. 18.75 (978-0-8239-5214-4(2) , PowerKids Pr.) Rosen Publishing Group, Inc., The.

HUMAN-ANIMAL RELATIONSHIPS—FICTION

Alily, Joseph. The Boy & the Wolf. 2007. 9.00 (***978-0-8059-9053-9(4)***) Dorrance Publishing Co., Inc.

Allen, Page. Madison's Descent: A Child's Journey. (J). 2006. pap. 25.00 (***978-0-9752516-2-1(7)***); 2004. lib. bdg. 60.00 (***978-0-9752516-1-4(9)***) Otis & Randolph Pr.

Almond, David. Secret Heart. 2004. 224p. (YA). (gr. 7). pap. 5.99 (978-0-440-41827-6(5) , Laurel Leaf) Random Hse. Children's Bks.

Aragones, Sergio. Groo & Rufferto. 2000. (Groo Ser.). (Illus.). 112p. (YA). (gr. 7 up). pap. 9.95 (978-1-56971-447-8(9)) Dark Horse Comics.

—The Groo Inferno. 1999. (Groo Ser.). 96p. (YA). (gr. 5 up). pap. 9.95 (978-1-56971-430-0(4)) Dark Horse Comics.

Baraba, Joseph Frank. Dusty. 2006. 59p. pap. 12.95 (978-1-4241-2018-5(7)) PublishAmerica, Inc.

Berry, Virginia B. Iggie's Big Adventure. King, Garry W., illus. ed. 2002. 20p. (J). (gr. k-6). pap. 5.00 (978-0-9726091-0-4(5)) Berry Enterprises.

—Iggie's Big Adventure Coloring Book: A True Story of Faith. Berry, Virginia B., ed. King, Garry W., illus. ed. 2002. 16p. (J). (gr. k-6). pap. 1.00 (978-0-9726091-1-1(3)) Berry Enterprises.

Borgo, Lacy Finn. Big Mama's Baby. Cote, Nancy, illus. 2007. (J). (gr. k-2). 15.95 (***978-1-59078-187-6(2)***) Boyds Mills Pr.

Boston, Lucy M. Stranger at Green Knowe. 2002. (gr. 3-6). lib. bdg. 14.15 (978-0-613-54691-1(1)) Tandem Library Bks.

—A Stranger at Green Knowe. Boston, Peter, illus. 2002. (Green Knowe Ser.). 208p. (YA). reprint ed. (gr. 3 up). 17.00 (978-0-15-202583-0(9) , Harcourt Young Classics); (gr. 4-7). pap. 6.95 (978-0-15-202589-2(8) , Odyssey Classics) Harcourt Children's Bks.

Browne, N. M. Hunted. 2004. 336p. (J). (gr. 5 up). reprint ed. pap. 7.95 (978-1-58234-903-9(7) , Bloomsbury Children) Bloomsbury Publishing.

Buchwald, Claire. Max Talks to Me. Ritz, Karen, illus. 2007. (Sit! Stay! Read! Ser.). 24p. (J). 15.95 (***978-0-940719-03-3(7)***) Gryphon Pr., The.

Carman, Patrick. The Dark Hills Divide. (Land of Elyon Ser.: Bk. 1). (J). 2006. 288p. pap. 6.99 (978-0-439-79175-5(8)); 2005. (Illus.). 253p. (978-0-439-75843-7(2) , Orchard Bks.) Scholastic, Inc.

—The Dark Hills Divide. l.t. ed. 2005. (Land of Elyon Ser.: Bk. 1). 356p. 23.95 (978-0-7862-7752-0(1) , Large Print Pr.) Thorndike Pr.

—The Tenth City. 2006. (Land of Elyon Ser.: Bk. 3). 208p. (J). pap. 11.99 (978-0-439-70095-5(7) , Orchard Bks.) Scholastic, Inc.

Christelow, Eileen. Letters from a Desperate Dog. 2006. (Illus.). 32p. (J). (gr. 3-5). 16.00 (978-0-618-51003-0(6) , Clarion Bks.) Houghton Mifflin Co. Trade & Reference Div.

Christie, Jacky. The Wind Blows North. 2007. (ENG.). 56p. per. 10.99 (***978-1-4141-0835-3(4)***) Pleasant Word.

Clamp. Art of Cardcaptor Sakura, 3 vols., Vol. 2. 2002. 120p. (gr. 2-6). pap. 19.99 (978-1-59182-013-0(8)) TOKYOPOP, Inc.

Clement-Davies, David. Fell. 2007. 542p. (YA). (gr. 7-17). 19.95 (***978-0-8109-1185-7(X)***) Abrams, Harry N. , Inc.

Clements, Andrew & Bynum, Janie. Slippers at Home. 2007. 32p. (J). pap. 5.99 (978-0-14-240781-3(X) , Puffin) Penguin Group (USA) Inc.

Corder, Zizou. Lionboy. (Lionboy Trilogy : Bk. 1). (Illus.). (gr. 3-6). 2003. 288p. (J). 15.99 (978-0-8037-2982-7(0) , Dial); 2004. 304p. (YA). reprint ed. pap. 7.99 (978-0-14-240226-9(5) , Puffin) Penguin Group (USA) Inc.

—Truth. 2006. (Lionboy Trilogy : Bk. 3). 240p. (J). (gr. 3). pap. 6.99 (978-0-14-240705-9(4) , Puffin) Penguin Group (USA) Inc.

Cross, Gillian. Pictures in the Dark. 1998. (978-0-606-13703-4(3)) Tandem Library Bks.

Damitz, Charlie. Diving for el Corazon. Diefendorf, Cathy, illus. 2007. 100p. (J). pap. 7.95 (978-0-9744446-3-5(4)) All About Kids Publishing.

Dark Horse Comics Staff & Aragones, Sergio. Jamboree. 2000. (Groo Ser.). (Illus.). 96p. (YA). (gr. 5 up). pap. 9.95 (978-1-56971-462-1(2)) Dark Horse Comics.

Davis, Lambert. Swimming with Dolphins. Davis, Lambert, illus. 2004. (Illus.). 32p. (J). pap. 15.95 (978-0-439-47257-9(1) , Blue Sky Pr., The) Scholastic, Inc.

Dawson, Joy. Maggie, the Color-Blind Cow: A loving heart—that didn't see Color. 2006. (ENG., Illus.). 36p. (J). per. 12.95 (***978-1-59800-892-0(7)***) Outskirts Press, Inc.

Donaldson, Julia & Richards, Lucy. The Quick Brown Fox Club. 2006. (Red Bananas Ser.). (Illus.). 48p. (J). (978-0-7787-1080-6(7)) Crabtree Publishing Co.

Donofrio, Beverly. Mary & the Mouse, the Mouse & Mary. McClintock, Barbara, illus. 2007. 32p. (J). (ps-2). 16.99 (***978-0-375-83609-1(8)***); lib. bdg. 19.99 (***978-0-375-93609-8(2)***) Random Hse. Children's Bks. (Schwartz & Wade Bks.).

Duey, Kathleen. HOOFBEATS: Margret & Flynn: 1875: Margret & Flynn: 1875. 2008. 144p. (YA). (gr. 3). 15.99 (***978-0-525-47936-9(8)***) , Dutton Juvenile) Penguin Group (USA) Inc.

Farley, Terri. Blue Wings. 2006. 242p. (J). lib. bdg. 16.92 (***978-1-4242-1035-0(6)***) Fitzgerald Bks.

—Firefly. 2005. 214p. (J). lib. bdg. 16.92 (***978-1-4242-0835-7(1)***) Fitzgerald Bks.

—Firefly. 2005. (Illus.). 214p. (J). (***978-1-4156-2263-6(9)***) , Avon Bks.) HarperCollins Pubs.

Faust, Laurie, illus. A New Home for Honey. 2006. (J). 9.95 (***978-0-9789227-0-2(0)***) Weeping Willow Publishing.

Foreman, Michael. Fox Tale. 2007. (Illus.). 32p. (J). (gr. k-2). pap. 16.95 (***978-1-84270-610-7(1)***) Andersen GBR. *Dist:* Independent Pubs. Group.

Frazier, Craig. Stanley Mows the Lawn. 2005. (Illus.). 40p. (J). 15.95 (978-0-8118-4846-6(9)) Chronicle Bks. LLC.

Frederick, Heather Vogel. The Black Paw. Comport, Sally Wern, illus. (Spy Mice Ser.). (J). 2006. 256p. pap. 5.99 (978-1-4169-2770-9(0) , Aladdin); 2006. 256p. pap. 2.99 (978-1-4169-2502-6(3) , Aladdin); 2005. 240p. 9.95 (978-0-689-87753-7(6) , Simon & Schuster Children's Publishing) Simon & Schuster Children's Publishing.

Gandolfi, Silvana & Schwartz, Lynne Sharon. Aldabra, or, the Tortoise Who Loved Shakespeare. 2004. 151p. (J). (978-0-439-49744-2(2) , Levine, Arthur A. Bks.) Scholastic, Inc.

Gerstein, Mordicai. Fox Eyes. 2001. (gr. k-3). lib. bdg. 11.80 (978-0-613-43036-4(0)) Tandem Library Bks.

Gipson, Fred. Old Yeller. Date not set. 192p. (J). 20.95 (978-0-8488-2273-6(0)) Amereon LTD.

—Old Yeller. 2001. 132p. (J). (ps-7). lib. bdg. 16.45 (978-0-613-85744-4(5)) Tandem Library Bks.

—Old Yeller. 1999. (J). lib. bdg. 21.95 (978-1-56723-204-2(3)) Yestermorrow, Inc.

Gipson, Fred & Polson, Steven. Old Yeller. 2001. (Perennial Classics Ser.). (Illus.). 144p. (gr. 4-7). pap. 8.00 (978-0-06-093547-4(2)) HarperCollins Pubs.

Gipson, Frederick. Old Yeller. Burger, Carl, illus. 2002. 14.47 (978-0-7587-0299-9(X)) Book Wholesalers, Inc.

Gleitzman, Morris. Toad Away. 208p. (J). (gr. 3-7). 2007. 4.99 (978-0-375-82767-9(6) , Yearling); 2006. 14.95 (978-0-375-82766-2(8) , Random Hse. Bks. for Young Readers); 2006. lib. bdg. 16.99 (978-0-375-92766-9(2) , Random Hse. Bks. for Young Readers) Random Hse. Children's Bks.

—Toad Heaven. 2006. 208p. (J). (gr. 3-7). reprint ed. 4.99 (978-0-375-82765-5(X) , Yearling) Random Hse. Children's Bks.

Golding, Julia. Secret of the Sirens. Wyatt, David, illus. 2007. 384p. (YA). (gr. 5 up). 16.99 (***978-0-7614-5371-0(7)***) Cavendish, Marshall Corp.

Golds, Cassandra. Clair de Lune. Blackall, Sophie, illus. 2007. 208p. (J). (gr. 4-7). 5.99 (978-0-440-42089-7(X) , Yearling) Random Hse. Children's Bks.

Graham, Bob. The "Trouble with Dogs..." Said Dad. Graham, Bob, illus. 2007. (Illus.). 32p. (J). (ps). 12.99 (***978-0-7636-3316-5(X)***) Candlewick Pr.

Gravdahl, John. The Tale of Dog Giovanni. 2000. (Illus.). 32p. (J). (gr. k-4). 16.95 (978-0-9678577-9-4(1)) Propeller Pr.

Grokett, Jan. Songs of the Orcas. l.t. ed. 2002. 48p. (J). per. 9.99 (978-1-893108-72-1(4)) Neighborhood Pr. Publishing.

Guzman, Lila. Kichi in Jungle Jeopardy. Johnson, Regan, illus. (J). 2007. per. 8.95 (978-0-9769417-2-9(4)); 2006. 144p. 13.95 (978-0-9769417-1-2(6)) Blooming Tree Pr.

Harcourt School Publishers Staff. Friendly Hands. 3rd ed. 2002. (Trophies English Language Learners Ser.). (Illus.). pap. 5.10 (978-0-15-327894-5(3)) Harcourt Schl. Pubs.

—My Cats: Below Level. 3rd ed. 2002. (Trophies Reading Program Ser.). (Illus.). (J). (gr. 1). pap. 4.10 (978-0-15-322957-2(8)) Harcourt Schl. Pubs.

Harper, Jessica. A Place Called Kindergarten. Karas, G. Brian, illus. 2006. 32p. (J). (ps-3). 15.99 (978-0-399-24226-7(0) , Putnam Juvenile) Penguin Group (USA) Inc.

Harperfestival. Good Boy! Dog's Best Friend. 2003. (ps-2). lib. bdg. 11.80 (978-0-613-71419-8(9)) Tandem Library Bks.

Hattersley, Ray. Buster's Diaries: The True Story of A Dog & His Man. 2001. (gr. 3-6). lib. bdg. 21.05 (978-0-613-51806-2(3)) Tandem Library Bks.

Hearne, Betsy Gould. The Canine Connection: Stories about Dogs & People. 2003. (Illus.). 128p. (YA). 15.95 (978-0-689-85258-9(4) , McElderry, Margaret K.) Simon & Schuster Children's Publishing.

Henderson, Malcolm. Katie & Her Friends. Moss, P. Buckley, illus. 1998. 32p. (J). (ps-3). 15.95 (978-0-9665198-0-8(9) , 0998001000) Moss Portfolio, The.

Hill, Amye Rose. The Amazing Mr. Buddy. 10th ed. 2005. (Illus.). (J). 6.99 (978-0-9769234-0-4(8)) Zany Angel Projects LLC.

Hill, Janet Muirhead. Miranda & Starlight: (the Starlight Books, 1), 6 vols. Lehmkuhl, Pat, illus. 2nd rev. ed. 2003. (Starlight Bks.: 1). 168p. (J). (gr. 3-7). per. 9.00 (978-0-9714161-4-7(1)) Raven Publishing Inc. of Montana.

Hodges, Meredith. Jasper: The Story of a Mule. Shields, Bonnie, illus. 2003. 245p. (J). (gr. k-7). 39.95 (978-0-9702309-8-0(2)) Lucky 3 Ranch, Inc.

Ihimaera, Witi. The Whale Rider. 2003. Orig. Title: Te Kaieke Tohora. (YA). (gr. 3-6). 152p. 17.00 (978-0-15-205017-7(5)); 168p. pap. 8.00 (978-0-15-205016-0(7) , Harcourt Paperbacks) Harcourt Children's Bks.

—Whale Rider. 2003. (gr. 5-8). lib. bdg. 16.45 (978-0-613-70660-5(9)) Tandem Library Bks.

Jacques, Brian. Voyage of Slaves. (Castaways of the Flying Dutchman Ser.: No. 3). 2007. 320p. (gr. 12). mass mkt. 7.99 (***978-0-441-01528-3(X)***) , Ace Bks.); 2006. (Illus.). 368p. (YA). (gr. 5). 23.99 (978-0-399-24549-7(9) , Philomel) Penguin Group (USA) Inc.

Job & Derib. Yakari & Great Eagle. 2007. (Illus.). 48p. pap. 9.99 (***978-1-905460-04-5(X)***) CineBook GBR. *Dist:* Biblio Distribution.

Johnson, Gwen & Johnson, Carl. The Treasure of Diamond's Shoal. l.t. ed. 2007. (ENG., Illus.). 24p. (J). 8.95 (***978-0-9795860-0-2(3)***) Fish Tales Publishing.

Jones, Chuck. The White Seal. Jones, Chuck, illus. 2006. (Illus.). 32p. (J). 8.95 (978-0-8249-6598-3(1) , Ideals Children's Bks.) Ideals Pubns.

Jordan, Sarah Clark. The BossQueen, Little BigBark, & the Sentinel Pup. 2004. (Illus.). 144p. (J). 14.95 (978-1-58246-115-1(5) , Tricycle Pr.) Ten Speed Pr.

Kadohata, Cynthia. Cracker! The Best Dog in Vietnam. 2007. 320p. (J). (gr. 5-8). 16.99 (978-1-4169-0637-7(1) , Atheneum) Simon & Schuster Children's Publishing.

Kendall, Stan P. Samson Gets a Family. 2005. 22p. (J). 13.50 (978-1-4116-5756-4(X)) Lulu.com.

Kerr, M. E. Snakes Don't Miss Their Mothers. 208p. (J). 2007. (Illus.). pap. 5.99 (978-0-06-052626-9(2) , Harper Trophy); 2003. 15.99 (978-0-06-052624-5(6)) HarperCollins Pubs.

Kerr, Mike. Mike & a Lynx Named Kitty. Vitt, Karren, illus. 2nd rev. ed. 2006. 112p. per. 13.50 (***978-1-931195-36-2(6)***) KiwE Publishing, Ltd.

Kimmel, Haven. Orville: A Dog Story. Parker, Robert Andrew, illus. 2003. 32p. (J). (gr. k-3). 15.00 (978-0-618-15955-0(X) , Clarion Bks.) Houghton Mifflin Co. Trade & Reference Div.

King-Smith, Dick. The Crowstarver. l.t. ed. 2000. (J). (Illus.). 243p. pap. (978-0-7540-6095-6(0) , Galaxy Children's Large Print); 216p. pap. incl. audio (978-0-7540-6228-8(7) , RA029, Chivers Children's Audio Bks.) BBC Audiobooks America.

Koja, Kathe. Straydog. 2002. (Illus.). 112p. (YA). (gr. 8-10). 16.00 (978-0-374-37278-1(0) , Farrar, Straus & Giroux (BYR)) Farrar, Straus & Giroux.

—Straydog. 2004. 128p. (YA). reprint ed. pap. 5.99 (978-0-14-240071-5(8) , Puffin) Penguin Group (USA) Inc.

Komechak, Marilyn Gilbert. Paisano Pete: Snake-Killer Bird. 2003. (Illus.). 100p. (J). 9.95 (978-1-57168-770-8(X) , Eakin Pr.) Eakin Pr.

Kondak, Margarida. The Wild Horses of Summer Bay. Kondak, Mary, illus. l.t. ed. 2002. 31p. 9.95 (978-1-890692-06-3(9)) Wizard Works.

Kurtz, Carmen. Brun. (SPA.). 128p. (YA). (gr. 5-8). (978-84-279-3367-5(3)) Noguer y Caralt Editores, S. A. ESP. *Dist:* Lectorum Pubns., Inc.

—Brun. 2001. (SPA.). (gr. 7-12). lib. bdg. 16.40 (978-0-613-84207-5(3)) Tandem Library Bks.

Lawson, Rob, illus. Duke Finds a Home. 2006. (Duke's Tails Ser.). 32p. (J). (978-0-9779308-0-7(7)) Bush Brothers & Co.

Lindskold, Jane. Through Wolf's Eyes. 2002. (gr. 5-8). lib. bdg. 16.45 (978-0-613-64450-1(6)) Tandem Library Bks.

Lloyd, Stacy K. A Girl & Her Dog. 2005. 32p. pap. 12.00 (978-1-4116-1359-1(7)) Lulu.com.

Lofting, Hugh. The Story of Doctor Dolittle No. 3: Doctor Dolittle's Great Adventure. Kanzler, John, illus. 2007. (Easy Reader Classics Ser.). 32p. (J). pap. 3.95 (978-1-4027-4122-7(7)) Sterling Publishing Co., Inc.

—The Story of Doctor Dolittle No. 4: Doctor Dolittle's Magical Cure. Kanzler, John, illus. 2007. (Easy Reader Classics Ser.). 32p. (J). pap. 3.95 (978-1-4027-4123-4(5)) Sterling Publishing Co., Inc.

Loizeaux, William. Wings. Bowman, Leslie, illus. 2006. 160p. (J). 16.00 (978-0-374-34802-1(2)) Farrar, Straus & Giroux.

London, Jack. Colmillo Blanco. 2003. (Advanced Reading Ser.: Vol. 56). (SPA., Illus.). 268p. (J). (gr. 4-7). 11.95 (978-84-239-9030-6(3)) Espasa Calpe, S.A. ESP. *Dist:* Planeta Publishing Corp., i.b.d., Ltd.

—Colmillo Blanco. 2000. (SPA., Illus.). 280p. (YA). (gr. 7 up). 9.95 (978-84-207-1229-1(9)) Grupo Anaya, S.A. ESP. *Dist:* Libros Sin Fronteras.

—Colmillo Blanco. (SPA.). (J). 8.00 (978-958-04-7143-1(6)) Norma S.A. COL. *Dist:* Distribuidora Norma, Inc.

—White Fang. Vera, Ross, illus. 2002. (Great Illustrated Classics Ser.). 240p. (J). (gr. 3-8). 21.35 (978-1-57765-810-8(8) , ABDO & Daughters) ABDO Publishing Co.

—White Fang. 2003. 192p. (J). 4.99 (978-1-57759-566-3(1)) Dalmatian Pr.

London, Jack & Olmos. Colmillo Blanco. 2004. (SPA.). 280p. pap. 13.95 (***978-84-263-5246-0(4)***) Vives, Luis Editorial (Edelvives) ESP. *Dist:* Lectorum Pubns., Inc.

MacDonald, James. Levi, Adventures of a Police Dog. 2005. 96p. (J). 16.95 (978-0-9716923-1-2(9)) Regency Hse., Ltd.

Madison's Descent: A Child's Journey. collector's ed. 2004. (J). 75.00 (***978-0-9752516-0-7(0)***) Otis & Randolph Pr.

Manzel, Michael, illus. Moby's Tale. 2004. 248p. (YA). pap. 19.95 (***978-0-9746345-0-6(6)***) River of Life Publishing.

Martel, Yann. Life of Pi: A Novel. 2003. (gr. 7-12). lib. bdg. 23.45 (978-0-613-59907-8(1)) Tandem Library Bks.

Martinello, Marian L. Ready's Gifts. 2003. (Illus.). 158p. (YA). (gr. 8 up). per. 12.95 (978-0-9724113-0-1(5)) MindCatcher Pr.

Masson, J. Moussaieff. The Cat Who Came in from the Cold: A Fable. 2004. 107p. (978-0-345-47867-2(3) , Ballantine Bks.) Random House Publishing Group.

Matthews, L. S. A Dog for Life. 2006. 176p. (J). (gr. 5). 16.99 (978-0-385-90381-3(2)); 14.95 (978-0-385-73366-3(6)) Random Hse. Children's Bks. (Delacorte Bks. for Young Readers).

Mazer, Anne. The Oxboy. 2000. (gr. 5-8). lib. bdg. 15.25 (978-0-613-90534-3(2)) Tandem Library Bks.

McBride, Anthony & McBride, Autumn. The Lost Cat. 2007. (Illus.). pap. 11.00 (***978-1-56411-540-9(2)***) , CB Publishing & Design) UBUS Communications Systems.

McCament, Janice. 'Ole Paint Rocks. 2007. (J). per. 9.99 (***978-1-59886-925-5(6)***) Tate Publishing & Enterprises, L.L.C.

Metz, Melinda. Ravens Point. 2005. pap. (978-0-06-052373-2(5)) HarperCollins Canada, Ltd.

Milgrim, David. My Dog, Buddy. 2008. (J). pap. (***978-0-545-03593-4(7)***) Scholastic, Inc.

Nielsen, Susin. Hank & Fergus. Laliberte, Louise-Andree, illus. 2003. 32p. (J). (ps-2). 16.95 (978-1-55143-245-8(5)) Orca Bk. Pubs. USA.

Nolan, Carrie Stewart. My Little Miracle. 2007. (J). per. 10.99 (***978-1-59886-848-7(9)***) Tate Publishing & Enterprises, L.L.C.

Nussbaum, Ben. Toko Hippo. Wenzel, Gregory, illus. 2006. 36p. (J). pap. 6.95 (978-1-59249-578-8(8)) Soundprints.

—Toko Hippo Micro Ppb. Wenzel, Gregory, illus. 2006. 32p. (J). pap. 2.95 (978-1-59249-579-5(6)) Soundprints.

—Toko the Hippo. Wenzel, Gregory, illus. 2006. (African Wildlife Foundation Kids Ser.). 27p. (J). pap. 8.95 incl. audio compact disk (978-1-59249-580-1(X)) Soundprints.

Old Yeller. 1999. (J). 9.95 (978-1-56137-081-8(9)) Novel Units, Inc.

Paraskevas, Betty. Chocolate at the Four Seasons. Paraskevas, Mickey, illus. 2007. 32p. (J). (ps-1). 16.99 (978-0-316-01375-8(7)) Little Brown & Co.

PC Treasures, prod. Little Red Riding Hood. 2007. (J). (***978-1-60072-031-4(5)***) PC Treasures, Inc.

Pennac, Daniel. Eye of the Wolf. Adams, Sarah, tr. from FRE. Grafe, Max, illus. 2003. 112p. (J). (gr. 5 up). 15.99 (978-0-7636-1896-4(9)) Candlewick Pr.

Peruski, Steven. My Friend & Teacher Sammie. 2006. (YA). 21.99 (***978-0-615-13428-4(9)***) Compassion Pets Publishing.

Pierce, Tamora. Emperor Mage. 2005. (Immortals Ser.: No. 2). 384p. (YA). pap. 6.99 (978-1-4169-0337-6(2) , Simon Pulse) Simon & Schuster Children's Publishing.

Polacco, Patricia. Ginger & Petunia. Polacco, Patricia, illus. 2007. (Illus.). 40p. (J). (ps-3). 16.99 (978-0-399-24539-8(1) , Philomel) Penguin Group (USA) Inc.

Powell, Glenda. Cassie & Mr. Ant. Mitchell, Hazel, illus. 2008. (J). 7.95 (978-0-9779445-6-9(5)) Zoe Life Publishing.

Pratchett, Terry. The Amazing Maurice & His Educated Rodents. 2003. 368p. (YA). (gr. 7 up). pap. 6.99 (978-0-06-001235-9(8)) HarperCollins Pubs.

—The Amazing Maurice & His Educated Rodents. 2003. (gr. 5-8). lib. bdg. 15.30 (978-0-613-65757-0(8)) Tandem Library Bks.

Price, Reynolds. Perfect Friend. 2002. (gr. 3-6). lib. bdg. 19.95 (978-0-613-90179-6(7)) Tandem Library Bks.

Rakusin, Sudie. Dear Calla Roo. . , Love, Savannah Blue: A Letter to a Pen Pal. Rakusin, Sudie, illus. 2000. (Illus.). 36p. (J). (ps-4). 16.95 (978-0-9664805-1-1(1)) Winged Willow Pr.

—Dear Calla Roo... Love, Savannah Blue No. 2: A Letter about Getting Sick & Feeling Better. Rakusin, Sudie, illus. 2003. (Illus.). 32p. (J). (ps-4). 16.95 (978-0-9664805-3-5(8)) Winged Willow Pr.

Raphael, Morris. Ti-Nute, the Angel of Devil's Pond. Ferry, Kate, illus. 2000. 47p. (J). (978-0-8187-0332-4(6)) Harlo Pr.

Richter, Jutta. The Cat, or, How I Lost Eternity. Brailovsky, Anna, tr. from GER. 2007. (Illus.). 80p. (J). (gr. 3 up). 14.00 (***978-1-57131-676-9(0)***) Milkweed Editions.

Roberts, Shelly. Sissy & the Old Crow. 2006. (Illus.). 36p. (J). per. 18.00 (978-0-9789798-2-9(6) , 978-9789798-2-9) Blackbird's World Publishing Co.

—Sissy & the Old Crow (Coloring Book) 2006. (Illus.). 36p. (J). per. 6.50 (978-0-9789798-3-6(4) , 978-0-9789798-3-6) Blackbird's World Publishing Co.

Robinson, Fiona. The Useful Moose: A Truthful, Moose Full Tale. 2004. (Illus.). 32p. (J). (ps-3). 14.95 (978-0-8109-4925-6(3)) Abrams, Harry N. , Inc.

Rozanski, Bonnie. Borderline. 2007. 224p. (YA). pap. 22.95 (***978-0-88984-293-9(0)***) Porcupine's Quill, Inc. CAN. *Dist:* Univ. of Toronto Pr.

Rumford, James. Dog-of-the-Sea-Waves. 2004. (ENG & HAW., Illus.). 48p. (J). (gr. k-3). tchr. ed. 16.00 (978-0-618-35611-9(8)) Houghton Mifflin Co. Trade & Reference Div.

Russell, Christopher. Dogboy. 2006. 272p. (J). 15.99 (978-0-06-084116-4(8)); lib. bdg. 16.89 (978-0-06-084117-1(6)) HarperCollins Pubs.

—Hunted. 2007. 272p. (J). (gr. 5-8). 15.99 (978-0-06-084119-5(2)); lib. bdg. 16.89 (978-0-06-084120-1(6)) HarperCollins Pubs.

Sander, Heather. Make Mine with Everything, Vol. 2. 2004. (Robbie Packford Ser.). (Illus.). 144p. (J). (gr. 3-7). pap., tchr. ed. 6.95 (978-1-55143-308-0(7) , 1234551) Orca Bk. Pubs. USA.

Sargent, Dave, et al. A Puppy for Bobby, 10. 2004. (Learn to Read Ser.: 10). (Illus.). 18p. (J). pap. 9.95 (978-1-56763-818-9(X)) Ozark Publishing.

Sarnoff, Lolo. Dara: Autobiography of a Chesapeake Bay Retriever. 1999. (Illus.). 94p. (YA). (gr. 4 up). 16.95 (978-0-9700667-9-4(1)) Dara's Canine Foundation, Inc.

Sensel, Joni. Bears Barge In. Bivins, Christopher, illus. 2003. 32p. (J). (ps up). 14.95 (978-0-9701195-0-6(X)) Dream Factory Bks.

Stephens, R.David. My Animal Friends. 2001. (Illus.). 32p. (J). 6.95 (978-1-896580-74-6(2)) Tradewind Bks. CAN. *Dist:* Orca Bk. Pubs. USA.

Stone, Jeff. Crane. 2007. (Five Ancestors Ser.: Bk. 4). 248p. (J). pap. (***978-0-375-83078-5(2)***) Random Hse., Inc.

—The Five Ancestors Book #1: Tiger. (Five Ancestors Ser.: Bk. 1). 208p. (gr. 5). 2005. (J). lib. bdg. 17.99 (978-0-375-93071-3(X) , Random Hse. Bks. for Young Readers); 2005. (Illus.). (J). 15.95 (978-0-375-83071-6(5) , Random Hse. Bks. for Young Readers); 2006. reprint ed. 5.99 (978-0-375-83072-3(3) , Yearling) Random Hse. Children's Bks.

—Monkey. (Five Ancestors Ser.: Bk. 1). 208p. (gr. 5). 2006. 5.99 (978-0-375-83074-7(X) , Yearling); 2005. (J). lib. bdg. 17.99 (978-0-375-93073-7(6) , Random Hse. Bks. for Young Readers); 2005. (J). 15.95 (978-0-375-83073-0(1) , Random Hse. Bks. for Young Readers) Random Hse. Children's Bks.

—Snake. (Five Ancestors Ser.: Bk. 3). 208p. (J). (gr. 5). 2007. 5.99 (978-0-375-83076-1(6) , Yearling); 2006. 15.95 (978-0-375-83075-4(8) , Random Hse. Bks. for Young Readers) Random Hse. Children's Bks.

Terri, Branson. Brother Dragon. l.t. ed. 2007. (Illus.). 24p. (J). 9.99 (***978-0-9787421-9-5(2)***) Dragonfly Publishing, Inc.

Torres, Jotam. Weagol's Big Mess. 2007. 28p. per. 12.99 (***978-1-59886-758-9(X)***) Tate Publishing & Enterprises, L.L.C.

Tyminski, Lori, illus. The Jungle Book 2. 2003. (J). 15.98 (978-0-7853-7968-3(1)) Publications International, Ltd.

Vande Velde, Vivian. Smart Dog. 2007. (Illus.). 160p. (J). pap. 5.95 (***978-0-15-206172-2(X)*** , Magic Carpet Bks.) Harcourt Children's Bks.

Velmans, Hester. Isabel of the Whales. 192p. 2006. (gr. 4-7). 5.99 (978-0-440-42025-5(3) , Yearling); 2005. (J). (gr. 3-7). 15.95 (978-0-385-73202-4(3) , Delacorte Bks. for Young Readers); 2005. (J). (gr. 3-7). lib. bdg. 17.99 (978-0-385-90233-5(6) , Delacorte Bks. for Young Readers) Random Hse. Children's Bks.

Villaseñor, Victor. Little Crow to the Rescue/el Cuervito Al Rescate. Munoz, Elizabeth Cummins, tr. Alcantara, Felipe Ugalde, illus. (SPA & ENG.). 32p. (J). (ps-3). per. 15.95 (978-1-55885-430-7(4) , Piñata Books) Arte Publico Pr.

Wallace, Carol & Wallace, Bob. Bub, Snow, & the Burly Bear Scare. 2003. (gr. 3-6). lib. bdg. 13.00 (978-0-613-70870-8(9)) Tandem Library Bks.

Walpole, Peter. Healer of Harrow Point. 2000. (gr. 7-12). lib. bdg. 21.05 (978-0-613-88748-9(4)) Tandem Library Bks.

Watts, Leander. Ten Thousand Charms. 2005. 240p. (YA). (gr. 5). 16.00 (978-0-618-44897-5(7)) Houghton Mifflin Co. Trade & Reference Div.

West, Jill Marie. Smokey. 2002. (Illus.). 32p. (J). per. (978-0-9719283-2-9(0)) Mishe-Mokwa Design Prepress & Publishing.

White, E. B. Some Pig! A Charlotte's Web Picture Book. Kneen, Maggie, illus. 2006. (Charlotte's Web Ser.). 32p. (J). 16.99 (978-0-06-078161-3(0)); lib. bdg. 17.89 (978-0-06-078162-0(9)) HarperCollins Pubs.

White, E. B. Wilbur's Adventure. Kneen, Maggie, illus. 2008. (Charlotte's Web Ser.). 32p. (J). (gr. k-2). 16.99 (***978-0-06-078164-4(5)***) HarperCollins Pubs.

Williams, Susan. Wind Rider. 2006. 320p. (J). 16.99 (978-0-06-087236-6(5)); (YA). lib. bdg. 17.89 (978-0-06-087237-3(3)) HarperCollins Pubs.

Willson, Sarah. What's with Dad? Marantz, Larissa & DiPaolo, Katharine, illus. 2006. (All Grown Up! Ser.). 32p. (J). pap. 3.99 (978-1-4169-0669-8(X) , Simon Spotlight/Nickelodeon) Simon & Schuster Children's Publishing.

Wood, Nancy C. How the Tiny People Grew Tall: An Original Creation Tale. Walsh, Rebecca, illus. 2005. 32p. (J). (ps-2). 16.99 (978-0-7636-1543-7(9)) Candlewick Pr.

Yates, Janet Lee. Skeeter Bug Loves Sarah. 2007. (ENG.). 88p. per. 11.99 (***978-1-4141-0820-9(6)***) Pleasant Word.

HUMAN BEINGS

Catalano, Angela. Community Space: How Land & Weather Shape Communities. 2005. (Communities at Work Ser.). (Illus.). 24p. (J). pap. (978-1-4042-5022-2(0) , PowerKids Pr.) Rosen Publishing Group, Inc., The.

Facchini, Fiorenzo. Early Humans, 4 vols. Bacchin, Giorgio & Baldanzi, Alessandro, illus. 2004. (YA). (gr. 6 up). (978-0-7613-3697-6(4) , Twenty-First Century Bks.) Lerner Publishing Group.

Frenkel, Karen A. What Makes a Human a Human. 2006. (Navigators Ser.). (J). pap. 42.00 (***978-1-4108-6231-0(3)***) Benchmark Education Co.

Hall, Derek. Being Human. 2000. (J). (978-0-7172-9421-3(8)); (J). (978-0-7172-9422-0(6)); (J). (978-0-7172-9423-7(4)); (J). (978-0-7172-9425-1(0)); (J). (978-0-7172-9426-8(9)); Set. (Illus.). 384p. (YA). (gr. 5-8). lib. bdg. 229.00 (978-0-7172-9419-0(6)) Scholastic Library Publishing. (Grolier).

The Letter Mm: People Who Help Us, 6 vols. (gr. k-2). 17.50 (978-0-7368-4112-2(1)) Red Brick Learning.

McCutcheon, Marc. The Beast in You: Activities & Questions to Explore Evolution. 1999. (J). 17.75 (978-0-606-22460-4(2)) Tandem Library Bks.

Netzley, Patricia D. Alien Abductions. 2000. (Mystery Library). (Illus.). 96p. (YA). (gr. 4-12). 27.45 (978-1-56006-767-2(5) , Lucent Bks.) Thomson Gale.

Olson, Nathan. People Patterns. 2007. 32p. (J). (978-0-7368-6731-3(7)) Capstone Pr., Inc.

People Are Living Things: Individual Title Six-Packs. (gr. k-1). 23.00 (978-0-7635-9038-3(X)) Rigby Education.

Rigby Education Staff. Spikes, Scales & Armor. (Sails Literacy Ser.). (Illus.). 16p. (gr. 1-2). 27.00 (978-0-7635-9919-5(0) , 699190C99) Rigby Education.

Romero, Libby. Characteristics of People. 2006. pap. 42.00 (***978-1-4108-6482-6(0)***) Benchmark Education Co.

Saunders-Smith, Gail. People, 4 vols., Set. 1998. (J). pap. 53.00 (978-0-516-29778-1(3) , Children's Pr.) Scholastic Library Publishing.

Thomas, Keltie. Super Humans. Hall, Greg, illus. 2006. (Planet Earth News Ser.). 64p. (J). 19.95 (978-1-897066-51-5(1)); pap. 9.95 (978-1-897066-52-2(X)) Maple Tree Pr. CAN. *Dist:* Perseus Distribution.

Ward, Beck, et al. People: Pull the Tabs! Change the Pictures! 2004. (Magic Windows Ser.). (Illus.). 8p. (J). pap. 4.95 (978-0-7624-1844-2(3) , Running Pr. Kids) Running Pr. Bk. Pubs.

HUMAN BEINGS—EFFECT OF ENVIRONMENT ON

see also Human Skin Color

Catalano, Angela. Community Space: How Physical Environment Affects a Community. 2005. (Communities at Work Ser.). (Illus.). 24p. (J). 19.95 (978-1-4042-2783-5(0) , PowerKids Pr.) Rosen Publishing Group, Inc., The.

Creative Media Applications Staff. The Human Body & Environment: Skeletal & Muscular Systems, 4 vols., Vol. 1. 2003. (Middle School Reference Ser.). (Illus.). (J). (gr. 4-8). 160.00 (978-0-313-32559-5(6)) Greenwood Publishing Group, Inc.

Creative Media Applications Staff, contrib. by. The Human Body & the Environment: How Our Surroundings Affect Our Health, 4 vols. 2003. (Middle School Reference Ser.). (Illus.). 576p. (J). (gr. 6-8). 167.95 (978-0-313-32558-8(8) , MS2558, Middle School Reference) Greenwood Publishing Group, Inc.

Desonie, Dana. Humans & the Natural Environment. 2007. (Our Fragile Planet Ser.). 176p. (gr. 6-12). 35.00 (***978-0-8160-6220-1(X)*** , Chelsea Hse.) Facts On File, Inc.

The Environment. 2004. (Atlases of the Earth & Its Resources Ser.). (Illus.). 80p. (J). (gr. 5 up). lib. bdg. 34.00 (978-0-8368-5616-3(3) , World Almanac Library) Stevens, Gareth Inc.

Harris, Nicholas. How Tall? 2003. (How? Ser.). (Illus.). 30p. (J). 11.20 (978-1-4103-0194-9(X) , Blackbirch Pr., Inc.) Thomson Gale.

Holt, Rinehart and Winston Staff. Holt Environmental Science: Spanish Student Edition. 4th ed. 2004. 74.20 (978-0-03-068063-2(8)) Holt, Rinehart & Winston.

MacQuitty, Miranda & Dorling Kindersley Publishing Staff. Desert. 2000. (Eyewitness Bks.). (Illus.). 64p. (J). (gr. 4-7). lib. bdg. 19.99 (978-0-7894-6600-6(7)) Dorling Kindersley Publishing, Inc.

Paraire, Philippe & Collin, Marie-Marthe. El Medio Ambiente Explicado a los Ninos. (SPA., Illus.). 62p. (J). (gr. 3-5). (978-84-406-5512-7(6) , EB1713) Ediciones B ESP. *Dist:* Lectorum Pubns., Inc.

HUMAN BEINGS—INFLUENCE ON NATURE

see Nature—Effect of Human Beings on

HUMAN BEINGS—ORIGIN

see also Anatomy, Comparative; Evolution; Prehistoric Peoples

Anderson, Dale. How Do We Know the Nature of Humankind. 2005. (Great Scientific Questions & the Scientists Who Answered Them Ser.). (Illus.). 112p. (J). (gr. 7-12). lib. bdg. 26.50 (978-1-4042-0077-7(0)) Rosen Publishing Group, Inc., The.

Barron's Educational Editorial Staff. Searching for Human Origins. 1998. (Megascope Ser.). (Illus.). 64p. (J). (gr. 3-7). 6.95 (978-0-7641-5092-0(8)) Barron's Educational Series, Inc.

Poynter, Margaret. The Leakeys: Uncovering the Origins of Humankind. 2001. (Great Minds of Science Ser.). (Illus.). 128p. (YA). (gr. 4-10). pap. 10.95 (978-0-7660-1873-0(3)) Enslow Pubs., Inc.

Steele, Philip. The Incas: What Life Was Like in the Spectacular South American Empire. 2003. (Find Out about...Ser.). (Illus.). 64p. (gr. 3-7). pap. 7.99 (978-1-84215-777-0(9) , Southwater) Anness Publishing GBR. *Dist:* National Bk. Network.

HUMAN BODY

see Body, Human

HUMAN ECOLOGY

see also Community Life; Human Beings—Effect of Environment on; Human Geography; Nature—Effect of Human Beings on; Population; Social Psychology

Boothroyd, Jennifer. People & the Environment. 2008. (First Step Nonfiction - Ecology Ser.). (J). lib. bdg. 18.60 (***978-0-8225-8601-2(0)*** , Lerner Pubns.) Lerner Publishing Group.

Brelsfoard, Sam. Life Inside the Arctic Circle. 2005. (Illus.). 24p. (J). (***978-0-328-13638-4(7)*** , Scott Foresman) Addison-Wesley Educational Pubs., Inc.

Caduto, Michael J. In the Beginning: The Story of Genesis & Earth Activities for Children. 2004. 48p. 16.95 (978-0-8091-6717-3(4) , 6717-4) Paulist Pr.

Due, Andrea. People & the Earth: An Environmental Atlas, 6 vols. 1998. (Illus.). (J). lib. bdg. 235.00 (978-0-7172-9204-2(5) , Grolier) Scholastic Library Publishing.

Hooper, Roseanne. Life in the Coastlines: Animals, People, Plants. 2000. (gr. 3-6). lib. bdg. 15.25 (978-0-613-43341-9(6)) Tandem Library Bks.

Jeffers, Susan. Brother Eagle, Sister Sky. Jeffers, Susan, illus. 2002. (Illus.). 32p. (J). (gr. k up). pap. 7.99 (978-0-14-230132-6(9) , Puffin) Penguin Group (USA) Inc.

—Brother Eagle, Sister Sky. 2002. (gr. 3-6). lib. bdg. 16.45 (978-0-613-45249-6(6)) Tandem Library Bks.

Morgan, Sally. Cities, 1 vols. 2001. (World Book Ecology Ser.). (Illus.). 32p. (J). (978-0-7166-5228-1(5)) World Bk., Inc.

—Life in the Cities: Animals, People, Plants. 2000. (gr. 3-6). lib. bdg. 12.95 (978-0-613-43466-9(8)) Tandem Library Bks.

Pirotta, Saviour. People in the Rain Forest. 1999. (Deep in the Rain Forest Ser.). (Illus.). 32p. (J). (gr. 2-5). 25.69 (978-0-8172-5137-6(5)) Raintree.

—People in the Rain Forest. 1999. (Deep in the Rain Forest Ser.). (Illus.). 32p. (gr. 2-5). pap. 7.95 (978-0-8172-8111-3(8)); (978-0-7502-2197-9(6)) Steck-Vaughn.

Raabe, Emily. Human Impact on the Environment. 2006. (Life Science Library). (J). 21.25 (978-1-4042-2822-1(5) , PowerKids Pr.) Rosen Publishing Group, Inc., The.

Ring, Susan. Places We Live. (J). (gr. k-2). 2006. (Illus.). 16p. 15.93 (978-0-7368-5850-2(4) , Yellow Umbrella Bks.); 2005. (978-0-7368-5316-3(2)); 2005. (Illus.). 16p. (978-0-7368-5280-7(8)) Capstone Pr., Inc.

Suzuki, David T. & Vanderlinden, Kathy. You Are the Earth: From Dinosaur Breath to Pizza from Dirt. 2001. (Illus.). 128p. (J). (gr. 4-7). 19.35 (978-0-606-22743-8(1)) Tandem Library Bks.

United Nations Development Programme Staff & Peace Child International Staff, contrib. by. Peace Child International. 2003. (Illus.). 96p. (J). pap. 16.99 (978-0-237-52317-6(5) , Evans Brothers, Limited) Evans Publishing Group GBR. *Dist:* Independent Pubs. Group.

Watson, Susan. Living Sustainably. 2003. 32p. (J). lib. bdg. 24.25 (978-1-58340-404-1(X)) Smart Apple Media.

Williams, Brenda. Your Environment. 1998. (Geography Starts Here Ser.). (Illus.). 32p. (J). (gr. 1-4). lib. bdg. 25.69 (978-0-8172-5117-8(0)) Raintree.

—Your Environment. 1998. (Geography Starts Here Ser.). (Illus.). 32p. (J). (978-0-7502-1995-2(5)) Steck-Vaughn.

Zeaman, John. Overpopulation. 2002. (Single Title - Science Ser.). (Illus.). 128p. (YA). (gr. 9-12). 26.00 (978-0-531-11893-1(2) , Watts, Franklin) Scholastic Library Publishing.

HUMAN EVOLUTION

see also Human Beings—Origin

Diagram Group. Life on Earth Set, 6 vols. 2004. (Life on Earth Ser.). (Illus.). 112-112p. (gr. 4-9). 210.00 (978-0-8160-5044-4(9)) Facts On File, Inc.

Diagram Group, contrib. by. The First Humans. 2004. (Life on Earth Ser.). (Illus.). 112p. (J). (gr. 4-9). 35.00 (978-0-8160-5050-5(3)) Facts On File, Inc.

Facchini, Fiorenzo. Early Humans, 4 vols. Bacchin, Giorgio & Baldanzi, Alessandro, illus. 2004. (YA). (gr. 6 up). (978-0-7613-3697-6(4) , Twenty-First Century Bks.) Lerner Publishing Group.

Gallant, Roy A. Early Humans. 1999. (Story of Science Ser.). (Illus.). 80p. (J). (gr. 5 up). lib. bdg. 29.93 (978-0-7614-0960-1(2) , Benchmark Bks.) Cavendish, Marshall Corp.

Holt, Rinehart and Winston Staff. Holt Science & Technology Chapter 8: Life Science: History of Life on Earth. 5th ed. 2004. (Illus.). pap. 12.86 (978-0-03-030196-4(3)) Holt, Rinehart & Winston.

McCutcheon, Marc. The Beast in You: Activities & Questions to Explore Evolution. 1999. (J). 17.75 (978-0-606-22460-4(2)) Tandem Library Bks.

Norton, James R. Looking at the Mechanisms & Patterns of Evolution with Graphic Organizers. 2005. (Using Graphic Organizers to Study the Living Environment Ser.). (Illus.). 48p. (J). (978-1-4042-0616-8(7) , 1253990) Rosen Publishing Group, Inc., The.

Pocket History. 2000. 128p. (J). 9.98 (978-0-7525-3970-6(1)) Parragon, Inc.

Pocket Library, 3 vols., Set. 2000. (J). 29.95 (978-0-7525-3734-4(2)) Parragon, Inc.

Schertle, Alice. We. Addison, Kenneth, illus. (J). 2007. 32p. (gr. 4-7). 16.95 (978-1-58430-060-1(4)); 2006. (978-978-158-430-5(0)) Lee & Low Bks., Inc.

Sloan, Christopher. The Human Story: Our Evolution from Prehistoric Ancestors to Today. Garrett, Kenneth, illus. Garrett, Kenneth, photos by. 2004. 80p. (J). (gr. 5). 21.95 (978-0-7922-6325-8(1) , National Geographic Children's Bks.) National Geographic Society.

HUMAN FIGURE IN ART

see Anatomy; Figure Drawing

HUMAN GEOGRAPHY

see also Human Beings—Effect of Environment on

Ajmera, Maya & Versola, Anna Rhesa. Children from Australia to Zimbabwe. (Illus.). 2004. 64p. (YA). 19.95 (978-1-57091-478-2(8)); 2001. (J). pap. (978-1-57091-479-9(6)) Charlesbridge Publishing, Inc.

Arthus-Bertrand, Yann. The Future of the Earth: An Introduction to Sustainable Development for Young Readers. Bataille, Sylvia, illus. 2004. 76p. (J). (gr. 3-7). 16.95 (978-0-8109-5018-4(9)) Abrams, Harry N. , Inc.

Arthus-Bertrand, Yann & Burleigh, Robert. Earth from above for Young Readers. Arthus-Bertrand, Yann, photos by. 2002. (Illus.). 78p. (J). (gr. 1-5). 14.95 (978-0-8109-3486-3(8)) Abrams, Harry N. , Inc.

Benduhn, Tea. Living in Deserts. 2007. (J). pap. (***978-0-8368-8346-6(2)***); 24p. (gr. 2-4). lib. bdg. 19.93 (***978-0-8368-8341-1(1)***) Stevens, Gareth Inc. (Weekly Reader Early Learning Library).

—Living in Mountains. 2007. (J). pap. (***978-0-8368-8347-3(0)***); 24p. (gr. 2-4). lib. bdg. 19.93 (***978-0-8368-8342-8(X)***) Stevens, Gareth Inc. (Weekly Reader Early Learning Library).

—Living in Tropical Rain Forests. 2007. (J). pap. (***978-0-8368-8349-7(7)***); 24p. (gr. 2-4). lib. bdg. 19.93 (***978-0-8368-8344-2(6)***) Stevens, Gareth Inc. (Weekly Reader Early Learning Library).

Country ABCs, 12 bks. Incl. Australia ABCs : A Book about the People & Places of Australia. Hiemen, Sara. Avila, Antonio, illus. 23.93 (978-1-4048-0018-2(2)); Canada ABCs : A Book about the People & Places of Canada. Haugen, Brenda. Shaw, David, illus. (J). 23.93 (978-1-4048-0285-8(1)); China ABCs : A Book about the People & Places of China. Schroeder, Holly. Yesh, Jeff, illus. (J). 23.93 (978-1-4048-0180-6(4)); Egypt ABCs : A Book about the People & Places of Egypt. Hiemen, Sara. Ouren, Todd, illus. 23.93 (978-1-4048-0019-9(0)); Germany ABCs : A Book about the People & Places of Germany. Hiemen, Sara. Miller, Jason, illus. 23.93 (978-1-4048-0020-5(4)); Israel ABCs : A Book about the People & Places of Israel. Schroeder, Holly. Wolf, Claudia, illus. (J). 23.93 (978-1-4048-0179-0(0)); Japan ABCs : A Book about the People & Places of Japan. Hiemen, Sara. Ouren, Todd, illus. 23.93 (978-1-4048-0021-2(2)); Kenya ABCs : A Book about the People & Places of Kenya. Hiemen, Sara. Avila, Antonio, illus. (J). 23.93 (978-1-4048-0022-9(0)); Mexico ABCs : A Book about the People & Places of Mexico. Hiemen, Sara. Ouren, Todd, illus. 23.93 (978-1-4048-0023-6(9)); New Zealand ABCs : A Book about the People & Places of New Zealand. Schroeder, Holly. Wolf, Claudia, illus. (J). 23.93 (978-1-4048-0178-3(2) , 1229507); Russia ABCs : A Book about the People & Places of Russia. Berge, Ann. Yesh, Jeff, illus. (J). 23.93 (978-1-4048-0284-1(3)); United States ABCs : A Book about the People & Places of the United States. Schroeder, Holly. Yesh, Jeff, illus. (J). 23.93 (978-1-4048-0181-3(2) , 1229509); 32p. (gr. k-5). 2004. 2002. 271.20 (978-1-4048-0177-6(4)) Picture Window Bks.

Creative Media Applications Staff. How Geography Affects the United States: The Midwest, 5 vols., Vol. 3. 2002. (Illus.). (J). (978-0-313-32253-2(8)) Greenwood Publishing Group, Inc.

—How Geography Affects the United States: The Northeast, 5 vols., Vol. 1. 2002. (Illus.). (J). (978-0-313-32251-8(1)) Greenwood Publishing Group, Inc.

—How Geography Affects the United States: The Northwest, 5 vols., Vol. 4. 2002. (Illus.). (J). (978-0-313-32254-9(6)) Greenwood Publishing Group, Inc.

—How Geography Affects the United States: The Southeast, 5 vols. 2002. (Illus.). 720p. (gr. 6-8). 209.95 (978-0-313-32250-1(3) , MS2250, Middle School Reference); Vol. 2. (J). (978-0-313-32252-5(X)) Greenwood Publishing Group, Inc.

—How Geography Affects the United States: The Southwest, 5 vols., Vol. 5. 2002. (Illus.). (J). (978-0-313-32255-6(4)) Greenwood Publishing Group, Inc.

de Blij, H. J. Human Geography: With AP Companion Guide Set. 7th ed. 2003. 608p. (YA). pap., stu. ed. 87.00 net. (978-0-471-27464-3(X)) Wiley, John & Sons, Inc.

Fowler, Allan. Living near a River. 2000. (Rookie Read-About Geography Ser.). (Illus.). 32p. (J). (gr. 1-2). pap. 5.95 (978-0-516-27052-4(4) , Children's Pr.) Scholastic Library Publishing.

—Living near a River. 2000. (gr. k-3). lib. bdg. 14.10 (978-0-613-54735-2(7)) Tandem Library Bks.

Freeman, Dena & Alexander, Bryan. How People Live. 2003. (Illus.). 304p. (J). 29.99 (978-0-7894-9867-0(7)) Dorling Kindersley Publishing, Inc.

Gall, Susan B. & Gall, Timothy L. Junior Worldmark Encyclopedia of World Cultures, 9 vols. 1998. (Illus.). 2090p. (J). (gr. 4-7). lib. bdg. 470.00 (978-0-7876-1756-1(3) , GML00502-111157, UXL) Thomson Gale.

Ganeri, Anita. Indian Subcontinent. 2005. (Illus.). 44p. (J). (gr. 6-9). lib. bdg. 29.95 (978-1-58340-602-1(6)) Smart Apple Media.

Green, Mary. Rivers in Action. 2004. (Earth's Changing Landscape Ser.). (Illus.). 46p. (J). lib. bdg. 28.50 (978-1-58340-477-5(5)) Smart Apple Media.

Harris, Nicholas, ed. People of the World. 2002. (Blackbirch Visual Encyclopedia Ser.). (Illus.). 64p. (J). 37.44 (978-1-56711-518-5(7) , Blackbirch Pr., Inc.) Thomson Gale.

Harris, P. M. G. The History of Human Populations Vol. II: Migration, Urbanization, & Structural Change. 2003. (Illus.). 584p. 119.95 (978-0-275-97191-5(0) , C7191) Greenwood Publishing Group, Inc.

Helgren. People, Places & Changes: Online Edition Plus. 3rd ed. 2003. 17.26 (978-0-03-037418-0(9)) Holt, Rinehart & Winston.

Helgren, David M. Holt People, Places & Change: World Studies - Texas Edition. 3rd ed. 2002. 73.86 (978-0-03-065503-6(X)) Holt, Rinehart & Winston.

—People, Places & Change: Enhanced Online Edition. 3rd ed. 2003. 70.53 (978-0-03-072533-3(X)) Holt, Rinehart & Winston.

Hollyer, Beatrice. Wake up, World! A Day in the Life of Children Around the World. rev. ed. 1999. (Illus.). 48p. (J). (gr. 1-4). 17.95 (978-0-8050-6293-9(9) , Holt, Henry & Co. Bks. For Young Readers) Holt, Henry & Co.

Jenson-Elliott, Cynthia L. East Africa. 2002. (Indigenous Peoples of Africa Ser.). (Illus.). 112p. (YA). (gr. 4-12). 29.95 (978-1-56006-969-0(4) , Lucent Bks.) Thomson Gale.

—Southern Africa. 2002. (Indigenous Peoples of Africa Ser.). (Illus.). 112p. (J). 29.95 (978-1-59018-084-6(4) , Lucent Bks.) Thomson Gale.

Lambert, David. People of the Deserts. 1999. (Wide World Ser.). (Illus.). 48p. (J). (gr. 3-7). 18.98 (978-0-8172-5063-8(8)) Raintree.

Learning Company Books Staff, ed. Carmen Sandiego USA Adventures. 2004. (Illus.). 64p. (J). pap. 6.99 (978-0-7630-7615-3(5)) Learning Co. Bks.

—Carmen Sandiego World Adventures. 2004. (Illus.). 64p. (J). pap. 6.99 (978-0-7630-7616-0(3)) Learning Co. Bks.

Mason, Antony. People Around the World. 2002. (Illus.). 256p. (J). (gr. 5-9). tchr. ed. 25.00 (978-0-7534-5497-8(1) , Kingfisher) Houghton Mifflin Co. Trade & Reference Div.

Morris, Neil. Living by Lakes. 2004. (J). lib. bdg. (978-1-58340-485-0(6)) Smart Apple Media.

—Living by Rivers. 2004. (J). lib. bdg. (978-1-58340-482-9(1)) Smart Apple Media.

—Living in Cities. 2004. (J). lib. bdg. (978-1-58340-483-6(X)) Smart Apple Media.

—Living in the Mountains. 2004. (J). lib. bdg. (978-1-58340-484-3(8)) Smart Apple Media.

—Living on Islands. 2004. (J). lib. bdg. 27.10 (978-1-58340-487-4(2)) Smart Apple Media.

Nathan, Emma. La Gente. 2002. (Abre los Ojos y Aprende Serie).Tr. of Eyeopeners: People. (SPA.). 24p. (J). (-3). 24.94 (978-1-4103-0019-5(6) , Blackbirch Pr., Inc.) Thomson Gale.

—People. 2002. (Eyeopeners Ser.). (Illus.). 24p. (J). 22.45 (978-1-56711-652-6(3) , Blackbirch Pr., Inc.) Thomson Gale.

Nations of the World: Includes: Argentina, Australia, Canada, China, France, Japan, Mexico, Russia, South Africa, Sweden, 10 bks., Set. 2000. (Illus.). (YA). (gr. 5-9). 239.80 (978-0-7398-2848-9(7)) Raintree.

Parker, Edward, photos by. People. 2002. (Rain Forest Pilot Ser.). (Illus.). 48p. (J). lib. bdg. 27.12 (978-0-7398-5242-2(6)) Raintree.

People of the World. (J). (gr. 6). (978-0-8374-1460-7(1) , 208) Weekly Reader Corp.

Pickering, Mel, contrib. by. Childrensatlas.com. 2004. (Interfact Ser.). (Illus.). 48p. (J). (gr. 3-6). 24.95 incl. cd-rom (978-1-58728-403-8(0) , Two Can Publishing) T&N Children's Publishing.

Regan, Colm. People of the Islands. 1998. (Wide World Ser.). (Illus.). 48p. (J). (gr. 3-7). 18.98 (978-0-8172-5064-5(6)) Raintree.

Sager. Holt People, Places & Change: World Studies. 3rd ed. 2002. 73.20 (978-0-03-065501-2(3)) Holt, Rinehart & Winston.

Smith, David J. If the World Were a Village: A Book about the World's People. Armstrong, Shelagh, illus. 2004. 32p. (J). (gr. 4-6). (978-1-55074-779-9(7)) Kids Can Pr., Ltd.

Waugh, David. Place & People: Comparative Case Studies. 2001. (Illus.). 96p. (YA). (gr. 9-11). pap. 23.50 (978-0-17-434320-2(5)) Nelson Thornes Ltd. GBR. *Dist:* Trans-Atlantic Pubns., Inc.

Weidenman, Lauren. People & Places. 2000. (Yellow Umbrella Books). (Illus.). 16p. (J). (gr. 1). lib. bdg. 14.60 (978-0-7368-0743-2(8) , Pebble Bks.) Capstone Pr., Inc.

Winne, Joanne. Living on an Island. 2000. (Welcome Bks.). (Illus.). 24p. (J). (ps-2). 17.00 (978-0-516-23305-5(X) , Children's Pr.) Scholastic Library Publishing.

Woods, Mae. People of the Rain Forest. 1999. (Rain Forest Ser.). (Illus.). 24p. (J). (gr. k-6). lib. bdg. 21.35 (978-1-57765-020-1(4) , Checkerboard Library) ABDO Publishing Co.

Zurlo, Tony. Native Peoples of West Africa. 2001. (Indigenous Peoples of Africa Ser.). (Illus.). 112p. (J). (gr. 4-12). 29.95 (978-1-56006-832-7(9) , LML00902-178164, Lucent Bks.) Thomson Gale.

HUMAN RACE

see Human Beings

HUMAN RELATIONS

see Interpersonal Relations

HUMAN RIGHTS

Here are entered works on the rights of persons regardless of their legal, socioeconomic or cultural status and as recognized by the international community. Works on citizens' rights as established by law and protected by constitution are entered under Civil rights. Some works on human rights cataloged before 1987 may be found under Civil Rights.

see also Civil Rights

Altman, Linda Jacobs. The American Civil Rights Movement: The African-American Struggle for Equality. 2004. (Issues in Focus Ser.). (Illus.). 128p. (J). lib. bdg. 26.60 (978-0-7660-1944-7(6)) Enslow Pubs., Inc.

—Human Rights: Issues for a New Millennium. 2002. (Issues in Focus Ser.). (Illus.). 128p. (YA). (gr. 6-12). lib. bdg. 26.60 (978-0-7660-1689-7(7)) Enslow Pubs., Inc.

Banks, Deena. Amnesty International. 2003. (International Organizations Ser.). (Illus.). 48p. (J). (gr. 5 up). pap. 14.60 (978-0-8368-5526-5(4)); lib. bdg. 30.00 (978-0-8368-5517-3(5)) Stevens, Gareth Inc. (World Almanac Library).

Barbour, Scott. Individual Rights & the Police. 2006. 244p. (gr. 10-12). 36.20 (978-0-7377-2505-6(2) , Greenhaven Pr., Inc.) Thomson Gale.

Berry, Joy. Mine & Yours: Human Rights for Kids. Richardson, Nicole, illus. 2005. 46p. (J). (gr. 3-7). pap. 8.95 (978-1-57687-260-4(2) , PowerHouse Kids) powerHouse Cultural Entertainment, Inc.

Bradley, Catherine. Freedom of Movement. 1998. (What Do We Mean by Human Rights? Ser.). (Illus.). 48p. (J). (gr. 4-8). 23.00 (978-0-531-14447-3(X) , Watts, Franklin) Scholastic Library Publishing.

—Freedom of Movement. 2005. (What Do We Mean by Human Rights? Ser.). (Illus.). 46p. (J). (gr. 5-9). lib. bdg. 29.95 (978-1-932889-64-2(7)) Sea-To-Sea Pubns.

Brownlie, Alison. Why Do People Abuse Human Rights? 2004. (Exploring Tough Issues Ser.). (Illus.). 28p. (J). 29.93 (978-0-7398-6684-9(2)) Raintree.

Castle, Caroline. For Every Child: The UN Convention on the Rights of the Child in Words & Pictures. 2004. (Illus.). 36p. (J). (gr. k-4). reprint ed. 17.00 (978-0-7567-7706-7(2)) DIANE Publishing Co.

Currie, Stephen. Religious Oppression. 2003. (Great Escapes Ser.). (Illus.). 112p. (J). 29.95 (978-1-59018-280-2(4) , Lucent Bks.) Thomson Gale.

Donohoe, Helen. Terrorism. 2007. (J). ***(978-1-59604-144-8(7))*** Stargazer Bks.

Donohoe, Helen. Terrorism: A Look at the Way the World Is Today. 2005. (Issues of the World Ser.). (Illus.). 48p. (J). (gr. 6-9). lib. bdg. 29.95 (978-1-59604-070-0(X)) Stargazer Bks.

Downing, David. The Debate about Terrorist Tactics. 2007. (J). lib. bdg. ***(978-1-4042-3757-5(7)*** , Rosen Central) Rosen Publishing Group, Inc., The.

Grant, Reg. Amnesty International. 2001. (World Organizations Ser.). (Illus.). 32p. (YA). (gr. 6-8). 24.00 (978-0-531-14619-4(7)); pap. 6.95 (978-0-531-14811-2(4)) Scholastic Library Publishing. (Watts, Franklin).

—Amnesty International. 2001. (gr. 5-8). lib. bdg. 15.25 (978-0-613-53905-0(2)) Tandem Library Bks.

Haughton, Emma & Clarke, Penny. Rights in the Home. 2005. (What Do We Mean by Human Rights? Ser.). (Illus.). 46p. (J). (gr. 5-9). lib. bdg. 29.95 (978-1-932889-65-9(5)) Sea-To-Sea Pubns.

Herumin, Wendy. Child Labor Today: A Human Rights Issue. 2007. (Issues in Focus Today Ser.). (Illus.). 104p. (J). (gr. 6). lib. bdg. 31.93 ***(978-0-7660-2682-7(5))*** Enslow Pubs., Inc.

Hinds, Maurene J. You Have the Right to Know Your Rights: What Teens Should Know. 2005. (Issues in Focus Today). (Illus.). 104p. (J). (gr. 6-12). lib. bdg. 31.93 (978-0-7660-2358-1(3)) Enslow Pubs., Inc.

Immell, Myra H. Ethnic Violence. 2000. (Contemporary Issues Companion Ser.). 160p. (YA). lib. bdg. 36.20 (978-0-7377-0165-4(X)); (Illus.). (gr. 10 up). lib. bdg. 24.95 (978-0-7377-0164-7(1)) Thomson Gale. (Greenhaven Pr., Inc.).

Kramer, Ann. Human Rights: Who Decides? 2006. (Behind the News Ser.). (Illus.). 56p. (YA). (gr. 5-8). lib. bdg. 32.86 (978-1-4034-8832-9(0)) Heinemann Library.

Langwith, Jacqueline. Human Rights. 2007. (Opposing Viewpoints Ser.). (Illus.). 240p. (gr. 10-12). 36.20 ***(978-0-7377-3745-5(X));*** pap. 24.95 ***(978-0-7377-3746-2(8))*** Thomson Gale. (Greenhaven Pr., Inc.).

Mastoon, Adam. Shared Heart: Portraits & Stories Celebrating Lesbian, Gay & Bisexual Young People. 2001. (YA). (978-0-606-21430-8(5)) Tandem Library Bks.

McGowan, Keith. Human Rights. 2002. (Overview Ser.). (Illus.). 128p. (J). (gr. 6-9). 29.95 (978-1-56006-858-7(2) , Lucent Bks.) Thomson Gale.

Nygren-Krug, Helena, et al. Right to Health. 2002. (ENG, FRE & SPA., Illus.). 16p. pap. 4.05 (978-92-4-159028-0(9) , 1150474) World Health Organization.

O'Connor, Maureen. Equal Rights. 1998. (What Do We Mean by Human Rights? Ser.). (Illus.). 48p. (J). (gr. 4-8). 23.00 (978-0-531-14448-0(8) , Watts, Franklin) Scholastic Library Publishing.

—Equal Rights. 2005. (What Do We Mean by Human Rights? Ser.). (Illus.). 46p. (J). (gr. 5-9). lib. bdg. 29.95 (978-1-932889-63-5(9)) Sea-To-Sea Pubns.

O'Shei, Tim. Jimmy Carter: A MyReportLinks.com Book. 2002. (Presidents Ser.). (Illus.). 48p. (J). (gr. 4-10). lib. bdg. 25.26 (978-0-7660-5051-8(3) , MyReportLinks.com Bks.) Enslow Pubs., Inc.

Parry, Ann. Amnesty International. 2005. (Humanitarian Organizations Ser.). (Illus.). 32p. (J). (ps-8). lib. bdg. 22.95 (978-0-7910-8813-5(8) , Chelsea Hse.) Facts On File, Inc.

Prior, Katherine. Workers' Rights. 2005. (What Do We Mean by Human Rights? Ser.). (Illus.). 46p. (J). (gr. 5-9). lib. bdg. 29.95 (978-1-932889-68-0(X)) Sea-To-Sea Pubns.

Rayner, Amanda, ed. A Life Like Mine. 2002. (Illus.). 128p. (J). (gr. 4-7). 24.99 (978-0-7894-8859-6(0)) Dorling Kindersley Publishing, Inc.

Soliz, Adela. Human Rights. 2006. (Contemporary Issues Companion Ser.). (Illus.). 244p. (gr. 10-12). 24.95 (978-0-7377-2459-2(5)); pap. 36.20 (978-0-7377-2458-5(7)) Thomson Gale. (Greenhaven Pr., Inc.).

Stewart, Gail B. Human Rights in the Middle East. 2004. (Lucent Library of Conflict in the Middle East). (Illus.). 112p. (J). (gr. 7-10). 29.95 (978-1-59018-488-2(2) , Lucent Bks.) Thomson Gale.

Two-Can Publishing Ltd. Staff, contrib. by. Stand up for Your Rights. 2004. (Stand Up... Ser.). (Illus.). 96p. (J). (gr. 3-6). 14.95 (978-1-58728-400-7(6)); pap. 9.95 (978-1-58728-401-4(4)) T&N Children's Publishing. (Two Can Publishing).

University of Connecticut Staff. Tikvah: Children's Book Creators Reflect on Human Rights. 2001. (978-0-606-22749-0(0)) Tandem Library Bks.

Watson, Susan. Understanding Human Rights. 2003. 32p. (J). lib. bdg. 24.25 (978-1-58340-402-7(3)) Smart Apple Media.

HUMAN SKIN COLOR

Neubauer, Julie. Ten Little Freckles. 2006. 30p. (J). per. 13.99 ***(978-1-59886-702-2(4))*** Tate Publishing & Enterprises, L.L.C.

Tyler, Michael. The Skin You Live In. Csicsko, David Lee, illus. 2005. 32p. (J). 14.95 (978-0-9759580-0-1(3)) Chicago Children's Museum.

HUMANISM

Here are entered works on culture founded on the study of the classics.

see also Learning and Scholarship; Renaissance

Bennett, Helen. Humanism, What's That? A Book for Curious Kids. 2005. 56p. (J). pap. 13.00 (978-1-59102-387-6(4)) Prometheus Bks., Pubs.

An Introduction to the Humanities. (J). (gr. 7-12). (978-0-673-29435-7(8)) Addison-Wesley Educational Pubs., Inc.

HUMMINGBIRDS

Aziz, Laurel & Forsyth, Adrian. Hummingbirds. 2002. (Illus.). 64p. (J). (gr. 4-7). lib. bdg. 19.95 (978-1-55209-487-7(1)) Firefly Bks., Ltd.

—Hummingbirds: A Beginner's Guide. 2002. (Illus.). 64p. (J). (gr. 4-7). pap. 9.95 (978-1-55209-372-6(7)) Firefly Bks., Ltd.

Berger, Bruce. A Dazzle of Hummingbirds: The Colorful Life of a Tiny Scrapper. Leon, Vicki, ed. 2nd ed. 2005. (Jean-Michel Cousteau Presents Ser.). (Illus.). 48p. (J). pap. 7.95 (978-0-9666490-7-9(9)) London Town Pr.

Himmelman, John. A Hummingbird's Life. Himmelman, John, illus. 2001. (Nature Upclose Ser.). (Illus.). 32p. (J). (gr. k-2). pap. 6.95 (978-0-516-27159-0(8) , Children's Pr.) Scholastic Library Publishing.

—A Hummingbird's Life. 2000. (gr. k-3). lib. bdg. 15.25 (978-0-613-54557-0(5)) Tandem Library Bks.

The Hummingbird: Individual Title Six-Packs. (On Deck Ser.). 24p. (gr. 4-5). 35.00 (978-0-7578-1065-7(9)) Rigby Education.

Hummingbird Garden: Big Book: Level J. Group 1. (Story Box(R) Ser.). 16p. 31.50 (978-0-322-02469-4(2)) Wright Group, The.

Jango-Cohen, Judith. Hovering Hummingbirds. 2003. (Pull Ahead Bks.). (Illus.). 32p. (J). 22.60 (978-0-8225-4666-5(3) , Lerner Pubns.) Lerner Publishing Group.

—Hovering Hummingbirds. 2003. (gr. k-3). lib. bdg. 14.10 (978-0-613-58916-1(5)) Tandem Library Bks.

Kalz, Jill. Hummingbirds. 2002. (Illus.). 23p. (J). lib. bdg. 21.35 (978-1-58340-130-9(X)) Smart Apple Media.

Kelly, Irene. It's a Hummingbird's Life. 2003. (Illus.). 36p. (J). (gr. k-3). tchr. ed. 16.95 (978-0-8234-1658-5(5)) Holiday Hse., Inc.

Macken, JoAnn Early. The Life Cycle of a Hummingbird. 2006. (Illus.). 24p. (J). pap. (978-0-8368-6390-1(9)); lib. bdg. 19.33 (978-0-8368-6383-3(6)) Stevens, Gareth Inc.

The Mini Hummingbird Feeder (Scholastic Edition) 2006. pap. ***(978-0-7624-3129-8(6)*** , Running Pr.) Running Pr. Bk. Pubs.

Murray, Julie. Hummingbirds. 2005. (Animal Kingdom Set Ii Ser.). (Illus.). 24p. (J). (gr. k-4). lib. bdg. 21.35 (978-1-59197-320-1(1)) ABDO Publishing Co.

Otfinoski, Steven. Hummingbirds. 2008. (J). ***(978-0-7614-2932-6(8))*** Cavendish, Marshall Bks., Ltd.

Paige, Joy. El Colibri: El Pajaro Mas Pequeno Del Mundo. 2004. (Campeones Del Mundo Animal Ser.). (SPA & ENG., Illus.). 24p. (J). (gr. 3-6). lib. bdg. 17.25 (978-0-8239-6894-7(4) , Buenas Letra) Rosen Publishing Group, Inc., The.

—The Hummingbird: World's Smallest Bird. 2002. (Reading Power Ser.). (Illus.). 24p. (J). (gr. 1). lib. bdg. 17.25 (978-0-8239-5960-0(0) , PowerKids Pr.) Rosen Publishing Group, Inc., The.

Sayre, April Pulley. The Hungry Hummingbird. Holland, Gay W., illus. 2001. (All about Animals Ser.). 32p. (ps-2). lib. bdg. 22.90 (978-0-7613-1951-1(4) , Millbrook Pr.) Lerner Publishing Group.

Schwartz, David M. Hummingbird. Kuhn, Dwight, photos by. 2001. (Springboards into Science Ser.). (Illus.). 24p. (J). (gr. 1 up). lib. bdg. 20.67 (978-0-8368-2975-4(1)) Stevens, Gareth Inc.

—El Picaflor. Kuhn, Dwight, photos by. 2001. (Springboards into Science Ser.). (SPA., Illus.). 24p. (J). (gr. 1 up). lib. bdg. 20.67 (978-0-8368-2999-0(9) , GHS31418) Stevens, Gareth Inc.

Sovak, Jan. Learning about Hummingbirds. 2004. (Learning about Ser.). (Illus.). 16p. (J). (gr. 3-5). pap. 1.50 (978-0-486-43315-8(3)) Dover Pubns., Inc.

Swanson, Diane. Hummingbirds. 2004. (Welcome to the World of Animals Ser.). (Illus.). 32p. (J). (gr. 3 up). lib. bdg. 23.33 (978-0-8368-4024-7(0)) Stevens, Gareth Inc.

—Welcome to the World of Hummingbirds. 2002. (Welcome to the World Ser.). (Illus.). 32p. (J). (ps-2). 9.95 (978-1-55285-319-1(5)); pap. 5.95 (978-1-55285-318-4(7)) Whitecap Bks., Ltd. CAN. *Dist:* Firefly Bks., Ltd.

HUMORISTS

Aykroyd, Clarissa. Savage Satire: The Story of Jonathan Swift. 2006. (World Writers Ser.). (Illus.). 160p. (J). (gr. 6-12). lib. bdg. 27.95 (978-1-59935-027-1(0)) Reynolds, Morgan Inc.

Donovan, Sandra. Will Rogers: Cowboy, Comedian, & Commentator. 2006. (Signature Lives Ser.). (Illus.). 112p. (J). (gr. 4-8). lib. bdg. 31.93 (978-0-7565-2463-0(6)) Compass Point Bks.

HUMOROUS PICTURES

see Cartoons and Comics; Comic Books, Strips, etc.

HUMOROUS POETRY

see also Limericks; Nonsense Verses

Agard, John. Points of View with Prof Peekaboo. Kitamura, Satoshi, illus. 2001. 64p. (J). pap. 9.99 (978-0-09-941326-4(4)) Random Hse. GBR. *Dist:* Independent Pubs. Group.

Bowman, Crystal. If Peas Could Taste Like Candy: And Other Funny Poems for Kids. Jeffery, Lynn, illus. 1998. 128p. (J). 12.99 (978-0-310-21950-7(7)) Zonderkidz.

Brown, Calef. Dutch Sneakers & Flea Keepers: 14 More Stories. 2000. (Illus.). 32p. (J). (gr. k-3). tchr. ed. 16.00 (978-0-618-05183-0(X)) Houghton Mifflin Co. Trade & Reference Div.

—Polka-Bats & Octopus Slacks: 14 Stories. 1998. (Illus.). 32p. (J). (gr. k-3). 16.00 (978-0-395-85403-7(2)) Houghton Mifflin Co. Trade & Reference Div.

Brown, Marc. Hand Rhymes. Brown, Marc, illus. 2002. (Illus.). (J). 13.19 (978-0-7587-2677-3(5)) Book Wholesalers, Inc.

Burgess, Gelett. Goops & How to Be Them: A Manual of Manners for Polite Infants. 2004. (Illus.). 108p. per. 17.95 (978-1-55709-392-9(X)) Applewood Bks.

Carpenter, Stephen, illus. If Kids Ruled the School: More Kids' Favorite Funny School Poems. 2004. 73p. (J). (978-0-88166-468-3(5)) Meadowbrook Pr.

—Mary Had a Little Jam, & Other Silly Rhymes. 2004. 32p. (J). (978-0-88166-470-6(7)) Meadowbrook Pr.

Cole, Joanna & Calmenson, Stephanie. Yours till Banana Splits: 201 Autograph Rhymes. Tiegreen, Alan, illus. 2004. 64p. (J). (gr. 6-8). reprint ed. pap. 7.00 (978-0-7567-7349-6(0)) DIANE Publishing Co.

Cyrus, Kurt. Hotel Deep: Light Verse from Dark Water. 2005. (Illus.). 40p. (J). 16.00 (978-0-15-216771-4(4)) Harcourt Trade Pubs.

Dahl, Roald. Vile Verses. 2005. 192p. (J). (gr. 3). 25.00 (978-0-670-06042-9(9) , Viking Juvenile) Penguin Group (USA) Inc.

Demarest, Chris L. I Invited a Dragon to Dinner: And Other Poems to Make You Laugh Out Loud. 2004. (Illus.). 40p. (J). reprint ed. pap. 6.99 (978-0-14-240062-3(9) , Puffin) Penguin Group (USA) Inc.

—I Invited a Dragon to Dinner: And Other Poems to Make You Laugh Out Loud. 2004. (gr. k-3). lib. bdg. 15.30 (978-0-613-86710-8(6)) Tandem Library Bks.

Dordick, Barry. Macaroni on the Moon. Amado, Defne, illus. 2003. 110p. pap. 11.95 (978-0-595-26886-3(2)) iUniverse, Inc.

Dotlich, Rebecca Kai. When Riddles Come Rumbling: Poems to Ponder. Dugan, Karen M., illus. 2003. 32p. (YA). (gr. 2-4). 15.95 (978-1-56397-846-3(6)) Boyds Mills Pr.

Everton, Terry. My Mom Has Lost Her Marbles. Everton, Debbie, illus. 2001. 148p. (YA). pap. 10.95 (978-0-595-12776-4(2)) iUniverse, Inc.

Fatchen, Max. Songs for My Dog & Other Wry Rhymes. 1999. (Illus.). 125p. (J). (gr. 3-7). pap. 12.95 (978-1-86254-478-9(6)) Wakefield Pr. Pty, Ltd. AUS. *Dist:* Independent Pubs. Group.

Florian, Douglas. Laugh-eteria. 2008. (Illus.). 160p. (J). pap. 8.00 ***(978-0-15-206148-7(7)*** , Harcourt Paperbacks) Harcourt Children's Bks.

Fuertes, Gloria. Poesias, Rimas y Disparates: Pienso Mesa y Digo Silla. 2003. (SPA.). 128p. (978-84-305-8535-9(4) , SU4859) Susaeta Ediciones, S.A. ESP. *Dist:* Lectorum Pubns., Inc.

Greenberg, David. Don't Forget Your Etiquette! The Essential Guide to Misbehavior. Westcott, Nadine Bernard, illus. 2006. 40p. (J). 16.00 (978-0-374-34990-5(8) , Farrar, Straus & Giroux (BYR)) Farrar, Straus & Giroux.

Grimly, Gris. Gris Grimly's Wicked Nursery Rhymes II. 2006. (Illus.). 32p. (J). 16.95 (978-0-9729388-3-9(4)) Baby Tattoo Bks.

Hoce, Charles E. Beyond Old McDonald: Silly Poems from down on the Farm. Fernandes, Eugenie, illus. 2004. 32p. (J). 16.95 (978-1-59078-312-2(3)) Boyds Mills Pr.

Kammeraad, Kevin. The Tomato Collection. 2003. (Illus.). 64p. (J). pap. 9.95 (978-0-9669504-3-4(7)) Cooperfly Bks.

—The Tomato Collection. Kammeraad, Kevin, illus. 1999. (Illus.). 64p. (J). (ps-6). per. 18.95 (978-0-9669504-0-3(2)) Cooperfly Bks.

Koontz, Dean. The Paper Doorway: Funny Verse & Nothing Worse. Parks, Phil, illus. 2001. 160p. (J). (gr. 5 up). 17.95 (978-0-06-029488-5(4)) HarperCollins Pubs.

Lansky, Bruce. Rolling in the Aisles: A Collection of Laugh-Out-Loud Poems. Carpenter, Stephen, illus. 2004. 116p. (J). (978-0-88166-473-7(1)) Meadowbrook Pr.

Lansky, Bruce. Funny Little Poems for Funny Little Kids. 2002. (gr. 3-6). lib. bdg. 14.10 (978-0-613-90382-0(X)) Tandem Library Bks.

—I Hope I Don't Strike Out! & Other Funny Sports Poems. Carpenter, Stephen, illus. 2008. ***(978-0-88166-535-2(5))*** Meadowbrook Pr.

—If Pigs Could Fly. Carpenter, Stephen, illus. 2000. xii, 83p. (J). pap. (978-0-88166-379-2(4)) Meadowbrook Pr.

—Miles of Smiles: Kids Pick the Funniest Poems. Carpenter, Stephen, illus. 1998. xi, 115p. (J). (gr. 3-7). 16.00 (978-0-88166-313-6(1)) Meadow Brook Pubns.

—My Dog Ate My Homework! A Collection of Funny Poems. Carpenter, Stephen, illus. 2nd ed. 2001. 83p. (J). (978-0-88166-406-5(5)) Meadowbrook Pr.

Lansky, Bruce, ed. A Bad Case of the Giggles. Carpenter, Stephen, illus. 2008. 126p. (J). pap. 9.95 ***(978-1-4169-5197-1(0))*** Meadowbrook Pr.

Lansky, Bruce, ed. Rolling in the Aisles. Carpenter, Stephen, illus. 2004. 128p. (J). 17.00 (978-0-689-03766-5(X)) Meadowbrook Pr.

Marshall, James. Pocketful of Nonsense. 2003. (Illus.). 32p. (J). (gr. k-3). pap. 5.95 (978-0-618-34186-3(2)); tchr. ed. 15.00 (978-0-618-34187-0(0)) Houghton Mifflin Co. Trade & Reference Div.

—Pocketful of Nonsense. 2003. (gr. k-3). lib. bdg. 14.10 (978-0-613-90053-9(7)) Tandem Library Bks.

McGough, Roger. The Kingfisher Book of Funny Poems. Holden, Caroline, illus. 2002. 256p. (J). (gr. 3-5). tchr. ed. 18.95 (978-0-7534-5480-0(7) , Kingfisher) Houghton Mifflin Co. Trade & Reference Div.

Meadowbrook Press Staff. If Kids Ruled the School. 2004. (Illus.). 80p. (YA). pap. 8.95 (978-0-689-03273-8(0)) Simon & Schuster Children's Publishing.

Moses, Brian, contrib. by. Minibeasts. 2003. (Illus.). 65p. (J). pap. 6.99 (978-0-330-37057-8(X) , Pan) Pan Macmillan GBR. *Dist:* Trafalgar Square Publishing.

Nathan, Jeff. Calling All Animals: The First Book of PunOETRY. Ball, Liz, illus. 2003. 92p. (J). per. 9.95 (978-0-9702730-1-7(0)) Chucklebks. Publishing.

Nesbitt, Kenn. The Aliens Have Landed! Poems. 2001. (Illus.). 87p. (J). (978-0-88166-396-9(4)) Meadowbrook Pr.

Numeroff, Laura Joffe. Sometimes I Wonder If Poodles Like Noodles. Bowers, Tim, illus. 2002. 32p. (J). (ps-3). pap. 7.99 (978-0-689-85123-0(5) , Aladdin) Simon & Schuster Children's Publishing.

—Sometimes I Wonder If Poodles Like Noodles. 2002. (ps-2). lib. bdg. 15.30 (978-0-613-46230-3(0)) Tandem Library Bks.

Paraskevas, Betty. Junior Kroll. 2000. (978-0-606-20329-6(X)) Tandem Library Bks.

Proimos, James. If I Were in Charge the Rules Would Be Different! 2002. (Illus.). 80p. (J). (gr. k up). pap. 16.95 (978-0-439-20864-2(5) , Scholastic Pr.) Scholastic, Inc.

Rosen, Michael. Walking the Bridge of Your Nose. 1999. (978-0-606-16560-0(6)) Tandem Library Bks.

Rosen, Michael J., ed. & illus. Food Fight: Poets Join the Fight Against Hunger with Poems to Favorite Foods. Rosen, Michael J., illus. 2000. 45p. (YA). (gr. 6-7). 17.00 (978-0-7881-9112-1(8)) DIANE Publishing Co.

H I

Shapiro, Karen Jo. Because I Could Not Stop My Bike: And Other Poems. Faulkner, Matt, illus. 2004. 32p. (J). (gr. 2-7). 15.95 (978-1-58089-035-9(0)) Charlesbridge Publishing, Inc.

Shields, Carol Diggory. Almost Late to School: And More School Poems. Meisel, Paul, illus. 2003. 32p. (J). (gr. k). 15.99 (978-0-525-45743-5(7) , Dutton Juvenile) Penguin Group (USA) Inc.

Silverstein, Shel. Don't Bump the Glump & Other Fantasies. Silverstein, Shel, illus. 2008. 64p. 17.99 (***978-0-06-149338-6(4)***) HarperCollins Pubs.

—Hay Luz en el Desvan. Alonso Blanco, Victoria, tr. 2006. (SPA.). 169p. (J). pap. 16.95 (978-84-666-0567-0(3) , EB31012) Ediciones B ESP. *Dist:* Independent Pubs. Group, Lectorum Pubns., Inc.

—Where the Sidewalk Ends: Poems & Drawings. Silverstein, Shel, illus. 30th anniv. ed. 2004. (Illus.). 192p. lib. bdg. 19.89 (978-0-06-058653-9(2)) HarperCollins Pubs.

Spinelli, Eileen. Do You Have a Hat? Valerio, Geraldo, illus. 2004. 40p. (J). 16.95 (978-0-689-86253-3(9)) Simon & Schuster Children's Publishing.

Steinberg, David. Club Pet & Other Funny Poems: All Aboard Poetry Reader Station Stop 2. Sinnott, Adrian C., illus. 2005. (All Aboard Poetry Reader Ser.). 48p. (J). (gr. 1-3). pap. 3.99 (978-0-448-43773-6(2) , Grosset & Dunlap) Penguin Group (USA) Inc.

—The Monster Mall & Other Spooky Poems. Sinnott, Adrian C., illus. 2004. (All Aboard Poetry Reader Ser.). 48p. (J). (gr. 1-3). 13.89 (978-0-448-43543-5(8) , Grosset & Dunlap) Penguin Group (USA) Inc.

Stone, Tiffany. Floyd the Flamingo & His Flock of Friends. Shoemaker, Kathryn E., illus. 2006. 64p. (J). 7.95 (978-1-896580-58-6(0)) Tradewind Bks. CAN. *Dist:* Orca Bk. Pubs. USA.

Walsh, Maria Elena. El Reino del Reves. Hilb, Nora, illus. 2001. (SPA.). 96p. (J). (gr. 3-5). pap. 10.95 (978-950-511-636-2(5)) Santillana USA Publishing Co., Inc.

Wayland, April Halprin. Girl Coming in for a Landing. Clayton, Elaine, illus. 2004. 144p. (YA). (gr. 7). reprint ed. pap. 5.50 (978-0-440-41903-7(4) , Yearling) Random Hse. Children's Bks.

Whiting, Jim. No Perfect People, Please! Poems & audio cd By. 2007. (Illus.). 64p. (J). 16.95 (***978-0-9759276-2-5(0)***) Culturelink Pr.

Wilbur, Richard. Opposites, More Opposites & a Few Differences. 2000. (978-0-606-18186-0(5)) Tandem Library Bks.

HUMOROUS STORIES

see also Wit and Humor

Abbott, Tony. Stinky Business. 2000. (Don't Touch That Remote Ser.: No. 3). 160p. (J). (gr. 3-6). pap. 3.99 (978-0-671-02783-4(2) , Aladdin) Simon & Schuster Children's Publishing.

Aboff, Marcie. Alex & Marty Run Wild. 2005. (Madagascar Ser.). 32p. (J). pap. 3.99 (978-0-439-69631-9(3)) Scholastic, Inc.

Acher, Gabriela. El Amor en Tiempos del Colesterol.Tr. of Love in Cholesterol Times. (SPA.). (978-950-07-1540-9(6)) Editorial Sudamericana S.A.

Ada, Alma Flor. Bajo las Palmas Reales. (SPA., Illus.). 96p. (J). (gr. 5-8). 15.95 (978-1-58105-656-3(7)) Santillana USA Publishing Co., Inc.

—Stories the Year 'Round. 2001. (J). (gr. k-3). stu. ed., act. bk. ed. 10.95 (978-1-58105-242-8(1)) Santillana USA Publishing Co., Inc.

—Stories the Year 'Round: Home Connection. 2001. (J). (gr. k-3). pap. 7.65 (978-1-58105-358-6(4)) Santillana USA Publishing Co., Inc.

Ada, Alma Flor & Campoy, F. Isabel. Roll 'n' Role. (Gateways to the Sun). 32p. (J). (gr. k-6). pap. 13.95 (978-1-58105-678-5(8)) Santillana USA Publishing Co., Inc.

Adams, H. J. Of Dragons, Kings, Sages & Little Folk. 1999. 120p. (J). 22.50 (978-0-923687-52-6(1)) Celo Valley Bks.

Adams, Michelle Medlock. Sister for Sale. Brooks, Karen Stormer, illus. 2004. 28p. (J). pap. 4.99 (978-0-310-70820-9(6)) Zonderkidz.

—Sister for Sale. 2002. (Illus.). 32p. 7.99 (978-0-310-70254-2(2)) Zondervan.

Adams, William J. Hate that Thunder. Stiglich, Tom, illus. 2005. 24p. (J). pap. 8.95 (978-0-9772757-0-0(1)) Mandy & Andy Bks., Inc.

Addis, Sandra. Flashlight One, Night Fright Off. 2005. 18.00 (978-0-8059-9782-8(2)) Dorrance Publishing Co., Inc.

Adventures of Abby Alligator. 2001. (ps-2). lib. bdg. 9.80 (978-0-613-32244-7(4)) Tandem Library Bks.

Agee, Jon. Milo's Hat Trick. 2001. (Illus.). 32p. (J). (ps-17). (978-0-7868-0902-8(7)) Hyperion Bks. for Children.

Agee, Jon. Nothing. 2007. 32p. (J). (ps up). 16.99 (***978-0-7868-3694-9(6)***) Hyperion Bks. for Children.

Ahlberg, Allan. The Cat Who Got Carried Away. McEwen, Katharine, illus. 2003. 96p. (J). (gr. 1-4). 15.99 (978-0-7636-2073-8(4)) Candlewick Pr.

—The Children Who Smelled a Rat. McEwen, Katharine, illus. 2005. 80p. (J). (gr. 2-4). 15.99 (978-0-7636-2870-3(0)) Candlewick Pr.

—Half a Pig. Ahlberg, Allan & Ahlberg, Jessica, trs. Ahlberg, Jessica, illus. 2004. 40p. (J). (gr. k-3). 16.99 (978-0-7636-2373-9(3)) Candlewick Pr.

—Previously. Ingman, Bruce, illus. 2007. 32p. (J). (ps-3). 16.99 (***978-0-7636-3542-8(1)***) Candlewick Pr.

Ahlberg, Allan. Starting School. braille ed. 2004. (J). (gr. k-3). spiral bd. (978-0-616-01526-1(7)) Canadian National Institute for the Blind/Institut National Canadien pour les Aveugles.

Ahlberg, Allan & Ahlberg, Janet. Starting School. (Illus.). 32p. (J). pap. 9.95 (978-0-14-050737-9(X)) Penguin Bks., Ltd. GBR. *Dist:* Trafalgar Square Publishing.

Aiken, Joan. Arabel & Mortimer. Blake, Quentin, illus. 2007. 192p. (J). pap. 5.95 (***978-0-15-206082-4(0)*** , Odyssey Classics) Harcourt Children's Bks.

—Arabel's Raven. Blake, Quentin, illus. 2007. 160p. (J). pap. 5.95 (***978-0-15-206094-7(4)*** , Odyssey Classics) Harcourt Children's Bks.

—Black Hearts in Battersea. 1999. 240p. (J). (gr. 5-9). pap. 5.95 (978-0-395-97128-4(4)) Houghton Mifflin Co. Trade & Reference Div.

—The Cuckoo Tree. 2000. (Illus.). 304p. (J). (gr. 5-9). 16.00 (978-0-618-07024-4(9)); pap. 6.95 (978-0-618-07023-7(0)) Houghton Mifflin Co. Trade & Reference Div.

Alapont, Pasqual. Un Verano Sin Francesas. Sola, Raquel, tr. from CAT. Molinero, David, illus. 2000. (Periscopio Ser.).Tr. of Summer Without French Girls. (SPA.). 112p. (YA). (gr. 9 up). (978-84-236-5512-0(1)) Edebé ESP. *Dist:* Baker & Taylor Bks.

Albee, Sarah. The Bunny Hop. Swanson, Maggie, illus. 2004. 24p. (J). (gr. k-ps). bds. 4.99 (978-0-375-82693-1(9) , Random Hse. Bks. for Young Readers) Random Hse. Children's Bks.

Alexander, Lloyd. The Fortune-Tellers. Hyman, Trina Schart, illus. 2005. 28p. (J). (gr. k-4). reprint ed. 16.00 (978-0-7567-9706-5(3)) DIANE Publishing Co.

—Gypsy Rizka. 2000. (Illus.). 208p. (J). (gr. 3-7). pap. 5.99 (978-0-14-130980-4(6) , Puffin) Penguin Group (USA) Inc.

—Gypsy Rizka. unabr. ed. 2000. (YA). pap. 58.99 incl. audio (978-0-7887-3954-5(9) , 41059X4) Recorded Bks., LLC.

—Gypsy Rizka. 2000. (gr. 3-6). lib. bdg. 14.15 (978-0-613-30458-0(6)) Tandem Library Bks.

Alfonsi, Alice. Lizzie Mcguire: The Orchids & Gumbo Poker Club. 2003. (gr. 3-6). lib. bdg. 13.00 (978-0-613-75010-3(1)) Tandem Library Bks.

Alfonsi, Alice, adapted by. 2 Good 2 Be True, Bk. 6. rev. ed. 2005. (That's So Raven Ser.: Bk. 6). (Illus.). 128p. (J). (gr. 3-7). pap. 4.99 (978-0-7868-4683-2(6)) Disney Pr.

Allan, Nicholas. Que Animales! Mayobre, Maria Francisca, tr. from ENG. Allan, Nicholas, illus. 2001. (Coleccion Primeras Lecturas). (SPA., Illus.). 28p. (J). pap. 7.50 (978-980-257-264-9(0)) Ekare, Ediciones VEN. *Dist:* AIMS International Bks., Inc., Lectorum Pubns., Inc.

—Where Willy Went. 2005. (Illus.). 32p. (J). (ps-3). 15.95 (978-0-375-83030-3(8)); lib. bdg. 17.99 (978-0-375-93030-0(2)) Random Hse. Children's Bks. (Knopf Bks. for Young Readers).

Allard, Harry. Starlight Goes to Town. Booth, George, illus. 2007. (J). (978-0-374-37187-6(3)) Farrar, Straus & Giroux.

Allen, Will. Swords for Hire: Two of the Most Unlikely Heroes you'll ever Meet. Beck, David Michael, illus. 2003. 168p. (gr. 3 up). pap. 6.95 (978-0-9724882-0-4(0)) Centerpunch Pr.

Alley, R. W., illus. A Know-Nothing Halloween. 2002. (Know-Nothings Ser.). (J). 12.30 (978-0-7587-6905-3(9)) Book Wholesalers, Inc.

—The Know-Nothings Talk Turkey. 2002. (Know-Nothings Ser.). (J). 12.30 (978-0-7587-6906-0(7)) Book Wholesalers, Inc.

Alligators All Around. 2004. (J). 24.95 incl. audio (978-0-7882-0568-2(4)); pap. 14.95 incl. audio (978-0-7882-0633-7(8)) Weston Woods Studios, Inc.

Allison, Jennifer. Gilda Joyce: Psychic Investigator. 2005. 208p. (YA). 12.99 (978-0-525-47375-6(0) , Dutton Juvenile); 2006. 336p. (J). (gr. 5). reprint ed. pap. 6.99 (978-0-14-240698-4(8) , Puffin) Penguin Group (USA) Inc.

Allison, Jennifer. Gilda Joyce: The Ghost Sonata. 2007. 288p. (J). (gr. 5-8). 15.99 (***978-0-525-47808-9(6)*** , Dutton Juvenile) Penguin Group (USA) Inc.

Alonso, Fernando. Sopaboba. 8th ed. 2003. (SPA., Illus.). 136p. (978-84-239-9025-2(7) , EC1519) Espasa Calpe, S.A. ESP. *Dist:* Lectorum Pubns., Inc.

Amato, Mary. Drooling & Dangerous: The Riot Brothers Return! Long, Ethan, illus. 2006. 176p. (J). 16.95 (978-0-8234-1986-9(X)) Holiday Hse., Inc.

Amato, Mary. Stinky & Successful: The Riot Brothers Never Stop! Long, Ethan, illus. 2007. 160p. (J). (gr. 1-5). 16.95 (***978-0-8234-2100-8(7)***) Holiday Hse., Inc.

American Heritage Dictionary Editors. What Day Is It? Zagarenski, Pamela, illus. 2005. (Good Beginnings/Un Buen Comienzo Ser.). (SPA & ENG.). 4p. (J). bds. 3.95 (978-0-618-44874-6(8)) Houghton Mifflin Co. Trade & Reference Div.

Amico, Tom & Proimos, James. The Day the Dog Dressed Like Dad. 2004. (Illus.). 32p. (J). 16.95 (978-1-58234-877-3(4) , Bloomsbury Children) Bloomsbury Publishing.

Andersen, Hans Christian. El Ruisenor. Mitchell, Stephen, ed. Fischer, Maite Rodriguez, tr. Ibattouline, Bagram, illus. 2004. (SPA.). 48p. 15.95 (978-84-95939-25-8(8)) Blume ESP. *Dist:* Independent Pubs. Group.

—El Ruisenor. (SPA.). 32p. (J). (gr. 2-3). 12.95 (978-84-233-1567-3(3)) Ediciones Destino ESP. *Dist:* Lectorum Pubns., Inc., Planeta Publishing Corp.

Anderson, Brian. The Adventures of Commander Zack Proton & the Red Giant. Holgate, Doug, illus. 2006. (Adventures of Commander Zack Proton Ser.). 128p. (J). (gr. 2-5). pap. 3.99 (978-1-4169-1364-1(5) , Aladdin) Simon & Schuster Children's Publishing.

—The Adventures of Commander Zack Proton & the Warlords of Nibblecheese. Holgate, Doug, illus. 2006. (Adventures of Commander Zack Proton Ser.). 112p. (J). pap. 3.99 (978-1-4169-1365-8(3) , Aladdin) Simon & Schuster Children's Publishing.

Anderson, John David. Standard Hero Behavior. 2007. 288p. (J). (gr. 5-9). 16.00 (***978-0-618-75920-0(4)*** , Clarion Bks.) Houghton Mifflin Co. Trade & Reference Div.

Anderson, M. T. Burger Wuss. Butler, David, illus. 2001. 208p. (YA). (gr. 9 up). pap. 6.99 (978-0-7636-1567-3(6)) Candlewick Pr.

—Burger Wuss. 2001. 13.64 (978-0-606-22539-7(0)); (gr. 7-12). lib. bdg. 14.15 (978-0-613-44380-7(2)) Tandem Library Bks.

—The Clue of the Linoleum Lederhosen: M. T. Anderson's Thrilling Tales. Cyrus, Kurt, illus. 2007. (M. T. Anderson's Thrilling Tales Ser.). 272p. (J). pap. 5.95 (978-0-15-205407-6(3) , Harcourt Paperbacks) Harcourt Children's Bks.

Andrews, John Nevins. History of the Sabbath & First Day of the Week. 2006. cd-rom (978-1-892824-58-5(2)) AFCHRON.

Anglemyer, Jordan, illus. Grandpa's Favorites: A collection of quotes, things to ponder, stories, bits of verse, & Humor. 2007. 77p. (YA). per. 10.95 (***978-0-9796251-2-1(2)***) Robertson Publishing.

Anholt, Laurence. Billy Beast. 2004. (Illus.). 64p. (C). (gr. 3-5). 13.26 (978-0-7565-0628-5(X)) Compass Point Bks.

—Eco-Wolf & the Three Pigs. 2004. (Illus.). 64p. (C). (gr. 3-5). 13.26 (978-0-7565-0630-8(1)) Compass Point Bks.

—The Emperor's New Underwear. Robins, Arthur, illus. 1999. (J). pap. (978-0-88166-347-1(6)) Meadowbrook Pr.

—Foolish Jack & the Bean Stack. 2004. (Illus.). 64p. (J). (gr. 3 up). 13.26 (978-0-7565-0629-2(8)) Compass Point Bks.

—Ghostyshocks & the Three Scares. 2004. (Illus.). 64p. (J). (gr. 3 up). 13.26 (978-0-7565-0631-5(X)) Compass Point Bks.

—Rumply Crumply Stinky Pin. 2004. (Illus.). 64p. (J). (gr. 3 up). 13.26 (978-0-7565-0633-9(6)) Compass Point Bks.

—Shampoozel. 2004. (Illus.). 64p. (J). (gr. 3 up). 13.26 (978-0-7565-0634-6(4)) Compass Point Bks.

—Snow White & the Seven Aliens. 2004. (Illus.). 64p. (J). (gr. 3 up). 13.26 (978-0-7565-0635-3(2)) Compass Point Bks.

Anonymous. Lazarillo de Tormes. 1998. (SPA.). (gr. 7-12). lib. bdg. 14.10 (978-0-613-80724-1(3)) Tandem Library Bks.

Apperley, Dawn. Don't Wake the Baby. Apperley, Dawn, illus. 2001. (Illus.). 32p. (J). (ps-k). 17.99 (978-0-7475-5003-7(4)) Bloomsbury Publishing Plc GBR. *Dist:* Trafalgar Square Publishing.

Archibold, Tim, illus. Knock Knock! The Best Knock Knock Jokes Ever! 2004. (Sidesplitters Ser.). 64p. (J). (gr. 3-5). pap. 3.95 (978-0-7534-5707-8(5) , Kingfisher) Houghton Mifflin Co. Trade & Reference Div.

Ardagh, Philip. Awful End. Roberts, David, illus. l.t. ed. 2002. 184p. (J). 16.95 (978-0-7540-7826-5(4) , Galaxy Children's Large Print) BBC Audiobooks America.

—Dreadful Acts. 2002. (Eddie Dickens Trilogy: Bk. 2). (Illus.). 144p. (J). (gr. 3-6). 5.99 (978-0-571-20947-7(5)) Faber & Faber, Inc.

—Dreadful Acts. Roberts, David, illus. 2003. (Eddie Dickens Trilogy: Bk. 2). 144p. (J). (gr. 4-9). 12.95 (978-0-8050-7155-9(5) , Holt, Henry & Co. Bks. For Young Readers) Holt, Henry & Co.

—Dreadful Acts. Roberts, David, illus. 2004. (Eddie Dickens Trilogy Ser.: Bk. 2). 144p. (J). reprint ed. mass mkt. 5.99 (978-0-439-53760-5(6)) Scholastic, Inc.

—The Fall of Fergal: Or Not So Dingly in the Dell. Roberts, David, illus. 2005. (Unlikely Exploits Trilogy Ser.). 144p. (J). (ps-7). reprint ed. pap. 5.99 (978-0-439-73014-3(7) , Scholastic Paperbacks) Scholastic, Inc.

—The Fall of Fergal: The First Unlikely Exploit. Roberts, David, tr. Roberts, David, illus. 2004. (Unlikely Exploits Ser.). 144p. (J). 9.95 (978-0-8050-7476-5(7) , Holt, Henry & Co. Bks. For Young Readers) Holt, Henry & Co.

—The Green Men of Gressingham. Phillips, Mike, illus. 2006. 72;88p. (J). (gr. 2-3). lib. bdg. (978-1-59889-000-6(X)) Stone Arch Bks.

—A House Called Awful End. Roberts, David, illus. 2002. (Eddie Dickens Trilogy: Bk. 1). 144p. (J). (gr. 4-7). 14.95 (978-0-8050-6828-3(7) , Holt, Henry & Co. Bks. For Young Readers) Holt, Henry & Co.

—A House Called Awful End. 2003. (Eddie Dickens Trilogy: Bk. 1). (gr. 3-6). lib. bdg. 14.15 (978-0-613-72215-5(9)) Tandem Library Bks.

—Rise of the House Mcnally. 2006. (Unlikely Exploits Trilogy Ser.). 160p. (J). pap. 5.99 (978-0-439-73018-1(X) , Scholastic Paperbacks) Scholastic, Inc.

—The Rise of the House of McNally. Roberts, David, illus. 2005. (Unlikely Exploits Ser.: Vol. 3). 160p. (J). 9.95 (978-0-8050-7478-9(3) , Holt, Henry & Co. Bks. For Young Readers) Holt, Henry & Co.

—Terrible Times. Roberts, David, illus. 2003. (Eddie Dickens Trilogy: Bk. 3). 160p. (J). (gr. 3-6). 12.95 (978-0-8050-7156-6(3) , Holt, Henry & Co. Bks. For Young Readers) Holt, Henry & Co.

Ardagh, Philip, et al. A House Called Awful End. Roberts, David, illus. 2003. (Eddie Dickens Trilogy Ser.: Bk. 1). 144p. (J). (gr. 3-6). mass mkt. 5.99 (978-0-439-53759-9(2) , Scholastic Paperbacks) Scholastic, Inc.

Armstrong, Jennifer. Once upon a Banana. Small, David, illus. 2006. 48p. (J). (ps-3). 16.95 (978-0-689-84251-1(1) , Simon & Schuster Children's Publishing) Simon & Schuster Children's Publishing.

Arnold, Marsha Diane. Roar of a Snore. Pratt, Pierre, illus. 2006. (J). (***978-1-4156-8271-5(2)*** , Dial) Penguin Group (USA) Inc.

Arnold, Tedd. Catalina Magdalina Hoopensteiner Wallendiner Hogan Logan Bogan Was Her Name. Arnold, Tedd, illus. 2004. (Illus.). 40p. (J). pap. 10.95 (978-0-590-10994-9(4) , Cartwheel Bks.) Scholastic, Inc.

—Huggly Gets Dressed. 1999. (Huggly Ser.). (Illus.). 24p. (J). (ps-1). pap. 3.25 (978-0-439-10268-1(5)) Scholastic, Inc.

Arnold, Tedd. There Was an Old Lady Who Swallowed Fly Guy. 2007. (Fly Guy Ser.). 32p. (J). pap. 5.99 (***978-0-439-63906-4(9)***) Scholastic, Inc.

Arrigan, Mary & Paul, Korky. The Mummy Family Find Fame. 2006. (Red Bananas Ser.). (Illus.). 48p. (J). pap. (978-0-7787-1090-5(4)) Crabtree Publishing Co.

Artful Doodlers Limited Staff. The Finster Who Stole Christmas. 2005. (All Grown Up! Ser.). (Illus.). 24p. (J). pap. 3.99 (978-1-4169-0212-6(0) , Simon Spotlight/Nickelodeon) Simon & Schuster Children's Publishing.

—First Brat. 2006. (Totally Spies! Ser.). (Illus.). 64p. (J). pap. 4.99 (978-1-4169-0792-3(0) , Simon Spotlight) Simon & Schuster Children's Publishing.

Ashburn, Boni. Hush, Little Dragon. Murphy, Kelly, illus. 2008. 32p. (J). 15.95 (***978-0-8109-9491-1(7)*** , Abrams Bks. for Young Readers) Abrams, Harry N. , Inc.

Ashman, Linda. Can You Make a Piggy Giggle? Cole, Henry, illus. 2002. 32p. (J). 12.99 (978-0-525-46881-3(1) , Dutton Juvenile) Penguin Group (USA) Inc.

—Maxwell's Magic Mix-up. Dunnick, Regan, illus. 2004. 30p. (J). (gr. k-3). reprint ed. 16.00 (978-0-7567-7156-0(0)) DIANE Publishing Co.

—To the Beach! Westcott, Nadine Bernard, illus. 2005. 32p. (J). 16.00 (978-0-15-216490-4(1)) Harcourt Children's Bks.

Athey, Victoria. No Peas, Please! Delaney, Molly, illus. 2005. (J). pap. 4.95 (978-1-57874-087-1(8)) Kaeden Corp.

Atwater, Richard. Mr. Popper's Penguins. Lawson, Robert, illus. 2002. (J). 12.30 (978-0-7587-0294-4(9)) Book Wholesalers, Inc.

Atwood, Margaret. Bashful Bob & Doleful Dorinda. Petricic, Dusan, illus. 2006. 32p. (J). 17.95 (978-1-59990-004-9(1) , Bloomsbury Children) Bloomsbury Publishing.

—Bashful Bob & Doleful Dorinda. Petricic, Dusan, illus. 2006. 32p. (J). (gr. 1-3). (***978-1-55263-609-1(7)***) Key Porter Bks.

Atwood, Margaret. Rude Ramsay & the Roaring Radishes. Petricic, Dusan, illus. 2004. 32p. (J). 16.95 (978-1-58234-950-3(9) , Bloomsbury Children) Bloomsbury Publishing.

Auch, Mary Jane. Chickerella. Auch, Herm and Mary Jane, illus. 2006. 32p. 6.95 (978-0-8234-2015-5(9)) Holiday Hse., Inc.

Auch, Mary Jane. The Plot Chickens. 2008. (J). (***978-0-8234-2087-2(6)***) Holiday Hse., Inc.

Auch, Mary Jane & Auch, Herm. The Princess & the Pizza. 2002. (Illus.). 32p. (J). (gr. k-3). 6.95 (978-0-8234-1798-8(0)) Holiday Hse., Inc.

Auch, Mary Jane & Auch, Herm, illus. Beauty & the Beaks: A Turkey's Cautionary Tale. 2007. 32p. (J). (ps-3). 16.95 (978-0-8234-1990-6(8)) Holiday Hse., Inc.

Auerbach, Annie. Cindy Big Hair: A Twisted (and Teased & Braided) Cinderella Story. Maxey, David, illus. 2005. 16p. (J). 12.95 (978-1-58117-387-1(3) , Intervisual/Piggy Toes) Dalmatian Pr.

—Fiona's Fairy-Tale Five. 2007. (Shrek the Third Ser.). 24p. (J). pap. 3.99 (978-0-06-122862-9(1) , Harper Entertainment) HarperCollins Pubs.

—Hall Monitor, Vol. 3. 2004. 64p. (J). (gr. 2-5). pap. 17.00 incl. audio (978-0-8072-1988-1(6) , Listening Library) Random Hse. Audio Publishing Group.

—Me, Myself, & the Bowler Hat Guy. Disney Storybook Artists Staff & Husband, Ron, illus. 2007. (Meet the Robinsons Ser.). 24p. (J). pap. 3.99 (978-0-06-112468-6(0)) HarperCollins Pubs.

—Royally Wrong. 2007. (Shrek 3 Ser.). 24p. (J). pap. 3.99 (978-0-06-122861-2(3) , Harper Entertainment) HarperCollins Pubs.

—Spongebob Superstar. O'Hare, Mark, illus. 2001. (SpongeBob SquarePants Chapter Bks.: Vol. 5). 64p. (J). (gr. 4-7). pap. 3.99 (978-0-689-84174-3(4) , Simon Spotlight) Simon & Schuster Children's Publishing.

—Spongebob Superstar, Vol. 5. 2004. 64p. (J). (gr. 2-5). pap. 17.00 incl. audio (978-1-4000-8628-3(0) , Listening Library) Random Hse. Audio Publishing Group.

Auth, Tony. My Curious Uncle Dudley. Yourgrau, Barry, illus. 2004. 224p. (J). (gr. 4-7). 15.99 (978-0-7636-1935-0(3)) Candlewick Pr.

Auth, Tony, illus. The Hoboken Chicken Emergency. 2007. 101p. (J). (gr. 1-4). per. 4.99 (***978-1-4169-2810-2(3)*** , Aladdin) Simon & Schuster Children's Publishing.

Avi. Never Mind! A Twin Novel. 2004. 208p. (J). (gr. 5 up). lib. bdg. 16.89 (978-0-06-054315-0(9)) HarperCollins Pubs.

Avi & Vail, Rachel. Never Mind! A Twin Novel. 2004. 208p. (J). (gr. 5 up). 15.99 (978-0-06-054314-3(0)) HarperCollins Pubs.

—Never Mind! A Twin Novel. 2005. 200p. (J). (gr. k-9). per. 12.64 (978-0-606-33941-4(8)) Tandem Library Bks.

Axelrod, Amy. Pigs in the Corner: Fun with Math & Dance. McGinley-Nally, Sharon, illus. 2005. 40p. (J). (ps-ps). pap., pap. 6.99 (978-1-4169-0335-2(6) , Aladdin) Simon & Schuster Children's Publishing.

Axis of Weasels. 2004. pap. 12.95 (978-0-9761414-0-2(X)) MacMenamin Pr.

Aylesworth, Jim. Naughty Little Monkeys. Cole, Henry, illus. 2003. 40p. (J). (ps). 16.99 (978-0-525-46940-7(0) , Dutton Juvenile) Penguin Group (USA) Inc.

Babbitt, Natalie. Elsie Times Eight. 2001. (Illus.). 32p. (J). (ps-17). (978-0-7868-0901-1(9)) Hyperion Bks. for Children.

Bachelet, Gilles. When the Silliest Cat Was Small. Bachelet, Gilles, illus. 2007. (FRE & ENG., Illus.). 32p. (J). (ps-3). 16.95 (***978-0-8109-9415-7(1)*** , Abrams Bks. for Young Readers) Abrams, Harry N. , Inc.

Bagdasarian, Adam. First French Kiss. 2005. 144p. (YA). (gr. 9). pap. 5.95 (978-0-374-42323-0(7) , Farrar, Straus & Giroux (BYR)) Farrar, Straus & Giroux.

—First French Kiss: And Other Traumas. 2002. 144p. (YA). (gr. 7 up). 16.00 (978-0-374-32338-7(0) , Farrar, Straus & Giroux (BYR)) Farrar, Straus & Giroux.

Bagdasarian, Adam & Best, Cari. Are You Going to Be Good? Karas, G. Brian, illus. 2005. 32p. (J). 16.00 (978-0-374-30394-5(0) , Farrar, Straus & Giroux (BYR)) Farrar, Straus & Giroux.

Bahz, Kahanni. Ants? in My Pants? An Antimated Tale. Fraser, Kevin, illus. 2005. 72p. (J). (gr. k-4). reprint ed. 22.00 (978-0-7567-8705-9(X)) DIANE Publishing Co.

Baicker, Karen & Williams, Sam. Wake-Ity Wake! 2004. (Illus.). 5p. (J). bds. 6.95 (978-1-59354-036-4(1)) Handprint Bks.

—Yum Tummy Tickly! 2004. (Illus.). 5p. (J). bds. 6.95 (978-1-59354-037-1(X)) Handprint Bks.

Bailey, Linda. Stanley's party. Slavin, Bill, illus. 2003. 32p. (J). (gr. k-3). (978-1-55337-382-7(0)) Kids Can Pr., Ltd.

—Stanley's Wild Ride. Slavin, Bill, illus. 2006. 32p. (J). 14.95 (978-1-55337-960-7(8)) Kids Can Pr., Ltd. CAN. *Dist:* Wybel Marketing Group.

Baker, E. D. Dragon's Breath. 2003. 250p. (J). 15.95 (978-1-58234-858-2(8) , Bloomsbury Children) Bloomsbury Publishing.

—Dragon's Breath: Read-Along/Homework Pack. unabr. ed. 2005. (YA). (gr. 5-8). 92.70 incl. audio (978-1-4193-3563-1(4) , 42041) Recorded Bks., LLC.

—The Frog Princess. 2002. 200p. (J). (gr. 3-9). 15.95 (978-1-58234-799-8(9) , Bloomsbury Children) Bloomsbury Publishing.

—No Place for Magic: The Fourth Tale of the Frog Princess. 2006. (Tales of the Frog Princess Ser.). 250p. (YA). 15.95 (978-1-58234-654-0(2)) Bloomsbury Publishing.

Baker, E. D. The Salamander Spell. 2007. (Tales of the Frog Princess Ser.). 250p. (J). (gr. 3-7). 16.95 (***978-1-59990-018-6(1)*** , Bloomsbury Children) Bloomsbury Publishing.

Baker, Keith. Lucky Days with Mr. & Mrs. Green. (Mr. & Mrs. Green Ser.). (Illus.). 72p. (J). 2006. pap. 5.95 (978-0-15-205604-9(1) , Harcourt Paperbacks); 2005. 16.00 (978-0-15-216500-0(2) , Gulliver Bks.) Harcourt Children's Bks.

—Lucky Days with Mr. & Mrs. Green. 2007. (Mr. & Mrs. Green Ser.). 72p. (J). (gr. 2-4). 27.07 (***978-1-59961-300-0(X)***) Spotlight.

Baker, Keith. On the Go with Mr. & Mrs. Green. 2007. (Mr. & Mrs. Green Ser.). (Illus.). 72p. (J). pap. 5.95 (978-0-15-205867-8(2) , Harcourt Paperbacks) Harcourt Children's Bks.

—On the Go with Mr. & Mrs. Green. 2006. (Mr. & Mrs. Green Ser.). (Illus.). 72p. (J). 16.00 (978-0-15-205762-6(5)) Harcourt Trade Pubs.

—On the Go with Mr. & Mrs. Green. 2007. (Mr. & Mrs. Green Ser.). 72p. (J). (gr. 2-4). 27.07 (***978-1-59961-303-1(4)***) Spotlight.

Balcerek, Tom. The Cat & the Christmas Tree. 2006. (ENG.). 28p. per. 15.00 (***978-1-4259-7334-6(5)***) AuthorHouse.

Balch, Betty Neff & Poythress, Jean Hill. Tales of the Cinnamon Dragon Book I: Adventures in Farr Elvenhome. Balch, Betty Neff, illus. 2004. (Illus.). 152p. (J). lib. bdg. 16.95 (978-1-930580-46-6(0) , Luminary Media Group) Pine Orchard, Inc.

Baldacci, David. The Mystery of Silas Finklebean. Harrington, Patrick, illus. 2nd ed. 2006. (Freddy & the French Fries Ser.: No. 2). 176p. (J). (gr. 3-7). pap. 4.99 (978-0-316-05900-8(5)) Little Brown & Co.

Baldacci, David & Baldacci, Rudy. Fries Alive! 2006. (Freddy & the French Fries Ser.). (Illus.). 192p. (J). (gr. 3-7). pap. 4.99 (978-0-316-05901-5(3)) Little Brown & Co.

Ball, Tom. The Marty Graw Book. 2003. 220p. pap. 14.95 (978-1-59113-252-3(5)) Booklocker.com, Inc.

Balukoff, Constance. Mooky's Bad Hair Day. 2004. 21p. pap. 14.95 (978-1-4137-1480-7(3)) PublishAmerica, Inc.

Banks, Steven. King of the Creeps. 2006. 176p. (YA). (gr. 7). 15.95 (978-0-375-83291-8(2)); lib. bdg. 17.99 (978-0-375-93291-5(7)) Random Hse. Children's Bks. (Knopf Bks. for Young Readers).

—SpongeBob Exposed! The Insider's Guide to SpongeBob SquarePants. Schigiel, Gregg & Bond, Clint, illus. 2004. (Spongebob Squarepants Ser.). 96p. (J). 8.99 (978-0-689-86870-2(7) , Simon Spotlight/Nickelodeon) Simon & Schuster Children's Publishing.

—SpongeBob Goes to the Doctor. Saunders, Zina, illus. 2005. (Spongebob Squarepants Ser.). 24p. (J). pap. 3.99 (978-1-4169-0359-8(3) , Simon Spotlight/Nickelodeon) Simon & Schuster Children's Publishing.

—Spongebob Goes to the Doctor. Saunders, Zina, illus. 2005. 22p. (J). lib. bdg. 15.00 (***978-1-4242-0976-7(5)***) Fitzgerald Bks.

—Stop the Presses! DePorter, Vince, illus. 2005. 22p. (J). lib. bdg. 15.00 (***978-1-4242-0973-6(0)***) Fitzgerald Bks.

Banks, Steven. Welcome to Fifth Grade! Marantz, Larissa & DiPaolo, Katharine, illus. 2005. (All Grown Up! Ser.: Vol. 2). 24p. (J). (ps-ps). pap. 3.99 (978-0-689-86609-8(7) , Simon Spotlight/Nickelodeon) Simon & Schuster Children's Publishing.

Banks, Steven & Artifact Group. Perdidos en el tiempo (Lost in Time) Una aventura Medieval. 2006. (SpongeBob SquarePants Ser.). (SPA.). 24p. (J). pap. 3.99 (978-1-4169-1505-8(2) , Libros Para Ninos) Simon & Schuster Children's Publishing.

Banks, Steven & Hillenburg, Stephen. SpongeBob Goes to the Doctor. Saunders, Zina, illus. 2005. (J). (***978-1-4156-3131-7(X)*** , Simon Spotlight/Nickelodeon) Simon & Schuster Children's Publishing.

Bar-El, Dan. Such a Prince. Manders, John, illus. 2007. 32p. (J). (ps-3). 16.00 (978-0-618-71468-1(5) , Clarion Bks.) Houghton Mifflin Co. Trade & Reference Div.

Barensfeld, Debrae. Fox: Lost & Found. 2006. 12.95 (978-0-9776617-0-1(9)) CreoXimius Publishing Company.

Bark, George. 2004. (J). pap. 38.75 incl. audio compact disk (978-1-55592-713-4(0)); pap. 32.75 incl. audio (978-1-55592-709-7(2)) Weston Woods Studios, Inc.

Barkaw, Henniette. Don't Cry Sly: Big Book English Only. Johnson, Richard, illus. 2004. (J). pap. (978-1-85269-999-4(X)) Mantra Publishing, Ltd.

Barkow, Henriette & Johnson, Richard, illus. The Giant Turnip: Le Navet Geant. 2004. (TAM, CZE, VIE, SPA & GUJ.). 23p. (J). (978-1-85269-738-9(5)) Mantra Publishing, Ltd.

Barlow, Steve & Skidmore, Steve. Star Bores: May the Farce Be with You. 2004. 416p. 9.95 (978-0-00-719208-3(8)) HarperCollins Pubs. Ltd. GBR. *Dist:* Independent Pubs. Group.

—Tales of Dark Forest Trillogy. 3rd ed. 2003. (Tales of the Dark Forest Ser.). (Illus.). 192p. (J). pap. 10.99 (978-0-00-710865-7(6)) HarperCollins Pubs. Ltd. GBR. *Dist:* Independent Pubs. Group.

—Whizzard. 2002. (Tales of the Dark Forest Ser.). (Illus.). 256p. pap. 11.00 (978-0-00-710864-0(8)) HarperCollins Pubs. Ltd. GBR. *Dist:* Independent Pubs. Group.

Barnes, Jennifer. Perfect Cover. 2008. (The Squad). 288p. (YA). (gr. 7). mass mkt. 6.99 (***978-0-385-73454-7(9)*** , Delacorte Pr.) Dell Publishing.

—Skin Deep. 2008. (J). (***978-0-385-90477-3(0)*** , Delacorte Pr.) Dell Publishing.

Barnes, Jennifer Lynn. Tattoo. 2007. 272p. (YA). (gr. 7 up). pap. 7.99 (978-0-385-73347-2(X)); lib. bdg. 12.99 (978-0-385-90363-9(4)) Random Hse. Children's Bks. (Delacorte Bks. for Young Readers).

Barnholdt, Lauren. The Secret Identity of Devon Delaney. 2007. 272p. (J). (gr. 4-8). pap. 5.99 (***978-1-4169-3503-2(7)*** , Aladdin) Simon & Schuster Children's Publishing.

Barrett, Judi. Cloudy with a Chance of Meatballs. Barrett, Ron, illus. 2005. (J). pap. 18.95 incl. audio compact disk (978-1-59112-701-7(7)) Live Oak Media.

—Things That Are Most in the World. Nickle, John, illus. 2001. 32p. (J). 6.99 (978-0-689-84449-2(2) , Aladdin) Simon & Schuster Children's Publishing.

—Things That Are Most in the World. 2001. (ps-2). lib. bdg. 15.30 (978-0-613-73328-1(2)) Tandem Library Bks.

Barry, Dave & Pearson, Ridley. Cave of the Dark Wind: A Never Land Adventure. Call, Greg, illus. 2007. 176p. (gr. 3 up). 9.99 (978-0-7868-3790-8(X)) Hyperion Bks. for Children.

—Escape from the Carnivale: A Never Land Book. Call, Greg, illus. 2006. 144p. (gr. 3-17). 9.99 (978-0-7868-3789-2(6)) Hyperion Bks. for Children.

—Peter & the Secret of Rundoon. rev. ed. 2007. 496p. (YA). (gr. 7-17). 18.99 (***978-0-7868-3788-5(8)*** , Disney Editions) Disney Pr.

—Peter & the Shadow Thieves. rev. ed. 2007. 592p. (gr. 5 up). pap. 8.99 (***978-1-4231-0855-9(8)*** , Disney Editions) Disney Pr.

Barry, Dave & Pearson, Ridley. Peter & the Starcatchers. Call, Greg, illus. 2006. 480p. (gr. 5-17). reprint ed. pap. 7.99 (978-0-7868-4907-9(X) , Disney Editions) Disney Pr.

—Peter & the Starcatchers. 2004. 464p. (gr. 5-17). 17.99 (978-0-7868-5445-5(6)) Hyperion Bks. for Children.

Baryshnikov, Mikhail. Because... Radunsky, Vladimir, illus. 2007. 32p. (J). (ps-3). 16.99 (978-0-689-87582-3(7) , Atheneum) Simon & Schuster Children's Publishing.

The Bash Street Kids Annual 2004. annual 2003. (Illus.). 96p. (978-0-85116-815-9(9)) Thomson, D.C. & Co., Ltd. GBR. *Dist:* APG Sales and Fulfillment.

Basu, Jayinee. HJBRL - A Nonsense Story by Sukumar Ray. 2005. 68p. pap. 10.98 (978-1-4116-3983-6(9)) Lulu-.com.

Basye, Dale E. Heck: Where the Bad Kids Go. Dob, Bob, illus. 2008. (J). (***978-0-375-84075-3(3)***); pap. (***978-0-375-84076-0(1)***); lib. bdg. (***978-0-375-94075-0(8)***) Random Hse., Inc.

Bathroom Readers' Institute Staff. Uncle John's Strange & Silly Bathroom Reader for Kids Only! 2006. (Illus.). 144p. (J). pap. 7.95 (978-1-59223-385-4(6) , Portable Pr.) Advantage Pubs. Group.

—Uncle John's Wild & Wooly Bathroom Reader for Kids Only! 2005. (Illus.). 144p. (J). pap. 7.95 (978-1-59223-384-7(8) , Portable Pr.) Advantage Pubs. Group.

Bauer, Joan. Peeled. 2008. 256p. (YA). (gr. 7). 16.99 (***978-0-399-23475-0(6)*** , Putnam Juvenile) Penguin Group (USA) Inc.

Bauer, Jutta. Madrechillona. 2nd ed. 2003. (Rosa y Manzana Ser.). (SPA., Illus.). 28p. (J). (gr. k-2). (978-84-89804-36-4(2) , LC30478) Loguez Ediciones ESP. *Dist:* Lectorum Pubns., Inc.

Bauer, Michael Gerard. Don't Call Me Ishmael! 2007. 272p. (gr. 9 up). (J). 16.99 (***978-0-06-134834-1(1)***); (YA). lib. bdg. 17.89 (***978-0-06-134835-8(X)***) HarperCollins Pubs. (HarperTeen).

Beard, George & Hutchins, Harold. The Adventures of Super Diaper Baby. Beard, George, illus. 2002. (Captain Underpants Ser.). (Illus.). 128p. (gr. 2-5). mass mkt. 4.99 (978-0-439-37606-8(8) , Blue Sky Pr., The) Scholastic, Inc.

Beaumont, Karen. Doggone Dogs! Catrow, David, illus. 2008. (J). (***978-0-8037-3157-8(4)*** , Dial) Penguin Group (USA) Inc.

Bechtold, Lisze. Sally & the Purple Socks. Bechtold, Lisze, illus. 2008. 32p. (J). (ps). 15.99 (***978-0-399-24734-7(3)*** , Philomel) Penguin Group (USA) Inc.

Beckhorn, Susan Williams. Moose Eggs or, Why Moose Has Flat Antlers. Stevens, Helen, illus. 2007. 32p. (gr. k-3). 15.95 (***978-0-89272-689-9(X)***) Down East Bks.

Bedard, Michael. Sitting Ducks. 2001. (J). (978-0-606-22064-4(X)); (gr. 3-6). lib. bdg. 15.30 (978-0-613-45548-0(7)) Tandem Library Bks.

Beech, Sandy. Worst Class Trip Ever. Holder, Jimmy, illus. 2005. (Castaways Ser.). 176p. pap. 4.99 (978-0-689-87596-0(7) , Aladdin) Simon & Schuster Children's Publishing.

Beechen, Adam. Vacation Frustration! Goldberg, Barry, illus. 2005. (Fairly OddParents Ser.). 64p. (J). pap. 4.99 (978-0-689-87719-3(6) , Simon Spotlight/Nickelodeon) Simon & Schuster Children's Publishing.

—Wild Thornberrys Survival Guide. 2000. (gr. 3-6). lib. bdg. 10.65 (978-0-613-27582-8(9)) Tandem Library Bks.

Behar, Joy. Sheetzucacapoopoo: My Kind of Dog. Barretta, Gene, illus. 2006. 32p. (J). (ps). 15.99 (978-0-525-47718-1(7) , Dutton Juvenile) Penguin Group (USA) Inc.

Beil, Karen Magnuson. Jack's House. Wohnoutka, Mike, illus. 2008. (J). (***978-0-8234-1913-5(4)***) Holiday Hse., Inc.

Beinstein, Phoebe. Meet Dora! Mangano, Tom, illus. 2005. (Dora the Explorer Ser.). 12p. (J). bds. 5.99 (978-1-4169-0998-9(2) , Simon Spotlight/Nickelodeon) Simon & Schuster Children's Publishing.

Bell, Jennifer. Pony Tale. 2004. (Illus.). 50p. 7.00 (978-1-84161-011-5(9)) Ravette Publishing, Ltd. GBR. *Dist:* Parkwest Pubns., Inc.

Bengts, Mandy. The Tale of the Greedy Raven & the Hungry Bear. Bennington, Michael, illus. 2002. 24p. pap. 7.95 (978-1-894303-17-0(2)) RRP Pubs.

Bennett, Jeffrey. Max Goes to the Moon. Okamoto, Alan, illus. 2003. (Science Adventures with Max the Dog Ser.). 32p. (J). (ps-7). 16.95 (978-0-9721819-0-7(3)) Big Kid Science.

Bennett, John Roy. Animal Sneezes. Wysotski, David, illus. 2001. 32p. (J). (ps-k). 14.95 (978-1-894222-44-0(X)) Lobster Pr. CAN. *Dist:* Univ. of Toronto Pr.

Benton, Jim. Am I the Princess or the Frog? Benton, Jim, illus. 2005. (Dear Dumb Diary Ser.: Bk. 3). (Illus.). 160p. 4.99 (978-0-439-62907-2(1)) Scholastic, Inc.

—Attack of the 50-Ft. Cupid. 2004. (Franny K. Stein, Mad Scientist Ser.: Bk. 2). (Illus.). 112p. (J). (gr. 2-5). pap. 3.99 (978-0-689-86296-0(2) , Aladdin) Simon & Schuster Children's Publishing.

—Attack of the 50-Ft. Cupid. Benton, Jim, illus. 2003. (Franny K. Stein, Mad Scientist Ser.: Bk. 2). (Illus.). 112p. (J). (gr. 2-5). 14.95 (978-0-689-86292-2(X)) Simon & Schuster Children's Publishing.

—Can Adults Become Human? 2006. (Dear Dumb Diary Ser.: Bk. 5). (Illus.). 144p. (J). (gr. 3-7). pap. 4.99 (978-0-439-79621-7(0) , Scholastic Paperbacks) Scholastic, Inc.

—The Fran That Time Forgot. Benton, Jim, illus. 2005. (Franny K. Stein, Mad Scientist Ser.: Bk. 4). (Illus.). 112p. (J). mass mkt. 3.99 (978-0-689-86298-4(9) , Aladdin); 14.95 (978-0-689-86294-6(6) , Simon & Schuster Children's Publishing) Simon & Schuster Children's Publishing.

—The Fran with Four Brains. Benton, Jim, illus. 2006. (Franny K. Stein, Mad Scientist Ser.: Bk. 6). 112p. (J). 14.95 (978-1-4169-0231-7(7)) Simon & Schuster Children's Publishing.

—Franny K. Stein's Crate of Danger Set: Lunch Walks among Us; Attack of the 50-Ft. Cupid; the Invisible Fran; the Fran That Time Forgot. Benton, Jim, illus. 2005. (Franny K. Stein, Mad Scientist Ser.). 448p. (J). pap. 14.99 (978-1-4169-1402-0(1) , Aladdin) Simon & Schuster Children's Publishing.

—Hagamos Come Si Esto Nunca Hubiera Pasado. Benton, Jim, illus. 2006. (Querido Diario Tonto Ser.: Bk. 1). (SPA.). 112p. (J). pap. 4.99 (978-0-439-78374-3(7) , Scholastic en Espanol) Scholastic, Inc.

—Howard Hubbins Half Hour Hero. 2008. (J). pap. (***978-0-06-059774-0(7)***) HarperCollins Pubs.

—The Invisible Fran. Benton, Jim, illus. 2004. (Franny K. Stein, Mad Scientist Ser.: Bk. 3). (Illus.). 112p. (J). (gr. 2-5). 14.95 (978-0-689-86293-9(8)) Simon & Schuster Children's Publishing.

—Let's Pretend This Never Happened. 2007. (Dear Dumb Diary Ser.: Bk. 1). 128p. (J). pap. 2.99 (***978-0-545-01030-6(6)***) Scholastic, Inc.

—Lunch Walks among Us. Benton, Jim, illus. (Franny K. Stein, Mad Scientist Ser.: Bk. 2). (Illus.). 112p. (J). 2004. (gr. 2-5). mass mkt. 3.99 (978-0-689-86295-3(4) , Aladdin); 2003. 15.99 (978-0-689-86291-5(1)) Simon & Schuster Children's Publishing.

—My Pants Are Haunted! 2004. (Dear Dumb Diary Ser.: Bk. 2). (Illus.). 144p. (gr. 4 up). mass mkt. 4.99 (978-0-439-62905-8(5) , Scholastic Paperbacks) Scholastic, Inc.

—Never Do Anything, Ever. Benton, Jim, illus. 2005. (Dear Dumb Diary Ser.: Bk. 4). (Illus.). 144p. (J). (gr. 4-7). pap. 4.99 (978-0-439-62908-9(X) , Scholastic Paperbacks) Scholastic, Inc.

—Never Underestimate Your Dumb. 2008. (Dear Dumb Diary Ser.: Bk. 7). 160p. (J). pap. 4.99 (***978-0-439-82596-2(2)***) Scholastic, Inc.

Benton, Jim. The Problem with Here Is That It's Where I'm From. 2007. (Dear Dumb Diary Ser.: Bk. 6). (Illus.). 128p. (J). 4.99 (978-0-439-79622-4(9) , Scholastic Paperbacks) Scholastic, Inc.

Bergstrom, Gunilla. Good Night, Alfie Atkins. Dyssegaard, Elisabeth Kallick, tr. from SWE. 2005. (Illus.). 32p. (J). 15.00 (978-91-29-66154-5(4)) R & S Bks. SWE. *Dist:* Macmillan.

—Very Tricky, Alfie Atkins. Dyssegaard, Elisabeth Kallick, tr. from SWE. 2005. (Illus.). 32p. (J). 15.00 (978-91-29-66152-1(8)) R & S Bks. SWE. *Dist:* Macmillan.

Bernasconi, Pablo. Captain Arsenio: Inventions & (Mis)adventures in Flight. 2005. (Illus.). 40p. (J). (gr. 3-5). 16.00 (978-0-618-50749-8(3)) Houghton Mifflin Co. Trade & Reference Div.

Betsy, Howie. Hi Hi Puffy Amiyumi Trifold with Pen. 2006. 80p. (J). pap. 9.99 (978-0-439-74665-6(5) , Scholastic Paperbacks) Scholastic, Inc.

Big Book of Backyard Adventures. 2007. (Backyardigans Ser.). 192p. (J). 10.99 (***978-1-4169-3842-2(7)*** , Simon Spotlight/Nickelodeon) Simon & Schuster Children's Publishing.

Binaohan, Simon & Tacang, Brian. The Misadventures of Millicent Madding No. 1: Bully-Be-Gone. 2006. (Illus.). 224p. (J). lib. bdg. 17.89 (978-0-06-073912-6(6)) HarperCollins Pubs.

—The Misadventures of Millicent Madding Vol. 1: Bully-Be-Gone. 2006. (Illus.). 224p. (J). 16.99 (978-0-06-073911-9(8)) HarperCollins Pubs.

Binder, Helga, illus. Wild Wicked Winifred & the Pirates. 1999. (J). (978-0-7608-3207-3(2)) Sundance/Newbridge Educational Publishing.

—Wild Wicked Winifred & the Treasure Map. 1999. (J). (978-0-7608-3205-9(6)) Sundance/Newbridge Educational Publishing.

Birdseye, Tom. Attack of the Mutant Underwear. 2006. (Illus.). 208p. (J). (gr. 3). pap. 6.99 (978-0-14-240734-9(8) , Puffin) Penguin Group (USA) Inc.

Birney, Betty G. The Princess & the Peabodys. 2007. 256p. (J). lib. bdg. 16.89 (***978-0-06-084721-0(2)***); (gr. 5 up). 15.99 (***978-0-06-084720-3(4)***) HarperCollins Pubs.

Black, Cassandra. Twinkle: A Chapter Book. 2003. 113p. (J). 7.99 (978-0-9742739-0-7(2)) Lavender Bks.

Black, Deirdre. Moon over Gloomsville #2. 2008. 80p. (J). (gr. 2-5). 3.99 (***978-0-448-44673-8(1)*** , Grosset & Dunlap) Penguin Group (USA) Inc.

Black, Simon. Dog-Child. Robledo, Honorio, illus. 2006. 32p. (J). 17.95 (978-0-938317-42-5(3)) Consortium Bk. Sales & Distribution.

Blacker, Terence & Ross, Tony. In Stitches with Ms. Wiz, 4 vols. 2003. (Illus.). 57p. (J). pap. 8.99 (978-0-330-34764-8(0) , Pan) Pan Macmillan GBR. *Dist:* Trafalgar Square Publishing.

Blake, Jon & Roberts, David. Holiday Mania at the House of Fun. 2007. (Illus.). 128p. pap. 6.95 (***978-0-340-93129-5(9)***) Hodder Children's Division GBR. *Dist:* Independent Pubs. Group.

Blankenship, LeeAnn. Mr. Tuggle's Trouble. Dugan, Karen, illus. 2005. 28p. (J). (ps-3). 15.95 (978-1-59078-196-8(1)) Boyds Mills Pr.

Bloor, Edward. Story Time. 2002. (J). 17.95 (978-0-439-26686-4(6)) Scholastic, Inc.

Blume, Judy. Double Fudge. (Fudge Ser.). 224p. 2007. (J). (gr. 2). 5.99 (***978-0-14-240878-0(6)*** , Puffin); 2002. (gr. 3-7). 15.99 (978-0-525-46926-1(5) , Dutton Juvenile) Penguin Group (USA) Inc.

—Double Fudge. 2004. (Fudge Ser.). 160p. (J). (gr. 3-7). pap. 36.00 incl. audio (978-0-8072-2036-8(1) , Listening Library) Random Hse. Audio Publishing Group.

—Freckle Juice. 47p. (J). (gr. 1-3). pap. 4.50 (978-0-8072-1330-8(6) , Listening Library) Random Hse. Audio Publishing Group.

—Fudge-a-Mania. (Fudge Ser.). 2007. 160p. (J). (gr. 2). pap. 5.99 (978-0-14-240877-3(8) , Puffin); 2004. 176p. (gr. 12). mass mkt. 5.99 (978-0-425-19382-2(9) , Berkley) Penguin Group (USA) Inc.

—Fudge-a-Mania. (Fudge Ser.). (gr. 3-6). 2004. lib. bdg. 14.15 (978-0-613-87580-6(X)); 2003. lib. bdg. 14.15 (978-0-613-63936-1(7)) Tandem Library Bks.

—Jugo de Pecas. (SPA.). (J). (gr. 3-5). 7.96 (978-1-56137-447-2(4)) Novel Units, Inc.

—Jugo de Pecas. (SPA.). 40p. (J). 6.95 (978-84-372-3050-4(0)) Santillana USA Publishing Co., Inc.

—Jugo de Pecas. Navarro, Cristina, illus. (SPA.). 36p. (J). (gr. 3-5). pap. 8.95 (978-1-58986-630-0(4)) Santillana USA Publishing Co., Inc.

—Superfudge. 2002. (Fudge Ser.). (Illus.). (J). 13.40 (978-0-7587-6668-7(8)) Book Wholesalers, Inc.

—Superfudge. l.t. ed. 2000. (Fudge Ser.). 216p. (YA). (gr. 5-10). lib. bdg. 28.95 (978-1-58118-061-9(6) , 23475) LRS.

—Superfudge. 1999. (Fudge Ser.). (J). 9.95 (978-1-56137-175-4(0)) Novel Units, Inc.

—Superfudge. 2002. (Fudge Ser.). (Illus.). 176p. (J). 15.99 (978-0-525-46930-8(3) , Dutton Juvenile) Penguin Group (USA) Inc.

—Superfudge. (Fudge Ser.). 166p. (J). (gr. 2-4). pap. 4.99 (978-0-8072-1457-2(4) , Listening Library) Random Hse. Audio Publishing Group.

—Superfudge. (Fudge Ser.). (SPA.). 159p. (J). (gr. 5-8). pap. 9.95 (978-1-56014-665-0(6)) Santillana USA Publishing Co., Inc.

Blundell, Tony, illus. Funny Stories. 2004. (Red Hot Reads Ser.). 256p. (J). (gr. k-3). pap. 6.95 (978-0-7534-5733-7(4) , Kingfisher) Houghton Mifflin Co. Trade & Reference Div.

Blyton, Enid. Mister Meddle's Muddles. (Illus.). 111p. (J). pap. 6.95 (978-0-7475-3860-8(3)) Bloomsbury Publishing Plc GBR. *Dist:* Trafalgar Square Publishing.

—Mr Pink-Whistle Interferes. (Illus.). 112p. (J). pap. 7.99 (978-0-7475-3859-2(X)) Bloomsbury Publishing Plc GBR. *Dist:* Trafalgar Square Publishing.

—Mr Twiddle in Trouble Again. 2000. (Enid Blyton's Happy Days Ser.). (Illus.). 95p. (J). (ps-3). pap. 7.99 (978-0-7475-4355-8(0)) Bloomsbury Publishing Plc GBR. *Dist:* Trafalgar Square Publishing.

Boczkowski, Tricia. Hello, SpongeBob! 2005. (Spongebob Squarepants Ser.). 12p. (J). bds. 5.99 (978-1-4169-1000-8(X) , Simon Spotlight/Nickelodeon) Simon & Schuster Children's Publishing.

—Jimmy's Backpack Book. 2003. (Jimmy Neutron Boy Genius Ser.). (Illus.). 16p. (J). 6.99 (978-0-689-85978-6(3) , Simon Spotlight/Nickelodeon) Simon & Schuster Children's Publishing.

Bond, Clint & Clark, Andy, illus. The Great Snail Race. 2005. (Spongebob Squarepants Ser.). 24p. (J). pap. 3.99 (978-0-689-87313-3(1) , Simon Spotlight/Nickelodeon) Simon & Schuster Children's Publishing.

Boniface, William. What Do You Want on Your Pizza? Palen, Debbie, illus. 2000. 12p. (J). (ps-3). bds. 9.99 (978-0-8431-7473-1(0) , Price Stern Sloan) Penguin Group (USA) Inc.

Bonk, John J. Dustin Grubbs: One Man Show. 2006. 272p. (J). (gr. 3-7). pap. 5.99 (978-0-316-15408-6(3)) Little Brown & Co.

Bott, Elizabeth. Vinnie in Egypt. Frosini, Guido & Cecchetti, Alessandra, illus. l.t. ed. 2000. (Laugh & Learn Travel Ser.: No. 1). 54p. (J). (gr. k-8). 15.95 (978-0-9704678-0-5(X)) Pageturner Bks.

—Vinnie in France. Frosini, Guido & Cecchetti, Alessandra, illus. 2001. (Vinnie Ser.: Vol. 2). 54p. (YA). (gr. 5 up). 15.95 (978-0-9704678-1-2(8)) Pageturner Bks.

Bouchard, David. Fairy. Griffiths, Dean, illus. 2001. 32p. (J). (ps-2). 16.95 (978-1-55143-212-0(9)) Orca Bk. Pubs. USA.

Boudreaux, Larry. Dat Boudreaux Ain't Me, It's Ma Cousin. 1999. 160p. per. 12.00 (978-0-9676002-0-8(0)) Boudreaux Cajun General Store.

Boyce, Frank Cottrell. Framed. 2006. 320p. pap. 15.95 (***978-0-330-43425-6(X)***) Macmillan Publishers Ltd. GBR. *Dist:* Trans-Atlantic Pubns., Inc.

Boyce, Frank Cottrell. Millions. (gr. 3 up). 2004. (Illus.). 256p. (J). 15.99 (978-0-06-073330-8(6)); 2004. (Illus.). 256p. (J). lib. bdg. 16.89 (978-0-06-073331-5(4)); 2005. 272p. (YA). reprint ed. pap. 6.99 (978-0-06-073332-2(2), Harper Trophy) HarperCollins Pubs.

Boynton, Sandra. Big Box of Boynton: Barnyard Dance! Pajama Time! Oh My Oh My Oh Dinosaurs! Boynton, Sandra, illus. 2005. (Illus.). 24p. (J). (ps-k). bds. 18.95 (978-0-7611-3989-8(3), 13989) Workman Publishing Co., Inc.

—Moo, Baa, La La La! Boynton, Sandra, illus. 2004. (Illus.). 16p. (J). 9.99 (978-0-689-87027-9(2), Little Simon) Simon & Schuster Children's Publishing.

The Boys from Brooklyn: The Great Robbery. 2004. (J). mass mkt. 9.95 (978-0-9761440-0-7(X)) Booksforboys.

Bradfield, Jolly Roger. Pickle-Chiffon Pie. 2004. (Illus.). 64p. (J). 18.95 (978-1-930900-30-1(9)) Purple Hse. Pr.

Bradley, Alex. Hot Lunch. 2007. 272p. (YA). (gr. 7 up). 16.99 (***978-0-525-47830-0(2)***, Dutton Juvenile) Penguin Group (USA) Inc.

Bradman, Tony. The Magnificent Mummies. Chatterton, Martin, illus. 2001. (Blue Bananas Ser.). 48p. (J). (gr. 1-2). (978-0-7787-0843-8(8)); pap. (978-0-7787-0889-6(6)) Crabtree Publishing Co.

—Magnificent Mummies. 2002. (gr. k-3). lib. bdg. 12.95 (978-0-613-52878-8(6)) Tandem Library Bks.

—Midnight in Memphis. Chatterton, Martin & Chatterton, Ann, illus. 2001. (Blue Bananas Ser.). 48p. (J). (gr. 1-2). (978-0-7787-0848-3(9)); pap. (978-0-7787-0894-0(2)) Crabtree Publishing Co.

—Midnight in Memphis. 2002. (gr. k-3). lib. bdg. 12.95 (978-0-613-52881-8(6)) Tandem Library Bks.

—The Surprise Party. 2005. (Red Bananas Ser.). (Illus.). 48p. (J). (ps). pap. (978-0-7787-1084-4(X)) Crabtree Publishing Co.

Bradman, Tony & Chatterton, Martin. The Mummy Family Finds Fame. 2006. (Illus.). 46p. (J). (978-0-7787-1076-9(9)) Crabtree Publishing Co.

Brami, Elisabeth. Mommy Time. Tschiegg, Anne-Sophie, illus. 2002. 48p. (J). (gr. k up). 9.95 (978-1-929132-22-5(0)) Kane/Miller Bk. Pubs., Inc.

Brand, Christianna. Nurse Matilda: The Collected Tales. Ardizzone, Edward, illus. ed. 2005. 300p. (J). 16.95 (978-1-58234-670-0(4)) Bloomsbury Publishing.

Brandreth, Gyles. Madcap Book of Laughs. Hawkins, Colin et al, illus. 288p. (J). pap. 6.95 (978-0-233-99569-4(2)) Andre Deutsch GBR. *Dist:* Trafalgar Square Publishing.

Bravo, Amelia Bedelia! 2002. (Amelia Bedelia Ser.). (Illus.). (J). 11.87 (978-0-7587-8899-3(1)) Book Wholesalers, Inc.

Breathed, Berkeley. Flawed Dogs: The Year-End Leftovers at the Piddleton Last Chance Dog Pound. 2003. (Illus.). 48p. (J). (ps-17). 18.95 (978-0-316-71359-7(7)) Little Brown & Co.

—The Last Basselope: One Ferocious Story. Breathed, Berkeley, illus. 2001. (Illus.). 32p. (J). (ps-17). pap. 6.99 (978-0-316-12664-9(0)) Little Brown & Co.

—Last Basselope: One Ferocious Story. 2001. (gr. 3-6). lib. bdg. 14.10 (978-0-613-35643-5(8)) Tandem Library Bks.

Breen, Steve. Stick. 2007. (Illus.). 40p. (J). (ps). 16.99 (978-0-8037-3124-0(8), Dial) Penguin Group (USA) Inc.

Brennan, Eileen. Dirtball Pete. 2008. (J). (978-0-375-83425-7(7)); lib. bdg. (978-0-375-93425-4(1)) Random Hse., Inc.

Brennan, Herbie. Fairy Nuff: A Tale of Bluebell Ball. Collins, Ross, illus. 2002. 128p. (J). (gr. 2-4). 13.95 (978-1-58234-770-7(0), Bloomsbury Children) Bloomsbury Publishing.

—Nuff Said. 2002. (gr. 3-6). lib. bdg. 15.25 (978-0-613-85268-5(0)) Tandem Library Bks.

—Nuff Said: Another Tale of Bluebell Wood. Collins, Ross, illus. 2002. 128p. (J). (gr. 2-5). 13.95 (978-1-58234-771-4(9), Bloomsbury Children) Bloomsbury Publishing.

—Zartog's Remote. Layton, Neal, illus. 2003. (Middle Grade Fiction Ser.). 96p. (J). (gr. 3-6). 14.95 (978-1-57505-507-7(4), Carolrhoda Bks.) Lerner Publishing Group.

Brewer, Elly. Jerry & the Jannans. 2006. 320p. (J). pap. 11.99 (***978-0-7475-8213-7(0)***) Bloomsbury Publishing Plc GBR. *Dist:* Independent Pubs. Group.

Brian, James. Catkid Book #4 Three's A Crowd. 2008. 96p. pap. 3.99 (***978-0-439-88857-8(3)***, Scholastic Paperbacks) Scholastic, Inc.

Bridwell, Norman. Clifford's Funny Adventures. 2007. 48p. (J). pap. 4.99 (***978-0-439-93438-1(9)***, Cartwheel Bks.) Scholastic, Inc.

Bright, Paul. I'm Not Going Out There! Cort, Ben, illus. 2006. 28p. (J). (ps-2). 16.00 (978-1-56148-535-2(7)) Good Bks.

—Under the Bed. Cort, Ben, illus. 2004. 32p. (J). 16.00 (978-1-56148-436-2(9)) Good Bks.

Brimner, Larry Dane. Cats! Payne, Tom, illus. 2001. (Rookie Reader Espanol Ser.). 24p. (J). (gr. k-2). pap. 4.95 (978-0-516-27075-3(3), Children's Pr.) Scholastic Library Publishing.

—Cats! Payne, Tom, illus. 2001. 23p. (J). (ps-3). lib. bdg. 12.95 (978-0-613-54114-5(6)) Tandem Library Bks.

Brisson, Pat. Hobbledy-Clop. Chambliss, Maxie, illus. 2003. 32p. (J). (ps up). 15.95 (978-1-56397-888-3(1)) Boyds Mills Pr.

Broach, Elise. When Dinosaurs Came with Everything. Small, David, illus. 2007. (Junior Library Guild Selection Ser.). 40p. (J). (ps-2). 16.99 (978-0-689-86922-8(3)) Simon & Schuster Children's Publishing.

Broadhurst, D. T. The Faringo Kid. 2006. pap. 13.49 (***978-1-4259-1836-1(0)***) AuthorHouse.

Brock, Melea J. Right-Side-Up Stories for Upside-Down-People. 2001. (YA). pap. 14.98 incl. audio (978-0-9667455-8-0(2)) Right-Side-Up Stories.

Brooks, Barbara. The Hawkins Series. 2000. (Illus.). 440p. (gr. 4-7). pap. 24.95 (978-0-595-00285-6(4), Backinprint.com) iUniverse, Inc.

Brooks, Mel & Reiner, Carl. The 2000 Year Old Man Goes to School. Bennett, James, illus. 2005. 40p. (J). (ps-3). 17.99 (978-0-06-076676-4(X)); lib. bdg. 18.89 (978-0-06-076677-1(8)) HarperCollins Pubs.

Brooks, Walter R. Freddy & the Bean Home News. Wiese, Kurt, illus. 2000. (Freddy Ser.). 230p. (J). (gr. 3-7). 23.95 (978-1-58567-081-9(2)) Overlook Pr., The.

—Freddy & the Popinjay. Wiese, Kurt, illus. 2001. 244p. (J). (gr. 4-7). 23.95 (978-1-58567-134-2(7)) Overlook Pr., The.

—Freddy & the Space Ship. Wiese, Kurt, illus. 2001. 262p. (J). (gr. 3). 23.95 (978-1-58567-105-2(3)) Overlook Pr., The.

—Freddy Plays Football. Wiese, Kurt, illus. 2001. 265p. (J). (gr. 4-7). 23.95 (978-1-58567-133-5(9)) Overlook Pr., The.

—Freddy Plays Football. 2002. (gr. 3-6). lib. bdg. 16.45 (978-0-613-54415-3(3)) Tandem Library Bks.

—Freddy's Cousin Weedly. Wiese, Kurt, illus. 2002. 220p. (J). 23.95 (978-1-58567-309-4(9)) Overlook Pr., The.

Brouillet, Chrystine & Sylvestre, Daniel. Clementine N'aime Pas Sa Voisine. 2002. (Premier Roman Ser.). (FRE., Illus.). 64p. (J). (gr. 1-4). pap. (978-2-89021-498-9(2)) Diffusion du livre Mirabel.

Brown, Amanda. Blonde Love. 4th rev. ed. 2007. 224p. (gr. 3-7). pap. 6.99 (978-0-7868-3888-2(4)) Hyperion Pr.

—Vote Blonde. 3rd rev. ed. 2006. 224p. (gr. 3-7). pap. 6.99 (978-0-7868-3887-5(6)) Hyperion Pr.

Brown, Jeff. Flat Stanley. Nash, Scott, illus. 2006. (Flat Stanley Ser.). 40p. (J). 16.99 (978-0-06-112904-9(6)) HarperCollins Pubs.

—The Flat Stanley Collection Box Set. Nash, Scott, illus. 2006. (Flat Stanley Ser.). (J). pap. 14.99 (978-0-06-083776-1(4), Harper Trophy) HarperCollins Pubs.

—Invisible Stanley. Nash, Scott, illus. 2003. (Stanley Lambchop Adventure Ser.). 96p. (J). pap. 4.99 (978-0-06-009792-9(2)) HarperCollins Pubs.

—Invisible Stanley. 2003. (gr. k-3). lib. bdg. 13.00 (978-0-613-68434-7(6)) Tandem Library Bks.

—Stanley, Flat Again! Nash, Scott, illus. (Stanley Lambchop Adventure Ser.). 96p. (J). 2004. pap. 4.99 (978-0-06-442173-7(2), Harper Trophy); 2003. 14.99 (978-0-06-009551-2(2)); 2003. lib. bdg. 15.89 (978-0-06-029826-5(X)) HarperCollins Pubs.

Brown, Marc. Los Calzoncillos de Arturo. Sarfatti, Esther, tr. (SPA.). (J). (gr. k-2). pap. 6.95 (978-1-930332-09-6(2), LC30188) Lectorum Pubns., Inc.

—El Cumpleanos de Arturo. 2000. (J). 13.75 (978-0-606-20187-2(4)) Tandem Library Bks.

Brown, Mik, illus. Hee! Hee! Hee! The Funniest Joke Book Ever. 2004. (Sidesplitters Ser.). 64p. (J). (gr. 3-5). pap. 3.95 (978-0-7534-5708-5(3), Kingfisher) Houghton Mifflin Co. Trade & Reference Div.

Bruel, Nick. Who Is Melvin Bubble? 2006. (Illus.). 32p. (J). 16.95 (978-1-59643-116-4(4)) Roaring Brook Pr.

Bryan, Sean. A Bear & His Boy. Murphy, Tom, illus. rev. ed. 2007. 32p. (J). (ps-1). 14.99 (***978-1-55970-838-8(7)***) Arcade Publishing, Inc.

—A Boy & His Bunny. Murphy, Tom, illus. rev. ed. 2005. 32p. (J). (ps-1). pap. 14.99 (978-1-55970-725-1(9)) Arcade Publishing, Inc.

—A Girl & Her Gator. Murphy, Tom, illus. rev. ed. 2006. 36p. (J). (ps-1). 14.99 (978-1-55970-798-5(4)) Arcade Publishing, Inc.

Bubble Trouble. 2001. (SpongeBob SquarePants Ser.). (Illus.). (J). pap. 3.99 (978-0-307-10981-1(X), 10981, Golden Bks.) Random Hse. Children's Bks.

Buckeridge, Anthony. Jennings' Little Hut. l.t. ed. 2005. (Dales Ser.). (Illus.). 272p. (J). 23.99 (978-1-84262-370-1(2)) Magna Large Print Bks. GBR. *Dist:* Ulverscroft Large Print Bks., Ltd.

Buckless, Andrea. Too Many Cooks! Jacobs, Kayne & Burns, Marilyn, illus. 2002. (Hello Reader! Science Ser.). 32p. (J). (gr. 1-3). pap. 3.99 (978-0-439-16966-0(6), Cartwheel Bks.) Scholastic, Inc.

—Too Many Cooks! 2000. (gr. k-3). lib. bdg. 11.80 (978-0-613-63571-4(X)) Tandem Library Bks.

Buehner, Caralyn. Dex: The Heart of a Hero. Buehner, Mark, illus. 2007. 32p. (J). (ps-3). pap. 6.99 (***978-0-06-443845-2(7)***, Harper Trophy) HarperCollins Pubs.

Buehner, Caralyn. The Snowmen Pop-up Book. Buehner, Mark, illus. 2006. 14p. (J). (ps). 21.99 (978-0-8037-3180-6(9), Dial) Penguin Group (USA) Inc.

Buehner, Caralyn & Buehner, Mark. A Box of Snowmen. 2005. (Illus.). 32p. (J). (ps-7). lthr. 32.99 (978-0-8037-3108-0(6), Dial) Penguin Group (USA) Inc.

The Bug Ball. 2003. (Daisy Board Books Ser.). 10p. (J). bds. 9.95 (978-0-7525-8296-2(8)) Parragon, Inc.

Bullard, Lisa. Not Enough Beds. Oeltjenbruns, Joni, illus. 2004. (Carolrhoda Picture Books Ser.). 32p. (J). (ps-3). pap. 6.95 (978-1-57505-797-2(2)) Lerner Publishing Group.

Bumble Bee Helps Out. 2002. (My First Tab Story Ser.). (J). bds. 3.98 (978-0-7525-8954-1(7)) Parragon, Inc.

Bumble's Sweet Surprise. 2003. (Daisy Board Books Ser.). 10p. (J). bds. 9.95 (978-0-7525-8297-9(6)) Parragon, Inc.

Bunting, Eve. My Backpack. Cocca-Leffler, Maryann, illus. 2005. 32p. (J). (ps-ps). pap. 9.95 (978-1-59078-369-6(7)) Boyds Mills Pr.

Burchett, Janet & Vogler, Sara. Scare Fair, Vol. 9. Brown, Judy, illus. 96p. (J). pap. 6.99 (978-0-330-37606-8(3), Pan) Pan Macmillan GBR. *Dist:* Trafalgar Square Publishing.

Burkett, Kathy. Whiz Bang, Zoom! Ethan Flask & Professor Von Offel's Energetic Experiments. 2001. (Mad Science Ser.). 66p. (J). pap. (978-0-439-27089-2(8)) Scholastic, Inc.

Burkett, Kathy & Korman, Gordon. What's the Big Idea? Ethan Flask & Professor Von Offel's Ingenious Inventions. 2001. (Mad Science Ser.). (Illus.). 65p. (J). pap. (978-0-439-23581-5(2)) Scholastic, Inc.

Burns, Ian. Lissie Pendle. 2006. 196p. pap. 13.04 (978-1-4116-5491-4(9)) Lulu.com.

Burns, Laura. A Fine State of Affairs, No. 3. 2006. (Darcy's Wild Life Ser.: Bk. 3). 176p. (J). (gr. 4-7). pap. 4.99 (978-0-448-44260-0(4), Grosset & Dunlap) Penguin Group (USA) Inc.

Burns, Laura J. Go West, Darcy! 2006. (Darcy's Wild Life Ser.: Bk. 6). 160p. (J). (***978-1-4156-8867-0(2)***, Grosset & Dunlap) Penguin Group (USA) Inc.

Busch, Lou & Sherman, Allan. Hello Muddah, Hello Faddah: (A Letter from Camp) Davis, Jack E., illus. 2006. 32p. (J). (ps). reprint ed. pap. 6.99 (978-0-14-240638-0(4), Puffin) Penguin Group (USA) Inc.

Bushell, Sharon. The Trouble with Bernie. 2004. (Illus.). 160p. (J). per. 6.99 (978-0-9721725-2-3(1)) Road Tunes Media.

Butschkow, Ralf. Something Is Not Quite Right. 2002. (Illus.). 28p. (J). 13.95 (978-1-929132-29-4(8)) Kane/Miller Bk. Pubs., Inc.

Butterworth, Nick. Percy's Bumpy Ride. 2003. (Illus.). 32p. (J). pap. 11.00 (978-0-00-715514-9(X), HarperSport) HarperCollins Pubs. Ltd. GBR. *Dist:* Trafalgar Square Publishing.

—Percy's Bumpy Ride. 2000. (Illus.). 28p. (J). (978-1-58048-091-8(8)) Sandvik Publishing.

Byars, Betsy. Ant Plays Bear. Simont, Marc, illus. 2005. (Ant Ser.). (J). pap. 18.95 incl. audio compact disk (978-1-59112-630-0(4)) Live Oak Media.

—Burbujas, el Pez de una Tonelada. 2003. (SPA., Illus.). 160p. (YA). (gr. 5-8). 6.80 (978-84-279-3191-6(3), NG3953) Noguer y Caralt Editores, S. A. ESP. *Dist:* Lectorum Pubns., Inc.

—The Eighteenth Emergency. 1999. (J). (gr. 5-8). 21.25 (978-0-8446-7026-3(X)) Smith, Peter Pub., Inc.

—My Brother, Ant. Simont, Marc, illus. 2005. (Ant Ser.). (J). pap. 18.95 incl. audio compact disk (978-1-59112-626-3(6)) Live Oak Media.

Byrne. Mad Mags: Purr. (Illus.). 80p. (J). 7.95 (978-0-14-130042-9(6)) Penguin Bks., Ltd. GBR. *Dist:* Trafalgar Square Publishing.

Cabot, Meg. All-am. 2008. 256p. (J). pap. 7.99 (***978-0-06-147989-2(6)***, HarperTeen) HarperCollins Pubs.

—All American Girl. 2003. 416p. (YA). (gr. 7 up). pap. 6.99 (978-0-06-447277-7(9)) HarperCollins Pubs.

—All American Girl. 2002. (gr. 7-12). lib. bdg. 15.30 (978-0-613-62192-2(1)) Tandem Library Bks.

—All American Girl. l.t. ed. 2003. 354p. (J). 25.95 (978-0-7862-6102-4(1), Large Print Pr.) Thorndike Pr.

—In Love. 2002. (Princess Diaries: Vol. 3). 240p. (YA). (gr. 7 up). 16.99 (978-0-06-029467-0(1)) HarperCollins Pubs.

—In Love, Vol. 3. 2004. (Princess Diaries: Vol. 3). 288p. (J). (gr. 7 up). pap. 38.00 incl. audio (978-0-8072-2284-3(4), Listening Library) Random Hse. Audio Publishing Group.

—Party Princess. l.t. rev. ed. 2007. (Princess Diaries: Vol. 7). 335p. (YA). 23.95 (***978-0-7862-9273-8(3)***) Thorndike Pr.

—The Princess Present. 2004. (Princess Diaries: Vol. 6 1/2). 96p. (J). (gr. 7 up). 8.99 (978-0-06-075433-4(8)) HarperCollins Pubs.

—Ready or Not. 2nd ed. 2005. 256p. (YA). (gr. 7 up). 16.99 (978-0-06-072450-4(1)) HarperCollins Pubs.

—Ready or Not. l.t. ed. 2006. 322p. (YA). 23.95 (978-0-7862-8282-1(7)) Thorndike Pr.

Caddy, David. Smash. 2000. (Illus.). 128p. (J). pap. 10.95 (978-1-86368-271-8(6)) Fremantle Pr. AUS. *Dist:* International Specialized Bk. Services.

—Whammy! (Illus.). 112p. (YA). pap. 10.72 (978-1-86368-163-6(9)) Fremantle Pr. AUS. *Dist:* International Specialized Bk. Services.

Caho, Cheryl. Jumbo's Tiny Tale - Volume 1: Family Fun. 2007. (Illus.). 84p. per. 15.97 (***978-0-9779960-7-0(7)***) Thornton Publishing.

—Jumbo's Tiny Tales - Volume 2: Furry Friends. 2007. (Illus.). 82p. per. 15.97 (***978-0-9779960-3-2(4)***) Thornton Publishing.

Calamari, Barbara. Fright Before Christmas. 2001. (gr. 3-6). lib. bdg. 11.80 (978-0-613-87772-5(1)) Tandem Library Bks.

Callahan, Thera S. All Wrapped Up. 2004. (Rookie Reader Espanol Ser.). (Illus.). 31p. (J). (gr. k-2). pap. 4.95 (978-0-516-21949-3(9), Children's Pr.) Scholastic Library Publishing.

—All Wrapped Up. Gordon, Mike, illus. 2003. (Rookie Reader - Level C Ser.). 32p. (J). 19.50 (978-0-516-22844-0(7), Children's Pr.) Scholastic Library Publishing.

Calvert, Deanna. Las Sombras: Shadows. Lester, Mike, illus. 2005. (Rookie Reader(R) Espanol Ser.). (SPA.). 24p. (gr. k-2). 19.50 (978-0-516-24448-6(5), Children's Pr.) Scholastic Library Publishing.

Calvert, Pam. Princess Peepers. Mourning, Tuesday, illus. 2008. (J). (***978-0-7614-5437-3(3)***) Cavendish, Marshall Corp.

Campbell, Kim, et al. Invasion of the Judy Snatchers. 2000. (Doug: 1). (Illus.). 96p. (gr. 2-5). pap. 4.99 (978-0-7868-4382-4(9)) Disney Pr.

Candlewick Books Staff, Books. Have You Seen the Crocodile? 2003. (gr. k-3). lib. bdg. 11.80 (978-0-613-74743-1(7)) Tandem Library Bks.

Canfield, Andrea. Sassy the Seahag. Hallinan, Susan, illus. 2003. Orig. Title: Sassy the Seahag. (J). per. (978-0-9721327-3-2(2)) Eight Dog Publishing.

Cannon, A. E. On the Go with Pirate Pete & Pirate Joe! Smith, Elwood H., illus. 2002. (Puffin Easy-to-Read Ser.). 32p. (J). pap. 3.99 (978-0-14-230136-4(1), Puffin) Penguin Group (USA) Inc.

—On the Go with Pirate Pete & Pirate Joe. 2002. (gr. k-3). lib. bdg. 11.80 (978-0-613-54424-5(2)) Tandem Library Bks.

—Way Out West with Pirate Pete & Pirate Joe. Smith, Elwood H., illus. 2006. (Viking Easy-To-Read Ser.). 32p. (J). (ps). 13.99 (978-0-670-06080-1(1), Viking Juvenile) Penguin Group (USA) Inc.

Cannon, Ann Edwards. Let the Good Times Roll with Pirate Pete & Pirate Joe. Smith, Elwood, illus. 2004. (Easy-to-Read,Viking Children's Ser.). 32p. (J). (ps-3). 13.99 (978-0-670-03679-0(X), Viking Juvenile) Penguin Group (USA) Inc.

Capucilli, Alyssa Satin. Biscuit's New Trick. 2001. (I Can Read Bks.). (Illus.). (J). 10.79 (978-0-606-21071-3(7)) Tandem Library Bks.

Carey, Graham. The Tails Book. 2002. (Illus.). 132p. (J). reprint ed. 18.00 (978-1-930873-63-6(8)) Neumann Pr., The.

Carlow, Emma. Kitty Princess & the Newspaper Dress. Dickinson, Trevor, illus. 2003. 32p. (J). (ps-1). 16.99 (978-0-7636-2077-6(7)) Candlewick Pr.

Carlson, Dale P. Oscar the Orphaned Oyster. Harris, Fran D., ed. Caldwell, Don, illus. l.t. ed. 2000. 24p. (YA). pap. 10.00 (978-0-9664196-4-1(2)) De Day Publishing.

Carlson, Julie. Story Seeds: Fun Pack #1. 2002. (J). pap. (978-0-9718074-0-2(X)) Smarty Pants Bks.

Carta, Karla K. Chocolate in My Pocket. 2006. 21p. (J). 10.68 (978-1-4116-9312-8(4)) Lulu.com.

Carter, David A., creator. Glitter Critters: Dave Carter's Pop-up Book! 2005. (Illus.). 14p. (J). 14.95 (978-1-58117-199-0(4), Intervisual/Piggy Toes) Dalmatian Pr.

Caveney, Philip. Sebastian Darke: Prince of Fools. 2008. 272p. (YA). (gr. 7). lib. bdg. 18.99 (***978-0-385-90465-0(7)***, Delacorte Pr.) Dell Publishing.

Cazenave, Florencia. Mi Mantita. 2000. Tr. of My Blanket. (SPA., Illus.). (J). (ps-k). pap. 6.36 (978-950-24-0733-3(4)) Lectorum Pubns., Inc.

—Tengo Fiebre. (Que Pasa Coleccion). (SPA., Illus.). (J). pap. 6.36 (978-950-24-0681-7(8)) Albatros ARG. *Dist:* Lectorum Pubns., Inc.

Cazet, Denys. Elvis the Rooster Almost Goes to Heaven. Cazet, Denys, illus. 2004. (I Can Read Bks.). (Illus.). 48p. (J). (gr. k-3). pap. 3.99 (978-0-06-000502-3(5), Harper Trophy) HarperCollins Pubs.

—Elvis the Rooster Almost Goes to Heaven. Cazet, Denys, illus. unabr. ed. 2006. (Readalongs for Beginning Readers Ser.). (Illus.). (J). (gr. k-3). 25.95 incl. audio (978-1-59519-686-6(2)); 28.95 incl. audio compact disk (978-1-59519-687-3(0)); pap. 16.95 incl. audio (978-1-59519-682-8(X)); pap. 18.95 incl. audio compact disk (978-1-59519-683-5(8)); Set. pap. 29.95 incl. audio (978-1-59519-684-2(6)); Set. pap. 31.95 incl. audio compact disk (978-1-59519-685-9(4)) Live Oak Media.

—Minnie & Moo: Minnie & Moo Go Dancing. Cazet, Denys, illus. 2001. (Live Oak Readalong Ser.). (Illus.). (J). pap. 18.95 incl. audio compact disk (978-1-59112-390-3(9)) Live Oak Media.

—Minnie & Moo: Minnie & Moo Go to Paris. Cazet, Denys, illus. 2001. (Live Oak Readalong Ser.). (Illus.). (J). pap. 18.95 incl. audio compact disk (978-1-59112-394-1(1)) Live Oak Media.

—Minnie & Moo: Minnie & Moo Go to the Moon. Cazet, Denys, illus. (Live Oak Readalong Ser.). (Illus.). (J). 18.95 incl. audio compact disk (978-1-59112-392-7(5)) Live Oak Media.

—Minnie & Moo: Minnie & Moo Save the Earth. Cazet, Denys, illus. 2001. (Live Oak Readalong Ser.). (Illus.). (J). pap. 18.95 incl. audio compact disk (978-1-59112-396-5(8)) Live Oak Media.

—Minnie & Moo: The Case of the Missing Jelly Donut. Cazet, Denys, illus. (I Can Read Bks.). 48p. (J). 2006. pap. 3.99 (978-0-06-073009-3(9), Harper Trophy); 2005. (Illus.). 15.99 (978-0-06-073007-9(2)) HarperCollins Pubs.

—Minnie & Moo: The Night Before Christmas. Cazet, Denys, illus. (Readalongs for Beginning Readers Ser.). (Illus.). 2005. (J). pap. 16.95 incl. audio (978-1-59112-883-0(8)); 2004. 25.95 incl. audio (978-1-59112-884-7(6)) Live Oak Media.

—Minnie & Moo: The Night of the Living Bed. Cazet, Denys, illus. (I Can Read Bks.). 48p. (J). (gr. k-3). 2004. pap. 3.99 (978-0-06-000505-4(X), Harper Trophy); 2003. (Illus.). 16.99 (978-0-06-000503-0(3)); 2003. (Illus.). lib. bdg. 16.89 (978-0-06-000504-7(1)) HarperCollins Pubs.

—Minnie & Moo & the Haunted Sweater. Cazet, Denys, illus. 2007. (I Can Read Bks.). 48p. (J). (ps-3). 15.99 (***978-0-06-073016-1(1)***); lib. bdg. 16.89 (***978-0-06-073017-8(X)***) HarperCollins Pubs.

—Minnie & Moo & the Seven Wonders of the World. Cazet, Denys, illus. 2003. (Illus.). 144p. (J). 16.95 (978-0-689-85330-2(0) , Atheneum/Richard Jackson Bks.) Simon & Schuster Children's Publishing.

—Minnie & Moo Go Dancing. 1999. (Illus.). 48p. (J). pap. 15.95 (978-0-7737-3105-9(9)) Dorling Kindersley Publishing, Inc.

—Minnie & Moo Go Dancing. Cazet, Denys, illus. 2001. (Illus.). 25.95 incl. audio (978-0-87499-722-4(4)); 28.95 incl. audio compact disk (978-1-59112-591-4(X)); pap. 29.95 incl. audio (978-0-87499-723-1(2)); pap. 31.95 incl. audio compact disk (978-1-59112-590-7(1)) Live Oak Media.

—Minnie & Moo Go to Paris. Cazet, Denys, illus. 2001. (Illus.). 28.95 incl. audio compact disk (978-1-59112-595-2(2)); pap. 31.95 incl. audio compact disk (978-1-59112-594-5(4)); pap. 29.95 incl. audio (978-0-87499-768-2(2)) Live Oak Media.

—Minnie & Moo Go to the Moon. Cazet, Denys, illus. 2002. (Minnie & Moo Ser.). (Illus.). (J). 11.32 (978-0-7587-1444-2(0)) Book Wholesalers, Inc.

—Minnie & Moo Go to the Moon. Cazet, Denys, illus. 2001. (Illus.). 25.95 incl. audio (978-0-87499-718-7(6)); pap. 29.95 incl. audio (978-0-87499-719-4(4)); pap. 31.95 incl. audio compact disk (978-1-59112-592-1(8)); pap. 18.95 incl. audio compact disk (978-1-59112-593-8(6)) Live Oak Media.

—Minnie & Moo Go to the Moon. 2001. (Live Oak Readalong Ser.). (Illus.). (J). (ps-4). pap. 16.95 incl. audio (978-0-87499-717-0(8)) Live Oak Media.

—Minnie & Moo Meet Frankenswine. Cazet, Denys, illus. 2002. (Minnie & Moo Ser.). (Illus.). 12.34 (978-1-4046-1308-9(0)) Book Wholesalers, Inc.

—Minnie & Moo Meet Frankenswine. Cazet, Denys, illus. (I Can Read Bks.: Bk. 3). (Illus.). 48p. (J). 2002. pap. 3.99 (978-0-06-444311-1(6)); 2001. 15.89 (978-0-06-623749-7(1)); 2001. 14.95 (978-0-06-623748-0(3)) HarperCollins Pubs.

—Minnie & Moo Meet Frankenswine. Cazet, Denys, illus. (Readalongs for Beginning Readers Ser.). (Illus.). 2005. (J). pap. 16.95 incl. audio (978-1-59112-261-6(9)); 2005. (J). pap. 18.95 incl. audio compact disk (978-1-59112-875-5(7)); 2004. 28.95 incl. audio compact disk (978-1-59112-876-2(5)); 2004. (J). 25.95 incl. audio (978-1-59112-262-3(7)); 2004. (J). pap. 29.95 incl. audio (978-1-59112-263-0(5)); 2004. (J). pap. 31.95 incl. audio compact disk (978-1-59112-877-9(3)) Live Oak Media.

—Minnie & Moo Meet Frankenswine. 2002. (gr. k-3). lib. bdg. 11.80 (978-0-613-62183-0(2)) Tandem Library Bks.

—Minnie & Moo Save the Earth. Cazet, Denys, illus. 2001. (Illus.). 25.95 incl. audio (978-0-87499-771-2(2)); 28.95 incl. audio compact disk (978-1-59112-597-6(9)); pap. 29.95 incl. audio (978-0-87499-772-9(0)); pap. 31.95 incl. audio compact disk (978-1-59112-596-9(0)) Live Oak Media.

—The Night of the Living Bed. Cazet, Denys, illus. unabr. ed. 2005. (Minnie & Moo Ser.). (gr. k-4). (Illus.). 25.95 incl. audio (978-1-59519-389-6(8)); (Illus.). 28.95 incl. audio compact disk (978-1-59519-393-3(6)); (Illus.). pap. 16.95 incl. audio (978-1-59519-388-9(X)); (Illus.). pap. 18.95 incl. audio compact disk (978-1-59519-392-6(8)); Set. pap. 31.95 incl. audio compact disk (978-1-59519-394-0(4)); Set. (Illus.). pap. 29.95 incl. audio (978-1-59519-390-2(1)) Live Oak Media.

—Shrunken Head. Cazet, Denys, illus. 2008. (I Can Read Bks.: No. 3). 48p. (J). pap. 3.99 (***978-0-06-073015-4(3)*** , Harper Trophy) HarperCollins Pubs.

Cazet, Denys. Shrunken Head No. 3: Grandpa Spanielson's Chicken Pox Stories. Cazet, Denys, illus. 2007. (I Can Read Bks.). (Illus.). 48p. (J). (gr. k-2). 15.99 (978-0-06-073013-0(7)); lib. bdg. 16.89 (978-0-06-073014-7(5)) HarperCollins Pubs.

Cazet, Denys & Dorling Kindersley Publishing Staff. Minnie & Moo Go Dancing. 1998. (Minnie & Moo Ser.: Vol. 2). (Illus.). 48p. (J). (gr. 1-3). 12.99 (978-0-7894-2515-7(7)) Dorling Kindersley Publishing, Inc.

—Minnie & Moo Go to the Moon. 1998. (Minnie & Moo Ser.: Vol. 1). (Illus.). 48p. (J). (gr. 1-3). 12.99 (978-0-7894-2516-4(5)); pap. 3.99 (978-0-7894-2537-9(8)) Dorling Kindersley Publishing, Inc.

—Minnie & Moo Save the Earth, Vol. 3. 1999. (Minnie & Moo Ser.: Vol. 3). (Illus.). 48p. (J). (gr. 1-3). 12.99 (978-0-7894-2594-2(7)); pap. 3.99 (978-0-7894-3929-1(8)) Dorling Kindersley Publishing, Inc.

Center for Learning Network Staff. A Connecticut Yankee in King Arthur's Court: Curriculum Unit —Teacher Guide. 2001. (Novel Ser.). 57p. (YA). tchr. ed., spiral bd. 19.95 (978-1-56077-690-1(0)) Ctr. for Learning, The.

Cepeda, Joe. The Swing. 2006. (Illus.). (J). (***978-1-4287-0187-8(7)*** , Levine, Arthur A. Bks.) Scholastic, Inc.

Cerasini, Marc. The SpongeBob Squarepants Movie: A Novelization of the Hit Movie! novel ed. 2004. (Spongebob Squarepants Ser.). (Illus.). 144p. (J). pap. 4.99 (978-0-689-86840-5(5) , Simon Spotlight) Simon & Schuster Children's Publishing.

Chamberlain, Margaret. Please Don't Tease Tootsie. 2008. 32p. (J). (ps). 16.99 (***978-0-525-47982-6(1)*** , Dutton Juvenile) Penguin Group (USA) Inc.

Chanane, Gloria. Fearful Frannie & Her Fateful Trip to Maui. 2003. 57p. 9.95 (978-1-4137-0162-3(0)) PublishAmerica, Inc.

Chandler, Paul. Mouse of Commons - Mouse of Lords. 2006. 186p. pap. 14.99 (978-1-4116-8447-8(8)) Lulu.com.

Chapman, Lynn. When You're Not Looking. 2006. (Illus.). 10p. (J). bds. 12.95 (978-0-7696-4638-1(7) , Gingham Dog Pr.) School Specialty Publishing.

Chapman, Lynne, illus. Funny Stories for Nine Year Olds. 2003. 280p. (J). 8.99 (978-0-330-37491-0(5) , Macmillan Children's Bks.) Pan Macmillan GBR. *Dist:* Trafalgar Square Publishing.

Charles, Norma M. All the Way to Mexico. 2003. (Illus.). 168p. (J). pap. 6.95 (978-1-55192-598-1(2)) Raincoast Bk. Distribution CAN. *Dist:* Perseus Distribution.

Charlie's Great Adventure: The Hilarious Tale of Life Through a Cat's Eyes. 2000. 112p. per. 6.95 (978-0-9702546-4-1(4)) GoodyGoody Bks.

Charlip, Remy. Little Old Beard & Big Young Little Beard. Rettenmund, Tamara, illus. 2006. 32p. (J). 5.95 (978-0-7614-5288-1(5)) Cavendish, Marshall Corp.

Chatterton, Martin. Holidaze! 2003. (Illus.). 48p. (J). pap. 8.99 (978-1-4052-0608-2(X)) Egmont Bks., Ltd. GBR. *Dist:* Independent Pubs. Group.

—The Surprise Party. Chatterton, Martin, illus. 2005. (Red Bananas Ser.). (Illus.). 48p. (J). (978-0-7787-1068-4(8)) Crabtree Publishing Co.

Cheshire, Simon. Kissing Vanessa. 2006. 144p. (YA). (gr. 7-11). mass mkt. 5.99 (978-0-440-23894-2(3) , Laurel Leaf) Random Hse. Children's Bks.

Chesterfield, Sadie. A Family for Lewis. Disney Storybook Artists Staff, illus. 2007. (I Can Read Bks.). 32p. (J). pap. 3.99 (978-0-06-112470-9(2) , Harper Trophy) HarperCollins Pubs.

Cheva, Cherry. She's So Money. 2008. 304p. (J). 16.99 (***978-0-06-128855-5(1)***); lib. bdg. 17.89 (***978-0-06-128852-4(7)***) HarperCollins Pubs. (HarperTeen).

Child, Lauren. Clarice Bean Spells Trouble. Child, Lauren, illus. (Clarice Bean Ser.). 192p. (J). (gr. 3-6). 2006. pap. 5.99 (978-0-7636-2903-8(0)); 2005. (Illus.). bds. 15.99 (978-0-7636-2813-0(1)) Candlewick Pr.

—I Will Never Not Ever Eat a Tomato. 2003. (Illus.). 32p. (J). (ps-3). reprint ed. pap. 6.99 (978-0-7636-2180-3(3)) Candlewick Pr.

—Utterly Me, Clarice Bean. Child, Lauren, illus. 2003. (Illus.). 192p. (J). (gr. 3-7). 15.99 (978-0-7636-2186-5(2)) Candlewick Pr.

—Utterly Me, Clarice Bean. 2002. (Illus.). 160p. (J). 5.99 (978-1-84121-918-9(5) , Orchard Bks.) Scholastic, Inc.

—What Planet Are You from, Clarice Bean? Child, Lauren, illus. 2002. (Illus.). 32p. (J). (gr. 1-5). 16.99 (978-0-7636-1696-0(6)) Candlewick Pr.

—Who's Afraid of the Big Bad Book? Child, Lauren, illus. 2003. (Illus.). 36p. (ps-2). 16.99 (978-0-7868-0926-4(4)) Hyperion Bks. for Children.

Chmielowski, Josef. Where in the Hell is Sourdough Alaska: Tales of Mischief, Males, & Mayhem. 2005. 224p. 14.95 (978-1-888125-79-5(9)) Publication Consultants.

Chrismer, Melanie. Phoebe Clappsaddle & The Tumbleweed Gang. Roeder, Virginia M., illus. 2002. 32p. (J). 14.95 (978-1-56554-966-1(X)) Pelican Publishing Co., Inc.

—Phoebe Clappsaddle for Sheriff. Roeder, Virginia M., illus. 2003. 32p. (J). pap. 14.95 (978-1-58980-127-1(X)) Pelican Publishing Co., Inc.

—Phoebe Clappsaddle Has a Tumbleweed Christmas. Roeder, Virginia M., illus. 2004. 32p. (J). 15.95 (978-1-58980-241-4(1)) Pelican Publishing Co., Inc.

Christelow, Eileen. Where's the Big Bad Wolf? Christelow, Eileen, illus. 2002. (Illus.). 40p. (J). (gr. k-3). tchr. ed. 16.00 (978-0-618-18194-0(6) , Clarion Bks.) Houghton Mifflin Co. Trade & Reference Div.

Church, Caroline Jayne. Digby Takes Charge. 2007. 32p. (J). (ps-2). 14.99 (978-1-4169-3441-7(3) , McElderry, Margaret K.) Simon & Schuster Children's Publishing.

Churchill, Ginger M. Carmen's Sticky Scab. Gott, Barry, illus. 2007. 32p. (ps-4). 15.95 (***978-1-933718-13-2(7)***) Tanglewood Pr.

Ciminera, Siobhan. Something's Wrong with Cavity Sam! Haefele, Steve, illus. 2007. 16p. (J). pap. 4.99 (978-0-448-44339-3(2) , Grosset & Dunlap) Penguin Group (USA) Inc.

Cirrone, Dorian. Dancing in Red Shoes Will Kill You. 2006. 224p. (J). pap. 7.99 (978-0-06-055703-4(6) , Harper Trophy) HarperCollins Pubs.

Civardi, Anne. First Experiences. ed. 2004. (First Experiences Ser.). 144p. (J). 8.95 (978-0-7945-0341-3(1)) EDC Publishing.

Clark, Emma Chichester. What Shall We Do, Blue Kangaroo? Clark, Emma Chichester, illus. 2003. (Illus.). 32p. (J). (gr. k-k). 15.95 (978-0-385-74635-9(0) , Doubleday Bks. for Young Readers) Random Hse. Children's Bks.

Clarke, Judith. Al Capsella & Watchdogs. 164p. pap. 9.95 (978-0-7022-2294-8(1)) Univ. of Queensland Pr. AUS. *Dist:* International Specialized Bk. Services.

Cleary, Beverly. The Ramona Collection: Ramona & Her Father; Ramona & Her Mother; Ramona Forever; Ramona's World, Vol. 2. Tiegreen, Alan, illus. 2002. (Cleary Reissue Ser.). (J). pap. 23.96 (978-0-06-441006-9(4) , Harper Trophy) HarperCollins Pubs.

—The Ramona Collection, Volume 1. Dockray, Tracy, illus. 2006. (J). pap. 19.99 (978-0-06-124647-0(6) , Harper Trophy) HarperCollins Pubs.

—The Ramona Collection, Volume 2. Dockray, Tracy, illus. 2006. (J). pap. 19.99 (978-0-06-124648-7(4) , Harper Trophy) HarperCollins Pubs.

Clement, Maryceleste. Mr. Tootles & Those Oodles of Noodles. 2002. (Tootle Tales Ser.: Vol. 1). (Illus.). 32p. (J). (ps-3). 14.95 (978-0-9721706-0-4(X)) Tootle Time Publishing Co.

Clement, Rod. Just Another Ordinary Day. 1998. (Illus.). 32p. (J). (ps-3). pap. 5.95 (978-0-06-443500-0(8)) HarperCollins Pubs.

Clemente, Horacio. La Gallina de los Huevos Duros. 2002. (SPA.). 64p. (J). pap. (978-1-4000-0018-0(1)) Editorial Sudamericana S.A.

Clements, Andrew. Bully Buster. Harvey, Amanda, illus. 2001. (Jake Drake Ser.: Bk. 1). 80p. (J). (gr. 4-7). 15.95 (978-0-689-83917-7(0)) Simon & Schuster Children's Publishing.

—Jake Drake, Class Clown. Avendano, illus. 2001. 96p. (J). mass mkt. 3.99 (978-0-689-84915-2(X) , Aladdin) Simon & Schuster Children's Publishing.

—Jake Drake, Know-It-All. Avendano, Dolores, illus. 2001. (Ready-for-Chapters Ser.). 88p. (J). (gr. 4-7). lib. bdg. 10.79 (978-0-606-21259-5(0)) Tandem Library Bks.

Cobot, Meg. All-American Girl. 2004. 416p. (J). (gr. 7 up). pap. 44.00 incl. audio (978-0-8072-2281-2(X) , Listening Library) Random Hse. Audio Publishing Group.

Cocca-Leffler, Maryann. Calling All Cats: All Aboard Picture Reader. 2004. (All Aboard Books Ser.). (Illus.). 32p. (J). (ps-1). mass mkt. 3.99 (978-0-448-43369-1(9) , Grosset & Dunlap) Penguin Group (USA) Inc.

Cochran, Jean M. Farmer Brown & His Little Red Truck. Enos, Daryl, illus. 2008. 32p. (J). 16.95 (***978-0-9792035-0-3(3)***) Pleasant St. Pr.

Cohen, Peter. Boris's Glasses. Sandin, Joan, tr. Landstrom, Olof, illus. 2003. 28p. (J). (gr. k-3). 15.00 (978-91-29-65942-9(6)) R & S Bks. SWE. *Dist:* Macmillan.

Colandro, Lucille. There Was a Cold Lady Who Swallowed Some Snow. Lee, Jared D., illus. 2003. 32p. (J). pap. 5.95 (978-0-439-56703-9(3)); pap. 5.95 (978-0-439-47109-1(5)) Scholastic, Inc. (Cartwheel Bks.).

—There Was a Cold Lady Who Swallowed Some Snow. unabr. ed. 2006. (J). (gr. k-2). pap. 9.95 incl. audio compact disk (978-0-439-89556-9(1)) Scholastic, Inc.

—There Was a Cold Lady Who Swallowed Some Snow. 2003. (gr. k-3). lib. bdg. 14.10 (978-0-613-72229-2(9)) Tandem Library Bks.

—There Was A Cold Lady Who Swallowed Some Snow -library. 2006. (J). 18.95 (978-0-439-89841-6(2)) Scholastic, Inc.

Colbert, Larry C. Insights from an Out-of-Sight Guy. 2005. 111p. per. 20.00 (978-0-9766329-0-0(X)) Driving Vision, Inc.

Cole, Babette. El Libro de Etiqueta de Lady Lupina. 2003. (Babette Cole Ser.). (SPA.). (J). 18.95 (978-84-233-3337-0(X)) Ediciones Destino ESP. *Dist:* Planeta Publishing Corp.

Cole, Brock. Buttons. Cole, Brock, illus. (Illus.). 32p. (J). 2004. pap. 6.95 (978-0-374-41013-1(5) , Sunburst); 2000. 16.00 (978-0-374-31001-1(7) , Farrar, Straus & Giroux (BYR)) Farrar, Straus & Giroux.

Collins, Terry. Tea at the Treedome. 2004. 64p. (J). (gr. 2-5). pap. 17.00 incl. audio (978-0-8072-1986-7(X) , Listening Library) Random Hse. Audio Publishing Group.

Collinson, Roger. Butterfingers. 2003. (Illus.). 80p. pap. 9.99 (978-1-84270-290-1(4)) Andersen GBR. *Dist:* Independent Pubs. Group.

Coman, Carolyn. The Big House. Shepperson, Rob, illus. 2004. 224p. (J). 16.95 (978-1-932425-09-3(8) , Lemniscaat) Boyds Mills Pr.

—The Big House. Rob, Shepperson, illus. 2007. 224p. (J). (gr. 3 up). pap. 6.99 (978-0-14-240740-0(2) , Puffin) Penguin Group (USA) Inc.

Coman, Carolyn. Sneaking Suspicions. Shepperson, Rob, illus. 2007. 204p. (J). (gr. 3-7). 16.95 (***978-1-59078-491-4(X)*** , Front Street) Boyds Mills Pr.

Come Back, Amelia Bedelia. 2002. (Amelia Bedelia Ser.). (Illus.). (J). 12.34 (978-0-7587-6057-9(4)) Book Wholesalers, Inc.

Condon, Bill. Snow Bright & the Seven Sumos. Forss, Ian, illus. 1999. (Supa Doopers Ser.). 64p. (J). (978-0-7608-1927-2(0)) Sundance/Newbridge Educational Publishing.

Condon, Tom. The Sandman: Stories to Read to Children. 2003. 136p. (J). pap. 11.95 (978-0-595-27291-4(6)) iUniverse, Inc.

Conford, Ellen. Annabel the Actress Starring in Camping It Up. Andriani, Renee W., illus. 2005. (Annabel the Actress Ser.). 64p. (J). pap. 3.99 (978-0-689-84792-9(0) , Aladdin) Simon & Schuster Children's Publishing.

Annabel the Actress Starring in Gorilla My Dreams. Andriani, Renee W., illus. 2000. (Annabel the Actress Ser.). 64p. (J). (gr. 2-5). pap. 3.99 (978-0-689-83883-5(2) , Aladdin) Simon & Schuster Children's Publishing.

—Annabel the Actress Starring in Gorilla My Dreams. 2000. (Ready-for-Chapters Ser.). (J). 10.79 (978-0-606-20029-5(0)) Tandem Library Bks.

—A Case for Jenny Archer. Palmisciano, Diane, illus. 2nd ed. 2006. 64p. (J). (gr. 1-4). pap. 3.99 (978-0-316-01486-1(9)) Little Brown & Co.

—Hound of the Barkervilles. Andriani, Renee W., illus. 2002. (Annabel the Actress Ser.). 96p. (J). (gr. 2-5). 15.00 (978-0-689-84734-9(3)) Simon & Schuster Children's Publishing.

—Jenny Archer, Author. Palisciano, Diane, illus. 2006. 64p. (J). (gr. 1-4). pap. 3.99 (978-0-316-01487-8(7)) Little Brown & Co.

—A Job for Jenny Archer. 2006. (Illus.). 80p. (J). (gr. 1-4). pap. 3.99 (978-0-316-01484-7(2)) Little Brown & Co.

—What's Cooking, Jenny Archer? Palmisciano, Diane, illus. 2006. 80p. (J). (gr. 1-4). pap. 3.99 (978-0-316-01488-5(5)) Little Brown & Co.

Connors, Jerrold. Now, Louie! Connors, Jerrold, illus. 2006. (Illus.). 40p. (J). 12.99 (978-0-9721416-1-1(8)) Alligator Boogaloo.

Contijoch, Josefa. Mariquilla en la Nieve. Filella, Lluis, illus. 2003. (Caballo Alado Ser.). (SPA & ENG.). 24p. 6.95 (978-84-7864-647-0(7)) Combel Editorial, S.A. ESP. *Dist:* Independent Pubs. Group.

—Mariquilla va de Fiesta. Filella, Lluis, illus. 2003. (Caballo Alado Ser.). (SPA & ENG.). 24p. 6.95 (978-84-7864-648-7(5)) Combel Editorial, S.A. ESP. *Dist:* Independent Pubs. Group.

—Mariquilla y el Pino. Filella, Lluis, illus. 2003. (Caballo Alado Ser.). (SPA & ENG.). 24p. 6.95 (978-84-7864-645-6(0)) Combel Editorial, S.A. ESP. *Dist:* Independent Pubs. Group.

Cook, Deanna F. & Meryman, Charlotte, eds. Family Fun: 350 Parents Share Their Creative Tips. 2005. (Illus.). 256p. (J). pap. 16.95 (978-0-7868-5541-4(X) , Disney Editions) Disney Pr.

Cook, Stephen. Day Out with Daddy. 2006. (Illus.). 32p. (J). 17.85 (978-0-8027-8060-7(1)); 16.95 (978-0-8027-8059-1(8)) Walker & Co.

Cooper, Terry, ed. Humorous Fiction: A Complete Unit That Helps Students Explore This Exciting Genre & Become Better Readers & Writers. 2001. (Illus.). 48p. (ps-3). pap. 12.95 (978-0-439-23806-9(4)) Scholastic, Inc.

Cooper, Wendy. My First Ride with Isaiah. Elizabeth Mobley, illus. 2006. 18p. (J). 11.95 (***978-0-9772964-8-4(2)***) Kingdom Publishing Group, Inc.

Corey, Shana. Horus's Horrible Day. Teague, Mark, illus. 2001. (First Graders from Mars Ser.: No. 1). 32p. (J). (gr. k-2). pap. 14.95 (978-0-439-26220-0(8)); pap. 4.99 (978-0-439-31955-3(2)) Scholastic, Inc. (Levine, Arthur A. Bks.).

Cosmic Debris Staff, contrib. by. Emily the Strange: Seeing/Deceiving. 2006. 64p. 12.95 (978-0-8118-5626-3(7)) Chronicle Bks. LLC.

Coulman, Valerie. I Am a Ballerina. Lamb, Sandra, illus. 2004. 32p. (J). (ps-2). pap. 6.95 (978-1-897073-20-9(8)) Lobster Pr. CAN. *Dist:* Univ. of Toronto Pr.

—When Pigs Fly. Roge, illus. 2001. 32p. (J). (ps-1). (978-1-894222-36-5(9)) Lobster Pr.

—When Pigs Fly. Roge, illus. 2004. 32p. (J). pap. 6.95 (978-1-894222-79-2(2)) Lobster Pr. CAN. *Dist:* Univ. of Toronto Pr.

Coville, Bruce. Don't Fry My Veeblax! Sansekers, Tony, illus. 2000. (I Was a Sixth Grade Alien Ser.: Vol. 6). (J). 10.64 (978-0-606-19849-3(0)) Tandem Library Bks.

—I Lost My Grandfather's Brain. unabr. ed. 2004. (I Was a Sixth Grade Alien Ser.). 160p. (J). (gr. 3-6). pap. 29.00 incl. audio (978-0-8072-8385-1(1) , YA180SP, Listening Library) Random Hse. Audio Publishing Group.

—I Lost My Grandfather's Brain. 1999. (I Was a Sixth Grade Alien Ser.). (Illus.). (J). 10.64 (978-0-606-18306-2(0X)) Tandem Library Bks.

—I Was a Sixth Grade Alien. (I Was a Sixth Grade Alien Ser.). 170p. (J). (gr. 4-6). pap. 3.99 (978-0-8072-8202-1(2)); 2004. (gr. 3-6). pap. 29.00 incl. audio (978-0-8072-8201-4(4) , S YA 138 SP) Random Hse. Audio Publishing Group. (Listening Library).

—I Was a Sixth Grade Alien. 1999. (I Was a Sixth Grade Alien Ser.). (J). 11.64 (978-0-606-17089-5(8)) Tandem Library Bks.

—My Teacher Fried My Brains. Pierard, John, illus. 2005. 138p. (J). (gr. 3-7). lib. bdg. 12.04 (978-0-606-33890-5(X)) Tandem Library Bks.

—My Teacher Is an Alien. Wimmer, Mike, illus. 2005. 124p. (J). (ps-7). lib. bdg. 12.04 (978-0-606-33889-9(6)) Tandem Library Bks.

—Peanut Butter Lover Boy. 2000. (I Was a Sixth Grade Alien Ser.). (Illus.). (J). (978-0-606-18307-9(8)) Tandem Library Bks.

—There's an Alien in My Underwear. 2001. (Illus.). 150p. (J). (gr. 3-6). lib. bdg. 11.04 (978-0-606-22824-4(1)) Tandem Library Bks.

—Zombies of the Science Fair. 2000. (I Was a Sixth Grade Alien Ser.). (Illus.). (J). (978-0-606-18308-6(6)) Tandem Library Bks.

Cowell, Cressida. How to Be a Pirate. 2005. (Illus.). 224p. (J). (gr. 3-7). 10.99 (978-0-316-15598-4(5)) Little Brown & Co.

—How to Speak Dragonese. 2006. (Illus.). 240p. (J). (gr. 3-7). 10.99 (978-0-316-15600-4(0)) Little Brown & Co.

—How to Train Your Dragon. 2004. (Illus.). 224p. (J). (gr. 3-7). 10.99 (978-0-316-73737-1(2)) Little Brown & Co.

Cowley, Joy. Agapanthus Hum & the Eyeglasses Hour. 2001. (Easy-to-Read Ser.). (C). (978-0-606-20535-1(7)) Tandem Library Bks.

Cowley, Joy. Chicken Feathers. Elliott, David W., illus. 2008. 160p. (J). (gr. 3-6). 15.99 (***978-0-399-24791-0(2)*** , Philomel) Penguin Group (USA) Inc.

Cox, Judy. Don't Be Silly, Mrs. Millie! Mathieu, Joe, illus. 2005. 32p. (J). (ps-2). 14.95 (978-0-7614-5166-2(8)) Cavendish, Marshall Corp.

—Mrs. Millie Goes to Philly! Mathieu, Joseph, illus. 2008. (J). (***978-0-7614-5372-7(5)***) Cavendish, Marshall Corp.

Cox, Judy. Weird Stories from the Lonesome Cafe. Kidd, Diane, illus. 2000. 80p. (J). (gr. 2-4). 15.00 (978-0-15-202134-4(5)) Harcourt Children's Bks.

Coyle, Carmela LaVigna. Thank You, Aunt Tallulah. MacPherson, Bruce, illus. 2006. 32p. 15.95 (978-0-87358-891-1(6) , Rising Moon Bks. for Young Readers) Northland Publishing.

Crimi, Carolyn. The Louds Move In! Dunnick, Regan, illus. 2006. 32p. (J). 14.95 (978-0-7614-5221-8(4)) Cavendish, Marshall Corp.

Croce, Warren. Opposite Day. 2007. (ENG.). 28p. per. 14.90 (***978-1-4303-0659-7(9)***) Lulu.com.

Cronin, Doreen. Dooby Dooby Moo. Lewin, Betsy, illus. 2006. 40p. (J). (ps-2). 16.95 (978-0-689-84507-9(3)) Simon & Schuster Children's Publishing.

—Pato para Presidente. Lewin, Betsy, illus. 2005. Tr. of Duck for President. (SPA.). 15.95 (978-1-930332-73-7(4)) Lectorum Pubns., Inc.

Cross, Gillian. Down with the Dirty Danes. (Illus.). 61p. (J). pap. 7.99 (978-0-00-675534-0(8) , HarperSport) HarperCollins Pubs. Ltd. GBR. *Dist:* Trafalgar Square Publishing.

Crummel, Susan Stevens & Stevens, Janet. Cook-a-Doodle-Doo! 2005. (Illus.). 48p. (J). (ps-ps). reprint ed. pap. 7.00 (978-0-15-205658-2(0) , Voyager Bks./Libros Viajeros) Harcourt Children's Bks.

H I

Cummings, Ferdinand: The Bottle-Headed Cat. 2004. 124p. per. 11.95 (978-1-59453-280-1(X) , 2093) Airleaf Publishing & Bookselling.

Cupper, Karin. The Thrilling Adventures of Life in Eidl. 2005. 151p. pap. 19.95 (978-1-4137-6862-6(8)) PublishAmerica, Inc.

Curious, George & Brazelton, T. Berry. George Was Here. 2007. (Curious George Ser.). 224p. (J). (ps-1). 4.99 (***978-1-4169-4847-6(3)*** , Simon Scribbles) Simon & Schuster Children's Publishing.

—Monkey Around. Obrero, Rudy, illus. 2007. (Curious George Ser.). 48p. (J). (ps-1). 3.99 (***978-1-4169-4846-9(5)*** , Simon Scribbles) Simon & Schuster Children's Publishing.

Curry, Jane. Down from the Lonely Mountain: California Indian Tales. 2000. (Illus.). 148p. (YA). pap. 10.95 (978-0-595-00440-9(7) , Backinprint.com) iUniverse, Inc.

Curtis & Driscoll. Mr. Bean, Level 2. 2000. (Illus.). 48p. (C). pap. 9.00 (978-0-582-34129-6(9)) Longman Publishing Group.

Curtis, Jamie Lee. Cuando Yo Era Pequena: Memorias de una Nina de Cuatro Anos. Cornell, Laura, illus. 2001. (CAT.). 32p. (J). 14.95 (978-84-95040-95-4(6)) Serres, Ediciones, S. L. ESP. *Dist:* Lectorum Pubns., Inc.

—Cuando Yo Era Pequena: Memorias de una Nina de Cuatro Anos. Rubio, Esther, tr. Cornell, Laura, illus. 2001. (SPA.). 32p. (J). (gr. k-1). (978-84-95040-94-7(8) , RR5222) Serres, Ediciones, S. L. ESP. *Dist:* Lectorum Pubns., Inc.

Cutbill, Andy. The Beast of Baloddan. 2003. (Hotel Chronicles). (Illus.). 208p. pap. (978-0-340-86570-5(9) , Hodder Children's Books) Hodder Children's Division.

Cutlip, Kimbra L. Firefighter's Night Before Christmas. Rice, James, illus. 2002. 32p. (J). (gr. k-3). 15.95 (978-1-58980-054-0(0)) Pelican Publishing Co., Inc.

D C Thomson Staff, ed. The Broons 2004. 2003. (Illus.). 96p. (J). 9.95 (978-0-85116-835-7(3)) Thomson, D.C. & Co., Ltd. GBR. *Dist:* APG Sales and Fulfillment.

—The Broons & Oor Wullie 2004: More Classics from the Fifties. 2003. (Illus.). 144p. (J). 12.95 (978-0-85116-836-4(1)) Thomson, D.C. & Co., Ltd. GBR. *Dist:* APG Sales and Fulfillment.

Dahl, Michael. Galactic Giggles: Far-Out & Funny Jokes about Outer Space. Reibeling, Brandon, illus. 2004. (Read-It! Joke Books). 24p. (C). (gr. k-3). 18.60 (978-1-4048-0126-4(X)) Picture Window Bks.

Dahl, Roald. Charlie & the Chocolate Factory. movie tie-in ed. Date not set. 174p. (J). 19.95 (978-0-8488-2241-5(2)) Amereon LTD.

—Charlie & the Chocolate Factory. Blake, Quentin, illus. 2007. 176p. (J). (gr. 2). 6.99 (***978-0-14-241031-8(4)*** , Puffin) Penguin Group (USA) Inc.

—Charlie & the Chocolate Factory. movie tie-in ed. 2005. (Illus.). 40p. (J). (gr. 3-6). 6.99 (978-0-14-240420-1(9) , Puffin) Penguin Group (USA) Inc.

—Charlie & the Chocolate Factory. Blake, Quentin, illus. novel movie tie-in ed. 2005. 176p. (gr. 3-6). 6.99 (978-0-14-240388-4(1) , Puffin) Penguin Group (USA) Inc.

—Charlie & the Chocolate Factory. movie tie-in ed. 2005. 176p. (J). (gr. 3-7). lib. bdg. 16.99 (978-0-375-93460-5(X) , Knopf Bks. for Young Readers) Random Hse. Children's Bks.

—Charlie & the Chocolate Factory. Blake, Quentin, illus. movie tie-in ed. 176p. (J). (gr. 3-7). 2005. 14.95 (978-0-375-83460-8(5)); 2001. 15.95 (978-0-375-81526-3(0)); 2001. lib. bdg. 17.99 (978-0-375-91526-0(5)) Random Hse. Children's Bks. (Knopf Bks. for Young Readers).

—Charlie & the Great Glass Elevator. Blake, Quentin, illus. 2007. 176p. (J). (gr. 2). 6.99 (***978-0-14-241032-5(2)*** , Puffin) Penguin Group (USA) Inc.

—Charlie & the Great Glass Elevator. Blake, Quentin, illus. 2001. 176p. (J). (gr. 3-7). 15.95 (978-0-375-81525-6(2) , Knopf Bks. for Young Readers) Random Hse. Children's Bks.

—Charlie & the Great Glass Elevator. Blake, Quentin, illus. 2005. (Puffin Modern Classics Ser.). 176p. (J). (gr. 3-6). pap. 6.99 (978-0-14-240412-6(8) , Puffin) Penguin Group (USA) Inc.

—Le Doigt Magique.Tr. of Magic Finger. pap. 16.95 (978-2-07-053723-5(4)) Gallimard, Editions FRA. *Dist:* Distribooks, Inc.

—Matilda. (J). pap. 29.95 incl. audio (978-0-7540-6216-5(3)) BBC Audiobooks America.

—Matilda. (FRE.). (J). pap. 19.95 (978-2-07-051254-6(1)) Gallimard, Editions FRA. *Dist:* Distribooks, Inc.

—Matilda. Blake, Quentin, illus. 240p. 2007. (J). (gr. 2). 6.99 (***978-0-14-241037-0(3));*** 2004. (gr. 3). pap. 6.99 (978-0-14-240253-5(2)) Penguin Group (USA) Inc. (Puffin).

—Matilda. 2000. (GER.). (J). pap. 12.95 (978-3-499-20855-3(5)) Rowohlt Taschenbuch Verlag GmbH DEU. *Dist:* Distribooks, Inc.

—The Twits. Blake, Quentin, illus. 2002. (J). 12.34 (978-0-7587-5237-6(7)) Book Wholesalers, Inc.

—The Twits. Blake, Quentin, illus. 2007. 96p. (J). (gr. 2). 5.99 (***978-0-14-241039-4(X)*** , Puffin) Penguin Group (USA) Inc.

—The Twits. Blake, Quentin, illus. 2002. 96p. (J). (gr. 2-6). 15.95 (978-0-375-82242-1(9)); lib. bdg. 17.99 (978-0-375-92242-8(3)) Random Hse. Children's Bks. (Knopf Bks. for Young Readers).

Dalmatian Press Staff. Have We Got a Surprise for You! Amazing Marker. 2004. (Bigidea's Veggietales(R) Ser.). (Illus.). 48p. (J). spiral bd. 4.99 (978-1-4037-0812-0(6)) Dalmatian Pr.

—Looney Tunes: Your Favorite Looney Tunes: Storybook Collection. (Looney Tunes Ser.). (Illus.). 217p. (J). 10.99 (978-1-4037-0524-2(0)) Dalmatian Pr.

—A Pond So Blue. 2002. (Illus.). 24p. (J). (gr. k-5). pap. 2.99 (978-1-57759-241-9(7)) Dalmatian Pr.

—Rainforest Friends. 2002. (Illus.). 24p. (J). (gr. k-5). pap. 2.99 (978-1-57759-278-5(6)) Dalmatian Pr.

—Rosie in the Way. 2002. (Illus.). 24p. (J). (gr. k-5). pap. 2.99 (978-1-57759-367-6(7)) Dalmatian Pr.

—The Three LIttle Pigs. 2002. (Illus.). 24p. (J). (gr. k-5). pap. 2.99 (978-1-57759-477-2(0)) Dalmatian Pr.

Dalmatian Press Staff, contrib. by. Fun Slate: Justice League. 2003. (Justice League Ser.). (J). pap. 1.99 (978-1-4037-0350-7(7)) Dalmatian Pr.

Daniel, Alan. Aaron's Hair. 2002. (ps-2). lib. bdg. 11.80 (978-0-613-49706-0(6)) Tandem Library Bks.

Danko, Dan & Mason, Tom. Sidekicks, Vol. 3. 2004. (Illus.). 112p. (J). 13.95 (978-0-316-73426-4(8)) Little Brown & Co.

—Sidekicks 6: Invasion of the Evil Teachers from Planet Buttface. 2005. 128p. (J). pap. 4.99 (978-0-316-15896-1(8)) Little Brown & Co.

Danziger, Paula. There's a Bat in Bunk Five. 2006. (J). 160p. (gr. 5). pap. 5.99 (978-0-14-240681-6(3)); 150p. (***978-1-4156-7491-8(4))*** Penguin Group (USA) Inc. (Puffin).

Daudet, Alphonse. The Siege of Berlin & Other Stories. 2004. reprint ed. pap. 15.95 (978-1-4191-8248-8(X)); pap. 1.99 (978-1-4192-8248-5(4)) Kessinger Publishing, LLC.

David, Lawrence. The Cupcaked Crusader. Gott, Barry, illus. 2002. (Horace Splattly Ser.: Vol. 1). 144p. (J). pap. 4.99 (978-0-14-230021-3(7) , Puffin) Penguin Group (USA) Inc.

—Horace Splattly: The Cupcaked Crusader. (gr. 3-6). 2003. lib. bdg. 13.00 (978-0-613-61708-6(8)); 2002. lib. bdg. 13.00 (978-0-613-45274-8(7)); 2002. lib. bdg. 13.00 (978-0-613-45275-5(5)) Tandem Library Bks.

—Invasion of the Shag Carpet Creature. 2004. (Horace Splattly Ser.). (Illus.). 160p. (J). pap. 4.99 (978-0-14-240042-5(4) , Puffin) Penguin Group (USA) Inc.

—When Second Graders Attack. Gott, Barry, illus. 2nd ed. 2002. (Horace Splattly Ser.). 160p. (J). pap. 4.99 (978-0-14-230118-0(3) , Puffin) Penguin Group (USA) Inc.

David, Mark. Crazy Cars. David, Mark, illus. 2006. (Illus.). 32p. (J). pap. 7.95 (978-1-933605-05-0(7)) Kane/Miller Bk. Pubs., Inc.

David, Yvonne. Out of the Apple Orchard. 2005. (Illus.). 72p. (J). 18.95 (978-0-9621385-4-6(1)) Arbiter Pr.

Davies, Jacqueline. The House Takes a Vacation. White, Lee, illus. 2006. (J). 16.99 (978-0-7614-5331-4(8)) Cavendish, Marshall Corp.

Davies, Tristan. Anoraknophobia. 1999. (Illus.). 48p. (J). pap. (978-0-340-72834-5(5) , Hodder & Stoughton) Hodder General Publishing Division.

—Wallace & Gromit: The Lost Slipper & The Curse of the Ramsbottoms. 1998. (Wallace & Gromit Comic Strip Bks.). (J). (ps-3). pap. 9.95 (978-0-8417-3035-9(0)) Adventure Medical Kits.

Davies, Tristan & Newman, Nick. Wallace & Gromit: Anoraknophobia. 1998. (Wallace & Gromit Comic Strip Bks.). (Illus.). 48p. (J). 9.95 (978-0-8417-2031-2(2)) Adler's Foreign Bks., Inc.

Davies, Tristan, et al. Crackers in Space. 2000. (Illus.). 48p. (J). pap. (978-0-340-71290-0(2) , Hodder & Stoughton) Hodder General Publishing Division.

—Crackers in Space. 2000. (Illus.). 48p. (J). 16.99 (978-0-340-71289-4(9) , Hodder & Stoughton) Hodder General Publishing Division GBR. *Dist:* Trafalgar Square Publishing.

Davis, Brian. My Shoes Got the Blues, Wheeler, Ron, illus. 2003. (Book of Matt Ser.: 2). 80p. (J). pap. 4.99 (978-1-59269-057-2(2)) Mcruffy Pr.

Davis, David. Rock n Roll Dogs. 2006. (Illus.). (J). 15.95 (978-1-58980-349-7(3)) Pelican Publishing Co., Inc.

Davis, Donald. Mama Learns to Drive: Stories That Celebrate Mothers. 2005. (Illus.). 128p. 17.95 (978-0-87483-745-2(6) , 1235376) August Hse. Pubs., Inc.

Davis, Jim. Fat Cat, No.1. 2003. (J). (gr. 5-8). lib. bdg. 24.55 (978-0-613-68581-8(4)) Tandem Library Bks.

—Garfield's Big Book of Excellent Excuses. 2000. (Illus.). (J). (978-0-606-18664-3(6)) Tandem Library Bks.

—Twelfth Garfield Fat Cat, 3 Packs. 2001. (gr. 5-8). lib. bdg. 19.90 (978-0-613-68627-3(6)) Tandem Library Bks.

Davis, Katie. Mabel the Tooth Fairy & How She Got Her Job. 2003. (Illus.). 40p. (J). (gr. k-3). 16.00 (978-0-15-216307-5(7)) Harcourt Children's Bks.

Davis, Stephie. Putting Boys on the Ledge. 2004. (YA). mass mkt. 5.99 (978-0-8439-5328-2(4)) Dorchester Publishing Co., Inc.

—Studying Boys. 2004. (YA). mass mkt. 5.99 (978-0-8439-5382-4(9)) Dorchester Publishing Co., Inc.

de Paola, Tomie. Guess Who's Coming to Santa's for Dinner? 2004. (Illus.). 48p. (J). (ps-3). 16.99 (978-0-399-24271-7(6) , Putnam Juvenile) Penguin Group (USA) Inc.

—The Knight & the Dragon. de Paola, Tomie, illus. 2002. (Illus.). 32p. (J). pap. 6.95 (978-1-931016-05-6(4) , MHC-05-4) Minnesota Humanities Commission.

De Regniers, Beatrice Schenk. What Can You Do with a Shoe? 2001. (ps-2). lib. bdg. 15.30 (978-0-613-73326-7(6)); (Illus.). (J). (978-0-606-21515-2(8)) Tandem Library Bks.

deGroat, Diane. Annie Pitts, Burger Kid. (Illus.). (J). 2001. 112p. (gr. 3-7). pap. 3.95 (978-1-58717-110-9(4)); 2000. 75p. pap. 14.95 (978-1-58717-016-4(7)) Chronicle Bks. LLC. (SeaStar Bks.).

—Annie Pitts, Burger Kid. 2001. (gr. 3-6). lib. bdg. 11.80 (978-0-613-43671-7(7)) Tandem Library Bks.

—Annie Pitts, Swamp Monster. 2001. (978-0-606-22334-8(7)) Tandem Library Bks.

—Last One in Is a Rotten Egg! deGroat, Diane, illus. 2007. (Illus.). 32p. (J). (ps-3). 15.99 (978-0-06-089294-4(3)); lib. bdg. 16.89 (978-0-06-089295-1(1)) HarperCollins Pubs.

Delaney, Kaz. My Life as a Snow Bunny. 2003. (YA). mass mkt. 5.99 (978-0-8439-5296-4(2)) Dorchester Publishing Co., Inc.

—My Life as a Snow Bunny. 2003. (gr. 7-12). lib. bdg. 14.15 (978-0-613-76908-2(2)) Tandem Library Bks.

Dem Bones. 2004. 24.95 incl. audio (978-1-55592-692-2(4)); 29.95 incl. cd-rom (978-1-55592-702-8(5)) Weston Woods Studios, Inc.

Denton, Terry. The Minotaur's Maze. 2004. (Storymaze Ser.). (Illus.). 144p. (J). pap. 6.95 (978-1-74114-088-0(9)) Allen & Unwin AUS. *Dist:* Independent Pubs. Group.

—The Obelisk of Eeeno. 2004. (Storymaze Ser.). (Illus.). 144p. (J). pap. 6.95 (978-1-74114-089-7(7)) Allen & Unwin AUS. *Dist:* Independent Pubs. Group.

Deogratias Simba. The Mystery Door. 2005. (Illus.). 22p. pap. 9.95 (978-9987-417-21-6(3)) Mkuki na Nyoka Pubs. TZA. *Dist:* Michigan State Univ. Pr.

DePaola, Tomie. Guess Who's Coming to Santa's for Dinner? DePaola, Tomie, illus. 2006. 40p. (J). (ps). pap. 6.99 (978-0-14-240699-1(6) , Puffin) Penguin Group (USA) Inc.

dePaola, Tomie. Tomie dePaola's Front Porch Stories & North Country Whoppers. dePaola, Tomie, illus. 2007. 64p. (J). (ps). 17.99 (***978-0-399-24754-5(8)*** , Putnam Juvenile) Penguin Group (USA) Inc.

Derby, Kenneth. The Top Ten Ways to Ruin the First Day of 5th Grade. 2004. 176p. (J). (gr. 4-6). tchr. ed. 16.95 (978-0-8234-1851-0(0)) Holiday Hse., Inc.

Derby, Sally. The Wacky Substitute. Herbert, Jennifer, illus. 2005. 32p. (J). (gr. k-3). 14.95 (978-0-7614-5219-5(2)) Cavendish, Marshall Corp.

Desplechin, Marie. Endlich Hexe! 2002. (GER.). 128p. pap. 15.00 (978-1-4000-3953-1(3) , New Media German Language) Random House Foreign Language Publishing.

Desrosiers, Sylvie. Qui Veut Entrer dans la Peau d'un Chien? Sylvestre, Daniel, illus. 2002. (Roman Jeunesse Ser.). (FRE.). 96p. (J). (gr. 4-7). pap. (978-2-89021-576-4(8)) Diffusion du livre Mirabel.

Desrosiers, Sylvie & Sylvestre, Daniel. Quelqu'un A-T-Il Vu Notdog? 2001. (Roman Jeunesse Ser.). (FRE., Illus.). 96p. (J). pap. (978-2-89021-453-8(2)) Diffusion du livre Mirabel.

Dhami, Narinder. Bhangra Babes. 2007. 192p. (J). (gr. 4-7). 5.99 (***978-0-440-42106-1(3)*** , Yearling) Random Hse. Children's Bks.

Dhami, Narinder. Bollywood Babes. 2006. 224p. (J). (gr. 4-7). pap. 5.50 (978-0-440-42020-0(2) , Yearling) Random Hse. Children's Bks.

DiCamillo, Kate. Mercy Watson Goes for a Ride. Van Dusen, Chris, illus. 2006. (Mercy Watson Ser.). 80p. (J). (gr. 1-3). 12.99 (978-0-7636-2332-6(6)) Candlewick Pr.

—Mercy Watson to the Rescue. Van Dusen, Chris, illus. 2005. 80p. (J). (gr. 1-3). 12.99 (978-0-7636-2270-1(2)) Candlewick Pr.

DiCamillo, Kate & Van Dusen, Chris. Mercy Watson: Fights Crime. Van Dusen, Chris, illus. 2006. (Illus.). 80p. (J). (gr. 1-3). 12.99 (978-0-7636-2590-6(6)) Candlewick Pr.

DiCamillo, Kate & Van Dusen, Chris. Princess in Disguise. Van Dusen, Chris, illus. 2007. (Mercy Watson Ser.). (Illus.). 80p. (J). (gr. 1-3). 12.99 (***978-0-7636-3014-0(4))*** Candlewick Pr.

Dickinson, Donald J. A Bird's Eye View of the Civil War in Loudon County & Campbell's Station, TN: A Book for Children. 2003. (Illus.). 251p. (J). per. (978-0-9637951-3-7(9)) Hart-Whitlow Pubs.

Dillman, Shanley Chris. The Black Pond. 2004. 126p. pap. 17.95 (978-1-4137-3861-2(3)) PublishAmerica, Inc.

DiSalvo-Ryan, DyAnne. The Sloppy Copy Slipup. 2005. (Illus.). 128p. (J). 16.95 (978-0-8234-1947-0(9)) Holiday Hse., Inc.

Disney Press Staff. Me Too, Woody! 2002. (gr. k-3). lib. bdg. 11.80 (978-0-613-73664-0(8)) Tandem Library Bks.

Disney Staff. Monkey Fist Strikes & Attack of the Killer Be, 8 vols. 2003. (Kim Possible Ser.). (Illus.). 100p. (gr. 2 up). pap. 7.99 (978-1-59182-146-5(0) , Tokyopop Kids) TOKYOPOP, Inc.

Disney Staff, et al, creators. Monkey Fist Strikes & Attack of the Killer Be, 8 vols. 2003. (Illus.). Vol. 1. 100p. (gr. 2 up). pap. 7.99 (978-1-59182-145-8(2)); Vol. 4. 192p. pap. 7.99 (978-1-59182-244-8(0)) TOKYOPOP, Inc. (Tokyopop Kids).

Display Measures. 2005. (YA). tchr. ed. (978-1-58246-136-6(8) , Tricycle Pr.) Ten Speed Pr.

Ditchfield, Christin. Cowlick! Beardshaw, Rosalind, illus. 2007. (Deluxe Golden Book Ser.). 40p. (J). (ps-k). 14.99 (978-0-375-83540-7(7)); lib. bdg. 17.99 (978-0-375-93540-4(1)) Random Hse. Children's Bks. (Golden Bks.).

DiTerlizzi, Tony. Jimmy Zangwow's Out-of-This-World Moon-Pie Adventure. DiTerlizzi, Tony, illus. 2003. (Illus.). 40p. (J). pap. 6.99 (978-0-689-85563-4(X) , Aladdin) Simon & Schuster Children's Publishing.

—Ted. 2004. (gr. k-3). lib. bdg. 15.30 (978-0-613-88653-6(4)) Tandem Library Bks.

Dodd, Lynley. Hairy Maclary, Sit. Dodd, Lynley, illus. 2001. (Gold Star First Readers Ser.). (Illus.). 32p. (J). (gr. 1 up). lib. bdg. 22.00 (978-0-8368-2808-5(9)) Stevens, Gareth Inc.

Dodd, Quentin. Beatnik Rutabagas from Beyond the Stars. 2001. (Illus.). 224p. (J). (gr. 4-6). 17.00 (978-0-374-30515-4(3) , Farrar, Straus & Giroux (BYR)) Farrar, Straus & Giroux.

—The Princess of Neptune. 2004. 224p. (J). 17.00 (978-0-374-36119-8(3) , Farrar, Straus & Giroux (BYR)) Farrar, Straus & Giroux.

Dodson, Emma. Badly Drawn Dog. 2004. (Illus.). 32p. (J). 14.95 (978-0-7641-5814-8(7)) Barron's Educational Series, Inc.

Doherty, Berlie. Coconut Comes to School. Bates, Ivan, illus. 2002. 32p. (J). 18.00 (978-0-00-710433-8(2)) HarperCollins Pubs. Ltd. GBR. *Dist:* Trafalgar Square Publishing.

Doherty, Paula. Going Places-Plane. Doherty, Paula, illus. 2005. (Going Places Board Bks.). (Illus.). 10p. (J). bds. 4.99 (978-0-7641-5886-5(4)) Barron's Educational Series, Inc.

—Going Places-Tractor. Doherty, Paula, illus. 2005. (Going Places Board Bks.). (Illus.). 10p. (J). bds. 4.99 (978-0-7641-5887-2(2)) Barron's Educational Series, Inc.

—Going Places-Train. Doherty, Paula, illus. 2005. (Going Places Board Bks.). (Illus.). 10p. (J). bds. 4.95 (978-0-7641-5888-9(0)) Barron's Educational Series, Inc.

Dominguez, Carlos. El Hombre de Otra Galaxia. 2001. Tr. of Men from Another Galaxy. (SPA.). 112p. (J). 7.95 (978-84-348-2709-7(3)) SM Ediciones ESP. *Dist:* AIMS International Bks., Inc.

Dominguez, Ramon Garcia. Una Pirana en mi Banera. (SPA.). (J). 7.95 (978-958-04-6022-0(1)) Norma S.A. COL. *Dist:* Distribuidora Norma, Inc.

Donaldson, Julia. El Grufalo. Scheffler, Axel, illus. 2003. (SPA.). 32p. (J). (gr. k-2). 7.96 (978-84-233-3145-1(8) , DS4478) Ediciones Destino ESP. *Dist:* Lectorum Pubns., Inc.

—The Spiffiest Giant in Town. Scheffler, Axel, illus. 2005. 32p. (J). reprint ed. pap. 5.99 (978-0-14-240275-7(3) , Puffin) Penguin Group (USA) Inc.

Dorion, Betty F. Whose Side Are You On? 2005. (Illus.). 216p. (J). (gr. 6 up). pap. 7.95 (978-1-55050-179-7(8)) Coteau Bks. CAN. *Dist:* Fitzhenry & Whiteside, Ltd.

Dorros, Arthur. When the Pigs Took Over. Greenseid, Diane, illus. 2002. (SPA.). 32p. (J). (ps-2). 15.99 (978-0-525-42030-9(4) , Dutton Juvenile) Penguin Group (USA) Inc.

Dower, Laura. Shrek & Fiona's Slide Show Projector Book. 2004. (Shrek 2 Ser.). (Illus.). 32p. (J). pap. 21.99 (978-0-439-57631-4(8)) Scholastic, Inc.

—Thanks for Nothing. Powers, Stephanie, illus. 2001. (From the Files of Madison Finn Ser.: Vol. 5). 165p. (J). (gr. 3-7). pap. 4.99 (978-0-7868-1557-9(4) , Volo) Hyperion Bks. for Children.

—Three's a Crowd, Bk. 16. rev. ed. 2004. (From the Files of Madison Finn Ser.: Vol. 16). 192p. (J). (gr. 3-7). pap. 4.99 (978-0-7868-0986-8(8)) Hyperion Bks. for Children.

Downard, Barry. Flash Harry Hare & Tom Tortoise. Downard, Barry, illus. 2008. 40p. (J). 15.99 (***978-1-4169-2509-5(0)*** , Simon & Schuster Children's Publishing) Simon & Schuster Children's Publishing.

Downing, Erin. Dancing Queen. 2006. (Romantic Comedies Ser.). 272p. (YA). pap. 6.99 (978-1-4169-2510-1(4) , Simon Pulse) Simon & Schuster Children's Publishing.

—Prom Crashers. 2007. (Romantic Comedies Ser.). 256p. (YA). pap. 6.99 (978-1-4169-3559-9(2) , Simon Pulse) Simon & Schuster Children's Publishing.

Downs, Celise. Secrets & Kisses. 2nd ed. 2004. Orig. Title: Undercover Love. (YA). per. 10.00 (978-0-9752907-2-9(X)) Gemini Mojo Pr.

Doyle, Roddy. The Giggler Treatment. Ajhar, Brian, illus. 2001. 112p. (J). (gr. 3-7). pap. 4.99 (978-0-439-16300-2(5) , Levine, Arthur A. Bks.) Scholastic, Inc.

—The Giggler Treatment. 2001. 10.79 (978-0-606-22178-8(6)); (gr. 3-6). lib. bdg. 11.80 (978-0-613-44359-3(4)) Tandem Library Bks.

—The Meanwhile Adventures. Ajhar, Brian, illus. 176p. (J). 2006. pap. 5.99 (978-0-439-66211-6(7)); 2004. (gr. 4-7). pap. 16.95 (978-0-439-66210-9(9)) Scholastic, Inc. (Levine, Arthur A. Bks.).

—Rover Saves Christmas. Ajhar, Brian, illus. 160p. (J). 2003. pap. 4.99 (978-0-439-30533-4(0)); 2001. (gr. 3-7). pap. 14.95 (978-0-439-30530-3(6)) Scholastic, Inc. (Levine, Arthur A. Bks.).

—Rover Saves Christmas. 2003. (gr. 3-6). lib. bdg. 13.00 (978-0-613-72061-8(X)) Tandem Library Bks.

Dr. Seuss Enterprises Staff. Hop on Pop. 2004. (Illus.). 24p. (J). (gr. k-ps). bds. 4.99 (978-0-375-82837-9(0) , Random Hse. Bks. for Young Readers) Random Hse. Children's Bks.

Drachman, Eric. It's Me! Isabelle, Decenciere, illus. 2004. 32p. 18.95 (978-0-9703809-2-0(5)) Kidwick Bks.

Driscoll, Laura. Slow down, Sara! 2003. (gr. k-3). lib. bdg. 13.00 (978-0-613-79273-8(4)) Tandem Library Bks.

Dubowski, Cathy East. Flubber. 2000. (SPA., Illus.). (J). pap. 9.95 (978-84-406-8184-3(4)) Ediciones B ESP. *Dist:* Distribooks, Inc.

Duffield, Katy. Farmer McPeepers' Milk Cows. Gray, Steve, illus. 2003. 32p. (gr. k-4). 15.95 (978-0-87358-825-6(8) , Rising Moon Bks. for Young Readers) Northland Publishing.

Dumbleton, Mike. Cat. Smith, Craig, illus. 2008. 32p. (J). 15.95 (***978-1-933605-73-9(1))*** Kane/Miller Bk. Pubs., Inc.

Dunbar, Joyce. Magic Lemonade. McCafferty, Jan, illus. 2001. (Blue Bananas Ser.). 48p. (J). (gr. 1-2). (978-0-7787-0839-1(X)); pap. (978-0-7787-0885-8(3)) Crabtree Publishing Co.

—Magic Lemonade. McCafferty, Jan, illus. 2001. 48p. (J). (ps-ps). lib. bdg. 12.95 (978-0-613-52875-7(1)) Tandem Library Bks.

—Where's My Sock? Rescek, Sanja, illus. 2006. 32p. (J). pap. 15.99 (978-0-439-74831-5(3) , Chicken Hse., The) Scholastic, Inc.

Dunfey, Beth, ed. Hi Hi Puffy Amiyumi Chapter Book. 2006. (Illus.). 64p. (J). pap. 3.99 (978-0-439-75021-9(0) , Scholastic Paperbacks) Scholastic, Inc.

Durand, Delphine. Bob & Co. 2007. (Illus.). 64p. (J). (ps-3). pap. 9.95 (***978-1-85437-723-4(X))*** Tate Gallery Publishing, Ltd. GBR. *Dist:* Hachette Bk. Group.

—My House. Adams, Sarah, tr. 2007. (Illus.). 44p. (J). (gr. k-2). 12.95 (***978-1-905341-09-2(1)***) WingedChariot Pr. GBR. *Dist:* Independent Pubs. Group.

Durango, Julia. Cha-Cha Chimps. Taylor, Eleanor, illus. 2006. 32p. (J). (ps-1). 15.95 (978-0-689-86456-8(6)) Simon & Schuster Children's Publishing.

—Dream Hop. Lee, Jared D., illus. 2005. 32p. (J). (gr. k-2). 15.95 (978-0-689-87163-4(5)) Simon & Schuster Children's Publishing.

Durant, Alan. Burger Boy. Matsuoka, Mei, illus. 2006. 32p. (J). (gr. k-3). 16.00 (978-0-618-71466-7(9) , Clarion Bks.) Houghton Mifflin Co. Trade & Reference Div.

—Creepe Hall for Ever! l.t. ed. 2005. (Illus.). 112p. (J). pap. (978-0-7540-6142-7(6) , CLP 333) BBC Audio.

Durrant, Sabine. Cross Your Heart, Connie Pickles. 2007. 272p. (J). (gr. 7 up). 16.99 (978-0-06-085479-9(0)); lib. bdg. 17.89 (978-0-06-085480-5(4)) HarperCollins Pubs. (HarperTeen).

Dutton, Sandra. Dear Miss Perfect: A Beast's Guide to Proper Behavior. 2007. (Illus.). 48p. (J). (gr. k-3). 16.00 (978-0-618-67717-7(8)) Houghton Mifflin Co.

Earls, Nick. 48 Shades of Brown. 2004. 288p. (YA). (gr. 7 up). pap. 6.99 (978-0-618-45295-8(8) , Graphia) Houghton Mifflin Co. Trade & Reference Div.

—48 Shades of Brown. 1999. 300p. (YA). pap. (978-0-14-028769-1(8)) Penguin Group (USA) Inc.

Edwards, Pamela. Oliver Has Something to Say! Pilon, Louis, illus. 2007. 24p. (J). (ps-1). (978-1-897073-52-0(6)) Lobster Pr.

Edwards, Pamela Duncan. Dinorella: A Prehistoric Fairy Tale. 1999. (gr. k-3). lib. bdg. 14.15 (978-0-613-74987-9(1)) Tandem Library Bks.

—Honk! The Story of a Prima Swanerina. 2000. (gr. k-3). lib. bdg. 14.15 (978-0-613-29978-7(7)) Tandem Library Bks.

Edwards, Pat. Monster from Mercury. 1999. (gr. 3-6). lib. bdg. 10.95 (978-0-613-19402-0(0)) Tandem Library Bks.

—Planet X. 1999. (gr. 3-6). lib. bdg. 10.95 (978-0-613-19422-8(5)) Tandem Library Bks.

—What's That? 1999. (gr. k-3). lib. bdg. 10.95 (978-0-613-30867-0(0)) Tandem Library Bks.

Egan, Tim. Burnt Toast on Davenport Street. Egan, Tim, illus. 2001. (Sandpiper Bks.). (Illus.). 32p. (J). (gr. k-3). pap. 6.95 (978-0-618-11121-3(2)) Houghton Mifflin Co. Trade & Reference Div.

Ehrlich, Amy. Bravo, Kazam! Saltzberg, Barney, illus. 2002. (Brand New Readers Ser.). (J). (ps-2). 8p. 12.99 (978-0-7636-1315-0(0)); 32p. pap. 5.99 (978-0-7636-1316-7(9)) Candlewick Pr.

Eliot, Jan. The First Collection of the Syndicated Cartoon Strip, No. 1. 2004. 128p. pap. 10.95 (978-0-9674102-2-7(3)) Four Panel Pr.

Elish, Dan. Attack of the Frozen Woodchucks. 2008. 256p. (J). 17.89 (***978-0-06-113871-3(1)*** , Geringer, Laura Book) HarperCollins Pubs.

—Attack of the Frozen Woodchucks. Call, Greg, illus. 2008. 256p. (J). 16.99 (***978-0-06-113870-6(3)*** , Geringer, Laura Book) HarperCollins Pubs.

Elliott, David. Evangeline Mudd: And the Golden-Haired Apes of the Ikkinasti Jungle. Wesson, Andrea, tr. Wesson, Andrea, illus. 2004. 208p. (J). (gr. 2-5). 15.99 (978-0-7636-1876-6(4)) Candlewick Pr.

—Evangeline Mudd & the Golden-Haired Apes of the Ikkinasti Jungle. Wesson, Andrea, illus. 2007. 208p. (J). (gr. 2-5). 5.99 (978-0-7636-2614-3(7)) Candlewick Pr.

—Evangeline Mudd & the Great Mink Escapade. Wesson, Andrea, illus. 2006. 192p. (J). (gr. 2-5). 15.99 (978-0-7636-2295-4(8)) Candlewick Pr.

—Hazel Nutt, Alien Hunter. Kelley, True, illus. 2005. 32p. (J). tchr. ed. 16.95 (978-0-8234-1843-5(X)) Holiday Hse., Inc.

Ellis, Deborah. A Company of Fools. 192p. (gr. 5 up). 2004. (J). pap. (978-1-55041-721-0(5)); 2002. (YA). (978-1-55041-719-7(3)) Fitzhenry & Whiteside, Ltd.

Ellis, Kiersten. Do Planets Hang on Strings? 2006. 24p. (J). per. 11.99 (***978-1-59886-688-9(5)***); 14.99 (***978-1-59886-992-7(2)***) Tate Publishing & Enterprises, L.L.C.

Ellis, Sarah. The Queen's Feet. Petricic, Dusan, illus. 2006. 32p. 17.95 (978-0-88995-320-8(1)) Red Deer Pr. CAN. *Dist:* F & W Pubns., Inc., Fitzhenry & Whiteside, Ltd.

Emmons, Katherine M. Keep Moving Forward. Husband, Ron, illus. 2007. (Meet the Robinsons Ser.). 24p. (J). pap. 3.99 (978-0-06-112469-3(9)) HarperCollins Pubs.

Emzer, Counselor. Duane, You Must be Insane. 2005. 20p. 7.97 (978-1-4116-3091-8(2)) Lulu.com.

Enderle, Judith Ross & Tessler, Stephanie Gordon. Six Creepy Sheep. O'Brien, John, illus. 2003. 24p. (J). (ps up). pap. 8.95 (978-1-56397-242-3(5)) Boyds Mills Pr.

English, David. Confessions English Eccentric. 2006. (Illus.). 256p. 44.50 (978-1-4050-5361-7(5)) Macmillan Publishers Ltd. GBR. *Dist:* Trans-Atlantic Pubns., Inc.

The Enormous Egg. 2004. (Literature Units Ser.). (Illus.). 48p. 7.99 (978-1-57690-632-3(9)) Teacher Created Materials, Inc.

Enormous Elephant Show. 2001. (ps-2). lib. bdg. 9.80 (978-0-613-32505-9(2)) Tandem Library Bks.

Enriquez, Jose. Saving the Mango Farm. 2006. 23p. (J). 10.98 (978-1-4116-5917-9(1)) Lulu.com.

Entara Ltd., photos by. Mind Your Manners. 2007. (Jakers! Ser.). 24p. (J). (ps-2). pap. 3.99 (***978-1-4169-4715-8(9)*** , Simon Spotlight) Simon & Schuster Children's Publishing.

Erickson, John R. The Case of the Black-Hooded Hangmans. Holmes, Gerald L., illus. 1998. (Hank the Cowdog Ser.: No. 24). 144p. (J). (gr. 2-5). 15.99 (978-0-670-88431-5(6) , Viking Juvenile); Vol. 24. pap. 4.99 (978-0-14-130400-7(6) , Puffin) Penguin Group (USA) Inc.

—The Case of the Black-Hooded Hangmans. 1999. (Hank the Cowdog Ser.: No. 24). (gr. 3-6). lib. bdg. 13.00 (978-0-7857-6345-1(7)) Tandem Library Bks.

—The Case of the Blazing Sky, No. 51. Holmes, Gerald L., illus. 2008. (Hank the Cowdog Ser.). 144p. (J). (gr. 3). 5.99 (***978-0-14-241015-8(2)*** , Puffin) Penguin Group (USA) Inc.

—The Case of the Blazing Sky #51. Holmes, Gerald L., illus. 2008. (Hank the Cowdog Ser.). 144p. (J). (gr. 3). 15.99 (***978-0-670-06260-7(X)*** , Viking Juvenile) Penguin Group (USA) Inc.

—The Case of the Burrowing Robot, Vol. 42. Holmes, Gerald L., illus. 2003. (Hank the Cowdog Ser.: No. 42). 144p. (J). (gr. 3). 15.99 (978-0-670-03632-5(3) , Viking Juvenile); (gr. 4-6). pap. 4.99 (978-0-14-250063-7(1) , Puffin) Penguin Group (USA) Inc.

—The Case of the Burrowing Robot. 2003. (Hank the Cowdog Ser.: No. 42). (gr. 3-6). lib. bdg. 13.00 (978-0-613-66353-3(5)) Tandem Library Bks.

—The Case of the Car-Barkaholic Dog. Holmes, Gerald L., illus. 1998. (Hank the Cowdog Ser.: No. 17). 144p. (J). (gr. 2-5). pap. 4.99 (978-0-14-130393-2(X) , Puffin) Penguin Group (USA) Inc.

—The Case of the Deadly Ha-Ha Game. 2001. (Hank the Cowdog Ser.: No. 37). (gr. 3-6). lib. bdg. 13.00 (978-0-613-33649-9(6)) Tandem Library Bks.

—The Case of the Double Bumblebee Sting. Holmes, Gerald L., illus. 1998. (Hank the Cowdog Ser.: No. 22). 144p. (J). (gr. 2-5). 14.99 (978-0-670-88429-2(4) , Viking Juvenile); Vol. 22. pap. 4.99 (978-0-14-130398-7(0) , Puffin) Penguin Group (USA) Inc.

—The Case of the Falling Sky. Holmes, Gerald L., illus. 2005. (Hank the Cowdog Ser.: No. 45). (J). 144p. pap. 4.99 (978-0-14-240296-2(6) , Puffin); 160p. (gr. 3-7). 15.99 (978-0-670-05999-7(4) , Viking Juvenile) Penguin Group (USA) Inc.

—The Case of the Garbage Monster from Outer Space. Holmes, Gerald L., illus. 1999. (Hank the Cowdog Ser.: No. 32). 144p. (J). (gr. 2-5). 13.99 (978-0-670-88488-9(X) , Viking Juvenile) Penguin Group (USA) Inc.

—The Case of the Halloween Ghost. Holmes, Gerald L., illus. 1998. (Hank the Cowdog Ser.: No. 9). 144p. (J). (gr. 2-5). 14.99 (978-0-670-88416-2(2) , Viking Juvenile); No. 9. pap. 4.99 (978-0-14-130385-7(9) , Puffin) Penguin Group (USA) Inc.

—The Case of the Haystack Kitties. Holmes, Gerald L., illus. 1998. (Hank the Cowdog Ser.: No. 30). 144p. (J). (gr. 2-5). 14.99 (978-0-670-88437-7(5) , Viking Juvenile); Vol. 30. pap. 4.99 (978-0-14-130406-9(5) , Puffin) Penguin Group (USA) Inc.

—The Case of the Hooking Bull, Vol. 18. Holmes, Gerald L., illus. 1998. (Hank the Cowdog Ser.: No. 18). 144p. (J). (gr. 2-5). pap. 4.99 (978-0-14-130394-9(8) , Puffin) Penguin Group (USA) Inc.

—The Case of the Kidnapped Collie. Holmes, Gerald L., illus. 1998. (Hank the Cowdog Ser.: No. 26). 144p. (J). (gr. 2-5). 14.99 (978-0-670-88433-9(2) , Viking Juvenile); Vol. 26. pap. 4.99 (978-0-14-130402-1(2) , Puffin) Penguin Group (USA) Inc.

—The Case of the Kidnapped Collie. 1999. (Hank the Cowdog Ser.: No. 26). (gr. 3-6). lib. bdg. 13.00 (978-0-7857-9075-4(6)) Tandem Library Bks.

—The Case of the Kidnapped Collie. Holmes, Gerald L., illus. 1999. (Hank the Cowdog Ser.: No. 26). (J). (gr. 2-5). 11.64 (978-0-606-09375-0(3)) Tandem Library Bks.

—The Case of the Measled Cowboy. Holmes, Gerald L., illus. 1999. (Hank the Cowdog Ser.: No. 33). 144p. (J). (gr. 2-5). 13.99 (978-0-670-88489-6(8) , Viking Juvenile); Vol. 33. pap. 4.99 (978-0-14-130423-6(5) , Puffin) Penguin Group (USA) Inc.

—The Case of the Measled Cowboy. 1999. (Hank the Cowdog Ser.: No. 33). (J). (gr. 2-5). 11.64 (978-0-606-17534-0(2)); (gr. 3-6). lib. bdg. 13.00 (978-0-613-14613-5(1)) Tandem Library Bks.

—The Case of the Midnight Rustler. Holmes, Gerald L., illus. 1998. (Hank the Cowdog Ser.: No. 19). 144p. (J). (gr. 2-5). 14.99 (978-0-670-88426-1(X) , Viking Juvenile); pap. 4.99 (978-0-14-130395-6(6) , Puffin) Penguin Group (USA) Inc.

—The Case of the Missing Bird Dog, Vol. 40. Holmes, Gerald L., illus. 2002. (Hank the Cowdog Ser.: No. 40). 144p. (J). 15.99 (978-0-670-03558-8(0) , Viking Juvenile); pap. 4.99 (978-0-14-230141-8(8) , Puffin) Penguin Group (USA) Inc.

—The Case of the Missing Cat. Holmes, Gerald L., illus. (Hank the Cowdog Ser.: No. 15). 144p. (J). (gr. 2-5). 2000. 14.99 (978-0-670-88422-3(7) , Viking Juvenile); 1998. pap. 4.99 (978-0-14-130391-8(3) , Puffin) Penguin Group (USA) Inc.

—The Case of the Missing Cat. 1999. (Hank the Cowdog Ser.: No. 15). (gr. 3-6). lib. bdg. 13.00 (978-0-8335-6828-1(0)) Tandem Library Bks.

—The Case of the Monkey Burglar. Holmes, Gerald L., illus. 2006. (Hank the Cowdog Ser.: NMo. 48). 129p. (J). lib. bdg. 17.00 (***978-1-4242-1604-8(4)***) Fitzgerald Bks.

—The Case of the Most Ancient Bone. Homes, Gerald L., illus. 2007. (Hank the Cowdog Ser.). 192p. (J). (gr. 3). 16.99 (978-0-670-06224-9(3) , Viking Juvenile) Penguin Group (USA) Inc.

—The Case of the Most Ancient Bone, No. 50. Holmes, Gerald L., illus. 2007. (Hank the Cowdog Ser.: No. 50). 256p. (J). (gr. 3). pap. 5.99 (978-0-14-240800-1(X) , Puffin) Penguin Group (USA) Inc.

—The Case of the Night-Stalking Bone Monster. Holmes, Gerald L., illus. 1998. (Hank the Cowdog Ser.: No. 27). 144p. (J). (gr. 2-5). 14.99 (978-0-670-88434-6(0) , Viking Juvenile); Vol. 27. pap. 4.99 (978-0-14-130403-8(0) , Puffin) Penguin Group (USA) Inc.

—The Case of the One-Eyed Killer Stud Horse, Vol. 8. Holmes, Gerald L., illus. 1998. (Hank the Cowdog Ser.: No. 8). 144p. (gr. 2-5). pap. 4.99 (978-0-14-130384-0(0) , Puffin) Penguin Group (USA) Inc.

—The Case of the Raging Rottweiler. Holmes, Gerald L., illus. 2000. (Hank the Cowdog Ser.: No. 36). (J). (gr. 2-5). 144p. 14.99 (978-0-670-89364-5(1) , Viking Juvenile); Vol. 36. 160p. pap. 4.99 (978-0-14-130668-1(8) , Puffin) Penguin Group (USA) Inc.

—The Case of the Raging Rottweiler. 2000. (Hank the Cowdog Ser.: No. 36). (gr. 3-6). lib. bdg. 13.00 (978-0-613-31048-2(9)); (Illus.). (J). 11.64 (978-0-606-20460-6(1)) Tandem Library Bks.

—The Case of the Saddle House Robbery. 2000. (Hank the Cowdog Ser.: No. 35). (gr. 3-6). lib. bdg. 13.00 (978-0-613-24495-4(8)) Tandem Library Bks.

—The Case of the Shipwrecked Tree. Holmes, Gerald L., illus. 2003. (Hank the Cowdog Ser.: No. 41). 144p. (J). (gr. 3-7). 14.99 (978-0-670-03603-5(X) , Viking Juvenile); (gr. 4-6). pap. 4.99 (978-0-14-230225-5(2) , Puffin) Penguin Group (USA) Inc.

—The Case of the Shipwrecked Tree. 2003. (Hank the Cowdog Ser.: No. 41). (gr. 3-6). lib. bdg. 13.00 (978-0-613-61613-3(8)) Tandem Library Bks.

—The Case of the Swirling Killer Tornado. Holmes, Gerald L., illus. 1998. (Hank the Cowdog Ser.: No. 25). 144p. (J). (gr. 2-5). 14.99 (978-0-670-88432-2(4) , Viking Juvenile); Vol. 25. pap. 4.99 (978-0-14-130401-4(4) , Puffin) Penguin Group (USA) Inc.

—The Case of the Tender Cheeping Chickies. Holmes, Gerald L., illus. 2005. (Hank the Cowdog Ser.: No. 47). 129p. (J). lib. bdg. 17.00 (***978-1-4242-1605-5(2)***) Fitzgerald Bks.

—The Case of the Tricky Trap. Holmes, Gerald L., illus. 2005. (Hank the Cowdog Ser.: No. 46). 126p. (J). lib. bdg. 17.00 (***978-1-4242-1603-1(6)***) Fitzgerald Bks.

—The Case of the Twisted Kitty. Holmes, Gerald L., illus. 2004. (Hank the Cowdog Ser.: No. 43). 131p. (J). lib. bdg. 17.00 (***978-1-4242-1600-0(1)***) Fitzgerald Bks.

—The Case of the Twisted Kitty, Vol. 43. Holmes, Gerald L., tr. Holmes, Gerald L., illus. 2004. (Hank the Cowdog Ser.: No. 43). 144p. (J). pap. 4.99 (978-0-14-240041-8(6) , Puffin) Penguin Group (USA) Inc.

—The Case of the Vampire Cat. Holmes, Gerald L., illus. 1998. (Hank the Cowdog Ser.: No. 21). 144p. (J). (gr. 2-5). 14.99 (978-0-670-88428-5(6) , Viking Juvenile); Vol. 21. pap. 4.99 (978-0-14-130397-0(2) , Puffin) Penguin Group (USA) Inc.

—The Case of the Vampire Vacuum Sweeper. Holmes, Gerald L., illus. 1998. (Hank the Cowdog Ser.: No. 29). 144p. (J). (gr. 2-5). 14.99 (978-0-670-88436-0(7) , Viking Juvenile); (gr. 3-7). pap. 4.99 (978-0-14-130405-2(7) , Puffin) Penguin Group (USA) Inc.

—The Case of the Vanishing Fishhook. Holmes, Gerald L., illus. 1999. (Hank the Cowdog Ser.: No. 31). 144p. (J). (gr. 2-5). 14.99 (978-0-670-88438-4(3) , Viking Juvenile); Vol. 31. pap. 4.99 (978-0-14-130356-7(5) , Puffin) Penguin Group (USA) Inc.

—The Case of the Vanishing Fishhook. 1999. (Hank the Cowdog Ser.: No. 31). (gr. 3-6). lib. bdg. 13.00 (978-0-613-11389-2(6)) Tandem Library Bks.

—The Curse of the Incredible Priceless Corncob. Holmes, Gerald L., illus. 1998. (Hank the Cowdog Ser.: No. 7). 144p. (J). (gr. 2-5). 14.99 (978-0-670-88414-8(6) , Viking Juvenile); Vol. 7. pap. 4.99 (978-0-14-130383-3(2) , Puffin) Penguin Group (USA) Inc.

—The Dungeon of Doom. Holmes, Gerald L., illus. 2004. (Hank the Cowdog Ser.: No. 44). 122p. (J). lib. bdg. 17.00 (***978-1-4242-1601-7(X)***) Fitzgerald Bks.

—Every Dog Has His Day. Holmes, Gerald L., illus. 1998. (Hank the Cowdog Ser.: No. 10). 144p. (J). (gr. 2-5). 15.99 (978-0-670-88417-9(0) , Viking Juvenile); pap. 4.99 (978-0-14-130386-4(7) , Puffin) Penguin Group (USA) Inc.

—Faded Love. Holmes, Gerald L., illus. 1998. (Hank the Cowdog Ser.: No. 5). 144p. (J). (gr. 2-5). 14.99 (978-0-670-88412-4(X) , Viking Juvenile); Vol. 5. pap. 4.99 (978-0-14-130381-9(6) , Puffin) Penguin Group (USA) Inc.

—The Fling, Vol. 38. Holmes, Gerald L., illus. 2001. (Hank the Cowdog Ser.: No. 38). 144p. (J). (gr. 2-5). pap. 4.99 (978-0-14-131174-6(6) , Puffin) Penguin Group (USA) Inc.

—The Further Adventures of Hank the Cowdog. Holmes, Gerald L., illus. (Hank the Cowdog Ser.: No. 2). 144p. (J). 1999. (gr. 2-5). pap. 4.99 (978-0-14-130378-9(6) , Puffin); 1998. (gr. 3-5). 14.99 (978-0-670-88409-4(X) , Viking Juvenile) Penguin Group (USA) Inc.

—The Further Adventures of Hank the Cowdog. Holmes, Gerald L., illus. 1999. (Hank the Cowdog Ser.: No. 2). (J). (gr. 2-5). lib. bdg. 13.00 (978-0-8335-6816-8(7)) Tandem Library Bks.

—The Garbage Monster from Outer Space, Vol. 32. Holmes, Gerald L., illus. 1999. (Hank the Cowdog Ser.: No. 32). 144p. (J). (gr. 2-5). pap. 4.99 (978-0-14-130422-9(7) , Puffin) Penguin Group (USA) Inc.

—The Garbage Monster from Outer Space. 1999. (Hank the Cowdog Ser.: No. 32). (J). (gr. 2-5). 11.64 (978-0-606-16827-4(3)); (gr. 3-6). lib. bdg. 13.00 (978-0-613-14748-4(0)) Tandem Library Bks.

—Hank Cowdog 50. Holmes, Gerard L., illus. 2007. 256p. 16.99 (***978-0-670-62249-8(4)*** , Viking Adult) Penguin Group (USA) Inc.

—Hank the Cowdog & Monkey Business. Holmes, Gerald L., illus. 1999. (Hank the Cowdog Ser.: No. 14). (J). (gr. 3-6). lib. bdg. 13.00 (978-0-8335-6827-4(2)) Tandem Library Bks.

—It's a Dog's Life. Holmes, Gerald L., illus. (Hank the Cowdog Ser.: No. 3). 100p. (J). (gr. 2-5). 9.95 (978-0-916941-04-8(3)) Maverick Bks., Inc.

—It's a Dog's Life. Holmes, Gerald L., illus. 1998. (Hank the Cowdog Ser.: No. 3). 144p. (J). (gr. 2-5). 14.99 (978-0-670-88410-0(3) , Viking Juvenile); pap. 4.99 (978-0-14-130379-6(4) , Puffin) Penguin Group (USA) Inc.

—Let Sleeping Dogs Lie. Holmes, Gerald L., illus. 1998. (Hank the Cowdog Ser.: No. 6). 144p. (J). (gr. 2-5). pap. 4.99 (978-0-14-130382-6(4) , Puffin) Penguin Group (USA) Inc.

—Lost in the Blinded Blizzard. Holmes, Gerald L., illus. 1998. (Hank the Cowdog Ser.: No. 16). 144p. (J). (gr. 2-5). 14.99 (978-0-670-88423-0(5) , Viking Juvenile); pap. 4.99 (978-0-14-130392-5(1) , Puffin) Penguin Group (USA) Inc.

—Lost in the Dark Unchanted Forest, Vol. 11. Holmes, Gerald L., illus. 1998. (Hank the Cowdog Ser.: No. 11). 144p. (J). (gr. 2-5). pap. 4.99 (978-0-14-130387-1(5) , Puffin) Penguin Group (USA) Inc.

—Monkey Business. Holmes, Gerald L., illus. 1998. (Hank the Cowdog Ser.: No. 14). 144p. (J). (gr. 2-5). 14.99 (978-0-670-88421-6(9) , Viking Juvenile); Vol. 14. pap. 4.99 (978-0-14-130390-1(5) , Puffin) Penguin Group (USA) Inc.

—Moonlight Madness. Holmes, Gerald L., illus. 1998. (Hank the Cowdog Ser.: No. 23). 144p. (J). (gr. 2-5). 15.99 (978-0-670-88430-8(8) , Viking Juvenile); Vol. 23. pap. 4.99 (978-0-14-130399-4(9) , Puffin) Penguin Group (USA) Inc.

—The Mopwater Files. Holmes, Gerald L., illus. 1998. (Hank the Cowdog Ser.: No. 28). 144p. (J). (gr. 2-5). 14.99 (978-0-670-88435-3(9) , Viking Juvenile); pap. 4.99 (978-0-14-130404-5(9) , Puffin) Penguin Group (USA) Inc.

—Murder in the Middle Pasture. Holmes, Gerald L., illus. 1998. (Hank the Cowdog Ser.: No. 4). 144p. (J). (gr. 2-5). 14.99 (978-0-670-88411-7(1) , Viking Juvenile); Vol. 4. pap. 4.99 (978-0-14-130380-2(8) , Puffin) Penguin Group (USA) Inc.

—Murder in the Middle Pasture. Holmes, Gerald L., illus. 1999. (Hank the Cowdog Ser.: No. 4). (J). (gr. 3-6). lib. bdg. 13.00 (978-0-8335-6817-5(5)) Tandem Library Bks.

—The Original Adventures of Hank the Cowdog. Holmes, Gerald L., illus. 1998. (Hank the Cowdog Ser.: No. 1). 144p. (J). (gr. 2-5). pap. 4.99 (978-0-14-130377-2(8) , Puffin) Penguin Group (USA) Inc.

—The Original Adventures of Hank the Cowdog. Holmes, Gerald L., illus. 1999. (Hank the Cowdog Ser.: No. 1). (J). (gr. 3-6). lib. bdg. 13.00 (978-0-8335-6815-1(9)) Tandem Library Bks.

—The Phantom in the Mirror. Holmes, Gerald L., illus. (Hank the Cowdog Ser.: No. 20). 144p. (J). (gr. 2-5). 2000. 14.99 (978-0-670-88427-8(8) , Viking Juvenile); Vol. 20. 1998. pap. 4.99 (978-0-14-130396-3(4) , Puffin) Penguin Group (USA) Inc.

—The Secret Laundry Monster Files, Vol. 39. Holmes, Gerald L., illus. 2002. (Hank the Cowdog Ser.: No. 39). 144p. (J). pap. 4.99 (978-0-14-230076-3(4) , Puffin) Penguin Group (USA) Inc.

—The Secret Laundry Monster Files. 2002. (Hank the Cowdog Ser.: No. 39). (gr. 3-6). lib. bdg. 13.00 (978-0-613-43642-7(3)) Tandem Library Bks.

—Slim's Good-Bye. Holmes, Gerald L., illus. 2000. (Hank the Cowdog Ser.: No. 34). 144p. (J). (gr. 2-5). 15.99 (978-0-670-88889-4(3) , Viking Juvenile); Vol. 34. pap. 4.99 (978-0-14-130677-3(7) , Puffin) Penguin Group (USA) Inc.

—Slim's Good-Bye. 2000. (Hank the Cowdog Ser.: No. 34). (gr. 3-6). lib. bdg. 13.00 (978-0-613-22391-1(8)); (Illus.). (J). (gr. 2-5). (978-0-606-18408-3(2)) Tandem Library Bks.

Ernst, Lisa Campbell. The Gingerbread Girl. Ernst, Lisa Campbell, illus. 2006. (Illus.). 36p. (J). (ps). 16.99 (978-0-525-47667-2(9) , Dutton Juvenile) Penguin Group (USA) Inc.

—Goldilocks Returns. Ernst, Lisa Campbell, illus. 2000. (Illus.). 40p. (J). (ps-3). 16.95 (978-0-689-82537-8(4)) Simon & Schuster Children's Publishing.

Esoldi, Vin. May Maisey Moo's Cowllection of Moo Tales Vol. I: The Convention. Bourdeaux, Robert, illus. 1999. (J). 48p. 17.95 (978-1-929745-00-5(1) , MMM 001); 99p. 29.95 (978-1-929745-01-2(X) , MM 001) Paula Pr. Pubs. (May Maisey Moo).

Evans, Douglas. The Elevator Family. 2001. (J). 11.30 (978-0-606-21173-4(X)) Tandem Library Bks.

Everett Hale, Edward. Last of the Peterkins with Others of the. 2006. pap. (***978-1-4068-1087-5(8)***) Echo Library.

Evers, Alf & Evers, Helen. The House the Pecks Built. 2001. (Illus.). 48p. (J). (gr. 3-7). 18.95 (978-0-87951-726-7(3)) Overlook Pr., The.

Fagan, Cary. Directed by Kaspar Snit. 2007. 160p. (J). (gr. 3-7). pap. 9.95 (978-0-88776-753-1(2) , Delacorte Bks. for Young Readers) Random Hse. Children's Bks.

—The Fortress of Kaspar Snit. 2004. (gr. 3-6). lib. bdg. 18.75 (978-0-613-77346-1(2)) Tandem Library Bks.

Failing, Barbara Larmon. Lasso Lou & Cowboy Mccoy. Arnold, Tedd, illus. 2003. 40p. (J). (gr. k-3). 16.99 (978-0-8037-2578-2(7) , Dial) Penguin Group (USA) Inc.

Fairbairn, John. Green Slime. Allen, Rosemary, illus. 96p. pap. 9.95 (978-0-7022-2488-1(X)) Univ. of Queensland Pr. AUS. *Dist:* International Specialized Bk. Services.

Falcon, Marilyn Perez. Cui-Cui-Cuidado! Animales al Volante. Repiso, Elena, illus. 2002. (SPA.). 32p. (J). pap. (978-980-257-269-4(1)) Ekare, Ediciones.

Falconer, Ian. Olivia fait son Cirque. (Olivia Ser.). 29.95 (978-2-02-051642-6(X)) Editions du Seuil FRA. *Dist:* Distribooks, Inc.

Fall Is Pumpkin Time! 2004. (YA). (978-0-8374-0011-2(2)); lib. bdg. (978-0-8374-0010-5(4)) Weekly Reader Corp.

Fallon, Jimmy. Snowball Fight! Stower, Adam, illus. 2005. 32p. (J). (ps). 15.99 (978-0-525-47456-2(0) , Dutton Juvenile) Penguin Group (USA) Inc.

Fallon, Joe & Scarborough, Ken. Halfway Hank. Davis, Jack E., illus. 2005. 40p. (J). 15.99 (978-0-06-623636-0(3)) HarperCollins Pubs.

Farrer, Vashti. Princess Euphorbia. Bodsworth, Nan, illus. 1999. (Supa Doopers Ser.). 64p. (J). (978-0-7608-1923-4(8)) Sundance/Newbridge Educational Publishing.

Faulkner, Keith & Lambert, Jonathan. Tap! Tap! Tap! 2003. (Illus.). 16p. (J). 8.95 (978-0-7641-5643-4(8)) Barron's Educational Series, Inc.

Fearnley, Jan. Colin & the Curly Claw. Fearnley, Jan, illus. 2001. (Blue Bananas Ser.). (Illus.). 48p. (J). (gr. 1-2). (978-0-7787-0840-7(3)); pap. (978-0-7787-0886-5(1)) Crabtree Publishing Co.

—Colin & the Curly Claw. 2002. (gr. k-3). lib. bdg. 12.95 (978-0-613-52821-4(2)) Tandem Library Bks.

—Mr Wolf's Pancakes. 2001. (gr. k-3). lib. bdg. 14.10 (978-0-613-53842-8(0)) Tandem Library Bks.

Feiffer, Jules. Bark, George. 2004. 24.95 incl. audio (978-1-55592-690-8(8)); 29.95 incl. cd-rom (978-1-55592-700-4(9)); pap. 14.95 incl. audio (978-1-55592-696-0(7)); pap. 18.95 incl. audio compact disk (978-1-55592-706-6(8)) Weston Woods Studios, Inc.

—By the Side of the Road. 2005. (Illus.). 59p. (J). (gr. k-4). reprint ed. 16.00 (978-0-7567-9371-5(8)) DIANE Publishing Co.

—By the Side of the Road. 2002. 64p. (J). (ps-17). (978-0-7868-0908-0(6)) Hyperion Bks. for Children.

Feiffer, Jules. A Room with a Zoo. Feiffer, Jules, illus. 2007. (Illus.). 182p. (J). (gr. 2-7). per. 7.99 ***(978-0-7868-3703-8(9))*** Hyperion Bks. for Children.

Feiffer, Kate. President Pennybaker. Preiss-Glasser, Robin, illus. 2008. (J). ***(978-1-4169-1354-2(8)*** , Simon & Schuster Children's Publishing) Simon & Schuster Children's Publishing.

Feiffer, Kate & Feiffer, Jules. Henry, the Dog with No Tail. 2007. 32p. (J). (ps-1). 16.99 (978-1-4169-1614-7(8) , Simon & Schuster Children's Publishing) Simon & Schuster Children's Publishing.

Feldman, Thea. Mummy with the Golden Mask. 2003. (gr. k-3). lib. bdg. 11.80 (978-0-613-71493-8(8)) Tandem Library Bks.

Ferriell, Phil. Bernie Bocks Makes the Team. 2007. 86p. 14.95 ***(978-1-4241-4991-9(6))*** PublishAmerica, Inc.

Ferris, Jean. Much Ado about Grubstake. 2006. (Illus.). 272p. (YA). 17.00 (978-0-15-205706-0(4)) Harcourt Children's Bks.

—Once upon a Marigold. 2002. 272p. (YA). (gr. 5 up). 17.00 (978-0-15-216791-2(9)); 2004. 288p. (J). reprint ed. pap. 5.95 (978-0-15-205084-9(1) , Harcourt Paperbacks) Harcourt Children's Bks.

—Once upon a Marigold. 2004. (gr. 5-8). lib. bdg. 14.10 (978-0-613-71637-6(X)) Tandem Library Bks.

Filippi, Sandra. Pedacitos de Magia. 2002. (SPA.). 32p. (J). pap. 8.95 (978-1-4000-0029-6(7)) Random Hse., Inc.

Finchler, Judy. Miss Malarkey Won't Be in Today. 2000. (J). (978-0-606-20294-7(3)); lib. bdg. 15.25 (978-0-613-30032-2(7)); (Illus.). (J). (978-0-606-20409-5(1)) Tandem Library Bks.

Finchler, Judy & O'Malley, Kevin. Miss Malarkey's Field Trip. 2006. (Illus.). 32p. (J). pap. 6.95 (978-0-8027-8917-4(X)) Walker & Co.

—Miss Malarkey's Field Trip. O'Malley, Kevin, illus. 2004. (Illus.). 32p. (J). 16.95 (978-0-8027-8912-9(9)) Walker & Co.

Fine, Anne. Frozen Billy. McBain, Georgina, illus. 2006. 192p. (J). 16.00 (978-0-374-32481-0(6)) Farrar, Straus & Giroux.

Fine, Anne. Jamie & Angus Together. Dale, Penny, illus. 2007. 112p. (J). (ps-1). 15.99 ***(978-0-7636-3374-5(7))*** Candlewick Pr.

Fine, Anne & Trimmer, Tony. Countdown. 2006. (Yellow Bananas Ser.). (Illus.). 48p. (J). pap. (978-0-7787-1004-2(1)) Crabtree Publishing Co.

Finney, Patricia. I, Jack. Bailey, Peter, illus. 192p. (J). 2005. pap. 5.99 (978-0-06-052209-4(7) , Harper Trophy); 2004. 15.99 (978-0-06-052207-0(0)); 2004. lib. bdg. 16.89 (978-0-06-052208-7(9)) HarperCollins Pubs.

Finney, Townsend. Disaster Run Amok. 2002. 35p. (J). per. 9.95 (978-0-9725830-0-8(9)) Buchavina Pr.

Fishbone, Greg. The Penguins of Doom. 2007. (From the Desk of Septina Nash Ser.). (Illus.). 192p. (J). (gr. 3-9). 13.95 ***(978-1-933831-03-9(0))*** Blooming Tree Pr.

Fishel, Dennis. Russell's Revenge, 1. 2005. (YA). 17.95 (978-0-9763398-2-3(X)) Dragonon, Inc.

Fisher, Carolyn. A Twisted Tale. 2004. (Illus.). 33p. (J). (gr. k-4). reprint ed. 16.00 (978-0-7567-8412-6(3)) DIANE Publishing Co.

—A Twisted Tale. 2002. (Illus.). 40p. (J). (ps-3). 15.95 (978-0-375-81540-9(6) , Knopf Bks. for Young Readers) Random Hse. Children's Bks.

Fitzgerald, John. Great Brain. 2006. 20.75 (978-0-8446-7293-9(9)) Smith, Peter Pub., Inc.

Fitzgerald, John D. The Great Brain. Mayer, Mercer, illus. (Great Brain Ser.). (J). 2004. 192p. (gr. 3-7). pap. 5.99 (978-0-14-240058-6(0) , Puffin); 2000. 1p. (ps-3). 16.99 (978-0-8037-2590-4(6) , Dial) Penguin Group (USA) Inc.

—The Great Brain. 175p. (J). (gr. 4-6). pap. 4.50 (978-0-8072-1422-0(1)); 2002. (YA). (gr. 3 up). pap. 35.00 incl. audio (978-0-8072-0859-5(0) , LYA 376 SP) Random Hse. Audio Publishing Group. (Listening Library).

—Me & My Little Brain. Mayer, Mercer, illus. 2004. (Great Brain Ser.). 144p. (J). (gr. 3-7). pap. 4.99 (978-0-14-240064-7(5) , Puffin) Penguin Group (USA) Inc.

—Me & My Little Brain. 2004. (gr. 3-6). lib. bdg. 14.15 (978-0-613-87832-6(9)) Tandem Library Bks.

Fitzgibbons, Michael. My Senior Year. 2000. 580p. (YA). pap. 32.95 (978-0-595-13739-8(3)) iUniverse, Inc.

Fleischman, Sid. Bo & Mzzz Mad. 112p. (J). (gr. 3 up). 2002. pap. 6.99 (978-0-06-440972-8(4)); 2001. lib. bdg. 15.89 (978-0-06-029398-7(5)) HarperCollins Pubs.

—Bo & Mzzz Mad. Hunt, Jonathan, illus. 2001. 112p. (J). (gr. 3 up). 14.99 (978-0-06-029397-0(7)) HarperCollins Pubs.

—Bo & Mzzz Mad. 2002. 103p. (J). (ps-7). lib. bdg. 13.00 (978-0-613-61838-0(6)) Tandem Library Bks.

—A Carnival of Animals. Hafner, Marylin, illus. 2000. 48p. (J). (gr. 2 up). 15.89 (978-0-688-16949-7(X)) HarperCollins Pubs.

—Here Comes McBroom! Three More Tall Tales. 1999. (J). (gr. 2-5). 21.75 (978-0-8446-7029-4(4)) Smith, Peter Pub., Inc.

—Here Comes Mcbroom! Three More Tall Tales. 1998. (Illus.). 79p. (J). (ps-k). lib. bdg. 13.00 (978-0-613-11625-1(9)) Tandem Library Bks.

—Here Comes McBroom! Three More Tall Tales. Blake, Quentin, illus. 1998. 80p. (J). (gr. 2-5). reprint ed. pap. 4.99 (978-0-688-16364-8(5)) HarperCollins Pubs.

—McBroom Tells a Lie. Wummer, Amy, illus. 1999. (Adventures of McBroom Ser.). 64p. (J). (gr. 2-6). pap. 4.99 (978-0-8431-7497-7(8) , Price Stern Sloan) Penguin Group (USA) Inc.

—McBroom Tells a Lie. 1999. (J). (978-0-606-19073-2(2)); (gr. 3-6). lib. bdg. 13.00 (978-0-613-14983-9(1)) Tandem Library Bks.

—McBroom Tells the Truth. Wummer, Amy, illus. 1998. (Adventures of McBroom Ser.). 62p. (J). (gr. 2-5). pap. 4.99 (978-0-8431-7947-7(3) , Price Stern Sloan) Penguin Group (USA) Inc.

—McBroom the Rainmaker. 1999. (J). (978-0-606-19074-9(0)) Tandem Library Bks.

Fleming, Candace. Muncha! Muncha! Muncha! 2004. (Illus.). (J). 25.95 incl. audio (978-1-59112-464-1(6)); 28.95 incl. audio compact disk (978-1-59112-924-0(9)) Live Oak Media.

—When Agnes Caws. Potter, Giselle, illus. 1999. 40p. (J). (ps-3). 16.00 (978-0-689-81471-6(2) , Atheneum/Anne Schwartz Bks.) Simon & Schuster Children's Publishing.

Fleming, Maria. Word Family Tales -Eep: To Sleep, Count Sheep. Pillo, Cary, illus. 2002. (Word Family Tales Ser.). 16p. (ps-2). pap. 2.95 (978-0-439-26268-2(2)) Scholastic, Inc.

Fleming, Sheila G. A Very Berra Holiday. 2002. 108p. pap. 9.95 (978-0-595-25600-6(7) , Weekly Reader Teacher's Pr) iUniverse, Inc.

Flesh, Chris P. Me So Pretty! 2007. (Pretty Freekin Scary Ser.: No. 2). 176p. (J). (gr. 3). pap. 4.99 ***(978-0-448-44683-7(9)*** , Grosset & Dunlap) Penguin Group (USA) Inc.

—You Smell Dead. 2007. (Pretty Freekin Scary Ser.: No. 1). 176p. (J). (gr. 3). pap. 4.99 ***(978-0-448-44682-0(0)*** , Grosset & Dunlap) Penguin Group (USA) Inc.

Flintstones Read Along. 2000. (J). (ps-3). pap. 6.98 incl. audio (978-0-7634-0675-2(9)) Walt Disney Records.

Ford, Bernette. No More Diapers for Ducky! Williams, Sam, illus. 2007. 26p. (J). bds. 6.95 ***(978-1-905417-38-4(1))*** Boxer Bks., Ltd. GBR. *Dist:* Sterling Publishing Co., Inc.

Forward, Toby. The Wolf's Story: What Really Happened to Little Red Riding Hood. Cohen, Izhar, illus. 2005. 32p. (J). (ps-3). 15.99 (978-0-7636-2785-0(2)) Candlewick Pr.

Fowles, Shelley, illus. The Seven Voyages of Sinbad. 2008. 64p. (J). 18.95 ***(978-1-84507-531-6(5))*** Lincoln, Frances Ltd. GBR. *Dist:* Perseus Distribution.

Fox, Dorothea Warren. Miss Twiggley's Tree. Fox, Dorothea Warren, illus. 2002. 17.95 (978-1-930900-17-2(1)) Purple Hse. Pr.

Fox, Mem. Boo to a Goose. 2001. (gr. k-3). lib. bdg. 14.15 (978-0-613-35910-8(0)) Tandem Library Bks.

Franco, Betsy. Silly Sally. Lamb, Stacey, illus. 2002. (Rookie Reader Espanol Ser.). 24p. (J). (gr. k-2). pap. 4.95 (978-0-516-27343-3(4) , Children's Pr.) Scholastic Library Publishing.

—Silly Sally. 2002. (gr. k-3). lib. bdg. 12.95 (978-0-613-53864-0(1)) Tandem Library Bks.

—Six Silly Seals & Other Read-Aloud ABC Story Skits. 2002. (Illus.). 64p. (ps-k). pap. 11.95 (978-0-439-31891-4(2)) Scholastic, Inc.

Frank, Lucy. Just Ask Iris. 2003. (Illus.). 224p. (J). pap. 4.99 (978-0-689-84454-6(9) , Aladdin) Simon & Schuster Children's Publishing.

—Just Ask Iris. 2003. (gr. 5-8). lib. bdg. 13.00 (978-0-613-66417-2(5)) Tandem Library Bks.

—Oy, Joy! 2001. (J). (978-0-606-21376-9(7)) Tandem Library Bks.

Frazee, Marla. Roller Coaster. 2006. (Illus.). 32p. (J). reprint ed. pap. 6.00 (978-0-15-205744-2(7) , Voyager Bks./Libros Viajeros) Harcourt Children's Bks.

Fredman, Marion. A Time to Hide. 2002. 32p. (J). 17.95 (978-1-57143-090-8(3)) RDR Bks.

Freeman, Michelle. The Ravioli Kid. Abbott, Jason, illus. 2005. 32p. (J). 15.95 (978-1-58685-438-6(0)) Gibbs Smith, Publisher.

French, Jackie. Pete the Sheep-Sheep. Whatley, Bruce, illus. 2005. 32p. (J). (gr. k-3). 14.00 (978-0-618-56862-8(X) , Clarion Bks.) Houghton Mifflin Co. Trade & Reference Div.

Freschet, Gina. Up & at 'Em with Winnie & Ernst. 2005. (Winnie & Ernst Ser.). (Illus.). 48p. (J). 15.00 (978-0-374-38446-3(0) , Farrar, Straus & Giroux (BYR)) Farrar, Straus & Giroux.

Friedman, Aimee. A Novel Idea. 2005. (Romantic Comedies Ser.). (Illus.). 256p. (YA). pap. 6.99 (978-1-4169-0785-5(8) , Simon Pulse) Simon & Schuster Children's Publishing.

Friedman, Kinky. Curse of the Missing Puppet Head. 2003. lib. bdg. 29.95 (978-0-9702383-6-8(3) , CMPH01) Vandam Pr., Inc.

Friesen, Ray. Another Dirt Sandwich: Some Rambling & Hilarious Exploits of Tbyrd Fearlessness. 2008. (ENG., Illus.). 100p. pap. 12.95 (978-0-9728177-4-5(3)) Don't Eat Any Bugs Prodns.

—Lookit!, Vol. 2. 2004. (YA). per. 4.95 (978-0-9728177-3-8(5)) Don't Eat Any Bugs Prodns.

—RQW, Vol. 3. 2003. (YA). 2.95 (978-0-9728177-2-1(7)) Don't Eat Any Bugs Prodns.

Fry, Sonali. Beyond Bikini Bottom! DePorter, Vince, illus. 2005. (Spongebob Squarepants Ser.). 16p. (J). (ps-ps). 7.99 (978-0-689-87738-4(2) , Simon Spotlight/Nickelodeon) Simon & Schuster Children's Publishing.

Fuertes, Gloria. Cuentos de Humor: Un Pulpo en un Garaje. 2003. (SPA.). 128p. 15.16 (978-84-305-7987-7(7) , SU5205) Susaeta Ediciones, S.A. ESP. *Dist:* Lectorum Pubns., Inc.

Fujishima, Kosuke. The Devil in Miss Urd. 2001. (Oh My Goddess! Ser.: Vol. 11). (Illus.). 176p. (J). (gr. 5 up). pap. 14.95 (978-1-56971-540-6(8)) Dark Horse Comics.

Gag, Wanda. The Funny Thing. 2003. (Illus.). 32p. 14.95 (978-0-8166-4241-0(9)) Univ. of Minnesota Pr.

Gaiman, Neil. The Day I Swapped My Dad for Two Goldfish. McKean, Dave, illus. 64p. (J). 2006. pap. 7.99 (978-0-06-058703-1(2) , Harper Trophy); 2004. 16.99 incl. audio compact disk (978-0-06-058701-7(6)); 2004. lib. bdg. 17.89 (978-0-06-058702-4(4)) HarperCollins Pubs.

Gall, Chris. Dear Fish. 2006. (Illus.). 36p. (J). (ps-1). 16.99 (978-0-316-05847-6(5)) Little Brown & Co.

Galvin, Kim. RJ's Farm. 2000. 208p. (J). (gr. 4-7). pap. 12.95 (978-0-595-13989-7(2) , Writers Club Pr.) iUniverse, Inc.

Gantos, Jack. Jack on the Tracks: Four Seasons of Fifth Grade. 1999. (Jack Henry Ser.). (Illus.). 192p. (J). (gr. 5-9). 16.00 (978-0-374-33665-3(2) , Farrar, Straus & Giroux (BYR)) Farrar, Straus & Giroux.

—Jack on the Tracks: Four Seasons of Fifth Grade. 2001. (gr. 5-8). lib. bdg. 14.10 (978-0-613-85137-4(4)) Tandem Library Bks.

—Jack on the Tracks: Four Seasons of Fifth Grade. l.t. ed. 2002. 210p. (J). 22.95 (978-0-7862-4394-5(5)) Thorndike Pr.

—Jack's Black Book. 1999. (Jack Henry Ser.). (Illus.). 176p. (J). (gr. 5-9). pap. 6.95 (978-0-374-43716-9(5) , Sunburst) Farrar, Straus & Giroux.

Gardner, Sally. El Nino Invisible. Tapia, Sonia, tr. 2005. (Ninos Magicos Ser.). (SPA.). 112p. (J). pap. 7.95 (978-84-666-1342-2(0)) Ediciones B ESP. *Dist:* Independent Pubs. Group.

Garfield, Leon. The Strange Affair of Adelaide Harris. 2001. (978-0-606-22822-0(5)) Tandem Library Bks.

Garmendia, Julio. Manzanita. Fuenmayor, Morella, illus. (SPA.). (J). pap. 7.96 (978-980-01-0972-4(2)) Monte Avila Editores Latinoamericana CA VEN. *Dist:* Lectorum Pubns., Inc.

Garriel, Barbara S. I Know a Shy Fellow Who Swallowed a Cello. O'Brian, John, illus. 2004. 32p. (J). (gr. k-2). 15.95 (978-1-59078-043-5(4)) Boyds Mills Pr.

Gates, Susan. Bill's Baggy Pants. Axworthy, Anni, illus. 2004. (Read-It! Readers Ser.). 32p. (C). (gr. k-3). 18.60 (978-1-4048-0050-2(6)) Picture Window Bks.

Gates, Susan, et al. Babi Bag Siwgwr. 2005. (WEL., Illus.). 75p. (978-1-902416-96-0(1)) Cymdeithas Lyfrau Ceredigion.

Gatou, Shouji. Full Metal Panic! Overload!, Vol. 5. 2006. (Illus.). 200p. (YA). pap. (978-1-4139-0342-3(8)) ADV Manga.

Gauthier, Bertrand & Dumont, Daniel. La, Si, Do, Place aux Jumeaux! 2002. (Premier Roman Ser.). (FRE., Illus.). 64p. pap. (978-2-89021-572-6(5)) Diffusion du livre Mirabel.

Gauthier, Gail. A Year with Butch & Spike. 2000. (978-0-606-17857-0(0)) Tandem Library Bks.

Gauthier, Gilles. Le Beau Valentino Sort Ses Crocs. Derome, Pierre-Andre, tr. 2003. (Premier Roman Ser.). (FRE., Illus.). 64p. (J). (gr. 1-4). pap. (978-2-89021-636-5(5)) Diffusion du livre Mirabel.

Gay, Marie-Louise. What Are You Doing, Sam? 2006. (Illus.). 32p. 14.95 (978-0-88899-734-0(5)) Groundwood Bks. CAN. *Dist:* Perseus Distribution.

Gaydos, Nora. My World. Sams, B. B., illus. 2004. (Now I'm Reading!Tm Beginning Reader Ser.). 128p. (J). (ps-1). 16.99 (978-1-58476-263-8(2)) Innovative Kids.

—Snack Attack, Level 2. Sams, B. B., illus. 2004. (Now I'm Reading! Ser.). 128p. (J). (ps-2). 16.99 (978-1-58476-264-5(0)) Innovative Kids.

Geoghegan, Adrienne. Dogs Don't Wear Glasses. 2000. (gr. k-3). lib. bdg. 16.40 (978-0-613-81226-9(3)) Tandem Library Bks.

George, Olivia. My Birthday Cake. Aviles, Martha, illus. 2005. (My First Reader Ser.). 31p. (J). (gr. k-1). pap. 3.95 (978-0-516-25276-6(3) , Children's Pr.) Scholastic Library Publishing.

—My Birthday Cake. Aviles Junco, Martha, illus. 2005. (My First Reader Ser.). 32p. (J). (gr. k-1). 18.50 (978-0-516-25178-3(3) , Children's Pr.) Scholastic Library Publishing.

Gershon, Gina & Gershon, Dann. Camp Creepy Time: The Adventures of Einstein P. Fleet. 2007. 224p. (J). (gr. 5 up). 16.99 (978-0-399-24737-8(8) , Putnam Juvenile) Penguin Group (USA) Inc.

Gibson, D. W., et al. Fundorado Island. 2006. (Illus.). 224p. (J). (gr. 3). lib. bdg. 16.99 (978-0-385-90284-7(0) , Delacorte Bks. for Young Readers) Random Hse. Children's Bks.

Gibson, Maggie. Alice Little & the Big Girls' Blouse. 2nd ed. 2001. 266p. (J). pap. 9.99 (978-0-575-40330-7(6) , Weidenfeld & Nicolson) Orion Publishing Group, Ltd. GBR. *Dist:* Independent Pubs. Group.

Giddens, Martha Anne. The Unluckiest Kid in the Universe. 2006. 56p. pap. ***(978-1-4120-7935-8(7))*** Trafford Publishing.

Gifaldi, David. Gregory, Maw & the Mean One. 2000. (Illus.). 148p. (J). (gr. 4-7). pap. 10.95 (978-0-595-14504-1(3) , Backinprint.com) iUniverse, Inc.

Gifford, Peggy. Moxy Maxwell Does Not Love Stuart Little. Fisher, Valorie, photos by. 2007. (Illus.). 104p. (J). (gr. 2-6). 12.99 (978-0-375-83915-3(1)); lib. bdg. 15.99 (978-0-375-93915-0(6)) Random Hse. Children's Bks. (Schwartz & Wade Bks.).

Gifford, Peggy. Moxy Maxwell Does Not Love Stuart Little. Fisher, Valorie, photos by. 2008. (Illus.). 112p. (J). (gr. 2-6). 5.50 ***(978-0-440-42230-3(2)*** , Yearling) Random Hse. Children's Bks.

Gifford, Peggy Elizabeth. Moxy Maxwell Does Not Love Writing Thank-You Notes. Fisher, Valorie, illus. Fisher, Valorie, photos by. 2008. (J). ***(978-0-375-84270-2(5)); (978-0-375-94552-6(0))*** Random Hse. Children's Bks. (Schwartz & Wade Bks.).

Gilden, Mel. Britney Spears Is a Three-Headed Alien: The Inside Story. 2001. (gr. 7-12). lib. bdg. 18.80 (978-0-613-82444-6(X)) Tandem Library Bks.

Gilson, Jamie. Wagon Train 911. 1998. 192p. (YA). (gr. 3 up). pap. 4.95 (978-0-688-15857-6(9)) HarperCollins Pubs.

—Wagon Train 911. 2001. (J). (978-0-606-20976-2(X)) Tandem Library Bks.

Ginkel, Anne. I've Got an Elephant. Bynum, Janie, illus. 2006. 32p. (J). 16.95 (978-1-56145-373-3(0) , Peachtree Junior) Peachtree Pubs., Ltd.

Glazer, Tom. On Top of Spaghetti. Johnson, Paul Brett, illus. 2006. 32p. (J). pap. 15.99 (978-0-439-74944-2(1) , Scholastic Pr.) Scholastic, Inc.

Gliori, Debi. Pure Dead Batty. 2007. (Illus.). 320p. (J). (gr. 4-7). 6.50 ***(978-0-440-42074-3(1)*** , Yearling) Random Hse. Children's Bks.

—Pure Dead Brilliant. l.t. ed. 2004. (Pure Dead Ser.: Vol. 5). (Illus.). 378p. (J). 21.95 (978-0-7862-6148-2(X)) Thorndike Pr.

—Siempre Te Querre. 2001. (SPA., Illus.). 32p. (J). (gr. k-2). (978-84-480-1632-6(7) , TM7120) Timun Mas, Editorial S.A. ESP. *Dist:* Lectorum Pubns., Inc.

Godwin, Parke. Disney's Main Street Storybook Collection. 2003. (Illus.). 320p. (J). 15.99 (978-0-7868-3431-0(5)) Disney Pr.

Goldberg, Barry, illus. Bubble Blowers, Beware! 2004. (Spongebob Squarepants Ser.). 24p. (J). pap. 3.99 (978-0-689-86862-7(6) , Simon Spotlight/Nickelodeon) Simon & Schuster Children's Publishing.

Golden Books Staff. Bounce Around, Tigger! 2000. (Disney Ser.). 24p. (J). (ps-3). pap. 3.29 (978-0-307-13173-7(4) , 13173, Golden Bks.) Random Hse. Children's Bks.

—The Good Humor Man. Gergely, Tibor, illus. 2005. (Big Little Golden Book Ser.). 32p. (J). (gr. k-k). 8.99 (978-0-375-83280-2(7) , Golden Bks.) Random Hse. Children's Bks.

—The Happy Man & His Dump Truck. Gergely, Tibor, illus. 2005. (Little Golden Book Classic Ser.). 24p. (J). (gr. k-k). 2.99 (978-0-375-83207-9(6) , Golden Bks.) Random Hse. Children's Bks.

—The House That Bob Built. 2004. (Bob the Builder Ser.). (Illus.). 8p. (J). (ps-1). bds. 10.99 (978-0-375-82732-7(3) , Golden Bks.) Random Hse. Children's Bks.

—Little Boy with a Big Horn. Yaccarino, Dan, illus. 2008. (Golden Classic Ser.). 48p. (J). (gr. k-k). lib. bdg. 17.99 ***(978-0-375-93903-7(2)*** , Golden Bks.) Random Hse., Inc.

—Little Golden Book Favorites by Richard Scarry. 2008. (Little Golden Book Ser.). (Illus.). 72p. (J). 5.99 ***(978-0-375-84580-2(1)*** , Golden Bks.) Random Hse., Inc.

—My Backpack. Ovresat, Laura, illus. 2006. 12p. (J). (gr. k-1). bds. 3.99 (978-0-375-87489-5(5) , Golden Bks.) Random Hse. Children's Bks.

—Traffic Trouble. 2004. (Illus.). 10p. (J). (ps-1). bds. 8.99 (978-0-375-82921-5(0) , Golden Bks.) Random Hse. Children's Bks.

Goldfinger, Jennifer P. My Dog Lyle. Goldfinger, Jennifer P., illus. 2007. (Illus.). 32p. (J). (ps-k). 16.00 (978-0-618-63983-0(7) , Clarion Bks.) Houghton Mifflin Co. Trade & Reference Div.

Goldman, Todd Harris. The Zoo I Drew. 2008. (J). ***(978-0-375-85201-5(8)); (978-0-375-95201-2(2))*** Random Hse., Inc.

Goldschmidt, Judy. Raisin Rodriguez & the Big-Time Smooch. 2007. 208p. (YA). pap. 5.99 (978-1-59514-125-5(1) , Razorbill) Penguin Group (USA) Inc.

—The Secret Blog of Raisin Rodriguez. (J). (gr. 5-12). 2006. 224p. pap. 5.99 (978-1-59514-071-5(9)); 2005. 208p. 12.99 (978-1-59514-018-0(2)) Penguin Group (USA) Inc. (Razorbill).

—Will the Real Raisin Rodriguez Please Stand Up? 2007. 208p. (YA). (gr. 5 up). 12.99 (978-1-59514-058-6(1) , Razorbill) Penguin Group (USA) Inc.

Goldstein, Arline. Keeping Time with JouJou. 2006. pap. 23.99 ***(978-1-4259-5043-9(4))*** AuthorHouse.

Gonick, Larry. Attack of the Smart Pies. 2005. (Illus.). 192p. (J). 15.95 (978-0-8126-2740-4(7)) Cricket Bks.

Gordon, Cambria. Reggie the Veggie. (J). 1999. pap. 3.99 (978-0-679-88848-2(9)); 1998. lib. bdg. 11.99 (978-0-679-98848-9(3)) Random Hse. Children's Bks. (Random Hse. Bks. for Young Readers).

Gore, Jim. Witch Snatchit & Mr Grabbit. 2005. (Illus.). 80p. pap. ***(978-1-84401-486-6(X))*** Athena Pr.

Goscinny, R. & Uderzo, A. Le Tour de Gaule d'Asterix. (FRE.). 21.95 (978-2-01-210005-3(8)) Hachette Groupe Livre FRA. *Dist:* Distribooks, Inc.

Goscinny, René. Asterix Chez les Belges. (FRE.). (J). pap. 21.95 ***(978-2-01-210156-2(9))*** Hachette Groupe Livre FRA. *Dist:* Distribooks, Inc.

—Asterix en Hispanie. (FRE.). (J). pap. 21.95 ***(978-2-01-210146-3(1))*** Hachette Groupe Livre FRA. *Dist:* Distribooks, Inc.

—Nicholas. Bell, Anthea, tr. from FRE. Sempé, Jean-Jacques, illus. 2005. 160p. 19.95 (978-0-7148-4482-4(9)) Phaidon Pr. GBR. *Dist:* Hachette Bk. Group.

H I

Goscinny, René. Nicholas & the Gang. 2007. (Illus.). 120p. (J). 19.95 ***(978-0-7148-4788-7(7))*** Phaidon Pr., Inc.

Goscinny, René, text. Asterix Chez les Belges. (FRE.). pap. 21.95 (978-2-01-210024-4(4) , DR24E) Hachette Groupe Livre FRA. *Dist:* Distribooks, Inc.

Goscinny, René & Sempé, Jean-Jacques. Nicholas Again. Bell, Anthea, tr. from FRE. rev. ed. 2006. (Illus.). 120p. 19.95 (978-0-7148-4564-7(7)) Phaidon Pr., Inc.

Goscinny, René & Uderzo. Asterix French. 21.95 (978-2-01-210022-0(8)) Hachette Groupe Livre FRA. *Dist:* Distribooks, Inc.

Goscinny, René & Uderzo, Albert. Asterix & the Falling Sky. 2006. (Illus.). 48p. pap. 9.95 (978-0-7528-7548-4(5)) Orion Bks. Ltd. GBR. *Dist:* Sterling Publishing Co., Inc.

—Asterix Chez les Helvetes. (FRE.). (J). pap. 21.95 (978-2-01-210016-9(3)) Hachette Groupe Livre FRA. *Dist:* Distribooks, Inc.

—Asterix en Corse. (FRE.). 21.95 (978-2-01-210020-6(1)) Hachette Groupe Livre FRA. *Dist:* Distribooks, Inc.

—Asterix en Hispanie. (FRE.). 21.95 (978-2-01-210014-5(7)) Hachette Groupe Livre FRA. *Dist:* Distribooks, Inc.

—Asterix et le Bombe. (FRE.). 21.95 (978-2-01-210008-4(2)) Hachette Groupe Livre FRA. *Dist:* Distribooks, Inc.

—Asterix French. 21.95 (978-2-01-210009-1(0)) Hachette Groupe Livre FRA. *Dist:* Distribooks, Inc.

Graham, Bob. Max. Graham, Bob, illus. 2002. (Illus.). 32p. (J). (ps-2). pap. 5.99 (978-0-7636-1857-5(8)) Candlewick Pr.

Grahame, Kenneth. The Wind in the Willows Bk. 1: The Riverbank. Iosa, Ann, illus. 2006. (Easy Reader Classics Ser.). 32p. (J). pap. 3.95 (978-1-4027-3293-5(7)) Sterling Publishing Co., Inc.

Gralley, Jean. Hogula: Dread Pig of Night. rev. ed. 2002. (Illus.). 32p. (J). (ps-3). pap. 6.95 (978-0-8050-7164-1(4) , Holt, Henry & Co. Bks. For Young Readers) Holt, Henry & Co.

—Hogula: Dread Pig of Night. 2002. (gr. k-3). lib. bdg. 15.25 (978-0-613-90145-1(2)) Tandem Library Bks.

Grant, Vicki. Dead-End Job. 2005. (Orca Soundings Ser.). 112p. (J). (gr. 7-12). pap. 7.95 (978-1-55143-378-3(8)) Orca Bk. Pubs. USA.

—Quid Pro Quo. 2005. 176p. (J). (gr. 3-7). pap. 7.95 (978-1-55143-370-7(2)); lib. bdg. 16.95 (978-1-55143-394-3(X)) Orca Bk. Pubs. USA.

Gravett, Emily. Wolves. Gravett, Emily, illus. 2006. (Illus.). 40p. (J). (gr. k-3). 16.99 (978-1-4169-1491-4(9) , Simon & Schuster Children's Publishing) Simon & Schuster Children's Publishing.

Gray, Margaret. The Lovesick Salesman. Cecil, Randy, illus. rev. ed. 2004. 192p. (J). 16.95 (978-0-8050-7558-8(5) , Holt, Henry & Co. Bks. For Young Readers) Holt, Henry & Co.

—The Ugly Princess & the Wise Fool. Cecil, Randy, illus. rev. ed. 2002. 176p. (J). (gr. 3-5). 16.95 (978-0-8050-6847-4(3) , Holt, Henry & Co. Bks. For Young Readers) Holt, Henry & Co.

Green, John. Terdellaline: A Free-Spirited, Energeti. 2005. 48p. pap. 12.95 (978-1-4137-9528-8(5)) PublishAmerica, Inc.

Greenberg, David T. Crocs! 2008. 32p. (J). (978-0-316-07306-6(7)) Little Brown & Co.

Greenburd, Dan. How I Fixed the Year 1000 Problem. 1999. (gr. 3-6). lib. bdg. 13.00 (978-0-613-21727-9(6)) Tandem Library Bks.

Greenburg, Dan. Attack of the Evil Elvises. Pamintuan, Macky, illus. 2007. (Weird Planet Ser.: No. 4). 96p. (J). (gr. 2-4). lib. bdg. 11.99 (978-0-375-93347-9(6)); 3.99 (978-0-375-83347-2(1)) Random Hse. Children's Bks. (Random Hse. Bks. for Young Readers).

—Chilling with the Great Ones. Pamintuan, Macky, illus. 2006. 96p. (J). (gr. 2-5). lib. bdg. 11.99 (978-0-375-93346-2(8)); (Weird Planet Ser.: No. 3). (gr. 1-4). pap. 3.99 (978-0-375-83346-5(3)) Random Hse. Children's Bks. (Random Hse. Bks. for Young Readers).

—The Day That Went from Bad to Verse. 2000. (Zack Files Ser.: No. 20). 11.79 (978-0-606-18851-7(7)) Tandem Library Bks.

—Just Add Water...and Scream! Davis, Jack E., illus. 2003. (Zack Files Ser.: No. 29). 64p. (gr. 1-4). mass mkt. 4.99 (978-0-448-42887-1(3) , Grosset & Dunlap) Penguin Group (USA) Inc.

—Just Add Water...and Scream! 2002. (gr. 3-6). lib. bdg. 13.00 (978-0-613-61637-9(5)) Tandem Library Bks.

—Maximum Girl Unmasked. 2002. (978-0-606-22272-3(3)) Tandem Library Bks.

—Me & My Mummy. Davis, Jack E., illus. 2002. (Zack Files Ser.: No. 26). 64p. (J). pap. 4.99 (978-0-448-42633-4(1) , Grosset & Dunlap) Penguin Group (USA) Inc.

—Me & My Mummy. 2002. (gr. 3-6). lib. bdg. 13.00 (978-0-613-50079-1(2)) Tandem Library Bks.

—My Grandma, Major League Slugger. Davis, Jack E., illus. 2001. (Zack Files Ser.: No. 24). 64p. (J). (gr. 2-5). pap. 4.99 (978-0-448-42550-4(5) , Grosset & Dunlap) Penguin Group (USA) Inc.

—My Grandma, Major League Slugger. 2001. (gr. 3-6). lib. bdg. 13.00 (978-0-613-58376-3(0)) Tandem Library Bks.

—My Teacher Ate My Homework, Vol. 27. Davis, Jack E., illus. 2002. (Zack Files Ser.: 27). 64p. (J). pap. 4.99 (978-0-448-42683-9(8) , Grosset & Dunlap) Penguin Group (USA) Inc.

—My Teacher Ate My Homework. 2002. (gr. 3-6). lib. bdg. 13.00 (978-0-613-61645-4(6)) Tandem Library Bks.

—This Body's Not Big Enough for the Both of Us. 2000. (gr. 3-6). lib. bdg. 13.00 (978-0-613-31803-7(X)); (Zack Files Ser.: No. 22). (J). (gr. 2-5). (978-0-606-20271-8(4)); (Zack Files Ser.). (Illus.). (J). (978-0-606-20406-4(7)) Tandem Library Bks.

—Weird Planet: Lights, Camera... Liftoff! Pamintuan, Macky, illus. 2007. (Weird Planet Ser.: No. 5). 96p. (J). (gr. 2-5). pap. 3.99 ***(978-0-375-84336-5(1)*** , Random Hse. Bks. for Young Readers) Random Hse. Children's Bks.

—Weird Planet No. 5: Lights, Camera... Liftoff! Pamintuan, Macky, illus. 2007. (Stepping Stone Bks.). 96p. (J). (gr. 2-5). lib. bdg. 11.99 ***(978-0-375-94336-2(6)*** , Random Hse. Bks. for Young Readers) Random Hse. Children's Bks.

Greenburg, Dan. The Worst Bully in the Entire Universe. 2003. (gr. 3-6). lib. bdg. 11.80 (978-0-613-84843-5(8)) Tandem Library Bks.

Greene, Renea Russ. Thunder in the Coffee Pot. Greene, Laura Hampton, illus. 2002. 36p. (J). pap. 8.95 (978-0-9723719-0-2(7)) FUN 4 5 Pubns.

Greene, Rhonda Gowler. This Is the Teacher. Lester, Mike, illus. 32p. (J). (gr. k). 2004. 15.99 (978-0-525-47125-7(1) , Dutton Juvenile); 2006. reprint ed. pap. 5.99 (978-0-14-240653-3(8) , Puffin) Penguin Group (USA) Inc.

Greene, Stephanie. Owen Foote, Super Spy. Weston, Martha, illus. 2005. 96p. (J). (gr. k-3). pap. 5.95 (978-0-618-55159-0(X) , Clarion Bks.) Houghton Mifflin Co. Trade & Reference Div.

—Pig Pickin' Mathieu, Joseph, illus. 2006. (Marshall Cavendish Chapter Book Ser.). 64p. (J). 14.99 (978-0-7614-5324-6(5)) Cavendish, Marshall Corp.

Greene, Stephanie. The Show-Off. Mathieu, Joseph, illus. 2007. (Moose & Hildy Ser.). 64p. (J). (gr. 1-4). 14.99 ***(978-0-7614-5374-1(1))*** Cavendish, Marshall Corp.

Greenwald, Sheila. The Mariah Delany Lending Library Disaster. 2000. (978-0-606-20450-7(4)) Tandem Library Bks.

Gregory, Jillian Louise. Dobbs Dog Detective: Operation Fido & Fifi. 2003. 67p. pap. 11.95 (978-1-4137-0644-4(4)) PublishAmerica, Inc.

Griffin, Kitty & Combs, Kathy. The Foot-Stomping Adventures of Clementine Sweet. Wohnoutka, Mike, tr. Wohnoutka, Mike, illus. 2004. 32p. (J). (gr. k-3). tchr. ed. 15.00 (978-0-618-24746-2(7) , Clarion Bks.) Houghton Mifflin Co. Trade & Reference Div.

Griffin, Kitty, et al. Cowboy Sam & Those Confounded Secrets. Wohnoutka, Mike, illus. 2001. 32p. (J). (gr. k-3). tchr. ed. 16.00 (978-0-618-08854-6(7) , Clarion Bks.) Houghton Mifflin Co. Trade & Reference Div.

Griffiths, Andy. The Day My Butt Went Psycho. 2003. (gr. 5-8). lib. bdg. 13.00 (978-0-613-62939-3(6)) Tandem Library Bks.

—The Day My Butt Went Psycho! 2003. 240p. (J). (gr. 4-7). 4.99 (978-0-439-42469-1(0)) Scholastic, Inc.

—Just Annoying! Denton, Terry, illus. 2003. (Just Books Ser.). 144p. (J). (gr. 3-5). pap. 4.99 (978-0-439-42471-4(2)) Scholastic, Inc.

—Just Disgusting! Denton, Terry, illus. 2005. 144p. (J). 4.99 (978-0-439-54954-7(X)) Scholastic, Inc.

—Just Joking! Denton, Terry, illus. 2003. (Just Books Ser.). 144p. (J). (gr. 3-5). 4.99 (978-0-439-42472-1(0)) Scholastic, Inc.

—Just Shocking! 2008. (Andy Griffith's Just! Ser.). 176p. (J). 4.99 ***(978-0-439-92623-2(8)*** , Scholastic Paperbacks) Scholastic, Inc.

—What Buttosaur Is That? 2008. (Teacher's Essential Guide Ser.). 208p. (J). (gr. 4-7). pap. 5.99 ***(978-0-439-92622-5(X)*** , Scholastic Paperbacks) Scholastic, Inc.

Griffiths, Andy. Zombie Butts from Uranus! 2004. 288p. (Orig.). (J). 4.99 (978-0-439-42470-7(4)) Scholastic, Inc.

Griggs, Terry. Cat's Eye Corner. 2003. (Cat's Eye Corner Ser.). (Illus.). 168p. (J). pap. 7.95 (978-1-55192-350-5(5)) Raincoast Bk. Distribution CAN. *Dist:* Perseus Distribution.

—Cat's Eye Corner. 2003. (gr. 3-6). lib. bdg. 16.40 (978-0-613-78641-6(6)) Tandem Library Bks.

Grimm, Lana & Bloch, Tania. How Butterbees Came to Bee! 2001. (Illus.). (J). (978-0-9662048-2-7(4)) Bee Unlimited, Inc.

—How Butterbees Came to Bee! Michener, David, illus. 2nd ed. 2001. 48p. 19.95 (978-0-9662048-3-4(2)) Bee Unlimited, Inc.

Groening, Matt. The Simpsons Treehouse of Horror Fun-Filled Frightfest. 2003. (Treehouse of Horror Ser.). (gr. 5-8). lib. bdg. 24.55 (978-0-613-68462-0(1)) Tandem Library Bks.

Grosgebauer, Clare Ham. Snickerdoodle! A Tall Tale about a Powerful Pee-Wee! Rissing, Karen, illus. 3rd ed. 2005. 40p. 12.99 (978-0-9741888-2-9(4)) Small Wonders Enterprises.

Gruber, Wilhelm. Tomas Lee al Reves. 2000. (978-0-606-18324-6(8)) Tandem Library Bks.

Guardo, Attilio. A Special Time in Clear Creek. 2004. 184p. pap. 19.95 (978-1-4137-2872-9(3)) PublishAmerica, Inc.

Gugler, Laurel Dee. Muddle Cuddle. van Kampen, Vlasta, illus. 2003. 24p. (J). (ps-1). lib. bdg. 16.95 (978-1-55037-435-3(4)) Annick Pr., Ltd. CAN. *Dist:* Firefly Bks., Ltd.

Gutierrez, Debbi Miller. Cactus Factory. 2007. (J). 6.00 ***(978-0-9740173-4-1(5))*** Prints By Mail.

Gutman, Dan. Dr. Carbles Is Losing His Marbles! Paillot, Jim, illus. 2007. (My Weird School Ser.: No.19). 112p. (J). lib. bdg. 15.89 ***(978-0-06-123478-1(8)*** ***);*** pap. 3.99 ***(978-0-06-123477-4(X)*** , Harper Trophy) HarperCollins Pubs.

—Funny Boy Meets the Airsick Alien from Andromeda. Dykes, John, illus. 3rd rev. ed. 1999. (L.A.F. Ser.: No. 3). 128p. (gr. 2-6). pap. 3.99 (978-0-7868-1330-8(X)) Hyperion Pr.

—Funny Boy Meets the Airsick Alien from Andromeda. 1999. (gr. 3-6). lib. bdg. 11.80 (978-0-613-21571-8(0)) Tandem Library Bks.

—Funny Boy Takes on the Chit-Chatting Cheese from Chattanooga. 2001. (L.A.F. Bks.). (Illus.). 128p. (gr. 2-6). pap. 4.99 (978-0-7868-1445-9(4)) Disney Pr.

—Funny Boy Takes on the Chit-Chatting Cheese from Chattanooga. 2000. (gr. 3-6). lib. bdg. 13.00 (978-0-613-31228-8(7)) Tandem Library Bks.

—The Homework Machine. 2007. 176p. (J). pap. 4.99 ***(978-0-689-87679-0(3)*** , Aladdin) Simon & Schuster Children's Publishing.

—The Million Dollar Strike. 2006. 224p. (gr. 3-7). pap. 5.99 (978-0-7868-3751-9(9)) Hyperion Pr.

—Million Dollar Strike. 2004. 176p. (J). lib. bdg. 18.46 ***(978-1-4242-2107-3(2))*** Fitzgerald Bks.

—Miss Daisy Is Crazy! Paillot, Jim, illus. 2004. (My Weird School Ser.: Bk. 1). 96p. (J). pap. 3.99 (978-0-06-050700-8(4)) HarperCollins Pubs.

—Miss Holly Is Too Jolly! Paillot, Jim, illus. 2006. (My Weird School Ser.: No.14). 112p. (J). lib. bdg. 15.89 (978-0-06-085383-9(2)) HarperCollins Pubs.

—Miss Lazar Is Bizarre! Paillot, Jim, illus. 2005. (My Weird School Ser.). 96p. (J). lib. bdg. 15.89 (978-0-06-082226-2(0)) HarperCollins Pubs.

—Miss Small Is off the Wall! Paillot, Jim, illus. 2005. (My Weird School Ser.). 112p. (J). lib. bdg. 15.89 (978-0-06-074519-6(3)); pap. 3.99 (978-0-06-074518-9(5) , Harper Trophy) HarperCollins Pubs.

—Miss Small Is off the Wall! Paillot, Jim, illus. 2005. 96p. (J). (gr. 2-5). lib. bdg. 11.19 (978-0-606-33326-9(6)) Tandem Library Bks.

—Mr. Docker Is off His Rocker! Paillot, Jim, illus. 2006. (My Weird School Ser.). 112p. (J). pap. 3.99 (978-0-06-082227-9(9) , Harper Trophy); lib. bdg. 15.89 (978-0-06-082228-6(7)) HarperCollins Pubs.

—Mr. Hynde Is Out of His Mind! Paillot, Jim, illus. 2005. (My Weird School Ser.: Bk. 6). 112p. (J). pap. 3.99 (978-0-06-074520-2(7) , Harper Trophy) HarperCollins Pubs.

—Mr. Hynde Is Out of His Mind! Paillot, Jim, illus. 2005. 97p. (J). (ps-k). lib. bdg. 10.64 (978-0-606-33934-6(5)) Tandem Library Bks.

—Mr. Louie Is Screwy! Paillot, Jim, illus. 2007. (My Weird School Ser.: No. 20). 112p. (J). lib. bdg. 15.89 ***(978-0-06-123480-4(X)*** ***);*** pap. 3.99 ***(978-0-06-123479-8(6)*** , Harper Trophy) HarperCollins Pubs.

—Mr. Macky Is Wacky! Paillot, Jim, illus. 2007. (My Weird School Ser.: No. 15). (J). 112p. lib. bdg. 15.89 (978-0-06-114152-2(6)); 96p. pap. 3.99 (978-0-06-114151-5(8) , Harper Trophy) HarperCollins Pubs.

—Mrs. Cooney Is Loony! Paillot, Jim, illus. 2005. (My Weird School Ser.). 112p. (J). pap. 3.99 (978-0-06-074522-6(3)); lib. bdg. 15.89 (978-0-06-074523-3(1)) HarperCollins Pubs. (Harper Trophy).

—Mrs. Kormel Is Not Normal! Paillot, Jim, illus. 2006. (My Weird School Ser.). 96p. (J). pap. 3.99 (978-0-06-082229-3(5) , Harper Trophy); lib. bdg. 15.89 (978-0-06-082230-9(9)) HarperCollins Pubs.

—Mrs. Patty Is Batty! Paillot, Jim, illus. 2006. (My Weird School Ser.: No. 13). 112p. (J). pap. 3.99 (978-0-06-085380-8(8) , Harper Trophy); lib. bdg. 15.89 (978-0-06-085381-5(6)) HarperCollins Pubs.

—Ms. Coco Is Loco! Paillot, Jim, illus. 2007. (My Weird School Ser.: No. 16). (J). 96p. pap. 3.99 (978-0-06-114153-9(4) , Harper Trophy); 112p. lib. bdg. 15.89 (978-0-06-114154-6(2)) HarperCollins Pubs.

—Ms. Hannah Is Bananas! Paillot, Jim, illus. 2004. (My Weird School Ser.: Bk. 4). 96p. (J). pap. 3.99 (978-0-06-050706-0(3) , Harper Trophy); lib. bdg. 15.89 (978-0-06-050707-7(1)) HarperCollins Pubs.

—Ms. Hannah Is Bananas! Paillot, Jim, illus. 2005. 84p. (J). (gr. 2-5). lib. bdg. 11.19 (978-0-606-33041-1(0)) Tandem Library Bks.

—Ms. Lagrange Is Strange! Paillot, Jim, illus. 2005. (My Weird School Ser.). 96p. (J). lib. bdg. 15.89 (978-0-06-082224-8(4)) HarperCollins Pubs.

Gutman, Dan. Ms. Todd Is Odd! Paillot, Jim, illus. 2006. (My Weird School Ser.: No. 12). (J). 112p. pap. 3.99 (978-0-06-082231-6(7) , Harper Trophy); 112p. lib. bdg. 15.89 (978-0-06-082232-3(5)); 98p. ***(978-1-4156-7916-6(9))*** HarperCollins Pubs.

Hachler, Bruno. Farley Farts. Muller, Birte, illus. 2003. 32p. (J). (gr. k-3). 15.95 (978-0-7358-1847-7(9)) North-South Bks., Inc.

Hachler, Bruno, et al. Farley Farts. 2004. (Illus.). 32p. (J). pap. 6.95 (978-0-7358-1969-6(6)) North-South Bks., Inc.

Haddad, Charles. Meet Calliope Day. 1999. (J). (978-0-606-16452-8(9)) Tandem Library Bks.

Hahn, Phil. Henrietta: The Homely Duckling. Coker, Paul, Jr., illus. 2004. (Weewisdom Bks.). 47p. (J). 16.95 (978-0-87159-293-4(2) , 168, Unity Hse.) Unity Schl. of Christianity.

Hale, Bruce. The Hamster of the Baskervilles: A Chet Gecko Mystery. (Chet Gecko Mystery Ser.: No. 5). (Illus.). (J). 2003. 144p. (gr. 3-7). pap. 4.95 (978-0-15-202509-0(X) , Harcourt Paperbacks); 2002. 132p. (gr. 4-7). 14.00 (978-0-15-202503-8(0)) Harcourt Children's Bks.

—Hiss Me Deadly: A Chet Gecko Mystery. Hale, Bruce, illus. 2007. (Chet Gecko Mystery Ser.: No. 13). (Illus.). 144p. (J). (gr. 3-7). 15.00 ***(978-0-15-205482-3(0))*** Harcourt Children's Bks.

—Key Lardo: A Chet Gecko Mystery. Hale, Bruce, illus. 2007. (Chet Gecko Mystery Ser.: No. 12). (Illus.). 128p. (J). (gr. 3-7). pap. 4.95 (978-0-15-205235-5(6) , Harcourt Paperbacks) Harcourt Children's Bks.

—Key Lardo: A Chet Gecko Mystery. 2006. (Chet Gecko Mystery Ser.: No. 12). (Illus.). 128p. (J). (gr. 3-7). 14.00 (978-0-15-205074-0(4)) Harcourt Children's Bks.

—The Malted Falcon: A Chet Gecko Mystery. (Chet Gecko Mystery Ser.: No. 7). (Illus.). (J). (gr. 3-7). 2004. 132p. pap. 4.95 (978-0-15-216712-7(9) , Harcourt Paperbacks); 2003. 128p. 14.00 (978-0-15-216706-6(4)) Harcourt Children's Bks.

—The Malted Falcon: A Chet Gecko Mystery. 2004. (Chet Gecko Mystery Ser.: No. 7). (J). (gr. 3-6). lib. bdg. 12.95 (978-0-613-71645-1(0)) Tandem Library Bks.

—Murder, My Tweet: A Chet Gecko Mystery. 2004. (Illus.). 117p. (J). (gr. 3-7). per. 12.00 (978-0-606-33413-6(0)) Tandem Library Bks.

—Pirates of Underwhere. Hillman, Shane, illus. 2008. (Underwhere Ser.). 160p. (J). 15.99 ***(978-0-06-085127-9(9)*** ***);*** lib. bdg. 16.89 ***(978-0-06-085128-6(7))*** HarperCollins Pubs.

—The Possum Always Rings Twice: A Chet Gecko Mystery. Hale, Bruce, illus. 2007. (Chet Gecko Mystery Ser.: No. 11). (Illus.). 144p. (J). (gr. 3-7). pap. 4.95 (978-0-15-205233-1(X) , Harcourt Paperbacks) Harcourt Children's Bks.

—The Possum Always Rings Twice: A Chet Gecko Mystery. 2006. (Chet Gecko Mystery Ser.: No. 11). (Illus.). 128p. (J). (gr. 3-7). 14.00 (978-0-15-205075-7(2)) Harcourt Children's Bks.

—Prince of Underwhere. Hillman, Shane, illus. 2008. (Underwhere Ser.). 176p. (J). lib. bdg. 16.89 ***(978-0-06-085125-5(2)*** ***);*** (gr. 3-7). 15.99 ***(978-0-06-085124-8(4))*** HarperCollins Pubs.

—This Gum for Hire: A Chet Gecko Mystery. (Chet Gecko Mystery Ser.: No. 6). (Illus.). (J). (gr. 3-7). 2003. 144p. pap. 4.95 (978-0-15-202497-0(2) , Harcourt Paperbacks); 2002. 136p. 15.00 (978-0-15-202491-8(3)) Harcourt Children's Bks.

—This Gum for Hire: A Chet Gecko Mystery. 2003. (Chet Gecko Mystery Ser.: No. 6). (J). (gr. 3-6). lib. bdg. 12.95 (978-0-613-59895-8(4)) Tandem Library Bks.

—Trouble Is My Beeswax: A Chet Gecko Mystery. 2004. (Chet Gecko Mystery Ser.: No. 8). (Illus.). 132p. (J). (gr. 3-6). pap. 4.95 (978-0-15-216724-0(2) , Harcourt Paperbacks) Harcourt Children's Bks.

—Trouble Is My Beeswax: A Chet Gecko Mystery. Weinman, Brad, illus. 2003. (Chet Gecko Mystery Ser.: No. 8). 128p. (J). (gr. 3-6). 14.00 (978-0-15-216718-9(8)) Harcourt Children's Bks.

—Trouble Is My Beeswax: A Chet Gecko Mystery. 2004. (Chet Gecko Mystery Ser.: No. 8). (J). (gr. 3-6). lib. bdg. 12.95 (978-0-613-71557-7(8)) Tandem Library Bks.

Hale, Lucretia. The Peterkin Papers. Brett, Harold M., illus. 2005. reprint ed. pap. 24.95 (978-1-4179-3265-8(1)) Kessinger Publishing, LLC.

Hale, Lucretia P. The Peterkin Papers. 2002. (ENG.). 23.99 ***(978-1-4043-2416-9(X)*** ***);*** pap. 18.99 ***(978-1-4043-2417-6(8))*** IndyPublish.com.

—The Peterkin Papers. 2004. reprint ed. pap. 20.95 (978-1-4191-7709-5(5)); pap. 1.99 (978-1-4192-7709-2(X)) Kessinger Publishing, LLC.

—The Peterkin Papers. 2006. (New York Review Children's Collection). (Illus.). 320p. (J). (gr. 4). 18.95 (978-1-59017-212-4(4) , NYR Children's Collection) New York Review of Bks., Inc., The.

Hale, Nathan. The Devil You Know. Hale, Nathan, illus. 2005. (Illus.). 32p. (J). (ps-3). 17.85 (978-0-8027-8983-9(8)); 16.95 (978-0-8027-8981-5(1)) Walker & Co.

Hall. Here Comes Zelda Claus: And Other Holiday Disasters. 2001. (J). pap. (978-0-15-216468-3(5)) Harcourt Trade Pubs.

Hall / Waltz. Mortimer Jones: The Bubble Gum Nerd, 1. l.t. ed. 2003. (Illus.). 32p. 19.95 (978-0-9741774-2-7(3)) D. W. Publishing.

Hall, John. Is He or Isn't He? 2006. 304p. (J). pap. 8.99 (978-0-06-078747-9(3)) HarperCollins Pubs.

Hall, Wesley. Cain McGee, Junior G-man: A Boy's Life in the River Bend. 2001. 287p. (J). pap. 15.95 (978-0-595-21275-0(1) , Writers Club Pr.) iUniverse, Inc.

Halperin, Wendy Anderson, tr. & illus. The Peterkins' Thanksgiving. Halperin, Wendy Anderson, illus. 2005. 32p. (J). (gr. 2-4). 17.95 (978-0-689-84142-2(6) , Atheneum) Simon & Schuster Children's Publishing.

Halverson, Deborah. Big Mouth. 2008. 144p. (J). (gr. 5). 15.99 ***(978-0-385-73394-6(1)*** ***);*** lib. bdg. 18.99 ***(978-0-385-90408-7(8))*** Random Hse. Children's Bks. (Delacorte Bks. for Young Readers).

Handford, Martin. Where's Waldo? Handford, Martin, illus. 2007. (Waldo Ser.). (Illus.). 32p. (J). (gr. k-7). pap. 7.99 ***(978-0-7636-3498-8(0))*** Candlewick Pr.

—Where's Waldo? The Fantastic Journey. Handford, Martin, illus. 2002. (Where's Waldo? Ser.). (Illus.). 32p. (J). (gr. 1-5). 5.99 (978-0-7636-1922-0(1)) Candlewick Pr.

—Where's Waldo? in Hollywood. Handford, Martin, illus. 2007. (Waldo Ser.). (Illus.). 32p. (J). (gr. k-7). pap. 7.99 ***(978-0-7636-3501-5(4))*** Candlewick Pr.

—Where's Waldo? Now. Handford, Martin, illus. 2007. (Waldo Ser.). (Illus.). 32p. (J). (gr. k-7). pap. 7.99 ***(978-0-7636-3499-5(9))*** Candlewick Pr.

—Where's Waldo? the Fantastic Journey. Handford, Martin, illus. 2007. (Illus.). 32p. (J). (gr. k-7). pap. 7.99 ***(978-0-7636-3500-8(6))*** Candlewick Pr.

—Where's Waldo? The Great Picture Hunt. Handford, Martin, illus. 2006. (Illus.). 24p. (J). (gr. 1-7). 14.99 (978-0-7636-3043-0(8)) Candlewick Pr.

—Where's Waldo? the Wonder Book. Handford, Martin, illus. 2007. (Waldo Ser.). (Illus.). 32p. (J). (gr. k-7). pap. 7.99 ***(978-0-7636-3502-2(2))*** Candlewick Pr.

Handford, Martin. Where's Waldo Now? Handford, Martin, illus. 2002. (Where's Waldo? Ser.). (Illus.). 32p. (J). (gr. 1-5). 5.99 (978-0-7636-1921-3(3)) Candlewick Pr.

Hands, Cynthia. Bubble Trouble. 2001. (SpongeBob SquarePants Ser.). (Illus.). 48p. (J). (ps-3). pap. 3.99 (978-0-307-28040-4(3) , Golden Bks.) Random Hse. Children's Bks.

—Coloring & Activity Book 3-in-1. Disney Storybook Artists Staff, illus. 2007. (Meet the Robinsons Ser.). 96p. (J). pap. 2.99 (978-0-06-112467-9(2)) HarperCollins Pubs.

—Coloring & Activity Book & Crayons. Clark, Jeff et al, illus. 2007. (Meet the Robinsons Ser.). 32p. (J). pap. 4.99 (978-0-06-112465-5(6)) HarperCollins Pubs.

—Coloring & Activity Book & Tattoos. Disney Storybook Artists Staff, illus. 2007. (Meet the Robinsons Ser.). 32p. (J). pap. 4.99 (978-0-06-112466-2(4)) HarperCollins Pubs.

Hands, Cynthia & Lodin, John. Coloring & Activity Book & Stickers. Disney Storybook Artists Staff, illus. 2007. (Meet the Robinsons Ser.). 32p. (J). pap., act. bk. ed. 4.99 (978-0-06-112463-1(X)) HarperCollins Pubs.

Hands, Cynthia & Melaranci, Elisabetta. Paint Book. Scuderi, Flavia & Vallorani, Giorgio, illus. 2007. (Meet the Robinsons Ser.). 32p. (J). pap. 4.99 (978-0-06-112464-8(8)) HarperCollins Pubs.

Hanna, James Milton, Sr. Once upon a Time in the South. l.t. ed. 2004. (Illus.). 235p. per. 12.95 (978-1-930052-15-4(4)) Cherokee Bks.

Hannan, Peter. Attack of the 50-Foot Alien Creep-Oids! Hannan, Peter, illus. 2007. (Super Goofballs Ser.: Bk. 4). 144p. (J). (gr. 2-6). pap. 4.99 (***978-0-06-085217-7(8)*** , Harper Trophy) HarperCollins Pubs.

—Goofballs in Paradise. Hannan, Peter, illus. 2007. (Super Goofballs Ser.: Bk. 2). (Illus.). (J). (gr. 2-6). 176p. 15.99 (978-0-06-085214-6(3)); 128p. pap. 4.99 (978-0-06-085213-9(5) , Harper Trophy) HarperCollins Pubs.

—Super Goofballs, Book 5: Doomed in Dreamland. Hannan, Peter, illus. 2008. (Super Goofballs Ser.). 144p. (J). pap. 4.99 (***978-0-06-085219-1(4)*** , Harper Trophy) HarperCollins Pubs.

—Super Underwear... & Beyond! Hannan, Peter, illus. 2007. (Super Goofballs Ser.). 160p. (J). pap. 4.99 (***978-0-06-085215-3(1)*** , Harper Trophy) HarperCollins Pubs.

Hannan, Peter. That Stinking Feeling. Hannan, Peter, illus. 2007. (Super Goofballs Ser.: Bk. 1). (Illus.). 160p. (J). (gr. 2-6). 15.99 (978-0-06-085212-2(7)); pap. 4.99 (978-0-06-085211-5(9) , Harper Trophy) HarperCollins Pubs.

Hansen, T. Cory. The Last Little Pumpkin. Foldvary-Anderson, Carol, illus. l.t. ed. 2002. 38p. (J). cd-rom 11.95 (978-0-9706612-8-9(2)) JetKor.

Hapka, Catherine. Shrek Babies. 2007. (I Can Read Bks.). 32p. (J). pap. 3.99 (***978-0-06-143687-1(9)*** , Harper Trophy) HarperCollins Pubs.

—Shrek the Halls. 2007. (Shrek the Third Ser.). 32p. (J). (ps-2). 15.99 (***978-0-06-143078-7(1)*** , Harper Entertainment) HarperCollins Pubs.

Harcourt School Publishers Staff. My Eggs: A Reader. 1999. (Collections Ser.). (Illus.). (J). pap. 2.10 (978-0-15-313449-4(6)) Harcourt Schl. Pubs.

Hargreaves, Roger. Little Miss Birthday. 2007. 32p. (J). pap. 3.99 (978-0-8431-2131-5(9) , Price Stern Sloan) Penguin Group (USA) Inc.

—Little Miss Brainy. Hargreaves, Roger, illus. 2002. (Mr. Men & Little Miss 3D Ser.). (Illus.). 32p. (J). pap. 3.99 (978-0-8431-7716-9(0) , Price Stern Sloan) Penguin Group (USA) Inc.

—Little Miss Contrary. Hargreaves, Roger, illus. 2000. (Mr. Men & Little Miss Ser.). (Illus.). 32p. (J). (gr. k-3). pap. 3.99 (978-0-8431-7619-3(9) , Price Stern Sloan) Penguin Group (USA) Inc.

—Little Miss Contrary. 2001. (gr. k-3). lib. bdg. 10.65 (978-0-613-31427-5(1)) Tandem Library Bks.

—Little Miss Fun. Hargreaves, Roger, illus. 2001. (Mr. Men & Little Miss Ser.). (Illus.). 32p. (J). (ps-3). pap. 3.99 (978-0-8431-7655-1(5) , Price Stern Sloan) Penguin Group (USA) Inc.

—Mr Bounce. 2000. (ps-2). lib. bdg. 10.65 (978-0-613-26231-6(X)) Tandem Library Bks.

—Mr Busy. 2000. (ps-2). lib. bdg. 10.65 (978-0-613-26232-3(8)) Tandem Library Bks.

—Mr. Cheerful. Hargreaves, Roger, illus. 2002. (Mr. Men & Little Miss Ser.). (Illus.). 32p. (J). pap. 3.99 (978-0-8431-7740-4(3) , Price Stern Sloan) Penguin Group (USA) Inc.

—Mr Clumsy. 2001. (gr. k-3). lib. bdg. 10.65 (978-0-613-31489-3(1)) Tandem Library Bks.

—Mr. Grumble. Hargreaves, Roger, illus. 2002. (Mr. Men & Little Miss Ser.). (Illus.). 32p. (J). pap. 3.99 (978-0-8431-7739-8(X) , Price Stern Sloan) Penguin Group (USA) Inc.

—Mr. Happy & the Wizard. 2007. (Mr. Men & Little Miss Ser.). 32p. (J). (ps). pap. 3.99 (978-0-8431-2491-0(1) , Price Stern Sloan) Penguin Group (USA) Inc.

—Mr. Perfect. Hargreaves, Roger, illus. 2001. (Mr. Men & Little Miss Ser.). (Illus.). 32p. (J). pap. 3.99 (978-0-8431-7689-6(X) , Price Stern Sloan) Penguin Group (USA) Inc.

—Mr Slow. 2000. (ps-2). lib. bdg. 10.65 (978-0-613-26241-5(7)) Tandem Library Bks.

—Mr. Sneeze. Hargreaves, Roger, illus. 2001. (Mr. Men & Little Miss Ser.). (Illus.). 32p. (J). pap. 3.99 (978-0-8431-7688-9(1) , Price Stern Sloan) Penguin Group (USA) Inc.

—Mr Strong. 1999. (ps-2). lib. bdg. 10.65 (978-0-613-22023-1(4)) Tandem Library Bks.

—Mr. Topsy-Turvy. Hargreaves, Roger, illus. 2001. (Mr. Men & Little Miss Ser.). (Illus.). 32p. (J). (ps-3). pap. 3.99 (978-0-8431-7654-4(7) , Price Stern Sloan) Penguin Group (USA) Inc.

Harley, Bill. Dirty Joe, the Pirate: A True Story. Davis, Jack E., illus. 2008. 32p. (J). 16.99 (***978-0-06-623780-0(7)***); lib. bdg. 17.89 (***978-0-06-623781-7(5)***) HarperCollins Pubs.

Harper, Charise Mericle. Flashcards of My Life. 2006. (Illus.). 240p. (J). (gr. 4-7). 15.99 (978-0-316-75621-1(0)) Little Brown & Co.

Harper, Jessica. A Place Called Kindergarten. Karas, G. Brian, illus. 2006. 32p. (J). (ps-3). 15.99 (978-0-399-24226-7(0) , Putnam Juvenile) Penguin Group (USA) Inc.

HarperCollins Staff & Auerbach, Annie. Royally Wrong. 2007. (Shrek 3 Ser.). (SPA.). 24p. (J). pap. 3.99 (978-0-06-122863-6(X) , Harper Entertainment) HarperCollins Pubs.

Harris, Bradley K. My Brother & I. Harris, Phyllis, illus. 2005. 26p. (J). 18.95 (978-0-9710278-6-2(2)) All About Kids Publishing.

Harris, Jay M. The Moon Is la Luna: A Fun & Easy Way to Learn 55 Spanish Words. Cordell, Matthew, illus. 2007. 32p. (J). (gr. 3-5). 15.00 (***978-0-618-64645-6(0)***) Houghton Mifflin Co.

Harris, Peter. Perfect Prudence. Allwright, Deborah, illus. 2003. 32p. (J). (gr. k-3). 15.95 (978-1-57768-437-4(0) , Gingham Dog Pr.) School Specialty Publishing.

Harrison, David. Miss Grubb, Super Sub! A Write-in Reader. O'Rourke, Page, illus. 2005. (Step into Reading Ser.: No. 3). 48p. (J). (gr. 1-3). pap. 3.99 (978-0-375-82894-2(X) , Random Hse. Bks. for Young Readers) Random Hse. Children's Bks.

Hart, Christopher. Merwin: Master of Disguise. 2002. (Illus.). 32p. (ps-2). 14.95 (978-0-8230-3049-1(0)) Watson-Guptill Pubns., Inc.

Haseley, Dennis. The Invisible Moose. Kellogg, Steven, illus. 40p. (J). (ps). 2008. pap. 6.99 (***978-0-14-241066-0(7)*** , Puffin); 2006. 16.99 (978-0-8037-2892-9(1) , Dial) Penguin Group (USA) Inc.

Hassler, Kurt. Hannah & the Homunculus. Darnell, K. L., illus. 2001. 32p. (J). 15.95 (978-1-58536-043-7(0)) Sleeping Bear Pr.

Hautman, Pete. Snatched. 2007. 224p. (J). pap. 6.99 (978-0-14-240795-0(X) , Puffin) Penguin Group (USA) Inc.

Hautzig, Deborah. Little Witch Loves to Write. Wickstrom, Sylvie, illus. 2004. (Stepping into Reading Ser.: Vol. 3). 48p. (J). (gr. 1-3). pap. 3.99 (978-0-375-82893-5(1) , Random Hse. Bks. for Young Readers) Random Hse. Children's Bks.

Havel, Geoff. The Facts of Life. Tholen, Shane, illus. 2001. 120p. (J). (gr. 3-5). pap. 13.95 (978-1-86368-321-0(6)) Fremantle Pr. AUS. *Dist:* International Specialized Bk. Services.

Haven, Paul. Two Hot Dogs with Everything. Ferguson, Peter, illus. 2007. 320p. (J). (gr. 4-7). 6.50 (978-0-375-83349-6(8) , Yearling) Random Hse. Children's Bks.

—Two Hot Dogs with Everything. 2006. (J). lib. bdg. (978-0-375-93350-9(6)) Random Hse. Children's Bks.

—Two Hot Dogs with Everything. Ferguson, Peter & Jessell, Tim, illus. 2006. 320p. (J). (gr. 3-7). 15.95 (978-0-375-83348-9(X) , Random Hse. Bks. for Young Readers) Random Hse. Children's Bks.

—Two Hot Dogs with Everything. Ferguson, Peter, illus. 2006. 320p. (J). (gr. 3-7). lib. bdg. 17.99 (978-0-375-93348-6(4) , Random Hse. Bks. for Young Readers) Random Hse. Children's Bks.

Hawkins, Colin. Mr Wolf's Birthday Surprise. 2004. (Illus.). 32p. (J). pap. 9.99 (978-1-4052-0685-3(3)) Egmont Bks., Ltd. GBR. *Dist:* Trafalgar Square Publishing.

—Mr Wolf's Week. 2004. (Illus.). 32p. (J). pap. 9.99 (978-1-4052-0683-9(7)) Egmont Bks., Ltd. GBR. *Dist:* Trafalgar Square Publishing.

—What's the Time, Mr Wolf? 2004. (Illus.). 32p. (J). 9.95 (978-1-4052-0684-6(5)) Egmont Bks., Ltd. GBR. *Dist:* Trafalgar Square Publishing.

Hayashi, Fumino. Neon Genesis Evangelion: Angelic Days. 2006. 184p. (YA). (Angelic Days Ser.: Vol. 2). (Illus.). pap. (978-1-4139-0348-5(7)); pap. (978-1-4139-0344-7(4)) ADV Manga.

—Neon Genesis Evangelion Vol. 3: Angelic Days. 2006. (Illus.). 184p. (YA). pap. (978-1-4139-0350-8(9)) ADV Manga.

Heck, Nancy & Taylor, Sandy. Sandy Convertible Finds Her Dream. Willison, Tom, illus. 1998. 22p. (J). (gr. k-4). pap. 6.00 (978-0-9670749-0-0(8)) Sandy Convertible, LLC.

Helakoski, Leslie. Big Chickens. Cole, Henry, illus. 2006. 32p. (J). (ps). 15.99 (978-0-525-47575-0(3) , Dutton Juvenile) Penguin Group (USA) Inc.

Heling, Kathryn & Hembrook, Deborah. I Wish I Had Freckles Like Abby/Quisiera tener pecas como Abby. de la Vega, Eida, tr. Adamson, Bonnie, illus. 2006. Tr. of Quisiera tener pecas como Abby. (SPA.). (J). 4.99 (978-0-9770906-6-2(3)) Raven Tree Pr.

—I Wish I Had Freckles Like Abby/Quisiera tener pecas como Abby. de la Vega, Eida, tr. Parins, Kris, illus. 2005. Tr. of Quisiera tener pecas como Abby. (SPA & ENG.). 32p. (J). 16.95 (978-0-9724973-8-1(2) , 626999) Raven Tree Pr.

—I Wish I Had Glasses Like Rosa/Quisiera tener lentes como Rosa. de la Vega, Eida, tr. Adamson, Bonnie, illus. Tr. of Quisiera tener lentes como Rosa. (SPA.). (J). 2006. 4.99 (978-0-9770906-5-5(5)); 2005. 32p. 16.95 (978-0-9724973-7-4(4) , 626999) Raven Tree Pr.

Heller, Linda. The Castle on Hester Street. Kulikov, Boris, illus. 2007. 40p. (J). 15.99 (978-0-689-87434-5(0) , Simon & Schuster Children's Publishing) Simon & Schuster Children's Publishing.

Heller, Sarah E. Disney Animal Friends Movie Theater Storybook & Projector. Disney Art Archives Staff, illus. 2003. (Movie Theater Storybooks & Movie Projectortm Ser.). 48p. (J). 24.99 incl. audio compact disk (978-0-7944-0122-1(8) , Reader's Digest Children's Bks.) Reader's Digest Children's Publishing, Inc.

Helmore, Jim. Letterbox Lil: A Cautionary Tale. 2006. (Illus.). (J). (***978-1-4156-4110-1(2)***) Barron's Educational Series, Inc.

Helquist, Brett. Roger, the Jolly Pirate. Helquist, Brett, illus. 40p. (J). 2007. pap. 6.99 (***978-0-06-443851-3(1)*** , Harper Trophy); 2004. (Illus.). 16.99 (978-0-06-623805-0(6)) HarperCollins Pubs.

Hendersen. Y. Tookay Is Coming! Hendersen, illus. 1999. (Illus.). (YA). (gr. 3-8). pap. 6.95 (978-1-890453-15-2(3)) Little Friend Pr.

Henkes, Kevin. A Box Full of Lilly. Henkes, Kevin, illus. 2006. (J). 24.99 (978-0-06-112852-3(X)) HarperCollins Pubs.

—A Box of Treats: Five Little Picture Books about Lilly & Her Friends. Henkes, Kevin, illus. 2004. (Illus.). (J). 14.99 (978-0-06-073211-0(3) , Harper Festival) HarperCollins Pubs.

Henry, William. Growing up Country: Life on the Farm. 2003. 108p. pap. 11.95 (978-0-595-26864-1(1) , Writers Club Pr.) iUniverse, Inc.

Hergé. Aventures de Tintin au Pays des Soviets. (FRE.). 21.95 (978-2-203-00100-8(3)) Casterman, Editions FRA. *Dist:* Distribooks, Inc.

Herman, Gail. Chutes & Ladders: The Magical Tree House Adventure. 2003. (Illus.). 12p. (J). pap. 9.95 (978-0-7624-1565-6(7) , Running Pr. Kids) Running Pr. Bk. Pubs.

Herrick, Steven. Naked Bunyip Dancing. Norling, Beth, illus. 2008. (J). (***978-1-59078-499-0(5)*** , Front Street) Boyds Mills Pr.

Hershey, Marilyn K. Oncology, Stupology... I Want to Go Home! Boris, Jill M., illus. Blodgea, Randy, photos by. 1999. 32p. (J). (ps-6). pap. 5.00 (978-0-9673550-0-9(1)) Butterfly Pr.

Hershey, Mary. The One Where the Kid Nearly Jumps to His Death & Lands in California. 2007. 288p. (YA). (gr. 5 up). 15.99 (978-1-59514-150-7(2) , Razorbill) Penguin Group (USA) Inc.

Hicks, Barbara Jean. The Secret Life of Walter Kitty. Santat, Dan, illus. 2007. (J). lib. bdg. (***978-0-375-03196-0(0)***) Knopf, Alfred A. Inc.

—The Secret Life of Walter Kitty. Santat, Dan, illus. 2007. 40p. (J). (gr. k-3). 16.99 (978-0-375-83196-6(7)); lib. bdg. 18.99 (978-0-375-93196-3(1)) Random Hse. Children's Bks. (Knopf Bks. for Young Readers).

Hicks, Betty. Busted ! rev. ed. 2004. 176p. (J). 15.95 (978-1-59643-004-4(4)) Roaring Brook Pr.

—Busted ! 2008. 192p. (J). pap. 6.99 (***978-0-312-38053-3(4)***) Square Fish.

Hill, Susanna Leonard. No Sword Fighting in the House. Kelley, True, illus. (Holiday House Reader Ser.: Level 2). 32p. (J). (gr. k-3). 14.95 (978-0-8234-1916-6(9)) Holiday Hse., Inc.

Hillenburg, Steven, creator. SpongeBob SquarePants: Tales from Bikini Bottom, 7 vols., Vol. 3. 2004. (Illus.). 96p. pap. 7.99 (978-1-59182-575-3(X) , Tokyopop Kids) TOKYOPOP, Inc.

—SpongeBob SquarePants Vol. 1: Krusty Krab Adventures, 2 vols. 2003. (Illus.). 96p. pap. 7.99 (978-1-59182-398-8(6) , Tokyopop Kids) TOKYOPOP, Inc.

—SpongeBob SquarePants Crime & Funishment Vol. 4, 7 vols. 2004. (Illus.). 96p. (gr. 2-5). pap. 7.99 (978-1-59182-576-0(8) , Tokyopop Kids) TOKYOPOP, Inc.

—SpongeBob SquarePantsTM: Friends Forever. 2003. (Illus.). 96p. pap. 7.99 (978-1-59182-399-5(4) , Tokyopop Kids) TOKYOPOP, Inc.

Hillerman, Tony. Buster Mesquite's Cowboy Band. Franklin, Ernest, illus. 2001. 32p. (J). 19.95 (978-0-914001-11-9(6)) Sidewinder Publishing LLC.

Himmelman, John. Chickens to the Rescue. 2006. (Illus.). 32p. (J). (ps-3). 16.95 (978-0-8050-7951-7(3)) Holt, Henry & Co.

Hinojosa, Francisco. Repugnante Pajarraco y Otros Regalos. Diego, Rapi, illus. (SPA.). 104p. (J). (gr. 3-5). pap. 9.95 (978-968-19-0293-3(9)) Santillana USA Publishing Co., Inc.

Hirsch, Odo. Hazel Green. 2004. 190p. (J). (gr. 3-7). lib. bdg. 13.60 (978-0-606-30296-8(4)) Tandem Library Bks.

Hitchcock, Coleen A. Bubbly Bubble. Yoh, Jason, illus. 2001. 16p. (J). 9.95 (978-1-929774-08-1(7)) Greenleaf Book Group Pr.

Hoberman, Mary Ann. There Once Was a Man Named Michael Finnegan. Westcott, Nadine Bernard, illus. 2006. 11p. (J). (ps-k). bds. 6.99 (978-0-316-73410-3(1)) Little Brown & Co.

—The Two Sillies. Cravath, Lynne W., illus. 2004. 28p. (J). (ps-2). reprint ed. 16.00 (978-0-7567-7869-9(7)) DIANE Publishing Co.

Hoeye, Michael. Time to Smell the Roses: A Hermux Tantamoq Adventure. 2007. 272p. (J). (gr. 3). 15.99 (***978-0-399-24490-2(5)*** , Putnam Juvenile) Penguin Group (USA) Inc.

Hoff, Syd. Sammy the Seal. Hoff, Syd, illus. 2002. (Illus.). (J). 12.34 (978-0-7587-4577-4(X)) Book Wholesalers, Inc.

—Sammy the Seal. 2000. (I Can Read Bks.). (Illus.). 64p. (J). (ps-1). pap. 3.99 (978-0-06-444270-1(5) , Harper Trophy) HarperCollins Pubs.

—Sammy the Seal. Hoff, Syd, illus. rev. ed. 2000. (I Can Read Bks.). (Illus.). 64p. (J). (ps-1). 16.99 (978-0-06-028545-6(1)); lib. bdg. 16.89 (978-0-06-028546-3(X)) HarperCollins Pubs.

—Sammy the Seal. 2000. (I Can Read Bks.). (978-0-606-17825-9(2)) Tandem Library Bks.

Holm, Jennifer L. Middle School Is Worse Than Meatloaf: A Year Told Through Stuff. Castaldi, Elicia, illus. 2007. 128p. (J). (gr. 3-7). 12.99 (978-0-689-85281-7(9) , Ginne Seo Bks) Simon & Schuster Children's Publishing.

Holmes, Andy. If You Give a Boy a Bible. 2004. 32p. 11.99 (978-0-8254-5513-1(8)) Kregel Pubns.

Holub, Joan. The Gingerbread Kid Goes to School, Vol. 1. Palen, Debbie, illus. 2002. (All Aboard Reading Ser.). 32p. (J). mass mkt. 3.99 (978-0-448-42674-7(9) , Grosset & Dunlap) Penguin Group (USA) Inc.

Holub, Joan & Buttler, Elizabeth. Yankee Doodle Riddles: American History Fun. 2003. (Illus.). 32p. (J). (gr. 2-5). 15.95 (978-0-8075-9260-1(9)) Whitman, Albert & Co.

Holzwarth, Werner & Erlbruch, Wolf. The Story of the Little Mole Who Went in Search of Whodunit. 2007. (J). (ps-5). 24p. 14.95 (***978-0-8109-1641-8(X)*** , Abrams Bks. for Young Readers); 22p. 9.95 (***978-0-8109-4457-2(X)*** , Abrams Image) Abrams, Harry N., Inc.

Homzie, H. B. & Phillips, Matthew. The Baby-Sitters Wore Diapers, No. 3. 2003. (Alien Clones from Outer Space Ser.). 80p. (J). pap. 3.99 (978-0-689-82344-2(4) , Aladdin) Simon & Schuster Children's Publishing.

Honey, Elizabeth. Don't Pat the Wombat! 2001. (Illus.). (J). 11.15 (978-0-606-21157-4(8)) Tandem Library Bks.

Honeywood, Varnette P., illus. Money Troubles. 2002. (Little Bill Ser.). (J). 11.91 (978-0-7587-1452-7(1)) Book Wholesalers, Inc.

Hooks, William H. Lo-Jack & the Pirates. Tusa, Tricia, illus. 1999. (Bank Street Reader Collection). 48p. (J). (gr. 2-4). lib. bdg. 22.60 (978-0-8368-1782-9(6)) Stevens, Gareth Inc.

Hoppe, Paul & Johnson, Henry. Travis & Freddy's Adventures in Vegas. 2006. 224p. (J). (gr. 5). 15.99 (978-0-525-47646-7(6) , Dutton Juvenile) Penguin Group (USA) Inc.

Hornik, Laurie Miller. The Secrets of Ms. Snickle's Class. Tilley, Debbie, illus. 2001. 144p. (J). (gr. 4-6). tchr. ed. 15.00 (978-0-618-03435-2(8) , Clarion Bks.) Houghton Mifflin Co. Trade & Reference Div.

—Zoo School. Tilley, Debbie, illus. 2004. 144p. (J). (gr. 3-5). tchr. ed. 16.00 (978-0-618-34204-4(4) , Clarion Bks.) Houghton Mifflin Co. Trade & Reference Div.

Horowitz, Anthony. Public Enemy Number Two. 2004. (Diamond Brothers Ser.). 208p. (J). (gr. 5). 16.99 (978-0-399-24154-3(X) , Philomel); pap. 6.99 (978-0-14-240218-4(4) , Puffin) Penguin Group (USA) Inc.

—South by Southeast. 2005. (Diamond Brothers Ser.). 160p. (J). (gr. 3-9). pap. 5.99 (978-0-14-240374-7(1) , Puffin) Penguin Group (USA) Inc.

—Three of Diamonds. 2005. (Diamond Brothers Ser.). 240p. (J). (gr. 5). pap. 6.99 (978-0-14-240298-6(2) , Puffin); (YA). (gr. 4). 16.99 (978-0-399-24157-4(4) , Philomel) Penguin Group (USA) Inc.

Horowitz, Dave. Five Little Gefiltes. Horowitz, Dave, illus. 2007. (Illus.). 32p. (J). (ps-2). 12.99 (978-0-399-24608-1(8) , Putnam Juvenile) Penguin Group (USA) Inc.

Horowitz, Ruth. Big Surprise in the Bug Tank. Holub, Joan, illus. 2005. (Easy-to-Read, Dial Ser.). 48p. (J). (gr. 1). 14.99 (978-0-8037-2874-5(3) , Dial) Penguin Group (USA) Inc.

Horvath, Polly. The Pepins & Their Problems. Hafner, Marylin, illus. 2004. 192p. (J). 16.00 (978-0-374-35817-4(6) , Farrar, Straus & Giroux (BYR)) Farrar, Straus & Giroux.

—The Pepins & Their Problems. Hafner, Marylin, illus. pap. 13.95 (978-0-88899-633-6(0)) Groundwood Bks. CAN. *Dist:* Transition Vendor.

—The Pepins & Their Problems. Hafner, Marylin, illus. 2008. 208p. (J). pap. 6.99 (***978-0-312-37751-9(7)***) Square Fish.

—The Pepins & Their Problems. Hafner, Marylin, illus. l.t. ed. 2004. 154p. (J). 22.95 (978-0-7862-7063-7(2)) Thorndike Pr.

Howe, James. Bud Barkin, Private Eye. Helquist, Brett, illus. (Tales from the House of Bunnicula Ser.). (J). 2004. 112p. pap. 3.99 (978-0-689-86989-1(4) , Aladdin); 2003. 96p. 9.95 (978-0-689-85632-7(6) , Atheneum) Simon & Schuster Children's Publishing.

—Bunnicula-in-a-Box: Bunnicula, the Celery Stalks at Midnight, Howliday Inn. 2006. 496p. (J). pap. 14.99 (978-1-4169-3498-1(7) , Aladdin) Simon & Schuster Children's Publishing.

—Bunnicula Meets Edgar Allan Crow. Fortune, Eric, illus. 2006. (Bunnicula Ser.). 160p. (J). 15.95 (978-1-4169-1458-7(7) , Ginne Seo Bks) Simon & Schuster Children's Publishing.

—Howie Monroe & the Doghouse of Doom. Helquist, Brett, illus. 2002. (Tales from the House of Bunnicula Ser.). 96p. (J). 9.95 (978-0-689-83951-1(0) , Atheneum) Simon & Schuster Children's Publishing.

—Howie Monroe & the Doghouse of Doom. 2002. (Tales from the House of Bunnicula Ser.). (Illus.). 90p. (J). (gr. 3-6). 9.95 (978-0-689-88395-8(1) , Atheneum) Simon & Schuster Children's Publishing.

—Howie Monroe & the Doghouse of Doom. 2004. (Tales from the House of Bunnicula Ser.). 85p. (J). (gr. 3-6). pap. 17.00 incl. audio (978-1-4000-8634-4(5) , Listening Library) Random Hse. Audio Publishing Group.

—Invasion of the Mind Swappers from Asteroid 6! 2004. (Tales from the House of Bunnicula Ser.). 112p. (J). (gr. 3-6). pap. 17.00 incl. audio (978-1-4000-8633-7(7) , Listening Library) Random Hse. Audio Publishing Group.

—Invasion of the Mind Swappers from Asteroid 6! Helquist, Brett, illus. (Tales from the House of Bunnicula Ser.). (J). 2003. 112p. pap. 3.99 (978-0-689-83950-4(2) , Aladdin); 2002. 96p. (gr. 2-4). 9.95 (978-0-689-83949-8(9) , Atheneum) Simon & Schuster Children's Publishing.

—Invasion of the Mind Swappers from Asteroid 6! 2003. (Tales from the House of Bunnicula Ser.). (gr. 3-6). lib. bdg. 11.80 (978-0-613-66414-1(0)) Tandem Library Bks.

—It Came from Beneath the Bed! Helquist, Brett, illus. 2002. (Tales from the House of Bunnicula Ser.). 96p. (J). (gr. 2-4). 9.95 (978-0-689-83947-4(2) , Atheneum) Simon & Schuster Children's Publishing.

—It Came from Beneath the Bed! 2003. (Tales from the House of Bunnicula Ser.). (gr. 3-6). lib. bdg. 11.80 (978-0-613-66415-8(9)) Tandem Library Bks.

—It Came from Beneath the Bed! 2004. (Tales from the House of Bunnicula Ser.). 112p. (J). (gr. 3-6). pap. 17.00 incl. audio (978-1-4000-8632-0(9) , Listening Library) Random Hse. Audio Publishing Group.

—The Odorous Adventures of Stinky Dog. Helquist, Brett, illus. 2003. (Tales from the House of Bunnicula Ser.). 112p. (J). bds. 9.95 (978-0-689-85633-4(4) , Atheneum) Simon & Schuster Children's Publishing.

—Screaming Mummies of the Pharaoh's Tomb II. Helquist, Brett, illus. 2003. (Tales from the House of Bunnicula Ser.). 112p. (J). 9.95 (978-0-689-83953-5(7) , Atheneum) Simon & Schuster Children's Publishing.

Howland, Naomi. The Matzah Man: A Passover Story. 2002. (Illus.). 32p. (J). (gr. k-3). 16.00 (978-0-618-11750-5(4) , Clarion Bks.) Houghton Mifflin Co. Trade & Reference Div.

Hoylie, Gerry. Byron Unleashed. 2005. 60p. pap. 14.95 (978-1-59113-670-5(9)) Booklocker.com, Inc.

Hudspeth, Elly Shafter & Peyton, Barbara. Colt Revolt: Memoirs of Three Mischievous, but Adorable Equine Siblings. Wilkins, Rhett, illus. 2007. 140p. pap. 12.95 (***978-1-60145-223-8(3)***) Booklocker.com, Inc.

Huelin, Jodi, adapted by. Piggley's Tough Break. 2008. (Jakers! Ser.). 24p. (J). pap. 3.99 (***978-1-4169-4770-7(1)*** , Simon Spotlight) Simon & Schuster Children's Publishing.

Hughes, Langston. Simple Speaks His Mind. (J). (gr. 5-6). reprint ed. lib. bdg. 22.95 (978-0-88411-061-3(3)) Amereon LTD.

Hughes, Susan. Earth to Audrey. Poulin, Stephane, illus. 2005. 32p. (J). (gr. k-3). (978-1-55337-843-3(1)) Kids Can Pr., Ltd.

—The Not-Quite World Famous Scientist. Taylor, Stephen, illus. 2002. (First Flight Ser.). 64p. (J). (gr. 4-6). pap. (978-1-55041-696-1(0)) Fitzhenry & Whiteside, Ltd.

Hurwitz, Johanna. Fourth-Grade Fuss. Hammond, Andy, illus. 2004. 144p. (J). 15.99 (978-0-06-052343-5(3)); lib. bdg. 16.89 (978-0-06-052344-2(1)) HarperCollins Pubs.

—Starting School. Dugan, Karen, illus. 2001. 102p. (J). (ps-ps). per. 10.39 (978-0-606-21464-3(X)) Tandem Library Bks.

Hutchens, Paul. The Bull Fighter. 1998. (gr. 3-6). lib. bdg. 13.00 (978-0-613-90324-0(2)) Tandem Library Bks.

Hutchins, Hazel. Robyn's Party-in-the-Park. Cathcart, Yvonne, illus. 2005. (First Novel Ser.). 64p. (J). (gr. 2-5). (***978-0-88780-663-6(5));*** 4.95 (978-0-88780-662-9(7)) Formac Publishing Co., Ltd. CAN. *Dist:* Casemate Pubs. & Bk. Distributors, LLC.

Hyman, Fracaswell. Adventure with Captain Brainstorm! 2001. (gr. k-3). lib. bdg. 14.15 (978-0-613-50399-0(6)) Tandem Library Bks.

Ibbotson, Eva. The Haunting of Granite Falls. Hawkes, Kevin, illus. 2005. 224p. (J). (gr. 3). pap. 5.99 (978-0-14-240371-6(7) , Puffin) Penguin Group (USA) Inc.

—Not Just a Witch. Hawkes, Kevin, illus. 2004. 192p. (gr. 3). pap. 5.99 (978-0-14-240232-0(X) , Puffin) Penguin Group (USA) Inc.

Impey, Rose. Who's a Clever Girl? Amstutz, Andre, illus. 2003. (Yellow Bananas Ser.). 48p. (J). (gr. 3-4). pap. (978-0-7787-0976-3(0)) Crabtree Publishing Co.

—Who's a Clever Girl? 2002. (gr. 3-6). lib. bdg. 12.95 (978-0-613-52935-8(9)) Tandem Library Bks.

Inches, Alison. Blue Talks! Style Guide Staff, illus. 2004. (Blue's Clues Ser.). 12p. (J). bds. 8.99 (978-0-689-86459-9(0) , Simon Spotlight/Nickelodeon) Simon & Schuster Children's Publishing.

Inns, Chris. The Jokers. 2005. (Illus.). 32p. (J). (ps-3). 16.95 (978-1-84507-287-2(1)) Lincoln, Frances Ltd. GBR. *Dist:* Perseus Distribution.

Inns, Christopher. The Jokers. 2006. (Illus.). 32p. pap. 7.95 (978-1-84507-429-6(7)) Lincoln, Frances Ltd. GBR. *Dist:* Perseus Distribution.

Inoue, Kazurou. Midori Days. 2006. (Midori Days Ser.). 208p. (YA). Vol. 6. pap. 9.99 (978-1-4215-0495-7(2)); Vol. 7. pap. 9.99 (978-1-4215-0496-4(0)) Viz Media.

Is That Funny? 2001. (J). per. 15.95 (978-0-9741319-2-4(X)) 4N Publishing LLC.

Ives, David. Monsieur Eek. Swearingen, Greg, illus. 2001. 192p. (J). (gr. 5 up). 15.89 (978-0-06-029530-1(9)) HarperCollins Pubs.

The J-Files: Individual Title, 6 Packs. (Bookweb Ser.). 32p. (gr. 3 up). 34.00 (978-0-7635-3941-2(4)) Rigby Education.

Jack Gantos. Jack's Black Book. l.t. ed. 2006. 160p. (J). 23.95 (978-0-7862-9033-8(1)) Thorndike Pr.

Jackson, A. Isaiah J. Jiffy: You, You, You. Bully! 2005. 50p. pap. 12.95 (978-1-4137-8524-1(7)) PublishAmerica, Inc.

Jackson, Alison. The Ballad of Valentine. Tusa, Tricia, illus. 2006. 32p. (J). (gr. 3). reprint ed. pap. 6.99 (978-0-14-240400-3(4) , Puffin) Penguin Group (USA) Inc.

—I Know an Old Lady Who Swallowed a Pie. Schachner, Judith B., illus. 2002. 32p. (J). (ps-3). pap. 6.99 (978-0-14-056595-9(7) , Puffin) Penguin Group (USA) Inc.

—I Know an Old Lady Who Swallowed a Pie. Schachner, Judith Byron, illus. 2002. (J). (ps-ps). lib. bdg. 15.30 (978-0-613-55215-8(6)) Tandem Library Bks.

Jackson, Melanie. The Spy in the Alley. 2002. (Dinah Galloway Mystery Ser.). 176p. (J). (gr. 3-7). pap. 6.95 (978-1-55143-207-6(2)) Orca Bk. Pubs. USA.

Jackson, Neta. Grandma Aggie & the Bless You. 2004. 11.99 (978-0-8254-2939-2(0)) Kregel Pubns.

Jacobs, Jimmy. Moonlight Through the Pines: Tales of the Georgia Evenings. Ward, Calvin H., illus. 2000. x, 116p. (J). (gr. 7-12). pap. 11.95 (978-0-9637477-3-0(8)) Franklin-Sarrett Pubs.

Jaffe, Michele. Bad Kitty. 2006. (Illus.). 288p. (J). 16.99 (978-0-06-078108-8(4)); lib. bdg. 17.89 (978-0-06-078109-5(2)) HarperCollins Pubs.

James, Charlie. Billy the Fish. Jolliffe, Ned, illus. 2006. 176p. (J). 14.95 (978-1-58234-732-5(8)); pap. 5.95 (978-1-58234-733-2(6)) Bloomsbury Publishing. (Bloomsbury Children).

James, Frank, illus. The Kingfisher Treasury of Funny Stories. 2003. (Kingfisher Treasury of Stories Ser.). 160p. (J). (gr. k-3). pap. 5.95 (978-0-7534-5631-6(1) , Kingfisher) Houghton Mifflin Co. Trade & Reference Div.

James, Simon. Baby Brains & RoboMom. 2008. (Illus.). 32p. (J). (ps-3). 15.99 (***978-0-7636-3463-6(8)***) Candlewick Pr.

Janisch, H. & Holland, C. Heave Ho! 2006. (Illus.). 32p. (J). 16.95 (978-0-7358-2091-3(0)) North-South Bks., Inc.

Janison, Kevin D. Deputy Dorkface: How Stinkville Got Cleaned Up. Doty, Eldon, illus. 2007. 32p. (J). (ps-1). 16.95 (***978-1-932173-82-6(X)***) Stephens Pr. LLC.

Jardine, Alan. Sloop John B: A Pirate's Tale. Pickering, Jimmy, illus. 2005. 32p. 17.95 (978-1-59687-181-6(4) , Milk & Cookies) ibooks, Inc.

Jarman, Julia. Class Two at the Zoo. Chapman, Lynne, illus. 2007. (Carolrhoda Picture Bks.). 32p. (J). (gr. k-3). 16.95 (***978-0-8225-7132-2(3)*** , Carolrhoda Bks.) Lerner Publishing Group.

Jennings, Sharon, et al. Franklin's Nickname. Southern, Shelley et al, trs. Southern, Shelley et al, illus. 2005. (Franklin TV StoryBks.). 32p. (J). (ps-3). (978-1-55337-489-3(4)) Kids Can Pr., Ltd.

Jethani, Rita. Baby has a Burp. 2006. (Illus.). 24p. (J). 12.00 (978-0-9774147-0-3(1)) Laasya Design.

Jett Jackson. 96p. (J). Bk. 1. 2000. pap. 4.99 (978-0-7868-4433-3(7)); Bk. 2. 2000. pap. 4.99 (978-0-7868-4434-0(5)); Bk. 4. 2001. pap. 4.99 (978-0-7868-4436-4(1)) Disney Pr.

Johansen, K. V. Torrie & the Firebird. Delezenne, Christine, illus. 2006. (Torrie Quests Ser.). 195p. (J). (gr. 3-5). 18.95 (978-1-55037-961-7(5)); pap. 7.95 (978-1-55037-960-0(7)) Annick Pr., Ltd. CAN. *Dist:* Firefly Bks., Ltd.

Johansen, Krista. Torrie & the Pirate Queen. Delezenne, Christine, illus. 2005. (Torrie Quests Ser.). 144p. (J). (gr. 4-6). 18.95 (978-1-55037-901-3(1)); pap. 7.95 (978-1-55037-900-6(3)) Annick Pr., Ltd. CAN. *Dist:* Firefly Bks., Ltd.

Johnson, Angela, et al. Tripping over the Lunch Lady. Mercado, Nancy, ed. 2006. 192p. (J). (gr. 5). pap. 5.99 (978-0-14-240624-3(4) , Puffin) Penguin Group (USA) Inc.

Johnson, Doug. Substitute Teacher Plans. Smith, Tammy, illus. rev. ed. 2002. 32p. (J). (gr. k-3). 16.95 (978-0-8050-6520-6(2) , Holt, Henry & Co. Bks. For Young Readers) Holt, Henry & Co.

Johnson, Gillian. Thora: A Half-Mermaid Tale. Johnson, Gillian, illus. 2005. (Illus.). 256p. (J). 15.99 (978-0-06-074378-9(6)); lib. bdg. 15.89 (978-0-06-074379-6(4)) HarperCollins Pubs.

Johnson, Linda & Hodges, Quae. 21st Century Parables: A Child's Book. 2006. 48p. pap. 14.95 (***978-1-60145-071-5(0)***) Booklocker.com, Inc.

Johnson, Paul Brett, tr. & illus. Little Bunny Foo Foo: Told & Sung by the Good Fairy. Johnson, Paul Brett, illus. 2004. 32p. (J). pap. 15.95 (978-0-439-37301-2(8)) Scholastic, Inc.

Johnson, Sandi. Beano Nenno: Wiggle & Walk. Johnson, Britt, ed. Johnson, Britt, illus. 1998. (Little Choo-Choo Bks.). 14p. (J). (ps-6). 8.99 (978-1-929063-15-4(6) , 115) Moons & Stars Publishing For Children.

Johnson, Suzanne C. Fribbity Ribbit! 1999. (J). 16.00 (978-0-517-70982-5(1)) Crown Publishing Group.

Johnston, Tony. Alien & Possum: Hanging Out. 2003. (gr. k-3). lib. bdg. 11.80 (978-0-613-66391-5(8)) Tandem Library Bks.

—Mummy's Mother. 2003. (Illus.). 160p. (J). pap. 15.95 (978-0-439-32462-5(9) , Blue Sky Pr., The) Scholastic, Inc.

Jonell, Lynne. Emmy & the Incredible Shrinking Rat. Bean, Jonathan, illus. 2007. 352p. (J). (gr. 4 up). 17.95 (***978-0-8050-8150-3(X)***) Holt, Henry & Co.

Jones, Brian and Brad. The Righteous Heroes. 2005. 36p. pap. 13.99 (978-1-4116-5423-5(4)) Lulu.com.

Jones, Diana Wynne. Stopping for a Spell. 2004. (gr. 3-6). lib. bdg. 14.15 (978-0-613-81137-8(2)) Tandem Library Bks.

Jones, Jasmine & Lodin, John. The Chapter Book. 2007. (Meet the Robinsons Ser.). 64p. (J). pap. 4.99 (978-0-06-112474-7(5)) HarperCollins Pubs.

Jones, Marcia Thornton & Dadey, Debbie. Double Trouble Monsters. 1999. (Bailey City Monsters Ser.: No. 5). (Illus.). 80p. (J). (gr. 2-4). pap. 3.99 (978-0-439-05870-4(8)) Scholastic, Inc.

—Double Trouble Monsters. 1999. (Bailey City Monsters Ser.: No. 5). (J). (gr. 2-4). (978-0-606-16604-1(1)) Tandem Library Bks.

—Dracula Doesn't Play Kickball. 2004. (Baily School Kids Ser.). 80p. (J). pap. 3.99 (978-0-439-56000-9(4) , Scholastic Paperbacks) Scholastic, Inc.

—The Hauntlys' Hairy Surprise. 1999. (Bailey City Monsters Super Special Ser.: No. 1). (Illus.). 112p. (J). (gr. 2-4). pap. 3.99 (978-0-590-04302-1(1)) Scholastic, Inc.

—The Hauntlys' Hairy Surprise. 1999. (Bailey City Monsters Super Special Ser.: No. 1). (J). (gr. 2-4). (978-0-606-19911-7(X)) Tandem Library Bks.

—Howling at the Hauntlys' Gurney, John Steven, illus. 1998. (Bailey City Monsters Ser.: No.2). (J). (gr. 2-4). pap. 3.99 (978-0-590-10845-4(X)) Scholastic, Inc.

—Kilmer's Pet Monster. 1999. (Bailey City Monsters Ser.: No. 4). (Illus.). 72p. (J). (gr. 2-4). pap. 3.99 (978-0-590-10847-8(6)) Scholastic, Inc.

—The Monsters Next Door. Gurney, John Steven, illus. 1998. (Bailey City Monsters Ser.: No. 1). 71p. (J). (gr. 2-4). pap. 3.99 (978-0-590-10787-7(9)) Scholastic, Inc.

—Snow Monster Mystery. 1999. (Bailey City Monsters Ser.: No. 8). (Illus.). (J). (gr. 2-4). (978-0-606-18514-1(3)) Tandem Library Bks.

—Spooky Spells. 1999. (Bailey City Monsters Ser.: No. 6). (Illus.). 80p. (J). (gr. 2-4). pap. 3.99 (978-0-439-05871-1(6)) Scholastic, Inc.

—Spooky Spells. 1999. (Bailey City Monsters Ser.: No. 6). (J). (gr. 2-4). (978-0-606-16656-0(4)) Tandem Library Bks.

—Vampire Baby. 1999. (Bailey City Monsters Ser.: No. 7). (Illus.). 80p. (J). (gr. 2-4). pap. 3.99 (978-0-439-05872-8(4)) Scholastic, Inc.

—Vampire Baby. 1999. (Bailey City Monsters Ser.: No. 7). (J). (gr. 2-4). (978-0-606-17059-8(6)) Tandem Library Bks.

—Vampire Trouble. 1998. (Bailey City Monsters Ser.: No. 3). (Illus.). 80p. (J). (gr. 2-4). pap. 3.99 (978-0-590-10846-1(8)) Scholastic, Inc.

Jonsberg, Barry. The Crimes & Punishments of Miss Payne. 2005. 272p. (J). (gr. 7-12). 15.95 (978-0-375-83240-6(8)); lib. bdg. 17.99 (978-0-375-93240-3(2)) Random Hse. Children's Bks. (Knopf Bks. for Young Readers).

Jordan, Apple. Journey to the Future. Disney Storybook Artists Staff, illus. 2007. (Meet the Robinsons Ser.). 32p. (J). pap. 3.99 (978-0-06-112472-3(9) , Harper Trophy) HarperCollins Pubs.

Jorisch, Stephane, illus. The Trial of the Stone: A Folk Tale. 2000. 32p. (J). (ps-1). lib. bdg. 19.95 (978-1-55037-647-0(0)) Annick Pr., Ltd. CAN. *Dist:* Firefly Bks., Ltd.

Joyce, William. A Day with Wilbur Robinson. Joyce, William, illus. 2006. (Illus.). 40p. (J). 16.99 (978-0-06-089098-8(3)); lib. bdg. 17.89 (978-0-06-089099-5(1)) HarperCollins Pubs. (Geringer, Laura Book).

Juby, Susan. Alice MacLeod, Realist at Last. (J). 2006. 320p. pap. 8.99 (978-0-06-051552-2(X)); 2005. 15.99 (978-0-06-051549-2(X)); 2005. 320p. lib. bdg. 16.89 (978-0-06-051550-8(3)) HarperCollins Pubs. (HarperTeen).

Jukes, Mavis. Cinderella 2000. 2001. (Illus.). (J). (978-0-606-20605-1(1)) Tandem Library Bks.

Kaczman, James. A Bird & His Worm. Kaczman, James, illus. 2002. (Illus.). 32p. (J). (gr. k-3). tchr. ed. 15.00 (978-0-618-09460-8(1)) Houghton Mifflin Co. Trade & Reference Div.

Kaczman, James. Lucky Monkey, Unlucky Monkey. 2008. 32p. (J). (gr. 3-5). 16.00 (***978-0-618-63153-7(4)***) Houghton Mifflin Co. Trade & Reference Div.

Kahl, Virginia. The Duchess Bakes a Cake. Kahl, Virginia, illus. 2002. 32p. 17.95 (978-1-930900-14-1(7)) Purple Hse. Pr.

Kain, P. G. The Social Experiments of Dorie Dilts: Dumped by Popular Demand. 2007. (Social Experiments of Dorie Dilts Ser.). 254p. (J). (gr. 4-8). per. 5.99 (***978-1-4169-3519-3(3)*** , Aladdin) Simon & Schuster Children's Publishing.

Kai's Cake. 2004. (Illus.). 23p. (J). pap. (978-0-9749469-0-0(7)) Crunchpeep Media.

Kako, Satoshi. Little Daruma & Little Kaminari. Howlett, Peter & McNamara, Richard B., trs. from JPN. 2003. (Illus.). 32p. (gr. 1-4). 10.95 (978-0-8048-3348-6(6)) Tuttle Publishing.

Kalman, Maira. La Ooh La. 2002. (gr. k-3). lib. bdg. 15.30 (978-0-613-43637-3(7)) Tandem Library Bks.

—Smartypants (Pete in School) Kalman, Maira, illus. 2003. (Illus.). 32p. (J). (gr. k-3). 15.99 (978-0-399-23478-1(0) , Putnam Juvenile) Penguin Group (USA) Inc.

Karim, Roberta. This Is a Hospital, Not a Zoo! 2002. (gr. k-3). lib. bdg. 14.10 (978-0-613-72912-3(9)) Tandem Library Bks.

Kasza, Keiko. Dorotea y Miguel. Aparicio, Cristina, tr. 2001. (SPA.). (J). (ps-2). 8.95 (978-958-04-6033-6(7)) Norma S.A. COL. *Dist:* Distribuidora Norma, Inc., Lectorum Pubns., Inc.

—No Te Rias, Pepe. (Buenas Noches Coleccion). (SPA.). (J). (gr. k-3). 8.95 (978-958-04-3623-2(1)) Norma S.A. COL. *Dist:* Distribuidora Norma, Inc., Lectorum Pubns., Inc.

Katschke, Judy. What's the Buzz? 2007. (Bee Movie Ser.). 64p. (J). (gr. 2-5). pap. 4.99 (***978-0-06-125177-1(1)*** , Harper Entertainment) HarperCollins Pubs.

Katschke, Judy & Artifact Group. Camp Sportacus. 2006. (LazyTown Ser.). 14p. (J). bds. 5.99 (978-1-4169-0662-9(2) , Simon Spotlight/Nickelodeon) Simon & Schuster Children's Publishing.

Katschke, Judy, et al. Help! There's a Ghost in My Room! 2003. (Full House Ser.: No. 1). (Illus.). 96p. mass mkt. 4.99 (978-0-06-054083-8(4) , 53751756, Harper Entertainment) HarperCollins Pubs.

Keane, Bil. The Family Circus by Request. Keane, Bil, illus. 2001. (Guideposts Ser.). (Illus.). 120p. 12.95 (978-0-8249-4603-6(0)) Ideals Pubns.

Keenan, Sheila. What's up with That Cup? 2001. (Hello Reader! Ser.). (Illus.). (J). (978-0-606-21519-0(0)) Tandem Library Bks.

Keene, Carolyn. Space Case. Jones, Jan Naimo, illus. 2004. 68p. (J). (ps-ps). lib. bdg. 12.00 (978-1-4176-3564-1(9)) Tandem Library Bks.

Keens-Douglas, Richardo. The Trial of the Stone: A Folk Tale. 2000. (gr. k-3). lib. bdg. 15.25 (978-0-613-50384-6(8)) Tandem Library Bks.

Keillor, Garrison. The Old Man Who Loved Cheese. braille ed. 2004. (Illus.). (J). (gr. k-3). spiral bd. (978-0-616-01687-9(5)) Canadian National Institute for the Blind/Institut National Canadien pour les Aveugles.

—The Old Man Who Loved Cheese. Wilsdorf, Anne, illus. 1998. (978-0-606-13674-7(6)) Tandem Library Bks.

Keller, Core F. Aviation Humor: Poking Fun at Airplane & Helicopter Pilots. 2002. 122p. (YA). pap. 10.95 (978-0-595-25631-0(7) , Writers Club Pr.) iUniverse, Inc.

Keller, Holly. Nosy Rosie. Keller, Holly, illus. 2006. (Illus.). 32p. (J). (gr. k-2). 16.99 (978-0-06-078758-5(9)); lib. bdg. 17.89 (978-0-06-078759-2(7)) HarperCollins Pubs.

Keller, Laurie. Arnie the Doughnut. Keller, Laurie, illus. 2005. (J). (gr. k-4). 24.95 incl. audio (978-0-439-76639-5(7) , WHRA649); 29.95 incl. audio compact disk (978-0-439-76641-8(9) , WHCD649) Weston Woods Studios, Inc.

—Arnie, the Doughnut. rev. ed. 2003. (Illus.). 40p. (J). (ps-3). 17.95 (978-0-8050-6283-0(1) , Holt, Henry & Co. Bks. For Young Readers) Holt, Henry & Co.

—Scrambled States of America. 2002. (gr. k-3). lib. bdg. 15.25 (978-0-613-75400-2(X)) Tandem Library Bks.

Kellogg, Steven. I Was Born about 10,000 Years Ago: A Tall Tale. 1998. (Illus.). 48p. (J). (ps-3). pap. 5.95 (978-0-688-16156-9(1) , Harper Trophy) HarperCollins Pubs.

—Missing Mitten Mystery. 2002. (gr. k-3). lib. bdg. 15.30 (978-0-613-83547-3(6)) Tandem Library Bks.

—Pinkerton & Friends: A Steven Kellogg Treasury. 2004. (Illus.). 336p. (J). (ps). 30.00 (978-0-8037-2979-7(0) , Dial) Penguin Group (USA) Inc.

Kelly, J. B. & Yamada, Takahiro. Roly & Renee Find a Way. 2002. 32p. 14.95 (978-1-931730-03-7(2)); (SPA.). pap. 5.95 (978-1-931730-05-1(9)) AMY Pr.

Kelly, John & Tincknell, Cathy. Scoop! An Exclusive by Monty Molenski. Kelly, John & Tincknell, Cathy, illus. 2007. (Illus.). 32p. (J). (gr. k-3). 15.99 (978-0-7636-3059-1(4)) Candlewick Pr.

Kelly, Mij. One More Sheep. Ayto, Russell, illus. 2006. 30p. (J). 16.95 (978-1-56145-378-8(1) , Peachtree Junior) Peachtree Pubs., Ltd.

Kenney, Cindy. Bob & Larry's Silly Slides. 2005. (Big Idea Bks.). (Illus.). 10p. 6.99 (978-0-310-70917-6(2)) Zonderkidz.

—Veggie Tales I Can! And So Can You! 2004. (Illus.). bds. 12.99 (978-0-310-70893-3(1)) Zonderkidz.

Kerrin, Jessica Scott. Martin Bridge: On the Lookout! Kelly, Joseph, illus. 2005. 144p. (J). (978-1-55337-689-7(7)) Kids Can Pr., Ltd.

Keselman, Gabriela. De Verdad Que No Podia. Villamuza, Noemi, illus. 2002. (SPA.). (J). (gr. k-2). 16.95 (978-84-88342-31-7(4) , KK30914) S.A. Kokinos ESP. *Dist:* Lectorum Pubns., Inc.

Kessler, Leonard. Sport Stories You'll Have a Ball With. 2001. (gr. 3-6). lib. bdg. 11.80 (978-0-613-56618-6(1)) Tandem Library Bks.

Kessler, Leonard P. Mrs. Pine Takes a Trip. Kessler, Leonard P., illus. 2005. (Illus.). (J). 16.00 (978-1-930900-25-7(2)) Purple Hse. Pr.

Kidd, Richard. Lobsters in Love: A Whirlpool Romance. Kidd, Lindsey, illus. 2004. 32p. (J). pap. 7.95 (978-1-84507-154-7(9)) Lincoln, Frances Ltd. GBR. *Dist:* Perseus Distribution.

Kidd, Ronald. The Best Adventure. 2002. (Illus.). 24p. (J). (ps). pap. 2.50 (978-1-888567-58-8(9)) Dalmatian Pr.

—Fantastic Friends. 2002. (Illus.). 24p. (J). (ps-4). pap. 2.50 (978-1-888567-59-5(7)) Dalmatian Pr.

Kim, Sun-Min & Horvath, David. Ugly Guide to the Uglyverse. 2008. (Illus.). 64p. (J). (gr. 2-5). pap. 5.99 (***978-0-375-84275-7(6)*** , Random Hse. Bks. for Young Readers) Random Hse. Children's Bks.

—The Ugly Guide to the Uglyverse. 2008. (Illus.). 64p. (J). (gr. 1). lib. bdg. 12.99 (***978-0-375-93683-8(1)*** , Random Hse. Bks. for Young Readers) Random Hse. Children's Bks.

—Ugly Guide to Things That Go & Things That Should Go But Don't. 2007. (Illus.). 64p. (J). (gr. 2-5). pap. 5.99 (***978-0-375-84370-9(1)*** , Random Hse. Bks. for Young Readers) Random Hse. Children's Bks.

Kimmel, Eric A. Bernal & Florinda: A Spanish Tale. Rayevsky, Robert, illus. 2004. 29p. (J). (gr. k-4). reprint ed. 16.00 (978-0-7567-7906-1(5)) DIANE Publishing Co.

—Hayyim's Ghost. 2005. (Illus.). 40p. (J). pap. 9.95 (978-1-932687-03-3(3) , Devora Publishing) Pitspopany Pr.

—Hayyim's Ghost. Binus, Ari, illus. 2005. 40p. (J). 16.95 (978-1-932687-02-6(5) , Devora Publishing) Pitspopany Pr.

Kimpton, Diana. The Lamb-A-Roo. Beardshaw, Rosalind, illus. 2006. 32p. (J). 15.95 (978-0-7696-4619-0(0) , Gingham Dog Pr.) School Specialty Publishing.

King, Charles. The Amazing Adventures of Joey & Joy. 2003. 128p. (J). pap. 9.99 (978-1-58832-087-2(1)); 19.99 (978-1-58832-086-5(3)) Unlimited Publishing LLC.

King, Emily. Mrs. Twiggenbotham Goes to Town. 2003. (Twiggenbotham Adventure Ser.). (Illus.). 32p. (J). 12.99 (978-0-8254-3064-0(X)) Kregel Pubns.

King-Smith, Dick. Funny Frank. Eastwood, John, illus. 2003. 112p. (gr. 2-5). pap. 5.50 (978-0-440-41880-1(1) , Yearling) Random Hse. Children's Bks.

—Funny Frank. Roth, Roger & Eastwood, John, illus. 2002. 112p. (J). (gr. 2-5). 14.95 (978-0-375-81460-0(4) , Knopf Bks. for Young Readers) Random Hse. Children's Bks.

—Funny Frank. 2003. (gr. 3-6). lib. bdg. 13.00 (978-0-613-72193-6(4)) Tandem Library Bks.

King, Stephen. Long Walk. 1999. (gr. 7-12). lib. bdg. 16.45 (978-0-613-17350-6(3)) Tandem Library Bks.

The Kingfisher Book of Funny Stories. 2003. 80p. (J). 17.95 (978-0-7534-5558-6(7)) Kingfisher Bks.

Kingfisher Editors, ed. What a Hoot! Over 150 Hilarious Animal Jokes. Chatterton, Martin, illus. 2005. (Sidesplitters Ser.). 64p. (J). (gr. 3-5). pap. 3.95 (978-0-7534-5892-1(6) , Kingfisher) Houghton Mifflin Co. Trade & Reference Div.

Kinney, Jeff. Diary of a Wimpy Kid. 2007. (Illus.). 224p. (J). (gr. 2-8). 12.95 (***978-0-8109-9313-6(9)*** , Abrams Bks. for Young Readers) Abrams, Harry N. , Inc.

Kirby, David & Woodman, Allen. The Cows Are Going to Paris. Demarest, Chris L., illus. 2003. 32p. (J). (gr. k-2). pap. 8.95 (978-1-56397-781-7(8)) Boyds Mills Pr.

Kirschner, Tanja. Bottoms. 2005. (Illus.). 24p. (YA). (ps-17). per. 3.99 (978-0-7358-2026-5(0)) North-South Bks., Inc.

HI

Kisseloff, Jeff & Wells, Rosemary. Ruby's Tea for Two. 2003. (Max & Ruby Ser.). 12p. (J). bds. 5.99 (978-0-670-03652-3(8) , Puffin) Penguin Group (USA) Inc.

Kizer, Amber. Gert Garibaldi's Rants & Raves: One Butt Cheek at a Time. 2007. (YA). 192p. (gr. 7). 15.99 (****978-0-385-73430-1(1));*** 304p. (gr. 9). lib. bdg. 18.99 (****978-0-385-90439-1(8))*** Random Hse. Children's Bks. (Delacorte Bks. for Young Readers).

Kline, Suzy. Horrible Harry Goes to Sea: Puffine Chapters. Remkiewicz, Frank, illus. 2003. (Horrible Harry Ser.). 64p. (J). (gr. 2-5). pap. 3.99 (978-0-14-250002-6(X) , Puffin) Penguin Group (USA) Inc.

—Horrible Harry Goes to Sea: Puffine Chapters. 2003. (gr. 3-6). lib. bdg. 11.80 (978-0-613-61629-4(4)) Tandem Library Bks.

—Horrible Harry Takes the Cake. Remkiewicz, Frank, illus. 2007. (Horrible Harry Ser.). 64p. (J). (gr. 2). 3.99 (****978-0-14-240939-8(1)*** , Puffin) Penguin Group (USA) Inc.

Kline, Suzy. Molly's in a Mess. Bluthenthal, Diana Cain, illus. 2002. (Chapters Ser.). 80p. (J). pap. 4.99 (978-0-698-11928-4(2) , Putnam Juvenile) Penguin Group (USA) Inc.

—Molly's in a Mess. 2002. (gr. 3-6). lib. bdg. 13.00 (978-0-613-64418-1(2)) Tandem Library Bks.

Klise, Kate. Regarding the Bathrooms: A Privy to the Past. Klise, M. Sarah, illus. 2006. (Regarding The ... Ser.). 160p. (YA). 15.00 (978-0-15-205164-8(3)) Harcourt Trade Pubs.

Klise, Kate & Klise, M. Sarah. Regarding the Trees: A Splintered Saga Rooted in Secrets. 2007. (Regarding The ... Ser.). (Illus.). 160p. (J). pap. 5.95 (****978-0-15-206090-9(1)*** , Harcourt Paperbacks) Harcourt Children's Bks.

Klise, Kate & Klise, M. Sarah, illus. Regarding the Bees: A Lesson, in Letters, on Honey, Dating, & Other Sticky Subjects. 2007. (Regarding The ... Ser.). 144p. (YA). (gr. 3-7). 15.00 (978-0-15-205711-4(0)) Harcourt Trade Pubs.

Klug, Eric. The Monster in My Closet. Klug, Eric, illus. 2007. (Illus.). 32p. (J). 15.95 (978-1-60108-007-3(7)) Red Cygnet Pr.

Knowles, Sheena. Edward the Emu. Clement, Rod, illus. 1998. 32p. (J). (ps-1). pap. 6.99 (978-0-06-443499-7(0)) HarperCollins Pubs.

—Edward the Emu. Clement, Rod, illus. 1998. 13.75 (978-0-606-11288-8(X)) Tandem Library Bks.

Koeppel, Ruth. SpongeBob's Day Off. DePorter, Vince, illus. 2004. (Spongebob Squarepants Ser.). 12p. (J). bds. 7.99 (978-0-689-87652-3(1) , Simon Spotlight/Nickelodeon) Simon & Schuster Children's Publishing.

Kogler, Jennifer Anne. Ruby Tuesday. 2005. 256p. (J). (gr. 7 up). lib. bdg. 16.89 (978-0-06-073957-7(6)) HarperCollins Pubs.

Kolar, Bob. Racer Dogs. Kolar, Bob, illus. 2003. (Illus.). 32p. (J). (ps-2). 15.99 (978-0-525-45939-2(1) , Dutton Juvenile) Penguin Group (USA) Inc.

Konnecke, Ole. Anthony & the Girls. Seitz, Nancy, tr. from GER. 2006. (Illus.). 32p. (J). 15.00 (978-0-374-30376-1(2)) Macmillan.

Koren, Edward. Very Hairy Harry. Koren, Edward, illus. 2003. (Illus.). (978-0-06-057744-5(4)); (J). (978-0-06-056868-9(2)) HarperCollins Pubs.

Korman, Gordon. The Chicken Doesn't Skate. 1998. 192p. (J). (gr. 4-8). pap. 4.50 (978-0-590-85301-9(5)) Scholastic, Inc.

—Invasion of the Nose Pickers. Vaccaro, Victor, illus. 2000. (L.A.F. Bks.). 138p. (J). (gr. 2-6). lib. bdg. 14.49 (978-0-7868-2590-5(1)) Hyperion Paperbacks for Children.

—Invasion of the Nose Pickers. 2001. (gr. 3-6). lib. bdg. 13.00 (978-0-613-31362-9(3)) Tandem Library Bks.

—Maxx Comedy: The Funniest Kid in America. 2006. 160p. (gr. 3-7). pap. 5.99 (978-0-7868-3895-0(7)) Hyperion Pr.

—No More Dead Dogs. Orig. Title: Touchdown Stage Left. 192p. (gr. 5-9). 2002. (J). pap. 5.99 (978-0-7868-1601-9(5)); 2000. (Illus.). 15.99 (978-0-7868-0531-0(5)) Hyperion Bks. for Children.

—No More Dead Dogs. 2002. Orig. Title: Touchdown Stage Left. (gr. 5-8). lib. bdg. 14.15 (978-0-613-61850-2(5)) Tandem Library Bks.

—The Sixth Grade Nickname Game. 2004. 160p. (gr. 3-7). pap. 5.99 (978-0-7868-5190-4(2)) Hyperion Paperbacks for Children.

Kotecki, Jason. Childhood Returns No. 2: Kim & Jason Annual #2. 2002. per. 13.95 (978-0-9715253-1-3(5)) JBiRD iNK, Ltd.

—Dreaming Big: Kim & Jason Annual #1. 2001. 118p. per. 13.95 (978-0-9715253-0-6(7)) JBiRD iNK, Ltd.

—Stupid Swimming Lessons: Kim & Jason Annual #3. 2004. 134p. per. 13.95 (978-0-9715253-2-0(3)) JBiRD iNK, Ltd.

Kotzwinkle, William & Murray, Glenn. Walter the Farting Dog: Trouble at the Yard Sale. Colman, Audrey, illus. 2004. 32p. (J). (gr. k). 16.99 (978-0-525-47217-9(7) , Dutton Juvenile) Penguin Group (USA) Inc.

—Walter the Farting Dog: Trouble at the Yard Sale. Coleman, Audrey, illus. 2006. 32p. (J). (gr. k). reprint ed. pap. 6.99 (978-0-14-240626-7(0) , Puffin) Penguin Group (USA) Inc.

Kowitt, Holly. Ask Angelica! 2005. (All Grown Up! Ser.). (Illus.). 48p. (J). (ps-ps). pap. 3.99 (978-0-689-86605-0(4) , Simon Spotlight) Simon & Schuster Children's Publishing.

—Belly Laughs from Bikini Bottom. 2003. (SpongeBob SquarePants Ser.). (Illus.). 48p. (J). pap. 3.99 (978-0-689-86165-9(6) , Simon Spotlight) Simon & Schuster Children's Publishing.

—Belly Laughs from Bikini Bottom. 2003. (gr. k-3). lib. bdg. 10.65 (978-0-613-85671-3(6)) Tandem Library Bks.

—SpongeBob's Book of Excuses. Style Guide Staff, illus. 2005. (Spongebob Squarepants Ser.). 48p. (J). pap. 3.99 (978-0-689-87211-2(9) , Simon Spotlight) Simon & Schuster Children's Publishing.

—2 Grrrls Locker Talk: Cool School Comics. 2002. (gr. 3-6). lib. bdg. 13.00 (978-0-613-72026-7(1)) Tandem Library Bks.

Krauss, Ruth. The Backward Day. Simont, Marc, illus. 2007. 40p. (J). (ps-2). 14.95 (****978-1-59017-237-7(X)*** , NYR Children's Collection) New York Review of Bks., Inc., The.

Krensky, Stephen. Bubble Trouble. 2004. (ps-2). lib. bdg. 11.80 (978-0-613-88999-5(1)) Tandem Library Bks.

—How Santa Got His Job. Schindler, S. D., illus. 2002. (J). 24.04 (978-0-7587-2770-1(4)) Book Wholesalers, Inc.

—How Santa Got His Job. Schindler, S. D., illus. 2002. 32p. (J). pap. 6.99 (978-0-689-84668-7(1) , Aladdin) Simon & Schuster Children's Publishing.

—How Santa Got His Job. 2002. (gr. k-3). lib. bdg. 15.30 (978-0-613-90196-3(7)) Tandem Library Bks.

—Noah's Bark. Rogé, illus. 2008. (J). lib. bdg. (****978-0-8225-7645-7(7)*** , Carolrhoda Bks.) Lerner Publishing Group.

Krensky, Stephen. What a Mess! 2001. (Step into Reading Ser.). (Illus.). (J). (978-0-606-21513-8(1)) Tandem Library Bks.

Krensky, Stephen & Pickering, Jimmy. Bubble Trouble. 2004. (Ready-to-Reads Ser.). (Illus.). 32p. (J). pap. 3.99 (978-0-689-85710-2(1) , Aladdin) Simon & Schuster Children's Publishing.

Krosoczka, Jarrett J. Baghead. Krosoczka, Jarrett J., illus. (Illus.). 40p. (J). (ps-2). 2002. 15.95 (978-0-375-81566-9(X) , Knopf Bks. for Young Readers); 2004. reprint ed. pap. 6.99 (978-0-553-11172-9(8) , Dragonfly Bks.) Random Hse. Children's Bks.

Krulik, Nancy E. Be Nice to Mice, No. 20. 2006. (Katie Kazoo, Switcheroo Ser.: No. 20). (Illus.). 78p. (J). (****978-1-4156-7185-6(0)*** , Grosset & Dunlap) Penguin Group (USA) Inc.

—Cat's Big Night. 1999. Tr. of Dog Behind Bars. (gr. 3-6). lib. bdg. 11.80 (978-0-613-21313-4(0)) Tandem Library Bks.

—Ice-Cream Dreams. Martinez, Heather, illus. 2004. 22p. (J). lib. bdg. 15.00 (****978-1-4242-0975-0(7))*** Fitzgerald Bks.

—Ice-Cream Dreams. 2007. 24p. (J). 21.35 (****978-1-59961-366-6(2))*** Spotlight.

Krulik, Nancy E. She's Got the Beat. 2005. (Romantic Comedies Ser.). 320p. (YA). pap. 6.99 (978-1-4169-0020-7(9) , Simon Pulse) Simon & Schuster Children's Publishing.

Kurtz, Jane. Does a Spider Wear a Seatbelt. 2004. (Illus.). (J). 14.00 (978-0-689-84482-9(4) , Aladdin) Simon & Schuster Children's Publishing.

Kurzweil, Allen. Leon & the Champion Chip. Bertholf, Bret, illus. 352p. (J). 2007. pap. 6.99 (****978-0-06-053935-1(6)*** , Harper Trophy); 2005. 15.99 (978-0-06-053933-7(X)); 2005. lib. bdg. 16.89 (978-0-06-053934-4(8)) HarperCollins Pubs.

Kurzweil, Allen. Leon & the Spitting Image. Bertholf, Bret, illus. 320p. (J). (gr. 3 up). 2005. pap. 6.99 (978-0-06-053932-0(1) , Harper Trophy); 2003. 16.99 (978-0-06-053930-6(5)); 2003. lib. bdg. 16.89 (978-0-06-053931-3(3)) HarperCollins Pubs.

Kuskin, Karla. Under My Hood I Have a Hat. Kosaka, Fumi, illus. 2004. 32p. (J). (ps-2). 14.99 (978-0-06-057242-6(6) , Geringer, Laura Book) HarperCollins Pubs.

Kvasnosky, Laura McGee. Zelda & Ivy One Christmas: A Story about the Fabulous Fox Sisters. Kvasnosky, Laura McGee, illus. 2002. (Illus.). 48p. (J). (gr. k-4). pap. 6.99 (978-0-7636-1344-0(4)) Candlewick Pr.

Labatt, Mary. Weekend at the Grand Hotel. 2001. (gr. 3-6). lib. bdg. 12.95 (978-0-613-37071-4(6)) Tandem Library Bks.

Laden, Nina. Private I Guana: The Case of the Missing Chameleon. 1999. (gr. k-3). lib. bdg. 15.25 (978-0-613-89998-7(9)) Tandem Library Bks.

Lambrou, M. A. Kokos. WWWWings: Anything Is Possible When You Believe. 2004. 128p. pap. 9.95 (978-1-932047-16-5(6) , Llumina Pr.) Media Creations, Inc.

Lamerton, Todd, illus. Wow! What a Cow- A Tale from Funky Farm. 2003. (J). (978-0-7575-0005-3(6)) Kendall/Hunt Publishing Co.

Lampman, Evelyn Sibley. The Shy Stegosaurus of Cricket Creek. Buel, Hubert, illus. 2001. 220p. (J). 17.95 (978-1-930900-09-7(0)) Purple Hse. Pr.

Landstrom, Olof & Landstrom, Lena. Boo & Baa Have Company. Sandin, Joan, tr. from SWE. 2006. (Illus.). 40p. (J). 15.00 (978-91-29-66546-8(9)) R & S Bks. SWE. *Dist:* Macmillan.

Lantz, Francess L. Stepbaby from Planet Weird. 2001. (Illus.). (J). 3.99 (978-0-375-81259-0(8) , Random Hse. Bks. for Young Readers) Random Hse. Children's Bks.

LaPadula, Tom, illus. Timmy Turner, Action Hero. 2005. (Fairly OddParents Ser.). 64p. (J). pap. 4.99 (978-0-689-87720-9(X) , Simon Spotlight/Nickelodeon) Simon & Schuster Children's Publishing.

LaRochelle, David. Absolutely, Positively Not. 2005. 219p. (YA). (978-0-439-59110-2(4)); 224p. (J). (gr. 7-12). pap. 16.95 (978-0-439-59109-6(0)) Scholastic, Inc. (Levine, Arthur A. Bks.).

Larson, Gary. There's a Hair in My Dirt! A Worm's Story. 1999. (Illus.). (J). (978-0-606-21603-6(0)) Tandem Library Bks.

Laske, Ernest. Life in Monkey Town. 2005. 174p. per. 12.95 (978-1-59886-010-8(0)) Tate Publishing & Enterprises, L.L.C.

Lasky, Kathryn. The Emperor's Old Clothes. Catrow, David, illus. 2002. 32p. (J). (ps-2). pap. 7.00 (978-0-15-216348-8(4) , Voyager Bks./Libros Viajeros) Harcourt Children's Bks.

—The Emperor's Old Clothes. 2002. (gr. k-3). lib. bdg. 14.15 (978-0-613-53806-0(4)) Tandem Library Bks.

Lauber, Patricia. Purrfectly Purrfect: Life at the Acatemy. Lewin, Betsy, illus. 2000. 80p. (J). (gr. 3-7). 15.89 (978-0-06-029209-6(1)); 15.95 (978-0-688-17299-2(7)) HarperCollins Pubs.

Lautanen, Michelle. Mom, What If I Swallowed an Icecube? A Humorous Tale of Worst Aid. l.t. ed. 2006. (Illus.). 25p. (J). per. 14.95 (978-1-933324-38-8(4)) Cedar Hill Publishing.

Law, Karina. The Truth about Hansel & Gretel. Counsell, Elke, illus. 2004. (Read-It! Readers Ser.). 32p. (C). (gr. k-3). 18.60 (978-1-4048-0559-0(1)) Picture Window Bks.

Lawrence, David. Beetle Boy. 1999. (Illus.). (J). (978-0-606-21055-3(5)) Tandem Library Bks.

Lawrence, Michael. The Toilet of Doom. 2004. 256p. (J). pap. 16.95 (978-0-7540-7913-2(9) , Galaxy Children's Large Print) BBC Audiobooks America.

Layne, Steven L. Thomas's Sheep & the Spectacular Science Project. Board, Perry, illus. 2004. 32p. (J). pap. 15.95 (978-1-58980-210-0(1)) Pelican Publishing Co., Inc.

Leaney, Cindy. An Amazing Machine. Whitehouse, Patty, ed. King, Sue & Wilks, Peter, illus. 2004. (Friendly Phonics Ser.). 24p. (J). lib. bdg. 14.95 (978-1-59054-194-4(4)) Fitzgerald Bks.

—The Circus. Whitehouse, Patty, ed. King, Sue & Wilks, Peter, illus. 2004. (Friendly Phonics Ser.). 24p. (J). lib. bdg. 14.95 (978-1-59054-114-2(6)) Fitzgerald Bks.

—Fun at the Fair. Whitehouse, Patty, ed. King, Sue & Wilks, Peter, illus. 2004. (Friendly Phonics Ser.). 24p. (J). lib. bdg. 14.95 (978-1-59054-153-1(7)) Fitzgerald Bks.

—The Giant's Garden. Whitehouse, Patty, ed. King, Sue & Wilks, Peter, illus. 2004. (Friendly Phonics Ser.). 24p. (J). lib. bdg. 14.95 (978-1-59054-181-4(2)) Fitzgerald Bks.

—Harry Has Hiccups. Whitehouse, Patty, ed. King, Sue & Wilks, Peter, illus. 2004. (Friendly Phonics Ser.). 24p. (J). lib. bdg. 14.95 (978-1-59054-182-1(0)) Fitzgerald Bks.

—Jungle Journey. Whitehouse, Patty, ed. King, Sue & Wilks, Peter, illus. 2004. (Friendly Phonics Ser.). 24p. (J). lib. bdg. 14.95 (978-1-59054-183-8(9)) Fitzgerald Bks.

—Just Lazy Luke. Whitehouse, Patty, ed. King, Sue & Wilks, Peter, illus. 2004. (Friendly Phonics Ser.). 24p. (J). lib. bdg. 14.95 (978-1-59054-105-0(7)) Fitzgerald Bks.

—A Long List. Whitehouse, Peter, ed. King, Sue & Wilks, Peter, illus. 2004. (Friendly Phonics Ser.). 24p. (J). lib. bdg. 14.95 (978-1-59054-190-6(1)) Fitzgerald Bks.

—Mr. Know-it-all Crow. Whitehouse, Patty, ed. King, Sue & Wilks, Peter, illus. 2004. (Friendly Phonics Ser.). 24p. (J). lib. bdg. 14.95 (978-1-59054-086-2(7)) Fitzgerald Bks.

—Nice News. Whitehouse, Patty, ed. King, Sue & Wilks, Peter, illus. 2004. (Friendly Phonics Ser.). 24p. (J). lib. bdg. 14.95 (978-1-59054-205-7(3)) Fitzgerald Bks.

—Note in a Bottle. Whitehouse, Patty, ed. King, Sue & Wilks, Peter, illus. 2004. (Friendly Phonics Ser.). 24p. (J). lib. bdg. 14.95 (978-1-59054-107-4(3)) Fitzgerald Bks.

—On the Beach. Whitehouse, Patty, ed. King, Sue & Wilks, Peter, illus. 2004. (Friendly Phonics Ser.). 24p. (J). lib. bdg. 14.95 (978-1-59054-108-1(1)) Fitzgerald Bks.

—Oodles of Noodles. Whitehouse, Patty, ed. King, Sue & Wilks, Peter, illus. 2004. (Friendly Phonics Ser.). 24p. (J). lib. bdg. 14.95 (978-1-59054-030-5(1)) Fitzgerald Bks.

—Picnic in the Park. Whitehouse, Patty, ed. King, Sue & Wilks, Peter, illus. 2004. (Friendly Phonics Ser.). 24p. (J). lib. bdg. 14.95 (978-1-59054-217-0(7)) Fitzgerald Bks.

—Rachel the Shy Jellyfish. Whitehouse, Patty, ed. King, Sue & Wilks, Peter, illus. 2004. (Friendly Phonics Ser.). 24p. (J). lib. bdg. 14.95 (978-1-59054-274-3(6)) Fitzgerald Bks.

—Rainy Day Play. Whitehouse, Patty, ed. King, Sue & Wilks, Peter, illus. 2004. (Friendly Phonics Ser.). 24p. (J). lib. bdg. 14.95 (978-1-59054-047-3(6)) Fitzgerald Bks.

—Rescue & Repair. Whitehouse, Patty, ed. King, Sue & Wilks, Peter, illus. 2004. (Friendly Phonics Ser.). 24p. (J). lib. bdg. 14.95 (978-1-59054-225-5(8)) Fitzgerald Bks.

—Station K. I. D. S. Whitehouse, Patty, ed. King, Sue & Wilks, Peter, illus. 2004. (Friendly Phonics Ser.). 24p. (J). lib. bdg. 14.95 (978-1-59054-186-9(3)) Fitzgerald Bks.

—Super Sale. Whitehouse, Patty, ed. King, Sue & Wilks, Peter, illus. 2004. (Friendly Phonics Ser.). 24p. (J). lib. bdg. 14.95 (978-1-59054-231-6(2)) Fitzgerald Bks.

—A Talking Telescope. Whitehouse, Patty, ed. King, Sue & Wilks, Peter, illus. 2004. (Friendly Phonics Ser.). 24p. (J). lib. bdg. 14.95 (978-1-59054-247-7(9)) Fitzgerald Bks.

—What Do You See? Whitehouse, Patty, ed. King, Sue & Wilks, Peter, illus. 2004. (Friendly Phonics Ser.). 24p. (J). lib. bdg. 14.95 (978-1-59054-039-8(5)) Fitzgerald Bks.

Leblanc, Louise. Le Tombeau en Peril, Vol. 56. Brochard, Philippe, illus. 2003. (Premier Roman Ser.). (FRE.). 64p. (J). (gr. 2-5). pap. (978-2-89021-282-4(3)) Diffusion du livre Mirabel.

Leblanc, Louise & Gay, Marie-Louise. Sophie Decouvre l'Envers du Decor. 2002. (Premier Roman Ser.). (FRE., Illus.). 64p. (J). (gr. 1-4). pap. (978-2-89021-569-6(5)) Diffusion du livre Mirabel.

Lee, Quinlan B. Bungee Boo Dance! 2004. (Boohbah Ser.). (Illus.). 22p. (J). bds. 4.99 (978-0-439-59089-1(2)) Scholastic, Inc.

—Scrunch Up, Stretch Out! 2004. (Boohbah Ser.: Bk. 2). (Illus.). 22p. (J). bds. 4.99 (978-0-439-59091-4(4)) Scholastic, Inc.

—Whizzy, Dizzy Fun. 2005. (Boohbah Ser.). (Illus.). 32p. (J). (ps-ps). pap. 3.99 (978-0-439-74411-9(3)) Scholastic, Inc.

Leeds, Robert X. HOW to Almost MAKE A MILLION DOLLARS: I Almost Did it. You Can Almost Do it Too!, 2005. 246p. pap. 16.95 (978-0-9674025-5-0(7)) EPIC Publishing Co.

—HOW to almost MAKE A MILLION DOLLARS: I almost did it. You can almost do it Too! 2005. (CHI.). 246p. 21.95 (978-0-9674025-6-7(5)) EPIC Publishing Co.

Lemieux, Jean. Pas de S pour Copernic. Casson, Sophie, illus. 2001. (Premier Roman Ser.). (FRE.). 64p. (J). (gr. 1-4). pap. (978-2-89021-454-5(0)) Diffusion du livre Mirabel.

Lendler, Ian. An Undone Fairy Tale. Martin, Whitney, illus. 2005. 32p. (J). (gr. 1-3). 15.95 (978-0-689-86677-7(1) , Simon & Schuster Children's Publishing) Simon & Schuster Children's Publishing.

Leno, Jay. If Roast Beef Could Fly. Whitehead, S. B., illus. 2005. 30p. (J). (gr. k-4). 18.00 (978-0-7567-9365-4(3)) DIANE Publishing Co.

Leno, Jay & Whitehead, S. B. If Roast Beef Could Fly. 2004. (Illus.). 32p. (J). 17.95 (978-0-689-86767-5(0)) Simon & Schuster Children's Publishing.

Leonard, Elise. Scared Stiff. 2007. (Al's World Ser.). 132p. (J). (gr. 5-9). per. 5.99 (****978-1-4169-3466-0(9)*** , Aladdin) Simon & Schuster Children's Publishing.

Lerner, Harriet. What's So Terrible about Swallowing an Apple Seed? 2001. (Illus.). (J). (978-0-606-21518-3(2)) Tandem Library Bks.

Lester, Julius. Sam & the Tigers. 2000. (978-0-606-18845-6(2)); lib. bdg. 15.30 (978-0-613-28630-5(8)) Tandem Library Bks.

—Sam & the Tigers: A New Telling of Little Black Sambo. Pinkney, Jerry, illus. 2002. (J). 14.04 (978-0-7587-0141-1(1)) Book Wholesalers, Inc.

Lester, Julius & Isadora, Rachel. Sam & the Tigers: A Retelling of 'Little Black Sambo' Pinkney, Jerry & Christiansen, Hans, illus. 2000. (Picture Puffin Ser.). 40p. (J). (ps-3). pap. 6.99 (978-0-14-056288-0(5) , Puffin) Penguin Group (USA) Inc.

Lesynski, Loris. Sopa de Niño o el Ogro con Gripe. Canetti, Yanitzia, tr. from ENG. Lesynski, Loris, illus. 2004. (ENG & SPA., Illus.). 32p. (J). (ps-3). pap. 5.95 (978-1-55037-855-9(4)) Annick Pr., Ltd. CAN. *Dist:* Firefly Bks., Ltd.

Levine, Martha Peaslee. Stop That Nose! White, Lee, illus. 2006. (J). (978-0-7614-5222-5(2)); 32p. 14.95 (978-0-7614-5280-5(X)) Cavendish, Marshall Corp.

Levithan, David. My Class Project. 2000. (Malcolm in the Middle Ser.). 48p. (J). (gr. 3-7). pap. 5.99 (978-0-439-22843-5(3)) Scholastic, Inc.

Levy, Elizabeth. A Hare-Raising Tale: A Fletcher Mystery. Gorstein, Mordicai, illus. unabr. ed. 2006. (First Chapter Bks.). (J). (gr. 2-4). pap. 17.95 incl. audio (****978-1-59519-704-7(4));*** pap. 20.95 incl. audio compact disk (****978-1-59519-705-4(2))*** Live Oak Media.

—The Mixed-Up Mask Mystery: A Fletcher Mystery. Gorstein, Mordicai, illus. unabr. ed. 2006. (First Chapter Bks.). (J). (gr. 2-4). pap. 20.95 incl. audio compact disk (****978-1-59519-711-5(7));*** pap. 17.95 incl. audio (****978-1-59519-710-8(9))*** Live Oak Media.

Levy, Elizabeth. My Life As a Fifth-Grade Comedian. 1998. 192p. (J). (ps-7). pap. 5.99 (978-0-06-440723-6(3) , Harper Trophy) HarperCollins Pubs.

—My Life As a Fifth-Grade Comedian. 1999. (J). pap., stu. ed. 41.20 incl. audio (978-0-7887-3180-8(7) , 40915) Recorded Bks., LLC.

Levy, Janice. The Man Who Lived in a Hat. Brown, Dave, illus. 2001. (Young Spirit Bks.). 40p. (J). (ps up). 16.95 (978-1-57174-211-7(5)) Hampton Roads Publishing Co., Inc.

Lewis, Jill. A Mom in a Million. Gulbis, Stephen, illus. 2005. 32p. (J). (978-1-84458-368-3(6)) Chrysalis Children's Bks.

Lewis, L. W. Poodles Tigers Monsters & You. Harris, Lorrayne R., illus. 2004. 64p. kivar 12.95 (978-0-9711572-1-7(9)) Red Pumpkin Pr.

Lewis, Steve, Sr. The Course of a Horse. 2006. (J). 65.00 (978-1-59971-897-2(9)) Aardvark Global Publishing.

Lewman, David. Bikini Bottom Riddles. Style Guide Staff, illus. 2005. (Spongebob Squarepants Ser.). 48p. (J). pap. 3.99 (978-0-689-87875-6(3) , Simon Spotlight) Simon & Schuster Children's Publishing.

—Blizzard Bluster! SpongeBob's Book of Frosty Funnies. 2008. (SpongeBob SquarePants Ser.). 48p. (J). pap. 3.99 (****978-1-4169-4747-9(7)*** , Simon Spotlight) Simon & Schuster Children's Publishing.

—Campfire Funnies. Style Guide Staff, illus. 2006. (SpongeBob SquarePants Ser.). 48p. (J). pap. 3.99 (978-1-4169-1315-3(7) , Simon Spotlight) Simon & Schuster Children's Publishing.

—Day in the Life of Tommy. 1999. (gr. k-3). lib. bdg. 10.65 (978-0-613-15768-1(0)) Tandem Library Bks.

—Fairly Odd Excuses. Style Guide Staff, illus. 2005. (Fairly OddParents Ser.). 48p. (J). pap. 3.99 (978-0-689-87874-9(5) , Simon Spotlight) Simon & Schuster Children's Publishing.

—SpongeBob & the Princess. Bond, Clint, illus. 2004. (SpongeBob SquarePants 8 X 8 Paperback ; #5 Ser.). 24p. (J). pap. 3.99 (978-0-689-86581-7(3) , Simon Spotlight/Nickelodeon) Simon & Schuster Children's Publishing.

—SpongeBob's Secret Valentine. Martinez, Heather, illus. 2003. (SpongeBob SquarePants Ser.). 24p. (J). pap. 3.99 (978-0-689-86326-4(8) , Simon Spotlight/Nickelodeon) Simon & Schuster Children's Publishing.

The Lil Dudes. 2006. (YA). per. (978-1-59872-308-3(1)) Instantpublisher.com.

Limb, Sue. Girl, 15, Charming but Insane. 2004. (Girl, 15 Ser.). 214p. (J). (gr. 5). per. 16.00 (978-0-606-33729-8(6)) Tandem Library Bks.

—Girl 15, Charming but Insane. 2007. (Girl, 15 Ser.). 224p. (YA). (gr. 7-11). mass mkt. 5.99 (978-0-440-23896-6(X) , Laurel Leaf) Random Hse. Children's Bks.

—Girl, Barely 15: Flirting for England. 2008. (Girl, 15 Ser.). 256p. (YA). (gr. 5). 15.99 (*978-0-385-73538-4(3)); lib. bdg. 18.99 (*978-0-385-90520-6(3)) Random Hse. Children's Bks. (Delacorte Bks. for Young Readers).

—Girl, Going on 17: Pants on Fire. (Girl, 15 Ser.). (gr. 5 up). 2007. 256p. (YA). pap. 8.99 (*978-0-385-73219-2(8)); 2006. 240p. (J). 14.95 (978-0-385-73218-5(X)); 2006. 240p. (YA). lib. bdg. 17.99 (978-0-385-90246-5(8)) Random Hse. Children's Bks. (Delacorte Bks. for Young Readers).

Limb, Sue. Girl, (Nearly) 16: Absolute Torture. (Girl, 15 Ser.). 224p. (YA). (gr. 5-11). 2008. mass mkt. 6.50 (*978-0-440-23897-3(8) , Laurel Leaf); 2006. pap. 8.95 (978-0-385-73217-8(1) , Delacorte Bks. for Young Readers) Random Hse. Children's Bks.

Lindenbaum, Pija. When Owen's Mom Breathed Fire. Dyssegaard, Elisabeth Kallick, tr. 2006. (Illus.). 32p. (J). 16.00 (978-91-29-66548-2(5)) R & S Bks. SWE. *Dist:* Macmillan.

Lindgren, Astrid. Happy Times in Noisy Village. Wikland, Ilon, illus. 2003. Orig. Title: Bullerby Boken. 128p. (J). pap. 10.95 (978-1-883937-66-9(3)) Bethlehem Bks.

—Pippi Goes to School. 1999. (J). (gr. k-3). lib. bdg. 14.15 (978-0-613-22923-4(1)) Tandem Library Bks.

—Pippi Goes to the Circus. 2000. (J). (gr. k-3). lib. bdg. 14.15 (978-0-613-28608-4(1)) Tandem Library Bks.

—Pippi Longstocking. Nunally, Tina, tr. from SWE. 2007. 208p. (J). (gr. k). 25.00 (*978-0-670-06276-8(6) , Viking Juvenile) Penguin Group (USA) Inc.

—Pippi Longstocking. Glanzman, Louis S., illus. 2005. (Puffin Modern Classics Ser.). 160p. (J). (*978-1-4155-8329-6(3) , Puffin) Penguin Group (USA) Inc.

Lindgren, Astrid. Pippi's Extraordinary Ordinary Day. Chesworth, Michael, illus. 2001. 32p. (J). (ps-3). lib. bdg. 12.79 (978-0-606-21381-3(3)) Tandem Library Bks.

Lindgren, Barbro. Benny's Had Enough! Dyssegaard, Elisabeth Kallick, tr. Landstrom, Olof, illus. 2005. 28p. (J). (ps-1). reprint ed. pap. 6.95 (978-91-29-66338-9(5)) R & S Bks. SWE. *Dist:* Macmillan.

Lindsay, Norman. The Magic Pudding. 2006. (Illus.). 144p. (J). pap. 7.95 (978-0-486-45281-4(6)) Dover Pubns., Inc.

—The Magic Pudding. 2006. 77.99 (*978-1-4280-3115-9(4)); 2005. (ENG.). pap. 70.99 (*978-1-4219-2134-1(0)) IndyPublish.com.

—The Magic Pudding. 2004. reprint ed. pap. 15.95 (978-1-4191-7119-2(4)); pap. 1.99 (978-1-4192-7119-9(9)) Kessinger Publishing, LLC.

—The Magic Pudding. Lindsay, Norman, illus. 2004. (New York Review Children's Collection). (Illus.). 184p. (J). (gr. 3-6). pap. 16.95 (978-1-59017-101-1(2) , NYR Children's Collection) New York Review of Bks., Inc., The.

Liput, Andrew L. Who Put the Snarfdoodle in My Lunch Box? 2nd ed. 2003. 108p. per. (978-1-932077-62-9(6)) Athena Pr.

Lithgow, John. Carnival of the Animals. Kulikov, Boris, illus. 2007. 40p. (J). (gr. k-5). pap. 7.99 (*978-0-689-87343-0(3) , Aladdin) Simon & Schuster Children's Publishing.

Little, Jean. I Know an Old Laddie. ed. 2004. (Illus.). (J). (gr. k-3). spiral bd. (978-0-616-01703-6(0)) Canadian National Institute for the Blind/Institut National Canadien pour les Aveugles.

Ljungkvist, Laura. Toni's Topsy-Turvy Telephone Day. 2001. (Illus.). 32p. (J). (ps-3). 15.95 (978-0-8109-4486-2(3)) Abrams, Harry N. , Inc.

Llewellyn, Sam. Little Darlings. 2005. 240p. (J). (gr. 3-7). pap. 5.99 (978-1-59514-066-1(2) , Razorbill) Penguin Group (USA) Inc.

Lodge, Bernard. Custard Surprise. Bowers, Tim, illus. 2007. (I Can Read Bks.). 48p. (J). (ps-3). lib. bdg. 16.89 (*978-0-06-073688-0(7)); 15.99 (*978-0-06-073687-3(9)) HarperCollins Pubs.

Loehr, Patrick. Mucumber Mcgee & the Half-Eaten Hot Dog. Loehr, Patrick, illus. 2007. (Illus.). 32p. (J). (ps-3). 15.99 (*978-0-06-082327-6(5)); lib. bdg. 16.89 (*978-0-06-082328-3(3)) HarperCollins Pubs. (Tegen, Katherine Bks).

Logue, Stephanie. Mango's Revenge. Murphy, Chris, illus. 2006. (J). pap. (978-1-59336-769-5(4)) Mondo Publishing.

London, Jonathan. Froggy Goes to the Doctor. ed. 2004. (Illus.). (J). (gr. k-3). spiral bd. (978-0-616-14585-2(3)); spiral bd. (978-0-616-14586-9(1)) Canadian National Institute for the Blind/Institut National Canadien pour les Aveugles.

—Froggy Goes to the Doctor. Remkiewicz, Frank, illus. (Froggy Ser.). 32p. (J). 2004. pap. 5.99 (978-0-14-240193-4(5) , Puffin); 2002. 15.99 (978-0-670-03578-6(5) , Viking Juvenile) Penguin Group (USA) Inc.

—Froggy's Sleepover. Remkiewicz, Frank, illus. 2007. (Froggy Ser.). 32p. (J). pap. 5.99 (978-0-14-240750-9(X) , Puffin) Penguin Group (USA) Inc.

London, Sara. Good Luck Glasses. (Hello Reader! Ser.). 2001. (Illus.). (J). 10.79 (978-0-606-21216-8(7)); 2000. lib. bdg. 11.80 (978-0-613-35519-3(9)) Tandem Library Bks.

Long, Ethan. Stop Kissing Me. 2007. 30p. (J). (ps). 10.99 (*978-0-316-00143-4(0)) Little, Brown Bks. for Young Readers.

Lopez, David Mark. Walk Like an Egyptian. 2006. (J). (gr. 3-7). (*978-0-9744097-0-2(7)) Lopez, David.

Loud Lips Lucy. 2002. (Smarties Ser.: Vol. 1). 32p. (J). (gr. k-3). 16.00 (978-0-9708296-0-3(4)) Savor Publishing Hse., Inc.

Loves, June. Mi Angel de la Guarda. (Torre de Papel Ser.). (SPA., Illus.). (J). (gr. 2). 7.95 (978-958-04-5048-1(X)) Norma S.A. COL. *Dist:* Distribuidora Norma, Inc.

Low, Alice. Aunt Lucy Went to Buy a Hat. Huliska-Beith, Laura, illus. 2004. 32p. (J). (ps-3). lib. bdg. 16.89 (978-0-06-008972-6(5)) HarperCollins Pubs.

—Aunt Lucy Went to Buy a Hat. Huliska-Beith, Laura, tr. Huliska-Beith, Laura, illus. 2004. 32p. (J). (ps-3). 15.99 (978-0-06-008971-9(7)) HarperCollins Pubs.

Lowrie, Paul & Nicholaus, Bret. Hooray for Minnesota Winters! For Minnesotans (and Those Who Wish They Were) of All Ages. Lindholm, Joe, ed. Awes, Jennifer, illus. 2005. 53p. (J). (ps-16). 16.95 (978-0-9755801-7-2(5)) Questmarc Publishing.

Lowry, Lois. Anastasia Tiene las Respuetas. Bustelo, Ana, tr. Alonso Díaz-Toledo, Juan Ramon, illus. 2003. (Espasa Juvenil Ser.: No. 149). Tr. of Anastasia Has the Answers. (SPA.). 160p. (J). 9.95 (978-84-239-6334-8(9)) Espasa Calpe, S.A. ESP. *Dist:* Continental Bk. Co., Inc., Lectorum Pubns., Inc., Planeta Publishing Corp.

—Gooney Bird & the Room Mother. Thomas, Middy Chilman, illus. 2005. 80p. (J). (gr. 3-5). 15.00 (978-0-618-53230-8(7) , Walter Lorraine) Houghton Mifflin Co. Trade & Reference Div.

—Gooney Bird & the Room Mother. 2006. 80p. (J). (gr. 2-5). 5.50 (978-0-440-42133-7(0) , Yearling) Random Hse. Children's Bks.

—Gooney Bird Greene. Thomas, Middy Chilman, illus. 2002. 96p. (J). (gr. 3-5). tchr. ed. 15.00 (978-0-618-23848-4(4) , Walter Lorraine) Houghton Mifflin Co. Trade & Reference Div.

—Gooney Bird Greene. 2004. (Illus.). 96p. (J). (gr. 2-5). reprint ed. pap. 5.50 (978-0-440-41960-0(3) , Yearling) Random Hse. Children's Bks.

—Gooney Bird Greene. 2004. (gr. 3-6). lib. bdg. 13.55 (978-0-613-82980-9(8)) Tandem Library Bks.

—Gooney the Fabulous. Thomas, Middy, illus. 2007. 96p. (J). (gr. 2-5). 15.00 (978-0-618-76691-8(X) , Walter Lorraine) Houghton Mifflin Co. Trade & Reference Div.

Lowry, Lois. The Willoughbys. 2008. (J). (*978-0-618-97974-5(3)) Houghton Mifflin Co.

Lubar, David. Monster Road. 1999. (Illus.). 144p. (J). (gr. 3-7). pap. 4.50 (978-0-590-28168-3(2)) Scholastic, Inc.

Lubner, Susan Emple. Ruthie Bon Bair: Do Not Go to Bed with Wringing Wet Hair! Whatley, Bruce, illus. 2006. 32p. (J). (ps-3). 15.95 (978-0-8109-5470-0(2)) Abrams, Harry N. , Inc.

Lucado, Max. Hermie & Wormie in the Flood of Lies. 2004. (Max Lucado's Hermie & Friends Ser.). 24p. (J). bds. 6.99 (978-1-4003-0287-1(0)) Nelson, Thomas Inc.

Lum, Kate. Princesses Are Not Quitters! Hellard, Sue, illus. 2005. 32p. (J). (ps-7). pap. 6.95 (978-1-58234-987-9(8) , Bloomsbury Children) Bloomsbury Publishing.

Luzzatto, Caroline. Interplanetary Avenger. 2005. (Illus.). 128p. (J). (gr. 3-7). 16.95 (978-0-8234-1933-3(9)) Holiday Hse., Inc.

Lynch, Clam. Ruby Gloom's Keys to Happiness. Hsu, Martin, illus. 2004. 48p. (J). (gr. 5-9). 12.95 (978-0-8109-5036-8(7)) Abrams, Harry N. , Inc.

Lynne, Rustyna. Bella's Birthday Manicure. Lynne, Rustyna, illus. l.t. ed. 2002. (Illus.). 14p. (J). (gr. k-2). spiral bd. 10.95 (978-0-9719657-6-8(5)) Red Carpet Publishing.

—Bella's Birthday Manicure: Special Needs Version. Lynne, Rustyna, illus. l.t. ed. 2002. (Illus.). 9p. (YA). (gr. 3-8). spiral bd. 10.95 (978-0-9719657-7-5(3)) Red Carpet Publishing.

—Giovanni's Pedicure. Lynne, Rustyna, illus. l.t. ed. 2002. (Illus.). 14p. (J). (gr. k-2). spiral bd. 10.95 (978-0-9719657-8-2(1)) Red Carpet Publishing.

—Giovanni's Pedicure: Special Needs Version. Lynne, Rustyna, illus. l.t. ed. 2002. (Illus.). 12p. (YA). (gr. 3-8). spiral bd. 10.95 (978-0-9719657-9-9(X)) Red Carpet Publishing.

—Tatiana's Shampoo. Lynne, Rustyna, illus. l.t. ed. 2002. (Illus.). 12p. (J). (gr. k-2). spiral bd. 10.95 (978-0-9719657-2-0(2)) Red Carpet Publishing.

—Tatiana's Shampoo: Special Needs Version. Lynne, Rustyna, illus. l.t. ed. 2002. (Illus.). 14p. (YA). (gr. 3-8). spiral bd. 10.95 (978-0-9719657-3-7(0)) Red Carpet Publishing.

—Tyler Brushes His Teeth. Lynne, Rustyna, illus. l.t. ed. 2002. (Illus.). 17p. (J). (gr. k-2). spiral bd. 10.95 (978-0-9719657-4-4(9)) Red Carpet Publishing.

—Tyler Brushes His Teeth: Special Needs Version. Lynne, Rustyna, illus. l.t. ed. 2002. 14p. (YA). (gr. 3-8). spiral bd. 10.95 (978-0-9719657-5-1(7)) Red Carpet Publishing.

Lyon, Tammie, illus. Eloise at the Wedding. 2006. (Ready-to-Reads Ser.). 32p. (J). (ps-1). lib. bdg. 11.89 (978-1-4169-2457-9(4) , Aladdin Library) Simon & Schuster Children's Publishing.

Macaulay, David. Black & White. 2005. (Illus.). 32p. (J). (gr. k-3). 6.95 (978-0-618-63687-7(0) , Walter Lorraine) Houghton Mifflin Co. Trade & Reference Div.

MacDonald, Amy. No More Nasty. Smith, Cat Bowman, illus. 2001. (J). (978-0-7894-2676-5(5)) Dorling Kindersley Publishing, Inc.

—No More Nice, No More Nasty. Smith, Cat Bowman, illus. 2005. 304p. (J). pap. 7.95 (978-0-374-45511-8(2) , Farrar, Straus & Giroux (BYR)) Farrar, Straus & Giroux.

MacDonald, Betty. Hello, Mrs. Piggle-Wiggle. Boiger, Alexandra, illus. 2007. 192p. (J). lib. bdg. 16.89 (*978-0-06-125124-5(0)) HarperCollins Pubs.

—Mrs. Piggle-Wiggle. Boiger, Alexandra, illus. 2007. 192p. (J). lib. bdg. 16.89 (*978-0-06-125123-8(2)) HarperCollins Pubs.

—Mrs. Piggle-Wiggle's Magic. Boiger, Alexandra, illus. 2007. 192p. (J). lib. bdg. 16.89 (*978-0-06-125125-2(9)) HarperCollins Pubs.

MacDonald, Betty Bard. Happy Birthday, Mrs. Piggle-Wiggle. Boiger, Alexandra, illus. 2007. (Mrs. Piggle-Wiggle Ser.). 208p. (J). (gr. 3-7). 15.99 (*978-0-06-072812-0(4)) HarperCollins Pubs.

—Hello, Mrs Piggle Wiggle. unabr. ed. 2004. 125p. (J). (gr. 2-5). pap. 29.00 incl. audio (978-0-8072-1184-7(2) , S YA 1018 SP, Listening Library) Random Hse. Audio Publishing Group.

—Mrs. Piggle-Wiggle. unabr. ed. 2004. (Illus.). 119p. (J). (gr. 2-5). pap. 29.00 incl. audio (978-0-8072-1180-9(X) , S YA 1022 SP, Listening Library) Random Hse. Audio Publishing Group.

MacHado, Ana Maria. Un Monton de Unicornios (A Bunch of Unicorns) Vasco, Irene, tr. Coll, Ivar Da, illus. 2001. (SPA.). 48p. (J). 8.95 (978-958-04-6261-3(5)) Norma S.A. COL. *Dist:* AIMS International Bks., Inc., Distribuidora Norma, Inc.

Mackerel, Seymour. Fish School. Horne, Philip & Loter, John, illus. 2003. (Finding Nemo). 24p. (J). (gr. k-k). pap. 3.25 (978-0-7364-2127-0(0) , RH/Disney) Random Hse. Children's Bks.

MacLean, Christine. Mary Margaret & the Perfect Pet Plan. 2004. (Illus.). 128p. (J). (gr. 3-7). 15.99 (978-0-525-47183-7(9) , Dutton Juvenile) Penguin Group (USA) Inc.

Maclean, Christine. Mary Margaret Meets Her Match. 2007. 176p. (J). (gr. 3-5). 15.99 (978-0-525-47775-4(6) , Dutton Juvenile) Penguin Group (USA) Inc.

MacLellan, Erin. Run from the Nun! 2003. 128p. (J). (gr. 4-6). tchr. ed. 16.95 (978-0-8234-1796-4(4)) Holiday Hse., Inc.

MacLeod, Doug. I'm Being Stalked by a Moonshadow. 2007. 212p. (YA). (gr. 8 up). 16.95 (*978-1-59078-501-0(0) , Front Street) Boyds Mills Pr.

MacPhail, Catherine. Get That Ghost to Go! Donnelly, Karen, illus. 2006. (Pathway Books). 83p. (J). 21.26 (978-1-59889-004-4(2)) Stone Arch Bks.

MacRae, Tom. The Opposite. Odriozola, Elena, illus. 2006. 32p. (J). 15.95 (978-1-56145-371-9(4) , Peachtree Junior) Peachtree Pubs., Ltd.

Maddern, Eric. The King with Horse's Ears. Hess, Paul, illus. 2004. 32p. (J). pap. 7.95 (978-1-84507-309-1(6)) Lincoln, Frances Ltd. GBR. *Dist:* Perseus Distribution.

Madison, Alan. The Littlest Grape Stomper. Potter, Giselle, illus. 2007. 40p. (J). (ps-3). lib. bdg. 18.99 (978-0-375-93675-3(0)); 16.99 (978-0-375-83675-6(6)) Random Hse. Children's Bks. (Schwartz & Wade Bks.).

—Pecorino Plays Ball. Cantone, Annalaura, illus. 2006. 40p. (J). (ps-3). 15.95 (978-0-689-86522-0(8) , Atheneum/Anne Schwartz Bks.) Simon & Schuster Children's Publishing.

—Pecorino's First Concert. Cantone, Annalaura, illus. 2005. 40p. (J). (ps-ps). 15.95 (978-0-689-85952-6(X) , Atheneum/Anne Schwartz Bks.) Simon & Schuster Children's Publishing.

Madison, Bennett. Lulu Dark & the Summer of the Fox. (YA). (gr. 7-12). 2007. 208p. 5.99 (978-1-59514-154-5(5)); 2006. 256p. 10.99 (978-1-59514-086-9(7)) Penguin Group (USA) Inc. (Razorbill).

—Lulu Dark Can See Through Walls. 256p. (YA). (gr. 7-12). 2006. pap. 5.99 (978-1-59514-104-0(9)); 2005. 9.99 (978-1-59514-010-4(7)) Penguin Group (USA) Inc. (Razorbill).

Magoo, Biz. Pajama Sam Out to Lunch! DiCicco, Sue, illus. 2001. (Humongous Ser.). 14p. (J). (ps-k). bds. 5.99 incl. cd-rom (978-1-58668-065-7(X)) Lyrick Studios.

Maguire, Gregory. A Couple of April Fools. Clayton, Elaine, illus. 2004. (Hamlet Chronicles Ser.). 192p. (J). (gr. 3-5). tchr. ed. 16.00 (978-0-618-27474-1(X) , Clarion Bks.) Houghton Mifflin Co. Trade & Reference Div.

—One Final Firecracker. 2007. (Hamlet Chronicles Ser.). 320p. (J). pap. 6.99 (*978-0-06-085284-9(4) , Harper Trophy) HarperCollins Pubs.

—One Final Firecracker. Clayton, Elaine, illus. 2005. 240p. (J). (gr. 4-6). 17.00 (978-0-618-27480-2(4) , Clarion Bks.) Houghton Mifflin Co. Trade & Reference Div.

—Seven Spiders Spinning: Y Gregory Maguire. l.t. ed. 2002. (J). 21.95 (978-0-7862-4419-5(4)) Thorndike Pr.

—Six Haunted Hairdos. 1999. (978-0-606-17470-1(2)) Tandem Library Bks.

—Six Haunted Hairdos. l.t. ed. 2002. 178p. (J). 21.95 (978-0-7862-4421-8(6)) Thorndike Pr.

—Three Rotten Eggs. Clayton, Elaine, illus. 2002. 192p. (J). (gr. 4-6). 16.00 (978-0-618-09655-8(8) , Clarion Bks.) Houghton Mifflin Co. Trade & Reference Div.

Maher, Mickle Brandt. Master Stitchum & the Moon. Dousias, Spiro, illus. 2003. (J). 19.99 (978-1-932188-01-1(0)) Bollix Bks.

Mahy, Margaret. The Great Piratical Rumbustification & the Librarian & the Robbers. Blake, Quentin, illus. 2000. 32p. (J). pap. 6.95 (978-1-56792-169-4(8)) Godine, David R. Pub.

—Summery Saturday Morning. 2000. (J). (978-0-606-19071-8(6)) Tandem Library Bks.

Malak, Annabel, illus. Goldilocks & the Three Bears. (Classic Stories Ser.). 48p. (J). audio, audio compact disk (978-2-921997-84-3(3)) Coffragants.

Maloney, Peter. Belly Button Boy. 2003. (gr. k-3). lib. bdg. 15.30 (978-0-613-61603-4(0)) Tandem Library Bks.

Maloney, Peter & Zekauskas, Felicia. Belly Button Boy. Maloney, Peter & Zekauskas, Felicia, illus. (Illus.). 40p. (J). (ps-2). 2003. pap. 6.99 (978-0-14-250017-0(8) , Puffin); 2000. 16.99 (978-0-8037-2542-3(6) , Dial) Penguin Group (USA) Inc.

Mamatas, Emanuel. By My Side: A Tale of the Heart. 2000. (Illus.). 132p. (YA). (gr. 5-10). pap. 8.95 (978-0-9706247-4-1(3)) Ikarian Pr. Of America.

—By My Side: A Tale of the Heart. 2000. (Illus.). 132p. (YA). (gr. 7-12). pap. 8.95 (978-1-891231-20-9(0)) Word Association Pubs.

Manuel, Lynn. The Lickety-Split Princess. 2005. (Illus.). 96p. (J). pap. 6.95 (978-1-55050-178-0(X)) Coteau Bks. CAN. *Dist:* Fitzhenry & Whiteside, Ltd.

Marantz, Larissa & DiPaolo, Katharine, illus. Singin' the Blues. 2005. (All Grown Up! Ser.). 24p. (J). (ps-ps). pap. 3.99 (978-0-689-86606-7(2) , Simon Spotlight/Nickelodeon) Simon & Schuster Children's Publishing.

Margaret, Linda. Footprints in the Pies: (and Other Excit. 2005. 64p. pap. 12.95 (978-1-4137-7151-0(3)) PublishAmerica, Inc.

Margolis, Leslie Goldman. Night at the Museum: A Junior Novelization. 2006. (Illus.). 128p. (J). mass mkt. 4.99 (978-0-7641-3576-7(7)) Barron's Educational Series, Inc.

Margulies, Teddy Slater. The Runaway Rabbit. Studio Orlando Staff, illus. 2001. (J). 10.79 (978-0-606-19915-5(2)) Tandem Library Bks.

Marino, Peter. Dough Boy. 2007. 176p. (YA). (gr. 7 up). pap. 6.95 (*978-0-8234-2096-4(5)) Holiday Hse., Inc.

Marino, Ricardo. Cuentos Ridiculos. 2002. (SPA.). 64p. (J). pap. 6.95 (978-1-4000-0035-7(1)) Random Hse., Inc.

—Cuentos Ridiculos. 2002. (SPA.). (gr. 3-6). lib. bdg. 15.25 (978-0-613-88210-1(5)) Tandem Library Bks.

Markas, Jenny. Scooby-Doo & the Monster of Mexico Jr Novelization. 2003. (gr. k-3). lib. bdg. 13.00 (978-0-613-66378-6(0)) Tandem Library Bks.

Markoe, Merrill. The Day My Dogs Became Guys. 2001. (978-0-606-20622-8(1)) Tandem Library Bks.

Marois, Andre. Avis de Recherche. Lemardele, Stephane, tr. 2003. (Roman Jeunesse Ser.). (FRE.). 96p. (J). (gr. 4-7). pap. (978-2-89021-646-4(2)) Diffusion du livre Mirabel.

Marois, Andre & Lemardele, Stephane. Meurtre a L'icluse 50. 2002. (Roman Jeunesse Ser.). (FRE., Illus.). 96p. pap. (978-2-89021-579-5(2)) Diffusion du livre Mirabel.

Marshall, James. Willis. 2001. (Illus.). 48p. (J). (gr. k-3). tchr. ed. 15.00 (978-0-618-12441-1(1)) Houghton Mifflin Co. Trade & Reference Div.

—Willis. 2001. (J). (978-0-606-21530-5(1)) Tandem Library Bks.

Marshall, James, illus. Miss Nelson Is Missing! 2002. (Miss Nelson Ser.). (J). 13.79 (978-0-7587-3147-0(7)) Book Wholesalers, Inc.

Marsoli, Lisa Ann & Bazaldua, Barbara. The Movie Storybook. Disney Storybook Artists Staff, illus. 2007. (Meet the Robinsons Ser.). 64p. (J). 8.99 (978-0-06-112476-1(1)) HarperCollins Pubs.

Martchenko, Michael. Ma, I'm a Farmer. Martchenko, Michael, illus. 2003. (Illus.). 32p. (J). (ps-2). pap. 5.95 (978-1-55037-696-8(9)) Annick Pr., Ltd. CAN. *Dist:* Firefly Bks., Ltd.

Martin, Andreu & Ribero, J. No Pidas Sardinas Fuera de Temporada. 35th ed. 2003. (SPA., Illus.). 178p. (J). (gr. 8-12). pap. 11.95 (978-84-204-4796-4(X)) Santillana USA Publishing Co., Inc.

Martin, David. Monkey Business. Nash, Scott, illus. 2000. (Brand New Readers Ser.). 32p. (J). (ps-2). pap. 5.99 (978-0-7636-0773-9(8)) Candlewick Pr.

Martin, Paul. Monster Manor: Beatrice's Spells. 2003. (gr. 3-6). lib. bdg. 13.00 (978-0-613-68193-3(2)) Tandem Library Bks.

Martin, Steve & Chast, Roz. The Alphabet from A to Y, with Bonus Letter Z! 2007. (Illus.). 64p. (J). 17.95 (*978-0-385-51662-4(2)); lib. bdg. 17.95 (*978-0-385-52377-6(7)) Doubleday Publishing. (Flying Dolphin Pr.).

Martinez, Heather, illus. Ice-Cream Dreams. 2004. (Spongebob Squarepants Ser.). 24p. (J). pap. 3.99 (978-0-689-86861-0(8) , Simon Spotlight/Nickelodeon) Simon & Schuster Children's Publishing.

—Road Trip. 2004. (Spongebob Squarepants Ser.). 24p. (J). pap. 5.99 (978-0-689-87382-9(4) , Simon Spotlight/Nickelodeon) Simon & Schuster Children's Publishing.

Marunas, Nathaniel. Manga Claus: The Blade of Kringle. Craddock, Erik, illus. 2006. 80p. (J). (gr. 4-12). 12.99 (978-1-59514-134-7(0) , Razorbill) Penguin Group (USA) Inc.

Marusak, Elaine. Truly Tales & Girl Fish Stories. 2006. 93p. pap. 14.95 (978-1-4241-3244-7(4)) PublishAmerica, Inc.

Marvin Redpost: A Magic Crystal. 2002. (Marvin Redpost Ser.). (Illus.). (J). 11.91 (978-0-7587-6198-9(8)) Book Wholesalers, Inc.

Marvin Redpost: Alone in His Teacher's House. 2002. (Marvin Redpost Ser.). (Illus.). (J). 11.91 (978-0-7587-1428-2(9)) Book Wholesalers, Inc.

Marvin Redpost: Class President. 2002. (Marvin Redpost Ser.). (Illus.). (J). 11.91 (978-0-7587-6195-8(3)) Book Wholesalers, Inc.

Marvin Redpost: Is He a Girl? 2002. (Marvin Redpost Ser.). (Illus.). (J). 11.91 (978-0-7587-6196-5(1)) Book Wholesalers, Inc.

Marvin Redpost: Super Fast, Out of Control! 2002. (Marvin Redpost Ser.). (Illus.). (J). 11.91 (978-0-7587-6199-6(6)) Book Wholesalers, Inc.

Marvin Redpost: Why Pick on Me? 2002. (Marvin Redpost Ser.). (Illus.). (J). 11.91 (978-0-7587-6197-2(X)) Book Wholesalers, Inc.

Maslen, Bobby Lynn & Maslen, John R. Long Vowels! 2006. (Bob Books Ser.: No. 5). 16p. (J). pap. 16.99 (978-0-439-86541-8(7) , Scholastic Paperbacks) Scholastic, Inc.

Maslen, John R. & Maslen, Bobby Lynn. Advancing Beginners. 2006. (Bob Books Set 2 Ser.). (Illus.). 16p. (J). pap. 16.99 (978-0-439-84502-1(5) , Scholastic Paperbacks) Scholastic, Inc.

—Beginning Readers. 2006. (Bob Books Set 1 Ser.). (Illus.). 16p. (J). pap. 16.99 (978-0-439-84500-7(9) , Scholastic Paperbacks) Scholastic, Inc.

—Compound Words. 2006. (Bob Books Set 4 Ser.). (Illus.). 16p. (J). pap. 16.99 (978-0-439-84506-9(8) , Scholastic Paperbacks) Scholastic, Inc.

H
I

Mason, Jane B. & Stephens, Sarah Hines. Bella Baxter & the Itchy Disaster. Shelley, John, illus. 2005. (Bella Baxter Ser.). 80p. (J). pap. 3.99 (978-0-689-86281-6(4) , Aladdin) Simon & Schuster Children's Publishing.

Mason, Simon. The Quigleys. Stephens, Helen, illus. 160p. (gr. k-7). 2003. 4.99 (978-0-440-41898-6(4) , Yearling); 2002. (J). 14.95 (978-0-385-75006-6(4) , Fickling, David Bks.) Random Hse. Children's Bks.

—Quigleys. 2003. (gr. 3-6). lib. bdg. 13.00 (978-0-613-82975-5(1)) Tandem Library Bks.

—The Quigleys: Not for Sale. Stephens, Helen, illus. 2006. 176p. (J). (gr. k-7). 5.50 (978-0-440-42084-2(9) , Yearling) Random Hse. Children's Bks.

—The Quigleys in a Spin. Stephens, Helen, illus. 2006. 192p. (J). (gr. k-7). lib. bdg. 16.99 (978-0-385-75099-8(4) , Fickling, David Bks.) Random Hse. Children's Bks.

Mason, Tom & Danko, Dan. Life Is Unfair! 2000. (Malcolm in the Middle Ser.: Vol. 1). 144p. (J). (gr. 3-7). pap. 4.99 (978-0-439-22840-4(9)) Scholastic, Inc.

—Waterpark. 2000. (Malcolm in the Middle Ser.: Vol. 2). 112p. (J). (gr. 3-7). pap. 4.99 (978-0-439-22842-8(5)) Scholastic, Inc.

Mason, Tom, et al. Laugh till You Drop! A Totally Spies! Joke Book. Artful Doodlers Limited Staff, illus. 2005. (Totally Spies! Ser.). 48p. (J). (ps-6). pap. 3.99 (978-1-4169-0027-6(6) , Simon Spotlight) Simon & Schuster Children's Publishing.

Mass, Wendy. Rapunzel: The One with All the Hair. 2006. (Twice upon a Time Ser.: No. 1). 208p. (J). pap. 5.99 (978-0-439-79656-9(3) , Scholastic Paperbacks) Scholastic, Inc.

Massicotte, Sylvie & Sottolichio, Rafael. Tu Rêves, Pitchounette? 2004. (Premier Roman Ser.). (FRE., Illus.). 64p. (J). (gr. 1-4). pap. (978-2-89021-581-8(4)) Diffusion du livre Mirabel.

Matsuoka, Kyoko. I Love to Take a Bath. Hayashi, Akiko, illus. 2006. 32p. (J). 17.95 (978-1-74126-023-6(X)) R.I.C. Pubns. AUS. *Dist:* SCB Distributors.

Maxwell-Hyslop, Miranda. Fish Go Woof! 2005. (Illus.). 36p. (J). (978-0-340-87338-0(8) , Hodder & Stoughton) Hodder General Publishing Division.

—Fish Go Woof! 2005. (Illus.). (J). pap. 9.99 (978-0-340-87339-7(6) , Hodder & Stoughton) Hodder General Publishing Division GBR. *Dist:* Trafalgar Square Publishing.

Maxwell, Katie. Eyeliner of the Gods. 2004. (YA). mass mkt. 5.99 (978-0-8439-5378-7(0)) Dorchester Publishing Co., Inc.

—Got Fangs? 2005. (YA). mass mkt. 5.99 (978-0-8439-5399-2(3)) Dorchester Publishing Co., Inc.

—The Taming of the Dru. 2004. (YA). mass mkt. 5.99 (978-0-8439-5298-8(9)) Dorchester Publishing Co., Inc.

—What's French for EW!? 2004. (YA). mass mkt. 5.99 (978-0-8439-5297-1(0)) Dorchester Publishing Co., Inc.

May, Scott. The Yuggs: A Bird in the Hat. 2000. mass mkt. 8.95 (978-1-931179-07-2(7)) Long Hill Productions, Inc.

—The Yuggs: A Bird in the Hat. Fisher, Brian Patrick, illus. 2000. 24p. (J). (gr. 1-3). pap. (978-0-9701450-3-1(9)) Long Hill Productions, Inc.

Mayer, Mercer. Just a Little Critter Collection. Mayer, Mercer, illus. 2005. (Illus.). 176p. (J). (ps-2). 9.99 (978-0-375-83255-0(6) , Golden Bks.) Random Hse. Children's Bks.

Mazer, Anne. The No-Nothings & Their Baby. Collins, Ross, illus. 2000. (J). (gr. k-3). 40p. pap. 15.95 (978-0-590-68049-3(8) , Scholastic Paperbacks); (978-0-590-68051-6(X)) Scholastic, Inc.

McAllister, Angela. Trust Me, Mom! Collins, Ross, illus. 2005. 32p. (J). (ps-2). 16.95 (978-1-58234-955-8(X)) Bloomsbury Publishing.

McAllister, Troon, pseud. Foursome. 2001. (gr. 7-12). lib. bdg. 23.40 (978-0-613-36809-4(6)) Tandem Library Bks.

McBratney, Sam. Guess How Much I Love You: My Baby Book. Jeram, Anita, illus. 10th anniv. ed. 2002. 48p. (J). (gr. k-12). 18.00 (978-0-7636-1909-1(4)) Candlewick Pr.

McCann, Jesse Leon. Ghastly Giant. del Sur, Duendes, illus. 2003. (Scooby Doo Ser.). 32p. (J). pap. 3.50 (978-0-439-45523-7(5)) Scholastic, Inc.

—Ghastly Giant. 2003. (gr. k-3). lib. bdg. 11.25 (978-0-613-66376-2(4)) Tandem Library Bks.

—Scooby-Doo & the Legend of Vampire Rock. 2003. (gr. 3-6). lib. bdg. 11.25 (978-0-613-58167-7(9)) Tandem Library Bks.

—Scooby-Doo & the Monster of Mexico. 2003. (gr. 3-6). lib. bdg. 11.25 (978-0-613-66377-9(2)) Tandem Library Bks.

McCarthy, Rebecca. Midnight Mystery #1. 2008. 80p. (J). (gr. 2-5). 3.99 (***978-0-448-44672-1(3)*** , Grosset & Dunlap) Penguin Group (USA) Inc.

McClements, George. Baron Von Baddie Wins. 2008. (J). (***978-0-15-206138-8(X)***) Harcourt Trade Pubs.

—Night of the Veggie Monster. 2008. (Illus.). 32p. (J). 15.85 (***978-1-59990-234-0(6)***) Bloomsbury Publishing.

—Night of the Veggie Monster. McClements, George, illus. 2008. (Illus.). 32p. (J). 14.95 (***978-1-59990-061-2(0)***) Bloomsbury Publishing.

McClements, George. Ridin' Dinos with Buck Bronco. 2007. (Illus.). 40p. (J). (ps-2). 16.00 (978-0-15-205989-7(X)) Harcourt Trade Pubs.

McCloskey, Robert. Centerburg Tales: More Adventures of Homer Price. 1999. (J). (gr. 3-6). lib. bdg. 14.15 (978-0-8085-8462-9(6)) Tandem Library Bks.

—Homer Price. 1998. (J). (gr. 4). pap. 3.95 (978-0-439-04464-6(2)) Scholastic, Inc.

—Homer Price. McCloskey, Robert, illus. 2005. 160p. (J). (gr. 3). pap. 5.99 (978-0-14-240415-7(2) , Puffin) Penguin Group (USA) Inc.

—Homer Price. l.t. ed. 2004. (Beeler Mystery Ser.). 158p. 29.95 (978-1-58118-123-4(X)) LRS.

—Homer Price. l.t. ed. (J). (gr. 4-6). reprint ed. 10.00 (978-0-89064-072-2(6)) National Assn. for Visually Handicapped.

McClymer, Kelly. Getting to Third Date. 2006. (Romantic Comedies Ser.). (Illus.). 304p. (YA). (gr. 9 up). pap. 5.99 (978-1-4169-1479-2(X) , Simon Pulse) Simon & Schuster Children's Publishing.

McDonald, Megan. Doctor Is In! Reynolds, Peter H., illus. 2006. (Judy Moody Ser.: No. 5). 176p. (J). (gr. 1-5). pap. 5.99 (978-0-7636-2615-0(5)) Candlewick Pr.

—Doctor Is In! Reynolds, Peter H., tr. Reynolds, Peter H., illus. 2004. (Judy Moody Ser.: No. 5). 176p. (J). (gr. 1-5). 15.99 (978-0-7636-2024-0(6)) Candlewick Pr.

—Doctor Is In! Reynolds, Peter, illus. 2004. (Judy Moody Ser.: No. 5). 151p. (J). lib. bdg. 23.08 (***978-1-4242-1145-6(X)***) Fitzgerald Bks.

—Judy Moody Declares Independence. Reynolds, Peter H., illus. (Judy Moody Ser.: No. 6). 160p. (J). (gr. 1-4). 2007. pap. 5.99 (978-0-7636-2800-0(X)); 2005. 15.99 (978-0-7636-2361-6(X)) Candlewick Pr.

—Judy Moody Saves the World! Reynolds, Peter H., illus. (Judy Moody Ser.: No. 3). 160p. (J). (gr. 1-5). 2004. pap. 5.99 (978-0-7636-2087-5(4)); 2002. 15.99 (978-0-7636-1446-1(7)) Candlewick Pr.

—The Judy Moody Star-Studded Collection: Judy Moody; Judy Moody Gets Famous!; Judy Moody Saves the World! Reynolds, Peter H., illus. 2004. (Judy Moody Ser.). 464p. (J). (gr. 1-5). pap. 17.97 (978-0-7636-2563-4(9)) Candlewick Pr.

—Stink & the Incredible Super-Galactic Jawbreaker. Reynolds, Peter H., illus. 2007. (Stink Ser.). 144p. (J). (gr. k-3). pap. 4.99 (978-0-7636-3236-6(8)) Candlewick Pr.

—Stink & the Incredible Super-Galactic Jawbreaker. Reynolds, Peter, illus. 2006. 128p. (J). (gr. k-3). 12.99 (978-0-7636-2158-2(7)) Candlewick Pr.

—Stink & the World's Worst Super-Stinky Sneakers. Reynolds, Peter H., illus. 2007. (Stink Ser.). 144p. (J). (gr. k-3). 12.99 (978-0-7636-2834-5(4)) Candlewick Pr.

McElligott, Matthew. Backbeard & the Birthday Suit: The Hairiest Pirate Who Ever Lived. 2007. (Illus.). 32p. (J). pap. 6.95 (***978-0-8027-9680-6(X)***) Walker & Co.

—Backbeard: Pirate for Hire. McElligott, Matthew, illus. 2007. (Illus.). 32p. (J). 17.85 (***978-0-8027-9633-2(8)***); 16.95 (***978-0-8027-9632-5(X)***) Walker & Co.

McFann, Jennifer. Laveidem. 2004. 192p. (J). (gr. 5 up). pap. 9.95 (978-0-439-63987-3(5)) Scholastic, Inc.

McFarlane, Arlene. My Name Is Not Magilla Gorilla. Wise, Noreen, ed. Silverman, Karen, illus. 2000. (Lemonade Collection). 48p. (J). (ps up). pap. 5.95 (978-1-58584-210-0(9)) Huckleberry Pr.

McGeorge, Constance W. Waltz of the Scarecrows. 2003. (Illus.). 32p. (J). pap. 6.95 (978-0-8118-4078-1(6)) Chronicle Bks. LLC.

McGuirk, Leslie. Ho, Ho, Ho, Tucker! McGuirk, Leslie, illus. 2005. (Illus.). 30p. (J). (gr. k-k). bds. 7.99 (978-0-7636-2582-5(5)) Candlewick Pr.

McKay, Hilary. Dolphin Luck. l.t. ed. 2005. (Illus.). 272p. (J). pap. incl. audio (978-0-7540-7865-4(5) , CLP 449) BBC Audio.

—Dolphin Luck. 2004. (J). pap. 29.95 incl. audio (978-0-7540-6273-8(2) , Chivers Children's Audio Bks.) BBC Audiobooks America.

—Dolphin Luck. 2000. (J). (978-0-606-20086-8(X)) Tandem Library Bks.

—Dolphin Luck. l.t. ed. 2001. (Illus.). 198p. (J). (gr. 4-7). 21.95 (978-0-7862-2703-7(6)) Thorndike Pr.

McKay, Sharon E. What Are Friends For? 2001. (Hippo Tub Co. Ser.). (Illus.). 40p. (J). pap. 6.95 (978-1-894454-00-1(6)) Balmur Entertainment, Ltd. CAN. *Dist:* General Distribution Services, Inc.

McKee, David. Isabel's Noisy Tummy. 2007. (Illus.). 26p. (J). (ps-k). pap. 6.99 (978-1-84270-576-6(8)) Andersen GBR. *Dist:* Independent Pubs. Group.

—Mr Benn: Gladiator. 2005. (Illus.). 32p. (J). pap. 9.99 (978-1-84270-372-4(2)) Trafalgar Square Publishing.

McKendry, Sam. Are You Ticklish? A Touch & Tickle Book. Mitchell, Melanie, illus. 2005. 12p. (J). (ps up). 10.95 (978-1-58117-376-5(8) , Intervisual/Piggy Toes) Dalmatian Pr.

McKenna, Colleen O'Shaughnessy. Doggone... Third Grade! Roth, Stephanie, illus. 2002. 80p. (J). (gr. 4-6). tchr. ed. 15.95 (978-0-8234-1696-7(8)) Holiday Hse., Inc.

McKenzie, Tim A. Baxter Barret Brown's Bass Fiddle. 2004. (Illus.). 32p. (J). 19.95 incl. audio compact disk (978-1-931721-06-6(8)) Bright Sky Pr.

McKissack, Patricia C. Porch Lies: Tales of Slicksters, Tricksters, & Other Wily Characters. Carrilho, Andre, illus. 2006. 160p. (J). (gr. 3-7). lib. bdg. 20.99 (978-0-375-93619-7(X) , Schwartz & Wade Bks.) Random Hse. Children's Bks.

McLarey, Kristina Thermaenius, et al. When You Take a Pig to a Party. Wunsch, Marjory, illus. 2000. 32p. (J). (gr. k-4). 16.99 (978-0-531-33257-3(8)); pap. 15.95 (978-0-531-30257-6(1)) Scholastic, Inc. (Orchard Bks.).

McMullan, Kate. Keep a Lid on It, Pandora! 2003. (Myth-o-Mania Ser.: No. 6). (Illus.). 160p. (J). 9.99 (978-0-7868-0862-5(4)) Hyperion Bks. for Children.

—Nice Shot, Cupid! LaFleur, David, illus. 2002. (Myth-o-Mania Ser.: Bk. 4). 160p. (J). (gr. 3-7). 9.99 (978-0-7868-0860-1(8) , Volo) Hyperion Bks. for Children.

—Say Cheese, Medusa! LaFleur, David, illus. 2002. (Myth-o-Mania Ser.: Bk. 3). 160p. (J). (gr. 3-7). pap. 9.99 (978-0-7868-0859-5(4) , Volo) Hyperion Bks. for Children.

McNaughton, Colin. Captain Abduls Pirate School. McNaughton, Colin, illus. 2004. (Illus.). 40p. (J). (gr. 1 up). pap. 6.99 (978-0-7636-2540-5(X)) Candlewick Pr.

—Jolly Roger & the Pirates of Captain Abdul. McNaughton, Colin, illus. 2nd ed. 2004. (Illus.). 40p. (J). (gr. 1 up). pap. 6.99 (978-0-7636-2539-9(6)) Candlewick Pr.

—Potty Poo-Poo Wee-Wee! McNaughton, Colin, illus. 2005. (Illus.). 40p. (J). (gr. k-ps). 9.99 (978-0-7636-2781-2(X)) Candlewick Pr.

—Preston's Goal! 2001. (978-0-606-22599-1(4)) Tandem Library Bks.

McPhail, David. Sylvie & True. 2007. (Illus.). 32p. (J). (ps). 15.00 (978-0-374-37364-1(7)) Farrar, Straus & Giroux.

McPhail, David M. Big Pig & Little Pig. McPhail, David M., illus. 2002. (Illus.). (J). 11.45 (978-0-7587-5345-8(4)) Book Wholesalers, Inc.

—Big Pig & Little Pig. 2003. (Green Light Readers Level 1 Ser.). (Illus.). 24p. (J). 11.95 (978-0-15-204818-1(9)); pap. 3.95 (978-0-15-204857-0(X)) Harcourt Children's Bks. (Green Light Readers).

McVeity, Jen. The Frogs of Betts. Denton, Terry, illus. 1999. (Supa Doopers Ser.). 64p. (J). (978-0-7608-1932-6(7)) Sundance/Newbridge Educational Publishing.

—Green with Red Spots Horrible. Hobbs, Leigh, illus. 1999. (Supa Doopers Ser.). 64p. (J). (978-0-7608-1937-1(8)) Sundance/Newbridge Educational Publishing.

—Green with Red Spots Horrible. 1999. (gr. 3-6). lib. bdg. 12.60 (978-0-613-19369-6(5)) Tandem Library Bks.

Meacham, Margaret. A Fairy's Guide to Understanding Humans. 2007. 160p. (YA). (gr. 5 up). 16.95 (***978-0-8234-2078-0(7)***) Holiday Hse., Inc.

Meacham, Margaret. A Mid-Semester Night's Dream. 2004. 160p. (J). (gr. 4-6). tchr. ed. 16.95 (978-0-8234-1815-2(4)) Holiday Hse., Inc.

Meeuwissen, Tony. Remarkable Animals. 2007. (Illus.). 24p. (J). spiral bd. 15.95 (978-1-84507-741-9(5)) Lincoln, Frances Ltd. GBR. *Dist:* Perseus Distribution.

Meister, Cari. Tiny on the Farm. Davis, Rich, illus. 2008. 32p. (J). (ps). 13.99 (***978-0-670-06246-1(4)*** , Viking Juvenile) Penguin Group (USA) Inc.

Meng, Cece. The Wonderful Thing about Hiccups. Pedersen, Janet, illus. 2007. 32p. (J). (gr. k-3). 16.00 (978-0-618-59544-0(9) , Clarion Bks.) Houghton Mifflin Co. Trade & Reference Div.

Mercado, Nancy, ed. Tripping over the Lunch Lady: And Other School Stories. 2004. 192p. (J). 16.99 (978-0-8037-2873-8(5) , Dial) Penguin Group (USA) Inc.

Merola, Caroline. Coco Bonneau, le Héros. Merola, Caroline, illus. 2001. (Premier Roman Ser.). (FRE., Illus.). 64p. (J). (gr. 1-4). pap. (978-2-89021-539-9(3)) Diffusion du livre Mirabel.

—La Magie de Tonie Biscotti. 2002. (Premier Roman Ser.). (FRE., Illus.). 64p. (J). (gr. 1-4). pap. (978-2-89021-573-3(3)) Diffusion du livre Mirabel.

—La Trahison de Laurent Lareau. Merola, Caroline, illus. 2003. (Premier Roman Ser.). (FRE., Illus.). 64p. (J). (gr. 1-4). pap. (978-2-89021-645-7(4)) Diffusion du livre Mirabel.

Metzler, Chris & Kim, Sunyoung. Me & 10 Babies. (Illus.). 36p. (978-0-9688338-4-1(5)) Cadence Publishing.

Meyer, Franklyn E. Me & Caleb. Smith, Lawrence Beall, illus. 2006. (J). kivar 16.95 (***978-0-9789388-0-2(1)***) Hester Publishing.

—Me & Caleb Again. Liese, Charles, illus. 2006. (J). kivar 16.95 (***978-0-9789388-1-9(X)***) Hester Publishing.

Mighty Fine, Inc. Staff. Ruby Gloom's Guide to Friendship. 2005. (Illus.). 72p. (J). (gr. 5-9). 12.95 (978-0-8109-5862-3(7)) Abrams, Harry N. , Inc.

Miglis, Jenny. And the Winner Is ... Meurer, Caleb, illus. 2004. (SpongeBob SquarePants Ser.). 24p. (J). pap. 3.50 (978-0-689-86327-1(6) , Simon Spotlight/Nickelodeon) Simon & Schuster Children's Publishing.

—And the Winner Is ... Meurer, Caleb, illus. 2004. 24p. (J). (gr. k-3). lib. bdg. 11.25 (978-0-613-73383-0(5)) Tandem Library Bks.

—Peekaboo, Blue! Pontillo, Jenine, illus. 2004. (Blue's Clues Ser.). 12p. (J). bds. 7.99 (978-0-689-85257-2(6) , Simon Spotlight/Nickelodeon) Simon & Schuster Children's Publishing.

Miles, Ellen. Flintstones in Viva Rock Vegas: Digest Edition. 2000. (Illus.). 80p. (J). (gr. 4-7). pap. 3.99 (978-0-439-17303-2(5)) Scholastic, Inc.

Milgrim, David. Young McDonald. Milgrim, David, illus. 2006. (Illus.). 32p. (J). (gr. k). 12.99 (978-0-525-47570-5(2) , Dutton Juvenile) Penguin Group (USA) Inc.

Miller, Ruth. The Bear on the Bed. Slavin, Bill, illus. 32p. (J). (gr. k-3). 2004. (978-1-55337-687-3(0)); 2002. (978-1-55337-036-9(8)) Kids Can Pr., Ltd.

Millionaire, Tony. That Darn Yarn. 2005. (Illus.). 40p. (J). (ps-17). 7.95 (978-1-59582-009-9(4)) DH Pr.

Mills, Nancy Libbey. Never Eat Cabbage on Thursday. Wells, Shan, illus. 32p. (J). 2002. pap. 7.95 (978-1-893815-07-0(2)); 2005. 12.95 (978-1-893815-08-7(0)) Pie in the Sky Publishing, LLC.

Minter, J. Girls We Love. 2006. (Insiders Novel Ser.). 256p. (YA). pap. 8.95 (978-1-58234-742-4(5) , Bloomsbury Children) Bloomsbury Publishing.

Miranda, Anne. Who Said Boo? 2003. (Illus.). 24p. (ps-k). 12.99 (978-0-7868-0811-3(X)) Hyperion Bks. for Children.

Mitchell, Richard, illus. The Man from Mars. 1999. (J). (978-0-7608-3201-1(3)) Sundance/Newbridge Educational Publishing.

—The Monster from Mercury. 1999. (J). (978-0-7608-3200-4(5)) Sundance/Newbridge Educational Publishing.

—Planet X. 1999. (J). (978-0-7608-3202-8(1)) Sundance/Newbridge Educational Publishing.

Mlynowski, Sarah. Bras & Broomsticks. 2005. 320p. (YA). (gr. 7). 15.95 (978-0-385-73181-2(7) , Delacorte Bks. for Young Readers) Random Hse. Children's Bks.

—Frogs & French Kisses. (gr. 7). 2007. 304p. (YA). pap. 8.99 (***978-0-385-73185-0(X)***); 2006. (Illus.). 288p. (J). 15.95 (978-0-385-73182-9(5)); 2006. (Illus.). 288p. (YA). lib. bdg. 17.99 (978-0-385-90219-9(0)) Random Hse. Children's Bks. (Delacorte Bks. for Young Readers).

Montes, Graciela. Mas Chiquito Que Una Arveja, Mas Grande Que Una Ballena. 2002. (SPA.). 64p. (J). pap. 6.95 (978-1-4000-0047-0(5)) Random Hse., Inc.

Montes, Marisa. Gabi esta Aqui! Un dia loco de palabras Mezcladas. Cepeda, Joe, illus. 2004. (Get Ready for Gabi Ser.).Tr. of Crazy Mixed-Up Spanglish Day. (SPA.). 144p. (J). (gr. 2-5). pap. 3.99 (978-0-439-66129-4(3) , Scholastic Paperbacks) Scholastic, Inc.

—Get Ready for Gabi! No.3: No More Spanish. 2004. (gr. 3-6). lib. bdg. 11.80 (978-0-613-84571-7(4)) Tandem Library Bks.

—Juan Bob Goes to Work. Cepeda, Joe, illus. 2006. 32p. (J). pap. 6.99 (978-0-06-088227-3(1) , Rayo) HarperCollins Pubs.

—Juan Bobo Busca Trabajo. Cepeda, Joe, illus. 2006. (SPA.). 32p. (J). pap. 6.99 (978-0-06-113681-8(6) , Rayo) HarperCollins Pubs.

Montgomery, Claire & Montgomery, Monte. Hubert Invents the Wheel. Shelly, Jeff, illus. 2005. 192p. (J). (gr. 4-7). 16.95 (978-0-8027-8990-7(0)) Walker & Co.

Morgan, Allen. Matthew & Midnight Wrestlers. Martchenko, Michael, illus. 2004. 40p. pap. (978-1-55041-916-0(1)) Fitzhenry & Whiteside, Ltd.

—Matthew & the Midnight Movie. Martchenko, Michael, illus. 2002. (Matthew's Midnight Adventures Ser.). 32p. (YA). 6.99 (978-0-7737-6273-2(6)) Stoddart Kids CAN. *Dist:* Fitzhenry & Whiteside, Ltd.

—Quackadack Duck. Beder, John, illus. 2003. 32p. (J). (ps-2). lib. bdg. 18.95 (978-1-55037-761-3(2)) Annick Pr., Ltd. CAN. *Dist:* Firefly Bks., Ltd.

Morgan, Allen, et al. Compte Tes Sous, Mathieu! 2001. (Drtles d'Histoires Ser.). (FRE., Illus.). 24p. (YA). (ps up). pap. (978-2-89021-456-9(7)) Diffusion du livre Mirabel.

Morgan, Christopher. Pirates Drive Buses. 2008. 80p. (J). 14.95 (***978-1-59643-313-7(2)***) Roaring Brook Pr.

—Pirates Eat Porridge. Curtis, Neil, illus. 2007. 80p. (J). (gr. 2-5). 14.95 (***978-1-59643-304-5(3)***) Roaring Brook Pr.

Morgenstern, Susie. A Book of Coupons. Rosner, Gill, tr. from FRE. Bloch, Serge, illus. 2001. 64p. (J). (gr. 3-6). 13.99 (978-0-670-89970-8(4) , Viking Juvenile) Penguin Group (USA) Inc.

—Princesses Are People, Too: Two Modern Fairy Tales. 2004. (gr. 3-6). lib. bdg. 13.00 (978-0-613-89800-3(1)) Tandem Library Bks.

Morris, Gerald. The Lioness & Her Knight. 2005. (Squire's Tales Ser.). 352p. (J). (gr. 5-7). 16.00 (978-0-618-50772-6(8)) Houghton Mifflin Co. Trade & Reference Div.

—The Quest of the Fair Unknown. 2006. 278p. (J). (gr. 5). 16.00 (978-0-618-63152-0(6)) Houghton Mifflin Co. Trade & Reference Div.

Moser, Lisa. Sticky Burr: Adventures in Burrwood Forest. Gorbachev, Valeri, illus. 2007. (J). (***978-0-7636-3567-1(7)***) Candlewick Pr.

Moses, Brian. Estoy Aburrido. 2001. (Mis Sentimientos Coleccion). (SPA., Illus.). (J). pap. 6.95 (978-950-24-0841-5(1)) Albatros ARG. *Dist:* Lectorum Pubns., Inc.

—Yo No Fui: Aprender a Ser Honesto. Gordon, Mike, illus. 2000. (SPA.). 32p. (J). (ps-k). 7.95 (978-950-24-0804-0(7)) Lectorum Pubns., Inc.

Moss, Marissa. Amelia's Must-Keep Resolutions for the Best Year Ever! Moss, Marissa, illus. 2006. (Amelia's Notebooks). 40p. (J). 9.95 (978-1-4169-3361-8(1) , Simon & Schuster/Paula Wiseman Bks.) Simon & Schuster Children's Publishing.

Moss, Miriam. Can I Have Some? American English Edition. 2000. (Cambridge Reading Ser.). (Illus.). 12p. pap. 5.00 (978-0-521-79526-5(5)) Cambridge Univ. Pr.

Mould, Wendy. Ants in My Pants. Mould, Wendy, illus. 2001. (Illus.). 32p. (J). (gr. k-3). tchr. ed. 15.00 (978-0-618-09640-4(X) , Clarion Bks.) Houghton Mifflin Co. Trade & Reference Div.

Moulton, Mark Kimball. Twisted Sistahs. Good, Karen Hillard, illus. 2006. 32p. (J). (gr. 2-3). 14.95 (978-0-8249-8676-6(8)) Ideals Pubns.

Mouse Works Staff. Noodle Dance! Chunky Roly Poly. 1999. (P B & J Otter Noodle Stories Ser.). (Illus.). 16p. (J). bds. 3.50 (978-0-7364-0011-4(7)) Mouse Works.

Muir, Sabine. Meeting Wolfie: A Story about Mozart. 2006. 129p. pap. 16.95 (978-1-4241-3968-2(6)) PublishAmerica, Inc.

Muldrow, Diane. Hangin' with Bugs. Style Guide Staff, illus. 2006. (Baby Looney Tunes Ser.). 32p. (J). act. bk. ed. 0.99 (978-1-4169-1841-7(8) , Simon Scribbles) Simon & Schuster Children's Publishing.

Mule Days: Stories about Survivors of the Great Depression. 2004. (YA). lib. bdg. 22.50 net. (978-0-9755117-0-1(X)) Hidden Forest Pubs.

Muller, Birte. Farley Farts BB W/sound. 2007. (Illus.). 18p. (J). bds. 9.95 (978-0-7358-2115-6(1)) North-South Bks., Inc.

Munsch, Robert. Aaron's Hair. Daniel, Alan & Daniel, Lea, illus. 2000. 32p. (J). (ps-1). pap. 11.95 (978-0-439-19258-3(7)) Scholastic, Inc.

—Aaron's Hair. Daniel, Alan, illus. 1998. 32p. (J). (ps-2). 4.99 (978-0-590-21103-1(X)) Scholastic, Inc.

—Alligator Baby. ed. 2004. (Illus.). (J). (gr. k-3). spiral bd. (978-0-616-01730-2(8)); spiral bd. (978-0-616-01731-9(6)) Canadian National Institute for the Blind/Institut National Canadien pour les Aveugles.

—Alligator Baby. Martchenko, Michael, illus. 2002. 32p. (J). pap. 4.99 (978-0-439-38849-8(X)) Scholastic, Inc.

—Alligator Baby. 1998. (Illus.). (J). pap. 3.99 (978-0-590-34195-0(2) , Cartwheel Bks.) Scholastic, Inc.

—Alligator Baby. Martchenko, Michael, illus. 1998. 32p. (J). (ps-3). pap. 4.99 (978-0-590-88594-2(4) , Cartwheel Bks.) Scholastic, Inc.
—Alligator Baby. 1998. 10.79 (978-0-606-13117-9(5)) Tandem Library Bks.
—Espera y Veras. Aguirre, Rigo, tr. from ENG. Martchenko, Michael, illus. 2004. (SPA.). 24p. (J). (ps-2). pap. 5.95 (978-1-55037-872-6(4)) Annick Pr., Ltd. CAN. *Dist:* Firefly Bks., Ltd.
—Get Out of Bed! ed. 2004. (Illus.). (J). (gr. k-3). spiral bd. (978-0-616-04557-2(3)); spiral bd. (978-0-616-03049-3(5)) Canadian National Institute for the Blind/Institut National Canadien pour les Aveugles.
—I'm So Embarrassed! Martchenko, Michael, illus. 2006. 32p. (J). pap. 4.99 (978-0-439-83578-7(X) , Cartwheel Bks.) Scholastic, Inc.
—Makeup Mess. ed. 2004. (Illus.). (J). (gr. k-3). spiral bd. (978-0-616-11125-3(8)) Canadian National Institute for the Blind/Institut National Canadien pour les Aveugles.
—Makeup Mess. Martchenko, Michael, illus. ed. 2004. (J). (gr. k-3). spiral bd. (978-0-616-11124-6(X)) Canadian National Institute for the Blind/Institut National Canadien pour les Aveugles.
—Mmmm, Cookies! Martchenko, Michael, illus. 2002. 32p. (J). pap. 3.99 (978-0-590-89604-7(0)) Scholastic, Inc.
—More Pies! ed. 2004. (Illus.). (J). (gr. k-3). spiral bd. (978-0-616-14589-0(6)) Canadian National Institute for the Blind/Institut National Canadien pour les Aveugles.
—More Pies! Martchenko, Michael, illus. 2003. 32p. (J). pap. 4.99 (978-0-439-53285-3(X) , Cartwheel Bks.) Scholastic, Inc.
—Smelly Socks. Martchenko, Michael, illus. 2005. 32p. (J). pap. 4.99 (978-0-439-64948-3(X) , Cartwheel Bks.) Scholastic, Inc.
—El Traje de Nieve de Tomas. 2004. (SPA.). (ps-2). lib. bdg. 14.10 (978-0-613-78528-0(2)) Tandem Library Bks.
—El Traje de Nieve de Tomas. Aguirre, Rigo, tr. from ENG. Martchenko, Michael, illus. 2004. (SPA.). 24p. (J). (ps-2). pap. 5.95 (978-1-55037-854-2(6)) Annick Pr., Ltd. CAN. *Dist:* Firefly Bks., Ltd.
Munsch, Robert, et al. Aaron's Hair. Daniel, Alan & Daniel, Lea, illus. 2002. 32p. (J). pap. 4.99 (978-0-439-38848-1(1) , Cartwheel Bks.) Scholastic, Inc.
—Get Out of Bed! Daniel, Alan & Daniel, Lea, illus. 2002. 32p. (J). pap. 3.99 (978-0-439-38851-1(1)) Scholastic, Inc.
Munsch, Robert N. Bola de Mugre. Lopez, Jose M., tr. Suomalainen, Sami, illus. 2004. (SPA.). 32p. (J). (ps-2). pap. 5.95 (978-1-55037-873-3(2)) Annick Pr., Ltd. CAN. *Dist:* Firefly Bks., Ltd.
Murray, Marjorie Dennis. Hippo Goes Bananas! O'Malley, Kevin, illus. 2006. 32p. (J). 14.95 (978-0-7614-5224-9(9)) Cavendish, Marshall Corp.
Mustian, James Marshall, Sr., compiled by. Scarecrow's Clean Jokes & Humorous Stories. 1999. 40p. (gr. 10 up). pap. 4.95 (978-1-929181-05-6(1)) White Oaks Creations.
Myers, Bill. The Case of the Hiccupping Ears, Vol. 5. 2004. (Secret Agent Dingledorf Ser.: Vol. 5). (Illus.). 96p. (J). pap. 4.99 (978-1-4003-0178-2(5)) Nelson, Thomas Inc.
—My Life as a Belching Baboon with Bad Breath. 2006. (Incredible Worlds of Wally McDoogle Ser.). pap. 6.99 (978-1-4003-0907-8(7)) Nelson, Thomas Inc.
—My Life as a Computer Cockroach, Vol. 17. 1999. (Incredible Worlds of Wally McDoogle Ser.: No. 17). 128p. (J). (gr. 3-7). pap. 6.99 (978-0-8499-4026-2(5)) Nelson, Thomas Inc.
—My Life as a Cowboy Cowpie, Vol. 19. 2001. (Incredible Worlds of Wally McDoogle Ser.: No. 19). 128p. (J). (gr. 3-7). pap. 6.99 (978-0-8499-5990-5(X)) Nelson, Thomas Inc.
—My Life As a Haunted Hamburger, Hold the Pickles. 2006. (Incredible Worlds of Wally McDoogle Ser.: No. 27). 128p. (J). pap. 6.99 (978-1-4003-0636-7(1)) Nelson, Thomas Inc.
—My Life As A Smashed Burrito. Mangiat, Jeff, illus. 2005. (Incredible Worlds of Wally McDoogle Ser.: Vol. 1). 128p. (J). 9.99 (978-1-4003-0571-1(3)) Nelson, Thomas Inc.
—My Life as a Splatted Flat Quarterback. 2006. (Incredible Worlds of Wally McDoogle Ser.). pap. 6.99 (978-1-4003-0906-1(9)) Nelson, Thomas Inc.
—My Life As a Stupendously Stomped Soccer Star. 2006. (Incredible Worlds of Wally McDoogle Ser.). 128p. (J). pap. 6.99 (978-1-4003-0635-0(3)) Nelson, Thomas Inc.
—My Life As a Tarantula Toe Tickler, Vol. 22. 2003. (Incredible Worlds of Wally McDoogle Ser.: Vol. 22). (Illus.). 128p. (J). pap. 6.99 (978-0-8499-5993-6(4)) Nelson, Thomas Inc.
—My Life as Crocodile Junk Food. Mangiat, Jeff, illus. 2005. (Incredible Worlds of Wally McDoogle Ser.). 128p. (J). 9.99 (978-1-4003-0613-8(2)) Nelson, Thomas Inc.
—My Life As Invisible Intestines (with Intense Indigestion), Vol. 20. 2001. (Incredible Worlds of Wally McDoogle Ser.). 128p. (J). (gr. 3-7). pap. 6.99 (978-0-8499-5991-2(8)) Nelson, Thomas Inc.
—Sky Surfing Skateboarder, Vol. 21. 2002. (Incredible Worlds of Wally McDoogle Ser.). (Illus.). 128p. (J). (gr. 3-7). pap. 6.99 (978-0-8499-5992-9(6)) Nelson, Thomas Inc.
Napoli, Donna Jo & Johnston, Shelagh. Hotel Jungle. Spengler, Kenneth, tr. Spengler, Kenneth, illus. 2004. 33p. (J). 15.95 (978-1-59336-002-3(9)); pap. (978-1-59336-003-0(7)) Mondo Publishing.
Nash, Mary. Lost Treasures Bk. 2: Mrs. Coverlet's Magician. 2001. 128p. (J). 13.49 (978-0-7868-2597-4(9)) Hyperion Pr.
—While Mrs Coverlet Was Away. 2002. (gr. 3-6). lib. bdg. 13.00 (978-0-613-75030-1(6)) Tandem Library Bks.
Nash, Naomi. Chloe, Queen of Denial. 2004. (YA). mass mkt. 5.99 (978-0-8439-5377-0(2)) Dorchester Publishing Co., Inc.
Natti, Susanna, illus. Lionel at Large. 2002. (J). 11.49 (978-0-7587-1389-6(4)) Book Wholesalers, Inc.
—Lionel at School. 2002. (Lionel Ser.). 11.49 (978-1-4046-0491-9(X)) Book Wholesalers, Inc.
—Lionel in the Fall. 2002. (Lionel Ser.). (J). 11.49 (978-0-7587-1390-2(8)) Book Wholesalers, Inc.
—Lionel in the Summer. 2002. (Lionel Ser.). (J). 11.49 (978-0-7587-4120-2(0)) Book Wholesalers, Inc.
—Lionel in the Winter. 2002. (Lionel Ser.). (J). 11.49 (978-0-7587-1393-3(2)) Book Wholesalers, Inc.
Naylor, Phyllis Reynolds. I Can't Take You Anywhere! 2001. (J). 12.79 (978-0-606-20714-0(7)); lib. bdg. 14.15 (978-0-613-34773-0(0)) Tandem Library Bks.
—Peril in the Bessledorf Parachute Factory. Bernardin, James, illus. 2000. 160p. (J). (gr. 3-7). 16.95 (978-0-689-82539-2(0) , Atheneum) Simon & Schuster Children's Publishing.
Neilon. The Day My Brain Ran Away. 2002. 7.95 (978-0-9721080-0-3(9)) Pat & Sunny Pr.
Neira, Maria. Mama Oca y el Pastel. 2002. (Caballo Alado Ser.). (SPA & ENG., Illus.). 24p. 5.95 (978-84-7864-403-2(2)) Combel Editorial, S.A. ESP. *Dist:* Independent Pubs. Group.
—Mama Oca y las Vocales. 2002. (Caballo Alado Ser.). (SPA & ENG., Illus.). 24p. 5.95 (978-84-7864-402-5(4)) Combel Editorial, S.A. ESP. *Dist:* Independent Pubs. Group.
, New Players Club LLC, New Players Club L. L. C. Coco Boom Boom. 2006. 32p. 12.99 (978-1-4116-8191-0(6)) Lulu.com.
Newhouse, Mark H. Dragons in the Neighborhood. Blair, June H., illus. 2001. 32p. (J). (ps-6). 14.95 (978-0-9704629-1-6(3)); pap. 8.95 (978-0-9704629-2-3(1)) Earthkids Publishing.
Newman, Marlene. Myron's Magic Cow. Jago, illus. 2005. 40p. (J). (ps-3). 16.99 (978-1-84148-496-9(2)) Barefoot Bks., Inc.
Newton, Jill. Gordon in Charge. Newton, Jill, illus. 2003. (Illus.). 32p. (J). 15.95 (978-1-58234-823-0(5) , Bloomsbury Children) Bloomsbury Publishing.
Newton, Jill & Roddie, Shen. Don't Chat to the Bus Driver. 2001. (Illus.). 32p. (J). (ps-k). pap. 10.95 (978-0-7475-5028-0(X)) Bloomsbury Publishing Plc GBR. *Dist:* Independent Pubs. Group.
Nick Jr. Ready-to-Read Boxed Set: Learn to Read with Dora & Friends! 2004. (Ready-to-Reads Ser.). (Illus.). 24p. (J). pap. 9.99 (978-0-689-87051-4(5) , Simon Spotlight/Nickelodeon) Simon & Schuster Children's Publishing.
Nick Ready-to-Read Boxed Set: Learn to Read with SpongeBob & Friends! 2004. (Ready-to-Reads Ser.). (Illus.). 32p. (J). pap. 9.99 (978-0-689-87053-8(1) , Simon Spotlight/Nickelodeon) Simon & Schuster Children's Publishing.
Nickel, Scott. Curse of the Red Scorpion. Harpster, Steve, illus. 2006. (Graphic Sparks Ser.). 33p. (J). 19.93 (978-1-59889-034-1(4)) Stone Arch Bks.
—Night of the Homework Zombies. Harpster, Steve, illus. 2006. (Graphic Sparks Ser.). 33p. (J). 19.93 (978-1-59889-035-8(2)) Stone Arch Bks.
Nishimura, Kae. Dinah! 2004. 32p. 14.00 (978-0-618-33613-5(3) , Clarion Bks.) Houghton Mifflin Co. Trade & Reference Div.
—Dinah! A Cat Adventure. 2004. (Illus.). 32p. (J). (gr. k-3). 14.00 (978-0-618-33612-8(5) , Clarion Bks.) Houghton Mifflin Co. Trade & Reference Div.
Nobisso, Josephine. En Ingles, por Supuesto. Ziborova, Dasha, illus. 2003. Orig. Title: In English, of Course. (SPA.). 32p. 16.95 (978-0-940112-14-8(0)) Gingerbread Hse.
—En ingles, por Supuesto. Ziborova, Dasha, illus. 2003. Orig. Title: In English, of Course. (SPA.). 32p. pap. 8.95 (978-0-940112-16-2(7)) Gingerbread Hse.
—In English, of Course. Ziborova, Dasha, illus. 2003. Tr. of En Ingles, Por Supuesto. 32p. (J). (SPA.). 16.95 (978-0-940112-07-0(8)); pap. 8.95 (978-0-940112-08-7(6)) Gingerbread Hse.
Nodelman, Perry. Behaving Bradley. 2000. (Illus.). (J). (978-0-606-17911-9(9)) Tandem Library Bks.
—Behaving Bradley. l.t. ed. 2002. 272p. (J). 22.95 (978-0-7862-4779-0(7)) Thorndike Pr.
Nolan, Lucy A. Down Girl & Sit: Smarter Than Squirrels. Reed, Mike, illus. 2004. 64p. (J). 14.95 (978-0-7614-5184-6(6)) Cavendish, Marshall Corp.
—A Fairy in a Dairy. Bryant, Laura J., illus. 2003. 32p. (J). 16.95 (978-0-7614-5130-3(7)) Cavendish, Marshall Corp.
—On the Road. Reed, Mike, illus. 2005. 54p. (J). (gr. 1-4). per. 14.95 (978-0-7614-5234-8(6)) Cavendish, Marshall Corp.
Nolen, Jerdine. Plantzilla. Catrow, David, illus. 2002. 32p. (J). (gr. k-3). 16.00 (978-0-15-202412-3(3) , Silver Whistle) Harcourt Trade Pubs.
—Plantzilla Goes to Camp. Catrow, David, illus. 2006. 32p. (J). (gr. k-3). 16.95 (978-0-689-86803-0(0)) Simon & Schuster Children's Publishing.
Nolen, Jerdine & Keliher, Brian. Plantzilla. Catrow, David, illus. 2005. 32p. (J). (ps-ps). reprint ed. pap., pap. 7.00 (978-0-15-205392-5(1) , Voyager Bks./Libros Viajeros) Harcourt Children's Bks.
Noonen, Tom. Pelicans Belly Can. Fredericksen, Alison, illus. 1999. 38p. (J). (ps-3). 14.95 (978-1-893385-04-7(3)) Little Leaf Pr., Inc.
Norman, Kimberly E. Jack of All Tails. Clark, David H., illus. 2007. 32p. (J). 15.99 (978-0-525-47793-8(4) , Dutton Juvenile) Penguin Group (USA) Inc.
Numeroff, Laura Joffe. Dogs Don't Wear Sneakers. Mathieu, Joe, illus. 2005. (Stories to Go! Ser.). 40p. (J). pap. 4.99 (978-0-689-87828-2(1) , Aladdin) Simon & Schuster Children's Publishing.
—If You Take a Mouse to the Movies. Bond, Felicia, illus. 2000. (Laura Geringer Bks.). (J). (ps-2). 9.95 (978-0-694-01531-3(8) , Harper Festival); 40p. lib. bdg. 16.89 (978-0-06-027868-7(4) , Geringer, Laura Book) HarperCollins Pubs.
—If You Take a Mouse to the Movies: Book & Doll. Bond, Felicia, illus. 2001. (J). (ps-2). 19.95 (978-0-694-01427-9(3)) HarperCollins Pubs.
—Laura Numeroff's 10-Step Guide to Living with Your Monster. Evans, Nate, illus. 2002. 32p. (J). (ps-2). 16.99 (978-0-06-623822-7(6) , Geringer, Laura Book) HarperCollins Pubs.
Numeroff, Laura Joffe. A Mouse Cookie First Library. Bond, Felicia, illus. 2007. (If You Give... Ser.). (J). 15.99 (*978-0-06-117479-7(3) , Harper Festival) HarperCollins Pubs.
Numeroff, Laura Joffe & Bond, Felicia. If You Give a Mouse a Cookie. l.t. ed. (FRE.). (J). bds. 29.99 (978-0-590-71930-8(0)) Scholastic, Inc.
Nunez, Alonso. El Invencible y Malvado Dragon Curiambro. (SPA.). (J). (gr. 2-4). 18.95 (978-968-494-096-3(3) , CI30452) Centro de Informacion y Desarrollo de la Comunicacion y la Literatura MEX. *Dist:* AIMS International Bks., Inc., Continental Bk. Co., Inc., Lectorum Pubns., Inc.
Nuttbucket, Oliver S., III. A Boy Scout's Handbook of Madcap Tales. Glover, Robert, illus. 2003. 48p. (YA). per. 7.95 (978-0-9741310-0-9(8) , 0-9741310-0-8) Lost Scout Pr.
Nybo, B. J. Elmo Jackson Great Yellow Ball. 2005. (978-0-9742322-0-1(3)) New Art & Vision, LLC.
O'Brien, John. Poof! 2005. (Illus.). 32p. (J). (ps-ps). reprint ed. pap. 8.95 (978-1-59078-374-0(3)) Boyds Mills Pr.
O'Brien, Tim. Tomcat in Love. 1999. (gr. 7-12). lib. bdg. 22.25 (978-0-613-62863-1(2)) Tandem Library Bks.
Ocampo, Silvina. La Naranja Maravillosa. 1998. Tr. of Marvelous Orange. (SPA.). 160p. (J). (gr. 4-7). 9.95 (978-84-204-3676-0(3)) Santillana USA Publishing Co., Inc.
O'Connell, Tyne. Dueling Princes: The Calypso Chronicles, Book 3. 2006. 272p. (YA). pap. 7.95 (978-1-58234-900-8(2) , Bloomsbury Children) Bloomsbury Publishing.
—Dumping Princes. (YA). 2007. 256p. pap. 7.95 (*978-1-59990-150-3(1) , Bloomsbury Children); 2006. (Calypso Chronicles Ser.: Bk. 4). (Illus.). 304p. (gr. 7-10). 16.95 (978-1-58234-852-0(9)) Bloomsbury Publishing.
—Pulling Princes. 2004. (Illus.). 208p. (J). 16.95 (978-1-58234-957-2(6) , Bloomsbury Children) Bloomsbury Publishing.
—Stealing Princes. 2006. (Calypso Chronicles Ser.: Bk. 2). 304p. (YA). reprint ed. pap. 7.95 (978-1-58234-905-3(3) , Bloomsbury Children) Bloomsbury Publishing.
O'Connor, Jane. Fancy Nancy & the Boy from Paris. Glasser, Robin Preiss & Enik, Ted, illus. 2008. (I Can Read Bks.). 32p. (J). 16.99 (*978-0-06-123610-5(1)) HarperCollins Pubs.
—Fancy Nancy & the Boy from Paris. Glasser, Robin Preiss, illus. 2008. (I Can Read Bks.). 32p. (J). pap. 3.99 (*978-0-06-123609-9(8) , Harper Trophy) HarperCollins Pubs.
O'Connor, Teddy. A New Brain for Igor. 2001. (Step into Reading Ser.). (Illus.). (J). (978-0-606-21347-9(3)) Tandem Library Bks.
O'Donnell, Barbara. Mrs Mumble, Bumble, Grumble. 2003. (Illus.). (J). pap. 5.98 (978-0-89914-503-7(5) , 503-5) 3rd Party Publishing Co.
Ogden, Charles. Mischief Manual. Carton, Rick, illus. 2007. (Edgar & Ellen Ser.). 112p. (J). pap. 7.99 (978-1-4169-3935-1(0) , Aladdin) Simon & Schuster Children's Publishing.
—Nod's Limbs. Carton, Rick, illus. 2007. (Edgar & Ellen Ser.). (J). 224p. 9.99 (978-1-4169-1501-0(X)); 210p. (*978-1-4287-3214-8(4)) Simon & Schuster Children's Publishing. (Aladdin).
—Pet's Revenge. Carton, Rick, illus. 2006. (Edgar & Ellen Ser.). 192p. (J). (gr. 3-7). 9.95 (978-1-4169-1408-2(0) , Aladdin) Simon & Schuster Children's Publishing.
—Rare Beasts. Carton, Rick, illus. ed. 2005. (Edgar & Ellen Ser.). 144p. (J). 9.95 (978-1-4169-1409-9(9) , Aladdin) Simon & Schuster Children's Publishing.
—Tourist Trap. Carton, Rick, illus. ed. 2005. (Edgar & Ellen Ser.). 176p. (J). 9.95 (978-1-4169-1411-2(0) , Aladdin) Simon & Schuster Children's Publishing.
—Triple Threat Vols. 1-3, Set: Their First Three Misadventures: Rare Beasts, Tourist Trap, under Town. Carton, Rick, illus. 2007. (Edgar & Ellen Ser.). 464p. (J). 29.99 (978-1-4169-3462-2(6) , Aladdin) Simon & Schuster Children's Publishing.
—Under Town. Carton, Rick, illus. ed. 2006. (Edgar & Ellen Ser.). 160p. (J). 9.95 (978-1-4169-1412-9(9) , Aladdin) Simon & Schuster Children's Publishing.
Ogilvy, Ian. Measle & the Dragodon. 2006. 352p. (J). pap. 6.99 (978-0-06-058690-4(7) , Harper Trophy) HarperCollins Pubs.
—Measle & the Wrathmonk. 2005. 224p. (J). reprint ed. pap. 5.99 (978-0-06-058687-4(7) , Harper Trophy) HarperCollins Pubs.
O'Hely, Eileen. Penny the Pencil. 2005. (Illus.). 197p. (J). pap. 15.95 (978-1-85635-475-2(X)) Mercier Pr., Ltd., The IRL. *Dist:* Irish Bks. & Media, Inc.
Ohi, Ruth. Me & My Sister. Ohi, Ruth, illus. 2005. (Illus.). 24p. (J). (gr. k-ps). pap. 5.95 (978-1-55037-892-4(9)); lib. bdg. 19.95 (978-1-55037-893-1(7)) Annick Pr., Ltd. CAN. *Dist:* Firefly Bks., Ltd.
Oirich, Alan. The Amnesia Countdown. Randall, Ron, illus. 2003. (Jewish Hero Corps. Ser.: 1). 24p. (J). pap. 3.95 (978-1-932443-06-6(1) , JHC1, Shayach Comics) Judaica Pr., Inc., The.
O'Keefe, Susan. Death by Eggplant. rev. ed. 2004. 144p. (J). 15.95 (978-1-59643-011-2(7)) Roaring Brook Pr.
Oldfield, Jenny. Don't Make Me Laugh, Liam. Layton, Neal, illus. 128p. (J). pap. 8.95 (978-0-340-85107-4(4)) Macmillan Publishers Ltd. GBR. *Dist:* Trafalgar Square Publishing.
Oliver, Lin. Attack of the Growling Eyeballs. 2008. (Who Shrunk Daniel Funk? Ser.). 112p. (J). 14.99 (*978-1-4169-0951-4(6) , Simon & Schuster Children's Publishing) Simon & Schuster Children's Publishing.
Olker, Constance. The Punctuation Pals Go Snow Skiing. 2005. (Illus.). (J). 44p. per. 18.95 (978-1-933449-14-2(4)); per. 17.95 (978-0-9761289-7-7(7)) Nightengale Pr.
Olsen, Mary-Kate & Olsen, Ashley. Two of a Kind No. 33: Heart to Heart. 2004. (gr. 3-6). lib. bdg. 13.00 (978-0-613-71364-1(8)) Tandem Library Bks.
Olson, David. Lazy Daisy. 2000. (Illus.). 32p. (ps-2). 9.95 (978-1-59093-052-6(5)) Warehousing & Fulfillment Specialists, LLC (WFS, LLC).
Olson, David. The Thunderstruck Stork. Munsinger, Lynn, illus. 2007. (J). (ps-2). 15.95 (*978-0-8075-7910-7(6)) Whitman, Albert & Co.
Olsson, Soren & Jacobsson, Anders. In Ned's Head. Read, Kevin, tr. 2004. 144p. (J). reprint ed. pap. 4.99 (978-0-689-87355-3(7) , Aladdin) Simon & Schuster Children's Publishing.
Olten, Manuela. Boys Are Best! 2007. (Illus.). 32p. (J). (ps-1). 14.95 (*978-1-905417-48-3(9)) Boxer Bks., Ltd. GBR. *Dist:* Sterling Publishing Co., Inc.
O'Malley, Kevin. Gimme Cracked Corn & I Will Share. O'Malley, Kevin, illus. 2007. (Illus.). 32p. (J). (gr. k-3). 17.85 (*978-0-8027-9685-1(0)); 16.95 (*978-0-8027-9684-4(2)) Walker & Co.
—Herbert Fieldmouse, Secret Agent. 2003. (Illus.). 32p. (J). pap. (978-1-59336-043-6(6)); (gr. 1-6). 15.95 (978-1-59336-042-9(8)) Mondo Publishing.
—Mount Olympus Basketball. O'Malley, Kevin, illus. (Illus.). 32p. (J). 2005. (gr. 1-4). pap., pap. 6.95 (978-0-8027-7728-7(7)); 2004. (gr. 2-6). 15.95 (978-0-8027-8844-3(0)) Walker & Co.
—Mount Olympus Basketball. 2004. (Illus.). 32p. (J). (gr. 2-6). 16.85 (978-0-8027-8845-0(9)) Walker & Co.
—Once upon a Cool Motorcycle Dude. O'Malley, Kevin et al, illus. 2005. 32p. (J). 16.95 (978-0-8027-8947-1(1)) Walker & Co.
O'Neil, Dave. Lies Your Parents Tell You. Morris, Kiran, illus. 2005. 160p. pap. (978-0-7344-0292-9(9) , Lothian Bks.) Hachette Livre Australia.
Oni Wa Soto, 6 vols. (Multicultural Programs Ser.). 16p. (gr. 1-6). 42.50 (978-0-7802-1478-1(1)) Wright Group, The.
Oram, Hiawyn & Ross, Tony. Boris: The Beetle Who Wouldn't Stay Down. 2000. (Illus.). 32p. (J). 17.99 (978-0-86264-977-7(3)) Andersen GBR. *Dist:* Independent Pubs. Group.
Orr, Wendy. Mokie & Bik. Bean, Jonathan, illus. 2007. 80p. (J). (gr. 2-5). 15.95 (978-0-8050-7979-1(3)) Holt, Henry & Co.
Osterweil, Adam. The Amulet of Komondor. Thorpe, Peter, illus. 2004. 112p. (J). (gr. 3-7). 15.95 (978-1-886910-81-2(2) , Lemniscaat) Boyds Mills Pr.
Ostow, Micol. Gettin' Lucky. 2007. (Romantic Comedies Ser.). 256p. (YA). (gr. 6-9). mass mkt. 5.99 (978-1-4169-3536-0(3) , Simon Pulse) Simon & Schuster Children's Publishing.
—30 Guys in 30 Days. 2005. (Romantic Comedies Ser.). 304p. (YA). pap. 6.99 (978-1-4169-0278-2(3) , Simon Pulse) Simon & Schuster Children's Publishing.
Ostrow, Kim. Ask Me Anything! Piluso, Piero, illus. 2004. (Fairly OddParents Ser.). 12p. (J). bds. 12.95 (978-0-689-86719-4(0) , Simon Spotlight/Nickelodeon) Simon & Schuster Children's Publishing.
Ostrow, Kim. Great Snail Race. 2007. 24p. (J). 21.35 (*978-1-59961-364-2(6)) Spotlight.
Owens, Greg. Rupert the Wrong-Word Pirate. Beaky, Suzanne, illus. 2006. (J). (978-1-58987-143-4(X)) Kindermusik International.
Oxenbury, Helen, illus. We're Going on a Bear Hunt. 2004. 33p. (J). (TAM, CZE, VIE, GUJ & PER.). (978-1-85269-707-5(5)); (TAM, CZE, VIE, GUJ & PER.). (978-1-85269-708-2(3)); (TAM, CZE, VIE, GUJ & PER.). (978-1-85269-709-9(1)); (TAM, CZE, VIE, GUJ & PER.). (978-1-85269-713-6(X)); (TAM, CZE, VIE, GUJ & PER.). (978-1-85269-714-3(8)); (CZE, TAM, VIE, GUJ & PER.). (978-1-85269-719-8(9)); (TAM, CZE, VIE, GUJ & PER.). (978-1-85269-721-1(0)) Mantra Publishing, Ltd.
Packard, Mary & Mitier, Matt. Same & Different: Comparison Rhymes. Banta, Susan & Cushman, Doug, illus. 2004. (Rhyme Time Learning Ser.). 16p. (J). (gr. 1 up). lib. bdg. 20.67 (978-0-8368-4097-1(6)) Stevens, Gareth Inc.
Packard, Mary & Mitter, Matt. Once upon a Rhyme: Story Rhymes. Banta, Susan & Cushman, Doug, illus. 2004. (Rhyme Time Learning Ser.). 16p. (J). (gr. 1 up). lib. bdg. 20.67 (978-0-8368-4096-4(8)) Stevens, Gareth Inc.
Palatini, Margie. Bedhead. Davis, Jack E., illus. 2nd ed. 2005. (Stories to Go! Ser.). (J). (*978-1-4156-2894-2(7) , Aladdin) Simon & Schuster Children's Publishing.
—The Cheese. Johnson, Steve & Fancher, Lou, illus. 2007. 32p. (J). (ps-3). 16.99 (978-0-06-052630-6(0)) HarperCollins Pubs.
—Earthquack! Moser, Barry, illus. 2005. 32p. (J). (ps-ps). pap., pap. 6.99 (978-1-4169-0260-7(0) , Aladdin) Simon & Schuster Children's Publishing.
—Moosestache. 32p. pap. (978-0-7868-1497-8(7)) Hyperion Bks. for Children.
—Oink? Cole, Henry, illus. 2006. 40p. (J). (ps-3). 15.95 (978-0-689-86258-8(X)) Simon & Schuster Children's Publishing.

HI

—Stinky Smelly Feet: A Love Story. Long, Ethan, illus. 2004. 32p. (J). (ps). 15.99 (978-0-525-47201-8(0) , Dutton Juvenile) Penguin Group (USA) Inc.

—The Three Silly Billies. Moser, Barry, illus. 2005. 32p. (J). (ps-3). 16.99 (978-0-689-85862-8(0) , Simon & Schuster Children's Publishing) Simon & Schuster Children's Publishing.

—The Web Files. Egielski, Richard, illus. 2001. 32p. 15.99 (978-0-7868-0419-1(X) , Volo) Hyperion Bks. for Children.

Palatini, Margie, ed. The Cheese. Johnson, Steve & Fancher, Lou, illus. 2007. 32p. (J). (ps-3). lib. bdg. 17.89 (978-0-06-052631-3(9)) HarperCollins Pubs.

Palatini, Margie & Davis, Jack E. Sweet Tooth. 2004. (Illus.). 40p. (J). 16.95 (978-0-689-85159-9(6)) Simon & Schuster Children's Publishing.

Palatini, Margie & Moser, Barry. Earthquack! 2002. (Illus.). 32p. (J). (ps-3). 15.95 (978-0-689-84280-1(5)) Simon & Schuster Children's Publishing.

Papademitriou, Lisa. Sixth-Grade Glommers, Norks, & Me. 2006. 224p. (gr. 5-7). pap. 5.99 (978-0-7868-5170-6(8)) Hyperion Pr.

Parent, Nancy. Orange You Glad? 2000. (Captain Kangaroo Ser.). 32p. (J). (gr. k-1). pap. 3.99 (978-0-06-107157-7(9) , Harper Entertainment) HarperCollins Pubs.

Parish, Herman. Amelia Bedelia 4 Mayor. Sweat, Lynn, illus. (I Can Read Bks.). (J). 2001. 64p. (gr. k-2). pap. 3.99 (978-0-06-444309-8(4) , Harper Trophy); 1999. 48p. (gr. 1 up). 15.99 (978-0-688-16721-9(7)) HarperCollins Pubs.

—Amelia Bedelia & the Cat. Sweat, Lynn, illus. 2008. 48p. (J). 16.99 (*978-0-06-084349-6(7)); lib. bdg. 17.89 (*978-0-06-084350-2(0)) HarperCollins Pubs. (Greenwillow Bks.).

—Amelia Bedelia, Bookworm. Sweat, Lynn, illus. 2005. 64p. (J). lib. bdg. 13.85 (*978-1-4242-0518-9(2)) Fitzgerald Bks.

—Amelia Bedelia, Bookworm. Sweat, Lynn, illus. 2003. 64p. (J). (gr. k-3). 16.99 (978-0-06-051890-5(1)); lib. bdg. 16.89 (978-0-06-051891-2(X)) HarperCollins Pubs.

—Amelia Bedelia Bookworm. Sweat, Lynn, illus. 2005. (I Can Read Bks.). 64p. (J). pap. 3.99 (978-0-06-051892-9(8) , Harper Trophy) HarperCollins Pubs.

—Amelia Bedelia, Rocket Scientist? Sweat, Lynn, illus. (I Can Read Bks.). 64p. (J). 2007. pap. 3.99 (978-0-06-051889-9(8) , Harper Trophy); 2005. (gr. 1 up). 15.99 (978-0-06-051887-5(1)); 2005. (gr. 1 up). lib. bdg. 16.89 (978-0-06-051888-2(X)) HarperCollins Pubs.

—Amelia Bedelia under Construction. Sweat, Lynn, illus. (I Can Read Bks.). 64p. (J). 2007. pap. 3.99 (*978-0-06-084346-5(2) , Harper Trophy); 2006. 15.99 (978-0-06-084344-1(6)); 2006. lib. bdg. 16.89 (978-0-06-084345-8(4)) HarperCollins Pubs.

—Amelia Bedelia's First Day of School. 2007. 32p. (J). pap. 6.99 (*978-0-06-154457-6(4) , Harper Trophy) HarperCollins Pubs.

—Amelia Bedelia's Masterpiece. Sweat, Lynn, illus. 2007. 64p. (J). 15.99 (978-0-06-084355-7(1)); lib. bdg. 16.89 (978-0-06-084356-4(X)) HarperCollins Pubs.

—Be My Valentine, Amelia Bedelia. Sweat, Lynn, illus. 2004. 20p. (J). (gr. 1 up). pap. 6.99 (978-0-06-051886-8(3) , Harper Festival) HarperCollins Pubs.

—Bravo, Amelia Bedelia. Sweat, Lynn, illus. 1999. (Amelia Bedelia Ser.). 48p. (J). (gr. k-2). pap. 3.95 (978-0-380-73215-9(7)) HarperCollins Pubs.

—Bravo, Amelia Bedelia. 1999. (Amelia Bedelia Ser.). (J). (gr. k-2). (978-0-606-15929-6(0)) Tandem Library Bks.

—Calling Doctor Amelia Bedelia. Sweat, Lynn, illus. (I Can Read Bks.). 64p. (J). 2004. (gr. k-3). pap. 3.99 (978-0-06-008780-7(3) , Harper Trophy); 2002. (gr. 1-2). 15.99 (978-0-06-001421-6(0)); 2002. (gr. 1-2). lib. bdg. 17.89 (978-0-06-001422-3(9)) HarperCollins Pubs.

—Happy Haunting, Amelia Bedelia. Sweat, Lynn, illus. (I Can Read Bks.). 64p. (J). 2006. pap. 3.99 (978-0-06-051895-0(2) , Harper Trophy); 2004. 15.99 (978-0-06-051893-6(6)); 2004. lib. bdg. 16.89 (978-0-06-051894-3(4)) HarperCollins Pubs.

Parish, Peggy. Amelia Bedelia. Siebel, Fritz, illus. 1999. (I Can Read Bks.). 64p. (J). (ps-3). 16.99 (978-0-694-01296-1(3) , Harper Festival) HarperCollins Pubs.

—Amelia Bedelia. Thomas, Barbara Siebel & Siebel, Fritz, illus. 2000. (Coleccion Ya Se Leer). (SPA.). (J). (gr. 1-3). 15.95 (978-1-880507-76-6(5) , LC0355); pap. 6.99 (978-1-880507-75-9(7) , LC0360) Lectorum Pubns., Inc.

—Amelia Bedelia. Siebel, Fritz, illus. 1999. (J). (gr. 1-3). 9.95 (978-1-56137-023-8(1)) Novel Units, Inc.

—Amelia Bedelia. 2001. (SPA., Illus.). (J). 13.75 (978-0-606-21546-6(8)) Tandem Library Bks.

—Amelia Bedelia. Siebel, Fritz, illus. 1999. (I Can Read Bks.). (J). (gr. 1-3). 11.50 (978-0-88103-916-0(0)) Tandem Library Bks.

—Amelia Bedelia 4 Mayor. 1999. (gr. k-3). lib. bdg. 11.80 (978-0-613-68400-2(1)) Tandem Library Bks.

—Amelia Bedelia & the Baby. Sweat, Lynn, illus. 2004. (I Can Read Bks.). 64p. (J). (gr. k-3). pap. 3.99 (978-0-06-051105-0(2) , Harper Trophy) HarperCollins Pubs.

—Amelia Bedelia Goes Camping. Sweat, Lynn, illus. 2003. (I Can Read Bks.). 64p. (J). (ps-ps). pap. 3.99 (978-0-06-051106-7(0) , Harper Trophy) HarperCollins Pubs.

—Amelia Bedelia Goes Camping. 2003. (gr. k-3). lib. bdg. 11.80 (978-0-613-62664-4(8)) Tandem Library Bks.

—Amelia Bedelia Helps Out. Sweat, Lynn, illus. 2005. 64p. (J). (ps-ps). lib. bdg. 11.19 (978-0-606-33266-8(9)) Tandem Library Bks.

—Amelia Bedelia's Family Album. Sweat, Lynn, illus. 2003. (I Can Read Bks.). 48p. (J). (gr. k-3). pap. 3.99 (978-0-06-051116-6(8) , Harper Trophy) HarperCollins Pubs.

—Amelia Bedelia's Family Album. 2003. (gr. k-3). lib. bdg. 11.80 (978-0-613-62129-8(8)) Tandem Library Bks.

—Thank You, Amelia Bedelia. 1999. (I Can Read Bks.). (J). (gr. 1-3). 11.55 (978-0-88103-910-8(1)) Tandem Library Bks.

Park, Barbara. Junie B. , First Grader (at Last!) unabr. ed. 2004. (Junie B. Jones Ser.: No. 18). 70p. (J). (gr. k-3). pap. 17.00 incl. audio (978-0-8072-1020-8(X) , S FTR 258 SP, Listening Library) Random Hse. Audio Publishing Group.

—Junie B. , First Grader (at Last!) 2001. (Junie B. Jones Ser.: No. 18). (J). (gr. k-3). lib. bdg. 11.80 (978-0-613-57510-2(5)) Tandem Library Bks.

—Junie B., First Grader: Aloha-Ha-Ha! 2006. (Junie B. Jones Ser.: No. 26). (Illus.). 128p. (J). (gr. k-3). lib. bdg. 13.95 (978-0-375-93403-2(0)); (gr. 2-5). 11.95 (978-0-375-83403-5(6)) Random Hse. Children's Bks. (Random Hse. Bks. for Young Readers).

—Junie B., First Grader: Boo... & I Mean It! Brunkus, Denise, illus. 2004. (Junie B. Jones Ser.: No. 24). 96p. (J). (gr. k-3). 11.95 (978-0-375-82806-5(0)); lib. bdg. 13.99 (978-0-375-92806-2(5)) Random Hse. Children's Bks. (Random Hse. Bks. for Young Readers).

—Junie B., First Grader: Boss of Lunch. unabr. ed. 2004. (Junie B. Jones Ser.: No. 19). 70p. (J). (gr. k-3). pap. 17.00 incl. audio (978-0-8072-1021-5(8) , S FTR 259 SP, Listening Library) Random Hse. Audio Publishing Group.

—Junie B., First Grader: Boss of Lunch. 2002. (Junie B. Jones Ser.: No. 19). (J). (gr. k-3). lib. bdg. 11.80 (978-0-613-63168-6(4)) Tandem Library Bks.

—Junie B., First Grader: Cheater Pants. Brunkus, Denise, tr. Brunkus, Denise, illus. 2004. (Junie B. Jones Ser.: No. 21). 96p. (J). (gr. 1-4). pap. 3.99 (978-0-375-82302-2(6) , Random Hse. Bks. for Young Readers) Random Hse. Children's Bks.

—Junie B., First Grader: Cheater Pants. Brunkus, Denise, illus. 2003. (Junie B. Jones Ser.: No. 21). 96p. (J). (gr. k-3). lib. bdg. 13.99 (978-0-375-92301-2(2)); (gr. 1-4). 11.95 (978-0-375-82301-5(8)) Random Hse. Children's Bks. (Random Hse. Bks. for Young Readers).

—Junie B., First Grader: One-Man Band. Brunkus, Denise, tr. Brunkus, Denise, illus. 2004. (Junie B. Jones Ser.: No. 22). 96p. (J). (gr. k-3). pap. 3.99 (978-0-375-82536-1(3) , Random Hse. Bks. for Young Readers) Random Hse. Children's Bks.

—Junie B., First Grader: One-Man Band. Brunkus, Denise, illus. 2003. (Junie B. Jones Ser.: No. 22). 96p. (J). (gr. k-3). 11.95 (978-0-375-82522-4(3)); (gr. 1-4). lib. bdg. 13.99 (978-0-375-92522-1(8)) Random Hse. Children's Bks. (Random Hse. Bks. for Young Readers).

—Junie B. Jones & a Little Monkey Business, Vol. 2. unabr. ed. 2004. (Junie B. Jones Ser.: Vol. 2). 68p. (J). (gr. k-3). pap. 17.00 incl. audio (978-0-8072-0779-6(9) , LFTR 238 SP, Listening Library) Random Hse. Audio Publishing Group.

—Junie B. Jones & Her Big Fat Mouth. unabr. ed. 2004. (Junie B. Jones Ser.: No. 3). 69p. (J). (gr. k-3). pap. 17.00 incl. audio (978-0-8072-0780-2(2) , LFTR 239 SP, Listening Library) Random Hse. Audio Publishing Group.

—Junie B. Jones & Some Sneaky Peeky Spying. unabr. ed. 2004. (Junie B. Jones Ser.: No. 4). 66p. (J). (gr. k-3). pap. 17.00 incl. audio (978-0-8072-0781-9(0) , LFTR 240 SP, Listening Library) Random Hse. Audio Publishing Group.

—Junie B. Jones & Some Sneaky Peeky Spying. Brunkus, Denise, illus. 2005. (Junie B. Jones Ser.: No. 4). (SPA.). 80p. (J). (gr. k-3). pap. 3.99 (978-0-439-42515-5(8) , Scholastic en Espanol) Scholastic, Inc.

—Junie B. Jones & the Mushy Gushy Valentime. unabr. ed. 2004. (Junie B. Jones Ser.: No. 14). 69p. (J). (gr. k-3). pap. 17.00 incl. audio (978-0-8072-0335-4(1) , Listening Library) Random Hse. Audio Publishing Group.

—Junie B. Jones & the Mushy Gushy Valentime. Brunkus, Denise, illus. 1999. (Junie B. Jones Ser.: No. 14). 80p. (J). (gr. k-3). pap. 3.99 (978-0-375-80039-5(5)); lib. bdg. 11.99 (978-0-375-90039-6(X)) Random Hse. Children's Bks. (Random Hse. Bks. for Young Readers).

—Junie B. Jones & the Mushy Gushy Valentime. Brunkus, Denise, illus. 1999. (Junie B. Jones Ser.: No. 14). 69p. (J). (gr. k-3). lib. bdg. 11.80 (978-0-613-21832-0(9)) Tandem Library Bks.

—Junie B. Jones & the Mushy Gushy Valentime. 1999. (Junie B. Jones Ser.: No. 14). (J). (gr. k-3). 10.79 (978-0-606-19516-4(5)) Tandem Library Bks.

—Junie B. Jones & the Stupid Smelly Bus. unabr. ed. 2004. (Junie B. Jones Ser.: Vol. 1). 69p. (J). (gr. k-3). pap. 17.00 incl. audio (978-0-8072-0778-9(0) , LFTR 237 SP, Listening Library) Random Hse. Audio Publishing Group.

—Junie B. Jones Collection, Bks. 17-20. abr. ed. 2002. (J). pap. 23.00 incl. audio (978-0-8072-0965-3(1) , Listening Library) Random Hse. Audio Publishing Group.

—Junie B. Jones Is a Beauty Shop Guy. Brunkus, Denise & Silverpin Studio Staff, illus. 1998. (Junie B. Jones Ser.: No. 11). 80p. (J). (gr. k-3). lib. bdg. 11.99 (978-0-679-98931-8(5) , Random Hse. Bks. for Young Readers) Random Hse. Children's Bks.

—Junie B. Jones Is a Beauty Shop Guy. Brunkus, Denise, illus. 1998. (Junie B. Jones Ser.: No. 11). 80p. (J). (gr. 1-4). pap. 3.99 (978-0-679-88931-1(0) , Random Hse. Bks. for Young Readers) Random Hse. Children's Bks.

—Junie B. Jones Is a Beauty Shop Guy. Brunkus, Denise, illus. 1998. (Junie B. Jones Ser.: No. 11). (J). (gr. k-3). 10.79 (978-0-606-13963-2(X)) Tandem Library Bks.

—Junie B. Jones Is a Graduation Girl. unabr. ed. 2004. (Junie B. Jones Ser.: No. 17). 69p. (J). (gr. k-3). pap. 17.00 incl. audio (978-0-8072-1019-2(6) , S FTR 257 SP, Listening Library) Random Hse. Audio Publishing Group.

—Junie B. Jones Is (Almost) a Flower Girl. Brunkus, Denise, illus. 1999. (Junie B. Jones Ser.: No. 13). 80p. (J). (gr. 1-4). lib. bdg. 11.99 (978-0-375-90038-9(1)); (gr. k-3). pap. 3.99 (978-0-375-80038-2(7)) Random Hse. Children's Bks. (Random Hse. Bks. for Young Readers).

—Junie B. Jones Is Captain Field Day. Brunkus, Denise, illus. 2001. (Junie B. Jones Ser.: No. 16). 80p. (J). (gr. k-3). pap. 3.99 (978-0-375-80291-1(6) , Random Hse. Bks. for Young Readers) Random Hse. Children's Bks.

—Junie B. Jones Is Captain Field Day. 2001. (Junie B. Jones Ser.: No. 16). (J). (gr. k-3). lib. bdg. 11.80 (978-0-613-33767-0(0)) Tandem Library Bks.

—Junie B. Jones Smells Something Fishy. Brunkus, Denise & Silverpin Studio Staff, illus. 1998. (Junie B. Jones Ser.: No. 12). 80p. (J). (gr. k-3). lib. bdg. 11.99 (978-0-679-99130-4(1) , Random Hse. Bks. for Young Readers) Random Hse. Children's Bks.

—Junie B. Jones Smells Something Fishy. Brunkus, Denise, illus. 1998. (Junie B. Jones Ser.: No. 12). 80p. (J). (gr. 1-4). pap. 3.99 (978-0-679-89130-7(7) , Random Hse. Bks. for Young Readers) Random Hse. Children's Bks.

—Junie B. Jones Tiene un Pio, Pio en el Bolsillo. 2006. (SPA., Illus.). 80p. (J). pap. 3.99 (978-0-439-66122-5(6) , Scholastic en Espanol) Scholastic, Inc.

—Junie B. Jones y el Cumpleanos del Malo de Jim. Brunkus, Denise, illus. 2005. (SPA.). 96p. (J). (ps-ps). pap. 3.99 (978-0-439-56028-3(4) , Scholastic en Espanol) Scholastic, Inc.

—Junie B. Jones's First Boxed Set Ever!, 4 bks., Set. Brunkus, Denise, illus. 2001. (Junie B. Jones Ser.). (J). (gr. 1-4). pap. 15.96 (978-0-375-81361-0(6) , Random Hse. Bks. for Young Readers) Random Hse. Children's Bks.

—Operation: Dump the Chump. 2001. (Illus.). (J). (978-0-606-20833-8(X)) Tandem Library Bks.

—Pssst! It's Me... the Bogeyman. Kroninger, Stephen, illus. 2001. 40p. (J). pap. 6.99 (978-0-689-84616-8(9) , Aladdin) Simon & Schuster Children's Publishing.

—Pssst! It's Me... the Bogeyman. 2001. (978-0-606-22102-3(6)) Tandem Library Bks.

Park, Eun Ah. Sweet & Sensitive, Vol. 1. 2004. 200p. pap. (978-1-4139-0074-3(7)) ADV Manga.

Park, Nick, et al. Close Shave. 2006. 31.95 (978-0-19-459239-0(1)) Oxford Univ. Pr., Inc.

Parker, Daniel. Wessex Papers No. 1: Trust Falls. 2002. (gr. 7-12). lib. bdg. 13.00 (978-0-613-71478-5(4)) Tandem Library Bks.

Parkinson, Curtis. Mr Reez's Sneezes. 1999. (ps-2). lib. bdg. 14.10 (978-0-613-78354-5(9)) Tandem Library Bks.

Parr, Todd. I Like Being Me! 2006. (Toddworld Ser.). 24p. (J). (ps-3). pap. 3.99 (978-0-316-05714-1(2)) Little Brown & Co.

—Otto Goes to the Beach. 2003. (Illus.). 24p. (J). (ps-1). 9.95 (978-0-316-73870-5(0) , Tingley, Megan Bks.) Little, Brown Bks. for Young Readers.

—Underwear Do's & Don'ts. 2005. 32p. (J). (ps-ps). 9.99 (978-0-316-05964-0(1) , Tingley, Megan Bks.) Little, Brown Bks. for Young Readers.

Pascoe, Elaine. Fooled You! Fakes & Hoaxes Through the Years. Keller, Laurie, illus. rev. ed. 2005. 96p. (J). 18.95 (978-0-8050-7528-1(3) , Holt, Henry & Co. Bks. For Young Readers) Holt, Henry & Co.

Pass, Erica. The Long, Hot Recess. Goldberg, Barry, illus. ed. 2005. (Fairly Odd Parents Ser.: 4). 24p. (J). lib. bdg. 15.00 (978-1-59054-806-6(X)) Fitzgerald Bks.

—The Scavenger Hunt. Marantz, Larissa & DiPaolo, Katharine, illus. 2006. (All Grown Up! Ser.). 24p. (J). pap. 3.99 (978-1-4169-0791-6(2) , Simon Spotlight/Nickelodeon) Simon & Schuster Children's Publishing.

Pass, Erica. Vote for SpongeBob! Moore, Harry, illus. 2008. (SpongeBob SquarePants Ser.). 24p. (J). pap. 3.99 (*978-1-4169-4986-2(0) , Simon Spotlight/Nickelodeon) Simon & Schuster Children's Publishing.

Pass, Erica & Artifact Group. Hooray for Dads! 2007. (SpongeBob SquarePants Ser.). 24p. (J). pap. 3.99 (978-1-4169-2782-2(4) , Simon Spotlight/Nickelodeon) Simon & Schuster Children's Publishing.

Pass, Erica & Hot Animation Staff, Animation. A World of Shapes. 2005. (Rubbadubbers Ser.). 22p. (J). bds. 4.99 (978-0-689-87429-1(4) , Simon Spotlight) Simon & Schuster Children's Publishing.

Passen, Lisa. The Incredible Shrinking Teacher. 2008. (Illus.). 32p. (J). pap. 6.99 (*978-0-312-38017-5(8)) Square Fish.

Patton, Lee. Toe Jam & Boo Boo's. 2004. 33p. pap. 17.95 (978-1-4137-1508-8(7)) PublishAmerica, Inc.

Patz, Nancy. Pumpernickel Tickle & Mean Green Cheese. Patz, Nancy, photos by. 2000. (Illus.). 40p. (J). reprint ed. 16.95 (978-1-893116-17-7(4)) Baltimore Sun, The.

Paul, Ann Whitford. Silly Sadie, Silly Samuel. 1999. (Ready-to-Read Ser.). (Illus.). (J). (978-0-606-20388-3(5)) Tandem Library Bks.

Paulsen, Gary. Molly McGinty Has a Good Day. 2004. 112p. (gr. 4-7). lib. bdg. 14.99 (978-0-385-90911-2(X) , Lamb, Wendy) Random Hse. Children's Bks.

—Molly Mcginty Has a Really Good Day. 112p. (gr. 3-7). 2006. 5.50 (978-0-440-41482-7(2) , Yearling); 2004. 12.95 (978-0-385-32588-2(6) , Lamb, Wendy) Random Hse. Children's Bks.

—The Schernoff Discoveries. 1998. 112p. (gr. 5-9). 4.99 (978-0-440-41463-6(6) , Yearling) Random Hse. Children's Bks.

—The Schernoff Discoveries. 1998. (978-0-606-13761-4(0)) Tandem Library Bks.

Pearson, Mary E. Generous Me. Krejca, Gary, illus. (Rookie Reader Espanol Ser.). (J). 2003. 32p. (gr. k-2). pap. 4.95 (978-0-516-27819-3(3)); 2002. 31p. (gr. 1-2). 19.50 (978-0-516-22253-0(8)) Scholastic Library Publishing. (Children's Pr.).

—Generous Me. 2002. (gr. k-3). lib. bdg. 12.95 (978-0-613-59484-4(3)) Tandem Library Bks.

Pearson, Tracey Campbell. Bob. Pearson, Tracey Campbell, illus. 2002. (Illus.). 32p. (J). (ps-1). 16.00 (978-0-374-39957-3(3) , Farrar, Straus & Giroux (BYR)) Farrar, Straus & Giroux.

—Bob. Pearson, Tracey Campbell, illus. 2006. (Illus.). 32p. (J). reprint ed. pap. 6.95 (978-0-374-40871-8(8)) Macmillan.

Peck, Richard. Fair Weather. (Illus.). 160p. 2003. (YA). pap. 5.99 (978-0-14-250034-7(8) , Puffin); 2001. (J). (gr. 4-8). 16.99 (978-0-8037-2516-4(7) , Dial) Penguin Group (USA) Inc.

—Fair Weather. 2003. (gr. 3-6). lib. bdg. 14.15 (978-0-613-57895-0(3)) Tandem Library Bks.

—Fair Weather. 2004. 146p. (J). (gr. 5-9). pap. 36.00 incl. audio (978-0-8072-2038-2(8) , Listening Library) Random Hse. Audio Publishing Group.

—Fair Weather. l.t. ed. 2002. 161p. (YA). 24.95 (978-0-7862-3922-1(0)) Thomson Gale.

—The Teacher's Funeral: A Comedy in Three Parts. 2004. 208p. (J). (gr. 5). 16.99 (978-0-8037-2736-6(4) , Dial); 2006. 224p. (YA). (gr. 3). reprint ed. pap. 6.99 (978-0-14-240507-9(8) , Puffin) Penguin Group (USA) Inc.

—The Teacher's Funeral: A Comedy in Three Parts. l.t. ed. 2005. 226p. 22.95 (978-0-7862-7750-6(5) , Large Print Pr.) Thorndike Pr.

Pelham, David. Applebee's Colors. 2006. (Illus.). 16p. (J). 12.95 (978-0-7624-2647-8(0) , Running Pr.) Running Pr. Bk. Pubs.

Pelletier, Marthe. Leo a la Mer. Cote, Genevieve, tr. 2003. (Premier Roman Ser.). (FRE., Illus.). 64p. (J). (gr. 1-4). pap. (978-2-89021-637-2(3)) Diffusion du livre Mirabel.

Penner, Fred. Proud. Bolling, Vickey, illus. 2001. 32p. (J). (ps). pap. 4.95 (978-1-55285-274-3(1)) Whitecap Bks., Ltd. CAN. *Dist:* Firefly Bks., Ltd.

Pennypacker, Sara. Clementine. Frazee, Marla, illus. 2006. 144p. (gr. 1-5). 14.99 (978-0-7868-3882-0(5)) Hyperion Pr.

Perlman, Rhea. The Brink of Ex-stink-tion. Santat, Dan, illus. 2007. (Otto Undercover Ser.: No. 5). 128p. (J). pap. 3.99 (978-0-06-075503-4(2) , Harper Trophy) HarperCollins Pubs.

—Canyon Catastrophe. Santat, Dan, illus. 2006. (Otto Undercover Ser.). 128p. (J). 14.99 (978-0-06-075498-3(2)); pap. 3.99 (978-0-06-075497-6(4)) HarperCollins Pubs.

Perret, Gene, text. Harvey Green, the Eating Machine. 2002. (Illus.). 32p. (J). 12.95 (978-1-893860-78-0(7)) Arizona Highways.

Pescetti, Luis Maria. Caperucita Roja (tal Como se le Contaron a Jorge) Pescetti, Luis Maria, illus. 2003. (SPA., Illus.). 30p. (J). (gr. k-3). pap. 9.95 (978-968-19-0518-7(0)) Santillana USA Publishing Co., Inc.

—Frin. Gedovious, Juan, illus. 2003. (SPA.). 202p. (J). (gr. 5-8). pap. 11.95 (978-968-19-0636-8(5)) Santillana USA Publishing Co., Inc.

Petty, J. T. Clemency Pogue: Fairy Killer. Davis, Will, illus. 2005. (Clemency Pogue Ser.). 128p. (J). 9.95 (978-0-689-87236-5(4) , Simon & Schuster Children's Publishing) Simon & Schuster Children's Publishing.

—The Scrivener Bees. Friend, David Michael, illus. 2007. (Clemency Pogue Ser.). 176p. (J). (gr. 3-7). 11.99 (978-1-4169-0769-5(6) , Simon & Schuster Children's Publishing) Simon & Schuster Children's Publishing.

Phinn, Gervase. What's the Matter, Royston Knapper? (J). 10.99 incl. audio (978-0-85953-556-4(8)) Child's Play-International.

—What's the Matter, Royston Knapper? Fisher, Chris, illus. 2001. 112p. (J). 9.99 (978-0-85953-883-1(4)) Child's Play-International.

Pierce, Angelica. Wizard in Blue Jeans. 2007. 184p. pap. 10.95 (*978-1-4303-0647-4(5)) Lulu.com.

Pilkey, Dav. The Adventures of Captain Underpants: An Epic Novel. 2004. (Captain Underpants Ser.: No. 1). (J). lib. bdg. 19.95 (978-0-439-68434-7(X) , Scholastic, Inc.) Scholastic, Inc.

—The Adventures of Super Diaper Baby. 2004. (J). lib. bdg. 19.95 (978-0-439-68435-4(8) , Scholastic, Inc.) Scholastic, Inc.

—The Adventures of Super Diaper Baby. Pilkey, Dav, illus. 2002. (Captain Underpants Ser.). (Illus.). 128p. (J). (gr. 2-5). pap. 16.95 (978-0-439-37605-1(X) , Blue Sky Pr., The) Scholastic, Inc.

—El Capitan Calzoncillos la Ridicula Historia De. 2008. 176p. (J). pap. 4.99 (*978-0-545-02583-6(4) , Scholastic en Espanol) Scholastic, Inc.

—El Capitan Calzoncillos y el Perverso Plan del Profesor Pipicaca. 2002. (Captain Underpants Ser.: No. 4). (SPA.). 160p. (J). (gr. 1-5). pap. 4.99 (978-0-439-41037-3(1) , Scholastic en Espanol) Scholastic, Inc.

—El Capitan Calzoncillos y la Furia de la Supermujer Macroelastica. 2003. (Captain Underpants Ser.). (SPA., Illus.). 176p. (J). (gr. 2-5). pap. 4.99 (978-0-439-53820-6(3) , Scholastic en Espanol) Scholastic, Inc.

—The Captain Underpants Set: The Adventures of Captain Underpants; Captain Underpants & the Attack of the Talking Toilets; Captain Underpants & the Invasion of the Incredibly Naughty Cafeteria Ladies from Outer Space; Captain Underpants & the Perilous Plot of Professor Poopypants, 4 vols. 2000. (Captain Underpants Ser.: Nos. 1-4). (J). (gr. 2-5). pap. 19.95 (978-0-439-22700-1(3) , Blue Sky Pr., The) Scholastic, Inc.

—Captain Underpants & the Attack of the Talking Toilets. (Captain Underpants Ser.: No. 2). (J). 2004. lib. bdg. 19.95 (978-0-439-68436-1(6) , Scholastic, Inc.); 1999. (Illus.). 144p. (gr. 2-5). pap. 16.95 (978-0-590-63136-5(5) , Blue Sky Pr., The) Scholastic, Inc.

—Captain Underpants & the Attack of the Talking Toilets. Pilkey, Dav, illus. 1999. (Captain Underpants Ser.: No. 2). (Illus.). 144p. (J). (gr. 2-5). pap. 4.99 (978-0-590-63427-4(5)) Scholastic, Inc.

—Captain Underpants & the Attack of the Talking Toilets. collector's ed. 2007. 144p. (J). pap. 9.99 (*978-0-545-02727-4(6)) Scholastic, Inc.

—Captain Underpants & the Attack of the Talking Toilets. 1999. (Captain Underpants Ser.: No. 2). (Illus.). (J). (gr. 2-5). 11.64 (978-0-606-15830-5(8)); (gr. 3-6). lib. bdg. 13.00 (978-0-613-11382-3(9)) Tandem Library Bks.

—Captain Underpants & the Big, Bad Battle of the Bionic Booger Boy Pt. 1: The Night of the Nasty Nostril Nuggets. 2004. (Captain Underpants Ser.: Bk. 6). (J). lib. bdg. 19.95 (978-0-439-68438-5(2) , Scholastic, Inc.) Scholastic, Inc.

—Captain Underpants & the Big, Bad Battle of the Bionic Booger Boy Pt. 1: The Night of the Nasty Nostril Nuggets. Pilkey, Dav, illus. 2003. (Captain Underpants Ser.: Bk. 6). (Illus.). 176p. (J). 4.99 (978-0-439-37610-5(6) , Blue Sky Pr., The) Scholastic, Inc.

—Captain Underpants & the Big, Bad Battle of the Bionic Booger Boy Pt. 1: The Night of the Nasty Nostril Nuggets. 2003. (Captain Underpants Ser.: Bk. 6). (gr. 3-6). lib. bdg. 13.00 (978-0-613-68836-9(8)) Tandem Library Bks.

—Captain Underpants & the Big, Bad Battle of the Bionic Booger Boy Pt. 2: The Revenge of the Ridiculous Robo-Boogers. 2004. (Captain Underpants Ser.: Bk. 7). (J). lib. bdg. 19.95 (978-0-439-68437-8(4) , Scholastic, Inc.) Scholastic, Inc.

—Captain Underpants & the Big, Bad Battle of the Bionic Booger Boy Pt. 2: The Revenge of the Ridiculous Robo-Boogers. Pilkey, Dav, illus. 2003. (Captain Underpants Ser.). (Illus.). 176p. (J). (gr. 3-6). 4.99 (978-0-439-37612-9(2)); pap. 16.95 (978-0-439-37611-2(4)) Scholastic, Inc. (Blue Sky Pr., The).

—Captain Underpants & the Big, Bad Battle of the Bionic Booger Boy Pt. 2: The Revenge of the Ridiculous Robo-Boogers. 2003. (Captain Underpants Ser.: Bk. 7). lib. bdg. 13.00 (978-0-613-68837-6(6)) Tandem Library Bks.

—Captain Underpants & the Invasion of the Incredibly Naughty Cafeteria Ladies from Outer Space: And the Subsequent Assault of the Equally Evil Lunchroom Zombie Nerds. 2004. (Captain Underpants Ser.: No. 3). (J). lib. bdg. 19.95 (978-0-439-68439-2(0) , Scholastic, Inc.) Scholastic, Inc.

—Captain Underpants & the Invasion of the Incredibly Naughty Cafeteria Ladies from Outer Space: And the Subsequent Assault of the Equally Evil Lunchroom Zombie Nerds. Pilkey, Dav, illus. 1999. (Captain Underpants Ser.: No. 3). (Illus.). 144p. (J). (gr. 2-5). 4.99 (978-0-439-04996-2(2) , Blue Sky Pr., The) Scholastic, Inc.

—Captain Underpants & the Invasion of the Incredibly Naughty Cafeteria Ladies from Outer Space: And the Subsequent Assault of the Equally Evil Lunchroom Zombie Nerds. 1999. (Captain Underpants Ser.: No. 3). (Illus.). 134p. (J). (gr. 2-5). pap. 16.95 (978-0-439-04995-5(4) , Blue Sky Pr., The) Scholastic, Inc.

—Captain Underpants & the Invasion of the Incredibly Naughty Cafeteria Ladies from Outer Space: And the Subsequent Assault of the Equally Evil Lunchroom Zombie Nerds. 1999. (Captain Underpants Ser.: No. 3). (gr. 3-6). lib. bdg. 13.00 (978-0-613-17900-3(5)) Tandem Library Bks.

—Captain Underpants & the Perilous Plot of Professor Poopypants. 2004. (Captain Underpants Ser.: No. 4). (J). lib. bdg. 19.95 (978-0-439-68440-8(4) , Scholastic, Inc.) Scholastic, Inc.

—Captain Underpants & the Perilous Plot of Professor Poopypants. Pilkey, Dav, illus. 2000. (Captain Underpants Ser.: No. 4). (Illus.). 160p. (J). (gr. 2-5). pap. 4.99 (978-0-439-04998-6(9)); pap. 16.95 (978-0-439-04997-9(0)) Scholastic, Inc. (Blue Sky Pr., The).

—Captain Underpants & the Perilous Plot of Professor Poopypants. 2000. (Captain Underpants Ser.: No. 4). (gr. 3-6). lib. bdg. 13.00 (978-0-613-21289-2(4)); (Illus.). (J). (gr. 2-5). 11.64 (978-0-606-18526-4(7)) Tandem Library Bks.

—Captain Underpants & the Preposterous Plight of the Purple Potty People. 2006. 176p. (J). 19.99 (978-0-439-90381-3(5) , Blue Sky Pr., The) Scholastic, Inc.

—Captain Underpants & the Wrath of the Wicked Wedgie Woman. 2004. (Captain Underpants Ser.: No. 5). (J). lib. bdg. 19.95 (978-0-439-68441-5(2) , Scholastic, Inc.) Scholastic, Inc.

—Captain Underpants & the Wrath of the Wicked Wedgie Woman. Pilkey, Dav, illus. 2001. (Captain Underpants Ser.: No. 5). (Illus.). 176p. (J). (gr. 2-5). 4.99 (978-0-439-05000-5(6)) Scholastic, Inc.

—Captain Underpants & the Wrath of the Wicked Wedgie Woman. 2001. (Captain Underpants Ser.: No. 5). (gr. 3-6). lib. bdg. 13.00 (978-0-613-35767-8(1)); (Illus.). (J). 11.64 (978-0-606-21101-7(2)) Tandem Library Bks.

—Captain Underpants Books 1-4 Boxset. 2007. (J). pap. 19.96 (*978-0-545-02287-3(8) , Blue Sky Pr., The) Scholastic, Inc.

—The Captain Underpants Extra-Crunchy Book O' Fun. 2001. (Captain Underpants Ser.). (gr. 3-6). lib. bdg. 11.80 (978-0-613-32369-7(6)) Tandem Library Bks.

—The Captain Underpants Extra-Crunchy Book O' Fun 'N Games. Pilkey, Dav, illus. 2001. (Captain Underpants Ser.). (Illus.). 96p. (J). (gr. 2-5). mass mkt. 3.99 (978-0-439-26761-8(7)) Scholastic, Inc.

—Dog Breath! The Horrible Trouble with Hally Tosis. Pilkey, Dav, illus. 2002. (Illus.). (J). 23.98 (978-0-7587-2398-7(9)) Book Wholesalers, Inc.

—Dog Breath! The Horrible Trouble with Hally Tosis. 2004. (Scholastic Bookshelf Ser.). 32p. (J). pap. 6.99 (978-0-439-59839-2(7) , Scholastic Paperbacks) Scholastic, Inc.

—Dog Breath! The Horrible Trouble with Hally Tosis. 2001. (Illus.). (J). (978-0-606-20688-4(4)) Tandem Library Bks.

—The Dumb Bunnies. 2007. 32p. (J). pap. 10.99 (*978-0-545-03938-3(X) , Levine, Arthur A. Bks.) Scholastic, Inc.

—The Dumb Bunnies. 2005. (Illus.). 30p. (J). (ps-ps). lib. bdg. 12.79 (978-0-606-33285-9(5)) Tandem Library Bks.

—Dumb Bunnies Collection. 2007. (J). pap. 12.99 (*978-0-439-75666-2(9) , Blue Sky Pr., The) Scholastic, Inc.

—Dumb Bunnies' Easter (Bkshelf) 2008. 32p. pap. 6.99 (*978-0-545-00880-8(8) , Scholastic Paperbacks) Scholastic, Inc.

—Dumb Bunnies Go to the Zoo, The. 2007. 32p. pap. 5.99 (*978-0-439-93049-9(9)) Scholastic, Inc.

—The First Captain Underpants Collection: Captain Underpants & the Perilous Plot of Professor Poopypants; Captain Underpants & the Invasion of the Incredibly Naughty Cafeteria Ladies from Outer Space; Captain Underpants & the Attack of the Talking Toilets; The Adventures of Captain Underpants. 2004. (Captain Underpants Ser.). (Illus.). (J). 19.96 (978-0-439-69862-7(6)) Scholastic, Inc.

—Giant Robot vs. the Mutant Mosquitoes from Mercury. Ontiveros, Martin, illus. 2000. (Ricky Ricotta Ser.: No. 2). 128p. (J). (ps-3). pap. 16.95 (978-0-590-30721-5(5) , Blue Sky Pr., The) Scholastic, Inc.

—Make Way for Dumb Bunnies. 2007. 32p. (J). pap. 10.99 (*978-0-545-03939-0(8) , Levine, Arthur A. Bks.) Scholastic, Inc.

—Mighty Robot vs. the Uranium Unicorns from Uranus. Ontiveros, Martin, illus. 2005. (Ricky Ricotta Ser.: Bk. 7). 128p. (J). pap. 16.99 (978-0-439-37646-4(7) , Blue Sky Pr., The) Scholastic, Inc.

—Ricky Ricotta Y el Poderoso Robot Contra Los Mecamonos de Marte. 2007. (Ricky Ricotta Ser.: No. 4). 144p. (J). pap. 3.99 (978-0-439-85105-3(X) , Scholastic en Espanol) Scholastic, Inc.

—Ricky Ricotta Y el Poderoso Robot Contra Los Mecamonos de Marte. Ontiveros, Martin, illus. 2002. (Ricky Ricotta Ser.: No. 4). 144p. (gr. 2-4). pap. 3.99 (978-0-439-25296-6(2)); (J). (ps-3). pap. 16.95 (978-0-439-25295-9(4)) Scholastic, Inc. (Blue Sky Pr., The).

—Ricky Ricotta Y el Poderoso Robot Contra Los Mecamonos de Marte. 2002. (Ricky Ricotta Ser.: No. 4). (978-0-606-22263-1(4)) Tandem Library Bks.

—Ricky Ricotta's Giant Robot vs. the Mutant Mosquitoes from Mercury. Ontiveros, Martin, illus. 2000. (Ricky Ricotta Ser.: No. 2). (J). (ps-3). pap. 47.88 (978-0-439-21522-0(6)) Scholastic, Inc.

—Ricky Ricotta's Giant Robot vs. the Mutant Mosquitoes from Mercury. Ontiveros, Martin, illus. 2000. (Ricky Ricotta Ser.: Bk. 2). 127p. (J). (ps). per. 11.80 (978-0-613-26747-2(8)) Tandem Library Bks.

—Ricky Ricotta's Giant Robot vs. the Mutant Mosquitoes from Mercury. 2000. (Ricky Ricotta Ser.: No. 2). (J). (ps-3). (978-0-606-19604-8(8)) Tandem Library Bks.

—Ricky Ricotta's Giant Robot vs. the Voodoo Vultures from Venus. Ontiveros, Martin, illus. 2001. (Ricky Ricotta Ser.: No. 3). 128p. (J). (ps-3). pap. 16.95 (978-0-439-23624-9(X)) Scholastic, Inc.

—Ricky Ricotta's Mighty Robot vs. the Mutant Mosquitoes from Mercury. Ontiveros, Martin, illus. 2000. (Ricky Ricotta Ser.: No. 2). 128p. (J). (ps-3). pap. 3.99 (978-0-590-30722-2(3)) Scholastic, Inc.

—Ricky Ricotta's Mighty Robot vs. the Stupid Stinkbugs from Saturn. Ontiveros, Martin, illus. 2003. (Ricky Ricotta Ser.: No. 6). 128p. (J). pap. 16.95 (978-0-439-37644-0(0)); mass mkt. 3.99 (978-0-439-37645-7(9)) Scholastic, Inc. (Blue Sky Pr., The).

—The Second Captain Underpants Collection: The Adventures of Super Diaper Baby; Captain Underpants & the Big, Bad Battle of the Bionic Booger Boy Part 2; Captain Underpants & the Big, Bad Battle of the Bionic Booger Boy Part 1; Captain Underpants & the Wrath of the Wicked Wedgie Woman. 2004. (Captain Underpants Ser.). (Illus.). 525p. (J). (gr. 3 up). 19.96 (978-0-439-69054-6(4) , Scholastic Paperbacks) Scholastic, Inc.

—The Silly Gooses. Pilkey, Dav, illus. 2000. (Illus.). 40p. (J). (ps-3). pap. 5.99 (978-0-590-95735-9(X)) Scholastic, Inc.

—The Silly Gooses. 2000. (978-0-606-18890-6(8)) Tandem Library Bks.

—The Wrath of the Wicked Wedgie Women. Pilkey, Dav, illus. 2001. (Captain Underpants Ser.: No. 5). (Illus.). 176p. (J). (gr. 2-5). pap. 16.95 (978-0-439-04999-3(7)) Scholastic, Inc.

Pilkey, Dav, illus. The All New Captain Underpants Extra-Crunchy Book O' Fun 2. 2002. (Captain Underpants Ser.). 96p. (J). (gr. 1-5). pap. 3.99 (978-0-439-37608-2(4)) Scholastic, Inc.

—Captain Underpants & the Big, Bad Battle of the Bionic Booger Boy Pt. 1: The Night of the Nasty Nostril Nuggets. 2003. (Captain Underpants Ser.: Bk. 6). 176p. (J). pap. 16.95 (978-0-439-37609-9(2) , Blue Sky Pr., The) Scholastic, Inc.

—The Dumb Bunnies Go to the Zoo. 2002. (Dumb Bunnies Ser.). (J). 22.91 (978-0-7587-2424-3(1)) Book Wholesalers, Inc.

—Make Way for Dumb Bunnies. 2002. (Dumb Bunnies Ser.). (J). 20.49 (978-0-7587-3078-7(0)) Book Wholesalers, Inc.

Pin, Isabel. When I Grow up, I Will Win the Nobel Peace Prize. Seitz, Nancy, tr. from GER. Pin, Isabel, illus. 2006. (Illus.). 32p. (J). (gr. 3-5). 16.00 (978-0-374-38313-8(8) , Farrar, Straus & Giroux (BYR)) Farrar, Straus & Giroux.

Pinkwater, Daniel M. The Artsy Smartsy Club. Pinkwater, Jill, illus. 2005. 176p. (J). 16.89 (978-0-06-053558-2(X)); 15.99 (978-0-06-053557-5(1)) HarperCollins Pubs.

—Bad Bears & a Bunny. Pinkwater, Jill, illus. 2005. (Irving & Muktuk Story Ser.). 32p. (J). (gr. k-3). 16.00 (978-0-618-33926-6(4)) Houghton Mifflin Co. Trade & Reference Div.

—Bad Bears Go Visiting. Pinkwater, Jill, illus. 2007. 32p. (J). (gr. k-3). 16.00 (978-0-618-43126-7(8)) Houghton Mifflin Co.

—Big Bob & the Magic Valentine's Day Potato. Pinkwater, Jill, illus. 2000. (Hello Reader! Ser.: Level 3). 32p. (J). (gr. 1-3). 3.99 (978-0-590-63275-1(2) , Cartwheel Bks.) Scholastic, Inc.

—Big Bob & the Magic Valentine's Day Potato. 2000. (Hello Reader! Ser.). (Illus.). (J). (978-0-606-18518-9(6)) Tandem Library Bks.

—Bongo Larry. Pinkwater, Jill, illus. 1998. (Accelerated Reader Bks.). 32p. (J). (ps up). 14.95 (978-0-7614-5020-7(3) , Cavendish Children's Bks.) Cavendish, Marshall Corp.

—Dancing Larry. Pinkwater, Daniel M. & Pinkwater, Jill, illus. 2006. 32p. (J). 16.95 (978-0-7614-5220-1(6)) Cavendish, Marshall Corp.

—Go West. Rash, Andy, illus. 2002. (Fat Camp Commandos Ser.). 96p. (J). (gr. 3-8). pap. 14.95 (978-0-439-29772-1(9) , Scholastic Pr.) Scholastic, Inc.

—Go West. 2003. (gr. 3-6). lib. bdg. 12.40 (978-0-613-62511-1(0)) Tandem Library Bks.

—The Hoboken Chicken Emergency. Auth, Tony, illus. 2007. 112p. (J). (gr. 1-4). 16.99 (*978-1-4169-2809-6(X) , Atheneum) Simon & Schuster Children's Publishing.

—The Hoboken Chicken Emergency. 1999. (gr. 3-6). lib. bdg. 13.00 (978-0-7857-9893-4(5)) Tandem Library Bks.

—Irving & Muktuk: Two Bad Bears. Pinkwater, Jill, illus. 2003. 32p. (J). (gr. k-3). 5.95 (978-0-618-35404-7(2)) Houghton Mifflin Co. Trade & Reference Div.

—Irving & Muktuk: Two Bad Bears. Pinkwater, Jill & Pinkwater, Daniel M., illus. 2001. 32p. (J). (gr. k-3). tchr. ed. 15.00 (978-0-618-09334-2(6)) Houghton Mifflin Co. Trade & Reference Div.

—Irving & Muktuk: Two Bad Bears. ed. 2004. (Illus.). (J). (gr. k-3). spiral bd. (978-0-616-11136-9(3)); spiral bd. (978-0-616-11137-6(1)) Canadian National Institute for the Blind/Institut National Canadien pour les Aveugles.

—Looking for Bobowicz: A Hoboken Chicken Story. Pinkwater, Jill, illus. (J). 2006. 224p. pap. 5.99 (978-0-06-053556-8(3) , Harper Trophy); 2004. 208p. 15.99 (978-0-06-053554-4(7)) HarperCollins Pubs.

—The Lunchroom of Doom. 2000. (gr. 3-6). lib. bdg. 11.80 (978-0-613-31437-4(9)) Tandem Library Bks.

—The Magic Pretzel. 2000. (gr. 3-6). lib. bdg. 11.80 (978-0-613-26097-8(X)); (Werewolf Club Ser.: No. 1). (978-0-606-17942-3(9)) Tandem Library Bks.

—The Magic Pretzel. Pinkwater, Jill, illus. 2000. (Werewolf Club Ser.). (J). (978-0-606-19734-2(6)) Tandem Library Bks.

—Mush, a Dog from Space. Pinkwater, Jill, illus. 2002. (Ready-for-Chapters Ser.). 64p. (J). (gr. 1-4). lib. bdg. 11.89 (978-0-689-84801-8(3) , Aladdin Library) Simon & Schuster Children's Publishing.

—Mush's Jazz Adventure. 2002. (gr. 3-6). lib. bdg. 11.80 (978-0-613-57577-5(6)) Tandem Library Bks.

—The Neddiad: How Neddie Took the Train, Went to Hollywood, & Saved Civilization. 2007. 320p. (J). (gr. 5). 16.00 (*978-0-618-59444-3(2)) Houghton Mifflin Co. Trade & Reference Div.

—Once upon a Blue Moose. 2006. 160p. (gr. 2-5). 6.50 (978-0-440-42083-5(0) , Yearling) Random Hse. Children's Bks.

—The Picture of Morty & Ray. Davis, Jack E., illus. 2003. 32p. (J). (gr. 1-5). 15.99 (978-0-06-623785-5(8)) HarperCollins Pubs.

—The Werewolf Club Meets Dorkula, No. 3. 2001. (Werewolf Club Ser.). (Illus.). (J). (978-0-606-20983-0(2)) Tandem Library Bks.

—The Werewolf Club Meets the Hound of the Basketballs. Pinkwater, Jill, illus. 4th ed. 2001. (Werewolf Club Ser.: Vol. 4). 64p. (J). pap. 7.95 (978-0-689-84473-7(5) , Aladdin) Simon & Schuster Children's Publishing.

—The Werewolf Club Meets the Hound of the Basketballs. 2001. (978-0-606-22089-7(5)) Tandem Library Bks.

—4: Fantastic Novels. 2000. (J). (978-0-606-19948-3(9)) Tandem Library Bks.

—4 Fantastic Novels. 2000. (Illus.). 640p. (J). (gr. 4-7). pap. 12.00 (978-0-689-83488-2(8) , Aladdin) Simon & Schuster Children's Publishing.

Pinkwater, Daniel M. & Pinkwater, Jill. The Magic Pretzel. 2000. (Werewolf Club Ready for Chapters Ser.: Bk. 1). (Illus.). 80p. (J). (gr. 2-4). pap. 3.99 (978-0-689-83790-6(9) , Aladdin) Simon & Schuster Children's Publishing.

—Mush's Jazz Adventure. 2002. (Ready-for-Chapters Ser.). (Illus.). 48p. (J). pap. 6.99 (978-0-689-84572-7(3) , Aladdin) Simon & Schuster Children's Publishing.

Pinkwater, Daniel M. & Pinkwater, Jill, illus. Bad Bear Detectives: An Irving & Muktuk Story. 2006. 32p. (J). (gr. k-3). 16.00 (978-0-618-43125-0(X)) Houghton Mifflin Co.

—Bad Bears Go Visiting: An Irving & Muktuk Story. 2007. (J). (*978-1-4287-3949-9(1)) Houghton Mifflin Co.

Pinkwater, Daniel M. & Pinkwater, Jill, illus. Bad Bears in the Big City: An Irving & Muktuk Story. 2004. 32p. (J). (gr. k-3). tchr. ed. 16.00 (978-0-618-25208-4(8)) Houghton Mifflin Co. Trade & Reference Div.

Pitchford, Dean. The Big One-Oh. 2007. 192p. (J). (gr. 3). 15.99 (978-0-399-24547-3(2) , Putnam Juvenile) Penguin Group (USA) Inc.

Pittar, Gill. Milly, Molly & Aunt Maude (book W/dolls) 2006. 28p. pap. (978-1-86972-101-5(2)) Milly Molly Bks.

—Milly, Molly & Taffy Bogle (book W/dolls) 2006. 28p. pap. (978-1-86972-092-6(X)) Milly Molly Bks.

Pittau, Francesco & Gervais, Bernadette. That's Dangerous! 2004. (Illus.). 80p. (J). bds. 7.95 (978-1-57912-350-5(3) , 81350) Black Dog & Leventhal Pubs., Inc.

Piven, Hanoch. The Scary Show of Mo & Jo. Piven, Hanoch, illus. 2005. (Illus.). 32p. (J). (ps-3). 18.95 (978-0-7624-2097-1(9) , Running Pr. Kids) Running Pr. Bk. Pubs.

Plante, Raymond. Le Grand Role de Marilou Polaire. Favreau, Marie-Claude, illus. 2003. (Premier Roman Ser.). (FRE.). 64p. (J). (gr. 2-5). pap. (978-2-89021-288-6(2)) Diffusion du livre Mirabel.

—Marilou Polaire et la Magie des Etoiles. Favreau, Marie-Claude, illus. 2002. (Premier Roman Ser.). (FRE.). 64p. (J). (gr. 1-4). pap. (978-2-89021-563-4(6)) Diffusion du livre Mirabel.

Play Ball, Amelia Bedelia. 2002. (Amelia Bedelia Ser.). (Illus.). (J). 12.34 (978-0-7587-6239-9(9)) Book Wholesalers, Inc.

Plourde, Josee. La Promesse des Iles. Lemelin, Linda, tr. 2003. (Premier Roman Ser.). (FRE., Illus.). 64p. (J). (gr. 1-4). pap. (978-2-89021-630-3(6)) Diffusion du livre Mirabel.

Plourde, Lynn. Book Fair Day. Wickstrom, Thor, illus. (J). 2008. 40p. (gr. 1-3). pap. 6.99 (*978-0-14-241139-1(6) , Puffin); 2006. (*978-1-4156-8095-7(7) , Dutton Juvenile) Penguin Group (USA) Inc.

Plourde, Lynn. Grandpappy Snippy Snappies. Santoro, Christopher, illus. (J). Date not set. 16.89 (978-0-06-029528-8(7)); 2002. 15.99 (978-0-06-028050-5(6)) HarperCollins Pubs.

Pluta, K. There's a Yak in my Bed. Stallop, Christy, illus. 2007. 32p. (J). 16.95 (978-0-9769417-4-3(0)) Blooming Tree Pr.

PM Emerald Anthology Funny Business: an Anthology of Humor: 1 Anthology. (gr. 3-4). 8.00 (978-0-7635-7805-3(3)) Rigby Education.

Pochenko. Conspiracy Prophecy II: WWIII & Rumors of WWIV in Revelation. 2003. 230p. (YA). pap. 14.95 (978-0-595-26419-3(0) , Writer's Showcase Pr.) iUniverse, Inc.

Poirier, Mark Jude. Goats: A Novel. 2002. (Illus.). 355p. pap. 13.00 (978-0-7868-8713-2(3)) Talk Miramax Bks.

Polacco, Patricia. Ginger & Petunia. Polacco, Patricia, illus. 2007. (Illus.). 40p. (J). (ps-3). 16.99 (978-0-399-24539-8(1) , Philomel) Penguin Group (USA) Inc.

—The Graves Family Goes Camping. Polacco, Patricia, illus. 2005. (Illus.). 48p. (J). (ps-5). 16.99 (978-0-399-24369-1(0) , Philomel) Penguin Group (USA) Inc.

—Oh, Look! Polacco, Patricia, illus. 2004. (Illus.). 32p. (J). (ps-3). 16.99 (978-0-399-24223-6(6) , Philomel) Penguin Group (USA) Inc.

Polhemus, Coleman. The Crocodile Blues. Polhemus, Coleman, illus. 2007. (Illus.). 48p. (J). (ps-1). 16.99 (*978-0-7636-3543-5(X)) Candlewick Pr.

Pollack, Pam. The Bad Luck Charm. 2001. (Malcolm in the Middle Ser.: No. 3). 144p. (J). (gr. 3-7). pap. 4.99 (978-0-439-23078-0(0)) Scholastic, Inc.

Ponti, Jamie. Animal Attraction. 2005. (Romantic Comedies Ser.). 272p. (YA). pap. 5.99 (978-1-4169-0987-3(7) , Simon Pulse) Simon & Schuster Children's Publishing.

Poth, Karen. The Puggslyville Fair: A Scratch-and-Sniff Storybook. McGee, Warner, illus. 2008. (VeggieTales Ser.). 14p. (J). (ps-2). bds. 7.99 (*978-1-4169-4870-4(8) , Little Simon Inspirations) Simon & Schuster Children's Publishing.

Pow, Tom. Callum's Big Day. Hedderick, Mairi, illus. 2002. 32p. (J). 12.95 (978-0-9535413-4-8(7)) iynx publishing GBR. *Dist:* Dufour Editions, Inc.

Powell, Anna. Don't Say That, Willy Nilly! Roberts, David, illus. 2005. 28p. (J). (gr. k-2). 16.00 (978-1-56148-488-1(1)) Good Bks.

Powell, Randy. Three Clams & an Oyster. 224p. (YA). 2006. pap. 6.95 (978-0-374-40007-1(5)); 2002. (gr. 7-10). 16.00 (978-0-374-37526-3(7)) Farrar, Straus & Giroux. (Farrar, Straus & Giroux (BYR)).

Prachett, Terry. Men at Arms. 2000. (gr. 7-12). lib. bdg. 15.30 (978-0-613-34006-9(X)) Tandem Library Bks.

Pratchett, Terry. The Amazing Maurice & His Educated Rodents. 2003. 368p. (YA). (gr. 7 up). pap. 6.99 (978-0-06-001235-9(8)) HarperCollins Pubs.

—The Amazing Maurice & His Educated Rodents. 2003. (gr. 5-8). lib. bdg. 15.30 (978-0-613-65757-0(8)) Tandem Library Bks.

—Johnny & the Dead. 224p. (J). 2007. pap. 5.99 (978-0-06-054190-3(3) , Harper Trophy); 2006. 15.99 (978-0-06-054188-0(1)); 2006. (gr. 5-7). lib. bdg. 16.89 (978-0-06-054189-7(X)) HarperCollins Pubs.

—Sourcery. 2001. (gr. 5-8). lib. bdg. 15.30 (978-0-613-57278-1(5)) Tandem Library Bks.

Preller, James. Case of the Great Sled Race. 2000. (gr. 3-6). lib. bdg. 11.80 (978-0-613-21298-4(3)) Tandem Library Bks.

Prestifilippo, Pablo. El Hombrecito Verde. 2004. (SPA., Illus.). 48p. (J). 8.50 (978-84-241-7905-2(6)) Everest de Ediciones y Distribucion, S.L. ESP. *Dist:* Lectorum Pubns., Inc.

Pride, Felicia. Everybody Hates First Girlfriends. 2007. (Everybody Hates Chris Ser.). 96p. (J). (gr. 2-5). pap. 5.99 (*978-1-4169-3798-2(6) , Simon Spotlight) Simon & Schuster Children's Publishing.

Primavera, Elise. Secret Order Gumm Street Girl, No. 2. 2006. (978-0-06-056949-5(2)); (978-0-06-056950-1(6)) HarperCollins Canada, Ltd.

Prince, Sarah. Mr Wolf Leaves Town. 1999. (gr. k-3). lib. bdg. 11.80 (978-0-613-19399-3(7)) Tandem Library Bks.

Princeler, Don C. Bodywork: And Other Adventures of Skippy Redcap. Johnson, Rita, illus. Princeler, Cynthia, photos by. 2001. 183p. (J). pap. 12.00 (978-1-884687-30-3(X)) New Horizons Publishing Co.

Pringle, Cindy & Pringle, Kirby. Happy Tails: Earl & Pearl on the Farm. l.t. ed. 2006. (Illus.). 32p. (J). 16.95 (978-0-9777126-0-1(5)) Dogtown Artworks.

Prinz, Yvonne. Still There, Clare Teacher Guide. 2005. 4p. (J). pap. (978-1-55192-821-0(3)) Raincoast Bk. Distribution CAN. *Dist:* Transition Vendor.

Proimos, James. Johnny Mutton, He's So Him! 2004. (Johnny Mutton Ser.). (Illus.). 48p. (J). reprint ed. pap. 5.95 (978-0-15-216766-0(8) , Harcourt Paperbacks) Harcourt Children's Bks.

—Johnny Mutton, He's So Him! 2004. (gr. 3-6). lib. bdg. 14.10 (978-0-613-71558-4(6)) Tandem Library Bks.

—Mutton Soup: More Adventures of Johnny Mutton. 2004. (Johnny Mutton Ser.). (Illus.). 48p. (J). 16.00 (978-0-15-216772-1(2)) Harcourt Children's Bks.

The Puffin Book of Funny Stories. 2006. 208p. (J). pap. 9.99 (978-0-14-333517-7(0) , Penguin Global) Penguin Group (USA) Inc.

Pullman, Philip. I Was a Rat! 2000. (Illus.). 176p. (gr. 3-5). 15.95 (978-0-375-80176-1(6) , Knopf Bks. for Young Readers) Random Hse. Children's Bks.

—I Was a Rat! Or the Scarlet Slippers. l.t. ed. 2005. 256p. (J). pap. (978-0-7540-6132-8(9) , CLP 326) BBC Audio.

—I Was a Rat! Or the Scarlet Slippers. unabr. l.t. ed. 2001. (Read-Along Ser.). 224p. (J). 29.95 incl. audio (978-0-7540-6233-2(3) , RA034, Chivers Children's Audio Bks.) BBC Audiobooks America.

—I Was a Rat! Or the Scarlet Slippers. 2002. (gr. 7-12). lib. bdg. 13.00 (978-0-613-64439-6(5)) Tandem Library Bks.

—The Scarecrow & His Servant. Bailey, Peter, illus. 240p. (J). (gr. 3-7). 2007. 6.50 (978-0-440-42130-6(6) , Yearling); 2005. 15.95 (978-0-375-81531-7(7) , Knopf Bks. for Young Readers); 2005. lib. bdg. 17.99 (978-0-375-91531-4(1) , Knopf Bks. for Young Readers) Random Hse. Children's Bks.

—Spring-Heeled Jack. Mostyn, David, illus. 2004. 112p. (gr. 3-7). 5.99 (978-0-440-41881-8(X) , Yearling) Random Hse. Children's Bks.

Pulver, Robin. Axle Annie & the Speed Grump. Arnold, Tedd, illus. 2005. 36p. (J). (ps-3). 16.99 (978-0-8037-2787-8(9) , Dial) Penguin Group (USA) Inc.

Puttock, Simon. "Here I Am!" Said Smedley. Chatterton, Martin & Chatterton, Ann, illus. 2001. (Blue Bananas Ser.). 48p. (J). (gr. 1-2). (978-0-7787-0838-4(1)); pap. (978-0-7787-0884-1(5)) Crabtree Publishing Co.

—Here I Am! Said Smedley. 2002. (gr. k-3). lib. bdg. 12.95 (978-0-613-52852-8(2)) Tandem Library Bks.

Rabe, Tish. Innovative Kids Readers: Milly's Silly Suitcase - Level 1. Janovitz, Marilyn, illus. 2006. (J). (ps-1). 6.99 (978-1-58476-493-9(7)) Innovative Kids.

—Milly's Silly Suitcase. Janovitz, Marilyn, illus. 2006. (innovativeKids readers ser.: level 1). 24p. (J). (ps-1). pap. 6.99 (978-1-58476-476-2(7) , IKIDS) Innovative Kids.

Rade, Erin P. Who Wants Some Pizza? Smith, Len, illus. 2007. (Meet the Robinsons Ser.). 20p. (J). pap. 6.99 (978-0-06-112480-8(X)) HarperCollins Pubs.

Rader, Laura. Santa's New Suit. Rader, Laura, illus. 2004. (Illus.). 32p. (J). (gr. k-3). reprint ed. 13.00 (978-0-7567-7154-6(4)) DIANE Publishing Co.

Radford, Sheri. Penelope & the Humongous Burp. Tripp, Christine, illus. 2005. 32p. pap. (978-1-897073-33-9(X)) Lobster Pr.

Rae, Amber. Stories for Kids by Kids. 2001. 16p. (J). (gr. 2-7). 3.75 (978-0-9660336-2-5(0)) Santa's Secret Creations.

Ragnar. Got Your Nose: A True Story. 2004. (Illus.). 32p. (ps-3). 9.00 (978-0-9729388-1-5(8)) Baby Tattoo Bks.

Random House Disney Staff. Disney/Pixar Fun Kit. (Fun Kit Ser.). (Illus.). 48p. (J). (ps-2). 2007. pap. 9.99 (*978-0-7364-2492-9(X)); 2006. 9.99 (978-0-7364-2412-7(1)) Random Hse. Children's Bks. (Golden/Disney).

Rankin, Laura, illus. The Cowgirl Aunt of Harriet Bean. 2007. 81p. (J). (gr. 2-4). per. 4.95 (*978-1-59990-055-1(6) , Bloomsbury Children) Bloomsbury Publishing.

Ransom, Jeanie Franz. What Do Parents Do When You're Not Home. Moore, Cyd, illus. 2007. 32p. (J). (gr. k-2). 16.95 (978-1-56145-409-9(5) , Peachtree Junior) Peachtree Pubs., Ltd.

Raskin, Ellen. Westing Game. 2003. 182p. (J). lib. bdg. 15.00 (*978-1-4242-2271-1(0)) Fitzgerald Bks.

Rateau, Loy. David's Prayers: A Boy's Perseverance of Conquering the Enemy. 2005. 17.00 (978-0-8059-9834-4(9)) Dorrance Publishing Co., Inc.

Rau, Dana Meachen. Clown Around, Level B. Evans, Nate, illus. 2001. (Early Reader Ser.). 32p. (J). (gr. k up). lib. bdg. 18.60 (978-0-7565-0074-0(5)) Compass Point Bks.

Ravel, Edeet. The Secret Journey of Pauline Siddhartha. 2007. 224p. pap. 9.95 (*978-1-55192-974-3(0)) Raincoast Bk. Distribution CAN. *Dist:* Perseus Distribution.

Rayner, Robert. Miss Little's Losers. 2003. (Sports Stories Ser.). 128p. (J). (gr. 4-8). 7.95 (978-1-55028-810-0(5)); (*978-1-55028-811-7(3)) Lorimer, James & Co., Ltd., Pubs. CAN. *Dist:* Casemate Pubs. & Bk. Distributors, LLC.

Ready Set Laugh. 2004. (J). per. (978-1-57657-458-4(X)) Paradise Pr., Inc.

Rees, Douglas. Uncle Pirate. Auth, Tony, illus. 2008. 112p. (J). (*978-1-4169-4762-2(0) , McElderry, Margaret K.) Simon & Schuster Children's Publishing.

Rees, Gwyneth. The Mum Hunt. l.t. ed. 2006. pap. 16.95 (978-1-4056-6061-7(9)) BBC Audio GBR. *Dist:* BBC Audiobooks America.

Regal, David. Jungle Mischief. 2000. (gr. k-3). lib. bdg. 11.25 (978-0-613-25834-0(7)) Tandem Library Bks.

Regan, Dian Curtis. Barnyard Slam. Meisel, Paul, illus. 2006. (J). (978-0-8234-1907-4(X)) Holiday Hse., Inc.

—The World According to Kaley. 2005. (Illus.). 112p. (J). (gr. 4-7). per. 14.99 (978-1-58196-039-6(5)) Darby Creek Publishing.

Regan, Michael. Pimp My Pumpkin. 2006. (Illus.). 32p. pap. 6.95 (978-0-7624-2824-3(4)) Running Pr. Bk. Pubs.

—The Power of Positive Winking. 2003. (J). 12.95 (978-0-375-82374-9(3)); lib. bdg. 16.99 (978-0-375-92374-6(8)) Random Hse. Children's Bks. (Random Hse. Bks. for Young Readers).

Reiche, Deitlof. Book Two in the Golden Hamster Saga. Cepeda, Joe, illus. 2006. 208p. (J). pap. 4.99 (978-0-439-53156-6(X) , Scholastic Paperbacks) Scholastic, Inc.

Reiss, Mike. The Great Show & Tell Disaster! Cressy, Mike, illus. 2001. 32p. (J). 13.99 (978-0-8431-7680-3(6) , Price Stern Sloan) Penguin Group (USA) Inc.

—Late for School. Austin, Michael, illus. 2003. 32p. (J). (gr. 1-5). 16.95 (978-1-56145-286-6(6) , Q35957) Peachtree Pubs., Ltd.

—Santa Claustrophobia. Catrow, David, illus. 2002. 32p. (J). (gr. 2-5). 10.99 (978-0-8431-7756-5(X) , Price Stern Sloan) Penguin Group (USA) Inc.

—Santa Claustrophobia. Catrow, David, illus. 2006. 32p. (J). (ps). pap. 5.99 (978-0-14-240376-1(8) , Puffin) Penguin Group (USA) Inc.

Reiss, Mike. Santa's Eleven Months Off. Montgomery, Michael, illus. 2007. 32p. (J). (ps-3). 16.95 (*978-1-56145-421-1(4) , Peachtree Junior) Peachtree Pubs., Ltd.

Rennison, Louise. Angus, Thongs & Full-Frontal Snogging. 2000. (Confessions of Georgia Nicolson Ser.). (Illus.). 256p. (J). (gr. 7 up). lib. bdg. 17.89 (978-0-06-028871-6(X)) HarperCollins Pubs.

—Angus, Thongs & Full-Frontal Snogging: Confessions of Georgia Nicolson. 2001. (Confessions of Georgia Nicolson Ser.). 272p. (J). (gr. 7 up). pap. 7.99 (978-0-06-447227-2(2) , HarperTeen) HarperCollins Pubs.

—Angus, Thongs & Full-Frontal Snogging: Confessions of Georgia Nicolson. 2003. (gr. 7-12). lib. bdg. 15.30 (978-0-613-71444-0(X)); 2001. (J). 13.64 (978-0-606-20508-5(X)) Tandem Library Bks.

—Angus, Thongs, & Full-Frontal Snogging: Confessions of Georgia Nicolson. 2001. (gr. 7-12). lib. bdg. 15.30 (978-0-613-35897-2(X)) Tandem Library Bks.

—Angus, Thongs & Full-Frontal Snogging (rack) Confessions of Georgia Nicolson. 2003. (Confessions of Georgia Nicolson Ser.). 256p. (J). pap. 6.99 (978-0-06-052184-4(8)) HarperCollins Pubs.

—Dancing in My Nuddy-Pants: Even Further Confessions of Georgia Nicolson. (Confessions of Georgia Nicolson Ser.). 2003. 224p. (J). 15.99 (978-0-06-009746-2(9)); 2004. 240p. (YA). reprint ed. pap. 7.99 (978-0-06-009748-6(5)) HarperCollins Pubs. (HarperTeen).

—Fabbity-Fab! A Big Box of Georgia. 2005. (Confessions of Georgia Nicolson Ser.). (J). pap. 19.99 (978-0-06-079724-9(X) , HarperTeen) HarperCollins Pubs.

—Further Confessions of Georgia Nicolson. ed. 2004. (Confessions of Georgia Nicolson Ser.). 416p. (J). pap. 13.99 (978-0-06-059007-9(6)) HarperCollins Pubs.

—Knocked Out by My Nunga-Nungas. 2004. (Confessions of Georgia Nicolson Ser.). (Illus.). 208p. (J). (gr. 8 up). reprint ed. pap. 6.99 (978-0-06-058991-2(4)) HarperCollins Pubs.

—Knocked Out by My Nunga-Nungas: Further, Further Confessions of Georgia Nicolson. 2002. (Confessions of Georgia Nicolson Ser.). 192p. (J). (gr. 8-10). 15.99 (978-0-06-623656-8(8)) HarperCollins Pubs.

—Knocked Out by My Nunga-Nungas: Further, Further Confessions of Georgia Nicolson. 2003. (gr. 7-12). lib. bdg. 15.30 (978-0-613-67208-5(9)) Tandem Library Bks.

—Love Is a Many Trousered Thing. 2007. (Confessions of Georgia Nicolson Ser.). (J). 288p. lib. bdg. 17.89 (*978-0-06-085388-4(3)); 256p. (gr. 7 up). 16.99 (*978-0-06-085387-7(5)) HarperCollins Pubs. (HarperTeen).

—On the Bright Side, I'm Now the Girlfriend of a Sex God: Further Confessions Of. 2002. (gr. 7-12). lib. bdg. 15.30 (978-0-613-49344-4(3)) Tandem Library Bks.

—On the Bright Side, I'm Now the Girlfriend of a Sex God: Further Confessions of Georgia Nicolson. (Confessions of Georgia Nicolson Ser.). 2003. 256p. (J). pap. 6.99 (978-0-06-052185-1(6)); 2002. 272p. (YA). pap. 7.99 (978-0-06-447226-5(4)); 2001. 256p. (J). (gr. 7 up). 17.99 (978-0-06-028813-6(2)) HarperCollins Pubs.

—Startled by His Furry Shorts. 2007. (Confessions of Georgia Nicolson Ser.). 304p. (J). pap. 7.99 (*978-0-06-085386-0(7) , HarperTeen) HarperCollins Pubs.

—Startled by His Furry Shorts! 2006. (Confessions of Georgia Nicolson Ser.). 288p. (J). 16.99 (978-0-06-085384-6(0)); lib. bdg. 17.89 (978-0-06-085385-3(9)) HarperCollins Pubs. (HarperTeen).

—Then He Ate My Boy Entrancers: More Mad, Marvy Confessions of Georgia Nicolson. (Confessions of Georgia Nicolson Ser.). 2006. 336p. (J). pap. 7.99 (978-0-06-058939-4(6)); 2005. 320p. (J). lib. bdg. 16.89 (978-0-06-058938-7(8)); No. 6. 2005. 320p. (YA). 15.99 (978-0-06-058937-0(X)) HarperCollins Pubs. (HarperTeen).

Resnikoff, Irene & Valas, Claudia. OG in Jerusalem. 2003. (OG the Terrible Ser.: Vol. 3). (HEB., Illus.). 24p. (J). pap. 4.50 (978-0-939144-43-3(3)) EKS Publishing Co.

Rex, Adam. Psst! 2007. (Illus.). 40p. (J). (gr. k-3). 16.00 (978-0-15-205817-3(6)) Harcourt Trade Pubs.

Rey, Margret. Curious George Goes to a Costume Party. Vipah Interactive Staff, illus. 2001. (Curious George Ser.). 24p. (J). (gr. k-3). tchr. ed. 12.95 (978-0-618-06564-6(4)) Houghton Mifflin Co. Trade & Reference Div.

Rey, Margret, et al. Curious George Goes to a Costume Party. Weston, Martha, illus. 2001. (Curious George Ser.). 24p. (J). (gr. k-3). pap. 3.95 (978-0-618-06569-1(5)) Houghton Mifflin Co. Trade & Reference Div.

Ricci, Laura. Dr. Mike's Adventures. 2006. 63p. pap. 12.95 (978-1-4241-2653-8(3)) PublishAmerica, Inc.

Richards, Chuck. Jungle Gym Jitters. Richards, Chuck, illus. 2004. (Illus.). 32p. (J). 17.85 (978-0-8027-8932-7(3)); 16.95 (978-0-8027-8931-0(5)) Walker & Co.

Richards, Pat. Bardolph Bedivere Wolf Returns. Richards, Charles, illus. 2007. 42p. (J). (*978-0-9790796-4-1(0)) PJR Assocs., Ltd.

Richardson, Bill. But If They Do. Mongeau, Marc, illus. 2003. 24p. (J). (ps-1). pap. 6.95 (978-1-55037-786-6(8)); lib. bdg. 18.95 (978-1-55037-787-3(6)) Annick Pr., Ltd. CAN. *Dist:* Firefly Bks., Ltd.

—Sally Dog Little. Malepart, Celine, illus. 2002. 24p. (J). (ps-2). lib. bdg. 14.95 (978-1-55037-759-0(0)) Annick Pr., Ltd. CAN. *Dist:* Firefly Bks., Ltd.

Richler, Mordecai. Jacob Two-Two & the Dinosaur. Eyolfson, Norman, illus. 2004. 96p. (J). (gr. 3-7). pap. 6.95 (978-0-88776-712-8(5)) Tundra Bks., Inc./Livres Toundra, Inc. CAN. *Dist:* Random Hse., Inc.

Richmond, Andrew. The Adventures of Bonga-Bo: Christopher, Front & Center! Now! 2004. (Illus.). 50p. (J). per. 9.95 (978-1-59453-366-2(0) , 2477) Airleaf Publishing & Bookselling.

Richter, Danny. The Big Gozonga. 2006. 16.95 (978-0-9786107-0-8(9)) Arbor Bks.

Riddell, Chris. Chris Riddell's Da Vinci Cod & Other Illustrations for Unwritten Books. Riddell, Chris, illus. 2006. (Illus.). 72p. (J). (gr. 7). 7.99 (978-0-7636-3053-9(5)) Candlewick Pr.

Riddleburger, Sam. The Qwikpick Adventure Society. 2007. (Illus.). 128p. (J). (gr. 4-6). 16.99 (978-0-8037-3178-3(7) , Dial) Penguin Group (USA) Inc.

Rider, Cynthia. The Crocodile's Sky Snack. Clementson, John, illus. 2001. (Cambridge Reading Ser.). 16p. pap. 6.00 (978-0-521-01402-1(6)) Cambridge Univ. Pr.

Riker, Richard K. School Days Daze. l.t. ed. 2005. (Illus.). 168p. (J). 15.95 (978-0-9760416-0-3(X)) Safe Harbor Pubns.

Rinck, Maranke. The Sweetest Kiss. Van Der Linden, Martijn, illus. 2007. 32p. (J). 16.95 (*978-1-59078-519-5(3)) Boyds Mills Pr.

Ring, Susan. Where's My Nose? Peterson, Stephanie, illus. 2001. 16p. (J). bds. 5.99 (978-0-448-42504-7(1) , Grosset & Dunlap) Penguin Group (USA) Inc.

Rivard, Ken. Mom, the School Flooded. Weissmann, Joe, illus. rev. ed. 2007. 24p. (J). (gr. k-2). pap. 6.95 (*978-1-55451-095-5(3)); lib. bdg. 19.95 (*978-1-55451-096-2(1)) Annick Pr., Ltd. CAN. *Dist:* Firefly Bks., Ltd.

Rivers, Karen. The Cure for Crushes: And Other Deadly Plagues. 2005. 304p. (J). (gr. 10 up). pap. 6.95 (978-1-55192-779-4(9)) Raincoast Bk. Distribution CAN. *Dist:* Perseus Distribution.

Rix, Jamie. Mr. Mumble's Fabulous Flybrows. 2003. (Illus.). 64p. (J). pap. 8.99 (978-0-552-54747-5(6) , Corgi) Transworld Publishers Ltd. GBR. *Dist:* Trafalgar Square Publishing.

Roberts, A. A. Bobo World. 2003. (Illus.). 190p. (J). (gr. 5-7). pap. 14.95 (978-0-9718544-0-6(8)) AntHill Publishing.

Roberts, Daniel. There's a Cookie Stuck to My Nose! 2006. (ENG., Illus.). 36p. per. 16.99 (*978-1-4259-7093-2(1)) AuthorHouse.

Roberts, Diane. Made You Look. 160p. (gr. 3-7). 2004. pap. 5.50 (978-0-440-41854-2(2) , Yearling); 2003. (J). 15.95 (978-0-385-72979-6(0) , Delacorte Bks. for Young Readers) Random Hse. Children's Bks.

Roberts, Lynn. Little Red: A Fizzingly Good Yarn. Roberts, David, illus. 2005. 32p. (J). (ps-3). 16.95 (978-0-8109-5783-1(3) , Abrams Bks. for Young Readers) Abrams, Harry N., Inc.

Robertson, M. P. Hieronymus Betts & His Unusual Pets. 2005. (Illus.). 32p. (J). (ps-3). 15.95 (978-1-84507-289-6(8)) Lincoln, Frances Ltd. GBR. *Dist:* Perseus Distribution.

Robins, Eleanor. A Very Good Year. 2004. 48p. (YA). per. (978-1-56254-784-4(4) , SP7844) Saddleback Educational Publishing.

Robinson, Barbara. My Brother Louis Measures Worms: And Other Louis Stories. 2005. 240p. (J). (ps-7). pap. 5.99 (978-0-06-076672-6(7) , Harper Trophy) HarperCollins Pubs.

Robinson, Fiona. The Useful Moose: A Truthful, Moose-Full Tale. 2004. (Illus.). 32p. (J). (ps-3). 14.95 (978-0-8109-4925-6(3)) Abrams, Harry N., Inc.

Robles, Eric. Billy Was Born to Be a Cowboy! 2007. (J). (978-0-375-83422-6(2)); lib. bdg. (978-0-375-93422-3(7)) Random Hse., Inc.

Rockwell, Thomas. How to Eat Fried Worms. 2006. 128p. (J). (gr. 2-5). 5.99 (978-0-440-42185-6(3) , Yearling) Random Hse. Children's Bks.

Roddie, Shen. Simon Says. Lambert, Sally Anne, illus. 32p. (J). (ps-3). 2001. pap. 8.99 (978-0-7112-1532-0(4)); 2000. 19.99 (978-0-7112-1529-0(4)) Lincoln, Frances Ltd. GBR. *Dist:* Transition Vendor, Antique Collectors' Club.

Roddie, Shen & Lambert, Sally Ann. Simon Says. 2004. (Illus.). 32p. (J). pap. 7.95 (978-1-84507-233-9(2)) Lincoln, Frances Ltd. GBR. *Dist:* Perseus Distribution.

Roman, Sela Anders. Where Are Grandpa's Teeth? Smith, Len, illus. 2007. (Meet the Robinsons Ser.). 20p. (J). pap. 6.99 (978-0-06-112478-5(8)) HarperCollins Pubs.

Root, Phyllis. Aunt Nancy & the Bothersome Visitors. Parkins, David, illus. 2007. 64p. (J). (gr. 2-5). 16.99 (*978-0-7636-3074-4(8)) Candlewick Pr.

Rosado, Maria. Wild Thornberrys Trivia Book. 2000. (gr. 3-6). lib. bdg. 10.65 (978-0-613-27583-5(7)) Tandem Library Bks.

Roselle, Gayle. Moozelville Playground. 2007. (Illus.). 74p. (J). pap. 12.95 (*978-0-9788628-8-6(0)) Just Write Bks.

Rosen, Michael. Ronquidos! Langley, Jonathan, illus. Tr. of Snore!. (SPA.). (J). (gr. 1-3). 8.95 (978-958-04-4646-0(6)) Norma S.A. COL. *Dist:* Distribuidora Norma, Inc., Lectorum Pubns., Inc.

—We're Going on a Bear Hunt. Oxenbury, Helen, illus. 2003. 36p. (J). pap. 7.99 (978-0-689-85349-4(1) , Aladdin) Simon & Schuster Children's Publishing.

Rosen, Michael, ed. Ribticklers: Funny Stories. 2007. 288p. (J). (gr. 7). pap. 6.95 (*978-0-7534-6139-6(0) , Kingfisher) Houghton Mifflin Co. Trade & Reference Div.

Rosen, Michael & Oxenbury, Helen. We're Going on a Bear Hunt. 2004. (POR, TAM, CZE, VIE & CHI., Illus.). 32p. (J). (978-1-85269-706-8(7)); (978-1-85269-710-5(5)); (978-1-85269-711-2(3)); (978-1-85269-716-7(4)); (978-1-85269-718-1(0)); (978-1-85269-720-4(2)) Mantra Publishing, Ltd.

Rosen, Michael & Rosen, Michael. Fantastically Funny Stories. Brown, Mik, illus. 2005. (Sidesplitters Ser.). 64p. (J). (gr. 3-5). pap. 3.95 (978-0-7534-5876-1(4) , Kingfisher) Houghton Mifflin Co. Trade & Reference Div.

Rosen, Michael J. We're Going on a Bear Hunt. Oxenbury, Helen, illus. gif. ed. 2002. 40p. (J). 9.99 (978-0-7636-1979-4(5)) Candlewick Pr.

Rosenthal, Betsy R. It's Not Worth Making a Tzimmes Over! Rivers, Ruth, illus. 2006. 32p. (J). 15.95 (978-0-8075-3677-3(6)) Whitman, Albert & Co.

Rosenthal, Marc. Phooey! Rosenthal, Marc, illus. 2007. 40p. (J). (ps-3). 16.99 (978-0-06-075248-4(3)); lib. bdg. 17.89 (978-0-06-075249-1(1)) HarperCollins Pubs. (Cotler, Joanna Books).

Rosoff, Meg. Jumpy Jack & Googily. Blackall, Sophie, illus. 2008. 32p. (J). 16.95 (*978-0-8050-8066-7(X)) Holt, Henry & Co.

—Meet Wild Boars. Blackall, Sophie, illus. rev. ed. 2005. 40p. (J). 15.95 (978-0-8050-7488-0(0) , Holt, Henry & Co. Bks. For Young Readers) Holt, Henry & Co.

—Untitled Rossoff 2 Wild Boars. Date not set. (J). 16.95 (978-0-8050-7523-6(2) , Holt, Henry & Co. Bks. For Young Readers) Holt, Henry & Co.

Ross, Jay. Bungalow 29. Klimko, Andrew Frank, illus. 2005. 125p. pap. 12.95 (978-0-9771994-0-2(1)) Visor Bks.

Ross, Jil. The Real 'Nitty Gritty' 2006. (Illus.). 62p. (J). per. 6.95 (978-1-933324-40-1(6)) Cedar Hill Publishing.

Ross, Jil M. What's the Matter, Mr. Ticklebritches? Another installment in the Shenanigans Series. 2006. (Illus.). 62p. (J). per. 6.95 (978-1-933324-26-5(0)) Cedar Hill Publishing.

Ross, Pat. M & M & the Mummy Mess. Hafner, Marylin, illus. 1999. (Puffin Chapters Ser.). 48p. (J). (gr. 2-5). pap. 4.99 (978-0-14-130654-4(8) , Puffin) Penguin Group (USA) Inc.

Ross, Tony. I Want My Potty. Ross, Tony, illus. 2007. (People Love Little Princess Books! Ser.). (Illus.). 28p. (J). pap. 4.95 (978-1-933605-23-4(5) , 05234) Kane/Miller Bk. Pubs., Inc.

—Say Please! Ross, Tony, illus. 2006. (People Love Little Princess Books! Ser.: 6). (Illus.). 28p. (J). pap. 4.95 (978-1-933605-16-6(2)) Kane/Miller Bk. Pubs., Inc.

—Super Dooper Jezebel. (Illus.). 32p. (J). pap. 9.99 (978-1-84270-096-9(0)) Andersen GBR. *Dist:* Trafalgar Square Publishing.

Rothstein, Nancy. My Daddy Snores. 2007. 32p. (J). pap. 5.99 (*978-0-545-02834-9(5)) Scholastic, Inc.

Rovetch, L. Bob. Hot Dog & Bob & the Dangerously Dizzy Attack of the Alien Hypno Hamsters. Whamond, Dave, illus. 2007. 96p. (J). pap. 4.95 (978-0-8118-5602-7(X)) Chronicle Bks. LLC.

—Hot Dog & Bob & the Exceptionally Eggy Attack of the Game Gators. Whamond, Dave, illus. 2007. 96p. (J). pap. 4.95 (978-0-8118-5604-1(6)) Chronicle Bks. LLC.

—Hot Dog & Bob & the Surprisingly Slobbery Attack of the Dog-Wash Doggies. Whamond, Dave, illus. 2007. (Hot Dog & Bob Ser.: No. 5). 96p. (J). (gr. 1-5). 15.50 (978-0-8118-5745-1(X)); pap. 4.95 (978-0-8118-5746-8(8)) Chronicle Bks. LLC.

Rovetch, Lissa. Hot Dog & Bob Adventure. Whamond, Dave, illus. (J). 2007. 96p. 15.50 (978-0-8118-5601-0(1)); No. 6. 2008. pap. 4.95 (978-0-8118-5748-2(4)) Chronicle Bks. LLC.

—Hot Dog & Bob Adventure 6 Le. Whamond, Dave, illus. 2008. (J). 15.50 (978-0-8118-5747-5(6)) Chronicle Bks. LLC.

—Hot Dog & Bob & the Exceptionally Eggy Attack of the Game Gators. Whamond, Dave, illus. 2007. 96p. (J). 15.50 (978-0-8118-5603-4(8)) Chronicle Bks. LLC.

Rowdy's Big day: Horses & Ponies. 2002. (Illus.). 24p. (J). (gr. k-5). pap. 2.99 (978-1-57759-377-5(4)) Dalmatian Pr.

Rowling, J. K. Harry Potter a l'Ecole des Sorciers. l.t. ed. 2005. (Harry Potter Ser.). (Illus.). 408p. 30.99 (978-2-84011-646-2(4)) Ulverscroft Large Print Bks. GBR. *Dist:* Ulverscroft Large Print Bks., Ltd.

—Harry Potter & the Sorcerer's Stone. GrandPré, Mary, illus. 2003. (Harry Potter Ser.: Year 1). 320p. (J). (ps-17). 24.95 (978-0-439-55493-0(4) , Levine, Arthur A. Bks.) Scholastic, Inc.

—Harry Potter & the Sorcerer's Stone. 2001. (Illus.). (J). 13.64 (978-0-606-21606-7(5)) Tandem Library Bks.

Roy, Ron. Fireworks at the FBI. Bush, Timothy, illus. 2006. 96p. (J). (gr. 1-4). pap. 3.99 (978-0-375-87527-4(1)); lib. bdg. 11.99 (978-0-375-97527-1(6)) Random Hse. Children's Bks. (Random Hse. Bks. for Young Readers).

Rubin, Cathy. Eleanor, Ellatony, Ellencake, & Me. Fowler, Christopher, illus. 2003. (Eleanor Ser.). 32p. (J). (gr. k-3). 14.95 (978-1-57768-412-1(5) , Gingham Dog Pr.) School Specialty Publishing.

Ruditis, Paul. Love, Hollywood Style. 2008. (Romantic Comedies Ser.). 272p. (YA). mass mkt. 6.99 (*978-1-4169-5138-4(5) , Simon Pulse) Simon & Schuster Children's Publishing.

Ruelle, Karen Gray. Mother's Day. (Illus.). 32p. (J). (gr. k-3). tchr. ed. 14.95 (978-0-8234-1773-5(5)) Holiday Hse., Inc.

Rumble, Chris. The Good, the Bad, & the Smelly. 2005. (Adventures of Uncle Stinky Ser.). (Illus.). 96p. (J). 15.95 (978-1-58246-120-5(1) , Tricycle Pr.) Ten Speed Pr.

—Moby Stink. 2005. (Illus.). 96p. (J). (ps-7). pap. 5.95 (978-1-58246-145-8(7) , Tricycle Pr.) Ten Speed Pr.

H
I

—Stink Trek: The Adventures of Uncle Stinky #2. 2005. (Illus.). 96p. (J). 5.95 (978-1-58246-123-6(6) , Tricycle Pr.) Ten Speed Pr.

Rundstrom, T. S. Baribold Jones & Big Big Booger Grabber. 2004. (Illus.). per. (978-1-932062-43-4(2)) Hability Solution Services, Inc.

Running Press Staff & Neusner, Dena. Johnny Tractors Fun Farm Day. 2006. (Illus.). 8p. (J). pap. 5.95 (978-0-7624-2630-0(6) , Running Pr. Kids) Running Pr. Bk. Pubs.

Rushton, Rosie. The Dashwood Sisters' Secrets of Love. 2006. 336p. (gr. 7-17). reprint ed. pap. 8.99 (978-0-7868-5137-9(6)) Hyperion Pr.

—How Could You Do This to Me, Mum? 2005. 224p. (J). pap. 5.99 (978-0-7868-5187-4(2)) Hyperion Bks. for Children.

—I Think I'll Just Curl up & Die. 2005. 176p. (J). pap. 5.99 (978-0-7868-5188-1(0)) Hyperion Bks. for Children.

—Just Don't Make a Scene, Mum! 2005. 224p. (J). pap. 5.99 (978-0-7868-5186-7(4)) Hyperion Bks. for Children.

—Melissa. 2000. (Fab Five Ser.). 224p. (gr. 5-9). pap. 4.99 (978-0-7868-1502-9(7)) Hyperion Bks. for Children.

—Melissa. 2000. (gr. 5-8). lib. bdg. 13.00 (978-0-613-31467-1(0)) Tandem Library Bks.

—Sophie. 2000. (gr. 5-8). lib. bdg. 13.00 (978-0-613-31732-0(7)) Tandem Library Bks.

—Where Do We Go from Here? 2005. 224p. (J). pap. 5.99 (978-0-7868-5189-8(9)) Hyperion Bks. for Children.

Ruttle, Keith. The Lord Mount Dragon. 2005. (Cambridge Storybooks Ser.). (Illus.). 32p. pap. 7.00 (978-0-521-67487-4(5)) Cambridge Univ. Pr.

Rylant, Cynthia. Mr. Putter & Tabby Feed the Fish. 2002. (Mr. Putter & Tabby Ser.). (Illus.). (J). 13.15 (978-0-7587-9914-2(4)) Book Wholesalers, Inc.

—Mr. Putter & Tabby Feed the Fish. Howard, Arthur, illus. (Mr. Putter & Tabby Ser.). 44p. (J). (gr. 1-4). 2002. pap. 5.95 (978-0-15-216366-2(2) , Harcourt Paperbacks); 2001. 15.00 (978-0-15-202408-6(5)) Harcourt Children's Bks.

—Mr. Putter & Tabby Feed the Fish. 2001. (Mr. Putter & Tabby Ser.). (gr. k-3). lib. bdg. 14.10 (978-0-613-44315-9(2)) Tandem Library Bks.

—Mr. Putter & Tabby Pour the Tea. Howard, Arthur, illus. 2002. (Mr. Putter & Tabby Ser.). (J). 13.15 (978-0-7587-0684-3(7)) Book Wholesalers, Inc.

—Mr. Putter & Tabby Row the Boat. Howard, Arthur, illus. 2002. (Mr. Putter & Tabby Ser.). (J). 13.15 (978-0-7587-0685-0(5)) Book Wholesalers, Inc.

—Mr. Putter & Tabby Take the Train. Howard, Arthur, illus. 2002. (Mr. Putter & Tabby Ser.). (J). 13.15 (978-0-7587-0686-7(3)) Book Wholesalers, Inc.

—Mr. Putter & Tabby Toot the Horn. Howard, Arthur, illus. 2002. (Mr. Putter & Tabby Ser.). (J). 13.15 (978-0-7587-0687-4(1)) Book Wholesalers, Inc.

—Mr. Putter & Tabby Walk the Dog. Howard, Arthur, illus. 2002. (Mr. Putter & Tabby Ser.). (J). 13.15 (978-0-7587-0688-1(X)) Book Wholesalers, Inc.

—Puppy Mudge Finds a Friend. Stevenson, Sucie, illus. 2004. (Puppy Mudge Ser.). 32p. (J). (ps-k). 14.95 (978-0-689-83982-5(0)) Simon & Schuster Children's Publishing.

—Puppy Mudge Loves His Blanket. Mones, Isidre, illus. 2005. (Puppy Mudge Ser.). 32p. (J). (ps). pap. 3.99 (978-1-4169-0336-9(4) , Aladdin) Simon & Schuster Children's Publishing.

—Puppy Mudge Wants to Play. Stevenson, Sucie, illus. 2005. (Puppy Mudge Ser.). 32p. (J). (ps-k). 14.95 (978-0-689-83984-9(7)) Simon & Schuster Children's Publishing.

Rylant, Cynthia & Mones, Isidre. Puppy Mudge Has a Snack. 2004. (Puppy Mudge Ser.). (Illus.). 32p. (J). pap. 3.99 (978-0-689-86995-2(9) , Aladdin) Simon & Schuster Children's Publishing.

Sachar, Louis. Class President. 1999. (Marvin Redpost Ser.: No. 5). (Illus.). 80p. (J). (gr. k-3). lib. bdg. 11.99 (978-0-679-98999-8(4) , Random Hse. Bks. for Young Readers) Random Hse. Children's Bks.

Class President. Wummer, Amy, illus. 1999. (Marvin Redpost Ser.: Vol. 5). 80p. (J). (gr. k-3). 3.99 (978-0-679-88999-1(X) , Random Hse. Bks. for Young Readers) Random Hse. Children's Bks.

—Class President. 1999. (Marvin Redpost Ser.: Bk. 5). (gr. 3-6). lib. bdg. 11.80 (978-0-613-16151-0(3)) Tandem Library Bks.

—A Magic Crystal? Loehr, Mallory, ed. Wummer, Amy, illus. 2000. (Marvin Redpost Ser.: No. 8). 96p. (J). (gr. k-3). 3.99 (978-0-679-89002-7(5) , Random Hse. Bks. for Young Readers) Random Hse. Children's Bks.

Sadler, Marilyn. Zenon Kar, Girl of the 21st Century No. 1: Bobo Crazy. 2001. (Stepping Stone Bks.). (Illus.). (J). 10.79 (978-0-606-21007-2(5)) Tandem Library Bks.

—Zenon Kar, Girl of the 21st Century No. 2: Spaceball Stars. 2001. (Stepping Stone Bks.). (Illus.). (J). (978-0-606-21542-8(5)) Tandem Library Bks.

Samuel, Catherine. Timmy's Eggs-Ray Vision. Saunders, Zina, illus. 2005. 16p. (J). lib. bdg. 12.00 (*978-1-4242-0968-2(4)) Fitzgerald Bks.

Samuel, Catherine & Hartman, Butch. Timmy's Eggs-Ray Vision. Saunders, Zina, illus. 2005. (J). (*978-1-4155-8053-0(7) , Simon Spotlight/Nickelodeon) Simon & Schuster Children's Publishing.

Sandburg, Carl. The Huckabuck Family & How They Raised: Popcorn in Nebraska & Quit & Came Back. Small, David, illus. 2006. 30p. (J). (gr. k-4). reprint ed. 16.00 (*978-1-4223-5854-2(2)) DIANE Publishing Co.

Sandburg, Carl & Sandburg, Carl. Rootabaga Stories. Petersham, Maud Fuller & Petersham, Miska, illus. 2003. 176p. (J). (ps-7). lib. bdg. 14.10 (978-0-613-67517-8(7)) Tandem Library Bks.

Sander, Sonia. Sports Heroes. Franchesco! & Hardin, Greg, illus. 2007. (VeggieTales Ser.). 96p. (J). 2.99 (978-1-4169-3512-4(6) , Simon Scribbles) Simon & Schuster Children's Publishing.

Sander, Sonia. Wonderful Wuzzleburg. 2008. (Wow! Wow! Wubbzy! Ser.). 224p. (J). 4.99 (*978-1-4169-4793-6(0) , Simon Scribbles) Simon & Schuster Children's Publishing.

Sanderson, Brandon. Alcatraz Versus the Evil Librarians. 2007. (Alcatraz Versus the Evil Librarians Ser.). 320p. (J). pap. 16.99 (*978-0-439-92550-1(9) , Scholastic Pr.) Scholastic, Inc.

Sastrias, Marta. Cuentos de Todo y de Nada. Martinez y Luis San Vicente, Enrique, illus. 2003. (SPA.). 82p. (J). (gr. 3-5). (978-968-19-0551-4(2)) Aguilar, Altea, Taurus, Alfaguara, S.A. de C.V.

Sato, Wakiko. Grandma Baba Wants Sunshine!, Vol. 5. 2004. (Grandma Baba Ser.). (JPN & ENG., Illus.). 32p. (J). 10.95 (978-0-8048-3568-8(3)) Tuttle Publishing.

—Grandma Baba's Big Cleanup!, Vol. 6. 2004. (Grandma Baba Ser.). (JPN & ENG., Illus.). 32p. (J). 10.95 (978-0-8048-3569-5(1)) Tuttle Publishing.

—Grandma Baba's Bird's Nest!, Vol. 9. Carpenter, Richard, tr. from JPN. 2004. (Grandma Baba Ser.). (Illus.). 32p. (J). 10.95 (978-0-8048-3571-8(3)) Tuttle Publishing.

—Grandma Baba's Birthday Party, Vol. 4. 2004. (Grandma Baba Ser.). (Illus.). 32p. 10.95 (978-0-8048-3562-6(4)) Tuttle Publishing.

—Grandma Baba's Busy Night, Bk. 1. 2004. (Grandma Baba Ser.). (Illus.). 32p. 10.95 (978-0-8048-3559-6(4)) Tuttle Publishing.

—Grandma Baba's Dream Mountain!, Vol. 7. 2004. (Grandma Baba Ser.). (JPN & ENG., Illus.). 32p. (J). 10.95 (978-0-8048-3570-1(5)) Tuttle Publishing.

—Grandma Baba's Magic Watermelon!, Vol. 8. Carpenter, Richard, tr. from JPN. 2004. (Grandma Baba Ser.). (Illus.). 28p. (J). 10.95 (978-0-8048-3567-1(5)) Tuttle Publishing.

—Grandma Baba's Sunny Spring, Vol. 2. 2004. (Grandma Baba Ser.). (Illus.). 32p. 10.95 (978-0-8048-3560-2(8)) Tuttle Publishing.

—Grandma Baba's Warming Ideas, Vol. 3. 2004. (Grandma Baba Ser.). (Illus.). 32p. 10.95 (978-0-8048-3561-9(6)) Tuttle Publishing.

Saunders, Zina, illus. Trouble at the Krusty Krab! 2004. (Ready-to-Read Ser.). 32p. (J). pap. 3.99 (978-0-689-86838-2(3) , Simon Spotlight/Nickelodeon) Simon & Schuster Children's Publishing.

Sawyer, Dawnn. Sparkly Boohball: Color & Activity Book with Glitter Stickers. 2004. (Boohbah Ser.). (Illus.). 32p. (J). pap. 3.99 (978-0-439-59086-0(8)) Scholastic, Inc.

—Twirling, Whirling, Swirl! Color & Activity Book with Cardstock Insert. 2004. (Boohbah Ser.). (Illus.). 32p. (J). pap. 3.99 (978-0-439-59087-7(6)) Scholastic, Inc.

Sayre, April Pulley. Noodle Man: The Pasta Superhero. Costanza, Stephen, illus. 2002. 40p. (J). (ps-2). 16.95 (978-0-439-29307-5(3) , Orchard Bks.) Scholastic, Inc.

Scagliotti, Loti. They Say He Said She Said. 2006. (Silly Word & Number Stories Ser.). (Illus.). 28p. (J). 12.95 (978-9974-7925-0-0(9)) Hardenville SA URY. *Dist:* Independent Pubs. Group.

Scarsbrook, Richard. Cheeseburger Subversive. 2005. 204p. pap. 13.95 (978-1-894345-54-5(1)) Thistledown Pr., Ltd. CAN. *Dist:* Literary Pr. Group of Canada.

Schachner, Judy. Skippy Jon Jones. 2003. (Illus.). 32p. (J). (ps). 15.99 (978-0-525-47134-9(0) , Dutton Juvenile) Penguin Group (USA) Inc.

Schachner, Judy. Skippyjon Jones & the Treasure Hunt. 2008. 16p. (J). (ps-1). 9.99 (*978-0-448-44817-6(3) , Grosset & Dunlap) Penguin Group (USA) Inc.

Schafer, Milton. I'm Big! Lew-Vriethoff, Joanne, illus. 2006. (J). (*978-1-4156-8150-3(3) , Dial) Penguin Group (USA) Inc.

Schares, Stephen Jon. Just Plain Crazy. 2000. 124p. (YA). (gr. 4-7). pap. 9.95 (978-0-595-14069-5(6)) iUniverse, Inc.

Schindler, Nina & Rushton, Rosie. Geliebte Brieffeindin: Ein E-Mail- Roman. 2002. (GER.). 228p. pap. 15.00 (978-1-4000-3956-2(8) , New Media German Language) Random House Foreign Language Publishing.

Schlaht, Kim. Ronnie's Rotten Recipes. Tijerina, Arnold G., 3rd, ed. Gregory, Chris, illus. 2006. 72p. (J). per. 18.95 (978-0-9777688-1-3(3)) TICO Publishing.

Schneider, Evanne. Pass the SAT the Humorous Way: Lampooning Fairy Tales. Yaras, Adam, illus. 2000. 315p. (YA). (gr. 8-11). pap. 18.95 (978-0-9700747-2-0(7)) Westcreek Industries/Westcreek Publishing.

Schneider, Howie. Wilky the White House Cockroach. Schneider, Howie, illus. 2006. (Illus.). 32p. (J). (ps-3). 16.99 (978-0-399-24388-2(7)) Penguin Group (USA) Inc.

Schnetzler, Pattie L. Widdermaker. Sealock, Rick, illus. 2005. 32p. (gr. k-2). 15.95 (978-0-87614-647-7(7)) Lerner Publishing Group.

Schnitzlein, Danny. The Monster Who Did My Math. Mayer, Bill, illus. 2007. 32p. (J). (gr. 1-5). 16.95 (*978-1-56145-420-4(6) , Peachtree Junior) Peachtree Pubs., Ltd.

Scholastic, Inc. Staff. Dear Mrs. Larue. 2005. (J). pap. 550.00 (978-0-439-70787-9(0) , Sidekicks TM) Scholastic, Inc.

Schories, Pat, illus. Bathtime for Biscuit. 2002. (Biscuit Ser.). (J). 11.91 (978-0-7587-6003-6(5)) Book Wholesalers, Inc.

Schorr, Melissa. Goy Crazy: But Please Don't Tell My Jewish Grandmother! 2006. 352p. (gr. 7-17). 15.99 (978-0-7868-3852-3(3)) Hyperion Pr.

Schujer, Silvia. El Monumento Encantado. Elizalde, Marcelo, illus. 2001. Tr. of Enchanted Monument. (SPA.). 64p. (J). (gr. 2-4). per. (978-950-07-1936-0(3)) Editorial Sudamericana S.A.

Schulz, Charles M. A Charlie Brown Thanksgiving. 2006. (Illus.). 128p. 4.95 (978-0-7624-2753-6(1)) Running Pr. Bk. Pubs.

Schwartz, Amy. Starring Miss Darlene. 2007. (Illus.). 32p. (J). (ps-3). 16.95 (*978-1-59643-230-7(6)) Roaring Brook Pr.

Schwartz, Roslyn. The Mole Sisters & the Question. Schwartz, Roslyn, illus. 2002. (Mole Sisters Ser.). (Illus.). 32p. (J). (ps-k). pap. 4.95 (978-1-55037-768-2(X)); lib. bdg. 14.95 (978-1-55037-769-9(8)) Annick Pr., Ltd. CAN. *Dist:* Firefly Bks., Ltd.

Schwarz, Larry. Ellen's 11-Star Spectacular Super Deluxe Hotel. Denato, Kelly, illus. 2006. 32p. (J). (ps-1). 15.99 (978-0-316-86902-7(3)) Little Brown & Co.

Schwarz, Laurence. Ellen's 11-Star Spectacular Super Deluxe Hotel. Denato, Kelly, illus. 2006. (J). (978-1-4156-8083-4(3)) Little Brown & Co.

Schwarz, Viviane. Shark & Lobster's Amazing Undersea Adventure. Schwarz, Viviane & Stewart, Joel, illus. 2006. 40p. (J). (ps-1). 15.99 (978-0-7636-2910-6(3)) Candlewick Pr.

—Shark & Lobster's Amazing Undersea Adventure. Stewart, Joel, illus. 2006. 34p. (J). (*978-1-4156-8140-4(6)) Candlewick Pr.

Scieszka, Jon. Birdman or Birdbrain? 2007. (Time Warp Trio). 48p. (J). pap. 3.99 (*978-0-06-111647-6(5) , Harper Trophy) HarperCollins Pubs.

—Cowboy & Octopus. Smith, Lane, illus. 2007. 40p. (J). (ps-5). 16.99 (*978-0-670-91058-8(9) , Viking Juvenile) Penguin Group (USA) Inc.

—Da Wild, Da Crazy, Da Vinci. McCauley, Adam, illus. 2006. (Time Warp Trio Ser.: No. 14). 96p. (J). (gr. 2). pap. 4.99 (978-0-14-240465-2(9) , Puffin) Penguin Group (USA) Inc.

—Hey Kid, Want to Buy a Bridge? McCauley, Adam, illus. 2002. (Time Warp Trio Ser.: No. 11). 80p. (J). (gr. 3-5). 15.99 (978-0-670-89916-6(X) , Viking Juvenile) Penguin Group (USA) Inc.

—It's All Greek to Me. Smith, Lane & McCauley, Adam, illus. 1999. (Time Warp Trio Ser.: No. 8). 80p. (J). (gr. 2-6). 14.99 (978-0-670-88596-1(7) , Viking Juvenile) Penguin Group (USA) Inc.

—Knights of the Kitchen Table. unabr. ed. 1998. (Time Warp Trio Ser.: No. 1). 55p. (J). (gr. 2-5). pap. 17.00 incl. audio (978-0-8072-0391-0(2) , FTR193SP, Listening Library) Random Hse. Audio Publishing Group.

—Me Oh Maya. McCauley, Adam, illus. (Time Warp Trio Ser.: No. 13). (J). 2005. 96p. pap. 4.99 (978-0-14-240300-6(8) , Puffin); 2003. 80p. (gr. 2-6). 14.99 (978-0-670-03629-5(3) , Viking Juvenile) Penguin Group (USA) Inc.

—Nos Vemos, Gladiador.Tr. of See you later, gladiator. (SPA.). (J). 7.95 (978-958-04-6484-6(7)) Norma S.A. COL. *Dist:* Distribuidora Norma, Inc.

—Oh Say, I Can't See. McCauley, Adam, illus. 2007. (Time Warp Trio Ser.: No. 15). 80p. (J). (gr. 2-6). pap. 4.99 (978-0-14-240808-7(5) , Puffin) Penguin Group (USA) Inc.

—El Pirata Barbanegra. Smith, Lane, illus. (SPA.). (J). (gr. 5-8). 7.95 (978-958-04-3401-6(8) , NR8584) Norma S.A. COL. *Dist:* Distribuidora Norma, Inc., Lectorum Pubns., Inc.

—Sam Samurai, Vol. 10. McCauley, Adam, illus. (Time Warp Trio Ser.: No. 10). (J). 2004. 112p. (gr. 2-6). pap. 4.99 (978-0-14-240088-3(2) , Puffin); 2001. 80p. (gr. 1-5). 14.99 (978-0-670-89915-9(1) , Viking Juvenile) Penguin Group (USA) Inc.

—See You Later, Gladiator. McCauley, Adam, illus. (Time Warp Trio Ser.: No. 9). 96p. (J). (gr. 2-5). 2000. 14.99 (978-0-670-89340-9(4) , Viking Juvenile); Vol. 9. 2004. pap. 4.99 (978-0-14-240117-0(X) , Puffin) Penguin Group (USA) Inc.

—Squids Will Be Squids: Fresh Morals, Beastly Fables. 2002. (Illus.). (J). 24.55 (978-0-7587-5392-2(6)) Book Wholesalers, Inc.

—Squids Will Be Squids: Fresh Morals, Beastly Fables. Smith, Lane, illus. 1998. 48p. (J). (gr. 3-3). 17.99 (978-0-670-88135-2(X) , Viking Juvenile) Penguin Group (USA) Inc.

—Squids Will Be Squids: Fresh Morals, Beastly Fables. 2003. (gr. k-3). lib. bdg. 16.45 (978-0-613-67305-1(0)) Tandem Library Bks.

—Tut, Tut. Smith, Lane, illus. 2004. (Time Warp Trio Ser.: No. 6). 74p. (J). (ps-7). lib. bdg. 11.79 (978-0-606-30136-7(4)) Tandem Library Bks.

Scieszka, Jon. Your Mother Was a Neanderthal. Smith, Lane, illus. 2006. (Time Warp Trio Ser.: No. 4). 78p. (J). (*978-1-4176-3603-7(3) , Puffin) Penguin Group (USA) Inc.

Scieszka, Jon & Smith, Lane. Squids Will Be Squids: Fresh Morals, Beastly Fables. 2003. (Illus.). 48p. (J). pap. 7.99 (978-0-14-250040-8(2) , Puffin) Penguin Group (USA) Inc.

Scooby Doo's Halloween Tricks & Treats. 2006. (Illus.). 128p. 4.95 (978-0-7624-2827-4(9)) Running Pr. Bk. Pubs.

Scott-Cameron, Nancy. Santa Claus Is on a Diet. Conlan, Craig, illus. 2007. 32p. (J). (ps-k). 19.95 (*978-0-9546576-9-7(1)) Mogzilla GBR. *Dist:* Independent Pubs. Group.

Scott, Jerry. Zits Vol. 7: Carretera y Manta. 2007. (SPA., Illus.). 128p. reprint ed. pap. 19.95 (*978-1-59497-337-6(7)) Public Square Bks.

Scott, Lori Z. Megan Rose has Ants in Her Pants. 2007. 96p. (J). pap. 4.99 (*978-0-7847-2105-6(X)) Standard Publishing.

Scrimger, Richard. The Boy from Earth. 2004. 168p. (J). (gr. 3-7). pap. 7.95 (978-0-88776-591-9(2)) Tundra Bks., Inc./Livres Toundra, Inc. CAN. *Dist:* Random Hse., Inc.

Scrimger, Richard. Into the Ravine. 2007. 144p. (YA). (gr. 6 up). pap. 9.95 (*978-0-88776-822-4(9)) Tundra Bks., Inc./Livres Toundra, Inc. CAN. *Dist:* Random Hse., Inc.

Scroggs, Kirk. Night of the Living Eggnog. 7th rev. ed. 2007. (Wiley & Grampa Ser.). 112p. (J). (gr. 1). pap. 3.99 (*978-0-316-00685-9(8)) Little, Brown Bks. for Young Readers.

Scroggs, Kirk Brandon. Bigfoot Backpacking Bonanza. 5th ed. 2007. (Wiley & Grampa Ser.: No. 5). 112p. (J). (gr. 3-7). pap. 3.99 (*978-0-316-05949-7(8)); 12.99 (*978-0-316-05948-0(X)) Little, Brown Bks. for Young Readers.

—Dracula vs. Grampa at the Monster Truck Spectacular. 2006. (Wiley & Grampa's Creature Features Ser.: No. 1). (Illus.). 112p. (J). (gr. 3-7). pap. 2.99 (978-0-316-05941-1(2)) Little Brown & Co.

—Grampa's Zombie BBQ. 2nd ed. 2006. (Wiley & Grampa's Creature Features Ser.: No. 2). (Illus.). 112p. (J). (gr. 3-7). 12.99 (978-0-316-05943-5(9)); pap. 3.99 (978-0-316-05942-8(0)) Little Brown & Co.

—Hair Ball from Outer Space. 6th ed. 2007. (Wiley & Grampa Ser.: No. 6). 112p. (J). (gr. 3-7). pap. 3.99 (*978-0-316-05951-0(X)); 12.99 (*978-0-316-05950-3(1)) Little, Brown Bks. for Young Readers.

—Monster Fish Frenzy. 3rd ed. 2006. (Wiley & Grampa's Creature Features Ser.: No. 3). (Illus.). 112p. (J). (gr. 3-7). 12.99 (978-0-316-05944-2(7)); pap. 3.99 (978-0-316-05945-9(5)) Little Brown & Co.

—Super Soccer Freak Show. 4th ed. 2007. (Wiley & Grampa's Creature Features Ser.: No. 4). (Illus.). 112p. (J). (gr. 3-7). 12.99 (978-0-316-05946-6(3)); pap. 3.99 (978-0-316-05947-3(1)) Little Brown & Co.

Scuderi, Lucia. Dos Ratones en la Luna. 2004. Tr. of Two Mice on the Moon. (SPA., Illus.). (J). 20.99 (978-84-261-3273-4(1)) Juventud, Editorial ESP. *Dist:* Lectorum Pubns., Inc.

See, Ee Lin. My Kiasu Teenage Life in Singapore. 2005. (Illus.). 176p. pap. 12.95 (978-981-05-3016-7(1)) Monsoon Bks. Pte. Ltd. SGP. *Dist:* Biblio Distribution.

Seibold, J. Otto. Quincy, the Hobby Photographer. 2006. (Illus.). 64p. 14.95 (978-0-15-101494-1(9)) Harcourt Trade Pubs.

Seltzer, Richard. Lizard of Oz, Now & Then, Hundreds & Hundreds of Gerbils, Tiger in the Intercom, See You Later Elevator. 2001. (J). cd-rom 20.00 (978-0-915232-93-2(6)) B & R Samizdat Express.

Selway, Martina, illus. Clean Out the Fridge, Fred! 1999. (J). (978-0-7608-3199-1(8)) Sundance/Newbridge Educational Publishing.

—Fred Fixes a Faucet. 1999. (J). (978-0-7608-3193-9(9)) Sundance/Newbridge Educational Publishing.

—Fred's Cold. 1999. (J). (978-0-7608-3192-2(0)) Sundance/Newbridge Educational Publishing.

—The Photograph. 1999. (J). (978-0-7608-3197-7(1)) Sundance/Newbridge Educational Publishing.

—Something Nasty! 1999. (J). (978-0-7608-3198-4(X)) Sundance/Newbridge Educational Publishing.

—The Visitor. 1999. (J). (978-0-7608-3194-6(7)) Sundance/Newbridge Educational Publishing.

—What's That? 1999. (J). (978-0-7608-3195-3(5)) Sundance/Newbridge Educational Publishing.

Sempé, Jean-Jacques & Goscinny, René. Nicholas. Bell, Anthea, tr. from FRE. rev. ed. 2005. (Illus.). 136p. (ps-7). 19.95 (978-0-7148-4529-6(9)) Phaidon Pr. GBR. *Dist:* Hachette Bk. Group.

Sendak, Maurice. Monsters in Space. 2003. (gr. k-3). lib. bdg. 11.80 (978-0-613-68264-0(5)) Tandem Library Bks.

Sensel, Joni. Reality Leak. Slade, Christian, illus. 2007. (J). 224p. 16.95 (978-0-8050-8125-1(9)); 218p. (*978-1-4287-3983-3(1)) Holt, Henry & Co.

Service, Pamela F. My Cousin, the Alien. 2008. (J). lib. bdg. (*978-0-8225-7627-3(9) , Carolrhoda Bks.) Lerner Publishing Group.

Seuling, Barbara. Robert & the Practical Jokes. Brewer, Paul, illus. 2006. (Robert Bks.). 150p. (J). 16.95 (978-0-8126-2741-1(5)) Cricket Bks.

Seuss, Dr. Battaglia dell Burro. pap. 24.95 (978-88-09-02449-6(4)) Giunti, Gruppo Editoriale ITA. *Dist:* Distribooks, Inc.

—Gerald McBoing Boing. Seuss, Dr., illus. 2004. (Little Golden Book Ser.). (Illus.). 24p. (J). (gr. k-k). 2.99 (978-0-375-82721-1(8) , Golden Bks.) Random Hse. Children's Bks.

—Gerald McBoing Boing. Crawford, Mel, illus. 2000. 32p. (J). (gr. k-3). 12.95 (978-0-679-89140-6(4) , Random Hse. Bks. for Young Readers) Random Hse. Children's Bks.

—Green Eggs & Ham. 2001. (Nifty Lift-and-Look Bks.). (Illus.). 12p. (J). (gr. k-ps). bds. 7.99 (978-0-375-81088-6(9) , Random Hse. Bks. for Young Readers) Random Hse. Children's Bks.

—Hop on Pop. 2005. (Illus.). 64p. (J). (ps-2). audio compact disk 9.95 (978-0-375-83493-6(1) , Random Hse. Bks. for Young Readers) Random Hse. Children's Bks.

—Your Favorite Seuss: A Baker's Dozen by the One & Only Dr. Seuss. 2004. (Illus.). 368p. (J). (gr. k-3). 34.95 (978-0-375-81061-9(7) , Random Hse. Bks. for Young Readers) Random Hse. Children's Bks.

Sexton, Brenda. Elephants in the Bathtub & Other Silly Riddles. Mills, Liz, ed. 2006. (Illus.). 12p. (J). pap. 5.99 (978-0-439-82312-8(9) , Cartwheel Bks.) Scholastic, Inc.

Shannon, David. Alicia el Hada. Shannon, David, illus. 2004. (SPA., Illus.). 40p. (J). (gr. k-ps). pap. 15.95 (978-0-439-66203-1(6) , Blue Sky Pr., The) Scholastic, Inc.

—David Huele! Shannon, David, illus. 2005. (David Smells! Ser.). (SPA., Illus.). 12p. (J). (ps-ps). bds. 6.99 (978-0-439-75511-5(5) , Scholastic en Espanol) Scholastic, Inc.

—David Va al Colegio. 2000. Tr. of David Goes to School. (SPA., Illus.). 32p. (J). (ps-3). 13.99 (978-84-241-5886-6(5)) Everest de Ediciones y Distribucion, S.L. ESP. *Dist:* Lectorum Pubns., Inc.

H I

—David Va Al Colegio. 1999. (SPA.). (gr. k-3). lib. bdg. 16.40 (978-0-613-64483-9(2)) Tandem Library Bks.

—Good Boy, Fergus! (muy Bien, Fergus!) 2006. 40p. (J). pap. 3.99 (978-0-439-80294-9(6) , Scholastic en Espanol) Scholastic, Inc.

Shannon, George. Wise Acres. Zemke, Deborah, illus. 2004. 40p. (J). 15.95 (978-1-59354-041-8(8)) Handprint Bks.

Shanower, Eric. The Salt Sorcerer of Oz & Other Stories. Shanower, Eric, illus. 2003. (Oz Ser.). (Illus.). 288p. (J). 24.95 (978-1-929527-06-9(3)) Hungry Tiger Pr.

Sharp, N. L. Ring Bear. Hassler, Michael T., illus. 2006. 32p. 17.95 (978-1-886225-91-6(5)) Prairieland Pr.

Sheldon, Dyan. Deep & Meaningful Diaries from Planet Janet. 2007. 464p. (YA). (gr. 9). pap. 8.99 (978-0-7636-3216-8(3)) Candlewick Pr.

Sheppard, Kate, illus. Funny Stories for Six Year Olds. 2003. 263p. (J). pap. 9.99 (978-0-330-36857-5(5) , Macmillan Children's Bks.) Pan Macmillan GBR. *Dist:* Trafalgar Square Publishing.

Sherwood, Ben. The Man Who Ate The 747. 2002. 258p. (gr. 7-12). per. 14.75 (978-0-613-49504-2(7)) Tandem Library Bks.

Shipton, Paul. The Pig Scrolls. 2007. (Illus.). 304p. (J). (gr. 5-9). 6.99 (***978-0-7636-3302-8(X)***) Candlewick Pr.

Shore, Monica G. The Tale of Grandpa's Hair. 2006. (ENG.). 28p. per. 13.99 (***978-1-4259-2997-8(4)***) AuthorHouse.

Shulman, Mark. Some Cows. Nguyen, Vincent, illus. 2003. (Some Animals Ser.). 24p. (J). 5.95 (978-0-7641-5650-2(0)) Barron's Educational Series, Inc.

—Some Pigs. Nguyen, Vincent, illus. 2003. (Some Animals Ser.). 24p. (J). 5.95 (978-0-7641-5651-9(9)) Barron's Educational Series, Inc.

Sierra, Judy. Mind Your Manners, B. B. Wolf. Seibold, J. Otto, illus. 2007. 40p. (J). (ps-3). 16.99 (978-0-375-83532-2(6)); lib. bdg. 19.99 (978-0-375-93532-9(0)) Random Hse. Children's Bks. (Knopf Bks. for Young Readers).

Silberberg, Alan. Pond Scum. 2007. 288p. (gr. 3-7). pap. 5.99 (978-0-7868-5635-0(1)) Hyperion Pr.

The Silly Swamp of Shapes. 2002. (Puppy Tales Ser.). (Illus.). 24p. (J). (gr. k-3). 1.49 (978-1-57759-270-9(0)) Dalmatian Pr.

Silverhardt, Lauryn. Playtime with Bob. 2004. (Bob the Builder Ser.). (Illus.). 10p. (J). bds. 8.99 (978-0-689-86530-5(9) , Simon Spotlight) Simon & Schuster Children's Publishing.

—SpongeBob SpookyPants. Style Guide Staff, illus. 2004. (Spongebob Squarepants Ser.). 16p. (J). bds. 5.99 (978-0-689-87320-1(4) , Simon Spotlight/Nickelodeon) Simon & Schuster Children's Publishing.

—SpongeBob's Best Day Ever! Reiss, William & Greenblatt, C. H., illus. 2004. (SpongeBob SquarePants Ser.). 12p. (J). bds. 6.99 (978-0-689-86754-5(9) , Simon Spotlight/Nickelodeon) Simon & Schuster Children's Publishing.

—Winona Makes Waves! Style Guide Staff, illus. 2005. (Rubbadubbers Ser.). 8p. (J). 6.99 (978-0-689-87616-5(5) , Simon Spotlight) Simon & Schuster Children's Publishing.

Silverhardt, Lauryn & Thompson Bros. Staff. Meet Boots! 2005. (Dora the Explorer Ser.). 12p. (J). bds. 5.99 (978-1-4169-0999-6(0) , Simon Spotlight/Nickelodeon) Simon & Schuster Children's Publishing.

Silverman, Erica. When the Chickens Went on Strike. Trueman, Matthew, illus. 2005. 32p. (J). pap. 6.99 (978-0-14-240279-5(6) , Puffin) Penguin Group (USA) Inc.

Simard, Remy. Mister Once-upon-A-Time. 2000. (ps-2). lib. bdg. 15.25 (978-0-613-26235-4(2)) Tandem Library Bks.

Simendinger, Ted. Jurassic Trout: A Flyfishing Comedy. 2004. per. 9.95 (978-0-9702405-5-2(4)) Airplane Reader Publishing.

—12 Miles to Paradise: A People Story about Horses & Horseracing. 2nd ed. 2004. 364p. per. 12.95 (978-0-9702405-4-5(6)) Airplane Reader Publishing.

Simmons, Andrew. Bullseye Express. 2001. (Woody's Roundup Ser.: Bk. 5). (Illus.). 64p. (gr. 2-5). reprint ed. pap. 4.99 (978-0-7868-4457-9(4)) Disney Pr.

Simmons, Don. Cockroach. 2003. (YA). per. 10.00 (978-1-59453-023-4(8) , 1631) Airleaf Publishing & Bookselling.

Simms Taback Staff, illus. There Was an Old Lady Who Swallowed a Fly. 2004. (J). pap. 18.95 incl. audio compact disk (978-1-55592-145-3(0)); pap. 18.95 incl. audio compact disk (978-1-55592-146-0(9)) Weston Woods Studios, Inc.

Simon, Annette. Mocking Birdies. 2005. (Illus.). 32p. (J). 16.95 (978-1-894965-29-3(9)) Simply Read Bks. CAN. *Dist:* Perseus Distribution.

Simon, Francesca. Horrid Henry's Head Lice. 2000. 96p. lib. bdg. 14.49 (978-0-7868-2453-3(0)) Hyperion Bks. for Children.

Simpson, Fiona, ed. My Swampy Valentine. 2006. (Shrek Ser.). 16p. (J). pap. 4.99 (978-0-439-82013-4(8) , Scholastic) Scholastic, Inc.

Singh, Vandana. Younguncle Comes to Town. Kamath, B. M., illus. 2006. 160p. (J). (gr. 3-5). 14.99 (978-0-670-06051-1(8) , Viking Juvenile) Penguin Group (USA) Inc.

Slate, Joseph. Miss Bindergarten's Wild Day. Wolff, Ashley, illus. 2005. 40p. (J). (ps). 16.99 (978-0-525-47084-7(0) , Dutton Juvenile) Penguin Group (USA) Inc.

Slater, David Michael. Cheese Louise! Cowden, Steve, illus. 2005. 32p. (J). (gr. 2-4). pap. 8.95 (978-1-55285-721-2(2) , Walrus Bks.) Whitecap Bks., Ltd. CAN. *Dist:* Firefly Bks., Ltd.

—Jacques & Spock. Tilley, Debbie, illus. 2004. 32p. (J). (gr. k-3). tchr. ed. 15.00 (978-0-618-15980-2(0) , Clarion Bks.) Houghton Mifflin Co. Trade & Reference Div.

—Ned Loses His Head. Brooks, S. G., illus. 2007. (Missy Swiss & More Ser.). 32p. (J). (ps-4). lib. bdg. 27.07 (***978-1-60270-011-6(7)*** , Looking Glass Library) Magic Wagon.

Slater, David Michael. The Ring Bear. Brooks, S. G., illus. 2004. 32p. (J). 15.95 (978-0-9729225-1-7(2) , 1231960) Flashlight Pr.

Slepian, Jan. Hungry Thing. 2001. (Illus.). (J). 12.79 (978-0-606-21242-7(6)) Tandem Library Bks.

Slobodkina, Esphyr. Caps for Sale. 2005. (Illus.). (J). pap. 18.95 incl. audio compact disk (978-1-59112-697-3(5)) Live Oak Media.

Small, David. Hoover's Bride. 2006. (Illus.). 40p. (J). pap. 5.99 (978-0-439-81218-4(6) , Scholastic Paperbacks) Scholastic, Inc.

—Imogene's Antlers. Small, David, illus. 2002. (Illus.). (J). 14.79 (978-0-7587-2836-4(0)) Book Wholesalers, Inc.

—Imogene's Antlers. 2000. (J). pap. 19.97 incl. audio (978-0-7366-9207-6(X)) Books on Tape, Inc.

—Imogene's Antlers. 2005. (Illus.). (J). pap. 18.95 incl. audio compact disk (978-1-59112-723-9(8)) Live Oak Media.

—Imogene's Antlers. Small, David, illus. 2005. (Illus.). (J). (gr. 1-6). pap. 16.95 incl. audio (978-0-87499-322-6(9)) Live Oak Media.

—Imogene's Antlers. Boughton, Simon, ed. Small, David, illus. 2000. (Illus.). 32p. (J). (ps-3). 15.95 (978-0-375-81048-0(X) , Crown Books For Young Readers) Random Hse. Children's Bks.

Smith, Alexander McCall. The Cowgirl Aunt of Harriet Bean. Rankin, Laura, illus. 2006. (Harriet Bean Ser.). 80p. (J). (gr. 2-4). 9.95 (978-1-58234-977-0(0) , Bloomsbury Children) Bloomsbury Publishing.

Smith, J. E. Complex City: All in a Day's Work. 2003. 120p. per. 12.95 (978-0-9728070-0-5(4)) Better Comics.

Smith, Jeff. Bone: Eyes of the Storm. Smith, Jeff, illus. 2002. (Bone Ser.). (Illus.). 27.19 (978-1-4046-2801-4(0)) Book Wholesalers, Inc.

—Bone: Old Man's Cave. Smith, Jeff, illus. 2002. (Bone Ser.). (Illus.). (YA). 26.06 (978-1-4046-2804-5(5)) Book Wholesalers, Inc.

—Bone: The Dragonslayer. Smith, Jeff, illus. 2002. (Bone Ser.). (Illus.). 27.19 (978-1-4046-2802-1(9)) Book Wholesalers, Inc.

—Bone: The Great Cow Race. Smith, Jeff, illus. 2002. (Bone Ser.). (Illus.). (YA). 24.94 (978-1-4046-2800-7(2)) Book Wholesalers, Inc.

—Bone: Treasure Hunters. Smith, Jeff, illus. 2002. (Bone Ser.). (Illus.). (YA). 26.06 (978-1-4046-2806-9(1)) Book Wholesalers, Inc.

—Bone Vol. 7: Ghost Circles. Smith, Jeff, illus. 2002. (Bone Ser.). (Illus.). 27.19 (978-1-4046-2805-2(3)) Book Wholesalers, Inc.

—Bone: Rock Jaw: Master of the Eastern Border. Smith, Jeff, illus. 2002. (Bone Ser.). (Illus.). 24.94 (978-1-4046-2803-8(7)) Book Wholesalers, Inc.

Smith, Lane. The Happy Hocky Family Moves to the Country! 2003. (Illus.). 64p. (J). 16.99 (978-0-670-03594-6(7) , Viking Juvenile) Penguin Group (USA) Inc.

—The Happy Hocky Family Moves to the Country. Smith, Lane, illus. 2005. 64p. (J). pap. 6.99 (978-0-14-240297-9(4) , Puffin) Penguin Group (USA) Inc.

—John, Paul, George & Ben. 2006. (Illus.). 40p. (J). (ps-k). 16.99 (978-0-7868-4893-5(6)) Hyperion Pr.

Smith, Linda. The Inside Tree. Brown, Kathryn, illus. Date not set. 32p. (J). (ps-3). 5.99 (978-0-06-443542-0(3)) HarperCollins Pubs.

—The Inside Tree. 2002. 32p. (J). (ps-3). 14.95 (978-0-06-028241-7(X)) HarperCollins Pubs.

Smith, Mary Ann & Milway, Katie Smith. Cappuccina Goes to Town. Fernandes, Eugenie, illus. 2004. 32p. (J). (gr. k-3). (978-1-55337-686-6(2)) Kids Can Pr., Ltd.

Smith, Mary Ann, et al. Cappuccina Goes to Town. Fernandes, Eugenie, illus. unabr. ed. 2002. 32p. (J). (gr. k-3). (978-1-55074-807-9(6)) Kids Can Pr., Ltd.

Smith, Robert Kimmel. Chocolate Fever. Fiammenghi, Gioia, illus. 2006. 93p. (J). (***978-1-4156-7192-4(3)*** , Puffin) Penguin Group (USA) Inc.

Smith, Robert Kimmel. Chocolate Fever. 2006. (Illus.). 96p. (J). (gr. 2). 4.99 (978-0-14-240595-6(7) , Puffin) Penguin Group (USA) Inc.

Smith, Stu & Wolff, Julian. The Bubble Gum Kid. 2006. (Illus.). 32p. 15.95 (978-0-7624-2046-9(4)) Running Pr. Bk. Pubs.

Sneezles & Wheezles. 2006. (J). 15.99 (978-1-55517-912-0(6) , Cedar Fort, Inc.) Cedar Fort, Inc./CFI Distribution.

Snicket, Lemony, pseud. The Austere Academy. Helquist, Brett, illus. 2008. (Series of Unfortunate Events Ser.: Bk. 5). 240p. (J). (gr. 5 up). pap. 6.99 (***978-0-06-114634-3(X)*** , Harper Trophy) HarperCollins Pubs.

—The Austere Academy. 2000. (Series of Unfortunate Events Ser.: Bk. 5). (J). (gr. 4-7). pupil's gde. ed. (978-0-06-029312-3(8)) HarperCollins Pubs.

—The Austere Academy. Helquist, Brett, illus. 2000. (Series of Unfortunate Events Ser.: Bk. 5). 240p. (J). (gr. 5 up). 12.99 (978-0-06-440863-9(9)); lib. bdg. 15.89 (978-0-06-028888-4(4)) HarperCollins Pubs.

—The Bad Beginning. Helquist, Brett, illus. l.t. ed. 2002. (Series of Unfortunate Events Ser.: Bk. 1). 168p. (J). 16.95 (978-0-7540-7812-8(4) , Galaxy Children's Large Print) BBC Audiobooks America.

—The Bad Beginning. Helquist, Brett, illus. 1999. (Series of Unfortunate Events Ser.: Bk. 1). 176p. (J). (gr. 5 up). 12.99 (978-0-06-440766-3(7)); lib. bdg. 15.89 (978-0-06-028312-4(2)) HarperCollins Pubs.

—The Beatrice Letters. Helquist, Brett, illus. 2006. (Series of Unfortunate Events Ser.). 72p. (J). 19.99 (978-0-06-058658-4(3)) HarperCollins Pubs.

—The Carnivorous Carnival. Helquist, Brett, illus. 2002. (Series of Unfortunate Events Ser.: Bk. 9). 304p. (J). (gr. 4-7). 12.99 (978-0-06-441012-0(9) , Harper Trophy); (ps-3). lib. bdg. 15.89 (978-0-06-029640-7(2)) HarperCollins Pubs.

—The Complete Wreck, Bks. 1-13. Helquist, Brett, illus. 2006. (Series of Unfortunate Events Ser.). (J). 150.00 (978-0-06-111906-4(7)) HarperCollins Pubs.

—The Dilemma Deepens, 3 vols., Bks. 7-9. Helquist, Brett, illus. 2003. (Series of Unfortunate Events Ser.: Bks. 7-9). (J). (gr. 3-6). 38.99 (978-0-06-055620-4(X)) HarperCollins Pubs.

—The End. Helquist, Brett, illus. 2006. (Series of Unfortunate Events Ser.: Bk. 13). (J). 368p. lib. bdg. 15.89 (978-0-06-029644-5(5)); 384p. (gr. 5 up). 12.99 (978-0-06-441016-8(1)) HarperCollins Pubs.

—The Ersatz Elevator. Helquist, Brett, illus. 2001. (Series of Unfortunate Events Ser.: Bk. 6). 272p. (J). (gr. 5 up). 12.99 (978-0-06-440864-6(7)); 6th ed. lib. bdg. 15.89 (978-0-06-028889-1(2)) HarperCollins Pubs.

—The Gloom Looms, Bks. 10-12. Helquist, Brett, illus. 2005. (Series of Unfortunate Events Ser.). (J). 38.99 (978-0-06-083909-3(0)) HarperCollins Pubs.

—The Grim Grotto. Helquist, Brett, illus. 2004. (Series of Unfortunate Events Ser.: Bk. 11). 352p. (gr. 3-6). (J). lib. bdg. 15.89 (978-0-06-029642-1(9)); (YA). 12.99 (978-0-06-441014-4(5) , HarperCollins) HarperCollins Pubs.

—La Habitacion de los Reptiles. Helquist, Brett, illus. 2002. (Series of Unfortunate Events Ser.). (SPA.). 208p. (J). (gr. 4-6). 10.95 (978-84-264-3741-9(9) , LM31164) Editorial Lumen ESP. *Dist:* Lectorum Pubns., Inc.

—The Hostile Hospital. Helquist, Brett, illus. 2001. (Series of Unfortunate Events Ser.: Bk. 8). (J). 272p. (gr. 5 up). 12.99 (978-0-06-440866-0(3)); 255p. (gr. 4-7). lib. bdg. (978-0-06-623919-4(2)); 8th ed. 272p. (gr. 5 up). lib. bdg. 15.89 (978-0-06-028891-4(4)) HarperCollins Pubs.

—Un Infausto Inizio. pap. 23.95 (978-88-7782-951-1(6)) Salani ITA. *Dist:* Distribooks, Inc.

—The Loathsome Library, Bks. 1-6. Helquist, Brett, illus. 2005. (Series of Unfortunate Events Ser.: Vol. 1). (J). 65.00 (978-0-06-083353-4(X)) HarperCollins Pubs.

—Un Mal Principio. Helquist, Brett, illus. 2002. (Series of Unfortunate Events Ser.). (SPA.). 224p. (J). (gr. 4-6). 10.95 (978-84-264-3740-2(0) , LM31162) Editorial Lumen ESP. *Dist:* Lectorum Pubns., Inc.

—Un Mal Principio. Busquets, Nestor, tr. Helquist, Brett, illus. 2004. (Catastroficas Desdichas Ser.). (SPA.). 176p. (J). pap. 7.95 (978-0-307-20934-4(2) , Montena) Random House Mondadori ESP. *Dist:* Random Hse., Inc.

—The Miserable Mill. Helquist, Brett, illus. 2000. (Series of Unfortunate Events Ser.: Bk. 4). 208p. (J). (gr. 3-6). 12.99 (978-0-06-440769-4(1)); (ps-2). lib. bdg. 15.89 (978-0-06-028315-5(7)) HarperCollins Pubs.

—The Notorious Notations. Helquist, Brett, illus. 2006. (Series of Unfortunate Events Ser.). 176p. (J). pap. 9.99 (978-0-06-087235-9(7) , Harper Festival) HarperCollins Pubs.

—Omnibus. Helquist, Brett, illus. movie tie-in ed. (Series of Unfortunate Events Ser.). (J). 2004. 35.99 (978-0-06-075773-1(6)); Bks. 1-3. 2001. 24p. (gr. 3-6). 38.99 (978-0-06-029809-8(X)) HarperCollins Pubs.

—Ouragan sur le Lac. pap. 24.95 (978-2-09-282356-9(6)) Nathan, Fernand FRA. *Dist:* Distribooks, Inc.

—The Penultimate Peril. Helquist, Brett, illus. 2005. (Series of Unfortunate Events Ser.: Bk. 12). 368p. (J). lib. bdg. 15.89 (978-0-06-029643-8(7)) HarperCollins Pubs.

—The Reptile Room. Helquist, Brett, illus. l.t. ed. 2002. (Series of Unfortunate Events Ser.: Bk. 2). 184p. (J). pap. 16.95 (978-0-7540-7823-4(X) , Galaxy Children's Large Print) BBC Audiobooks America.

—The Reptile Room. Helquist, Brett, illus. 1999. (Series of Unfortunate Events Ser.: Bk. 2). 208p. (J). (gr. 5 up). 12.99 (978-0-06-440767-0(5)); lib. bdg. 15.89 (978-0-06-028313-1(0)) HarperCollins Pubs.

—Der Schlimme Anfang. (978-3-407-79815-2(6)) Beltz, Julius GmbH & Company KG.

—The Situation Worsens, 3 vols., Bks. 4-6. Helquist, Brett, illus. 2002. (Series of Unfortunate Events Ser.). (J). (gr. 3-6). 38.99 (978-0-06-009556-7(3)) HarperCollins Pubs.

—The Slippery Slope. Helquist, Brett, illus. 2003. (Series of Unfortunate Events Ser.: Bk. 10). (YA). (gr. 5 up). 197.82 (978-0-06-057743-8(6)); 352p. (J). (gr. 3-6). 12.99 (978-0-06-441013-7(7)); 352p. (J). (gr. 3-6). lib. bdg. 15.89 (978-0-06-029641-4(0)) HarperCollins Pubs.

—The Vile Village. Helquist, Brett, illus. 2001. (Series of Unfortunate Events Ser.: Bk. 7). 272p. (J). (gr. 5 up). 12.99 (978-0-06-440865-3(5)); 7th ed. lib. bdg. 15.89 (978-0-06-028890-7(6)) HarperCollins Pubs.

—The Wide Window. l.t. ed. 2003. (Series of Unfortunate Events Ser.: Bk. 3). (Illus.). 216p. (J). 16.95 (978-0-7540-7850-0(7) , Galaxy Children's Large Print) BBC Audiobooks America.

—The Wide Window. Helquist, Brett, illus. 2000. (Series of Unfortunate Events Ser.: Bk. 3). 224p. (J). (gr. 5 up). 12.99 (978-0-06-440768-7(3)) HarperCollins Pubs.

—The Wide Window. Helquist, Brett & Kupperman, Michael, illus. 2000. (Series of Unfortunate Events Ser.: Bk. 3). 224p. (J). (ps-2). lib. bdg. 15.89 (978-0-06-028314-8(9)) HarperCollins Pubs.

Snicket, Lemony, pseud, creator. Lemony Snicket: The Unauthorized Autobiography. 2002. (Series of Unfortunate Events Ser.). (Illus.). 240p. (J). (gr. 5 up). 12.99 (978-0-06-000719-5(2)) HarperCollins Pubs.

The Socksnatchers. 2005. (Illus.). 40p. (J). (ps-ps). 15.95 (978-1-59572-003-0(0)) Star Bright Bks., Inc.

Sommer, Carl. Your Job Is Easy Read-along, 1 bk. 2003. (Another Sommer-Time Story Ser.). (Illus.). 48p. (J). lib. bdg. 23.95 incl. audio compact disk (978-1-57537-717-9(9)); lib. bdg. 23.95 incl. audio (978-1-57537-767-4(5)) Advance Publishing, Inc.

Soto, Gary. Chato & the Party Animals. 2005. (J). pap. 18.95 incl. audio compact disk (978-1-59112-919-6(2)); (Illus.). pap. 16.95 incl. audio (978-1-59112-459-7(X)) Live Oak Media.

Soule, Jean Conder. Never Tease a Weasel. Booth, George, illus. 2007. (Picture Book Ser.). 40p. (J). (ps-2). 15.99 (978-0-375-83420-2(6)); lib. bdg. 18.99 (978-0-375-93420-9(0)) Random Hse. Children's Bks. (Random Hse. Bks. for Young Readers).

Sowa, Elizabeth. The Hexagon. 2004. 24p. (J). pap. 14.95 (978-1-4137-2130-0(3)) PublishAmerica, Inc.

Spafford-Fitz, Karen. Dog Walker. 2006. 112p. (J). (gr. 5-10). pap. 7.95 (978-1-55143-522-0(5)); lib. bdg. 14.95 (978-1-55143-533-6(0)) Orca Bk. Pubs. USA.

Spanyol, Jessica. Come on, Bugs! Let's Have Some Fun! Spanyol, Jessica, illus. 2006. (Illus.). 32p. (J). (gr. k-k). 15.99 (978-0-7636-3055-3(1)) Candlewick Pr.

Sparks, Kerry. Dimples. 2002. 108p. pap. 9.95 (978-0-595-22461-6(X) , Writers Club Pr.) iUniverse, Inc.

Spearman, Andy. Barry Boyhound. 2007. 240p. (J). (gr. 3-7). 5.50 (***978-0-440-42058-3(X)*** , Yearling) Random Hse. Children's Bks.

Spelvin, Justin & Hot Animation Staff, Animation. Star of the Show. 2005. (Rubbadubbers). 24p. (J). pap. 3.99 (978-0-689-87427-7(8)) Simon & Schuster, Inc.

Spencer, George. The Bossman Ballads. 2005. 48p. 5.49 (978-1-4116-4583-7(9)) Lulu.com.

Spinelli, Eileen. Six Hogs on a Scooter. Nash, Scott, illus. 2000. 40p. (J). (gr. k-4). 16.99 (978-0-531-33212-2(8)); pap. 15.95 (978-0-531-30212-5(1)) Scholastic, Inc. (Orchard Bks.).

—Thanksgiving at the Tappletons' Lloyd, Megan, illus. 32p. (J). (ps-3). 2003. 16.99 (978-0-06-008670-1(X)); 2004. pap. 6.99 (978-0-06-008672-5(6) , Harper Trophy) HarperCollins Pubs.

Spirn, Michele. The Know-Nothings Talk Turkey. Alley, R. W., illus. 2001. 48p. (J). (gr. k-3). lib. bdg. 11.80 (978-0-613-62145-8(X)) Tandem Library Bks.

Spirn, Michele Sobel. A Know-Nothing Halloween. Alley, R. W., illus. 2000. (I Can Read Bks.). 48p. (J). (gr. k-3). 14.95 (978-0-06-028185-4(5)) HarperCollins Pubs.

—The Know-Nothings Talk Turkey. Alley, R. W., illus. (I Can Read Bks.). 48p. (J). (ps-3). 2001. pap. 3.99 (978-0-06-444251-0(9) , Harper Trophy); 2000. 14.95 (978-0-06-028183-0(9)); 2000. 14.89 (978-0-06-028184-7(7)) HarperCollins Pubs.

—The Know-Nothings Talk Turkey. Alley, Robert W., illus. 2000. 48p. (J). (gr. k-3). lib. bdg. 11.19 (978-0-606-22291-4(X)) Tandem Library Bks.

Spooner, Joe. The Elephant Walk. Spooner, Joe, illus. 2004. (Illus.). (J). pap. 14.95 (978-0-9745686-3-8(5)) Arnica Publishing, Inc.

A Spoonful of Melancholy in a Bucketful of Laughs at a House Called Awful End. 2003. (Eddie Dickens Trilogy: Bk. 1). (J). pap. (978-0-439-41268-1(4)) Scholastic, Inc.

St. Aubin, Bruno. Daddy's an Alien. St. Aubin, Bruno, illus. 2005. (Read-It! Readers Ser.). (Illus.). 32p. (J). (gr. k-3). 18.60 (978-1-4048-1067-9(6)) Picture Window Bks.

Stadler, John. The Cats of Mrs. Calamari. Stadler, John, illus. 1999. (Illus.). 32p. (J). (ps-1). pap. 5.95 (978-0-531-07140-3(5) , Orchard Bks.) Scholastic, Inc.

—The Cats of Mrs. Calamari. 1999. (Illus.). (J). (978-0-606-18332-1(9)) Tandem Library Bks.

Stahnke, Rich. Furious Fist of the Drunken Monkey: Origin of the Species #3. 2007. 2.95 (***978-0-9791192-4-8(3)***) Silent Devil Productions.

Stanley, Diane. Raising Sweetness. Karas, G. Brian, illus. 2004. (Live Oak Readalong Ser.). (J). (ps-3). audio compact disk 18.95 (978-1-59112-494-8(8)) Live Oak Media.

—Raising Sweetness. 2003. (Live Oak Readalong Ser.). (Illus.). (J). pap. 16.95 incl. audio (978-1-59112-265-4(1)) Live Oak Media.

—Saving Sweetness. Karas, G. Brian, illus. 2002. 13.19 (978-1-4046-0940-2(7)) Book Wholesalers, Inc.

—Saving Sweetness. Karas, G. Brian, illus. 2005. (J). pap. 18.95 incl. audio compact disk (978-1-59112-330-9(5)); 2002. 28.95 incl. audio compact disk (978-1-59112-548-8(0)); 2002. pap. 39.95 incl. audio compact disk (978-1-59112-547-1(2)) Live Oak Media.

—Saving Sweetness. Karas, G. Brian, illus. 2001. 32p. (J). (ps-ps). pap. 5.99 (978-0-698-11767-9(0) , Putnam Juvenile) Penguin Group (USA) Inc.

—Saving Sweetness. Karas, G. Brian, illus. 2001. (J). (ps-ps). lib. bdg. 14.15 (978-0-613-44412-5(4)) Tandem Library Bks.

Stanley, John. Little Lulu Vol. 14: Queen Lulu. 2007. 240p. pap. 9.95 (978-1-59307-683-2(5)) Dark Horse Comics.

—Little Lulu Volume 13: Too Much Fun. Too Much Fun. 2006. (Illus.). 208p. pap. 9.95 (978-1-59307-621-4(5)) Dark Horse Comics.

Stanley, Lesa, told to. You Have That in Your Purse, Mrs. Connor? 2004. (J). pap. 16.00 (978-0-8059-6466-0(5)) Dorrance Publishing Co., Inc.

Stanton, Andy. You're a Bad Man, Mr. Gum! Dezern, Chad, illus. 2008. 144p. (J). 9.99 (***978-0-06-115240-5(4)***); lib. bdg. 14.89 (***978-0-06-115243-6(9)***) HarperCollins Pubs.

Stauffacher, Sue. Donuthead. 2003. (Illus.). 160p. (J). (gr. 3-7). 15.95 (978-0-375-82468-5(5)); lib. bdg. 17.99 (978-0-375-92468-2(X)) Random Hse. Children's Bks. (Knopf Bks. for Young Readers).

—Donutheart. 2006. 208p. (J). (gr. 3-7). 15.95 (978-0-375-83275-8(0)); lib. bdg. 17.99 (978-0-375-93275-5(5)) Random Hse. Children's Bks. (Knopf Bks. for Young Readers).

Staunton, Ted. Hope Springs a Leak. 1998. (Northern Lights Young Novels Ser.). 148p. (J). (gr. 4-9). pap. 7.95 (978-0-88995-174-7(8)) Red Deer Pr. CAN. *Dist:* Fitzhenry & Whiteside, Ltd.

HI

—Morgan Makes a Deal. Slavin, Bill, illus. 2005. (First Novel Ser.). 64p. (J). (gr. 2-5). (***978-0-88780-667-4(8)***); 4.95 (978-0-88780-666-7(X)) Formac Publishing Co., Ltd. CAN. *Dist:* Casemate Pubs. & Bk. Distributors, LLC.

Steadman, Ralph. Little. Com. Steadman, Ralph, illus. 2005. (Illus.). 32p. (J). pap. 9.99 (***978-1-84270-484-4(2)***) Andersen GBR. *Dist:* Independent Pubs. Group.

Steele, Michael. A Tale of Two Kitties. novel movie tie-in ed. 2006. (Garfield's A Tail of Two Kitties Ser.). 112p. (J). pap. 4.99 (978-0-439-87395-6(9)) Scholastic, Inc.

Steig, William. Shrek! Steig, William, illus. 2002. (Illus.). (J). 14.43 (978-0-7587-3617-8(7)) Book Wholesalers, Inc.

—Shrek! Steig, William, illus. (Illus.). 2005. (J). pap. 18.95 incl. audio compact disk (978-1-59112-328-6(3)); 1998. pap. 35.95 incl. audio compact disk (978-1-59112-551-8(0)) Live Oak Media.

—Shrek! 1998. (Illus.). pap., tchr. ed. 33.95 incl. audio (978-0-87499-456-8(X)); (J). pap. 16.95 incl. audio (978-0-87499-454-4(3)) Live Oak Media.

Steinberg, Laya. Thesaurus Rex Finds a Friend. Harter, Debbie, illus. 2006. (J). (978-1-905236-48-0(4)) Barefoot Bks., Inc.

Stephens, Becky. Me Again! 2003. (gr. 3-6). lib. bdg. 13.00 (978-0-613-87298-0(3)) Tandem Library Bks.

Stephens, Evelyn. Five Little Yaks. 2007. (Illus.). 56p. (J). per. 15.00 (***978-0-9716039-2-9(8)***) Lawrence Publishing.

Stephenson, Neal. Snow Crash. 2000. (Illus.). 468p. (gr. 7-12). pr. 23.40 (978-0-613-36162-0(8)) Tandem Library Bks.

Steptoe, Javaka. The Jones Family Express. Steptoe, Javaka, illus. 2005. (Illus.). 40p. (J). 7.95 (978-1-58430-262-9(3)) Lee & Low Bks., Inc.

Stern, Ricki. Beryl E. Bean. 2nd ed. 2002. (Beryl E. Bean Ser.). (Illus.). 64p. (J). 14.89 (978-0-06-028772-6(1)) HarperCollins Pubs.

—Mission Impossible. Date not set. (Beryl E. Bean Ser.: Vol. 3). (Illus.). (J). lib. bdg. 15.89 (978-0-06-028773-3(X) , Harper Trophy) HarperCollins Pubs.

Stern, Ricki & Worcester, Heidi P. Adventure: Lonely Leader. Bates, Amy June, illus. 2003. (Beryl E. Bean Ser.: No. 3). 64p. (J). lib. bdg. 16.89 (978-0-06-028774-0(8)) HarperCollins Pubs.

—Beryl E. Bean: Mission Impossible Friendship. Bates, Amy June, illus. 2002. (J). pap. 5.99 (978-0-06-442122-5(8) , Harper Trophy) HarperCollins Pubs.

—Beryl E. Bean Book 1: Mighty Adventurer of the Planet. Bates, Amy June, illus. 2002. (Beryl E. Bean Ser.). 64p. (J). (gr. 2-4). pap. 5.95 (978-0-06-442120-1(1)) HarperCollins Pubs.

Stevens, Janet & Crummel, Susan Stevens. The Great Fuzz Frenzy. 2005. (Illus.). 56p. (J). (ps-ps). 17.00 (978-0-15-204626-2(7) , Harcourt Children's Bks) Harcourt Children's Bks.

—The Great Fuzz Frenzy. unabr. ed. 2006. (J). (gr. k-3). 27.99 incl. audio (***978-0-8045-6940-8(1)*** , SAC6941); 29.95 incl. audio compact disk (***978-0-8045-4154-1(X)*** , SACD4155) Spoken Arts, Inc.

—Help Me, Mr. Mutt! Expert Answers for Dogs with People Problems. 2008. 56p. (J). 17.00 (***978-0-15-204628-6(3)***) Harcourt Trade Pubs.

Stevens, Janet & Crummel, Susan Stevens. Jackalope. Stevens, Janet, illus. 2003. (Illus.). 56p. (J). (gr. k-3). 17.00 (978-0-15-216736-3(6)) Harcourt Children's Bks.

Stillerman, Robbie. Willie the Wizard: With 14 Stickers. 2001. 4p. (J). pap. 1.50 (978-0-486-41764-6(6)) Dover Pubns., Inc.

Stilton, Geronimo. All Because of a Cup of Coffee. 2004. (Geronimo Stilton Ser.: No. 10). (Illus.). 112p. (J). (gr. 2-5). lib. bdg. 13.94 (978-0-606-33273-6(1)) Tandem Library Bks.

—Attack of the Bandit Cats. Wolf, Matt, illus. 2004. (Geronimo Stilton Ser.: No. 8). 115p. (J). lib. bdg. 10.00 (***978-1-4242-0277-5(9)***) Fitzgerald Bks.

—Christmas Catastrophe. ed. 2007. (Geronimo Stilton Ser.). 128p. (J). pap. 6.99 (***978-0-545-00902-7(2)*** , Scholastic Paperbacks) Scholastic, Inc.

—The Christmas Toy Factory. 2006. (Geronimo Stilton Ser.: No. 27). (Illus.). 95p. (J). (***978-1-4156-8969-1(5)***) Scholastic, Inc.

—The Curse of the Cheese Pyramid. Wolf, Matt, illus. 2004. (Geronimo Stilton Ser.: No. 2). 113p. (J). lib. bdg. 10.00 (***978-1-4242-0696-4(0)***) Fitzgerald Bks.

—A Fabumouse Vacation for Geronimo. 2004. (Geronimo Stilton Ser.: No. 9). (Illus.). 113p. (J). (gr. 2-5). lib. bdg. 13.94 (978-0-606-33272-9(3)) Tandem Library Bks.

—I'm Too Fond of My Fur! Wolf, Matt, illus. 2004. (Geronimo Stilton Ser.: No. 4). 116p. (J). lib. bdg. 10.00 (***978-1-4242-0698-8(7)***) Fitzgerald Bks.

—It's Halloween, You 'Fraidy Mouse! Wolf, Matt, illus. 2004. 113p. (J). lib. bdg. 10.00 (***978-1-4242-0280-5(9)***) Fitzgerald Bks.

—It's Halloween, You 'Fraidy Mouse! 2004. (Geronimo Stilton Ser.: No. 11). (Illus.). 113p. (J). (gr. 2-5). lib. bdg. 13.94 (978-0-606-33274-3(X)) Tandem Library Bks.

—Lost Treasure of the Emerald Eye. Wolf, Matt, illus. 2004. (Geronimo Stilton Ser.: No. 1). 116p. (J). lib. bdg. 10.00 (***978-1-4242-0695-7(2)***) Fitzgerald Bks.

—Lost Treasure of the Emerald Eye. 2007. (Geronimo Stilton Ser.: No. 1). 128p. (J). pap. 2.99 (***978-0-545-01032-0(2)*** , Scholastic Paperbacks) Scholastic, Inc.

—Lost Treasure of the Emerald Eye. Wolf, Matt & Keys, Larry, illus. 2004. (Geronimo Stilton Ser.: No. 1). 128p. (J). (gr. 2-5). pap. 6.99 (978-0-439-55963-8(4) , Scholastic Paperbacks) Scholastic, Inc.

—The Mona Mousa Code. Wolf, Matt, illus. 2005. (Geronimo Stilton Ser.: No. 15). 113p. (J). lib. bdg. 10.00 (***978-1-4242-0284-3(1)***) Fitzgerald Bks.

—The Mona Mousa Code. Wolf, Matt, illus. 2005. (Geronimo Stilton Ser.: No. 15). 113p. (J). (ps-k). lib. bdg. 13.54 (978-0-606-33278-1(2)) Tandem Library Bks.

—The Phantom of the Subway. Wolf, Matt, illus. 2004. (Geronimo Stilton Ser.: No. 13). 112p. (J). lib. bdg. 10.00 (***978-1-4242-0282-9(5)***) Fitzgerald Bks.

—The Phantom of the Subway. 2004. (Geronimo Stilton Ser.: No. 13). (Illus.). 112p. (J). (gr. 2-5). lib. bdg. 13.94 (978-0-606-33276-7(6)) Tandem Library Bks.

—Surf's up, Geronimo! 2005. (Geronimo Stilton Ser.: No. 20). (Illus.). 109p. (J). (978-1-4156-0622-3(6)) Scholastic, Inc.

—The Temple of the Ruby of Fire. Wolf, Matt, illus. 2004. (Geronimo Stilton Ser.: No. 14). 109p. (J). lib. bdg. 10.00 (***978-1-4242-0283-6(3)***) Fitzgerald Bks.

—Valentine's Day Disaster. Keys, Larry et al, illus. 2006. (Geronimo Stilton Ser.: No. 23). 122p. (J). lib. bdg. 18.46 (***978-1-4242-0292-8(2)***) Fitzgerald Bks.

—Valentine's Day Disaster. 2006. (Geronimo Stilton Ser.: No. 23). (Illus.). 91p. (J). (978-1-4156-4780-6(1)) Scholastic, Inc.

—Watch Your Whiskers, Stilton! 2005. (Geronimo Stilton Ser.: No. 17). (Illus.). 111p. (J). (978-1-4155-8205-3(X)) Scholastic, Inc.

Stilton, Geronimo. The Wild, Wild West. Stilton, Geronimo et al, illus. 2005. (Geronimo Stilton Ser.: No. 21). 121p. (J). lib. bdg. 18.46 (***978-1-4242-0290-4(6)***) Fitzgerald Bks.

Stilton, Geronimo & Wolf, Matt. All Because of a Cup of Coffee. 2004. (Geronimo Stilton Ser.: No. 10). (Illus.). 112p. (J). lib. bdg. 10.00 (***978-1-4242-0279-9(5)***) Fitzgerald Bks.

Stine, R. L. Punk'd & Skunked. Park, Trip, illus. 2007. (Rotten School Ser.: No. 11). 128p. (J). 6.99 (978-0-06-078830-8(5)); lib. bdg. 14.89 (978-0-06-078831-5(3)) HarperCollins Pubs.

—Rottenest Angel. Park, Trip, illus. 2007. (Rotten School Ser.: No. 10). 128p. (J). lib. bdg. 14.89 (978-0-06-078828-5(3)) HarperCollins Pubs.

—The Rottenest Angel. Park, Trip, illus. 2007. (Rotten School Ser.: Vol. 10). 128p. (J). 6.99 (978-0-06-078827-8(5)) HarperCollins Pubs.

—Terror Trips. 2007. (Goosebumps Graphix Ser.). 144p. (J). pap. 16.99 (978-0-439-85777-2(5)); (Illus.). pap. 8.99 (978-0-439-85780-2(5)) Scholastic, Inc. (Graphix).

Stine, R.L. Punk'd & Skunked. Park, Trip, illus. 2007. 108p. (J). pap. (***978-0-06-078832-2(1)***) HarperCollins Pubs.

Stirnkorb, Patricia. Stranger Danger: The reluctantly written but absolutly necessary book for todays boys & Girls. 2005. (Illus.). 32p. (J). 12.99 (978-0-9758709-9-0(8)) Journey Stone Creations, LLC.

Stoeke, Janet Morgan. Minerva Louise. 2001. (J). (978-0-606-21330-1(9)) Tandem Library Bks.

Strand, Jeff. Elrod Mcbugle on the Loose. 2006. (ENG.). 136p. (YA). per. 9.25 (***978-0-7599-4325-4(7)***) Hard Shell Word Factory.

Strasser, Todd. Don't Get Caught Driving the School Bus. 2000. (Don't Get Caught Ser.). (J). 11.15 (978-0-606-19556-0(4)) Tandem Library Bks.

—Don't Get Caught in the Girl's Locker Room. 2001. (Don't Get Caught Ser.). (Illus.). (J). 11.15 (978-0-606-21155-0(1)) Tandem Library Bks.

Strong, Jeremy. Stuff: The Life of a Cool Demented Dude. Armstrong, Matthew S., illus. 2007. 240p. (J). (gr. 7 up). 15.99 (978-0-06-084105-8(2) , HarperTeen) HarperCollins Pubs.

—Stuff: The Life of a Cool Demented Dude. Armstrong, Matthew, illus. 2007. 240p. (J). (gr. 7 up). lib. bdg. 16.89 (978-0-06-084106-5(0) , HarperTeen) HarperCollins Pubs.

Stroud, Scott. Baby Kong. Hunt, Jim, illus. 2006. (J). 12.95 (978-1-60131-001-9(3)) Big Tent Bks.

Students in Conjunction with 826 Valencia Staff. Some Things You Should Know about Captain Rick: An Informational Booklet Provided for the Safety of the Republic. 2006. 46p. (J). pap. 8.00 (978-0-9770844-1-8(8)) 826 Valencia.

Students of New York City High School, ed. Sonny Paine, Issue Two: Sonny Applies to College. 2007. 86p. (J). (gr. 8-12). pap. 8.00 (***978-0-9790073-5-4(6)***) 826 Valencia.

Style Guide Staff, illus. Patricks Backpack Book. 2003. (SpongeBob SquarePants Ser.). 16p. (J). bds. 6.99 (978-0-689-85649-5(0) , Simon Spotlight/Nickelodeon) Simon & Schuster Children's Publishing.

—Spongebob Squarepants: Backpack Book. 2003. (SpongeBob SquarePants Ser.). 16p. (J). bds. 6.99 (978-0-689-85648-8(2) , Simon Spotlight/Nickelodeon) Simon & Schuster Children's Publishing.

Suarez, Perla. Blum! Rojas, Maria, illus. 2001. (SPA.). 40p. (J). 15.95 (978-950-511-517-4(2)) Alfaguara S.A. de Ediciones ARG. *Dist:* Santillana USA Publishing Co., Inc.

Sula, Sondra. The Expanders: Quest for the Flubulator. 2000. mass mkt. 8.95 (978-1-931179-11-9(5)) Long Hill Productions, Inc.

—The Expanders: Quest for the Flubulator. Johnson, Terri L., illus. 2000. 32p. (J). (gr. 1-3). pap. (978-0-9701450-2-4(0)) Long Hill Productions, Inc.

Sullivan, Michael. Escapade Johnson & Mayhem at Mount Moosilauke. Kolitsky, Joy, illus. 2007. (Escapade Johnson Ser.). 96p. (J). pap. 3.95 (978-1-929945-70-2(1)) Big Guy Bks., Inc.

Swallow, Pamela C. Groundhog Gets a Say. Bunkus, Denise, illus. 2007. 40p. (J). (ps). pap. 6.99 (***978-0-14-240896-4(4)*** , Puffin) Penguin Group (USA) Inc.

Sweetland, Nancy Rose. Yelly Kelly/Kelly, el Griton. de la Vega, Eida, tr. Sweetland, Robert, illus. rev. ed. 2004. Tr. of Kelly, el Griton. (SPA & ENG.). 32p. (J). (gr. k-3). 16.95 (978-0-9720192-0-0(0) , 626999) Raven Tree Pr.

Swift, John. Tea with a Vampire. 2007. pap. 9.00 (***978-0-8059-8963-2(3)***) Dorrance Publishing Co., Inc.

Swope, Sam. Krazees. 2003. lib. bdg. 15.25 (978-0-613-59656-5(0)) Tandem Library Bks.

Sydor, Colleen. Raising a Little Stink. Constantin, Pascale, illus. 2006. 32p. 16.95 (978-1-55337-896-9(2)) Kids Can Pr., Ltd. CAN. *Dist:* Wybel Marketing Group.

Tafuri, Nancy. Silly Little Goose! 2001. (Illus.). (J). 15.95 (978-0-439-06305-0(1)) Scholastic, Inc.

Tayleur, Karen. Excuses! Survive & Succeed with David Mortimore Baxter. Garvey, Brann, illus. 2007. (David Mortimore Baxter Ser.). 71p. (J). (gr. 3-6). lib. bdg. 23.93 (978-1-59889-073-0(5)) Stone Arch Bks.

—Liar! David Mortimore Baxter. Garvey, Brann, illus. 2007. 71p. (J). pap. (***978-1-59889-206-2(1)***) Stone Arch Bks.

—Manners! David Mortimore Baxter. Garvey, Brann, illus. 2007. 77p. (J). pap. (***978-1-59889-207-9(X)***) Stone Arch Bks.

—Promises! David Mortimore Baxter. Garvey, Brann, illus. 2007. 87p. (J). pap. (***978-1-59889-208-6(8)***) Stone Arch Bks.

Tayleur, Karen. Secrets! The Secret Life of David Mortimore Baxter. Garvey, Brann, illus. 2007. (David Mortimore Baxter Ser.). 82p. (J). (gr. 3-6). lib. bdg. 23.93 (978-1-59889-077-8(8)) Stone Arch Bks.

Taylor, Alastair. Swollobog. 2001. (Illus.). 32p. (J). (gr. k-3). tchr. ed. 15.00 (978-0-618-04348-4(9)) Houghton Mifflin Co. Trade & Reference Div.

Taylor, Marshall, illus. & photos by. Adventures of Cow. Taylor, Marshall, photos by. 2005. 32p. (J). 12.95 (978-1-58246-139-7(2) , Tricycle Pr.) Ten Speed Pr.

—Adventures of Cow, Too. Taylor, Marshall, photos by. 2007. 32p. (J). (ps-1). 12.95 (978-1-58246-189-2(9) , Tricycle Pr.) Ten Speed Pr.

Taylor, Sean. When a Monster Is Born. Sharratt, Nick, illus. 2007. 32p. (J). (ps-1). 16.95 (***978-1-59643-254-3(3)***) Roaring Brook Pr.

Teach Us, Amelia Bedelia. 2002. (Amelia Bedelia Ser.). (Illus.). (J). 11.91 (978-0-7587-1726-9(1)) Book Wholesalers, Inc.

Teague, Mark. Dear Mrs. La Rue: Letters from Obedience School. Teague, Mark, illus. 2002. (Dear Mrs. Larue Ser.). (Illus.). 32p. (J). (gr. k-3). 16.99 (978-0-439-20663-1(4) , Scholastic Pr.) Scholastic, Inc.

—Detective LaRue: Letters from the Investigation. Teague, Mark, illus. 2004. (Detective Larue Ser.). (Illus.). 32p. (J). (ps-3). pap. 15.95 (978-0-439-45868-9(4) , Scholastic Pr.) Scholastic, Inc.

—Larue para Alcalde: Cartas de la Campana: Cartas de la Campana. 2008. (Larue for Mayor Ser.). 32p. (J). pap. 4.99 (***978-0-545-02214-9(2)*** , Scholastic en Espanol) Scholastic, Inc.

—The Letters from the Campaign. 2008. (Larue for Mayor Ser.). 32p. (J). pap. 16.99 (***978-0-439-78315-6(1)*** , Blue Sky Pr., The) Scholastic, Inc.

Temple, Bob. The Day Mom Finally Snapped. Harpster, Steve, illus. 2006. (Graphic Sparks Ser.). 33p. (J). 19.93 (978-1-59889-038-9(7)) Stone Arch Bks.

Terasaki, Stanley Todd. Ghosts for Breakfast. Shinjo, Shelly, illus. 2002. 32p. (J). (gr. k-4). 16.95 (978-1-58430-046-5(9)) Lee & Low Bks., Inc.

Thaler, Mike. The Custodian from the Black Lagoon. 2001. (Black Lagoon Ser.). (Illus.). (J). 10.05 (978-0-606-22044-6(5)) Tandem Library Bks.

—The Field Day from the Black Lagoon. Lee, Jared D., illus. 2008. (Little Apple Ser.). 64p. (J). 3.99 (***978-0-439-68076-9(X)***) Scholastic, Inc.

—Field Day from the Black Lagoon. Lee, Jared D., illus. 2005. 64p. (J). lib. bdg. 15.00 (***978-1-4242-2261-2(3)***) Fitzgerald Bks.

—The Librarian from the Black Lagoon. Lee, Jared D., illus. unabr. ed. 2007. (J). (gr. k-2). pap. 18.95 incl. audio compact disk (***978-0-439-02774-8(8)***); pap. 14.95 incl. audio (***978-0-439-02773-1(X)***) Scholastic, Inc.

—The Music Teacher from the Black Lagoon. Lee, Jared D., illus. 2000. (Black Lagoon Ser.). 32p. (J). (ps-3). pap. 3.99 (978-0-439-18873-9(3)) Scholastic, Inc.

—The Music Teacher from the Black Lagoon. 2000. (Black Lagoon Ser.). (J). (ps-3). (978-0-606-18882-1(7)) Tandem Library Bks.

—Music Teacher from the Black Lagoon. 2000. (gr. 3-6). lib. bdg. 10.95 (978-0-613-24063-5(4)) Tandem Library Bks.

—The School Secretary from the Black Lagoon. Lee, Jared D., illus. 2006. (J). (***978-0-439-80077-8(3)***) Scholastic, Inc.

—The Teacher from the Black Lagoon. Lee, Jared D., illus. 2004. (YA). (gr. k up). pap. 14.95 incl. audio (978-1-55592-172-9(8)) Weston Woods Studios, Inc.

—The Teacher from the Black Lagoon. Lee, Jared D., illus. 2004. (J). (gr. k-3). pap. 18.95 incl. audio compact disk (978-1-55592-495-9(6)) Weston Woods Studios, Inc.

Thank You, Amelia Bedelia. 2002. (Amelia Bedelia Ser.). (J). 12.34 (978-0-7587-6292-4(5)) Book Wholesalers, Inc.

Theriault, Francis Patrick. The Candy Coated Castle's Catastrophe: A Christmas Crisis. 2006. (ENG.). 48p. pap. 10.95 (978-1-59800-555-4(3)) Outskirts Press, Inc.

Thomas, Cameron. The Utt Jungle Airline: The Jungle of Utt. Krystoforski, Andrej, illus. 2004. (Jungle of Utt Ser.). 48p. (J). 16.95 (978-0-921800-03-3(7)) MGT Developments, Ltd. CAN. *Dist:* Independent Pubs. Group.

Thomas, Frances. Polly's Absolutely Worst Birthday Ever. Gardner, Sally, illus. 2003. 96p. (gr. 1-4). lib. bdg. 16.99 (978-0-385-90122-2(4) , Delacorte Bks. for Young Readers) Random Hse. Children's Bks.

Thomas, Shelley Moore. Happy Birthday, Good Knight. Plecas, Jennifer, illus. 2006. 48p. (J). (ps). 13.99 (978-0-525-47184-4(7) , Dutton Juvenile) Penguin Group (USA) Inc.

Thomas, Valerie. Winnie Flies Again. 2000. (978-0-606-19823-3(7)) Tandem Library Bks.

Thompson. My Friend Mr. Morris. (Illus.). 32p. (J). pap. 7.95 (978-0-14-038887-9(7)) Penguin Bks., Ltd. GBR. *Dist:* Trafalgar Square Publishing.

Thompson, Clarence. Leave Me Alone You Fat Baboon! 2004. 193p. pap. 19.95 (978-1-4137-4610-5(1)) PublishAmerica, Inc.

Thompson, Colin. The Floods #1: Good Neighbors. Scrambly, Crab, illus. 2008. (Floods Ser.). 224p. (J). 15.99 (***978-0-06-113196-7(2)***); lib. bdg. 16.89 (***978-0-06-113199-8(7)***) HarperCollins Pubs.

Thompson, Colin. The Great Montefiasco. Redlich, Ben, illus. 2004. 40p. (J). (ps-ps). 16.95 (978-1-59572-008-5(1)) Star Bright Bks., Inc.

Thompson, Joan. Lucy Russell: Lucy in the Wings. 2003. 129p. (YA). pap. 10.95 (978-0-595-26906-8(0) , Authors Choice Pr.) iUniverse, Inc.

—Lucy Russell: The Starstruck Summer. 2003. 129p. (YA). pap. 10.95 (978-0-595-26903-7(6) , Authors Choice Pr.) iUniverse, Inc.

Thompson, Kay. Eloise at the Wedding. Lyon, Tammie, illus. 2006. (Eloise Ser.). 32p. (J). (ps-1). pap. 3.99 (978-0-689-87449-9(9) , Aladdin) Simon & Schuster Children's Publishing.

—Eloise en Paris. Knight, Hilary, illus. 2002. (SPA.). 84p. (J). (gr. k-3). 17.00 (978-84-264-3739-6(7) , LM30421) Editorial Lumen ESP. *Dist:* Distribooks, Inc., Lectorum Pubns., Inc.

—Eloise the Ultimate Edition. Knight, Hilary, illus. 2000. 304p. (J). (ps-3). 39.99 (978-0-689-83990-0(1)) Simon & Schuster Children's Publishing.

Thompson, Kay. Eloise's Christmas Trinkles. Knight, Hilary, illus. 2007. (Eloise Ser.). 48p. (J). (ps-3). 9.99 (***978-0-689-87425-3(1)***) Simon & Schuster Children's Publishing.

Thornhill, Samantha. Everybody Hates School Presentations. 2008. (Everybody Hates Chris Ser.). 96p. (J). pap. 5.99 (***978-1-4169-4983-1(6)*** , Simon Spotlight) Simon & Schuster Children's Publishing.

Thottam, Meena. The Last Dancer. 2006. (J). 3.95 (***978-0-9776917-7-7(2)*** , Curcumin Bks.) Davlaw Press.

Thottam, Meena, adapted by. Brothers of the Jungle. 2006. (J). 3.95 (***978-0-9776917-4-6(8)*** , Curcumin Bks.) Davlaw Press.

—Chameil's Choice. 2006. (J). 3.95 (***978-0-9776917-6-0(4)*** , Curcumin Bks.) Davlaw Press.

—Death, Where are You? 2006. (J). 3.95 (***978-0-9776917-5-3(6)*** , Curcumin Bks.) Davlaw Press.

—Maybe I am, Maybe I am Not. 2006. (J). 3.95 (***978-0-9776917-8-4(0)*** , Curcumin Bks.) Davlaw Press.

—The Pretender. 2006. (J). 3.95 (***978-0-9776917-3-9(X)*** , Curcumin Bks.) Davlaw Press.

—Road to Riches. 2006. (J). 3.95 (***978-0-9776917-9-1(9)*** , Curcumin Bks.) Davlaw Press.

—The Sage's Daughter. 2006. (J). 3.95 (***978-0-9776917-2-2(1)*** , Curcumin Bks.) Davlaw Press.

Todd, Barbara. The Rainmaker. Roge, illus. 2003. 32p. (J). (ps-2). lib. bdg. 18.95 (978-1-55037-775-0(2)) Annick Pr., Ltd. CAN. *Dist:* Firefly Bks., Ltd.

Tokyopop Staff. Spongebob Squarepants. 2003. (gr. 3-6). lib. bdg. 16.45 (978-0-613-79933-1(X)); lib. bdg. 16.45 (978-0-613-79935-5(6)) Tandem Library Bks.

Toliver, Wendy. The Secret Life of a Teenage Siren. 2007. (Romantic Comedies Ser.). 304p. (YA). mass mkt. 6.99 (***978-1-4169-5065-3(6)*** , Simon Pulse) Simon & Schuster Children's Publishing.

Tolstoy, Alexei. El Nabo Gigante (The Gigantic Turnip) Sarfatti, Esther, tr. Sharkey, Niamh, illus. 2001. Tr. of Gigantic Turnip. (SPA.). 40p. (J). (ps-1). reprint ed. pap. 6.99 (978-1-84148-396-2(6) , BFP0577) Barefoot Bks., Inc.

Tolstoy, Alexei, ed. El Nabo Gigante. 2000. Tr. of Gigantic Turnip. (J). (978-0-606-19703-8(6)) Tandem Library Bks.

Tondreau Levert, Louise & Perkes, Carolyn. Parents Do the Weirdest Things! Girard, Roge, illus. 2001. (Little Wolf Bks.: Level 2). 32p. (J). (gr. 1 up). pap. (978-1-894363-75-4(2)) Dominique & Friends.

Toy Story 2 Read Along. 1999. (J). (ps-3). pap. 6.98 incl. audio (978-0-7634-0535-9(3)) Walt Disney Records.

Trasler, Janee. Ghost Eats It All: Little Boo Books. 2006. (Illus.). 24p. (J). (ps-1). 5.99 (978-0-316-01844-9(9)) Little Brown & Co.

Trembath, Don. One Missing Finger. 2001. (Black Belt Ser.). 160p. (J). (gr. 3-7). pap. 6.95 (978-1-55143-194-9(7)) Orca Bk. Pubs. USA.

—One Missing Finger. 2001. (gr. 3-6). lib. bdg. 15.25 (978-0-613-88906-3(1)) Tandem Library Bks.

Tremblay, Alain Ulysse. L' Héritage de Julien. Malépart, Céline, illus. 2004. (Roman Jeunesse Ser.). (FRE.). 96p. (J). (gr. 4-7). pap. (978-2-89021-682-2(9)) Diffusion du livre Mirabel.

—Mon Pere Est un Jupi. 2002. (Roman Jeunesse Ser.). (FRE., Illus.). 96p. (J). (gr. 4-7). pap. (978-2-89021-589-4(X)) Diffusion du livre Mirabel.

Tremblay, Carole. Theodore the Millipede. Malepart, Celine, illus. 2005. (Read-It! Readers Ser.). 32p. (J). (gr. k-3). 18.60 (978-1-4048-1026-6(9)) Picture Window Bks.

Tremblay, Carole, et al. Theodore the Millipede. Malepart, Celine, illus. 2001. (Little Wolf Bks.: Level 3). 32p. (J). (gr. 1 up). pap. (978-1-894363-69-3(8)) Dominique & Friends.

Trimble, Irene & Olin, Mary. The Junior Novel. 2007. (Meet the Robinsons Ser.). 144p. (J). pap. 4.99 (978-0-06-112475-4(3)) HarperCollins Pubs.

Trine, Greg. The Curse of the Bologna Sandwich. Montijo, Rhode, illus. 2006. (Melvin Beederman, Superhero Ser.). 144p. (J). 15.95 (978-0-8050-7928-9(9)); pap. 5.99 (978-0-8050-7836-7(3)) Holt, Henry & Co.

H
I

—The Fake Cape Caper. Montijo, Rhode, illus. 5th rev. ed. 2007. (Melvin Beederman, Superhero Ser.). 144p. (J). pap. 5.99 (*978-0-8050-8159-6(3)); (gr. 2 up). 16.95 (*978-0-8050-8158-9(5)) Holt, Henry & Co. (Holt, Henry & Co. Bks. For Young Readers).

—The Grateful Fred. Montijo, Rhode, illus. 3rd rev. ed. 2006. (Melvin Beederman, Superhero Ser.). 144p. (J). 15.95 (978-0-8050-7921-0(1)) Holt, Henry & Co.

—The Grateful Fred. Montijo, Rhode, illus. 3rd rev. ed. 2006. (Melvin Beederman, Superhero Ser.). 144p. (J). pap. 5.99 (978-0-8050-7922-7(X)) Holt, Henry & Co.

—The Revenge of the McNasty Brothers. Montijo, Rhode, illus. 2nd rev. ed. 2006. (Melvin Beederman, Superhero Ser.). 144p. (J). 15.95 (978-0-8050-7929-6(7)); pap. 5.99 (978-0-8050-7837-4(1)) Holt, Henry & Co.

—Terror in Tights. Montijo, Rhode, illus. 4th rev. ed. 2007. (Melvin Beederman, Superhero Ser.). 144p. (J). (gr. 2-4). 16.95 (978-0-8050-7923-4(8)); pap. 5.99 (978-0-8050-7924-1(6)) Holt, Henry & Co.

Tripp, Valerie. Very Funny, Elizabeth! Andreasen, Dan, illus. 2005. (American Girls Collection). 81p. (J). (gr. 3). 12.95 (978-1-59369-067-0(3)); pap. 6.95 (978-1-59369-061-8(4)) American Girl Publishing, Inc. (American Girl).

Troiano, Joe. Little Scribbles: Halloween Fun with Spookley the Square Pumpkin. Banta, Susan, illus. 2006. (Little Scribbles Ser.). 12p. (J). bds. 5.95 (978-1-4027-4017-6(4)) Sterling Publishing Co., Inc.

Trudel, Sylvain & Langlois, Suzane. Un Secret dans Mon Jardin. 2001. (Premier Roman Ser.). (FRE., Illus.). 64p. (J). pap. (978-2-89021-452-1(4)) Diffusion du livre Mirabel.

Tryon, Micro, et al. Fundorado Island. 2006. (Illus.). 224p. (J). (gr. 3). 14.95 (978-0-385-73267-3(8) , Delacorte Bks. for Young Readers) Random Hse. Children's Bks.

Twain, Mark. Mark Twain. Hall, Tracy, illus. 2004. (Great American Short Stories Ser.). 80p. (J). lib. bdg. 23.33 (978-0-8368-4255-5(3)) Stevens, Gareth Inc.

—Mark Twain. Camfield, Gregg, ed. Comport, Sally Wern, illus. 2005. (Stories for Young People Ser.). 80p. (J). (gr. 7-9). 14.95 (978-1-4027-1178-7(6)) Sterling Publishing Co., Inc.

—The Prince & the Pauper. abr. ed. 2001. (gr. 7-12). lib. bdg. 15.25 (978-0-613-43870-4(1)) Tandem Library Bks.

Twystd. 2001. (ENG.). per. 12.95 (978-0-9673711-2-2(0)) Osprey Pr.

Tyner, Christopher. I'll Do It Tommarra Laura. 2004. 37p. (J). pap. 17.95 (978-1-4137-2753-1(0)) PublishAmerica, Inc.

Uhlberg, Myron. Lemuel the Fool. Lamut, Sonja, illus. 2001. 32p. (J). (ps-3). 15.95 (978-1-56145-220-0(3)) Peachtree Pubs., Ltd.

Umansky, Kaye. Donkey-Ride to Disaster. Fisher, Chris, illus. l.t. ed. 2005. 120p. (J). pap. (978-0-7540-6184-7(1) , CLP 378) BBC Audio.

—Donkey-Ride to Disaster. 2003. (J). pap. 24.95 incl. audio (978-0-7540-6246-2(5) , Galaxy Children's Large Print) BBC Audiobooks America.

—Madness in the Mountains. l.t. ed. 2005. (Illus.). 128p. (J). pap. (978-0-7540-7852-4(3)' , CLP 442) BBC Audio.

—Madness in the Mountains. 2004. (J). 24.95 incl. audio (978-0-7540-6271-4(6) , Chivers Children's Audio Bks.) BBC Audiobooks America.

Underwood, Deborah. Pirate Mom. Gilpin, Stephen, illus. 2006. (Step into Reading Ser.). 48p. (J). (gr. 1-3). lib. bdg. 11.99 (978-0-375-93323-3(9)); 3.99 (978-0-375-83323-6(4)) Random Hse. Children's Bks. (Random Hse. Bks. for Young Readers).

Universal Dreamworks Pictures Staff. Cat in the Hat: Official Movie Book. 2004. (Illus.). 128p. pap. 12.95 (978-1-57243-609-1(3) , 53846352) Triumph Bks.

Urban, Linda. A Crooked Kind of Perfect. 2007. (Illus.). 224p. (J). (gr. 3-7). 16.00 (*978-0-15-206007-7(3)) Harcourt Children's Bks.

Ure, Jean. Secret Life of Sally Tomato. 2001. (Diary Ser.). (Illus.). 160p. (J). pap. 9.99 (978-0-00-675150-2(4) , Collins) HarperCollins Pubs. Ltd. GBR. Dist: Independent Pubs. Group.

Vaes, Alain. The Princess & the Pea. Vaes, Alain, illus. 2001. (Illus.). 32p. (J). (gr. 1-3). 15.95 (978-0-316-89633-7(0)) Little, Brown Bks. for Young Readers.

Vail, Rachel. Never Mind! A Twin Novel. 2005. 208p. (J). (gr. 5 up). reprint ed. pap. 5.99 (978-0-06-054316-7(7) , Harper Trophy) HarperCollins Pubs.

—Over the Moon. Nash, Scott, illus. 2001. 32p. (J). (ps-2). pap. 5.95 (978-0-531-07184-7(7) , Orchard Bks.) Scholastic, Inc.

van de Ruit, John. Spud. 2007. 352p. (YA). (gr. 7 up). 16.99 (*978-1-59514-170-5(7) , Razorbill) Penguin Group (USA) Inc.

Van Draanen, Wendelin. Attack of the Tagger. 2004. (Shredderman Ser.: Bk. 2). (Illus.). 176p. (J). (gr. 2-5). lib. bdg. 14.99 (978-0-375-92352-4(7) , Knopf Bks. for Young Readers) Random Hse. Children's Bks.

—Attack of the Tagger. Biggs, Brian, illus. 2004. (Shredderman Ser.: Bk. 2). 176p. (J). (gr. 2-5). 12.95 (978-0-375-82352-7(2) , Knopf Bks. for Young Readers) Random Hse. Children's Bks.

—Confessions of a Serial Kisser. 2008. 272p. (J). (gr. 7). 15.99 (*978-0-375-84248-1(9)); lib. bdg. 18.99 (*978-0-375-94248-8(3)) Random Hse. Children's Bks. (Knopf Bks. for Young Readers).

—Enemy Spy. 2005. (Shredderman Ser.: Bk. 4). (Illus.). 192p. (J). (gr. 2-5). 12.95 (978-0-375-82354-1(9)); lib. bdg. 14.99 (978-0-375-92354-8(3)) Random Hse. Children's Bks. (Knopf Bks. for Young Readers).

—Secret Identity. Biggs, Brian, illus. 2004. (Shredderman Ser.: Bk. 1). 144p. (J). (gr. 2-5). 12.95 (978-0-375-82351-0(4) , Knopf Bks. for Young Readers) Random Hse. Children's Bks.

Van-Leeuwen, Jan. Lost Treasures Bk. 4: The Great Cheese Conspiracy. 2001. 96p. (J). 13.49 (978-0-7868-2555-4(3)) Hyperion Pr.

Vande Velde, Vivian. Wizard at Work. 2003. (Illus.). 144p. (YA). 16.00 (978-0-15-204559-3(7)) Harcourt Children's Bks.

—Wizard at Work: A Novel in Stories. 2004. (Illus.). 144p. (J). pap. 5.95 (978-0-15-205309-3(3) , Magic Carpet Bks.) Harcourt Children's Bks.

Venokur, Ross. The Cookie Company. 2001. (Illus.). (J). (978-0-606-21120-8(9)) Tandem Library Bks.

Viky Toma Unas Vacaciones Divetidas. 2003. (SPA.). 62p. (J). (ps-1). (978-968-5308-80-9(2) , Silver Dolphin en Español) Advanced Marketing, S. de R. L. de C. V.

Viorst, Judith. Alexander & the Terrible, Horrible, No Good, Very Bad Day & Other Stories & Poems. Cruz, Ray, illus. 2002. (J). 14.47 (978-0-7587-1915-7(9)) Book Wholesalers, Inc.

—Alexander & the Terrible, Horrible, No Good, Very Bad Day & Other Stories & Poems. 2000. (Alexander Ser.). 76p. (J). (gr. k-3). pap. 6.25 (978-0-87129-979-6(8) , A83) Dramatic Publishing Co.

—Alexander & the Terrible, Horrible, No Good, Very Bad Day & Other Stories & Poems. 1999. (Alexander Ser.). (J). (gr. k-3). pap. 23.24 incl. audio (978-0-7887-3177-8(7) , 40912) Recorded Bks., LLC.

—Alexander & the Terrible, Horrible, No Good, Very Bad Day & Other Stories & Poems. Cruz, Ray, illus. 2002. 32p. (J). mass mkt. 1.00 (978-0-689-85525-2(7) , Aladdin) Simon & Schuster Children's Publishing.

—Alexander & the Terrible, Horrible, No Good, Very Bad Day & Other Stories & Poems. Cruz, Ray, illus. 1999. (Alexander Ser.). (J). (gr. k-3). lib. bdg. 14.15 (978-0-8085-2406-9(2)) Tandem Library Bks.

von Konigslow, Andrea Wayne. Bing & Chutney off to Moosonee. von Konigslow, Andrea Wayne, illus. 2001. (Bing & Chutney Adventures Ser.). (Illus.). 24p. (J). (gr. k-ps). lib. bdg. 18.95 (978-1-55037-679-1(9)) Annick Pr., Ltd. CAN. Dist: Firefly Bks., Ltd.

Wagner, Brian. 10 Things Not to Do with Your Eyeball. 2005. 20p. 9.99 (978-1-4116-5977-3(5)) Lulu.com.

Walker, Sally M. Meet the Vowels. Luthardt, Kevin, illus. 2008. (J). lib. bdg. (*978-0-8225-7982-3(0) , Millbrook Pr.) Lerner Publishing Group.

Wall, Jean Jones. I Can Stand by a Rase. 2004. (Illus.). 60p. (J). (gr. 3-5). pap. 12.00 (978-0-9760518-0-0(X)) JWall Publishing.

Wallace, Bill. No Dogs Allowed! 2005. 224p. (J). pap. 5.99 (978-1-4169-0381-9(X) , Aladdin) Simon & Schuster Children's Publishing.

Wallace, Karen. King Cudgel's Challenge. Flook, Helen, illus. 2007. (J). lib. bdg. (*978-1-4048-3706-5(X)) Picture Window Bks.

—Prince Marvin's Great Moment. Flook, Helen, illus. 2007. (J). lib. bdg. (*978-1-4048-3707-2(8)) Picture Window Bks.

—Princess Gusty Ox's Strange Change. Flook, Helen, illus. 2007. (J). lib. bdg. (*978-1-4048-3708-9(6)) Picture Window Bks.

—Queen Carrion's Big Bear Hug. Flook, Helen, illus. 2007. (J). lib. bdg. (*978-1-4048-3709-6(4)) Picture Window Bks.

Walsh, Ann. Flower Power. 2005. (Orca Currents Ser.). 112p. (J). (gr. 4-10). pap. 7.95 (978-1-55143-386-8(9)) Orca Bk. Pubs. USA.

Walsh, Maria Elena. Cuentopos de Gulubu. Lavandeira, Sandra, illus. 2003. (SPA.). 120p. (J). (gr. 3-5). 14.95 (978-950-511-630-0(6)) Alfaguara S.A. de Ediciones ARG. Dist: Santillana USA Publishing Co., Inc.

Walsh, Marissa. A Field Guide to High School. 2007. 144p. (YA). (gr. 7). lib. bdg. 18.99 (*978-0-385-90427-8(4)); 15.99 (*978-0-385-73410-3(7)) Random Hse. Children's Bks. (Delacorte Bks. for Young Readers).

Walt Disney Records Staff, prod. A Bug's Life Read Along. 1998. 24p. (J). (ps-3). 6.98 incl. audio (978-0-7634-0441-3(1)) Walt Disney Home Video.

Walton, Rick. Bullfrog Pops. McAllister, Chris, illus. 2005. 32p. pap. 6.95 (978-1-58685-840-7(8)) Gibbs Smith, Publisher.

Wang, Margaret. Who Stole the Cookie from the Cookie Jar? Schneider, Christine, illus. 2005. 22p. (J). 10.95 (978-1-58117-383-3(0) , Intervisual/Piggy Toes) Dalmatian Pr.

Ward, Nick. No Te Comas a la Maestra. Fabiancic, Miriam, tr. Ward, Nick, illus. 2001. (SPA., Illus.). (J). (gr. k-1). pap. 3.99 (978-0-439-26363-4(8) , SO30706) Scholastic, Inc.

Wardlaw, Lee. 101 Ways to Bug Your Parents. 2002. 160p. (J). pap. (978-0-14-038739-1(0) , Putnam Juvenile) Penguin Group (USA) Inc.

—101 Ways to Bug Your Teacher. 256p. 2005. (gr. 5-7). pap. 6.99 (978-0-14-240331-0(8) , Puffin); 2004. (Illus.). (J). (gr. 4). 16.99 (978-0-8037-2658-1(9) , Dial) Penguin Group (USA) Inc.

Warren, Prue. Heart's Desire Cottage. 2006. pap. 8.95 (978-0-533-15240-7(2)) Vantage Pr., Inc.

Watase, Yuu. Alice 19th Vol. 6: Blindness. Watase, Yuu, illus. 2004. (Alice 19th Ser.). (Illus.). 200p. (YA). pap. 9.99 (978-1-59116-243-8(2)) Viz Media.

—The Lost Word. Watase, Yuu, illus. 2004. (Alice 19th Ser.). (Illus.). 200p. (YA). pap. 9.99 (978-1-59116-244-5(0)) Viz Media.

Waterton, Betty. A Bumblebee Sweater. LaFave, Kim, illus. 2007. 32p. (J). (ps-3). (*978-1-55455-028-9(9)) Fitzhenry & Whiteside, Ltd.

Watkins, Kate. Dooley Makes Friends. 2002. (Illus.). 24p. (J). (gr. k-5). pap. 2.99 (978-1-57759-472-7(X)) Dalmatian Pr.

Watson, Esther Pearl. Trouble at Sugar-Dip Well. 2002. (Illus.). 32p. (J). (gr. k-3). 15.00 (978-0-618-11863-2(2)) Houghton Mifflin Co. Trade & Reference Div.

Watson, J. D. My Socks Don't Match. 2004. 41p. pap. 19.95 (978-1-4137-1935-2(X)) PublishAmerica, Inc.

Watson, Sally. The Hornet's Nest. 2002. (J). pap. 12.95 (978-1-930009-66-0(6) , 800-691-7779) Image Cascade Publishing.

Watterson, Bill. La Buena Vida. 2000. (Calvin y Hobbes Ser.: Vol. 12). Tr. of Good Life. (SPA., Illus.). 64p. (J). 6.95 (978-84-406-8543-8(2)) Ediciones B ESP. Dist: Distribooks, Inc.

—En Todas Partes Hay Tesoros. 3rd ed. 2000. (Calvin y Hobbes Ser.: Vol. 1). Tr. of There's Treasure Everywhere. (SPA., Illus.). 48p. (J). 6.95 (978-84-406-7413-5(9)) Ediciones B ESP. Dist: Distribooks, Inc.

—Hay un Tigre en Mi Sopa. 2000. (Calvin y Hobbes Ser.: Vol. 7). Tr. of There's a Tiger in My Soup. (SPA., Illus.). 48p. (J). 6.95 (978-84-406-8250-5(6)) Ediciones B ESP. Dist: Distribooks, Inc.

—Matando el Tiempo. 2000. (Calvin y Hobbes Ser.: Vol. 5). Tr. of Killing Time. (SPA., Illus.). 48p. (J). 6.95 (978-84-406-8047-1(3)) Ediciones B ESP. Dist: Distribooks, Inc.

—Munecos de Nieve Suicidas. 2000. (Calvin y Hobbes Ser.: Vol. 3). (SPA., Illus.). 48p. (J). 6.95 (978-84-406-7411-1(2)) Ediciones B ESP. Dist: Distribooks, Inc.

Wax, Wendy. Class Picture Day. Petrosino, Tamara, illus. 2005. 40p. (J). (ps-3). pap. 6.99 (978-0-8431-1351-8(0) , Grosset & Dunlap) Penguin Group (USA) Inc.

—Fairly Odd Funnies. Style Guide Staff, illus. 2005. (Fairly OddParents Ser.). 48p. (J). pap. 3.99 (978-0-689-87599-1(1) , Simon Spotlight) Simon & Schuster Children's Publishing.

—A Fairly Odd Recess: A Funny Fill-ins Book. Style Guide Staff, illus. 2005. (Fairly OddParents Ser.). 48p. (J). pap. 3.99 (978-1-4169-0646-9(0) , Simon Spotlight) Simon & Schuster Children's Publishing.

—Top-Secret Handbook. Artful Doodlers Limited Staff, illus. 2005. (Totally Spies! Ser.). 48p. (J). pap. 3.99 (978-0-689-87729-2(3) , Simon Spotlight) Simon & Schuster Children's Publishing.

Weathers, Regina Lorick. Safety Sam, I Am: How to Avoid A Sticky Jelly Jam. Short, Gregory T., illus. 2004. (J). per. 7.95 (978-0-9665909-6-8(1)) Kalawantis Publishing Services, Inc.

Webb, Mack H., Jr. Webb's Wondrous Tales Book 2. Webb, Celia, illus. 2007. 156p. (J). per. 14.95 (*978-0-9779576-3-7(2)) Pilinut Pr., Inc.

Weeks, Sarah. Fink's Funk. 2006. (Boyds Will Be Boyds Ser.: No. 4). 144p. (J). pap. 4.99 (978-0-439-57472-3(2) , Scholastic Paperbacks) Scholastic, Inc.

—Mrs. McNosh Hangs up Her Wash. Westcott, Nadine Bernard, illus. 2002. 24p. (J). pap. 6.99 (978-0-06-000479-8(7) , Harper Trophy) HarperCollins Pubs.

—Mrs. McNosh Hangs up Her Wash. 2002. (ps-2). lib. bdg. 18.75 (978-0-613-57646-8(2)) Tandem Library Bks.

—Oh My Gosh, Mrs. McNosh. Westcott, Nadine Bernard, illus. 2002. 32p. (J). (ps up). 15.99 (978-0-694-01204-6(1)); lib. bdg. 15.89 (978-0-06-008858-3(3)) HarperCollins Pubs. (Geringer, Laura Book).

Wegman, William. Dress up Batty. Wegman, William, illus. 2004. (Illus.). 18p. (ps-17). 19.99 (978-0-7868-1849-5(2)) Hyperion Bks. for Children.

—Wegman's Party in a Box Surprise Party Kit. 2000. (J). 24.99 (978-0-7868-0657-7(5)) Hachette Bk. Group.

Wehner, Adrienna. Elephants & Roses. 2003. (Illus.). (YA). (gr. 2 up). 22.00 (978-0-9653866-3-0(5)) Wehner, Adrienna.

Weigelt, Udo. Spring Fever. 2005. (Illus.). 32p. (J). (ps up). 15.95 (978-0-7358-2033-3(3)) North-South Bks., Inc.

Weinstock, Robert. Giant Meatball. 2008. (J). (*978-0-15-205595-0(9)) Harcourt Trade Pubs.

Weis, Carol. When the Cows Got Loose. Hoyt, Ard, illus. 2006. 40p. (J). (ps-1). 16.95 (978-0-689-85166-7(9)) Simon & Schuster Children's Publishing.

Weiss, David Cody, et al. It's about Time. 2006. (All Grown Up! Ser.). 64p. (J). pap. 4.99 (978-1-4169-0668-1(1) , Simon Spotlight/Nickelodeon) Simon & Schuster Children's Publishing.

Weiss, Ellen. Eloise & the Very Secret Room. Lyon, Tammie, illus. 2006. (Eloise Ser.). 32p. (J). pap. 3.99 (978-0-689-87450-5(2) , Aladdin) Simon & Schuster Children's Publishing.

Weiss, J. G. Lizzie Mcguire Movie: Junior Novelization. 2003. (gr. 3-6). lib. bdg. 13.00 (978-0-613-82908-3(5)) Tandem Library Bks.

Welling, Peter J. Joe Van der Katt & the Grat Picket Fence. 2005. (Illus.). 32p. (J). 15.95 (978-1-58980-281-0(0)) Pelican Publishing Co., Inc.

—Michael le Souffle & the April Fool. Welling, Peter J., illus. 2003. (Illus.). 32p. (J). 15.95 (978-1-58980-105-9(9)) Pelican Publishing Co., Inc.

—Shawn O'Hisser, the Last Snake in Ireland. Welling, Peter J., illus. 2002. (Illus.). 32p. (J). (gr. k-3). 15.95 (978-1-58980-014-4(1)) Pelican Publishing Co., Inc.

Wesley, Valerie Wilson. How to (Almost) Ruin Your School Play. Roos, Maryn, illus. 4th rev. ed. 2005. (Willimena Rules! Ser.). 112p. (gr. 2-5). pap. 3.99 (978-0-7868-5259-8(3) , Jump at the Sun) Hyperion Bks. for Children.

West, Greg. Hooky. 2000. (gr. 7-12). lib. bdg. 21.60 (978-0-613-79758-0(2)) Tandem Library Bks.

West, Tracey. Jelly-Bean Jam. Durk, Jim & Roper, Robert, illus. 2008. (Totally Spies! Ser.). 24p. (J). pap. 5.99 (978-1-4169-3340-3(9) , Simon Spotlight) Simon & Schuster Children's Publishing.

—Me & My Robot No.2: The Show-and-Tell Show-off. 2003. (ps-2). lib. bdg. 11.80 (978-0-613-72529-3(8)) Tandem Library Bks.

Weston, Martha & Greene, Stephanie. Owen Foote, Super Spy. Weston, Martha, illus. 2001. (Illus.). 96p. (J). (gr. 4-6). tchr. ed. 15.00 (978-0-618-11752-9(0) , Clarion Bks.) Houghton Mifflin Co. Trade & Reference Div.

Weston, Tamson. Hey, Pancakes! Gammell, Stephen, illus. 2003. 32p. (J). 17.00 (978-0-15-216502-4(9)) Harcourt Trade Pubs.

Weyn, Suzanne & Gonzalez, Diana. South Beach Sizzle. 2005. 249p. (YA). (978-1-4155-7724-0(2) , Simon Pulse) Simon & Schuster Children's Publishing.

Weyn, Suzanne & Gonzalez, Diana. South Beach Sizzle. 2005. 249p. (YA). (gr. 9-12). per. 14.45 (978-1-4176-6059-9(7)) Tandem Library Bks.

What Is Fun? Individual Title Six-Packs. (gr. 1-2). 22.00 (978-0-7635-9094-9(0)) Rigby Education.

Wheeler, Lisa. Avalanche Annie: A Not-So-Tall Tale. Cyrus, Kurt, illus. 2005. 30p. (J). (gr. k-4). reprint ed. 16.00 (978-0-7567-8536-9(7)) DIANE Publishing Co.

—Avalanche Annie: A Not-So-Tall Tale. Cyrus, Kurt, illus. 2003. 32p. (J). 16.00 (978-0-15-216735-6(8)) Harcourt Children's Bks.

Wheeler, Lisa & Floca, Brian. Uncles & Antlers. 2004. (Illus.). 40p. (J). 15.95 (978-0-689-86469-8(8) , Atheneum/Richard Jackson Bks.) Simon & Schuster Children's Publishing.

Where's Waldo: the Complete Set. 2006. (J). 82.94 (*978-0-7636-3510-7(3)) Candlewick Pr.

Whint, Ana Lee. Espalemit. 2003. (ENG.). 112p. pap. 9.95 (*978-0-595-26259-5(7) , Writers Club Pr.) iUniverse, Inc.

Whippo, Walt. Little White Duck. Paley, Joan, illus. 2002. (J). 20.81 (978-0-7587-3019-0(5)) Book Wholesalers, Inc.

Whippo, Walt & Zaritzky, Bernard. Little White Duck. Paley, Joan, illus. 2005. 22p. (J). (ps-k). bds. 6.99 (978-0-316-73397-7(0)) Little, Brown Bks. for Young Readers.

White, Kathy. Little Green Riding Hood. 2006. 42.00 (*978-1-4108-6182-5(1)) Benchmark Education Co.

Whiting, Sue & Martin, Stuart. That's Funny! 2003. (Illus.). 14p. 12.95 (978-1-74047-272-2(1)) Book Co. Publishing Pty, Ltd., The AUS. Dist: Penton Overseas, Inc.

Whitlock, Matt. Punk's Christmas Carol. 2006. 32p. 16.95 (978-0-9769057-1-4(X)) Little Hero.

Who Put the Snarfdoodle in My Lunch Box? (and Other Lost Tales of the Legendary Snarfdoodle) 2002. per. (978-1-930493-55-1(X)) Athena Pr.

Whytock, Cherry. My Cup Runneth Over: The Life of Angelica Cookson Potts. 2005. 192p. (YA). mass mkt. 3.99 (978-1-4169-0521-9(9) , Simon Pulse) Simon & Schuster Children's Publishing.

—My Saucy Stuffed Ravioli: The Life of Angelica Cookson Potts. Whytock, Cherry, illus. 2005. (Illus.). 176p. (YA). 14.95 (978-0-689-86550-3(3)) Simon & Schuster Children's Publishing.

—My Scrumptious Scottish Dumplings: The Life of Angelica Cookson Potts. Whytock, Cherry, illus. 2006. 192p. (YA). mass mkt. 5.99 (978-0-689-86552-7(X) , Simon Pulse) Simon & Schuster Children's Publishing.

Whytock, Cherry, illus. My Scrumptious Scottish Dumplings: The Life of Angelica Cookson Potts. 2004. 176p. (YA). 14.95 (978-0-689-86549-7(X)) Simon & Schuster Children's Publishing.

Wiebe, Trina. Max the Mighty Superhero. Cole, Kathryn, ed. Flook, Helen, illus. 2004. (Max-A-Million Ser.). 96p. (J). pap. 5.95 (978-1-894222-68-6(7)) Lobster Pr. CAN. Dist: Univ. of Toronto Pr.

—Max the Mighty Superhero. 2003. (gr. k-3). lib. bdg. 14.10 (978-0-613-85826-7(3)) Tandem Library Bks.

—Max the Movie Director. Cole, Kathryn, ed. Flook, Helen, illus. 2004. (Max-A-Million Ser.). 96p. (J). (gr. 2-4). pap. 5.95 (978-1-894222-69-3(5)) Lobster Pr. CAN. Dist: Univ. of Toronto Pr.

—Max the Movie Director. 2003. (gr. k-3). lib. bdg. 14.10 (978-0-613-87390-1(4)) Tandem Library Bks.

Wiggin, Kate Douglas. Rebecca of Sunnybrook Farm. 2003. lib. bdg. 11.80 (978-0-613-90467-4(2)); 1999. (gr. 5-8). lib. bdg. 10.65 (978-0-613-17468-8(2)) Tandem Library Bks.

Wilcox, Leah. Falling for Rapunzel. Monks, Lydia, illus. 32p. (J). (gr. k-3). 2005. pap. 5.99 (978-0-14-240399-0(7) , Puffin); 2003. 14.99 (978-0-399-23794-2(1) , Putnam Juvenile) Penguin Group (USA) Inc.

Wilcox, Leah. Waking Beauty. Monks, Lydia, illus. 2008. 32p. (J). (ps). 16.99 (*978-0-399-24615-9(0) , Putnam Juvenile) Penguin Group (USA) Inc.

The Wild, Wild West. 2005. (Illus.). 106p. (J). (978-1-4156-0684-1(6)) Scholastic, Inc.

Wilder, Rae. Soccer Girls. 2000. 252p. (J). (gr. 4-7). pap. 13.95 (978-0-595-00566-6(7)) iUniverse, Inc.

Wiley, Debra D. Peanut Butter Boogers. 2006. 24p. per. 11.99 (*978-1-59886-730-5(X)) Tate Publishing & Enterprises, L.L.C.

Willems, Mo. Knuffle Bunny: A Cautionary Tale. 2004. (Illus.). 36p. (J). (ps-1). 15.99 (978-0-7868-1870-9(0)) Hyperion Bks. for Children.

Willever, Lisa. You Can't Walk a Fish! 2002. (Illus.). 32p. 11.95 (978-0-9679227-1-3(2) , 329-011) Franklin Mason Pr.

Williams, Carol Lynch. A Mother to Embarrass Me. 2003. 144p. (J). (gr. 3-7). pap. 4.99 (978-0-440-41810-8(0) , Yearling) Random Hse. Children's Bks.

—My Angelica. 2001. (978-0-606-21340-0(6)) Tandem Library Bks.

Willis, Jeanne. Delilah D. at the Library. Reeve, Rosie, illus. 2007. 32p. (J). (gr. k-3). 16.00 (978-0-618-78195-9(1) , Clarion Bks.) Houghton Mifflin Co. Trade & Reference Div.

—Gorilla! Gorilla! Ross, Tony, illus. 2006. 32p. (J). (ps-3). 15.95 (978-1-4169-1490-7(0) , Atheneum) Simon & Schuster Children's Publishing.

Willis, Jeanne & Ross, Tony. Como Era Yo Cuando Era un Bebe? (Buenas Noches Coleccion). (SPA., Illus.). (J). (gr. k-3). 8.95 (978-958-04-6031-2(0)) Norma S.A. COL. Dist: Distribuidora Norma, Inc., Lectorum Pubns., Inc.

Willson, Sarah. Class Confusion. Dress, Robert, illus. 2006. (SpongeBob SquarePants Ser.). 24p. (J). pap. 3.99 (978-1-4169-1239-2(8) , Simon Spotlight/Nickelodeon) Simon & Schuster Children's Publishing.

—Just Say Please! Moore, Harry, illus. 2007. (SpongeBob SquarePants Ser.). 32p. (J). pap. 3.99 (978-1-4169-4129-3(0) , Simon Spotlight/Nickelodeon) Simon & Schuster Children's Publishing.

—A Super Silly Fiesta. Roper, Robert, illus. 2004. (Dora the Explorer Ser.). 12p. (J). bds. 11.95 (978-0-689-86371-4(3) , Simon Spotlight/Nickelodeon) Simon & Schuster Children's Publishing.

Wilson, David Henry. Never Steal Wheels from a Dog. Scheffler, Axel, illus. l.t. ed. 2005. 168p. (J). pap. (978-0-7540-7821-0(3) , CLP 411) BBC Audio.

Wilson, Jacqueline. The Story of Tracy Beaker. Sharratt, Nick, illus. 2002. 144p. (gr. 3-7). 5.50 (978-0-440-41807-8(0) , Yearling) Random Hse. Children's Bks.

Wings: A Tale of Two Chickens. 2004. (J). pap. 14.95 incl. audio (978-1-56008-045-9(0)); pap. 14.95 incl. audio (978-1-56008-082-4(5)) Weston Woods Studios, Inc.

Winkler, Henry & Oliver, Lin. The Curtain Went Up, My Pants Fell Down. Watson, Jesse Joshua, illus. 2007. (Hank Zipzer Ser.: No. 11). 160p. (J). 13.99 (978-0-448-44268-6(X)); pap. 4.99 (978-0-448-44267-9(1)) Penguin Group (USA) Inc. (Grosset & Dunlap).

—Help! Somebody Get Me Out of Fourth Grade! 2004. (Hank Zipzer Ser.: No. 7). 160p. (J). (gr. 3-8). mass mkt. 4.99 (978-0-448-43619-7(1) , Grosset & Dunlap) Penguin Group (USA) Inc.

—Help! Somebody Get Me Out of Fourth Grade! 2006. (Hank Zipzer Ser.: No. 7). (J). (gr. 3-8). 24.21 (978-1-59961-106-8(6)) Spotlight.

—Help! Somebody Get Me Out of Fourth Grade! Heyer, Carol, illus. 2004. (Hank Zipzer Ser.: No. 7). 156p. (J). (ps-7). lib. bdg. 11.64 (978-0-606-32738-1(X)) Tandem Library Bks.

—Holy Enchilada! Heyer, Carol & Watson, Jesse Joshua, illus. 2004. (Hank Zipzer Ser.: No. 6). 160p. (J). (gr. 3-8). pap. 4.99 (978-0-448-43353-0(2) , Grosset & Dunlap) Penguin Group (USA) Inc.

—Holy Enchilada!, No. 6. Watson, Jesse Joshua, illus. 2004. (Hank Zipzer Ser.: No. 6). 160p. (J). (gr. 3-7). 13.99 (978-0-448-43554-1(3) , Grosset & Dunlap) Penguin Group (USA) Inc.

—Holy Enchilada! 2006. (Hank Zipzer Ser.: No. 6). (J). (gr. 3-8). 24.21 (978-1-59961-105-1(8)) Spotlight.

—Holy Enchilada! 2003. (Hank Zipzer Ser.: No. 6). (gr. 3-6). lib. bdg. 13.00 (978-0-613-72546-0(8)) Tandem Library Bks.

—I Got a "D" in Salami. 2003. (Hank Zipzer Ser.: No. 2). (Illus.). 176p. (gr. 2-5). mass mkt. 4.99 (978-0-448-43163-5(7) , Grosset & Dunlap) Penguin Group (USA) Inc.

—I Got a "D" in Salami. Carol, Heyer, illus. 2003. (Hank Zipzer Ser.: No. 2). 176p. (J). (gr. 2-5). 12.99 (978-0-448-43233-5(1) , Grosset & Dunlap) Penguin Group (USA) Inc.

—My Dog's a Scaredy-Cat: A Halloween Tail. Watson, Jesse Joshua, illus. 2006. (Hank Zipzer Ser.: No. 10). 160p. (J). 13.99 (978-0-448-43879-5(8) , Grosset & Dunlap) Penguin Group (USA) Inc.

—My Dog's a Scaredy-Cat: A Halloween Tail. Heyer, Carol & Watson, Jesse Joshua, illus. 2006. (Hank Zipzer Ser.: No. 10). 160p. (J). (gr. 3-7). pap. 4.99 (978-0-448-43878-8(X) , Grosset & Dunlap) Penguin Group (USA) Inc.

—Niagara Falls, or Does It? 2003. (Hank Zipzer Ser.: No. 1). (Illus.). 144p. (J). (gr. 2-5). pap. 4.99 (978-0-448-43162-8(9) , Grosset & Dunlap) Penguin Group (USA) Inc.

—Niagara Falls, or Does It? Carol, Heyer, illus. 2003. (Hank Zipzer Ser.: No. 1). 144p. (J). (gr. 2-5). 12.99 (978-0-448-43232-8(3) , Grosset & Dunlap) Penguin Group (USA) Inc.

—Niagara Falls, or Does It? 2004. (Hank Zipzer Ser.: No. 1). 128p. (J). (gr. 2-6). pap. 29.00 incl. audio (978-1-4000-9006-8(7) , Listening Library) Random Hse. Audio Publishing Group.

—Niagara Falls, or Does It? 2006. (Hank Zipzer Ser.: No. 1). (J). (gr. 3-8). 24.21 (978-1-59961-108-2(2)) Spotlight.

—Niagara Falls, or Does It? 2003. (Hank Zipzer Ser.: No. 1). lib. bdg. 13.00 (978-0-613-63737-4(2)) Tandem Library Bks.

—The Night I Flunked My Field Trip. Heyer, Carol, illus. 2004. (Hank Zipzer Ser.: No. 5). 176p. (J). (gr. 3-7). 13.99 (978-0-448-43502-2(0) , Grosset & Dunlap) Penguin Group (USA) Inc.

—The Night I Flunked My Field Trip. 2006. (Hank Zipzer Ser.: No. 5). (J). (gr. 3-8). 24.21 (978-1-59961-104-4(X)) Spotlight.

—Summer School! What Genius Thought That Up? Heyer, Carol, illus. 2005. (Hank Zipzer Ser.: No. 8). 160p. (gr. 3-7). mass mkt. 4.99 (978-0-448-43739-2(2)); (J). (ps-7). 13.99 (978-0-448-43740-8(6)) Penguin Group (USA) Inc. (Grosset & Dunlap).

—Summer School! What Genius Thought That Up? 2006. (Hank Zipzer Ser.: No. 8). (J). (gr. 3-8). 24.21 (978-1-59961-107-5(4)) Spotlight.

—Summer School! What Genius Thought That Up? 2005. (Hank Zipzer Ser.: No. 8). (Illus.). 157p. (J). (ps-7). per. 11.64 (978-0-606-33097-8(6)) Tandem Library Bks.

—The Zippity Zinger. 2003. (Hank Zipzer Ser.: No. 4). (Illus.). 160p. (J). (gr. 3-8). mass mkt. 4.99 (978-0-448-43193-2(9) , Grosset & Dunlap) Penguin Group (USA) Inc.

—The Zippity Zinger. Heyer, Carol, illus. 2003. (Hank Zipzer Ser.: No. 4). 160p. (J). 13.99 (978-0-448-43287-8(0) , Grosset & Dunlap) Penguin Group (USA) Inc.

Winnick, Karen B. Barn Sneeze. Winnick, Karen B., illus. 2003. (Illus.). 32p. (J). (gr. k-2). 15.95 (978-1-56397-948-4(9)) Boyds Mills Pr.

Wishinsky, Frieda. A Bee in Your Ear. Laliberte, Louise, illus. 2004. (Orca Echoes Ser.). 64p. (J). (gr. 2-3). pap. 4.99 (978-1-55143-324-0(9)) Orca Bk. Pubs. USA.

Wisniewski, David. Halloweenies. Wisniewski, David, illus. 2002. (Illus.). 71p. (J). (gr. 2-4). lib. bdg. 16.89 (978-0-06-000514-6(9)) HarperCollins Pubs.

Wittek, Lee. Critter Capers: Tales from the Dogcatcher Who Captures Your Heart. 2002. (Illus.). 230p. (J). pap. 15.95 (978-0-9722872-1-0(3)) BBM Pr.

Wittlinger, Ellen. Hard Love. unabr. ed. 2004. 240p. (J). (gr. 7 up). pap. 38.00 incl. audio (978-0-8072-0865-6(5) , LYA 283 SP, Listening Library) Random Hse. Audio Publishing Group.

—Hard Love. 2001. (YA). 14.65 (978-0-606-20689-1(2)); (gr. 7-12). lib. bdg. 16.45 (978-0-613-34759-4(5)) Tandem Library Bks.

Wojciechowski, Susan. Beany & the Dreaded Wedding. Natti, Susanna, illus. ed. 2005. 128p. (J). (gr. 1-4). pap. 4.99 (978-0-7636-2569-6(8)) Candlewick Pr.

—Beany Goes to Camp. Natti, Susanna, illus. ed. 2005. (Beany Ser.). 112p. (J). (gr. 1-4). pap. 4.99 (978-0-7636-2570-2(1)) Candlewick Pr.

—Beany Not Beanhead. Natti, Susanna, illus. ed. 2005. (Beany Ser.). 96p. (J). (gr. 1-4). pap. 4.99 (978-0-7636-2567-2(1)) Candlewick Pr.

Wolf, Ema. Los Imposibles. 2002. (SPA.). 48p. (J). pap. 6.95 (978-1-4000-0067-8(X)) Random Hse., Inc.

Wollman, Jessica. Bunches of Fun. MacNeil, Chris, illus. 2006. (Penelope Fritter Ser.). 160p. (J). pap. 4.99 (978-1-4169-0091-7(8) , Aladdin) Simon & Schuster Children's Publishing.

—The Chipster's Sister. MacNeil, Chris, illus. 2005. (Penelope Fritter, Super-Sitter Ser.). 128p. (J). pap. 4.99 (978-1-4169-0089-4(6) , Aladdin) Simon & Schuster Children's Publishing.

—Meet the Phonees. MacNeil, Chris, illus. 2005. (Penelope Fritter, Super-Sitter Ser.). 144p. (J). pap. 4.99 (978-1-4169-0090-0(X) , Aladdin) Simon & Schuster Children's Publishing.

Wood, Audrey. Cerditos. Campoy, F. Isabel, tr. Wood, Don, illus. 2006. 34p. (J). bds. 6.95 (978-0-15-205731-2(5) , Voyager Bks./Libros Viajeros) Harcourt Children's Bks.

—The Napping House. Wood, Don, illus. 2005. 32p. (J). bds. 10.95 (978-0-15-205620-9(3) , Red Wagon Bks.) Harcourt Children's Bks.

—Silly Sally. Wood, Audrey, illus. 2002. (Illus.). (J). 23.40 (978-0-7587-3621-5(5)) Book Wholesalers, Inc.

—Silly Sally. braille ed. 2004. (J). (gr. 1). spiral bd., bds. (978-0-616-01864-4(9)) Canadian National Institute for the Blind/Institut National Canadien pour les Aveugles.

—Silly Sally. 1999. (Illus.). 30p. (J). (ps). bds. 6.95 (978-0-15-201990-7(1) , Red Wagon Bks.) Harcourt Children's Bks.

—Silly Sally: Lap-Sized Board Book. 2007. (Illus.). 30p. (J). bds. 10.95 (978-0-15-205902-6(4) , Red Wagon Bks.) Harcourt Children's Bks.

Wood, Brian. The Cramp Twins. 2001. (J). pap. 9.95 (978-0-385-32714-5(5) , Random Hse. Bks. for Young Readers) Random Hse. Children's Bks.

—Swamp Fever. 2001. (Cramp Twins Ser.). (J). pap. (978-0-385-32717-6(X) , Dell Books for Young Readers) Random Hse. Children's Bks.

Wood, Doug. When Mama Mirabelle Comes Home. 2007. (Illus.). 32p. (J). (ps-1). 16.95 ***(978-1-4263-0194-0(4));*** lib. bdg. 24.90 ***(978-1-4263-0195-7(2))*** National Geographic Society. (National Geographic Children's Bks.).

Wood, Jane R. Voices in St. Augustine. 2004. (Illus.). 144p. (J). per. 6.99 (978-0-9707267-6-6(7)) Bluefish Bay Publishing.

Wood, Nancy. Mr. & Mrs. God in the Creation Kitchen. Ering, Timothy Basil, illus. 2006. 32p. (J). (gr. k). 16.99 (978-0-7636-1258-0(8)) Candlewick Pr.

Woolfe, Angela. Avril Crump & Her Amazing Clones. 2008. (Illus.). 192p. (J). pap. 9.95 ***(978-1-4052-0747-8(7))*** Egmont Bks., Ltd. GBR. *Dist:* Independent Pubs. Group.

—Avril Crump & the Slumber Code. 2008. (Illus.). 256p. (J). pap. 9.95 ***(978-1-4052-1893-1(2))*** Egmont Bks., Ltd. GBR. *Dist:* Independent Pubs. Group.

Worth, Bonnie. Who Cares? Pooh Cares! Hollister, Samantha, illus. 2007. 16p. (J). (gr. k-ps). bds. 6.99 (978-0-7364-2283-3(8) , RH/Disney) Random Hse. Children's Bks.

Worthington, Lisa & Moon, Susan. People Do Silly Things. Totire, Valerie, illus. 2003. 16p. (J). (gr. k-2). pap. 4.95 (978-1-57874-037-6(1)) Kaeden Corp.

Wright, Chris. Operation Overflow. 2003. per. 14.25 (978-1-932301-90-8(9) , 1555) Airleaf Publishing & Bookselling.

Wright, Joshua. Hapless, Hopeless, Horrible. 2004. (Illus.). 192p. (J). pap. 6.95 (978-1-74114-082-8(X)) Allen & Unwin AUS. *Dist:* Independent Pubs. Group.

—Plotless, Pointless, Pathetic. 2004. (Illus.). 180p. (J). pap. 6.95 (978-1-86508-785-6(8)) Allen & Unwin AUS. *Dist:* Independent Pubs. Group.

Yaccarino, Dan. Oswald. Yaccarino, Dan, illus. 2004. (Oswald Ser.: Vol. 5). (Illus.). 24p. (J). pap. 3.99 (978-0-689-87331-7(X) , Simon Spotlight/Nickelodeon) Simon & Schuster Children's Publishing.

Yee, Wong Herbert. Mrs Brown Went to Town. 2003. (gr. k-3). lib. bdg. 14.10 (978-0-613-91047-7(8)) Tandem Library Bks.

Yolen, Jane. How Do Dinosaurs Eat Their Food? Teague, Mark, illus. 2006. (SPA.). 40p. (J). pap. 4.99 (978-0-439-76404-9(1) , Scholastic en Espanol) Scholastic, Inc.

—How Do Dinosaurs Get Well Soon? Teague, Mark, illus. 2004. 40p. (J). pap. 4.99 (978-0-439-54563-1(3)) Scholastic, Inc.

—Twelve Impossible Things Before Breakfast. 2001. (978-0-606-21496-4(8)) Tandem Library Bks.

Yoo, Tae-Eun, illus. The Little Red Fish. 2007. 40p. (J). (ps). 15.99 (978-0-8037-3145-5(0) , Dial) Penguin Group (USA) Inc.

Yorinks, Arthur. Company's Coming. 2000. (Illus.). 32p. (gr. k-4). 16.49 (978-0-7868-2433-5(6)) Hyperion Bks. for Children.

—Company's Coming. Small, David, illus. 2000. 32p. (gr. k-4). 15.99 (978-0-7868-0500-6(5)) Hyperion Bks. for Children.

—Company's Going. (J). pap. 14.99 (978-0-06-205125-7(3)) HarperCollins Pubs.

—Company's Going. Small, David, illus. 2001. 40p. (gr. k-4). 15.99 (978-0-7868-0415-3(7)); 16.49 (978-0-7868-2363-5(1)) Hyperion Bks. for Children.

—Mommy? Sendak, Maurice, illus. 2006. 32p. (J). pap. 24.95 (978-0-439-88050-3(5) , Di Capua, Michael) Scholastic, Inc.

Yorinks, Arthur, et al. Company's Going. Date not set. (J). lib. bdg. 15.89 (978-0-06-205126-4(1)) HarperCollins Pubs.

Yost-Filgate, Susan. Rip Squeak & His Friends. Filgate, Leonard, illus. 2004. 32p. (J). 16.95 (978-1-59384-058-7(6)) Parklane Publishing.

—Rip Squeak & His Friends. Filgate, Leonard, illus. 2004. 32p. (J). 16.95 (978-0-9672422-3-1(1)) Rip Squeak, Inc.

Yost-Filgate, Susan & Filgate, Leonard. Rip Squeak & His Friends. 1999. 32p. (J). pap. (978-1-931290-01-2(6)) Tallfellow Pr.

Young, Dianne. Honey Trouble. 2002. (Early Chapters Bks.). (Illus.). 96p. (J). pap. 5.95 (978-1-896184-01-2(4)) Roussan Pubs., Inc./Roussan Editeur, Inc. CAN. *Dist:* Orca Bk. Pubs. USA.

Young, Kirk. The Chronicles of His Excellency: Almost-an-Eighth-of-a-Memoir. 2003. 120p. (YA). pap. 12.95 (978-0-595-27583-0(4)) iUniverse, Inc.

Young, Steve. Winchell Mink: The Misadventure Begins. 2004. 144p. (J). 16.89 (978-0-06-053500-1(8)) HarperCollins Pubs.

—15 Minutes. 2006. 176p. (J). 15.99 (978-0-06-072508-2(7)); lib. bdg. 16.89 (978-0-06-072509-9(5)) HarperCollins Pubs.

Yourgrau, Barry. Another NASTYbook: The Curse of the Tweeties. DeJesus, Robert, illus. 2006. 176p. (J). 11.99 (978-0-06-057981-4(1)); lib. bdg. 13.89 (978-0-06-057982-1(X)) HarperCollins Pubs. (Cotler, Joanna Books).

—Nasty Book. 2005. 192p. (J). (gr. k-9). 11.99 (978-0-06-057978-4(1) , Cotler, Joanna Books) HarperCollins Pubs.

—Nasty Book, No. 3. Swaab, Neil, illus. 2007. 160p. (J). 12.99 ***(978-0-06-077676-3(5)*** , Cotler, Joanna Books) HarperCollins Pubs.

—NASTYbook. 192p. (J). 2007. pap. 5.99 ***(978-0-06-057980-7(3)*** , Harper Trophy); 2005. lib. bdg. 13.89 (978-0-06-057979-1(X)) HarperCollins Pubs.

—Yet Another NASTYbook: MiniNasties. Swaab, Neil, illus. 2007. 160p. (J). lib. bdg. 13.89 ***(978-0-06-077677-0(3)*** , Cotler, Joanna Books) HarperCollins Pubs.

Zhaohua, Ji & Xu, Cui. No! That's Wrong! Zhaohua, Ji & Xu, Cui, illus. 2008. (Illus.). 32p. (J). 15.95 ***(978-1-933605-66-1(9))*** Kane/Miller Bk. Pubs., Inc.

Ziegler, Mark. Fur, Feathers, & Fun! A Book of Animal Jokes. Haugen, Ryan, illus. 2005. (Read-It! Readers Ser.). 24p. (J). (ps). lib. bdg. 18.60 (978-1-4048-1161-4(3)) Picture Window Bks.

—Nutty Names: A Book of Name Jokes. Haugen, Ryan, illus. 2005. (Read-It! Readers Ser.). 24p. (J). (ps). lib. bdg. 18.60 (978-1-4048-1163-8(X)) Picture Window Bks.

Zimet, Sara Goodman. Hannah & the Perfect Picture Pony: A Story of the Great Depression. Fuller, Sandy Ferguson, illus. 2005. 24p. (J). lib. bdg. 16.95 (978-0-9645159-2-5(X)) Discovery Pr. Pubns., Inc.

Zimmer, Elizabeth. The Turtle & the Deep Blue Sky. Zimmer, Eric, illus. 2007. 24p. (J). (ps-2). 12.95 ***(978-1-55591-597-1(3))*** Fulcrum Publishing.

Zion, Gene. Harry the Dirty Dog Board Book. Graham, Margaret Bloy, illus. 50th ed. 2006. 32p. (J). 6.99 (978-0-06-084244-4(X) , Harper Festival) HarperCollins Pubs.

Zobel-Nolan, Allia. What I Like about Me! A Book Celebrating Differences. 2005. (Illus.). 14p. (J). 14.99 (978-0-7944-0763-6(3)) Reader's Digest Assn., Inc., The.

Zoehfeld, Kathleen Weidner. Billy. 2001. (Rolie Polie Olie Ser.). (Illus.). 12p. (J). (gr. k-2). bds. 3.99 (978-0-7364-1023-6(6)) Mouse Works.

—The Movie Novel. 2006. (Ice Age 2 Ser.). (Illus.). 112p. (J). pap. 4.99 (978-0-06-083974-1(0)) HarperCollins Pubs.

—Where Are You Pooh? Pooh's First Discovery. 1999. (Disney's Winnie the Pooh Ser.). (Illus.). 12p. (J). (ps-1). 5.99 (978-0-7364-0051-0(6)) Mouse Works.

Zucker, Zoey. Daffy Does It Again. Style Guide Staff, illus. 2006. (Baby Looney Tunes Ser.). 48p. (J). act. bk. ed. 3.99 (978-1-4169-1843-1(4) , Simon Scribbles) Simon & Schuster Children's Publishing.

Zuravicky, Orli. The Krabby Patty Special (with Extra Plankton) Galan, Manny, illus. 2007. (SpongeBob SquarePants Ser.). 18p. (J). 9.99 ***(978-1-4169-3666-4(1)*** , Simon Spotlight/Nickelodeon) Simon & Schuster Children's Publishing.

HUNDRED YEARS' WAR, 1339-1453

Lace, William W. Joan of Arc & the Hundred Years' War in World History. 2003. (In World History Ser.). (Illus.). 128p. (J). (gr. 5-12). lib. bdg. 26.60 (978-0-7660-1938-6(1)) Enslow Pubs., Inc.

Roberts, Jeremy. Saint Joan of Arc. 2000. (Biography Ser.). (Illus.). 112p. (J). (gr. 6-12). lib. bdg. 25.26 (978-0-8225-4981-9(6) , Lerner Pubns.) Lerner Publishing Group.

Whiting, Jim. The Life & Times of Joan of Arc. 2005. (Biography from Ancient Civilizations Ser.). (Illus.). 48p. (J). (gr. 4-8). lib. bdg. 29.95 (978-1-58415-345-0(8)) Mitchell Lane Pubs., Inc.

HUNDRED YEARS' WAR, 1339-1453—FICTION

Russell, Christopher. Dogboy. 2006. 272p. (J). 15.99 (978-0-06-084116-4(8)); lib. bdg. 16.89 (978-0-06-084117-1(6)) HarperCollins Pubs.

HUNGARIANS—UNITED STATES—FICTION

Cheng, Andrea. Eclipse. 2006. 320p. (J). 16.95 (978-1-932425-21-5(7) , Front Street) Boyds Mills Pr.

Couric, Katie. The Brand New Kid. Priceman, Marjorie, illus. 2000. 32p. (J). (gr. 2-3). 15.95 (978-0-385-50030-2(0) , Doubleday) Doubleday Publishing.

Konigsburg, E. L. The Outcasts of 19 Schuyler Place. 2004. 304p. 16.95 (978-0-689-86636-4(4) , Atheneum) Simon & Schuster Children's Publishing.

HUNGARY

Ake, Anne. Hungary. 2002. (Modern Nations of the World Ser.). (Illus.). 120p. (J). (gr. 7-10). 29.95 (978-1-56006-970-6(8) , Lucent Bks.) Thomson Gale.

Brimson, Samuel. Hungary-Kiribati. 8 vols. 2003. (Nations of the World Ser.: Vol. 4). (Illus.). 64p. (J). (gr. 5 up). lib. bdg. 30.00 (978-0-8368-5488-6(8) , World Almanac Library) Stevens, Gareth Inc.

Chung, Shuh Cheng & Condra-Peters, Amy. Welcome to Hungary. 2003. (Welcome to My Country Ser.). (Illus.). 48p. (J). (gr. 2 up). lib. bdg. 26.00 (978-0-8368-2544-2(6)) Stevens, Gareth Inc.

Docalavich, Heather. Hungary. 2006. (European Union Ser.). (Illus.). 88p. (J). (gr. 5 up). lib. bdg. (978-1-4222-0050-6(7) , 1248003) Mason Crest Pubs.

Esbenshade, Richard S. Hungary. 2nd ed. 2005. (Cultures of the World Ser.). (Illus.). 144p. (YA). 37.07 (978-0-7614-1846-7(6) , Benchmark Bks.) Cavendish, Marshall Corp.

Grolier Educational Staff, contrib. by. Hungary. 2003. (Illus.). 32p. (J). (978-0-7172-5793-5(2) , Grolier) Scholastic Library Publishing.

Lundrigan, Nicole. Hungary. 2002. (Countries of the World Ser.). (Illus.). 96p. (J). (gr. 6 up). lib. bdg. 30.00 (978-0-8368-2344-8(3)) Stevens, Gareth Inc.

Stalcup, Ann. Hungary. 2005. (Enchantment of the World, Second Ser.). (Illus.). 144p. (J). (gr. 5-9). 36.00 (978-0-516-23683-4(0) , Children's Pr.) Scholastic Library Publishing.

Van Cleaf, Kristin. Hungary. 2007. (Countries Set VI Ser.). (Illus.). 40p. (J). (gr. k-6). lib. bdg. 24.21 ***(978-1-59928-783-6(8)*** , Checkerboard Library) ABDO Publishing Co.

HUNGARY—FICTION

Cheng, Andrea. Eclipse. 2006. 320p. (J). 16.95 (978-1-932425-21-5(7) , Front Street) Boyds Mills Pr.

—The Lace Dowry. 2005. 120p. (J). 16.95 (978-1-932425-20-8(9) , Lemniscaat) Boyds Mills Pr.

—Marika. 1998. 148p. (YA). (gr. 5 up). 16.95 (978-1-886910-78-2(2) , Lemniscaat) Boyds Mills Pr.

Libby, Alisa. The Blood Confession. 2006. 360p. (YA). (gr. 9). 18.99 (978-0-525-47732-7(2) , Dutton Juvenile) Penguin Group (USA) Inc.

Szablya, Helen M. & Anderson, Peggy King. The Fall of the Red Star. 2003. 168p. (YA). (gr. 4-6). pap. 9.95 (978-1-56397-977-4(2)) Boyds Mills Pr.

—The Fall of the Red Star. 2002. 166p. (J). (gr. 4-7). lib. bdg. 18.75 (978-0-613-53809-1(9)) Tandem Library Bks.

Wiseman, Eva. Kanada. 2006. (Illus.). 264p. (J). (gr. 5). pap. 9.95 (978-0-88776-729-6(X)) Tundra Bks., Inc./Livres Toundra, Inc. CAN. *Dist:* Random Hse., Inc.

—My Canary Yellow Star. 2002. (gr. 5-8). lib. bdg. 15.25 (978-0-613-62688-0(5)) Tandem Library Bks.

—My Canary Yellow Star. 2001. (Illus.). 240p. (J). (gr. 3-7). pap. 6.95 (978-0-88776-533-9(5)) Tundra Bks., Inc./Livres Toundra, Inc. CAN. *Dist:* Random Hse., Inc.

HUNGARY—HISTORY

Klaudy, Kinga. Budapest: A City Set in Time. 1999. (J). pap. 21.00 (978-963-13-4569-8(6)) Corvina Books HUN. *Dist:* State Mutual Bk. & Periodical Service, Ltd.

HUNGARY—HISTORY—REVOLUTION, 1956

Kalman, Bobbie. Refugee Child: My Memories of the 1956 Hungarian Revolution. Bedell, Barbara, illus. 2006. 224p. (J). (gr. 5 up). pap. (978-0-7787-2760-6(2)) Crabtree Publishing Co.

Kalman, Bobbie. Refugee Child Activity Guide. 2006. (Illus.). 32p. (gr. 5-8). ***(978-0-7787-2759-0(9))*** Crabtree Publishing Co.

HUNS

Harvey, Bonnie. Attila the Hun. 2003. (Ancient World Leaders Ser.). (Illus.). 112p. (gr. 6-12). 30.00 (978-0-7910-7221-9(5)); pap. 30.00 (978-0-7910-7495-4(1)) Facts On File, Inc. (Chelsea Hse.).

Oliver, Marilyn Tower. Attila the Hun. 2005. (Heroes & Villains Ser.). (Illus.). 96-112p. (gr. 7-10). 29.95 (978-1-59018-638-1(9) , Blackbirch Pr., Inc.) Thomson Gale.

HUNS—FICTION

Griffin, Philip. Ursula's Maiden Army. 2005. 288p. (J). pap. 14.95 (978-0-9749610-1-9(9)) Beagle Bay Bks.

Slade, Arthur G. Villainology: Fabulous Lives of the Big, the Bad, & the Wicked. Mah, Derek, illus. 2007. 96p. (J). (gr. 4-7). pap. 9.95 ***(978-0-88776-809-5(1))*** Tundra Bks., Inc./Livres Toundra, Inc. CAN. *Dist:* Random Hse., Inc.

HUNTING

see also Game Protection; Tracking and Trailing; Trapping

The Advantage Max-4 HD Waterfowl Coloring & Activity Book. 2003. (J). pap. (978-0-9745863-0-4(7)) Cypress Knees Publishing.

Bear Hunting in Alaska: The Brown & Grizzly Bear Hunter's Guide. 2004. (Illus.). 280p. bds. 30.00 (978-0-9741684-0-1(8)) Northern Publishing.

Bright, Michael. Hunters: Encyclopedia of Nature's Predators in the Wild. 2005. (Illus.). 512p. 24.99 (978-0-7548-1506-8(4) , Lorenz Bks.) Anness Publishing GBR. *Dist:* National Bk. Network.

Ceaser, Jonathan. Essential Deer Hunting for Teens. 2000. (High Interest Bks.). (Illus.). 48p. (YA). (gr. 7-12). pap. 6.95 (978-0-516-23554-7(0) , Children's Pr.) Scholastic Library Publishing.

Complete Guide to Hunting, 3 vols., Set. (Illus.). 96,112p. (YA). (gr. 7 up). lib. bdg. (978-1-59084-499-1(8)) Mason Crest Pubs.

Edwards, Yvonne, et al. Going for Kalta: Hunting for Sleepy Lizards at Yalata. 1999. (Illus.). 30p. (J). reprint ed. pap. 11.50 (978-1-86465-012-9(5)) IAD Pr. AUS. *Dist:* International Specialized Bk. Services.

Frahm, Randy. Deer Hunting. (J). 2008. (***978-1-4296-0817-6(X));*** 2001. (Illus.). 48p. (gr. 3-4). lib. bdg. 21.26 (978-0-7368-0912-2(0) , Capstone High-Interest Bks.) Capstone Pr., Inc.

—Duck Hunting. (J). 2008. (***978-1-4296-0818-3(8));*** 2001. (Illus.). 48p. (gr. 3-4). lib. bdg. 21.26 (978-0-7368-0913-9(9) , Capstone High-Interest Bks.) Capstone Pr., Inc.

Gilpin, Daniel. Food & Clothing. 2004. (History of Invention Ser.). (Illus.). 96p. (YA). (gr. 6-12). 35.00 (978-0-8160-5441-1(X)) Facts On File, Inc.

Hackenberg, Richard. Moose Hunting in Alaska: The Secrets to Success. Russ, Tony & O'Loughlin, Diane, eds. 2003. (Illus.). 280p. per. 22.95 (978-0-9639869-9-3(6)) Northern Publishing.

Hahn, Michael T. Dad's Deer Tactics 1000: Tom Hahn's Hunting Secrets Revealed by His Son. Hahn, Michael T., photos by. unabr. ed. 2003. (Illus.). 295p. (YA). pap. 19.95 (978-0-9721716-0-1(6) , 1) In Cider Pr.

Hanmer, Trudy J. The Hunting Debate: Aiming at the Issues. 1999. (Issues in Focus Ser.). (Illus.). 112p. (YA). (gr. 6-12). lib. bdg. 26.60 (978-0-7660-1110-6(0)) Enslow Pubs., Inc.

Hunters. (Amazing Animals Ser.). 32p. (J). (gr. 1). pap. (978-1-882210-78-7(6)) Action Publishing, Inc.

Keoke, Emory Dean & Porterfield, Kay Marie. Food, Farming, & Hunting. 2005. (American Indian Contributions to the World Ser.). (Illus.). 160p. (J). (gr. 4-9). 35.00 (978-0-8160-5393-3(6)) Facts On File, Inc.

Laney, Dawn. Hunting. 2007. (Opposing Viewpoints Ser.). (Illus.). 240p. (gr. 10-12). 36.20 (***978-0-7377-3896-4(0));*** pap. 24.95 (***978-0-7377-3897-1(9))*** Thomson Gale. (Greenhaven Pr., Inc.).

Lewis, Joan. Hunting. (Get Going! Hobbies Ser.). (Illus.). 32p. (J). 2005. (gr. 4-6). pap. 7.85 (978-1-4034-6125-4(2)); 2004. 27.79 (978-1-4034-6118-6(X)) Heinemann Library.

Marrin, Albert. Saving the Buffalo. 2006. (Illus.). 128p. (J). (gr. 5-7). pap. 18.99 (978-0-439-71854-7(6)) Scholastic, Inc.

Martin, Michael. Pheasant Hunting. 2008. (J). (***978-1-4296-0823-7(4))*** Capstone Pr., Inc.

The Outdoor Youth Adventures Young Hunter's Colorinig Book. 2004. (J). pap. (978-0-9745863-6-6(6)) Cypress Knees Publishing.

Prohibited! Individual Title Six-Packs. (Bookweb Ser.). 32p. (gr. 6 up). 34.00 (978-0-7578-0908-8(1)) Rigby Education.

The Realtree Deer Hunting Activity & Coloring Book. 2003. (J). pap. (978-0-9745863-1-1(5)) Cypress Knees Publishing.

The Realtree Hunting Coloring Book. 2003. (J). pap. (978-0-9745863-3-5(1)) Cypress Knees Publishing.

Rock Hunters: Individual Title Six-Packs. (Rigby Infoquest Ser.). 24p. (gr. 3 up). 34.00 (978-0-7578-5777-5(9)) Rigby Education.

Russ, Tony. Bear Hunting in Alaska: How to Hunt Brown & Grizzly Bears. O'Loughlin, Diane, ed. 2004. (Illus.). 296p. per. 22.95 (978-0-9639869-8-6(8)) Northern Publishing.

—Sheep Hunting in Alaska: The Dall Sheep Hunters Guide: 2nd Edition. 2nd rev. ed. 2002. pap. 19.95 (978-0-9639869-6-2(1)) Northern Publishing.

Slade, Suzanne. Let's Go Hunting. 2007. (Adventures Outdoors Ser.). (Illus.). 32p. (J). (gr. 4-6). lib. bdg. 23.95 (978-1-4042-3646-2(5) , PowerKids Pr.) Rosen Publishing Group, Inc., The.

Spencer, Jim. A Young Hunter's Guide to Waterfowling & Conservation. Cox, Gary, illus. 2004. 104p. pap. 12.95 (978-1-932052-18-3(6)) Ducks Unlimited, Inc.

Strom, Laura Layton. Caught with a Catch: Poaching in Africa. 2007. (Shockwave: Economics & Geography Ser.). (Illus.). 36p. (J). (gr. 4-6). lib. bdg. 25.00 (***978-0-531-17798-3(X)*** , Children's Pr.) Scholastic Library Publishing.

Trout, John, Jr. Hunting Rutting Bucks: Secrets for Tagging the Biggest Buck of Your Life! 2004. (Illus.). 224p. 24.95 net. (978-0-9722804-6-4(4)) Woods N' Water, Inc.

Walters, Keith. Chesapeake Outdoors: Tales of Fishing & Hunting on Maryland's Eastern Shore & Beyond. 2003. (Illus.). 288p. pap. 19.95 (978-0-9627039-4-2(X)) Aerie Hse.

Weaver, Jack. Hunting: Have Fun, Be Smart. (Explore the Outdoors Ser.). (Illus.). 64p. 2005. (YA). (gr. 7-12). lib. bdg. 26.50 (978-0-8239-3760-8(7)); 2000. (J). (gr. 4-6). lib. bdg. 26.50 (978-0-8239-3167-5(6) , EOHUNT) Rosen Publishing Group, Inc., The.

Weintraub, Aileen. Bow Hunting. 2004. (Great Outdoors Ser.). (Illus.). 48p. (J). 16.95 (978-0-7368-2410-1(3) , Capstone High/Low Bks.) Capstone Pr., Inc.

Weintraub, Aileen. Bowhunting. 2008. (J). (***978-1-4296-0814-5(5))*** Capstone Pr., Inc.

Wheeler, Donald G. Tales from the Golden Age of Rattlesnake Hunting. 2001. (Illus.). 169p. 28.00 (978-0-9713197-3-8(1)); pap. 12.95 (978-0-9713197-0-7(7)) ECO Herpetological Pub. & Dist.

Wilson, Jef. Hunting for Fun! 2006. (For Fun! Ser.). (Illus.). 48p. (J). (gr. 3-5). 22.60 (978-0-7565-1680-2(3)) Compass Point Bks.

HUNTING—FICTION

Allende, Isabel. Forest of the Pygmies. Peden, Margaret Sayers, tr. from SPA. 2005. 304p. (J). (gr. 5 up). 19.99 (978-0-06-076196-7(2) , Rayo) HarperCollins Pubs.

—Forest of the Pygmies. l.t. ed. 2005. 304p. (J). (gr. 5 up). pap. 19.99 (978-0-06-076200-1(4) , Rayo) HarperCollins Pubs.

Auger, Dale. Mwakwa—Talks to the Loon: A Cree Story for Children. Auger, Dale, illus. 2006. (ENG & CRE., Illus.). 32p. (J). (gr. 1-6). 21.95 (978-1-894974-04-2(2)) Heritage Hse. Publishing Co., Ltd. CAN. *Dist:* Midpoint Trade Bks., Inc.

Auger, Dale. Mwakwa Talks to the Loon: A Cree Story for Children. 2007. (Illus.). 32p. (J). pap. 9.95 (***978-1-894974-32-5(8))*** Heritage Hse. Publishing Co., Ltd. CAN. *Dist:* Midpoint Trade Bks., Inc.

Azean, Evon, Sr. Pissuryugtua. Mute, Frank, Jr., illus. l.t. ed. 2000. 8p. (J). pap. 14.50 (978-1-58084-189-4(9)) Lower Kuskokwim Schl. District.

Ballantyne, Michael. Blown to Bits or the Lonely Man of Rakat. 2006. 36.99 (***978-1-4280-4221-6(0));*** pap. 30.99 (***978-1-4280-4226-1(1))*** IndyPublish.com.

Ballantyne, R. M. Blown to Bits; or, the Lonely Man of Rak. 2006. pap. (***978-1-4065-0515-3(3))*** Dodo Pr.

—Gorilla Hunters A Tale of the Wilds of A. 2006. pap. 36.95 (***978-1-4286-5952-0(8))*** Kessinger Publishing, LLC.

Barnum, P. T. Dick Broadhead: A Story of Perilous Adve. 2006. pap. 30.95 (***978-1-4286-1959-3(3))*** Kessinger Publishing, LLC.

Bartlett, Susan. Opening Day. Wrenn, Luanne, illus. 2007. 32p. (J). 16.95 (***978-0-88448-288-8(X))*** Tilbury Hse. Pubs.

Barton, Stacy. Babba & I Went Hunting Today. O'Brien, Maureen, illus. 2004. 32p. 13.99 (978-0-8254-2037-5(7)) Kregel Pubns.

Beckman, Dean A. The Making of a Deer Hunter. 2006. 83p. pap. 14.95 (978-1-4241-1403-0(9)) PublishAmerica, Inc.

Bonehill, Ralph. Four Boy Hunters. 2006. (Illus.). 242p. (J). pap. 14.95 (978-1-55753-390-6(3)) Purdue Univ. Pr.

—Four Boy Hunters or the Outing of the Gu. 2006. 78.99 (***978-1-4280-0015-5(1));*** pap. 72.99 (***978-1-4280-0023-0(2))*** IndyPublish.com.

—Guns & Snowshoes: Or, the Winter Outing of the Young Hunters. 2006. 160p. pap. 11.99 (978-1-4264-3173-9(2)); 174p. pap. 14.99 (978-1-4264-3208-8(9)) BiblioBazaar.

—Out with Gun & Camera. 2006. 264p. (C). pap. 14.95 (978-1-55753-392-0(X)) Purdue Univ. Pr.

—Young Hunters of the Lake. rev. ed. 2006. 212p. 27.95 (978-1-4218-1805-4(1)); pap. 12.95 (978-1-4218-1905-1(8)) 1st World Publishing, Inc. (1st World Library - Literary Society).

Bonehill, Ralph. Young Hunters of the Lake or Out with Ro. 2006. 78.99 (***978-1-4280-0115-2(8));*** pap. 71.99 (***978-1-4280-0100-8(X))*** IndyPublish.com.

Brin, Susannah. The Seal Killers. Taylor, Marjorie, illus. rev. ed. 1999. (Take Ten Ser.). 50p. (YA). (gr. 4-12). pap. 3.95 (978-1-58659-014-7(6)) Artesian Pr.

Buffalo Hunt. 1998. (J). (gr. 5). pap. 3.95 (978-0-439-04480-6(4)) Scholastic, Inc.

Burgess, Thornton W. Adventures of Poor Mrs. Quack. 2004. reprint ed. pap. 15.95 (978-1-4191-5160-6(6)); pap. 1.99 (978-1-4192-5160-3(0)) Kessinger Publishing, LLC.

Burningham, John. Harquin: Fox Who Went Down. 2000. (Illus.). 32p. (J). pap. 8.99 (978-0-09-982510-4(4) , Red Fox) Random Hse. Children's Bks. GBR. *Dist:* Trafalgar Square Publishing.

Carson, Jana. We Both Read-the Mighty Little Lion Hunter. Staake, Bob, illus. 2000. (We Both Read Ser.). 44p. (J). (gr. 1 up). 7.99 (978-1-891327-21-6(6)); pap. 3.99 (978-1-891327-22-3(4)) Treasure Bay, Inc.

Casanova, Mary. Wolf Shadows. 1999. (978-0-606-16667-6(X)) Tandem Library Bks.

Clark, Ann Nolan. Young Hunter of Picuris. Ma-Pe-Wi, illus. rev. ed. 1999. 32p. (J). (gr. k-5). 6.95 (978-1-885772-15-2(7)) Kiva Publishing, Inc.

Clark, Patricia Nikolina. In the Shadow of the Mammoth. LeTourneau, Anthony Alex, illus. 2003. 190p. (J). pap. 6.99 (978-0-9674602-4-6(7)) Blue Marlin Pubns.

Climer, Steven Lee. Young of Heart. 2006. (YA). pap. (***978-0-9790649-5-1(3))*** Mardi Gras Publishing, LLC.

Connell, Richard. The Most Dangerous Game. 2006. pap. 9.99 (978-1-59986-969-8(1)) Filiquarian Publishing, LLC.

—Most Dangerous Game. 2006. pap. 15.95 (***978-1-4304-5151-8(3))*** Kessinger Publishing, LLC.

Connell, Richard. The Most Dangerous Game. 2004. reprint ed. pap. 15.95 (978-1-4191-7460-5(6)); pap. 1.99 (978-1-4192-7460-2(0)) Kessinger Publishing, LLC.

Cozzens, Woodworth Samu. Young Trail Hunters or the Wild Riders O. 2006. pap. 26.99 (***978-1-4280-3343-6(2))*** IndyPublish.com.

Crawford, Laura. In Arctic Waters. Hodson, Ben, illus. 2007. 32p. (J). pap. 8.95 (***978-1-934359-34-1(3))*** Sylvan Dell Pubng.

Crum, Shutta. Click! Beder, John, tr. Beder, John, illus. 2003. 24p. (J). (978-1-55005-074-5(5)) Fitzhenry & Whiteside, Ltd.

Dahl, Roald. Le Doigt Magique. 6th ed. 1998. Tr. of Magic Finger. (FRE., Illus.). (J). (gr. 4-7). pap. 17.95 (978-2-07-051784-8(5)) Gallimard, Editions FRA. *Dist:* Distribooks, Inc.

Duey, Kathleen. Silver Bracelet. 2002. (gr. 3-6). lib. bdg. 11.80 (978-0-613-58388-6(4)) Tandem Library Bks.

Elliott, Dean. Grampa Dean's Hunting Adventures. 1999. (Grampa Dean Ser.: Vol. 1). (Illus.). 176p. pap. 12.95 (978-0-9671996-0-3(3)) Rascal Publishing.

Farshtey, Greg. Dark Hunters. Simpson, Fiona, ed. 2006. (Bionicle Ser.: No. 4). (Illus.). 128p. (J). pap. 6.99 (978-0-439-82803-1(1) , Scholastic) Scholastic, Inc.

Gantschev, Ivan. The Rabbit & the Bear: A Christmas Tale. Gantschev, Ivan, illus. 2007. (Illus.). 32p. (J). (ps). 16.95 (***978-0-7358-2145-3(3))*** North-South Bks., Inc.

Green, Julia. Hunter's Heart. 2007. 264p. (YA). (gr. 7-12). 16.95 (***978-0-7613-9493-8(1)*** , Carolrhoda Bks.) Lerner Publishing Group.

Gross, Philip. The Lastling. 2006. 256p. (YA). (gr. 7). 16.00 (978-0-618-65998-2(6) , Clarion Bks.) Houghton Mifflin Co. Trade & Reference Div.

Harvey, Damian. Oggy & the Dinosaur. Hall, Francois, illus. 2005. (Reading Corner Ser.). 24p. (J). (gr. k-3). lib. bdg. 22.80 (978-1-59771-008-4(3)) Sea-To-Sea Pubns.

Holt, Rinehart and Winston Staff. Where the Red Fern Grows: With Connections. 1998. pap., stu. ed. 13.20 (978-0-03-054053-0(4)) Holt, Rinehart & Winston.

Hunter, Helen W. Duck Hunting with Grandpa. Rozeboom, Grant, illus. 1998. (Young American Hunting & Fishing Ser.: Vol. 1). 102p. (J). (gr. 2-7). pap. 7.99 (978-0-9662769-0-9(6)) Hunter Hse. Pubns.

—Turkey Hunting with Grandpa. Rozeboom, Grant, illus. 2000. (Young American Hunting & Fishing Ser.: Vol. 2). (J). (gr. 2-7). pap. 9.99 (978-0-9662769-2-3(2)) Hunter Hse. Pubns.

Kazenbroot, Nelly. Down the Chimney with Googal & Googolplex. 2004. 63p. (J). lib. bdg. 20.00 (***978-1-4242-1257-6(X))*** Fitzgerald Bks.

Kellerhals-Stewart, Heather. Muktu: The Backward Muskok. Muntean, Karen, illus. 1999. 32p. (J). pap. 5.99 (978-0-9686209-0-8(6)) Chauntaluf Publishing CAN. *Dist:* Milestone Pubns., Ltd.

Lachenmeyer, Nathaniel. Searching for Sasquatch. Bradley, Vicki, illus. 2007. 32p. 16.95 (***978-1-57061-442-2(3))*** Sasquatch Bks.

Laswell, Wendy Jo. Gone Hunting. 2004. (Illus.). (J). lib. bdg. (978-1-932252-42-2(8)) Creative Continuum, Inc.

Leslie, Lawrence J. With Trapper Jim in the North Woods. 2004. reprint ed. pap. 19.95 (978-1-4191-9451-1(8)); pap. 1.99 (978-1-4192-9451-8(2)) Kessinger Publishing, LLC.

Malone, Geoffrey. Elephant Ben. 2nd ed. 2002. 160p. (J). pap. (978-0-340-86059-5(6) , Hodder & Stoughton) Hodder General Publishing Division.

The Mammoth Hunters: Individual Title Six-Packs. (Bookweb Ser.). 32p. (gr. 5 up). 34.00 (978-0-7635-3778-4(0)) Rigby Education.

Martin, Francesca. Los Cazadores de Miel. (SPA., Illus.). 27p. (J). pap. 11.95 (978-980-257-175-8(X) , EK2944) Ekare, Ediciones VEN. *Dist:* Kane/Miller Bk. Pubs., Inc., Lectorum Pubns., Inc.

Milani, Mino. El Ultimo Lobo. (Barco de Vapor).Tr. of Last Wolf. (SPA.). 144p. (YA). (gr. 5-8). (978-84-348-4520-6(2)) SM Ediciones.

Milway, Alex. The Mouse Hunter. 2007. 384p. (J). pap. 5.99 (***978-0-316-02455-6(4))*** Little, Brown Bks. for Young Readers.

Myers, Tim. The Outfoxed Fox. Pang, Ariel Ya-Wen, illus. 2007. 32p. (J): (gr. k-3). 16.99 (***978-0-7614-5356-7(3))*** Cavendish, Marshall Corp.

Nohel, Andre & Back, Francis. L' Orphelin des Mers. 2000. (Roman Jeunesse Ser.). (FRE.). 96p. (J). (gr. 4-7). pap. (978-2-89021-413-2(3)) Diffusion du livre Mirabel.

Olaizola, José Luis. El Cazador Urbano.Tr. of Urban Hunter. (SPA.). 160p. (J). 6.50 (978-84-355-0814-8(5)) Minon, S.A. ESP. *Dist:* AIMS International Bks., Inc.

Oliver, Narelle. The Hunt. Oliver, Narelle, illus. 1998. (Illus.). 32p. (J). (ps-3). pap. 6.95 (978-1-887734-43-1(0)) Star Bright Bks., Inc.

Oxenbury, Helen, illus. We're Going on a Bear Hunt. 2004. 33p. (J). (TAM, CZE, VIE, GUJ & PER.). (978-1-85269-707-5(5)); (TAM, CZE, VIE, GUJ & PER.). (978-1-85269-708-2(3)); (TAM, CZE, VIE, GUJ & PER.). (978-1-85269-709-9(1)); (TAM, CZE, VIE, GUJ & PER.). (978-1-85269-713-6(X)); (TAM, CZE, VIE, GUJ & PER.). (978-1-85269-714-3(8)); (CZE, TAM, VIE, GUJ & PER.). (978-1-85269-719-8(9)); (TAM, CZE, VIE, GUJ & PER.). (978-1-85269-721-1(0)) Mantra Publishing, Ltd.

Oxley, MacDonald J. Young Woodsman or Life in the Forests of. 2006. 24.99 (***978-1-4280-3300-9(9));*** pap. 18.99 (***978-1-4280-3280-4(0))*** IndyPublish.com.

Paulsen, Gary. Brian's Hunt. 2005. 112p. (J). (gr. 5). pap. 5.99 (978-0-553-49415-0(5) , Laurel Leaf) Random Hse. Children's Bks.

—Brian's Hunt: A Novel. 2005. 103p. (YA). (gr. 4-8). reprint ed. 15.00 (978-0-7567-9570-2(2)) DIANE Publishing Co.

Paulsen, Gary. Tracker. 2007. 96p. (J). pap. 4.99 (***978-1-4169-3940-5(7)*** , Aladdin) Simon & Schuster Children's Publishing.

Reich, J. J. Snort, Wheeze, Rattle & Grunt. Hillmann, Joe & Cox, Chad, illus. 2006. (J). 8.99 (978-0-9762971-1-6(6)) Outdoor Originals LLC.

Reich, J. J. Snort, Wheeze, Rattle & Grunt: Kampp Tales: Outdoor Adventures. Johnathan, Kuehl, illus. 2006. 64p. (J). (***978-0-9762971-2-3(4))*** Outdoor Originals LLC.

Reid, Mayne. Young Yagers or A Narrative of Hunting A. 2006. (Illus.). pap. 31.95 (***978-1-4286-2205-0(5))*** Kessinger Publishing, LLC.

Remolina, Tere. Un Cambio de Piel. Martinez, Enrique, illus. (Barril Sin Fondo Ser.). (SPA.). (J). (gr. 3-5). pap. (978-968-6465-20-4(0)) Casa de Estudios de Literatura y Talleres Artisticos Amaquemecan A.C. MEX. *Dist:* Lectorum Pubns., Inc.

Rosen, Michael. We're Going on a Bear Hunt. Oxenbury, Helen, illus. 2003. 36p. (J). pap. 7.99 (978-0-689-85349-4(1) , Aladdin) Simon & Schuster Children's Publishing.

—We're Going on a Bear Hunt. 2003. (gr. k-3). lib. bdg. 16.45 (978-0-613-61665-2(0)) Tandem Library Bks.

Rosen, Michael & Oxenbury, Helen. We're Going on a Bear Hunt. 2004. (POR, TAM, CZE, VIE & CHI., Illus.). 32p. (J). (978-1-85269-706-8(7)); (978-1-85269-710-5(5)); (978-1-85269-711-2(3)); (978-1-85269-716-7(4)); (978-1-85269-718-1(0)); (978-1-85269-720-4(2)) Mantra Publishing, Ltd.

Rosen, Michael & Oxenbury, Helen, illus. La Chasse a L'ours. 2004. Orig. Title: We're Going on a Bear Hunt. (POR, TAM, CZE, VIE & CHI.). 33p. (J). (978-1-85269-712-9(1)) Mantra Publishing, Ltd.

—Chung Ta Di Sian Gau. 2004. Orig. Title: We're Going on a Bear Hunt. (TAM, CZE, VIE, GUJ & PER.). 33p. (J). (978-1-85269-722-8(9)) Mantra Publishing, Ltd.

—Vamos a Caca de Um Urso. 2004. Orig. Title: We're Going on a Bear Hunt. (POR, TAM, CZE, VIE & CHI.). 33p. (J). (978-1-85269-715-0(6)) Mantra Publishing, Ltd.

Rosen, Michael J. We're Going on a Bear Hunt. Oxenbury, Helen, illus. gif. ed. 2002. 40p. (J). 9.99 (978-0-7636-1979-4(5)) Candlewick Pr.

Ruark, Robert C. I Didn't Know It Was Loaded. (J). 22.95 (978-0-89190-958-3(3)) Amereon LTD.

Sam, Joe, illus. The Invisible Hunters (Los Cazadores Invisibles) (YA). (gr. 1 up). 25.95 incl. audio (978-0-89239-036-6(0)) Children's Bk. Pr.

Santillo, LuAnn. The Big Hunt. Santillo, LuAnn, ed. 2003. (Half-Pint Kids Readers Ser.). (Illus.). 7p. (J). (ps-1). pap. (978-1-59256-076-9(8)) Half-Pint Kids, Inc.

Sargent, Pat. The Bobcat, 8, Vol. 5. Lenoir, Jane, illus. 2003. (Barney the Bear Killer Ser.: Vol. 5). 136p. (J). lib. bdg. 25.25 (978-1-56763-971-1(2)) Ozark Publishing.

Scheer, Julian. A Thanksgiving Turkey. Himler, Ronald, illus. 2001. 32p. (J). (gr. k-3). tchr. ed. 16.95 (978-0-8234-1674-5(7)) Holiday Hse., Inc.

Searcher Hunter. 2004. (Caravan Ser.). 80p. pap. 9.50 (978-0-8341-2124-9(7)) Beacon Hill Pr. of Kansas City.

Simons, Jamie & Scollon, E. W. The Hunt is On. Evans, Michael, illus. 1998. (Goners Ser.: No. 2). (J). (gr. 3-7). (978-0-606-13436-1(0)) Tandem Library Bks.

Skipper, Cecil. The Deer Lick. 2004. 166p. (YA). pap. 12.95 (978-0-595-30949-8(6)) iUniverse, Inc.

Spinner, Stephanie. Quiver. 2002. 192p. (YA). (gr. 7). lib. bdg. 17.99 (978-0-375-91489-8(7) , Knopf Bks. for Young Readers) Random Hse. Children's Bks.

Standish, Burt L. Frank Merriwell's Hunting Tour. Rudman, Jack, ed. (Frank Merriwell Ser.). (YA). (gr. 9 up). 29.95 (978-0-8373-9307-0(8)); 2003. pap. 9.95 (978-0-8373-9007-9(9) , FM-007) Merriwell, Frank Inc.

Talbot, Amy. Deer & Friends: A Folktale from India. 2006. 23.00 (***978-1-4108-6173-3(2))*** Benchmark Education Co.

Taylor, Theodore. Lord of the Kill. 2004. 256p. (J). pap. 5.99 (978-0-439-55956-0(1) , Scholastic Paperbacks) Scholastic, Inc.

Truax, Doug. A Good Day for Ducks. Smith, Jack K., illus. 2003. 32p. (gr. k-4). 16.95 (978-1-932052-12-1(7)) Ducks Unlimited, Inc.

Tutt, Keith. Pablo Goes Hunting. Giffard, Hannah, illus. 2005. 32p. (J). 15.95 (978-1-84507-284-1(7)) Lincoln, Frances Ltd. GBR. *Dist:* Perseus Distribution.

Walpole, Peter. The Healer of Harrow Point. 2000. 144p. (J). (gr. 5 up). pap. 11.95 (978-1-57174-167-7(4)) Hampton Roads Publishing Co., Inc.

—Healer of Harrow Point. 2000. (gr. 7-12). lib. bdg. 21.05 (978-0-613-88748-9(4)) Tandem Library Bks.

Wilder, Laura Ingalls. The Deer in the Wood. 1999. (gr. k-3). lib. bdg. 14.15 (978-0-613-11467-7(1)) Tandem Library Bks.

HURON, LAKE (MICH. AND ONT.)

Ylvisaker, Anne. Lake Huron. 2003. (Fact Finders Ser.). (Illus.). 32p. (J). lib. bdg. 22.60 (978-0-7368-2209-1(7) , Bridgestone Bks.) Capstone Pr., Inc.

HURRICANES

Allberti, Frances C. Finding Rover. Gremillion, Barry, illus. 2006. (J). per. (978-0-9785937-1-1(5)) Open Pages Publishing.

Allen, Jean. Hurricanes. 2000. (Natural Disasters Ser.). (Illus.). 48p. (J). (gr. 3-4). lib. bdg. 21.26 (978-0-7368-0587-2(7) , Capstone High-Interest Bks.) Capstone Pr., Inc.

Armentrout, David & Armentrout, Patricia. Hurricanes. 2007. (Illus.). 32p. (J). (978-1-60044-232-2(3)) Rourke Publishing, LLC.

Beech, Sandy. Weather's Here, Wish You Were Great. 2005. (Illus.). 186p. (J). (***978-1-4156-1165-4(3)*** , Aladdin) Simon & Schuster Children's Publishing.

Berger, Melvin. Do Tornadoes Really Twist? 2000. (gr. 3-6). lib. bdg. 14.10 (978-0-613-32476-2(5)) Tandem Library Bks.

Berger, Melvin & Berger, Gilda. Do Tornadoes Really Twist? Questions & Answers about Tornadoes & Hurricanes. Bond, Barbara Higgins, illus. 2000. (Question & Answer Ser.). 48p. (J). (gr. 2-5). pap. 14.95 (978-0-439-09584-6(0)) Scholastic, Inc.

—Do Tornadoes Really Twist? Questions & Answers about Tornadoes & Hurricanes. 2000. (Scholastic Question & Answer Ser.). (J). 10.01 (978-0-439-09585-3(9)) Scholastic, Inc.

—Hurricanes Have Eyes but Can't See: And Other Amazing Facts about Wild Weather. 2003. (Illus.). 48p. (J). (978-0-439-54980-6(9)) Scholastic, Inc.

Brennan, Joseph K. Hurricanes. 2003. (Science Links Ser.). (Illus.). 32p. (gr. 3-5). 23.00 (978-0-7910-7424-4(2) , Chelsea Hse.) Facts On File, Inc.

Brennan, Kristine. The Galveston Hurricane. 2002. (Great Disasters, Reforms & Ramifications Ser.). (Illus.). 112p. (J). 30.00 (978-0-7910-6740-6(8) , Chelsea Hse.) Facts On File, Inc.

Challen, Paul C. Hurricane & Typhoon Alert! 2004. (Disaster Alert! Ser.). (Illus.). 32p. (J). (978-0-7787-1575-7(2)) Crabtree Publishing Co.

—Hurricanes & Typhoon Alert! 2004. (Disaster Alert! Ser.). (Illus.). 32p. (J). pap. (978-0-7787-1607-5(4)) Crabtree Publishing Co.

Chambers, Catherine. Hurricane. (Wild Weather Ser.). (Illus.). 32p. (J). 2007. (gr. 2-4). pap. 7.99 ***(978-1-4034-9588-4(2));*** 2007. (gr. 2-4). lib. bdg. 25.36 ***(978-1-4034-9579-2(3));*** 2002. (gr. k-2). lib. bdg. 21.36 (978-1-58810-651-3(9)) Heinemann Library.

Chambers, Catherine. Hurricanes. (Disasters in Nature Ser.). (Illus.). 48p. (J). (gr. 4-7). 2002. pap. 8.50 (978-1-58810-334-5(X) , 91080); 2000. lib. bdg. 24.22 (978-1-57572-429-4(4)) Heinemann Library.

—Hurricanes. 2005. (What on Earth? Ser.). (Illus.). 32p. (J). 25.50 (978-0-516-25320-6(4) , Children's Pr.) Scholastic Library Publishing.

—Hurricanes. 2001. (gr. 3-6). lib. bdg. 17.05 (978-0-613-86814-3(5)) Tandem Library Bks.

Demarest, Chris L. Hurricane Hunters! Riders on the Storm. Demarest, Chris L., illus. 2006. 40p. (J). (ps-5). 17.95 (978-0-689-86168-0(0) , McElderry, Margaret K.) Simon & Schuster Children's Publishing.

Dineen, Jacqueline. Hurricanes & Typhoons. 2004. (Natural Disasters Ser.). (J). lib. bdg. 27.10 (978-1-932799-06-4(0)) Stargazer Bks.

Doeden, Matt. Hurricanes. 2008. (Pull Ahead Books-Forces of Nature Ser.). (J). lib. bdg. 22.60 ***(978-0-8225-7906-9(5)*** , Lerner Pubns.) Lerner Publishing Group.

Donnelly, Karen J. Storms of the Past & the Future. 2003. (Earths Changing Weather & Climate Ser.). (Illus.). 24p. (J). lib. bdg. 18.75 (978-0-8239-6216-7(4) , PowerKids Pr.) Rosen Publishing Group, Inc., The.

Dorling Kindersley Publishing Staff, ed. Hurricane & Tornado. 2004. (Dk Eyewitness Books Ser.). (Illus.). 72p. (J). 15.99 (978-0-7566-0690-9(X)) Dorling Kindersley Publishing, Inc.

Dudley, William. Hurricane Katrina. 2006. (At Issue Ser.). 91p. (YA). (gr. 6-10). lib. bdg. 29.95 (978-0-7377-3551-2(1) , Greenhaven Pr., Inc.) Thomson Gale.

Fine, Jil. Hurricanes. 2007. (Natural Disasters Ser.). (Illus.). 48p. (J). pap. (978-0-531-18722-7(5)) Children's Pr., Ltd.

—Hurricanes. 2006. (Natural Disasters Ser.). (Illus.). 48p. (J). (978-0-531-12436-9(3) , Children's Pr.) Scholastic Library Publishing.

Fradin, Dennis & Fradin, Judith. Hurricanes. 2007. (Witness to Disaster Ser.). (Illus.). 48p. (J). (gr. 3-6). 16.95 ***(978-1-4262-0111-0(7));*** lib. bdg. 26.90 ***(978-1-4262-0112-7(5))*** National Geographic Society. (National Geographic Children's Bks.).

Gaffney, Timothy R. Hurricane Hunters. 2001. (Aircraft Ser.). (Illus.). 48p. (YA). (gr. 4-10). lib. bdg. 23.93 (978-0-7660-1569-2(6)) Enslow Pubs., Inc.

Galiano, Dean. Hurricanes. rev. ed. 2005. (Weather Watchers' Library). (Illus.). 48p. (YA). (gr. 5-8). lib. bdg. 23.95 (978-0-8239-3095-1(5) , WEHURR) Rosen Publishing Group, Inc., The.

Gentle, Victor & Perry, Janet. Hurricanes. 2001. (Natural Disasters Ser.). (Illus.). 24p. (J). (gr. 2 up). lib. bdg. 22.00 (978-0-8368-2834-4(8)) Stevens, Gareth Inc.

Gibson, Karen Bush. The Fury of Hurricane Andrew 1992. 2005. (Natural Disasters Ser.). (Illus.). 32p. (J). (gr. 1-4). lib. bdg. (978-1-58415-416-7(0)) Mitchell Lane Pubs., Inc.

Gigliotti, Jim. Hurricanes. 2006. (Boys Rock! Ser.). (Illus.). 32p. (J). (gr. 1-5). 24.21 (978-1-59296-731-5(0)) Child's World, Inc.

Green, Jen. Hurricane Andrew. 2005. (Illus.). 32p. (J). lib. bdg. 24.67 (978-0-8368-4497-9(1)) Stevens, Gareth Inc.

Group/McGraw-Hill, Wright. Savage Storms: Tornadoes & Hurricanes, 6 vols. (Book2WebTM Ser.). (gr. 4-8). 36.50 (978-0-322-04424-1(3)) Wright Group, The.

Harcourt School Publishers Staff. Hurricane! Below Level. 3rd ed. 2002. (Trophies Reading Program Ser.). (Illus.). pap. 5.10 (978-0-15-323069-1(X)) Harcourt Schl. Pubs.

—Living with Hurricanes Advanced Level. 3rd ed. 2002. (Trophies Reading Program Ser.). (Illus.). pap. 5.10 (978-0-15-323383-8(4)) Harcourt Schl. Pubs.

—The Most Dangerous Storms on Earth Advanced Level. 3rd ed. 2002. (Trophies Reading Program Ser.). (Illus.). pap. 5.10 (978-0-15-323486-6(5)) Harcourt Schl. Pubs.

—Storm Watch: Below Level. 3rd ed. 2002. (Trophies Reading Program Ser.). (Illus.). (J). pap. 4.10 (978-0-15-322969-5(1)) Harcourt Schl. Pubs.

—Storm Watch 5-Pack, Below Level. 3rd ed. 2002. (Trophies Reading Program Ser.). (Illus.). (gr. 1). pap. 20.10 (978-0-15-326819-9(0)) Harcourt Schl. Pubs.

Harper, Kristine. Hurricane Andrew. 2005. (Environmental Disasters Ser.). (Illus.). 112p. (gr. 6-12). 35.00 (978-0-8160-5759-7(1)) Facts On File, Inc.

Hoffman, Mary Ann. Hurricane Katrina. 2006. (Nature in the News Ser.). (Illus.). 32p. (J). lib. bdg. (978-1-4042-3537-3(X) , PowerKids Pr.) Rosen Publishing Group, Inc., The.

Hopping, Lorraine Jean. Huracanes!, Level 4. Wheeler, Jody, illus. 2002. (Hello Reader! Ser.). (SPA.). 48p. (J). pap. 3.99 (978-0-439-41134-9(3) , Scholastic en Espanol) Scholastic, Inc.

Huracan a la Vista! 6 Small Books. (Saludos Ser.: Vol. 2). (SPA.). (gr. 3-5). 31.00 (978-0-7635-2069-4(1)) Rigby Education.

Hurricane on Its Way!, 6 Packs. (Greetings Ser.: Vol. 2). (gr. 3-5). 31.00 (978-0-7635-2063-2(2)) Rigby Education.

Jennings, Terry. Hurricanes & Tornadoes. 1999. (Natural Disasters Ser.). (Illus.). 32p. (J). lib. bdg. 16.95 (978-1-929298-47-1(1)) Chrysalis Education.

Kerrod, Robin. Shaking Earth: Volcanoes, Earthquakes, Hurricanes Etc. 2005. (Illus.). 128p. pap. 17.99 (978-1-84476-097-8(9) , Southwater) Anness Publishing GBR. *Dist:* National Bk. Network.

Kliman, Gilbert. My Personal Story about Hurricanes Katrina & Rita: A Guided Activity Workbook for Middle & High School Students. 2005. (YA). spiral bd. 19.00 ***(978-0-9790846-9-0(5))*** Children's Psychological Health Ctr., Inc., The.

Larson, Erik. Isaac's Storm: A Man, a Time, & the Deadliest Hurricane in History. 2000. 323p. (gr. 7-12). per. 22.25 (978-0-613-29271-9(5)) Tandem Library Bks.

Lassieur, Allison. Storm Tracker. 2006. (Illus.). 32p. (J). (978-1-4109-2576-3(5)); pap. (978-1-4109-2605-0(2)) Steck-Vaughn.

Latham, Donna. Hurricane! The 1900 Galveston Night of Terror. 2005. (X-Treme Disasters That Changed America Ser.). (Illus.). 32p. (J). (gr. 3-7). lib. bdg. 25.27 (978-1-59716-071-1(7)) Bearport Publishing Co., Inc.

London, Jonathan. Hurricane. Sorenson, Henri, illus. 1998. 32p. (J). (gr. k-3). 16.89 (978-0-688-12978-1(1)) HarperCollins Pubs.

—Hurricane! Sorensen, Henri, illus. 1998. 32p. (J). (gr. k-3). 16.99 (978-0-688-12977-4(3)) HarperCollins Pubs.

Markle, Sandra. Can You Believe? Hurricanes. Bosson, Jo-Ellen C., tr. Bosson, Jo-Ellen C., illus. 2002. 48p. (J). (978-0-439-35610-7(5)) Scholastic, Inc.

McGrath, Barbara Barbieri. The Storm: Students of Biloxi, Mississippi, Remember Hurricane Katrina. 2006. (Illus.). 64p. (J). pap. 9.95 (978-1-58089-173-8(X)) Charlesbridge Publishing, Inc.

Meister, Cari. Hurricanes. 1999. (Nature's Fury Ser.). (Illus.). 32p. (J). (gr. 3-8). lib. bdg. 24.21 (978-1-57765-080-5(8) , ABDO & Daughters) ABDO Publishing Co.

Mezzanotte, Jim. Huracanes. 2006. (ENG & SPA.). (J). lib. bdg. ***(978-0-8368-8071-7(4));*** (Illus.). 24p. (gr. 2). pap. ***(978-0-8368-8078-6(1))*** Stevens, Gareth Inc. (Weekly Reader Early Learning Library).

—Hurricanes. 2006. (J). lib. bdg. ***(978-0-8368-7913-1(9));*** (Illus.). 24p. (gr. 2). pap. ***(978-0-8368-7920-9(1))*** Stevens, Gareth Inc. (Weekly Reader Early Learning Library).

Miller, Debra A. Hurricane Katrina: Devastation on the Gulf Coast. 2006. 112p. (J). (gr. 7-10). 29.95 (978-1-59018-936-8(1) , Lucent Bks.) Thomson Gale.

Miller, Mara. Hurricane Katrina Strikes the Gulf Coast: Disaster & Survival. 2006. (Deadly Disasters Ser.). (Illus.). 48p. (J). lib. bdg. 23.93 (978-0-7660-2803-6(8) , 1251895) Enslow Pubs., Inc.

Morris, Neil. Hurricanes & Tornadoes. 1999. (Natural Disasters Ser.). (Illus.). 31p. (J). (gr. 5 up). pap. 5.95 (978-0-7641-1060-3(8)) Barron's Educational Series, Inc.

—Hurricanes & Tornadoes. 1998. (Wonders of Our World Ser.). (Illus.). 32p. (J). (gr. 3-4). lib. bdg. (978-0-86505-831-6(8)) Crabtree Publishing Co.

—Inside Hurricanes & Tornadoes. 2006. (Inside Nature's Disasters Ser.). (Illus.). 36p. (J). lib. bdg. (978-0-8368-7249-1(5)) Stevens, Gareth Inc.

Nicolson, Cynthia Pratt. Hurricane! 2002. (Disaster Ser.). (Illus.). 32p. (J). (gr. 4-6). (978-1-55074-970-0(6)); (978-1-55074-906-9(4)) Kids Can Pr., Ltd.

Olson, Nathan. Hurricanes. 2005. (Weather Update Ser.). (Illus.). 24p. (J). (ps-7). lib. bdg. 21.26 (978-0-7368-4332-4(9) , Bridgestone Bks.) Capstone Pr., Inc.

Ouellette, Jeannine. Hurricane Katrina. 2007. (Essential Events Ser.). (ENG., Illus.). 112p. (YA). (gr. 8-12), lib. bdg. 32.79 ***(978-1-59928-852-9(4)*** , Essential Library) ABDO Publishing Co.

Oxlade, Chris. Violent Skies: Hurricanes. 2004. (Turbulent Planet Ser.). (Illus.). 48p. (J). 28.56 (978-1-4109-1100-1(4)); pap. 8.50 (978-1-4109-1205-3(1)) Harcourt Schl. Pubs.

—Violent Skies: Hurricanes. 2005. (Turbulent Planet Ser.). (Illus.). 48p. (J). pap. (978-1-4109-1747-8(9)) Steck-Vaughn.

—Violent Skies-Hurricanes. 2005. (Turbulent Planet Ser.). (Illus.). 48p. (J). (ps-1). lib. bdg. 31.43 (978-1-4109-1737-9(1)) Steck-Vaughn.

Palser, Barb. Hurricane Katrina: Aftermath of Disaster. 2006. (Snapshots in History Ser.). (J). 31.93 (978-0-7565-2101-1(7)) Compass Point Bks.

Park, Louise. Hurricanes. 2007. (J). ***(978-1-59920-112-2(7))*** Smart Apple Media.

Parks, Peggy J. Hurricanes. 2006. (KidHaven Science Library). (Illus.). 48p. (J). (gr. 4-8). 26.20 (978-0-7377-3550-5(3) , Kidhaven) Thomson Gale.

Phelan, Glen. Extreme Weather. 2004. (National Geographic Reading Expeditions Ser.). (Illus.). 32p. (J). pap. (978-0-7922-4575-9(X)) National Geographic Society.

Pitt, Steve. Rain Tonight: A Story of Hurricane Hazel. 2004. (gr. 3-6). lib. bdg. 22.20 (978-0-613-77307-2(1)) Tandem Library Bks.

—Rain Tonight: A Story of Hurricane Hazel. Collins, Heather, illus. 2004. 48p. (J). (gr. 3-7). pap. 6.95 (978-0-88776-641-1(2)) Tundra Bks., Inc./Livres Toundra, Inc. CAN. *Dist:* Random Hse., Inc.

Richards, Julie. Howling Hurricanes. 2001. (Natural Disasters Ser.). (Illus.). 32p. (J). (gr. 5 up). 28.00 (978-0-7910-6584-6(7) , 010452, Chelsea Hse.) Facts On File, Inc.

Rodger, Ellen. Hurricane Katrina. 2006. (Disaster Alert! Ser.). (Illus.). 32p. (J). (gr. 4). pap. (978-0-7787-1618-1(X)); (gr. 3-9). ***(978-0-7787-1586-3(8))*** Crabtree Publishing Co.

Rooney, Anne. Hurricane! 2007. (Illus.). 32p. (978-1-84193-564-5(6)) Arcturus Pubs., Ltd.

Rose, Sally. El Nino! & la Nina. 1999. (978-0-606-17528-9(8)) Tandem Library Bks.

Rotter, Charles. Hurricanes: Storms of the Sea. 2002. (Life-Views Ser.). (Illus.). 32p. (J). lib. bdg. (978-1-58341-020-2(1) , Creative Education) Creative Co., The.

Sherrow, Victoria. Hurricane Andrew: Nature's Rage. 1998. (American Disasters Ser.). (Illus.). 48p. (YA). (gr. 4-10). lib. bdg. 23.93 (978-0-7660-1057-4(0)) Enslow Pubs., Inc.

Simon, Seymour. Hurricanes. 32p. (J). 2007. 16.99 ***(978-0-06-117072-0(0));*** 2007. pap. 6.99 ***(978-0-06-117071-3(2));*** 2003. (Illus.). 15.99 (978-0-688-16291-7(6)); 2003. (Illus.). lib. bdg. 17.89 (978-0-688-16292-4(4)) HarperCollins Pubs.

Sood, Malini. Hurricanes & Tornadoes. 2008. (J). lib. bdg. ***(978-1-4042-3900-5(6)*** , PowerKids Pr.) Rosen Publishing Group, Inc., The.

Spilsbury, Louise & Spilsbury, Richard. Howling Hurricanes. 2004. (Heinemann Infosearch Ser.). (Illus.). 32p. (J). pap. 7.50 (978-1-4034-5445-4(0)); lib. bdg. (978-1-4034-4785-2(3)) Heinemann Library.

Steele, Christy. Hurricanes. 2000. (Nature on the Rampage Ser.). (Illus.). 32p. (J). (gr. 4-7). lib. bdg. 22.83 (978-0-7398-1793-0(0)) Raintree.

Strom, Laura Layton. Built below Sea Level: New Orleans. 2007. (Shockwave: People & Communities Ser.). 36p. (J). pap. 6.95 ***(978-0-531-18774-6(8));*** (Illus.). (gr. 4-6). lib. bdg. 25.00 ***(978-0-531-17746-4(7))*** Scholastic Library Publishing. (Children's Pr.).

Thomas, Rick. Eye of the Storm: A Book about Hurricanes. Shea, Denise, illus. 2005. (Amazing Science Ser.). 24p. (C). (gr. k-3). 22.60 (978-1-4048-0928-4(7)) Picture Window Bks.

Thoron, Joe. Hurricanes. 2006. (Kaleidoscope Natural Disasters Ser.). (Illus.). 48p. (J). lib. bdg. 28.50 (978-0-7614-2103-0(3) , Benchmark Bks.) Cavendish, Marshall Corp.

Torres, John. Hurricane Katrina 2005. 2006. (Natural Disasters Ser.). (Illus.). 32p. (J). (gr. 1-4). lib. bdg. (978-1-58415-498-3(5)) Mitchell Lane Pubs., Inc.

—Hurricane Katrina & the Devastation of New Orleans 2005. 2006. (Monumental Milestones Ser.). (Illus.). 48p. (J). lib. bdg. 20.95 (978-1-58415-473-0(X)) Mitchell Lane Pubs., Inc.

Treaster, Joseph B. Hurricane Force: In the Path of America's Deadliest Storms. 2007. (New York Times Ser.). (Illus.). 128p. (J). (gr. 7). 16.95 (978-0-7534-6086-3(6) , Kingfisher) Houghton Mifflin Co. Trade & Reference Div.

Trueit, Trudi Strain. Storm Chasers. 2002. (Watts Library). (Illus.). 64p. (J). (gr. 5-7). 25.50 (978-0-531-11971-6(8) , Watts, Franklin) Scholastic Library Publishing.

Wall, Suzy. Hurricanes. ed. 2004. (Shared Connections Ser.). (J). pap. 27.00 (978-1-4108-1643-6(5)) Benchmark Education Co.

—Hurricanes (Big Book) ed. 2004. (Shared Connections Ser.). (J). pap., instr.'s gde. ed. 27.00 (978-1-4108-1619-1(2)) Benchmark Education Co.

Weather Wise: Historic Hurricanes! 2001. (J). pap. 5.95 (978-1-56911-726-2(8)) Learning Resources, Inc.

Wescovich Dill, Pamela. Katrina's Rainbow: The Miracle of the Storm Crosses. 2006. (Illus.). 46p. (J). 17.99 ***(978-1-59879-302-4(0))*** Lifevest Publishing, Inc.

Why the Wild Winds Blow: Six-Pack. (Greetings Ser.: Vol. 1). (gr. 3-5). 31.00 (978-0-7635-1838-7(7)) Rigby Education.

Wilson, Cristi. Just Because. Wilson, Cristi, illus. l.t. ed. 2006. (Illus.). 24p. (J). per. 10.99 ***(978-1-59879-251-5(2))*** Lifevest Publishing, Inc.

Woods, Michael & Woods, Mary B. Hurricanes. 2007. (Disasters up Close Ser.). (Illus.). 64p. (J). (gr. 4-6). 27.93 (978-0-8225-4710-5(4) , Lerner Pubns.) Lerner Publishing Group.

World Book, Inc Staff, contrib. by. Hurricanes, Typhoons, & Other Tropical Cyclones. 2007. (J). ***(978-0-7166-9808-1(0))*** World Bk., Inc.

HURRICANES—FICTION

Anastasia School, Amerigo. Powerful Hands. l.t. ed. 2006. (Illus.). 16p. (J). 19.95 (978-1-59879-120-4(6)); per. 10.99 (978-1-59879-096-2(X)) Lifevest Publishing, Inc.

Anderson, Laurie Halse. Storm Rescue. 2003. (Wild at Heart Ser.). (Illus.). 105p. (J). (gr. 4 up). lib. bdg. 23.33 (978-0-8368-3260-0(4)) Stevens, Gareth Inc.

—Storm Rescue. 2001. (American Girl Wild at Heart Ser.: Bk. 6). (Illus.). (YA). (978-0-606-21528-2(X)) Tandem Library Bks.

Beserra, Donna. Twirly Shirley In Hurricane Shirley. 2005. 22p. (J). 8.00 (978-0-9729484-4-9(9)) Seventh Street Pr.

Brouwer, Sigmund. Legend of the Gilded Saber. 2002. (gr. 3-6). lib. bdg. 14.15 (978-0-613-89740-2(4)) Tandem Library Bks.

Candy, Wolf. The Tree, the House & the Hurricane. l.t. ed. 2005. (Illus.). 24p. (J). 7.00 (978-0-9762292-3-0(4)) New Global Publishing.

Cooke, Trish. Zoom! 2001. (Illus.). 25p. (J). pap. 9.99 (978-0-00-664621-1(2)) HarperCollins Pubs. Ltd. GBR. *Dist:* Independent Pubs. Group.

Davis, Mike. Land of the Lost Mammoths: A Science Adventure. 2003. (Illus.). 174p. (J). 15.95 (978-0-9747078-0-8(5)) Perceval Pr.

Demas, Corinne. Hurricane! Strohmeier, Lenice U., illus. 2000. (Accelerated Reader Bks.). 32p. (J). (gr. k-3). 15.95 (978-0-7614-5052-8(1) , Cavendish Children's Bks.) Cavendish, Marshall Corp.

Donald, Margaret. Tipsy: The Hurricane Hero. 2007. 26p. (J). 14.95 ***(978-81-8386-050-5(8))*** India Research Pr. IND. *Dist:* Independent Pubs. Group.

Duey, Kathleen. Louisiana Hurricane, 1860. 2000. (Illus.). (J). (978-0-606-18802-9(9)) Tandem Library Bks.

Duey, Kathleen & Bale, Karen. Hurricane: New Bedford, Massachusetts, 1784. 1999. (Survival! Ser.: No. 9). (J). (gr. 4-7). (978-0-606-16280-7(1)) Tandem Library Bks.

Duey, Kathleen & Bale, Karen A. Hurricane, New Bedford, Massachusetts, 1784. 1999. (Survival! Ser.: No. 9). 160p. (J). (gr. 4-7). per. 4.50 (978-0-689-82544-6(7) , Simon Pulse) Simon & Schuster Children's Publishing.

Eleanor, Coalson. Simon Says Run. 2006. (Illus.). (J). 8.95 (978-1-56167-944-7(5)) American Literary Pr.

Escott, John. Hannah & the Hurricane. abr. ed. 1998. (Illus.). 16p. (C). pap. 9.00 (978-0-582-35290-2(8)) Pearson ESL.

Faris, Debi. Kaya & Nannas First Excellent Adventur. 2006. pap. 18.99 ***(978-1-4259-7780-1(4))*** AuthorHouse.

Ford, Sandy Lee, illus. Gullah, the Nawleans Cat Meets Katrina. 2007. 32p. (J). ***(978-0-9793637-0-2(5))*** Hart Street Pubs.

Gershator, Phillis. Tiny & Bigman. Cravath, Lynne W., illus. 1999. (Accelerated Reader Bks.). 32p. (J). (gr. k-3). 15.95 (978-0-7614-5044-3(0) , Cavendish Children's Bks.) Cavendish, Marshall Corp.

Gildea, Kathy. The Adventures of Baylee Beagle—Hurricane Hound. Larson, Amanda, illus. 2005. 28p. (J). 7.95 (978-0-9767096-2-6(7)) Maxim Pr.

El gran huracan de Galveston 12: Leveled Books. 2001. (McGraw-Hill. Lectura Ser.). (ENG & SPA.). (gr. 5 up). (978-0-02-188284-7(3)) Macmillan/McGraw-Hill Schl. Div.

Greene, Janice. The Eye of the Hurricane, Set 2. 2002. 32p. (YA). 2.95 (978-1-56254-418-8(7) , SP 4187) Saddleback Educational Publishing.

Hanson, Ed. Hurricane. 2004. 64p. (YA). per. 3.95 (978-1-56254-805-6(0) , SP8050) Saddleback Educational Publishing.

Harcourt School Publishers Staff. Hurricane! Take-Home Book. 1999. (Collections Ser.). (Illus.). (J). pap. 1.90 (978-0-15-317247-2(9)) Harcourt Schl. Pubs.

Harlow, Joan Hiatt. Blown Away! 2007. 272p. (J). (gr. 4-7). 15.99 (978-1-4169-0781-7(5) , McElderry, Margaret K.) Simon & Schuster Children's Publishing.

Haydel, Catherine. Uno the Cat & Hurricane Katrina. 2006. 18.00 (978-0-8059-7341-9(9)) Dorrance Publishing Co., Inc.

El heros de los Huracanes. 2000. (McGraw-Hill Ciencias Ser.). (ENG & SPA.). (gr. 3 up). (978-0-02-279637-2(1)) Macmillan/McGraw-Hill Schl. Div.

Hurricane Harbor: Coloring/Activity Book incl Stickers. 2007. (Illus.). (J). ***(978-1-933934-69-3(7))*** Educational Adventures.

Hurricane Harbor: Picture Book (English) 8x8. 2007. (Illus.). (J). ***(978-1-933934-68-6(9))*** Educational Adventures.

Hurricane Katrina Dogs. 2006. (J). per. ***(978-1-932570-78-6(0))*** Literacy Footprints Inc.

Jones, Martha Tannery. Terror from the Gulf: A Hurricane in Galveston. 1999. (Illus.). 134p. (YA). (gr. 4-7). 17.95 (978-1-885777-21-8(3)) Hendrick-Long Publishing Co.

Lake, Julie. Galveston's Summer of the Storm. 2003. (Chaparral Book for Young Readers Ser.). 210p. 16.95 (978-0-87565-272-6(7)) Texas Christian Univ. Pr.

Lakin, Patricia. Hurricane! Lubach, Vanessa, illus. 2000. (Our World Ser.). 32p. (gr. k-4). lib. bdg. (978-0-7613-1616-9(7) , Millbrook Pr.) Lerner Publishing Group.

Lamson, Sharon E. Roach Approach/Squiggz Rides Storm. Barry, Bruce, illus. 2006. 40p. (J). pap. 4.99 (978-0-310-71384-5(6)) Zonderkidz.

Lance, Scott. Pourman's Library. 2003. 108p. (YA). pap. 10.95 (978-0-595-30148-5(7)) iUniverse, Inc.

Laurie, Peter. Mauby & the Hurricane. 2007. 56p. pap. 16.00 ***(978-1-4050-7718-7(2))*** Macmillan Caribbean GBR. *Dist:* Interlink Publishing Group, Inc.

Martin, Ann M. Karen's Hurricane. 1999. (Baby-Sitters Little Sister Ser.: No. 113). (Illus.). 106p. (J). (gr. 3-7). pap. 3.99 (978-0-590-52379-0(1)) Scholastic, Inc.

Mau, Connie. Catch me if you Can. Lemus, Kristina, illus. l.t. ed. 2006. 28p. (J). 14.95 (978-0-9778843-0-8(9)) Mau, C. Publishing Co.

Mercier, Deirdre. Yesterday We Had A Hurricane: Bilingual (English & Spanish) Edition. Huffman, Cindy, ed. Mercier, Deirdre, illus. 2006. (SPA & ENG., Illus.). 40p. (J). 17.95 (978-0-9754342-9-1(2)) Bumble Bee Publishing.

Mercier, Deirdre McLaughlin. Yesterday We Had A Hurricane: English Edition. 2006. (Illus.). (J). 17.95 (978-0-9754342-5-3(X)) Bumble Bee Publishing.

Miller, D. C. Hurricane Hunters: A Craig Hancock Adventure. 2005. (YA). pap. 9.95 (978-1-59088-646-5(1)) Wings ePress, Inc.

Morrison, P. R. The Wind Tamer. 2006. 336p. (YA). 16.95 (978-1-58234-781-3(6)) Bloomsbury Publishing.

Morrison, P. R. Wind Tamer. 2007. 336p. (YA). pap. 7.95 ***(978-1-59990-147-3(1)*** , Bloomsbury Children) Bloomsbury Publishing.

Myers, Anna. Stolen by the Sea. 2006. 144p. (J). pap. 6.95 (978-0-8027-8976-1(5)) Walker & Co.

Paterson, Diane. Hurricane Wolf. Paterson, Diane, illus. 2006. (Illus.). 32p. (J). 16.95 (978-0-8075-3438-0(2)) Whitman, Albert & Co.

Pippin, Sheila. Katrina: Through Mango's Eyes. 2007. (J). 12.95 ***(978-1-56167-956-0(9))*** American Literary Pr.

Robison, Peggy. Prince Cody Runs Ahead of the Hurricane. Clay, Doris, illus. 2005. 64p. (J). per. 9.95 (978-0-9764982-7-8(8)) Legacy Publishing Services, Inc.

H I

Rogers, Lisa Waller. The Great Storm: The Hurricane Diary of J. T. King, Galveston, Texas, 1900. 2002. (Lone Star Journals). (Illus.). 192p. (J). 14.50 (978-0-89672-478-5(6)) Texas Tech Univ. Pr.

Ryherd, Tim. My Hurricane Book. 2006. (J). 12.95 (978-0-9749974-1-4(2)) Ryherd, Tim Publishing.

Shah, Meera. And, Then Came Katrina. l.t. ed. 2005. (Illus.). 32p. (YA). pap. 12.99 (978-0-9774219-0-9(2)) Shah, Meera.

Smith, Debra West. Hattie Marshall & the Hurricane. 2000. 144p. (J). (gr. 4-7). pap. 7.95 (978-1-56554-675-2(X)) Pelican Publishing Co., Inc.

Strong, Jeremy. Giant Jim & the Hurricane. (Illus.). 96p. (J). pap. 7.95 (978-0-14-038248-8(8)) Penguin Bks., Ltd. GBR. *Dist:* Trafalgar Square Publishing.

Trueman, Terry. Hurricane. 2008. 144p. (J). 15.99 ***(978-0-06-000018-9(X)***); lib. bdg. 16.89 ***(978-0-06-000019-6(8))*** HarperCollins Pubs.

Wallner, Alexandra. Sergio & the Hurricane. 2006. (Illus.). 32p. (J). pap. 6.95 (978-0-8050-7984-5(X) , Holt, Henry & Co. Bks. For Young Readers) Holt, Henry & Co.

—Sergio & the Hurricane. Wallner, Alexandra, illus. rev. ed. 2000. (Illus.). 32p. (J). (ps-2). 17.95 (978-0-8050-6203-8(3) , Holt, Henry & Co. Bks. For Young Readers) Holt, Henry & Co.

Webb, Terry. Weathering the Storms. 2005. 148p. (YA). pap. 13.99 (978-1-4141-0393-8(X)) Pleasant Word.

What Young Hearts Whisper. 2006. (Illus.). (J). per. 23.00 (978-0-9785269-0-0(2)) Phi Sigma Omega, Alpha Kappa Alpha Sorority, Inc.

What Young Hearts Whisper - Stories of Survival - Hurricanes Katrina & Rita Special Edition. ed. 2006. per. 27.50 (978-0-9785269-1-7(0)) Phi Sigma Omega, Alpha Kappa Alpha Sorority, Inc.

HUSSEIN, SADDAM, 1937-2006

Anderson, Dale. Saddam Hussein. 2004. (A&E Biography Ser.). (Illus.). 112p. (J). 29.27 (978-0-8225-5005-1(9) , Lerner Pubns.) Lerner Publishing Group.

Downing, David. Saddam Hussein & Iraq. 2003. (Troubled World Ser.). (Illus.). 64p. (J). lib. bdg. 28.56 (978-1-4109-0184-2(X)) Raintree.

Richie, Jason. Iraq & the Fall of Saddam Hussein. 2003. (Illus.). 112p. (J). (gr. 5 up). lib. bdg. 24.95 (978-1-881508-63-2(3)) Oliver Pr., Inc.

Shields, Charles J. Saddam Hussein. (Major World Leaders Ser.). (Illus.). (gr. 6-12). 2003. 144p. 30.00 (978-0-7910-6943-1(5)); 2003. 144p. pap. 30.00 (978-0-7910-7526-5(5)); 2nd ed. 2005. 162p. (J). pap. 30.00 (978-0-7910-8572-1(4)) Facts On File, Inc. (Chelsea Hse.).

—Saddam Hussein. 2003. (gr. 5-8). lib. bdg. 18.75 (978-0-613-81041-8(4)) Tandem Library Bks.

Shields, Charles J. & Koestler-Grack, Rachel A. Saddam Hussein. 2nd ed. 2005. (Major World Leaders Ser.). (Illus.). 112p. (J). 30.00 (978-0-7910-8576-9(7) , Chelsea Hse.) Facts On File, Inc.

Stewart, Gail B. Saddam Hussein. 2003. (Heroes & Villains Ser.). (Illus.). 96p. (J). 29.95 (978-1-59018-350-2(9) , Lucent Bks.) Thomson Gale.

Wheeler, Jill C. Saddam Hussein. 2004. (War in Iraq Ser.). (Illus.). 48p. (J). (gr. 4-8). lib. bdg. 25.65 (978-1-59197-499-4(2)) ABDO Publishing Co.

HUTCHINSON, ANNE MARBURY, 1591-1643

Capstone Press, contrib. by. Anne Hutchinson. (Colonial America Biographies Ser.). 48p. (YA). pap. 7.95 (978-0-7368-4483-3(X)) Capstone Pr., Inc.

Clark, Beth. Anne Hutchinson. 1999. (Colonial Leaders Ser.). (Illus.). 80p. (J). (gr. 3 up). pap. 27.50 (978-0-7910-5685-1(6) , Chelsea Hse.) Facts On File, Inc.

—Anne Hutchinson: Religious Leader. 2000. (Colonial Leaders Ser.). (Illus.). 80p. (YA). (gr. 3 up). 27.50 (978-0-7910-5342-3(3) , Chelsea Hse.) Facts On File, Inc.

—Anne Hutchinson: Religious Leader. 2000. (gr. 3-6). lib. bdg. 17.60 (978-0-613-83456-8(9)) Tandem Library Bks.

Kiely Miller, Barbara. Anne Hutchinson. 2007. (J). pap. ***(978-0-8368-8324-4(1)*** , Weekly Reader Early Learning Library) Stevens, Gareth Inc.

Miller, Barbara Kiely. Anne Hutchinson. 2007. (Great Americans Ser.). 24p. (J). (gr. 2-4). lib. bdg. 19.93 ***(978-0-8368-8317-6(9)*** , Weekly Reader Early Learning Library) Stevens, Gareth Inc.

Raum, Elizabeth. Anne Hutchinson. 2004. (Illus.). 32p. (J). pap. 7.50 (978-1-4034-5966-4(5)); lib. bdg. (978-1-4034-5958-9(4)) Heinemann Library.

Stille, Darlene R. Anne Hutchinson: Puritan Protester. 2006. (Signature Lives Ser.). (Illus.). 112p. (J). (gr. 5-7). 30.60 (978-0-7565-1577-5(7)) Compass Point Bks.

Walsh, Kieran. Anne Hutchinson. 2005. (Discover the Life of a Colonial American Ser.). (Illus.). 24p. (gr. 2-5). 14.95 (978-1-59515-137-7(0)) Rourke Publishing, LLC.

HYDRAULIC ENGINEERING

see also Hydrostatics; Rivers; Water; Water-Supply Engineering; Wells

Mahaney, Ian F. Water Power. 2007. (Energy in Action Ser.). (Illus.). 24p. (J). (gr. 4-6). lib. bdg. 21.25 (978-1-4042-3481-9(0) , PowerKids Pr.) Rosen Publishing Group, Inc., The.

Matthews, Stuart. Hydraulics. 2001. (How Does It Work? Ser.). (Illus.). 24p. (J). (gr. 2-7). lib. bdg. 21.30 (978-1-58340-067-8(2)) Smart Apple Media.

HYDROELECTRIC POWER

see Water Power

HYDROLOGY

see Water

HYDROSTATICS

Bryant-Mole, Karen & Ansary, Mir Tamim. Floating & Sinking. 2002. (Illus.). 24p. (J). (gr. 1-3). pap. 6.50 (978-1-4034-0049-9(0) , 91493) Heinemann Library.

Cole, Joanna. The Magic School Bus Ups & Downs: A Book about Floating & Sinking. 2002. (Magic School Bus Ser.). (Illus.). (J). 11.45 (978-0-7587-9336-2(7)) Book Wholesalers, Inc.

Murray, Julie. Floating & Sinking. 2007. (J). 21.35 (978-1-59679-823-6(8) , Buddy Bks.) ABDO Publishing Co.

Nelson, Robin. Flotar y Hundirse (Float & Sink) 2007. (Mi Primer Paso al Mundo Real - Fuerzas y Movimiento (First Step Nonfiction - Forces & Motion) Ser.). (SPA.). 24p. (J). (gr. k-2). lib. bdg. 18.60 ***(978-0-8225-7808-6(5)*** , Ediciones Lerner) Lerner Publishing Group.

HYENAS

Holmes, Kevin J. Hyenas. 1998. (Animals Ser.). (Illus.). 24p. (J). (gr. 2-3). lib. bdg. 18.60 (978-0-7368-0064-8(6) , Bridgestone Bks.) Capstone Pr., Inc.

Hyenas. (Animals Ser.). 32p. (J). 6.95 (978-0-7368-8409-9(2)) Capstone Pr., Inc.

Hyenas. 2006. (J). pap. 7.95 (978-0-8225-3468-6(1) , First Avenue Editions) Lerner Publishing Group.

Markle, Sandra. Hyenas. 2005. (Animal Scavengers Ser.). (Illus.). 39p. (J). (ps-7). 25.26 (978-0-8225-3194-4(1) , Lerner Pubns.) Lerner Publishing Group.

Morgan, Sally. Hyenas. 2003. (Predators Ser.). (Illus.). 32p. (J). lib. bdg. 25.70 (978-0-7398-6601-6(X)) Raintree.

Prudom, Sharla. Jambo! Hyena. Prudom, Sharla, photos by. 2002. (Jambo! Ser.). (SWA & ENG.). (J). cd-rom 12.50 (978-1-931792-25-7(9)) E-Digital Bks., LLC.

Richardson, Adele D. Hyenas: Hunters & Scavengers. 2001. (Wild World of Animals Ser.). (Illus.). 24p. (J). (gr. 1-2). lib. bdg. 18.60 (978-0-7368-0963-4(5) , Bridgestone Bks.) Capstone Pr., Inc.

HYENAS—FICTION

Atwood, Debbie A. No More Diapers. Cherry, Richard, illus. 2000. 10p. (J). (ps-k). 6.95 (978-0-9701013-1-0(7)) Novel Approach Pubns., LLC.

Brandon, Taylor. The Hyena Who Wouldn't Laugh. Sandow, Paris, illus. 1999. (World's Greatest Children's Bks.). 48p. (J). (gr. k-5). 14.99 (978-1-889945-68-2(4)) Imperius.

Cannon, Janell. Pinduli. Cannon, Janell, illus. 2004. (Illus.). 48p. (J). 16.00 (978-0-15-204668-2(2)) Harcourt Children's Bks.

Lamb-Shapiro, Jessica. The Hyena Who Lost Her Laugh: A Story about Changing Your Negative Thinking. Gilgannon, Denise, illus. 2000. (Early Prevention Ser.). 53p. (J). pap. 11.50 (978-1-58815-005-9(4)) Childswork/Childsplay.

Laughing Hyena: Individual Title Six-Pack Pouch - Level J. (Lighthouse Ser.). 16p. (gr. 2 up). 28.00 (978-0-7578-0858-6(1)) Rigby Education.

Ringbom, Antonia & Wiklund, Alison. The Hiding Hyena (Chichewa) 2005. (J). (978-0-9753285-5-2(7)) H.B.P., Inc.

Schnurre, Wolfdietrich. La Princesa Viene a las Cuatro. Berner, Rotraut Susanne, illus. 2002. (Rosa y Manzana Ser.). (SPA.). 32p. (J). (gr. k-2). (978-84-89804-32-6(X) , LG30138) Loguez Ediciones ESP. *Dist:* Lectorum Pubns., Inc.

Tini Sisters Staff. How Hilda Hushed Her Hiccups. Mauterer, Erin Marie, illus. 2000. (Letter-Sound Listen & Retell Adventure Ser.). 32p. (J). (ps-2). 18.95 incl. audio compact disk (978-0-9678459-1-3(2)); 24.95 (978-0-9678459-0-6(4)) Atori Publishing, Inc.

Wiklund, Alison & Ringbom, Antonia. The Hiding Hyena. 2004. (Illus.). 48p. (J). (978-0-9753285-3-8(0)) H.B.P., Inc.

HYGIENE

see Health

HYGIENE—FICTION

Anderson, Peggy Perry. To the Tub. 2001. (Illus.). 32p. (J). (gr. k-ps). reprint ed. pap. 4.95 (978-0-618-13844-9(7) , Walter Lorraine) Houghton Mifflin Co. Trade & Reference Div.

—To the Tub. 2001. (gr. k-3). lib. bdg. 12.95 (978-0-613-35583-4(0)) Tandem Library Bks.

Arcure, Suzanne. Little Angels. 2002. 36p. pap. 9.95 (978-0-7414-0791-7(4)) Infinity Publishing.

Arnold, Tedd. No More Water in the Tub! Sequel to No Jumping on the Bed! Buehner, Mark, illus. 1998. (Picture Puffin Ser.). 32p. (J). (ps-3). pap. 6.99 (978-0-14-056430-3(6) , Puffin) Penguin Group (USA) Inc.

Bain, Michelle. Las aventuras de Juanito el Pulgarcito: Liborio el Microbio y el apreton de Manos. Lizana, Lorenzo, illus. 2007. Tr. of Jimmy Jam Germ & the Happy Handshake!. (SPA.). (J). 16.95 ***(978-0-9795832-1-6(7))*** Pixie Stuff LLC.

Balukoff, Constance. Mooky's Bad Hair Day. 2004. 21p. pap. 14.95 (978-1-4137-1480-7(3)) PublishAmerica, Inc.

Beck, Andrea. Elliot's Bath. Beck, Andrea, illus. 2004. (Elliot Moose Ser.). (Illus.). 32p. (J). (gr. k-3). (978-1-55337-070-3(8)) Kids Can Pr., Ltd.

—Elliot's Bath. 2004. (Elliot Moose Story Ser.). (Illus.). 32p. (J). (gr. k-3). (978-1-55074-802-4(5)) Kids Can Pr., Ltd.

Bevan, Jan Atchley. Corky the Bathtub Who Couldn't Swallow. Yovanovic, Christine, illus. 2001. (J). 14.95 (978-0-9653895-5-6(3)) Bookmark Publishing.

Brown, Margaret Wise. The Dirty Little Boy. Salerno, Steven, illus. 2005. 32p. (J). (ps-1). pap. 5.95 (978-0-7614-5180-8(3)) Cavendish, Marshall Corp.

—The Dirty Little Boy. Salerno, Steven, illus. 2001. 40p. (J). (ps-3). 16.95 (978-1-890817-52-7(X)) Winslow Pr.

Burge, Kenneth Dean. Lena's Star. Burge, Deborah Lynn, illus. l.t. ed. 2001. 36p. (J). per. 10.00 (978-0-9715953-0-9(5) , Verner Publishing) Verner Advertising, LLC.

Burningham, John. Time to Get Out of the Bath, Shirley. 2004. (Red Fox Picture Book Ser.). (Illus.). 24p. (J). pap. 8.99 (978-0-09-920051-2(1) , Red Fox) Random Hse. Children's Bks. GBR. *Dist:* Trafalgar Square Publishing.

Capucilli, Alyssa Satin. Bathtime for Biscuit. 1999. (My First I Can Read Bks.). (J). (ps-k). 10.79 (978-0-606-17116-8(9)) Tandem Library Bks.

Church, Caroline Jane. One Smart Goose. 2005. (Illus.). 32p. (J). 16.95 (978-0-439-68765-2(9) , Orchard Bks.) Scholastic, Inc.

Cocca-Leffler, Maryann. Dog Wash Day: All Aboard Picture Reader. 2004. (All Aboard Reading Ser.). (Illus.). 32p. (J). (ps-1). pap. 3.99 (978-0-448-43370-7(2) , Grosset & Dunlap) Penguin Group (USA) Inc.

Cook, Julia. I'm a Booger... Treat Me with Respect! 2007. (J). pap. 9.95 ***(978-1-934073-11-7(3))*** CTC Publishing.

Cousins, Lucy. Maisy Cleans Up. 2002. (Maisy Ser.). (Illus.). 24p. (J). (ps-k). pap. 3.99 (978-0-7636-1712-7(1)) Candlewick Pr.

—Maisy Cleans Up. 2002. (ps-2). lib. bdg. 11.00 (978-0-613-51315-9(0)) Tandem Library Bks.

—Maisy Takes a Bath. Cousins, Lucy, illus. 2000. (Maisy Bks.). (Illus.). 24p. (J). (gr. k-k). pap. 3.99 (978-0-7636-1084-5(4)) Candlewick Pr.

—Maisy Takes a Bath. 2000. (Maisy Bks.). (Illus.). (J). (ps). 9.99 (978-0-7636-0182-9(9)) Candlewick Pr.

—Maisy Takes a Bath. 2000. (ps-2). lib. bdg. 11.00 (978-0-613-27962-8(X)) Tandem Library Bks.

Cowley, Joy. Mrs. Wishy-Washy's Scrubbing Machine. Fuller, Elizabeth, illus. 2005. 18p. (J). (ps-1). bds. 5.99 (978-0-399-24203-8(1) , Philomel) Penguin Group (USA) Inc.

—Mrs. Wishy-Washy's Splishy Sploshy Day. Fuller, Elizabeth, illus. 2005. 16p. (J). (ps-1). pap. 5.99 (978-0-399-24202-1(3) , Philomel) Penguin Group (USA) Inc.

Cummings, Pat. Clean Your Room, Harvey Moon! Cummings, Pat, illus. 2002. (Illus.). (J). 14.47 (978-0-7587-2248-5(6)) Book Wholesalers, Inc.

—Clean Your Room, Harvey Moon! 1998. (J). pap. 4.95 (978-0-87628-335-6(0)) Ctr. for Applied Research in Education, The.

Dague, Paige A. & Dague, James. ScribbleMonster Takes a Bath. 2001. (Illus.). 32p. (J). (ps). pap. 5.50 (978-0-9706406-2-8(5)) ScribbleBooks Co., The.

DeFelice, Cynthia C. Casey in the Bath. Demarest, Chris L., illus. 1998. 32p. (J). (ps-k). pap. 6.95 (978-0-374-41049-0(6) , Sunburst) Farrar, Straus & Giroux.

Dorling Kindersley Publishing Staff. Baby's Bathtime. 1999. (Bath Bks.). (Illus.). 10p. (J). (ps-k). 6.99 (978-0-7894-4323-6(6)) Dorling Kindersley Publishing, Inc.

Edwards, Frank B. Mortimer Mooner Stopped Taking a Bath. 2000. (978-0-606-22925-8(6)) Tandem Library Bks.

Fanning, Tena. Booger Boogie. 2007. 32p. (ps-3). 14.95 ***(978-1-933721-13-2(8))*** Playdate Kids Publishing.

Foster, Bill. The Boy Who Wouldn't Comb His Hair. Kilgore, Jeannette Vrlin, illus. 2002. 32p. (J). (gr. k-6). 14.95 (978-1-931650-15-1(2)) Coastal Publishing Carolina, Inc.

Gaspard, Helen. Doctor Dan the Bandage Man. 2004. (Illus.). 24p. (J). (gr. k-k). 2.99 (978-0-375-82880-5(X) , Golden Bks.) Random Hse. Children's Bks.

Goodman, Joan Elizabeth. Bernard's Bath. Catalano, Dominic, illus. 2003. 32p. (J). (ps up). reprint ed. pap. 8.95 (978-1-56397-854-8(7)) Boyds Mills Pr.

—Bernard's Bath. 2000. (Illus.). (J). (978-0-606-18011-5(7)) Tandem Library Bks.

Hargreaves, Roger. Mr. Messy. 1998. (Mr. Men & Little Miss Ser.). (Illus.). 32p. (J). (gr. k up). pap. 3.99 (978-0-8431-7421-2(8) , Price Stern Sloan) Penguin Group (USA) Inc.

Harman, Chuck. Clean up That Mess! 2000. (Adventures of Artie the Airplane & His Friends Ser.). (Illus.). 32p. (J). (ps-6). pap. 6.95 (978-1-891736-11-7(6)) Studio Five/Fourteen.

Heller, Andrew. A Mouthful of Teeth. 2002. (Illus.). 16p. (J). 7.99 (978-0-9722038-4-5(2)) Mr Do It All, Inc.

—No Bones about It. Rene, Perez, illus. l.t. ed. 2003. 12p. (J). 7.99 (978-0-9722038-5-2(0)) Mr Do It All, Inc.

I'm a Booger... Treat Me with Respect! 2007. (J). 15.95 ***(978-1-934073-12-4(1))*** CTC Publishing.

Jensen, Patricia. The Mess. 2004. (My First Reader Ser.). (Illus.). 32p. (J). (gr. k-1). pap. 3.95 (978-0-516-24634-5(8) , Children's Pr.) Scholastic Library Publishing.

Kreloff, Elliot, illus. I'm Going to Read (Level 2): Tic & Tac Clean Up. 2007. (I'm Going to Read Ser.). 32p. (J). pap. 3.95 (978-1-4027-4243-9(6)) Sterling Publishing Co., Inc.

Llewellyn, Claire. A Banarse! Aprender Sobre Higiene Personal.Tr. of Who Wash! Learning about Personal Hygiene. (SPA.). (J). (gr. k-2). pap. 6.36 (978-950-24-0947-4(7)) Albatros ARG. *Dist:* Lectorum Pubns., Inc.

Lynne, Rustyna. Bella's Birthday Manicure. Lynne, Rustyna, illus. l.t. ed. 2002. (Illus.). 14p. (J). (gr. k-2). spiral bd. 10.95 (978-0-9719657-6-8(5)) Red Carpet Publishing.

—Bella's Birthday Manicure: Special Needs Version. Lynne, Rustyna, illus. l.t. ed. 2002. (Illus.). 9p. (YA). (gr. 3-8). spiral bd. 10.95 (978-0-9719657-7-5(3)) Red Carpet Publishing.

—Derrick & Sierra Take Baths. Lawrence, Mary, illus. l.t. ed. 2002. 15p. (J). (gr. k-2). spiral bd. 11.95 (978-0-9719657-0-6(6)) Red Carpet Publishing.

—Derrick & Sierra Take Baths: Special Needs Version. Lawrence, Mary, illus. l.t. ed. 2002. 15p. (YA). (gr. 3-8). spiral bd. 11.95 (978-0-9719657-1-3(4)) Red Carpet Publishing.

—Giovanni's Pedicure. Lynne, Rustyna, illus. l.t. ed. 2002. (Illus.). 14p. (J). (gr. k-2). spiral bd. 10.95 (978-0-9719657-8-2(1)) Red Carpet Publishing.

—Giovanni's Pedicure: Special Needs Version. Lynne, Rustyna, illus. l.t. ed. 2002. (Illus.). 12p. (YA). (gr. 3-8). spiral bd. 10.95 (978-0-9719657-9-9(X)) Red Carpet Publishing.

—Janel's Shampoo: Special Needs Version. Lynne, Rustyna, illus. 2002. (Illus.). 17p. (J). spiral bd. 12.95 (978-0-9722829-1-8(2)) Red Carpet Publishing.

MacDonald, Betty Bard. The Won't-Pick-up-Toys Cure. Whatley, Bruce, illus. 1998. (Mrs. Piggle-Wiggle Adventure Ser.). (J). lib. bdg. (978-0-06-027629-4(0)) HarperCollins Pubs.

Markels, Bobby. How to Be a Human Bean. Leek, Kenny, illus. Date not set. 24p. (J). (gr. 3 up). reprint ed. pap. 4.50 (978-1-880991-01-5(2)) Stone Publishing Co.

McAffee, Diane. Kaylee, Clean Your Room. Francis, Guy, illus. 1999. 24p. (J). (978-1-57008-688-5(5)) Scribbulations LLC.

McKissack, Patricia C. & McKissack, Fredrick. Messy Bessey. Regan, Dana, illus. rev. ed. 1999. (Rookie Readers Ser.). 32p. (J). (gr. 1-2). 19.50 (978-0-516-21650-8(3) , Children's Pr.) Scholastic Library Publishing.

—Messy Bessey, Vol. 2. 2006. 96p. (J). (gr. 1-2). 8.95 (978-0-516-25301-5(8) , Children's Pr.) Scholastic Library Publishing.

McKissack, Patricia C. & McKissack, Fredrick L. Messy Bessey. Regan, Dana, illus. rev. ed. 2000. (Rookie Reader Espanol Ser.). 32p. (J). (gr. k-2). pap. 4.95 (978-0-516-27003-6(6) , Children's Pr.) Scholastic Library Publishing.

McOmber, Rachel B., ed. McOmber Phonics Storybooks: The Haircut. rev. ed. (Illus.). (J). (978-0-944991-53-4(X)) Swift Learning Resources.

—McOmber Phonics Storybooks: The Tub. rev. ed. (Illus.). (J). (978-0-944991-24-4(6)) Swift Learning Resources.

Meister, Cari. Tiny's Bath. Davis, Rich, illus. 1999. (Viking Easy-to-Read Ser.). 32p. (J). (ps-2). 13.89 (978-0-670-87962-5(2) , Viking Juvenile); pap. 3.99 (978-0-14-130267-6(4) , Puffin) Penguin Group (USA) Inc.

—Tiny's Bath. Davis, Rich, illus. 1999. (J). (ps-ps). lib. bdg. 11.80 (978-0-613-15238-9(7)) Tandem Library Bks.

Noonan, Julia. Bath Day. Noonan, Julia, illus. 2000. (Puppy & Me Ser.). (Illus.). 20p. (J). (ps-1). pap. 6.99 (978-0-439-11492-9(6) , Cartwheel Bks.) Scholastic, Inc.

Overland, Sarah. Pamela la Impaciente y los Microbios. Conway, Aaron, illus. 2007. (SPA.). 32p. (J). pap. 7.95 ***(978-1-930650-39-8(6))*** Trellis Publishing, Inc.

Random House Disney Staff & Winston, Helena. Castle Cleanup! BKN International Staff, illus. 2002. 32p. (J). (ps-k). pap. 3.99 (978-0-7364-1290-2(5) , Golden/Disney) Random Hse. Children's Bks.

Rudisill, J. J., et al, illus. No More Chores. 1999. (Wimzie's House Bks.). 24p. (J). pap. 3.99 (978-0-88724-542-8(0) , CD-4848) Carson-Dellosa Publishing Co., Inc.

Sarda, Rosa. I Like Getting Dirty: Me Gusta Ensuciarme. 2002. (gr. k-3). lib. bdg. 12.95 (978-0-613-50535-2(2)) Tandem Library Bks.

Speakes, Leslie. The Hygiene Mystery. 2004. 31p. pap. 17.95 (978-1-4137-1860-7(4)) PublishAmerica, Inc.

Staunton, Ted. The Puddleman. Clark, Brenda, illus. 2004. 32p. (J). (ps-4). pap. 6.95 (978-0-88995-190-7(X)) Red Deer Pr. CAN. *Dist:* Fitzhenry & Whiteside, Ltd.

Suen, Anastasia. Toddler Two: Dos Anos. Cheon, Winnie, illus. 2002. (ENG & SPA.). (J). bds. 5.95 (978-1-58430-054-0(X)) Lee & Low Bks., Inc.

Teague, Mark. El Chiquero. 2002. (SPA., Illus.). 32p. (J). (gr. k-2). pap. 5.99 (978-0-439-27000-7(6) , SO30911, Scholastic en Espanol) Scholastic, Inc.

—Pigsty. Teague, Mark, illus. 2002. (Illus.). (J). 24.00 (978-0-7587-3417-4(4)) Book Wholesalers, Inc.

—Pigsty. 2004. (Scholastic Bookshelf Ser.). 32p. (J). pap. 6.99 (978-0-439-59843-9(5) , Scholastic Paperbacks) Scholastic, Inc.

Teckentrup, Britta. Big Smelly Bear. 2007. (Illus.). 32p. (J). (ps-1). 12.95 (978-1-905417-37-7(3)) Boxer Bks., Ltd. GBR. *Dist:* Sterling Publishing Co., Inc.

Twinn, Michael. No Smoking. 2000. (Illus.). 32p. (J). 26.99 (978-0-85953-848-6(5)) Child's Play-International.

Vogel, Elizabeth. Al Agua Patos. 2004. (Limpieza y Salud Todo el Dia Ser.). (SPA & ENG., Illus.). 24p. (J). lib. bdg. 16.00 (978-0-8239-6617-2(8)); (gr. 1-2). lib. bdg. 16.00 (978-0-8239-6616-5(X)) Rosen Publishing Group, Inc., The. (Buenas Letra).

Watt, F. Al Agua Patos! 2004. (Mundo del Pequenin Ser.). (SPA., Illus.). 16p. (J). (ps up). 4.95 (978-0-7460-3867-3(4)) EDC Publishing.

Watt, Fiona. Baby's Bathtime Kid Kit. 1998. (Baby's World Ser.). (Illus.). 16p. (J). (ps). 14.95 (978-1-58086-220-2(9)) EDC Publishing.

Watt, Fiona & Wells, Rachel, eds. Potty Time. 2004. (Baby's World Ser.). (Illus.). 16p. (J). (ps up). pap. 4.95 (978-0-7460-3839-0(9)) EDC Publishing.

Weeks, Sarah. Splish, Splash! Wolff, Ashley, illus. 2000. (My First I Can Read Bks.). 32p. (J). (ps up). pap. 3.99 (978-0-06-444282-4(9) , Harper Trophy) HarperCollins Pubs.

—Splish, Splash! 2000. (gr. k-3). lib. bdg. 11.80 (978-0-613-27034-2(7)) Tandem Library Bks.

Wells, Rosemary. Max Cleans Up. Wells, Rosemary, illus. 2002. (Max the Bunny Ser.). (Illus.). 13.19 (978-1-4046-0741-5(2)) Book Wholesalers, Inc.

—Max Cleans Up. (Max & Ruby Ser.). (Illus.). 32p. (J). 2002. pap. 5.99 (978-0-14-230133-3(7) , Puffin); 2000. 15.99 (978-0-670-89218-1(1) , Viking Juvenile) Penguin Group (USA) Inc.

HYGIENE, MENTAL

see Mental Health

HYGIENE, PUBLIC

see Public Health

HYGIENE, SOCIAL

see Public Health; Sexually Transmitted Diseases

HYMENOPTERA

see Ants; Bees; Wasps

HYMNOLOGY

see Hymns

HYMNS

see also Carols; Church Music

Alexander, Cecil. All Things Bright & Beautiful. Vojtech, Anna, illus. 2004. 24p. (J). (ps-3). 15.95 (978-0-7358-1892-7(4)) North-South Bks., Inc.

Alexander, Cecil Frances. All Things Bright & Beautiful. Whatley, Bruce, illus. 2004. 32p. (J). pap. 6.99 (978-0-06-008339-7(5) , Harper Trophy) HarperCollins Pubs.

—All Things Bright & Beautiful. Heyer, Carol, illus. 2002. 26p. (ps-3). 9.95 (978-1-59093-019-9(3)) Warehousing & Fulfillment Specialists, LLC (WFS, LLC).

—All Things Bright & Beautiful. McDaniels, Preston, illus. 2000. (Hymns for Children Ser.). 32p. (J). (ps-2). 17.95 (978-0-8192-1834-6(0) , 6257) Morehouse Publishing.

—All Things Bright & Beautiful. McDaniels, Preston, illus. 2nd ed. 2001. (Hymns for Children Ser.). 32p. (ps-2). pap. 4.95 (978-0-8192-1884-1(7)) Morehouse Publishing.

—All Things Bright & Beautiful. Vojtech, Anna, illus. ed. 2006. 24p. (J). (ps-2). pap. 6.95 (978-0-7358-2045-6(7)) North-South Bks., Inc.

Bartlett, E. M., contrib. by. Victory in Jesus. 7.50 (978-0-8054-5926-5(X)) B&H Publishing Grp.

Bergerac. My First Book of Hymns & Spirituals: 26 Favorite Songs in Easy Piano Arrangements. 1999. (Illus.). 48p. pap. 4.95 (978-0-486-40849-1(3)) Dover Pubns., Inc.

Bond, Douglas. Mr. Pipes & the British Hymn Makers. 1999. (Illus.). 256p. (J). (gr. 6-9). pap. 9.95 (978-1-930092-12-9(1) , CLP29760) Christian Liberty Pr.

Brokering, Herbert F. Earth & All Stars. 2004. 144p. 14.95 (978-0-8006-5929-5(5) , Augsburg Bks.) Augsburg Fortress, Pubs.

Bryan, Ashley. Let It Shine: Three Favorite Spirituals. Bryan, Ashley, illus. 2007. (Illus.). 48p. (J). (ps-3). 16.99 (978-0-689-84732-5(7) , Atheneum) Simon & Schuster Children's Publishing.

Compact Disc Staff. Hymns & Bible Songs. 1998. (Growing Minds with Music Ser.). (J). audio compact disk 12.99 (978-1-57583-065-0(5)) Twin Sisters Productions, LLC.

Cross, Elsa. El Himno de las Ranas. Zacchi, Lucia, illus. 2005. (SPA.). (J). (gr. k-2). pap. 10.95 (978-968-494-052-9(1) , CI2003) Centro de Informacion y Desarrollo de la Comunicacion y la Literatura MEX. *Dist:* Lectorum Pubns., Inc., Iaconi, Mariuccia Bk. Imports.

Cunningham, Edie. One Day. McInturff, Linda & Brownlie, Ian, illus. 2004. 28p. (J). pap. (978-1-932381-09-2(0) , 6340) Bible Visuals International, Inc.

Davis, Rebecca Henry. Fanny Crosby: Queen of Gospel Songs. 2003. (Illus.). 107p. (J). 6.49 (978-1-57924-970-0(1)) Jones, Bob Univ. Pr.

Elkins, Stephen. The Word & Song Songbook Vol. 2: The New Testament. 2004. (Illus.). 64p. (J). 12.99 (978-0-8054-1695-4(1)) B&H Publishing Grp.

Feldstein, Sandy & Clark, Larry. Festival Chorale & March. 2004. (YA). pap. 40.00 (978-1-932895-02-5(7)) Playin-Time Productions, Inc.

Fitchwell, Jennifer, illus. Praise God. 2002. (Play-A-Song Ser.). 11p. (J). 7.99 (978-0-7853-6375-0(0)) Publications International, Ltd.

Flanagan, Katie, illus. Songs of Praise. 2002. (J). 7.99 (978-0-7853-6376-7(9)) Publications International, Ltd.

Granfield, Linda. Amazing Grace: The Story of the Hymn. braille ed. 2004. (Illus.). (J). (gr. 2-4). spiral bd. (978-0-616-01661-9(1)) Canadian National Institute for the Blind/Institut National Canadien pour les Aveugles.

Horman, John D., et al. Something Old, Something New Vol. 2: Hymns to Explore, Things to Do. Keithahn, Mary Nelson, ed. 2004. 96p. (gr. 2-5). pap. 17.00 (978-0-687-09101-0(2)) Abingdon Pr.

Jesus Wants Me for a Sunbeam: A Sing-along Book of Songs about the Savior. 2006. 14p. (J). bds. 15.95 (978-1-59038-634-7(5) , Shadow Mountain) Deseret Bk. Co.

Living Stream Ministry Staff. Hymns: #1-1348. 1311p. (J). (gr. 6). per. 22.50 (978-0-7363-1122-9(X) , 02-003-001); per. 20.00 (978-0-7363-1123-6(8) , 02 004-001) Living Stream Ministry.

—Hymns: 100 Selected. 150p. (J). (gr. 6). per. 6.25 (978-0-87083-234-5(4) , 02-007-001) Living Stream Ministry.

—Hymns #1-1348. 1311p. (J). (gr. 6). per. 25.00 (978-0-7363-1121-2(1) , 02-017-001) Living Stream Ministry.

MacGilton, Alice K. A Study in Latin Hymns. 2001. 116p. (YA). reprint ed. 88.00 (978-0-7222-6138-5(1)) Library Reprints, Inc.

Mandoyan, Antranik, ed. Daily Devotionals. 2000. (Illus.). 430p. (J). (gr. 5-7). pap. (978-1-883131-07-4(3)) Armenian Missionary Assn. of America.

Marshall, Mark. God Knows What It's Like to Be a Teenager: Teen Life & the Psalms. 2002. (gr. 7-12). lib. bdg. 24.55 (978-0-613-77808-4(1)) Tandem Library Bks.

McDaniels, Preston, illus. Now the Day Is Over. 2001. (Hymns for Children Ser.). 32p. (J). (ps-2). 17.95 (978-0-8192-1868-1(5)) Morehouse Publishing.

McInturff, Linda, illus. Wounded for Me. 2000. 12p. (J). pap. (978-1-932381-19-1(8)) Bible Visuals International, Inc.

McInturff, Linda, illus. O Little Town of Bethlehem. 2002. 16p. (J). pap. (978-1-932381-98-6(8)) Bible Visuals International, Inc.

McInturff, Linda & Tweed, Sean, illus. The Light of the World Is Jesus. 2004. 16p. (J). pap. (978-1-932381-08-5(2)) Bible Visuals International, Inc.

McKay, Graham. A Hymn a Day. 2003. 99p. pap. (978-0-9717444-1-7(6)) O'More Publishing.

Moss, Donna. How I Praise You! 150 Little Psalms in Song. Moss, Rebecca, illus. 1998. 240p. (J). (ps-8). pap. (978-0-9663809-2-7(4)) Apex Publishing Services.

Pinkney, Gloria Jean. Music from Our Lord's Holy Heaven. Pinkney, Jerry et al, illus. 2005. 48p. (J). (ps up). lib. bdg. 18.89 incl. audio compact disk (978-0-06-000769-0(9)) HarperCollins Pubs.

Psalms: Experiencing God. 1999. (Club 56 Ser.). 28p. (J). (gr. 5-6). pap., stu. ed., wbk. ed. 2.79 (978-1-57405-364-7(7)) CharismaLife Pubs.

Raschka, Chris. Simple Gifts. rev. ed. 2001. (Illus.). 32p. (J). (ps-2). pap. 8.95 (978-0-8050-6817-7(1) , Holt, Henry & Co. Bks. For Young Readers) Holt, Henry & Co.

—Simple Gifts. Raschka, Chris, illus. 2003. (Illus.). pap. 41.95 incl. audio (978-0-87499-642-5(2)); pap. 43.95 incl. audio compact disk (978-1-59112-604-1(5)) Live Oak Media.

—Simple Gifts. (Live Oak Readalong Ser.). (Illus.). (J). 2003. pap. 16.95 incl. audio (978-0-87499-640-1(6)); 2003. pap. 18.95 incl. audio compact disk (978-1-59112-414-6(X)); 2000. 24.95 incl. audio (978-0-87499-641-8(4)) Live Oak Media.

—Simple Gifts: A Shaker Hymn. 2001. (gr. k-3). lib. bdg. 16.40 (978-0-613-75396-8(8)) Tandem Library Bks.

Roberts, Philip L. Hymns for Handbells, Vol. 1. 2002. 65p. per. 12.00 (978-1-57999-165-4(3) , G-5770) GIA Pubns., Inc.

—Hymns for Handbells, Vol. 2. 2002. 80p. per. 14.00 (978-1-57999-198-2(X) , G-5899) GIA Pubns., Inc.

Sas, Alfredo C., ed. Reformation Hymnal. 2003. Tr. of No Temals, Manada Pequeña. (ENG.). 14.95 (978-0-9745295-0-9(8)) Reformation Herald Publishing Assn.

Songs from God's Garden. 2002. (Illus.). (J). (978-0-7853-6415-3(3)) Publications International, Ltd.

Spring Psalm. 7.50 (978-0-8054-5939-5(1)) B&H Publishing Grp.

Summer Psalm. 7.50 (978-0-8054-5922-7(7)) B&H Publishing Grp.

Tada, Joni Eareckson & Wolgemuth, Bobbie. Hymns for a Kid's Heart, 2 vols. Martinez, Sergio, illus. 2005. (Great Hymns of Our Faith Ser.). 96p. (J). 21.99 (978-1-58134-505-6(4)); Vol. 2. 21.99 incl. audio compact disk (978-1-58134-582-7(8)) Crossway Bks. (Crossway Bibles).

—Passion Hymns for a Kid's Heart. Martinez, Sergio, illus. 2005. 96p. 21.99 (978-1-58134-665-7(4) , Crossway Bibles) Crossway Bks.

Warnes, Tim, illus. Jesus Loves Me! 2006. 32p. (J). 12.95 (978-1-4169-0065-8(9)) Simon & Schuster Children's Publishing.

—Jesus Loves Me. 2008. 26p. (J). bds. 7.99 (***978-1-4169-5367-8(1)*** , Little Simon Inspirations) Simon & Schuster Children's Publishing.

Warnes, Tim, illus. Rise & Shine! 2007. 32p. (J). 12.99 (978-1-4169-1377-1(7) , Simon & Schuster Children's Publishing) Simon & Schuster Children's Publishing.

Watts, I. Divine Songs. 2006. 52p. pap. (978-1-84702-997-3(3)) Echo Library.

Wezeman, Phylllis Vos & Liechty, Anna L. Hymn Stories for Children: The Apostles' Creed. 2004. (Illus.). 64p. (J). 10.95 (978-0-9752605-8-6(8)) LOGOS System Assocs.

Wilger, Jennifer Root. Wiggle Worms Learn the Psalms. 2003. (Godprints Bible Funstuff Ser.). 112p. pap., pap. 16.99 (978-0-7814-3960-2(4) , 0781439604) Cook, David C. Publishing Co.

I

ICE

see also Glaciers; Icebergs

Bundey, Nikki. Ice & People. 2005. (Science of Weather Ser.). (Illus.). 32p. (gr. 4-6). lib. bdg. 21.27 (978-1-57505-497-1(3)) Lerner Publishing Group.

Frost, Helen. Ice. Saunders-Smith, Gail, ed. 2004. (Weather Ser.). (Illus.). 24p. (J). (gr. k-1). lib. bdg. 15.93 (978-0-7368-2094-3(9) , Pebble Bks.) Capstone Pr., Inc.

—Water As a Solid. 1999. pap. 13.25 (978-0-516-21917-2(0) , Children's Pr.) Scholastic Library Publishing.

Hopwood, James. Cool Dry Ice Devices: Fun Science Projects with Dry Ice. 2007. (Cool Science Ser.). (Illus.). 32p. (J). (gr. k-6). lib. bdg. 24.21 (***978-1-59928-907-6(5)*** , Checkerboard Library) ABDO Publishing Co.

Lilly, Melinda. Water & Ice. (Read & Do Science Ser.). (Illus.). (J). 20.64 (978-1-58952-639-6(2)) Rourke Publishing, LLC.

—Water & Ice. Thompson, Scott M., photos by. 2006. (Rourke Discovery Library). (Illus.). 24p. (gr. 1-4). 14.95 (978-1-59515-406-4(X) , 1244277) Rourke Publishing, LLC.

Merk, A. Rain, Snow & Ice. 2003. (Weather Report Discovery Library). (Illus.). 24p. (gr. 1-4). 14.95 (978-1-58952-571-9(X)) Rourke Publishing, LLC.

Steele, Philip. Snow & Ice. 1998. (Living with the Weather Ser.). (Illus.). 48p. (J). (gr. 4-7). lib. bdg. 18.98 (978-0-8172-5052-2(2)) Raintree.

Water, Ice, & Steam. (Rosen Real Readers Big Bookstm Ser.). 12p. (J). (gr. 1-2). 31.95 (978-1-4042-6215-7(6)) Rosen Publishing Group, Inc., The.

ICE AGE

see Glacial Epoch

ICE CREAM, ICES, ETC.

Boekhoff, P. M. Ben & Jerry. 2004. (Inventors & Creators Ser.). (Illus.). 48p. (J). (gr. 4-7). 26.20 (978-0-7377-2611-4(3) , Greenhaven Pr., Inc.) Thomson Gale.

Boniface, William. What Do You Want on Your Sundae? Palen, Debbie, illus. 2001. 12p. (J). (ps-3). bds. 9.99 (978-0-8431-7638-4(5) , Price Stern Sloan) Penguin Group (USA) Inc.

Cooper, Elisha. Ice Cream. Cooper, Elisha, illus. 2002. (Illus.). 40p. (J). (gr. k up). 16.99 (978-0-06-001423-0(7)) HarperCollins Pubs.

—Ice Cream. 2002. (Illus.). 40p. (J). (ps up). 15.89 (978-0-06-001424-7(5)) HarperCollins Pubs.

Fleisher, Paul. Ice Cream Treats: The Inside Scoop. Saunders, David O., photos by. 2001. (Photo Bks.). (Illus.). 48p. (J). (gr. 2-5). lib. bdg. 23.93 (978-1-57505-268-7(7) , Carolrhoda Bks.) Lerner Publishing Group.

Gibbons, Gail. Ice Cream: The Full Scoop. 2006. (Illus.). 32p. (J). (ps-3). 16.95 (978-0-8234-2000-1(0)) Holiday Hse., Inc.

Greenstein, Elaine. Ice Cream Cones for Sale! 2003. (Illus.). (J). (978-0-439-32729-9(6)) Scholastic, Inc.

Greenstein, Elaine, et al. Ice Cream Cones for Sale! 2003. (Illus.). 32p. (J). pap. 15.95 (978-0-439-32728-2(8) , Levine, Arthur A. Bks.) Scholastic, Inc.

Ice Cream: First Wave Satellite Individual Title Six-Packs. (Sails Literacy Ser.). 16p. (gr. k up). 27.00 (978-0-7578-6866-5(5)) Rigby Education.

Keller, Kristin Thoennes. Milk to Ice Cream. 2004. (First Facts Ser.). (Illus.). 24p. (J). lib. bdg. 21.26 (978-0-7368-2635-8(1)) Capstone Pr., Inc.

Landau, Elaine. Ice Cream: The Creamy Cold Treat. 2001. (Tasty Treats Ser.). (Illus.). 24p. (J). (gr. 1-4). lib. bdg. 23.93 (978-1-57103-338-3(6)) Rourke Publishing, LLC.

Lee, Frances. Ice Cream. 1999. (ps-2). lib. bdg. 11.20 (978-0-613-30506-8(X)) Tandem Library Bks.

Marks, Ed. Ice Cream Collectibles. 2003. (Schiffer Book for Collectors Ser.). (Illus.). 160p. (gr. 10-13). pap. 29.95 (978-0-7643-1856-6(X)) Schiffer Publishing, Ltd.

Murray, Julie. Milk to Ice Cream. 2007. (Beginning to End Ser.). (Illus.). 24p. (J). (gr. k-3). lib. bdg. 21.35 (978-1-59679-838-0(6) , Buddy Bks.) ABDO Publishing Co.

Older, Jules. Ice Cream. Severance, Lyn, illus. 2002. 31p. (J). (gr. 2-5). 16.95 (978-0-88106-111-6(5)) Charlesbridge Publishing, Inc.

—Ice Cream. 2002. (gr. 3-6). lib. bdg. 15.25 (978-0-613-56432-8(4)) Tandem Library Bks.

Parker, Marjorie Blain. Ice Cream Everywhere! Roth, Stephanie, illus. 2002. (Rhyme Time Readers Ser.). (J). 1.95 (978-0-439-33397-9(0)) Scholastic, Inc.

Pickering, Robin. I Like Ice Cream. 2000. (Welcome Bks.). (Illus.). 24p. (J). (ps-2). pap. 4.95 (978-0-516-23010-8(7)); 17.00 (978-0-516-23085-6(9)) Scholastic Library Publishing. (Children's Pr.).

—I Like Ice Cream. 2000. (gr. k-3). lib. bdg. 12.95 (978-0-613-52087-4(4)) Tandem Library Bks.

Rau, Dana Meachen. Ice Cream. 2008. (J). (***978-0-7614-2893-0(3)***) Cavendish, Marshall Bks., Ltd.

Richards, Kitty. Ice Cream Fun Day. Goldberg, Barry, illus. 1999. (Rugrats Ser.). 16p. (J). (ps-2). 3.99 (978-0-689-82388-6(6) , 076714003996, Simon Spotlight/Nickelodeon) Simon & Schuster Children's Publishing.

Shofner, Shawndra. How it Happens: At the Ice Cream Factory. 2008. (How It Happens Ser.). (J). lib. bdg. 19.95 net. (***978-1-934545-06-5(6)***) Oliver Pr., Inc.

Snyder, Inez. Milk to Ice Cream. 2003. (How Things Are Made Ser.). (Illus.). 24p. (J). 18.00 (978-0-516-24268-2(7) , Children's Pr.); pap. 4.95 (978-0-516-24360-3(8) , Watts, Franklin) Scholastic Library Publishing.

—Milk to Ice Cream. 2003. (gr. k-3). lib. bdg. 12.95 (978-0-613-59684-8(6)) Tandem Library Bks.

Taus-Bolstad, Stacy. From Milk to Ice Cream. (From Start to Finish Ser.). (J). 2003. (Illus.). 24p. 18.60 (978-0-8225-0714-7(5) , Lerner Pubns.); 2002. pap. 4.95 (978-0-8225-0668-3(8)) Lerner Publishing Group.

Wardlaw, Lee. We All Scream for Ice Cream! The Scoop on America's Favorite Dessert. Forrest, Sandra, illus. 2000. 224p. (J). (gr. 3-7). pap. 4.95 (978-0-380-80250-0(3) , Harper Trophy) HarperCollins Pubs.

ICE HOCKEY

see Hockey

ICE SKATING

see Skating

ICE SPORTS

see Winter Sports

ICEBERGS

Fowler, Allan. Icebergs, Ice Caps, & Glaciers. 1998. (Rookie Read-About Science Ser.). (Illus.). 32p. (J). (gr. 1-2). pap. 4.95 (978-0-516-26257-4(2) , Children's Pr.) Scholastic Library Publishing.

Princess, Takamado Hih & Takamado, Hisako de. LulieThe Iceburg: Her Imperial Highness Princess. Aska, Warabe, illus. 1998. 44p. (ps-3). 17.00 (978-1-56836-272-4(2)) Kodansha America, Inc.

Simon, Seymour. Icebergs & Glaciers. 1999. (Illus.). 32p. (J). (ps-3). pap. 6.99 (978-0-688-16705-9(5) , Harper Trophy) HarperCollins Pubs.

—Icebergs & Glaciers. 1999. (J). 13.79 (978-0-606-16760-4(9)); lib. bdg. 15.25 (978-0-613-18255-3(3)) Tandem Library Bks.

ICEBOXES

see Refrigeration and Refrigerating Machinery

ICELAND

Deady, Kathleen W. Iceland. (True Book(R): Geography Ser.). (J). 2005. (Illus.). 48p. (gr. 3-5). pap. 6.95 (978-0-516-25832-4(X)); 2004. 25.00 (978-0-516-22811-2(0)) Scholastic Library Publishing. (Children's Pr.).

Harcourt School Publishers Staff. Fire & Ice Advanced Level. 3rd ed. 2002. (Trophies Reading Program Ser.). (Illus.). pap. 5.10 (978-0-15-323288-6(9)) Harcourt Schl. Pubs.

Harper, Judith. Unique Places. 2005. (Real Deal - Green Plus Ser.). (Illus.). 32p. (gr. 4-8). 19.00 (978-0-7910-8903-3(7)) Facts On File, Inc.

Harper, Judith E. Unique Places. 2005. (Real Deal Ser.). (Illus.). 32p. (J). pap. (978-0-7608-9635-8(6)) Sundance/Newbridge Educational Publishing.

McMillan, Bruce. Going Fishing. 2005. (Illus.). 32p. (J). (gr. k-3). 16.00 (978-0-618-47201-7(0) , Walter Lorraine) Houghton Mifflin Co. Trade & Reference Div.

Somervill, Barbara A. Iceland. 2003. (Enchantment of the World, Second Ser.). (Illus.). 144p. (J). (gr. 5-9). 36.00 (978-0-516-22694-1(0) , Children's Pr.) Scholastic Library Publishing.

Van Cleaf, Kristin. Iceland. 2007. (Countries Set VI Ser.). (Illus.). 40p. (J). (gr. k-6). lib. bdg. 24.21 (***978-1-59928-784-3(6)*** , Checkerboard Library) ABDO Publishing Co.

Wilcox, Jonathan & Latif, Zawiah Abdul. Iceland. 2nd ed. 2007. (Cultures of the World Ser.). 144p. (J). lib. bdg. 39.93 (978-0-7614-2074-3(6) , Benchmark Bks.) Cavendish, Marshall Corp.

ICELAND—FICTION

Erlings, Fridrik. Benjamin Dove. 2007. 224p. (YA). (gr. 5-9). pap. 7.95 (***978-0-7358-2149-1(6)***) North-South Bks., Inc.

Harcourt School Publishers Staff. Bird on the Beach: Take-Home Book. 2001. (Collections Ser.). (Illus.). (J). pap. 1.90 (978-0-15-319490-0(1)) Harcourt Schl. Pubs.

Hauger, Torill Thorstad. Escape from the Vikings. Hamnes, Lisa, ed. Born, Anne, tr. from NOR. Hauger, Torill Thorstad, illus. 2000. Orig. Title: Flukten Fra Vikingene. (Illus.). 175p. (J). (gr. 4-12). pap. (978-1-57534-013-5(5)) Skandisk, Inc.

McMillan, Bruce. How the Ladies Stopped the Wind. Gunnella, illus. 2007. 32p. (J). (gr. k-3). 16.00 (***978-0-618-77330-5(4)***) Houghton Mifflin Co.

McMillan, Bruce. The Problem with Chickens. Gunnella, illus. 2005. 32p. (J). (gr. k-3). 16.00 (978-0-618-58581-6(8) , Walter Lorraine) Houghton Mifflin Co. Trade & Reference Div.

Ruepp, Krista. Runaway Pony PB. 2007. (J). pap. 6.95 (978-0-7358-2106-4(2)) North-South Bks., Inc.

—Winter Pony. James, J. Alison, tr. from GER. Heyne, Ulrike, illus. 2002. 32p. (J). 15.95 (978-0-7358-1691-6(3)) North-South Bks., Inc.

Spirn, Michele Sobel. Race to the Sea. 2001. (gr. 3-6). lib. bdg. 11.80 (978-0-613-43952-7(X)) Tandem Library Bks.

ICHTHYOLOGY

see Fishes

ICONOGRAPHY

see Art; Christian Art and Symbolism; Portraits

IDAHO

Boone, Mary. Uniquely Idaho. 2004. (Heinemann State Studies). (Illus.). 48p. (J). 27.07 (978-1-4034-4646-6(6)); pap. 9.00 (978-1-4034-4715-9(2)) Heinemann Library.

Brown, Jonatha A. Idaho. 2006. (Portraits of the States Ser.). (J). pap. (978-0-8368-4717-8(2)); lib. bdg. (978-0-8368-4700-0(8)) Stevens, Gareth Inc.

Brown, Vanessa. Idaho. Brusca, Maria Cristina, tr. 2005. (Bilingual Library of the United States of America: Set 1). (ENG & SPA., Illus.). 32p. (J). (gr. 2-5). lib. bdg. 22.50 (978-1-4042-3077-4(7) , Buenas Letra) Rosen Publishing Group, Inc., The.

Crutcher, Chris. King of the Mild Frontier: An Ill-Advised Autobiography. 2004. 272p. (J). reprint ed. pap. 6.99 (978-0-06-050251-5(7) , HarperTeen) HarperCollins Pubs.

Edwards, Karen. Idaho: The Gem State. 2003. (World Almanac Library of the States). (Illus.). 48p. (J). (gr. 5 up). pap. 14.95 (978-0-8368-5321-6(0)); lib. bdg. 30.00 (978-0-8368-5150-2(1)) Stevens, Gareth Inc. (World Almanac Library).

Foran, Jill. A Guide to Idaho. 2001. (American States Ser.). (Illus.). 32p. (J). lib. bdg. 16.95 (978-1-930954-33-5(6)); per. 7.95 (978-1-930954-76-2(X)) Weigl Pubs., Inc.

Fradin, Dennis Brindell. Idaho. 1998. (From Sea to Shining Sea Ser.). (Illus.). 64p. (J). (gr. 3-5). pap. 7.95 (978-0-516-26290-1(4) , Children's Pr.) Scholastic Library Publishing.

Heinrichs, Ann. Idaho. 2005. (Welcome to the USA Ser.). 40p. (J). (gr. 1-5). 27.07 (978-1-59296-471-0(0)) Child's World, Inc.

—Idaho. 2003. (This Land Is Your Land Ser.). (Illus.). 48p. (J). (gr. 3 up). lib. bdg. 22.60 (978-0-7565-0352-9(3)) Compass Point Bks.

Hodgkins, Fran. Idaho. 2003. (Land of Liberty Ser.). (Illus.). 64p. (J). (gr. 3-4). lib. bdg. 23.93 (978-0-7368-1580-2(5) , Bridgestone Bks.) Capstone Pr., Inc.

Idaho. 2000. (Switched on Schoolhouse Ser.). (Illus.). (YA). (gr. 7-12). pap. 24.95 incl. cd-rom (978-0-7403-0264-0(7) , SOSID) Alpha Omega Pubns., Inc.

Kule, Elaine A. Idaho Facts & Symbols. (States & Their Symbols Ser.). 24p. (J). 2000. (Illus.). (gr. 2-3). lib. bdg. 18.60 (978-0-7368-0636-7(9) , Bridgestone Bks.); 2003. lib. bdg. 19.93 (978-0-7368-2242-8(9)) Capstone Pr., Inc.

Kummer, Patricia K. Idaho. rev. ed. 2002. (One Nation Ser.). (Illus.). 48p. (J). (gr. 3-4). lib. bdg. 22.60 (978-0-7368-1236-8(9) , Bridgestone Bks.) Capstone Pr., Inc.

MacGregor, Carol Lynn. Lewis & Clark's Bittersweet Crossing. Hoopes, Gaye, tr. Hoopes, Gaye, illus. 2004. 32p. (J). 16.95 (978-0-87004-437-3(0) , 043700) Caxton Pr.

Marsh, Carole. The Big Idaho Reproducible Activity Book. 2001. (Carole Marsh Idaho Bks.). (Illus.). 96p. (J). (gr. 2-6). pap. 9.95 (978-0-7933-9940-6(8)) Gallopade International.

—Idaho Classic Christmas Trivia. 2002. (Carole Marsh Idaho Bks.). (Illus.). 32p. pap. 6.95 (978-0-635-01391-0(6) , 13916); lib. bdg. 14.95 (978-0-635-01392-7(4) , 13924) Gallopade International. (Marsh, Carole Bks.).

—Idaho Current Events Projects: 30 Cool, Activities, Crafts, Experiments & More for Kids to Do to Learn about Your State! 2003. (Idaho Experience Ser.). 32p. (gr. k-5). pap. 5.95 (978-0-635-02031-4(9) , Marsh, Carole Bks.) Gallopade International.

—The Idaho Experience Pocket Guide. 2001. (Carole Marsh Idaho Bks.). (Illus.). 96p. (J). (gr. 3-8). pap. 6.95 (978-0-7933-9911-6(4)) Gallopade International.

—Idaho Geography Projects: 30 Cool, Activities, Crafts, Experiments & More for Kids to Do to Learn about Your State! 2003. (Idaho Experience Ser.). 32p. (gr. k-5). pap. 5.95 (978-0-635-01831-1(4) , Marsh, Carole Bks.) Gallopade International.

—Idaho Government Projects: 30 Cool, Activities, Crafts, Experiments & More for Kids to Do to Learn about Your State! 2003. (Idaho Experience Ser.). 32p. (gr. k-5). pap. 5.95 (978-0-635-01931-8(0) , Marsh, Carole Bks.) Gallopade International.

—Idaho Jeopardy! Answers & Questions about Our State! 2001. (Carole Marsh Idaho Bks.). (Illus.). 32p. (J). (gr. 3-8). pap. 7.95 (978-0-7933-9795-2(2)) Gallopade International.

—Idaho "Jography" A Fun Run Thru Our State! 2001. (Carole Marsh Idaho Bks.). (Illus.). 32p. (J). (gr. 3-8). pap. 7.95 (978-0-7933-9824-9(X)) Gallopade International.

—Idaho Millionaire: Game Book. 2001. (Carole Marsh Idaho Bks.). (Illus.). 32p. (J). (gr. 3-8). pap., act. bk. ed. 9.95 (978-0-635-00040-8(7)) Gallopade International.

—Idaho People Projects: 30 Cool, Activities, Crafts, Experiments & More for Kids to Do to Learn about Your State! 2003. (Idaho Experience Ser.). 32p. (gr. k-5). pap. 5.95 (978-0-635-01981-3(7) , Marsh, Carole Bks.) Gallopade International.

—Idaho Survivor: Game Book. 2001. (Carole Marsh Idaho Bks.). (Illus.). 32p. (J). (gr. 3-8). pap., act. bk. ed. 9.95 (978-0-635-00533-5(6)) Gallopade International.

—Idaho Symbols & Facts Projects: 30 Cool, Activities, Crafts, Experiments & More for Kids to Do to Learn about Your State! 2003. (Idaho Experience Ser.). 32p. (gr. k-5). pap. 5.95 (978-0-635-01881-6(0) , Marsh, Carole Bks.) Gallopade International.

—My First Book about Idaho. 2001. (Carole Marsh Idaho Bks.). (Illus.). 32p. (J). (gr. k-4). pap. 7.95 (978-0-7933-9882-9(7)) Gallopade International.

—The Survivor: A Class Challenge. 2001. (Carole Marsh Idaho Bks.). lib. bdg. 29.95 (978-0-635-00658-5(8)) Gallopade International.

Miller, Amy. Idaho. 2003. (From Sea to Shining Sea Ser.: 2). (Illus.). 80p. (J). 30.50 (978-0-516-22391-9(7) , Children's Pr.) Scholastic Library Publishing.

Pelta, Kathy. Idaho. 2nd rev. exp. ed. 2002. (Hello U. S. A. Ser.). (Illus.). 84p. (J). (gr. 3-6). lib. bdg. 25.26 (978-0-8225-4080-9(0)) Lerner Publishing Group.

—Idaho. rev. ed. 2002. (gr. 3-6). lib. bdg. 15.25 (978-0-613-46077-4(4)) Tandem Library Bks.

Peterson, Sheryl. Idaho. 2008. (J). (*978-1-58341-637-2(4) , Creative Education) Creative Co., The.

Sanders, Doug. Idaho. 2004. (It's My State! Ser.). (Illus.). 80p. (J). 27.07 (978-0-7614-1824-5(5)) Cavendish, Marshall Corp.

Schaffer, David. Idaho: A MyReportLinks. Com Book. 2003. (States Ser.). (Illus.). 48p. (J). lib. bdg. 25.26 (978-0-7660-5134-8(X) , MyReportLinks.com Bks.) Enslow Pubs., Inc.

Spence, Clark C. For Wood River or Bust: Idaho's Silver Boom of the 1880s. 2004. (Idaho Legacy Ser.). (Illus.). 278p. 29.95 (978-0-89301-215-1(7)) Univ. of Idaho Pr.

Stefoff, Rebecca. Idaho. 2000. (Celebrate the States Ser.). (Illus.). 144p. (gr. 4-8). lib. bdg. 37.07 (978-0-7614-0663-1(8) , Benchmark Bks.) Cavendish, Marshall Corp.

Steiner, Stan, et al. P Is for Potato: An Idaho Alphabet. Stack, Jocelyn, illus. 2005. (Discover America State by State Ser.). 40p. (J). 17.95 (978-1-58536-155-7(0)) Sleeping Bear Pr.

Wadsworth, Ginger. River Discoveries. Kratter, Paul, illus. 2002. (J). pap. 6.95 (978-1-57091-419-5(2)); (gr. 1-4). 16.95 (978-1-57091-418-8(4)) Charlesbridge Publishing, Inc.

—River Discoveries. 2002. (gr. k-3). lib. bdg. 15.25 (978-0-613-62645-3(1)) Tandem Library Bks.

Young, Virgil M. The Story of Idaho. 4th ed. 2004. (Illus.). 257p. 29.95 (978-0-89301-259-5(9)) Univ. of Idaho Pr.

Zollman, Pam. Idaho. 2006. 32p. (gr. 1-2). (YA). pap. 5.95 (978-0-516-26609-1(8)); (Illus.). (J). 20.50 (978-0-516-24965-0(7)) Scholastic Library Publishing. (Children's Pr.).

IDAHO—FICTION

Creech, Sharon. Walk Two Moons. 2002. (Illus.). (J). 15.00 (978-0-7587-0223-4(X)) Book Wholesalers, Inc.

—Walk Two Moons. 2004. 304p. (J). (gr. 7 up). pap. 6.99 (978-0-06-056013-3(4) , Harper Trophy) HarperCollins Pubs.

—Walk Two Moons. 1999. (J). 9.95 (978-1-56137-770-1(8)) Novel Units, Inc.

—Walk Two Moons. 2004. (gr. 7-12). lib. bdg. 14.75 (978-0-613-81971-8(3)) Tandem Library Bks.

—Walk Two Moons. l.t. ed. 2003. 287p. pap. 10.95 (978-0-7862-6185-7(4)) Thorndike Pr.

Crutcher, Chris. The Sledding Hill. 2005. 240p. (J). (gr. 7 up). 16.99 (978-0-06-050243-0(6)); lib. bdg. 17.89 (978-0-06-050244-7(4)) HarperCollins Pubs.

—Sledding Hill. 2006. 256p. (J). pap. 6.99 (978-0-06-050245-4(2) , HarperTeen) HarperCollins Pubs.

Dorie & Me. 2003. (YA). per. (978-1-59431-071-3(8) , Ebks. On The Net) ebooksonthe.net.

Duey, Kathleen. Celou Sudden Shout: Idaho, 1826. 1998. (American Diaries Ser.: No. 9). (J). (gr. 3-7). (978-0-606-13121-6(3)) Tandem Library Bks.

Farrell, Mary Cronk. Fire in the Hole! 2004. 176p. (YA). (gr. 5-9). tchr. ed. 15.00 (978-0-618-44634-6(6) , Clarion Bks.) Houghton Mifflin Co. Trade & Reference Div.

George, Jean Craighead. Fire Storm. Minor, Wendell, illus. 2003. (Outdoor Adventures Ser.). 32p. (J). 15.99 (978-0-06-000263-3(8)); lib. bdg. 16.89 (978-0-06-000264-0(6)) HarperCollins Pubs.

—Snowboard Twist. Minor, Wendell, illus. 2004. (Outdoor Adventures Ser.). 32p. (J). 15.99 (978-0-06-050595-0(8)) HarperCollins Pubs.

Hamilton, Morse. The Garden of Eden Motel. 1999. (Illus.). 160p. (J). (gr. 5 up). 16.00 (978-0-688-16814-8(0)) HarperCollins Pubs.

Hite, Sid. The King of Slippery Falls. 2004. 224p. (J). pap. 16.95 (978-0-439-34257-5(0)) Scholastic, Inc.

Ingold, Jeanette. The Big Burn. 2003. (Illus.). 320p. (YA). pap. 6.95 (978-0-15-204924-9(X) , Harcourt Paperbacks) Harcourt Children's Bks.

—The Big Burn. 2003. (gr. 5-8). lib. bdg. 15.25 (978-0-613-55148-9(6)) Tandem Library Bks.

Littke, Lael. Searching for Selene. 2003. 203p. (J). pap. 13.95 (978-1-59038-179-3(3)) Deseret Bk. Co.

Oblich, Kathleen. Jake & the Scarecrow. 2007. 48p. pap. 12.95 (*978-1-4241-3101-3(4)) PublishAmerica, Inc.

Patneaude, David. Colder Than Ice. 2003. (J). (gr. 4-7). 168p. 15.95 (978-0-8075-8135-3(6)); 167p. pap. 6.95 (978-0-8075-8136-0(4)) Whitman, Albert & Co.

Romano, Elaine. The Magic Potato - la Papa Magica: Story & coloring book in English & Spanish, 1. Nielsen, Emily, tr. Winchel, Heidi, illus. 2nd ed. 2004. (SPA.). 20p. (J). 3.00 (978-0-9728225-3-4(4)) Mill Park Publishing.

IDAHO—HISTORY

Crutcher, Chris. King of the Mild Frontier: An Ill-Advised Autobiography. 2003. (Illus.). 208p. (J). (gr. 7-12). 16.99 (978-0-06-050249-2(5)) HarperCollins Pubs.

Hall, Carol S. & Hansen, T. J. This Is Idaho. 342p. (J). (gr. 1-6). pap. 49.95 (978-1-56861-051-1(3)) Swift Learning Resources.

Marsh, Carole. Idaho History Projects: 30 Cool, Activities, Crafts, Experiments & More for Kids to Do to Learn about Your State! 2003. (Idaho Experience Ser.). 32p. (gr. k-5). pap. 5.95 (978-0-635-01781-9(4) , Marsh, Carole Bks.) Gallopade International.

—My First Pocket Guide Idaho. 2000. (Idaho Experience! Ser.). (Illus.). 96p. (J). (gr. 3-8). 12.95 (978-0-635-01302-6(9) , 13029) Gallopade International.

Quasha, Jennifer. How to Draw Idahos Sights & Symbols. 2002. (Kids Guide to Drawing America Ser.). 32p. (J). lib. bdg. 25.25 (978-0-8239-6068-2(4) , PowerKids Pr.) Rosen Publishing Group, Inc., The.

IDENTITY (PSYCHOLOGY)

see also Individuality

Kirberger, Kimberly. No Body's Perfect: Stories by Teens about Body Image, Self-Acceptance, & the Search for Identity. 2003. (No Body's Perfect Ser.). 304p. (YA). 12.95 (978-0-439-42638-1(3) , Scholastic Paperbacks) Scholastic, Inc.

Landis, Leanne. The Plainest Piece of the Puzzle. 2002. 32p. (J). pap. 8.95 (978-0-9723707-2-1(2)) White Door Publishing.

Pryor, Tamara & Konek, Jana. Respect Self Value People Middle School Student Lesson & Activity Guide. 2002. (Illus.). XV, 173p. (YA). (gr. 6-8). pap. 55.00 (978-0-9722617-0-8(2)) Healing Path Foundation.

Weedn, Lisa. Finding My Groove: Who I Am & Where I'm Going. Weedn, Flavia M., illus. 2001. 64p. (gr. 8 up). pap. 14.95 (978-0-7683-2237-8(5)) CEDCO Publishing.

IDENTITY—FICTION

Ahrens, Robin Isabel. Dee & Bee. Haley, Amanda, illus. 2000. 40p. (J). (ps-1). 14.95 (978-1-890817-26-8(0)) Winslow Pr.

Alger, Horatio. Hector's Inheritance: Or, The Boys of Smith Institute. 2006. pap. (*978-1-4065-0708-9(3)) Dodo Pr.

—Hector's Inheritance: Or, The Boys of Smith Institute. unabr. ed. 2002. (Polyglot Press Alger Ser.). (Illus.). (J). pap. 17.95 (978-1-4115-0004-4(0)) Polyglot Pr., Inc.

Alger Jr. Horatio Staff. Hector's Inheritance. rev. ed. 2006. 276p. 28.95 (978-1-4218-1758-3(6)); pap. 13.95 (978-1-4218-1858-0(2)) 1st World Publishing, Inc. (1st World Library - Literary Society).

Allen, M. E. Gotta Get Some Bish Bash Bosh. 2005. (Illus.). 208p. (J). 15.99 (978-0-06-073198-4(2) , HarperTeen); lib. bdg. 16.89 (978-0-06-073201-1(6)) HarperCollins Pubs.

Alphin, Elaine Marie. Simon Says. (YA). (gr. 9-12). 2005. 264p. pap. 6.95 (978-0-15-204678-1(X) , Harcourt Paperbacks); 2002. (Illus.). 272p. 17.00 (978-0-15-216355-6(7)) Harcourt Children's Bks.

An, Na. The Fold. 2008. 192p. (J). (gr. 5). 16.99 (*978-0-399-24276-2(7) , Putnam Juvenile) Penguin Group (USA) Inc.

Anderson, Janet. Going Through the Gate. 2000. (Illus.). (J). (978-0-606-18407-6(4)) Tandem Library Bks.

Apelqvist, Eva. Swede Dreams. 2007. (S. A. S. S. (Students Across the Seven Seas) Ser.). (Illus.). (YA). 224p. pap. 6.99 (978-0-14-240746-2(1)); 202p. (*978-1-4287-2702-1(7)) Penguin Group (USA) Inc. (Puffin).

Avi. Crispin: La Cruz de Plomo. 2004. Tr. of Crispin: The Cross of Lead. (SPA., Illus.). (YA). pap. 7.99 (978-84-348-9601-7(X)) SM Ediciones ESP. *Dist:* Lectorum Pubns., Inc.

—Crispin: The Cross of Lead. 2002. 256p. (gr. 5-9). 16.49 (978-0-7868-2647-6(9)) Disney Pr.

—Crispin: The Cross of Lead. 2002. (Illus.). 272p. (gr. 5-9). 15.99 (978-0-7868-0828-1(4)) Hyperion Bks. for Children.

—Crispin: The Cross of Lead. 2004. 320p. (J). (gr. 3-7). reprint ed. pap. 6.99 (978-0-7868-1658-3(9)) Hyperion Paperbacks for Children.

—Crispin: The Cross of Lead. 2004. (gr. 3-6). lib. bdg. 15.30 (978-0-613-74965-7(0)) Tandem Library Bks.

—Crispin: The Cross of Lead. 2003. 303p. (J). 25.95 (978-0-7862-5501-6(3)) Thorndike Pr.

Banerjee, Anjali. Maya Running. 2006. 224p. (YA). (gr. 7). reprint ed. mass mkt. 5.99 (978-0-553-49424-2(4) , Laurel Leaf) Random Hse. Children's Bks.

Bang, Molly Garrett. Goose. Bang, Molly Garrett, illus. 2002. (Illus.). (J). 19.72 (978-0-7587-2626-1(0)) Book Wholesalers, Inc.

Banks, Kate. Dillon Dillon. 160p. (J). 2002. (gr. 3-6). 16.00 (978-0-374-31786-7(0) , Farrar, Straus & Giroux (BYR)); 2005. reprint ed. pap. 5.95 (978-0-374-41715-4(6) , Sunburst) Farrar, Straus & Giroux.

Baptiste, Tracey. Angel's Grace. 2005. 176p. (J). 15.95 (978-0-689-86773-6(5) , Simon & Schuster/Paula Wiseman Bks.) Simon & Schuster Children's Publishing.

Baskin, Nora Raleigh. The Truth about My Bat Mitzvah. 2008. 144p. (J). 15.99 (*978-1-4169-3558-2(4) , Simon & Schuster Children's Publishing) Simon & Schuster Children's Publishing.

Baskin, Nora Raleigh. What Every Girl. 2002. (gr. 5-8). lib. bdg. 13.00 (978-0-613-89779-2(X)) Tandem Library Bks.

Bateson, Catherine. The Boyfriend Rules of Good Behavior. 2006. 192p. (YA). 16.95 (978-0-8234-2026-1(4)) Holiday Hse., Inc.

Bath, K. P. Escape from Castle Cant. 2006. (Illus.). 304p. (J). (gr. 3-7). 16.99 (978-0-316-10857-7(X)) Little Brown & Co.

—The Secret of Castle Cant. 2006. 304p. (J). (gr. 3-7). reprint ed. pap. 6.99 (978-0-316-05991-6(9)) Little Brown & Co.

Batson, Wayne Thomas. Isle of Swords. 2007. 352p. (J). 16.99 (*978-1-4003-1018-0(0)) Nelson, Thomas Inc.

Beale, Fleur. I Am Not Esther. 2004. 256p. (gr. 7-17). reprint ed. pap. 6.99 (978-0-7868-1673-6(2)) Hyperion Bks. for Children.

Beaumont, Karen. I Like Myself! Catrow, David, illus. 2004. 32p. (J). 16.00 (978-0-15-202013-2(6)) Harcourt Children's Bks.

Bell, Alison. The Zibby Payne & the Wonderful, Terrible Tomboy Experiment. 2006. 96p. (J). (gr. 2-5). pap. (978-1-897073-39-1(9)) Lobster Pr.

Belle Prater's Boy. 1999. (Pathways to Critical Thinking Ser.). 32p. (YA). pap., stu. ed., tchr.'s training gde. ed. 19.95 (978-1-58303-081-3(6)) Pathways Publishing.

Benton, Jim. Lunch Walks among Us. Benton, Jim, illus. (Franny K. Stein, Mad Scientist Ser.: Bk. 2). (Illus.). 112p. (J). 2004. (gr. 2-5). mass mkt. 3.99 (978-0-689-86295-3(4) , Aladdin); 2003. 15.99 (978-0-689-86291-5(1)) Simon & Schuster Children's Publishing.

Besser, Kenneth/R. Arnie Carver & the Plague of Demeverde. 2007. (Illus.). x, 338p. (J). (*978-1-934316-02-3(4)) RTMC Organization, LLC.

Bode, N. E. The Anybodies. Ferguson, Peter, illus. 288p. (J). 2004. 16.99 (978-0-06-055735-5(4)); 2004. lib. bdg. 17.89 (978-0-06-055736-2(2)); 2005. reprint ed. pap. 6.99 (978-0-06-055737-9(0)) HarperCollins Pubs.

Brian, Kate. The Princess & the Pauper. 2004. 272p. (YA). reprint ed. mass mkt. 6.99 (978-0-689-87042-2(6) , Simon Pulse) Simon & Schuster Children's Publishing.

—The Princess & the Pauper. l.t. ed. 2003. 345p. (J). 22.95 (978-0-7862-6101-7(3) , Large Print Pr.) Thorndike Pr.

Brooks, Kevin. Being. 2008. 352p. (J). pap. 7.99 (*978-0-439-90342-4(4) , PUSH) Scholastic, Inc.

Burgess, Melvin. Sara's Face. 2007. 272p. (YA). (gr. 7 up). 16.99 (978-1-4169-3617-6(3)) Simon & Schuster Children's Publishing.

Burns, Joanne. Pamela Platypus' Problem. 2005. 21p. (J). 8.99 (978-1-4116-5226-2(6)) Lulu.com.

Butcher, Kristin. Chat Room. 2006. 112p. (gr. 5-10). pap. 7.95 (978-1-55143-485-8(7)); lib. bdg. 14.95 (978-1-55143-529-9(2)) Orca Bk. Pubs. USA.

Cabot, Meg. Avalon High. (J). 2007. 320p. pap. 8.99 (*978-0-06-075588-1(1) , HarperTeen); 2006. 304p. 16.99 (978-0-06-075586-7(5)); 2006. 304p. lib. bdg. 17.89 (978-0-06-075587-4(3)) HarperCollins Pubs.

—Avalon High. l.t. ed. 2006. 335p. (YA). 23.95 (978-0-7862-9032-1(3)) Thorndike Pr.

—In Love. 2002. (Princess Diaries: Vol. 3). (YA). (gr. 7 up). 272p. mass mkt. 5.99 (978-0-06-052568-2(1)); 240p. 16.99 (978-0-06-029467-0(1)) HarperCollins Pubs.

—In Love, Vol. 3. 2004. (Princess Diaries: Vol. 3). 288p. (J). (gr. 7 up). pap. 38.00 incl. audio (978-0-8072-2284-3(4) , Listening Library) Random Hse. Audio Publishing Group.

—The Princess Diaries. (Princess Diaries: Vol. I). 2008. 256p. (J). pap. 7.99 (*978-0-06-147993-9(4) , HarperTeen); 2000. 240p. (J). (gr. 7 up). lib. bdg. 17.89 (978-0-06-029210-2(5)); 2001. 320p. (YA). (gr. 7 up). pap. 6.99 (978-0-380-81402-2(1) , Harper Trophy); 2000. (Illus.). 240p. (J). (gr. 7 up). 16.99 (978-0-380-97848-9(2)) HarperCollins Pubs.

—The Princess Diaries. unabr. ed. 2004. (Princess Diaries: Vol. I). 240p. (J). (gr. 7 up). pap. 38.00 incl. audio (978-0-8072-0669-0(5) , Listening Library) Random Hse. Audio Publishing Group.

—The Princess Diaries. 2001. (Princess Diaries: Vol. I). (gr. 7-12). lib. bdg. 15.30 (978-0-613-37165-0(8)); (Illus.). (J). (978-0-606-21844-3(0)) Tandem Library Bks.

—The Princess Diaries. l.t. ed. 2002. (Princess Diaries: Vol. I). 325p. (J). 24.95 (978-0-7862-4058-6(X)) Thomson Gale.

—Princess diaries, volume Ii: 2008. (Princess Diaries). 240p. (J). pap. 7.99 (*978-0-06-147994-6(2) , HarperTeen) HarperCollins Pubs.

—Princess diaries, volume Iii. 2008. (Princess Diaries). 240p. (J). pap. 7.99 (*978-0-06-147995-3(0) , HarperTeen) HarperCollins Pubs.

—Princess in the Spotlight. 2001. (Princess Diaries: Vol. II). 240p. (J). (gr. 7 up). 16.99 (978-0-06-029465-6(5)) HarperCollins Pubs.

—Princess in the Spotlight. unabr. ed. 2004. (Princess Diaries: Vol. II). 272p. (J). (gr. 7 up). pap. 38.00 incl. audio (978-0-8072-1197-7(4) , S YA 332 SP, Listening Library) Random Hse. Audio Publishing Group.

—Princess in Training. (Princess Diaries: Vol. 6). (Illus.). (J). 2006. 320p. pap. 6.99 (978-0-06-009615-1(2) , Harper Trophy); 2005. 288p. (gr. 7 up). 16.99 (978-0-06-009613-7(6)) HarperCollins Pubs.

—Princess in Training. l.t. ed. 2005. (Princess Diaries: Vol. 6). 355p. (YA). (gr. 7-12). per. 22.95 (978-0-7862-7753-7(X) , Large Print Pr.) Thorndike Pr.

—Princess in Waiting. 2003. (Princess Diaries: Vol. 4). (Illus.). 240p. (J). (gr. 7 up). 16.99 (978-0-06-009607-6(1)) HarperCollins Pubs.

—Princess in Waiting. l.t. ed. 2003. (Princess Diaries: Vol. 4). 287p. (J). 25.95 (978-0-7862-5682-2(6)) Thorndike Pr.

Cabot, Meg. Princess on the Brink. 2008. (Princess Diaries: Vol. 8). (J). 288p. 16.99 (*978-0-06-072461-0(7)); 272p. pap. 7.99 (*978-0-06-072460-3(9) , Harper Trophy) HarperCollins Pubs.

Calhoun, Dia. Firegold. 2003. 304p. (YA). pap. 8.95 (978-0-374-42311-7(3) , Sunburst) Farrar, Straus & Giroux.

—Firegold. (YA). 2003. 285p. (gr. 8-12). per. 17.60 (978-0-613-59617-6(X)); 1999. (Illus.). (gr. 6 up). (978-0-606-18341-3(8)) Tandem Library Bks.

—Firegold. l.t. ed. 2005. 415p. (YA). (gr. 7-12). per. 21.95 (978-0-7862-7696-7(7) , Large Print Pr.) Thorndike Pr.

—Firegold. 2001. 352p. (J). (gr. 7-12). pap. 5.95 (978-1-58837-003-7(8)) Winslow Pr.

Calonita, Jen. Secrets of My Hollywood Life. 2006. 256p. (J). (gr. 7-17). 16.99 (978-0-316-15442-0(3)) Little Brown & Co.

—Secrets of My Hollywood Life. 2007. 256p. (J). (gr. 7 up). pap. 7.99 (*978-0-316-15443-7(1) , Poppy) Little, Brown Bks. for Young Readers.

Cannon, A. E. The Loser's Guide to Life & Love. 2008. 272p. (J). 16.99 (*978-0-06-112846-2(5)); lib. bdg. 17.89 (*978-0-06-112847-9(3)) HarperCollins Pubs. (HarperTeen).

Carvell, Marlene. Sweetgrass Basket. 2005. 256p. (J). (gr. 3-6). 16.99 (978-0-525-47547-7(8) , Dutton Juvenile) Penguin Group (USA) Inc.

—Who Will Tell My Brother? 2004. 160p. (gr. 7-17). pap. 5.99 (978-0-7868-1657-6(0)) Hyperion Bks. for Children.

Cassidy, Anne. Looking for JJ. 2007. (Illus.). 336p. (YA). (gr. 9 up). 17.00 (*978-0-15-206190-6(8)) Harcourt Children's Bks.

Castellucci, Cecil. Boy Proof. 208p. (YA). (gr. 9 up). 2005. 15.99 (978-0-7636-2333-3(4)); 2006. reprint ed. pap. 7.99 (978-0-7636-2796-6(8)) Candlewick Pr.

Catalanotto, Peter. Matthew A. B. C. Catalanotto, Peter, illus. 2002. (Illus.). 32p. (J). (ps-2). 15.95 (978-0-689-84582-6(0) , Atheneum/Richard Jackson Bks.) Simon & Schuster Children's Publishing.

Cheng, Andrea. Marika. 1998. 148p. (YA). (gr. 5 up). 16.95 (978-1-886910-78-2(2) , Lemniscaat) Boyds Mills Pr.

Cheshire, Simon. The Prince & the Snowgirl. 2007. 176p. (J). (gr. 7). pap. 8.99 (978-0-385-73342-7(9)); lib. bdg. 12.99 (978-0-385-90359-2(6)) Random Hse. Children's Bks. (Delacorte Bks. for Young Readers).

Chima, Cinda Williams. The Warrior Heir. 2006. 432p. (gr. 7-17). 16.99 (978-0-7868-3916-2(3)) Hyperion Bks. for Children.

—The Warrior Heir. 2007. 448p. (gr. 7-17). pap. 8.99 (*978-0-7868-3917-9(1)) Hyperion Pr.

Choyce, Lesley. Deconstructing Dylan. 2006. 180p. (YA). pap. 12.99 (*978-1-55002-603-0(8) , Boardwalk Bks.) Dundurn Group, The CAN. *Dist:* Univ. of Toronto Pr.

Christopher, Matt. Skateboard Renegade. ed. 2000. (Sports Classics IV Ser.). 139p. (J). lib. bdg. 15.00 (978-1-59054-768-7(3)) Fitzgerald Bks.

—Skateboard Renegade. 2000. (Matt Christopher Sports Classics Ser.). 144p. (J). (gr. 3-7). 15.95 (978-0-316-13487-3(2)) Little, Brown Bks. for Young Readers.

—Skateboard Renegade. 2000. (J). (978-0-606-19843-1(1)) Tandem Library Bks.

—Skateboard Renegade: Is Image Everything? 2000. 144p. (J). (gr. 3-7). pap. 4.99 (978-0-316-13549-8(6)) Little Brown & Co.

Clements, Andrew. Things Hoped For. 176p. (gr. 5). 2008. (J). 6.99 (*978-0-14-241073-8(X) , Puffin); 2006. (YA). 16.99 (978-0-399-24350-9(X) , Philomel) Penguin Group (USA) Inc.

Cobb, Nyelah. True Identity. 2003. 104p. pap. 9.95 (978-0-595-28227-2(X)) iUniverse, Inc.

Cofer, Judith Ortiz. Call Me Maria. 2006. 144p. (J). pap. 6.99 (978-0-439-38578-7(4) , Scholastic Paperbacks) Scholastic, Inc.

Comrie, Margaret S. The Heroes of Castle Bretten. 2003. (Illus.). 229p. (J). (978-1-894666-65-7(8)) Inheritance Pubns.

Cooney, Caroline B. The Face on the Milk Carton. l.t. ed. 2006. 225p. (YA). 21.95 (978-0-7862-8504-4(4)) Thorndike Pr.

—The Voice on the Radio. 1998. 224p. (YA). (gr. 7-12). mass mkt. 6.50 (978-0-440-21977-4(9) , Laurel Leaf) Random Hse. Children's Bks.

—The Voice on the Radio. 1998. (J). (978-0-606-13886-4(2)) Tandem Library Bks.

—What Janie Found. 2002. 192p. (YA). (gr. 7). pap. 6.50 (978-0-440-22772-4(0) , Laurel Leaf) Random Hse. Children's Bks.

—What Janie Found. 2002. (gr. 7-12). lib. bdg. 14.15 (978-0-613-64454-9(9)) Tandem Library Bks.

Cooper, Ilene. Sam I Am. 256p. (J). 2006. pap. 5.99 (978-0-439-43968-8(X)); 2004. (gr. 4-7). pap. 15.95 (978-0-439-43967-1(1) , Scholastic Pr.) Scholastic, Inc.

Cornish, D. M. Lamplighter: Monster Blood Tattoo, Book 2: Monster Blood Tattoo, Book 2. 2008. 400p. (YA). (gr. 7). 18.99 (*978-0-399-24639-5(8) , Putnam Juvenile) Penguin Group (USA) Inc.

Cory, Kim Delmar. Home to Mackinac: The Tale of Young Jack Murphy's Discovery of Loyalty, Family & Forgiveness. Evans, Laura, illus. 2007. 175p. (J). pap. 9.95 (978-0-911872-87-3(6)) Mackinac State Historic Parks.

Cosgrove, Stephen. Tee Tee. 2003. (gr. k-3). lib. bdg. 13.00 (978-0-613-64604-8(5)) Tandem Library Bks.

Croggon, Alison. The Naming. 2006. (Pellinor Ser.: Bk. 1). 528p. (YA). (gr. 7). pap. 8.99 (978-0-7636-3162-8(0)) Candlewick Pr.

Croggon, Allison. Naming: The First Book of Pellinor, No. 1. 2005. 528p. (YA). (gr. 7 up). 17.99 (978-0-7636-2639-6(2)) Candlewick Pr.

Crossley-Holland, Kevin. At the Crossing Places. 2002. (Arthur Trilogy: Bk. 2). 416p. (J). (gr. 9 up). 17.95 (978-0-439-26598-0(3) , Levine, Arthur A. Bks.) Scholastic, Inc.

—At the Crossing-Places. 2004. (Illus.). 394p. (YA). (gr. 7-12). lib. bdg. 13.64 (978-0-606-32761-9(4)) Tandem Library Bks.

—At the Crossing Places. 2004. (Arthur Trilogy: Bk. 2). 416p. (J). (gr. 4-7). reprint ed. pap. 7.99 (978-0-439-26599-7(1) , Levine, Arthur A. Bks.) Scholastic, Inc.

—King of the Middle March. 432p. (J). 2006. pap. 7.99 (978-0-439-26601-7(7)); Book 3. 2004. (gr. 7 up). 17.95 (978-0-439-26600-0(9) , Levine, Arthur A. Bks.) Scholastic, Inc.

—The Seeing Stone. 2002. (Arthur Trilogy: Vol. 1). 368p. (J). (gr. 5 up). mass mkt. 6.99 (978-0-439-43524-6(2) , Levine, Arthur A. Bks.) Scholastic, Inc.

—Seeing Stone. 2002. (gr. 7-12). lib. bdg. 15.30 (978-0-613-50642-7(1)) Tandem Library Bks.

Cruz, Maria Colleen. Border Crossing. 128p. (YA). pap. 9.95 (978-1-55885-405-5(3) , Piñata Books) Arte Publico Pr.

—Border Crossing. 2003. (gr. 7-12). lib. bdg. 18.75 (978-0-613-90255-7(6)) Tandem Library Bks.

Davis, Terry. If Rock & Roll Were a Machine: A Novel. 2003. 174p. (YA). pap. 15.95 (978-0-910055-86-4(6)) Eastern Washington Univ. Pr.

Dessen, Sarah. Dreamland. 2000. (Illus.). 256p. (J). (gr. 7-12). 15.99 (978-0-670-89122-1(3) , Viking Juvenile) Penguin Group (USA) Inc.

Dole, Mayra Lazara. Down to the Bone. 2008. 384p. (J). 16.99 (*978-0-06-084310-6(1) , HarperTeen) HarperCollins Pubs.

Doyle, Malachy. Who Is Jesse Flood? 2002. 176p. (J). (gr. 5-10). 14.95 (978-1-58234-776-9(X) , Bloomsbury Children) Bloomsbury Publishing.

Dunbar, Joyce. A Chick Called Saturday. Granstrom, Brita, illus. 2004. 32p. (J). 16.00 (978-0-8028-5260-1(2)) Eerdmans, William B. Publishing Co.

Dunnington, Gwenyth. Second Chance: Girl with the Heart of a Dragon. 2003. 422p. (YA). pap. 22.95 (978-0-595-29525-8(8)) iUniverse, Inc.

Durrant, Lynda. Turtle Clan Journey. 1999. 192p. (J). (gr. 5-9). tchr. ed. 15.00 (978-0-395-90369-8(6) , Clarion Bks.) Houghton Mifflin Co. Trade & Reference Div.

Edmonds, Lyra. An African Princess. Wilson, Anne, illus. 2004. 32p. (J). (ps-2). 15.99 (978-0-7636-2595-5(7)) Candlewick Pr.

Edwards, Pamela Duncan. Gigi & Lulu's Gigantic Fight. Cole, Henry, tr. Cole, Henry, illus. 2004. 40p. (J). (ps-2). 14.99 (978-0-06-050752-7(7)) HarperCollins Pubs.

Emerson, Carl. What Are You, Patty? A Platypus Tale. Trover, Zachary, illus. 2007. (Animal Underdogs Ser.). 32p. (J). (ps-4). lib. bdg. 27.07 (*978-1-60270-020-8(6) , Looking Glass Library) Magic Wagon.

Farrell, Mame. Bradley & the Billboard. 2002. 224p. (J). pap. 5.95 (978-0-374-40912-8(9) , Sunburst) Farrar, Straus & Giroux.

—Bradley & the Billboard. 1999. (YA). pap., stu. ed. 58.00 incl. audio (978-0-7887-3060-3(6) , 40894) Recorded Bks., LLC.

Feiffer, Kate & Feiffer, Jules. Henry, the Dog with No Tail. 2007. 32p. (J). (ps-1). 16.99 (978-1-4169-1614-7(8) , Simon & Schuster Children's Publishing) Simon & Schuster Children's Publishing.

Ferrer, Caridad. It's Not about the Accent. 2007. 288p. (YA). (gr. 7 up). pap. 9.95 (*978-1-4165-2491-5(6) , MTV) Simon & Schuster.

Finley, Mary Pearce. Soaring Eagle. 1998. 176p. (gr. 5-7). pap. 8.95 (978-1-57168-281-9(3)) Eakin Pr.

—White Grizzly. 2000. (gr. 5-9). (Illus.). 215p. (J). 15.95 (978-0-86541-053-4(4)); 216p. (YA). pap. 8.95 (978-0-86541-058-9(5)) Filter Pr., LLC.

Fisk, Pauline. The Red Judge. 2005. 208p. (YA). 16.95 (978-1-58234-942-8(8) , Bloomsbury Children) Bloomsbury Publishing.

—The Secret of Sabrina Fludde. 2002. 250p. (J). (gr. 5 up). 15.95 (978-1-58234-754-7(9) , Bloomsbury Children) Bloomsbury Publishing.

Flake, Sharon G. Bang! 2005. 320p. (gr. 7-17). 16.99 (978-0-7868-1844-0(1) , Jump at the Sun) Hyperion Bks. for Children.

Franklin, Emily. Labor of Love: The Principles of Love. 2007. 256p. (gr. 12 up). pap. 9.99 (*978-0-451-22211-4(3) , N A L Trade) Penguin Group (USA) Inc.

—The Other Half of Me. 2007. 256p. (YA). (gr. 9). 15.99 (*978-0-385-73445-5(X)); lib. bdg. 18.99 (*978-0-385-90449-0(5)) Random Hse. Children's Bks. (Delacorte Bks. for Young Readers).

Friedman, Robin. The Girlfriend Project. 2007. 192p. (YA). (gr. 7 up). 15.95 (978-0-8027-9624-0(9)) Walker & Co.

Friedrich, Molly. You're Not My Real Mother! Hale, Christy, tr. Hale, Christy, illus. 2004. 32p. (J). (ps-3). 15.99 (978-0-316-60553-3(0) , Tingley, Megan Bks.) Little, Brown Bks. for Young Readers.

García, Cristina. I Wanna Be Your Shoebox. 2008. 208p. (J). (*978-1-4169-3928-3(8) , Simon & Schuster Children's Publishing) Simon & Schuster Children's Publishing.

Garden, Nancy. Holly's Secret. 2000. 144p. (YA). (gr. 3-7). 16.00 (978-0-374-33273-0(8) , Farrar, Straus & Giroux (BYR)) Farrar, Straus & Giroux.

Gehrman, Jody. Confessions of a Triple Shot Betty. 2008. 256p. (J). (gr. 9). 16.99 (*978-0-8037-3247-6(3) , Dial) Penguin Group (USA) Inc.

Gerber, Linda. Now & Zen. Pilkington, Roger, ed. 2006. (S. A. S. S. (Students Across the Seven Seas) Ser.). 224p. (YA). (gr. 7). pap. 6.99 (978-0-14-240657-1(0) , Puffin) Penguin Group (USA) Inc.

Gerstein, Mordicai. Fox Eyes. 2001. (gr. k-3). lib. bdg. 11.80 (978-0-613-43036-4(0)) Tandem Library Bks.

Giles, Gail. Right Behind You. 2007. 304p. (YA). (gr. 10 up). 15.99 (*978-0-316-16636-2(7)) Little, Brown Bks. for Young Readers.

Glenn, Sharlee Mullins. Just What Mama Needs. Hirao, Amiko, illus. 2008. 32p. (J). 16.00 (978-0-15-205759-6(5)) Harcourt Trade Pubs.

Goldblatt, Stacey. Stray. 2007. 288p. (YA). (gr. 7-10). 15.99 (978-0-385-73443-1(3)); lib. bdg. 18.99 (978-0-385-90448-3(7)) Random Hse. Children's Bks. (Delacorte Bks. for Young Readers).

Gonzalez, Julie. Wings. 208p. (gr. 7). 2006. (YA). mass mkt. 5.99 (978-0-440-23904-8(4) , Laurel Leaf); 2005. (J). 15.95 (978-0-385-73227-7(9) , Delacorte Bks. for Young Readers) Random Hse. Children's Bks.

Goobie, Beth. Flux. 2004. 224p. (J). (gr. 7-12). lib. bdg. 16.95 (978-1-55143-314-1(1)) Orca Bk. Pubs. USA.

Gould, Peter L. Write Naked. 2008. 256p. (YA). 16.95 (*978-0-374-38483-8(5)) Farrar, Straus & Giroux.

Grant, Vicki. I. D. 2007. (Orca Soundings Ser.). 112p. (YA). pap. (*978-1-55143-694-4(9)) Orca Bk. Pubs.

—I.D. 2007. (Orca Soundings Ser.). 112p. (YA). (gr. 7 up). lib. bdg. (*978-1-55143-696-8(5)) Orca Bk. Pubs.

Grealish, Maureen M. Just Plain Worm. 25p. (J). (gr. k-2). (978-0-9667780-0-7(6)) Ballenwyck Publishing Corp.

Grey, Christopher Peter. Leonardo's Shadow: Or, My Astonishing Life as Leonardo da Vinci's Servant. 2006. 400p. (YA). 16.95 (978-1-4169-0543-1(X) , Atheneum) Simon & Schuster Children's Publishing.

Griffin, Adele. The Other Shepards. 1999. (978-0-606-17144-1(4)) Tandem Library Bks.

—The Other Shepards. l.t. ed. 2000. (Illus.). 209p. (J). (gr. 4-7). 20.95 (978-0-7862-2914-7(4)) Thorndike Pr.

Grimes, Nikki. Bronx Masquerade. 2003. 176p. (YA). (gr. 6-11). pap. 5.99 (978-0-14-250189-4(1) , Puffin) Penguin Group (USA) Inc.

—Bronx Masquerade. Myers, Chris, illus. 2001. 176p. (J). (gr. 7 up). 16.99 (978-0-8037-2569-0(8) , Dial) Penguin Group (USA) Inc.

—Bronx Masquerade. 2003. (gr. 7-12). lib. bdg. 14.15 (978-0-613-81701-1(X)) Tandem Library Bks.

Guest, Jacqueline. Dream Racer. 2006. (SideStreets Ser.). 136p. (YA). (gr. 7-12). (*978-1-55028-945-9(4)); 7.95 (*978-1-55028-942-8(X)) Lorimer, James & Co., Ltd., Pubs. CAN. *Dist:* Casemate Pubs. & Bk. Distributors, LLC.

Haddix, Margaret Peterson. Double Identity. (J). (gr. 5-9). 2007. 192p. pap. 5.99 (978-0-689-87379-9(4) , Aladdin); 2005. 224p. 15.95 (978-0-689-87374-4(3)) Simon & Schuster Children's Publishing.

Halvorsen Schreck, Karen. Lucy's Family Tree. Gassler, Stephen, illus. 2006. 40p. (J). 7.95 (*978-0-88448-292-5(8)) Tilbury Hse. Pubs.

Hamilton, Virginia. Plain City. (Barco de Vapor). (SPA.). 176p. (YA). (gr. 5-8). 6.95 (978-84-348-4686-9(1) , LEC6861) SM Ediciones ESP. *Dist:* Continental Bk. Co., Inc.

—Plain City. 2003. 208p. (J). (gr. 4-7). pap. 5.99 (978-0-590-47365-1(4) , Scholastic Paperbacks) Scholastic, Inc.

Harcourt School Publishers Staff. What Do I Look Like? Advanced Level. 3rd ed. 2002. (Trophies Reading Program Ser.). (Illus.). pap. 5.10 (978-0-15-323101-8(7)) Harcourt Schl. Pubs.

Harrison, Troon. The Twilight Box: Tales of Terre II. 2007. (Tales of Terre Ser.: 2). 376p. (YA). per. 10.95 (*978-0-9768126-7-8(3)) Brown Barn Bks.

Hemphill, Stephanie. Things Left Unsaid: A Novel in Poems. 2005. 272p. (gr. 7-17). 16.99 (978-0-7868-1850-1(6)) Hyperion Bks. for Children.

—Things Left Unsaid: A Novel in Poems. 2007. 272p. (gr. 7-17). pap. 7.99 (*978-0-7868-3745-8(4)) Hyperion Pr.

Hicks, Betty. Get Real. 2006. 192p. (J). 16.95 (978-1-59643-089-1(3)) Roaring Brook Pr.

Hidier, Tanuja Desai. Born Confused. 2003. (gr. 7-12). lib. bdg. 16.45 (978-0-613-72235-3(3)) Tandem Library Bks.

Hidier, Tanuja Desai, et al. Born Confused. Hidier, Tanuja Desai, illus. 2002. 432p. (J). pap. 16.95 (978-0-439-35762-3(4) , Scholastic Pr.) Scholastic, Inc.

Hite, Sid. The King of Slippery Falls. 2004. 224p. (J). pap. 16.95 (978-0-439-34257-5(0)) Scholastic, Inc.

Hobbs, Valerie. Anything but Ordinary. 2007. 176p. (YA). (gr. 7 up). 16.00 (978-0-374-30374-7(6)) Farrar, Straus & Giroux.

—Carolina Crow Girl. 2000. (Illus.). 144p. (J). (gr. 5-9). pap. 5.99 (978-0-14-130976-7(8) , Puffin) Penguin Group (USA) Inc.

—Carolina Crow Girl. 2000. (J). (ps-7). 137p. per. 14.15 (978-0-613-29902-2(7)); 12.64 (978-0-606-19066-4(X)) Tandem Library Bks.

Hoffman, Alice. Incantation. rev. ed. 2007. (Illus.). 166p. (YA). (gr. 7-17). per. 8.99 (*978-0-316-15428-4(8)) Little, Brown Bks. for Young Readers.

Hoffman, Mary. Amazing Grace. (Illus.). 32p. (J). (ARA & ENG.). (978-1-85430-334-9(1) , 93433); (ENG & VIE.). (978-1-85430-340-0(6) , 93435) Magi Pubns.

—Amazing Grace. Binch, Caroline, illus. 1998. (ENG & TUR.). 32p. (J). (ps-3). (978-1-85430-338-7(4)) Magi Pubns.

—Amazing Grace. 1999. (YA). pap. 32.99 incl. audio (978-0-7887-4097-8(0) , 41103) Recorded Bks., LLC.

Hoffman, Mary & Youngblood, Shay. Amazing Grace. 1998. 44p. pap. 6.25 (978-0-87129-809-6(0) , A64) Dramatic Publishing Co.

Horowitz, Anthony. Ravens Gate. (Power of Five Ser.: Vol. 1). 2006. 272p. (J). pap. 6.99 (978-0-439-68009-7(3) , Scholastic Paperbacks); 2005. 256p. (YA). pap. 17.95 (978-0-439-67995-4(8)) Scholastic, Inc.

—Ravens Gate. l.t. ed. 2006. (Power of Five Ser.: Vol. 1). (YA). 23.95 (978-0-7862-8584-6(2)) Thorndike Pr.

Horowitz, Dave. The Ugly Pumpkin: A Thanksgiving Story. Horowitz, Dave, illus. 2005. (Illus.). 40p. (J). (ps-2). 16.99 (978-0-399-24267-0(8) , Putnam Juvenile) Penguin Group (USA) Inc.

Horrocks, Anita. What They Don't Know. braille ed. 2003. (J). (gr. 2). spiral bd. (978-0-616-15267-6(1)) Canadian National Institute for the Blind/Institut National Canadien pour les Aveugles.

—What They Don't Know. 1999. (Illus.). 240p. (YA). (gr. 7-10). pap. 8.95 (978-0-7737-6001-1(6)) Stoddart Kids CAN. *Dist:* Fitzhenry & Whiteside, Ltd.

—What They Don't Know. 1999. (J). (978-0-606-19101-2(1)) Tandem Library Bks.

Howe, James. Pinky & Rex & the Bully. 2006. (J). (gr. 1-4). 24.21 (978-1-59961-074-0(4)) Spotlight.

Howe, Norma. Blue Avenger & the Theory of Everything. 2002. (Illus.). 240p. (J). (gr. 7-10). 17.95 (978-0-8126-2654-4(0)) Cricket Bks.

Hudson, Wade. The Two Tyrones. Page, Mark, illus. 2004. 32p. (J). lib. bdg. 15.00 (*978-1-4242-0239-3(6)) Fitzgerald Bks.

—The Two Tyrones. Page, Mark, illus. 2004. 32p. (J). (gr. 2). lib. bdg. 11.19 (978-0-606-33361-0(4)) Tandem Library Bks.

Hutchins, Pat. There's Only One of Me! Hutchins, Pat, illus. 2003. (Illus.). 24p. (J). 16.99 (978-0-06-029819-7(7)) HarperCollins Pubs.

—There's Only One of Me! Hutchins, Pat, illus. 2006. (J). (ps-2). 25.95 incl. audio (978-1-59519-490-9(8)); (Illus.). 28.95 incl. audio compact disk (978-1-59519-494-7(0)) Live Oak Media.

Ibbotson, Eva. The Star of Kazan. 2006. (Illus.). 416p. (J). (gr. 3). reprint ed. 6.99 (978-0-14-240582-6(5) , Puffin) Penguin Group (USA) Inc.

Inkpen, Mick. Nothing. 1998. (Illus.). 32p. (J). (ps-1). pap. 14.95 (978-0-531-30076-3(5) , Orchard Bks.) Scholastic, Inc.

Jacobs, Deborah Lynn. Choices. 2007. 208p. (YA). (gr. 7 up). 16.95 (*978-1-59643-217-8(9)) Roaring Brook Pr.

Jahn-Clough, Lisa. Country Girl, City Girl. 2004. 192p. (YA). (gr. 5). tchr. ed. 15.00 (978-0-618-44791-6(1) , Walter Lorraine) Houghton Mifflin Co. Trade & Reference Div.

Jinks, Catherine. Evil Genius. 2008. (Illus.). 512p. (YA). pap. 7.95 (*978-0-15-206185-2(1) , Harcourt Paperbacks) Harcourt Children's Bks.

—Evil Genius. 2007. (Illus.). 496p. (YA). (gr. 7 up). 17.00 (978-0-15-205988-0(1)); 486p. (J). (*978-1-4287-3510-1(0)) Harcourt Trade Pubs.

Jones, Frewin. The Faerie Path. 2008. (Faerie Path Ser.: Bk. 1). 336p. (J). pap. 8.99 (*978-0-06-087104-8(0) , Eos) HarperCollins Pubs.

—The Lost Queen. 2007. (Faerie Path Ser.: Bk. 2). 352p. (J). lib. bdg. 17.89 (*978-0-06-087106-2(7)); 335p. (YA). (gr. 7 up). 16.99 (*978-0-06-087105-5(9)) HarperCollins Pubs. (Eos).

Karns, Marie. The Incredible Peepers of Penelope Budd. Wummer, Amy, illus. 2005. 32p. (J). 15.95 (978-1-58685-405-8(4)) Gibbs Smith, Publisher.

King-Smith, Dick. Funny Frank. Eastwood, John, illus. 2003. 112p. (gr. 2-5). pap. 5.50 (978-0-440-41880-1(1) , Yearling) Random Hse. Children's Bks.

—Funny Frank. Roth, Roger & Eastwood, John, illus. 2002. 112p. (J). (gr. 2-5). 14.95 (978-0-375-81460-0(4) , Knopf Bks. for Young Readers) Random Hse. Children's Bks.

—Funny Frank. 2003. (gr. 3-6). lib. bdg. 13.00 (978-0-613-72193-6(4)) Tandem Library Bks.

Kline, Lisa Williams. The Princesses of Atlantis. 2002. (Illus.). 192p. (J). 16.95 (978-0-8126-2855-5(1)) Cricket Bks.

Korman, Gordon. Born to Rock. 272p. 2008. pap. 8.99 (*978-0-7868-0921-9(3)); 2006. (gr. 7 up). 15.99 (978-0-7868-0920-2(5)) Hyperion Bks. for Children.

Krauss, Ruth. I'll Be You & You Be Me. Sendak, Maurice, illus. rev. ed. 2001. 40p. (J). (ps-3). 14.89 (978-0-06-028458-9(7)); 15.95 (978-0-06-028459-6(5)) HarperCollins Pubs.

Kuskin, Karla. I Am Me. Wolcott, Dyanna, illus. 2000. 32p. (J). (ps-3). 15.99 (978-0-689-81473-0(9)) Simon & Schuster Children's Publishing.

Lachtman, Ofelia Dumas. The Summer of El Pintor. 2001. (Illus.). 240p. (J). (gr. 11 up). pap. 9.95 (978-1-55885-327-0(8) , Piñata Books) Arte Publico Pr.

—Summer of el Pintor. 2001. (gr. 5-8). lib. bdg. 18.75 (978-0-613-59023-5(6)) Tandem Library Bks.

Lawrence, Michael. The Toilet of Doom. 2004. 256p. (J). pap. 16.95 (978-0-7540-7913-2(9) , Galaxy Children's Large Print) BBC Audiobooks America.

Leavitt, Martine. Tom Finder. 2004. 220p. (YA). (gr. 5 up). pap. 7.95 (978-0-88995-262-1(0)) Red Deer Pr. CAN. *Dist:* Fitzhenry & Whiteside, Ltd.

—Tom Finder. 2003. (gr. 7-12). lib. bdg. 16.40 (978-0-613-84451-2(3)) Tandem Library Bks.

Leverich, Kathleen. The New You. 1998. 112p. (YA). (gr. 5 up). 15.00 (978-0-688-16076-0(X)) HarperCollins Pubs.

—New You. 2000. (978-0-606-18587-5(9)) Tandem Library Bks.

Levine, Gail Carson. Fairest. 2006. 336p. (J). (gr. 3-9). 16.99 (978-0-06-073408-4(6)); lib. bdg. 17.89 (978-0-06-073409-1(4)) HarperCollins Pubs.

—Fairest. l.t. rev. ed. 2007. 356p. (YA). 23.95 (*978-0-7862-9270-7(9)) Thorndike Pr.

Lin, Grace. The Year of the Rat. rev. ed. 2008. 208p. (J). (gr. 3-7). 14.99 (*978-0-316-11426-4(X)) Little, Brown Bks. for Young Readers.

Lisle, Janet Taylor. The Crying Rocks. 2003. (Illus.). 208p. (YA). 16.95 (978-0-689-85319-7(X) , Atheneum/Richard Jackson Bks.) Simon & Schuster Children's Publishing.

—The Crying Rocks. l.t. ed. 2004. (Thorndike Press Large Print Literacy Bridge Ser.). 273p. (J). 22.95 (978-0-7862-6140-6(4)) Thorndike Pr.

Lithgow, John. Marsupial Sue. Davis, Jack E., illus. 2001. 40p. (J). (ps-3). 17.95 incl. audio compact disk (978-0-689-84394-5(1)) Simon & Schuster Children's Publishing.

Lithgow, John & Davis, Jack E. Marsupial Sue. 2004. (Illus.). 40p. (J). reprint ed. pap. 6.99 (978-0-689-87410-9(3) , Aladdin) Simon & Schuster Children's Publishing.

Littman, Sarah. Confessions of a Closet Catholic. 2006. 208p. (J). (gr. 5). reprint ed. pap. 5.99 (978-0-14-240597-0(3) , Puffin) Penguin Group (USA) Inc.

Lollino, Jessica. Lily & the Lost Identity. Lollino, Jessica, ed. 2006. (Little Lily Mays Ser.: vol. 3). (Illus.). 32p. (J). pap. 20.00 (978-0-9712383-3-6(2)) Culture Connection, The.

Losi, Carol A. Salt & Pepper at the Pike Place Market. Meissner, Amy, illus. 2004. 32p. (J). 15.95 (978-1-55868-800-1(5)); pap. 8.95 (978-1-55868-801-8(3)) Graphic Arts Ctr. Publishing Co. (West Winds Pr.).

Love, D. Anne. A Little Rebellion. 2008. 272p. (YA). 16.99 (*978-1-4169-3481-3(2) , McElderry, Margaret K.) Simon & Schuster Children's Publishing.

Lucado, Max. A Hat for Ivan. Wenzel, David, illus. 2005. 32p. 15.99 (978-1-58134-414-1(7) , Crossway Bibles) Crossway Bks.

Lynch, Chris. Slot Machine. 2003. 21.75 (978-0-8446-7249-6(1)) Smith, Peter Pub., Inc.

Lynne Rae Perkins. Criss Cross. l.t. ed. 2006. 325p. (YA). 23.95 (978-0-7862-8728-4(4)) Thorndike Pr.

Magnus, Kellie. Little Lion Goes to School. Robinson, Michael, illus. l.t. ed. 2003. 16p. (J). 9.99 (978-0-9744211-0-0(3)) Media Magic New York.

Malone, Patricia. The Legend of Lady Ilena. 2003. (Illus.). 240p. (YA). (gr. 7). mass mkt. 5.50 (978-0-440-22909-4(X) , Laurel Leaf) Random Hse. Children's Bks.

—The Legend of Lady Ilena. 2003. (gr. 7-12). lib. bdg. 13.55 (978-0-613-72280-3(9)) Tandem Library Bks.

Maloney, Peter & Zekauskas, Felicia. His Mother's Nose. Maloney, Peter & Zekauskas, Felicia, illus. 2001. (Illus.). 40p. (J). (ps-3). 15.99 (978-0-8037-2545-4(0) , Dial) Penguin Group (USA) Inc.

Marsden, Carolyn. The Gold-Threaded Dress. 2006. 80p. (J). (gr. 2-4). reprint ed. pap. 5.99 (978-0-7636-2993-9(6)) Candlewick Pr.

—The Quail Club. 2006. 144p. (J). (gr. 3-5). 15.99 (978-0-7636-2635-8(X)) Candlewick Pr.

Marsden, Carolyn & Loh, Virginia Shin-Mui. The Jade Dragon. 2006. 176p. (J). (gr. 2-5). 15.99 (978-0-7636-3012-6(8)) Candlewick Pr.

Marsden, Carolyn & Mackler, Carolyn. The Gold-Threaded Dress. 2002. 80p. (J). (gr. 2-4). 14.99 (978-0-7636-1569-7(2)) Candlewick Pr.

Martin, Ann M. Here Today. (J). 2005. 336p. (gr. 5-9). pap. 5.99 (978-0-439-57945-2(7) , Scholastic Paperbacks); 2004. 320p. (gr. 4-7). pap. 16.95 (978-0-439-57944-5(9) , Scholastic Pr.) Scholastic, Inc.

Marvin Redpost: Is He a Girl? 2002. (Marvin Redpost Ser.). (Illus.). (J). 11.91 (978-0-7587-6196-5(1)) Book Wholesalers, Inc.

Mason, Ashley. Everybody Is Somebody Special. 2004. 33p. pap. 14.95 (978-1-4137-3044-9(2)) PublishAmerica, Inc.

May, Eleanor. The Real Me. Gott, Barry, illus. 2006. (Social Studies Connects). 32p. (J). (gr. k-3). pap. 4.99 (978-1-57565-186-6(6)) Kane Pr., The.

McDonald, Janet. Off-Color. 2007. 176p. (YA). (gr. 7 up). 16.00 (*978-0-374-37196-8(2)) Farrar, Straus & Giroux.

McGraw, Eloise. The Moorchild. 2007. 256p. (J). pap. 2.99 (*978-1-4169-4819-3(8) , Aladdin) Simon & Schuster Children's Publishing.

McGraw, Eloise Jarvis. The Moorchild. 2002. (Illus.). (J). 13.40 (978-0-7587-4123-3(5)) Book Wholesalers, Inc.

—The Moorchild. 256p. (J). 2006. pap. 5.99 (978-1-4169-2768-6(9)); 1998. (gr. 4-7). pap. 5.99 (978-0-689-82033-5(X)) Simon & Schuster Children's Publishing. (Aladdin).

—The Moorchild. 1998. (J). (978-0-606-13621-1(5)) Tandem Library Bks.

—The Moorchild. l.t. ed. 2002. 291p. (YA). 24.95 (978-0-7862-4787-5(8)) Thorndike Pr.

McNamee, Barbara Oakley. Kelsey & Seattle. 2007. (J). pap. 15.00 (*978-0-8059-7428-7(8)) Dorrance Publishing Co., Inc.

Meister, Cari. What Can I Be? Phillips, Matt, illus. 2003. (Rookie Reader Ser.). 24p. (J). 19.50 (978-0-516-22876-1(5) , Children's Pr.) Scholastic Library Publishing.

Metzger, Steve. It's Snowing. Wilhelm, Hans, illus. 1998. (Dinofours Ser.: No. 14). (J). (ps-1). pap. 3.25 (978-0-590-03550-7(9)) Scholastic, Inc.

Meyer, Carolyn. Jubilee Journey. 2007. (Illus.). 288p. (YA). pap. 6.95 (978-0-15-205845-6(1) , Harcourt Paperbacks) Harcourt Children's Bks.

Miklowitz, Gloria. Secrets in the House of Delgado. 2001. (gr. 5-8). lib. bdg. 15.30 (978-0-613-55662-0(3)) Tandem Library Bks.

Miklowitz, Gloria D. Secrets in the House of Delgado. 2004. 192p. (J). (gr. 4 up). pap. 8.00 (978-0-8028-5210-6(6)) Eerdmans, William B. Publishing Co.

Miller, Kirsten. The Empress's Tomb. 2007. (Kiki Strike Ser.). 350p. (J). (gr. 5-9). 16.95 (***978-1-59990-047-6(5)***, Bloomsbury Children) Bloomsbury Publishing.

Miller, Kirsten. Kiki Strike: Inside the Shadow City. (J). 2007. 400p. (gr. 5-9). pap. 7.95 (***978-1-59990-092-6(0))***; 2006. 250p. 16.95 (978-1-58234-960-2(6)) Bloomsbury Publishing. (Bloomsbury Children).

Mills, Claudia. You're a Brave Man, Julius Zimmerman. 2001. 160p. (gr. 3-7). pap. 5.99 (978-0-7868-1448-0(9)) Hyperion Bks. for Children.

Morris, Gerald. The Quest of the Fair Unknown. 2006. 278p. (J). (gr. 5). 16.00 (978-0-618-63152-0(6)) Houghton Mifflin Co. Trade & Reference Div.

Murphy, Rita. Looking for Lucy Buick. 176p. (YA). (gr. 7). 2007. mass mkt. 6.50 (***978-0-440-22924-7(3)***, Laurel Leaf); 2005. 15.95 (978-0-385-72939-0(1), Delacorte Bks. for Young Readers); 2005. lib. bdg. 17.99 (978-0-385-90176-5(3), Delacorte Bks. for Young Readers) Random Hse. Children's Bks.

Myracle, Lauren. Kissing Kate. 2007. 208p. (YA). (gr. 7). pap. 7.99 (978-0-14-240869-8(7), Puffin) Penguin Group (USA) Inc.

Namioka, Lensey. Half & Half. 2004. 144p. (gr. 3-7). pap. 5.50 (978-0-440-41890-0(9), Yearling) Random Hse. Children's Bks.

Naylor, Phyllis Reynolds. Outrageously Alice. 1998. (Alice Ser.). 144p. (J). (gr. 5-9). pap. 5.99 (978-0-689-80596-7(9), Aladdin) Simon & Schuster Children's Publishing.

—Sang Spell. 224p. (YA). (gr. 5 up). pap. 4.99 (978-0-8072-8294-6(4), Listening Library) Random Hse. Audio Publishing Group.

Naylor, Phyllis Reynolds & Duda, Jana. Sang Spell. 2000. (Illus.). 224p. (YA). (gr. 6-12). pap. 5.99 (978-0-689-82006-9(2), Simon Pulse) Simon & Schuster Children's Publishing.

Neasi, Barbara J. So Many Me's. Ochoa, Ana, illus. 2003. (Rookie Reader - Level C Ser.). 32p. (J). 19.50 (978-0-516-22883-9(8), Children's Pr.) Scholastic Library Publishing.

Newbery, Linda. Set in Stone. 2006. 368p. (YA). (gr. 9). lib. bdg. 18.99 (978-0-385-75103-2(6)) Knopf, Alfred A. Inc.

—Set in Stone. 2006. 368p. (YA). (gr. 9). 16.95 (978-0-385-75102-5(8), Fickling, David Bks.) Random Hse. Children's Bks.

Nishimura, Kae. Dinah! A Cat Adventure. 2004. (Illus.). 32p. (J). (gr. k-3). 14.00 (978-0-618-33612-8(5), Clarion Bks.) Houghton Mifflin Co. Trade & Reference Div.

Numeroff, Laura Joffe. Why a Disguise? 1999. (978-0-606-16317-0(4)) Tandem Library Bks.

Oates, Joyce Carol. Where Is Little Reynard? Graham, Mark, illus. 2003. 32p. (J). 16.89 (978-0-06-029583-7(X)) HarperCollins Pubs.

Okimoto, Jean Davies. Talent Night. 2000. (gr. 7-12). lib. bdg. 22.20 (978-0-613-83512-1(3)) Tandem Library Bks.

—Talent Night. 2000. 180p. (gr. 7-12). pap. 12.95 (978-0-595-00795-0(3), Backinprint.com) iUniverse, Inc.

Orona-Ramirez, Kristy. Kiki's Journey. Warm Day, Jonathan, illus. 2006. 32p. (J). 16.95 (978-0-89239-214-8(2)) Children's Bk. Pr.

Ortiz Cofer, Judith. Call Me Maria. 2004. (First Person Fiction Ser.). 144p. (J). (gr. 4-7). pap. 16.95 (978-0-439-38577-0(6), Orchard Bks.) Scholastic, Inc.

Ostow, Micol. Emily Goldberg Learns to Salsa. 2007. 288p. (J). (gr. 7). pap. 7.99 (***978-1-59514-144-6(8)***, Razorbill) Penguin Group (USA) Inc.

Palmer Preiss, Leah, illus. Escape from Castle Cant. rev. ed. 2007. 287p. (J). (gr. 3-7). per. 6.99 (***978-0-316-15436-9(9))*** Little, Brown Bks. for Young Readers.

Paterson, Katherine. Jacob Have I Loved. l.t. ed. 2000. (LRS Large Print Cornerstone Ser.). 266p. (J). (gr. 5-12). lib. bdg. 29.95 (978-1-58118-073-2(X), 23658) LRS.

—Jip, His Story. (gr. 5-9). 2005. 192p. (YA). pap. 5.99 (978-0-14-240411-9(X)); 1998. 208p. (J). pap. 6.99 (978-0-14-038674-5(2)) Penguin Group (USA) Inc. (Puffin).

Patterson, Christina. Jazz, a Horse of a Different Color. Nguyaen, Huy, illus. 2001. 31p. (J). (978-0-89802-759-4(4)) Beautiful America Publishing Co.

Paulsen, Gary. The Island. 2006. 208p. (J). pap. 5.99 (978-0-439-78662-1(2), Scholastic Paperbacks) Scholastic, Inc.

Payne, Tony & Payne, Jan. The Hippo-Not-Amus. Parker-Rees, Guy, illus. 2004. 32p. (J). pap. 16.95 (978-0-439-56418-2(2), Orchard Bks.) Scholastic, Inc.

Perkins, Lynne. Criss Cross. 2008. 368p. (J). pap. 6.99 (***978-0-06-009274-0(2)***, Greenwillow Bks.) HarperCollins Pubs.

Perkins, Lynne Rae. Criss Cross. 2005. (Illus.). 352p. (J). 16.99 (978-0-06-009272-6(6)); lib. bdg. 17.89 (978-0-06-009273-3(4)) HarperCollins Pubs.

Perkins, Mitali. First Daughter: Extreme American Makeover. (YA). (gr. 7). 2008. 288p. pap. 7.99 (***978-0-14-241154-4(X)***, Puffin); 2007. 192p. 16.99 (978-0-525-47800-3(0), Dutton Juvenile) Penguin Group (USA) Inc.

Peters, Julie Anne. Luna. 2006. 254p. (J). (gr. 9-17). reprint ed. pap. 7.99 (978-0-316-01127-3(4), Tingley, Megan Bks.) Little, Brown Bks. for Young Readers.

Portman, Frank. King Dork. 352p. (YA). (gr. 9). 2007. pap. 8.99 (***978-0-385-73450-9(6))***; 2006. (Illus.). 16.95 (978-0-385-73291-8(0)); 2006. (Illus.). lib. bdg. 18.99 (978-0-385-90312-7(X)) Random Hse. Children's Bks. (Delacorte Bks. for Young Readers).

Powell, Randy. Run If You Dare. 2001. 192p. (YA). (gr. 7 up). 16.00 (978-0-374-39981-8(6), Farrar, Straus & Giroux (BYR)) Farrar, Straus & Giroux.

—Run If You Dare. 2006. 192p. (YA). pap. 6.95 (978-0-374-46375-5(1)) Macmillan.

—Run If You Dare. l.t. ed. 2001. 216p. (J). 22.95 (978-0-7862-3716-6(3)) Thorndike Pr.

Prue, Sally. Call on the Stars. 2003. 192p. (J). (gr. 5 up). 15.95 (978-0-439-48268-4(2)) Scholastic, Inc.

—Cold Tom. 2004. 192p. (J). reprint ed. mass mkt. 5.99 (978-0-439-48269-1(0), Scholastic Paperbacks) Scholastic, Inc.

Pullman, Philip. The Broken Bridge. 2002. 20.50 (978-0-8446-7229-8(7)) Smith, Peter Pub., Inc.

Rabe, Tish. Pigs of a Feather. 1998. (J). 7.99 (978-0-679-89089-8(0), Random Hse. Bks. for Young Readers) Random Hse. Children's Bks.

Ramsay, Paulette. Aunt Jen. 2003. (Caribbean Writers Ser.). 105p. pap. 11.95 (978-0-435-91012-9(4), 91012) Heinemann.

Ransom, Candice F. More Than a Name. 1999. 115p. (J). (gr. 2-5). reprint ed. 14.00 (978-0-7881-6609-9(3)) DIANE Publishing Co.

Regan, Dian Curtis. Cam's Quest: The Continuing Story of Princess Nevermore & the Wizard's Apprentice. 2007. 256p. (J). (gr. 4-8). 17.95 (***978-1-58196-056-3(5))*** Darby Creek Publishing.

Reiss, Mike. The Boy Who Looked Like Lincoln. Catrow, David, tr. Catrow, David, illus. 2003. 32p. (J). (ps-6). 10.99 (978-0-8431-0271-0(3), Price Stern Sloan) Penguin Group (USA) Inc.

—The Boy Who Looked Like Lincoln. Catrow, David, illus. 2006. 32p. (J). (ps). reprint ed. pap. 5.99 (978-0-14-240416-4(0), Puffin) Penguin Group (USA) Inc.

Richardson, Nigel. The Wrong Hands. 272p. (YA). (gr. 7). 2008. mass mkt. 6.50 (***978-0-553-49500-3(3)***, Laurel Leaf); 2006. 15.95 (978-0-375-83459-2(1), Knopf Bks. for Young Readers); 2006. lib. bdg. 17.99 (978-0-375-93459-9(6), Knopf Bks. for Young Readers) Random Hse. Children's Bks.

Richter, Conrad. The Light in the Forest. 2005. (Illus.). 176p. 14.95 (978-1-4000-4426-9(X), Everyman's Library) Knopf Publishing Group.

Roberts, Laura Peyton. The Queen of Second Place. 336p. (gr. 7). 2006. (YA). pap. 5.99 (978-0-440-23871-3(4), Laurel Leaf); 2005. (J). lib. bdg. 17.99 (978-0-385-90200-7(X), Delacorte Bks. for Young Readers); 2005. (YA). 15.95 (978-0-385-73162-1(0), Delacorte Bks. for Young Readers) Random Hse. Children's Bks.

Robinson, Ronnie D. Yankee Doodle Boychik. 2002. (gr. 7-12). lib. bdg. 24.00 (978-0-613-74651-9(1)) Tandem Library Bks.

Sansone, Adele. The Little Green Goose. James, J. Alison, tr. Marks, Alan, illus. 2001. (J). (ps-ps). lib. bdg. 15.25 (978-0-613-36468-3(6)) Tandem Library Bks.

Savage, Deborah. Kotuku. 2002. 304p. (YA). (gr. 7 up). 16.00 (978-0-618-04756-7(5)) Houghton Mifflin Co. Trade & Reference Div.

Savery, Constance. Enemy Brothers. 2001. (Living History Library). (Illus.). 304p. (J). (gr. 5-12). reprint ed. pap. 13.95 (978-1-883937-50-8(7), 50-7) Bethlehem Bks.

Schirripa, Steve & Fleming, Charles. Nicky Deuce: Welcome to the Family. 2006. 176p. (gr. 5-8). 5.99 (978-0-440-42053-8(9), Yearling) Random Hse. Children's Bks.

Schmidt, Gary D. Anson's Way. 1999. 224p. (J). (gr. 5-9). tchr. ed. 15.00 (978-0-395-91529-5(5), Clarion Bks.) Houghton Mifflin Co. Trade & Reference Div.

Scholastic, Inc. Staff & Hudson, Wade. The Two Tyrones. Page, Mark, illus. 2004. (Just for You! Ser.). 32p. (gr. k-3). pap. 3.99 (978-0-439-56866-1(8), Teaching Resources) Scholastic, Inc.

Scott, Kieran. I Was a Non-Blonde Cheerleader. 2007. 272p. (YA). (gr. 7). 7.99 (***978-0-14-240910-7(3)***, Puffin); 2006. 272p. (YA). (gr. 7). pap. 6.99 (978-0-14-240641-0(4), Puffin); 2005. 256p. (J). 15.99 (978-0-399-24279-3(1), Putnam Juvenile) Penguin Group (USA) Inc.

Scott, Kieran. I was a Non Blonde Cheerleader (Splashproof Edition) 2007. 1p. (J). (gr. 7). pap. 6.99 (978-0-14-240832-2(8), Puffin) Penguin Group (USA) Inc.

Scraper, Katherine. Remember the Rules. 2006. (Early Explorers Ser.). (J). 30.00 (***978-1-4108-6031-6(0))*** Benchmark Education Co.

Sedgwick, Marcus. The Dark Flight Down. 240p. 2008. (YA). (gr. 7). pap. 7.99 (***978-0-553-48784-8(1))***; 2005. (J). (gr. 5-7). 15.95 (978-0-385-74645-8(8)) Random Hse. Children's Bks. (Lamb, Wendy).

Serfozo, Mary. A Head Is for Hats. Bratun, Katy, illus. 2000. (Hello Reader! Ser.). 32p. (J). (gr. k-2). pap. 3.99 (978-0-439-09909-7(9)) Scholastic, Inc.

—A Head Is for Hats. 2000. (Hello Reader! Ser.). (Illus.). (J). (978-0-606-18876-0(2)) Tandem Library Bks.

Service, Pamela F. My Cousin, the Alien. 2008. (J). lib. bdg. (***978-0-8225-7627-3(9)***, Carolrhoda Bks.) Lerner Publishing Group.

Shands, Linda I. Wild Fire. 2001. (Wakara of Eagle Lodge Ser.: Vol. 1). (Illus.). 176p. (J). (gr. 7-9). pap. 5.99 (978-0-8007-5746-5(7)) Revell.

Shaskan, Trisha Speed. This Is Anna. 2007. (Illus.). 24p. (J). (***978-1-4048-1244-4(X))*** Picture Window Bks.

Sheldon, Dyan. Confessions of a Teenage Drama Queen. braille ed. 2003. (J). (gr. 2). spiral bd. (978-0-616-15873-9(4)) Canadian National Institute for the Blind/Institut National Canadien pour les Aveugles.

—Confessions of a Teenage Drama Queen. 2002. (Illus.). 272p. (YA). (gr. 7-12). pap. 7.99 (978-0-7636-1848-3(9)) Candlewick Pr.

—Confessions of a Teenage Drama Queen. l.t. ed. 2004. 324p. 22.95 (978-0-7862-6903-7(0), Large Print Pr.) Thorndike Pr.

Shin, Sun Yung. Cooper's Lesson. Cogan, Kim & Paek, Min, trs. from ENG. Cogan, Kim, illus. 2004. (ENG & KOR.). 32p. (J). 16.95 (978-0-89239-193-6(6)) Children's Bk. Pr.

Shusterman, Neal. The Dark Side of Nowhere. 2002. 192p. (J). (gr. 5 up). 5.99 (978-0-7653-4243-0(X), Starscape) Doherty, Tom Assocs., LLC.

Simons, Moya. The Boy Who Would Live Forever: Is Daniel Destined to Be 12-Years-Old Forever? 2006. (Chomps Ser.). (Illus.). 108p. (J). (gr. 3-7). pap. 3.95 (978-0-7624-2624-9(1), Running Pr. Kids) Running Pr. Bk. Pubs.

Singleton, Linda Joy. Sea Switch. 2005. (Illus.). 264p. (ps-7). pap. 5.99 (978-0-7387-0712-9(0)) Llewellyn Pubns.

Smith, Lane. Pinocchio: The Boy. 2002. (Illus.). 40p. (J). (gr. k-3). 16.99 (978-0-670-03585-4(8), Viking Juvenile) Penguin Group (USA) Inc.

Smith, Roland. Zach's Lie. 2003. 224p. (J). (gr. 5-17). pap. 5.99 (978-0-7868-1440-4(3)) Hyperion Bks. for Children.

—Zach's Lie. 2003. (gr. 5-8). lib. bdg. 14.15 (978-0-613-63491-5(8)) Tandem Library Bks.

Sonnenblick, Jordan. Zen & the Art of Faking It. 2007. 272p. (J). pap. 16.99 (***978-0-439-83707-1(3)***, Scholastic Pr.) Scholastic, Inc.

Sorrells, Walter. Fake ID. 2005. (Hunted Ser.: 1). 192p. (YA). (gr. 6). 12.99 (978-0-525-47514-9(1), Dutton Juvenile) Penguin Group (USA) Inc.

—Fake ID: A Mystery. 2007. (Hunted Ser.). 336p. (YA). (gr. 7 up). pap. 6.99 (978-0-14-240762-2(3), Puffin) Penguin Group (USA) Inc.

Staunton, Ted. Sounding Off. 2004. 184p. (J). pap. 7.95 (978-0-88995-293-5(0)) Red Deer Pr. CAN. *Dist:* Fitzhenry & Whiteside, Ltd.

Stewart, Paul & Riddell, Chris. Edge Chronicles 1: Beyond the Deepwoods. 2008. (Edge Chronicles Ser.). 288p. (J). (gr. 5-7). 6.99 (***978-0-440-42087-3(3)***, Yearling) Random Hse. Children's Bks.

Strasser, Todd. How I Changed My Life. 2008. 240p. (YA). mass mkt. 6.99 (***978-1-4169-5409-5(0)***, Simon Pulse) Simon & Schuster Children's Publishing.

Tashiro, Chisato. Chameleon's Colors. Martens, Marianne, tr. from GER. 2003. (Illus.). 32p. (J). 15.95 (978-0-7358-1887-3(8)) North-South Bks., Inc.

—Chameleon's Colors bilingual L. 2007. (J). 16.50 (978-0-7358-2104-0(6)) North-South Bks., Inc.

—Chameleons Colors bilingual PB. 2007. (SPA.). (J). pap. 6.95 (978-0-7358-2105-7(4)) North-South Bks., Inc.

—Chameleons Colors PB. 2007. (Illus.). (J). pap. 6.95 (978-0-7358-2111-8(9)) North-South Bks., Inc.

Tashjian, Janet. The Gospel According to Larry. rev. ed. 2001. (Illus.). 192p. (YA). (gr. 7 up). 16.95 (978-0-8050-6378-3(1), Holt, Henry & Co. Bks. For Young Readers) Holt, Henry & Co.

—The Gospel According to Larry. 2003. (Illus.). 256p. (YA). (gr. 7). mass mkt. 6.50 (978-0-440-23792-1(0), Laurel Leaf) Random Hse. Children's Bks.

—The Gospel According to Larry. 2003. (gr. 7-12). lib. bdg. 14.15 (978-0-613-72333-6(3)) Tandem Library Bks.

—The Gospel According to Larry. l.t. ed. 2005. (Illus.). 235p. (YA). (gr. 8-12). lib. bdg. 22.95 (978-0-7862-7543-4(X)) Thorndike Pr.

Tesch, Lisa. The Little Princess. 2005. 54p. (J). per. 12.95 (978-1-933290-01-0(3)) Tate Publishing & Enterprises, L.L.C.

Tharp, Tim. Knights of the Hill Country. 2006. 240p. (YA). (gr. 7). 16.95 (978-0-375-83653-4(5)); lib. bdg. 18.99 (978-0-375-93653-1(X)) Random Hse. Children's Bks. (Knopf Bks. for Young Readers).

Thompson, Kay. Eloise's What I Absolutely Love Love Love. Knight, Hilary, illus. 2004. 32p. (J). 9.95 (978-0-689-84965-7(6), Simon & Schuster Children's Publishing) Simon & Schuster Children's Publishing.

Throwing Shadows. 2007. 150p. (J). (gr. 3-7). per. 5.99 (***978-1-4169-4959-6(3)***, Aladdin) Simon & Schuster Children's Publishing.

Tomlinson, Heather. The Swan Maiden. 2007. 304p. (YA). (gr. 7 up). 17.95 (***978-0-8050-8275-3(1))*** Holt, Henry & Co.

Triana, Gaby. Cubanita. 2006. 208p. (J). pap. 7.99 (978-0-06-056022-5(3)); 2005. 195p. (YA). (gr. 7-17). 15.99 (978-0-06-056020-1(7), Rayo) HarperCollins Pubs.

Tung, Angela. Song of the Stranger. Artenstein, Michael, ed. 1999. (Roxbury Park Bks.). (J). 192p. (gr. 3-7). pap. 4.95 (978-1-56565-948-3(1), 09481W); 96p. (gr. 5-8). 12.95 (978-1-56565-774-8(8), 07748W) Lowell Hse. (Roxbury Park).

Twain, Mark. The Prince & the Pauper. (J). 19.95 (978-0-8488-0849-5(5)) Amereon LTD.

—The Prince & the Pauper. 2007. (Bantam Classics Ser.). 224p. (J). (gr. 4-11). pap. 3.95 (978-0-553-21256-3(7), Bantam Classics) Bantam Bks.

—The Prince & the Pauper. 2000. (Thrift Edition Ser.). 176p. (gr. 6). pap. 2.50 (978-0-486-41110-1(9)) Dover Pubns., Inc.

—The Prince & the Pauper. (YA). (gr. 5-12). pap. 6.50 (978-0-8224-9344-0(6)) Globe Fearon Educational Publishing.

—The Prince & the Pauper. (J). 9.95 (978-1-56156-311-1(0)) Kidsbooks, Inc.

—The Prince & the Pauper. l.t. ed. 2000. (Large Print Heritage Ser.). 364p. (J). lib. bdg. 33.95 (978-1-58118-068-8(3), 23662) LRS.

—The Prince & the Pauper. l.t. ed. 2000. (Perennial Bestsellers Ser.). 307p. (J). 26.95 (978-0-7838-9061-6(3)) Thorndike Pr.

—The Prince & the Pauper. 1998. (Children's Library). 288p. (J). pap. 3.95 (978-1-85326-147-3(5), 1475WW) Wordsworth Editions, Ltd. GBR. *Dist:* Combined Publishing.

Umansky, Kaye. The Silver Spoon of Solomon Snow. Nash, Scott, illus. 2005. 304p. (J). (gr. 2-7). 14.99 (978-0-7636-2792-8(5)) Candlewick Pr.

—Solomon Snow & the Silver Spoon. Nash, Scott, illus. 2007. 304p. (J). (gr. 2-7). 12.99 (978-0-7636-3218-2(X)) Candlewick Pr.

Updale, Eleanor. Montmorency: Thief, Liar, Gentleman. 2004. (Montmorency Ser.). 240p. (J). pap. 16.95 (978-0-439-58035-9(8), Orchard Bks.) Scholastic, Inc.

—Montmorency & the Assassins: Master, Criminal, Spy. 2006. 416p. (J). (gr. 4-7). pap. 16.99 (978-0-439-68343-2(2), Orchard Bks.) Scholastic, Inc.

—Montmorency on the Rocks: Doctor, Aristocrat, Murderer? 2006. 368p. (J). pap. 6.99 (978-0-439-60677-6(2), Scholastic Paperbacks) Scholastic, Inc.

—Montmorency on the Rocks: Doctor, Aristocrat, Murderer? Hardcastle, Nick, illus. 2005. (Montmorency Ser.). 368p. (J). pap. 16.95 (978-0-439-60676-9(4), Orchard Bks.) Scholastic, Inc.

—Montmorency's Revenge. 2007. (Montmorency Ser.: Vol. 4). 304p. (J). (gr. 7 up). pap. 16.99 (978-0-439-81373-0(5), Orchard Bks.) Scholastic, Inc.

—Thief, Liar, Gentleman? 2005. (Montmorency Ser.). 240p. (J). reprint ed. pap. 6.99 (978-0-439-58036-6(6), Scholastic Paperbacks) Scholastic, Inc.

—Thief, Liar, Gentleman? l.t. ed. 2006. 261p. 23.95 (978-0-7862-8643-0(1)) Thorndike Pr.

Vail, Rachel. Please, Please, Please. (Friendship Ring Ser.: No. 2). 240p. (J). (gr. 4-8). 1999. pap. 3.99 (978-0-439-08762-9(7)); 1998. pap. 14.95 (978-0-590-00327-8(5)); 1998. pap. 4.99 (978-0-590-37452-1(4)) Scholastic, Inc.

Vail, Rachel. You, Maybe: The Profound Asymmetry of Love in High School. (J). 2007. 240p. pap. 7.99 (***978-0-06-056919-8(0)***, HarperTeen); 2006. 208p. (gr. 2). 15.99 (978-0-06-056917-4(4)); 2006. 208p. (gr. 2). lib. bdg. 16.89 (978-0-06-056918-1(2)) HarperCollins Pubs.

Van Steenwyk, Elizabeth. Maggie in the Morning. 2002. (gr. 3-6). lib. bdg. 14.15 (978-0-613-88116-6(8)) Tandem Library Bks.

Weeks, Sarah. I'm a Pig. Berry, Holly, illus. 2005. 32p. (J). (ps-2). lib. bdg. 16.89 (978-0-06-074344-4(1)); 15.99 (978-0-694-01075-2(8)) HarperCollins Pubs. (Geringer, Laura Book).

—Regular Guy. (Harper Trophy Bks.). 128p. (J). 2000. (gr. 5 up). pap. 4.99 (978-0-06-440782-3(9), Harper Trophy); 1999. (Illus.). (gr. 3-7). 14.89 (978-0-06-028368-1(8), Geringer, Laura Book); 1999. (Illus.). (gr. 3-7). 14.95 (978-0-06-028367-4(X), Geringer, Laura Book) HarperCollins Pubs.

—Regular Guy. 2000. (978-0-606-18715-2(4)); (gr. 3-6). lib. bdg. 13.00 (978-0-613-28621-3(9)) Tandem Library Bks.

—So B. It. (J). 2005. 272p. pap. 6.99 (978-0-06-441047-2(1), Harper Trophy); 2004. 256p. (gr. 5 up). 16.99 (978-0-06-623622-3(3), Geringer, Laura Book); 2004. 256p. (gr. 5 up). lib. bdg. 16.89 (978-0-06-623623-0(1), Geringer, Laura Book) HarperCollins Pubs.

Weil, Sylvie. My Guardian Angel. 208p. (J). 2007. pap. 5.99 (***978-0-439-57682-6(2)***, Scholastic Paperbacks); 2004. (gr. 4-7). pap. 16.95 (978-0-439-57681-9(4), Levine, Arthur A. Bks.) Scholastic, Inc.

Weyn, Suzanne. The Bar Code Revolution. 2006. 272p. (J). pap. 6.99 (978-0-439-80385-4(3), Scholastic Paperbacks) Scholastic, Inc.

—The Bar Code Tattoo. 2004. (Point Thriller Ser.). 256p. (J). (gr. 7 up). pap. 5.99 (978-0-439-39562-5(3)) Scholastic, Inc.

White, Ruth. Belle Prater's Boy. unabr. ed. 2004. 196p. (J). (gr. 5-9). pap. 38.00 incl. audio (978-0-8072-8682-1(6), YA234SP, Listening Library) Random Hse. Audio Publishing Group.

—Belle Prater's Boy. 1998. (YA). 12.15 (978-0-606-12610-6(4)) Tandem Library Bks.

—Belle Prater's Boy. l.t. ed. 2000. (Illus.). 221p. (YA). (gr. 4-7). 21.95 (978-0-7862-2885-0(7)) Thorndike Pr.

—Way down Deep. 2007. (Illus.). 208p. (J). (gr. 5 up). 16.00 (978-0-374-38251-3(4), Farrar, Straus & Giroux (BYR)) Farrar, Straus & Giroux.

Wilkins, Rose. So Super Starry. 2006. (YA). 230p. (***978-1-4156-6975-4(9)***); 240p. (gr. 7). reprint ed. pap. 6.99 (978-0-14-240581-9(7)) Penguin Group (USA) Inc. (Puffin).

Willems, Mo. Knuffle Bunny Too: A Case of Mistaken Identity. Willems, Mo, illus. rev. ed. 2007. (Illus.). 48p. (J). (ps-1). 16.99 (***978-1-4231-0299-1(1))*** Hyperion Pr.

Wilson, Diane Lee. Black Storm Comin'. (J). 2006. 240p. pap. 5.99 (978-0-689-87138-2(4), Aladdin); 2005. 304p. (gr. 5-9). 17.99 (978-0-689-87137-5(6), McElderry, Margaret K.) Simon & Schuster Children's Publishing.

Wilson, Gina. Ignis. Lynch, P. J., illus. 2003. 40p. (J). (ps). pap. 6.99 (978-0-7636-2192-6(7)) Candlewick Pr.

Winston, Sherri. Acting: A Novel. 2004. 256p. (YA). 15.95 (978-0-7614-5173-0(0)) Cavendish, Marshall Corp.

Winston, Sherri. Kayla Chronicles. 2008. 208p. (YA). (gr. 7-17). 16.99 (***978-0-316-11430-1(8))*** Little, Brown Bks. for Young Readers.

Winthrop, Elizabeth. Squashed in the Middle. Cummings, Pat, illus. 2005. 32p. (J). 16.95 (978-0-8050-6497-1(4), Holt, Henry & Co. Bks. For Young Readers) Holt, Henry & Co.

Wittlinger, Ellen. Gracie's Girl. Hamlin, Janet, illus. 2000. 192p. (J). (gr. 3-7). 16.95 (978-0-689-82249-0(9)) Simon & Schuster Children's Publishing.

—Gracie's Girl. l.t. ed. 2002. 224p. (J). 22.95 (978-0-7862-3761-6(9)) Thomson Gale.

—Hard Love. 2001. (Illus.). 240p. (YA). (gr. 8-12). reprint ed. pap. 8.99 (978-0-689-84154-5(X), Simon Pulse) Simon & Schuster Children's Publishing.

—Parrotfish. 2007. 304p. (YA). (gr. 7 up). 16.99 (978-1-4169-1622-2(9) , Simon & Schuster Children's Publishing) Simon & Schuster Children's Publishing.

Wong, Benedict Norbert. Lo & Behold. Wong, Benedict Norbert, illus. l.t. ed. 2003. (Illus.). 38p. (gr. 1 up). 16.95 (978-0-9728192-0-6(7) , LOBE) Taiji Arts Publishing.

—Lo & Behold: Good Enough to Eat. Wong, Benedict Norbert, illus. l.t. ed. 2003. (Illus.). 40p. (J). (gr. 1-12). 16.95 (978-0-9728192-1-3(5) , 1002LB) Taiji Arts Publishing.

Woods, Noah. Tom Cat. 2004. (Illus.). 32p. (J). (ps-2). lib. bdg. 16.99 (978-0-375-92497-2(3) , Random Hse. Bks. for Young Readers) Random Hse. Children's Bks.

Wright, Bil. When the Black Girl Sings. 2008. 272p. (YA). (gr. 7 up). 16.99 (***978-1-4169-3995-5(4)*** , Simon & Schuster Children's Publishing) Simon & Schuster Children's Publishing.

Wyeth, Sharon Dennis. The World of Daughter McGuire. 2001. 176p. (gr. 3-7). pap. 12.00 (978-0-375-89502-9(7) , Delacorte Bks. for Young Readers) Random Hse. Children's Bks.

Yang, Gene Luen. American Born Chinese. Pien, Lark, illus. rev. ed. 2006. 240p. (J). pap. 17.95 (978-1-59643-152-2(0) , First Second Bks.) Roaring Brook Pr.

—American Born Chinese, Collector's Edition. rev. ed. 2006. 240p. (J). 29.95 (978-1-59643-208-6(X) , First Second Bks.) Roaring Brook Pr.

Yoo, David. Girls for Breakfast. 304p. (YA). (gr. 9). 2005. 15.95 (978-0-385-73192-8(2) , Delacorte Bks. for Young Readers); 2005. lib. bdg. 17.99 (978-0-385-90227-4(1) , Delacorte Bks. for Young Readers); 2006. reprint ed. pap. 5.99 (978-0-440-23883-6(8) , Laurel Leaf) Random Hse. Children's Bks.

Zalben, Jane Breskin. Leap. 2007. 272p. (J). (gr. 5). 15.99 (978-0-375-83871-2(6)); lib. bdg. 18.99 (978-0-375-93871-9(0)) Random Hse. Children's Bks. (Knopf Bks. for Young Readers).

IDENTITY, PERSONAL

see Identity (Psychology); Personality

IDIOMS

see names of languages with the subdivision Idioms, e.g. English Language—Idioms

Bridgman, Beth, contrib. by. Figures of Speech. rev. ed. 1998. (Horizons Ser.). (Illus.). 24p. (J). (gr. 4-6). pap. 5.95 (978-1-58086-067-3(2)) EDC Publishing.

Harcourt School Publishers Staff. It's Raining Cats & Dogs. 3rd ed. 2002. (Trophies English Language Learners Ser.). (Illus.). pap. 5.10 (978-0-15-327704-7(1)) Harcourt Schl. Pubs.

Just the Bee's Knees: Individual Title Six-Packs. (Story Steps Ser.). (gr. k-2). 32.00 (978-0-7635-9844-0(5)) Rigby Education.

Realtime Associates and Mazer Corporation Staff & LeapFrog Staff, compiled by. Understand Idioms. 2002. (J). (gr. 3). 66.75 (978-1-58605-383-3(3) , LeapFrog Schl. Hse.) LeapFrog Enterprises, Inc.

—Understand Idioms & Analogies. 2002. (J). (gr. 4). 66.75 (978-1-58605-441-0(4)); (gr. 5). 66.75 (978-1-58605-504-2(6)) LeapFrog Enterprises, Inc. (LeapFrog Schl. Hse.).

Sebastiani, Laura, creator. Penny & Drew's Penciltips: Idioms. 2006. 80p. (J). 4.95 (978-0-9766793-2-5(9)) ThoughtRockets, Inc.

Snodgrass, Catherine S. Super Silly Sayings That Are over Your Head: A Children's Illustrated Book of Idioms. 2004. (Illus.). 29p. (J). (gr. 1-4). bds. 16.95 (978-0-9666529-4-9(0)) Starfish Specialty Pr., LLC.

IGNATIUS, OF LOYOLA, SAINT, 1491-1556

Giaimo, Donna, et al. Saint Ignatius of Loyola: For the Greater Glory of God. 2001. (Encounter the Saints Ser.: Vol. 8). (Illus.). 108p. (J). pap. 5.95 (978-0-8198-7043-8(9) , 332-348) Pauline Bks. & Media.

Sklar, Peggy A. St. Ignatius of Loyola: In God's Service. Kelley, Patrick, illus. 2001. 104p. 7.95 (978-0-8091-6686-6(7) , 6688-7) Paulist Pr.

ILLEGAL ALIENS

Egendorf, Laura K. Illegal Immigration. 2006. (Writing the Critical Essay Ser.). (Illus.). 144p. (gr. 6-10). 29.95 (978-0-7377-3582-6(1) , Greenhaven Pr., Inc.) Thomson Gale.

Haerens, Margaret. Illegal Immigration. 2006. (Opposing Viewpoints Ser.). 244p. (YA). (gr. 7 up). pap. 24.95 (978-0-7377-3357-0(8)); lib. bdg. 36.20 (978-0-7377-3356-3(X)) Thomson Gale. (Greenhaven Pr., Inc.).

Kenney, Karen. Illegal Immigration. 2007. (Essential Viewpoints Ser.). (Illus.). 112p. (YA). (gr. 7-9). lib. bdg. 32.79 (***978-1-59928-861-1(3)*** , Essential Library) ABDO Publishing Co.

Miller, Debra. Illegal Immigration. 2007. (Current Controversies Ser.). (Illus.). 240p. (J). (gr. 10-12). 36.20 (***978-0-7377-3723-3(9));*** pap. 24.95 (***978-0-7377-3724-0(7))*** Thomson Gale. (Greenhaven Pr., Inc.).

Miller, Debra A. Illegal Immigration. 2007. (Compact Research Ser.). 112p. (YA). lib. bdg. (***978-1-60152-009-8(3))*** ReferencePoint Pr., Inc.

Ouellette, Jeannine. A Day Without Immigrants: Rallying Behind America's Newcomers. 2007. (J). lib. bdg. (***978-0-7565-2498-2(9))*** Compass Point Bks.

ILLEGAL ALIENS—FICTION

Beatty, P. Lupita Manana. 6 vols., Set. 3rd ed. 2000. (J). pap. 29.70 (978-0-13-772484-0(5)) Prentice Hall (Schl. Div.).

Budhos, Marina. Ask Me No Questions. 2006. (Illus.). 176p. (YA). (gr. 5-9). 16.95 (978-1-4169-0351-2(8) , Atheneum) Simon & Schuster Children's Publishing.

Buss, Fran Leeper. Journey of the Sparrows. 2002. (gr. 5-8). lib. bdg. 15.30 (978-0-613-60810-7(0)) Tandem Library Bks.

Harper, Jo. Delfino's Journey. 2000. viii, 184p. (J). (gr. 8-12). 15.95 (978-0-89672-437-2(9)) Texas Tech Univ. Pr.

—Delfino's Journey, Grades 8-12. 2000. (Illus.). viii, 184p. (J). tchr. ed. 5.95 (978-0-89672-442-6(5)) Texas Tech Univ. Pr.

Hobbs, Will. Crossing the Wire. 224p. (J). 2007. pap. 5.99 (978-0-06-074140-2(6) , Harper Trophy); 2006. (Illus.). lib. bdg. 16.89 (978-0-06-074139-6(2)) HarperCollins Pubs.

Lupica, Mike. Heat. 2007. 240p. (J). pap. 6.99 (978-0-14-240757-8(7) , Puffin); 2006. 220p. (YA). (gr. 5). 16.99 (978-0-399-24301-1(1) , Philomel) Penguin Group (USA) Inc.

Lupita Manana. 3rd ed. (J). pap., stu. ed. (978-0-13-772500-7(0)) Prentice Hall (Schl. Div.).

Rushford, Patricia H. Secrets of Ghost Island. 2007. (J). (***978-88-02-46255-4(0))*** Moody Pubs.

Vanished. 64p. (YA). (gr. 6-12). pap. (978-0-8224-2367-6(7)) Globe Fearon Educational Publishing.

ILLINOIS

Alter, Judy. Illinois: A MyReportLinks.com Book. 2003. (States Ser.). (Illus.). 48p. (J). (gr. 4-10). lib. bdg. 25.26 (978-0-7660-5111-9(0) , MyReportLinks.com Bks.) Enslow Pubs., Inc.

Anderson, Kathy P. Illinois. 2nd rev. exp. ed. (Hello U. S. A. Ser.). (Illus.). 84p. (J). (gr. 3-6). 2003. pap. 6.95 (978-0-8225-4154-7(8)); 2002. lib. bdg. 25.26 (978-0-8225-4054-0(1)) Lerner Publishing Group.

Baldridge, Carol. Illinois Through the Decades Fact Cards. 2000. (Illus.). 70p. (J). (gr. 4-8). ring bd. 34.00 (978-1-884925-73-3(1)) Toucan Valley Pubns., Inc.

Boekhoff, P. M. Illinois. 2005. (Portraits of the States Ser.). (Illus.). 32p. (J). pap. (978-0-8368-4643-0(5)); lib. bdg. 23.33 (978-0-8368-4624-9(9)) Stevens, Gareth Inc.

Boekhoff, P. M. & Kallen, Stuart A. Illinois, 8 bks. 2001. (Seeds of a Nation Ser.). (Illus.). 48p. (J). (gr. 3-5). 26.20 (978-0-7377-0279-8(6) , LML00902-178547, Kidhaven) Thomson Gale.

Brill, Marlene Targ. Illinois. 2nd ed. 2005. (Celebrate the States Ser.). (Illus.). 144p. (J). (gr. 4-7). lib. bdg. 37.07 (978-0-7614-1735-4(4) , Benchmark Bks.) Cavendish, Marshall Corp.

Brown, Vanessa. Illinois. (Bilingual Library of the United States of America). (J). 2006. (SPA.). lib. bdg. (978-1-4042-3140-5(4) , PowerKids Pr.); 2005. (ENG & SPA., Illus.). 32p. lib. bdg. 22.50 (978-1-4042-3078-1(5) , Buenas Letra) Rosen Publishing Group, Inc., The.

Bruun, Erik & Peterson, Rick. Illinois. 2000. (Illus.). 48p. (J). (gr. 3-7). 9.95 (978-1-57912-101-3(2) , 81101) Black Dog & Leventhal Pubs., Inc.

Burgan, Michael. Illinois. 2007. (America the Beautiful, Third Ser.). (Illus.). 144p. (YA). (gr. 5-8). lib. bdg. 38.00 (***978-0-531-18559-9(1)*** , Children's Pr.) Scholastic Library Publishing.

Craats, Rennay. A Guide to Illinois. 2001. (American States Ser.). (Illus.). 32p. (J). lib. bdg. (978-1-930954-87-8(5)); per. 7.95 (978-1-930954-78-6(6)) Weigl Pubs., Inc.

Deinard, Jenny. How to Draw Illinois' Sights & Symbols. 2002. (Kid's Guide to Drawing America Ser.). (Illus.). 32p. (J). (gr. 3-5). lib. bdg. 25.25 (978-0-8239-6069-9(2) , PowerKids Pr.) Rosen Publishing Group, Inc., The.

—Illinois's Sights & Sounds. 2004. 48p. pap. 8.95 (978-1-4042-8502-6(4)) Rosen Publishing Group, Inc., The.

Feeley, Kathleen. Illinois. Porras, Carlos & D'Andrea, Patricia, trs. 2003. (World Almanac Biblioteca de los Estados). (SPA., Illus.). 48p. (J). (gr. 5 up). lib. bdg. 30.00 (978-0-8368-5544-9(2) , World Almanac Library) Stevens, Gareth Inc.

—Illinois: The Prairie State. 2002. (World Almanac Library of the States). (Illus.). 48p. (J). (gr. 5 up). pap. 14.95 (978-0-8368-5284-4(2)); lib. bdg. 30.00 (978-0-8368-5115-1(3)) Stevens, Gareth Inc. (World Almanac Library).

—Illinois: The Prairie State. 2002. (Illus.). 48p. (J). (gr. 4-7). lib. bdg. 24.15 (978-0-613-52403-2(9)) Tandem Library Bks.

Fowler, Allan. Illinois. (Rookie Read-About Geography Ser.). (Illus.). 32p. (J). (gr. 1-2). 2000. pap. 5.95 (978-0-516-26555-1(5)); 1999. 20.50 (978-0-516-21554-9(X)) Scholastic Library Publishing. (Children's Pr.).

Heinrichs, Ann. Illinois. 2005. (Welcome to the USA Ser.). 40p. (J). (gr. 1-5). 27.07 (978-1-59296-285-3(8)) Child's World, Inc.

—Illinois. 2002. (This Land Is Your Land Ser.). (Illus.). 48p. (J). (gr. 3 up). lib. bdg. 22.60 (978-0-7565-0313-0(2)) Compass Point Bks.

Illinois. 2000. (Switched on Schoolhouse Ser.). (Illus.). (YA). (gr. 7-12). pap. 24.95 incl. cd-rom (978-0-7403-0265-7(5) , SOSIL) Alpha Omega Pubns., Inc.

Illinois. 2003. (World Almanac Biblioteca de los Estados). (SPA., Illus.). 48p. (J). (gr. 5 up). pap. 0.00 (978-0-8368-5551-7(5) , World Almanac Library) Stevens, Gareth Inc.

Koopmans, Andy. The Leopold & Loeb Case. 2003. (Famous Trials Ser.). (Illus.). 112p. (J). 29.95 (978-1-59018-227-7(8) , Lucent Bks.) Thomson Gale.

Kummer, Patricia K. Illinois. rev. ed. 2002. (One Nation Ser.). (Illus.). 48p. (J). (gr. 3-4). lib. bdg. 22.60 (978-0-7368-1237-5(7) , Bridgestone Bks.) Capstone Pr., Inc.

Marsh, Carole. The Big Illinois Reproducible Activity Book. 2004. (Carole Marsh Illinois Bks.). (Illus.). 96p. (J). (gr. 2-6). pap. 9.95 (978-0-7933-9460-9(0)) Gallopade International.

—Illinois Classic Christmas Trivia. 2002. (Carole Marsh Illinois Bks.). (Illus.). 32p. pap. 6.95 (978-0-635-01393-4(2) , 13932); lib. bdg. 21.95 (978-0-635-01394-1(0) , 13940) Gallopade International.

—Illinois Current Events Projects: 30 Cool, Activities, Crafts, Experiments & More for Kids to Do to Learn about Your State! 2003. (Illinois Experience Ser.). 32p. (gr. k-5). pap. 5.95 (978-0-635-02032-1(7) , Marsh, Carole Bks.) Gallopade International.

—The Illinois Experience Pocket Guide. 2000. (Carole Marsh Illinois Bks.). (Illus.). 96p. (J). (gr. 3-8). pap. 6.95 (978-0-7933-9450-0(3)) Gallopade International.

—Illinois Geography Projects: 30 Cool, Activities, Crafts, Experiments & More for Kids to Do to Learn about Your State! 2003. (Illinois Experience Ser.). 32p. (gr. k-5). pap. 5.95 (978-0-635-01832-8(2) , Marsh, Carole Bks.) Gallopade International.

—Illinois Government Projects: 30 Cool, Activities, Crafts, Experiments & More for Kids to Do to Learn about Your State! 2003. (Illinois Experience Ser.). 32p. (gr. k-5). pap. 5.95 (978-0-635-01932-5(9) , Marsh, Carole Bks.) Gallopade International.

—Illinois Jeopardy! Answers & Questions about Our State! 2000. (Carole Marsh Illinois Bks.). (Illus.). 32p. (J). (gr. 3-8). pap. 7.95 (978-0-7933-9513-2(5)) Gallopade International.

—Illinois "Jography" A Fun Run Thru Our State! 2000. (Carole Marsh Illinois Bks.). (Illus.). 32p. (J). (gr. 3-8). pap. 7.95 (978-0-7933-9514-9(3)) Gallopade International.

—Illinois Millionaire: Game Book. 2001. (Carole Marsh Illinois Bks.). (Illus.). 32p. (J). (gr. 3-8). pap., act. bk. ed. 9.95 (978-0-635-00042-2(3)) Gallopade International.

—Illinois People Projects: 30 Cool, Activities, Crafts, Experiments & More for Kids to Do to Learn about Your State! 2003. (Illinois Experience Ser.). 32p. (gr. k-5). pap. 5.95 (978-0-635-01982-0(5) , Marsh, Carole Bks.) Gallopade International.

—Illinois Symbols & Facts Projects: 30 Cool, Activities, Crafts, Experiments & More for Kids to Do to Learn about Your State! 2003. (Illinois Experience Ser.). 32p. (gr. k-5). pap. 5.95 (978-0-635-01882-3(9) , Marsh, Carole Bks.) Gallopade International.

—The Incredible Illinois Coloring Book. 2000. (Carole Marsh Illinois Bks.). (Illus.). 32p. (J). (gr. k-2). pap. 3.95 (978-0-7933-9470-8(8)) Gallopade International.

—My First Book about Illinois. 2000. (Carole Marsh Illinois Bks.). (Illus.). 32p. (J). (gr. k-4). pap. 7.95 (978-0-7933-9512-5(7)) Gallopade International.

—My First Pocket Guide Illinois. 2000. (Illinois Experience Ser.). 96p. (J). (gr. 3-8). 12.95 (978-0-635-01303-3(7) , 13037) Gallopade International.

—The Survivor: A Class Challenge. 2001. (Carole Marsh Illinois Bks.). lib. bdg. 29.95 (978-0-635-00659-2(6)); lib. bdg. 29.95 (978-0-635-00661-5(8)) Gallopade International.

—Who Wants to Be a Millionaire? 2001. (Carole Marsh Illinois Bks.). lib. bdg. 29.95 (978-0-635-00043-9(1)) Gallopade International.

McAuliffe, Emily. Illinois: Facts & Symbols. 1998. (States & Their Symbols Ser.). 24p. (J). lib. bdg. 14.00 (978-0-531-11551-0(8) , Watts, Franklin) Scholastic Library Publishing.

—Illinois Facts & Symbols. rev. ed. 2003. (States & Their Symbols Ser.). 24p. (J). lib. bdg. 19.93 (978-0-7368-2243-5(7)) Capstone Pr., Inc.

Price-Groff, Claire. Illinois. 2002. (It's My State! Ser.). (Illus.). 80p. (J). 27.07 (978-0-7614-1422-3(3)) Cavendish, Marshall Corp.

Santella, Andrew. All Around Illinois: Regions & Resources. 2002. (Heinemann State Studies). (Illus.). 48p. (J). (gr. 3-5). lib. bdg. 27.07 (978-1-4034-0007-9(5)); pap. 8.50 (978-1-4034-0568-5(9) , 91872) Heinemann Library.

—Illinois, 6 bks., Set. 2002. (Heinemann State Studies). (J). (gr. 3-5). lib. bdg. 162.42 (978-1-58810-482-3(6)) Heinemann Library.

—Uniquely Illinois. 2002. (Heinemann State Studies). (Illus.). 48p. (J). (gr. 3-5). lib. bdg. 27.07 (978-1-4034-0012-3(1)); pap. 8.50 (978-1-4034-0573-9(5) , 91877) Heinemann Library.

Shofner, Shawndra. Illinois. 2008. (J). (***978-1-58341-638-9(2)*** , Creative Education) Creative Co., The.

Sievert, Terri. Illinois. 2003. (Land of Liberty Ser.). (Illus.). 64p. (J). (gr. 3-4). lib. bdg. 23.93 (978-0-7368-1581-9(3) , Bridgestone Bks.) Capstone Pr., Inc.

Somervill, Barbara A. Illinois. 80p. (J). 2008. (From Sea to Shining Sea, Second Ser.). pap. 7.95 (***978-0-531-18804-0(3));*** 2001. (From Sea to Shining Sea Ser.: 2). (Illus.). (gr. 3-5). 30.50 (978-0-516-22320-9(8)) Scholastic Library Publishing. (Children's Pr.).

Wargin, Kathy-Jo. L Is for Lincoln: An Illinois Alphabet. van Frankenhuyzen, Gijsbert, illus. 40p. (J). 2004. pap. 7.95 (978-1-58536-250-9(6)); 2000. 16.95 (978-1-58536-016-1(3)) Sleeping Bear Pr.

—Prairie Numbers: An Illinois Number Book. O'Malley, Kathy, illus. 2006. 40p. (J). 17.95 (978-1-58536-180-9(1)) Sleeping Bear Pr.

ILLINOIS—FICTION

Aryal, Aimee. Let's Go Illini! Shrestha, Anuj, illus. 2004. (J). 19.95 (978-1-932888-21-8(7)) Mascot Bks., Inc.

Bauer, Marion Dane. Killing Miss Kitty & Other Sins. 2007. 176p. (YA). (gr. 7). 16.00 (***978-0-618-69000-8(X)*** , Clarion Bks.) Houghton Mifflin Co. Trade & Reference Div.

—The Secret of the Painted House. Gore, Leonid, illus. 2007. (Stepping Stone Bks.). 112p. (J). (gr. 1-4). 11.99 (***978-0-375-84079-1(6));*** lib. bdg. 14.99 (***978-0-375-94079-8(0))*** Random Hse. Children's Bks. (Random Hse. Bks. for Young Readers).

Brodland, Rita, ed. State Fair Time Warp. Freeman, Troy, illus. l.t. ed. 2002. (WeWrite Kids! Ser.). 64p. (J). (gr. k-3). pap. 8.95 (978-1-57635-059-1(2)) WeWrite LLC.

Brokaw, Nancy Steele. Leaving Emma. 1999. 144p. (J). (gr. 4-6). tchr. ed. 15.00 (978-0-395-90699-6(7) , Clarion Bks.) Houghton Mifflin Co. Trade & Reference Div.

Center for Learning Network Staff. A Long Way from Chicago/A Year down Yonder: Curriculum Unit. 2002. (Novel Ser.). 84p. (J). tchr. ed., spiral bd. 19.95 (978-1-56077-723-6(0)) Ctr. for Learning, The.

Dell, Pamela. Liam's Watch: A Strange Story of the Great Chicago Fire. 2002. (Scrapbooks of America Ser.). (Illus.). 48p. (J). (gr. 2-6). 28.50 (978-1-59187-014-2(3)) Child's World, Inc.

Dower, Laura. Just Visiting. rev. ed. 2002. (From the Files of Madison Finn Ser.). 176p. (J). (gr. 3-7). pap. 4.99 (978-0-7868-1683-5(X) , Volo) Hyperion Bks. for Children.

—Just Visiting. 2002. (gr. 3-6). lib. bdg. 13.00 (978-0-613-90688-3(8)) Tandem Library Bks.

Fenner, Carol. Yolonda's Genius. unabr. ed. 2004. 211p. (J). (gr. 4-6). pap. 38.00 incl. audio (978-0-8072-0462-7(5) , Listening Library) Random Hse. Audio Publishing Group.

Gingold, Katharine Kendzy. Ruth by Lake & Prairie: True Stories of Early Naperville, Illinois. 2006. (J). per. 12.95 (***978-0-9792419-0-1(1))*** Gnu Ventures Co.

Greenlee, Don. This Countryboy Guardian Was Heaven Sent. 2007. (Illus.). 114p. (YA). per. 14.95 net. (***978-0-9795574-0-8(2))*** Country Boy Publishing Co.

Henity, Kristi. Kimi's Grand Adventures, Vol. 1. 2004. 55p. pap. 12.95 (978-1-4137-2869-9(3)) PublishAmerica, Inc.

Hornburg, Michael. Downers Grove. 2001. (gr. 7-12). lib. bdg. 21.10 (978-0-613-36949-7(1)) Tandem Library Bks.

Hunt, Irene. Across Five Aprils. 2002. 224p. (gr. 12). pap. 4.99 (978-0-425-18278-9(9) , Berkley) Penguin Group (USA) Inc.

—Across Five Aprils. 1999. (J). pap. 1.95 (978-0-590-05178-1(4)) Scholastic, Inc.

Jenkins, Jerry B. Wildfire! Into the Great Tribulation. 2003. (Left Behind Ser.: Bk. 27). (gr. 5-8). lib. bdg. 14.15 (978-0-613-63532-5(9)) Tandem Library Bks.

Kirby. Ida Lou's Story. 2000. (American Quilts Ser.: Vol. 4). (J). 11.64 (978-0-606-20082-0(7)) Tandem Library Bks.

Kirby, Susan E. Ellen's Story. 2000. (gr. 3-6). lib. bdg. 13.00 (978-0-613-31156-4(6)) Tandem Library Bks.

—Hattie's Story. 2000. (American Quilts Ser.: Vol. 2). (J). 11.64 (978-0-606-20080-6(0)) Tandem Library Bks.

Kirk, Donald. Hinsdale: The Summer of '58. 2003. (Illus.). (YA). pap. 7.95 (978-0-9654341-4-0(1) , Sweetwater Stagelines) The Old West Co.

Klise, Kate. Deliver Us from Normal. 2005. 240p. (YA). (gr. 5-9). 16.95 (978-0-439-52322-6(2)) Scholastic, Inc.

—Deliver Us from Normal: Read-Along/Homework Pack. unabr. ed. 2005. (YA). (gr. 5-8). 65.70 incl. audio (978-1-4193-3619-5(3) , 42050) Recorded Bks., LLC.

Leitch, Will. Catch. 2005. 304p. (YA). (gr. 9-12). pap. 7.99 (978-1-59514-069-2(7) , Razorbill) Penguin Group (USA) Inc.

Lems, Kristin. Piano Teacher's Daughter. Daoudi, Karima Lems & Daoudi, Kennan Lems, illus. 2002. pap. 18.00 (978-0-9637048-2-5(6)) Lems-Dworkin, Carol Pubs.

Lorenz, Albert & Schleh, Joy. Hero, Hawk, & Open Hand: A Story about Cahokia. 2004. (J). (978-0-8109-4842-6(7)) Abrams, Harry N. , Inc.

Moranville, Sharelle Byars. Over the River. rev. ed. 2002. 240p. (J). (gr. 4-9). 16.95 (978-0-8050-7049-1(4) , Holt, Henry & Co. Bks. For Young Readers) Holt, Henry & Co.

—Over the River. 2004. 240p. (gr. 5). 5.99 (978-0-440-41977-8(8) , Yearling) Random Hse. Children's Bks.

Park, Linda Sue. Project Mulberry. 2005. 240p. (J). (gr. 5-9). 16.00 (978-0-618-47786-9(1) , Clarion Bks.) Houghton Mifflin Co. Trade & Reference Div.

—Project Mulberry. 2007. 240p. (J). (gr. 4-7). pap. 6.50 (978-0-440-42163-4(2) , Yearling) Random Hse. Children's Bks.

Peck, Richard. A Long Way from Chicago. 2002. (Illus.). (J). 13.19 (978-0-7587-6520-8(7)) Book Wholesalers, Inc.

—A Long Way from Chicago. (Puffin Modern Classics Ser.). 2004. 160p. (gr. 3-6). pap. 6.99 (978-0-14-240110-1(2) , Puffin); 2000. (Illus.). 176p. (J). (gr. 5-9). pap. 6.99 (978-0-14-130352-9(2) , Puffin); 1998. 192p. (J). (gr. 4-7). 16.99 (978-0-8037-2290-3(7) , Dial) Penguin Group (USA) Inc.

—A Long Way from Chicago. 2000. (J). (978-0-606-19769-4(9)); (gr. 3-6). lib. bdg. 14.15 (978-0-613-30011-7(4)) Tandem Library Bks.

—On the Wings of Heroes. 2007. 160p. (J). (gr. 4-8). 16.99 (978-0-8037-3081-6(0) , Dial) Penguin Group (USA) Inc.

—The River Between Us. 2005. 164p. (J). (ps-7). lib. bdg. 12.64 (978-0-606-33120-3(4)) Tandem Library Bks.

—A Year down Yonder. 2002. (Illus.). (YA). 13.19 (978-1-4046-1795-7(7)) Book Wholesalers, Inc.

—A Year down Yonder. 2002. 144p. (gr. 5-8). pap. 6.99 (978-0-14-230070-1(5) , Puffin) Penguin Group (USA) Inc.

—A Year down Yonder. Cieslawski, Steve, illus. 2000. 144p. (J). (gr. 5-9). 16.99 (978-0-8037-2518-8(3) , Dial) Penguin Group (USA) Inc.

—A Year down Yonder. unabr. ed. 2004. (Middle Grade Cassette Librariestm Ser.). 144p. (J). (gr. 5-9). pap. 29.00 incl. audio (978-0-8072-0991-2(0) , S YA 256 SP, Listening Library) Random Hse. Audio Publishing Group.

—A Year down Yonder. l.t. ed. 2001. 160p. (J). 24.95 (978-0-7862-3282-6(X)) Thorndike Pr.

Rapp, Adam. Under the Wolf, under the Dog. 320p. (YA). (gr. 9). 2007. pap. 8.99 (978-0-7636-3365-3(8)); 2004. 16.99 (978-0-7636-1818-6(7)) Candlewick Pr.

Rogo, Thomas Paul. The Surfrider: A Midwestern Odyssey. Rogo, Thomas Paul, illus. 1999. (Illus.). 80p. (J). (gr. 3 up). 19.95 (978-1-57306-082-0(8)); 4.95 (978-1-57306-110-0(7)) Bess Pr., Inc.

H I

Schraff, Anne. Freedom Knows No Color. 2000. 118p. (J). pap. (978-0-7891-5136-0(7)); (gr. 5-12). lib. bdg. 13.95 (978-0-7807-9270-8(X)) Perfection Learning Corp.

Sinclair, Upton, et al. The Jungle. (Classics Illustrated Ser.). (Illus.). 52p. (YA). pap. 4.95 (978-1-57209-025-5(1)) Classics International Entertainment, Inc.

Smith, Greg Leitich. Ninjas, Piranhas, & Galileo. 2005. 192p. (J). (gr. 5-8). pap. 6.99 (978-0-316-01181-5(9)) Little Brown & Co.

Straub, Peter. Mr X. 2000. (gr. 7-12). lib. bdg. 16.45 (978-0-613-27980-2(8)) Tandem Library Bks.

Van Steenwyk, Elizabeth. Maggie in the Morning. 2002. (gr. 3-6). lib. bdg. 14.15 (978-0-613-88116-6(8)) Tandem Library Bks.

Williams, Maiya. The Hour of the Outlaw. 2007. 360p. (YA). (gr. 4-9). 16.95 (*978-0-8109-9355-6(4)) Abrams, Harry N. , Inc.

ILLINOIS—HISTORY

Adams, Colleen. A Weekend in the City: Adding & Subtracting Times to the Nearest Minute. 2004. (PowerMath Ser.). (Illus.). 24p. (J). lib. bdg. 21.25 (978-0-8239-8974-4(7) , PowerKids Pr.) Rosen Publishing Group, Inc., The.

Bechtold, Phyliss. Seymour Bluffs & the Legend of the Piasa Bird. 2007. 26p. 9.95 (*978-0-9728532-8-6(6)) New Horizons Christian Ctr.

Bial, Raymond. Nauvoo: Mormon City on the Mississippi River. 2006. (Illus.). 48p. (J). (gr. 4-6). 17.00 (978-0-618-39685-6(3)) Houghton Mifflin Co.

Hershenhorn, Esther. Illinois Fun Facts & Games. Balcom-Vetillo, Eileen, illus. 2000. (Fun Facts & Games Ser.). 64p. (J). (gr. 1-5). pap. 5.95 (978-1-892920-45-4(X)) GHB Publishers, LLC.

Marsh, Carole. Illinois History Projects: 30 Cool, Activities, Crafts, Experiments & More for Kids to Do to Learn about Your State! 2003. (Illinois Experience Ser.). 32p. (gr. k-5). pap. 5.95 (978-0-635-01782-6(2) , Marsh, Carole Bks.) Gallopade International.

Santella, Andrew. Illinois History. 2002. (State Studies). (Illus.). 48p. (J). (gr. 3-5). lib. bdg. 27.07 (978-1-4034-0008-6(3)) Heinemann Library.

—People of Illinois. 2002. (State Studies). (Illus.). 48p. (J). (gr. 3-5). pap. 8.50 (978-1-4034-0571-5(9) , 91876); lib. bdg. 27.07 (978-1-4034-0010-9(5)) Heinemann Library.

Turner, Glennette Tilley. The Underground Railroad in Illinois. 1999. (Illus.). xvii, 200p. (J). pap. 16.95 (978-0-938990-05-5(5)) Newman Educational Publishing Co.

ILLITERACY

see Literacy

ILLITERATE SOCIETIES

see Primitive Societies

ILLUMINATION

see Lighting

ILLUSIONS

see Optical Illusions

ILLUSTRATED BOOKS, CHILDREN'S—HISTORY AND CRITICISM

Aldana, Patricia, ed. Under the Spell of the Moon: Art for Children from the World's Great Illustrators. Dragland, Stan, tr. from MUL. 2004. (Illus.). 72p. (J). (ps up). 25.00 (978-0-88899-559-9(8)) Groundwood Bks. CAN. *Dist:* Perseus Distribution.

Christelow, Eileen. What Do Illustrators Do? Christelow, Eileen, illus. 1999. (Illus.). 40p. (J). (gr. k-3). tchr. ed. 15.00 (978-0-395-90230-1(4) , Clarion Bks.) Houghton Mifflin Co. Trade & Reference Div.

Curtain, Eleanor. Graeme Base: Writer & Illustrator. 2001. (gr. k-3). lib. bdg. 11.65 (978-0-613-33371-9(3)) Tandem Library Bks.

Marciano, John Bemelmans. Bemelmans: The Life & Art of Madeline's Creator. 1999. (Illus.). 256p. (J). 40.00 (978-0-670-88460-5(X) , Viking Juvenile) Penguin Group (USA) Inc.

ILLUSTRATION OF BOOKS

see also Caldecott Medal Books; Drawing

Christelow, Eileen. What Do Illustrators Do? Christelow, Eileen, illus. 40p. (J). (ps-3). 2007. pap. 6.95 (*978-0-618-87423-1(2)); 1999. tchr. ed. 15.00 (978-0-395-90230-1(4)) Houghton Mifflin Co. Trade & Reference Div. (Clarion Bks.).

Cummings, Pat. Talking with Artists. 1999. (Talking with Artists Ser.: Vol. 3). (Illus.). 96p. (J). (gr. 5-9). tchr. ed. 22.00 (978-0-395-89132-2(9) , Clarion Bks.) Houghton Mifflin Co. Trade & Reference Div.

Curtain, Eleanor. Graeme Base, Writer & Illustrator. Tonkin, Ross, photos by. 2001. (Alphakids Ser.). (Illus.). 16p. (J). (978-0-7608-5121-0(2)) Sundance/Newbridge Educational Publishing.

Dean, Tanya. Theodor Geisel (Dr. Seuss) 2002. (Who Wrote That? Ser.). (Illus.). 112p. (gr. 6-12). 30.00 (978-0-7910-6724-6(6) , Chelsea Hse.) Facts On File, Inc.

Elleman, Barbara. Tomie dePaola: His Art & His Stories. 1999. (Illus.). 1p. (J). 35.00 (978-0-399-23129-2(3) , Putnam Juvenile) Penguin Group (USA) Inc.

—Virginia Lee Burton: A Life in Art. 2002. (Illus.). 144p. (J). (gr. 7 up). tchr. ed. 20.00 (978-0-618-00342-6(8)) Houghton Mifflin Co. Trade & Reference Div.

Ford, Carin T. Dr. Seuss: Best-Loved Author. 2003. (People to Know Ser.). (Illus.). 128p. (J). (gr. 6-12). lib. bdg. 26.60 (978-0-7660-2106-8(8)) Enslow Pubs., Inc.

Frank, Vivien & Jaffe, Deborah. Make a Book: Six Different Books to Make, Write, & Illustrate. 2004. (Illus.). 32p. (J). (gr. 2-8). reprint ed. pap. 15.00 (978-0-7567-7703-6(8)) DIANE Publishing Co.

Gaines, Ann Graham. Dr. Seuss. 2001. (Real-Life Reader Biography Ser.). (Illus.). 32p. (J). (gr. 3-8). lib. bdg. 15.95 (978-1-58415-074-9(2)) Mitchell Lane Pubs., Inc.

—Maurice Sendak. l.t. ed. 2001. (Real-Life Reader Biography Ser.). (Illus.). 32p. (gr. 3-8). lib. bdg. 24.95 (978-1-58415-079-4(3)) Mitchell Lane Pubs., Inc.

Krull, Kathleen. The Boy on Fairfield Street: How Ted Geisel Grew up to Become Dr. Seuss. Johnson, Steve & Fancher, Lou, illus. 2004. 48p. (J). (gr. 1-7). 16.95 (978-0-375-82298-8(4) , Random Hse. Bks. for Young Readers) Random Hse. Children's Bks.

Leedy, Loreen. Look at My Book: How Kids Can Write & Illustrate Terrific Books. 2005. (Illus.). 32p. (J). 6.95 (978-0-8234-1959-3(2)) Holiday Hse., Inc.

Marcus, Leonard S. A Caldecott Celebration: Seven Artists & their Paths to the Caldecott Medal. 10th ed. 2007. (Illus.). 64p. (J). 19.95 (*978-0-8027-9703-2(2)) Walker & Co.

—A Caldecott Celebration: Seven Artists & Their Paths to the Caldecott Medal. 10th ed. 2007. 56p. (J). 20.85 (*978-0-8027-9704-9(0)) Walker & Co.

Marcus, Leonard S. Side by Side: Five Favorite Picture-Book Teams Go to Work. 2001. (Illus.). 64p. (J). (gr. 3 up). 22.95 (978-0-8027-8778-1(9)) Walker & Co.

Stalcup, Ann & Politi, Leo. Leo Politi: Artist of the Angels. 2004. (J). 24.95 (978-1-893110-38-0(9)) Silver Moon Pr.

ILLUSTRATIONS, HUMOROUS

see Cartoons and Comics

IMAGINARY ANIMALS

see Animals, Mythical

IMAGINARY VOYAGES

see Voyages, Imaginary

IMAGINATION

see also Creation (Literary, Artistic, etc.)

Black, Jessica L. Just Imagine. Linke, Don, Jr., illus. l.t. ed. 2000. (Cuddle Bks.). 7p. (J). (ps-1). pap. 10.95 (978-1-57332-181-5(8)) HighReach Learning, Inc.

Edgar, Kathleen J., et al. Imagination. 2003. (J). (978-1-59203-058-3(0)) Learning Challenge, Inc.

Freed, Shirley & Moon, Louise. My Favorite Place. Morelan, Bill, ed. Harrell, Rob, illus. 2003. 8p. (J). (gr. 1 up). pap. 3.99 (978-1-58938-105-6(X)) Concerned Communications.

Hahn, Beverly. Twenty Acres of Love: Irrigation Time. Hahn, Beverly, illus. 2003. (Illus.). v, 65p. (J). (ps-6). spiral bd. 12.95 (978-0-9722494-0-9(0)) Hahn, Beverly.

Harcourt School Publishers Staff. Observe, Think, Try. 3rd ed. 2002. (Trophies English Language Learners Ser.). (Illus.). pap. 5.10 (978-0-15-327765-8(3)) Harcourt Schl. Pubs.

McNulty, John. I Am Your Imagination. Gilmour, Karen, illus. 2006. 32p. (J). lib. bdg. (*978-0-9769580-3-1(1)) I Am Your Playground LLC.

Nayer, Judy. Projects for Preschoolers Make-Believe. 1999. (Projects for Preschoolers Ser.). (Illus.). 48p. (J). (ps-1). mass mkt. 4.99 (978-0-7681-0081-5(X) , 67306, McClanahan Bk.) Learning Horizons, Inc.

Rinaldo, Denise. Leonardo Da Vinci: With a Discussion of Imagination. 2003. (Values in Action Ser.). (J). (978-1-59203-066-8(1)) Learning Challenge, Inc.

Sawyer, Dawn. What Will I Be? Langer S.L., Jutta, illus. 2004. (Barney Ser.). 80p. (J). pap. 2.99 (978-0-439-62502-9(5)) Scholastic, Inc.

Spinelli, Eileen. In My New Yellow Shirt. Takahashi, Hideko, illus. rev. ed. 2001. 32p. (J). (ps-k). 17.95 (978-0-8050-6242-7(4) , Holt, Henry & Co. Bks. For Young Readers) Holt, Henry & Co.

IMAGINATION—FICTION

Abercrombie, Barbara. The Show-and-Tell Lion. Cravath, Lynne Avril, illus. 2006. 32p. (J). (ps-2). 16.95 (978-0-689-86408-7(6) , McElderry, Margaret K.) Simon & Schuster Children's Publishing.

Ahlberg, Allan. The Shopping Expedition. Amstutz, Andre, illus. 2005. 32p. (J). (ps-1). 16.99 (978-0-7636-2586-3(8)) Candlewick Pr.

Alcantara, Ricardo. El Hijo Del Viento. 2003. (SPA., Illus.). 64p. (978-84-207-6971-4(1) , GS2762) Grupo Anaya, S.A. ESP. *Dist:* Lectorum Pubns., Inc.

Aldis, Dorothy & Collins, Heather. Hiding. (FRE.). (J). pap. 7.99 (978-0-590-24195-3(8)) Scholastic, Inc.

Alexander, Lloyd. The Gawgon & the Boy. (Illus.). (J). (gr. 5-8). 2003. 208p. pap. 5.99 (978-0-14-250000-2(3) , Puffin); 2001. 256p. 17.99 (978-0-525-46677-2(0) , Dutton Juvenile) Penguin Group (USA) Inc.

—The Gawgon & the Boy. 2003. (gr. 3-6). lib. bdg. 14.15 (978-0-613-59809-5(1)) Tandem Library Bks.

—The Gawgon & the Boy. l.t. ed. 2003. 204p. (J). 23.95 (978-0-7862-5433-0(5)) Thorndike Pr.

Alexander, Martha G. I'll Protect You from the Jungle Beasts. Alexander, Martha G., illus. 2006. (Illus.). 32p. (J). 9.95 (978-1-57091-677-9(2)) Charlesbridge Publishing, Inc.

Amelio-Ortiz, Osvaldo P. Tato y su bata de Lata. 2005. (SPA., Illus.). 28p. (J). 18.95 (978-9974-7799-1-4(X)) Hardenville SA URY. *Dist:* Independent Pubs. Group.

Anderson, Eric B. Alena & the Favorite Thing. 2007. 48p. pap. 23.95 (*978-0-615-15153-3(1)) EBA Creative.

Andreae, Giles. Captain Flinn & the Pirate Dinosaurs. Ayto, Russell, illus. 2005. 32p. (J). (gr. k-3). 15.95 (978-1-4169-0713-8(0) , McElderry, Margaret K.) Simon & Schuster Children's Publishing.

Anglund, Joan Walsh. The Brave Cowboy. 2000. (Illus.). 40p. (J). (ps-3). 6.99 (978-0-7407-0649-3(7)) Andrews McMeel Publishing.

—Cowboy's Secret Life. Anglund, Joan Walsh, illus. anniv. ed. 2002. (Illus.). 40p. (gr. k-3). 6.95 (978-0-7407-2680-4(3)) Andrews McMeel Publishing.

Asch, Frank. Monsieur Saguette & His Baguette. Asch, Frank, illus. 2006. (Illus.). 32p. 6.95 (978-1-55337-978-2(0)) Kids Can Pr., Ltd. CAN. *Dist:* Wybel Marketing Group.

Ashley, Bernard. That's the One! 2007. (J). lib. bdg. 16.95 (*978-1-59566-370-2(3)) QEB Publishing Inc.

Awesome Authors. 2007. (J). per. 5.00 net. (*978-0-9778155-6-2(0)) HATCHBACK Publishing.

Baguley, Elizabeth. Meggie Moon. Mabire, Gregoire, illus. 2005. 28p. (J). (ps-ps). 16.00 (978-1-56148-474-4(1)) Good Bks.

Baker, Francis. Alakazam! Alakazoo! Kasznica, Justine, illus. 2002. 24p. (J). (ps-2). per. 7.95 (978-0-9722928-0-1(2)) Possibilities Publishing.

Bandsuh, Jim. Helmet Hank. 2007. (J). per. 15.99 (*978-1-933156-19-4(8) , Visikid Bks.) GSVQ Publishing.

Banks, Kate. Max's Dragon. Kulikov, Boris, illus. 2008. 32p. (J). 16.95 (*978-0-374-39921-4(2)) Farrar, Straus & Giroux.

Barrett, Anna Pearl. Neecie & the Swarming Germs. Carmical, Phillip, ed. 1998. (Illus.). 50p. (J). (gr. 2-4). pap. 9.95 (978-0-9661330-0-4(5)) Over the Rainbow Productions.

Bastedo, Jaya. The How 'Bout Sisters. Pacey, Janet, illus. 2000. 12p. (J). (ps-3). pap. (978-1-894303-26-2(1)) Raven Rock Publishing.

Baud, Jane Scroggins. The Girl Who Wanted to be a Horse. Darr, Cynthia G., illus. l.t. ed. 2001. 32p. (J). (gr. k-6). 17.95 (978-1-929701-04-9(7)) Under the Green Umbrella.

Beaty, Andrea. Dr. Ted. Lemaître, Pascal, illus. 2008. 32p. (J). 14.99 (978-1-4169-2820-1(0)) Simon & Schuster Children's Publishing.

Beddor, Frank. Seeing Redd. 2007. (Looking Glass Wars Trilogy: Bk. 2). 384p. (YA). (gr. 6 up). 17.99 (*978-0-8037-3155-4(8) , Dial) Penguin Group (USA) Inc.

Behind My Eyelids. 2005. (J). 15.00 (978-0-9773608-0-2(6)) Shiny Red Ball Publishing.

Beletic, Kittie/N. What Color Is Your Dream. 2007. (J). 16.95 (*978-1-933285-56-6(7)) Brown Bks. Publishing Group.

Bell, Wade. No Place Fit for a Child. 2007. (Prose Ser.). 200p. pap. 18.00 (*978-1-55071-266-7(7)) Guernica Editions, Inc. CAN. *Dist:* Independent Pubs. Group.

Bennett, John Roy. Jason Mason Middleton-Tapp. Pavanel, Jane, ed. Charbonneau, Isabelle, illus. 2000. 32p. (J). (ps-k). pap. 8.95 (978-1-894222-12-9(1)) Lobster Pr. CAN. *Dist:* Univ. of Toronto Pr.

Bingham, Deanne Lee. Just Imagine. Below, Halina, illus. 24p. (J). (ps-k). 2000. pap. (978-1-55041-544-5(1)); 1998. (978-1-55041-381-6(3)) Fitzhenry & Whiteside, Ltd.

Black, Thom. 55 Waverly Street. Chambers, Mary, illus. 1998. 48p. (J). 14.99 (978-0-310-20792-4(4)) Zondervan.

Blanchet, Sylvia Roberge. Rachel's Adventure Ring. St. Aubin, Bruno, illus. 2005. (Read-It! Readers Ser.). 32p. (J). (gr. k-3). 18.60 (978-1-4048-1070-9(6)) Picture Window Bks.

Bode, N. E. The Slippery Map. 2007. 288p. (J). lib. bdg. 17.89 (*978-0-06-079109-4(8)) HarperCollins Pubs.

—The Slippery Map. Dorman, Brandon, illus. 2007. 288p. (J). (gr. 3-7). 16.99 (*978-0-06-079108-7(X)) HarperCollins Pubs.

Bond, Tammy. I Wish of Things That I Could Be. 2003. 32p. pap. 9.00 (978-0-8059-5919-2(X)) Dorrance Publishing Co., Inc.

Bowdish, Lynea. The Carousel Ride. Bowdish, Lynea & Girouard, Patrick, illus. 1998. (Rookie Readers Ser.). 32p. (J). (gr. 1-2). 19.50 (978-0-516-20967-8(1) , Children's Pr.) Scholastic Library Publishing.

Brami, Elisabeth. Mommy Time. Tschiegg, Anne-Sophie, illus. 2002. 48p. (J). (gr. k up). 9.95 (978-1-929132-22-5(0)) Kane/Miller Bk. Pubs., Inc.

Brisson, Pat. Little Sister, Big Sister. Bluthenthal, Diana Cain, illus. rev. ed. 1999. (Redfeather Chapter Book Ser.). 64p. (J). (gr. 1-3). 16.95 (978-0-8050-5887-1(7) , Holt, Henry & Co. Bks. For Young Readers) Holt, Henry & Co.

Browne, Anthony. Changes. Browne, Anthony, illus. 2002. (Illus.). 32p. (J). (ps-1). reprint ed. pap. 6.95 (978-0-374-41177-0(8) , Sunburst) Farrar, Straus & Giroux.

—Changes. 2002. (ps-2). lib. bdg. 15.25 (978-0-613-71857-8(7)) Tandem Library Bks.

Brunelle, Lynn. I Go Places: A Fun Sticker Book. Espinosa, Leo, illus. 1999. 20p. (J). reprint ed. 7.95 (978-1-892374-23-3(4)) Weldon Owen, Inc.

Bunting, Eve. Little Badger, Terror of the Seven Seas. Pham, LeUyen, illus. 2006. (Badger Bks.). 32p. (J). pap. 6.00 (978-0-15-205702-2(1) , Voyager Bks./Libros Viajeros) Harcourt Children's Bks.

Burleigh, Robert. It's Funny Where Ben's Train Takes Him. Yardley, Joanna, illus. 1999. 32p. (J). (ps-2). pap. 15.95 (978-0-531-30106-7(0) , Orchard Bks.) Scholastic, Inc.

Burlinson, J. Imagination Goodnight. Perron, Debra, illus. 2005. 24p. (J). 14.95 (978-1-59879-068-9(4)) Lifevest Publishing, Inc.

Burton, Yvette M. A Twinkle in His Eye. Burton, Yvette M., illus. l.t. ed. 2000. (Illus.). 28p. (J). 10.00 (978-0-615-11477-4(6)) Shooting Star Publishing.

Byars, Betsy. Ant Plays Bear. 2002. (Illus.). (J). 11.49 (978-0-7587-0886-1(6)) Book Wholesalers, Inc.

—Ant Plays Bear. Simont, Marc, illus. 2000. (J). pap. 19.97 incl. audio (978-0-7366-9213-7(4)) Books on Tape, Inc.

—Ant Plays Bear. Simont, Marc, illus. (Ant Ser.). (J). 2005. pap. 18.95 incl. audio compact disk (978-1-59112-630-0(4)); 1999. 25.95 incl. audio (978-0-87499-542-8(6)); 1999. pap. 16.95 incl. audio (978-0-87499-541-1(8)); 1999. pap., tchr. ed. 29.95 incl. audio (978-0-87499-543-5(4)) Live Oak Media.

—Ant Plays Bear. Simont, Marc, illus. 1999. (Easy-to-Read Ser.). 32p. (J). (gr. 1-4). pap. 3.99 (978-0-14-130351-2(4) , Puffin) Penguin Group (USA) Inc.

—Boo's Dinosaur. Brooks, Erik, illus. 2006. 48p. (J). 15.95 (978-0-8050-7958-6(0) , Holt, Henry & Co. Bks. For Young Readers) Holt, Henry & Co.

Carroll, Lewis, pseud. Alice's Adventures in Wonderland: With a Discussion of Imagination. Schneider, Rex, tr. Schneider, Rex, illus. 2003. (J). (978-1-59203-046-0(7)) Learning Challenge, Inc.

Charles, Donald. Adventures in a Bubble. 2007. (J). per. 7.99 (*978-1-59886-877-7(2)) Tate Publishing & Enterprises, L.L.C.

Chen, Chih-Yuan. On My Way to Buy Eggs. Chen, Chih-Yuan, illus. 2007. (Illus.). 40p. (J). (ps-3). pap. 7.95 (978-1-933605-41-8(3)) Kane/Miller Bk. Pubs., Inc.

Chwast, Seymour. Harry, I Need You! Chwast, Seymour, illus. 2002. (Illus.). 32p. (J). (gr. k-3). tchr. ed. 15.00 (978-0-618-17917-6(8) , Walter Lorraine) Houghton Mifflin Co. Trade & Reference Div.

Civardi, Anne, et al. More Nightlights: Stories for You to Read to Your Child to Encourage Calm, Confidence & Creativity. 2007. (Illus.). 144p. pap. 14.95 (978-1-84483-407-5(7)) Duncan Baird Pubs. GBR. *Dist:* Sterling Publishing Co., Inc.

Cleary, Beverly. Emily's Runaway Imagination. 2002. (J). 13.83 (978-0-7587-9141-2(0)) Book Wholesalers, Inc.

—Emily's Runaway Imagination. 221p. (J). (gr. 2-4). pap. 4.95 (978-0-8072-1416-9(7) , Listening Library) Random Hse. Audio Publishing Group.

Cocca-Leffler, Maryann. Princess for a Day. 1998. (All Aboard Reading Ser.: Level 1). (Illus.). 32p. (J). (ps-1). pap. 3.99 (978-0-448-41604-5(2) , Grosset & Dunlap) Penguin Group (USA) Inc.

Cohen, Miriam. Eddy's Dream. Cohen, Adam, photos by. l.t. ed. 2000. (Illus.). 32p. (J). (gr. k-2). 16.95 (978-1-887734-57-8(0)) Star Bright Bks., Inc.

Cole, Gina, illus. Adapt. 2005. 40p. (J). 17.00 (978-0-9659538-3-2(1)) Soul Vision Works Publishing.

Conford, Ellen. Get the Picture, Jenny Archer? 2000. (J). 11.79 (978-0-606-19838-7(5)) Tandem Library Bks.

—Jenny Archer, Author. Palisciano, Diane, illus. 2006. 64p. (J). (gr. 1-4). pap. 3.99 (978-0-316-01487-8(7)) Little Brown & Co.

Cooper, Helen. Boy Who Wouldn't Go to Bed. 2000. (gr. k-3). lib. bdg. 14.15 (978-0-613-33679-6(8)) Tandem Library Bks.

—The Boy Who Wouldn't Go to Bed: Pictures & Story. Cooper, Helen, illus. 2000. (Illus.). 32p. (J). (ps-2). pap. 5.99 (978-0-14-056771-7(2) , Puffin) Penguin Group (USA) Inc.

—Tatty Ratty. Cooper, Helen, illus. 2002. (Illus.). 32p. (J). (ps-3). 16.00 (978-0-374-37386-3(8) , Farrar, Straus & Giroux (BYR)) Farrar, Straus & Giroux.

Cosgrove, Stephen. Snugg N. Flitter: Facing Your Fears. Arroyo, Fian, illus. 2004. (J). (978-1-58804-377-1(0)) PCI Educational Publishing.

Coté, Geneviève, illus. The Magic Beads. 2007. 32p. (J). (gr. 2 up). 16.95 (*978-1-894965-47-7(7)) Simply Read Bks. CAN. *Dist:* Perseus Distribution.

Courtney, Richard, illus. The Monster under the Shed. 2001. (Pictureback Bk.). 24p. (J). (ps-3). pap. 3.25 (978-0-375-81371-9(3) , Random Hse. Bks. for Young Readers) Random Hse. Children's Bks.

Cowan, Catherine. My Life with the Wave. ed. 2004. (Illus.). (J). (gr. k-3). spiral bd. (978-0-616-01621-3(2)) Canadian National Institute for the Blind/Institut National Canadien pour les Aveugles.

—My Life with the Wave. Buehner, Mark, illus. 2004. 32p. (J). (ps-3). reprint ed. pap. 6.99 (978-0-06-056200-7(5) , Harper Trophy) HarperCollins Pubs.

—My Life with the Wave. 2004. (gr. k-3). lib. bdg. 15.30 (978-0-613-83570-1(0)) Tandem Library Bks.

Cowen-Fletcher, Jane. Farmer Will. Cowen-Fletcher, Jane, illus. 2003. (Illus.). 32p. (J). (gr. k-k). pap. 5.99 (978-0-7636-2055-4(6)) Candlewick Pr.

—Nell's Elf. Cowen-Fletcher, Jane, illus. 2006. (Illus.). 32p. (J). (ps-2). 14.99 (978-0-7636-2391-3(1)) Candlewick Pr.

Crabtree, Sally. Magic Train Ride. Esplugas, Sonia, illus. 2006. 0032p. (J). 16.99 (978-1-905236-52-7(2)) Barefoot Bks., Inc.

Creech, Sharon. Fishing in the Air. Raschka, Chris, illus. 32p. (J). (ps-3). 2003. pap. 6.99 (978-0-06-051606-2(2) , Harper Trophy); 2000. 15.89 (978-0-06-028112-0(X) , Cotler, Joanna Books) HarperCollins Pubs.

—Fishing in the Air. 2003. (Live Oak Readalong Ser.). (Illus.). (J). pap. 16.95 incl. audio (978-1-59112-224-1(4)); pap. 18.95 incl. audio compact disk (978-1-59112-512-9(X)) Live Oak Media.

—Fishing in the Air. Raschka, Chris, illus. 2003. pap. 9.95 incl. audio (978-1-59112-223-4(6)) Live Oak Media.

—Fishing in the Air. 2000. (gr. k-3). lib. bdg. 15.30 (978-0-613-66967-2(3)) Tandem Library Bks.

Crews, Nina. I'll Catch the Moon. 1999. (Metro Reading Program Ser.). (J). (gr. k). 29.95 (978-1-58120-105-5(2)); 7.98 (978-1-58120-968-6(1)); 45.95 (978-1-58830-014-0(5)) Metropolitan Teaching & Learning Co.

Crockett, Johns. Harold et le crayon Rose. pap. 13.95 (978-2-266-09592-1(7)) Presses Pocket FRA. *Dist:* Distribooks, Inc.

Cruickshank, Margrit. Don't Dawdle Dorothy. Harvey, Amanda, illus. 1999. 28p. (J). (978-0-7112-1215-2(5)) Lincoln, Frances Ltd.

—Don't Dawdle Dorothy. Harvey, Amanda, illus. 2001. 32p. (J). (ps-1). pap. 8.99 (978-0-7112-1404-0(2)) Lincoln, Frances Ltd. GBR. *Dist:* Transition Vendor.

Crumpacker, Bunny. Alexander's Great Pretending Day. Andersen, Dan, illus. 2005. 32p. (J). (ps). 15.99 (978-0-525-46936-0(2) , Dutton Juvenile) Penguin Group (USA) Inc.

Curtis, Duane. Mr. Wishmadoo Takes You to Zarr Zoo. 2002. (Illus.). 40p. (J). lib. bdg. 12.95 (978-0-9718438-0-6(5) , 1001) Wail Hse. Publishing Co.

Custer, Jason. Everyday Monsters. 2005. (J). lib. bdg. 19.95 (***978-0-9754728-3-5(6)*** , Bear Hug Bks.) MidAmerica Publishing Co.

Davis, Jacky. Ladybug Girl. Soman, David, illus. 2008. 40p. (J). (ps). 16.99 (***978-0-8037-3195-0(7)*** , Dial) Penguin Group (USA) Inc.

Dean, Lani. One Misty Morning. Cassidy, Al, illus. 2004. 36p. (J). 14.95 (978-0-9645844-9-5(2)) Manor Hse. Publishing Co., Inc.

DeCesare, Angelo. Flip's Fantastic Journal. DeCesare, Angelo, illus. 1999. (Illus.). 48p. (J). (gr. 1-4). pap. 6.99 (978-0-14-056655-0(4) , Puffin) Penguin Group (USA) Inc.

—Flip's Fantastic Journal. 1999. (gr. 3-6). lib. bdg. 14.15 (978-0-613-21547-3(8)) Tandem Library Bks.

DeFelice, Cynthia C. The Ghost of Fossil Glen. 1998. (Ghost Mysteries Ser.). 176p. (J). (gr. 3-7). 16.00 (978-0-374-31787-4(9) , Farrar, Straus & Giroux (BYR)) Farrar, Straus & Giroux.

—The Ghost of Fossil Glen. 1999. 160p. (J). (gr. 3-7). pap. 5.99 (978-0-380-73175-6(4) , Harper Trophy) HarperCollins Pubs.

—The Ghost of Fossil Glen. 2000. (YA). (gr. 6 up). pap. 52.00 incl. audio (978-0-7887-4334-4(1) , 41129) Recorded Bks., LLC.

—The Ghost of Fossil Glen. 1999. (J). 11.60 (978-0-606-16359-0(X)); (gr. 5-8). lib. bdg. 14.15 (978-0-7857-0557-4(0)) Tandem Library Bks.

—The Ghost of Fossil Glen. l.t. ed. 2000. (Juvenile Ser.). (Illus.). 185p. (J). (gr. 4-7). 21.95 (978-0-7862-2768-6(0)) Thorndike Pr.

Delton, Judy. Angel Spreads Her Wings. Weber, Jill, illus. 2002. 160p. (J). (gr. 2-5). pap. 4.95 (978-0-618-21617-8(0)) Houghton Mifflin Co. Trade & Reference Div.

—Angel Spreads Her Wings. 2002. (gr. 3-6). lib. bdg. 12.95 (978-0-613-90475-9(3)) Tandem Library Bks.

DePalma, Johnny. The Raindrop Keeper. Crabapple, Molly, illus. 2006. (J). per. 8.50 (***978-0-9791127-1-3(0)***) Umbrelly Bks.

—The Raindrop Keeper: (Limited Edition Hardcover) Crabapple, Molly, illus. 2006. 50p. (J). 16.50 (***978-0-9791127-8-2(8)***) Umbrelly Bks.

Desimini, Lisa. The Sun & Moon: A Giant Love Story. 1999. (Illus.). 40p. (YA). (ps-3). pap. 16.95 (978-0-590-18720-6(1) , Blue Sky Pr., The) Scholastic, Inc.

Dingles, Molly. Jinka, Jinka Jelly Bean. Bingler, Aimee, illus. 1998. 38p. (J). (ps-6). 23.00 (978-1-891997-03-7(3)) Dingles & Co.

Dischler, Patricia. The Patty Cake Kids & the Lost Imagination Cap. 2007. (Illus.). 24p. (J). per. 9.95 (***978-1-59598-064-9(4)***) Goblin Fern Pr., Inc.

Diviny, Sean. Snow Inside the House. Rocco, Joe, illus. 1998. 32p. (J). (ps-3). 14.95 (978-0-06-027354-5(2)) HarperCollins Pubs.

DK Publishing Staff. Backyardigans: The Essential Guide. 2007. (Illus.). 48p. (J). 8.99 (978-0-7566-2703-4(6)) Dorling Kindersley Publishing, Inc.

Dodd, Lynley. A Dragon in a Wagon. Dodd, Lynley, illus. 2000. (Gold Star First Readers Ser.). (Illus.). 32p. (J). (gr. 1 up). lib. bdg. 22.00 (978-0-8368-2687-6(6)) Stevens, Gareth Inc.

Dorros, Arthur. Abuela. Kleven, Elisa, illus. 2002. (J). 14.04 (978-0-7587-1901-0(9)) Book Wholesalers, Inc.

Dream Catchers - Evaluation Guide: Evaluation Guide. 2006. (J). (978-1-55942-403-5(6)) Marsh Media.

Dream Catchers - Teaching Guide. 2001. (J). 17.95 (978-1-55942-183-6(5)) Marsh Media.

Dunbar, Polly. Dog Blue. Dunbar, Polly, illus. 2004. (Illus.). 40p. (J). (gr. k-k). 14.99 (978-0-7636-2476-7(4)) Candlewick Pr.

—Flyaway Katie. Dunbar, Polly, illus. 2004. (Illus.). 40p. (J). (gr. k-k). 14.99 (978-0-7636-2366-1(0)) Candlewick Pr.

Eaton, Deborah J. My Wild Woolly. Karas, G. Brian, illus. 2005. (Green Light Readers Level 2 Ser.). 24p. (J). (ps-ps). 12.95 (978-0-15-205148-8(1)); pap. 3.95 (978-0-15-205147-1(3)) Harcourt Trade Pubs.

Ebeltoft, Christine. Koo & Jay in the Rainforest. 2004. 34p. pap. 17.95 (978-1-4137-3698-4(X)) PublishAmerica, Inc.

Eckert, Allan W. The Crossbreed. 2000. (Illus.). 256p. (YA). (gr. 7-12). pap. 15.95 (978-0-595-08992-5(5) , Backinprint.com) iUniverse, Inc.

Eman, Leisa M. Pugsley's Imagination. 2007. 52p. per. 8.95 (***978-0-595-44247-8(1)***) iUniverse, Inc.

Estes, Eleanor. The Witch Family. Ardizzone, Edward, illus. 2000. 240p. (YA). (gr. 3 up). pap. 6.00 (978-0-15-202610-3(X) , Odyssey Classics) Harcourt Children's Bks.

—The Witch Family. 2000. (978-0-606-20338-8(9)); (J). (978-0-606-20176-6(9)); (gr. 3-6). lib. bdg. 14.15 (978-0-613-30884-7(0)) Tandem Library Bks.

Estes-Hill, Katrina. My Imagination. Kwong, Alvina, illus. 2007. 32p. (J). (ps-2). 15.95 (***978-0-9745715-6-0(3)***) KRBY Creations, LLC.

Falwell, Cathryn. Shape Capers. Falwell, Cathryn, illus. 2007. 32p. (J). (ps-k). 16.99 (***978-0-06-123699-0(3)*** , Greenwillow Bks.) HarperCollins Pubs.

—Shape Capers. 2007. 32p. (J). (ps-k). lib. bdg. 17.89 (***978-0-06-123700-3(0)*** , Greenwillow Bks.) HarperCollins Pubs.

Falwell, Cathryn. Word Wizard. (Illus.). 32p. (J). (gr. k-3). 2006. pap. 5.95 (978-0-618-68924-8(9)); 1998. tchr. ed. 16.00 (978-0-395-85580-5(2)) Houghton Mifflin Co. Trade & Reference Div. (Clarion Bks.).

Fancher, Lou. Star Climbing. Johnson, Steve, illus. 2006. 32p. (J). 15.99 (978-0-06-073901-0(0)); lib. bdg. 16.89 (978-0-06-073902-7(9)) HarperCollins Pubs. (Geringer, Laura Book).

Farmer, Karen, ed. If I Could Be Anything What Would I Be. 2007. 12p. pap. 8.95 (***978-1-59125-914-5(2)***) Penton Overseas, Inc.

Fearnley, Jan. A Special Something. 2004. (Illus.). 32p. 7.95 (978-0-7497-4639-1(4)) Egmont Bks., Ltd. GBR. *Dist:* Trafalgar Square Publishing.

—A Special Something. 2000. (Illus.). 32p. (ps-2). 15.99 (978-0-7868-0589-1(7)) Hyperion Pr.

Feiffer, Jules. I'm Not Bobby. Feiffer, Jules, illus. 2001. (Illus.). 32p. (J). (ps-17). (978-0-7868-0907-3(8)) Hyperion Bks. for Children.

—I'm Not Bobby! Feiffer, Jules, illus. 2006. (Illus.). 28p. (J). (gr. k-4). reprint ed. 16.00 (978-0-7567-9853-6(1)) DIANE Publishing Co.

—Meanwhile... Feiffer, Jules, illus. 1999. (Michael di Capua Bks.). (Illus.). 32p. (J). (ps-k). pap. 6.99 (978-0-06-205933-8(5)) HarperCollins Pubs.

—Meanwhile... 1999. (978-0-606-17882-2(1)); lib. bdg. 14.15 (978-0-613-22891-6(X)) Tandem Library Bks.

Ferraby, Sue. Run! Fiorin, Fabiano, illus. 2004. (Read-It! Readers Ser.). 32p. (C). (gr. k-3). 18.60 (978-1-4048-0552-1(4)) Picture Window Bks.

Ferrone, John M. Gus & the Pteranodon. Ferrone, John M., illus. 1999. (Illus.). 36p. (ps-5). pap. 16.95 (978-1-928811-00-8(0)) Story Stuff, Inc.

Fine, Anne & Trimmer, Tony. Countdown. 2006. (Yellow Bananas Ser.). (Illus.). 44p. (J). (978-0-7787-0958-9(2)) Crabtree Publishing Co.

Finks, Jan. Rainy Day Magic. 2000. II17p. (J). (ps-5). spiral bd. 15.00 (978-0-615-11137-7(8)) Hope Chest Publishing.

Fite, Anna. Ada y Max en el Pueblo Marinero. 2002. (Ada y Max Ser.). (SPA & ENG.). 10p. 4.95 (978-84-7864-335-6(4)) Combel Editorial, S.A. ESP. *Dist:* Independent Pubs. Group.

—Ada y Max Van de Excursion Al Rio. 2002. (Ada y Max Ser.). (SPA & ENG.). 10p. 4.95 (978-84-7864-334-9(6)) Combel Editorial, S.A. ESP. *Dist:* Independent Pubs. Group.

—Ada y Max Viajan en Tren. 2002. (Ada y Max Ser.). (SPA & ENG.). 10p. 4.95 (978-84-7864-333-2(8)) Combel Editorial, S.A. ESP. *Dist:* Independent Pubs. Group.

Fitzpatrick, Marie-Louise. I'm a Tiger, Too! Fitzpatrick, Marie-Louise, illus. 2002. (Illus.). 6.95 (978-0-86327-871-6(X)) Interlink Publishing Group, Inc.

Florczak, Robert. Yikes!!! Florczak, Robert, illus. 2003. (Illus.). 32p. (J). pap. 15.95 (978-0-590-05043-2(5) , Blue Sky Pr., The) Scholastic, Inc.

Floyd, Marla K. The Pink Poodle. 2000. (Illus.). 28p. (J). (ps-6). pap. 9.95 (978-0-9704399-0-1(3)) Daisy Pubns.

Fontes, Justine. Jordan's Silly Sick Day. Lee, Jared D., illus. 2005. (Rookie Reader Espanol Ser.). 32p. (J). (gr. k-2). pap. 4.95 (978-0-516-26821-7(X) , Children's Pr.) Scholastic Library Publishing.

—Jordan's Silly Sick Day. Lee, Jared D., tr. Lee, Jared D., illus. 2004. (Rookie Reader Ser.). 31p. (J). 19.50 (978-0-516-25897-3(4) , Children's Pr.) Scholastic Library Publishing.

Fox, Christyan & Fox, Diane. Around the World PiggyWiggy. 2002. (Illus.). 24p. (J). 14.95 (978-1-929766-58-1(0)) Handprint Bks.

—Bathtime PiggyWiggy: A Pull-the-Page Book. 2001. (Illus.). 24p. (J). 12.95 (978-1-929766-32-1(7)) Handprint Bks.

—Pirate PiggyWiggy. 2003. (Illus.). 24p. (J). 11.95 (978-1-929766-76-5(9)) Handprint Bks.

Fox, Diane. Firefighter Piggywiggy. Fox, Christyan, illus. 2001. 24p. (J). (ps-k). 9.95 (978-1-929766-16-1(5)) Handprint Bks.

Fox, Diane, et al. Goodnight PiggyWiggy: A Pull-the-Page Book. Fox, Christyan, illus. 2000. 24p. (J). (ps-k). 12.95 (978-1-929766-06-2(8)) Handprint Bks.

Freed, Shirley & Moon, Louise. I Like to Ride. Morelan, Bill, ed. Harrell, Rob, illus. 2003. 8p. (J). (-k). pap. 3.99 (978-1-58938-103-2(3)) Concerned Communications.

Freedman, Deborah. Scribble. 2007. (Illus.). 40p. (J). (ps-1). 15.99 (978-0-375-83966-5(6)); lib. bdg. 18.99 (978-0-375-93966-2(0)) Random Hse. Children's Bks. (Knopf Bks. for Young Readers).

Fuchs, Menucha. Just a Pinch. 2004. (Illus.). 20p. (J). 6.95 (978-1-932443-22-6(3) , JAPH) Judaica Pr., Inc., The.

Fuge, Charles. I Know a Rhino. 2003. (Illus.). 32p. (J). bds. 5.95 (978-1-4027-0861-9(0)) Sterling Publishing Co., Inc.

—I Know a Rhino. Fuge, Charles, illus. 2002. (Illus.). 32p. (J). (ps-1). 12.95 (978-1-4027-0137-5(3)) Sterling Publishing Co., Inc.

Fuglestad, R. A., illus. Over the Rainbow with Joey. l.t. ed. 2004. 22p. (J). bds. 8.99 (978-0-9729093-0-3(3)) Tike-Time.

Fulmer, Jeffrey. My Imagination Kit. Pickering, Jimmy, tr. Pickering, Jimmy, illus. 2003. (J). 24p. 15.95 (978-1-59336-008-5(8)); 23p. pap. (978-1-59336-009-2(6)) Mondo Publishing.

Garfield, Valerie. Harold & the Purple Crayon: The Giant Garden. 2002. (ps-2). lib. bdg. 11.80 (978-0-613-50439-3(9)) Tandem Library Bks.

Gauthier, Gail. A Girl, a Boy, & a Monster Cat. Cepeda, Joe, illus. 2007. 96p. (J). (gr. 2-4). 14.99 (978-0-399-24689-0(4) , Putnam Juvenile) Penguin Group (USA) Inc.

Gauthier, Gail. A Girl, A Boy, & Three Robbers. Cepeda, Joe, illus. 2008. 64p. (J). (gr. 1-3). 14.99 (***978-0-399-24690-6(8)*** , Putnam Juvenile) Penguin Group (USA) Inc.

Gay, Marie-Louise. On My Island. Gay, Marie-Louise, illus. 2001. (Illus.). 36p. (J). (ps-4). 16.95 (978-0-88899-396-0(X)) Groundwood Bks. CAN. *Dist:* Perseus Distribution.

Geisert, Arthur. The Etcher's Studio. 2005. (Illus.). 32p. (J). (gr. k-3). reprint ed. 5.95 (978-0-618-55614-4(1) , Walter Lorraine) Houghton Mifflin Co. Trade & Reference Div.

Gemmen, Heather. But It's True. Lagares, Luciano, illus. 2004. (Tough Stuff for Kids Ser.). 36p. (J). (gr. 4-7). pap., pap. 5.99 (978-0-7814-4033-2(5) , 0781440335) Cook, David C. Publishing Co.

George, Audra. Vagabonding. George, Audra, illus. 2006. (Illus.). 32p. (J). 17.95 (978-1-60108-010-3(7)) Red Cygnet Pr.

Geter, Maurice. My Friend Buddy. Geter, Maurice, illus. 2006. (Illus.). 24p. (J). (978-1-4120-9646-1(4)) Trafford Publishing.

Girmay, Aracelis. Changing, Changing. Girmay, Aracelis, illus. 2005. (Illus.). 48p. (J). (ps-17). 19.95 (978-0-8076-1553-9(6)) Braziller, George Inc.

Gittemeier, Tausha. Hmmm, I was Thinking... What If? 2004. 20p. pap. 14.95 (978-1-4137-3429-4(4)) PublishAmerica, Inc.

Glass, Beth Raisner & Lubner, Susan. Noises at Night. Whatley, Bruce, illus. 2005. 32p. (J). (ps-3). 15.95 (978-0-8109-5750-3(7) , Abrams Bks. for Young Readers) Abrams, Harry N. , Inc.

Glenn, Sharlee Mullins. Just What Mama Needs. Hirao, Amiko, illus. 2008. 32p. (J). 16.00 (978-0-15-205759-6(5)) Harcourt Trade Pubs.

Goddard, Mary Beth. How Would It Feel? Mycek-Wodecki, Anna, illus. 2005. 32p. (J). 15.95 (978-1-59143-050-6(X) , Bear Cub Bks.) Bear & Co.

Godwin, Patricia, I Feel Orange Today. Macaulay, Kitty, illus. 24p. (J). (ps-k). 2001. lib. bdg. 14.95 (978-1-55037-284-7(X)); 2000. pap. 1.25 (978-1-55037-640-1(3)) Annick Pr., Ltd. CAN. *Dist:* Firefly Bks., Ltd.

Gold, Bernice. My Four Lions. Stanbridge, Joanne, illus. 1999. 24p. (J). (ps-1). lib. bdg. 17.95 (978-1-55037-603-6(9)) Annick Pr., Ltd. CAN. *Dist:* Firefly Bks., Ltd.

—My Four Lions. 1999. (978-0-606-18141-9(5)) Tandem Library Bks.

Gonzalez, Rigoberto. Soledad Sigh-Sighs / Soledad Suspiros. Ibarra, Rosa, illus. 2003. Tr. of Soledad Suspiros. (ENG & SPA.). 32p. (J). 16.95 (978-0-89239-180-6(4)) Children's Bk. Pr.

Gore, Leonid. Danny's First Snow. Gore, Leonid, illus. 2007. 40p. (J). (ps-2). 16.99 (978-1-4169-1330-6(0)) Simon & Schuster Children's Publishing.

Goss, Leon. In Your Seat, Mr. Pete! Velez, Jill Ondercin, illus. 2005. (J). pap. (978-1-933156-11-8(2)); per. (978-1-933156-04-0(X)) GSVQ Publishing. (VisionQuest Kids).

Gray, Kes & Parsons, Garry. Billy's Bucket. 2003. (Illus.). 32p. (J). 24.95 (978-0-370-32596-5(6)) Random Hse. GBR. *Dist:* Random Hse. of Canada, Ltd.

Grindley, Sally. Reve de Glace et Patins Blancs. Duchesne, Christiane, tr. from ENG. Hieta, Heli, illus. (FRE.). 28p. (J). pap. 6.95 (***978-2-922435-06-1(7)***) Editions Homard CAN. *Dist:* Univ. of Toronto Pr.

Guy, Ginger Foglesong. Go Back to Bed! Bernardin, James, illus. 2006. (J). 15.95 (978-1-57505-750-7(6) , Carolrhoda Bks.) Lerner Publishing Group.

Hagerup, Klaus. Markus & Diana. Chace, Tara, tr. from NOR. 2006. 192p. (J). 17.95 (978-1-932425-59-8(4) , Front Street) Boyds Mills Pr.

Hagin, Karen. If I Could Reach the Sky. 2005. (J). lib. bdg. 19.95 (***978-0-9754728-7-3(9)*** , Bear Hug Bks.) MidAmerica Publishing Co.

Hall, Kirsten. Duck, Duck, Goose! Rader, Laura, illus. 2003. (My First Reader Ser.). 32p. (J). 18.50 (978-0-516-22925-6(7) , Children's Pr.) Scholastic Library Publishing.

—My Trucks. Boyd, Patti, illus. 2003. (My First Reader Ser.). 32p. (J). 18.50 (978-0-516-22935-5(4) , Children's Pr.) Scholastic Library Publishing.

Hanken, Sandra. Sky Castle. Bergsma, Jody Lynn, illus. 1998. 32p. (ps-3). 15.95 (978-0-935699-14-2(7)) Illumination Arts Publishing Co., Inc.

Hanson, Dave. We're Going Camping. McNicholas, Shelagh, illus. 2005. (Reading Corner Ser.). 24p. (J). (gr. k-3). lib. bdg. 22.80 (978-1-59771-015-2(6)) Sea-To-Sea Pubns.

Hargreaves, Roger. Mr Daydream. 2000. (ps-2). lib. bdg. 10.65 (978-0-613-26233-0(6)) Tandem Library Bks.

Hébert, Marie-Francine. Bird Brain. 1999. (Illus.). 48p. (YA). (gr. 3-6). pap. 4.95 (978-1-896764-17-7(7)) Second Story Pr. CAN. *Dist:* Orca Bk. Pubs. USA.

Henkes, Kevin. Jessica. Henkes, Kevin, illus. 1998. (Illus.). 24p. (J). (ps-ps). pap. 6.99 (978-0-688-15847-7(1) , Harper Trophy) HarperCollins Pubs.

—Jessica. 1998. 12.79 (978-0-606-13536-8(7)) Tandem Library Bks.

Hilbrandt, Sarah Perrin. Jacob & the Taboo. 2006. 24p. per. 11.99 (***978-1-59886-818-0(7)***) Tate Publishing & Enterprises, L.L.C.

Hirsch, Odo. Antonio S. & the Mysterious Theodore Guzman. 2001. (Illus.). 224p. (J). lib. bdg. 16.49 (978-0-7868-2605-6(3)) Hyperion Bks. for Children.

—Antonio S. & the Mysterious Theodore Guzman. Hall, August, illus. 2001. 208p. (gr. 3-7). 15.99 (978-0-7868-0747-5(4)) Hyperion Bks. for Children.

Holm, Jennifer L. & Holm, Matthew. Queen of the World! 2005. (Babymouse Ser.). (Illus.). 96p. (J). (gr. 2-5). pap. 5.95 (978-0-375-83229-1(7)); lib. bdg. 12.99 (978-0-375-93229-8(1)) Random Hse. Children's Bks. (Random Hse. Bks. for Young Readers).

Honeywood, Varnette P., illus. The Best Way to Play. 2002. (Little Bill Ser.). (J). 11.91 (978-0-7587-0983-7(8)) Book Wholesalers, Inc.

Hood, Thomas. Before I Go to Sleep. Begin, Mary Jane, illus. 1999. 32p. (J). (ps-k). 15.95 (978-0-688-12424-3(0)) HarperCollins Pubs.

Howell, Lauren. If I Was the Mayor. Dawson, Sheldon, illus. 2005. 32p. (J). per. (978-0-9735798-1-9(1)) Three Bears Publishing.

Hull, Maureen. Rainy Days with Bear. Franson, Leanne, illus. 2004. 32p. (J). 15.95 (978-1-894222-85-3(7)) Lobster Pr. CAN. *Dist:* Univ. of Toronto Pr.

Hutchins, Hazel J. I'd Know You Anywhere. Ohi, Ruth, illus. 2002. 24p. (J). (ps-k). pap. 7.95 (978-1-55037-746-0(9)); lib. bdg. 19.95 (978-1-55037-747-7(7)) Annick Pr., Ltd. CAN. *Dist:* Firefly Bks., Ltd.

—I'd Know You Anywhere. ed. 2004. (Illus.). (J). (ps up). spiral bd. (978-0-616-14577-7(2)); spiral bd. (978-0-616-14578-4(0)) Canadian National Institute for the Blind/Institut National Canadien pour les Aveugles.

The Imaginary Zoo. 2007. (J). 16.95 (978-0-9789880-0-5(0)) Wild About Learning, Inc.

Inns, Christopher. What Will I Be? 2005. (Mirror, Mirror Ser.). (Illus.). 12p. (J). (ps-k). bds. 5.95 (978-0-7534-5893-8(4) , Kingfisher) Houghton Mifflin Co. Trade & Reference Div.

Jackson, Shirley. 9 Magic Wishes. Hyman, Miles, illus. 2001. 32p. (J). (ps-2). 16.00 (978-0-374-35525-8(8) , Farrar, Straus & Giroux (BYR)) Farrar, Straus & Giroux.

Jarman, Julia. Jack in a Box. (Illus.). (J). 2005. 28p. 19.95 (978-0-00-710410-9(3)); 2004. 32p. pap. 11.00 (978-0-00-710411-6(1)) HarperCollins Pubs. Ltd. GBR. *Dist:* Independent Pubs. Group.

Jenkins, Emily. Daffodil, Crocodile. Bogacki, Tomek, illus. 2007. 32p. (J). (ps-3). 16.00 (978-0-374-39944-3(1) , Farrar, Straus & Giroux (BYR)) Farrar, Straus & Giroux.

Jinkins, Jim. Pinky Dinky Doo: Polka Dot Pox. 2004. (Illus.). 48p. (J). (gr. 1-3). pap. 3.99 (978-0-375-82713-6(7) , Random Hse. Bks. for Young Readers) Random Hse. Children's Bks.

—Pinky Dinky Doo: Think Pink! 2006. (Step into Reading Ser.). (Illus.). 48p. (J). (gr. 1-3). pap. 3.99 (978-0-375-83573-5(3)); lib. bdg. 11.99 (978-0-375-93573-2(8)) Random Hse. Children's Bks. (Random Hse. Bks. for Young Readers).

—Pinky Dinky Doo: Where Are My Shoes? 2004. (Illus.). 48p. (J). (gr. 1-3). pap. 3.99 (978-0-375-82712-9(9) , Random Hse. Bks. for Young Readers) Random Hse. Children's Bks.

—Pinky Dinky Doo: Shrinky Pinky! 2005. (Step into Reading Ser.). (Illus.). 48p. (J). (gr. 1-3). pap. 3.99 (978-0-375-83235-2(1) , Random Hse. Bks. for Young Readers) Random Hse. Children's Bks.

Johnson, Angela. Lily Brown's Paintings. Lewis, E. B., illus. 2007. 32p. (J). (ps-3). pap. 16.99 (978-0-439-78225-8(2) , Orchard Bks.) Scholastic, Inc.

Johnston, Tony. Boo! Croll, Carolyn, illus. 1998. (Hello Reader! Ser.). (J). 3.99 (978-0-590-37998-4(4)) Scholastic, Inc.

Jones, Katina. Cool School Story: Little Lucy & Friends. Ottinger, Jon, illus. Zaidan, Rick, photos by. 2001. (Little Lucy & Friends Ser.). 24p. (J). (ps-3). 9.99 (978-1-57151-700-5(6)) Playhouse Publishing.

Jones, Sylvie. Who's in the Tub? Constantin, Pascale, illus. 2007. 38p. (ps-3). 15.95 (***978-1-59354-612-0(2)***) Handprint Bks.

Kalz, Jill. Mike's Nightlight. Spence, Tom, illus. 2006. (Read-It! Readers Ser.). 32p. (J). (ps-3). 18.60 (978-1-4048-1726-5(3)) Picture Window Bks.

—Tuckerbean. Mahan, Ben, illus. 2006. (Read-It! Readers Ser.). 24p. (J). (ps-3). 18.60 (978-1-4048-1591-9(0)) Picture Window Bks.

Karns, Marie. The Incredible Peepers of Penelope Budd. Wummer, Amy, illus. 2005. 32p. (J). 15.95 (978-1-58685-405-8(4)) Gibbs Smith, Publisher.

Kay, Catherine. When I'm by Myself. Morgan, Ron, illus. 1998. (Sis & Beezie Ser.: Vol. 1). 32p. (J). (ps-6). 17.95 (978-0-9663651-0-8(0)) Portos Publishing Co.

Kay, Julia. Gulliver Snip & the Clipper Ship. 2008. 32p. (J). 16.95 (***978-0-8050-7992-0(0)***) Holt, Henry & Co.

Kimmel, Haven. Kaline Klattermaster's Tree House. Brown, Peter, illus. 2008. 160p. (J). 15.99 (***978-0-689-87402-4(2)*** , Atheneum) Simon & Schuster Children's Publishing.

Klingel, Cynthia Fitterer & Noyed, Robert B. Imagination & the Letter I. 2003. (Alphaphonics Ser.). (Illus.). 24p. (J). (ps-2). 21.36 (978-1-59296-099-6(5)) Child's World, Inc.

Korman, Gordon. Liar, Liar, Pants on Fire. 1999. (gr. 3-6). lib. bdg. 11.80 (978-0-613-11773-9(5)) Tandem Library Bks.

Langley, Jonathan. Missing! Langley, Jonathan, illus. 2000. (Illus.). 32p. (J). (ps-k). 15.95 (978-0-7614-5078-8(5) , Cavendish Children's Bks.) Cavendish, Marshall Corp.

—Missing! 2007. (Illus.). 32p. (J). pap. 7.95 (***978-1-84507-740-2(7)***) Lincoln, Frances Ltd. GBR. *Dist:* Perseus Distribution.

Lawson, Janet. Audrey & Barbara. Lawson, Janet, illus. 2002. (Illus.). 32p. (J). (ps-3). 13.95 (978-0-689-83896-5(4) , Atheneum) Simon & Schuster Children's Publishing.

Lazo, Caroline. Someday When My Cat Can Talk. Brooker, Kyrsten, illus. 2008. 32p. (J). (ps-3). lib. bdg. 19.99 (***978-0-375-93754-5(4)*** , Schwartz & Wade Bks.) Random Hse. Children's Bks.

Lazo, Caroline Evensen. Someday When My Cat Can Talk. Brooker, Kyrsten, illus. 2008. 32p. (J). (***978-0-375-83754-8(X)*** , Schwartz & Wade Bks.) Random Hse. Children's Bks.

Lee, Hector Viveros. I Had a Hippopotamus. 1999. (Metro Reading Program Ser.). (J). (gr. k). 29.95 (978-1-58120-109-3(5)) Metropolitan Teaching & Learning Co.

Lee, Ingrid. Dragon Tide. Meister, Soizik, illus. 2006. 32p. (ps-2). 17.95 (978-1-55143-352-3(4)) Orca Bk. Pubs. USA.

H I

Leon, Loni. Can you Imagine..., 1. Leon, Loni & Huston, Kyle, illus. 2006. 49p. (J). 21.95 (978-0-9728556-0-0(2)) Sullivan, Kelley Enterprises.

Leonard, Marcia. Dress-Up. Handelman, Dorothy, photos by. 1999. (Real Kids Readers Ser.). (Illus.). 32p. (J). (ps-1). lib. bdg. 18.90 (978-0-7613-2053-1(9)); pap. 4.99 (978-0-7613-2078-4(4)) Lerner Publishing Group. (Millbrook Pr.).

—Dress-Up. 1999. (J). 11.79 (978-0-606-19154-8(2)) Tandem Library Bks.

Leverich, Kathleen. Hilary & the Troublemakers. 1999. (Beech Tree Chapter Bks.). (Illus.). 144p. (J). (gr. 1-4). pap. 4.95 (978-0-688-16453-9(6) , Harper Trophy) HarperCollins Pubs.

Levert, Mireille. An Island in the Soup. 2001. (Illus.). 24p. (J). (ps-k). 15.95 (978-0-88899-403-5(6)) Groundwood Bks. CAN. *Dist:* Perseus Distribution.

Levine, Terri. Abigail & the Purple Fairy. Harr, Lynn, illus. 2007. 34p. (J). (ps-3). per. 14.99 (***978-1-60002-314-9(2)*** , Airleaf Publishing) Airleaf Publishing & Bookselling.

Lewis, H. B. Winnie Mae. 2001. (Illus.). 40p. (J). (gr. 3). pap. 8.95 (978-0-89812-013-4(6) , Creative Paperbacks) Creative Co., The.

Leybas, Veronica. Let's Imagine. 2007. (J). per. 6.99 (***978-1-59886-888-3(8))*** Tate Publishing & Enterprises, L.L.C.

Liberto, Lorenzo. Matt the Rat & His Magic Cloud / Raton Mateo y Su Nube Magica: A Day at School / un Dia de Escuela. Gomez, Rocio, ed. Torres, Irving, illus. 2003. (Matt the Rat Ser. / La Serie de Raton Mateo). (ENG & SPA.). 32p. (J). lib. bdg. 20.00 (978-0-9743668-0-7(3)) Harvest Sun Pr., LLC.

Liberto, Lorenzo, et al. Matt the Rat's Incredible Creations / Las Creaciones Increíbles de Raton Mateo. Torres, Irving, illus. 2004. (ENG & SPA.). 32p. (J). lib. bdg. 20.00 (978-0-9743668-3-8(8)) Harvest Sun Pr., LLC.

Lithgow, John. The Carnival of the Animals. Kulikov, Boris, illus. 2004. 40p. (J). (ps-3). 17.95 (978-0-689-86721-7(2)) Simon & Schuster Children's Publishing.

—I'm a Manatee. Hoyt, Ard, illus. 2003. 32p. (J). 17.95 incl. audio compact disk (978-0-689-85427-9(7)) Simon & Schuster Children's Publishing.

—I'm a Manatee. Hoyt, Ard, illus. 2007. 32p. (J). 9.99 (978-0-689-85452-1(8) , Aladdin) Simon & Schuster Children's Publishing.

London, Jonathan. My Big Rig. Garofoli, Viviana, illus. 2007. 32p. (J). (ps-3). 14.99 (***978-0-7614-5346-8(6))*** Cavendish, Marshall Corp.

—My Big Rig. Garofoli, Viviana, illus. 2007. (J). (***978-1-4287-3689-4(1))*** Cavendish, Marshall Corp.

Lowenstein, Sallie, illus. Sir Kyle & Lady Madeline. Lowenstein, Sallie, . 2007. 32p. (J). 18.95 (978-0-9658486-6-4(3)) Lion Stone Bks.

Lukas, Catherine. Race to the Tower of Power. 2007. 24p. (J). 21.35 (***978-1-59961-159-4(7))*** Spotlight.

MacLean, Christine Kole. Even Firefighters Hug Their Moms. Reed, Mike, illus. 2002. 32p. (J). 16.99 (978-0-525-46996-4(6) , Dutton Juvenile) Penguin Group (USA) Inc.

Macmillan, Lesley. What Would You Be? Holcomb, Michele, illus. 2006. 32p. (J). per. 12.99 (***978-1-59879-228-7(8))*** Lifevest Publishing, Inc.

Maier, Inger M. When Fuzzy Was Afraid of Big & Loud Things. Candon, Jennifer, illus. 2005. 32p. (J). 14.95 (978-1-59147-322-0(5)); pap. 8.95 (978-1-59147-323-7(3)) American Psychological Assn. (Magination Pr.).

Marlowe, Pete. One Arabian Morning. Bell, Charles, illus. 2000. 32p. (J). (gr. k-3). pap. 6.95 (978-1-55037-658-6(6)) Annick Pr., Ltd. CAN. *Dist:* Firefly Bks., Ltd.

Marshall, Mark. Imagine! 2006. (Illus.). 10p. (J). (gr. k-k). bds. 12.95 (978-0-7696-4647-3(6) , Gingham Dog Pr.) School Specialty Publishing.

Martella, Liz. Izabella & her Wardrobe. 2007. 18p. 12.95 (***978-0-615-14941-7(3))*** Martella, Liz.

Marx, Patricia. Meet My Staff. Chast, Roz, illus. 1998. 40p. (J). (ps-3). 14.95 (978-0-06-027484-9(0) , Cotler, Joanna Books) HarperCollins Pubs.

Mathes, Charles. In Every Moon There Is a Face. Graston, Arlene, illus. 2003. 32p. 15.95 (978-0-9701907-4-1(3)) Illumination Arts Publishing Co., Inc.

May, Kyla. Introducing Kyla May Miss. Behaves. 2005. (Illus.). 64p. (J). (gr. 4-7). pap. 4.99 (978-0-8431-1370-9(7) , Price Stern Sloan) Penguin Group (USA) Inc.

Mayer, Mercer. A Silly Story. 2003. (Illus.). (J). pap. (978-1-57768-337-7(4)) School Specialty Publishing.

McAllister, Angela. Harry's Box. Jones, Jenny, illus. 2003. 32p. (J). (gr. k-3). 16.95 (978-1-58234-772-1(7) , Bloomsbury Children) Bloomsbury Publishing.

McCardell, Kenneth/W. Bible Rhymes' Christmas Story. Chirco, Antonella, illus. 2007. 32p. (J). 17.95 (***978-0-9790605-2-6(4)*** , BibleRhymes) BibleRhymes Publishing, L.L.C.

—Bible Rhymes' Creation. Chirco, Antonella, illus. 2007. 32p. (J). 17.95 (***978-0-9790605-0-2(8)*** , BibleRhymes) BibleRhymes Publishing, L.L.C.

McCourt, Lisa. Happy Halloween, Stinky Face. Moore, Cyd, illus. 2007. 32p. (J). (ps-3). pap. 15.99 (978-0-439-77977-7(4)) Scholastic, Inc.

—It's Time for School, Stinky Face. Moore, Cyd, illus. 2004. 32p. (J). pap. 15.95 (978-0-439-63574-5(8)); pap. 5.99 (978-0-439-63575-2(6)) Scholastic, Inc.

McEwan, Ian. The Daydreamer. Browne, Anthony, illus. 2002. 208p. (J). (gr. 3 up). pap. 8.99 (978-0-06-053015-0(4) , Harper Trophy) HarperCollins Pubs.

—The Daydreamer. 2000. 160p. (gr. 4-7). pap. 10.95 (978-0-385-49805-0(5) , Anchor) Knopf Publishing Group.

McLerran, Alice. Roxaboxen. Cooney, Barbara, illus. 2004. 32p. (J). (ps-3). pap. 6.99 (978-0-06-052633-7(5) , Harper Trophy) HarperCollins Pubs.

McNaughton, Colin. Lemmy Was a Diver. (Illus.). 32p. (J). 17.99 (978-1-84270-301-4(3)) Andersen GBR. *Dist:* Trafalgar Square Publishing.

—Lemmy Was a Diver. 2005. (Illus.). 32p. (J). pap. 6.99 (***978-1-84270-422-6(2))*** Transworld Publishers Ltd. GBR. *Dist:* Independent Pubs. Group.

McPhail, David M. Edward in the Jungle. McPhail, David M., illus. 2004. (Illus.). 28p. (J). (gr. k-4). reprint ed. lib. bdg. 16.00 (978-0-7567-8009-8(8)) DIANE Publishing Co.

Militzer, Jill. Kizzy's Castle. 2005. 35p. 13.24 (978-1-4116-5538-6(9)) Lulu.com.

Miranda, Anne. Beep! Beep! 2000. (ps-2). lib. bdg. 16.40 (978-0-613-27731-0(7)) Tandem Library Bks.

—Beep! Beep! A Vehicle Imagination Book. Murphy, David, illus. 2000. 32p. (J). (ps up). pap. 7.95 (978-1-890515-20-1(5)) Turtle Bks.

Morgan, Michaela. The Thing in the Basement. Weir, Doffy, illus. 2006. 48p. (J). (***978-1-4048-3133-9(9))*** Picture Window Bks.

Mould, Wendy. Ants in My Pants. Mould, Wendy, illus. 2001. (Illus.). 32p. (J). (gr. k-3). tchr. ed. 15.00 (978-0-618-09640-4(X) , Clarion Bks.) Houghton Mifflin Co. Trade & Reference Div.

Murawski, Kevin, illus. Harold & the Purple Crayon: The Giant Garden. 128p. (J). (978-0-06-059705-4(4)) HarperCollins Pubs.

Musgrave, Susan. Dreams Are More Real Than Bathtubs. braille ed. 2004. (Illus.). (J). (gr. k-3). spiral bd. (978-0-616-01748-7(0)) Canadian National Institute for the Blind/Institut National Canadien pour les Aveugles.

—Dreams Are More Real Than Bathtubs. Gay, Marie-Louise, illus. 1999. 32p. (J). (ps-2). 14.95 (978-1-55143-107-9(6)) Orca Bk. Pubs. USA.

Myer, Ellen. Freddie's Friends. Simmons, Marcia, illus. 2002. (J). (ps-3). 6.95 (978-0-9721586-1-9(8)) Family Treasures Publishing Co.

Namm, Diane. Guess Who? Sheldon, David, illus. 2004. (My First Reader Ser.). 32p. (J). (gr. k-1). pap. 3.95 (978-0-516-25503-3(7) , Children's Pr.) Scholastic Library Publishing.

—Guess Who? Sheldon, David, tr. Sheldon, David, illus. 2004. (My First Reader Ser.). 31p. (J). 18.50 (978-0-516-24412-9(4) , Children's Pr.) Scholastic Library Publishing.

Napoli, Donna Jo. Playing Games. Ben-Ami, Doren & Klementz-Harte, Lauren, illus. 2000. (Angelwings Ser.: No. 8). 80p. (J). (gr. 2-5). mass mkt. 7.95 (978-0-689-83208-6(7) , Aladdin) Simon & Schuster Children's Publishing.

—Playing Games. 2000. (Angelwings Ser.: No. 8). (Illus.). (J). (978-0-606-20386-9(9)) Tandem Library Bks.

Neitzel, Shirley. I'm Taking a Trip on My Train. Parker, Nancy Winslow, illus. 1999. 40p. (J). (ps-3). 14.89 (978-0-688-15834-7(X)) HarperCollins Pubs.

Nesbit, E. Story of the Treasure Seekers. 2006. pap. (***978-1-4068-3507-6(2))*** Echo Library.

Nesbit, E. The Story of the Treasure Seekers: Being the Adventures of the Bastable Children in Search of A Fortune. l.t. ed. 2005. 288p. pap. (978-1-84637-207-0(0)) Echo Library.

Ness, Evaline. Sam, Bangs y Hechizo de Luna. 2000. (978-0-606-20896-3(8)) Tandem Library Bks.

Neubecker, Robert. Beasty Bath. 2005. (Illus.). 32p. (J). (ps-1). pap. 14.99 (978-0-439-64000-8(8) , Orchard Bks.) Scholastic, Inc.

Numeroff, Laura Joffe. Chimps Don't Wear Glasses. Mathieu, Joe, illus. 2006. (Stories to Go! Ser.). 32p. (J). pap. 4.99 (978-1-4169-1859-2(0) , Aladdin) Simon & Schuster Children's Publishing.

Nuttle, Jim, illus. If I Were... A Book of Make-Believe. Shorten, Chris, photos by. 1999. (J). reprint ed. 5.95 (978-1-892374-24-0(2)) Weldon Owen, Inc.

Obiols, Anna. Dali & the Path of Dreams. Dunn, Andrew, tr. from SPA. Subirana, Joan, illus. 2007. 32p. (J). pap. 7.95 (***978-1-84507-777-8(6))*** Lincoln, Frances Ltd. GBR. *Dist:* Perseus Distribution.

Offen, Hilda. There Might Be Giants. (Illus.). 25p. (J). pap. (978-0-340-68149-7(7) , Hodder & Stoughton) Hodder General Publishing Division.

Oliver, Mark Herren. Trish & the Wishing Star. 2006. (ENG.). 32p. per. 18.65 (***978-1-4134-9402-0(1))*** Xlibris Corp.

Orme, David. Dinosaur Planet. Fiorin, Fabiano, illus. 2005. 32p. (J). (gr. 1-2). lib. bdg. 11.15 (978-0-606-33601-7(X)) Tandem Library Bks.

Ormerod, Jan. Ballet Sisters No. 1: The Duckling & the Swan. 2007. (Scholastic Reader Ser.). 32p. (J). (gr. k-2). pap. 5.99 (978-0-439-82281-7(5)) Scholastic, Inc.

—Lizzie Nonsense. Ormerod, Jan, illus. 2004. (Illus.). 40p. (J). (***978-1-877003-59-2(X))*** Little Hare Bks.

Ormerod, Jan. Lizzie Nonsense: A Story of Pioneer Days. 2005. (Illus.). 40p. (J). (gr. k-3). 15.00 (978-0-618-57493-3(X) , Clarion Bks.) Houghton Mifflin Co. Trade & Reference Div.

Palatini, Margie. Zak's Lunch. Fine, Howard, illus. 1998. 32p. (J). (gr. k-3). tchr. ed. 16.00 (978-0-395-81674-5(2) , Clarion Bks.) Houghton Mifflin Co. Trade & Reference Div.

—Zak's Lunch. Fine, Howard, illus. 2004. 32p. (J). (gr. k-3). reprint ed. pap. 6.95 (978-0-618-48603-8(8) , Clarion Bks.) Houghton Mifflin Co. Trade & Reference Div.

—Zak's Lunch. unabr. ed. 1999. (J). pap., stu. ed. 32.00 incl. audio (978-0-7887-2983-6(7) , 40865) Recorded Bks., LLC.

Papademetriou, Lisa. Really? 1999. (Real Kids Readers Ser.: 3). (Illus.). 32p. (J). (gr. 2-4). pap. 4.99 (978-0-7613-2097-5(0) , Millbrook Pr.) Lerner Publishing Group.

—Really? Handelman, Dorothy, photos by. 1999. (Real Kids Readers Ser.). (Illus.). 48p. (gr. 1-3). lib. bdg. 18.90 (978-0-7613-2072-2(5) , Millbrook Pr.) Lerner Publishing Group.

—Really? 1999. (J). (978-0-606-19171-5(2)); (gr. 3-6). lib. bdg. 11.80 (978-0-613-18163-1(8)) Tandem Library Bks.

Parazette, Joan. Aldo! Nascimbene, Yan, illus. 2006. (J). (978-1-56846-197-7(6) , Creative Editions) Creative Co., The.

Paterson, Katherine. The Smallest Cow in the World. Brown, Jane Clark, illus. 2002. (J). 12.34 (978-0-7587-1673-6(7)) Book Wholesalers, Inc.

Patricelli, Leslie. The Birthday Box. Patricelli, Leslie, illus. 2007. (Illus.). 32p. (J). (gr. k-k). 15.99 (978-0-7636-2825-3(5)) Candlewick Pr.

Perry, Sarah. Y Si... 1999. (Books for Young Readers Ser.). (SPA., Illus.). 44p. (gr. 2-4). 16.95 (978-0-89236-542-5(0) , OX2455) Oxford Univ. Pr., Inc.

Pesko, Mila. Little Mary of the Rose & the Giant Baked Bean. 2007. per. 14.95 (***978-1-932762-75-4(2))*** Elderberry Press, Inc.

Philpot, Graham. Troglobytes. 1998. (Illus.). 32p. (J). pap. 11.99 (978-1-85881-621-0(1)) Orion Children's Bks. GBR. *Dist:* Independent Pubs. Group.

Piscetta, Colleen McCauley. Dandelion Delilah: The Tale of the Dandelion Fairies. Wolf, Gwynn, illus. 2002. (J). 24.95 (978-1-888683-87-5(2)) Wooster Bk. Co., The.

Polacco, Patricia. Appelemando's Dreams. pap. 6.99 (978-0-14-240003-6(3) , Puffin) Penguin Group (USA) Inc.

—Emma Kate. Polacco, Patricia, illus. 2005. (Illus.). 40p. (J). (ps-1). 16.99 (978-0-399-24452-0(2) , Philomel) Penguin Group (USA) Inc.

Portis, Antoinette. Not a Stick. 2008. 32p. (J). (ps-1). 14.89 (***978-0-06-112326-9(9))*** HarperCollins Pubs.

—Not Stick. 2008. 32p. (J). 12.99 (***978-0-06-112325-2(0))*** HarperCollins Pubs.

Povandra, Shirley. My Imaginary Friend. 2007. 17.95 (***978-1-59526-669-9(0))*** Media Creations, Inc.

Prince, Sarah. If I Were Invisible. 2001. (gr. k-3). lib. bdg. 11.80 (978-0-613-33379-5(9)) Tandem Library Bks.

—I'm Brave. 1999. (ps-2). lib. bdg. 11.55 (978-0-613-30510-5(8)) Tandem Library Bks.

Purdy, Jo. A Day in a Night. 2005. 352p. pap. 24.95 (978-1-4137-6263-1(8)) PublishAmerica, Inc.

Ragin, M. K. Mildred Row & Improper Bounds. 2006. 185p. pap. 19.95 (978-1-4137-9724-4(5)) PublishAmerica, Inc.

Rasmussen, Anne & Nemiroff, Marc. The Very Lonely Bathtub. Flanagan, Kate, illus. 1999. 32p. (J). (ps-2). (978-1-55798-607-8(X) , 441-6070, Magination Pr.) American Psychological Assn.

Rau, Dana Meachen. Moon Walk. Buchs, Thomas, illus. 3rd ed. 2005. (Soundprints' Read-and-Discover Ser.). 48p. (J). (gr. 2-4). pap. 3.95 (978-1-59249-015-8(8) , S2006) Soundprints.

Rex, Michael. You Can Do Anything, Daddy! Rex, Michael, illus. 2007. 32p. (J). (ps). 14.99 (978-0-399-24298-4(8) , Putnam Juvenile) Penguin Group (USA) Inc.

Riley, Christine. Chester's Field, O'Brien, Laurel, illus. 2004. 296p. (J). per. 17.50 (978-0-9740683-6-7(5)) Authors & Artists Publishers of New York, Inc.

—Chester's Field. 2002. 103p. per. 10.00 (978-0-9724680-3-9(X)) Lifevest Publishing, Inc.

Robbins, Beth. Tom Is Afraid of the Dark. Stuart, Jon, illus. 2001. (It's OK! Ser.). 24p. (J). (ps-k). pap. 3.95 (978-0-7894-7420-9(4) , D K Ink) Dorling Kindersley Publishing, Inc.

Robinson, Hilary. Croc by the Rock. Gordon, Mike, illus. 2005. 32p. (J). lib. bdg. 9.00 (***978-1-4242-0885-2(8))*** Fitzgerald Bks.

Robinson, Hilary. The Croc by the Rock, Level 1. Gordon, Mike, illus. 2005. (Lightning Readers Ser.). 32p. (J). (ps-k). pap., pap. 3.95 (978-0-7696-4219-2(5) , Gingham Dog Pr.) School Specialty Publishing.

Roep, Nada. Kisses. Cate, Marijke Ten, illus. 1998. 32p. (J). 15.95 (978-1-886910-85-0(5) , Lemniscaat) Boyds Mills Pr.

Rogers, Karen M. Quien Puedo Aer? Alvarado, Ana María, tr. Bulat, Getty, illus. 2000. (Think-Kids Book Collection).Tr. of Who Can I Be?. (SPA.). 16p. (J). (gr. 1-4). pap. 2.95 (978-1-58237-051-4(6)) Creative Thinkers, Inc.

Romain, Trevor. The Boy Who Swallowed a Rainbow. 2003. (Illus.). 32p. (J). (gr. k-2). 15.95 (978-1-56397-920-0(9)) Boyds Mills Pr.

Roorda, Julie. Wings of a Bee: A Young Adult Novel. 2007. (Illus.). 232p. pap. 9.95 (***978-1-894549-68-4(6))*** Sumach Pr. CAN. *Dist:* Univ. of Toronto Pr.

Rue, Nancy. Sophie Tracks a Thief, Vol. 8. 2005. (Faithgirlz Ser.). (Illus.). 144p. (J). pap. 6.99 (978-0-310-71023-3(5)) Zonderkidz.

Rue, Nancy N. Sophie & the Scoundrels, Bk. 3. Chen, Grace, illus. 2005. (Faithgirlz Ser.). 128p. (J). pap. 6.99 (978-0-310-70758-5(7)) Zonderkidz.

—Sophie Breaks the Code, Vol. 7. 2005. (Faithgirlz Ser.). (Illus.). 144p. (J). pap. 6.99 (978-0-310-71022-6(7)) Zonderkidz.

Rugrats. 2007. (J). 128.10 (***978-1-59961-354-3(9))*** Spotlight.

Ryan, Susan Jane. Esmeralda & the Enchanted Pond. Cook, Sandra, illus. 2001. 48p. (J). (gr. 2-5). 14.95 (978-1-56164-236-6(3)) Pineapple Pr., Inc.

Ryan, Susan Jane & Cook, Sandra G. Esmeralda & the Enchanted Pond. 2001. (Illus.). 48p. (gr. 4-7). pap., act. bk. ed. 5.00 (978-1-56164-247-2(9)) Pineapple Pr., Inc.

Sargent, Dave & Sargent, Pat. Bo Bo's Big Imagination, 10, 13. Robinson, Laura, illus. 2004. (Learn to Read Ser.: 10). Tr. of La Gran Imaginacion de Bo Bo. 18p. (J). pap. 9.95 (978-1-56763-822-6(8)); lib. bdg. 19.95 (978-1-56763-821-9(X)) Ozark Publishing.

Sauer, Cat. Flip Flop & Hoot. Jankowski, Dan, illus. l.t. ed. 2003. (Brown Bag Bedtime Bks.: 1). 35p. (YA). spiral bd. 16.95 (978-0-9704460-6-0(3)) Writer's Ink. Studios, Inc.

—A Possum in the Roses. Jankowski, Dan, illus. l.t. ed. 2003. (Brown Bag Bedtime Bks.: 1). 27p. (YA). spiral bd. 16.95 (978-0-9704460-7-7(1)) Writer's Ink. Studios, Inc.

—What's a Jaybird to Do? Jankowski, Dan, illus. l.t. ed. 2003. (Brown Bag Bedtime Bks.: 1). 31p. (YA). spiral bd. 16.95 (978-0-9704460-8-4(X)) Writer's Ink. Studios, Inc.

Schachner, Judith B. Mr. Emerson's Cook. 2002. (J). per. 7.95 (978-1-930654-27-3(8)) Reading Matters, Inc.

Schachner, Judy. Skippy Jon Jones. Schachner, Judy, illus. 2005. (Illus.). 32p. (J). reprint ed. pap. 5.99 (978-0-14-240403-4(9) , Puffin) Penguin Group (USA) Inc.

—Skippyjon Jones: Up & Down. 2007. 12p. (J). (ps). pap. 6.99 (978-0-525-47807-2(8) , Dutton Juvenile) Penguin Group (USA) Inc.

Schaefer, Carole Lexa. Someone Says. Morgan, Pierr, illus. 2003. 32p. (J). (gr. k-2). 15.99 (978-0-670-03664-6(1) , Viking Juvenile) Penguin Group (USA) Inc.

—Squiggle. 1999. (978-0-606-16574-7(6)); lib. bdg. 15.30 (978-0-613-18193-8(X)) Tandem Library Bks.

Schaefer, Carole Lexa & Morgan, Peirr. The Squiggle. 1999. (Illus.). 32p. (J). (gr. k-3). pap. 6.99 (978-0-517-88579-6(4) , Dragonfly Bks.) Random Hse. Children's Bks.

Schecter, Ellen. Swim Like a Fish. Cymerman, John E., illus. 1998. (Bank Street Reader Collection). 48p. (J). (ps-2). lib. bdg. 22.60 (978-0-8368-1767-6(2)) Stevens, Gareth Inc.

Schuepbach, Lynnette. Cat Time. 2006. 28p. pap. 12.95 (978-0-9759613-2-2(2)) Creative Sources.

Schwartz, Roslyn. Yo Baby! Schwartz, Roslyn, illus. 2002. (Illus.). 24p. (J). (gr. k-ps). pap. 5.95 (978-1-55037-754-5(X)); lib. bdg. 18.95 (978-1-55037-755-2(8)) Annick Pr., Ltd. CAN. *Dist:* Firefly Bks., Ltd.

Seidler, Tor. The Tar Pit. 2000. (J). 15.95 (978-0-06-623611-7(8)); lib. bdg. 15.89 (978-0-06-623612-4(6)) HarperCollins Pubs.

—The Tar Pit. 2001. (978-0-606-22299-0(5)) Tandem Library Bks.

Seuss, Dr. Y Pensar Que lo Vi por la Calle Porvenir. Canetti, Yanitzia, tr. Seuss, Dr., illus. 2006. (SPA., Illus.). (J). 14.99 (***978-1-933032-07-8(3))*** Lectorum Pubns., Inc.

Shalant, Phyllis. When Pirates Came to Brooklyn. 2002. 176p. (J). (gr. 4-7). 16.99 (978-0-525-46920-9(6) , Dutton Juvenile) Penguin Group (USA) Inc.

Shanahan, Lisa & Guthridge, Bettina. My Mom Tarzan. 2007. (J). bds. 12.95 (***978-1-59692-239-6(7))*** MacAdam/Cage Publishing, Inc.

Shannon, David. Alice the Fairy. 2004. (Illus.). 40p. (J). pap. 15.95 (978-0-439-49025-2(1) , Blue Sky Pr., The) Scholastic, Inc.

Simon, Charnan. The Sillies. Petelinsek, Kathleen, illus. 2006. (Magic Door to Learning Ser.). 24p. (J). 21.36 (978-1-59296-627-1(6)) Child's World, Inc.

Simpson, Lesley. The Shabbat Box. Bosch, Nicole in den, illus. 2001. 32p. (J). (ps-1). pap. 6.95 (978-1-58013-027-1(5)) Kar-Ben Publishing.

Sis, Peter. Dinosaur! Sis, Peter, illus. (J). (ps-1). 2005. 28p. bds. 6.99 (978-0-06-075967-4(4) , Harper Festival); 2000. (Illus.). 24p. 16.99 (978-0-688-17049-3(8)) HarperCollins Pubs.

—Madlenka's Music. 2005. (J). (978-0-375-82855-3(9)); lib. bdg. (978-0-375-92855-0(3)) Random Hse., Inc.

—Madlenka's Soccer Ball. 2005. (J). (978-0-375-82852-2(4)); lib. bdg. (978-0-375-92852-9(9)) Random Hse., Inc.

Slater, Dashka. Firefighters in the Dark. Ceccoli, Nicoletta, illus. 2006. 32p. (J). (gr. k-3). 16.00 (978-0-618-55459-1(9)) Houghton Mifflin Co.

Smith, Jennifer Lynne. Things I Wonder. Perez, Angela J., ed. Gray, Angela M., illus. 2007. 36p. (J). 17.95 (***978-0-9778328-5-9(6))*** His Work Christian Publishing.

Smith, Linda. Kelly's Cabin. Krasulja, Zorica, illus. 2006. 62p. (J). lib. bdg. 20.00 (***978-1-4242-1248-4(0))*** Fitzgerald Bks.

—Kelly's Cabin. Krasulja, Zorica, illus. 2006. 64p. (gr. 2-3). pap. 4.99 (978-1-55143-408-7(3)) Orca Bk. Pubs. USA.

Spalding, Andrea. It's Raining It's Pouring. Watts, Leslie Elizabeth, illus. 2002. 32p. (J). (ps-2). 7.95 (978-1-55143-229-8(3)) Orca Bk. Pubs. USA.

Spangler, Brie. Peg Leg Peke. 2008. 40p. (J). (ps-1). lib. bdg. 18.99 (***978-0-375-94888-6(0)*** , Knopf Bks. for Young Readers) Random Hse. Children's Bks.

Spelvin, Justin. Pirate Treasure. 2007. 24p. (J). 21.35 (***978-1-59961-158-7(9))*** Spotlight.

Spinelli, Eileen. Someday. Winstead, Rosie, illus. 2007. 32p. (J). (ps). 16.99 (978-0-8037-2941-4(3) , Dial) Penguin Group (USA) Inc.

St. Pierre, Stephanie. Rugrats Blast Off. 2007. 24p. (J). 21.35 (***978-1-59961-358-1(1))*** Spotlight.

Stadler, Alexander. Beverly Billingsly Takes the Cake. 2005. (Gulliver Books). (Illus.). 32p. (J). 16.00 (978-0-15-205357-4(3)) Harcourt Trade Pubs.

Steadman, Ralph. That's My Dad. 2001. (Illus.). 32p. (J). pap. 8.99 (978-1-84270-011-2(1)) Andersen GBR. *Dist:* Independent Pubs. Group.

Steele, Alexander. Unleashed in Space. 1999. (Super Adventures of Wishbone Ser.: No. 3). (J). (gr. 4-7). (978-0-606-19032-9(5)) Tandem Library Bks.

Stern, Shirley. Let's Get Moving: Carry-along Coloring Kit. 2008. (Franny's Feet Ser.). 80p. (J). (ps-1). 5.99 (***978-1-4169-4918-3(6)*** , Simon Scribbles) Simon & Schuster Children's Publishing.

Stewart, Joel. Dexter Bexley & the Big Blue Beastie. Stewart, Joel, illus. 2007. (Illus.). 32p. (J). (ps-3). 16.95 (***978-0-8234-2068-1(X))*** Holiday Hse., Inc.

Stone, David Lee. The Ratastrophe Catastrophe. Lea, Bob, illus. 2004. (Illmoor Chronicles Ser.: Bk. 1). 288p. (gr. 5-9). 16.99 (978-0-7868-5128-7(7)) Hyperion Bks. for Children.

Stone, Phoebe. Go Away, Shelley Boo! Stone, Phoebe, illus. 1999. (Illus.). 32p. (J). (ps-3). 15.95 (978-0-316-81677-9(9)) Little, Brown Bks. for Young Readers.

Stussy, Virginia. Wishes & Wonder. 2007. (ENG.). 52p. per. 12.95 ***978-1-4241-6086-0(3))*** PublishAmerica, Inc.

Sutherland, Marc. The Waiting Place. Sutherland, Marc, illus. 2004. (Illus.). 24p. (J). (gr. k-4). reprint ed. 15.00 (978-0-7567-8382-2(8)) DIANE Publishing Co.

Tandi's World. 2006. (J). (978-0-9772634-0-0(1)) Hall, Monique P. Productions.

Teitelbaum, Michael. If I Could Drive a Crane! Klavins, Uldis & Walker, Jeff, illus. 2002. (Tonka Ser.). 24p. (J). (ps-3). pap. 3.50 (978-0-439-34174-5(4) , Cartwheel Bks.) Scholastic, Inc.

Theroux, Phyllis. Serefina under the Circumstances. Priceman, Marjorie, illus. 2004. 30p. (J). (gr. k-4). reprint ed. (978-0-7567-7756-2(9)) DIANE Publishing Co.

—Serefina under the Circumstances. 2000. (J). 16.00 (978-0-689-80450-2(4) , Simon & Schuster Children's Publishing) Simon & Schuster Children's Publishing.

Thiesing, Lisa. A Dark & Noisy Night: A Silly Thriller with Peggy the Pig. 2005. (Dutton Easy Reader Ser.). (Illus.). 32p. (J). ***(*978-1-4156-1784-7(8)*** , Dutton Juvenile) Penguin Group (USA) Inc.

Thompson, John M. & Schultz, George M. Just Imagine. Wodin, illus. 2006. 32p. 16.95 ***(*978-0-9740190-6-2(2))*** Illumination Arts Publishing Co., Inc.

Thompson, Kate. Switchers. 220p. (J). (gr. 4-7). pap. 5.99 (978-0-8072-1553-1(8)); 2004. (Switchers Ser.: Vol. 1). (gr. 5-9). pap. 38.00 incl. audio (978-0-8072-8138-3(7) , YA115SP) Random Hse. Audio Publishing Group. (Listening Library).

—Switchers. 1999. (978-0-606-17387-2(0)); (gr. 5-8). lib. bdg. 14.15 (978-0-613-20224-4(4)) Tandem Library Bks.

Thomson, Sarah L. Imagine a Day. Gonsalves, Robert, illus. 2005. 40p. (J). 18.99 (978-0-689-85219-0(3) , Atheneum) Simon & Schuster Children's Publishing.

—Imagine a Night. Gonsalves, Rob, illus. 2003. 40p. (J). 18.99 (978-0-689-85218-3(5) , Atheneum) Simon & Schuster Children's Publishing.

Thorpe, Kiki. Let's Go, Little Bill! Oxley, Jennifer & Kanemoto, Dan, illus. 2002. (Little Bill Ser.). 14p. (J). (ps-2). bds. 12.95 (978-0-689-84776-9(9) , Simon Spotlight/Nickelodeon) Simon & Schuster Children's Publishing.

Tibo, Gilles. Simon's Disguise. ed. 2004. (J). (ps-2). spiral bd. (978-0-616-01790-6(1)); spiral bd. (978-0-616-01791-3(X)) Canadian National Institute for the Blind/ Institut National Canadien pour les Aveugles.

—Simon's Disguise. 2001. (gr. k-3). lib. bdg. 12.95 (978-0-613-70587-5(4)) Tandem Library Bks.

—Simon's Disguise. Fischman, Sheila, tr. from FRE. 2001. (Illus.). 24p. (J). (ps-1). pap. 4.95 (978-0-88776-545-2(9)) Tundra Bks., Inc./Livres Toundra, Inc. CAN. *Dist:* Random Hse., Inc.

—Simon's Disguise. Tibo, Gilles, illus. 1999. (Simon Ser.). (Illus.). 24p. (J). (ps-1). 10.95 (978-0-88776-472-1(X)) Tundra Bks., Inc./Livres Toundra, Inc. CAN. *Dist:* Random Hse., Inc.

Tich, Jan. Que mira Miranda? Jantti, Mariana, illus. 2005. (SPA.). 28p. (J). 14.95 (978-9974-7799-0-7(1)) Hardenville SA URY. *Dist:* Independent Pubs. Group.

Time for Your Mind. l.t. ed. 2006. (Illus.). 35p. (J). (978-0-9785480-1-8(9)) Mielcarek, David.

Tong, Kevin. The Earth Machine. Tong, Kevin, illus. 2007. (Illus.). 32p. (J). 15.95 (978-1-60108-001-1(8)) Red Cygnet Pr.

Tregebov, Rhea. What-If Sara. Franson, Leanne, illus. 2000. 12p. (J). (ps-3). 10.95 (978-1-896764-22-1(3)); pap. 4.95 (978-1-896764-20-7(7)) Second Story Pr. CAN. *Dist:* Orca Bk. Pubs. USA.

Trondheim, Lewis. Harum Scarum: The Spiffy Adventures of McConey, Vol. 1. (Illus.). 48p. (gr. 10 up). pap. 10.95 (978-1-56097-288-4(2)) Fantagraphics Bks.

Tusa, Tricia. Bunnies in My Head, 1. Tusa, Tricia et al, illus. 1998. (Illus.). (J). (gr. k-5). 20.00 (978-0-9664551-8-2(5)) Univ. of Texas, M.D. Anderson Cancer Ctr.

Twain, Mark. The Adventures of Tom Sawyer: With a Discussion of Imagination. Butterfield, Ned, illus. 2003. (Values in Action Illustrated Classics Ser.). 190p. (J). (978-1-59203-027-9(0)) Learning Challenge, Inc.

Uhlberg, Myron. Flying over Brooklyn. 2003. (Illus.). 32p. (J). (gr. k-3). pap. 6.95 (978-1-56145-294-1(7)) Peachtree Pubs., Ltd.

—Flying over Brooklyn. Fitzgerald, Gerald, illus. 1999. 32p. (J). (ps-3). 15.95 (978-1-56145-194-4(0)) Peachtree Pubs., Ltd.

Van Leeuwen, Jean. Oliver the Mighty Pig, Level. 2. Schweninger, Ann, illus. 2004. (Easy-to-Read Ser.). 48p. (J). (gr. k-3). 14.99 (978-0-8037-2886-8(7) , Dial) Penguin Group (USA) Inc.

Van Steenhoven, Tom. Moon Adventure. 1999. (Billy Bks.). (Illus.). (J). 15.99 (978-0-9672652-0-9(7)) Nation of Imagi, LLC, The.

Vivian, Bart. Imagine. Vivian, Bart, illus. 1998. (Illus.). 32p. (J). (ps-4). 14.95 (978-1-885223-72-2(2)) Beyond Words Publishing, Inc.

Waddell, Martin. Bee Frog. Firth, Barbara, illus. 2007. 32p. (J). (ps-2). 14.99 (978-0-7636-3310-3(0)) Candlewick Pr.

Wallace & Bostock. Imagine You Are a Dolphin. (Illus.). 25p. (J). pap. (978-0-340-67833-6(X) , Hodder & Stoughton) Hodder General Publishing Division.

Walton, Rick. You Don't Always Get What You Hope For. Mario, Heidi S., illus. 2nd ed. 2001. 32p. (J). (ps-3). pap. 5.95 (978-1-58685-108-8(X)) Gibbs Smith, Publisher.

—You Don't Always Get What You Hope For. 2001. (gr. k-3). lib. bdg. 14.10 (978-0-613-52649-4(X)) Tandem Library Bks.

Ward, Helen. The Dragon Machine. Anderson, Wayne, illus. 2005. 32p. (J). pap. 6.99 (978-0-14-240364-8(4) , Puffin) Penguin Group (USA) Inc.

Watson, T. E. The Monster in the Mailbox. Lancaster, Mari & Lancaster, Linus, illus. 2002. 32p. (J). (gr. 2-6). 16.95 (978-1-58478-011-3(8) , Paw Prints Pr.) Heather & Highlands Publishing.

Wax, Wendy. Secret Agents. 2007. 24p. (J). 21.35 ***(*978-1-59961-161-7(9))*** Spotlight.

Weeks, Sarah. If I Were a Lion. Solomon, Heather M., illus. 2004. 40p. (J). 16.99 (978-0-689-84836-0(6) , Atheneum) Simon & Schuster Children's Publishing.

Weiss, David & Weiss, Bobbi. Foster's Home for Imaginary Friends 8x8, No. 1. 2006. (Illus.). 24p. (J). pap. 3.99 (978-0-439-77580-9(9) , Scholastic) Scholastic, Inc.

Wells, Rosemary. The Small World of Binky Braverman. Egielski, Richard, illus. 40p. (J). (ps-3). 2003. 15.99 (978-0-670-03636-3(6) , Viking Juvenile); 2006. reprint ed. pap. 6.99 (978-0-14-240380-8(6) , Puffin) Penguin Group (USA) Inc.

West, Tracey. Roxy Hunter & the Mystery of the Moody Ghost. 2007. 128p. (J). (gr. 2-5). 4.99 ***(*978-0-8431-2663-1(9)*** , Price Stern Sloan) Penguin Group (USA) Inc.

Whatley, Bruce & Smith, Rosie. Captain Pajamas. 2000. (Illus.). 32p. (J). (ps-3). 15.89 (978-0-06-026614-1(7)) HarperCollins Pubs.

Williams, Regina. What If... Keith, Doug, illus. l.t. ed. 2001. 32p. (J). (ps up). 15.95 (978-0-935699-22-7(8)) Illumination Arts Publishing Co., Inc.

Williams, Suzanne. Master of Minds? Carter, Abby, illus. 2004. 58p. (J). lib. bdg. 15.00 ***(*978-1-4242-0911-8(0))*** Fitzgerald Bks.

Willis, Jeanne. Delilah D. at the Library. Reeve, Rosie, illus. 2007. 32p. (J). (gr. k-3). 16.00 (978-0-618-78195-9(1) , Clarion Bks.) Houghton Mifflin Co. Trade & Reference Div.

Wilson, Budge & LaFave, Kim. Duff's Monkey Business. 2000. (New First Novels Ser.). (Illus.). 63p. (gr. 1-5). 4.95 (978-0-88780-498-4(5)); (978-0-88780-499-1(3)) Formac Publishing Co., Ltd. CAN. *Dist:* Casemate Pubs. & Bk. Distributors, LLC.

Wilson, Karma. Princess Me. Unzner-Fischer, Christa, illus. 2007. 32p. (J). (ps-2). 16.99 (978-1-4169-4098-2(7) , McElderry, Margaret K.) Simon & Schuster Children's Publishing.

Wing, Natasha. Go to Bed, Monster! Kantorovitz, Sylvie, illus. 2007. 40p. (J). (ps-2). 16.00 (978-0-15-205775-6(7)) Harcourt Trade Pubs.

Wlodarski, Loran. If A Dolphin Were A Fish. Klein, Laurie Allen, illus. 2006. 32p. (J). 15.95 (978-0-9768823-2-9(9)) Sylvan Dell Pubng.

Wlodarski, Loran. If a Dolphin Were a Fish. Klein, Laurie Allen, illus. 2007. 1p. (J). 8.95 ***(*978-1-934359-03-7(3))*** Sylvan Dell Pubng.

Wood, Douglas. A Quiet Place. Andreasen, Dan, illus. 32p. (J). 2002. 16.95 (978-0-689-81511-9(5)); 2005. reprint ed. pap. 7.99 (978-0-689-87609-7(2) , Aladdin) Simon & Schuster Children's Publishing.

Wyss, Tyan. Night Flyer. Immelman, Sarita, illus. 2006. 40p. (J). per. 14.95 ***(*978-1-58939-916-7(1))*** Virtualbookworm.com Publishing, Inc.

Yamamoto, Lani. Albert. Yamamoto, Lani, illus. 2004. (Illus.). 32p. (J). 10.95 (978-1-58536-251-6(4)) Sleeping Bear Pr.

Yang, James. Joey & Jet in Space. Yang, James, illus. 2006. (Illus.). 32p. (J). (ps-k). 15.95 (978-0-689-86927-3(4) , Atheneum/Richard Jackson Bks.) Simon & Schuster Children's Publishing.

Zimmerman, Andrea. Digger Man. Clemesha, David, illus. 2007. 32p. (J). (ps-k). pap. 6.95 ***(*978-0-8050-8203-6(4)*** , Holt, Henry & Co. Bks. For Young Readers) Holt, Henry & Co.

Zimmerman, Andrea Griffing. Fire Engine Man. Clemesha, David, illus. 2007. 32p. (J). (ps-1). 15.95 (978-0-8050-7905-0(X)) Holt, Henry & Co.

Zimmerman, Andrea Griffing & Clemesha, David. Digger Man. rev. ed. 2003. (Illus.). 32p. (J). 15.95 (978-0-8050-6628-9(4) , Holt, Henry & Co. Bks. For Young Readers) Holt, Henry & Co.

Zolotow, Charlotte. Do You Know What I'll Do? Steptoe, Javaka, illus. rev. ed. 2000. 32p. (J). (ps-2). 16.99 (978-0-06-027879-3(X)) HarperCollins Pubs.

Zuehlke, Karen. Welcome to Janie's World. 2006. (ENG.). 76p. per. 14.95 ***(*978-1-4241-4587-4(2))*** PublishAmerica, Inc.

IMBECILITY

see People with Mental Disabilities

IMMERSION, BAPTISMAL

see Baptism

IMMIGRANTS

see Emigration and Immigration

IMMIGRATION AND EMIGRATION

see Emigration and Immigration

IMMUNITY

see also Allergy; Communicable Diseases; Vaccination

Balkwill, Fran & Rolph, Mic. Germ Zappers. 2001. (Enjoy Your Cells Ser.: Vol. 2). (Illus.). 32p. (J). 13.95 (978-0-87969-613-9(3)); pap. 8.95 (978-0-87969-598-9(6)) Cold Spring Harbor Laboratory Pr.

Ballard, Carol. The Immune System. 2003. (Body Focus Ser.). (Illus.). 48p. (J). lib. bdg. 27.07 (978-1-4034-0751-1(7)); pap. (978-1-4034-3299-5(6)) Heinemann Library.

Benchmark Education Staff. Fighting Disease. 2005. 2.00 ***(*978-1-4108-4657-0(1))*** Benchmark Education Co.

Boudreau, Gloria. The Immune System. 2004. (Kidhaven Science Library). (Illus.). 48p. (J). 26.20 (978-0-7377-2077-8(8) , Greenhaven Pr., Inc.) Thomson Gale.

Cole, Joanna. The Magic School Bus Inside Ralphie: A Book about Germs. 2002. (Magic School Bus Ser.). (Illus.). (J). 11.45 (978-0-7587-6980-0(6)) Book Wholesalers, Inc.

Defenses. (Amazing Animals Ser.). 32p. (J). (gr. 1). pap. (978-1-882210-79-4(4)) Action Publishing, Inc.

Donnellan, William Lorne. The Miracle of Immunity. 2002. (Story of Science Ser.). (Illus.). 79p. (J). 29.93 (978-0-7614-1425-4(8) , Benchmark Bks.) Cavendish, Marshall Corp.

Jerome, Kate Boehm. Fighting Disease. 2003. (Human Body Ser.). (Illus.). 32p. (J). pap. (978-0-7922-8865-7(3)) National Geographic Society.

Lombardo, Michelle. The OrganWise Guys - Basic Training for Better Health Vol. 2, 2 vols. Herron, Mark, illus. 1998. 35p. (J). (gr. 2-5). (978-0-9648438-3-7(8)) Wellness, Inc.

Parker, Steve. Defend Yourself! The Immune System. 2006. (Illus.). 48p. (J). (978-1-4109-1880-2(7)); pap. (978-1-4109-1887-1(4)) Steck-Vaughn.

Parsons, Michelle Hyde. Fighting Disease. 2005. 42.00 ***(*978-1-4108-4609-9(1))*** Benchmark Education Co.

Thames, Susan. Our Immune System. 2008. (J). ***(*978-1-60044-511-8(X))*** Rourke Publishing, LLC.

IMPERIAL TRANS-ANTARCTIC EXPEDITION, 1914-1917

Armstrong, Jennifer. Shipwreck at the Bottom of the World: The Extraordinary True Story of Shackleton & the Endurance. 2000. (gr. 5-8). lib. bdg. 21.05 (978-0-613-30126-8(9)) Tandem Library Bks.

Calvert, Patricia. Sir Ernest Shackleton: By Endurance We Conquer. 2002. (Great Explorations Ser.). (Illus.). 80p. (J). 29.93 (978-0-7614-1485-8(1) , Benchmark Bks.) Cavendish, Marshall Corp.

Fine, Jil. Shackleton Expedition. 2002. (gr. 7-12). lib. bdg. 15.25 (978-0-613-58800-3(2)) Tandem Library Bks.

Hoena, B. A. Shackleton & the Lost Antarctic Expedition. Hoover, Dave & Barnett, Charles, illus. 2006. (Graphic Library). 32p. (J). (978-0-7368-5482-5(7)) Capstone Pr., Inc.

Kimmel, Elizabeth Cody. Ice Story: Shackleton's Lost Expedition. 1999. (Illus.). 128p. (J). (gr. 4-6). tchr. ed. 19.00 (978-0-395-91524-0(4) , Clarion Bks.) Houghton Mifflin Co. Trade & Reference Div.

McCurdy, Michael. Trapped by the Ice: Shackleton's Amazing Antarctic Adventure. 2002. (gr. 3-6). lib. bdg. 17.60 (978-0-613-75493-4(X)) Tandem Library Bks.

Penner, Lucille Recht. Ice Wreck. LaFleur, David, illus. 2004. (Stepping Stones Ser.). 48p. (J). (gr. k-3). pap. 3.99 (978-0-307-26408-4(4) , Random Hse. Bks. for Young Readers) Random Hse. Children's Bks.

IMPLEMENTS, UTENSILS, ETC.

see Agricultural Machinery; Household Equipment and Supplies; Tools

IMPORTS

see Commerce

IMPOSTORS AND IMPOSTURE

see also Fraud

Blackwood, Gary L. Perplexing People. 2005. (Unsolved History Ser.). (Illus.). 72p. (J). (gr. 3-7). lib. bdg. (978-0-7614-1890-0(3) , Benchmark Bks.) Cavendish, Marshall Corp.

Standiford, Natalie. The Stone Giant. 2000. (J). (978-0-606-18928-6(9)) Tandem Library Bks.

Thompson, Lisa. Hoaxes, Fibs & Fakes. 2005. (Real Deal Ser.). (Illus.). 32p. (J). 18.50 (978-0-7910-8428-1(0) , Chelsea Hse.) Facts On File, Inc.

Weil, Ann. Fakes. 2007. (J). pap. ***(*978-1-4109-2988-4(4))***; lib. bdg. ***(*978-1-4109-2967-9(1))*** Steck-Vaughn.

IMPRESSIONISM (ART)

see also Post-Impressionism (Art)

Burleigh, Robert. Seurat & la Grande Jatte: Connecting the Dots. 2004. (Illus.). 32p. (J). (gr. k-4). 17.95 (978-0-8109-4811-2(7)) Abrams, Harry N. , Inc.

Dover Staff. Impressionist Art Masterpieces to Color. 2007. (Illus.). 128p. pap. 8.95 (978-0-486-45135-0(6)) Dover Pubns., Inc.

Gunderson, Jessica. Impressionism. 2008. (J). ***(*978-1-58341-611-2(0)*** , Creative Education) Creative Co., The.

Harris, Lois V. Mary Cassatt: Impressionist Painter. 2007. 32p. (J). (gr. k-3). 15.95 ***(*978-1-58980-452-4(X))*** Pelican Publishing Co., Inc.

Hyde, Margaret E., ed. Impressionists for Kids. 2004. (Great Art for Kids Ser.). (Illus.). 14p. ring bd. 8.95 (978-1-58980-265-0(9)); 12p. (J). pap. 8.95 (978-1-58980-203-2(9)) Pelican Publishing Co., Inc.

Klein, Adam G. & Monet, Claude. Claude Monet. 2007. (Illus.). 32p. (J). 22.78 (978-1-59679-732-1(0)) ABDO Publishing Co.

Klein, Adam G. & Renoir, Auguste. Pierre-Auguste Renoir. 2007. (Illus.). 32p. (J). 22.78 (978-1-59679-736-9(3)) ABDO Publishing Co.

Knapp, Ruthie & Lehmberg, Janice. Impressionist Art. 1998. (Off the Wall Museum Guides for Kids). (Illus.). 72p. (J). pap. 10.95 (978-0-87192-385-1(8)) Davis Pubns., Inc.

Lacey, Sue. In the Time of Renoir. 2001. (gr. 3-6). lib. bdg. 17.60 (978-0-613-45192-5(9)) Tandem Library Bks.

Marotske, Michelle R. & Yoakum, Kimberly H. Impressionism. Marotske, Michelle R. & Yoakum, Kimberly H., illus. 1998. (Illus.). 20p. (J). (gr. 1-6). mass mkt. (978-1-893397-01-9(7)) Painted in the Corner Productions, L.L.C.

Mason, Antony. El arte Impresionista: En los tiempos de Renoir. Llaca, Martha, tr. 2005. (Arte Alrededor del Mundo Ser.). 48p. (J). pap. 9.95 (978-85-7416-229-4(9)) Callis Editora Ltda BRA. *Dist:* Independent Pubs. Group.

Parks, Peggy J. Impressionism. 2006. (Illus.). 112p. (J). (gr. 7-10). 32.45 (978-1-59018-958-0(2) , Lucent Bks.) Thomson Gale.

Raimondo, Joyce. Picture This! Activities & Adventures in Impressionism. 2004. (Art Explorers Ser.). (Illus.). 48p. (J). (gr. 1-5). 12.95 (978-0-8230-2503-9(9)) Watson-Guptill Pubns., Inc.

Sabbeth, Carol. Monet & the Impressionists for Kids: Their Lives & Ideas, 21 Activities. 2002. (For Kids Ser.). (Illus.). 152p. (J). (gr. 4 up). pap. 17.95 (978-1-55652-397-1(1)) Chicago Review Pr., Inc.

—Monet & the Impressionists for Kids: Their Lives & Ideas, 21 Activities. 2002. (gr. 3-6). lib. bdg. 28.00 (978-0-613-64194-4(9)) Tandem Library Bks.

Salvi, Francesco. The Impressionists. 2008. (YA). lib. bdg. 24.95 net. ***(*978-1-934545-03-4(1))*** Oliver Pr., Inc.

Sateren, Shelley Swanson. Monet. 2001. (Masterpieces). (Illus.). 24p. (J). (gr. 2-3). lib. bdg. 18.60 (978-0-7368-1123-1(0) , Bridgestone Bks.) Capstone Pr., Inc.

Spence, David. Renoir: Color y Naturaleza. (Coleccion Grandes Artistas).Tr. of Renoir: Colot & Nature. (SPA.). (YA). (gr. 5-8). 12.76 (978-84-8211-137-7(X)) Celeste Ediciones, S.A. ESP. *Dist:* Lectorum Pubns., Inc.

Wallis, Jeremy. Impressionists. 2002. (Artists in Profile Ser.). (Illus.). 64p. (J). lib. bdg. 28.50 (978-1-58810-642-1(X)) Heinemann Library.

IMPRISONMENT

see Prisons

IN-LINE SKATING

Aggressive in-Line Skating. (To the Extreme Ser.). 32p. (YA). 7.95 (978-0-7368-6173-1(4)) Capstone Pr., Inc.

Blackall, Bernie & Bizley, Kirk. In-Line Skating. 1999. (Illus.). 32p. (J). (gr. 5-7). lib. bdg. 24.22 (978-1-57572-942-8(3)) Heinemann Library.

Blomquist, Christopher. In-Line Skating in the X Games. 2003. (Kids Guide to the X Games Ser.). (Illus.). 24p. (J). lib. bdg. 19.95 (978-0-8239-6302-7(0) , PowerKids Pr.) Rosen Publishing Group, Inc., The.

Cook, Nick. Downhill In-Line Skating. 2000. (Extreme Sports Ser.). (Illus.). 48p. (J). (gr. 3-4). lib. bdg. 21.26 (978-0-7368-0482-0(X) , Capstone High-Interest Bks.) Capstone Pr., Inc.

Craats, Rennay. Inline Skating. 2001. (For the Love of Sports Ser.). (Illus.). 24p. (J). lib. bdg. 15.95 (978-1-930954-32-8(8)) Weigl Pubs., Inc.

Crossingham, John. Extreme in-Line Skating. 2003. (gr. 3-6). lib. bdg. 15.25 (978-0-613-82413-2(X)) Tandem Library Bks.

—In-Line Skating in Action. 2002. (Sports in Action Ser.). (Illus.). 32p. (J). pap. (978-0-7787-0348-8(7)) Crabtree Publishing Co.

—In-Line Skating in Action. Rouse, Bonna & Crabtree, Marc, illus. Crabtree, Marc, photos by. 2002. (Sports in Action Ser.). 32p. (J). (gr. 4-7). (978-0-7787-0328-0(2)) Crabtree Publishing Co.

—In-Line Skating in Action. 2003. (gr. 3-6). lib. bdg. 15.25 (978-0-613-52860-3(3)) Tandem Library Bks.

Crossingham, John & Kalman, Bobbie. Extreme in-Line Skating. 2003. (Extreme Sports - No Limits Ser.). (Illus.). 32p. (J). (gr. 3). (978-0-7787-1667-9(8)); pap. (978-0-7787-1713-3(5)) Crabtree Publishing Co.

David, Jack. In-Line Skating. 2008. (Illus.). 24p. (J). lib. bdg. 19.95 ***(*978-1-60014-137-9(4))*** Bellwether Media.

Eck, Kristin. In-Line Skating: Check It Out. 2001. (Reading Power Ser.). (Illus.). 24p. (J). (gr. 1). lib. bdg. 17.25 (978-0-8239-5699-9(7) , PKINSK, Rosen Central) Rosen Publishing Group, Inc., The.

Gedatus, Gus. In-Line Skating for Fitness. 2000. (Nutrition & Fitness Ser.). (Illus.). 64p. (J). (gr. 4-6). lib. bdg. 23.93 (978-0-7368-0707-4(1) , LifeMatters Bks.) Capstone Pr., Inc.

Glidewell, Steve. Inline Skating. 2004. (Extreme Sports Ser.). (Illus.). 32p. (J). (gr. 3-6). lib. bdg. 22.60 (978-0-8225-1244-8(0)) Lerner Publishing Group.

Herran, Joe & Thomas, Ron. In-Line Skating. 2002. (Action Sports Ser.). (Illus.). 32p. (gr. 4-8). 28.00 (978-0-7910-6999-8(0) , Chelsea Hse.) Facts On File, Inc.

Hughes, Morgan. In-Line Skating. 2003. (Wheels in Motion Ser.). (Illus.). 24p. (J). 20.64 (978-1-58952-666-2(X)) Rourke Publishing, LLC.

In-Line Skating. 2004. (I-Quest Ser.). (Illus.). 48p. (J). per. (978-1-84229-755-1(4)) Top That! Publishing PLC.

Kaelberer, Angie Peterson. Aggressive In-Line Skating. 2006. (Blazers—To the Extreme Ser.). (Illus.). 32p. (J). (978-0-7368-4396-6(5)) Capstone Pr., Inc.

Kaminker, Laura. In-Line Skating! Get Aggressive. 1999. (Extreme Sports Collection). (Illus.). 64p. (YA). (gr. 5-8). lib. bdg. 26.50 (978-0-8239-3012-8(2) , EXSKAT, Rosen Central) Rosen Publishing Group, Inc., The.

—In-Line Skating! Get Aggressive. 2000. (Illus.). 64p. (YA). per. 9.95 (978-1-56254-302-0(4) , SP 3024) Saddleback Educational Publishing.

Maurer, Tracy. In-Line Skating. 2002. (Radsports Guides). (Illus.). 48p. (gr. 4-8). 20.95 (978-1-58952-103-2(X)) Rourke Publishing, LLC.

McKenna, Anne T. Aggressive In-Line Skating. 1999. (Extreme Sports Ser.). (Illus.). 48p. (J). (gr. 3-4). lib. bdg. 21.26 (978-0-7368-0164-5(2) , Capstone High-Interest Bks.) Capstone Pr., Inc.

H I

Miller, Chuck. In-Line Skating. 2001. (Extreme Sports Ser.). (Illus.). 48p. (J). lib. bdg. 24.26 (978-0-7398-4688-9(4)) Raintree.

Miller, Liz. Advanced in-Line Skating. 2000. (gr. 7-12). lib. bdg. 24.55 (978-0-613-27695-5(7)) Tandem Library Bks.

Morgan, Jed. In-Line Skating. 2006. (Illus.). 32p. (J). (978-1-58340-957-2(2)) Smart Apple Media.

Murdico, Suzanne J. In-Line Skating. 2005. (Rad Sports Techniques & Tricks Ser.). (Illus.). 48p. (YA). (gr. 5-8). lib. bdg. 26.50 (978-0-8239-3844-5(1)) Rosen Publishing Group, Inc., The.

Parr, Danny. Extreme In-Line Skating Moves. 2001. (Behind the Moves Ser.). (Illus.). 32p. (J). (gr. 3-4). lib. bdg. 21.26 (978-0-7368-0782-1(9) , Capstone High-Interest Bks.) Capstone Pr., Inc.

Roberts, Ben. In-Line Skating. 1999. (Extreme Sports Ser.). (Illus.). 32p. (YA). (gr. 5-9). 6.95 (978-0-7641-0798-6(4)) Barron's Educational Series, Inc.

Savage, Jeff. Top 10 In-Line Skaters. 1999. (Sports Top 10 Ser.). (Illus.). 48p. (YA). (gr. 4-10). lib. bdg. 23.93 (978-0-7660-1129-8(1)) Enslow Pubs., Inc.

Shafran, Michael. Skate! Your Guide to Blading, Aggressive, Vert, Street, Roller Hockey, Speed Skating, Dance, Fitness Training, & More. 2003. (Illus.). 64p. (J). (gr. 4-7). pap. 8.95 (978-0-7922-5107-1(5) , National Geographic Children's Bks.) National Geographic Society.

Smith, Martin. In-Line Skating. 2001. (To the Limit Ser.). (Illus.). 32p. (J). (gr. 4-7). lib. bdg. 25.69 (978-0-7398-3166-3(6)) Raintree.

Thomas, Keltie. Blades, Boards & Scooters. Attoe, Steve & Moon, Allan, illus. 2005. (Popular Mechanics for Kids Ser.). 64p. (J). pap., pap. 9.95 (978-1-897066-34-8(1)) Maple Tree Pr. CAN. *Dist:* Perseus Distribution.

Van Cleaf, Kristin. In-Line Skating. 2003. (X-Treme Sports Ser.). (Illus.). 32p. (J). (gr. k-6). lib. bdg. 22.78 (978-1-57765-927-3(9)) ABDO Publishing Co.

Weil, Ann. Aggressive In-Line Skating. 2004. (Edge Books, X-Sports). (Illus.). 32p. (J). lib. bdg. 22.60 (978-0-7368-2708-9(0)) Capstone Pr., Inc.

Witt, Alexa. It's Great to Skate! 2000. (Ready-to-Read Ser.). (J). (978-0-606-19713-7(3)) Tandem Library Bks.

Woods, Bob. In-Line Skating. 2003. (Extreme Sports Ser.). (Illus.). 24p. (J). (gr. 2 up). lib. bdg. 22.00 (978-0-8368-3722-3(3)) Stevens, Gareth Inc.

IN-LINE SKATING—FICTION

Christopher, Matt. Inline Skater. 2001. (J). 11.15 (978-0-606-21247-2(7)) Tandem Library Bks.

INCANDESCENT LAMPS

see Electric Lamps

INCAS

Ackroyd, Peter. Cities of Blood. 2005. (Voyages through Time Ser.). (Illus.). 144p. (J). (gr. 4-7). pap. 9.99 (978-0-7566-1367-9(1)) Dorling Kindersley Publishing, Inc.

Allison, Amy. Machu Picchu. 2003. (Building History Ser.). (Illus.). 112p. (YA). 32.45 (978-1-59018-020-4(8) , Lucent Bks.) Thomson Gale.

Apte, Sunita. The Inca. 2005. (Navigators Ser.). (J). pap. 42.00 (***978-1-4108-5100-0(1)***) Benchmark Education Co.

Baquedano, Elizabeth & Buller, Laura. Aztec, Inca, & Maya. 2005. (Dk eyewitness Bks.). (Illus.). 72p. (J). lib. bdg. 19.99 (978-0-7566-1392-1(2)) Dorling Kindersley Publishing, Inc.

Baquedano, Elizabeth & Clarke, Barry. Aztec, Inca, & Maya. Zabe, Michel, photos by. 2005. (Dk eyewitness Bks.). (Illus.). 72p. (J). (gr. 4-7). 15.99 (978-0-7566-1383-9(3)) Dorling Kindersley Publishing, Inc.

Benchmark Education Staff. The Inca World. 2005. 2.00 (***978-1-4108-4673-0(3)***) Benchmark Education Co.

Bingham, Jane. The Inca Empire. 2007. (Time Travel Guides Ser.). (Illus.). 64p. (YA). (gr. 5-8). lib. bdg. 34.29 (***978-1-4109-2731-6(8)***) Raintree.

—The Inca Empire. 2007. (Time Travel Guides Ser.). (Illus.). 64p. (J). (***978-1-4109-2738-5(5)***) Steck-Vaughn.

Brannon, Barbara. Discover the Inca. 2005. 39.00 (***978-1-4108-5148-2(6)***) Benchmark Education Co.

Byers, Helen. Peru. 2004. (National Geographic Reading Expeditions Ser.). (Illus.). 24p. (J). pap. (978-0-7922-4538-4(5)) National Geographic Society.

Calvert, Patricia. The Ancient Inca. (People of the Ancient World Ser.). (Illus.). 128p. 2005. (J). (gr. 6-8). pap. 9.95 (978-0-531-16740-3(2)); 2004. 29.50 (978-0-531-12358-4(8)) Scholastic Library Publishing. (Watts, Franklin).

Conklin, Wendy. Mayas, Aztecs, Incas: All-in-One Resource with Background Information, Map Activities, Simulations & Games, & a Read-Aloud Play to Support Comprehension & Critical Thinking in Social Studies. 2006. 80p. pap. 12.99 (978-0-439-53994-4(3) , Teaching Resources) Scholastic, Inc.

Corrick, James A. The Inca. 2002. (Lost Civilizations Ser.). (Illus.). 112p. (YA). (gr. 6-8). 29.95 (978-1-56006-850-1(7) , LML00902-178181, Lucent Bks.) Thomson Gale.

Dean, Arlan. Terra-Cotta Soldiers: Army of Stone. 2005. (High Interest Books Ser.). (Illus.). 48p. (J). (ps-7). 24.00 (978-0-516-25124-0(4) , Children's Pr.) Scholastic Library Publishing.

Dworkin, Mark J. Mayas, Aztecs & Incas: Mysteries of Ancient Civilizations of Central & South America. 1999. (Illus.). 144p. (J). (gr. 10-12). reprint ed. pap. 17.00 (978-0-7881-6589-4(5)) DIANE Publishing Co.

Ganeri, Anita. The Incas. 2006. (J). (978-0-7565-1951-3(9)) Compass Point Bks.

Glencoe McGraw-Hill Staff & McGraw-Hill - Jamestown Education Staff. Jamestown's Early Civilizations: Inca Life. 2001. (gr. 5-12). pap. 11.96 (978-0-8092-9492-3(3) , 9780809294923) Jamestown.

Grant, Neil. Everyday Life of the Aztecs, Incas & Mayans. Cappon, Manuela et al, illus. 2003. (Uncovering History Ser.). 46p. (J). lib. bdg. 28.50 (978-1-58340-253-5(5)) Smart Apple Media.

Gruber, Beth, et al. Ancient Inca: Archaeology Unlocks the Secrets of Inca's Past. 2006. (National Geographic Investigates Ser.). (Illus.). 64p. (J). (gr. 3-7). 17.95 (978-0-7922-7827-6(5)); lib. bdg. 27.90 (978-0-7922-7873-3(9)) National Geographic Society. (National Geographic Children's Bks.).

Halls, Kelly Milner. Mysteries of the Mummy Kids. 2007. (Illus.). 72p. (J). (gr. 4-8). 18.95 (***978-1-58196-059-4(X)***) Darby Creek Publishing.

Hoogenboom, Lynn. Francisco Pizarro: A Primary Source Biography. 2006. (J). lib. bdg. (978-1-4042-3038-5(6) , PowerKids Pr.) Rosen Publishing Group, Inc., The.

Ingram, Scott. Francisco Pizarro. 2002. (History's Villains Ser.). (Illus.). 112p. 29.94 (978-1-56711-627-4(2) , Blackbirch Pr., Inc.) Thomson Gale.

Kachurek, Sandra J. Francisco Pizarro: Explorer of South America. 2004. (Explorers! Ser.). (Illus.). 48p. (J). lib. bdg. 23.93 (978-0-7660-2178-5(5)) Enslow Pubs., Inc.

Keller, Mary Jo, et al. Inca, Aztec, Maya: Arts, Crafts, Cooking, & Historical Aids. Lorseyedi, Barbara, illus. 1999. (Hands-On Heritage Ser.). 48p. (J). (gr. 2-6). pap., act. bk. ed. 6.95 (978-1-56472-150-1(7) , EP150) Edupress, Inc.

Kline, Trish. Francisco Pizarro. 2003. (Rourke Discovery Library). (Illus.). 24p. (gr. 2-5). 14.95 (978-1-58952-297-8(4)) Rourke Publishing, LLC.

Lourie, Peter. Lost Treasure of the Inca. 2003. (Illus.). 48p. (J). (gr. 4-6). 18.95 (978-1-56397-743-5(5)); pap. 10.95 (978-1-56397-983-5(7)) Boyds Mills Pr.

—Lost Treasure of the Inca. 2001. (gr. 3-6). lib. bdg. 18.75 (978-0-613-53831-2(5)) Tandem Library Bks.

MacDonald, Fiona & Salariya, David. Inca Town. Bergin, Mark, illus. 1998. (Metropolis Ser.). 45p. (J). (gr. 4-7). 25.00 (978-0-531-14481-7(X) , Watts, Franklin) Scholastic Library Publishing.

Mann, Elizabeth. Machu Picchu: The Story of the Amazing Inkas & Their City in the Clouds. Crehore, Amy, illus. 2000. (Wonders of the World Ser.: Vol. 6). 48p. (J). (gr. 4-7). 22.95 (978-0-9650493-9-9(6)) Mikaya Pr.

Martell, Hazel Mary. Civilizations of Peru Before 1535. 1999. (Looking Back Ser.). (Illus.). 64p. (YA). (gr. 6-9). 19.98 (978-0-8172-5428-5(5)) Raintree.

Meltzer, Milton. Francisco Pizarro: The Conquest of Peru. 2003. (Great Explorations Ser.). (J). 29.93 (978-0-7614-1607-4(2) , Benchmark Bks.) Cavendish, Marshall Corp.

Mountjoy, Shane. Francisco Pizarro & the Conquest of the Inca. Goetzmann, William H., ed. 2005. (Explorers of New Lands Ser.). (Illus.). 150p. (J). (gr. 4-8). 30.00 (978-0-7910-8614-8(3) , Chelsea Hse.) Facts On File, Inc.

Nicholson, Sue. Aztecs & Incas: A Guide to the Pre-Colonized Americas in 1504. 2000. (Sightseers Ser.). (Illus.). 32p. (J). (gr. 3-5). tchr. ed. 8.95 (978-0-7534-5236-3(7) , Kingfisher) Houghton Mifflin Co. Trade & Reference Div.

Nishi, Dennis. The Incan Empire. 1999. (World History Ser.). (Illus.). 112p. (YA). (gr. 8-11). 27.45 (978-1-56006-538-8(9) , LML00902-177895, Lucent Bks.) Thomson Gale.

Peterson, Sheryl. Machu Picchu. 2005. (Ancient Wonders of the World Ser.). (Illus.). 32p. (gr. 4-7). 18.95 (978-1-58341-357-9(X) , Creative Education) Creative Co., The.

Rees, Rosemary. The Incas. 2006. (Illus.). 64p. (J). (***978-1-4034-8750-6(2)***) Heinemann Library.

Richardson, Hazel. Life in Ancient South America. 2005. (Peoples of the Ancient World Ser.). (Illus.). 32p. (J). (ps-9). (978-0-7787-2042-3(X)); pap. (978-0-7787-2072-0(1)) Crabtree Publishing Co.

Rosemary Rees. The Incas. 2nd ed. 2006. (Illus.). 64p. (J). pap. (***978-1-4034-8756-8(1)***) Heinemann Library.

Saunders, Nicholas. Pizarro & the Incas. 2006. (Stories from History Ser.). 48p. (J). pap. 6.95 (***978-0-7696-4642-8(5)***) School Specialty Publishing.

Saunders, Nicholas J. The Inca City of Cuzco. 2005. (Places in History Ser.). (Illus.). 48p. (J). pap. (978-0-8368-5819-8(0)); lib. bdg. 30.00 (978-0-8368-5812-9(3)) Stevens, Gareth Inc. (World Almanac Library).

Sayer, Chloe. The Incas. 1999. (Ancient World Ser.). (Illus.). 64p. (gr. 5-10). lib. bdg. 27.12 (978-0-8172-5125-3(1)) Raintree.

—The Incas. 1999. (Ancient World Ser.). (Illus.). 64p. (J). (978-0-7502-2171-9(2)) Steck-Vaughn.

Scheff. The Inca. 2001. (Ancient Civilizations Ser.). (Illus.). (J). pap. (978-0-7398-4145-7(9)) Steck-Vaughn.

Scheff, Duncan. Incas. 2001. (Ancient Civilizations Ser.). (Illus.). 48p. (J). lib. bdg. 22.83 (978-0-7398-3582-1(3)) Raintree.

Somervill, Barbara A. Machu Picchu: City in the Clouds. 2005. (High Interest Books). (Illus.). 48p. (J). (ps-7). 24.00 (978-0-516-25123-3(6)); (YA). (gr. 7-12). pap. 6.95 (978-0-516-25092-2(2)) Scholastic Library Publishing. (Children's Pr.).

Steele, Philip. Inca World. 2000. (Step into Ser.). (Illus.). 64p. (gr. 3-7). 12.95 (978-0-7548-0476-5(3)) Anness Publishing, Inc.

—The Incas: What Life Was Like in the Spectacular South American Empire. 2003. (Find Out about...Ser.). (Illus.). 64p. (gr. 2-7). pap. 7.99 (978-1-84215-777-0(9) , Southwater) Anness Publishing GBR. *Dist:* National Bk. Network.

Steele, Philip & MacDonald, Fiona. Sungods & Sacrifice: Lost World of the Aztecs, Incas & Maya. 2004. (Illus.). 128p. pap. 17.99 (978-1-84476-005-3(7) , Southwater) Anness Publishing GBR. *Dist:* National Bk. Network.

Takacs, Stefanie. The Inca. 2003. (True Book Ser.). (Illus.). 48p. (J). 25.00 (978-0-516-22776-4(9) , Children's Pr.) Scholastic Library Publishing.

Thomas, Emma. Temple of the Sun. 2003. (History Hunters Ser.). (Illus.). 32p. (J). (gr. 3 up). lib. bdg. 24.67 (978-0-8368-3744-5(4)) Stevens, Gareth Inc.

Trumbauer, Lisa. The Inca World. 2005. 39.00 (***978-1-4108-4625-9(3)***) Benchmark Education Co.

Von Hagen, Victor Wolfgang. The Incas: People of the Sun. 2003. 127p. pap. 29.00 (978-0-7581-0248-5(8)) Textbook Pubs.

Worth, Richard. Pizarro & the Conquest of the Incan Empire in World History. 2000. (In World History Ser.). (Illus.). 128p. (YA). (gr. 5-12). lib. bdg. 26.60 (978-0-7660-1396-4(0)) Enslow Pubs., Inc.

Zronik, John Paul. Francisco Pizarro: Journeys Through Peru & South America. 2005. (In the Footsteps of Explorers Ser.). (Illus.). 32p. (J). (ps-9). (978-0-7787-2411-7(5)); pap. (978-0-7787-2447-6(6)) Crabtree Publishing Co.

INCAS—FICTION

Becket, Jim. Inca Gold: Choose Your Own Adventure #20. 2007. (Choose Your Own Adventure Ser.: 20). (Illus.). 144p. (J). per. 6.99 (***978-1-933390-20-8(4)*** , CHCL20) Chooseco LLC.

Burgess, Robert F. Where Condors Fly. 2000. (Illus.). 196p. (gr. 4-7). pap. 12.95 (978-0-595-00347-1(8) , Backinprint.com) iUniverse, Inc.

Clark, Ann Nolan. Secret of the Andes. 2001. (gr. 5-9). 21.75 (978-0-8446-7172-7(X)) Smith, Peter Pub., Inc.

Ficklin, Jonene H. Orinoco Intrigue. 2005. (YA). 14.95 (978-0-9761188-1-7(5)) Victor's Crown Publishing.

Horowitz, Anthony. Evil Star. 2006. (Power of Five Ser.: Vol. 2). 320p. (J). pap. 17.99 (978-0-439-67996-1(6) , Scholastic Pr.) Scholastic, Inc.

Vandersteen, Willy. The Secret of the Incas. Geerts, Paul, illus. 1998. (Greatest Adventures of Spike & Suzy Ser.: Vol. 3). 56p. (J). (gr. 2-9). 11.95 (978-0-9533178-2-0(X)) Intes International (UK) Ltd. GBR. *Dist:* Diamond Comic Distributors, Inc.

INCEST

Lynn Slaughter. Teen Rape. 2004. (Illus.). 112p. (J). (978-1-56006-513-5(3)) Thomson Gale.

Marcy-Webster, Susan & Phillips, Emily. If I Tell. 2006. (Illus.). 32p. (J). pap. 3.95 (978-1-55864-178-5(5) , K1785, KIDSRIGHTS) JIST Publishing.

Rosen, Marvin. Dealing with the Effects of Rape & Incest. 2002. (Focus on Family Matters Ser.). (Illus.). 64p. (J). (gr. 5 up). 25.00 (978-0-7910-6693-5(2) , Chelsea Hse.) Facts On File, Inc.

INCEST—FICTION

Amateau, Gigi. Claiming Georgia Tate. 208p. (YA). (gr. 9). 2007. pap. 7.99 (***978-0-7636-3311-0(9)***); 2005. 15.99 (978-0-7636-2339-5(3)) Candlewick Pr.

Block, Francesca Lia. Wasteland. 160p. (J). 2003. 15.99 (978-0-06-028644-6(X) , Cotler, Joanna Books); 2003. (Illus.). 16.89 (978-0-06-028645-3(8) , Cotler, Joanna Books); 2004. reprint ed. pap. 7.99 (978-0-06-440839-4(6)) HarperCollins Pubs.

Hurwin, Davida Wills. Circle the Soul Softly. 2006. 176p. (J). 15.99 (978-0-06-077505-6(X)); lib. bdg. 16.89 (978-0-06-077506-3(8)) HarperCollins Pubs.

Newbery, Linda. Set in Stone. 2006. 368p. (YA). (gr. 9). lib. bdg. 18.99 (978-0-385-75103-2(6)) Knopf, Alfred A. Inc.

—Set in Stone. 2006. 368p. (YA). (gr. 9). 16.95 (978-0-385-75102-5(8) , Fickling, David Bks.) Random Hse. Children's Bks.

INCINERATION

see Refuse and Refuse Disposal

INDEPENDENCE DAY (U. S.)

see Fourth of July

INDEPENDENCE HALL (PHILADELPHIA, PA.)

Britton, Tamara L. Independence Hall. 2005. (Checkerboard History Library). (Illus.). 32p. (J). (gr. k-6). lib. bdg. 22.78 (978-1-57765-853-5(1)) ABDO Publishing Co.

Marcovitz, Hal. Independence Hall. 2002. (American Symbols & Their Meanings Ser.). (Illus.). 48p. (J). (gr. 4 up). lib. bdg. (978-1-59084-030-6(5)) Mason Crest Pubs.

INDIA

Abdul Kalam, A. P. J. Children Ask Kalam. Kathuria, Rohit, illus. 2006. 109p. (J). (***978-81-7758-245-1(3)***) Pearson Education.

Aboff, Marcie. India ABCs: A Book about the People & Places of India. Moore, Frances, illus. 2006. (Country ABCs Ser.). 32p. (J). (gr. k-5). 23.93 (978-1-4048-1571-1(6)) Picture Window Bks.

Allard, Denise. India. 2000. (Postcards from...Ser.). (Illus.). 32p. (J). (gr. 2-4). pap. 6.95 (978-0-8172-6222-8(9)) Steck-Vaughn.

Anita Roy. India. 2006. (Illus.). 48p. (J). pap. (***978-1-4109-2467-4(X)***) Steck-Vaughn.

Arnold, Caroline & Comora, Madeleine. Taj Mahal. Bhushan, Rahul, illus. 2007. 32p. (J). (gr. k up). spiral bd. 17.95 (978-0-7613-2609-0(X) , Millbrook Pr.) Lerner Publishing Group.

Axworthy, Anni. Anni's India Diary. 2000. (J). (978-0-606-18747-3(2)) Tandem Library Bks.

Barker, Amanda. India. 1998. (Worldfocus Ser.). (Illus.). 32p. (J). pap. (978-1-57572-028-9(0)) Heinemann Library.

—India. (World Focus Ser.). (Illus.). 32p. (J). (gr. 3-7). 3.99 (978-0-431-07258-6(2)) Oxfam Publishing GBR. *Dist:* Stylus Publishing, LLC.

Brace, Steven. India. 1999. (Country Studies). (Illus.). 64p. (YA). lib. bdg. 27.07 (978-1-57572-893-3(1)) Heinemann Library.

Brooks, Susie. India. 2006. (Our Lives, Our World Ser.). (Illus.). (J). (978-1-59389-288-3(8)) Chrysalis Education.

Brownlie Bojang, Ali & Barber, Nicola. Focus on India. 2006. (Illus.). 64p. (J). pap. (978-0-8368-6728-2(9)); lib. bdg. (978-0-8368-6721-3(1)) Stevens, Gareth Inc. (World Almanac Library).

Caldwell, John, pseud. India. 1999. (Major World Nations Ser.). (Illus.). 144p. (YA). (gr. 4-7). lib. bdg. 21.95 (978-0-7910-4988-4(4) , Chelsea Hse.) Facts On File, Inc.

Caper, William. India & China. 2005. (Navigators Ser.). (J). pap. 44.00 (***978-1-4108-5112-3(5)***) Benchmark Education Co.

Castelain, Celine & Liutkus, Aurelien. Asha: A Child of the Himalayas. 2005. (Children of the World Ser.). (Illus.). 24p. (J). (gr. k-3). 22.45 (978-1-4103-0286-1(5) , Blackbirch Pr., Inc.) Thomson Gale.

Clark, Leon E., ed. African Eyes Vol. 2: Culture & Society. 1999. (Illus.). 346p. (J). (gr. 11 up). pap. 24.95 (978-0-938960-28-7(8)) Ctr. for International Training & Education.

Conboy, Fiona & Arora Lal, Sunandini. Welcome to India. 1999. (Welcome to My Country Ser.). (Illus.). 48p. (J). (gr. 2 up). lib. bdg. 26.00 (978-0-8368-2497-1(0)) Stevens, Gareth Inc.

Costain, Meredith & Collins, Paul, eds. Welcome to India. 2001. (Countries of the World Ser.). (Illus.). 32p. (J). 28.00 (978-0-7910-6875-5(7) , Chelsea Hse.) Facts On File, Inc.

Cumming, David. The Ganges. 2003. (Great Rivers of the World Ser.). (Illus.). 48p. (gr. 5 up). (J). pap. 14.95 (978-0-8368-5450-3(0)); (YA). lib. bdg. 30.00 (978-0-8368-5443-5(8)) Stevens, Gareth Inc. (World Almanac Library).

—India. 2004. (Letters from Around the World Ser.). 32p. (J). lib. bdg. (978-1-84234-248-0(7) , Cherrytree Books) Evans Publishing Group.

—India. 1999. (We Come from Ser.). (Illus.). 32p. (J). (gr. 1-4). lib. bdg. 25.69 (978-0-8172-5213-7(4)) Raintree.

Dalal, Anita. India. 2001. (Nations of the World Ser.). (Illus.). 128p. (YA). (gr. 6-8). lib. bdg. 34.26 (978-0-7398-1289-1(0)) Raintree.

Das, Prodeepta. A Child's Day in an Indian Village. 2001. (Child's Day Ser.). (Illus.). 32p. (J). (gr. k-2). lib. bdg. 25.64 (978-0-7614-1220-5(4) , Benchmark Bks.) Cavendish, Marshall Corp.

—I Is for India. 2004. (World Alphabets Ser.). (Illus.). 32p. (J). pap. 7.95 (978-1-84507-320-6(7)) Lincoln, Frances Ltd. GBR. *Dist:* Perseus Distribution.

—Prita Goes to India. 2006. (Children Return to their Roots Ser.). (Illus.). 40p. 15.95 (978-1-84507-128-8(X)) Lincoln, Frances Ltd. GBR. *Dist:* Perseus Distribution.

De Capua, Sarah. India. 2003. (First Reports). (Illus.). 48p. (J). (gr. 3 up). lib. bdg. 22.60 (978-0-7565-0424-3(4)) Compass Point Bks.

Doak, Robin S. Indian Americans. 2008. (J). (***978-1-60044-612-2(4)***) Rourke Publishing, LLC.

Downing, David. India & Pakistan Conflict. 2004. (Troubled World Ser.). (Illus.). 64p. (J). 28.56 (978-1-4109-0181-1(5)) Raintree.

Engfer, LeeAnne. India in Pictures. 2nd rev. ed. 2003. (Visual Geography Ser.). (Illus.). 80p. (J). (gr. 5-12). 27.93 (978-0-8225-0371-2(9)) Lerner Publishing Group.

Fairclough, Chris, illus. & photos by. India. Fairclough, Chris, photos by. 2002. (Changing Face Of... Ser.). 48p. (J). lib. bdg. 27.12 (978-0-7398-4966-8(2)) Raintree.

Flatt, Lizann. India. 2002. (Country Files Ser.). 32p. (J). lib. bdg. 24.25 (978-1-58340-201-6(2)) Smart Apple Media.

Fontes, Justine & Fontes, Ron. India. 2004. (to Z Ser.). (Illus.). 40p. (J). (gr. 2-4). pap. 6.95 (978-0-516-26809-5(0) , Children's Pr.) Scholastic Library Publishing.

Ganeri, Anita. India. 2000. (Exploration Into... Ser.). (Illus.). 48p. (J). (gr. 4-7). 25.00 (978-0-7910-6022-3(5) , Chelsea Hse.) Facts On File, Inc.

—India. 2007. (J). (***978-1-59920-017-0(1)***) Smart Apple Media.

Ganeri, Anita. Indira Gandhi. 2003. (Leading Lives Ser.). (Illus.). 64p. (J). lib. bdg. 28.50 (978-1-4034-0833-4(5)) Heinemann Library.

Ganeri, Anita & Wright, Rachel. India. 2005. (Illus.). 32p. (J). (gr. 4-7). lib. bdg. 27.10 (978-1-932889-96-3(5)) Sea-To-Sea Pubns.

Godard, Philippe. We Live in India. Duffet, Sophie, illus. 2006. (Kids Around the World Ser.). 48p. (gr. 3-6). 15.95 (978-0-8109-5736-7(1) , Abrams Bks. for Young Readers) Abrams, Harry N. , Inc.

Green, Jen. Mumbai. Fairclough, Chris, photos by. 2007. (Global Cities Ser.). (Illus.). 64p. (J). (gr. 5-8). 30.00 (978-0-7910-8851-7(0) , Chelsea Hse.) Facts On File, Inc.

Guile, Melanie. Culture in India. 2004. (Culture In Ser.). (Illus.). (J). 25.70 (978-1-4109-1134-6(9)) Harcourt Schl. Pubs.

Harkrader, Lisa. India: A MyReportLinks. com Book. 2004. (Top Ten Countries of Recent Immigrants Ser.). (Illus.). 48p. (J). lib. bdg. 25.26 (978-0-7660-5180-5(3) , MyReportLinks.com Bks.) Enslow Pubs., Inc.

Harvey, Miles. Look What Came from India. 1999. (Look What Came from Ser.). 32p. (gr. 2-4). (Illus.). pap. 6.95 (978-0-531-15965-1(5)); (J). 22.00 (978-0-531-11587-9(9)) Scholastic Library Publishing. (Watts, Franklin).

Hill, Valerie. India. 2002. (Ask about Asia Ser.). (Illus.). 48p. (J). (gr. 4 up). lib. bdg. (978-1-59084-204-1(9)) Mason Crest Pubs.

Italia, Bob. India. 2002. (Countries Ser.). (Illus.). 40p. (J). (gr. k-6). lib. bdg. 22.78 (978-1-57765-752-1(7) , Checkerboard Library) ABDO Publishing Co.

Jackson, Elaine. India. 2004. (QEB Travel Through Ser.). (Illus.). 32p. (J). lib. bdg. 18.95 (978-1-59566-060-2(7)) QEB Publishing Inc.

Kalman, Bobbie. India: The Culture. 2001. (gr. 3-6). lib. bdg. 16.40 (978-0-613-32686-5(5)) Tandem Library Bks.

—India: The Land. 2001. (gr. 3-6). lib. bdg. 16.40 (978-0-613-32687-2(3)) Tandem Library Bks.

—India: The People. 2001. (gr. 3-6). lib. bdg. 16.40 (978-0-613-32688-9(1)) Tandem Library Bks.

—India - The Culture. 2nd rev. ed. 2000. (Lands, Peoples & Cultures Ser.). (Illus.). 32p. (J). (gr. 4-5). (978-0-7787-9383-0(4)); pap. (978-0-7787-9751-7(1)) Crabtree Publishing Co.

—India - The Land. 2nd rev. ed. 2000. (Lands, Peoples & Cultures Ser.). (Illus.). 32p. (J). (gr. 4-5). (978-0-7787-9381-6(8)); pap. (978-0-7787-9749-4(X)) Crabtree Publishing Co.

—India - The People. 2nd rev. ed. 2000. (Lands, Peoples & Cultures Ser.). (Illus.). 32p. (J). (gr. 4-5). (978-0-7787-9382-3(6)); pap. (978-0-7787-9750-0(3)) Crabtree Publishing Co.

Lal, Sunandini A. India. 1999. (Countries of the World Ser.). (Illus.). 96p. (J). (gr. 6 up). lib. bdg. 30.00 (978-0-8368-2262-5(5)) Stevens, Gareth Inc.

Landau, Elaine. India. 2000. (True Bks.). (Illus.). 48p. (J). (gr. 3-5). pap. 6.95 (978-0-516-26764-7(7) , Children's Pr.) Scholastic Library Publishing.

Littlefield, Holly. Colors of India. Porter, Janice Lee, illus. (Colors of the World Ser.). 24p. 2003. (J). (gr. 1-4). 5.95 (978-1-57505-368-4(3)); 1999. (gr. 3-6). lib. bdg. 19.93 (978-1-57505-344-8(6)) Lerner Publishing Group.

—Colors of India. (Colors of the World Ser.). 2000. (Illus.). (J). 12.75 (978-0-606-21926-6(9)); 1999. (gr. 3-6). lib. bdg. 14.10 (978-0-613-68205-3(X)) Tandem Library Bks.

Lynette, Rachel. The Taj Mahal. 2005. (Great Structures in History Ser.). (Illus.). 48p. (J). (ps-8). lib. bdg. 26.20 (978-0-7377-3154-5(0) , Greenhaven Pr., Inc.) Thomson Gale.

Madavan, Vijay. Cooking the Indian Way. 2nd rev. expurg. ed. 2002. (Easy Menu Ethnic Cookbooks). (Illus.). 72p. (J). (gr. 5-12). 25.26 (978-0-8225-4110-3(6) , Lerner Pubns.) Lerner Publishing Group.

Mahadevan, Madhavi S. Hanuman's Adventures in the Nether World: A 600 Year Old Classic Retold. Srivi, illus. 2005. (J). (978-81-89020-30-9(7)) Katha.

Mattern, Joanne. India. 2003. (Countries & Cultures Ser.). (Illus.). 64p. (J). (gr. 3-4). lib. bdg. 23.95 (978-0-7368-1548-2(1) , Bridgestone Bks.) Capstone Pr., Inc.

McCulloch, Julie. India. 2002. (Illus.). 48p. (J). (gr. 4-6). pap. (978-1-58810-387-1(0) , 91137) Heinemann Library.

McNeil, Niki, et al. HOCPP 1114 Ancient India. 2006. spiral bd. 20.00 (***978-1-60308-114-6(3)***) In the Hands of a Child.

Mehta, Anurag & Prajapati, Rajesh. India after Independence: For Children. 2004. (Illus.). 216p. (J). (978-81-7676-036-2(6)) Nita Mehta Publications.

Murphy, Patricia J. India. 2003. (Discovering Cultures Ser.). 48p. (J). 25.64 (978-0-7614-1516-9(5) , Benchmark Bks.) Cavendish, Marshall Corp.

Nelson, Julie. India. 2001. (Ancient Civilizations Ser.). (Illus.). 48p. (J). lib. bdg. 22.83 (978-0-7398-3583-8(1)) Raintree.

Olson, Nathan. India. 2005. (Fact Finders Ser.). (Illus.). 32p. (J). 22.60 (978-0-7368-3751-4(5)) Capstone Pr., Inc.

Park. Taking Your Camera To..., 6 vols., Set 3. 2000. pap. (978-0-7398-4136-5(X)) Steck-Vaughn.

Park, Ted. Taking Your Camera To..., Set 3. 2000. pap., tchr. ed. (978-0-7398-4135-8(1)) Steck-Vaughn.

—Taking Your Camera to India. Sloan, Frank, ed. 2001. (Taking Your Camera to Ser.). (Illus.). 32p. (J). (gr. 4-7). lib. bdg. 22.83 (978-0-7398-3570-8(X)) Raintree.

—Taking Your Camera to India. 2000. (Illus.). (J). pap. (978-0-7398-4132-7(7)) Steck-Vaughn.

Phillips, Douglas A. & Gritzner, Charles F. India. 2003. (Modern World Nations Ser.). (Illus.). (gr. 6-12). 150p. 30.00 (978-0-7910-7237-0(1)); 200p. pap. 30.00 (978-0-7910-7503-6(6)) Facts On File, Inc. (Chelsea Hse.).

Popper, Garry. Mina in India. Johnson, Andi, illus. 2004. 36p. (ps-7). 4.00 (978-1-84161-079-5(8)) Ravette Publishing, Ltd. GBR. *Dist:* Parkwest Pubns., Inc.

Powell, Jillian. Looking at India. 2006. (J). pap. (***978-0-8368-7676-5(8)***); lib. bdg. (***978-0-8368-7669-7(5)***) Stevens, Gareth Inc.

Roy, Anita. India. 2005. (Destination Detectives Ser.). (Illus.). 48p. (J). lib. bdg. 31.43 (978-1-4109-1861-1(0)) Raintree.

—India. 2006. (Illus.). 48p. (J). (***978-1-4109-2460-5(2)***) Steck-Vaughn.

Roza, Greg. A Primary Source Guide to India. 2003. (Countries of the World : A Primary Source Journey Ser.). (Illus.). 24p. (J). pap. (978-0-8239-8080-2(4)); lib. bdg. 19.95 (978-0-8239-6596-0(1)) Rosen Publishing Group, Inc., The. (PowerKids Pr.).

Ryan, Patrick. Welcome to India. 2007. (Welcome to the World Ser.). 32p. (J). (gr. 1-5). 27.07 (***978-1-59296-914-2(3)***) Child's World, Inc.

Sapre, Reshma. India. 2002. (Steadwell Books World Tour). (Illus.). 48p. (J). lib. bdg. 24.26 (978-0-7398-5535-5(2)) Raintree.

Shores, Lori. Teens in India. 2007. (Global Connections Ser.). (Illus.). 96p. (J). pap. (***978-0-7565-2071-7(1)***) Compass Point Bks.

Spilsbury, Louise & Spilsbury, Richard. Living on the Ganges River. 2007. (J). (***978-1-4109-2820-7(9)***); (***978-1-4109-2829-0(2)***) Steck-Vaughn.

Srinivasan, Tadhika & Jermyn, L. India. 2nd ed. 2001. (Cultures of the World Ser.). (Illus.). 144p. (gr. 5 up). lib. bdg. 37.07 (978-0-7614-1354-7(5) , Benchmark Bks.) Cavendish, Marshall Corp.

Stefoff, Rebecca. Asian Empires. 2004. (Illus.). 48p. (J). 27.07 (978-0-7614-1643-2(9) , Benchmark Bks.) Cavendish, Marshall Corp.

Streissguth, Thomas. India. (Country Explorers Ser.). (J). 2008. lib. bdg. 27.93 (***978-0-8225-8662-3(2)*** , Lerner Pubns.); 1998. (Illus.). 48p. (gr. 3-5). lib. bdg. 22.60 (978-1-57505-111-6(7) , Carolrhoda Bks.) Lerner Publishing Group.

Streissguth, Thomas & Streissguth, Tom. India. 1998. (Ticket to Ser.). (Illus.). 48p. (J). (gr. k-2). 22.60 (978-1-57505-136-9(2) , Carolrhoda Bks.) Lerner Publishing Group.

Swan, Erin Pembrey. India. 2002. (Enchantment of the World, Second Ser.). (Illus.). 144p. (J). (gr. 5-9). 36.00 (978-0-516-21121-3(8) , Children's Pr.) Scholastic Library Publishing.

Tagliaferro, Linda. Taj Mahal: India's Majestic Tomb. 2005. (Castles, Palaces, & Tombs Ser.). (Illus.). 32p. (J). lib. bdg. 25.27 (978-1-59716-004-9(0)) Bearport Publishing Co., Inc.

Taking Your Camera To... Includes: Argentina, China, Germany, India, South Africa, Vietnam, 6 bks., Set. 2001. (Taking Your Camera to Ser.). (Illus.). (J). (gr. 4-7). 136.98 (978-0-7398-3573-9(4)) Raintree.

Thomson, Ruth. India. 2006. (Living In- Ser.). (Illus.). 32p. (J). (978-1-59771-046-6(6)) Sea-To-Sea Pubns.

Weber, Valerie J. I Come from India. 2006. (This Is My Story Ser.). (Illus.). 24p. (J). (gr. k-2). pap. 5.95 (978-0-8368-7242-2(8)); lib. bdg. 19.93 (978-0-8368-7235-4(5)) Stevens, Gareth Inc. (Weekly Reader Early Learning Library).

Williams, Brian. Guide to India. 1999. (World Guides Ser.). (Illus.). 32p. (J). (gr. 2-6). lib. bdg. 21.27 (978-1-884756-46-7(8)) Davidson Titles, Inc.

INDIA—BIOGRAPHY

Benge, Janet & Benge, Geoff. Sundar Singh: Footprints over the Mountains. 2005. (Christian Heroes, Then & Now Ser.). (Illus.). 183p. (J). (978-1-57658-318-0(X)) YWAM Publishing.

Burleigh, Robert. Tiger of the Snows: Tenzing Norgay: the Boy Whose Dream Was Everest. Young, Ed, illus. 2006. 40p. (J). (gr. 2-5). 16.95 (978-0-689-83042-6(4) , Atheneum) Simon & Schuster Children's Publishing.

Dommermuth-Costa, Carol. Indira Gandhi: Daughter of India. 2001. (Lerner Biographies Ser.). (Illus.). 128p. (YA). (gr. 6-12). 6.95 (978-0-8225-4963-5(8) , Lerner Pubns.) Lerner Publishing Group.

Downing, David. Mohandas Gandhi. 2002. (Leading Lives Ser.). (Illus.). 64p. (J). (gr. 5-7). lib. bdg. 28.50 (978-1-58810-581-3(4)); pap. (978-1-4034-0124-3(1) , 91615) Heinemann Library.

Nelson, Robin. Mother Teresa: A Life of Caring. 2007. (Pull Ahead Books). (Illus.). 32p. (J). 22.60 (978-0-8225-6384-6(3) , Lerner Pubns.) Lerner Publishing Group.

Rivera, Sheila. Mohandas Gandhi: A Life of Integrity. 2007. (Pull Ahead Books). (Illus.). 32p. (J). 22.60 (978-0-8225-6383-9(5) , Lerner Pubns.) Lerner Publishing Group.

Shaw, Maura D. Gandhi: India's Great Soul. Marchesi, Stephen, illus. 2003. (Spiritual Biographies for Young Readers Ser.). 32p. (J). (gr. 1-3). 12.95 (978-1-893361-91-1(8)) SkyLight Paths Publishing.

Slavicek, Louise Chipley. Mother Teresa: Caring for the World's Poor. 2007. (Modern Peacemakers Ser.). (Illus.). 120p. (YA). (gr. 9 up). 30.00 (***978-0-7910-9433-4(2)*** , Chelsea Hse.) Facts On File, Inc.

Somervill, Barbara A. Indira Gandhi: Political Leader in India. (Illus.). 112p. (J). 2007. pap. (***978-0-7565-2207-0(2));*** 2006. (978-0-7565-1885-1(7)) Compass Point Bks.

Wheeler, Jill C. Gandhi. 2003. (Breaking Barriers Ser.). 64p. (J). (gr. 3-8). lib. bdg. 25.65 (978-1-57765-906-8(6)) ABDO Publishing Co.

Wilkinson, Philip. World History Biographies: Gandhi: The Young Protester Who Founded a Nation. 2007. (NG World History Biographies Ser.). (Illus.). 64p. (J). (gr. 3-7). pap. 6.95 (***978-1-4263-0132-2(4)*** , National Geographic Children's Bks.) National Geographic Society.

Woog, Adam. Jyotirmayee Mohapatra, Advocate for India's Young Women. 2006. (Young Heroes Ser.). (Illus.). 64p. (J). (gr. 4-8). lib. bdg. 27.45 (978-0-7377-3611-3(9) , Kidhaven) Thomson Gale.

INDIA—DESCRIPTION AND TRAVEL

Bowden, Rob. The Ganges. 2003. (River Journey Ser.). (Illus.). 48p. (J). lib. bdg. 28.56 (978-0-7398-6070-0(4)) Raintree.

Corwin, Jeff. Into Wild India. Pascoe, Elaine, ed. 2003. (Jeff Corwin Experience Ser.). (Illus.). 48p. (J). 24.95 (978-1-56711-854-4(2)); 11.20 (978-1-4103-0171-0(0)) Thomson Gale. (Blackbirch Pr., Inc.).

Cumming, David. India. 2004. (Letters from Around the World Ser.). 32p. (J). lib. bdg. (978-1-84234-248-0(7) , Cherrytree Books) Evans Publishing Group.

Fairclough, Chris, illus. & photos by. India. Fairclough, Chris, photos by. 2002. (Changing Face Of... Ser.). 48p. (J). lib. bdg. 27.12 (978-0-7398-4966-8(2)) Raintree.

Ganeri, Anita. Indian Subcontinent. 2005. (Illus.). 44p. (J). (gr. 6-9). lib. bdg. 29.95 (978-1-58340-602-1(6)) Smart Apple Media.

Kalman, Bobbie. India - The Land. 2nd rev. ed. 2000. (Lands, Peoples & Cultures Ser.). (Illus.). 32p. (J). (gr. 4-5). (978-0-7787-9381-6(8)); pap. (978-0-7787-9749-4(X)) Crabtree Publishing Co.

Mathur-Kamat, Ambika. Miss Panda in India. Crawford, K. Michael, illus. 2001. (Miss Panda Ser.). 40p. (J). pap. 11.99 (978-1-59092-027-5(9) , Little Blue Works) Windstorm Creative.

Park, Ted. Taking Your Camera to India. Sloan, Frank, ed. 2001. (Taking Your Camera to Ser.). (Illus.). 32p. (J). (gr. 4-7). lib. bdg. 22.83 (978-0-7398-3570-8(X)) Raintree.

Parker. The Golden Temple. 2003. (Holy Places Ser.). (Illus.). 32p. (J). pap. 6.95 (978-1-4109-0052-4(5)) Raintree.

Ross. Bodh Gaya. 2003. (Holy Places Ser.). (Illus.). 32p. (J). pap. 6.95 (978-1-4109-0050-0(9)) Raintree.

Shofner, Shawndra. Taj Mahal. 2005. (Ancient Wonders of the World Ser.). (Illus.). 32p. (J). (gr. 4-7). 18.95 (978-1-58341-361-6(8) , Creative Education) Creative Co., The.

Webster, Christine. Taj Mahal. 2007. (J). (***978-1-59036-729-2(4)); (*978-1-59036-730-8(8))*** Weigl Pubs., Inc.

INDIA—FICTION

Alsius, Lourdes. Unos Padres Para Aruna. 2005. (SPA.). 32p. (J). 18.95 (978-84-8418-096-8(4)) Zendrera Zariquiey, Editorial ESP. *Dist:* Iaconi, Mariuccia Bk. Imports.

Amazing Mallika - Evaluation Guide: Evaluation Guide. 2006. (J). (978-1-55942-398-4(6)) Marsh Media.

Atkins, Jeannine. Aani & the Tree Huggers. Pinto, Venantius J., illus. 2000. 32p. (J). (ps-5). 6.95 (978-1-58430-004-5(3)); 15.95 (978-1-880000-24-3(5)) Lee & Low Bks., Inc.

—Aani & the Tree Huggers. 2000. (Illus.). (J). 13.75 (978-0-606-18245-4(4)) Tandem Library Bks.

Bain, F. A Digit of the Moon. 2002. 436p. per. 39.95 (978-1-932080-29-2(5)) Ross & Perry, Inc.

Ballard, John H. SoulMates: A Novel to End World Hunger, 2 bks. in 1. Ellen, Joan, ed. Litzenger, Roseanne, illus. 1998. (Soul to Soul Adventure Ser.). 524p. (YA). (gr. 7 up). 19.95 (978-0-932279-06-4(6)); (gr. 4-7). pap. 14.95 (978-0-932279-05-7(8)) World Citizens.

Bannerman, Helen. Little Black Sambo (Illustrated Edition) 2006. (Illus.). pap. (***978-1-4065-0769-0(5)***) Dodo Pr.

—The Story of Little Babaji. Marcellino, Fred, illus. 2002. 72p. (J). (ps up). pap. 7.99 (978-0-06-008093-8(0) , Harper Trophy) HarperCollins Pubs.

—Story of Little Babaji. 2002. (gr. k-3). lib. bdg. 16.40 (978-0-613-85154-1(4)) Tandem Library Bks.

—The Story of Little Babaji. ed. 2004. (Illus.). (J). (ps up). spiral bd. (978-0-616-14615-6(9)) Canadian National Institute for the Blind/Institut National Canadien pour les Aveugles.

—The Story of Little Black Sambo. 2004. (Wee Books for Wee Folks). (Illus.). 61p. (J). (gr. 1-3). reprint ed. 6.95 (978-1-55709-414-8(4)) Applewood Bks.

—The Story of Little Black Sambo. 2007. pap. 7.99 (***978-1-59986-912-4(8)*** , FQ Classics) Fillquarian Publishing, LLC.

—The Story of Little Black Sambo. Bing, Christopher H., illus. 2003. 40p. (J). (ps up). 17.95 (978-1-929766-55-0(6)) Handprint Bks.

—The Story of Little Black Sambo. Bannerman, Helen, illus. 2003. (Illus.). 64p. (J). (gr. k-3). 15.99 (978-0-397-30006-8(9)) HarperCollins Pubs.

Benchimol, Brigitte. Jadyn & the Magic Bubble: Discovering India. Benchimol, Brigitte & Zima, Siegfried, illus. 2007. 58p. (J). (gr. 3-4). 19.95 (***978-0-9701654-9-7(8)***) East West Discovery Pr.

Bjerkvold, Belinda & Kipling, Rudyard. The Jungle Book. Larrea, Miguel & Andrada, Javier, illus. 2006. (J). lib. bdg. (***978-0-8368-7663-5(6)***) Stevens, Gareth Inc.

Blackford, Harriet. Tiger's Story. Stojic, Manya, illus. 2007. 32p. (J). 12.95 (978-1-905417-39-1(X)) Boxer Bks., Ltd. GBR. *Dist:* Sterling Publishing Co., Inc.

Bond, Ruskin. Cherry Tree. Eitzen, Allan, illus. 2003. 32p. (J). (gr. 2-4). pap. 9.95 (978-1-56397-621-6(8)) Boyds Mills Pr.

—Rusty, the Boy from the Hills. 2002. (Illus.). viii, 209p. (J). (978-0-14-333547-4(2) , Puffin) Penguin Group (USA) Inc.

Bosse, Malcolm. Tusk & Stone. 2004. 256p. (YA). reprint ed. pap. 8.95 (978-1-886910-74-4(X) , Lemniscaat) Boyds Mills Pr.

Brian, Kate. Lucky T. 2007. 304p. (YA). (gr. 9 up). pap. 8.99 (978-1-4169-3545-2(2) , Simon Pulse) Simon & Schuster Children's Publishing.

Brooks, John. The Sundarbans Tiger. 2006. 115p. (J). pap. 13.58 (978-0-9661789-4-4(7)) Lulu.com.

Byng, Georgia. Molly Moon Viaja a Traes del Tiempo. Crispin, Maria Dolores, tr. 2005. (SPA.). 350p. (978-84-675-0570-2(2)) SM Ediciones.

—Molly Moon's Hypnotic Time Travel Adventure. 2007. 400p. (J). (gr. 3-7). pap. 6.99 (978-0-06-075034-3(0) , Harper Trophy) HarperCollins Pubs.

Chadha, Radhika. Basava & the Dots of Fire. Phatak, Bhakti, illus. 2005. 24p. (J). (***978-81-8146-165-0(7)***) Tulika Pubs.

Chadha, Radhika & Kuriyan, Priya. I'm So Sleepy. 2004. (Illus.). 24p. (J). (978-81-8146-033-2(2)) Tulika Pubs.

Charles, Veronika Martenova. The Birdman. Galouchko, Annouchka Gravel & Daigle, Stephan, illus. 2006. 32p. (J). (gr. k-3). 17.95 (978-0-88776-740-1(0)) Tundra Bks., Inc./Livres Toundra, Inc. CAN. *Dist:* Random Hse., Inc.

Cherrington, Janelle. Drawing the Line. Goldberg, Barry, illus. 2000. (Wild Thornberrys Ready-to-Read Ser. : Vol. 2). 32p. (J). (gr. 4-6). pap. 3.99 (978-0-689-83231-4(1) , Simon Spotlight/Nickelodeon) Simon & Schuster Children's Publishing.

—Drawing the Line. 2000. (gr. k-3). lib. bdg. 11.80 (978-0-613-24899-0(6)) Tandem Library Bks.

Chidvilasananda, Swami. The Great Hiss. Cornelis, Susan, illus. 2002. 32p. (J). 18.95 (978-0-911307-90-0(7) , 205221, Siddha Yoga Pubn.) SYDA Foundation.

Corry, Beatrice J. Old Friends. 2002. (Babu the Buffalo, Tales of India Ser.: Bk. 1). (Illus.). 21p. (J). (978-0-9722880-0-2(7)); pap. (978-0-9722880-1-9(5)) Babu Bks.

Cowcher, Helen. Tigress. 2001. (Illus.). 40p. (YA). (BEN, ENG, URD, TUR & VIE.). 16.95 (978-1-84059-024-1(6)); (GRE, ENG, URD, TUR & VIE., 16.95 (978-1-84059-026-5(2)); (GUJ, ENG, URD, TUR & VIE., 16.95 (978-1-84059-027-2(0)); (TUR, ENG, URD, VIE & CHI., 16.95 (978-1-84059-028-9(9)); (URD, ENG, TUR, VIE & CHI., 16.95 (978-1-84059-029-6(7)) Milet Publishing.

Daswani, Kavita. Indie Girl. 2007. 208p. (YA). (gr. 7 up). pap. 8.99 (***978-1-4169-4892-6(9)*** , Simon Pulse) Simon & Schuster Children's Publishing.

De Souza, Eunice. 101 Folktales from India. 2005. (Illus.). 350p. (YA). 14.00 (978-0-670-04967-7(0) , Penguin Global) Penguin Group (USA) Inc.

Dharmarajan, Geeta. The Magic Raindrop. Thapar, Bindia, illus. 2005. (J). (978-81-89020-28-6(5)) Katha.

Divakaruni, Chitra Banerjee. The Conch Bearer. 2005. 272p. (J). reprint ed. pap. 5.99 (978-0-689-87242-6(9) , Aladdin) Simon & Schuster Children's Publishing.

—The Conch Bearer. 2005. 265p. (J). (gr. 3-7). per. 14.45 (978-1-4176-6930-1(6)); per. 12.64 (978-0-606-33382-5(7)) Tandem Library Bks.

—The Mirror of Fire & Dreaming. 2005. (Brotherhood of the Conch Ser.: Bk. 2). (Illus.). 336p. (J). (ps-17). 16.95 (978-1-59643-067-9(2)) Roaring Brook Pr.

—The Mirror of Fire & Dreaming. 2007. 336p. (J). (gr. 3-7). pap. 5.99 (978-1-4169-1768-7(3) , Aladdin) Simon & Schuster Children's Publishing.

Dutta, Arup Kumar. The Boy Who Became King. Arya, Viki, illus. 2004. 122p. (J). (***978-81-291-0405-2(9)***) Rupa & Co.

Dwivedi, S. The Broken Flute. 1998. (Illus.). 122p. (J). pap. 30.00 (978-81-86982-22-8(1)) Business Pubns. Inc. IND. *Dist:* State Mutual Bk. & Periodical Service, Ltd.

Faye, Thomas. Pirates of the Caribbean: The Secret Files of the East India Trading Company. rev. ed. 2007. 28p. (gr. 8). 19.99 (***978-1-4231-0499-5(4)***) Disney Pr.

Ganeri, Anita. Hindu Stories. Gray, Carole, illus. 2006. 42p. (J). (gr. 4-6). 23.95 (978-1-4048-1309-0(8)) Picture Window Bks.

Gangopadhyay, Narayan. 4 Heroes & the Haunted House. 1998. 114p. (J). pap. (978-81-86211-34-2(9)) Tara Publishing.

Ganguli, Taraknath & Gangapadhyay, Narayan. 4 Heroes & a Green Beard. Bhattacharjee, Swati, tr. from BEN. 1999. (Translations from Indian Languages Ser.). (Illus.). 92p. (J). pap. (978-81-86211-52-6(7)) Tara Publishing.

Gavin, Jamila. The Blood Stone. 2005. (Illus.). 352p. (YA). (gr. 6-8). 18.00 (978-0-374-30846-9(2)) Farrar, Straus & Giroux.

—Fine Feathered Friend. Williams, Dan, illus. 2002. (Yellow Bananas Ser.). 48p. (J). (gr. 3-4). pap. (978-0-7787-0985-5(X)); lib. bdg. (978-0-7787-0939-8(6)) Crabtree Publishing Co.

—Fine Feathered Friend. 2002. (gr. 3-6). lib. bdg. 12.95 (978-0-613-52842-9(5)) Tandem Library Bks.

Ghosh, Premola, illus. Ten Timeless Tales. 2005. 38p. (J). (***978-81-89013-35-6(1)***) Zubaan.

Guillain, Adam. Bella Balistica & the Indian Summer. 2005. (Bella Balistica Ser.). (Illus.). 272p. (J). pap. 9.95 (978-1-84059-407-2(1)) Milet Publishing.

Hamilton, Martha & Weiss, Mitch. The Ghost Catcher: A Bengali Folktale. Balouch, Kristen, illus. 2008. 32p. (***978-0-87483-835-0(5)*** , August Hse. Little Folk) August Hse. Pubs., Inc.

Hammerslough, Jane. Langur Monkey's Day. Buelt, Laura, illus. 2005. (Wild Reading Adventures! Ser.). (J). (ps-2). 32p. 2.95 (978-1-59249-143-8(X) , S7156); 36p. 9.95 (978-1-59249-144-5(8) , PS7156); 32p. 19.95 incl. audio (978-1-59249-221-3(5) , BC7106) Soundprints.

—Langur Monkey's Day. Buelt, Laura, tr. Buelt, Laura, illus. 2005. (Wild Reading Adventures! Ser.). 36p. (J). (ps-2). 15.95 (978-1-59249-141-4(3) , B7106); pap. 6.95 (978-1-59249-142-1(1) , S7106) Soundprints.

Heine, Teresa. Elephant Dance: Remembering India. Moxley, Sheila, illus. 2004. 40p. (J). 16.99 (978-1-84148-917-9(4)) Barefoot Bks., Inc.

Heine, Theresa. Elephant Dance. Moxley, Sheila, illus. 2006. 0040p. pap. 6.99 (978-1-905236-79-4(4)) Barefoot Bks., Inc.

Henty, G. A. With Clive in India. 2006. pap. (***978 1 4068-1316-6(8)***) Echo Library.

Hirshkowith, Sandra. Premlata & the Festival of Lights. Andrew, Ian, illus. 1999. (Chapter Bks.). 96p. (J). (gr. 2-5). pap. 4.25 (978-0-06-442091-4(4) , Harper Trophy) HarperCollins Pubs.

Howard, Ginger. A Basket of Bangles: How a Business Begins. Noll, Cheryl Kirk, illus. 2002. (Around the World Ser.). 32p. (gr. k-3). lib. bdg. 21.90 (978-0-7613-1902-3(6) , Millbrook Pr.) Lerner Publishing Group.

Husain, Zakir & Mishra, Samina. Sunshine for Amma. Pottenkulam, Pooja, illus. 2004. 16p. (J). (978-81-89013-41-7(6)) Zubaan.

Infante, Begona. Minu Yo Soy de India (I'm from India) (SPA.). 32p. (J). 12.95 (978-84-246-9401-2(5)) La Galera, S.A. Editorial ESP. *Dist:* AIMS International Bks., Inc.

Ishwaran, Wobine. Spunky Sprout in India. 2006. pap. 19.50 (***978-1-4259-4237-3(7)***) AuthorHouse.

Jaffrey, Madhur. Robi Dobi: The Marvellous Adventures of an Indian Elephant. Hall, Amanda, illus. 2001. 64p. (YA). (gr. 1 up). pap. 13.00 (978-1-86205-160-7(7) , Pavilion Bks., Ltd.) Anova Bks. GBR. *Dist:* Trafalgar Square Publishing.

Jeeva Raghunath & Nayar, Deeya. Malli: Malli. Nancy Raj, illus. 2005. (HIN & ENG.). 16p. (J). (***978-81-8146-089-9(8)***) Tulika Pubs.

Jenisch, Betty. Rennie. 2007. 9.00 (***978-0-8059-8947-2(1)***) Dorrance Publishing Co., Inc.

Jeyaveeran, Ruth. The Road to Mumbai. 2004. (Illus.). 32p. (J). (gr. k-3). tchr. ed. 16.00 (978-0-618-43419-0(4)) Houghton Mifflin Co. Trade & Reference Div.

Keen, Karl D. They Call Me Chief. 2004. (YA). per. 10.95 (978-0-9742791-3-8(7)) Litho Tech, LLC.

H I

Kipling, Rudyard. The Jungle Book. Pablo Marcos Studio Staff, illus. 2002. (Great Illustrated Classics Ser.).Tr. of 192. 240p. (J). (gr. 3-8). 21.35 (978-1-57765-812-2(4) , ABDO & Daughters) ABDO Publishing Co.

—The Jungle Book. Alexander, Gregory, illus. 1999. (Classics Ser.).Tr. of 192. 160p. (J). 12.95 (978-0-7892-0558-2(0)); pap. 7.95 (978-0-7892-0548-3(3)) Abbeville Pr., Inc. (Abbeville Kids).

—The Jungle Book. 2000. (Dover Juvenile Classics Ser.).Tr. of 192. 160p. (J). (gr. 4-7). pap. 2.50 (978-0-486-41024-1(2)) Dover Pubns., Inc.

—The Jungle Book. 1998. (Children's Classics).Tr. of 192. (ENG., Illus.). 192p. (J). (gr. 4-7). pap. (978-1-85326-119-0(X) , 119XWW) Wordsworth Editions, Ltd.

—The Jungle Book. Corvino, Lucy, illus. 2008. (Classic Starts Ser.). 160p. (J). 5.95 (***978-1-4027-4576-8(1)***) Sterling Publishing Co., Inc.

—The Jungle Book.Tr. of 192. (J). reprint ed. lib. bdg. 24.95 (978-0-88411-819-0(3)) Amereon LTD.

—The Jungle Book: #1 Rikki-Tikki-Tavi Moves In. 2007. (Easy Reader Classics Ser.). 32p. (J). (ps-3). 21.35 (***978-1-59961-336-9(0)***) Spotlight.

—The Jungle Book: Mowgli's Story. Bayley, Nicola, illus. unabr. ed. 2005. 160p. (J). (gr. 4-7). 19.99 (978-0-7636-2317-3(2)) Candlewick Pr.

—The Jungle Book Mowgli's Big Birthday, No. 3. Hale, Nathan, illus. 2007. (Easy Reader Classics Ser.). 32p. (J). pap. 3.95 (978-1-4027-4124-1(3)) Sterling Publishing Co., Inc.

—The Jungle Books. (Borders Classics Ser.). 276p. 7.95 (978-1-58726-165-7(0)) Ann Arbor Media Group, LLC.

—The Jungle Books. 2004. (Barnes & Noble Classics Ser.). (Illus.). 432p. pap. 5.95 (978-1-59308-109-6(X)) Barnes & Noble, Inc.

—The Jungle Books. 2005. 336p. (gr. 12). pap. 4.95 (978-0-451-52975-6(8) , Signet Classics) Penguin Group (USA) Inc.

—Kim. unabr. ed. 1998. (Wordsworth Classics Ser.).Tr. of 384. (YA). (gr. 6-12). 5.27 (978-0-89061-099-2(1) , R0991WW) Jamestown.

—Rikki-Tikki-Tavi. Pinkney, Jerry, illus. 2004. 48p. (J). (ps-3). reprint ed. pap. 6.99 (978-0-06-058785-7(7) , Harper Trophy) HarperCollins Pubs.

—Rudyard Kipling Collected Short Stories. Court, Robert, illus. 2001. (Great Author Ser.). (J). (978-0-9709033-6-5(7)) Peterson Publishing Co., Inc.

Kipling, Rudyard & Hedge, Tricia. The Jungle Book, Level 2. 2nd abr. ed. 2000. (Bookworms Ser.).Tr. of 192. (Illus.). 64p. 6.50 (978-0-19-422977-7(7)) Oxford Univ. Pr., Inc.

Krishnaswami, Uma. Chachaji's Cup. Sitaraman, Soumya, illus. 2003. 32p. (J). (gr. 1 up). 16.95 (978-0-89239-178-3(2)) Children's Bk. Pr.

—Monsoon. Akib, Jamel, illus. 2003. 32p. (J). 16.00 (978-0-374-35015-4(9) , Farrar, Straus & Giroux (BYR)) Farrar, Straus & Giroux.

—Naming Maya. 2004. (Illus.). 192p. (J). 16.00 (978-0-374-35485-5(5) , Farrar, Straus & Giroux (BYR)) Farrar, Straus & Giroux.

Kroll, Virginia L. Selvakumar Knew Better. Li, Xiaojun, illus. 2006. (J). 17.95 (978-1-885008-29-9(5)) Shen's Bks.

Landolf, Diane Wright. The Jungle Book. Rowe, John, illus. 2008. 112p. (J). (***978-0-375-84276-4(4)***); lib. bdg. (***978-0-375-94062-0(6)***) Random Hse., Inc.

McCormick, Patricia. Sold. 2006. 272p. (gr. 7 up). 15.99 (978-0-7868-5171-3(6)) Hyperion Pr.

Milbourne, Anna. Stories from India. 2005. (Stories for Young Children Ser.). 96p. (J). 16.95 (978-0-7945-0925-5(8) , Usborne) EDC Publishing.

Montgomery, R. A. Caravan. 2007. (Choose Your Own Adventure - Dragonlarks Ser.). (Illus.). 64p. (J). pap. 5.99 (***978-1-933390-54-3(9)***) Chooseco LLC.

Moverley, Richard. The Reluctant Rajput. Dean, David, illus. 2005. (Yellow Go Bananas Ser.). 48p. (J). pap. (978-0-7787-2745-3(9)); lib. bdg. (978-0-7787-2723-1(8)) Crabtree Publishing Co.

Mukerji, Dhan Gopal. Jungle Beasts & Men. Allen, J. E., illus. 2005. reprint ed. pap. 22.95 (978-0-7661-9403-8(5)) Kessinger Publishing, LLC.

Namjoshi, Suniti & Jain, Shefalee. Aditi & the Marine Sage. 2004. (Simply a Story Ser.). (Illus.). 80p. (J). (978-81-8146-040-0(5)) Tulika Pubs.

Nanji, Shenaaz. Indian Tales. Corr, Christopher, illus. 2007. 96p. (YA). (gr. 2 up). 19.99 (***978-1-84686-083-6(0)***) Barefoot Bks., Inc.

Noyes, Deborah. When I Met the Wolf Girls. Hall, August, illus. 2007. 40p. (J). (gr. 3-5). 17.00 (978-0-618-60567-5(3)) Houghton Mifflin Co.

Osborne, Mary Pope. Tigers at Twilight, Vol. 19. unabr. ed. 2004. (Magic Tree House Ser. : No. 19). 72p. (J). (gr. k-3). pap. 17.00 incl. audio (978-0-8072-0928-8(7) , S FTR 251 SP, Listening Library) Random Hse. Audio Publishing Group.

—Tigers at Twilight. Murdocca, Sal, illus. 1999. (Magic Tree House Ser.: No. 19). 96p. (J). (gr. k-3). lib. bdg. 11.99 (978-0-679-99065-9(8)); mass mkt. 3.99 (978-0-679-89065-2(3)) Random Hse. Children's Bks. (Random Hse. Bks. for Young Readers).

—Tigers at Twilight. 1999. (Magic Tree House Ser. : No. 19). (J). (gr. k-3). (Illus.). 71p. lib. bdg. 10.79 (978-0-606-16957-8(1)); lib. bdg. 11.80 (978-0-613-16224-1(2)) Tandem Library Bks.

Padma, T. V. The Forbidden Temple: Stories from the Past. Vyas, Bhavana, illus. 2004. 95p. (J). (***978-81-8146-041-7(3)***) Tulika Pubs.

Panamkat, Matthew. Karan Quma & the Meluha Tree. 2007. 348p. per. 19.95 (***978-0-595-41816-9(3)***) iUniverse, Inc.

Parmar, Tavisha, illus. The Class Photograph. 2005. (J). (***978-81-902492-1-8(5)***) Vivera Bks.

Perkins, Mitali. Monsoon Summer. 2006. 272p. (YA). (gr. 7). mass mkt. 6.50 (978-0-440-23840-9(4) , Laurel Leaf) Random Hse. Children's Bks.

Philip, Jimmy. Precious Moments: An Adventure in Wellmore. 2001. 132p. pap. 10.95 (978-0-595-19555-8(5) , Writers Club Pr.) iUniverse, Inc.

Pinkney, Jerry. Rikki-Tikki-Tavi. 2004. (gr. k-3). lib. bdg. 15.30 (978-0-613-83560-2(3)) Tandem Library Bks.

Point, Virginia. Molly's Metamorphosis in India. 2005. 193p. pap. 19.95 (978-1-4137-3729-5(3)) PublishAmerica, Inc.

Ramanujam, Geeta. The Wise Monkey & Other Animal Stories. Guhathakurta, Ajanta, illus. 2002. 112p. (J). (978-0-14-333545-0(6) , Puffin) Penguin Group (USA) Inc.

Ravishankar, Anushka. Excuse Me, Is This India? Leutwiler, Anita, illus. 2003. 28p. (J). 7.99 (978-81-86211-56-4(X)) Penguin Group (USA) Inc.

Ray, Satyajit. Unicorn Expedition & Other Stories: The Exploits of Professor Shonku. 2004. (Illus.). x, 237p. (J). pap. (978-0-14-333584-9(7) , Puffin) Penguin Group (USA) Inc.

Rumford, James. Nine Animals & the Well. 2003. (Illus.). 32p. (J). (gr. k-3). tchr. ed. 16.00 (978-0-618-30915-3(2)) Houghton Mifflin Co. Trade & Reference Div.

Schomer Wendel, Gretchen & Schomer, Adam Anthony. Becka & the Big Bubble: Becka Goes to India. 2007. (Illus.). 32p. (J). 11.99 (***978-1-933754-13-0(3)***) Waterside Publishing.

Sheth, Kashmira. Blue Jasmine. 2004. 192p. (gr. 4-7). 15.99 (978-0-7868-1855-6(7)) Hyperion Bks. for Children.

—Koyal Dark, Mango Sweet. 224p. (gr. 7-17). 2006. 15.99 (978-0-7868-3857-8(4)); 2007. pap. 7.99 (***978-0-7868-3858-5(2)***) Hyperion Pr.

Shiva's Fire. 2002. stu. ed. (978-1-58130-747-4(0)) Novel Units, Inc.

Siegel, Elizabeth. Taj. Toye, Derek, illus. 2007. 48p. (J). lib. bdg. 23.08 (***978-1-4242-1632-1(X)***) Fitzgerald Bks.

Somaiah, Rosemarie. Indian Children's Favorite Stories. 2006. (Illus.). 80p. (J). 16.95 (978-0-8048-3687-6(6)) Tuttle Publishing.

Souhami, Jessica. Rama & the de Mon King: An Ancient Tale from India. 2006. (Illus.). 30p. (J). (gr. k-4). reprint ed. 15.00 (978-0-7567-9813-0(2)) DIANE Publishing Co.

Staples, Suzanne Fisher. Shiva's Fire. 2000. (Illus.). 288p. (YA). (gr. 7-12). 18.00 (978-0-374-36824-1(4) , Farrar, Straus & Giroux (BYR)) Farrar, Straus & Giroux.

—Shiva's Fire. 2001. 288p. (J). (gr. 5 up). pap. 6.99 (978-0-06-440979-7(1) , Harper Trophy) HarperCollins Pubs.

—Shiva's Fire. 2001. (978-0-606-22295-2(2)); (gr. 7-12). lib. bdg. 14.10 (978-0-613-44414-9(0)) Tandem Library Bks.

Stewart, Angela. The Curious Adventures of India Sophia. Stuart, Mitchell, illus. 2004. (Juvenile Novel Ser.). 176p. (J). (gr. 4-6). pap. 9.95 (978-1-895836-78-3(6)) River Bks. CAN. *Dist:* Coteau Bks., Fitzhenry & Whiteside, Ltd.

Thompson, Lisa, illus. Incredible India. 2006. (Read-It! Chapter Books). 80p. (J). (gr. 2-4). 19.95 (978-1-4048-1676-3(3)) Picture Window Bks.

Thornhill, Jan, illus. The Rumor: A Jataka Tale from India. 2005. 32p. pap. 6.95 (978-1-897066-27-0(9)) Maple Tree Pr. CAN. *Dist:* Perseus Distribution.

Thottam, Meena. The Last Dancer. 2006. (J). 3.95 (***978-0-9776917-7-7(2)*** , Curcumin Bks.) Davlaw Press.

Thottam, Meena, adapted by. Brothers of the Jungle. 2006. (J). 3.95 (***978-0-9776917-4-6(8)*** , Curcumin Bks.) Davlaw Press.

—Chameli's Choice. 2006. (J). 3.95 (***978-0-9776917-6-0(4)*** , Curcumin Bks.) Davlaw Press.

—Death, Where are You? 2006. (J). 3.95 (***978-0-9776917-5-3(6)*** , Curcumin Bks.) Davlaw Press.

—Maybe I am, Maybe I am Not. 2006. (J). 3.95 (***978-0-9776917-8-4(0)*** , Curcumin Bks.) Davlaw Press.

—The Pretender. 2006. (J). 3.95 (***978-0-9776917-3-9(X)*** , Curcumin Bks.) Davlaw Press.

—Road to Riches. 2006. (J). 3.95 (***978-0-9776917-9-1(9)*** , Curcumin Bks.) Davlaw Press.

—The Sage's Daughter. 2006. (J). 3.95 (***978-0-9776917-2-2(1)*** , Curcumin Bks.) Davlaw Press.

Trimble, Irene. Jungle Friends. 2003. (gr. k-3). lib. bdg. 11.80 (978-0-613-65128-8(6)) Tandem Library Bks.

Tyminski, Lori, illus. The Jungle Book 2. 2003. (J). 15.98 (978-0-7853-7968-3(1)) Publications International, Ltd.

Whelan, Gloria. Homeless Bird. (gr. 5 up). 2001. 192p. pap. 5.99 (978-0-06-440819-6(1)); 2000. 240p. (J). 16.99 (978-0-06-028454-1(4)) HarperCollins Pubs.

—Homeless Bird. unabr. ed. 2004. 240p. (J). (gr. 5-9). pap. 29.00 incl. audio (978-0-8072-8859-7(4) , Listening Library) Random Hse. Audio Publishing Group.

—Homeless Bird. 2001. 186p. (YA). (gr. 8-12). lib. bdg. 14.15 (978-0-613-44393-7(4)) Tandem Library Bks.

—Homeless Bird. l.t. ed. 2002. 147p. (J). 23.95 (978-0-7862-4060-9(1)) Thomson Gale.

Whitaker, Zai. Kali & the Rat Snake. Natarajan, Srividya, illus. 2006. 32p. (J). 15.95 (978-1-933605-10-4(3)) Kane/Miller Bk. Pubs., Inc.

Wolf, Gita. Very Hungry Lion. Roy, Indrapramit, illus. 2006. 24p. 20.95 (978-81-86211-02-1(0)) Tara Publishing IND. *Dist:* Consortium Bk. Sales & Distribution.

YKids Staff. Mother Teresa. 2008. (Great Figures in History Ser.). 144p. (J). pap. 14.95 (***978-981-05-7552-6(1)***) Youngjin (Singapore) Pte Ltd. SGP. *Dist:* Independent Pubs. Group.

Young, Ed. Seven Blind Mice. Young, Ed, illus. 2007. pap. 18.95 incl. audio compact disk (***978-0-439-02785-4(3)***); (Illus.). pap. 14.95 incl. audio (***978-0-439-02784-7(5)***) Scholastic, Inc.

INDIA—HISTORY

Ali, Daud. Ancient India. 2001. (Step into Ser.). (Illus.). 64p. (gr. 3-7). 14.95 (978-0-7548-0658-5(8) , Lorenz Bks.) Anness Publishing, Inc.

—Ancient India: What Life Was Like in One of the Earliest Civilizations on Earth. 2003. (Find Out about...Ser.). (Illus.). 64p. (gr. 3-7). pap. 7.99 (978-1-84215-778-7(7) , Southwater) Anness Publishing GBR. *Dist:* National Bk. Network.

Ancient India DBA. 2003. spiral bd. 16.95 (978-1-56004-153-5(6)) Social Studies Schl. Service.

Ancient Mesopotamia/India. 2003. (Mr. Donn & Maxie's Always Something You Can Use Ser.). spiral bd. 19.95 (978-1-56004-166-5(8)) Social Studies Schl. Service.

Bailey, Katharine. Vasco da Gama: Quest for the Spice Trade. 2007. (Illus.). 32p. (J). (gr. 3-9). (***978-0-7787-2421-6(2)***); pap. (***978-0-7787-2457-5(3)***) Crabtree Publishing Co.

Barr, Marilynn G. India. 2003. (Illus.). 48p. (J). pap. 7.95 (978-1-57310-413-5(2)) Teaching & Learning Co.

Bryan, Nichol. Bhopal: Chemical Plant Accident. 2003. (Environmental Disasters Ser.). (Illus.). 48p. (gr. 5 up). (YA). lib. bdg. 30.00 (978-0-8368-5503-6(5)); (J). pap. 11.95 (978-0-8368-5510-4(8)) Stevens, Gareth Inc. (World Almanac Library).

Conklin, Wendy. China * India * Mesopotamia * Africa: All-in-One Resource with Background Information, Map Activities, Simulations & Games, & a Read-Aloud Play to Support Comprehension & Critical Thinking in Social Studies. 2006. (Ancient Civilizations Ser.). 96p. pap. 13.99 (978-0-439-53993-7(5) , Teaching Resources) Scholastic, Inc.

Corrick, James A. Ancient India. 2005. (Illus.). (J). (978-1-59018-435-6(1) , Lucent Bks.) Thomson Gale.

Dalal, A. Kamala. India. 2007. (Countries of the World Ser.). (Illus.). 64p. (YA). (gr. 5 up). lib. bdg. 27.90 (***978-1-4263-0127-8(8)*** , National Geographic Children's Bks.) National Geographic Society.

Dalal, Anita. Ancient India: Archaeology Unlocks the Secrets of India's Past. 2007. (National Geographic Investigates Ser.). (Illus.). 64p. (YA). (gr. 5 up). 17.95 (***978-1-4263-0070-7(0)***); lib. bdg. 27.90 (***978-1-4263-0071-4(9)***) National Geographic Society. (National Geographic Children's Bks.).

Dalal, Roshen. The Puffin History of India for Children: 3000 BC - AD 1947. Phadke, Aarohi et al, illus. 2002. x, 404p. (J). pap. (978-0-14-333544-3(8) , Puffin) Penguin Group (USA) Inc.

Demi. Gandhi. Demi, illus. 2001. (Illus.). 40p. (J). (gr. 2-5). 21.99 (978-0-689-84149-1(3) , McElderry, Margaret K.) Simon & Schuster Children's Publishing.

Diamond, Arthur. The Bhopal Chemical Leak. 2002. (World Disasters Ser.). (Illus.). 64p. (YA). (gr. 4-12). lib. bdg. 26.20 (978-1-56006-009-3(3) , Lucent Bks.) Thomson Gale.

Fine, Jil. Writing in Ancient India. 2003. (Writing in the Ancient World Ser.). (Illus.). 24p. (J). lib. bdg. 17.25 (978-0-8239-6508-3(2) , PowerKids Pr.) Rosen Publishing Group, Inc., The.

Ganeri, Anita. India under the Mughal Empire, 1526-1858. 1999. (Looking Back Ser.). (J). 19.98 (978-0-8172-5432-2(3)) Raintree.

Gassos, Dolores. The Mayas. 2005. (Ancient Civilizations Ser.). (Illus.). 32p. (J). (gr. 4-8). lib. bdg. 28.00 (978-0-7910-8489-2(2) , Chelsea Clubhouse) Facts On File, Inc.

Goodwim, William. India. 1999. (Modern Nations of the World Ser.). (Illus.). 112p. (YA). (gr. 7-10). 27.45 (978-1-56006-598-2(2) , Lucent Bks.) Thomson Gale.

Harcourt School Publishers Staff. The People of India. 3rd ed. 2002. (Horizons Ser.). (Illus.). (J). pap. 7.30 (978-0-15-333636-2(6)) Harcourt Schl. Pubs.

Heinrichs, Ann. Mahatma Gandhi. 2001. (Trailblazers of the Modern World Ser.). (Illus.). 48p. (J). (gr. 5 up). pap. 14.95 (978-0-8368-5224-0(9)); lib. bdg. 30.00 (978-0-8368-5064-2(5)) Stevens, Gareth Inc. (World Almanac Library).

Heydlauff, Lisa. Going to School in India. 2005. 98p. (J). 21.95 (978-1-57091-666-3(7)) Charlesbridge Publishing, Inc.

Hirsch, E. D., ed. Ancient India. 2003. tchr. ed. 9.95 (978-0-7690-5045-4(X)); stu. ed. 49.95 (978-0-7690-2949-8(3)) Pearson Learning.

Hirst, Mike. A Flavor of India. 1999. (Food & Festivals Ser.). (Illus.). 32p. (J). (gr. 1-4). lib. bdg. 25.69 (978-0-8172-5551-0(6)) Raintree.

Hughes, Christopher. India & Pakistan. 2003. (Nations in Conflict Ser.). (Illus.). 48p. (J). 24.95 (978-1-56711-539-0(X) , Blackbirch Pr., Inc.) Thomson Gale.

India, 1835-1952, Vol. IV, Pt. II. (J). (gr. k). 95.00 (978-0-932106-63-6(3)) Durst, Sanford J.

Indian Independence & the Question of Pakistan, 2. 2005. (Illus.). 100p. (YA). pap. (978-1-891306-89-1(8)) Choices Education Program, Watson Institute, Brown Univ.

Kilgallon, Conor. India & Sri Lanka. 2002. (Cultures & Costumes Ser.). (Illus.). 64p. (J). (gr. 7 up). lib. bdg. (978-1-59084-443-4(2)) Mason Crest Pubs.

Malaspina, Ann. Mahatma Gandhi & India's Independence in World History. 2000. (In World History Ser.). (Illus.). 128p. (YA). (gr. 5-12). lib. bdg. 26.60 (978-0-7660-1398-8(7)) Enslow Pubs., Inc.

Martin, Michael. India & Pakistan: Conflict over Kashmir. 2006. (J). (978-1-59018-643-5(5) , Lucent Bks.) Thomson Gale.

McDaniel, Jan. Indian Immigration. 2004. (Changing Face of North America Ser.). (Illus.). 112p. (YA). lib. bdg. (978-1-59084-683-4(4)) Mason Crest Pubs.

Nelson. India. 2001. (Ancient Civilizations Ser.). (Illus.). (J). pap. (978-0-7398-4151-8(3)) Steck-Vaughn.

Nicholson, Michael. Mahatma Gandhi. (Pacificadores Mundiales Ser.). 64p. (gr. 5-8). 28.70 (978-1-4103-0541-1(4) , Blackbirch Pr., Inc.) Thomson Gale.

Parker, Victoria. The Golden Temple. 2003. (Holy Places Ser.). (Illus.). 32p. (J). 24.28 (978-0-7398-6079-3(8)) Raintree.

Richardson, Hazel. Life in the Ancient Indus River Valley. 2005. (Peoples of the Ancient World Ser.). (Illus.). 32p. (J). (ps-9). pap. (978-0-7787-2070-6(5)); lib. bdg. (978-0-7787-2040-9(3)) Crabtree Publishing Co.

Rossi, Ann. India. 2004. (National Geographic Reading Expeditions Ser.). (Illus.). 24p. (J). pap. (978-0-7922-4537-7(7)) National Geographic Society.

Schomp, Virginia. Ancient India. 2005. (People of the Ancient World Ser.). (Illus.). 112p. (J). (gr. 6-8). pap. 9.95 (978-0-531-16846-2(8)); 30.50 (978-0-531-12379-9(0)) Scholastic Library Publishing. (Watts, Franklin).

Shores, Lori. Teens in India. 2006. (Illus.). 96p. (J). (gr. 5-7). (978-0-7565-2063-2(0)) Compass Point Bks.

Todd, Anne M. Mohandas Gandhi. 2004. (Spiritual Leaders & Thinkers Ser.). (Illus.). 120p. (gr. 9-13). (J). 30.00 (978-0-7910-7864-8(7)); 30.00 (978-0-7910-7865-5(5)) Facts On File, Inc. (Chelsea Hse.).

Wheeler, Jill C. Gandhi. 2003. (Breaking Barriers Ser.). 64p. (J). (gr. 3-8). lib. bdg. 25.65 (978-1-57765-906-8(6)) ABDO Publishing Co.

—Indira Gandhi. 2004. (Women of the World Ser.). (J). (978-1-59197-614-1(6)) ABDO Publishing Co.

Writing in Ancient India, 6 Packs. (On Deck Ser.: Vol. 2). 24p. (gr. 4-5). 35.00 (978-0-7578-5868-0(6)) Rigby Education.

INDIAN DANCE

Cox, Rhonda. Powwow. 2001. (Books for Young Learners). (Illus.). 12p. (978-1-57274-392-2(1)) Owen, Richard C. Pubs., Inc.

Gait, Darlene, illus. Secret of the Dance. 2006. 32p. (YA). (gr. 4 up). 17.95 (978-1-55143-396-7(6)) Orca Bk. Pubs. USA.

Greene, Jacqueline Dembar. Powwow: A Good Day to Dance. Greene, Jacqueline Dembar, photos by. 1998. (First Bks.). (Illus.). 64p. (J). (gr. 5-7). 22.00 (978-0-531-20337-8(9) , Watts, Franklin) Scholastic Library Publishing.

INDIA RUBBER

see Rubber

INDIAN SIGN LANGUAGE

Coulter, Lavrie. Secrets in Stone: All about Maya Hieroglyphs. English, Sarah Jane, illus. 2003. 48p. (gr. 4-8). 18.00 (978-0-7567-9000-4(X)) DIANE Publishing Co.

Kelly, Michael. Native American Talking Signs. 1999. (Looking Into the Past Ser.). (Illus.). 64p. (YA). (gr. 5 up). lib. bdg. 19.75 (978-0-7910-4681-4(8) , Chelsea Hse.) Facts On File, Inc.

INDIANA

Boekhoff, P. M. & Kallen, Stuart A. Indiana. 2001. (Seeds of a Nation Ser.). (Illus.). 48p. (J). (gr. 3-5). 26.20 (978-0-7377-0663-5(5) , LML00902-178559, Kidhaven) Thomson Gale.

Brill, Marlene Targ. Indiana. 2nd ed. 2006. (Celebrate the States Ser.). (Illus.). 144p. (J). (978-0-7614-2020-0(7) , Benchmark Bks.) Cavendish, Marshall Corp.

Brown, Jonatha A. & Orr, Tamra. Indiana. 2005. (Portraits of the States Ser.). (Illus.). 32p. (J). pap. (978-0-8368-4644-7(3)) Stevens, Gareth Inc.

Brown, Jonatha A. & Orr, Tamra B. Indiana. 2005. (Portraits of the States Ser.). (Illus.). 32p. (J). (ps-17). lib. bdg. 23.33 (978-0-8368-4625-6(7)) Stevens, Gareth Inc.

Brown, Vanessa. Indiana. 2005. (Bilingual Library of the United States of America: Set 1). (ENG & SPA., Illus.). 32p. (J). (gr. 2-5). lib. bdg. 22.50 (978-1-4042-3079-8(3) , Buenas Letra) Rosen Publishing Group, Inc., The.

Brunelle, Lynn. Indiana: The Hoosier State. 2002. (World Almanac Library of the States). (Illus.). 48p. (J). (gr. 5 up). pap. 14.95 (978-0-8368-5285-1(0)); lib. bdg. 30.00 (978-0-8368-5116-8(1)) Stevens, Gareth Inc. (World Almanac Library).

—Indiana: The Hoosier State. 2002. (gr. 5-8). lib. bdg. 24.15 (978-0-613-52406-3(3)) Tandem Library Bks.

Capstone Press Staff, contrib. by. Indiana. rev. ed. 2002. (One Nation Ser.). (Illus.). 48p. (J). (gr. 3-4). lib. bdg. 22.60 (978-0-7368-1238-2(5) , Bridgestone Bks.) Capstone Pr., Inc.

Craats, Rennay. A Guide to Indiana. 2001. (American States Ser.). 32p. (J). (Illus.). (gr. 4-7). lib. bdg. 16.95 (978-1-930954-65-6(4)); per. 7.95 (978-1-930954-51-9(4)) Weigl Pubs., Inc.

Derzipilski, Kathleen. Indiana. 2006. (Its My State! Ser.). (Illus.). 80p. (J). (gr. 3-6). lib. bdg. 29.93 (978-0-7614-1927-3(6) , Benchmark Bks.) Cavendish, Marshall Corp.

Dhilawala, Sakina. Armenia. 2nd ed. 2006. (Celebrate the States Ser.). (Illus.). 144p. (J). lib. bdg. 39.93 (978-0-7614-2029-3(0) , Benchmark Bks.) Cavendish, Marshall Corp.

Furlong Reynolds, Cynthia. H Is for Hoosier: An Indiana Alphabet. Langton, Bruce, illus. 2001. 40p. (J). 17.95 (978-1-58536-041-3(4)) Sleeping Bear Pr.

Harcourt School Publishers Staff. Horizons: We Are in Indiana. 3rd ed. 2002. (Illus.). pap. 5.60 (978-0-15-333539-6(4)) Harcourt Schl. Pubs.

Heinrichs, Ann. Indiana. 2005. (Welcome to the USA Ser.). 40p. (J). (gr. 1-5). 27.07 (978-1-59296-472-7(9)) Child's World, Inc.

—Indiana. 2003. (This Land Is Your Land Ser.). (Illus.). 48p. (J). (gr. 3 up). lib. bdg. 22.60 (978-0-7565-0325-3(6)) Compass Point Bks.

Hyde, Judith Jensen. Indiana. (Rookie Read-about' Geography: States Ser.). 32p. (J). 2007. pap. 5.95 (***978-0-516-21618-8(X));*** 2006. (Illus.). (gr. 1-2). 20.50 (978-0-516-21846-5(8)) Scholastic Library Publishing. (Children's Pr.).

Indiana. 2000. (Switched on Schoolhouse Ser.). (Illus.). (YA). (gr. 7-12). pap. 24.95 incl. cd-rom (978-0-7403-0266-4(3) , SOSIN) Alpha Omega Pubns., Inc.

Indiana - Fishing Map Guide - Northeastern Region Vol. 1: Lake Maps & Fishing Information for over 200 Lakes in Northeastern Indiana. 2002. (Illus.). 184p. (YA). spiral bd. 21.95 (978-1-885010-48-3(6)) Sportsman's Connection.

Indiana - Fishing Map Guide - Outside of the NE Region Vol. 2: Lake Maps & Fishing Information for Inland Aleks & Reservoirs Outside of the NE Region Plus Lake Michigan & Ohio River Coverage. 2002. (Illus.). 192p. (YA). spiral bd. 21.95 (978-1-885010-49-0(4)) Sportsman's Connection.

Indianapolis Sold C 2005. 2004. 420p. (YA). pap. 15.00 (978-1-58553-955-0(4) , 05GC0018) Entertainment Publications, Inc.

Knapp, Ron. Indiana: A MyReportLinks.com Book. 2003. (States Ser.). (Illus.). 48p. (J). (gr. 4-10). lib. bdg. 25.26 (978-0-7660-5118-8(8) , MyReportLinks.com Bks.) Enslow Pubs., Inc.

Ling, Bettina. Indiana. 2003. (From Sea to Shining Sea Ser.: 2). (Illus.). 80p. (J). 30.50 (978-0-516-22387-2(9) , Children's Pr.) Scholastic Library Publishing.

Marsh, Carole. The Big Indiana Reproducible Activity Book! 2001. (Indiana Experience! Ser.). (Illus.). 96p. (J). (gr. 2-6). pap., act. bk. ed. 9.95 (978-0-7933-9941-3(6)) Gallopade International.

—Indiana Classic Christmas Trivia. 2002. (Carole Marsh Indiana Bks.). (Illus.). 32p. pap. 6.95 (978-0-635-01395-8(9) , 13959); lib. bdg. 21.95 (978-0-635-01396-5(7) , 13967) Gallopade International. (Marsh, Carole Bks.).

—Indiana Current Events Projects: 30 Cool, Activities, Crafts, Experiments & More for Kids to Do to Learn about Your State! 2003. (Indiana Experience Ser.). 32p. (gr. k-5). pap. 5.95 (978-0-635-02033-8(5) , Marsh, Carole Bks.) Gallopade International.

—Indiana Geography Projects: 30 Cool, Activities, Crafts, Experiments & More for Kids to Do to Learn about Your State! 2003. (Indiana Experience Ser.). 32p. (gr. k-5). pap. 5.95 (978-0-635-01833-5(0) , Marsh, Carole Bks.) Gallopade International.

—Indiana Government Projects: 30 Cool, Activities, Crafts, Experiments & More for Kids to Do to Learn about Your State! 2003. (Indiana Experience Ser.). 32p. (gr. k-5). pap. 5.95 (978-0-635-01933-2(7) , Marsh, Carole Bks.) Gallopade International.

—Indiana Jeopardy! Answers & Questions about Our State! 2004. (Illus.). 32p. (J). (gr. 3-8). pap., act. bk. ed. 7.95 (978-0-7933-9796-9(0)) Gallopade International.

—Indiana "Jography" A Fun Run Through Our State! 2004. (Illus.). 32p. (J). (gr. 3-8). pap., act. bk. ed. 7.95 (978-0-7933-9825-6(8)) Gallopade International.

—Indiana People Projects: 30 Cool, Activities, Crafts, Experiments & More for Kids to Do to Learn about Your State! 2003. (Indiana Experience Ser.). 32p. (gr. k-5). pap. 5.95 (978-0-635-01983-7(3) , Marsh, Carole Bks.) Gallopade International.

—Indiana Survivor: Game Book. 2001. (Carole Marsh Indiana Bks.). (Illus.). 32p. (J). (gr. 3-8). pap., act. bk. ed. 9.95 (978-0-635-00535-9(2)) Gallopade International.

—Indiana Symbols & Facts Projects: 30 Cool, Activities, Crafts, Experiments & More for Kids to Do to Learn about Your State! 2003. (Indiana Experience Ser.). 32p. (gr. k-5). pap. 5.95 (978-0-635-01883-0(7) , Marsh, Carole Bks.) Gallopade International.

—My First Book about Indiana. 2004. (Illus.). 32p. (J). (gr. k-4). pap. 7.95 (978-0-7933-9883-6(5)) Gallopade International.

—Who Wants to Be a Millionaire? 2001. (Carole Marsh Indiana Bks.). lib. bdg. 29.95 (978-0-635-00045-3(8)) Gallopade International.

Marsh, Carole & Gentzke, Sue. Indiana: The Indiana Experience. 2001. (Illus.). 96p. (J). (gr. 3-8). pap., act. bk. ed. 6.95 (978-0-7933-9912-3(2)) Gallopade International.

McAuliffe, Bill. Indiana: Facts & Symbols. 1999. (J). lib. bdg. 14.00 (978-0-531-11802-3(9)) Capstone Pr., Inc.

—Indiana Facts & Symbols. (States & Their Symbols Ser.). 24p. (J). 1999. (Illus.). (gr. 2-3). lib. bdg. 18.60 (978-0-7368-0218-5(5) , Bridgestone Bks.); 2003. lib. bdg. 19.93 (978-0-7368-2244-2(5)) Capstone Pr., Inc.

McNamara, Connie. My First Indiana University Words. 2004. (J). bds. 11.95 (978-0-9743244-8-7(5)) Shamrock Publishing, Inc.

—My First Purdue University Words. 2004. (J). bds. 11.95 (978-0-9743244-9-4(3)) Shamrock Publishing, Inc.

Messer, Luke. Hoosier Heart. 2006. (Illus.). (J). 16.95 (***978-0-9786799-1-0(1)***) Eva Publishing, LLC.

Murray, Julie. Indiana. 2006. (Buddy Book Ser.). (Illus.). 32p. (J). (gr. k-4). lib. bdg. 22.78 (978-1-59197-673-8(1) , Buddy Bks.) ABDO Publishing Co.

Nicodemus, Laura Konger. Grandma's House Had No Electricity, 4 vols. Nicodemus, Laura Konger, illus. 2002. (Illus.). 16p. (J). 3.99 (978-0-9722216-2-7(X)) Grandma's Stories, Inc.

—Grandma's House Had No Water, 4 vols. Nicodemus, Laura Konger, illus. 2002. (Illus.). 16p. (J). (gr. 1-4). 3.99 (978-0-9722216-1-0(1)) Grandma's Stories, Inc.

—Grandma's Onion Patch, 4 vols. Nicodemus, Laura Konger, illus. 2002. (Illus.). 16p. (J). (gr. 1-4). 3.99 (978-0-9722216-3-4(8)) Grandma's Stories, Inc.

—Grandma's Scary Mean Gander, 4 vols., Set. Nicodemus, Laura Konger, illus. 2002. (Illus.). 16p. (J). (gr. 1-4). 3.99 (978-0-9722216-0-3(3)) Grandma's Stories, Inc.

Pell, Ed. Indiana. 2003. (Land of Liberty Ser.). (Illus.). 64p. (J). (gr. 3-4). lib. bdg. 23.93 (978-0-7368-1582-6(1) , Bridgestone Bks.) Capstone Pr., Inc.

Ross, D. J. Uniquely Indiana. 2003. (State Studies). (Illus.). 48p. (J). pap. 8.50 (978-1-4034-4505-6(2)); 27.07 (978-1-4034-4490-5(0)) Heinemann Library.

Shofner, Shawndra. Indiana. 2008. (J). (***978-1-58341-639-6(0)*** , Creative Education) Creative Co., The.

Swain, Gwenyth. Indiana. 2nd rev. ed. 2002. (Hello U. S. A. Ser.). (Illus.). 84p. (J). (gr. 3-6). lib. bdg. 25.26 (978-0-8225-4081-6(9)) Lerner Publishing Group.

—Indiana. 2002. (Illus.). 84p. (J). (gr. 3-6). lib. bdg. 15.25 (978-0-613-46079-8(0)) Tandem Library Bks.

INDIANA—FICTION

Aryal, Aimee. Let's Go Hoosiers! Shrestha, Anuj, illus. 2004. (J). 19.95 (978-1-932888-32-4(2)) Mascot Bks., Inc.

Blakeslee, Ann R. Summer Battles. 2000. (Illus.). 128p. (YA). (gr. 5-9). 14.95 (978-0-7614-5064-1(5) , Cavendish Children's Bks.) Cavendish, Marshall Corp.

Brown, Marc. Buster on the Farm. 2005. (Postcards from Buster Ser.). (Illus.). 32p. (J). (gr. 1-4). 14.99 (978-0-316-15884-8(4)); pap. 3.99 (978-0-316-00108-3(2)) Little, Brown Bks. for Young Readers.

—Buster on the Town. 2005. (Postcards from Buster Ser.). (Illus.). 32p. (J). (gr. 1-4). 14.99 (978-0-316-15882-4(8)) Little, Brown Bks. for Young Readers.

Cabot, Meg. Teen Idol. l.t. ed. 2006. 366p. (YA). 23.95 (978-0-7862-7760-5(2)) Thorndike Pr.

Clifford, Eth. The Year of the Three-Legged Deer. Cuffari, Richard, tr. Cuffari, Richard, illus. 2003. (Library of Indiana Classics). 176p. (YA). 32.95 (978-0-253-34251-5(1)); pap. 14.95 (978-0-253-21604-5(4)) Indiana Univ. Pr.

Cullen, Lynn. Diary of Nelly Vandorn. (gr. 3 up). Date not set. 128p. mass mkt. 4.99 (978-0-06-440926-1(0)); 2002. 192p. (J). 15.95 (978-0-06-029133-4(8)) HarperCollins Pubs.

Faces of War. 2004. (Illus.). 210p. per. 10.97 (978-0-9754291-1-2(6)) Booth, John Harvey.

Finley, Martha. Mildred Keith, Vol. 1. (Mildred Classics Ser.: Vol. 1). 288p. pap. 6.95 (978-1-58182-227-4(8)) Cumberland Hse. Publishing.

Giles, Gail. Right Behind You. 2007. 304p. (YA). (gr. 10 up). 15.99 (***978-0-316-16636-2(7))*** Little, Brown Bks. for Young Readers.

Johns, W. E. The Boy Biggles. 2001. 148p. pap. (978-0-7551-0735-3(7)) House of Stratus, Inc.

Kipling, Rudyard. Rikki Tikki Tavi. Jones, Chuck, illus. 2006. 32p. (J). 8.95 (978-0-8249-6597-6(3) , Ideals Children's Bks.) Ideals Pubns.

Kjellberg, B. Abe: A Farm Boy. 2006. (J). per. (978-0-912868-07-3(4)) Kjellberg, Inc.

—Apple Acres: The Farm. 2006. (J). per. 7.95 (***978-0-912868-10-3(4))*** Kjellberg, Inc.

—Courtnee: A Farm Girl. 2005. (Illus.). 84p. (J). per. 7.95 (978-0-912868-06-6(6)) Kjellberg, Inc.

—Sandy: A City Girl. 2005. (Illus.). 94p. (J). per. 7.95 (978-0-912868-08-0(2) , 8080) Kjellberg, Inc.

Kornblatt, Marc. Izzy's Place. 2003. (Illus.). 128p. (J). 16.95 (978-0-689-84639-7(8) , McElderry, Margaret K.) Simon & Schuster Children's Publishing.

Lewis, Calvin, Jr. & Wilhite, Susan L. It Comes in the Night: Speaking Eagle, Book One. 2006. pap. 9.95 (***978-1-934130-03-2(6)*** , 3002) Flood Crest Pr.

Major, Charles. Bears of Blue River. reprint ed. lib. bdg. 23.95 (978-0-88411-094-1(X)) Amereon LTD.

May, Sophie. Dotty Dimple Out West. 2005. reprint ed. pap. 22.95 (978-1-4179-8845-7(2)) Kessinger Publishing, LLC.

Peck, Richard. Here Lies the Librarian. 160p. (J). (gr. 5 up). 2007. 6.99 (***978-0-14-240908-4(1)*** , Puffin); 2006. 16.99 (978-0-8037-3080-9(2) , Dial) Penguin Group (USA) Inc.

—Here Lies the Librarian. rev. ed. 175p. 23.95 (***978-0-7862-9183-0(4))*** Thorndike Pr.

Peck, Richard. The Teacher's Funeral: A Comedy in Three Parts. 2004. 208p. (J). (gr. 5). 16.99 (978-0-8037-2736-6(4) , Dial); 2006. 224p. (YA). (gr. 3). reprint ed. pap. 6.99 (978-0-14-240507-9(8) , Puffin) Penguin Group (USA) Inc.

—The Teacher's Funeral: A Comedy in Three Parts. l.t. ed. 2005. 226p. 22.95 (978-0-7862-7750-6(5) , Large Print Pr.) Thorndike Pr.

Penrose, Margaret. The Motor Girls on Cedar Lake, or the He. 2006. 63.99 (***978-1-4219-9401-7(1));*** pap. 56.99 (***978-1-4219-9422-2(4))*** IndyPublish.com.

Porter, Gene. Freckles. 2006. pap. (***978-1-4250-2281-5(2))*** Assistedreadingbooks.com Inc.

Sanders, Scott Russell. Bad Man Ballad. 2004. (Library of Indiana Classics). 256p. (J). reprint ed. pap. 32.95 (978-0-253-21688-5(5)) Indiana Univ. Pr.

Smith, Jane. Adventure on White High Island. 2006. (YA). per. (978-0-9777074-0-9(7)) Beverly Hills Publishing.

Stratton-Porter. At the Foot of the Rainbow. 2006. 19.99 (***978-1-4219-7512-2(2))*** IndyPublish.com.

Stratton Porter, Gene. At the Foot of the Rainbow. 2007. 180p. 18.95 (***978-1-934169-52-0(8));*** pap. 7.95 (***978-1-934169-53-7(6))*** Norilana Bks.

—A Daughter of the Land. 2007. 340p. 22.95 (***978-1-934169-46-9(3));*** pap. 11.95 (***978-1-934169-47-6(1))*** Norilana Bks.

—Freckles. 2006. 236p. (YA). 19.95 (***978-1-934169-32-2(3));*** pap. 8.95 (***978-1-934169-33-9(1))*** Norilana Bks.

Stratton-Porter, Gene. Freckles. (J). reprint ed. lib. bdg. 24.95 (978-0-89190-949-1(4) , Rivercity Pr.) Amereon LTD.

—Freckles EasyRead Comfort Edition. 2006. pap. (***978-1-4250-1125-3(X))*** Assistedreadingbooks.com Inc.

—Freckles EasyRead Edition. 2006. pap. (***978-1-4250-0577-1(2))*** Assistedreadingbooks.com Inc.

—Freckles EasyRead Large Edition. 2006. pap. (***978-1-4250-1603-6(0))*** Assistedreadingbooks.com Inc.

Stratton-Porter, Gene. A Girl of the Limberlost. 2003. (Twelve-Point Ser.). (J). lib. bdg. 25.00 (978-1-58287-232-2(5)) North Bks.

Stratton Porter, Gene. A Girl of the Limberlost. 2006. 336p. (YA). 21.95 (***978-1-934169-30-8(7));*** pap. 10.95 (***978-1-934169-31-5(5))*** Norilana Bks.

Stratton-Porter, Gene. A Girl of the Limberlost. (J). reprint ed. lib. bdg. 33.95 (978-0-89190-948-4(6) , Rivercity Pr.) Amereon LTD.

—A Girl of the Limberlost. Benda, Wladyslaw T., illus. 2005. reprint ed. pap. 38.95 (978-0-7661-9424-3(8)) Kessinger Publishing, LLC.

—A Girl of the Limberlost. l.t. ed. 2004. (Large Print Ser.). 463p. 26.00 (978-1-58287-716-7(5)) North Bks.

Stratton-Porter, Gene. Harvester. 2006. pap. (***978-1-4068-3133-7(6))*** Echo Library.

Stratton-Porter, Gene & Matthews, Andrew. Freckles. 2000. (Illus.). 32p. (C). pap. 9.00 (978-0-582-42655-9(3)) Pearson ESL.

Swain, Gwenyth. Chig & the Second Spread. 2003. 208p. (J). (gr. 3-7). 14.95 (978-0-385-73065-5(9) , Delacorte Bks. for Young Readers) Random Hse. Children's Bks.

Thrasher, Crystal. The Dark Didn't Catch Me. 2004. (Library of Indiana Classics). 192p. (J). reprint ed. pap. 14.95 (978-0-253-21685-4(0)) Indiana Univ. Pr.

Walker, Cheryl. The Little Black & White Pony. 2003. 28p. (J). pap. 2.50 (978-0-9726326-1-4(1)) TechArts International LLC.

Waltman, Kevin. Learning the Game. 2005. 224p. (J). (gr. 7 up). pap. 16.95 (978-0-439-73109-6(7) , Scholastic Pr.) Scholastic, Inc.

Woodworth, Chris. When Ratboy Lived Next Door. 2005. (Illus.). 192p. (J). 16.00 (978-0-374-34677-5(1) , Farrar, Straus & Giroux (BYR)) Farrar, Straus & Giroux.

INDIANA—HISTORY

Deinard, Jenny. How to Draw Indianas Sights & Symbols. 2002. (Kids Guide to Drawing America Ser.). 32p. (J). lib. bdg. 25.25 (978-0-8239-6070-5(6) , PowerKids Pr.) Rosen Publishing Group, Inc., The.

Harcourt School Publishers Staff. Horizons: Indiana Edition. 3rd ed. 2003. (Illus.). 69.80 (978-0-15-321348-9(5)) Harcourt Schl. Pubs.

Marsh, Carole. Indiana History Projects: 30 Cool, Activities, Crafts, Experiments & More for Kids to Do to Learn about Your State! 2003. (Indiana Experience Ser.). 32p. (gr. k-5). pap. 5.95 (978-0-635-01783-3(0) , Marsh, Carole Bks.) Gallopade International.

—My First Pocket Guide Indiana. 2000. (Indiana Experience! Ser.). (Illus.). 96p. (J). (gr. 3-8). 12.95 (978-0-635-01304-0(5) , 13045) Gallopade International.

INDIANAPOLIS COLTS (FOOTBALL TEAM)

Hawkes, Brian. The History of the Indianapolis Colts. 2004. (NFL Today Ser.). (Illus.). 32p. 18.95 (978-1-58341-299-2(9) , Creative Education) Creative Co., The.

Indianapolis Colts Staff. Indianapolis Colts. CWC Sports Inc., ed. 1998. (NFL Team Yearbooks Ser.). (J). (gr. 1-12). pap. 9.99 (978-1-891613-10-4(3)) Everett Sports Publishing & Marketing.

Stewart, Mark. The Indianapolis Colts. 2006. (Team Spirit Ser.). (Illus.). 48p. (J). lib. bdg. 25.27 (978-1-59953-005-5(8)) Norwood Hse. Pr.

Stewart, Mark. Indianapolis Colts. 2007. 48p. pap. 9.95 (***978-1-60357-002-2(0))*** Norwood Hse. Pr.

INDIANAPOLIS SPEEDWAY RACE

Fish, Bruce. Indy Car Racing. (Race Car Legends Ser.). (Illus.). (J). 2001. pap. 7.95 (978-0-7910-5846-6(8)); 2000. 64p. (gr. 4-7). 25.00 (978-0-7910-5845-9(X)) Facts On File, Inc. (Chelsea Hse.).

Harcourt School Publishers Staff. Horizons: The Indianapolis 500. 3rd ed. 2002. (Illus.). pap. 5.60 (978-0-15-333545-7(9)) Harcourt Schl. Pubs.

King, Mike. I Is for Indy. Rodgers, John, illus. 2006. 48p. (J). (gr. 4 up). 18.95 (978-1-891390-21-0(X)) Witness Productions.

INDIANS

see also Indians of Central America; Indians of Mexico; Indians of North America; Indians of South America

Benson, Sonia & Baker, Deborah J. Almanac, Early Civilizations, 2 vols. 2005. (Early Civilizations in the Americas Reference Library). (Illus.). xli, 551p. (J). lib. bdg. 67.00 (978-0-7876-7679-7(9) , UXL) Thomson Gale.

—Early Civilizations in the, 2 vols. 2005. (Early Civilizations in the Americas Reference Library). (Illus.). xli, 551p. (J). 120.00 (978-0-7876-9252-0(2) , UXL) Thomson Gale.

—Primary Sources, Early Americas, 2 vols. 2005. (Early Civilizations in the Americas Reference Library). (Illus.). xli, 551p. (J). lib. bdg. 67.00 (978-0-7876-7681-0(0) , UXL) Thomson Gale.

Long, Cathryn J. Ancient America. 2002. (World History Ser.). (Illus.). 112p. (YA). (gr. 8-11). 32.45 (978-1-56006-889-1(2) , LML00902-178210, Lucent Bks.) Thomson Gale.

Nextext Staff, contrib. by. The Ancient Americas: 30,000 B.C.-A.D.1600. 2004. (Stories in History Ser.). (Illus.). 192p. (gr. 6-12). tchr. ed. (978-0-618-25525-2(7) , 2-00331) McDougal Littell Inc.

Remington, Gwen. The Cheyenne. 2000. (Indigenous Peoples of North America Ser.). (Illus.). 96p. (J). (gr. 4-12). 28.70 (978-1-56006-750-4(0) , LML00902-178100, Lucent Bks.) Thomson Gale.

Wood, Geraldine. Science of the Early Americas. 1999. (gr. 5-8). lib. bdg. 17.60 (978-0-613-54346-0(7)) Tandem Library Bks.

INDIANS, TREATMENT OF

Anderson, Dale. The California Missions. 2002. (Landmark Events in American History Ser.). (Illus.). 48p. (J). (gr. 5 up). lib. bdg. 30.00 (978-0-8368-5339-1(3)); pap. 14.60 (978-0-8368-5353-7(9)) Stevens, Gareth Inc. (World Almanac Library).

Ditchfield, Christin. Spanish Missions. 2006. 48p. (gr. 3-5). (YA). pap. 6.95 (978-0-516-21746-8(1)); (Illus.). (J). 25.00 (978-0-516-22834-1(X)) Scholastic Library Publishing. (Children's Pr.).

Ingram, Scott. Francisco Pizarro. 2002. (History's Villains Ser.). (Illus.). 112p. 29.94 (978-1-56711-627-4(2) , Blackbirch Pr., Inc.) Thomson Gale.

Kelley, Alison Turnbull. Native Americans & the United States. 2002. (People at Odds Ser.). (Illus.). 112p. (J). (gr. 5 up). 30.00 (978-0-7910-6707-9(6) , Chelsea Hse.) Facts On File, Inc.

McIntosh, Kenneth. First Encounters Between Spain & the Americas: Two Worlds Meet. 2005. (Illus.). 112p. (J). (ps-7). lib. bdg. (978-1-59084-925-5(6)) Mason Crest Pubs.

Scarbrough, Mary Hertz. A California Mission. 2005. (Daily Life Ser.). (J). (978-0-7377-3090-6(0) , Greenhaven Pr., Inc.) Thomson Gale.

Waldman, Stuart. We Asked for Nothing: The Remarkable Journey of Cabeza de Vaca. McNeely, Tom, illus. 2003. (Great Explorers Ser.). 48p. (J). (gr. 4-8). 19.95 (978-1-931414-07-4(6)) Mikaya Pr.

INDIANS OF CANADA

see Indians of North America—Canada

INDIANS OF CENTRAL AMERICA

Fine, Jil. Mayan Writing in Mesoamerica. 2003. (Writing in the Ancient World Ser.). (Illus.). 24p. (J). lib. bdg. 17.25 (978-0-8239-6511-3(2) , PowerKids Pr.) Rosen Publishing Group, Inc., The.

Fourstar, Jerome & Blue Talk, Richard. How the Morning & Evening Stars Came to Be: And Other Assiniboine Indian Stories. 2003. (Indian Reading Ser.). (Illus.). 48p. pap. 9.95 (978-0-917298-96-7(9)) Montana Historical Society Pr.

Keoke, Emory Dean & Porterfield, Kay Marie. American Indian Contributions to the World: Buildings, Clothing, & Art. 2005. (American Indian Contributions to the World Ser.). (Illus.). 160p. (J). (gr. 4-9). 35.00 (978-0-8160-5394-0(4)) Facts On File, Inc.

Shuter, Jane. The Maya. 2002. (History Opens Windows Ser.). (Illus.). 32p. (J). (gr. 2-4). lib. bdg. 22.79 (978-1-58810-591-2(1)) Heinemann Library.

Swanton, John R. Indian Tribes of Mexico, Central America & the West Indies. (Shorey Indian Ser.). 40p. (J). reprint ed. pap. 10.00 (978-0-8466-0087-9(0) , S87) Shorey's Bookstore.

INDIANS OF CENTRAL AMERICA—FICTION

Cameron, Ann. Colibri. 2003. 240p. (J). (gr. 5-8). 17.00 (978-0-374-31519-1(1) , 53501559, Farrar, Straus & Giroux (BYR)) Farrar, Straus & Giroux.

—Colibri. 2005. 256p. (YA). (gr. 7). pap. 5.99 (978-0-440-42052-1(0) , Laurel Leaf) Random Hse. Children's Bks.

—Colibri. Rioja, Alberto Jimenez, tr. from ENG. 2005. (SPA., Illus.). 256p. (J). (gr. 6-9). pap. 14.99 (978-0-439-68314-2(9) , Scholastic en Espanol) Scholastic, Inc.

Eboch, Chris. The Well of Sacrifice. Barnard, Bryn, illus. 1999. 240p. (J). (gr. 5-9). tchr. ed. 16.00 (978-0-395-90374-2(2) , Clarion Bks.) Houghton Mifflin Co. Trade & Reference Div.

Greene, Michele Dominguez. Chasing the Jaguar. 240p. (J). 2008. pap. 7.99 (***978-0-06-076355-8(8)*** , Rayo); 2006. 15.99 (978-0-06-076353-4(1)) HarperCollins Pubs.

—Chasing the Jaguar. Greene, Michele Dominguez, illus. 2006. 240p. (J). lib. bdg. 16.89 (978-0-06-076354-1(X)) HarperCollins Pubs.

Guzman, Lila. Kichi in Jungle Jeopardy. Johnson, Regan, illus. (J). 2007. per. 8.95 (978-0-9769417-2-9(4)); 2006. 144p. 13.95 (978-0-9769417-1-2(6)) Blooming Tree Pr.

Mikaelsen, Ben. Tree Girl. 2005. 240p. (J). pap. 7.99 (978-0-06-009006-7(5) , HarperTeen) HarperCollins Pubs.

O'Neill, Katrina. Decoding the Mayan Marvels. Cantell, Brenda, illus. 2005. (Treasure Trackers Ser.). 80p. (gr. 5-9). 19.00 (978-0-7910-8871-5(5) , Chelsea Hse.) Facts On File, Inc.

INDIANS OF CENTRAL AMERICA—MAYAS

see Indians of Mexico—Mayas

INDIANS OF MEXICO

Chapman, Gillian. Aztec Crafts from the Past. 2000. (Crafts from the Past Ser.). (Illus.). 37p. (J). (gr. 4-7). pap. 9.95 (978-0-688-17748-5(4)) HarperCollins Pubs.

Fine, Jil. Mayan Writing in Mesoamerica. 2003. (Writing in the Ancient World Ser.). (Illus.). 24p. (J). lib. bdg. 17.25 (978-0-8239-6511-3(2) , PowerKids Pr.) Rosen Publishing Group, Inc., The.

Larson, Bonnie. When Animals Were People: A Huichol Indian Tale. Rivera Lemos, Modesto, illus. 2002. Tr. of Cuando los Animales Fueron Gente. (ENG & SPA.). 32p. (J). (gr. 1-3). pap. 16.95 (978-1-57416-051-2(6)) Clear Light Pubs.

Licon, Ernesto Gonzales, ed. The Vanished Mesoamerican Civilizations: The Unknown Empires of the Zapotecs & Mixtecs. 2001. (Illus.). 240p. lib. bdg. 95.00 (978-0-7656-8035-8(1) , Sharpe Reference) Sharpe, M.E. Inc.

MacDonald, Fiona. You Wouldn't Want to Be an Aztec Sacrifice! 2001. (gr. 3-6). lib. bdg. 18.75 (978-0-613-44279-4(2)) Tandem Library Bks.

Miller, Janet K., illus. Efrain of the Sonoran Desert: A Lizard's Life among the Seri Indians. 2001. 32p. (J). (gr. 3-5). 15.95 (978-0-938317-55-5(5)) Cinco Puntos Pr.

Padilla, Stan. Yaqui Coloring Book. 1999. (Illus.). 28p. (J). (ps-3). 4.95 (978-1-57067-068-8(4)) Book Publishing Co., The.

Peppas, Lynn. Life in Ancient Mesoamerica. 2004. (Peoples of the Ancient World Ser.). (Illus.). 32p. (J). (978-0-7787-2039-3(X)) Crabtree Publishing Co.

Quezada, Juan. Juan Quezada. Dale, Shelley, illus. 2003. (SPA.). 40p. (J). 16.95 (978-0-9708617-0-2(2)); pap. 9.95 (978-0-9708617-1-9(0)) Norman Bks.

—Juan Quezada. Mlawer, Teresa, tr. Dale, Shelley, illus. 2003. 40p. (J). (gr. k-6). 16.95 (978-0-9708617-4-0(5)); pap. 9.95 (978-0-9708617-5-7(3)) Norman Bks.

Swanton, John R. Indian Tribes of Mexico, Central America & the West Indies. (Shorey Indian Ser.). 40p. (J). reprint ed. pap. 10.00 (978-0-8466-0087-9(0) , S87) Shorey's Bookstore.

INDIANS OF MEXICO—AZTECS

Ackroyd, Peter. Cities of Blood. 2005. (Voyages through Time Ser.). (Illus.). 144p. (J). (gr. 4-7). pap. 9.99 (978-0-7566-1367-9(1)) Dorling Kindersley Publishing, Inc.

Allan, Tony. The Aztec Empire. 2004. (Excavating the Past Ser.). (J). pap. 8.50 (978-1-4034-5459-1(0)); lib. bdg. 27.07 (978-1-4034-4839-2(6)) Heinemann Library.

Amado, Elisa. Sun Stone Days/Dias de Piedra/Tonaltin. Espinosa, Peggy, tr. Andreadis, Ianna, illus. Davalos, Felipe, photos by. 2007. (ENG & SPA.). 48p. (J). 8.95 (978-0-88899-810-1(4)) Groundwood Bks. CAN. *Dist:* Perseus Distribution.

Anton, Ferdinand. The Secret World of the Aztecs. Wynne, Christopher, ed. Aston, Paul, tr. from GER. 2006. (Illus.). 28p. (J). (gr. 4-8). reprint ed. 17.00 (978-1-4223-5338-7(9)) DIANE Publishing Co.

—The Secret World of the Aztecs. 2002. (Adventures in Art Ser.). (Illus.). 30p. 14.95 (978-3-7913-2702-0(X)) Prestel Publishing.

Ardagh, Philip. The Aztecs. 2001. (History Detectives Ser.). (Illus.). 64p. (J). (gr. 3 up). 16.95 (978-0-87226-632-2(X) , 6632XB, Bedrick, Peter Bks.) School Specialty Publishing.

Armentrout, David & Armentrout, Patricia. Aztecs. 2003. (Timelines of Ancient Civilizations Ser.). (Illus.). 32p. (J). 28.50 (978-1-58952-718-8(6)) Rourke Publishing, LLC.

—Treasures from Mexico. 2000. (Treasures from the Past Ser.). (Illus.). 48p. (J). (gr. 4-8). lib. bdg. 29.93 (978-1-55916-290-6(2)) Rourke Publishing, LLC.

Baquedano, Elizabeth & Buller, Laura. Aztec, Inca, & Maya. 2005. (Dk eyewitness Bks.). (Illus.). 72p. (J). lib. bdg. 19.99 (978-0-7566-1392-1(2)) Dorling Kindersley Publishing, Inc.

Baquedano, Elizabeth & Clarke, Barry. Aztec, Inca, & Maya. Zabe, Michel, photos by. 2005. (Dk eyewitness Bks.). (Illus.). 72p. (J). (gr. 4-7). 15.99 (978-0-7566-1383-9(3)) Dorling Kindersley Publishing, Inc.

Benchmark Education Staff. The Aztec World. 2005. 2.00 ***(978-1-4108-4666-2(0))*** Benchmark Education Co.

Bingham, Jane. The Aztec Empire. 2007. (Time Travel Guides Ser.). (Illus.). 64p. (YA). (gr. 5-8). lib. bdg. 34.29 ***(978-1-4109-2730-9(X))*** Raintree.

—The Aztec Empire. 2007. (Time Travel Guides Ser.). (Illus.). 64p. (J). ***(978-1-4109-2737-8(7))*** Steck-Vaughn.

Brannon, Barbara. Discover the Aztec. 2005. 39.00 ***(978-1-4108-5147-5(8))*** Benchmark Education Co.

Caper, William. The Aztec. 2005. (Navigators Ser.). (J). pap. 42.00 ***(978-1-4108-5099-7(4))*** Benchmark Education Co.

Chrisp, Peter. The Aztecs. 1999. (History Beneath Your Feet Ser.). (Illus.). 48p. (J). (gr. 3-7). lib. bdg. 27.12 (978-0-8172-5753-8(5)) Raintree.

Clarke, Catriona. Aztecs - Internet Referenced (Level 2) 2007. 32p. (J). 4.99 (978-0-7945-1579-9(7) , Usborne) EDC Publishing.

Conklin, Wendy. Mayas, Aztecs, Incas: All-in-One Resource with Background Information, Map Activities, Simulations & Games, & a Read-Aloud Play to Support Comprehension & Critical Thinking in Social Studies. 2006. 80p. pap. 12.99 (978-0-439-53994-4(3) , Teaching Resources) Scholastic, Inc.

Dalal, Anita. Myths of Pre-Columbian America. 2001. (Mythic World Ser.). (Illus.). 48p. (J). lib. bdg. 27.12 (978-0-7398-3193-9(3)) Raintree.

Daning, Tom. Mesoamerican Mythology: Quetzalcoatl. 2007. (Jr. Graphic Mythologies Ser.). (Illus.). 24p. (J). (978-1-4042-2344-8(4)); pap. (978-1-4042-2154-3(9)); (gr. 2-6). lib. bdg. 21.25 (978-1-4042-3401-7(2)) Rosen Publishing Group, Inc., The. (PowerKids Pr.).

Dawson, Imogen. Food & Feasts with the Aztecs. 2004. (Illus.). 32p. (J). (gr. 4-8). reprint ed. 14.00 (978-0-7567-7143-0(9)) DIANE Publishing Co.

Dawson, Imogene. Clothes & Crafts in Aztec Times. 2000. (Clothes & Crafts in History Ser.). (Illus.). 32p. (J). (gr. 4 up). lib. bdg. 24.67 (978-0-8368-2735-4(X)) Stevens, Gareth Inc.

Deedrick, Tami. The Aztec. 2001. (Ancient Civilizations Ser.). (Illus.). (J). pap. (978-0-7398-4144-0(0)) Steck-Vaughn.

—Aztecs. 2001. (Ancient Civilizations Ser.). (Illus.). 48p. (J). lib. bdg. 22.83 (978-0-7398-3579-1(3)) Raintree.

Dworkin, Mark J. Mayas, Aztecs & Incas: Mysteries of Ancient Civilizations of Central & South America. 1999. (Illus.). 144p. (J). (gr. 10-12). reprint ed. pap. 17.00 (978-0-7881-6589-4(5)) DIANE Publishing Co.

Eleanor Hall. Life among the Aztec. 2004. (Way People Live Ser.). (Illus.). 112p. (J). 29.95 (978-1-59018-160-7(3)) Thomson Gale.

Fisher, Leonard Everett, illus. The Two Mountains: An Aztec Legend. 2000. 32p. (J). (gr. k-3). tchr. ed. 16.95 (978-0-8234-1504-5(X)) Holiday Hse., Inc.

Flowers, Charles. Cortes & the Conquest of the Aztec Empire in World History. 2001. (In World History Ser.). (Illus.). 128p. (J). (gr. 5-12). lib. bdg. 26.60 (978-0-7660-1395-7(2)) Enslow Pubs., Inc.

Ganeri, Anita. Aztecs. 2000. (History Starts Here Ser.). (Illus.). 32p. (J). (ps-3). pap. 8.95 (978-0-7398-2031-5(1)) Steck-Vaughn.

—Aztecs. 2000. (J). (978-0-606-20558-0(6)) Tandem Library Bks.

—The Aztecs. 2006. (J). (978-0-7565-1950-6(0)) Compass Point Bks.

—The Aztecs. 1999. (History Starts Here Ser.). (Illus.). 32p. (J). (ps-3). lib. bdg. 25.69 (978-0-7398-1352-2(8)) Raintree.

Glencoe McGraw-Hill Staff & McGraw-Hill - Jamestown Education Staff. Jamestown's Early Civilizations: Aztec Life. 2001. (gr. 5-12). pap. 11.96 (978-0-8092-9489-3(3) , 9780809294893) Jamestown.

Gonzalbo, Pablo Escalante. An Aztec. Dulin, Laura, tr. De Gante, Guillermo, illus. 2000. (Day with Ser.). 48p. (J). (gr. 5-7). lib. bdg. (978-0-8225-1921-8(6)) Lerner Publishing Group.

Grant, Neil. Everyday Life of the Aztecs, Incas & Mayans. Cappon, Manuela et al, illus. 2003. (Uncovering History Ser.). 46p. (J). lib. bdg. 28.50 (978-1-58340-253-5(5)) Smart Apple Media.

Hull, Robert. The Aztecs. 1998. (Ancient World Ser.). (Illus.). 63p. (YA). (gr. 5-10). lib. bdg. 27.12 (978-0-8172-5056-0(5)) Raintree.

Jovinelly, Joann & Netelkos, Jason. The Crafts & Culture of the Aztecs. 2002. (Crafts of the Ancient World Ser.). (Illus.). 48p. (YA). (gr. 5-8). lib. bdg. 29.25 (978-0-8239-3512-3(4) , Rosen Central) Rosen Publishing Group, Inc., The.

Keller, Mary Jo, et al. Inca, Aztec, Maya: Arts, Crafts, Cooking, & Historical Aids. Lorseyedi, Barbara, illus. 1999. (Hands-On Heritage Ser.). 48p. (J). (gr. 2-6). pap., act. bk. ed. 6.95 (978-1-56472-150-1(7) , EP150) Edupress, Inc.

Kimmel, Eric A. Montezuma & the Fall of the Aztecs. San Souci, Daniel, illus. 2000. 32p. (J). (gr. 4-6). tchr. ed. 16.95 (978-0-8234-1452-9(3)) Holiday Hse., Inc.

King, David C. Projects about the Ancient Aztecs. 2006. (Hands-On Projects Ser.). (Illus.). 48p. (J). lib. bdg. 29.93 (978-0-7614-2256-3(0) , Benchmark Bks.) Cavendish, Marshall Corp.

Klobuchar, Lisa. History & Activities of the Aztecs. 2006. (Hands-On Ancient History Ser.). (Illus.). 32p. (J). (978-1-4034-7921-1(6)); pap. (978-1-4034-7929-7(1)) Heinemann Library.

Landau, Elaine. Exploring the World of the Aztecs with Elaine Landau. 2005. (Exploring Ancient Civilizations with Elaine Landau Ser.). (Illus.). 48p. (J). (gr. 4-7). lib. bdg. 23.93 (978-0-7660-2341-3(9) , Enslow Elementary) Enslow Pubs., Inc.

Macdonald, F. Step into the Aztec & Maya Worlds. 2007. (Illus.). 64p. pap. 10.99 ***(978-1-84476-420-4(6)*** , Southwater) Anness Publishing GBR. *Dist:* National Bk. Network.

MacDonald, Fiona. The Aztecs. 2003. (Strange Histories Ser.). (Illus.). 32p. (J). lib. bdg. 25.70 (978-0-7398-6439-5(4)) Raintree.

Macdonald, Fiona. The Aztecs. 2007. (J). lib. bdg. 19.95 ***(978-1-59566-351-1(7))*** QEB Publishing Inc.

MacDonald, Fiona. How to Be an Aztec Warrior. Bergin, Mark & Antram, Dave, illus. 2005. (How to Be Ser.). 32p. (J). (gr. 3-7). 21.90 (978-0-7922-3632-0(7) , National Geographic Children's Bks.) National Geographic Society.

—How to Be an Aztec Warrior. Bergin, Mark & Antram, David, illus. 2005. (How to Be Ser.). 32p. (J). (gr. 3-7). 14.95 (978-0-7922-3617-7(3) , National Geographic Children's Bks.) National Geographic Society.

—You Wouldn't Want to Be an Aztec Sacrifice! 2001. (gr. 3-6). lib. bdg. 18.75 (978-0-613-44279-4(2)) Tandem Library Bks.

—You Wouldn't Want to Be an Aztec Sacrifice! Gruesome Things You'd Rather Not Know. Antram, David, illus. 2001. (You Wouldn't Want to Ser.). 32p. (J). (gr. 2-5). 28.50 (978-0-531-14602-6(2)); pap. 9.95 (978-0-531-16209-5(5)) Scholastic Library Publishing. (Watts, Franklin).

Mathews, Sally Schofer. The Sad Night: The Story of an Aztec Victory & a Spanish Loss. 2001. (J). (978-0-606-21406-3(2)) Tandem Library Bks.

Moore, Heidi. Blood & Celebration: Aztec Beliefs. 2007. (J). ***(978-1-4109-2891-7(8))***; pap. ***(978-1-4109-2898-6(5))*** Steck-Vaughn.

Morris, Ting & Young, E. Aztecs & Maya. 2006. (Illus.). 32p. (J). (978-1-58340-915-2(7) , 1262694) Smart Apple Media.

Naden, Corinne J. & Blue, Rose. The Aztecs & Tenochtitlan. 2003. (J). pap. (978-1-58417-321-2(1)); lib. bdg. (978-1-58417-320-5(3)) Lake Street Pubs.

Nicholson, Robert. The Aztecs. 2004. (Interfact Ser.). (SPA., Illus.). 48p. (J). (gr. 3-6). pap. 14.95 incl. cd-rom (978-1-58728-450-2(2) , Two Can Publishing) T&N Children's Publishing.

Owens, L. L. The Great Aztecs. 2002. (Cover-To-Cover Chapter Books). (Illus.). 56p. (J). pap. (978-0-7891-5742-3(X)); (gr. 1-4). lib. bdg. 16.95 (978-0-7569-0910-9(4)) Perfection Learning Corp.

Rees, Rosemary. The Aztecs. (Illus.). 64p. 2006. (J). ***(978-1-4034-8749-0(9));*** 2002. (J). (gr. 4-6). pap. 8.95 (978-1-58810-317-8(X) , 91123); 1999. (gr. 4-6). lib. bdg. 27.07 (978-1-57572-888-9(5)) Heinemann Library.

Reid, Struan. Montezuma. 2002. (Historical Biographies Ser.). (Illus.). 32p. (J). (gr. 2-4). lib. bdg. 22.79 (978-1-58810-566-0(0)) Heinemann Library.

Rosemary Rees. The Aztecs. 2nd ed. 2006. (Illus.). 64p. (J). pap. ***(978-1-4034-8755-1(3))*** Heinemann Library.

Russell, Henry. Ancient Aztec: Archaeology Unlocks the Secrets of the Aztec Past. 2007. (National Geographic Investigates Ser.). (Illus.). 64p. (YA). (gr. 5 up). 17.95 ***(978-1-4263-0072-1(7));*** lib. bdg. 27.90 ***(978-1-4263-0073-8(5))*** National Geographic Society. (National Geographic Children's Bks.).

Santella, Andrew. The Aztec. (True Bks.). (Illus.). (J). (gr. 3-5). 2003. 48p. pap. 6.95 (978-0-516-26973-3(9)); 2002. 47p. pap. 25.00 (978-0-516-22500-5(6)) Scholastic Library Publishing. (Children's Pr.).

—The Aztec. 2003. (Illus.). 47p. (J). (gr. 4-7). lib. bdg. 15.25 (978-0-613-59447-9(9)) Tandem Library Bks.

Schuman, Michael A. Mayan & Aztec Mythology. Bock, William Sauts, illus. 2001. (Mythology Ser.). 128p. (J). (gr. 6-12). lib. bdg. 26.60 (978-0-7660-1409-1(6)) Enslow Pubs., Inc.

Shuter, Jane. The Aztecs. 2002. (History Opens Windows Ser.). (Illus.). 32p. (J). (gr. 2-4). lib. bdg. 22.79 (978-1-58810-589-9(X)) Heinemann Library.

Shuter, Jane & Taylor, Pat. The Aztecs, Set 2. 2002. (History Opens Windows Ser.). (Illus.). 32p. (J). (gr. 2-4). pap. 7.50 (978-1-4034-0024-6(5) , 91609) Heinemann Library.

Smalley, Roger. The Aztecs: Rise & Fall of a Great Empire. 2003. (High Five Reading (Red Level) Ser.). (Illus.). (J). 64p. lib. bdg. 22.60 (978-0-7368-2785-0(4)); 48p. pap. 15.93 (978-0-7368-2828-4(1)) Capstone Pr., Inc.

—The Aztecs: Rise & Fall of a Great Empire, 6 vols. (gr. 4 up). 49.95 (978-0-7368-2838-3(9) , High Five) Red Brick Learning.

Sonneborn, Liz. The Ancient Aztecs. 2005. (People of the Ancient World Ser.). (Illus.). 112p. (gr. 6-8). (YA). pap. 9.95 (978-0-531-16844-8(1)); 30.50 (978-0-531-12362-1(6)) Scholastic Library Publishing. (Watts, Franklin).

Steedman, Scott. Aztec News: Invaders Flee City. 2000. (gr. 5-8). lib. bdg. 15.30 (978-0-613-74678-6(3)) Tandem Library Bks.

Steele, Philip. The Aztec News. 2001. (History News Ser.). (Illus.). 32p. (J). (gr. 3 up). lib. bdg. 24.67 (978-0-8368-2777-4(5)) Stevens, Gareth Inc.

—The Aztec News. 2000. (News Ser.). (J). (978-0-606-19308-5(1)) Tandem Library Bks.

Steele, Philip & MacDonald, Fiona. Sungods & Sacrifice: Lost World of the Aztecs, Incas & Maya. 2004. (Illus.). 128p. pap. 17.99 (978-1-84476-005-3(7) , Southwater) Anness Publishing GBR. *Dist:* National Bk. Network.

Stout, Mary A. Aztec. 2003. (Native American Peoples Ser.). (Illus.). 32p. (J). (gr. 4 up). lib. bdg. 24.67 (978-0-8368-3699-8(5)) Stevens, Gareth Inc.

Tanaka, Shelley. The Lost Temple of the Aztecs: What It Was When the Spaniards Invaded Mexico. 2001. (I Was There Bk.). (Illus.). (J). (978-0-606-20773-7(2)) Tandem Library Bks.

Tenochtitlan. 2002. (Illus.). 112p. (J). 30.00 (978-0-7910-6681-2(9) , Chelsea Hse.) Facts On File, Inc.

Thomson, Ruth. The Aztecs. (Illus.). 32p. (YA). (gr. 3 up). lib. bdg. 27.10 (978-1-932889-09-3(4)) Sea-To-Sea Pubns.

Top That Publishing Staff, ed. Aztec Madness. 2004. (Wicked Tattoos Ser.). (Illus.). 16p. (J). pap. (978-1-84510-109-1(X)) Top That! Publishing PLC.

Trumbauer, Lisa. The Aztec World. 2005. 39.00 ***(978-1-4108-4618-1(0))*** Benchmark Education Co.

Tucker, Mary. Mayans & Aztecs. Mitchell, Judy, ed. Mohrman, Gary, illus. 2002. (Exploring Ancient Civilizations Ser.). 48p. (J). (gr. 3-6). pap. 7.95 (978-1-57310-355-8(1)) Teaching & Learning Co.

Wood, Marion & Mitchell, Peter. Ancient Aztec & Mayan Civilizations. 3rd rev. ed. 2007. (Cultural Atlas for Young People Ser.). (Illus.). 96p. (YA). (gr. 5-8). 35.00 ***(978-0-8160-6820-3(8)*** , Chelsea Hse.) Facts On File, Inc.

Wyborny, Sheila. Life During the Aztec Empire. 2003. (Life During the Great Civilizations Ser.). (Illus.). 48p. (J). (gr. 3-5). 24.95 (978-1-56711-736-3(8) , Blackbirch Pr., Inc.) Thomson Gale.

INDIANS OF MEXICO—AZTECS—FICTION

Burnett, Eric. Trapped in Tenochtitlan: An Aztec Adventure. 2002. 113p. pap. 9.95 (978-0-595-22161-5(0) , Writers Club Pr.) iUniverse, Inc.

Grimm, Jacob W. & Grimm, Wilhelm K. The Fisherman & the Turtle. Avilel[81]s Junco, Martha, illus. 2008. (J). ***(978-0-7614-5387-1(3))*** Cavendish, Marshall Corp.

INDIANS OF MEXICO—FICTION

Aimard, Gustave. The Indian Scout: a Story of the Aster City. 2006. (ENG.). 464p. per. 37.95 ***(978-1-4286-1776-6(0))*** Kessinger Publishing, LLC.

Bernard, Virginia. Eliza & the Sacred Mountain. 2000. (Going to Ser.). (Illus.). 121p. (J). (gr. 4-8). pap. 6.95 (978-1-893577-05-3(8)) Four Corners Publishing Co., Inc.

Harper, Jo. Delfino's Journey. 2000. viii, 184p. (J). (gr. 8-12). 15.95 (978-0-89672-437-2(9)) Texas Tech Univ. Pr.

—Delfino's Journey, Grades 8-12. 2000. (Illus.). viii, 184p. (J). tchr. ed. 5.95 (978-0-89672-442-6(5)) Texas Tech Univ. Pr.

Harper, Josephin & Harper, Jo. Teresa's Journey. 2006. 192p. (YA). pap. 17.95 (978-0-89672-591-1(X)) Texas Tech Univ. Pr.

Kline, Trish. I Am Called Calpulli. 2001. (Illus.). 112p. (J). (gr. 4-7). 15.95 (978-0-8234-1570-0(8)) Holiday Hse., Inc.

Montgomery, R. A. Mystery of the Maya. 2006. (Choose Your Own Adventure Ser.: No. 5). (Illus.). 144p. (J). (gr. 4-7). mass mkt. 5.99 (978-1-933390-05-5(0) , CHCL05) Chooseco LLC.

Race to Moonrise Rev. 2006. 9.95 (978-1-932738-31-5(2)) Western Reflections Publishing Co.

Ramirez, Antonio. Napí. Domi, illus. 2004. 32p. (J). 15.95 (978-0-88899-610-7(1)) Groundwood Bks. CAN. *Dist:* Perseus Distribution.

Ramirez, Antonio & Domi. Napí. 2004. (SPA., Illus.). 32p. (J). 15.95 (978-0-88899-611-4(X)) Groundwood Bks. CAN. *Dist:* Perseus Distribution.

Scieszka, Jon. Me Oh Maya. McCauley, Adam, illus. (Time Warp Trio Ser.: No. 13). (J). 2005. 96p. pap. 4.99 (978-0-14-240300-6(8) , Puffin); 2003. 80p. (gr. 2-6). 14.99 (978-0-670-03629-5(3) , Viking Juvenile) Penguin Group (USA) Inc.

INDIANS OF MEXICO—LEGENDS

Dalal, Anita. Myths of Pre-Columbian America. 2001. (Mythic World Ser.). (Illus.). 48p. (J). lib. bdg. 27.12 (978-0-7398-3193-9(3)) Raintree.

Johnston, Tony. The Tale of Rabbit & Coyote. DePaola, Tomie, illus. 1998. 32p. (J). (ps-ps). pap. 6.99 (978-0-698-11630-6(5) , Putnam Juvenile) Penguin Group (USA) Inc.

—The Tale of Rabbit & Coyote. de Paola, Tomie, illus. 1998. (978-0-606-13834-5(X)) Tandem Library Bks.

Petersen, Patricia. Voladores. Petersen, Sheli, illus. 2002. (Legends of the Americas Ser.). 32p. (J). (gr. k-7). 18.95 (978-1-57768-972-0(0) , Bedrick, Peter Bks.) School Specialty Publishing.

Unger, David, tr. Popol Vuh: A Sacred Book of the Maya. Garay, Luis, illus. 1999. 88p. (J). (gr. 2-7). 19.95 (978-0-88899-334-2(X)) Groundwood Bks. CAN. *Dist:* Perseus Distribution.

INDIANS OF MEXICO—MAYAS

Ackroyd, Peter. Cities of Blood. 2005. (Voyages through Time Ser.). (Illus.). 144p. (J). (gr. 4-7). pap. 9.99 (978-0-7566-1367-9(1)) Dorling Kindersley Publishing, Inc.

Andrade, Mary J. Day of the Dead in Mexico-Yucatan: Through the Eyes of the Soul. Andrade, Mary J., ed. 2003. (Through the Eyes of the Soul, Day of the Dead in Mexico Ser.: Vol. 5). (SPA & ENG., Illus.). 110p. 26.95 (978-0-9665876-6-1(9)) La Oferta Publishing Co.

Armentrout, David & Armentrout, Patricia. Treasures from Mexico. 2000. (Treasures from the Past Ser.). (Illus.). 48p. (J). (gr. 4-8). lib. bdg. 29.93 (978-1-55916-290-6(2)) Rourke Publishing, LLC.

Baquedano, Elizabeth & Buller, Laura. Aztec, Inca, & Maya. 2005. (Dk eyewitness Bks.). (Illus.). 72p. (J). lib. bdg. 19.99 (978-0-7566-1392-1(2)) Dorling Kindersley Publishing, Inc.

Baquedano, Elizabeth & Clarke, Barry. Aztec, Inca, & Maya. Zabe, Michel, photos by. 2005. (Dk eyewitness Bks.). (Illus.). 72p. (J). (gr. 4-7). 15.99 (978-0-7566-1383-9(3)) Dorling Kindersley Publishing, Inc.

Bell-Rehwoldt, Sheri. Amazing Maya Inventions You Can Build Yourself. 2007. (Build It Yourself Ser.). (Illus.). 128p. (J). pap. 14.95 (978-0-9771294-6-1(2)) Nomad Pr.

Benchmark Education Staff. The Maya World. 2005. 2.00 ***(978-1-4108-4680-8(6))*** Benchmark Education Co.

Braman, Arlette N. Secrets of Ancient Cultures: The Maya-Activities & Crafts from a Mysterious Land. Nidenoff, Michele, illus. 2003. 118p. pap. 12.95 (978-0-471-21981-1(9) , Wiley) Wiley, John & Sons, Inc.

Brannon, Barbara. Discover the Maya. 2005. 39.00 ***(978-1-4108-5149-9(4))*** Benchmark Education Co.

Chrisp, Peter. Look into the Past Maya. 1999. (J). (gr. 4-7). 22.83 (978-0-7398-1410-9(9)) Raintree.

Conklin, Wendy. Mayas, Aztecs, Incas: All-in-One Resource with Background Information, Map Activities, Simulations & Games, & a Read-Aloud Play to Support Comprehension & Critical Thinking in Social Studies. 2006. 80p. pap. 12.99 (978-0-439-53994-4(3) , Teaching Resources) Scholastic, Inc.

Coulter, Lavrie. Secrets in Stone: All about Maya Hieroglyphs. English, Sarah Jane, illus. 2003. 48p. (gr. 4-8). 18.00 (978-0-7567-9000-4(X)) DIANE Publishing Co.

Crandell, Rachel. Hands of the Maya: Villagers at Work & Play. rev. ed. 2002. (Illus.). 32p. (J). (gr. k-4). 16.95 (978-0-8050-6687-6(X) , Holt, Henry & Co. Bks. For Young Readers) Holt, Henry & Co.

Dalal, Anita. Myths of Pre-Columbian America. 2001. (Mythic World Ser.). (Illus.). 48p. (J). lib. bdg. 27.12 (978-0-7398-3193-9(3)) Raintree.

Day, Nancy. Your Travel Guide to the Ancient Mayan Civilization. 2005. (Passport to History Ser.). (Illus.). 96p. (gr. 5-8). lib. bdg. 26.50 (978-0-8225-3077-0(5)) Lerner Publishing Group.

Deedrick, Tami. Maya. Sloan, Frank, ed. 2001. (Ancient Civilizations Ser.). (Illus.). 48p. (J). (gr. 4-6). lib. bdg. 22.83 (978-0-7398-3585-2(8)) Raintree.

—The Maya. 2000. (Ancient Civilizations Ser.). (Illus.). (J). pap. (978-0-7398-4146-4(7)) Steck-Vaughn.

Dworkin, Mark J. Mayas, Aztecs & Incas: Mysteries of Ancient Civilizations of Central & South America. 1999. (Illus.). 144p. (J). (gr. 10-12). reprint ed. pap. 17.00 (978-0-7881-6589-4(5)) DIANE Publishing Co.

Eboch, Chris. Life among the Maya. 2005. (Way People Live Ser.). (Illus.). 112p. (YA). (gr. 7-10). lib. bdg. 29.95 (978-1-59018-162-1(X) , Lucent Bks.) Thomson Gale.

Englar, Mary. The Mayas. 2004. (J). (978-0-7368-2695-2(5)) Capstone Pr., Inc.

Ganeri, Anita. The Ancient Maya. 2005. (Ancient Civilizations Ser.). (Illus.). 32p. (J). (gr. 4-6). 26.60 (978-0-7565-1677-2(3)) Compass Point Bks.

George, Linda. Maya. 2003. (Life During the Great Civilizations Ser.). (Illus.). 48p. (J). (gr. 3-5). 24.95 (978-1-56711-738-7(4) , Blackbirch Pr., Inc.) Thomson Gale.

Grant, Neil. Everyday Life of the Aztecs, Incas & Mayans. Cappon, Manuela et al, illus. 2003. (Uncovering History Ser.). 46p. (J). lib. bdg. 28.50 (978-1-58340-253-5(5)) Smart Apple Media.

Hoffman, Mary Ann. The History of the Maya: Using Computational Skills in Problem Solving. 2005. (Powermath Ser.). (Illus.). 32p. (J). 22.50 (978-1-4042-5149-6(6)); (978-1-4042-5149-6(9)); pap. (978-1-4042-5148-9(0)) Rosen Publishing Group, Inc., The. (PowerKids Pr.).

Keller, Mary Jo, et al. Inca, Aztec, Maya: Arts, Crafts, Cooking, & Historical Aids. Lorseyedi, Barbara, illus. 1999. (Hands-On Heritage Ser.). 48p. (J). (gr. 2-6). pap., act. bk. ed. 6.95 (978-1-56472-150-1(7) , EP150) Edupress, Inc.

Kirkpatrick, Naida. The Maya. 2003. (Understanding People in the Past Ser.: Set. 3). (J). pap. 8.95 (978-1-4034-0606-4(5)); (Illus.). 64p. pap. 28.50 (978-1-4034-0386-5(4)) Heinemann Library.

Kops, Deborah. Palenque. 2008. (J). lib. bdg. (***978-0-8225-7504-7(3)***) Twenty First Century Bks.

Lechner, Judith. The Maya. 2005. (Navigators Ser.). (J). pap. 42.00 (***978-1-4108-5101-7(X)***) Benchmark Education Co.

Levchuck, Caroline M. Kids in the Time of the Maya. 1999. (Kids Throughout History Ser.). (Illus.). 24p. (J). (gr. 3). lib. bdg. 18.75 (978-0-8239-5258-8(4) , PowerKids Pr.) Rosen Publishing Group, Inc., The.

Linares, Frederico Navarrete. A Maya. Dulin, Laura, tr. Sachez de Tagle, Andres, illus. 2000. (Day with Ser.). 48p. (J). (gr. 5-7). lib. bdg. 22.60 (978-0-8225-1922-5(4)) Lerner Publishing Group.

Lourie, Peter. The Mystery of the Maya: Uncovering the Lost City of Palenque. 2004. (Exploration Ser.). (Illus.). 48p. (YA). (gr. 4-6). pap. 11.95 (978-1-59078-265-1(8)) Boyds Mills Pr.

—The Mystery of the Maya: Uncovering the Lost City of Palenque. Lourie, Peter, photos by. 2003. (Illus.). 48p. (J). (gr. 4-6). 19.95 (978-1-56397-839-5(3)) Boyds Mills Pr.

Macdonald, F. Step into the Aztec & Maya Worlds. 2007. (Illus.). 64p. pap. 10.99 (***978-1-84476-420-4(6)*** , Southwater) Anness Publishing GBR. *Dist:* National Bk. Network.

Matthews, Rupert. You Wouldn't Want to Be a Mayan Soothsayer! Fortunes You'd Rather Not Tell. Antram, David, illus. 2007. (You Wouldn't Want to...: Ancient Civilization Ser.). 32p. (J). 29.00 (***978-0-531-18746-3(2));*** (gr. 2-5). pap. 9.95 (***978-0-531-13925-7(5))*** Scholastic Library Publishing. (Watts, Franklin).

Menchu, Rigoberta. The Girl from Chimel. Unger, David, tr. from SPA. Domi, illus. 2005. 56p. (J). (ps-7). 18.95 (978-0-88899-666-4(7)) Groundwood Bks. CAN. *Dist:* Perseus Distribution.

Montejo, Victor. Popol Vuj: Libro Sagrado de los Mayas. Unger, David, tr. Garay, Luis, illus. 1999. (SPA.). 96p. (J). (gr. 4-7). pap. 12.95 (978-0-88899-362-5(5) , GRO6252, Libros Tigrillo) Groundwood Bks. CAN. *Dist:* Lectorum Pubns., Inc., Perseus Distribution.

Morris, Ting & Young, E. Aztecs & Maya. 2006. (Illus.). 32p. (J). (978-1-58340-915-2(7) , 1262694) Smart Apple Media.

Naden, Corinne J. & Blue, Rose. Ancient Maya & Tikal. 2003. (J). pap. (978-1-58417-319-9(X)); lib. bdg. (978-1-58417-318-2(1)) Lake Street Pubs.

Nicholson, Sue. Aztecs & Incas: A Guide to the Pre-Colonized Americas in 1504. 2000. (Sightseers Ser.). (Illus.). 32p. (J). (gr. 3-5). tchr. ed. 8.95 (978-0-7534-5236-3(7) , Kingfisher) Houghton Mifflin Co. Trade & Reference Div.

Orr, Tamra. The Maya. 2005. (Watts Library). (Illus.). 64p. (J). (gr. 5-7). 25.50 (978-0-531-12296-9(4) , Watts, Franklin) Scholastic Library Publishing.

Parramon Staff. Mayas. 2006. (SPA.). 32p. (J). (gr. 6-8). 10.40 (978-84-342-2738-5(X) , PR33933) Parramon Ediciones S.A. ESP. *Dist:* Lectorum Pubns., Inc.

Perl, Lila. The Ancient Maya. 2005. (People of the Ancient World Ser.). (Illus.). 112p. (J). (gr. 6-8). pap. 9.95 (978-0-531-16848-6(4)); 30.50 (978-0-531-12381-2(2)) Scholastic Library Publishing. (Watts, Franklin).

Petra Press Staff. The Maya. 2001. (First Reports). (Illus.). 48p. (J). (gr. 3 up). lib. bdg. 22.60 (978-0-7565-0081-8(8)) Compass Point Bks.

Schuman, Michael A. Mayan & Aztec Mythology. Bock, William Sauts, illus. 2001. (Mythology Ser.). 128p. (J). (gr. 6-12). lib. bdg. 26.60 (978-0-7660-1409-1(6)) Enslow Pubs., Inc.

Shuter, Jane. The Maya. 2002. (History Opens Windows Ser.). (Illus.). 32p. (J). (gr. 2-4). lib. bdg. 22.79 (978-1-58810-591-2(1)) Heinemann Library.

Solbiati, Romano. Mayan Tikal. Ripamonti, Aldo, illus. 2001. (Journey to the Past Ser.). 56p. (J). (gr. 6-8). lib. bdg. 27.12 (978-0-7398-1955-5(0)) Raintree.

Steele, Philip & MacDonald, Fiona. Sungods & Sacrifice: Lost World of the Aztecs, Incas & Maya. 2004. (Illus.). 128p. pap. 17.99 (978-1-84476-005-3(7) , Southwater) Anness Publishing GBR. *Dist:* National Bk. Network.

Swisher, Clarice. Mayan Civilization. 2003. (Understanding Great Literature Ser.). (Illus.). 128p. (J). 29.95 (978-1-56006-782-5(9) , Lucent Bks.) Thomson Gale.

Takacs, Stefanie. The Maya. 2003. (True Book Ser.). (Illus.). 48p. (J). 25.00 (978-0-516-22778-8(5) , Children's Pr.) Scholastic Library Publishing.

Trumbauer, Lisa. The Maya World. 2005. 42.00 (***978-1-4108-4632-7(6))*** Benchmark Education Co.

Unger, David, tr. Popol Vuh: A Sacred Book of the Maya. Garay, Luis, illus. 1999. 88p. (J). (gr. 2-7). 19.95 (978-0-88899-334-2(X)) Groundwood Bks. CAN. *Dist:* Perseus Distribution.

Wagner, Heather Lehr. Rigoberta Menchu Tum: Activist for Indigenous Rights in Guatemala. 2007. (Modern Peacemakers Ser.). (Illus.). 120p. (J). (gr. 9 up). 30.00 (***978-0-7910-8998-9(3)*** , Chelsea Hse.) Facts On File, Inc.

Where Did the Maya Go? Individual Title Six-Packs. (Action Packs Ser.). 104p. (gr. 3-5). 44.00 (978-0-7635-8416-0(9)) Rigby Education.

Wood, Marion & Mitchell, Peter. Ancient Aztec & Mayan Civilizations. 3rd rev. ed. 2007. (Cultural Atlas for Young People Ser.). (Illus.). 96p. (YA). (gr. 5-8). 35.00 (***978-0-8160-6820-3(8)*** , Chelsea Hse.) Facts On File, Inc.

INDIANS OF MEXICO—MAYAS—ANTIQUITIES

Swisher, Clarice. Mayan Civilization. 2002. (World History Ser.). (Illus.). 112p. (YA). (gr. 8-11). 32.45 (978-1-56006-806-8(X) , LML00902-178138, Lucent Bks.) Thomson Gale.

INDIANS OF MEXICO—MAYAS—FICTION

Buja, John E. & Morrison, Melody. Ballcourt of Death: Novel. 2000. (Illus.). 128p. (J). (gr. 7-12). pap. (978-1-894303-23-1(7)) Raven Rock Publishing.

Eboch, Chris. The Well of Sacrifice. Barnard, Bryn, illus. 1999. 240p. (J). (gr. 5-9). tchr. ed. 16.00 (978-0-395-90374-2(2) , Clarion Bks.) Houghton Mifflin Co. Trade & Reference Div.

Greene, Michele Dominguez. Chasing the Jaguar. 2008. 240p. (J). pap. 7.99 (***978-0-06-076355-8(8)*** , Rayo) HarperCollins Pubs.

Mayan Pyramid Mystery. 2001. (Illus.). 10p. (J). 12.99 (978-0-307-10617-9(9) , 10617, Golden Bks.) Random Hse. Children's Bks.

Montejo, Victor. White Flower: A Maya Princess. Yockteng, Rafael, illus. 2005. 36p. (J). (gr. 1). 16.95 (978-0-88899-599-5(7)) Groundwood Bks. CAN. *Dist:* Perseus Distribution.

Thompson, Susan, et al. Mayan Folktales: Cuentos Folkloricos Mayas. 2007. (World Folklore Ser.). (SPA & ENG.). 236p. 35.00 (***978-1-59158-138-3(9)*** , LU1389) Libraries Unlimited, Inc.

Unger, David, tr. Popol Vuj: Libro Sagrado de los Maya. Garay, Luis, illus. 1999. (SPA.). 88p. (J). (gr. 4-7). 19.95 (978-0-88899-344-1(7) , GRO1579) Groundwood Bks. CAN. *Dist:* Lectorum Pubns., Inc., Perseus Distribution.

INDIANS OF NORTH AMERICA

see also Cliff Dwellers and Cliff Dwellings; Indians of North America—Canada; Mounds and Mound Builders

Adare, Sierra. Ojibwe. 2003. (Native American Peoples Ser.). (Illus.). 32p. (J). (gr. 4 up). lib. bdg. 24.67 (978-0-8368-3667-7(7)) Stevens, Gareth Inc.

African American & American Indian Relations. 2000. (My Ancestors—My Heroes Ser.: Vol. 50). (J). (gr. 3-4). (978-1-893091-49-8(X)) Parker Publishing Co.

Alfrey, Eunice, et al. The Turtle Who Went to War: And Other Sioux Stories. 2003. (Indian Reading Ser.). (Illus.). 48p. pap. 9.95 (978-0-917298-95-0(0)) Montana Historical Society Pr.

Alvarez, Juan. Chocolate, Chipmunks, & Canoes: An American Indian Words Coloring Book. Alvarez, Juan, illus. 2004. (Illus.). 32p. (ps-3). pap. 3.95 (978-1-878610-03-4(1)) Red Crane Bks., Inc.

American Indian Nations. (Social Studies Collections). (Illus.). (J). (gr. 3-4). lib. bdg. 382.88 (978-0-7368-2341-8(7)) Capstone Pr., Inc.

American Indian Nations, 12 bks. Incl. Apache : Nomadic Hunters of the Southwest. Englar, Mary. 2003. lib. bdg. 22.60 (978-0-7368-1563-5(5)); Arapaho : Hunters of the Great Plains. Gibson, Karen Bush. 2003. lib. bdg. 22.60 (978-0-7368-1564-2(3)); Blackfeet : People of the Dark Moccasins. Gibson, Karen Bush. 2003. lib. bdg. 22.60 (978-0-7368-1565-9(1)); Cherokee : An Independent Nation. Todd, Anne M. 2002. lib. bdg. 22.60 (978-0-7368-1355-6(1)); Creek : Farmers of the Southeast. Boraas, Tracey. 2003. lib. bdg. 22.60 (978-0-7368-1566-6(X)); Iroquois : The Six Nations Confederacy. Englar, Mary. 2002. lib. bdg. 22.60 (978-0-7368-1353-2(5)); Ojibwa : People of the Great Lakes. Todd, Anne M. 2002. lib. bdg. 22.60 (978-0-7368-1356-3(X)); Powhatan : A Confederacy of Native American Tribes. Boraas, Tracey. 2003. lib. bdg. 22.60 (978-0-7368-1567-3(8)); Pueblo : Farmers of the Southwest. Englar, Mary. 2002. lib. bdg. 22.60 (978-0-7368-1357-0(8)); Seminole : The First People in Florida. Englar, Mary. 2002. lib. bdg. 22.60 (978-0-7368-1358-7(6)); Sioux : People of the Great Plains. Todd, Anne M. 2002. lib. bdg. 22.60 (978-0-7368-1354-9(3)); Wampanoag : The People of the First Light. Riehecky, Janet. 2003. lib. bdg. 22.60 (978-0-7368-1568-0(6)); 48p. (J). (gr. 3-4). (Illus.). Set lib. bdg. 271.20 (978-0-7368-1602-1(X) , Bridgestone Bks.) Capstone Pr., Inc.

American Indians. (J). (ps 12). 2.95 (978-0-936672-83-0(8)) Aerial Photography Services, Inc.

Anderson, Madelyn Klein. The Omaha. 2000. (Watts Library). (Illus.). 64p. (gr. 5-7). (YA). pap. 8.95 (978-0-531-16481-5(0)); (J). 25.50 (978-0-531-20404-7(9)) Scholastic Library Publishing. (Watts, Franklin).

—Omaha. 2000. (gr. 5-8). lib. bdg. 17.60 (978-0-613-37484-2(3)) Tandem Library Bks.

Ansary, Mir Tamim. California Indians. (Native Americans Ser.). (Illus.). 32p. (J). 2002. (gr. 1-4). pap. 7.50 (978-1-58810-349-9(8) , 91109); 2000. (gr. 2-4). lib. bdg. 21.36 (978-1-57572-927-5(X)) Heinemann Library.

—California Indians. 2001. (gr. k-3). lib. bdg. 15.90 (978-0-613-87923-1(6)); (Illus.). (J). 14.30 (978-0-606-21983-9(8)) Tandem Library Bks.

—Eastern Woodlands Indians. (Native Americans Ser.). (Illus.). 32p. (J). 2002. (gr. 1-4). pap. 7.50 (978-1-58810-451-9(6) , 91170); 2000. (gr. 2-4). lib. bdg. 21.36 (978-1-57572-930-5(X)) Heinemann Library.

—Eastern Woodlands Indians. 2001. (Native Americans Ser.). (Illus.). (J). 13.75 (978-0-606-21991-4(9)) Tandem Library Bks.

—Great Basin Indians. (Native Americans Ser.). (Illus.). 32p. (J). 2002. (gr. 1-4). pap. 7.50 (978-1-58810-452-6(4) , 91171); 1999. (gr. 2-4). lib. bdg. 21.36 (978-1-57572-922-0(9)) Heinemann Library.

—Great Basin Indians. 2001. (gr. k-3). lib. bdg. 15.90 (978-0-613-84256-3(1)); (Illus.). (J). 13.75 (978-0-606-21998-3(6)) Tandem Library Bks.

—Northwest Coast Indians. 2002. (Native Americans Ser.). (Illus.). 32p. (J). (gr. 1-4). pap. 7.50 (978-1-58810-350-5(1) , 91110) Heinemann Library.

—Northwest Coast Indians. 2001. (Native Americans Ser.). (Illus.). (J). (978-0-606-22012-5(7)) Tandem Library Bks.

—Plains Indians. (Native Americans Ser.). (Illus.). 32p. (J). 2002. (gr. 1-4). pap. 7.50 (978-1-58810-351-2(X) , 91111); 2000. (gr. 2-4). lib. bdg. 21.36 (978-1-57572-929-9(6)) Heinemann Library.

—Plains Indians. 2001. (Native Americans Ser.). (Illus.). (J). (978-0-606-22015-6(1)) Tandem Library Bks.

—Plateau Indians. (Native Americans Ser.). (Illus.). 32p. (J). 2002. (gr. 1-4). pap. 7.50 (978-1-58810-453-3(2) , 91172); 2000. (gr. 2-4). lib. bdg. 21.36 (978-1-57572-928-2(8)) Heinemann Library.

—Southeast Indians. (Native Americans Ser.). (Illus.). 32p. (J). 2002. (gr. 1-4). pap. 7.50 (978-1-58810-454-0(0) , 91173); 1999. (gr. 2-4). lib. bdg. 21.36 (978-1-57572-924-4(5)) Heinemann Library.

—Southeast Indians. 2001. (gr. k-3). lib. bdg. 15.90 (978-0-613-89425-8(1)); (Illus.). (J). (978-0-606-22021-7(6)) Tandem Library Bks.

—Southwest Indians. (Native Americans Ser.). (Illus.). 32p. (J). 2002. (gr. 1-4). pap. 7.50 (978-1-58810-352-9(8) , 91112); 1999. (gr. 2-4). lib. bdg. 21.36 (978-1-57572-923-7(7)) Heinemann Library.

—Southwest Indians. 2001. (Native Americans Ser.). (Illus.). (J). (978-0-606-22022-4(4)) Tandem Library Bks.

Ansary, Mir Tamim, contrib. by. Northwest Coast Indians. 1999. (Native Americans Ser.). (Illus.). 32p. (J). (gr. 2-4). lib. bdg. 21.36 (978-1-57572-921-3(0)) Heinemann Library.

Arenstam, Peter, et al. Mayflower 1620: A New Look at a Pilgrim Voyage. Brimberg, Sisse & Coulson, Cotton, illus. Brimberg, Sisse & Coulson, Cotton, photos by. 2003. 48p. (J). (gr. 3-7). 17.95 (978-0-7922-6142-1(9) , National Geographic Children's Bks.) National Geographic Society.

Austin and Company Inc. Staff. The Courage of Sarah Noble Literature. 2000. (Illus.). 48p. (J). (gr. k-3). pap., tchr. ed. 7.99 (978-1-57690-642-2(6) , TCA2642) Teacher Created Materials, Inc.

Aykroyd, Clarissa. Native American Horsemanship. 2002. (Native American Life Ser.). (Illus.). 64p. (J). (gr. 5 up). lib. bdg. (978-1-59084-121-1(2)) Mason Crest Pubs.

Baquedano, Elizabeth. Aztecas, Incas y Mayas. 2004. (DK Guides Ser.). 64p. (J). lib. bdg. 19.99 (978-0-7566-0411-0(7)) Dorling Kindersley Publishing, Inc.

Bedry, Christa. The Pueblo. 2004. (American Indian Art & Culture Ser.). (Illus.). 32p. (J). (gr. 3-5). 25.50 (978-0-7910-7964-5(3) , Chelsea Hse.) Facts On File, Inc.

Benchmark Education Staff, compiled by. Native AMER. 2006. spiral bd. 119.00 (***978-1-4108-7112-1(6)***) Benchmark Education Co.

Bial, Raymond. The Blackfeet. 2002. (Lifeways Ser.). (Illus.). 128p. (J). 34.21 (978-0-7614-1416-2(9) , Benchmark Bks.) Cavendish, Marshall Corp.

—Lifeways, 4 bks., Group 7. Incl. Cree. 128p. (978-0-7614-1902-0(0)); Crow. 124p. (978-0-7614-1901-3(2)); Menominee. 127p. (978-0-7614-1903-7(9)); (Illus.). (J). 2005. 2005. (978-0-7614-1900-6(4) , Benchmark Bks.) Cavendish, Marshall Corp.

—Lifeways - Group 1, 4 bks., Set. Incl. Cherokee. lib. bdg. 34.21 (978-0-7614-0801-7(0)); Iroquois. lib. bdg. 34.21 (978-0-7614-0802-4(9)); Navajo. lib. bdg. 34.21 (978-0-7614-0803-1(7)); Sioux. lib. bdg. 34.21 (978-0-7614-0804-8(5)); 128p. (J). (gr. 5-9). 1998. (Illus.). 1999. Set lib. bdg. 136.86 (978-0-7614-0800-0(2) , Benchmark Bks.) Cavendish, Marshall Corp.

—The Long Walk: The Story of Navajo Captivity. 2002. (Great Journeys Ser.). (Illus.). 94p. (J). 32.79 (978-0-7614-1322-6(7) , Benchmark Bks.) Cavendish, Marshall Corp.

—The Mandan. 2002. (Lifeways Ser.). (Illus.). 126p. (J). 34.21 (978-0-7614-1415-5(0) , Benchmark Bks.) Cavendish, Marshall Corp.

—The Ojibwe. 1999. (Lifeways Ser.). (Illus.). 128p. (J). (gr. 5-9). lib. bdg. 34.21 (978-0-7614-0863-5(0) , Benchmark Bks.) Cavendish, Marshall Corp.

—The Shoshone. 2001. (Lifeways Ser.). (Illus.). 128p. (J). (gr. 5-9). lib. bdg. 34.21 (978-0-7614-1211-3(5) , Benchmark Bks.) Cavendish, Marshall Corp.

Binns, Tristan Boyer. Mission San Juan Capistrano. 2002. (Visiting the Past Ser.). (Illus.). 32p. (J). (gr. 5-7). pap. 6.95 (978-1-58810-410-6(9) , 91183) Heinemann Library.

—San Juan Capistrano. 2001. (Visiting the Past Ser.). (Illus.). 32p. (J). (gr. 5-7). lib. bdg. 24.22 (978-1-58810-272-0(6)) Heinemann Library.

—St. Augustine. (Visiting the Past Ser.). (Illus.). 32p. (J). (gr. 5-7). 2002. pap. 6.95 (978-1-58810-411-3(7) , 91184); 2001. lib. bdg. 24.22 (978-1-58810-273-7(4)) Heinemann Library.

Bishop, Amanda & Kalman, Bobbie. Life of the Navajo. 2003. (Native Nations of North America Ser.). (Illus.). 32p. (J). (gr. 5). pap. (978-0-7787-0468-3(8)); lib. bdg. (978-0-7787-0376-1(2)) Crabtree Publishing Co.

—Nations of the Northwest Coast. 2003. (Native Nations of North America Ser.). (Illus.). 32p. (J). (gr. 5). (978-0-7787-0378-5(9)) Crabtree Publishing Co.

Boraas, Tracey. The Creek: Farmers of the Southeast. 2003. (American Indian Nations Ser.). (Illus.). 48p. (J). (gr. 3-4). lib. bdg. 22.60 (978-0-7368-1566-6(X) , Bridgestone Bks.) Capstone Pr., Inc.

—The Powhatan: A Confederacy of Native American Tribes. 2003. (American Indian Nations Ser.). (Illus.). 48p. (J). (gr. 3-4). lib. bdg. 22.60 (978-0-7368-1567-3(8) , Bridgestone Bks.) Capstone Pr., Inc.

Boule, Mary Null. Native Americans of North America: Basin Region: Northern Paiute. Harding, Virginia, ed. Liddell, Daniel & Basta, Mary, illus. 1999. 64p. (gr. 3-6). 7.95 (978-1-877599-55-2(7)) Merryant Pubs.

Bowen, Richard. The Native Americans. 2002. (Welcome to America Ser.). (Illus.). 64p. (J). (gr. 5 up). lib. bdg. (978-1-59084-115-0(8)) Mason Crest Pubs.

Brody, J. J. A Mimbres. Bacchin, Giorgio, illus. adapted ed. 1999. (Day with Ser.). 48p. (J). (gr. 5-7). lib. bdg. (978-0-8225-1917-1(8)) Lerner Publishing Group.

Brown, Robin C. The Crafts of Florida's First People. 2003. (Illus.). 64p. (J). pap. 9.95 (978-1-56164-282-3(7)) Pineapple Pr., Inc.

Bruchac, Joseph. Many Nations. Goetzl, Robert F., illus. 2004. 32p. (J). pap. 5.99 (978-0-439-63590-5(X)) Scholastic, Inc.

—Many Nations: An Alphabet of Native America. Goetzl, Robert F., illus. 2004. 32p. (J). (ps-ps). lib. bdg. 12.79 (978-0-606-30986-8(1)) Tandem Library Bks.

Buller, Laura. Native Americans: An Inside Look at the Tribes & Traditions. 2003. (Illus.). 96p. (J). (ps-7). lib. bdg. 14.10 (978-0-613-45603-6(3)) Tandem Library Bks.

Carlson, Laurie M. More Than Moccasins: A Kid's Activity Guide to Traditional North American Indian Life. 2003. (Kid's Guide Ser.). (Illus.). 200p. (J). (gr. k-7). pap. 14.95 (978-1-55652-213-0(4)) Chicago Review Pr., Inc.

Carole Marsh. Alabama Indians. 2004. (Alabama Experience Ser.). 36p. (gr. 3-8). 29.95 (978-0-635-02247-9(8)); pap. 7.95 (978-0-635-02246-2(X)) Gallopade International.

—Alaska Indians. 2004. (Alaska Experience Ser.). 36p. (gr. 3-8). pap. 7.95 (978-0-635-02248-6(6)); lib. bdg. 29.95 (978-0-635-02249-3(4)) Gallopade International.

—Arizona Indians. 2004. (Arizona Experience Ser.). lib. bdg. 29.95 (978-0-635-02251-6(6)); 36p. (gr. 3-8). pap. 7.95 (978-0-635-02250-9(8)) Gallopade International.

—Arkansas Indians. 2004. (Arkansas Experience Ser.). lib. bdg. 29.95 (978-0-635-02253-0(2)); 36p. (gr. 3-8). pap. 7.95 (978-0-635-02252-3(4)) Gallopade International.

—Best Book of Native American Biographies. 2004. (Native American Heri Ser.). 32p. (gr. 3-8). pap. 7.95 (978-0-635-02400-8(4)) Gallopade International.

—Big Book of Native American Activities. 2004. (Native American Heri Ser.). 48p. (gr. 2-6). pap. 9.95 (978-0-635-02397-1(0)) Gallopade International.

—California Indians. 2004. (California Experienc Ser.). 36p. (gr. 3-8). 29.95 (978-0-635-02255-4(9)) Gallopade International.

—Celebrating Native American Heritage. 2004. (Native American Heri Ser.). 24p. (gr. 3-8). pap. 5.95 (978-0-635-02399-5(7)) Gallopade International.

—Colorado Indians. 2004. (Colorado Experience Ser.). 36p. (gr. 3-8). 29.95 (978-0-635-02257-8(5)); pap. 7.95 (978-0-635-02256-1(7)) Gallopade International.

—Florida Indians. 2004. (Florida Experience Ser.). lib. bdg. 29.95 (978-0-635-02263-9(X)); 36p. (gr. 3-8). pap. 7.95 (978-0-635-02262-2(1)) Gallopade International.

—Georgia Indians. 2004. (Georgia Experience Ser.). 36p. (gr. 3-8). 29.95 (978-0-635-02265-3(6)); pap. 7.95 (978-0-635-02264-6(8)) Gallopade International.

—Hawaii Indians. 2004. (Hawaii Experience Ser.). 36p. (gr. 3-8). pap. 7.95 (978-0-635-02266-0(4)); lib. bdg. 29.95 (978-0-635-02267-7(2)) Gallopade International.

—Idaho Indians. 2004. (Idaho Experience Ser.). 36p. (gr. 3-8). pap. 7.95 (978-0-635-02268-4(0)); lib. bdg. 29.95 (978-0-635-02269-1(9)) Gallopade International.

—Illinois Indians. 2004. (Illinois Experience Ser.). 36p. (gr. 3-8). 29.95 (978-0-635-02271-4(0)); pap. 7.95 (978-0-635-02270-7(2)) Gallopade International.

—Indiana Indians. 2004. (Indiana Experience Ser.). 36p. (gr. 3-8). 29.95 (978-0-635-02273-8(7)); pap. 7.95 (978-0-635-02272-1(9)) Gallopade International.

—Iowa Indians. 2004. (Iowa Experience Ser.). 36p. (gr. 3-8). pap. 7.95 (978-0-635-02274-5(5)); 29.95 (978-0-635-02275-2(3)) Gallopade International.

—Kansas Indians. 2004. (Kansas Experience Ser.). 36p. (gr. 3-8). 29.95 (978-0-635-02277-6(X)); pap. 7.95 (978-0-635-02276-9(1)) Gallopade International.

—Kentucky Indians. 2004. (Kentucky Experience Ser.). 36p. (gr. 3-8). pap. 7.95 (978-0-635-02278-3(8)); lib. bdg. 29.95 (978-0-635-02279-0(6)) Gallopade International.

—Louisiana Indians. 2004. (Louisiana Experience Ser.). 36p. (gr. 3-8). 29.95 (978-0-635-02281-3(8)); pap. 7.95 (978-0-635-02280-6(X)) Gallopade International.

—Maine Indians. 2004. (Maine Experience Ser.). lib. bdg. 29.95 (978-0-635-02283-7(4)); 36p. (gr. 3-8). pap. 7.95 (978-0-635-02282-0(6)) Gallopade International.

—Maryland Indians. 2004. (Maryland Experience Ser.). lib. bdg. 29.95 (978-0-635-02285-1(0)); 36p. (gr. 3-8). pap. 7.95 (978-0-635-02284-4(2)) Gallopade International.

—Massachusetts Indians. 2004. (Massachusetts Experi Ser.). 36p. (gr. 3-8). 29.95 (978-0-635-02287-5(7)); pap. 7.95 (978-0-635-02286-8(9)) Gallopade International.

—Michigan Indians. 2004. (Michigan Experience Ser.). lib. bdg. 29.95 (978-0-635-02289-9(3)); 36p. (gr. 3-8). pap. 7.95 (978-0-635-02288-2(5)) Gallopade International.

—Minnesota Indians. 2004. (Minnesota Experience Ser.). lib. bdg. 29.95 (978-0-635-02291-2(5)); 36p. (gr. 3-8). pap. 7.95 (978-0-635-02290-5(7)) Gallopade International.

—Mississippi Indians. 2004. (Mississippi Experien Ser.). 36p. (gr. 3-8). pap. 7.95 (978-0-635-02292-9(3)); lib. bdg. 29.95 (978-0-635-02293-6(1)) Gallopade International.

—Missouri Indians. 2004. (Missouri Experience Ser.). 36p. (gr. 3-8). 29.95 (978-0-635-02295-0(8)); pap. 7.95 (978-0-635-02294-3(X)) Gallopade International.

—Montana Indians. 2004. (Montana Experience Ser.). 36p. (gr. 3-8). pap. 7.95 (978-0-635-02296-7(6)); lib. bdg. 29.95 (978-0-635-02297-4(4)) Gallopade International.

—Native American Heritage Coloring Book. 2004. (Native American Heri Ser.). 24p. (gr. k-2). pap. 3.95 (978-0-635-02398-8(9)) Gallopade International.

—Nebraska Indians. 2004. (Nebraska Experience Ser.). 36p. (gr. 3-8). pap. 7.95 (978-0-635-02298-1(2)); lib. bdg. 29.95 (978-0-635-02299-8(0)) Gallopade International.

—Nevada Indians. 2004. (Nevada Experience Ser.). 36p. (gr. 3-8). pap. 7.95 (978-0-635-02300-1(8)); lib. bdg. 29.95 (978-0-635-02301-8(6)) Gallopade International.

—New Hampshire Indians. 2004. (New Hampshire Experi Ser.). lib. bdg. 29.95 (978-0-635-02303-2(2)); 36p. (gr. 3-8). pap. 7.95 (978-0-635-02302-5(4)) Gallopade International.

—New Jersey Indians. 2004. (New Jersey Experienc Ser.). 36p. (gr. 3-8). 29.95 (978-0-635-02305-6(9)); pap. 7.95 (978-0-635-02304-9(0)) Gallopade International.

—New Mexico Indians. 2004. (New Mexico Experienc Ser.). 36p. (gr. 3-8). pap. 7.95 (978-0-635-02306-3(7)); lib. bdg. 29.95 (978-0-635-02307-0(5)) Gallopade International.

—New York Indians. 2004. (New York Experience Ser.). lib. bdg. 29.95 (978-0-635-02309-4(1)); 36p. (gr. 3-8). pap. 7.95 (978-0-635-02308-7(3)) Gallopade International.

—North Carolina Indians. 2004. (North Carolina Exper Ser.). 36p. (gr. 3-8). 29.95 (978-0-635-02311-7(3)); pap. 7.95 (978-0-635-02310-0(5)) Gallopade International.

—North Dakota Indians. 2004. (North Dakota Experie Ser.). 36p. (gr. 3-8). pap. 7.95 (978-0-635-02312-4(1)); lib. bdg. 29.95 (978-0-635-02313-1(X)) Gallopade International.

—Ohio Indians. 2004. (Ohio Experience Ser.). 36p. (gr. 3-8). 29.95 (978-0-635-02315-5(6)); pap. 7.95 (978-0-635-02314-8(8)) Gallopade International.

—Oklahoma Indians. 2004. (Oklahoma Experience Ser.). 36p. (gr. 3-8). 29.95 (978-0-635-02317-9(2)); pap. 7.95 (978-0-635-02316-2(4)) Gallopade International.

—Oregon Indians. 2004. (Oregon Experience Ser.). lib. bdg. 29.95 (978-0-635-02319-3(9)); 36p. (gr. 3-8). pap. 7.95 (978-0-635-02318-6(0)) Gallopade International.

—Pennsylvania Indians. 2004. (Pennsylvania Experie Ser.). 36p. (gr. 3-8). 29.95 (978-0-635-02321-6(0)); pap. 7.95 (978-0-635-02320-9(2)) Gallopade International.

—Rhode Island Indians. 2004. (Rhode Island Experie Ser.). 36p. (gr. 3-8). pap. 7.95 (978-0-635-02322-3(9)); lib. bdg. 29.95 (978-0-635-02323-0(7)) Gallopade International.

—South Carolina Indians. 2004. (South Carolina Exper Ser.). 36p. (gr. 3-8). 29.95 (978-0-635-02325-4(3)); pap. 7.95 (978-0-635-02324-7(5)) Gallopade International.

—South Dakota Indians. 2004. (South Dakota Experie Ser.). 36p. (gr. 3-8). pap. 7.95 (978-0-635-02326-1(1)); 29.95 (978-0-635-02327-8(X)) Gallopade International.

—Tennessee Indians. 2004. (Tennessee Experience Ser.). 36p. (gr. 3-8). pap. 7.95 (978-0-635-02328-5(8)); lib. bdg. 29.95 (978-0-635-02329-2(6)) Gallopade International.

—Texas Indians. 2004. (Texas Experience Ser.). 36p. (gr. 3-8). 29.95 (978-0-635-02331-5(8)); pap. 7.95 (978-0-635-02330-8(X)) Gallopade International.

Chelsea House Publishing Staff. The New England Indians. 1999. (Illustrated Living History Ser.). (Illus.). 144p. (YA). (gr. 1-4). 21.95 (978-0-7910-4525-1(0) , Chelsea Hse.) Facts On File, Inc.

The Cherokee Indians, 6 vols. (gr. 2-5). 36.95 (978-0-7368-8166-1(2)) Red Brick Learning.

Coe, Charles. Red Patriots the Story of Osceola & the Seminole Indian Wars. 2006. (Illus.). cd-rom (978-1-892824-36-3(1)) AFCHRON.

The Comanche Indians, 6 vols. (gr. 2-5). 36.95 (978-0-7368-8167-8(0)) Red Brick Learning.

Cooper, Michael L. Indian School: Teaching the White Man's Way. 1999. (Illus.). 112p. (J). (gr. 5-9). tchr. ed. 18.00 (978-0-395-92084-8(1) , Clarion Bks.) Houghton Mifflin Co. Trade & Reference Div.

Corrigan, Jim. Europeans & Native Americans. 2002. (Native American Life Ser.). (Illus.). 64p. (YA). (gr. 5 up). lib. bdg. (978-1-59084-124-2(7)) Mason Crest Pubs.

Coupe, Robert. Native Americans. 2002. (Junior Adventure Ser.). (Illus.). 32p. (J). (gr. 3 up). lib. bdg. (978-1-59084-167-9(0)) Mason Crest Pubs.

Covert, Kim. The Powhatan People. 1998. (Native Peoples Ser.). (Illus.). 24p. (J). (gr. 2-3). lib. bdg. 18.60 (978-0-7368-0078-5(6) , Bridgestone Bks.) Capstone Pr., Inc.

Craats, Rennay. The Navajo. 2004. (American Indian Art & Culture Ser.). (Illus.). 32p. (gr. 3-5). 25.50 (978-0-7910-7961-4(9) , Chelsea Hse.) Facts On File, Inc.

Dalton, Anne. The Lenni-Lenape of Pennsylvania, New Jersey, New York, Delaware, Wisconsin, Oklahoma, & Ontario. 2005. (Library of Native Americans). (Illus.). 64p. (J). 26.50 (978-1-4042-2872-6(1) , PowerKids Pr.) Rosen Publishing Group, Inc., The.

Davies, Gill. Native America 900 BC- the Present. Aronson, Marc, ed. 2005. (National Geographic Timelines Ser.). (Illus.). 64p. (J). 27.90 (978-0-7922-7078-2(9)) National Geographic Society.

—Native America 9000 BC - the Present. Aronson, Marc, ed. 2005. (National Geographic Timelines Ser.). (Illus.). 64p. (J). 17.95 (978-0-7922-6456-9(8)) National Geographic Society.

Davis, Kenneth C. Don't Know Much about the Pioneers & Indians. 48p. (J). Date not set. (gr. 1-4). pap. 5.99 (978-0-06-446232-7(3)); 2003. (Picture Bks.: No. 6). (Illus.). (ps-1). 16.89 (978-0-06-028618-7(0)) HarperCollins Pubs.

Davis, Lucile. The Caddo of Texas. 2003. (Library of Native Americans). (Illus.). 64p. (J). lib. bdg. 26.50 (978-0-8239-6435-2(3) , PowerKids Pr.) Rosen Publishing Group, Inc., The.

De Angelis, Therese. The Cherokee: Native Basket Weavers. 2003. (America's First Peoples Ser.). (Illus.). 32p. (J). (gr. 2-3). lib. bdg. 23.93 (978-0-7368-1535-2(X) , Bridgestone Bks.) Capstone Pr., Inc.

—The Ojibwa: Wild Rice Gatherers. 2003. (America's First Peoples Ser.). (Illus.). 32p. (J). (gr. 2-3). lib. bdg. 23.93 (978-0-7368-1537-6(6) , Bridgestone Bks.) Capstone Pr., Inc.

De Capua, Sarah. The Shoshone. 2007. (First Americans Ser.). 48p. (J). lib. bdg. 29.93 ***(978-0-7614-2683-7(3)*** , Benchmark Bks.) Cavendish, Marshall Corp.

DeKeyser, Stacy. The Wampanoag. 2005. (Watts Library). (Illus.). 64p. (J). (gr. 5-7). 25.50 (978-0-531-12298-3(0) , Watts, Franklin) Scholastic Library Publishing.

Dennis, Yvonne Wakim & Hirschfelder, Arlene. Children of Native America Today. 2004. (Illus.). 64p. (J). 19.95 (978-1-57091-499-7(0)) Charlesbridge Publishing, Inc.

Dimartino, Catherine. Early American Alliances. 2005. (Illus.). 16p. (J). pap. ***(978-0-328-14893-6(8))*** Pearson Education.

Ditchfield, Christin. The Shoshone. 2003. (True Book Ser.). (Illus.). 48p. (J). 25.00 (978-0-516-22987-4(7) , Children's Pr.) Scholastic Library Publishing.

—Spanish Missions. 2006. (True Book - Westward Expansion Ser.). (Illus.). 48p. (J). (gr. 3-5). 25.00 (978-0-516-22834-1(X) , Children's Pr.) Scholastic Library Publishing.

Doherty, Craig A. Northwest Coast Indians. Facts on File, Inc. Staff, ed. 2008. (Native America Ser.). 136p. (J). (gr. 5-8). 35.00 (978-0-8160-5977-5(2)) Facts On File, Inc.

—Southwest Indians. Facts on File, Inc. Staff, ed. 2008. (Native America Ser.). 136p. (J). (gr. 5-8). 35.00 (978-0-8160-5975-1(6)) Facts On File, Inc.

—Subarctic Peoples. Facts on File, Inc. Staff, ed. 2008. (Native America Ser.). 136p. (J). (gr. 5-8). 35.00 (978-0-8160-5978-2(0)) Facts On File, Inc.

Dorling Kindersley Publishing Staff. North American Indian. 2005. (Eyewitness Books). 72p. (J). 15.99 (978-0-7566-1081-4(8)) Dorling Kindersley Publishing, Inc.

Englar, Mary. The Cheyenne Indians: Hunter Gatherers of the Northern Plains. 2003. (American Indian Nations Ser.). (Illus.). 48p. (J). lib. bdg. 23.93 (978-0-7368-2178-0(3) , Bridgestone Bks.) Capstone Pr., Inc.

—The Comanche Indians: Nomads of the Southern Plains. 2003. (American Indian Nations Ser.). (Illus.). 48p. (J). lib. bdg. 23.93 (978-0-7368-2180-3(5) , Bridgestone Bks.) Capstone Pr., Inc.

—The Iroquois: The Six Nations Confederacy. 2002. (American Indian Nations Ser.). (Illus.). 48p. (J). (gr. 3-4). lib. bdg. 22.60 (978-0-7368-1353-2(5) , Bridgestone Bks.) Capstone Pr., Inc.

—The Pueblo: Southwestern Potters. 2003. (America's First Peoples Ser.). (Illus.). 32p. (J). (gr. 2-3). lib. bdg. 23.93 (978-0-7368-1538-3(4) , Bridgestone Bks.) Capstone Pr., Inc.

First North Americans Kid Kit. 32p. (YA). (gr. 1). 14.95 (978-1-58086-449-7(X)); (Illus.). (YA). (gr. 1 up). 14.95 (978-1-58086-442-8(2)); 2003. (Illus.). 14.95 (978-1-58086-532-6(1)); 2003. (Illus.). 15.95 (978-1-58086-533-3(X)) EDC Publishing.

Fitterer, C. Ann. Tecumseh: Chief of the Shawnee. 2002. (Spirit of America: Our People Ser.). (Illus.). 32p. (J). (gr. 2-6). 27.07 (978-1-56766-168-2(8)) Child's World, Inc.

Fitzpatrick, Marie-Louise. The Long March: The Choctaw's Gift to Irish Famine Relief. 2004. (Illus.). 32p. (J). 7.95 (978-1-58246-065-9(5) , Tricycle Pr.) Ten Speed Pr.

Flanagan, Alice K. The Shawnee. January, Brendan, ed. 1998. (True Bks.). (Illus.). 48p. (J). (gr. 3-5). pap. 6.95 (978-0-516-26384-7(6) , Children's Pr.) Scholastic Library Publishing.

—The Utes. January, Brendan, ed. 1998. (True Bks.). (Illus.). 48p. (J). (gr. 3-5). pap. 6.95 (978-0-516-26386-1(2) , Children's Pr.) Scholastic Library Publishing.

—The Wampanoags. January, Brendan, ed. 1998. (True Bks.). (Illus.). 48p. (J). (gr. 3-5). pap. 6.95 (978-0-516-26388-5(9) , Children's Pr.) Scholastic Library Publishing.

—The Zunis. January, Brendan, ed. 1998. (True Bks.). (Illus.). 48p. (J). (gr. 3-5). pap. 6.95 (978-0-516-26389-2(7) , Children's Pr.) Scholastic Library Publishing.

—The Zunis. 1998. (True Bks.). (Illus.). 48p. (J). (gr. 3-5). 25.00 (978-0-516-20630-1(3) , Children's Pr.) Scholastic Library Publishing.

Fourstar, Jerome & Blue Talk, Richard. How the Morning & Evening Stars Came to Be: And Other Assiniboine Indian Stories. 2003. (Indian Reading Ser.). (Illus.). 48p. pap. 9.95 (978-0-917298-96-7(9)) Montana Historical Society Pr.

Fourstar, Jerome, et al. How the Summer Season Came: And Other Assiniboine Indian Stories. 2003. (Indian Reading Ser.). (Illus.). 104p. pap. 9.95 (978-0-917298-94-3(2)) Montana Historical Society Pr.

Fowler, Loretta. The Arapaho. 2005. (Indians of North America, Heritage Edition Ser.). (Illus.). 148p. (YA). (gr. 9-12). lib. bdg. 30.00 (978-0-7910-8593-6(7) , Chelsea Hse.) Facts On File, Inc.

Fowler, Verna. The Menominee. 2000. (Indian Nations Ser.). (Illus.). 48p. (J). (gr. 3-7). lib. bdg. 25.69 (978-0-8172-5458-2(7)) Raintree.

Gaines, Richard. The Algonquin. 2000. (Native Americans Ser.). (Illus.). 32p. (J). (gr. k-6). lib. bdg. 22.78 (978-1-57765-383-7(1) , Checkerboard Library) ABDO Publishing Co.

—Apache. 2000. (Native Americans Ser.). (Illus.). 32p. (J). (gr. k-6). lib. bdg. 22.78 (978-1-57765-381-3(5) , Checkerboard Library) ABDO Publishing Co.

—Cheyenne. 2000. (Native Americans Ser.). (Illus.). 32p. (J). (gr. k-6). lib. bdg. 22.78 (978-1-57765-378-3(5) , Checkerboard Library) ABDO Publishing Co.

—Comanche. 2000. (Native Americans Ser.). (Illus.). 32p. (J). (gr. k-6). lib. bdg. 22.78 (978-1-57765-372-1(6) , Checkerboard Library) ABDO Publishing Co.

—Iroquois. Fadden, John Kahionhes & Gray, Barbara, illus. 2000. (Native Americans Ser.). 32p. (J). (gr. k-6). lib. bdg. 22.78 (978-1-57765-373-8(4) , Checkerboard Library) ABDO Publishing Co.

—Navajo. Fadden, David K., illus. 2000. (Native Americans Ser.). 30p. (J). (gr. k-6). lib. bdg. 22.78 (978-1-57765-374-5(2) , Checkerboard Library) ABDO Publishing Co.

—Seminole. 2000. (Native Americans Ser.). (Illus.). 32p. (J). (gr. k-6). lib. bdg. 22.78 (978-1-57765-376-9(9) , Checkerboard Library) ABDO Publishing Co.

Gaines, Richard & Fadden, David K. Nez Perce. 2000. (Native Americans Ser.). (Illus.). 32p. (J). (gr. k-6). lib. bdg. 22.78 (978-1-57765-375-2(0) , Checkerboard Library) ABDO Publishing Co.

George, Lynn. Calendars of Native Americans: Timekeeping Methods of Ancient North America. 2004. (PowerMath Ser.). (Illus.). 32p. (J). pap. (978-0-8239-7446-7(4) , PowerKids Pr.) Rosen Publishing Group, Inc., The.

Gibson, Karen Bush. The Arapaho: Hunters of the Great Plains. 2003. (American Indian Nations Ser.). (Illus.). 48p. (J). (gr. 3-4). lib. bdg. 22.60 (978-0-7368-1564-2(3) , Bridgestone Bks.) Capstone Pr., Inc.

—The Blackfeet: People of the Dark Moccasins. 2003. (American Indian Nations Ser.). (Illus.). 48p. (J). (gr. 3-4). lib. bdg. 22.60 (978-0-7368-1565-9(1) , Bridgestone Bks.) Capstone Pr., Inc.

—The Chickasaw Nation. 2002. (Native Peoples Ser.). (Illus.). 24p. (J). (gr. 2-3). lib. bdg. 18.60 (978-0-7368-1365-5(9) , Bridgestone Bks.) Capstone Pr., Inc.

—The Chumash Indians: Seafarers of the Pacific Coast. 2003. (American Indian Nations Ser.). 48p. (J). lib. bdg. 23.93 (978-0-7368-2179-7(1) , Bridgestone Bks.) Capstone Pr., Inc.

—The Pawnee Indians: Farmer Hunters of the Central Plains. 2003. (American Indian Nations Ser.). (Illus.). 48p. (J). lib. bdg. 23.93 (978-0-7368-2181-0(3) , Bridgestone Bks.) Capstone Pr., Inc.

—The Potawatomi. 2002. (Native Peoples Ser.). (Illus.). 24p. (J). (gr. 2-3). lib. bdg. 18.60 (978-0-7368-1368-6(3) , Bridgestone Bks.) Capstone Pr., Inc.

Glencoe McGraw-Hill Staff & McGraw-Hill - Jamestown Education Staff. Jamestown's Early Civilizations: North American Indian Life. 2001. (gr. 5-12). pap. 11.96 (978-0-8092-9491-6(5) , 9780809294916) Jamestown.

Gourley, Catherine. Who Is Maria Tallchief? Taylor, Val Paul & Harrison, Nancy, illus. 2002. (Who Was...? Ser.). 112p. (J). mass mkt. 4.99 (978-0-448-42675-4(7) , Grosset & Dunlap) Penguin Group (USA) Inc.

—Who Is Maria Tallchief? 2002. (gr. 3-6). lib. bdg. 13.00 (978-0-613-45330-1(1)) Tandem Library Bks.

Gray-Kanatiiosh, Barbara A. Modoc. 2007. (Illus.). 32p. (J). 22.78 (978-1-59197-656-1(1)) ABDO Publishing Co.

—Native Americans Set II, 10 vols. Incl. Blackfoot. lib. bdg. 22.78 (978-1-57765-604-3(0)); Creek. lib. bdg. 22.78 (978-1-57765-605-0(9)); Hopi. Chimerica, Charles, illus. lib. bdg. 22.78 (978-1-57765-598-5(2)); Inuit. Kanietakeron, David, illus. lib. bdg. 22.78 (978-1-57765-599-2(0)); Maidu. lib. bdg. 22.78 (978-1-57765-602-9(4)); Miwok. lib. bdg. 22.78 (978-1-57765-601-2(6)); Ohlone. lib. bdg. 22.78 (978-1-57765-603-6(2)); Pawnee. lib. bdg. 22.78 (978-1-57765-607-4(5)); Pomo. lib. bdg. 22.78 (978-1-57765-600-5(8)); Pueblo. lib. bdg. 22.78 (978-1-57765-606-7(7)); 32p. (J). (gr. k-6). (Illus.). 2002. Set lib. bdg. 227.80 (978-1-57765-520-6(6) , Checkerboard Library) ABDO Publishing Co.

—Native Americans Set III, 10 vols. 2004. (Illus.). (J). (gr. k-6). lib. bdg. 227.80 (978-1-57765-932-7(5) , Checkerboard Library) ABDO Publishing Co.

—Pawnee. 2002. (Native Americans Ser.). (Illus.). 32p. (J). (gr. k-6). lib. bdg. 22.78 (978-1-57765-607-4(5) , Checkerboard Library) ABDO Publishing Co.

Green, Rayna & Fernandez, Melanie. The Encyclopedia of the First Peoples of North America. 35.00 (978-0-88899-380-9(3)) Groundwood Bks. CAN. *Dist:* Transition Vendor.

Greene, Jacqueline Dembar. Powwow: A Good Day to Dance. Greene, Jacqueline Dembar, photos by. 1998. (First Bks.). (Illus.). 64p. (J). (gr. 5-7). 22.00 (978-0-531-20337-8(9) , Watts, Franklin) Scholastic Library Publishing.

—The Tohono O'Odham. 1998. (First Bks.). (Illus.). 64p. (J). (gr. 5-7). 22.00 (978-0-531-20326-2(3) , Watts, Franklin) Scholastic Library Publishing.

Hansen-Krening, Nancy, et al, eds. Kaleidoscope: A Multicultural Booklist for Grades K-8. 4th ed. 2003. (NCTE Bibliography Ser.). (Illus.). 118p. (J). pap. 30.95 (978-0-8141-2539-7(5) , 25395) National Council of Teachers of English.

Harcourt School Publishers Staff. Meet My Family - 5 Pack - Grade 1. 3rd ed. 2002. (Trophies English Language Learners Ser.). 20.10 (978-0-15-327617-0(7)) Harcourt Schl. Pubs.

—El Pueblo: Advance-Level. 3rd ed. 2002. (SPA.). (gr. 3). pap. 6.80 (978-0-15-324124-6(1)) Harcourt Schl. Pubs.

Harris, Christie. Mouse Woman & the Mischief-Makers. Tait, Douglas, illus. 2005. 152p. (J). pap. 7.95 (978-1-55192-751-0(9)) Raincoast Bk. Distribution CAN. *Dist:* Perseus Distribution.

Haslam, Andrew. Native Americans. 2004. (Make It Work! History Ser.). (Illus.). 64p. (J). (gr. 3-6). 14.95 (978-1-58728-308-6(5) , Two Can Publishing) T&N Children's Publishing.

Hatt, Christine. The Peoples of North America Before Columbus. 1999. (Looking Back Ser.). (Illus.). 64p. (J). (gr. 6-9). 19.98 (978-0-8172-5426-1(9)) Raintree.

Hayden, Kate. Plains Indians. rev. ed. 2004. (Come & Discover My World Ser.). (Illus.). 32p. (gr. 2-5). (J). pap. 7.95 (978-1-58728-070-2(1)); 14.95 (978-1-58728-064-1(7)) T&N Children's Publishing. (Two Can Publishing).

Higgins, Nadia. Spanish Missions of the Old West. 2007. (Events in American History Ser.). (Illus.). 48p. (J). (gr. 4-6). lib. bdg. 29.93 (978-1-60044-128-8(9)) Rourke Publishing, LLC.

Holling, Holling C. The Book of Indians. 2000. (YA). 20.95 (978-0-8488-2968-1(9)) Amereon LTD.

Hook, Jason. Native Americans. 2001. (People Who Made History Ser.). (Illus.). 48p. (J). (gr. 4-7). lib. bdg. 27.12 (978-0-7398-2750-5(2)) Raintree.

Hughes, Michael A., ed. Indian War's Civil War. 1999. (Journal of the Indian Wars Ser.: Vol. 1, No. 3). (Illus.). 188p. (YA). pap. 12.99 (978-1-882810-81-9(3)) Savas Beatie.

Indians of the Americas. 2005. (Illus.). (J). (gr. 5-7). 98.00 (978-0-531-18756-2(X) , Watts, Franklin) Scholastic Library Publishing.

The Iroquois Indians, 6 vols. (gr. 2-5). 36.95 (978-0-7368-8447-1(5)) Red Brick Learning.

Iverson, Peter. The Navajo. 2005. (Indians of North America, Heritage Edition Ser.). (Illus.). 139p. (J). (gr. 5-13). lib. bdg. 30.00 (978-0-7910-8595-0(3) , Chelsea Hse.) Facts On File, Inc.

Johnson, Michael. Native Tribes of North America, 6 bks. Incl. Native Tribes of California & the Southwest. Yenne, Bill. lib. bdg. 32.67 (978-0-8368-5609-5(0)); Native Tribes of the Great Basin & Plateau. Clarke, Duncan. lib. bdg. 32.67 (978-0-8368-5610-1(4)); Native Tribes of the North & Northwest Coast. Burkinshaw, Jane. lib. bdg. 32.67 (978-0-8368-5611-8(2)); Native Tribes of the Northeast. lib. bdg. 32.67 (978-0-8368-5612-5(0)); Native Tribes of the Plains & Prairie. lib. bdg. 32.67 (978-0-8368-5613-2(9)); Native Tribes of the Southeast. Clarke, Duncan. lib. bdg. 32.67 (978-0-8368-5614-9(7)); 64p. (J). (gr. 5 up). (Illus.). 2004. Set lib. bdg. 196.02 (978-0-8368-5608-8(2) , World Almanac Library) Stevens, Gareth Inc.

Johnson, Troy. Native American Life, 15 vols., Set. 2002. (Illus.). 64p. (YA). (gr. 5 up). lib. bdg. (978-1-59084-117-4(4)) Mason Crest Pubs.

Jones, Donald M., photos by. Buffalo Country: America's National Bison Range. 2005. (Illus.). 72p. per. 13.95 (978-1-931832-56-4(0) , 8667872363) Riverbend Publishing.

Junior Library of American Indians. 2005. 80p. pap. 450.00 (978-0-7910-8471-7(X) , Chelsea Hse.) Facts On File, Inc.

The Kalapuyans: A Sourcebook on the Indians of the Willamette Valley. 2nd exp. ed. 2004. pap. 12.95 (978-0-9753484-0-6(X)) Mission Mill Museum.

Kallen, Stuart A. Native Americans of the Great Lakes. 1999. (Indigenous Peoples of North America Ser.). (Illus.). 144p. (J). (gr. 4-12). 28.70 (978-1-56006-568-5(0) , LML00902-177923, Lucent Bks.) Thomson Gale.

Kalman, Bobbie. Life in a Plains Camp. 2001. (Native Nations of North America Ser.). (Illus.). 32p. (J). (gr. 5). (978-0-7787-0369-3(X)); pap. (978-0-7787-0461-4(0)) Crabtree Publishing Co.

—Life in a Plains Camp. 2001. (gr. 3-6). lib. bdg. 16.40 (978-0-613-43465-2(X)) Tandem Library Bks.

—Life in an Anishinabe Camp. 2002. (Native Nations of North America Ser.). (Illus.). 32p. (J). (gr. 5). (978-0-7787-0373-0(8)); pap. (978-0-7787-0465-2(3)) Crabtree Publishing Co.

—Life in an Anishinabe Camp. 2003. (gr. 3-6). lib. bdg. 16.40 (978-0-613-52868-9(9)) Tandem Library Bks.

—Nations of the Plains. 2001. (Native Nations of North America Ser.). (Illus.). 32p. (J). (gr. 5). pap. (978-0-7787-0460-7(2)); (978-0-7787-0368-6(1)) Crabtree Publishing Co.

—Nations of the Plains. 2001. (gr. 3-6). lib. bdg. 16.40 (978-0-613-43479-9(X)) Tandem Library Bks.

—Nations of the Southwest. 2003. (Native Nations of North America Ser.). (Illus.). 32p. (J). (gr. 3-9). (978-0-7787-0374-7(6)); pap. (978-0-7787-0466-9(1)) Crabtree Publishing Co.

—Nations of the Southwest. 2003. (gr. 3-6). lib. bdg. 17.60 (978-0-613-59133-1(X)) Tandem Library Bks.

Kamma, Anne. If You Lived with the Hopi. 1999. (gr. 3-6). lib. bdg. 14.15 (978-0-613-21749-1(7)); (Illus.). (J). 12.79 (978-0-606-18563-9(1)) Tandem Library Bks.

Kamma, Anne & Johnson, Pamela. If You Lived with the Indians of the Northwest Coast. Johnson, Pamela, illus. 2002. (If You Ser.). (Illus.). 64p. (J). pap. 5.99 (978-0-439-26077-0(9)) Scholastic, Inc.

Kamma, Anne & Koedt, A. P. If You Lived with the Hopi Indians. Gardner, Linda, illus. 1999. (If You Lived Ser.: Vol. 1). 80p. (J). (gr. 2-5). pap. 5.99 (978-0-590-39726-1(5)) Scholastic, Inc.

Kavasch, E. Barrie. Zuni Children & Elders Talk Together. 1999. (Library of Intergenerational Learning). 24p. (J). (gr. k-4). lib. bdg. 19.95 (978-0-8239-5227-4(4) , PowerKids Pr.) Rosen Publishing Group, Inc., The.

Keating, Susan K. Native American Rivalries. 2002. (Native American Life Ser.). (Illus.). 64p. (J). (gr. 5 up). lib. bdg. (978-1-59084-129-7(8)) Mason Crest Pubs.

Kent, Deborah. The Trail of Tears. 2007. (Cornerstones of Freedomtrade;, Second Ser.). 48p. (J). 5.95 ***(978-0-531-18693-0(8)*** , Children's Pr.) Scholastic Library Publishing.

Keoke, Emory Dean & Porterfield, Kay Marie. American Indian Contributions to the World: Buildings, Clothing, & Art. 2005. (American Indian Contributions to the World Ser.). (Illus.). 160p. (J). (gr. 4-9). 35.00 (978-0-8160-5394-0(4)) Facts On File, Inc.

Keremitsis, Eileen. Life in a California Mission. 2002. (Way People Live Ser.). (Illus.). 112p. (J). (gr. 7-10). 29.95 (978-1-59018-159-1(X) , Lucent Bks.) Thomson Gale.

Kessel Joyce K. Squanto y el primer Día de Accion de Gracias (Squanto & the First Thanksgiving) Donze, Lisa, illus. 2007. (Yo solo Festividades (on My Own Holidays) Ser.). (J). pap. 6.95 ***(978-0-8225-7795-9(X)*** , Ediciones Lerner) Lerner Publishing Group.

Kessel, Joyce K. Squanto y el Primer Día de Accion de Gracias (Squanto & the First Thanksgiving) Donze, Lisa, illus. 2007. (Yo Solo Festividades (On My Own Holidays) Ser.). (SPA.). 48p. (J). (gr. 2-4). lib. bdg. 25.26 ***978-0-8225-7792-8(5)*** , Ediciones Lerner) Lerner Publishing Group.

King, David C. The Powhatan. 2007. (First Americans Ser.). 48p. (J). lib. bdg. 29.93 ***978-0-7614-2681-3(7)*** , Benchmark Bks.) Cavendish, Marshall Corp.

Koestler-Grack, Rachel A. The Seminole: Patchworkers of the Everglades. 2003. (America's First Peoples Ser.). (Illus.). 32p. (J). (gr. 2-3). lib. bdg. 23.93 (978-0-7368-1539-0(2) , Bridgestone Bks.) Capstone Pr., Inc.

—The Sioux: Nomadic Buffalo Hunters. 2003. (America's First Peoples Ser.). (Illus.). 32p. (J). (gr. 2-3). lib. bdg. 23.93 (978-0-7368-1540-6(6) , Bridgestone Bks.) Capstone Pr., Inc.

Labastida, Roberta. My Ancestor's Village. 2003. (Illus.). 32p. (J). 9.95 (978-0-932653-61-1(8)) Sunbelt Pubns., Inc.

Lacey, Theresa Jensen. The Pawnee. 2005. (Indians of North America, Heritage Edition Ser.). (Illus.). 105p. (YA). (gr. 9-12). lib. bdg. 30.00 (978-0-7910-8599-8(6) , Chelsea Hse.) Facts On File, Inc.

Landau, Elaine. Celebrate the First Thanksgiving with Elaine Landau. 2006. (Explore Colonial America with Elaine Landau Ser.). (Illus.). 48p. (J). lib. bdg. 23.93 (978-0-7660-2556-1(X) , Enslow Elementary) Enslow Pubs., Inc.

Lange, Karen E. 1607: A New Look at Jamestown. Block, Ira, photos by. 2007. (Illus.). 48p. (J). (gr. 3-7). 17.95 (978-1-4263-0012-7(3) , National Geographic Children's Bks.) National Geographic Society.

Lassieur, Allison. The Arapaho Tribe. 2001. (Native Peoples Ser.). (Illus.). 24p. (J). (gr. 2-3). lib. bdg. 18.60 (978-0-7368-0945-0(7) , Bridgestone Bks.) Capstone Pr., Inc.

—The Nez Perce Tribe. 2000. (Native Peoples Ser.). (Illus.). 24p. (J). (gr. 2-3). lib. bdg. 18.60 (978-0-7368-0500-1(1) , Bridgestone Bks.) Capstone Pr., Inc.

—The Pequot Tribe. 2001. (Native Peoples Ser.). (Illus.). 24p. (J). (gr. 2-3). lib. bdg. 18.60 (978-0-7368-0948-1(1) , Bridgestone Bks.) Capstone Pr., Inc.

Lee, Georgia. A Chumash. Bacchin, Giorgio, illus. 1999. (Day with Ser.). 48p. (J). (gr. 5-7). lib. bdg. (978-0-8225-1918-8(6)) Lerner Publishing Group.

Legay, Gilbert. Atlas de los Indios Norteamericanos. (SPA., Illus.). 96p. (YA). (gr. 5-8). (978-84-261-2924-6(2) , IV1599) Juventud, Editorial ESP. *Dist:* Lectorum Pubns., Inc.

The Library of Native Americans: Set 4. (J). (gr. k-5). 159.00 (978-1-4042-2961-7(2)) Rosen Publishing Group, Inc., The.

Liddell, Daniel & Basta, Mary, illus. Native Americans of North America, Set, 11. 2003. (Native Americans of North America). 48p. (J). (gr. 3-6). pap. 6.45 (978-1-877599-61-3(1)) Merryant Pubs.

Lindeen, Carol K. Native American Powwows Set F, 6 vols. (Phonics Readers Ser.). (gr. k-2). 28.95 (978-0-7368-4082-8(6)) Red Brick Learning.

Lomberg, Michelle. The Ojibwa. 2004. (American Indian Art & Culture Ser.). (Illus.). 32p. (gr. 3-5). 25.50 (978-0-7910-7962-1(7) , Chelsea Hse.) Facts On File, Inc.

MacGregor, Carol. Shoshoni Pony: First Horse in the Northwest. Lee, Dick, illus. 2004. 32p. 15.95 (978-0-87004-431-1(1) , 043110) Caxton Pr.

Malinowski, Sharon, et al, eds. Arctic, Subarctic & Great Plains, 1999, Vol. 3. 1999. (U-X-L Encyclopedia of Native American Tribes Ser.: Vol. 3). (Illus.). 832p. (J). (gr. 5-9). lib. bdg. 67.00 (978-0-7876-2841-3(7) , GML00502-112401, UXL) Thomson Gale.

—California & the Pacific Northwest, 1999. 1999. (U-X-L Encyclopedia of Native American Tribes Ser.: Vol. 4). (Illus.). 832p. (J). (gr. 5-9). 67.00 (978-0-7876-2842-0(5) , GML00502-112402, UXL) Thomson Gale.

—Encyclopedia of Native American Tribes, 4 vols., Set. 1999. (Illus.). 832p. (YA). (gr. 6). 235.00 (978-0-7876-2838-3(7) , GML00502-112398, UXL) Thomson Gale.

—Great Basin & Southwest, Vol. 2. 1999. (U-X-L Encyclopedia of Native American Tribes Ser.: Vol. 2). (Illus.). 832p. (J). (gr. 5-9). lib. bdg. 67.00 (978-0-7876-2840-6(9) , GML00502-112400, UXL) Thomson Gale.

—Northeast & Southeast, 1999, Vol. 1. 1999. (U-X-L Encyclopedia of Native American Tribes Ser.: Vol. 1). (Illus.). 832p. (J). (gr. 5-9). lib. bdg. 67.00 (978-0-7876-2839-0(5) , GML00502-112399, UXL) Thomson Gale.

Marcovitz, Hal. Coronado to Escalate: Francisco Coronado & the Exploration of the American Southwest. 1999. (Explorers of the New World Ser.). (Illus.). 64p. (J). (gr. 4 up). 31.00 (978-0-7910-5515-1(9) , Chelsea Hse.) Facts On File, Inc.

—George a Custer. 2002. (gr. 5-8). lib. bdg. 17.60 (978-0-613-50916-9(1)) Tandem Library Bks.

Marsh, Carole. Chief Powhatan. 2002. (One Thousand Readers Ser.). (Illus.). 12p. (J). (gr. k-4). 2.95 (978-0-635-01498-6(X) , 1498X) Gallopade International.

Mattern, Joanne. The Shoshone People. 2001. (Native Peoples Ser.). (Illus.). 24p. (J). (gr. 2-3). lib. bdg. 18.60 (978-0-7368-0834-7(5) , Bridgestone Bks.) Capstone Pr., Inc.

Mayer, Cassie. Tecumseh. 2007. (J). ***(978-1-4034-9975-2(6))***; pap. ***(978-1-4034-9984-4(5))*** Heinemann Library.

Mayrl, Damon. The Potawatomi of Wisconsin. 2003. (Library of Native Americans). (Illus.). 64p. (J). lib. bdg. 26.50 (978-0-8239-6428-4(0) , PowerKids Pr.) Rosen Publishing Group, Inc., The.

McCarthy, Cathy. The Ojibwa. 2000. (Indian Nations Ser.). (Illus.). 48p. (J). (gr. 3-7). lib. bdg. 25.69 (978-0-8172-5460-5(9)) Raintree.

McCay, William. Pueblos del Mundo. ed. 2004. (SPA.). 32p. (J). pap. 6.00 (978-1-4108-2346-5(6) , A23466) Benchmark Education Co.

McLeese, Tex. Monta en Silla y a Pelo. Palacios, Argentina, tr. Tr. of Bronc & Bareback Riding. (SPA., Illus.). 24p. (J). (gr. 1-3). lib. bdg. 19.27 (978-1-57103-386-4(6)) Rourke Publishing, LLC.

McLester, L. Gordon. The Oneida. 2000. (Indian Nations Ser.). (Illus.). 48p. (J). (gr. 3-7). lib. bdg. 25.69 (978-0-8172-5457-5(9)) Raintree.

McMillan, Bruce. Salmon Summer. 1998. (Illus.). 32p. (J). (gr. k-3). tchr. ed. 17.00 (978-0-395-84544-8(0) , Walter Lorraine) Houghton Mifflin Co. Trade & Reference Div.

McNeil, Niki, et al. HOCPP 1090 Native Americans of California. 2006. spiral bd. 19.50 ***(978-1-60308-090-3(2))*** In the Hands of a Child.

Media Projects, Inc., Staff. Student Almanac of Native American History: From Prehistoric Times to the Trail of Tears, 30,000 B. C.-1838, 2 vols., Vol. 1. 2003. (Middle School Reference Ser.). (Illus.). 144p. (J). (978-0-313-32600-4(2)) Greenwood Publishing Group, Inc.

—Student Almanac of Native American History: From the Trial of Tears to Today, 1839 to the Present, 2 vols., Vol. 2. 2003. (Middle School Reference Ser.). (Illus.). 144p. (J). (978-0-313-32601-1(0)) Greenwood Publishing Group, Inc.

Melody, Michael Edward. The Apache. 2005. (Indians of North America, Heritage Edition Ser.). (Illus.). 112p. (YA). (gr. 9-12). lib. bdg. 30.00 (978-0-7910-8597-4(X) , Chelsea Hse.) Facts On File, Inc.

Morris, Ann. Grandma Maxine Remembers: A Native American Family Story. Linenthal, Peter, illus. 2002. (What Was It Like, Grandma? Ser.). 32p. (gr. k-3). lib. bdg. 22.90 (978-0-7613-2317-4(1) , Millbrook Pr.) Lerner Publishing Group.

Morris, Ting. Native Americans. Young, E., illus. 2006. 32p. (J). (978-1-58340-916-9(5)) Smart Apple Media.

Munz, Casey "Naanaage Binesik", illus. Sshtaa taa Haa! Oh No! 2004. Tr. of Sshtaa taa Haa!. (OJI & ENG.). 16p. (J). per. (978-0-9758801-0-4(1)) Bay Mills Indian Community.

Murdoch, David & Dorling Kindersley Publishing Staff. North American Indian. 2005. (Eyewitness Books). (Illus.). 72p. (J). (ps-7). lib. bdg. 19.99 (978-0-7566-1082-1(6)) Dorling Kindersley Publishing, Inc.

National Geographic Society Staff. Indian Tribes of the Americas. 1999. (Cultural & Geographical Exploration Ser.). (Illus.). 144p. (YA). (gr. 7-12). 21.95 (978-0-7910-5447-5(0) , Chelsea Hse.) Facts On File, Inc.

Native America Set, 4-Volumes. 2007. (Native America Ser.). 136p. (gr. 5-8). 140.00 (978-0-8160-6813-5(5)) Facts On File, Inc.

Native American Baskets, 6 vols., Set. C. (Phonics Readers Ser.). (gr. k-2). 17.50 (978-0-7368-3220-5(3)) Red Brick Learning.

Native American Life. 2005. (Illus.). (J). (gr. 2-3). lib. bdg. 127.56 (978-0-7368-3815-3(5)) Capstone Pr., Inc.

Native American Peoples, 12 bks. Incl. Apache. Birchfield, D. L. lib. bdg. 24.67 (978-0-8368-3664-6(2)); Aztec. Stout, Mary A. lib. bdg. 24.67 (978-0-8368-3699-8(5)); Cherokee. Birchfield, D. L. lib. bdg. 24.67 (978-0-8368-3700-1(2)); Cheyenne. Birchfield, D. L. lib. bdg. 24.67 (978-0-8368-3701-8(0)); Comanche. Birchfield, D. L. lib. bdg. 24.67 (978-0-8368-3702-5(9)); Cree. Stout, Mary A. lib. bdg. 24.67 (978-0-8368-3703-2(7)); Mohawk. Adare, Sierra. lib. bdg. 24.67 (978-0-8368-3665-3(0)); Navajo. Birchfield, D. L. lib. bdg. 24.67 (978-0-8368-3704-9(5)); Nez Perce. Stout, Mary A. lib. bdg. 24.67 (978-0-8368-3666-0(9)); Ojibwe. Adare, Sierra. lib. bdg. 24.67 (978-0-8368-3667-7(7)); Seminole. Birchfield, D. L. lib. bdg. 24.67 (978-0-8368-3668-4(5)); Sioux. Birchfield, D. L. lib. bdg. 24.67 (978-0-8368-3669-1(3)); 32p. (J). (gr. 4 up). 2003. (Illus.). 2002. Set lib. bdg. 287.20 (978-0-8368-3879-4(3)) Stevens, Gareth Inc.

Native American Peoples New Releases: Aztec; Cherokee; Cheyenne; Comanche; Cree; Navajo, 6 bks. 2003. (Illus.). (J). (gr. 4 up). lib. bdg. 143.60 (978-0-8368-3698-1(7)) Stevens, Gareth Inc.

Native Americans. 2004. (Illus.). lib. bdg. 7.95 (978-0-8225-4276-6(5)) Lerner Publishing Group.

Native Americans. (Mini Question & Answers America Ser.). 32p. Date not set. (J). 3.98 (978-0-7525-9873-4(2)); 2000. (YA). 7.49 (978-0-7525-4648-3(1)) Parragon, Inc.

Native Americans. 2004. (Thematic Units Ser.). (Illus.). 80p. 9.99 (978-1-57690-581-4(0)) Teacher Created Materials, Inc.

The Native Americans, 4 bks. Incl. Indians of the Great Plains : Traditions, History, Legends & Life. Sita, Lisa. lib. bdg. 27.33 (978-0-8368-2645-6(0)); Indians of the Northeast : Traditions, History, Legends & Life. Sita, Lisa. lib. bdg. 27.33 (978-0-8368-2646-3(9)); Indians of the Northwest : Traditions, History, Legends & Life. Press, Petra. lib. bdg. 27.33 (978-0-8368-2647-0(7)); Indians of the Southwest : Traditions, History, Legends & Life. Sita, Lisa. lib. bdg. 27.33 (978-0-8368-2648-7(5)); 64p. (J). (gr. 5 up). (Illus.). 1999. Set lib. bdg. 109.32 (978-0-8368-2644-9(2)) Stevens, Gareth Inc.

Native Americans, 10 vols., Set. 1999. (Illus.). 800p. (YA). (gr. 5-10). lib. bdg. 325.00 (978-0-7172-9395-7(5) , Grolier) Scholastic Library Publishing.

The Native Americans: Fourth Grade Newcomer Books. (On Our Way to English Ser.). (gr. 4 up). 34.50 (978-0-7578-7261-7(1)) Rigby Education.

Native Americans I. (YA). tchr. ed. 41.95 (978-0-382-40674-4(5)) Cobblestone Publishing Co.

Native Americans II. (J). tchr. ed. 41.95 (978-0-382-40675-1(3)) Cobblestone Publishing Co.

Native Americans of the Great Plains, 11 bks. 1999. (Indians of North America Ser.). (YA). (gr. 5 up). 219.45 (978-0-7910-3824-6(6) , Chelsea Hse.) Facts On File, Inc.

Native Americans Set 4. 2007. (J). 227.80 ***(978-1-59197-648-6(0)*** , Checkerboard Library) ABDO Publishing Co.

Los Nativos Americanos: El Pueblo Indigena de Norteamerica.Tr. of Native Americans: The Native People of North America. (SPA.). 256p. (YA). (gr. 5-8). 36.00 (978-84-7630-201-9(0)) Libsa, Editorial S.A. ESP. *Dist:* Lectorum Pubns., Inc.

Nelson, Sharlene P. & Nelson, Ted W. The Makah. 2003. (Watts Library). (Illus.). 64p. (J). 25.50 (978-0-531-12168-9(2) , Watts, Franklin) Scholastic Library Publishing.

Newman, Shirlee. Pequots in Southern New England. 2000. (gr. 5-8). lib. bdg. 17.60 (978-0-613-37496-5(7)) Tandem Library Bks.

Newman, Shirlee Petkin. The Pequots. 2000. (Watts Library). (Illus.). 64p. (YA). (gr. 5-7). pap. 8.95 (978-0-531-16482-2(9) , Watts, Franklin) Scholastic Library Publishing.

Nishnawbe: A Story of Indians in Michigan. pap., tchr. ed. (978-0-938682-59-2(8)) River Road Pubns., Inc.

Noble, David G. 101 Questions about Ancient Indians of the Southwest. 1998. (Illus.). 32p. (J). (gr. 1-6). pap. 9.95 (978-1-877856-87-7(8)) Western National Parks Assn.

Nottage, Cindy & Morse, Virginia. Let's Research Native Americans. 3rd rev. ed. 2002. 65p. (gr. 3-6). 19.95 (978-1-57652-013-0(7)) Active Learning Systems, LLC.

Nottage, Cindy, et al. Let's Research Native Americans - Primary. 2nd rev. ed. 2002. 42p. 13.95 (978-1-57652-010-9(2)) Active Learning Systems, LLC.

The Ojibwa Indians, 6 vols. (gr. 2-5). 36.95 (978-0-7368-8448-8(3)) Red Brick Learning.

Orr, Tamra. Native American Medicine. 2002. (Native American Life Ser.). (Illus.). 64p. (J). (gr. 5 up). lib. bdg. (978-1-59084-119-8(0)) Mason Crest Pubs.

Otfinoski, Steven. Native AMER at the Time of the Explorers. 2005. (Navigators Ser.). (J). pap. 42.00 ***(978-1-4108-5106-2(0))*** Benchmark Education Co.

Parsons, Alexandra. Native Americans. Haslam, Andrew, illus. 2004. (Make It Work! History Ser.). 64p. (J). (gr. 3-6). pap. 7.95 (978-1-58728-301-7(8) , Two Can Publishing) T&N Children's Publishing.

Pasqua, Sandra M. The Navajo Nation. 2000. (Native Peoples Ser.). (Illus.). 24p. (J). (gr. 2-3). lib. bdg. 18.60 (978-0-7368-0499-8(4) , Bridgestone Bks.) Capstone Pr., Inc.

Patrick, Bethanne Kelly. Native American Languages. 2002. (Native American Life Ser.). (Illus.). 64p. (J). (gr. 5 up). lib. bdg. (978-1-59084-130-3(1)) Mason Crest Pubs.

Perrin, Pat & Bowers, Arden C., eds. Native Americans. 2000. (Researching American History Ser.). (Illus.). 56p. (J). 7.95 (978-1-57960-063-1(8)) History Compass, LLC.

Petra Press Staff. The Zuni. 2002. (First Reports). (Illus.). 48p. (J). (gr. 3 up). lib. bdg. 22.60 (978-0-7565-0189-1(X)) Compass Point Bks.

Philip, Neil, ed. In a Sacred Manner I Live: Native American Wisdom. 2005. (Illus.). 93p. (J). (gr. 5-7). pap., pap. 8.95 (978-0-618-60483-8(9) , Clarion Bks.) Houghton Mifflin Co. Trade & Reference Div.

Price, Sean. The Birth of a State: California Missions. 2007. (J). ***(978-1-4109-2694-4(X))***; pap. ***(978-1-4109-2705-7(9))*** Steck-Vaughn.

Prior, Jennifer Overend. Native Americans. 1998. (Technology Connections Ser.). 48p. (J). (gr. 3-8). pap. 7.95 (978-1-57690-398-8(2) , TCM2398) Teacher Created Materials, Inc.

The Pueblo Indians, 6 vols. (gr. 2-5). 36.95 (978-0-7368-8449-5(1)) Red Brick Learning.

Raczek, Linda T. & Hook, Richard. Stories from Native North America. 2000. (Multicultural Stories Ser.). (Illus.). 48p. (J). (ps-3). 9.95 (978-0-7398-2033-9(8)) Steck-Vaughn.

Raintree Steck-Vaughn Staff. Indian Nations. 1999. (YA). 102.76 (978-0-7398-1713-1(2)); Set. 2000. (Illus.). (J). 102.76 (978-0-8172-5541-1(9)) Raintree.

Remington, Gwen. The Cheyenne. 2000. (Indigenous Peoples of North America Ser.). (Illus.). 96p. (J). (gr. 4-12). 28.70 (978-1-56006-750-4(0) , LML00902-178100, Lucent Bks.) Thomson Gale.

Riehecky, Janet. The Osage. 2002. (Native Peoples Ser.). (Illus.). 24p. (J). (gr. 2-3). lib. bdg. 18.60 (978-0-7368-1367-9(5) , Bridgestone Bks.) Capstone Pr., Inc.

—The Wampanoag: The People of the First Light. 2003. (American Indian Nations Ser.). (Illus.). 48p. (J). (gr. 3-4). lib. bdg. 22.60 (978-0-7368-1568-0(6) , Bridgestone Bks.) Capstone Pr., Inc.

Rosinsky, Natalie M. The Arapaho & Their History. 2004. (We the People Ser.). (Illus.). 48p. (J). 22.60 (978-0-7565-0831-9(2)) Compass Point Bks.

—The Chumash & Their History. 2004. (We the People Ser.). (Illus.). 48p. (J). 22.60 (978-0-7565-0835-7(5)) Compass Point Bks.

—The Creek & Their History. 2004. (We the People Ser.). (Illus.). 48p. (J). 22.60 (978-0-7565-0836-4(3)) Compass Point Bks.

—The Ojibwe & Their History. 2004. (We the People Ser.). (Illus.). 48p. (J). 22.60 (978-0-7565-0843-2(6)) Compass Point Bks.

—The Powhatan & Their History. 2004. (We the People Ser.). (Illus.). 48p. (J). 22.60 (978-0-7565-0844-9(4)) Compass Point Bks.

—The Wampanoag & Their History. 2004. (We the People Ser.). (Illus.). 48p. (J). 22.60 (978-0-7565-0847-0(9)) Compass Point Bks.

Ruffenach, Jessie, ed. Baby Learns to Count. Thomas, Peter, tr. Blacksheep, Beverly, illus. l.t. ed. 2003. (NAV & ENG.). 16p. (J). bds. 7.95 (978-1-893354-47-0(4)) Salina Bookshelf.

Rutsala, David. Native American Confederacies. 2002. (Native American Life Ser.). (Illus.). 64p. (YA). (gr. 5 up). lib. bdg. (978-1-59084-128-0(X)) Mason Crest Pubs.

Ryan, Marla, ed. Cahuilla. 2002. (Tribes of North America Ser.). (Illus.). 48p. (J). 23.70 (978-1-56711-613-7(2) , Blackbirch Pr., Inc.) Thomson Gale.

Santella, Andrew. The First Thanksgiving. 2003. (Cornerstones of Freedom). (Illus.). 48p. (J). (gr. 4-6). 26.00 (978-0-516-24204-0(0) , Children's Pr.) Scholastic Library Publishing.

—Illinois Native People. 2002. (Heinemann State Studies). (Illus.). 48p. (J). (gr. 3-5). lib. bdg. 27.07 (978-1-4034-0009-3(1)) Heinemann Library.

—Navajo. 2002. (gr. 3-6). lib. bdg. 15.25 (978-0-613-59528-5(9)) Tandem Library Bks.

Schonberg, Marcia. Michigan Native Peoples. 2003. (Heinemann State Studies). (Illus.). 48p. (J). 27.07 (978-1-4034-0660-6(X)) Heinemann Library.

—Ohio Native Peoples. 2003. (Heinemann State Studies). (Illus.). 48p. (J). pap. 8.50 (978-1-4034-2690-1(2)); lib. bdg. 27.07 (978-1-4034-0667-5(7)) Heinemann Library.

Seale, Doris & Slapin, Beverly. A Broken Flute: The Native Experience in Books for Children. 2005. (Contemporary Native American Communities Ser.). (Illus.). 480p. 49.95 (978-0-7591-0778-6(5)) AltaMira Pr.

The Seminole Indians, 6 vols. (gr. 2-5). 36.95 (978-0-7368-8168-5(9)) Red Brick Learning.

Serrano, Francisco. The Poet King of Tezcoco: A Great Leader of Ancient Mexico. Serrano, Pablo, illus. 2007. 48p. (J). 18.95 (978-0-88899-787-6(6)) Groundwood Bks. CAN. *Dist:* Perseus Distribution.

Silver, Donald M. & Wynne, Patricia J. Northeast Indians: Reproducible Models That Help Students Build Content Area Knowledge & Vocabulary & Learn about the Traditional Life of Native American Peoples. 2005. (Easy Make & Learn Projects Ser.). (Illus.). 80p. (gr. 3-5). pap. 12.99 (978-0-439-24116-8(2) , Teaching Resources) Scholastic, Inc.

—Southwest Indians: Reproducible Models That Help Students Build Content Area Knowledge & Vocabulary & Learn about the Traditional Life of Native American Peoples. 2005. (Easy Make & Learn Projects Ser.). (Illus.). 80p. (gr. 3-5). pap. 12.99 (978-0-439-24115-1(4) , Teaching Resources) Scholastic, Inc.

Silverstone, Michael. Winona Laduke: Restoring Land & Culture in Native America. 2001. (Women Changing the World Ser.). (Illus.). 112p. (gr. 4-7). pap. 10.95 (978-1-55861-261-7(0)) Feminist Pr. at The City Univ. of New York.

The Sioux Indians, 6 vols. (gr. 2-5). 36.95 (978-0-7368-8165-4(4)) Red Brick Learning.

Sjonger, Rebecca & Kalman, Bobbie. Nations of the Eastern Great Lakes. 2004. (Native Nations of North America Ser.). (Illus.). 32p. pap. (978-0-7787-0473-7(4)) Crabtree Publishing Co.

Smith, Karla. People of Virginia. 2003. (Heinemann State Studies). (Illus.). 48p. (J). pap. 8.50 (978-1-4034-0581-4(6)); (gr. 3-5). lib. bdg. (978-1-4034-0359-9(7)) Heinemann Library.

—Virginia Native Peoples. 2003. (Heinemann State Studies). (Illus.). 48p. (J). (gr. 3-5). lib. bdg. (978-1-4034-0363-6(5)) Heinemann Library.

Smithyman, Kathryn & Kalman, Bobbie. Native North American Foods & Recipes. 2005. (Native Nations of North America Ser.). (Illus.). 32p. (J). (gr. 3-9). lib. bdg. (978-0-7787-0383-9(5)) Crabtree Publishing Co.

Spradlin, Michael P. The Legend of Blue Jacket. Himler, Ronald, illus. 2002. 32p. (J). (gr. k-4). 18.99 (978-0-688-15835-4(8)) HarperCollins Pubs.

Staeger, Rob. Native American Tools & Weapons. 2002. (Native American Life Ser.). (Illus.). 64p. (J). (gr. 5 up). lib. bdg. (978-1-59084-132-7(8)) Mason Crest Pubs.

Stein, R. Conrad. Spanish Missionaries: Bringing Spanish Culture to the Americas. 2005. (Proud Heritage: the Hispanic Library Ser.). (Illus.). 40p. (J). (gr. 3-7). 28.50 (978-1-59296-387-4(0)) Child's World, Inc.

Steward, Mark. New York Native Peoples. 2003. (Heinemann State Studies). (Illus.). 48p. (J). (gr. 3-5). lib. bdg. (978-1-4034-0354-4(6)) Heinemann Library.

Stewart, Mark. New York Native Peoples. 2003. (Heinemann State Studies). (Illus.). 48p. (J). pap. 8.50 (978-1-4034-0576-0(X)) Heinemann Library.

—New York Native Peoples. 2003. (gr. 3-6). lib. bdg. 17.05 (978-0-613-60975-3(1)) Tandem Library Bks.

Stone, Lynn M. Bison. 2003. (Animals in U.S. History Ser.). (Illus.). 24p. (J). 25.64 (978-1-58952-698-3(8)) Rourke Publishing, LLC.

Stotter, Mike. Native Americans. 2002. (Find Out about-...Ser.). (Illus.). 64p. pap. 7.99 (978-1-84215-669-8(1) , Southwater) Anness Publishing GBR. *Dist:* National Bk. Network.

Streissguth, Thomas. The Comanche. 2000. (Indigenous Peoples of North America Ser.). (Illus.). 96p. (J). (gr. 4-12). 28.70 (978-1-56006-633-0(4) , LML00902-177988, Lucent Bks.) Thomson Gale.

Taylor, C. J. How We Saw the World Vol. 4: Nine Native Stories of the Way Things Began. 1999. (gr. 3-6). lib. bdg. 17.60 (978-0-613-77276-1(8)) Tandem Library Bks.

Taylor, Colin, et al. Plains Indians. 2008. (Native America Ser.). 136p. (J). (gr. 5-8). 35.00 (978-0-8160-5976-8(4)) Facts On File, Inc.

Terry, Michael. Daily Life in a Plains Indian Village 1868. 1999. (gr. 3-6). lib. bdg. 18.75 (978-0-613-21396-7(3)) Tandem Library Bks.

Thomas, Marjorie & Ruffenach, Jessie. What Does 'died' Mean? Hañsha oolyé Daaztsaa? Begay, Patrick, illus. 2005. (ENG & NAV.). 32p. (J). pap. 9.00 (978-1-893354-56-2(3)) Salina Bookshelf.

Tieck, Sarah. Sacagawea. 2007. (Buddy Book Ser.). (Illus.). 32p. (J). 22.78 (978-1-59679-789-5(4)) ABDO Publishing Co.

H
I

Todd, Anne M. The Ojibwa: People of the Great Lakes. 2002. (American Indian Nations Ser.). (Illus.). 48p. (J). (gr. 3-4). lib. bdg. 22.60 (978-0-7368-1356-3(X), Bridgestone Bks.) Capstone Pr., Inc.

—The Sioux: People of the Great Plains. 2002. (American Indian Nations Ser.). (Illus.). 48p. (J). (gr. 3-4). lib. bdg. 22.60 (978-0-7368-1354-9(3), Bridgestone Bks.) Capstone Pr., Inc.

Torr, James D. Westward Expansion. 2002. (gr. 7-12). lib. bdg. 33.25 (978-0-613-73610-7(9)) Tandem Library Bks.

Torr, James D., ed. Westward Expansion. 2003. (Interpreting American History Through Primary Documents Ser.x). (Illus.). 208p. (J). 32.45 (978-0-7377-1134-9(5), Greenhaven Pr., Inc.) Thomson Gale.

Ueda, Reed & Stotsky, Sandra, eds. Native American Answer Book. 1999. (Ethnic Answer Book Ser.). (Illus.). 136p. (YA). (gr. 5 up). pap. 8.95 (978-0-7910-4792-7(X)); lib. bdg. 17.95 (978-0-7910-4791-0(1)) Facts On File, Inc. (Chelsea Hse.).

Waldman, Carl. Encyclopedia of Native American Tribes. Braun, Molly, illus. (Facts on File Ser.). 2nd rev. ed. 1999. xxiii, 312p. pap. 19.95 (978-0-8160-3964-7(X)); 3rd rev. ed. 384p. (J). (gr. 9). pap. 21.95 (978-0-8160-6274-4(9), Checkmark Bks.); 3rd rev. ed. 2006. 384p. (J). (gr. 9). 75.00 (978-0-8160-6273-7(0)) Facts On File, Inc.

Walker, Paul Robert. Remember Little Bighorn: Indians, Soldiers, & Scouts Tell Their Stories. 2006. (Illus.). 64p. (J). (gr. 4-8). 17.95 (978-0-7922-5521-5(6)); lib. bdg. 27.90 (978-0-7922-5522-2(4)) National Geographic Society. (National Geographic Children's Bks.).

Wallace, Mary. The Inuksuk Book. 2004. (Wow Canada! Collection). (Illus.). 64p. (J). pap. 13.95 (978-1-897066-13-3(9)) Maple Tree Pr. CAN. *Dist:* Perseus Distribution.

Walters, Anna Lee. The Pawnee Nation. 2000. (Native Peoples Ser.). (Illus.). 24p. (J). (gr. 2-3). lib. bdg. 18.60 (978-0-7368-0501-8(X), Bridgestone Bks.) Capstone Pr., Inc.

Ward, Gail. Native Americans along the Lewis & Clark Trail. 2002. 32p. (978-1-886609-31-0(4)) Tamarack Bks., Inc.

Weber, Valerie J. & Anderson, Dale. The California Missions. 2002. (Events That Shaped America Ser.). (Illus.). 32p. (J). (gr. 3 up). lib. bdg. 24.67 (978-0-8368-3223-5(X)) Stevens, Gareth Inc.

Weist, Tom. History of the Cheyenne People. 2002nd ed. 2002. pap. 14.95 (978-0-89992-157-0(4)) Council for Indian Education.

Weitzel, Kelley G. Journeys with Florida's Indians. 2002. (Illus.). 200p. 24.95 (978-0-8130-2581-0(8)) Univ. Pr. of Florida.

Welch, Deborah. Economic Issues & Development. 2005. (Contemporary Native American Issues Ser.). (Illus.). 160p. (J). (gr. 9-12). 30.00 (978-0-7910-7973-7(2), Chelsea Hse.) Facts On File, Inc.

Whitcraft, Melissa. The Mayflower Compact. 2003. (Cornerstones of Freedom). (Illus.). 48p. (J). (gr. 4-6). 26.00 (978-0-516-24203-3(2), Children's Pr.) Scholastic Library Publishing.

White, Tekla N. San Francisco Bay Area Missions. 2007. (Exploring California Missions Ser.). (J). 27.93 ***(978-0-8225-0900-4(8)***, Lerner Pubns.) Lerner Publishing Group.

Wilds, Mary. The Creek. 2005. (Indigenous Peoples of North America Ser.). (J). (978-1-59018-611-4(7), Lucent Bks.) Thomson Gale.

Williams, Colleen Madonna Flood. Homes of the Native Americans. 2002. (Native American Life Ser.). (Illus.). 64p. (J). (gr. 5 up). lib. bdg. (978-1-59084-120-4(4)) Mason Crest Pubs.

—Native American Family Life. 2002. (Native American Life Ser.). (Illus.). 64p. (J). (gr. 5 up). lib. bdg. (978-1-59084-126-6(3)) Mason Crest Pubs.

—What the Native Americans Wore. 2002. (Native American Life Ser.). (Illus.). 64p. (J). (gr. 5 up). lib. bdg. (978-1-59084-125-9(5)) Mason Crest Pubs.

Williams, Jack S. The Esselen of California. 2003. (Library of Native Americans). (Illus.). 64p. (J). lib. bdg. 26.50 (978-0-8239-6433-8(7)) Rosen Publishing Group, Inc., The.

—The Luiseano of California. 2003. (Library of Native Americans). (Illus.). 64p. (J). lib. bdg. 26.50 (978-0-8239-6431-4(0), PowerKids Pr.) Rosen Publishing Group, Inc., The.

—The Modoc of California. 2004. (Library of Native Americans). (Illus.). 64p. (J). lib. bdg. 26.50 (978-1-4042-2660-9(5)) Rosen Publishing Group, Inc., The.

—The Mojavo of California. 2004. (Library of Native Americans). (Illus.). 64p. (J). lib. bdg. 26.50 (978-1-4042-2661-6(3)) Rosen Publishing Group, Inc., The.

—The Mono of California. 2004. (Library of Native Americans). (Illus.). 64p. (J). lib. bdg. 26.50 (978-1-4042-2662-3(1)) Rosen Publishing Group, Inc., The.

—The Pomo of California. 2003. (Library of Native Americans). (Illus.). 64p. (J). lib. bdg. 26.50 (978-0-8239-6436-9(1), PowerKids Pr.) Rosen Publishing Group, Inc., The.

—The Shasta of California. 2004. (Library of Native Americans of California). (Illus.). 64p. (J). lib. bdg. 26.50 (978-1-4042-2663-0(X)) Rosen Publishing Group, Inc., The.

—The Shoshone of California. 2004. (Library of Native Americans of California). (Illus.). 64p. (J). lib. bdg. 26.50 (978-1-4042-2664-7(8)) Rosen Publishing Group, Inc., The.

—The Tongva of California. 2003. (Library of Native Americans). (Illus.). 64p. (J). lib. bdg. 26.50 (978-0-8239-6429-1(9), PowerKids Pr.) Rosen Publishing Group, Inc., The.

Williams, Jack S. & Davis, Thomas L. Indians of the California Mission Frontier. 2004. (People of the California Missions Ser.). (Illus.). 64p. (J). lib. bdg. 25.50 (978-0-8239-6281-5(4), PowerKids Pr.) Rosen Publishing Group, Inc., The.

Willis, Michelle "Osawazhinkwaa-Ikwe. Kwezenhs Bimose. Willis, Michelle "Osawazhinkwaa-Ikwe, illus. 2004. Tr. of Kwezenhs Bimose. (OJI., Illus.). 8p. (J). per. (978-0-9758801-1-1(X)) Bay Mills Indian Community.

Wolf, Linda Little. Visions of the Buffalo People: Activity Book. 2nd ed. 2003. (Illus.). 128p. (J). pap. 14.95 (978-1-58980-124-0(5)) Pelican Publishing Co., Inc.

Wolfson, Evelyn. Native Americans. 2005. (First Look at History Ser.). (Illus.). 24p. (J). lib. bdg. 22.00 (978-0-8368-4528-0(5)) Stevens, Gareth Inc.

Wood-Trost, Lucille. Native Americans of the Plains. 1999. (Indigenous Peoples of North America Ser.). (Illus.). 112p. (YA). (gr. 4-12). 27.45 (978-1-56006-627-9(X), LML00902-177982, Lucent Bks.) Thomson Gale.

Woods, Geraldine. Navajo. 2002. (gr. 5-8). lib. bdg. 17.60 (978-0-613-54044-5(1)) Tandem Library Bks.

Yacowitz, Caryn. The Comanche. 2002. (Illus.). 32p. (J). pap. (978-1-4034-0509-8(3)) Heinemann Library.

—Comanche Indians. 2003. (Native Americans Ser.). (Illus.). 32p. (J). (gr. 2-4). lib. bdg. 24.22 (978-1-4034-0302-5(3)) Heinemann Library.

—Iroquois Indians. (Native Americans Ser.). (Illus.). 32p. (J). 2003. (gr. 2-4). lib. bdg. 24.22 (978-1-4034-0303-2(1)); 2002. pap. 6.95 (978-1-4034-0510-4(7)) Heinemann Library.

—Lakota Indians. 2002. (Illus.). 32p. (J). pap. 6.95 (978-1-4034-0512-8(3)) Heinemann Library.

—Lakota Indians. 2003. (gr. 3-6). lib. bdg. 15.25 (978-0-613-60928-9(X)) Tandem Library Bks.

—The Seminole. 2002. (Illus.). 32p. (J). pap. 6.95 (978-1-4034-0511-1(5)) Heinemann Library.

—Seminole Indians. 2003. (Native Americans Ser.). (Illus.). 32p. (J). (gr. 2-4). lib. bdg. 24.22 (978-1-4034-0304-9(X)) Heinemann Library.

—Sioux Indians. 2003. (Native Americans Ser.). (Illus.). 32p. (J). (gr. 2-4). lib. bdg. 24.22 (978-1-4034-0305-6(8)) Heinemann Library.

Yue, Charlotte & Yue, David. The Wigwam & the Longhouse. Yue, Charlotte & Yue, David, illus. 2000. (Illus.). 128p. (J). (gr. 5-9). tchr. ed. 15.00 (978-0-395-84169-3(0)) Houghton Mifflin Co. Trade & Reference Div.

Zappler, Georg. Learn about ... Texas Indians. Poole, Juliann, ed. Ivy, Elena T., illus. 2007. 48p. pap. 10.95 ***(978-0-292-71684-1(2))*** Univ. of Texas Pr.

INDIANS OF NORTH AMERICA—ABNAKI INDIANS—FICTION

Bruchac, Joseph. The Winter People. 2004. (Illus.). 176p. (J). (gr. 5). pap. 5.99 (978-0-14-240229-0(X), Puffin) Penguin Group (USA) Inc.

—The Winter People. Bernardin, James, illus. 2002. 176p. (J). 16.99 (978-0-8037-2694-9(5), Dial) Penguin Group (USA) Inc.

Dubois, Muriel L. Abenaki Captive. 16.00 (978-0-9723410-0-4(5)) Apprentice Shop Bks., LLC.

INDIANS OF NORTH AMERICA—ACOMA INDIANS—FICTION

Little, Kimberley Griffiths. The Last Snake Runner: A Novel. 2006. 201p. (YA). (gr. 7-10). reprint ed. 16.00 ***(978-1-4223-5838-2(0))*** DIANE Publishing Co.

INDIANS OF NORTH AMERICA—AGRICULTURE

Keoke, Emory Dean. American Indian Contributions to the World, 5 Vols., Set. 2005. (American Indian Contributions to the World Ser.). 128-160p. (J). (gr. 4-9). 175.00 (978-0-8160-5392-6(8)) Facts On File, Inc.

Keoke, Emory Dean & Porterfield, Kay Marie. Food, Farming, & Hunting. 2005. (American Indian Contributions to the World Ser.). (Illus.). 160p. (J). (gr. 4-9). 35.00 (978-0-8160-5393-3(6)) Facts On File, Inc.

INDIANS OF NORTH AMERICA—ALGONKIN INDIANS

see Indians Of North America—Algonquian Indians

INDIANS OF NORTH AMERICA—ALGONQUIAN INDIANS

Harcourt School Publishers Staff. Trading Days Advanced Level. 3rd ed. 2002. (Trophies Reading Program Ser.). (Illus.). pap. 5.10 (978-0-15-323214-5(5)) Harcourt Schl. Pubs.

Kalman, Bobbie. Nations of the Western Great Lakes. (Native Nations of North America Ser.). (Illus.). 32p. (J). (gr. 5). 2003. pap. (978-0-7787-0464-5(5)); 2002. (978-0-7787-0372-3(X)) Crabtree Publishing Co.

—Nations of the Western Great Lakes. 2003. (gr. 3-6). lib. bdg. 17.60 (978-0-613-52886-3(7)) Tandem Library Bks.

McCurdy, Michael. An Algonquian Year: The Year According to the Full Moon. 2000. (Illus.). 32p. (J). (gr. k-3). tchr. ed. 15.00 (978-0-618-00705-9(9)) Houghton Mifflin Co. Trade & Reference Div.

McLeese, Tex. Monta deToro y Toreo. Palacios, Argentina, tr. (SPA., Illus.). 24p. (J). (gr. 1-3). lib. bdg. 19.27 (978-1-57103-388-8(2)) Rourke Publishing, LLC.

The Puritans, Algonkians & Roger Williams (NCHS) (J). (gr. 5-8). spiral bd., tchr.'s planning gde. ed. 13.50 (978-0-382-44447-0(7)) Cobblestone Publishing Co.

The Puritans, Algonkians & Roger Williams (NCHS) Grades 5-8. (J). tchr. ed. 18.00 (978-0-382-44537-8(6)) Cobblestone Publishing Co.

Rosinsky, Natalie M. The Algonquin. 2004. (First Reports). 48p. (J). (gr. 3 up). lib. bdg. 22.60 (978-0-7565-0642-1(5)) Compass Point Bks.

INDIANS OF NORTH AMERICA—ALGONQUIAN INDIANS—FICTION

Dorris, Michael. Guests. 1999. 128p. (gr. 4-17). pap. 4.99 (978-0-7868-1356-8(3)) Hyperion Pr.

Hassinger, Peter W. The Book of Alfar: A Tale of the Hudson Highlands. 2002. (Illus.). 272p. (J). (gr. 4 up). 15.89 (978-0-06-028470-1(6), Geringer, Laura Book) HarperCollins Pubs.

Lowden, Stephanie. Time of the Eagle: A Story of an Ojibwe Winter. 2004. 128p. (J). pap. 12.00 (978-1-883953-34-8(0)) Midwest Traditions, Inc.

INDIANS OF NORTH AMERICA—AMUSEMENTS

see Indians of North America—Games; Indians of North America—Social Life and Customs

INDIANS OF NORTH AMERICA—ANTIQUITIES

see also Mounds and Mound Builders

Alexander, Suzanna M., et al. Prehistoric People of Moccasin Bend, Chattanooga, Tennessee: An Educational Coloring Book. 2006. (J). ***(978-0-9779189-3-5(9))*** Waldenhouse Pub., Inc.

Boule, Mary Null. Native Americans of North America: Plateau Tribes: Cayuse, Walla Walla & Umatilla People. Harding, Virginia, ed. Liddell, Daniel & Basta, Mary, illus. 1999. 64p. (J). (gr. 3-6). pap. 7.95 (978-1-877599-54-5(9)) Merryant Pubs.

—Navajo People: SW Region, Set. Liddell, Daniel & Basta, Mary, illus. (Native Americans of North America Ser.). 50-60p. (J). (gr. 3-6). pap. 7.95 (978-1-877599-59-0(X)) Merryant Pubs.

—Washoe People. Harding, Virginia, ed. Liddell, Daniel & Basta, Mary, illus. 2000. 64p. (J). 7.95 (978-1-877599-56-9(5)) Merryant Pubs.

Holliday, Diane Young & Malone, Bobbie. Digging & Discovery: Wisconsin Archaeology. 2nd ed. 2006. (New Badger History Ser.). (Illus.). 120p. pap. 15.95 (978-0-87020-376-3(2)) Wisconsin Historical Society.

Innes, Brian. Native American Monuments. 1999. (Unsolved Mysteries Ser.). (Illus.). 48p. (YA). (gr. 3 up). lib. bdg. 25.69 (978-0-8172-5482-7(X)) Raintree.

Lauber, Patricia. Who Came First? New Clues to Prehistoric Americans. 2003. (Illus.). 64p. (J). (gr. 5). 18.95 (978-0-7922-8228-0(0), National Geographic Children's Bks.) National Geographic Society.

Levy, Elizabeth & Havlan, J. R. Awesome Ancient Ancestors. McFeeley, Daniel, illus. 2001. (America's Horrible Histories Ser.: No. 2). 156p. (J). (gr. 4-6). pap. 12.95 (978-0-439-30349-1(4)) Scholastic, Inc.

Miller, Connie R. The Lakota. 2003. (Digging up Native American History Ser.). (J). pap. (978-1-58417-109-6(X)); lib. bdg. (978-1-58417-046-4(8)) Lake Street Pubs.

Rosebrough, Amy & Malone, Bobbie. Water Panthers, Bears, & Thunderbirds: Exploring the Effigy Mounds of Wisconsin. 2003. (New Badger History Ser.). (Illus.). 32p. (J). pap. 9.95 (978-0-87020-357-2(6)) Wisconsin Historical Society.

Wood, Marion & Williams, Brian. Ancient America. 2nd ed. 2003. (Cultural Atlases for Young People Ser.). (Illus.). (J). (gr. 4-9). 672p. 245.00 (978-0-8160-5144-1(5)); 96p. 35.00 (978-0-8160-5145-8(3)) Facts On File, Inc.

INDIANS OF NORTH AMERICA—APACHE INDIANS

Bial, Raymond. The Apache. 2001. (Lifeways Ser.). (Illus.). 128p. (J). (gr. 5-9). lib. bdg. 34.21 (978-0-7614-0939-7(4), Benchmark Bks.) Cavendish, Marshall Corp.

Birchfield, D. L. Apache. 2003. (Native American Peoples Ser.). (Illus.). 32p. (J). (gr. 4 up). lib. bdg. 24.67 (978-0-8368-3664-6(2)) Stevens, Gareth Inc.

Cuevas, Lou. Apache Legends: Songs of the Wind Dancer. Brown, Keven, ed. Cleveland, Fred, illus. 2003. 128p. (Orig.). (YA). pap. 8.95 (978-0-87961-219-1(3)) Naturegraph Pubs., Inc.

Englar, Mary. The Apache: Nomadic Hunters of the Southwest. 2003. (American Indian Nations Ser.). (Illus.). 48p. (J). (gr. 3-4). lib. bdg. 22.60 (978-0-7368-1563-5(5), Bridgestone Bks.) Capstone Pr., Inc.

Gaines, Richard. Apache. 2000. (Native Americans Ser.). (Illus.). 32p. (J). (gr. k-6). lib. bdg. 22.78 (978-1-57765-381-3(5), Checkerboard Library) ABDO Publishing Co.

Golston, Sydele E. Changing Woman of the Apache: Women's Lives in Past & Present. 2001. (Illus.). 144p. (J). (gr. 5-7). reprint ed. 25.00 (978-0-7881-9686-7(3)) DIANE Publishing Co.

Jastrzembski, Joseph C. The Apache Wars: The Final Resistance. 2007. (Landmark Events in Native American History Ser.). 136p. (gr. 9). 35.00 ***(978-0-7910-9343-6(3)***, Chelsea Hse.) Facts On File, Inc.

Kavasch, E. Barrie. Apache Children & Elders Talk Together. 1999. (Library of Intergenerational Learning). 24p. (J). (gr. k-4). lib. bdg. 19.95 (978-0-8239-5225-0(8), PowerKids Pr.) Rosen Publishing Group, Inc., The.

Martin, Jo. Apache Women Warriors. 2000. (To Know the Land Ser.). (Illus.). 62p. (YA). (gr. 8 up). 23.00 (978-0-934272-53-7(0)); pap. 15.00 (978-0-934272-52-0(2)) Burke, John Gordon Pub., Inc.

McIntosh, Kenneth. Apache. 2003. (North American Indians Today Ser.). (Illus.). 96p. (YA). (gr. 7-9). lib. bdg. (978-1-59084-664-3(8)) Mason Crest Pubs.

McLeese, Tex. Enlace en el Rodeo. Palacios, Argentina, tr. Tr. of Rodeo Roping. (SPA., Illus.). 24p. (J). (gr. 1-3). lib. bdg. 19.27 (978-1-57103-384-0(X)) Rourke Publishing, LLC.

Miller, Connie R. The Apache. 2003. (Uncovering Native American History Ser.). (J). pap. (978-1-58417-113-3(8)); lib. bdg. (978-1-58417-050-1(6)) Lake Street Pubs.

Moskal, Greg. An Apache Indian Community. 2002. (Reading Room Collection). (Illus.). 24p. (J). lib. bdg. 18.75 (978-0-8239-3719-6(4)) Rosen Publishing Group, Inc., The.

Netzley, Patricia D. Apache Warrior. 2002. (Daily Life Ser.). (Illus.). 48p. (J). (gr. 3-5). 26.20 (978-0-7377-0989-6(8), Greenhaven Pr., Inc.) Thomson Gale.

Petra Press Staff. The Apache. 2001. (First Reports). (Illus.). 48p. (J). (gr. 3 up). lib. bdg. 22.60 (978-0-7565-0077-1(X)) Compass Point Bks.

Ryan, Marla Felkins & Schmittroth, Linda, eds. Apache. 2002. (Tribes of Native America Ser.). (Illus.). 32p. (J). 23.70 (978-1-56711-604-5(3), Blackbirch Pr., Inc.) Thomson Gale.

Santella, Andrew. The Apache. 2001. (True Bks.). (Illus.). 48p. (J). (gr. 3-5). pap. 6.95 (978-0-516-27311-2(6), Children's Pr.) Scholastic Library Publishing.

—Apache. 2001. (gr. 3-6). lib. bdg. 15.25 (978-0-613-53475-8(1)) Tandem Library Bks.

Sonneborn, Liz. The Apache. 2005. (Watts Library). (Illus.). 64p. (gr. 5-7). 25.50 (978-0-531-12295-2(6), Watts, Franklin) Scholastic Library Publishing.

Stanley, George Edward. Geronimo: Young Warrior. 2001. 11.64 (978-0-606-22097-2(6)) Tandem Library Bks.

Tayac, Gabrielle. Meet Naiche: A Native Boy from the Chesapeake Bay Area. Harrington, John, photos by. 2007. (Illus.). 48p. (J). 15.95 (978-1-57178-146-8(3)) Council Oak Bks.

Tayac, Gabrielle & Secakuku, Susan. Meet Naiche. Harrington, John, photos by. 2003. (My World). (Illus.). 32p. (J). (gr. 4 up). lib. bdg. 24.67 (978-0-8368-3795-7(9)) Stevens, Gareth Inc.

INDIANS OF NORTH AMERICA—APACHE INDIANS—FICTION

Dearen, Patrick. Hidden Treasure of the Chisos. 2001. (gr. 3-6). lib. bdg. 17.60 (978-0-613-83165-9(9)) Tandem Library Bks.

—The Hidden Treasure of the Chisos, Bk. 3. 2001. (Lone Star Heroes Ser.). 117p. pap. 8.95 (978-1-55622-829-2(5), Republic of Texas Pr.) Wordware Publishing, Inc.

Holmas, Stig. Son-of-Thunder. Born, Anne, tr. from NOR. Hurford, John, illus. 2001. (Chiricahua Apache Series / Stig Holmas Ser.: Vol. 1). 139p. (gr. 7 up). 16.95 (978-0-943173-88-7(4)) Rinehart, Roberts Pubs.

Taschek, Karen. Horse of Seven Moons. 2005. (Illus.). 192p. (YA). pap. 14.95 (978-0-8263-3215-8(3)) Univ. of New Mexico Pr.

Wood, Elizabeth Lamb. There Go the Apaches. 2005. pap. 26.95 (978-1-4191-5979-4(8)) Kessinger Publishing, LLC.

INDIANS OF NORTH AMERICA—ARAPAHOE INDIANS—FICTION

Henty, G. A. In the Heart of the Rockies. 2002. 370p. 29.95 (978-1-59087-073-0(5), GAH073); per. 19.95 (978-1-59087-072-3(7), GAH072) Althouse Pr.

—In the Heart of the Rockies. Hindley, G. C., illus. 1998. 388p. (YA). (gr. 8-12). reprint ed. per. 16.95 (978-1-890623-08-1(3)) Lost Classics Bk. Co.

—In the Heart of the Rockies. collector's ed. 2002. (Illus.). im. lthr. 38.85 (978-1-4115-1341-9(X)); pap. 19.95 (978-1-4115-0577-3(8)); 25.95 (978-1-4115-0949-8(8)); pap. 17.95 (978-1-4115-0174-4(8)) Polyglot Pr., Inc.

Korman, Susan. Horse Raid: An Arapaho Camp in the 1800s. Farnsworth, Bill, illus. 1998. (Smithsonian Odyssey Ser.: Vol. 10). 32p. (J). (gr. 2-5). 14.95 (978-1-56899-613-4(6), B6011); 19.95 incl. audio (978-1-56899-615-8(2), BC6011); pap. 6.95 (978-1-56899-614-1(4), S6011); pap. 10.95 incl. audio (978-1-56899-616-5(0)) Soundprints.

Ryan, Marla Felkins & Schmittroth, Linda, eds. Arapaho. 2003. (Tribes of Native America Ser.). (Illus.). 32p. (J). 23.70 (978-1-56711-587-1(X), Blackbirch Pr., Inc.) Thomson Gale.

INDIANS OF NORTH AMERICA—ARAWAK INDIANS

Swanton, John R. Indian Tribes of Mexico, Central America & the West Indies. (Shorey Indian Ser.). 40p. (J). reprint ed. pap. 10.00 (978-0-8466-0087-9(0), S87) Shorey's Bookstore.

INDIANS OF NORTH AMERICA—ART

American Indian Crafts. 2005. (Book Treks Ser.). (J). (gr. 3 up). stu. ed. 34.95 (978-0-673-62838-1(8)) Celebration Pr.

Anton, Ferdinand. The Secret World of the Aztecs. 2002. (Adventures in Art Ser.). (Illus.). 30p. 14.95 (978-3-7913-2702-0(X)) Prestel Publishing.

Brooklyn Museum Staff, et al. The Native American Look Book: Art & Activities for Kids from the Brooklyn Museum. 2000. (Illus.). 48p. (gr. 4-7). pap. 12.95 (978-1-56584-604-3(4)) New Pr., The.

Cherrington, Janelle. Native American Baskets. 2003. (Compass Point Phonics Readers Ser.). (Illus.). 16p. (J). (gr. 1 up). 13.26 (978-0-7565-0514-1(3)) Compass Point Bks.

Downs, Dorothy. Patchwork: Seminole & Miccosukee Art & Activities. 2005. (Illus.). 55p. (J). (gr. 3-7). pap. 9.95 (978-1-56164-332-5(7)) Pineapple Pr., Inc.

Falconer, Shelley & White, Shawna. Stones, Bones & Stitches: Storytelling Through Inuit Art. 2007. 40p. (YA). (gr. 3 up). 22.95 ***(978-0-88776-854-5(7))*** Tundra Bks. of Northern New York.

Finley, Carol. Art of the Far North: Inuit Sculpture, Drawing, & Printmaking. 1998. (Art Around the World Ser.). (Illus.). 56-64p. (gr. 4-8). 23.93 (978-0-8225-2075-7(3)) Lerner Publishing Group.

Gaspas, Dianne. Southwest Indian Designs Coloring Book. 2003. (Illus.). 32p. (J). pap. 3.95 (978-0-486-43042-3(1)) Dover Pubns., Inc.

Gnojewski, Carol. American Indian Crafts Kids Can Do! 2006. (Multicultural Crafts Kids Can Do! Ser.). (Illus.). 32p. (J). lib. bdg. 22.60 (978-0-7660-2458-8(X), Enslow Elementary) Enslow Pubs., Inc.

Hall, Margaret. Venom & Visions. 2007. (Shockwave: Arts & Culture Ser.). (Illus.). 36p. (J). (gr. 4-6). lib. bdg. 25.00 (*978-0-531-17788-4(2) , Children's Pr.) Scholastic Library Publishing.

Levy, Janey. Native American Art from the Pueblos. 2003. (Reading Room Collection). (Illus.). 24p. (J). lib. bdg. 18.75 (978-0-8239-3702-8(X)) Rosen Publishing Group, Inc., The.

Native American Art & Artists, 6 vols. (Book2WebTM Ser.). (gr. 4-8). 36.50 (978-0-322-02981-1(3)) Wright Group, The.

Oppelt, Norman T. Earth, Water & Fire: The Prehistoric Pottery of Mesa Verde. rev. ed. 1998. (Illus.). 91p. (YA). reprint ed. pap. 14.95 (978-0-9662845-0-8(X)) Oppelt Pubns.

Petra Press. Native American Art. 2nd ed. 2006. (Illus.). 32p. (J). pap. (*978-1-4034-8777-3(4)) Heinemann Library.

Press, Petra. Native American Art. 2006. (Illus.). 32p. (J). (*978-1-4034-8769-8(3)) Heinemann Library.

Trottier, Maxine. Native Crafts: Inspired by North America's First People. Melo, Esperanca, illus. unabr. ed. 2000. (Kids Can Do It Ser.). (J). (gr. 4-6). 132p. (978-1-55074-549-8(2)); 40p. (978-1-55074-854-3(8)) Kids Can Pr., Ltd.

—Native Crafts: Inspired by North America's First People. 2000. (gr. 3-6). lib. bdg. 14.10 (978-0-613-26345-0(6)); (Illus.). (J). (978-0-606-18228-7(4)) Tandem Library Bks.

INDIANS OF NORTH AMERICA—BANNOCK INDIANS—FICTION

Thomasma, Kenneth. Doe Sia: Bannock Girl & the Handcart Pioneer. 1999. (Amazing Indian Children: 8). (J). (gr. 3-8). pap. 7.99 (978-1-880114-20-9(8)) Grandview Publishing Co.

INDIANS OF NORTH AMERICA—BIOGRAPHY

Adler, David A. A Picture Book of Sacagawea. Brown, Dan, illus. 2000. (Picture Book Biography Ser.). 32p. (J). (gr. k-3). tchr. ed. 16.95 (978-0-8234-1485-7(X)) Holiday Hse., Inc.

Allen, Paula Gunn. As Long As the Rivers Flow: The Stories of Nine Native Americans. 2001. (YA). 11.15 (978-0-606-22174-0(3)) Tandem Library Bks.

Alter, Judy. Great Women of the Old West. 2001. (We the People Ser.). (Illus.). 48p. (J). (gr. 4 up). lib. bdg. 22.60 (978-0-7565-0099-3(0)) Compass Point Bks.

—Sacagawea: Native American Interpreter. 2002. (Spirit of America: Our People Ser.). (Illus.). 32p. (J). (gr. 2-6). 27.07 (978-1-56766-166-8(1)) Child's World, Inc.

American Indian Biographies, 10 bks. Incl. Chief Joseph 1840-1904. Englar, Mary. 2004. lib. bdg. 23.93 (978-0-7368-2444-6(8)); Chief Red Cloud 1822-1909. Monroe, Judy. 2004. lib. bdg. 23.93 (978-0-7368-2445-3(6)); Crazy Horse 1842-1877. Todd, Anne M. 2002. lib. bdg. 23.93 (978-0-7368-1210-8(5)); Osceola 1804-1838. Koestler-Grack, Rachel A. 2002. lib. bdg. 23.93 (978-0-7368-1211-5(3)); Pocahontas 1595-1617. Sonneborn, Liz. 2002. lib. bdg. 23.93 (978-0-7368-1214-6(8)); Sacagawea 1788-1812. Wallner, Rosemary. 2002. lib. bdg. 23.93 (978-0-7368-1213-9(X)); Sequoyah, 1770-1843. Dennis, Yvonn Wakim. 2004. lib. bdg. 23.93 (978-0-7368-2447-7(2)); Sitting Bull 1831-1890. Todd, Anne M. 2002. lib. bdg. 23.93 (978-0-7368-1215-3(6)); Squanto1585-1622. Hirschfelder, Arlene B. 2004. lib. bdg. 23.93 (978-0-7368-2446-0(4)); Tecumseh 1768-1813. Koestler-Grack, Rachel A. 2002. lib. bdg. 23.93 (978-0-7368-1212-2(1)); 32p. (J). (gr. 3-4). (Illus.). Set lib. bdg. 239.30 (978-0-7368-2552-8(5) , Blue Earth Bks.) Capstone Pr., Inc.

Avery, Susan & Skinner, Linda. Extraordinary American Indians. 2001. (Illus.). 252p. (YA). (gr. 6-8). reprint ed. 25.00 (978-0-7881-9698-0(7)) DIANE Publishing Co.

Banks, Sara Harrell. Tomo-Chi-Chi: Gentle Warrior. (J). pap. 12.95 (978-0-913720-79-0(8)) Beil, Frederic C. Pub., Inc.

Basel, Roberta. Sequoyah: Inventor of Written Cherokee. 2006. (Signature Lives Ser.). 112p. (YA). (gr. 5-8). lib. bdg. 31.93 (*978-0-7565-1887-5(3)) Compass Point Bks.

Becker, Sandra. Pocahontas. 2003. (Folk Heroes Ser.). (Illus.). 24p. (J). lib. bdg. 15.95 (978-1-59036-074-3(5)) Weigl Pubs., Inc.

Belarde-Lewis, Miranda. Meet Lydia: A Native Girl from Southeast Alaska. Harrington, John, photos by. 2004. (My World—Young Native Americans Today Ser.). (Illus.). 48p. (J). 15.95 (978-1-57178-147-5(1)) Council Oak Bks.

Birchfield, D. L. Crazy Horse. 2002. (Raintree Biographies Ser.). (Illus.). 32p. (J). lib. bdg. 25.69 (978-0-7398-5673-4(1)) Raintree.

—Sacagawea. 2002. (Raintree Biographies Ser.). (Illus.). 32p. (J). lib. bdg. 25.69 (978-0-7398-5680-2(4)) Raintree.

Black, Sonia W. Let's Read About— Squanto. Doucet, Bob, illus. 2002. (Scholastic First Biographies Ser.). (J). pap. (978-0-439-45952-5(4)) Scholastic, Inc.

Bloom Fradin, Judith & Brindell Fradin, Dennis. Who Was Sacagawea? Taylor, Van Paul & Harrison, Nancy, illus. 2002. (Who Was...? Ser.). 112p. (J). pap. 4.99 (978-0-448-42485-9(1) , Grosset & Dunlap) Penguin Group (USA) Inc.

Brown, Don. Bright Path: Young Jim Thorpe. Brown, Don, illus. 2006. (Illus.). 40p. (J). 17.95 (978-1-59643-041-9(9)) Roaring Brook Pr.

Bruchac, Joseph. Bowman's Store: A Journey to Myself. 2001. (Illus.). 328p. (YA). (gr. 7 up). pap. 6.95 (978-1-58430-027-4(2)) Lee & Low Bks., Inc.

—Bowman's Store: A Journey to Myself. 2001. (gr. 3-6). lib. bdg. 15.25 (978-0-613-84717-9(2)) Tandem Library Bks.

—Buffalo Song. Farnsworth, Bill, illus. 2008. (J). Lee & Low Bks., Inc.

—Geronimo. 2006. 240p. (J). (gr. 7 up). pap. 16.99 (978-0-439-35360-1(2)) Scholastic, Inc.

—Jim Thorpe, Original All-American. 2006. (Illus.). 288p. (J). (gr. 5). 16.99 (978-0-8037-3118-9(3) , Dial) Penguin Group (USA) Inc.

—Seeing the Circle. Fine, John Christopher, photos by. 1999. (Meet the Author Ser.). (Illus.). 32p. (J). (gr. 2-5). 14.95 (978-1-57274-327-4(1) , 724) Owen, Richard C. Pubs., Inc.

Capaldi, Gina, illus. A Boy Named Beckoning: The True Story of Dr. Carlos Montezuma, Native American Hero. 2008. (Exceptional Social Studies Titles for Intermediate Grades Ser.). (J). lib. bdg. 16.95 (*978-0-8225-7644-0(9) , Carolrhoda Bks.) Lerner Publishing Group.

Collard, Sneed B., III. Sacagawea: Brave Shoshone Girl. 2006. (American Heroes Ser.). (Illus.). 48p. (J). (gr. 3-5). lib. bdg. 28.50 (978-0-7614-2166-5(1) , Benchmark Bks.) Cavendish, Marshall Corp.

Collier, James Lincoln. The Tecumseh You Never Knew. Copeland, Greg, illus. 2004. (You Never Knew Ser.). (J). 25.50 (978-0-516-24426-6(4) , Children's Pr.) Scholastic Library Publishing.

Collins, David R., et al. Ishi: The Last of His People. Welch, Kelly, illus. 2004. (Notable Americans Ser.). 96p. (YA). (gr. 6-12). 23.95 (978-1-883846-54-1(4) , First Biographies) Reynolds, Morgan Inc.

Crosby, Michael T. Sacagawea: Lewis & Clark's Pathfinder. 2007. 144p. (J). 25.95 (*978-1-59556-026-1(2)) OTTN Publishing.

Davis, Kenneth C. Don't Know Much about Sitting Bull Sitting Bull, Vol. 2. 2003. (Don't Know Much About Ser.). (Illus.). 144p. (J). (gr. 3-7). 16.89 (978-0-06-028818-1(3)) HarperCollins Pubs.

DeKeyser, Stacy. Sacagawea. 2004. (Watts Library). (Illus.). 64p. (J). 25.50 (978-0-531-12290-7(5) , Watts, Franklin) Scholastic Library Publishing.

Dennis, Yvonn Wakim. Sequoyah, 1770-1843. 2004. (American Indian Biographies Ser.). (Illus.). 32p. (J). (gr. 3-4). lib. bdg. 23.93 (978-0-7368-2447-7(2) , Blue Earth Bks.) Capstone Pr., Inc.

Durrant, Lynda. Beaded Moccasins. 2000. (Illus.). 192p. (gr. 4-7). 5.99 (978-0-440-41591-6(8) , Yearling) Random Hse. Children's Bks.

—The Beaded Moccasins: The Story of Mary Campbell. 1998. 192p. (J). (gr. 4-6). tchr. ed. 15.00 (978-0-395-85398-6(2) , Clarion Bks.) Houghton Mifflin Co. Trade & Reference Div.

Durrett, Deanne & Kallen, Stuart A. Native American Chiefs & Warriors. 1999. (History Makers Ser.). (Illus.). 112p. (YA). (gr. 7-10). 28.70 (978-1-56006-364-3(5) , Lucent Bks.) Thomson Gale.

Egan, Tracie. Cynthia Ann Parker: Cautiva de los Comanches. Gonzalez, Tomas, tr. 2003. (Grandes Personajes en la Historia de los Estados Unidos Ser.). (ENG & SPA.). (J). pap. (978-0-8239-4225-1(2)) Rosen Publishing Group, Inc., The.

Erdrich, Lise. Sacagawea. Buffalohead, Julie, illus. 2003. 40p. (J). (gr. 3-6). 16.95 (978-0-87614-646-0(9) , Carolrhoda Bks.) Lerner Publishing Group.

Famous Indians: A Collection of Short Biographies. 2000. 64p. (J). 7.95 (978-1-885772-23-7(8)) Kiva Publishing, Inc.

Feinstein, Stephen. Lee sobre Sacagawea/Read about Sacagawea. 2006. (I Like Biographies! Bilingual Ser.). (ENG & SPA., Illus.). 24p. (J). (gr. 1-3). lib. bdg. 21.26 (978-0-7660-2674-2(4) , Enslow Elementary) Enslow Pubs., Inc.

—Read about Sacagawea. 2004. (I Like Biographies Ser.!). (Illus.). 24p. (J). lib. bdg. 21.26 (978-0-7660-2297-3(8)) Enslow Pubs., Inc.

First Americans Group 2, 6 bks., Set. Incl. Cheyenne. De Capua, Sarah. lib. bdg. 29.93 (978-0-7614-2248-8(X)); Comanche. De Capua, Sarah. lib. bdg. 29.93 (978-0-7614-2249-5(8)); Haida. King, David C. lib. bdg. 29.93 (978-0-7614-2250-1(1)); Huron. King, David C. lib. bdg. 29.93 (978-0-7614-2251-8(X)); Ojibwe. King, David C. lib. bdg. 29.93 (978-0-7614-2252-5(8)); Seminole. King, David C. lib. bdg. 29.93 (978-0-7614-2253-2(6)); (Illus.). 48p. (J). 2006. 2007. Set lib. bdg. 179.57 (*978-0-7614-2247-1(1) , Benchmark Bks.) Cavendish, Marshall Corp.

Fitterer, C. Ann. Tecumseh: Chief of the Shawnee. 2002. (Spirit of America: Our People Ser.). (Illus.). 32p. (J). (gr. 2-6). 27.07 (978-1-56766-168-2(8)) Child's World, Inc.

Ford, Carin T. Sacagawea: Meet an American Legend. 2003. (Meeting Famous People Ser.). (Illus.). 32p. (J). lib. bdg. 22.60 (978-0-7660-2004-7(5)) Enslow Pubs., Inc.

Fradin, Dennis Brindell. Who Was Sacagawea? 2002. (gr. 3-6). lib. bdg. 13.00 (978-0-613-43655-7(5)) Tandem Library Bks.

Franklin, Virgil. The Story of Sacagawea. 2002. (Reading Room Collection). (Illus.). 24p. (J). pap. (978-0-8239-8162-5(2)); lib. bdg. 18.75 (978-0-8239-3725-7(9)) Rosen Publishing Group, Inc., The.

Frazier, Neta Lohnes. Path to the Pacific: The Story of Sacagawea. 2007. (Sterling Point Bks.). (Illus.). 177p. (J). (*978-1-4287-2899-8(6)) Sterling Publishing Co., Inc.

—Path to the Pacific: The Story of Sacajawea. 2007. (Sterling Point Bks.). (Illus.). 192p. (J). pap. 6.95 (978-1-4027-4138-8(3)) Sterling Publishing Co., Inc.

—Sterling Point Books: Path to the Pacific: The Story of Sacajawea. 2007. (Sterling Point Bks.). (Illus.). 192p. (J). 12.95 (978-1-4027-4518-8(4)) Sterling Publishing Co., Inc.

Fritz, Jean. The Double Life of Pocahontas. 2004. 24.95 incl. audio (978-1-56008-189-0(9)) Weston Woods Studios, Inc.

Furbee, Mary Rodd. Wild Rose: Nancy Ward & the Cherokee Nation. 2004. (Women of the Frontier Ser.). (Illus.). 112p. (YA). (gr. 6-12). 23.95 (978-1-883846-71-8(4) , First Biographies) Reynolds, Morgan Inc.

Geronimo, Level 2. 1999. (SmartReader Ser.). (J). pap., tchr. ed. 19.95 incl. audio (978-0-7887-0127-6(4) , 79315T3) Recorded Bks., LLC.

Gosda, Randy T. Sitting Bull. 2002. (First Biographies Ser.). (Illus.). 32p. (J). (gr. k-4). lib. bdg. 22.78 (978-1-57765-737-8(3) , Buddy Bks.) ABDO Publishing Co.

Haugen, Brenda. Geronimo: Apache Warrior. 2005. (Signature Lives Ser.). (Illus.). 112p. (J). (gr. 5-7). 30.60 (978-0-7565-1002-2(3)) Compass Point Bks.

Hayhurst, Chris. Toro Sentado: Jefe Sioux. 2003. (ENG & SPA.). (J). pap. (978-0-8239-4238-1(4)) Rosen Publishing Group, Inc., The.

Hirschfelder, Arlene B. Squanto1585-1622. 2004. (American Indian Biographies Ser.). (Illus.). 32p. (J). (gr. 3-4). lib. bdg. 23.93 (978-0-7368-2446-0(4) , Blue Earth Bks.) Capstone Pr., Inc.

Holliday, Diane. Mountain Wolf Woman: A Ho-Chunk Girlhood. 2007. (Badger Biographies Ser.). (Illus.). 80p. (J). pap. 12.95 (*978-0-87020-381-7(9)) Wisconsin Historical Society.

Howard, Annabelle. Cry Out Liberty: Sarah Winnemucca, Indian Princess. 2005. 40.00 (*978-1-4108-4204-6(5)) Benchmark Education Co.

Hubbard-Brown, Janet. Native American Leaders. 1999. (Costume, Tradition & Culture). (Illus.). 64p. (YA). (gr. 5 up). 12.95 (978-0-7910-5209-9(5) , Chelsea Hse.) Facts On File, Inc.

Jeffrey, Gary & Petty, Kate. Sitting Bull: The Life of a Lakota Sioux Chief. 2005. (Graphic Nonfiction Ser.). (Illus.). 48p. (J). (gr. 4-6). lib. bdg. 26.50 (978-1-4042-0247-4(1)) Rosen Publishing Group, Inc., The.

Jenner, Caryn. The Story of Pocahontas, Vol. 2. Martin, Linda, ed. 2000. (Readers Ser.). (Illus.). 32p. (J). (gr. 1-3). pap. 3.99 (978-0-7894-6636-5(8)) Dorling Kindersley Publishing, Inc.

—The Story of Pocahontas. 2000. (Illus.). 32p. (J). (ps-ps). lib. bdg. 11.80 (978-0-613-33108-1(7)) Tandem Library Bks.

Jenner, Caryn & Dorling Kindersley Publishing Staff. The Story of Pocahontas. 2000. (Readers Ser.). (Illus.). 32p. (J). (gr. 1-3). 14.99 (978-0-7894-6637-2(6)) Dorling Kindersley Publishing, Inc.

Juettner, Bonnie. 100 Native Americans Who Changed History. 2005. (People Who Changed History Ser.). (Illus.). 112p. (J). lib. bdg. 30.00 (978-0-8368-5770-2(4) , World Almanac Library) Stevens, Gareth Inc.

—100 Native-Americans Who Shaped American History. 2003. (100 Ser.). (Illus.). 112p. (J). 7.95 (978-0-912517-51-3(4)) Bluewood Bks.

—100 Native-Americans Who Shaped American History. 2003. (gr. 7-12). lib. bdg. 16.40 (978-0-613-58682-5(4)) Tandem Library Bks.

Kalman, Bobbie. Famous Native North Americans. 2003. (gr. 3-6). lib. bdg. 17.60 (978-0-613-85049-0(1)) Tandem Library Bks.

Kalman, Bobbie & Aloian, Molly. Famous Native North Americans. 2003. (Native Nations of North America Ser.). (Illus.). 32p. (J). (gr. 5). (978-0-7787-0379-2(7)); pap. (978-0-7787-0471-3(8)) Crabtree Publishing Co.

Kiely Miller, Barbara. Chief Joseph. 2007. (J). pap. (*978-0-8368-8321-3(7) , Weekly Reader Early Learning Library) Stevens, Gareth Inc.

Klingel, Cynthia Fitterer & Noyed, Robert B. Chief Joseph: Chief of the Nez Perce. 2002. (Spirit of America: Our People Ser.). (Illus.). 32p. (J). (gr. 2-6). 27.07 (978-1-56766-165-1(3)) Child's World, Inc.

Koestler-Grack, Rachel A. Chief John Ross. 2004. (Illus.). 32p. (J). pap. 7.50 (978-1-4034-5007-4(2)); lib. bdg. 24.22 (978-1-4034-5000-5(5)) Heinemann Library.

—Chief Joseph. 2004. (Illus.). 32p. (J). pap. 7.50 (978-1-4034-5008-1(0)); lib. bdg. 24.22 (978-1-4034-5001-2(3)) Heinemann Library.

—Osceola 1804-1838. 2002. (American Indian Biographies Ser.). (Illus.). 32p. (J). (gr. 3-4). lib. bdg. 23.93 (978-0-7368-1211-5(3) , Blue Earth Bks.) Capstone Pr., Inc.

—Sacagawea. 2004. (Illus.). 32p. (J). pap. 7.50 (978-1-4034-5011-1(0)); lib. bdg. 24.22 (978-1-4034-5004-3(8)) Heinemann Library.

Krull, Kathleen. Pocahontas: Princess of the New World. Diaz, David, illus. 2007. 40p. (J). (gr. 1-6). 17.85 (978-0-8027-9555-7(2)); 16.95 (978-0-8027-9554-0(4)) Walker & Co.

Littlechild, George. This Land Is My Land. Littlechild, George, illus. 2003. (Illus.). 32p. (J). pap. 7.95 (978-0-89239-184-4(7)) Children's Bk. Pr.

—This Land Is My Land. 2003. (gr. 3-6). lib. bdg. 16.40 (978-0-613-61390-3(2)) Tandem Library Bks.

Marcovitz, Hal. Sacagawea: Guide for the Lewis & Clark Expedition. 2007. (Illus.). 63p. (J). pap. 12.00 (*978-1-4223-6712-4(6)) DIANE Publishing Co.

—Sacagawea: Guide for the Lewis & Clark Expedition. 2000. (Explorers of the New World Ser.). (Illus.). (J). 63p. (gr. 4-7). pap. 25.00 (978-0-7910-6169-5(8)); 64p. (gr. 8-12). 25.00 (978-0-7910-5959-3(6)) Facts On File, Inc. (Chelsea Hse.).

—Sacagawea: Guide for the Lewis & Clark Expedition. 2001. (gr. 3-6). lib. bdg. 17.60 (978-0-613-33014-5(5)) Tandem Library Bks.

Marsh, Carole. Tecumseh. 2002. (One Thousand Readers Ser.). (Illus.). 12p. (J). (gr. k-4). 2.95 (978-0-635-01563-1(3) , 15633) Gallopade International.

McLeese, Don. Jim Thorpe. 2003. (Rourke Discovery Library). (Illus.). 24p. (gr. 2-5). 14.95 (978-1-58952-305-0(9)) Rourke Publishing, LLC.

—Sacagawea. 2003. (Native American Legends Ser.). (Illus.). 32p. (J). 28.50 (978-1-58952-729-4(1)) Rourke Publishing, LLC.

Metaxas, Eric. Squanto & the First Thanksgiving: The Legendary American Tale. Donato, Michael A., illus. 2004. 36p. (J). (gr. 3-8). reprint ed. 19.00 (978-0-7567-7123-2(4)) DIANE Publishing Co.

Miller, Barbara Kiely. Chief Joseph. 2007. (Great Americans Ser.). 24p. (J). (gr. 2-4). lib. bdg. 19.93 (*978-0-8368-8314-5(4) , Weekly Reader Early Learning Library) Stevens, Gareth Inc.

Milton, Joyce. Sacajawea. Hehenberger, Shelly, illus. 2001. (All Aboard Reading Ser.). 48p. (J). (gr. 1-3). pap. 3.99 (978-0-448-42539-9(4) , Grosset & Dunlap) Penguin Group (USA) Inc.

Monceaux, Morgan & Katcher, Ruth. My Heroes, My People: African Americans & Native Americans in Thewest. Monceaux, Morgan, illus. 2004. (Illus.). 63p. (J). (gr. k-4). reprint ed. 18.00 (978-0-7567-7868-2(9)) DIANE Publishing Co.

Moody, Ralph. Geronimo: Wolf of the Warpath. 2006. (Sterling Point Bks.). (Illus.). 192p. (J). 12.95 (978-1-4027-3184-6(1)); pap. 6.95 (978-1-4027-3612-4(6)) Sterling Publishing Co., Inc.

Moskal, Greg. An Apache Indian Community. 2002. (Reading Room Collection). (J). (978-0-8239-8156-4(8)); (978-0-8239-8558-6(X)) Rosen Publishing Group, Inc., The.

—Un Pueblo Apache. Gonzalez, Tomas, tr. 2002. (Buenas Letras Reading Room Ser.). (SPA., Illus.). 24p. (J). (gr. 4-7). lib. bdg. 18.75 (978-0-8239-6512-0(0) , Buenas Letra) Rosen Publishing Group, Inc., The.

Native American Biographies, 6 bks., Set. (Illus.). (YA). (gr. 6-12). lib. bdg. 125.70 (978-0-89490-965-8(7)) Enslow Pubs., Inc.

Nelson, S. D. Quiet Hero: The Ira Hayes Story. Nelson, S. D., illus. 2006. (Illus.). (J). lib. bdg. 16.95 (978-1-58430-263-6(1)) Lee & Low Bks., Inc.

Niethammer, Carolyn J. Keeping the Rope Straight: Annie Dodge Wauneka's Life of Service to the Navajo. Ruffenach, Jessie, ed. 2006. (Illus.). 128p. 22.95 (978-1-893354-72-2(5)) Salina Bookshelf.

Petrie, Kristin. Sacagawea. 2007. (Illus.). 32p. (J). 22.78 (978-1-59679-749-9(5)) ABDO Publishing Co.

Philip, Neil, ed. A Braid of Lives: Native American Childhood. 2000. (Illus.). 96p. (J). (gr. 7 up). 20.00 (978-0-395-64528-4(X) , Clarion Bks.) Houghton Mifflin Co. Trade & Reference Div.

Phillips, Larissa. Cochise: Jefe Apache. de la Vega, Eida, tr. from ENG. 2003. (Grandes Personajes en la Historia de Los Estados Unidos Ser.). (ENG & SPA., Illus.). 32p. (J). pap. (978-0-8239-4223-7(6)) Rosen Publishing Group, Inc., The.

Rappaport, Doreen. The Flight of Red Bird: The Life of Zitkala-sa. 1999. (J). (978-0-606-16777-2(3)) Tandem Library Bks.

—We Are the Many: A Picture Book of American Indians. Van Wright, Cornelius, illus. 2002. 32p. (J). (gr. k-4). 15.99 (978-0-688-16559-8(1)); lib. bdg. 17.89 (978-0-06-001139-0(4)) HarperCollins Pubs.

Rausch, Monica. Sacagawea. 2006. (Illus.). 24p. (J). pap. (*978-0-8368-7692-5(X)); lib. bdg. (*978-0-8368-7685-7(7)) Stevens, Gareth Inc. (Weekly Reader Early Learning Library).

Roop, Peter & Roop, Connie. Thank You, Squanto! 2005. (Before I Made History Ser.). (Illus.). 57p. (J). pap. (978-0-439-79254-7(1)) Scholastic, Inc.

Rosinsky, Natalie M. Sarah Winnemucca: Scout, Activist, & Teacher. 2005. (Signature Lives Ser.). (Illus.). 112p. (J). (gr. 5-7). (978-0-7565-1003-9(1)) Compass Point Bks.

Rucker, Jeffrey A. The Story of Sitting Bull. 2002. (Reading Room Collection). (J). pap. (978-0-8239-8169-4(X)); (Illus.). 24p. lib. bdg. 18.75 (978-0-8239-3732-5(1)) Rosen Publishing Group, Inc., The.

Sacajawea, Traductora Y Guia. 2003. (Notas Biograficas Ser.). (YA). pap. 48.95 (978-0-8136-5915-2(9)) Modern Curriculum Pr.

Schaefer, Lola M. Pocahontas. Saunders-Smith, Gail, ed. 2002. (First Biographies Ser.). (Illus.). 24p. (J). (gr. k-1). lib. bdg. 15.93 (978-0-7368-1175-0(3) , Pebble Bks.) Capstone Pr., Inc.

Schilling, Vincent. Native Athletes in Action! 2007. (Native Trailblazers Ser.). (Illus.). 128p. (J). (gr. 4-8). pap. 9.95 (*978-0-9779183-0-0(0)) 7th Generation.

Shull, Jodie A. Peacemaker Princess: A Story about Sarah Winnemucca. 2007. (Creative Minds Biography Ser.). (J). spiral bd. 22.60 (978-0-8225-5990-0(0)) Lerner Publishing Group.

Silverstone, Michael. Winona Laduke: Restoring Land & Culture in Native America. 2001. (Women Changing the World Ser.). (Illus.). 112p. (gr. 4-7). 19.95 (978-1-55861-260-0(2)) Feminist Pr. at The City Univ. of New York.

Simmons, Marc. Friday, the Arapaho Boy: A Story from History. Kil, Ronald R., illus. 2004. 56p. (J). (gr. 4 up). 18.95 (978-0-8263-3609-5(4)) Univ. of New Mexico Pr.

Sonneborn, Liz. Pocahontas 1595-1617. 2002. (American Indian Biographies Ser.). (Illus.). 32p. (J). (gr. 3-4). lib. bdg. 23.93 (978-0-7368-1214-6(8) , Blue Earth Bks.) Capstone Pr., Inc.

Stanley, George E. Crazy Horse: Young War Chief. Henderson, Meryl, illus. 2005. (Childhood of Famous Americans Ser.). 208p. (J). pap. 5.99 (978-0-689-85746-1(2) , Aladdin) Simon & Schuster Children's Publishing.

Stanley, George Edward. Crazy Horse: Young War Chief. Henderson, Meryl, illus. 2005. 199p. (J). (978-1-4156-2931-4(5) , Aladdin) Simon & Schuster Children's Publishing.

—Geronimo: Young Warrior. 2001. (gr. 3-6). lib. bdg. 13.00 (978-0-613-63409-0(8)) Tandem Library Bks.

Sutcliffe, Jane. Chief Joseph. 2004. (History Maker Bios Ser.). (J). pap. 6.95 (978-0-8225-2068-9(0)) Lerner Publishing Group.

—Chief Joseph. Parlin, Tim, tr. Parlin, Tim, illus. 2004. (History Maker Bios Ser.). 48p. (J). (gr. 3-5). lib. bdg. 26.60 (978-0-8225-0696-6(3)) Lerner Publishing Group.

Tallchief, Maria. Tallchief: America's Prima Ballerina. 2001. (J). (978-0-606-22511-3(0)) Tandem Library Bks.

H
I

Tallchief, Maria & Well, Rosemary. Tallchief: America's Prima Ballerina. Kelley, Gary, illus. 2001. 28p. (J). (gr. k-4). lib. bdg. 15.30 (978-0-613-44420-0(5)) Tandem Library Bks.

Tallchief, Maria & Wells, Rosemary. Tallchief: America's Prima Ballerina. Kelley, Gary, illus. 1999. 32p. (J). (gr. k-4). 16.99 (978-0-670-88756-9(0) , Viking Juvenile) Penguin Group (USA) Inc.

Tayac, Gabrielle. Meet Naiche: A Native Boy from the Chesapeake Bay Area. Harrington, John, photos by. 2007. (Illus.). 48p. (J). 15.95 (978-1-57178-146-8(3)) Council Oak Bks.

Tayac, Gabrielle & Secakuku, Susan. Meet Naiche. Harrington, John, photos by. 2003. (My World). (Illus.). 32p. (J). (gr. 4 up). lib. bdg. 24.67 (978-0-8368-3795-7(9)) Stevens, Gareth Inc.

Tieck, Sarah. Sacagawea. 2007. (Buddy Book Ser.). (Illus.). 32p. (J). 22.78 (978-1-59679-789-5(4)) ABDO Publishing Co.

Todd, Anne M. Crazy Horse 1842-1877. 2002. (American Indian Biographies Ser.). (Illus.). 32p. (J). (gr. 3-4). lib. bdg. 23.93 (978-0-7368-1210-8(5) , Blue Earth Bks.) Capstone Pr., Inc.

—Osceola. 2004. (Illus.). 32p. (J). pap. 7.50 (978-1-4034-5010-4(2)); lib. bdg. 24.22 (978-1-4034-5003-6(X)) Heinemann Library.

—Sequoyah. 2004. (Illus.). 32p. (J). pap. 7.50 (978-1-4034-5012-8(9)); lib. bdg. 24.22 (978-1-4034-5005-0(6)) Heinemann Library.

—Sitting Bull 1831-1890. 2002. (American Indian Biographies Ser.). (Illus.). 32p. (J). (gr. 3-4). lib. bdg. 23.93 (978-0-7368-1215-3(6) , Blue Earth Bks.) Capstone Pr., Inc.

Townsend, Dana E. Sequoyah & the Cherokee Alphabet. Gabriel, Andrea, illus. 2005. (Voices Reading Ser.). 32p. (J). (978-0-7367-2953-6(4)) Zaner-Bloser, Inc.

Trumbauer, Lisa. Sitting Bull. (First Biographies Ser.). 24p. (J). pap. 5.95 (978-0-7368-5088-9(0)) Capstone Pr., Inc.

Van Steenwyck, Elizabeth. Seneca Chief, Army General: A Story about Ely Parker. 2001. (gr. 3-6). lib. bdg. 15.25 (978-0-613-68385-2(4)) Tandem Library Bks.

Wallner, Rosemary. Sacagawea 1788-1812. 2002. (American Indian Biographies Ser.). (Illus.). 32p. (J). (gr. 3-4). lib. bdg. 23.93 (978-0-7368-1213-9(X) , Blue Earth Bks.) Capstone Pr., Inc.

Witteman, Barbara. Sacagawea. 2002. (Photo-Illustrated Biographies Ser.). (Illus.). 24p. (J). (gr. 2-3). lib. bdg. 18.60 (978-0-7368-1112-5(5) , Bridgestone Bks.) Capstone Pr., Inc.

Zemlicka, Shannon. Pocahontas. Reeves, Jeni, illus. 2002. (On My Own Biographies Ser.). 47p. (J). lib. bdg. 23.93 (978-0-87614-598-2(5) , Carolrhoda Bks.) Lerner Publishing Group.

—Pocahontas. 2002. (gr. 3-6). lib. bdg. 14.10 (978-0-613-52481-0(0)) Tandem Library Bks.

—Quanah Parker. 2004. (History Maker Bios Ser.). (J). pap. 6.95 (978-0-8225-2070-2(2)); (Illus.). 48p. 26.60 (978-0-8225-0724-6(2) , Carolrhoda Bks.) Lerner Publishing Group.

INDIANS OF NORTH AMERICA—CANADA

Ansary, Mir Tamim. Subarctic Indians. (Native Americans Ser.). (Illus.). 32p. (J). 2002. (gr. 1-4). pap. 7.50 (978-1-58810-455-7(9) , 91174); 2000. (gr. 2-4). lib. bdg. 21.36 (978-1-57572-926-8(1)) Heinemann Library.

Bailey, Katie. Radisson & Groseilliers: Fur Traders of the North. 2006. (In the Footsteps of Explorers Ser.). (Illus.). 32p. (J). (gr. 3-14). pap. (978-0-7787-2458-2(1) , 1253444); (978-0-7787-2422-3(0) , 1253444) Crabtree Publishing Co.

Bial, Raymond. The Inuit. 2001. (Lifeways Ser.). (Illus.). 128p. (J). (gr. 5-9). lib. bdg. 34.21 (978-0-7614-1212-0(3) , Benchmark Bks.) Cavendish, Marshall Corp.

Englar, Mary. The Iroquois: The Six Nations Confederacy. 2002. (American Indian Nations Ser.). (Illus.). 48p. (J). (gr. 3-4). lib. bdg. 22.60 (978-0-7368-1353-2(5) , Bridgestone Bks.) Capstone Pr., Inc.

Johnson, Michael & Burkinshaw, Jane. Native Tribes of the North & Northwest Coast. 2004. (Native Tribes of North America Ser.). (Illus.). 64p. (J). (gr. 5 up). lib. bdg. 32.67 (978-0-8368-5611-8(2) , World Almanac Library) Stevens, Gareth Inc.

Koestler-Grack, Rachel A. The Iroquois: Longhouse Builders. 2003. (America's First Peoples Ser.). (Illus.). 32p. (J). (gr. 2-3). lib. bdg. 23.93 (978-0-7368-1536-9(8) , Bridgestone Bks.) Capstone Pr., Inc.

Littlechild, George. This Land Is My Land. Littlechild, George, illus. 2003. (Illus.). 32p. (J). pap. 7.95 (978-0-89239-184-4(7)) Children's Bk. Pr.

—This Land Is My Land. 2003. (gr. 3-6). lib. bdg. 16.40 (978-0-613-61390-3(2)) Tandem Library Bks.

Meuse, Theresa. The Sharing Circle: Stories about First Nations Culture. Stevens, Arthur, illus. 2003. pap. 11.95 (978-1-55109-450-2(9)) Down East Bks.

Riehecky, Janet. The Cree Tribe. 2002. (Native Peoples Ser.). (Illus.). 24p. (J). (gr. 2-3). lib. bdg. 18.60 (978-0-7368-1366-2(7) , Bridgestone Bks.) Capstone Pr., Inc.

Schilling, Vincent. Native Athletes in Action! 2007. (Native Trailblazers Ser.). (Illus.). 128p. (J). (gr. 4-8). pap. 9.95 (***978-0-9779183-0-0(0)***) 7th Generation.

Schmittroth, Felkins Ryan. Cree. 2003. (Tribes of Native America Ser.). (Illus.). 32p. (J). 23.70 (978-1-56711-690-8(6) , Blackbirch Pr., Inc.) Thomson Gale.

Stout, Mary A. Cree. 2003. (Native American Peoples Ser.). (Illus.). 32p. (J). (gr. 4 up). lib. bdg. 24.67 (978-0-8368-3703-2(7)) Stevens, Gareth Inc.

INDIANS OF NORTH AMERICA—CANADA—FICTION

Campbell, Nicola I. Shi-Shi-Etko. LaFave, Kim, illus. 2005. 32p. (ps-3). 16.95 (978-0-88899-659-6(4)) Groundwood Bks. CAN. *Dist:* Perseus Distribution.

Dubois, Muriel L. Abenaki Captive. 16.00 (978-0-9723410-0-4(5)) Apprentice Shop Bks., LLC.

Eckert, Allan W. Return to Hawk's Hill. 1998. (Illus.). 160p. (J). (gr. 7-12). 15.95 (978-0-316-21593-0(7)) Little Brown & Co.

—Return to Hawk's Hill. 2000. (978-0-606-17850-1(3)) Tandem Library Bks.

—Return to Hawk's Hill: Sequel to the Newbery Honor-Winning Incident at Hawk's Hill. 2000. 208p. (J). (gr. 7-17). pap. 15.99 (978-0-316-00689-7(0)) Little Brown & Co.

Hartson. Willa's New World: The Novel Study. 124p. stu. ed. 29.95 (978-1-55378-058-8(2)) Edmonton Public Schls. Centre for Education CAN. *Dist:* Coteau Bks.

Langrish, Katherine. Troll Blood. Stevens, Tim, illus. 2008. 352p. (J). 16.99 (***978-0-06-111674-2(2)***); lib. bdg. 17.89 (***978-0-06-111675-9(0)***) HarperCollins Pubs. (Eos).

Nervelle, Rosemarie. The Witch of Beaver Creek Mine. 2007. 160p. (gr. 5-9). 14.95 (***978-0-89272-741-4(1)***) Down East Bks.

Richardson, Faith. Tree Root & River Rat. 2003. (Illus.). 248p. (J). 21.95 (978-0-9744989-4-2(7)); pap. 12.95 (978-0-9744989-5-9(5)) Fox Song Bks.

Schultz Nicholson, Lorna. Northern Star. 2006. (Sports Stories Ser.). 112p. (J). (gr. 3-8). (***978-1-55028-911-4(X)***); 7.95 (978-1-55028-910-7(1)) Lorimer, James & Co., Ltd., Pubs. CAN. *Dist:* Casemate Pubs. & Bk. Distributors, LLC.

Schwartz, Virginia Frances. Initiation. 2003. 268p. (YA). (978-1-55005-053-0(2)) Fitzhenry & Whiteside, Ltd.

Trottier, Maxine. By the Standing Stone. 2001. (gr. 3-6). lib. bdg. 16.40 (978-0-613-51481-1(5)) Tandem Library Bks.

Trottier, Maxine. Death of My Country: The Plains of Abraham Diary of Geneviève Aubuchon. 2005. (Dear Canada Ser.). (Illus.). 208p. pap. (***978-0-439-96762-4(7)***) Scholastic Canada, Ltd.

Walters, Eric. War of the Eagles. 1998. 160p. (YA). (gr. 7-12). 14.00 (978-1-55143-118-5(1)) Orca Bk. Pubs. USA.

INDIANS OF NORTH AMERICA—CAPTIVITIES

Aller, Susan Bivin. Living with the Senecas: A Story about Mary Jemison. Harden, Laurie, illus. 2007. (Creative Minds Biographies Ser.). (J). spiral bd. 22.60 (978-0-8225-5989-4(7)) Lerner Publishing Group.

INDIANS OF NORTH AMERICA—CAPTIVITIES—FICTION

Buckey, Sarah Masters. Enemy in the Fort. 2001. (American Girl Collection). (Illus.). (J). 12.60 (978-0-606-21180-2(2)) Tandem Library Bks.

Cooney, Caroline B. The Ransom of Mercy Carter. 2002. (gr. 7-12). lib. bdg. 13.55 (978-0-613-60395-9(8)) Tandem Library Bks.

Durrant, Lynda. The Beaded Moccasins: The Story of Mary Campbell. 2000. (J). 11.64 (978-0-606-20017-2(7)) Tandem Library Bks.

—Beaded Moccasins: The Story of Mary Campbell. 2000. (gr. 5-8). lib. bdg. 13.00 (978-0-613-33670-3(4)) Tandem Library Bks.

Smith, Mary P. Boy Captive of Old Deerfield. (Illus.). (J). (gr. 5-6). reprint ed. lib. bdg. 22.95 (978-0-89190-961-3(3) , Rivercity Pr.) Amereon LTD.

Wheeler, Arville. White Squaw: The True Story of Jennie Wiley. 2000. (Illus.). 163p. (J). 14.95 (978-0-945084-82-2(X)) Stuart, Jesse Foundation, The.

INDIANS OF NORTH AMERICA—CHEROKEE INDIANS

American Indian Nations: The Cherokee; The Iroquois; The Ojibwa; The Pueblo; The Seminole; The Sioux, 6 bks. (Illus.). (J). (gr. 3-4). lib. bdg. 101.70 (978-0-7368-1359-4(4) , Bridgestone Bks.) Capstone Pr., Inc.

Bial, Raymond. The Cherokee. 1998. (Lifeways Ser.). (Illus.). 128p. (J). (gr. 5-9). lib. bdg. 34.21 (978-0-7614-0801-7(0) , Benchmark Bks.) Cavendish, Marshall Corp.

Birchfield, D. L. Cherokee. 2003. (Native American Peoples Ser.). (Illus.). 32p. (J). (gr. 4 up). lib. bdg. 24.67 (978-0-8368-3700-1(2)) Stevens, Gareth Inc.

—The Trail of Tears. 2003. (Landmark Events in American History Ser.). (Illus.). 48p. (J). (gr. 5 up). pap. 14.95 (978-0-8368-5409-1(8)); lib. bdg. 30.00 (978-0-8368-5381-0(4)) Stevens, Gareth Inc. (World Almanac Library).

Bruchac, Joseph. The Trail of Tears. 1999. (Step into Reading Ser.). (Illus.). 48p. (J). (gr. 3-5). pap. 3.99 (978-0-679-89052-2(1) , Random Hse. Bks. for Young Readers) Random Hse. Children's Bks.

—The Trail of Tears. 1999. (Step into Reading Ser.). (978-0-606-17525-8(3)) Tandem Library Bks.

Burgan, Michael. The Trail of Tears. 2001. (We the People Ser.). (Illus.). 48p. (J). (gr. 4 up). lib. bdg. 22.60 (978-0-7565-0101-3(6)) Compass Point Bks.

Cloud Tapper, Suzanne & Tapper, Suzanne Cloud. The Cherokee: A Proud People. 2005. (American Indians Ser.). (Illus.). 48p. (J). (ps-7). lib. bdg. 23.93 (978-0-7660-2454-0(7) , Enslow Elementary) Enslow Pubs., Inc.

Dennis, Yvonn Wakim. Sequoyah, 1770-1843. 2004. (American Indian Biographies Ser.). (Illus.). 32p. (J). (gr. 3-4). lib. bdg. 23.93 (978-0-7368-2447-7(2) , Blue Earth Bks.) Capstone Pr., Inc.

Duvall, Deborah L. How Medicine Came to the People: A Tale of the Ancient Cherokees. 2004. (Grandmother Stories Ser.: Vol. 2). (Illus.). 32p. (J). 14.95 (978-0-8263-3007-9(X)) Univ. of New Mexico Pr.

Elish, Dan, et al. The Trail of Tears: The Story of the Cherokee Removal. 2001. (Great Journeys Ser.). (Illus.). 96p. (J). (gr. 5 up). lib. bdg. 32.79 (978-0-7614-1228-1(X) , Benchmark Bks.) Cavendish, Marshall Corp.

Fischer, Laura. Life on the Trail of Tears. 2003. (Picture the Past Ser.). (Illus.). 32p. (J). pap. 6.95 (978-1-4034-4288-8(6)); lib. bdg. 22.79 (978-1-4034-3800-3(5)) Heinemann Library.

—Life on the Trail of Tears. 2003. (gr. k-3). lib. bdg. 35.30 (978-0-613-88783-0(2)) Tandem Library Bks.

Flanagan, Alice K. Mrs. Scott's Beautiful Art. Flanagan, Romie, illus. 1999. (Our Neighborhood Ser.). 32p. (J). (gr. 1-2). 20.00 (978-0-516-21135-0(8) , Children's Pr.) Scholastic Library Publishing.

Gaines, Richard. Cherokee. 2000. (Native Americans Ser.). (Illus.). 32p. (J). (gr. k-6). lib. bdg. 22.78 (978-1-57765-377-6(7) , Checkerboard Library) ABDO Publishing Co.

Griffis, Molly Levite. Great American Bunion Derby. 2003. (Illus.). viii, 87p. (J). 15.95 (978-1-57168-801-9(3) , Eakin Pr.) Eakin Pr.

Isaacs, Sally Senzell. The Trail of Tears. 2004. (Illus.). 32p. (J). pap. 7.50 (978-1-4034-4792-0(6)); lib. bdg. (978-1-4034-2507-2(8)) Heinemann Library.

Kent, Deborah. The Trail of Tears. 2005. (Cornerstones of Freedom Ser.). (Illus.). 48p. (J). (gr. 4-6). 26.00 (978-0-516-23624-7(5) , Children's Pr.) Scholastic Library Publishing.

Kucharczyk, Emily Rose. Wilma Mankiller: Native American Leader. 2002. (Famous Women Juniors Ser.). (Illus.). 32p. (J). (gr. 3-5). 23.70 (978-1-56711-593-2(4) , Blackbirch Pr., Inc.) Thomson Gale.

McLaughlin, Kari Massie. My Adventure with the Cherokee. 2007. 44p. (J). 8.99 (978-1-59092-446-4(0) , Orchard Academy Pr.) Windstorm Creative.

Miller, Connie R. The Cherokee. 2003. (Uncovering Native American History Ser.). (J). pap. (978-1-58417-111-9(1)); lib. bdg. (978-1-58417-048-8(4)) Lake Street Pubs.

O'Neill, Linda. Imagine Being Blind. 2000. (Imagine Ser.). (Illus.). 32p. (J). (gr. 1-4). lib. bdg. 26.60 (978-1-57103-376-5(9)) Rourke Publishing, LLC.

Petra Press Staff. The Cherokee. 2001. (First Reports). (Illus.). 48p. (J). (gr. 3 up). lib. bdg. 22.60 (978-0-7565-0079-5(6)) Compass Point Bks.

Petrini, Catherine M., tr. The Cherokee. 2003. (North American Indians Ser.). (Illus.). 48p. (J). 26.20 (978-0-7377-1511-8(1) , Greenhaven Pr., Inc.) Thomson Gale.

Roop, Peter & Roop, Connie. Cherokee. 1998. (If You Lived Ser.). (Illus.). 80p. (J). (gr. 2-5). pap. 5.99 (978-0-590-95606-2(X)) Scholastic, Inc.

Rumford, James. Sequoyah: The Cherokee Man Who Gave His People Writing. Huckaby, Anna Sixkiller, tr. 2004. (ENG & CHR., Illus.). 32p. (J). (gr. k-3). tchr. ed. 16.00 (978-0-618-36947-8(3)) Houghton Mifflin Co. Trade & Reference Div.

Ryan, Marla, ed. Cherokee. 2002. (Tribes of North America Ser.). (Illus.). 48p. (J). 23.70 (978-1-56711-614-4(0) , Blackbirch Pr., Inc.) Thomson Gale.

Ryan, Marla Felkins & Schmittroth, Linda, eds. Cheyenne. 2002. (Tribes of Native America Ser.). (Illus.). 32p. (J). 23.70 (978-1-56711-606-9(X) , Blackbirch Pr., Inc.) Thomson Gale.

Salas, Laura Purdie. The Trail of Tears 1838. 2003. (Let Freedom Ring Ser.). (Illus.). 48p. (J). (gr. 3-4). lib. bdg. 22.60 (978-0-7368-1559-8(7) , Bridgestone Bks.) Capstone Pr., Inc.

Santella, Andrew. The Cherokee. 2001. (True Bks.). (Illus.). 48p. (J). (gr. 3-5). pap. 6.95 (978-0-516-27315-0(9) , Children's Pr.) Scholastic Library Publishing.

—Cherokee. 2001. (gr. 3-6). lib. bdg. 15.25 (978-0-613-53490-1(5)) Tandem Library Bks.

Stewart, Philip. Cherokee. 2003. (North American Indians Today Ser.). (Illus.). 96p. (J). lib. bdg. (978-1-59084-665-0(6)) Mason Crest Pubs.

Todd, Anne M. The Cherokee: An Independent Nation. 2002. (American Indian Nations Ser.). (Illus.). 48p. (J). (gr. 3-4). lib. bdg. 22.60 (978-0-7368-1355-6(1) , Bridgestone Bks.) Capstone Pr., Inc.

—Sequoyah. 2004. (Illus.). 32p. (J). pap. 7.50 (978-1-4034-5012-8(9)); lib. bdg. 24.22 (978-1-4034-5005-0(6)) Heinemann Library.

Waxman, Laura Hamilton. Sequoyah. 2004. (History Maker Bios Ser.). (Illus.). 48p. (J). 26.60 (978-0-8225-0697-3(1) , Carolrhoda Bks.) Lerner Publishing Group.

INDIANS OF NORTH AMERICA—CHEROKEE INDIANS—FICTION

Anderson, Dee, retold by. Otter Gets Tricked! A Cherokee Trickster Story. l.t. ed. 2004. (Illus.). 32p. (J). pap. 6.00 (978-0-9755934-1-7(2)) Colonel Davenport Historical Foundation.

Bannon, Kay Thorpe. Curious One: A Cherokee Story. Sneed, Ravina Rene, illus. 2001. 38p. (J). (ps-5). pap. 12.95 (978-0-9669946-3-6(9)) Lobster Cove Publishing Co.

Bruchac, Joseph. The Journal of Jesse Smoke: A Cherokee Boy: Trail of Tears, 1838. 2001. (My Name Is America Ser.). (Illus.). 176p. (J). (gr. 4-8). pap. 10.95 (978-0-439-12197-2(3)) Scholastic, Inc.

Cahill, Byron. The Legend of Skywoman. 2005. 40.00 (***978-1-4108-4232-9(0)***) Benchmark Education Co.

Carter, Forrest. The Education of Little Tree. 2001. (gr. 7-12). lib. bdg. 23.40 (978-0-613-59067-9(8)) Tandem Library Bks.

Cornelissen, Cornelia. Soft Rain. 1999. (gr. 3-6). lib. bdg. 12.40 (978-0-613-23036-0(1)) Tandem Library Bks.

Ellington, Charlotte Jane. Dancing Leaf: A Novel. 2007. 192p. (YA). 15.95 (978-1-57072-311-7(7)) Overmountain Pr.

Haines, J. D. Flight of the Eagle. 2002. (Illus.). 88p. 15.95 (978-1-57168-744-9(0)) Eakin Pr.

Hanington, John G. The Adventures of Quick Fox. 2006. 80p. pap. 9.95 (***978-0-7414-3223-0(4)***) Infinity Publishing.

Johnston, Tony. Trail of Tears. Moser, Barry, illus. 1998. (J). (978-0-590-48519-7(9) , Blue Sky Pr., The) Scholastic, Inc.

Leppard, Lois Gladys. Mandie & the Cherokee Legend. 2007. (Mandie Bks.: No. 2). 144p. (J). (gr. 4-7). reprint ed. mass mkt. 5.99 (978-0-87123-321-9(5)) Bethany Hse. Pubs.

Moore, Lonnie W. & Moore, Iola. A Cherokee Spirit: The Saga of Oroville Annie & White Wolf. 1999. (Illus.). 45p. (J). pap. 15.95 (978-0-9661244-2-2(1)) I & L Publishing.

Penn, Audrey. The Whistling Tree. Gibson, Barbara, illus. 2006. 32p. 16.95 (978-0-9749303-9-8(3)) Tanglewood Pr.

Rockwood, Joyce. To Spoil the Sun. l.t. ed. 2004. 259p. 20.95 (978-0-7862-6433-9(0)) Thorndike Pr.

Smith, Florence B. Painted Eagle's Dream. 2001. 220p. (J). pap. 8.00 (978-1-893463-41-7(9)) Prickly Pr.

Tanner, Miriam. A Rose after Midnight. 2006. 100p. pap. 14.95 (978-1-4241-0693-6(1)) PublishAmerica, Inc.

Wood, D. K. Nightmare at Indian Cave. 2006. pap. 10.00 (***978-1-4257-1640-0(7)***) Xlibris Corp.

INDIANS OF NORTH AMERICA—CHEYENNE INDIANS

Bial, Raymond. The Cheyenne. 2001. (Lifeways Ser.). (Illus.). 128p. (J). (gr. 5-9). lib. bdg. 34.21 (978-0-7614-0938-0(6) , Benchmark Bks.) Cavendish, Marshall Corp.

Birchfield, D. L. Cheyenne. 2003. (Native American Peoples Ser.). (Illus.). 32p. (J). (gr. 4 up). lib. bdg. 24.67 (978-0-8368-3701-8(0)) Stevens, Gareth Inc.

Lassieur, Allison. The Cheyenne. 2001. (Native Peoples Ser.). (Illus.). 24p. (J). (gr. 2-3). lib. bdg. 18.60 (978-0-7368-0831-6(0) , Bridgestone Bks.) Capstone Pr., Inc.

McIntosh, Kenneth & McIntosh, Marsha. Cheyenne. 2003. (North American Indians Today Ser.). (Illus.). 96p. (J). lib. bdg. (978-1-59084-666-7(4)) Mason Crest Pubs.

—Seminoles, 15 vols., Set. 2004. (North American Indians Today Ser.). (Illus.). 96p. (J). lib. bdg. (978-1-59084-663-6(X)) Mason Crest Pubs.

McLeese, Tex. Carrera de Barril. Palacios, Argentina, tr. Tr. of Rodeo Barrel Racing. (SPA., Illus.). 24p. (J). (gr. 1-3). lib. bdg. 19.27 (978-1-57103-387-1(4)) Rourke Publishing, LLC.

Meli, Franco. A Cheyenne. Bacchin, Giorgio, illus. 1999. (Day with Ser.). 48p. (J). (gr. 5-7). lib. bdg. (978-0-8225-1920-1(8)) Lerner Publishing Group.

Petra Press Staff. The Cheyenne. 2002. (First Reports). (Illus.). 48p. (J). (gr. 3 up). lib. bdg. 22.60 (978-0-7565-0186-0(5)) Compass Point Bks.

Santella, Andrew. Cheyenne. 2002. (gr. 3-6). lib. bdg. 15.25 (978-0-613-59457-8(6)) Tandem Library Bks.

INDIANS OF NORTH AMERICA—CHEYENNE INDIANS—FICTION

Bunting, Eve. Cheyenne Again. Toddy, Irving, illus. 2002. 32p. (J). (gr. k-3). pap. 5.95 (978-0-618-19465-0(7) , Clarion Bks.) Houghton Mifflin Co. Trade & Reference Div.

Finley, Mary Pearce. Little Fox's Secret: The Mystery of Bent's Fort. Spurlock, Martha J., illus. 1999. 68p. (J). (gr. 3-4). lib. bdg. 15.95 (978-0-86541-049-7(6)) Filter Pr., LLC.

—Soaring Eagle. 1998. 176p. (gr. 5-7). pap. 8.95 (978-1-57168-281-9(3)) Eakin Pr.

Gilliland, Hap. Alone in the Wilderness. 2003. (Illus.). 160p. (YA). (gr. 6-10). pap. 14.95 (978-0-87961-257-3(6)) Naturegraph Pubs., Inc.

High, Linda Oatman. Winter Shoes for Shadow Horse. Lewin, Ted, illus. 2003. 32p. (J). (gr. 2-4). 15.95 (978-1-56397-472-4(X)) Boyds Mills Pr.

INDIANS OF NORTH AMERICA—CHILDREN

Dennis, Yvonne Wakim & Hirschfelder, Arlene. Children of Native America Today. 2004. (Illus.). 64p. (J). 19.95 (978-1-57091-499-7(0)) Charlesbridge Publishing, Inc.

Littlefield, Holly. Children of the Indian Boarding Schools. 2005. (Picture the American Past Ser.). (Illus.). 48p. (J). (gr. 2-5). lib. bdg. 22.60 (978-1-57505-467-4(1)) Lerner Publishing Group.

INDIANS OF NORTH AMERICA—CHIPPEWA INDIANS—FICTION

Sargent, Dave, et al. Knocking the Rice Vol. 9: (Chippewa) Be Powerful, 20. Lenoir, Jane, illus. l.t. ed. 2003. (Story Keeper Ser.: 9). 42p. (J). pap. 6.95 (978-1-56763-920-9(8)) Ozark Publishing.

INDIANS OF NORTH AMERICA—CHOCTAW INDIANS

Ditchfield, Christin. Choctaw. 2006. 48p. (J). (gr. 3-5). pap. 6.95 (978-0-516-25589-7(4) , Children's Pr.) Scholastic Library Publishing.

Koestler-Grack, Rachel A. The Choctaw: Stickball Players of the South. 2003. (America's First Peoples Ser.). (Illus.). 32p. (J). (gr. 2-3). lib. bdg. 23.93 (978-0-7368-2170-4(8) , Bridgestone Bks.) Capstone Pr., Inc.

Lassieur, Allison. The Choctaw Nation. 2001. (Native Peoples Ser.). (Illus.). 24p. (J). (gr. 2-3). lib. bdg. 18.60 (978-0-7368-0832-3(9) , Bridgestone Bks.) Capstone Pr., Inc.

Schmittroth, Felkins Ryan. Choctaw. 2003. (Tribes of Native America Ser.). (Illus.). 32p. (J). 23.70 (978-1-56711-688-5(4) , Blackbirch Pr., Inc.) Thomson Gale.

INDIANS OF NORTH AMERICA—CHUMASHAN INDIANS

Gray-Kanatiiosh, Barbara A. Chumash. 2004. (Native Americans Set Iii Ser.). (Illus.). 32p. (J). (gr. k-6). lib. bdg. 22.78 (978-1-57765-933-4(3)) ABDO Publishing Co.

Hicks, Terry Allan. The Chumash. 2007. (First Americans Ser.). 48p. (J). lib. bdg. 29.93 (***978-0-7614-2678-3(7)*** , Benchmark Bks.) Cavendish, Marshall Corp.

Miller, Connie R. The Chumash. 2003. (Uncovering Native American History Ser.). (J). pap. (978-1-58417-112-6(X)); lib. bdg. (978-1-58417-049-5(2)) Lake Street Pubs.

Williams, Jack S. The Chumash of California. 2003. (Library of Native Americans). (Illus.). 64p. (J). lib. bdg. 26.50 (978-0-8239-6426-0(4) , PowerKids Pr.) Rosen Publishing Group, Inc., The.

Young, Robert. A Personal Tour of la Purisima. 1999. (How It Was Ser.). (Illus.). 64p. (J). (gr. 4-6). lib. bdg. (978-0-8225-3576-8(9) , Lerner Pubns.) Lerner Publishing Group.

INDIANS OF NORTH AMERICA—COMANCHE INDIANS

Bial, Raymond. The Comanche. 1999. (Lifeways Ser.). (Illus.). 128p. (J). (gr. 5-9). lib. bdg. 34.21 (978-0-7614-0864-2(9) , Benchmark Bks.) Cavendish, Marshall Corp.

Birchfield, D. L. Comanche. 2003. (Native American Peoples Ser.). (Illus.). 32p. (J). (gr. 4 up). lib. bdg. 24.67 (978-0-8368-3702-5(9)) Stevens, Gareth Inc.

Ditchfield, Christin. Comanche. 2006. 48p. (J). (gr. 3-5). pap. 6.95 (978-0-516-25590-3(8) , Children's Pr.) Scholastic Library Publishing.

Egan, Tracie. Cynthia Ann Parker: Comanche Captive. 2003. (Primary Sources of Famous People in American History Ser.). (Illus.). 32p. (J). pap. (978-0-8239-4179-7(5)) Rosen Publishing Group, Inc., The.

George, Charles. The Comanche. 2003. (North American Indians Ser.). (Illus.). 48p. (J). 26.20 (978-0-7377-1474-6(3) , Greenhaven Pr., Inc.) Thomson Gale.

Libal, Joyce. Comanche. 2003. (North American Indians Today Ser.). (Illus.). 96p. (J). lib. bdg. (978-1-59084-667-4(2)) Mason Crest Pubs.

Rollings, Willard H. The Comanche. (Indians of North America, Revised Ser.). (Illus.). 120p. (J). (gr. 9-13). 2005. pap. 13.25 (978-0-7910-8349-9(7)); 2004. 30.00 (978-0-7910-7996-6(1)) Facts On File, Inc. (Chelsea Hse.).

Schmittroth, Felkins Ryan. Comanche. 2003. (Tribes of Native America Ser.). (Illus.). 32p. (J). 23.70 (978-1-56711-689-2(2) , Blackbirch Pr., Inc.) Thomson Gale.

Zemlicka, Shannon. Quanah Parker. 2004. (History Maker Bios Ser.). (J). pap. 6.95 (978-0-8225-2070-2(2)); (Illus.). 48p. 26.60 (978-0-8225-0724-6(2) , Carolrhoda Bks.) Lerner Publishing Group.

INDIANS OF NORTH AMERICA—COMANCHE INDIANS—FICTION

Dearen, Patrick. Comanche Peace Pipe. 2001. (gr. k-3). lib. bdg. 17.60 (978-0-613-86879-2(X)) Tandem Library Bks.

—Comanche Peace Pipe. 2001. (Lone Star Heroes Ser.). 128p. (ps-3). pap. 8.95 (978-1-55622-831-5(7) , Republic of Texas Pr.) Wordware Publishing, Inc.

Lewis, Preston. Blanca Is My Name: Or, How I Saved the Buffalo on the Texas Plains. Eckhardt, Jason C., illus. 2002. (Animal Legends Ser.: Vol. 2). 188p. 15.95 (978-1-57168-699-2(1)); 9.95 (978-1-57168-700-5(9)) Eakin Pr.

Shefelman, Janice J., et al. Comanche Song. 2000. (Illus.). 256p. (J). (gr. 4-7). 17.95 (978-1-57168-397-7(6)) Eakin Pr.

Werkley, Vicki. Girl-on-Fire. Laidig, Jean & HighPine, Gayle, eds. 1999. 230p. (YA). pap. 14.95 (978-1-58436-400-9(9)) Haven Bks.

INDIANS OF NORTH AMERICA—COSTUME AND ADORNMENT

Greene, Jacqueline Dembar. Powwow: A Good Day to Dance. Greene, Jacqueline Dembar, photos by. 1998. (First Bks.). (Illus.). 64p. (J). (gr. 5-7). 22.00 (978-0-531-20337-8(9) , Watts, Franklin) Scholastic Library Publishing.

INDIANS OF NORTH AMERICA—CREE INDIANS—FICTION

Wheeler, Jordan & Jackson, Dennis. Christmas at Wapos Bay. 2006. 176p. (J). pap. ***(978-1-55050-324-1(3))*** Coteau Bks.

Wiebe, Rudy. Hidden Buffalo. Lonechild, Michael, illus. 2006. 32p. pap. 8.95 (978-0-88995-334-5(1)) Red Deer Pr. CAN. *Dist:* F & W Pubns., Inc.

—Hidden Buffalo. Lonechild, Michael, tr. 2004. (Illus.). 32p. (J). (gr. k-2). 17.95 (978-0-88995-285-0(X)) Red Deer Pr. CAN. *Dist:* Fitzhenry & Whiteside, Ltd.

INDIANS OF NORTH AMERICA—CREEK INDIANS

Gray-Kanatiiosh, Barbara A. Creek. 2002. (Native Americans Ser.). (Illus.). 32p. (J). (gr. k-6). lib. bdg. 22.78 (978-1-57765-605-0(9) , Checkerboard Library) ABDO Publishing Co.

Lassieur, Allison. The Creek Nation. 2001. (Native Peoples Ser.). (Illus.). 24p. (J). (gr. 2-3). lib. bdg. 18.60 (978-0-7368-0947-4(3) , Bridgestone Bks.) Capstone Pr., Inc.

Libal, Autumn. Creek. 2003. (North American Indians Today Ser.). (Illus.). 96p. (J). lib. bdg. (978-1-59084-668-1(0)) Mason Crest Pubs.

Robinson, Deborah B. The Cree of North America. 2002. (First Peoples Ser.). (Illus.). 48p. (J). (gr. 4-8). lib. bdg. 23.93 (978-0-8225-4178-3(5)) Lerner Publishing Group.

INDIANS OF NORTH AMERICA—CROW INDIANS

Ditchfield, Christin. The Crow. 2005. (True Book Ser.). (Illus.). 47p. (J). (ps-7). 25.00 (978-0-516-23645-2(8) , Children's Pr.) Scholastic Library Publishing.

—Crow. 2006. 48p. (J). (gr. 3-5). pap. 6.95 (978-0-516-25591-0(6) , Children's Pr.) Scholastic Library Publishing.

Kavasch, E. Barrie. Crow Children & Elders Talk Together. 1999. (Library of Intergenerational Learning). 24p. (J). (gr. k-4). lib. bdg. 19.95 (978-0-8239-5231-1(2) , PowerKids Pr.) Rosen Publishing Group, Inc., The.

Lassieur, Allison. The Apsaalooke (Crow) Nation. 2002. (Native Peoples Ser.). (Illus.). 24p. (J). (gr. 2-3). lib. bdg. 18.60 (978-0-7368-1103-3(6) , Bridgestone Bks.) Capstone Pr., Inc.

Maher, Erin. Traditions of the Crow People. 2002. (Reading Room Collection). (Illus.). 24p. (J). lib. bdg. 18.75 (978-0-8239-3741-7(0)) Rosen Publishing Group, Inc., The.

McIntosh, Kenneth & McIntosh, Marsha. Crow. 2003. (North American Indians Today Ser.). (Illus.). 96p. (J). lib. bdg. (978-1-59084-669-8(9)) Mason Crest Pubs.

Ryan, Marla Felkins & Schmittroth, Linda, eds. Crow. 2002. (Tribes of Native America Ser.). (Illus.). 32p. (J). 23.70 (978-1-56711-623-6(X) , Blackbirch Pr., Inc.) Thomson Gale.

Tarbescu, Edith. Crow. 2000. (gr. 5-8). lib. bdg. 17.60 (978-0-613-37320-3(0)) Tandem Library Bks.

INDIANS OF NORTH AMERICA—CROW INDIANS—FICTION

Duey, Kathleen. Celou Sudden Shout: Idaho, 1826. 1998. (American Diaries Ser.: No. 9). (J). (gr. 3-7). (978-0-606-13121-6(3)) Tandem Library Bks.

Matcheck, Diane. The Sacrifice. 1999. (978-0-606-17598-2(9)) Tandem Library Bks.

INDIANS OF NORTH AMERICA—CUSTOMS

see Indians of North America—Social Life and Customs

INDIANS OF NORTH AMERICA—DAKOTA INDIANS

Aller, Susan Bivin. Sitting Bull. 2004. (History Maker Bios Ser.). (J). pap. 6.95 (978-0-8225-2072-6(9)) Lerner Publishing Group.

—Sitting Bull. Parlin, Tim, tr. Parlin, Tim, illus. 2004. (History Maker Bios Ser.). 47p. (J). 26.60 (978-0-8225-0700-0(5) , Carolrhoda Bks.) Lerner Publishing Group.

Birchfield, D. L. Sioux. 2003. (Native American Peoples Ser.). (Illus.). 32p. (J). (gr. 4 up). lib. bdg. 24.67 (978-0-8368-3669-1(3)) Stevens, Gareth Inc.

Bruchac, Joseph. A Boy Called Slow: The True Story of Sitting Bull. 1998. (Illus.). 32p. (J). (ps-3). pap. 6.99 (978-0-698-11616-0(X) , Putnam Juvenile) Penguin Group (USA) Inc.

—A Boy Called Slow: The True Story of Sitting Bull. 1998. (J). 13.79 (978-0-606-13223-7(6)) Tandem Library Bks.

Bryant, Charles S. & Murch, Abel B. Indian Massacre in Minnesota: A History of the Great Massacre by the Sioux Indians in Minnesota. 2001. 524p. (YA). reprint ed. (978-1-58218-410-4(0)); (978-1-58218-411-1(9)) Digital Scanning, Inc.

Calvert, Patricia. Stand-off at Standing Rock. 2001. (Single Titles Ser.: up). (Illus.). 144p. (gr. 8-12). lib. bdg. (978-0-7613-1360-1(5) , Millbrook Pr.) Lerner Publishing Group.

Gaines, Richard. Sioux. 2000. (Native Americans Ser.). (Illus.). 32p. (J). (gr. k-6). lib. bdg. 22.78 (978-1-57765-382-0(3) , Checkerboard Library) ABDO Publishing Co.

Isaacs, Sally Senzell. Life in a Sioux Village. (Picture the Past Ser.). (Illus.). 32p. (J). 2002. (gr. k-3). pap. 7.50 (978-1-58810-415-1(X) , 91188); 2001. (gr. 2-4). lib. bdg. 21.36 (978-1-58810-250-8(5)) Heinemann Library.

Koopmans, Anna. The Sioux. 2004. (American Indian Art & Culture Ser.). (Illus.). 32p. (gr. 3-5). 25.50 (978-0-7910-7963-8(5) , Chelsea Hse.) Facts On File, Inc.

Nobleman, Marc Tyler. The Battle of the Little Bighorn. 2001. (We the People Ser.). (Illus.). 48p. (J). (gr. 4 up). lib. bdg. 22.60 (978-0-7565-0150-1(4)) Compass Point Bks.

Petra Press Staff. The Sioux. 2001. (First Reports). (Illus.). 48p. (J). (gr. 3 up). lib. bdg. 22.60 (978-0-7565-0084-9(2)) Compass Point Bks.

Roop, Connie. Sitting Bull. 2002. (gr. 3-6). lib. bdg. 12.40 (978-0-613-50833-9(5)) Tandem Library Bks.

Roop, Connie & Roop, Peter. Sitting Bull. 2002. (In Their Own Words Ser.). (Illus.). 128p. (J). pap. 4.99 (978-0-439-26322-1(0) , Scholastic Reference) Scholastic, Inc.

Rose, Lavera. Grandchildren of the Lakota. Bellville, Cheryl Walsh, photos by. 1998. (World's Children Ser.). (Illus.). 40p. (J). (gr. 3-6). lib. bdg. 23.93 (978-1-57505-279-3(2) , Carolrhoda Bks.) Lerner Publishing Group.

Santella, Andrew. Lakota Sioux. 2001. (gr. 3-6). lib. bdg. 15.25 (978-0-613-53521-2(9)) Tandem Library Bks.

Stein, R. Conrad. The Sioux: A Proud People. 2005. (American Indians Ser.). (Illus.). 48p. (J). lib. bdg. 23.93 (978-0-7660-2452-6(0) , Enslow Elementary) Enslow Pubs., Inc.

Swain, Gwenyth. Little Crow: Leader of the Dakota. 2004. (Illus.). 102p. pap. 12.95 (978-0-87351-503-0(X) , Borealis Bk.) Minnesota Historical Society Pr.

Todd, Anne M. The Sioux: People of the Great Plains. 2002. (American Indian Nations Ser.). (Illus.). 48p. (J). (gr. 3-4). lib. bdg. 22.60 (978-0-7368-1354-9(3) , Bridgestone Bks.) Capstone Pr., Inc.

—Sitting Bull 1831-1890. 2002. (American Indian Biographies Ser.). (Illus.). 32p. (J). (gr. 3-4). lib. bdg. 23.93 (978-0-7368-1215-3(6) , Blue Earth Bks.) Capstone Pr., Inc.

INDIANS OF NORTH AMERICA—DAKOTA INDIANS—FICTION

Calvert, Patricia. Betrayed! 2004. (gr. 5-8). lib. bdg. 13.00 (978-0-613-88652-9(6)) Tandem Library Bks.

Howe, James. Dances with Wolves: The Movie Story. 2004. (Medallion Edition Ser.). 160p. 7.95 (978-1-55704-633-8(6)) Newmarket Pr.

Howe, James, adapted by. Dances with Wolves: The Children's Picture Book. 2004. (Illus.). 64p. (gr. 2 up). 14.95 (978-1-55704-104-3(0)) Newmarket Pr.

Matthaei, Gay & Grutman, Jewel. The Sketchbook of Thomas Blue Eagle. Cvijanovic, Adam, illus. 2001. 60p. (YA). (gr. 5-8). reprint ed. 17.00 (978-0-7567-6295-7(2)) DIANE Publishing Co.

Oldfield, J. Silver Cloud. 2002. (Illus.). 229p. pap. (978-0-340-85108-1(2) , Hodder & Stoughton) Hodder General Publishing Division.

Osborne, Mary Pope. Buffalo Before Breakfast. 2004. (Magic Tree House Ser. : No. 18). 72p. (J). (gr. k-3). pap. 17.00 incl. audio (978-0-8072-0927-1(9) , Listening Library) Random Hse. Audio Publishing Group.

—Buffalo Before Breakfast. Murdocca, Sal, illus. 1999. (Magic Tree House Ser.: No. 18). (J). (gr. k-3). 20.00 (978-0-375-80041-2(7)); 96p. lib. bdg. 11.99 (978-0-679-99064-2(X)); Vol. 18. 96p. mass mkt. 3.99 (978-0-679-89064-5(5)) Random Hse. Children's Bks. (Random Hse. Bks. for Young Readers).

—Buffalo Before Breakfast. Murdocca, Salvatore, illus. 1999. (Magic Tree House Ser. : No. 18). 72p. (J). (gr. k-3). lib. bdg. 11.80 (978-0-613-16067-4(3)) Tandem Library Bks.

—Buffalo Before Breakfast. 1999. (Magic Tree House Ser. : No. 18). (J). (gr. k-3). lib. bdg. 10.79 (978-0-606-16841-0(9)) Tandem Library Bks.

Schultz, Jan Neubert. Battle Cry. 2006. (Illus.). 240p. (J). 15.95 (978-1-57505-928-0(2) , Carolrhoda Bks.) Lerner Publishing Group.

Wangerin, Walter, Jr. The Crying for a Vision: A Novel. 2003. 346p. 16.95 (978-1-55725-342-2(0)) Paraclete Pr., Inc.

Whelan, Gloria. Miranda's Last Stand. 144p. (J). (gr. 3-7). 2000. pap. 4.95 (978-0-06-442097-6(3) , Harper Trophy); 1999. (Illus.). 14.89 (978-0-06-028252-3(5)) HarperCollins Pubs.

—Miranda's Last Stand. 2000. (J). (978-0-606-19267-5(0)); (978-0-606-19988-9(8)) Tandem Library Bks.

INDIANS OF NORTH AMERICA—DANCES

see Indian Dance

INDIANS OF NORTH AMERICA—DELAWARE INDIANS

Carole Marsh. Delaware Indians. 2004. (Delaware Experience Ser.). 36p. (gr. 3-8). pap. 7.95 (978-0-635-02260-8(5)); lib. bdg. 29.95 (978-0-635-02261-5(3)) Gallopade International.

Lassieur, Allison. The Delaware People. 2002. (Native Peoples Ser.). (Illus.). 24p. (J). (gr. 2-3). lib. bdg. 18.60 (978-0-7368-1104-0(4) , Bridgestone Bks.) Capstone Pr., Inc.

Myers, Albert C., ed. William Penn's Own Account of Lenni Lenape or Delaware Indians. 2005. (Illus.). 96p. (J). pap. (978-0-912608-13-6(7)) Middle Atlantic Pr.

Spizzirri, Linda, ed. Northeast Indians. (Illus.). 32p. (J). (gr. 1-8). pap. 4.98 incl. audio (978-0-86545-040-0(4)) Spizzirri Pr., Inc.

INDIANS OF NORTH AMERICA—DELAWARE INDIANS—FICTION

Durrant, Lynda. The Beaded Moccasins: The Story of Mary Campbell. 2000. (J). 11.64 (978-0-606-20017-2(7)) Tandem Library Bks.

—Beaded Moccasins: The Story of Mary Campbell. 2000. (gr. 5-8). lib. bdg. 13.00 (978-0-613-33670-3(4)) Tandem Library Bks.

Johnston, Norma. Feather in the Wind. 2001. (Illus.). 172p. (J). (gr. 5-9). 14.95 (978-0-7614-5063-4(7) , Cavendish Children's Bks.) Cavendish, Marshall Corp.

Messinger, Carla & Katz, Susan. When the Shadbush Blooms. Fadden, David Kanietakeron, illus. 2007. 32p. (J). (ps-2). 15.95 (978-1-58246-192-2(9) , Tricycle Pr.) Ten Speed Pr.

Osborne, Mary Pope. Standing in the Light: The Captive Diary of Catherine Carey Logan, Delaware Valley, Pennsylvania, 1763. (Dear America Ser.). (J). 2000. 9.95 (978-0-439-17968-3(8)); 1998. (Illus.). 192p. (gr. 4-9). pap. 10.95 (978-0-590-13462-0(0)) Scholastic, Inc.

Richter, Conrad. The Light in the Forest. (YA). (gr. 7 up). 21.95 (978-0-89190-333-8(X)) Amereon LTD.

INDIANS OF NORTH AMERICA—DWELLINGS

Adams, McCrea. Tipi. Dawson, Kimberly L., illus. 2000. (Native American Homes Ser.). 32p. (J). (gr. 3-6). lib. bdg. 28.50 (978-1-55916-275-3(9)) Rourke Publishing, LLC.

Beres, Cynthia Breslin. Longhouse. Dawson, Kimberly L., illus. 2000. (Native American Homes Ser.). 32p. (J). (gr. 3-6). lib. bdg. 28.50 (978-1-55916-247-0(3)) Rourke Publishing, LLC.

Harcourt School Publishers Staff. Trofeos Below Level: Una Casa/Tipi. 3rd ed. 2002. (SPA., Illus.). pap. 5.50 (978-0-15-323870-3(4)) Harcourt Schl. Pubs.

Kalman, Bobbie. Life in a Longhouse Village. Parker, Lewis, illus. 2001. (Native Nations of North America Ser.). 32p. (J). (gr. 5). (978-0-7787-0370-9(3)); pap. (978-0-7787-0462-1(9)) Crabtree Publishing Co.

—Native Homes. 2001. (Native Nations of North America Ser.). (Illus.). 32p. (J). (gr. 5). (978-0-7787-0371-6(1)); pap. (978-0-7787-0463-8(7)) Crabtree Publishing Co.

Koestler-Grack, Rachel A. The Iroquois: Longhouse Builders. 2003. (America's First Peoples Ser.). (Illus.). 32p. (J). (gr. 2-3). lib. bdg. 23.93 (978-0-7368-1536-9(8) , Bridgestone Bks.) Capstone Pr., Inc.

Mitchell, Kevin M. Wickiup. 2000. (Native American Homes Ser.). (Illus.). 32p. (J). (gr. 3-6). lib. bdg. 28.50 (978-1-55916-276-0(7)) Rourke Publishing, LLC.

Rau, Dana Meachen. Bookworms: The Inside Story, 6 bks., Set. Incl. Castle. 32p. lib. bdg. 22.79 (978-0-7614-2272-3(2)); Igloo. 24p. lib. bdg. 22.79 (978-0-7614-2273-0(0)); Log Cabin. 24p. lib. bdg. 22.79 ***(978-0-7614-2274-7(9));*** Pyramid. 32p. lib. bdg. 22.79 ***(978-0-7614-2275-4(7));*** Skyscraper. 32p. lib. bdg. 22.79 (978-0-7614-2276-1(5)); Tepee. 32p. lib. bdg. 22.79 (978-0-7614-2277-8(3)); (Illus.). (J). (gr. k-2). 2006. 2006. Set lib. bdg. 136.71 ***(978-0-7614-2271-6(4)*** , Benchmark Bks.) Cavendish, Marshall Corp.

Rau, Dana Meachen. Tepee. 2006. (Bookworms Ser.). (Illus.). 32p. (J). (gr. k-2). lib. bdg. 22.79 (978-0-7614-2277-8(3) , Benchmark Bks.) Cavendish, Marshall Corp.

Steltzer, Ulli. Building an Igloo. rev. ed. 1999. (Illus.). 32p. (J). (gr. k-3). pap. 7.95 (978-0-8050-6313-4(7) , Holt, Henry & Co. Bks. For Young Readers) Holt, Henry & Co.

INDIANS OF NORTH AMERICA—EDUCATION

Littlefield, Holly. Children of the Indian Boarding Schools. 2005. (Picture the American Past Ser.). (Illus.). 48p. (J). (gr. 2-5). lib. bdg. 22.60 (978-1-57505-467-4(1)) Lerner Publishing Group.

INDIANS OF NORTH AMERICA—EDUCATION—FICTION

Hobbs, William. Far North. 2004. (Illus.). 304p. (J). (gr. 7 up). pap. 6.99 (978-0-06-054096-8(6) , Harper Trophy) HarperCollins Pubs.

INDIANS OF NORTH AMERICA—FICTION

Aardema, Verna. Bringing the Rain to Kapiti Plain. 2002. (Illus.). (J). 14.04 (978-0-7587-2153-2(6)) Book Wholesalers, Inc.

Adams, M.F.T., C.A.C. III, Juanita Beasley, MA. Clancy & the Bear Dance: One Ute Mountain Boy's Journey from Alcoholism & Abuse to Wholeness! 2007. 104p. pap. 11.95 ***(978-0-615-14729-1(1))*** Out-of-Body Travel Foundation, The.

Alarid, Carilyn & Markel, Marilyn. Old Grandfather Teaches a Lesson: Mimbres Children Learn Respect. Alarid, Carilyn & Markel, Marilyn, illus. 2004. (Illus.). 116p. (J). pap. 16.95 (978-0-86534-418-1(3)) Sunstone Pr.

—Talks All Day Has the Courage to Speak: Mimbres Children Learn Citizenship. Alarid, Carilyn & Markel, Marilyn, illus. 2006. (Illus.). 125p. (J). pap. 16.95 (978-0-86534-470-9(1)) Sunstone Pr.

Albers, Everett C. Lewis & Clark Meet the American Indians: As Told by Seaman the Dog. Eslinger, Kimberly, illus. 1999. 32p. (J). (ps-11). pap. 3.95 (978-0-9674002-0-4(1)) United Printing.

Alder, Elizabeth. Crossing the Panther's Path. 2002. (Illus.). 240p. (J). 18.00 (978-0-374-31662-4(7) , Farrar, Straus & Giroux (BYR)) Farrar, Straus & Giroux.

—Crossing the Panther's Path. 2003. (YA). 24.95 (978-0-7862-5013-4(5)) Thorndike Pr.

Alexie, Sherman. The Absolutely True Diary of a Part-Time Indian. Forney, Ellen, illus. 2007. 240p. (YA). (gr. 7 up). 16.99 ***(978-0-316-01368-0(4))*** Little, Brown Bks. for Young Readers.

Allende, Isabel. La Ciudad de las Bestias. 2003. (SPA.). (gr. 5-8). lib. bdg. 16.45 (978-0-613-83866-5(1)) Tandem Library Bks.

Amado, Elisa, tr. from SPA. Napí Goes to the Mountain. Domi, illus. 2006. 48p. (J). (gr. 1-3). 18.95 (978-0-88899-713-5(2)) Groundwood Bks. CAN. *Dist:* Perseus Distribution.

Anastasio, Dina. Por qué el cuervo es negro y el buho tiene manchitas & How Raven Became Black & Owl Got Its Spots. 2005. spiral bd. 66.00 ***(978-1-4108-5626-5(7))*** Benchmark Education Co.

Anderson, Jane. Iktomi Takes to the Sky: A Native AMER Folktale. 2006. spiral bd. 23.00 ***(978-1-4108-7164-0(9))*** Benchmark Education Co.

Applegate, Stan. The Devil's Highway. Watling, James, illus. 1998. 224p. (J). (gr. 3-7). pap. 8.95 (978-1-56145-184-5(3) , Q21196) Peachtree Pubs., Ltd.

Armstrong, Alan W. Raleigh's Page. Jessell, Tim, illus. 2007. (J). 336p. (gr. 1-5). lib. bdg. 19.99 (978-0-375-93319-6(0)); 328p. (gr. 5-7). 16.99 (978-0-375-83319-9(6)) Random Hse. Children's Bks. (Random Hse. Bks. for Young Readers).

Ashabranner, Brent K. & Davis, Russell G. The Choctaw Code. 2006. 121p. (J). (978-1-59166-621-9(X)) Jones, Bob Univ. Pr.

Awiakta, Marilou. Rising Fawn & the Fire Mystery. 96p. (J). per. 14.95 (978-1-55591-600-8(7)) Fulcrum Publishing.

Ballantyne, R. M. The Norsemen in the West or America Before Columbus. 2004. reprint ed. pap. 1.99 (978-1-4192-7571-5(2)) Kessinger Publishing, LLC.

—Silver Lake. 2004. reprint ed. pap. 15.95 (978-1-4191-4729-6(3)); pap. 1.99 (978-1-4192-4729-3(8)) Kessinger Publishing, LLC.

Banks, Lynne Reid. The Indian in the Cupboard. 1999. (Indian in the Cupboard Ser.: No. 1). (J). (gr. 4-7). pap. 4.95 (978-5-553-81211-9(9)) HarperCollins Pubs.

—The Indian in the Cupboard. (Indian in the Cupboard Ser.: No. 1). 44p. (J). (gr. 4-7). 1999. 9.95 (978-1-56137-225-6(0)); 1998. 11.95 (978-1-56137-693-3(0) , NU6930SP) Novel Units, Inc.

—The Indian in the Cupboard. 181p. (J). (Indian in the Cupboard Ser.: No. 1). (gr. 4-7). pap. 4.99 (978-0-8072-1433-6(7)); 2004. (Indian in the Cupboard Ser.). (gr. 3-7). pap. 36.00 incl. audio (978-0-8072-7308-1(2) , YA809SP) Random Hse. Audio Publishing Group. (Listening Library).

—The Key to the Indian. Watling, James, illus. 1999. (Indian in the Cupboard Ser.: No. 5). 288p. (J). (gr. 4 up). pap. 6.99 (978-0-380-80373-6(9)) HarperCollins Pubs.

—The Key to the Indian. 1998. (Indian in the Cupboard Ser.: No. 5). 240p. (J). (gr. 4-7). 16.00 (978-0-380-97717-8(6)) HarperCollins Pubs.

—The Key to the Indian. (Indian in the Cupboard Ser.: No. 5). 240p. (J). (gr. 4-7). pap. 4.99 (978-0-8072-1551-7(1) , Listening Library) Random Hse. Audio Publishing Group.

—The Key to the Indian. 1999. (gr. 3-6). lib. bdg. 13.00 (978-0-613-23006-3(X)) Tandem Library Bks.

—The Return of the Indian. 1999. (Indian in the Cupboard Ser.: No. 2). (J). (gr. 4-7). 9.95 (978-1-56137-232-4(3)) Novel Units, Inc.

H I

—The Return of the Indian. (Indian in the Cupboard Ser.: No. 2). 189p. (J). (gr. 4-7). pap. 4.99 (978-0-8072-1434-3(5) , Listening Library) Random Hse. Audio Publishing Group.

Banks, Sara Harrell. Remember My Name. 2nd ed. 2003. (YA). pap. 10.95 (978-0-89992-158-7(2)) Council for Indian Education.

Batdorf, Carol. Tinka Coloring Book: A Day in a Little Girl's Life. 2005. (Illus.). 24p. (Orig.). (gr. 1-6). pap. 5.95 (978-0-88839-249-7(4)) Hancock Hse. Pubs., Ltd. CAN. *Dist:* Hancock Hse. Pubs.

Bauer Mueller, Pamela. An Angry Drum Echoed: Mary Musgrove, Queen of the Creeks. 2007. (Illus.). 296p. (J). (978-0-9685097-7-7(0)) Pinata Publishing.

Bickel, Karla. Handmade Necklace. Bickel, Karla, illus. l.t. ed. 2004. (Illus.). 16p. (J). (ps-6). pap. 5.00 (978-1-891452-11-6(8) , 1) Heart Arbor Bks.

Bjornson, Nancy. Llamas, Ponies & Pyrite. 2007. (J). (*978-1-930596-82-5(0)) Amherst Pr.

—Mustangs, Fires & Snakes. 2007. (J). (*978-1-930596-84-9(7)) Amherst Pr.

Blue, Martha. Little Prankster Girl: At'Eed Adilahi Yazhi. Ruffenach, Jessie, ed. Thomas, Peter, tr. Smith, Keith, illus. 2003. (NAV & ENG.). 32p. 17.95 (978-1-893354-36-4(9)) Salina Bookshelf.

BlueWolf, James Don. Speaking for Fire. Greenlee, Carolyn Wing, illus. 2003. 44p. (J). (gr. 2-7). 14.95 (978-1-887400-31-2(1)) Earthen Vessel Production, Inc.

Bly, Stephen A. The Buffalo's Last Stand. 2002. (Retta Barre's Oregon Trail Ser.: 2). 111p. pap. 5.99 (978-1-58134-392-2(2)) Crossway Bks.

—The Lost Wagon Train. 2005. (Retta Barre's Oregon Trail Ser.: Vol. 1). 110p. pap. 5.99 (978-1-58134-391-5(4) , Crossway Bibles) Crossway Bks.

Bombay, Cal & Sharpe, Margaret. Slave, Brave & Free, 10 bks. 2003. 256p. (J). per. 12.99 (978-1-929125-41-8(0) , Multnomah) WaterBrook Pr.

Bond, Douglas. Guns of Thunder. 2007. (J). 11.99 (978-1-59638-013-4(6)) P & R Publishing.

Bouchard, David & Lonechild, Michael. Qu'Appelle. 2002. (Illus.). 32p. (J). (gr. 3-6). 15.95 (978-1-55192-475-5(7)) Raincoast Bk. Distribution CAN. *Dist:* Perseus Distribution.

Bowman, Andy. Indian Slim. Travis, Stephanie, illus. 29p. (J). (gr. 1-6). pap. 6.95 (978-1-931650-06-9(3)); lib. bdg. 14.95 (978-1-931650-07-6(1)) Coastal Publishing Carolina, Inc.

Bowman, Eva Jean. Chief Ninham: Forgotten Hero. Bowler Elementary School Students Staff, illus. Walling, Richard et al, photos by. 1999. 43p. (YA). (gr. 2 up). pap. 14.00 (978-0-935790-04-7(7)) Muh-He-Con-Neew Pr.

Boyd, Jones Veda. Nellie the Brave: The Cherokee Trail of Tears. 2006. (Sisters in Time Ser.). 144p. (J). pap. 4.97 (978-1-59789-070-0(7)) Barbour Publishing, Inc.

Boyden, Linda. The Blue Roses. Cordova, Amy, illus. 2002. 32p. (J). (gr. 1-5). 16.95 (978-1-58430-037-3(X)) Lee & Low Bks., Inc.

Brezenoff, Steven. Burning Secrets. Vue, Tou, illus. 2008. (J). pap. (*978-1-59889-920-7(1)); (YA). (gr. 5-9). lib. bdg. 17.95 (*978-1-59889-854-5(X)) Stone Arch Bks.

Brooks, Martha. Bone Dance. 2005. 184p. (J). (gr. 7-16). pap. 6.95 (978-0-88899-336-6(6)) Groundwood Bks. CAN. *Dist:* Perseus Distribution.

—The Bone Dance. 1999. (J). (978-0-606-16716-1(1)) Tandem Library Bks.

Bruchac, James & Bruchac, Joseph. When the Chenoo Howls: Native American Tales of Terror. Sauts, William, illus. 1999. 136p. (J). (gr. 3-7). 16.95 (978-0-8027-8638-8(3)); pap. 10.95 (978-0-8027-7576-4(4)) Walker & Co.

Bruchac, Joseph. The Arrow over the Door. Watling, James, illus. 2002. 96p. (J). pap. 4.99 (978-0-14-130571-4(1) , Puffin) Penguin Group (USA) Inc.

—The Arrow over the Door. 1998. (Illus.). 96p. (J). (gr. 2-4). 15.99 (978-0-8037-2078-7(5) , Dial) Penguin Group (USA) Inc.

—The Arrow over the Door. Watling, James, illus. 2002. 89p. (J). (ps-7). lib. bdg. 13.00 (978-0-613-45242-7(9)) Tandem Library Bks.

—Code Talker: A Novel about the Navajo Marines of World War Two. 2006. 240p. (YA). (gr. 5). pap. 7.99 (978-0-14-240596-3(5) , Puffin) Penguin Group (USA) Inc.

—Crazy Horse's Vision. ed. 2004. (Illus.). (J). (gr. 1-3). spiral bd. (978-0-616-07251-6(1)) Canadian National Institute for the Blind/Institut National Canadien pour les Aveugles.

—Crazy Horse's Vision. 2005. (J). 28.95 incl. audio compact disk (978-1-59112-912-7(5)); 25.95 incl. audio (978-1-59112-452-8(2)) Live Oak Media.

—The First Strawberries: A Cherokee Story. Vojtech, Anna, illus. 1998. (Picture Bks.). 32p. (J). (ps-3). pap. 6.99 (978-0-14-056409-9(8) , Puffin) Penguin Group (USA) Inc.

—The First Strawberries: A Cherokee Story. 1998. (Picture Puffin Ser.). 13.79 (978-0-606-13388-3(7)) Tandem Library Bks.

—The Heart of a Chief. 2001. (J). 12.64 (978-0-606-21230-4(2)); (gr. 5-8). lib. bdg. 14.15 (978-0-613-44212-1(1)) Tandem Library Bks.

—Heroes & Heroines, Monsters & Magic: Native American Legends & Folktales. Burgevin, Daniel, illus. 2004. 200p. (gr. 3-7). reprint ed. pap. 12.95 (978-0-89594-995-0(4) , Crossing Pr., Inc.) Ten Speed Pr.

—Sacajawea. 2001. (Illus.). 208p. (J). (gr. 7 up). pap. 4.99 (978-0-439-28068-6(0)) Scholastic, Inc.

—Sacajawea: The Story of Bird Woman & the Lewis & Clark Expedition. 2003. 199p. (YA). (gr. 7-17). lib. bdg. 13.00 (978-0-613-44368-5(3)) Tandem Library Bks.

—Squanto's Journey: The Story of the First Thanksgiving. Shed, Greg, illus. 2000. 32p. (J). (gr. 2-5). 16.00 (978-0-15-201817-7(4) , Silver Whistle) Harcourt Trade Pubs.

—Squanto's Journey: The Story of the First Thanksgiving. Shed, Greg, illus. 2000. 32p. (J). (gr. 1-4). 19.98 (978-0-7398-3072-7(4)) Raintree.

—Wabi: A Hero's Tale. 208p. (gr. 7). 2007. (YA). 6.99 (*978-0-14-240947-3(2) , Puffin); 2006. (J). 16.99 (978-0-8037-3098-4(5) , Dial) Penguin Group (USA) Inc.

—The Warriors. 2004. (Junior Library Guild Selection Ser.). 120p. (J). (gr. 4 up). 15.95 (978-1-58196-002-0(6)); pap. 4.99 (978-1-58196-022-8(0)) Darby Creek Publishing.

—Whisper in the Dark. Comport, Sally Wern, illus. 2005. 192p. (J). (gr. 5 up). 15.99 (978-0-06-058087-2(9)); lib. bdg. 16.89 (978-0-06-058088-9(7)) HarperCollins Pubs.

Buchanan, William J. Diablo: The Devil Steer. 2004. 151p. (J). (gr. 6-10). 9.95 (978-0-8263-3139-7(4)) Univ. of New Mexico Pr.

Butler, Amy. Virginia Bound. 2003. 192p. (J). (gr. 5-9). tchr. ed. 15.00 (978-0-618-24752-3(1) , Clarion Bks.) Houghton Mifflin Co. Trade & Reference Div.

Calvert, Patricia. Betrayed! 2004. (gr. 5-8). lib. bdg. 13.00 (978-0-613-88652-9(6)) Tandem Library Bks.

Cameron, Anne. Dreamspeaker. unabr. ed. 2005. 128p. pap. 9.95 (978-1-55017-364-2(2)) Harbour Publishing Co., Ltd. CAN. *Dist:* Graphic Arts Ctr. Publishing Co.

—Dreamspeaker. 2000. 128p. (YA). (gr. 7-9). mass mkt. 5.95 (978-0-7736-7482-0(9)) Stoddart Kids CAN. *Dist:* Fitzhenry & Whiteside, Ltd.

Campbell Hale, Janet. The Owl's Song. 1998. 153p. (C). pap. 13.95 (978-0-8263-1861-9(4)) Univ. of New Mexico Pr.

Campoy, F. Isabel, et al. Celebrate a Powwow with Sandy Starbright. Alvarez, María Jesus, illus. 2006. 31p. (J). (*978-1-59820-127-7(1)) Santillana USA Publishing Co., Inc.

Carbone, Elisa. Blood on the River: James Town, 1607. 2006. (Illus.). 256p. (YA). (gr. 7-8). 16.99 (978-0-670-06060-3(7) , Viking Adult) Penguin Group (USA) Inc.

Carbone, Elisa. Blood on the River: James Town 1607. 2007. 237p. (J). (gr. 4). per. 6.99 (*978-0-14-240932-9(4) , Puffin) Penguin Group (USA) Inc.

Carlson, Lori Marie. Moccasin Thunder: Amercian Indian Stories for Today. 176p. (J). (gr. 9 up). 2005. 16.99 (978-0-06-623957-6(5)); 2000. lib. bdg. 16.89 (978-0-06-623959-0(1)) HarperCollins Pubs.

Carson, William C. Peter Becomes a Trail Man: The Story of a Boy's Journey on the Santa Fe Trail. Oliphant, Pat, illus. 2002. 192p. (J). (gr. 6 up). 12.95 (978-0-8263-2895-3(4)) Univ. of New Mexico Pr.

Carvell, Marlene. Sweetgrass Basket. 2005. 256p. (J). (gr. 3-6). 16.99 (978-0-525-47547-7(8) , Dutton Juvenile) Penguin Group (USA) Inc.

Caszatt-Allen, Wendy. Last Voyage of the Griffon. 2007. (Illus.). 140p. (J). pap. 6.95 (*978-1-934133-08-8(6)) Mackinac Island Pr., Inc.

Chibbaro, Julie. Redemption. 2004. (Illus.). 272p. (YA). 17.99 (978-0-689-85736-2(5) , Atheneum) Simon & Schuster Children's Publishing.

Chickasaw Adventures: More than Warriors. 2005. (J). (978-1-4265-0002-2(5)) Layne Morgan Media, Inc.

Chickasaw Adventures: Tears at Fort Coffee. 2004. (J). (978-0-9762904-2-1(1)) Layne Morgan Media, Inc.

Chickasaw Adventures: The Civil War. 2005. (J). (978-1-4265-0000-8(9)) Layne Morgan Media, Inc.

Chickasaw Adventures: War with the Creeks. 2005. (J). (978-1-4265-0001-5(7)) Layne Morgan Media, Inc.

Chickasaw Adventures No. 1: The Journey Begins. 2004. (J). (978-0-9762904-0-7(5)) Layne Morgan Media, Inc.

Chief & the Storyteller: Not All Wanderers Are Lost. 2004. (Illus.). 150p. (YA). per. 16.95 (978-0-9747972-0-5(0)) Great Adventures Publishing.

Clark, Ann Nolan. Bringer of the Mystery Dog. Howe, Oscar, illus. 2000. 48p. (J). (gr. k-5). 6.95 (978-1-885772-20-6(3)) Kiva Publishing, Inc.

Clark, N. Laurie. It's Wesley! The Adirondack Guide. Clark, N. Laurie, illus. 1998. (Illus.). 32p. (J). (gr. k up). per. 14.95 (978-0-9641197-1-0(4)) Clark Pubs.

Clifford, Eth. The Year of the Three-Legged Deer. Cuffari, Richard, tr. Cuffari, Richard, illus. 2003. (Library of Indiana Classics). 176p. (YA). 32.95 (978-0-253-34251-5(1)); pap. 14.95 (978-0-253-21604-5(4)) Indiana Univ. Pr.

Clifford, Mary. Lonesome Road. 2005. 185p. pap. 19.95 (978-1-4137-6419-2(3)) PublishAmerica, Inc.

Cooney, Caroline B. The Ransom of Mercy Carter. 2002. 256p. (YA). (gr. 7 up). mass mkt. 5.99 (978-0-440-22775-5(5) , Laurel Leaf) Random Hse. Children's Bks.

Cooper, James Fenimore. The Last of the Mohicans. 2002. (Great Illustrated Classics Ser.). (Illus.). 240p. (J). (gr. 3-8). 21.35 (978-1-57765-692-0(X) , ABDO & Daughters) ABDO Publishing Co.

—The Last of the Mohicans. 2001. (Saddleback Classics). (Illus.). (J). (978-0-606-21559-6(X)) Tandem Library Bks.

—The Last of the Mohicans. Howell, Troy, illus. 2008. (Classic Starts Ser.). 160p. (J). 5.95 (*978-1-4027-4577-5(X)) Sterling Publishing Co., Inc.

Cooper, James Fenimore. The Last of the Mohicans. Carrillo, Fred, illus. 2nd ed. 1998. (Illustrated Classic Book Ser.). 61p. (J). (gr. 3 up). reprint ed. pap. 4.95 (978-1-56767-249-7(3)) Educational Insights, Inc.

Cooper, James Fenimore & Bowler, Bill. The Last of the Mohicans. 2003. (Illus.). 80p. 6.50 (978-0-19-424403-9(2)) Oxford Univ. Pr., Inc.

Corll, Vivian. Himmarshee. 2002. 109p. pap. 16.95 (978-1-59129-959-2(4)) PublishAmerica, Inc.

Cornelissen, Cornelia. Soft Rain: A Story of the Cherokee Trail of Tears. 1999. (Illus.). 128p. (gr. 3-7). 5.50 (978-0-440-41242-7(0) , Yearling) Random Hse. Children's Bks.

—Soft Rain: A Story of the Cherokee Trail of Tears. 1999. (J). (978-0-606-18968-2(8)) Tandem Library Bks.

Crawford, Ann Fears. Keechee: The Witch of the Woods. 2005. (J). (978-1-931823-21-0(9)) Halcyon Pr.

Crazy Horse's Vision. pap. 16.95 incl. audio (978-1-59112-451-1(4)); pap. incl. audio (978-1-59112-453-5(0)); pap. 18.95 incl. audio compact disk (978-1-59112-911-0(7)); pap. incl. audio compact disk (978-1-59112-913-4(3)) Live Oak Media.

Creech, Sharon. Chasing Redbird. 1998. (J). 12.64 (978-0-606-13265-7(1)) Tandem Library Bks.

—Sharon Creech Box Set: Absolutely Normal Chaos, Walk Two Moons, Chasing Redbird. 2001. (J). (gr. 3-7). pap. 18.48 (978-0-06-441008-3(0) , Harper Trophy) HarperCollins Pubs.

Creel, Ann Howard. Under a Stand Still Moon. 2005. 192p. (YA). pap. 8.95 (978-0-9746481-8-7(3)) Brown Barn Bks.

—Water at the Blue Earth. 1998. (Illus.). 148p. (gr. 5-9). pap. 8.95 (978-1-57098-224-8(4)) Rinehart, Roberts Pubs.

Crew, Linda. Nekomah Creek. Robinson, Charles, illus. 2001. 192p. (gr. 4-7). pap. 12.00 (978-0-375-89506-7(X) , Yearling) Random Hse. Children's Bks.

Crook, Connie Brummel. Maple Moon. Cameron, Scott, illus. unabr. ed. 1998. 32p. (YA). (ps-2). (978-0-7737-3017-5(6)) Stoddart Kids.

—Maple Moon. 2000. (Illus.). 30p. (J). (ps-3). 6.95 (978-0-7737-6098-1(9)) Stoddart Kids CAN. *Dist:* Fitzhenry & Whiteside, Ltd.

Dalgliesh, Alice. The Courage of Sarah Noble. Weisgard, Leonard, illus. 2002. (J). 13.40 (978-0-7587-0249-4(3)) Book Wholesalers, Inc.

Dalton, Sheila. Trial by Fire. 1998. 208p. (YA). (gr. 9-12). pap. 6.95 (978-0-929141-63-3(6)) Napoleon Publishing/Rendezvous Pr. CAN. *Dist:* AtlasBooks Distribution.

Danticat, Edwidge. Anacaona: Golden Flower, Haiti 1490. 2005. (Royal Diaries). (Illus.). 192p. (J). pap. 10.95 (978-0-439-49906-4(2)) Scholastic, Inc.

DeFelice, Cynthia C. The Ghost of Poplar Point. 2007. (Ghost Mysteries Ser.). (Illus.). 192p. (J). (gr. 3-7). 16.00 (*978-0-374-32540-4(5)) Farrar, Straus & Giroux.

Dell, Pamela. Giles & Metacom: A Story of Plimoth & the Wampanoag. 2002. (Scrapbooks of America Ser.). (Illus.). 48p. (J). (gr. 2-6). 28.50 (978-1-59187-012-8(7)) Child's World, Inc.

Deschaine, Scott. Screaming Eagle. Roy, Mike, illus. 1999. 296p. (J). 19.95 (978-1-878181-04-6(1)) Discovery Comics.

Desoto, Ernestine. Sugar Bear Story. 2004. (NAI & ENG.). 32p. pap. 9.95 (978-0-932653-70-3(7)) Sunbelt Pubns., Inc.

DeVore, Maggie. White Crow. Barron, Lynn, ed. DeVore, Jeffrey, illus. 2002. (J). 17.00 (978-0-9708940-3-8(1)) Gently Worded Bks., LLC.

Dewey, Jennifer Owings. Navajo Summer. 2000. (gr. 3-6). lib. bdg. 18.75 (978-0-8085-8012-6(4)) Tandem Library Bks.

Dexter, Anthony. The Adventures of Manny the Manatee. 2004. 45p. pap. 19.95 (978-1-4137-2751-7(4)) PublishAmerica, Inc.

Dodge, Mary Mapes. Po No Kah an Indian Tale of Long Ago. 2004. reprint ed. pap. 15.95 (978-1-4191-4185-0(6)) Kessinger Publishing, LLC.

Dodge, Mary Mapes. PoNoKah an Indian Tale of Long Ago. 2006. pap. 21.95 (*978-1-4286-5828-8(9)) Kessinger Publishing, LLC.

Domiteaux, Diane & Wallis, Karen. Washoe Seasons of Life: A Native American Story. 2004. (Illus.). 44p. (J). lib. bdg. 19.95 (978-0-9749610-3-3(5) , 1234960) Beagle Bay Bks.

Doolittle, Bev & Maclay, Elise. The Earth Is My Mother. Doolittle, Bev, illus. 2000. (Illus.). 176p. (J). (gr. 4-7). tchr. ed. 17.95 (978-0-86713-044-7(X) , 85163) Greenwich Workshop Pr.

Dorris, Michael. Sees Behind Trees. rev. ed. 1999. 128p. (gr. 4-17). pap. 4.99 (978-0-7868-1357-5(1)) Disney Pr.

—Sees Behind Trees. 104p. (J). (gr. 4-6). pap. 4.95 (978-0-8072-1516-6(3)); 1998. pap. 28.00 incl. audio (978-0-8072-7957-1(9) , YA949SP) Random Hse. Audio Publishing Group. (Listening Library).

Down, Heather. A Deadly Distance. 2006. 133p. (J). (gr. 4-8). per. 9.99 (*978-1-55002-637-5(2) , Sandcastle Bks.) Dundurn Group, The CAN. *Dist:* Univ. of Toronto Pr.

Downie, Mary Alice. Scared Sarah. Wood, Muriel, illus. 2002. 65p. pap. (978-1-55041-714-2(2)); 64p. (J). (gr. 3-6). (978-1-55041-712-8(6)) Fitzhenry & Whiteside, Ltd.

Downing, Sybil & Barker, Jane Valentine. Mesas to Mountains. (Colorado Heritage Ser.). (Illus.). 47p. (J). (ps-8). reprint ed. pap. 7.95 (978-1-878611-04-8(6)) Silver Rim Pr.

Durrant, Lynda. Turtle Clan Journey. 1999. 192p. (J). (gr. 5-9). tchr. ed. 15.00 (978-0-395-90369-8(6) , Clarion Bks.) Houghton Mifflin Co. Trade & Reference Div.

Erdrich, Lise. Bears Make Rock Soup: And Other Stories. Fifield, Lisa, illus. 2002. 32p. (J). (gr. 1 up). 16.95 (978-0-89239-172-1(3)) Children's Bk. Pr.

Erdrich, Louise. The Birchbark House. 2002. (gr. 5-8). lib. bdg. 15.00 (978-0-613-59384-7(7)) Tandem Library Bks.

—The Game of Silence. l.t. ed. 2005. (Illus.). 319p. (J). (gr. 3-7). per. 22.95 (978-0-7862-7768-1(8) , Large Print Pr.) Thorndike Pr.

Eustache, Harold. Shuswap Journey. 2004. 176p. pap. 15.95 (978-1-894778-15-2(4)) Theytus Bks., Ltd. CAN. *Dist:* Orca Bk. Pubs. USA.

Faber, Gail & Lasagna, Michele. Clara Rides the Rancho. Faber, Gail, illus. (Whispers Ser.). (Illus.). (J). (gr. 3-7). 2002. 52p. pap., tchr.'s training gde. ed. 10.95 (978-0-936480-17-6(3)); 2001. 185p. 12.95 (978-0-936480-16-9(5)); 2001. 185p. pap. 9.95 (978-0-936480-15-2(7)) Magpie Pubns.

Farber, Erica. Golden Eagle. Mayer, Mercer, illus. 2006. (Critter Kids Adventure Ser.). 32p. (J). (gr. 2-5). pap. 4.95 (978-0-7696-4764-7(2) , Gingham Dog Pr.) School Specialty Publishing.

Farley, Walter. Little Black, a Pony. Whitethorne, Baje, illus. unabr. ed. 2006. (ENG & NAV.). 64p. (J). (ps-3). 21.95 incl. audio compact disk (978-1-893354-90-6(3)) Salina Bookshelf.

Feagan, Robert. Mystery at Shildii Rock. 2007. 168p. (J). pap. 9.99 (*978-1-55002-668-9(2) , Sandcastle Bks.) Dundurn Group, The CAN. *Dist:* Univ. of Toronto Pr.

Feagan, Robert. Napachee. 2005. 128p. (YA). (gr. 3-8). pap., tchr. ed. (978-0-88878-403-2(1) , Sandcastle Bks.) Dundurn Group, The.

Feder, Harriet K. Death on Sacred Ground. 2003. (Young Adult Fiction Ser.). (Illus.). 192p. (J). (gr. 7 up). 14.95 (978-0-8225-0741-3(2) , Carolrhoda Bks.) Lerner Publishing Group.

Forester, MaMa Eagle. Young Eagle, Pretty Flower. Spears, Ashley E., illus. 2004. 16p. (J). 7.95 (978-0-9762389-4-2(2)) Trent's Prints.

Fox, Lee White. Toby Erdrich & the Golden Eclipse. Selyov, Trebor E., ed. 2005. 170p. (YA). (gr. 7-12). pap. 11.95 (978-0-9665055-7-3(3) , 5) Hallmark Emporium.

Freeman, Bill. Sioux Winter. 1999. (Bains Series by Bill Freeman Ser.). (Illus.). 141p. (J). (gr. 3-8). 6.95 (978-1-55028-652-6(8)); (*978-1-55028-653-3(6)) Lorimer, James & Co., Ltd., Pubs. CAN. *Dist:* Casemate Pubs. & Bk. Distributors, LLC.

Frost, Helen. Diamond Willow. 2008. 128p. (J). 16.00 (*978-0-374-31776-8(3)) Farrar, Straus & Giroux.

Frye, Mary M. The Boy Who Almost Lost His Name, 5 vols., Vol .2. Willis, Henry J., tr. from ENG. Howard, Norma, illus. 2001. 40p. (J). 20.00 (978-0-9710250-1-1(0)) Choctaw Crafts & Bks.

George, Jean Craighead. Julie of the Wolves. Schoenherr, John, illus. 2003. (Julie of the Wolves Ser.). 208p. (YA). (gr. 7 up). pap. 5.99 (978-0-06-054095-1(8) , Harper Trophy) HarperCollins Pubs.

—Julie's Wolf Pack. Minor, Wendell, illus. 1999. (Julie of the Wolves Ser.). 208p. (J). (gr. 5 up). pap. 5.99 (978-0-06-440721-2(7) , Harper Trophy) HarperCollins Pubs.

Gilliland, Hap. Flint's Rock. Livers-Lambert, Paulette, illus. 2001. (Council for Indian Education Ser.). 144p. (gr. 4 up). pap. 8.95 (978-1-879373-82-2(3)) Rinehart, Roberts Pubs.

Goble, Paul. The Girl Who Loved Horses. Goble, Paul, illus. 2001. (Illus.). (J). pap. 18.95 incl. audio compact disk (978-1-59112-314-9(3)) Live Oak Media.

—The Girl Who Loved Wild Horses. Goble, Paul, illus. 2001. (Illus.). 28.95 incl. audio compact disk (978-1-59112-752-9(1)); pap. 39.95 incl. audio compact disk (978-1-59112-534-1(0)) Live Oak Media.

—Legend of the White Buffalo Woman. 2002. (gr. k-3). lib. bdg. 16.40 (978-0-613-81335-8(9)) Tandem Library Bks.

Golio, Janet & Golio, Mike. Present from the Past. 2nd ed. 2007. 120p. (YA). pap. 14.99 (*978-1-59092-145-6(3) , Blue Works) Windstorm Creative.

—Puzzle from the Past. 2nd ed. 2007. 120p. (YA). pap. 14.99 (*978-1-59092-146-3(1) , Blue Works) Windstorm Creative.

Golio, Janet, et al. A Present from the Past: Multimedia Edition. 2000. (Illus.). III, 157p. (J). (gr. 4-7). cd-rom 14.95 (978-0-9704202-0-6(X)) GAGA.

Gregory, Kristiana. Jenny of the Tetons. 2002. (Great Episodes Ser.). 192p. (YA). pap. 6.00 (978-0-15-216770-7(6) , Gulliver Bks.) Harcourt Children's Bks.

—Jenny of the Tetons. 2002. (gr. 5-8). lib. bdg. 14.15 (978-0-613-83778-1(9)) Tandem Library Bks.

—The Legend of Jimmy Spoon. 2002. (Great Episodes Ser.). 224p. (YA). pap. 6.00 (978-0-15-216776-9(5) , Gulliver Bks.) Harcourt Children's Bks.

Griese, Arnold A. Anna's Athabaskan Summer. Ragins, Charles, illus. 2003. 32p. (J). (gr. k-2). pap. 9.95 (978-1-56397-650-6(1)) Boyds Mills Pr.

Grinnell, George Bird. Jack among the Indians. 2006. (Illus.). pap. 30.95 (*978-1-4286-3276-9(X)) Kessinger Publishing, LLC.

Grokett, Jan. Songs of the Orcas. l.t. ed. 2002. 48p. (J). per. 9.99 (978-1-893108-72-1(4)) Neighborhood Pr. Publishing.

Guest, Jacqueline. Lightning Rider. 2000. (SideStreets Ser.). (gr. 7-12). 168p. 7.95 (978-1-55028-720-2(6)); 162p. (YA). (978-1-55028-721-9(4)) Lorimer, James & Co., Ltd., Pubs. CAN. *Dist:* Casemate Pubs. & Bk. Distributors, LLC.

—Lightning Rider. 2001. (gr. 7-12). lib. bdg. 13.00 (978-0-613-78316-3(6)); (gr. 3-6). lib. bdg. 13.00 (978-0-613-54819-9(1)) Tandem Library Bks.

Haig-Brown, Roderick L. The Whale People. unabr. ed. (Illus.). 206p. (YA). pap. 14.95 (*978-1-55017-277-5(8)) Harbour Publishing Co., Ltd. CAN. *Dist:* Graphic Arts Ctr. Publishing Co.

Halter, Loretta. A Voice for the Redwoods. du Houx, Emily, illus. 2003. 64p. pap. 14.00 (978-1-882190-66-9(1)) Polar Bear & Co.

Hamilton, Elizabeth L. Secret of Cachuma Lake. 2001. (Travel Adventure Ser.: Bk. 1). (Illus.). 144p. (YA). per. 9.95 (978-0-9713749-7-3(X)) Quiet Impact, Inc.

Harcourt School Publishers Staff. The Trading Post On Level. 3rd ed. 2002. (Trophies Reading Program Ser.). (Illus.). pap. 5.10 (978-0-15-323184-1(X)) Harcourt Schl. Pubs.

Hennessy, B. G. One Little, Two Little, Three Little Pilgrims. 2001. (gr. k-3). lib. bdg. 15.30 (978-0-613-85724-6(0)) Tandem Library Bks.

Henty, G. A. In the Heart of the Rockies. l.t. ed. 2006. 322p. pap. 17.99 (978-1-4264-3253-8(4)) BiblioBazaar.

—In the Heart of the Rockies. 2003. (ENG.). pap. 15.99 (***978-1-4142-0081-1(1)***) IndyPublish.com.

—In the Heart of the Rockies. 2004. reprint ed. pap. 27.95 (978-1-4191-2600-0(8)); pap. 1.99 (978-1-4192-2600-7(2)) Kessinger Publishing, LLC.

Herr, Melody. Summer of Discovery. 2006. 111p. (J). pap. 10.95 (978-0-8032-2437-7(0)); 112p. pap. 10.95 (978-0-8032-7362-7(2) , A Bison Original) Univ. of Nebraska Pr.

Hewitt, William. Across the Wide River. 2004. 104p. (J). 11.95 (978-0-8263-2978-3(0)) Univ. of New Mexico Pr.

Hill, Kirkpatrick. The Year of Miss Agnes. 2002. 128p. (J). (ps-7). mass mkt. 4.99 (978-0-689-85124-7(3) , Aladdin) Simon & Schuster Children's Publishing.

—The Year of Miss Agnes. Knorr, Peter, illus. 2000. 128p. (J). (gr. 3-7). 16.00 (978-0-689-82933-8(7) , McElderry, Margaret K.) Simon & Schuster Children's Publishing.

Hillerman, Tony. The Wailing Wind. 2003. 334p. (gr. 7-12). per. 16.45 (978-0-613-59827-9(X)) Tandem Library Bks.

Hobbs, Will. Beardream. 2000. (gr. k-3). lib. bdg. 15.30 (978-0-613-28414-1(3)) Tandem Library Bks.

—Kokopelli's Flute. 2005. 160p. (J). (gr. k-9). pap. 4.99 (978-1-4169-0250-8(3) , Aladdin) Simon & Schuster Children's Publishing.

Hobbs, William. Far North. 2004. (Illus.). 304p. (J). (gr. 7 up). pap. 6.99 (978-0-06-054096-8(6) , Harper Trophy) HarperCollins Pubs.

—Ghost Canoe. 1998. (Avon Camelot Bks.). 208p. (J). (gr. 5-9). pap. 5.99 (978-0-380-72537-3(1)) HarperCollins Pubs.

—Ghost Canoe. 1998. (J). 12.64 (978-0-606-13420-0(4)) Tandem Library Bks.

Holm, Jennifer L. Boston Jane. 2002. (gr. 3-6). lib. bdg. 15.30 (978-0-613-56251-5(8)) Tandem Library Bks.

—Wilderness Days. (Boston Jane Ser.). 256p. (J). (gr. 5 up). 2004. pap. 5.99 (978-0-06-440881-3(7) , Harper Trophy); 2002. 16.99 (978-0-06-029043-6(9)); 2002. lib. bdg. 18.89 (978-0-06-029044-3(7)) HarperCollins Pubs.

Hopkins, Suzette. Little Wolf's Christmas. Taylor, Jill, illus. 2004. 19p. (J). 12.95 (978-1-932133-72-1(0)) Writers' Collective, The.

Hudson, Jan. Dawn Rider. 2000. (Illus.). (J). (978-0-606-18399-4(X)) Tandem Library Bks.

Hutchens, Paul. The Indian Cemetery. rev. ed. 1998. (Sugar Creek Gang Ser.: Vol. 13). 96p. (J). (gr. 4-7). 4.99 (978-0-8024-7017-1(3)) Moody Pubs.

Hutchinson, Emily. Last of the Mohicans. abr. ed. 2001. (gr. 7-12). lib. bdg. 15.25 (978-0-613-36461-4(9)) Tandem Library Bks.

The Indian in the Cupboard. 1998. (J). pap. 3.95 (978-0-439-04474-5(X)) Scholastic, Inc.

Irbinskas, Heather. How Jackrabbit Got His Very Long Ears. Spengler, Kenneth J., illus. 1999. 32p. (gr. k up). 15.95 (978-0-87358-566-8(6) , Rising Moon Bks. for Young Readers) Northland Publishing.

—The Lost Kachina. Albert, Robert & Anthis, Brian, illus. 2004. 32p. (J). 15.95 (978-1-885772-33-6(5)) Kiva Publishing, Inc.

Jackson, Dave & Jackson, Neta. Exiled to the Red River: Chief Spokane Garry. 2003. (Trailblazer Bks.). (Illus.). 144p. (J). pap. 6.99 (978-0-7642-2235-1(X)) Bethany Hse. Pubs.

Jacobs, Paul S. James Printer: A Novel of King Philip's War. 2000. 224p. (J). (gr. 4-7). 4.50 (978-0-590-97541-4(2)) Scholastic, Inc.

Jaffe, Nina. Flor de Oro. Sanchez, Enrique, illus. (SPA.). (J). 15.95 (978-1-55885-463-5(0) , Piñata Books) Arte Publico Pr.

James, Betsy. Mud Family. 1998. (gr. k-3). lib. bdg. 19.90 (978-0-613-70810-4(5)) Tandem Library Bks.

Jeffers, Susan, illus. Brother Eagle, Sister Sky: A Message from Chief Seattle. 2002. 20p. (J). (gr. 3-5). reprint ed. 16.00 (978-0-7567-5580-5(8)) DIANE Publishing Co.

Jelinek, Donald A. Survivor of the Alamo: The Saga of Moses Rose, Who Fought for France with Napoleon Bonaparta - & Then for Texas with Jim Bowle, Davy Crockett & William Barret Travis at the Alamo. 1999. (Illus.). 253p. (J). pap. (978-0-9704607-0-7(8)) Jelinck, Donald A.

Jennings, Paulla. Strawberry Thanksgiving. Peters, Ramona, illus. 2005. (Multicultural Celebrations Ser.). 32p. (J). 4.95 (978-1-59373-010-9(1)) Bunker Hill Publishing, Inc.

Job & Derib. Yakari & Great Eagle. 2007. (Illus.). 48p. pap. 9.99 (***978-1-905460-04-5(X)***) CineBook GBR. *Dist:* Biblio Distribution.

John, Roberta. Proud to Be a Blacksheep. Ruffenach, Jessie, ed. Smith, Keith, illus. 2006. (NAV & ENG.). 32p. 17.95 (978-1-893354-05-0(9)) Salina Bookshelf.

Johnson, Rodney. Curse of the Royal Ruby: A Rinnah Two Feathers Mystery. 2002. (gr. 7-12). lib. bdg. 19.90 (978-0-613-90288-5(2)) Tandem Library Bks.

—The Secret of Dead Man's Mine. Thompson, Jill, illus. 2001. 248p. (J). (gr. 4-7). pap. 12.00 (978-0-9663473-3-3(1)) Uglytown Productions.

Jones, Jennifer Berry. Heetunka's Harvest: A Tale of the Plains Indians. Keegan, Shannon, illus. 1998. (Council for Indian Education Ser.). 32p. (gr. k-7). pap. 8.95 (978-1-57098-235-4(X)) Rinehart, Roberts Pubs.

—Heetunka's Harvest: A Tale of the Plains Indians. 1998. (gr. 3-6). lib. bdg. 17.60 (978-0-613-82654-9(X)) Tandem Library Bks.

Jones, Kimberly K. Sand Dollar Summer. 2006. 224p. (J). 15.95 (978-1-4169-0362-8(3) , McElderry, Margaret K.) Simon & Schuster Children's Publishing.

Kadohata, Cynthia. Weedflower. 2006. (J). (978-0-689-04937-8(4)); (Illus.). 272p. (gr. 5 up). 16.95 (978-0-689-86574-9(0)) Simon & Schuster Children's Publishing. (Atheneum).

Karr, Kathleen. Worlds Apart. 2005. 208p. (J). 15.95 (978-0-7614-5195-2(1)) Cavendish, Marshall Corp.

Katschke, Judy. The Case of the Wild Wolf River. 1998. (New Adventures of Mary-Kate & Ashley Ser.). 87p. (J). (gr. 2-7). pap. 3.99 (978-0-590-29401-0(6)) Scholastic, Inc.

Ketchum, Liza. Where the Great Hawk Flies. 2005. 272p. (J). (gr. 5-9). 16.00 (978-0-618-40085-0(0) , Clarion Bks.) Houghton Mifflin Co. Trade & Reference Div.

Kimmel, Eric A. The Lady in the Blue Cloak: Legends from the Texas Missions. Guevera, Susan, illus. 2005. 40p. (J). 16.95 (978-0-8234-1738-4(7)) Holiday Hse., Inc.

Kirkpatrick, Katherine. Trouble's Daughter: The Story of Susanna Hutchinson, Indian Captive. 2000. (978-0-606-17896-9(1)) Tandem Library Bks.

Kotzwinkle, William. The Return of Crazy Horse. 2001. (Illus.). 32p. (J). (ps-3). 16.95 (978-1-58394-047-1(2) , Frog Ltd.) North Atlantic Bks.

Kroll, Steven. John Quincy Adams: Letters from a Southern Planter's Son. 2001. (Dear Mr. President Ser.). (Illus.). 128p. (J). (gr. 4-6). 9.95 (978-1-890817-93-0(7)) Winslow Pr.

Kudlinski, Kathleen V. My Lady, Pocahontas. 400th anniv. ed. 2006. 208p. (YA). (gr. 6-8). 16.95 (978-0-7614-5293-5(1)) Cavendish, Marshall Corp.

Kusugak, Michael Arvaarluk. Arctic Stories. Krykorka, Vladyana Langer, illus. 1998. 40p. (J). (gr. k-4). pap. 7.95 (978-1-55037-452-0(4)); lib. bdg. 19.95 (978-1-55037-453-7(2)) Annick Pr., Ltd. CAN. *Dist:* Firefly Bks., Ltd.

—Arctic Stories. 1999. (J). (978-0-606-16482-5(0)) Tandem Library Bks.

L'Allier, Peter. Rotten Robbie & the Legend of Wanibinoo. 2006. (Illus.). (YA). 18.95 (978-0-9724022-8-6(4)) Dr. Todd, LLC.

Lamberti, B. J. Nelson Paige & the Treasure Trove. 2006. 174p. per. 12.95 (978-1-59886-193-8(X)) Tate Publishing & Enterprises, L.L.C.

Landrey, Wanda A. The Ghost of Spindletop Hill. 2000. (Illus.). 144p. (J). 15.95 (978-1-57168-449-3(2)) Eakin Pr.

Lapallo, Connie. Dark Enough to See the Stars in a Jamestown Sky. 2006. (YA). (gr. 7 up). pap. 19.95 (***978-1-59526-421-3(3)***) Media Creations, Inc.

Larrabee, Lisa. Grandmother Five Baskets. Sawyer, Lori, illus. 2000. 60p. (gr. 3-7). pap. 9.95 (978-0-943173-90-0(6)) Rinehart, Roberts Pubs.

The Last of the Mohicans. 2000. (Illus.). (YA). 48p. stu. ed., per. 17.95 (978-1-56254-294-8(X) , SP294X); 80p. per. 6.95 (978-1-56254-293-1(1) , SP2931) Saddleback Educational Publishing.

Lawlor, Laurie. Wind on the River. 2004. 156p. (J). lib. bdg. 16.92 (***978-1-4242-0771-8(1)***) Fitzgerald Bks.

Lawlor, Laurie. Wind on the River: A Story of the Civil War. 2001. (American Portraits Ser.). (Illus.). iv, 156p. (J). (gr. 5-8). 15.32 (978-0-8092-0582-0(3) , 9780809205820) Jamestown.

—Wind on the River: A Story of the Civil War. 2000. (gr. 5-8). lib. bdg. 15.70 (978-0-613-36904-6(1)) Tandem Library Bks.

Lawlor, Laurie & McGraw-Hill Staff. Wind on the River: A Story of the Civil War. 2001. (Jamestown Classics Ser.). (Illus.). iv, 156p. (J). (gr. 5-8). pap. 10.00 (978-0-8092-0624-7(2) , 9780809206247) Jamestown.

Lenington, Amber. The White Indian: Lost in the Reality of My Own Dream. 2005. (YA). (978-0-9616620-1-1(8)) Constellation Pr.

Letts, Billie. The Honk & Holler Opening Soon. 1999. (gr. 7-12). lib. bdg. 23.40 (978-0-613-17283-7(3)) Tandem Library Bks.

Lewis, Floyd. The Foundered Mule. 2006. (YA). (***978-0-9788283-2-5(1)***) Acacia Publishing, Inc.

Lewis, Paul Owen. Frog Girl. Lewis, Paul Owen, illus. 1999. (Illus.). 32p. (J). (gr. 2 up). lib. bdg. 24.67 (978-0-8368-2228-1(5)) Stevens, Gareth Inc.

—Frog Girl. 2001. (gr. k-3). lib. bdg. 15.25 (978-0-613-37144-5(5)) Tandem Library Bks.

—Frog Girl. 2004. (Illus.). 38p. (J). tchr. ed., tchr.'s planning gde. ed. 2.95 (978-1-58246-009-3(4) , Tricycle Pr.) Ten Speed Pr.

—Frog Girl. (Illus.). 32p. (J). (ps-5). 18.95 (978-1-55110-658-2(2)) Whitecap Bks., Ltd. CAN. *Dist:* Graphic Arts Ctr. Publishing Co.

—Storm Boy. Lewis, Paul Owen, illus. 1999. (Illus.). 32p. (J). (gr. 2 up). lib. bdg. 22.60 (978-0-8368-2229-8(3)) Stevens, Gareth Inc.

—Storm Boy. 2003. (gr. k-3). lib. bdg. 15.25 (978-0-613-85264-7(8)) Tandem Library Bks.

—Storm Boy. 2004. (Illus.). (J). tchr. ed. 2.95 (978-1-58246-008-6(6)); 32p. (gr. k-5). 6.95 (978-1-58246-057-4(4)); 32p. (gr. 1-4). 14.95 (978-1-883672-96-6(1)) Ten Speed Pr. (Tricycle Pr.).

—Storm Boy. 2005. (Illus.). 32p. (ps-5). pap. 8.95 (978-1-55285-268-2(7)) Whitecap Bks., Ltd. CAN. *Dist:* Graphic Arts Ctr. Publishing Co.

Lincoln Collier, James. The Corn Raid. 2004. 142p. (J). lib. bdg. 16.92 (***978-1-4242-0768-8(1)***) Fitzgerald Bks.

Lisle, Janet Taylor. The Crying Rocks. 2003. (Illus.). 208p. (YA). 16.95 (978-0-689-85319-7(X) , Atheneum/Richard Jackson Bks.) Simon & Schuster Children's Publishing.

—The Crying Rocks. l.t. ed. 2004. (Thorndike Press Large Print Literacy Bridge Ser.). 273p. (J). 22.95 (978-0-7862-6140-6(4)) Thorndike Pr.

Little, Kimberley Griffiths. Enchanted Runner. 1999. (Avon Camelot Bks.). 149p. (J). (gr. 5-7). 15.00 (978-0-380-97623-2(4)) HarperCollins Pubs.

—The Last Snake Runner. 2004. 208p. (YA). (gr. 7). pap. 5.99 (978-0-440-23782-2(3) , Laurel Leaf) Random Hse. Children's Bks.

London, Jonathan. Giving Thanks. Manchess, Gregory, illus. 2003. 32p. (J). (ps-2). 16.99 (978-0-7636-1680-9(X)) Candlewick Pr.

Long, Devata. Seeing Is Sometimes Believing. Garza, Amy Ammons, ed. Cain, Doreyl Ammons, illus. l.t. ed. 2001. 32p. (J). (gr. k-3). pap. 6.95 (978-0-9651232-8-0(6) , AC505, Catch the Spirit of Appalachia) Ammons Communications, Ltd.

Long, Olivia. Thunderbirds & Thunderbeings. Long, Olivia, illus. Date not set. (Our Precious Planet Ser.). (Illus.). 32p. (J). (ps-4). (978-1-880042-10-6(X)) Shelf-Life Bks.

Lopez, David Mark. Maddie's Magic Markers: Ride Like an Indian. 2006. (J). (gr. 3-7). (***978-0-9744097-1-9(5)***) Lopez, David.

Lorenz, Albert & Schleh, Joy. Hero, Hawk, & Open Hand: A Story about Cahokia. 2004. (J). (978-0-8109-4842-6(7)) Abrams, Harry N. , Inc.

Lough, Loree. Dream Seekers: Roger William's Stand for Freedom. 1999. (American Adventure Ser.: No. 3). (Illus.). 144p. (J). (gr. 3-7). lib. bdg. 15.95 (978-0-7910-5043-9(2) , Chelsea Hse.) Facts On File, Inc.

Loyie, Larry & Brissenden, Constance. The Gathering Tree. Holmlund, Heather D., illus. 2006. 48p. (J). bds. 18.95 (978-1-894778-28-2(6)) Theytus Bks., Ltd. CAN. *Dist:* Orca Bk. Pubs. USA.

Maracle, Lee. Will's Garden. 2002. (gr. 7-12). lib. bdg. 18.75 (978-0-613-88445-7(0)) Tandem Library Bks.

Mark of the Stone. 2000. 45p. (J). (gr. 3-6). per. 9.99 (978-0-9707770-0-3(0)) Blue Horse Mukwa Publishing.

Markle, Sandra. The Fledglings. 2003. 144p. (YA). (gr. 4-6). pap. 9.95 (978-1-56397-696-4(X)) Boyds Mills Pr.

—The Fledglings. 2001. (J). (978-0-606-22053-8(4)) Tandem Library Bks.

Marsden, Carolyn. Bird Springs. 2007. 128p. (J). (gr. 3 up). 14.99 (978-0-670-06193-8(X) , Viking Juvenile) Penguin Group (USA) Inc.

Marsh, Carole. Pocahontas. 2002. (One Thousand Readers Ser.). (Illus.). 12p. (J). (gr. k-4). 2.95 (978-0-635-01506-8(4) , 15064) Gallopade International.

—Pocahontas. (Read-Along Ser.). (J). 7.99 incl. audio (978-1-55723-739-2(5)) Walt Disney Records.

Marsh, Carole. The Puzzle of the Indian Arrowhead. 2006. 64p. (gr. 1-3). 14.95 (***978-0-635-06201-7(1)***) Gallopade International.

Matcheck, Diane. The Sacrifice. 2005. 208p. (YA). pap. 6.95 (978-0-374-46440-0(5) , Sunburst) Farrar, Straus & Giroux.

Matthaei, Gay & Grutman, Jewel. The Sketchbook of Thomas Blue Eagle. Cvijanovic, Adam, illus. 2001. 60p. (YA). (gr. 5-8). reprint ed. 17.00 (978-0-7567-6295-7(2)) DIANE Publishing Co.

Matthews, Kay. An Anasazi Welcome. Belknap, Barbara, illus. 2004. 40p. (gr. 4-7). pap. 6.95 (978-1-878610-27-0(9)) Red Crane Bks., Inc.

Max, Jill, compiled by. Spider Spins a Story: Fourteen Legends from Native America. 2007. (J). pap. 7.95 (***978-0-87358-936-9(X)*** , Rising Moon Bks. for Young Readers) Northland Publishing.

Maxson, H. A. & Young, Claudia H. Lenapehoking: Land of the Delawares. Etherson, Lesley, illus. 2001. 64p. (J). per. 8.95 (978-0-9704692-1-2(7)) Bay Oak Pubs., Ltd.

Mayaprua, Alejandro Taish. Nantu & Auju: How the Moon & the Potoo Bird Came to Be. Youth of the Achuar Tribe of Ecuador, illus. 2005. (J). 15.95 (978-0-9745477-0-1(0)) Arutam Pr.

Mccabe, Jr. Planting the Wilderness or, the Pioneer Boys: a Story of Frontier Life. 2007. pap. 27.95 (***978-1-4304-8187-4(0)***) Kessinger Publishing, LLC.

McCain, Becky Ray. Grandmother's Dreamcatcher. 2001. (Illus.). (J). (978-0-606-21858-0(0)) Tandem Library Bks.

McLeod, Elaine. Lessons from Mother Earth. Wood, Colleen, illus. 2002. (J). (ps-1). 15.95 (978-0-88899-312-0(9)) Groundwood Bks. CAN. *Dist:* Transition Vendor.

McLerran, Alice. The Ghost Dance. Morin, Paul, illus. 2001. 40p. (J). (gr. k-3). pap. 6.95 (978-0-618-11143-5(3) , Clarion Bks.) Houghton Mifflin Co. Trade & Reference Div.

McMurtry, Robby, tr. Song of Moon Pony. 2003. (Illus.). 17.95 (978-1-57168-740-1(8)) Eakin Pr.

Medearis, Angela Shelf. Dancing with the Indians. Byrd, Samuel, illus. 2000. pap. 18.95 incl. audio compact disk (978-1-59519-248-6(4)); pap. 39.95 incl. audio compact disk (978-1-59519-249-3(2)); (J). (gr. 1-6). 24.95 incl. audio (978-0-87499-333-2(4)); (J). (gr. 1-6). pap. 16.95 incl. audio (978-0-87499-332-5(6)) Live Oak Media.

—Dancing with the Indians, Grades 1-6. Byrd, Samuel, illus. unabr. ed. 2000. (J). pap., tchr. ed. 37.95 incl. audio (978-0-87499-334-9(2)) Live Oak Media.

Mesta, Robert I. Condor: Spirit of the Canyon. Ormsby, Lawrence, illus. 2007. (J). (***978-0-938216-85-8(6)***) Grand Canyon Assn.

Metaxas, Eric. Princess Scargo & the Birthday Pumpkin. Barbour, Karen, illus. 2005. (Rabbit Ears-A Classic Tale Ser.). 40p. (J). (gr. k-5). 25.65 (978-1-59197-769-8(X)) Spotlight.

Mikaelsen, Ben. Touching Spirit Bear. 2001. 256p. (J). (gr. 5 up). 16.99 (978-0-380-97744-4(3)); lib. bdg. 17.89 (978-0-06-029149-5(4)) HarperCollins Pubs.

—Touching Spirit Bear. l.t. ed. 2004. 305p. pap. 10.95 (978-0-7862-6351-6(2)) Thorndike Pr.

Momaday, N. Scott. Circle of Wonder: A Native American Christmas Story. Momaday, N. Scott, illus. 2001. (Illus.). 44p. 24.95 incl. audio compact disk (978-0-8263-2796-3(6)) Univ. of New Mexico Pr.

Montgomery, Rutherford G. Broken Fang. Hunt, Lynn Bogue, illus. 2004. (Classic Ser.). 312p. (gr. 4-7). pap. 15.95 (978-0-87004-416-8(8)) Caxton Pr.

Moonshower, Candie. The Legend of Zoey. 2007. 224p. (J). (gr. 4-7). 5.99 (***978-0-440-23924-6(9)*** , Yearling) Random Hse. Children's Bks.

Moore, Billy Loran. Little Brother Real Snake. 144p. 10.95 (978-1-58838-147-7(1)) NewSouth, Inc.

Munro, Ken. The Cross Keys Caper. 2006. (Sammy & Brian Mystery Ser.: 18). 154p. pap. 5.95 (***978-1-932864-94-6(6)***) Masthof Pr.

Murphy, Barbara Beasley. Ace Flies Like an Eagle. 2003. (Can't Stop Ace Ser.: No. 3). 180p. (J). pap. 16.95 (978-0-86534-409-9(4)) Sunstone Pr.

Nelson, S. D. The Star People: A Lakota Story. 2003. (Illus.). 36p. (J). (ps-3). 14.95 (978-0-8109-4584-5(3)) Abrams, Harry N. , Inc.

Nielsen, Gwyn English. Serendipity & the Dream Catcher. Nielsen, Gwyn English, ed. Colby, Devon English, illus. 2003. 176p. (gr. 3-7). pap. 5.95 (978-0-9660726-2-4(6)) C.G.S. Pr.

Noble, Trinka Hakes. The Legend of Michigan. Frankenhuyzen, Gijsbert van, illus. 2006. 48p. (J). 17.95 (978-1-58536-278-3(6)) Sleeping Bear Pr.

Noble, Trinka Hakes. The Legend of the Cape May Diamond. Lewis, Earl B, illus. rev. ed. 2007. 40p. (J). 17.95 (***978-1-58536-279-0(4)***) Sleeping Bear Pr.

O'Dell, Scott. Island of the Blue Dolphins. 2002. (Illus.). (J). 15.00 (978-0-7587-0194-7(2)) Book Wholesalers, Inc.

—Island of the Blue Dolphins. 184p. (J). (gr. 3-5). pap. 5.99 (978-0-8072-8327-1(4)); 2004. (gr. 5-9). pap. 36.00 incl. audio (978-0-8072-8326-4(6) , YA163SP) Random Hse. Audio Publishing Group. (Listening Library).

—Sing Down the Moon. 2006. 21.75 (978-0-8446-7288-5(2)) Smith, Peter Pub., Inc.

Oldfield, Jenny. Iron Eyes. 2002. (Illus.). 240p. (J). pap. 13.99 (978-0-340-85109-8(0) , Hodder & Stoughton) Hodder General Publishing Division GBR. *Dist:* Trafalgar Square Publishing.

Olsen, Sylvia. The Girl with a Baby. 2004. 208p. (J). pap. 7.95 (978-1-55039-142-8(9)) Sono Nis Pr. CAN. *Dist:* Orca Bk. Pubs. USA.

—No Time to Say Goodbye. 2002. (Illus.). 175p. (J). pap. 6.95 (978-1-55039-121-3(6)) Sono Nis Pr. CAN. *Dist:* Orca Bk. Pubs. USA.

—Yellow Line. 2005. (Orca Soundings Ser.). 112p. (J). (gr. 7-12). pap. 7.95 (978-1-55143-462-9(8)) Orca Bk. Pubs. USA.

Orona-Ramirez, Kristy. Kiki's Journey. Warm Day, Jonathan, illus. 2006. 32p. (J). 16.95 (978-0-89239-214-8(2)) Children's Bk. Pr.

Ortakales, Denise. The Legend of the Old Man of the Mountain. Crawford, Robert, illus. 2004. 40p. (J). 17.95 (978-1-58536-236-3(0)) Sleeping Bear Pr.

Ortiz, Simon J. The Good Rainbow Road. Lacapa, Michael & Montejo, Victor, trs. Lacapa, Michael, illus. 2004. (NAI, ENG & SPA.). 64p. (J). 16.95 (978-0-8165-2340-5(1)) Univ. of Arizona Pr.

Osborne, Mary Pope. Adaline Falling Star. unabr. ed. 2004. (Middle Grade Cassette Librariestm Ser.). 176p. (J). (gr. 3-7). pap. 29.00 incl. audio (978-0-8072-1195-3(8) , S YA 319 SP, Listening Library) Random Hse. Audio Publishing Group.

Osofsky, Audrey. Dreamcatcher. 1999. (J). lib. bdg. (978-0-606-16921-9(0)) Tandem Library Bks.

Otte, Wanda. Hidden Secrets of the Knob. 2007. (ENG.). 228p. (J). per. 17.99 (***978-1-4141-0810-0(9)***) Pleasant Word.

Otten, Charlotte. Home in a Wilderness Fort: Copper Harbor 1844. 2006. (J). pap. 14.95 (978-0-9766104-5-8(0)) Arbutus Pr.

Pearsall, Shelley. Crooked River. 2005. 256p. (J). (gr. 5-9). 15.95 (978-0-375-82389-3(1)); lib. bdg. 17.99 (978-0-375-92389-0(6)) Random Hse. Children's Bks. (Knopf Bks. for Young Readers).

Penn, Audrey. The Whistling Tree. Gibson, Barbara, illus. 2003. 32p. 16.95 (978-0-87868-852-4(8) , 8528, Child & Family Pr.) Child Welfare League of America, Inc.

Perkins, Elavina & Johnson, Jerrold T., eds. Ashkii's Journey. Clinton, Verna, illus. 2001. (ENG & NAV.). 36p. 17.95 (978-1-893354-31-9(8)) Salina Bookshelf.

Peschke, M. Dead Man's Map. Smith, Tod, illus. 2008. (J). pap. (***978-1-59889-921-4(X)***); (YA). (gr. 5-9). lib. bdg. 17.95 (***978-1-59889-855-2(8)***) Stone Arch Bks.

Powell, Neva. The Long Crossing. Powell, Eugene, illus. 1998. 128p. (YA). (gr. 4-7). pap. 12.95 (978-0-9661072-2-7(5)) Avocet Pr., Inc.

Price, Joan. Medicine Man. 1999. 124p. (YA). (gr. 7-10). pap. 9.99 (978-0-88092-069-8(6)) Royal Fireworks Publishing Co.

Priest, George E. The Great Winged Monster of the Piasa Valley: The Legend of the Piasa. 1998. (Illus.). 123p. (YA). (gr. 4-12). 17.00 (978-0-9678461-0-1(2)); pap. 15.00 (978-0-9678461-1-8(0)) Alton Museum of History & Art, Inc.

Race to Moonrise Rev. 2006. 9.95 (978-1-932738-31-5(2)) Western Reflections Publishing Co.

Raczek, Linda Theresa. Rainy's Powwow. Bennett, Gary, illus. 1999. 32p. (J). (gr. k-3). 15.95 (978-0-87358-686-3(7) , Rising Moon Bks. for Young Readers) Northland Publishing.

Raffa, Edwina & Rigsby, Annelle. Escape to the Everglades. 2006. pap., tchr. ed., act. bk. ed. 6.00 (978-1-56164-362-2(9)) Pineapple Pr., Inc.

Ramírez, Antonio. Napi va a la Montagna. Domi, illus. 2006. (SPA.). 48p. (J). 18.95 (978-0-88899-715-9(9)) Groundwood Bks. CAN. *Dist:* Perseus Distribution.

Ramthun, Bonnie. The White Gates. 2008. (J). (*978-0-375-84554-3(2)*); pap. (*978-0-375-84555-0(0)*); lib. bdg. (*978-0-375-94554-0(7)*) Random Hse., Inc.

Razzell, Mary. Haida Quest. unabr. ed. 2002. 144p. (YA). (978-1-55017-249-2(2)) Harbour Publishing Co., Ltd.

Rees, Celia. Sorceress. (Illus.). 352p. (YA). (gr. 9). 2003. pap. 8.99 (978-0-7636-2183-4(8)); 2002. 15.99 (978-0-7636-1847-6(0)) Candlewick Pr.

Rice, Bebe Faas. The Place at the Edge of the Earth. 2002. 192p. (YA). (gr. 5-9). tchr. ed. 15.00 (978-0-618-15978-9(9), Clarion Bks.) Houghton Mifflin Co. Trade & Reference Div.

Rice, Mel. Fire on the Hillside. 2001. (gr. 3-6). lib. bdg. 17.60 (978-0-613-86878-5(1)) Tandem Library Bks.

Richter, Conrad. The Light in the Forest. 2005. (Illus.). 176p. 14.95 (978-1-4000-4426-9(X), Everyman's Library) Knopf Publishing Group.

Riefe, Barbara. Amelia Dale Archer Story. 1998. 304p. (YA). (gr. 8 up). 22.95 (978-0-312-86077-6(3), Forge Bks.) Doherty, Tom Assocs., LLC.

Robison, C. Dan, Jr. Wind Seer: The Story of One Boy's Contribution to the Anasazi Culture. 2005. 132p. (J). per. 18.95 (978-0-922993-27-7(0)) Marquette Bks., LLC.

Rogerson, George. Stillness of the Dawn - Book One - White Man Coming. 2007. 144p. (YA). pap. 12.95 (*978-1-60145-165-1(2)*) Booklocker.com, Inc.

Ross, Sylvia. Lion Singer. 2005. (Illus.). 33p. (J). (gr. 1-4). 12.95 (978-1-59714-009-6(0), Great Valley Bks.) Heyday Bks.

Rubcic, Michael. Native Soul. 2004. 216p. (Orig.). (J). pap. 14.95 (978-0-9746848-0-2(5)) Native Sun Pr.

Rue, Nancy N. The Discovery. 2001. (Christian Heritage Ser.). (Illus.). 192p. (J). (gr. 3-7). pap. (978-1-56179-862-9(2)) Focus on the Family Publishing.

Ruffenach, Jessie, ed. Baby Learns about Animals. Thomas, Peter, tr. from NAV. Blacksheep, Beverly, illus. 2004. (ENG & NAV.). 16p. 7.95 (978-1-893354-49-4(0)) Salina Bookshelf.

Rylant, Cynthia & Siegel, Mark. Long Night Moon. 2004. (Illus.). 40p. (J). 16.95 (978-0-689-85426-2(9)) Simon & Schuster Children's Publishing.

Salonen, Roxane Beauclair. First Salmon. 2005. (Illus.). 29p. (J). (gr. 3-7). 15.95 (978-1-59078-171-5(6)) Boyds Mills Pr.

Sargent, Dave & Sargent, Pat. Charlie: (Appaloosa) Be Brave, 25, 14. Lenoir, Jane, illus. 2001. (Saddle Up Ser.: 14). 36p. (J). pap. 6.95 (978-1-56763-608-6(X)); lib. bdg. 22.60 (978-1-56763-607-9(1)) Ozark Publishing.

—Hoot: (Grullo) Be Creative, 30, 35. Lenoir, Jane, illus. 2003. (Saddle Up Ser.: Vol. 35). 42p. (J). pap. 6.95 (978-1-56763-696-3(9)); lib. bdg. 22.60 (978-1-56763-695-6(0)) Ozark Publishing.

—Kiowa: (Paint) Be Trustworthy, 25, 37. Lenoir, Jane, illus. 2001. (Saddle Up Ser.: 37). 36p. (J). pap. 6.95 (978-1-56763-618-5(7)); lib. bdg. 22.60 (978-1-56763-617-8(9)) Ozark Publishing.

—Mack: (Medicine Hat Paint) Be a Leader, 30, 39. Lenoir, Jane, illus. 2003. (Saddle Up Ser.: Vol. 39). 42p. (J). pap. 6.95 (978-1-56763-700-7(0)); lib. bdg. 22.60 (978-1-56763-699-4(3)) Ozark Publishing.

—Whiskers: (Roan) Pride & Peace, 30, 59. Lenoir, Jane, illus. (Saddle Up Ser.: Vol. 59). 42p. (J). 2003. pap. 6.95 (978-1-56763-806-6(6)); 2002. lib. bdg. 22.60 (978-1-56763-805-9(8)) Ozark Publishing.

Sargent, Dave, et al. Counting Coup Vol. 4: (Cheyenee) Be Proud, 20. Lenoir, Jane, illus. l.t. ed. 2003. (Story Keeper Ser.). 42p. (J). lib. bdg. 22.60 (978-1-56763-909-4(7)) Ozark Publishing.

Savageau, Cheryl. Muskrat Will Be Swimming. Hynes, Robert, illus. 2006. 32p. (J). pap. (978-0-88448-280-2(4)) Tilbury Hse. Pubs.

Say, Allen. Home of the Brave. 2002. (Illus.). 32p. (J). (gr. k-3). 17.00 (978-0-618-21223-1(X), Walter Lorraine) Houghton Mifflin Co. Trade & Reference Div.

Sayles, Carol L. Turn the Turtle Rightside. 2007. 156p. (J). pap. 9.95 (978-1-933255-25-5(0)) DNA Pr.

Scieszka, Jon. The Good, the Bad, & the Goofy, Vol. 3. 2004. (Time Warp Trio Ser.: No. 3). (Illus.). 80p. (J). (gr. 2-6). pap. 4.99 (978-0-14-240046-3(7), Puffin) Penguin Group (USA) Inc.

—You Can't, but Genghis Khan. 2006. (Time Warp Trio). 80p. (J). (gr. 2-5). pap. 4.99 (978-0-06-111636-0(X), Harper Trophy) HarperCollins Pubs.

Scott, Ann Herbert. On Mother's Lap. Coalson, Glo, illus. 2002. (J). 14.74 (978-0-7587-3318-4(6)) Book Wholesalers, Inc.

—On Mother's Lap. Coalson, Glo, illus. 2000. 14p. (J). (gr. k-ps). bds. 5.95 (978-0-618-05159-5(7), Clarion Bks.) Houghton Mifflin Co. Trade & Reference Div.

Shaw, Janet. Kaya's Short Story Collection. Farnsworth, Bill & Graef, Renee, illus. 2006. 256p. (J). 12.95 (*978-1-59369-119-6(X)*) American Girl Publishing, Inc.

Shaw, Janet. Kaya's Story Collection. Farnsworth, Bill, illus. 2005. (American Girls Collection). 407p. (J). (gr. 3-17). 29.95 (978-1-59369-046-5(0), American Girl) American Girl Publishing, Inc.

Shaw, Janet Beeler. Changes for Kaya. 2002. (gr. 3-6). lib. bdg. 14.10 (978-0-613-46214-3(9)) Tandem Library Bks.

—Kaya's Escape. 2002. (gr. 3-6). lib. bdg. 14.10 (978-0-613-46223-5(8)) Tandem Library Bks.

—Kaya's Hero. 2002. (gr. 3-6). lib. bdg. 14.10 (978-0-613-46224-2(6)) Tandem Library Bks.

Sheely, Robert. In the Hands of the Enemy. Killcoyne, Hope L., ed. Martin, John F., illus. 2003. (Adventures in America Ser.: Vol. 8). 75p. (J). 14.95 (978-1-893110-31-1(1)) Silver Moon Pr.

Shefelman, Janice J. & Shefelman, Tom, illus. Son of Spirit Horse. 2004. 74p. (J). (978-1-57168-833-0(1), Eakin Pr.) Eakin Pr.

Siegelson, Kim L. Escape South. Jackson, Shelley, illus. 2004. (Road to Reading Ser.). 80p. (J). (gr. k-3). pap. 3.99 (978-0-307-26504-3(8), Random Hse. Bks. for Young Readers) Random Hse. Children's Bks.

—Escape South. 2000. (J). 10.79 (978-0-606-18931-6(9)) Tandem Library Bks.

Simmons, Marc. Billy Blackfeet in the Rockies: A Story from History. Kil, Ronald R., illus. 2006. 56p. (J). 18.95 (978-0-8263-4105-1(5)) Univ. of New Mexico Pr.

—Millie Cooper's Ride: A True Story from History. Kil, Ronald R., illus. 2002. 56p. (J). 16.95 (978-0-8263-2925-7(X)) Univ. of New Mexico Pr.

Skurzynski, Gloria & Ferguson, Alane. Ghost Horses. 2000. (National Parks Mysteries Ser.: Vol. 6). (Illus.). 160p. (J). (gr. 3-7). 15.95 (978-0-7922-7055-3(X), National Geographic Children's Bks.) National Geographic Society.

Smelcer, John. The Trap. 2006. 176p. (YA). (gr. 4-7). 15.95 (978-0-8050-7939-5(4)) Holt, Henry & Co.

—The Trap. 2007. 192p. (YA). pap. 7.99 (*978-0-312-37755-7(X)*) Square Fish.

Smith, Cynthia Leitich. Indian Shoes. Madsen, Jim, illus. 2002. 80p. (J). (gr. 2-5). 15.99 (978-0-06-029531-8(7)) HarperCollins Pubs.

—Rain Is Not My Indian Name. Earley, Lori, illus. 2001. 144p. (J). (gr. 5-9). 16.99 (978-0-688-17397-5(7)) HarperCollins Pubs.

Smith, Patricia Clark. Weetamoo, Heart of the Pocassets: Massachusetts, 1653. 2003. (Royal Diaries Ser.). (Illus.). 208p. (J). pap. 10.95 (978-0-439-12910-7(9)) Scholastic, Inc.

Smith, Roland. The Last Lobo. 2001. (gr. 3-6). lib. bdg. 14.15 (978-0-613-74960-2(X)); (J). (978-0-606-21289-2(2)) Tandem Library Bks.

Snedden, Genevra Sis. Docas the Indian Boy of Santa Clara. 2005. pap. 21.95 (978-1-4179-2695-4(3)) Kessinger Publishing, LLC.

Sneve, Virginia Driving Hawk. Bad River Boys. Farnsworth, Bill, illus. 2005. 32p. (YA). 16.95 (978-0-8234-1856-5(1)) Holiday Hse., Inc.

Sneve, Virginia Driving Hawk. Lana's Lakota Moons. 2007. (Illus.). 127p. (J). (gr. 3 up). pap. 12.95 (*978-0-8032-6028-3(8)*) Univ. of Nebraska Pr.

Stainer, M. L. The Lyon's Cub. Melvin, James, illus. unabr. ed. 1998. (Book 2 of the Lyon Saga Ser.: Bk. 2). 162p. (YA). (gr. 5-10). pap. 6.95 (978-0-9646904-6-2(2)); lib. bdg. 9.95 (978-0-9646904-5-5(4)) Chicken Soup Pr., Inc.

—The Lyon's Throne. Melvin, James, illus. 1999. (Lyon Saga Ser.: Bk. 4). 153p. (YA). (gr. 5-9). pap. 6.95 (978-1-893337-02-2(2)) Chicken Soup Pr., Inc.

Steele, Alexander. The Last of the Breed. Punchatz, Don, illus. l.t. ed. 1999. (Adventures of Wishbone Ser.: No. 16). 163p. (J). (gr. 4 up). lib. bdg. 22.60 (978-0-8368-2594-7(2)) Stevens, Gareth Inc.

Steele, D. Kelley. Fire in Her Hair: A Story of Friendship. James, Margaret Ray, illus. l.t. ed. 2002. 40p. (J). (gr. 1-6). 18.95 (978-0-9711534-0-0(X)) Hidden Path Pubn., Inc.

Stenhouse, Ted. A Dirty Deed. 2005. (Illus.). 192p. (YA). (gr. 13 up). (978-1-55337-360-5(X)); (gr. 5-9). (978-1-55337-361-2(8)) Kids Can Pr., Ltd.

Sterling, Shirley. My Name Is Seepeetza. 1998. 126p. (J). (gr. 5-7). pap. 8.95 (978-0-88899-165-2(7), Libros Tigrillo) Groundwood Bks. CAN. *Dist:* Perseus Distribution.

Stiegemeyer, Julie. Thanksgiving: A Harvest Celebration. Benoit, Renne, illus. 2006. (ENG.). 32p. (J). pap. 6.99 (978-0-7586-0916-8(7)) Concordia Publishing Hse.

Stilwell, Norma. It Was Powwow Time in Plymouth. 2004. 43p. pap. 19.95 (978-1-4137-3534-5(7)) PublishAmerica, Inc.

Stites, Clara. Katya of Fort Ross. 2001. (Illus.). 80p. (J). pap. 8.95 (978-1-56474-379-4(9)) Fithian Pr.

Stone, Marie. On Their Own: A Journey to Jamestown. 2006. (J). (978-1-57249-385-8(2); White Mane Kids) White Mane Publishing Co., Inc.

Swanson, Bruce. Gray Wolf's Search. Peterson, Gary, illus. 2007. 24p. (J). (gr. 1-5). 14.95 (978-0-9779183-1-7(9)) Seventh Generation Design.

Sweeney, Joyce. Waiting for June. 2006. 160p. 5.99 (978-0-7614-5329-1(6)) Cavendish, Marshall Corp.

Taylor, Bonnie Highsmith. Kodi's Mare. Marks, Dea, illus. 2000. (Cover-to-Cover Novel Ser.). 82p. (J). pap. (978-0-7891-2929-1(9)); (gr. 2-5). lib. bdg. 13.95 (978-0-7807-8962-3(8)) Perfection Learning Corp.

Taylor, C. J. All the Stars in the Sky: Native Stories from the Heavens. Thisdale, Francois, illus. 2006. 40p. (J). (gr. 3). 17.95 (978-0-88776-759-3(1)) Tundra Bks., Inc./Livres Toundra, Inc. CAN. *Dist:* Random Hse., Inc.

Taylor, Drew Hayden. The Boy in the Treehouse/The Girl Who Loved Her Horses. 2000. 160p. pap. 13.95 (978-0-88922-441-4(2)) Talonbooks, Ltd. CAN. *Dist:* Chicago Distribution Ctr.

Thomas, Lowell P. The Panther & the Windigo. 2002. (Illus.). 264p. (YA). (gr. 5-9). per. 10.99 (978-0-9668559-3-7(0)) East of the Sun Publishing.

Thomasma, Kenneth. Doe Sia: Bannock Girl & the Handcart Pioneer. 1999. (Amazing Indian Children: Vol. 8). (J). (gr. 3-8). 12.99 (978-1-880114-21-6(6)) Grandview Publishing Co.

Tingle, Tim. Crossing Bok Chitto: A Choctaw Tale of Friendship & Freedom. Bridges, Jeanne Rorex, illus. 2006. (SPA & ENG.). 40p. (J). 17.95 (978-0-938317-77-7(6)) Cinco Puntos Pr.

Tolson, Aaron J. Washington Putter. 2005. 248p. (YA). per. 22.00 (978-1-58982-243-6(9), Bedside Bks.) American Bk. Publishing Group.

Trotter, Deborah W. A Summer's Trade. Manavi, Lorraine Begay, tr. Toddy, Irving, illus. 2008. (ENG & NAV.). 32p. (gr. 2-5). 17.95 (*978-1-893354-71-5(7)*) Salina Bookshelf.

Tsinajinnie, Veronica, et al. Johonaa'éí: Bringer of Dawn. Howard, Winston, illus. 2008. (ENG & NAV.). 32p. 17.95 (978-1-893354-54-8(7)) Salina Bookshelf.

Turner, Ginger. Gold Mine! The California Gold Rush Story. 2004. (Illus.). 46p. (J). per. 15.95 (978-0-9742502-2-9(8)) Gossamer Bks., LLC.

Turner, Ginger & Shimpi, Shekhar. Gold Mine! The California Gold Rush Story. 2004. (Illus.). 44p. (J). pap. 15.95 (978-0-9742502-3-6(6)) Gossamer Bks., LLC.

Urban, Betsy. Waiting for Deliverance. 2000. (Illus.). iv, 186p. (J). (gr. 7-12). 18.99 (978-0-531-33310-5(8)); pap. 17.95 (978-0-531-30310-8(1)) Scholastic, Inc. (Orchard Bks.).

Van Camp, Richard. What's the Most Beautiful Thing You Know about Horses? Littlechild, George, illus. 32p. (J). 2003. pap. 7.95 (978-0-89239-185-1(5)); 1998. (gr. 1 up). 15.95 (978-0-89239-154-7(5)) Children's Bk. Pr.

—What's the Most Beautiful Thing You Know about Horses? 2003. (gr. k-3). lib. bdg. 16.40 (978-0-613-70988-0(8)) Tandem Library Bks.

Vaughan, Marcia. Night Dancer: Mythical Piper of the Native American Southwest. Desimini, Lisa, illus. 2002. 32p. (J). (ps-2). pap. 16.95 (978-0-439-35248-2(7), Orchard Bks.) Scholastic, Inc.

Vick, Helen Hughes. Shadow. 1998. (Courage of the Stone Ser.). 128p. (gr. 4-9). 15.95 (978-1-57098-218-7(X)) Rinehart, Roberts Pubs.

Von Ahnen, Katherine & Young Bear, Joan A. Charlie Young Bear. Lambert, Paulette L., illus. 2000. (Council for Indian Education Ser.). 48p. (gr. 2-4). pap. 4.95 (978-1-57098-001-5(2)) Rinehart, Roberts Pubs.

Von Burg, Frederick E. Keep My White Sneakers, Kit Carson: An Adventure with the Blackfeet. 2002. 160p. pap. 12.95 (978-0-595-24264-1(2), Writers Club Pr.) iUniverse, Inc.

Waboose, Jan Bourdeau. Firedancers. Taylor, C. J., illus. 2000. 26p. (J). (ps-3). 14.95 (978-0-7737-3138-7(5)) Stoddart Kids CAN. *Dist:* Fitzhenry & Whiteside, Ltd.

—Morning on the Lake. Reczuch, Karen, illus. 32p. (J). (gr. k-3). 2002. (978-1-55074-588-7(3)); 1998. (978-1-55074-373-9(2)) Kids Can Pr., Ltd.

—Morning on the Lake. 2002. (gr. k-3). lib. bdg. 14.10 (978-0-613-83962-4(5)) Tandem Library Bks.

—Sky Sisters. Deines, Brian, illus. 2000. 32p. (J). (gr. k-3). (978-1-55074-697-6(9)) Kids Can Pr., Ltd.

—Skysisters. Deines, Brian, illus. 2002. 32p. (J). (gr. k-3). (978-1-55074-699-0(5)) Kids Can Pr., Ltd.

Wallace, Bill. The Legend of Thunderfoot. 2007. 150p. (J). (gr. 3-7). per. 5.99 (*978-1-4169-0692-6(4)*, Aladdin) Simon & Schuster Children's Publishing.

Walt Disney Company Staff. Pocahontas. 2005. (WEL., Illus.). 24p. (978-1-899877-04-1(5)) Y Ddraig Fach.

Walters, Scott. Woman Too Young of Panther Cave. 2007. (YA). per. 16.95 (*978-1-934248-09-6(6)*) Mill City Pr., Inc.

—Woman Too Young of Panther Cave. 2007. 20.95 (*978-1-934248-14-0(2)*) Mill City Pr., Inc.

Wargin, Kathy-Jo. The Legend of the Lady's Slipper. van Frankenhuyzen, Gijsbert, illus. (Great Lakes Legend Ser.). 48p. (J). (gr. k-5). 2003. pap. 7.95 (978-1-58536-168-7(2)); 2001. 17.95 (978-1-886947-74-0(0)) Sleeping Bear Pr.

Waterton, Betty. A Salmon for Simon. rev. ed. 1998. (Illus.). 32p. (J). (ps-1). pap. 6.95 (978-0-88899-276-5(9)) Groundwood Bks. CAN. *Dist:* Perseus Distribution.

Weber, Lou, ed. Tonka Construction. 2004. (Illus.). 12p. (J). bds. 7.98 (978-0-7853-9006-0(5), 7194400) Publications International, Ltd.

—Tonka Rescue. 2004. (Illus.). 12p. (J). bds. 7.98 (978-0-7853-9008-4(1), 7194500) Publications International, Ltd.

Weir, Joan. Maybe Tomorrow. 2001. 209p. (YA). (gr. 5-9). pap. 5.95 (978-0-7736-7486-8(1)) Stoddart Kids CAN. *Dist:* Fitzhenry & Whiteside, Ltd.

—Maybe Tomorrow. 2001. (gr. 5-8). lib. bdg. 14.10 (978-0-613-63629-2(5)) Tandem Library Bks.

Whelan, Gloria. Miranda's Last Stand. 144p. (J). (gr. 3-7). 2000. pap. 4.95 (978-0-06-442097-6(3), Harper Trophy); 1999. (Illus.). 14.89 (978-0-06-028252-3(5)) HarperCollins Pubs.

—Miranda's Last Stand. 2000. (J). (978-0-606-19267-5(0)); (978-0-606-19988-9(8)) Tandem Library Bks.

—Return to the Island. 192p. (J). (gr. 4-7). 2002. pap. 5.95 (978-0-06-440761-8(6)); 2000. 15.89 (978-0-06-028254-7(1)) HarperCollins Pubs.

Williamson, Ray A. & Monroe, Jean Guard. They Dance in the Sky: Native American Star Myths. Stewart, Edgar, illus. 2007. 144p. (J). (gr. 4-6). pap. 8.95 (*978-0-618-80912-7(0)*) Houghton Mifflin Co. Trade & Reference Div.

Wisniewski, David. The Wave of the Sea-Wolf. 1999. (978-0-606-22855-8(1)) Tandem Library Bks.

Wisniewski, David & Wisniewski, David. Wave of the Sea-Wolf. Wisniewski, David, illus. 1999. (Illus.). (J). (gr. k-4). lib. bdg. 14.10 (978-0-613-19489-1(6)) Tandem Library Bks.

Wolfel, Ursula. Fliegender Stern. pap. 14.95 (978-3-570-26064-7(X)) Bertelsman, Verlagsgruppe C. GmbH DEU. *Dist:* Distribooks, Inc.

Wood, Audrey. The Rainbow Bridge. 2000. (gr. 3-6). lib. bdg. 15.30 (978-0-613-28618-3(9)) Tandem Library Bks.

Woods, Brenda. My Name Is Sally Little Song. 192p. (J). 2007. (gr. 2). 5.99 (*978-0-14-240943-5(X)*, Puffin); 2006. (gr. 3-6). 15.99 (978-0-399-24312-7(7), Putnam Juvenile) Penguin Group (USA) Inc.

Woolley, Barbara B. Freedom West. 2006. 22.99 (*978-1-4257-0124-6(8)*); pap. 15.99 (*978-1-4257-0123-9(X)*) Xlibris Corp.

Worcester, Donald Emmet. Lone Hunter Books: War Pony. 2000. Tr. of Lone Hunter's Gray Pony. (gr. 3-6). lib. bdg. 32.65 (978-0-613-90540-4(7)) Tandem Library Bks.

Wright, Caleb E. Marcus Blair A Story of Provincial Times. 2006. pap. 22.95 (*978-1-4286-6303-9(7)*) Kessinger Publishing, LLC.

Wyss, Thelma Hatch. Bear Dancer: The Story of a Ute Girl. 2005. (Illus.). 192p. (J). 15.95 (978-1-4169-0285-0(6), McElderry, Margaret K.) Simon & Schuster Children's Publishing.

Yazzie, Seraphine G. The Three Little Sheep. Smith, Ryan Huna, illus. 2006. (ENG & NAV.). 32p. 12.95 (978-1-893354-09-8(1)) Salina Bookshelf.

Yeahpau, Thomas M. X-Indian Chronicles: The Book of Mausape. 2006. 240p. (YA). (gr. 9). 16.99 (978-0-7636-2706-5(2)) Candlewick Pr.

Youmans, Marly. The Curse of the Raven Mocker. 2003. 288p. (J). 18.00 (978-0-374-31667-9(8), Farrar, Straus & Giroux (BYR)) Farrar, Straus & Giroux.

—The Curse of the Raven Mocker. 2006. 288p. (YA). (gr. 7). pap. 7.99 (978-0-14-240696-0(1), Puffin) Penguin Group (USA) Inc.

Zima, Gordon. Sunbirds & Evergreens. 2006. (J). (978-0-9742894-5-8(0)) Hutton Electronic Publishing.

Zima, Gordon & Zima, Paula, illus. Sun Birds & Evergreens: The Nuk-Chuk Stories. 2005. (J). (978-0-9742894-3-4(4)) Hutton Electronic Publishing.

INDIANS OF NORTH AMERICA—FOLKLORE

see also Indians of North America—Legends

Arroyo, Andrea, illus. The Legend of the Lady Slipper. 1999. 32p. (J). (gr. k-3). tchr. ed. 15.00 (978-0-395-90512-8(5)) Houghton Mifflin Co. Trade & Reference Div.

Bannon, Kay Thorpe. Yonder Mountain: A Cherokee Legend. Lombardo, Anna, illus. 1999. iv, 23p. (J). pap. (978-0-9669946-0-5(4)) Lobster Cove Publishing Co.

Beaverhead, Peter, et al. Mary Quequesah's Love Story: A Pend d'Oreille Indian Tale. 2000. (Illus.). 32p. pap. 5.95 (978-0-917298-71-4(3)) Montana Historical Society Pr.

Berk, Ari & Anderson, Carolyn Dunn. Coyote Speaks: Wonders of the Native American World. 2008. (J). (*978-0-8109-9372-3(4)*, Abrams Bks. for Young Readers) Abrams, Harry N., Inc.

Bruchac, Joseph & Bruchac, James. How Chipmunk Got His Stripes. Aruego, Jose & Dewey, Ariane, illus. 2003. 32p. (J). (gr. k-3). pap. 6.99 (978-0-14-250021-7(6), Puffin) Penguin Group (USA) Inc.

—How Chipmunk Got His Stripes: A Tale of Bragging & Teasing. Aruego, Jose & Dewey, Ariane, illus. 2001. 32p. (J). (gr. k-3). 16.99 (978-0-8037-2404-4(7), Dial) Penguin Group (USA) Inc.

—Raccoon's Last Race: A Traditional Abenaki Story. Aruego, Jose & Dewey, Ariane, illus. 2004. 32p. (J). (ps). 16.99 (978-0-8037-2977-3(4), Dial) Penguin Group (USA) Inc.

Bruchac, Joseph & Ross, Gayle. The Girl Who Married the Moon: Tales from Native North America. 2006. 128p. (YA). pap. 9.95 (978-1-55591-566-7(3), 800.992.2908) Fulcrum Publishing.

Carpelan, Mary J. Coyote Fights the Sun: A Shasta Indian Tale. 2002. (Illus.). 32p. (J). pap. 9.95 (978-1-890771-60-7(0)) Heyday Bks.

Charles, Veronika Martenova. Maiden of the Mist: A Legend of Niagara Falls. 2001. (Illus.). 32p. (J). (ps-3). 6.95 (978-0-7737-6207-7(8)); 13.95 (978-0-7737-3297-1(7)) Stoddart Kids CAN. *Dist:* Fitzhenry & Whiteside, Ltd.

Clark, Ann Nolan. Little Boy with Three Names: Stories of Taos Pueblo. Lujan, Tonita, illus. 2005. 75p. (J). (gr. 2-6). reprint ed. pap. 15.00 (978-0-7567-9717-1(9)) DIANE Publishing Co.

Crow, Joe M. Brave Wolf & the Thunderbird. Martin, Linda R., illus. 1998. (Tales of the People Ser.). 30p. (ps-3). 14.95 (978-0-7892-0160-7(7)) Abbeville Pr., Inc.

Curry, Jane Louise. Hold up the Sky. Watts, James, illus. 2003. 176p. (J). 18.95 (978-0-689-85287-9(8), McElderry, Margaret K.) Simon & Schuster Children's Publishing.

Curtin, Jeremiah, ed. Seneca Indian Myths. l.t. ed. 2001. (Illus.). 530p. pap. 16.95 (978-0-486-41602-1(X)) Dover Pubns., Inc.

Dalal, Anita. Myths of Native Americans. 2001. (Mythic World Ser.). (Illus.). 48p. (J). lib. bdg. 27.12 (978-0-7398-3190-8(9)) Raintree.

De Montano, Marty K. The Butterfly Dance. 2001. (Tales of the People Ser.). (Illus.). 32p. (ps-5). 14.95 (978-0-7892-0161-4(5)) Abbeville Pr., Inc.

—Coyote in Love with a Star. Coffin, Tom, illus. 1998. (Tales of the People Ser.). 30p. (ps up). 14.95 (978-0-7892-0162-1(3)) Abbeville Pr., Inc.

Dewey, Jennifer Owings. The Shaman & the Water Serpent. Yazzie, Benton, illus. 2007. 40p. (J). 16.95 (978-0-8263-4211-9(6)) Univ. of New Mexico Pr.

Duncan, Lois. The Magic of Spider Woman. 2000. (gr. 3-6). lib. bdg. 14.15 (978-0-613-31439-8(5)) Tandem Library Bks.

Duvall, Deborah L. How Medicine Came to the People: A Tale of the Ancient Cherokees. 2004. (Grandmother Stories Ser.: Vol. 2). (Illus.). 32p. (J). 14.95 (978-0-8263-3007-9(X)) Univ. of New Mexico Pr.

Duvall, Deborah L., text. The Great Ball Game of the Birds & Animals. 2004. (Grandmother Stories Ser.: Vol. 1). (Illus.). 32p. (J). 14.95 (978-0-8263-2913-4(6)) Univ. of New Mexico Pr.

—Rabbit & the Bears: A Traditional Cherokee Legend. 2004. (Grandmother Stories Ser.). (Illus.). 32p. (J). 14.95 (978-0-8263-3131-1(9)) Univ. of New Mexico Pr.

Earth, Red. Selu & Kana'Ti: Cherokee Corn Mother & Lucky Hunter. Earth, Red, illus. 1998. (Mondo Folktales Ser.). (Illus.). 32p. (J). (gr. k-4). pap. 4.95 (978-1-57255-167-1(4)) Mondo Publishing.

Endredy, James. The Journey of Tunuri & the Blue Deer: A Huichol Indian Story. Hernandez de la Cruz, Maria & Cruz Lopez, Casimiro de la, trs. Hernandez de la Cruz, Maria & Cruz Lopez, Casimiro de la, illus. 2003. 32p. 15.95 (978-1-59143-016-2(X)) Bear & Co.

Gary, Ken, tr. & illus. The Fire Stealers: A Hopi Story. Gary, Ken, illus. 2003. (J). 15.95 (978-1-885772-13-8(0)) Kiva Publishing, Inc.

Goble, Paul. The Lost Children: The Boys Who Were Neglected. Goble, Paul, illus. 1998. (Illus.). 40p. (J). (ps-3). 6.99 (978-0-689-81999-5(4) , Aladdin) Simon & Schuster Children's Publishing.

—Mystic Horse. Goble, Paul, illus. 2003. (Illus.). 40p. (J). lib. bdg. 17.89 (978-0-06-029814-2(6)); 16.99 (978-0-06-029813-5(8)) HarperCollins Pubs.

—The Return of the Buffaloes: A Plains Indian Story about Famine & Renewal of the Earth. 2002. (Illus.). 32p. (J). (gr. 3-7). pap. 7.95 (978-0-7922-6554-2(8) , National Geographic Children's Bks.) National Geographic Society.

Grey, Herman. American Indian Love Stories: Traditional Stories of Love & Romance from Tribes Across America. 2002. 160p. (YA). pap. 14.95 (978-1-57416-063-5(X)) Clear Light Pubs.

Grinnell, George Bird. Blackfeet Indian Stories. 2005. 144p. per. 10.95 (978-1-931832-57-1(9) , 8667872363) Riverbend Publishing.

Harris, Christie. The Mouse Woman Trilogy: 30th Anniversary Edition. Tait, Douglas, illus. 30th ed. 2008. 464p. pap. 21.95 (***978-1-55192-880-7(9)***) Raincoast Bk. Distribution CAN. *Dist:* Perseus Distribution.

Hausman, Gerald. The Story of Blue Elk. Rodanas, Kristina, illus. 1998. 32p. (J). (gr. k-3). tchr. ed. 15.00 (978-0-395-84512-7(2) , Clarion Bks.) Houghton Mifflin Co. Trade & Reference Div.

Hayes, Joe. Soft Child: How Rattlesnake Got Its Fangs. Sather, Kay, illus. 2000. 32p. (ps-3). pap. 8.95 (978-0-943173-89-4(2)) Rinehart, Roberts Pubs.

Hinton, Leanne, tr. Ishi's Tale of Lizard. Roth, Susan L., illus. 2000. 32p. (J). (gr. 1-4). pap. 5.95 (978-1-890771-32-4(5)) Heyday Bks.

Keams, Geri. The Snail Girl Brings Water: A Navajo Story. Ziehler-Martin, Richard, illus. 1998. (J). (gr. k-3). 15.95 (978-0-87358-662-7(X) , Rising Moon Bks. for Young Readers) Northland Publishing.

Kootenai Culture Committee Staff. How Marten Got His Spots: And Other Kootenai Indian Stories. Finley, Debbie Joseph & Kallowatt, Howard, illus. 2002. 48p. pap. 8.95 (978-0-917298-92-9(6)) Montana Historical Society Pr.

Kuharski, Janice. El Regalo del Cuervo. de la Vega, Eida, tr. Kitchel, JoAnn, illus. 2001. (Books for Young Learners). Tr. of Raven's Gift. (SPA.). 16p. (J). (gr. k-2). pap. 5.00 (978-1-57274-451-6(0) , 2896) Owen, Richard C. Pubs., Inc.

Lee, Frances. Crow & the Daylight. 2001. (gr. k-3). lib. bdg. 11.95 (978-0-613-33354-2(3)) Tandem Library Bks.

Lilly, Melinda. Huatya Curi & the Five Condors: A Huarochiri Myth. Reasoner, Charles, illus. 1999. (Latin American Tales & Myths Ser.). 31p. (J). (gr. 2-5). lib. bdg. 26.60 (978-1-57103-263-8(0)) Rourke Publishing, LLC.

Lind, Michael. The Bluebonnet Girl. Kiesler, Kate, illus. rev. ed. 2003. 40p. (J). (ps-4). 16.95 (978-0-8050-6573-2(3) , Holt, Henry & Co. Bks. For Young Readers) Holt, Henry & Co.

Longfellow, Henry Wadsworth. The Song of Hiawatha. 2003. (Illus.). 32p. (J). 16.95 (978-1-59354-002-9(7)) Handprint Bks.

Marchand, Barbara, illus. Kou Skelowh: We Are the People. 2005. 88p. (J). pap. 12.95 (978-1-894778-18-3(9)) Theytus Bks., Ltd. CAN. *Dist:* Orca Bk. Pubs. USA.

Martin, Rafe. The World Before This One. Nicholls, Calvin, illus. 2002. 208p. (J). pap. 16.95 (978-0-590-37976-2(3) , Levine, Arthur A. Bks.) Scholastic, Inc.

—The World Before This One: A Novel Told in Legend. 2005. (Illus.). 208p. (J). (ps-7). pap. 5.99 (978-0-590-37980-9(1) , Levine, Arthur A. Bks.) Scholastic, Inc.

McDermott, Gerald. Arrow to the Sun: A Pueblo Indian Tale. McDermott, Gerald, illus. 2002. (Illus.). (J). 14.04 (978-0-7587-0038-4(5)) Book Wholesalers, Inc.

—Arrow to the Sun: A Pueblo Indian Tale. McDermott, Gerald, illus. 2004. (Illus.). 37p. (J). (gr. k-3). reprint ed. pap. 14.00 (978-0-7567-7103-4(X)) DIANE Publishing Co.

—Arrow to the Sun: A Pueblo Indian Tale. 2004. (J). (ps-4). pap. 14.95 incl. audio (978-1-56008-047-3(7) , PRA184) Weston Woods Studios, Inc.

—Coyote: A Trickster Tale from the American Southwest. 1999. (J). 13.80 (978-0-606-16530-3(4)) Tandem Library Bks.

—Raven: A Trickster Tale from the Pacific Northwest. McDermott, Gerald, illus. 2002. (Illus.). (J). 21.70 (978-0-7587-0138-1(1)) Book Wholesalers, Inc.

—Raven: A Trickster Tale from the Pacific Northwest. McDermott, Gerald, illus. 2001. (Illus.). 32p. (J). (ps-3). pap. 7.00 (978-0-15-202449-9(2) , Voyager Bks./Libros Viajeros) Harcourt Children's Bks.

—Raven: A Trickster Tale from the Pacific Northwest. 2001. (J). (978-0-606-22605-9(2)) Tandem Library Bks.

McDermott, Gerald & McDermott, Gerald. Raven: A Trickster Tale from the Pacific Northwest. McDermott, Gerald, illus. 2001. (Illus.). (J). (ps-ps). lib. bdg. 15.30 (978-0-613-45428-5(6)) Tandem Library Bks.

Mead, Alice & Neptume, Arnold, eds. Giants of the Dawnland: Ancient Wabanaki Tales. Date not set. 76p. (YA). pap. 8.00 (978-1-888034-01-1(7)) Loose Cannon Pr.

Mohican Nation Youth. Stories of Our Elders. Ganley, Beatrice et al, photos by. 1999. (Illus.). 21p. (YA). (gr. 4). pap. 10.00 (978-0-935790-06-1(3)) Muh-He-Con-Neew Pr.

Norman, Howard. Trickster & the Fainting Birds. Pohrt, Tom, illus. 1999. 82p. (YA). (gr. 5-8). reprint ed. 20.00 (978-0-7567-6419-7(X)) DIANE Publishing Co.

—Trickster & the Fainting Birds. 2000. (Illus.). 96p. (J). (ps-3). 20.98 (978-0-7398-1363-8(3)) Raintree.

Olson, Dennis L. Wisdom Warrior. 1999. (Illus.). 64p. 9.95 (978-1-55971-709-0(2) , NorthWord Bks. for Young Readers) T&N Children's Publishing.

Parker, Robert Andrew, illus. The People with Five Fingers: A Native Californian Creation Tale. 2000. (Accelerated Reader Bks.). 32p. (J). (ps-k). 15.95 (978-0-7614-5058-0(0) , Cavendish Children's Bks.) Cavendish, Marshall Corp.

Philip, Neil. The Great Mystery: Myths of Native America. 2001. (Illus.). 160p. (J). (gr. 7 up). 25.00 (978-0-395-98405-5(X) , Clarion Bks.) Houghton Mifflin Co. Trade & Reference Div.

Powell, Patricia Hruby. Zinnia: How the Corn Was Saved. Ruffenach, Jessie, ed. Thomas, Peter, tr. Benally, Kendrick, illus. 2004. (ENG & NAV.). 32p. 17.95 (978-1-893354-38-8(5)) Salina Bookshelf.

Rayner, Olivia, illus. North American Myths & Legends. 2001. (World Book Myths & Legends Ser.). 64p. (J). (978-0-7166-2611-4(X)) World Bk., Inc.

Rodanas, Kristina, illus. Yonder Mountain: A Cherokee Legend. 2005. 32p. (J). (gr. k-3). 16.95 (978-0-7614-5113-6(7)) Cavendish, Marshall Corp.

Rudolph, Nancy Lyn. Paper Animal Masks from Northwest Tribal Tales. 2004. (Illus.). 80p. (J). (gr. 4-8). reprint ed. 20.00 (978-0-7567-7073-0(4)) DIANE Publishing Co.

Salish Culture Committee & Montana Historical Society Staff. Coyote Stories of the Montana Salish Indians. 1999. (Illus.). 64p. (ps up). pap. 9.95 (978-0-917298-61-5(6)) Montana Historical Society Pr.

Sanchez, Enrique O., illus. The Golden Flower: A Taino Myth from Puerto Rico. 32p. (J). (ps). 15.95 (978-1-55885-452-9(5) , Piñata Books) Arte Publico Pr.

Sherman, Pat. The Sun's Daughter. Christie, R. Gregory, illus. 2005. 32p. (J). (gr. k-3). 16.00 (978-0-618-32430-9(5) , Clarion Bks.) Houghton Mifflin Co. Trade & Reference Div.

Smith, Ronnie. Twin Warriors. 2001. (gr. 7-12). lib. bdg. 18.75 (978-0-613-87283-6(5)) Tandem Library Bks.

—Twin Warriors. 2001. 108p. pap. 9.95 (978-0-595-18471-2(5) , Writers Club Pr.) iUniverse, Inc.

St. Romain, Rose Anne. Moon's Cloud Blanket. Waites, Joan C., illus. 2003. 32p. (J). 15.95 (978-1-56554-922-7(8)) Pelican Publishing Co., Inc.

Stoodt, Jeffrey. How the Rattlesnake Got Its Rattle. 1998. (Illus.). 24p. (ps-3). pap. 4.95 (978-0-8172-7978-3(4)) Steck-Vaughn.

Taylor, C. J. How We Saw the World: Nine Native Stories of the Way Things Began. Taylor, C. J., illus. 1999. (Native Legends Ser.: Vol. 4). (Illus.). 32p. (J). (gr. 3-6). reprint ed. pap. 8.95 (978-0-88776-373-1(1)) Tundra Bks., Inc./Livres Toundra, Inc. CAN. *Dist:* Random Hse., Inc.

—Peace Walker: The Legend of Hiawatha & Tekanawita. 2004. (Illus.). 48p. (J). (gr. 3). 15.95 (978-0-88776-547-6(5)) Tundra Bks., Inc./Livres Toundra, Inc. CAN. *Dist:* Random Hse., Inc.

Van Laan, Nancy. Shingebiss: An Ojibwe Legend. Bowen, Betsy, illus. 2002. 32p. (J). (gr. k-3). pap. 6.95 (978-0-618-21616-1(2)) Houghton Mifflin Co. Trade & Reference Div.

Vanasse, Deb. A Totem Tale: A Tall Story from Alaska. Brooks, Erik, illus. 2006. 32p. (J). pap. 10.95 (978-1-57061-439-2(3)) Sasquatch Bks.

Vidal, Cesar. Gray Feather & the Big Dog. Torrecilla, Pablo, illus. 2002. (Legends of the Americas Ser.). 32p. (J). (gr. k-7). 18.95 (978-1-57768-973-7(9) , Bedrick, Peter Bks.) School Specialty Publishing.

Vogel, Carole Garbuny. Weather Legends: Native American Lore & the Science of Weather. 2001. (Illus.). 80p. (gr. 4-6). lib. bdg. 29.90 (978-0-7613-1900-9(X) , Millbrook Pr.) Lerner Publishing Group.

Wade, Mary Hazelton. Indian Fairy Tales As Told to Little Chi. 2006. (Illus.). pap. 27.95 (***978-1-4254-9031-7(X)***) Kessinger Publishing, LLC.

Wargin, Kathy-Jo. The Legend of Leelanau. 2003. (Great Lakes Legend Ser.). (Illus.). 48p. (J). 17.95 (978-1-58536-150-2(X)) Sleeping Bear Pr.

Webb, Shirley G. Tales from the Keeper of the Myths: Cherokee Stories for Children. 2003. 104p. (J). pap. 9.95 (978-0-595-27264-8(9)) iUniverse, Inc.

INDIANS OF NORTH AMERICA—GAMES

Anderson, Madelyn Klein. North American Indian Games. 2000. (Watts Library). (Illus.). 64p. (J). (gr. 5-7). pap. 8.95 (978-0-531-16474-7(8) , Watts, Franklin) Scholastic Library Publishing.

—North American Indian Games. 2000. (gr. 5-8). lib. bdg. 17.60 (978-0-613-37479-8(7)) Tandem Library Bks.

Hoyt-Goldsmith, Diane. Lacrosse: The National Game of the Iroquois. Migdale, Lawrence, photos by. 1998. (Illus.). 31p. (J). (gr. 4-7). tchr. ed. 16.95 (978-0-8234-1360-7(8)) Holiday Hse., Inc.

Titus, David. Native Alaskan String Figures. 2007. (Illus.). 32p. (J). 5.99 (***978-0-9744562-7-0(6)***) WRDSMTH Productions.

INDIANS OF NORTH AMERICA—GOVERNMENT RELATIONS

Burgan, Michael. The Trail of Tears. 2001. (We the People Ser.). (Illus.). 48p. (J). (gr. 4 up). lib. bdg. 22.60 (978-0-7565-0101-3(6)) Compass Point Bks.

Elish, Dan, et al. The Trail of Tears: The Story of the Cherokee Removal. 2001. (Great Journeys Ser.). (Illus.). 96p. (J). (gr. 5 up). lib. bdg. 32.79 (978-0-7614-1228-1(X) , Benchmark Bks.) Cavendish, Marshall Corp.

Funk, Jack. Outside, the Women Cried: The Story of the Surrender by Chief Thunderchild's Band of Their Reserve near Delmas, Saskatchewan 1908. 2007. 108p. per. 12.95 (***978-0-595-43557-9(2)***) iUniverse, Inc.

Gregson, Susan R. Tecumseh: Shawnee Leader. 2003. (Let Freedom Ring Ser.). (Illus.). 48p. (J). (gr. 3-4). lib. bdg. 22.60 (978-0-7368-1556-7(2) , Bridgestone Bks.) Capstone Pr., Inc.

Kelley, Alison Turnbull. Native Americans & the United States. 2002. (People at Odds Ser.). (Illus.). 112p. (J). (gr. 5 up). 30.00 (978-0-7910-6707-9(6) , Chelsea Hse.) Facts On File, Inc.

Koestler-Grack, Rachel A. Chief John Ross. 2004. (Illus.). 32p. (J). pap. 7.50 (978-1-4034-5007-4(2)); lib. bdg. 24.22 (978-1-4034-5000-5(5)) Heinemann Library.

McAmis, Herb. The Cherokee. 2000. (Indian Nations Ser.). (Illus.). 48p. (J). (gr. 3-6). lib. bdg. 25.69 (978-0-8172-5456-8(0)) Raintree.

O'Neal, Bill. Long Before the Pilgrims: The First Thanksgiving, el Paso del Norte, 1598. Martinez, Lynn O'Neal, tr. Morgan, Polsky, illus. 2000. (ENG & SPA.). 48p. (J). 15.95 (978-1-57168-448-6(4)) Eakin Pr.

Petra Press Staff. The Seminole. 2001. (First Reports). (Illus.). 48p. (J). (gr. 3 up). lib. bdg. 22.60 (978-0-7565-0083-2(4)) Compass Point Bks.

Roza, Greg. The Karankawa of Texas. 2005. (Library of Native Americans). (Illus.). 64p. (J). 26.50 (978-1-4042-2870-2(5) , PowerKids Pr.) Rosen Publishing Group, Inc., The.

Torr, James D. Westward Expansion. 2002. (gr. 7-12). lib. bdg. 33.25 (978-0-613-73610-7(9)) Tandem Library Bks.

Torr, James D., ed. Westward Expansion. 2003. (Interpreting American History Through Primary Documents Ser.x). (Illus.). 208p. (J). 32.45 (978-0-7377-1134-9(5) , Greenhaven Pr., Inc.) Thomson Gale.

Wilson, Mike. Broken Promises: The U. S. Government & Native Americans. 2002. (History of the Old West Ser.). (Illus.). 64p. (YA). (gr. 5 up). lib. bdg. (978-1-59084-064-1(X)) Mason Crest Pubs.

INDIANS OF NORTH AMERICA—HISTORY

see also Indians of North America—Wars

Abbink, Emily. Monterey Bay Area Missions. 2007. (Exploring California Missions Ser.). (J). 27.93 (***978-0-8225-0887-8(7)*** , Lerner Pubns.) Lerner Publishing Group.

Adil, Janeen R. The Northeast Indians: Daily Life in the 1500s. 2006. (Bridgestone Books). (Illus.). 24p. (J). (978-0-7368-4314-0(0)) Capstone Pr., Inc.

Aloian, Molly & Kalman, Bobbie. Life of the California Coast Nations. 2004. (Native Nations of North America Ser.). (Illus.). 32p. (J). (978-0-7787-0382-2(7)); pap. (978-0-7787-0474-4(2)) Crabtree Publishing Co.

American Indian Art & Culture. 2005. (Illus.). 32p. (gr. 3-5). pap. 153.00 (978-0-7910-7959-1(7) , Chelsea Hse.) Facts On File, Inc.

The Apache Indians. (Native Peoples Ser.). 24p. (J). 6.95 (978-0-7368-8441-9(6)) Capstone Pr., Inc.

Arnold, Caroline. Ancient Cliff Dwellers of Mesa Verde. 2000. (gr. 3-6). lib. bdg. 15.25 (978-0-613-29870-4(5)) Tandem Library Bks.

Art, Suzanne Strauss. Ancient Times: The Story of the First Americans. Art, Suzanne Strauss, illus. 1999. (Illus.). 178p. (YA). (gr. 5-8). pap. 14.95 (978-0-9656557-7-4(6)) Pemblewick Pr.

Bailey, Katie. Radisson & Groseilliers: Fur Traders of the North. 2006. (In the Footsteps of Explorers Ser.). (Illus.). 32p. (J). (gr. 3-14). pap. (978-0-7787-2458-2(1) , 1253444) Crabtree Publishing Co.

Barnett, Michelle Noble, et al. Theme Pockets - November: The First Thanksgiving; Native Americans; the Food Pyramid. Evans, Marilyn, ed. Larsen, Jo, illus. 1999. (Making Books with Pockets). 96p. (J). pap., tchr. ed. 12.99 (978-1-55799-708-1(X) , EMC 594) Evan-Moor Educational Pubs.

Bedry, Christa. The Pueblo. 2003. (American Indian Art & Culture Ser.). (Illus.). 32p. (J). pap. (978-1-59036-179-5(2)) Weigl Pubs., Inc.

Behnke, Alison. The Apaches. 2007. (Native American Histories Ser.). (Illus.). 56p. (J). 27.93 (978-0-8225-5915-3(3) , Lerner Pubns.) Lerner Publishing Group.

Behrens, June. Central Coast Missions in California. 2007. (Exploring California Missions Ser.). (J). 27.93 (***978-0-8225-0897-7(4)*** , Lerner Pubns.) Lerner Publishing Group.

Benchmark Education Staff, compiled by. Native Land & Native AMER HIST. 2005. spiral bd. 225.00 (***978-1-4108-5810-8(3)***) Benchmark Education Co.

Benjamin, Lisa. People of the Wetlands. 2005. (Voices Reading Ser.). (Illus.). 32p. (J). (978-0-7367-2947-5(X)) Zaner-Bloser, Inc.

Bial, Raymond. The Blackfeet. 2002. (Lifeways Ser.). (Illus.). 128p. (J). 34.21 (978-0-7614-1416-2(9) , Benchmark Bks.) Cavendish, Marshall Corp.

—The Cree. 2005. (Lifeways Ser.). (Illus.). 128p. (J). (978-0-7614-1902-0(0) , Benchmark Bks.) Cavendish, Marshall Corp.

—The Crow. 2005. (Lifeways Ser.). (Illus.). 124p. (J). (978-0-7614-1901-3(2) , Benchmark Bks.) Cavendish, Marshall Corp.

—The Menominee. 2005. (Lifeways Ser.). (Illus.). 127p. (J). (978-0-7614-1903-7(9) , Benchmark Bks.) Cavendish, Marshall Corp.

Bishop, Amanda & Kalman, Bobbie. Life of the Navajo. 2003. (Native Nations of North America Ser.). (Illus.). 32p. (J). (gr. 5). lib. bdg. (978-0-7787-0376-1(2)) Crabtree Publishing Co.

—Nations of the Northwest Coast. 2003. (Native Nations of North America Ser.). (Illus.). 32p. (J). (gr. 5). pap. (978-0-7787-0470-6(X)) Crabtree Publishing Co.

Boekhoff, P. M. & Kallen, Stuart A. Native Americans of the Great Lakes. 2003. (North American Indians Ser.). (Illus.). 48p. (J). lib. bdg. 26.20 (978-0-7377-1510-1(3)) Thomson Gale.

Bonvillain, Nancy. The Zuni. 2005. (Indians of North America, Heritage Edition Ser.). (Illus.). 127p. (YA). (gr. 7-12). lib. bdg. 30.00 (978-0-7910-8594-3(5) , Chelsea Hse.) Facts On File, Inc.

Boule, Mary Null. California Native American Tribes: Mohave Tribe, 28 booklets. Liddell, Daniel & Basta, Mary, illus. (California Native American Tribes). 52p. (J). (gr. 3-6). pap. 7.95 (978-1-877599-73-6(5)) Merryant Pubs.

—Native Americans of North America: Hopi People, Set, 11. Liddell, Daniel, illus. 2002. 52p. (Orig.). (J). (gr. 3-6). pap. 6.45 (978-1-877599-58-3(1)) Merryant Pubs.

—Native Americans of North America: Ute Tribe, 11 booklets. Liddell, Daniel & Basta, Mary, illus. 2002. (Native Americans of North America). (J). (gr. 3-6). pap. 7.95 (978-1-877599-60-6(3)) Merryant Pubs.

Broida, Marian. The Pueblo. 2005. (First Americans Ser.). (Illus.). 48p. (J). (gr. 3-7). lib. bdg. (978-0-7614-1898-6(9) , Benchmark Bks.) Cavendish, Marshall Corp.

Brower, Pauline. Inland Valley Missions in California. 2007. (Exploring California Missions Ser.). (J). 27.93 (***978-0-8225-0899-1(0)*** , Lerner Pubns.) Lerner Publishing Group.

Bruchac, Joseph. Lasting Echoes. 1999. (J). (978-0-606-22201-3(4)) Tandem Library Bks.

—Navajo Long Walk: The Tragic Story of a Proud People's Forced March from Their Homeland. Begay, Shonto W., illus. 2002. 64p. (J). (gr. 3-7). 18.95 (978-0-7922-7058-4(4) , National Geographic Children's Bks.) National Geographic Society.

—Trail of Tears. 1999. (gr. 3-6). lib. bdg. 11.80 (978-0-613-22518-2(X)) Tandem Library Bks.

Burnill, Richard. Ishi Rediscovered: Biography of the Last Reported Yahi Indian of California. 2001. (Illus.). (J). (gr. 4-12). pap. 25.00 (978-1-878464-51-4(5)) Anthro Co., The.

Capstone Press, contrib. by. The Iroquois Indians. (Native Peoples Ser.). 24p. (J). pap. 6.95 (978-0-7368-8442-6(4)) Capstone Pr., Inc.

—The Ojibwa Indians. (Native Peoples Ser.). 24p. (J). pap. 6.95 (978-0-7368-8443-3(2)) Capstone Pr., Inc.

Carole Marsh. Connecticut Indians. 2004. (Connecticut Experien Ser.). 36p. (gr. 3-8). 29.95 (978-0-635-02259-2(1)); pap. 7.95 (978-0-635-02258-5(3)) Gallopade International.

—Vermont Indians. 2004. (Vermont Experience Ser.). 36p. (gr. 3-8). pap. 7.95 (978-0-635-02334-6(2)); lib. bdg. 29.95 (978-0-635-02335-3(0)) Gallopade International.

—Virginia Indians. 2004. (Virginia Experience Ser.). 36p. (gr. 3-8). 29.95 (978-0-635-02337-7(7)); pap. 7.95 (978-0-635-02336-0(9)) Gallopade International.

—Washington Indians. 2004. (Washington Experienc Ser.). lib. bdg. 29.95 (978-0-635-02339-1(3)); 36p. (gr. 3-8). pap. 7.95 (978-0-635-02338-4(5)) Gallopade International.

—West Virginia Indians. 2004. (West Virginia Experi Ser.). 36p. (gr. 3-8). pap. 7.95 (978-0-635-02340-7(7)); lib. bdg. 29.95 (978-0-635-02341-4(5)) Gallopade International.

—Wisconsin Indians. 2004. (Wisconsin Experience Ser.). 36p. (gr. 3-8). 29.95 (978-0-635-02343-8(1)); pap. 7.95 (978-0-635-02342-1(3)) Gallopade International.

—Wyoming Indians. 2004. (Wyoming Experience Ser.). 36p. (gr. 3-8). 29.95 (978-0-635-02345-2(8)); pap. 7.95 (978-0-635-02344-5(X)) Gallopade International.

Casey, Carolyn. The Apache. 2005. (First Americans Ser.). (Illus.). 48p. (J). (gr. 3-7). lib. bdg. (978-0-7614-1894-8(6) , Benchmark Bks.) Cavendish, Marshall Corp.

Cipriano, Jeri. Three Historical Communities of North America. 2005. (Navigators Ser.). (J). pap. 38.00 (***978-1-4108-5095-9(1)***) Benchmark Education Co.

Clare, John D. The Native Peoples of North America. 2002. (Illus.). 48p. pap. 23.50 (***978-0-340-80329-5(0)*** , Hodder Murray) Hodder Education GBR. *Dist:* Trans-Atlantic Pubns., Inc.

Collins, James. The Trail of Tears with Buffalo Bill & Farley's Raiders. 2006. (Time Traveler's Adventure Ser.). (Illus.). 56p. (J). 13.50 incl. audio compact disk (978-1-932332-31-5(6)) Toy Box Productions.

Craats, Rennay. The Cherokee. 2003. (American Indian Art & Culture Ser.). (Illus.). 32p. (J). pap. (978-1-59036-180-1(6)) Weigl Pubs., Inc.

—The Navajo. 2003. (American Indian Art & Culture Ser.). (Illus.). 32p. (J). pap. 7.95 (978-1-59036-182-5(2)) Weigl Pubs., Inc.

Crewe, Sabrina & Birchfield, D. L. The Trail of Tears. 2004. (Events That Shaped America Ser.). (Illus.). 32p. (J). (gr. 3 up). lib. bdg. 24.67 (978-0-8368-3400-0(3)) Stevens, Gareth Inc.

Crewe, Sabrina & Riehecky, Janet. The Settling of St. Augustine. 2003. (Events That Shaped America Ser.). (Illus.). 32p. (J). (gr. 3 up). lib. bdg. 24.67 (978-0-8368-3395-9(3)) Stevens, Gareth Inc.

Croy, Anita. Ancient Pueblo: Archaeology Unlocks the Secrets of America's Past. 2007. (National Geographic Investigates Ser.). (Illus.). 64p. (YA). (gr. 5 up). 17.95 (***978-1-4263-0130-8(8)***); lib. bdg. 27.90 (***978-1-4263-0131-5(6)***) National Geographic Society. (National Geographic Children's Bks.).

De Capua, Sarah. The Cheyenne. 2006. (First Americans Ser.). (Illus.). 48p. (J). lib. bdg. 29.93 (978-0-7614-2248-8(X) , Benchmark Bks.) Cavendish, Marshall Corp.

—The Comanche. 2006. (First Americans Ser.). (Illus.). 48p. (J). lib. bdg. 29.93 (978-0-7614-2249-5(8) , Benchmark Bks.) Cavendish, Marshall Corp.

De Capua, Sarah E. The Cherokee. 2005. (First Americans Ser.). (Illus.). 48p. (J). (gr. 3-7). lib. bdg. (978-0-7614-1895-5(4) , Benchmark Bks.) Cavendish, Marshall Corp.

—The Iroquois. 2005. (First Americans Ser.). (Illus.). 48p. (J). (gr. 3-7). lib. bdg. (978-0-7614-1896-2(2) , Benchmark Bks.) Cavendish, Marshall Corp.

Deer, Ada E., intro. Indians of North America. (Illus.). (gr. 9-13). pap. 59.70 (978-0-7910-8399-4(3)); lib. bdg. 137.70 (978-0-7910-8417-5(5)) Facts On File, Inc. (Chelsea Hse.).

Denetdale, Jennifer. The Long Walk: The Forced Navajo Exile. 2007. (Landmark Events in Native American History Ser.). 136p. (J). (gr. 9). 35.00 (***978-0-7910-9344-3(1)*** , Chelsea Hse.) Facts On File, Inc.

Ditchfield, Christin. The Arapaho. 48p. (J). 2006. (gr. 3-5). pap. 6.95 (978-0-516-25586-6(X)); 2005. (Illus.). (ps-7). 25.00 (978-0-516-23642-1(3)) Scholastic Library Publishing. (Children's Pr.).

—The Blackfoot. 2005. (True Book Ser.). (ENG., Illus.). 47p. (J). (ps-7). 25.00 (978-0-516-23643-8(1) , Children's Pr.) Scholastic Library Publishing.

—The Chippewa. 2005. (True Book Ser.). (Illus.). 47p. (J). (ps-7). 25.00 (978-0-516-22817-4(X) , Children's Pr.) Scholastic Library Publishing.

—The Choctaw. 2005. (True Book Ser.). (Illus.). 47p. (J). (ps-7). 25.00 (978-0-516-22818-1(8) , Children's Pr.) Scholastic Library Publishing.

—The Comanche. 2005. (True Book Ser.). (Illus.). 47p. (J). (ps-7). 25.00 (978-0-516-23644-5(X) , Children's Pr.) Scholastic Library Publishing.

—The Crow. 2005. (True Book Ser.). (Illus.). 47p. (J). (ps-7). 25.00 (978-0-516-23645-2(8) , Children's Pr.) Scholastic Library Publishing.

—Spanish Missions. 2006. 48p. (YA). (gr. 3-5). pap. 6.95 (978-0-516-21746-8(1) , Children's Pr.) Scholastic Library Publishing.

Doherty, Craig A. California Indians. Facts on File, Inc. Staff, ed. 2008. (Native America Ser.). 136p. (J). (gr. 5-8). 35.00 (978-0-8160-5973-7(X)) Facts On File, Inc.

—Great Basin Indians. Facts on File, Inc. Staff, ed. 2008. (Native America Ser.). 136p. (J). (gr. 5-8). 35.00 (978-0-8160-5974-4(8)) Facts On File, Inc.

Doherty, Craig A. & Doherty, Katherine M. Arctic Peoples. 2008. (Native America Ser.). 136p. (J). (gr. 5-8). 35.00 (978-0-8160-5970-6(5)) Facts On File, Inc.

—Plateau Indians. 2008. (Native America Ser.). 136p. (J). (gr. 5-8). 35.00 (978-0-8160-5971-3(3)) Facts On File, Inc.

—Southeast Indians. 2008. (Native America Ser.). 136p. (J). (gr. 5-8). 35.00 (978-0-8160-5969-0(1)) Facts On File, Inc.

Donlan, Leni. Cherokee Rose: The Trail of Tears. 2007. (J). (***978-1-4109-2702-6(4)***); pap. (***978-1-4109-2713-2(X)***) Steck-Vaughn.

Donlan, Leni. Counting Coup: Customs of the Crow Nation. 2006. (American History Through Primary Sources Ser.). (Illus.). 32p. (J). (978-1-4109-2421-6(1)); pap. (978-1-4109-2432-2(7)) Steck-Vaughn.

Englar, Mary. The Cherokee & Their History. 2005. (We the People Ser.). (Illus.). 48p. (J). (gr. 4-6). 23.93 (978-0-7565-1273-6(5) , 1244090) Compass Point Bks.

—The Great Plains Indians: Daily Life in The 1700s. 2005. (Native American Life Ser.). (Illus.). 24p. (J). (gr. 2-4). lib. bdg. 21.26 (978-0-7368-4315-7(9) , Bridgestone Bks.) Capstone Pr., Inc.

—The Sioux & Their History. 2005. (We the People Ser.). (Illus.). 48p. (J). (gr. 4-6). 23.93 (978-0-7565-1275-0(1) , 1244094) Compass Point Bks.

—The Southwest Indians: Daily Life in the 1500s. 2006. (Bridgestone Books). (J). (978-0-7368-4319-5(1)) Capstone Pr., Inc.

First Reports-Native Americans Complete Set. (First Reports-Native Americans Ser.). (gr. 3-5). 361.60 (978-0-7565-0725-1(1)) Compass Point Bks.

Foran, Jill. Native-American Life. 2003. (Real Life Stories Ser.). (Illus.). 24p. (J). lib. bdg. 15.95 (978-1-59036-080-4(X)) Weigl Pubs., Inc.

Fuhr, Ute, et al. Native Americans. 1998. (First Discovery Book Ser.). (Illus.). 24p. (J). (ps-2). 12.95 (978-0-590-38153-6(9)) Scholastic, Inc.

Furbee, Mary Rodd. Shawnee Captive: The Story of Mary Draper Ingles. 2003. (Illus.). 112p. (YA). per. 9.95 (978-1-891852-29-9(9)) Quarrier Pr.

—Shawnee Captive: The Story of Mary Draper Ingles. 2004. (Women of the Frontier Ser.). (Illus.). 112p. (J). (gr. 6-12). 23.95 (978-1-883846-69-5(2) , First Biographies) Reynolds, Morgan Inc.

Georgiady, Nicholas P., et al. Michigan's First Settlers: The Indians - Native Americans, Vol. 3. Nixon, Buford, illus. 2nd rev. ed. 1998. 31p. (J). (gr. 4-8). pap. 4.50 (978-0-917961-09-0(9)) Argee Pubs.

Gibson, Karen Bush. The Great Basin Indians: Daily Life in The 1700s. 2005. (Native American Life Ser.). (Illus.). 24p. (J). (gr. 2-4). lib. bdg. 21.26 (978-0-7368-4318-8(3) , Bridgestone Bks.) Capstone Pr., Inc.

Gray-Kanatiiosh, Barbara A. Cahuilla. 2007. (Illus.). 32p. (J). lib. bdg. 22.78 (978-1-59197-651-6(0) , Checkerboard Library) ABDO Publishing Co.

—Chickasaw. 2007. (ENG., Illus.). 32p. (J). lib. bdg. 22.78 (978-1-59197-652-3(9) , Checkerboard Library) ABDO Publishing Co.

—Kiowa. 2007. (Illus.). 32p. (J). 22.78 (978-1-59197-654-7(5)) ABDO Publishing Co.

—Paiute. 2007. (Illus.). 32p. (J). 22.78 (978-1-59197-657-8(X)) ABDO Publishing Co.

—Yurok. 2007. (Illus.). 32p. (J). 22.78 (978-1-59197-658-5(8)) ABDO Publishing Co.

Green, Jen. How Ancient Americans Lived. 2006. (Illus.). 128p. pap. 17.99 (978-1-84476-212-5(2) , Southwater) Anness Publishing GBR. *Dist:* National Bk. Network.

Hakim, Joy. The First Americans Prehistory-1600 Teaching Guide. 3rd ed. 2002. (History of US Ser.). (Illus.). 112p. (Orig.). pap., tchr. ed. 16.95 (978-0-19-515351-4(0)) Oxford Univ. Pr., Inc.

—A History of US Bk. 1: The First Americans. 3rd rev. ed. (History of US Ser.). (Illus.). 192p. 2006. 19.95 (978-0-19-518230-9(8)); 2005. 19.95 (978-0-19-518894-3(2)) Oxford Univ. Pr., Inc.

Hakim, Joy. A History of US Vol. 1: The First Americans. rev. ed. 2007. (History of US Ser.). 192p. pap. 15.95 (***978-0-19-532715-1(2)***) Oxford Univ. Pr., Inc.

Harcourt School Publishers Staff. The Bison, People & the Plains Advanced Level. 3rd ed. 2002. (Trophies Reading Program Ser.). (Illus.). pap. 5.10 (978-0-15-323399-9(0)) Harcourt Schl. Pubs.

Hargrove, Julia. Wounded Knee Historic Site. Mohrman, Gary, illus. 2004. (Historic Monuments Ser.). 48p. (J). pap. 6.95 (978-1-57310-431-9(0) , 1238117) Teaching & Learning Co.

Indian Nations, 4 vols. 2000. (Illus.). (J). 102.76 (978-0-7398-2845-8(2)) Raintree.

Indian Nations, 12 bks., Set. Incl. Cherokee. McAmis, Herb. 2000. lib. bdg. 25.69 (978-0-8172-5456-8(0)); Cheyenne. Limberhand, Dennis. 2000. lib. bdg. 25.69 (978-0-8172-5469-8(2)); Dakota Sioux. Eder, Jeanne Oyawin. 2000. lib. bdg. 25.69 (978-0-8172-5467-4(6)); Makah. Eder, Jeanne Oyawin. 1999. lib. bdg. 25.69 (978-0-8172-5459-9(5)); Menominee. Fowler, Verna. 2000. lib. bdg. 25.69 (978-0-8172-5458-2(7)); Navajo. Griffin, Lana T. & Nockideneh, Tommy J. 1999. lib. bdg. 25.69 (978-0-8172-5463-6(3)); Ojibwa. McCarthy, Cathy. 2000. lib. bdg. 25.69 (978-0-8172-5460-5(9)); Oneida. McLester, L. Gordon. 2000. lib. bdg. 25.69 (978-0-8172-5457-5(9)); Pomo. Castillo, Edward D. 1999. lib. bdg. 25.69 (978-0-8172-5455-1(2)); Seminoles. Kavasch, E. Barrie. 1999. lib. bdg. 25.69 (978-0-8172-5464-3(1)); Shoshone. Blackhawk, Ned. 2000. lib. bdg. 25.69 (978-0-8172-5468-1(4)); Zuni. Ladd, Edmund J. 1999. lib. bdg. 25.69 (978-0-8172-5454-4(4)); 48p. (J). (gr. 3-7). (Illus.). 2000. Set lib. bdg. 308.28 (978-0-7398-3134-2(8)) Raintree.

Isaacs, Sally Senzell. The Great Land Rush. 2003. (Illus.). 32p. (J). pap. 7.50 (978-1-4034-4771-5(3)); lib. bdg. 25.64 (978-1-4034-2505-8(1)) Heinemann Library.

—Life in a California Mission. (Picture the Past Ser.). (Illus.). 32p. (J). 2002. (gr. k-3). pap. 7.50 (978-1-58810-414-4(1) , 91187); 2001. (gr. 2-4). lib. bdg. 21.36 (978-1-58810-249-2(1)) Heinemann Library.

—Life in St. Augustine. (Picture the Past Ser.). (Illus.). 32p. (J). 2003. lib. bdg. (978-1-58810-694-0(2)); 2002. (gr. 1-3). pap. 7.50 (978-1-4034-0526-5(3)) Heinemann Library.

Johnson, Michael. Native Tribes of the Northeast. 2004. (Native Tribes of North America Ser.). (Illus.). 64p. (J). (gr. 5 up). lib. bdg. 32.67 (978-0-8368-5612-5(0) , World Almanac Library) Stevens, Gareth Inc.

—Native Tribes of the Plains & Prairie. 2004. (Native Tribes of North America Ser.). (Illus.). 64p. (J). (gr. 5 up). lib. bdg. 32.67 (978-0-8368-5613-2(9) , World Almanac Library) Stevens, Gareth Inc.

Johnson, Michael & Burkinshaw, Jane. Native Tribes of the North & Northwest Coast. 2004. (Native Tribes of North America Ser.). (Illus.). 64p. (J). (gr. 5 up). lib. bdg. 32.67 (978-0-8368-5611-8(2) , World Almanac Library) Stevens, Gareth Inc.

Johnson, Michael & Clarke, Duncan. Native Tribes of the Great Basin & Plateau. 2004. (Native Tribes of North America Ser.). (Illus.). 64p. (J). (gr. 5 up). lib. bdg. 32.67 (978-0-8368-5610-1(4) , World Almanac Library) Stevens, Gareth Inc.

—Native Tribes of the Southeast. 2004. (Native Tribes of North America Ser.). (Illus.). 64p. (J). (gr. 5 up). lib. bdg. 32.67 (978-0-8368-5614-9(7) , World Almanac Library) Stevens, Gareth Inc.

Johnson, Michael & Yenne, Bill. Native Tribes of California & the Southwest. 2004. (Native Tribes of North America Ser.). (Illus.). 64p. (J). (gr. 5 up). lib. bdg. 32.67 (978-0-8368-5609-5(0) , World Almanac Library) Stevens, Gareth Inc.

Kalman, Bobbie. Native Homes. 2001. (J). (978-0-606-21345-5(7)); (gr. 3-6). lib. bdg. 16.40 (978-0-613-43480-5(3)) Tandem Library Bks.

Kalman, Bobbie. A Visual Dictionary of a Plains Native Community. 2007. (Visual Dictionaries Ser.). (Illus.). 32p. (J). (gr. 1-7). pap. (***978-0-7787-3525-0(7)***) Crabtree Publishing Co.

Kavin, Kim. Tools of Native Americans: A Kid's Guide to the History & Culture of the First Americans. 2006. (Tools of Discovery Ser.). (Illus.). 144p. (J). (gr. 5-8). pap. 16.95 (978-0-9749344-8-8(8)) Nomad Pr.

King, David C. The Haida. 2006. (First Americans Ser.). (Illus.). 48p. (J). lib. bdg. 29.93 (978-0-7614-2250-1(1) , Benchmark Bks.) Cavendish, Marshall Corp.

—The Huron. 2006. (First Americans Ser.). (Illus.). 48p. (J). lib. bdg. 29.93 (978-0-7614-2251-8(X) , Benchmark Bks.) Cavendish, Marshall Corp.

—The Navajo. 2005. (First Americans Ser.). (Illus.). 48p. (J). (gr. 3-7). lib. bdg. (978-0-7614-1897-9(0) , Benchmark Bks.) Cavendish, Marshall Corp.

—The Ojibwe. 2006. (First Americans Ser.). (Illus.). 48p. (J). lib. bdg. 29.93 (978-0-7614-2252-5(8) , Benchmark Bks.) Cavendish, Marshall Corp.

—Projects about the Eastern Woodland Indians. 2005. (Hands-On History Ser.). (Illus.). 44p. (J). (978-0-7614-1979-2(9) , Benchmark Bks.) Cavendish, Marshall Corp.

—The Seminole. 2006. (First Americans Ser.). (Illus.). 48p. (J). lib. bdg. 29.93 (978-0-7614-2253-2(6) , Benchmark Bks.) Cavendish, Marshall Corp.

—The Sioux. 2005. (First Americans Ser.). (Illus.). 48p. (J). (gr. 3-7). lib. bdg. (978-0-7614-1899-3(7) , Benchmark Bks.) Cavendish, Marshall Corp.

Koopmans, Anna. The Sioux. 2003. (American Indian Art & Culture Ser.). (Illus.). 32p. (J). pap. (978-1-59036-184-9(9)) Weigl Pubs., Inc.

Lange, Karen E. 1607: A New Look at Jamestown. Block, Ira, photos by. 2007. (Illus.). 48p. (J). (gr. 3-7). lib. bdg. 27.90 (978-1-4263-0013-4(1) , National Geographic Children's Bks.) National Geographic Society.

Lemke, Nancy. Southern Coast Missions in California. 2007. (Exploring California Missions Ser.). (J). 27.93 (***978-0-8225-1935-5(6)*** , Lerner Pubns.) Lerner Publishing Group.

Lepore, Jill. Encounters in the New World: A History in Documents. 2002. (Pages from History Ser.). (Illus.). 176p. pap. 19.95 (978-0-19-515491-7(6)) Oxford Univ. Pr., Inc.

—Encounters in the New World: A History in Documents. 2002. (Illus.). 175p. (YA). (gr. 7-12). lib. bdg. 30.35 (978-0-613-57356-6(0)) Tandem Library Bks.

Levine, Michelle. The Sioux. 2007. (Native American Histories Ser.). (Illus.). 56p. (J). 27.93 (978-0-8225-2864-7(9) , Lerner Pubns.) Lerner Publishing Group.

Levy, Elizabeth. Are We There Yet? The Europeans Meet the Americans. 2002. (America's Horrible Histories Ser.: No. 3). 160p. (J). 12.95 (978-0-439-30350-7(8) , Scholastic Paperbacks) Scholastic, Inc.

Levy, Janey. The Wampanoag of Massachusetts & Rhode Island. 2005. (Library of Native Americans). (Illus.). 64p. (J). 26.50 (978-1-4042-2871-9(3) , PowerKids Pr.) Rosen Publishing Group, Inc., The.

The Library of Native Americans: Set 3. (J). (gr. k-5). 159.00 (978-1-4042-2657-9(5)) Rosen Publishing Group, Inc., The.

Lilly, Melinda. Spanish Missions. 2003. (Rourke Discovery Library). (Illus.). 24p. (gr. 1-4). 14.95 (978-1-58952-369-2(5)) Rourke Publishing, LLC.

Limberhand, Dennis. The Cheyenne. 2000. (Indian Nations Ser.). (Illus.). 48p. (J). (gr. 3-7). lib. bdg. 25.69 (978-0-8172-5469-8(2)) Raintree.

Lomberg, Michelle. The Iroquois. 2003. (American Indian Art & Culture Ser.). (Illus.). 32p. (J). pap. (978-1-59036-181-8(4)) Weigl Pubs., Inc.

—The Ojibwa. 2003. (American Indian Art & Culture Ser.). (Illus.). 32p. (J). pap. (978-1-59036-183-2(0)) Weigl Pubs., Inc.

Lund, Bill. The Cherokee Indians. (Native Peoples Ser.). 24p. (J). pap. 6.95 (978-0-7368-8054-1(2)) Capstone Pr., Inc.

—The Comanche Indians. (Native Peoples Ser.). 24p. (J). pap. 6.95 (978-0-7368-8055-8(0)) Capstone Pr., Inc.

MacGregor, Carol Lynn. Lewis & Clark's Bittersweet Crossing. Hoopes, Gaye, tr. Hoopes, Gaye, illus. 2004. 32p. (J). 16.95 (978-0-87004-437-3(0) , 043700) Caxton Pr.

MacMillan, Dianne M. Los Angeles Area Missions. 2007. (Exploring California Missions Ser.). (J). 27.93 (***978-0-8225-0898-4(2)*** , Lerner Pubns.) Lerner Publishing Group.

McAmis, Herb. The Cherokee. 2000. (Indian Nations Ser.). (Illus.). 48p. (J). (gr. 3-6). lib. bdg. 25.69 (978-0-8172-5456-8(0)) Raintree.

McCarthy, Kevin M. Native Americans in Florida. 1999. (Illus.). 216p. (J). (gr. 3-7). 25.95 (978-1-56164-181-9(2)); pap. 18.95 (978-1-56164-182-6(0)) Pineapple Pr., Inc.

McNamara, Margaret. Discover the Iroquois. 2006. pap. 39.00 (***978-1-4108-6443-7(X)***) Benchmark Education Co.

—Discover the Lakota. 2006. pap. 39.00 (***978-1-4108-6442-0(1)***) Benchmark Education Co.

—Discover the Navajo. 2006. pap. 39.00 (***978-1-4108-6441-3(3)***) Benchmark Education Co.

Media Projects, Inc., Staff. Student Almanac of Native American History, 2 vols. 2003. (Middle School Reference Ser.). (Illus.). 144p. (J). (gr. 6-8). 86.95 (978-0-313-32599-1(5) , MS2599, Middle School Reference) Greenwood Publishing Group, Inc.

Miller, Amy. Trail of Tears. 2002. (Instant Social Studies Activities Folders Ser.). (Illus.). 6p. (gr. 4-8). 3.95 (978-0-439-37089-9(2)) Scholastic, Inc.

Miller, Raymond H. The Apache. 2005. (North American Indians Ser.). (Illus.). 48p. (J). (ps-8). lib. bdg. 26.20 (978-0-7377-2625-1(3) , Greenhaven Pr., Inc.) Thomson Gale.

Monroe, Judy. The Northwest Indians: Daily Life in The 1700s. 2005. (Native American Life Ser.). (Illus.). 24p. (J). (gr. 2-4). lib. bdg. 21.26 (978-0-7368-4316-4(7) , Bridgestone Bks.) Capstone Pr., Inc.

Morris, Neil. Everyday Life of the Native Americans. 2005. (Uncovering History Ser.). (Illus.). 46p. (J). (gr. 6-9). lib. bdg. 29.95 (978-1-58340-708-0(1)) Smart Apple Media.

My People: A History of the Native Americans. 1998. (Illus.). 192p. (YA). (gr. 5-9). 18.95 (978-2-215-05128-2(0)) Continental Enterprises Group, Inc. (CEG).

Nash, Alice & Strobel, Christoph. Daily Life of Native Americans from Post-Columbian Through Nineteenth-Century America. 2006. (Greenwood Press "Daily Life Through History" Ser.). (Illus.). 312p. (J). 49.95 (978-0-313-33515-0(X) , GR3515, Greenwood Pr.) Greenwood Publishing Group, Inc.

Nelson, Sheila. Before Canada: First Nations & First Contacts, Prehistory-1523. 2005. (Illus.). 87p. (J). (gr. 3-7). lib. bdg. 21.95 (978-1-4222-0001-8(9) , 1247963) Mason Crest Pubs.

O'Neal, Bill. Long Before the Pilgrims: The First Thanksgiving, el Paso del Norte, 1598. Martinez, Lynn O'Neal, tr. Morgan, Polsky, illus. 2000. (ENG & SPA.). 48p. (J). 15.95 (978-1-57168-446-6(4)) Eakin Pr.

Palazzo-Craig, Janet. The Ojibwe of Michigan, Wisconsin, Minnesota, & North Dakota. 2005. (Library of Native Americans). (Illus.). 64p. (J). 26.50 (978-1-4042-2873-3(X) , PowerKids Pr.) Rosen Publishing Group, Inc., The.

Parsons Yazzie, Evangeline. Dzaní Yázhí Naazbaa' Little Woman Warrior Who Came Home. Ruffenach, Jessie, ed. Toddy, Irving, illus. 2005. (NAV & ENG.). 32p. (gr. 4-7). 17.95 (978-1-893354-55-5(5)) Salina Bookshelf.

Patent, Dorothy Hinshaw. The Buffalo & the Indians: A Shared Destiny. Munoz, William, photos by. 2006. (Illus.). 96p. (J). (gr. 4-6). 18.00 (978-0-618-48570-3(8) , Clarion Bks.) Houghton Mifflin Co. Trade & Reference Div.

Philip, Neil. The Great Circle: A History of the First Nations. 2006. (Illus.). 176p. (J). (gr. 5-9). 25.00 (978-0-618-15941-3(X) , Clarion Bks.) Houghton Mifflin Co. Trade & Reference Div.

Press, Petra. Indians of the Northwest: Traditions, History, Legends & Life. 1999. (Native Americans Ser.). (Illus.). 64p. (J). (gr. 5 up). lib. bdg. 27.33 (978-0-8368-2647-0(7)) Stevens, Gareth Inc.

The Pueblo Indians. (Native Peoples Ser.). 24p. (J). 6.95 (978-0-7368-8444-0(0)) Capstone Pr., Inc.

Rappaport, Doreen. We Are the Many: A Picture Book of American Indians. Van Wright, Cornelius, illus. 2002. 32p. (J). (gr. k-4). 15.99 (978-0-688-16559-8(1)); lib. bdg. 17.89 (978-0-06-001139-0(4)) HarperCollins Pubs.

Riehecky, Janet. The Cree Tribe. 2002. (Native Peoples Ser.). (Illus.). 24p. (J). (gr. 2-3). lib. bdg. 18.60 (978-0-7368-1366-2(7) , Bridgestone Bks.) Capstone Pr., Inc.

Rosinsky, Natalie M. The Ojibwe & Their History. 2005. (We the People Ser.). (YA). (978-0-7565-0876-0(2)) Compass Point Bks.

Rossi, Ann. Native American & Europeans 1492-1700: Cultures Collide. 2004. (Crossroads America Ser.). (Illus.). 40p. (J). (gr. 5-9). 21.90 (978-0-7922-7198-7(X) , National Geographic Children's Bks.) National Geographic Society.

Ruppel, Maxine. Vostaas: White Buffalo's Story of the Plains Indians. (Indian Culture Ser.). (J). (gr. 4-10). pap. 4.95 (978-0-89992-001-6(2)) Council for Indian Education.

Saffer, Barbara. Life on the Reservation. 2002. (History of the Old West Ser.). (Illus.). 64p. (J). (gr. 5 up). lib. bdg. (978-1-59084-070-2(4)) Mason Crest Pubs.

Salas, Laura Purdie. The Trail of Tears 1838. 2003. (Let Freedom Ring Ser.). (Illus.). 48p. (J). (gr. 3-4). lib. bdg. 22.60 (978-0-7368-1559-8(7) , Bridgestone Bks.) Capstone Pr., Inc.

Schmittroth, Felkins Ryan. Narragansett. 2003. (Tribes of Native America Ser.). (Illus.). 32p. (J). 23.70 (978-1-56711-698-4(1) , Blackbirch Pr., Inc.) Thomson Gale.

—Ojibway. 2003. (Tribes of Native America Ser.). (Illus.). 32p. (J). 23.70 (978-1-56711-725-7(2) , Blackbirch Pr., Inc.) Thomson Gale.

—Ute. 2003. (Tribes of Native America Ser.). (Illus.). 32p. (J). 23.70 (978-1-56711-723-3(6) , Blackbirch Pr., Inc.) Thomson Gale.

Schomp, Virginia. The Native Americans. 2007. (Myths of the World Ser.). 96p. (J). lib. bdg. 32.79 (***978-0-7614-2550-2(0)*** , Benchmark Bks.) Cavendish, Marshall Corp.

Schonberg, Marcia. Michigan Native Peoples. 2003. (Heinemann State Studies). (Illus.). 48p. (J). 27.07 (978-1-4034-0660-6(X)); pap. 8.50 (978-1-4034-2678-9(3)) Heinemann Library.

The Seminole Indians. (Native Peoples Ser.). 24p. (J). 6.95 (978-0-7368-8056-5(9)) Capstone Pr., Inc.

Shull, Jodie A. Peacemaker Princess: A Story about Sarah Winnemucca. 2007. (Creative Minds Biography Ser.). (J), spiral bd. 22.60 (978-0-8225-5990-0(0)) Lerner Publishing Group.

The Sioux Indians. (Native Peoples Ser.). 24p. (J). 6.95 (978-0-7368-8053-4(4)) Capstone Pr., Inc.

Sita, Lisa. Indians of the Great Plains: Traditions, History, Legends & Life. 1999. (Native Americans Ser.). (Illus.). 64p. (J). (gr. 5 up). lib. bdg. 27.33 (978-0-8368-2645-6(0)) Stevens, Gareth Inc.

—Indians of the Northeast: Traditions, History, Legends & Life. 1999. (Native Americans Ser.). (Illus.). 64p. (J). (gr. 5 up). lib. bdg. 27.33 (978-0-8368-2646-3(9)) Stevens, Gareth Inc.

—Indians of the Southwest: Traditions, History, Legends & Life. 1999. (Native Americans Ser.). (Illus.). 64p. (J). (gr. 5 up). lib. bdg. 27.33 (978-0-8368-2648-7(5)) Stevens, Gareth Inc.

Sjonger, Rebecca & Kalman, Bobbie. Nations of the Eastern Great Lakes. 2004. (Native Nations of North America Ser.). (Illus.). 32p. (J). (978-0-7787-0381-5(9)) Crabtree Publishing Co.

Slusher-Haas, Kathy Jo. The Southeast Indians: Daily Life in the 1500s. 2006. (Bridgestone Books). (Illus.). 24p. (J). (978-0-7368-4317-1(5)) Capstone Pr., Inc.

Sneve, Virginia Driving Hawk. Enduring Wisdom: Sayings from American Indians. Saint James, Synthia, illus. 2005. 32p. (YA). (gr. k-3). tchr. ed. 16.95 (978-0-8234-1455-0(8)) Holiday Hse., Inc.

Soeder, Pamela. Discover American Indian Ways: A Carnegie Activity Book. Powless, William, illus. 1998. (Carnegie Discover Ser.). 28p. (gr. 4-7). pap. 4.95 (978-1-57098-199-9(X)) Rinehart, Roberts Pubs.

Sonneborn, Elizabeth. New York Public Library Amazing Native American History. 1999. (gr. 5-8). lib. bdg. 22.20 (978-0-613-26381-8(2)) Tandem Library Bks.

Sonneborn, Liz. The Choctaws. 2007. (Native American Histories Ser.). (Illus.). 56p. (J). 27.93 (978-0-8225-5911-5(0) , Lerner Pubns.) Lerner Publishing Group.

—The Shoshones. 2007. (Native American Histories Ser.). (Illus.). 56p. (J). 27.93 (978-0-8225-2849-4(5) , Lerner Pubns.) Lerner Publishing Group.

Sonneborn, Liz & New York Public Library Staff. The New York Public Library Amazing Native American History: A Book of Answers for Kids. 1999. (New York Public Library Books for Kids Ser.: Vol. 8). (Illus.). 176p. (gr. 5-9). pap. 16.95 (978-0-471-33204-6(6) , Wiley) Wiley, John & Sons, Inc.

St. Lawrence, Genevieve. The Iroquois & Their History. 2005. (We the People Ser.). (Illus.). 48p. (J). (gr. 4-6). (978-0-7565-1272-9(7) , 1244092) Compass Point Bks.

—The Pueblo & Their History. 2005. (We the People Ser.). (Illus.). 48p. (J). (gr. 4-6). (978-0-7565-1274-3(3) , 1244093) Compass Point Bks.

Steins, Richard. Exploration & Settlement. 2000. (Making of America Ser.). (Illus.). 96p. (J). (gr. 4-7). lib. bdg. 28.54 (978-0-8172-5700-2(4)) Raintree.

Stone, Amy. Creek. 2004. (Native American Peoples Ser.). (Illus.). 32p. (J). 24.67 (978-0-8368-4217-3(0)) Stevens, Gareth Inc.

—Oneida. 2004. (Native American Peoples Ser.). (Illus.). 32p. (J). lib. bdg. 24.67 (978-0-8368-4220-3(0)) Stevens, Gareth Inc.

Stone, Lynn M. Mustang. 2003. (Animals in U.S. History Ser.). (Illus.). 24p. (J). 25.64 (978-1-58952-700-3(3)) Rourke Publishing, LLC.

Stout, Mary. Blackfoot. 2004. (Native American Peoples Ser.). (Illus.). 32p. (J). lib. bdg. 24.67 (978-0-8368-4216-6(2)) Stevens, Gareth Inc.

—Hopi. 2004. (Native American Peoples Ser.). (Illus.). 32p. (J). lib. bdg. 24.67 (978-0-8368-4218-0(9)) Stevens, Gareth Inc.

—Shoshone. 2004. (Native American Peoples Ser.). (Illus.). 32p. (J). lib. bdg. 24.67 (978-0-8368-4221-0(9)) Stevens, Gareth Inc.

Sundling, Charles W. Native Americans of the Frontier. 2000. (Frontier Land Ser.). (Illus.). 32p. (J). (gr. 3-8). lib. bdg. 24.21 (978-1-57765-042-3(5) , ABDO & Daughters) ABDO Publishing Co.

Tayac, Gabrielle & Bowes, John P. Black Hawk & the War of 1832: Removal in the North. 2007. (Landmark Events in Native American History Ser.). 136p. (gr. 9). 35.00 (***978-0-7910-9342-9(5)** , Chelsea Hse.) Facts On File, Inc.

Thompson, Linda. People of the Plateau. 2003. (Illus.). 48p. (J). 29.93 (978-1-58952-758-4(5)) Rourke Publishing, LLC.

Todd, Anne M. The Ojibwa: People of the Great Lakes. 2002. (American Indian Nations Ser.). (Illus.). 48p. (J). (gr. 3-4). lib. bdg. 22.60 (978-0-7368-1356-3(X) , Bridgestone Bks.) Capstone Pr., Inc.

—The Sioux: People of the Great Plains. 2002. (American Indian Nations Ser.). (Illus.). 48p. (J). (gr. 3-4). lib. bdg. 22.60 (978-0-7368-1354-9(3) , Bridgestone Bks.) Capstone Pr., Inc.

Traylor, Waverley. Indian Legends of the Great Dismal Swamp. Traylor, Margaret, ed. Hancock, Stefanie, illus. 2004. 72p. (gr. 8 up). pap. 9.95 (978-0-9715068-3-1(3)) Traylor, Waverley Publishing.

Trumbauer, Lisa. The First Americans. 2007. (J). (***978-1-4034-9665-2(X)**); pap. (***978-1-4034-9673-7(0)**) Heinemann Library.

Turner, Ann Warren. Sitting Bull Remembers. Date not set. 32p. (J). (ps-3). 15.99 (978-0-06-029153-2(2)); pap. 5.99 (978-0-06-443725-7(6)); lib. bdg. 16.89 (978-0-06-029154-9(0)) HarperCollins Pubs.

Waldman, Stuart. We Asked for Nothing: The Remarkable Journey of Cabeza de Vaca. McNeely, Tom, illus. 2003. (Great Explorers Ser.). 48p. (J). (gr. 4-8). 19.95 (978-1-931414-07-4(6)) Mikaya Pr.

Walker, Niki & Kalman, Bobbie. Native North American Wisdom & Gifts. 2005. (Native Nations of North America Ser.). (Illus.). 32p. (J). (gr. 3-9). lib. bdg. (978-0-7787-0384-6(3)); pap. (978-0-7787-0476-8(9)) Crabtree Publishing Co.

Weintraub, Aileen. The Choctaw. 2005. (Indigenous Peoples of North America Ser.). (J). (978-1-59018-610-7(9) , Lucent Bks.) Thomson Gale.

Weitzel, Kelley G. The Timucua Indians: A Native American Detective Story. 2000. (UPF Young Readers Library). (Illus.). 176p. (gr. 4-7). pap. 12.95 (978-0-8130-1738-9(6)) Univ. Pr. of Florida.

Whittock, Martyn J. The Native Peoples of North America. 2002. (Illus.). 48p. pap. 23.50 (***978-0-340-80330-1(4)** , Hodder Murray) Hodder Education GBR. *Dist:* Trans-Atlantic Pubns., Inc.

Wilcox, Charlotte. The Seminoles. 2007. (Native American Histories Ser.). 56p. (J). 27.93 (978-0-8225-2848-7(7) , Lerner Pubns.) Lerner Publishing Group.

Wingate, Philippa & Reid, Struan. Who Were the First North Americans? 2004. (Starting Point History Ser.). (Illus.). 32p. (J). pap. 4.99 (978-0-7945-0397-0(7) , Usborne); lib. bdg. 12.95 (978-1-58086-512-8(7)) EDC Publishing.

Wirkner, Linda. Learning about the Settlement of the Americas, with Graphic Organizers. 2005. (Graphic Organizers in Social Studies). (J). 19.95 (978-1-4042-2814-6(4) , PowerKids Pr.) Rosen Publishing Group, Inc., The.

Wolf, Linda Little. Visions of the Buffalo People. 2003. (gr. 5-8). lib. bdg. 24.55 (978-0-613-67129-3(5)) Tandem Library Bks.

INDIANS OF NORTH AMERICA—HISTORY—FICTION

Brown, Alvin R. Native American Action Stories: Exciting Events in Nine Different Tribes. 2005. 254p. per. 15.95 (978-1-59453-885-8(9) , 3307, Airleaf Publishing) Airleaf Publishing & Bookselling.

Cultures of the World, 6 vols., Set. 2nd ed. Incl. Argentina. Gofen, E. & Jermyn, L. lib. bdg. 37.07 (978-0-7614-1358-5(8) , Benchmark Bks.); Brazil. Richard, Christopher & Jermyn, L. lib. bdg. 37.07 (978-0-7614-1359-2(6) , Cavendish, Marshall Reference Bks.); Chile. Winter, J. Kohen & Roraff, S. lib. bdg. 37.07 (978-0-7614-1360-8(X) , Benchmark Bks.); Colombia. DuBois, Jill & Jermyn, L. lib. bdg. 37.07 (978-0-7614-1361-5(8) , Benchmark Bks.); Mexico. Reilly, M. J. & Jermyn, L. lib. bdg. 37.07 (978-0-7614-1363-9(4) , Benchmark Bks.); Venezuela. Winter, J. Kohen & Baguley, K. lib. bdg. 37.07 (978-0-7614-1362-2(6) , Cavendish, Marshall Reference Bks.); 144p. (gr. 5 up). (Illus.). 2001. 222.43 (978-0-7614-1357-8(X) , Benchmark Bks.) Cavendish, Marshall Corp.

Hamilton, Elizabeth L. Mystery at Lake Cachuma. 2003. (Character Mystery Ser.: No. 1). (Illus.). 114p. (J). (gr. 3-6). per. 9.95 (978-0-9713749-4-2(5) , Character-in-Action) Quiet Impact, Inc.

Harcourt School Publishers Staff. Tisquantum & the Pilgrims On Level. 3rd ed. 2002. (Trophies Reading Program Ser.). (Illus.). pap. 5.10 (978-0-15-323366-1(4)) Harcourt Schl. Pubs.

Howe, LeAnne. Shell Shaker. 2001. (gr. 7-12). lib. bdg. 21.05 (978-0-613-62703-0(2)) Tandem Library Bks.

Lowden, Stephanie Golightly. Time of the Eagle: A Story of an Ojibwe Winter. 2006. 128p. (J). 18.95 (978-1-883953-38-6(3) , Blue Horse Bks.) Midwest Traditions, Inc.

Shaffer, Elizabeth N. Hannah & the Indian King, Vol. 2. Pratt, Fran, ed. 2002. (Historical Novel Ser.). pap. 9.95 (978-0-936369-35-8(3)) Son-Rise Pubns. & Distribution Co.

INDIANS OF NORTH AMERICA—HOPI INDIANS

Boule, Mary Null. Native Americans of North America: Hopi People, Set, 11. Liddell, Daniel, illus. 2002. 52p. (Orig.). (J). (gr. 3-6). pap. 6.45 (978-1-877599-58-3(1)) Merryant Pubs.

Gray-Kanatiiosh, Barbara A. Hopi. Chimerica, Charles, illus. 2002. (Native Americans Ser.). 32p. (J). (gr. k-6). lib. bdg. 22.78 (978-1-57765-598-5(2) , Checkerboard Library) ABDO Publishing Co.

Lassieur, Allison. The Hopi. 2002. (Native Peoples Ser.). (Illus.). 24p. (J). (gr. 2-3). lib. bdg. 18.60 (978-0-7368-1102-6(8) , Bridgestone Bks.) Capstone Pr., Inc.

Santella, Andrew. Hopi. 2002. (gr. 3-6). lib. bdg. 15.25 (978-0-613-59497-4(5)) Tandem Library Bks.

Schmittroth, Felkins Ryan. Hopi. 2003. (Tribes of Native America Ser.). (Illus.). 32p. (J). 23.70 (978-1-56711-691-5(4) , Blackbirch Pr., Inc.) Thomson Gale.

Secakuku, Susan. Meet Mindy: A Native Girl from the Southwest. Harrington, John, illus. Harrington, John, photos by. 2002. (My World: Young Native Americans Today Ser.). 48p. (J). 15.95 (978-1-58270-091-5(5)) Beyond Words Publishing, Inc.

—Meet Mindy: A Native Girl from the Southwest. Harrington, John, photos by. 2006. (Illus.). 48p. (J). 15.95 (978-1-57178-148-2(X)) Council Oak Bks.

Secakuku, Susan & Tayac, Gabrielle. Meet Mindy. Harrington, John, photos by. 2003. (My World). (Illus.). 32p. (J). (gr. 4 up). lib. bdg. 24.67 (978-0-8368-3794-0(0)) Stevens, Gareth Inc.

St. Lawrence, Genevieve. The Hopi. 2003. (Uncovering Native American History Ser.). (J). pap. (978-1-58417-115-7(4)); lib. bdg. (978-1-58417-052-5(2)) Lake Street Pubs.

INDIANS OF NORTH AMERICA—HOPI INDIANS—FICTION

Price, Joan. Truth Is a Bright Star. 2nd rev. ed. 2004. (Illus.). 156p. (J). (gr. 3-7). 8.95 (978-1-58246-055-0(8) , Tricycle Pr.) Ten Speed Pr.

Smith, Roland. The Last Lobo. 2001. (gr. 3-6). lib. bdg. 14.15 (978-0-613-74960-2(X)) Tandem Library Bks.

INDIANS OF NORTH AMERICA—HURON INDIANS

Gray-Kanatiiosh, Barbara A. Huron. 2004. (Native Americans Set Iii Ser.). (Illus.). 32p. (J). (gr. k-6). lib. bdg. 22.78 (978-1-57765-935-8(X)) ABDO Publishing Co.

Libal, Autumn. Huron. 2003. (North American Indians Today Ser.). (Illus.). 96p. (J). lib. bdg. (978-1-59084-670-4(2)) Mason Crest Pubs.

INDIANS OF NORTH AMERICA—INDUSTRIES

Corwin, Judith Hoffman. Native American Crafts of California, the Great Basin, & the Southwest. 2002. (gr. 3-6). lib. bdg. 16.40 (978-0-613-59523-0(8)) Tandem Library Bks.

—Native American Crafts of the Northeast & Southeast. Corwin, Judith Hoffman, illus. 2003. (Native American Crafts Ser.). (Illus.). 48p. (J). (gr. 3-6). pap. 7.95 (978-0-531-15593-6(5) , Watts, Franklin) Scholastic Library Publishing.

—Native American Crafts of the Northeast & Southeast. 2002. (gr. 3-6). lib. bdg. 16.40 (978-0-613-59524-7(6)) Tandem Library Bks.

—Native American Crafts of the Northwest Coast, the Arctic, & the Subarctic. 2002. (gr. 3-6). lib. bdg. 16.40 (978-0-613-59525-4(4)) Tandem Library Bks.

—Native American Crafts of the Plains & Plateau. Corwin, Judith Hoffman, illus. 2003. (Native American Crafts Ser.). (Illus.). 48p. (J). (gr. 3-6). pap. 7.95 (978-0-531-15595-0(1) , Watts, Franklin) Scholastic Library Publishing.

—Native American Crafts of the Plains & Plateau. 2002. (gr. 3-6). lib. bdg. 16.40 (978-0-613-59526-1(2)) Tandem Library Bks.

Gnojewski, Carol. American Indian Crafts Kids Can Do! 2006. (Multicultural Crafts Kids Can Do! Ser.). (Illus.). 32p. (J). lib. bdg. 22.60 (978-0-7660-2458-8(X) , Enslow Elementary) Enslow Pubs., Inc.

Hoffman-Corwin, Judith. Native American Crafts of the Northwest Coast, the Arctic & the Subarctic. 1999. (J). (978-0-531-11340-0(X) , Watts, Franklin) Scholastic Library Publishing.

Schiffer, Nancy N. Contemporary Hopi Kachina Dolls. 2003. (Illus.). 208p. (gr. 10-13). 39.95 (978-0-7643-1848-1(9)) Schiffer Publishing, Ltd.

INDIANS OF NORTH AMERICA—IROQUOIS INDIANS

American Indian Nations: The Cherokee; The Iroquois; The Ojibwa; The Pueblo; The Seminole; The Sioux, 6 bks. (Illus.). (J). (gr. 3-4). lib. bdg. 101.70 (978-0-7368-1359-4(4) , Bridgestone Bks.) Capstone Pr., Inc.

Beres, Cynthia Breslin. Longhouse. Dawson, Kimberly L., illus. 2000. (Native American Homes Ser.). 32p. (J). (gr. 3-6). lib. bdg. 28.50 (978-1-55916-247-0(3)) Rourke Publishing, LLC.

Bial, Raymond. The Iroquois. 1998. (Lifeways Ser.). (Illus.). 128p. (J). (gr. 5-9). lib. bdg. 34.21 (978-0-7614-0802-4(9) , Benchmark Bks.) Cavendish, Marshall Corp.

—Longhouses. 2004. (American Community Ser.). (Illus.). 48p. (J). (gr. 2-5). 29.00 (978-0-516-23707-7(1) , Children's Pr.) Scholastic Library Publishing.

Bowman, David. Native AMER of the Eastern Woodlands. 2006. (Navigators Ser.). (J). pap. 42.00 (***978-1-4108-6252-5(6)**) Benchmark Education Co.

Bruchac, Joseph. The Boy Who Lived with the Bears: And Other Iroquois Stories. Jacob, Murv, illus. 2003. (Storytime Ser.). 63p. (J). pap. 11.95 (978-0-930407-61-2(X)) Parabola Bks.

Eames-Sheavly, Marcia. The Three Sisters: Exploring an Iroquois Garden. Eames-Sheavly, Marcia, illus. 2000. (Illus.). 24p. (J). (gr. 4-7). pap. 5.50 (978-1-57753-269-9(4) , 142LM15) Resource Centre, The.

Hoyt-Goldsmith, Diane. Lacrosse: The National Game of the Iroquois. Migdale, Lawrence, photos by. 1998. (Illus.). 31p. (J). (gr. 4-7). tchr. ed. 16.95 (978-0-8234-1360-7(8)) Holiday Hse., Inc.

Kalman, Bobbie. Life in a Longhouse. 2001. (gr. 3-6). lib. bdg. 16.40 (978-0-613-43464-5(1)) Tandem Library Bks.

—Life in a Longhouse Village. Parker, Lewis, illus. 2001. (Native Nations of North America Ser.). 32p. (J). (gr. 5). (978-0-7787-0370-9(3)); pap. (978-0-7787-0462-1(9)) Crabtree Publishing Co.

Koestler-Grack, Rachel A. The Iroquois: Longhouse Builders. 2003. (America's First Peoples Ser.). (Illus.). 32p. (J). (gr. 2-3). lib. bdg. 23.93 (978-0-7368-1536-9(8) , Bridgestone Bks.) Capstone Pr., Inc.

Levine, Ellen. If You Lived with the Iroquois. 1999. (If You Lived Ser.). (Illus.). 80p. (J). (gr. 2-5). pap. 5.99 (978-0-590-67445-4(5)) Scholastic, Inc.

McIntosh, Kenneth & McIntosh, Marsha. Iroquois: The Haudenosaunee. 2003. (North American Indians Today Ser.). (Illus.), 96p. (J). lib. bdg. (978-1-59084-671-1(0)) Mason Crest Pubs.

McNamara, Margaret. Native AMER of the Eastern Woodlands: The Iroquois. 2006. pap. 42.00 (***978-1-4108-6440-6(5)**) Benchmark Education Co.

Miller, Connie R. The Iroquois. 2003. (Digging up Native American History Ser.). (J). (978-1-58417-045-7(X)); pap. (978-1-58417-108-9(1)) Lake Street Pubs.

O'Neill, Linda. Imagine Being Paralyzed. 2000. (Imagine Ser.). (Illus.). 32p. (J). (gr. 1-4). lib. bdg. 26.60 (978-1-57103-378-9(5)) Rourke Publishing, LLC.

Petra Press Staff. The Iroquois. 2001. (First Reports). (Illus.). 48p. (J). (gr. 3 up). lib. bdg. 22.60 (978-0-7565-0080-1(X)) Compass Point Bks.

Randolph, Joanne. The Iroquois League. 2003. (Reading Room Collection). (Illus.). 24p. (J). lib. bdg. 18.75 (978-0-8239-3703-5(8)) Rosen Publishing Group, Inc., The.

Ryan, Marla, ed. Mohawk. 2002. (Tribes of North America Ser.). (Illus.). 48p. (J). 23.70 (978-1-56711-615-1(9) , Blackbirch Pr., Inc.) Thomson Gale.

Sonneborn, Liz. Iroquois. 2002. (gr. 5-8). lib. bdg. 17.60 (978-0-613-53052-1(7)) Tandem Library Bks.

Takacs, Stefanie. The Iroqious. 2004. (True Bks.). (J). (gr. 3-5). pap. 6.95 (978-0-516-27824-7(X) , Children's Pr.) Scholastic Library Publishing.

—The Iroquois. 2003. (True Book Ser.). (Illus.). 48p. (J). 25.00 (978-0-516-22777-1(7) , Children's Pr.) Scholastic Library Publishing.

INDIANS OF NORTH AMERICA—IROQUOIS INDIANS—FICTION

Andreasen, Dan, illus. Eagle Song. 1999. (Puffin Chapters Ser.). (J). 11.79 (978-0-606-16833-5(8)); (gr. 3-6). lib. bdg. 13.00 (978-0-613-17790-0(8)) Tandem Library Bks.

Bruchac, Joseph. Eagle Song. Andreasen, Dan, illus. 1999. 96p. (J). (gr. 2-5). pap. 4.99 (978-0-14-130169-3(4) , Puffin) Penguin Group (USA) Inc.

Kelsey, Avonelle. Iroquois Medicine Woman. Kelsey, Avonelle, illus. (Illus.). 300p. (Orig.). (YA). (978-0-9640610-5-7(8)) Cheval International.

Preble Mike. Why the Owl Has Big Ears. McCann Shawn, illus. 2005. 32p. 8.75 (978-0-9771466-0-4(X)) Goulasche Pr.

Pryor, Bonnie. Thomas in Danger, 1779. Dodson, Bert, illus. 2000. (American Adventures Ser.). 176p. (J). (gr. 3-7). pap. 4.95 (978-0-380-73212-8(2)) HarperCollins Pubs.

INDIANS OF NORTH AMERICA—KARANKAWA

Roza, Greg. The Karankawa of Texas. 2005. (Library of Native Americans). (Illus.). 64p. (J). 26.50 (978-1-4042-2870-2(5) , PowerKids Pr.) Rosen Publishing Group, Inc., The.

INDIANS OF NORTH AMERICA—KIOWA INDIANS—FICTION

Momaday, N. Scott. House Made of Dawn. 1999. 198p. (gr. 7-12). per. 22.25 (978-0-613-37149-0(6)) Tandem Library Bks.

Momaday, N. Scott, illus. Four Arrows & Magpie: A Kiowa Story. 2006. 48p. (ps-3). pap. 9.95 (978-1-930709-63-8(3)) HAWK Publishing Group.

INDIANS OF NORTH AMERICA—KIOWA INDIANS—LEGENDS

Ryan, Marla Felkins & Schmittroth, Linda, eds. Kiowa. 2003. (Tribes of Native America Ser.). (Illus.). 32p. (J). 23.70 (978-1-56711-692-2(2) , Blackbirch Pr., Inc.) Thomson Gale.

INDIANS OF NORTH AMERICA—LEGENDS

see also Indians of North America—Folklore

Bruchac, James & Bruchac, Joseph. When the Chenoo Howls: Native American Tales of Terror. Sauts, William, illus. 1999. 136p. (J). (gr. 3-7). 16.95 (978-0-8027-8638-8(3)) Walker & Co.

Bruchac, Joseph. The Boy Who Lived with the Bears: And Other Iroquois Stories. Jacob, Murv, illus. 2003. (Storytime Ser.). 63p. (J). pap. 11.95 (978-0-930407-61-2(X)) Parabola Bks.

Bruchac, Joseph & Ross, Gayle. The Girl Who Married the Moon: Tales from Native North America. 2006. 128p. (YA). pap. 9.95 (978-1-55591-566-7(3) , 800.992.2908) Fulcrum Publishing.

Caduto, Michael J. & Bruchac, Joseph. Keepers of the Earth: Native American Stories & Environmental Activities for Children. Fadden, John Kahionhes & Wood, Carol, illus. (Keepers Ser.). 240p. (gr. 1-3). reprint ed. pap. 21.95 (978-1-55591-385-4(7)) Fulcrum Publishing.

Cuevas, Lou. Apache Legends: Songs of the Wind Dancer. Brown, Keven, ed. Cleveland, Fred, illus. 2003. 128p. (Orig.). (YA). pap. 8.95 (978-0-87961-219-1(3)) Naturegraph Pubs., Inc.

Curry, Jane Louise. Back in the Beforetime. 2001. (J). 11.64 (978-0-606-20560-3(8)) Tandem Library Bks.

De Montano, Marty K. Coyote in Love with a Star. Coffin, Tom, illus. 1998. (Tales of the People Ser.). 30p. (ps up). 14.95 (978-0-7892-0162-1(3)) Abbeville Pr., Inc.

Dover Staff. Listen & Color: Native American Legends. Green, John, illus. 2004. 48p. (J). pap. 6.95 incl. audio compact disk (978-0-486-43892-4(9)) Dover Pubns., Inc.

Duvall, Deborah L., text. Rabbit & the Bears: A Traditional Cherokee Legend. 2004. (Grandmother Stories Ser.). (Illus.). 32p. (J). 14.95 (978-0-8263-3131-1(9)) Univ. of New Mexico Pr.

Ehlert, Lois. Mole's Hill: A Woodland Tale. Ehlert, Lois, illus. 2002. (Illus.). (J). 14.04 (978-0-7587-3153-1(1)) Book Wholesalers, Inc.

—Mole's Hill: A Woodland Tale. Ehlert, Lois, illus. 2004. (Illus.). 30p. (J). (gr. k-4). 15.00 (978-0-7567-7725-8(9)) DIANE Publishing Co.

Goble, Paul. Iktomi & the Buzzard: A Plains Indian Story. 1998. (Illus.). 32p. (J). (ps-2). pap. 6.95 (978-0-531-07100-7(6) , Orchard Bks.) Scholastic, Inc.

—Iktomi & the Buzzard: A Plains Indian Story. 1998. (978-0-606-13516-0(2)) Tandem Library Bks.

—Iktomi & the Coyote: A Plains Indian Story. 1998. (Illus.). 32p. (J). (ps-2). 17.99 (978-0-531-33108-8(3)); pap. 16.95 (978-0-531-30108-1(7)) Scholastic, Inc. (Orchard Bks.).

Harris, Christie. Mouse Woman & the Mischief-Makers. Tait, Douglas, illus. 2005. 152p. (J). pap. 7.95 (978-1-55192-751-0(9)) Raincoast Bk. Distribution CAN. *Dist:* Perseus Distribution.

Jepperson, Richard. Black Robe Woman, Lakota Warrior: Being the Second Part of the Crazy Horse Chronicles. Mundie, Ken, illus. 2001. viii, 152p. (YA). (gr. 7-12). 18.95 (978-0-9672012-1-4(7)) String of Beads Pubns.

—The War of the Mormon Cow: The First Part of the Crazy Horse Chronicles. Mundie, Ken, illus. 1999. viii, 56p. (J). (gr. 7-12). 16.95 (978-0-9672012-0-7(9)) String of Beads Pubns.

Keeper, Berry. The Old Ones Told Me: American Indian Stories for Children. Keeper, Berry, illus. 3rd ed. 2000. (Illus.). 36p. (J). (gr. 4-7). reprint ed. pap. 6.95 (978-0-8323-0473-6(5)) Binford & Mort Publishing.

Kuharski, Janice. Raven's Gift. Kitchel, JoAnn, illus. 1999. (Books for Young Learners). 16qp. (J). (gr. k-2). pap. 5.00 (978-1-57274-144-7(9) , 2896) Owen, Richard C. Pubs., Inc.

Marchand, Barbara, illus. Kou-Skelowh/We Are the People: A Trilogy of Okanagan Legends. 2000. 88p. (J). (ps-3). pap. 10.95 (978-0-919441-81-1(5)) Theytus Bks., Ltd. CAN. *Dist:* Orca Bk. Pubs. USA.

Mead, Alice & Neptume, Arnold, eds. Giants of the Dawnland: Ancient Wabanaki Tales. Date not set. 76p. (YA). pap. 8.00 (978-1-888034-01-1(7)) Loose Cannon Pr.

Mohican Nation Youth. Stories of Our Elders. Ganley, Beatrice et al, photos by. 1999. (Illus.). 21p. (YA). (gr. 4). pap. 10.00 (978-0-935790-06-1(3)) Muh-He-Con-Neew Pr.

Moon, Grace Purdie. Indian Legends in Rhyme. Moon, Carl, illus. 2000. 63p. (J). (gr. 4-7). 7.95 (978-1-885772-22-0(X)) Kiva Publishing, Inc.

Murphy, Claire Rudolf. The Prince & the Salmon People. Pasco, Duane, illus. 2002. 48p. (J). pap. 19.95 (978-0-910055-83-3(1)) Eastern Washington Univ. Pr.

Neitzel, Shirley. From the Land of the White Birch: Three Ojibwa Legends. Powers, Daniel, illus. 2000. 32p. (J). (gr. 2-5). pap. 8.95 (978-0-938682-56-1(3)) River Road Pubns., Inc.

Rodanas, Kristina, reader. Follow the Stars: A Native American Woodlands Tale. 1998. (Accelerated Reader Bks.). (Illus.). 32p. (J). (gr. k-3). lib. bdg. 15.95 (978-0-7614-5029-0(7) , Cavendish Children's Bks.) Cavendish, Marshall Corp.

Ross, Gayle. How Rabbit Tricked Otter: And Other Cherokee Trickster Stories. 2003. (Storytime Ser.). (Illus.). 78p. (J). pap. 12.95 (978-0-930407-60-5(1)) Parabola Bks.

Scheer, George F. Cherokee Animal Tales. 2003. (gr. 3-6). lib. bdg. 16.40 (978-0-613-77669-1(0)) Tandem Library Bks.

Taylor, C. J. All the Stars in the Sky: Native Stories from the Heavens. Thisdale, Francois, illus. 2006. 40p. (J). (gr. 3). 17.95 (978-0-88776-759-3(1)) Tundra Bks., Inc./Livres Toundra, Inc. CAN. *Dist:* Random Hse., Inc.

Van Laan, Nancy. Shingebiss: An Ojibwe Legend. Bowen, Betsy, illus. 2002. 32p. (J). (gr. k-3). pap. 6.95 (978-0-618-21616-1(2)) Houghton Mifflin Co. Trade & Reference Div.

H
I

Wargin, Kathy-Jo. The Legend of Sleeping Bear. van Frankenhuyzen, Gijsbert, illus. 1998. (Great Lakes Legend Ser.). 48p. (J). (ps-3). 17.95 (978-1-886947-35-1(X)) Sleeping Bear Pr.

Wolf, Linda Little. The Great Spirit Horse. 2nd ed. 2003. (Illus.). 152p. (J). pap. 10.95 (978-1-58980-123-3(7)) Pelican Publishing Co., Inc.

—The Great Spirit Horse. Spatrisano-Graham, Kimberly, illus. 2001. 120p. (J). (gr. 4-7). per. 9.95 (978-0-9671978-7-6(2)) Syncopated Pr.

Wood, Douglas. The Rabbit & the Moon. Baker, Leslie A., illus. 2001. 40p. (J). (ps-3). 12.99 (978-0-689-84304-4(6), Aladdin) Simon & Schuster Children's Publishing.

Wooldridge, Jack. Broken Words: A Potawatomi Fable. Wooldridge, Jack, illus. 2002. (Illus.). 29p. (J). pap. 7.00 (978-1-887963-19-0(7)) Pota Pr.

INDIANS OF NORTH AMERICA—MIWOK INDIANS

Covert, Kim. The Coast Miwok. 1998. (Native Peoples Ser.). (Illus.). 24p. (J). (gr. 2-3). lib. bdg. 18.60 (978-0-7368-0077-8(8), Bridgestone Bks.) Capstone Pr., Inc.

Gray-Kanatiiosh, Barbara A. Miwok. 2002. (Native Americans Ser.). (Illus.). 32p. (J). (gr. k-6). lib. bdg. 22.78 (978-1-57765-601-2(6), Checkerboard Library) ABDO Publishing Co.

Williams, Jack S. The Miwok of California. 2004. (Library of Native Americans). (Illus.). 64p. (J). lib. bdg. 26.50 (978-1-4042-2659-3(1)) Rosen Publishing Group, Inc., The.

INDIANS OF NORTH AMERICA—MOHAVE INDIANS

Boule, Mary Null. California Native American Tribes: Mohave Tribe, 28 booklets. Liddell, Daniel & Basta, Mary, illus. (California Native American Tribes). 52p. (J). (gr. 3-6). pap. 7.95 (978-1-877599-73-6(5)) Merryant Pubs.

—Mohave Tribe Vol. 1: California Tribes or CA Region. Liddell, Daniel & Basta, Mary, illus. 2000. (Native Americans of North America Ser.). 52p. (J). (gr. 3-6). pap. 7.95 (978-1-877599-57-6(3)) Merryant Pubs.

Gray-Kanatiiosh, Barbara A. Mohave. 2004. (Native Americans Set Iii Ser.). (Illus.). 32p. (J). (gr. k-6). lib. bdg. 22.78 (978-1-57765-936-5(8)) ABDO Publishing Co.

INDIANS OF NORTH AMERICA—MOHAWK INDIANS

Adare, Sierra. Mohawk. 2003. (Native American Peoples Ser.). (Illus.). 32p. (J). (gr. 4 up). lib. bdg. 24.67 (978-0-8368-3665-3(0)) Stevens, Gareth Inc.

Kirk, Connie A. The Mohawks of North America. 2002. (First Peoples Ser.). (Illus.). 48p. (J). (gr. 4-8). lib. bdg. 23.93 (978-0-8225-4853-9(4)) Lerner Publishing Group.

Ryan, Marla, ed. Mohawk. 2002. (Tribes of North America Ser.). (Illus.). 48p. (J). 23.70 (978-1-56711-615-1(9), Blackbirch Pr., Inc.) Thomson Gale.

INDIANS OF NORTH AMERICA—MOHAWK INDIANS—FICTION

Bruchac, Joseph. Bearwalker. Comport, Sally Wern, illus. 2007. 224p. (J). (gr. 5-8). 15.99 (***978-0-06-112309-2(9)***); lib. bdg. 16.89 (***978-0-06-112311-5(0)***) HarperCollins Pubs.

Bruchac, Joseph. The Return of Skeleton Man. Comport, Sally Wern, illus. 2006. 144p. (J). 15.99 (978-0-06-058090-2(9)) HarperCollins Pubs.

Carvell, Marlene. Who Will Tell My Brother? 2004. 160p. (gr. 7-17). pap. 5.99 (978-0-7868-1657-6(0)) Hyperion Bks. for Children.

Kirk, Connie Ann. Sky Dancers. Hale, Christy, illus. 2004. (J). (gr. 1-4). 16.95 (978-1-58430-162-2(7)) Lee & Low Bks., Inc.

Wax, Wendy. Empire Dreams. Doney, Todd, illus. 2000. (Adventures in America Ser.). 96p. (J). (gr. 4-7). lib. bdg. 14.95 (978-1-893110-19-9(2)) Silver Moon Pr.

INDIANS OF NORTH AMERICA—MUSIC

Ench, Rick. North American Indian Music. 2002. (gr. 5-8). lib. bdg. 17.60 (978-0-613-53068-2(3)) Tandem Library Bks.

Ench, Rick & Cravath, Jay. North American Indian Music: Indians of the Americas. 2002. (Watts Library). (Illus.). 64p. (J). (gr. 5-7). 25.50 (978-0-531-11772-9(3), Watts, Franklin) Scholastic Library Publishing.

Ench, Rick, et al. North American Indian Music. 2002. (Watts Library). (J). (gr. 5-7). pap. 8.95 (978-0-531-16230-9(3), Watts, Franklin) Scholastic Library Publishing.

Tyrrell, Frances, illus. The Huron Carol. 2004. 32p. 16.00 (978-0-8028-5263-2(7)) Eerdmans, William B. Publishing Co.

INDIANS OF NORTH AMERICA—MYTHOLOGY

see Indians of North America—Folklore; Indians of North America—Legends; Indians of North America—Religion and Mythology

INDIANS OF NORTH AMERICA—NAVAHO INDIANS

Aaseng, Nathan. Navajo Code Talkers. 2000. (Illus.). 96p. (J). (gr. 3-6). reprint ed. pap. 7.95 (978-0-8027-7589-4(6)) Walker & Co.

Abbink, Emily. Colors of the Navajo. Porter, Janice Lee, illus. 1998. (Colors of the World Ser.). 24p. (J). (gr. 1-4). 5.95 (978-1-57505-269-4(5)); (gr. 3-6). lib. bdg. 19.93 (978-1-57505-207-6(5)) Lerner Publishing Group.

—Colors of the Navajo. Porter, Janice Lee, illus. 1998. 24p. (J). (ps-3). lib. bdg. 14.10 (978-0-613-68208-4(4)) Tandem Library Bks.

Bial, Raymond. The Navajo. 1998. (Lifeways Ser.). (Illus.). 128p. (J). (gr. 5-9). lib. bdg. 34.21 (978-0-7614-0803-1(7), Benchmark Bks.) Cavendish, Marshall Corp.

Birchfield, D. L. Navajo. 2003. (Native American Peoples Ser.). (Illus.). 32p. (J). (gr. 4 up). lib. bdg. 24.67 (978-0-8368-3704-9(5)) Stevens, Gareth Inc.

Boekhoff, P. M. & Kallen, Stuart A. The Navajo. 2003. (North American Indians Ser.). (J). 26.20 (978-0-7377-1512-5(X), Greenhaven Pr., Inc.) Thomson Gale.

Boule, Mary Null. Navajo People: SW Region, Set. Liddell, Daniel & Basta, Mary, illus. (Native Americans of North America Ser.). 50-60p. (J). (gr. 3-6). pap. 7.95 (978-1-877599-59-0(X)) Merryant Pubs.

Bruchac, Joseph. Navajo Long Walk: The Tragic Story of a Proud People's Forced March from Their Homeland. Begay, Shonto W., illus. 2002. 64p. (J). (gr. 3-7). 18.95 (978-0-7922-7058-4(4), National Geographic Children's Bks.) National Geographic Society.

De Angelis, Therese. The Navajo: Weavers of the Southwest. 2003. (America's First Peoples Ser.). (Illus.). 32p. (J). (gr. 2-3). lib. bdg. 23.93 (978-0-7368-2172-8(4), Bridgestone Bks.) Capstone Pr., Inc.

Griffin, Lana T. & Nockideneh, Tommy J. The Navajo. 1999. (Indian Nations Ser.). (Illus.). 48p. (J). (gr. 3-6). lib. bdg. 25.69 (978-0-8172-5463-6(3)) Raintree.

Knowles, Gerald M. The Navajo of North America. 2005. (First Peoples Ser.). (Illus.). 48p. (gr. 4-8). lib. bdg. 23.95 (978-0-8225-0662-1(9)) Lerner Publishing Group.

McIntosh, Kenneth. Navajo. 2003. (North American Indians Today Ser.). (Illus.). 96p. (J). lib. bdg. (978-1-59084-672-8(9)) Mason Crest Pubs.

McNamara, Margaret. Native AMER of the Southwest: The Navajo. 2006. pap. 39.00 (***978-1-4108-6438-3(3)***) Benchmark Education Co.

Rossi, Ann. Native AMER of the Southwest. 2006. (Navigators Ser.). (J). pap. 42.00 (***978-1-4108-6251-8(8)***) Benchmark Education Co.

Ryan, Marla Felkins & Schmittroth, Linda, eds. Navajo. 2002. (Tribes of Native America Ser.). (Illus.). 32p. (J). 23.70 (978-1-56711-624-3(8), Blackbirch Pr., Inc.) Thomson Gale.

Santella, Andrew. Navajo Code Talkers. 2004. (We the People Ser.). (Illus.). 48p. (J). (gr. 4 up). lib. bdg. 22.60 (978-0-7565-0611-7(5)) Compass Point Bks.

Woods, Geraldine. The Navajo. 2002. (Watts Library). (J). (gr. 5-7). pap. 8.95 (978-0-531-16227-9(3), Watts, Franklin) Scholastic Library Publishing.

Yacowitz, Caryn. Navajo Indians. 2003. (Native Americans Ser.). (Illus.). 32p. (J). pap. 7.50 (978-1-4034-4172-0(3)); lib. bdg. 24.22 (978-1-4034-0864-8(5)) Heinemann Library.

INDIANS OF NORTH AMERICA—NAVAHO INDIANS—FICTION

Armstrong, Nancy. Navajo Long Walk. Livers-Lambert, Paulette, illus. 2nd ed. 2001. (Council for Indian Education Ser.). 128p. (gr. 4-7). pap. 10.95 (978-1-879373-56-3(4)) Rinehart, Roberts Pubs.

Browne, Vee. The Stone Cutter & the Navajo Maiden. Brycelea, Clifford, illus. 2008. (NAV.). 32p. (***978-1-893354-92-0(X)***) Salina Bookshelf.

Crowder, Jack L., et al. Stephanie & the Coyote. Morgan, William, tr. 3rd rev. ed. (ENG & NAV., Illus.). 32p. (J). (gr. 3 up). reprint ed. pap. 4.95 (978-0-9616589-0-8(8)) Crowder, Jack L.

Davidson, A. L., et al. The Spirit Line. 2004. 224p. (YA). (gr. 7). 16.99 (978-0-670-03645-5(5), Viking Juvenile) Penguin Group (USA) Inc.

Dewey, Jennifer Owings. Navajo Summer. 2003. (Illus.). 136p. (YA). (gr. 6-9). 10.95 (978-1-56397-855-5(5)) Boyds Mills Pr.

—Navajo Summer. 2000. (J). (978-0-606-19306-1(5)) Tandem Library Bks.

Grammer, Maurine. The Navajo Brothers & the Stolen Herd. Cleveland, Fred, illus. 2004. 120p. (gr. 4-7). pap. 9.95 (978-1-878610-23-2(6)) Red Crane Bks., Inc.

Hausman, Gerald. The Coyote Bead. 1999. (Young Spirit Books Ser.). 144p. (J). (gr. 5-10). pap. 11.95 (978-1-57174-145-5(3)) Hampton Roads Publishing Co., Inc.

—Coyote Bead. 1999. (gr. 5-8). lib. bdg. 21.05 (978-0-613-50289-4(2)) Tandem Library Bks.

Kent, Renee Holmes. J. J. Navajo Princess, Vol. 3. 2004. (Adventures in Misty Falls Ser.: Vol. 3). (Illus.). 100p. (gr. 4-7). pap. 4.99 (978-1-56309-763-8(X), N007105) New Hope Pubs.

Maher, Ramona. Alice Yazzie's Year. Begay, Shonto, illus. 2004. 40p. (J). 15.95 (978-1-58246-080-2(9), Tricycle Pr.) Ten Speed Pr.

Schick, Eleanor. Navajo Wedding Day: A Dine Marriage Ceremony. 1999. (Accelerated Reader Bks.). (Illus.). 40p. (J). (gr. k-3). 15.95 (978-0-7614-5031-3(9), Cavendish Children's Bks.) Cavendish, Marshall Corp.

Tapahonso, Luci. Songs of Shiprock Fair. Emerson, Anthony C., illus. 1999. 32p. (J). (ps-3). 15.95 (978-1-885772-11-4(4)) Kiva Publishing, Inc.

Thomas, Marjorie W. Bidii. Begay, Patrick S., illus. 2000. (ENG & NAV.). 32p. (J). pap. 9.00 (978-1-893354-16-6(4)) Salina Bookshelf.

—White Nose the Sheep Dog: Chiilgai, Na'nilkaadii. 2000. (ENG & NAV., Illus.). 40p. (J). pap. 9.00 (978-1-893354-17-3(2)) Salina Bookshelf.

Whitethorne, Baje, Sr. Father's Boots: Azhe'e bikenidoots'osii. Marvin, Yellowhair & Jerrold, Johnson, eds. Darlene, Redhair, tr. Whitethorne, Baje, Sr., illus. 2001. (ENG & NAV., Illus.). 32p. (gr. 1-6). 17.95 (978-1-893354-29-6(6)) Salina Bookshelf.

Whitethorne, Baje, Sr., illus. Sunpainters: Eclipse of the Navajo Sun. 2002. 32p. 17.95 (978-1-893354-33-3(4)) Salina Bookshelf.

INDIANS OF NORTH AMERICA—NAVAHO INDIANS—LEGENDS

Cohlene, Terri & Scholastic, Inc. Staff. Turquoise Boy. Reasoner, Charles, illus. 2004. 48p. (J). pap. 5.99 (978-0-439-63588-2(8)) Scholastic, Inc.

INDIANS OF NORTH AMERICA—NEZ PERCE INDIANS

Bial, Raymond. The Nez Perce. 2002. (Lifeways Ser.). (Illus.). 128p. (J). (gr. 5-9). lib. bdg. 34.21 (978-0-7614-1210-6(7), Benchmark Bks.) Cavendish, Marshall Corp.

Bond, Fred G. Flatboating on the Yellowstone, 1877. 1998. (Illus.). 64p. (YA). (gr. 6 up). 19.95 (978-1-886747-03-6(2)) Ward Hill Pr.

Boule, Mary Null. Native Americans of North America: Plateau Tribes: Cayuse, Walla Walla & Umatilla People. Harding, Virginia, ed. Liddell, Daniel & Basta, Mary, illus. 1999. 64p. (J). (gr. 3-6). pap. 7.95 (978-1-877599-54-5(9)) Merryant Pubs.

—Native Americans of North America: Plateau Tribes: Nez Perce People. Liddell, Daniel & Basta, Mary, illus. 1999. 64p. (J). (gr. 3-6). pap. 7.95 (978-1-877599-53-8(0)) Merryant Pubs.

King, David C. The Nez Perce. 2007. (First Americans Ser.). (Illus.). 48p. (J). (gr. 4-7). lib. bdg. 29.93 (***978-0-7614-2680-6(9)***, Benchmark Bks.) Cavendish, Marshall Corp.

Klingel, Cynthia Fitterer & Noyed, Robert B. Chief Joseph: Chief of the Nez Perce. 2002. (Spirit of America: Our People Ser.). (Illus.). 32p. (J). (gr. 2-6). 27.07 (978-1-56766-165-1(3)) Child's World, Inc.

MacGregor, Carol Lynn. Lewis & Clark's Bittersweet Crossing. Hoopes, Gaye, tr. Hoopes, Gaye, illus. 2004. 32p. (J). 16.95 (978-0-87004-437-3(0), 043700) Caxton Pr.

Miller, Connie R. The Nez Perce. 2003. (Digging up Native American History Ser.). (J). pap. (978-1-58417-110-2(3)); lib. bdg. (978-1-58417-047-1(6)) Lake Street Pubs.

Nelson, Sharlene & Nelson, Ted. The Nez Perce. 2004. (Watts Library Ser.). (Illus.). 63p. (J). (gr. 5-7). pap. 8.95 (978-0-531-16216-3(8), Watts, Franklin) Scholastic Library Publishing.

Nelson, Ted W. & Nelson, Sharlene P. The Nez Perce. 2003. (Watts Library: Indians of the Americas Ser.). (Illus.). 64p. (J). 25.50 (978-0-531-12169-6(0), Watts, Franklin) Scholastic Library Publishing.

Petra Press Staff. The Nez Perce. 2002. (First Reports). (Illus.). 48p. (J). (gr. 3 up). lib. bdg. 22.60 (978-0-7565-0187-7(3)) Compass Point Bks.

Raymer, Dottie. Welcome to Kaya's World 1764: Growing up in a Native American Homeland. Evert, Jodi, ed. 2003. (American Girls Collection). (Illus.). 64p. (J). (gr. 2 up). 16.95 (978-1-58485-722-8(6)) American Girl Publishing, Inc.

Rife, Douglas M. Chief Joseph Surrenders. Mitchell, Judy, ed. Smith, Bron, illus. 2002. 48p. (J). (gr. 4-8). pap. 6.95 (978-1-57310-348-0(9)) Teaching & Learning Co.

Ryan, Marla Felkins & Schmittroth, Linda, eds. Nez Perce. 2002. (Tribes of Native America Ser.). (Illus.). 48p. (J). 23.70 (978-1-56711-616-8(7), Blackbirch Pr., Inc.) Thomson Gale.

Stout, Mary A. Nez Perce. 2003. (Native American Peoples Ser.). (Illus.). 32p. (J). (gr. 4 up). lib. bdg. 24.67 (978-0-8368-3666-0(9)) Stevens, Gareth Inc.

Takacs, Stefanie. The Nez Perce. (True Bks.). (Illus.). (J). 2004. 47p. (gr. 3-5). pap. 6.95 (978-0-516-27825-4(8)); 2003. 48p. 25.00 (978-0-516-22779-5(3)) Scholastic Library Publishing. (Children's Pr.).

Troy, Don & Court, Rob. Art of Early Egypt. 2003. (Scribbles Institute : Art in Ancient Civilizations Ser.). 32p. (J). (gr. 1-5). 21.36 (978-1-56766-553-6(5)) Child's World, Inc.

INDIANS OF NORTH AMERICA—NEZ PERCE INDIANS—FICTION

Shaw, Janet Beeler. Changes for Kaya Bk. 6: A Winter Story. Farnsworth, Bill & McAliley, Susan, illus. 2002. (American Girls Collection: Bk. 6). 80p. (gr. 2-7). (J). 12.95 (978-1-58485-434-0(0)); 6.95 (978-1-58485-433-3(2)) American Girl Publishing, Inc.

—Kaya: An American Girl. 2002. (American Girls Collection). (Illus.). (J). (gr. 2). pap. 39.95 (978-1-58485-511-8(8)) American Girl Publishing, Inc.

—Kaya & Lone Dog Bk. 4: A Friendship Story. Farnsworth, Bill & McAliley, Susan, illus. 2002. (American Girls Collection: Bk. 4). 96p. (J). (gr. 2-7). 12.95 (978-1-58485-430-2(8)); 6.95 (978-1-58485-429-6(4)) American Girl Publishing, Inc.

—Kaya Shows the Way Bk. 5: A Sister Story. Farnsworth, Bill & McAliley, Susan, illus. 2002. (American Girls Collection: Bk. 5). 88p. (gr. 2-7). (J). 12.95 (978-1-58485-432-6(4)); 6.95 (978-1-58485-431-9(6)) American Girl Publishing, Inc.

—Kaya's Escape! A Survival Story, Bk. 2. Farnsworth, Bill & McAliley, Susan, illus. 2002. (American Girls Collection: Bk. 2). 88p. (gr. 2-7). (J). 12.95 (978-1-58485-426-5(X)); 6.95 (978-1-58485-425-8(1)) American Girl Publishing, Inc.

—Kaya's Hero Bk. 3: A Story of Giving. Farnsworth, Bill & McAliley, Susan, illus. 2002. (American Girls Collection: Bk. 3). 88p. (gr. 2-7). (J). 12.95 (978-1-58485-428-9(6)); 6.95 (978-1-58485-427-2(8)) American Girl Publishing, Inc.

—Meet Kaya. 2002. (gr. 3-6). lib. bdg. 14.10 (978-0-613-46227-3(0)) Tandem Library Bks.

—Meet Kaya: An American Girl. Farnsworth, Bill & McAliley, Susan, illus. 2002. (American Girls Collection: Bk. 1). 80p. (gr. 2-7). (J). 12.95 (978-1-58485-424-1(3)); 6.95 (978-1-58485-423-4(5)) American Girl Publishing, Inc.

INDIANS OF NORTH AMERICA—OGLALA INDIANS

Birchfield, D. L. Crazy Horse. 2002. (Raintree Biographies Ser.). (Illus.). 32p. (J). lib. bdg. 25.69 (978-0-7398-5673-4(1)) Raintree.

Cunningham, Chet. Chief Crazy Horse. 2005. (Biography Ser.). (Illus.). 112p. (gr. 6-12). lib. bdg. 27.93 (978-0-8225-4978-9(6)) Lerner Publishing Group.

Kavasch, E. Barrie. Lakota Sioux Children & Elders Talk Together. 1999. (Library of Intergenerational Learning). 24p. (J). (gr. k-4). lib. bdg. 19.95 (978-0-8239-5226-7(6), PowerKids Pr.) Rosen Publishing Group, Inc., The.

Oldfield, Jenny. Crazy Horse. 2001. (Illus.). 152p. (J). pap. 9.99 (978-0-340-71618-2(5), Hodder & Stoughton) Hodder General Publishing Division GBR. *Dist:* Trafalgar Square Publishing.

Todd, Anne M. Crazy Horse 1842-1877. 2002. (American Indian Biographies Ser.). (Illus.). 32p. (J). (gr. 3-4). lib. bdg. 23.93 (978-0-7368-1210-8(5), Blue Earth Bks.) Capstone Pr., Inc.

INDIANS OF NORTH AMERICA—OGLALA INDIANS—FICTION

Bruchac, Joseph. Crazy Horse's Vision. Nelson, S. D., illus. 2000. 40p. (YA). (gr. 1 up). 16.95 (978-1-880000-94-6(6)) Lee & Low Bks., Inc.

Kath, Sharon. Teepees on the Moon. 2001. 186p. (J). (gr. 8-12). 15.95 (978-0-936389-85-1(0)) Tudor Pubs., Inc.

INDIANS OF NORTH AMERICA—OJIBWAY INDIANS—FICTION

Carter, Alden R. Crescent Moon. 1999. 160p. (YA). (gr. 7 up). tchr. ed. 16.95 (978-0-8234-1521-2(X)) Holiday Hse., Inc.

—Crescent Moon. 1999. (J). 15.95 (978-0-590-29882-7(8)) Scholastic, Inc.

Erdrich, Louise. The Birchbark House. Erdrich, Louise, illus. 2002. (Illus.). 256p. (gr. 4-17). pap. 6.99 (978-0-7868-1454-1(3)) Hyperion Paperbacks for Children.

—The Game of Silence. 2005. (Illus.). 272p. (J). lib. bdg. 16.89 (978-0-06-029790-9(5)); 2005. (Illus.). 272p. 15.99 (978-0-06-029789-3(1)); 2006. 288p. (J). reprint ed. pap. 5.99 (978-0-06-441029-8(3), Harper Trophy) HarperCollins Pubs.

—The Game of Silence. l.t. ed. 2000. 272p. (YA). (gr. 7-12). 20.95 (978-0-7862-2178-3(X)) Thorndike Pr.

—The Last Report on the Miracles at Little No Horse: A Novel. 2002. (gr. 7-12). lib. bdg. 22.20 (978-0-613-62146-5(8)) Tandem Library Bks.

Ernst, Kathleen. Trouble at Fort la Pointe. 2000. (American Girl Collection). (Illus.). (J). (978-0-606-20956-4(5)) Tandem Library Bks.

Gerber, Carole. Firefly Night. Husted, Marty, illus. 2000. 32p. (J). (ps-1). 16.95 (978-1-58089-051-9(2)); pap. 6.95 (978-1-58089-066-3(0)) Charlesbridge Publishing, Inc.

—Firefly Night. Husted, Marty, illus. 2000. (J). (ps-3). lib. bdg. 15.25 (978-0-613-35117-1(7)) Tandem Library Bks.

—Firefly Night. 2000. (J). (978-0-606-19687-1(0)) Tandem Library Bks.

McCain, Becky Ray. Grandmother's Dreamcatcher. Schuett, Stacey, illus. 32p. (J). (gr. k-3). 2004. pap. 6.95 (978-0-8075-3032-0(8)); 1998. 15.95 (978-0-8075-3031-3(X)) Whitman, Albert & Co.

Pearsall, Shelley. Crooked River. 2007. 272p. (J). (gr. 5-9). pap. 6.50 (978-0-440-42101-6(2), Yearling) Random Hse. Children's Bks.

Slipperjack, Ruby. Little Voice. Racette, Sherry Farrell, illus. 2005. (In the Same Boat Ser.: No. 4). 256p. (J). (gr. 4-6). pap. 8.95 (978-1-55050-182-7(8)) Coteau Bks. CAN. *Dist:* Fitzhenry & Whiteside, Ltd.

Van Laan, Nancy. Shingebiss: An Ojibwe Legend. Bowen, Betsy, illus. 2002. 32p. (J). (gr. k-3). pap. 6.95 (978-0-618-21616-1(2)) Houghton Mifflin Co. Trade & Reference Div.

INDIANS OF NORTH AMERICA—ORIGIN

Lauber, Patricia. Who Came First? New Clues to Prehistoric Americans. 2003. (Illus.). 64p. (J). (gr. 5). 18.95 (978-0-7922-8228-0(0), National Geographic Children's Bks.) National Geographic Society.

Sattler, Helen Roney. The Earliest Americans. Zallinger, Jean Day, illus. 2001. 128p. (J). (gr. 4-6). pap. 8.95 (978-0-618-11146-6(8), Clarion Bks.) Houghton Mifflin Co. Trade & Reference Div.

INDIANS OF NORTH AMERICA—PAIUTE INDIANS—FICTION

Fuchs, Bernie. Ride Like the Wind: A Tale of the Pony Express. Fuchs, Bernie, illus. 2004. (Illus.). 32p. (J). pap. 16.95 (978-0-439-26645-1(9), Blue Sky Pr., The) Scholastic, Inc.

INDIANS OF NORTH AMERICA—PAPAGO INDIANS—FICTION

Cowley, Joy. Big Moon Tortilla. Strongbow, Dyanne, illus. 2003. 32p. (J). (gr. 1-4). 14.95 (978-1-56397-601-8(3)); (gr. 2-4). pap. 8.95 (978-1-59078-037-4(X)) Boyds Mills Pr.

—Big Moon Tortilla. 2002. (gr. 3-6). lib. bdg. 16.40 (978-0-613-58456-2(2)) Tandem Library Bks.

INDIANS OF NORTH AMERICA—PAWNEE INDIANS—FICTION

Remington, Gwen. The Pawnee. 2000. (Indigenous Peoples of North America Ser.). (Illus.). 96p. (YA). (gr. 4-12). 28.70 (978-1-56006-825-9(6), LML00902-178157, Lucent Bks.) Thomson Gale.

INDIANS OF NORTH AMERICA—PIEGAN INDIANS

Lacey, Theresa Jensen. The Blackfeet. 2005. (Indians of North America, Heritage Edition Ser.). (Illus.). 110p. (YA). (gr. 9-12). lib. bdg. 30.00 (978-0-7910-8596-7(1), Chelsea Hse.) Facts On File, Inc.

INDIANS OF NORTH AMERICA—POETRY

Bruce, Lisa & Waterhouse, Stephen R., illus. Engines, Engines: An Indian Counting Rhyme. 2001. 32p. (J). (ps-k). pap. 10.99 (978-0-7475-5013-6(1)) Bloomsbury Publishing Plc GBR. *Dist:* Independent Pubs. Group.

Bruchac, Joseph. The Earth under Sky Bear's Feet: Native American Poems of the Land. Locker, Thomas, illus. 1998. 32p. (J). (gr. k-3). pap. 6.99 (978-0-698-11647-4(X) , Putnam Juvenile) Penguin Group (USA) Inc.

Clark, Ann Nolan. In My Mother's House. Herrera, Velino, illus. 2004. 56p. (J). (gr. k-3). reprint ed. pap. 14.00 (978-0-7567-7104-1(8)) DIANE Publishing Co.

Longfellow, Henry Wadsworth & Remington, Frederic. The Song of Hiawatha. 2004. (Nonpareil Book Ser.). (Illus.). 288p. pap. 14.95 (978-1-56792-258-5(9)); 23.95 (978-1-56792-273-8(2)) Godine, David R. Pub.

McCauley, Marlene. Song of Kateri: Princess of the Eucharist. McCauley, R. Allan, ed. McCauley, Marlene & Children's Art-Friends of Kateri, illus. unabr. ed. 2005. 300p. (YA). (gr. 4-7). per. 14.95 (978-0-9633633-2-9(8)) Grace Hse. Publishing.

INDIANS OF NORTH AMERICA—POMO INDIANS

Gray-Kanatiiosh, Barbara A. Pomo. 2002. (Native Americans Ser.). (Illus.). 32p. (J). (gr. k-6). lib. bdg. 22.78 (978-1-57765-600-5(8) , Checkerboard Library) ABDO Publishing Co.

Ryan, Marla Felkins & Schmittroth, Linda, eds. Pomo. 2002. (Tribes of Native America Ser.). (Illus.). 32p. (J). 23.70 (978-1-56711-629-8(9) , Blackbirch Pr., Inc.) Thomson Gale.

INDIANS OF NORTH AMERICA—PUEBLO INDIANS

American Indian Nations: The Cherokee; The Iroquois; The Ojibwa; The Pueblo; The Seminole; The Sioux, 6 bks. (Illus.). (J). (gr. 3-4). lib. bdg. 101.70 (978-0-7368-1359-4(4) , Bridgestone Bks.) Capstone Pr., Inc.

Arnold, Caroline. The Ancient Cliff Dwellers of Mesa Verde. Hewett, Richard, illus. 2000. 64p. (YA). (gr. 7-7). pap. 7.95 (978-0-618-05149-6(X) , Clarion Bks.) Houghton Mifflin Co. Trade & Reference Div.

Bial, Raymond. The Pueblo. 1999. (Lifeways Ser.). (Illus.). 128p. (J). (gr. 5-9). lib. bdg. 34.21 (978-0-7614-0861-1(4) , Benchmark Bks.) Cavendish, Marshall Corp.

Flanagan, Alice K. The Pueblos. 1998. (True Bks.). (Illus.). 48p. (J). (gr. 3-5). 25.00 (978-0-516-20626-4(5) , Children's Pr.) Scholastic Library Publishing.

—The Pueblos. 1998. (Illus.). 47p. (J). (ps-ps). lib. bdg. 15.25 (978-0-613-37516-0(5)) Tandem Library Bks.

Folsom, Franklin. Red Power on the Rio Grande. 2003. (YA). pap. 13.95 (978-0-89992-156-3(6)) Council for Indian Education.

Gray-Kanatiiosh, Barbara A. Pueblo. 2002. (Native Americans Ser.). (Illus.). 32p. (J). (gr. k-6). lib. bdg. 22.78 (978-1-57765-606-7(7) , Checkerboard Library) ABDO Publishing Co.

Harcourt School Publishers Staff. Pueblo Storyteller Dolls. 3rd ed. 2002. (Horizons Ser.). (Illus.). (J). pap. 3.70 (978-0-15-333210-4(7)) Harcourt Schl. Pubs.

Kalman, Bobbie. Life in a Pueblo. 2003. (Native Nations of North America Ser.). (Illus.). 32p. (J). (gr. 3-9). pap. (978-0-7787-0467-6(X)); (gr. 5-9). (978-0-7787-0375-4(4)) Crabtree Publishing Co.

—Life in a Pueblo. 2003. (gr. 3-6). lib. bdg. 17.60 (978-0-613-59131-7(3)) Tandem Library Bks.

Lavender, David. Mother Earth, Father Sky: The Pueblo Indians of the American Southwest. 1998. (Illus.). 96p. (J). (gr. 4-7). tchr. ed. 16.95 (978-0-8234-1365-2(9)) Holiday Hse., Inc.

Levy, Janey. Native American Art from the Pueblos. 2003. (Reading Room Collection). (Illus.). 24p. (J). lib. bdg. 18.75 (978-0-8239-3702-8(X)) Rosen Publishing Group, Inc., The.

Lourie, Peter. Anasazi: Exploring the Mysteries of Chaco Canyon. 2003. (Illus.). 48p. (J). (gr. 4-6). 19.95 (978-1-56397-972-9(1)) Boyds Mills Pr.

McIntosh, Kenneth. Pueblo. 2003. (North American Indians Today Ser.). (Illus.). 96p. (J). lib. bdg. (978-1-59084-676-6(1)) Mason Crest Pubs.

McLeese, Tex. Lucha con Novillos. Palacios, Argentina, tr. Tr. of Steer Wrestling. (SPA., Illus.). 24p. (J). (gr. 1-3). lib. bdg. 19.27 (978-1-57103-385-7(8)) Rourke Publishing, LLC.

Peterson, David. Chaco Culture National Historical Park. 1999. (True Bks.). (Illus.). 48p. (J). (gr. 3-5). 25.00 (978-0-516-20942-5(6) , Children's Pr.) Scholastic Library Publishing.

Petra Press Staff. The Pueblo. 2001. (First Reports). (Illus.). 48p. (J). (gr. 3 up). lib. bdg. 22.60 (978-0-7565-0082-5(0) Compass Point Bks.

Rasmussen, R. Kent. Pueblo. Kurnizki, Kimberly L. Dawson, illus. 2001. (Native American Homes Ser.). 32p. (J). (gr. 3-6). lib. bdg. 28.50 (978-1-55916-249-4(X)) Rourke Publishing, LLC.

Ross, Pamela. The Pueblo Indians. 1999. (Native Peoples Ser.). (Illus.). 24p. (J). (gr. 2-3). lib. bdg. 18.60 (978-0-7368-0079-2(4) , Bridgestone Bks.) Capstone Pr., Inc.

Ryan, Marla Felkins & Schmittroth, Linda, eds. Pueblo. 2002. (Tribes of Native America Ser.). (Illus.). 48p. (J). 23.70 (978-1-56711-617-5(5) , Blackbirch Pr., Inc.) Thomson Gale.

Shuter, Jane. Mesa Verde. (Visiting the Past Ser.). (Illus.). 32p. (J). (gr. 5-7). 2002. pap. 6.95 (978-1-58810-407-6(9) , 91182); 1999. lib. bdg. 24.22 (978-1-57572-858-2(3)) Heinemann Library.

Sloan, Frank, ed. Anasazis. 2001. (Ancient Civilizations Ser.). (Illus.). 48p. (J). (gr. 4-6). lib. bdg. 22.83 (978-0-7398-3575-3(0)) Raintree.

INDIANS OF NORTH AMERICA—PUEBLO INDIANS—ANTIQUITIES

Ancient Civilizations, 10 vols., Set. 2000. (Illus.). (YA). (gr. 5-9). lib. bdg. 319.00 (978-0-7172-9471-8(4) , Grolier) Scholastic Library Publishing.

Anderson, Dale. The Anasazi Culture at Mesa Verde. 2003. (Landmark Events in American History Ser.). (Illus.). 48p. (J). (gr. 5 up). pap. 14.95 (978-0-8368-5399-5(7)); lib. bdg. 30.00 (978-0-8368-5371-1(7)) Stevens, Gareth Inc. (World Almanac Library).

Crewe, Sabrina & Anderson, Dale. The Anasazi Culture at Mesa Verde. 2003. (Events That Shaped America Ser.). (Illus.). 32p. (J). (gr. 3 up). lib. bdg. 24.67 (978-0-8368-3390-4(2)) Stevens, Gareth Inc.

Dewey, Jennifer Owings. Stories on Stone: Rock Art Images from the Ancient Ones. 2003. (Illus.). 32p. 16.95 (978-0-8263-3024-6(X)) Univ. of New Mexico Pr.

Goodman, Susan E. Digging into Southwest Archaeology. 2000. (Ultimate Field Trip Ser.: Vol. 2). (YA). 13.79 (978-0-606-19252-1(2)) Tandem Library Bks.

Lavender, David. Mother Earth, Father Sky: The Pueblo Indians of the American Southwest. 1998. (Illus.). 96p. (J). (gr. 4-7). tchr. ed. 16.95 (978-0-8234-1365-2(9)) Holiday Hse., Inc.

Sloan, Frank, ed. Ancient Civilizations, 6 bks., Set. Incl. Anasazis. lib. bdg. 22.83 (978-0-7398-3575-3(0)); China. Deedrick, Tami. lib. bdg. 22.83 (978-0-7398-3580-7(7)); Egypt. Steele, Christy. lib. bdg. 22.83 (978-0-7398-3576-0(9)); Greece. Steele, Christy. lib. bdg. 22.83 (978-0-7398-3577-7(7)); Maya. Deedrick, Tami. lib. bdg. 22.83 (978-0-7398-3585-2(8)); Rome. Steele, Christy. lib. bdg. 22.83 (978-0-7398-3578-4(5)); (J). (gr. 4-7). (Illus.). 48p. 2001. Set lib. bdg. 95.88 (978-0-7398-3587-6(4)) Raintree.

Young, Robert. A Personal Tour of Mesa Verde. 1999. (How It Was Ser.). (Illus.). 64p. (J). (gr. 4-6). lib. bdg. (978-0-8225-3577-5(7) , Lerner Pubns.) Lerner Publishing Group.

INDIANS OF NORTH AMERICA—PUEBLO INDIANS—FICTION

Bronson, Wilfrid S. Pinto's Journey. 2007. (J). pap. ***(978-0-86534-557-7(0))*** Sunstone Pr.

Bryant, Kathleen. Kokopelli's Gift. Sisneros, Michelle Tsosie, illus. 2002. 32p. (J). 15.95 (978-1-885772-29-9(7)) Kiva Publishing, Inc.

Kita, Suzanne. The Mystery of the Anasazi at Frijoles Canyon. Chang, Glenn K. M., photos by. 2002. (Illus.). 105p. (J). 14.95 (978-1-885772-26-8(2)) Kiva Publishing, Inc.

Lehr, Norma. Dance of the Crystal Skull. rev. exp. ed. 2003. (Illus.). 238p. (J). (gr. 3-7). lib. bdg. 15.95 (978-0-87358-724-2(3) , Rising Moon Bks. for Young Readers) Northland Publishing.

—Dance of the Crystal Skull. 1999. (Illus.). (J). (978-0-606-18310-9(8)) Tandem Library Bks.

Lyon, George Ella. Dreamplace. 1998. (J). 13.75 (978-0-606-13348-7(8)) Tandem Library Bks.

McDermott, Gerald. Arrow to the Sun. 30th anniv. ed. 2004. 48p. (J). (gr. k). 16.99 (978-0-670-05938-6(2) , Viking Juvenile) Penguin Group (USA) Inc.

—Arrow to the Sun: A Pueblo Indian Tale. 2002. 48p. 15.95 (978-957-632-204-4(9)) Formosan Magazine Pr., Ltd. CHN. *Dist:* Shen's Bks.

Montgomery, R. A. Indian Trail. 2007. (Choose Your Own Adventure - Dragonlarks Ser.). (Illus.). 64p. (J). pap. 5.99 ***(978-1-933390-53-6(0))*** Chooseco LLC.

Preston, Douglas & Child, Lincoln. Thunderhead. 2000. (gr. 7-12). lib. bdg. 15.90 (978-0-613-28102-7(0)) Tandem Library Bks.

Vick, Helen Hughes. Shadow. 1998. (Courage of the Stone Ser.). 128p. (gr. 4-9). 15.95 (978-1-57098-218-7(X)) Rinehart, Roberts Pubs.

INDIANS OF NORTH AMERICA—PUEBLO INDIANS—LEGENDS

Haley, Gail E., tr. & illus. Kokopelli, Drum in Belly. Haley, Gail E., illus. 2003. (J). 18.95 (978-0-86541-068-8(2)); pap. 12.95 (978-0-86541-069-5(0)) Filter Pr., LLC.

INDIANS OF NORTH AMERICA—RECREATIONS

see Indians of North America—Games

INDIANS OF NORTH AMERICA—RELIGION AND MYTHOLOGY

see also Indian Dance; Totems and Totemism

Berk, Ari & Anderson, Carolyn Dunn. Coyote Speaks: Wonders of the Native American World. 2008. (J). ***(978-0-8109-9372-3(4))*** , Abrams Bks. for Young Readers) Abrams, Harry N. , Inc.

Dalal, Anita. Myths of Native Americans. 2001. (Mythic World Ser.). (Illus.). 48p. (J). lib. bdg. 27.12 (978-0-7398-3190-8(9)) Raintree.

Golston, Sydele E. Changing Woman of the Apache: Women's Lives in Past & Present. 2001. (Illus.). 144p. (J). (gr. 5-7). reprint ed. 25.00 (978-0-7881-9686-7(3)) DIANE Publishing Co.

Kessler, Timothy. When God Made the Dakotas. Morin, Paul, illus. 2006. 32p. (J). 17.00 (978-0-8028-5275-5(0) , Eerdmans Bks For Young Readers) Eerdmans, William B. Publishing Co.

Novesky, Amy & Wedman, Belgin K. Elephant Prince: The Story of Ganesh. 2005. (Illus.). 32p. (J). 16.95 (978-1-932771-16-9(6)) Mandala Publishing.

Peacock, Thomas & Wisuri, Marlene. The Good Path. 2004. (Illus.). 128p. pap. 17.95 (978-1-890434-53-3(1)) Afton Historical Society Pr.

Perez, Jaime O. Traditional Ceremonial Pathways: A Pilgrim's Journey. l.t. ed. 2003. (Illus.). 170p. per. 9.99 net. (978-0-9729612-0-2(8) , 44444) Sun Circle Pr.

Philip, Neil. The Great Mystery: Myths of Native America. 2001. (Illus.). 160p. (J). (gr. 7 up). 25.00 (978-0-395-98405-5(X) , Clarion Bks.) Houghton Mifflin Co. Trade & Reference Div.

Schomp, Virginia. The Native Americans. 2007. (Myths of the World Ser.). 96p. (J). lib. bdg. 32.79 ***(978-0-7614-2550-2(0)*** , Benchmark Bks.) Cavendish, Marshall Corp.

Staeger, Rob. Native American Religions. 2002. (Native American Life Ser.). (Illus.). 64p. (YA). (gr. 5 up). lib. bdg. (978-1-59084-122-8(0)) Mason Crest Pubs.

Webster, M. L. On the Trail Made of Dawn: Native American Creation Stories. 2001. (Illus.). 96p. (J). (gr. 4 up). 19.50 (978-0-208-02497-8(2) , Linnet Bks.) Shoe String Pr., Inc.

Wolfson, Evelyn. American Indian Mythology. Bock, William Sauts, illus. 2001. (Mythology Ser.). 128p. (YA). (gr. 6-12). lib. bdg. 26.60 (978-0-7660-1411-4(8)) Enslow Pubs., Inc.

INDIANS OF NORTH AMERICA—SAUK INDIANS

Poulakidas, Georgene. Black Hawk's War. 2004. (Primary Sources of American Wars Ser.). (Illus.). 24p. (J). lib. bdg. (978-1-4042-2682-1(6)) Rosen Publishing Group, Inc., The.

INDIANS OF NORTH AMERICA—SCHOOLS

see Indians of North America—Education

INDIANS OF NORTH AMERICA—SEMINOLE INDIANS

American Indian Nations: The Cherokee; The Iroquois; The Ojibwa; The Pueblo; The Seminole; The Sioux, 6 bks. (Illus.). (J). (gr. 3-4). lib. bdg. 101.70 (978-0-7368-1359-4(4) , Bridgestone Bks.) Capstone Pr., Inc.

Bial, Raymond. The Seminole. 1999. (Lifeways Ser.). (Illus.). 128p. (J). (gr. 5-9). lib. bdg. 34.21 (978-0-7614-0862-8(2) , Benchmark Bks.) Cavendish, Marshall Corp.

Birchfield, D. L. Seminole. 2003. (Native American Peoples Ser.). (Illus.). 32p. (J). (gr. 4 up). lib. bdg. 24.67 (978-0-8368-3668-4(5)) Stevens, Gareth Inc.

Englar, Mary. The Pueblo: Farmers of the Southwest. 2002. (American Indian Nations Ser.). (Illus.). 48p. (J). (gr. 3-4). lib. bdg. 22.60 (978-0-7368-1357-0(8) , Bridgestone Bks.) Capstone Pr., Inc.

—The Seminole: The First People in Florida. 2002. (American Indian Nations Ser.). (Illus.). 48p. (J). (gr. 3-4). lib. bdg. 22.60 (978-0-7368-1358-7(6) , Bridgestone Bks.) Capstone Pr., Inc.

Kavasch, E. Barrie. Seminole Children & Elders Talk Together. 1999. (Library of Intergenerational Learning). 24p. (J). (gr. k-4). lib. bdg. 19.95 (978-0-8239-5229-8(0) , PowerKids Pr.) Rosen Publishing Group, Inc., The.

Koestler-Grack, Rachel A. Osceola 1804-1838. 2002. (American Indian Biographies Ser.). (Illus.). 32p. (J). (gr. 3-4). lib. bdg. 23.93 (978-0-7368-1211-5(3) , Blue Earth Bks.) Capstone Pr., Inc.

Libal, Joyce. Seminoles. 2003. (North American Indians Today Ser.). (Illus.). 96p. (J). lib. bdg. (978-1-59084-677-3(X)) Mason Crest Pubs.

Petra Press Staff. The Seminole. 2001. (First Reports). (Illus.). 48p. (J). (gr. 3 up). lib. bdg. 22.60 (978-0-7565-0083-2(4)) Compass Point Bks.

Ryan, Marla Felkins & Schmittroth, Linda, eds. Seminole. 2002. (Tribes of Native America Ser.). (Illus.). 32p. (J). 23.70 (978-1-56711-630-4(2) , Blackbirch Pr., Inc.) Thomson Gale.

Sonneborn, Liz. Seminole. 2002. (gr. 5-8). lib. bdg. 17.60 (978-0-613-54354-5(8)) Tandem Library Bks.

—The Seminole: Indians of the Americas. 2002. (Watts Library). (J). (gr. 5-7). pap. 8.95 (978-0-531-16228-6(1)); (Illus.). 64p. 25.50 (978-0-531-13951-6(4)) Scholastic Library Publishing. (Watts, Franklin).

Takacs, Stefanie. The Seminole. (True Bks.). (J). 2004. (gr. 3-5). pap. 6.95 (978-0-516-27908-4(4)); 2003. (Illus.). 48p. 25.00 (978-0-516-22781-8(5)) Scholastic Library Publishing. (Children's Pr.).

Todd, Anne M. Osceola. 2004. (Illus.). 32p. (J). pap. 7.50 (978-1-4034-5010-4(2)); lib. bdg. 24.22 (978-1-4034-5003-6(X)) Heinemann Library.

Weisman, Brent R. Unconquered People: Florida's Seminole & Miccosukee Indians. 1999. (Native Peoples, Cultures, & Places of the Southeastern United States Ser.). (Illus.). 184p. (YA). pap. 19.95 (978-0-8130-1663-4(0)) Univ. Pr. of Florida.

Wickman, Patricia R. Seminole Colors: A Coloring & Learning Book for Young Minds. 1999. (Illus.). 36p. (J). (gr. 1-6). (978-0-9659981-3-0(4)) Seminole Tribe of Florida, Dept. of Anthropology & Genealogy.

Yacowitz, Caryn. Seminole. 2003. (gr. 3-6). lib. bdg. 15.25 (978-0-613-60926-5(3)) Tandem Library Bks.

INDIANS OF NORTH AMERICA—SEMINOLE INDIANS—FICTION

Moeller, Kathleen H. Hoketichee & the Manatee. Soper, Pat, illus. 1998. (Books for Young Learners). 16p. (J). (gr. k-2). pap. 5.00 (978-1-57274-117-1(1) , A2745) Owen, Richard C. Pubs., Inc.

Raffa, Edwina & Rigsby, Annelle. Escape to the Everglades. 2006. (Illus.). 100p. (J). 12.95 (978-1-56164-351-6(3)) Pineapple Pr., Inc.

INDIANS OF NORTH AMERICA—SENECA INDIANS

Van Steenwyck, Elizabeth. Seneca Chief, Army General: A Story about Ely Parker. 2001. (gr. 3-6). lib. bdg. 15.25 (978-0-613-68385-2(4)) Tandem Library Bks.

Van Steenwyk, Elizabeth. Seneca Chief, Army General: A Story about Ely Parker. Ritz, Karen, illus. 2000. (Creative Minds Biographies Ser.). 64p. (J). (gr. 3-6). lib. bdg. 22.60 (978-1-57505-431-5(0) , Carolrhoda Bks.) Lerner Publishing Group.

INDIANS OF NORTH AMERICA—SENECA INDIANS—FICTION

Charles, Veronika Martenova. Maiden of the Mist: A Legend of Niagara Falls. 2001. (gr. 3-6). lib. bdg. 15.25 (978-0-613-52136-9(6)) Tandem Library Bks.

INDIANS OF NORTH AMERICA—SHAWNEE INDIANS

De Capua, Sarah. The Shawnee. 2007. (First Americans Ser.). 48p. (J). lib. bdg. 29.93 ***(978-0-7614-2682-0(5)*** , Benchmark Bks.) Cavendish, Marshall Corp.

Flanagan, Alice K. The Shawnee. 1998. (True Bks.). (Illus.). 48p. (J). (gr. 3-5). 25.00 (978-0-516-20627-1(3) , Children's Pr.) Scholastic Library Publishing.

Mattern, Joanne. The Shawnee Indians. 2001. (Native Peoples Ser.). (Illus.). 24p. (J). (gr. 2-3). lib. bdg. 18.60 (978-0-7368-0833-0(7) , Bridgestone Bks.) Capstone Pr., Inc.

Petra Press Staff. The Shawnee. 2002. (First Reports). (Illus.). 48p. (J). (gr. 3 up). lib. bdg. 22.60 (978-0-7565-0188-4(1)) Compass Point Bks.

Ryan, Marla Felkins & Schmittroth, Linda, eds. Shawnee. 2002. (Tribes of Native America Ser.). (Illus.). 32p. (J). 23.70 (978-1-56711-631-1(0) , Blackbirch Pr., Inc.) Thomson Gale.

Yacowitz, Caryn. Shawnee Indians. 2003. (Native Americans Ser.). (Illus.). 32p. (J). pap. 7.50 (978-1-4034-4175-1(8)); lib. bdg. 24.22 (978-1-4034-0867-9(X)) Heinemann Library.

INDIANS OF NORTH AMERICA—SHAWNEE INDIANS—BIOGRAPHY

Aller, Susan Bivin. Tecumseh. 2004. (History Maker Bios Ser.). (J). pap. 6.95 (978-0-8225-2073-3(7)); (Illus.). 48p. 26.60 (978-0-8225-0699-7(8) , Carolrhoda Bks.) Lerner Publishing Group.

Koestler-Grack, Rachel A. Tecumseh 1768-1813. 2002. (American Indian Biographies Ser.). (Illus.). 32p. (J). (gr. 3-4). lib. bdg. 23.93 (978-0-7368-1212-2(1) , Blue Earth Bks.) Capstone Pr., Inc.

Todd, Anne M. Chief Tecumseh. 2004. (Illus.). 32p. (J). pap. 7.50 (978-1-4034-5009-8(9)); lib. bdg. 24.22 (978-1-4034-5002-9(1)) Heinemann Library.

INDIANS OF NORTH AMERICA—SHAWNEE INDIANS—FICTION

Bruchac, Joseph. The Dark Pond. Comport, Sally Wern, illus. 160p. (J). (gr. 5 up). 2005. pap. 5.99 (978-0-06-052998-7(9) , Harper Trophy); 2004. lib. bdg. 16.89 (978-0-06-052997-0(0)) HarperCollins Pubs.

Rinaldi, Ann. The Second Bend in the River. 1999. 288p. (J). (gr. 5-9). pap. 4.99 (978-0-590-74259-7(0)) Scholastic, Inc.

INDIANS OF NORTH AMERICA—SIGN LANGUAGE

see Indian Sign Language

INDIANS OF NORTH AMERICA—SIKSIKA INDIANS—FICTION

Ackerman, Ned. Spirit Horse. 2002. 176p. (J). pap. 4.99 (978-0-590-39720-9(6)) Scholastic, Inc.

Oke, Janette. Drums of Change: The Story of Running Fawn. 2003. (Classics for Girls Ser.). (Illus.). 176p. (J). 9.99 (978-0-7642-2714-1(9)) Bethany Hse. Pubs.

INDIANS OF NORTH AMERICA—SIKSIKA INDIANS

Bial, Raymond. The Blackfeet. 2002. (Lifeways Ser.). (Illus.). 128p. (J). 34.21 (978-0-7614-1416-2(9) , Benchmark Bks.) Cavendish, Marshall Corp.

Gray-Kanatiiosh, Barbara A. Blackfoot. 2002. (Native Americans Ser.). (Illus.). 32p. (J). (gr. k-6). lib. bdg. 22.78 (978-1-57765-604-3(0) , Checkerboard Library) ABDO Publishing Co.

Lacey, Theresa Jensen. The Blackfeet. 2005. (Indians of North America, Heritage Edition Ser.). (Illus.). 110p. (YA). (gr. 9-12). lib. bdg. 30.00 (978-0-7910-8596-7(1) , Chelsea Hse.) Facts On File, Inc.

Lassieur, Allison. The Blackfeet Nation. 2001. (Native Peoples Ser.). (Illus.). 24p. (J). (gr. 2-3). lib. bdg. 18.60 (978-0-7368-0946-7(5) , Bridgestone Bks.) Capstone Pr., Inc.

Petra Press Staff. The Blackfeet. 2001. (First Reports). (Illus.). 48p. (J). (gr. 3 up). lib. bdg. 22.60 (978-0-7565-0078-8(8)) Compass Point Bks.

Ryan, Marla Felkins & Schmittroth, Linda, eds. Blackfoot. 2002. (Tribes of Native America Ser.). (Illus.). 32p. (J). 23.70 (978-1-56711-605-2(1) , Blackbirch Pr., Inc.) Thomson Gale.

INDIANS OF NORTH AMERICA—SIOUX INDIANS

American Indian Nations: The Cherokee; The Iroquois; The Ojibwa; The Pueblo; The Seminole; The Sioux, 6 bks. (Illus.). (J). (gr. 3-4). lib. bdg. 101.70 (978-0-7368-1359-4(4) , Bridgestone Bks.) Capstone Pr., Inc.

Kops, Deborah. Native AMER of the Plains. 2006. (Navigators Ser.). (J). pap. 42.00 ***(978-1-4108-6250-1(X))*** Benchmark Education Co.

LoneHill, Karen. Sioux. 2003. (North American Indians Today Ser.). (Illus.). 96p. (J). lib. bdg. (978-1-59084-678-0(8)) Mason Crest Pubs.

McNamara, Margaret. Native AMER of the Plains: The Lakota. 2006. pap. 39.00 ***(978-1-4108-6439-0(1))*** Benchmark Education Co.

Miller, Connie R. The Lakota. 2003. (Digging up Native American History Ser.). (J). lib. bdg. (978-1-58417-046-4(8)) Lake Street Pubs.

Santella, Andrew. The Lakota Sioux. 2001. (True Bks.). (Illus.). 48p. (J). (gr. 3-5). pap. 6.95 (978-0-516-27323-5(X) , Children's Pr.) Scholastic Library Publishing.

—The Lakota Sioux: American Indians. 2001. (American Indians Ser.). (Illus.). 48p. (J). (gr. 3-5). 25.00 (978-0-516-22218-9(X) , Children's Pr.) Scholastic Library Publishing.

INDIANS OF NORTH AMERICA—SIOUX INDIANS—FICTION

Bunting, Eve. Moonstick: The Seasons of the Sioux. Sandford, John B., illus. 2000. (Trophy Picture Bk.). 32p. (J). (gr. k-4). pap. 6.99 (978-0-06-443619-9(5) , Harper Trophy) HarperCollins Pubs.

—Moonstick: The Seasons of the Sioux. 2000. (978-0-606-18706-0(5)); (gr. 3-6). lib. bdg. 14.10 (978-0-613-34014-4(0)) Tandem Library Bks.

Kretzer-Malvehy, Terry. Passage to Little Bighorn. 1999. (978-0-606-18313-0(2)) Tandem Library Bks.

INDIANS OF NORTH AMERICA—SOCIAL CONDITIONS

America's First Peoples, 10 bks. Incl. Cherokee : Native Basket Weavers. De Angelis, Therese. lib. bdg. 23.93 (978-0-7368-1535-2(X)); Choctaw : Stickball Players of the South. Koestler-Grack, Rachel A. lib. bdg. 23.93 (978-0-7368-2170-4(8)); Inuit : Ivory Carvers of the Far North. Koestler-Grack, Rachel A. lib. bdg. 23.93 (978-0-7368-2171-1(6)); Iroquois : Longhouse Builders. Koestler-Grack, Rachel A. lib. bdg. 23.93 (978-0-7368-1536-9(8)); Navajo : Weavers of the Southwest. De Angelis, Therese. lib. bdg. 23.93 (978-0-7368-2172-8(4)); Ojibwa : Wild Rice Gatherers. De Angelis, Therese. lib. bdg. 23.93 (978-0-7368-1537-6(6)); Pueblo : Southwestern Potters. Englar, Mary. lib. bdg. 23.93 (978-0-7368-1538-3(4)); Seminole : Patchworkers of the Everglades. Koestler-Grack, Rachel A. lib. bdg. 23.93 (978-0-7368-1539-0(2)); Shoshone : Pine Nut Harvesters of the Great Basin. Keller, Kristin Thoennes. lib. bdg. 23.93 (978-0-7368-2173-5(2)); Sioux : Nomadic Buffalo Hunters. Koestler-Grack, Rachel A. lib. bdg. 23.93 (978-0-7368-1540-6(6)); 32p. (J). (gr. 2-3). (Illus.). 2003. Set lib. bdg. 239.30 (978-0-7368-2339-5(5) , Bridgestone Bks.) Capstone Pr., Inc.

Bruchac, Joseph. Buffalo Song. Farnsworth, Bill, illus. 2008. (J). Lee & Low Bks., Inc.

Kalman, Bobbie. Native Homes. 2001. (J). (978-0-606-21345-5(7)); (gr. 3-6). lib. bdg. 16.40 (978-0-613-43480-5(3)) Tandem Library Bks.

Kelley, Alison Turnbull. Native Americans & the United States. 2002. (People at Odds Ser.). (Illus.). 112p. (J). (gr. 5 up). 30.00 (978-0-7910-6707-9(6) , Chelsea Hse.) Facts On File, Inc.

Keoke, Emory Dean & Porterfield, Kay Marie. American Indian Contributions to the World. 2005. (American Indian Contributions to the World Ser.). (Illus.). 160p. (gr. 4-9). (J). 35.00 (978-0-8160-5395-7(2)); (YA). 35.00 (978-0-8160-5397-1(9)) Facts On File, Inc.

Sioux, Tracee. Native American Migration. 2004. (Primary Sources of Immigration & Migration in America Ser.). (Illus.). 24p. (J). lib. bdg. 19.95 (978-0-8239-6825-1(1) , PowerKids Pr.) Rosen Publishing Group, Inc., The.

Thompson, Linda. People of the Plains & Prairies. 2003. (Native People, Native Lands Ser.). (Illus.). 48p. (J). 29.93 (978-1-58952-757-7(7)) Rourke Publishing, LLC.

INDIANS OF NORTH AMERICA—SOCIAL LIFE AND CUSTOMS

see also Indian Dance; Indians of North America—Games

Adil, Janeen R. The Northeast Indians: Daily Life in the 1500s. 2006. (Bridgestone Books). (Illus.). 24p. (J). (978-0-7368-4314-0(0)) Capstone Pr., Inc.

Aloian, Molly & Kalman, Bobbie. Life of the California Coast Nations. 2004. (Native Nations of North America Ser.). (Illus.). 32p. (J). (978-0-7787-0382-2(7)); pap. (978-0-7787-0474-4(2)) Crabtree Publishing Co.

American Indian Art & Culture. 2005. (Illus.). 32p. (gr. 3-5). pap. 153.00 (978-0-7910-7959-1(7) , Chelsea Hse.) Facts On File, Inc.

American Indian Lives, 8 vols., Set. Incl. Artists & Craftspeople. Hirschfelder, Arlene. 160p. 1994. 25.00 (978-0-8160-2960-0(1)); Athletes. Aaseng, Nathan. 144p. 1995. 25.00 (978-0-8160-3019-4(7)); Performers. Sonneborn, Liz. 128p. 1995. 25.00 (978-0-8160-3045-3(6)); Political Leaders & Peacemakers. Sherrow, Victoria. 160p. 1994. 25.00 (978-0-8160-2943-3(1)); Reformers & Activists. Nielsen, Nancy J. 128p. 1997. 25.00 (978-0-8160-3440-6(0)); Scholars, Writers & Professionals. Bolton, Jonathan W. & Wilson, Claire M. 160p. 1994. 25.00 (978-0-8160-2896-2(6)); Spiritual Leaders. Walker, Paul R. 160p. 1994. 25.00 (978-0-8160-2875-7(3)); (Illus.). (YA). (gr. 5-12). 2001. 175.00 (978-0-8160-4631-7(X)) Facts On File, Inc.

Bedry, Christa. The Pueblo. 2004. (American Indian Art & Culture Ser.). (Illus.). 32p. (J). (gr. 3-5). 25.50 (978-0-7910-7964-5(3) , Chelsea Hse.) Facts On File, Inc.

—The Pueblo. 2003. (American Indian Art & Culture Ser.). (Illus.). 32p. (J). pap. (978-1-59036-179-5(2)) Weigl Pubs., Inc.

Behnke, Alison. The Apaches. 2007. (Native American Histories Ser.). (Illus.). 56p. (J). 27.93 (978-0-8225-5915-3(3) , Lerner Pubns.) Lerner Publishing Group.

Belarde-Lewis, Miranda. Meet Lydia: A Native Girl from Southeast Alaska. Harrington, John, photos by. 2004. (My World—Young Native Americans Today Ser.). (Illus.). 48p. (J). 15.95 (978-1-57178-147-5(1)) Council Oak Bks.

Benjamin, Lisa. People of the Wetlands. 2005. (Voices Reading Ser.). (Illus.). 32p. (J). (978-0-7367-2947-5(X)) Zaner-Bloser, Inc.

Berk, Ari & Anderson, Carolyn Dunn. Coyote Speaks: Wonders of the Native American World. 2008. (J). (***978-0-8109-9372-3(4)*** , Abrams Bks. for Young Readers) Abrams, Harry N., Inc.

Bial, Raymond. The Blackfeet. 2002. (Lifeways Ser.). (Illus.). 128p. (J). 34.21 (978-0-7614-1416-2(9) , Benchmark Bks.) Cavendish, Marshall Corp.

—The Choctaw. 2002. (Lifeways Ser.). (Illus.). 128p. (J). 34.21 (978-0-7614-1413-1(4) , Benchmark Bks.) Cavendish, Marshall Corp.

—Lifeways - Group 2, 4 bks., Set. Incl. Comanche. lib. bdg. 34.21 (978-0-7614-0864-2(9)); Ojibwe. lib. bdg. 34.21 (978-0-7614-0863-5(0)); Pueblo. lib. bdg. 34.21 (978-0-7614-0861-1(4)); Seminole. lib. bdg. 34.21 (978-0-7614-0862-8(2)); 128p. (J). (gr. 5-9). 1999. (Illus.). 2000. Set lib. bdg. 136.86 (978-0-7614-0860-4(6) , Benchmark Bks.) Cavendish, Marshall Corp.

—Lifeways - Group 4, 4 bks., Set. Incl. Inuit. 2001. lib. bdg. 34.21 (978-0-7614-1212-0(3)); Nez Perce. 2002. lib. bdg. 34.21 (978-0-7614-1210-6(7)); Powhatan. 2000. lib. bdg. 34.21 (978-0-7614-1209-0(3)); Shoshone. 2001. lib. bdg. 34.21 (978-0-7614-1211-3(5)); 128p. (J). (gr. 5-9). (Illus.). 2001. 136.86 (978-0-7614-1208-3(5) , Benchmark Bks.) Cavendish, Marshall Corp.

—The Powhatan. 2000. (Lifeways Ser.). (Illus.). 128p. (J). (gr. 5-9). lib. bdg. 34.21 (978-0-7614-1209-0(3) , Benchmark Bks.) Cavendish, Marshall Corp.

—The Shoshone. 2001. (Lifeways Ser.). (Illus.). 128p. (J). (gr. 5-9). lib. bdg. 34.21 (978-0-7614-1211-3(5) , Benchmark Bks.) Cavendish, Marshall Corp.

—The Tlingit. 2002. (Lifeways Ser.). (Illus.). 128p. (J). 34.21 (978-0-7614-1414-8(2) , Benchmark Bks.) Cavendish, Marshall Corp.

Bishop, Amanda & Kalman, Bobbie. Life of the Navajo. 2003. (Native Nations of North America Ser.). (Illus.). 32p. (J). (gr. 5). lib. bdg. (978-0-7787-0376-1(2)) Crabtree Publishing Co.

—Nations of the Northwest Coast. 2003. (Native Nations of North America Ser.). (Illus.). 32p. (J). (gr. 5). (978-0-7787-0378-5(9)) Crabtree Publishing Co.

Bonvillain, Nancy. The Zuni. 2005. (Indians of North America, Heritage Edition Ser.). (Illus.). 127p. (YA). (gr. 7-12). lib. bdg. 30.00 (978-0-7910-8594-3(5) , Chelsea Hse.) Facts On File, Inc.

Boule, Mary Null. California Native American Tribes: Mohave Tribe, 28 booklets. Liddell, Daniel & Basta, Mary, illus. (California Native American Tribes). 52p. (J). (gr. 3-6). pap. 7.95 (978-1-877599-73-6(5)) Merryant Pubs.

—California's Native American Tribes, 26 vols. Liddell, Daniel & Basta, Mary, illus. 2000. 52p. (J). (gr. 3-6). pap. 108.00 (978-1-877599-23-1(9)) Merryant Pubs.

—Native Americans of North America: Hopi People, Set, 11. Liddell, Daniel, illus. 2002. 52p. (Orig.). (J). (gr. 3-6). pap. 6.45 (978-1-877599-58-3(1)) Merryant Pubs.

—Native Americans of North America: Plateau Tribes: Nez Perce People. Liddell, Daniel & Basta, Mary, illus. 1999. 64p. (J). (gr. 3-6). pap. 7.95 (978-1-877599-53-8(0)) Merryant Pubs.

—Native Americans of North America: Ute Tribe, 11 booklets. Liddell, Daniel & Basta, Mary, illus. 2002. (Native Americans of North America). (J). (gr. 3-6). pap. 7.95 (978-1-877599-60-6(3)) Merryant Pubs.

Boyden, Linda. Powwow's Coming. 2007. (Illus.). 32p. (J). (gr. 3 up). 16.95 (***978-0-8263-4265-2(5)***) Univ. of New Mexico Pr.

Brown, Chris. Chief Hawah's Book of Native American Indians. 2006. (Illus.). 32p. (J). 14.99 (978-0-7145-3308-7(4)) Boyars, Marion Pubs., Inc.

Burgan, Michael. Inuit. 2004. (Native American Peoples Ser.). (Illus.). 32p. (J). lib. bdg. 24.67 (978-0-8368-4219-7(7)) Stevens, Gareth Inc.

Cherrington, Janelle. The Drum Beats On. Casilla, Robert, illus. 2002. 16p. (J). (978-0-439-35125-6(1)) Scholastic, Inc.

Cloud Tapper, Suzanne & Tapper, Suzanne Cloud. The Cherokee: A Proud People. 2005. (American Indians Ser.). (Illus.). 48p. (J). (ps-7). lib. bdg. 23.93 (978-0-7660-2454-0(7) , Enslow Elementary) Enslow Pubs., Inc.

Cornell, George & Henry, Gordon. Ojibwa. 2003. (North American Indians Today Ser.). (Illus.). 96p. (J). lib. bdg. (978-1-59084-673-5(7)) Mason Crest Pubs.

Coupe, Robert. Native Americans. 1999. (Explorers Ser.). (Illus.). 32p. (J). (978-0-7699-0571-6(4)) Shortland Pubns. (U. S. A.) Inc.

Craats, Rennay. The Cherokee. 2003. (American Indian Art & Culture Ser.). (Illus.). 32p. (J). pap. (978-1-59036-180-1(6)) Weigl Pubs., Inc.

—The Navajo. 2003. (American Indian Art & Culture Ser.). (Illus.). 32p. (J). pap. 7.95 (978-1-59036-182-5(2)) Weigl Pubs., Inc.

Das, Prodeepta. A Child's Day in an Indian Village. 2001. (Child's Day Ser.). (Illus.). 32p. (J). (gr. k-2). lib. bdg. 25.64 (978-0-7614-1220-5(4) , Benchmark Bks.) Cavendish, Marshall Corp.

Davis, Lucile. The Kiowa of Texas. 2003. (Library of Native Americans). (Illus.). 64p. (J). lib. bdg. 26.50 (978-0-8239-6434-5(5) , PowerKids Pr.) Rosen Publishing Group, Inc., The.

De Capua, Sarah. The Cheyenne. 2006. (First Americans Ser.). (Illus.). 48p. (J). lib. bdg. 29.93 (978-0-7614-2248-8(X) , Benchmark Bks.) Cavendish, Marshall Corp.

—The Comanche. 2006. (First Americans Ser.). (Illus.). 48p. (J). lib. bdg. 29.93 (978-0-7614-2249-5(8) , Benchmark Bks.) Cavendish, Marshall Corp.

Delgado, James P. Native American Shipwrecks. 2000. (Watts Library). (Illus.). 64p. (J). (gr. 5-7). 25.50 (978-0-531-20379-8(4) , Watts, Franklin) Scholastic Library Publishing.

—Native American Shipwrecks. 2000. (Illus.). 63p. (J). (gr. 4-7). lib. bdg. 17.60 (978-0-613-54041-4(7)) Tandem Library Bks.

Dennis, Yvonne Wakim & Hirschfelder, Arlene. Children of Native America Today. 2004. (Illus.). 64p. (J). 19.95 (978-1-57091-499-7(0)) Charlesbridge Publishing, Inc.

Ditchfield, Christin. The Arapaho. 48p. (J). 2006. (gr. 3-5). pap. 6.95 (978-0-516-25586-6(X)); 2005. (Illus.). (ps-7). 25.00 (978-0-516-23642-1(3)) Scholastic Library Publishing. (Children's Pr.).

—The Blackfoot. 2005. (True Book Ser.). (ENG., Illus.). 47p. (J). (ps-7). 25.00 (978-0-516-23643-8(1) , Children's Pr.) Scholastic Library Publishing.

—Blackfoot. 2006. 48p. (J). (gr. 3-5). pap. 6.95 (978-0-516-25587-3(8) , Children's Pr.) Scholastic Library Publishing.

—The Chippewa. 2005. (True Book Ser.). (Illus.). 47p. (J). (ps-7). 25.00 (978-0-516-22817-4(X) , Children's Pr.) Scholastic Library Publishing.

—Chippewa. 2006. 48p. (J). (gr. 3-5). pap. 6.95 (978-0-516-25588-0(6) , Children's Pr.) Scholastic Library Publishing.

—Choctaw. 2006. 48p. (J). (gr. 3-5). pap. 6.95 (978-0-516-25589-7(4) , Children's Pr.) Scholastic Library Publishing.

—Comanche. 2006. 48p. (J). (gr. 3-5). pap. 6.95 (978-0-516-25590-3(8) , Children's Pr.) Scholastic Library Publishing.

—The Crow. 2005. (True Book Ser.). (Illus.). 47p. (J). (ps-7). 25.00 (978-0-516-23645-2(8) , Children's Pr.) Scholastic Library Publishing.

—Crow. 2006. 48p. (J). (gr. 3-5). pap. 6.95 (978-0-516-25591-0(6) , Children's Pr.) Scholastic Library Publishing.

—The Shoshone. (Watts Library). 2005. (Illus.). 64p. (gr. 5-7). 25.50 (978-0-531-12297-6(2) , Watts, Franklin); 2004. (J). (gr. 3-5). pap. 6.95 (978-0-516-24643-7(7) , Children's Pr.) Scholastic Library Publishing.

Donlan, Leni. Counting Coup: Customs of the Crow Nation. 2006. (American History Through Primary Sources Ser.). (Illus.). 32p. (J). (978-1-4109-2421-6(1)); pap. (978-1-4109-2432-2(7)) Steck-Vaughn.

Englar, Mary. The Cherokee & Their History. 2005. (We the People Ser.). (Illus.). 48p. (J). (gr. 4-6). 23.93 (978-0-7565-1273-6(5) , 1244090) Compass Point Bks.

—The Great Plains Indians: Daily Life in The 1700s. 2005. (Native American Life Ser.). (Illus.). 24p. (J). (gr. 2-4). lib. bdg. 21.26 (978-0-7368-4315-7(9) , Bridgestone Bks.) Capstone Pr., Inc.

—The Sioux & Their History. 2005. (We the People Ser.). (Illus.). 48p. (J). (gr. 4-6). 23.93 (978-0-7565-1275-0(1) , 1244094) Compass Point Bks.

—The Southwest Indians: Daily Life in the 1500s. 2006. (Bridgestone Books). (J). (978-0-7368-4319-5(1)) Capstone Pr., Inc.

Feinstein, Stephen. California Native Peoples. 2003. (Heinemann State Studies). (Illus.). 48p. (J). (gr. 3-5). lib. bdg. (978-1-4034-0341-4(4)) Heinemann Library.

Finley, Carol. Art of the Far North: Inuit Sculpture, Drawing, & Printmaking. 1998. (Art Around the World Ser.). (Illus.). 56-64p. (gr. 4-8). 23.93 (978-0-8225-2075-7(3)) Lerner Publishing Group.

Flood, Nancy Bo. The Navajo Year: Walk Through Many Seasons. Whitethorne, Billy, illus. 2006. 32p. 17.95 (978-1-893354-06-7(7)) Salina Bookshelf.

Foran, Jill. Native-American Life. 2003. (Real Life Stories Ser.). (Illus.). 24p. (J). lib. bdg. 15.95 (978-1-59036-080-4(X)) Weigl Pubs., Inc.

Fowler, Verna. The Menominee. 2000. (Indian Nations Ser.). (Illus.). 48p. (J). (gr. 3-7). lib. bdg. 25.69 (978-0-8172-5458-2(7)) Raintree.

Fuhr, Ute, et al. Native Americans. 1998. (First Discovery Book Ser.). (Illus.). 24p. (J). (ps-2). 12.95 (978-0-590-38153-6(9)) Scholastic, Inc.

Gibson, Karen Bush. The Great Basin Indians: Daily Life in The 1700s. 2005. (Native American Life Ser.). (Illus.). 24p. (J). (gr. 2-4). lib. bdg. 21.26 (978-0-7368-4318-8(3) , Bridgestone Bks.) Capstone Pr., Inc.

Glatzer, Jenna. Native American Festivals & Ceremonies. 2002. (Native American Life Ser.). (Illus.). 64p. (YA). (gr. 5 up). lib. bdg. (978-1-59084-123-5(9)) Mason Crest Pubs.

Gray-Kanatiiosh, Barbara A. Caddo. 2007. (Illus.). 32p. (J). lib. bdg. 22.78 (978-1-59197-650-9(2) , Checkerboard Library) ABDO Publishing Co.

—Cahuilla. 2007. (Illus.). 32p. (J). lib. bdg. 22.78 (978-1-59197-651-6(0) , Checkerboard Library) ABDO Publishing Co.

—Chickasaw. 2007. (ENG., Illus.). 32p. (J). lib. bdg. 22.78 (978-1-59197-652-3(9) , Checkerboard Library) ABDO Publishing Co.

—Choctaw. 2007. (Illus.). 32p. (J). 22.78 (978-1-59197-653-0(7)) ABDO Publishing Co.

—Gabrielino. 2004. (Native Americans Set Iii Ser.). (Illus.). 32p. (J). (gr. k-6). lib. bdg. 22.78 (978-1-57765-934-1(1)) ABDO Publishing Co.

—Kiowa. 2007. (Illus.). 32p. (J). 22.78 (978-1-59197-654-7(5)) ABDO Publishing Co.

—Kumeyaay. 2007. (Illus.). 32p. (J). 22.78 (978-1-59197-655-4(3)) ABDO Publishing Co.

—Maidu. 2002. (Native Americans Ser.). (Illus.). 32p. (J). (gr. k-6). lib. bdg. 22.78 (978-1-57765-602-9(4) , Checkerboard Library) ABDO Publishing Co.

—Paiute. 2007. (Illus.). 32p. (J). 22.78 (978-1-59197-657-8(X)) ABDO Publishing Co.

—Salinan. 2004. (Native Americans Set Iii Ser.). (Illus.). 32p. (J). (gr. k-6). lib. bdg. 22.78 (978-1-57765-937-2(6)) ABDO Publishing Co.

—Shoshone. 2004. (Native Americans Set Iii Ser.). (J). (gr. k-6). lib. bdg. 22.78 (978-1-57765-939-6(2)) ABDO Publishing Co.

—Ute. 2004. (Native Americans Set Iii Ser.). (Illus.). 32p. (J). (gr. k-6). lib. bdg. 22.78 (978-1-57765-940-2(6)) ABDO Publishing Co.

—Yokut. 2004. (Native Americans Set Iii Ser.). (Illus.). 32p. (J). (gr. k-6). lib. bdg. 22.78 (978-1-57765-942-6(2)) ABDO Publishing Co.

—Yurok. 2007. (Illus.). 32p. (J). 22.78 (978-1-59197-658-5(8)) ABDO Publishing Co.

Green, Jen. How Ancient Americans Lived. 2006. (Illus.). 128p. pap. 17.99 (978-1-84476-212-5(2) , Southwater) Anness Publishing GBR. *Dist:* National Bk. Network.

Greene, Jacqueline Dembar. Powwow: A Good Day to Dance. Greene, Jacqueline Dembar, photos by. 1998. (First Bks.). (Illus.). 64p. (J). (gr. 5-7). 22.00 (978-0-531-20337-8(9) , Watts, Franklin) Scholastic Library Publishing.

Greig, Charlotte. Native America. 2002. (Cultures & Costumes Ser.). (Illus.). 64p. (J). (gr. 7 up). lib. bdg. (978-1-59084-435-9(1)) Mason Crest Pubs.

Gunderson, Mary. American Indian Cooking Before 1500. 2000. (Blue Earth Books). (Illus.). 32p. (J). (gr. 3-4). lib. bdg. 22.60 (978-0-7368-0605-3(9) , Bridgestone Bks.) Capstone Pr., Inc.

Hall, Margaret. Venom & Visions. 2007. (Shockwave: Arts & Culture Ser.). (Illus.). 36p. (J). (gr. 4-6). lib. bdg. 25.00 (***978-0-531-17788-4(2)*** , Children's Pr.) Scholastic Library Publishing.

Hayden, Kate. Les Indiens des Plaines. 2000. (Come & Discover My World Ser.). (FRE., Illus.). 32p. (J). pap. 7.95 (978-1-58728-194-5(5) , Two Can Publishing) T&N Children's Publishing.

Hirsch, E. D., ed. Native Americans: Cultures & Conflicts, Level 5. tchr. ed. 9.95 (978-0-7690-5083-6(2)); stu. ed. 49.95 (978-0-7690-2854-5(3)) Pearson Learning.

Holliday, Diane. Mountain Wolf Woman: A Ho-Chunk Girlhood. 2007. (Badger Biographies Ser.). (Illus.). 80p. (J). pap. 12.95 (***978-0-87020-381-7(9)***) Wisconsin Historical Society.

Houghton, Gillian. The Oneida of Wisconsin. 2003. (Library of Native Americans). (Illus.). 64p. (J). lib. bdg. 26.50 (978-0-8239-6432-1(9) , PowerKids Pr.) Rosen Publishing Group, Inc., The.

Hummingbird, Jesse & Hummingbird, Sandy. Cherokee Clothing. 2006. 32p. (J). act. bk. ed. 4.95 (978-1-57067-180-7(X) , Native Voices) Book Publishing Co., The.

Hummingbird, Sandy & Hummingbird, Jesse. Powwow Activity Book. 1999. (Illus.). 28p. (ps-3). 4.95 (978-1-57067-078-7(1)) Book Publishing Co., The.

Indians of North America Heritage Edition. 2005. pap. 420.00 (978-0-7910-9186-9(4) , Chelsea Hse.) Facts On File, Inc.

Isaacs, Sally Senzell. Life in a Hopi Village. (Picture the Past Ser.). (Illus.). 32p. (J). 2002. (gr. k-3). pap. 7.50 (978-1-58810-298-0(X) , 91064); 2000. (gr. 2-4). lib. bdg. 21.36 (978-1-57572-314-3(X)) Heinemann Library.

—Life in a Hopi Village. 2001. (gr. k-3). lib. bdg. 15.90 (978-0-613-86819-8(6)); (Illus.). (J). (978-0-606-22004-0(6)) Tandem Library Bks.

Issues in Native American Life, 7 bks. (Indians of North America Ser.). (YA). (gr. 5 up). 139.65 (978-0-7910-3828-4(9) , Chelsea Hse.) Facts On File, Inc.

Iverson, Peter. The Navajo. 2005. (Indians of North America, Heritage Edition Ser.). (Illus.). 139p. (J). (gr. 5-13). lib. bdg. 30.00 (978-0-7910-8595-0(3) , Chelsea Hse.) Facts On File, Inc.

Johnson, Michael. Native Tribes of the Northeast. 2004. (Native Tribes of North America Ser.). (Illus.). 64p. (J). (gr. 5 up). lib. bdg. 32.67 (978-0-8368-5612-5(0) , World Almanac Library) Stevens, Gareth Inc.

—Native Tribes of the Plains & Prairie. 2004. (Native Tribes of North America Ser.). (Illus.). 64p. (J). (gr. 5 up). lib. bdg. 32.67 (978-0-8368-5613-2(9) , World Almanac Library) Stevens, Gareth Inc.

Johnson, Michael & Burkinshaw, Jane. Native Tribes of the North & Northwest Coast. 2004. (Native Tribes of North America Ser.). (Illus.). 64p. (J). (gr. 5 up). lib. bdg. 32.67 (978-0-8368-5611-8(2) , World Almanac Library) Stevens, Gareth Inc.

Johnson, Michael & Clarke, Duncan. Native Tribes of the Great Basin & Plateau. 2004. (Native Tribes of North America Ser.). (Illus.). 64p. (J). (gr. 5 up). lib. bdg. 32.67 (978-0-8368-5610-1(4) , World Almanac Library) Stevens, Gareth Inc.

—Native Tribes of the Southeast. 2004. (Native Tribes of North America Ser.). (Illus.). 64p. (J). (gr. 5 up). lib. bdg. 32.67 (978-0-8368-5614-9(7) , World Almanac Library) Stevens, Gareth Inc.

Johnson, Michael & Yenne, Bill. Native Tribes of California & the Southwest. 2004. (Native Tribes of North America Ser.). (Illus.). 64p. (J). (gr. 5 up). lib. bdg. 32.67 (978-0-8368-5609-5(0) , World Almanac Library) Stevens, Gareth Inc.

Kallen, Stuart A. Native Americans of the Great Lakes. 1999. (Indigenous Peoples of North America Ser.). (Illus.). 144p. (J). (gr. 4-12). 28.70 (978-1-56006-568-5(0) , LML00902-177923, Lucent Bks.) Thomson Gale.

Kalman, Bobbie. Life in a Plains Camp. 2001. (Native Nations of North America Ser.). (Illus.). 32p. (J). (gr. 5). (978-0-7787-0369-3(X)); pap. (978-0-7787-0461-4(0)) Crabtree Publishing Co.

—Life in a Plains Camp. 2001. (gr. 3-6). lib. bdg. 16.40 (978-0-613-43465-2(X)) Tandem Library Bks.

Kavasch, E. Barrie. Blackfoot Children & Elders Talk Together. 1999. (Library of Intergenerational Learning). 24p. (J). (gr. k-4). lib. bdg. 19.95 (978-0-8239-5228-1(2) , PowerKids Pr.) Rosen Publishing Group, Inc., The.

—Lakota Sioux Children & Elders Talk Together. 1999. (Library of Intergenerational Learning). 24p. (J). (gr. k-4). lib. bdg. 19.95 (978-0-8239-5226-7(6) , PowerKids Pr.) Rosen Publishing Group, Inc., The.

Keller, Kristin Thoennes. The Shoshone: Pine Nut Harvesters of the Great Basin. 2003. (America's First Peoples Ser.). (Illus.). 32p. (J). (gr. 2-3). lib. bdg. 23.93 (978-0-7368-2173-5(2) , Bridgestone Bks.) Capstone Pr., Inc.

Keoke, Emory Dean & Porterfield, Kay Marie. Food, Farming, & Hunting. 2005. (American Indian Contributions to the World Ser.). (Illus.). 160p. (J). (gr. 4-9). 35.00 (978-0-8160-5393-3(6)) Facts On File, Inc.

King, David C. The Haida. 2006. (First Americans Ser.). (Illus.). 48p. (J). lib. bdg. 29.93 (978-0-7614-2250-1(1) , Benchmark Bks.) Cavendish, Marshall Corp.

—The Huron. 2006. (First Americans Ser.). (Illus.). 48p. (J). lib. bdg. 29.93 (978-0-7614-2251-8(X) , Benchmark Bks.) Cavendish, Marshall Corp.

—The Navajo. 2005. (First Americans Ser.). (Illus.). 48p. (J). (gr. 3-7). lib. bdg. (978-0-7614-1897-9(0) , Benchmark Bks.) Cavendish, Marshall Corp.

—The Ojibwe. 2006. (First Americans Ser.). (Illus.). 48p. (J). lib. bdg. 29.93 (978-0-7614-2252-5(8) , Benchmark Bks.) Cavendish, Marshall Corp.

—The Seminole. 2006. (First Americans Ser.). (Illus.). 48p. (J). lib. bdg. 29.93 (978-0-7614-2253-2(6) , Benchmark Bks.) Cavendish, Marshall Corp.

—The Sioux. 2005. (First Americans Ser.). (Illus.). 48p. (J). (gr. 3-7). lib. bdg. (978-0-7614-1899-3(7) , Benchmark Bks.) Cavendish, Marshall Corp.

Knotts, Bob. Florida Native Peoples. 2002. (State Studies). (Illus.). 48p. (J). pap. 8.50 (978-1-4034-0564-7(6)); (gr. 3-5). lib. bdg. (978-1-4034-0348-3(1)) Heinemann Library.

Knowles, Gerald M. The Navajo of North America. 2005. (First Peoples Ser.). (Illus.). 48p. (gr. 4-8). lib. bdg. 23.95 (978-0-8225-0662-1(9)) Lerner Publishing Group.

Koopmans, Anna. The Sioux. 2003. (American Indian Art & Culture Ser.). (Illus.). 32p. (J). pap. (978-1-59036-184-9(9)) Weigl Pubs., Inc.

La Vere, David. The Texas Indians. 2004. (Centennial Series of the Association of Former Students: 95). (Illus.). 328p. 29.95 (978-1-58544-301-7(8)) Texas A&M Univ. Pr.

Lassieur, Allison. The Cheyenne. 2001. (Native Peoples Ser.). (Illus.). 24p. (J). (gr. 2-3). lib. bdg. 18.60 (978-0-7368-0831-6(0) , Bridgestone Bks.) Capstone Pr., Inc.

—The Delaware People. 2002. (Native Peoples Ser.). (Illus.). 24p. (J). (gr. 2-3). lib. bdg. 18.60 (978-0-7368-1104-0(4) , Bridgestone Bks.) Capstone Pr., Inc.

Levy, Janey. The Wampanoag of Massachusetts & Rhode Island. 2005. (Library of Native Americans). (Illus.). 64p. (J). 26.50 (978-1-4042-2871-9(3) , PowerKids Pr.) Rosen Publishing Group, Inc., The.

Limberhand, Dennis. The Cheyenne. 2000. (Indian Nations Ser.). (Illus.). 48p. (J). (gr. 3-7). lib. bdg. 25.69 (978-0-8172-5469-8(2)) Raintree.

Loew, Patty. Native People of Wisconsin. 2003. (New Badger History Ser.). (Illus.). 136p. (J). pap. 15.95 (978-0-87020-348-0(7)) Wisconsin Historical Society.

Lomberg, Michelle. The Iroquois. 2003. (American Indian Art & Culture Ser.). (Illus.). 32p. (J). pap. (978-1-59036-181-8(4)) Weigl Pubs., Inc.

—The Ojibwa. 2003. (American Indian Art & Culture Ser.). (Illus.). 32p. (J). pap. (978-1-59036-183-2(0)) Weigl Pubs., Inc.

McAmis, Herb. The Cherokee. 2000. (Indian Nations Ser.). (Illus.). 48p. (J). (gr. 3-6). lib. bdg. 25.69 (978-0-8172-5456-8(0)) Raintree.

McCarthy, Cathy. The Ojibwa. 2000. (Indian Nations Ser.). (Illus.). 48p. (J). (gr. 3-7). lib. bdg. 25.69 (978-0-8172-5460-5(9)) Raintree.

McIntosh, Marsha. Teen Life on Reservations & First Nation Communities: Growing up Native. 2008. (Youth in Rural North America Ser.). (J). (978-1-4222-0018-6(3)) Mason Crest Pubs.

McLester, L. Gordon. The Oneida. 2000. (Indian Nations Ser.). (Illus.). 48p. (J). (gr. 3-7). lib. bdg. 25.69 (978-0-8172-5457-5(9)) Raintree.

Meuse, Theresa. The Sharing Circle: Stories about First Nations Culture. Stevens, Arthur, illus. 2003. pap. 11.95 (978-1-55109-450-2(9)) Down East Bks.

Miller, Connie R. The Lakota. 2003. (Digging up Native American History Ser.). (J). pap. (978-1-58417-109-6(X)); lib. bdg. (978-1-58417-046-4(8)) Lake Street Pubs.

Miller, Raymond H. The Apache. 2005. (North American Indians Ser.). (Illus.). 48p. (J). (ps-8). lib. bdg. 26.20 (978-0-7377-2625-1(3) , Greenhaven Pr., Inc.) Thomson Gale.

Monroe, Judy. The Northwest Indians: Daily Life in The 1700s. 2005. (Native American Life Ser.). (Illus.). 24p. (J). (gr. 2-4). lib. bdg. 21.26 (978-0-7368-4316-4(7) , Bridgestone Bks.) Capstone Pr., Inc.

Moore, Sharon. Native American Foods & Recipes. 2002. (Reading Room Collection). (Illus.). 24p. (J). pap. (978-0-8239-8164-9(9)); lib. bdg. 18.75 (978-0-8239-3727-1(5)) Rosen Publishing Group, Inc., The.

Morris, Neil. Everyday Life of the Native Americans. 2005. (Uncovering History Ser.). (Illus.). 46p. (J). (gr. 6-9). lib. bdg. 29.95 (978-1-58340-708-0(1)) Smart Apple Media.

Nash, Alice & Strobel, Christoph. Daily Life of Native Americans from Post-Columbian Through Nineteenth Century America. 2006. (Greenwood Press "Daily Life Through History" Ser.). (Illus.). 312p. (J). 49.95 (978-0-313-33515-0(X) , GR3515, Greenwood Pr.) Greenwood Publishing Group, Inc.

Oestreicher, David M. The Algonquin of New York. 2003. (Library of Native Americans). (Illus.). 64p. (J). lib. bdg. 26.50 (978-0-8239-6427-7(2)) Rosen Publishing Group, Inc., The.

Palazzo-Craig, Janet. The Ojibwe of Michigan, Wisconsin, Minnesota, & North Dakota. 2005. (Library of Native Americans). (Illus.). 64p. (J). 26.50 (978-1-4042-2873-3(X) , PowerKids Pr.) Rosen Publishing Group, Inc., The.

Peacock, Thomas & Wisuri, Marlene. The Good Path. 2004. (Illus.). 128p. pap. 17.95 (978-1-890434-53-3(1)) Afton Historical Society Pr.

Petra Press Staff. The Iroquois. 2001. (First Reports). (Illus.). 48p. (J). (gr. 3 up). lib. bdg. 22.60 (978-0-7565-0080-1(X)) Compass Point Bks.

Rau, Dana Meachen. Tepee. 2006. (Bookworms Ser.). (Illus.). 32p. (J). (gr. k-2). lib. bdg. 22.79 (978-0-7614-2277-8(3) , Benchmark Bks.) Cavendish, Marshall Corp.

Regional Tribes: Native American Life. 2005. (Illus.). (J). (gr. 2-3). lib. bdg. 127.56 (978-0-7368-4418-5(X)) Capstone Pr., Inc.

Riehecky, Janet. The Cree Tribe. 2002. (Native Peoples Ser.). (Illus.). 24p. (J). (gr. 2-3). lib. bdg. 18.60 (978-0-7368-1366-2(7) , Bridgestone Bks.) Capstone Pr., Inc.

—The Osage. 2002. (Native Peoples Ser.). (Illus.). 24p. (J). (gr. 2-3). lib. bdg. 18.60 (978-0-7368-1367-9(5) , Bridgestone Bks.) Capstone Pr., Inc.

Rose, Lavera. Grandchildren of the Lakota. Bellville, Cheryl Walsh, photos by. 1998. (World's Children Ser.). (Illus.). 40p. (J). (gr. 3-6). lib. bdg. 23.93 (978-1-57505-279-3(2) , Carolrhoda Bks.) Lerner Publishing Group.

Rosinsky, Natalie M. The Algonquin. 2004. (First Reports). 48p. (J). (gr. 3 up). lib. bdg. 22.60 (978-0-7565-0642-1(5)) Compass Point Bks.

—The Arapaho & Their History. 2004. (We the People Ser.). (Illus.). 48p. (J). 22.60 (978-0-7565-0831-9(2)) Compass Point Bks.

—The Chumash & Their History. 2004. (We the People Ser.). (Illus.). 48p. (J). 22.60 (978-0-7565-0835-7(5)) Compass Point Bks.

—The Creek & Their History. 2004. (We the People Ser.). (Illus.). 48p. (J). 22.60 (978-0-7565-0836-4(3)) Compass Point Bks.

—The Ojibwe & Their History. 2004. (We the People Ser.). (Illus.). 48p. (J). 22.60 (978-0-7565-0843-2(6)) Compass Point Bks.

—The Powhatan & Their History. 2004. (We the People Ser.). (Illus.). 48p. (J). 22.60 (978-0-7565-0844-9(4)) Compass Point Bks.

—The Wampanoag & Their History. 2004. (We the People Ser.). (Illus.). 48p. (J). 22.60 (978-0-7565-0847-0(9)) Compass Point Bks.

Ross, Pamela. The Chinook People. 1998. (Native Peoples Ser.). (Illus.). 24p. (J). (gr. 2-3). lib. bdg. 18.60 (978-0-7368-0076-1(X) , Bridgestone Bks.) Capstone Pr., Inc.

Rossi, Ann. Native American & Europeans 1492-1700: Cultures Collide. 2004. (Crossroads America Ser.). (Illus.). 40p. (J). (gr. 5-9). 21.90 (978-0-7922-7198-7(X) , National Geographic Children's Bks.) National Geographic Society.

—Two Cultures Meet: Native American & European. 2002. (Reading Expeditions Ser.). (Illus.). 40p. (J). (978-0-7922-8679-0(0)) National Geographic Society.

Roza, Greg. The Karankawa of Texas. 2005. (Library of Native Americans). (Illus.). 64p. (J). 26.50 (978-1-4042-2870-2(5) , PowerKids Pr.) Rosen Publishing Group, Inc., The.

Rutsala, David. Hunting with the Native Americans. 2002. (Native American Life Ser.). (Illus.). 64p. (J). (gr. 5 up). lib. bdg. (978-1-59084-127-3(1)) Mason Crest Pubs.

Ryan, Marla, ed. Cahuilla. 2002. (Tribes of North America Ser.). (Illus.). 48p. (J). 23.70 (978-1-56711-613-7(2) , Blackbirch Pr., Inc.) Thomson Gale.

—Cherokee. 2002. (Tribes of North America Ser.). (Illus.). 48p. (J). 23.70 (978-1-56711-614-4(0) , Blackbirch Pr., Inc.) Thomson Gale.

—Mohawk. 2002. (Tribes of North America Ser.). (Illus.). 48p. (J). 23.70 (978-1-56711-615-1(9) , Blackbirch Pr., Inc.) Thomson Gale.

Ryan, Marla Felkins & Schmittroth, Linda, eds. Abenaki. 2003. (Tribes of Native America Ser.). (Illus.). 32p. (J). 23.70 (978-1-56711-574-1(8) , Blackbirch Pr., Inc.) Thomson Gale.

—Chickasaw. 2003. (Tribes of Native America Ser.). (Illus.). 32p. (J). 23.70 (978-1-56711-590-1(X) , Blackbirch Pr., Inc.) Thomson Gale.

—Chinook. 2003. (Tribes of Native America Ser.). (Illus.). 32p. (J). 23.70 (978-1-56711-685-4(X) , Blackbirch Pr., Inc.) Thomson Gale.

—Menominee. 2003. (Tribes of Native America Ser.). (Illus.). 32p. (J). 23.70 (978-1-56711-697-7(3) , Blackbirch Pr., Inc.) Thomson Gale.

Sanna, Ellyn. Potawatomi. 2003. (North American Indians Today Ser.). (Illus.). 96p. (J). lib. bdg. (978-1-59084-675-9(3)) Mason Crest Pubs.

Schmittroth, Felkins Ryan. Ojibway. 2003. (Tribes of Native America Ser.). (Illus.). 32p. (J). 23.70 (978-1-56711-725-7(2) , Blackbirch Pr., Inc.) Thomson Gale.

—Shoshone. 2003. (Tribes of Native America Ser.). (Illus.). 32p. (J). 23.70 (978-1-56711-722-6(8) , Blackbirch Pr., Inc.) Thomson Gale.

Schomp, Virginia. The Native Americans. 2007. (Myths of the World Ser.). 96p. (J). lib. bdg. 32.79 (***978-0-7614-2550-2(0)*** , Benchmark Bks.) Cavendish, Marshall Corp.

Schonberg, Marcia. Michigan Native Peoples. 2003. (Heinemann State Studies). (Illus.). 48p. (J). 27.07 (978-1-4034-0660-6(X)); pap. 8.50 (978-1-4034-2678-9(3)) Heinemann Library.

Shoulders, Michael & Shoulders, Debbie. D Is for Drum: A Native American Alphabet. Toddy, Irving, illus. rev. ed. 2006. 40p. (J). (gr. k-5). 16.95 (978-1-58536-274-5(3)) Sleeping Bear Pr.

Sjonger, Rebecca & Kalman, Bobbie. Nations of the Eastern Great Lakes. 2004. (Native Nations of North America Ser.). (Illus.). 32p. (J). (978-0-7787-0381-5(9)); pap. (978-0-7787-0473-7(4)) Crabtree Publishing Co.

Slusher-Haas, Kathy Jo. The Southeast Indians: Daily Life in the 1500s. 2006. (Bridgestone Books). (Illus.). 24p. (J). (978-0-7368-4317-1(5)) Capstone Pr., Inc.

Soeder, Pamela. Discover American Indian Ways: A Carnegie Activity Book. Powless, William, illus. 1998. (Carnegie Discover Ser.). 28p. (gr. 4-7). pap. 4.95 (978-1-57098-199-9(X)) Rinehart, Roberts Pubs.

Sonneborn, Liz. The Choctaws. 2007. (Native American Histories Ser.). (Illus.). 56p. (J). 27.93 (978-0-8225-5911-5(0) , Lerner Pubns.) Lerner Publishing Group.

—The Shoshones. 2007. (Native American Histories Ser.). (Illus.). 56p. (J). 27.93 (978-0-8225-2849-4(5) , Lerner Pubns.) Lerner Publishing Group.

Sonneborn, Liz & New York Public Library Staff. The New York Public Library Amazing Native American History: A Book of Answers for Kids. 1999. (New York Public Library Books for Kids Ser.: Vol. 8). (Illus.). 176p. (gr. 5-9). pap. 16.95 (978-0-471-33204-6(6) , Wiley) Wiley, John & Sons, Inc.

St. Lawrence, Genevieve. The Iroquois & Their History. 2005. (We the People Ser.). (Illus.). 48p. (J). (gr. 4-6). (978-0-7565-1272-9(7) , 1244092) Compass Point Bks.

—The Pueblo & Their History. 2005. (We the People Ser.). (Illus.). 48p. (J). (gr. 4-6). (978-0-7565-1274-3(3) , 1244093) Compass Point Bks.

Staeger, Rob. Native American Sports & Games. 2002. (Native American Life Ser.). (Illus.). 64p. (J). (gr. 5 up). lib. bdg. (978-1-59084-118-1(2)) Mason Crest Pubs.

Staub, Frank. Children of the Tlingit. 1998. (World's Children Ser.). (Illus.). 56p. (J). (gr. 3-6). lib. bdg. (978-1-57505-333-2(0) , Carolrhoda Bks.) Lerner Publishing Group.

Stewart, Mark. New Jersey Native Peoples. 2003. (State Studies). (Illus.). 48p. (J). pap. 8.50 (978-1-4034-2684-0(8)); lib. bdg. 27.07 (978-1-4034-0674-3(X)) Heinemann Library.

Stewart, Philip. Osage. 2003. (North American Indians Today Ser.). (Illus.). 96p. (J). lib. bdg. (978-1-59084-674-2(5)) Mason Crest Pubs.

Stone, Amy. Creek. 2004. (Native American Peoples Ser.). (Illus.). 32p. (J). 24.67 (978-0-8368-4217-3(0)) Stevens, Gareth Inc.

—Oneida. 2004. (Native American Peoples Ser.). (Illus.). 32p. (J). lib. bdg. 24.67 (978-0-8368-4220-3(0)) Stevens, Gareth Inc.

Stout, Mary. Blackfoot. 2004. (Native American Peoples Ser.). (Illus.). 32p. (J). lib. bdg. 24.67 (978-0-8368-4216-6(2)) Stevens, Gareth Inc.

—Hopi. 2004. (Native American Peoples Ser.). (Illus.). 32p. (J). lib. bdg. 24.67 (978-0-8368-4218-0(9)) Stevens, Gareth Inc.

—Shoshone. 2004. (Native American Peoples Ser.). (Illus.). 32p. (J). lib. bdg. 24.67 (978-0-8368-4221-0(9)) Stevens, Gareth Inc.

Sugobono, Nahuel. Leyendas, Mitos, Cuentos y Otros Relatos de las Praderas Norteamericanas. Huadi, illus. 2003. (SPA.). 96p. pap. 11.95 (978-987-550-278-9(2)) Longseller S.A. ARG. *Dist:* Bilingual Pubns. Co., The.

Sundling, Charles W. Native Americans of the Frontier. 2000. (Frontier Land Ser.). (Illus.). 32p. (J). (gr. 3-8). lib. bdg. 24.21 (978-1-57765-042-3(5) , ABDO & Daughters) ABDO Publishing Co.

Swamp, Jake. Giving Thanks: A Native American Good Morning Message. braille ed. 2004. (Illus.). (J). (gr. k-3). spiral bd. (978-0-616-03096-7(3)) Canadian National Institute for the Blind/Institut National Canadien pour les Aveugles.

—Giving Thanks: A Native American Good Morning Message. (gr. k-3). lib. bdg. 15.25 (978-0-613-05061-6(4)) Tandem Library Bks.

Tayac, Gabrielle & Secakuku, Susan. My World: Young Native Americans Today, 2 bks. Harrington, John, photos by. Incl. Meet Mindy. lib. bdg. 24.67 (978-0-8368-3794-0(0)); Meet Naiche. lib. bdg. 24.67 (978-0-8368-3795-7(9)); 32p. (J). (gr. 4 up). (Illus.). 2003. Set lib. bdg. 49.34 (978-0-8368-3793-3(2)) Stevens, Gareth Inc.

Terry, Michael. Daily Life in a Plains Indian Village, 1868. 1999. (978-0-89919-960-3(7)) Houghton Mifflin Co.

—Daily Life in a Plains Indian Village 1868. 1999. (Illus.). 48p. (J). (gr. 5-9). pap. 10.95 (978-0-395-97499-5(2) , Clarion Bks.) Houghton Mifflin Co. Trade & Reference Div.

Thompson, Linda. The California People. 2003. (Illus.). 48p. (J). 29.93 (978-1-58952-753-9(4)) Rourke Publishing, LLC.

—People of the Great Basin. 2003. (Illus.). 48p. (J). 29.93 (978-1-58952-754-6(2)) Rourke Publishing, LLC.

—People of the Northeast Woodlands. 2003. (Illus.). 48p. (J). 29.93 (978-1-58952-755-3(0)) Rourke Publishing, LLC.

—People of the Northwest & Subarctic. 2003. (Illus.). 48p. (J). 29.93 (978-1-58952-756-0(9)) Rourke Publishing, LLC.

—People of the Plateau. 2003. (Illus.). 48p. (J). 29.93 (978-1-58952-758-4(5)) Rourke Publishing, LLC.

—People of the Southeast. 2003. (Native People, Native Lands Ser.). (Illus.). 48p. (J). 29.93 (978-1-58952-759-1(3)) Rourke Publishing, LLC.

—People of the Southwest. 2003. (Illus.). 48p. (J). 29.93 (978-1-58952-760-7(7)) Rourke Publishing, LLC.

Todd, Anne M. The Cherokee: An Independent Nation. 2002. (American Indian Nations Ser.). (Illus.). 48p. (J). (gr. 3-4). lib. bdg. 22.60 (978-0-7368-1355-6(1) , Bridgestone Bks.) Capstone Pr., Inc.

—The Ojibwa: People of the Great Lakes. 2002. (American Indian Nations Ser.). (Illus.). 48p. (J). (gr. 3-4). lib. bdg. 22.60 (978-0-7368-1356-3(X) , Bridgestone Bks.) Capstone Pr., Inc.

—The Sioux: People of the Great Plains. 2002. (American Indian Nations Ser.). (Illus.). 48p. (J). (gr. 3-4). lib. bdg. 22.60 (978-0-7368-1354-9(3) , Bridgestone Bks.) Capstone Pr., Inc.

Trumbauer, Lisa. The First Americans. 2007. (J). (***978-1-4034-9665-2(X)***); pap. (***978-1-4034-9673-7(0)***) Heinemann Library.

Wade, Mary Dodson. Texas Native Peoples. 2003. (Heinemann State Studies). (Illus.). 48p. (J). pap. 8.50 (978-1-4034-2697-0(X)); lib. bdg. 27.07 (978-1-4034-0688-0(X)) Heinemann Library.

—Texas Native Peoples. 2003. (gr. 3-6). lib. bdg. 17.05 (978-0-613-88568-3(6)) Tandem Library Bks.

Weinberger, Kimberly. Let's Read About— Pocahontas. Marchesi, Stephen, illus. 2003. (Scholastic First Biographies Ser.). (J). pap. (978-0-439-56148-8(5)) Scholastic, Inc.

Weintraub, Aileen. The Choctaw. 2005. (Indigenous Peoples of North America Ser.). (J). (978-1-59018-610-7(9) , Lucent Bks.) Thomson Gale.

Wilcox, Charlotte. The Seminoles. 2007. (Native American Histories Ser.). (Illus.). 56p. (J). 27.93 (978-0-8225-2848-7(7) , Lerner Pubns.) Lerner Publishing Group.

Williams, Jack S. The Miwok of California. 2004. (Library of Native Americans). (Illus.). 64p. (J). lib. bdg. 26.50 (978-1-4042-2659-3(1)) Rosen Publishing Group, Inc., The.

—The Ohlone of California. 2003. (Library of Native Americans). (Illus.). 64p. (J). lib. bdg. 26.50 (978-0-8239-6430-7(2) , PowerKids Pr.) Rosen Publishing Group, Inc., The.

Williams, Suzanne. Cherokee Indians. (Native Americans Ser.). (Illus.). 32p. (J). 2003. (gr. 2-4). lib. bdg. 24.22 (978-1-4034-0301-8(5)); 2002. pap. 6.95 (978-1-4034-0508-1(5)) Heinemann Library.

—The Chinook. 2002. (Illus.). 32p. (J). pap. 6.95 (978-1-4034-0507-4(7)) Heinemann Library.

—Chinook Indians. 2003. (Native Americans Ser.). (Illus.). 32p. (J). (gr. 2-4). lib. bdg. 24.22 (978-1-4034-0300-1(7)) Heinemann Library.

—Ojibwe Indians. 2003. (Native Americans Ser.). (Illus.). 32p. (J). pap. 7.50 (978-1-4034-4173-7(1)); lib. bdg. 22.79 (978-1-4034-0865-5(3)) Heinemann Library.

—Powhatan Indians. 2003. (Native Americans Ser.). (Illus.). 32p. (J). pap. 7.50 (978-1-4034-4174-4(X)); lib. bdg. 24.22 (978-1-4034-0866-2(1)) Heinemann Library.

—Tlingit Indians. 2003. (Native Americans Ser.). (Illus.). 32p. (J). pap. 7.50 (978-1-4034-4176-8(6)); lib. bdg. 22.79 (978-1-4034-0868-6(8)) Heinemann Library.

Wolf, Linda Little. Visions of the Buffalo People. 2003. (gr. 5-8). lib. bdg. 24.55 (978-0-613-67129-3(5)) Tandem Library Bks.

Yacowitz, Caryn. Shawnee Indians. 2003. (Native Americans Ser.). (Illus.). 32p. (J). pap. 7.50 (978-1-4034-4175-1(8)); lib. bdg. 24.22 (978-1-4034-0867-9(X)) Heinemann Library.

INDIANS OF NORTH AMERICA—SPORTS

see Indians of North America—Games

INDIANS OF NORTH AMERICA—SUQUAMISH INDIANS

Jeffers, Susan. Brother Eagle, Sister Sky. Jeffers, Susan, illus. 2002. (Illus.). 32p. (J). (gr. k up). pap. 7.99 (978-0-14-230132-6(9) , Puffin) Penguin Group (USA) Inc.

—Brother Eagle, Sister Sky. 2002. (gr. 3-6). lib. bdg. 16.45 (978-0-613-45249-6(6)) Tandem Library Bks.

INDIANS OF NORTH AMERICA—TAOS INDIANS

Warm Day, Jonathan. Painted Stories from Taos Pueblo. 2003. (Illus.). 32p. (J). 16.95 (978-1-57416-080-2(X)) Clear Light Pubs.

INDIANS OF NORTH AMERICA—UTE INDIANS

Krudwig, Vickie Leigh. Searching for Chipeta: The Story of a Ute & Her People. 2004. (Illus.). 128p. (J). (gr. 4). pap. 12.95 (978-1-55591-466-0(7)) Fulcrum Publishing.

INDIANS OF NORTH AMERICA—UTE INDIANS—FICTION

Creel, Ann Howard. Water at the Blue Earth. 1998. (Illus.). 148p. (gr. 5-9). pap. 8.95 (978-1-57098-224-8(4)) Rinehart, Roberts Pubs.

Hobbs, Will. Beardance. 2004. (Illus.). 197p. (J). (gr. 4-7). lib. bdg. 12.04 (978-0-606-32685-8(5)) Tandem Library Bks.

Hobbs, William. Bearstone. 2004. 160p. (J). pap. 5.99 (978-0-689-87071-2(X) , Aladdin) Simon & Schuster Children's Publishing.

INDIANS OF NORTH AMERICA—WAMPANOAG INDIANS

Flanagan, Alice K. The Wampanoags. 1998. (True Bks.). (Illus.). 48p. (J). (gr. 3-5). 25.00 (978-0-516-20629-5(X) , Children's Pr.) Scholastic Library Publishing.

Gray-Kanatiiosh, Barbara A. Wampanoag. 2004. (Native Americans Set Iii Ser.). (Illus.). 32p. (J). (gr. k-6). lib. bdg. 22.78 (978-1-57765-941-9(4)) ABDO Publishing Co.

Greene, Jacqueline Dembar. Powwow: A Good Day to Dance. Greene, Jacqueline Dembar, photos by. 1998. (First Bks.). (Illus.). 64p. (J). (gr. 5-7). 22.00 (978-0-531-20337-8(9) , Watts, Franklin) Scholastic Library Publishing.

Hirschfelder, Arlene B. Squanto1585-1622. 2004. (American Indian Biographies Ser.). (Illus.). 32p. (J). (gr. 3-4). lib. bdg. 23.93 (978-0-7368-2446-0(4) , Blue Earth Bks.) Capstone Pr., Inc.

Kamma, Anne. If You Lived at the Time of Squanto. Johnson, Pamela Ford, illus. 2006. 63p. (J). pap. (***978-0-439-87628-5(1)***) Scholastic, Inc.

Levy, Janey. The Wampanoag of Massachusetts & Rhode Island. 2005. (Library of Native Americans). (Illus.). 64p. (J). 26.50 (978-1-4042-2871-9(3) , PowerKids Pr.) Rosen Publishing Group, Inc., The.

Metaxas, Eric. Squanto & the First Thanksgiving. Donato, Michael A., illus. 2005. (Rabbit Ears-A Classic Tale Ser.). 40p. (J). (gr. k-5). 25.65 (978-1-59197-771-1(1)) Spotlight.

—Squanto & the First Thanksgiving: The Legendary American Tale. Donato, Michael A., illus. 2004. 36p. (J). (gr. 3-8). reprint ed. 19.00 (978-0-7567-7123-2(4)) DIANE Publishing Co.

Sewall, Marcia. People of the Breaking Day. 1998. pap. 5.99 (978-0-87628-988-4(X)) Ctr. for Applied Research in Education, The.

Whitehurst, Susan. The First Thanksgiving. 2002. (Library of the Pilgrims). (Illus.). 24p. (J). (gr. 3). lib. bdg. 19.95 (978-0-8239-5807-8(8) , PowerKids Pr.) Rosen Publishing Group, Inc., The.

INDIANS OF NORTH AMERICA—WAMPANOAG INDIANS—FICTION

Bruchac, Joseph. Squanto's Journey: The Story of the First Thanksgiving. Shed, Greg, illus. 2007. 32p. (J). pap. 6.00 (***978-0-15-206044-2(8)*** , Voyager Bks./Libros Viajeros) Harcourt Children's Bks.

H
I

INDIANS OF NORTH AMERICA—WARS

see also Little Bighorn, Battle of the, Mont., 1876; United States—History—French and Indian War, 1755-1763

Alter, Judy. The Indian Wars: A MyReportLinks.com Book. 2002. (U. S. Wars Ser.). (Illus.). 48p. (J). (gr. 4-10). lib. bdg. 25.26 (978-0-7660-5099-0(8) , MyReportLinks.com Bks.) Enslow Pubs., Inc.

Behrman, Carol H. The Indian Wars. 2005. (Chronicle of America's Wars Ser.). (Illus.). 96p. (J). (gr. 5-12). 27.93 (978-0-8225-0847-2(8)) Lerner Publishing Group.

Bruchac, Joseph. Geronimo. 2006. 240p. (J). (gr. 7 up). pap. 16.99 (978-0-439-35360-1(2)) Scholastic, Inc.

Buffalo Soldiers & the Western Frontier Vol. 2: Individual Title Six-Packs. (On Deck Ser.: Vol. 2). 24p. (gr. 4-5). 35.00 (978-0-7578-5805-5(8)) Rigby Education.

Connell, Kate. These Lands Are Ours: Tecumseh's Fight for the Old Northwest. 2001. (Nonfiction Bookbag Ser.). (J). (gr. 5-6). per. 8.45 (978-1-58830-206-9(7)) Metropolitan Teaching & Learning Co.

Deitch, JoAnne Weisman, ed. The Indian Wars: Researching American History. 2002. (Researching American History Ser.). (Illus.). 60p. (J). (978-1-57960-087-7(5)) History Compass, LLC.

Dolan, Edward F., Jr. The American Indian Wars. 2003. (Single Titles Ser.). 112p. (gr. 5-8). lib. bdg. 29.90 (978-0-7613-1968-9(9) , Twenty-First Century Bks.) Lerner Publishing Group.

Donovan, Jim. Custer & the Little Bighorn: The Man, the Mystery, the Myth. 2001. (Illus.). 224p. (gr. 8 up). 35.00 (978-0-89658-531-7(X)) Voyageur Pr., Inc.

Feinstein, Stephen. Read about Geronimo. 2006. (I Like Biographies! Ser.). (Illus.). 24p. (J). lib. bdg. 21.26 (978-0-7660-2598-1(5) , Enslow Elementary) Enslow Pubs., Inc.

Flanagan, Alice K. The Buffalo Soldiers. 2004. (We the People Ser.). (Illus.). 48p. (J). 22.60 (978-0-7565-0833-3(9)) Compass Point Bks.

Glaser, Jason. The Buffalo Soldiers & the American West. Smith, Tod & Barnett, Charles, illus. 2005. (Graphic Library). 32p. (J). (gr. 3-7). lib. bdg. 25.26 (978-0-7368-4966-1(1)) Capstone Pr., Inc.

Haugen, Brenda. Geronimo: Apache Warrior. 2005. (Signature Lives Ser.). (Illus.). 112p. (J). (gr. 5-7). 30.60 (978-0-7565-1002-2(3)) Compass Point Bks.

January, Brendan. Little Bighorn: June 25, 1876. 2004. (American Battlefields Ser.). (Illus.). 32p. (J). 14.95 (978-1-59270-028-8(4)) Enchanted Lion Bks., LLC.

Jastrzembski, Joseph C. The Apache Wars: The Final Resistance. 2007. (Landmark Events in Native American History Ser.). 136p. (gr. 9). 35.00 (***978-0-7910-9343-6(3)*** , Chelsea Hse.) Facts On File, Inc.

Kiely Miller, Barbara. Chief Joseph. 2007. (J). pap. (***978-0-8368-8321-3(7)*** , Weekly Reader Early Learning Library) Stevens, Gareth Inc.

Koestler-Grack, Rachel A. Chief Joseph. 2004. (Illus.). 32p. (J). pap. 7.50 (978-1-4034-5008-1(0)); lib. bdg. 24.22 (978-1-4034-5001-2(3)) Heinemann Library.

Landau, Elaine. The Wounded Knee Massacre. 2004. (Cornerstones of Freedom Ser.). (Illus.). 48p. (J). 26.00 (978-0-516-24244-6(X) , Children's Pr.) Scholastic Library Publishing.

Lawlor, Laurie & McGraw-Hill Staff. Wind on the River: A Story of the Civil War. 2001. (Jamestown Classics Ser.). (Illus.). iv, 156p. (J). (gr. 5-8). pap. 10.00 (978-0-8092-0624-7(2) , 9780809206247) Jamestown.

Marker, Sherry. Plains Indian Wars. 2nd ed. 2003. (America at War Ser.). (Illus.). 176p. (J). (gr. 6-12). 35.00 (978-0-8160-4931-8(9)) Facts On File, Inc.

McPherson, James M. Into the West: From Reconstruction to the Final Days of the American Frontier. 2006. 96p. (J). (gr. 4-9). 22.95 (978-0-689-86543-5(0) , Atheneum) Simon & Schuster Children's Publishing.

Miller, Barbara Kiely. Chief Joseph. 2007. (Great Americans Ser.). 24p. (J). (gr. 2-4). lib. bdg. 19.93 (***978-0-8368-8314-5(4)*** , Weekly Reader Early Learning Library) Stevens, Gareth Inc.

—Jefe Joseph. 2007. (Grandes Personajes (Great Americans) Ser.). (SPA.). 24p. (J). (gr. 2-4). lib. bdg. 19.93 (***978-0-8368-8331-2(4)*** , Weekly Reader Early Learning Library) Stevens, Gareth Inc.

—Jefe Joseph (Chief Joseph) 2007. (Grandes Personajes (Great Americans) Ser.). (SPA.). 24p. (J). (gr. 2-4). pap. 5.95 (***978-0-8368-8338-1(1)*** , Weekly Reader Early Learning Library) Stevens, Gareth Inc.

Nardo, Don. The Native Americans. 2002. (History of Weapons & Warfare Ser.). (Illus.). 112p. (J). 29.95 (978-1-59018-070-9(4) , Lucent Bks.) Thomson Gale.

Netzley, Patricia D. Apache Warrior. 2002. (Daily Life Ser.). (Illus.). 48p. (J). (gr. 3-5). 26.20 (978-0-7377-0989-6(8) , Greenhaven Pr., Inc.) Thomson Gale.

Nobleman, Marc Tyler. The Battle of the Little Bighorn. 2001. (We the People Ser.). (Illus.). 48p. (J). (gr. 4 up). lib. bdg. 22.60 (978-0-7565-0150-1(4)) Compass Point Bks.

Philbrick, Nathaniel. The Mayflower & the Pilgrims' New World. 2008. 304p. (J). (gr. 4-6). 19.99 (***978-0-399-24795-8(5)*** , Putnam Juvenile) Penguin Group (USA) Inc.

Raabe, Emily. Buffalo Soldiers & the Western Frontier. 2003. (Reading Power Ser.). (Illus.). 24p. (J). lib. bdg. 17.25 (978-0-8239-6495-6(7) , PowerKids Pr.) Rosen Publishing Group, Inc., The.

—The U. S. Cavalry & the Indian Wars. 2003. (Reading Power Ser.). (Illus.). 24p. (J). lib. bdg. 17.25 (978-0-8239-6496-3(5) , PowerKids Pr.) Rosen Publishing Group, Inc., The.

Stanley, George Edward. Crazy Horse: Young War Chief. Henderson, Meryl, illus. 2005. 199p. (J). (978-1-4156-2931-4(5) , Aladdin) Simon & Schuster Children's Publishing.

Stefoff, Rebecca. The Indian Wars. 2002. (North American Historical Atlases Ser.). (Illus.). 48p. (J). 27.07 (978-0-7614-1348-6(0) , Benchmark Bks.) Cavendish, Marshall Corp.

Swain, Gwenyth. Little Crow: Leader of the Dakota. 2004. (Illus.). 102p. pap. 12.95 (978-0-87351-503-0(X) , Borealis Bk.) Minnesota Historical Society Pr.

Todd, Anne M. Chief Tecumseh. 2004. (Illus.). 32p. (J). pap. 7.50 (978-1-4034-5009-8(9)); lib. bdg. 24.22 (978-1-4034-5002-9(1)) Heinemann Library.

INDIANS OF NORTH AMERICA—WARS—FICTION

Lawlor, Laurie. Wind on the River: A Story of the Civil War. 2004. (Jamestown's American Portraits Ser.). (Illus.). 160p. (J). (gr. 5-7). pap. 4.95 (978-0-7696-3425-8(7) , Waterbird Bks.) School Specialty Publishing.

—Wind on the River: A Story of the Civil War. 2000. (978-0-606-21880-1(7)) Tandem Library Bks.

Raffa, Edwina & Rigsby, Annelle. Escape to the Everglades. 2006. pap., tchr. ed., act. bk. ed. 6.00 (978-1-56164-362-2(9)) Pineapple Pr., Inc.

INDIANS OF SOUTH AMERICA

Byers, Helen. Peru. 2004. (National Geographic Reading Expeditions Ser.). (Illus.). 24p. (J). pap. (978-0-7922-4538-4(5)) National Geographic Society.

Castner, James L. Native Peoples: Deep in the Amazon. 2001. (Deep in the Amazon Ser.). (Illus.). 32p. (J). (gr. 5 up). lib. bdg. 28.50 (978-0-7614-1128-4(3) , Benchmark Bks.) Cavendish, Marshall Corp.

Corrick, James A. The Inca. 2002. (Lost Civilizations Ser.). (Illus.). 112p. (YA). (gr. 6-8). 29.95 (978-1-56006-850-1(7) , LML00902-178181, Lucent Bks.) Thomson Gale.

Davies, Gill. Native America 900 BC- the Present. Aronson, Marc, ed. 2005. (National Geographic Timelines Ser.). (Illus.). 64p. (J). 27.90 (978-0-7922-7078-2(9)) National Geographic Society.

—Native America 9000 BC - the Present. Aronson, Marc, ed. 2005. (National Geographic Timelines Ser.). (Illus.). 64p. (J). 17.95 (978-0-7922-6456-9(8)) National Geographic Society.

Eagen, James. The Aymara of South America. 2002. (First Peoples Ser.). (Illus.). 48p. (J). (gr. 4-8). lib. bdg. 23.93 (978-0-8225-4174-5(2)) Lerner Publishing Group.

Ganeri, Anita. Living in the Amazon Rainforest. 2007. (J). pap. (***978-1-4109-2826-9(8)***); lib. bdg. (***978-1-4109-2817-7(9)***) Steck-Vaughn.

Indians of the Americas. 2005. (Illus.). (J). (gr. 5-7). 98.00 (978-0-531-18756-2(X) , Watts, Franklin) Scholastic Library Publishing.

Kachurek, Sandra J. Francisco Pizarro: Explorer of South America. 2004. (Explorers! Ser.). (Illus.). 48p. (J). lib. bdg. 23.93 (978-0-7660-2178-5(5)) Enslow Pubs., Inc.

Kallen, Stuart A. Life in the Amazon Rain Forest. 1999. (Way People Live Ser.). (Illus.). 96p. (YA). (gr. 7-10). 27.45 (978-1-56006-387-2(4) , LML00902-177770, Lucent Bks.) Thomson Gale.

Keoke, Emory Dean & Porterfield, Kay Marie. American Indian Contributions to the World: Buildings, Clothing, & Art. 2005. (American Indian Contributions to the World Ser.). (Illus.). 160p. (J). (gr. 4-9). 35.00 (978-0-8160-5394-0(4)) Facts On File, Inc.

Mann, Elizabeth. Machu Picchu: The Story of the Amazing Inkas & Their City in the Clouds. Crehore, Amy, illus. 2000. (Wonders of the World Ser.: Vol. 6). 48p. (J). (gr. 4-7). 22.95 (978-0-9650493-9-9(6)) Mikaya Pr.

Munduruku, Daniel. Tales of the Amazon: How the Munduruku Indians Live. Springer, Jane, tr. Laurabeatriz, illus. 2000. 72p. (J). (gr. 3-7). 18.95 (978-0-88899-392-2(7) , Libros Tigrillo) Groundwood Bks. CAN. *Dist:* Perseus Distribution.

Nishi, Dennis. The Incan Empire. 1999. (World History Ser.). (Illus.). 112p. (YA). (gr. 8-11). 27.45 (978-1-56006-538-8(9) , LML00902-177895, Lucent Bks.) Thomson Gale.

Raintree Steck-Vaughn Staff. Indian Nations. 2000. (Illus.). (J). 205.52 (978-0-8172-5462-9(5)) Raintree.

Rees, Rosemary. The Incas. 2006. (Illus.). 64p. (J). (***978-1-4034-8750-6(2)***) Heinemann Library.

Reynolds, Jan. Amazon Basin: Vanishing Cultures. 2007. 32p. (J). (***978-1-60060-125-5(1)***); (***978-1-60060-140-8(5)***) Lee & Low Bks., Inc.

Rosemary Rees. The Incas. 2nd ed. 2006. (Illus.). 64p. (J). pap. (***978-1-4034-8756-8(1)***) Heinemann Library.

Sayer, Chloe. The Incas. 1999. (Ancient World Ser.). (Illus.). 64p. (J). (978-0-7502-2171-9(2)) Steck-Vaughn.

Scheff, Duncan. Incas. 2001. (Ancient Civilizations Ser.). (Illus.). 48p. (J). lib. bdg. 22.83 (978-0-7398-3582-1(3)) Raintree.

Shuter, Jane. The Incas. 2002. (History Opens Windows Ser.). (Illus.). 32p. (J). (gr. 2-4). lib. bdg. 22.79 (978-1-58810-590-5(3)); Set 2. pap. 7.50 (978-1-4034-0025-3(3) , 91610) Heinemann Library.

Sirimarco, Elizabeth. Yanomamis. 1999. (Endangered Cultures Ser.). (Illus.). 32p. (YA). (gr. 4 up). lib. bdg. 16.95 (978-1-887068-96-3(1)) Smart Apple Media.

Tahan, Raya. The Yanomami of South America. 2002. (First Peoples Ser.). (Illus.). 48p. (J). (gr. 4-8). lib. bdg. 23.93 (978-0-8225-4851-5(8)) Lerner Publishing Group.

Webster, Christine. Yanomami. 2004. (Indigenous Peoples Ser.). (J). pap. 7.95 (978-1-59036-159-7(8)); (Illus.). 32p. lib. bdg. 18.20 (978-1-59036-124-5(5)) Weigl Pubs., Inc.

INDIANS OF SOUTH AMERICA—FICTION

Allende, Isabel. City of the Beasts. 2005. Tr. of Ciudad de las Bestias. 464p. (J). (gr. 7-17). pap. 7.99 (978-0-06-077645-9(5) , Rayo) HarperCollins Pubs.

—City of the Beasts. Peden, Margaret Sayers, tr. from SPA. 2002. Tr. of Ciudad de las Bestias. 416p. (J). (gr. 5 up). 19.99 (978-0-06-050918-7(X)) HarperCollins Pubs.

—City of the Beasts. l.t. ed. 2002. Tr. of Ciudad de las Bestias. 400p. (J). (gr. 5). pap. 19.99 (978-0-06-051195-1(8)) HarperCollins Pubs.

—City of the Beasts. Peden, Margaret Sayers, tr. from SPA. 2004. Tr. of Ciudad de las Bestias. 432p. (J). (gr. 5 up). reprint ed. pap. 7.99 (978-0-06-053503-2(2)) HarperCollins Pubs.

—City of the Beasts. 2004. Tr. of Ciudad de las Bestias. (gr. 5-8). lib. bdg. 16.45 (978-0-613-71427-3(X)) Tandem Library Bks.

Andrews, Jan. Very Last First Time. 1998. (978-0-606-13885-7(4)) Tandem Library Bks.

Arrieta, Maria Luz. El Ultimo Cacique de la Sabana. 2003. (SPA.). 208p. (978-958-30-0581-7(9) , PV30149) Centro de Informacion y Desarrollo de la Comunicacion y la Literatura MEX. *Dist:* Lectorum Pubns., Inc.

Brown, Virginia Pounds. The Gold Disc of Coosa. 2007. 112p. (J). pap. 11.95 (***978-1-60306-018-9(9)***) NewSouth, Inc.

Garcia, Alfredo. Erase una Vez Entre los Chibchas. 2003. (SPA.). 116p. (978-958-30-0298-4(4) , PV30144) Centro de Informacion y Desarrollo de la Comunicacion y la Literatura MEX. *Dist:* Lectorum Pubns., Inc.

Horowitz, Anthony. Evil Star. 2006. (Power of Five Ser.: Vol. 2). 320p. (J). pap. 17.99 (978-0-439-67996-1(6) , Scholastic Pr.) Scholastic, Inc.

McDermott, Gerald. Jabuti the Tortoise: A Trickster Tale from the Amazon. 2005. (Illus.). 32p. (J). (ps-ps). pap., pap. 7.00 (978-0-15-205374-1(3) , Voyager Bks./Libros Viajeros) Harcourt Children's Bks.

Palermo, Miguel Angel. Lo Que Cuentan los Mapuches. Rojas, María P, illus. 2000. (Cuentamerica Ser.). (SPA.). 62p. (YA). (gr. 4). 7.95 (978-950-07-1738-0(7) , SA30065) Editorial Sudamericana S.A. ARG. *Dist:* Lectorum Pubns., Inc.

Parker, Vic. Traditional Tales from South America. 2006. 48p. (J). (ps-4). reprint ed. 20.00 (978-1-4223-5596-1(9)) DIANE Publishing Co.

Platt, Richard. The Vanishing Rainforest. van Wyk, Rupert, illus. 32p. 2004. (J). pap. 7.95 (978-1-84507-321-3(5)); 2003. (YA). 14.99 (978-0-7112-1960-1(5)) Lincoln, Frances Ltd. GBR. *Dist:* Perseus Distribution, Antique Collectors' Club.

Thomas, Rob. Green Thumb. unabr. ed. 2000. (YA). pap. 59.00 incl. audio (978-0-7887-3641-4(8) , 41007) Recorded Bks., LLC.

—Green Thumb. 2000. (978-0-606-20048-6(7)) Tandem Library Bks.

INDIANS OF SOUTH AMERICA—FOLKLORE

Arnold, Syrah, illus. South American Myths & Legends. 2001. (World Book Myths & Legends Ser.). 64p. (J). (978-0-7166-2612-1(8)) World Bk., Inc.

Jaekel, Susan M., illus. Tug of War: A Tale about Being Resourceful. 2006. (J). (***978-1-59939-091-8(4)*** , Reader's Digest Young Families, Inc.) Reader's Digest Children's Publishing, Inc.

Knutson, Barbara. Love & Roast Chicken: A Trickster Tale from the Andes Mountains. 2004. (Carolrhoda Picture Books Ser.). (Illus.). 40p. (J). (ps-3). 16.95 (978-1-57505-657-9(7)) Lerner Publishing Group.

Pirotta, Saviour. Stories from the Amazon. 2000. (Multicultural Stories Ser.). (Illus.). 48p. (J). (ps-3). pap. 9.95 (978-0-7398-1815-2(4)) Steck-Vaughn.

Pirotta, Saviour & Gryspeerdt, Becky, illus. Stories from the Amazon. 1999. (Multicultural Stories Ser.). 48p. (J). (ps-3). lib. bdg. 27.12 (978-0-7398-1332-4(3)) Raintree.

INDIANS OF SOUTH AMERICA—PERU

Jepson-Gilbert, Anita. Maria & the Stars of Nazca (Maria y las Estrellas de Nazca) Casis, Carmen A., tr. Osban, Rodger, illus. 2004. Tr. of Maria y las Estrellas de Nazca. (SPA & ENG.). 32p. (J). pap. incl. audio compact disk (978-0-9749745-0-7(1)) TAE Nazca Resources.

—Maria & the Stars of Nazca (Maria y las Estrellas de Nazca), without audio CD. Osban, Rodger, illus. 2004. Tr. of Maria y las Estrellas de Nazca. (ENG & SPA.). pap. 14.95 (978-0-9749745-1-4(X)) TAE Nazca Resources.

Martell, Hazel Mary. Civilizations of Peru Before 1535. 1999. (Looking Back Ser.). (Illus.). 64p. (YA). (gr. 6-9). 19.98 (978-0-8172-5428-5(5)) Raintree.

INDIC LITERATURE—COLLECTIONS

Bujjai. Panchatantra, Asampreksha Karyatva. 2000. (Illus.). (J). mass mkt. 7.00 (978-81-7767-020-2(4)) Devamala Bks. Private, Ltd. IND. *Dist:* Ameya, LLC.

—Panchatantra, Labhdanasa. 2000. (Illus.). (J). mass mkt. 7.00 (978-81-7767-019-6(0)) Devamala Bks. Private, Ltd. IND. *Dist:* Ameya, LLC.

—Panchatantra, Mitrabedha. 2000. (Illus.). (J). mass mkt. 9.00 (978-81-7767-017-2(4)) Devamala Bks. Private, Ltd. IND. *Dist:* Ameya, LLC.

—Panchatantra, Mitralabha. 2000. (Illus.). (J). mass mkt. 7.00 (978-81-7767-016-5(6)) Devamala Bks. Private, Ltd. IND. *Dist:* Ameya, LLC.

—Panchatantra, Sandhivigraha. 2000. (Illus.). (J). mass mkt. 7.00 (978-81-7767-018-9(2)) Devamala Bks. Private, Ltd. IND. *Dist:* Ameya, LLC.

Mukherjee, Meera. Catching Fish & Other Stories. 2000. (Illus.). 51p. (J). pap. 8.50 (978-81-7046-180-7(4)) Seagull Bks. IND. *Dist:* South Asia Bks.

—Little Flower Shefali & Other Stories. 2000. (Illus.). 52p. (J). pap. 7.50 (978-81-7046-179-1(0)) Seagull Bks. IND. *Dist:* South Asia Bks.

INDIGENOUS PEOPLES

Bartlett, Anne. The Aboriginal Peoples of Australia. 2002. (First Peoples Ser.). (Illus.). 48p. (J). (gr. 4-8). lib. bdg. 23.93 (978-0-8225-4854-6(2)) Lerner Publishing Group.

Doudna, Kelly. People Around the World. 2004. (Around the World Ser.). (Illus.). 23p. (J). (ps-3). lib. bdg. 19.93 (978-1-59197-567-0(0)) ABDO Publishing Co.

Einarson, Earl. The Moccasins. Einarson, Earl, illus. 2005. (Illus.). 16p. (J). pap. 7.95 (978-1-894778-14-5(6)) Theytus Bks., Ltd. CAN. *Dist:* Orca Bk. Pubs. USA.

Jenson-Elliott, Cynthia L. Southern Africa. 2002. (Indigenous Peoples of Africa Ser.). (Illus.). 112p. (J). 29.95 (978-1-59018-084-6(4) , Lucent Bks.) Thomson Gale.

Kroll, Virginia L. With Love, to Earth's Endangered People. 1998. (gr. 5-8). lib. bdg. 17.60 (978-0-613-70737-4(0)) Tandem Library Bks.

—With Love, to Earth's Endangered Peoples. Collier-Morales, Roberta, illus. 1998. 48p. (YA). (gr. 4-7). pap. 8.95 (978-1-883220-82-2(3)); 17.95 (978-1-883220-83-9(1)) Dawn Pubns.

Loughran, Donna. Living in the Tundra. 2004. (Rookie Read-About Geography Ser.). (Illus.). 31p. (J). (gr. 1-2). pap. 5.95 (978-0-516-27331-0(0) , Children's Pr.) Scholastic Library Publishing.

Nile, Richard. Threatened Cultures. 1999. pap. 152.82 (978-0-8172-9645-2(X)) Raintree.

Reynolds, Jan. Far North: Vanishing Cultures. 2007. 32p. (J). (***978-1-60060-127-9(8)***); (***978-1-60060-142-2(1)***) Lee & Low Bks., Inc.

Spilsbury, Louise & Spilsbury, Richard. Living in the Himalaya. 2007. (J). (***978-1-4109-2818-4(7)***); (***978-1-4109-2827-6(6)***) Steck-Vaughn.

Strudwick, Leslie & Webster, Christine. Indigenous Peoples Series, 4 vols. 2003. (J). lib. bdg. (978-1-59036-149-8(0)) Weigl Pubs., Inc.

Zurlo, Tony. Native Peoples of West Africa. 2001. (Indigenous Peoples of Africa Ser.). (Illus.). 112p. (J). (gr. 4-12). 29.95 (978-1-56006-832-7(9) , LML00902-178164, Lucent Bks.) Thomson Gale.

INDIVIDUALITY

Here are entered works on the sum total of characteristics which distinguish an individual from all others.

see also Identity (Psychology); Personality

Ajmera, Maya. Extraordinary Girls. 2000. (J). 14.75 (978-0-606-19326-9(X)) Tandem Library Bks.

Ajmera, Maya, et al. Extraordinary Girls: A Celebration of Girlhood Around the World. 2004. (Illus.). 48p. (YA). (ps-3). 16.95 (978-0-88106-065-2(8)) Charlesbridge Publishing, Inc.

Box, Su. You Are Very Special. Poole, Susie, illus. 2003. 32p. (J). pap. 6.95 (978-0-8198-8807-5(9) , 332-417) Pauline Bks. & Media.

Burton, Margie, et al. No One Else Like Me. Evento, Susan, ed. 1998. (Early Connections Ser.). 16p. (gr. k-2). pap. 4.25 (978-1-892393-69-2(7)) Benchmark Education Co.

Charlip, Remy & Moore, Lilian. Hooray for Me! Williams, Vera B., illus. 2004. 40p. (YA). (ps up). 14.95 (978-1-883672-43-0(0) , Tricycle Pr.) Ten Speed Pr.

Danzig, Robert J. There Is Only One You: You Are Unique in the Universe. 2003. (Illus.). 72p. 9.95 (978-0-87868-884-5(6) , 8846, Child & Family Pr.) Child Welfare League of America, Inc.

Dwight, Laura, photos by. We Are All Alike... We Are All Different. 2002. (Illus.). 32p. (J). 15.95 (978-0-439-41780-8(5)) Scholastic, Inc.

Fox, Mem. Whoever You Are. 2001. (gr. k-3). lib. bdg. 14.15 (978-0-613-53881-7(1)) Tandem Library Bks.

Fox, Mem & Staub, Leslie. Quienquiera Que Seas. Ada, Alma Flor & Campoy, F. Isabel, trs. Staub, Leslie, illus. 2002. (ENG & SPA., Illus.). 32p. (J). pap. 7.00 (978-0-15-216460-7(X) , HB31513, Voyager Bks./Libros Viajeros) Harcourt Children's Bks.

Fox, Mem & Staub, Leslie. Whoever You Are. 2007. (Illus.). 28p. (J). (ps). bds. 6.95 (***978-0-15-206066-4(9)*** , Red Wagon Bks.) Harcourt Children's Bks.

Landis, Leanne. The Plainest Piece of the Puzzle. 2002. 32p. (J). pap. 8.95 (978-0-9723707-2-1(2)) White Door Publishing.

Lionni, Leo. Pezzettino. 2006. (Illus.). 40p. (J). (gr. k-3). lib. bdg. 17.99 (978-0-394-93156-2(4) , Pantheon) Knopf Publishing Group.

Mills, Andy & Osborn, Becky. Shapesville. Neitz, Erica, tr. Neitz, Erica, illus. 2003. 32p. 14.95 (978-0-936077-47-5(6)); pap. 7.95 (978-0-936077-44-4(1)) Shelter Pubns., Inc.

Muharrar, Aisha. More Than a Label: Why What You Wear & Who You're with Doesn't Define Who You Are. 2004. (Illus.). 152p. (YA). (gr. 8 up). pap. 13.95 (978-1-57542-110-0(0)) Free Spirit Publishing, Inc.

O'Keefe, Susan. Be the Star That You Are: A Book for Kids Who Feel Different. Alley, R. W., illus. 2005. (Elf-Help Books for Kids). (J). per. 7.95 (978-0-87029-391-7(5)) Abbey Pr.

Onuoha-Ezemma, Glory. Don't Make Fun of My Name: My Name Is Special to My Parents & Me. unabr. ed. 2003. (Illus.). 47p. (J). (gr. k-6). pap. 9.95 (978-0-9661598-6-8(1)) Ekwike Bks. & Publishing.

Read Magazine Editorial Staff. Read in A Different Light: Stories of Loners, Outcasts & Rebels. 2000. (Best of READ Ser.). 160p. (gr. 5 up). lib. bdg. 24.90 (978-0-7613-1615-2(9) , Millbrook Pr.) Lerner Publishing Group.

Rotner, Shelley & Kelly, Sheila M. What I Can Do? A Book about Discovering What You Do Well. 2001. (Contemporary Issues for Young Children Ser.). (Illus.). 24p. (gr. k-3). lib. bdg. 22.90 (978-0-7613-2119-4(5) , Millbrook Pr.) Lerner Publishing Group.

Scott, Foresman and Company Staff. Work & Play, Big & Little, You & Me. (J). 18.82 (978-0-673-21373-0(0) , Scott Foresman) Addison Wesley Schl.

Waters, Jennifer. All Kinds of People: What Makes Us Different. 2002. (Spyglass Books). (Illus.). 24p. (J). (gr. 1 up). lib. bdg. 18.60 (978-0-7565-0377-2(9)) Compass Point Bks.

INDIVIDUALITY—FICTION

Ada, Alma Flor. A Surprise for Mother Rabbit. 2000. (gr. k-3). lib. bdg. 17.60 (978-0-613-79391-9(9)) Tandem Library Bks.

HI

Alborough, Jez. Some Dogs Do. Alborough, Jez, illus. 2003. (Illus.). 40p. (J). (ps-2). 15.99 (978-0-7636-2201-5(X)) Candlewick Pr.

Andreae, Giles. Giraffes Can't Dance. Parker-Rees, Guy, illus. unabr. ed. 2007. (J). (ps-1). 29.95 incl. audio compact disk (*978-0-439-02734-2(9)); 24.95 incl. audio (*978-0-439-02733-5(0)) Scholastic, Inc.

Appelt, Kathi. Incredible Me! Karas, G. Brian, illus. 2003. 32p. (J). (ps-1). 15.99 (978-0-06-028622-4(9)) HarperCollins Pubs.

Arnold, Marsha D. The Pumpkin Runner. 1998. (Illus.). 32p. (J). (ps-3). 16.99 (978-0-8037-2124-1(2) , Dial) Penguin Group (USA) Inc.

Atkinson, Greg. Skuborm & His Super Hat. Ford Wilson, Melanie, illus. l.t. ed. 2002. 32p. per. (978-0-9730527-0-1(8)) Red Hare Pr.

Banana-Tail. 2003. lib. bdg. 13.95 (978-0-9727681-0-8(6)) Active Media Publishing, LLC.

Banks, Quentin. Ace of the Woods. 2005. 32p. (J). pap. 13.99 (978-1-4116-5211-8(8)) Lulu.com.

Bauer, Joan. Stand Tall. 192p. (YA). 2005. (gr. 5). pap. 7.99 (978-0-14-240427-0(6) , Puffin); 2002. (gr. 6-9). 16.99 (978-0-399-23473-6(X) , Putnam Juvenile) Penguin Group (USA) Inc.

Bea, Holly. Lucy Goose Goes to Texas. Boddy, Joe, illus. 2005. 32p. (J). 15.95 (978-1-932073-15-7(9)) New World Library.

Berger, Barbara Helen. Thunder Bunny. Berger, Barbara Helen, illus. 2007. (Illus.). 32p. (J). (ps-3). 16.99 (978-0-399-22035-7(6) , Philomel) Penguin Group (USA) Inc.

Birrer, Cynthia & Birrer, Bill, illus. The Confused Zebra. 1999. (J). 16.95 (978-0-86543-795-1(5)) Africa World Pr.

Bloom, Suzanne, illus. A Splendid Friend, Indeed. 2007. 32p. (J). 15.95 (978-1-59078-286-6(0)) Boyds Mills Pr.

Bloomfield, Denise. More Than A Spoonful. 2007. 28p. (J). mass mkt. 12.95 (*978-0-9778113-0-4(1)) HeartFelt Stories LLC.

Boynton, Sandra. Yay, You! Moving Out, Moving up, Moving On. Boynton, Sandra, illus. 2001. (Illus.). 32p. (J). (ps-3). 14.95 (978-0-689-84283-2(X) , Little Simon) Simon & Schuster Children's Publishing.

Brashares, Ann. The Second Summer of the Sisterhood. (Sisterhood of Traveling Pants Ser.: Bk. 2). (YA). (gr. 7 up). 2006. 448p. mass mkt. 6.99 (978-0-553-49501-0(1) , Dell Books for Young Readers); 2004. 416p. pap. 8.95 (978-0-385-73105-8(1) , Delacorte Bks. for Young Readers) Random Hse. Children's Bks.

—The Second Summer of the Sisterhood. l.t. ed. 2003. (Sisterhood of Traveling Pants Ser. : Bk. 2). 379p. (YA). (gr. 7 up). 25.95 (978-0-7862-5545-0(5)) Thorndike Pr.

Bridges, Shirin Yim. The Umbrella Queen. Yoo, Tae-Eun, illus. 2008. 32p. (J). 16.99 (978-0-06-075040-4(5)); lib. bdg. 17.89 (978-0-06-075041-1(3)) HarperCollins Pubs.

Brimner, Larry Dane. Nana's Hog. Miller, Susan, illus. (Rookie Reader Skill Set Ser.). 32p. (J). 1999. (gr. k-2). pap. 4.95 (978-0-516-26412-7(5)); 1998. (gr. 1-2). 19.50 (978-0-516-20755-1(5)) Scholastic Library Publishing. (Children's Pr.).

Bullard, Lisa. Marvelous Me: Inside & Out. Wesley, Omarr, illus. 2004. (All about Me Ser.). 24p. (C). (gr. k-1). 21.26 (978-1-4048-0042-7(5)) Picture Window Bks.

Bynum, Janie. Otis. 2003. (Illus.). 40p. (J). pap. 7.00 (978-0-15-204604-0(6) , Voyager Bks./Libros Viajeros) Harcourt Children's Bks.

—Otis. 2003. (gr. k-3). lib. bdg. 14.15 (978-0-613-70501-1(7)) Tandem Library Bks.

Cabot, Meg, et al. Shining On: 11 Star Author's Illuminating Stories. 2007. 176p. (YA). (gr. 7 up). 8.99 (978-0-385-73472-1(7) , Delacorte Bks. for Young Readers) Random Hse. Children's Bks.

Cave, Kathryn. Henry's Song. Hendra, Sue, illus. 2000. 32p. (J). (ps-3). 16.00 (978-0-8028-5198-7(3) , Eerdmans Bks For Young Readers) Eerdmans, William B. Publishing Co.

Cazet, Denys. Will You Read to Me? Cazet, Denys, illus. 2007. 32p. (J). (ps-1). 16.99 (978-1-4169-0935-4(4)) Simon & Schuster Children's Publishing.

Chodos-Irvine, Margaret. Ella Sarah Gets Dressed. 2003. (Illus.). 40p. (J). 16.00 (978-0-15-216413-3(8)) Harcourt Children's Bks.

Clarke, Jane & Gale, Cathy. Plodney Creeper, Supersloth. 2006. (Blue Bananas Ser.). (Illus.). 47p. (J). (978-0-7787-0850-6(0)) Crabtree Publishing Co.

Collins-Varni, H. Elizabeth. The Doll Lady. Kuusisto, Judy, illus. 2001. 32p. (J). (ps-3). 15.95 (978-0-935699-24-1(4) , 0935699244) Illumination Arts Publishing Co., Inc.

Cosgrove, Stephen. Cricket Clickett: Finding Your Talents. Arroyo, Fian, illus. 2004. (J). (978-1-58804-382-5(7)) PCI Educational Publishing.

—Shimmeree. James, Robin, illus. ed. 2003. (Serendipity Bks.). 32p. (J). (gr. k-5). pap. 4.99 (978-0-8431-0251-2(9) , Price Stern Sloan) Penguin Group (USA) Inc.

Crimi, Carolyn. Get Busy, Beaver! Bynum, Janie, illus. 2004. 32p. (J). (ps-3). pap. 15.95 (978-0-439-54866-3(7) , Orchard Bks.) Scholastic, Inc.

Damjan, Mischa. The Clown Said No. ed. 2004. (Illus.). (J). (gr. k-3). spiral bd. (978-0-616-14569-2(1)) Canadian National Institute for the Blind/Institut National Canadien pour les Aveugles.

—The Clown Said No. Casty, Gian, illus. 2007. 32p. (J). 17.99 (*978-0-698-40063-4(1) , Minedition) Penguin Group (USA) Inc.

Danielles Show & Tell Lesson. 2005. (YA). per. (978-1-59872-256-7(5)) Instantpublisher.com.

Danziger, Paula. Can You Sue Your Parents for Malpractice? 1998. 160p. (J). (gr. 4-7). pap. 4.99 (978-0-698-11688-7(7) , Putnam Juvenile) Penguin Group (USA) Inc.

—Can You Sue Your Parents for Malpractice? (gr. 5-6). 144p. (J). pap. 3.99 (978-0-8072-1375-9(6)); 152p. (YA). pap. 3.99 (978-0-8072-1540-1(6)) Random Hse. Audio Publishing Group. (Listening Library).

de Paola, Tomie. The Art Lesson. de Paola, Tomie, illus. 2002. (Illus.). (J). 13.19 (978-0-7587-1969-0(8)) Book Wholesalers, Inc.

Dolenz, Micky. Gakky Two-Feet. Clark, David, illus. 2006. (J). (*978-1-4156-8089-6(2) , Putnam Juvenile) Penguin Group (USA) Inc.

Donahue, Jill L. Last in Line. Previn, Stacey, illus. 2006. (Read-It! Readers Ser.). (J). 19.93 (978-1-4048-2415-7(4)) Picture Window Bks.

Doudna, Kelly. Goat Cheese. Haberstroh, Anne, illus. 2006. (Fact & Fiction Ser.). 24p. (J). 21.35 (978-1-59679-937-0(4) , SandCastle); pap. (978-1-59679-938-7(2)) ABDO Publishing Co.

Downey, Joni J. Will You Be My Friend? —We Really Are No Different. Brudos, Susan E., illus. 2004. (J). pap. (978-0-932991-34-8(3)) Place In The Woods, The.

Downey, Lynn. Most Loved Monster. Davis, Jack E., illus. 2004. 32p. (J). (ps). 16.99 (978-0-8037-2728-1(3) , Dial) Penguin Group (USA) Inc.

Dubner, Stephen J. The Boy with Two Belly Buttons. Niemann, Christoph, illus. 2007. 32p. (J). lib. bdg. 17.89 (*978-0-06-113403-6(1)); 16.99 (*978-0-06-113402-9(3)) HarperCollins Pubs.

Dupuy, Diane. The Little Girl Who Did... What?!!! Stockelbach, Ed, illus. 2004. 32p. 12.95 (978-0-9730736-0-7(8)) Beyond Light CAN. *Dist:* Hushion Hse. Publishing, Ltd.

Eastman, Peter. Fred & Ted Go Camping. 2005. (Bright & Early Bks.). (Illus.). 48p. (J). (gr. k-3). 8.99 (978-0-375-82965-9(2)); lib. bdg. 12.99 (978-0-375-92965-6(7)) Random Hse. Children's Bks. (Random Hse. Bks. for Young Readers).

Eastman, Peter Anthony. Fred & Ted Like to Fly. 2007. (Beginner Books(R) Ser.). (Illus.). 48p. (J). (gr. k-3). 8.99 (978-0-375-84064-7(8)); lib. bdg. 12.99 (978-0-375-94064-4(2)) Random Hse. Children's Bks. (Random Hse. Bks. for Young Readers).

Ehlert, Lois. Oodles of Animals. 2008. (J). (*978-0-15-206274-3(2)) Harcourt Trade Pubs.

Emerson, Carl. Speed up, Sammy the Tree Sloth! Trover, Zachary, illus. 2007. (Animal Underdogs Ser.). 32p. (J). (ps-4). lib. bdg. 27.07 (*978-1-60270-019-2(2) , Looking Glass Library) Magic Wagon.

Ering, Timothy B. Necks Out for Adventure: The True Story of Edwin Wiggleskin. 2007. 48p. (J). (*978-0-7636-2355-5(5)) Candlewick Pr.

Evans, Nate & Numeroff, Laura Nate. Sherman Crunchley. Bowers, Tim, illus. 2005. 32p. (J). pap. 5.99 (978-0-14-240385-3(7) , Puffin) Penguin Group (USA) Inc.

Fogg, K. L. Serpent Tide. 2006. 16.95 (978-1-59156-861-2(7)) Covenant Communications, Inc.

Fox, Mem. The Straight Line Wonder. (978-1-57255-567-9(X)) Mondo Publishing.

—The Straight Line Wonder. 2002. (gr. 3-6). lib. bdg. 14.15 (978-0-613-82650-1(7)) Tandem Library Bks.

Fredericks, Mariah. The True Meaning of Cleavage. (YA). 2003. (Illus.). 224p. 15.95 (978-0-689-85092-9(1) , Atheneum/Richard Jackson Bks.); 2004. 240p. reprint ed. pap. 6.99 (978-0-689-86958-7(4) , Simon Pulse) Simon & Schuster Children's Publishing.

Friedman, Laurie B. A Style All Her Own. Watts, Sharon, illus. 2005. 32p. (J). (ps-3). lib. bdg. 15.95 (978-1-57505-599-2(6)) Lerner Publishing Group.

Gardeski, Christina Mia. All Kinds of Kids. McMahon, Bob, illus. 2002. 19.95 (978-1-932715-38-5(X)) UMI (Urban Ministries, Inc.).

—All Kinds of Kids Level A. McMahon, Bob, illus. 2002. (Rookie Readers Ser.). 24p. (J). (gr. k-1). 19.50 (978-0-516-22370-4(4) , Children's Pr.) Scholastic Library Publishing.

—Toda Clase de Ninos. 2002. Tr. of All Kinds of Kids. (gr. k-3). lib. bdg. 12.95 (978-0-613-59552-0(1)) Tandem Library Bks.

Genechten, Guido van. Flop-Ear. 2002. (Illus.). (J). (978-0-7641-5543-7(1)) Barron's Educational Series, Inc.

Gikow, Louise. The Big Game. Garner, Phil, tr. Garner, Phil, illus. 2004. (My First Reader Ser.). 31p. (J). 18.50 (978-0-516-24408-2(6) , Children's Pr.) Scholastic Library Publishing.

Goss, Leon. I'm Good, I'm Beautiful, I'm Smart. Mailey, Maria C. & Neuburger, Jenny, illus. 2005. (J). per. (978-1-933156-02-6(3) , VisionQuest Kids) GSVQ Publishing.

Graham, Wendy. My Weird Mother. Burgemeestre, Kevin, illus. 1999. (Supa Doopers Ser.). 56p. (J). (978-0-7608-1921-0(1)) Sundance/Newbridge Educational Publishing.

Gray, Libba Moore. Miss Tizzy. Rowland, Jada, illus. 1998. 40p. (J). (ps-3). 6.99 (978-0-689-81897-4(1) , Aladdin) Simon & Schuster Children's Publishing.

—Miss Tizzy. 1998. (978-0-606-13611-2(8)) Tandem Library Bks.

Green, George & Brooke, Amy/ J. George Green's, the Lion Who Couldn't Roar. 2007. (J). per. 17.99 (*978-1-933156-14-9(7) , Visikid Bks.) GSVQ Publishing.

Haber, Melissa. Heroic Adventures of Hercules Amsterdam. 2004. 224p. (J). (gr. 5). pap. 5.99 (978-0-14-240216-0(8) , Puffin) Penguin Group (USA) Inc.

Hacker, Michael. Who Am I? Dillard, Karen, illus. 2000. 24p. (J). (ps). 7.99 (978-1-56309-736-2(2)) New Hope Pubs.

Hall, Kirsten. First Day of School: All about Shapes & Sizes. Luedecke, Bev, illus. 2003. (Beastieville Ser.). 32p. (J). (ps-1). 19.50 (978-0-516-22893-8(5) , Children's Pr.) Scholastic Library Publishing.

Hallem, J. Horsing Around. Squire, Stan, illus. 2006. (Read-It! Chapter Books). 64p. (J). (gr. 2-4). 19.95 (978-1-4048-1666-4(6)) Picture Window Bks.

Hallowell, Edward & Mayer, Bill. A Walk in the Rain with a Brain. 2004. (Illus.). 32p. (J). (gr. 1-3). 16.95 (978-0-06-000731-7(1) , ReganBooks) HarperCollins Pubs.

Hautman, Pete. Rash. (YA). 2007. 272p. pap. 8.99 (*978-0-689-86904-4(5) , Simon Pulse); 2006. 256p. (gr. 7 up). 16.99 (978-0-689-86801-6(4) , Simon & Schuster Children's Publishing) Simon & Schuster Children's Publishing.

—Rash. l.t. rev. ed. 2007. 307p. (YA). 22.95 (*978-0-7862-9312-4(8)) Thorndike Pr.

Haynes, Eva Johns. The Turkey That Crowed. Bozarth, Kelly Paige, illus. 2000. 32p. (J). (ps-3). pap. 6.95 (978-0-9679211-0-5(4)) Haynes, Eva Johns.

Helakoski, Leslie. Woolbur. Harper, Lee, illus. 2008. 32p. (J). 16.99 (*978-0-06-084726-5(3)) HarperCollins Pubs.

Heling, Kathryn & Hembrook, Deborah. I Wish I Had Freckles Like Abby/Quisiera tener pecas como Abby. de la Vega, Eida, tr. Adamson, Bonnie, illus. 2006. Tr. of Quisiera tener pecas como Abby. (SPA.). (J). 4.99 (978-0-9770906-6-2(3)) Raven Tree Pr.

—I Wish I Had Freckles Like Abby/Quisiera tener pecas como Abby. de la Vega, Eida, tr. Parins, Kris, illus. 2005. Tr. of Quisiera tener pecas como Abby. (SPA & ENG.). 32p. (J). 16.95 (978-0-9724973-8-1(2) , 626999) Raven Tree Pr.

—I Wish I Had Glasses Like Rosa/Quisiera tener lentes como Rosa. de la Vega, Eida, tr. Adamson, Bonnie, illus. Tr. of Quisiera tener lentes como Rosa. (SPA.). (J). 2006. 4.99 (978-0-9770906-5-5(5)); 2005. 32p. 16.95 (978-0-9724973-7-4(4) , 626999) Raven Tree Pr.

Henshon, Suzanna E. Spiders on the Ceiling. 2006. (J). (978-0-88092-614-0(7)) Royal Fireworks Publishing Co.

Herman, Gail. Just Like Mike. 2001. (978-0-606-21277-9(9)) Tandem Library Bks.

Herrick, Steven. Naked Bunyip Dancing. Norling, Beth, illus. 2008. (J). (*978-1-59078-499-0(5) , Front Street) Boyds Mills Pr.

Hume, Lachie. Clancy the Courageous Cow. Hume, Lachie, illus. 2007. (Illus.). 32p. (gr. k-1). 16.99 (978-0-06-117249-6(9)) HarperCollins Pubs.

Hurst, Carol Otis. Terrible Storm. Schindler, S. D., illus. 2007. 32p. (J). (gr. k-3). 16.99 (978-0-06-009001-2(4)); lib. bdg. 17.89 (978-0-06-009002-9(2)) HarperCollins Pubs.

Iyengar, Malathi. Romina's Rangoli/By Malathi Michelle Iyengar ; Illustrated by Jennifer Wanardi. Wanardi, Jennifer, illus. 2007. (J). (*978-1-885008-32-9(5)) Shen's Bks.

Jenkins, Emily. Daffodil. Bogacki, Tomek, illus. 2004. 32p. (J). 16.00 (978-0-374-31676-1(7) , Farrar, Straus & Giroux (BYR)) Farrar, Straus & Giroux.

—Daffodil, Crocodile. Bogacki, Tomek, illus. 2007. 32p. (J). (ps-3). 16.00 (978-0-374-39944-3(1) , Farrar, Straus & Giroux (BYR)) Farrar, Straus & Giroux.

Jones, Christianne C. Emma's New Look. 2007. (Illus.). 24p. (J). (*978-1-4048-1230-7(X)) Picture Window Bks.

—Emma's New Look. Yilmaz, Necdet, illus. 2006. (Read It! Readers Ser.). 32p. (J). (gr. 1-2). 19.93 (*978-1-4048-3138-4(X)) Picture Window Bks.

Jones, Christianne C. Tricia's Talent. Ramos, Beatriz Helena, illus. 2005. (Read-It! Readers Ser.). (J). (978-1-4048-1727-2(1)) Picture Window Bks.

Kann, Elizabeth. Purplicious. Kann, Victoria, illus. 2007. 40p. (J). lib. bdg. 17.89 (*978-0-06-124406-3(6)) HarperCollins Pubs.

Kann, Elizabeth & Kann, Victoria. Purplicious. Kann, Victoria, illus. 2007. 40p. (J). (gr. k-3). 16.99 (*978-0-06-124405-6(8)) HarperCollins Pubs.

Karns, Marie. The Incredible Peepers of Penelope Budd. Wummer, Amy, illus. 2005. 32p. (J). 15.95 (978-1-58685-405-8(4)) Gibbs Smith, Publisher.

Keller, John G. The Rubber-Legged Duck. Cole, Henry, illus. 2008. (J). (*978-0-15-205289-8(5)) Harcourt Trade Pubs.

Kenah, Katharine. The Best Chef in Second Grade. Carter, Abby, illus. 2007. (I Can Read Bks.). 48p. (J). lib. bdg. 16.89 (*978-0-06-053562-9(8)); 15.99 (*978-0-06-053561-2(X)) HarperCollins Pubs.

Kessler, Leonard, illus. & text. Mr. Pine's Mixed-up Signs. Kessler, Leonard, text. anniv. ed. 2001. 61p. (J). 16.00 (978-1-930900-03-5(1)) Purple Hse. Pr.

King-Smith, Dick. Funny Frank. Eastwood, John, illus. 2003. 112p. (gr. 2-5). pap. 5.50 (978-0-440-41880-1(1) , Yearling) Random Hse. Children's Bks.

—Funny Frank. Roth, Roger & Eastwood, John, illus. 2002. 112p. (J). (gr. 2-5). 14.95 (978-0-375-81460-0(4) , Knopf Bks. for Young Readers) Random Hse. Children's Bks.

—Funny Frank. 2003. (gr. 3-6). lib. bdg. 13.00 (978-0-613-72193-6(4)) Tandem Library Bks.

Koch, Edward T. & Koch Thaler, Pat. Eddie: Harold's Little Brother. Warhola, James, illus. 2004. 32p. (J). (ps). 16.99 (978-0-399-24210-6(4) , Putnam Juvenile) Penguin Group (USA) Inc.

Koja, Kathe. Straydog. 2002. (Illus.). 112p. (YA). (gr. 8-10). 16.00 (978-0-374-37278-1(0) , Farrar, Straus & Giroux (BYR)) Farrar, Straus & Giroux.

—Straydog. 2004. 128p. (YA). reprint ed. pap. 5.99 (978-0-14-240071-5(8) , Puffin) Penguin Group (USA) Inc.

Konigsburg, E. L. The Outcasts of 19 Schuyler Place. 304p. 2004. 16.95 (978-0-689-86636-4(4) , Atheneum); 2005. (J). reprint ed. pap. 5.99 (978-0-689-86637-1(2) , Aladdin) Simon & Schuster Children's Publishing.

—The Outcasts of 19 Schuyler Place. l.t. ed. 2004. (Thorndike Press Large Print the Literary Bridge Ser.). 346p. (J). 22.95 (978-0-7862-6483-4(7)) Thorndike Pr.

Kostecki-Shaw, Jenny Sue. My Travelin' Eye. 2008. 40p. (J). 16.95 (*978-0-8050-8169-5(0)) Holt, Henry & Co.

Krauser, Susan A. Lilith A. Wilith. 2002. (J). lib. bdg. 16.95 (978-0-9717860-0-4(3)) Lilith & Co.

Krensky, Stephen. Milo the Really Big Bunny. Suber, Melissa, illus. 2006. 32p. (J). (ps-1). 14.95 (978-0-689-87345-4(X)) Simon & Schuster Children's Publishing.

Kupchella, Rick. Girls Can! Make it Happen. Brown, Marilyn, illus. 2004. 40p. (J). 16.95 (978-0-9726504-3-4(1)) Tristan Publishing, Inc.

Laybourn, Emma. Missing Magic. 2007. 192p. (J). (gr. 4 up). 16.99 (978-0-8037-3219-3(8) , Dial) Penguin Group (USA) Inc.

Lechner, John. Sticky Burr: Adventures in Burrwood Forest. Lechner, John, illus. 2007. (Illus.). 56p. (J). (gr. 1-5). 15.99 (978-0-7636-3054-6(3)) Candlewick Pr.

Leonard, Marcia. Best Friends. Handelman, Dorothy, photos by. 1999. (Real Kids Readers Ser.). (Illus.). 32p. (ps-1). lib. bdg. 18.90 (978-0-7613-2064-7(4) , Millbrook Pr.) Lerner Publishing Group.

—Best Friends. (J). (978-0-606-19144-9(5)); 1999. lib. bdg. 13.00 (978-0-613-18155-6(7)) Tandem Library Bks.

Lester, Helen. El Pinguino Taky. Munsinger, Lynn, illus. 2001. (SPA.). 32p. (J). (gr. k-3). pap. 5.95 (978-0-618-12531-9(0) , HM30384); tchr. ed. 15.00 (978-0-618-12530-2(2) , HM30383) Houghton Mifflin Co. Trade & Reference Div.

Livingston, Irene. Finklehopper Frog. Lies, Brian, illus. 2004. 30p. (J). (ps-2). 14.95 (978-1-58246-075-8(2) , Tricycle Pr.) Ten Speed Pr.

Lowry, Lois. A Summer to Die. 2007. 160p. (YA). (gr. 7). pap. 7.99 (978-0-385-73420-2(4) , Delacorte Bks. for Young Readers) Random Hse. Children's Bks.

—A Summer to Die. 1999. mass mkt. (978-0-553-14304-1(2)); mass mkt. (978-0-553-24389-5(6)); mass mkt. (978-0-553-25447-1(2)) Random Hse., Inc.

Lowry, Lois, frwd. Shining On: 11 Star Authors' Illuminating Stories. 2007. 176p. (YA). (gr. 7). lib. bdg. 11.99 (978-0-385-90470-4(3) , Delacorte Bks. for Young Readers) Random Hse. Children's Bks.

Lucado, Max. Punchinello & the Most Marvelous Gift: And, Your Special Gift. Martinez, Sergio, illus. 2007. (J). (*978-1-58134-877-4(0)) Crossway Bks.

Lucado, Max. Your Special Gift. Wenzel, David, illus. 2006. 31p. (J). 15.99 (978-1-58134-698-5(0)) Crossway Bks.

Lucas, David. Halibut Jackson. 2004. (Illus.). 32p. (J). (ps-3). 16.95 (978-0-375-82690-0(4) , Knopf Bks. for Young Readers) Random Hse. Children's Bks.

MacDonald, Alan. Trolls Go Home! Beech, Mark, illus. 2007. 128p. (J). 14.95 (*978-1-59990-077-3(7)); pap. 5.95 (*978-1-59990-078-0(5)) Bloomsbury Publishing.

Madison, Alan. Velma Gratch & the Way Cool Butterfly. Hawkes, Kevin, illus. 2007. 40p. (J). (ps-3). 16.99 (*978-0-375-83597-1(0) , Schwartz & Wade Bks.) Random Hse. Children's Bks.

Maguire, Arlene. Special People, Special Ways. Carpenter, Christina D., ed. Bailey, Sheila, illus. 1999. 32p. (J). (ps-3). 14.95 (978-1-886440-00-5(X)) Portunus Publishing Co.

Manning, Mick. Cock-a-Doodle-Hooooooo! Granstrom, Brita, illus. 2007. 28p. (J). (ps-2). 16.95 (*978-1-56148-568-0(3)) Good Bks.

Marien, Donna. Waiting at the Bay: A Young Woman's Reflections on Journeys in the Sea of Life. 2003. 108p. (YA). pap. 10.95 (978-0-595-26304-2(6) , Writers Club Pr.) iUniverse, Inc.

Martin, Bill, Jr. Chicken Chuck. Salerno, Steven, illus. 40p. (J). (ps-3). 2001. pap. 7.95 (978-1-58837-017-4(8)); 2000. 16.95 (978-1-890817-31-2(7)) Winslow Pr.

Martin, Bill. Chicken Chuck. Salerno, Steven, illus. 2005. 32p. (J). pap. 5.95 (978-0-7614-5216-4(8)) Cavendish, Marshall Corp.

Martin, Bill, Jr. & Sampson, Michael. The Little Squeegy Bug. Corrigan, Patrick, illus. 2001. 32p. (J). (ps-2). reprint ed. pap. 5.95 (978-0-7614-5243-0(5)) Cavendish, Marshall Corp.

Marvelous Me. (All about Me Ser.). 24p. (J). 6.95 (978-1-4048-0157-8(X)) Picture Window Bks.

Mayfield, Sue & Padua, Rochelle. I Can, You Can, Toucan! 2006. (Green Bananas Ser.). (Illus.). 47p. (J). (978-0-7787-1032-5(7)) Crabtree Publishing Co.

McCabe, Lauren A. How Many Spots Have I Got? Foulke, Nancy, illus. 2005. (J). 16.00 (978-1-893516-02-1(4)) Our Child Pr.

McKenna, Mark, et al, illus. Banana Tail. 2003. 32p. (J). 12.95 (978-0-9727681-3-9(0)) Active Media Publishing, LLC.

Meister, Cari. What Can I Be? Phillips, Matt, illus. 2003. (Rookie Reader Ser.). 24p. (J). 19.50 (978-0-516-22876-1(5) , Children's Pr.) Scholastic Library Publishing.

Meomi. The Octonauts & the Only Lonely Monster. 2006. (Illus.). 36p. (J). (ps-3). 15.95 (978-1-59702-005-3(2)) Immedium.

Merrell, Victoria Jane. The Buffalo & the Butterfly. Bilisoly, Harvey, illus. 2002. 12p. (J). (ps-4). 21.95 (978-0-9717556-0-4(4)) VJM Pubns.

Mills, Claudia. Lizzie at Last. 2002. 152p. (J). (gr. 4-7). lib. bdg. 14.15 (978-0-613-50150-7(0)) Tandem Library Bks.

—Lizzie Mcguire at Last. 2002. 160p. (gr. 3-7). pap. 5.99 (978-0-7868-1672-9(4)) Hyperion Paperbacks for Children.

Mitchell, Lori. Different Just Like Me. (Illus.). 32p. (J). (ps-3). 2001. pap. 6.95 (978-1-57091-490-4(7)); 1999. 15.95 (978-0-88106-975-4(2)) Charlesbridge Publishing, Inc.

—Different Just Like Me. 2001. (gr. k-3). lib. bdg. 16.40 (978-0-613-79208-0(4)) Tandem Library Bks.

Mochizuki, Ken. Beacon Hill Boys. 208p. (J). 2004. (gr. 7 up). 5.99 (978-0-439-24906-5(6)); 2002. (gr. 9 up). pap. 16.95 (978-0-439-26749-6(8) , Scholastic Pr.) Scholastic, Inc.

H I

Montserrat, Pep. Ms. Rubinstein's Beauty. 2006. (Illus.). 32p. (J). (gr. k-2). 14.95 (978-1-4027-3063-4(2)) Sterling Publishing Co., Inc.

Morgan, Michaela. Silly Sausage in Trouble. Shulman, Dee, illus. 2006. (Read-It! Chapter Books). (J). 21.26 (978-1-4048-2737-0(4)) Picture Window Bks.

Munsch, Robert N. Stephanie's Ponytail. Martchenko, Michael, illus. 2007. (Annikins Ser.). 24p. (J). (ps-2). pap. 1.50 (*978-1-55451-114-3(3)) Annick Pr., Ltd. CAN. *Dist:* Firefly Bks., Ltd.

Murray, Andrew. The Very Sleepy Sloth. Tickle, Jack, tr. Tickle, Jack, illus. 2003. 32p. (J). tchr. ed. 15.95 (978-1-58925-033-8(8) , tiger tales) ME Media LLC.

Murray, Martine. Henrietta: There's No One Better. 2006. (Illus.). (J). 88p. 9.99 (978-0-439-80749-4(2)); 96p. pap. 9.99 (978-0-439-80747-0(6)) Scholastic, Inc. (Levine, Arthur A. Bks.).

Namm, Diane. My Best Friend. Gordon, Mike, illus. 2004. (My First Reader Ser.). 32p. (J). (gr. k-1). pap. 3.95 (978-0-516-25504-0(5) , Children's Pr.) Scholastic Library Publishing.

—My Best Friend. Gordon, Mike, tr. Gordon, Mike, illus. 2004. (My First Reader Ser.). 31p. (J). 18.50 (978-0-516-24416-7(7) , Children's Pr.) Scholastic Library Publishing.

Naylor, Phyllis Reynolds. Anyone Can Eat Squid! Ramsey, Marcy Dunn, illus. 2005. 80p. (J). 14.95 (978-0-7614-5182-2(X)) Cavendish, Marshall Corp.

Neasi, Barbara J. Just Like Me. Hantel, Johanna, illus. rev. ed. 2003. (Rookie Reader Espanol Ser.). 32p. (J). (gr. k-2). pap. 4.95 (978-0-516-27495-9(3) , Children's Pr.) Scholastic Library Publishing.

—Just Like Me. rev. ed. 2002. (Rookie Readers Ser.). (J). lib. bdg. 19.00 (978-0-516-22564-7(2) , Children's Pr.) Scholastic Library Publishing.

—Just Like Me. Hantel, Johanna, illus. rev. ed. 2002. (Rookie Readers Ser.). 31p. (J). (gr. 1-2). 19.50 (978-0-516-22669-9(X) , Children's Pr.) Scholastic Library Publishing.

O'Connor, Jane. Fancy Nancy. Glasser, Robin Preiss, illus. 2005. (Fancy Nancy Ser.). 32p. (J). 16.99 (978-0-06-054209-2(8)); lib. bdg. 17.89 (978-0-06-054210-8(1)) HarperCollins Pubs.

—Fancy Nancy & the Posh Puppy. Glasser, Robin Preiss, illus. 2007. (Fancy Nancy Ser.). 32p. (J). lib. bdg. 17.89 (*978-0-06-054215-3(2)); 16.99 (*978-0-06-054213-9(6)) HarperCollins Pubs.

—Fancy Nancy Loves! Loves!! Loves!!! Glasser, Robin Preiss, illus. 2007. (Fancy Nancy Ser.). 12p. (J). (ps-3). pap. 6.99 (*978-0-06-123599-3(7) , Harper Festival) HarperCollins Pubs.

—Fancy Nancy's Glamorous Gift. Glasser, Robin Preiss, illus. gif. ed. 2007. (Fancy Nancy Ser.). 32p. (J). (ps-2). 24.99 (*978-0-06-137182-0(3)) HarperCollins Pubs.

O'Neill, Peggy. Little Squarehead. Freeman, Denise, illus. 2001. 32p. (J). (ps up). 15.95 (978-0-935699-21-0(X) , 093569921x) Illumination Arts Publishing Co., Inc.

Oram, Hiawyn. The Wrong Overcoat. Birchall, Mark, illus. 2000. (Picture Bks.). 32p. (J). (ps-3). lib. bdg. 15.95 (978-1-57505-453-7(1) , Carolrhoda Bks.) Lerner Publishing Group.

Parks, Charlsie Austin. The Beautiful Duckling. Moisan, Elizabeth, illus. 2001. 64p. (J). 20.95 (978-1-57736-210-4(1) , Hillsboro Pr.) Providence Hse Pubs.

Parr, Todd. The Family Book. Parr, Todd, illus. 2003. (Illus.). 32p. (J). (ps-1). 15.99 (978-0-316-73896-5(4)) Little Brown & Co.

—It's Okay to Be Different. Parr, Todd, illus. 2001. (Illus.). 32p. (J). (ps-1). 15.99 (978-0-316-66603-9(3) , Tingley, Megan Bks.) Little, Brown Bks. for Young Readers.

Paul, Ann Whitford. Hop! Hop! Hop! Gerardi, Jan, illus. 2005. 32p. (J). (ps-1). pap. 3.99 (978-0-375-82857-7(5) , Random Hse. Bks. for Young Readers) Random Hse. Children's Bks.

Peterson, Bruce & Peterson, Marilyn. The Adventures of Bo the Cloud: The Rainbow Bird. Horton, Pamela, ed. Panasiti, Peg, illus. 2001. 28p. (J). mass mkt. 9.95 incl. audio (978-0-9708417-0-4(1)) High Hopes Publishing.

Piven, Hanoch. My Dog Is As Smelly As Dirty Socks: And Other Funny Family Portraits. 2007. (Illus.). 40p. (J). (ps-3). 15.99 (978-0-375-84052-4(4)); lib. bdg. 18.99 (978-0-375-94052-1(9)) Random Hse. Children's Bks. (Schwartz & Wade Bks.).

Proimos, James. The Many Adventures of Johnny Mutton. Proimos, James, illus. 2001. (Johnny Mutton Ser.). (Illus.). 48p. (J). (gr. k-4). pap. 6.00 (978-0-15-202413-0(1) , Harcourt Paperbacks) Harcourt Children's Bks.

Raintree Steck-Vaughn Staff. I'm Special! 2000. (Read All about It Ser.). (Illus.). (J). pap. 4.95 (978-0-8114-3739-4(6)) Steck-Vaughn.

Raschka, Chris. New York Is English, Chattanooga Is Creek. 2005. (Illus.). 40p. (J). (gr. k-4). 16.95 (978-0-689-84600-7(2) , Atheneum) Simon & Schuster Children's Publishing.

Rau, Dana Meachen. Wonderful Things. Woodworth, Viki, illus. 2001. (Early Reader Ser.). 32p. (J). (gr. k up). lib. bdg. 18.60 (978-0-7565-0075-7(3)) Compass Point Bks.

Rawlinson, Julia. Mule School. Chapman, Lynne, illus. 2008. (J). (*978-1-56148-597-0(7)) Good Bks.

Read, Nicholas. Saving Emily. Klem, Ellen, illus. 2004. (Young Readers Ser.). 150p. (J). (gr. 5 up). pap. 16.00 (978-1-57392-897-7(6) , Pyr Bks.) Prometheus Bks., Pubs.

Reiser, Lynn. My Way/Mi Manera: A Margaret & Margarita Story/Un Cuento de Margarita y Margaret. Reiser, Lynn, illus. 2007. Tr. of A mi Manera: Un cuento de Margarita y Margaret. (ENG & SPA., Illus.). 32p. (J). (ps-1). 15.99 (978-0-06-084101-0(X)) HarperCollins Pubs.

Reiss-Weimann, Elayne. I'm Different. Yeagle, Dean, illus. 2002. (Read-To-Me Ser.). 25p. (J). (978-0-7665-1224-5(X)) Abrams, Harry N. , Inc.

Reynolds, Cynthia Furlong. Grammie's Secret Cupboard. Dodson, Bert, illus. 2007. 32p. (J). 17.95 (*978-1-58726-310-1(6) , Mitten Pr.) Ann Arbor Media Group, LLC.

Richardson, John. Grunt. Rogers, Emma, illus. 2002. 32p. (J). (gr. k-3). 15.00 (978-0-618-15974-1(6) , Clarion Bks.) Houghton Mifflin Co. Trade & Reference Div.

Rix, Jamie. Mr. Mumble's Fabulous Flybrows. 2003. (Illus.). 64p. (J). pap. 8.99 (978-0-552-54747-5(6) , Corgi) Transworld Publishers Ltd. GBR. *Dist:* Trafalgar Square Publishing.

Robbins, Jacqui. Two of a Kind. Phelan, Matt, illus. 2008. (J). (*978-1-4169-2437-1(X)) Simon & Schuster Children's Publishing.

Rogers, Karen M. Mingo y Yo. Alvarado, Ana María, tr. Bulet, Getty, illus. 2000. (Think-Kids Book Collection).Tr. of Max & Me. (SPA.). 16p. (J). (gr. 1-4). pap. 2.95 (978-1-58237-050-7(8)) Creative Thinkers, Inc.

Rohmann, Eric. Pumpkinhead. 2003. 32p. (J). (gr. k-4). 14.95 (978-0-375-82416-6(2) , Knopf Bks. for Young Readers) Random Hse. Children's Bks.

Rovetch, Lissa. Frog Went A-Dancing. Berry, Holly, illus. 2006. (J). (978-1-58987-008-6(5)) Kindermusik International.

Saltzberg, Barney. Star of the Week. Saltzberg, Barney, illus. 2006. (Illus.). 32p. (J). (gr. k-3). 15.99 (978-0-7636-2914-4(6)) Candlewick Pr.

Savadier, Elivia. Time to Get Dressed! Savadier, Elivia, illus. 2006. (Illus.). 32p. (J). 14.95 (978-1-59643-161-4(X)) Roaring Brook Pr.

Schaefer, Lola M. Frankie Stein. Atteberry, Kevan, illus. 2007. 32p. (J). (ps-2). 16.99 (*978-0-7614-5358-1(X)) Cavendish, Marshall Corp.

Schick, Alice & Schick, Joel. The Penguin Child & the Albatross Child. 2007. (J). bds. 13.95 (*978-1-59692-228-0(1)) MacAdam/Cage Publishing, Inc.

Shannon, David. A Bad Case of Stripes. 2007. (J). 9.95 (978-0-439-92494-8(4)) Scholastic, Inc.

Shannon, David. Bad Case of Stripes - Library Edition. 2007. (J). 18.95 (*978-0-439-02328-3(9)) Scholastic, Inc.

Shaskan, Trisha Speed. This Is Anna. Senturk, Burak, illus. 2006. 24p. (J). (*978-1-4048-3168-1(1)) Picture Window Bks.

Shay, Ruth Ann. The Littlest Susan. Mertes, Charles, illus. 2000. 32p. (J). (ps-4). lib. bdg. 20.00 (978-0-9701167-0-3(5)) Guided Pen Pr.

Silvermetz, Marcia A. Gertrude the Albino Frog & Her Friend Rupert the Turtle. Doyel, Ginger, illus. 2003. 48p. (J). (gr. 2-3). 19.95 (978-0-9718724-0-0(6)) Hiccup Cottage Pubns.

Singer, Marilyn. The One & Only Me. Rubel, Nicole, illus. 2000. (Growing Tree Ser.). 24p. (J). (ps-k). 9.95 (978-0-694-01279-4(3) , Harper Festival) HarperCollins Pubs.

Smallman, Steve. Bumbletum. Warnes, Tim, illus. 2006. 32p. (J). 15.95 (978-1-58925-060-4(5) , tiger tales) ME Media LLC.

Spelman, Cornelia Maude. When I Feel Good about Myself. Parkinson, Kathy, illus. 2003. (Way I Feel Ser.). 24p. (J). (ps-1). 15.95 (978-0-8075-8887-1(3)) Whitman, Albert & Co.

Spinelli, Eileen. I Like Noisy, Mom Likes Quiet. Halverson, Lydia, illus. 2006. 32p. (J). 8.95 (978-0-8249-5517-5(X) , 1256103, Ideals Children's Bks.) Ideals Pubns.

Spinelli, Jerry. Star Girl. 2000. 192p. (J). (gr. 5-8). 15.95 (978-0-679-88637-2(0) , Knopf Bks. for Young Readers) Random Hse. Children's Bks.

—Stargirl. 2002. (EMC Masterpiece Series Access Editions). xiv, 199p. (YA). 10.95 (978-0-8219-2504-1(0) , 35378) EMC/Paradigm Publishing.

—Stargirl. unabr. ed. 2004. 192p. (J). (gr. 7 up). pap. 40.00 incl. audio (978-0-8072-0855-7(8) , LYA 323 SP, Listening Library) Random Hse. Audio Publishing Group.

—Stargirl. (YA). 2004. 208p. (gr. 5). mass mkt. 6.99 (978-0-440-41677-7(9) , Laurel Leaf); 2000. 192p. (gr. 5-8). lib. bdg. 17.99 (978-0-679-98637-9(5) , Knopf Bks. for Young Readers); 2002. 208p. (gr. 7 up). reprint ed. pap. 8.95 (978-0-375-82233-9(X) , Knopf Bks. for Young Readers) Random Hse. Children's Bks.

—Stargirl. Tino, illus. (SPA.). 224p. (J). (gr. 5-8). pap. 9.95 (978-1-59437-815-7(0)) Santillana USA Publishing Co., Inc.

—Stargirl. 2002. (gr. 7-12). lib. bdg. 17.60 (978-0-613-49417-5(2)) Tandem Library Bks.

—Stargirl. l.t. ed. 2001. 240p. (J). (gr. 8-12). 24.95 (978-0-7862-3218-5(8)) Thorndike Pr.

Spruill, Ed & Spruill, Sonya. Jordan's Hair. Peringer, Stephen Mercer, illus. 2005. 16p. (J). 8.00 (978-0-8170-1484-1(5)) Judson Pr.

Sula, Sondra. Katie: Katie & the Ogre. Ruiz, Marcus, illus. 2000. 32p. (J). (gr. 1-3). pap. (978-1-931179-01-0(8)) Long Hill Productions, Inc.

Sundgaard, Arnold & Sundgaard, Carle. The Lamb & the Butterfly. Carle, Eric, illus. 1999. 32p. (J). (ps-1). pap. 16.95 (978-0-531-05779-7(8) , Orchard Bks.) Scholastic, Inc.

Tafuri, Nancy. You Are Special, Little One. Tafuri, Nancy, illus. 2003. (Illus.). 32p. (J). pap. 16.95 (978-0-439-39879-4(7)) Scholastic, Inc.

Taylor-Butler, Christine. I Am Smart. Borlasca, Hector, illus. (J). (gr. k-1). 2006. 32p. pap. 3.95 (978-0-516-24971-1(1)); 2005. 31p. 18.50 (978-0-516-25176-9(7)) Scholastic Library Publishing. (Children's Pr.).

Tetro, Marc. A Barbecue for Charlotte. 1999. (Illus.). 32p. 19.95 (978-1-55278-112-8(7)) McArthur & Co. CAN. *Dist:* National Bk. Network.

Thomas, Frances. Little Monster's Book of Numbers. Collins, Ross, illus. 2005. 10p. (J). (ps-k). bds. 5.95 (978-1-58234-979-4(7)) Bloomsbury Publishing.

Tiano, Danielle. Tillie Is Terrific. 2006. (Illus.). (J). 16.99 (978-0-9788789-0-0(6)) Beyond Your Words.

Umbrellabird's Umbrella. 2001. (ps-2). lib. bdg. 9.80 (978-0-613-33177-7(X)) Tandem Library Bks.

Velthuijs, Max. Frog & the Stranger. ed. 2006. (Illus.). 32p. (J). 8.99 (*978-1-84270-466-0(4)) Andersen GBR. *Dist:* Independent Pubs. Group.

—Frog & the Stranger. Iqbal, Gulshan, tr. 2005. (Frog Ser.). (URD, ENG, VIE, CHI & BEN., Illus.). 32p. (J). 13.50 (978-1-84059-190-3(0)) Milet Publishing.

—Frog & the Stranger. 2000. (Frog Ser.). (Illus.). 32p. (J). (BEN, ENG, VIE, CHI & URD.). 13.50 (978-1-84059-187-3(0)); (VIE, ENG, CHI, BEN & URD., 13.50 (978-1-84059-191-0(9)); (ALB & ENG., 13.50 (978-1-84059-186-6(2)); (VIE, CHI, BEN, ENG & URD., 13.50 (978-1-84059-189-7(7)) Milet Publishing.

Waddell, Martin. Tough Ronald. Mould, Chris, illus. 2006. (Read-It! Chapter Books). 64p. (J). lib. bdg. (*978-1-4048-3127-8(4) , 1265816) Picture Window Bks.

Wallace, Karen. Marvin, the Blue Pig. Williams, Lisa, illus. 2004. (Read-It! Readers Ser.). 32p. (C). (gr. k-3). 18.60 (978-1-4048-0564-4(8)) Picture Window Bks.

Wallace, Karen. Princess Gusty Ox's Strange Change. Flook, Helen, illus. 2007. (J). lib. bdg. (*978-1-4048-3708-9(6)) Picture Window Bks.

Warnes, Tim. Chalk & Cheese. 2008. (J). (*978-1-4169-1378-8(5) , Simon & Schuster Children's Publishing) Simon & Schuster Children's Publishing.

Weatherly, Lee. Missing Abby. 2006. 208p. (YA). (gr. 7). mass mkt. 5.99 (978-0-553-49488-4(0) , Laurel Leaf) Random Hse. Children's Bks.

Weaver, Tess. Frederick Finch, Loudmouth. 2008. (J). (*978-0-618-45239-2(7) , Clarion Bks.) Houghton Mifflin Co. Trade & Reference Div.

Wells, Rosemary. Doris's Dinosaur. Wheeler, Jody & Nez, John, illus. 2001. (Yoko & Friends School Days Ser.: No. 4). 32p. (gr. k-2). 9.99 (978-0-7868-0726-0(1) , Volo) Hyperion Bks. for Children.

—Doris's Dinosaur. 2001. (J). 10.79 (978-0-606-22550-2(1)) Tandem Library Bks.

Welsh, David J. The Boy Who Burned Too Brightly: A Modern Allegory. Bolt, Brandon, illus. 2001. 67p. 19.95 (978-0-9656442-0-4(0)) Alisam Pr.

Weninger, Brigitte. Why Are You Fighting, Davy? Lanning, Rosemary, tr. from GER. Tharlet, Eve, illus. 2002. 32p. (J). pap. 6.95 (978-0-7358-1601-5(8)) North-South Bks., Inc.

—Why Are You Fighting, Davy? 2002. (gr. k-3). lib. bdg. 15.25 (978-0-613-87277-5(0)) Tandem Library Bks.

Wheatley, Nadia & Ottley, Matt. Luke's Way of Looking. 2001. (Illus.). 36p. (J). (gr. k up). 15.95 (978-1-929132-18-8(2)) Kane/Miller Bk. Pubs., Inc.

Whitney, Kim Ablon. See You down the Road: A Novel. 2004. 192p. (J). (gr. 7). lib. bdg. 17.99 (978-0-375-92467-5(1) , Knopf Bks. for Young Readers) Random Hse. Children's Bks.

Wilson, Jacqueline. Double Act. Sharrat, Nick & Heap, Sue, illus. 1999. 192p. (gr. 3-7). 5.50 (978-0-440-41374-5(5) , Yearling) Random Hse. Children's Bks.

Winfrey, Michelle Whitaker. It's My Birthday. . . Finally! A Leap Year Story. Turley, Joyce M., illus. 2003. 88p. (J). (gr. 3-7). per. 11.95 (978-0-9727179-0-8(0)) Hobby Hse. Publishing Group.

Woloson, Eliza. My Friend Isabelle. Gough, Bryan, tr. Gough, Bryan, illus. 2003. 28p. (J). 14.95 (978-1-890627-50-8(X)) Woodbine Hse.

Wong, Janet S. Minn & Jake. Cote, Genevieve, illus. 2003. 160p. (J). (gr. 2-5). 16.00 (978-0-374-34987-5(8) , Farrar, Straus & Giroux (BYR)) Farrar, Straus & Giroux.

Zachmeyer, Mary L. The Star That Sparkled. Ruzicka, Delores F., illus. Date not set. 26p. (J). pap. 5.00 (978-0-9646864-1-0(4)) Zachmeyer, Mary L.

Zimmer, Elizabeth. The Turtle & the Deep Blue Sky. Zimmer, Eric, illus. 2007. 24p. (J). (ps-2). 12.95 (*978-1-55591-597-1(3)) Fulcrum Publishing.

INDOCHINA

see Southeast Asia

INDONESIA

Arnot, Susie. Indonesia. 1998. (Worldfocus Ser.). (Illus.). 32p. (978-1-57572-075-3(2)) Heinemann Library.

Boast, Clare. Indonesia. 1998. (Next Stop! Ser.). (Illus.). 32p. (J). (ps-3). lib. bdg. 19.92 (978-1-57572-676-2(9)) Heinemann Library.

Bohn, Diana M. Islands of the Rainbow: An Indonesian Adventure. 1998. (J). 5.90 (978-0-377-00323-1(9)) Friendship Pr.

Brimson, Samuel. Brazil-East Timor, 8 vols. 2003. (Nations of the World Ser.: Vol. 2). (Illus.). 64p. (J). (gr. 5 up). lib. bdg. 30.00 (978-0-8368-5486-2(1) , World Almanac Library) Stevens, Gareth Inc.

Burton, Tristan. Indonesia. 2006. (Countries of the World Ser.). 64p. (gr. 6-12). 30.00 (978-0-8160-6016-0(9)) Facts On File, Inc.

Canavan, Roger. Indonesia. 2008. (J). (*978-1-60044-615-3(9)) Rourke Publishing, LLC.

Cassanos, Lynda. Indonesia. 2005. (Growth & Influence of Islam in the Nations of Asia & Central Asia Ser.). (Illus.). 128p. (J). (ps-7). lib. bdg. 25.95 (978-1-59084-835-7(7)) Mason Crest Pubs.

Costain, Meredith & Collins, Paul. Welcome to Indonesia. 2001. (Countries of the World Ser.). (Illus.). 32p. (J). (gr. 4 up). 28.00 (978-0-7910-6543-3(X) , 010206, Chelsea Hse.) Facts On File, Inc.

Cumming, David. Indonesia. Etchart, Julio, illus. Etchart, Julio, photos by. 2004. (Letters from Around the World Ser.). (J). lib. bdg. (978-1-84234-241-1(X) , Cherrytree Books) Evans Publishing Group.

Doak, Robin S. Indonesia. 2004. (First Reports). (Illus.). 48p. (J). (gr. 3 up). lib. bdg. 22.60 (978-0-7565-0582-0(8)) Compass Point Bks.

Fisher, Frederick. Indonesia. 1999. (Countries of the World Ser.). (Illus.). 96p. (J). (gr. 6 up). lib. bdg. 30.00 (978-0-8368-2317-2(6)) Stevens, Gareth Inc.

Furgang, Kathy. Mt. Tamabora: A Killer Volcano from Indonesia. 2001. (Volcanoes of the World Ser.). 24p. (J). lib. bdg. 19.95 (978-0-8239-5661-6(X) , PowerKids Pr.) Rosen Publishing Group, Inc., The.

Gelman, Rita Golden. Rice Is Life. Choi, Yangsook, illus. 2004. 25p. (J). reprint ed. 16.00 (978-0-7567-7202-4(8)) DIANE Publishing Co.

Guile, Melanie. Indonesia. 2003. (Illus.). 32p. (J). lib. bdg. 25.70 (978-1-4109-0469-0(5)) Raintree.

Horton, Edward. Indonesia. 2003. (Nations of the World Ser.). (Illus.). 128p. (J). pap. 34.28 (978-0-7398-6998-7(1)) Steck-Vaughn.

Into Wild Indonesia. 2004. 11.20 (978-1-4103-0244-1(X) , Blackbirch Pr., Inc.) Thomson Gale.

Lim, Robin. Indonesia. (Ticket to Ser.). (Illus.). 48p. 2005. (gr. 2-4). 22.60 (978-1-57505-175-8(3)); 2000. (J). (gr. 3-5). lib. bdg. 22.60 (978-1-57505-150-5(8) , Carolrhoda Bks.) Lerner Publishing Group.

Lyle, Garry. Indonesia. 1999. (Major World Nations Ser.). (Illus.). 144p. (YA). (gr. 4-7). lib. bdg. 21.95 (978-0-7910-4987-7(6) , Chelsea Hse.) Facts On File, Inc.

Lynch, Emma. We're from Indonesia. 2005. (We're from Ser.). (Illus.). 32p. (J). pap. (978-1-4034-5813-1(8)); lib. bdg. (978-1-4034-5804-9(9)) Heinemann.

McGuinn, Taro. East Timor: Island in Turmoil. 1998. (World in Conflict Ser.). (Illus.). 104p. (YA). (gr. 7-12). 25.26 (978-0-8225-3555-3(6) , Lerner Pubns.) Lerner Publishing Group.

Mesenas, Geraldine & Fisher, Frederick. Welcome to Indonesia. 2001. (Welcome to My Country Ser.). (Illus.). 48p. (J). (gr. 2 up). lib. bdg. 26.00 (978-0-8368-2517-6(9)) Stevens, Gareth Inc.

Miller, Debra A. Indonesia. 2005. (Modern Nations of the World Ser.). (Illus.). 112p. (J). (gr. 5-8). lib. bdg. 29.95 (978-1-59018-442-4(4) , Lucent Bks.) Thomson Gale.

Mirpuri, Gouri & Cooper, R. Indonesia. 2nd ed. 2001. (Cultures of the World Ser.). (Illus.). 144p. (gr. 5 up). lib. bdg. 37.07 (978-0-7614-1355-4(3) , Benchmark Bks.) Cavendish, Marshall Corp.

Morgan, Sally. Focus on Indonesia. 2007. (J). pap. (*978-0-8368-6757-2(2)); 64p. (gr. 5-8). lib. bdg. 33.27 (*978-0-8368-6750-3(5)) Stevens, Gareth Inc. (World Almanac Library).

Orr, Tamra & Greenblatt, Miriam. Indonesia. 2005. (Enchantment of the World, Second Ser.). (Illus.). 144p. (J). (gr. 5-9). 36.00 (978-0-516-23684-1(9) , Children's Pr.) Scholastic Library Publishing.

Phillips, Douglas A. Indonesia. 2004. (Modern World Nations Ser.). (Illus.). 120p. (gr. 6-12). 30.00 (978-0-7910-8022-1(6) , Chelsea Hse.) Facts On File, Inc.

Riehecky, Janet. Indonesia. 2002. (Countries of the World Ser.). (Illus.). 126p. (J). (gr. 2-3). 18.60 (978-0-7368-1106-4(0) , Bridgestone Bks.) Capstone Pr., Inc.

Ryan, Patrick. Welcome to Indonesia. 2007. (Welcome to the World Ser.). 32p. (J). (gr. 1-5). 27.07 (*978-1-59296-915-9(1)) Child's World, Inc.

Simpson, Judith. Indonesia. 2002. (Ask about Asia Ser.). (Illus.). 48p. (J). (gr. 4 up). lib. bdg. (978-1-59084-202-7(2)) Mason Crest Pubs.

Wade, Mary Dodson. Indonesia: A Question & Answer Book. 2007. (Fact Finders Ser.). (Illus.). 32p. (J). 22.60 (978-0-7368-6409-1(1)) Capstone Pr., Inc.

INDONESIA—FICTION

Ballantyne, Michael. Blown to Bits or the Lonely Man of Rakat. 2006. 36.99 (*978-1-4280-4221-6(0)); pap. 30.99 (*978-1-4280-4226-1(1)) IndyPublish.com.

Ballantyne, R. M. Blown to Bits; or, the Lonely Man of Rak. 2006. pap. (*978-1-4065-0515-3(3)) Dodo Pr.

Conrad, Joseph & West, Clare. Lord Jim. 2nd abr. ed. 2000. (Bookworms Ser.). (Illus.). 6.50 (978-0-19-423037-7(6)) Oxford Univ. Pr., Inc.

Fama, Elizabeth. Overboard. 2002. (Illus.). 192p. (YA). (gr. 6-9). 15.95 (978-0-8126-2652-0(4)) Cricket Bks.

—Overboard. 2005. 160p. (YA). (gr. 7). pap. 5.50 (978-0-553-49436-5(8) , Laurel Leaf) Random Hse. Children's Bks.

Jenkins, Jerry B. Crash at Cannibal Valley. 2006. (AirQuest Adventures Ser.). 160p. (J). pap. 6.99 (978-0-310-71347-0(1)) Zonderkidz.

Lewis, Richard. The Killing Sea: A Novel of the Tsunami. 2006. 192p. (YA). (gr. 6-10). 15.95 (978-1-4169-1165-4(0)) Simon & Schuster Children's Publishing.

Richards, Kitty. Bird Who Cried Wolf. 2000. (gr. k-3). lib. bdg. 11.80 (978-0-613-24367-4(6)) Tandem Library Bks.

Taylor, Diane. Singapore Children's Favorite Stories. Tay-Audouard, L. K., illus. 2003. 96p. (gr. 1-5). 16.95 (978-0-7946-0097-6(2)) Tuttle Publishing.

Valerio, Geraldo, illus. Go to Sleep, Gecko! A Balinese Folktale. 2006. 32p. (gr. 4-7). 16.95 (978-0-87483-780-3(4)) August Hse. Pubs., Inc.

Youngberg, Norma. The Tiger of Bitter Valley. 2004. (Illus.). 251p. (J). (gr. 3-6). reprint ed. per. 13.95 (978-1-57258-186-9(7) , 945-6048) TEACH Services, Inc.

INDUCTION (LOGIC)

see Logic

INDUCTION MOTORS

see Electric Motors

INDUS RIVER

Aronovsky, Ilona. The Indus Valley. 2004. (Excavating the Past Ser.). (J). pap. 8.50 (978-1-4034-5460-7(4)); lib. bdg. 27.07 (978-1-4034-4840-8(X)) Heinemann Library.

H I

Bowden, Rob. Settlements of the Indus River. (Rivers Through Time Ser.). 48p. (J). 2005. pap. 8.50 (978-1-4034-5723-3(9)); 2004. (Illus.). lib. bdg. 29.93 (978-1-4034-5718-9(2)); 2004. (Illus.). pap. (978-1-4034-6249-7(6)) Heinemann Library.

INDUSTRIAL CHEMISTRY

see Chemical Industries

INDUSTRIAL COUNCILS

see Management—Employee Participation

INDUSTRIAL DRAWING

see Mechanical Drawing

INDUSTRIAL EDUCATION

see Technical Education

INDUSTRIAL ENGINEERING

see Industrial Management

INDUSTRIAL MANAGEMENT

Here are entered works on the application of the principles of management to industrial enterprises, including production, office management, marketing, finance, etc. Works on the technical control of manufacturing processes are entered under Factory Management.

see also Business; Machinery; Marketing

Bruce Woodcock's Business Network Writers Staff. The Great Universal Business Network: And How It Grew. Fisher, Suzanne, ed. Ritterbusch, Mark, illus. l.t. ed. 1999. (WeWrite Kids! Ser.: Vol. 43). 45p. (J). (gr. 3-8). pap. 3.95 (978-1-57635-051-5(7)) WeWrite LLC.

Leave a Mark, Not a Stain. 2005. (YA). 14.95 (978-1-59872-138-6(0)) Instantpublisher.com.

McGraw-Hill Staff. Entrepreneurship & Small Business Management. 2nd ed. 1999. (C). pap., stu. ed., wbk. ed. 17.32 (978-0-02-644070-7(9), 9780026440707) Glencoe/McGraw-Hill.

Pincus, Marilyn. Your Bright Future in Business Administration. 2002. (gr. 7-12). lib. bdg. 21.10 (978-0-613-56711-4(0)) Tandem Library Bks.

Wesley, Sonya L. Business Management Ethical Marketing: A Discussion & Activity Tool. 2000. (Sport Ser.). (Illus.). (C). spiral bd. (978-0-9706421-8-9(0)) Game Plan Pubns.

INDUSTRIAL MATERIALS

see Materials

INDUSTRIAL ORGANIZATION

see Industrial Management

INDUSTRIAL REVOLUTION

see Great Britain—History—19th Century; Industry—History

INDUSTRIAL SCHOOLS

see Technical Education

INDUSTRIAL WASTES

see Waste Products

INDUSTRIES

see Industry

INDUSTRIES, CHEMICAL

see Chemical Industries

INDUSTRY

see also Industrial Management; Manufactures

Brezina, Corona. The Industrial Revolution in America. 2005. (Illus.). 64p. (J). (gr. 5-8). lib. bdg. 29.25 (978-1-4042-0179-8(3)) Rosen Publishing Group, Inc., The.

Coster, Patience. Farming & Industry. Aldous, Kate & Farmer, Andrew, illus. 1998. (Step-by-Step Geography Ser.). 32p. (J). (gr. 1-3). 18.50 (978-0-516-20354-6(1) , Children's Pr.) Scholastic Library Publishing.

Daiber, Robert A. & Erekson. Manufacturing Technology: Today & Tomorrow. 1999. (Illus.). 192p. (YA). (gr. 6-12). stu. ed., wbk. ed. 8.87 (978-0-02-675753-9(2)) Glencoe/McGraw-Hill.

Edge, Laura Bufano. Andrew Carnegie. 2004. (Lerner Biographies Ser.). (Illus.). 128p. (J). (gr. 6-12). lib. bdg. 27.93 (978-0-8225-4965-9(4)) Lerner Publishing Group.

Gedacht, Daniel C. Economy & Industry in Ancient Rome. 2004. (Primary Sources of Ancient Civilizations Ser.). (Illus.). 24p. (J). lib. bdg. (978-0-8239-8946-1(1)); lib. bdg. 19.95 (978-0-8239-6780-3(8)) Rosen Publishing Group, Inc., The. (PowerKids Pr.).

Gillis, Jennifer Blizin. Edwin Binney: The Man Who Brought Us Crayons in Many Colors. 2005. (Illus.). 32p. (J). (978-1-4034-6346-3(8)); pap. (978-1-4034-6360-9(3)) Heinemann Library.

Hayward, Linda. I Am a Pencil. Nicklaus, Carol, illus. 2003. (Silly Millies Ser.). 32p. lib. bdg. 17.90 (978-0-7613-2904-6(8) , Millbrook Pr.) Lerner Publishing Group.

Juettner, Bonnie. Energy. 2004. (Our Environment Ser.). (Illus.). 48p. (J). (ps-7). lib. bdg. 26.20 (978-0-7377-1821-8(8) , Greenhaven Pr., Inc.) Thomson Gale.

Peterson, Tiffany. Clarence Birdseye. 2003. (Illus.). 32p. (J). lib. bdg. 22.79 (978-1-4034-3247-6(3)) Heinemann Library.

—Clarence Birdseye. 2003. (gr. k-3). lib. bdg. 14.75 (978-0-613-86558-6(8)) Tandem Library Bks.

Roberts-Davis, Tanya. We Need to Go to School: Voices of the Rugmark Children. 2003. (Illus.). 48p. (J). (gr. 5 up). pap. 7.95 (978-0-88899-426-4(5)) Groundwood Bks. CAN. *Dist:* Perseus Distribution.

Teichmann, Iris. Expanding Industry. 2004. (Earth's Changing Landscape Ser.). (J). lib. bdg. 28.50 (978-1-58340-481-2(3)) Smart Apple Media.

INDUSTRY—HISTORY

Bacchin, Giorgio, illus. Industrial Revolution, 1800-1850: A Social History. 2002. (Road to Globalization Ser.). 32p. (YA). 22.95 (978-0-7910-7092-5(1)) Facts On File, Inc.

Brezina, Corona. The Industrial Revolution in America. 2005. (Illus.). 64p. (J). (gr. 5-8). lib. bdg. 29.25 (978-1-4042-0179-8(3)) Rosen Publishing Group, Inc., The.

Brown, Jonatha A. Bill Gates. 2004. (Illus.). 24p. (J). pap. (978-0-8368-4317-0(7)); (YA). lib. bdg. 19.33 (978-0-8368-4310-1(X)) Stevens, Gareth Inc.

Buckley, Susan Washburn. The Industrial Revolution: 1790-1850. 2002. (Reading Expeditions Ser.). (Illus.). 40p. (J). (978-0-7922-8685-1(5)) National Geographic Society.

Collier, Christopher & Collier, James Lincoln. The Rise of Industry: 1860-1900. 1999. (Drama of American History Ser.). (Illus.). 96p. (J). (gr. 5-9). lib. bdg. 31.36 (978-0-7614-0820-8(7) , Benchmark Bks.) Cavendish, Marshall Corp.

Connolly, Sean. Industrial Revolution. 2003. (gr. 5-8). lib. bdg. 17.60 (978-0-613-60968-5(9)) Tandem Library Bks.

—The Industrial Revolution. 2003. (Illus.). 56p. (J). pap. (978-1-4034-3638-2(X)); (YA). (gr. 6-8). lib. bdg. 27.07 (978-1-4034-0974-4(9)) Heinemann Library.

The Industrial Revolution: PowerPoint Presentations in World History. 2005. cd-rom 49.95 net. (978-1-56004-210-5(9)) Social Studies Schl. Service.

Jarnow, Jesse. Oil, Steel, & Railroads: America's Big Businesses in the Late 1800s. 2003. (America's Industrial Society in the Nineteenth Century Ser.). (Illus.). 32p. (J). pap. (978-0-8239-4276-3(7)) Rosen Publishing Group, Inc., The.

Peters, Craig. Bill Gates: Software Genius of Microsoft. 2003. (Internet Biographies Ser.). (Illus.). 48p. (J). (gr. 4-10). lib. bdg. 23.93 (978-0-7660-1969-0(1)) Enslow Pubs., Inc.

—Larry Ellison: Database Genius of Oracle. 2003. (Internet Biographies Ser.). (Illus.). 48p. (J). (gr. 4-10). lib. bdg. 23.93 (978-0-7660-1974-4(8)) Enslow Pubs., Inc.

Peterson, Tiffany. W. K. Kellogg. 2003. (Lives & Times Ser.). (Illus.). (J). 24p. pap. (978-1-4034-4259-8(2)); 32p. lib. bdg. 22.79 (978-1-4034-3249-0(X)) Heinemann Library.

Pierce, Alan. The Industrial Revolution. 2005. (American Moments Ser.). (Illus.). 48p. (J). (gr. 4-8). lib. bdg. 25.65 (978-1-59197-933-3(1)) ABDO Publishing Co.

Price, Sean. Smokestacks & Spinning Jennys: Industrial Revolution. 2006. (American History Through Primary Sources Ser.). (Illus.). 32p. (J). (978-1-4109-2413-1(0)); pap. (978-1-4109-2424-7(6)) Steck-Vaughn.

Richardson, Adele D. The Story of Microsoft. 2003. (Built for Success Ser.). (Illus.). 48p. (J). 28.50 (978-1-58340-294-8(2)) Smart Apple Media.

Sakolsky, Josh. Critical Perspectives on the Industrial Revolution. 2005. (Critical Anthologies of Nonfiction Writing Ser.). (Illus.). 176p. (gr. 7-12). lib. bdg. 30.60 (978-1-4042-0062-3(2)) Rosen Publishing Group, Inc., The.

Sheppard, Paul. Access to Geography: Economic Activity & Change. 2004. (Illus.). 144p. pap. 27.50 (***978-0-340-81500-7(0)*** , Hodder Murray) Hodder Education GBR. *Dist:* Trans-Atlantic Pubns., Inc.

Sioux, Tracee. Immigrants, Migration, & the Industrial Revolution. 2004. (Primary Sources of Immigration & Migration in America Ser.). (Illus.). 24p. (J). lib. bdg. 19.95 (978-0-8239-6826-8(X) , PowerKids Pr.) Rosen Publishing Group, Inc., The.

—Immigration, Migration, & the Industrial Revolution. 2004. (Primary Sources of Immigration & Migration in America Ser.). (Illus.). 24p. (J). lib. bdg. (978-0-8239-8998-0(4) , PowerKids Pr.) Rosen Publishing Group, Inc., The.

Stein, R. Conrad. The Industrial Revolution: Manufacturing a Better America. 2006. (American Saga Ser.). (Illus.). 128p. (J). lib. bdg. 31.93 (978-0-7660-2571-4(3)) Enslow Pubs., Inc.

Sutcliffe, Jane. Milton Hershey. Parlin, Tim, illus. 2004. (History Maker Bios Ser.). 48p. (J). 26.60 (978-0-8225-0247-0(X) , Lerner Pubns.) Lerner Publishing Group.

Thomson Gale Staff. Age of Reform & Industrialization: 1896-1920. 2002. (gr. 7-12). lib. bdg. 39.05 (978-0-613-73612-1(5)) Tandem Library Bks.

Wirkner, Linda. Learning about America's Industrial Growth with Graphic Organizers. 2005. (Graphic Organizers in Social Studies). (J). 19.95 (978-1-4042-2812-2(8) , PowerKids Pr.) Rosen Publishing Group, Inc., The.

INDUSTRY—ORGANIZATION

see Industrial Management

INDUSTRY AND ART

see Art Industries and Trade

INEBRIATES

see Alcoholism

INEQUALITY

see Equality

INFANTILE PARALYSIS

see Poliomyelitis

INFANTS

Here are entered works on children from birth through two years of age.

Aigner-Clark, Julie. Bebes. 2004. (Baby Einstein Ser.). (SPA., Illus.). 20p. (J). bds. 3.95 (978-970-718-155-7(9) , Silver Dolphin en Español) Advanced Marketing, S. de R. L. de C. V. MEX. *Dist:* Perseus Distribution.

—365 Days of Baby Einstein. 2003. (Illus.). 176p. (ps-17). 16.99 (978-0-7868-1908-9(1) , Disney Editions) Disney Pr.

Allen, Joy. Baby Signs: A Baby-Sized Guide to Speaking with Sign Language. 2008. 16p. (J). (ps). bds. 6.99 (***978-0-8037-3193-6(0)*** , Dial) Penguin Group (USA) Inc.

Ariel Books Staff. Baby. 2003. (Illus.). 80p. 5.99 (978-0-7407-3362-8(1)) Andrews McMeel Publishing.

Arlon, Penelope & Dorling Kindersley Publishing Staff. Baby Days. King, Dave & Crawford, Andy, photos by. 2003. (DK Baby Ser.). (Illus.). 487p. (J). bds. 12.99 (978-0-7894-9815-1(4)) Dorling Kindersley Publishing, Inc.

Ashbe, Jeanne. And after That. Ashbe, Jeanne, illus. 2002. (Illus.). 12p. (J). 9.95 (978-1-929132-24-9(7)) Kane/Miller Bk. Pubs., Inc.

Ault, Kelly. Let's Sign! Every Baby's Guide to Communicating with Grownups. Landry, Leo, illus. 2005. 80p. (J). (gr. k-ps). 17.00 (978-0-618-50774-0(4)) Houghton Mifflin Co. Trade & Reference Div.

Babies: Kindergarten Newcomer Books. (On Our Way to English Ser.). (gr. k up). 23.50 (978-0-7578-7197-9(6)) Rigby Education.

Babies on the Move. 2000. (J). bds. 5.95 (978-0-439-15524-3(X)) Scholastic, Inc.

Baby Shakespeare. (Baby Einstein Ser.). (Illus.). 28p. (J). (ps). pap. 19.98 incl. audio, VHS (978-1-892309-15-0(7)) Baby Einstein Co., LLC, The.

Barrett, John E., photos by. Babies! 2000. (Elmo's World Ser.). (Illus.). 12p. (J). (gr. k-ps). bds. 4.99 (978-0-375-80572-1(9) , Random Hse. Bks. for Young Readers) Random Hse. Children's Bks.

Bauer, Marion Dane. If You Were Born a Kitten. Stammen, JoEllen McAllister, illus. 1999. 32p. (J). (gr. k-3). per. 16.00 (978-0-689-82725-9(3) , Simon & Schuster Children's Publishing) Simon & Schuster Children's Publishing.

—If You Were Born a Kitten. 2001. (Illus.). (J). 13.79 (978-0-606-20719-5(8)) Tandem Library Bks.

Blakeslee, Ann R. Play, Baby, Play! Palma, Anna, illus. 2005. (Play, Baby, Play Ser.). 4p. (J). (ps-ps). bds. 8.99 (978-0-439-72593-4(3) , Cartwheel Bks.) Scholastic, Inc.

Brighter Vision Publishing Staff. Babies. 1998. (Year of Fun Ser.). (Illus.). 32p. (ps-k). pap. 3.99 (978-1-55254-013-8(8)) Brighter Vision Pubns.

Buck, Nola. How a Baby Grows. 1998. (Growing Tree Ser.). (Illus.). 14p. (J). (ps up). bds. 5.95 (978-0-694-00873-5(7) , Harper Festival) HarperCollins Pubs.

Burns Knight, Margy. Welcoming Babies. Sibley O'Brien, Anne, illus. 2005. 40p. (J). (gr. k-4). 7.95 (978-0-88448-124-9(7)) Tilbury Hse. Pubs.

Campbell Books Staff & Fry, Carolyn. Babies First Word. 2001. (Illus.). 10p. (J). bds. 9.95 (978-0-333-73343-1(6)) Macmillan Publishers Ltd. GBR. *Dist:* Independent Pubs. Group.

Campbell, Rod. Baby's Busy Book. 2003. (Illus.). 8p. (J). 13.00 (978-0-333-65997-7(X)) Macmillan Publishers Ltd. GBR. *Dist:* Independent Pubs. Group.

—This Baby! 2000. (Illus.). 20p. (J). pap. (978-0-333-67488-8(X) , Macmillan Children's Bks.) Pan Macmillan.

Canizares, Susan & Chanko, Pamela. Babies. 1999. (Learning Center Emergent Readers Ser.). (J). pap. 2.50 (978-0-439-04588-9(6)) Scholastic, Inc.

Canizares, Susan & Daniel, Moreton. Babies on the Move. 1999. (ps-2). lib. bdg. 10.10 (978-0-613-21152-9(9)) Tandem Library Bks.

Canizares, Susan & Moreton, Daniel. Babies on the Move. 1999. (Social Studies Emergent Readers). (J). 2.50 (978-0-439-04556-8(8)) Scholastic, Inc.

Christopher, Matt. All Keyed Up. Vasconcellos, Daniel, illus. 7th ed. 2003. (Soccer 'Cats Ser.: No. 7). 64p. (J). (gr. 1-4). pap. 4.99 (978-0-316-73821-7(2)) Little, Brown Bks. for Young Readers.

—All Keyed Up. 2003. (gr. k-3). lib. bdg. 13.00 (978-0-613-71890-5(9)) Tandem Library Bks.

Civardi, Anne. The New Baby. Bates, Michelle, ed. Cartwright, Stephen, illus. rev. ed. 2005. 16p. (J). (ps-17). pap. 4.95 (978-0-7945-1003-9(5) , Usborne) EDC Publishing.

Cole, Joanna. New Baby at Your House. 1999. (gr. k-3). lib. bdg. 14.10 (978-0-613-15030-9(9)) Tandem Library Bks.

—The New Baby at Your House. Miller, Margaret, photos by. rev. ed. 1998. (Illus.). 48p. (J). (ps-3). 15.89 (978-0-688-13898-1(5)) HarperCollins Pubs.

Dawson, Richard. My Baby Brother: A Fill-In & Keep Book. 2000. (Illus.). 30p. (J). (gr. k up). pap. (978-0-330-36970-1(9) , Macmillan Children's Bks.) Pan Macmillan.

—My Baby Sister: Fill-In & Keep Book. 2000. (Illus.). 32p. (YA). (gr. k up). pap. (978-0-330-36971-8(7) , Macmillan Children's Bks.) Pan Macmillan.

DK Publishing Staff. The New Baby. 2007. (Illus.). 12p. (J). 6.99 (978-0-7566-2584-9(X)) Dorling Kindersley Publishing, Inc.

Dorling Kindersley Publishing Staff. Baby Faces. 1998. (Soft-to-Touch Books Ser.). (Illus.). 16p. (J). (ps). bds. 4.99 (978-0-7894-3650-4(7)) Dorling Kindersley Publishing, Inc.

—Baby Says Peekaboo! 2006. (Illus.). 12p. (J). bds. 6.99 (978-0-7566-1621-2(2)) Dorling Kindersley Publishing, Inc.

—Out & About. 2003. (Baby's World Ser.). (Illus.). 36p. (J). bds. 6.99 (978-0-7894-8578-6(8)) Dorling Kindersley Publishing, Inc.

Douglas, Ann. Baby Science: How Babies Really Work! Desputeaux, Helene, illus. 2004. 32p. (J). (gr. k-4). reprint ed. pap. 7.00 (978-0-7567-8455-3(7)) DIANE Publishing Co.

—Baby Science: How Babies Really Work! Desputeaux, Helene, illus. 1998. 32p. (J). (ps-3). 18.95 (978-1-895688-83-2(3)); pap. 6.95 (978-1-895688-84-9(1)) Maple Tree Pr. CAN. (Owl Bks.). *Dist:* Firefly Bks., Ltd.

Drake, Jane & Love, Ann. My Baby Sister & Me. Ritchie, Scot, illus. 2000. (Memory Scrapbks. for Kids). 32p. (J). (gr. k-3). (978-1-55074-641-9(3)) Kids Can Pr., Ltd.

Ellwand, David. Big Book of Beautiful Babies. 2003. bds. 8.99 (978-0-525-47229-2(0) , Dutton Juvenile) Penguin Group (USA) Inc.

Endersbe, Julie. Teen Mothers: Raising a Baby. 1999. (Perspectives on Healthy Sexuality Ser.). (Illus.). 64p. (J). (gr. 4-6). lib. bdg. 23.93 (978-0-7368-0270-3(3) , LifeMatters Bks.) Capstone Pr., Inc.

Engelbreit, Mary. Booky. Engelbreit, Mary, illus. 2002. (Illus.). 14p. (J). (ps up). 6.99 (978-0-06-008133-1(3) , Harper Festival) HarperCollins Pubs.

Frasier, Debra. El Dia en Que Tu Naciste. Ada, Alma Flor & Campoy, F. Isabel, trs. 1998. (SPA., Illus.). 32p. (J). (gr. k-2). pap. 7.00 (978-0-15-201709-5(7) , HB7090, Red Wagon Bks.) Harcourt Children's Bks.

Frazee, Marla. Walk On! A Guide for Babies of All Ages. 2006. (Illus.). 40p. (J). 16.00 (978-0-15-205573-8(8)) Harcourt Trade Pubs.

Frazee, Marla. Walk On! (Gift Edition) 2008. (Illus.). 40p. (J). 9.95 (***978-0-15-206528-7(8)***) Harcourt Children's Bks.

Gentieu, Penny. Grow! Babies! 2002. (Illus.). 22p. (J). (gr. k-ps). bds. 5.99 (978-0-375-82208-7(9) , Crown Books For Young Readers) Random Hse. Children's Bks.

Global Fund for Children Staff. Global Babies. 2007. 18p. (J). (ps). bds. 6.95 (***978-1-58089-174-5(8)***) Charlesbridge Publishing, Inc.

Harwood, Beth. Amazing Baby Go Baby Go. 2005. (Illus.). 16p. (J). bds. 5.95 (978-1-59223-526-1(3)) Advantage Pubs. Group.

Helmer, Diana Star. Let's Talk about Having a New Brother or Sister. 1999. (Let's Talk Library). (Illus.). 24p. (J). (gr. 3). lib. bdg. 18.75 (978-0-8239-5191-8(X) , PowerKids Pr.) Rosen Publishing Group, Inc., The.

Henderson, Kathy. Look at You! A Baby Body Book. Howard, Paul, illus. 2007. 40p. (J). (ps). 15.99 (978-0-7636-2745-4(3)) Candlewick Pr.

Holtz, Lara, ed. Babies. 2002. (Baby's World Ser.). (Illus.). 36p. (J). bds. 6.99 (978-0-7894-8575-5(3)) Dorling Kindersley Publishing, Inc.

Hughes, Monica. My First Brother or Sister. 2003. (Illus.). 24p. (J). pap. 5.50 (978-1-4109-0670-0(1)); lib. bdg. 18.56 (978-1-4109-0644-1(2)) Raintree.

Hunter, Rebecca. My New Sister. Fairclough, Chris, photos by. 2007. (First Times Ser.). (Illus.). 24p. (J). pap. 10.95 (***978-0-237-52695-5(6)*** , Evans Brothers, Limited) Evans Publishing Group GBR. *Dist:* Independent Pubs. Group.

I Love Babies. 2004. per. 9.95 (978-0-9754779-1-5(9)) Chosen Word Publishing.

Intrater, Roberta Grobel. Cucu! 2002. (Baby Faces Ser.). (SPA.). 8p. (J). pap. 4.95 (978-0-439-15553-3(3)) Scholastic, Inc.

—Sonrie! 2002. (Baby Faces Ser.). (SPA., Illus.). (J). bds. 4.95 (978-0-439-15552-6(5) , Cartwheel Bks.) Scholastic, Inc.

Jamison, Jocelyn. Baby Mood Swings. 2003. (Illus.). 64p. (J). (gr. 1). spiral bd. 7.99 (978-0-8431-0479-0(1) , Price Stern Sloan) Penguin Group (USA) Inc.

Keller, Kristin Thoennes. Health Care for Infants & Toddlers. 2000. (Skills for Teens Who Parent Ser.). (Illus.). 64p. (J). (gr. 4-6). lib. bdg. 23.93 (978-0-7368-0704-3(7) , LifeMatters Bks.) Capstone Pr., Inc.

—Parenting an Infant. 2000. (Skills for Teens Who Parent Ser.). (Illus.). 64p. (J). (gr. 4-6). lib. bdg. 23.93 (978-0-7368-0702-9(0) , LifeMatters Bks.) Capstone Pr., Inc.

Knight, Margy Burns. Welcoming Babies. O'Brien, Anne Sibley, illus. 2003. 32p. (J). (ps-4). lib. bdg. 15.15 (978-0-606-22818-3(7)) Tandem Library Bks.

Lafferty, Lida & Flood, Bo. Born Early: A Premature Baby's Story. Young, Rebecca, photos by. 1998. (Illus.). 48p. pap. 9.95 (978-1-57749-064-7(9)) Fairview Pr.

Lasky, Kathryn. Love That Baby! A Book about Babies for New Brothers, Sisters, Cousins, & Friends. Plecas, Jennifer, illus. 2003. 32p. (J). (ps-3). 15.99 (978-1-56402-679-8(5)) Candlewick Pr.

Lindsay, Jeanne Warren. Your Baby's First Year: A Guide for Teenage Parents. Blum, Carole, photos by. 3rd ed. 2004. (Teen Pregnancy & Parenting Series Ser.). 224p. (J). 18.95 (978-1-932538-04-5(6)); pap. 12.95 (978-1-932538-03-8(8)) Morning Glory Pr., Inc.

Lindsay, Jeanne Warren & Brunelli, Jean. Nurturing Your Newborn: Young Parents' Guide to Baby's First Month. 2nd ed. 2006. (Illus.). 96p. (J). pap. (978-1-932538-38-0(0)) Morning Glory Pr., Inc.

Lorenz Editors. Babies: With over 50 Reusable Stickers. 2001. (Sticker Fun Ser.). (Illus.). 16p. pap. 2.95 (978-0-7548-0844-2(0) , Lorenz Bks.) Anness Publishing, Inc.

MacKenzie, Catherine. Our New Baby. 2000. 16p. (J). (ps-3). pap. (978-1-85792-607-1(2) , Christian Focus) Christian Focus Pubns.

Macmillan Children's Books Staff & Pilbrow, Giles. The Little Guide to Babies. 2000. (Little Guides Ser.). (Illus.). 20p. (J). (ps-3). (978-0-333-73422-3(X) , Macmillan Children's Bks.) Pan Macmillan.

Magabala Books Staff. Australian Babies. 2005. (Illus.). 10p. (J). 8.00 (978-1-875641-92-5(0)) Magabala Bks. AUS. *Dist:* International Specialized Bk. Services.

Miller, Margaret. Baby Faces. Miller, Margaret, photos by. 1998. (Look Baby Bks.). (Illus.). 14p. (J). (ps-4). 6.99 (978-0-689-81911-7(0) , Little Simon) Simon & Schuster Children's Publishing.

Molinet, Michael & Molinet, Kelly. Just Like You. Molinet, Michael, illus. 2004. (Illus.). 22p. (J). 15.99 (978-1-932587-34-0(9)) Green Key Bks.

Morris, Alison. I Love to Learn. 2004. (Look at Me... I Love Ser.). (Illus.). 10p. (J). bds. 4.99 (978-1-85854-343-7(6)) Brimax Books Ltd. GBR. *Dist:* Byeway Bks.

Murkoff, Heidi. What to Expect When Mommy's Having a Baby. Rader, Laura, illus. (What to Expect Kids Ser.). (J). (ps-k). 2004. 24p. pap. 3.99 (978-0-06-053802-6(3)); 2000. 32p. 7.99 (978-0-694-01321-0(8)) HarperCollins Pubs. (Harper Festival).

HI

Our Baby: Individual Title Six-Packs. (Literatura 2000 Ser.). (ps-1). 28.00 (978-0-7635-0011-5(9)) Rigby Education.

Peekaboo Baby. 2004. (J). bds. 6.99 (978-0-9753127-1-1(5)) Family Bks. at Home.

Priddy, Roger. Baby Active Centre. rev. ed. 2002. 12p. (J). bds. 10.95 (978-0-312-49073-7(9) , Priddy Bks.) St. Martin's Pr.

Rauch, Jennifer, et al. Before You Were Born. 1998. (Illus.). 36p. (J). (ps-1). 10.95 (978-0-7611-1200-6(6) , 11200) Workman Publishing Co., Inc.

Robert, Naima Bint. Welcome to the World, Baby. Brazell, Derek, illus. 2005. 32p. (J). (ENG & ALB.). pap. 12.95 (978-1-84444-268-3(3)); (ENG & ARA.). pap. 12.95 (978-1-84444-269-0(1)); (ENG & BEN.). pap. 12.95 (978-1-84444-270-6(5)); (ENG & CHI.). pap. 12.95 (978-1-84444-271-3(3)); (ENG & CHI.). pap. 12.95 (978-1-84444-272-0(1)); (CRO, ENG & SER.). pap. 12.95 (978-1-84444-273-7(X)); (ENG, PER & FAR.). pap. 12.95 (978-1-84444-274-4(8)); (ENG & FRE.). pap. 12.95 (978-1-84444-275-1(6)); (ENG & GER.). pap. 12.95 (978-1-84444-276-8(4)); (ENG & GUJ.). pap. 12.95 (978-1-84444-278-2(0)); (ENG & HIN.). pap. 12.95 (978-1-84444-279-9(9)); (ENG & ITA.). pap. 12.95 (978-1-84444-280-5(2)); (JPN & ENG.). pap. 12.95 (978-1-84444-281-2(0)); (ENG & KOR.). pap. 12.95 (978-1-84444-282-9(9)); (ENG & PAN.). pap. 12.95 (978-1-84444-283-6(7)); (ENG & POL.). pap. 12.95 (978-1-84444-284-3(5)); (POR & ENG.). pap. 12.95 (978-1-84444-285-0(3)); (ENG, RUM & ROM.). pap. 12.95 (978-1-84444-286-7(1)); (RUS & ENG.). pap. 12.95 (978-1-84444-287-4(X)); (ENG & SOM.). pap. 12.95 (978-1-84444-288-1(8)); (ENG & SPA.). pap. 12.95 (978-1-84444-289-8(6)); (ENG & SWA.). pap. 12.95 (978-1-84444-290-4(X)); (ENG & TUR.). pap. 12.95 (978-1-84444-293-5(4)); (ENG & URD.). pap. 12.95 (978-1-84444-295-9(0)); (ENG & VIE.). pap. 12.95 (978-1-84444-296-6(9)); (YOR & ENG.). pap. 12.95 (978-1-84444-297-3(7)); (SHO & ENG.). pap. 12.95 (978-1-84444-450-2(3)); (ENG, KOR & KUR.). pap. 12.95 (978-1-84444-633-9(6)) Mantra Lingua GBR. *Dist:* Mantra Publishing, Ltd.

Robert, Naima Bint & Petrova-Browning, Nina. Welcome to the World, Baby. Brazell, Derek, illus. 2005. (ENG & BUL.). 32p. (J). pap. 12.95 (978-1-84444-721-3(9)) Mantra Lingua GBR. *Dist:* Mantra Publishing, Ltd.

Rock, Lois. Now We Have a Baby. Massey, Jane, illus. 2005. 32p. (J). (ps-3). 7.95 (978-1-56148-451-5(2)) Good Bks.

Sears, William, et al. Baby on the Way. Andriani, Renee W., illus. 2001. 32p. (J). (ps-3). 12.99 (978-0-316-78767-3(1)) Little, Brown Bks. for Young Readers.

—What Baby Needs. Andriani, Renee W., illus. 2001. 32p. (J). (ps-3). 12.99 (978-0-316-78828-1(7)) Little, Brown Bks. for Young Readers.

Sheldon, Annette. Big Sister Now: A Story about Me & Our New Baby. Maizel, Karen, illus. 2005. 32p. (J). (ps). 14.95 (978-1-59147-243-8(1)); pap. 8.95 (978-1-59147-244-5(X)) American Psychological Assn. (Magination Pr.).

Siegen Smith, Nikki, compiled by. Welcome to the World: A Celebration of Birth & Babies from Many Cultures. 2005. (Illus.). 48p. (J). 18.99 (978-1-84148-890-5(9)) Barefoot Bks., Inc.

Sirett, Dawn. Baby's Busy World. 2005. (Illus.). 26p. (J). 12.99 (978-0-7566-1018-0(4)) Dorling Kindersley Publishing, Inc.

Takahashi, Hideko, illus. Hello, New Baby. 2005. 12p. (J). (ps up). 9.95 (978-1-58117-345-1(8) , Intervisual/Piggy Toes) Dalmatian Pr.

Thomas, Shelley Moore. A Baby's Coming to Your House! Futran, Eric, photos by. 2001. (Illus.). 32p. (J). (ps-1). 15.95 (978-0-8075-0502-1(1)) Whitman, Albert & Co.

Tuxworth, Nicola. Babies, 12 vols. 2006. (Illus.). 12p. bds. 6.99 (978-0-7548-1368-2(1) , Lorenz Bks.) Anness Publishing GBR. *Dist:* National Bk. Network.

Verdick, Elizabeth. Pacifiers Are Not Forever. Heinlen, Marieka, illus. 2007. 24p. (J). (ps). bds. 7.95 (***978-1-57542-257-2(3))** Free Spirit Publishing, Inc.

Watt, Fiona. Christmas Baby Jigsaw Book. Wells, Rachel, illus. 2004. (Jigsaw Books Ser.). 14p. (J). 10.95 (978-0-7945-0809-8(X) , Usborne) EDC Publishing.

Welcome to the World, Baby. 2004. (J). (ALB & ENG.). (978-1-84444-621-6(2)); (ARA & ENG.). (978-1-84444-622-3(0)); (BEN & ENG.). (978-1-84444-623-0(9)); (CHI & ENG.). (978-1-84444-624-7(7)); (CHI & ENG.). (978-1-84444-625-4(5)); (CRO & ENG.). (978-1-84444-626-1(3)); (ENG & PER.). (978-1-84444-627-8(1)); (ENG & FRE.). (978-1-84444-645-2(X)); (ENG & GRE.). (978-1-84444-628-5(X)); (ENG & GUJ.). (978-1-84444-629-2(8)); (ENG & HIN.). (978-1-84444-630-8(1)); (ENG & ITA.). (978-1-84444-631-5(X)); (ENG & JPN.). (978-1-84444-632-2(8)); (ENG & KUR.). (978-1-84444-634-6(4)); (ENG & PAN.). (978-1-84444-635-3(2)); (ENG & POL.). (978-1-84444-636-0(0)); (ENG & POR.). (978-1-84444-637-7(9)); (ENG & RUS.). (978-1-84444-638-4(7)); (ENG & SOM.). (978-1-84444-639-1(5)); (ENG & SPA.). (978-1-84444-640-7(9)); (ENG & TAM.). (978-1-84444-641-4(7)); (ENG & TUR.). (978-1-84444-642-1(5)); (ENG & URD.). (978-1-84444-643-8(3)); (ENG & VIE.). (978-1-84444-644-5(1)) Mantra Publishing, Ltd.

Where Do We Come From ? 2006. (J). per. 9.99 (978-0-9777650-0-3(8)) El Assali, Amira.

Williams, Rhonda, photos by. Mommy, Daddy, Where Do Babies Come From? Activity Book. Date not set. (Wonderful World of True Love Ser.). (Illus.). 16p. (J). (gr. k-4). pap. 3.95 (978-0-9675068-0-7(8)) Media For Life.

Windsor, Jo. Taking Care of Babies: Early Level Satellite Individual Title Six-Packs. (Sails Literacy Ser.). 16p. (gr. 1-2). 27.00 (978-0-7578-6513-8(5)) Rigby Education.

Wolff, Ashley. Me Baby, You Baby. Wolff, Ashley, illus. 2004. (Illus.). 32p. (J). (ps). 14.99 (978-0-525-46952-0(4) , Dutton Juvenile) Penguin Group (USA) Inc.

Zondervan. A Baby Is a Blessing from Above: Reflections & Prayers for Parents & Baby. 2003. (Noah's Ark Baby Ser.). 96p. 9.99 (978-0-310-98790-1(3)) Zondervan.

INFANTS—DISEASES

see Children—Diseases

INFANTS—FICTION

Adler, David A. Andy & Tamika. Hillenbrand, Will, illus. 1999. (Andy Russell Ser.). 144p. (YA). (gr. 2-5). 14.00 (978-0-15-201735-4(6) , Gulliver Bks.) Harcourt Children's Bks.

Ahlberg, Janet & Ahlberg, Allan. Adios Pequeño! Ahlberg, Janet, illus. 2003. (Picture Books Collection). (SPA., Illus.). 32p. (J). (gr. k-3). 12.95 (978-84-372-2315-5(6)) Altea, Ediciones, S.A. - Grupo Santillana ESP. *Dist:* Santillana USA Publishing Co., Inc.

Aigner-Clark, Julie. Babies. 2002. (Baby Einstein Ser.). (Illus.). 20p. (J). (ps-17). bds. 3.99 (978-0-7868-0838-0(1)) Hyperion Bks. for Children.

—Mimi's Toes: A Splash & Giggle Bath Book. Zaidi, Nadeem, illus. 2003. (Baby Einstein Ser.). 10p. (J). (ps-ps). 6.99 (978-0-7868-1909-6(X)) Hyperion Bks. for Children.

—Who Lives in the Pond? A Splash & Giggle Bath Book. Zaidi, Nadeem, illus. 2003. (Baby Einstein Ser.). 10p. (ps-ps). pap. 6.99 (978-0-7868-1910-2(3)) Hyperion Bks. for Children.

Alexander, Martha. When the New Baby Comes, I'm Moving Out. Alexander, Martha, illus. 2006. (Illus.). 32p. (J). 9.95 (978-1-57091-678-6(0)) Charlesbridge Publishing, Inc.

Allen, Page. Madison's Descent: A Child's Journey. (J). 2006. pap. 25.00 (***978-0-9752516-2-1(7));** 2004. lib. bdg. 60.00 (***978-0-9752516-1-4(9))** Otis & Randolph Pr.

—The Way to Davis: On the River of Stars. collector's ed. 2007. (J). 75.00 (***978-0-9752516-3-8(5))** Otis & Randolph Pr.

Allison, Alida. Toddler's Potty Book. Parmentier, Henry, illus. 2003. Tr. of Libro de Basinica del Pequenito. (SPA.). 16p. (J). (ps-1). bds. 5.99 (978-0-8431-0502-5(X) , Price Stern Sloan) Penguin Group (USA) Inc.

Amadeo, Diana M. My Baby Sister Is a Preemie. Bladholm, Cheri, illus. 2005. (Helping Kids Heal Ser.). 32p. (J). 9.99 (978-0-310-70867-4(2)) Zonderkidz.

Andreae, Giles. There's a House Inside My Mommy. Cabban, Vanessa, illus. 2002. (Concept Book Ser.). 32p. (J). (ps-3). 15.95 (978-0-8075-7853-7(3)) Whitman, Albert & Co.

Anness Publishing Staff & Tuxworth, Nicola. Babies. 2000. (Very First Picture Board Bks.). (Illus.). 20p. (gr. 2-7). bds. 5.00 (978-0-7548-0707-0(X)) Anness Publishing GBR. *Dist:* National Bk. Network.

Appelt, Kathi. Hushabye, Baby Blue. Gottlieb, Dale, illus. 2000. (Growing Tree Ser.). 14p. (J). (ps up). 5.95 (978-0-694-01341-8(2) , Harper Festival) HarperCollins Pubs.

—Someone's Come to Our House. Carpenter, Nancy, illus. 1999. 24p. (J). (ps-3). 16.00 (978-0-8028-5144-4(4) , Eerdmans Bks For Young Readers) Eerdmans, William B. Publishing Co.

Apperley, Dawn. Don't Wake the Baby. Apperley, Dawn, illus. 2001. (Illus.). 32p. (J). (ps-k). 17.99 (978-0-7475-5003-7(4)) Bloomsbury Publishing Plc GBR. *Dist:* Trafalgar Square Publishing.

Arrington, Frances. Prairie Whispers. 2005. 192p. (J). (gr. 5). pap. 6.99 (978-0-14-240306-8(7) , Puffin) Penguin Group (USA) Inc.

Ashbe, Jeanne. Adios! 2003. (SPA.). 48p. (J). 15.95 (978-84-95150-68-4(9)) Corimbo, Editorial S.L. ESP. *Dist:* Distribooks, Inc., Lectorum Pubns., Inc.

—Eso No Se Hace! 2003. (SPA.). 32p. (978-84-95150-35-6(2)) Corimbo, Editorial S.L.

Asquith, Ros. Ball! 2000. (Toddlers Storybook Ser.). (Illus.). 24p. (J). pap. 5.95 (978-0-7894-5749-3(0) , D K Ink) Dorling Kindersley Publishing, Inc.

Aston, Dianna Hutts. When You Were Born. Lewis, Earl, illus. 2004. 32p. (J). (ps up). 15.99 (978-0-7636-1438-6(6)) Candlewick Pr.

Baek, Matthew J. Be Gentle with the Dog, Dear. 2008. 32p. (J). (ps-k). 14.99 (***978-0-8037-3250-6(3)** , Dial) Penguin Group (USA) Inc.

Ballard, Robin. I Used to Be the Baby. Ballard, Robin, illus. 2002. (Illus.). 24p. (J). (ps up). 15.99 (978-0-06-029586-8(4)); 15.89 (978-0-06-029587-5(2)) HarperCollins Pubs.

Banks, Lynne Reid. Angela & Diabola. 163p. (J). (gr. 4-6). pap. 4.50 (978-0-8072-1515-9(5) , Listening Library) Random Hse. Audio Publishing Group.

—Angela & Diabola. 1998. (J). (978-0-606-13124-7(8)) Tandem Library Bks.

Banks, Steven. In Search of Reptar. 2002. (gr. 3-6). lib. bdg. 11.80 (978-0-613-50538-3(7)) Tandem Library Bks.

Barney Meets the New Baby. 2002. (Barney Ser.). 32p. (J). (ps-k). bds. 5.95 (978-1-58668-246-0(6)) Scholastic, Inc.

Baskerville. New Baby. (Illus.). 32p. (J). pap. 4.95 (978-0-7136-4111-0(8) , 93347) A & C Black GBR. *Dist:* Lubrecht & Cramer, Ltd., Talman Co.

Bateman, Colin. Running with the Reservoir Pups. 2005. 272p. (J). (gr. 5-9). lib. bdg. 17.99 (978-0-385-90268-7(9) , Delacorte Bks. for Young Readers) Random Hse. Children's Bks.

Bauld, Jane Scoggins. Never, Ever Shake a Baby. Romain, Trevor, illus. l.t. ed. 1999. 32p. (J). (gr. k-6). pap. (978-0-9651123-1-4(4)) Allen, Evelyn W.

Beck, Scott. Little House, Little Town. 2004. (Illus.). 32p. (J). (ps-1). 14.95 (978-0-8109-4930-0(X)) Abrams, Harry N. , Inc.

Berenstain, Stan & Berenstain, Jan. The Berenstain Bears & Baby Makes Five. 2000. (Berenstain Bears First Time Bks.). (Illus.). 32p. (J). (gr. k-1). pap. 3.25 (978-0-679-88960-1(4) , Random Hse. Bks. for Young Readers) Random Hse. Children's Bks.

—The Berenstain Bears & Baby Makes Five. 2000. (Berenstain Bears First Time Bks.). (J). (ps-2). lib. bdg. 10.95 (978-0-613-24332-2(3)); (Illus.). 10.05 (978-0-606-18485-4(6)) Tandem Library Bks.

—The Berenstain Bears & the Baby Chipmunk. Berenstain, Stan, illus. 2005. (Illus.). 32p. (J). lib. bdg. 13.85 (***978-1-4242-0817-3(3))** Fitzgerald Bks.

Berenstain, Stan & Berenstain, Jan. The Berenstain Bears' Easter Surprise. l.t. ed. 1998. (Berenstain Bears Ser.). (Illus.). 48p. (J). (ps-3). pap. 10.95 (978-0-590-94730-5(3)) Scholastic, Inc.

Bergren, Lisa Tawn. God Gave Us Two. Bryant, Laura J., illus. 2001. 40p. (J). 9.99 (978-1-57856-507-8(3) , WaterBrook Pr.) WaterBrook Pr.

Bergstein, Rita. Your Own Big Bed. Hartung, Susan Kathleen, illus. 2008. 32p. (J). (ps). 15.99 (***978-0-670-06079-5(8)** , Viking Juvenile) Penguin Group (USA) Inc.

Bertrand, Lynne. Granite Baby. Hawkes, Kevin, illus. 2005. 40p. (J). 16.00 (978-0-374-32761-3(0) , Farrar, Straus & Giroux (BYR)) Farrar, Straus & Giroux.

Bilik-Franklin, MidiAna & Griffith, Indigo, photos by. The Carseat Tourist. 2006. (Illus.). (J). bds. 7.95 (978-0-9772825-0-0(3)) Critter Camp Inc.

Black, Jessica L. What Can Baby Do? Board Book & Felt Puppet Set. Metzger, Jeanne, illus. 2005. (J). bds. (978-1-57332-366-6(7)) HighReach Learning, Inc.

Blackaby, Susan. Coco on the Go. Muehlenhardt, Amy Bailey, illus. 2006. (Read-It! Readers Ser.). 24p. (J). (ps-3). 18.60 (978-1-4048-1580-3(5)) Picture Window Bks.

—One up for Brad. Epstein, Len, illus. 2006. (Read-It! Readers Ser.). (J). 19.93 (978-1-4048-2418-8(9)) Picture Window Bks.

Blake, Michel. Baby's Day. Blake, Michel, illus. 2007. (Easy-Open Ser.). (Illus.). 16p. (J). (ps). bds. 5.99 (978-0-7636-3368-4(2)) Candlewick Pr.

Boelts, Maribeth. Why Did You Bring Home a New Baby? A Book about Becoming a Sibling. Bladholm, Cheri, illus. 2006. 32p. (J). 9.99 (978-0-310-70901-5(6)) Zonderkidz.

Bond, Rebecca. Just Like a Baby. Bond, Rebecca, illus. 1999. (Illus.). 32p. (J). (ps-3). 15.95 (978-0-316-10416-6(7)) Little Brown & Co.

Borders, Christine Kareem. Gram Makes a House Call. Borders, Christine Kareem, illus. 1999. (Illus.). 77p. (J). (gr. 2-4). pap. 5.95 (978-0-9671160-0-6(7)) Greenhills Pr.

Borgardt, Marianne. My Funny Faces. Guyer, Terry, illus. Shorten, Chris, photos by. 1999. 12p. (J). 5.95 (978-1-892374-17-2(X)) Weldon Owen, Inc.

Bourgeois, Paulette & Clark, Brenda, creators. Franklin & the Baby. 1999. (Illus.). (J). (978-0-439-12065-4(9)) Scholastic, Inc.

Bowen & Simon and Schuster Children's Staff. Dancing Baby Flip Book. 1998. (Illus.). 80p. (J). (gr. 3-7). pap. 2.99 (978-0-689-82452-4(1) , Simon Pulse) Simon & Schuster Children's Publishing.

Bowen, Anne. Christmas Is Coming. Bogacki, Tomasz, illus. 2007. (Carolrhoda Picture Bks.). 32p. (J). (ps-4). 16.95 (***978-1-57505-934-1(7)** , Carolrhoda Bks.) Lerner Publishing Group.

Bowen, Anne. When You Visit Grandma & Grandpa. Bogacki, Tomasz, tr. Bogacki, Tomasz, illus. 2004. (Carolrhoda Picture Books Ser.). 32p. (J). (ps-3). 15.95 (978-1-57505-610-4(0)) Lerner Publishing Group.

Bowen, Anne M. I Loved You Before You Were Born. Shed, Greg, illus. 32p. (J). (ps-3). 2001. 16.99 (978-0-06-028720-7(9)); 2004. reprint ed. pap. 6.99 (978-0-06-443631-1(4)) HarperCollins Pubs.

—I Loved You Before You Were Born. 2004. (gr. 3-6). lib. bdg. 14.15 (978-0-613-81977-0(2)) Tandem Library Bks.

Bridge, Michael. Moses Goodleaf Learns to Walk: A Short Tale of Discovery. Brennan, Christine, illus. 2000. 32p. (J). pap. 16.95 (978-0-944963-19-7(6)); pap. 7.95 incl. audio (978-0-944963-33-3(1)); lib. bdg. 22.95 (978-0-944963-18-0(8)) Glastonbury Pr.

Bridges, Margaret Park. Am I Big or Little? Dockray, Tracy, illus. 2002. 32p. (J). (ps-2). pap. 5.95 (978-1-58717-147-5(3) , SeaStar Bks.) Chronicle Bks. LLC.

Bridges, Margaret Park & Dockray, Tracy. Am I Big or Little? 2000. (Illus.). 32p. (J). (ps-3). 16.50 (978-1-58717-020-1(5) , SeaStar Bks.) Chronicle Bks. LLC.

Brown, Craig. In the Spring. Brown, Craig, illus. 2004. (Illus.). 21p. (J). reprint ed. 14.00 (978-0-7567-8298-6(8)) DIANE Publishing Co.

Brown, Marc. Arthur's Baby. 1998. (Arthur Adventure Ser.). (Illus.). 30p. (J). (ps-k). bds. 5.95 (978-0-316-11858-3(3)) Little, Brown Bks. for Young Readers.

—Arthur's Lost Puppy. 2001. (Arthur Ser.). (J). (ps-1). spiral bd. 14.99 (978-1-58605-223-2(3)) LeapFrog Enterprises, Inc.

Brown, Margaret Wise. Another Important Book. Raschka, Chris, illus. 1999. (Joanna Cotler Bks.). 32p. (J). (ps-k). lib. bdg. 16.89 (978-0-06-026283-9(4)); 16.99 (978-0-06-026282-2(6)) HarperCollins Pubs. (Cotler, Joanna Books).

Bruha, Ginger. Lilly's Breakfast Time. 2004. 20p. pap. 14.95 (978-1-4137-3133-0(3)) PublishAmerica, Inc.

Bruna, Dick. My Miffy. 2000. (Illus.). (J). (ps-k). pap. 10.95 (978-1-56836-307-3(9)) Kodansha America, Inc.

Bunting, Eve. Baby Can. Chambliss, Maxie, illus. 2007. 32p. (J). 15.95 (978-1-59078-322-1(0)) Boyds Mills Pr.

—Doll Baby. 2000. (Illus.). 48p. (J). (gr. 7-4). tchr. ed. 15.00 (978-0-395-93094-6(4) , Clarion Bks.) Houghton Mifflin Co. Trade & Reference Div.

—Our Teacher's Having a Baby. deGroat, Diane, illus. 2001. 32p. (J). (gr. k-3). pap. 6.95 (978-0-618-11138-1(7) , Clarion Bks.) Houghton Mifflin Co. Trade & Reference Div.

—Our Teacher's Having a Baby. 2001. (gr. k-3). lib. bdg. 14.10 (978-0-613-35547-6(4)); (Illus.). (J). (978-0-606-21372-1(4)) Tandem Library Bks.

—Twinnies. 2001. (Illus.). (J). (978-0-606-21497-1(6)) Tandem Library Bks.

Burne-Jones, Edward C. Illustrations: Series 2. fac. ed. 2001. 68p. pap. 15.95 (978-1-4021-4059-4(2) , Elibron Classics) Adamant Media.

Burningham, John. Avocado Baby. 2000. (Illus.). 32p. (J). pap. 8.99 (978-0-09-920061-1(9) , Red Fox) Random Hse. Children's Bks. GBR. *Dist:* Trafalgar Square Publishing.

Byars, Betsy. Bingo Brown Amante Gitano. 2003. (gr. 3-6). lib. bdg. 19.90 (978-0-613-63015-3(7)) Tandem Library Bks.

Bye-Bye, Bottle. 2001. (Illus.). 12p. bds. 4.99 (978-0-307-13476-9(8) , Golden Bks.) Random Hse. Children's Bks.

Cabal, Graciela Beatriz. Tomasito. Lavandeira, Sandra, illus. (SPA.). (J). (gr. k-3). 2003. 37p. pap. 9.95 (978-950-511-348-4(X)); 2002. pap. 9.95 (978-9972-847-12-7(8)) Santillana USA Publishing Co., Inc.

Canizares, Susan & Daniel, Moreton. Babies on the Move. 1999. (ps-2). lib. bdg. 10.10 (978-0-613-21152-9(9)) Tandem Library Bks.

Canizares, Susan & Moreton, Daniel. Babies on the Move. 1999. (Social Studies Emergent Readers). (J). 2.50 (978-0-439-04556-8(8)) Scholastic, Inc.

Capucilli, Alyssa Satin. Biscuit & the Baby. Schories, Pat, illus. 2005. 24p. (J). lib. bdg. 13.85 (***978-1-4242-0702-2(9))** Fitzgerald Bks.

—Biscuit & the Baby. Schories, Pat, illus. 2005. (My First I Can Read Bks.). 32p. (J). (ps up). 14.99 (978-0-06-009459-1(1)); lib. bdg. 15.89 (978-0-06-009460-7(5)) HarperCollins Pubs.

Carlstrom, Nancy White & Saport, Linda. Before You Were Born. Saport, Linda, illus. 2004. (Illus.). 32p. (ps-k). 17.00 (978-0-8028-5185-7(1)) Eerdmans, William B. Publishing Co.

Carter, Dorothy. Wilhe'mina Miles: After the Stork Night. Stevenson, Harvey, illus. 2005. 30p. (J). (gr. k-4). reprint ed. 16.00 (978-0-7567-9421-7(8)) DIANE Publishing Co.

Ceelen, Vicky. Baby! Baby! 2008. (Illus.). 24p. (J). (gr. k-ps). bds. 6.99 (***978-0-375-84207-8(1)** , Random Hse. Bks. for Young Readers) Random Hse. Children's Bks.

Celcer, Irene. The Gift of Egg Donation. Gatto, Horacio, illus. 2007. (Hope & Will Have a Baby Ser.). 32p. (J). (gr. k-3). pap. 19.95 (978-0-9755810-1-8(5) , 9780975581018) Graphite Pr.

—The Gift of Embryo Donation. Gatto, Horacio, illus. 2007. (Hope & Will Have a Baby Ser.). 32p. (J). (gr. k-3). pap. 19.95 (978-0-9755810-2-5(3) , 9780975581025) Graphite Pr.

—The Gift of Sperm Donation. Gatto, Horacio, illus. 2007. (Hope & Will Have a Baby Ser.). 32p. (J). (gr. k-3). pap. 19.95 (978-0-9755810-3-2(1) , 9780975581032) Graphite Pr.

—The Gift of Surrogacy. Gatto, Horacio, illus. 2007. (Hope & Will Have a Baby Ser.). 32p. (J). (gr. k-3). pap. 19.95 (978-0-9755810-4-9(X) , 9780975581049) Graphite Pr.

Chardiet, Jon. Parker Penguin, Big Brother Blues. Micucci, Charles, illus. 1998. (Read with Me Paperback Ser.). (J). (978-0-590-14924-2(5)) Scholastic, Inc.

Charlip, Remy. Baby Hearts & Baby Flowers. 2001. (Illus.). 24p. (J). (ps-3). 15.89 (978-0-06-029592-9(9)) HarperCollins Pubs.

Choi, Jin. Where's the Baby? (Korean) 2004. (KOR., Illus.). 12p. (J). bds. 5.50 (978-1-932065-80-0(6)) Star Bright Bks., Inc.

Christian, Cheryl. Donde esta el Bebé? Fiol, María A., tr. Dwight, Laura, photos by. 2000. (Photoflaps Ser.). (SPA., Illus.). 12p. (J). (ps). bds. 5.50 (978-1-887734-26-4(0)) Star Bright Bks., Inc.

—Donde Esta el Perrito? Fiol, María A., tr. from ENG. Dwight, Laura, photos by. 2000. (Photoflaps Ser.). (SPA., Illus.). 12p. (J). (ps). bds. 5.50 (978-1-887734-29-5(5)) Star Bright Bks., Inc.

—What Happens Next? Kisa Kap Rive Apre? Dwight, Laura, photos by. 2005. (Illus.). 12p. (J). (ps). per. 5.50 (978-1-59572-025-2(1)) Star Bright Bks., Inc.

—Where Does It Go? (English/Haitian Creole) 2005. (CRP., Illus.). 12p. (J). bds. 5.50 (978-1-59572-026-9(X)) Star Bright Bks., Inc.

—Where's the Baby? Dwight, Laura, photos by. 2005. (Photoflaps Ser.). (RUS., Illus.). 12p. (J). (ps). per. 5.50 (978-1-932065-86-2(5)) Star Bright Bks., Inc.

—Where's the Baby? (Simplified Chinese) Dwight, Laura, photos by. 2004. (CHI., Illus.). 12p. (J). bds. 5.50 (978-1-932065-68-8(7)) Star Bright Bks., Inc.

—Where's the Baby? (Vietnamese) Dwight, Laura, photos by. 2004. (VIE., Illus.). 12p. (J). bds. 5.50 (978-1-932065-74-9(1)) Star Bright Bks., Inc.

—Where's the Baby?/Kote Tibebe a Ye? Dwight, Laura, photos by. 2005. (CRP., Illus.). 12p. (J). (ps). per. 5.50 (978-1-59572-027-6(8)) Star Bright Bks., Inc.

—Y Ahora, Qué Pasara? Fiol, María A., tr. from ENG. Dwight, Laura, photos by. 2000. (Photoflaps Ser.). (SPA., Illus.). 12p. (J). (ps). bds. 5.50 (978-1-887734-27-1(9)) Star Bright Bks., Inc.

Chronicle Books LLC Staff. I'm Such a Silly Baby. 2008. 32p. (J). 15.99 (978-0-8118-5134-3(6)) Chronicle Bks. LLC.

Claire, Onge. Caillou Que manque t Il. pap. 9.95 (978-2-89450-267-9(2)) Chouette Publishing CAN. *Dist:* Distribooks, Inc.

Clark, Brenda, illus. Franklin's Baby Sister. 2002. (Franklin Ser.). (J). 14.40 (978-0-7587-6436-2(7)) Book Wholesalers, Inc.

Clerk, Jessica. The Wriggly, Wriggly Baby. Rankin, Laura, illus. 2002. 32p. (J). pap. 16.95 (978-0-590-96067-0(9) , Levine, Arthur A. Bks.) Scholastic, Inc.

Cohen, Caron Lee. Happy to You! Litzinger, Rosanne, illus. 2001. 40p. (J). (gr. k-ps). tchr. ed. 15.00 (978-0-618-04229-6(6) , Clarion Bks.) Houghton Mifflin Co. Trade & Reference Div.

Cohen, Miriam. Backpack Baby. Cohen, Miriam, illus. 1999. (Backpack Baby Stories Ser.). (Illus.). 12p. (J). (ps). bds. 5.95 (978-1-887734-58-5(9)) Star Bright Bks., Inc.

—Mine! A Backpack Baby Story. Cohen, Miriam, illus. 1999. (Backpack Baby Stories Ser.). (Illus.). 12p. (J). (ps). bds. 5.95 (978-1-887734-59-2(7)) Star Bright Bks., Inc.

—Say Hi, Backpack Baby! Cohen, Miriam, illus. l.t. ed. 2001. (Backpack Baby Stories Ser.). (Illus.). 12p. (J). (ps). bds. 5.95 (978-1-887734-82-0(1)) Star Bright Bks., Inc.

Cohn, Arlen. Firsts: Reflections of a 7-Year Old. Vasconsellos, Daniel, tr. Vasconsellos, Daniel, illus. gif. ed. 2004. 28p. bds. 9.99 (978-1-57939-168-3(0)) Accord Publishing, Ltd.

Cole, Babette. Princess Smartypants Rules. Cole, Babette, illus. 2005. (Illus.). 32p. (J). (ps-3). 15.99 (978-0-399-24349-3(6) , Putnam Juvenile) Penguin Group (USA) Inc.

Cole, Brock. Larky Mavis. Cole, Brock, illus. 2001. (Illus.). 32p. (J). (ps-3). 16.00 (978-0-374-34365-1(9) , Farrar, Straus & Giroux (BYR)) Farrar, Straus & Giroux.

Cole, Joanna. I'm a Big Brother. Strevens-Marzo, Bridget, illus. 2008. 32p. (J). 6.99 (***978-0-06-134906-5(2)***) HarperCollins Pubs.

—I'm a Big Brother Lap Edition. Chambliss, Maxie, illus. 2006. 28p. (J). 12.99 (978-0-06-085412-6(X) , Harper Festival) HarperCollins Pubs.

—I'm a Big Brother (Spanish Edition) Strevens-Marzo, Bridget, illus. 2008. (SPA.). 32p. (J). 6.99 (***978-0-06-134908-9(9)*** , Rayo) HarperCollins Pubs.

—I'm a Big Sister. Strevens-Marzo, Bridget, illus. 2008. 32p. (J). 6.99 (***978-0-06-134907-2(0)***) HarperCollins Pubs.

—I'm a Big Sister Lap Edition. Chambliss, Maxie, illus. 2006. 28p. (J). 12.99 (978-0-06-085413-3(8) , Harper Festival) HarperCollins Pubs.

Cole, Joanna. I'm a Big Sister (Spanish Edition) Strevens-Marzo, Bridget, illus. 2008. (SPA.). 32p. (J). 6.99 (***978-0-06-134909-6(7)*** , Rayo) HarperCollins Pubs.

Coleman, Michael. One, Two, Three, Oops! Williamson, Gwyneth, illus. 1999. 32p. (J). (ps-2). 14.95 (978-1-888444-45-2(2)) Little Tiger Pr.

Colman, Michelle Sinclair. Beach Babies Wear Shades. Dion, Nathalie, illus. 2007. 20p. (J). (ps). 6.95 (***978-1-58246-204-2(6)*** , Tricycle Pr.) Ten Speed Pr.

—Country Babies Wear Plaid. Dion, Nathalie, illus. 2006. 20p. (J). (ps). bds. 6.95 (978-1-58246-172-4(4) , Tricycle Pr.) Ten Speed Pr.

—Urban Babies Wear Black. Dion, Nathalie, illus. 2005. 20p. (J). (ps). 6.95 (978-1-58246-158-8(9) , Tricycle Pr.) Ten Speed Pr.

Cooney, Caroline B. Hush Little Baby. 1999. 272p. (J). (gr. 6-10). pap. 4.99 (978-0-590-81974-9(7)) Scholastic, Inc.

—Hush Little Baby. 1999. (J). 11.64 (978-0-606-15580-9(5)) Tandem Library Bks.

Corso, Erika. The Day You Came. 2006. (ENG., Illus.). 28p. per. 12.95 (978-1-59800-242-3(2)) Outskirts Press, Inc.

Cosgrove, Stephen. The Glitterby Baby. James, Robin, illus. ed. 2001. (Serendipity Bks.). 32p. (J). pap. 4.99 (978-0-8431-7685-8(7) , Price Stern Sloan) Penguin Group (USA) Inc.

Costales, Amy. Hello Night: Hola Noche. McDonald, Mercedes, illus. 2007. (ENG & SPA.). 24p. 12.95 (***978-0-87358-927-7(0)*** , Luna Rising) Northland Publishing.

Cowell, Cressida. What Shall We Do with the Boo-Hoo Baby? Godon, Ingrid, illus. (J). 2003. 12p. bds. 7.99 (978-0-439-44266-4(4)); 2000. 32p. 15.95 (978-0-439-15311-9(5)) Scholastic, Inc.

Cowell, Cressida & Godon, Ingrid, illus. What Shall We Do with the Boo-Hoo Baby? 2000. (J). pap. (978-0-439-15312-6(3)) Scholastic, Inc.

Cowen, Fletcher. Baby Angels. 2005. (Illus.). 16p. (J). (gr. k-ps). bds. 6.99 (978-0-7636-2896-3(4)) Candlewick Pr.

Cronin, Doreen. Bounce. Menchin, Scott, illus. 2007. 40p. (J). (ps). 14.00 (978-1-4169-1627-7(X) , Atheneum) Simon & Schuster Children's Publishing.

Crystal, Billy. Grandpa's Little One. 2008. 40p. (J). (ps-k). pap. 6.99 (978-0-06-078175-0(0) , Harper Trophy) HarperCollins Pubs.

—Grandpa's Little One. Porfirio, Guy, illus. 2006. 40p. (J). (ps-k). lib. bdg. 17.89 (978-0-06-078174-3(2)) HarperCollins Pubs.

Crystal, Billy. I Already Know I Love You Board Book. Sayles, Elizabeth, illus. 2008. 32p. (J). 7.99 (***978-0-06-145057-0(X)*** , Harper Festival) HarperCollins Pubs.

Cuantos Juguetes. 2000. (Mundo del Pequenin Ser.).Tr. of Baby's Toys. (SPA., Illus.). 16p. (YA). (ps up). pap. 4.95 (978-0-7460-3865-9(8)) EDC Publishing.

Cummings, Pat. Angel Baby. 2000. (Illus.). 24p. (J). (gr. k-2). 15.89 (978-0-688-14822-5(0)) HarperCollins Pubs.

Curtis, Jamie Lee. When I Was Little: A Four-Year-Old's Memoir of Her Youth. braille ed. 2004. (Illus.). (J). (gr. k-3). spiral bd. (978-0-616-01625-1(5)); spiral bd. (978-0-616-01626-8(3)) Canadian National Institute for the Blind/Institut National Canadien pour les Aveugles.

—When I Was Little: A Four-Year-Old's Memoir of Her Youth. Cornell, Laura, illus. 1999. (Joanna Cotler Bks.). 32p. (J). (ps-k). 7.99 (978-0-694-01216-9(5) , Harper Festival) HarperCollins Pubs.

Cutler, Jane. Darcy & Gran Don't Like Babies. Ryan, Susannah, illus. rev. ed. 2002. 32p. (J). (ps-2). 16.50 (978-0-374-31696-9(1) , Farrar, Straus & Giroux (BYR)); pap. 6.95 (978-0-374-41686-7(9) , Sunburst) Farrar, Straus & Giroux.

Dalmatian Press Staff. Baby's Goodnight Blessings. 2000. (Illus.). (J). (ps-k). bds. 2.99 (978-1-57759-374-4(X)) Dalmatian Pr.

—Goodnight Baby. 2000. (Illus.). 20p. (J). bds. 2.99 (978-1-57759-370-6(7)) Dalmatian Pr.

—I'm a Baby. 2000. (Illus.). 20p. (J). (ps-k). bds. 2.99 (978-1-57759-371-3(5)) Dalmatian Pr.

Dalmatian Press Staff. Sesame Street My Baby Brother Is a Little Monster. 2007. 24p. pap. 3.50 (***978-1-4037-3213-2(2)***) Dalmatian Pr.

Danziger, Paula. Barfburger Baby, I Was Here First. Karas, G. Brian, tr. Karas, G. Brian, illus. 2004. 32p. (J). (ps-3). 16.99 (978-0-399-23204-6(4) , Putnam Juvenile) Penguin Group (USA) Inc.

—Barfburger Baby, I Was Here First. Karas, G. Brian, illus. 2007. 32p. (J). pap. 5.99 (978-0-14-240739-4(9) , Puffin) Penguin Group (USA) Inc.

David, Luke. Tommy's New Playmate. 2007. 24p. (J). 21.35 (***978-1-59961-360-4(3)***) Spotlight.

Davis, David. Ten Redneck Babies: A Southern Counting Book. Ward, Sue Marshall, illus. 2004. 32p. (J). (gr. k-3). pap. 15.95 (978-1-58980-232-2(2)) Pelican Publishing Co., Inc.

Davis, Jennifer. Before You Were Big. Cornell, Laura, illus. 2003. 36p. (J). 11.95 (978-0-7611-2732-1(1) , 12732) Workman Publishing Co., Inc.

de Brunhoff, Laurent. Babar's Little Girl. 2001. (Babar Ser.). (Illus.). 38p. (J). (ps-3). 16.95 (978-0-8109-5703-9(5)) Abrams, Harry N. , Inc.

de Paola, Tomie. The Baby Sister. 1999. (gr. k-3). lib. bdg. 14.15 (978-0-8085-0222-7(0)) Tandem Library Bks.

Delios, Kim, photos by. Aussie Toddlers Can. l.t. ed. 2006. (Illus.). 10p. (J). (978-1-875641-88-8(2)) Magabala Bks.

Delton, Judy. Angel's Mother's Baby. Weber, Jill, illus. 2003. 144p. (J). (gr. 3-5). pap. 4.95 (978-0-618-36919-5(8)) Houghton Mifflin Co. Trade & Reference Div.

Desimini, Lisa. My Beautiful Child. Mahurin, Matt, tr. Mahurin, Matt, illus. 2004. 32p. (J). pap. 16.95 (978-0-439-45893-1(5) , Blue Sky Pr., The) Scholastic, Inc.

Deutschbein, Mary J. Maggie's Weaning. Baty-Barr, Caroline, illus. 2nd ed. 1999. 24p. (J). (ps-1). pap. 6.95 (978-0-912500-58-4(1)) La Leche League International.

Devine, Monica. Carry Me, Mama. Paquin, Pauline, illus. 2002. 22p. (ps-3). 15.95 (978-0-7737-3317-6(5)) Stoddart Kids CAN. *Dist:* Fitzhenry & Whiteside, Ltd.

Dewan, Ted. Crispin & the 3 Little Piglets. Dewan, Ted, illus. 2003. (Illus.). 32p. (J). (gr. k-3). 15.95 (978-0-385-74633-5(4) , Doubleday Bks. for Young Readers) Random Hse. Children's Bks.

Dodd, Emma. Amazing Baby: on the Move! Jolley, Mike, illus. 2007. (Amazing Baby Ser.). 10p. (J). bds. 6.95 (***978-1-59223-800-2(9)*** , Silver Dolphin Bks.) Advantage Pubs. Group.

—Amazing Baby: Rain or Shine! Jolley, Mike, illus. 2007. (Amazing Baby Ser.). 10p. (J). bds. 6.95 (***978-1-59223-801-9(7)*** , Silver Dolphin Bks.) Advantage Pubs. Group.

Doman, Regina. Mi Angelito en las aquas. 2006. (SPA.). 46p. pap. 6.95 (***978-1-933184-22-7(1)***) Sophia Institute Pr.

Dorling Kindersley Publishing Staff. Babies Love. 2003. (Baby's World Ser.). (Illus.). 12p. (J). bds. 6.99 (978-0-7894-9212-8(1)) Dorling Kindersley Publishing, Inc.

—Baby Talk. 2005. (Baby Fun Ser.). (Illus.). 20p. (J). (ps-3). bds. 4.99 (978-0-7566-0986-3(0)) Dorling Kindersley Publishing, Inc.

—Baby's Bathtime. 1999. (Bath Bks.). (Illus.). 10p. (J). (ps-k). 6.99 (978-0-7894-4323-6(6)) Dorling Kindersley Publishing, Inc.

—Bedtime Peekaboo! 2006. (Illus.). 12p. (J). bds. 6.99 (978-0-7566-1622-9(0)) Dorling Kindersley Publishing, Inc.

—Look at Me: I Can Clap. 2002. (Baby's World Board Books Ser.). (Illus.). 12p. (J). bds. 6.99 (978-0-7894-8827-5(2)) Dorling Kindersley Publishing, Inc.

Doyle, Charlotte. It's Twins! Gorton, Julia, illus. 2003. 32p. (J). (ps-1). 10.99 (978-0-399-23718-8(6) , Putnam Juvenile) Penguin Group (USA) Inc.

Duke, Shirley Smith. No Bows! Mattheson, Jenny, illus. 2006. 32p. (J). 15.95 (978-1-56145-356-6(0) , Peachtree Junior) Peachtree Pubs., Ltd.

Dunbar, Joyce. Shoe Baby. Dunbar, Polly, illus. 2005. 40p. (J). (gr. k-k). 15.99 (978-0-7636-2779-9(8)) Candlewick Pr.

Duncan, Alice Faye. Honey Baby Sugar Child. Keeter, Susan, illus. 2005. 32p. (J). 15.95 (978-0-689-84678-6(9)) Simon & Schuster Children's Publishing.

Elizabeti's Doll. 2004. 24.95 incl. audio (978-1-55592-053-1(5)); (J). pap. 14.95 incl. audio (978-1-55592-716-5(5)) Weston Woods Studios, Inc.

Elya, Susan Middleton. Bebe Goes Shopping. Salerno, Steven, illus. 2008. 36p. (J). pap. 6.00 (***978-0-15-206142-5(8)*** , Voyager Bks./Libros Viajeros) Harcourt Children's Bks.

Enderle, Judith Ross & Gordon, Stephanie Jacob. Smile, Principessa! Litzinger, Rosanne & Curmi, Serena, illus. 2007. 40p. (J). (ps-3). 16.99 (978-1-4169-1004-6(2) , McElderry, Margaret K.) Simon & Schuster Children's Publishing.

Fallon, Joan & Feltenstein, Arlene. Will the New Baby Be Bigger Than Me? Escriva, Viví, illus. 1998. (J). (ps-3). 9.95 (978-1-56492-252-6(9)) Laredo Publishing Co., Inc.

Falwell, Cathryn. We Have a Baby. Falwell, Cathryn, illus. 2002. (Illus.). (J). 13.79 (978-0-7587-3939-1(7)) Book Wholesalers, Inc.

—We Have a Baby. Falwell, Cathryn, illus. 1999. (Illus.). 32p. (J). (gr. k-ps). 6.95 (978-0-395-73970-9(5) , Clarion Bks.) Houghton Mifflin Co. Trade & Reference Div.

Fearnley, Jan. A Special Something. 2004. (Illus.). 32p. 7.95 (978-0-7497-4639-1(4)) Egmont Bks., Ltd. GBR. *Dist:* Trafalgar Square Publishing.

—A Special Something. 2000. (Illus.). 32p. (ps-2). 15.99 (978-0-7868-0589-1(7)) Hyperion Pr.

Fennell, Kristen & Petruccelli, Jessica, illus. A World of Hope: Written by Hope's Parents Laurie & Mike. l.t. ed. 2005. 18p. (J). per. 9.99 (978-1-59879-069-6(2)) Lifevest Publishing, Inc.

Fine, Anne. Flour Babies. l.t. ed. 2000. 238p. (J). pap. 16.95 (978-0-7540-6110-6(8) , Galaxy Children's Large Print) BBC Audiobooks America.

Finley, Martha. Mildred's Married Life, Vol. 4. (Mildred Classics Ser.: Vol. 4). 288p. pap. 6.95 (978-1-58182-230-4(8)) Cumberland Hse. Publishing.

Fisher, Valorie. My Big Sister. Fisher, Valorie, photos by. 2003. (Illus.). 40p. (J). 14.95 (978-0-689-85479-8(X) , Atheneum/Anne Schwartz Bks.) Simon & Schuster Children's Publishing.

Fleming, Candace & Smith, Maggie. This Is the Baby. 2004. (Illus.). 40p. (J). 16.50 (978-0-374-37486-0(4) , Farrar, Straus & Giroux (BYR)) Farrar, Straus & Giroux.

Formby, Caroline. Tristan's Bedtime Story. Formby, Caroline, illus. l.t. ed. 1998. (Children's Stories Published in Other Lands Ser.). (Illus.). 32p. (J). (gr. 2 up). lib. bdg. 12.95 (978-1-56674-269-6(2)) Forest Hse. Publishing Co., Inc.

—Tristan's Temper Tantrum. Formby, Caroline, illus. l.t. ed. 1998. (Children's Stories Published in Other Lands Ser.). (Illus.). 32p. (J). (gr. 2 up). lib. bdg. 12.95 (978-1-56674-224-5(2)) Forest Hse. Publishing Co., Inc.

Fox, Mem. Ten Little Fingers & Ten Little Toes. Oxenbury, Helen, illus. 2008. (J). (***978-0-15-206057-2(X)***) Harcourt Trade Pubs.

Franco, Betsy. Silly Sally Level 3. Lamb, Stacey, illus. 2002. (Rookie Readers Ser.). 24p. (J). (gr. k-1). 19.50 (978-0-516-22492-3(1) , Children's Pr.) Scholastic Library Publishing.

Frasier, Debra. On the Day You Were Born. 2006. (Illus.). 24p. (J). bds. 7.95 (978-0-15-205944-6(X) , Red Wagon Bks.) Harcourt Children's Bks.

Frazee, Marla. Hush, Little Baby: A Folk Song with Pictures. 2007. (Illus.). 42p. (J). bds. 6.95 (978-0-15-205887-6(7) , Red Wagon Bks.) Harcourt Children's Bks.

Freed, Shirley Ann & Moon, Louise. Baby Is Sleeping. Morelan, Bill, ed. l.t. ed. 2002. (Illus.). 16p. (J). (gr. 5). pap. 3.99 (978-1-58938-006-6(1)) Concerned Communications.

Freedman, Claire. Oops-a-Daisy! Hansen, Gaby, illus. 32p. (J). 2004. tchr. ed. 15.95 (978-1-58925-037-6(0)); 2006. reprint ed. 6.95 (978-1-58925-398-8(1)) ME Media LLC. (tiger tales).

Freeman, Martha. The Trouble with Babies. Smith, Cat Bowman, illus. 2002. 80p. (J). (gr. 4-6). tchr. ed. 15.95 (978-0-8234-1698-1(4)) Holiday Hse., Inc.

French, Simon. Guess the Baby. Rawlins, Donna, illus. 2002. 32p. (J). (gr. k-3). 14.00 (978-0-618-25989-2(9) , Clarion Bks.) Houghton Mifflin Co. Trade & Reference Div.

Fuller, Rachel. Little Hands Library. 2007. 26p. (J). 13.99 (***978-0-7641-9381-1(3)***) Barron's Educational Series, Inc.

Gaither, Gloria & Zondervan. Ordinary Baby, Extraordinary Gift. Hranilovich, Barbara, illus. ed. 2000. 40p. (J). 14.99 (978-0-310-23086-1(1)) Zonderkidz.

Gallagher, Mary. Mulhern Twins. 2007. (Illus.). 126p. pap. 10.95 (***978-1-905172-17-7(6)***) Collins Pr., The IRL. *Dist:* Dufour Editions, Inc.

Garcia Sanchez, J. L. El Nino Gigante (The Giant Child) (Derechos del Nino Ser.). (SPA., Illus.). 32p. (J). (gr. 3-5). pap. 8.95 (978-1-56014-580-6(3)) Santillana USA Publishing Co., Inc.

Gates, Susan, et al. Babi Bag Siwgwr. 2005. (WEL., Illus.). 75p. (978-1-902416-96-0(1)) Cymdeithas Lyfrau Ceredigion.

Gentieu, Penny. Baby! Talk! Gentieu, Penny, illus. 2000. (Illus.). 22p. (J). (gr. k-ps). bds. 5.99 (978-0-517-80079-9(9) , Crown Books For Young Readers) Random Hse. Children's Bks.

—Wow! Babies! Gentieu, Penny, illus. 2000. (Illus.). 22p. (J). (gr. k-ps). bds. 5.99 (978-0-517-80080-5(2) , Crown Books For Young Readers) Random Hse. Children's Bks.

Gikow, Louise. Bye-Bye, Pacifier. 1999. (Naptime Tales Bks.). 14p. (J). bds. 3.49 (978-0-307-13468-4(7) , 13468, Golden Bks.) Random Hse. Children's Bks.

Gilman, Phoebe. Algo de Nada. Roehrich-Rubio, Esther, tr. from ENG. Gilman, Phoebe, illus. 1999. Tr. of Something from Nothing. (SPA., Illus.). 40p. (J). (gr. k-3). lib. bdg. 15.95 (978-1-880507-53-7(6) , LC8621) Lectorum Pubns., Inc.

Gliori, Debi. Pure Dead Frozen. 2007. (J). (gr. 5). 320p. 15.99 (***978-0-375-83317-5(X)***); 304p. lib. bdg. 18.99 (***978-0-375-93317-2(4)***) Random Hse. Children's Bks. (Knopf Bks. for Young Readers).

Gobo Books Staff. Santa Baby. 2006. 8p. 9.95 (978-1-932915-30-3(3)) Sandvik Innovations, LLC.

Gold, Becky. Babies in Reptarland. Goldberg, Barry, illus. 2000. (Rugrats Ser.). 32p. (J). (ps-2). 5.99 (978-0-689-83337-3(7) , Simon Spotlight/Nickelodeon) Simon & Schuster Children's Publishing.

—Babies in Reptarland. 2000. (gr. k-3). lib. bdg. 14.15 (978-0-613-30972-1(3)) Tandem Library Bks.

—Take a Bow, Babies! 2000. (gr. k-3). lib. bdg. 11.80 (978-0-613-27155-4(6)) Tandem Library Bks.

Gold, Rebecca. Take a Bow, Babies! 2000. (Ready-to-Read Ser.). (Illus.). 32p. (J). (ps-3). pap. (978-0-7434-0854-7(3) , Simon & Schuster Children's Publishing) Simon & Schuster Children's Publishing.

Gold, Rebecca & Gold, Becky. Take a Bow, Babies! Lesniewski, Bill & De la Paz, Orlando, illus. 2000. (Ready-to-Read Ser.). 32p. (J). (ps-3). pap. 3.99 (978-0-689-82830-0(6) , Simon Spotlight/Nickelodeon) Simon & Schuster Children's Publishing.

Goodman, Joan. Bernard Wants a Baby. Catalano, Dominic, illus. 2004. 32p. (J). (ps up). 15.95 (978-1-59078-088-6(4)) Boyds Mills Pr.

Gordon, Jeffie Ross. Two Badd Babies. Demarest, Chris L., illus. 2003. 32p. (J). (gr. k-2). pap. 8.95 (978-1-56397-895-1(4)) Boyds Mills Pr.

Gordon, Wendy. I'm Safe! with the New Baby. Gordon, Paul, illus. 1999. (I'm Safe! Ser.). 32p. (J). (ps-3). pap. 5.95 (978-1-891596-04-9(7)) BackYard Bks.

—I'm Safe! with the New Baby. 1999. 24p. (ps-3). pap., act. bk. ed. 2.49 (978-1-891596-05-6(5)) Backyard Pub. Co., Inc.

Gosline, Andrea Alban. January's Child: The Birthday Month Book. Bossi, Lisa Burnett, illus. 2007. 32p. (J). (ps-3). pap. 12.99 (978-0-439-67268-9(6) , Scholastic Pr.) Scholastic, Inc.

—Ten Little Wishes: A Baby Animal Counting Book. Bossi, Lisa Burnett, illus. 2007. 40p. (J). (ps-k). 15.99 (978-0-06-053410-3(9)); lib. bdg. 16.89 (978-0-06-053411-0(7)) HarperCollins Pubs.

Grambling, Lois G. Grandma Tells a Story. Willingham, Fred, illus. 2004. (J). pap. 6.95 (978-1-58089-072-4(5)); 15.95 (978-1-58089-057-1(1)) Charlesbridge Publishing, Inc.

Greenstein, Elaine. As Big As You. Greenstein, Elaine, illus. 2004. (Illus.). 32p. (J). (gr. k-ps). pap. 6.99 (978-0-553-11234-4(1) , Dragonfly Bks.) Random Hse. Children's Bks.

Gregory, Mary. Robinson & the Baby. Asunce, Jodi, illus. 2001. 16p. (J). (ps-4). pap. 5.95 (978-0-9713356-0-8(5)) Berenger Co.

Gregory, Valiska. Shirley's Wonderful Baby. Degen, Bruce, illus. 2002. 32p. (J). (ps-2). 14.99 (978-0-06-028132-8(4)) HarperCollins Pubs.

Greulich, Deborah Ripoll. I Choose You. 2007. 28p. per. 12.99 (***978-1-59886-953-8(1)***) Tate Publishing & Enterprises, L.L.C.

Griffin, Claire Janosik. Kidding Around. Wright, Jane Chambless, illus. 2000. (Rollicking Rhymes Ser.). 20p. (J). (gr. k-1). 3.99 (978-1-56822-978-2(X) , IF40212-E4, Instructional Fair) Schaffer, Frank Pubns.

Grimes, Nikki. Discussion of the Committee on Daubert Standards: Summary of Meet. Collier, Bryan, illus. 2006. ix, 35p. (J). pap. (***978-0-309-10248-3(0)*** , Orchard Bks.) Scholastic, Inc.

Grimes, Nikki. Welcome, Precious. 2006. 32p. (J). pap. 16.99 (978-0-439-55702-3(X) , Orchard Bks.) Scholastic, Inc.

Guest, Elissa Haden. Iris & Walter, Lost & Found. Davenier, Christine, illus. 2004. (Iris & Walter Ser.). 44p. (J). 15.00 (978-0-15-216701-1(3) , Gulliver Bks.) Harcourt Children's Bks.

Hakala, Joann. A Baby Brother! Oh No! Shaw-Peterson, Kimberly, illus. 2006. 32p. (J). per. 10.95 (978-1-59298-152-6(6)) Beaver's Pond Pr., Inc.

Haley, Amanda. It's a Baby's World. 2001. (Illus.). 24p. (J). (ps). 12.95 (978-0-316-34596-5(2)) Little Brown & Co.

Harcourt School Publishers Staff. Andy & Tamika: Reader's Choice Book. 2001. (Collections Ser.). (Illus.). pap. 12.10 (978-0-15-314359-5(2)) Harcourt Schl. Pubs.

Harper, Anita. It's Not Fair! McQuillan, Mary, illus. 2007. 32p. (J). (ps-k). 16.95 (***978-0-8234-2094-0(9)***) Holiday Hse., Inc.

Harris, Dorothy Joan. Cameron & Me. ed. 2004. (Illus.). (J). (gr. k-3). spiral bd. (978-0-616-01667-1(0)); spiral bd. (978-0-616-01668-8(9)) Canadian National Institute for the Blind/Institut National Canadien pour les Aveugles.

Harris, Robie H. Happy Birth Day! Emberley, Michael, illus. 2002. (J). 24.94 (978-0-7587-2684-1(8)) Book Wholesalers, Inc.

—Happy Birth Day! Emberley, Michael, illus. 2002. 32p. (J). (ps-3). pap. 6.99 (978-0-7636-0974-0(9)) Candlewick Pr.

—Happy Birth Day! Emberley, Michael, illus. 2002. (J). (ps-ps). lib. bdg. 15.30 (978-0-613-74733-2(X)) Tandem Library Bks.

—Hi New Baby! 2003. (gr. k-3). lib. bdg. 15.30 (978-0-613-74817-9(4)) Tandem Library Bks.

—Hi New Baby. Emberley, Michael, illus. 2003. 32p. (J). (gr. k-2). pap. 6.99 (978-0-7636-1826-1(8)) Candlewick Pr.

Hawkes, Kevin. The Wicked Big Toddlah. 2007. 40p. (J). (ps-3). 16.99 (978-0-375-82427-2(8)); lib. bdg. 19.99 (978-0-375-92427-9(2)) Random Hse. Children's Bks. (Knopf Bks. for Young Readers).

Hawkins-Walsh, Elizabeth & Pierson-Solís, Lennard. Katie's Premature Brother = el Hermano Prematuro de Katie. Blake, Anne Catharine, illus. 2006. (J). (978-1-56123-197-3(5)) Centering Corp.

Hegg, Tom & Hanson, Warren. Peef & the Baby Sister. Hegg, Tom & Hanson, Warren, illus. 2006. (J). (978-0-931674-67-9(0)) Waldman Hse. Pr., Inc.

Henderson, Kathy. The Baby Dances. Barton, Jill, illus. 1998. (J). (978-1-56402-335-3(4)) Candlewick Pr.

Henkes, Kevin. Julius, the Baby of the World. 2003. (Live Oak Readalong Ser.). (Illus.). (J). pap. 16.95 incl. audio (978-1-59112-249-4(X)) Live Oak Media.

—Julius: the Baby of the World. 2004. (Live Oak Readalong Ser.). (Illus.). (J). (ps-2). audio compact disk 18.95 (978-1-59112-492-4(1)) Live Oak Media.

—Julius, the Baby of the World. braille ed. 2004. (J). (ps-2). spiral bd. (978-0-616-07239-4(2)) Canadian National Institute for the Blind/Institut National Canadien pour les Aveugles.

Henson, Heather. Angel Coming. Gaber, Susan, illus. 2005. 40p. (J). 15.95 (978-0-689-85531-3(1) , Atheneum) Simon & Schuster Children's Publishing.

Herndon, Barbara & Gorey, Jill. Be My Valentine! del Carmen, Louis & Peters, James, illus. 2000. 30p. (J). (gr. k-3). per. 5.99 (978-0-671-77321-2(6) , Simon & Schuster Children's Publishing) Simon & Schuster Children's Publishing.

Hest, Amy. You're the Boss, Baby Duck! 2001. (978-0-606-22536-6(6)) Tandem Library Bks.

Hillert, Margaret. I Need You, Dear Dragon. Helton, David, illus. rev. exp. ed. 2007. (Beginning to Read Ser.). 32p. (J). lib. bdg. (978-1-59953-039-0(2)) Norwood Hse. Pr.

Hindley, Judy. Baby Talk: A Book of First Words & Phrases. Granstrom, Brita, illus. 2006. 32p. (J). (gr. k-k). 15.99 (978-0-7636-2971-7(5)) Candlewick Pr.

Hodes, Loren. Too Big, Too Little. . . Just Right! Hodes, Loren, illus. 2002. (Illus.). (J). 9.95 (978-1-880582-72-5(4) , TTTH) Judaica Pr., Inc., The.

Holt, Kimberly Willis. Waiting for Gregory. Swiatkowska, Gabriela, illus. 2006. (J). (***978-1-4156-7424-6(8)***) Holt, Henry & Co.

—Waiting for Gregory. Swiatkowska, Gabi, illus. rev. ed. 2006. 32p. (J). 16.95 (978-0-8050-7388-1(4) , Holt, Henry & Co. Bks. For Young Readers) Holt, Henry & Co.

Hood, Susan. Noisy Baby. 1999. (Lamaze Ser.). (Illus.). 14p. (J). (ps). 8.99 (978-1-56799-893-1(3) , Friedman-Fairfax) Friedman, Michael Publishing Group, Inc.

Hopkinson, Deborah. A Packet of Seeds. Andersen, Bethanne, illus. 2004. 32p. (J). 15.99 (978-0-06-009089-0(8)) HarperCollins Pubs.

Hornby, Nick. Slam. 2007. 304p. (J). (gr. 6). 19.99 (***978-0-399-25048-4(4)*** , Putnam Juvenile) Penguin Group (USA) Inc.

Howe, James. Pinky & Rex & the New Baby. Sweet, Melissa, illus. 1999. (Pinky & Rex Ser.). (J). (gr. 1-4). (978-0-606-15941-8(X)) Tandem Library Bks.

—Pinky & Rex & the New Baby. 2006. (J). (gr. 1-4). 24.21 (978-1-59961-076-4(0)) Spotlight.

Howe, James & Sweet, Melissa. Pinky & Rex & the New Baby. 1999. (Pinky & Rex Ser.). (Illus.). 48p. (J). (gr. 1-4). pap. 3.99 (978-0-689-82548-4(X) , Aladdin) Simon & Schuster Children's Publishing.

Hughes, Mair Wynn & Davies, Tracy. Brawd Newydd. 2005. (WEL., Illus.). 15p. pap. (978-0-86243-453-3(X)) Y Lolfa.

Hutchins, Hazel J. Two So Small. 2000. (gr. k-3). lib. bdg. 16.40 (978-0-613-50386-0(4)) Tandem Library Bks.

Hutchins, Pat. Where's the Baby? 1999. (Illus.). 32p. (J). (ps-3). pap. 4.95 (978-0-688-17063-9(3) , Harper Trophy) HarperCollins Pubs.

—Where's the Baby? 1999. (978-0-606-17398-8(6)) Tandem Library Bks.

Intrater, Roberta Grobel. Baby Faces. 2002. (Baby Faces Ser.). 10p. (J). bds. 4.95 (978-0-439-42005-1(9) , Cartwheel Bks.) Scholastic, Inc.

—Besitos y Abrozos. 2002. (Baby Faces Ser.). (SPA.). 12p. (J). bds. 4.95 (978-0-439-39079-8(6)) Scholastic, Inc.

—Dulces Suenos. 2002. (Baby Faces Ser.). (SPA.). 12p. (J). bds. 4.95 (978-0-439-39076-7(1)) Scholastic, Inc.

—Eat! 2002. (Baby Faces Ser.). 10p. (J). bds. 4.95 (978-0-439-42006-8(7) , Cartwheel Bks.) Scholastic, Inc.

—Hugs & Kisses. 2002. (Baby Faces Ser.). 10p. (J). bds. 4.95 (978-0-439-42003-7(2) , Cartwheel Bks.) Scholastic, Inc.

—Peek-a-Boo, You! Intrater, Roberta Grobel, photos by. 2nd rev. l.t. ed. 2005. (Illus.). 14p. (J). 14.99 (978-0-9764985-0-6(2)) 1212 Pr.

—Peek-a-Boo, You! Intrater, Roberta Grobel, photos by. 2002. (Illus.). 7p. (J). pap. 9.95 (978-0-439-33961-2(8) , Cartwheel Bks.) Scholastic, Inc.

—Que Rico. 2002. (Baby Faces Ser.). (SPA.). 12p. (J). bds. 4.95 (978-0-439-39078-1(8)) Scholastic, Inc.

—Sleep. 2002. (Baby Faces Ser.). (Illus.). 10p. (J). bds. 4.95 (978-0-439-42004-4(0) , Cartwheel Bks.) Scholastic, Inc.

Intrater, Roberta Grobel & Danko, Dan. Splish Splash: El Agua Patos. 2002. (Baby Faces Ser.). (SPA., Illus.). 12p. (J). bds. 4.95 (978-0-439-39077-4(X)) Scholastic, Inc.

Isadora, Rachel. Peekaboo Bedtime. Isadora, Rachel, illus. 2008. 32p. (J). (ps-k). 16.99 (***978-0-399-24384-4(4)*** , Putnam Juvenile) Penguin Group (USA) Inc.

—Peekaboo Morning. Isadora, Rachel, illus. 2008. 32p. (J). (ps-ps). bds. 6.99 (***978-0-399-25153-5(7)*** , Putnam Juvenile) Penguin Group (USA) Inc.

Jacobs, Julie. My Heart Is a Magic House. Pons, Bernadette, illus. 2007. 32p. (J). (ps-1). 15.95 (978-0-8075-5335-0(2)) Whitman, Albert & Co.

Jam, Teddy. Night Cars. Beddows, Eric, illus. 2006. 32p. 9.95 (978-0-88899-748-7(5)) Groundwood Bks. CAN. *Dist:* Perseus Distribution.

James, Simon. Baby Brains. James, Simon, illus. 2007. (Illus.). 32p. (J). (ps-3). pap. 6.99 (***978-0-7636-3682-1(7)***) Candlewick Pr.

—Baby Brains: The Smartest Baby in the Whole World. James, Simon, illus. 2004. (Illus.). 32p. (J). (ps-3). 15.99 (978-0-7636-2507-8(8)) Candlewick Pr.

—Baby Brains & RoboMom. 2008. (Illus.). 32p. (J). (ps-3). 15.99 (***978-0-7636-3463-6(8)***) Candlewick Pr.

—Baby Brains Superstar: The Smartest Baby in the Whole World. James, Simon, illus. 2005. (Illus.). 32p. (J). (ps-3). 15.99 (978-0-7636-2894-9(8)) Candlewick Pr.

—Jake & His Cousin Sidney. 2002. (gr. 3-6). lib. bdg. 13.00 (978-0-613-53737-7(8)) Tandem Library Bks.

Jenkins, Emily. That New Animal. Pratt, Pierre, illus. 2005. 32p. (J). 16.00 (978-0-374-37443-3(0) , Farrar, Straus & Giroux (BYR)) Farrar, Straus & Giroux.

—That New Animal. Jenkins, Emily, illus. 2006. (Illus.). (J). (ps-4). 29.95 incl. audio compact disk (978-0-439-84925-8(X) , WHCD687); 24.95 incl. audio (978-0-439-84924-1(1) , WHRA687) Weston Woods Studios, Inc.

Jennings, Sharon. Don't Wake the Baby. Zaman, Farida, illus. 2002. 24p. (J). (ps-k). bds. (978-1-55041-687-9(1)) Fitzhenry & Whiteside, Ltd.

—When You Get a Baby. Fitzgerald, Joanne, illus. 2002. 24p. (J). (ps-k). bds. (978-1-55041-702-9(9)) Fitzhenry & Whiteside, Ltd.

Jethani, Rita. Baby has a Burp. 2006. (Illus.). 24p. (J). 12.00 (978-0-9774147-0-3(1)) Laasya Design.

Johnson, Angela. The First Part Last. 144p. (YA). 2003. (Illus.). (gr. 6 up). 15.95 (978-0-689-84922-0(2)); 2004. reprint ed. pap. 5.99 (978-0-689-84923-7(0) , Simon Pulse) Simon & Schuster Children's Publishing.

Joly, Fanny. Atencion, Bebe Ataca! Capdevila, Roser, illus. 2003. (Coleccion Bebe). (SPA.). (J). (gr. 1-3). (978-84-246-3652-4(X) , GL30758) La Galera, S.A. Editorial ESP. *Dist:* Lectorum Pubns., Inc.

—Un Bebe? Que Mala Idea! Capdevila, Roser, illus. 2003. (Coleccion Bebe). (SPA.). (J). (gr. 1-3). (978-84-246-3651-7(1) , GL30757) La Galera, S.A. Editorial ESP. *Dist:* Lectorum Pubns., Inc.

Jones, Marcia Thornton & Dadey, Debbie. Vampire Baby. 1999. (Bailey City Monsters Ser.: No. 7). (Illus.). 80p. (J). (gr. 2-4). pap. 3.99 (978-0-439-05872-8(4)) Scholastic, Inc.

—Vampire Baby. 1999. (Bailey City Monsters Ser.: No. 7). (J). (gr. 2-4). (978-0-606-17059-8(6)) Tandem Library Bks.

Kallok, Emma & Bower, Joel. Gem. 2004. (Illus.). 32p. (J). (gr. k-2). 14.95 (978-1-58246-027-7(2) , Tricycle Pr.) Ten Speed Pr.

Katz, Karen. Baby's Box of Family Fun. Katz, Karen, illus. 2006. 56p. (J). bds. 19.95 (978-1-4169-2795-2(6) , Little Simon) Simon & Schuster Children's Publishing.

—Baby's Day. Katz, Karen, illus. 2007. 10p. (J). 14.99 (***978-1-4169-3580-3(0)*** , Little Simon) Simon & Schuster Children's Publishing.

—Excuse Me: A Little Book of Manners. Katz, Karen, illus. 2002. (Lift-the-Flap Bks.). (Illus.). 14p. (J). (ps-1). 5.99 (978-0-448-42585-6(8) , Grosset & Dunlap) Penguin Group (USA) Inc.

—No Biting. Katz, Karen, illus. 2002. (Illus.). 14p. (J). (ps-1). 5.99 (978-0-448-42584-9(X) , Grosset & Dunlap) Penguin Group (USA) Inc.

—Over the Moon: An Adoption Tale. 2001. lib. bdg. 15.25 (978-0-613-37027-1(9)) Tandem Library Bks.

—Peek-a-Baby. Katz, Karen, illus. 2007. 14p. (J). 6.99 (***978-1-4169-3622-0(X)*** , Little Simon) Simon & Schuster Children's Publishing.

—Ten Tiny Tickles. 2005. (Illus.). 32p. (J). 14.95 (978-0-689-85976-2(7) , McElderry, Margaret K.) Simon & Schuster Children's Publishing.

—Where Is Baby's Belly Button? Katz, Karen, illus. 2000. (Lift-the-Flap Bks.). (Illus.). 14p. (J). bds. 5.99 (978-0-689-83560-5(4) , Little Simon) Simon & Schuster Children's Publishing.

—Where Is Baby's Valentine? A Lift-the-Flap Book. Katz, Karen, illus. 2006. (Illus.). 14p. (J). 6.99 (978-1-4169-0971-2(0) , Little Simon) Simon & Schuster Children's Publishing.

Kaye, Buddy. You're Adorable. Alexander, Martha, illus. 1998. 22p. (J). (gr. k-ps). bds. 6.99 (978-0-7636-0674-9(X)) Candlewick Pr.

Keats, Ezra Jack. Peter's Chair. 2001. (Illus.). 40p. (J). (gr. k-3). pap. 6.95 (978-1-931016-07-0(0) , MHC-07-0) Minnesota Humanities Commission.

—Peter's Chair. Keats, Ezra Jack, illus. 1998. (Illus.). 40p. (J). (ps-3). 15.99 (978-0-670-88064-5(7) , Viking Juvenile); pap. 6.99 (978-0-14-056441-9(1) , Puffin) Penguin Group (USA) Inc.

—Peter's Chair. Keats, Ezra Jack, illus. 1998. (Picture Puffin Ser.). (Illus.). (978-0-606-13701-0(7)) Tandem Library Bks.

—Peter's Chair. (J). (ps-3). pap. 12.95 incl. audio Weston Woods Studios, Inc.

—Silla de Pedro. 1999. (SPA.). (gr. k-3). lib. bdg. 15.30 (978-0-613-22936-4(3)) Tandem Library Bks.

Kemp, Jane & Walters, Clare. 99 Mostly Fun Things I'll Do Today. Uff, Caroline, illus. 2007. 32p. (J). 22.95 (***978-1-4052-2806-0(7)***); pap. 12.95 (***978-1-4052-2807-7(5)***) Egmont Bks., Ltd. GBR. *Dist:* Independent Pubs. Group.

Kent, Renee Holmes. Girl Talk, Vol. 7. 2004. (Adventures in Misty Falls Ser.: Vol. 7). (Illus.). 100p. (J). (gr. 4-7). pap. 4.99 (978-1-56309-455-2(X) , N017103) New Hope Pubs.

Kinsey-Warnock, Natalie. Canada Geese Quilt. 2000. 11.79 (978-0-606-20354-8(0)) Tandem Library Bks.

Kleinberg, Naomi. Baby Says. 2007. (Illus.). 12p. (J). (gr. k-ps). bds. 4.99 (***978-0-375-84201-6(2)*** , Random Hse. Bks. for Young Readers) Random Hse. Children's Bks.

Klevin, Elisa. Monster in the House. 2001. (Illus.). (J). (978-0-606-20808-6(9)) Tandem Library Bks.

Klingel, Cynthia Fitterer & Noyed, Robert B. Cute! The Sound of Long U. 1999. (Wonder Books Phonics: Vowels Ser.). (Illus.). 24p. (J). (ps-3). 21.36 (978-1-56766-734-9(1)) Child's World, Inc.

Koller, Jackie French. Baby for Sale. Pedersen, Janet, illus. 2002. 32p. (J). (ps-2). 16.95 (978-0-7614-5106-8(4)) Cavendish, Marshall Corp.

Kopper, Lisa. Daisy Is a Mommy. Kopper, Lisa, illus. 2002. (Illus.). (J). 21.36 (978-0-7587-2336-9(9)) Book Wholesalers, Inc.

Krailing, Tessa. Disgusting Denzil. Phillips, Mike, illus. 2006. 48p. (J). lib. bdg. (***978-1-4048-3117-9(7)***) Picture Window Bks.

Kraushaar, Sabine. Good Morning Baby. 2007. (Illus.). (J). bds. 3.99 (978-0-7358-2119-4(4)) North-South Bks., Inc.

—Good Night Baby. 2007. (Illus.). (J). bds. 3.99 (978-0-7358-2120-0(8)) North-South Bks., Inc.

Krishnaswami, Uma. Bringing Asha Home. Akib, Jamal, illus. 2006. 32p. (J). (978-1-58430-259-9(3)) Lee & Low Bks., Inc.

Kroll, Virginia L. On the Way to Kindergarten. Schlossberg, Elisabeth, illus. 2006. 32p. (J). (ps). 15.99 (978-0-399-24168-0(X) , Putnam Juvenile) Penguin Group (USA) Inc.

—She Is Born: A Celebration of Daughters. Rowe, John, illus. 2000. 32p. (J). (gr. 9 up). 15.95 (978-1-885223-94-4(3)) Beyond Words Publishing, Inc.

Krulik, Nancy E. Oh, Baby! John and Wendy Staff, illus. 2002. (Katie Kazoo, Switcheroo Ser.: No. 3). 80p. (J). pap. 3.99 (978-0-448-42704-1(4) , Grosset & Dunlap) Penguin Group (USA) Inc.

Kubler, Annie, illus. My New Baby. 2000. 14p. (J). (ps-k). bds. 3.99 (978-0-85953-974-6(1)) Child's Play-International.

Kueffner, Sue. Look, Baby! 1999. (Lamaze Ser.). (Illus.). 8p. (J). (ps). 8.99 (978-1-56799-882-5(8) , Friedman-Fairfax) Friedman, Michael Publishing Group, Inc.

Lach, William. Baby Loves. Cassatt, Mary, illus. 2002. (J). (978-1-58839-052-3(7)) Metropolitan Museum of Art, The.

Laden, Nina. Grow Up. 2003. (Illus.). 26p. (J). bds. 6.95 (978-0-8118-3761-3(0)) Chronicle Bks. LLC.

Landolf, Diane Wright. What a Good Big Brother! Johnson, Steve & Fancher, Lou, illus. 2008. (J). (978-0-375-84258-0(6)); lib. bdg. (978-0-375-94258-7(0)) Random Hse. Children's Bks.

Lane, Queen, illus. & creator. It's Christmas Time (Babytown Storybook) Lane, Queen, creator. 2005. (BABYTOWN Ser.: Bk. 4). 36p. (J). spiral bd. 15.00 (978-0-9772738-1-2(4)) Quebla.

Lane, Queen & Boykin, Brian, illus. No No Baby (Babytown Storybook) 2005. (BABYTOWN Ser.: Bk. 1). 30p. (J). spiral bd. 15.00 (978-0-9772738-0-5(6)) Quebla.

Langrish, Katherine. Troll Mill. 2008. 384p. (J). 7.99 (***978-0-06-058309-5(6)*** , Eos) HarperCollins Pubs.

Lansky, Bruce. When I'm a Big Brother. 2003. 22p. (J). bds. 9.95 (978-0-684-01868-3(3)) Meadowbrook Pr.

—When I'm a Big Sister. 2003. 22p. (J). bds. 9.95 (978-0-684-01865-2(9)) Meadowbrook Pr.

Lantz, Francess L. Stepbaby from Planet Weird. 2001. (Illus.). (J). 3.99 (978-0-375-81259-0(8) , Random Hse. Bks. for Young Readers) Random Hse. Children's Bks.

Lawrence, Michael. Baby Loves. 2000. (Toddlers Storybook Ser.). (Illus.). 24p. (J). (ps). pap. 5.95 (978-0-7894-5744-8(X) , D K Ink) Dorling Kindersley Publishing, Inc.

—Baby Loves Visiting. Reynolds, Adrian, illus. 2002. (Toddler Story Books). 24p. (J). (ps). pap. 5.99 (978-0-7894-8860-2(4) , D K Ink) Dorling Kindersley Publishing, Inc.

Layne, Steven L. Love the Baby. Hoyt, Ard, illus. 2007. 32p. (J). (ps-k). 15.95 (978-1-58980-392-3(2)) Pelican Publishing Co., Inc.

—Over Land & Sea: The Story of International Adoption. Bower, Jan, illus. 2005. 32p. (J). 15.95 (978-1-58980-182-0(2)) Pelican Publishing Co., Inc.

Lee, Spike & Lee, Tonya Lewis. Please, Baby, Please. Nelson, Kadir, illus. 2007. (Classic Board Bks.). 32p. (J). bds. 7.99 (***978-1-4169-4911-4(9)*** , Little Simon) Simon & Schuster Children's Publishing.

L'Engle, Madeleine. The Other Dog. Davenier, Christine, illus. 2006. 48p. (J). reprint ed. pap. 6.95 (978-0-8118-5228-9(8) , SeaStar Bks.) Chronicle Bks. LLC.

—The Other Dog. Davenier, Christine, illus. 2003. 37p. (J). (gr. 2-5). reprint ed. 16.00 (978-0-7567-6970-3(1)) DIANE Publishing Co.

Leonard, Barry, contrib. by. Rock a Bye Baby. 2006. (Illus.). 61p. (J). reprint ed. 25.00 (978-1-4223-5246-5(3)) DIANE Publishing Co.

Leonard, Marcia. Let's Go Baby-O! 2000. (Hanna Bks.). (Illus.). 24p. (J). (ps-k). 7.95 (978-0-694-01367-8(6) , Harper Festival) HarperCollins Pubs.

Leslie, Amanda. Babies' Day. 2002. (Illus.). 10p. (J). 5.95 (978-1-58925-671-2(9) , tiger tales) ME Media LLC.

Lewis, Kim. Quilt for Baby. Lewis, Kim, illus. 2002. (Illus.). 32p. (J). (gr. k-k). 15.99 (978-0-7636-1925-1(6)) Candlewick Pr.

Lewison, Wendy Cheyette. Baby Faces. Moroney, Christopher, illus. 2002. 14p. (J). (gr. k). bds. 6.99 (978-0-375-81538-6(4) , Random Hse. Bks. for Young Readers) Random Hse. Children's Bks.

—Peekaboo! I See You! Moroney, Christopher, illus. 2002. (Sesame Beginnings Ser.). 14p. (J). (gr. k). bds. 7.99 (978-0-375-81512-6(0) , Random Hse. Bks. for Young Readers) Random Hse. Children's Bks.

Lillegard, Dee. Who Will Sing a Lullaby? Yaccarino, Dan, illus. 2007. 32p. (J). (ps-1). 15.99 (***978-0-375-81573-7(2)***); lib. bdg. 18.99 (***978-0-375-91573-4(7)***) Random Hse. Children's Bks. (Knopf Bks. for Young Readers).

Lloyd-Jones, Sally. How to Be a Baby—By Me, the Big Sister. Heap, Sue, illus. 2007. 40p. (J). (ps-3). 15.99 (978-0-375-83843-9(0) , Schwartz & Wade Bks.) Random Hse. Children's Bks.

—How to Be a Baby—by Me, the Big Sister. Heap, Sue, illus. 2007. 40p. (J). (ps-3). lib. bdg. 17.99 (978-0-375-93843-6(5) , Schwartz & Wade Bks.) Random Hse. Children's Bks.

Lohans, Alison. Waiting for the Sun. Mets, Marilyn & Lawson, Peter, illus. 2007. 32p. pap. (***978-0-88995-358-1(9)***) Fitzhenry & Whiteside, Ltd.

London, Jonathan. Froggy's Baby Sister. Remkiewicz, Frank, illus. (Froggy Ser.). 32p. (J). 2005. pap. 5.99 (978-0-14-240342-6(3) , Puffin); 2003. 15.99 (978-0-670-03659-2(5) , Viking Juvenile) Penguin Group (USA) Inc.

Long, D. J. I Wish I Was the Baby. Johnson, Gary, illus. 2002. 32p. (J). 5.95 (978-0-8249-5441-3(6)) Ideals Pubns.

Long, Melinda. Pirates Don't Change Diapers. Shannon, David, illus. 2007. 44p. (J). (ps-2). 16.00 (978-0-15-205353-6(0)) Harcourt Trade Pubs.

Look, Lenore. Henry's First-Moon Birthday. Heo, Yumi, illus. 2001. 40p. (J). (ps-2). 16.99 (978-0-689-82294-0(4) , Atheneum/Anne Schwartz Bks.) Simon & Schuster Children's Publishing.

Lowry, Lois. The Silent Boy. 2003. (Illus.). 192p. (YA). (gr. 5-12). tchr. ed. 15.00 (978-0-618-28231-9(9) , Walter Lorraine) Houghton Mifflin Co. Trade & Reference Div.

Mack, Todd. Princess Penelope Takes Charge. Gran, Julia, illus. 2006. 32p. (J). pap. 16.99 (978-0-439-67380-8(1) , Scholastic Pr.) Scholastic, Inc.

MacKenzie, Catherine. Going to the Doctor. 2000. 16p. (J). (ps-3). pap. (978-1-85792-608-8(0) , Christian Focus) Christian Focus Pubns.

MacLachlan, Patricia. Two Novels: Baby/Journey. 2007. 224p. (J). (gr. 4-7). 16.99 (978-0-385-73423-3(9)); lib. bdg. 19.99 (978-0-385-90436-0(3)) Random Hse. Children's Bks. (Delacorte Bks. for Young Readers).

MacLachlan, Patricia & MacLachlan, Emily. Bittle. Yaccarino, Dan, illus. 2004. 40p. (J). (ps-3). 16.99 (978-0-06-000961-8(6)); lib. bdg. 16.89 (978-0-06-000962-5(4)) HarperCollins Pubs. (Cotler, Joanna Books).

Maclean, Christine. Mary Margaret & the Perfect Pet Plan. Vicky, Lowe, illus. 2007. 192p. (J). (gr. 3). pap. 5.99 (978-0-14-240767-7(4) , Puffin) Penguin Group (USA) Inc.

Madison's Descent: A Child's Journey. collector's ed. 2004. (J). 75.00 (***978-0-9752516-0-7(0)***) Otis & Randolph Pr.

Magsamen, Sandra. Little Blossom: Huggable, Lovable, Snuggable Books. 2007. (Messages from the Heart Ser.). (Illus.). 6p. (J). (ps-17). 10.99 (***978-0-316-06593-1(5)*** Little, Brown Bks. for Young Readers.

—Messages from the Heart: Baby Love:Huggable, Lovable, Snuggable Books. 2nd ed. 2006. (Message from the Heart Ser.). (Illus.). 10p. (J). (ps-17). 10.99 (978-0-316-16633-1(2)) Little Brown & Co.

—My Blanket: Huggable, Lovable, Snuggable Books. 2006. (Message from the Heart Ser.). (Illus.). 6p. (J). (ps-17). 10.99 (978-0-316-01459-5(1)) Little Brown & Co.

Mallard, Paula M. Don't Step on the Diaper. 1999. 122p. (J). (gr. 8-12). per. 12.00 (978-1-886623-04-0(X)) Canal Side Pubs.

Manushkin, Fran. Baby, Come Out! Himler, Ronald, illus. 2002. 40p. (J). 15.95 (978-1-887734-71-4(6)) Star Bright Bks., Inc.

Manzano, Sonia. A Box Full of Kittens. Phelan, Matt, illus. 2007. 40p. (J). (ps-2). 16.99 (978-0-689-83089-1(0) , Atheneum) Simon & Schuster Children's Publishing.

Mario, Heidi S. I'd Rather Have an Iguana. 1999. (Illus.). 32p. (J). (ps-3). 14.95 (978-0-88106-357-8(6)) Charlesbridge Publishing, Inc.

Marx, David F. Baby in the House. Fisher, Cynthia, illus. 2000. (Rookie Reader Skill Set Ser.). 32p. (J). (gr. k-2). pap. 4.95 (978-0-516-27045-6(1) , Children's Pr.) Scholastic Library Publishing.

—Baby in the House. Fisher, Cynthia, illus. 2000. 31p. (J). (ps-3). lib. bdg. 12.95 (978-0-613-62265-3(0)) Tandem Library Bks.

Marzollo, Jean. Do You Know New? Takabayashi, Mari, illus. 1998. (Growing Tree Ser.). 14p. (J). (ps up). 6.99 (978-0-694-00870-4(2)) HarperCollins Pubs.

Massicotte, Sylvie & Faniel, Lucie. C'est la Vie, Pitchounette. 2001. (Premier Roman Ser.). (FRE.). 64p. (J). (gr. 1-4). pap. (978-2-89021-434-7(6)) Diffusion du livre Mirabel.

Mathias, B. J. Jeffrey William & The Little Prince. 2002. 10.00 (978-0-9711320-9-2(7)) Electronic Publishing Services.

Mayer, Mercer. The New Baby. Mayer, Mercer, illus. 2001. (Little Critter Ser.). (Illus.). 24p. (J). (gr. k-k). reprint ed. pap. 3.29 (978-0-307-11942-1(4) , 11942, Random Hse. Bks. for Young Readers) Random Hse. Children's Bks.

Mayne, William. Pandora. Blech, Dietlind, illus. 2001. (SPA.). 32p. (J). (gr. k-3). (978-84-89675-63-6(5) , ZZ0542) Zendrera Zariquiey, Editorial ESP. *Dist:* Lectorum Pubns., Inc.

Mazer, Anne. The No-Nothings & Their Baby. Collins, Ross, illus. 2000. (J). (gr. k-3). 40p. pap. 15.95 (978-0-590-68049-3(8) , Scholastic Paperbacks); (978-0-590-68051-6(X)) Scholastic, Inc.

McAfee, Annalena. Busy Baby. Lewis, Anthony, illus. 1998. 18p. (J). pap. 9.99 (978-1-58048-055-0(1)) Sandvik Publishing.

McCarty, Peter. Baby Steps. rev. ed. 2000. (Illus.). 32p. (J). (ps up). 16.00 (978-0-8050-5953-3(9) , Holt, Henry & Co. Bks. For Young Readers) Holt, Henry & Co.

McCormick, Wendy. The Night You Were Born. Williams, Sophy, illus. 2000. 32p. (J). (ps-2). 15.95 (978-1-56145-225-5(4)) Peachtree Pubs., Ltd.

McElmurry, Jill. I'm Not a Baby! 2005. (J). 15.95 (978-0-689-87008-8(6) , Atheneum) Simon & Schuster Children's Publishing.

—I'm Not a Baby. McElmurry, Jill, illus. 2006. (Illus.). 40p. (J). (ps-3). 16.95 (978-0-375-83614-5(4) , Schwartz & Wade Bks.) Random Hse. Children's Bks.

McGill, Alice. Here We Go Round. Evans, Shane W., illus. 2002. 128p. (J). (gr. 3-5). 15.00 (978-0-618-16064-8(7)) Houghton Mifflin Co. Trade & Reference Div.

McMullan, Kate. If You Were My Bunny. McPhail, David M., illus. 2002. 15.70 (978-0-7587-2831-9(X)) Book Wholesalers, Inc.

—If You Were My Bunny. McPhail, David M., illus. 1998. (Hello Reader! Ser.). 26p. (J). reprint ed. bds. 6.99 (978-0-590-34126-4(X)) Scholastic, Inc.

McNamara, Joan. Borya & the Burps: An Eastern European Adoption Story. Majewski, Dawn, illus. 2005. 30p. (J). (ps-ps). 18.00 (978-0-944934-31-9(5)) Perspectives Pr., Inc.

Melmed, Laura Krauss. The Rainbabies. LaMarche, Jim, illus. 2004. 32p. (J). (ps-3). pap. 6.99 (978-0-688-15113-3(2)) HarperCollins Pubs.

Mendes, Valerie. Look at Me, Grandma! Fletcher, Claire, illus. 2001. 32p. (J). (ps-1). pap. 15.95 (978-0-439-29654-0(4) , Chicken Hse., The) Scholastic, Inc.

Merritt, Kate, illus. Peekaboo, Baby! A Rhyming Flap Book. 2002. (DK Ladybird Ser.). 12p. (J). bds. 6.95 (978-0-7894-8467-3(6)) Dorling Kindersley Publishing, Inc.

Michels, Dia L. Look What I See! Where Can I Be? at Home. Bowles, Michael J. N., photos by. 2002. 32p. 16.95 (978-1-930775-06-0(7)) Platypus Media, L.L.C.

—Look What I See! Where Can I Be? in the Neighborhood. Bowles, Michael J. N., illus. 2001. (Look What I See! Where Can I Be? Ser.: Vol. 1). 32p. 16.95 (978-1-930775-00-8(8)) Platypus Media, L.L.C.

—Look What I See! Where Can I Be? with My Animal Friends. Bowles, Michael J. N. & Bowles, Michael J. N., photos by. 2007. (Illus.). (J). pap. 9.95 (978-1-930775-08-4(3)) Platypus Media, L.L.C.

Michels-Gualtieri, Akaela S. I Was Born to Be a Sister. Ramsey, Marcy Dunn, illus. 2001. 32p. (ps-7). 16.95 (978-1-930775-03-9(2)) Platypus Media, L.L.C.

—I was Born to be a Sister. Ramsey, Marcy Dunn, illus. 2006. 32p. 18.95 (978-1-930775-11-4(3)) Platypus Media, L.L.C.

—I was Born to Be a Sister. 2005. 32p. pap. 9.95 incl. audio compact disk (978-1-930775-24-4(5)) Platypus Media, L.L.C.

Miller, Margaret. I Love Colors, Vol. 1. Miller, Margaret, illus. 1999. (Look Baby Books Ser.). (Illus.). 14p. (J). (gr. k-3). 6.99 (978-0-689-82356-5(8) , 076714004993, Little Simon) Simon & Schuster Children's Publishing.

Milord, Susan. Love That Baby! 2005. (Illus.). 16p. (J). (gr. k-ps). pap. 7.95 (978-0-618-56323-4(9)) Houghton Mifflin Co. Trade & Reference Div.

Mimi. Jake Is Up! Dubin, Jill, illus. 1999. (Jake's World Ser.: Vol. 2). 26p. (J). (ps-k). bds. 6.95 (978-1-892780-01-0(1)) Giggles Group, Inc., The.

Miriam Cohen. Backpack Baby. 2005. (ENG, SAI & SPA., Illus.). 12p. (J). (ps-ps). per. 5.95 (978-1-59572-018-4(9)) Star Bright Bks., Inc.

Moore, Eva. Franklin & the Baby. 2004. (Franklin TV Story-Bks.). (Illus.). 32p. (J). (gr. k-3). (978-1-55074-706-5(1)) Kids Can Pr., Ltd.

—Franklin & the Baby. 1999. (Franklin TV-Tie In Ser.). (Illus.). 32p. (J). (ps-3). pap. 4.50 (978-0-439-08365-2(6)) Scholastic, Inc.

Moore, Eva & Nelvana Staff. Franklin & the Baby. 2000. (Franklin TV Storybook Ser.). (Illus.). 96p. (J). (ps-3). (978-1-55074-708-9(8)) Kids Can Pr., Ltd.

Morgan, Gwyn & Owen, Dai. Babi Ben. 2005. (WEL., Illus.). 64p. (978-1-85596-611-6(5)) Dref Wen.

Morris, Kerry Nicole. The Baby Who Just... WON't Sleep! Parker's Story. 2004. 35p. pap. 17.95 (978-1-4137-3724-0(2)) PublishAmerica, Inc.

Munsch, Robert. Alligator Baby. ed. 2004. (Illus.). (J). (gr. k-3). spiral bd. (978-0-616-01730-2(8)); spiral bd. (978-0-616-01731-9(6)) Canadian National Institute for the Blind/Institut National Canadien pour les Aveugles.

—Alligator Baby. Martchenko, Michael, illus. 2002. 32p. (J). pap. 4.99 (978-0-439-38849-8(X)) Scholastic, Inc.

—Love You Forever. McGraw, Sheila, illus. gif. ed. 2000. 32p. (J). (ps-1). 19.95 (978-1-55209-109-8(0)) Firefly Bks., Ltd.

Murphy, Mary. I Kissed the Baby! Murphy, Mary, illus. 2003. (Illus.). 24p. (J). (gr. k-k). 14.99 (978-0-7636-2122-3(6)) Candlewick Pr.

Murphy, Mary Elizabeth. I Kissed the Baby! Murphy, Mary Elizabeth, illus. 2004. (Illus.). 24p. (J). (gr. k-ps). bds. 6.99 (978-0-7636-2443-9(8)) Candlewick Pr.

Myers, Tim. Good Babies: A Tale of Trolls, Humans, a Witch & a Switch. Murphy, Kelly, illus. 2005. 32p. (J). (ps-3). 15.99 (978-0-7636-2227-5(3)) Candlewick Pr.

Nelson, Scott. Bye-Bye, Pacifier. 2001. (Illus.). 12p. bds. 4.99 (978-0-307-13475-2(X) , Golden Bks.) Random Hse. Children's Bks.

Newman, Marjorie. Just Like Me. Wilson-Max, Ken, illus. 2006. 32p. (J). 16.85 (978-0-8027-8081-2(4)); 15.95 (978-0-8027-8080-5(6)) Walker & Co.

Newman, Nanette. Good Baby, Bad Baby. 2003. (Illus.). 32p. (J). 17.99 (978-0-00-711538-9(5)) HarperCollins Pubs. Ltd. GBR. *Dist:* Independent Pubs. Group.

—Up to the Skies. Williams, Sam, illus. 2002. 24p. (J). pap. 7.99 (978-0-340-80506-0(4) , Hodder & Stoughton) Hodder General Publishing Division GBR. *Dist:* Trafalgar Square Publishing.

Nishimura, Kae, illus. Baby, I'm Bigger. 2007. (I'm Going to Read Ser.). 28p. (J). (gr. 1-2). pap. 3.95 (***978-1-4027-4244-6(4)***) Sterling Publishing Co., Inc.

North, Sherry. Because You Are My Baby. Hall, Marcellus, illus. 2008. 32p. (J). 15.95 (***978-0-8109-9482-9(8)*** , Abrams Bks. for Young Readers) Abrams, Harry N. , Inc.

Nye, Naomi Shihab. Baby Radar. Carpenter, Nancy, illus. 2003. 32p. (J). lib. bdg. 16.89 (978-0-688-15949-8(4)) HarperCollins Pubs.

O'Book, Irene. Maybe My Baby. Hible, Paula, illus. 1998. (Growing Tree Ser.). 14p. (J). (ps up). 6.99 (978-0-694-00872-8(9) , Harper Festival) HarperCollins Pubs.

O'Connell, Rebecca. The Baby Goes Beep. Wilson-Max, Ken, illus. rev. ed. 2003. 32p. (J). (ps up). 22.90 (978-0-7613-2867-4(X)); 14.95 (978-0-7613-1789-0(9)) Roaring Brook Pr.

Offerman, Lynn. Where Is It? Hers. Chambers, Sally, illus. 1998. (Nuk Bks.). 8p. (J). 6.95 (978-0-7641-7233-5(6)) Barron's Educational Series, Inc.

O'Hair, Margaret. Star Baby. Kono, Erin Eitter, illus. 2005. 32p. (J). (gr. k-ps). 16.00 (978-0-618-30668-8(4) , Clarion Bks.) Houghton Mifflin Co. Trade & Reference Div.

O'Keefe, Susan Heyboer. Baby Day. Spowart, Robin, illus. 2006. 32p. (J). 15.95 (978-1-56397-981-1(0)) Boyds Mills Pr.

Olsen, Madeline. Busy Baby! Rutten, Nicole, illus. 2001. (Starring Me! Ser.). 10p. (J). (ps-k). bds. 7.95 (978-1-57145-463-8(2) , Silver Dolphin Bks.) Advantage Pubs. Group.

—Peek-a-Boo Baby! Rutten, Nicole, illus. 2001. (Starring Me! Ser.). 10p. (J). (ps-k). bds. 7.95 (978-1-57145-462-1(4) , Silver Dolphin Bks.) Advantage Pubs. Group.

Olson-Brown, Ellen. Ten Stinky Babies. 2005. (Illus.). 28p. (J). (ps-ps). 12.95 (978-1-58246-137-3(6) , Tricycle Pr.) Ten Speed Pr.

Orgill, Roxane. Go-Go Baby! Salerno, Steven, tr. Salerno, Steven, illus. 2004. 32p. (J). 14.95 (978-0-7614-5157-0(9)) Cavendish, Marshall Corp.

Ostow, Micol & Burge, Constance M. Changeling Places: An Original Novel. 2005. 152p. (J). (978-1-4155-8183-4(5) , Simon Spotlight) Simon & Schuster Children's Publishing.

Ostrow, Kim. Chuckie's New Mommy. 2007. 24p. (J). 21.35 (***978-1-59961-356-7(5)***) Spotlight.

Ostrow, Kim. Dil in a Pickle. 2000. (Rugrats Chapter Bks.). (Illus.). (J). 10.79 (978-0-606-20628-0(0)) Tandem Library Bks.

Oxenbury, Helen. All Fall Down. Oxenbury, Helen, illus. 1999. (Oxenbury Board Bks.). (Illus.). 10p. (J). (ps-k). bds. 6.99 (978-0-689-81985-8(4) , Little Simon) Simon & Schuster Children's Publishing.

Packard, Mary. The New Baby. Haley, Amanda, illus. 2004. (My First Reader Ser.). 32p. (J). (gr. k-1). pap. 3.95 (978-0-516-25506-4(1) , Children's Pr.) Scholastic Library Publishing.

—The New Baby. Haley, Amanda, tr. Haley, Amanda, illus. 2004. (My First Reader Ser.). 31p. (J). 18.50 (978-0-516-24409-9(4) , Children's Pr.) Scholastic Library Publishing.

Palatini, Margie. Goldie Is Mad. Palatini, Margie, illus. 2001. (Illus.). 32p. (ps-k). 15.49 (978-0-7868-2490-8(5)); 14.99 (978-0-7868-0565-5(X)) Hyperion Bks. for Children.

—The Wonder Worm Wars. 1999. (978-0-606-16660-7(2)) Tandem Library Bks.

Pandell, Karen. I Love You Baby from Head to Toe. Fletcher, Jane, illus. 2004. 16p. (J). (gr. k-ps). bds. 5.99 (978-0-7636-1588-8(9)) Candlewick Pr.

Park, Barbara. Junie B. Jones & a Little Monkey Business, Vol. 2. unabr. ed. 2004. (Junie B. Jones Ser.: Vol. 2). 68p. (J). (gr. k-3). pap. 17.00 incl. audio (978-0-8072-0779-6(9) , LFTR 238 SP, Listening Library) Random Hse. Audio Publishing Group.

—Junie B. Jones y el Negocio del Mono. Brunkus, Denise, illus. 2005. (Junie B. Jones Ser.).Tr. of Junie B Jones Little Monkey Business. (SPA.). 80p. (J). pap. 3.99 (978-0-439-42514-8(X) , Scholastic en Espanol) Scholastic, Inc.

Park, Barbara. Ma! There's Nothing to Do Here! A Word from Your Baby-In-Waiting. Garofoli, Viviana, illus. 2008. 40p. (J). (***978-0-375-83852-1(X));*** lib. bdg. (***978-0-375-93852-8(4)***) Random Hse., Inc.

Partis, Joanne. Look at Me! 2007. (Illus.). 10p. (J). bds. 4.99 (***978-1-84458-365-2(1)***) Anova Bks. GBR. *Dist:* Independent Pubs. Group.

Patz, Nancy & Roth, Susan L. Babies Can't Eat Kimchee! Patz, Nancy & Roth, Susan L., illus. 2006. (Illus.). 32p. (J). (ps-2). 16.95 (978-1-59990-017-9(3)) Bloomsbury Publishing.

Paulits, John. Philip & the Case of the Mistaken Identity & Philip & the Baby. 2007. (YA). pap. 7.50 (***978-1-59705-109-5(8));*** pap. 13.95 (***978-1-59705-897-1(1)***) Wings ePress, Inc.

Pearce, Emily Smith. Isabel & the Miracle Baby. 2007. 144p. (YA). (gr. 3 up). 15.95 (***978-1-932425-44-4(6)*** , Front Street) Boyds Mills Pr.

Peddicord, Jane Ann & So, Meilo. That Special Little Baby. 2007. (Illus.). 40p. (J). (ps-2). 16.00 (978-0-15-205430-4(8)) Harcourt Trade Pubs.

Phillips, Samantha. Crow: Part 1, Vol. 1. 2006. (ENG.). 24p. (YA). 3.50 (978-0-9785891-0-3(6) , 0001) MANGA-CANDY, LLC.

Pinczuk, Jane. Michele, the Nursing Toddler: A Story about Sharing Love. Murray, Barbara, illus. 1998. 32p. (J). (gr. 1-5). 14.95 (978-0-912500-40-9(9) , 253) La Leche League International.

Piper, Sophie. When You Were Very Small. Stephenson, Kristina, illus. 2006. 28p. (J). 7.95 (978-1-56148-515-4(2)) Good Bks.

Powell, Jillian. Izzy's Idea. Shearing, Leonie, illus. 2004. (Read-It! Readers Ser.). 32p. (C). (gr. k-3). 18.60 (978-1-4048-0644-3(X)) Picture Window Bks.

Price, Mathew. What Does Baby Do? Morozumi, Atsuko, illus. 2003. (Tommy Board Bks.). 10p. (J). bds., bds. 4.99 (978-0-7696-2958-2(X)) School Specialty Publishing.

Priddy, Roger. Baby Gund Baby Boy. 2006. 22p. (J). bds. 5.95 (978-0-312-49704-0(0) , Priddy Bks.) St. Martin's Pr.

—Baby Gund Baby Girl. 2006. 22p. (J). bds. 5.95 (978-0-312-49703-3(2) , Priddy Bks.) St. Martin's Pr.

—Baby Gund Mirror Bathtime. rev. ed. 2006. 12p. (J). bds. 6.95 (978-0-312-49708-8(3) , Priddy Bks.) St. Martin's Pr.

—Baby Hugs. 2004. 10p. (J). 7.95 (978-0-312-49335-6(5) , Priddy Bks.) St. Martin's Pr.

—Happy Baby - Faces. 2001. (Baby Shakers Ser.). (Illus.). 24p. (J). bds. 5.95 (978-0-312-49019-5(4) , Priddy Bks.) St. Martin's Pr.

Puttock, Simon. The Day the Baby Blew Away. Gale, Cathy, illus. 2004. 32p. (J). 15.95 (978-1-84507-046-5(1)) Lincoln, Frances Ltd. GBR. *Dist:* Transition Vendor.

Quattlebaum, Mary. Grover G. Graham & Me. 2003. 192p. (J). (gr. 3-7). pap. 5.99 (978-0-440-41918-1(2) , Yearling) Random Hse. Children's Bks.

Rabe, Tish. I'm a Baby: A Mix & Match Book. Larranaga, Ana, illus. 2006. 14p. (J). (ps-ps). bds. 9.99 (978-1-58476-355-0(8) , IKIDS) Innovative Kids.

Ramirez, Linda M. & Salcines, Maria Luisa. Playtime for Molly: A Story about Filial Therapy: How a Parent & Child Play to Improve Their Relationship. 2001. (Illus.). 24p. pap. 8.95 (978-0-9713839-0-6(1)) MarLin Bks.

Rana, Binni. How BabyKrishna Got His Blue. Debgupta, Shub, illus. 1999. 12p. (J). (978-1-929981-00-7(7)) kahani.com, Inc.

Random House Staff. Baby Party. Barrett, John E., illus. 2006. 12p. (J). (gr. k-ps). bds. 4.99 (978-0-375-83764-7(7) , Random Hse. Bks. for Young Readers) Random Hse. Children's Bks.

Ransom, Jeanie Franz. Grandma U. Corvino, Lucy, illus. 2002. 32p. (J). 15.95 (978-1-56145-214-9(9)) Peachtree Pubs., Ltd.

Reader's Digest Editors. Busy, Busy Baby. 2004. (Small Miracles Ser.: No. 6). 10p. (J). 7.99 (978-1-4003-0319-9(2)) Nelson, Thomas Inc.

Reddekopp, Sharon. A New Baby for Paige. Pamplin, Terry, illus. 2000. 16p. (J). (ps-3). pap. (978-1-894303-07-1(5)) Raven Rock Publishing.

Reiser, Lynn. My Baby & Me. Gentieu, Penny, illus. 2008. 32p. (J). (ps-1). 16.99 (***978-0-375-85205-3(0)*** , Knopf Bks. for Young Readers) Random Hse. Children's Bks.

Reiser, Lynn. You & Me, Baby. Gentieu, Penny, illus. 2006. 40p. (J). (gr. k-ps). lib. bdg. 17.99 (978-0-375-93401-8(4) , Knopf Bks. for Young Readers) Random Hse. Children's Bks.

—You & Me, Baby. Gentieu, Penny, photos by. 2006. (Illus.). 40p. (J). (gr. k-ps). 15.95 (978-0-375-83401-1(X) , Knopf Bks. for Young Readers) Random Hse. Children's Bks.

Reynolds, Lisa Rene. My Little Firstborn. Orth, Donna, illus. 2001. 32p. (J). (ps-3). per. 11.95 (978-0-9703178-7-2(5) , Ramona's Bk. Co.) RBC Publishing Co., Inc.

Reynolds, Marilyn. Baby Help. 2003. (True-To-Life Ser.: Vol. 6). 192p. (J). (gr. 7-12). 15.95 (978-1-885356-26-0(9)); pap. 8.95 (978-1-885356-27-7(7)) Morning Glory Pr., Inc.

Rhoton, Lesa. Angus & the Triplets. Switzer, Bobby, illus. 2006. 28p. per. 13.95 (978-1-58939-852-8(1)) Virtualbookworm.com Publishing, Inc.

Richards, Laura E. Jiggle Joggle Jee! 2001. (Illus.). 32p. (J). (ps-3). 15.89 (978-0-688-17833-8(2)) HarperCollins Pubs.

Ries, Lori. Super Sam! Rama, Sue, illus. (J). 2007. pap. 6.95 (***978-1-58089-171-4(3));*** 2004. 32p. 14.95 (978-1-58089-041-0(5)) Charlesbridge Publishing, Inc.

Robbins, Beth. Tom, Ally, & the New Baby. Stuart, Jon, illus. 2001. (It's OK! Ser.). 24p. (J). (ps-k). pap. 3.95 (978-0-7894-7430-8(1) , D K Ink) Dorling Kindersley Publishing, Inc.

Roberts, Willo Davis. The One Left Behind. 2007. 139p. (J). (gr. 3-7). per. 5.99 (978-0-689-85083-7(2)) Simon & Schuster Children's Publishing.

Robinson, Marcus. Samurai Baby the Adventure Begins. 2007. 87p. pap. 11.98 (***978-1-4303-0350-3(6)***) Lulu.com.

Rock, Lois & Buckingham, Gabriella. Now You Are. 2002. (Illus.). 28p. 4.99 (978-1-56148-394-5(X)); 2nd ed. 4.99 (978-1-56148-395-2(8)); 3rd ed. 4.99 (978-1-56148-396-9(6)) Good Bks.

Rockwell, Lizzy. Hello Baby! Rockwell, Lizzy, illus. 2002. (Illus.). (J). 14.79 (978-0-7587-4439-5(0)) Book Wholesalers, Inc.

—Hello Baby! Rockwell, Lizzy, illus. 2000. (Illus.). 32p. (J). (gr. k-k). pap. 6.99 (978-0-517-80074-4(8) , Dragonfly Bks.) Random Hse. Children's Bks.

—Hello Baby! 2000. (J). (978-0-606-18980-4(7)); lib. bdg. 15.30 (978-0-613-25484-7(8)) Tandem Library Bks.

Romanova, Yelena. The Perfect Friend. Kulikov, Boris, illus. 2005. 32p. (J). (ps-1). 15.00 (978-0-374-35821-1(4) , Frances Foster Bks.) Farrar, Straus & Giroux.

Root, Phyllis. What Baby Wants. Barton, Jill, illus. 2002. (J). 23.40 (978-0-7587-3955-1(9)) Book Wholesalers, Inc.

—What Baby Wants. Barton, Jill, illus. 1998. 18p. (J). (ps-3). pap. 12.98 (978-1-58048-027-6(0)) Sandvik Publishing.

—What Baby Wants. 2001. (J). (978-0-606-21514-5(X)) Tandem Library Bks.

Roper, Janice. Dancing on the Moon. Grimm, Laurence G., illus. 2001. iv, 31p. (J). (ps-3). 19.95 (978-0-9641218-6-7(7)) SIDS Educational Services, Inc.

Rosado, Maria. Book 'Em Tommy. 2000. (Rugrats Chapter Bks.). (Illus.). (J). 10.79 (978-0-606-20577-1(2)) Tandem Library Bks.

Rosen, Michael. Howler. Layton, Neal, illus. 2004. 32p. (J). (ps-2). 15.95 (978-1-58234-851-3(0) , Bloomsbury Children) Bloomsbury Publishing.

Ross, Tony. I Want a Sister. 2002. (Illus.). 22p. (J). 9.99 (978-1-84270-103-4(7)) Andersen GBR. *Dist:* Independent Pubs. Group.

Rouss, Sylvia A. My Baby Brother: What a Miracle! Dubois, Liz Goulet, illus. 2002. (J). 14.95 (978-0-8246-0445-5(8)) David, Jonathan Publishers, Inc.

Russo-Stark, Marisabina. Come Back, Hannah! 2001. (Illus.). 32p. (J). (ps-3). 15.89 (978-0-688-17384-5(5)) HarperCollins Pubs.

Ryan, Darlene & Manchester, Peter. Kisses, Kisses, Kisses. 2004. (Illus.). 24p. (J). (***978-1-55131-092-3(9)***) Univ. of New Brunswick, Dept. of Graphic Services.

S. I. Artists Staff. Baby Strawberry's Rainbow Day. 2006. (Strawberry Shortcake Baby Ser.). (Illus.). 10p. (J). (ps-ps). bds. 5.99 (978-0-448-44356-0(2) , Grosset & Dunlap) Penguin Group (USA) Inc.

Salerno, Steven. Harry Hungry. 2008. (J). (***978-0-15-206257-6(2)***) Harcourt Trade Pubs.

Schafer, Milton. Bath Time for Baby Strawberry. S. I. Artists Staff, illus. 2006. (Strawberry Shortcake Baby Ser.). 6p. (J). (ps-ps). bds. 4.99 (978-0-448-44357-7(0) , Grosset & Dunlap) Penguin Group (USA) Inc.

Schlein, Miriam. The Story about Me. Stephenson, Kristina, illus. 2004. 32p. (J). (ps-1). 15.95 (978-0-8075-7631-1(X)) Whitman, Albert & Co.

Schoberle, Cecile. Thank You, Angelica. 2007. 24p. (J). 21.35 (***978-1-59961-359-8(X)***) Spotlight.

Scholastic, Inc. Staff. My Happy Baby! Berg, Michelle, illus. 2004. 4p. (J). 12.95 (978-0-439-57733-5(0) , Cartwheel Bks.) Scholastic, Inc.

Schroeder, Lisa. Baby Can't Sleep. Garofoli, Viviana, illus. 2007. 24p. (J). bds. 5.95 (978-1-4027-4323-8(8)) Sterling Publishing Co., Inc.

Schwartz, Amy. A Teeny, Tiny Baby. 2006. (Illus.). 32p. (J). 12.95 (978-1-59643-193-5(8)) Roaring Brook Pr.

—A Teeny Tiny Baby. Schwartz, Amy, illus. 2002. (Illus.). 14.74 (978-1-4046-0277-9(1)) Book Wholesalers, Inc.

—A Teeny Tiny Baby. Schwartz, Amy, illus. 2000. (Illus.). 32p. (J). (ps-1). pap. 6.95 (978-0-531-07177-9(4) , Orchard Bks.) Scholastic, Inc.

Schwartz, Roslyn. Yo Baby! Schwartz, Roslyn, illus. 2002. (Illus.). 24p. (J). (gr. k-ps). pap. 5.95 (978-1-55037-754-5(X)); lib. bdg. 18.95 (978-1-55037-755-2(8)) Annick Pr., Ltd. CAN. *Dist:* Firefly Bks., Ltd.

Shapiro, Jody Fickes. Family Lullaby. Felstead, Cathie, illus. 2007. 40p. (J). (ps). 16.99 (978-0-06-051482-2(5)); lib. bdg. 17.89 (978-0-06-051483-9(3)) HarperCollins Pubs.

Shea, Pegi Deitz. I See Me! 2000. (Growing Tree Ser.). (Illus.). 14p. (J). (ps up). 5.95 (978-0-694-01278-7(5) , Harper Festival) HarperCollins Pubs.

Shields, Gillian. Angel Baby. 2006. (Illus.). 24p. (J). (ps). pap. 9.99 (978-0-00-718006-6(3) , HarperCollins Children's Bks.) HarperCollins Pubs. Ltd. GBR. *Dist:* Independent Pubs. Group.

—The Starlight Baby. Harbour, Elizabeth, illus. 2006. 32p. (J). 15.95 (978-1-4169-1456-3(0)) Simon & Schuster Children's Publishing.

Silverman, Manuel S. Rosie & the Mole: The Story of a Bris. 1999. (Illus.). 48p. (J). (gr. 1-4). 16.95 (978-0-943706-22-1(X) , Devora Publishing) Pitspopany Pr.

—Rosie & the Mole: The Story of a Bris. Kahn, Katherine Janus, illus. 1999. 48p. (J). (gr. 1-4). pap. 9.95 (978-0-943706-20-7(3) , Devora Publishing) Pitspopany Pr.

Simon & Collins. Don't Wake up the Baby. (Illus.). 25p. (J). (978-0-340-70935-1(9)); pap. (978-0-340-69842-6(X)) Hodder General Publishing Division. (Hodder & Stoughton).

Singer, Marilyn. City Lullaby. Cneut, Carll, illus. 2007. 32p. (J). (ps-3). 16.00 (***978-0-618-60703-7(X)*** , Clarion Bks.) Houghton Mifflin Co. Trade & Reference Div.

Slattery, Karen. Piper's Diapers. 2003. (J). pap. 9.00 (978-0-8059-5765-5(0)) Dorrance Publishing Co., Inc.

Slingsby, Janet. Hush-a-Bye Babies. Beckett, Andy, illus. 2001. 32p. (J). (ps-2). 14.95 (978-0-7641-5410-2(9)) Barron's Educational Series, Inc.

Smith, Maggie. One Naked Baby. 2007. (Illus.). 40p. (J). (ps-k). 15.99 (978-0-375-83329-8(3)); lib. bdg. 17.99 (978-0-375-93329-5(8)) Random Hse. Children's Bks. (Knopf Bks. for Young Readers).

Sockabasin, Allen. Thanks to the Animals. Raye, Rebekah, illus. 2005. 32p. (J). (ps-2). 16.95 (978-0-88448-270-3(7)) Tilbury Hse. Pubs.

Spicer, Lin. Faerie Baby. 2006. pap. (***978-1-84426-384-4(3)***) Upfront Publishing Ltd.

Spicher, Kolleen. Baby Write-in Album. 2003. (Illus.). (YA). 14.95 (978-1-931722-35-3(8) , Sixth Avenue Bks.) Grand Central Publishing.

Spinelli, Eileen. Lizzie Logan, Second Banana. 2000. (978-0-606-17827-3(9)) Tandem Library Bks.

St John, Patricia. A Home for Virginia. Smith, Helen, illus. 2005. 24p. (J). (ps-7). per. (978-1-85792-961-4(6) , Christian Focus) Christian Focus Pubns.

Stockham, Leslie C. What's the Matter with the Baby? 1999. Tr. of Que le Pasa Al Bebito?. (Illus.). 18p. (J). (ps). 19.98 (978-1-893447-00-4(6)) Bilingual Language Materials.

Sturges, Philemon. How Do You Make a Baby Smile? Strevens-Marzo, Bridget, illus. 2007. 24p. (J). (ps). 16.99 (***978-0-06-076072-4(9));*** lib. bdg. 17.89 (***978-0-06-076073-1(7)***) HarperCollins Pubs.

Stuve-Bodeen, Stephanie. Mama Elizabeti. Hale, Christy, illus. 2000. 32p. (J). (ps up). 12.76 (978-1-58430-002-1(7)) Lee & Low Bks., Inc.

Suen, Anastasia. Baby Born. Chang, Chih-Wei, illus. 2000. Orig. Title: Recien Nacido. 18p. (J). (ps-4). 5.56 (978-1-880000-68-7(7)) Lee & Low Bks., Inc.

Sykes, Julie. Little Tiger's Big Surprise! Warnes, Tim, illus. 2001. 32p. (J). (ps-2). tchr. ed. 14.95 (978-1-58925-002-4(8) , tiger tales) ME Media LLC.

Sykes, Julie & Warnes, Tim. Little Tiger's Big Surprise! 2001. (Illus.). 32p. (J). (ps-2). 5.95 (978-1-58925-352-0(3) , tiger tales) ME Media LLC.

Taback, Simms. Peekaboo Who? 2006. (Illus.). 14p. bds. 8.95 (978-1-59354-180-4(5)) Blue Apple Bks.

H I

Tabby, Abigail. Who's That Pretty Baby? Book & Frame Gift Set. Beeke, Tiphanie, illus. 2007. (Little Simon Baby Ser.). 12p. (J). 9.99 (***978-1-4169-3790-6(0)*** , Little Simon) Simon & Schuster Children's Publishing.

Taylor, Ann & HarperCollins Staff. Baby Dance. Van Heerden, Marjorie, illus. 1999. (Growing Tree Ser.). 16p. (J). (ps up). 6.99 (978-0-694-01206-0(8) , Harper Festival) HarperCollins Pubs.

Taylor, Donna. Dream Come True. 2000. (gr. k-3). lib. bdg. 11.25 (978-0-613-31140-3(X)) Tandem Library Bks.

Teal, Joyce Willard. The Point System. 1998. (Illus.). (J). pap. 8.80 (978-1-56763-399-3(4)); lib. bdg. 25.25 (978-1-56763-398-6(6)) Ozark Publishing.

thomas, Dalandra, illus. Noonimals: The New Baby. thomas, Dalandra, . rev. ed. 2007. 40p. (J). pap. 14.99 (***978-0-9796832-0-6(3)***) Nooni Publishing.

Thomas, Joyce Carol. You Are My Perfect Baby. Bennett, Nneka, photos by. 1999. (Joanna Cotler Bks.). (Illus.). 14p. (J). (ps up). 5.95 (978-0-694-01096-7(0) , Harper Festival) HarperCollins Pubs.

Tildes, Phyllis L. Cara de BeBe. Tildes, Phyllis L., illus. 2004. (SPA., Illus.). 10p. (J). bds. 5.95 (978-1-57091-428-7(1)) Charlesbridge Publishing, Inc.

Trebi-Ollennu, Flora. Shogologo Babies. Vandenberg, Jan, illus. 2002. 64p. pap. (***978-1-894718-03-5(8)***) Amerley Treb Bks.

Tremblay, Carole, et al. A Monster in the House. 2000. (Illus.). 32p. (J). (ps-3). pap. (978-1-894363-46-4(9)) Dominique & Friends.

Truscott, Lucian K., IV. Itty Bitty Baby. 2003. (J). lib. bdg. 17.99 (978-0-375-92197-1(4) , Random Hse. Bks. for Young Readers) Random Hse. Children's Bks.

Tuxworth, Nicola. Babies. 2001. (Very First Picture Bks.). (Illus.). 20p. 5.95 (978-0-7548-0937-1(4)) Anness Publishing GBR. *Dist:* National Bk. Network.

—Funny Faces: A Very First Picture Book. 1999. (Pictures & Words Ser.). (Illus.). 24p. (J). (ps up). lib. bdg. 22.00 (978-0-8368-2272-4(2)) Stevens, Gareth Inc.

Vagnozzi, Barbara. Hungry Baby. 2002. (Baby's Day Ser.). (Illus.). 16p. (J). (ps up). 3.95 (978-1-84089-238-3(2) , Zero to Ten, Limited) Evans Publishing Group GBR. *Dist:* Independent Pubs. Group.

—Messy Baby. 2002. (Baby's Day Ser.). (Illus.). 16p. (J). (ps up). 3.95 (978-1-84089-237-6(4) , Zero to Ten, Limited) Evans Publishing Group GBR. *Dist:* Independent Pubs. Group.

—Morning Baby. 2002. (Baby's Day Ser.). (Illus.). 16p. (J). (ps up). 3.95 (978-1-84089-236-9(6) , Zero to Ten, Limited) Evans Publishing Group GBR. *Dist:* Independent Pubs. Group.

—Sleepy Baby. 2002. (Baby's Day Ser.). (Illus.). 16p. (J). (ps up). 3.95 (978-1-84089-239-0(0) , Zero to Ten, Limited) Evans Publishing Group GBR. *Dist:* Independent Pubs. Group.

Van Draanen, Wendelin. Sammy Keyes & the Search for Snake Eyes. (Sammy Keyes Ser.: Bk. 7). (gr. 5). 2003. 320p. (J). pap. 5.99 (978-0-440-41900-6(X) , Yearling); 2002. 272p. lib. bdg. 17.99 (978-0-375-91175-0(8) , Knopf Bks. for Young Readers) Random Hse. Children's Bks.

Vaughan, Kathryn Mademann. Little One... Good Night: A Lullaby from Vermont. Edson, Anharad, illus. 2004. (J). per. 19.95 incl. audio compact disk (978-0-9747447-0-4(0)) Chaser Media LLC.

Voake, Charlotte. Hello Twins. Voake, Charlotte, illus. 2006. (Illus.). 32p. (J). (gr. k-k). 15.99 (978-0-7636-3003-4(9)) Candlewick Pr.

Vogel, Elizabeth. Al Agua Patos. 2004. (Limpieza y Salud Todo el Dia Ser.). (SPA & ENG., Illus.). 24p. (J). lib. bdg. 16.00 (978-0-8239-6617-2(8)); (gr. 1-2). lib. bdg. 16.00 (978-0-8239-6616-5(X)) Rosen Publishing Group, Inc., The. (Buenas Letra).

Wahl, Jan. Mabel Ran Away with the Toys. Woodruff, Liza, illus. 2000. 32p. (J). (ps-3). 16.95 (978-1-58089-059-5(8)); pap. 6.95 (978-1-58089-067-0(9)) Charlesbridge Publishing, Inc.

—Mabel Ran Away with the Toys. 2000. (gr. k-3). lib. bdg. 15.25 (978-0-613-35177-5(0)) Tandem Library Bks.

Wallace, Nancy Elizabeth. Baby Day! 2003. (Illus.). 32p. (J). (gr. k-ps). 9.95 (978-0-618-27576-2(2)) Houghton Mifflin Co. Trade & Reference Div.

Walsh, Joanna. All Asleep. rev. ed. 2008. 24p. (J). (ps). bds. 6.99 (***978-0-316-11871-2(0)***) Little, Brown Bks. for Young Readers.

Wardlaw, Lee. The Chair Where Bear Sits. Benfanti, Russell, illus. 2001. 56p. (J). (ps-2). 23.00 (978-1-890817-85-5(6)) Winslow Pr.

Watt, F. Al Agua Patos! 2004. (Mundo del Pequenin Ser.). (SPA., Illus.). 16p. (J). (ps up). 4.95 (978-0-7460-3867-3(4)) EDC Publishing.

—Felices Suenos! 2004. (Mundo del Pequenin Ser.).Tr. of Baby's Bedtime. (SPA., Illus.). 16p. (YA). (ps up). pap. 4.95 (978-0-7460-3869-7(0)) EDC Publishing.

Watt, Fiona. Baby's Bathtime Kid Kit. 1998. (Baby's World Ser.). (Illus.). 16p. (J). (ps). 14.95 (978-1-58086-220-2(9)) EDC Publishing.

—Baby's Mealtime. 2004. (Baby's World Bathbooks Ser.). (Illus.). 10p. (YA). (ps-k). 7.95 (978-0-7460-4176-5(4)) EDC Publishing.

—Sleepy Baby Board Bk. Mackinnon, Catherine-Anne, illus. 2006. 10p. (J). bds. 8.99 (978-0-7945-1071-8(X) , Usborne) EDC Publishing.

Watt, Fiona & Wells, Rachel. Baby's Bedtime. 2004. (Baby's World Ser.). (Illus.). 16p. (J). (ps up). pap. 4.95 (978-0-7460-3374-6(5)) EDC Publishing.

Wax, Wendy. Runaway Turkey. 2003. (ps-2). lib. bdg. 11.80 (978-0-613-73407-3(6)) Tandem Library Bks.

—Valentine for Tommy. 2003. (gr. k-3). lib. bdg. 11.80 (978-0-613-57563-8(6)) Tandem Library Bks.

Weatherford, Carole Boston. Jazz Baby. Freeman, Laura, illus. 2002. 24p. (J). (ps). 11.95 (978-1-58430-039-7(6)) Lee & Low Bks., Inc.

Weber, Jill. Angel's Mother's Baby. 2003. (gr. 3-6). lib. bdg. 12.95 (978-0-613-86977-5(X)) Tandem Library Bks.

Weiss, Ellen & Cooke, Tom. Bye-Bye, Bottle. 1998. (Muppets Ser.). 14p. (J). (ps). bds. 3.49 (978-0-307-13469-1(5) , 13469, Golden Bks.) Random Hse. Children's Bks.

Wells, Rosemary. Max Cleans Up. Wells, Rosemary, illus. 2002. (Max the Bunny Ser.). (Illus.). 13.19 (978-1-4046-0741-5(2)) Book Wholesalers, Inc.

—Max Cleans Up. (Max & Ruby Ser.). (Illus.). 32p. (J). 2002. pap. 5.99 (978-0-14-230133-3(7) , Puffin); 2000. 15.99 (978-0-670-89218-1(1) , Viking Juvenile) Penguin Group (USA) Inc.

—McDuff & the Baby. Jeffers, Susan, illus. 2006. 32p. (ps-k). 9.99 (978-0-7868-3834-9(5)) Hyperion Bks. for Children.

—McDuff & the Baby. Jeffers, Susan, illus. 2020. 24p. (J). pap. 4.99 (978-0-7868-1191-5(9)) Hyperion Paperbacks for Children.

West, Cathy. All Growed Up. 2001. (gr. k-3). lib. bdg. 14.15 (978-0-613-43915-2(5)) Tandem Library Bks.

Wheeler, Lisa. Jazz Baby. Christie, Gregory R., illus. 2007. 40p. (J). (ps-2). 16.00 (978-0-15-202522-9(7)) Harcourt Trade Pubs.

Whelan, Olwyn. The Star Child. Maidment, Stella, illus. 2004. 40p. (J). 14.95 (978-1-84458-039-2(3)) Chrysalis Children's Bks. GBR. *Dist:* Transition Vendor.

Whybrow, Ian. A Baby for Grace. Birmingham, Christian, illus. 1998. 32p. (J). (gr. k-ps). tchr. ed. 15.95 (978-0-7534-5142-7(5) , Kingfisher) Houghton Mifflin Co. Trade & Reference Div.

Wigand, Molly. Be My Valentine! 2000. (gr. k-3). lib. bdg. 14.15 (978-0-613-21177-2(4)) Tandem Library Bks.

Wild, Margaret. Midnight Babies. James, Ann, illus. 2001. 32p. (J). (gr. k-3). tchr. ed. 15.00 (978-0-618-10412-3(7) , Clarion Bks.) Houghton Mifflin Co. Trade & Reference Div.

Wilkowski, Susan. Baby's Bris. Friedman, Judith, illus. 1999. 32p. (J). (ps-5). 16.95 (978-1-58013-052-3(6)); pap. 6.95 (978-1-58013-053-0(4)) Kar-Ben Publishing.

Willis, Jeanne & Ross, Tony. Dr. Xargles Book of Earthlets. 2003. (Illus.). 32p. (J). pap. 9.99 (978-1-84270-067-9(7)) Andersen GBR. *Dist:* Trafalgar Square Publishing.

Willson, Sarah. Brand-New Daddy. 2001. lib. bdg. 14.15 (978-0-613-43921-3(X)) Tandem Library Bks.

—Picture Perfect Tommy. 2001. (gr. k-3). lib. bdg. 11.80 (978-0-613-43949-7(X)) Tandem Library Bks.

—Rugrats' Easter Surprise. 2002. (gr. k-3). lib. bdg. 14.15 (978-0-613-51321-0(5)) Tandem Library Bks.

—Tricked for Treats! A Rugrats Halloween. 1999. (gr. k-3). lib. bdg. 14.15 (978-0-613-22524-3(4)) Tandem Library Bks.

Wilson, Sarah. Chuckie Meets the Beastie Bunny. 2000. (Rugrats Chapter Bks.). (Illus.). (J). 10.30 (978-0-606-20604-4(3)) Tandem Library Bks.

Winter, Susan. A Baby Just Like Me. (J). 2002. (TUR & ENG.). 13.95 (978-1-85269-295-7(2)); 2000. (ARA & ENG.). 13.99 (978-1-85269-297-1(9)); 2000. (BEN & ENG.). 13.95 (978-1-85269-248-3(0)); 2000. (CHI.). 13.99 (978-1-85269-259-9(6)); 2000. (GUJ & ENG.). 13.95 (978-1-85269-290-2(1)); 2000. (SOM & ENG.). 19.95 (978-1-85269-292-6(8)); 2000. (URD & ENG.). 13.95 (978-1-85269-296-4(0)) Mantra Publishing, Ltd. GBR. *Dist:* AIMS International Bks., Inc.

Wood, Amanda. Baby's Day! Dodd, Emma, illus. 2006. (Amazing Baby Ser.). 16p. (J). bds. 5.95 (978-1-59223-588-9(3) , Silver Dolphin Bks.) Advantage Pubs. Group.

Wood, Jacqueline & Wood, Jakki. Baby Parade. 2003. (Illus.). 32p. (J). 14.95 (978-0-7112-2065-2(4)) Lincoln, Frances Ltd. GBR. *Dist:* Transition Vendor.

Wood, Jakki. Baby Parade. 2004. (Illus.). 32p. (J). 14.95 (978-1-84507-273-5(1)); reprint ed. pap. 7.95 (978-1-84507-042-7(9)) Lincoln, Frances Ltd. GBR. *Dist:* Transition Vendor, Perseus Distribution.

Yolen, Jane. Grandma's Hurrying Child. Johnson, Stephen T. & Chorao, Kay, illus. 2005. 32p. (J). 16.00 (978-0-15-201813-9(1) , Gulliver Bks.) Harcourt Children's Bks.

Young, Dianne. Purple Hair? I Don't Care! Hartmann, Barbara, illus. 1998. 32p. (J). (ps-k). pap. 7.95 (978-0-916291-55-6(3)) Kane/Miller Bk. Pubs., Inc.

Young, Selina. All about Me: A Hundred Things That Heppened to Me Between 9 & 3. 2007. (Illus.). 80p. (J). (ps-k). 12.00 (***978-1-84255-118-9(3)***) Orion Publishing Group, Ltd. GBR. *Dist:* Independent Pubs. Group.

INFECTION AND INFECTIOUS DISEASES

see Communicable Diseases

INFIRMARIES

see Hospitals

INFORMATION SERVICES

Wolinsky, Art. Locating & Evaluating Information on the Internet. 1999. (Internet Library). (Illus.). 64p. (YA). (gr. 4-12). lib. bdg. 22.60 (978-0-7660-1259-2(X)) Enslow Pubs., Inc.

INFORMATION STORAGE AND RETRIEVAL SYSTEMS

Arnone, Marilyn P. Mac, Information Detective, In— the Curious Kids & the Squiggly Question. Stockley, Gerry, illus. 2005. 32p. (J). (***978-1-59158-296-0(2)***) Libraries Unlimited, Inc.

Arnone, Marilyn P. Mac, Information Detective, in the Curious Kids—Digging for Answers: A Storybook Approach to Introducing Research Skills. Stockley, Gerry & Reeves, Andrea, illus. 2006. 71p. (J). 35.00 (978-1-59158-188-8(5)) Libraries Unlimited, Inc.

Arnone, Marilyn P. & Coatney, Sharon. MAC, Information Detective, in the Case Of— Curious Kids & the Squiggly Question: Picture Book. 2005. 32p. (J). 35.00 (978-1-59158-189-5(3)) Libraries Unlimited, Inc.

Mackall, Joe. Research & Information Management. 2nd ed. 2004. (Career Skills Library). (Illus.). 128p. (YA). (gr. 6-12). 21.95 (978-0-8160-5518-0(1) , Ferguson Publishing Co.) Facts On File, Inc.

Patrice Cassedy. Computer Technology. 2004. (Careers for the Twenty-First Century Ser.). (Illus.). 112p. (J). 29.95 (978-1-56006-896-9(5)) Thomson Gale.

QEB Let's Start! Computing National Book Stores Edition: Sorting Information. 2006. (J). per. (978-1-59566-296-5(0)) QEB Publishing Inc.

INFORMATION TECHNOLOGY

Apel, Melanie Ann. Careers in Information Science. 2000. (Careers Ser.). (Illus.). 105p. (YA). (gr. 7-12). lib. bdg. 18.95 (978-0-8239-2892-7(6) , CAINSC, PowerKids Pr.) Rosen Publishing Group, Inc., The.

—Careers in Information Technology. rev. ed. 2005. (Career Resource Library). (Illus.). 192p. (J). (gr. 7-12). lib. bdg. 26.50 (978-0-8239-4085-1(3)) Rosen Publishing Group, Inc., The.

Bidder, Jane. Inventions We Use for Information & Entertainment. 2006. (Illus.). 32p. (J). lib. bdg. (978-0-8368-6899-9(4)) Stevens, Gareth Inc.

Bowden, Gregory Laurence & Maguire, Kerryn. Practice IT. (Cambridge Secondary It Ser.). Bk. 1. 2001. tchr. ed. 288.20 incl. cd-rom (978-0-521-75027-1(X)); Bk. 1. 2001. (Illus.). 136p. pap. 12.80 (978-0-521-75025-7(3)); Bk. 2. 2002. tchr. ed. 143.90 incl. cd-rom (978-0-521-75028-8(8)); Bk. 2. 2001. (Illus.). 192p. pap. 17.05 (978-0-521-75026-4(1)) Cambridge Univ. Pr.

Corwin, Gene. Your Bright Future in Information Technology. 2002. (gr. 7-12). lib. bdg. 21.10 (978-0-613-56713-8(7)) Tandem Library Bks.

Doyle, Stephen. Ict Framework Solutions: Year 7. 2006. (Illus.). 290p. (YA). pap., stu. ed. 32.50 (978-0-7487-8083-9(1)) Nelson Thornes Ltd. GBR. *Dist:* Trans-Atlantic Pubns., Inc.

—Understanding Information & Communication Technology: For A Level. 2000. (Illus.). 334p. (C). pap. 59.50 (978-0-7487-3609-6(3)) Nelson Thornes Ltd. GBR. *Dist:* Trans-Atlantic Pubns., Inc.

Goodwin, Ann. How to Dazzle at Information Technology. 2004. (Illus.). 48p. pap. 30.00 (978-1-897675-67-0(4)) Brilliant Pubns. GBR. *Dist:* Parkwest Pubns., Inc.

Information Technology Careers (AVA) 2001. (YA). pap. 6.00 (978-1-57078-014-1(5) , CEV00014); pap. 8.00 (978-1-57078-015-8(3) , CEV00015) C E V Multimedia, Ltd.

J.G. Ferguson Publishing Company Staff, contrib. by. What Can I Do Now? 2007. (What Can I Do Now Ser.). 208p. (J). (gr. 6-12). 29.95 (***978-0-8160-6027-6(4)*** , Ferguson Publishing Co.) Facts On File, Inc.

McBride, P. K. Skills Award in Information Technology: Foundation Level. 2002. (Cambridge International Examinations Ser.). (Illus.). 156p. pap. 15.00 (978-0-521-52529-9(2)) Cambridge Univ. Pr.

—Skills Award in Information Technology: Standard Level. 2003. (Cambridge International Examinations Ser.). (Illus.). 144p. pap. 16.00 (978-0-521-52528-2(4)) Cambridge Univ. Pr.

Page, Alison & Shepard, Tristram. Information & Communications Technology: Skills Book 2 Levels 4-5. 2000. (Getting It Right Ser.). (Illus.). 144p. (YA). (gr. 9-11). pap. 22.50 (978-0-7487-4423-7(1)); pap. 22.50 (978-0-7487-4421-3(5)) Nelson Thornes Ltd. GBR. *Dist:* Trans-Atlantic Pubns., Inc.

Page, Alison, et al. Information & Communications Technology: Skills Book 3 Levels 5 Plus. 2000. (Getting It Right Ser.). (Illus.). 144p. (YA). (gr. 9-11). pap. 22.50 (978-0-7487-4530-2(0)) Nelson Thornes Ltd. GBR. *Dist:* Trans-Atlantic Pubns., Inc.

Potts, Colin. Cambridge Checkpoints VCE Information Processing & Management 2005. 2004. (Cambridge Checkpoints Ser.). 184p. pap., stu. ed. 11.85 (978-0-521-60960-9(7)) Cambridge Univ. Pr.

Reeves, Diane Lindsey, et al. Career Ideas for Teens in Information Technology. (Career Ideas for Teens Ser.). (gr. 6-12). 192p. pap. 16.95 (978-0-8160-6921-7(2) , Checkmark Bks.); 2005. (Illus.). 184p. (J). per. 40.00 (978-0-8160-5293-6(X) , Ferguson Publishing Co.) Facts On File, Inc.

Stoyles, Pennie, et al. Information Technology Issues. 2003. 32p. (J). lib. bdg. 24.25 (978-1-58340-329-7(9)) Smart Apple Media.

Ward-Johnson, Chris & Gould, William. The Magic Mouse Dictionary of Computers & Information Technology. Laughing Gravy Design Staff, illus. 2003. (Magic Mouse Guides). 64p. (J). lib. bdg. 27.93 (978-0-7660-2264-5(1)) Enslow Pubs., Inc.

Wilson, Barbara. City & Guilds: Information Technology. 2nd rev. ed. (Illus.). 144p. pap. (978-1-86152-699-1(7) , Arden Shakespeare, The) Thomson Learning EMEA, Ltd.

Wilson, Carole. Exploring Information & Software Technology Teacher CD-ROM. 4th rev. ed. 2007. tchr. ed. 74.00 incl. cd-rom (***978-0-521-69264-9(4)***) Cambridge Univ. Pr.

Woodford, Chris. Digital Technology. 2006. (Science in Focus Ser.). 48p. (J). 27.00 (978-0-7910-8861-6(8) , Chelsea Hse.) Facts On File, Inc.

INITIAL TEACHING ALPHABET

Flora, Sherrill B. Alphabet Fun. 1999. (Basic Skills Ser.). 48p. (J). (ps-2). pap. 6.99 (978-0-513-02254-6(6) , TSD22546, Instructional Fair) Schaffer, Frank Pubns.

School Zone Publishing Company Staff. Alphabet Fun. 2000. (Flash Cards 4-Pack Ser.). (J). 12.99 (978-0-88743-813-4(X) , 04030) School Zone Publishing Co.

Titzer, Robert C. A Book Your Baby Can Read! Dozier, Brendan et al, photos by. 2003. (Early Language Development Ser.: Vol. 2). (Illus.). 14p. (J). pap. 7.95 (978-0-9657510-5-6(8) , 0-9657510-5-8) Infant Learning Co., The.

—A Book Your Baby Can Read! Dozier, Brendan et al, photos by. 1998. (Early Language Development Ser.: Vol. 1). (Illus.). 14p. (J). (ps). pap. 7.95 (978-0-9657510-1-8(5) , 0-9657510-1-5) Infant Learning Co., The.

—A Book Your Baby Can Read! Early Language Development Series. Dozier, Lisa et al, photos by. 2003. (Early Language Development Ser.: Vol. 3). (Illus.). 14p. (J). pap. 7.95 (978-0-9657510-9-4(0) , 0-9657510-9-0) Infant Learning Co., The.

—A Book Your Baby Can Read! 5 Book Set: Early Language Development Series, 5 vols., Vol. 1. 2003. (Illus.). 80p. (J). pap. 29.95 (978-1-931026-05-5(X) , 1-931026-05-X) Infant Learning Co., The.

—A Book Your Baby Can Read! Review: Early Language Development Series. Dozier, Brendan et al, photos by. 2003. (Early Language Development Ser.). (Illus.). 14p. (J). pap. 7.95 (978-1-931026-04-8(1) , 1-931026-04-1) Infant Learning Co., The.

—A Book Your Baby Can Read! Starter: Early Language Development Series, 1, Starter Book. Dozier, Lisa et al, photos by. 2003. (Book Your Baby Can Read!: Starter Book). (Illus.). 14p. (J). pap. 7.95 (978-1-931026-03-1(3) , 1-931026-03-3) Infant Learning Co., The.

INJURIES

see First Aid

INJURIOUS INSECTS

see Insects, Injurious and Beneficial

INLAND NAVIGATION

see also Canals; Lakes

Heat-Moon, William Least. River-Horse: The Logbook of a Boat Across America. 2001. (gr. 7-12). lib. bdg. 23.45 (978-0-613-36633-5(6)) Tandem Library Bks.

INNS

see Hotels, Motels, etc.

INOCULATION

see Vaccination

INORGANIC CHEMISTRY

see Chemistry, Inorganic

INQUISITION

Don Nardo. The Trial of Galileo. 2004. (Famous Trials Ser.). (Illus.). 112p. (J). 29.95 (978-1-59018-423-3(8)) Thomson Gale.

INQUISITION—FICTION

Hoffman, Alice. Incantation. rev. ed. 2007. (Illus.). 166p. (YA). (gr. 7-17). per. 8.99 (***978-0-316-15428-4(8)***) Little, Brown Bks. for Young Readers.

Lasky, Kathryn. Blood Secret. 2006. 304p. (J). pap. 5.99 (978-0-06-000063-9(5) , Harper Trophy) HarperCollins Pubs.

Matas, Carol. The Burning Time. 2007. 112p. (YA). (gr. 7 up). pap. (***978-1-55143-624-1(8)***) Orca Bk. Pubs.

Miklowitz, Gloria. Secrets in the House of Delgado. 2001. (gr. 5-8). lib. bdg. 15.30 (978-0-613-55662-0(3)) Tandem Library Bks.

INQUISITION—SPAIN

Melchiore, Susan McCarthy. The Spanish Inquisition. 2001. (Great Disasters, Reforms & Ramifications Ser.). (Illus.). 114p. (YA). (gr. 6-10). 32.00 (978-0-7910-6327-9(5) , Chelsea Hse.) Facts On File, Inc.

Miklowitz, Gloria D. Secrets in the House of Delgado. 2004. 192p. (J). (gr. 4 up). pap. 8.00 (978-0-8028-5210-6(6)) Eerdmans, William B. Publishing Co.

INSANE

see Mental Illness

INSECTS

see also names of insects, e.g. Bees; Butterflies; Wasps

Acorn, John Harrison. Bugs of Ontario. Sheldon, Ian, illus. rev. ed. 2003. 160p. (gr. 4). pap. 11.95 (978-1-55105-287-8(3)) Lone Pine Publishing USA.

Acorn, John Harrison & Sheldon, Ian. Bugs of British Columbia. Sheldon, Ian, illus. rev. ed. 2001. (Illus.). 160p. (J). (gr. 4). pap. 11.95 (978-1-55105-231-1(8)) Lone Pine Publishing USA.

Act-Two Staff. Bug Safari. 2004. (Illus.). (J). (gr. 1-4). pap. 8.99 incl. cd-rom (978-0-7868-3415-0(3)) Hyperion Bks. for Children.

Adam, Winky. Bugs. 2000. (Dover Little Activity Bks.). (Illus.). 64p. (J). pap., act. bk. ed. 1.50 (978-0-486-40969-6(4)) Dover Pubns., Inc.

Advantage Publishers Group & Pledger, Maurice. All about Bugs & Beetles. 2007. (All About Ser.). (Illus.). 80p. (J). 12.95 (978-1-59223-459-2(3) , Silver Dolphin Bks.) Advantage Pubs. Group.

Allen, Francesca, illus. Creepy-Crawlies. 2005. 10p. (J). 4.99 (978-0-7945-0856-2(1) , Usborne) EDC Publishing.

Allen, Judy. Are you a Dragonfly? Humphries, Tudor, illus. 2004. (Backyard Bks.). 32p. (J). (ps up). 5.95 (978-0-7534-5805-1(5) , Kingfisher) Houghton Mifflin Co. Trade & Reference Div.

—Are You a Ladybug? Humphries, Tudor, illus. 2000. (Backyard Bks.). 32p. (J). (gr. k-3). tchr. ed. 9.95 (978-0-7534-5241-7(3) , Kingfisher) Houghton Mifflin Co. Trade & Reference Div.

Allman, Toney. From Bug Legs to Walking Robots. 2005. (Imitating Nature Ser.). (Illus.). 32p. (J). (gr. 3-6). 24.95 (978-0-7377-3385-3(3) , Kidhaven) Thomson Gale.

Aloian, Molly & Kalman, Bobbie. Helpful & Harmful Insects. 2005. (World of Insects Ser.). (Illus.). 32p. (J). (978-0-7787-2341-7(0)); pap. (978-0-7787-2375-2(5)) Crabtree Publishing Co.

H
I

—Insect Bodies. 2005. (World of Insects Ser.). (Illus.). 32p. (J). (978-0-7787-2340-0(2)); pap. (978-0-7787-2374-5(7)) Crabtree Publishing Co.

—Insect Life Cycles. 2005. (World of Insects Ser.). (Illus.). 32p. (J). (978-0-7787-2343-1(7)); pap. (978-0-7787-2377-6(1)) Crabtree Publishing Co.

—Insects That Work Together. 2005. (World of Insects Ser.). (Illus.). 32p. (J). (978-0-7787-2342-4(9)); pap. (978-0-7787-2376-9(3)) Crabtree Publishing Co.

Armentrout, David & Armentrout, Patricia. Insects. 2003. (50 Words about Ser.). (Illus.). 32p. (gr. 2-4). 19.95 (978-1-58952-344-9(X)) Rourke Publishing, LLC.

Artell, Mike. Backyard Bloodsuckers: Questions, Facts & Tongue Twisters about Creepy Crawlers. 2004. (Illus.). 80p. pap. (978-0-673-59248-4(0)) Good Year Bks.

Ashley, Susan. Let's Read about Insects, 6 bks. Incl. Ants. lib. bdg. 19.33 (978-0-8368-4050-6(X)); Bees. lib. bdg. 19.93 (978-0-8368-4051-3(8)); Butterflies. lib. bdg. 19.33 (978-0-8368-4052-0(6)); Fireflies. lib. bdg. 19.93 (978-0-8368-4053-7(4)); Grasshoppers. lib. bdg. 19.33 (978-0-8368-4054-4(2)); Ladybugs. lib. bdg. 19.33 (978-0-8368-4055-1(0)); 24p. (YA). (gr. 1 up). (Illus.). 2004. Set lib. bdg. 115.98 (978-0-8368-4049-0(6) , Weekly Reader Early Learning Library) Stevens, Gareth Inc.

—Let's Read about Insects, 6 bks. Incl. Ants. pap. 5.95 (978-0-8368-4057-5(7)); Bees. pap. 5.95 (978-0-8368-4058-2(5)); Butterflies. pap. 5.95 (978-0-8368-4059-9(3)); Fireflies. pap. 5.95 (978-0-8368-4060-5(7)); Grasshoppers. pap. 5.95 (978-0-8368-4061-2(5)); Ladybugs. pap. 5.95 (978-0-8368-4062-9(3)); 24p. (J). (gr. 1 up). (Illus.). 2004. pap. (978-0-8368-4056-8(9) , Weekly Reader Early Learning Library) Stevens, Gareth Inc.

Atari Classic Arcades: Millipede, 2004. cd-rom 4.99 (978-1-59150-400-9(7)) TOPICS Entertainment.

Backyard Bugs. (J). 21.95 (978-0-8136-4252-9(3)) Modern Curriculum Pr.

Bailey, Jill. Bug Dictionary: An A to Z of Insects & Creepy Crawlies. Atkinson, Mike, tr. 2002. (Illus.). 64p. (J). pap. (978-0-439-36859-9(6)) Scholastic, Inc.

—Bug Dictionary: An A to Z of Insects & Creepy Crawlies. 2002. (Illus.). 64p. (J). 26.20 (978-1-56711-547-5(0) , Blackbirch Pr., Inc.) Thomson Gale.

—How Insects Work Together. 1998. (Nature's Mysteries Ser.). (Illus.). 32p. (J). (gr. 3-5). lib. bdg. 22.79 (978-0-7614-0859-8(2) , Benchmark Bks.) Cavendish, Marshall Corp.

Baker, Charles F., ed. Bugs. 2005. (Illus.). 32p. (J). 17.95 (978-0-8126-7926-7(1)) Cobblestone Publishing Co.

Baker, Nancy & Hoffman, Richard L. Exploring Virginia Insects. Date not set. 32p. (J). (gr. 4-6). pap., act. bk. ed. 4.95 (978-0-9625801-8-5(X)) Virginia Museum of Natural History.

Baker, Wendy. Experimenta con Insectos (Experiment with Insects) (SPA.). 56p. (J). 17.50 (978-84-348-3996-0(2)) SM Ediciones ESP. *Dist:* AIMS International Bks., Inc.

—Insects. Haslam, Andrew, illus. 2004. (Make It Work! Science Ser.). 48p. (J). (gr. 3-6). pap. 6.95 (978-1-58728-356-7(5) , Two Can Publishing) T&N Children's Publishing.

—Insects: The Hands-on Approach to Science. 2000. (gr. 3-6). lib. bdg. 15.25 (978-0-613-43334-1(3)) Tandem Library Bks.

Baker, Wendy & Haslam, Andrew. Insects. (Make It Work! Ser.). (Illus.). (J). 48p. pap. 15.95 (978-0-590-24204-2(0)); (FRE., pap. 9.99 (978-0-590-24330-8(6)) Scholastic, Inc.

Ball, Jacqueline A. Migrating Animals of the Air. 2007. (J). pap. (*978-0-8368-8422-7(1)); 24p. (gr. 2-4). lib. bdg. 19.93 (*978-0-8368-8417-3(5)) Stevens, Gareth Inc. (Weekly Reader Early Learning Library).

Barbaresi, Nina. Glow-in-the-Dark Bugs Stickers. 2006. (Dover Little Activity Bks.). 2p. (J). pap. 1.50 (978-0-486-44912-8(2)) Dover Pubns., Inc.

—Shiny Bugs. 2004. (Shiny Stickers Ser.). (Illus.). 2p. (J). (ps-5). pap. 1.50 (978-0-486-43539-8(3)) Dover Pubns., Inc.

Barner, Bob. Bug Safari. Barner, Bob, illus. 2006. (Illus.). 36p. (J). reprint ed. pap. 6.95 (978-0-8234-2038-4(8)) Holiday Hse., Inc.

—Bugs! Bugs! Bugs! 1999. (Illus.). 32p. (J). (ps-3). 14.95 (978-0-8118-2238-1(9)) Chronicle Bks. LLC.

Barnett, Michelle Noble, et al. Theme Pockets - August: One of a Kind; Ocean Habitats; Insect Riddles. Evans, Marilyn, ed. Larsen, Jo, illus. 1999. (Making Books with Pockets). 96p. (J). pap., tchr. ed. 12.99 (978-1-55799-705-0(5) , EMC 591) Evan-Moor Educational Pubs.

Bater, Lucy. Incredible Insects. 2007. (J). (*978-1-60044-260-5(9)) Rourke Publishing, LLC.

Batten, Mary. About Insects: A Guide for Children. Bond, Higgins, illus. 2002. (About...Ser.). 48p. (J). pap. 7.95 (978-1-56145-232-3(7)) Peachtree Pubs., Ltd.

Beall, Pamela Conn & Nipp, Susan Hagen. Wee Sing & Learn Bugs. Pongmee, Yudthana, illus. 2007. (Wee Sing & Learn Ser.). 20p. (J). (ps-2). 9.99 (978-0-8431-2185-8(8) , Price Stern Sloan) Penguin Group (USA) Inc.

Bedry, Christa. Insects. 2004. (Prehistoric Life Ser.). (J). pap. 7.95 (978-1-59036-173-3(3)); (Illus.). 32p. lib. bdg. 15.95 (978-1-59036-113-9(X)) Weigl Pubs., Inc.

Benchmark Education Staff, compiled by. Insects Measure up! & ¡Vamos a medir Insectos! 2005. 52.00 (*978-1-4108-4496-5(X)) Benchmark Education Co.

Berger, Melvin. Buzz! A Book about Insects. 2000. (Hello Reader! Science Ser.). (Illus.). 40p. (J). (gr. 1-3). pap. 3.99 (978-0-439-08748-3(1)) Scholastic, Inc.

—Buzz! A Book about Insects. 2000. (Hello Reader! Ser.). (Illus.). (J). 10.79 (978-0-606-18521-9(6)) Tandem Library Bks.

—How Do Flies Walk Upside Down? Questions & Answers about Insects. 1999. (Question & Answer Ser.). (J). 12.75 (978-0-606-20062-2(2)) Tandem Library Bks.

Berger, Melvin & Berger, Gilda. How Do Flies Walk Upside Down? Questions & Answers about Insects. Effler, Jim, illus. 1999. (Scholastic Question & Answer Ser.). 48p. (J). (gr. 2-4). pap. 12.95 (978-0-590-13082-0(X) , Scholastic Reference) Scholastic, Inc.

Berkowitz, Henry. Insects & Spiders: An Educational Coloring Book. Berkowitz, Henry, illus. 2001. (Illus.). 32p. (J). (ps-3). pap. 4.95 (978-0-932855-67-1(9)) Winner Enterprises.

Bernard, Robin. Creepy Crawlies. 2003. (Learn All About Ser.). 88p. pap. 10.95 (978-0-439-51882-6(2)) Scholastic, Inc.

—Insects. 2001. (Illus.). 16p. (J). (gr. 3-7). pap. 5.95 (978-0-7922-6670-9(6) , National Geographic Children's Bks.) National Geographic Society.

—Insects. 2001. (ps-2). lib. bdg. 14.10 (978-0-613-49332-1(X)) Tandem Library Bks.

Beylon, Cathy. Color Your Own Bugs Stickers. 2006. 2p. (J). pap. 2.95 (978-0-486-44843-5(6)) Dover Pubns., Inc.

Biel, Timothy Levi. Aranas. Rountree, Monica, tr. 2003. (Zoobooks). Orig. Title: Spiders. (SPA., Illus.). 24p. (J). (gr. 1-7). lib. bdg. 15.95 (978-1-888153-82-8(2)) Wildlife Education, Ltd.

Billions of Bugs: Fifth Grade Guided Comprehension Level N. (On Our Way to English Ser.). (gr. 5 up). 34.50 (978-0-7578-6600-5(X)) Rigby Education.

Bishop, Nic, illus. The Backyard Detective: Critters up Close. 2002. (Backyard Detective Ser.). 48p. (J). (gr. 3-6). pap. 16.95 (978-0-439-17478-7(3) , Scholastic Pr.) Scholastic, Inc.

Blobaum, Cindy. Insectigations: 40 Hands-on Activities to Explore the Insect World. 2005. (Illus.). 144p. (J). (ps-ps). pap. 12.95 (978-1-55652-568-1(0)) Chicago Review Pr., Inc.

Boor, Daniele. Bajo la Tierra. (Coleccion Mundo Maravilloso). (SPA., Illus.). 40p. (J). (gr. 2-4). (978-84-348-3469-9(3) , SM5474) SM Ediciones ESP. *Dist:* Lectorum Pubns., Inc.

Brennan, Patricia. Grasshoppers & Their Relatives, Vol. 5. World Book, Inc. Staff, ed. 2001. (World Book's Animals of the World Ser.: Set 2). (Illus.). 64p. (J). (978-0-7166-1219-3(4)) World Bk., Inc.

—Stink Bugs & Other True Bugs, Vol. 10. World Book, Inc. Staff, ed. 2002. (World Book's Animals of the World Ser.: Set 3). (Illus.). 64p. (J). (978-0-7166-1233-9(X)) World Bk., Inc.

Brighter Minds. 3-D Bugs! 2007. (Illus.). 15p. (J). 9.95 (978-1-57791-208-8(X)) Brighter Minds Children's Publishing.

Brighter Vision Publishing Staff. Bugs. 1999. (Stick'n Learn Stories Ser.). (Illus.). (J). (ps-1). pap. 2.50 (978-1-55254-068-8(5)) Brighter Vision Pubns.

Brown Bear Books (Firm) Staff, contrib. by. Insects. 2007. (J). (*978-1-933834-14-6(5)) Brown Bear Books.

Brown, Susan. Insectos/Insects. 2005. 80p. (J). per. 9.99 (978-1-59441-434-3(3) , FI-704005) Carson-Dellosa Publishing Co., Inc.

Bruce, Jim. Creepy Crawlies. Kingfisher Editors, ed. 2001. (Question Time Ser.). (Illus.). 32p. (J). pap. 6.95 (978-0-7534-5413-8(0)); tchr. ed. 11.95 (978-0-7534-5342-1(8)) Houghton Mifflin Co. Trade & Reference Div. (Kingfisher).

Bruton, Mike. Insects: South African Edition. 1998. (Cambridge Reading Routes Ser.). (Illus.). 24p. pap. 5.00 (978-0-521-63663-6(9)) Cambridge Univ. Pr.

Bueche, Shelley. Bedbugs. 2005. (Parasites Ser.). (Illus.). 32p. (J). (ps-8). lib. bdg. 24.95 (978-0-7377-3168-2(0) , Greenhaven Pr., Inc.) Thomson Gale.

Bug Mania. (Flip Flap Fun Book Ser.). 10p. (J). bds. (978-2-7643-0183-8(9)) Phidal Publishing, Inc./Editions Phidal, Inc.

Bug Viewer. 2002. 64p. (J). pap. 9.98 (978-0-7525-6294-0(0)) Parragon, Inc.

Bugs! (Early Intervention Levels Ser.). 31.86 (978-0-7362-0626-6(4)) Hampton-Brown Bks.

Bugs. 2005. (J). per. 4.99 (978-1-933581-22-4(0)) Byeway Bks.

Bugs - Set1: Bugs & Critters. 2005. (J). spiral bd. 23.40 (978-0-9770248-0-3(6)) Sidedoor Publishing LLC.

Bugs, Beware! Fifth Grade Guided Comprehension Level T. (On Our Way to English Ser.). (gr. 5 up). 34.50 (978-0-7578-6631-9(X)) Rigby Education.

Bugs Know It Alls Learning Kit. 2001. (Illus.). 24p. (YA). 7.95 (978-1-58610-512-9(4) , 85013) Learning Horizons, Inc.

Bugs Life. 1998. (Flip Bks.). (J). 3.99 (978-0-7364-0103-6(2)) Mouse Works.

Bulion, Leslie. Hey There, Stink Bug! Evans, Leslie, illus. 2006. 45p. (J). 12.95 (978-1-58089-304-6(X)) Charlesbridge Publishing, Inc.

Burnie, David. Insect. 2007. (Dk Online Ser.). (Illus.). 96p. (J). pap. 9.99 (978-0-7566-2294-7(8)) Dorling Kindersley Publishing, Inc.

Burnie, David & Dorling Kindersley Publishing Staff. Insect. 2005. (Google E Guides). (Illus.). 96p. (J). 17.99 (978-0-7566-1010-4(9)) Dorling Kindersley Publishing, Inc.

Burton, Margie, et al. Insects All Around. Adams, Alison, ed. 1999. (Early Connections Ser.). 16p. (J). (gr. k-2). pap. 4.50 (978-1-58344-067-4(4)) Benchmark Education Co.

Busy Bugs. Date not set. (Sticker Shapes Ser.). (Illus.). 16p. (J). 2.98 (978-0-7525-8138-5(4)) Parragon, Inc.

Busy Bugs Giant Sticker Shapes. 2002. (Sticker Shapes Ser.). 16p. (J). pap. 5.98 (978-0-7525-7926-9(6)) Parragon, Inc.

Camper, Cathy. Bugs Before Time: Prehistoric Insects & Their Relatives. Kirk, Steve, illus. 2002. 40p. (J). (gr. 4-7). 17.95 (978-0-689-82092-2(5)) Simon & Schuster Children's Publishing.

Capeci, Anne. Insect Invaders. Speirs, John, illus. 2002. (Magic School Bus Chapter Bks.: No. 11). 96p. (J). (gr. 2-5). 4.99 (978-0-439-31431-2(3) , Scholastic Paperbacks) Scholastic, Inc.

Carter, David A. Birthday Bugs: A Pop-up Party. Carter, David A., illus. 2004. (Illus.). 16p. (J). 10.95 (978-0-689-81858-5(0) , Little Simon) Simon & Schuster Children's Publishing.

—Glitter Bugs: Make 6 Fab Bugs. Carter, David A., illus. 1998. (Bugs in a Box Bks.). (Illus.). 16p. (J). (ps-3). 7.99 (978-0-689-81857-8(2) , Little Simon) Simon & Schuster Children's Publishing.

—Novelty Bugs Book. 1999. (Illus.). (J). (978-0-689-81867-7(X) , Little Simon) Simon & Schuster Children's Publishing.

Catchpole, Heather & Woods, Vanessa. It's True! There are Bugs in Your Bed. Smith, Craig, illus. 2006. (It's True! Ser.). 88p. (J). (gr. 5-8). 19.95 (978-1-55037-951-8(8)); pap. 5.95 (978-1-55037-950-1(X)) Annick Pr., Ltd. CAN. *Dist:* Firefly Bks., Ltd.

Childrens Press Staff, ed. Insects, Spiders & Worms. 1998. (Rookie Read-About Science Ser.). pap. 19.90 (978-0-516-29985-3(9) , Children's Pr.) Scholastic Library Publishing.

Clarke, Ginjer L. Bug Out! The World's Creepiest, Crawliest Critters. Mueller, Pete, illus. 2007. (All Aboard Science Reader Ser.). 48p. (J). pap. 3.99 (978-0-448-44543-4(3) , Grosset & Dunlap) Penguin Group (USA) Inc.

Clarke, Jacqueline. Early Themes: Creepy Crawless. 2002. 40p. (J). 9.95 (978-0-439-16235-7(1)) Scholastic, Inc.

Clarke, Penny. Spiders, Insects, & Minibeasts. Bergin, Mark, illus. 2002. (Scary Creatures Ser.). 32p. (J). (gr. 2-4). pap. 22.50 (978-0-531-14674-3(X) , Watts, Franklin) Scholastic Library Publishing.

—Spiders, Insects, & Minibeasts. 2003. (gr. 3-6). lib. bdg. 15.25 (978-0-613-54362-0(9)) Tandem Library Bks.

Claybourne, Anna. Beetles & Other Bugs. 2004. (Awesome Bugs Ser.). (J). lib. bdg. 27.10 (978-1-932799-54-5(0)) Stargazer Bks.

—Insects. (Weird Wildlife Ser.). (Illus.). 32p. (J). 2003. pap. 7.95 (978-1-4109-0077-7(0)); 2002. 25.69 (978-0-7398-4855-5(0)) Raintree.

—Insects - Weird Wildlife, 6 bks. 2003. (Illus.). (J). pap. 48.30 (978-1-4109-0296-2(X)) Harcourt Schl. Pubs.

Conan, Sally Ann. God Made Creepy Crawlies. 2005. (Illus.). 40p. (J). 9.99 (978-0-8066-4986-3(0) , Augsburg Bks.) Augsburg Fortress, Pubs.

Coombs, Rachel & Harris, Nicholas. The World of Bugs. 2006. 32p. (gr. 2-4). 23.70 (978-1-4103-0353-0(5) , Blackbirch Pr., Inc.) Thomson Gale.

Cooper, Jason. Libelulas. 2005. (Biblioteca del Descubrimiento de los Insectos Ser.). (SPA.). 24p. pap. 5.45 (978-1-59515-696-9(8)) Rourke Publishing, LLC.

—Mantis Religiosas. 2005. (Biblioteca del Descubrimiento de los Insectos Ser.). (SPA.). 24p. pap. 5.45 (978-1-59515-699-0(2)) Rourke Publishing, LLC.

—Mariposas. 2005. (Biblioteca del Descubrimiento de los Insectos Ser.). (SPA.). 24p. pap. 5.45 (978-1-59515-695-2(X)) Rourke Publishing, LLC.

—Praying Mantises. (Insects Ser.). 24p. (gr. k-2). 2006. (Illus.). 14.95 (978-1-59515-429-3(9)); 2005. pap. 5.45 (978-1-59515-743-0(3)) Rourke Publishing, LLC.

Creasy, Mary-Anne. My Worm Farm. 2001. (gr. k-3). lib. bdg. 11.80 (978-0-613-33401-3(9)) Tandem Library Bks.

Creepy & Crawly. 2002. (Questions & Answers Ser.). 12p. (J). pap. 3.98 (978-0-7525-7898-9(7)) Parragon, Inc.

Creepy Crawlies Kid Kit. 24p. (J). 8.99 (978-1-58086-757-3(X) , Usborne) EDC Publishing.

Critters & Bugs of the Tropical Rainforest. 2003. (J). spiral bd. 12.95 (978-1-931334-33-4(1)) Pieces of Learning.

Curry, Don L. & Kaufman, Johanna. Bugs, More or Less? 1999. (Illus.). 32p. (J). 13.25 (978-0-7368-7053-5(9)) Capstone Pr., Inc.

Dalgleish, Sharon. Creepy Creatures. 2002. (Junior Adventure Ser.). (Illus.). 32p. (J). (gr. 3 up). lib. bdg. (978-1-59084-163-1(8)) Mason Crest Pubs.

—Creepy Creatures. Cavaluzzo, Laura & McEwen, Rebecca, eds. 1999. (Explorers Ser.). (Illus.). 32p. (J). (978-0-7699-0469-6(6)) Shortland Pubns. (U. S. A.) Inc.

Daly, Catherine. Bug, Bugs, Bugs. 2000. (gr. k-3). lib. bdg. 11.25 (978-0-613-31031-4(4)) Tandem Library Bks.

—Bugs, Bugs, Bugs. Smath, Jerry, illus. 2000. (Reading Railroad Bks.). 32p. (J). (ps-8). pap. 3.99 (978-0-448-42189-6(5) , Grosset & Dunlap) Penguin Group (USA) Inc.

Daronco, Mickey & Ohanesian, Diane. Bugs. 2nd rev. ed. 2003. (BuildUp Ser.). (J). pap. 22.00 (978-1-4108-0739-7(8)) Benchmark Education Co.

Dell, Pamela. Do Bed Bugs Bite? A Book about Insects. 2007. (First Facts Ser.). (Illus.). 24p. (J). (978-0-7368-6785-6(6) , 1264903) Capstone Pr., Inc.

Denchfield, Nick & Sharp, Anne, illus. Pop-up Minibeast Adventure. 2004. 16p. (J). (gr. k-4). reprint ed. 25.00 (978-0-7567-8204-7(X)) DIANE Publishing Co.

Dickins, R. Bugs. 2004. (Discovery Program Ser.). (Illus.). 48p. (J). pap. 8.95 (978-0-7945-0267-6(9) , Usborne); lib. bdg. 16.95 (978-1-58086-469-5(4)) EDC Publishing.

Dickins, Rosie. Bugs. Woodcock, John, illus. 2002. (Usborne Discovery Ser.). 48p. (J). pap. (978-0-439-57320-7(3)) Scholastic, Inc.

Discovery Channel. Animal Planet the Most Extreme Bugs. Nichols, Catherine, ed. 2007. (Animal Planet Extreme Animals Ser.). 80p. 15.95 (*978-0-7879-8663-6(1) , Jossey-Bass) Wiley, John & Sons, Inc.

Dixon, Norma. Focus on Flies. 2006. (Illus.). 32p. (J). (gr. 3-7). 17.95 (978-1-55005-128-5(8)) Fitzhenry & Whiteside, Ltd. CAN. *Dist:* F & W Pubns., Inc.

DK Publishing. Insect. 2008. 48p. (J). (gr. 2-8). pap. 9.99 (*978-0-7566-3821-4(6)) Dorling Kindersley Publishing, Inc.

DK Publishing Staff. Buzz. 2007. 144p. (J). (gr. 2-7). 19.99 (978-0-7566-2912-0(8)) Dorling Kindersley Publishing, Inc.

DK Publishing Staff. World of Bugs: Cub Scout Activity Series. 2007. 16p. (J). pap. 2.49 (*978-0-7566-3190-1(4)) Dorling Kindersley Publishing, Inc.

Dorling Kindersley Publishing Staff. Bug. 2004. (Ultimate Sticker Bks.). 16p. (J). pap. 6.99 (978-0-7566-0234-5(3)) Dorling Kindersley Publishing, Inc.

—Bugs. 2001. 32p. (J). pap. 19.80 (978-0-439-31813-6(0)) Scholastic, Inc.

—Bugs & Slugs. 2006. (Ultimate Sticker Bks.). 16p. (J). pap. 6.99 (978-0-7566-2098-1(8)) Dorling Kindersley Publishing, Inc.

—Creepy Crawly. 2005. (Ultimate sticker Bks.). 16p. (J). pap. 6.99 (978-0-7566-1456-0(2)) Dorling Kindersley Publishing, Inc.

—Glow in the Dark Bugs. 2002. (Ultimate Sticker Bks.). (Illus.). 16p. (J). pap. 6.99 (978-0-7894-8856-5(6)) Dorling Kindersley Publishing, Inc.

—Insect. 2006. (Eye Know Ser.). (Illus.). 24p. (J). 8.99 (978-0-7566-2226-8(3)) Dorling Kindersley Publishing, Inc.

—Insectos! 2003. (DK Readers Ser.). (SPA., Illus.). 48p. (J). pap. 3.99 (978-0-7894-9519-8(8)) Dorling Kindersley Publishing, Inc.

—Insects. 2nd rev. ed. 2003. (DK Pockets Ser.). (Illus.). 160p. (J). pap. 6.99 (978-0-7894-9594-5(5)) Dorling Kindersley Publishing, Inc.

—Smithsonian Bug Hunter. 2005. (Nature Activity Ser.). (Illus.). 72p. (J). pap. 9.99 (978-0-7566-1030-2(3)) Dorling Kindersley Publishing, Inc.

—What's Inside Insects? 1999. (978-0-606-17817-4(1)) Tandem Library Bks.

Dorling Kindersley Publishing Staff, ed. Bugs. 2004. (Dk Picture Stickers Ser.). 16p. (J). pap. 3.99 (978-0-7566-0558-2(X)) Dorling Kindersley Publishing, Inc.

Dorling Kindersley Publishing Staff & Greenaway, Theresa. The Big Book of Bugs. 2000. (Illus.). 32p. (J). (gr. 4-7). 14.99 (978-0-7894-6520-7(5)) Dorling Kindersley Publishing, Inc.

Draw 50 Creepy Crawlies. 2002. (Draw 50 Ser.). (Illus.). (J). 17.60 (978-0-7587-4561-3(3)) Book Wholesalers, Inc.

Driscoll, Laura. Looking at Bugs. Drew-Brook-Cormack, Deborah et al, illus. 2001. (My First Field Guides Ser.). 64p. (J). pap. 5.99 (978-0-448-42487-3(8) , Grosset & Dunlap) Penguin Group (USA) Inc.

Dunn, Gary A. Insect Life Cycle Studies Unit III: Entomology. 1998. (Illus.). 36p. (J). (gr. 5-7). reprint ed. pap. 15.00 (978-0-7881-4323-6(9)) DIANE Publishing Co.

Dussling, Jennifer. Bugs! Bugs! Bugs! 1998. (Eyewitness Readers). (Illus.). 32p. (J). (gr. 1-3). pap. 3.99 (978-0-7894-3438-8(5) , 0-7894-4760-6) Dorling Kindersley Publishing, Inc.

—Insectos! 2003. (SPA.). (gr. k-3). lib. bdg. 11.80 (978-0-613-62449-7(1)) Tandem Library Bks.

Dussling, Jennifer & Dorling Kindersley Publishing Staff. Bugs! Bugs! Bugs! 1998. (Eyewitness Readers). (Illus.). 32p. (J). (gr. 1-3). 12.99 (978-0-7894-3762-4(7)) Dorling Kindersley Publishing, Inc.

Dussling, Jennifer & Royston, Angela. Bugs! Bugs! Bugs! & Slinky, Scaly Snakes! 2007. (Read & Listen Bks.). 64p. (J). 9.99 (978-0-7566-2669-3(2)) Dorling Kindersley Publishing, Inc.

Einhorn, Kama. My First Book about Insects. Moroney, Christopher, illus. 2007. (Sesame Subjects Ser.). 24p. (J). (gr. k-k). 7.99 (*978-0-375-84029-6(X) , Random Hse. Bks. for Young Readers) Random Hse. Children's Bks.

Encyclopedia of Tiny Creatures, 6 Pks. (Discovery World Ser.). 16p. (gr. 1-2). 28.00 (978-0-7635-8468-9(1)) Rigby Education.

Evans, Arthur V., et al. Grzimek's Student Animal Life Resource, 2 vols. 2005. (Illus.). l, 442p. (J). (978-0-7876-9244-5(1)); (978-0-7876-9245-2(X)) Thomson Gale. (UXL).

Facklam, Margery. Bugs for Lunch. Long, Sylvia, illus. 1999. 32p. (J). (ps-3). 15.95 (978-0-88106-271-7(5)) Charlesbridge Publishing, Inc.

—Bugs for Lunch. 1999. (J). 13.75 (978-0-606-16409-2(X)); lib. bdg. 15.25 (978-0-613-16331-6(1)) Tandem Library Bks.

Facklam, Margery & Facklam, Paul. The Big Bug Book. 1998. (J). 13.50 (978-0-606-13202-2(3)) Tandem Library Bks.

Farndon, J., et al. Bugs & Minibeasts. 2003. (Illustrated Wildlife Encyclopedia... Ser.). (Illus.). 256p. pap. 19.99 (978-1-84215-724-4(8) , Southwater) Anness Publishing GBR. *Dist:* National Bk. Network.

Farndon, John. Insect Kingdom. 2004. (Illus.). 128p. pap. 17.99 (978-1-84476-033-6(2) , Southwater) Anness Publishing GBR. *Dist:* National Bk. Network.

—Insects. 2004. 32p. (J). 23.70 (978-1-4103-0120-8(6) , Blackbirch Pr., Inc.) Thomson Gale.

Faulkner, Keith. Amazing 3D Bugs. Weston, Steve, illus. 2004. (J). (978-0-439-66811-8(5)) Scholastic, Inc.

—Big Bugs! Giant Creepy Crawly Pop-Ups. Holmes, Stephen, illus. 2004. 14p. (J). pap. 10.95 (978-0-439-49905-7(4)) Scholastic, Inc.

Ferguson, Richard. Backyard Bugs. 2007. (Illus.). 14p. (J). (gr. k-3). 12.99 (978-0-7566-2538-2(6)) Dorling Kindersley Publishing, Inc.

Fisher, Diana. Insects: Step-by-Step Instructions for 26 Creepy Crawlies. 2007. (Draw & Color Ser.). (Illus.). 40p. (J). (gr. k-1). pap. 4.95 (978-1-60058-507-4(8)) Foster, Walter Publishing, Inc.

Florian, Douglas. Insectlopedia. 2002. (Illus.). 48p. (J). (gr. k-3). pap. 7.00 (978-0-15-216335-8(2) , Voyager Bks./Libros Viajeros) Harcourt Children's Bks.

—Insectlopedia. 2000. (Illus.). 47p. (J). (gr. 1-5). 16.98 (978-0-7398-2201-2(2)) Raintree.

—Insectlopedia. 2002. (gr. 3-6). lib. bdg. 15.30 (978-0-613-44304-3(7)) Tandem Library Bks.

Foley, Cate. Find the Insect. 2000. (Welcome Bks.). (Illus.). 24p. (J). (ps-2). 17.00 (978-0-516-23096-2(4) , Children's Pr.) Scholastic Library Publishing.

—Find the Insect. 2000. (gr. k-3). lib. bdg. 12.95 (978-0-613-52045-4(9)) Tandem Library Bks.

Follow the Bee. 2004. 10p. (J). bds. 5.99 (978-1-85997-874-0(6)) Byeway Bks.

Fredericks, Anthony D. On One Flower: Butterflies, Ticks & a Few More Icks. DiRubbio, Jennifer, illus. 2006. 32p. (J). (gr. k-4). 16.95 (978-1-58469-086-3(0)); pap. 7.95 (978-1-58469-087-0(9)) Dawn Pubns.

Frost, Helen. Cicadas. Saunders-Smith, Gail, ed. 2001. (Insects Ser.). (Illus.). 24p. (J). (gr. k-1). lib. bdg. 15.93 (978-0-7368-0851-4(5) , Pebble Bks.) Capstone Pr., Inc.

—Cicadas. 2005. (Bugs, Bugs, Bugs Ser.). 24p. (YA). (gr. k-3). pap. (978-0-7368-9086-1(6) , Pebble Bks.) Capstone Pr., Inc.

—Walkingsticks. Saunders-Smith, Gail, ed. 2001. (Insects Ser.). (Illus.). 24p. (J). (gr. k-1). lib. bdg. 15.93 (978-0-7368-0854-5(X) , Pebble Bks.) Capstone Pr., Inc.

—Walkingsticks, Vol. 2. 2005. (Bugs, Bugs, Bugs Ser.). 24p. (YA). (gr. k-3). pap. (978-0-7368-9089-2(0) , Pebble Bks.) Capstone Pr., Inc.

—Water Bugs. Saunders-Smith, Gail, ed. 2001. (Insects Ser.). (Illus.). 24p. (J). (gr. k-1). lib. bdg. 15.93 (978-0-7368-0856-9(6) , Pebble Bks.) Capstone Pr., Inc.

—Water Bugs, Vol. 2. 2005. (Bugs, Bugs, Bugs Ser.). 24p. (YA). (gr. k-3). pap. (978-0-7368-9091-5(2) , Pebble Bks.) Capstone Pr., Inc.

Fun with Insects & Bugs. 2001. (Learning Adventures Grade 1 Ser.). (Illus.). (J). (ps-3). pap. 2.25 (978-1-55254-239-2(4)) Brighter Vision Pubns.

Funny Bugs. 2005. (Early Library). (YA). (ps-3). 23.94 (978-0-8215-8943-4(1)) Sadlier, William H. Inc.

Gareth Stevens Publishing Staff, contrib. by. Insects. 2002. (Discovery Channel School Science Ser.). (Illus.). 32p. (J). (gr. 5 up). lib. bdg. 24.67 (978-0-8368-3215-0(9)) Stevens, Gareth Inc.

Gikow, Louise. Ripley's Incredible Insects. 2004. (Illus.). 60p. (J). (978-0-439-63359-8(1)) Scholastic, Inc.

Gilpin, Daniel. Centipedes, Millipedes, Scorpions & Spiders. 2005. (Illus.). 48p. (J). (gr. 4-6). (978-0-7565-1254-5(9)) Compass Point Bks.

Godkin, Celia. What about Ladybugs? Godkin, Celia, illus. 2001. (Illus.). 40p. (J). (ps-3). pap. 6.95 (978-0-87156-921-9(3)) Sierra Club Bks. for Children.

—What about Ladybugs? 1998. (J). (978-0-606-13894-9(3)) Tandem Library Bks.

Goldberg, Howard A. Bugs: Pull the Tabs! Change the Pictures! 2004. (Magic Windows Ser.). (Illus.). 8p. (J). pap. 4.95 (978-0-7624-1578-6(9) , Running Pr. Kids) Running Pr. Bk. Pubs.

Gordon, David George. Creepy Critters of the Southwest. 2004. (Illus.). 16p. pap. 4.95 (978-1-58369-053-6(0)) Western National Parks Assn.

—La Tarantula. 2004. (Al Descubierto Ser.).Tr. of Uncover a Tarantula. (SPA., Illus.). 16p. (J). bds. 18.95 (978-970-718-212-7(1) , Silver Dolphin Bks.) Advantage Pubs. Group.

Gordon, Melanie Apel. Let's Talk about Scratches, Scrapes & Bug Bites. 2000. (Let's Talk Library). (Illus.). 24p. (J). (gr. 3). lib. bdg. 18.75 (978-0-8239-5416-2(1) , PowerKids Pr.) Rosen Publishing Group, Inc., The.

Gould, Robert. Bugs, Vol. 7. Epstein, Eugene, illus. 2007. (Big Stuff Ser.: 7 vols.). 16p. (J). bds. 7.95 (978-1-929945-66-5(3)) Big Guy Bks., Inc.

Grambo, Rebecca L., et al. Animal Kingdom. 2000. (Eyes on Nature Ser.). (Illus.). 109p. (J). (978-1-56156-882-6(1)) Kidsbooks, Inc.

Gray, Susan H. Emerald Ash Borer. 2008. (J). lib. bdg. 26.26 ***978-1-60279-112-1(0))** Cherry Lake Publishing.

Green, Emily K. Walkingsticks. 2006. (Blastoff! Readers Ser.). (Illus.). 24p. (J). lib. bdg. 16.95 (978-1-60014-015-0(7)) Bellwether Media.

—Walkingsticks. 2006. (Blastoff! Readers Ser.). (Illus.). 24p. (J). (gr. k-2). 18.50 ***978-0-531-17865-2(X))** Scholastic Library Publishing.

Green, Jen. Insects. 1999. (Young Scientist Concepts & Projects Ser.). (Illus.). 68p. (J). (gr. 4 up). lib. bdg. 26.60 (978-0-8368-2266-3(8)) Stevens, Gareth Inc.

—Insects: Fantastic Facts. 2000. (Fantastic Facts Ser.). (Illus.). 64p. (gr. 2-7). pap. 6.95 (978-1-84215-090-0(1) , Southwater) Anness Publishing GBR. *Dist:* National Bk. Network.

Green, Jen & Corbet, Sarah A. Insect Societies: Nature Watch. 2003. (Nature Watch Ser.). (Illus.). 64p. 14.99 (978-0-7548-1085-8(2) , Lorenz Bks.) Anness Publishing GBR. *Dist:* National Bk. Network.

Green, John. Bugs Stained Glass Coloring Book. 2000. (Shiny Stickers Ser.). (Illus.). 8p. (J). pap. 1.50 (978-0-486-41257-3(1)) Dover Pubns., Inc.

Grolier Educational Staff, contrib. by. Insects & Other Invertebrates, 50 vols. 2004. (J). (World of Animals Ser.: Vol. 3). (Illus.). 499.00 (978-0-7172-5894-9(7)); (978-0-7172-5895-6(5) , Grolier); (978-0-7172-5896-3(3) , Grolier); (978-0-7172-5897-0(1) , Grolier); (978-0-7172-5898-7(X) , Grolier); (978-0-7172-5899-4(8) , Grolier); (978-0-7172-5900-7(5) , Grolier); (978-0-7172-5901-4(3) , Grolier); (978-0-7172-5902-1(1) , Grolier); (978-0-7172-5903-8(X) , Grolier); (978-0-7172-5904-5(8) , Grolier) Scholastic Library Publishing.

—Under the Microscope. 1999. (J). (978-0-7172-9430-5(7)); (978-0-7172-9431-2(5)); (978-0-7172-9432-9(3)); (978-0-7172-9433-6(1)); (978-0-7172-9434-3(X)); (978-0-7172-9435-0(8)); (978-0-7172-9436-7(6)) Scholastic Library Publishing. (Grolier).

Gross Bugs. (Illus.). (J). (gr. k-6). 112.50 (978-1-4042-3292-1(3)) Rosen Publishing Group, Inc., The.

Grosset and Dunlap Staff & Heller, Ruth. Insects & Spiders. 2000. (Designs for Coloring Ser.). (Illus.). 64p. (J). (ps-3). pap. 5.99 (978-0-448-42250-3(6) , Grosset & Dunlap) Penguin Group (USA) Inc.

Group/McGraw-Hill, Wright. La Vida de Los Insectos, 6 vols., Vol. 2. (First Explorers. Primeros Exploradores Nonfiction Sets Ser.). (SPA.). (gr. 1-2). 34.95 (978-0-7699-1479-4(9)) Shortland Pubns. (U. S. A.) Inc.

Haffmann, Janet & Richardson, Adele D. Bugbooks, Set. (Illus.). 32p. (J). lib. bdg. 170.40 (978-1-887068-49-9(X)) Smart Apple Media.

Hall, Margaret. Cicadas. 2006. (Illus.). 24p. (J). (978-0-7368-5349-1(9)) Capstone Pr., Inc.

Hamilton, Inga. Bugs. 2004. (Brainbusters Ser.). (Illus.). 16p. (J). (gr. 3-6). pap. 5.95 (978-1-58728-679-7(3) , Two Can Publishing) T&N Children's Publishing.

Harcourt School Publishers Staff. Bug Surprises: Practice Book. 3rd ed. 2001. (Trophies Reading Program Ser.). (Illus.). (J). pap. 1.80 (978-0-15-325087-3(9)) Harcourt Schl. Pubs.

—Bug Surprises: Practice Book: Florida Edition. 3rd ed. 2002. (Trophies Reading Program Ser.). (Illus.). (J). pap. 2.00 (978-0-15-326602-7(3)) Harcourt Schl. Pubs.

—Bugs - Grade 1. 3rd ed. 2002. (Trophies English Language Learners Ser.). pap. 3.20 (978-0-15-327564-7(2)) Harcourt Schl. Pubs.

—Insectos/Sorpresas, Theme Bk. 11. 1999. (Vamos Ser.). (SPA., Illus.). (J). pap. 3.60 (978-0-15-315853-7(0)) Harcourt Schl. Pubs.

—Insects & Spiders: Independent Reader. 3rd ed. 2002. (Trophies Reading Program Ser.). (Illus.). (J). pap. 2.90 (978-0-15-325486-4(6)) Harcourt Schl. Pubs.

—Trofeos Advanced Level: Inventa/Insecto. 3rd ed. 2002. (SPA., Illus.). (J). pap. 6.80 (978-0-15-323930-4(1)) Harcourt Schl. Pubs.

Harris, Monica. Walking Stick. 2003. (Bug Books). (Illus.). 32p. (J). lib. bdg. 22.79 (978-1-4034-0766-5(5)); pap. 6.50 (978-1-4034-0995-9(1)) Heinemann Library.

Harris, Trudy. Pattern Bugs. Green, Anne Canevari, illus. 2001. (Fun Early Math Concepts Ser.). 40p. (J). (gr. k-3). 22.60 (978-0-7613-2107-1(1) , Millbrook Pr.) Lerner Publishing Group.

Hartley, Karen, et al. Head Louse. 2006. (Illus.). 32p. (J). ***978-1-4034-8298-3(5));** 2nd ed. pap. ***978-1-4034-8311-9(6))** Heinemann Library.

Haslam, Andrew. Insects. 2004. (Make It Work! Science Ser.). (Illus.). 48p. (J). (gr. 3-6). 12.95 (978-1-58728-365-9(4) , Two Can Publishing) T&N Children's Publishing.

Healy, Nick. The World's Most Dangerous Bugs. 2006. (Edge Books, the World's Top Tens). (Illus.). 32p. (978-0-7368-5456-6(8)) Capstone Pr., Inc.

Heiskell Rickey, Ann. Bugs & Critters I Have Known. Rickey Hawkins, Lamar, ed. Heiskell Smith, Ardeane, illus. 1998. 93p. (J). (gr. 1-8). 12.95 (978-0-9667834-1-4(7)) Old Canyon Pr.

Helbrough, Emma, et al. 1001 Bugs to Spot. Gower, Teri, illus. 2005. 31p. (J). ***978-0-439-79104-5(9))** Scholastic, Inc.

Heller, Ruth. How to Hide a Butterfly: And Other Insects. unabr. ed. 2001. (How to Hide Ser.). (J). (gr. k-3). pap. 14.45 incl. audio (978-0-8045-6573-8(2) , 6573) Spoken Arts, Inc.

Hepworth, Cathi. Bug Off! A Swarm of Insect Words. 1998. (Illus.). 1p. (J). (ps-3). 15.99 (978-0-399-22640-3(0) , Putnam Juvenile) Penguin Group (USA) Inc.

Heurtelou, Maude. Insect: Ensek. 1999. (Big Book Ser.). (CRP & ENG., Illus.). 8p. (J). (gr. k-2). 19.50 (978-1-58432-067-8(2)) Educa Vision.

Hewitt, Sally. Bugs Pop-up: Creepy Crawlers Face to Face. Gilvan-Cartwright, Chris, illus. 2004. 12p. (J). (ps-1). 14.95 (978-0-8109-5032-0(4)) Abrams, Harry N. , Inc.

—Minibeasts. (Illus.). 32p. (YA). (gr. 2 up). lib. bdg. 27.10 (978-1-932333-26-9(0)) Chrysalis Education.

Hickman, Pamela. Bug Book. 1999. (Illus.). (J). (978-0-606-16550-1(9)); (gr. 3-6). lib. bdg. 14.10 (978-0-613-16330-9(3)) Tandem Library Bks.

—Starting with Nature Bug Book. Collins, Heather, illus. unabr. ed. 1999. (Starting with Nature Ser.). 32p. (J). (gr. 4-6). (978-1-55074-653-2(7)); (978-1-55074-475-0(5)) Kids Can Pr., Ltd.

Hide to Survive, 6 Packs. (gr. k-1). 23.00 (978-0-7635-8857-1(1)) Rigby Education.

Hilton, Samantha. World of Insects. Holmes, Steve, illus. 2003. (Interfact Ladder Ser.). 48p. (J). (ps-2). 14.95 incl. cd-rom (978-1-58728-419-9(7) , Two Can Publishing) T&N Children's Publishing.

Himmelman, John. A Ladybug's Life. Stewart, Melissa, ed. Himmelman, John, illus. 1998. (Nature Upclose Ser.). (Illus.). 32p. (J). (gr. k-2). pap. 6.95 (978-0-516-26353-3(6) , Children's Pr.) Scholastic Library Publishing.

—A Mealworm's Life. 2001. (gr. k-3). lib. bdg. 15.25 (978-0-613-54015-5(8)) Tandem Library Bks.

—A Pill Bug's Life. 2000. (Nature Upclose Ser.). (Illus.). 32p. (J). (gr. k-2). pap. 6.95 (978-0-516-26798-2(1) , Children's Pr.) Scholastic Library Publishing.

—A Slug's Life. Stewart, Melissa, ed. Himmelman, John, illus. 1998. (Nature Upclose Ser.). (Illus.). 32p. (J). (gr. k-2). pap. 6.95 (978-0-516-26356-4(0) , Children's Pr.) Scholastic Library Publishing.

Hipp, Andrew. Assassin Bugs. 2003. (Really Wild Life Of... Ser.). (Illus.). 24p. (J). lib. bdg. 18.75 (978-0-8239-6240-2(7) , PowerKids Pr.) Rosen Publishing Group, Inc., The.

—Leafhoppers. 2003. (Really Wild Life Of... Ser.). (Illus.). 24p. (J). lib. bdg. 18.75 (978-0-8239-6241-9(5) , PowerKids Pr.) Rosen Publishing Group, Inc., The.

—Orchid Mantises. 2003. (Really Wild Life Of... Ser.). (Illus.). 24p. (J). lib. bdg. 18.75 (978-0-8239-6239-6(3) , PowerKids Pr.) Rosen Publishing Group, Inc., The.

—Peanut-Head Bugs. 2003. (Really Wild Life Ser.). (Illus.). 24p. (J). lib. bdg. 18.75 (978-0-8239-6242-6(3)) Rosen Publishing Group, Inc., The.

—Really Wild Life of Insects, 4 vols., set. 80.70 (978-0-8239-7275-3(5)) Rosen Publishing Group, Inc., The.

Holland, Gay W., illus. An Introduction to Bug-Watching. 2003. (Look Closer Ser.: 4). 32p. lib. bdg. 22.90 (978-0-7613-2664-9(2) , Millbrook Pr.) Lerner Publishing Group.

Holmes, Anita. Insect Detector. 2000. (We Can Read about Nature! Ser.). (Illus.). 32p. (J). (gr. 1). lib. bdg. 21.36 (978-0-7614-1110-9(0) , Benchmark Bks.) Cavendish, Marshall Corp.

Howard, Fran. Walkingsticks. 2005. (Pebble Plus: Bugs, Bugs, Bugs! Ser.). (Illus.). 24p. (J). 19.93 (978-0-7368-3645-6(4)) Capstone Pr., Inc.

Howard, Pam. Bugs, Bugs, Bugs. Gray, Stacy A., illus. 2003. 10p. (J). (ps-1). bds. 10.95 (978-1-57332-226-3(1)) High-Reach Learning, Inc.

Hudak, Heather C. Insects. 2004. (Animal Facts Ser.). (Illus.). 24p. (J). lib. bdg. 24.45 (978-1-59036-199-3(7)) Weigl Pubs., Inc.

Huggins-Cooper, Lynn. Beastly Bugs. 2007. (Killer Nature! Ser.). (Illus.). 32p. (J). (gr. 3-5). lib. bdg. 28.50 ***978-1-58340-936-7(X))** Smart Apple Media.

Huggins-Cooper, Lynn. Minibeasts. McNicholas, Shelagh & Burroughs, Dave, trs. McNicholas, Shelagh & Burroughs, Dave, illus. 2004. 30p. (J). lib. bdg. (978-1-58340-444-7(9)) Smart Apple Media.

—Minibeasts. 2003. (Starters Ser.). 24p. (J). lib. bdg. 21.35 (978-1-58340-263-4(2)) Smart Apple Media.

Hughes, Huw John, et al. Bwystfilod Bychain. 2005. (WEL., Illus.). 39p. (978-1-85596-665-9(4)) Dref Wen.

Hughes, Monica. Bugs. 2006. (I Love Reading Ser.). (Illus.). 24p. (J). lib. bdg. 19.96 (978-1-59716-149-7(7)) Bearport Publishing Co., Inc.

Hutnick, Theresa & Phillips, Karen. Insectos Insolitos. Fox, Peter, photos by. 2005. (SPA., Illus.). 38p. (J). spiral bd. 17.95 (978-987-1078-43-1(9)) Klutz Latino MEX. *Dist:* Independent Pubs. Group.

Hyperion Staff, ed. Bug. 1999. 12p. (J). 6.95 (978-0-7868-3207-1(X)) Hyperion Pr.

Imes, Rick. Incredible Bugs: An Eye-Opening Guide to the Amazing World of Insects. 2000. (Illus.). 160p. (YA). (gr. 7-9). 23.00 (978-0-7881-6985-4(8)) DIANE Publishing Co.

Innovative Kids Staff, et al. Bugs in the Garden. Filipowich, Bob, illus. 2003. (J). (ps). 8.99 (978-1-58476-171-6(7)) Innovative Kids.

The Insect Army 6 Packs. Individual Title. (Rigby Infoquest Ser.). 24p. (gr. 3 up). 34.00 (978-0-7578-5781-2(7)) Rigby Education.

El insecto Palo 6 Packs. Individual Title. (On Deck en Espanol Ser.).Tr. of Stick Insect. (SPA.). 24p. (gr. 4-5). 35.00 (978-0-7578-6439-1(2)) Rigby Education.

Insects, Set. 2005. (Bugs, Bugs, Bugs Ser.). (YA). (gr. k-3). 297.00 (978-0-7368-4203-7(9) , Pebble Bks.) Capstone Pr., Inc.

Insects, Set. (gr. k-2). 288.95 (978-0-7368-9040-3(8)) Red Brick Learning.

Insects. 2001. (gr. 3-6). lib. bdg. 11.25 (978-0-613-58119-6(9)) Tandem Library Bks.

Insects, 16 bks. Incl. Ants. Coughlan, Cheryl. Saunders-Smith, Gail, ed. 1999. lib. bdg. 15.93 (978-0-7368-0234-5(7)); Beetles. Coughlan, Cheryl. Saunders-Smith, Gail, ed. 1999. lib. bdg. 15.93 (978-0-7368-0235-2(5)); Bumble Bees. Coughlan, Cheryl. Saunders-Smith, Gail, ed. 1999. lib. bdg. 15.93 (978-0-7368-0236-9(3)); Butterflies. Schuh, Mari C. 2003. lib. bdg. 15.93 (978-0-7368-1664-9(X)); Cicadas. Frost, Helen. Saunders-Smith, Gail, ed. 2001. lib. bdg. 15.93 (978-0-7368-0851-4(5)); Cockroaches. Rustad, Martha E. H. 2003. lib. bdg. 15.93 (978-0-7368-1665-6(8)); Crickets. Coughlan, Cheryl. Saunders-Smith, Gail, ed. 1999. lib. bdg. 15.93 (978-0-7368-0237-6(1)); Dragonflies. Coughlan, Cheryl. Saunders-Smith, Gail, ed. 1999. lib. bdg. 15.93 (978-0-7368-0238-3(X)); Fireflies. Coughlan, Cheryl & Frost, Helen. Saunders-Smith, Gail, ed. 1999. lib. bdg. 15.93 (978-0-7368-0239-0(8)); Flies. Coughlan, Cheryl. Saunders-Smith, Gail, ed. 1999. lib. bdg. 15.93 (978-0-7368-0240-6(1)); Grasshoppers. Coughlan, Cheryl. Saunders-Smith, Gail, ed. 1999. lib. bdg. 15.93 (978-0-7368-0241-3(X)); Honey Bees. Rustad, Martha E. H. 2003. lib. bdg. 15.93 (978-0-7368-1666-3(6)); Ladybugs. Coughlan, Cheryl. Saunders-Smith, Gail, ed. 1999. lib. bdg. 15.93 (978-0-7368-0242-0(8)); Mosquitoes. Coughlan, Cheryl & Frost, Helen. Saunders-Smith, Gail, ed. 1999. lib. bdg. 15.93 (978-0-7368-0243-7(6)); Moths. Frost, Helen. Saunders-Smith, Gail, ed. 2001. lib. bdg. 15.93 (978-0-7368-0852-1(3)); Praying Mantises. Frost, Helen. Saunders-Smith, Gail, ed. 2001. lib. bdg. 15.93 (978-0-7368-0853-8(1)); Termites. Schuh, Mari C. 2003. lib. bdg. 15.93 (978-0-7368-1667-0(4)); Walkingsticks. Frost, Helen. Saunders-Smith, Gail, ed. 2001. lib. bdg. 15.93 (978-0-7368-0854-5(X)); Wasps. Frost, Helen. Saunders-Smith, Gail, ed. 2001. lib. bdg. 15.93 (978-0-7368-0855-2(8)); Water Bugs. Frost, Helen. Saunders-Smith, Gail, ed. 2001. lib. bdg. 15.93 (978-0-7368-0856-9(6)); 24p. (J). (gr. k-1). (Illus.). Set lib. bdg. 318.60 (978-0-7368-1674-8(7) , Pebble Bks.) Capstone Pr., Inc.

Insects! (Creatures Corner Ser.). 16p. (J). (978-2-7643-0123-4(5)) Phidal Publishing, Inc./Editions Phidal, Inc.

Insects. 2007. (My First Sticker Encyclopedia Ser.). (Illus.). 18p. (J). pap. 5.95 ***978-1-59496-146-5(8))** Teora USA LLC.

Insects, Set, Vol. 2. 2005. (Bugs, Bugs, Bugs Ser.). (YA). (gr. k-3). 297.00 (978-0-7368-4204-4(7) , Pebble Bks.) Capstone Pr., Inc.

Insects: Individual Title Six-Packs. (Rigby Focus Ser.). 16p. (gr. 1 up). 28.00 (978-0-7578-5303-6(X)); 30.00 (978-0-7578-5535-1(0)) Rigby Education.

Insects & Spiders. (Action Bks.). 64p. (J). (gr. 3-7). pap. (978-1-882210-67-1(0)) Action Publishing, Inc.

Insects & Spiders. 2005. 32p. pap. 140.00 (978-0-7910-8522-6(8) , Chelsea Hse.) Facts On File, Inc.

Insects Change. 2002. (Illus.). (J). pap. 5.43 (978-0-7398-5926-1(9)) Steck-Vaughn.

Insects Classroom Library. (gr. k-2). lib. bdg. 128.95 (978-0-7368-1826-1(X)) Red Brick Learning.

Insects Complete Unit. (gr. k-2). 642.95 (978-0-7368-1827-8(8)) Red Brick Learning.

Insects II Set. (gr. k-2). 172.95 (978-0-7368-9120-2(X)) Red Brick Learning.

Interesting Insects: Individual Title Six-Pack. (Story Steps Ser.). (gr. k-2). 23.00 (978-0-7635-9847-1(X)) Rigby Education.

Jackson, Donna M. The Bug Scientists. 2002. (Scientists in the Field Ser.). (Illus.). 48p. (J). (gr. 4-6). 16.00 (978-0-618-10868-8(8)) Houghton Mifflin Co. Trade & Reference Div.

Jarrow, Gail. Chiggers. 2003. (Parasites Ser.). (Illus.). 32p. (J). 24.95 (978-0-7377-1778-5(5) , Greenhaven Pr., Inc.) Thomson Gale.

Jay, Michael. Flying Creatures. 2003. (Illus.). 32p. (J). lib. bdg. 25.70 (978-1-4109-0007-4(X)) Raintree.

Johnson-Farris, Nancy. Critters & Bugs of Africa. 2003. (J). spiral bd. 12.95 (978-1-931334-35-8(8)) Pieces of Learning.

—Critters & Bugs of the Great Sonoran Desert. 2003. (J). spiral bd. 12.95 (978-1-931334-32-7(3)) Pieces of Learning.

Johnson, Jinny. Creepy Crawlies. 1999. (Weird & Wonderful! Ser.). (Illus.). 45p. (YA). (gr. 3 up). pap. 7.99 (978-0-7681-0186-7(7) , 57003, McClanahan Bk.) Learning Horizons, Inc.

Jones, Jeff. Just Bugs: Learning the Short U Sound. (Power-Phonics Ser.). (Illus.). (J). 2002. 24p. (gr. 1). lib. bdg. 18.50 (978-0-8239-5911-2(2)); 2001. 23p. lib. bdg. 26.40 (978-0-8239-8256-1(4)) Rosen Publishing Group, Inc., The. (PowerKids Pr.).

Kahn, Sarah. Creepy Crawlies. Scott, Peter David, illus. 2006. (J). ***978-0-439-78702-4(5))** Scholastic, Inc.

Kalman, Bobbie. El Ciclo de Vida de la Mariposa. Reiach, Margaret Amy, illus. 2005. (Serie Ciclos de Vida Ser.). (SPA.). 32p. (J). (ps-ps). pap. (978-0-7787-8708-2(7)) Crabtree Publishing Co.

—El Ciclo de Vida de la Mariposa. 2005. (Serie Ciclos de Vida Ser.). (SPA., Illus.). 32p. (J). (978-0-7787-8662-7(5)) Crabtree Publishing Co.

Kalman, Bobbie & Aloian, Molly. El Ciclo de Vida de los Insectos. 2006. (Mundo de los Insectos Ser.). (SPA & ENG., Illus.). 32p. (J). (gr. k-6). pap. (978-0-7787-8515-6(7)); (978-0-7787-8499-9(1)) Crabtree Publishing Co.

—El Cuerpo de los Insectos. 2006. (Mundo de los Insectos Ser.). (SPA., Illus.). 32p. (J). (gr. k-6). pap. (978-0-7787-8512-5(2)); (978-0-7787-8496-8(7)) Crabtree Publishing Co.

—Insectos Que Trabajan en Equipo. 2006. (Mundo de los Insectos Ser.). (SPA., Illus.). 32p. (J). (gr. k-6). (978-0-7787-8498-2(3)) Crabtree Publishing Co.

—Insectos que Trabajan en Equipo. 2006. (Mundo de los Insectos Ser.). (SPA., Illus.). 32p. (J). (gr. k-6). pap. (978-0-7787-8514-9(9)) Crabtree Publishing Co.

—Insectos Utiles y Dañinos. 2006. (Mundo de los Insectos Ser.). (SPA., Illus.). 32p. (J). (gr. k-6). pap. (978-0-7787-8513-2(0)); (978-0-7787-8497-5(5)) Crabtree Publishing Co.

Kalman, Bobbie & Crossingham, John. Los hagares de los Insectos. 2006. (SPA., Illus.). 32p. (gr. 1-2). pap. (978-0-7787-8516-3(5)) Crabtree Publishing Co.

—Insect Homes. 2006. (World of Insects Ser.). (Illus.). 32p. (J). (gr. k-6). pap. (978-0-7787-2379-0(8)); (978-0-7787-2345-5(3)) Crabtree Publishing Co.

Kalman, Bobbie & Sjonger, Rebecca. Everyday Insects. 2006. (World of Insects Ser.). (Illus.). 32p. (J). (gr. k-6). pap. (978-0-7787-2370-7(4)); (978-0-7787-2336-3(4)) Crabtree Publishing Co.

—Insect Defenses. 2006. (World of Insects Ser.). (Illus.). 32p. (J). (gr. k-6). pap. (978-0-7787-2368-4(2)); (978-0-7787-2334-9(8)) Crabtree Publishing Co.

—Insectos Comunes. 2006. (SPA., Illus.). 32p. (gr. 1-2). pap. (978-0-7787-8517-0(3)) Crabtree Publishing Co.

Kelly, Diane A. Stick Insect (Bugs) 2004. (Bugs Ser.). (Illus.). 32p. (J). (gr. 4-7). 24.95 (978-0-7377-1774-7(2)) Thomson Gale.

Ketch, Ann. Lightning Bugs. Hood, Joyce, illus. 2003. 12p. (J). (gr. k-2). pap. 4.95 (978-1-57874-038-3(X)) Kaeden Corp.

Khan, Sarah. Creepy Crawlies Lift-the-Flap. Scott, Peter, illus. 2005. (Luxury Lift-the-Flap Learners Ser.). 16p. (J). (gr. 1 up). 11.95 (978-0-7945-0763-3(8) , Usborne) EDC Publishing.

Kilpatrick, Cathy. Creepy Crawlies. rev. ed. 2006. (First Nature Ser.). 24p. (J). pap. 4.99 (978-0-7945-1494-5(4) , Usborne) EDC Publishing.

Kite, L. Patricia. Insect Facts & Folklore. 2001. (Illus.). 80p. (gr. 3-6). lib. bdg. 29.90 (978-0-7613-1822-4(4) , Millbrook Pr.) Lerner Publishing Group.

Kneidel, Sally. More Pet Bugs. 1999. (gr. 3-6). lib. bdg. 22.20 (978-0-613-16528-0(4)) Tandem Library Bks.

Kravetz, Jonathan. Mosquitoes. 2006, (Illus.). 24p. (J). lib. bdg. (978-1-4042-3044-6(0) , PowerKids Pr.) Rosen Publishing Group, Inc., The.

—Stink Bugs. 2006. (Illus.). 24p. (J). lib. bdg. (978-1-4042-3045-3(9)) Rosen Publishing Group, Inc., The.

Kuhn, Dwight & Pascoe, Elaine. Ant Lions & Lacewings. 2004. (Illus.). 48p. (J). (gr. 2-4). 24.95 (978-1-4103-0310-3(1) , Blackbirch Pr., Inc.) Thomson Gale.

Kuwahara, Ryuichi. In Front of the Ant: Walking with Beetles & Other Insects. Kuribayashi, Satoshi, photos by. 2004. (Illus.). 28p. (J). pap. 8.95 (978-1-929132-63-8(4)) Kane/Miller Bk. Pubs., Inc.

Ladybugs & Other Insects. 2007. (First Discovery Book Ser.). 24p. (J). pap. 5.99 (*978-0-439-91086-6(2)) Scholastic, Inc.

Landau, Elaine. Minibeasts as Pets. 1998. (True Bks.). (Illus.). 48p. (J). (gr. 3-5). pap. 6.95 (978-0-516-26268-0(8) , Children's Pr.) Scholastic Library Publishing.

Lara, Enrique & Garcia, Luis. Leaves. 2004. (Illus.). (J). (978-81-89020-07-1(2)) Katha.

Larousse Mexico Staff, ed. Los Insectos (Insects) 2006. (Mi Pequena Enciclopedia Ser.). (Illus.). 38p. (ps-k). pap. 3.95 (978-970-22-1188-4(3)) Larousse, Ediciones, S. A. de C. V. MEX. *Dist:* Houghton Mifflin Co. Trade & Reference Div.

Lasebny, Andy & McMonigle, Orin A. Praying Mantids Keeping Aliens. 2001. 40p. (YA). 10.00 (978-0-9719129-2-2(0)) Elytra & Antenna.

Lee, Celeste & Herndon, Ryan, compiled by. Guinness World Records: Bizarre Bug Records. 2006. (Illus.). 29p. (J). (*978-0-439-87416-8(5)) Scholastic, Inc.

Lee, Justin. How to Draw Insects. 2002. (Kid's Guide to Drawing Ser.). (Illus.). 24p. (J). lib. bdg. 21.25 (978-0-8239-5791-0(8) , PowerKids Pr.) Rosen Publishing Group, Inc., The.

Legg, Gerald. The World of Insect Life. 2002. (Inside Look Ser.). (Illus.). 48p. (J). (gr. 4 up). lib. bdg. 26.00 (978-0-8368-3179-5(9)) Stevens, Gareth Inc.

Levine, Shar, et al. Extreme 3-D Scary Bugs. 2005. (Extreme 3-D Ser.). (Illus.). 48p. (gr. 4-7). 14.95 (978-1-59223-365-6(1) , Silver Dolphin Bks.) Advantage Pubs. Group.

Listen-Read-Think Science: Bugs & Slugs. 2006. pap. 4.49 (978-1-4206-8149-9(4)) Teacher Created Materials, Inc.

Littlefield, Angie & Littlefield, Jennifer. The 10 Grossest Bugs. 2008. (Tentrade; Ser.). 48p. (J). pap. 14.99 (*978-1-55448-462-1(6) , Watts, Franklin) Scholastic Library Publishing.

Llewellyn, Claire. The Best Book of Bugs. (Best Book of... Ser.). (Illus.). 32p. (J). (gr. k-3). 2005. pap. 6.95 (978-0-7534-5901-0(9)); 1998. tchr. ed. 12.95 (978-0-7534-5118-2(2)) Houghton Mifflin Co. Trade & Reference Div. (Kingfisher).

Loewen, Nancy. Backyard Bugs, 6 bks. Reibeling, Brandon, illus. Incl. Busy Buzzers : Bees in Your Backyard. 22.60 (978-1-4048-0143-1(X)); Hungry Hoppers : Grasshoppers in Your Backyard. 22.60 (978-1-4048-0146-2(4)); Living Lights : Fireflies n Your Backyard. 22.60 (978-1-4048-0145-5(6)); Night Flyers : Moths in Your Backyard. 22.60 (978-1-4048-0144-8(8)); Spotted Beetles : Ladybugs in Your Backyard. 22.60 (978-1-4048-0142-4(1)); Tiny Workers : Ants in Your Backyard. 22.60 (978-1-4048-0141-7(3)); 24p. (C). (gr. k-3). 2004. (Illus.). 2003. 135.60 (978-1-4048-0140-0(5)) Picture Window Bks.

Loman, Roberta K. Lots of Bugs! 1999. (Illus.). 48p. (J). (ps-2). 2.99 (978-0-7847-0888-0(6) , 22060, Bean Sprouts) Standard Publishing.

Looking at Insects: Individual Title Six-Packs. (Discovery World Ser.). 24p. (gr. 1-2). 33.00 (978-0-7635-8474-0(6)) Rigby Education.

Looking for Insects. 2003. (J). 28.95 (978-0-673-78112-3(7)) Celebration Pr.

Lucy, Bowman. Bugs (Level 1) - Internet Referenced. 2007. (Beginners Nature Ser.). 32p. (J). 4.99 (*978-0-7945-1705-2(6) , Usborne) EDC Publishing.

Lunis, Natalie. Bugs All Around. Date not set. (Thinking Like a Scientist Ser.). (Illus.). 20p. (J). pap. 16.95 (978-1-58273-091-2(1)) Sundance/Newbridge Educational Publishing.

Macken, JoAnn Early. The Life Cycle of a Cicada. 2006. (Illus.). 24p. (J). pap. (978-0-8368-6387-1(9)); lib. bdg. 19.33 (978-0-8368-6380-2(1)) Stevens, Gareth Inc.

MacRo, Hartley & MacRo, Taylor. Head Louse. 2002. (Bug Bks.). (Illus.). 32p. (J). (gr. k-2). pap. 6.95 (978-1-58810-320-8(X) , 91031) Heinemann Library.

Made by God: Insects. 2004. 32p. (C). pap. 5.99 (978-0-7424-2799-0(4)) School Specialty Publishing.

Madsen, Chris. Bugs. 2005. (Glow in the Dark Ser.). (Illus.). 23p. (J). (ps-7). bds. 5.95 (978-1-902626-75-8(3)) Red Bird Publishing GBR. *Dist:* Perseus Distribution.

Mariner Books Staff & Leahy, Christopher. Peterson First Guide to Insects of North America. White, Richard E., illus. 2nd ed. 1998. (Peterson First Guides). 128p. pap. 5.95 (978-0-395-90664-4(4)) Houghton Mifflin Co. Trade & Reference Div.

Markle, Sandra. Can You Believe? Insects. Bosson, Jo-Ellen, tr. Bosson, Jo-Ellen, illus. 2002. 48p. (J). (978-0-439-35612-1(1)) Scholastic, Inc.

—Creepy, Crawly Baby Bugs. 2003. (Illus.). 32p. (J). pap. 6.95 (978-0-8027-7659-4(0)) Walker & Co.

Markle, Sandra. Stick Insects: Masters of Defense. 2008. (Insect World Ser.). (J). lib. bdg. 27.93 (*978-0-8225-7296-1(6) , Lerner Pubns.) Lerner Publishing Group.

Marshall Cavendish Corporation Staff, contrib. by. Insects & Spiders of the World, 11 vols., Set. 2003. (Illus.). 704p. lib. bdg. 471.36 (978-0-7614-7334-3(3) , Cavendish, Marshall Reference Bks.) Cavendish, Marshall Corp.

Martin, James W. R. Ticks. 2004. (Nature's Children Ser.). (J). (978-0-7172-5975-5(7) , Grolier) Scholastic Library Publishing.

Martin, Michael. Insect Evidence. 2007. 32p. (J). (978-0-7368-6789-4(9)) Capstone Pr., Inc.

Masiello, Ralph. Bug Drawing Book: Simple Steps to Make Anyone an Artist. Masiello, Ralph, illus. 2004. (Illus.). 32p. (J). 16.95 (978-1-57091-525-3(3)); pap. 6.95 (978-1-57091-526-0(1)) Charlesbridge Publishing, Inc.

Matuszak, Pat. Bugs! Sheldon, David, illus. 2004. (Bible Critters Ser.). 36p. (J). pap. 4.99 (978-0-310-70811-7(7)) Zonderkidz.

Maynard, Christopher. Bugs: A Close up View of the Insect World. 2001. (gr. 3-6). lib. bdg. 14.10 (978-0-613-45578-7(9)) Tandem Library Bks.

McEvey, Shane F. Bugs. 2001. (Insects & Spiders Ser.). (Illus.). 32p. (J). (gr. 4 up). 28.00 (978-0-7910-6595-2(2) , 010552, Chelsea Hse.) Facts On File, Inc.

—Insects & Spiders Series, 6 bks. Incl. Beetles. 32p. 28.00 (978-0-7910-6600-3(2) , 010551); Bugs. 32p. 28.00 (978-0-7910-6595-2(2) , 010552); Dragonflies. 32p. 28.00 (978-0-7910-6597-6(9) , 010553); Flies. 32p. 28.00 (978-0-7910-6596-9(0) , 010554); Moths & Butterflies. 16.95 (978-0-7910-6598-3(7) , 010555); Spiders. 32p. 28.00 (978-0-7910-6599-0(5) , 010556); (J). (gr. 4 up). 2001. (Illus.). 101.70 (978-0-7910-6594-5(4) , 010550S, Chelsea Hse.) Facts On File, Inc.

McKissack, Patricia C. Bugs! rev. ed. 2000. (gr. k-3). lib. bdg. 12.95 (978-0-613-37299-2(9)) Tandem Library Bks.

McKissack, Patricia C. & McKissack, Fredrick L. Bugs! Cressy, Mike, illus. 2000. (Rookie Readers Ser.). 32p. (J). rev. ed. (gr. 1-2). 19.50 (978-0-516-21658-4(9)); 2nd rev. ed. (gr. k-2). pap. 4.95 (978-0-516-27046-3(X)) Scholastic Library Publishing. (Children's Pr.).

McLaurin, Thad, ed. Investigating Science - Insects. 2000. 48p. 9.95 (978-1-56234-388-0(2) , Mailbox Bks., The) Education Ctr., Inc.

McMonigle, Orin A. Assassins, Waterscorpions, & Other True Bugs. 2001. 36p. (J). 10.00 (978-0-9719129-3-9(9)) Elytra & Antenna.

McNab, Chris. Dangerous Insects & Spiders. 2006. (Nature's Monsters Ser.). (Illus.). 32p. (J). lib. bdg. (978-0-8368-6848-7(X)) Stevens, Gareth Inc.

—Giant Spiders & Insects. 2006. (Nature's Monsters Ser.). (Illus.). 32p. (J). lib. bdg. (978-0-8368-6850-0(1)) Stevens, Gareth Inc.

Meister, Cari. Insects, Set. Incl. Butterflies. lib. bdg. 21.35 (978-1-57765-459-9(5)); Crickets. lib. bdg. 21.35 (978-1-57765-460-5(9)); Dragonflies. lib. bdg. 21.35 (978-1-57765-461-2(7)); Fireflies. lib. bdg. 21.35 (978-1-57765-462-9(5)); Ladybugs. lib. bdg. 21.35 (978-1-57765-463-6(3)); Mosquitoes. lib. bdg. 21.35 (978-1-57765-464-3(1)); 24p. (J). (gr. k-6). 2001. (Illus.). 2001. Set lib. bdg. 128.10 (978-1-57765-295-3(9) , Checkerboard Library) ABDO Publishing Co.

Meredith Books Staff, ed. Buggin' with Ruud. 2007. 48p. pap. 6.99 (*978-0-696-23690-7(7)) Meredith Bks.

Merlino, Kim. Insects & Spiders: Grades 2 & 3. (Illus.). (J). pap., wbk. ed. 4.99 (978-0-88743-960-5(8)) School Zone Publishing Co.

Merrick, Patrick. Leeches. 2000. (Naturebooks: Creepy Crawlers Ser.). (Illus.). 32p. (J). (gr. 1-5). 25.64 (978-1-56766-633-5(7)) Child's World, Inc.

—Lice. 2000. (Naturebooks: Creepy Crawlers Ser.). (Illus.). 32p. (J). (gr. 1-5). 25.64 (978-1-56766-634-2(5)) Child's World, Inc.

—Walkingsticks. 2006. (New Naturebooks). (Illus.). 32p. (J). (gr. 1-5). 27.07 (978-1-59296-654-7(3)) Child's World, Inc.

Microscopic Investigations: Insects & Spiders. 2001. (J). pap. 5.95 (978-1-56911-744-6(6)) Learning Resources, Inc.

Miller, Connie Colwell. Mosquitoes. 2005. (Illus.). 24p. (J). 21.26 (978-0-7368-3709-5(4)) Capstone Pr., Inc.

Miller, Gary. Unwelcome Guests. 2005. (Real Deal Ser.). (Illus.). 32p. (J). 18.50 (978-0-7910-8772-5(7) , Chelsea Hse.) Facts On File, Inc.

Miller, Heather. Daddy Longlegs (Bugs) 2005. (Bugs Ser.). (Illus.). 32p. (J). (gr. 3-6). 24.95 (978-0-7377-1769-3(6) , Greenhaven Pr., Inc.) Thomson Gale.

Miller, Heather & Chesworth, Michael, illus. Good Evening Larvae, Nymphs, & Insects! This Is Bob Beetle Welcoming You to Another Episode of This Is Your Life Cycle, the Show That Follows the Life Cycle of Everybody's Favorite Class of Animals, the Insects! 2008. (J). (*978-0-618-72485-7(0) , Clarion Bks.) Houghton Mifflin Co. Trade & Reference Div.

Miller, Sara Swan. Ants, Bees, & Wasps of North America. 2003. (Animals in Order Ser.). 48p. (gr. 4-6). pap. 6.95 (978-0-531-16658-1(9) , Watts, Franklin) Scholastic Library Publishing.

—Cicadas & Aphids: What They Have in Common. 1999. (Animals in Order Ser.). (Illus.). 48p. (J). (gr. 4-6). pap. 6.95 (978-0-531-15944-6(2)); (gr. 3-5). 26.50 (978-0-531-11519-0(4)) Scholastic Library Publishing. (Watts, Franklin).

—Cicadas & Aphids: What They Have in Common. 1999. (gr. 3-6). lib. bdg. 15.25 (978-0-613-34642-9(4)) Tandem Library Bks.

—True Bugs: When Is a Bug Really a Bug? (Animals in Order Ser.). (Illus.). 48p. (J). (gr. 4-6). 1999. pap. 6.95 (978-0-531-15922-4(1)); 1998. 26.50 (978-0-531-11479-7(1)) Scholastic Library Publishing. (Watts, Franklin).

—True Bugs: When Is a Bug Really a Bug? 1999. (Illus.). 47p. (J). (gr. 3-5). lib. bdg. 15.25 (978-0-613-35013-6(8)) Tandem Library Bks.

—Will You Sting Me? Will You Bite? The Truth about Some Scary-Looking Insects. Chrustowski, Rick, illus. 2001. (Curious Little Critters Ser.). 48p. (J). (gr. k-7). 18.95 (978-0-88045-144-4(0)); pap. 9.95 (978-0-88045-145-1(9)) Stemmer Hse. Pubs., Inc.

Minnis, Ivan. I Like Bugs. 2007. 24p. (J). (978-1-4034-9280-7(8)); (978-1-4034-9271-5(9)) Heinemann Library.

Mishica, Clare. Billions of Bugs. Caldwell, Lise, ed. Loman, Roberta K., illus. rev. ed. 1998. (Happy Day Bks.). 24p. (J). (ps-2). 2.49 (978-0-7847-0798-2(7) , 04256, Bean Sprouts) Standard Publishing.

Mitzo Thompson, Kim. Bugs. 2006. (Sing along Activity Books with CDs Ser.). 32p. (J). pap. 4.99 (978-0-7696-4577-3(1)) School Specialty Publishing.

Moffatt, Judith. Bugs: A Read & Do Book. 2001. (Hello Reader! Ser.). (Illus.). (J). (978-0-606-21088-1(1)) Tandem Library Bks.

Morgan, Sally. Butterflies & Other Insects. 2001. (Illus.). 32p. (J). lib. bdg. 24.25 (978-1-930643-42-0(X)) Chrysalis Education.

—Looking at Minibeasts, 4 vols., Set. Incl. Butterflies & Moths. lib. bdg. 16.95 (978-1-929298-80-8(3)); Ladybugs & Beetles. lib. bdg. 16.95 (978-1-929298-79-2(X)); Slugs & Snails. lib. bdg. 16.95 (978-1-929298-81-5(1)); Spiders, Centipedes, & Millipedes. lib. bdg. 16.95 (978-1-929298-82-2(X)); 32p. (J). (gr. 1-4). (Illus.). 2000. Set lib. bdg. 67.80 (978-1-929298-83-9(8)) Chrysalis Education.

—Spiders, Centipedes, & Millipedes. 2000. (Looking at Minibeasts Ser.). (Illus.). 32p. (J). (gr. 1-4). lib. bdg. 16.95 (978-1-929298-82-2(X)) Chrysalis Education.

Morley, Warner Marga. The Insect Folk. 2006. 95.99 (*978-1-4280-4438-8(8)); pap. 89.99 (*978-1-4280-4449-4(3)) IndyPublish.com.

Morris, Neil. Minibeasts. 2004. (Knowledge Masters Ser.). (Illus.). 32p. (YA). pap. incl. cd-rom (978-1-903954-51-5(7)) Chrysalis Children's Bks.

Morris, Rod, photos by. Weta: A Knight in Shining Armour. 2002. (Illus.). 31p. (J). (978-1-86943-547-9(8)) Scholastic, Inc.

Mound, L. A. & Dorling Kindersley Publishing Staff. Insect. 2004. (Eyewitness Books). (Illus.). 72p. (J). (ps-7). lib. bdg. 19.99 (978-0-7566-0691-6(8)) Dorling Kindersley Publishing, Inc.

Mound, Laurence. Insect. 2007. (DK Eyewitness Bks.). 72p. (J). (gr. 3-8). 15.99 incl. cd-rom (978-0-7566-3004-1(5)) Dorling Kindersley Publishing, Inc.

—Insectos. 2005. (Dk eyewitness Bks.). 72p. (J). 15.99 (978-0-7566-1487-4(2)); lib. bdg. 19.99 (978-0-7566-1493-5(7)) Dorling Kindersley Publishing, Inc.

Mouse Works Staff. A Bugs Life: Can You Find the Difference? 1998. (Seek & See Book Ser.). (Illus.). 24p. (J). (gr. k-3). 3.99 (978-1-57082-937-6(3)) Mouse Works.

—Bug's Life: Can You Find the Difference Seek & See. 1998. 24p. (J). 3.99 (978-0-7364-0069-5(9)) Mouse Works.

Murawski, Darlyne A. Bug Faces. 2000. (Illus.). 32p. (J). (gr. 5-9). 16.95 (978-0-7922-7557-2(8) , National Geographic Children's Bks.) National Geographic Society.

Murphy. Bug Dance. 2003. (J). pap., tchr. ed. (978-0-7398-6545-3(5)); 2002. (Illus.). pap. (978-0-7398-6789-1(X)) Steck-Vaughn.

Murphy, Patricia J. Investigating Insects with a Scientist. 2004. (I Like Science! Ser.). (Illus.). 24p. (J). (gr. 1-3). lib. bdg. 21.26 (978-0-7660-2270-6(6)) Enslow Pubs., Inc.

Murray, Peter & Primm, E. Russell. Insects. 2004. (Science Around Us Ser.). 32p. (J). (gr. 2-6). 27.07 (978-1-59296-215-0(7)) Child's World, Inc.

Needham, Karen Merrie & Lucas, Launi. Strange Beginnings. Lucas, Launi, illus. 2001. (Illus.). 32p. (J). (978-1-896580-11-1(4)) Tradewind Bks.

Newman-D'Amico, Fran. Bugs Activity & Coloring Book. 2007. 32p. (J). pap. 3.95 (*978-0-486-46199-1(8)) Dover Pubns., Inc.

Noble, Marty. Fun with Bugs Stencils. 1999. (Illus.). 6p. (J). pap. 1.50 (978-0-486-40759-3(4)) Dover Pubns., Inc.

O'Donnell, Kerri. Ugly Bugs. 2006. (Ugly Animals Ser.). (Illus.). 24p. (J). (gr. k-2). lib. bdg. 21.25 (978-1-4042-3527-4(2)) Rosen Publishing Group, Inc., The.

Ohare, Ted. Insectos. 2005. (Que Es un Animal? Biblioteca del Descubrimiento Ser.). (SPA.). 24p. pap. 5.45 (978-1-59515-688-4(7)) Rourke Publishing, LLC.

O'Hare, Ted. Insectos. 2006. (Que es un Animal? Biblioteca del Descubrimiento Ser.). (gr. 1-4). 14.95 (978-1-59515-630-3(5)) Rourke Publishing, LLC.

—Insects. 2006. (What Is an Animal Ser.). (Illus.). 24p. (gr. 1-4). 14.95 (978-1-59515-418-7(3)) Rourke Publishing, LLC.

Ohare, Ted. Insects. 2005. 24p. pap. 5.45 (978-1-59515-732-4(8)) Rourke Publishing, LLC.

Olson, Carl. 50 Common Insects of the Southwest. 2004. (Illus.). 64p. pap. 11.95 (978-1-58369-042-0(5)) Western National Parks Assn.

O'Neil, Sarah. Insects. 2000. (gr. k-3). lib. bdg. 11.80 (978-0-613-29652-6(4)) Tandem Library Bks.

O'Neill, Amanda. Insects & Bugs. 2002. (Curious Kids Guides). (Illus.). 32p. (J). tchr. ed. 6.95 (978-0-7534-5466-4(1) , Kingfisher) Houghton Mifflin Co. Trade & Reference Div.

Packard, Mary. The Real Thing! Stinkbugs: And Other Bugs. 2006. (Illus.). 47p. (J). (*978-0-439-88064-0(5) , Scholastic) Scholastic, Inc.

Paige, Joy. El Insecto Palo: El Insecto Mas Largo Del Mundo. 2004. (Campeones Del Mundo Animal Ser.). (SPA & ENG., Illus.). 24p. (J). (gr. 3-6). lib. bdg. 17.25 (978-0-8239-6897-8(9) , Buenas Letra) Rosen Publishing Group, Inc., The.

—The Stick Insect: World's Longest Insect. 2002. (Reading Power Ser.). (Illus.). 24p. (J). (gr. 1). lib. bdg. 17.25 (978-0-8239-5963-1(5) , PowerKids Pr.) Rosen Publishing Group, Inc., The.

Pallotta, Jerry. Icky Bug Colors. Biedryzycki, David, illus. 2004. 32p. (J). pap. 5.99 (978-0-439-38917-4(8) , Cartwheel Bks.) Scholastic, Inc.

—The Icky Bug Counting Board Book. Masiello, Ralph, illus. 2004. (J). bds. 6.95 (978-1-57091-624-3(1)) Charlesbridge Publishing, Inc.

—Icky Bug Shapes. Bersani, Shennen, illus. 2004. 32p. (J). pap. 5.99 (978-0-439-38918-1(6) , Cartwheel Bks.) Scholastic, Inc.

Parker, Edward, photos by. Insects & Spiders. 2002. (Rain Forest Pilot Ser.). (Illus.). 48p. (J). lib. bdg. 27.12 (978-0-7398-5240-8(X)) Raintree.

Parker, Janice. Cockroaches, Cocoons & Honeycombs: The Science of Insects. 1998. (Science @ Work Ser.). (Illus.). 48p. (J). (gr. 4-6). 27.12 (978-0-7398-0135-2(X)) Raintree.

—Insects. 2007. (J). (*978-1-59036-707-0(3)); (*978-1-59036-708-7(1)) Weigl Pubs., Inc.

Parker, Janice. The Science of Insects. 1999. (Living Science Ser.). (Illus.). 32p. (J). (gr. 2 up). lib. bdg. 23.93 (978-0-8368-2466-7(0)) Stevens, Gareth Inc.

Parker, Steve. Ant Lions, Wasps & Other Insects. 2005. (Animal Kingdom Classification Ser.). (Illus.). 48p. (J). (gr. 4-6). (978-0-7565-1250-7(6)) Compass Point Bks.

—Insects, Bugs, & Art Activities. 2002. (gr. 3-6). lib. bdg. 17.60 (978-0-613-82415-6(0)) Tandem Library Bks.

Parker, Steve & Goodman, Polly. Insects, Bugs, & Art Activities. 2002. (Arty Facts Ser.). (Illus.). 48p. (J). (gr. 3-4). pap. (978-0-7787-1137-7(4)); lib. bdg. (978-0-7787-1109-4(9)) Crabtree Publishing Co.

Pascoe, Elaine. Bugs. Kuhn, Dwight, illus. Kuhn, Dwight, photos by. 2003. 48p. (J). 23.70 (978-1-56711-458-4(X) , Blackbirch Pr., Inc.) Thomson Gale.

—How & Why Insects Grow & Change. Kupperstein, Joel, ed. Kuhn, Dwight, photos by. 2000. (How & Why Ser.). (Illus.). 16p. (J). (gr. 1-3). pap. 2.99 (978-1-57471-665-8(4) , 2972) Creative Teaching Pr., Inc.

—Insects Grow & Change. Kuhn, Dwight, photos by. 2002. (Springboards into Science Ser.). (Illus.). 24p. (J). (gr. 1 up). lib. bdg. 20.67 (978-0-8368-3009-5(1)) Stevens, Gareth Inc.

—Insects Visit Flowers. Kuhn, Dwight, photos by. 2002. (Springboards into Science Ser.). (Illus.). 24p. (J). (gr. 1 up). lib. bdg. 20.67 (978-0-8368-3010-1(5)) Stevens, Gareth Inc.

—Mantids. Kuhn, Dwight, photos by. 2004. (Illus.). 48p. (J). (gr. 2-4). 24.95 (978-1-4103-0307-3(1) , Blackbirch Pr., Inc.) Thomson Gale.

—Spittlebugs & Other Sap Tappers. 2003. (Illus.). 48p. (J). 24.95 (978-1-56711-430-0(X) , Blackbirch Pr., Inc.) Thomson Gale.

Pebble Books: Bugs, Bugs, Bugs. 2005. (YA). (gr. k-3). 831.60 (978-0-7368-4220-4(9) , Pebble Bks.) Capstone Pr., Inc.

Penner, Lucille Recht & Rabe, Tish. On Beyond Bugs: All about Insects. Ruiz, Aristides, illus. 1999. 48p. (J). (gr. k-3). lib. bdg. 11.99 (978-0-679-97303-4(6) , Random Hse. Bks. for Young Readers) Random Hse. Children's Bks.

Perios, Sylvaine. Mariquita. (Coleccion Mundo Maravilloso). (SPA., Illus.). 40p. (J). (gr. 2-4). 13.00 (978-84-348-3467-5(7) , SM5480) SM Ediciones ESP. *Dist:* Lectorum Pubns., Inc., i.b.d., Ltd.

Phillips, Dee. Bugs & Spiders (Blue Zoo Guides) 2006. (Blue Zoo Guides Ser.). (Illus.). 96p. 18.95 (978-1-58728-520-2(7) , Two Can Publishing) T&N Children's Publishing.

Pierre, Stephanie S. Earwig. 2002. (Bug Bks.). (Illus.). 32p. (J). (gr. k-2). pap. 6.95 (978-1-58810-925-5(9) , 91523) Heinemann Library.

—Firefly. 2002. (Bug Bks.). (Illus.). 32p. (J). (gr. k-2). pap. 6.95 (978-1-58810-926-2(7) , 91524) Heinemann Library.

—Pillbug. 2002. (Bug Bks.). (Illus.). 32p. (J). (gr. k-2). pap. 6.95 (978-1-58810-927-9(5) , 91525) Heinemann Library.

Pike, Katy. Insects. (Make it Work Ser.). 42p. (J). (gr. 4-8). pap. 18.95 (978-1-882210-39-8(5)) Action Publishing, Inc.

—Insects. 2003. (Animal Facts Ser.). (Illus.). 24p. (gr. 2-4). 23.00 (978-0-7910-7281-3(9) , Chelsea Hse.) Facts On File, Inc.

—Insects. 2004. (Illus.). lib. bdg. 7.95 (978-0-8225-4526-2(8)) Lerner Publishing Group.

—Insects. 2000. (Illus.). (J). (gr. 1-5). reprint ed. pap. (978-1-57584-710-8(8)) Reader's Digest Children's Publishing, Inc.

—Insects. 2002. (Super Science Activities Ser.). 48p. (J). (gr. 2-5). 7.99 (978-0-7439-3661-3(2) , 3661) Teacher Created Materials, Inc.

Praying Mantises, Vol. 2. 2005. (Bugs, Bugs, Bugs Ser.). (YA). (gr. k-3). (978-0-7368-9088-5(2) , Pebble Bks.) Capstone Pr., Inc.

Praying Mantises, 6 vols. (gr. k-2). 28.95 (978-0-7368-9109-7(9)) Red Brick Learning.

Preston-Mafham, Rod, et al. Insects & Other Invertebrates. 2006. (Facts at Your Fingertips Ser.). (Illus.). 64p. (J). (*978-1-933834-02-3(1)) Brown Bear Books.

Priddy, Roger. Bug IQ. 2006. (J). 14p. bds. 9.95 (978-0-312-49883-2(7)); 16p. bds. 14.95 (978-0-312-49697-5(4)) St. Martin's Pr. (Priddy Bks.).

—Busy Bugs. 2005. (Sticker Activity Fun Workbooks). (Illus.). 48p. (J). pap., act. bk. ed. 3.47 (978-0-312-49661-6(3) , Priddy Bks.) St. Martin's Pr.

—Trucks, Bugs, Dinosaurs. 2006. 132p. (J). act. bk. ed. 12.95 (978-0-312-49741-5(5) , Priddy Bks.) St. Martin's Pr.

Priddy, Roger & Priddy Books Staff. Sticker Activity Fun Busy Bugs: Play & Learn. rev. ed. 2006. 48p. (J). bds. 3.47 (978-0-312-49796-5(2) , Priddy Bks.) St. Martin's Pr.

Prior, Jennifer Overend. Bugs. Bauer, Larry, illus. 1999. (Thematic Units Ser.). 80p. (J). (ps-1). pap., tchr. ed. 9.99 (978-1-57690-620-0(5) , TCA2620) Teacher Created Materials, Inc.

—Technology Connections for Creepy Crawlies. 1998. (Technology Connections Ser.). 48p. (J). (gr. 3-8). pap. 7.95 (978-1-57690-399-5(0) , TCM2399) Teacher Created Materials, Inc.

Pugliano-Martin, Carol. Being a Bug Scout. 2004. (Navigators Ser.). (J). pap. 42.00 (978-1-4108-0424-2(0)) Benchmark Education Co.

H I

Pugliano-Martin, Carol. Como ser un explorador de animalitos & Being a Bug Scout. 2005. spiral bd. 84.00 (*978-1-4108-5695-1(X)) Benchmark Education Co.

Pyers, Greg. Why Am I an Insect? 2005. (Raintree Perspectives Ser.). (Illus.). 32p. (J). (978-1-4109-2019-5(4)); (gr. 6-8). pap. 7.85 (978-1-4109-2026-3(7)) Steck-Vaughn.

Que es un insecto? Science, 6 vols.Tr. of What Is an Insect? Science. (SPA.). (gr. k-2). 28.95 (978-0-7368-3128-4(2) , Yellow Umbrella Bks.) Capstone Pr., Inc.

Quire, Ann O. Cicadas. 2004. (True Bks.). (J). (gr. 3-5). pap. 6.95 (978-0-516-27766-0(9) , Children's Pr.) Scholastic Library Publishing.

Raintree Steck-Vaughn Staff. Donde Viven los Insectos? 1999. (Coleccion en Parejas). (SPA.). (J). pap., stu. ed. 21.50 (978-0-7398-0841-2(9)) Steck-Vaughn.

Ramsden, Julie & Ramsden, Michael. Mini Beasts. 2005. (X-Zone Ser.). (Illus.). 30p. (gr. 4-8). 23.00 (978-0-7910-8994-1(0)) Facts On File, Inc.

Reyes, Blanca Matilde. Insects. 2006. (Illus.). 16p. (J). act. bk. ed. 0.75 (978-1-933984-04-9(X)) Two Lands.

Rice, Judith Anne. Those Itsy-Bitsy Teeny-Tiny Not-So-Nice Head Lice/Esos Pequenines Chiquitines para Nada Simpaticos Piojos. Stricklin, Julie A. & Ytsma, Petronella J., illus. 2004. (SPA & ENG.). 32p. (J). (gr. k-3). pap. 12.95 (978-1-884834-54-7(X)) Redleaf Pr.

Richardson, Adele D. Insects. 2004. (First Facts Ser.). (Illus.). 24p. (J). lib. bdg. 21.26 (978-0-7368-2623-5(8)) Capstone Pr., Inc.

—Walking Sticks. 1998. (Bugs Ser.). (Illus.). 32p. (YA). (gr. 3-12). lib. bdg. 16.95 (978-1-887068-37-6(6)) Smart Apple Media.

Richardson, Joy. Insects. 2005. (Illus.). 32p. (J). lib. bdg. 23.33 (978-0-8368-4505-1(6)) Stevens, Gareth Inc.

Rigby Education Staff. Bugs on the Menu. (Sails Literacy Ser.). (Illus.). 16p. (gr. 2-3). 27.00 (978-0-7635-9954-6(9) , 699549C99) Rigby Education.

—Discovery World Red Insect Body. (Discovery World Ser.). (Illus.). 12p. (gr. 1-2). 31.00 (978-0-7635-2704-4(1)) Rigby Education.

—Pebble Soup Ever Changing Big Book: Ants & Grasshoppers. (Pebble Soup Explorations Ser.). 16p. (ps up). tchr. ed. 21.00 (978-0-7635-6474-2(5)) Rigby Education.

—Upside Down. (Sails Literacy Ser.). (Illus.). 16p. (gr. k-1). 27.00 (978-0-7635-9863-1(1) , 698631C99) Rigby Education.

Robertson, Matthew. The Big Book of Bugs. 2000. (Illus.). 443p. (gr. 4-7). 29.95 (978-0-941807-33-3(9) , Welcome Bks.) Welcome Enterprises, Inc.

Robinson, W. Wright. How Insects Build Their Amazing Homes. Iverson, Carlyn, illus. 1999. (Animal Architects Ser.). 64p. (J). (gr. 5-9). 24.95 (978-1-56711-375-4(3) , Blackbirch Pr., Inc.) Thomson Gale.

Rockwell, Anne F. Bugs Are Insects. Jenkins, Steve, illus. 2001. (Let's-Read-and-Find-Out Science Ser.). 40p. (J). (ps-1). 15.95 (978-0-06-028568-5(0)); pap. 5.99 (978-0-06-445203-8(4) , Harper Trophy); lib. bdg. 16.89 (978-0-06-028569-2(9)) HarperCollins Pubs.

—Bugs Are Insects. 2001. (gr. k-3). lib. bdg. 13.00 (978-0-613-46252-5(1)); (Illus.). (J). 11.79 (978-0-606-21089-8(X)) Tandem Library Bks.

Rompella, Natalie. Don't Squash That Bug! The Curious Kid's Guide to Insects. Burian, Margo, illus. 2007. (Little Lobster Learners Ser.). 32p. (J). (gr. 2-4). (978-1-897073-50-6(X)) Lobster Pr.

Rompella, Natalie, et al. Droles de Bestioles! Petit Guide des Insectes. Burian, Margo, illus. 2007. (FRE.). 32p. pap. (*978-2-922435-15-3(6)) Lobster Pr.

Ross, Kathy. Crafts for Kids Who Are Learning about Insects. Barger, Jan, illus. 2008. (J). lib. bdg. (*978-0-8225-7591-7(4) , Millbrook Pr.) Lerner Publishing Group.

Ross, Kathy & Holm, Sharon Lane. Crafts for Kids Who Are Learning about Insects & Other Creepy Crawlies. 2008. (Crafts for Kids Who Are Learning about... Ser.). (J). lib. bdg. 25.26 (*978-0-8225-6809-4(8) , Millbrook Pr.) Lerner Publishing Group.

Ross, Michael Elsohn. Millipedology. Erickson, Darren, illus. Grogan, Brian, photos by. 2003. (Backyard Buddies Ser.). 48p. (YA). (gr. 3-5). 6.95 (978-1-57505-436-0(1) , Carolrhoda Bks.) Lerner Publishing Group.

—Rolypolyology. 2003. (Backyard Buddies Ser.). 48p. (YA). (gr. 3-5). 6.95 (978-0-87614-901-0(8) , Carolrhoda Bks.) Lerner Publishing Group.

Royston, Angela. Insects. (Illus.). 32p. (YA). (gr. 2 up). lib. bdg. 27.10 (978-1-932333-36-7(3)) Chrysalis Education.

Running Press Staff. Bugs. 2000. (Fit-a-Shape Ser.). (Illus.). 10p. (J). (ps-k). pap. 6.95 (978-0-7624-0817-7(0) , Running Pr. Kids) Running Pr. Bk. Pubs.

Running Press Staff & Mann, Holly. Bugs: Pull the Tabs! Change the Pictures! 2004. (Magic Windows Ser.). (Illus.). 8p. (J). (ps-k). pap. 4.95 (978-0-7624-1577-9(0) , Running Pr. Kids) Running Pr. Bk. Pubs.

Ruth, Angie. My Adventure with Bugs. 2006. 44p. (J). 8.99 (978-1-59092-448-8(7) , Orchard Academy Pr.) Windstorm Creative.

Salzmann, Mary Elizabeth. What Has Wings? 2007. (Creature Features Ser.). (ENG., Illus.). 24p. (J). (ps-3). lib. bdg. 24.21 (*978-1-59928-876-5(1) , Super SandCastle) ABDO Publishing Co.

Saunders-Smith, Gail. Insects Science. (gr. k-2). 19.95 (978-0-7368-9214-8(1)) Red Brick Learning.

Saunders-Smith, Gail, ed. Bugs, Bugs, Bugs! 2005. (Pebble Plus Ser.). (Illus.). (J). (gr. k-1). lib. bdg. 279.02 (978-0-7368-4404-8(X)) Capstone Pr., Inc.

Savage, Stephen. Insects. 1999. (What's the Difference? Ser.). (Illus.). 32p. (J). (gr. 2-4). lib. bdg. 25.69 (978-0-7398-1355-3(2)) Raintree.

—Insects. 1999. (What's the Difference? Ser.). (Illus.). 32p. (J). (gr. k-3). pap. 7.95 (978-0-7398-1477-2(X)) Steck-Vaughn.

Sayre, April Pulley. Ant, Ant, Ant! An Insect Chant. Park, Trip, illus. 2005. 32p. (gr. k-3). 15.95 (978-1-55971-922-3(2) , NorthWord Bks. for Young Readers) T&N Children's Publishing.

Scarborough, Sheryl. About Bugs. 1999. (gr. k-3). lib. bdg. 11.80 (978-0-613-82081-3(9)) Tandem Library Bks.

—We Both Read-about Bugs. (We Both Read Ser.). (Illus.). 44p. (J). (gr. 2 up). 1998. 7.99 (978-1-891327-07-0(0)); 2nd ed. 1999. pap. 3.99 (978-1-891327-11-7(9)) Treasure Bay, Inc.

Schaefer, Lola M. What Is an Insect? Saunders-Smith, Gail, ed. 2001. (Animal Kingdom Ser.). (Illus.). 24p. (J). (gr. k-1). lib. bdg. 14.60 (978-0-7368-0866-8(3) , Pebble Bks.) Capstone Pr., Inc.

Schiller, Pam. Bugs, Bugs, Bugs! 2006. (NOODLEBUG Activities for Hands-on Learning Ser.). (Illus.). 32p. (J). pap. 4.99 (978-0-7696-4237-6(3)) School Specialty Publishing.

Scholastic, Inc. Staff. Insects, 2. 1998. (Pocket Charts Ser.). (J). 7.95 (978-0-590-04128-7(2)) Scholastic, Inc.

School Specialty Publishing. Insects. 2004. (On-File Ser.). 4p. (J). (gr. 3-5). ring bd. 4.99 (978-0-7424-2898-0(2) , Instructional Fair) Schaffer, Frank Pubns.

School Zone Publishing Company Staff. Insects & Spiders. (Illus.). (J). 19.99 incl. audio compact disk (978-0-88743-944-5(6)); 19.99 incl. audio compact disk (978-0-88743-977-3(2)) School Zone Publishing Co.

Schulte, Mary Knudson. Ants & Other Insects. 2005. (Scholastic News Nonfiction Readers Ser.). (Illus.). 24p. (J). (gr. 1-2). 19.00 (978-0-516-24935-3(5) , Children's Pr.) Scholastic Library Publishing.

Science Stories Foss Spanish Insects EA CR05. 2005. (J). (978-1-59242-584-6(4)) Delta Education, LLC.

Selsam, Millicent E. & Goor, Ronald. Backyard Insects. Goor, Ronald, photos by. 2000. (Illus.). 40p. (J). (ps-3). pap. 4.99 (978-0-590-42256-7(1)) Scholastic, Inc.

Sexton, Colleen. Cicadas. 2007. (Illus.). 24p. (J). lib. bdg. 16.95 (978-1-60014-051-8(3)) Bellwether Media.

—Cicadas. 2007. (Blastoff! Readers Ser.). 24p. (J). (gr. k-2). 18.50 (*978-0-531-17567-5(7) , Children's Pr.) Scholastic Library Publishing.

—World of Insects, Level 2, 4 bks., Set. Incl. Beetles. 18.50 (*978-0-531-17566-8(9)); Cicadas. 18.50 (*978-0-531-17567-5(7)); Honey Bees. 18.50 (*978-0-531-17568-2(5)); Praying Mantises. 18.50 (*978-0-531-17569-9(3)); 24p. (J). (gr. k-2). (Blastoff! Readers Ser.). 2007. 74.00 (*978-0-531-17743-3(2) , Children's Pr.) Scholastic Library Publishing.

Sheehan, Thomas F. Little Neighbors. 2006. (City Science Ser.). (Illus.). 24p. (gr. k-3). 14.95 (978-1-59515-408-8(6)) Rourke Publishing, LLC.

—Pequenos Vecinos: Little Neighbors. 2006. (Rourke Discovery Library). (SPA., Illus.). 24p. (J). (978-1-59515-664-8(X)) Rourke Publishing, LLC.

Shepherd, Matthew, et al. Pollinator Conservation Handbook: A Guide to Understanding, Protecting, & Providing Habitat for Native Pollinator Insects, 2003. (Illus.). 145p. pap. 19.95 (978-0-9744475-0-6(1)) Xerces Society, The.

Sherman, Janice. Draco the Dragonfly. 2007. (ENG., Illus.). 15p. (J). pap. 4.99 (*978-0-9797139-6-5(X)) Jan's Looks & Bks.

—Kyle the Caterpillar. 2007. (ENG., Illus.). 10p. (J). pap. 4.99 (*978-0-9797139-5-8(1)) Jan's Looks & Bks.

Sill, Cathryn. About Arachnids: A Guide for Children. Sill, John, illus. 2006. 40p. (J). 7.95 (978-1-56145-364-1(1)) Peachtree Pubs., Ltd.

Sill, Cathryn P. About Insects: A Guide for Children. Sill, John, illus. 2000. 48p. (J). (ps-3). 15.95 (978-1-56145-207-1(6)) Peachtree Pubs., Ltd.

—About Insects: A Guide for Children. 2003. (gr. k-3). lib. bdg. 16.40 (978-0-613-60379-9(6)) Tandem Library Bks.

Silver Dolphin en Español Staff, ed. Libro y modelos 3-D: Bichos y Mas: Books & 3-D Models: Bugs & More. 2007. (Illus.). 24p. (J). 12.95 (*978-970-718-506-7(6) , Silver Dolphin en Español) Advanced Marketing, S. de R. L. de C. V. MEX. *Dist:* Perseus Distribution.

Silverstein, Alvin, et al. Creepy Crawlies. 2003. (What a Pet! Ser.). (Illus.). 48p. (gr. 5-8). lib. bdg. 23.90 (978-0-7613-2511-6(5) , Millbrook Pr.) Lerner Publishing Group.

Simon. Seemore Big Bugs. 2005. (Illus.). (J). 32p. 14.50 (978-1-58717-253-3(4)); 40p. pap. 3.95 (978-1-58717-265-6(8)) Chronicle Bks. LLC. (SeaStar Bks.).

Smith. Insects & Spiders: Sticker Book. 1998. (J). pap. 2.99 (978-0-87628-444-5(6)) Ctr. for Applied Research in Education, The.

Smithyman, Kathryn & Kalman, Bobbie. Insects in Danger. 2006. (World of Insects Ser.). (Illus.). 32p. (J). (gr. k-6). pap. (978-0-7787-2378-3(X)); (978-0-7787-2344-8(5)) Crabtree Publishing Co.

Snedden, Robert. Insects. 2007. (J). (*978-1-59920-079-8(1)); (*978-1-59920-080-4(5)) Smart Apple Media.

Solway, Andrew. Classifying Insects. 2003. (Classifying Living Things Ser.). (Illus.). 32p. (J). (gr. 3-5). lib. bdg. 24.22 (978-1-4034-0849-5(1)); pap. (978-1-4034-3346-6(1)) Heinemann Library.

—Deadly Insects. 2005. (Illus.). 48p. (J). (ps-6). lib. bdg. 31.43 (978-1-4034-6566-5(5)); pap. (978-1-4034-6572-6(X)) Heinemann Library.

—What's Living in Your Classroom? 2004. (Hidden Life Ser.). (Illus.). 32p. (J). pap. 7.50 (978-1-4034-5485-0(X)); lib. bdg. 25.64 (978-1-4034-4846-0(9)) Heinemann Library.

—What's Living on Your Body? 2004. (Hidden Life Ser.). (Illus.). 32p. (J). pap. 7.50 (978-1-4034-5487-4(6)); lib. bdg. (978-1-4034-4848-4(5)) Heinemann Library.

Somervill, Barbara A. Leeches: Waiting in the Water. 2008. (J). lib. bdg. (*978-1-4042-3801-5(8) , PowerKids Pr.) Rosen Publishing Group, Inc., The.

Soundprints Staff, ed. Backyard Collection: Daddy Longlegs, Owl, Armadillo & Ladybug Books, 4 microbks., No. III. (Smithsonian's Backyard Ser.). (Illus.). 128p. (J). (ps-2). 18.95 (978-1-56899-634-9(9)) Soundprints.

Southwater Staff. Look & Learn about Creepy Crawlies. 2001. (Look & Learn Ser.). (Illus.). 32p. (ps). 7.95 (978-1-84215-284-3(X) , Southwater) Anness Publishing GBR. *Dist:* National Bk. Network.

Sovak, Jan. Insects Stained Glass Coloring Book. 2003. (Illus.). 16p. (J). (gr. 3). pap. 5.95 (978-0-486-43047-8(2)) Dover Pubns., Inc.

Spiders & Other Creepy-Crawlies. 2002. (Wild, Wild World Ser.). 32p. (J). 9.95 (978-0-7525-4680-3(5)) Parragon, Inc.

Spilsbury, Louise & Spilsbury, Richard. The Life Cycle of Insects. 2003. (From Egg to Adult Ser.). (J). lib. bdg. 24.22 (978-1-4034-0786-3(X)); (Illus.). 32p. pap. 7.50 (978-1-4034-3406-7(9)) Heinemann Library.

—Scientists at Work: Insect Investigators: Entomologists Hardback. 2007. (Illus.). 32p. (J). (*978-0-431-14925-7(9)) Heinemann Library.

—Scientists at Work: Insect Investigators: Entomologists Paperback. 2007. (Illus.). 32p. (J). (*978-0-431-14932-5(1)) Heinemann Library.

Spilsbury, Richard & Spilsbury, Louise. Insect Investigators: Entomologists. 2007. (J). (*978-1-4034-9949-3(7)); pap. (*978-1-4034-9956-1(X)) Heinemann Library.

Squire, Ann O. Cicadas. 2003. (True Book Ser.). (Illus.). 48p. (J). 25.00 (978-0-516-22782-5(3) , Children's Pr.) Scholastic Library Publishing.

St. Pierre, Stephanie. Earwig. 2002. (gr. k-3). lib. bdg. 14.75 (978-0-613-61419-1(4)) Tandem Library Bks.

St Pierre, Stephanie. Earwig. 2002. (Heinemann First Library). (Illus.). 32p. (J). (gr. k-2). lib. bdg. 21.36 (978-1-58810-172-3(X)) Heinemann Library.

St. Pierre, Stephanie. Material Changes & Reactions. 2002. (Chemicals in Action Ser.). (Illus.). 48p. (J). (gr. 6-8). lib. bdg. 25.64 (978-1-58810-197-6(5)) Heinemann Library.

—Pillbug. 2002. (Heinemann First Library). (Illus.). 32p. (J). (gr. k-2). lib. bdg. 21.36 (978-1-58810-174-7(6)) Heinemann Library.

—Pillbug. 2002. (gr. k-3). lib. bdg. 14.75 (978-0-613-61450-4(X)) Tandem Library Bks.

—States of Matter. 2002. (Bug Books Ser.). (Illus.). 48p. (J). (gr. 6-8). lib. bdg. 25.64 (978-1-58810-199-0(1)) Heinemann Library.

Steck-Vaughn Staff. Insects up Close. 2002. (Illus.). (J). pap. 3.74 (978-0-7398-5892-9(0)) Steck-Vaughn.

Steedman, Scott. Backpack Books: 1,001 Facts about Insects. 2003. (gr. 3-6). lib. bdg. 17.60 (978-0-613-55688-0(7)) Tandem Library Bks.

Steiner, Jeanette. Bug's Life Book & Plush Set. 1998. 96p. (J). 7.99 (978-0-7364-0080-0(X)) Mouse Works.

Stevens, Kathryn. Bugs Rule! 2007. (Boys Rock! Ser.). 32p. (J). (gr. 1-5). 24.21 (*978-1-59296-856-5(2)) Child's World, Inc.

Stewart, Jennifer, ed. Backyard Bugs. Birmingham, Lloyd, illus. 1999. 28p. (J). (ps-2). 3.29 (978-0-7847-1093-7(7) , 22077, Bean Sprouts) Standard Publishing.

Stewart, Melissa. Daddy Longlegs Isn't a Spider. 2004. 32p. lib. bdg. 23.90 (978-0-7613-2561-1(1) , Millbrook Pr.) Lerner Publishing Group.

—Insects. 2001. (Animals Ser.). (Illus.). 48p. (J). (gr. 3-5). 25.00 (978-0-516-22040-6(3) , Children's Pr.) Scholastic Library Publishing.

—Insects. 2001. (gr. 3-6). lib. bdg. 15.25 (978-0-613-54576-1(1)) Tandem Library Bks.

—Maggots, Grubs, & More: The Secret Lives of Young Insects. 2003. 64p. lib. bdg. 24.90 (978-0-7613-2658-8(8) , Millbrook Pr.) Lerner Publishing Group.

Stewart, Melissa. My Bug Book. 2008. 16p. (J). 6.99 (*978-0-06-089979-0(4)) HarperCollins Pubs.

Stewart, Pat. Invisible Bugs Magic Picture Book. 2003. (Dover Little Activity Bks.). (Illus.). 16p. (J). pap. 1.50 (978-0-486-42635-8(1)) Dover Pubns., Inc.

—Invisible Insects Magic Picture Book. 2000. (Dover Little Activity Bks.). (Illus.). 16p. (J). pap. 1.50 (978-0-486-41008-1(0)) Dover Pubns., Inc.

The Stick Insect: Individual Title Six-Packs. (On Deck Ser.). 24p. (gr. 4-5). 35.00 (978-0-7578-1068-8(3)) Rigby Education.

Stillerman, Robbie. Silly Bugs Stickers. 2003. (Dover Little Activity Bks.). (Illus.). 4p. (J). (ps-5). pap. 1.50 (978-0-486-42624-2(6)) Dover Pubns., Inc.

Stone, Lynn M. Amazing Insects. 2001. (Six Legged World Ser.). (Illus.). 24p. (J). (gr. 1-4). lib. bdg. 20.64 (978-1-55916-309-5(7)) Rourke Publishing, LLC.

—Edificios de la Granja. Sarfatti, Esther & de la Vega, Eida, trs. 2002. (Vida en la Granja (Life on the Farm) Ser.).Tr. of Farm Buildings. (SPA., Illus.). 24p. (J). mass mkt. 5.95 (978-1-58952-241-1(9) , RK31457) Rourke Publishing, LLC.

—Granjas de Ayer y de Hoy. Sarfatti, Esther & de la Vega, Eida, trs. (Vida en la Granja (Life on the Farm) Ser.).Tr. of Farms Old & New. (SPA., Illus.). 24p. (J). 2002. mass mkt. 5.95 (978-1-58952-244-2(3) , RK31460); 2001. (gr. 1-3). lib. bdg. 19.27 (978-1-58952-185-8(4) , RK5070) Rourke Publishing, LLC.

—Insects & People. 2000. (Six Legged World Ser.). (Illus.). 24p. (J). (gr. 1-4). lib. bdg. 19.27 (978-1-55916-311-8(9)) Rourke Publishing, LLC.

—The Insect's Body. 2000. (Six Legged World Ser.). (Illus.). 24p. (J). (gr. 1-4). lib. bdg. 19.27 (978-1-55916-314-9(3)) Rourke Publishing, LLC.

—Insects of All Kinds. 2000. (Six Legged World Ser.). (Illus.). 24p. (J). (gr. 1-4). lib. bdg. 20.64 (978-1-55916-312-5(7)) Rourke Publishing, LLC.

—Lives of Insects. 2000. (Six Legged World Ser.). (Illus.). 24p. (J). (gr. 1-4). lib. bdg. 20.64 (978-1-55916-313-2(5)) Rourke Publishing, LLC.

—Maquinaria de la Granja. Sarfatti, Esther & de la Vega, Eida, trs. 2002. (Vida en la Granja (Life on the Farm) Ser.).Tr. of Farm Machinery. (SPA., Illus.). 24p. (J). mass mkt. 5.95 (978-1-58952-243-5(5) , RK31459) Rourke Publishing, LLC.

Storad, Conrad J. Little Lords of the Desert. Atwood, Donna S., illus. 1998. 32p. (J). (gr. 1-6). pap. 8.95 (978-0-9660293-2-1(1)) Atwood, Donna Design.

Sund, Mike, illus. Creepy Crawly Creatures. 2007. 7p. 16.95 (*978-1-58117-623-0(6) , Intervisual/Piggy Toes) Dalmatian Pr.

Sutherland, Jonathan. Flying Insects. 2006. (Nature's Monsters Ser.). (Illus.). 32p. (J). lib. bdg. (978-0-8368-6849-4(8)) Stevens, Gareth Inc.

—Social Insects. 2006. (Nature's Monsters Ser.). (Illus.). 32p. (J). lib. bdg. (978-0-8368-6851-7(X)) Stevens, Gareth Inc.

Swanson, Diane. Bug Bites: Insects Hunting Insects... & More. 2001. (gr. k-3). lib. bdg. 22.20 (978-0-613-78507-5(X)) Tandem Library Bks.

Swanson, Diane. Bugs up Close. Davidson, Paul, photos by. 2007. (Illus.). 40p. (J). (gr. 2-5). pap. (*978-1-55453-139-4(X)); (ps-3). (*978-1-55453-138-7(1)) Kids Can Pr., Ltd.

Tabletop Zoo: Add-on Package. 2003. (J). 26.95 (978-0-673-76189-7(4)) Celebration Pr.

Tabletop Zoo: Individual 6-pack: Cicadas. 2003. 43.95 (978-0-673-57975-1(1)) Celebration Pr.

Tabletop Zoo: Stick Insects. 2003. (J). 43.95 (978-0-673-57976-8(X)) Celebration Pr.

Tabletop Zoo: Tabletop Zoo Complete Package. 2003. (J). 167.95 (978-0-673-76172-9(X)) Celebration Pr.

Tatchell, Judy. Bugs & Slugs Lift-the-Flap. 2004. (Luxury Lift-the-Flap Ser.). 16p. (J). (gr. 1 up). 11.95 (978-0-7945-0762-6(X) , Usborne) EDC Publishing.

Taylor, Barbara. Birds & Other Flying Animals. 2002. (J). 24.95 (978-1-57768-965-2(8) , Bedrick, Peter Bks.) School Specialty Publishing.

—Bug Athletes. (Illus.). 32p. (YA). (gr. 1 up). lib. bdg. 27.10 (978-1-932333-10-7(X)) Chrysalis Education.

—Bug Hunters. (Illus.). 32p. (YA). (gr. 1 up). lib. bdg. 27.10 (978-1-932333-12-1(6)) Chrysalis Education.

—Bugs & Spiders. Eye View Staff, ed. 2003. (Eye View Ser.). (Illus.). 32p. (J). 14.95 (978-1-57768-564-7(4) , Waterbird Bks.) School Specialty Publishing.

—Bugs Snakes Spiders & Crocodiles. 2008. (Illus.). 512p. 29.99 (*978-0-7548-1781-9(4) , Lorenz Bks.) Anness Publishing GBR. *Dist:* National Bk. Network.

—Insects. 2006. (Kingfisher Young Knowledge Ser.). (Illus.). 48p. (J). (gr. k-3). 9.95 (978-0-7534-5933-1(7) , Kingfisher) Houghton Mifflin Co. Trade & Reference Div.

—Poisonous Bugs. (Illus.). 32p. (YA). (gr. 1 up). lib. bdg. 27.10 (978-1-932333-14-5(2)) Chrysalis Education.

—Water Bugs. (Illus.). 32p. (YA). (gr. 1 up). lib. bdg. 27.10 (978-1-932333-11-4(8)) Chrysalis Education.

Telford & Theodorou, Rod. Through a Termite City. 2002. (Amazing Journeys Ser.). (Illus.). 32p. (J). (gr. k-3). pap. 7.50 (978-1-58810-303-1(X) , 91068) Heinemann Library.

Theodorou, Rod. Insects. 2007. (Illus.). 32p. (J). (*978-1-4034-9251-7(4)); (*978-1-4034-9244-9(1)) Heinemann Library.

Time-Life Books Editors. Insect World. 1999. (Illus.). 88p. (J). (ps-3). 14.95 (978-0-8094-4841-8(6)) Time-Life, Inc.

Titherington, Jeanne. Bonkers Fellini. Titherington, Jeanne, illus. 2001. (Illus.). 24p. (J). (ps up). 16.89 (978-0-688-15029-7(2)) HarperCollins Pubs.

Tokuda, Yukihisa. I'm a Pill Bug. Takahashi, Kiyoshi, illus. 2006. 28p. (J). pap. 7.95 (978-1-929132-95-9(6)) Kane/Miller Bk. Pubs., Inc.

Top That Publishing Staff, ed. Creepy Crawlies. 2005. (Illus.). 24p. (978-1-84510-539-6(7)) Top That! Publishing PLC.

—Incredible Insects. 2005. 48p. pap. (978-1-84510-190-9(1)) Top That! Publishing PLC.

Totally Amazing Bug Books, 4 bks., Set. 2001. (Illus.). (J). (gr. 1-4). bds. 19.99 (978-0-307-20080-8(9) , Golden Bks.) Random Hse. Children's Bks.

Townsend. Incredible Insects, 6 Pack. 2004. (Illus.). (J). pap. 51.30 (978-1-4109-0863-6(1)) Harcourt Schl. Pubs.

Townsend, John. Incredible Insects. 2004. (J). pap. 9.50 (978-1-4109-0854-4(2)); (Illus.). 56p. lib. bdg. 31.36 (978-1-4109-0530-7(6)) Harcourt Schl. Pubs.

—Incredible Insects. 2005. (J). 56p. (978-1-4109-1724-9(X)); (978-1-4109-1715-7(0)) Steck-Vaughn.

Trumbauer, Lisa. What Is an Insect? 2006. (Yellow Umbrella Books for Early Readers). (Illus.). 18p. (J). (978-0-7368-5975-2(6)) Yellow Umbrella Pr.

—What Is an Insect. 2006. (Yellow Umbrella Books for Early Readers). (ENG & SPA., Illus.). 18p. (J). (978-0-7368-6011-6(8)) Yellow Umbrella Pr.

Tuxworth, Nicola & Lorenz Editors. Bugs. 2004. (Let's Look at... Ser.). (Illus.). 20p. 5.99 (978-0-7548-1281-4(2)) Anness Publishing GBR. *Dist:* National Bk. Network.

Under the Microscope: Insects, 8 vols., Set. 1999. (Illus.). 384p. (J). (gr. 4-6). lib. bdg. 235.00 (978-0-7172-9428-2(5) , Grolier) Scholastic Library Publishing.

Underwood, Dessie & Cohen, Judith Love. You Can Be a Woman Entomologist. Katz, David Arthur, illus. 2002. 40p. (J). (gr. 4-6). lib. bdg. 13.95 (978-1-880599-60-0(0)); per. 7.00 (978-1-880599-59-4(7)) Cascade Pass, Inc.

Urton, Andrea. Bugs. 2001. (Illus.). 48p. (J). (gr. 4-7). pap. 8.95 (978-0-7373-0537-1(1)) Lowell Hse. Juvenile.

—Bugs & Animals. 2001. (Stick'n Learn Stories Ser.). (Illus.). 96p. (J). (gr. 3-7). pap. 6.95 (978-1-55254-235-4(1)) Brighter Vision Pubns.

VanCleave, Janice Pratt. Janice VanCleave's Play & Find Out about Bugs: Easy Experiments for Young Children. 1999. (Play & Find Out Ser.: Vol. 9). (Illus.). 122p. (ps-2). pap. 12.95 (978-0-471-17663-3(X) , Wiley) Wiley, John & Sons, Inc.

Vaughan, Jenny. Why Don't Worms Have Legs? 2003. (What? Where? Why? Ser.). (Illus.). 24p. (J). (gr. 1 up). lib. bdg. 20.67 (978-0-8368-3791-9(6)) Stevens, Gareth Inc.

Visca, Curt & Visca, Kelley. How to Draw Cartoon Insects. 2003. (Kid's Guide to Drawing Ser.). (Illus.). 24p. (J). lib. bdg. 21.25 (978-0-8239-6157-3(5) , PowerKids Pr.) Rosen Publishing Group, Inc., The.

Wagner, Kathi. The Everything Kids' Bugs Book: Puzzles, Games, & Trivia for Hours of Squishy Fun. 2003. (Everything Ser.). (Illus.). 144p. pap. 6.95 (978-1-58062-892-1(3) , 53392107) Adams Media Corp.

Walking Sticks. (Bugs, Bugs, Bugs! Ser.). 24p. (J). 6.95 (978-0-7368-5103-9(8)) Capstone Pr., Inc.

Ward, Allison, ed. Investigating Science - Insects & Spiders. 2003. 48p. 9.95 (978-1-56234-571-6(0) , Mailbox Bks., The) Education Ctr., Inc.

Ward, Beck. A Bug's World. 2005. (Illus.). 10p. (J). pap. 7.95 (978-0-7624-1985-2(7) , Running Pr. Kids) Running Pr. Bk. Pubs.

Warren, Jean. Bugs. Cubley, Kathleen, ed. 1998. (Sticker Book Ser.). (Illus.). 32p. (J). (ps). pap. 3.95 (978-1-57029-214-9(0) , WPH 3704, Totline Pubns.) Schaffer, Frank Pubns.

Watts, Barrie. Ladybugs. (Illus.). 32p. (YA). (gr. 2 up). lib. bdg. 27.10 (978-1-932889-19-2(1)) Sea-To-Sea Pubns.

Wawrychuk, Carol & McSweeney, Cherie. Insects & Spiders: Active Learning about Nature. Chalk, Philip, illus. 1999. 48p. (J). (ps-1). pap. 7.95 (978-1-57612-074-3(0) , MM2088) Monday Morning Bks., Inc.

Weber, Rebecca. Tricky Insects: And Other Fun Creatures. 2002. (Spyglass Books). (Illus.). 24p. (J). (gr. 1 up). lib. bdg. 18.60 (978-0-7565-0388-8(4)) Compass Point Bks.

Weber, Valerie. Giant Tubeworms. 2005. (Weird Wonders of the Deep Ser.). (Illus.). 24p. (J). lib. bdg. 22.00 (978-0-8368-4562-4(5)) Stevens, Gareth Inc.

Webster, Jean. DaddyLongLegs. 2006. 80p. pap. (978-1-84637-590-3(8)) Echo Library.

Wechsler, Doug. Bizarre Bugs. 2003. (Illus.). 48p. (YA). (gr. 4-6). 17.95 (978-1-59078-095-4(7)) Boyds Mills Pr.

Weingartz, Jill. Ant Colonies. 2001. (Created Environments Ser.). (Illus.). 24p. (J). 21.35 (978-1-58340-103-3(2)) Smart Apple Media.

Wexo, John Bonnett. Insects, Vol. 2. 2001. (Zoobooks Ser.). 24p. (J). (gr. 1-7). 15.95 (978-1-888153-01-9(6)) Wildlife Education, Ltd.

What Is an Insect? 2005. (Animals, Animals, Animals Ser.). (YA). (gr. k-3). (978-0-7368-9095-3(5) , Pebble Bks.) Capstone Pr., Inc.

What Is an Insect?, 6 vols. (gr. k-2). 28.95 (978-0-7368-9116-5(1)); 2006. 8,16p. (J). 6.50 (978-0-7368-1708-0(5)) Red Brick Learning.

Whayne, Susanne Santoro. World of Insects. 1998. (J). 9.95 (978-0-87628-396-7(2)) Ctr. for Applied Research in Education, The.

White, Nancy. The Magic School Bus Explores the World of Bugs. 2002. (Illus.). 32p. (J). pap. 5.99 (978-0-439-22517-5(5)) Scholastic, Inc.

Whitehouse, Patricia. BugBooks. Abello, Patricia, tr. 2003. (Illus.). (J). pap. 23.40 (978-1-4034-3031-1(4)) Heinemann Library.

—Los Insectos, 4 bks., Set. Abello, Patricia, tr. 2003. (Illus.). (J). lib. bdg. 91.16 (978-1-4034-3008-3(X)) Heinemann Library.

Wildlife Education, Ltd. Staff, contrib. by. Insects, Set. 2002. (All about Animals Ser.). (Illus.). (J). (gr. k-6). 16.95 incl. VHS (978-1-888153-86-6(5)) Wildlife Education, Ltd.

Wilkes, Sarah. Insects. 2006. (J). pap. (978-0-8368-6230-0(9)); (Illus.). 48p. lib. bdg. 30.00 (978-0-8368-6211-9(2)) Stevens, Gareth Inc. (World Almanac Library).

Wilsdon, Christina & National Audubon Society Staff. Insects. 1998. (Audubon Society First Field Guide Ser.). (Illus.). 160p. (J). (gr. 3-7). pap. 8.95 (978-0-590-05483-6(X) , Scholastic Reference) Scholastic, Inc.

Windsor, Jo. Animal Lights: Early Level Satellite Individual Title Six-Packs. (Sails Literacy Ser.). 16p. (gr. 1-2). 27.00 (978-0-7578-2938-3(4)) Rigby Education.

—Horns: Early Level Satellite Individual Title Six-Packs. (Sails Literacy Ser.). 16p. (gr. 1-2). 27.00 (978-0-7578-2915-4(5)) Rigby Education.

—How Many Legs? Early Level Satellite Individual Title Six-Packs. (Sails Literacy Ser.). 16p. (gr. 1-2). 27.00 (978-0-7578-2929-1(5)) Rigby Education.

Winner, Cherie. Everything Bug. 2004. (Kids' FAQs Ser.). (Illus.). 64p. (YA). (gr. 2-6). ring bd. 10.95 (978-1-55971-890-5(0) , NorthWord Bks. for Young Readers) T&N Children's Publishing.

Woods, Mae. Insects of the Rain Forest. 1999. (Rain Forest Ser.). (Illus.). 24p. (J). (gr. k-6). lib. bdg. 21.35 (978-1-57765-023-2(9) , Checkerboard Library) ABDO Publishing Co.

World Book, Inc. Staff, contrib. by. Insects of the United States & Canada. 2004. (World Book's Science & Nature Guides Ser.). (Illus.). 80p. (J). (978-0-7166-4214-5(X)) World Bk., Inc.

World Book, Inc Staff, contrib. by. Insects, Spiders, & Creepy Crawlers: A Supplement to Childcraft, the How & Why Library. 2007. (J). (***978-0-7166-0618-5(6)***) World Bk., Inc.

—World of Insects. 2007. (J). (***978-0-7166-7735-2(0)***) World Bk., Inc.

World of Insects. 2005. (Illus.). (J). (gr. 2-3). lib. bdg. 212.60 (978-0-7368-4422-2(8)) Capstone Pr., Inc.

World of Insects, 8 vols., Set. 2006. (Blastoff! Readers Ser.). (Illus.). (J). (gr. k-2). 148.00 (***978-0-531-16876-9(X)***) Scholastic Library Publishing.

Wray, Paul. It's a Bugs World: A Directory of Awesome Insects. 2000. (Illus.). 128p. (YA). (gr. 3 up). pap. 4.95 (978-1-902618-88-3(2)) Element Children's Bks.

Wyse, Liz & Barnes, Jon. Insects. (Make It Work! Ser.). (Illus.). 48p. (J). pap. 7.95 (978-0-590-24402-2(7)) Scholastic, Inc.

York, Penelope. Bugs. Ling, Mary, ed. 2002. (Eye Wonder Ser.). (Illus.). 48p. (J). (gr. k-3). 9.99 (978-0-7894-8552-6(4)) Dorling Kindersley Publishing, Inc.

York, Penelope & Dorling Kindersley Publishing Staff. Bugs. 2002. (Eye Wonder Ser.). (Illus.). 48p. (J). (gr. k-3). lib. bdg. 17.99 (978-0-7894-8553-3(2)) Dorling Kindersley Publishing, Inc.

Young, Caroline & Khanduri, Kamini. The Big Bug Search. Jackson, Ian, illus. 2003. 32p. (J). (978-0-590-12076-0(X)) Scholastic, Inc.

Zabludoff, Marc. The Insect Class. 2005. (Family Trees Ser.). (Illus.). 96p. (J). (gr. 3-7). lib. bdg. 29.93 (978-0-7614-1819-1(9) , Benchmark Bks.) Cavendish, Marshall Corp.

Zakowski, Connie. Insects on Display: A Guide to Mounting & Displaying Insects. 2000. (Illus.). 71p. (J). pap. 8.95 (978-1-56825-041-0(X) , 041-X) Rainbow Bks., Inc.

Zappler, Goerg, ed. Learn about Texas Insects. 1999. (Illus.). 60p. (J). (gr. 4-7). pap. 7.95 (978-1-885696-27-4(2)) Texas Parks & Wildlife Pr.

Ziefert, Harriet. Bugs, Beetles, & Butterflies. Flather, Lisa, illus. 1998. (Easy-to-Read Ser.). 32p. (J). (ps-2). pap. 3.99 (978-0-14-038691-2(2) , Puffin) Penguin Group (USA) Inc.

—Bugs, Beetles, & Butterflies. Flather, Lisa, illus. 1998. (Puffin Easy-to-Read Ser.). 32p. (J). (ps-2). lib. bdg. 10.79 (978-0-606-20458-3(X)); lib. bdg. 11.80 (978-0-613-11368-7(3)) Tandem Library Bks.

Zim, Herbert S. & Cottam, Clarence. Insects: A Golden Guide from St. Martin's Press. rev. ed. 2001. (Golden Guides Ser.). (Illus.). 160p. pap. 6.95 (978-1-58238-129-9(1) , Golden Guides from Saint Martin's Pr.) St. Martin's Pr.

Zimmerman, Dottie, creator. Interactive Sing-along Big Books Here Come the Bugs! 2007. (J). spiral bd. 12.95 (***978-1-58650-714-5(1)***) Super Duper Pubns.

INSECTS—COLLECTION AND PRESERVATION

Blanchard, Patricia & Suhr, Joanne. My Bug Box. Sloat, Teri, illus. (Books for Young Learners). 12p. (J). 2003. pap. 20.00 net. (978-1-57274-701-2(3) , BB2473); 1999. pap. 5.00 (978-1-57274-273-4(9)) Owen, Richard C. Pubs., Inc.

Canizares, Susan & Chanko, Pamela. What Do Insects Do? 1998. (Science Emergent Readers Ser.). (Illus.). (J). pap. 2.50 (978-0-590-39794-0(X)) Scholastic, Inc.

Canizares, Susan & Reid, Mary. Where Do Insects Live? 1998. (Science Emergent Readers Ser.). (Illus.). (J). pap. 2.50 (978-0-590-39793-3(1)) Scholastic, Inc.

Carre, Kathy & Ansary, Mir Tamim. Insects. 1998. (Cool Collections). (978-1-57572-117-0(1)) Heinemann Library.

Pascoe, Elaine. Ants. Kuhn, Dwight, photos by. 1998. (Nature Close-Up Ser.). (Illus.). 48p. (J). (gr. 4-8). 23.70 (978-1-56711-183-5(1) , Blackbirch Pr., Inc.) Thomson Gale.

Zakowski, Connie. Insects on Display: A Guide to Mounting & Displaying Insects. 2000. (Illus.). 71p. (J). pap. 8.95 (978-1-56825-041-0(X) , 041-X) Rainbow Bks., Inc.

INSECTS—FICTION

Aardema, Verna. Por Que Zumban los Mosquitos en los Oidos de la Gente. Blanco, Osvaldo, tr. 1998. (SPA., Illus.). 32p. (J). (ps-3). 18.99 (978-0-8037-2298-9(2) , VK7503, Dial) Penguin Group (USA) Inc.

—Why Mosquitoes Buzz in People's Ears. 1999. (J). 9.95 (978-1-56137-478-6(4)) Novel Units, Inc.

—Why Mosquitoes Buzz in People's Ears. 2004. 29.95 incl. cd-rom (978-1-55592-491-1(3)); pap. 32.75 incl. audio (978-1-55592-494-2(8)); (J). pap. 18.95 incl. audio compact disk (978-1-55592-490-4(5)); (J). pap. 18.95 incl. audio compact disk (978-1-55592-493-5(X)); (J). pap. 32.75 incl. audio (978-1-55592-492-8(1)) Weston Woods Studios, Inc.

Ace Lacewing: Bug Detective. 2005. (Illus.). 40p. (J). (ps-k). 15.95 (978-1-57091-569-7(5)) Charlesbridge Publishing, Inc.

Ada, Alma Flor. El Canto del Mosquito. (Libros para Contar Ser.). (J). (gr. k-3). (SPA., Illus.). 16p. pap. 6.95 (978-1-58105-196-4(4)); 1998. (ENG & SPA.). pap. 5.95 (978-0-88272-806-3(7)) Santillana USA Publishing Co., Inc.

Adams, John. The Dragonfly Door. Gibson, Barbara Leonard, illus. rev. ed. 2007. 40p. (J). (gr. k-5). 17.95 (***978-1-934066-12-6(5)***) Feather Rock Bks., Inc.

Adams, Pam, illus. There Was an Old Lady Storysack. (J). 65.00 (978-0-85953-835-0(4)) Child's Play-International.

—There Was an Old Lady Who Swallowed a Fly. (J). 2005. bds. 12.99 (978-0-85953-314-0(X)); 2000. 16p. bds. 5.99 (978-0-85953-727-8(7)) Child's Play-International.

Adams, Pam, tr. & illus. There Was an Old Lady Who Swallowed a Fly. Adams, Pam, illus. 2003. (Classic Books with Holes). (J). 4.99 (978-0-85953-134-4(1)) Child's Play-International.

The Ants. 2001. 32p. (J). 15.95 (978-0-9653422-7-8(1) , Quarter-Inch Publishing) Quarter-Inch Publishing.

Applefield, Annie. The Beetle & the Berry. Applefield, Annie, illus. 2007. (Illus.). 28p. (J). per. 15.95 (***978-0-9748933-9-6(0)***) E & E Publishing.

Archambault, Jeanne. The Leaping Grasshopper. Smith, Dwight, illus. 2006. 32p. (J). bds. 15.95 (978-0-9763031-2-1(4)) Jitterbug Bks.

Arena, Felice. Sally & Dave: A Slug Story. Arena, Felice, illus. 2008. (Illus.). 32p. (J). 7.95 (***978-1-933605-71-5(5)***) Kane/Miller Bk. Pubs., Inc.

Arnold, Nick. Ugly Bugs. 1998. (J). (gr. 5-9). pap. 3.99 (978-0-590-13858-1(8) , Scholastic Paperbacks) Scholastic, Inc.

Arnold, Tedd. Fly High, Fly Guy! 2008. (Fly Guy Ser.). 32p. (J). 5.99 (***978-0-545-00722-1(4)***) Scholastic, Inc.

—Hi, Fly Guy! Arnold, Tedd, illus. 2005. (Fly Guy Ser.: No. 1). (Illus.). 32p. (J). pap. 5.99 (978-0-439-63903-3(4) , Cartwheel Bks.) Scholastic, Inc.

—Shoo, Fly Guy! 2006. (Fly Guy Ser.: No. 3). (Illus.). 32p. (J). pap. 5.99 (978-0-439-63905-7(0) , Cartwheel Bks.) Scholastic, Inc.

Avi. A Beginning, a Muddle, & an End: The Return of the End of the Beginning. Tusa, Tricia, illus. 2008. 176p. (J). 14.95 (***978-0-15-205555-4(X)***) Harcourt Trade Pubs.

—The End of the Beginning: Being the Adventures of a Small Snail (and an Even Smaller Ant) Tusa, Tricia, illus. 144p. (J). 2008. pap. 6.95 (***978-0-15-205532-5(0)*** , Harcourt Paperbacks); 2004. 14.95 (978-0-15-204968-3(1)) Harcourt Children's Bks.

Aylesworth, Jim. Old Black Fly. 2002. (Illus.). (J). 15.49 (978-0-7587-3302-3(X)) Book Wholesalers, Inc.

Bahrampour, Ali. Luna Likes Bugs. 2008. (J). (978-0-374-34672-0(0) , Farrar, Straus & Giroux (BYR)) Farrar, Straus & Giroux.

Bailey, Arthur Scott. The Tale of Freddie Firefly. 2004. reprint ed. pap. 15.95 (978-1-4191-8478-9(4)); pap. 1.99 (978-1-4192-8478-6(9)) Kessinger Publishing, LLC.

Bailey, Arthur Scott. Tuck-Me-in Tales: The Tale of Freddie Fi. 2006. pap. (***978-1-4065-0449-1(1)***) Dodo Pr.

Banks, Lynne Reid. Harry the Poisonous Centipede's Big Adventure: Another Story to Make You Squirm. l.t. ed. 2005. (Illus.). 176p. (J). pap. (978-0-7540-6197-7(3) , CLP 388) BBC Audio.

—Harry the Poisonous Centipede's Big Adventure: Another Story to Make You Squirm. Ross, Tony, illus. 2001. 192p. (J). (ps-1). 14.95 (978-0-06-029139-6(7)); (gr. 4-7). 14.89 (978-0-06-029394-9(2)) HarperCollins Pubs.

Bass, Keisha Y., creator. Ladybug Ladybug. 2005. (Illus.). 60p. (J). per. 7.95 (978-0-9768129-0-6(8)) KB Publishing.

The Bee & the Bug, 6 vols. 8p. (gr. k-1). 21.50 (978-0-322-02076-4(X)) Wright Group, The.

Bell, Rebecca. Message from Miami - the Adventures of Sharp-Eye - Book2. Bell, Rebecca, illus. 2005. (Adventures of Sharp-Eye). 30p. (J). per. 9.95 (***978-1-934138-09-0(6)***) Bouncing Ball Bks., Inc.

—A Regular Bug - the Adventures of Sharp-Eye - Book1. Bell, Rebecca, illus. 2005. (Adventures of Sharp-Eye: Bk. 1). (Illus.). 25p. (J). per. 9.95 (***978-1-934138-08-3(8)***) Bouncing Ball Bks., Inc.

Bennett, Elizabeth. The New Bug. Scherer, Jeffrey, illus. 2003. 32p. (J). (978-0-439-46641-7(5)) Scholastic, Inc.

Bernstein, Nina. Magic by the Book. Kulikov, Boris, illus. 2005. 240p. (J). 17.00 (978-0-374-34718-5(2) , Farrar, Straus & Giroux (BYR)) Farrar, Straus & Giroux.

—Magic by the Book. unabr. ed. 2005. (J). 63.75 incl. audio (978-1-4193-3607-2(X) , 42048) Recorded Bks., LLC.

—Magic by the Book. l.t. ed. 2006. 248p. (J). 22.95 (978-0-7862-8382-8(3)) Thorndike Pr.

Bishop, Nick. Katydids. Bishop, Nick, photos by. 1998. (Books for Young Learners). (Illus.). 8p. (J). (gr. k-2). pap. 5.00 (978-1-57274-135-5(X) , A2170) Owen, Richard C. Pubs., Inc.

The Black Bug SAT. Date not set. 5.95 (978-0-89868-319-6(X)) ARO Publishing Co.

Black, Cassandra. Twinkle: A Chapter Book. 2003. 113p. (J). 7.99 (978-0-9742739-0-7(2)) Lavender Bks.

Blake-Brekke, Carri. Billy Bully Bug: Learns a Lesson in Hawaii. Melton, Jodi, illus. 2003. (Mrs. B's Story Time... With a Twist! Ser.). 20p. (J). pap. 11.95 incl. audio compact disk (978-0-9720549-2-8(8)) Mom's Pride Enterprises.

—Bugs on the Farm: Mrs. B's Story Time... with a Twist! Melton, Jodi, illus. 2002. 20p. (J). (gr. k-7). pap. 11.95 incl. audio compact disk (978-0-9720549-0-4(1)) Mom's Pride Enterprises.

—Juanita Maria Sophia Bug Diva: Lived down South in the West. Melton, Jo Lynn, illus. 2004. (Mrs. B'S Story Time-. . with A Twist! Ser.). 20p. (J). pap. 11.95 incl. audio compact disk (978-0-9720549-3-5(6)) Mom's Pride Enterprises.

Blanchard, Patricia & Suhr, Joanne. Mi Caja de Insectas. Romo, Alberto, tr. Sloat, Teri, illus. 1999. (Books for Young Learners).Tr. of My Bug Box. (SPA.). 12p. (J). (gr. k-2). pap. 5.00 (978-1-57274-341-0(7) , A2877) Owen, Richard C. Pubs., Inc.

Blechman, R. O. Franklin the Fly. 2007. 40p. (YA). (gr. 2 up). 17.95 (***978-1-56846-148-9(8)*** , Creative Editions) Creative Co., The.

Bogart, Jo Ellen. The Big Tree Gang. Griffiths, Dean, illus. 2005. (Orca Echoes Ser.). 64p. (J). (gr. 2-3). pap. 4.99 (978-1-55143-345-5(1)) Orca Bk. Pubs. USA.

Bolduc, Dylan. Moth & the Flame. 2000. (Publish-a-Book Ser.). (Illus.). 24p. (J). (ps-3). pap. 7.95 (978-0-7398-2369-9(8)) Steck-Vaughn.

Bonnell, Kris. Bugs in My Backyard. 2005. (J). 3.75 (978-1-933727-02-8(0)) Reading Reading Bks., LLC.

Bono, Mary. Ugh! a Bug. 2001. (Illus.). (J). 16.85 (978-0-8027-8800-9(9)) Walker & Co.

Book Company Staff. Be Bop Bugs. 2003. (Novelty Bks.). (J). 15.95 (978-1-74047-329-3(9)) Book Co. Publishing Pty, Ltd., The AUS. *Dist:* Penton Overseas, Inc.

—Busy Bugs. 2003. (Puzzles Ser.). (Illus.). (J). bds. 10.95 (978-1-74047-335-4(3)) Book Co. Publishing Pty, Ltd., The AUS. *Dist:* Penton Overseas, Inc.

—Counting. 2003. (Bug Chunkie Board Bks.). (Illus.). (J). bds. 2.95 (978-1-74047-346-0(9)) Book Co. Publishing Pty, Ltd., The AUS. *Dist:* Penton Overseas, Inc.

—Percival the Plain Little Caterpillar. Brawley, Helen, illus. 2005. (Sparkle Bks.). 16p. (J). (gr. 4-11). bds. 12.95 (978-1-74047-109-1(1)) Book Co. Publishing Pty, Ltd., The AUS. *Dist:* Penton Overseas, Inc.

Book Company Staff & Turner, Jill. Percival the Plain Little Caterpillar. 2005. (Sparkle Books Minis Ser.). (Illus.). 16p. (J). (gr. 3-9). bds. 7.95 (978-1-74047-576-1(3) , Penton Kids) Penton Overseas, Inc.

Bosca, Francesca. The Three Grasshoppers. Ferri, Giuliano, illus. 2006. 32p. (J). 16.50 (978-1-933327-14-3(6)); 15.95 (978-1-933327-13-6(8)) Purple Bear Bks., Inc.

Boulter, Steve, illus. Busy Bugs. 2007. (Rattle Bks.). 8p. (J). (ps). bds. 4.99 (***978-0-7641-6075-2(3)***) Barron's Educational Series, Inc.

Box, Marty & McKenna, Allen. The Little Red Beetle Goes Shopping. Box, Marty, illus. 2005. (ENG., Illus.). 40p. pap. (***978-1-84401-521-4(1)***) Athena Pr.

Brandt-Taylor, Diane. The Bunny, the Bear, the Bug & the Bee. Brandt, Michael, illus. 2005. (J). cd-rom 9.88 (978-0-9773236-0-9(9)) TaySysCo Publishing.

Breckenridge, Trula & Lynch, Todd. Ricca the Ladybug. Breckenridge, Trula & Lynch, Todd, illus. 2004. (J). per. (978-0-9749480-8-9(X) , MSPpress) Mama Specific Productions.

Brereton, Shannon. Story Rids: Treat Me Wrong & You'll Put Me in a Jar? 1998. (Illus.). 32p. (J). (gr. 1-3). pap. 7.50 (978-0-8059-4422-8(2)) Dorrance Publishing Co., Inc.

Brown, Margaret Wise. I Like Bugs. Karas, G. Brian, illus. 1999. (Road to Reading Ser.). 32p. (J). (ps-1). pap. 3.99 (978-0-307-26107-6(7) , Random Hse. Bks. for Young Readers) Random Hse. Children's Bks.

—I Like Bugs. 1999. (ps-2). lib. bdg. 11.80 (978-0-613-27895-9(X)) Tandem Library Bks.

Bryant, Megan E. & Blau, Judith. Meet the Mudsters. Nunn, Paul E., illus. 2008. 32p. (J). (gr. 1-4). 7.99 (***978-0-448-44822-0(X)*** , Grosset & Dunlap) Penguin Group (USA) Inc.

Bug Business. 2002. (Illus.). (J). pap. (978-0-7398-5138-8(1)) Steck-Vaughn.

The Bug Guy. Date not set. 9.95 (978-0-89868-285-4(1)); pap. 3.95 (978-0-89868-284-7(3)) ARO Publishing Co.

Bugs & Other Stories: Individual Title Six-Pack. (Story Steps Ser.). (gr. k-2). 48.00 (978-0-7635-9616-3(7)) Rigby Education.

Bug's Life. 1999. 32p. (J). 3.99 (978-0-7364-1027-4(9)) Mouse Works.

Bugtime Adventures - Blessing in Disguise. 2005. (J). 3.95 (978-1-933262-26-0(5)) Lightning Bug Flix.

Bugz. 2002. (Illus.). (J). pap. (978-0-7398-5137-1(3)) Steck-Vaughn.

Burton, Margie, et al. Counting Insects. Adams, Alison, ed. 1999. (Early Connections Ser.). 16p. (J). (gr. k-2). pap. 4.50 (978-1-58344-059-9(3)) Benchmark Education Co.

Butterworth, MyLinda & Day, Linda S. Frogazoom! Day, Linda S., illus. l.t. ed. 2003. (Illus.). 32p. (J). (gr. k-3). 16.95 (978-1-890905-03-3(8) , Eco Fiction Bks.) Day to Day Enterprises.

The Cake: Individual Title Six-Packs. (Story Steps Ser.). (gr. k-2). 29.00 (978-0-7635-9601-9(9)) Rigby Education.

Campbell, Rod. Colour Bugs. 2003. (Illus.). 10p. (J). bds. 4.95 (978-0-333-73338-7(X)) Macmillan Publishers Ltd. GBR. *Dist:* Trafalgar Square Publishing.

—Counting Bugs. 1999. (Illus.). 12p. (J). 6.99 (978-0-333-73337-0(1)) Macmillan Publishers Ltd. GBR. *Dist:* Independent Pubs. Group.

Capeci, Anne. Insect Invaders. 2001. (gr. 3-6). lib. bdg. 11.80 (978-0-613-63304-8(0)) Tandem Library Bks.

Capeci, Anne & Speirs, John. Insect Invaders. 2001. 87p. (J). pap. (978-0-439-26551-5(7)) Scholastic, Inc.

Carle, Eric. Coccinelle Mal Lune. pap. 18.95 (978-2-87142-287-7(7)) Mijade Editions BEL. *Dist:* Distribooks, Inc.

—Piccolo Ragno Tesse e Tace. pap. 18.95 (978-88-04-33198-8(4)) Mondadori ITA. *Dist:* Distribooks, Inc.

—The Very Clumsy Click Beetle. Carle, Eric, illus. 1999. (Illus.). 32p. (J). (ps-3). 21.99 (978-0-399-23201-5(X) , Philomel) Penguin Group (USA) Inc.

—The Very Little Library: The Very Hungry Caterpillar, The Very Lonely Firefly, The Very Busy Spider. Carle, Eric, illus. 2002. (Illus.). 1p. (J). (ps-1). bds. 34.99 (978-0-399-24204-5(X) , Philomel) Penguin Group (USA) Inc.

Carter. Fun Bug Pack. 1998. (J). 17.97 (978-0-689-82615-3(X) , Little Simon) Simon & Schuster Children's Publishing.

Carter, David A. Alpha Bugs: A Pop-Up Alphabet. Carter, David A., illus. ed. 2006. (Illus.). 28p. (J). (ps-2). 11.95 (978-1-4169-0973-6(7) , Little Simon) Simon & Schuster Children's Publishing.

—Bugs Novelty, Bk. 3. 1999. (Illus.). (978-0-689-81861-5(0) , Little Simon) Simon & Schuster Children's Publishing.

—Chanukah Bugs: A Pop-up Celebration. Carter, David A., illus. 2002. (Illus.). 16p. (J). (ps-2). 10.95 (978-0-689-81860-8(2) , Little Simon) Simon & Schuster Children's Publishing.

—Feely Bugs: To Touch & Feel. Carter, David A., illus. ed. 2005. (Illus.). 14p. (J). (ps-ps). pap. 9.99 (978-1-4169-0326-0(7) , Little Simon) Simon & Schuster Children's Publishing.

—Giggle Bugs: A Lift-&-Laugh Book. 1999. (Illus.). 32p. (gr. k-3). per. 12.95 (978-0-689-82717-4(2) , Simon & Schuster Children's Publishing) Simon & Schuster Children's Publishing.

—Giggle Bugs: A Lift-and-Laugh Book. Carter, David A., illus. 1999. (Bugs in a Box Bks.). (Illus.). 20p. (J). (ps-2). 13.95 (978-0-689-81859-2(9) , Little Simon) Simon & Schuster Children's Publishing.

—Jingle Bugs: A Merry Pop-up Book with Lights & Music! Carter, David A., illus. 2004. (Illus.). 22p. (J). pap. 10.95 (978-0-689-87416-1(2) , Little Simon) Simon & Schuster Children's Publishing.

—Love Bugs. Carter, David A., illus. ed. 2003. (Illus.). 12p. (J). (gr. k-3). 6.99 (978-0-689-85815-4(9) , Little Simon) Simon & Schuster Children's Publishing.

—Peekaboo Bugs: A Hide-and-Seek Book by David A. Carter. Carter, David A., illus. 2002. (Bugs in a Box Bks.). (Illus.). 10p. (J). (ps-k). 13.95 (978-0-689-85035-6(2) , Little Simon) Simon & Schuster Children's Publishing.

—The 12 Bugs of Christmas: A Pop up Christmas Counting Book. Carter, David A., illus. 1999. (Bugs in a Box Books Ser.). (Illus.). 12p. (J). (ps-k). 14.95 (978-0-689-83104-1(8) , Little Simon) Simon & Schuster Children's Publishing.

Chadwick, Robert. Vengeful Impulse. 2003. (gr. 7-12). lib. bdg. 17.60 (978-0-613-83499-5(2)) Tandem Library Bks.

Chronicle Books LLC Staff. Paleo Bugs. 2008. 48p. (J). 15.99 (978-0-8118-6022-2(1)) Chronicle Bks. LLC.

Clarke, Jane. Scratching's Catching! Kingfisher Editors, ed. Lewis, Jan, illus. 2007. (I Am Reading Ser.). 48p. (J). (gr. k-3). pap. 3.95 (978-0-7534-5958-4(2) , Kingfisher) Houghton Mifflin Co. Trade & Reference Div.

Clifton, Dorinda. Ginger Bird & the Big Bad Bug with the Hard, Hard Heart. 2006. (J). 6.95 (978-0-9771973-1-6(X)) Bedbug Pr., Inc.

Coleman, Candace. Zubie the Lightning Bug - I Want to Remember Your Thoughts. ed. 2006. (J). 15.99 (978-0-9774998-0-9(4)) Parent Brigade Company, The.

Coman, Carolyn. Bee & Jacky. 2006. 104p. pap. 9.95 (978-1-932425-37-6(3) , Lemniscaat) Boyds Mills Pr.

Connelly, Wendy. Fiona the Firefly! 2003. (Illus.). (J). 12.95 (978-1-929039-16-6(6)) Ambassador Bks., Inc.

Contijoch, Josefa. Mariquilla en la Nieve. Filella, Lluis, illus. 2003. (Caballo Alado Ser.). (SPA & ENG.). 24p. 6.95 (978-84-7864-647-0(7)) Combel Editorial, S.A. ESP. *Dist:* Independent Pubs. Group.

—Mariquilla va de Fiesta. Filella, Lluis, illus. 2003. (Caballo Alado Ser.). (SPA & ENG.). 24p. 6.95 (978-84-7864-648-7(5)) Combel Editorial, S.A. ESP. *Dist:* Independent Pubs. Group.

—Mariquilla y el Pino. Filella, Lluis, illus. 2003. (Caballo Alado Ser.). (SPA & ENG.). 24p. 6.95 (978-84-7864-645-6(0)) Combel Editorial, S.A. ESP. *Dist:* Independent Pubs. Group.

Copeland, Mark. The Bundle at Blackthorpe Heath. 2006. (Illus.). 208p. (J). (gr. 5). 15.00 (978-0-618-56302-9(4)) Houghton Mifflin Co.

Cosgrove, Stephen. Bee Double Bopp: Respecting Others. Arroyo, Fian, illus. 2004. (J). (978-1-58804-350-4(9)) PCI Educational Publishing.

—Big Bubba Bigg, Jr: Dealing with Bullies. Arroyo, Fian, illus. 2004. (J). (978-1-58804-352-8(5)) PCI Educational Publishing.

—The Bigg Family: Getting along with Others. Arroyo, Fian, illus. 2004. (J). (978-1-58804-354-2(1)) PCI Educational Publishing.

—The Bugglar Brothers: Consequences of Stealing. Arroyo, Fian, illus. 2007. (J). (978-1-58804-381-8(9)) PCI Educational Publishing.

—Cricket Clickett: Finding Your Talents. Arroyo, Fian, illus. 2004. (J). (978-1-58804-382-5(7)) PCI Educational Publishing.

—Flutterby Fly. 2001. (Orig.). (gr. k-3). lib. bdg. 13.00 (978-0-613-35688-6(8)) Tandem Library Bks.

—Flynn "Flea" Flicker: Sticking to the Truth. Arroyo, Fian, illus. 2004. (J). (978-1-58804-353-5(3)) PCI Educational Publishing.

—Hickory B. Hopp: Paying Attention. Arroyo, Fian, illus. 2004. (J). (978-1-58804-379-5(7)) PCI Educational Publishing.

—Hucklebug. James, Robin, illus. rev. ed. 2001. (Serendipity Bks.). 1p. (J). pap. 4.99 (978-0-8431-7649-0(0) , Price Stern Sloan) Penguin Group (USA) Inc.

—Hucklebug. 2001. (gr. k-3). lib. bdg. 13.00 (978-0-613-85011-7(4)) Tandem Library Bks.

—Katy Didd Bigg: Standing up for Yourself. Arroyo, Fian, illus. 2004. (J). (978-1-58804-378-8(9)) PCI Educational Publishing.

—Melody Moth: Practice Makes Perfect. Arroyo, Fian, illus. 2004. (J). (978-1-58804-351-1(7)) PCI Educational Publishing.

—Mizz Buggly: Doing Your Best. Arroyo, Fian, illus. 2004. (J). (978-1-58804-380-1(0)) PCI Educational Publishing.

—Snugg N. Flitter: Facing Your Fears. Arroyo, Fian, illus. 2004. (J). (978-1-58804-377-1(0)) PCI Educational Publishing.

Cosgrove, Stephen & James, Robin. Flutterby Fly. rev. ed. 2001. (Serendipity Bks.). (Illus.). 1p. (Orig.). (J). pap. 4.99 (978-0-8431-7662-9(8) , Price Stern Sloan) Penguin Group (USA) Inc.

Cronin, Doreen. Diary of a Fly. Bliss, Harry, illus. 2007. 40p. (J). (ps-3). 15.99 ***(978-0-06-000156-8(9));*** lib. bdg. 16.89 ***(978-0-06-000157-5(7))*** HarperCollins Pubs. (Cotler, Joanna Books).

Cronin, Doreen. Diary of a Spider. Bliss, Harry, illus. 2005. 40p. (J). (ps-3). 15.99 (978-0-06-000153-7(4)); lib. bdg. 16.89 (978-0-06-000154-4(2)) HarperCollins Pubs. (Cotler, Joanna Books).

—Diary of a Spider. Bliss, Harry, illus. unabr. ed. 2006. (Picture Book Readalong Ser.). (J). (ps-3). 25.95 incl. audio (978-1-59519-482-4(7)); 28.95 incl. audio compact disk (978-1-59519-486-2(X)) Live Oak Media.

—Diary of a Spider. Bliss, Harry, illus. unabr. ed. 2006. (J). (ps-3). 24.95 incl. audio ***(978-0-439-90573-2(7));*** 29.95 incl. audio compact disk ***(978-0-439-90579-4(6))*** Weston Woods Studios, Inc.

Crowley, Ned. Ugh!, a Bug. 2005. (Silly Millies Ser.). 32p. (J). (ps-4). pap. 4.99 (978-0-7613-2475-1(5) , First Avenue Editions) Lerner Publishing Group.

—Ugh! a Bug! 2005. (Silly Millies Ser.). (Illus.). 32p. (J). (ps-ps). lib. bdg. 18.60 (978-0-7613-3450-7(5) , Millbrook Pr.) Lerner Publishing Group.

Cummings, Catherine M. A Flea's Lament. Conner, Wendy Simpson, illus. 2002. (Flea Books: Vol. 1). 24p. (J). (ps-2). pap. 7.95 (978-0-9725155-0-4(X)) Junibird Productions.

Cushman, Doug. Inspector Hopper. Cushman, Doug, illus. 2000. (I Can Read Bks.). (Illus.). 64p. (J). (gr. k-3). 14.95 (978-0-06-028382-7(3)) HarperCollins Pubs.

Daddy Is a Doodlebug Doodle Pad. 2000. (J). (978-0-06-029068-9(4)) HarperCollins Pubs.

D'Agata, Tabatha. Ick the Stick. Croxcatto, Maria Ivana, tr. Lineberger, Judy, illus. 2007. (Yes, I Can Read! Ser.: 1). 24p. (J). 6.95 ***(978-1-934138-01-4(0))*** Bouncing Ball Bks., Inc.

Dahl, Roald. James & the Giant Peach. Blake, Quentin, illus. 2002. (J). 13.19 (978-0-7587-6619-9(X)) Book Wholesalers, Inc.

—James & the Giant Peach. 2001. (gr. 3-6). lib. bdg. 14.15 (978-0-613-35965-8(8)); (Illus.). (J). 12.64 (978-0-606-20734-8(1)) Tandem Library Bks.

The Daisy Bug Kids Say Hello New York. 2004. (J). (978-0-9712349-2-5(2)) Univ. At Buffalo, Child Care Ctr.

Dakos, Kalli. The Bug in Teacher's Coffee: And Other School Poems. Reed, Mike, illus. 2002. (I Can Read Bks.: Bk. 2). 48p. (J). (gr. k-3). pap. 3.99 (978-0-06-444305-0(1)) HarperCollins Pubs.

Dargon, J. Beetle & Lady Bug. 2005. 48p. pap. 12.95 (978-1-4137-6701-8(X)) PublishAmerica, Inc.

Day, Robert O. & Day, Linda S. There's a Frog on a Log in the Bog. Day, Linda S., illus. 2003. (Just So Wild Ser.: Vol. 1). (Illus.). (J). (gr. 3-6). 212p. pap. 8.95 (978-1-890905-50-7(X)); 14.95 (978-1-890905-51-4(8)) Day to Day Enterprises. (Eco Fiction Bks.).

De Vicq de Cumptich, Roberto. Counting Insects. Date not set. (J). 15.95 (978-0-8050-6560-2(1) , Holt, Henry & Co. Bks. For Young Readers) Holt, Henry & Co.

Deem, Saitofi Anne. Myrtle Learns about Lice. 1998. (Teachable Moments Ser.). (Illus.). 12p. (J). (ps-3). pap. 7.95 (978-1-930694-11-8(3)) Myrtle Learns.

DeMatteis, J.M. Stardust Kid. 2008. (Stardust Kind Ser. : Ser.). (Illus.). 128p. pap. 14.99 ***(978-1-934506-04-2(4))*** Boom! Studios.

Depisco, Dorothea. Beetle Bugs Party: A Counting Book. Parry, Jo, illus. 2005. 10p. (J). (ps-ps). 10.95 (978-1-58117-415-1(2) , Intervisual/Piggy Toes) Dalmatian Pr.

Derrick, Patricia. Sly the Dragonfly. 2007. 32p. 18.95 (978-1-933818-16-0(6)) Animalations.

DeSica, Melissa. Gecko & Mosquito. Desica, Melissa, illus. 2007. (J). 14.95 ***(978-0-9790647-6-0(7))*** Watermark Publishing, LLC.

Disney Publishing Staff. The Big Bug Hunt, 15 vols. 2003. (It's Fun to Learn Ser.). (Illus.). 32p. (J). (ps-3). 3.99 (978-1-57973-139-7(2)) Advance Pubs. LLC.

Dodd, Lynley. Zachary Quack Minimonster. 2006. (Gold Star First Readers Ser.). (Illus.). 31p. (J). 22.00 (978-0-8368-6187-7(6)) Stevens, Gareth Inc.

Douglas, Babette. Rosebud. 2004. (J). 9.99 (978-1-890343-12-5(9)) Kiss A Me Productions, Inc.

Dragonfly Dreams & Other Stories: Individual Title Six-Pack. (Story Steps Ser.). (gr. k-2). 48.00 (978-0-7635-9843-3(7)) Rigby Education.

Durango, Julia. Pest Fest. Cyrus, Kurt, illus. 2007. 40p. (J). (ps-2). 16.99 ***(978-0-689-85569-6(9))*** Simon & Schuster Children's Publishing.

Edgecombe, Jane. Fly Away Home. Martin, Stuart, illus. 2003. (J). 15.95 (978-1-74047-152-7(0)) Book Co. Publishing Pty, Ltd., The AUS. *Dist:* Penton Overseas, Inc.

—What's Bugging You? Cassettari, Noeline, illus. 2002. (Touch & Feel Bk.). (J). 12.95 (978-1-74047-151-0(2)) Book Co. Publishing Pty, Ltd., The AUS. *Dist:* Penton Overseas, Inc.

—Whoops! 2003. (J). pap. 12.95 (978-1-74047-258-6(6)) Book Co. Publishing Pty, Ltd., The AUS. *Dist:* Penton Overseas, Inc.

Edwards, Frank B. Bug. Bianchi, John, illus. 2004. (Bug & Frogger Ser.). 144p. (J). (gr. 3-6). pap. 4.95 (978-1-894323-17-8(3)) Pokeweed Pr. CAN. *Dist:* Fitzhenry & Whiteside, Ltd.

—Snug As a Big Red Bug. Bianchi, John, illus. 1999. (New Reader Ser.). (J). (gr. k-1). Pokeweed Pr.

—Snug As a Big Red Bug. Bianchi, John, illus. 1999. (New Reader Ser.). 24p. (J). (ps-1). lib. bdg. 14.95 (978-1-894323-01-7(7)) Pokeweed Pr. CAN. *Dist:* Fitzhenry & Whiteside, Ltd.

—Snug As a Big Red Bug. 1999. (gr. k-3). lib. bdg. 12.95 (978-0-613-37045-5(7)); (Illus.). (J). (978-0-606-22038-5(0)) Tandem Library Bks.

Edwards, Frank B. & Bianchi, John. Bug. 2004. (Bug & Frogger Ser.). (Illus.). 144p. (J). (gr. 3-6). 14.95 (978-1-894323-18-5(1)) Pokeweed Pr. CAN. *Dist:* Fitzhenry & Whiteside, Ltd.

—Snug As a Big Red Bug. 1999. (New Reader Ser.). (Illus.). 24p. (J). (ps-1). pap. 4.95 (978-1-894323-00-0(9)) Pokeweed Pr. CAN. *Dist:* Fitzhenry & Whiteside, Ltd.

Efird, Carrie. Wiggly, Squiggly Bugs. Lent, Marion W., illus. l.t. ed. 1998. (Big Bks.). (J). (ps-k). pap. 10.95 (978-1-57332-117-4(6)) HighReach Learning, Inc.

Egielski, Richard. Buz. Egielski, Richard, illus. 1999. (Illus.). 32p. (J). (ps-2). pap. 6.99 (978-0-06-443479-9(6) , Harper Trophy) HarperCollins Pubs.

—Buz. 1999. (J). 13.79 (978-0-606-15842-8(1)); lib. bdg. 15.30 (978-0-613-11376-2(4)) Tandem Library Bks.

—Jazper. Egielski, Richard, illus. 1998. (Illus.). 32p. (J). (ps-2). 14.95 (978-0-06-027817-5(X)) HarperCollins Pubs.

Eliasen, Lorena. Chameleon & the Dragonfly: A Pop-Up Book. 2004. (Illus.). 12p. (J). pap. 16.95 (978-0-439-52320-2(6) , Orchard Bks.) Scholastic, Inc.

Elliott, David. The Transmogrification of Roscoe Wizzle. 2004. (Illus.). 128p. (J). (gr. 2-5). reprint ed. pap. 5.99 (978-0-7636-1880-3(2)) Candlewick Pr.

Fairchild, Simone. Queen Bee's Mystery in the Lilac Tree. Key, Pamela, illus. 2007. 42p. (J). per. 19.95 ***(978-0-9788985-7-1(5))*** A Better Be Write Pub.

Fernandezil, Vivian. Bugs in a Jug. McIntyre, Mark, illus. 1999. (Eyes on Science Ser.). (J). (gr. 1-6). 6.95 (978-1-58295-017-4(2) , Beehive Bk.) Pace Products, Inc.

Finn, Isobel. Very Lazy Ladybug. 2003. (ps-2). lib. bdg. 15.25 (978-0-613-84708-7(3)) Tandem Library Bks.

Five Little Ladybugs. 2005. 12p. (J). 14.95 (978-1-58117-218-8(4) , Intervisual/Piggy Toes) Dalmatian Pr.

Fleming, Denise. Beetle Bop. 2007. (Illus.). 32p. (J). (ps-2). 16.00 (978-0-15-205936-1(9)) Harcourt Trade Pubs.

Frederick, Cynthia. The Gray Beetle. 2005. 20p. 15.00 (978-1-4116-5732-8(2)) Lulu.com.

Freeman, Don. Manuelo, the Playing Mantis. McCue, Lisa, illus. 2004. 32p. (J). (ps-8). 15.99 (978-0-670-03684-4(6) , Viking Juvenile) Penguin Group (USA) Inc.

—Manuelo, the Playing Mantis. 2006. (Illus.). 32p. (J). reprint ed. pap. 5.99 (978-0-14-240560-4(4) , Puffin) Penguin Group (USA) Inc.

Frenkel, Yetti. The Big, Blue Lump. Frenkel, Yetti, illus. 2004. (Illus.). 32p. (J). 16.95 (978-0-9749006-0-5(5)) Snow Tree Bks.

Friedrich, Joachim. 4 1/2 Friends & the Secret Cave. 2001. 144p. (J). (gr. 4-7). lib. bdg. 15.49 (978-0-7868-2419-9(0)) Hyperion Pr.

Frontiera, Deborah K. The Re-Creation of Roacheria. 2nd ed. 2004. (Chronicles of Henry Roach-Dairier: Bk. 3). 247p. (YA). (gr. 5 up). per. 15.95 (978-0-9753410-3-2(0)) Jade Enterprises.

—To Build a Tunnel. 2nd ed. 2004. (Chronicles of Henry Roach-Dairier: Bk. 1). 218p. (YA). (gr. 5 up). per. 15.95 (978-0-9753410-1-8(4)) Jade Enterprises.

Funari Willever, Lisa. The Culprit Was a Fly: Theodore Meets His Match. Corsi, Adam, illus. 1998. (Theodore Ser.). 32p. (J). (ps-4). pap. 6.95 (978-1-889383-08-8(2)) Angel Pubns.

A Garden Circus. 2003. (J). 9.99 (978-0-9740847-5-6(1)) GiGi Bks.

Gerth, Melanie. Diez Pequeñas Mariquitas. Huliska-Beith, Laura, illus. 2005. Orig. Title: Ten Little Ladybugs. (SPA.). 22p. (J). (ps). 10.95 (978-1-58117-006-1(8) , Intervisual/Piggy Toes) Dalmatian Pr.

Gill, Janie S. The Blue Green Housefly. 2001. (Predictable Readers Ser.). (Illus.). (J). (gr. k-2). lib. bdg. 11.95 (978-0-89868-537-4(0)) ARO Publishing Co.

Godkin, Celia. What about Ladybugs? 1998. (J). (978-0-606-13894-9(3)) Tandem Library Bks.

Gollub, Matthew. The Jazz Fly. Hanke, Karen, illus. 2000. 32p. (J). (ps-1). 17.95 incl. audio compact disk (978-1-889910-17-8(1)) Tortuga Pr.

Goodnight, Little Bug & Wheres the Chick? 2005. (J). bds. 19.99 (978-0-9767325-8-7(0)) Toy Quest.

Gran, Julia. Big Bug Surprise. 2007. 32p. (J). (ps-3). pap. 12.99 (978-0-439-67609-0(6) , Scholastic Pr.) Scholastic, Inc.

Grasshopper Learns a Lesson: Second Grade Guided Reading Level L. (On Our Way to English Ser.). (gr. 2 up). 34.50 (978-0-7578-7101-6(1)) Rigby Education.

Graves, Sue. Bug in a Rug. 2007. (Fun with Phonics Ser.). 20p. (J). pap. 4.99 ***(978-0-439-02550-8(8))*** Scholastic, Inc.

Gray, Nigel. Fly. Smith, Craig, illus. 32p. (J). 18.95 (978-1-875560-39-4(4)) Univ. of Western Australia Pr. AUS. *Dist:* International Specialized Bk. Services.

Greban, Quentin. Mommy, I Love You. 2005. (Illus.). 28p. (ps-3). 9.95 (978-1-59687-184-7(9) , Milk & Cookies) ibooks, Inc.

Greenberg, David T. Bugs! Munsinger, Lynn, illus. 2002. 32p. (J). (ps-3). pap. 6.99 (978-0-316-35576-6(3)) Little, Brown Bks. for Young Readers.

Greenburg, J. C. In the Kitchen. 2002. (Andrew Lost Ser.: Bk. 3). (Illus.). 96p. (J). (gr. 2-5). lib. bdg. 11.99 (978-0-375-91279-5(7) , Random Hse. Bks. for Young Readers) Random Hse. Children's Bks.

—In the Kitchen. Palen, Debbie, illus. 2002. (Andrew Lost Ser.: Bk. 3). 96p. (J). (gr. 2-5). pap. 3.99 (978-0-375-81279-8(2) , Random Hse. Bks. for Young Readers) Random Hse. Children's Bks.

—In the Kitchen. 2002. (Andrew Lost Ser.: Bk. 3). (J). (gr. 3-6). lib. bdg. 11.80 (978-0-613-86248-6(1)) Tandem Library Bks.

Groat, Deborah. Bugs in My Back Yard. Senesi, Susan, illus. 2000. 32p. (J). (ps-5). pap. 9.95 (978-1-56167-632-3(2) , Five Star Special Edition) American Literary Pr.

Group/McGraw-Hill, Wright. Bugs don't Bug Me: Level K, 6 vols., Vol. 2. (First Explorers Ser.). 24p. (gr. 1-2). 34.95 (978-0-7699-1455-8(1)) Shortland Pubns. (U. S. A.) Inc.

Hall, John. Jeffrey Takes on the World. 2005. 48p. pap. 12.95 (978-1-4137-9832-6(2)) PublishAmerica, Inc.

Hamilton, Leo. Leo Hamilton's Odd Collection of Animal & Insect Stories. Larkin, Jessica, illus. l.t. ed. (J). (ps-5). Vol. I. 2000. 36p. pap. 7.99 (978-0-9671660-0-1(4)); Vol. II. 2000. 40p. pap. 8.99 (978-0-9671660-1-8(2)); Vol. III. 2002. 24p. pap. 8.99 (978-0-9671660-3-2(9)) Story Place, The.

Hanson, Warren. Bugtown Boogie. 2008. 32p. (J). 16.99 ***(978-0-06-059937-9(5));*** lib. bdg. 17.89 ***(978-0-06-059938-6(3))*** HarperCollins Pubs. (Geringer, Laura Book).

Harcourt School Publishers Staff. A Bug & a Pup: Below Level. 3rd ed. 2002. (Trophies Reading Program Ser.). (Illus.). (J). pap. 3.20 (978-0-15-322947-3(0)) Harcourt Schl. Pubs.

—A Bug Needs a Home: Independent Reader. 3rd ed. 2002. (Trophies Reading Program Ser.). (Illus.). (J). pap. 2.90 (978-0-15-325487-1(4)) Harcourt Schl. Pubs.

—Bug Surprises: Theme Book. 1999. (Collections Ser.). (Illus.). (J). pap. 3.00 (978-0-15-314027-3(5)) Harcourt Schl. Pubs.

—Fly Ladybug, Fly Below Level. 3rd ed. 2002. (Trophies Reading Program Ser.). (Illus.). pap. 5.10 (978-0-15-323048-6(7)) Harcourt Schl. Pubs.

—Invent an Insect Advanced Level. 3rd ed. 2002. (Trophies Reading Program Ser.). (Illus.). pap. 5.10 (978-0-15-323019-6(3)) Harcourt Schl. Pubs.

—Trofeos Advanced Level: Que Mira Topi? 3rd ed. 2002. (SPA., Illus.). pap. 5.50 (978-0-15-323919-9(0)) Harcourt Schl. Pubs.

—Trofeos Below Level: Goni y Chispa. 3rd ed. 2002. (SPA., Illus.). (J). pap. 3.50 (978-0-15-323858-1(5)) Harcourt Schl. Pubs.

—What Can Matt Do? Advanced Level. 3rd ed. 2002. (Trophies Reading Program Ser.). (Illus.). (J). pap. 3.70 (978-0-15-323008-0(8)) Harcourt Schl. Pubs.

Harrison, Paul. Hmm, que rica mosca, Level P. Worsley, Belinda, illus. 2006. (Lightning Readers Ser.). 32p. (J). pap. 3.95 (978-0-7696-4228-4(4) , Gingham Dog Pr.) School Specialty Publishing.

—Yummy, Yummy Fly. Worsley, Belinda, illus. 2006. (Lightning Readers Ser.). 32p. (J). (ps-k). pap. 3.95 (978-0-7696-4198-0(9) , Gingham Dog Pr.) School Specialty Publishing.

Harter, Gage. Sly the Fly: The Doctor's Office. Teich, Melle, illus. 2003. 16p. (J). 7.95 (978-1-59466-009-2(3) , Little Ones) Port Town Publishing.

Harvey, Jane. Busy Bugs: A Book about Patterns. 2003. (gr. k-3). lib. bdg. 11.80 (978-0-613-67531-4(2)) Tandem Library Bks.

Hawley, Greg. Don't Let the Bedbugs Bite. Regan, Dana, illus. 2004. (J). (978-0-9657612-7-7(4)) Paddle Wheel Publishing.

Hayes, Cheri. There's a Louse in My House: A Kid's Story about Head Lice. Gosselin, Kim, ed. Dineen, Tom, illus. 2001. (Healthy Habits for Kids Ser.: Vol. 1). 24p. (J). (ps-5). pap. 6.95 (978-1-891383-10-6(8)) JayJo Bks., LLC.

Heiner, Garth Farr. Look Out Below. Melander, Eric, illus. l.t. unabr. ed. 2001. (Fun-with-the-Law Ser.: No. 6). 32p. (J). (gr. k-7). pap. 5.95 (978-1-929905-06-5(8)) Fun With the Law, Inc.

Hensley, Terri Anne. The silliest bug & insect book Ever. 2007. (J). per. 6.95 ***(978-0-9789057-7-4(6))*** Huntington Ludlow Media Group.

Hilario. Beetle's Short Cut. 2006. (Stories for Smaller Kids Ser.). (Illus.). 16p. (J). bds. 5.95 (978-9974-7925-6-2(8)) Hardenville SA URY. *Dist:* Independent Pubs. Group.

Hino, Hideshi. The Bug Boy No. 2: Hino Horror: A Graphic Novel. Hino, Hideshi, illus. 2005. (Illus.). 204p. (YA). (gr. 4-9). reprint ed. pap. 10.00 (978-0-7567-9709-6(8)) DIANE Publishing Co.

Holm, Jennifer L. & Hamel, Jonathan. You Only Have Nine Lives. Weinman, Brad, illus. 2005. (Stink Files Ser.). 144p. (J). lib. bdg. 15.89 (978-0-06-052986-4(5)) HarperCollins Pubs.

Hood, Susan. Caterpillar Spring, Butterfly Summer. Gévry, Claudine, illus. 2003. 10p. (J). (gr. k-3). bds. 12.99 (978-0-7944-0149-8(X) , Reader's Digest Children's Bks.) Reader's Digest Children's Publishing, Inc.

Hooker, Karen. Look! Bugs... Durney, Ryan, illus. 1999. 8p. (J). (gr. k-2). pap. 3.75 (978-1-58323-002-2(5) , Seedling Pubns.) Continental Pr., Inc.

La Hormiga y el Saltamontes: Lap Book. (Pebble Soup Exploraciones Ser.). (SPA.). 16p. (ps up). 21.00 (978-0-7578-1682-6(7)) Rigby Education.

La hormiga y el Saltamontes: Small Book. (Pebble Soup Exploraciones Ser.). (SPA.). 16p. (ps up). 5.00 (978-0-7578-1722-9(X)) Rigby Education.

Horowitz, Ruth. Breakout at the Bug Lab. Holub, Joan, illus. 2002. (Easy-to-Read, Puffin Ser.). 48p. (J). pap. 3.99 (978-0-14-230200-2(7) , Puffin) Penguin Group (USA) Inc.

—Breakout at the Bug Lab. 2001. (Illus.). 48p. (J). (gr. k-3). 13.99 (978-0-8037-2510-2(8) , Dial) Penguin Group (USA) Inc.

Hull, Donna L. Wally WaddleSnout & the Peppermint Race! Smith, Geoffrey P., illus. l.t. ed. 2001. 32p. (J). (ps-5). 13.95 (978-0-9710017-0-1(7)) TDH Bks.

I Can Fly: Individual Title Six-Pack Pouch - Level C. (Lighthouse Ser.). 12p. (gr. k-1). 24.00 (978-0-7578-0821-0(2)) Rigby Education.

Jackson, Donna M. The Bug Scientists. 2004. (Scientists in the Field Ser.). (Illus.). 48p. (J). (gr. 4-6). pap. 5.95 (978-0-618-43232-5(9)) Houghton Mifflin Co. Trade & Reference Div.

Jackson, Tyrone. Save Our Home. 2006. (ENG.). 88p. per. 14.95 ***(978-1-4241-0875-6(6))*** PublishAmerica, Inc.

James, Ian. Why Mosquitos Buzz in People's Ears: A Folktale from West Africa. 2006. spiral bd. 42.00 ***(978-1-4108-7161-9(4))*** Benchmark Education Co.

Janssen, Charlotta. The Secret of Three Butterpillars: A Never Ending Tale. 2001. (Illus.). 18p. (J). 12.95 (978-0-7611-2113-8(7) , 12113) Workman Publishing Co., Inc.

Jenkins, Amanda. Mutant Bugs. 2005. 22.00 ***(978-1-4108-4219-0(3))*** Benchmark Education Co.

Johnston, Tony. Sparky & Eddie: Trouble with Rats. Ryan, Susannah, illus. 32p. (J). 1999. op-p. 4.95 (978-0-590-47981-3(4)); 1998. 13.95 (978-0-590-47980-6(0)) Scholastic, Inc.

Jordan, Apple. Bug Stew! 2003. (gr. k-3). lib. bdg. 11.80 (978-0-613-73701-2(6)) Tandem Library Bks.

Joyce, William. Leaf Men & the Brave Good Bugs. 2001. (gr. k-3). lib. bdg. 15.25 (978-0-613-35969-6(0)) Tandem Library Bks.

Kamau, G. Why Beetles Roll Cowdung. 2004. 18p. 13.95 (978-9966-25-167-1(7)) Heinemann Kenya, Limited (East African Educational Publishers Ltd E.A.E.P.) KEN. *Dist:* Michigan State Univ. Pr.

Kamke, Bridget. The Story of the Infinipede. Ospital, Genev-eive, illus. 2003. (J). 19.95 (978-0-9744306-0-7(9)) You Can Do It! Productions.

Kelly, Theresa. Tony the Pony: Bugs Are Not Bad. Sampson, Jody, illus. 2005. (J). per. 7.95 (978-1-59466-030-6(1)) Port Town Publishing.

Kent, Jack. The Caterpillar & the Polliwog. Kent, Jack, illus. 2002. (Illus.). (J). 14.43 (978-0-7587-2206-5(0)) Book Wholesalers, Inc.

—The Caterpillar & the Polliwog. 2004. (J). (ps-3). pap. 14.95 incl. audio (978-0-89719-762-5(3) , PBC312) Weston Woods Studios, Inc.

Kimmel, Eric A. Bernal & Florinda: A Spanish Tale. Rayevsky, Robert, illus. 2004. 29p. (J). (gr. k-4). reprint ed. 16.00 (978-0-7567-7906-1(5)) DIANE Publishing Co.

Kirk, David. Bedtime Story/David Kirk. 2006. (Illus.). 32p. (J). ***(978-1-4156-8869-4(9)); (*978-0-448-44514-4(X))*** Penguin Group (USA) Inc.

—Captain Sunny Patch. 2006. (Illus.). 32p. (J). ***(*978-1-4156-8868-7(0)); (*978-0-448-44515-1(8))*** Callaway Editions, Inc.

—Cry Buggie. 2006. (Miss Spider Ser.). (Illus.). 32p. (J). (ps-1). 6.99 (978-0-448-44427-7(5)) Callaway Editions, Inc.

—Eight Legs Up. 2006. (Miss Spider Ser.). (Illus.). 32p. (J). pap. 6.99 (978-0-448-44426-0(7)) Callaway Editions, Inc.

—Humbug! 2006. (Miss Spider Ser.). (Illus.). 32p. (J). (ps-1). 17.99 (978-0-448-44428-4(3)) Callaway Editions, Inc.

—Little Miss Spider. (Miss Spider Ser.). (J). 2003. (Illus.). 32p. pap. 5.99 (978-0-439-54315-6(0)); 1999. 155.40 (978-0-439-11737-1(2)) Scholastic, Inc.

—Little Miss Spider. Kirk, David, illus. 1999. (Miss Spider Ser.). (Illus.). 32p. (J). (ps-2). pap. 12.95 (978-0-439-08389-8(3)) Scholastic, Inc.

—Little Miss Spider at Sunny Patch School. Kirk, David, illus. (Miss Spider Ser.). (Illus.). 32p. (J). 2003. pap. 5.99 (978-0-439-54316-3(9)); 2000. pap. 12.95 (978-0-439-08727-8(9)) Scholastic, Inc.

—Little Miss Spider at Sunnypatch School. Kirk, David, illus. 2002. (Little Miss Spider Ser.). (Illus.). (J). 21.85 (978-0-7587-3008-4(X)) Book Wholesalers, Inc.

—Miss Spider Boxset: The Counting Book; New Car; ABC. 2003. (Illus.). (J). 12.95 (978-0-439-54317-0(7)) Scholastic, Inc.

—Miss Spider's ABC. Kirk, David, illus. 1998. (Miss Spider Ser.). (Illus.). 32p. (J). (ps-2). pap. 16.95 (978-0-590-28279-6(4)) Scholastic, Inc.

—Miss Spider's ABC: New Board Book Edition. Kirk, David, illus. 2000. (Miss Spider Ser.). (Illus.). 32p. (J). (ps-2). bds. 8.95 (978-0-439-13747-8(0) , Scholastic Reference) Scholastic, Inc.

—Miss Spider's New Car. Kirk, David, illus. 1999. (Miss Spider Ser.). (Illus.). 32p. (J). (ps-2). bds. 8.95 (978-0-439-04675-6(0)) Scholastic, Inc.

—Top O' Big Tree. 2006. (Miss Spider Ser.). (Illus.). 32p. (J). 6.99 (978-0-448-44120-7(9) , Grosset & Dunlap) Penguin Group (USA) Inc.

Kitten chased a Fly 6 Packs. Individual Title. (gr. 1-2). 22.00 (978-0-7635-9163-2(7)) Rigby Education.

Klier, Kimberly Wagner & Dobkin, Bonnie. Bug. 2006. 96p. (J). (gr. 1-2). 8.95 (978-0-516-25385-5(9) , Children's Pr.) Scholastic Library Publishing.

Kline, Suzy. Horrible Harry & the Ant Invasion. 1998. (Horrible Harry Ser.: No. 2). (Illus.). 64p. (J). (gr. 2-4). pap. 3.99 (978-0-14-130082-5(5) , Puffin) Penguin Group (USA) Inc.

Kompelien, Tracy. Fly Paper. Haberstroh, Anne, illus. (Fact & Fiction Ser.). 24p. (J). 2007. 21.35 (978-1-59928-438-5(3)); 2006. (978-1-59928-439-2(1)) ABDO Publishing Co.

Krings, Antoon. Abeja Teresa. 2005. (Bichitos curiosos Ser.). (SPA., Illus.). 32p. (J). 5.95 (978-84-932442-7-9(9)) Blume ESP. *Dist:* Independent Pubs. Group.

—Duendecillo Membrillo. 2005. (Bichitos curiosos Ser.). (SPA., Illus.). 32p. (J). 5.95 (978-84-932442-6-2(0)) Blume ESP. *Dist:* Independent Pubs. Group.

—Gilberto Mariposa. 2005. (Bichitos curiosos Ser.). (SPA., Illus.). 32p. (J). 5.95 (978-84-932442-9-3(5)) Blume ESP. *Dist:* Independent Pubs. Group.

Langham, Tony. Creepy Crawly Calypso. Harter, Debbie, illus. 2004. 32p. (J). 16.99 incl. audio compact disk (978-1-84148-699-4(X)) Barefoot Bks., Inc.

Langham, Tony & Harter, Debbie. Creepy Crawly Calypso. 2006. 32p. pap. 9.99 incl. cd-rom (978-1-902283-46-3(5)) Barefoot Bks., Inc.

Langner-Urso, Denise. Jeffrey's Journey with the Wind. 2005. 78p. pap. 14.95 (978-1-4137-4112-4(6)) PublishAmerica, Inc.

Lawler, Janet. A Mama Bug's Love. Peterson, Rick, illus. 2006. (Preschool Pop-Ups Ser.). 14p. (J). 7.99 (978-1-4169-1548-5(6) , Little Simon) Simon & Schuster Children's Publishing.

Layton, Neal. Bartholomew & the Bug. 2006. (Illus.). (J). (ps). 14.99 (978-0-340-87328-1(0)); pap. 9.99 (978-0-340-87329-8(9)) Hodder General Publishing Division GBR. (Hodder & Stoughton). *Dist:* Trafalgar Square Publishing.

Le Neouanic, Lionel. Little Smudge. 2006. (Illus.). 48p. (J). (ps-1). 14.95 (978-1-905417-22-3(5)) Boxer Bks., Ltd. GBR. *Dist:* Sterling Publishing Co., Inc.

Leach, Ann. Oh, Doug! A Dragonfly's Day. Aldredge, Russell, illus. 1999. 26p. (J). (gr. k-3). pap. 10.95 (978-1-929150-00-7(8)) Take Flight Pubns.

Lechner, John. Sticky Burr: Adventures in Burrwood Forest. Lechner, John, illus. 2007. (Illus.). 56p. (J). (gr. 1-5). 15.99 (978-0-7636-3054-6(3)) Candlewick Pr.

Leske, Staci. Butterfly That Loved the Firefly. 2006. 21.95 ***(*978-1-4259-7645-3(X))***; pap. 11.95 ***(*978-1-4259-7644-6(1))*** AuthorHouse.

Levy, Constance & Nakata, Hiroe. The Story of Red Rubber Ball. 2004. (Illus.). 32p. (J). 16.00 (978-0-15-216589-5(4) , Silver Whistle) Harcourt Trade Pubs.

Lionni, Leo. The Alphabet Tree. 2004. (Illus.). 40p. (J). (ps-3). reprint ed. 15.95 (978-0-394-81016-4(3) , Knopf Bks. for Young Readers) Random Hse. Children's Bks.

Llewellyn, Claire & Bailey, Peter. What's Creepy Crawly ? 2004. (Illus.). 24p. (J). 14.95 (978-1-84507-245-2(6)) Lincoln, Frances Ltd. GBR. *Dist:* Perseus Distribution.

Lluch, Alex. Big Bugs, Small Bugs: If You Could Be a Bug, Which Bug Would You Be? Defenbaugh, David, illus. 2005. 28p. (ps-7). bds. 7.95 (978-1-887169-62-2(8)) Wedding Solutions Publishing, Inc.

Lobel, Arnold. Saltamontes Va Da Viage. Date not set. (SPA.). 68p. 9.95 (978-84-204-3053-9(6)) Santillana USA Publishing Co., Inc.

Lockhart, E. Fly on the Wall. 2007. 192p. (YA). (gr. 7). pap. 8.99 ***(*978-0-385-73282-6(1)*** , Delacorte Bks. for Young Readers) Random Hse. Children's Bks.

Lockhart, E. Fly on the Wall: How One Girl Saw Everything. 2006. 192p. (YA). (gr. 7). 15.95 (978-0-385-73281-9(3)); lib. bdg. 17.99 (978-0-385-90299-1(9)) Random Hse. Children's Bks. (Delacorte Bks. for Young Readers).

Lonborg, Rosemary. Helpin' Bugs. Houghton, Diane R., illus. 32p. (J). (ps-3). reprint ed. 2006. pap. 7.00 (978-1-4223-5405-6(9)); 2004. 15.00 (978-0-7567-8176-7(0)) DIANE Publishing Co.

Long, Olivia. Billy Bumble Is Missing! Long, Olivia, illus. Date not set. (Kaleidoscope Ser.). (Illus.). 32p. (J). (ps-4). (978-1-880042-02-1(9)) Shelf-Life Bks.

Loper, Kathleen. Angelina Katrina: Bugs in My Backyard. Waltz, Dan, illus. l.t. ed. 2004. 24p. (J). 17.95 (978-0-9741774-4-1(X)) D. W. Publishing.

Lord, John Vernon & Burroway, Janet. The Giant Jam Sandwich. 2007. (Illus.). 32p. (J). (ps-k). pap. 9.95 incl. audio compact disk ***(*978-0-618-83952-0(6))*** Houghton Mifflin Co. Trade & Reference Div.

Lorimer, Janet. Bugged! 2001. (PageTurner Science Fiction Ser.). 80p. (YA). per. 3.95 (978-1-56254-130-9(7) , SP 1307) Saddleback Educational Publishing.

—Bugged! 2001. (gr. 7-12). lib. bdg. 11.80 (978-0-613-34096-0(5)) Tandem Library Bks.

Lou Weber Staff, ed. Busy Bugs Play a Puzzle. 2004. 12p. (J). bds. 9.98 (978-1-4127-3149-2(6) , 7231900) Publications International, Ltd.

Lozoff, Bo. The Wonderful Life of a Fly Who Couldn't Fly. Stover, Beth, illus. 2002. 44p. (J). (ps-5). 17.95 (978-1-57174-286-5(7)) Hampton Roads Publishing Co., Inc.

Lucado, Max. Buzby & the Grumble Bees. 2007. (Max Lucado's Hermie & Friends Ser.). 38p. (J). bds. 12.99 ***(*978-1-4003-0913-9(1))*** Nelson, Thomas Inc.

—Flo the Lyin' Fly. 2004. (Max Lucado's Hermie & Friends Ser.). (Illus.). 48p. (J). 12.99 (978-1-4003-0286-4(2)) Nelson, Thomas Inc.

—Stanley una chinche Apestosa. 2006. (Max Lucado's Hermie & Friends Ser.).Tr. of Stanley the Stink Bug. (SPA.). 48p. 10.99 (978-0-88113-950-1(5)) Grupo Nelson.

—The Twelve Bugs of Christmas. 2004. 20p. (J). bds. 9.99 (978-1-4003-0492-9(X)); (Illus.). bds. 6.99 (978-1-4003-0493-6(8)) Nelson, Thomas Inc.

Lucado, Max, creator. Flo, the Lyin' Fly. 2006. 38p. (J). bds. 12.99 (978-1-4003-0889-7(5)) Nelson, Thomas Inc.

—Stanley the Stinkbug. 2006. (Hermie & Friends Ser.). (Illus.). 48p. (J). 12.99 (978-1-4003-0734-0(1)) Nelson, Thomas Inc.

Lucado, Max & Max Lucado's Hermie and Friends Staff, creators. Stanley the Stinkbug. 2006. (Hermie & Friends Ser.). 24p. (J). bds. 6.99 (978-1-4003-0735-7(X)) Nelson, Thomas Inc.

Lucado, Max & Schmidt, Troy. Webster, the Scaredy Spider. 2005. 32p. (J). pap. 3.99 (978-1-4003-0665-7(5)) Nelson, Thomas Inc.

Luebke, Gayle M. There's A Bug in My Bed. 2005. 17p. 9.58 (978-1-4116-2635-5(4)) Lulu.com.

Mansour, Vivian. La Vida Util de Pillo Polilla. Flores, Lupita, illus. rev. ed. 2004. (Castillo de la Lectura Naranja Ser.). (SPA.). 112p. (J). (gr. 3-5). pap. 7.95 (978-970-20-0129-4(3)) Castillo, Ediciones, S. A. de C. V. MEX. *Dist:* Macmillan.

Marquess, Dana. Night of the Lighted Freedom: A Firefly Fantasy. 2006. (Illus.). 32p. (J). 19.95 (978-1-932278-06-4(0)) Mayhaven Publishing.

Martin, Bill, Jr. & Sampson, Michael. The Little Squeegy Bug. Corrigan, Patrick, illus. 2001. 32p. (J). (ps-2). reprint ed. pap. 5.95 (978-0-7614-5243-0(5)) Cavendish, Marshall Corp.

Martin, Bill, Jr., et al. The Little Squeegy Bug. 2001. (Illus.). 40p. (J). (ps-2). 16.95 (978-1-890817-90-9(2)) Winslow Pr.

Martín Larrañaga, Ana. Beautiful Bugs. 2000. (Ana's Animals Bks.). (Illus.). (J). (ps-k). 3.95 (978-1-58646-002-0(1)) Polka Dot Pr.

Matute, Ana M. El Saltamontes Verde. (SPA.). (YA). (gr. 5-8). pap. 7.96 (978-84-264-3410-4(X)); 2003. 96p. (978-84-264-3001-4(5) , LM0622); 2003. (Illus.). 133p. (978-84-264-5051-7(2) , LM30549) Editorial Lumen ESP. *Dist:* Lectorum Pubns., Inc.

Max Lucado's Hermie & Friends. The Straight Path. 2005. (Illus.). 14p. (J). (ps-ps). 9.99 (978-1-4003-0511-7(X)) Nelson, Thomas Inc.

McDonald, Megan. Beetle McGrady Eats Bugs! Manning, Jane K., illus. 2005. 32p. (J). 15.99 (978-0-06-001354-7(0)); lib. bdg. 17.89 (978-0-06-001355-4(9)) HarperCollins Pubs.

McElligott, Matthew. Bean Thirteen. McElligott, Matthew, illus. 2007. 32p. (J). (gr. k-3). 15.99 (978-0-399-24535-0(9) , Putnam Juvenile) Penguin Group (USA) Inc.

McLean, Wendy. Whizz! 2003. (J). pap. 12.95 (978-1-74047-276-0(4)) Book Co. Publishing Pty, Ltd., The AUS. *Dist:* Penton Overseas, Inc.

McLean, Wendy & Book Company Staff. Whizz! 2002. (Sparkle Bks.). 10p. (J). bds. 9.95 (978-1-74047-273-9(X)) Book Co. Publishing Pty, Ltd., The AUS. *Dist:* Penton Overseas, Inc.

McOmber, Rachel B., ed. McOmber Phonics Storybooks: A Hum-Bug. rev. ed. (Illus.). (J). (978-0-944991-20-6(3)) Swift Learning Resources.

—McOmber Phonics Storybooks: Bug. rev. ed. (Illus.). (J). (978-0-944991-19-0(X)) Swift Learning Resources.

—McOmber Phonics Storybooks: The Hum-Bug Hop. rev. ed. (Illus.). (J). (978-0-944991-31-2(9)) Swift Learning Resources.

MCP Staff. Good Night Little Bug, Level 4, Bk. 42. (J). (ps-3). 24.50 (978-0-8136-1971-2(8)) Modern Curriculum Pr.

—That Fly, Level 3, Bk. 12. (J). (ps-3). 24.50 (978-0-8136-1943-9(2)) Modern Curriculum Pr.

McPhail, David M. A Bug, a Bear & a Boy. 1998. (Hello Reader! Ser.). (Illus.). 32p. (J). (ps-1). pap. 3.99 (978-0-590-14904-4(0)) Scholastic, Inc.

—A Bug, a Bear & a Boy. 1998. (Hello Reader! Ser.). (J). (ps-1). 10.79 (978-0-606-13231-2(7)) Tandem Library Bks.

—A Bug, a Bear & a Boy Go to School. 1999. (Illus.). (J). 10.79 (978-0-606-20469-9(5)) Tandem Library Bks.

—A Bug, a Bear, & a Boy Go to School. 2004. 32p. (J). lib. bdg. 15.00 (978-1-59054-668-0(7)) Fitzgerald Bks.

Mercer, Rita C. Earl the Squatchem. 2007. 9.00 ***(*978-0-8059-8823-9(8))*** Dorrance Publishing Co., Inc.

Metzger, Steve. Ladybug's Birthday. Williamson, James, illus. 2000. (Side-by-Side Ser.). (J). pap. 3.50 (978-0-590-02599-7(6)) Scholastic, Inc.

Miller, Dorothy Anne. Stories to Read 'Round the Campfire. 2006. pap. 12.95 (978-1-4137-7554-9(3)) PublishAmerica, Inc.

Miraglia, Matthew. Maria & the Carrot Patch. 2007. (J). per. 17.99 ***(*978-1-59886-984-2(1))*** Tate Publishing & Enterprises, L.L.C.

Miss Spider's Tea Party. 2003. (J). pap. 19.95 (978-0-439-54314-9(2)) Scholastic, Inc.

Mitchell, Marianne. Firebug. 2004. (Illus.). 176p. (YA). (gr. 4-6). 16.95 (978-1-59078-170-8(8)) Boyds Mills Pr.

Moffatt, Judith. Bugs. 2001. (Hello Reader! Ser.). (Illus.). 32p. (J). (gr. k-2). pap. 3.99 (978-0-439-09859-5(9)) Scholastic, Inc.

Mouse Works Staff. Bug's Life. 1998. (Disney's Bug's Life Ser.). (Illus.). 96p. (J). (ps-4). 7.99 (978-1-57082-979-6(9)) Mouse Works.

—Where Are the Bugs? 1998. (Illus.). 10p. (J). bds. 4.99 (978-0-7364-0068-8(0)) Mouse Works.

Muench-Williams, Heather. The Tod Squad Can See Bugs. 2007. (J). bds. ***(*978-1-57332-446-5(9))*** HighReach Learning, Inc.

Muhs, Lisa. What If Ladybugs Were Blue? 2001. (J). 7.95 (978-0-7880-2001-8(3)) CSS Publishing Co.

Muldrow, Diane. Hangin' with Bugs. Style Guide Staff, illus. 2006. (Baby Looney Tunes Ser.). 32p. (J). act. bk. ed. 0.99 (978-1-4169-1841-7(8) , Simon Scribbles) Simon & Schuster Children's Publishing.

Mullican, Judy. Bugs in the Garden. 2006. (J). pap. (978-1-57332-419-9(1)) HighReach Learning, Inc.

Murdock, Kita Helmetag & Helmetag, Patricia. Cecily Cicada, 2004th l.t. ed. 2004. (Illus.). 28p. (J). pap. 9.95 (978-0-615-12548-0(4)) Possum Products.

Murphy. Best Bug Parade: Comparing Sizes Big Book. 2002. (Illus.). (J). pap. (978-0-7398-6775-4(X)) Steck-Vaughn.

Murphy, Kelly. The Boll Weevil Ball. rev. ed. 2002. (Illus.). 32p. (J). (ps-2). 15.95 (978-0-8050-6712-5(4) , Holt, Henry & Co. Bks. For Young Readers) Holt, Henry & Co.

Myers, Bill. The House That Went Ker-Splat! The Parable of the Wise & Foolish Builder. Smith, Andy J., illus. 2008. (J). ***(*978-0-310-71220-6(3))*** Zonderkidz.

—Stink Bug Saves the Day! The Parable of the Good Samaritan. Smith, Andy J., illus. 2008. (J). ***(*978-0-310-71219-0(X))*** Zonderkidz.

Nazoa, Aquiles. Fabula de la Avispa Ahogada. 2002. (SPA., Illus.). 36p. (J). 6.50 (978-980-257-099-7(0) , EK4926) Ekare, Ediciones VEN. *Dist:* Lectorum Pubns., Inc.

Nettrour, Nelani. Dragonfly Flight. Lesnick, Tina, illus. l.t. ed. 2003. 62p. (J). pap. 11.94 (978-1-932657-02-9(9)) Third Millennium Pubns.

—Jodi's Bugs. Nettrour, Heather, illus. l.t. ed. 2003. 66p. (J). pap. 11.95 (978-1-932657-04-3(5)) Third Millennium Pubns.

Newgarden, Mark & Cash, Megan Montague. Bow-Wow Bugs a Bug. 2007. (Illus.). 56p. (J). (ps-2). 12.95 (978-0-15-205813-5(3)) Harcourt Trade Pubs.

Nickel, Scott. Backyard Bug Battle: A Buzz Beaker Brainstorm. Smith, Andy J., illus. 2007. (Graphic Sparks Ser.). 33p. (J). (gr. 2-5). lib. bdg. 19.93 (978-1-59889-054-9(9)) Stone Arch Bks.

Noguera, Pablo. Las Aventuras de Romeo Palote. 2000. (J). (978-956-240-299-6(1)) Arrayan Editores S.A.

Noyes, Diana. The Tickle Bug. Noyes, Diana, illus. l.t. ed. 2005. (Illus.). 20p. (J). per. 9.99 (978-1-59879-080-1(3)) Lifevest Publishing, Inc.

O'Malley, Kevin. Leo Cockroach... Toy Tester. O'Malley, Kevin, illus. 1999. (Illus.). 32p. (J). (gr. k-3). lib. bdg. 16.85 (978-0-8027-8690-6(1)) Walker & Co.

Osborne, Mary Pope. Spider Kane & the Mystery at Jumbo Nightcrawler's. 1999. (J). (978-0-606-19083-1(X)) Tandem Library Bks.

—Spider Kane & the Mystery under the May-Apple. 1999. (J). (978-0-606-19084-8(8)) Tandem Library Bks.

Owen, Dan. Ellen. 2006. 32p. (J). pap. 11.99 (978-1-4116-9069-1(9)) Lulu.com.

Palatini, Margie. The Perfect Pet. Whatley, Bruce, illus. 2003. 32p. (J). (ps-2). 15.99 (978-0-06-000108-7(9)); lib. bdg. 16.89 (978-0-06-000109-4(7)) HarperCollins Pubs.

Parker, Andy. Ciberbichos: Cyber Bugs, Spanish-Language Edition. 2005. (Mekanimals Ser.). (SPA., Illus.). 8p. (J). bds. 12.95 (978-970-718-323-0(3) , Silver Dolphin en Español) Advanced Marketing, S. de R. L. de C. V. MEX. *Dist:* Perseus Distribution.

Parker, Andy, illus. Mekanimals Cyber Bugs. 2004. 8p. (J). bds. 12.95 (978-1-59223-146-1(2) , Silver Dolphin Bks.) Advantage Pubs. Group.

Penton Overseas, Inc. Staff, contrib. by. There Was an Old Lady Who Swallowed a Fly. rev. ed. 2007. 14p. 10.95 ***(*978-1-74181-191-9(0))*** Hinkler Bks. Pty, Ltd. AUS. *Dist:* Penton Overseas, Inc.

Perez, Jessica. Goodnight, Little Bug. Shelly, Jeff, illus. 2005. (J). bds. 14.99 (978-0-9767325-2-5(1)) Toy Quest.

Peters, Lisa Westberg. Sleepyhead Bear. Schoenherr, Ian, illus. 2006. (J). 32p. 16.99 (978-0-06-059675-0(9)); 40p. lib. bdg. 17.89 (978-0-06-059676-7(7)) HarperCollins Pubs.

Pettersson, Aline. Ontario, la Mariposa Viajera. Valderrama, Rosario, illus. 2003. (SPA.). 72p. (J). (gr. 3-5). pap. 11.95 (978-968-19-0276-6(9)) Santillana USA Publishing Co., Inc.

Pfeffer, Wendy. Firefly at Stonybrook Farm: Smithsonian's Backyard. Mikec, Larry, illus. 2005. (Smithsonian's Backyard Ser.). 32p. (J). (ps-2). 9.95 (978-1-59249-308-1(4) , PB5076) Soundprints.

Phillips, Gina & Martin, Stuart. Bees & Butterflies. 2003. (Busy Bugs Ser.). 12p. (J). bds. 14.95 (978-1-74047-239-5(X)) Book Co. Publishing Pty, Ltd., The AUS. *Dist:* Penton Overseas, Inc.

Pichon, Liz. The Very Ugly Bug. 2005. (Illus.). 32p. (J). 15.95 (978-1-58925-048-2(6) , tiger tales) ME Media LLC.

Pinczes, Elinor J. One Hundred Hungry Ants. MacKain, Bonnie, illus. 1999. 32p. (J). (gr. k-3). pap. 6.95 (978-0-395-97123-9(3)) Houghton Mifflin Co. Trade & Reference Div.

—A Remainder of One. MacKain, Bonnie, illus. 2002. 32p. (J). (gr. k-3). pap. 5.95 (978-0-618-25077-6(8)) Houghton Mifflin Co. Trade & Reference Div.

—Remainder of One. 2002. (gr. k-3). lib. bdg. 14.10 (978-0-613-90724-8(8)) Tandem Library Bks.

Pixton, Amy, creator. Things with Wings. 2006. (J). (978-0-9779631-2-6(8)) TyBook.

Polly Hollybug, the Winter Adventure. 2000. 32p. (J). per. 8.95 (978-0-9705740-0-8(2)) Hollybug, Polly Inc.

Powell, Glenda. Cassie & Mr. Ant. Mitchell, Hazel, illus. 2008. (J). 7.95 (978-0-9779445-6-9(5)) Zoe Life Publishing.

Priddy Book. In the Yard; Fuzzy Bee & Friends. (Illus.). (J). 17.90 (978-0-312-49377-6(0) , Priddy Bks.) St. Martin's Pr.

Prince, Sarah. Butterfly, the Bird, the Beetle, & Me. 2000. (gr. k-3). lib. bdg. 11.80 (978-0-613-29568-0(4)) Tandem Library Bks.

Provost, Elizabeth. Ten Little Sleepyheads. Saaf, Donald, illus. 2005. 32p. (J). 16.95 (978-1-58234-838-4(3)) Bloomsbury Publishing.

Quit Bugging Me. 2007. 150p. (YA). pap. 8.99 ***(*978-0-9776043-6-4(5))*** Aspirations Media, Inc.

Reader's Digest Editors. Bugillions ! 2004. (Look & See (Googly Eyes) Ser.). (Illus.). 10p. (J). bds. 7.99 (978-0-7944-0283-9(6) , Reader's Digest Children's Bks.) Reader's Digest Children's Publishing, Inc.

Reece, Stephen. The Bedbugs Save Sidney. 1998. (Illus.). 16p. (J). (ps-3). pap. 3.65 (978-1-892388-07-0(3)) Little Trucker Bks.

Reynolds, Aaron. Breaking Out of the Bungle Bird: Based on Proverbs 13:10. Whitehead, Peter, illus. 2005. (Insect-Inside Ser.). 40p. (J). 9.99 (978-0-310-70956-5(3)) Zonderkidz.

—The Dung Beetle Bandits. Lervold, Eric, illus. 2007. (J). 40p. ***(*978-1-59889-317-5(3))***; 33p. pap. ***(*978-1-59889-412-7(9))*** Stone Arch Bks.

—The Fortune Cookies of Weevil. Lervold, Eric, illus. 2007. 33p. (J). ***(*978-1-59889-318-2(1))***; pap. ***(*978-1-59889-413-4(7))*** Stone Arch Bks.

Richards, Lucy, illus. Busy Bugs (W/Header Card) 2004. (Cuddly Cuffs Ser.: 6). 12p. (J). tchr. ed. 5.95 (978-1-58925-730-6(8) , tiger tales) ME Media LLC.

Richards, Lucy & Finn, Rebecca, illus. Busy Bugs (W/Hang Tag) 2004. (Cuddly Cuffs Ser.: 6). 6p. (J). tchr. ed. 5.95 (978-1-58925-726-9(X) , tiger tales) ME Media LLC.

Rigby Education Staff. Animals of the Rainforest. (Sails Literacy Ser.). (Illus.). 16p. (gr. k-1). 27.00 (978-0-7635-9867-9(4) , 698674C99) Rigby Education.

Rigby, Peter. Stanley Sticks Out. Smith, Craig, illus. 2000. 32p. (YA). 12.95 (978-1-876268-43-5(3)) Univ. of Western Australia Pr. AUS. *Dist:* International Specialized Bk. Services.

Rights, Lenz-Mulligan & van der Put, Klaartje. Little Ladybug. 2005. (Illus.). 12p. (J). bds. 6.95 (978-0-8118-4848-0(5)) Chronicle Bks. LLC.

H I

Rinehart, Susie Caldwell. Eliza & the Dragonfly. Hovemann, Anisa Claire, illus. 2004. (Sharing Nature with Children Book Ser.). 32p. (J). 16.95 (978-1-58469-060-3(7)); 8.95 (978-1-58469-059-7(3)) Dawn Pubns.

Rowe, Papa. Itchy Lee & Itchy Dee Mcgee. Wilkins, Kevan & Mason, Shannon, eds. Shortell, Stephen, illus. ed. 2006. (J). 15.99 (978-0-9778858-0-0(1)) WowZee Works Inc.

Russ, Tim. Bugsters! 2008. (Illus.). 32p. (J). (***978-0-9795131-7-6(0)***) Woods N' Water, Inc.

Sanders, Terri L. Night Flies. 2003. (J). E-Book 4.95 incl. cd-rom (978-1-59201-010-3(5)) Bks. Unbound E-Publishing Co.

Santillo, LuAnn. The Seeds. Santillo, LuAnn, ed. 2003. (Half-Pint Kids Readers Ser.). (Illus.). 7p. (J). (ps-1). pap. (978-1-59256-109-4(8)) Half-Pint Kids, Inc.

Sargent, Dave & Sargent, Pat. Lizzy Lightning Bug/Lizzy la Luciérnaga, 10 vols., Vol. 17. Robinson, Laura, illus. 2004. (Learn to Read Ser.: 10). Tr. of Lizzy la Luciernaga. (ENG & SPA.). 18p. (J). (gr. k-2). lib. bdg. 19.95 (978-1-56763-993-3(3)) Ozark Publishing.

Savage, Bridgette Z. Fly Like the Wind. Savage, Bridgette Z., illus. 2005. (Illus.). 112p. (J). per. 16.99 (978-0-9771494-0-7(4)) Buckbeech Studios.

Schreiber, Anne. Picnics on the Hill. Lewis, Anthony, illus. 2000. (Scholastic At-Home Phonics Reading Program Ser.: Vol. 57). 24p. (J). (978-0-590-68859-8(6)) Scholastic, Inc.

See, Linda. Cindy & Sean Centipede's: It Was Magical, Granny Wise Owl. 1998. (Illus.). 32p. (J). (gr. k-3). pap. 8.00 (978-0-8059-4458-7(3)) Dorrance Publishing Co., Inc.

Serfozo, Mary. Big Bug Dug. Maccarone, Grace, ed. Scherer, Jeffrey, illus. 2003. 32p. (J). pap. 3.99 (978-0-439-59426-4(X)) Scholastic, Inc.

Serwacki, Kevin, illus. Doorknob the Rabbit & the Carnival of Bugs. 2003. 32p. (J). 14.95 (978-1-58246-143-4(0) , Tricycle Pr.) Ten Speed Pr.

Shaw, Irene. Cosy Cottage. 2006. (Illus.). 48p. pap. (***978-1-84401-792-8(3)***) Athena Pr.

Shepherd, Donna J. The Lonely Lightning Bug. 2005. (Illus.). 16p. (J). E-Book 9.95 incl. cd-rom (978-1-933090-30-6(8)) Guardian Angel Publishing, Inc.

Shi, Sharon. The Little Tattoo Bug Book. Garofalo, Francesco, illus. rev. ed. 2000. 24p. (J). (gr. k-2). mass mkt. 4.99 (978-0-9678636-6-5(X) , B007, Tattootles Bks.) Tattoo Manufacturing.

Shields, Carol Diggory. The Bugliest Bug. Nash, Scott, illus. 32p. (J). (ps-3). 2005. pap. 6.99 (978-0-7636-2293-0(1)); 2002. 16.99 (978-0-7636-0784-5(3)) Candlewick Pr.

Shreeve, Elizabeth. Hector Finds a Fortune. Levy, Pamela R., illus. 2004. 68p. (J). lib. bdg. 15.00 (***978-1-4242-0903-3(X)***) Fitzgerald Bks.

—Hector on Thin Ice. Levy, Pamela R., illus. 2004. 71p. (J). lib. bdg. 15.00 (***978-1-4242-0904-0(8)***) Fitzgerald Bks.

Shreeve, Elizabeth. Hector Springs Loose. Levy, Pamela R., illus. 2004. (Ready-for-Chapters Ser.). 80p. (J). pap. 3.99 (978-0-689-86414-8(0) , Aladdin) Simon & Schuster Children's Publishing.

Shubert's Choice. 2004. (YA). 9.00 (978-1-889609-26-3(9)) Loving Guidance, Inc.

Shubert's Helpful Day. 2001. (J). 9.00 (978-1-889609-19-5(6)) Loving Guidance, Inc.

Shulman, Mark. The Insect Invaders. Collins, Mark, illus. 2005. (Storytime Stickers Ser.). 16p. (J). (gr. k-2). pap. 4.95 (978-1-4027-2746-7(1)) Sterling Publishing Co., Inc.

Siegel, Phil. Simon the Daredevil Centipede: He Learned to Skate - & Much, Much More. Caiarelli, Alisa, illus. 1998. 28p. (J). pap. 8.95 (978-0-932991-58-4(0) , Different Bks.) Place In The Woods, The.

Silberberg, Alan. Pond Scum. 2007. 288p. (gr. 3-7). pap. 5.99 (978-0-7868-5635-0(1)) Hyperion Pr.

Sillyhead, Uncle, III. Here Come the Tickle Bugs! Sillyhead, Uncle, III, illus. 1999. (Illus.). 48p. (J). (gr. 1). (978-0-9677127-0-3(X)) Tickle Bugs.

Sloat, Teri. The Thing That Bothered Farmer Brown. Westcott, Nadine Bernard, illus. 2001. 32p. (J). (ps-2). pap. 5.95 (978-0-531-07183-0(9) , Orchard Bks.) Scholastic, Inc.

Smith, Beth Esh. Red Bug Board Book & Felt Puppet Set. Coates, Jennifer, illus. 2005. (J). bds. (978-1-57332-368-0(3)) HighReach Learning, Inc.

Smith, Simon. Jimmy's Lost Bug: A Retelling of the Parable of the Lost Sheep. 2004. (Clay Pot Parables Ser.). (Illus.). 32p. (J). 9.99 (978-0-310-70661-8(0)) Zonderkidz.

Sneed, Brad. Deputy Harvey & the Ant Cow Caper. 2005. (Illus.). 32p. (J). (ps). 16.99 (978-0-8037-3023-6(3) , Dial) Penguin Group (USA) Inc.

Sonenklar, Carol. Bug Girl. 2000. (Illus.). (J). (978-0-606-18100-6(8)) Tandem Library Bks.

Spanyol, Jessica. Come on, Bugs! Let's Have Some Fun! Spanyol, Jessica, illus. 2006. (Illus.). 32p. (J). (gr. k-k). 15.99 (978-0-7636-3055-3(1)) Candlewick Pr.

The Sparkling Beauty. 2006. Orig. Title: Televisual Book. (J). 18.99 (978-0-9779672-0-9(4)) Karsonkina, Tatiana.

Speck, Katie. Maybelle in the Soup. Ratz de Tagyos, Paul, illus. 2007. 64p. (J). (gr. 2-5). 15.95 (***978-0-8050-8092-6(9)***) Holt, Henry & Co.

Stanley, Mandy. Busy Bugs. 2003. (Illus.). 12p. (J). (ps-k). bds. 4.95 (978-0-7534-5678-1(8) , Kingfisher) Houghton Mifflin Co. Trade & Reference Div.

Steck-Vaughn Staff. Mud Is Much Fun/Gus Funny. 1999. (Take Me Home Ser.). (Illus.). (J). pap. (978-0-7398-2675-1(1)) Steck-Vaughn.

Stone, Jodi. Lady Bug. Herring, Kip, illus. 2005. 36p. (J). per. 15.00 (978-0-9754298-7-7(6) , Ithaca Pr.) Authors & Artists Publishers of New York, Inc.

Sturges, Philemon. I Love Bugs! Halpern, Shari, illus. 2005. 32p. (J). (ps-1). 14.99 (978-0-06-056168-0(8)); lib. bdg. 14.89 (978-0-06-056169-7(6)) HarperCollins Pubs.

Suarez de la Prida, Isabel. Los Diminutos. Bouchain, Nava, illus. 2003. (SPA.). 32p. (J). (gr. k-3). pap. 6.95 (978-968-19-0631-3(4)) Santillana USA Publishing Co., Inc.

Super Fly Guy. 2007. 32p. (J). per. (***978-0-439-90374-5(2)***) Scholastic, Inc.

Sweeney, Jacqueline. Meadow Magic. 2001. (We Can Read! Ser.). (Illus.). 32p. (J). (gr. 1-2). lib. bdg. 21.36 (978-0-7614-1124-6(0) , Benchmark Bks.) Cavendish, Marshall Corp.

Tada, Satoshi. Mr. Beetle. Hirano, Cathy, tr. from JPN. Tada, Satoshi, illus. 2001. (Picture Bks.). (Illus.). 48p. (J). (ps-3). lib. bdg. 15.95 (978-1-57505-561-9(9) , Carolrhoda Bks.) Lerner Publishing Group.

Taylor, Susie. The Grimy-Slimy Bug Safari. Lyon, Tammie, illus. 2004. (Topsy-Turvy Tracy Ser.). 40p. (J). 12.99 (978-0-310-70443-0(X)) Zonderkidz.

Ten Little Lady Bugs. (Mini Whizz Ser.). (Illus.). (J). (978-1-58209-076-4(9)) Books Are Fun, Ltd.

Thorpe, Kiki. Bugged by Bugs. 2001. (gr. k-3). lib. bdg. 11.25 (978-0-613-51295-4(2)) Tandem Library Bks.

Toy Box Innovations Staff, creator. Disney Pixar: Finding Nemo/A Bug's Life/Monsters, Inc. unabr. abr. ed. 2005. (Disney's Read along Collection). (J). audio compact disk 14.99 (978-0-7634-1151-0(5)) Walt Disney Records.

Tozer, Al. Mr. Ant & His Friends: A Fun Insect Story. 2002. (J). 19.95 (978-0-9720493-0-6(4)) Junebug Pr.

Tsubakiyama, Margaret. Lice Are Lousy: All about Headlice. 1999. 3. (Illus.). 32p. (gr. k-3). lib. bdg. 23.90 (978-0-7613-1316-8(8) , Millbrook Pr.) Lerner Publishing Group.

Tyson, Leigh Ann. An Interview with Harry the Tarantula. Drescher, Henrik, illus. 2003. 32p. (J). (ps-3). 15.95 (978-0-7922-5122-4(9) , National Geographic Children's Bks.) National Geographic Society.

Uncle Bobby. Herman & Hariett. 2004. 43p. pap. 19.95 (978-1-4137-2931-3(2)) PublishAmerica, Inc.

Uribe, Veronica. Buzz, Buzz, Buzz. Calderon, Gloria, illus. 2001. 32p. (J). (ps-k). 15.95 (978-0-88899-430-1(3)) Groundwood Bks. CAN. *Dist:* Perseus Distribution.

—El Mosquito Zumbador. Calderon, Gloria, illus. 1999. (SPA.). 28p. (J). (gr. 1-4). pap. 6.99 (978-980-257-232-8(2)) Ekare, Ediciones VEN. *Dist:* Kane/Miller Bk. Pubs., Inc., Lectorum Pubns., Inc.

van Kampen, Vlasta. Marigold's Wings. 2005. (Illus.). 31p. (J). lib. bdg. 24.67 (978-0-8368-4500-6(5)) Stevens, Gareth Inc.

Van Turennout, Paola, illus. One Little Bug. 2004. 40p. (J). 15.95 (978-1-894965-12-5(4)) Simply Read Bks. CAN. *Dist:* Perseus Distribution.

Varner, Carla. The Worrisome Worm. 2003. (J). 11.95 (978-0-9745787-3-6(8)) I Can Do All Things Productions.

Voake, Steve. The Dreamwalker's Child. (Illus.). 320p. (YA). 2007. pap. 7.95 (978-1-59990-038-4(6)); 2006. 16.95 (978-1-58234-661-8(5)) Bloomsbury Publishing. (Bloomsbury Children).

Voake, Steve & Voake, Steven. The Web of Fire. Watkinson, Mark, illus. 2007. 336p. (YA). (gr. 5-8). 17.95 (978-1-58234-737-0(9) , Bloomsbury Children) Bloomsbury Publishing.

Walker, E. G. Mario & the Tarantula. Leigh, Chris, illus. 1999. 46p. (ps-5). pap. 6.95 (978-0-7392-0268-5(5) , PO3351) Morris Publishing.

Walsh, Ellen Stoll. Dot & Jabber & the Big Bug Mystery. 2003. (Dot & Jabber Ser.). (Illus.). 40p. (J). 15.00 (978-0-15-216518-5(5)) Harcourt Trade Pubs.

Walt Disney Records Staff, prod. A Bug's Life Read Along. 1998. 24p. (J). (ps-3). 6.98 incl. audio (978-0-7634-0441-3(1)) Walt Disney Home Video.

Ward, Jennifer. Over in the Garden. Spengler, Kenneth J., illus. 2002. 32p. (ps-2). 15.95 (978-0-87358-793-8(6) , Rising Moon Bks. for Young Readers) Northland Publishing.

Waring, Geoff. Oscar & the Moth: A Book about Light & Dark. Waring, Geoff, illus. 2007. (Illus.). 32p. (J). (ps). 11.99 (***978-0-7636-3559-6(6)***) Candlewick Pr.

Watson-Dubisch, Carolyn. Bug-a-boo, 1. l.t. ed. 2006. (Illus.). 32p. (J). per. 9.95 (978-0-9779295-1-1(5)) Medusa Road Pr.

Weaver, Ann. A Wiggly Spider a Slug a Salamander & the Bug! Hildebrand, Sharon, illus. 2000. 16p. (J). pap. 5.95 (978-0-87012-649-9(0)) McClain Printing Co.

Whiting, Sue & Book Company Staff. Bugs at Play. Mosley, Dudley, illus. 2002. (Button Bks.). 12p. (J). bds. 12.95 (978-1-74047-219-7(5)) Book Co. Publishing Pty, Ltd., The AUS. *Dist:* Penton Overseas, Inc.

—My Place. Mosley, Dudley, illus. 2002. (Button Bks.). 12p. (J). bds. 12.95 (978-1-74047-194-7(6)) Book Co. Publishing Pty, Ltd., The AUS. *Dist:* Penton Overseas, Inc.

Whiting, Sue & Martin, Stuart. That's Funny! 2003. (Illus.). 14p. 12.95 (978-1-74047-272-2(1)) Book Co. Publishing Pty, Ltd., The AUS. *Dist:* Penton Overseas, Inc.

Willis, Jeanne & Ross, Tony. Mayfly Day. 2006. (Illus.). 32p. (J). (978-1-84270-492-9(3)) Andersen.

Wilson, Karma. A Frog in the Bog. Rankin, Joan, illus. 2003. 32p. (J). 16.95 (978-0-689-84081-4(0) , McElderry, Margaret K.) Simon & Schuster Children's Publishing.

Wilson, Karma & Rankin, Joan. A Frog in the Bog. 2007. 32p. (J). pap. 6.99 (978-1-4169-2727-3(1) , Aladdin) Simon & Schuster Children's Publishing.

Wilson, Mary. Paper Dragonfly. 2007. 32p. 15.95 (***978-0-9726614-3-0(3)***) Shenanigan Bks.

Woodson, Jacqueline. I Hadn't Meant to Tell You This. 2006. (YA). 176p. (gr. 7). 11.99 (978-0-399-24499-5(9) , Putnam Juvenile); 128p. (gr. 7). pap. 5.99 (978-0-14-240555-0(8) , Puffin) Penguin Group (USA) Inc.

Wright, Bill, Sr. Gleedus the Happy Grasshopper. Fraser, Jess, illus. 2006. (J). cd-rom 9.99 (***978-0-9795190-6-2(3)***) Color & Learn.

Yep, Laurence. Cockroach Cooties. 2001. 144p. (gr. 3-7). pap. 5.99 (978-0-7868-1338-4(5)) Hyperion Bks. for Children.

—Cockroach Cooties. 2001. (gr. 3-6). lib. bdg. 14.15 (978-0-613-45730-9(7)) Tandem Library Bks.

Zollman, Pam. Don't Bug Me! 2001. (Illus.). 144p. (J). (gr. 4-6). tchr. ed. 15.95 (978-0-8234-1584-7(8)) Holiday Hse., Inc.

INSECTS—HABITS AND BEHAVIOR

Act-Two Staff. Bug Safari. 2004. (Illus.). (J). (gr. 1-4). pap. 8.99 incl. cd-rom (978-0-7868-3415-0(3)) Hyperion Bks. for Children.

Coughlan, Cheryl. Ladybugs. Saunders-Smith, Gail, ed. 1999. (Insects Ser.). (Illus.). 24p. (J). (gr. k-1). lib. bdg. 15.93 (978-0-7368-0242-0(8) , Pebble Bks.) Capstone Pr., Inc.

Forsyth, Adrian. Exploring the World of Insects: The Equinox Guide to Insect Behaviour. 2004. (Illus.). 64p. (J). (gr. 4-8). reprint ed. pap. 10.00 (978-0-7567-8497-3(2)) DIANE Publishing Co.

Glaser, Linda. Spectacular Spiders. Holland, Gay W., illus. 1998. (Linda Glaser's Classic Creatures Ser.). 32p. (ps-3). lib. bdg. 22.90 (978-0-7613-0353-4(7) , Millbrook Pr.) Lerner Publishing Group.

Grassy, John. Insects. 2001. (Smart Start Reader Ser.). (Illus.). 31p. (J). (978-0-439-27894-2(5)) Scholastic, Inc.

Green, Jen & Frith, Mathew. Beetles & Bugs. (Nature Fact File Ser.). (Illus.). 64p. 2004. pap. 7.99 (978-1-84215-894-4(5) , Southwater); 2001. (gr. 3-7). 14.95 (978-0-7548-0838-1(6)) Anness Publishing GBR. *Dist:* National Bk. Network.

Halfmann, Janet & Richardson, Adele D. The Bugbook, 8 vols. in 1. 1999. (Illus.). 232p. (J). (gr. 2-7). lib. bdg. 25.95 (978-1-887068-99-4(6)) Smart Apple Media.

Miller, Connie Colwell. Disgusting Bugs. 2007. (Illus.). 32p. (J). (978-0-7368-6798-6(8)); (***978-0-7368-7876-0(9)***) Capstone Pr., Inc.

Stone, Lynn M. Homes & Habits of Insects. 2000. (Six Legged World Ser.). (Illus.). 24p. (J). (gr. 1). lib. bdg. 20.64 (978-1-55916-310-1(0)) Rourke Publishing, LLC.

Tagliaferro, Linda. Ants & Their Nests. 2004. (Pebble Plus, Animal Homes Ser.). (Illus.). 29p. (J). 13.95 (978-0-7368-2380-7(8)) Capstone Pr., Inc.

—Bees & Their Hives. 2004. (Pebble Plus, Animal Homes Ser.). (Illus.). 24p. (J). 13.95 (978-0-7368-2382-1(4)) Capstone Pr., Inc.

INSECTS, INJURIOUS AND BENEFICIAL

see also Insects As Carriers of Disease

also names of insects, e.g. Locusts; Silkworms, etc.

Birch. Head Lice up Close 6 Pack. 2004. pap. 40.50 (978-1-4109-1154-4(3)) Harcourt Schl. Pubs.

Miller, Sara Swan. Will You Sting Me? Will You Bite? The Truth about Some Scary-Looking Insects. Chrustowski, Rick, illus. 2001. (Curious Little Critters Ser.). 48p. (J). (gr. k-7). 18.95 (978-0-88045-144-4(0)); pap. 9.95 (978-0-88045-145-1(9)) Stemmer Hse. Pubs., Inc.

Pascoe, Elaine. Grubs & Other Garden Pests. Kuhn, Dwight, photos by. 2005. (Nature Close-up Ser.). (Illus.). 48p. (J). (ps-7). lib. bdg. 24.95 (978-1-4103-0536-7(8) , Blackbirch Pr., Inc.) Thomson Gale.

Schaefer, Lola M. Honey Bees & Hives. Saunders-Smith, Gail, ed. 1999. (Honey Bees Ser.). (Illus.). 24p. (J). (gr. k-1). lib. bdg. 14.60 (978-0-7368-0230-7(4) , Pebble Bks.) Capstone Pr., Inc.

Silverstein, Alvin, et al. Bites & Stings. 2001. (My Health Ser.). (Illus.). 48p. (J). (gr. 3-5). 25.50 (978-0-531-11861-0(4) , Watts, Franklin) Scholastic Library Publishing.

INSECTS—POETRY

Cricket Magazine Group. Ladybug, Ladybug & Other Favorite Poems. 2007. (Illus.). 40p. (J). 17.95 (978-0-8126-7936-6(9)) Cricket Bks.

Cyrus, Kurt. Oddhopper Opera: A Bug's Garden of Verses. 2007. (Illus.). 32p. (J). pap. 7.00 (978-0-15-205855-5(9) , Voyager Bks./Libros Viajeros) Harcourt Children's Bks.

Dakos, Kalli. The Bug in Teacher's Coffee: And Other School Poems. 1999. (I Can Read Bks.). (Illus.). 48p. (J). (gr. k-3). 16.89 (978-0-06-027940-0(0)) HarperCollins Pubs.

DiTerlizzi, Tony. The Spider & the Fly. 2002. (Illus.). 40p. (J). 17.99 (978-0-689-85289-3(4)) Simon & Schuster Children's Publishing.

Florian, Douglas. Insectlopedia. 1998. (Illus.). 56p. (J). (gr. k-5). 16.00 (978-0-15-201306-6(7)) Harcourt Children's Bks.

—Laugh-Eteria. 2000. (gr. 3-6). lib. bdg. 15.30 (978-0-613-33708-3(5)) Tandem Library Bks.

Greenberg, David. Bugs! 2002. (gr. k-3). lib. bdg. 14.10 (978-0-613-44808-6(1)) Tandem Library Bks.

Moses, Brian, contrib. by. Minibeasts. 2003. (Illus.). 65p. (J). pap. 6.99 (978-0-330-37057-8(X) , Pan) Pan Macmillan GBR. *Dist:* Trafalgar Square Publishing.

Pollsar, Barry L. Insect Soup: Bug Poems. Clark, David, illus. 1999. (Rainbow Morning Music Picture Bks.). 32p. (J). (gr. 1-7). 14.95 (978-0-938663-22-5(4)) Rainbow Morning Music Alternatives.

Reffett, Frances. Insectaside. Losh, Eric, illus. l.t. ed. 2006. 28p. (J). 8.00 net. (***978-0-9785886-0-1(6)***) Chicory Pr.

INSECTS AS CARRIERS OF DISEASE

see also Flies; Mosquitoes

Hirschmann, Kris. Ticks. 2003. (Parasites Ser.). (Illus.). 32p. (J). 24.95 (978-0-7377-1782-2(3) , Greenhaven Pr., Inc.) Thomson Gale.

INSPECTION OF SCHOOLS

see School Management And Organization

INSPIRATION

see Creation (Literary, Artistic, etc.)

INSTRUCTION

see Education; Teaching

INSTRUMENTS, ASTRONOMICAL

see Astronomical Instruments

INSTRUMENTS, MEASURING

see Measuring Instruments

INSTRUMENTS, METEOROLOGICAL

see Meteorological Instruments

INSTRUMENTS, MUSICAL

see Musical Instruments

INSTRUMENTS, SCIENTIFIC

see Scientific Apparatus and Instruments

INSULIN

Bankston, John. Frederick Banting & the Discovery of Insulin. 2002. (Unlocking the Secrets of Science Ser.). (Illus.). 56p. (gr. 4-10). lib. bdg. 25.70 (978-1-58415-094-7(7)) Mitchell Lane Pubs., Inc.

Yuwiler, Janice. Insulin. 2005. (Great Medical Discoveries Ser.). (Illus.). 112p. (YA). (gr. 7-10). lib. bdg. 29.95 (978-1-56006-930-0(9) , Lucent Bks.) Thomson Gale.

INSURANCE

Schwartz, Stuart B. Buying Insurance. 1998. (Life Skills Ser.). (J). lib. bdg. 20.95 (978-0-516-21461-0(6) , Children's Pr.) Scholastic Library Publishing.

Schwartz, Stuart B. & Conley, Craig. Buying Insurance. (Life Skills-Career Bks.). 48p. pap. 6.95 (978-0-7368-8507-2(2)); 1998. (Illus.). 32p. (J). (gr. 3-4). lib. bdg. 21.26 (978-0-7368-0045-7(X)) Capstone Pr., Inc. (Life-Matters Bks.).

INTEGRATED CIRCUITS

Charlton, Windsor. The Invention of the Silicon Chip: A Revolution in Daily Life. 2002. (Point of Impact Ser.). (Illus.). 32p. (J). (gr. 5-7). lib. bdg. 25.64 (978-1-58810-554-7(7)); pap. 7.50 (978-1-4034-0073-4(3) , 91553) Heinemann Library.

INTEGRATION, RACIAL

see Race Relations

INTEGRATION IN EDUCATION

see Segregation in Education

INTELLECT

see also Creation (Literary, Artistic, etc.); Imagination; Knowledge, Theory of; Logic; Perception; Reasoning; Senses and Sensation; Thought and Thinking

Carter, Philip J. & Russell, Kenneth A. IQ Tests to Keep You Sharp. 2002. (Illus.). 96p. pap. 7.95 (978-0-8069-5789-0(1)) Sterling Publishing Co., Inc.

Falone, John J. The Genius Frequency: An Owner's Manual for the Cosmic Mind. unabr. ed. 2000. 416p. (YA). (gr. 8 up). pap. 19.75 (978-0-9704176-0-2(8)) Global Light Network.

Hancock, Jonathan. How to Be a Genius. Rowe, Alan, illus. 2001. (How to Ser.). 96p. (J). (gr. 5-7). 16.00 (978-0-531-14648-4(0)); pap. 4.95 (978-0-531-13996-7(4)) Scholastic Library Publishing. (Watts, Franklin).

—How to Be a Genius. 2001. (gr. 5-8). lib. bdg. 12.95 (978-0-613-54542-6(7)) Tandem Library Bks.

Kim, Jeannie. Body & Mind. 2003. (Whole You Ser.). 160p. (J). pap. 4.50 (978-0-439-40464-8(9) , Scholastic Paperbacks) Scholastic, Inc.

Knecht, Andromeda. Pathways for Kids & Other People Too... Knecht, Sherry, ed. 1999. (Illus.). 52p. (J). (gr. 3-6). pap. 9.95 (978-1-929589-03-6(4)) Branching Leat Pubns.

—Pathways for Kids & Other People Too... 2nd rev. ed. 1999. 58p. (J). (gr. 3-6). pap. 9.95 (978-1-929589-17-3(4)) Branching Leat Pubns.

Romanek, Trudee. Aha! The Most Interesting Book You'll Ever Read about Intelligence. Cowles, Rose, tr. Cowles, Rose, illus. 2004. (Mysterious You Ser.). 40p. (J). (gr. 4-6). (978-1-55337-569-2(6)); (978-1-55337-485-5(1)) Kids Can Pr., Ltd.

INTELLECTUAL LIFE

see Culture; Learning and Scholarship

INTELLIGENCE

see Intellect

INTELLIGENCE OF ANIMALS

see Animal Intelligence

INTELLIGENCE SERVICE—UNITED STATES

Baker, David. CIA & FBI. 2006. (Fighting Terrorism Ser.). (Illus.). 48p. (gr. 4-8). 20.95 (978-1-59515-482-8(5)) Rourke Publishing, LLC.

Fridell, Ron. Spying, Modern World of Espionage. 2002. (Single Titles Ser.). (Illus.). 144p. (gr. 7 up). lib. bdg. 24.90 (978-0-7613-1662-6(0) , Millbrook Pr.) Lerner Publishing Group.

Hines, Janet. Inside America's CIA: The Central Intelligence Agency. 2005. (Inside the World's Most Famous Intelligence Agencies Ser.). (Illus.). 64p. (YA). (gr. 7-12). lib. bdg. 26.50 (978-0-8239-3811-7(5)) Rosen Publishing Group, Inc., The.

Lang, Patrick, tr. The Human Side of Intelligence. 2003. (Securing the Nation Ser.). (Illus.). 112p. (gr. 9-13). 30.00 (978-0-7910-7616-3(4) , Chelsea Hse.) Facts On File, Inc.

Lockwood, Brad. Domestic Spying & Wiretapping. 2006. (In the News Ser.). (Illus.). 64p. (J). (gr. 7-12). lib. bdg. 27.95 (***978-1-4042-0973-2(5)***) Rosen Publishing Group, Inc., The.

Rabiger, Joanna. Government Intelligence Agencies. 2002. (Crime & Detection Ser.). (Illus.). 96p. (J). (gr. 7 up). lib. bdg. (978-1-59084-374-1(6)) Mason Crest Pubs.

Streissguth, Thomas. America's Security Agencies: The Department of Homeland Security, FBI, NSA, & CIA. 2008. (Federal Government Ser.). 128p. (J). (gr. 6 up). lib. bdg. 33.27 (***978-1-59845-058-3(1)*** , MyReportLinks.com Bks.) Enslow Pubs., Inc.

INTEMPERANCE

see Alcoholism

INTERCOLLEGIATE ATHLETICS

see Athletics

INTERCULTURAL EDUCATION

see Multicultural Education

INTEREST GROUPS

see Lobbying

INTERIOR DECORATION

see also Coverlets; Furniture; Rugs; Tapestry

Banner, Shawn. Room for You: Find Your Style & Make Your Room Say You! 2001. (gr. 3-6). lib. bdg. 16.40 (978-0-613-83324-0(4)) Tandem Library Bks.

Banner, Shawn, illus. Room for You: Find Your Style & Make Your Room Say You! 2001. (American Girl Library). 80p. (J). (gr. 3 up). pap. 7.95 (978-1-58485-369-5(7)) American Girl Publishing, Inc.

Bond, Fiona. The Arts in Your Church: A Practical Guide. 2001. (Illus.). 128p. 14.99 (978-1-903689-00-4(7)) Piquant Editions Ltd. GBR. *Dist:* Gabriel Resources.

Craig, Rebecca. Dream Bedroom: Use Recycled Materials to Make Cool Crafts. 2007. (EcoCrafts Ser.). (Illus.). 48p. (J). (gr. 3-5). pap. 7.95 (***978-0-7534-5966-9(3)*** , Kingfisher) Houghton Mifflin Co. Trade & Reference Div.

Everett, Felicity & Woods, P., eds. Decorate Your Room. 1999. (Practical Guides Ser.). (Illus.). 64p. (YA). (gr. 6 up). lib. bdg. 16.95 (978-0-88110-392-2(6)) EDC Publishing.

Freixenet, Anna. Creating with Mosaics. 2000. (Crafts for All Seasons Ser.). (Illus.). 32p. (J). (gr. 3-8). lib. bdg. 23.70 (978-1-56711-440-9(7) , Blackbirch Pr., Inc.) Thomson Gale.

Greene, Michael. Gee! I Wish I Had a Bedroom That Was All My Own: An Education Adventure in Interior Environment. 1998. (Illus.). 112p. (YA). (gr. 6-12). lib. bdg. 20.00 (978-1-881134-03-9(2)) Tuesday's Child Publishing, Ltd.

Grover, Jill Williams. Tween Friends: Ideas & Projects for Room Decorating. 2006. (Illus.). 128p. (J). pap. (978-1-4027-2364-3(4)) Sterling Publishing Co., Inc.

Gunzi, Christiane. My Home. (My Very First Look at Ser.). (SPA., Illus.). 24p. (ps-k). 2004. (J). pap. 5.95 (978-1-58728-685-8(8)); 2003. 9.95 (978-1-58728-671-1(8)) T&N Children's Publishing. (Two Can Publishing).

Hantman, Clea. I Wanna Re-Do My Room. Houshyar, Azadeh, illus. 2006. 144p. (J). pap. 9.99 (978-0-689-87463-5(4) , Aladdin) Simon & Schuster Children's Publishing.

Harte, May. ABCs in My House. 2004. (Look-And-Learn Books). (Illus.). (J). lib. bdg. 7.95 (978-1-4042-2824-5(1) , PowerKids Pr.) Rosen Publishing Group, Inc., The.

—1, 2, 3 in My House. 2004. (Look-And-Learn Books). (Illus.). (J). lib. bdg. 7.95 (978-1-4042-2823-8(3) , PowerKids Pr.) Rosen Publishing Group, Inc., The.

Hufford, Deborah. Room Decorating: Make Your Space Unique. 2005. (Snap Books Craft Ser.). (Illus.). 32p. (J). (gr. 3-5). 22.60 (978-0-7368-4386-7(8)) Capstone Pr., Inc.

Hunt, Sara, ed. Room Crafts: Add Some Simple Style to Your Space. 2004. (American Girl Library(R) Ser.). (Illus.). 64p. spiral bd. 9.95 (978-1-58485-911-6(3)) American Girl Publishing, Inc.

Jennings, Lynette. Have Fun with Your Room. 2001. 64p. (J). (gr. 6-10). 12.00 (978-0-689-82585-9(4) , Simon Pulse) Simon & Schuster Children's Publishing.

Kane, Andy. Changing Rooms: Handy Andy's Homework. 2003. (Illus.). 192p. bds. 24.95 (978-0-563-55192-8(5)) BBC Worldwide Americas.

Lee, Jacqueline, ed. Decorate Your Locker: So It's Completely & Totally Your Own (at Least for a Year) 2004. (Klutz Ser.). (Illus.). 24p. (J). 9.95 (978-1-59174-270-8(6)) Klutz.

Montano, Mark. Super Suite. 2002. (gr. 7-12). lib. bdg. 28.00 (978-0-613-87742-8(X)) Tandem Library Bks.

Scholastic, Inc. Staff. Trading Spaces: Boys vs. Girls. 2003. (gr. 3-6). lib. bdg. 22.20 (978-0-613-81181-1(X)) Tandem Library Bks.

Skinner, Tina. Kids Decor: Interior Inspirations, Infants Through Teens. 2002. (Schiffer Design Book Ser.). (Illus.). 160p. (gr. 10-13). pap. 24.95 (978-0-7643-1613-5(3)) Schiffer Publishing, Ltd.

Sutherland, Gill & Aitken, Kirstie. The Best Friends Guide to Bedroom Decorating. 2004. (Illus.). 127p. (J). (978-0-439-68946-5(5)) Scholastic, Inc.

Warwick, Ellen. Stuff for Your Space. Lum, Bernice, tr. Lum, Bernice, illus. 2004. (Kids Can Do It Ser.). 40p. (J). (gr. 4-6). (978-1-55337-399-5(5)); (978-1-55337-398-8(7)) Kids Can Pr., Ltd.

Weaver, Janice & Wishinsky, Frieda. It's Your Room: A Decorating Guide for Real Kids. Davila, Claudia, illus. 2006. 64p. (J). (gr. 4-7). pap. 14.95 (978-0-88776-711-1(7)) Tundra Bks., Inc./Livres Toundra, Inc. CAN. *Dist:* Random Hse., Inc.

Weekly Reader Early Learning Library (Firm) Staff, contrib. by. Things at Home. 2006. (Things in My World Ser.). (Illus.). 16p. (J). pap. (978-0-8368-6814-2(5)); lib. bdg. (978-0-8368-6807-4(2)) Stevens, Gareth Inc.

—Things at Home: Las Cosas de Mi Casa. 2006. (ENG & SPA., Illus.). 16p. pap. (978-0-8368-7226-2(6) , Weekly Reader Early Learning Library) Stevens, Gareth Inc.

—Things at Home (Las Cosas de Mi Casa) 2006. (ENG & SPA., Illus.). 16p. (J). lib. bdg. 17.27 (978-0-8368-7219-4(3) , Weekly Reader Early Learning Library) Stevens, Gareth Inc.

INTERIOR DECORATION—FICTION

Kompelien, Tracy. Octopus's Garden. Nobens, C. A., illus. 2007. (Fact & Fiction Ser.). 24p. (J). 21.35 (978-1-59928-456-9(1) , SandCastle) ABDO Publishing Co.

Krauss, Ruth. I Want to Paint My Bathroom Blue. Sendak, Maurice, illus. 2001. (Sendak Reissues Ser.). 24p. 15.95 (978-0-06-028634-7(2)) HarperCollins Pubs.

Krauss, Ruth & Sendak, Maurice. I Want to Paint My Bathroom Blue. 2001. (Sendak Reissues Ser.). (Illus.). 24p. (J). 14.89 (978-0-06-028635-4(0)) HarperCollins Pubs.

Law, Felicia. Rumble Meets Lucas Lizard. Pak, Yoon Mi, illus. 2006. (Read-It! Readers Ser.). 32p. (J). (gr. 2-4). 18.60 (978-1-4048-1334-2(9)) Picture Window Bks.

Lawton, Wendy. Flip Flop. 2004. (Real Tv - Real Transformations Series (Take 2) Ser.). 208p. (J). pap. 10.99 (978-0-8024-5414-0(3)) Moody Pubs.

Rylant, Cynthia. Annie & Snowball & the Prettiest House: The Second Book of Their Adventures. Stevenson, Sucie, illus. 2007. (Annie & Snowball Ser.). 40p. (J). (gr. k-2). 15.99 (***978-1-4169-0939-2(7)*** , Simon & Schuster Children's Publishing) Simon & Schuster Children's Publishing.

Santucci, Barbara. Abby's Chairs. Santini, Debrah L., illus. 2004. 32p. 16.00 (978-0-8028-5205-2(X)) Eerdmans, William B. Publishing Co.

Slonim, David. He Came with the Couch. Slonim, David, illus. 2005. (Illus.). 36p. (J). (ps-ps). 15.95 (978-0-8118-4430-7(7)) Chronicle Bks. LLC.

INTERMARRIAGE

see also Interracial Marriage

Alderman, Bruce. Interracial Relationships. 2006. (Social Issues Firsthand Ser.). 224p. (YA). (gr. 7 up). 29.95 (978-0-7377-2895-8(7) , Greenhaven Pr., Inc.) Thomson Gale.

INTERMARRIAGE—FICTION

Otey Little, Mimi. Yoshiko & the Foreigner. Otey Little, Mimi, illus. 2004. (Illus.). 31p. (J). (gr. 4-8). reprint ed. 16.00 (978-0-7567-7510-0(8)) DIANE Publishing Co.

INTERMARRIAGE, RACIAL

see Interracial Marriage

INTERMITTENT FEVER

see Malaria

INTERNATIONAL COOPERATION

Here are entered works on international cooperative activities with or without the participation of governments.

see also International Organization; United Nations

Alagna, Magdalena. The Monroe Doctrine: An End to European Colonies in America. 2003. (Life in the New American Nation Ser.). (Illus.). 32p. (YA). pap. 6.50 (978-0-8239-4258-9(9)) Rosen Publishing Group, Inc., The.

Cole, Michael D. International Space Station: A Space Mission. 1999. (Countdown to Space Ser.). (Illus.). 48p. (YA). (gr. 4-10). lib. bdg. 23.93 (978-0-7660-1117-5(8)) Enslow Pubs., Inc.

INTERNATIONAL ECONOMIC RELATIONS

Downing, David. Global Business: Who Benefits? 2006. (Illus.). 56p. (J). lib. bdg. (978-1-4034-8831-2(2)) Heinemann Library.

Garlake, Teresa. Global Debt. 2003. (21st Century Debates Ser.). (Illus.). 64p. (J). lib. bdg. 28.56 (978-0-7398-6035-9(6)) Raintree.

Harris, Nathaniel. Globalization. 2007. (J). lib. bdg. (***978-1-4042-3753-7(4)*** , Rosen Central) Rosen Publishing Group, Inc., The.

Teichmann, Iris. Globalization. 2003. (In the News Ser.). (J). lib. bdg. 24.25 (978-1-58340-397-6(3)) Smart Apple Media.

INTERNATIONAL EXHIBITIONS

see Exhibitions

INTERNATIONAL FEDERATION

see International Organization

INTERNATIONAL LAW

see also International Cooperation; International Organization; International Relations; Pirates; Salvage; Slave Trade; War

Kolba, Boris. International Courts. 2003. (International Organizations Ser.). (Illus.). 48p. (J). (gr. 5 up). pap. 11.95 (978-0-8368-5528-9(0) , World Almanac Library) Stevens, Gareth Inc.

Stearman, Kaye. Military Intervention. 2007. (J). lib. bdg. (***978-1-4042-3756-8(9)*** , Rosen Central) Rosen Publishing Group, Inc., The.

INTERNATIONAL ORGANIZATION

Here are entered works on theories and efforts leading toward world-wide or regional political organization of nations.

see also International Cooperation; International Law; World Politics

also names of specific organizations, e.g. United Nations, etc.

International Organizations, 8 bks. Incl. Amnesty International. Banks, Deena. lib. bdg. 30.00 (978-0-8368-5517-3(5)); European Union. Petra Press Staff. lib. bdg. 30.00 (978-0-8368-5518-0(3)); International Courts. Kolba, Boris. lib. bdg. 30.00 (978-0-8368-5519-7(1)); Interpol. Blashfield, Jean F. lib. bdg. 30.00 (978-0-8368-5520-3(5)); Red Cross & Red Crescent. Blashfield, Jean F. lib. bdg. 30.00 (978-0-8368-5521-0(3)); "UNICEF (International Organizations) (Library Binding) " Grahame, Deborah A. lib. bdg. 30.00 (978-0-8368-5522-7(1)); United Nations. Tarsitano, Frank. lib. bdg. 30.00 (978-0-8368-5523-4(X)); World Health Organization. Grahame, Deborah A. lib. bdg. 30.00 (978-0-8368-5524-1(8)); 48p. (J). (gr. 5 up). (Illus.). 2003. Set lib. bdg. 240.00 (978-0-8368-5516-6(7) , World Almanac Library) Stevens, Gareth Inc.

January, Brendan. Globalize It! The Stories of the IMF, the World Bank, the WTO - And Those Who Protest. 2003. (Single Titles Ser.). (Illus.). 144p. (gr. 7 up). 26.90 (978-0-7613-2417-1(8) , Twenty-First Century Bks.) Lerner Publishing Group.

INTERNATIONAL RELATIONS

see also Diplomats; Disarmament; International Cooperation; International Economic Relations; International Law; International Organization; Monroe Doctrine; Peace; Security, International

also names of countries with the subdivision Foreign Relations, e.g. U. S.—Foreign Relations, etc.

Alagna, Magdalena. The Monroe Doctrine: An End to European Colonies in America. 2003. (Life in the New American Nation Ser.). (Illus.). 32p. (YA). pap. 6.50 (978-0-8239-4258-9(9)) Rosen Publishing Group, Inc., The.

Breen, Jennifer. England & India. 2002. (People at Odds Ser.). (Illus.). 112p. (J). (gr. 5 up). 30.00 (978-0-7910-6708-6(4) , Chelsea Hse.) Facts On File, Inc.

Connolly, Sean. United Nations - Keeping the Peace. 2002. (Troubled World Ser.). (Illus.). 64p. (J). (gr. 6 up). lib. bdg. 28.54 (978-0-7398-6342-8(8)) Raintree.

Foreign Policy Association Staff. Great Decisions. Rohan, Karen M., ed. 2001. (Illus.). 104p. (YA). (gr. 8-12). pap. 15.00 (978-0-87124-194-8(3) , 31498) Foreign Policy Assn.

Foreign Policy Research Institute Staff, ed. Modern Middle East Nations & Their Strategic Places in the World, 25 vols., Set. 2003. (Illus.). 112,128p. (YA). (gr. 7 up). lib. bdg. (978-1-59084-504-2(8)) Mason Crest Pubs.

Global Beat. 1998. 34p. (J). pap. 10.00 (978-0-87104-742-7(X) , Branch Libraries) New York Public Library.

Harmon, Daniel E. Turkey. 2003. (Modern Middle East Nations & Their Strategic Place in the World Ser.). (Illus.). 112,128p. (YA). (gr. 7 up). lib. bdg. (978-1-59084-524-0(2)) Mason Crest Pubs.

Hoffman, Aaron M. Building Trust: Overcoming Suspicion in International Conflict. 2005. (SUNY Series in Israeli Studies). (Illus.). 224p. (C). 55.00 (978-0-7914-6635-3(3)) State Univ. of New York Pr.

Marks, James Lynn. Opposites. 2000. (Education Through Creation Ser.: Bk. 7). (Illus.). 16p. (J). (ps-6). pap. 9.95 (978-0-9706412-6-7(5) , 1007) Seventh Sun Productions.

Nelson, Robin. Working with Others. 2006. (Pull Ahead Bks.). (Illus.). 32p. (J). 22.60 (978-0-8225-3486-0(X) , Lerner Pubns.) Lerner Publishing Group.

Walker, Tim. International Relations: Understanding the Behavior of Nations. 4th ed. 2001. (Illus.). 95p. (J). 13.95 (978-0-932765-97-0(1)) Close Up Foundation.

Watson, Susan. Being Active Citizens. 2003. 32p. (J). lib. bdg. 24.25 (978-1-58340-398-3(1)) Smart Apple Media.

—Making Global Connections. 2003. 32p. (J). lib. bdg. 24.25 (978-1-58340-405-8(8)) Smart Apple Media.

INTERNATIONAL RELATIONS—FICTION

Caletti, Deb. Honey, Baby, Sweetheart. 320p. (YA). 2005. pap. 7.99 (978-0-689-86474-2(4) , Simon Pulse); 2004. 15.95 (978-0-689-86765-1(4)) Simon & Schuster Children's Publishing.

—Honey, Baby, Sweetheart. l.t. ed. 2005. 367p. 22.95 (978-0-7862-7308-9(9) , Large Print Pr.) Thorndike Pr.

Crutcher, Chris. Ironman. 2004. 288p. (J). pap. 6.99 (978-0-06-059840-2(9) , HarperTeen) HarperCollins Pubs.

Durrant, Sabine. Bon Voyage, Connie Pickles. 2008. 240p. (J). 16.99 (***978-0-06-085482-9(0)***); lib. bdg. 17.89 (***978-0-06-085483-6(9)***) HarperCollins Pubs. (HarperTeen).

Franklin, Emily. The Principles of Love. 2005. 256p. (gr. 12-12). pap. 9.99 (978-0-451-21517-8(6) , N A L Trade) Penguin Group (USA) Inc.

Jones, Jennifer B. The Short Story of My Life. 2004. 160p. (J). 16.95 (978-0-8027-8903-1(6)) Walker & Co.

Klassen, Kirsten L. Katelyn's Affection. 2004. 280p. pap. 11.99 (978-0-8361-9281-0(8)) Herald Pr.

Lowry, Brigid. Things You Either Hate or Love. 2007. 192p. (YA). (gr. 4-7). pap. 8.95 (978-0-312-36308-6(7) , St. Martin's Griffin) St. Martin's Pr.

Sanchez, Alex & Louth, Jack. Rainbow Road. 2005. 256p. (J). 16.95 (978-0-689-86565-7(1)) Simon & Schuster Children's Publishing.

Shaffer, Jeanne E. The Swimmer with a Rope in His Teeth: A Shadow Fable. Cruse, Howard, illus. 2004. 70p. pap. 14.00 (978-1-59102-181-0(2) , Pyr Bks.) Prometheus Bks., Pubs.

Sheldon, Dyan. Confessions of a Teenage Drama Queen. l.t. ed. 2004. 324p. 22.95 (978-0-7862-6903-7(0) , Large Print Pr.) Thorndike Pr.

Standiford, Natalie. Ex Rating. 4th rev. ed. 2006. (Dating Game Ser.: No. 4). 224p. (J). (gr. 8-17). pap. 9.99 (978-0-316-15876-3(3)) Little Brown & Co.

INTERNATIONAL SECURITY

see Security, International

INTERNATIONAL TRADE

see Commerce

INTERNET

see also World Wide Web

Adams, Cynthia. Exploring the World on the Net. 1999. (gr. 3-6). lib. bdg. 23.40 (978-0-613-25099-3(0)) Tandem Library Bks.

Albee, Michael J. Elements of Research: The Student's Guide to Avoiding Plagiarism in the Information Age. 2003. (Illus.). 140p. per. (978-0-9745405-0-4(1)) Albee, Michael.

Allman, Toney. Internet Predators. 2007. (Ripped from the Headlines Ser.). 64p. (J). (gr. 5). 23.95 (***978-1-60217-000-1(2)***) Erickson Pr.

APTE, Inc. Staff. Internet Coach: Discover Literacy & Culture. 2001. (Illus.). 16p. (J). (gr. 4-8). pap. 9.95 (978-1-889651-78-1(8)) APTE, Inc.

—Internet Coach: Discover the Web. 2001. (Illus.). 16p. (J). (gr. 4-8). pap. 9.95 (978-1-889651-79-8(6)) APTE, Inc.

Austin and Nelson Publishers Staff. 101 Cool Sites for Kids on the Internet. 1998. (Illus.). 96p. (gr. 4-6). 9.99 (978-1-56822-755-9(8) , IF22378) School Specialty Publishing.

Axelrod-Contrada, Joan. Reno v. ACLU: Internet Censorship. 2006. (Supreme Court Milestones Ser.). (Illus.). 144p. (J). lib. bdg. 39.93 (978-0-7614-2144-3(0) , Benchmark Bks.) Cavendish, Marshall Corp.

Bingham, Jane, et al. Encyclopedia of World History: Prehistoric, Ancient, Medieval, Last 500 Years. 2004. (World History Ser.). (Illus.). 415p. (J). (gr. 3 up). 39.95 (978-0-7460-4168-0(3)) EDC Publishing.

Bins Not To Be On Royalty Rep, prod. Internet Workbook. (YA). 24.95 (978-0-7365-3284-6(6)) Films Media Group.

Bodden, Valerie. Internet. 2008. (J). (***978-1-58341-557-3(2)*** , Creative Education) Creative Co., The.

Brimner, Larry Dane. E-Mail. rev. ed. 2000. (True Bks.). (Illus.). 48p. (J). (gr. 3-5). 25.00 (978-0-516-21937-0(5) , Children's Pr.) Scholastic Library Publishing.

—The World Wide Web. rev. ed. 2000. (gr. 3-6). lib. bdg. 15.25 (978-0-613-37599-3(8)) Tandem Library Bks.

Bucy, Erik P. Living in the Information Age: A New Media Reader. 2001. 352p. (YA). pap. 33.95 (978-0-534-59050-5(0)) Thomson Wadsworth.

Buell, Tonya. Careers with Successful Dot-Com Companies. 2005. (Library of E-Commerce & Internet Careers). (Illus.). 64p. (YA). (gr. 7-12). lib. bdg. 26.50 (978-0-8239-3424-9(1)) Rosen Publishing Group, Inc., The.

Bullock, Linda. Careers on the Web. 2002. (Technology & You Ser.). (Illus.). 48p. (J). lib. bdg. 27.12 (978-0-7398-4694-0(9)) Raintree.

Carson, Mary Kay. Weather: Quick & Easy Internet Activities for the One Computer Classroom. 2002. (Technology Ser.). (Illus.). 48p. (J). 9.95 (978-0-439-27856-0(2)) Scholastic, Inc.

Chabot, Jean-Phillipe. Internet. Grant, Donald, illus. 2000. (First Discovery Book Ser.). 30p. (J). (ps-3). 12.95 (978-0-439-14824-5(3)) Scholastic, Inc.

Chang, Maria L. Science. 2002. (Internet Scavenger Hunts Ser.). (Illus.). 64p. (gr. 4-8). pap. 10.95 (978-0-439-13846-8(9)) Scholastic, Inc.

Ciovacco, Justine. Surf the Internet. 2003. (Step Back Science Ser.). (Illus.). 48p. (J). 24.95 (978-1-56711-679-3(5) , Blackbirch Pr., Inc.) Thomson Gale.

Cook, Catherine Halloran & Pfeifer, Janet McGivney. Internet Quest: 101 Adventures Around the World Wide Web. Reiner, Angela & Streams, Jennifer, eds. Harvey, Gayle S., illus. 2000. 144p. (J). (gr. 2-4). pap. 14.95 (978-0-86530-456-7(4) , IP 456-4) Incentive Pubns., Inc.

Craig, Tom. Internet: Technology, People, Process. 2003. (Media Wise Ser.). 64p. (J). lib. bdg. 28.50 (978-1-58340-257-3(8)) Smart Apple Media.

Croft, Jennifer. Everything You Need to Know about Staying Safe in Cyberspace. rev. ed. 1999. (Need to Know Library). (Illus.). 64p. (YA). (gr. 7-12). lib. bdg. 25.25 (978-0-8239-2957-3(4) , NTCYBE) Rosen Publishing Group, Inc., The.

Davis, Steve. Using the Internet. 1998. (Illus.). 64p. (YA). (gr. 5). pap. 8.95 (978-1-58037-078-3(0)) Twain, Mark Media, Inc. Pubs.

Deedrick, Tami. The Internet. 2001. (Great Inventions Ser.). (J). 22.83 (978-0-7398-4699-5(X)) Raintree.

Doherty, Gillian. Birds. 2004. (Discovery Program Ser.). (SPA., Illus.). 64p. (J). (gr. 2 up). pap. 8.95 (978-0-7460-3738-6(4)); lib. bdg. 16.95 (978-1-58086-334-6(5)) EDC Publishing.

Dorling Kindersley Publishing Staff. Kid's Guide to the Internet. 2001. (Illus.). (J). (978-0-606-20752-2(X)) Tandem Library Bks.

Dougherty, Karla. The Rules to Be Cool: Etiquette & Netiquette. 2001. (Teen Issues Ser.). (Illus.). 64p. (J). (gr. 6-12). lib. bdg. 22.60 (978-0-7660-1607-1(2)) Enslow Pubs., Inc.

Douglas, Julie. The Internet. 2002. (Transportation & Communication Ser.). (Illus.). 48p. (J). (gr. 1-4). lib. bdg. 23.93 (978-0-7660-1889-1(X)) Enslow Pubs., Inc.

Eck, Michael. The Internet: Inside & Out. 2005. (Technology Ser.). (Illus.). 48p. (YA). (gr. 4-8). lib. bdg. 26.50 (978-0-8239-6108-5(7)) Rosen Publishing Group, Inc., The.

—The Internet: Por Dentro y por Fuera. 2002. (Tecnología Ser.). (SPA., Illus.). 48p. (YA). lib. bdg. 26.50 (978-0-8239-6150-4(8) , PowerKids Pr.) Rosen Publishing Group, Inc., The.

Ehrenhafte, Daniel. Marc Andreessen: Web Warrior. 2001. (Techies Ser.: up). (Illus.). 80p. (gr. 5 up). lib. bdg. 23.90 (978-0-7613-1964-1(6) , Twenty-First Century Bks.) Lerner Publishing Group.

Ekman, Joseph Anthony. Kids Ultimate Online Homework Resource Guide 2004. 2003. spiral bd. 14.95 (978-0-9745406-0-3(9)) Duke Publishing & Software Corp.

French, Laura. Internet Pioneers: The Cyber-Elite. 2001. (Collective Biographies Ser.). (Illus.). 112p. (J). (gr. 6-12). lib. bdg. 26.60 (978-0-7660-1540-1(8)) Enslow Pubs., Inc.

Friedman, Lauri S. The Internet. 2007. (Introducing Issues with Opposing Viewpoints Ser.). (Illus.). 144p. (gr. 7-10). 33.70 (***978-0-7377-3567-3(8)*** , Greenhaven Pr., Inc.) Thomson Gale.

Gabler, Laura R., ed. Career Exploration on the Internet: A Student's Guide to More Than 500 Web Sites. 2nd ed. (Illus.). 752p. (YA). pap. (978-0-89434-305-6(X) , Ferguson Publishing Co.) Facts On File, Inc.

H I

Gilbert, Sara. The Story of Google. 2008. (J). (***978-1-58341-605-1(6)*** , Creative Education) Creative Co., The.

Goranson, Christopher D. Careers as a Webmaster: Maintaining the Site. 2005. (Library of E-Commerce & Internet Careers). (Illus.). 64p. (YA). (gr. 7-12). lib. bdg. 26.50 (978-0-8239-3419-5(5)) Rosen Publishing Group, Inc., The.

—Everything You Need to Know about Misinformation on the Internet. 2005. (Need to Know Library). (Illus.). 64p. (YA). (gr. 4-6). lib. bdg. 25.25 (978-0-8239-3521-5(3)) Rosen Publishing Group, Inc., The.

Graham, Ian. Internet: The Impact on Our Lives. 2001. (Twenty-First Century Debates Ser.). (Illus.). 64p. (J). (978-0-7502-2771-1(0)) Steck-Vaughn.

—The Internet: The Impact on Our Lives. 2001. (Twenty-First Century Debates Ser.). (Illus.). 64p. (J). (gr. 6-8). lib. bdg. 27.12 (978-0-7398-3173-1(9)) Raintree.

—The Internet Revolution. 2003. (Science at the Edge Ser.). (Illus.). 64p. (J). (gr. 6-8). lib. bdg. 27.86 (978-1-4034-0325-4(2)) Heinemann Library.

Gralla, Preston. Online Activities for Kids: Projects for School, Extra Credit, or Just Plain Fun! 2001. (Illus.). 256p. pap. 16.95 (978-0-471-39073-2(9) , Wiley) Wiley, John & Sons, Inc.

—Online Kids: A Young Surfer's Guide to Cyberspace. 2nd rev. ed. 1999. (Illus.). 288p. 29.95 (978-0-471-33329-6(8) , Wiley) Wiley, John & Sons, Inc.

Haegele, Katie. E-Advertising & E-Marketing: Online Opportunities. 2005. (Library of E-Commerce & Internet Careers). (Illus.). 64p. (YA). (gr. 7-12). lib. bdg. 26.50 (978-0-8239-3426-3(8)) Rosen Publishing Group, Inc., The.

Hamilton, John. Internet. 2005. (Straight to the Source Ser.). (Illus.). 32p. (J). (gr. k-6). lib. bdg. 22.78 (978-1-59197-544-1(1)) ABDO Publishing Co.

Hankison, Whitney. Surfing the Internet Safely: A Workbook for Children. 2007. 68p. per. 9.95 (***978-0-595-44630-8(2)***) iUniverse, Inc.

Harcourt School Publishers Staff. The Internet. 3rd ed. 2002. (Horizons Ser.). (Illus.). (J). pap. 7.30 (978-0-15-333604-1(8)) Harcourt Schl. Pubs.

Heese, VaReane. Internet Cruises. 2000. (Illus.). (J). (gr. 4-8). 56.00 (978-1-57336-313-6(8) , 5057) Interaction Pubs., Inc.

Herumin, Wendy. Censorship on the Internet: From Filters to Freedom of Speech. 2004. (Issues in Focus Ser.). (Illus.). 128p. (J). lib. bdg. 26.60 (978-0-7660-1946-1(2)) Enslow Pubs., Inc.

Hillstrom, Kevin. The Internet Revolution. 2005. (Defining Moments Ser.). (Illus.). 203p. (YA). lib. bdg. 49.00 (978-0-7808-0767-9(7)) Omnigraphics, Inc.

Hoh, John L., Jr. The Church on the Web: A Hands-On Tutor for the Novice. 2001. (YA). ring bd. 44.95 (978-1-57052-206-2(5)) Church Growth Institute.

Horvitz, Leslie Alan. Meg Whitman: President & CEO of EBAY. 2005. (Ferguson Career Biographies Ser.). (Illus.). 128p. (J). (gr. 6-12). 25.00 (978-0-8160-5891-4(1) , Ferguson Publishing Co.) Facts On File, Inc.

Hovanec, Erin M. Careers as Content Provider for the Web. 2005. (Commerce & Internet Careers Ser.). (Illus.). 64p. (YA). (gr. 7-12). lib. bdg. 26.50 (978-0-8239-3418-8(7)) Rosen Publishing Group, Inc., The.

—Internet Field Trips, 7 bks. Incl. Online Visit to Africa. lib. bdg. 18.75 (978-0-8239-5651-7(2)); Online Visit to Antarctica. lib. bdg. 18.75 (978-0-8239-5656-2(3)); Online Visit to Asia. lib. bdg. 18.75 (978-0-8239-5652-4(0)); Online Visit to Australia. lib. bdg. 18.75 (978-0-8239-5653-1(9)); Online Visit to Europe. lib. bdg. 18.75 (978-0-8239-5657-9(1)); Online Visit to North America. lib. bdg. 18.75 (978-0-8239-5654-8(7)); Online Visit to South America. lib. bdg. 18.75 (978-0-8239-5655-5(5)); 24p. (J). (gr. 3). 2001. (Illus.). 2001. Set lib. bdg. 131.25 (978-0-8239-7069-8(8) , PowerKids Pr.) Rosen Publishing Group, Inc., The.

Internet: Building A Website. 2000. (gr. 7-12). lib. bdg. 15.25 (978-0-613-25716-9(2)) Tandem Library Bks.

Internet Guide. (Internet Guide Ser.). (gr. k-6). 2004. 30.00 (978-0-328-02542-8(9)); 2000. (SPA.). tchr. ed. 30.00 (978-0-673-62225-9(8)) Addison-Wesley Educational Pubs., Inc.

Internet Made Easy. 2005. (Illus.). 128p. per. (978-0-7853-8843-2(5) , 7192000) Publications International, Ltd.

Internet Projects. (Information Technology Ser.). 64p. (gr. 3-5). 7.99 (978-0-7424-0207-2(X) , IF19330); (gr. 6-12). 7.99 (978-0-7424-0208-9(8) , IF19331) School Specialty Publishing.

J. G. Ferguson Publishing Company Staff, ed. Careers in Focus. 3rd ed. 2006. (Careers in Focus Ser.). (Illus.). 192p. (J). (gr. 6-12). 29.95 (978-0-8160-6564-6(0) , Ferguson Publishing Co.) Facts On File, Inc.

Jablonski, Carla. Esther Dyson: Web Guru. 2002. (Techies Ser.). (Illus.). 80p. (gr. 5 up). lib. bdg. 23.90 (978-0-7613-2657-1(X) , Twenty-First Century Bks.) Lerner Publishing Group.

Jefferis, David. Internet: Electronic Global Village. 2002. (Megatech Ser.). (Illus.). 32p. (J). (gr. 4-5). pap. (978-0-7787-0062-3(3)); lib. bdg. (978-0-7787-0052-4(6)) Crabtree Publishing Co.

—Internet: Electronic Global Village. 2002. (gr. 3-6). lib. bdg. 17.60 (978-0-613-52962-4(6)) Tandem Library Bks.

Kay, Heidi & DelVecchio, Karen. The World at Your Fingertips: Learning Research & Internet Skills. 2002. 80p. (J). (gr. 1-6). pap. 15.95 (978-1-57950-071-9(4) , Upstart Bks.) Highsmith Inc.

Kazunas, Charnan & Kazunas, Thomas. The Internet for Kids. 2nd rev. ed. 2000. (True Bks.). (Illus.). 48p. (J). (gr. 3-5). 25.00 (978-0-516-21936-3(7) , Children's Pr.) Scholastic Library Publishing.

Kelly, Deirdre. 10 Quick & Fun Internet Field Trips. 2001. 48p. pap. 9.95 (978-0-439-27165-3(7)) Scholastic, Inc.

Komorn, Julie. Chat Chat Chat. 1999. (gr. 3-6). lib. bdg. 12.40 (978-0-613-21325-7(4)) Tandem Library Bks.

Lathrop, Ann. Student Cheating & Plagiarism in the Internet Era: A Wake-up Call. 2000. (gr. 7-12). lib. bdg. 42.00 (978-0-613-64771-7(8)) Tandem Library Bks.

LaVan, Ken & Colbin, Kaila. The Real People's Guide to the Internet. LaVan, Ken & Colbin, Kaila, illus. 1999. (Illus.). 96p. (YA). (gr. 5 up). pap. 19.95 (978-0-9669483-2-5(7)) ThoughtSource, Inc.

Lawler, Jennifer. Cyberdanger & Internet Safety. 2000. (Hot Issues Ser.). (Illus.). 64p. (YA). (gr. 6-12). lib. bdg. 27.93 (978-0-7660-1368-1(5)) Enslow Pubs., Inc.

Learning Resources for Kids on the Net. 2003. per. 14.95 (978-0-9722803-0-3(8)) Resources on the Net Publishing.

Leiviska, Karen. Internet Made Easy: Internet Scavenger Hunts for the Topics You Teach:Step-by-Step Reproducibles for 10 Exciting Internet Explorations That Enrich Learning & Get Kids Web-Savvy. 2000. 64p. pap. 10.95 (978-0-439-17034-5(6)) Scholastic, Inc.

Lewis, Ian. How to Conquer the Internet. Benton, Tim, illus. 2001. (How to Ser.). 96p. (J). (gr. 5-7). 16.00 (978-0-531-14639-2(1)); pap. 4.95 (978-0-531-14817-4(3)) Scholastic Library Publishing. (Watts, Franklin).

—How to Conquer the Internet. 2001. (gr. 5-8). lib. bdg. 12.95 (978-0-613-54547-1(8)) Tandem Library Bks.

Lockman, Darcy. The Internet. 2000. (Kaleidoscope Ser.). (Illus.). 48p. (J). (gr. 3 up). lib. bdg. 25.64 (978-0-7614-1046-1(5) , Benchmark Bks.) Cavendish, Marshall Corp.

Loughran, Donna. Internet History. 2002. (Technology & You Ser.). (Illus.). 48p. (J). lib. bdg. 27.12 (978-0-7398-4696-4(5)) Raintree.

—Using the Internet Safely. 2002. (Technology & You Ser.). (Illus.). 48p. (J). lib. bdg. 27.12 (978-0-7398-4697-1(3)) Raintree.

Lubka, Willie. Kiss Guide to the Internet. 2000. (gr. 7-12). lib. bdg. 29.20 (978-0-613-32750-3(0)) Tandem Library Bks.

Marshall, Elizabeth L. & Heweston, Nicholas. A Student's Guide to the Internet. rev. ed. 2000. (Single Titles Ser.: up). (Illus.). 128p. (gr. 5 up). lib. bdg. 24.90 (978-0-7613-1661-9(2) , Twenty-First Century Bks.) Lerner Publishing Group.

Marzilli, Alan. Policing the Internet. 2004. (Point/Counterpoint Ser.). (Illus.). 112p. (gr. 9-13). 32.95 (978-0-7910-8088-7(9) , Chelsea Hse.) Facts On File, Inc.

McCormick, Anita Louise. The Internet: Surfing the Issues. 1998. (Issues in Focus Ser.). (Illus.). 128p. (YA). (gr. 6-12). lib. bdg. 26.60 (978-0-89490-956-6(8)) Enslow Pubs., Inc.

McGraw-Hill Staff. Connect Online! Classroom. 2002. 130.00 (978-0-07-830907-6(7)) Glencoe/McGraw-Hill.

Menhard, Francha Roffe. Internet Issues: Pirates, Censors & Cybersquatters. 2001. (Issues in Focus Ser.). (Illus.). 128p. (J). (gr. 6-12). lib. bdg. 26.60 (978-0-7660-1687-3(0)) Enslow Pubs., Inc.

Miller, Deborah J. Careers with an Internet Service Provider. 2005. (Library of E-Commerce & Internet Careers). (Illus.). 64p. (YA). (gr. 7-12). lib. bdg. 26.50 (978-0-8239-3425-6(X)) Rosen Publishing Group, Inc., The.

Miller, Jonathan. Sharks. 2004. (Discovery Program Ser.). (SPA., Illus.). 64p. (J). (gr. 2 up). pap. 8.95 (978-0-7460-3723-2(6)); lib. bdg. 16.95 (978-1-58086-335-3(3)) EDC Publishing.

Morales, Leslie. Esther Dyson: Internet Visionary. 2003. (Internet Biographies Ser.). (Illus.). 48p. (J). (gr. 4-10). lib. bdg. 23.93 (978-0-7660-1973-7(X)) Enslow Pubs., Inc.

More Simple Internet Activities. 2003. (Illus.). 96p. (J). (gr. 3-5). 14.99 (978-0-7439-3871-6(2)) Teacher Created Materials, Inc.

Morgan, Sally. Internet. 2001. (Behind Media Ser.). (Illus.). 48p. (J). (gr. 6-8). lib. bdg. 24.22 (978-1-58810-032-0(4)) Heinemann Library.

Murray, Guillermo. Internet para Nino.Tr. of Internet for Children. (SPA.). 8.98 (978-970-643-110-3(1)) Selector, S.A. de C.V. MEX. *Dist:* AIMS International Bks., Inc.

Nicholson, Sue, ed. Encyclopedia: The Ultimate Online Learning Resource. 2003. (Illus.). 448p. 29.99 (978-0-7894-9869-4(3)) Dorling Kindersley Publishing, Inc.

Oxlade, Chris. My First Email Guide. 2007. (J). (***978-1-4329-0017-5(X)***); pap. (***978-1-4329-0021-2(8)***) Heinemann Library.

—My First Internet Guide. 2007. (J). (***978-1-4329-0019-9(6)***); pap. (***978-1-4329-0023-6(4)***) Heinemann Library.

Parks, Peggy J. The Internet. (Lucent Library of Science & Technology Ser.). (J). 2005. 112p. (gr. 7-10). lib. bdg. 29.95 (978-1-59018-441-7(6) , Lucent Bks.); 2003. 48p. 23.70 (978-0-7377-1015-1(2) , Greenhaven Pr., Inc.) Thomson Gale.

Pedersen, Ted. How to Find Almost Anything on the Internet: A Kid's Guide to Safe Searching. 2000. (Illus.). (J). 11.79 (978-0-606-18468-7(6)) Tandem Library Bks.

Pelusey, Michael & Pelusey, Jane. Internet (Media) 2005. (Media Ser.). (Illus.). 32p. (J). (ps-8). lib. bdg. 21.95 (978-0-7910-8803-6(0) , Chelsea Hse.) Facts On File, Inc.

Perry, Robert. Build Your Own Website. 2000. (Watts Library). (Illus.). 64p. (YA). (gr. 5-7). pap. 8.95 (978-0-531-16469-3(1) , Watts, Franklin) Scholastic Library Publishing.

—Build Your Own Website. 2000. (gr. 5-8). lib. bdg. 17.60 (978-0-613-37300-5(6)) Tandem Library Bks.

Peters, Craig. Steve Case: Internet Genius of America Online. 2003. (Internet Biographies Ser.). (Illus.). 48p. (YA). (gr. 4-10). lib. bdg. 23.93 (978-0-7660-1971-3(3)) Enslow Pubs., Inc.

Polly, Jean Armour. Internet Kids & Family Yellow Pages. 3rd ed. 1999. 744p. (J). pap. 34.99 (978-0-07-212206-0(4)) McGraw-Hill School Education Group.

Pondiscio, Robert. Get on the Net: Everything You Need to Know about the Internet, Including Hundreds of Fun & Useful Sites. 1999. 240p. (J). (gr. 5-9). pap. 5.99 (978-0-380-80334-7(8)) HarperCollins Pubs.

—Get on the Net: Everything You Need to Know about the Internet, Including the World Wide Web & Addresses for Hours of Fun & Ease. 1999. (Illus.). (J). (978-0-606-17972-0(0)) Tandem Library Bks.

Quadrillion Media Staff. Internet (Das Internet) Surfin' the Web. 1998. (Start Me Up Ser.). 64p. (J). (gr. 3-8). pap. 15.95 (978-1-58185-023-9(9) , Tessloff Publishing) Quadrillion Media LLC.

Restrepo, Jaime A. Internet para Todos. 1999. (Illus.). (J). (978-0-606-18498-4(8)) Tandem Library Bks.

Robinette, Michelle. Internet Scavengr Hunt American History. 2002. (Internet Scavenger Hunts Ser.). (Illus.). 64p. (gr. 4-8). pap. 10.95 (978-0-439-31665-1(0)) Scholastic, Inc.

Rominger, Lynne. Extraordinary Blogs & Ezines. 2006. 128p. (gr. 8-12). pap. 9.95 (978-0-531-13904-2(2) , Watts, Franklin) Scholastic Library Publishing.

Rosner, Marc Alan. Science Fair Success Using the Internet. (Science Fair Success Ser.). (Illus.). 112p. (gr. 6-12). 1999. (YA). lib. bdg. 26.60 (978-0-7660-1172-4(0)); 2006. (J). lib. bdg. 26.60 (978-0-7660-2425-0(3)) Enslow Pubs., Inc.

Rothman, Kevin F. Coping with Dangers on the Internet. 2005. (Coping Ser.). (Illus.). 192p. (YA). (gr. 7-12). lib. bdg. 26.50 (978-0-8239-3201-6(X)) Rosen Publishing Group, Inc., The.

Royston, Angela. Internet & E-Mail. 2001. (In Touch Ser.). (Illus.). 32p. (J). (gr. 1-3). lib. bdg. 22.79 (978-1-58810-063-4(4)) Heinemann Library.

Roza, Greg. The Incredible Story of Computers & the Internet. 2004. (Kid's Guide to Incredible Technology Ser.). (Illus.). 24p. (J). lib. bdg. 19.95 (978-0-8239-6717-9(4) , PowerKids Pr.) Rosen Publishing Group, Inc., The.

Salvador, Roberta. The Best Ever Web Sites for the Topics You Teach. 2000. pap. 10.95 (978-0-439-13115-5(4)) Scholastic, Inc.

Sheikh-Miller, Jonathan. Snakes. 2004. (Discovery Program Ser.). (SPA., Illus.). 64p. (J). (gr. 2 up). pap. 8.95 (978-0-7945-0004-7(8) , Usborne); lib. bdg. 16.95 (978-1-58086-344-5(2)) EDC Publishing.

Sherman, Josepha. The History of the Internet. 2003. (Illus.). 63p. (J). (ps-7). lib. bdg. 17.60 (978-0-613-67630-4(0)) Tandem Library Bks.

—Internet Safety. 2003. (gr. 5-8). lib. bdg. 17.60 (978-0-613-67636-6(X)) Tandem Library Bks.

—It's a www. World. 2004. (YA). lib. bdg. 25.90 (978-0-7613-2353-2(8) , Millbrook Pr.) Lerner Publishing Group.

Snedden, Robert. The Internet. 2001. (Technoworld Ser.). (Illus.). 32p. (J). lib. bdg. 25.69 (978-0-7398-3253-0(0)) Raintree.

Solomon, Gwen, et al. Connect Online! 2002. stu. ed. 41.32 (978-0-07-824520-6(6) , 9780078245206) Glencoe/McGraw-Hill.

Souter, Gerry, et al. Researching on the Internet Using Search Engines, Bulletin Boards, & Listservs. 2003. (Internet Library). (Illus.). 64p. (J). (gr. 4-12). lib. bdg. 22.60 (978-0-7660-2081-8(9)) Enslow Pubs., Inc.

Space, Cy B. Dump It: Cool Stuff from the Net. 2000. (Illus.). 96p. (J). (gr. 3 up). pap. 4.95 (978-1-902618-48-7(3)) Element Children's Bks.

Spangenburg, Ray & Moser, Diane. Savvy Surfing on the Internet: Searching & Evaluating Web Sites. 2001. (Issues in Focus Ser.). (Illus.). 112p. (YA). (gr. 6-12). lib. bdg. 26.60 (978-0-7660-1590-6(4)) Enslow Pubs., Inc.

Stephens, Catherine. Inside the Internet. 2003. (Science Issues Today Ser.). (Illus.). 32p. (J). pap. (978-0-7922-8875-6(0)) National Geographic Society.

Stephens, Michael. The Library Internet Trainer's Toolkit. 2001. (Netguide Ser.). (Illus.). 223p. cd-rom 149.95 (978-1-55570-415-5(8)) Neal-Schuman Pubs., Inc.

Story-Huffman, Ru. Caldecott on the Net: Reading & Internet Activities. 2nd rev. ed. 2002. 93p. (J). (gr. k-5). pap. 17.95 (978-1-57950-076-4(5) , Upstart Bks.) Highsmith Inc.

—Newbery on the Net: Reading & Internet Activities. 2nd rev. ed. 2002. 96p. (J). (gr. 4-8). pap. 17.95 (978-1-57950-077-1(3) , Upstart Bks.) Highsmith Inc.

Stoyles, Pennie, et al. Information Technology Issues. 2003. 32p. (J). lib. bdg. 24.25 (978-1-58340-329-7(9)) Smart Apple Media.

Tatchell, Judy. Science Encyclopedia. 2004. (Library of Science Ser.). (Illus.). 448p. (J). (gr. 4 up). 39.95 (978-0-7460-3833-8(X)); lib. bdg. 47.95 (978-1-58086-337-7(X)) EDC Publishing.

Toby, Edna & Stevens, Robert. What's the Internet? Stevens, Robert, illus. 1998. (Illus.). 32p. (J). (gr. k-3). 19.95 (978-0-9662813-1-6(4)) New Traditions Pr., Inc.

Toronto Public Library Staff. The Research Virtuoso: Brilliant Methods for Normal Brains. Weissmann, Joe, illus. 2006. 88p. (gr. 12). 19.95 (978-1-55037-957-0(7)); pap. 10.95 (978-1-55037-956-3(9)) Annick Pr., Ltd. CAN. *Dist:* Firefly Bks., Ltd.

Tracy, Kathleen. Marc Andreessen & the Development of the Web Browser. 2002. (Unlocking the Secrets of Science Ser.). (Illus.). 56p. (gr. 4-10). lib. bdg. 25.70 (978-1-58415-092-3(0)) Mitchell Lane Pubs., Inc.

Trumbauer, Lisa. Computer Fun Social Studies. 2000. (J). (978-0-606-19151-7(8)) Tandem Library Bks.

—Homework Help for Kids on the Net. 2000. (gr. 3-6). lib. bdg. 12.95 (978-0-613-25545-5(3)); (Illus.). (J). (978-0-606-20708-9(2)) Tandem Library Bks.

Vander Hook, Sue. Internet. 1999. (Making Contact Ser.). (Illus.). 32p. (YA). (gr. 4-7). lib. bdg. 16.95 (978-1-887068-61-1(9)) Smart Apple Media.

Vitual Tours. 2001. (J). (978-0-307-10542-4(3) , Golden Bks.) Random Hse. Children's Bks.

Wallace, Mark. 101 Things to Do on the Internet. 1999. (gr. 3-6). lib. bdg. 19.90 (978-0-613-74408-9(X)) Tandem Library Bks.

Ward-Johnson, Chris. Internet: A Magic Mouse Guide. Laughing Gravy Design Staff, illus. 2003. (Magic Mouse Guides). 32p. (J). lib. bdg. 22.60 (978-0-7660-2260-7(9)) Enslow Pubs., Inc.

Weber, Sandra. The Internet. 2003. (Transforming Power of Technology Ser.). (Illus.). 112p. (J). (gr. 9-13). 30.00 (978-0-7910-7449-7(8) , Chelsea Hse.) Facts On File, Inc.

Wingate, Philippa & Wallace, Mark. The Internet. 1999. (Computer Guides Ser.). (Illus.). 112p. (YA). (gr. 5 up). pap. 14.95 (978-0-7460-4091-1(1)) EDC Publishing.

Wolinsky, Art. Communicating on the Internet. (Internet Library). (Illus.). 64p. (YA). (gr. 4-12). 2000. pap. 11.93 (978-0-7660-1743-6(5)); 1999. lib. bdg. 22.60 (978-0-7660-1260-8(3)) Enslow Pubs., Inc.

—Creating & Publishing Web Pages on the Internet. (Internet Library). (Illus.). 64p. (YA). (gr. 4-12). 2000. pap. 11.93 (978-0-7660-1744-3(3)); 1999. lib. bdg. 22.60 (978-0-7660-1262-2(X)) Enslow Pubs., Inc.

—The History of the Internet & the World Wide Web. (Internet Library). (Illus.). 64p. (YA). (gr. 4-12). 2000. pap. 11.93 (978-0-7660-1746-7(X)); 1999. lib. bdg. 22.60 (978-0-7660-1261-5(1)) Enslow Pubs., Inc.

—The Internet Library, 4 bks., Set. Incl. Communicating on the Internet. pap. 11.93 (978-0-7660-1743-6(5)); Creating & Publishing Web Pages on the Internet. pap. 11.93 (978-0-7660-1744-3(3)); History of the Internet & the World Wide Web. pap. 11.93 (978-0-7660-1746-7(X)); Locating & Evaluating Information on the Internet. pap. 11.93 (978-0-7660-1745-0(1)); 64p. (YA). (gr. 4-12). 2000. (Illus.). 1999. Set pap. 39.80 (978-0-7660-1795-5(8)) Enslow Pubs., Inc.

—Internet Power Research Using the Big Approach. rev. ed. 2005. (Internet Library). (Illus.). 64p. (J). lib. bdg. 22.60 (978-0-7660-1563-0(7)) Enslow Pubs., Inc.

—Internet Power Research Using the Big6 Approach. 2005. (Internet Library). (Illus.). 64p. pap. (978-0-7660-1564-7(5)) Enslow Pubs., Inc.

—Locating & Evaluating Information on the Internet. (Internet Library). (Illus.). 64p. (YA). (gr. 4-12). 2000. pap. 11.93 (978-0-7660-1745-0(1)); 1999. lib. bdg. 22.60 (978-0-7660-1259-2(X)) Enslow Pubs., Inc.

—Safe Surfing on the Internet. 2003. (Internet Library). (Illus.). 64p. (YA). (gr. 4-12). lib. bdg. 22.60 (978-0-7660-2030-6(4)) Enslow Pubs., Inc.

Wood, Ira. How to Stay Safe at Home & On-Line. 2002. (Illus.). 24p. (J). pap. (978-0-8239-8159-5(2)); lib. bdg. 18.75 (978-0-8239-3722-6(4)) Rosen Publishing Group, Inc., The.

INTERNET—FICTION

Amato, Mary. The Naked Mole Rat Letters. 2007. 208p. (J). (gr. 3-7). pap. 6.95 (***978-0-8234-2098-8(1)***) Holiday Hse., Inc.

Anzalone, Karen. Time in a Bottle. 2003. 100p. (YA). pap. 9.00 (978-0-7599-3840-3(7)) Hard Shell Word Factory.

Barlow, Steve & Skidmore, Steve. The Doomsday Virus. Buckley, Harriet, illus. 2008. (J). pap. (***978-1-59889-907-8(4)***); lib. bdg. (***978-1-59889-871-2(X)***) Stone Arch Bks.

Baxter, Stephen. The Web: Gulliverzone. 2005. 128p. (J). (gr. 4-6). mass mkt. 5.99 (978-0-7653-4941-5(8) , Tor Bks.) Doherty, Tom Assocs., LLC.

—Web Webcrash. 1998. 128p. (J). pap. 7.99 (978-1-85881-632-6(7)) Orion Children's Bks. GBR. *Dist:* Trafalgar Square Publishing.

Berenstain, Stan & Berenstain, Jan. The Berenstain Bears Lost in Cyberspace. 1999. (Berenstain Bears Big Chapter Bks.). (J). (gr. 2-6). (978-0-606-16839-7(7)) Tandem Library Bks.

Brown, Terry, creator. Stranger Online. 2005. (Todays-Girls.com Ser.: Vol. 1). 144p. (J). pap. 5.99 (978-1-4003-0755-5(4)) Nelson, Thomas Inc.

Butcher, Kristin. Chat Room. 2006. 112p. (gr. 5-10). pap. 7.95 (978-1-55143-485-8(7)); lib. bdg. 14.95 (978-1-55143-529-9(2)) Orca Bk. Pubs. USA.

Capeci, Anne. Case of the Cyber-Hacker. l.t. ed. 2000. (Wishbone Mysteries Ser.: No. 19). (Illus.). 141p. (J). (gr. 4 up). lib. bdg. 23.33 (978-0-8368-2702-6(3)) Stevens, Gareth Inc.

—Case of the Cyber-Hacker. 2000. (gr. 3-6). lib. bdg. 11.80 (978-0-613-27764-8(3)) Tandem Library Bks.

Carson, D. Mathew. Cyber Angel. 2006. pap. 8.95 (978-0-533-15218-6(6)) Vantage Pr., Inc.

Clancy, Tom. Shadow of Honor. 1999. (Tom Clancy's Net Force Ser.). (978-0-606-20428-6(8)) Tandem Library Bks.

Cray, Jordan. Bad Intent. 1998. (Danger.com Ser.: No. 6). (YA). (gr. 6 up). (978-0-606-13310-4(0)) Tandem Library Bks.

—Most Wanted. 1998. (Danger.com Ser.: No. 7). (YA). (gr. 6 up). (978-0-606-13311-1(9)) Tandem Library Bks.

—Stalker. 1998. (Danger.com Ser.: No. 5). (YA). (gr. 6 up). (978-0-606-13309-8(7)) Tandem Library Bks.

Cregar, Elyse. Feline Online: What Happens When a Smart Cat Surfs the Internet? 2001. 149p. (J). (gr. 2-7). pap. 8.95 (978-0-9621292-1-6(6)) Tamerac Publishing Co.

Draper, Sharon M. Romiette & Julio. 2009. 320p. (YA). pap. 8.99 (***978-1-4169-5514-6(3)*** , Simon Pulse) Simon & Schuster Children's Publishing.

—Romiette & Julio. Lowenbein, Adam, illus. (YA). (gr. 7-12). 2001. 336p. mass mkt. 6.99 (978-0-689-84209-2(0) , Simon Pulse); 1999. 240p. 18.99 (978-0-689-82180-6(8) , Atheneum) Simon & Schuster Children's Publishing.

Duracell and the National Center for Missing & Exploited Children (NCMEC), creator. The Great Tomato Adventure: A Story about Smart Safety Choices. 2007. 0.00 (*978-0-9795307-0-8(9)) Duracell & the National Ctr. for Missing & Exploited Children (NCMEC).

Ferrari, Vincent. Blogosfear. 2005. 143p. (YA). pap. 15.00 (978-1-4116-6814-0(6)) Lulu.com.

Fink, Jeri & Paltrowitz, Donna. Mathew's Tangled Trails. (YA). pap. 11.95 (978-0-7925-5279-6(2)) Educational Activities, Inc.

Fuzy, Jim. An Internet Adventure with Safari Sam. Melvin, Anita Flannery, illus. 2004. 24p. (J). per. 14.95 (978-0-9760129-7-9(9)) Avant Garde Publishing.

Haddix, Margaret Peterson. Among the Hidden. Nielsen, Cliff, illus. 2000. (Shadow Children Ser.). 160p. (J). (gr. 3-7). mass mkt. 5.99 (978-0-689-82475-3(0) , Aladdin) Simon & Schuster Children's Publishing.

Hooper, Mary. Amy. 2004. 176p. (J). (gr. 5-10). reprint ed. pap. 6.95 (978-1-58234-915-2(0) , Bloomsbury Children) Bloomsbury Publishing.

iKeepSafe.Org Staff, et al. Faux Paw Meets the First Lady: Keeping Children Safe Online. Sandman Studios Staff, illus. 2006. 45p. pap., pap., pap. 14.95 incl. cd-rom (978-0-470-05138-2(8) , Wiley) Wiley, John & Sons, Inc.

—Faux Paw's Adventures in the Internet: Keeping Children Safe Online. 2006. 32p. pap., pap., pap. 14.95 incl. cd-rom (978-0-470-05137-5(X) , Wiley) Wiley, John & Sons, Inc.

Jenkins, Jerry B. & Fabry, Chris. Instant Menace. 2006. (Tyndale Kids Ser.). 256p. (J). pap. 5.99 (978-1-4143-0148-8(0)) Tyndale Hse. Pubs.

Leblanc, Louise. Maddie Surfs for Cyber Pals. Gay, Marie-Louise, illus. 2004. 64p. (J). lib. bdg. 12.00 (*978-1-4242-1226-2(X)) Fitzgerald Bks.

—Maddie Surfs for Cyber Pals. Cummins, Sarah, tr. from FRE. Gay, Marie-Louise, illus. 2004. (First Novels Ser.: Vol. 52). 64p. (gr. 2-5). (J). 4.95 (978-0-88780-638-4(4)); (*978-0-88780-639-1(2)) Formac Publishing Co., Ltd. CAN. *Dist:* Casemate Pubs. & Bk. Distributors, LLC.

Mackall, Dandi Daley. Grace Notes. 2006. (Faithgirlz Ser.). (Illus.). 128p. (J). pap. 6.99 (978-0-310-71093-6(6)) Zonderkidz.

Matthew's Web Unplugged. 2003. (J). per. (978-0-9716567-7-2(0)) Book Web Publishing, Ltd.

McNeece, Alexander. Sam Iver: Imminent Threat. 2007. 140p. per. 11.95 (*978-0-595-43260-8(3)) iUniverse, Inc.

Messinger, Robert. I've Got Mail! Salerno, John, illus. 2003. 40p. 12.95 (978-1-893237-01-8(X)) Little Mai Pr.

Miss O, Harlie, Justine, and Isabella, with Devra Newberger Speregen, Juliette. Caught in the Net. 2006. (Miss O & Friends Ser.). (Illus.). 144p. (J). pap. 5.99 (978-0-8230-2948-8(4)) Watson-Guptill Pubns., Inc.

Myracle, Lauren. Ttyl. (Internet Girls Ser.). (YA). (gr. 8-17). 2005. 234p. pap. 6.95 (978-0-8109-8788-3(0)); 2004. 224p. 15.95 (978-0-8109-4821-1(4) , Amulet Bks.) Abrams, Harry N. , Inc.

Sanschagrin, Joceline. Le Visage Masqué. Brignaud, Pierre, illus. 2004. (Mon Roman Ser.). (FRE.). 160p. (J). (gr. 2). pap. (978-2-89021-651-8(9)) Diffusion du livre Mirabel.

Skurzynski, Gloria. Over the Edge. 2002. (gr. 3-6). lib. bdg. 14.10 (978-0-613-62819-8(5)) Tandem Library Bks.

Skurzynski, Gloria & Ferguson, Alane. Over the Edge. 2002. (Mysteries in Our National Parks Ser.: Vol. 7). 160p. (J). (gr. 3-7). pap. 5.95 (978-0-7922-6686-0(2)); Vol. 7. 15.95 (978-0-7922-6677-8(3)) National Geographic Society. (National Geographic Children's Bks.).

Stewart, Sharon. Spider's Web. 1998. 160p. (J). (gr. 4-9). pap. 7.95 (978-0-88995-177-8(2)) Red Deer Pr. CAN. *Dist:* Fitzhenry & Whiteside, Ltd.

Tashjian, Janet. The Gospel According to Larry. rev. ed. 2001. (Illus.). 192p. (YA). (gr. 7 up). 16.95 (978-0-8050-6378-3(1) , Holt, Henry & Co. Bks. For Young Readers) Holt, Henry & Co.

—The Gospel According to Larry. 2003. (Illus.). 256p. (YA). (gr. 7). mass mkt. 6.50 (978-0-440-23792-1(0) , Laurel Leaf) Random Hse. Children's Bks.

—The Gospel According to Larry. l.t. ed. 2005. (Illus.). 235p. (YA). (gr. 8-12). lib. bdg. 22.95 (978-0-7862-7543-4(X)) Thorndike Pr.

Ure, Jean. Secret Meeting. 2004. (Diary Ser.). (Illus.). 176p. (J). pap. 8.99 (978-0-00-715620-7(0) , Collins) HarperCollins Pubs. Ltd. GBR. *Dist:* Independent Pubs. Group.

Walters, Eric. Stuffed. 2006. 112p. (gr. 3-6). lib. bdg. 14.95 (978-1-55143-519-0(5)); (gr. 7-12). pap. 7.95 (978-1-55143-500-8(4)) Orca Bk. Pubs. USA.

Wilhelm, Doug. The Revealers. 224p. (J). 2003. 16.00 (978-0-374-36255-3(6) , Farrar, Straus & Giroux (BYR)); 2005. reprint ed. pap. 6.95 (978-0-374-46243-7(7) , Sunburst) Farrar, Straus & Giroux.

Wilson, Jacqueline. The Worry Web Site. 2005. 112p. (gr. 3-7). pap. 5.50 (978-0-440-41929-7(8) , Yearling) Random Hse. Children's Bks.

—The Worry Website. l.t. ed. 2003. (Illus.). 168p. (J). 16.95 (978-0-7540-7842-5(6) , Galaxy Children's Large Print) BBC Audiobooks America.

Yates, Janet Lee. Skeeter Bug Loves Sarah. 2007. (ENG.). 88p. per. 11.99 (*978-1-4141-0820-9(6)) Pleasant Word.

Zondervan. 2:52 Laptop 1 Reality Shift/Laptop 2 Double Take - Focus on the Family: 52 Laptop 1 Reality Shift/ Laptop 2 Double Take - Focus on the Family. 2004. (J). pap. 9.98 (978-0-310-70934-3(2)) Zonderkidz.

INTERNMENT CAMPS

see Concentration Camps

INTERPERSONAL RELATIONS

Here are entered works that deal with the integration of people so that they can live and work together with psychological, social and economic satisfaction.

Acevedo, Eddie. The Ultimate Teen Relationship Guide! Step-by-Step Handbook for Love & Dating That Young People Can Really Use! 2002. (gr. 7-12). lib. bdg. 32.70 (978-0-613-77555-7(4)) Tandem Library Bks.

Algranati, Melissa J. Talk about It: Family Fun for Girls 8-11. 2005. (Illus.). 49p. (J). (978-0-88441-696-8(8)) Girl Scouts of the USA.

Allenbaugh, Kay. Chocolate for a Teen's Dreams: Heartwarming Stories about Making Your Wishes Come True. 2003. (Illus.). 224p. pap. 12.00 (978-0-7432-3703-1(X) , Fireside) Simon & Schuster.

Amos, Janine. ¡Es Mio! Coffee, Carol & Carrillo, Consuelo, trs. Spenceley, Annabel, illus. 2002. (Weekly Reader Early Learning Library). (SPA.). 32p. (J). (ps up). lib. bdg. 23.33 (978-0-8368-3678-3(2)) Stevens, Gareth Inc.

—Separations, 4 bks. Green, Gwen, illus. Hampton, Angela, photos by. Incl. Death. lib. bdg. 23.33 (978-0-8368-3089-7(X)); Divorce. lib. bdg. 23.33 (978-0-8368-3090-3(3)); Hospital. lib. bdg. 23.33 (978-0-8368-3091-0(1)); Moving. lib. bdg. 23.33 (978-0-8368-3092-7(X)); 32p. (J). (gr. 3 up). (Illus.). 2002. Set lib. bdg. 93.32 (978-0-8368-3088-0(1)) Stevens, Gareth Inc.

Anonymous. Diary of a Junior Year. (Real Teens Ser.: Vol. 4). (YA). (gr. 7 up). 2000. 196p. pap. 4.99 (978-0-439-08411-6(3) , Scholastic Paperbacks); 1999. pap. 59.88 (978-0-439-13483-5(8)); 1999. mass mkt. 59.88 (978-0-439-11746-3(1)); 1999. mass mkt. 59.88 (978-0-439-09275-3(2)) Scholastic, Inc.

—Diary of a Junior Year. 1999. (Real Teens Ser.: Vol. 1). (YA). (gr. 7 up). 11.64 (978-0-606-17278-3(5)); (978-0-606-17547-0(4)) Tandem Library Bks.

Artsrunik, Valentina. How to Flirt & Be Seductive. 2001. (Illus.). 100p. (YA). pap. 11.99 (978-1-903906-02-6(4)) Artnik Media GBR. *Dist:* De Breff, Vanko.

Asugha, Ruby. Little Sisters, Listen Up! A Message of Hope for Girls Growing up in Poverty Racism, & Despair. 2004. 138p. 9.95 (978-1-889322-61-2(X) , 25-017) Boys Town Pr.

Baish, Vanessa. Frequently Asked Questions about Dating: Teen Life. 2006. (FAQ Ser.). (Illus.). 64p. (J). (gr. 7-12). lib. bdg. 27.95 (*978-1-4042-1969-4(2)) Rosen Publishing Group, Inc., The.

Baker, Jed. The Social Skills Picture Book: For High School & Beyond. 2006. (Illus.). 177p. (J). (gr. 4-7). per. 39.95 (*978-1-932565-35-5(3)) Future Horizons, Inc.

Bartel, Blaine. Little Black Book on How to Get Along with Your Parents. 2004. (Illus.). 80p. (J). pap. 4.99 (978-1-57794-626-7(X)) Harrison Hse., Inc.

Bawden, Jennifer. Un Hombre no es la Solucion: Construye una Vida Propia y Luego, una Relacion con Alguien. (SPA.). (J). 12.00 (978-958-04-7015-1(4)) Norma S.A. COL. *Dist:* Distribuidora Norma, Inc.

Becker, Leah B. & Beck, Carol. My Grandma's Angels. 2000. 48p. (J). (ps-3). 12.00 (978-1-57921-308-4(1)) WinePress Publishing.

Beisswenger, Iffer & Eldred, Margaret. The Way We See Things: Middle Schoolers Look at Themselves & Issues They Face Everyday. Krusi, Carolynne, ed. 2004. 96p. pap. 14.95 (978-0-9759264-0-6(3)) Rope Ferry Pr.

Bender, Janet. Getting Yourself Together When Your Family Comes Apart: Coping with Family Changes. 2004. (Illus.). 50p. (J). per. 19.95 (978-1-931636-28-5(1)) National Center For Youth Issues.

Bennett, Vicki. Life Smart: Choices for Young People about Friendship, Family & Future. 2003. (Illus.). 192p. (J). pap. 14.95 (978-1-876451-13-4(0)) Finch Publishing AUS. *Dist:* Independent Pubs. Group.

Benton, Jim. Love Bites. 2005. (It's Happy Bunny Ser.: No. 1). (Illus.). 72p. (J). 7.99 (978-0-439-69345-5(4)) Scholastic, Inc.

Berry, Joy Wilt. A Book about Being Mean. 2005. (Illus.). (J). (978-0-7172-8591-4(X)) Scholastic, Inc.

—A Book about Complaining. 2005. (Illus.). (J). (978-0-7172-8595-2(2)) Scholastic, Inc.

—A Book about Interrupting. 2005. (Illus.). (J). (978-0-7172-8599-0(5)) Scholastic, Inc.

Blackburn, Tammie. It Takes Two. Coffman, Dennis, illus. 2000. 16p. (J). pap. 5.95 (978-1-891846-16-8(7)) Business Word, The.

Blatt, Jessica. The Teen Girl's Gotta-Have-It Guide to Boys: From Getting Them to Getting over Them! Frenette, Cynthia, illus. 2007. (Teen Girl's Gotta-Have-It Guides). 96p. (YA). (gr. 7 up). pap. 8.95 (978-0-8230-1725-6(7)) Watson-Guptill Pubns., Inc.

Block, Joel D. & Bartell, Susan S. Stepliving for Teens: Getting along with Stepparents & Siblings. 2001. (Plugged in Ser.). (Illus.). 96p. (J). (gr. 4-12). pap. 4.99 (978-0-8431-7568-4(0) , Price Stern Sloan) Penguin Group (USA) Inc.

Bode, Janet. Heartbreak & Roses: Real Life Stories of Troubled Love. 2000. (YA). (978-0-606-19403-7(7)) Tandem Library Bks.

Borlenghi, Patricia. Dear Aunty. 2001. 128p. (J). pap. 10.99 (978-0-7475-4735-8(1)) Bloomsbury Publishing Plc GBR. *Dist:* Independent Pubs. Group.

Burns, Peggy. Make Friends, Break Friends. 2004. (Kids' Guides Ser.). (Illus.). 32p. (J). (gr. 1-4). lib. bdg. 25.64 (978-1-4109-0571-0(3)) Raintree.

—Playground Survival. 2004. (Kids' Guides Ser.). (Illus.). 32p. (J). (gr. 1-4). lib. bdg. 25.64 (978-1-4109-0572-7(1)) Raintree.

Canfield, Jack L., et al. Chicken Soup for the Teenage Soul: Stories about Disses, Losses, Messes, Stresses & More. 2006. 280p. (YA). pap. 14.95 (978-0-7573-0407-1(9)) Health Communications, Inc.

Carlson, Dale Bick. Talk: Teen Art of Communication. Khairnar, Kishore, ed. Nicklaus, Carol, illus. 2006. 154p. (YA). (gr. 7 up). pap. 14.95 (978-1-884158-32-2(3)) Bick Publishing Hse.

Cassella, Lynn. When Parents Divorce. 2003. (YA). pap. 1.95 net. (978-0-7648-1061-9(8)) Liguori Pubns.

Cavallaro, Gloria. My Beloved's Israel. Wootten, Batya R. et al, eds. Lenhart, Crystal & Yisrael, Miriam, illus. 2001. 384p. (YA). pap. 16.95 (978-1-886987-05-0(X)) House of David.

Clark, Chap. Next Time I Fall in Love: How to Handle Sex, Intimacy, & Feelings in Dating Relationships. 2004. 144p. pap. 18.00 (978-1-59244-684-1(1) , Wipf and Stock) Wipf & Stock Pubs.

Clark, Jan. Family Survival. 2004. (Illus.). 32p. (J). lib. bdg. 25.64 (978-1-4109-0569-7(1)) Raintree.

Clement, Claude & Daly, Melissa. Don't Be Shy: How to Fit in, Make Friends, & Have Fun-Even If You Weren't Born Outgoing. Quennehen, Christian, illus. 2005. (Sunscreen Ser.). 112p. (J). (gr. 5-9). pap. 9.95 (978-0-8109-5860-9(0)) Abrams, Harry N. , Inc.

Cobb, Carlene. Coping with an Abusive Relationship. 2005. (Coping Ser.). (Illus.). 192p. (YA). (gr. 7-12). lib. bdg. 26.50 (978-0-8239-2822-4(5)) Rosen Publishing Group, Inc., The.

Colwell, Todd. Get Real about Relationships: Leader's Guide. 2005. (YA). 7.95 (978-0-9748825-6-7(9)) Ampelon Publishing, LLC.

Cook, Julia. Personal Space Camp. 2006. (J). 15.95 (*978-1-934073-06-3(7)) CTC Publishing.

—Personal Space Camp: Teaching Children the Concepts of Personal Space. ed. 2006. 32p. (J). (ps up). pap. 9.95 (*978-1-934073-05-6(9)) CTC Publishing.

Cooper, Scott. Speak up & Get Along! Learn the Mighty Might, Thought Chop, & More Tools to Make Friends, Stop Teasing, & Feel Good about Yourself! 2005. (Illus.). 128p. (J). (gr. 3-7). pap. 12.95 (978-1-57542-182-7(8)) Free Spirit Publishing, Inc.

CosmoGIRL! Editors. All about Guys. Cosmopolitan Editors, ed. 2004. (CosmoGIRL Quiz Book Ser.). (Illus.). 128p. pap. 5.95 (978-1-58816-382-0(2)) Hearst Bks.

—All about You. Cosmopolitan Editors, ed. 2004. (CosmoGIRL Quiz Book Ser.). (Illus.). 128p. pap. 5.95 (978-1-58816-381-3(4)) Hearst Bks.

Cotta, Susan. I Can Show You I Care: Compassionate Touch for Children. Crawford, Gregory, illus. 2003. 32p. (gr. 1-5). 16.95 (978-1-55643-433-4(2)) North Atlantic Bks.

Crissy, Pat. Real-World Social Skills Curriculum. 2004. (J). ring bd. 69.95 (978-1-58804-368-9(1)) PCI Educational Publishing.

Davidson, Tish. School Conflict. 2004. (Life Balance Ser.). (Illus.). 79p. (YA). (gr. 5-8). pap. 6.95 (978-0-531-15571-4(4) , Watts, Franklin) Scholastic Library Publishing.

Dee, Catherine. Girls' Book of Love: Cool Quotes, Super Stories, Awesome Advice, & More. 2002. (gr. 3-6). lib. bdg. 18.75 (978-0-613-71776-2(7)) Tandem Library Bks.

Diary of a Junior Year. 2000. (Real Teens Ser.: Vol. 6). 160p. (YA). (gr. 7 up). pap. 4.99 (978-0-439-08413-0(X)) Scholastic, Inc.

Drew, Naomi. The Kids' Guide to Working Out Conflicts: How to Keep Cool, Stay Safe, & Get Along. 2004. (Illus.). 160p. (J). (gr. 5-9). pap. 13.95 (978-1-57542-150-6(X)) Free Spirit Publishing, Inc.

Educators for Social Responsibility, told to. The Courage to Be Yourself: True Stories by Teens about Cliques, Conflicts, & Overcoming Peer Pressure. 2005. 160p. (YA). (gr. 8 up). pap. 13.95 (978-1-57542-185-8(2)) Free Spirit Publishing, Inc.

Espeland, Pamela. Knowing Me, Knowing You: The I-Sight Way to Understand Yourself & Others. 2004. (Illus.). 128p. (YA). (gr. 8-12). pap. 13.95 (978-1-57542-090-5(2)) Free Spirit Publishing, Inc.

—A Leader's Guide to Knowing Me, Knowing You. 2004. 112p. (gr. 6-12). tchr. ed. 21.95 (978-1-57542-091-2(0)) Free Spirit Publishing, Inc.

Espeland, Pamela & Verdick, Elizabeth. Making Choices & Making Friends. 2006. (Illus.). 80p. (J). (gr. 3-7). pap. 9.95 (978-1-57542-201-5(8)) Free Spirit Publishing, Inc.

Everly, Nita. Early Social Behavior Books Can You Be a Friend? 2005. (J). spiral bd. 10.95 (978-0-7606-0633-9(1)) LinguiSystems, Inc.

—Early Social Behavior Books Can you Be Polite? 2005. (J). spiral bd. 10.95 (978-0-7606-0637-7(4)) LinguiSystems, Inc.

—Early Social Behavior Books Can You Listen with Your Eyes? 2005. (J). spiral bd. 10.95 (978-0-7606-0630-8(7)) LinguiSystems, Inc.

—Early Social Behavior Books Can You Share? 2005. (J). spiral bd. 10.95 (978-0-7606-0635-3(8)) LinguiSystems, Inc.

—Early Social Behavior Books Can You Take Turns? 2005. (J). spiral bd. 10.95 (978-0-7606-0634-6(X)) LinguiSystems, Inc.

—Early Social Behavior Books Can You Tell How Someone Feels? 2005. (J). spiral bd. 14.95 (978-0-7606-0636-0(6)) LinguiSystems, Inc.

—Early Social Behavior Books Can You Use a Good Voice? 2005. (J). spiral bd. 10.95 (978-0-7606-0632-2(3)) LinguiSystems, Inc.

—Early Social Behavior Books Can You Use Your Words? 2005. (J). spiral bd. 10.95 (978-0-7606-0631-5(5)) LinguiSystems, Inc.

Family Relationships Classroom Library. (gr. k-2). lib. bdg. 82.95 (978-0-7368-1832-2(4)) Red Brick Learning.

Family Relationships Complete Unit. (gr. k-2). 381.95 (978-0-7368-1833-9(2)) Red Brick Learning.

Fiedler, Julie & Kravetz, Jonathan. How to Deal with Insults. 2007. (Let's Work It Out Ser.). (Illus.). 24p. (J). (gr. 2-5). lib. bdg. 21.25 (*978-1-4042-3673-8(2) , PowerKids Pr.) Rosen Publishing Group, Inc., The.

Fields, Doug & Eastman, Brett. Connecting Your Heart to Others: 6 Small Group Sessions on Fellowship. 2003. (Life Together Ser.). 144p. pap., stu. ed. 7.99 (978-0-310-25334-1(9)) Zondervan.

—Growing to Be Like Jesus: 6 Small Group Sessions on Discipleship. 2003. (Life Together Ser.). 144p. pap., stu. ed. 7.99 (978-0-310-25335-8(7)) Zondervan.

—Starting to Go Where God Wants You to Be: 6 Small Group Lessons on Beginning Life Together. 2003. (Life Together Ser.). 144p. pap., stu. ed. 7.99 (978-0-310-25333-4(0)) Zondervan.

Finding a Partner in Later Life. 2005. (YA). per. (978-1-59872-108-9(9)) Instantpublisher.com.

Finnis, Anne & Bond, Denis. It's A Boy/Girl Thing. 2003. (Illus.). 144p. (J). pap. 10.95 (978-0-09-943212-8(9) , Red Fox) Random Hse. Children's Bks. GBR. *Dist:* Random Hse. of Canada, Ltd.

Frank, Kim T. & Smith-Rex, Susan J. Getting with It! A Kid's Guide to Forming Good Relationships & Fitting In. Jackson, Ruth A. & Elliott, Jan H., illus. 1998. 200p. (J). (gr. k-5). pap. 9.95 (978-0-932796-77-6(X)) Educational Media Corp.

Frazier, Jessica. Inside a Sista's Soul. Gray, Etha, ed. 2002. 59p. (YA). pap. 8.95 (978-1-879940-10-9(8)) Concepts 'N' Publishing.

Gainer, Cindy. I'm Like You, You're Like Me: A Child's Book about Understanding & Celebrating Each Other. Gainer, Cindy, illus. 1998. (Illus.). 48p. (J). (ps-3). 12.95 (978-1-57542-039-4(2)) Free Spirit Publishing, Inc.

Galloway, L. A. This Is NOT Your Parents' Prom: A Handbook to Proms, Parties & Promises, 2 vols. Medick, Mike G., illus. 2002. 152p. (YA). (gr. 8-13). per. 14.99 (978-0-9718915-0-0(8)) Have Vision Pubns.

Garwood, Ben & Garwood, Mary. Not Like You. 2004. 172p. (YA). per. 11.95 (978-1-933094-00-7(1)) Tarbutton Pr.

George, Michele Naylor. The Rainbow of Respect & Responsibility. 1999. (J). (978-0-9672049-0-1(9)) Grace & Mercy Publishing.

Gilmore, Susan K. & Fraleigh, Patrick W. Communication Style Profile for Students. 3rd ed. 1999. (Illus.). 40p. (Orig.). (YA). (gr. 8 up). pap. 10.00 (978-0-938070-04-7(5)) Friendly Pr.

Girls Know Best, 7 bks. l.t. ed. Incl. Boys Know It All : Wise Thoughts & Wacky Ideas from Guys Like You. Roehm, Michelle, compiled by. 167p. 1999. lib. bdg. 23.33 (978-0-8368-2455-1(5)); Girls Know Best Vol. 2 : Tips on Life & Fun Stuff to Do. Monson-Burton, Marianne, compiled by. 1999. lib. bdg. 23.33 (978-0-8368-2453-7(9)); Girls Know Best Vol. 3 : Your Words, Your World. Monson-Burton, Marianne, compiled by. 153p. 2000. lib. bdg. 23.33 (978-0-8368-2672-2(8)); Girls Knows Best : Advice for Girls from Girls on Just about Everything. Roehm, Michelle, compiled by. 160p. 1999. lib. bdg. 23.33 (978-0-8368-2452-0(0)); Girls Who Rocked the World : Heroines from Sacagawea to Sheryl Swoopes. Welden, Amelie. McCann, Jerry, illus. 117p. 1999. lib. bdg. 23.33 (978-0-8368-2454-4(7)); Girls Who Rocked the World Vol. 2 : Heroines from Harriet Tubman to Mia Hamm. Roehm, Michelle, compiled by. 152p. 2000. lib. bdg. 23.33 (978-0-8368-2673-9(6)); Throw Like a Girl : Discovering the Body, Mind & Spirit of the Athlete in You! Frost, Shelley & Troussieux, Ann. 128p. 2000. lib. bdg. 23.33 (978-0-8368-2674-6(4)); (J). (gr. 3 up). (Illus.). Set lib. bdg. 163.31 (978-0-8368-2741-5(4)) Stevens, Gareth Inc.

Girolamo, Catherine. Answers...a Handbook for Men. 2001. 140p. (YA). pap. 9.95 (978-0-595-13990-3(6)) iUniverse, Inc.

Gizicki-Lipson, Coryn & Gizicki, Carlie. An Angel in the Sky. Gizicki-Lipson, Coryn, illus. 2003. (Illus.). 32p. (J). 14.95 (978-0-9740438-0-7(X)) In the Sky Publishing.

Godfrey, Christopher J. That's Where I Live: A Guide to Good Relationships. 1999. 175p. (YA). (Illus.). (gr. 7-12). pap. 8.95 (978-0-9676435-0-2(3)); pap. 8.95 (978-0-9676443-5-6(6)) Life Athletes Pr.

Goodwin, Evelyn. Meet the Children from the Fifty States in Poetry. 2007. 106p. pap. 37.50 (*978-0-615-16145-7(6)) Goodwin, Evelyn.

Graham, Stedman. Move Without the Ball: Put Your Skills & Your Magic to Work for You. 2004. (Illus.). 208p. pap. 14.00 (978-0-7432-3440-5(5) , Fireside) Simon & Schuster.

Gurian, Michael. Understanding Guys: A Guide for Teenage Girls. 1999. (J). (978-0-606-19512-6(2)) Tandem Library Bks.

Hacker, Caryn Sabes. A Bully Grows Up: Erik Meets the Wizard: Adult Guide Edition, 1. Boureau, Silvere, illus. 2006. 34p. (J). tchr. ed. 15.95 (*978-0-9791046-0-2(2)) Caryn Solutions, LLC.

—A Bully Grows Up: Erik Meets the Wizard: Student Edition. Boureau, Silvere, illus. 2006. 52p. (J). stu. ed. 12.95 (*978-0-9791046-1-9(0)) Caryn Solutions, LLC.

Hansen, Holly T. & Johnson, Jennifer Hunt. Remembering Father, 14 vols. 2002. (Illus.). 32p. 9.95 (978-0-9741172-1-8(8) , CMB14) Tapis & Assocs., Inc.

Harpster, Steve, illus. Growing up Happy: Arnold Gets Angry, Betty Stops the Bully & Catherine Finds Her Courage: the Emotional Literacy Series, 3, 3 vols., Set. 2004. (Emotional Literacy Ser.). 135p. (J). lib. bdg. 52.00 (978-0-9747789-9-0(0)) CTC Publishing.

Hartman, Jack & Hartman, Judy. Exchange Your Worries for God's Perfect Peace. 2003. 436p. per. 12.00 (978-0-915445-09-7(3) , Lamplight Ministries, Inc.) Lamplight Pubns.

Hauver, Sandy. Dating & Relationships, 8 vols., Vol. 4. 2002. (Illus.). (J). per. (978-1-932062-29-8(7)) Hability Solution Services, Inc.

Havelin, Kate. Perspectives on Relationships, 7 bks. Incl. Assertiveness : "How Can I Say What I Mean?" lib. bdg. 23.93 (978-0-7368-0290-1(8)); Child Abuse : "Why Do My Parents Hit Me?" lib. bdg. 23.93 (978-0-7368-0287-1(8)); Dating : "What Is a Healthy Rela-

H I

tionship?" lib. bdg. 23.93 (978-0-7368-0292-5(4)); Family Violence : "My Parents Hurt Each Other!" lib. bdg. 23.93 (978-0-7368-0286-4(X)); Parents : "They're Driving Me Crazy!" lib. bdg. 23.93 (978-0-7368-0285-7(1)); Peer Pressure : "How Can I Say No?" lib. bdg. 23.93 (978-0-7368-0291-8(6)); Sexual Harassment : "This Doesn't Feel Right!" lib. bdg. 23.93 (978-0-7368-0289-5(4)); 64p. (J). (gr. 4-6). 1999. (Illus.). Set lib. bdg. 167.57 (978-0-7368-1816-2(2) , LifeMatters Bks.) Capstone Pr., Inc.

Hernandez, Roger E. Teens & Relationships. 2005. (Gallup Youth Survey, Major Issues & Trends Ser.). (Illus.). 112p. (J). (ps-7). lib. bdg. 22.95 (978-1-59084-875-3(6)) Mason Crest Pubs.

Hipp, Earl. Understanding the Human Volcano: What Teens Can Do about Violence. Hanson, L. K., illus. 2000. 190p. (gr. 8-12). pap. 16.00 (978-1-56838-359-0(2) , Z1613) Hazelden Publishing & Educational Services.

—Understanding the Human Volcano: What Teens Can Do about Violence. 2000. (gr. 7-12). lib. bdg. 25.75 (978-0-613-79022-2(7)) Tandem Library Bks.

Holyoke, Nancy. A Smart Girl's Guide to Boys: Surviving Crushes, Staying True to Yourself & Other Stuff! Timmons, Bonnie, illus. 2001. (American Girl Library). 112p. (J). (gr. 3 up). 9.95 (978-1-58485-368-8(9)) American Girl Publishing, Inc.

—A Smart Girl's Guide to Boys: Surviving Crushes, Staying True to Yourself & Other Stuff! 2001. (gr. 3-6). lib. bdg. 18.75 (978-0-613-50064-7(4)) Tandem Library Bks.

Jeffrey, R. Stephen. Rules of the Game. 1999. 145p. (J). pap. 11.95 (978-1-893455-01-6(7)) Aloha Publishing & Marketing.

—Rules of the Game: The ABC's of Relationships. 1999. vii, 140p. (YA). (gr. 7-12). 15.00 (978-1-893455-00-9(9)) Aloha Publishing & Marketing.

Johnson, Charlotte Russell. The Flip Side: A Journey to Hell & Back. 2004. 256p. (YA). per. 15.95 (978-0-9741893-2-1(4)) Reaching Beyond, Inc.

Jukes, Mavis. The Guy Book: An Owner's Manual: Maintenance, Safety, & Operating Instructions for Boys. 2002. (Illus.). 160p. (YA). (gr. 7 up). 12.95 (978-0-679-89028-7(9) , Crown Books For Young Readers) Random Hse. Children's Bks.

Kemp, Kristen. What to Do When Your Best Friend Hates You. 2002. (Genny in a Bottle Ser.: No. 2). (Illus.). 144p. (J). (gr. 3-7). pap. 4.50 (978-0-439-21179-6(4) , Scholastic Paperbacks) Scholastic, Inc.

Khidekel, Marina. The Quiz Life. 2008. 224p. (J). lib. bdg. (***978-0-375-94063-7(4)***); (YA). (gr. 5). pap. 6.99 (***978-0-375-84263-4(2)***) Dell Publishing. (Delacorte Pr.).

Kihm, Steve. The Lost Candy Bar. 2004. (J). mass mkt. 6.95 (978-0-9786794-0-8(7)) Lost Candy Bar Pr., LLC.

Kirberger, Kimberly. Teen Love: On Friendship. 2000. (gr. 7-12). lib. bdg. 22.20 (978-0-613-30774-1(7)) Tandem Library Bks.

—Teen Love, on Relationships: A Book for Teenagers. 1999. (Teen Love Ser.). (Illus.). 300p. (YA). (gr. 8-12). pap. 14.95 (978-1-55874-734-0(6)) Health Communications, Inc.

Kirberger, Kimberly & Mortensen, Colin. On Friendship. 2000. (Teen Love Ser.). (Illus.). 400p. (YA). (gr. 7-12). pap. 12.95 (978-1-55874-815-6(6)) Health Communications, Inc.

Koubek, Christine Wickert. Friends, Cliques & Peer Pressure: Be True to Yourself. 2002. (Teen Issues Ser.). (Illus.). 64p. (YA). (gr. 6-12). lib. bdg. 22.60 (978-0-7660-1669-9(2)) Enslow Pubs., Inc.

Krulik, Nancy E. Who Do You Love? 2001. (gr. 5-8). lib. bdg. 11.80 (978-0-613-73318-2(5)) Tandem Library Bks.

Landalf, Helen. Moving Is Relating: Developing Interpersonal Skills Through Movementfor Children. 1998. (Young Actors Ser.). 90p. (J). (gr. 3-6). pap. 19.95 (978-1-57525-123-3(X)) Smith and Kraus Publishers, Incorporated.

Leeper, Angela. I Care. 2004. (You & Me Ser.). (J). pap. (978-1-4034-6090-5(6)) Heinemann Library.

Levy, Barrie. In Love & in Danger: A Teen's Guide to Breaking Free of Abusive Relationships. 3rd rev. ed. 2006. (Illus.). 150p. (Orig.). (YA). pap. 12.95 (978-1-58005-187-3(1)) Seal Pr.

Liles, Rebecca. My Daddy's a Soldier, 2 bks. 2003. (Illus.). 16p. (J). 4.99 (978-0-9744346-0-5(4)) Rebecca's Bks.

—My Mommy's a Soldier, 2 bks. 2003. (Illus.). 16p. (J). 4.99 (978-0-9744346-1-2(2)) Rebecca's Bks.

Lookadoo, Justin & DiMarco, Hayley. The Dateable Rules: A Guide to the Sexes. 2004. (Illus.). 176p. (YA). reprint ed. pap. 11.99 (978-0-8007-5915-5(X)) Revell.

Macavinta, Courtney & Pluym, Andrea R. Vander. Respect: A Girl's Guide to Getting Respect & Dealing When Your Line Is Crossed. Lepage, Catherine, illus. 2005. 240p. (YA). (gr. 8). pap. 15.95 (978-1-57542-177-3(1)) Free Spirit Publishing, Inc.

MacDonald, Fiona. Home, Family & Everyday Life. 2001. (Through the Ages Ser.). (Illus.). 64p. (gr. 3-7). 12.95 (978-0-7548-0816-9(5)) Anness Publishing GBR. *Dist:* National Bk. Network.

MacKall, Dandi Daley. Teamwork Skills. 2nd ed. 2004. (Career Skills Library). (Illus.). 144p. (YA). (gr. 6-12). 21.95 (978-0-8160-5524-1(6) , Ferguson Publishing Co.) Facts On File, Inc.

Marcovitz, Hal. Teens & Family Issues. 2004. (Gallup Youth Survey, Major Issues & Trends Ser.). (Illus.). 112,128p. (J). (gr. 7-9). lib. bdg. 22.95 (978-1-59084-725-1(3)) Mason Crest Pubs.

Marks, James Lynn. I Love to Give. 2000. (Education Through Creation Ser.: Bk. 3). (Illus.). 16p. (J). (ps-6). pap. 9.95 (978-0-9706412-2-9(2) , 1003) Seventh Sun Productions.

Martin, Elena. Trabajando Juntos. 2005. Tr. of Working Together. (SPA., Illus.). 16p. (J). (gr. 1 up). lib. bdg. 15.93 (978-0-7368-4182-5(2)) Capstone Pr., Inc.

—Working Together. 2003. (Yellow Umbrella Books for Early Readers). (Illus.). 17p. (J). 15.93 (978-0-7368-2930-4(X)); pap. (978-0-7368-2889-5(3)) Yellow Umbrella Pr.

Marx, Trish. Reaching for the Sun: Kids in Cuba. 2003. (Single Titles Ser.: 6). (Illus.). 48p. lib. bdg. 25.90 (978-0-7613-2261-0(2) , Millbrook Pr.) Lerner Publishing Group.

McCloud, Carol. Have You Filled a Bucket Today? A Guide to Daily Happiness for Kids. Messing, Dave, illus. 2006. (J). pap. 9.95 (978-0-9785075-1-0(7) , Ferne Pr.) Nelson Publishing & Marketing.

McDowell, Josh & Stewart, Ed. Friendship 911 Collection: My Friend Is Struggling With... Conflicts with Others. 2000. (Friendship 911 Ser.). (Illus.). 64p. (gr. 8-12). pap. 7.98 (978-0-8499-3795-8(7)) Nelson, Thomas Inc.

McGraw-Hill Staff & Sasse, Connie R. Families Today, 2 vols. 4th ed. 2003. 728p. (C). (gr. 9-12). stu. ed. 61.32 (978-0-07-829840-0(7) , 9780078298400) Glencoe/ McGraw-Hill.

Meier, Katie. A Girl's Guide to Life: The Real Dish on Growing up, Being True, & Making Your Teen Years Fabulous! 2004. (Illus.). 208p. (YA). pap. 13.99 (978-0-8499-4443-7(0)) Nelson, Thomas Inc.

Meiners, Cheri. Talk & Work It Out. Johnson, Meredith, illus. 2005. (Learning to Get Along Ser.). 40p. (J). (ps-3). pap. 10.95 (978-1-57542-176-6(3)) Free Spirit Publishing, Inc.

Meiners, Cheri J. Be Polite & Kind. 2004. (Learning to Get Along Ser.). (Illus.). 40p. (J). (ps-3). pap. 10.95 (978-1-57542-151-3(8)) Free Spirit Publishing, Inc.

—Join in & Play. 2004. (Learning to Get Along Ser.). (Illus.). 40p. (J). (ps-3). pap. 10.95 (978-1-57542-152-0(6)) Free Spirit Publishing, Inc.

Meiners, Cheryl J. Accept & Value Each Person. 2006. (Learning to Get Along Ser.). (Illus.). 40p. (J). (ps-3). pap. 10.95 (978-1-57542-203-9(4)) Free Spirit Publishing, Inc.

Middleton, Don. Dealing with Feeling Left Out. 1998. (Conflict Resolution Library). (Illus.). 24p. (J). (gr. k-4). pap. 6.95 (978-1-56838-270-8(7)) Hazelden Publishing & Educational Services.

—Dealing with Feeling Left Out. 1999. (Conflict Resolution Library). 24p. (J). lib. bdg. 18.75 (978-0-8239-5269-4(X) , PowerKids Pr.) Rosen Publishing Group, Inc., The.

—Dealing with Secrets. 1998. (Conflict Resolution Library). (Illus.). 24p. (J). (gr. k-4). pap. 6.95 (978-1-56838-271-5(5)) Hazelden Publishing & Educational Services.

—Dealing with Secrets. 1999. (Conflict Resolution Library). 24p. (J). lib. bdg. 18.75 (978-0-8239-5265-6(7) , PowerKids Pr.) Rosen Publishing Group, Inc., The.

—Dealing with Tattling. 1999. (Conflict Resolution Library). 24p. (J). lib. bdg. 18.75 (978-0-8239-5266-3(5) , PowerKids Pr.) Rosen Publishing Group, Inc., The.

Miller, Deanna. Time to Tell 'Em Off! A Pocket Guide to Overcoming Peer Ridicule. l.t. ed. 2002. 108p. (YA). per. (978-0-9725424-0-1(X)) Miller, Deanna.

Moe, Barbara. Coping with Rejection. 2005. (Coping Ser.). (Illus.). 192p. (YA). (gr. 7-12). lib. bdg. 26.50 (978-0-8239-3362-4(8)) Rosen Publishing Group, Inc., The.

Moehn, Heather. Everything You Need to Know about Cliques. 2005. (Need to Know Library). (Illus.). 64p. (J). (gr. 7-12). 25.25 (978-0-8239-3326-6(1)) Rosen Publishing Group, Inc., The.

Monckeberg, Paulina. Artilugia 2007 Spanish. 2006. (Pascualina Family of Products Ser.). (SPA., Illus.). 274p. (J). spiral bd. 14.99 (978-956-8222-46-8(4)) Pascualina Producciones S.A.

—Pascualina 2007 English. 2006. (Pascualina Family of Products Ser.). 274p. (J). spiral bd. 16.99 (978-956-8222-48-2(0)) Pascualina Producciones S.A.

Monson-Burton, Marianne. Girls Know Best Vol. 3: Your Words, Your World. 1999. (gr. 3-6). lib. bdg. 17.60 (978-0-613-33368-9(3)) Tandem Library Bks.

Monson-Burton, Marianne, compiled by. Girls Know Best Vol. 2: Tips on Life & Fun Stuff to Do. l.t. ed. 1999. (Girls Know Best Ser.). (Illus.). (J). (gr. 3 up). lib. bdg. 23.33 (978-0-8368-2453-7(9)) Stevens, Gareth Inc.

—Girls Know Best Vol. 3: Your Words, Your World. l.t. ed. 2000. (Girls Know Best Ser.). (Illus.). 153p. (J). (gr. 3 up). lib. bdg. 23.33 (978-0-8368-2672-2(8)) Stevens, Gareth Inc.

Moore-Malinos, Jennifer. When My Parents Forgot How to Be Friends. Fabrega, Marta, illus. 2005. (Let's Talk about It! Ser.). 32p. (J). (ps-3). pap. 6.95 (978-0-7641-3172-1(9)) Barron's Educational Series, Inc.

Mosatche, Harriet S. & Lawner, Elizabeth K. Getting to Know the Real You: 50 Fun Quizzes Just for Girls. 2002. (Illus.). 240p. pap. 12.95 (978-0-7615-2954-5(3) , Three Rivers Pr.) Crown Publishing Group.

Moses, Brian. Excuse Me. 2000. (gr. k-3). lib. bdg. 14.45 (978-0-613-30388-0(1)) Tandem Library Bks.

Navarra, Tova. Young People. 2002. Tr. of Tough Problems. (gr. 5-8). lib. bdg. 15.25 (978-0-613-83481-0(X)) Tandem Library Bks.

Olien, Rebecca. Kids Care! 2007. (Illus.). 128p. (J). (gr. 2-7). 16.99 (***978-0-8249-6793-2(3)*** , Williamson Bks.) Ideals Pubns.

—Kids Care! Kline, Michael, illus. 2007. 128p. (J). pap. 12.99 (***978-0-8249-6792-5(5)*** , Williamson Bks.) Ideals Pubns.

Olson, David H., et al. Building Relationships: Developing Skills for Life. 1999. (Illus.). 258p. (YA). (gr. 6 up). pap. 14.95 (978-0-9671983-0-9(5)) Life Innovations, Inc.

Palmer-Kuhn, Glenda. Let's Be Friends — a Jungle Legend. Lunsford, Stacy, illus. 2002. (J). 7.95 (978-0-9643029-5-2(0)) SpritSBo.

Peacock, Judith. Dating & Sex: Defining & Setting Boundaries. (Perspectives on Healthy Sexuality Ser.). pap. 8.95 (978-0-7368-8845-5(4)); 2000. (Illus.). 64p. (J). (gr. 4-6). lib. bdg. 23.93 (978-0-7368-0716-6(0)) Capstone Pr., Inc. (LifeMatters Bks.).

Peavler, Amy & Peavler, Jan. The King the Queen & the Princess. Peavler, Amy & Peavler, Jan, illus. 2006. (Illus.). 40p. (J). per. (978-0-9787672-2-8(5)) Lotus Petal Publishing.

Penchina, Sharon. Dogs & Bugs Go Together, Really They Do! 2007. 28p. 12.95 (978-0-9740684-8-0(9)) 2 Imagine.

Polsky, Milton & Gilead, Jack. The Improv Workshop Handbook: Creative Movement & Verbal Interaction for Students K-8: The Object Is Teamwork. Cordero, Chris, ed. Rockwell, Richard, illus. l.t. ed. 2003. 112p. (J). (gr. k-8). pap. 15.00 (978-0-88734-691-0(X)) Players Pr., Inc.

Powell. Is Kissing a Girl Who Smokes Like Licking an Ashtray? 2003. (gr. 7-12). lib. bdg. 14.10 (978-0-613-71864-6(X)) Tandem Library Bks.

Priest, Saira, photos by & des. If We Were... Priest, Saira, des. l.t. ed. 2003. 20p. 12.95 (978-0-9726628-7-1(1)) Native Nature.

Richmond, Marianne. Thank You Mom. 2004. (Illus.). 40p. (YA). 7.95 (978-0-9741465-6-0(0)) Marianne Richmond Studios, Inc.

Richmond, Marianne R. The DIY Guide to Understanding a Woman. 2005. (Illus.). 40p. (YA). 7.95 (978-0-9763101-6-7(3)) Marianne Richmond Studios, Inc.

—I Care about You. 2004. (Illus.). 40p. (YA). 7.95 (978-0-9753528-1-6(4)) Marianne Richmond Studios, Inc.

Riso, Walter. Amar o Depender? Como Superar el Apego Afectivo y Hacer del Amor una Experiencia Plena y Saludable. (SPA.). (J). 10.00 (978-958-04-5425-0(6)) Norma S.A. COL. *Dist:* Distribuidora Norma, Inc.

Roehm, Michelle, compiled by. Boys Know It All: Wise Thoughts & Wacky Ideas from Guys Like You. l.t. ed. 1999. (Girls Know Best Ser.). (Illus.). 167p. (J). (gr. 3 up). lib. bdg. 23.33 (978-0-8368-2455-1(5)) Stevens, Gareth Inc.

—Girls Knows Best: Advice for Girls from Girls on Just about Everything. 1999. (Girls Know Best Ser.). (Illus.). 160p. (J). (gr. 3 up). lib. bdg. 23.33 (978-0-8368-2452-0(0)) Stevens, Gareth Inc.

Roehm, Michelle, ed. Girls Know Best: Advice for Girls on Just about Everything. Roth, Marci Doane, illus. 1999. 160p. (J). (gr. 4-7). 6.98 (978-1-56731-313-0(2) , MJF Bks.) Fine Communications.

Romain, Trevor. Cliques, Phonies, & Other Baloney. Romain, Trevor, illus. 1998. (Laugh & Learn Ser.). (Illus.). 136p. (YA). (gr. 3-8). pap. 8.95 (978-1-57542-045-5(7)) Free Spirit Publishing, Inc.

—Cliques, Phonies, & Other Baloney. 1998. (gr. 5-8). lib. bdg. 18.75 (978-0-613-87131-0(6)) Tandem Library Bks.

Ross, Allison J. Everything You Need to Know about Social Anxiety. 2005. (Need to Know Library). (Illus.). 64p. (YA). (gr. 7-12). 25.25 (978-0-8239-3324-2(5)) Rosen Publishing Group, Inc., The.

Roy, Jennifer Rozines. Difficult People: Dealing with Almost Anyone. 2001. (Teen Issues Ser.). (Illus.). 64p. (J). (gr. 6-12). lib. bdg. 22.60 (978-0-7660-1583-8(1)) Enslow Pubs., Inc.

Rue, Nancy N. Everything You Need to Know about Peer Mediation. rev. ed. 2001. (Need to Know Library). (Illus.). 64p. (YA). (gr. 4-6). lib. bdg. 25.25 (978-0-8239-3464-5(0)) Rosen Publishing Group, Inc., The.

Scheunemann, Pam. Learning about Differences. 2004. (Keeping the Peace Ser.). (Illus.). 23p. (J). (ps-3). lib. bdg. 19.93 (978-1-59197-561-8(1)) ABDO Publishing Co.

Schneider, Meg. Rules for Teens. 2000. (gr. 7-12). lib. bdg. 13.00 (978-0-613-26794-6(X)) Tandem Library Bks.

Seduction by Shakespeare: Advice, Observations & Quotes on Love, Lust, Beauty & Desire. 2004. 128p. (YA). (gr. 11 up). per. 11.95 (978-0-9674898-6-5(5)) TCB-Cafe Publishing.

Seventeen Magazine. True Love. 2007. 128p. (J). pap. 4.95 (978-1-58816-629-6(5)) Hearst Communications, Inc.

Seymour, Peter & Dodi, Emily, compiled by. Welcome Baby! A Three-Dimensional Scene & Pop-Up Book. 1998. (From Me to You Ser.). (Illus.). 6p. 5.95 (978-1-888443-06-6(5) , Intervisual/Piggy Toes) Dalmatian Pr.

Sherman, Dean. Relationships: The Key to Love, Sex, & Everything Else. 2003. 208p. pap. 12.99 (978-1-57658-275-6(2)) YWAM Publishing.

Sheva, Marie, mem. The Year of the Dogs: A Chronicle of Redemption, a Story of Love. 2003. (Illus.). 247p. (YA). per. 15.95 (978-0-9741736-0-3(6) , 9900) Sheva, Marie.

Simmons, Rachel. Odd Girl Speaks Out. 2004. (gr. 7-12). lib. bdg. 15.10 (978-0-613-70533-2(5)) Tandem Library Bks.

Slavens, Elaine. Arguing: Word by Word. Murray, Steven, illus. 2004. (Deal with It Ser.). 32p. (J). (gr. 4-8). 12.95 (978-1-55028-820-9(2)) Lorimer, James & Co., Ltd., Pubs. CAN. *Dist:* Casemate Pubs. & Bk. Distributors, LLC.

Snipes, Carol. Mary's Rockin' ABC's. 2005. (Illus.). (J). 17.95 (978-0-9702324-5-8(4)) Pinpoint Printing.

Sommers, Michael A. Great Interpersonal Skills. 2008. (J). (***978-1-4042-1423-1(2)***) Rosen Publishing Group, Inc., The.

Spencer, Lauren. Everything You Need to Know about Falling in Love. 2001. (Need to Know Library). (Illus.). 64p. (YA). (gr. 4-6). lib. bdg. 25.25 (978-0-8239-3395-2(4)) Rosen Publishing Group, Inc., The.

Sperekas, Nicole B. But He Says He Loves Me: Girls Speak Out on Dating Abuse. 2002. viii, 162p. (J). 15.00 (978-1-884444-66-1(0)) Safer Society Pr.

Stenzel, Pam. Sex Has a Price Tag: Discussions about Sexuality, Spirituality, & Self Respect. 2003. (gr. 7-12). lib. bdg. 18.80 (978-0-613-86016-1(0)) Tandem Library Bks.

Strong, Jennifer, ed. Love Stories: How Love Conquers All. 2001. (Teen People Ser.). 160p. (YA). (gr. 7 up). pap. 6.95 (978-0-06-447320-0(1) , Avon) HarperCollins Pubs.

Stuchin, Mallory. We're in This Together: 15 Teens Reveal How They Get Along with Their Parents (And Other Sanity-Saving Insights) 2003. 112p. (J). pap. 14.95 (978-1-932181-03-6(2)) Personhood Pr.

Turkovitz, Karen. What's So Special about Mitchell? Ryan, Linda et al, eds. Marshall, Ian, illus. l.t. ed. 2002. 26p. (J). (gr. k-4). pap. 6.95 (978-0-9679115-5-7(9)) Fivedegressbelowzero Pr.

Tyler, John C. Friendships: Lovers, Huggers & Others. 2000. (Illus.). 126p. (YA). (gr. 7 up). 9.95 (978-0-9674350-0-8(5)) Tyler, John C.

Verdick, Elizabeth. Words Are Not for Hurting. Heinlen, Marieka, illus. 2004. (Best Behavior Ser.). 24p. (J). 7.95 (978-1-57542-155-1(0)) Free Spirit Publishing, Inc.

Wandberg, Robert. Peer Mediation: Agreeing on Solutions. 2000. (Contemporary Issues Ser.). (Illus.). 64p. (J). (gr. 4-6). lib. bdg. 23.93 (978-0-7368-1023-4(4) , LifeMatters Bks.) Capstone Pr., Inc.

Webster-Doyle, Terrence. Why Is Everybody Picking on Me: Guide to Handling Bullies. Cameron, Rod, illus. 1999. 144p. pap. 18.95 (978-0-8348-0467-8(0) , Weatherhill, Inc.) Shambhala Pubns., Inc.

Weedn, Lisa. Just Hangin' Out: Chick Chat Between Best Friends. Weedn, Flavia M., illus. 2001. 60p. (gr. 7-12). pap. 14.95 (978-0-7683-2238-5(3)) CEDCO Publishing.

Westfall, Tom C. Mostly Sand & Gravel. 2002. 243p. (YA). pap. 16.95 (978-0-595-21573-7(4) , Writer's Showcase Pr.) iUniverse, Inc.

White, Kelly & Stacy, Lori. Ask Lucky! The Girls'life Guide to Dealing with Dilemmas. 2003. (Illus.). 120p. (J). (978-0-439-44982-3(0)) Scholastic, Inc.

Why Relationships Matter. 1998. (Core Belief Bible Study Ser.). (YA). (gr. 10-12). pap. 11.99 (978-0-7644-0896-0(8)) Group Publishing, Inc.

Williams, Gaylyn & Williams, Ken L. Sharpening Your Interpersonal Skills. 2001. (SPA & FRE.). ring bd. 20.00 net. (978-0-9721728-0-6(7)) Relationship Resources, Inc.

Williams, Julie. A Smart Girl's Guide to Starting Middle School: Everything You Need to Know about Making the Grade, Staying Cool at a New School, & Juggling More Homework, More Teachers, & More Friends! Martini, Angela, illus. 2004. (Americangirl Library(R) Ser.). 96p. (J). 9.95 (978-1-58485-877-5(X)) American Girl Publishing, Inc.

Wilson, Rebekah. The Hope Chest: A Legacy of Love, 2nd ed. 2003. (Illus.). 380p. (YA). per. 15.00 (978-1-59565-001-6(6)) Hope Chest Legacy, Inc.

Worthy of Honor. 2003. (Humble Heart Ser.). (J). spiral bd., wbk. ed. (978-0-9746148-2-3(3)) Common Courtesy.

Zielin, Lara. Make Things Happen: The Key to Networking for Teens. 2004. (Illus.). 108p. (J). pap. 9.95 (978-1-894222-43-3(1)) Lobster Pr. CAN. *Dist:* Univ. of Toronto Pr.

111 Things Every Woman Must Know about Men. 2000. 128p. (YA). (gr. 10 up). mass mkt. 7.99 (978-0-9675537-1-9(7)) Upstart Publishing Co.

INTERPERSONAL RELATIONS—FICTION

Abela, Deborah. Mission: the Nightmare Vortex. O'Connor, George, illus. 2007. (Spy Force Ser.). 256p. (J). pap. 5.99 (978-1-4169-3484-4(7) , Aladdin) Simon & Schuster Children's Publishing.

Adee, Donna & Adee, Ed. Jonathan Finds True Treasure. Rectenbaugh, Marci, illus. 2004. (Jonathan Ser.: Bk. 2). 344p. (J). per. 10.95 (978-0-9654272-5-8(0)) Harvest Pubns.

Adoff, Jaime. Names Will Never Hurt Me. 2004. 144p. (J). (gr. 7). 16.99 (978-0-525-47175-2(8) , Dutton Juvenile) Penguin Group (USA) Inc.

Alexander, Martha. I Sure Am Glad to See You, Blackboard Bear. Alexander, Martha, illus. 2nd rev. ed. 2004. (Illus.). 30p. (J). (gr. k-3). reprint ed. 11.00 (978-0-7567-7153-9(6)) DIANE Publishing Co.

Alfonsi, Alice. Trust Your Heart. novel rev. ed. 2007. (W. I. T. C. H. Ser.: Bk. 24). 144p. (gr. 3-7). pap. 4.99 (***978-1-4231-0288-5(6)***) Hyperion Pr.

Allen, M. E. Gotta Get Some Bish Bash Bosh. 2005. (Illus.). 208p. (J). 15.99 (978-0-06-073198-4(2) , HarperTeen); lib. bdg. 16.89 (978-0-06-073201-1(6)) HarperCollins Pubs.

An, Na. The Fold. 2008. 192p. (J). (gr. 5). 16.99 (***978-0-399-24276-2(7)*** , Putnam Juvenile) Penguin Group (USA) Inc.

Andersen, Hans Christian. La Reina de las Nieves. (SPA., Illus.). 48p. (J). (gr. 3-5). (978-84-241-5526-1(2) , EV1028) Everest de Ediciones y Distribucion, S.L. ESP. *Dist:* Lectorum Pubns., Inc.

—La Reina de las Nieves. Bravo-Villasante, Carmen, tr. Catagan, Tino, illus. (SPA.). (J). (gr. 2-4). 6.50 (978-84-355-0695-3(9)) Minon, S.A. ESP. *Dist:* Lectorum Pubns., Inc.

Anderson, Jodi. Peaches. 2005. 320p. (J). (gr. 7 up). lib. bdg. 16.89 (978-0-06-073306-3(3)) HarperCollins Pubs.

Anderson, Jodi & Anderson, Jodi Lynn. Peaches. 2005. 320p. (YA). (gr. 7-12). 15.99 (978-0-06-073305-6(5)) HarperCollins Pubs.

Anderson, Jodi Lynn. Peaches. 2006. 320p. (J). reprint ed. pap. 8.99 (978-0-06-073307-0(1) , Harper Trophy) HarperCollins Pubs.

Anderson, Laurie Halse. Speak. 2002. (YA). 14.89 (978-1-4046-1072-9(3)) Book Wholesalers, Inc.

—Speak. 1999. 208p. (YA). (gr. 8-12). 17.00 (978-0-374-37152-4(0) , Farrar, Straus & Giroux (BYR)) Farrar, Straus & Giroux.

—Speak. 2006. 224p. (YA). pap. 10.00 (978-0-14-240732-5(1) , Puffin) Penguin Group (USA) Inc.

—Speak. 2001. (J). (978-0-606-21444-5(5)) Tandem Library Bks.

—Speak. l.t. ed. 2000. 276p. (YA). (gr. 8-12). 20.95 (978-0-7862-2525-5(4)) Thorndike Pr.

Anfousse, Ginette. Les Barricades d'Arthur. 2001. (Premier Roman Ser.). (FRE.). 64p. (J). (gr. 2-5). pap. (978-2-89021-163-6(0)) Diffusion du livre Mirabel.

—A Terrible Secret. Hutchison, Jennifer, tr. from FRE. 2000. (SideStreets Ser.). (gr. 7-12). 112p. 7.95 (978-1-55028-704-2(4)); 108p. (YA). (*978-1-55028-705-9(2)) Lorimer, James & Co., Ltd., Pubs. CAN. *Dist:* Casemate Pubs. & Bk. Distributors, LLC.

—Terrible Secret. 2001. (gr. 7-12). lib. bdg. 13.00 (978-0-613-42804-0(8)) Tandem Library Bks.

Apelqvist, Eva. Swede Dreams. 2007. (S. A. S. S. (Students Across the Seven Seas) Ser.). (Illus.). (YA). 224p. pap. 6.99 (978-0-14-240746-2(1)); 202p. (*978-1-4287-2702-1(7)) Penguin Group (USA) Inc. (Puffin).

Apostolina, M. Hazing Meri Sugarman. 2005. 272p. (YA). pap. 8.99 (978-1-4169-0610-0(X) , Simon Pulse) Simon & Schuster Children's Publishing.

Arena, Felice & Kettle, Phil. Basketball Buddies. Gordon, Gus, illus. 2004. (J). pap. (978-1-59336-369-7(9)) Mondo Publishing.

Arterburn, Stephen & Hunt, Angela Elwell. Noah. 2004. (Young Believer on Tour Ser.). (J). pap. 3.99 (978-0-8423-8337-0(9)) Tyndale Hse. Pubs.

Asher, Jay. Thirteen Reasons Why. 2007. 256p. (YA). (gr. 7). 16.99 (*978-1-59514-171-2(5) , Razorbill) Penguin Group (USA) Inc.

Atkins, Catherine. Alt Ed. 2004. 208p. (J). (gr. 8-12). reprint ed. pap. 6.99 (978-0-14-240235-1(4) , Puffin) Penguin Group (USA) Inc.

Atkinson, Chryssa. Lindsey. 2001. (American Girl Today Ser.). (Illus.). 128p. (J). pap. 6.95 (978-1-58485-450-0(2)) American Girl Publishing, Inc.

—Lindsey. 2003. (gr. 3-6). lib. bdg. 15.25 (978-0-613-85868-7(9)) Tandem Library Bks.

Austen, Jane. Pride & Prejudice. Miralles, Joseph, illus. 2005. (Great Illustrated Classics Ser.). 236p. (J). (gr. 3-8). 21.35 (978-1-59679-249-4(3) , ABDO & Daughters) ABDO Publishing Co.

Awdry, Wilbert V. James & the Red Balloon & Other Thomas the Tank Engine Stories. 2004. (Thomas & Friends Ser.). (Illus.). 24p. (J). (ps-2). pap. 3.99 (978-0-375-82753-2(6) , Random Hse. Bks. for Young Readers) Random Hse. Children's Bks.

Banim, Lisa & Minsky, Terri. The Case of the Kate Haters. 2005. (Illus.). 124p. (J). (*978-1-4156-3927-6(2)) Disney Pr.

Banks, Kate. Friends of the Heart: Amici Del Cuore. 2005. 144p. (J). 16.00 (978-0-374-32455-1(7)) Farrar, Straus & Giroux.

Barham, Lisa. Accidentally Fabulous. 2008. (Fashion-Forward Adventures of Imogene Ser.). 256p. (YA). pap. 9.99 (*978-1-4169-1445-7(5) , Simon Pulse) Simon & Schuster Children's Publishing.

Barnholdt, Lauren. Two-Way Street. 2007. 304p. (YA). pap. 8.99 (978-1-4169-1318-4(1) , Simon Pulse) Simon & Schuster Children's Publishing.

Barshaw, Ruth McNally. Ellie McDoodle: Have Pen, Will Travel. Barshaw, Ruth McNally, illus. 2007. (Illus.). 176p. (J). (gr. 3-7). 11.95 (*978-1-58234-745-5(X)) Bloomsbury Publishing.

Baskin, Nora Raleigh. Basketball (or Something Like It) 176p. (J). 2007. (gr. 4-7). pap. 5.99 (978-0-06-059612-5(0) , Harper Trophy); 2005. 15.99 (978-0-06-059610-1(4)); 2005. lib. bdg. 16.89 (978-0-06-059611-8(2)) HarperCollins Pubs.

Bateson, Catherine. The Boyfriend Rules of Good Behavior. 2006. 192p. (YA). 16.95 (978-0-8234-2026-1(4)) Holiday Hse., Inc.

—Rain May & Captain Daniel. 2002. 144p. (YA). pap. 15.50 (978-0-7022-3337-1(4)) Univ. of Queensland Pr. AUS. *Dist:* International Specialized Bk. Services.

Bateson, Catherine. Stranded in Boringsville. 144p. (gr. 5-9). (J). 16.95 (978-0-8234-1969-2(X)); 2007. (YA). pap. 6.95 (*978-0-8234-2113-8(9)) Holiday Hse., Inc.

Bauer, Joan. Squashed. 2005. 208p. (YA). (gr. 7). pap. 7.99 (978-0-14-240426-3(8) , Puffin) Penguin Group (USA) Inc.

—Squashed. 2001. (978-0-606-22520-5(X)) Tandem Library Bks.

—Squashed! 2001. 208p. (YA). 16.99 (978-0-399-23750-8(X) , Putnam Juvenile) Penguin Group (USA) Inc.

Bauer, Marion Dane. The Double-Digit Club. 2004. 126p. (J). (gr. 4-6). tchr. ed. 15.95 (978-0-8234-1805-3(7)) Holiday Hse., Inc.

Bauer, Marion Dane. Killing Miss Kitty & Other Sins. 2007. 176p. (YA). (gr. 7). 16.00 (*978-0-618-69000-8(X) , Clarion Bks.) Houghton Mifflin Co. Trade & Reference Div.

Beam, Matt. Getting to First Base with Danalda Chase. 2007. (Illus.). 192p. (J). (gr. 5-8). 16.99 (978-0-525-47578-1(8) , Dutton Juvenile) Penguin Group (USA) Inc.

Bell, Julia. Dirty Work. 2007. 192p. (YA). 16.95 (*978-0-8027-9741-4(5)) Walker & Co.

Beller, Jasmine. Bring It On. 2006. (Hip-Hop Kidz Ser.: Vol. 1). 160p. (J). (gr. 4-7). pap. 4.99 (978-0-448-44362-1(7) , Grosset & Dunlap) Penguin Group (USA) Inc.

—Bust a Move. 2006. 156p. (J). (*978-1-4156-9619-4(5) , Grosset & Dunlap) Penguin Group (USA) Inc.

—Freaky #3. 2007. (Illus.). 160p. (J). pap. 4.99 (978-0-448-44364-5(3) , Grosset & Dunlap) Penguin Group (USA) Inc.

—Raise the Roof, No. 4. 2007. 160p. (J). pap. 4.99 (978-0-448-44445-1(3) , Grosset & Dunlap) Penguin Group (USA) Inc.

Bellingham, Brenda. Lilly in the Middle. Owen, Elizabeth, illus. 2003. (First Novel Ser.). 64p. (J). (gr. 1-5). 4.95 (978-0-88780-589-9(2)); (*978-0-88780-590-5(6)) Formac Publishing Co., Ltd. CAN. *Dist:* Casemate Pubs. & Bk. Distributors, LLC.

Bennet-Boltinghouse, JoAnn. A Pooch Finds Her Purpose. Julich, Jennifer, illus. 2006. (YolandaBaby Ser.). 32p. (J). 16.00 (978-0-9785151-0-2(2)) Ginger Pr., The.

Bernardo, Anilu. Loves Me, Loves Me Not. 1998. 169p. (YA). (gr. 6-12). 16.95 (978-1-55885-258-7(1) , Piñata Books) Arte Publico Pr.

—Loves Me, Loves Me Not. 1999. (gr. 7-12). lib. bdg. 18.75 (978-0-613-23737-6(4)) Tandem Library Bks.

Bingham, Kelly. Shark Girl. 2007. (Illus.). 288p. (YA). (gr. 7 up). 16.99 (*978-0-7636-3207-6(4)) Candlewick Pr.

Bingham, Kelly L. Shark Girl. 2007. 276p. (YA). (*978-1-4287-4705-0(2)) Candlewick Pr.

Birdseye, Tom. Attack of the Mutant Underwear. 2006. (Illus.). 208p. (J). (gr. 3). pap. 6.99 (978-0-14-240734-9(8) , Puffin) Penguin Group (USA) Inc.

Birney, Betty G. Surprises According to Humphrey. 2008. 192p. (J). (gr. 3). 14.99 (*978-0-399-24730-9(0) , Putnam Juvenile) Penguin Group (USA) Inc.

Birney, Betty G. Trouble According to Humphrey. (J). 2008. 192p. (gr. 3-4). 5.99 (*978-0-14-241089-9(6) , Puffin); 2007. 176p. (gr. 2-4). 14.99 (978-0-399-24505-3(7)) Penguin Group (USA) Inc.

Blackman, Malorie. Black & White. 2007. 512p. (YA). (gr. 9 up). pap. 7.99 (978-1-4169-0017-7(9) , Simon Pulse) Simon & Schuster Children's Publishing.

Blake, Emily. Playing with Fire. 2008. (Little Secrets Ser.: No. 1). 224p. (J). pap. 4.99 (*978-0-545-02824-0(8) , Scholastic Paperbacks) Scholastic, Inc.

Blume, Judy. Double Fudge. 2004. (Fudge Ser.). 192p. (gr. 12). mass mkt. 5.99 (978-0-425-19647-2(X) , Berkley) Penguin Group (USA) Inc.

Bodett, Tom. Norman Tuttle on the Last Frontier. 208p. (YA). (gr. 7). 2006. mass mkt. 5.99 (978-0-553-49493-8(7) , Laurel Leaf); 2004. 15.95 (978-0-679-89031-7(9) , Knopf Bks. for Young Readers) Random Hse. Children's Bks.

—Norman Tuttle on the Last Frontier: A Novel in Stories. 2004. 208p. (J). (gr. 7). lib. bdg. 17.99 (978-0-679-99031-4(3) , Knopf Bks. for Young Readers) Random Hse. Children's Bks.

Boggess, Eileen. Mia the Meek. 2006. (Mia Fullerton Ser.: Bk. 1). 155p. (YA). (gr. 6-9). 16.95 (*978-1-890862-46-6(0)) Bancroft Pr.

Bondoux, Anne-Laure. The Destiny of Linus Hoppe. Temerson, Catherine, tr. from FRE. 2005. 160p. (J). (gr. 3-7). lib. bdg. 17.99 (978-0-385-90255-7(7) , Delacorte Bks. for Young Readers) Random Hse. Children's Bks.

—The Killer's Tears. Maudet, Y., tr. 176p. (YA). (gr. 7). 2007. pap. 8.99 (978-0-385-73384-7(4)); 2006. (Illus.). 15.95 (978-0-385-73293-2(7)); 2006. (Illus.). lib. bdg. 17.99 (978-0-385-90314-1(6)) Random Hse. Children's Bks. (Delacorte Bks. for Young Readers).

Bondoux, Anne-Laure. The Second Life of Linus Hoppe. Temerson, Catherine, tr. 2007. 208p. (gr. 4-7). 5.99 (*978-0-440-42039-2(3) , Yearling) Random Hse. Children's Bks.

Bonin, Liane. Celebrity Skin: Fame Unlimited. 2007. 288p. (YA). pap. 9.99 (978-0-451-22032-5(3) , N A L Trade) Penguin Group (USA) Inc.

Bonin, Liane. Pretty on the Outside: Fame Unlimited. 2007. 288p. (YA). pap. 9.99 (*978-0-451-22122-3(2) , N A L Trade) Penguin Group (USA) Inc.

Bonk, John J. Dustin Grubbs: Take Two! 2006. 256p. (J). (gr. 3-7). 15.99 (978-0-316-15637-0(X)) Little Brown & Co.

Bowers, Laura. Beauty Shop for Rent: ... Fully Equipped, Inquire Within. 2007. (Illus.). 336p. (J). (gr. 6-10). 17.00 (978-0-15-205764-0(1)) Harcourt Trade Pubs.

Bowers, Laura. Beauty Shop for Rent: ... fully equipped, inquire Within. 2008. (Illus.). 336p. (J). pap. 6.95 (*978-0-15-206385-6(4) , Harcourt Paperbacks) Harcourt Children's Bks.

Bowie, C. W. Laboriosos deditos de las Manos. Canetti, Yanitzia, tr. Willingham, Fred, illus. 2004. Tr. of Busy Fingers. (SPA.). 32p. (J). pap. 7.95 (978-1-58089-043-4(1)) Charlesbridge Publishing, Inc.

—Laboriosos deditos de los Pies. Canetti, Yanitzia, tr. Willingham, Fred, illus. 2004. Tr. of Busy Toes. (SPA.). 32p. (J). pap. 7.95 (978-1-58089-098-4(9)) Charlesbridge Publishing, Inc.

Bowler, Tim. Midget. 2000. (978-0-606-17929-4(1)) Tandem Library Bks.

Bradbury, Bianca. Flight into Spring. 2005. 184p. (YA). pap. (*978-1-932350-01-2(2)) Bethlehem Bks.

Brande, Robin. Evolution, Me & Other Freaks of Nature. 2007. 272p. (gr. 7). (J). lib. bdg. 18.99 (*978-0-375-94349-2(8)); (YA). 15.99 (*978-0-375-84349-5(3)) Random Hse. Children's Bks. (Knopf Bks. for Young Readers).

Breslin, Theresa. Remembrance. 2004. 304p. (YA). (gr. 7). mass mkt. 6.50 (978-0-440-23778-5(5) , Laurel Leaf) Random Hse. Children's Bks.

Brian, Kate. Megan Meade's Guide to the McGowan Boys. 2005. (Illus.). 272p. (YA). 15.99 (978-1-4169-0030-6(6)) Simon & Schuster Children's Publishing.

—Megan Meade's Guide to the Mcgowan Boys. 2006. 288p. (YA). pap. 8.99 (978-1-4169-0031-3(4) , Simon Pulse) Simon & Schuster Children's Publishing.

Brimner, Larry Dane. The Big, Beautiful, Brown Box. Tripp, Christine, illus. (Rookie Choices Ser.). 32p. (J). (gr. 1-2). 2002. pap. 5.95 (978-0-516-25973-4(3)); 2001. 19.50 (978-0-516-22160-1(4)) Scholastic Library Publishing. (Children's Pr.).

Broach, Elise. Shakespeare's Secret. rev. ed. 2005. (Illus.). 256p. (J). 16.95 (978-0-8050-7387-4(6) , Holt, Henry & Co. Bks. For Young Readers) Holt, Henry & Co.

Brontë, Emily. Wuthering Heights. abr. ed. (Classics Illustrated Ser.). (Illus.). 52p. (YA). pap. 4.95 (978-1-57209-011-8(1)) Classics International Entertainment, Inc.

—Wuthering Heights: Abridged for Children. 1998. (Illus.). 48p. (YA). (gr. 4-7). pap. 6.95 (978-0-8114-6847-3(X)) Steck-Vaughn.

Brooks, Martha. Being with Henry. 1999. (J). (978-0-88899-377-9(3)) Douglas & McIntyre, Ltd.

—Being with Henry. pap. 8.95 (978-0-88899-502-5(4)) Groundwood Bks. CAN. *Dist:* Transition Vendor.

—Mistik Lake. 2007. 224p. (J). (gr. 9 up). 16.00 (*978-0-374-34985-1(1) , Farrar, Straus & Giroux (BYR)) Farrar, Straus & Giroux.

Brooks, Martha. True Confessions of a Heartless Girl. braille ed. 2003. (J). (gr. 2). spiral bd. (978-0-616-15264-5(7)) Canadian National Institute for the Blind/Institut National Canadien pour les Aveugles.

—True Confessions of a Heartless Girl. 2003. 192p. (YA). (gr. 9 up). 16.00 (978-0-374-37806-6(1) , Farrar, Straus & Giroux (BYR)) Farrar, Straus & Giroux.

—True Confessions of a Heartless Girl. pap. 8.95 (978-0-88899-569-8(5)) Groundwood Bks. CAN. *Dist:* Transition Vendor.

—True Confessions of a Heartless Girl. 2004. 224p. (J). reprint ed. pap. 6.99 (978-0-06-059497-8(7) , HarperTeen) HarperCollins Pubs.

—True Confessions of a Heartless Girl. 2004. 216p. (YA). (gr. 7-12). lib. bdg. 13.64 (978-0-606-32642-1(1)) Tandem Library Bks.

Brouillet, Chrystine. Le Cameleon. 2003. (Roman Jeunesse Ser.). (FRE., Illus.). 96p. (YA). (gr. 4-7). pap. (978-2-89021-072-1(3)) Diffusion du livre Mirabel.

—Le Complot. Brochard, Philippe, illus. 2001. (Roman Jeunesse Ser.). (FRE.). 96p. (J). (gr. 4-7). pap. (978-2-89021-471-2(0)) Diffusion du livre Mirabel.

—Une Nuit Tres Longue. 2002. (Roman Plus Ser.). (FRE.). 160p. (YA). (gr. 8 up). pap. (978-2-89021-174-2(6)) Diffusion du livre Mirabel.

Brown, Marc. Arthur & the New Kid. 2004. (Arthur Ser.). (Illus.). 24p. (J). (gr. k-3). pap. 3.99 (978-0-375-81381-8(0)); lib. bdg. 11.99 (978-0-375-91381-5(5)) Random Hse. Children's Bks. (Random Hse. Bks. for Young Readers).

Brugman, Alyssa. Being Bindy. 2006. 208p. (YA). (gr. 7). 15.95 (978-0-385-73294-9(5)); lib. bdg. 17.99 (978-0-385-90315-8(4)) Random Hse. Children's Bks. (Delacorte Bks. for Young Readers).

Bryant, Megan E. Dance with Me! 2007. (All Aboard Reading Ser.). 32p. (J). (ps-1). pap. 3.99 (*978-0-448-44665-3(0) , Grosset & Dunlap) Penguin Group (USA) Inc.

Buchanan, Kathy Wierenga & Johnson, Lissa Halls. When Stars Fall, Vol. 11. 2005. (Brio Girls Ser.). 208p. (YA). pap. 7.99 (978-1-58997-090-8(X)) Focus on the Family Publishing.

Bunting, Eve. Noche de Humo. Andujar, Gloria de Aragon, tr. Diaz, David, illus. 1999. (SPA.). 36p. (J). (gr. 2-4). pap. 7.00 (978-0-15-201946-4(4) , Voyager Bks./Libros Viajeros) Harcourt Children's Bks.

—Noche de Humo. 1999. (978-0-606-16516-7(9)); (SPA.). lib. bdg. 14.15 (978-0-613-16782-6(1)) Tandem Library Bks.

—Smoky Night. 2002. (Illus.). (J). 13.19 (978-0-7587-0073-5(3)) Book Wholesalers, Inc.

—Smoky Night. Diaz, David, illus. 1999. 36p. (J). (ps-3). pap. 7.00 (978-0-15-201884-9(0) , Harcourt Paperbacks) Harcourt Children's Bks.

—Smoky Night. 1999. (978-0-606-16515-0(0)); lib. bdg. 14.15 (978-0-613-18279-9(0)) Tandem Library Bks.

Burgess, Melvin. Doing It. 336p. (YA). 2006. reprint ed. pap. 6.95 (978-0-8050-8079-7(1)); 2004. 15.95 (978-0-8050-7565-6(8)) Holt, Henry & Co. (Holt, Henry & Co. Bks. For Young Readers).

—Lady: My Life As A Bitch. 2002. (gr. 7-12). lib. bdg. 15.30 (978-0-613-68355-5(2)) Tandem Library Bks.

Burnham, Niki. Goddess Games. 2007. 288p. (YA). (gr. 9 up). 15.99 (978-1-4169-2700-6(X)) Simon & Schuster Children's Publishing.

Burningham, John. Edwardo: The Horriblest Boy in the Whole Wide World. 2007. (Illus.). 32p. (J). (ps-3). 16.99 (978-0-375-84053-1(2)); lib. bdg. 19.99 (978-0-375-94053-8(7)) Random Hse. Children's Bks. (Knopf Bks. for Young Readers).

Byars, Betsy. The Animal, the Vegetable, & John D. Jones. 150p. (J). (gr. 4-6). pap. 3.50 (978-0-8072-1414-5(0) , Listening Library) Random Hse. Audio Publishing Group.

Cabot, Meg. All-am. 2008. 256p. (J). pap. 7.99 (*978-0-06-147989-2(6) , HarperTeen) HarperCollins Pubs.

—All American Girl. 2003. 416p. (YA). (gr. 7 up). pap. 6.99 (978-0-06-447277-7(9)) HarperCollins Pubs.

—All American Girl. 2002. (gr. 7-12). lib. bdg. 15.30 (978-0-613-62192-2(1)) Tandem Library Bks.

—All American Girl. l.t. ed. 2003. 354p. (J). 25.95 (978-0-7862-6102-4(1) , Large Print Pr.) Thorndike Pr.

—Princess in Training. l.t. ed. 2005. (Princess Diaries: Vol. 6). 355p. (YA). (gr. 7-12). per. 22.95 (978-0-7862-7753-7(X) , Large Print Pr.) Thorndike Pr.

—Ready or Not. 2nd ed. 2005. 256p. (J). (gr. 7 up). lib. bdg. 16.89 (978-0-06-072451-1(X)) HarperCollins Pubs.

—Teen Idol. (J). (gr. 7 up). 2004. 304p. 15.99 (978-0-06-009616-8(0)); 2005. (Illus.). 320p. reprint ed. pap. 8.99 (978-0-06-009618-2(7) , Harper Trophy) HarperCollins Pubs.

—Teen Idol. l.t. ed. 2006. 366p. (YA). 23.95 (978-0-7862-7760-5(2)) Thorndike Pr.

Calonita, Jen. Secrets of My Hollywood Life: On Location. 2nd ed. 2007. 240p. (J). (gr. 7 up). 16.99 (*978-0-316-15439-0(3)) Little, Brown Bks. for Young Readers.

Cameron, Peter. Someday This Pain Will Be Useful to You. 2007. 240p. (YA). (gr. 9 up). 16.00 (978-0-374-30989-3(2)) Farrar, Straus & Giroux.

Campbell, Joanna. Bridal Dreams. 2004. (Thoroughbred Ser.: No. 65). 176p. (J). pap. 4.99 (978-0-06-059524-1(8) , Harper Entertainment) HarperCollins Pubs.

Canady, Pat. Upside - Downside, Downside - Upside. Zawiki, Neil, illus. 2000. 42p. (J). (ps-4). pap. 10.00 (978-1-929889-00-6(3)) Canady SW Publishing.

Canalin, Philip. Just Hug A Bubble. 2006. pap. 15.49 (*978-1-4259-7453-4(8)) AuthorHouse.

Candlewick Press Staff. Love & Kisses Ams Ed. 2002. (J). bds. 12.99 (978-0-7636-1823-0(3)) Candlewick Pr.

Cann, Kate. Grecian Holiday: Or, How I Turned down the Best Possible Thing Only to Have The. 2002. (gr. 7-12). lib. bdg. 14.15 (978-0-613-71506-5(3)) Tandem Library Bks.

—Grecian Holiday: Or, How I Turned down the Best Possible Thing Only to Have the Time of My Life. 2002. 352p. (J). (gr. 8 up). pap. 5.99 (978-0-06-447302-6(3)) HarperCollins Pubs.

—Spanish Holiday: Or, How I Transformed the Worst Vacation Ever into the Best Sum. 2004. (gr. 7-12). lib. bdg. 14.15 (978-0-613-71954-4(9)) Tandem Library Bks.

Cannon, A. E. The Loser's Guide to Life & Love. 2008. 272p. (J). 16.99 (*978-0-06-112846-2(5)); lib. bdg. 17.89 (*978-0-06-112847-9(3)) HarperCollins Pubs. (HarperTeen).

Carlson, Melody. Becoming Me. 2000. (Diary of a Teenage Girl Ser.: Bk. 1). (Illus.). 256p. (YA). pap. 12.99 (978-1-57673-735-4(7) , Multnomah) WaterBrook Pr.

—I Do. 2005. (Diary of a Teenage Girl Ser.). 272p. (YA). pap. 12.99 (978-1-59052-320-9(2) , Multnomah) WaterBrook Pr.

—Just Ask. 2005. (Diary of a Teenage Girl Ser.). 256p. (J). pap. 12.99 (978-1-59052-321-6(0) , Multnomah) WaterBrook Pr.

—My Name Is Chloe. 2005. 288p. (YA). mass mkt. 7.99 (978-1-59052-736-8(4) , Multnomah) WaterBrook Pr.

—My Name Is Chloe: Diary of a Teenage Girl. 2003. (gr. 7-12). lib. bdg. 22.25 (978-0-613-87416-8(1)) Tandem Library Bks.

—On My Own. 2002. (gr. 7-12). lib. bdg. 22.25 (978-0-613-85855-7(7)) Tandem Library Bks.

—On My Own: Diary Number 4. 2002. (Diary of a Teenage Girl Ser.: Bk. 4). 300p. (J). pap. 12.99 (978-1-59052-017-8(3) , Multnomah) WaterBrook Pr.

Carlton, Susan. Lobsterland. 2007. 224p. (YA). (gr. 9 up). 16.95 (*978-0-8050-8096-4(1)) Holt, Henry & Co.

Carr, Jon & Carr, Debra. Sammy the Elephant in a Lesson on Personal Differences. 2000. 13p. 6.00 (978-1-885072-39-9(2)) Creflo Dollar Ministries Pubns.

Carson, Carole. Remembering When I Was Young, 2 vols. Kenfield, Peggy, illus. gif. ed. 2006. 92p. (J). 24.95 (978-0-9766030-6-1(3)) Hound Pr.

Caseley, Judith. The Kissing Diary. 2007. 208p. (J). (gr. 5 up). 16.00 (978-0-374-36346-8(3)) Farrar, Straus & Giroux.

Castellucci, Cecil. Boy Proof. 208p. (YA). (gr. 9 up). 2005. 15.99 (978-0-7636-2333-3(4)); 2006. reprint ed. pap. 7.99 (978-0-7636-2796-6(8)) Candlewick Pr.

Challenge of Choice. 2002. (YA). per. 11.95 (978-0-9656307-3-3(0)) Sunrise Selections.

Chambers, Aidan. Postcards from No Man's Land. 2004. 320p. (J). (gr. 9 up). reprint ed. pap. 7.99 (978-0-14-240145-3(5) , Puffin) Penguin Group (USA) Inc.

Chan, Gillian. An Ocean Apart: The Gold Mountain Diary of Chin Mei-Ling. 2004. (Dear Canada Ser.). (Illus.). 217p. (J). pap. (978-0-7791-1353-8(5)) Scholastic Canada, Ltd.

Charlip, Remy & Moore, Lilian. Hooray for Me! 2007. (Illus.). 40p. (J). pap. 7.95 (*978-1-58246-201-1(1) , Tricycle Pr.) Ten Speed Pr.

Cheripko, Jan. Sun Moon Stars Rain. 2006. (Illus.). 160p. (YA). 16.95 (978-1-932425-53-6(5) , Lemniscaat) Boyds Mills Pr.

Cheshire, Simon. Kissing Vanessa. 2004. 144p. (YA). (gr. 7). 15.95 (978-0-385-73212-3(0) , Delacorte Bks. for Young Readers) Random Hse. Children's Bks.

—The Prince & the Snowgirl. 2007. 176p. (J). (gr. 7). pap. 8.99 (978-0-385-73342-7(9)); lib. bdg. 12.99 (978-0-385-90359-2(6)) Random Hse. Children's Bks. (Delacorte Bks. for Young Readers).

Chessen, Sherri. Gorp's Dream: A Tale of Diversity, Tolerance, & Love in Pumpernickel Park. Masel, Christy, illus. 2003. 36p. (J). pap. 7.95 (978-0-9724249-1-2(1)) Gorp Group Pr., The.

Chotjewitz, David & Orgel, Doris. Crazy Diamond. 2008. 272p. (YA). 17.99 (*978-1-4169-1176-0(6)) Simon & Schuster Children's Publishing.

Choyce, Lesley. The End of the World As We Know It. 2007. 224p. (YA). (gr. 7 up). pap. 9.95 (*978-0-88995-379-6(1)) Red Deer Pr. CAN. *Dist:* Fitzhenry & Whiteside, Ltd.

Christopher, Matt. Slam Dunk. 2004. (Illus.). 128p. (J). (gr. 4-7). pap. 4.99 (978-0-316-60762-9(2)) Little Brown & Co.

Clairday, Robynn. Confessions of a Boyfriend Stealer. 2005. 240p. (YA). (gr. 7-12). pap. 7.95 (978-0-385-73242-0(2) , Delacorte Bks. for Young Readers) Random Hse. Children's Bks.

Clark, Abbie. Way down Yonder in the Paw Paw Patch. 2006. (J). per. 16.95 (*978-1-59858-129-4(5)) Dog Ear Publishing, LLC.

Clark, Billy C. The Champion of Sourwood Mountain. 2003. (Illus.). 251p. (J). (978-1-931672-19-1(9)) Stuart, Jesse Foundation, The.

Clarke, Judith. Night Train. 2007. (J). pap. 9.95 (*978-1-932425-92-5(6) , Front Street) Boyds Mills Pr.

H I

Clarke, Nicole & Veron, Alexa. Close up & Personal, Vol. 2. 2006. (Flirt Ser.: No. 2). 224p. (J). (gr. 7). pap. 6.99 (978-0-448-44264-8(7) , Grosset & Dunlap) Penguin Group (USA) Inc.

Clements, Andrew. Jake Drake, Bully Buster. Pedersen, Janet, illus. 2007. (Jake Drake Ser.). 80p. (J). pap. 3.99 (***978-1-4169-3933-7(4)*** , Aladdin) Simon & Schuster Children's Publishing.

—Lunch Money. Selznick, Brian, illus. 2007. 240p. (J). (gr. 3-7). pap. 5.99 (***978-0-689-86685-2(2)*** , Aladdin) Simon & Schuster Children's Publishing.

—Lunch Money. Selznick, Brian, illus. l.t. ed. 2005. 231p. (J). (gr. 3-7). 21.95 (978-0-7862-8036-0(0) , Large Print Pr.) Thorndike Pr.

Cobot, Meg. All-American Girl. 2004. 416p. (J). (gr. 7 up). pap. 44.00 incl. audio (978-0-8072-2281-2(X) , Listening Library) Random Hse. Audio Publishing Group.

Coburn, Jake. LoveSick. 2005. 240p. (YA). (gr. 8-12). 16.99 (978-0-525-47383-1(1) , Dutton Juvenile) Penguin Group (USA) Inc.

—Prep. 2005. 192p. (YA). (gr. 7). pap. 5.99 (978-0-14-240307-5(5) , Puffin) Penguin Group (USA) Inc.

Codell, Esmé Raji. Sahara Special. (J). (gr. 3-7). 2004. 192p. pap. 5.99 (978-0-7868-1611-8(2)); 2003. (Illus.). 208p. lib. bdg. 16.49 (978-0-7868-2627-8(4)) Hyperion Bks. for Children.

—Sahara Special. 2003. (gr. 3-6). lib. bdg. 14.10 (978-0-613-65611-5(3)) Tandem Library Bks.

Cohen, Tish. The Invisible Rules of the Zoe Lama. 2007. 208p. (J). (gr. 4-7). 15.99 (978-0-525-47810-2(8) , Dutton Juvenile) Penguin Group (USA) Inc.

Cohn, Rachel. Cupcake. 2007. 256p. (YA). 15.99 (978-1-4169-1217-0(7) , Simon & Schuster Children's Publishing) Simon & Schuster Children's Publishing.

—Gingerbread. 2002. (Illus.). 176p. (J). (gr. 9 up). 15.95 (978-0-689-84337-2(2)) Simon & Schuster Children's Publishing.

—Gingerbread. 2003. (gr. 7-12). lib. bdg. 15.30 (978-0-613-60473-4(3)) Tandem Library Bks.

—Pop Princess. 2004. (Illus.). 320p. (J). 16.95 (978-0-689-85205-3(3)) Simon & Schuster Children's Publishing.

—Shrimp. 288p. (YA). (gr. 7 up). 2005. 15.95 (978-0-689-86612-8(7) , Simon & Schuster Children's Publishing); 2006. reprint ed. pap. 6.99 (978-0-689-86613-5(5) , Simon Pulse) Simon & Schuster Children's Publishing.

Cohn, Rachel. You Know Where to Find Me. 2008. 208p. (YA). 15.99 (***978-0-689-87859-6(1)*** , Simon & Schuster Children's Publishing) Simon & Schuster Children's Publishing.

Cohn, Rachel & Wattenberg, Jane. Gingerbread. 2003. 176p. (YA). pap. 6.99 (978-0-689-86020-1(X) , Simon Pulse) Simon & Schuster Children's Publishing.

Colasanti, Susane. Tara's Triumph. 2006. 320p. (J). (gr. 7). 17.99 (978-0-670-06029-0(1) , Viking Juvenile) Penguin Group (USA) Inc.

Colasanti, Susane & Jeffries, Cindy. Tara's Triumph, Vol. 5. 2007. (Fame School Ser.). 128p. (J). (gr. 7). 5.99 (***978-0-14-240837-7(9)***) Penguin Group (USA) Inc.

Cole, Stephen. Thieves Like Us. 352p. (YA). 2007. (Illus.). pap. 7.95 (978-1-59990-041-4(6)); 2006. 16.95 (978-1-58234-653-3(4)) Bloomsbury Publishing. (Bloomsbury Children).

Cole, Stephen. Thieves Till We Die. 2007. 320p. (YA). 16.95 (***978-1-59990-082-7(3)*** , Bloomsbury Children) Bloomsbury Publishing.

Coleman, Michael. Weirdo's War. 1998. (Illus.). 192p. (J). (gr. 4-8). pap. 16.95 (978-0-531-30103-6(6) , Orchard Bks.) Scholastic, Inc.

Collins, Yvonne & Rideout, Sandy. The New & Improved Vivien Leigh Reid: Diva in Control. 2007. 240p. (gr. 7-10). pap. 9.95 (978-0-312-35828-0(8) , St. Martin's Griffin); 231p. (YA). (***978-1-4287-1928-6(8)***) St. Martin's Pr.

Cooper, Ilene. Sam I Am. 256p. (J). 2006. pap. 5.99 (978-0-439-43968-8(X)); 2004. (gr. 4-7). pap. 15.95 (978-0-439-43967-1(1) , Scholastic Pr.) Scholastic, Inc.

Cooper, Wendy. My First Ride with Isaiah. Elizabeth Mobley, illus. 2006. 18p. (J). 11.95 (***978-0-9772964-8-4(2)***) Kingdom Publishing Group, Inc.

Copeland, Cynthia L. Elin's Island. 2003. (Single Titles Ser.: up). 144p. (gr. 6 up). lib. bdg. 22.90 (978-0-7613-2522-2(0) , Millbrook Pr.) Lerner Publishing Group.

—The 15 Best Things about Being the New Kid. Vargo, Sharon Hawkins, illus. 2006. (Silly Millies Ser.). 32p. (J). 21.27 (978-0-7613-2889-6(0) , Millbrook Pr.) Lerner Publishing Group.

Corbet, Robert. Fifteen Love. 2005. 192p. (YA). pap. 6.95 (978-0-8027-7714-0(7)) Walker & Co.

—Shelf Life. 2005. 190p. (YA). 16.95 (978-0-8027-8959-4(5)) Walker & Co.

Corbett, Sue. 12 Again. 2007. 240p. (J). (gr. 5 up). pap. 5.99 (978-0-14-240729-5(1) , Puffin) Penguin Group (USA) Inc.

Corrigan, Eireann. Splintering. 192p. (J). 2005. pap. 7.99 (978-0-439-48992-8(X)); 2004. pap. 16.95 (978-0-439-53597-7(2)) Scholastic, Inc.

—Splintering. 2005. 184p. (YA). (gr. 8-12). lib. bdg. 15.04 (978-0-606-33304-7(5)) Tandem Library Bks.

Cote, Denis. Les Yeux d'Emeraude. 2003. (Roman Jeunesse Ser.). (FRE.). 96p. (YA). (gr. 4-7). pap. (978-2-89021-165-0(7)) Diffusion du livre Mirabel.

Crane, E. M. Skin Deep. 2008. (YA). (***978-0-385-73479-0(4)*** , Delacorte Pr.) Dell Publishing.

Crawford, Ann Fears. Vangie: The Ghost of the Pines. 2002. 142p. (J). 17.95 (978-1-57168-710-4(6) , Eakin Pr.) Eakin Pr.

Crilley, Mark. Spring. Crilley, Mark, illus. 2007. (Miki Falls Ser.). (Illus.). 176p. (J). (gr. 7 up). pap. 7.99 (***978-0-06-084616-9(X)*** , HarperTeen) HarperCollins Pubs.

—Summer. Crilley, Mark, illus. 2007. (Miki Falls Ser.). (Illus.). 176p. (J). (gr. 7 up). pap. 7.99 (***978-0-06-084617-6(8)*** , HarperTeen) HarperCollins Pubs.

Cross, Gillian. Tightrope. 1999. 224p. (J). (gr. 7 up). 16.95 (978-0-8234-1512-0(0)) Holiday Hse., Inc.

—Tightrope. 1999. 210p. (YA). (978-0-19-271804-4(5)) Oxford Univ. Pr., Inc.

Croteau, Marie-Danielle. Un Vent de Liberte. 2003. (Roman Plus Ser.). (FRE.). 160p. (YA). (gr. 8 up). pap. (978-2-89021-204-6(1)) Diffusion du livre Mirabel.

Crowe, Carole. Waiting for Dolphins. 2003. 144p. (YA). (gr. 4-6). pap. 9.95 (978-1-59078-073-2(6)); (Illus.). pap. 16.95 (978-1-56397-847-0(4)) Boyds Mills Pr.

—Waiting for Dolphins. 2003. (gr. 3-6). lib. bdg. 18.75 (978-0-613-59368-7(5)) Tandem Library Bks.

Crutcher, Chris. Ironman. 2004. 280p. (YA). (gr. 10). lib. bdg. 14.04 (978-0-606-32640-7(5)) Tandem Library Bks.

—Staying Fat for Sarah Byrnes. 2003. 304p. (J). (ps-3). pap. 6.99 (978-0-06-009489-8(3)) HarperCollins Pubs.

Culver, Carol. Rich Girl: A BFF Novel. 2008. 240p. pap. 9.99 (***978-0-425-21915-7(1)*** , Berkley Trade) Penguin Group (USA) Inc.

Cummings, Catherine M. A Flea's Lament. Conner, Wendy Simpson, illus. 2002. (Flea Books: Vol. 1). 24p. (J). (ps-2). pap. 7.95 (978-0-9725155-0-4(X)) Junibird Productions.

Cutler, Dave. When I Wished I Was Alone. Cutler, Dave, illus. 2003. (Illus.). 36p. (J). 16.95 (978-0-9671851-0-1(6)) GreyCore Pr.

Cutler, Jane. Common Sense & Fowls. Barasch, Lynne, illus. 2005. 144p. (J). 16.00 (978-0-374-32262-5(7) , Farrar, Straus & Giroux (BYR)) Farrar, Straus & Giroux.

Danziger, Paula. Earth to Matthew. 1998. (Matthew Martin Ser.: No. 3). 154p. (J). (gr. 3-7). pap. 5.99 (978-0-698-11692-4(5) , Putnam Juvenile) Penguin Group (USA) Inc.

Davidson, Dana. Jason & Kyra. 2005. 352p. (gr. 7-17). pap. 5.99 (978-0-7868-3653-6(9) , Jump at the Sun) Hyperion Bks. for Children.

Davies, Jacqueline. Where the Ground Meets the Sky. 2002. 224p. (YA). (gr. 5-9). 14.95 (978-0-7614-5105-1(6) , Cavendish Children's Bks.) Cavendish, Marshall Corp.

De Lint, Charles. Waifs & Strays. 2004. 416p. (YA). (gr. 7 up). pap. 8.99 (978-0-14-240158-3(7) , Puffin) Penguin Group (USA) Inc.

Dean, Zoey. The A-List: A Novel. 2003. (A-List Ser.: Bk. 1). (YA). lib. bdg. 17.60 (978-0-613-70574-5(2)) Tandem Library Bks.

—Back in Black. 2005. (A-List Ser.: No. 5). 304p. (YA). (gr. 9-17). pap. 9.99 (978-0-316-01092-4(8) , Poppy) Little, Brown Bks. for Young Readers.

—Blonde Ambition. 2004. (A-List Ser.: No. 3). 240p. (YA). (gr. 9-17). pap. 9.99 (978-0-316-73474-5(8) , Poppy) Little, Brown Bks. for Young Readers.

—Blonde Ambition. 2004. (A-List Ser.: No. 3). 233p. (YA). (gr. 8-12). per. 16.64 (978-0-606-33461-7(0)) Tandem Library Bks.

—Girls on Film. 2004. 250p. (YA). (gr. 8-12). per. 16.64 (978-0-606-33460-0(2)) Tandem Library Bks.

—Some Like It Hot. 6th ed. 2006. (A-List Ser.: No. 6). 320p. (J). (gr. 9-17). pap. 9.99 (978-0-316-01093-1(6) , Poppy) Little, Brown Bks. for Young Readers.

—Tall Cool One. No. 4. 2005. (A-List Ser.: No. 4). 304p. (YA). (gr. 9-17). pap. 9.99 (978-0-316-73508-7(6) , Poppy) Little, Brown Bks. for Young Readers.

—Tall Cool One. 2005. (A-List Ser.: No. 4). 295p. (YA). (gr. 7-17). per. 16.64 (978-0-606-33462-4(9)) Tandem Library Bks.

DeAngelo, Jeremy. The Out Crowd. 2006. (J). pap. (978-0-88092-613-3(9)); lib. bdg. (978-0-88092-612-6(0)) Royal Fireworks Publishing Co.

Decampi, Alex & Federica Manfredi. Kat & Mouse, Vol. 2. 2007. (Illus.). pap. 5.99 (978-1-59816-549-4(6) , Tokyopop Kids) TOKYOPOP, Inc.

Decary, Marie. Nuisance Publik. 2002. (Roman Plus Ser.). (FRE., Illus.). 160p. (YA). (gr. 8 up). pap. (978-2-89021-249-7(1)) Diffusion du livre Mirabel.

DeLaCroix, Alice. How to Survive a Totally Boring Summer. Fisher, Cynthia, illus. 2007. 96p. (J). (gr. 1-4). 16.95 (***978-0-8234-2024-7(8)***) Holiday Hse., Inc.

Dellasega, Cheryl. Nugrl90 (Sadie) LaPierre, Karina, illus. 2007. (Bloggrls Ser.). (YA). (gr. 7 up). 200p. 15.99 (***978-0-7614-5375-8(X)***); 190p. per. 6.99 (***978-0-7614-5396-3(2)***) Cavendish, Marshall Corp.

Desplechin, Marie. Poor Little Witch Girl. Rosner, Gillian, tr. 2007. 144p. (J). pap. 6.95 (***978-1-59990-128-2(5)*** , Bloomsbury Children) Bloomsbury Publishing.

Desrosiers, Sylvie. Le Long Silence. 2002. (Roman Plus Ser.). (FRE., Illus.). 160p. (YA). (gr. 8 up). pap. (978-2-89021-256-5(4)) Diffusion du livre Mirabel.

—La Patte dans le Sac. Sylvestre, Daniel, illus. 2001. (Roman Jeunesse — Special Editions Ser.). (FRE.). 96p. (J). (gr. 4-7). pap. (978-2-89021-507-8(5)) Diffusion du livre Mirabel.

—Qui a Peur des Fantomes? 2002. (Roman Jeunesse Ser.). (FRE.). 96p. (YA). (gr. 4-7). pap. (978-2-89021-073-8(1)) Diffusion du livre Mirabel.

Dessen, Sarah. Dreamland. 2000. (Illus.). 256p. (J). (gr. 7-12). 15.99 (978-0-670-89122-1(3) , Viking Juvenile) Penguin Group (USA) Inc.

—Just Listen. 384p. (YA). (gr. 7). 2008. pap. 8.99 (***978-0-14-241097-4(7)*** , Puffin); 2006. 17.99 (978-0-670-06105-1(0) , Viking Juvenile) Penguin Group (USA) Inc.

—Keeping the Moon. 2004. 240p. (YA). (gr. 7 up). pap. 7.99 (978-0-14-240176-7(5) , Puffin) Penguin Group (USA) Inc.

—Lock & Key. 2008. 432p. (YA). (gr. 7). 18.99 (***978-0-670-01088-2(X)*** , Viking Juvenile) Penguin Group (USA) Inc.

—That Summer. 208p. (YA). (gr. 7). 2006. 16.99 (978-0-670-06110-5(7) , Viking Juvenile); 2004. pap. 7.99 (978-0-14-240172-9(2) , Puffin) Penguin Group (USA) Inc.

—That Summer. 1998. (J). (978-0-606-13842-0(0)) Tandem Library Bks.

—This Lullaby. (J). 2002. 304p. 16.99 (978-0-670-03530-4(0) , Viking Juvenile); 2004. 352p. reprint ed. pap. 7.99 (978-0-14-250155-9(7) , Puffin) Penguin Group (USA) Inc.

—The Truth about Forever. 2006. 400p. (YA). (gr. 7). reprint ed. pap. 7.99 (978-0-14-240625-0(2) , Puffin) Penguin Group (USA) Inc.

Deuker, Carl. Night Hoops. 2001. 256p. (gr. 7 up). pap. 6.99 (978-0-06-447275-3(2) , Harper Trophy) HarperCollins Pubs.

—Night Hoops. 2000. (Illus.). 224p. (J). (gr. 7-12). tchr. ed. 15.00 (978-0-395-97936-5(6)) Houghton Mifflin Co. Trade & Reference Div.

—Night Hoops. 2001. (978-0-606-22927-2(2)); 250p. (gr. 7-12). lib. bdg. 14.15 (978-0-613-61919-6(6)) Tandem Library Bks.

Disher, Garry. The Divine Wind: A Love Story. 2004. 160p. (J). pap. 5.99 (978-0-439-36916-9(9)); 2002. 176p. (YA). (gr. 9 up). pap. 15.95 (978-0-439-36915-2(0)) Scholastic, Inc. (Levine, Arthur A. Bks.).

Disney Press Staff, et al. Raven Rocks. 19th rev. ed. 2007. 128p. (gr. 3-7). pap. 4.99 (***978-0-7868-3839-4(6)*** Disney Pr.

D'Lacey, Chris. From E to You. 2001. (gr. 7-12). lib. bdg. 13.00 (978-0-613-85076-6(9)) Tandem Library Bks.

D'Lacey, Chris & Newbery, Linda. From E to You. 2001. 208p. (YA). (gr. 7 up). mass mkt. 4.99 (978-0-7434-2285-7(6) , Simon Pulse) Simon & Schuster Children's Publishing.

Donovan, Stacey. Who I Am Keeps Happening. 2004. (YA). (978-0-7636-1988-6(4)) Candlewick Pr.

Dorfman, Joaquín. Playing It Cool. 2006. 352p. (gr. 7-11). (J). lib. bdg. 17.99 (978-0-375-93641-8(6)); (YA). 15.95 (978-0-375-83641-1(1)) Random Hse. Children's Bks. (Random Hse. Bks. for Young Readers).

Dorfman, Joaquin. Playing it Cool. 2007. 352p. (J). (gr. 7-11). pap. 7.99 (978-0-375-84024-1(9) , Random Hse. Bks. for Young Readers) Random Hse. Children's Bks.

Dower, Laura. From the Files of Madison Finn: Heart to Heart. 2003. (gr. 3-6). lib. bdg. 13.00 (978-0-613-75026-4(8)) Tandem Library Bks.

Downing, Erin. Dancing Queen. 2006. (Romantic Comedies Ser.). 272p. (YA). pap. 6.99 (978-1-4169-2510-1(4) , Simon Pulse) Simon & Schuster Children's Publishing.

Duder, Tessa. Tiggie Thompson All at Sea. 2001. 232p. (YA). pap. (978-0-14-131323-8(4) , Puffin) Penguin Group (USA) Inc.

Dunmore, Helen. The Tide Knot. 2008. (J). (***978-0-06-081857-9(3)***); 336p. 16.99 (***978-0-06-081855-5(7)***); 336p. lib. bdg. 17.89 (***978-0-06-081856-2(5)***) HarperCollins Pubs.

DuPrau, Jeanne. Car Trouble. 288p. (J). 2006. pap. 6.99 (978-0-06-073675-0(5) , HarperTeen); 2005. 15.99 (978-0-06-073672-9(0)); 2005. lib. bdg. 16.89 (978-0-06-073674-3(7)) HarperCollins Pubs.

Eager, Edward. The Well-Wishers. Bodecker, N. M., illus. 1999. 220p. (J). (ps-7). per. 14.15 (978-0-613-22594-6(5)) Tandem Library Bks.

Earls, Nick. After Summer. 2005. 240p. (YA). (gr. 7). pap. 6.99 (978-0-618-45781-6(X) , Graphia) Houghton Mifflin Co. Trade & Reference Div.

—48 Shades of Brown. 2004. 288p. (YA). (gr. 7 up). pap. 6.99 (978-0-618-45295-8(8) , Graphia) Houghton Mifflin Co. Trade & Reference Div.

Edgeworth, Maria. Tomorrow. 2004. reprint ed. pap. 15.95 (978-1-4191-9032-2(6)); pap. 1.99 (978-1-4192-9032-9(0)) Kessinger Publishing, LLC.

Efaw, Amy. Battle Dress. 2000. (Illus.). 304p. (J). (gr. 7 up). 16.99 (978-0-06-027943-1(5)) HarperCollins Pubs.

—Battle Dress. 2004. (Illus.). 382p. (YA). (gr. 8-12). per. 14.04 (978-0-606-30102-2(X)) Tandem Library Bks.

Ellis, Ann Dee. This Is What I Did. 2007. 176p. (YA). (gr. 7 up). 16.99 (978-0-316-01363-5(3)) Little Brown & Co.

Ellis, Kim. Bernard & His Dad. 2005. 49p. pap. 12.95 (978-1-4137-7058-2(4)) PublishAmerica, Inc.

Emery, Anne. Senior Year. 2006. (YA). per. 11.95 (***978-1-59511-005-3(4)***) Image Cascade Publishing.

—Sorority Girl. 2006. (YA). per. 11.95 (***978-1-59511-007-7(0)***) Image Cascade Publishing.

Emmanuel, Linda. The Angel Children: I Love Who I Am. 2005. (Illus.). (J). E-Book 12.95 incl. cd-rom (978-0-9767418-0-0(6)) Wintermantel Group, LLC, The.

Emmy's Question. 2007. (J). 16.99 (***978-0-9790395-2-2(5)***) Morningtide Pr.

Erik & Isabelle Senior Year at Foresthill High. 2007. (YA). per. 12.00 (***978-0-9755848-3-5(9)***) Foglight Pr.

Farnes, Catherine. Over the Divide. 2001. 146p. (J). (gr. 7-12). 6.49 (978-1-57924-646-4(X)) Jones, Bob Univ. Pr.

—Over the Divide. 2001. (gr. 7-12). lib. bdg. 14.70 (978-0-613-85517-4(5)) Tandem Library Bks.

Faye, Charlet. The Feather-Dusted Easter. Letterman, Kimberlee, illus. 1999. 48p. (J). (gr. k-3). 16.95 (978-0-9655222-0-5(2)) FayeHouse. Pr. International.

Fehler, Gene. Beanball. 2008. 128p. (J). (gr. 7 up). 16.00 (***978-0-618-84348-0(5)*** , Clarion Bks.) Houghton Mifflin Co. Trade & Reference Div.

Ferguson, Alane. The Angel of Death. 2006. (Forensic Mystery Ser.). 272p. (YA). (gr. 7). 15.99 (978-0-670-06055-9(0) , Viking Adult) Penguin Group (USA) Inc.

Ferguson, Alane. Angel of Death. 2008. (Forensic Mystery Ser.). 272p. (YA). (gr. 7). pap. 6.99 (***978-0-14-241087-5(X)*** , Puffin) Penguin Group (USA) Inc.

Ferraro, Tina. How to Hook a Hottie. 2008. 208p. (J). pap. (***978-0-385-73438-7(7)*** , Delacorte Pr.) Dell Publishing.

—How to Hook a Hottie. 2008. 208p. (YA). (gr. 7). lib. bdg. 11.99 (***978-0-385-90444-5(4)*** , Delacorte Bks. for Young Readers) Random Hse. Children's Bks.

—Top Ten Uses for an Unworn Prom Dress. 2007. 240p. (YA). (gr. 7). pap. 7.99 (978-0-385-73368-7(2)); lib. bdg. 12.99 (978-0-385-90383-7(9)) Random Hse. Children's Bks. (Delacorte Bks. for Young Readers).

Ferraro, Tina. Top Ten Uses for an Unworn Prom Dress: A Novel. 2006. 222p. (YA). (***978-1-4287-2694-9(2)*** , Delacorte Pr.) Dell Publishing.

Ferris, Aimee. Girl Overboard. 2007. (S. A. S. S. (Students Across the Seven Seas) Ser.). 224p. (YA). (gr. 7). pap. 6.99 (978-0-14-240799-8(2) , Puffin) Penguin Group (USA) Inc.

Fitch, Sheree. One More Step. 2002. (Orca Soundings Ser.). 96p. (J). (gr. 7-12). pap. 7.95 (978-1-55143-248-9(X)) Orca Bk. Pubs. USA.

—One More Step. 2002. (gr. 7-12). lib. bdg. 16.40 (978-0-613-62978-2(7)) Tandem Library Bks.

Fleischman, Paul. Breakout. 2005. (Illus.). 137p. (YA). (gr. 7-12). lib. bdg. 15.60 (978-1-4176-6932-5(2)) Tandem Library Bks.

—Mind's Eye. 2001. (gr. 7-12). lib. bdg. 13.55 (978-0-613-34013-7(2)) Tandem Library Bks.

Flesh, Chris P. The Mystery of the Mystery Meat #3. 2008. 176p. (J). (gr. 3). pap. 4.99 (***978-0-448-44811-4(4)*** , Grosset & Dunlap) Penguin Group (USA) Inc.

Fletcher, Susan. Shadow Spinner. unabr. ed. 1999. (J). (gr. 5). pap., stu. ed. 59.24 incl. audio (978-0-7887-3007-8(X) , 40889) Recorded Bks., LLC.

—Shadow Spinner. Kramer, Dave, illus. 1999. (Jean Karl Bks.). 224p. (J). (gr. 5-9). pap. 5.99 (978-0-689-83051-8(3) , Aladdin) Simon & Schuster Children's Publishing.

—Shadow Spinner. 1999. (978-0-606-17195-3(9)); (gr. 5-8). lib. bdg. 13.00 (978-0-613-23034-6(5)) Tandem Library Bks.

Flinn, Alex. Diva. 2007. 288p. (J). pap. 7.99 (***978-0-06-056846-7(1)***); 2006. 272p. (YA). 16.99 (978-0-06-056843-6(7)); 2006. 272p. (YA). lib. bdg. 17.89 (978-0-06-056845-0(3)) HarperCollins Pubs. (HarperTeen).

Fogelin, Adrian. The Big Nothing. 2004. 224p. (J). 14.95 (978-1-56145-326-9(9)) Peachtree Pubs., Ltd.

—Big Nothing. 2006. 224p. (YA). pap. 6.95 (978-1-56145-388-7(9)) Peachtree Pubs., Ltd.

—My Brother's Hero. (Peachtree Junior Publication Ser.). 224p. (J). 2002. (gr. 3-7). 14.95 (978-1-56145-274-3(2)); 2005. reprint ed. pap. 6.95 (978-1-56145-352-8(8)) Peachtree Pubs., Ltd.

—The Real Question. 2006. 240p. (YA). 15.95 (978-1-56145-383-2(8) , Peachtree Junior) Peachtree Pubs., Ltd.

Foley, John. Hoops of Steel. 2007. 240p. (J). (gr. 9 up). pap. 8.95 (978-0-7387-0981-9(6) , Flux) Llewellyn Pubns.

Ford, Juwanda G. Shop Talk. Hoston, Jim, illus. 2004. 32p. (J). lib. bdg. 15.00 (***978-1-4242-0236-2(1)***) Fitzgerald Bks.

Frank, Christian M. Catholic (Reluctantly) 2007. (YA). pap. 11.95 (***978-1-928832-99-7(7)***) Sophia Institute Pr.

Frank, E. R. Friction. 208p. (YA). 2003. (Illus.). 16.95 (978-0-689-85384-5(X) , Atheneum/Richard Jackson Bks.); 2004. reprint ed. pap. 6.99 (978-0-689-85385-2(8) , Simon Pulse) Simon & Schuster Children's Publishing.

—Life Is Funny. 2002. 272p. (YA). pap. 7.99 (978-0-14-230083-1(7) , Puffin) Penguin Group (USA) Inc.

Frank, E. R. & Dorling Kindersley Publishing Staff. Life Is Funny. 2000. (Richard Jackson Bks.). (Illus.). 272p. (J). (gr. 7-12). 19.99 (978-0-7894-2634-5(X)) Dorling Kindersley Publishing, Inc.

Frank, Hillary. Better Than Running at Night. Frank, Hillary, illus. 2002. (Illus.). 272p. (YA). (gr. 7 up). pap. 7.99 (978-0-618-25073-8(5)); (gr. 9 up). tchr. ed. 17.00 (978-0-618-10439-0(9)) Houghton Mifflin Co. Trade & Reference Div.

—Better Than Running at Night. 2002. (gr. 7-12). lib. bdg. 18.80 (978-0-613-90721-7(3)) Tandem Library Bks.

—I Can't Tell You. 2004. 208p. (YA). (gr. 7). 16.00 (978-0-618-41202-0(6)); pap. 7.99 (978-0-618-49491-0(X) , Graphia) Houghton Mifflin Co. Trade & Reference Div.

Frankel, Valerie. American Fringe. 2008. 272p. (gr. 12 up). 9.99 (***978-0-451-22292-3(X)*** , N A L Trade) Penguin Group (USA) Inc.

Frankel, Valerie. Fringe Girl in Love. 2007. 256p. (YA). pap. 9.99 (978-0-451-22046-2(3) , N A L Trade) Penguin Group (USA) Inc.

Franklin, Emily. Labor of Love: The Principles of Love. 2007. 256p. (gr. 12 up). pap. 9.99 (***978-0-451-22211-4(3)*** , N A L Trade) Penguin Group (USA) Inc.

Franklin, Emily. Summer of Love: The Principles of Love. 2007. 256p. (YA). pap. 9.99 (978-0-451-22040-0(4) , N A L Trade) Penguin Group (USA) Inc.

Frederick, Heather Vogel. The Mother-Daughter Book Club. 2007. 256p. (J). (gr. 4-7). 15.99 (978-0-689-86412-4(4)) Simon & Schuster Children's Publishing.

Fredericks, Mariah. Crunch Time. 336p. (YA). 2007. (gr. 7 up). pap. 7.99 (***978-1-4169-3973-3(3)*** , Simon Pulse); 2005. (Illus.). 16.99 (978-0-689-86938-9(X) , Atheneum) Simon & Schuster Children's Publishing.

Fredericks, Mariah. The True Meaning of Cleavage. (YA). 2003. (Illus.). 224p. 15.95 (978-0-689-85092-9(1) , Atheneum/Richard Jackson Bks.); 2004. 240p. reprint ed. pap. 6.99 (978-0-689-86958-7(4) , Simon Pulse) Simon & Schuster Children's Publishing.

Freeman, Martha. 1,000 Reasons Never to Kiss a Boy. 2007. 240p. (YA). (gr. 7 up). 16.95 (978-0-8234-2044-5(2)) Holiday Hse., Inc.

Freymann-Weyr, Garret. The Kings Are Already Here. 2003. 160p. (YA). (gr. 7). tchr. ed. 15.00 (978-0-618-26363-9(2)) Houghton Mifflin Co. Trade & Reference Div.

—My Heartbeat. 2002. 160p. (YA). (gr. 7-12). 15.00 (978-0-618-14181-4(2)) Houghton Mifflin Co. Trade & Reference Div.

—Stay with Me. 2006. 320p. (YA). (gr. 8). 16.00 (978-0-618-60571-2(1)) Houghton Mifflin Co.

—Stay with Me. 2007. 320p. (YA). (gr. 9 up). pap. 8.99 ***(978-0-618-88404-9(1))*** Houghton Mifflin Co. Trade & Reference Div.

Frost, Helen. Keesha's House. 2003. (Illus.). 128p. (YA). 16.00 (978-0-374-34064-3(1) , Farrar, Straus & Giroux (BYR)) Farrar, Straus & Giroux.

Fuqua, Jonathon Scott. King of the Pygmies. 2007. (Illus.). 256p. (YA). (gr. 9). pap. 7.99 ***(*978-0-7636-3412-4(3))*** Candlewick Pr.

G Studios & Crouch, Cheryl. Double-Booked. 2007. (Chosen Girls' Ser.). 144p. (J). pap. 6.99 (978-0-310-71268-8(8)) Zonderkidz.

—Unplugged. 2007. (Chosen Girls' Ser.). 144p. (J). pap. 6.99 (978-0-310-71269-5(6)) Zonderkidz.

Gallagher, Diana G. Camp Can't: The Complicated Life of Claudia Cristina Cortez. Garvey, Brann, illus. 2008. (J). pap. ***(*978-1-59889-878-1(7));*** 81p. (gr. 4-8). lib. bdg. 23.93 ***(*978-1-59889-840-8(X))*** Stone Arch Bks.

—Dance Trap: The Complicated Life of Claudia Cristina Cortez. Garvey, Brann, illus. 2008. (J). pap. ***(*978-1-59889-879-8(5));*** 81p. (gr. 4-8). lib. bdg. 23.93 ***(*978-1-59889-841-5(8))*** Stone Arch Bks.

Gallagher, Liz. The Opposite of Invisible. 2008. (YA). ***(*978-0-375-84152-1(0)); (*978-0-375-94329-4(3))*** Dell Publishing. (Delacorte Pr.).

Gantos, Jack. Hole in My Life. 2004. 208p. (YA). (gr. 7-12). reprint ed. pap. 8.00 (978-0-374-43089-4(6) , Farrar, Straus & Giroux (BYR)) Farrar, Straus & Giroux.

Gauthier, Bertrand. Ani Croche. 2002. (Roman Jeunesse Ser.). (FRE.). 96p. (YA). (gr. 4-7). pap. (978-2-89021-054-7(5)) Diffusion du livre Mirabel.

—Le Cent Pour Cent d'Ani Croche. 2002. (Roman Jeunesse Ser.). (FRE.). 96p. (YA). (gr. 4-7). pap. (978-2-89021-213-8(0)) Diffusion du livre Mirabel.

—Le Journal Intime d'Ani Croche. 2002. (Roman Jeunesse Ser.). (FRE., Illus.). 96p. (YA). (gr. 4-7). pap. (978-2-89021-062-2(6)) Diffusion du livre Mirabel.

—La Revanche d'Ani Croche. 2003. (Roman Jeunesse Ser.). (FRE.). 96p. (YA). (gr. 4-7). pap. (978-2-89021-078-3(2)) Diffusion du livre Mirabel.

Gauthier, Gail. Saving the Planet & Stuff. 2003. 240p. (YA). (gr. 4 up). 17.99 (978-0-399-23761-4(5) , Putnam Juvenile) Penguin Group (USA) Inc.

Gehrman, Jody. Confessions of a Triple Shot Betty. 2008. 256p. (J). (gr. 9). 16.99 ***(*978-0-8037-3247-6(3)*** , Dial) Penguin Group (USA) Inc.

Geras, Adele. Other Echoes. 2005. 144p. (J). (gr. 7). 15.95 (978-0-385-75054-7(4) , Fickling, David Bks.) Random Hse. Children's Bks.

Giles, Gail. Playing in Traffic. 2006. (Illus.). 176p. (YA). reprint ed. pap. 6.99 (978-1-4169-0926-2(5) , Simon Pulse) Simon & Schuster Children's Publishing.

Giles, Gail. Right Behind You. 2007. 304p. (YA). (gr. 10 up). 15.99 ***(*978-0-316-16636-2(7))*** Little, Brown Bks. for Young Readers.

Going, K. L. Fat Kid Rules the World. (YA). 2004. (gr. 8-12). 17.99 (978-0-8037-2948-3(0) , Dial); 2003. 224p. (gr. 4 up). 17.99 (978-0-399-23990-8(1) , Putnam Juvenile); 2004. 192p. (gr. 6). reprint ed. pap. 6.99 (978-0-14-240208-5(7) , Puffin) Penguin Group (USA) Inc.

Golding, Theresa Martin. Kat's Surrender. 2002. (gr. 3-6). lib. bdg. 18.75 (978-0-613-53826-8(9)) Tandem Library Bks.

Goldschmidt, Judy. Raisin Rodriguez & the Big-Time Smooch. 2007. 208p. (YA). pap. 5.99 (978-1-59514-125-5(1) , Razorbill) Penguin Group (USA) Inc.

—The Secret Blog of Raisin Rodriguez. (J). (gr. 5-12). 2006. 224p. pap. 5.99 (978-1-59514-071-5(9)); 2005. 208p. 12.99 (978-1-59514-018-0(2)) Penguin Group (USA) Inc. (Razorbill).

Gonzales, David. Mijos Handbook. Gonzales, David, illus. 2004. (Mijos Ser.). (Illus.). 80p. (J). (gr. 2-5). pap. 5.99 (978-0-439-56232-4(5) , Scholastic Paperbacks) Scholastic, Inc.

Gonzalez, Gabriela & Triana, Gaby. Backstage Pass. 2004. (Illus.). 224p. (J). (gr. 7 up). 15.99 (978-0-06-056017-1(7)); lib. bdg. 16.89 (978-0-06-056018-8(5)) HarperCollins Pubs.

Goode, Caroline. Cupidity. 2005. (Romantic Comedies Ser.). 288p. (YA). mass mkt. 3.99 (978-1-4169-1147-0(2) , Simon Pulse) Simon & Schuster Children's Publishing.

Goode, Caroline & Saidens, Amy. Cupidity. 2004. (Romantic Comedies Ser.). 288p. (YA). pap. 6.99 (978-0-689-87228-0(3) , Simon Pulse) Simon & Schuster Children's Publishing.

Gore, Elizabeth Griffin. Niara. Brown, Marietta, ed. 2000. 227p. (YA). (gr. 8 up). pap. (978-0-9701447-0-6(9)) Gore Pubns.

Gould, Jason. Jinx. 2004. 215p. (YA). (gr. 9-17). per. 14.04 (978-0-606-30072-8(4)) Tandem Library Bks.

Gould, Peter L. Write Naked. 2008. 256p. (YA). 16.95 ***(*978-0-374-38483-8(5))*** Farrar, Straus & Giroux.

Green, John. An Abundance of Katherines. 256p. (YA). 2008. pap. 8.99 ***(*978-0-14-241070-7(5)*** , Puffin); 2006. (gr. 9). 16.99 (978-0-525-47688-7(1) , Dutton Juvenile) Penguin Group (USA) Inc.

Green, John. Looking for Alaska. 2005. 160p. (YA). (gr. 8-12). 15.99 (978-0-525-47506-4(0) , Dutton Juvenile) Penguin Group (USA) Inc.

Green, Julia. Hunter's Heart. 2007. 264p. (YA). (gr. 7-12). 16.95 ***(*978-0-7613-9493-8(1)*** , Carolrhoda Bks.) Lerner Publishing Group.

Griffin, Adele. My Almost Epic Summer. 2008. 176p. (YA). (gr. 7). pap. 6.99 ***(*978-0-14-240805-6(0)*** , Puffin); 2006. 192p. (J). (gr. 4). 15.99 (978-0-399-23784-3(4) , Putnam Juvenile) Penguin Group (USA) Inc.

Griffin, Adele. My Almost Epic Summer (Splashproof Ed.) 2007. 1p. (YA). (gr. 7). pap. 6.99 (978-0-14-240860-5(3) , Puffin) Penguin Group (USA) Inc.

Griffis, Molly Levite. The Feester Filibuster. 2002. (Illus.). 224p. 18.95 (978-1-57168-693-0(2)) Eakin Pr.

—The Feester Filibuster. 2002. (gr. 3-6). lib. bdg. 17.60 (978-0-613-79188-5(6)) Tandem Library Bks.

Gugler, Laurel Dee. Muddle Cuddle. van Kampen, Vlasta, illus. 2003. 24p. (J). (ps-1). pap. 6.95 (978-1-55037-434-6(6)) Annick Pr., Ltd. CAN. *Dist:* Firefly Bks., Ltd.

Gunn, Robin Jones. A Heart Full of Hope. rev. ed. 1999. (Christy Miller Ser.: Bk. 6). 160p. (YA). (gr. 7-12). pap. 6.99 (978-1-56179-719-6(7)) Bethany Hse. Pubs.

—Open Your Heart. 1998. (Sierra Jensen Ser.: Bk. 7). 160p. (YA). (gr. 7-11). pap. (978-1-56179-562-8(3)) Focus on the Family Publishing.

—Sierra Jensen Collection: Close Your Eyes; Without a Doubt; With This Ring, Vol. 2. 2006. (Sierra Jensen Ser.: Bks. 4-6). 496p. (J). 14.99 (978-1-59052-589-0(2) , Multnomah Fiction) WaterBrook Pr.

—Sierra Jensen Collection: Hold on Tight; Closer Than Ever; Take My Hand, Vol. 4. 2006. (Sierra Jensen Ser.: Bks. 10-12). 464p. (J). 14.99 (978-1-59052-591-3(4) , Multnomah Fiction) WaterBrook Pr.

—Sierra Jensen Collection: Only You; Sierra, In Your Dreams; Don't You Wish, Vol. 1. 2006. (Sierra Jensen Ser.: Bks. 1-3). 432p. (J). 14.99 (978-1-59052-588-3(4) , Multnomah Fiction) WaterBrook Pr.

—Sierra Jensen Collection: Open Your Heart; Time Will Tell; Now Picture This, Vol. 3. 2006. (Sierra Jensen Ser.: Bks. 7-9). 480p. (J). 14.99 (978-1-59052-590-6(6) , Multnomah Fiction) WaterBrook Pr.

—Time Will Tell. 1998. (Sierra Jensen Ser.: Bk. 8). 160p. (YA). (gr. 7-11). pap. (978-1-56179-568-0(2)) Focus on the Family Publishing.

—Whispers. 2004. (Glenbrooke Ser.: Bk. 2). 288p. pap. 12.99 (978-1-59052-192-2(7) , Multnomah) WaterBrook Pr.

—Without a Doubt. 1998. (Sierra Jensen Ser.: Bk. 5). 160p. (YA). (gr. 7-11). pap. (978-1-56179-519-2(4)) Focus on the Family Publishing.

Gutman, Dan. The Homework Machine. 2006. (Illus.). 160p. (J). (gr. 3-7). 15.95 (978-0-689-87678-3(5)) Simon & Schuster Children's Publishing.

—The Homework Machine. 2006. (YA). 21.95 (978-0-7862-8883-0(3)) Thorndike Pr.

Haddad, Charles. Calliope Day Falls... in Love? 2003. (Illus.). 160p. (gr. 3-7). lib. bdg. 16.99 (978-0-385-90100-0(3) , Delacorte Bks. for Young Readers) Random Hse. Children's Bks.

Haddix, Margaret Peterson. Among the Impostors. (Shadow Children Ser.). (J). (gr. 3-7). 2002. 192p. mass mkt. 5.99 (978-0-689-83908-5(1) , Aladdin); 2001. (Illus.). 176p. 16.95 (978-0-689-83904-7(9)) Simon & Schuster Children's Publishing.

—Among the Impostors. 2002. (Shadow Children Ser.). (gr. 3-6). lib. bdg. 13.00 (978-0-613-61844-1(0)) Tandem Library Bks.

Hall, Barbara. Dixie Storms. 2006. (Illus.). 224p. (J). pap. 6.95 (978-0-15-205756-5(0) , Harcourt Paperbacks) Harcourt Children's Bks.

Halpern, Sue. Introducing Sasha Abramowitz. 2005. 288p. (J). (gr. 5-8). 17.00 (978-0-374-38432-6(0) , Frances Foster Bks.) Farrar, Straus & Giroux.

Halpin, Brendan. How Ya Like Me Now. 2007. 208p. (YA). (gr. 7 up). 16.00 (978-0-374-33495-6(1)) Farrar, Straus & Giroux.

Hamanaka, Sheila. All the Colors of the Earth. Hamanaka, Sheila, illus. 1999. (Illus.). 32p. (J). (ps-3). pap. 6.99 (978-0-688-17062-2(5) , Harper Trophy) HarperCollins Pubs.

—All the Colors of the Earth. 1999. (J). 12.79 (978-0-606-17242-4(4)); (gr. 3-6). lib. bdg. 14.15 (978-0-613-22808-4(1)) Tandem Library Bks.

Hansen, Sara J. Sand Mermaids. 2004. 122p. pap. 17.95 (978-1-4137-1799-0(3)) PublishAmerica, Inc.

Harmon, Michael B. The Last Exit to Normal. 2008. (YA). ***(*978-0-375-84098-2(2));*** lib. bdg. ***(*978-0-375-94098-9(7))*** Knopf, Alfred A. Inc.

Harold, Gwyneth. Bad Girls in School. 2006. 148p. (YA). pap. (978-0-435-21517-0(5)) Heinemann.

Harrison, Lisi. Best Friends for Never. 2004. (Clique Ser.: Bk. 2). 208p. (J). (gr. 5-8). pap. 9.99 (978-0-316-70131-0(9) , Poppy) Little, Brown Bks. for Young Readers.

—Bratfest at Tiffany's. 2008. (Clique Ser.: No. 9). 300p. (gr. 7-12). pap. 9.99 ***(*978-0-316-00680-4(7)*** , Poppy) Little, Brown Bks. for Young Readers.

Harrison, Lisi. Revenge of the Wannabes. 2005. (Clique Ser.: No. 3). 304p. (YA). (gr. 5-8). pap. 9.99 (978-0-316-70133-4(5) , Poppy) Little, Brown Bks. for Young Readers.

Harrison, Mette Ivie. The Monster in Me. 2003. 160p. (J). (gr. 7 up). tchr. ed. 16.95 (978-0-8234-1713-1(1)) Holiday Hse., Inc.

Hautman, Pete. Sweetblood. 2003. (Illus.). 192p. (YA). 16.95 (978-0-689-85048-6(4)) Simon & Schuster Children's Publishing.

Hautzig, Deborah. Little Witch Goes to Camp. 2002. (gr. k-3). lib. bdg. 10.95 (978-0-613-82447-7(4)) Tandem Library Bks.

Hayes, Sonia. Urban Goddess. 2007. 224p. (YA). per. 9.95 ***(*978-0-9777573-1-2(5))*** NUA Multimedia.

Haynes, Eva Johns. The Turkey That Crowed. Bozarth, Kelly Paige, illus. 2000. 32p. (J). (ps-3). pap. 6.95 (978-0-9679211-0-5(4)) Haynes, Eva Johns.

Headley, Justina Chen. Girl Overboard. 2008. 352p. (J). (gr. 7-17). 16.99 ***(*978-0-316-01130-3(4))*** Little Brown & Co.

Hébert, Marie-Francine & Germain, Philippe. Un Blouson dans la Peau. 2001. (Premier Roman — Special Editions Ser.). (FRE., Illus.). 64p. (J). (gr. 1-4). pap. (978-2-89021-476-7(1)) Diffusion du livre Mirabel.

—Un Monstre dans les Cereales. 2001. (FRE., Illus.). 64p. (J). pap. (978-2-89021-475-0(3)) Diffusion du livre Mirabel.

Heldring, Thatcher. Toby Wheeler: Eighth-Grade Benchwarmer. 2007. 224p. (J). (gr. 4-7). 14.99 ***(*978-0-385-73390-8(9));*** lib. bdg. 17.99 ***(*978-0-385-90405-6(3))*** Random Hse. Children's Bks. (Delacorte Bks. for Young Readers).

Hennessy, Claire. Afterwards. 2005. 188p. (YA). pap. ***(*978-1-84223-207-1(X))*** Poolbeg Pr.

Henty, G. A. With Wolfe in Canada: The Winning of a Continent. 2001. (Illus.). 353p. (J). (978-0-921100-86-7(8)); pap. (978-0-921100-87-4(6)) Inheritance Pubns.

—With Wolfe in Canada: The Winning of a Continent. (Illus.). 353p. (J). 2000. (gr. 8-12). pap. 14.99 (978-1-887159-30-2(4)); 1998. lib. bdg. 20.99 (978-1-887159-18-0(5)) Preston-Speed Pubns.

—With Wolfe in Canada: The Winning of a Continent. 2006. per. 8.95 (978-1-57646-980-4(8)) Quiet Vision Publishing.

Hergenrader, Christina. Dangerous Roads. 2004. 224p. (J). 6.99 (978-0-7586-0715-7(6)) Concordia Publishing Hse.

—Double Shift. 2004. 208p. (J). 6.99 (978-0-7586-0716-4(4)) Concordia Publishing Hse.

—Lies & Deceptions. 2003. (Novel Devotions Ser.). 176p. (YA). 6.99 (978-0-7586-0229-9(4)) Concordia Publishing Hse.

—Lies & Deceptions. 2003. (gr. 7-12). lib. bdg. 15.30 (978-0-613-74602-1(3)) Tandem Library Bks.

—Temptations. 2003. (Novel Devotions Ser.). 176p. (YA). 6.99 (978-0-7586-0230-5(8)) Concordia Publishing Hse.

—Temptations. 2003. (gr. 7-12). lib. bdg. 15.30 (978-0-613-74603-8(1)) Tandem Library Bks.

Heynen, Jim. Cosmos Coyote & William the Nice. 2002. (gr. 7-12). lib. bdg. 16.45 (978-0-613-71513-3(6)) Tandem Library Bks.

Hills, Tad. Duck & Goose. Hills, Tad, illus. 2006. 40p. (J). (ps-2). lib. bdg. 16.99 (978-0-375-93611-1(4)); (Illus.). 14.95 (978-0-375-83611-4(X)) Random Hse. Children's Bks. (Schwartz & Wade Bks.).

Hirsch, Odo. Have Courage, Hazel Green! (J). 2007. (Illus.). 256p. pap. 6.95 (978-1-59990-003-2(3)); 2006. 262p. 15.95 (978-1-58234-659-5(3)) Bloomsbury Publishing. (Bloomsbury Children).

Hite, Sid. I'm Exploding Now. 2007. 192p. (YA). (gr. 5-9). 16.99 ***(*978-0-7868-3757-1(8))*** Hyperion Pr.

Hobbs, Valerie. Anything but Ordinary. 2007. 176p. (YA). (gr. 7 up). 16.00 (978-0-374-30374-7(6)) Farrar, Straus & Giroux.

Hobbs, Will. Leaving Protection. 2005. 192p. (J). (gr. 5 up). pap. 5.99 (978-0-380-73312-5(9) , Harper Trophy) HarperCollins Pubs.

—River Thunder. 1999. (Learn-Along Board Bks. Ser.). 224p. (YA). (gr. 7-12). pap. 5.99 (978-0-440-22681-9(3) , Laurel Leaf) Random Hse. Children's Bks.

—River Thunder. 1999. (gr. 7-12). lib. bdg. 13.55 (978-0-613-12037-1(X)) Tandem Library Bks.

Hogan, Mary. The Serious Kiss. 2005. 256p. (J). pap. 7.99 (978-0-06-072208-1(8) , Harper Trophy); (YA). (gr. 7 up). 16.99 (978-0-06-072206-7(1)) HarperCollins Pubs.

Hohl, Richard. The Prairie: A Novelette. 2006. (Illus.). 67p. pap. ***(*978-1-4120-9073-5(3))*** Trafford Publishing.

Holder, Nancy. Pretty Little Devils. 2007. (YA). 1p. pap. 6.99 (978-1-59514-152-1(9)); 256p. pap. 6.99 (978-1-59514-149-1(9)) Penguin Group (USA) Inc. (Razorbill).

Holmes, Linda. Jazz & Sam. 2002. (Reading Explosion Beginner Readers: Book 2). 32p. (J). pap. 9.95 (978-1-57921-445-6(2)) WinePress Publishing.

Hooper, Mary. Amy. 2004. 176p. (J). (gr. 5-10). reprint ed. pap. 6.95 (978-1-58234-915-2(0) , Bloomsbury Children) Bloomsbury Publishing.

Hopkins, Cathy. Mates, Dates & Cosmic Kisses. 2003. (Mates, Dates Ser.). (YA). (gr. 7-12). lib. bdg. 13.00 (978-0-613-61796-3(7)) Tandem Library Bks.

—Mates, Dates & Sizzling Summers. 2006. (Mates, Dates Ser.). 224p. (YA). mass mkt. 5.99 (978-0-689-87698-1(X) , Simon Pulse) Simon & Schuster Children's Publishing.

Hopkins, Ellen. Impulse. 2007. 672p. (YA). (gr. 9 up). 16.99 (978-1-4169-0356-7(9) , McElderry, Margaret K.) Simon & Schuster Children's Publishing.

Horvath, Polly. Everything on a Waffle. 2001. 160p. (J). (gr. 5 up). 16.00 (978-0-374-32236-6(8) , Farrar, Straus & Giroux (BYR)) Farrar, Straus & Giroux.

—Everything on a Waffle. 2008. 176p. (J). pap. 6.99 ***(*978-0-312-38004-5(6))*** Square Fish.

Horvath, Polly. The Vacation. 2005. 208p. (J). 16.00 (978-0-374-38070-0(8) , Farrar, Straus & Giroux (BYR)) Farrar, Straus & Giroux.

Houston, Pam. Waltzing the Cat. 1999. (gr. 7-12). lib. bdg. 23.45 (978-0-613-27451-7(2)) Tandem Library Bks.

Howe, Norma. Blue Avenger & the Theory of Everything. 2002. (Illus.). 240p. (J). (gr. 7-10). 17.95 (978-0-8126-2654-4(0)) Cricket Bks.

Hughes, Mark Peter. Lemonade Mouth. 2007. 352p. (J). (gr. 7). 15.99 (978-0-385-73392-2(5)); lib. bdg. 18.99 (978-0-385-90404-9(5)) Random Hse. Children's Bks. (Delacorte Bks. for Young Readers).

Hughes, Pat. Open Ice. 288p. (YA). (gr. 9). 2007. mass mkt. 6.50 ***(*978-0-553-49444-0(9)*** , Laurel Leaf); 2005. 15.95 (978-0-385-74675-5(X) , Lamb, Wendy) Random Hse. Children's Bks.

Hunter, Terri. One Starry Night. 2000. 32p. (J). 16.95 (978-0-9705974-0-3(1)) Baby Star Productions, LLC.

Hyde, Diana. Sex Without Love. 2001. 304p. pap. 12.95 (978-0-9705435-4-7(9)) Heicron, Inc.

I Am Just Like U. 2003. per. (978-0-9740182-2-5(8)) Hunt-ForMo Creations.

I Like You & I Love You. 2003. (J). per. 5.95 (978-0-9742714-1-5(1)) I C Creative, Inc.

Jacobson, Jennifer Richard. Stained. 208p. (YA). (gr. 8 up). 2005. (Illus.). 16.95 (978-0-689-86745-3(X) , Atheneum); 2006. reprint ed. pap. 6.99 (978-1-4169-1337-5(8) , Simon Pulse) Simon & Schuster Children's Publishing.

—Stained. l.t. ed. 2006. 201p. (YA). 21.95 (978-0-7862-8283-8(5)) Thorndike Pr.

Jahn-Clough, Lisa. Country Girl, City Girl. 2004. 192p. (YA). (gr. 5). tchr. ed. 15.00 (978-0-618-44791-6(1) , Walter Lorraine) Houghton Mifflin Co. Trade & Reference Div.

Jahn-Clough, Lisa. Me, Penelope. 2007. 208p. (YA). (gr. 7 up). 16.00 ***(*978-0-618-77366-4(5)*** , Walter Lorraine) Houghton Mifflin Co. Trade & Reference Div.

Jantti, Mariana. Cuanta gente! Quienes Son? Amelio-Ortiz, Osvaldo P. & Rodriguez Vidal, Andrea, illus. 2005. (SPA.). 28p. (J). 14.95 (978-9974-7799-2-1(8) , nicanitas) Hardenville SA URY. *Dist:* Independent Pubs. Group.

Jenkins, A. M. Out of Order. 256p. (J). 2005. pap. 6.99 (978-0-06-447374-3(0)); 2003. lib. bdg. 16.89 (978-0-06-623969-9(9)) HarperCollins Pubs.

Jennings, Patrick. Barb & Dingbat's Crybaby Hotline. 2007. 208p. (YA). (gr. 7 up). 16.95 ***(*978-0-8234-2055-1(8))*** Holiday Hse., Inc.

Jennings, Sharon. Into My Mother's Arms. Ohi, Ruth, illus. 2000. 32p. (J). (ps-k). (978-1-55041-533-9(6)) Fitzhenry & Whiteside, Ltd.

—Into My Mother's Arms: With Sticker & Card. Ohi, Ruth, illus. 2001. 32p. (J). (ps-k). (978-1-55041-669-5(3)) Fitzhenry & Whiteside, Ltd.

Johnson, Angela. Bird. 2004. 144p. (J). (gr. 4). 16.99 (978-0-8037-2847-9(6) , Dial) Penguin Group (USA) Inc.

Johnson-Choong, Shelly. The Jewelry Box. 2nd ed. 2004. (YA). reprint ed. pap. 10.95 (978-1-932280-40-1(5) , 80405) Granite Publishing & Distribution.

Johnson, D. B. Eddie's Kingdom. 2005. (Illus.). 32p. (J). (gr. k-3). 16.00 (978-0-618-56299-2(0)) Houghton Mifflin Co. Trade & Reference Div.

Johnson, Lissa Halls & Lambert, David. Opportunity Knocks Twice, Vol. 3. 2005. (Brio Girls Ser.). 192p. (YA). pap. 7.99 (978-1-56179-953-4(X)) Focus on the Family Publishing.

Johnson, Lissa Halls & Wierenga, Kathy. No Lifeguard on Duty, Vol. 8. 2005. (Brio Girls Ser.). 192p. (YA). (gr. 6-11). pap. 7.99 (978-1-58997-081-6(0)) Focus on the Family Publishing.

Johnson, Peter. What Happened. 2007. 133p. (YA). (gr. 9 up). 16.95 (978-1-932425-67-3(5) , Front Street) Boyds Mills Pr.

Johnson, Varian. My Life as a Rhombus. 2008. 312p. (J). pap. 9.95 ***(*978-0-7387-1160-7(8)*** , Flux) Llewellyn Pubns.

Johnston, Julie. Adam & Eve & Pinch-Me. 2003. 232p. (J). (gr. 6). pap. 9.95 (978-0-88776-648-0(X)) Tundra Bks., Inc./Livres Toundra, Inc. CAN. *Dist:* Random Hse., Inc.

Jones, Carrie. Love (and Other Uses for Duct Tape) 2008. 264p. (J). 16.95 ***(*978-0-7387-1257-4(4)*** , Flux) Llewellyn Pubns.

Jones, Patrick. Cheated. 2008. 208p. (YA). 16.95 ***(*978-0-8027-9699-8(0))*** Walker & Co.

Jones, Patrick. Things Change. (J). 2004. 216p. 16.95 (978-0-8027-8901-3(3)); 2006. 228p. reprint ed. pap. 7.95 (978-0-8027-7746-1(5)) Walker & Co.

Jonsberg, Barry. Am I Right or Am I Right? 2007. 256p. (gr. 7). (J). lib. bdg. 18.99 (978-0-375-93637-1(8)); (YA). 15.99 (978-0-375-83637-4(3)) Random Hse. Children's Bks. (Knopf Bks. for Young Readers).

Joyce, Eunice. Jack & the Silly Hat. Joyce, Eunice, ed. Joyce, Derrick, illus. 2001. 19p. (Orig.). (J). pap. 18.99 (978-0-9712932-0-5(1)) Four Sons Publishing, Inc.

Juby, Susan. Miss Smithers. 2004. (Illus.). 336p. (J). 15.99 (978-0-06-051546-1(5)); lib. bdg. 16.89 (978-0-06-051547-8(3)) HarperCollins Pubs. (HarperTeen).

Jukes, Mavis. Planning the Impossible. 2000. (J). (978-0-606-20022-6(3)) Tandem Library Bks.

Kalish, Ginny. Rachel Rude Rowdy. 2001. (Illus.). 128p. (J). pap. 15.95 (978-1-56976-127-4(2) , 1148, Zephyr Pr.) Chicago Review Pr., Inc.

Kantor, Melissa. Confessions of a Not It Girl. 2006. 256p. (gr. 7-17). pap. 8.99 (978-0-7868-1808-2(5)) Hyperion Pr.

Karasyov, Carrie & Kargman, Jill. Summer Intern. 2007. 192p. (gr. 7 up). (J). lib. bdg. 17.89 ***(*978-0-06-115376-1(1));*** (YA). 16.99 ***(*978-0-06-115375-4(3))*** HarperCollins Pubs. (HarperTeen).

Kass, Pnina Moed. Real Time. 2006. 192p. (YA). (gr. 7). reprint ed. pap. 7.99 (978-0-618-69174-6(X)) Houghton Mifflin Co.

Kelly, Katy. Lucy Rose: Working Myself to Pieces & Bits. Ferguson, Peter, illus. 2007. (J). (gr. 3-7). 208p. 12.99 ***(*978-0-385-73408-0(5));*** 128p. lib. bdg. 15.99 ***(*978-0-385-90425-4(8))*** Random Hse. Children's Bks. (Delacorte Bks. for Young Readers).

Kelly, Theresa. Forget Me Not, Vol. 5. 2000. (Aloha Cove Ser.: Vol. 5). (Illus.). 272p. (YA). (gr. 7-11). 5.99 (978-0-570-07033-7(3)) Concordia Publishing Hse.

—Forget Me Not. 2000. (gr. 7-12). lib. bdg. 14.15 (978-0-613-72782-2(7)) Tandem Library Bks.

—Good-Bye Is Not Forever. 2000. (Aloha Cove Ser.: Vol. 8). 272p. (J). (gr. 7-11). pap. 5.99 (978-0-570-07073-3(2)) Concordia Publishing Hse.

—Place in the Heart. 1999. (gr. 7-12). lib. bdg. 14.15 (978-0-613-72783-9(5)) Tandem Library Bks.

H I

—A Place in the Heart, Vol. 6. 2000. (Aloha Cove Ser.: Vol. 6). (Illus.). 272p. (YA). (gr. 7-11). 5.99 (978-0-570-07034-4(1)) Concordia Publishing Hse.

Kennedy, Mary. Tales of a Hollywood Gossip Queen. 2006. 256p. (YA). (gr. 12). pap. 9.99 (978-0-425-20993-6(8) , Berkley Trade) Penguin Group (USA) Inc.

Kenney, Cindy. Love Your Neighbor. 2004. (Illus.). 22p. bds. 4.99 (978-0-310-70783-7(8)) Zonderkidz.

Kerr, B. Modern Persona: Valhalla High School. 2007. 296p. (YA). per. 18.95 ***(978-0-595-44412-0(1))*** iUniverse, Inc.

Kerr, M. E. I Stay near You: One Story in Three. 2006. (Illus.). 216p. (YA). pap. 6.95 (978-0-15-205589-9(4) , Harcourt Paperbacks) Harcourt Children's Bks.

—What Became of Her. 2000. 256p. (J). (gr. 7 up). 15.95 (978-0-06-028435-0(8)) HarperCollins Pubs.

—What Became of Her. 2002. (gr. 7-12). lib. bdg. 14.10 (978-0-613-87324-6(6)) Tandem Library Bks.

Killian, Beth. Boy Trouble. 2007. 256p. pap. 9.95 (978-1-4165-3497-6(0) , MTV) Simon & Schuster.

Kimmel, Elizabeth Cody. Lily B. on the Brink of Love. (J). 2006. 208p. pap. 5.99 (978-0-06-075545-4(8) , Harper Trophy); 2005. 224p. 15.99 (978-0-06-075541-6(5)); 2005. 192p. lib. bdg. 16.89 (978-0-06-075543-0(1)) HarperCollins Pubs.

—Mary Leaves Little House. 2008. (Little House Ser.). 192p. (J). lib. bdg. 16.89 ***(978-0-06-000906-9(3));*** (gr. 3-7). 15.99 ***(978-0-06-000905-2(5))*** HarperCollins Pubs.

—Spin the Bottle. 2008. 240p. (J). (gr. 5). 16.99 ***(978-0-8037-3191-2(4)*** , Dial) Penguin Group (USA) Inc.

Kipling, Rudyard. Captains Courageous. Landgraf, Ken, illus. 2002. (Great Illustrated Classics Ser.).Tr. of 200. 240p. (J). (gr. 3-8). 21.35 (978-1-57765-683-8(0) , ABDO & Daughters) ABDO Publishing Co.

—Captains Courageous. 1999. (Dover Juvenile Classics Ser.).Tr. of 200. (J). (Illus.). 176p. (gr. 4-7). pap. 2.50 (978-0-486-40786-9(1)); (978-0-04-864078-9(6)) Dover Pubns., Inc.

—Captains Courageous. 1999. Tr. of 200. (gr. 3-6). lib. bdg. 10.10 (978-0-613-90755-2(8)) Tandem Library Bks.

Klass, David. Whirlwind. 2008. (Caretaker Trilogy Ser.). 304p. (YA). 17.95 ***(978-0-374-32308-0(9))*** Farrar, Straus & Giroux.

Klein, Rachel. The Moth Diaries. 2002. 256p. (YA). (978-1-58243-205-2(8)) Counterpoint.

Kline, Suzy. Herbie Jones & the Second Grade Slippers. Sweeten, Sami, illus. 2006. 64p. (J). (gr. 1-4). 14.99 (978-0-399-23132-2(3) , Putnam Juvenile) Penguin Group (USA) Inc.

Klinger, Shula. The Kingdom of Strange. 2008. (YA). ***(978-0-7614-5395-6(4))*** Cavendish, Marshall Corp.

Klise, Kate. Deliver Us from Normal. 2005. 240p. (YA). (gr. 5-9). 16.95 (978-0-439-52322-6(2)) Scholastic, Inc.

—Deliver Us from Normal: Read-Along/Homework Pack. unabr. ed. 2005. (YA). (gr. 5-8). 65.70 incl. audio (978-1-4193-3619-5(3) , 42050) Recorded Bks., LLC.

—Far from Normal. 2006. 240p. (J). pap. 16.99 (978-0-439-79447-3(1) , Scholastic Pr.) Scholastic, Inc.

Koertge, Ronald. Confess-O-Rama. 1998. (978-0-606-13291-6(0)) Tandem Library Bks.

Koja, Kathe. Kissing the Bee. 2007. 128p. (YA). (gr. 9 up). 16.00 ***(978-0-374-39938-2(7)*** , Farrar, Straus & Giroux (BYR)) Farrar, Straus & Giroux.

Koss, Amy Goldman. The Girls. 128p. (J). 2002. pap. 5.99 (978-0-14-230033-6(0) , Puffin); 2000. (Illus.). (gr. 5-9). 16.99 (978-0-8037-2494-5(2) , Dial) Penguin Group (USA) Inc.

—Gossip Times Three. 176p. (J). 2003. (gr. 6). 16.99 (978-0-8037-2849-3(2) , Dial); 2005. (gr. 5). reprint ed. pap. 5.99 (978-0-14-240295-5(8) , Puffin) Penguin Group (USA) Inc.

Kroll, Steven. The Biggest Valentine Ever. Bassett, Jeni, illus. 2006. 32p. (J). pap. 3.99 (978-0-439-76419-3(X)) Scholastic, Inc.

Krovatin, Christopher. Heavy Metal & You. 2005. 192p. (J). (gr. 7-12). pap. 16.95 (978-0-439-73648-0(X)) Scholastic, Inc.

Krulik, Nancy E. Boys, Boys, Boys. 2000. (gr. 5-8). lib. bdg. 13.00 (978-0-613-31021-5(7)) Tandem Library Bks.

—Girls Don't Have Cooties, No. 4. 2002. (Katie Kazoo, Switcheroo Ser.: No. 4). (Illus.). 80p. (J). pap. 3.99 (978-0-448-42705-8(2) , Grosset & Dunlap) Penguin Group (USA) Inc.

—Girls Don't Have Cooties, No. 4. 2002. (Katie Kazoo, Switcheroo Ser.: No. 4). (J). (gr. 3-6). lib. bdg. 11.80 (978-0-613-60291-4(9)) Tandem Library Bks.

—Newly Wed. 2005. 304p. (YA). (gr. 11 up). pap. 5.99 (978-0-689-87660-8(2) , Simon Pulse) Simon & Schuster Children's Publishing.

Lachtman, Ofelia Dumas, et al. Pepita Takes Time (Pepita, Siempre Tarde) 2000. (SPA & ENG., Illus.). 32p. (J). (ps-2). 14.95 (978-1-55885-304-1(9) , Piñata Books) Arte Publico Pr.

Lamba, Marie. What I Meant... 2007. 320p. (gr. 5-11). (J). 16.99 (978-0-375-84091-3(5)); (YA). lib. bdg. 19.99 (978-0-375-94091-0(X)) Random Hse. Children's Bks. (Random Hse. Bks. for Young Readers).

Lamba, Marie. What I Said- 2008. (J). ***(978-0-375-84093-7(1));*** lib. bdg. ***(978-0-375-94093-4(6))*** Random Hse., Inc.

Lanagan, Margo. Black Juice. 2005. 208p. (J). (gr. 7 up). 15.99 (978-0-06-074390-1(5)); lib. bdg. 16.89 (978-0-06-074391-8(3)) HarperCollins Pubs.

—White Time. 2006. 224p. (J). (gr. 7 up). 15.99 (978-0-06-074393-2(X) , Eos); lib. bdg. 16.89 (978-0-06-074394-9(8)) HarperCollins Pubs.

Lane, Dakota. The Secret Life of It Girls. 2007. 128p. (YA). (gr. 9 up). 14.99 ***(978-1-4169-1492-1(7))*** Simon & Schuster Children's Publishing.

Lane, Sharmen. Why Am I Special? l.t. ed. 2006. (Illus.). 23p. (J). per. 14.95 (978-0-9764103-8-6(9)) Daylight Pubs.

Langan, Paul. Someone to Love Me. 2007. (Bluford Ser.: No. 4). 208p. (J). pap. 3.99 (978-0-439-90486-5(2)) Scholastic, Inc.

Lantz, Francess L. Stepbaby from Planet Weird. 2001. (Illus.). (J). 3.99 (978-0-375-81259-0(8) , Random Hse. Bks. for Young Readers) Random Hse. Children's Bks.

Lavigne, Guy. Pas de Quartier pour les Poires. 2003. (Roman Plus Ser.). (FRE., Illus.). 160p. (YA). (gr. 8 up). pap. (978-2-89021-250-3(5)) Diffusion du livre Mirabel.

Lawrence, Iain. B for Buster. (Illus.). 336p. (YA). (gr. 7). 2004. 15.95 (978-0-385-73086-0(1) , Delacorte Bks. for Young Readers); 2006. reprint ed. 5.99 (978-0-440-23810-2(2) , Laurel Leaf) Random Hse. Children's Bks.

Lawton, Wendy. Changing Faces: Real TV, Take 1. 2004. (Real Tv - Real Transformations Series (Take 1) Ser.). 224p. (J). pap. 10.99 (978-0-8024-5413-3(5)) Moody Pubs.

Le, Ny Jeanine. Date. 2008. (Once upon A Prom Ser.). 240p. (J). pap. 5.99 ***(978-0-545-03182-0(6)*** , Scholastic Paperbacks) Scholastic, Inc.

—Once upon A Prom #2 Dress. 2008. (Once upon A Prom Ser.). 240p. (J). pap. 5.99 ***(978-0-545-03181-3(8)*** , Scholastic Paperbacks) Scholastic, Inc.

Leaney, Cindy. Everyone Makes a Difference: A Story about Community. Wilks, Peter, illus. 2004. 32p. (J). 28.50 (978-1-58952-733-1(X)) Rourke Publishing, LLC.

—It's Your Turn Now: Politeness. Wilks, Peter, tr. Wilks, Peter, illus. 2003. 31p. (J). 28.50 (978-1-58952-735-5(6)) Rourke Publishing, LLC.

Leavitt, Martine. Keturah & Lord Death. 2006. 216p. (YA). (gr. 7 up). 16.95 (978-1-932425-29-1(2) , Front Street) Boyds Mills Pr.

Leedahl, Shelley A. The Bone Talker. Slavin, Bill, illus. 2004. (Northern Lights Books for Children Ser.). 32p. (ps-3). 15.95 (978-0-88995-214-0(0)) Red Deer Pr. CAN. *Dist:* Fitzhenry & Whiteside, Ltd.

Lefeuvre, Amy. Probable Sons. 2004. reprint ed. pap. 15.95 (978-1-4191-4306-9(9)); pap. 1.99 (978-1-4192-4306-6(3)) Kessinger Publishing, LLC.

Lenhard, Elizabeth. It's a Purl Thing. (YA). 2006. 288p. (gr. 7). pap. 6.99 (978-0-14-240695-3(3) , Puffin); 2005. (Illus.). 272p. (gr. 6-10). 16.99 (978-0-525-47622-1(9) , Dutton Juvenile) Penguin Group (USA) Inc.

—Knit Two Together. 272p. (gr. 7). 2008. (YA). pap. 7.99 ***(978-0-14-241013-4(6)*** , Puffin); 2006. (J). 16.99 (978-0-525-47764-8(0) , Dutton Juvenile) Penguin Group (USA) Inc.

—Knitwise. 2007. 272p. (YA). (gr. 7). 16.99 ***(978-0-525-47838-6(8)*** , Dutton Juvenile) Penguin Group (USA) Inc.

Lerman, Drew. Magic City. 2007. 288p. (YA). (gr. 9 up). pap. 7.99 (978-0-439-89027-4(6) , PUSH) Scholastic, Inc.

Leventhal, Debra. What Is Your Language? 1998. (Picture Puffin Ser.). (J). (978-0-606-13901-4(X)) Tandem Library Bks.

Levinson, Marilyn. No Boys Allowed. 2005. 144p. (J). pap. 4.99 (978-0-439-71965-0(8) , Scholastic Paperbacks) Scholastic, Inc.

Levithan, David. Realm of Possibility. 2006. 224p. (YA). (gr. 7). reprint ed. pap. 8.95 (978-0-375-83657-2(8) , Knopf Bks. for Young Readers) Random Hse. Children's Bks.

Levithan, David & Cohn, Rachel. Naomi & Ely's No Kiss List. 2007. (YA). (gr. 9 up). 240p. 16.99 ***(978-0-375-84440-9(6));*** 192p. lib. bdg. 19.99 ***(978-0-375-94440-6(0))*** Random Hse. Children's Bks. (Knopf Bks. for Young Readers).

Levy, Janice. Totally Uncool. Monroe, Chris, illus. (Picture Bks.). 32p. (J). (ps-3). 1999. 15.95 (978-1-57505-306-6(3)); 2003. reprint ed. 6.95 (978-1-57505-555-8(4)) Lerner Publishing Group. (Carolrhoda Bks.).

Lewis, Beverly. No Guys Pact. 2003. (Holly's Heart Ser.: Bk. 9). 160p. (YA). (gr. 5-9). pap. 6.99 (978-0-7642-2616-8(9)) Bethany Hse. Pubs.

Lewis, Richard. The Demon Queen. 2008. 252p. (J). ***(978-1-4169-3589-6(4)*** , Simon & Schuster Children's Publishing) Simon & Schuster Children's Publishing.

Linch, Tanya. Owl, the Aat & the Roar. 2005. (Illus.). 32p. (ps-k). pap. 12.99 (978-0-7475-6324-2(1)) Bloomsbury Publishing Plc GBR. *Dist:* Independent Pubs. Group.

Lockhart, E. The Boy Book: A Study of Habits & Behaviors, Plus Techniques for Taming Them. (YA). (gr. 7). 2008. 224p. pap. 8.99 ***(978-0-385-73209-3(0));*** 2006. 208p. 15.95 (978-0-385-73208-6(2)); 2006. 208p. 17.99 (978-0-385-90239-7(5)) Random Hse. Children's Bks. (Delacorte Bks. for Young Readers).

—The Boyfriend List. (gr. 7). 2005. 240p. (J). lib. bdg. 17.99 (978-0-385-90238-0(7)); 2006. 256p. (YA). reprint ed. pap. 8.95 (978-0-385-73207-9(4)) Random Hse. Children's Bks. (Delacorte Bks. for Young Readers).

—The Boyfriend List: (15 Guys, 11 Shrink Appointments, 4 Ceramic Frogs, & Me, Ruby Oliver) 2005. 240p. (YA). (gr. 7). 15.95 (978-0-385-73206-2(6) , Delacorte Bks. for Young Readers) Random Hse. Children's Bks.

—Fly on the Wall. 2007. 192p. (YA). (gr. 7). pap. 8.99 ***(978-0-385-73282-6(1)*** , Delacorte Bks. for Young Readers) Random Hse. Children's Bks.

Lockhart, E. Fly on the Wall: How One Girl Saw Everything. 2006. 192p. (YA). (gr. 7). 15.95 (978-0-385-73281-9(3)); lib. bdg. 17.99 (978-0-385-90299-1(9)) Random Hse. Children's Bks. (Delacorte Bks. for Young Readers).

Lockwood, Cara. The Scarlet Letterman. 2007. (Bard Academy Ser.). 320p. pap. 9.95 (978-1-4165-2490-8(8) , MTV) Simon & Schuster.

Long, John Arthur & Meyer, Chet. The Tooth Fairy Legend: The Touch of Kindness. Zenobi, Nadine, illus. 2002. 56p. (J). 14.95 (978-0-9710749-1-0(7)) L & M Creations.

Love, D. Anne. Picture Perfect. 2007. (YA). 304p. (gr. 7 up). 16.99 (978-0-689-87390-4(5)); 291p. ***(978-1-4287-3275-9(6))*** Simon & Schuster Children's Publishing. (McElderry, Margaret K.).

Lovelace, Maud Hart. Carney's House Party. 2000. (gr. 3-6). lib. bdg. 15.25 (978-0-613-31046-8(2)) Tandem Library Bks.

Lowry, Brigid. Follow the Blue. 2004. 205p. (J). (gr. 7 up). tchr. ed. 16.95 (978-0-8234-1827-5(8)) Holiday Hse., Inc.

—Follow the Blue. 2006. 208p. (YA). pap. 8.95 (978-0-312-34297-5(7) , St. Martin's Griffin) St. Martin's Pr.

Lubar, David. Dunk. (YA). (gr. 7-10). 2002. 256p. tchr. ed. 15.00 (978-0-618-19455-1(X) , Clarion Bks.); 2004. 272p. reprint ed. pap. 6.99 (978-0-618-43909-6(9) , Graphia) Houghton Mifflin Co. Trade & Reference Div.

—Sleeping Freshmen Never Lie. (YA). 2007. 288p. pap. 6.99 (978-0-14-240780-6(1) , Puffin); 2005. 160p. (gr. 6-10). 16.99 (978-0-525-47311-4(4) , Dutton Juvenile) Penguin Group (USA) Inc.

Ludwig, Trudy. Big Mouth. Prevost, Mikela, illus. 2007. (J). ***(978-1-58246-240-0(2)*** , Tricycle Pr.) Ten Speed Pr.

Ludwig, Trudy. Just Kidding. Gustavson, Adam, illus. 2006. 32p. (J). 15.95 (978-1-58246-163-2(5) , Tricycle Pr.) Ten Speed Pr.

Ludwig Trudy. Solo Bromeando. Gustavson Adam, illus. 2006. (SPA.). 32p. 15.95 (978-1-58246-177-9(5) , Tricycle Pr.) Ten Speed Pr.

Luper, Eric. Big Slick. 2007. 240p. (YA). (gr. 9 up). 16.00 ***(978-0-374-30799-8(7))*** Farrar, Straus & Giroux.

Lupica, Mike. Miracle on 49th Street. 256p. (gr. 5). 2007. (J). pap. 7.99 ***(978-0-14-240942-8(1)*** , Puffin); 2006. (YA). 17.99 (978-0-399-24488-9(3) , Philomel) Penguin Group (USA) Inc.

Lurie, April. Dancing in the Streets of Brooklyn. 208p. (gr. 3-7). 2004. pap. 5.99 (978-0-440-41825-2(9) , Yearling); 2002. lib. bdg. 17.99 (978-0-385-90066-9(X) , Delacorte Bks. for Young Readers) Random Hse. Children's Bks.

Lurie, April. The Latent Powers of Dylan Fontaine. 2008. 224p. (YA). (gr. 9). 15.99 ***(978-0-385-73125-6(6)*** , Delacorte Bks. for Young Readers) Random Hse. Children's Bks.

Lyga, Barry. The Astonishing Adventures of Fanboy & Goth Girl. 2006. 320p. (YA). (gr. 8). 16.95 (978-0-618-72392-8(7)) Houghton Mifflin Co.

—The Astonishing Adventures of Fanboy & Goth Girl. 2007. 320p. (YA). (gr. 9-12). pap. 8.99 ***(978-0-618-91652-8(0))*** Houghton Mifflin Co. Trade & Reference Div.

Lynch, Chris. Whitechurch. 1999. 256p. (YA). (gr. 12 up). 14.95 (978-0-06-028330-8(0)); (gr. 7 up). 14.89 (978-0-06-028331-5(9)) HarperCollins Pubs.

—Who the Man. 2002. 192p. (J). (gr. 5 up). 15.99 (978-0-06-623938-5(9)) HarperCollins Pubs.

—Who the Man. 2004. (gr. 5-8). lib. bdg. 14.15 (978-0-613-81982-4(9)) Tandem Library Bks.

MacCullough, Carolyn. Stealing Henry. rev. ed. 2005. 208p. (YA). 16.95 (978-1-59643-045-7(1)) Roaring Brook Pr.

Mackall, Dandi Daley. Crazy in Love. 2008. 240p. (YA). (gr. 7). pap. 6.99 ***(978-0-14-241157-5(4)*** , Puffin) Penguin Group (USA) Inc.

—Grace Notes. 2006. (Faithgirlz Ser.). (Illus.). 128p. (J). pap. 6.99 (978-0-310-71093-6(6)) Zonderkidz.

—Grace under Pressure. 2007. (Faithgirlz!#8482; / Blog On! Ser.). 128p. (J). pap. 6.99 (978-0-310-71263-3(7)) Zonderkidz.

—Just Jazz Bk. 3: Blog On! 2006. (Faithgirlz Ser.). (Illus.). 128p. (J). pap. 6.99 (978-0-310-71095-0(2)) Zonderkidz.

—Love, Annie. 2006. (Faithgirlz Ser.: Bk. 2). 128p. (J). pap. 6.99 (978-0-310-71094-3(4)) Zonderkidz.

MacKall, Dandi Daley. Sierra's Story. 2004. (Degrees of Betrayal Ser.). 336p. (YA). pap. 9.99 (978-0-8423-8726-2(9)) Tyndale Hse. Pubs.

Mackall, Dandi Daley. Storm Rising Bk. 4: Blog On! 2006. (Faithgirlz Ser.). (Illus.). 128p. (J). pap. 6.99 (978-0-310-71096-7(0)) Zonderkidz.

Mackey, Weezie Kerr. Throwing a Like Girl. 2007. 272p. (J). (gr. 7 up). 16.99 ***(978-0-7614-5342-0(3))*** Cavendish, Marshall Corp.

Mackler, Carolyn. Love & Other Four-Letter Words. 2005. 256p. (YA). (gr. 7). pap. 7.95 (978-0-385-73266-6(X) , Delacorte Bks. for Young Readers) Random Hse. Children's Bks.

—Love & Other Four-Letter Words. 2002. (gr. 7-12). lib. bdg. 13.55 (978-0-613-72272-8(8)) Tandem Library Bks.

MacLachlan, Patricia. Who Loves Me? Shepherd, Amanda, illus. 2005. 40p. (J). (ps-3). lib. bdg. 15.89 (978-0-06-027977-6(X)); 14.99 (978-0-06-027976-9(1)) HarperCollins Pubs. (Cotler, Joanna Books).

Maclean, Christine. Mary Margaret, Center Stage. Vicky, Lowe, illus. 2007. 176p. (J). (gr. 3). pap. 5.99 (978-0-14-240768-4(2) , Puffin) Penguin Group (USA) Inc.

—Mary Margaret, Center Stage. 2006. (Illus.). 160p. (J). (gr. 3). 15.99 (978-0-525-47597-2(4) , Dutton Juvenile) Penguin Group (USA) Inc.

Madison, Bennett. Lulu Dark & the Summer of the Fox. 2007. 208p. (YA). (gr. 7-12). 5.99 (978-1-59514-154-5(5) , Razorbill) Penguin Group (USA) Inc.

—Lulu Dark Can See Through Walls. 256p. (YA). (gr. 7-12). 2006. pap. 5.99 (978-1-59514-104-0(9)); 2005. 9.99 (978-1-59514-010-4(7)) Penguin Group (USA) Inc. (Razorbill).

Maguire, Arlene. Special People, Special Ways. Carpenter, Christina D., ed. Bailey, Sheila, illus. 1999. 32p. (J). (ps-3). 14.95 (978-1-886440-00-5(X)) Portunus Publishing Co.

Mallat, Kathy. Mama Love. Mallat, Kathy, illus. 2004. (Illus.). 24p. (J). 15.95 (978-0-8027-8902-0(1)) Walker & Co.

Mammay, Judith. Knowing Joseph. 2008. (Illus.). 256p. (YA). (gr. 2-7). 16.95 ***(978-1-933831-05-3(7))*** Blooming Tree Pr.

Manners I. Care. 2005. (J). pap. 5.99 ***(978-0-9771143-4-4(1))*** Child LIfe Bks., LLC.

Manning, Sarra. Let's Get Lost. 2006. 320p. (YA). (gr. 9). 16.99 (978-0-525-47666-5(0) , Dutton Juvenile) Penguin Group (USA) Inc.

—Pretty Things (Splashproof Ed.) 2007. 1p. (YA). (gr. 7). pap. 6.99 (978-0-14-240859-9(X) , Puffin) Penguin Group (USA) Inc.

Margles, Samantha & Wasserman, Robin. Unfabulous: The Perfect Moment. 2007. (Teenick Ser.). 128p. (J). pap. 4.99 (978-0-439-89340-4(2)) Scholastic, Inc.

Marien, Donna. Waiting at the Bay: A Young Woman's Reflections on Journeys in the Sea of Life. 2003. 108p. (YA). pap. 10.95 (978-0-595-26304-2(6) , Writers Club Pr.) iUniverse, Inc.

Martin, Nora. Flight of the Fisherbird. 2003. (Illus.). 200p. (J). 16.95 (978-1-58234-814-8(6) , Bloomsbury Children) Bloomsbury Publishing.

Masel, Christy, illus. Gorp's Dream: A Tale of Diversity, Tolerance, & Love in Pumpernickel Park. 2003. 36p. (J). 14.95 (978-0-9724249-0-5(3)) Gorp Group Pr., The.

Mason, Jane. Zoey 101: Chapter Book. 2006. (Zoey 101 Ser.). 112p. (J). pap. 4.99 (978-0-439-84872-5(5)) Scholastic, Inc.

Mass, Wendy. Leap Day. 2006. 224p. (J). (gr. 5-8). pap. 7.99 (978-0-316-05828-5(9)) Little Brown & Co.

Matson, Nancy. The Boy Trap. Chesworth, Michael, illus. 1999. 128p. (J). (gr. 3-7). 14.95 (978-0-8126-2663-6(X)) Cricket Bks.

Matthews, L. S. The Outcasts. 2007. 272p. (YA). (gr. 7). 15.99 ***(978-0-385-73367-0(4));*** lib. bdg. 18.99 ***(978-0-385-90382-0(0))*** Random Hse. Children's Bks. (Delacorte Bks. for Young Readers).

Mayer, Melody. The Nannies: Friends with Benefits. 2006. (Nannies Ser.). 288p. (YA). (gr. 9). pap. 8.95 (978-0-385-73284-0(8) , Delacorte Bks. for Young Readers) Random Hse. Children's Bks.

—The Nannies: Have to Have It. 2006. (Nannies Ser.). 256p. (YA). (gr. 7). 8.95 (978-0-385-73351-9(8) , Delacorte Bks. for Young Readers) Random Hse. Children's Bks.

—The Nannies: Have to Have It. 2006. (Nannies Novel Ser.). 256p. (YA). (gr. 9). lib. bdg. 10.99 (978-0-385-90366-0(9) , Delacorte Bks. for Young Readers) Random Hse. Children's Bks.

Mayer, Melody. Tainted Love: A Nannies Novel. 2007. (Nannies Ser.). 272p. (gr. 9). (J). lib. bdg. 11.99 ***(978-0-385-90367-7(7));*** (YA). 8.99 ***(978-0-385-73352-6(6))*** Random Hse. Children's Bks. (Delacorte Bks. for Young Readers).

Mazer, Norma Fox. Babyface. 2007. (Illus.). 176p. (YA). pap. 6.95 (978-0-15-206277-4(7) , Harcourt Paperbacks) Harcourt Children's Bks.

McBratney, Sam. Weisst du Eigentlich, Wie Lieb Ich Dich Hab? 2000. Tr. of Guess How Much I Love You?. (GER.). (J). pap. 24.95 (978-3-7941-4217-0(9)) Sauerlander AG CHE. *Dist:* Distribooks, Inc.

McCann, Daryl & Forbes, Debbie. Wish You Weren't Here. 2000. 144p. (YA). pap. 14.95 (978-0-7022-3103-2(7)) Univ. of Queensland Pr. AUS. *Dist:* International Specialized Bk. Services.

McCarthy, Maureen. Rose by Any Other Name. 2008. 336p. (YA). 16.95 ***(978-1-59643-372-4(8))*** Roaring Brook Pr.

McClure, Brian D. Who Am I? 2006. (Illus.). 52p. (J). 12.95 (978-1-933426-03-7(9)) Universal Flag Publishing.

McDaniel, Lurlene. Hit & Run. 2007. 192p. (YA). (gr. 7). 13.99 (978-0-385-90198-7(4)); 10.99 (978-0-385-73161-4(2)) Random Hse. Children's Bks. (Delacorte Bks. for Young Readers).

—Letting Go of Lisa. (YA). (gr. 7). 2007. 176p. mass mkt. 6.50 ***(978-0-440-23868-3(4)*** , Laurel Leaf); 2006. 192p. 10.95 (978-0-385-73159-1(0) , Delacorte Bks. for Young Readers); 2006. 192p. lib. bdg. 12.99 (978-0-385-90196-3(8) , Delacorte Bks. for Young Readers) Random Hse. Children's Bks.

—Prey. 2008. 208p. (YA). ***(978-0-385-73453-0(0)*** , Delacorte Pr.) Dell Publishing.

McDaniel, Lurlene. Raina's Story. 2005. (Angels in Pink Ser.). 208p. (J). (gr. 7). lib. bdg. 12.99 (978-0-385-90194-9(1) , Delacorte Bks. for Young Readers) Random Hse. Children's Bks.

McDonald, Janet. Off-Color. 2007. 176p. (YA). (gr. 7 up). 16.00 ***(978-0-374-37196-8(2))*** Farrar, Straus & Giroux.

McGraw-Hill Staff & Sasse, Connie R. Families Today, 2 vols. 4th ed. 2003. 728p. (C). (gr. 9-12). stu. ed. 61.32 (978-0-07-829840-0(7) , 9780078298400) Glencoe/McGraw-Hill.

McKayhan, Monica. Trouble Follows. 2007. 256p. pap. 9.99 ***(978-0-373-83087-9(4))*** Harlequin Enterprises, Ltd. CAN. *Dist:* Simon & Schuster, Inc.

McNeal, Laura & McNeal, Tom. Crooked. 2007. 352p. (J). (gr. 7). pap. 7.99 (978-0-375-84191-0(1) , Knopf Bks. for Young Readers) Random Hse. Children's Bks.

—Crushed. (gr. 7). 2007. 336p. (J). pap. 7.99 (978-0-375-83121-8(5)); 2006. 320p. (YA). 15.95 (978-0-375-83105-8(3)); 2006. 320p. (YA). lib. bdg. 17.99 (978-0-375-93105-5(8)) Random Hse. Children's Bks. (Knopf Bks. for Young Readers).

—Zipped. 2003. 288p. (J). (gr. 7). 15.95 (978-0-375-81491-4(4)); lib. bdg. 17.99 (978-0-375-91491-1(9)) Random Hse. Children's Bks. (Knopf Bks. for Young Readers).

McTighe, Carolyn. The Sakura Tree. Brownlee, Karen, illus. 2008. 32p. (J). (ps-3). 17.95 (***978-0-88995-354-3(6)***) Red Deer Pr. CAN. *Dist:* Fitzhenry & Whiteside, Ltd.

Meacham, Margaret. A Mid-Semester Night's Dream. 2004. 160p. (J). (gr. 4-6). tchr. ed. 16.95 (978-0-8234-1815-2(4)) Holiday Hse., Inc.

Mechling, Lauren & Moser, Laura. All Q, No A: More Tales of a 10th-Grade Social Climber. 2006. 288p. (YA). (gr. 7). pap. 7.99 (978-0-618-66378-1(9) , Graphia) Houghton Mifflin Co. Trade & Reference Div.

Mechling, Lauren & Moser, Laura. Foreign Exposure: The Social Climber Abroad. 2007. 320p. (YA). (gr. 7 up). pap. 8.99 (***978-0-618-66379-8(7)*** , Graphia) Houghton Mifflin Co. Trade & Reference Div.

Mercado, Nancy. Every Man for Himself: Ten Short Stories about Being a Guy. 2007. 176p. (J). (gr. 4-7). pap. 6.99 (978-0-14-240813-1(1) , Puffin) Penguin Group (USA) Inc.

Merrell, Victoria Jane. The Buffalo & the Butterfly. Bilisoly, Harvey, illus. 2002. 12p. (J). (ps-4). 21.95 (978-0-9717556-0-4(4)) VJM Pubns.

Meyer, Brad. A Matchless Age. 2006. 302p. pap. 24.95 (978-1-4241-0523-6(4)) PublishAmerica, Inc.

Meyer, Stephenie. Eclipse. rev. ed. 2007. (Twilight Saga Ser.). 640p. (YA). (gr. 7 up). 18.99 (***978-0-316-16020-9(2)***) Little, Brown Bks. for Young Readers.

Michaels, Jamie. Kiss My Book. 2007. 288p. (YA). (gr. 7). pap. 7.99 (***978-0-385-73499-8(9)***); lib. bdg. 10.99 (***978-0-385-90493-3(2)***) Random Hse. Children's Bks. (Delacorte Bks. for Young Readers).

Miles, Linda, et al. Amanda Salamander & the Secret of Happily Ever After. 2005. (J). cd-rom 7.99 (978-0-9778623-4-4(8)) Miles and Associates.

Mills, Claudia. Alex Ryan, Stop That! 2003. 160p. (J). 16.00 (978-0-374-34655-3(0) , Farrar, Straus & Giroux (BYR)) Farrar, Straus & Giroux.

—Makeovers by Marcia. 2005. 160p. (J). 16.00 (978-0-374-34654-6(2) , Farrar, Straus & Giroux (BYR)) Farrar, Straus & Giroux.

Mills, Claudia. The Totally Made-Up Civil War Diary of Amanda MacLeish. 2008. 208p. (J). 16.00 (***978-0-374-37696-3(4)***) Farrar, Straus & Giroux.

Moeyaert, Bart & Boeke, Wanda. Dani Bennoni. 2008. (YA). (***978-1-932425-97-0(7)*** , Front Street) Boyds Mills Pr.

Moloney, James. Touch Me. 2000. 256p. (YA). pap. 16.95 (978-0-7022-3151-3(7)) Univ. of Queensland Pr. AUS. *Dist:* International Specialized Bk. Services.

Montes, Marisa. A Crazy Mixed-Up Spanglish Day. Cepeda, Joe, illus. 2003. (Get Ready for Gabi Ser.: No. 1). 128p. (J). pap. 3.99 (978-0-439-47519-8(8)) Scholastic, Inc.

Montgomery, L. M. Anne of the Island. Date not set. mass mkt. (978-0-8125-6563-8(0) , Tor Bks.) Doherty, Tom Assocs., LLC.

—Anne of the Island. 2006. (ENG.). pap. (***978-1-4068-2171-0(3)***); pap. (***978-1-4068-3175-7(1)***) Echo Library.

—Anne of the Island. 2006. (ENG.). 102.99 (***978-1-4219-3295-8(4)***) IndyPublish.com.

—Anne of the Island. 2004. reprint ed. pap. 1.99 (978-1-4192-0718-1(0)); pap. 30.95 (978-1-4179-0885-1(8)) Kessinger Publishing, LLC.

—Anne of the Island. (Twelve-Point Ser.). 2001. 240p. lib. bdg. 25.00 (978-1-58287-157-8(4)); 2004. 396p. 26.00 (978-1-58287-640-5(1)) North Bks.

—Anne of the Island. abr. ed. 1998. (Avonlea Ser.: No. 4). 304p. (J). (gr. 5-8). pap. 4.99 (978-0-14-036777-5(2) , Puffin) Penguin Group (USA) Inc.

—Anne of the Island. 2000. (Anne of Green Gables Ser.: Vol. No. 3). (gr. 5-8). 182p. 24.95 (978-1-57646-309-3(5)); 182p. pap. 14.99 (978-1-57646-308-6(7)); 336p. pap. 19.99 (978-1-57646-310-9(9)) Quiet Vision Publishing.

—Anne of the Island. 2001. (gr. 7-12). lib. bdg. 30.40 (978-0-613-79774-0(4)) Tandem Library Bks.

—Anne of the Island Book & Charm. 2005. (Charming Classics). 304p. (J). pap. 6.99 (978-0-06-075859-2(7) , Harper Festival) HarperCollins Pubs.

Moore, Stephanie Perry. Purity Reigns. 2002. (Laurel Shadrach Ser.: Vol. 1). 240p. (YA). pap. 6.99 (978-0-8024-4035-8(5)) Moody Pubs.

—Purity Reigns. 2002. (gr. 7-12). lib. bdg. 15.30 (978-0-613-90559-6(8)) Tandem Library Bks.

—Saved Race, Vol. 3. 2001. (Payton Skky Ser.). 160p. (YA). (gr. 7-13). pap. 6.99 (978-0-8024-4238-3(2)) Moody Pubs.

—Saved Race. 2001. (gr. 7-12). lib. bdg. 15.30 (978-0-613-88831-8(6)) Tandem Library Bks.

—Surrendered Heart. 2002. (gr. 7-12). lib. bdg. 15.30 (978-0-613-84490-1(4)) Tandem Library Bks.

Moriarty, Jaclyn. The Murder of Bindy MacKenzie. (J). 2008. 496p. 8.99 (978-0-439-74052-4(5)); 2006. 352p. pap. 16.99 (978-0-439-74051-7(7)) Scholastic, Inc. (Levine, Arthur A. Bks.).

Moriarty, Jaclyn. The Spell Book of Listen Taylor. 2007. (YA). (***978-0-439-84679-0(X)***); 496p. (J). (gr. 9 up). 16.99 (***978-0-439-84678-3(1)***) Scholastic, Inc. (Levine, Arthur A. Bks.).

Morty, Ducktor. Can Do & Friends to the Rescue! A Story about Getting along & Working Together. l.t. ed. 2005. Orig. Title: Can Do & the Mall. (Illus.). 34p. (J). pap. (978-0-9768384-2-5(7)) Can Do Duck Publishing.

Moss, Alexandra. Boys or Ballet? 2006. 142p. (J). (***978-1-4156-8361-3(1)*** , Grosset & Dunlap) Penguin Group (USA) Inc.

Murdock, Catherine Gilbert. The Off Season. 2007. 288p. (YA). (gr. 7-10). 16.00 (***978-0-618-68695-7(9)***) Houghton Mifflin Co. Trade & Reference Div.

Murrell, Diane. Tobin Learns to Make Friends. 2001. (Illus.). (J). (ps-3). per. 16.95 (978-1-885477-79-8(1)) Future Horizons, Inc.

Myers, Anna. Tulsa Burning. 2004. 184p. (J). pap. 7.95 (978-0-8027-7696-9(5)); (Illus.). (gr. 3-7). 16.95 (978-0-8027-8829-0(7)) Walker & Co.

Myers, Bill. My Life as a Cowboy Cowpie, Vol. 19. 2001. (Incredible Worlds of Wally McDoogle Ser.: No. 19). 128p. (J). (gr. 3-7). pap. 6.99 (978-0-8499-5990-5(X)) Nelson, Thomas Inc.

Myers, Edward. Duck & Cover. 2004. 200p. (J). per. 11.95 (978-0-9674477-8-0(X)) Montemayor Pr.

Myers, Walter Dean. The Beast. 2005. 192p. (YA). (gr. 7-12). 6.99 (978-0-439-36842-1(1) , Scholastic Paperbacks) Scholastic, Inc.

—Every Man for Himself: 10 Short Stories about Being a Guy. Mercado, Nancy, ed. 2005. (Illus.). 176p. (YA). (gr. 9). 16.99 (978-0-8037-2896-7(4) , Dial) Penguin Group (USA) Inc.

—Somewhere in the Darkness. 2003. (gr. 7-12). lib. bdg. 14.15 (978-0-613-67300-6(X)) Tandem Library Bks.

Myracle, Lauren. L8r, G8r. 2007. (Ttyl Ser.). 288p. (J). (gr. 2-8). 15.95 (***978-0-8109-1266-3(X)*** , Amulet Bks.) Abrams, Harry N. , Inc.

—Rhymes with Witches. (YA). (gr. 8-17). 2006. 272p. pap. 6.95 (978-0-8109-9215-3(9)); 2005. 224p. 16.95 (978-0-8109-5859-3(7) , Amulet Bks.) Abrams, Harry N. , Inc.

—Thirteen. 2008. 224p. (J). (gr. 5). 15.99 (***978-0-525-47896-6(5)*** , Dutton Juvenile) Penguin Group (USA) Inc.

—TTFN (Ta-Ta for Now) 2006. (Internet Girls Ser.). 240p. (YA). (gr. 9-17). 15.95 (978-0-8109-5971-2(2) , Amulet Bks.) Abrams, Harry N. , Inc.

—Ttyl. (Internet Girls Ser.). (YA). (gr. 8-17). 2005. 234p. pap. 6.95 (978-0-8109-8788-3(0)); 2004. 224p. 15.95 (978-0-8109-4821-1(4) , Amulet Bks.) Abrams, Harry N. , Inc.

Myracle, Lauren. Twelve. 2008. 224p. (YA). (gr. 5-8). 6.99 (***978-0-14-241091-2(8)*** , Puffin) Penguin Group (USA) Inc.

Naliboff, Jane. The Only One Club. Hopkins, Jeff, illus. 2004. 32p. (J). 15.95 (978-0-9729225-3-1(9)) Flashlight Pr.

Namioka, Lensey. An Ocean Apart, a World Away. 2003. (gr. 7-12). lib. bdg. 13.55 (978-0-613-72264-3(7)) Tandem Library Bks.

Naylor, Phyllis Reynolds. Alice Alone. (Alice Ser.). 240p. 2002. mass mkt. 5.99 (978-0-689-85189-6(8) , Simon Pulse); 2001. (Illus.). (J). (gr. 5-9). 16.00 (978-0-689-82634-4(6) , Atheneum) Simon & Schuster Children's Publishing.

—Alice Alone. 2002. (Alice Ser.). (gr. 5-8). lib. bdg. 13.00 (978-0-613-73352-6(5)) Tandem Library Bks.

—Alice on the Outside. (Alice Ser.). 176p. (gr. 5-9). 2000. (YA). mass mkt. 5.99 (978-0-689-80594-3(2) , Simon Pulse); 1999. (J). 16.00 (978-0-689-80359-8(1) , Atheneum) Simon & Schuster Children's Publishing.

—Alice on the Outside. 2000. (Alice Ser.). (YA). (gr. 5-9). 11.64 (978-0-606-19706-9(0)); (gr. 7-12). lib. bdg. 13.00 (978-0-613-29866-7(7)) Tandem Library Bks.

—All but Alice. 2002. (Alice Ser.). 160p. (J). (gr. 4-7). pap. 5.99 (978-0-689-85044-8(1) , Aladdin) Simon & Schuster Children's Publishing.

—All but Alice. 2002. (Alice Ser.). (gr. 7-12). lib. bdg. 13.00 (978-0-613-44999-1(1)) Tandem Library Bks.

—Blizzard's Wake. (YA). 2004. (Illus.). 240p. pap. 5.99 (978-0-689-85221-3(5) , Simon Pulse); 2002. 224p. 16.95 (978-0-689-85220-6(7) , Atheneum) Simon & Schuster Children's Publishing.

—Blizzard's Wake. 2004. (gr. 7-12). lib. bdg. 14.15 (978-0-613-73409-7(2)) Tandem Library Bks.

—Blizzard's Wake. l.t. ed. 2003. 260p. (J). 22.95 (978-0-7862-5815-4(2)) Thorndike Pr.

—Including Alice. 2004. (Alice Ser.). 288p. (YA). 15.95 incl. audio compact disk (978-0-689-82637-5(0) , Atheneum) Simon & Schuster Children's Publishing.

—Reluctantly Alice. 2000. (Alice Ser.). 192p. (J). (gr. 5-9). pap. 5.99 (978-0-689-81688-8(X) , Aladdin) Simon & Schuster Children's Publishing.

—Reluctantly Alice. 2000. (Alice Ser.). (YA). (gr. 5-9). (978-0-606-19951-3(9)); (gr. 7-12). lib. bdg. 13.00 (978-0-613-30105-3(6)) Tandem Library Bks.

—Simply Alice. (Alice Ser.). 240p. (YA). 2003. (Illus.). mass mkt. 5.99 (978-0-689-85965-6(1) , Simon Pulse); 2002. (gr. 6-9). 16.00 (978-0-689-82635-1(4) , Atheneum) Simon & Schuster Children's Publishing.

—Simply Alice. 2003. (Alice Ser.). (gr. 7-12). lib. bdg. 13.00 (978-0-613-73415-8(7)) Tandem Library Bks.

Naylor, Phyllis Reynolds & Vaccaro, Nick. Including Alice. 2005. (Alice Ser.). 288p. (YA). mass mkt. 5.99 (978-0-689-87074-3(4) , Simon Pulse) Simon & Schuster Children's Publishing.

Nelson, Blake. The New Rules of High School. 2004. 240p. (YA). reprint ed. pap. 6.99 (978-0-14-240242-9(7) , Puffin) Penguin Group (USA) Inc.

—Prom Anonymous. 272p. (gr. 7 up). 2007. (YA). pap. 6.99 (978-0-14-240745-5(3) , Puffin); 2006. (J). 16.99 (978-0-670-05945-4(5) , Viking Adult) Penguin Group (USA) Inc.

Nelson, Suzanne. The Sound of Munich. Henderson, Jeanine, illus. 2006. (S. A. S. S. (Students Across the Seven Seas) Ser.). 224p. (J). (gr. 7). pap. 6.99 (978-0-14-240576-5(0) , Puffin) Penguin Group (USA) Inc.

Nelson, Theresa. Ruby Electric. 272p. (J). 2003. (Illus.). 16.95 (978-0-689-83852-1(2) , Atheneum/Richard Jackson Bks.); 2004. reprint ed. pap. 5.99 (978-0-689-87146-7(5) , Aladdin) Simon & Schuster Children's Publishing.

Nerz, Ryan A. & SparkNotes Editors. Head over Heels. 2004. (SAT Vocabulary Novels Ser.). (Illus.). 240p. pap. 7.95 (978-1-4114-0082-5(8)) Spark Publishing Group.

Newbery, Linda. The Shell House. 2004. 352p. (YA). (gr. 7-11). reprint ed. mass mkt. 6.50 (978-0-440-23786-0(6) , Laurel Leaf) Random Hse. Children's Bks.

Newhall, Mary. Calamity Jinx. 2005. (Thoroughbred Ser.: Vol. 71). (Illus.). 165p. (J). (***978-1-4155-9659-3(X)*** , Harper Entertainment) HarperCollins Pubs.

Nields, Nerissa. Plastic Angel. 2005. (Plastic Angel Ser.). 256p. (J). (ps-7). pap. 17.95 (978-0-439-70913-2(X) , Orchard Bks.) Scholastic, Inc.

Nilsson, Per. Seventeen. Chace, Tara, tr. 2007. 264p. (YA). (gr. 7 up). 17.95 (***978-1-932425-89-5(6)***) Boyds Mills Pr.

Nitz, Kristin Wolden. Defending Irene. 2004. 224p. (J). (gr. 4-6). 14.95 (978-1-56145-309-2(9)) Peachtree Pubs., Ltd.

Noel, Alyson. Saving Zoe: A Novel. 2007. 240p. (YA). (gr. 8 up). pap. 8.95 (***978-0-312-35510-4(6)*** , St. Martin's Griffin) St. Martin's Pr.

Norris, Shana. Libby Fawcett's Secret Blog. 2008. 208p. (J). 15.95 (***978-0-8109-9474-4(7)***) Abrams, Harry N. , Inc.

Northrop, Nancy. Connie - the Three Legged Turtle. Duckworth, Jeff, illus. 2002. 41p. (J). (gr. k-3). 8.25 (978-0-9627894-5-8(3)) LNR Pubns.

Norton, Tamra. Molly Married? 2003. 158p. (J). pap. 12.95 (978-1-55517-694-5(1) , 76941, Bonneville Bks.) Cedar Fort, Inc./CFI Distribution.

O'Connell, Tyne. Dumping Princes. (YA). 2007. 256p. pap. 7.95 (***978-1-59990-150-3(1)*** , Bloomsbury Children); 2006. (Calypso Chronicles Ser.: Bk. 4). (Illus.). 304p. (gr. 7-10). 16.95 (978-1-58234-852-0(9)) Bloomsbury Publishing.

—Pulling Princes. 2004. (Illus.). 208p. (J). 16.95 (978-1-58234-957-2(6) , Bloomsbury Children) Bloomsbury Publishing.

—Stealing Princes. (Calypso Chronicles : Bk. 2). (ps-7). 2005. (Illus.). 250p. (J). 16.95 (978-1-58234-992-3(4)); 2006. 304p. (YA). reprint ed. pap. 7.95 (978-1-58234-905-3(3)) Bloomsbury Publishing. (Bloomsbury Children).

O'Connor, Barbara. Fame & Glory in Freedom, Georgia. 2003. 112p. (J). 16.00 (978-0-374-32258-8(9) , Farrar, Straus & Giroux (BYR)) Farrar, Straus & Giroux.

—Greetings from Nowhere. 2008. 208p. (J). 16.00 (***978-0-374-39937-5(9)***) Farrar, Straus & Giroux.

O'Connor, Barbara. How to Steal a Dog. 2007. 176p. (J). (gr. 3-7). 16.00 (978-0-374-33497-0(8)) Farrar, Straus & Giroux.

O'Dell, Kathleen. Agnes Parker... Keeping Cool in Middle School. 160p. (J). (gr. 4-6). 2008. pap. 5.99 (***978-0-14-241181-0(7)*** , Puffin); 2007. 16.99 (978-0-8037-3078-6(0) , Dial) Penguin Group (USA) Inc.

O'Dell, Kathleen. Bad Tickets. 2007. 240p. (YA). (gr. 7). 15.99 (978-0-375-83801-9(5)); lib. bdg. 18.99 (978-0-375-93801-6(X)) Random Hse. Children's Bks. (Knopf Bks. for Young Readers).

O'Keefe, Susan. My Life & Death by Alexandra Canarsie. 2006. 224p. pap. 7.95 (978-1-56145-387-0(0) , Peachtree Junior) Peachtree Pubs., Ltd.

O'Keefe, Susan Heyboer. My Life & Death, by Alexandra Canarsie. 2002. 217p. (YA). (gr. 7-10). 14.95 (978-1-56145-264-4(5) , Q32889) Peachtree Pubs., Ltd.

Okimoto, Jean Davies. Dear Ichiro. Keith, Doug, illus. 2006. 29p. (J). (gr. 4-8). reprint ed. 17.00 (***978-1-4223-5803-0(8)***) DIANE Publishing Co.

—Dear Ichiro. Keith, Doug, illus. 2002. 32p. (J). 16.95 (978-1-57061-373-9(7)) Sasquatch Bks.

—The Eclipse of Moonbeam Dawson. 1998. 187p. (YA). (gr. 8-12). per. 13.00 (978-0-613-17196-0(9)) Tandem Library Bks.

One Starry Night Gift Box. 2000. 32p. 29.95 (978-0-9705974-1-0(X)) Baby Star Productions, LLC.

Ostow, Micol. Crush du Jour. 2007. (Romantic Comedies Ser.). 224p. (YA). mass mkt. 6.99 (***978-1-4169-5027-1(3)*** , Simon Pulse) Simon & Schuster Children's Publishing.

Otto, Gina. Cassandra's Angel. Joost, Trudy, illus. 2001. 32p. (ps-3). 15.95 (978-0-935699-20-3(1)) Illumination Arts Publishing Co., Inc.

Padian, Maria. Brett McCarthy: Work In Progress. 2008. (J). 288p. (***978-0-375-84675-5(1)***); (***978-0-375-94675-2(6)***) Knopf, Alfred A. Inc.

Paratore, Coleen Murtagh. Willa by Heart. 2008. (Wedding Planner's Daughter Ser.). 240p. (J). 15.99 (***978-1-4169-4076-0(6)***) Simon & Schuster Children's Publishing.

Park, Barbara. Operation: Dump the Chump. 2001. 128p. (J). (gr. 3-7). reprint ed. 5.50 (978-0-394-82592-2(6) , Yearling) Random Hse. Children's Bks.

Parker, Francis W. Uncle Robert's Geography, Uncle Robert's, Vol. 3. 2004. reprint ed. pap. 20.95 (978-1-4191-9175-6(6)) Kessinger Publishing, LLC.

—Uncle Robert's Geography, Uncle Robert's Visit, Vol. 3. 2004. reprint ed. pap. 1.99 (978-1-4192-9175-3(0)) Kessinger Publishing, LLC.

Pascal, Francine. Elizabeth. 2000. (Secret Love Diaries). (gr. 7-12). lib. bdg. 12.40 (978-0-613-33043-5(9)) Tandem Library Bks.

Patneaude, David. Colder Than Ice. 2003. (J). (gr. 4-7). 168p. 15.95 (978-0-8075-8135-3(6)); 167p. pap. 6.95 (978-0-8075-8136-0(4)) Whitman, Albert & Co.

Patneaude, David. Deadly Drive. 184p. (J). 2007. pap. 6.95 (***978-0-8075-0845-9(4)***); 2005. (gr. 6-8). 15.95 (978-0-8075-0844-2(6)) Whitman, Albert & Co.

Patron, Susan. The Higher Power of Lucky. Phelan, Matt, illus. 2006. 144p. (J). (gr. 4-6). 16.95 (978-1-4169-0194-5(9) , Atheneum/Richard Jackson Bks.) Simon & Schuster Children's Publishing.

Pearsall, Shelley. All of the Above: A Novel. Steptoe, Javaka, illus. 2006. 256p. (J). (gr. 3-7). 15.99 (978-0-316-11524-7(5)) Little Brown & Co.

—All of the Above: A Novel. 2008. 128p. (J). (gr. 3-7). pap. 5.99 (***978-0-316-11526-1(6)***) Little, Brown Bks. for Young Readers.

Pearson, Mary E. A Room on Lorelei Street. rev. ed. 2005. 272p. (YA). 16.95 (978-0-8050-7667-7(0)) Holt, Henry & Co.

Peet, Mal. Keeper. 2007. 240p. (J). (gr. 5). pap. 6.99 (978-0-7636-3286-1(4)) Candlewick Pr.

Perez, Marlene. Dead Is the New Black. 2008. (Illus.). 204p. (YA). pap. 7.95 (***978-0-15-206408-2(7)*** , Harcourt Paperbacks) Harcourt Children's Bks.

Peters, Julie Anne. Grl2Grl. 2007. 160p. (YA). (gr. 10 up). pap. 11.99 (***978-0-316-01343-7(9)***) Little, Brown Bks. for Young Readers.

Peters, Julie Anne. Keeping You a Secret. 2005. 272p. (YA). (gr. 9-17). pap. 7.99 (978-0-316-00985-0(7) , Tingley, Megan Bks.) Little, Brown Bks. for Young Readers.

—Keeping You a Secret. 2005. 250p. (YA). (gr. 8-12). per. 14.64 (978-0-606-33459-4(9)) Tandem Library Bks.

Pfister, Marcus. Rainbow Fish Undersea Fun Sticker Storybook. 2003. (Illus.). (J). pap. 6.95 (978-1-59014-147-2(4)) North-South Bks., Inc.

Pinkney, Andrea Davis. Raven in a Dove House. 1999. (978-0-606-17789-4(2)) Tandem Library Bks.

Pinkston, Ronald. A Police Officer That's What I'll Be! Rivera, Israel, illus. 1999. 26p. (J). (gr. k-2). 12.99 (978-0-9671708-0-0(X)) Pinkston Publishing.

Plum-Ucci, Carol. The She. 2003. (Illus.). 288p. (YA). 17.00 (978-0-15-216819-3(2)) Harcourt Children's Bks.

Porter, Eleanor H. Classic Starts: Pollyanna. Akib, Jamel, illus. 2007. (Classic Starts Ser.). 160p. (J). 4.95 (978-1-4027-3692-6(4)) Sterling Publishing Co., Inc.

Porter, Eleanor H. Miss Billys Decision. 2006. pap. (***978-1-4068-3240-2(5)***) Echo Library.

Poupart, Jean-Marie. Des Crayons Qui Trichent. 2003. (Roman Jeunesse Ser.). (FRE.). 96p. (YA). (gr. 4-7). pap. (978-2-89021-197-1(5)) Diffusion du livre Mirabel.

—Des Photos Qui Parlent. 2003. (Roman Jeunesse Ser.). (FRE.). 96p. (YA). (gr. 4-7). pap. (978-2-89021-162-9(2)) Diffusion du livre Mirabel.

Powell, Randy. The Whistling Toilets. 2001. (Aerial Fiction Ser.). 256p. (YA). (gr. 7 up). pap. 5.95 (978-0-374-48369-2(8) , Aerial) Farrar, Straus & Giroux.

Prue, Sally. The Devil's Toenail. 2004. (Illus.). 208p. (J). 16.95 (978-0-439-48634-7(3)) Scholastic, Inc.

Qualey, Marsha. Just Like That. 240p. (YA). (gr. 7). 2007. pap. 6.99 (978-0-14-240830-8(1) , Puffin); 2005. 16.99 (978-0-8037-2840-0(9) , Dial) Penguin Group (USA) Inc.

Rabb, Margo. Cures for Heartbreak. 2007. 256p. (YA). (gr. 9). 15.99 (978-0-385-73402-8(6)); lib. bdg. 18.99 (978-0-385-90414-8(2)) Random Hse. Children's Bks. (Delacorte Bks. for Young Readers).

Radford, Michelle. Almost Fabulous. 2008. 256p. (J). pap. 8.99 (***978-0-06-125235-8(2)*** , HarperTeen) HarperCollins Pubs.

Rahlens, Holly-Jane. Prince William, Maximilian Minsky, & Me. (YA). (gr. 7-11). 2007. 320p. pap. 7.99 (***978-0-7636-3299-1(6)***); 2005. 160p. 16.99 (978-0-7636-2704-1(6)) Candlewick Pr.

Rallison, Janette. It's a Mall World after All. 2006. 240p. (YA). 16.95 (978-0-8027-8853-5(X)) Walker & Co.

Randle, Kristen D. Slumming. 2003. (Illus.). 240p. (J). 16.99 (978-0-06-001022-5(3) , HarperTeen) HarperCollins Pubs.

Ray, Belinda & SparkNotes Staff. Sun-Kissed. 2004. (SparkNotes SAT Vocabulary Novels Ser.). (Illus.). 200p. pap. 7.95 (978-1-4114-0080-1(1)) Spark Publishing Group.

Rayban, Chloe. Drama Queen. 2004. 208p. pap. 12.99 (978-0-7475-6325-9(X)) Bloomsbury Publishing Plc GBR. *Dist:* Independent Pubs. Group.

Rees, Gwyneth. The Mum Hunt. l.t. ed. 2006. pap. 16.95 (978-1-4056-6061-7(9)) BBC Audio GBR. *Dist:* BBC Audiobooks America.

Reetz, Kurt. Lenny's Neighborhood: Lenny's New Hairdo. 2000. mass mkt. 8.95 (978-1-931179-09-6(3)) Long Hill Productions, Inc.

—Lenny's Neighborhood: Lenny's New Hairdo. Farkas, Josh, illus. 2000. 32p. (J). (gr. 1-3). pap. (978-0-9701450-8-6(X)) Long Hill Productions, Inc.

Refrrolo, C. T. Grandchild of Mine: You & I. 2006. (J). 12.00 (978-0-8059-6845-3(8)) Dorrance Publishing Co., Inc.

Reinhardt, Dana. How to Build a House. 2008. 240p. (YA). (gr. 7). lib. bdg. 18.99 (***978-0-375-94454-3(0)*** , Lamb, Wendy) Random Hse. Children's Bks.

Reisner, Molly & Ostrow, Kim. Camp SpongeBob. Martinez, Heather, illus. 2004. (SpongeBob SquarePants Ready-To-Read Ser.: Vol. 5). 32p. (J). pap. 3.99 (978-0-689-86593-0(7) , Simon Spotlight/Nickelodeon) Simon & Schuster Children's Publishing.

Rennison, Louise. Dancing in My Nuddy-Pants: Even Further Confessions of Georgia Nicolson. (Confessions of Georgia Nicolson Ser.). 2003. 224p. (J). 15.99 (978-0-06-009746-2(9)); 2004. 240p. (YA). reprint ed. pap. 7.99 (978-0-06-009748-6(5)) HarperCollins Pubs. (HarperTeen).

—Knocked Out by My Nunga-Nungas: Further, Further Confessions of Georgia Nicolson. 2002. (Confessions of Georgia Nicolson Ser.). 192p. (J). (gr. 8-10). 15.99 (978-0-06-623656-8(3)) HarperCollins Pubs.

—Knocked Out by My Nunga-Nungas: Further, Further Confessions of Georgia Nicolson. 2003. (gr. 7-12). lib. bdg. 15.30 (978-0-613-67208-5(9)) Tandem Library Bks.

—Startled by His Furry Shorts. 2007. (Confessions of Georgia Nicolson Ser.). 304p. (J). pap. 7.99 (***978-0-06-085386-0(7)*** , HarperTeen) HarperCollins Pubs.

—Startled by His Furry Shorts! 2006. (Confessions of Georgia Nicolson Ser.). 288p. (J). 16.99 (978-0-06-085384-6(0)); lib. bdg. 17.89 (978-0-06-085385-3(9)) HarperCollins Pubs. (HarperTeen).

H I

—Then He Ate My Boy Entrancers: More Mad, Marvy Confessions of Georgia Nicolson. (Confessions of Georgia Nicolson Ser.). 2006. 336p. (J). pap. 7.99 (978-0-06-058939-4(6)); 2005. 320p. (J). lib. bdg. 16.89 (978-0-06-058938-7(8)); No. 6. 2005. 320p. (YA). 15.99 (978-0-06-058937-0(X)) HarperCollins Pubs. (HarperTeen).

Rettig, Liz. My Desperate Love Diary. 2007. 314p. (YA). (gr. 9 up). 16.95 (978-0-8234-2033-9(7)) Holiday Hse., Inc.

Ripslinger, Jon. Derailed. 2006. 288p. (J). pap. 8.95 (978-0-7387-0888-1(7) , Flux) Llewellyn Pubns.

Riso, Walter. Cuestion de Dignidad: Aprenda a decir NO y gane autoestima siendo Asertivo. 2002. (SPA.). (J). 12.99 (978-958-04-6597-3(5)) Norma S.A. COL. *Dist:* Distribuidora Norma, Inc.

Ritter, John H. Under the Baseball Moon. 2008. 320p. (J). (gr. 6). 6.99 (*978-0-14-241090-5(X)* , Puffin); 2006. (Illus.). 224p. (YA). (gr. 5). 16.99 (978-0-399-23623-5(6) , Philomel) Penguin Group (USA) Inc.

Roberts, G. Sillwee Wobbert the Happy Heart Kid. Lucas, Glenn E., illus. 2001. (Sillwsee Wobbert Ser.: 1). 32p. (J). (ps-5). pap. 10.00 (978-0-9704861-1-0(1)) Dream Publishing Co.

Roberts, Laura Peyton. Queen B. 368p. (gr. 7-11). 2007. (YA). mass mkt. 6.50 (*978-0-440-23872-0(2)* , Laurel Leaf); 2006. (J). lib. bdg. 17.99 (978-0-385-90201-4(8) , Delacorte Bks. for Young Readers); 2006. (YA). 15.95 (978-0-385-73163-8(9) , Delacorte Bks. for Young Readers) Random Hse. Children's Bks.

Roberts, Laura Peyton. The Queen of Second Place. 336p. (gr. 7). 2006. (YA). pap. 5.99 (978-0-440-23871-3(4) , Laurel Leaf); 2005. (J). lib. bdg. 17.99 (978-0-385-90200-7(X) , Delacorte Bks. for Young Readers); 2005. (YA). 15.95 (978-0-385-73162-1(0) , Delacorte Bks. for Young Readers) Random Hse. Children's Bks.

Robison, Dan. Death Chant: Kimo's Battle with the Shamanic Forces. 2006. 194p. (J). pap. (978-0-922993-52-9(1)) Marquette Bks., LLC.

Rodowsky, Colby F. That Fernhill Summer. 2006. 176p. (J). 16.00 (978-0-374-37442-6(2)) Farrar, Straus & Giroux.

Rogers, Lisa Waller. The Great Storm: The Hurricane Diary of J. T. King, Galveston, Texas, 1900. 2002. (Lone Star Journals). (Illus.). 192p. (J). 14.50 (978-0-89672-478-5(6)) Texas Tech Univ. Pr.

Rosenberg, Liz. Seventeen: A Novel in Prose Poems. 2002. 160p. (YA). (gr. 9 up). 16.95 (978-0-8126-4915-4(X)) Cricket Bks.

Rosenbloom, Fiona. We Are So Crashing Your Bar Mitzvah! 2007. 224p. (gr. 5 up). 15.99 (*978-0-7868-3890-5(6)*) Hyperion Pr.

Rosenbloom, Fiona. You Are So Not Invited to My Bat Mitzvah! 2005. 208p. (gr. 7-17). 15.99 (978-0-7868-5616-9(5)) Hyperion Pr.

Ross, Dave. A Book of Hugs. Rader, Laura, illus. 2000. 40p. (J). pap. 6.99 (978-0-06-443514-7(8) , Harper Trophy) HarperCollins Pubs.

Rottman, S. L. Slalom. 2004. 256p. (YA). (gr. 7). 16.99 (978-0-670-05913-3(7) , Viking Juvenile) Penguin Group (USA) Inc.

Rowlands, Samuel. The Bride. 2004. reprint ed. pap. 15.95 (978-1-4191-5524-6(5)); pap. 1.99 (978-1-4192-5524-3(X)) Kessinger Publishing, LLC.

Ruby, Laura. Good Girls. 2008. 304p. (J). pap. 8.99 (*978-0-06-088225-9(5)*); 2006. 288p. (J). lib. bdg. 17.89 (978-0-06-088224-2(7)); 2006. 288p. (YA). 16.99 (978-0-06-088223-5(9)) HarperCollins Pubs. (HarperTeen).

Ruby, Laura. Lily's Ghosts. 2003. 272p. (J). (gr. 5 up). 16.99 (978-0-06-051829-5(4)) HarperCollins Pubs.

Rue, Nancy N. & Youth Specialties Staff. New Girl in Town. 2004. (Invert / 'Nama Beach High Ser.: No. 1). 176p. (J). pap. 6.99 (978-0-310-24399-1(8)) Zondervan.

Ruel, Francine. Des Graffiti A Suivre. 2002. (Roman Plus Ser.). (FRE.). 160p. (YA). (gr. 8 up). pap. (978-2-89021-166-7(5)) Diffusion du livre Mirabel.

Runyon, Brent. Maybe. 2006. 208p. (YA). (gr. 9). 18.99 (978-0-375-93543-5(6)); 16.95 (978-0-375-83543-8(1)) Random Hse. Children's Bks. (Knopf Bks. for Young Readers).

Rushton, Rosie. Friends, Enemies. 2004. 240p. (gr. 5-17). 15.99 (978-0-7868-5177-5(5)) Hyperion Paperbacks for Children.

—Friends, Enemies. 2006. 240p. (gr. 5-17). pap. 5.99 (978-0-7868-5178-2(3)) Hyperion Pr.

Russell, Cheryl & Brouch, Dan. The Story of the Starhearts. l.t. ed. 1999. 30p. (J). (ps-3). 15.95 (978-0-9713181-0-6(7)) StarHeart Productions.

Russo, Marisabina. A Portrait of Pia. 2007. (Illus.). 240p. (YA). (gr. 6-8). 17.00 (978-0-15-205577-6(0)) Harcourt Trade Pubs.

Russon, Penni. Breathe. 2007. (Illus.). 368p. (J). (gr. 9 up). 16.99 (978-0-06-079393-7(7)); lib. bdg. 17.89 (978-0-06-079394-4(5)) HarperCollins Pubs.

—Undine. 2006. (Illus.). 336p. (J). 16.99 (978-0-06-079389-0(9)); lib. bdg. 17.89 (978-0-06-079390-6(2)) HarperCollins Pubs.

Ryan, Sarah. The Rules for Hearts: A Family Drama. 2007. 224p. (YA). (gr. 9 up). 16.99 (978-0-670-05906-5(4) , Viking Juvenile) Penguin Group (USA) Inc.

Rylant, Cynthia. A Fine White Dust. 2006. 112p. (J). pap. 4.99 (978-1-4169-2769-3(7) , Aladdin); 2000. (Illus.). (YA). (gr. 5-9). 25.00 (978-0-689-84087-6(X) , Atheneum/Richard Jackson Bks.) Simon & Schuster Children's Publishing.

Sachar, Louis. Small Steps. (YA). 2008. 288p. (gr. 7). pap. 8.99 (*978-0-385-73315-1(1)*); 2006. 272p. (gr. 5). 16.95 (978-0-385-73314-4(3)); 2006. 272p. (gr. 7). lib. bdg. 19.99 (978-0-385-90333-2(2)) Random Hse. Children's Bks. (Delacorte Bks. for Young Readers).

—Small Steps. rev. l.t. ed. 2006. 339p. 23.95 (978-0-7862-8297-5(5)) Thorndike Pr.

Saenz, Benjamin Alire. He Forgot to Say Good-Bye. 2008. 272p. (YA). (*978-1-4169-4963-3(1)* , Simon & Schuster Children's Publishing) Simon & Schuster Children's Publishing.

Sage, Elizabeth. Finding Home. 2002. (Five Star First Edition Women's Fiction Ser.). 225p. (J). 26.95 (978-0-7862-4111-8(X) , Five Star) Thomson Gale.

Salisbury, Graham. Night of the Howling Dogs. 2007. 208p. (J). (gr. 3-7). 16.99 (*978-0-385-73122-5(1)*); lib. bdg. 19.99 (*978-0-385-90146-8(1)*) Random Hse. Children's Bks. (Lamb, Wendy).

Salisbury, Linda G. No Sisters Sisters Club: A Bailey Fish Adventure. Grotke, Christopher A., illus. 2005. 188p. (J). per. 8.95 (978-1-881539-40-7(7)) Tabby Hse. Bks.

Salmansohn, Karen. Girl Wonders. 2007. 128p. (J). 6.95 (*978-1-58246-162-5(7)* , Tricycle Pr.) Ten Speed Pr.

—One Puppy, Three Tales Bk. 1: Alexandra Rambles On! 2004. (Alexandra Rambles on! Ser.: Bk. 1). (Illus.). 70p. (J). (gr. 4-6). 12.95 (978-1-58246-044-4(2) , Tricycle Pr.) Ten Speed Pr.

—Wherever I Go, There I Am. 2004. (Alexandra Rambles on! Ser.). (Illus.). 70p. (YA). (gr. 4-7). 12.95 (978-1-58246-079-6(5) , Tricycle Pr.) Ten Speed Pr.

Salmansohn, Karen, et al. Crashed, Smashed, & Mashed: A Trip to Junkyard Heaven. 2004. (Alexandra Rambles on! Ser.). (Illus.). 32p. (J). (gr. 3-6). 14.95 (978-1-58246-034-5(5) , Tricycle Pr.) Ten Speed Pr.

Sanchez, Alex. Rainbow Boys. (YA). 2003. 272p. 8.99 (978-0-689-85770-6(5) , Simon Pulse); 2001. 256p. (gr. 9 up). 17.00 (978-0-689-84100-2(0)) Simon & Schuster Children's Publishing.

—Rainbow Boys. 2003. (gr. 7-12). lib. bdg. 16.45 (978-0-613-66434-9(5)) Tandem Library Bks.

—Rainbow High. 2003. (Illus.). 272p. (YA). 16.95 (978-0-689-85477-4(3)) Simon & Schuster Children's Publishing.

—Rainbow Road. 2007. 272p. (YA). pap. 8.99 (978-1-4169-1191-3(X) , Simon Pulse) Simon & Schuster Children's Publishing.

—So Hard to Say. 240p. 2004. (J). 15.95 (978-0-689-86564-0(3)); 2006. (Illus.). (YA). reprint ed. pap. 7.99 (978-1-4169-1189-0(8) , Aladdin) Simon & Schuster Children's Publishing.

Sanschagrin, Joceline. Atterrissage Force. 1998. (Roman Jeunesse Ser.). (FRE., Illus.). 96p. (J). (gr. 4-7). pap. (978-2-89021-064-6(2)) Diffusion du livre Mirabel.

—Le Karateka. 1998. (Roman Jeunesse Ser.). (FRE., Illus.). 96p. (J). (gr. 4-7). pap. (978-2-89021-118-6(5)) Diffusion du livre Mirabel.

Sarfati, Sonia. Comme une Peau De Chagrin. 2003. (Roman Plus Ser.). (FRE.). 160p. (YA). (gr. 8 up). pap. (978-2-89021-242-8(4)) Diffusion du livre Mirabel.

Scholastic, Inc. Staff & Ford, Juwanda G. Shop Talk. Hoston, Jim, illus. 2004. (Just for You! Ser.). 32p. (gr. k-3). pap. 3.99 (978-0-439-56873-9(0) , Teaching Resources) Scholastic, Inc.

Schraff, Anne. The Boy from Planet Nowhere. 1999. 125p. (J). pap. (978-0-7891-4927-5(3)); (gr. 5-12). lib. bdg. 13.95 (978-0-7807-8004-0(3)) Perfection Learning Corp.

—Just Another Name for Lonely. 1999. 107p. (J). pap. (978-0-7891-4923-7(0)); (gr. 5-12). lib. bdg. 13.95 (978-0-7807-8007-1(8)) Perfection Learning Corp.

—Secrets in the Shadows. 2007. (Bluford Ser.: No. 3). 208p. (J). pap. 3.99 (978-0-439-90485-8(4)) Scholastic, Inc.

—Secrets in the Shadows. Langan, Paul, ed. 2002. (Bluford Ser.: 3). 126p. (YA). mass mkt. 4.95 (978-0-944210-05-5(8)) Townsend Pr.

—Someone to Love Me. Langan, Paul, ed. 2002. (Bluford Ser.: 4). 162p. (YA). mass mkt. 4.95 (978-0-944210-06-2(6)) Townsend Pr.

—Until We Meet Again. Langan, Paul, ed. 2002. (Bluford Ser.: 7). 144p. (YA). mass mkt. 4.95 (978-0-944210-07-9(4)) Townsend Pr.

—Wait until Spring. 2000. 125p. (J). pap. (978-0-7891-5139-1(1)); (gr. 5-12). lib. bdg. 13.95 (978-0-7807-9282-1(3)) Perfection Learning Corp.

Schreiber, Ellen. Comedy Girl. 2004. (Illus.). 288p. (J). (gr. 7 up). 15.99 (978-0-06-009338-9(2) , Tegen, Katherine Bks) HarperCollins Pubs.

—Vampire Kisses. (Vampire Kisses Ser.: Bk. 1). (gr. 7 up). 2003. 208p. (J). 16.99 (978-0-06-009334-1(X) , Tegen, Katherine Bks); 2003. 208p. (J). lib. bdg. 16.89 (978-0-06-009335-8(8) , Tegen, Katherine Bks); 2005. 272p. (YA). reprint ed. pap. 5.99 (978-0-06-009336-5(6) , Harper Trophy) HarperCollins Pubs.

Schreiber, Mark. Starcrossed. 2007. 336p. (J). (gr. 9 up). pap. 8.95 (978-0-7387-1001-3(6) , Flux) Llewellyn Pubns.

Schubert, Ulli. Harry's Got a Girlfriend! 2000. (gr. 3-6). lib. bdg. 14.10 (978-0-613-29976-3(0)) Tandem Library Bks.

Scott, Kieran. Brunettes Strike Back. (YA). 2007. 272p. (gr. 7). pap. 7.99 (978-0-14-240778-3(X) , Puffin); 2006. 256p. (gr. 5). 16.99 (978-0-399-24493-3(X) , Putnam Juvenile) Penguin Group (USA) Inc.

—A Non-Blonde Cheerleader in Love. 2007. 272p. (YA). (gr. 7-10). 16.99 (978-0-399-24494-0(8) , Putnam Juvenile) Penguin Group (USA) Inc.

Scott, Mary Ann. New Girl. 2003. 208p. (YA). (978-1-55041-725-8(8)) Fitzhenry & Whiteside, Ltd.

Searle-White, Joshua. Magic Wanda's Travel Emporium: Tales of Love, Hate & Things in Between. 2006. (Illus.). 144p. (J). pap. (978-1-55896-510-2(6) , Skinner Hse. Bks.) Unitarian Universalist Assn.

Second Look. 64p. (YA). (gr. 6-12). pap. (978-0-8224-2385-0(5)) Globe Fearon Educational Publishing.

Selfors, Suzanne. Saving Juliet. 2008. 256p. (YA). 16.95 (*978-0-8027-9740-7(7)*) Walker & Co.

Sellers, Mandy Lauren. The Boy Beside Me. 2000. (gr. 7-12). lib. bdg. 23.40 (978-0-613-84106-1(9)) Tandem Library Bks.

Seymour, Tres. The Revelation of Saint Bruce. 1998. (Illus.). 128p. (YA). (gr. 7-12). pap. 16.95 (978-0-531-30109-8(5) , Orchard Bks.) Scholastic, Inc.

Shapiro, Laurie Gwen. Brand X: The Boyfriend Account. 2006. 240p. (YA). (gr. 7). 15.95 (978-0-385-73288-8(0)); lib. bdg. 17.99 (978-0-385-90309-7(X)) Random Hse. Children's Bks. (Delacorte Bks. for Young Readers).

Shapiro, Lawrence E. Freddy Fights Fat: An Emotional Literacy Book. Harpster, Steve, illus. 2004. (Emotional Literacy Ser.). 54p. (J). (gr. 2 up). 14.95 (978-0-9747789-5-2(8) , 67873) CTC Publishing.

Sheldon, Dyan. Confessions of a Teenage Drama Queen. 2005. 272p. (YA). (gr. 7 up). pap. 7.99 (978-0-7636-2827-7(1)); 2004. (J). 107.82 (978-0-7636-2538-2(8)); 2004. (Illus.). 308p. (YA). (gr. 7 up). pap. 5.99 (978-0-7636-2416-3(0)) Candlewick Pr.

—Confessions of a Teenage Drama Queen. 2002. (gr. 7-12). lib. bdg. 15.30 (978-0-613-74762-2(3)) Tandem Library Bks.

—Confessions of a Teenage Hollywood Star. 2007. (Illus.). 208p. (YA). (gr. 7 up). pap. 7.99 (*978-0-7636-3408-7(5)*) Candlewick Pr.

—My Perfect Life. (YA). (gr. 7). 2004. 208p. pap. 5.99 (978-0-7636-2436-1(5)); 2002. (Illus.). 224p. 16.99 (978-0-7636-1839-1(X)); 2005. 208p. reprint ed. pap. 7.99 (978-0-7636-2828-4(X)) Candlewick Pr.

—Planet Janet. 240p. (YA). (gr. 9 up). 2004. (Illus.). pap. 6.99 (978-0-7636-2556-6(6)); 2003. 14.99 (978-0-7636-2048-6(3)) Candlewick Pr.

Sheldon, Dyan. Sophie Pitt-Turnbull Discovers America. 192p. (YA). (gr. 7). 2007. pap. 7.99 (*978-0-7636-3295-3(3)*); 2005. 15.99 (978-0-7636-2740-9(2)) Candlewick Pr.

Sheth, Kashmira. Koyal Dark, Mango Sweet. 224p. (gr. 7-17). 2006. 15.99 (978-0-7868-3857-8(4)); 2007. pap. 7.99 (*978-0-7868-3858-5(2)*) Hyperion Pr.

Shields, Carol Diggory. Lucky Pennies & Hot Chocolate. Nakata, Hiroe, illus. 2002. 32p. (J). pap. 5.99 (978-0-14-230190-6(6) , Puffin) Penguin Group (USA) Inc.

Shields, Gillian. The Actual Real Reality of Jennifer James: A Reality TV Novel. 2006. 384p. (J). lib. bdg. 17.89 (978-0-06-082241-5(4) , Tegen, Katherine Bks) HarperCollins Pubs.

Shipley, Jocelyn. Getting a Life: A Young Adult Novel. 2003. 224p. (J). pap. 7.95 (978-1-894549-18-9(X)) Sumach Pr. CAN. *Dist:* Orca Bk. Pubs. USA.

Shulman, Polly. Enthusiasm. (YA). 2007. 208p. (gr. 7 up). 7.99 (*978-0-14-240935-0(9)* , Puffin); 2006. 212p. (gr. 6). 15.99 (978-0-399-24389-9(5) , Putnam Juvenile) Penguin Group (USA) Inc.

Simmons, Vikk. Divided Loyalties. 2004. 150p. (YA). per. 12.95 (978-1-58749-484-0(1) , Byte/Me Teen Bk.) Awe-Struck E-Books, Inc.

Simner, Janni Lee. Secret of the Three Treasures. 2005. 160p. (J). 16.95 (978-0-8234-1914-2(2)) Holiday Hse., Inc.

Slater, David Michael. The Sharpest Tool in the Shed. Reibeling, Brandon, illus. 2007. (Missy Swiss & More Ser.). 32p. (J). (ps-4). lib. bdg. 27.07 (*978-1-60270-013-0(3)* , Looking Glass Library) Magic Wagon.

Sloan, Brian. A Really Nice Prom Mess. 2005. 272p. (YA). (gr. 7 up). 14.95 (978-0-689-87438-3(3) , Simon & Schuster Children's Publishing) Simon & Schuster Children's Publishing.

Smallcomb, Pam. Camp Buccaneer. Lichtenheld, Tom, illus. 2002. (Ready-for-Chapters Ser.). 64p. (J). (gr. 1-3). lib. bdg. 11.89 (978-0-689-84383-9(6) , Aladdin Library) Simon & Schuster Children's Publishing.

Smiletown's Upside Down. 2007. (J). per. 14.95 (*978-0-9785132-3-8(1)*) Smile-a-Lot, LLP.

Smith, Anne Warren. Tails of Spring Break. 2005. 136p. (J). (gr. 2-5). 15.95 (978-0-8075-6358-8(7)) Whitman, Albert & Co.

Smith, D. James. Probably the World's Best Story about a Dog & the Girl Who Loved Me. 2006. 240p. (J). (gr. 4-7). 15.95 (978-1-4169-0542-4(1)) Simon & Schuster Children's Publishing.

Smith, Jennifer E. The Comeback Season. 2008. 256p. (YA). 15.99 (*978-1-4169-3847-7(8)* , Simon & Schuster Children's Publishing) Simon & Schuster Children's Publishing.

Smith, Sherri L. Hot, Sour, Salty, Sweet. 2008. 176p. (J). (*978-0-385-73417-2(4)*); lib. bdg. (*978-0-385-90431-5(2)*) Dell Publishing. (Delacorte Pr.).

Smith, Stephen & Caldwell, Lise. Strike Three. 2006. (Game on for Girls Ser.). 128p. (J). pap. 5.99 (978-0-7847-1729-5(X) , 42146) Standard Publishing.

Sones, Sonya. One of Those Hideous Books Where the Mother Dies. 272p. (YA). 2004. (Illus.). 16.95 (978-0-689-85820-8(5)); 2005. (gr. 7-12). reprint ed. pap. 6.99 (978-1-4169-0788-6(2) , Simon Pulse) Simon & Schuster Children's Publishing.

Sonnenblick, Jordan. Drums, Girls & Dangerous Pie. 2004. 208p. (J). 15.95 (978-0-9761030-1-1(X)) Scholastic, Inc.

Sorrells, Walter. Static. 2006. 224p. (J). lib. bdg. 23.08 (*978-1-4242-2215-5(X)*) Fitzgerald Bks.

Sparrow, Rebecca. The Year Nick McGowan Came to Stay. 2008. (YA). (*978-0-375-84570-3(4)*); lib. bdg. (*978-0-375-94570-0(9)*) Knopf, Alfred A. Inc.

Spinelli, Jerry. Jason & Marceline. 2000. 233p. (J). (gr. 4-7). pap. 6.99 (978-0-316-80662-6(5)) Little Brown & Co.

Spollen, Anne. The Shape of Water. 2008. 312p. (J). pap. 9.95 (*978-0-7387-1101-0(2)* , Flux) Llewellyn Pubns.

St. Anthony, Jane. Grace above All. 2007. 176p. (J). (gr. 5-8). 16.00 (978-0-374-39940-5(9) , Farrar, Straus & Giroux (BYR)) Farrar, Straus & Giroux.

Stanley, Diane. A Time Apart. 1999. (Illus.). 256p. (J). (gr. 5 up). 15.95 (978-0-688-16997-8(X)) HarperCollins Pubs.

Stauffacher, Sue. Donutheart. 2006. 208p. (J). (gr. 3-7). 15.95 (978-0-375-83275-8(0)); lib. bdg. 17.99 (978-0-375-93275-5(5)) Random Hse. Children's Bks. (Knopf Bks. for Young Readers).

Steinhofel, Andreas. The Center of the World. 2007. 480p. (YA). (gr. 9). pap. 7.99 (978-0-440-22932-2(4) , Laurel Leaf) Random Hse. Children's Bks.

Stevens, Travis. I Aint Mad at Ya. 2006. 208p. pap. 15.00 (978-0-9745075-5-2(5)) Amiaya Entertainment.

Stine, Megan. Prom Night: Making Out. 2006. 256p. (YA). (gr. 12). pap. 9.99 (978-0-425-21179-3(7) , Berkley Trade) Penguin Group (USA) Inc.

—Prom Night: All the Way: All the Way. 2007. 240p. (YA). pap. 9.99 (978-0-425-21363-6(3) , Berkley Trade) Penguin Group (USA) Inc.

Stine, R.L. Killer's Kiss. 2005. 149p. (J). lib. bdg. 13.00 (*978-1-4242-0997-2(8)*) Fitzgerald Bks.

Stoehr, Shelley. Tomorrow Wendy: A Love Story. 2003. lib. bdg. 24.55 (978-0-613-87785-5(3)) Tandem Library Bks.

—Tomorrow Wendy: A Love Story. 2003. 176p. (YA). pap. 14.95 (978-0-595-26954-9(0) , Backinprint.com) iUniverse, Inc.

Stokes, Anthony, ed. Voices on Violence: The Lives of Children in Their Own Words. l.t. ed. 2002. (Illus.). 80p. 10.00 (978-0-9724803-0-7(7)) Orange Boy Bks.

Stolarz, Laurie Faria. Project 17. rev. ed. 2007. 256p. (gr. 7 up). 15.99 (*978-0-7868-3856-1(6)*) Hyperion Bks. for Children.

Stork, Francisco X. Behind the Eyes. 2006. 256p. (YA). (gr. 9). 16.99 (978-0-525-47735-8(7) , Dutton Adult) Penguin Group (USA) Inc.

Strasser, Todd. Boot Camp. 2007. 256p. (YA). (gr. 8 up). 15.99 (978-1-4169-0848-7(X)) Simon & Schuster Children's Publishing.

Stratton-Porter. At the Foot of the Rainbow. 2006. 19.99 (*978-1-4219-7512-2(2)*) IndyPublish.com.

Stratton Porter, Gene. At the Foot of the Rainbow. 2007. 180p. 18.95 (*978-1-934169-52-0(8)*); pap. 7.95 (*978-1-934169-53-7(6)*) Norilana Bks.

Streblow, Mary. The Family of Man. 2005. 28p. 14.01 (978-1-4116-5564-5(8)) Lulu.com.

Strickland, Brad, et al. The Storm: A Novelization. 2006. (Flight 29 down Ser.: Vol. 4). 224p. (J). (*978-1-4156-8721-5(8)* , Grosset & Dunlap) Penguin Group (USA) Inc.

Strong, Jeremy. Stuff: The Life of a Cool Demented Dude. Armstrong, Matthew S., illus. 2007. 240p. (J). (gr. 7 up). 15.99 (978-0-06-084105-8(2) , HarperTeen) HarperCollins Pubs.

—Stuff: The Life of a Cool Demented Dude. Armstrong, Matthew, illus. 2007. 240p. (J). (gr. 7 up). lib. bdg. 16.89 (978-0-06-084106-5(0) , HarperTeen) HarperCollins Pubs.

Sunderland, Margot & Hancock, Nicky. Helping Children Who Yearn for Someone They Love & the Frog Who Longed for the Moon to Smile, 2 vols. Armstrong, Nicky, tr. Armstrong, Nicky, illus. 76p. (978-0-86388-502-0(0) , 002-4776) Speechmark Publishing Ltd.

Sutherland, Tui. This Must Be Love. 256p. (J). 2005. pap. 7.99 (978-0-06-056477-3(6) , Harper Trophy); 2004. (gr. 7 up). 15.99 (978-0-06-056475-9(X)); 2004. (gr. 7 up). lib. bdg. 16.89 (978-0-06-056476-6(8)) HarperCollins Pubs.

Swallow, Pamela Curtis. It Only Looks Easy. rev. ed. 2003. 176p. (J). (gr. 3-7). 15.95 (978-0-7613-1790-6(2)) Roaring Brook Pr.

Tarshis, Lauren. Emma-Jean Lazarus Fell Out of a Tree. 2008. 208p. (YA). (gr. 7). pap. 6.99 (*978-0-14-241150-6(7)* , Puffin) Penguin Group (USA) Inc.

Taylor, Michelle. What's Happily Ever After, Anyway? 2005. (Illus.). 192p. (YA). pap. 10.95 (978-0-9746481-3-2(2)) Brown Barn Bks.

Teenage Bluez: Series 2, 2. 2006. 200p. (YA). pap. 10.99 (978-0-9741394-8-7(3)) Power Play Media.

Theo & the Sisters of Sage: From the Creator of We Are All the Same Inside. 2003. (We Are All the Same Inside Ser.: Vol. 3). (Illus.). 32p. (J). pap. 7.95 (978-0-9718232-1-1(9)) T.I.M.M.-E. Co., Inc.

Thesman, Jean. The Tree of Bells. 1999. 240p. (J). (gr. 5-9). tchr. ed. 15.00 (978-0-395-90510-4(9)) Houghton Mifflin Co. Trade & Reference Div.

Thompson, Julian F. Hard Time. 2003. (Illus.). 256p. (YA). 16.95 (978-0-689-85424-8(2) , Atheneum) Simon & Schuster Children's Publishing.

Tiller, Steve. Connectada al Corazon. Cremeans, Robert, illus. Date not set. (SPA.). (J). 15.95 (978-1-932317-01-5(5)) MichaelsMind LLC.

Tobias, Jerry E. There's No Better Place Than the U. S. of A. 2004. (Illus.). 30p. (J). 4.95 (978-0-9700582-2-5(5)) Factors Pr.

Townsend, Wendy. Lizard Love. 2008. (J). (*978-1-932425-34-5(9)* , Front Street) Boyds Mills Pr.

Triana, Gaby. Cubanita. 2006. 208p. (J). pap. 7.99 (978-0-06-056022-5(3)); 2005. 195p. (YA). (gr. 7-17). 15.99 (978-0-06-056020-1(7) , Rayo) HarperCollins Pubs.

Trimble, Marcia. Flower Green: A Flower for All Seasons. Dubin, Jill, illus. 2002. 32p. (J). (ps-2). 15.95 (978-1-891577-67-3(0)) Images Pr.

Trueman, Terry. 7 Days at the Hot Corner, No. 2. 2007. 160p. (J). (gr. 7 up). 15.99 (978-0-06-057494-9(1)); lib. bdg. 16.89 (978-0-06-057495-6(X)) HarperCollins Pubs. (HarperTeen).

Tullos, Matt. Wrong Turn in the Fast Lane. 1998. (Summit High Ser.). 144p. (Orig.). (J). (gr. 7-9). pap. 4.99 (978-0-8054-0180-6(6)) B&H Publishing Grp.

—Wrong Turn in the Fast Lane. 1998. (Orig.). (gr. 7-12). lib. bdg. 14.15 (978-0-613-90148-2(7)) Tandem Library Bks.

Uhlig, Richard Allen. Last Dance at the Frosty Queen. 2007. 368p. (YA). (gr. 9). lib. bdg. 18.99 (*978-0-375-93967-9(9)); 15.99 (*978-0-375-83967-2(4)) Random Hse. Children's Bks. (Knopf Bks. for Young Readers).

Unknow. Berry Sweet Baby Kisses. Si, Artists, illus. 2006. (Strawberry Shortcake Baby Ser.). 10p. (J). (ps-ps). bds. 5.99 (978-0-448-44417-8(8) , Grosset & Dunlap) Penguin Group (USA) Inc.

Urban, Linda. A Crooked Kind of Perfect. 2007. (Illus.). 224p. (J). (gr. 3-7). 16.00 (*978-0-15-206007-7(3)) Harcourt Children's Bks.

Vail, Rachel. If We Kiss. 2005. 272p. (J). 15.99 (978-0-06-056914-3(X)) HarperCollins Pubs.

—If You Only Knew: Zoe. 1998. (Friendship Ring Ser.: No. 1). 240p. (J). (gr. 4-8). pap. 14.95 (978-0-590-03370-1(0)); pap. 4.99 (978-0-590-37451-4(6)) Scholastic, Inc.

—Not That I Care: Morgan. 1998. (Friendship Ring Ser.: No. 3). (J). (gr. 4-8). 59.88 (978-0-590-95214-9(5)); 240p. pap. 4.99 (978-0-590-37453-8(2)); 240p. pap. 14.95 (978-0-590-03476-0(6)) Scholastic, Inc.

—Popularity Contest: Zoe. 2000. (Friendship Ring Ser.: No. 5). (J). (gr. 4-8). (Illus.). 240p. pap. 3.99 (978-0-590-68911-3(8) , Scholastic Paperbacks); Vol. 5. pap. 47.88 (978-0-439-16067-4(7)) Scholastic, Inc.

Vail, Rachel. You, Maybe: The Profound Asymmetry of Love in High School. (J). 2007. 240p. pap. 7.99 (*978-0-06-056919-8(0) , HarperTeen); 2006. 208p. (gr. 2). 15.99 (978-0-06-056917-4(4)); 2006. 208p. (gr. 2). lib. bdg. 16.89 (978-0-06-056918-1(2)) HarperCollins Pubs.

Valdes-Rodriguez, Alisa. Haters. 2006. 368p. (J). (gr. 7-17). 16.99 (978-0-316-01307-9(2)) Little Brown & Co.

Valgardson, W. D. Divorced Kids Club: And Other Stories. 2000. (gr. 5-8). lib. bdg. 15.25 (978-0-613-33888-2(X)) Tandem Library Bks.

Van Draanen, Wendelin. Flipped. 224p. (gr. 5-9). 2003. (J). pap. 8.95 (978-0-375-82544-6(4)); 2001. (J). 14.95 (978-0-375-81174-6(5)); 2001. lib. bdg. 16.99 (978-0-375-91174-3(X)) Random Hse. Children's Bks. (Knopf Bks. for Young Readers).

Van Etten, David. Likely Story (Book 1) 2008. (Likely Story Ser.). 208p. (J). (gr. 7). 15.99 (*978-0-375-84676-2(X)); lib. bdg. 18.99 (*978-0-375-94676-9(4)) Random Hse. Children's Bks. (Knopf Bks. for Young Readers).

Van Lieshout, Elle & Van Os, Erik. Nice Party. 1998. (Illus.). 32p. (J). 15.95 (978-1-886910-89-8(8) , Lemniscaat) Boyds Mills Pr.

Vanished. 64p. (YA). (gr. 6-12). pap. (978-0-8224-2367-6(7)) Globe Fearon Educational Publishing.

Vaughan, Kathryn Mademann. What's under the Sea? 2005. (Illus.). (J). per. 19.95 incl. audio compact disk (978-0-9747447-2-8(7)) Chaser Media LLC.

Vaught, Susan. Big Fat Manifesto. 2007. 320p. (YA). 16.95 (*978-1-59990-206-7(0) , Bloomsbury Children) Bloomsbury Publishing.

Vega, Denise. Click Here: To Find Out How I Survived Seventh Grade. 2006. 224p. (J). (gr. 5-8). reprint ed. pap. 7.99 (978-0-316-98559-8(7)) Little Brown & Co.

Vivian, Siobhan. A Little Friendly Advice. 2008. 256p. (J). pap. 16.99 (*978-0-545-00404-6(7) , PUSH) Scholastic, Inc.

Vizzini, Ned. Be More Chill. 2004. 304p. (gr. 8-17). 16.95 (978-0-7868-0995-0(7)) Hyperion Bks. for Children.

—Be More Chill. 2005. 304p. (gr. 8-17). pap. 7.99 (978-0-7868-0996-7(5)) Miramax Bks.

Voigt, Cynthia & Marcus, Barry David. Bad Girls in Love. (Bad Girls Ser.). 240p. 2003. (Illus.). (J). pap. 5.99 (978-0-689-86620-3(8) , Aladdin); 2002. (YA). (gr. 4-8). 15.95 (978-0-689-82471-5(8) , Atheneum/Anne Schwartz Bks.) Simon & Schuster Children's Publishing.

von Ziegesar, Cecily. The It Girl Collection. 2006. (It Girl Ser.). (YA). (gr. 10-17). pap. 29.99 (978-0-316-02068-8(0) , Poppy) Little, Brown Bks. for Young Readers.

—Lucky. 2007. (It Girl Ser.: No. 5). 256p. (YA). (gr. 10-17). pap. 9.99 (*978-0-316-11347-2(6) , Poppy) Little, Brown Bks. for Young Readers.

—Notorious. 2nd ed. 2006. (It Girl Ser.: No. 2). 288p. (J). (gr. 7-17) pap. 9.99 (978-0-316 01186 0(X) , Poppy) Little, Brown Bks. for Young Readers.

—Reckless. 2006. (It Girl Ser.: No. 3). 288p. (J). (gr. 7-17). pap. 9.99 (978-0-316-01187-7(8) , Poppy) Little, Brown Bks. for Young Readers.

Voorhees, Coert. Los Torres. 2008. 320p. 16.99 (*978-1-4231-0304-2(1)) Hyperion Pr.

Waite, Judy. A Trick of the Mind. 2005. (Illus.). 272p. (YA). (gr. 7). 16.95 (978-0-689-87014-9(0) , Atheneum) Simon & Schuster Children's Publishing.

—Trick of the Mind. 2006. 288p. (YA). pap. 6.99 (978-0-689-87015-6(9) , Simon Pulse) Simon & Schuster Children's Publishing.

Walker, Melissa. Violet on the Runway. 2007. 240p. (YA). (gr. 12 up). pap. 9.99 (*978-0-425-21704-7(3) , Berkley Trade) Penguin Group (USA) Inc.

Wallace, Rich. Losing Is Not an Option. 2003. 144p. (YA). (gr. 5-9). 15.95 (978-0-375-81351-1(9) , Knopf Bks. for Young Readers) Random Hse. Children's Bks.

Wallington, Aury & Schwartz, Josh. The OC: Bait & Switch. 2005. 163p. (YA). (978-1-4156-2363-3(5)) Scholastic, Inc.

Walsh, Marissa. A Field Guide to High School. 2007. 144p. (YA). (gr. 7). lib. bdg. 18.99 (*978-0-385-90427-8(4)); 15.99 (*978-0-385-73410-3(7)) Random Hse. Children's Bks. (Delacorte Bks. for Young Readers).

Waltman, Kevin. Learning the Game. 2005. 224p. (J). (gr. 7 up). pap. 16.95 (978-0-439-73109-6(7) , Scholastic Pr.) Scholastic, Inc.

Warner, Sally. Only Emma. Harper, Jamie, illus. 2006. 144p. (J). (gr. 3). pap. 5.99 (978-0-14-240711-0(9) , Puffin) Penguin Group (USA) Inc.

Warner, Sally & Harper, Jamie. Only Emma. 2005. (Illus.). 128p. (J). (gr. 3-7). 14.99 (978-0-670-05979-9(X) , Viking Juvenile) Penguin Group (USA) Inc.

Wasserman, Robin. Pride. 2006. (Seven Deadly Sins Ser.). 256p. (YA). pap. 8.99 (978-0-689-87784-1(6) , Simon Pulse) Simon & Schuster Children's Publishing.

—Sloth. 2006. (Seven Deadly Sins Ser.). 256p. (YA). pap. 7.99 (978-1-4169-0718-3(1) , Simon Pulse) Simon & Schuster Children's Publishing.

—Wrath. 2006. (Seven Deadly Sins Ser.). (Illus.). 256p. (YA). pap. 8.99 (978-0-689-87785-8(4) , Simon Pulse) Simon & Schuster Children's Publishing.

Watkins, Dawn L., et al. Pollyanna. 2006. (J). (978-1-59166-669-1(4)) Jones, Bob Univ. Pr.

Wax, Wendy & Artful Doodlers Limited Staff. Coolest Girl in School. 2005. (Ready-To-Read Ser.). (Illus.). 32p. (J). (ps-ps). pap. 3.99 (978-0-689-86647-0(X) , Simon Spotlight/Nickelodeon) Simon & Schuster Children's Publishing.

Weatherly, Lee. Kat Got Your Tongue. 2007. 208p. (YA). (gr. 7-9). lib. bdg. 18.99 (978-0-385-75122-3(2)); 15.99 (978-0-385-75117-9(6)) Random Hse. Children's Bks. (Fickling, David Bks.).

—Missing Abby. 2006. 208p. (YA). (gr. 7). mass mkt. 5.99 (978-0-553-49488-4(0) , Laurel Leaf) Random Hse. Children's Bks.

Weaver, Will. Saturday Night Dirt. 2008. (Motor Novel Ser.). 176p. (YA). 14.95 (*978-0-374-35060-4(4)) Farrar, Straus & Giroux.

Weeks, Sarah. Guy Time. 2001. 176p. (J). (gr. 3-7). pap. 5.99 (978-0-06-440783-0(7) , Harper Trophy) HarperCollins Pubs.

Wein, Elizabeth. The Empty Kingdom. 2008. (YA). (gr. 5). 16.99 (*978-0-670-06273-7(1) , Viking Juvenile) Penguin Group (USA) Inc.

Weinheimer, Beckie. Converting Kate. 2007. 288p. (YA). (gr. 7 up). 16.99 (978-0-670-06152-5(2) , Viking Juvenile) Penguin Group (USA) Inc.

Weisberg, E. Gathering Roses. 2007. pap. (*978-1-84747-118-5(8)) Chipmunkapublishing.

Welcome Home, Mrs. Jordon. 2000. (Tippy Parrish Story Ser.). (YA). (gr. 6-10). per. 12.95 (978-1-930009-23-3(2)) Image Cascade Publishing.

Wells, Helen. Cherry Ames, Boarding School Nurse. 2007. (YA). (*978-0-8261-0413-7(4)) Springer.

—Cherry Ames, Cruise Nurse. 2007. (YA). (*978-0-8261-0411-3(8)) Springer.

Weyr, Garret. My Heartbeat. 2003. 176p. (YA). pap. 7.99 (978-0-14-240066-1(1) , Puffin) Penguin Group (USA) Inc.

—My Heartbeat. 2003. (gr. 7-12). lib. bdg. 16.45 (978-0-613-81700-4(1)) Tandem Library Bks.

Wharton, Edith. Ethan Frome, Level 3. 2nd abr. ed. 2000. (Bookworms Ser.). (Illus.). 80p. 6.50 (978-0-19-423002-5(3)) Oxford Univ. Pr., Inc.

White, Ellen Emerson. White House Autumn. 2008. (YA). pap. 8.99 (*978-0-312-37489-1(5)) Feiwel & Friends.

Whitney, Kim Ablon. The Perfect Distance. 2007. 256p. (YA). (gr. 7). pap. 5.99 (978-0-553-49467-9(8) , Laurel Leaf) Random Hse. Children's Bks.

Whittenberg, Allison. Life Is Fine. 2008. 192p. (YA). (gr. 7). 15.99 (*978-0-385-73480-6(8) , Delacorte Bks. for Young Readers) Random Hse. Children's Bks.

Who Needs a Hug. 2003. (J). per. (978-1-57657-877-3(1)) Paradise Pr., Inc.

Whytock, Cherry. My Cup Runneth Over: The Life of Angelica Cookson Potts. Whytock, Cherry, illus. (YA). 2003. (Illus.). 176p. 14.95 (978-0-689-86546-6(5)); 2004. 192p. reprint ed. mass mkt. 5.99 (978-0-689-86551-0(1) , Simon Pulse) Simon & Schuster Children's Publishing.

—My Saucy Stuffed Ravioli: The Life of Angelica Cookson Potts. Whytock, Cherry, illus. 2005. (Illus.). 176p. (YA). 14.95 (978-0-689-86550-3(3)) Simon & Schuster Children's Publishing.

—My Scrumptious Scottish Dumplings: The Life of Angelica Cookson Potts. Whytock, Cherry, illus. 2006. 192p. (YA). mass mkt. 5.99 (978-0-689-86552-7(X) , Simon Pulse) Simon & Schuster Children's Publishing.

Whytock, Cherry, illus. My Scrumptious Scottish Dumplings: The Life of Angelica Cookson Potts. 2004. 176p. (YA). 14.95 (978-0-689-86549-7(X)) Simon & Schuster Children's Publishing.

Wild, Margaret. Jinx. Gould, Jason, photos by. 2004. (Illus.). 224p. (YA). reprint ed. pap. 11.95 (978-0-689-86541-1(4) , Simon Pulse) Simon & Schuster Children's Publishing.

—Jinx. 2004. (gr. 7-12). lib. bdg. 15.30 (978-0-613-73451-6(3)) Tandem Library Bks.

Wildner, Martina & Skofield, James. Shooting Stars Everywhere. 2006. 192p. (J). (gr. 7). 15.95 (978-0-385-73250-5(3) , Delacorte Bks. for Young Readers) Random Hse. Children's Bks.

Wilhelm, Doug. Falling. 2007. 256p. (YA). (gr. 9 up). 17.00 (978-0-374-32251-9(1)) Farrar, Straus & Giroux.

Wilkins, Rose. So Super Starry. 2006. (YA). 230p. (*978-1-4156-6975-4(9)); 240p. (gr. 7). reprint ed. pap. 6.99 (978-0-14-240581-9(7)) Penguin Group (USA) Inc. (Puffin).

Williams, Dar. Lights, Camera, Amalee. 2006. (Amalee Ser.: No. 2). 192p. (J). pap. 16.99 (978-0-439-80352-6(7) , Scholastic Pr.) Scholastic, Inc.

Williams-Garcia, Rita. Every Time a Rainbow Dies. (Amistad Ser.). (Illus.). 176p. 2002. (J). pap. 6.99 (978-0-06-447303-3(1) , HarperTeen); 2001. (YA). (gr. 9 up). 15.95 (978-0-688-16245-0(2)) HarperCollins Pubs.

—Every Time a Rainbow Dies. 2002. (gr. 7-12). lib. bdg. 15.25 (978-0-613-62381-0(9)) Tandem Library Bks.

Williams, Jacklyn. Happy Birthday, Gus! Cushman, Doug, illus. 2005. (Read-It! Readers Ser.). 32p. (J). (gr. k-3). 18.60 (978-1-4048-0957-4(0)) Picture Window Bks.

Wilson, Jacqueline. Girls in Tears. 176p. (YA). (gr. 7). 2004. (Girls Quartet: Bk. 4). mass mkt. 4.99 (978-0-440-23807-2(2) , Laurel Leaf); 2003. lib. bdg. 11.99 (978-0-385-90104-8(6) , Delacorte Bks. for Young Readers) Random Hse. Children's Bks.

—Girls in Tears. 2004. (gr. 7-12). lib. bdg. 13.00 (978-0-613-72253-7(1)) Tandem Library Bks.

—Girls Out Late. 2003. 224p. (YA). (gr. 7). mass mkt. 5.50 (978-0-440-22959-9(6) , Laurel Leaf) Random Hse. Children's Bks.

—Girls Out Late. Sharratt, Nick, illus. 2003. 192p. (YA). mass mkt. (978-0-552-54523-5(6) , Corgi) Transworld Publishers Ltd. GBR. *Dist:* Random Hse. of Canada, Ltd.

Windle, Jeanette. Jana's Journal: A Novel for Teens. 2002. 256p. pap. 12.99 (978-0-8254-4117-2(X)) Kregel Pubns.

Wittlinger, Ellen. Heart on My Sleeve. 2005. (Illus.). 240p. (YA). reprint ed. pap. 6.99 (978-0-689-84999-2(0) , Simon Pulse) Simon & Schuster Children's Publishing.

—Love & Lies: Marisol's Story. 2008. 256p. (YA). (*978-1-4169-1623-9(7) , Simon & Schuster Children's Publishing) Simon & Schuster Children's Publishing.

—Sandpiper. 2005. 240p. (YA). (gr. 7 up). 16.95 (978-0-689-86802-3(2) , Simon & Schuster Children's Publishing) Simon & Schuster Children's Publishing.

—Zigzag. (Illus.). (YA). 2003. 272p. 16.95 (978-0-689-84996-1(6)); 2005. 288p. reprint ed. pap. 6.99 (978-0-689-84998-5(2) , Simon Pulse) Simon & Schuster Children's Publishing.

Wojciechowski, Susan. Beany & the Meany. Natti, Susanna, illus. 112p. (J). (gr. 1-4). 2006. pap. 4.99 (978-0-7636-2974-8(X)); 2005. 15.99 (978-0-7636-2630-3(9)) Candlewick Pr.

Wolff, Virginia Euwer. Probably Still Nick Swansen. Katz, illus. 2003. 160p. mass mkt. 10.00 (978-0-689-85227-5(4) , Simon Pulse) Simon & Schuster Children's Publishing.

Wood, Maryrose. Sex Kittens & Horn Dawgs Fall in Love. 256p. (YA). (gr. 7). 2007. pap. 8.99 (*978-0-385-73277-2(5)); 2006. 15.95 (978-0-385-73276-5(7)); 2006. lib. bdg. 17.99 (978-0-385-90296-0(4)) Random Hse. Children's Bks. (Delacorte Bks. for Young Readers).

Woods, Brenda. Emako Blue. 128p. (YA). 2005. (gr. 6). pap. 5.99 (978-0-14-240418-8(7) , Puffin); 2004. (gr. 5-12). 15.99 (978-0-399-24006-5(3) , Putnam Juvenile) Penguin Group (USA) Inc.

Woodson, Jacqueline. Behind You. 128p. (YA). 2006. (gr. 7). pap. 5.99 (978-0-14-240390-7(3) , Puffin); 2004. (gr. 5-12). 15.99 (978-0-399-23988-5(X) , Putnam Juvenile) Penguin Group (USA) Inc.

Wynne-Jones, Tim. Rex Zero, the King of Nothing. 2008. 224p. (J). 16.95 (*978-0-374-36259-1(9)) Farrar, Straus & Giroux.

Zarr, Sara. Story of a Girl. 2007. 208p. (J). (gr. 7-17). 16.99 (978-0-316-01453-3(2)) Little Brown & Co.

Zephaniah, Benjamin. Gangsta Rap. 2004. 200p. (J). (gr. 9 up). pap. 7.95 (978-1-58234-886-5(3) , Bloomsbury Children) Bloomsbury Publishing.

Ziegler, Jennifer. Alpha Dog. 2006. 336p. (YA). (gr. 7). pap. 7.95 (978-0-385-73285-7(6)); lib. bdg. 9.99 (978-0-385-90302-8(2)) Random Hse. Children's Bks. (Delacorte Bks. for Young Readers).

Zindel, Lizabeth. Girl of the Moment. 288p. (YA). (gr. 7). 2008. pap. 8.99 (*978-0-14-241104-9(3) , Puffin); 2007. 16.99 (978-0-670-06210-2(3) , Viking Juvenile) Penguin Group (USA) Inc.

Zusak, Markus. Getting the Girl. 2004. 256p. (J). pap. 6.99 (978-0-439-38950-1(X) , Levine, Arthur A. Bks.) Scholastic, Inc.

The 15 Best Things about Being the New Kid. 2006. (J). pap. 5.95 (978-0-8225-6473-7(4) , First Avenue Editions) Lerner Publishing Group.

INTERPLANETARY COMMUNICATION

see Interstellar Communication

INTERPLANETARY VOYAGES

see also Outer Space—Exploration; Rockets (Aeronautics); Space Flight

Allman, Toney. Space Travel. 2005. (Science on the Edge Ser.). (Illus.). 48p. (J). (gr. 4-7). 24.95 (978-1-4103-0532-9(5) , Blackbirch Pr., Inc.) Thomson Gale.

Atkinson, Stuart. Space Travel. 2002. (Young Library - Space Busters Ser.). (Illus.). 32p. (J). lib. bdg. 25.69 (978-0-7398-4852-4(6)) Raintree.

Dorling Kindersley Publishing Staff. Space Travel. 2004. (Google E Guides Ser.). (Illus.). 96p. (J). 17.99 (978-0-7566-0533-9(4)) Dorling Kindersley Publishing, Inc.

Graham, Ian. Space Travel. 2004. (Interfact Ser.). (SPA., Illus.). 48p. (J). (gr. 3-6). 14.95 incl. cd-rom (978-1-58728-465-6(0) , Two Can Publishing) T&N Children's Publishing.

Hamilton, John. Spaceships. 2007. (World of Science Fiction Ser.). (Illus.). 32p. (J). 24.21 (978-1-59679-995-0(1)) ABDO Publishing Co.

Hunt, Gene. Accidental Space Ship. 2006. 150p. (J). (gr. 4-6). 16.95 (978-1-59354-119-4(8)) Handprint Bks.

Jackson, Ellen B. The World Around Us: A Space Voyage. Miller, Ron, illus. 2006. (Exceptional Science Title for Intermediate Grades). 40p. (J). lib. bdg. 23.93 (978-0-7613-3405-7(X) , Millbrook Pr.) Lerner Publishing Group.

Solway, Andrew. Can We Travel to the Stars? Space Flight & Space Exploration. 2006. (Stargazers Guides Ser.). (Illus.). 48p. (J). (978-1-4034-7711-8(6)); pap. (978-1-4034-7718-7(3)) Heinemann Library.

Space Travel. (Jump Ser.). 36p. (J). (gr. 2-7). pap. (978-1-882210-22-0(0)) Action Publishing, Inc.

INTERRACIAL MARRIAGE

Alonso, Karen. Loving vs. Virginia: Interracial Marriage. 2000. (Landmark Supreme Court Cases Ser.). (Illus.). 112p. (J). (gr. 6-12). lib. bdg. 26.60 (978-0-7660-1338-4(3)) Enslow Pubs., Inc.

Fuyo Gaskins, Pearl, ed. What Are You? Voices of Mixed-Race Young People. rev. ed. 1999. (Illus.). 288p. (YA). (gr. 7-12). 18.95 (978-0-8050-5968-7(7) , Holt, Henry & Co. Bks. For Young Readers) Holt, Henry & Co.

Gold, Susan Dudley. Loving v. Virginia: Intermarriage Upheld. 2007. (Supreme Court Milestones Ser.). 144p. (YA). (gr. 9 up). lib. bdg. 39.93 (*978-0-7614-2586-1(1) , Benchmark Bks.) Cavendish, Marshall Corp.

Haugen, David M. Interracial Relationships. 2006. 128p. (YA). (gr. 7 up). 21.20 (978-0-7377-2391-5(2)); pap. 29.95 (978-0-7377-2390-8(4)) Thomson Gale. (Greenhaven Pr., Inc.).

INTERRACIAL MARRIAGE—FICTION

Igus, Toyomi. Two Mrs Gibsons. 2001. (gr. k-3). lib. bdg. 16.40 (978-0-613-65372-5(6)) Tandem Library Bks.

Woodson, Jacqueline. The House You Pass on the Way. 2003. 112p. (YA). reprint ed. pap. 5.99 (978-0-14-250191-7(3) , Puffin) Penguin Group (USA) Inc.

—The House You Pass on the Way. Lt. ed. 2004. 109p. (J). 22.95 (978-0-7862-6428-5(4)) Thorndike Pr.

Wyeth, Sharon Dennis. The World of Daughter McGuire. 2001. 176p. (gr. 3-7). pap. 12.00 (978-0-375-89502-9(7) , Delacorte Bks. for Young Readers) Random Hse. Children's Bks.

Yep, Laurence. The Cook's Family. 1998. (J). (978-0-03-992907-7(8)) Holt, Rinehart & Winston.

—The Cook's Family. 1999. (J). (978-0-606-18932-3(7)) Tandem Library Bks.

INTERSTELLAR COMMUNICATION

Branley, Franklyn M. Is There Life in Outer Space. 1999. (Let's-Read-and-Find-Out Science Ser.). (Illus.). 40p. (J). (ps-1). 15.95 (978-0-06-028146-5(4)) HarperCollins Pubs.

Firestone, Mary. SETI Science. 2005. (Weird Careers in Science Ser.). (Illus.). 81p. (J). (gr. 4-8). lib. bdg. 25.00 (978-0-7910-8701-5(8) , Chelsea Hse.) Facts On File, Inc.

Zelon, Helen. The Endeavour Mission STS-61: Fixing the Hubble Space Telescope. 2002. (Space Missions Ser.). (Illus.). 24p. (J). (gr. 2-4). lib. bdg. 19.95 (978-0-8239-5774-3(8) , PowerKids Pr.) Rosen Publishing Group, Inc., The.

INTERSTELLAR VOYAGES

see Interplanetary Voyages

INTERVIEWING (JOURNALISM)

see Reporters and Reporting

INTOLERANCE

see Toleration

INTOXICATION

see Alcoholism; Drug Addiction

INUIT

Here are entered works limited to the indigenous Arctic peoples of Greenland, Canada, and northern Alaska. Works discussing collectively the Inuit peoples and the related Eskimo peoples of southern and western Alaska and adjacent regions of Siberia, or works for which the individual group cannot be identified, are entered under Eskimos.

Ansary, Mir Tamim. Arctic Peoples. (Native Americans Ser.). (Illus.). 32p. (J). 2002. (gr. 1-4). pap. 7.50 (978-1-58810-450-2(8) , 91169); 1999. (gr. 2-4). lib. bdg. 21.36 (978-1-57572-920-6(2)) Heinemann Library.

Bial, Raymond. The Inuit. 2001. (Lifeways Ser.). (Illus.). 128p. (J). (gr. 5-9). lib. bdg. 34.21 (978-0-7614-1212-0(3) , Benchmark Bks.) Cavendish, Marshall Corp.

Burgan, Michael. Inuit. 2004. (Native American Peoples Ser.). (Illus.). 32p. (J). lib. bdg. 24.67 (978-0-8368-4219-7(7)) Stevens, Gareth Inc.

Corriveau, Danielle. The Inuit of Canada. 2005. (First Peoples Ser.). (Illus.). 48p. (gr. 4-8). lib. bdg. 23.95 (978-0-8225-4850-8(X)) Lerner Publishing Group.

Falconer, Shelley & White, Shawna. Stones, Bones & Stitches: Storytelling Through Inuit Art. 2007. 40p. (YA). (gr. 3 up). 22.95 (*978-0-88776-854-5(7)) Tundra Bks. of Northern New York.

Furgang, Kathy. The Inupiaq Live Here. 2003. (Early Connections Ser.). (J). pap. 33.00 (978-1-4108-1087-8(9)) Benchmark Education Co.

George, Charles & George, Linda. The Inuit. 2005. (North American Indians Ser.). (Illus.). 48p. (J). (ps-7). lib. bdg. 26.20 (978-0-7377-2626-8(1) , Greenhaven Pr., Inc.) Thomson Gale.

Gray-Kanatiiosh, Barbara A. Inuit. Kanietakeron, David, illus. 2002. (Native Americans Ser.). 32p. (J). (gr. k-6). lib. bdg. 22.78 (978-1-57765-599-2(0) , Checkerboard Library) ABDO Publishing Co.

Hancock, Lyn. Nunavut. 2nd rev. ed. (Hello Canada Ser.). 72p. (J). pap. (978-1-55041-760-9(6)) Fitzhenry & Whiteside, Ltd.

Harper, Judith E. Inuit. 1999. (Endangered Cultures Ser.). (Illus.). 32p. (YA). (gr. 4 up). lib. bdg. 16.95 (978-1-887068-74-1(0)) Smart Apple Media.

Ipellie, Alootook & MacDonald, David. The Inuit Thought of It: Amazing Arctic Innovations. 2007. (Illus.). 32p. (J). (gr. 4-6). pap. 8.95 (*978-1-55451-087-0(2)); lib. bdg. 19.95 (*978-1-55451-088-7(0)) Annick Pr., Ltd. CAN. *Dist:* Firefly Bks., Ltd.

Kent, Deborah. The Inuit: A Proud People. 2005. (American Indians Ser.). (Illus.). 48p. (J). lib. bdg. 23.93 (978-0-7660-2451-9(2) , Enslow Elementary) Enslow Pubs., Inc.

H
I

King, David C. The Inuit. 2007. (First Americans Ser.). 48p. (J). lib. bdg. 29.93 (*978-0-7614-2679-0(5) , Benchmark Bks.) Cavendish, Marshall Corp.

Koestler-Grack, Rachel A. The Inuit: Ivory Carvers of the Far North. 2003. (America's First Peoples Ser.). (Illus.). 32p. (J). (gr. 2-3). lib. bdg. 23.93 (978-0-7368-2171-1(6) , Bridgestone Bks.) Capstone Pr., Inc.

Lassieur, Allison. The Inuit. 2000. (Native Peoples Ser.). (Illus.). 24p. (J). (gr. 2-3). lib. bdg. 18.60 (978-0-7368-0498-1(6) , Bridgestone Bks.) Capstone Pr., Inc.

Miller, Connie R. The Inuit. 2003. (Uncovering Native American History Ser.). (J). pap. (978-1-58417-114-0(6)); lib. bdg. (978-1-58417-051-8(4)) Lake Street Pubs.

Morris, Neil. Living in the Arctic. 2007. (J). pap. (*978-1-4109-2824-5(1)); lib. bdg. (*978-1-4109-2815-3(2)) Steck-Vaughn.

Oberman, Sheldon. Shaman's Nephew: A Life in the Far North. 2000. (gr. 3-6). lib. bdg. 23.40 (978-0-613-65096-0(4)) Tandem Library Bks.

Reynolds, Jan. Frozen Land: Vanishing Cultures. 2007. 32p. (J). (*978-1-60060-128-6(6)); (*978-1-60060-143-9(X)) Lee & Low Bks., Inc.

Rhodes, Sam. Native American Rhymes: The People of the Far North, 9 vols. Howard, Kimberley, ed. Haas, Deborah, illus. 2003. 92p. (J). (gr. 3-5). mass mkt. 7.50 (978-0-9743214-0-0(0)) Rhodes Educational Pubns.

Santella, Andrew. The Inuit. 2001. (True Bks.). (Illus.). 48p. (J). (gr. 3-5). pap. 6.95 (978-0-516-27319-8(1) , Children's Pr.) Scholastic Library Publishing.

—Inuit. 2001. (gr. 3-6). lib. bdg. 15.25 (978-0-613-53513-7(8)) Tandem Library Bks.

Strudwick, Leslie. Inuit. 2003. (Indigenous Peoples Ser.). (Illus.). 32p. (J). lib. bdg. 18.20 (978-1-59036-122-1(9)) Weigl Pubs., Inc.

Wallace, Mary. Make Your Own Inuksuk. 2004. (Wow Canada! Collection). (Illus.). 32p. (J). pap. 8.95 (978-1-897066-14-0(7)) Maple Tree Pr. CAN. *Dist:* Perseus Distribution.

Williams, Suzanne Morgan. The Inuit. 2003. (Watts Library: Indians of the Americas Ser.). (Illus.). 64p. (J). 25.50 (978-0-531-12172-6(0) , Watts, Franklin) Scholastic Library Publishing.

Yacowitz, Caryn. Inuit Indians. 2003. (Native Americans Ser.). (Illus.). 32p. (J). pap. 7.50 (978-1-4034-4171-3(5)); lib. bdg. 24.22 (978-1-4034-0863-1(7)) Heinemann Library.

INUIT—FICTION

Bania, Michael. Kumak's Fish: A Tall Tale from the Far North. 2005. (Illus.). 32p. 15.95 (978-0-88240-583-4(7)); pap. 8.95 (978-0-88240-584-1(5)) Graphic Arts Ctr. Publishing Co.

Bushey, Jeanne. Orphans in the Sky. Krykorka, Vladyana, illus. 2004. 32p. (J). (gr. 1-3). 17.95 (978-0-88995-291-1(4)) Red Deer Pr. CAN. *Dist:* Fitzhenry & Whiteside, Ltd.

—The Polar Bear's Gift. Krykorka, Vladyana Langer, illus. 2004. (Northern Lights Books for Children Ser.). 32p. (J). (ps-3). pap. 16.95 (978-0-88995-220-1(5)) Red Deer Pr. CAN. *Dist:* Fitzhenry & Whiteside, Ltd.

Devine, Monica. Carry Me, Mama. Paquin, Pauline, illus. 2002. 22p. (ps-3). 15.95 (978-0-7737-3317-6(5)) Stoddart Kids CAN. *Dist:* Fitzhenry & Whiteside, Ltd.

Dewey, Jennifer Owings. Minik's Story. 2003. (Illus.). 160p. (YA). 15.95 (978-0-7614-5134-1(X)) Cavendish, Marshall Corp.

Easley, Mary Ann. I Am the Ice Worm. 2003. 128p. (J). (gr. 4-7). 16.95 (978-1-56397-412-0(6)) Boyds Mills Pr.

—I Am the Ice Worm. 1998. (978-0-606-13500-9(6)) Tandem Library Bks.

Edwardson, Debby Dahl. Whale Snow. Patterson, Annie, illus. 2004. 32p. (J). (ENG.). pap. 7.95 (978-1-57091-496-6(6)); pap. (978-1-57091-394-5(3)); 15.95 (978-1-57091-393-8(5)) Charlesbridge Publishing, Inc.

Feagan, Robert. Napachee. 2006. 128p. (J). pap. 9.99 (*978-1-55002-636-8(4) , Sandcastle Bks.) Dundurn Group, The CAN. *Dist:* Univ. of Toronto Pr.

George, Jean Craighead. Arctic Son. 1999. (J). (978-0-606-17381-0(1)) Tandem Library Bks.

Golding, Theresa Martin & Easley, Mary Ann. I Am the Ice Worm. 2004. (Illus.). 128p. (YA). (gr. 4-6). pap. 9.95 (978-1-59078-281-1(X)) Boyds Mills Pr.

Hamel, Mike. Rylan the Renegade: Matterhorn, the Brave Series, 6. 2007. 192p. (J). pap. 12.99 (*978-0-89957-838-5(1)) AMG Pubs.

Heinz, Brian J. Kayuktuk: An Arctic Quest. Van Zyle, Jon, illus. 2004. (J). pap. 6.95 (978-0-936335-09-4(2)); 14.95 (978-0-936335-08-7(4)) Ballyhoo BookWorks, Inc.

—Nanuk, Lord of the Ice. Manchess, Gregory, illus. 2005. (J). (978-0-936335-13-1(0)); pap. (978-0-936335-14-8(9)) Ballyhoo BookWorks, Inc.

Nelson, Kelly. Boreal, Dragon of the North. 2005. 68p. (YA). pap. 9.99 (978-1-4141-0292-4(5)) Pleasant Word.

Pasquali, Elena. Ituku's Christmas Journey. Kolanovic, Dubravka, illus. 2005. 32p. (J). (ps-3). 16.00 (978-1-56148-495-9(4)) Good Bks.

Rivera, Raquel. Arctic Adventures: Tales from the Lives of Inuit Artists. Marton, Jirina, illus. 2007. 36p. (gr. 3 up). 18.95 (978-0-88899-714-2(0)) Groundwood Bks. CAN. *Dist:* Perseus Distribution.

Stafford, Liliana. Snow Bear. Davis, Lambert, illus. 32p. (J). pap. (978-0-88899-441-7(9)) Groundwood Bks.

—Snow Bear. Davis, Lambert, illus. 2001. 32p. (J). (gr. 1-3). 15.95 (978-0-439-26977-3(6)) Scholastic, Inc.

Taylor, Theodore. Ice Drift. (Illus.). 240p. (J). 2006. pap. 5.95 (978-0-15-205550-9(9) , Harcourt Paperbacks); 2005. 16.00 (978-0-15-205081-8(7)) Harcourt Children's Bks.

Ulmer, Michael. The Gift of the Inuksuk. Rose-Popp, Melanie, illus. rev. ed. 2004. 32p. (J). 17.95 (978-1-58536-214-1(X)) Sleeping Bear Pr.

Wood, Ellen. Hundreds of Fish. Felix, Monique, illus. 2000. (Notebooks Ser.). 40p. (gr. 4 up). 17.95 (978-1-56846-162-5(3) , Creative Editions) Creative Co., The.

INVALID COOKERY

see Cookery for the Sick

INVALIDS

see People with Disabilities; Sick

INVASION OF PRIVACY

see Privacy, Right of

INVENTIONS

see also Creation (Literary, Artistic, etc.); Inventors

Allman, Toney. From Barbs on a Weed to Velcro. 2005. (Imitating Nature Ser.). (Illus.). 32p. (J). (ps-8). lib. bdg. 24.95 (978-0-7377-3118-7(4) , Greenhaven Pr., Inc.) Thomson Gale.

—From Boxfish Bodies to Bionic Cars. 2006. (Imitating Nature Ser.). 32p. (J). (gr. 3-6). 24.95 (978-0-7377-3609-0(7) , Greenhaven Pr., Inc.) Thomson Gale.

Bailey, Gerry. Age of New Ideas. Boulter, Steve et al, illus. 2005. (Crafty Inventions Ser.). 48p. (C). (gr. 4-6). 26.60 (978-1-4048-1037-2(4)) Picture Window Bks.

—Early Civilizations. Boulter, Steve et al, illus. 2005. (Crafty Inventions Ser.). 48p. (C). (gr. 4-6). 26.60 (978-1-4048-1038-9(2)) Picture Window Bks.

—First Thousand Years. Smith, Jan & Keylock, Andrew, illus. 2005. (Crafty Inventions Ser.). 48p. (C). (gr. 4-6). 26.60 (978-1-4048-1039-6(0)) Picture Window Bks.

—Long, Long Ago. Boulter, Steve et al, illus. 2005. (Crafty Inventions Ser.). 48p. (C). (gr. 4-6). 26.60 (978-1-4048-1043-3(9)) Picture Window Bks.

—Modern Times. Boulter, Steve et al, illus. 2005. (Crafty Inventions Ser.). 48p. (C). (gr. 4-6). 26.60 (978-1-4048-1044-0(7)) Picture Window Bks.

—The Top Ten Inventors. Boulter, Steve & Smith, Jan, illus. 2005. (Crafty Inventions Ser.). 48p. (C). (gr. 4-6). 26.60 (978-1-4048-1046-4(3)) Picture Window Bks.

—Trade & Industry. Boulter, Steve et al, illus. 2005. (Crafty Inventions Ser.). 48p. (C). (gr. 4-6). 26.60 (978-1-4048-1047-1(1)) Picture Window Bks.

Banting, Erinn. Inventing the Automobile. 2006. (Breakthrough Inventions Ser.). (Illus.). 32p. (J). (gr. 3-9). pap. (978-0-7787-2834-4(X)); (978-0-7787-2812-2(9)) Crabtree Publishing Co.

—Inventing the Telephone. 2006. (Breakthrough Inventions Ser.). (Illus.). 32p. (J). (gr. 3-9). pap. (978-0-7787-2837-5(4)); (978-0-7787-2815-3(3)) Crabtree Publishing Co.

Barretta, Gene. Now & Ben: The Modern Inventions of Benjamin Franklin. 2006. (Illus.). 40p. (J). 16.95 (978-0-8050-7917-3(3)) Holt, Henry & Co.

Benchmark Education Staff, compiled by. Invention & Technology. 2006. spiral bd. 145.00 (*978-1-4108-7100-8(2)) Benchmark Education Co.

Bender, Lionel. Invention. Dorling Kindersley Publishing Staff, ed. 2005. (Eyewitness Bks.). (Illus.). 72p. (J). (ps-7). 15.99 (978-0-7566-1075-3(3)) Dorling Kindersley Publishing, Inc.

Bender, Lionel & Dorling Kindersley Publishing Staff. Invention. 2005. (Eyewitness Books). (Illus.). 72p. (J). (ps-7). lib. bdg. 19.99 (978-0-7566-1076-0(1)) Dorling Kindersley Publishing, Inc.

Bergen, Lara Rice. My Book of Inventions. Fruchter, Jason, illus. 2001. (Jimmy Neutron Boy Genius Ser.). 24p. (J). pap. 3.50 (978-0-689-84540-6(5) , Simon Spotlight/Nickelodeon) Simon & Schuster Children's Publishing.

—My Book of Inventions. 2001. (ps-2). lib. bdg. 11.25 (978-0-613-43942-8(2)) Tandem Library Bks.

Berger, Melvin. Think Factory: Amazing Inventions. 2006. (Illus.). 47p. (*978-0-439-51913-7(6)) Scholastic, Inc.

Beshore, George W. Science in Ancient China. 1998. (Science of the Past Ser.). (Illus.). 64p. (J). (gr. 5-7). pap. 8.95 (978-0-531-15914-9(0) , Watts, Franklin) Scholastic Library Publishing.

—Science in Ancient China. 1998. (gr. 3-6). lib. bdg. 17.60 (978-0-613-72684-9(7)) Tandem Library Bks.

Bidder, Jane. Inventions We Use at Home. 2006. (Illus.). 32p. (J). lib. bdg. (978-0-8368-6898-2(6)) Stevens, Gareth Inc.

—Inventions We Use for Information & Entertainment. 2006. (Illus.). 32p. (J). lib. bdg. (978-0-8368-6899-9(4)) Stevens, Gareth Inc.

Bingham, Caroline & Dorling Kindersley Publishing Staff. Invention. 2005. (Eye Wonder Ser.). (Illus.). 48p. (J). 9.99 (978-0-7566-0619-0(5)) Dorling Kindersley Publishing, Inc.

Bridgman, Roger. How Nearly Everything Was Invented. Lazar, Ralph & Swerling, Lisa, illus. 2006. 64p. (J). 19.99 (978-0-7566-2077-6(5)) Dorling Kindersley Publishing, Inc.

—1,000 Inventions & Discoveries. 2006. (Illus.). 256p. (J). pap. 14.99 (978-0-7566-1705-9(7)) Dorling Kindersley Publishing, Inc.

Bridgman, Roger Francis. 1,000 Inventions & Discoveries. 2006. (Illus.). 256p. (J). (*978-1-4156-4955-8(3)) Dorling Kindersley Publishing, Inc.

Brown Reference Group. History of Invention Set. 2004. (History of Invention Ser.). 96-96p. (gr. 6-12). 280.00 (978-0-8160-5435-0(5)) Facts On File, Inc.

Brubaker, Elizabeth A. & Garmire, Diane Rowen. Inventing for Kids. 2003. 176p. (J). pap. 26.95 (978-1-56976-163-2(9) , Zephyr Pr.) Chicago Review Pr., Inc.

Campbell, Guy & Devins, Mark, compiled by. World's Most Amazing Inventions Facts for Kids. 2003. (World's Most Amazing Ser.). (Illus.). 112p. (J). pap. 3.99 (978-0-603-56099-6(7)) Egmont Bks., Ltd. GBR. *Dist:* Independent Pubs. Group.

Carlson, Laurie M. Queen of Inventions: How the Sewing Machine Changed the World. 2003. (Illus.). 32p. lib. bdg. 22.90 (978-0-7613-2706-6(1) , Millbrook Pr.) Lerner Publishing Group.

Casanellas, Antonio. Great Discoveries & Inventions, 5 bks. Garousi, Ali, illus. Incl. Great Discoveries & Inventions That Advanced Industry & Technology. lib. bdg. 24.67 (978-0-8368-2583-1(7)); Great Discoveries & Inventions That Helped Explore Earth & Space. lib. bdg. 24.67 (978-0-8368-2584-8(5)); Great Discoveries & Inventions That Improved Human Health. lib. bdg. 24.67 (978-0-8368-2585-5(3)); Great Discoveries & Inventions That Improved Our Daily Lives. lib. bdg. 24.67 (978-0-8368-2586-2(1)); Great Discoveries & Inventions That Improved Transportation. lib. bdg. 24.67 (978-0-8368-2587-9(X)); 32p. (J). (gr. 4 up). (Illus.). 2000. Set lib. bdg. 123.35 (978-0-8368-2582-4(9)) Stevens, Gareth Inc.

—Great Discoveries & Inventions That Advanced Industry & Technology. Garousi, Ali, illus. 2000. (Great Discoveries & Inventions Ser.). 32p. (J). (gr. 4 up). lib. bdg. 24.67 (978-0-8368-2583-1(7)) Stevens, Gareth Inc.

—Great Discoveries & Inventions That Improved Our Daily Lives. Garousi, Ali, illus. 2000. (Great Discoveries & Inventions Ser.). 32p. (J). (gr. 4 up). lib. bdg. 24.67 (978-0-8368-2586-2(1)) Stevens, Gareth Inc.

Casey, Susan. Kids Inventing! A Handbook for Young Inventors. 2005. (Illus.). 144p. (ps-7). pap. 14.95 (978-0-471-66086-6(8) , Wiley) Wiley, John & Sons, Inc.

—Women Invent: Two Centuries of Discoveries That Have Shaped Our World. 2003. (Illus.). 144p. (J). (gr. 4-8). pap. 14.95 (978-1-55652-317-5(3)) Chicago Review Pr., Inc.

Catala, Ellen. What Has Changed? 2005. (Yellow Umbrella Ser.). (Illus.). 17p. (978-0-7368-5271-5(9)); (978-0-7368-5307-1(3)) Capstone Pr., Inc.

Claybourne, Anna & Larkum, Adam. Story of Inventions. 2007. (Story of Inventions Ser.). 96p. (J). 10.99 (*978-0-7945-1710-6(2) , Usborne) EDC Publishing.

Clements, Gillian. The Picture History of the Great Inventors. Clements, Gillian, illus. 2005. (Illus.). 80p. (J). (gr. 3-17). pap., pap. 12.95 (978-1-84507-439-5(4)) Lincoln, Frances Ltd. GBR. *Dist:* Perseus Distribution.

Coppin, Brigitte. Inventing Our World. Gibson, Sarah et al, trs. 1998. (Discoveries Ser.). Orig. Title: The Great Inventions. (Illus.). 75p. (J). (gr. 2-9). lib. bdg. 23.95 (978-0-88682-948-3(8) , Creative Education) Creative Co., The.

Daynes, Katie. Toilets, Telephones & Other Useful Inventions. 2005. (Young Reading Series 1 Ser.). 48p. (J). (gr. 2 up). pap. 5.95 (978-0-7945-0888-3(X) , Usborne) EDC Publishing.

Deitch, JoAnne Weisman, ed. A Nation of Inventors. 2001. (Researching American History Ser.). (Illus.). 56p. (J). 7.95 (978-1-57960-077-8(8)) History Compass, LLC.

Deprisco, Dorothea. Inventions & Great Ideas. 2001. (Know-It-All Ser.). (Illus.). vii, 53p. (J). (978-0-439-20213-8(2)) Scholastic, Inc.

Dorling Kindersley Publishing Staff. Invention. 2005. (Eye Wonder Ser.). 48p. (J). lib. bdg. 17.99 (978-0-7566-0621-3(7)) Dorling Kindersley Publishing, Inc.

Dorn, Rebekah. The Sewing Machine. 2004. (Fact Finders Ser.). 32p. (J). lib. bdg. 22.60 (978-0-7368-2670-9(X)) Capstone Pr., Inc.

Douglas, Vincent & School Specialty Publishing Staff. Inventions & Discoveries. 2006. (Just the Facts Ser.). (Illus.). 64p. (J). (gr. 5-8). pap. 9.95 (978-0-7696-4256-7(X)) School Specialty Publishing.

Dowswell, Paul. Everyday Life. 2001. (Great Inventions Ser.). (Illus.). 48p. (YA). (gr. 6-8). lib. bdg. 25.64 (978-1-58810-212-6(2)) Heinemann Library.

—Transportation. 2001. (Great Inventions Ser.). (Illus.). 48p. (YA). (gr. 6-8). lib. bdg. 25.64 (978-1-58810-216-4(5)) Heinemann Library.

Draze, Dianne. Inventions, Inventors & You. 2005. 64p. (Orig.). 11.95 (978-1-59363-082-9(4)) Prufrock Pr.

Driscoll, Dan, et al. The Inventor's Times. Ashburn, Bryn & Shell, Christine, illus. 2003. 64p. (J). pap. 9.99 (978-0-439-38474-2(5) , Scholastic Paperbacks) Scholastic, Inc.

Early Inventions: Individual Title Six-Packs. (Rigby Focus Ser.). 24p. (gr. 2 up). 28.00 (978-0-7578-5356-2(0)); 30.00 (978-0-7578-5586-3(5)) Rigby Education.

Erlbach, Arlene. The Kids' Invention Book. 1999. (Kids' Ventures Ser.). (Illus.). 64p. (J). (gr. 3-6). pap. (978-0-8225-9844-2(2) , Lerner Pubns.) Lerner Publishing Group.

—The Kids' Invention Book. 1999. (978-0-606-22544-1(7)) Tandem Library Bks.

Ford, Barbara. Keeping Things Cool: Inventions That Changed Our Lives. (J). lib. bdg. 20.90 (978-0-8027-6616-8(1)) Walker & Co.

Frank, Marjorie Slavick, et al. Science Leveled Libraries: Inventing a Better Tomorrow. 3rd ed. 2002. (Harcourt Science Ser.). (gr. 4 up). pap. 25.60 (978-0-15-327277-6(5)) Harcourt Schl. Pubs.

Godwin, Beth. Livewire Investigates Australian Inventions. 2003. (Livewires Ser.). 32p. pap. 4.75 (978-0-521-53834-3(3)) Cambridge Univ. Pr.

Goldish, Meish. Inventions. 2002. (Illus.). 16p. (J). pap. (978-0-439-35136-2(7)) Scholastic, Inc.

Goldschlager, Amy. Inventions Science Experiment Log. Aycock, Daniel & Ward, Sam, illus. 2001. (Mad Science Ser.). 48p. (J). (978-0-439-22461-1(6)) Scholastic, Inc.

Gomez, Rebecca. Thomas Edison. 2003. (First Biographies Ser.). (Illus.). 32p. (J). (gr. k-4). lib. bdg. 22.78 (978-1-57765-945-7(7)) ABDO Publishing Co.

Great Inventions, 5 bks., Group 2. Incl. Airplane. Faber, Harold. 128p. (J). (gr. 3-7). lib. bdg. (978-0-7614-1876-4(8)); Automobile. Collier, James Lincoln. 112p. (J). (gr. 3-7). lib. bdg. (978-0-7614-1877-1(6)); Electricity & the Lightbulb. Collier, James Lincoln. 112p. (YA). (gr. 8-12). lib. bdg. (978-0-7614-1878-8(4)); Steam Engine. Collier, James Lincoln. 112p. (J). (gr. 8-12). lib. bdg. (978-0-7614-1880-1(6)); Telephone. Stefoff, Rebecca. 127p. (J). (gr. 8-12). lib. bdg. (978-0-7614-1879-5(2)); (Illus.). 2005. (978-0-7614-1875-7(X) , Benchmark Bks.) Cavendish, Marshall Corp.

Great Inventions Classroom Library. (gr. 2-5). lib. bdg. 34.95 (978-0-7368-4545-8(3)) Red Brick Learning.

Great Inventions Complete Unit. (gr. 2-5). 198.95 (978-0-7368-4544-1(5)) Red Brick Learning.

Great Inventions Group 3, 5 bks., Set. Incl. Medical Imaging. Sherrow, Victoria. 127p. lib. bdg. 39.93 (978-0-7614-2231-0(5)); Microscopes & Telescopes. Stefoff, Rebecca. 128p. lib. bdg. 39.93 (978-0-7614-2230-3(7)); Rockets. Otfinoski, Steven. 111p. lib. bdg. 39.93 (978-0-7614-2232-7(3)); Submarines. Stefoff, Rebecca. 127p. lib. bdg. 39.93 (978-0-7614-2229-7(3)); Television. Otfinoski, Steven. 111p. lib. bdg. 39.93 (978-0-7614-2228-0(5)); (Illus.). (J). 2006. 2007. Set lib. bdg. 199.64 (*978-0-7614-2227-3(7) , Benchmark Bks.) Cavendish, Marshall Corp.

Green, Jen. Medicine. 2004. (Routes of Science Ser.). (Illus.). 40p. (J). (gr. 4-7). 23.70 (978-1-4103-0168-0(0) , Blackbirch Pr., Inc.) Thomson Gale.

Happy Accidents!, 6 Pack. (Action Packs Ser.). 104p. (gr. 3-5). 44.00 (978-0-7635-3303-8(3)) Rigby Education.

Harcourt School Publishers Staff. Inventing a Better Tomorrow: Take-Home Book. 2001. (Collections Ser.). (Illus.). (J). pap. 1.90 (978-0-15-319498-6(7)) Harcourt Schl. Pubs.

—Inventors & Inventions. 3rd ed. 2002. (Horizons Ser.). (Illus.). (J). pap. 5.50 (978-0-15-333322-4(7)) Harcourt Schl. Pubs.

—The Mother of Invention: Take-Home Book. 2001. (Collections Ser.). (Illus.). (J). pap. 1.90 (978-0-15-319560-0(6)) Harcourt Schl. Pubs.

—Observe, Think, Try. 3rd ed. 2002. (Trophies English Language Learners Ser.). (Illus.). pap. 5.10 (978-0-15-327765-8(3)) Harcourt Schl. Pubs.

—Whose Bright Idea? 3rd ed. 2002. (Trophies English Language Learners Ser.). (Illus.). pap. 5.10 (978-0-15-327887-7(0)) Harcourt Schl. Pubs.

Harper, Charise Mericle. Imaginative Inventions: The Who, What, Where, When, & Why of Roller Skates, Potato Chips, Marbles, & Pie. Harper, Charise Mericle, illus. 2001. (Illus.). 32p. (J). (ps-3). 16.99 (978-0-316-34725-9(6)) Little, Brown Bks. for Young Readers.

Harris, David & Thomson, Russell. Who Invented That? 2005. (X-Zone Ser.). (Illus.). 30p. (gr. 4-8). 23.00 (978-0-7910-8980-4(0)) Facts On File, Inc.

Harrison, Peter. Inventions. 2000. (All about Ser.). (Illus.). 64p. (gr. 3-7). pap. 7.95 (978-1-84215-289-8(0) , Southwater) Anness Publishing GBR. *Dist:* National Bk. Network.

Harrison, Peter, et al. Great Inventions That Shaped the World. 2003. (Illustrated Science Encyclopedia Ser.). (Illus.). 264p. pap. 19.99 (978-0-7548-1265-4(0)) Anness Publishing GBR. *Dist:* National Bk. Network.

Haskins, Jim. Outward Dreams: Black Inventors & Their Inventions. 2003. (gr. 5-8). lib. bdg. 17.60 (978-0-613-75330-2(5)) Tandem Library Bks.

—Outward Dreams: Black Inventors & Their Inventions. 2003. (Illus.). 112p. (J). pap. 8.95 (978-0-8027-7673-0(6)) Walker & Co.

Haywood, John. Science & Technology. 2004. (Illus.). 64p. pap. 8.99 (978-1-84215-956-9(9) , Southwater) Anness Publishing GBR. *Dist:* National Bk. Network.

Hegedus, Alannah. Bleeps & Blips to Rocket Ships: Greant Investions in Communications. 2001. (gr. 3-6). lib. bdg. 28.00 (978-0-613-77267-9(9)) Tandem Library Bks.

Hegedus, Alannah, et al. Bleeps & Blips to Rocket Ships: Great Inventions in Communications. Slavin, Bill, illus. 2001. 88p. (J). (gr. 4 up). pap. 17.95 (978-0-88776-452-3(5)) Tundra Bks., Inc./Livres Toundra, Inc. CAN. *Dist:* Random Hse., Inc.

Henderson & Yount. Milestones in Discovery & Invention, 4 Vols., Set. 2006. 176p. (gr. 6-12). 140.00 (978-0-8160-7014-5(8)) Facts On File, Inc.

Hibbert, Clare & Dorling Kindersley Publishing Staff. Green Lantern's Book of Great Inventions. 2005. (Dk Readers Ser.). (Illus.). 48p. (J). 12.99 (978-0-7566-1012-8(5)); pap. 3.99 (978-0-7566-1013-5(3)) Dorling Kindersley Publishing, Inc.

Hills, Larry. The Bicycle. 2004. (Fact Finders Ser.). (Illus.). 32p. (J). (gr. 3-5). lib. bdg. 22.60 (978-0-7368-2668-6(8) , Fact Finders) Capstone Pr., Inc.

—The Camera. 2004. (Fact Finders Ser.). (Illus.). 32p. (J). (gr. 3-5). lib. bdg. 22.60 (978-0-7368-2669-3(6) , Fact Finders) Capstone Pr., Inc.

Houghton, Sarah. Inventions: Great Ideas & Where They Came From. 2002. (High Five Reading Ser.). (Illus.). 48p. (J). pap. (978-0-7368-9532-3(9)) Capstone Pr., Inc.

—Inventions: Great Ideas & Where They Came From, 6 vols. (gr. 4 up). 49.95 (978-0-7368-9543-9(4) , High Five) Red Brick Learning.

—Inventions: Great Ideas & Where They Came from. 2002. (High Five Reading Ser.). (Illus.). 48p. (J). (gr. 3-4). lib. bdg. 22.60 (978-0-7368-9554-5(X) , Capstone High-Interest Bks.) Capstone Pr., Inc.

How Ohio Helped Invent the World: From the Airplane to the Yo-Yo. 2001. 84p. (YA). per. 11.95 (978-0-9715702-0-7(5)) Dalton, Curt.

Inventions & Discoveries. (Action Bks.). 64p. (J). (gr. 3-7). pap. (978-1-882210-68-8(9)) Action Publishing, Inc.

Inventions That Shaped the World, 4 bks., Set. Incl. Camera. Trueit, Trudi Strain. 30.50 (978-0-531-12409-3(6)); Cotton Gin. Robinson Masters, Nancy. 30.50 (978-0-531-12406-2(1)); Microscope. Petersen, Christine. 30.50 (978-0-531-12408-6(8)); Telephone. Kummer, Patricia K. 30.50 (978-0-531-12407-9(X)); (Illus.). 80p. (J). (gr. 5-8). 2006. 2006. 122.00 (978-0-531-16826-4(3) , Watts, Franklin) Scholastic Library Publishing.

Inventions That Shaped the World: Introduce Readers to Revolutionary, Impactful Inventions, 4 Bks., Set. 2005. (YA). 118.00 (978-0-531-18753-1(5)); 2004. (J). 118.00 (978-0-531-19331-0(4) , Children's Pr.) Scholastic Library Publishing.

Inventors & Inventions - Group 2, 6 bks., Set. Incl. Biotechnology. Wells, Donna K. lib. bdg. 25.64 (978-0-7614-0046-2(X)); Nuclear Power. Holland, Gini. lib. bdg. 25.64 (978-0-7614-0047-9(8)); Radiology. Winkler, Kathy. lib. bdg. 25.64 (978-0-7614-0075-2(3)); Satellites. Fox, Mary Virginia. lib. bdg. 25.64 (978-0-7614-0049-3(4)); Television. Riehecky, Janet. lib. bdg. 25.64 (978-0-7614-0045-5(1)); Video. Biel, Jackie. lib. bdg. 25.64 (978-0-7614-0048-6(6)); 64p. (YA). (gr. 5-9). 1996. (Illus.). Set lib. bdg. 153.86 (978-0-7614-0044-8(3) , Benchmark Bks.) Cavendish, Marshall Corp.

Jango-Cohen, Judith. Ben Franklin's Big Shock. Lepp, Kevin, illus. 2006. (On My Own Science Ser.). 48p. (J). (gr. 2-4). 25.26 (978-1-57505-873-3(1) , Millbrook Pr.) Lerner Publishing Group.

Jedicke, Peter. Scientific American. 2007. (Scientific American Ser.). 72p. (J). (gr. 5-8). 30.00 (978-0-7910-9048-0(5) , Chelsea Hse.) Facts On File, Inc.

Jefferis, David. Machines & Inventions. 2002. (Young Library). (Illus.). 32p. (J). lib. bdg. 25.69 (978-0-7398-6323-7(1)) Raintree.

Kassinger, Ruth. Build a Better Mousetrap: Make Classic Inventions, Discover Your Problem-Solving Genius, & Take the Inventors' Challenge. 2002. (Illus.). 128p. pap. 14.95 (978-0-471-39538-6(2) , Wiley) Wiley, John & Sons, Inc.

—Reinvent the Wheel: Make Classic Inventions, Discover Your Problem-Solving Genius, & Take the Inventor's Challenge. 2001. (Illus.). 128p. pap. 14.95 (978-0-471-39539-3(0) , Wiley) Wiley, John & Sons, Inc.

Keener, Joan N. God Thought of It First. Petrova, Valeria, illus. 2006. 28p. (J). 14.99 (978-0-7847-1432-4(0) , 04016) Standard Publishing.

Konigsburg, E. L. Samuel Todd's Book of Great Inventions. ed. 2000. (J). (gr. 2). spiral bd. (978-0-616-03043-1(6)) Canadian National Institute for the Blind/Institut National Canadien pour les Aveugles.

—Samuel Todd's Book of Great Inventions. 1999. (gr. k-3). lib. bdg. 14.15 (978-0-613-22304-1(7)) Tandem Library Bks.

Larousse Kingfisher Chambers Staff & Madgwick, Wendy. Inventions. 2000. (Questions & Answers about... Ser.). (Illus.). 40p. (J). (gr. 4-6). pap. 7.95 (978-0-7534-5311-7(8) , Kingfisher) Houghton Mifflin Co. Trade & Reference Div.

Lethbridge, Lucy & Robinson, James. Inventions. 2006. (Kingfisher Knowledge Ser.). (Illus.). 64p. (J). (gr. 5-9). 12.95 (978-0-7534-5973-7(6) , Kingfisher) Houghton Mifflin Co. Trade & Reference Div.

Lucas, Debra. One Thing Leads to Another. 2003. (Science Links Ser.). (Illus.). 32p. (gr. 3-5). 23.00 (978-0-7910-7425-1(0) , Chelsea Hse.) Facts On File, Inc.

Lunis, Natalie. Household Inventions: From Toilets to Toasters. 2006. (Which Came First? Ser.). (Illus.). 32p. (J). lib. bdg. 25.27 (978-1-59716-131-2(4)) Bearport Publishing Co., Inc.

MacLeod, Jilly. Great Inventions. (Eyes on Adventure Ser.). 32p. (J). (gr. 1). pap. (978-1-882210-80-0(8)) Action Publishing, Inc.

Madgwick, Wendy. Inventions. 2000. (gr. 3-6). lib. bdg. 16.40 (978-0-613-90909-9(7)) Tandem Library Bks.

—Questions & Answers: Inventions. 2000. (J). (978-0-606-20872-7(0)) Tandem Library Bks.

Major Inventions Through History, 7 bks., Set. 2006. (J). (gr. 5-7). 61.95 (***978-0-8225-5822-4(X)***) Lerner Publishing Group.

Major Inventions Through History, 7 bks., Set. Incl. History of Communication. Woods, Michael & Woods, Mary B. (gr. 4-7). 26.60 (978-0-8225-3807-3(5)); History of Energy. Landau, Elaine. (gr. 3-7). 26.60 (978-0-8225-3806-6(7)); History of Food. Jango-Cohen, Judith. (ps-7). 26.60 (978-0-8225-2484-7(8)); History of Medicine. Woods, Michael & Woods, Mary B. (gr. 3-7). 26.60 (978-0-8225-2636-0(0)); History of Transportation. Herbst, Judith. (gr. 5-8). 26.60 (978-0-8225-2496-0(1)); History of Weapons. Herbst, Judith. (gr. 3-7). 26.60 (978-0-8225-3805-9(9)); (Illus.). 56p. (J). 2006. 186.20 (978-0-8225-2475-5(9) , Twenty-First Century Bks.) Lerner Publishing Group.

Mara, Wil. Clock. 2006. 80p. (YA). (gr. 5-8). pap. 9.95 (978-0-531-16743-4(7) , Watts, Franklin) Scholastic Library Publishing.

Maule, David. Inventions That Changed the World: Level 4 Book. 2005. (Illus.). 64p. (C). pap. 9.00 (***978-0-582-85489-5(X)***) Pearson ESL.

Mercury Books, creator. Age of New Ideas. (Crafty Inventions Ser.). (Illus.). 48p. (J). (ps-9). 12.95 (978-1-904668-71-8(2)) Mercury Bks. Ltd. GBR. *Dist:* International Publishers Marketing.

—Early Discoveries. (Crafty Inventions Ser.). (Illus.). 48p. (J). (ps-9). 12.95 (978-1-904668-70-1(4)) Mercury Bks. Ltd. GBR. *Dist:* International Publishers Marketing.

—Expanding World. (Crafty Inventions Ser.). (Illus.). 48p. (J). (ps-9). 12.95 (978-1-904668-72-5(0)) Mercury Bks. Ltd. GBR. *Dist:* International Publishers Marketing.

—Into the Future. (Crafty Inventions Ser.). (Illus.). 48p. (J). (ps-9). 12.95 (978-1-904668-73-2(9)) Mercury Bks. Ltd. GBR. *Dist:* International Publishers Marketing.

—Long Long Ago. (Crafty Inventions Ser.). (Illus.). 48p. (J). (ps). 12.95 (978-1-904668-68-8(2)) Mercury Bks. Ltd. GBR. *Dist:* International Publishers Marketing.

—Working Things Out. (Crafty Inventions Ser.). (Illus.). 48p. (J). (ps-9). 12.95 (978-1-904668-69-5(0)) Mercury Bks. Ltd. GBR. *Dist:* International Publishers Marketing.

Mom, Science. The Science in Your Shoes: And 49 Other Places in a Kid's Everyday Life. Mom, Science & Girl, Science, illus. 1999. 12p. (J). (gr. 3-6). pap. 10.95 (978-0-9659630-2-2(0)) Tomorrow's Girl.

Morrison, Ian. Skiing in the Desert: Asian Innovation. 2007. (Shockwave: Science in Practice Ser.). (Illus.). 36p. (J). (gr. 4-6). lib. bdg. 25.00 (***978-0-531-17583-5(9)*** , Children's Pr.) Scholastic Library Publishing.

Norman, Penny. Science One Two Three Inventions. Einstein, Ann, ed. 2005. 32p. 15.95 (978-1-886978-67-6(0)) Norman & Globus, Inc.

Orr, Tamra. Steam Engine. 2006. 80p. (YA). (gr. 5-8). pap. 9.95 (978-0-531-16724-3(0) , Watts, Franklin) Scholastic Library Publishing.

Osborne, J. E. Inventions. Date not set. (Early Science Big Bks.). (Illus.). 16p. (J). (ps-2). pap. 16.95 (978-1-58273-117-9(9)) Sundance/Newbridge Educational Publishing.

Oxlade, Chris. The Inside & Out Guide to Inventions. 2006. (Inside & Out Guides Ser.). (Illus.). 32p. (J). pap. (978-1-4034-9092-6(9)); lib. bdg. (978-1-4034-9085-8(6)) Heinemann Library.

—Inventions. 2003. (Knowledge Masters Ser.). (Illus.). 32p. (YA). pap. incl. cd-rom (978-1-903954-59-1(2)) Chrysalis Children's Bks.

—Inventions & Machines: The Changing World. 2005. (Illus.). 128p. pap. 17.99 (978-1-84476-059-6(6) , Southwater) Anness Publishing GBR. *Dist:* National Bk. Network.

Packard, Mary. High-Tech Inventions: A Chapter Book. 2005. (True Tales Ser.). (Illus.). 48p. (J). (gr. 2-4). pap. 4.95 (978-0-516-24684-0(4) , Children's Pr.) Scholastic Library Publishing.

Parker, Steve. 1900-20: A Shrinking World. 2001. (Twentieth Century Science & Technology Ser.). (Illus.). 32p. (J). (gr. 5 up). lib. bdg. 26.00 (978-0-8368-2942-6(5)) Stevens, Gareth Inc.

—1920-40: Atoms to Automation. 2001. (Twentieth Century Science & Technology Ser.). (Illus.). 32p. (J). (gr. 5 up). lib. bdg. 26.00 (978-0-8368-2943-3(3)) Stevens, Gareth Inc.

—1940-60: The Nuclear Age. 2001. (Twentieth Century Science & Technology Ser.). (Illus.). 32p. (J). (gr. 5 up). lib. bdg. 26.00 (978-0-8368-2944-0(1)) Stevens, Gareth Inc.

—1960s: Space & Time. 2001. (Twentieth Century Science & Technology Ser.). (Illus.). 32p. (J). (gr. 5 up). lib. bdg. 26.00 (978-0-8368-2945-7(X)) Stevens, Gareth Inc.

—1970-90: Computers & Chips. 2001. (Twentieth Century Science & Technology Ser.). (Illus.). 32p. (J). (gr. 5 up). lib. bdg. 26.00 (978-0-8368-2946-4(8)) Stevens, Gareth Inc.

—1990-2000: The Electronic Age. 2001. (Twentieth Century Science & Technology Ser.). (Illus.). 32p. (J). (gr. 5 up). lib. bdg. 26.00 (978-0-8368-2947-1(6)) Stevens, Gareth Inc.

Perry, Andrea J. Here's What You Do When You Can't Find Your Shoe. Snow, Alan, illus. 2003. 40p. (J). (gr. k-3). 16.95 (978-0-689-83067-9(X) , Atheneum) Simon & Schuster Children's Publishing.

Platt, Richard. Eureka! Great Inventions & How They Happened. 2003. (Illus.). 96p. (J). (gr. 5-9). tchr. ed. 18.95 (978-0-7534-5580-7(3) , Kingfisher) Houghton Mifflin Co. Trade & Reference Div.

Play Bac Edu-Team, ed. Inventions: From Rocks to Rockets. 2007. (Illus.). 10p. (Orig.). (J). 6.95 (***978-1-60214-008-0(1)***) Play Bac Publishing, USA.

Puzzle Track Staff, ed. Around the World Adv. 2007. (Puzzle Track Ser.). 20p. (J). bds. 18.95 (***978-0-7696-5589-5(0)***) School Specialty Publishing.

Reid, Struan, tr. Inventions & Trade. 2002. (World Issues Ser.). (Illus.). 43p. (J). lib. bdg. 28.50 (978-1-931983-33-4(X)) Chrysalis Education.

Richter, Joanne. Inventing the Camera. 2006. (Breakthrough Inventions Ser.). (Illus.). 32p. (J). (gr. 3-9). pap. (978-0-7787-2836-8(6)) Crabtree Publishing Co.

Ring, Susan. Nature Did It First. 2003. (Science Links Ser.). (Illus.). 32p. (gr. 3-5). 23.00 (978-0-7910-7427-5(7) , Chelsea Hse.) Facts On File, Inc.

Ross, Frank. Oracle Bones, Stars, & Wheelbarrows: Ancient Chinese Science & Technology. (gr. 5-8). lib. bdg. 15.25 (978-0-8335-6082-7(4)) Tandem Library Bks.

Rossi, Ann. The Age of Inventions. 2002. (Illus.). 40p. (J). (978-0-7922-8696-7(0)) National Geographic Society.

Schonberg, Marcia. I Is for Idea: An Inventions Alphabet. Radzinski, Kandy, illus. 2005. (National Alphabet Bks.). 48p. (J). (gr. k-5). 16.95 (978-1-58536-257-8(3)) Sleeping Bear Pr.

Science Stories Foss Spanish Ideas & Inventions EA CR05. 2005. (J). (978-1-59242-588-4(7)) Delta Education, LLC.

Shuter, Jane. Discoveries & Inventions. 1999. (Ancient Egypt Ser.). 32p. (J). (gr. 3-5). lib. bdg. 22.79 (978-1-57572-729-5(3)) Heinemann Library.

—Discoveries, Inventions & Ideas. 1999. (Ancient Greece Ser.). (Illus.). 32p. (J). lib. bdg. 22.79 (978-1-57572-739-4(0)) Heinemann Library.

Sobey, Edwin J. C. How to Enter & Win an Invention Contest. 1999. (Science Fair Success Ser.). (Illus.). 104p. (YA). (gr. 6-12). lib. bdg. 26.60 (978-0-7660-1173-1(9)) Enslow Pubs., Inc.

—Inventing Toys: Kids Having Fun Learning Science. Miller, Levi, illus. 2001. 144p. (J). (gr. 4-8). pap. 24.95 (978-1-56976-124-3(8) , 1121, Zephyr Pr.) Chicago Review Pr., Inc.

St. George, Judith. So You Want to Be an Inventor? Small, David, illus. 2002. 56p. (J). 16.99 (978-0-399-23593-1(0) , Philomel) Penguin Group (USA) Inc.

—So You Want to Be an Inventor? Small, David, illus. 2005. 56p. (J). pap. 7.99 (978-0-14-240460-7(8) , Puffin) Penguin Group (USA) Inc.

Steck-Vaughn Staff. Ancient Inventions: Ahead of Their Time. 2002. pap. (978-0-7398-6156-1(5)) Steck-Vaughn.

—Darren Swayne Debaker/Amazing Inventions. 2002. (J). pap. (978-0-7398-6155-4(7)) Steck-Vaughn.

Stevens, Ian. Amazing Inventions. 2005. (Top Tens Ser.). (Illus.). 32p. (J). (gr. 3-7). lib. bdg. 25.27 (978-1-59716-067-4(9)) Bearport Publishing Co., Inc.

Taylor, Barbara. I Wonder Why Zippers Have Teeth: And Other Questions about Inventions. 2003. (I Wonder Why Ser.). 32p. (J). (gr. k-3). pap. 6.95 (978-0-7534-5665-1(6) , Kingfisher) Houghton Mifflin Co. Trade & Reference Div.

Thompson, Lisa. Inventing the Future. 2006. (Real Deal - Yellow Ser.). (Illus.). 32p. (J). (gr. 4-8). 19.00 (978-0-7910-9062-6(0)) Facts On File, Inc.

Tomecek, Stephen M. What a Great Idea! Inventions That Changed the World. Stuckenschneider, Dan, illus. 2003. 112p. (J). (gr. 4-9). pap. 18.95 (978-0-590-68144-5(3) , Scholastic Reference) Scholastic, Inc.

Top That Publishing Staff, ed. Inventions. 2004. (Know How Know Why Ser.). (Illus.). 48p. (J). pap. (978-1-84510-030-8(1)) Top That! Publishing PLC.

Townsend, John. Outrageous Inventions. 2006. (Illus.). 56p. (J). pap. (978-1-4109-2384-4(3)); lib. bdg. (978-1-4109-2379-0(7)) Steck-Vaughn.

Trueit, Trudi Strain. Gunpowder. 2006. 80p. (YA). (gr. 5-8). pap. 9.95 (978-0-531-16744-1(5) , Watts, Franklin) Scholastic Library Publishing.

Ubac, Claire. Brilliant & Crazy Inventions. 1999. (Megascope Ser.). (Illus.). 64p. (J). (gr. 5-9). 6.95 (978-0-7641-5183-5(5)) Barron's Educational Series, Inc.

Unlocking the Secrets of Science, 40 Bks, Set. (Illus.). (gr. 4-10). lib. bdg. (978-1-58415-255-2(9)) Mitchell Lane Pubs., Inc.

Vogt, Greg & Shearer, Deborah. Robotix Workshop: An Inventor's Kit. 2002. (Discovery Kit Ser.). (Illus.). 64p. (J). pap. 19.95 (978-0-7624-1326-3(3) , Running Pr. Kids) Running Pr. Bk. Pubs.

Watts, Claire & Nicholson, Robert. Incredible Inventions. 2000. (Info Adventure Ser.). (Illus.). 32p. (J). (gr. 3-6). pap. 3.95 (978-1-58728-109-9(0) , Two Can Publishing) T&N Children's Publishing.

Which Came First? 2006. (Which Came First? Ser.). (J). lib. bdg. 143.76 (978-1-59716-134-3(9)) Bearport Publishing Co., Inc.

Williams, Brian. Science. 2001. (Great Inventions Ser.). (Illus.). 48p. (YA). (gr. 6-8). lib. bdg. 25.64 (978-1-58810-214-0(9)) Heinemann Library.

Woodford, Chris, et al. Cool Stuff & How It Works. Jones, Kevin, illus. 2005. 256p. (J). (gr. 8-7). 24.99 (978-0-7566-1465-2(1)) Dorling Kindersley Publishing, Inc.

Wulffson, Don. Toys! Amazing Stories Behind Some Great Inventions. Keller, Laurie, illus. rev. ed. 2000. 144p. (J). (gr. 3-7). 16.95 (978-0-8050-6196-3(7) , Holt, Henry & Co. Bks. For Young Readers) Holt, Henry & Co.

Wulffson, Don L. Kid Who Invented the Popsicle: And Other Surprising Stories about Inventions. 1999. 128p. (J). (gr. 3-7). pap. 5.99 (978-0-14-130204-1(6) , Puffin) Penguin Group (USA) Inc.

—Kid Who Invented the Popsicle & Other Extraordinary Stories Behind Everyday Th. 1999. (gr. 3-6). lib. bdg. 13.00 (978-0-613-17816-7(5)) Tandem Library Bks.

—The Kid Who Invented the Popsicle & Other Extraordinary Stories Behind Everyday Things. 1999. (J). (978-0-606-16835-9(4)) Tandem Library Bks.

Wyatt, Valerie. Inventions. Fernandes, Matthew, illus. 2004. (FAQ Ser.). 40p. (J). (gr. 4-6). (978-1-55337-404-6(5)); (978-1-55337-403-9(7)) Kids Can Pr., Ltd.

—Inventions. 2003. (gr. 3-6). lib. bdg. 15.25 (978-0-613-84967-8(1)) Tandem Library Bks.

Young Discovery Library, 6 bks. (Illus.). (J). (gr. k-6). lib. bdg. 17.94 (978-1-56674-941-1(7)) Forest Hse. Publishing Co., Inc.

Your Little Black Book on African American Inventions & Inventors. 2006. (J). per. 9.95 (***978-0-9791883-0-5(X)***) Disciple One Publishing.

Zdrok, Jodie L. 1880-1900 (Events That Changed the World) 2004. (gr. 10-12). 22.45 (978-0-7377-2038-9(7) , Greenhaven Pr., Inc.) Thomson Gale.

INVENTIONS—FICTION

Alger Jr. Horatio Staff. Herbert Carter's Legacy. rev. ed. 2006. 264p. 28.95 (978-1-4218-1756-9(X)); pap. 13.95 (978-1-4218-1856-6(6)) 1st World Publishing, Inc. (1st World Library - Literary Society).

Anholt, Laurence. Leonardo & the Flying Boy. 2007. (Anholt's Artists Books for Children Ser.). 32p. (J). (ps-3). pap. 7.99 (***978-0-7641-3851-5(0)***) Barron's Educational Series, Inc.

—Leonardo & the Flying Boy: A Story about Leonardo da Vinci. 2000. (Illus.). 32p. (J). (ps-2). 15.99 (978-0-7641-5225-2(4)) Barron's Educational Series, Inc.

—Leonardo y el Aprendiz Volador: Un Cuento Sobre Leonardo Da Vinci. 2000. Tr. of Leonardo & the Flying Boy. (CAT., Illus.). 30p. (J). (gr. 3-5). 14.95 (978-84-95040-79-4(4)) Serres, Ediciones, S. L. ESP. *Dist:* Lectorum Pubns., Inc.

Appleton, Victor. Tom Swift & His Great Searchlight or O. 2006. pap. (***978-1-4065-0903-8(5)***) Dodo Pr.

Baker, Keith. On the Go with Mr. & Mrs. Green. 2007. (Mr. & Mrs. Green Ser.). (Illus.). 72p. (J). pap. 5.95 (978-0-15-205867-8(2) , Harcourt Paperbacks) Harcourt Children's Bks.

—On the Go with Mr. & Mrs. Green. 2006. (Mr. & Mrs. Green Ser.). (Illus.). 72p. (J). 16.00 (978-0-15-205762-6(5)) Harcourt Trade Pubs.

—On the Go with Mr. & Mrs. Green. 2007. (Mr. & Mrs. Green Ser.). 72p. (J). (gr. 2-4). 27.07 (***978-1-59961-303-1(4)***) Spotlight.

Ballard, Mignon F. Aunt Matilda's Ghost. 2000. (Illus.). vii, 136p. (J). 22.50 (978-1-57072-116-8(5)); pap. 12.50 (978-1-57072-132-8(7)) Overmountain Pr.

Carney, Mary Lou. Dr Welch & the Great Grape Story. Meidell, Sherry, illus. 2004. 32p. (J). 16.95 (978-1-59078-039-8(6)) Boyds Mills Pr.

Clancy, Tom. Safe House. 2000. (gr. 7-12). lib. bdg. 13.00 (978-0-613-33493-8(0)) Tandem Library Bks.

Cross, Gillian. Sam Sorts It Out. Mier, Colin, illus. 2005. 24p. (J). lib. bdg. 22.65 (***978-1-59646-702-6(9)***) Dingles & Co.

Davies, Tristan & Newman, Nick. Wallace & Gromit: Anoraknophobia. 1998. (Wallace & Gromit Comic Strip Bks.). (Illus.). 48p. (J). 9.95 (978-0-8417-2031-2(2)) Adler's Foreign Bks., Inc.

Downing, Wick. Leonardo's Hand. 2001. (Illus.). 208p. (J). (gr. 5-9). tchr. ed. 15.00 (978-0-618-07893-6(2)) Houghton Mifflin Co. Trade & Reference Div.

Dubowski, Cathy East. Flubber. 2000. (SPA., Illus.). (J). pap. 9.95 (978-84-406-8184-3(4)) Ediciones B ESP. *Dist:* Distribooks, Inc.

Duffey, Betsy. The Gadget War. Wilson, Janet, illus. 2000. 80p. (J). (gr. 2-5). pap. 4.99 (978-0-14-130708-4(0) , Puffin) Penguin Group (USA) Inc.

Feinman, Myke. In Search of the First Teddy Bear. Feinman, Anthony, photos by. 2002. (Illus.). 16p. (J). 4.95 (978-0-9664974-4-1(9)) Ink & Feathers Comics.

Geisert, Arthur. Lights Out. 2005. (Illus.). 32p. (J). (gr. k-3). 16.00 (978-0-618-47892-7(2) , Walter Lorraine) Houghton Mifflin Co. Trade & Reference Div.

Greenburg, J. C. In the Kitchen. 2002. (Andrew Lost Ser.: Bk. 3). (Illus.). 96p. (J). (gr. 2-5). lib. bdg. 11.99 (978-0-375-91279-5(7) , Random Hse. Bks. for Young Readers) Random Hse. Children's Bks.

—In the Kitchen. Palen, Debbie, illus. 2002. (Andrew Lost Ser.: Bk. 3). 96p. (J). (gr. 2-5). pap. 3.99 (978-0-375-81279-8(2) , Random Hse. Bks. for Young Readers) Random Hse. Children's Bks.

—In the Kitchen. 2002. (Andrew Lost Ser.: Bk. 3). (J). (gr. 3-6). lib. bdg. 11.80 (978-0-613-86248-6(1)) Tandem Library Bks.

—In Time. Gerardi, Jan, illus. 2004. (Andrew Lost Ser.: Bk. 9). 96p. (J). (gr. 2-5). pap. 3.99 (978-0-375-82949-9(0)); 9th ed. lib. bdg. 11.99 (978-0-375-92949-6(5)) Random Hse. Children's Bks. (Random Hse. Bks. for Young Readers).

—In Time. Gerardi, Jan, illus. 2004. (Andrew Lost Ser.: Bk. 9). 80p. (J). (gr. 2-5). lib. bdg. 11.19 (978-0-606-32799-2(1)) Tandem Library Bks.

—On Earth. Gerardi, Jan, illus. 2005. (Andrew Lost Ser.: Bk. 10). 96p. (J). (gr. 2-4). 10th ed. pap. 3.99 (978-0-375-82950-5(4)); No. 10. lib. bdg. 11.99 (978-0-375-92950-2(9)) Random Hse. Children's Bks. (Random Hse. Bks. for Young Readers).

—On Earth. Gerardi, Jan, illus. 2005. (Andrew Lost Ser.: Bk.. 10). 85p. (J). (gr. 2-4). lib. bdg. 11.19 (978-0-606-33239-2(1)) Tandem Library Bks.

—On the Dog. Palen, Debbie, illus. 2002. (Andrew Lost Ser.: Bk. 1). 96p. (J). (gr. 1-4). pap. 3.99 (978-0-375-81277-4(6) , Random Hse. Bks. for Young Readers) Random Hse. Children's Bks.

—On the Dog. 2002. (Andrew Lost Ser.: Bk. 1). (J). (ps-2). lib. bdg. 11.80 (978-0-613-50405-8(4)) Tandem Library Bks.

—On the Reef. Reed, Mike, tr. Reed, Mike & Gerardi, Jan, illus. 2004. (Andrew Lost Ser.: Bk. 7). 96p. (J). (gr. 2-5). pap. 3.99 (978-0-375-82525-5(8) , Random Hse. Bks. for Young Readers) Random Hse. Children's Bks.

—Under Water. Reed, Mike, illus. 2003. (Andrew Lost Ser.: Bk. 5). 96p. (J). (gr. 2-5). mass mkt. 3.99 (978-0-375-82523-1(1) , Random Hse. Bks. for Young Readers) Random Hse. Children's Bks.

Hall / Watts. Mortimer Jones: The Bubble Gum Nerd, 1. l.t. ed. 2003. (Illus.). 32p. 19.95 (978-0-9741774-2-7(3)) D. W. Publishing.

Harcourt School Publishers Staff. The Best Invention Ever Below Level. 3rd ed. 2002. (Trophies Reading Program Ser.). (Illus.). (gr. 6). pap. 5.10 (978-0-15-323401-9(6)) Harcourt Schl. Pubs.

Harlen, Jonathan. Brain Scam. 2004. (Illus.). 204p. (Orig.). (J). pap. 7.95 (978-1-86508-687-3(8)) Allen & Unwin AUS. *Dist:* Independent Pubs. Group.

Hicks, Clifford B. Alvin Fernald Foreign Trader. Schluenderfritz, Theodore, illus. 2007. (J). pap. 11.95 (***978-1-883937-74-4(4)***) Bethlehem Bks.

Hicks, Clifford B. The Marvelous Inventions of Alvin Fernald. Geer, Charles, illus. 2006. 119p. (J). 16.95 (978-1-930900-21-9(X)) Purple Hse. Pr.

Hoban, Russell. A Near Thing for Captain Najork. Blake, Quentin, illus. 2006. 32p. (J). pap. (***978-1-56792-323-0(2)***) Godine, David R. Pub.

Hughes, Carol. Dirty Magic. 2006. (Illus.). 432p. (J). (gr. 4-9). 17.95 (978-0-375-83187-4(8)); (gr. 5-8). lib. bdg. 19.99 (978-0-375-93187-1(2)) Random Hse. Children's Bks. (Random Hse. Bks. for Young Readers).

—Dirty Magic. 2008. (Illus.). 432p. (J). (gr. 5-9). 5.99 (978-0-375-83188-1(6)) Random Hse., Inc.

Hutchins, Hazel J. TJ & the Rockets. 2004. (Orca Young Readers Ser.). (Illus.). 144p. (J). (gr. 3-6). pap., tchr. ed. 4.99 (978-1-55143-300-4(1) , 1234543) Orca Bk. Pubs. USA.

Joyce, William. Sleepy Time Olie. Joyce, William, illus. 2001. (Rolie Polie Olie Ser.). (Illus.). 40p. (J). (ps-3). 15.95 (978-0-06-029613-1(5) , Geringer, Laura Book) HarperCollins Pubs.

—Sleepy Time Olie. 2001. (Rolie Polie Olie Ser.). (Illus.). 40p. (J). (ps-3). 15.89 (978-0-06-029614-8(3) , Geringer, Laura Book) HarperCollins Pubs.

—Sleepy Time Olie. Joyce, William, illus. 2006. (Rolie Polie Olie Ser.). 40p. (J). pap. 6.99 (978-0-06-084222-2(9) , Harper Trophy) HarperCollins Pubs.

Kerr, Bob. Mechanical Harry. Kerr, Bob, illus. 1999. (Illus.). 28p. (J). (gr. 2 up). lib. bdg. 23.33 (978-0-8368-2248-9(X)) Stevens, Gareth Inc.

Kidd, Ronald. Undercover Kid: Comic Book King. Sklar, Andy, illus. 2007. (All Aboard Mystery Reader Ser.). 48p. (J). pap. 3.99 (*978-0-448-44438-3(0) , Grosset & Dunlap) Penguin Group (USA) Inc.

Kimpton, Diana. Edison's Fantastic Phonograph. Robertson, M. P., illus. 2004. 32p. (J). pap. 7.95 (978-1-84507-262-9(6)) Lincoln, Frances Ltd. GBR. *Dist:* Perseus Distribution.

Lennon, Joan. There's a Kangaroo in My Soup! Rasmussen, Wendy, illus. 2000. 128p. (J). (gr. 1-4). 16.95 (978-0-8126-2898-2(5)) Cricket Bks.

Lewison, Wendy Cheyette. Easter Bunny's Amazing Egg Machine. 2002. (ps-2). lib. bdg. 10.95 (978-0-613-83538-1(7)) Tandem Library Bks.

Liberto, Lorenzo, et al. Matt the Rat's Incredible Creations / Las Creaciones Increíbles de Raton Mateo. Torres, Irving, illus. 2004. (ENG & SPA.). 32p. (J). lib. bdg. 20.00 (978-0-9743668-3-8(8)) Harvest Sun Pr., LLC.

McCall, Bruce. Marveltown Forever. 2008. (J). (*978-0-374-39925-2(5)) Farrar, Straus & Giroux.

McGough, Roger. Dotty Inventions: And Some Real Ones Too! Swain, Holly, illus. 2004. 32p. (J). 15.95 (978-1-84507-036-6(4)) Lincoln, Frances Ltd. GBR. *Dist:* Perseus Distribution.

Montgomery, Claire & Montgomery, Monte. Hubert Invents the Wheel. Shelly, Jeff, illus. 2005. 192p. (J). (gr. 4-7). 16.95 (978-0-8027-8990-7(0)) Walker & Co.

Moore, Ulysses. Isle of Masks. 2008. (Ulysses Moore Book Ser.). 256p. (J). 5.99 (*978-0-439-77671-4(6) , Scholastic Paperbacks) Scholastic, Inc.

Oppel, Kenneth. Skybreaker. (J). 2007. 560p. (gr. 7 up). pap. 6.99 (978-0-06-053229-1(7)); 2005. (Illus.). 384p. (gr. 6-10). 16.99 (978-0-06-053227-7(0)); 2005. (Illus.). 384p. (gr. 6-10). lib. bdg. 17.89 (978-0-06-053228-4(9)) HarperCollins Pubs.

Parent, Nancy. Treasure House. 2000. (Captain Kangaroo Ser.). 32p. (J). (gr. k-1). pap. 3.99 (978-0-06-107158-4(7) , Harper Entertainment) HarperCollins Pubs.

The Perfect Person, 6 Packs. (Bookweb Ser.). 32p. (gr. 4 up). 34.00 (978-0-7635-3734-0(9)) Rigby Education.

The Perfect Pet, 6 Packs. (Bookweb Ser.). 32p. (gr. 5 up). 34.00 (978-0-7635-3781-4(0)) Rigby Education.

Preller, James. The Case of the Million Dollar Mystery. 2002. (Jigsaw Jones Mystery Super Special Ser.: No. 2). (Illus.). 112p. (J). (gr. 1-5). pap. 3.99 (978-0-439-42629-9(4) , Scholastic Paperbacks) Scholastic, Inc.

—Case of the Million Dollar Mystery. 2002. (gr. 3-6). lib. bdg. 11.80 (978-0-613-63267-6(2)) Tandem Library Bks.

Prince, Sarah. Sherman Shrinker. 2001. (gr. k-3). lib. bdg. 11.65 (978-0-613-33429-7(9)) Tandem Library Bks.

Stewart, Paul & Riddell, Chris. Far-Flung Adventures: Fergus Crane. 2006. (Illus.). 240p. (J). (gr. 3-7). 14.95 (978-0-385-75088-2(9) , Fickling, David Bks.) Random Hse. Children's Bks.

Stine, R.L. Punk'd & Skunked. Park, Trip, illus. 2007. 108p. (J). pap. (*978-0-06-078832-2(1)) HarperCollins Pubs.

Thompson, Lisa. Look Out! Thompson, Lisa & Stapleton, Matthew, illus. 2005. (Read-It! Chapter Bks.). 48p. (J). (ps-k). lib. bdg. 19.95 (978-1-4048-1343-4(8)) Picture Window Bks.

—What's Next? Thompson, Lisa & Stapleton, Matthew, illus. 2005. (Read-It! Chapter Bks.). 48p. (J). (ps-k). lib. bdg. 19.95 (978-1-4048-1350-2(0)) Picture Window Bks.

—Wild Ideas. Thompson, Lisa & Stapleton, Matthew, illus. 2005. (Read-It! Chapter Bks.). 48p. (J). (ps-k). lib. bdg. 19.95 (978-1-4048-1346-5(2)) Picture Window Bks.

Villeneuve, Mireille. Felicio's Incredible Invention. Villeneuve, Anne, illus. 2005. (Read-It! Readers Ser.). 32p. (J). (gr. k-3). 18.60 (978-1-4048-1030-3(7)) Picture Window Bks.

—Felicio's Incredible Invention. 2000. (gr. k-3). lib. bdg. 14.10 (978-0-613-25149-5(0)) Tandem Library Bks.

Villeneuve, Mireille, et al. Felicio's Incredible Invention. 2000. (Illus.). 32p. (J). (ps-3). pap. (978-1-894363-39-6(6)) Dominique & Friends.

Willson, Sarah. Perfect Formula. 1999. (gr. 3-6). lib. bdg. 11.80 (978-0-613-15939-5(X)) Tandem Library Bks.

Younger, Marshal. The Last Days of Eugene Meltsner. 2000. (Adventures in Odyssey Ser.). (Illus.). 96p. (J). (gr. 3-7). pap. 4.99 (978-1-56179-911-4(4)) Focus on the Family Publishing.

—The Last Days of Eugene Meltsner. 2000. (Adventures in Odyssey Ser.). (Illus.). (J). pap. (978-0-8423-4048-9(3)) Tyndale Hse. Pubs.

INVENTORS

see also Inventions

Abbey, Cherie D., ed. Biography Today: Profiles of People of Interest to Young Readers. (Scientists & Inventors Ser.: Vol. 9). 2004. (J). (gr. 3 up). lib. bdg. (978-0-7808-0711-2(1)); 2003. (YA). lib. bdg. (978-0-7808-0656-6(5)); 2002. 200p. (YA). lib. bdg. (978-0-7808-0636-8(0)); 2002. 200p. (YA). lib. bdg. (978-0-7808-0514-9(3)) Omnigraphics, Inc.

Adams, Colleen. Benjamin Franklin: American Inventor. 2002. (Reading Room Collection). (Illus.). 24p. (J). lib. bdg. 18.75 (978-0-8239-3745-5(3)) Rosen Publishing Group, Inc., The.

Adler, David A. B. Franklin, Printer. 2001. (Illus.). 136p. (J). (gr. 4-6). tchr. ed. 19.95 (978-0-8234-1675-2(5)) Holiday Hse., Inc.

African-American Inventors. 2000. (My Ancestors—My Heroes Ser.: Vol. 8). (J). (gr. 3-4). (978-1-893091-07-8(4)) Parker Publishing Co.

Aldrich, Lisa J. Nikola Tesla & the Taming of Electricity. 2005. (Profiles in Science Ser.). (Illus.). 160p. (J). (ps-7). lib. bdg. 26.95 (978-1-931798-46-4(X)) Reynolds, Morgan Inc.

Aller, Susan Bivin. George Eastman. 2004. (History Maker Bios Ser.). (Illus.). 48p. (J). (gr. 3-5). lib. bdg. 26.60 (978-0-8225-0200-5(3)) Lerner Publishing Group.

Alter, Judy. Samuel F. B. Morse: Inventor & Code Creator. 2003. (Spirit of America: Our People Ser.). (Illus.). 32p. (J). (gr. 2-6). 27.07 (978-1-56766-446-1(6)) Child's World, Inc.

Auch, Allison. Personalidades electrizantes & Electrifying Personalities. 2005. spiral bd. 84.00 (*978-1-4108-5713-2(1)) Benchmark Education Co.

Bailey, Gerry. The Top Ten Inventors. Boulter, Steve & Smith, Jan, illus. 2005. (Crafty Inventions Ser.). 48p. (C). (gr. 4-6). 26.60 (978-1-4048-1046-4(3)) Picture Window Bks.

Baker, Henry E. American Black Inventors Pictorials Drawings & Illustrations Volume I. 2007. (Illus.). 369p. (YA). lib. bdg. (978-1-892824-30-1(2) , AFCHRON-.COM) AFCHRON.

Bankston, John. Alexander Graham Bell & the Story of the Telephone. 2004. (Uncharted, Unexplored, & Unexplained Ser.). (Illus.). 48p. (J). (gr. 4-8). lib. bdg. 29.95 (978-1-58415-243-9(5)) Mitchell Lane Pubs., Inc.

—Karl Benz & the Single Cylinder Engine. 2004. (Uncharted, Unexplored, & Unexplained Ser.). (Illus.). 48p. (J). (gr. 4-8). lib. bdg. 29.95 (978-1-58415-244-6(3)) Mitchell Lane Pubs., Inc.

Barretta, Gene. Now & Ben: The Modern Inventions of Benjamin Franklin. 2006. (Illus.). 40p. (J). 16.95 (978-0-8050-7917-3(3)) Holt, Henry & Co.

Beardsley, Laura E. Benjamin Franklin. 2007. (Essential Lives Ser.). (ENG., Illus.). 112p. (YA). (gr. 8-12). lib. bdg. 32.79 (*978-1-59928-840-6(0) , Essential Library) ABDO Publishing Co.

Benge, Janet & Benge, Geoff. Benjamin Franklin: A Useful Life. 2005. (Illus.). 197p. (J). (978-1-932096-14-9(0)) Emerald Bks.

Benge, Janet & Benge, Geoff. Thomas Edison: Inspiration & Hard Work. 2007. (J). pap. (*978-1-932096-37-8(X)) Emerald Bks.

Berger, Melvin & Berger, Gilda. Did You Invent the Phone All Alone, Alexander Graham Bell? 2007. (Scholastic Science Supergiants Ser.). 48p. (J). pap. 4.99 (978-0-439-83381-3(7) , Scholastic Nonfiction) Scholastic, Inc.

—What Makes the Light Bright, Mr. Edison? Dorman, Brandon, illus. 2007. (Scholastic Science Supergiants Ser.). 48p. (J). pap. 4.99 (978-0-439-83380-6(9)) Scholastic, Inc.

Bingham, Caroline & Dorling Kindersley Publishing Staff. Invention. 2005. (Eye Wonder Ser.). (Illus.). 48p. (J). 9.99 (978-0-7566-0619-0(5)) Dorling Kindersley Publishing, Inc.

Black American Inventors. 2001. 96p. (YA). (gr. 6-12). pap. 10.95 (978-0-87460-367-5(6)) Lion Bks.

Boekhoff, P. M. & Kallen, Stuart A. Benjamin Franklin. 2006. (Illus.). 48p. (J). (gr. 4-8). 17.00 (978-1-4223-5322-6(2)) DIANE Publishing Co.

Boothroyd, Jennifer. Robert Fulton: A Life of Innovation. 2007. (Pull Ahead Books-Biographies Ser.). (J). 22.60 (978-0-8225-6458-4(0) , Lerner Pubns.) Lerner Publishing Group.

Borden, Louise & Blegvad, Erik. Sea Clocks. 2004. (Illus.). 48p. (J). 18.95 (978-0-689-84216-0(3) , McElderry, Margaret K.) Simon & Schuster Children's Publishing.

Braun, Sandra. Incredible Women Inventors. 2006. (Women's Hall of Fame Ser.). (Illus.). 112p. (J). pap. 7.95 (978-1-897187-15-9(7)) Second Story Pr. CAN. *Dist:* Orca Bk. Pubs. USA.

Brill, Marlene Targ. Margaret Knight, Girl Inventor. Friar, Joanne, illus. 2001. 32p. (gr. 2-4). lib. bdg. 22.90 (978-0-7613-1756-2(2) , Twenty-First Century Bks.) Lerner Publishing Group.

Bryant, Tamera. Thomas Alva Edison. 2003. (World Was Never the Same Ser.). (J). (978-1-58417-260-4(6)); pap. (978-1-58417-261-1(4)) Lake Street Pubs.

Buchanan, Ben. My Year with Harry Potter: How I Discovered My Own Magical World. 2001. (Illus.). 112p. (ps-3). 12.95 (978-1-930051-50-8(6)) Lantern Bks.

Burgan, Michael. Thomas Alva Edison: Great American Inventor. 2006. (J). (978-0-7565-1884-4(9)) Compass Point Bks.

Camp, Carole Ann. American Women Inventors. 2004. (Collective Biographies Ser.). (Illus.). 104p. (J). lib. bdg. 26.60 (978-0-7660-1913-3(6)) Enslow Pubs., Inc.

Carson, Mary Kay. Sterling Biographies: Alexander Graham Bell: Giving Voice to the World. 2007. (Sterling Biographies Ser.). (Illus.). 128p. (J). 12.95 (*978-1-4027-4951-3(1)); pap. 5.95 (*978-1-4027-3230-0(9)) Sterling Publishing Co., Inc.

Casey, Susan. Women Invent: Two Centuries of Discoveries That Have Shaped Our World. 2003. (Illus.). 144p. (J). (gr. 4-8). pap. 14.95 (978-1-55652-317-5(3)) Chicago Review Pr., Inc.

Cefrey, Holly. The Inventions of Alexander Graham Bell: The Telephone. 2003. (19th Century American Inventors Ser.). (Illus.). 24p. (J). lib. bdg. 17.25 (978-0-8239-6441-3(8) , PowerKids Pr.) Rosen Publishing Group, Inc., The.

—The Inventions of Granville Woods: The Railroad Telegraph System & the "Third Rail" 2003. (19th Century American Inventors Ser.). (Illus.). 24p. (J). lib. bdg. 17.25 (978-0-8239-6442-0(6) , PowerKids Pr.) Rosen Publishing Group, Inc., The.

—The Inventions of Martha Coston: Signal Flares That Saved Sailors' Lives. 2003. (19th Century American Inventors Ser.). (Illus.). 24p. (J). lib. bdg. 17.25 (978-0-8239-6444-4(2) , PowerKids Pr.) Rosen Publishing Group, Inc., The.

—The Inventions of Thomas Alva Edison. 2003. (19th Century American Inventors Ser.). (Illus.). 24p. (J). lib. bdg. 17.25 (978-0-8239-6440-6(X) , PowerKids Pr.) Rosen Publishing Group, Inc., The.

Champion, Neil. James Watt. 2000. (Groundbreakers Ser.). (Illus.). 48p. (J). (gr. 5-7). lib. bdg. 25.64 (978-1-57572-371-6(9)) Heinemann Library.

Champion, Neil & Babbage, Charles. Charles Babbage. 2000. (Groundbreakers Ser.). (Illus.). 48p. (J). (gr. 5-7). lib. bdg. 25.64 (978-1-57572-367-9(0)) Heinemann Library.

Claybourne, Anna & Larkum, Adam. Story of Inventions. 2007. (Story of Inventions Ser.). 96p. (J). 10.99 (*978-0-7945-1710-6(2) , Usborne) EDC Publishing.

Clements, Gillian. The Picture History of the Great Inventors. Clements, Gillian, illus. 2005. (Illus.). 80p. (J). (gr. 3-17). pap., pap. 12.95 (978-1-84507-439-5(4)) Lincoln, Frances Ltd. GBR. *Dist:* Perseus Distribution.

Collard, Sneed B., III. Benjamin Franklin: The Man Who Could Do Just about Anything. 2006. (American Heroes Ser.). (Illus.). 48p. (J). (gr. 3-5). lib. bdg. 28.50 (*978-0-7614-2161-0(0) , Benchmark Bks.) Cavendish, Marshall Corp.

Collier, James Lincoln. The Benjamin Franklin You Never Knew. 2004. (You Never Knew Ser.). (Illus.). 80p. (J). 25.50 (978-0-516-24427-3(2) , Children's Pr.) Scholastic Library Publishing.

Crompton, Samuel Willard. The Wright Brothers: First in Flight. 2007. (Milestones in American History Ser.). 120p. (gr. 6-12). 35.00 (*978-0-7910-9356-6(5) , Chelsea Hse.) Facts On File, Inc.

Currie, Stephen. Women Inventors. 2001. (History Makers Ser.). (Illus.). 96p. (YA). (gr. 7-10). 27.45 (978-1-56006-865-5(5) , Lucent Bks.) Thomson Gale.

Dash, Joan. The Longitude Prize: The Race Between the Moon & the Watch-Machine. Petricic, Dusan, illus. 2000. 208p. (J). (gr. 4-7). 17.00 (978-0-374-34636-2(4) , Farrar, Straus & Giroux (BYR)) Farrar, Straus & Giroux.

Davis, Marc & Santella, Andrew. The Wright Brothers: Inventors & Aviators. 2003. (Spirit of America: Our People Ser.). (Illus.). 32p. (J). (gr. 2-6). 27.07 (978-1-56766-369-3(9)) Child's World, Inc.

Deitch, JoAnne Weisman, ed. A Nation of Inventors. 2001. (Researching American History Ser.). (Illus.). 56p. (J). 7.95 (978-1-57960-077-8(8)) History Compass, LLC.

Delano, Marfe Ferguson. Inventing the Future: A Photobiography of Thomas Alva Edison. 2006. 64p. (J). (gr. 5). pap. 7.95 (978-0-7922-5934-3(3) , National Geographic Children's Bks.) National Geographic Society.

Dolan, Ellen M. Thomas Alva Edison: Inventor. 1998. (Historical American Biographies Ser.). (Illus.). 128p. (YA). (gr. 6-12). lib. bdg. 26.60 (978-0-7660-1014-7(7)) Enslow Pubs., Inc.

Donlan, Leni. A Life Well Lived: Ben Franklin. 2007. (J). (*978-1-4109-2698-2(2)); pap. (*978-1-4109-2709-5(1)) Steck-Vaughn.

Dooling, Michael. Young Thomas Edison. 2005. (Illus.). 40p. (J). (ps-3). 16.95 (978-0-8234-1868-8(5)) Holiday Hse., Inc.

Doyle, Alfreda C. Black American Inventors - Based on Black American Inventors - A Rhyme. 1999. (Illus.). 20p. pap., wbk. ed. 15.95 (978-1-56820-389-8(6)) Story Time Stories That Rhyme.

Draze, Dianne. Inventions, Inventors & You. 2005. 64p. (Orig.). 11.95 (978-1-59363-082-9(4)) Prufrock Pr.

Dunn, Joeming W. The Wright Brothers. Dunn, Joeming W. & Dunn, Ben, illus. 2007. (Bio-Graphics Ser.). 32p. (J). (gr. 3-6). lib. bdg. 27.07 (*978-1-60270-071-0(0) , Graphic Planet) Magic Wagon.

Edwards, Pamela Duncan. The Wright Brothers. Cole, Henry, illus. 2003. 40p. (gr. k-4). 16.49 (978-0-7868-2682-7(7)) Hyperion Bks. for Children.

Erlbach, Arlene. The Kids' Invention Book. 1999. (978-0-606-22544-1(7)) Tandem Library Bks.

Espinosa, Rod. Benjamin Franklin. 2007. (Bio-Graphics Ser.). (Illus.). 32p. (J). (gr. 3-6). lib. bdg. 27.07 (*978-1-60270-066-6(4) , Graphic Planet) Magic Wagon.

Fandel, Jennifer. Alexander Graham Bell & the Telephone. Tucker, Keith & Barnett, Charles, illus. 2007. (Graphic Library). 32p. (J). 25.26 (978-0-7368-6478-7(4)) Capstone Pr., Inc.

—The Light Bulb. 2004. (What in the World? Ser.). (Illus.). 48p. 19.95 (978-1-58341-271-8(9) , Creative Education) Creative Co., The.

Feinstein, Stephen. Alexander Graham Bell: Genius Behind the Bell. 2008. (Inventors Who Changed the World Ser.). 128p. (gr. 6 up). lib. bdg. 33.27 (*978-1-59845-055-2(7) , MyReportLinks.com Bks.) Enslow Pubs., Inc.

Fish, Bruce. Benjamin Franklin: American Statesman, Scientist & Writer. 1999. (Colonial Leaders Ser.). (Illus.). 80p. (gr. 3 up). (J). pap. 8.95 (978-0-7910-5690-5(2)); (YA). 27.50 (978-0-7910-5347-8(4)) Facts On File, Inc. (Chelsea Hse.).

Flammang, James M. Robert Fulton: Inventor & Steamboat Builder. 1999. (Historical American Biographies Ser.). (Illus.). 128p. (YA). (gr. 6-12). lib. bdg. 26.60 (978-0-7660-1141-0(0)) Enslow Pubs., Inc.

Fleming, Candace. Ben Franklin's Almanac. 2003. (Illus.). 128p. (J). (gr. 5-9). 19.95 (978-0-689-83549-0(3) , Atheneum/Anne Schwartz Bks.) Simon & Schuster Children's Publishing.

Fleming, Thomas. Sterling Point Books: Ben Franklin: Inventing America. 2007. (Sterling Point Bks.). (Illus.). 192p. (J). 12.95 (978-1-4027-4523-2(0)); pap. 6.95 (978-1-4027-4143-2(X)) Sterling Publishing Co., Inc.

Fleming, Thomas J. Benjamin Franklin: Inventing America. 2007. (Sterling Point Bks.). (Illus.). viii, 177p. (J). (*978-1-4287-2411-2(7)) Sterling Publishing Co., Inc.

Ford, Carin T. Alexander Graham Bell: Inventor of the Telephone. 2002. (Meeting Famous People Ser.). (Illus.). 32p. (J). (gr. 1-4). lib. bdg. 22.60 (978-0-7660-1858-7(X)) Enslow Pubs., Inc.

—George Eastman: The Kodak Camera Man. 2004. (Famous Inventors Ser.). (Illus.). 32p. (J). lib. bdg. 22.60 (978-0-7660-2247-8(1)) Enslow Pubs., Inc.

—Thomas Edison: Inventor. 2002. (Famous Inventors Ser.). (Illus.). 32p. (J). (gr. 1-4). lib. bdg. 22.60 (978-0-7660-1860-0(1)) Enslow Pubs., Inc.

—The Wright Brothers: Heroes of Flight. 2003. (Famous Inventors Ser.). (Illus.). 32p. (J). (gr. 1-4). lib. bdg. 22.60 (978-0-7660-2002-3(9)) Enslow Pubs., Inc.

Fradin, Dennis Brindell. Who Was Ben Franklin? 2002. (gr. 3-6). lib. bdg. 13.00 (978-0-613-43654-0(7)) Tandem Library Bks.

Gaines, Ann Graham. Alexander Graham Bell. 2001. (Discover the Life of an Inventor Ser.). (Illus.). 24p. (J). (gr. 1-4). lib. bdg. 20.64 (978-1-58952-117-9(X)) Rourke Publishing, LLC.

—Alexander Graham Bell. Sarfatti, Esther & de la Vega, Eida, trs. 2001. (Inventores Famosos Ser.). (SPA & ENG., Illus.). 24p. (J). (gr. 1-4). lib. bdg. 19.27 (978-1-58952-173-5(0) , RK5266) Rourke Publishing, LLC.

—Alexander Graham Bell. 2002. (SPA.). (gr. k-3). lib. bdg. 14.10 (978-0-613-79408-4(7)) Tandem Library Bks.

—Alexander Graham Bell. Sarfatti, Esther & de la Vega, Eida, trs. 2002. (Inventores Famosos Ser.). (SPA., Illus.). 24p. (J). mass mkt. 5.95 (978-1-58952-233-6(8) , RK31450) Rourke Publishing, LLC.

—Eli Whitney. Sarfatti, Esther & de la Vega, Eida, trs. from ENG. 2001. (Inventores Famosos Ser.). (SPA., Illus.). 24p. (J). (gr. 1-4). lib. bdg. 19.27 (978-1-58952-177-3(3) , RK7727) Rourke Publishing, LLC.

—Eli Whitney. 2002. (SPA.). (gr. k-3). lib. bdg. 14.10 (978-0-613-79830-3(9)) Tandem Library Bks.

—Hedy Lamarr. Sarfatti, Esther & de la Vega, Eida, trs. 2002. (Inventores Famosos Ser.). (SPA., Illus.). 24p. (J). mass mkt. 5.95 (978-1-58952-236-7(2) , RK31453) Rourke Publishing, LLC.

—Hedy Lamarr. 2001. (Discover the Life of an Inventor Ser.). (Illus.). 24p. (J). (gr. 1-4). lib. bdg. 20.64 (978-1-58952-119-3(6)) Rourke Publishing, LLC.

—Hedy Lamarr. Sarfatti, Esther & de la Vega, Eida, trs. from ENG. 2001. (Inventores Famosos Ser.). (SPA., Illus.). 24p. (J). lib. bdg. 19.27 (978-1-58952-176-6(5) , RK7040) Rourke Publishing, LLC.

—Thomas Edison. 2001. (Inventores Famosos Ser.). (Illus.). 24p. (J). (gr. 1-4). (SPA & ENG.). lib. bdg. 19.27 (978-1-58952-174-2(9) , RK2159); lib. bdg. 20.64 (978-1-58952-122-3(6)) Rourke Publishing, LLC.

Gaines, Ann Graham & Whitney, Eli. Eli Whitney. 2001. (Illus.). 24p. (J). (gr. 1-4). lib. bdg. 20.64 (978-1-58952-118-6(8)) Rourke Publishing, LLC.

Gaustad, Edwin S. Benjamin Franklin: Inventing America. 2006. 143p. (J). (gr. 4-8). reprint ed. 22.00 (978-1-4223-5227-4(7)) DIANE Publishing Co.

Gibson, Karen Bush. Eli Whitney. 2006. (Profiles in American History Ser.). (Illus.). 48p. (J). (gr. 4-8). lib. bdg. 20.95 (978-1-58415-434-1(9)) Mitchell Lane Pubs., Inc.

Gillis, Jennifer Blizin. Benjamin Franklin. 2004. (Illus.). 32p. (J). pap. 6.50 (978-1-4034-5332-7(2)); lib. bdg. 22.79 (978-1-4034-5324-2(1)) Heinemann Library.

—George Eastman. 2004. (Illus.). 32p. (J). pap. 6.50 (978-1-4034-5334-1(9)); lib. bdg. 22.79 (978-1-4034-5326-6(8)) Heinemann Library.

—Robert Fulton. 2004. (Illus.). 32p. (J). pap. 6.50 (978-1-4034-5336-5(5)); lib. bdg. 22.79 (978-1-4034-5328-0(4)) Heinemann Library.

Goldish, Meish. Inventions. 2002. (Illus.). 16p. (J). pap. (978-0-439-35136-2(7)) Scholastic, Inc.

Goldsmith, Howard. Thomas Edison to the Rescue! DiVito, Anna, illus. 2003. (Ready-to-Read Cofa Ser.). 32p. (J). pap. 3.99 (978-0-689-85331-9(9) , Aladdin) Simon & Schuster Children's Publishing.

—Thomas Edison to the Rescue! 2003. (gr. k-3). lib. bdg. 11.80 (978-0-613-61591-4(3)) Tandem Library Bks.

Goldsmith, Mike. Guglielmo Marconi. 2002. (Scientists Who Made History Ser.). (Illus.). 48p. (J). lib. bdg. 27.12 (978-0-7398-5227-9(2)) Raintree.

Graham, Amy. Thomas Edison: Wizard of Light & Sound. 2007. (Inventors Who Changed the World Ser.). (Illus.). 128p. (J). lib. bdg. 33.27 (978-1-59845-052-1(2) , MyReportLinks.com Bks.) Enslow Pubs., Inc.

Grandes Inventos, 6 vols. (Explorers. Exploradores Nonfiction Sets Ser.). (SPA.). 32p. (gr. 3-6). 44.95 (978-0-7699-0634-8(6)) Shortland Pubns. (U. S. A.) Inc.

Great Inventions Group 3, 5 bks., Set. Incl. Medical Imaging. Sherrow, Victoria. 127p. lib. bdg. 39.93 (978-0-7614-2231-0(5)); Microscopes & Telescopes. Stefoff, Rebecca. 128p. lib. bdg. 39.93 (978-0-7614-2230-3(7)); Rockets. Otfinoski, Steven. 111p. lib. bdg. 39.93 (978-0-7614-2232-7(3)); Submarines. Stefoff, Rebecca. 127p. lib. bdg. 39.93 (978-0-7614-2229-7(3)); Television. Otfinoski, Steven. 111p. lib. bdg. 39.93 (978-0-7614-2228-0(5)); (Illus.). (J). 2006. 2007. Set lib. bdg. 199.64 (*978-0-7614-2227-3(7) , Benchmark Bks.) Cavendish, Marshall Corp.

Great Life Stories: Inventors & Scientists, 3 bks. 2004. (J). 88.50 (978-0-531-12397-3(9) , Children's Pr.); (Illus.). 118.00 (978-0-531-19329-7(2)) Scholastic Library Publishing.

Gregson, Susan R. Benjamin Franklin. 2000. (Let Freedom Ring Ser.). (Illus.). 48p. (J). (gr. 3-4). lib. bdg. 22.60 (978-0-7368-1031-9(5) , Bridgestone Bks.) Capstone Pr., Inc.

Groundbreakers Series, 24 bks., Set. (Illus.). (J). (gr. 4-6). lib. bdg. 612.96 (978-1-58810-133-4(9)) Heinemann Library.

Gunderson, Jessica. Eli Whitney & the Cotton Gin. 2007. (Illus.). 32p. (J). (978-0-7368-6843-3(7)) Capstone Publishing.

Hall, Margaret. Eli Whitney. 2004. (Illus.). 32p. (J). pap. 6.50 (978-1-4034-5333-4(0)); lib. bdg. 22.79 (978-1-4034-5325-9(X)) Heinemann Library.

—John Deere. 2004. (Illus.). 32p. (J). pap. 6.50 (978-1-4034-5335-8(7)); lib. bdg. 22.79 (978-1-4034-5327-3(6)) Heinemann Library.

—Leonardo Da Vinci. 2007. (Essential Lives Ser.). (ENG., Illus.). 112p. (J). (gr. 6-8). lib. bdg. 32.79 (*978-1-59928-844-4(3) , Essential Library) ABDO Publishing Co.

Hall, Margaret. Samuel Morse. 2004. (J). pap. 6.50 (978-1-4034-5337-2(3)); lib. bdg. 22.79 (978-1-4034-5329-7(2)) Heinemann Library.

Hantula, Richard. Thomas Edison. 2004. (Trailblazers of the Modern World Ser.). (Illus.). 48p. (J). pap. 11.95 (978-0-8368-5265-3(6)); lib. bdg. 30.00 (978-0-8368-5496-1(9)) Stevens, Gareth Inc. (World Almanac Library).

Harcourt School Publishers Staff. Almqu/Ben Franklin On Level. 3rd ed. 2002. (Trofeos Ser.). (SPA., Illus.). pap. 6.80 (978-0-15-324086-7(5)) Harcourt Schl. Pubs.

—Bright Ideas Below Level. 3rd ed. 2002. (Trophies Reading Program Ser.). (Illus.). pap. 5.10 (978-0-15-323418-7(0)) Harcourt Schl. Pubs.

—Bright Ideas, Grades 1-3. 1999. (Collections Ser.). tchr. ed. 152.60 (978-0-15-312079-4(7)) Harcourt Schl. Pubs.

—Garrett Morgan. 3rd ed. 2002. (Horizons Ser.). (Illus.). (J). (gr. 1). pap. 3.70 (978-0-15-333146-6(1)) Harcourt Schl. Pubs.

—Inventing a Better Tomorrow Below Level. 3rd ed. 2002. (Trophies Reading Program Ser.). (Illus.). pap. 5.10 (978-0-15-323236-7(6)) Harcourt Schl. Pubs.

—Inventive Americans Advanced Level. 3rd ed. 2002. (Trophies Reading Program Ser.). (Illus.). pap. 5.10 (978-0-15-323398-2(2)) Harcourt Schl. Pubs.

—Inventors & Inventions. 3rd ed. 2002. (Horizons Ser.). (Illus.). (J). pap. 5.50 (978-0-15-333322-4(7)) Harcourt Schl. Pubs.

—The Surprising Mr. Bird. 3rd ed. 2002. (Horizons Ser.). (Illus.). (J). pap. 7.30 (978-0-15-333585-3(8)) Harcourt Schl. Pubs.

Harness, Cheryl. The Remarkable Benjamin Franklin. 2005. (Illus.). 48p. (J). (gr. 2 up). 17.95 (978-0-7922-7882-5(8)); 27.90 (978-0-7922-7884-9(4)) National Geographic Society. (National Geographic Children's Bks.).

Harris, Laurie Lanzen. Biography for Beginners: Inventors. 2006. (J). (978-1-931360-27-2(8)) Favorable Impressions.

Harris, Laurie Lanzen, ed. Biography Today: Profiles of People of Interest to Young Readers. (Illus.). (YA). (gr. 4 up). 2001. (Scientists & Inventors Ser.: Vol. 5). 200p. lib. bdg. (978-0-7808-0434-0(1)); 1999. (Scientist Inventors Ser.: Vol. 3). 206p. lib. bdg. (978-0-7808-0364-0(7)) Omnigraphics, Inc.

Haskins, Jim. Black Stars. 2001. (Black Stars Ser.: Vol. 1). 272p. 59.95 (978-0-471-21145-7(1) , Wiley) Wiley, John & Sons, Inc.

—Outward Dreams: Black Inventors & Their Inventions. 2003. (gr. 5-8). lib. bdg. 17.60 (978-0-613-75330-2(5)) Tandem Library Bks.

—Outward Dreams: Black Inventors & Their Inventions. 2003. (Illus.). 112p. (J). pap. 8.95 (978-0-8027-7673-0(6)) Walker & Co.

Haven, Kendall F. Alexander Graham Bell: Inventor & Visionary. 2003. (Great Life Stories: Inventors & Scientists Ser.). (Illus.). 128p. (J). 30.50 (978-0-531-12314-0(6) , Watts, Franklin) Scholastic Library Publishing.

Hegedus, Alannah. Bleeps & Blips to Rocket Ships: Greant Investions in Communications. 2001. (gr. 3-6). lib. bdg. 28.00 (978-0-613-77267-9(9)) Tandem Library Bks.

Higgins, Maria Mihalik. Sterling Biographies: Benjamin Franklin: Revolutionary Inventor. 2007. (Sterling Biographies Ser.). (Illus.). 128p. (J). 12.95 (*978-1-4027-4952-0(X)) Sterling Publishing Co., Inc.

Hirschmann, Kris. Jonathan Ive: Designer of the IPod. 2007. (Innovators Ser.). 64p. (J). (gr. 4-8). 27.45 (978-0-7377-3533-8(3) , Kidhaven) Thomson Gale.

Inventors & Inventions - Group 2, 6 bks., Set. Incl. Biotechnology. Wells, Donna K. lib. bdg. 25.64 (978-0-7614-0046-2(X)); Nuclear Power. Holland, Gini. lib. bdg. 25.64 (978-0-7614-0047-9(8)); Radiology. Winkler, Kathy. lib. bdg. 25.64 (978-0-7614-0075-2(3)); Satellites. Fox, Mary Virginia. lib. bdg. 25.64 (978-0-7614-0049-3(4)); Television. Riehecky, Janet. lib. bdg. 25.64 (978-0-7614-0045-5(1)); Video. Biel, Jackie. lib. bdg. 25.64 (978-0-7614-0048-6(6)); 64p. (YA). (gr. 5-9). 1996. (Illus.). Set lib. bdg. 153.86 (978-0-7614-0044-8(3) , Benchmark Bks.) Cavendish, Marshall Corp.

Inventors & Scientists, 2 bks., Set. 2005. (YA). 59.00 (978-0-531-18750-0(0)) Scholastic Library Publishing.

Jenner, Caryn. First Flight: The Wright Brothers. 2003. (gr. k-3). lib. bdg. 11.80 (978-0-613-67328-0(X)) Tandem Library Bks.

—First Flight Vol. 4: The Story of the Wright Brothers. 2003. (DK Readers Ser.). (Illus.). 48p. (J). (gr. 5). pap. 3.99 (978-0-7894-9291-3(1)) Dorling Kindersley Publishing, Inc.

Jenner, Caryn & Dorling Kindersley Publishing Staff. First Flight: The Wright Brothers. 2003. (Readers Ser.). (Illus.). 48p. (J). 14.99 (978-0-7894-9541-9(4)) Dorling Kindersley Publishing, Inc.

John Logie Baird. 2002. (Scientists Who Made History Ser.). (Illus.). 48p. lib. bdg. (978-0-7398-5222-4(1)) Raintree.

Kelly, Jack. Benjamin Franklin. Tafalla, Ortiz, illus. 2005. (Heroes of America Ser.). 240p. (J). (gr. 3-8). lib. bdg. 21.35 (978-1-59679-257-9(4)) ABDO Publishing Co.

Kendall, Martha E. Steve Wozniak: Inventor of the Apple Computer. 2000. (Illus.). 112p. (YA). (gr. 4 up). pap. 10.95 (978-0-945783-08-4(6)) Highland Publishing Group.

Kjelle, Marylou Morano. Raymond Damadian & the Development of the MRI. l.t. ed. 2002. (Unlocking the Secrets of Science Ser.). (Illus.). 56p. (gr. 4-10). lib. bdg. 25.70 (978-1-58415-141-8(2)) Mitchell Lane Pubs., Inc.

Klingel, Cynthia Fitterer. Alexander Graham Bell: Inventor. 2003. (Spirit of America: Our People Ser.). (Illus.). 32p. (J). (gr. 2-6). 27.07 (978-1-56766-367-9(2)) Child's World, Inc.

Klingel/Noyed. Thomas Edison: Inventor. 2003. (Spirit of America: Our People Ser.). (Illus.). 32p. (J). (gr. 2-6). 27.07 (978-1-56766-449-2(0)) Child's World, Inc.

Koestler-Grack, Rachel A. Leonardo Da Vinci: Artist, Inventor, & Renaissance Man. 2005. (Makers of the Middle Ages & Renaissance Ser.). (Illus.). 146p. (J). (gr. 4-8). lib. bdg. 30.00 (978-0-7910-8626-1(7) , Chelsea Hse.) Facts On File, Inc.

Kozar, Richard. Inventors & Their Discoveries. 1999. (Costume, Tradition & Culture). (Illus.). 64p. (YA). (gr. 5 up). 28.00 (978-0-7910-5163-4(3) , Chelsea Hse.) Facts On File, Inc.

Kroll, Steven. Robert Fulton: From Submarine to Steamboat. Farnsworth, Bill, illus. 1999. 32p. (J). (gr. 4-6). tchr. ed. 16.95 (978-0-8234-1433-8(7)) Holiday Hse., Inc.

Kulling, Monica. Listen Up! Alexander Graham Bell's Talking Machine. Walz, Richard, illus. 2007. (Step into Reading Ser.). 48p. (J). (gr. 1-3). pap. 3.99 (978-0-375-83115-7(0)); lib. bdg. 11.99 (978-0-375-93115-4(5)) Random Hse. Children's Bks. (Random Hse. Bks. for Young Readers).

Landau, Elaine. Meet Ben Franklin with Elaine Landau. 2006. (Explore Colonial America with Elaine Landau Ser.). (Illus.). 48p. (J). lib. bdg. 23.93 (978-0-7660-2555-4(1) , Enslow Elementary) Enslow Pubs., Inc.

MacLeod, Elizabeth. Alexander Graham Bell. Krystoforski, Andrej, illus. 2007. 32p. pap. (*978-1-55453-002-1(4)) Kids Can Pr., Ltd.

Mara, Wil. Alexander Graham Bell. 2002. (Rookie Biographies Ser.). (Illus.). 32p. (J). (gr. 1-2). 20.50 (978-0-516-22524-1(3) , Children's Pr.) Scholastic Library Publishing.

—Benjamin Franklin. rev. ed. 2006. (Rookie Biography Ser.). (Illus.). 31p. (J). (978-0-531-12450-5(9)) Children's Pr., Ltd.

—Thomas Alva Edison. 2004. (Rookie Biographies Ser.). (Illus.). 31p. (J). 20.50 (978-0-516-21843-4(3) , Children's Pr.) Scholastic Library Publishing.

Marcovitz, Hal. Benjamin Franklin: Scientist, Inventor, Printer, & Statesman. 2006. (Leaders of the American Revolution Ser.). (Illus.). 176p. (J). (gr. 5-8). 30.00 (978-0-7910-9219-4(4) , Chelsea Hse.) Facts On File, Inc.

Martin, Justin. Easy Reader Biographies: Alexander Graham Bell: A Famous Inventor. 2007. 16p. pap. 2.99 (*978-0-439-77415-4(2) , Teaching Resources) Scholastic, Inc.

Martin, Michael J. The Wright Brothers. 2002. (Importance of Ser.). (Illus.). 112p. (J). (gr. 7-10). 32.45 (978-1-56006-847-1(7) , Lucent Bks.) Thomson Gale.

Matthews, Tom L. Always Inventing: A Photobiography of Alexander Graham Bell. 2006. 64p. (J). (gr. 5). pap. 7.95 (978-0-7922-5932-9(7) , National Geographic Children's Bks.) National Geographic Society.

Mayer, Cassie. Benjamin Franklin. 2007. (J). (*978-1-4034-9970-7(5)); pap. (*978-1-4034-9979-0(9)) Heinemann Library.

Mayo, Gretchen Will. The Wright Brothers. 2003. (Trailblazers of the Modern World Ser.). (Illus.). 48p. (J). (gr. 5 up). lib. bdg. 30.00 (978-0-8368-5094-9(7)); pap. 11.95 (978-0-8368-5254-7(0)) Stevens, Gareth Inc. (World Almanac Library).

McClure, Judy. Theoreticians & Builders: Mathematicians, Physical Scientists, Inventors. 2002. (Remarkable Women). (Illus.). 80p. (YA). (gr. 6-9). lib. bdg. 32.85 (978-0-8172-5728-6(4)) Raintree.

McCully, Emily Arnold. Marvelous Mattie: How Margaret E. Knight Became an Inventor. 2006. (Illus.). 32p. (J). 16.00 (978-0-374-34810-6(3)) Farrar, Straus & Giroux.

McCurdy, Michael. So Said Ben. 2007. (Illus.). 32p. (YA). (gr. 4 up). 17.95 (*978-1-56846-147-2(X) , Creative Editions) Creative Co., The.

McDonough, Yona Zeldis. The Life of Benjamin Franklin: An American Original. Zeldis, Malcah, illus. 2006. 48p. (J). 17.95 (978-0-8050-7856-5(8)) Holt, Henry & Co.

McLeese, Don. Louis Daguerre. (Discover the Life of an Inventor Ser.). 2006. (Illus.). 24p. (gr. 2-5). 14.95 (978-1-59515-432-3(9)); 2005. (ENG & SPA.). (J). (978-1-59515-672-3(0)) Rourke Publishing, LLC.

—Robert Fulton. 2006. (Rourke Discovery Library). (Illus.). 24p. (gr. 2-5). 14.95 (978-1-59515-434-7(5) , 1244323) Rourke Publishing, LLC.

McPherson, Stephanie Sammartino. Alexander Graham Bell. Butler, Tad, illus. 2007. (History Maker Biographies Ser.). (J). 26.60 (*978-0-8225-7606-8(6) , Lerner Pubns.) Lerner Publishing Group.

Micklos, John. Alexander Graham Bell Inventor of the Telephone. 2006. 44p. (J). lib. bdg. 15.00 (*978-1-4242-0686-5(3)) Fitzgerald Bks.

Mortensen, Lori. Thomas Edison: Inventor, Scientist, & Genius. Thompson, Jeffrey, illus. 2006. (Biographies Ser.). 24p. (J). (gr. k-3). lib. bdg. 23.93 (978-1-4048-3105-6(3)) Picture Window Bks.

Murphy, Patricia J. Garrett Morgan: Inventor of the Traffic Light & Gas Mask. 2004. (Famous Inventors Ser.). (Illus.). 32p. (J). lib. bdg. 22.60 (978-0-7660-2274-4(9)) Enslow Pubs., Inc.

—Grace Hopper: Computer Pioneer. 2004. (Famous Inventors Ser.). (Illus.). 32p. (J). lib. bdg. 22.60 (978-0-7660-2273-7(0)) Enslow Pubs., Inc.

Niz, Ellen Sturm. Philo Farnsworth & the Television. Tucker, Keith, illus. 2007. (Graphic Library). 32p. (J). 25.26 (978-0-7368-6487-9(3)) Capstone Pr., Inc.

Olson, Kay Melchisedech. Benjamin Franklin: An American Genius. Purcell, Gordon & Schulz, Barbara, illus. 2005. (Graphic Library). 32p. (J). (gr. 3-7). lib. bdg. 25.26 (978-0-7368-4629-5(8)) Capstone Pr., Inc.

Olson, Kay Melchisedech. Frank Zamboni & the Ice-Resurfacing Machine. Dominguez, Richard & Barnett, Charles, III, illus. 2008. (J). (*978-1-4296-0147-4(7)) Capstone Pr., Inc.

Orr, Tamra B. The Dawn of Aviation: The Story of the Wright Brothers. 2005. (Illus.). 48p. (YA). (ps-7). lib. bdg. 29.95 (978-1-58415-396-2(2) , 1244922) Mitchell Lane Pubs., Inc.

O'Shei, Tim. Marconi & Tesla: Pioneers of Radio Communication. 2008. (Inventors Who Changed the World Ser.). (Illus.). 128p. (J). (gr. 6 up). lib. bdg. 33.27 (*978-1-59845-076-7(X) , MyReportLinks.com Bks.) Enslow Pubs., Inc.

—Philo T. Farnsworth: Visionary Inventor of Television. 2008. (Inventors Who Changed the World Ser.). 128p. (J). (gr. 6 up). lib. bdg. 33.27 (*978-1-59845-075-0(1) , MyReportLinks.com Bks.) Enslow Pubs., Inc.

Parker, Lewis K. The Inventions of Amanda Jones: The Vacuum Method of Canning & Food Preservation. 2003. (19th Century American Inventors Ser.). (Illus.). 24p. (J). lib. bdg. 17.25 (978-0-8239-6445-1(0) , PowerKids Pr.) Rosen Publishing Group, Inc., The.

Parks, Peggy J. Benjamin Franklin: Genius Inventor & Electricity Pioneer. 2002. (Giants of Science Ser.). (Illus.). 64p. (J). 26.20 (978-1-56711-658-8(2) , Blackbirch Pr., Inc.) Thomson Gale.

—Robert Fulton: Innovator with Steam Power. 2003. (Giants of Science Ser.). (Illus.). 64p. (J). 26.20 (978-1-56711-492-8(X) , Blackbirch Pr., Inc.) Thomson Gale.

Pederson, Charles E. Thomas Edison. 2007. (Essential Lives Ser.). (ENG., Illus.). 112p. (YA). (gr. 8-12). lib. bdg. 32.79 (*978-1-59928-845-1(1) , Essential Library) ABDO Publishing Co.

Peterson, Tiffany. Clarence Birdseye. 2003. (Lives & Times Ser.). (Illus.). (J). 24p. pap. (978-1-4034-4255-0(X)); 32p. lib. bdg. 22.79 (978-1-4034-3247-6(3)) Heinemann Library.

—Clarence Birdseye. 2003. (gr. k-3). lib. bdg. 14.75 (978-0-613-86558-6(8)) Tandem Library Bks.

Pierce, Morris A. Robert Fulton & the Development of the Steamboat. 2005. (Library of American Lives & Times). (Illus.). 112p. (YA). (gr. 4-8). lib. bdg. 31.95 (978-0-8239-5737-8(3)) Rosen Publishing Group, Inc., The.

Platt, Richard. Eureka! Great Inventions & How They Happened. 2003. (Illus.). 96p. (J). (gr. 5-9). tchr. ed. 18.95 (978-0-7534-5580-7(3) , Kingfisher) Houghton Mifflin Co. Trade & Reference Div.

Polette, Nancy. Blunder or Brainstorm: Fact & Fiction of Famous Inventors & Inventions. Dillon, Paul, illus. 2006. (YA). pap. 11.95 (*978-1-931334-91-4(9)) Pieces of Learning.

Pollard, Michael. Alexander Graham Bell: Father of Modern Communication. 2000. (Giants of Science Ser.). (Illus.). 64p. (J). (gr. 5-8). 27.44 (978-1-56711-334-1(6) , Blackbirch Pr., Inc.) Thomson Gale.

Price-Groff, Claire. Thomas Alva Edison: Inventor & Entrepreneur. 2003. (Great Life Stories Ser.). 128p. (J). 30.50 (978-0-531-12275-4(1) , Watts, Franklin) Scholastic Library Publishing.

Raatma, Lucia. Alexander Graham Bell. 2004. (Compass Point Early Biographies Ser.). (Illus.). 32p. (J). (gr. 2 up). lib. bdg. 21.26 (978-0-7565-0569-1(0)) Compass Point Bks.

—Thomas Edison. 2004. (Compass Point Early Biographies Ser.). (Illus.). 32p. (J). (gr. 2 up). lib. bdg. 21.26 (978-0-7565-0567-7(4)) Compass Point Bks.

Randolph, Ryan P. Benjamin Franklin: Inventor, Writer & Patriot. 2005. (Library of American Lives & Times). (Illus.). 112p. (YA). (gr. 4-8). lib. bdg. 31.95 (978-0-8239-5751-4(9)) Rosen Publishing Group, Inc., The.

Rausch, Monica. Benjamin Franklin. 2006. (J). (ENG & SPA.). pap. (*978-0-8368-7988-9(0)); (ENG & SPA.). lib. bdg. (*978-0-8368-7981-0(3)); (Illus.). 24p. pap. (*978-0-8368-7689-5(X)); (Illus.). 24p. lib. bdg. (*978-0-8368-7682-6(2)) Stevens, Gareth Inc. (Weekly Reader Early Learning Library).

—George Eastman & the Camera. 2006. (Illus.). 24p. (J). pap. (*978-0-8368-7730-4(6)); lib. bdg. (*978-0-8368-7499-0(4)) Stevens, Gareth Inc. (Weekly Reader Early Learning Library).

—George Eastman y la Camara. 2006. (ENG & SPA.). (J). pap. (*978-0-8368-7999-5(6)); lib. bdg. (*978-0-8368-7994-0(5)) Stevens, Gareth Inc. (Weekly Reader Early Learning Library).

—Henry Ford & the Model T Car. 2006. (Illus.). 24p. (J). pap. (*978-0-8368-7731-1(4)); lib. bdg. (*978-0-8368-7500-3(1)) Stevens, Gareth Inc. (Weekly Reader Early Learning Library).

—Henry Ford y el Modelo T. 2006. (ENG & SPA.). (J). pap. (*978-0-8368-8000-7(5)); lib. bdg. (*978-0-8368-7995-7(3)) Stevens, Gareth Inc. (Weekly Reader Early Learning Library).

—Thomas Edison & the Light Bulb. 2006. (Illus.). 24p. (J). pap. (*978-0-8368-7732-8(2)); lib. bdg. (*978-0-8368-7501-0(X)) Stevens, Gareth Inc. (Weekly Reader Early Learning Library).

—Thomas Edison y la Bombilla Eléctrica. 2006. (J). pap. (*978-0-8368-8002-1(1)); lib. bdg. (*978-0-8368-7997-1(X)) Stevens, Gareth Inc. (Weekly Reader Early Learning Library).

—The Wright Brothers & the Airplane. 2006. (Illus.). 24p. (J). pap. (*978-0-8368-7733-5(0)); lib. bdg. (*978-0-8368-7502-7(8)) Stevens, Gareth Inc. (Weekly Reader Early Learning Library).

Reid, Struan. Alexander Graham Bell. (Groundbreakers Ser.). (Illus.). 48p. (J). (gr. 5-7). 2002. pap. 8.50 (978-1-58810-989-7(5) , 91464); 2000. lib. bdg. 25.64 (978-1-57572-366-2(2)) Heinemann Library.

—John Logie Baird. 2000. (Groundbreakers Ser.). (Illus.). 48p. (J). (gr. 5-7). lib. bdg. 25.64 (978-1-57572-372-3(7)) Heinemann Library.

Riley, Gail Blasser. Benjamin Franklin & Electricity. 2004. (Cornerstones of Freedom Ser.). (Illus.). 48p. (J). 26.00 (978-0-516-24240-8(7) , Children's Pr.) Scholastic Library Publishing.

Riley, John B. Benjamin Franklin: A Photo Biography. l.t. ed. 2004. (First Biographies Ser.). (Illus.). 24p. (YA). (gr. 5 up). 16.95 (978-1-883846-64-0(1) , First Biographies) Reynolds, Morgan Inc.

Ring, Susan. Nature Did It First. 2003. (Science Links Ser.). (Illus.). 32p. (gr. 3-5). 23.00 (978-0-7910-7427-5(7) , Chelsea Hse.) Facts On File, Inc.

Rivera, Sheila. Alexander Graham Bell: A Life of Helpfulness. 2007. (Pull Ahead Books-Biographies Ser.). (J). 22.60 (978-0-8225-6463-8(7) , Lerner Pubns.) Lerner Publishing Group.

Robinson Masters, Nancy. The Cotton Gin. 2006. (Inventions That Shaped the World Ser.). (Illus.). 80p. (J). (gr. 5-8). 30.50 (978-0-531-12406-2(1) , Watts, Franklin) Scholastic Library Publishing.

Ross, Stewart. Alexander Graham Bell. 2001. (Scientists Who Made History Ser.). (Illus.). 48p. (J). lib. bdg. 27.12 (978-0-7398-4415-1(6)) Raintree.

Rossi, Ann. The Age of Inventions. 2002. (Illus.). 40p. (J). (978-0-7922-8696-7(0)) National Geographic Society.

Ryan, Bernard. The Wright Brothers: Inventors of the Airplane. 2003. (Great Life Stories Ser.). (Illus.). 128p. (J). 30.50 (978-0-531-12254-9(9) , Watts, Franklin) Scholastic Library Publishing.

Sabin, Louis & Macken, JoAnn Early. Thomas Edison: Incredible Inventor. 2006. (Illus.). 52p. (J). (*978-0-439-88006-0(8)) Scholastic, Inc.

Samuel, Charlie. Inventors & Inventions in Colonial America. 2003. (Primary Sources of Everyday Life in Colonial America Ser.). (Illus.). 24p. (J). lib. bdg. 21.25 (978-0-8239-6601-1(1) , PowerKids Pr.) Rosen Publishing Group, Inc., The.

Sandler, Martin. Inventors. 1999. (gr. 5-8). lib. bdg. 19.95 (978-0-613-22876-3(6)) Tandem Library Bks.

Sandler, Martin W. Inventors. 1999. (Library of Congress Classics). (Illus.). 96p. (J). (gr. 3 up). pap. 12.99 (978-0-06-446746-9(5)) HarperCollins Pubs.

—Inventors. 1999. (Illus.). (J). 17.64 (978-0-606-18698-8(0)) Tandem Library Bks.

Satterfield, Kathryn Hoffman. Benjamin Franklin A Man of Many Talents. 2005. 44p. (J). lib. bdg. 15.00 (*978-1-4242-0846-3(7)) Fitzgerald Bks.

Saunders-Smith, Gail, ed. Thomas Edison. 2002. (First Biographies Ser.). (Illus.). 24p. (J). (gr. k-1). lib. bdg. 15.93 (978-0-7368-1436-2(1) , Pebble Bks.) Capstone Pr., Inc.

Schaefer, Lola M. Alexander Graham Bell. Saunders-Smith, Gail, ed. 2003. (First Biographies Ser.). (Illus.). 24p. (J). (gr. k-1). lib. bdg. 15.93 (978-0-7368-1644-1(5) , Pebble Bks.) Capstone Pr., Inc.

Schuman, Michael A. Alexander Graham Bell: Inventor & Teacher. 1999. (Historical American Biographies Ser.). (Illus.). 128p. (YA). (gr. 6-12). lib. bdg. 20.95 (978-0-7660-1096-3(1)) Enslow Pubs., Inc.

Scientists & Inventors, 10 bks., Set 1. 2000. (Illus.). (J). (gr. 5-7). lib. bdg. 256.40 (978-1-58810-132-7(0)) Heinemann Library.

Seidman, David. Samuel Morse & the Telegraph. 2007. 32p. (J). (978-0-7368-6846-4(1)) Capstone Pr., Inc.

Sherrow, Victoria. Alexander Graham Bell. Verstraete, Elaine, illus. (On My Own Biographies Ser.). 48p. 2005. (gr. 2-5). lib. bdg. 23.93 (978-1-57505-460-5(4)); 2003. (J). (gr. 1-3). 5.95 (978-1-57505-533-6(3)) Lerner Publishing Group.

—Alexander Graham Bell. 2001. (gr. 3-6). lib. bdg. 14.10 (978-0-613-79235-6(1)) Tandem Library Bks.

—Benjamin Franklin. 2002. (History Maker Bios Ser.). (Illus.). (J). 47p. pap. 6.95 (978-0-8225-0383-5(2) , Lerner Pubns.); 48p. (gr. 3-5). lib. bdg. 26.60 (978-0-8225-0198-5(8)) Lerner Publishing Group.

Shuter, Jane. Alexander Graham Bell. 2000. (Lives & Times Ser.). (Illus.). 24p. (J). (gr. k-2). lib. bdg. 19.92 (978-1-57572-228-3(3)) Heinemann Library.

—Thomas Edison. (Lives & Times Ser.). (Illus.). 24p. (J). 2000. lib. bdg. 19.92 (978-1-57572-230-6(5)); Set 1. 2002. pap. 6.50 (978-1-58810-347-5(1) , 91107) Heinemann Library.

Sonneborn, Liz. Guglielmo Marconi: Inventor of Wireless Technology. 2005. (Great Life Stories Ser.). (Illus.). 111p. (J). 30.50 (978-0-531-16752-6(6) , Watts, Franklin) Scholastic Library Publishing.

St. George, Judith. So You Want to Be an Inventor? Small, David, illus. 2002. 56p. (J). 16.99 (978-0-399-23593-1(0) , Philomel) Penguin Group (USA) Inc.

—So You Want to Be an Inventor? Small, David, illus. 2005. 56p. (J). pap. 7.99 (978-0-14-240460-7(8) , Puffin) Penguin Group (USA) Inc.

Stanley, George Edward. Leonardo Da Vinci: Young Artist, Writer, & Inventor. 2005. (Childhood of World Figures Ser.). 166p. (J). (978-1-4156-3039-6(9) , Aladdin) Simon & Schuster Children's Publishing.

Stephen, Krensky. Dk Bio: Benjamin Franklin Hc. 2007. 128p. 14.99 (*978-0-7566-3529-9(2)) Dorling Kindersley Publishing, Inc.

—Dk Bio: Benjamin Franklin Pb. 2007. 128p. pap. 4.99 (*978-0-7566-3528-2(4)) Dorling Kindersley Publishing, Inc.

The Story of Benjamin Franklin. 2002. (Illus.). 24p. (J). (ps-k). 6.95 (978-0-8249-4227-4(2)) Ideals Pubns.

Streissguth, Tom. Benjamin Franklin. 2005. (Bios for Challenged Readers Ser.). (Illus.). 112p. (J). (gr. 6-12). lib. bdg. 27.93 (978-0-8225-2210-2(1)) Lerner Publishing Group.

Sullivan, Erin. Mathematical Thinkers/Los Matematicos: English/Spanish Pair, 12 texts, 2 titles, Vol. 2. ed. 2004. (Navigators Ser.). (J). pap., instr.'s gde. ed. 84.00 (978-1-4108-1773-0(3) , 17733) Benchmark Education Co.

H
I

Sullivan, George E. Thomas Edison. 2002. (In Their Own Words Ser.). (Illus.). 128p. (J). (gr. 3-5). 4.99 (978-0-439-26319-1(0) , Scholastic Reference) Scholastic, Inc.

Tagliaferro, Linda. Thomas Edison: Inventor of the Age of Electricity. 2003. (Lerner Biographies Ser.). (Illus.). 128p. (J). 27.93 (978-0-8225-4689-4(2) , Lerner Pubns.) Lerner Publishing Group.

Thatcher Murcia, Rebecca. Thomas Edison: Great Inventor. 2004. (Uncharted, Unexplored, & Unexplained Ser.). (Illus.). 48p. (J). (gr. 4-8). lib. bdg. 29.95 (978-1-58415-306-1(7)) Mitchell Lane Pubs., Inc.

Thayer, William M. From Boyhood to Manhood - the Life of Be. 2006. pap. (*978-1-4068-0906-0(3)) Echo Library.

Thimmesh, Catherine. Girls Think of Everything: Stories of Ingenious Inventions by Women. Sweet, Melissa, illus. 2002. 64p. (YA). (gr. 4-6). reprint ed. pap. 6.95 (978-0-618-19563-3(7)) Houghton Mifflin Co. Trade & Reference Div.

—Girls Think of Everything: Stories of Ingenious Inventions by Women. 2000. (gr. 3-6). lib. bdg. 15.25 (978-0-613-60676-9(0)) Tandem Library Bks.

Time for Kids Editors. Alexander Graham Bell. 2006. (Time for Kids Ser.). (Illus.). 48p. (J). 14.99 (978-0-06-057619-6(7)); pap. 3.99 (978-0-06-057618-9(9) , Harper Trophy) HarperCollins Pubs.

—Benjamin Franklin: A Man of Many Talents. 2005. (Time for Kids Ser.). (Illus.). 48p. (J). 14.99 (978-0-06-057610-3(3)); pap. 3.99 (978-0-06-057609-7(X)) HarperCollins Pubs.

—Thomas Edison: A Brilliant Inventor. 2005. (Time for Kids Ser.). (Illus.). 48p. (J). 14.99 (978-0-06-057612-7(X)); pap. 3.99 (978-0-06-057611-0(1)) HarperCollins Pubs.

Tracy, Kathleen. Henry Bessemer: Making Steel from Iron. 2005. (Uncharted, Unexplored, & Unexplained Ser.). (Illus.). 48p. (J). (gr. 4-8). lib. bdg. 29.95 (978-1-58415-366-5(0)) Mitchell Lane Pubs., Inc.

—William Hewlett: Pioneer of the Computer Age. 2002. (Unlocking the Secrets of Science Ser.). (J). (978-1-58415-178-4(1)); (Illus.). 56p. (gr. 4-10). lib. bdg. 25.70 (978-1-58415-142-5(0)) Mitchell Lane Pubs., Inc.

Unlocking the Secrets of Science: Set of 15 Inventors. (Illus.). 26p. (gr. 4-10). lib. bdg. (978-1-58415-232-3(X)) Mitchell Lane Pubs., Inc.

Van Steenwyk, Elizabeth. One Fine Day: A Radio Play. Farnsworth, Bill, illus. 2004. 32p. (gr. 3-5). 16.00 (978-0-8028-5234-2(3)) Eerdmans, William B. Publishing Co.

Van Vleet, Carmella. Amazing Ben Franklin Inventions You Can Build Yourself. 2007. (Build It Yourself Ser.). 128p. (J). (gr. 4-7). pap. 14.95 (*978-0-9771294-7-8(0)) Nomad Pr.

Wadsworth, Ginger. The Wright Brothers. 2004. (History Maker Bios Ser.). (Illus.). 47p. (J). 26.60 (978-0-8225-0199-2(6) , Lerner Pubns.) Lerner Publishing Group.

Webster, Christine. Alexander Graham Bell & the Telephone. 2004. (Cornerstones of Freedom Ser.). (Illus.). 48p. (J). 26.00 (978-0-516-24227-9(X) , Children's Pr.) Scholastic Library Publishing.

Welch, Catherine A. Rise of the Reaper: A Story about Cyrus Hall McCormick. Jones, Jan Naimo, illus. 2007. (Creative Minds Biography Ser.). (J). spiral bd. 22.60 (978-0-8225-5988-7(9)) Lerner Publishing Group.

Welvaert, Scott R. Thomas Edison & the Lightbulb. 2007. (Graphic Library). (Illus.). 32p. 25.26 (978-0-7368-6489-3(X)) Capstone Pr., Inc.

Whiting, Jim. Benjamin Franklin. 2006. (Profiles in American History Ser.). (Illus.). 48p. (J). (gr. 4-8). lib. bdg. 20.95 (978-1-58415-435-8(7)) Mitchell Lane Pubs., Inc.

—James Watt & the Steam Engine. 2005. (Uncharted, Unexplored, & Unexplained Ser.). (Illus.). 48p. (J). (gr. 4-8). lib. bdg. 29.95 (978-1-58415-371-9(7)) Mitchell Lane Pubs., Inc.

Williams, Brian. Bell & the Science of the Telephone. Antram, David, illus. 2006. (Explosion Zone Ser.). 32p. (J). 12.99 (978-0-7641-5972-5(0)) Barron's Educational Series, Inc.

—Science. 2001. (Great Inventions Ser.). (Illus.). 48p. (YA). (gr. 6-8). lib. bdg. 25.64 (978-1-58810-214-0(9)) Heinemann Library.

—Thomas Alva Edison. 2002. (Groundbreakers Ser.). (Illus.). 48p. (J). (gr. 5-7). pap. 8.50 (978-1-58810-996-5(8) , 91471) Heinemann Library.

Williams, Brian, contrib. by. Thomas Alva Edison. 2000. (Groundbreakers Ser.). (Illus.). 48p. (J). (gr. 5-7). lib. bdg. 25.64 (978-1-57572-377-8(8)) Heinemann Library.

Williams, Marcia. Hooray for Inventors! Williams, Marcia, illus. 2005. (Illus.). 40p. (J). (gr. 3-7). 16.99 (978-0-7636-2760-7(7)) Candlewick Pr.

Woodside, Martin. Sterling Biographies: Thomas Edison: The Man Who Lit up the World. 2007. (Sterling Biographies Ser.). (Illus.). 128p. (J). 12.95 (*978-1-4027-4955-1(4)); pap. 5.95 (*978-1-4027-3229-4(5)) Sterling Publishing Co., Inc.

Wooldridge, Connie N. Thank You Very Much, Captain Ericsson! Glass, Andrew, photos by. 2004. (Illus.). 32p. (J). (gr. k-3). tchr. ed. 16.95 (978-0-8234-1626-4(7)) Holiday Hse., Inc.

Wyckoff, Edwin Brit. Electric Guitar Man: The Genius of les Paul. 2008. (Genius at Work! Great Inventor Biographies Ser.). (Illus.). 32p. (J). (gr. 3-4). lib. bdg. 22.60 (*978-0-7660-2847-0(X) , Enslow Elementary) Enslow Pubs., Inc.

—Stopping Bullets with a Thread: Stephanie Kwolek & Her Incredible Invention. 2008. (Genius at Work! Great Inventor Biographies Ser.). (Illus.). 32p. (J). (gr. 3-4). lib. bdg. 22.60 (*978-0-7660-2850-0(X) , Enslow Elementary) Enslow Pubs., Inc.

—The Teen Who Invented Television: Philo T. Farnsworth & His Awesome Invention. 2007. (Genius at Work! Great Inventor Biographies Ser.). (Illus.). 32p. (J). (gr. 3-4). lib. bdg. 22.60 (*978-0-7660-2845-6(3) , Enslow Elementary) Enslow Pubs., Inc.

Yolen, Jane. My Brothers' Flying Machine: Wilbur, Orville, & Me. Burke, Jim, illus. 2003. 32p. (J). (gr. 1-4). 17.99 (978-0-316-97159-1(6)) Little, Brown Bks. for Young Readers.

Young, Jeff C. Inspiring African-American Inventors. 2008. (J). (*978-1-59845-080-4(8)) Enslow Pubs., Inc.

Your Little Black Book on African American Inventions & Inventors. 2006. (J). per. 9.95 (*978-0-9791883-0-5(X)) Disciple One Publishing.

Zannos, Susan. Chester Carlson & the Development of Xerography. l.t. ed. 2002. (Unlocking the Secrets of Science Ser.). (Illus.). 56p. (gr. 4-10). lib. bdg. 25.70 (978-1-58415-117-3(X)) Mitchell Lane Pubs., Inc.

—Guglielmo Marconi & Radio Waves. 2004. (Uncharted, Unexplored, & Unexplained Ser.). (Illus.). 48p. (J). (gr. 4-8). lib. bdg. 29.95 (978-1-58415-265-1(6)) Mitchell Lane Pubs., Inc.

—Samuel Morse & the Telegraph. 2004. (Uncharted, Unexplored, & Unexplained Ser.). (Illus.). 48p. (J). (gr. 4-8). lib. bdg. 29.95 (978-1-58415-269-9(9)) Mitchell Lane Pubs., Inc.

Zemlicka, Shannon. Thomas Edison. 2003. (History Maker Bios Ser.). (Illus.). 48p. (J). lib. bdg. 25.26 (978-0-8225-0239-5(9) , Lerner Pubns.) Lerner Publishing Group.

INVENTORS—FICTION

Appleton, Victor. Into the Abyss. 2006. (Tom Swift, Young Inventor Ser.). 176p. (J). (gr. 3-7). pap. 4.99 (978-1-4169-1518-8(4) , Aladdin) Simon & Schuster Children's Publishing.

—Into the Abyss. 2007. (Tom Swift, Young Inventor Ser.). 160p. (J). (gr. 4-7). 27.07 (*978-1-59961-350-5(6)) Spotlight.

—The Robot Olympics. 2006. (Tom Swift, Young Inventor Ser.). 176p. (J). pap. 4.99 (978-1-4169-1361-0(0) , Aladdin) Simon & Schuster Children's Publishing.

—The Robot Olympics. 2007. (Tom Swift, Young Inventor Ser.). 160p. (J). (gr. 4-7). 27.07 (*978-1-59961-351-2(4)) Spotlight.

—Rocket Racers. 2007. (Tom Swift, Young Inventor Ser.: No. 4). 160p. (J). pap. 4.99 (978-1-4169-3488-2(X) , Aladdin) Simon & Schuster Children's Publishing.

—Rocket Racers. 2007. (Tom Swift, Young Inventor Ser.). 160p. (J). (gr. 4-7). 27.07 (*978-1-59961-352-9(2)) Spotlight.

—The Space Hotel. 2007. (Tom Swift, Young Inventor Ser.). 160p. (J). (gr. 4-7). 27.07 (*978-1-59961-353-6(0)) Spotlight.

Appleton, Victor & Appleton, Victor, II. Under the Radar. 2007. (Tom Swift, Young Inventor Ser.: No. 6). 146p. (J). (gr. 3-7). per. 4.99 (*978-1-4169-3644-2(0) , Aladdin) Simon & Schuster Children's Publishing.

Baldacci, David. The Mystery of Silas Finklebean. Harrington, Patrick, illus. 2nd ed. 2006. (Freddy & the French Fries Ser.: No. 2). 176p. (J). (gr. 3-7). pap. 4.99 (978-0-316-05900-8(5)) Little Brown & Co.

Baldacci, David & Baldacci, Rudy. Fries Alive! 2006. (Freddy & the French Fries Ser.). (Illus.). 192p. (J). (gr. 3-7). pap. 4.99 (978-0-316-05901-5(3)) Little Brown & Co.

Banks, Steve. Battle of the Band. 2003. (ps-2). lib. bdg. 11.25 (978-0-613-58144-8(X)) Tandem Library Bks.

Beechen, Adam. Jimmy on Ice. Marderosian, Mark, illus. 2003. (Jimmy Neutron Ser.: Vol. 2). 32p. (J). pap. 3.99 (978-0-689-85294-7(0) , Simon Spotlight/Nickelodeon) Simon & Schuster Children's Publishing.

—Jimmy on Ice. 2003. (ps-2). lib. bdg. 11.80 (978-0-613-58154-7(7)) Tandem Library Bks.

Binaohan, Simon & Tacang, Brian. The Misadventures of Millicent Madding No 1: Bully-Be-Gone. 2006. (Illus.). 224p. (J). lib. bdg. 17.89 (978-0-06-073912-6(6)) HarperCollins Pubs.

—The Misadventures of Millicent Madding Vol. 1: Bully-Be-Gone. 2006. (Illus.). 224p. (J). 16.99 (978-0-06-073911-9(8)) HarperCollins Pubs.

Carlson, Drew. Attack of the Turtle. Johnson, David A., illus. 2007. 160p. (J). (gr. 3-7). 16.00 (978-0-8028-5308-0(0) , Eerdmans Bks For Young Readers) Eerdmans, William B. Publishing Co.

Cullimore, Stan. Killer Sharks. Savage, Paul, illus. 2006. 40p. (J). (gr. 2-3). lib. bdg. (978-1-59889-013-6(1)) Stone Arch Bks.

Deutsch, Stacia & Cohon, Rhody. Bell's Breakthrough. Wenzel, David, illus. 2005. 105p. (J). (*978-1-4156-2913-0(7) , Aladdin) Simon & Schuster Children's Publishing.

D'Lacey, Chris. Franklin's Bear. Taylor, Thomas, illus. 2005. (Red Go Bananas Ser.). 42p. (J). lib. bdg. (978-0-7787-2674-6(6)) Crabtree Publishing Co.

Dodds, Dayle Ann. Henry's Amazing Machine. Brooker, Kyrsten, illus. 2004. 32p. (J). 16.50 (978-0-374-32953-2(2) , Nelanie Kroupa Bks.) Farrar, Straus & Giroux.

Doubleday, Russell. Stories of Inventors. 2004. reprint ed. pap. 1.99 (978-1-4192-4959-4(2)); pap. 15.95 (978-1-4191-4959-7(8)) Kessinger Publishing, LLC.

Duffey, Betsy. Gadget War. 2000. (gr. 3-6). lib. bdg. 13.00 (978-0-7857-9891-0(9)) Tandem Library Bks.

Fardell, John. Flight of the Silver Turtle. 2006. 212p. (J). (gr. 3). 15.99 (978-0-399-24382-0(8) , Putnam Juvenile) Penguin Group (USA) Inc.

Garinger, Alan. Jeremiah Stokely, Inventor. 2002. (J). per. 14.95 (978-1-57860-105-9(3)) Emmis Bks.

Glass, Andrew. The Wondrous Whirligig: The Wright Brothers' First Flying Machine. Glass, Andrew, illus. 2007. (Illus.). 30p. (J). reprint ed. 17.00 (*978-1-4223-6765-0(7)) DIANE Publishing Co.

Gutman, Dan. Back in Time. Thorkelson, illus. 2002. 208p. (J). pap. 5.99 (978-0-689-84125-5(6) , Aladdin) Simon & Schuster Children's Publishing.

—The Edison Mystery: Back in Time. 2002. (Illus.). 201p. lib. bdg. 13.00 (978-0-613-62098-7(4)) Tandem Library Bks.

James, Simon. Baby Brains & RoboMom. 2008. (Illus.). 32p. (J). (ps-3). 15.99 (*978-0-7636-3463-6(8)) Candlewick Pr.

Lasky, Kathryn. Humphrey, Albert, & the Flying Machine. Manders, John, illus. 2004. 40p. (J). 16.00 (978-0-15-216235-1(6) , Harcourt Children's Bks) Harcourt Children's Bks.

Loesch, Joe. The Benjamin Franklin Project. Hutchinson, Cheryl, ed. Cox, Brian T., illus. unabr. ed. 2002. (Backyard Adventure Ser.). 60p. (J). (gr. k-5). reprint ed. 16.95 incl. audio compact disk (978-1-932332-01-8(4) , 1-932332-01-4) Toy Box Productions.

—The Benjamin Franklin Project. Hutchinson, Cheryl J., ed. Cox, Brian T., illus. unabr. ed. 2002. (Backyard Adventure Ser.). 60p. (J). pap. 16.95 incl. audio compact disk (978-1-887729-86-4(0)); pap. 14.95 incl. audio (978-1-887729-85-7(2)) Toy Box Productions.

—George Washington Carver: The Great Peanut Adventure. Hutchinson, Cheryl J., ed. Cox, Brian T., illus. 2002. (Backyard Adventure Ser.). 60p. (J). (gr. k-5). pap. 14.95 incl. audio (978-1-887729-87-1(9)); pap. 16.95 incl. audio compact disk (978-1-887729-88-8(7)) Toy Box Productions.

—George Washington Carver: The Great Peanut Adventure. Hutchinson, Cheryl, ed. Cox, Brian T., illus. unabr. ed. 2002. (Backyard Adventure Ser.). 60p. (J). (gr. k-5). reprint ed. 16.95 incl. audio compact disk (978-1-932332-02-5(2)) Toy Box Productions.

May, Scott. Sten Gizzle, Time Traveler: The Egyptian Adventure. Farkas, Josh, illus. 2000. 24p. (J). (gr. 1-3). pap. (978-0-9701450-4-8(7)) Long Hill Productions, Inc.

Montgomery, R. A. The Brilliant Dr. Wogan. 2005. (Illus.). 112p. (J). pap. (*978-0-7608-9705-8(0)) Sundance/Newbridge Educational Publishing.

Nix, Garth. One Beastly Beast: Two Aliens, Three Inventors, Four Fantastic Tales. Biggs, Brian, illus. 2007. 176p. (J). (gr. 2-6). 15.99 (*978-0-06-084319-9(5)); lib. bdg. 16.89 (*978-0-06-084320-5(9)) HarperCollins Pubs. (Eos).

Orton, J. R. Trial Trip of the Flying Cloud. 2004. reprint ed. pap. 15.95 (978-1-4191-9109-1(8)); pap. 1.99 (978-1-4192-9109-8(2)) Kessinger Publishing, LLC.

Park, Nick, et al. Close Shave. 2006. 31.95 (978-0-19-459239-0(1)) Oxford Univ. Pr., Inc.

Pettenati, Jeanne. Galileo's Journal, 1609-1610. Rui, Paolo, illus. 2006. 30p. (J). 16.95 (978-1-57091-879-7(1)); pap. 6.95 (978-1-57091-880-3(5)) Charlesbridge Publishing, Inc.

Sabuda, Robert. Uh-Oh Leonardo! 2003. (Illus.). 48p. (J). 16.95 (978-0-689-81160-9(8) , Atheneum) Simon & Schuster Children's Publishing.

Sargent, Dave & Sargent, Pat. Ginger: (Lilac Roan) Be Likeable. 30 vols., Vol. 27. Lenoir, Jane, illus. 2003. (Saddle Up Ser.: Vol. 27). 42p. (J). pap. 6.95 (978-1-56763-812-7(0)); lib. bdg. 22.60 (978-1-56763-811-0(2)) Ozark Publishing.

Teitelbaum, Michael. Party on, America! 2005. (Ready-To-Read Ser.: Vol. 7). (J). pap. 3.99 (978-0-689-86594-7(5) , Simon Spotlight/Nickelodeon) Simon & Schuster Children's Publishing.

Thompson, Lisa. Gadget Hero. Thompson, Lisa & Stapleton, Matthew, illus. 2005. (Read-It! Chapter Bks.). 48p. (J). (ps-k). lib. bdg. 19.95 (978-1-4048-1349-6(7)) Picture Window Bks.

—Game Plan. Thompson, Lisa & Stapleton, Matthew, illus. 2005. (Read-It! Chapter Bks.). 48p. (J). (ps-k). lib. bdg. 19.95 (978-1-4048-1344-1(6)) Picture Window Bks.

Walters, Eric. Hydrofoil Mystery. 2003. 224p. mass mkt. 4.99 (978-0-14-130220-1(8) , Penguin Global) Penguin Group (USA) Inc.

Young, Emma. STORM: the Infinity Code: The Infinity Code. 2008. (J). (gr. 5). 16.99 (*978-0-8037-3265-0(1) , Dial) Penguin Group (USA) Inc.

INVERTEBRATES

see also Corals; Insects; Mollusks; Protozoa; Worms

Blaxland, Beth. Annelids: Earthworms, Leeches, & Sea Worms. 2002. (Invertebrates Ser.). (Illus.). 32p. (gr. 4-8). 28.00 (978-0-7910-6993-6(1) , Chelsea Hse.) Facts On File, Inc.

—Myriapods: Centipedes, Millipedes, & Their Relatives. 2002. (Invertebrates Ser.). (Illus.). 32p. (gr. 4-8). 28.00 (978-0-7910-6995-0(8) , Chelsea Hse.) Facts On File, Inc.

Boothroyd, Jennifer. Under the Ground. 2006. (First Step Nonfiction Ser.). (Illus.). 8p. (J). pap. (978-0-8225-5661-9(8) , Lerner Pubns.) Lerner Publishing Group.

Coldiron, Deborah. Sea Sponges. 2007. (Underwater World Ser.). (Illus.). 32p. (J). (gr. k-4). lib. bdg. 24.21 (*978-1-59928-812-3(5) , Buddy Bks.) ABDO Publishing Co.

Galko, Francine. Invertebrates. 2003. (Classifying Living Things Ser.). (Illus.). 32p. (J). pap. 6.95 (978-1-4034-3278-0(3)) Heinemann Library.

Gareth Stevens Publishing Staff, contrib. by. Invertebrates. 2002. (Discovery Channel School Science Ser.). (Illus.). 32p. (J). (gr. 5 up). lib. bdg. 24.67 (978-0-8368-3216-7(7)) Stevens, Gareth Inc.

Grolier Educational Staff, contrib. by. Insects & Other Invertebrates, 50 vols. 2004. (J). (World of Animals Ser.: Vol. 3). (Illus.). 499.00 (978-0-7172-5894-9(7)); (978-0-7172-5895-6(5) , Grolier); (978-0-7172-5896-3(3) , Grolier); (978-0-7172-5897-0(1) , Grolier); (978-0-7172-5898-7(X) , Grolier); (978-0-7172-5899-4(8) , Grolier); (978-0-7172-5900-7(5) , Grolier); (978-0-7172-5901-4(3) , Grolier); (978-0-7172-5902-1(1) , Grolier); (978-0-7172-5903-8(X) , Grolier); (978-0-7172-5904-5(8) , Grolier) Scholastic Library Publishing.

Holt, Rinehart and Winston Staff. Biology: Simple Invertebrates: Resources for Chapter 28. 4th ed. 2004. (Illus.). pap. 9.20 (978-0-03-069962-7(2)) Holt, Rinehart & Winston.

—Holt Science & Technology Chapter 15: Life Science: Invertebrates. 5th ed. 2004. (Illus.). pap. 12.86 (978-0-03-030219-0(6)) Holt, Rinehart & Winston.

—Holt Science & Technology Chptr. 8: Invertebrates: Chapter Resources - Tennessee Edition. 3rd ed. 2003. (YA). (gr. 7). pap. 11.40 (978-0-03-069138-6(9)) Holt, Rinehart & Winston.

Insects, Amphibians & Reptiles. 2001. 63p. (YA). 8.65 (978-0-7525-4875-3(1)) Parragon, Inc.

Invertebrates. 2005. (Illus.). 32p. (gr. 4-8). pap. 168.00 (978-0-7910-7058-1(1) , Chelsea Hse.) Facts On File, Inc.

Invertebrates. 2001. (Inquiry Science Ser.). 32p. (gr. 4-5). 4.99 (978-1-56822-680-4(2) , IF20851) School Specialty Publishing.

Kalman, Bobbie. What Is an Anthropod? 2003. (gr. 3-6). lib. bdg. 14.10 (978-0-613-52933-4(2)) Tandem Library Bks.

Kilpatrick, Cathy. Creepy Crawlies. rev. ed. 2006. (First Nature Ser.). 24p. (J). pap. 4.99 (978-0-7945-1494-5(4) , Usborne) EDC Publishing.

McNeil, Niki, et al. HOCPP 1131 Invertebrates. 2006. spiral bd. 22.00 (*978-1-60308-131-3(3)) In the Hands of a Child.

Morgan, Sally. Butterflies, Bugs, & Worms. 2002. (Young Discoverers Ser.). (Illus.). 32p. (J). (gr. k-3). pap. 7.95 (978-0-7534-5499-2(8) , Kingfisher) Houghton Mifflin Co. Trade & Reference Div.

—Under a Stone & Other Rocky Places. 2006. (Hidden Habitats Ser.). (J). (978-1-59389-285-2(3)) Chrysalis Education.

Murray, Peter. Mollusks & Crustaceans. 2004. (Science Around Us Ser.). 32p. (J). (gr. 2-6). 27.07 (978-1-59296-217-4(3)) Child's World, Inc.

Ohare, Ted. Invertebrados. 2005. (Que Es un Animal? Biblioteca del Descubrimiento Ser.). (SPA.). 24p. pap. 5.45 (978-1-59515-689-1(5)) Rourke Publishing, LLC.

O'Hare, Ted. Invertebrates. 2006. (What Is an Animal Ser.). (Illus.). 24p. (gr. 1-4). 14.95 (978-1-59515-419-4(1)) Rourke Publishing, LLC.

Ohare, Ted. Invertebrates. 2005. 24p. pap. 5.45 (978-1-59515-733-1(6)) Rourke Publishing, LLC.

Parker, Steve. Insects, Bugs, & Art Activities. 2002. (gr. 3-6). lib. bdg. 17.60 (978-0-613-82415-6(6)) Tandem Library Bks.

—Nematodes, Leeches & Other Worms. 2006. (Animal Kingdom Classification Ser.). (Illus.). 48p. (J). (gr. 4-6). 26.60 (978-0-7565-1615-4(3)) Compass Point Bks.

—Sponges, Jellyfish & Other Simple Animals. 2006. (Animal Kingdom Classification Ser.). (Illus.). 48p. (J). (gr. 4-6). 26.60 (978-0-7565-1614-7(5)) Compass Point Bks.

Parker, Steve & Goodman, Polly. Insects, Bugs, & Art Activities. 2002. (Arty Facts Ser.). (Illus.). 48p. (J). (gr. 3-4). pap. (978-0-7787-1137-7(4)); lib. bdg. (978-0-7787-1109-4(9)) Crabtree Publishing Co.

Pascoe, Elaine. Animals Without Backbones. 2003. (Kids Guide to the Classification of Living Things Ser.). 32p. (J). lib. bdg. 21.25 (978-0-8239-6311-9(X) , PowerKids Pr.) Rosen Publishing Group, Inc., The.

Petersen, Christine. Invertebrates. 2002. (Single Title - Science Ser.). (Illus.). 144p. (YA). (gr. 8-12). pap. 25.00 (978-0-531-12021-7(X) , Watts, Franklin) Scholastic Library Publishing.

Pugliano-Martin, Carol. Como ser un explorador de animalitos & Being a Bug Scout. 2005. spiral bd. 84.00 (*978-1-4108-5695-1(X)) Benchmark Education Co.

Schaefer, Lola M. Ooey-Gooey Animals 123. 2002. (Ooey-Gooey Animals Ser.). (Illus.). 24p. (J). (ps-1). pap. 5.25 (978-1-58810-720-6(5) , 91370); lib. bdg. 17.08 (978-1-58810-511-0(3)) Heinemann Library.

—Ooey-Gooey Animals ABC. 2002. (Ooey-Gooey Animals Ser.). (Illus.). 24p. (J). (ps-1). pap. 5.25 (978-1-58810-719-0(1) , 91371); lib. bdg. 17.08 (978-1-58810-510-3(5)) Heinemann Library.

—Slugs. 2002. (Ooey-Gooey Animals Ser.). (Illus.). 24p. (J). (ps-1). pap. 5.25 (978-1-58810-718-3(3) , 91373); lib. bdg. 17.08 (978-1-58810-509-7(1)) Heinemann Library.

Schlepp, Tammy J. Minibeasts. 2000. (gr. k-3). lib. bdg. 13.00 (978-0-613-45203-8(8)) Tandem Library Bks.

Silverstein, Alvin, et al. Creepy Crawlies. 2003. (What a Pet! Ser.). (Illus.). 48p. (gr. 5-8). lib. bdg. 23.90 (978-0-7613-2511-6(5) , Millbrook Pr.) Lerner Publishing Group.

Solway, Andrew. Spiders & Other Invertebrates. 2006. (Illus.). 48p. (J). (978-1-4034-8223-5(3)); pap. (978-1-4034-8230-3(6)) Heinemann Library.

Taylor, Barbara, et al. Bugs. 2006. (Illus.). 264p. pap. 19.99 (978-0-7548-1149-7(2) , Lorenz Bks.) Anness Publishing GBR. *Dist:* National Bk. Network.

Townsend, John. Incredible Arachnids. 2005. (J). 56p. (978-1-4109-1717-1(7)); lib. bdg. (978-1-4109-1708-9(8)) Steck-Vaughn.

INVESTIGATIONS

Harvey, Gill. True Stories of Crime & Detection. 2004. (True Adventure Stories Ser.). 144p. (J). lib. bdg. 12.95 (978-1-58086-644-6(1) , Usborne) EDC Publishing.

Mason, Paul. Investigating UFOs. 2004. (Forensic Files Ser.). (Illus.). 48p. (J). pap. 8.50 (978-1-4034-5474-4(4)) Heinemann Library.

—UFOs. 2004. (Forensic Files Ser.). (Illus.). 48p. (J). lib. bdg. (978-1-4034-4834-7(5)) Heinemann Library.

Morrison, Yvonne. The DNA Gave It Away! Teens Solve Crime. 2008. (Shockwave: Science in Practice Ser.). 32p. (J). pap. 6.95 (*978-0-531-18842-2(6) , Children's Pr.) Scholastic Library Publishing.

Sherrow, Victoria. The Oklahoma City Bombing: Terror in the Heartland. 1998. (American Disasters Ser.). (Illus.). 48p. (YA). (gr. 4-10). lib. bdg. 23.93 (978-0-7660-1061-1(9)) Enslow Pubs., Inc.

—The World Trade Center Bombing: Terror in the Towers. 1998. (American Disasters Ser.). (Illus.). 48p. (YA). (gr. 4-10). lib. bdg. 23.93 (978-0-7660-1056-7(2)) Enslow Pubs., Inc.

Whitehouse, Patricia. Investigations, 4 bks., Set. 2004. (J). (ps-1). lib. bdg. 82.57 (978-1-4034-5101-9(X)) Heinemann Library.

INVESTMENTS

see also Bonds; Securities; Stock Exchanges; Stocks

Bailey, Gerry & Law, Felicia. Get Rich Quick? Earning Money. Phillips, Mike & Brooks, Rosie, illus. 2006. (My Money Ser.). 24p. (J). (gr. 4-6). 27.93 (978-0-7565-1674-1(9)) Compass Point Bks.

Bamber, Lori. Sleep-Easy Investing: The Canadian Guide to Lower-Risk & Income Investing. 2004. 288p. pap. 17.38 (978-0-470-83431-2(5)) Wiley, John & Sons, Inc.

Burgauer, Steven. The Wealth Builder's Guide: An Investment Primer. Burgauer, Kate R., illus. 1998. 50p. spiral bd. 10.95 (978-1-892086-02-0(6)) Zero-g Pr.

Fabris, Judith. Money...Cool! Brolin, Carol, illus. l.t. ed. 2003. 155p. (YA). pap. 9.95 (978-1-893335-12-7(7)) Archipelago Pr.

Gardner, David. Motley Fool Investment Guide for Teen: 8 Steps to Having More Money Than Your Pa. 2002. (gr. 7-12). lib. bdg. 23.45 (978-0-613-56819-7(2)) Tandem Library Bks.

Gardner, David, et al. The Motley Fool Investment Guide for Teens: 8 Steps to Having More Money Than Your Parents Ever Dreamed Of. 2002. (Illus.). 256p. (YA). (gr. 9-12). pap. 14.95 (978-0-7432-2996-8(7) , Fireside) Simon & Schuster.

Hagenbuch, Rod & Capalbo, Richard J. Investment Survival: How to Use Investment Research to Create Winning Portfolio for the Coming Bull Market. 2002. (Illus.). 253p. (YA). 42.50 (978-0-9725769-0-1(8)) Quantum Group.

Honig, Debbie. Growing Money: A Complete Investing Guide For Kids. 2001. 14.64 (978-0-606-22480-2(7)) Tandem Library Bks.

Kiyosaki, Robert T. & Lechter, Sharon L. Rich Dad's Escape from the Rat Race: How to Become a Rich Kid by Following Rich Dad's Advice. Hoseley, Rantz, illus. 2005. 56p. (J). (gr. 4-7). pap. 9.99 (978-0-316-00047-5(7)) Little, Brown Bks. for Young Readers.

Loewen, Nancy. Ups & Downs: A Book about the Stock Market. Fitzpatrick, Brad, illus. 2004. (Money Matters Ser.). 24p. (J). 22.60 (978-1-4048-0954-3(6)) Picture Window Bks.

Minden, Cecilia. Investing: Making Your Money Work for You. 2008. (J). lib. bdg. 25.26 (*978-1-60279-003-2(5)) Cherry Lake Publishing.

Rosinsky, Natalie M. Saving Money. 2003. (Let's See Library). (Illus.). 24p. (J). (gr. 1 up). 19.93 (978-0-7565-0484-7(8)) Compass Point Bks.

Tobias. The Only Investment Guide Teens Will Ever Need. 2003. (YA). pap. (978-0-15-600711-5(8)) Harcourt Trade Pubs.

Yan, Adrianne. It's a Money Thing. 2008. 96p. (YA). 12.99 (978-0-8118-4427-7(7)) Chronicle Bks. LLC.

IOWA

Balcavage, Dynise. Iowa. 2002. (From Sea to Shining Sea Ser.: 2). (Illus.). 80p. (J). (gr. 3-5). 30.50 (978-0-516-22481-7(6) , Children's Pr.) Scholastic Library Publishing.

Brown, Vanessa. Iowa. 2005. (Bilingual Library of the United States of America: Set 1). (ENG & SPA., Illus.). 32p. (J). (ps-k). lib. bdg. 22.50 (978-1-4042-3080-4(7) , Buenas Letra) Rosen Publishing Group, Inc., The.

Christian, Sandra J. Iowa. 2003. (Land of Liberty Ser.). (Illus.). 64p. (J). (gr. 3-4). lib. bdg. 23.93 (978-0-7368-1583-3(X) , Bridgestone Bks.) Capstone Pr., Inc.

Daily Nonpareil Staff, prod. Heroes Remembered. 2003. (Illus.). 192p. per. 27.95 (978-0-9745410-2-0(8)) Omaha Bks.

Dykstra, Mary. Iowa. 2006. (Portraits of the States Ser.). (Illus.). 32p. (J). pap. 8.95 (978-0-8368-4663-6(4)); (gr. 1 up). lib. bdg. 23.33 (978-0-8368-4664-5(8)) Stevens, Gareth Inc.

Haack, Kelly J. Iowa: A MyReportLinks. Com Book. 2003. (States Ser.). (Illus.). 48p. (J). lib. bdg. 25.26 (978-0-7660-5146-1(3) , MyReportLinks.com Bks.) Enslow Pubs., Inc.

Heinrichs, Ann. Iowa. 2005. (Welcome to the USA Ser.). 40p. (J). (gr. 1-5). 27.07 (978-1-59296-473-4(7)) Child's World, Inc.

—Iowa. 2003. (This Land Is Your Land Ser.). (Illus.). 48p. (J). (gr. 3 up). lib. bdg. 22.60 (978-0-7565-0342-0(6)) Compass Point Bks.

Horton, Loren N. Uniquely Iowa. 2004. (Heinemann State Studies). (Illus.). 48p. (J). 27.07 (978-1-4034-4647-3(4)) Heinemann Library.

Horton, Loren N. & Hutt, Sarah. Uniquely Iowa. 2004. (Heinemann State Studies). (Illus.). 48p. (J). (gr. 3-7). pap. 9.00 (978-1-4034-4716-6(0)) Heinemann Library.

Iowa. 2000. (Switched on Schoolhouse Ser.). (Illus.). (YA). (gr. 7-12). pap. 24.95 incl. cd-rom (978-0-7403-0267-1(1) , SOSIA) Alpha Omega Pubns., Inc.

King, David C. Iowa. 2006. (It's My State! Ser.). (Illus.). 80p. (J). lib. bdg. 29.93 (978-0-7614-1928-0(4) , Benchmark Bks.) Cavendish, Marshall Corp.

Kule, Elaine A. Iowa Facts & Symbols. (States & Their Symbols Ser.). 24p. (J). 2000. (Illus.). (gr. 2-3). lib. bdg. 18.60 (978-0-7368-0637-4(7) , Bridgestone Bks.); 2003. lib. bdg. 19.93 (978-0-7368-2245-9(3)) Capstone Pr., Inc.

Kummer, Patricia K. Iowa. rev. ed. 2002. (One Nation Ser.). (Illus.). 48p. (J). (gr. 3-4). lib. bdg. 22.60 (978-0-7368-1239-9(3) , Bridgestone Bks.) Capstone Pr., Inc.

LaDoux, Rita C. Iowa. 2nd rev. exp. ed. 2002. (Hello U. S. A. Ser.). (Illus.). 84p. (J). (gr. 3-6). lib. bdg. 25.26 (978-0-8225-4078-6(9)) Lerner Publishing Group.

—Iowa. rev. ed. 2002. (gr. 3-6). lib. bdg. 15.25 (978-0-613-46080-4(4)) Tandem Library Bks.

Marsh, Carole. The Big Iowa Reproducible Activity Book. 2001. (Carole Marsh Iowa Bks.). (Illus.). 96p. (J). (gr. 2-6). pap., act. bk. ed. 9.95 (978-0-7933-9942-0(4)) Gallopade International.

—Iowa Classic Christmas Trivia. 2002. (Carole Marsh Iowa Bks.). (Illus.). 32p. pap. 6.95 (978-0-635-01397-2(5) , 13975, Marsh, Carole Bks.); lib. bdg. 21.95 (978-0-635-01398-9(3)) Gallopade International.

—Iowa Current Events Projects: 30 Cool, Activities, Crafts, Experiments & More for Kids to Do to Learn about Your State! 2003. (Iowa Experience Ser.). 32p. (gr. k-5). pap. 5.95 (978-0-635-02034-5(3) , Marsh, Carole Bks.) Gallopade International.

—The Iowa Experience Pocket Guide. 2001. (Carole Marsh Iowa Bks.). 96p. (J). (gr. 3-8). pap. 6.95 (978-0-7933-9913-0(0)) Gallopade International.

—Iowa Geography Projects: 30 Cool, Activities, Crafts, Experiments & More for Kids to Do to Learn about Your State! 2003. (Iowa Experience Ser.). 32p. (gr. k-5). pap. 5.95 (978-0-635-01834-2(9) , Marsh, Carole Bks.) Gallopade International.

—Iowa Government Projects: 30 Cool, Activities, Crafts, Experiments & More for Kids to Do to Learn about Your State! 2003. (Iowa Experience Ser.). 32p. (gr. k-5). pap. 5.95 (978-0-635-01934-9(5) , Marsh, Carole Bks.) Gallopade International.

—Iowa Jeopardy! Answers & Questions about Our State! 2001. (Carole Marsh Iowa Bks.). (Illus.). 32p. (J). (gr. 3-8). pap. 7.95 (978-0-7933-9797-6(9)) Gallopade International.

—Iowa "Jography" A Fun Run Thru Our State! 2001. (Carole Marsh Iowa Bks.). (Illus.). 32p. (J). (gr. 3-8). pap. 7.95 (978-0-7933-9826-3(6)) Gallopade International.

—Iowa Millionaire: Game Book. 2001. (Carole Marsh Iowa Bks.). (Illus.). 32p. (J). (gr. 3-8). pap., act. bk. ed. 9.95 (978-0-635-00046-0(6)) Gallopade International.

—Iowa People Projects: 30 Cool, Activities, Crafts, Experiments & More for Kids to Do to Learn about Your State! 2003. (Iowa Experience Ser.). 32p. (gr. k-5). pap. 5.95 (978-0-635-01984-4(1) , Marsh, Carole Bks.) Gallopade International.

—Iowa Survivor: Game Book. 2001. (Carole Marsh Iowa Bks.). (Illus.). 32p. (J). (gr. 3-8). pap., act. bk. ed. 9.95 (978-0-635-00536-6(0)) Gallopade International.

—Iowa Symbols & Facts Projects: 30 Cool, Activities, Crafts, Experiments & More for Kids to Do to Learn about Your State! 2003. (Iowa Experience Ser.). 32p. (gr. k-5). pap. 5.95 (978-0-635-01884-7(5) , Marsh, Carole Bks.) Gallopade International.

—My First Book about Iowa. 2001. (Illus.). 32p. (J). (gr. k-4). pap. 7.95 (978-0-7933-9884-3(3)) Gallopade International.

—Who Wants to Be a Millionaire? 2001. (Carole Marsh Iowa Bks.). lib. bdg. 29.95 (978-0-635-00047-7(4)) Gallopade International.

Martin, Michael A. Iowa: The Hawkeye State. 2002. (World Almanac Library of the States). (Illus.). 48p. (J). (gr. 5 up). lib. bdg. 30.00 (978-0-8368-5133-5(1)); pap. 14.95 (978-0-8368-5303-2(2)) Stevens, Gareth Inc. (World Almanac Library).

—Iowa: The Hawkeye State. 2003. (gr. 3-6). lib. bdg. 37.95 (978-0-613-76724-8(1)) Tandem Library Bks.

Morrice, Polly. Iowa. 1998. (Celebrate the States Ser.). (Illus.). 144p. (gr. 4-8). lib. bdg. 37.07 (978-0-7614-0421-7(X) , Benchmark Bks.) Cavendish, Marshall Corp.

Morrice, Polly Alison & Hart, Joyce. Iowa. 2nd ed. 2007. (Celebrate the States Ser.). (J). lib. bdg. 39.93 (978-0-7614-2350-8(8) , Benchmark Bks.) Cavendish, Marshall Corp.

Murray, Julie. Iowa. 2006. (Illus.). 32p. (J). (gr. k-4). lib. bdg. 22.78 (978-1-59197-674-5(X) , Buddy Bks.) ABDO Publishing Co.

Peterson, Sheryl. Iowa. 2008. (J). (*978-1-58341-640-2(4) , Creative Education) Creative Co., The.

Pierce, Patricia A. Numbers in a Row: An Iowa Number Book. Rohner, Dorothia, illus. 2006. 40p. (J). 17.95 (978-1-58536-164-9(X)) Sleeping Bear Pr.

Pierce, Patricia A. & Langton, Bruce, trs. H Is for Hawkeye: An Iowa Alphabet. Langton, Bruce, illus. 2003. (Illus.). 40p. (J). 17.95 (978-1-58536-114-4(3)) Sleeping Bear Pr.

Sapre, Reshma. Iowa. 2005. (Rookie Read-About Geography Ser.). (Illus.). 32p. (J). (gr. 1-2). pap. 5.95 (978-0-516-25930-7(X) , Children's Pr.) Scholastic Library Publishing.

Sapre, Reshma & Vargus, Nanci Reginelli. Iowa. 2004. (Rookie Read-About Geography Ser.). (J). 20.50 (978-0-516-22753-5(X) , Children's Pr.) Scholastic Library Publishing.

Winans, Jay D. A Guide to Iowa. 2001. (American States Ser.). (Illus.). 32p. (J). lib. bdg. 16.95 (978-1-930954-38-0(7)); per. 7.95 (978-1-930954-81-6(6)) Weigl Pubs., Inc.

Woods, Jessica I. Iowa. 2003. (Seeds of a Nation Ser.). (Illus.). 48p. (J). 23.70 (978-0-7377-1396-1(8) , Greenhaven Pr., Inc.) Thomson Gale.

IOWA—FICTION

Adee, Donna J. Miriam & Timothy Face Life, Vol. 3. Babcock, Marci, illus. 2000. 384p. (J). pap. 12.95 (978-0-9654272-3-4(4)) Harvest Pubns.

Andersen, C. B. The Book of Mormon Sleuth. 2000. v, 279p. (J). pap. 9.95 (978-1-57345-664-7(0)) Deseret Bk. Co.

Bauer, Joan. Squashed. 2005. 208p. (YA). (gr. 7). pap. 7.99 (978-0-14-240426-3(8) , Puffin) Penguin Group (USA) Inc.

—Squashed. 2001. (978-0-606-22520-5(X)) Tandem Library Bks.

—Squashed! 2001. 208p. (YA). 16.99 (978-0-399-23750-8(X) , Putnam Juvenile) Penguin Group (USA) Inc.

Butler, Dori Hillestad. Sliding into Home. 2005. 192p. (J). pap. 5.95 (978-1-56145-341-2(2)) Peachtree Pubs., Ltd.

Dallas, Sandra. Alice's Tulips. 2000. (gr. 7-12). lib. bdg. 22.20 (978-0-613-42657-2(6)) Tandem Library Bks.

Duey, Kathleen. Katie & the Mustang, Bk. 1. 2004. (Hoofbeats Ser.: Bk 1). 128p. pap. 4.99 (978-0-14-240090-6(4) , Puffin) Penguin Group (USA) Inc.

—Lara at Athenry Castle, Vol. 3. 2005. (Hoofbeats Ser.: No. 7). 128p. (J). (gr. 3-6). 15.99 (978-0-525-47340-4(8) , Dutton Juvenile) Penguin Group (USA) Inc.

Francis, Dorothy. The Case of the Bad-Luck Bike Ride Across Iowa. 2001. (YA). pap. 12.95 (978-0-7891-5323-4(8)) Perfection Learning Corp.

Gorman, Carol & Findley, Ron. The Stumptown Kid. 2005. 224p. (J). (gr. 3-7). 14.95 (978-1-56145-337-5(4)) Peachtree Pubs., Ltd.

Hello, Cy! 2007. (J). 14.95 (*978-1-932888-53-9(5)) Mascot Bks., Inc.

Hewitt, William. Across the Wide River. 2004. 104p. (J). 11.95 (978-0-8263-2978-3(0)) Univ. of New Mexico Pr.

Heynen, Jim. Cosmos Coyote & William the Nice. 2002. (gr. 7-12). lib. bdg. 16.45 (978-0-613-71513-3(6)) Tandem Library Bks.

Horvath, Polly. Occasional Cow. 2003. (gr. 5-8). lib. bdg. 14.10 (978-0-613-71875-2(5)) Tandem Library Bks.

Johnson, Tim. Never So Green. 2002. 240p. (YA). 18.00 (978-0-374-35509-8(6) , Farrar, Straus & Giroux (BYR)) Farrar, Straus & Giroux.

MacKall, Dandi Daley. Kyra's Story. 2003. (Degrees of Guilt Ser.). (YA). pap. 9.99 (978-0-8423-8284-7(4)) Tyndale Hse. Pubs.

Pfeiffer, Joseph R. & Pfeiffer, Robert J. Billy's Unusual Adventure. Pfeiffer, Joseph R., illus. l.t. ed. 1998. (Illus.). 32p. (J). (gr. k-4). 11.95 (978-0-9659772-1-0(8)); pap. 5.95 (978-0-9659772-2-7(6)) Chessmore Publishing.

Rylant, Cynthia. Old Town in the Green Groves: Laura Ingalls Wilder's Lost Little House Years. 2007. (Little House Ser.). 192p. (J). pap. 6.99 (978-0-06-088546-5(7) , Harper Trophy) HarperCollins Pubs.

—Old Town in the Green Groves: Laura Ingalls Wilder's Lost Little House Years. LaMarche, Jim, illus. (Little House Ser.). 176p. (J). 2004. pap. 5.99 (978-0-06-440990-2(2) , Harper Trophy); 2002. 15.99 (978-0-06-029561-5(9)) HarperCollins Pubs.

Warner, Gertrude Chandler. The Clue in the Corn Maze, Vol. 101. 2004. (Boxcar Children Mysteries Ser.: 101). (Illus.). 128p. (J). (gr. 2-7). 14.95 (978-0-8075-5556-9(8)); pap., lib. bdg. 4.50 (978-0-8075-5557-6(6)) Whitman, Albert & Co.

IOWA—HISTORY

Gensicke, Mary Ann. Fun Facts & Games: Iowa. Griffin, Sandra Ure, illus. 2000. (Fun Facts & Games Ser.). 64p. (J). (gr. 1-5). pap. 5.95 (978-1-892920-46-1(8)) GHB Publishers, LLC.

Iowa City, A Sense of Place: A Pictorial History of Iowa City the Surrounding Area. 2001. per. 34.99 (978-0-9712727-0-5(0)) Iowa City Pr.-Citizen.

Marsh, Carole. Iowa History Projects: 30 Cool, Activities, Crafts, Experiments & More for Kids to Do to Learn about Your State! 2003. (Iowa Experience Ser.). 32p. (gr. k-5). pap. 5.95 (978-0-635-01784-0(9) , Marsh, Carole Bks.) Gallopade International.

—My First Pocket Guide Iowa. 2000. (Iowa Experience! Ser.). (Illus.). 96p. (J). (gr. 3-8). 12.95 (978-0-635-01305-7(3) , 13053) Gallopade International.

Poole, Marcia. Building a Dream: The Story of the Sioux City Lewis & Clark Interpretive Center. 2004. (Illus.). 60p. per. 10.95 (978-0-9753860-0-2(X)) Sioux City Lewis & Clark Interpretive Ctr., The.

Wagner, Jay. H Is for Hawkeye. Potts Dawson, Eileen, illus. 2003. (J). 16.95 (978-1-931599-11-5(4) , Trails Bks.) Big Earth Publishing.

Wetterer, Margaret K. Kate Shelley & the Midnight Express. 2005. (On My Own History Ser.). (Illus.). (J). pap. 18.95 incl. audio compact disk (978-1-59112-663-8(0)) Live Oak Media.

IRAN

Bauder, Julia. Is Iran a Threat to Global Security? 2006. (Illus.). 128p. (gr. 10-12). 21.20 (978-0-7377-3527-7(9)); pap. 29.95 (978-0-7377-3526-0(0)) Thomson Gale. (Greenhaven Pr., Inc.).

Bauer, Brandy. Iran. 2005. (Fact Finders Ser.). (Illus.). 32p. (J). 22.60 (978-0-7368-3752-1(3)) Capstone Pr., Inc.

Cartlidge, Cherese & Clark, Charles. Iran. 2002. (Modern Nations of the World Ser.). (Illus.). 120p. (YA). (gr. 7-10). 29.95 (978-1-56006-971-3(6) , Lucent Bks.) Thomson Gale.

Doak, Robin S. Iran. 2004. (First Reports). (Illus.). 48p. (J). (gr. 3 up). lib. bdg. 22.60 (978-0-7565-0581-3(X)) Compass Point Bks.

Egendorf, Laura K., ed. Iran. 2006. (Opposing Viewpoints Ser.). (Illus.). 244p. (YA). (gr. 9 up). pap. 24.95 (978-0-7377-3418-8(3)); lib. bdg. 36.20 (978-0-7377-3417-1(5)) Thomson Gale. (Greenhaven Pr., Inc.).

Fast, April. Iran — The Land. 2005. (Lands, Peoples, & Cultures Ser.). (Illus.). 32p. (J). (ps-9). per. (978-0-7787-9315-1(X) , 1242060) Crabtree Publishing Co.

—Iran — The People. 2005. (Lands, Peoples, & Cultures Ser.). (Illus.). 32p. (J). (ps-9). per. (978-0-7787-9316-8(8)) Crabtree Publishing Co.

Grolier Educational Staff, contrib. by. Iran. 2003. (Illus.). 32p. (J). (978-0-7172-5794-2(0) , Grolier) Scholastic Library Publishing.

Habeeb, William Mark. Iran. 2003. (Modern Middle East Nations & Their Strategic Place in the World Ser.). (Illus.). 112,128p. (J). (gr. 7 up). lib. bdg. (978-1-59084-551-6(X)) Mason Crest Pubs.

Italia, Bob. Iran. 2001. (Countries Ser.). (Illus.). 40p. (J). (gr. k-6). lib. bdg. 22.78 (978-1-57765-495-7(1) , Checkerboard Library) ABDO Publishing Co.

Kaplan, Leslie C. Iran, a Primary Source Guide. 2005. (Countries of the World, a Primary Source Journey Ser.). (J). 19.95 (978-1-4042-2754-5(7) , PowerKids Pr.) Rosen Publishing Group, Inc., The.

Kheirabadi, Masoud. Iran. 2003. (Modern World Nations Ser.). (Illus.). (gr. 6-12). 150p. 30.00 (978-0-7910-7234-9(7)); 200p. pap. 30.00 (978-0-7910-7502-9(8)) Facts On File, Inc. (Chelsea Hse.).

—Iran. 2003. (gr. 7-12). lib. bdg. 21.05 (978-0-613-83447-6(X)) Tandem Library Bks.

King, John. Iran & the Islamic Revolution. 2005. (Middle East Ser.). (Illus.). 56p. (J). (978-1-4109-1623-5(5)); (gr. 4-7). pap. 9.90 (978-1-4109-1629-7(4)) Steck-Vaughn.

Lyle, Gary. Iran. 1999. (Major World Nations Ser.). (Illus.). 144p. (YA). (gr. 4-7). 29.95 (978-0-7910-4740-8(7) , Chelsea Hse.) Facts On File, Inc.

Mara, Wil. Iran. 2006. (Discovering Cultures Ser.). (Illus.). 48p. (J). lib. bdg. 28.50 (978-0-7614-1986-0(1) , Benchmark Bks.) Cavendish, Marshall Corp.

Miller, William. Tales of Persia: Missionary Stories from Islamic Iran. Van Patten, Bruce, illus. 2005. 163p. pap. 9.99 (978-0-87552-615-7(2)) P & R Publishing.

Moritz, Patricia M. Iran. 2000. (Dropping in on Ser.). (Illus.). 32p. (J). (gr. 2-5). lib. bdg. 28.50 (978-1-55916-285-2(6)) Rourke Publishing, LLC.

O'Shea, Maria. Iran. 2000. (Countries of the World Ser.). (Illus.). 96p. (J). (gr. 6 up). lib. bdg. 30.00 (978-0-8368-2325-7(7)) Stevens, Gareth Inc.

Reece, Katherine E. The Persians: Warriors of the Ancient World. 2005. (Ancient Civilizations Ser.). (Illus.). 48p. (gr. 4-8). 20.95 (978-1-59515-238-1(5)) Rourke Publishing, LLC.

Richardson, Adele. Iran. 2006. (My First Look at Countries Ser.). (Illus.). 24p. (J). (gr. 1-2). lib. bdg. 15.95 (978-1-58341-446-0(0) , Creative Education) Creative Co., The.

Richter, Joanne. Iran — The Culture. 2005. (Lands, Peoples, & Cultures Ser.). (Illus.). 32p. (J). (978-0-7787-9317-5(6) , 1242062) Crabtree Publishing Co.

Schemenauer, Elma. Welcome to Iran. 2008. (Welcome to the World Ser.). 32p. (J). (gr. 1-5). 27.07 (*978-1-59296-972-2(0)) Child's World, Inc.

Seidman, David. Teens in Iran. 2007. lib. bdg. (*978-0-7565-3300-7(7)) Compass Point Bks.

Walsh, Kieran. Iran. 2003. (Countries in the News Ser.). (Illus.). 24p. (J). 25.64 (978-1-58952-677-8(5)) Rourke Publishing, LLC.

Yip, Dora & O'Shea, Maria. Welcome to Iran. 2001. (Welcome to My Country Ser.). (Illus.). 48p. (J). (gr. 2 up). lib. bdg. 26.00 (978-0-8368-2525-1(X)) Stevens, Gareth Inc.

IRAN—FICTION

Ahour, Paravish. All Children of the World Smile in the Same Language: Iran; the Cradle of Civilization. 2006. 103p. (J). per. 16.95 (978-1-60002-015-5(1) , 3593, Airleaf Publishing) Airleaf Publishing & Bookselling.

Chowdhury, Rohini. The Three Princes of Persia. 2005. (Illus.). 176p. (J). pap. 8.00 (978-0-14-333493-4(X) , Penguin Global) Penguin Group (USA) Inc.

Fletcher, Susan. Alphabet of Dreams. 2008. 432p. (YA). mass mkt. 6.99 (*978-0-689-85152-0(9) , Simon Pulse) Simon & Schuster Children's Publishing.

Fletcher, Susan. Shadow Spinner. unabr. ed. 1999. (J). (gr. 5). pap., stu. ed. 59.24 incl. audio (978-0-7887-3007-8(X) , 40889) Recorded Bks., LLC.

—Shadow Spinner. Kramer, Dave, illus. 1999. (Jean Karl Bks.). 224p. (J). (gr. 5-9). pap. 5.99 (978-0-689-83051-8(3) , Aladdin) Simon & Schuster Children's Publishing.

—Shadow Spinner. 1999. (978-0-606-17195-3(9)); (gr. 5-8). lib. bdg. 13.00 (978-0-613-23034-6(5)) Tandem Library Bks.

Mead, Alice. Dawn & Dusk. 2007. (Illus.). 151p. (J). (*978-1-4287-3319-0(1)) Farrar, Straus & Giroux.

Moore, Diane. Sophie's Sojourn in Persia. 2004. 143p. pap. 19.95 (978-1-4137-4458-3(3)) PublishAmerica, Inc.

Napoli, Donna Jo. Beast. 272p. (YA). 2004. pap. 6.99 (978-0-689-87005-7(1)); 2002. (gr. 7 up). pap. 8.99 (978-0-689-83590-2(6)) Simon & Schuster Children's Publishing. (Simon Pulse).

Pakulak, Eric. At the Side of Esther: A Multiple-Ending Bible Adventure. Bulanadi, Danny, illus. 2000. 96p. (J). pap. 6.95 (978-0-8198-0769-4(9)) Pauline Bks. & Media.

Sayres, Meghan Nuttall. Anahita's Woven Riddle. 2006. 368p. (YA). (gr. 5-9). 16.95 (978-0-8109-5481-6(8)) Abrams, Harry N. , Inc.

Shary, Christie. The Blue Mosaic Vase. 2002. per. 18.99 (978-0-7443-0357-5(5)) SynergEbks.

Tenney, Tommy. Hadassah: The Girl Who Became Queen Esther. 2005. (Illus.). 168p. (J). 9.99 (978-0-7642-2738-7(6)) Bethany Hse. Pubs.

IRAN—HISTORY

Abbott, Jacob. History of Xerxes the Great. 2003. 302p. 99.00 (978-0-7950-4614-8(6)) New Library Press.Net.

Barter, James. The Ancient Persians. 2005. (Lost Civilizations Ser.). 112p. (YA). (gr. 5-8). lib. bdg. 29.95 (978-1-59018-621-3(4) , Lucent Bks.) Thomson Gale.

Barth, Linda. Mohammed Reza Pahlavi. 2002. (Major World Leaders Ser.). (Illus.). 112p. (gr. 6-12). 30.00 (978-0-7910-6948-6(6) , Chelsea Hse.) Facts On File, Inc.

H I

Bramwell, Neil D. Ancient Persia: A MyReportLinks. com Book. 2004. (Civilizations of the Ancient World Ser.). (Illus.). 48p. (YA). lib. bdg. 25.26 (978-0-7660-5251-2(6) , MyReportLinks.com Bks.) Enslow Pubs., Inc.

Cool Root, Margaret. Handbook to Life in the Persian Empire. Facts on File, Inc. Staff, ed. 2008. (Handbook to Life Ser.). 400p. (gr. 9). 70.00 (978-0-8160-5584-5(X)) Facts On File, Inc.

Graham, Amy. Iran in the News: Past, Present, & Future. 2006. (Middle East Nations in the News Ser.). (Illus.). 128p. (J). lib. bdg. 33.27 (978-1-59845-022-4(0) , MyReportLinks.com Bks.) Enslow Pubs., Inc.

Haskins, James, et al. Count Your Way Through Iran. 2007. (Count Your Way Ser.). (Illus.). 24p. (J). 19.93 (978-1-57505-881-8(2) , Millbrook Pr.) Lerner Publishing Group.

Khanlari, Parviz-Natel. A Young Persons History of Iran. Yazdanfar, Farzin, tr. 2006. (YA). pap. (978-1-58814-042-5(3)) IBEX Pubs., Inc.

Nardo, Don. Life in Ancient Persia. 2003. (Life During the Great Civilizations Ser.). (Illus.). 48p. (J). (gr. 3-5). 24.95 (978-1-56711-740-0(6) , Blackbirch Pr., Inc.) Thomson Gale.

Piddock, Charles. Iran. 2006. (Illus.). 48p. pap. (978-0-8368-6714-5(9)); lib. bdg. (978-0-8368-6707-7(6)) Stevens, Gareth Inc. (World Almanac Library).

Sam, Amini. Pictorial History of Iran: Ancient Pers. 2006. pap. 17.95 (***978-1-4259-6722-2(1)***) AuthorHouse.

Sheen, Barbara. Foods of Iran. 2006. (Taste of Culture Ser.). (Illus.). 64p. (J). (gr. 3-6). 27.45 (978-0-7377-3453-9(1) , Greenhaven Pr., Inc.) Thomson Gale.

Wagner, Heather Lehr. Iran. 2002. (Creation of the Modern Middle East Ser.). (Illus.). 125p. (gr. 6-12). 35.00 (978-0-7910-6514-3(6) , Chelsea Hse.) Facts On File, Inc.

IRAQ

Arbuthnot, Felicity & Van Der Gaag, Nikki. Baghdad. 2005. (Great Cities of the World Ser.). (Illus.). 48p. (J). (ps-7). 30.00 (978-0-8368-5049-9(1) , World Almanac Library) Stevens, Gareth Inc.

Balcavage, Dynise. Iraq. 2002. (Countries of the World Ser.). (Illus.). 96p. (J). (gr. 6 up). lib. bdg. 30.00 (978-0-8368-2359-2(1)) Stevens, Gareth Inc.

Bean, I. R. Iraq. 2008. (J). (***978-1-60044-616-0(7)***) Rourke Publishing, LLC.

Britton, Tamara L. Iraq. 2000. (Countries Ser.). (Illus.). 40p. (J). (gr. k-6). lib. bdg. 22.78 (978-1-57765-392-9(0) , Checkerboard Library) ABDO Publishing Co.

Coleman, Wim & Perrin, Pat. Iraq in the News: Past, Present, & Future. 2006. (Middle East Nations in the News Ser.). (Illus.). 128p. (J). lib. bdg. 33.27 (978-1-59845-027-9(1) , MyReportLinks.com Bks.) Enslow Pubs., Inc.

Corzine, Phyllis. Iraq. 2003. (Modern Nations of the World Ser.). (Illus.). 112p. (J). 29.95 (978-1-59018-114-0(X) , Lucent Bks.) Thomson Gale.

Docherty, J. P. Iraq. 1999. (Major World Nations Ser.). (Illus.). 144p. (YA). (gr. 4-7). 29.95 (978-0-7910-4979-2(5) , Chelsea Hse.) Facts On File, Inc.

Farndon, John. Mesopotamia. 2007. (DK Eyewitness Bks.). 72p. (J). (gr. 3-8). 15.99 incl. cd-rom (978-0-7566-2972-4(1)) Dorling Kindersley Publishing, Inc.

Fast, April. Iraq — The Culture. 2004. (Lands, Peoples, & Cultures Ser.). (Illus.). 32p. (J). (978-0-7787-9320-5(6)) Crabtree Publishing Co.

—Iraq — The Land. 2004. (Lands, Peoples, & Cultures Ser.). (Illus.). 32p. (J). (978-0-7787-9318-2(4)) Crabtree Publishing Co.

—Iraq — The People. 2004. (Lands, Peoples, & Cultures Ser.). (Illus.). 32p. (J). (978-0-7787-9319-9(2)) Crabtree Publishing Co.

Foster, Leila Merrell & Augustin, Byron. Iraq. 2006. (Enchantment of the World, Second Ser.). (Illus.). 144p. (J). (gr. 5-9). 36.00 (978-0-516-24852-3(9) , Children's Pr.) Scholastic Library Publishing.

Gaag, Nikki Van Der & Arbuthnot, Felicity. Baghdad. 2005. (Great Cities of the World Ser.). (Illus.). 48p. (J). pap. (978-0-8368-5209-7(5) , World Almanac Library) Stevens, Gareth Inc.

Kotapish, Dawn. Daily Life in Ancient & Modern Baghdad. Webb, Ray, illus. 2005. (Cities Through Time Ser.). 64p. (gr. 5-12). 25.26 (978-0-8225-3219-4(0)) Lerner Publishing Group.

Lightfoot, Dale. Iraq. 2nd rev. ed. 2006. (Modern World Nations Ser.). (Illus.). 120p. (J). (gr. 6-12). 30.00 (978-0-7910-9247-7(X) , Chelsea Hse.) Facts On File, Inc.

Malaspina, Ann. The Iroquois: A Proud People. 2005. (American Indians Ser.). (Illus.). 48p. (J). lib. bdg. 23.93 (978-0-7660-2450-2(4) , Enslow Elementary) Enslow Pubs., Inc.

Malhotra, Sonali. Welcome to Iraq. 2004. (Welcome to My Country Ser.). (Illus.). 48p. (J). (gr. 2 up). lib. bdg. 26.00 (978-0-8368-2559-6(4)) Stevens, Gareth Inc.

Mance, Angelia L. Iraq. 2002. (Modern World Nations Ser.). (Illus.). 150p. (gr. 6-12). 30.00 (978-0-7910-6928-8(1) , Chelsea Hse.) Facts On File, Inc.

Parks, Peggy J. Iraq. 2003. (Nations in Conflict Ser.). (Illus.). 48p. (J). 24.95 (978-1-4103-0078-2(1) , Blackbirch Pr., Inc.) Thomson Gale.

Phillips, Larissa. A Historical Atlas of Iraq. 2003. (Historical Atlases of South Asia, Central Asia & the Middle East Ser.). (Illus.). 64p. (YA). lib. bdg. 30.60 (978-0-8239-3865-0(4)) Rosen Publishing Group, Inc., The.

Ponsford, Simon. Iraq. 2007. (J). (***978-1-59920-021-7(X)***) Smart Apple Media.

Reece, Katherine E. The Mesopotamians: Conquerors of the Middle East. 2005. (Ancient Civilizations Ser.). (Illus.). 48p. (gr. 4-8). 20.95 (978-1-59515-237-4(7)) Rourke Publishing, LLC.

Roraback, Amanda. Iraq in a Nutshell. 2nd rev. exp. ed. 2004. (Nutshell Notes). (Illus.). 60p. (YA). pap. 7.95 (978-0-9702908-6-1(1)) Enisen Publishing.

Sapre, Reshma. Iraq. 2003. (World Tour Ser.). (J). lib. bdg. 25.70 (978-0-7398-6811-9(X)) Raintree.

Spengler, Kremena. Iraq: A Question & Answer Book. 2004. (Fact Finders Ser.). (Illus.). 32p. (J). lib. bdg. 22.60 (978-0-7368-2691-4(2)) Capstone Pr., Inc.

Steele, Philip. Mesopotamia. 2007. (DK Eyewitness Bks.). 72p. (J). (gr. 3-8). lib. bdg. 19.99 (978-0-7566-2971-7(3)) Dorling Kindersley Publishing, Inc.

Stevens, Kathryn. Welcome to Iraq. 2007. (Welcome to the World Ser.). 32p. (J). (gr. 1-5). 27.07 (***978-1-59296-916-6(X)***) Child's World, Inc.

Stewart, Gail B. Saddam Hussein. 2003. (Heroes & Villains Ser.). (Illus.). 96p. (J). 29.95 (978-1-59018-350-2(9) , Lucent Bks.) Thomson Gale.

Taus-Bolstad, Stacy. Iraq in Pictures. 2nd ed. 2004. (Visual Geography Series, Second Ser.). (Illus.). 80p. (J). (gr. 5-12). 27.93 (978-0-8225-0934-9(2)) Lerner Publishing Group.

Thompson, William & Thompson, Dorcas. Iraq. 2003. (Modern Middle East Nations & Their Strategic Place in the World Ser.). (Illus.). 112,128p. (YA). (gr. 5 up). lib. bdg. (978-1-59084-508-0(0)) Mason Crest Pubs.

Walsh, Kieran. Iraq. 2003. (Countries in the News Ser.). (Illus.). 48p. (J). 25.64 (978-1-58952-678-5(3)) Rourke Publishing, LLC.

IRAQ—HISTORY

Bryant, Tamera. The Life & Times of Hammurabi. 2005. (Biography from Ancient Civilizations Ser.). (Illus.). 48p. (J). (ps-7). lib. bdg. 29.95 (978-1-58415-338-2(5) , 1244807) Mitchell Lane Pubs., Inc.

Downing, David. Saddam Hussein & Iraq. 2003. (Troubled World Ser.). (Illus.). 64p. (J). lib. bdg. 28.56 (978-1-4109-0184-2(X)) Raintree.

Fattah, Hala. A Brief History of Iraq. 2008. (Brief History Ser.). 320p. (gr. 9). 45.00 (978-0-8160-5767-2(2)) Facts On File, Inc.

Gruber, Beth. Ancient Iraq: Archaeology Unlocks the Secrets of Iraq's Past. 2007. (NG Investigates Ser.). (Illus.). 64p. (J). (gr. 1-5). 17.95 (978-0-7922-5382-2(5)); (gr. 5). lib. bdg. 27.90 (978-0-7922-5383-9(3)) National Geographic Society. (National Geographic Children's Bks.).

Hardwick, Susan. Iraq: World-Wise Kids Guides. 2004. 96p. (978-1-59258-093-4(9)) Hylas Publishing.

Hynson, Colin. Mesopotamia. 2006. (Illus.). 48p. (J). pap. (978-0-8368-6244-7(9)); lib. bdg. 30.00 (978-0-8368-6192-1(2)) Stevens, Gareth Inc. (World Almanac Library).

King, John. Iraq Then & Now. 2005. (Middle East Ser.). (Illus.). (J). 55p. (978-1-4109-1622-8(7)); 56p. (gr. 4-7). pap. 9.90 (978-1-4109-1628-0(6)) Steck-Vaughn.

Malam, John. Ancient Mesopotamia. 2004. (Historic Civilizations Ser.). (Illus.). 32p. (J). lib. bdg. 24.67 (978-0-8368-4199-2(9)) Stevens, Gareth Inc.

Matthews, Rupert. You Wouldn't Want to Be an Assyrian Soldier! An Ancient Army You'd Rather Not Join. Antram, David, illus. 2007. (You Wouldn't Want to Ser.). 32p. (J). (gr. 2-5). 28.50 (***978-0-531-18727-2(6)*** , Watts, Franklin) Scholastic Library Publishing.

Oakes, Lorna. Step Into: Mesopotamia. 2006. (Illus.). 64p. pap. 12.99 (978-1-84476-305-4(6) , Southwater) Anness Publishing GBR. *Dist:* National Bk. Network.

Samuel, Charlie. Iraq. 2007. (Countries of the World Ser.). (Illus.). 64p. (YA). (gr. 5 up). lib. bdg. 27.90 (***978-1-4263-0061-5(1)*** , National Geographic Children's Bks.) National Geographic Society.

Schomp, Virginia. Ancient Mesopotamia: The Sumerians, Babylonians, & Assyrians. 2005. (People of the Ancient World Ser.). (Illus.). 112p. (J). (gr. 6-8). pap. 9.95 (978-0-531-16741-0(0) , Watts, Franklin) Scholastic Library Publishing.

Spencer, William. Iraq: Old Land, New Nation in Conflict. 2000. (Single Titles Ser.). (Illus.). 144p. (gr. 7 up). lib. bdg. (978-0-7613-1356-4(7) , Twenty-First Century Bks.) Lerner Publishing Group.

Wagner, Heather Lehr. Iraq. 2002. (Creation of the Modern Middle East Ser.). (Illus.). 125p. (gr. 6-12). 35.00 (978-0-7910-6506-8(5) , Chelsea Hse.) Facts On File, Inc.

Writing in Ancient Mesopotamia: Individual Title Six-Packs. (On Deck Ser.: Vol. 2). 24p. (gr. 4-5). 35.00 (978-0-7578-5870-3(8)) Rigby Education.

IRAQ—HISTORY—TO 634

Ancient Mesopotamia/India. 2003. (Mr. Donn & Maxie's Always Something You Can Use Ser.). spiral bd. 19.95 (978-1-56004-166-5(8)) Social Studies Schl. Service.

Apte, Sunita. Mesopotamia. 2005. (Navigators Ser.). (J). pap. 44.00 (***978-1-4108-5111-6(7)***) Benchmark Education Co.

Bargallo I Chaves, Eva. Mesopotamia. 2005. (Ancient Civilizations Ser.). (Illus.). 32p. (J). (gr. 4-8). lib. bdg. 28.00 (978-0-7910-8604-9(6) , Chelsea Clubhouse) Facts On File, Inc.

Benchmark Education Staff. The Empires of Mesopotamia. 2005. 2.00 (***978-1-4108-4661-7(X)***) Benchmark Education Co.

Brannon, Barbara. Discover the Empires of Mesopotamia. 2005. 39.00 (***978-1-4108-5161-1(3)***) Benchmark Education Co.

Conklin, Wendy. China * India * Mesopotamia * Africa: All-in-One Resource with Background Information, Map Activities, Simulations & Games, & a Read-Aloud Play to Support Comprehension & Critical Thinking in Social Studies. 2006. (Ancient Civilizations Ser.). 96p. pap. 13.99 (978-0-439-53993-7(5) , Teaching Resources) Scholastic, Inc.

Dargie, Richard. Rich & Poor in Mesopotamia: Iraq in Ancient Times. 2005. (Rich & Poor in Ser.). (Illus.). 32p. (J). (gr. 4-7). lib. bdg. 27.10 (978-1-58340-723-3(5)) Smart Apple Media.

Deedrick, Tami. Mesopotamia. 2001. (Ancient Civilizations Ser.). (Illus.). 48p. (J). lib. bdg. 22.83 (978-0-7398-3584-5(X)) Raintree.

—Mesopotamia. 2000. (Ancient Civilizations Ser.). (Illus.). (J). pap. 7.20 (978-0-7398-4155-6(6)) Steck-Vaughn.

Faiella, Graham. The Technology of Mesopotamia. 2005. (Technology of the Ancient World Ser.). (Illus.). 48p. (J). (978-1-4042-0560-4(8)) Rosen Publishing Group, Inc., The.

Feinstein, Stephen. Ancient Mesopotamia: A Myreportlinks. com Book. 2005. (Civilizations of the Ancient World Ser.). (Illus.). 48p. (J). (ps-10). lib. bdg. 25.26 (978-0-7660-5254-3(0) , MyReportLinks.com Bks.) Enslow Pubs., Inc.

Green, Jen & Oakes, Lorna. Mesopotamia. 2004. (Find Out about...Ser.). (Illus.). 64p. pap. 7.99 (978-1-84215-917-0(8) , Southwater) Anness Publishing GBR. *Dist:* National Bk. Network.

Greene, Jacqueline Dembar. Slavery in Ancient Egypt & Mesopotamia. 2000. (History of Slavery Library). (Illus.). 64p. (J). (gr. 5-7). 25.50 (978-0-531-11692-0(1) , Watts, Franklin) Scholastic Library Publishing.

—Slavery in Ancient Egypt & Mesopotamia. 2000. (gr. 3-6). lib. bdg. 17.60 (978-0-613-34472-2(3)) Tandem Library Bks.

Hunt, Norman Bancroft. Living in Ancient Mesopotamia. 2007. (Living in the Ancient World Ser.). 96p. (gr. 6-12). 35.00 (978-0-8160-6337-6(0)) Facts On File, Inc.

Hunter, Erica C. D. Ancient Mesopotamia. 3rd rev. ed. 2007. (Cultural Atlas for Young People Ser.). (Illus.). 96p. (YA). (gr. 5-8). 35.00 (***978-0-8160-6824-1(0)*** , Chelsea Hse.) Facts On File, Inc.

Klingel, Cynthia Fitterer & Noyed, Robert B. Ancient Mesopotamia. 2002. (Let's See Library). (Illus.). 24p. (J). (gr. 1 up). lib. bdg. 19.93 (978-0-7565-0294-2(2)) Compass Point Bks.

Mehta-Jones, Shilpa. Life in Ancient Mesopotamia. 2004. (Peoples of the Ancient World Ser.). (Illus.). 32p. (J). (978-0-7787-2036-2(5)); pap. (978-0-7787-2066-9(7)) Crabtree Publishing Co.

Mesopotamia. (Ancient Civilizations Ser.). 48p. (gr. 5 up). 6.99 (978-0-7647-0147-4(9) , FS10501) Schaffer, Frank Pubns.

Morley, Jacqueline. You Wouldn't Want to Be a Sumerian Slave! A Life of Hard Labor You'd Rather Avoid. Antram, David, illus. 2007. (You Wouldn't Want to... Ser.). 32p. (J). (gr. 2-5). 28.50 (***978-0-531-18728-9(4)*** , Watts, Franklin) Scholastic Library Publishing.

Nardo, Don. Ancient Mesopotamia. 2006. (Greenhaven Encyclopedia of Ser.). (Illus.). 324p. (YA). (gr. 9 up). 77.45 (978-0-7377-3441-6(8) , Greenhaven Pr., Inc.) Thomson Gale.

—Empires of Mesopotamia. 2000. (Lost Civilizations Ser.). (Illus.). 112p. (J). (gr. 6-9). 28.70 (978-1-56006-820-4(5) , LML00902-178152, Lucent Bks.) Thomson Gale.

Oakes, Lorna. Assyria & Mesopotamia. 2001. (Step into Ser.). (Illus.). 64p. (gr. 3-7). 14.95 (978-0-7548-0656-1(1) , Lorenz Bks.) Anness Publishing, Inc.

Ryall, Michael. The Empires of Mesopotamia. 2005. 42.00 (***978-1-4108-4613-6(X)***) Benchmark Education Co.

Service, Pamela F. Mesopotamia. 1998. (Cultures of the Past Ser.). (Illus.). 80p. (J). (gr. 5 up). lib. bdg. 29.93 (978-0-7614-0301-2(9) , Benchmark Bks.) Cavendish, Marshall Corp.

IRAQ-KUWAIT CRISIS, 1990-1991

Press, Skip. The Kuwaiti Oil Fires. Taylor, Marjorie, illus. rev. ed. 1999. (Take Ten Ser.). 46p. (YA). (gr. 4 up). pap. 3.95 (978-1-58659-024-6(3)) Artesian Pr.

IRAQ-KUWAIT CRISIS, 1990-1991—FICTION

Alshalabi, Firyal M. Summer 1990. 1999. 138 p. pap. 6.99 (978-0-9669988-0-1(4)) Aunt Strawberry Bks.

Simmons, Ted. Sandstorm. 2006. (Illus.). 140p. (YA). pap. 13.95 (***978-0-9776958-4-3(0)***) CyPress Pubns.

IRAQ WAR, 2003

Al-Windawi, Thura. Thura's Diary. 2004. (Illus.). 144p. (J). (gr. 3-7). 15.99 (978-0-670-05886-0(6) , Viking Juvenile) Penguin Group (USA) Inc.

Carlisle, Rodney P. Iraq War. 2nd rev. ed. 2007. (America at War Ser.). (Illus.). 208p. (J). (gr. 6-12). 35.00 (***978-0-8160-7129-6(2)***) Facts On File, Inc.

Doak, Robin S. Conflicts in Iraq & Afghanistan. 2006. (Wars That Changed American History Ser.). (Illus.). 48p. (J). pap. (978-0-8368-7305-4(X)); lib. bdg. (978-0-8368-7296-5(7)) Stevens, Gareth Inc. (World Almanac Library).

Fiscus, James W. Iraqi Insurgents: Iraqi Resistance to America after the Defeat of Saddam Hussein. 2004. (Frontline Coverage of Current Events Ser.). (Illus.). 48p. (YA). lib. bdg. 26.50 (978-1-4042-0277-1(3)) Rosen Publishing Group, Inc., The.

Gunderson, Cory Gideon. Battle in Baghdad. 2004. (War in Iraq Ser.). (Illus.). 48p. (J). (gr. 4-8). lib. bdg. 25.65 (978-1-59197-494-9(1)) ABDO Publishing Co.

—When Diplomacy Fails. 2004. (War in Iraq Ser.). (Illus.). 48p. (J). (gr. 4-8). lib. bdg. 25.65 (978-1-59197-502-1(6)) ABDO Publishing Co.

Hamilton, John. Allied Forces. 2004. (War in Iraq Ser.). (Illus.). 48p. (J). (gr. 4-8). lib. bdg. 25.65 (978-1-59197-491-8(7)) ABDO Publishing Co.

—America's Military. 2004. (War in Iraq Ser.). (Illus.). 48p. (J). (gr. 4-8). lib. bdg. 25.65 (978-1-59197-492-5(5)) ABDO Publishing Co.

—Real-Time Reporting. 2004. (War in Iraq Ser.). (Illus.). 48p. (J). (gr. 4-8). lib. bdg. 25.65 (978-1-59197-497-0(6)) ABDO Publishing Co.

—Weapons of the Twenty-First Century. 2004. (War in Iraq Ser.). (Illus.). 48p. (J). (gr. 4-8). lib. bdg. 25.65 (978-1-59197-501-4(8)) ABDO Publishing Co.

Martin, Michael J. The Iraqi Prisoner Abuse Scandal. 2005. (Lucent Terrorism Library). (Illus.). 109p. (YA). (gr. 7-10). lib. bdg. 29.95 (978-1-59018-769-2(5) , Lucent Bks.) Thomson Gale.

Miller, Debra A. Middle East. 2007. (Current Controversies Ser.). (Illus.). 240p. (gr. 10-12). 36.20 (***978-0-7377-3960-2(6));*** pap. 24.95 (***978-0-7377-3961-9(4)***) Thomson Gale. (Greenhaven Pr., Inc.).

—Rebuilding Iraq. 2004. (Illus.). 112p. (J). (gr. 7-10). 29.95 (978-1-59018-543-8(9) , Lucent Bks.) Thomson Gale.

—The War Against Iraq. 2003. (Lucent Terrorism Library). (Illus.). 112p. (J). 29.95 (978-1-59018-522-3(6) , Lucent Bks.) Thomson Gale.

Moe, Barbara A. The Search for Weapons of Mass Destruction in Iraq. 2004. (Library of Weapons of Mass Destruction). (Illus.). 64p. (J). lib. bdg. 26.50 (978-1-4042-0295-5(1)) Rosen Publishing Group, Inc., The.

Monteverde, Matthew. American Presence in Iraq: Winning the Peace. 2004. (Frontline Coverage of Current Events Ser.). (Illus.). 48p. (J). lib. bdg. 26.50 (978-1-4042-0276-4(5)) Rosen Publishing Group, Inc., The.

Payment, Simone. Finding & Capturing Saddam Hussein: A Successful Military Manhunt. 2004. (Frontline Coverage of Current Events Ser.). (Illus.). 48p. (J). lib. bdg. 26.50 (978-1-4042-0280-1(3)) Rosen Publishing Group, Inc., The.

Poffenberger, Nancy. Iraq, 2003. Gottesman, Val, illus. 2003. 32p. (YA). per. 9.95 (978-0-938293-11-8(7)) Fun Publishing Co.

—Iraq 2003. 2003. (gr. 3-6). lib. bdg. 18.75 (978-0-613-77719-3(0)) Tandem Library Bks.

Rivera, Sheila. Operation Iraqi Freedom. 2004. (War in Iraq Ser.). (Illus.). 48p. (J). (gr. 4-8). lib. bdg. 25.65 (978-1-59197-496-3(8)) ABDO Publishing Co.

—Rebuilding Iraq. 2004. (War in Iraq Ser.). (Illus.). 48p. (J). (gr. 4-8). lib. bdg. 25.65 (978-1-59197-498-7(4)) ABDO Publishing Co.

Schafer, Christopher. Attack in Iraq. 2004. (War in Iraq Ser.). (Illus.). 48p. (J). (gr. 4-8). lib. bdg. 25.65 (978-1-59197-493-2(3)) ABDO Publishing Co.

—War Protesters. 2004. (War in Iraq Ser.). (Illus.). 48p. (J). (gr. 4-8). lib. bdg. 25.65 (978-1-59197-500-7(X)) ABDO Publishing Co.

Shostak, Arthur B. Defeating Terrorism: Developing Dreams, 4 vols. 2004. (Defeating Terrorism/Developing Dreams Ser.). (Illus.). 120p. (YA). (gr. 9-13). 31.95 (978-0-7910-7955-3(4)); 31.95 (978-0-7910-7956-0(2)); 31.95 (978-0-7910-7957-7(0)) Facts On File, Inc. (Chelsea Hse.).

—Defeating Terrorism/Developing Dreams: Beyond 9/11 & the Iraq War, 4 vols. 2004. (Defeating Terrorism/ Developing Dreams Ser.). (Illus.). 120p. (YA). (gr. 9-13). 31.95 (978-0-7910-7958-4(9) , Chelsea Hse.) Facts On File, Inc.

Shostak, Arthur B., ed. Defeating Terrorism/Developing Dreams: Beyond 9/11 & the Iraq War. 2005. (Illus.). 120 to 185p. (gr. 9-13). pap. 159.75 (978-0-7910-8421-2(3) , Chelsea Hse.) Facts On File, Inc.

Stamaty, Mark A. Muhimat Al Sayyda Alia: Inkaz Kuttub Al Iraq. 2005. 32p. pap. 12.00 (978-977-6171-01-5(X) , 706-001) Al-Balsam Pubng. Hse. EGY. *Dist:* Bookworld Trade, Inc.

Stamaty, Mark Alan. Alia's Mission: Saving the Books of Iraq. 2004. (Illus.). 32p. (J). (gr. 1). 12.95 (978-0-375-83217-8(3)); lib. bdg. 14.99 (978-0-375-93217-5(8)) Random Hse. Children's Bks. (Knopf Bks. for Young Readers).

Uschan, Michael V. Life of an American Soldier in Iraq. 2004. (Illus.). 112p. (YA). (gr. 7-10). lib. bdg. 29.95 (978-1-59018-541-4(2) , Lucent Bks.) Thomson Gale.

Wheeler, Jill C. Coalition Leaders. 2004. (War in Iraq Ser.). (Illus.). 48p. (J). (gr. 4-8). lib. bdg. 25.65 (978-1-59197-495-6(X)) ABDO Publishing Co.

—Saddam Hussein. 2004. (War in Iraq Ser.). (Illus.). 48p. (J). (gr. 4-8). lib. bdg. 25.65 (978-1-59197-499-4(2)) ABDO Publishing Co.

Winter, Jeanette. The Librarian of Basra: A True Story from Iraq. 2005. (Illus.). 32p. (J). (gr. 2-4). 16.00 (978-0-15-205445-8(6)) Harcourt Children's Bks.

Yancey, Diane. The Home Front. 2004. (American War Library). (Illus.). 128p. (YA). (gr. 7-12). lib. bdg. 29.95 (978-1-59018-542-1(0) , Lucent Bks.) Thomson Gale.

Young, Jeff C. Operation Iraqi Freedom: A MyReportLinks. Com Book. 2003. (U. S. Wars Ser.). (Illus.). 48p. (J). lib. bdg. 25.26 (978-0-7660-5088-4(2) , MyReportLinks.com Bks.) Enslow Pubs., Inc.

Zwier, Lawrence J. & Weltig, Matthew Scott. The Persian Gulf & Iraqi Wars. 2005. (Chronicle of America's Wars Ser.). (Illus.). 96p. (J). (gr. 5-12). 27.93 (978-0-8225-0848-9(6)) Lerner Publishing Group.

IRELAND

Adams, Simon. Northern Ireland. 2005. (Illus.). 44p. (J). (gr. 6-9). lib. bdg. 29.95 (978-1-58340-604-5(2)) Smart Apple Media.

Banting, Erinn. Ireland: The Land. 2002. (gr. 3-6). lib. bdg. 16.40 (978-0-613-52965-5(0)) Tandem Library Bks.

—Ireland: The People. 2002. (gr. 3-6). lib. bdg. 16.40 (978-0-613-52966-2(9)) Tandem Library Bks.

—Ireland - The Culture. 2002. (Lands, Peoples & Cultures Ser.). (Illus.). 32p. (J). (gr. 4-5). pap. (978-0-7787-9719-7(8)) Crabtree Publishing Co.

—Ireland - The Land. 2002. (Lands, Peoples & Cultures Ser.). (Illus.). 32p. (J). (gr. 4-5). (978-0-7787-9349-6(4)); pap. (978-0-7787-9717-3(1)) Crabtree Publishing Co.

—Ireland - The People. 2002. (Lands, Peoples & Cultures Ser.). (Illus.). 32p. (J). (gr. 4-5). (978-0-7787-9350-2(8)); (978-0-7787-9351-9(6)); pap. (978-0-7787-9718-0(X)) Crabtree Publishing Co.

Barnham, Kay. Ireland. 2003. (Changing Face Of... Ser.). (Illus.). 48p. (J). lib. bdg. 28.56 (978-0-7398-6044-1(5)) Raintree.

Blashfield, Jean F. Ireland. 2002. (Enchantment of the World, Second Ser.). (Illus.). 144p. (J). (gr. 5-9). 36.00 (978-0-516-21127-5(7) , Children's Pr.) Scholastic Library Publishing.

Blomquist, Christopher. The United Kingdom, a Primary Source Guide. 2005. (Countries of the World, a Primary Source Journey Ser.). (J). 19.95 (978-1-4042-2760-6(1) , PowerKids Pr.) Rosen Publishing Group, Inc., The.

Britton, Tamara L. Northern Ireland. 2004. (Countries Ser.). (Illus.). 40p. (J). (gr. k-6). lib. bdg. 22.78 (978-1-59197-296-9(5)) ABDO Publishing Co.

Bunting, Eve. S Is for Shamrock: An Ireland Alphabet. Faulkner, Matt, illus. rev. ed. 2007. 40p. (J). 17.95 (978-1-58536-290-5(5)) Sleeping Bear Pr.

Campbell, Kumari. United Kingdom in Pictures. 2nd rev. expurg. ed. 2004. (Visual Geography Ser.). (Illus.). 80p. (J). (gr. 5-12). 27.93 (978-0-8225-1995-9(X)) Lerner Publishing Group.

Cummins, Richard. Ireland. 2000. (Let's Investigate Ser.). (Illus.). 32p. (J). (gr. 4-7). lib. bdg. (978-1-58341-032-5(5) , Creative Education) Creative Co., The.

Deady, Kathleen W. Ireland. 2001. (Countries of the World Ser.). (Illus.). 126p. (J). (gr. 2-3). 18.60 (978-0-7368-0814-9(0) , Bridgestone Bks.) Capstone Pr., Inc.

Faiella, Graham. Ireland: A Primary Source Cultural Guide. 2005. (Primary Sources of World Cultures Ser.). (J). (978-1-4042-0477-5(6)) Rosen Publishing Group, Inc., The.

Fontes, Justine & Fontes, Ron. Ireland. (to Z Ser.). (J). 2004. (gr. 2-4). pap. 6.95 (978-0-516-26810-1(4)); 2003. (Illus.). 40p. 24.50 (978-0-516-24561-4(9)) Scholastic Library Publishing. (Children's Pr.).

Fouberg, Erin Hogan & Hogan, Edward Patrick. Ireland. 2003. (Modern World Nations Ser.). (Illus.). 150p. (gr. 6-12). 30.00 (978-0-7910-7377-3(7) , Chelsea Hse.) Facts On File, Inc.

Friedman, Lita. Mary Robinson: Fighter for Human Rights. 2004. (Avisson Young Adult Ser.). (Illus.). 142p. (YA). pap. 19.95 (978-1-888105-65-0(8)) Avisson Pr., Inc.

Givens, David. For the Kids: A Family-Friendly Guide to Outings & Activities. 2003. (Illus.). 220p. (YA). pap. 20.95 (978-1-904148-27-2(1)) Liffey Pr., The. IRL. *Dist:* Dufour Editions, Inc.

Green, Yuko. Kathleen from Ireland Sticker Paper Doll. 1998. (Illus.). 4p. (J). (gr. k-5). pap. 1.50 (978-0-486-40320-5(3)) Dover Pubns., Inc.

Hardwick, Susan, ed. Ireland. 2005. (World-Wise Kids Project Guides). (Illus.). 96p. (978-1-59258-068-2(8)) Hylas Publishing.

Harvey, Miles. Look What Came from Ireland. 2003. (Look What Came from Ser.). (Illus.). 32p. (J). (gr. 2-4). pap. 6.95 (978-0-531-16628-4(7) , Watts, Franklin) Scholastic Library Publishing.

—Look What Came from Ireland. 2002. (gr. 3-6). lib. bdg. 15.25 (978-0-613-59508-7(4)) Tandem Library Bks.

Italia, Bob. Ireland. 2001. (Countries Ser.). (Illus.). 40p. (J). (gr. k-6). lib. bdg. 22.78 (978-1-57765-496-4(X) , Checkerboard Library) ABDO Publishing Co.

January, Brendan. Ireland. 1999. (True Bks.). (Illus.). 48p. (J). (gr. 3-5). 25.00 (978-0-516-21186-2(2) , Children's Pr.) Scholastic Library Publishing.

—Ireland. 1999. (gr. 3-6). lib. bdg. 15.25 (978-0-613-54581-5(8)) Tandem Library Bks.

Lace, William W. Ireland. 1999. (Modern Nations of the World Ser.). (Illus.). 128p. (YA). (gr. 7-10). 27.45 (978-1-56006-448-0(X) , Lucent Bks.) Thomson Gale.

Lovelace, Jesse. Keep to the Left! Freewheeling Through Ireland. 2002. 222p. pap. 14.95 (978-0-595-23931-3(5) , Writers Club Pr.) iUniverse, Inc.

March, Michael. Ireland. 2002. (Country Files Ser.). (Illus.). 32p. (J). lib. bdg. 24.25 (978-1-58340-203-0(9)) Smart Apple Media.

Mattern, Joanne. Ireland. 2003. (Countries & Cultures Ser.). (Illus.). 64p. (J). (gr. 3-4). lib. bdg. 23.95 (978-0-7368-1549-9(X) , Bridgestone Bks.) Capstone Pr., Inc.

Murphy, Patricia J. Ireland. 2003. (Discovering Cultures Ser.). (Illus.). 48p. (J). 25.64 (978-0-7614-1515-2(7) , Benchmark Bks.) Cavendish, Marshall Corp.

Olson, Kay Melchisedech. Ireland. 2003. (Many Cultures, One World Ser.). (Illus.). 32p. (J). (gr. 2-3). lib. bdg. 23.93 (978-0-7368-2168-1(6) , Bridgestone Bks.) Capstone Pr., Inc.

Pomeray, J. K. Ireland. 1999. (Major World Nations Ser.). (Illus.). 144p. (YA). (gr. 4-7). 29.95 (978-0-7910-4741-5(5) , Chelsea Hse.) Facts On File, Inc.

Rose, Elizabeth. A Primary Source Guide to Ireland. 2004. (Primary Sources of Countries of the World Ser.). (Illus.). 24p. (J). (gr. k). lib. bdg. 19.95 (978-0-8239-6731-5(X) , PowerKids Pr.) Rosen Publishing Group, Inc., The.

Ross, Michael Elsohn. Children of Ireland. Rigau, Felix, photos by. 2001. (World's Children Ser.). (Illus.). 48p. (J). (gr. 3-6). lib. bdg. (978-1-57505-521-3(X) , Carolrhoda Bks.) Lerner Publishing Group.

Rough Guides Staff, contrib. by. Ireland. 2005. (Our Lives, Our World Ser.). (Illus.). 32p. (J). (gr. 3 up). lib. bdg. 27.10 (978-1-59389-229-6(2)) Chrysalis Education.

Ryan, Patrick. Ireland. 1999. (Countries: Faces & Places Ser.). (Illus.). 32p. (J). (gr. 1-5). 25.64 (978-1-56766-599-4(3)) Child's World, Inc.

Sasek, M. This Is Ireland. 2005. (Illus.). 64p. (J). (gr. k). 17.95 (978-0-7893-1224-2(7)) Universe Publishing.

Simons, Rae. United Kingdom. 2006. (European Union Ser.). (Illus.). 88p. (YA). (gr. 5 up). lib. bdg. (978-1-4222-0064-3(7)) Mason Crest Pubs.

Spencer, Shannon. Ireland. 1999. (Countries of the World Ser.). (Illus.). 96p. (J). (gr. 6 up). lib. bdg. 30.00 (978-0-8368-2318-9(4)) Stevens, Gareth Inc.

Ueda, Reed & Stotsky, Sandra, eds. Irish-American Answer Book. 1999. (Ethnic Answer Book Ser.). (Illus.). 136p. (YA). (gr. 5 up). pap. 9.95 (978-0-7910-4796-5(2)); lib. bdg. 19.75 (978-0-7910-4795-8(4)) Facts On File, Inc. (Chelsea Hse.).

Wade, Mary Dodson. Ireland: A Question & Answer Book. 2007. (Fact Finders Ser.). (Illus.). 32p. (J). 22.60 (978-0-7368-6410-7(5)) Capstone Pr., Inc.

Walker, Ida. Ireland. 2006. (European Union Ser.). (Illus.). 88p. (YA). (gr. 5 up). lib. bdg. (978-1-4222-0051-3(5)) Mason Crest Pubs.

Walters, Johanna O'Mahony. Tales of Travel & Trust: Our Celtic Heritage. 1999. (Illus.). 54p. (YA). (gr. 5-12). pap. 8.95 (978-1-85390-459-2(7)) Veritas Pubns. IRL. *Dist:* Irish Bks. & Media, Inc.

Yip, Dora & Spencer, Shannon. Welcome to Ireland. 2001. (Welcome to My Country Ser.). (Illus.). 48p. (J). (gr. 2 up). lib. bdg. 26.00 (978-0-8368-2518-3(7)) Stevens, Gareth Inc.

IRELAND—FICTION

Arrigan, Mary. The Spirits of the Attic. 2001. 128p. (J). pap. 9.95 (978-1-901737-27-1(6)) Anvil Bks., Ltd. IRL. *Dist:* Dufour Editions, Inc.

Arrigan, Mary & Myler, Terry. Seascape with Barber's Harp. 1998. 160p. pap. 9.95 (978-1-901737-02-8(0)) Anvil Bks., Ltd. IRL. *Dist:* Dufour Editions, Inc.

Aryal, Aimee. Let's Go Irish! Shrestha, Anuj, illus. 2004. (J). 19.95 (978-0-9743442-5-6(7)) Mascot Bks., Inc.

Baglio, Ben M. Ponies at the Point No.10. 1999. (gr. 3-6). lib. bdg. 11.80 (978-0-613-16990-5(5)) Tandem Library Bks.

Banks, Lynne Reid. Maura's Angel. 1999. (J). (978-0-606-16353-8(0)) Tandem Library Bks.

Banville, Vincent. Hennessy. 180p. pap. 12.95 (978-0-7022-2505-5(3)) Univ. of Queensland Pr. AUS. *Dist:* International Specialized Bk. Services.

Barnard, Victoria. Joe on Holiday. Barnard, Victoria & Stephens, Andrew, illus. 2005. 18p. (J). (gr. k-4). reprint ed. 19.00 (978-0-7567-8531-4(6)) DIANE Publishing Co.

Bateman, Colin. Bring Me the Head of Oliver Plunkett. 2005. 272p. (J). (gr. 4-7). 15.95 (978-0-385-73245-1(7) , Delacorte Bks. for Young Readers) Random Hse. Children's Bks.

Bateman, Teresa. Fiona's Luck. Murphy, Kelly, illus. 2007. 32p. (J). (ps-3). 15.95 (978-1-57091-651-9(9)) Charlesbridge Publishing, Inc.

Bennett, Holly. The Warrior's Daughter. 2007. 240p. (YA). (gr. 7 up). pap. ***(978-1-55143-607-4(8))*** Orca Bk. Pubs.

Binchy, Maeve. The Return Journey. 1999. (gr. 7-12). lib. bdg. 15.30 (978-0-613-29333-4(9)) Tandem Library Bks.

Bo, Ben. Skullcrack. 2003. 168p. (J). pap. 6.95 (978-0-8225-3311-5(1)); (gr. 9-12). 14.95 (978-0-8225-3308-5(1)) Lerner Publishing Group.

—Skullcrack. 2000. (gr. 5-8). lib. bdg. 15.25 (978-0-613-58938-3(6)) Tandem Library Bks.

Brennan, Ann. The Hawthorn Bush. 2005. (Illus.). 163p. pap. ***(978-0-88887-316-3(6))*** Borealis Pr.

Bunting, Eve. Market Day. 1999. (J). (978-0-606-14263-2(0)) Tandem Library Bks.

—That's What Leprechauns Do. McCully, Emily Arnold, illus. 2006. 32p. (J). (gr. k-3). 16.00 (978-0-618-35410-8(7) , Clarion Bks.) Houghton Mifflin Co. Trade & Reference Div.

—Walking to School. Dooling, Michael, illus. 2005. 32p. (J). (gr. k-3). 20.01 (978-0-618-26144-4(3) , Clarion Bks.) Houghton Mifflin Co. Trade & Reference Div.

Burgard, Anna Marlis. Flying Feet: A Story of Irish Dance. Dees, Leighanne, illus. 2006. 31p. (J). (gr. 4-8). 16.00 (978-1-4223-5255-7(2)) DIANE Publishing Co.

Carroll, Yvonne. Great Irish Legends for Children. Lawrie, Robin, illus. 2005. 64p. (J). (ps-ps). 16.95 (978-1-58980-345-9(0)) Pelican Publishing Co., Inc.

—Irish Legends for Children. Su, Lucy, illus. 2004. 64p. 16.95 (978-1-58980-278-0(0)) Pelican Publishing Co., Inc.

Carville, Declan. A Day to Remember at the Giant's Causeway. Ellis, Brendan, illus. 29p. (J). (gr. 2-5). pap. 7.95 (978-0-9538222-0-1(6)) Discovery Pubns. GBR. *Dist:* Irish Bks. & Media, Inc.

Cassidy, Cathy. Scarlett. 2006. 272p. (YA). 16.99 (978-0-670-06068-9(2) , Viking Juvenile) Penguin Group (USA) Inc.

Colfer, Eoin. Benny & Babe. 2007. 288p. (gr. 5-17). 18.95 ***(978-1-4231-0283-0(5)); pap. 7.95 (978-1-4231-0284-7(3))*** Miramax Bks.

—Half-Moon Investigations. 2007. 304p. (gr. 5-17). pap. 7.99 ***(978-0-7868-4960-4(6))*** Miramax Bks.

Collins, Yvonne & Rideout, Sandy. Introducing Vivien Leigh Reid: Daughter of the Diva. 2005. 240p. pap. 9.95 (978-0-312-33837-4(6) , St. Martin's Griffin) St. Martin's Pr.

Conlon-McKenna, Marita. Under the Hawthorn Tree. 2003. (Illus.). 160p. pap. 5.95 (978-0-86278-206-1(6)) O'Brien Pr., Ltd., The. IRL. *Dist:* Independent Pubs. Group.

Conroy, Don. When the Sea Calls. 1999. (Illus.). 156p. (J). (gr. 4-8). per. (978-0-947548-99-5(8)) Mentor Bks.

Cosgrove, Stephen. Jake O'Shawnasey. 2002. (gr. k-3). lib. bdg. 13.00 (978-0-613-64531-7(6)) Tandem Library Bks.

Cowley, Joy. The Wishing of Biddy Malone. Denise, Christopher, illus. 2006. 40p. (J). reprint ed. pap. 6.99 (978-0-14-240589-5(2) , Puffin) Penguin Group (USA) Inc.

de Paola, Tomie. Jamie O'Rourke & the Pooka. Frith, Margaret, ed. de Paola, Tomie, illus. 2000. (Illus.). 32p. (J). (ps-3). 16.99 (978-0-399-23467-5(5) , Putnam Juvenile) Penguin Group (USA) Inc.

Denenberg, Barry. So Far from Home: The Diary of Mary Driscoll, an Irish Mill Girl. 2003. (Dear America Ser.). 144p. (J). 12.95 (978-0-439-55506-7(X)) Scholastic, Inc.

Dillon, Eilis. Island of Horses. 2004. (New York Review Children's Collection). 224p. (J). pap. 17.95 (978-1-59017-102-8(0) , NYR Children's Collection) New York Review of Bks., Inc., The.

—The Lost Island. 2006. (New York Review Children's Collection). 208p. (J). (gr. 5). 17.95 (978-1-59017-205-6(1) , NYR Children's Collection) New York Review of Bks., Inc., The.

Dinsdale, Christopher. Stolen Away. 2006. (Illus.). 229p. (YA). pap. 8.95 (978-1-894917-20-9(0)) Napoleon Publishing/Rendezvous Pr. CAN. *Dist:* AtlasBooks Distribution.

Dowd, Siobhan. A Swift Pure Cry. 2007. 320p. (YA). (gr. 7). 16.99 (978-0-385-75108-7(7)); lib. bdg. 19.99 (978-0-385-75109-4(5)) Random Hse. Children's Bks. (Fickling, David Bks.).

Doyle, Malachy. Who Is Jesse Flood? 2002. 176p. (J). (gr. 5-10). 14.95 (978-1-58234-776-9(X) , Bloomsbury Children) Bloomsbury Publishing.

Doyle, Roddy. The Giggler Treatment. 2001. (gr. 3-6). lib. bdg. 11.80 (978-0-613-44359-3(4)) Tandem Library Bks.

—The Meanwhile Adventures. Ajhar, Brian, illus. 176p. (J). 2006. pap. 5.99 (978-0-439-66211-6(7)); 2004. (gr. 4-7). pap. 16.95 (978-0-439-66210-9(9)) Scholastic, Inc. (Levine, Arthur A. Bks.).

Duane, Diane. A Wizard Abroad. 2001. (Young Wizards Ser.: Bk. 4). 368p. (YA). (gr. 5 up). pap. 6.95 (978-0-15-216238-2(0) , Magic Carpet Bks.) Harcourt Children's Bks.

—A Wizard Abroad. 2001. (gr. 5-8). lib. bdg. 14.75 (978-0-613-36083-8(4)) Tandem Library Bks.

Edwards, Pamela Duncan. The Leprechaun's Gold. Cole, Henry, illus. 2004. 32p. (J). (ps-2). 15.99 (978-0-06-623974-3(5)); lib. bdg. 16.89 (978-0-06-623975-0(3)) HarperCollins Pubs.

Emery, Joanna. Brothers of the Falls. Erickson, David, illus. 2004. (Adventures in America Ser.). (J). 14.95 (978-1-893110-37-3(0)) Silver Moon Pr.

Flegg, Aubrey. Katie's War: A Story of the Irish Civil War. 2003. 192p. (YA). (gr. 5 up). pap. 7.95 (978-0-86278-525-3(1)) O'Brien Pr., Ltd., The. IRL. *Dist:* Independent Pubs. Group, Irish American Bk. Co.

Flynn, Arthur. Luke in the Movies. 1999. (YA). (gr. 5-9). per. (978-1-902586-59-5(X)) Mentor Bks.

Giff, Patricia Reilly. Maggie's Door. 176p. (gr. 3-7). 2005. (J). pap. 5.99 (978-0-440-41581-7(0) , Yearling); 2003. (Illus.). (YA). lib. bdg. 17.99 (978-0-385-90095-9(3) , Lamb, Wendy) Random Hse. Children's Bks.

—Nory Ryan's Song. 2004. 160p. (J). (gr. 4-7). pap. 36.00 incl. audio (978-0-8072-2093-1(0) , Listening Library) Random Hse. Audio Publishing Group.

—Nory Ryan's Song. 2002. 176p. (J). (gr. 3-7). pap. 5.99 (978-0-440-41829-0(1) , Yearling) Random Hse. Children's Bks.

—Nory Ryan's Song. 2002. 148p. (J). (ps-7). per. 13.55 (978-0-613-57915-5(1)) Tandem Library Bks.

—Nory Ryan's Song. l.t. ed. 2001. 176p. (J). 23.95 (978-0-7862-3459-2(8)) Thorndike Pr.

Harrison, Cora. The Famine Secret. 1998. (Drumshee Timeline Ser.: Bk. 5). (Illus.). 128p. (J). (gr. 4-8). pap. 6.95 (978-0-86327-649-1(0)) Wolfhound Pr. IRL. *Dist:* Irish American Bk. Co.

—Milleniumdrumshee. 1999. (Drumshee Timeline Ser.). (Illus.). 143p. (J). (978-0-86327-715-3(2)) Wolfhound Pr.

—Nuala & Her Secret Wolf. 1998. (Drumshee Timeline Ser.: Bk. 1). (Illus.). 128p. (J). (gr. 4-8). pap. 6.95 (978-0-86327-585-2(0)) Wolfhound Pr. IRL. *Dist:* Irish American Bk. Co.

—The Secret of 1798. 1998. (Drumshee Timeline Ser.: Bk. 4). (Illus.). 128p. (J). (gr. 4-8). pap. 6.95 (978-0-86327-638-5(5)) Wolfhound Pr. IRL. *Dist:* Irish American Bk. Co.

—The Secret of Drumshee Castle. 1998. (Drumshee Timeline Ser.: Bk. 3). (Illus.). 128p. (J). (gr. 3-9). pap. 6.95 (978-0-86327-632-3(6)) Wolfhound Pr. IRL. *Dist:* Interlink Publishing Group, Inc., Irish American Bk. Co.

—The Secret of the Seven Crosses. 1998. (Drumshee Timeline Ser.: Bk. 2). (Illus.). 128p. (J). (gr. 4-8). pap. 6.95 (978-0-86327-616-3(4)) Wolfhound Pr. IRL. *Dist:* Irish American Bk. Co.

—Secret Spy from Drumshee. 2003. (Drumshee Timeline Ser.: No. 13). 144p. (J). pap. 6.95 (978-0-86327-902-7(3)) Wolfhound Pr. IRL. *Dist:* Interlink Publishing Group, Inc.

Heneghan, James. The Grave. 2000. (Illus.). (J). (gr. 7-10). pap. 7.95 (978-0-88899-414-1(1)) Groundwood Bks. CAN. *Dist:* Transition Vendor.

—Safe House. 2006. 176p. (J). pap. 7.95 (978-1-55143-640-1(X)) Orca Bk. Pubs. USA.

—Torn Away. 2003. 256p. (J). (gr. 4-7). pap. 6.95 (978-1-55143-263-2(3)) Orca Bk. Pubs. USA.

—Torn Away. 2003. (gr. 7-12). lib. bdg. 15.25 (978-0-613-84756-8(3)) Tandem Library Bks.

Hennessy, Claire. Afterwards. 2005. 188p. (YA). pap. ***(978-1-84223-207-1(X))*** Poolbeg Pr.

Higgins, Jack. The White House Connection. 2000. (gr. 7-12). lib. bdg. 16.45 (978-0-613-29382-2(5)) Tandem Library Bks.

Hodges, Margaret & Root, Kimberly B. The Wee Christmas Cabin. 2001. (Illus.). (J). (978-0-8234-1528-1(7)) Holiday Hse., Inc.

Holmes, Victoria. The Horse from the Sea. (J). 2006. (Illus.). 336p. pap. 6.99 (978-0-06-052030-4(2)); 2005. 320p. (gr. 5 up). 15.99 (978-0-06-052028-1(0)) HarperCollins Pubs.

—The Horse from the Sea: An Epic Horse Story. 2005. 320p. (J). (gr. k-9). lib. bdg. 16.89 (978-0-06-052029-8(9)) HarperCollins Pubs.

Hyland, Betty. Tressa & the Lost Circus of Ireland. 2004. 85p. (YA). pap. 10.95 (978-0-7414-2268-2(9)) Infinity Publishing.

Jacobs, Joseph. Irish Fairy Tales. Batten, John D., illus. 2001. (Children's Classics). (ENG.). 240p. (J). (gr. 3-6). pap. (978-1-84022-434-4(7)) Wordsworth Editions, Ltd.

Johnson, Lois Walfrid. Raider's Promise. 2006. (Raiders from the Sea Ser.). (Illus.). 304p. (J). pap. 8.99 (978-0-8024-3116-5(X)) Moody Pubs.

Jones, Heulwen. O'Grady's Well. 2005. (Illus.). 96p. pap. ***(978-1-84401-578-6(5))*** Athena Pr.

Kavanagh, Herminie Templeton. Darby O'Gill. rev. ed. 2006. 224p. 5.99 (978-0-7653-5462-4(4) , Tor Bks.) Doherty, Tom Assocs., LLC.

—Darby O'Gill & the Crocks of Gold: And Other Irish Tales. Schluenderfritz, Ted, illus. 2003. ix, 155p. (J). pap. 14.95 (978-1-928832-85-0(7)) Sophia Institute Pr.

Kissane, Dan. Jimmy's Leprechaun Trap. 2001. (Illus.). 95p. (gr. 8-12). pap. 5.95 (978-0-86278-512-3(X)) O'Brien Pr., Ltd., The. IRL. *Dist:* Independent Pubs. Group.

Krensky, Stephen. Too Many Leprechauns: Or How That Pot o' Gold Got to the End of the Rainbow. Andreasen, Dan, illus. 2007. 32p. (J). 12.99 (978-0-689-85112-4(X) , Simon & Schuster Children's Publishing) Simon & Schuster Children's Publishing.

Krull, Kathleen. A Pot O'Gold: A Treasury of Irish Stories, Poetry, Folklore, & of Course Blarney. McPhail, David M., illus. 2004. 192p. (gr. 2-5). 19.99 (978-0-7868-0625-6(7)) Hyperion Pr.

Lavin, Kevin. Desiroscope. 2002. 288p. (J). (gr. 3-9). pap. 6.95 (978-0-86327-885-3(X)) Interlink Publishing Group, Inc.

Lenihan, Edmund. Humorous Irish Tales for Children. 1998. 128p. pap. (978-1-85635-238-3(2)) Irish American Bk. Co.

Lyons, Mary E. Knockabeg: A Famine Tale. 2001. (Illus.). 128p. (J). (gr. 4-6). tchr. ed. 15.00 (978-0-618-09283-3(8)) Houghton Mifflin Co. Trade & Reference Div.

MacGill-Callahan, Sheila. The Last Snake in Ireland: A Story about St. Patrick. Hillenbrand, Will, illus. 1999. 32p. (J). (gr. k-3). 6.95 (978-0-8234-1555-7(4)) Holiday Hse., Inc.

Maclachlan, Kate. Love My Enemy. 2006. 268p. (J). pap. 9.99 ***(978-1-84270-340-3(4))*** Andersen GBR. *Dist:* Independent Pubs. Group.

McCann, David. Garda Gaby: The Danger of Playing Truant. Brundige, Britt, ed. Bauknecht, Julie, illus. l.t. ed. 2003. 14p. (J). (gr. k-5). spiral bd. 5.99 (978-1-929063-92-5(X) , 324) Moons & Stars Publishing For Children.

McCaughren, Tom. Children of the Forge. (Illus.). 128p. 3.95 (978-0-900068-98-0(1)) Penguin Group (USA) Inc.

—Legend of the Corrib King. (Illus.). 96p. 2.25 (978-0-900068-86-7(8)) Penguin Group (USA) Inc.

—Ride a Pale Horse. 1999. (Illus.). 144p. (YA). (gr. 4 up). 14.95 (978-1-901737-08-0(X)) Anvil Bks., Ltd. IRL. *Dist:* Dufour Editions, Inc., Irish Bks. & Media, Inc.

—Ride a Pale Horse. 2001. (Illus.). 144p. pap. 11.95 (978-1-901737-09-7(8)) Dufour Editions, Inc.

—Run with the Wind. 2002. (Illus.). 144p. pap. 7.95 (978-0-86327-568-5(0)) Interlink Publishing Group, Inc.

McCourt, Frank. Angela & the Baby Jesus. Long, Loren, illus. 2007. 40p. (J). 14.95 ***(978-1-4165-7470-5(0)*** , Scribner) Simon & Schuster.

—Angela & the Baby Jesus. Colon, Raul, illus. 2007. 32p. (J). (gr. k-5). 17.99 ***(978-1-4169-3789-0(7))*** Simon & Schuster Children's Publishing.

McDermott, Gerald. Tim O'Toole & the Wee Folk: An Irish Tale. McDermott, Gerald, illus. 2002. (Illus.). (J). 13.19 (978-0-7587-3812-7(9)) Book Wholesalers, Inc.

—Tim O'Toole & the Wee Folk: An Irish Tale. McDermott, Gerald, illus. 2004. (Illus.). 32p. (J). (ps-ps). lib. bdg. 13.19 (978-0-606-30057-5(0)) Tandem Library Bks.

McGinley, Carol. Allyn's Embarrassing & Mysterious Irish Adventures. Murray, Linda, illus. 1999. 202p. (J). (gr. 4-6). pap. 7.95 (978 1 892671 00-4(X)) AGA Publishing.

McKinty, Adrian. The Lighthouse Land. 2007. 416p. (YA). (gr. 7-17). pap. 7.95 ***(978-0-8109-9361-7(9))*** Abrams, Harry N. , Inc.

—The Lighthouse War. 2007. 403p. (J). (gr. 7-17). 16.95 ***(978-0-8109-9354-9(6))*** Abrams, Harry N. , Inc.

McMahon, Kate & Myler, Terry. Timber Twig. 1998. 142p. pap. 10.95 (978-1-901737-01-1(2)) Anvil Bks., Ltd. IRL. *Dist:* Dufour Editions, Inc.

Melling, O. R. The Hunter's Moon. 2005. (Chronicles of Faerie Ser.: No. 1). (Illus.). 296p. (J). (gr. 5-10). 16.95 (978-0-8109-5857-9(0)) Abrams, Harry N. , Inc.

—Hunter's Moon. 2006. (Chronicles of Faerie Ser.: No. 1). 304p. (J). (gr. 5-10). pap. 7.95 (978-0-8109-9214-6(0)) Abrams, Harry N. , Inc.

—The Light-Bearer's Daughter. 2007. (Chronicles of Faerie Ser.). (Illus.). 304p. (J). (gr. 2-8). 16.95 ***(978-0-8109-0781-2(X)*** , Amulet Bks.) Abrams, Harry N. , Inc.

Melling, O. R. The Summer King. (Chronicles of Faerie Ser.). 2007. 368p. (J). (gr. 2-8). pap. 7.95 ***(978-0-8109-9321-1(X)*** , Amulet Bks.); 2006. (Illus.). 380p. (YA). (gr. 5-10). 16.95 (978-0-8109-5969-9(0)) Abrams, Harry N. , Inc.

Molly's Magic: Evaluation Guide. 2006. (J). (978-1-55942-417-2(6)) Marsh Media.

Morpurgo, Michael. Twist of Gold. 2004. 304p. (J). pap. 8.99 (978-0-7497-4687-2(4)) Egmont Bks., Ltd. GBR. *Dist:* Trafalgar Square Publishing.

Murphy, Jim. Fergus & the Night-Demon: An Irish Ghost Story. Manders, John, illus. 2006. 32p. (J). (gr. 3-5). 16.00 (978-0-618-33955-6(8) , Clarion Bks.) Houghton Mifflin Co. Trade & Reference Div.

H I

Murphy, T. M. The Secrets of Cain's Castle. 2001. (Belltown Mystery Ser.). 144p. (J). (978-1-880158-38-8(8)) Townsend, J.N. Publishing.

Murray, Kirsty. Bridie's Fire. 2005. 264p. (J). pap. 8.95 (978-1-86508-727-6(0)) Allen & Unwin AUS. *Dist:* Independent Pubs. Group.

Napoli, Donna Jo. Hush: An Irish Princess' Tale. 2007. 320p. (YA). (gr. 7 up). 16.99 (***978-0-689-86176-5(1)***) Simon & Schuster Children's Publishing.

Neale, Cynthia G. The Irish Dresser: A Story of Hope During the Great Hunger (an Gorta Mor, 1845-1850) 2003. 148p. (J). pap. 7.95 (978-1-57249-344-5(5) , White Mane Kids) White Mane Publishing Co., Inc.

No Way Home: Individual Title Six-Packs. (Bookweb Ser.). 32p. (gr. 6 up). 34.00 (978-0-7578-0896-8(4)) Rigby Education.

Nolan, Janet. The St. Patrick's Day Shillelagh. Stahl, Ben, illus. 2002. 32p. (J). (gr. 2-5). 16.95 (978-0-8075-7344-0(2)) Whitman, Albert & Co.

—The St. Patrick's Day Shillelagh. Stahl, Ben F., illus. 2002. 32p. (J). (gr. 2-5). pap. 6.95 (978-0-8075-7345-7(0)) Whitman, Albert & Co.

O'Dwyer, Bridget. A Celtic Night: A fifteen-year old girl's modern retelling of Shakespeare's A Midsummer Night's Dream. 2006. 160p. (J). pap. 5.95 (978-1-932802-94-8(0) , Holy Macro! Bks.) MrExcel.com Publishing.

O'Neill, Alexis. Liam McLafferty's Choice. 2006. (J). (978-0-8028-5281-6(5) , Eerdmans Bks For Young Readers) Eerdmans, William B. Publishing Co.

O'Neill, Joan. Daisy Chain Days. 2004. (Daisy Chain War Bks.: Bk. 4). (J). pap. (978-0-340-88178-1(X) , Hodder Children's Books) Hodder Children's Division.

—Daisy Chain Dream. 2003. mass mkt. (978-0-340-85468-6(5) , Hodder Children's Books) Hodder Children's Division.

O'Neill, Joan. Dream Chaser. 2007. 272p. pap. 10.95 (***978-0-340-91148-8(4)***) Hodder Children's Division GBR. *Dist:* Independent Pubs. Group.

Osborne, Mary Pope. Viking Ships at Sunrise, Vol. 15. unabr. ed. 2004. (Magic Tree House Ser. : No. 15). 71p. (J). (gr. k-3). pap. 17.00 incl. audio (978-0-8072-0784-0(5) , LFTR 243 SP, Listening Library) Random Hse. Audio Publishing Group.

—Viking Ships at Sunrise. Murdocca, Salvatore, illus. 1998. (Magic Tree House Ser. : No. 15). 71p. (J). lib. bdg. 10.79 (978-0-606-15755-1(7)) Tandem Library Bks.

Parkinson, Siobhan. Second Fiddle: Or How to Tell a Blackbird from a Sausage. 2007. 192p. (J). (gr. 6-9). 16.95 (978-1-59643-122-5(9)) Roaring Brook Pr.

Raphael, Marie. A Boy from Ireland: A Novel. 2007. 224p. (YA). (gr. 7 up). 19.95 (978-0-89255-331-0(6)) Persea Bks., Inc.

Reeve, Phyllis Cardoze. One for Sorrow, Two for Joy. 2002. 150p. (YA). (gr. 6-9). pap. 14.95 (978-0-9725590-0-3(0)) Reeve, Phyllis.

Robertson, Ivan T. Jack & the Leprechaun. Bratun, Katy, illus. 2000. (Pictureback Ser.). 24p. (J). (gr. k-3). pap. 3.99 (978-0-375-80328-4(9) , Random Hse. Bks. for Young Readers) Random Hse. Children's Bks.

—Jack & the Leprechaun. 2000. (gr. k-3). lib. bdg. 10.95 (978-0-613-21788-0(8)) Tandem Library Bks.

Rose, Deborah Lee. The People Who Hugged the Trees: An Environmental Folk Tale. Saflund, Birgitta, illus. 2001. 32p. (gr. 4-7). pap. 7.95 (978-1-879373-50-1(5)) Rinehart, Roberts Pubs.

Ruttle, Keith. The Lord Mount Dragon. 2005. (Cambridge Storybooks Ser.). (Illus.). 32p. pap. 7.00 (978-0-521-67487-4(5)) Cambridge Univ. Pr.

Ryan, Emer & Newman, Clive, eds. From Two Islands: The Best of Irish-Australian Writers with New Fiction for Younger Readers. 2000. 180p. (J). pap. 12.95 (978-1-86368-282-4(1)) Fremantle Pr. AUS. *Dist:* International Specialized Bk. Services.

Sawyer, Ruth. The Wee Christmas Cabin of Carn-Na-Ween. Grafe, Max, illus. 2005. 40p. (J). (gr. 3 up). 14.99 (978-0-7636-2553-5(1)) Candlewick Pr.

Schlesinger, Gretchen. Send Me the Soap #1: The Emerald Isle Adventure. Pietila, David, illus. 2006. (J). 11.95 (978-0-9778536-0-1(8)) Eco-thumb Publishing Co.

—Send Me the Soap #1: The Emerald Isle Adventure (lib. Bdg.) Pietila, David, illus. 2006. (J). lib. bdg. (978-0-9778536-1-8(6)) Eco-thumb Publishing Co.

Schmidt, Gary D. Anson's Way. 1999. 224p. (J). (gr. 5-9). tchr. ed. 15.00 (978-0-395-91529-5(5) , Clarion Bks.) Houghton Mifflin Co. Trade & Reference Div.

—Anson's Way. 2001. (J). 12.64 (978-0-606-21039-3(3)) Tandem Library Bks.

—The Wonders of Donal O'Donnell: A Folktale of Ireland. Long, Loren, illus. rev. ed. 2002. 40p. (J). (gr. 3-6). 17.95 (978-0-8050-6516-9(4) , Holt, Henry & Co. Bks. For Young Readers) Holt, Henry & Co.

Schneider, Mical. Annie Quinn in America. (Adventures in Time Ser.). (J). 2003. (Illus.). 252p. (gr. 4-7). 15.95 (978-1-57505-510-7(4)); 2001. 6.95 (978-1-57505-535-0(X)) Lerner Publishing Group. (Carolrhoda Bks.).

Smith, Cathy Jo. Seamus Mcseamus, an Irish Rover. 2005. (Illus.). 104p. per. 11.95 (978-0-9766666-0-8(X)) Arcadian Hse.

Talbott, Hudson. O'sullivan Stew. 2001. (gr. k-3). lib. bdg. 15.30 (978-0-613-33718-2(2)) Tandem Library Bks.

Thompson, Kate. The New Policeman. 2007. 448p. (gr. 7-10). (J). lib. bdg. 17.89 (978-0-06-117428-5(9)); (YA). 16.99 (978-0-06-117427-8(0) , Greenwillow Bks.) HarperCollins Pubs.

—Switchers. 220p. (J). (gr. 4-7). pap. 5.99 (978-0-8072-1553-1(8)); 2004. (Switchers Ser.: Vol. 1). (gr. 5-9). pap. 38.00 incl. audio (978-0-8072-8138-3(7) , YA115SP) Random Hse. Audio Publishing Group. (Listening Library).

—Switchers. 1999. (978-0-606-17387-2(0)); (gr. 5-8). lib. bdg. 14.15 (978-0-613-20224-4(4)) Tandem Library Bks.

—Wild Blood. 2002. 272p. (gr. 5-17). pap. 5.99 (978-0-7868-1422-0(5)) Hyperion Paperbacks for Children.

—Wild Blood. 2002. (gr. 3-6). lib. bdg. 14.15 (978-0-613-74970-1(7)) Tandem Library Bks.

Town, Florida Ann. With a Silent Companion. 1999. (gr. 7-12). lib. bdg. 16.40 (978-0-613-89150-9(3)) Tandem Library Bks.

Wall, Bill. The Slave Coast. 1998. 144p. (YA). (gr. 4-7). pap. 7.95 (978-1-85635-196-6(3)) Mercier Pr., Ltd., The IRL. *Dist:* Irish Bks. & Media, Inc.

Welling, Peter J. Shawn O'Hisser, the Last Snake in Ireland. Welling, Peter J., illus. 2002. (Illus.). 32p. (J). (gr. k-3). 15.95 (978-1-58980-014-4(1)) Pelican Publishing Co., Inc.

Whelan, Gerard. A Winter of Spies. 2003. 191p. (YA). (gr. 5 up). pap. 6.95 (978-0-86278-566-6(9)) O'Brien Pr., Ltd., The IRL. *Dist:* Independent Pubs. Group.

Wiggin, Kate Douglas. Penelope's Irish Experiences. 2004. reprint ed. pap. 22.95 (978-1-4191-4072-3(8)); pap. 1.99 (978-1-4192-4072-0(2)) Kessinger Publishing, LLC.

Wilson, Laura. The Great Hunger. 2000. (Time Travellers Ser.). (Illus.). 36p. (J). (ps up). pap. 9.95 (978-0-688-17750-8(6) , Harper Trophy) HarperCollins Pubs.

—How I Survived the Irish Famine: Journal of Mary O'Flynn. 2000. (Time Travellers Ser.). (Illus.). 36p. (J). (ps-3). 14.89 (978-0-06-029534-9(1)) HarperCollins Pubs.

Wood, Lena. The Haunted Soul, Vol. 5. 2005. (Elijah Creek & the Armor of God Ser.: 5). (Illus.). 189p. (J). (gr. 3-7). pap. 6.99 (978-0-7847-1760-8(5) , 42155) Standard Publishing.

Woodruff, Elvira. Small Beauties: The Journey of Darcy Heart O'Hara. Rex, Adam, illus. 2006. 40p. (J). (gr. 1-4). 15.95 (978-0-375-82686-3(6)); lib. bdg. 17.99 (978-0-375-92686-0(0)) Random Hse. Children's Bks. (Knopf Bks. for Young Readers).

IRELAND—HISTORY

Allan, Tony. The Irish Famine: The Birth of Irish America. (Point of Impact Ser.). 32p. pap. 7.50 (978-1-4034-4113-3(8)); 2006. (Illus.). (J). (***978-1-4034-9144-2(5)***); 2001. (Illus.). (J). (gr. 5-7). lib. bdg. 24.22 (978-1-58810-077-1(4)) Heinemann Library.

—The Troubles in Northern Ireland. 2004. (Illus.). 56p. (J). lib. bdg. 27.07 (978-1-4034-4867-5(1)) Heinemann Library.

Banting, Erinn. Ireland: The Culture. 2002. (gr. 3-6). lib. bdg. 16.40 (978-0-613-52964-8(2)) Tandem Library Bks.

Bartoletti, Susan Campbell. Black Potatoes: The Story of the Great Irish Famine, 1845-1850. (Illus.). 192p. (J). (gr. 5-9). 2005. pap. 9.95 (978-0-618-54883-5(1)); 2001. tchr. ed. 18.00 (978-0-618-00271-9(5)) Houghton Mifflin Co. Trade & Reference Div.

Bladey, Conrad Jay. The Good Saint Brigid of Kildare: A Guide to the Primary Stories & Instructions for Celebrat. 2000. (Illus.). 20p. pap. 4.00 (978-0-9702386-1-0(4)) Hutman Productions.

Bowden, Rob. United Kingdom. 2006. (Destination Detectives Ser.). (Illus.). 48p. (J). pap. (978-1-4109-2343-1(6)); lib. bdg. (978-1-4109-2332-5(0)) Steck-Vaughn.

Bowden, Rob & Foley, Ronan. Focus on Ireland. 2007. (J). pap. (***978-0-8368-6758-9(0)***); 64p. (gr. 5-8). lib. bdg. 33.27 (***978-0-8368-6751-0(3)***) Stevens, Gareth Inc. (World Almanac Library).

Bowden, Rob & Foley, Ronan. Ireland. 2006. (Destination Detectives Ser.). (Illus.). 48p. (J). pap. (978-1-4109-2346-2(0)); lib. bdg. (978-1-4109-2335-6(5)) Steck-Vaughn.

Brassey, Richard. The Story of Ireland. 2002. (Illus.). 40p. 19.99 (978-1-85881-848-1(6)) Orion Bks. Ltd. GBR. *Dist:* Trafalgar Square Publishing.

Cronin, Mike. A History of Ireland. 2000. (Essential Histories Ser.). (Illus.). (YA). (978-0-312-23799-8(5)) St. Martin's Pr.

Crosbie, Duncan. Life on a Famine Ship: A Journal of the Irish Famine 1845-1850. Lee, Brian & Peter Bull Art Studio Staff, illus. 2006. 26p. (J). 16.99 (978-0-7641-6004-2(4)) Barron's Educational Series, Inc.

Darraj, Susan Muaddi. Mairead Corrigan & Betty Williams: Partners for Peace in Northern Ireland. 2006. (Modern Peacemakers Ser.). (Illus.). 112p. (J). (gr. 9 up). 30.00 (978-0-7910-9001-5(9) , Chelsea Hse.) Facts On File, Inc.

Derkins, Susie. The Irish Republican Army. 2005. (Inside the World's Most Infamous Terrorist Organizations Ser.). (Illus.). 64p. (YA). (gr. 7-12). lib. bdg. 26.50 (978-0-8239-3822-3(0)) Rosen Publishing Group, Inc., The.

Dolan, Edward F., Jr. The Irish Potato Famine: The Story of Irish-American Immigration. 2002. (Great Journeys Ser.). (Illus.). 109p. (J). 32.79 (978-0-7614-1323-3(5) , Benchmark Bks.) Cavendish, Marshall Corp.

Gallagher, Carole S. The Irish Potato Famine. 2001. (Great Disasters, Reforms & Ramifications Ser.). (Illus.). 112p. (J). 30.00 (978-0-7910-5788-9(7) , Chelsea Hse.) Facts On File, Inc.

Gottfried, Ted. Northern Ireland: Peace in Our Time? 2002. (Headliners Ser.). (Illus.). 64p. (gr. 5-8). lib. bdg. 25.90 (978-0-7613-2252-8(3) , Millbrook Pr.) Lerner Publishing Group.

Harrison, Cara. The Drumshee Rebels. 1999. 128p. (YA). (gr. 3 up). pap. 6.95 (978-0-86327-746-7(2)) Irish Bks. & Media, Inc.

Hill, George. The Fall of Irish Chiefs & Clans & the Plantation of Ulster: Including the Names of Irish Catholics, & Protestant Settlers. 2004. Orig. Title: An Historical Account of the Plantation in Ulster at the Commencement of the 17th Century. (Illus.). 276p. lib. bdg. 39.00 (978-0-940134-42-3(X)) Irish Genealogical Foundation.

Lisson, Deborah. Red Hugh: The Kidnap of Hugh O'Donnell. 2003. (Illus.). 224p. (YA). (gr. 5 up). pap. 7.95 (978-0-86278-604-5(5)) O'Brien Pr., Ltd., The IRL. *Dist:* Independent Pubs. Group.

Lyons, Mary E., ed. Feed the Children First: Irish Memories of the Great Hunger. 2002. (Illus.). 48p. (J). (gr. 4-7). 17.95 (978-0-689-84226-9(0) , Atheneum) Simon & Schuster Children's Publishing.

McConnell, Richard. War & Change: Ireland 1918-1924. 2007. (Illus.). 32p. (J). 22.95 (***978-0-237-53390-8(1)*** , Evans Brothers, Limited) Evans Publishing Group GBR. *Dist:* Independent Pubs. Group.

Minnis, Ivan. The Troubles of North Ireland. 2002. (Troubled World Ser.). (Illus.). 64p. (YA). (gr. 6 up). lib. bdg. 28.54 (978-0-7398-6341-1(X)) Raintree.

Noble, Marty. Invisible Irish Magic Picture Book. 1999. (Illus.). 16p. (J). pap. 1.00 (978-0-486-40765-4(9)) Dover Pubns., Inc.

O'Neill, Mary. Pick Your Brains about Ireland. Williams, Caspar, illus. 2005. (Pick Your Brains Ser.). 128p. pap. 9.95 (978-1-86011-221-8(8)) Cadogan Guides GBR. *Dist:* Globe Pequot Pr., The.

Pipe, Jim. You Wouldn't Want to Sail on an Irish Famine Ship! A Trip Across the Atlantic You'd Rather Not Make. (You Wouldn't Want to... : History of the World Ser.). 32p. (J). 2008. pap. 9.95 (***978-0-531-14854-9(8)*** , Watts, Franklin); 2007. spiral bd. 29.00 (***978-0-531-13913-4(1)*** , Children's Pr.) Scholastic Library Publishing.

Pollard, Michael. Rivers of Britain & Ireland: The Avon, Yorkshire Ouse, Tyne, Wye, Forth, Liffey, Lagan. (Illus.). 46p. (J). (978-0-237-51805-9(8) , Evans Brothers, Limited) Evans Publishing Group.

Tames, Richard. History of Ireland. 2nd ed. 2001. (Illus.). 32p. (J). (gr. 3-6). pap. 11.95 (978-0-7171-3244-7(7)) Gill & MacMillan, Ltd. IRL. *Dist:* Irish Bks. & Media, Inc.

Tony Allen. The Irish Famine. 2nd ed. 2006. (Illus.). 32p. (J). pap. (***978-1-4034-9153-4(4)***) Heinemann Library.

Wagner, Heather Lehr. The IRA & England. 2002. (People at Odds Ser.). (Illus.). 112p. (J). (gr. 5 up). 30.00 (978-0-7910-6706-2(8) , Chelsea Hse.) Facts On File, Inc.

IRISH AMERICANS

Allan, Tony. The Irish Famine: The Birth of Irish America. (Point of Impact Ser.). 32p. pap. 7.50 (978-1-4034-4113-3(8)); 2006. (Illus.). (J). (***978-1-4034-9144-2(5)***); 2001. (Illus.). (J). (gr. 5-7). lib. bdg. 24.22 (978-1-58810-077-1(4)) Heinemann Library.

De Capua, Sarah. Irish Americans. 2002. (Spirit of America: Our Cultural Heritage Ser.). (Illus.). 32p. (J). (gr. 2-6). 27.07 (978-1-56766-155-2(6)) Child's World, Inc.

Goldstein, Margaret J. Irish in America. 2005. (In America Ser.). (Illus.). 80p. (J). (gr. 5-8). lib. bdg. 27.93 (978-0-8225-3950-6(0)) Lerner Publishing Group.

Graves, Kerry A. Irish Americans. (Immigrants in America Ser.). 2004. 126p. (J). pap. 9.95 (978-0-7910-7511-1(7)); 2003. (Illus.). 112p. (gr. 6-12). 30.00 (978-0-7910-7128-1(6)) Facts On File, Inc. (Chelsea Hse.).

Hall, M. C. Irish Americans. 2003. (We Are America Ser.). 32p. pap. 6.95 (978-1-4034-3135-6(3)) Heinemann Library.

Hall, Margaret. Irish Americans. 2003. (We Are America Ser.). (Illus.). 32p. (J). lib. bdg. 24.22 (978-1-4034-0734-4(7)) Heinemann Library.

—Irish Americans. 2003. (gr. 3-6). lib. bdg. 15.25 (978-0-613-67417-1(0)) Tandem Library Bks.

Hossell, Karen Price. The Irish Americans. 2003. (Immigrants in America Ser.). (Illus.). 112p. (J). 29.95 (978-1-56006-752-8(7) , Lucent Bks.) Thomson Gale.

Nichol, Bryan. Irish Americans. 2004. (One Nation Ser.). (Illus.). 32p. (J). (gr. k-6). lib. bdg. 22.78 (978-1-59197-528-1(X) , Checkerboard Library) ABDO Publishing Co.

Nickles, Greg. The Irish. 2001. (We Came to North America Ser.). (Illus.). 32p. (J). (gr. 4). (978-0-7787-0190-3(5)); pap. (978-0-7787-0204-7(9)) Crabtree Publishing Co.

—Irish. 2001. (gr. 3-6). lib. bdg. 17.60 (978-0-613-43455-3(2)) Tandem Library Bks.

—The Irish: We Came to North America. 2006. (Illus.). 32p. (J). (gr. 4-8). reprint ed. 19.00 (978-0-7567-9909-0(0)) DIANE Publishing Co.

Parker, Lewis K. Why Irish Immigrants Came to America. 2003. (Reading Power Ser.). (Illus.). 24p. (J). lib. bdg. 17.25 (978-0-8239-6462-8(0) , PowerKids Pr.) Rosen Publishing Group, Inc., The.

Paulson, Timothy J. Irish Immigrants. 2004. (Immigration to the United States Ser.). (Illus.). 96p. (J). (gr. 4-9). per. 35.00 (978-0-8160-5682-8(X)) Facts On File, Inc.

Price Hossell, Karen. The Irish. 2004. (Illus.). 207p. (gr. 10-12). 34.95 (978-0-7377-2154-6(5) , Greenhaven Pr., Inc.) Thomson Gale.

Raum, Elizabeth. Irish Immigrants in America: An Interactive History Adventure. 2008. (You Choose Bks.). 112p. (J). (gr. 3-7). lib. bdg. 27.23 (***978-1-4296-0161-0(2)***) Capstone Pr., Inc.

Temple, Bob. The Irish-Americans. 2002. (Welcome to America Ser.). (Illus.). 64p. (YA). (gr. 5 up). lib. bdg. (978-1-59084-101-3(8)) Mason Crest Pubs.

Thornton, Jeremy. The Irish Potato Famine: Irish Immigrants Come to America (1845-1850) 2004. (Primary Sources of Immigration & Migration in America Ser.). (Illus.). 24p. (J). lib. bdg. 19.95 (978-0-8239-6831-2(6) , PowerKids Pr.) Rosen Publishing Group, Inc., The.

—The Irish Potato Famine: Irish Immigrants Come to America, 1845-1850. 2004. (Primary Sources of Immigration & Migration in America Ser.). (Illus.). 24p. (J). lib. bdg. (978-0-8239-8957-7(7) , PowerKids Pr.) Rosen Publishing Group, Inc., The.

Tony Allen. The Irish Famine. 2nd ed. 2006. (Illus.). 32p. (J). pap. (***978-1-4034-9153-4(4)***) Heinemann Library.

Trumbauer, Lisa. Hopes Fulfilled: The Irish Immigrants in Boston. 2005. (Illus.). 32p. (J). pap. (***978-0-7367-2881-2(3)***) Zaner-Bloser, Inc.

Uschan, Michael V. Irish Americans. 2006. (World Almanac Library of American Immigration). (Illus.). 48p. (J). pap. (978-0-8368-7324-5(6)); lib. bdg. (978-0-8368-7311-5(4)) Stevens, Gareth Inc. (World Almanac Library).

IRISH AMERICANS—FICTION

Alger, Horatio. Only an Irish Boy: Or, Andy Burke's Fortunes & Misfortunes. 2006. pap. (***978-1-4065-0716-4(4)***) Dodo Pr.

Alger Jr. Horatio Staff. Only an Irish Boy. rev. ed. 2006. 284p. 28.95 (978-1-4218-1759-0(4)); pap. 13.95 (978-1-4218-1859-7(0)) 1st World Publishing, Inc. (1st World Library - Literary Society).

Auch, Mary Jane. Ashes of Roses. rev. ed. 2002. 256p. (YA). (gr. 7-10). 16.95 (978-0-8050-6686-9(1) , Holt, Henry & Co. Bks. For Young Readers) Holt, Henry & Co.

—Ashes of Roses. 2004. 256p. (YA). (gr. 7). reprint ed. pap. 5.99 (978-0-440-23851-5(X) , Laurel Leaf) Random Hse. Children's Bks.

—Ashes of Roses. 2004. (gr. 7-12). lib. bdg. 14.15 (978-0-613-72252-0(3)) Tandem Library Bks.

Dillon, Jana. Lucky O'Leprechaun Comes to America. 2001. (Illus.). 32p. (J). (ps-1). pap. 15.95 (978-1-56554-816-9(7)) Pelican Publishing Co., Inc.

Durrant, Lynda. My Last Skirt: The Story of Jennie Hodgers, Union Soldier. 2006. 192p. (J). (gr. 5). 16.00 (978-0-618-57490-2(5) , Clarion Bks.) Houghton Mifflin Co. Trade & Reference Div.

—My Last Skirt: The Story of Jennie Hodgers, Union Soldier. 2006. 245p. (YA). 21.95 (978-0-7862-8880-9(9)) Thorndike Pr.

Emery, Joanna. Brothers of the Falls. Erickson, David, illus. 2004. (Adventures in America Ser.). (J). 14.95 (978-1-893110-37-3(0)) Silver Moon Pr.

Fenton, Edward. Duffy's Rocks. l.t. ed. 1999. (Golden Triangle Bks.). 240p. (YA). (gr. 8-12). pap. 9.95 (978-0-8229-5706-5(X)) Univ. of Pittsburgh Pr.

Giff, Patricia Reilly. Water Street. (gr. 4-7). 2008. 144p. 6.50 (***978-0-440-41921-1(2)*** , Yearling); 2006. 176p. (J). 15.95 (978-0-385-73068-6(3) , Lamb, Wendy); 2006. 176p. (J). lib. bdg. 17.99 (978-0-385-90097-3(X) , Lamb, Wendy) Random Hse. Children's Bks.

—Water Street. l.t. rev. ed. 2007. 193p. (YA). 23.95 (***978-0-7862-9277-6(6)***) Thorndike Pr.

Haas, Jessie. Chase. 2007. 256p. (J). (gr. 5-9). 16.99 (978-0-06-112850-9(3)); lib. bdg. 17.89 (978-0-06-112851-6(1)) HarperCollins Pubs.

Holland, Isabelle. Paperboy. 1999. 144p. (J). (gr. 7 up). tchr. ed. 16.95 (978-0-8234-1422-2(1)) Holiday Hse., Inc.

Hungry No More (Irish) 76p. (YA). (gr. 6-12). pap. 9.95 (978-0-8224-3680-5(9)) Globe Fearon Educational Publishing.

Hurst, Carol Otis. Torchlight. 2006. 160p. (J). (gr. 4-6). 16.00 (978-0-618-27601-1(7)) Houghton Mifflin Co.

Ingle, Sheila C. Courageous Kate: A Daughter of the American Revolution. 2006. (J). (***978-1-891885-52-5(9)***) Hub City Writers Project.

Loughrey, Eithne. Annie Moore: New York City Girl. 2006. (YA). (***978-0-8368-7737-3(3)***) Stevens, Gareth Inc.

—Annie Moore: The Golden Dollar Girl. l.t. ed. 2006. (Dales Ser.). 208p. (J). 23.99 (978-1-84262-447-0(4)) Magna Large Print Bks. GBR. *Dist:* Ulverscroft Large Print Bks., Ltd.

—Annie Moore First in Line for America. l.t. ed. 2006. (Dales Ser.). 224p. (J). 23.99 (978-1-84262-446-3(6)) Magna Large Print Bks. GBR. *Dist:* Ulverscroft Large Print Bks., Ltd.

—Annie Moore, First in Line for Ellis Island. 2006. (J). lib. bdg. (***978-0-8368-7735-9(7)***) Stevens, Gareth Inc.

—Annie Moore New York City Girl. l.t. ed. 2006. (Dales Ser.). 208p. 23.99 (978-1-84262-448-7(2)) Dales Large Print Bks. GBR. *Dist:* Ulverscroft Large Print Bks., Ltd.

Loughrey, Eithne. Annie Moore, the Golden Dollar Girl. 2006. (J). lib. bdg. (***978-0-8368-7736-6(5)***) Stevens, Gareth Inc.

McNamara, Margaret & Gordon, Mike. The Luck of the Irish. 2007. (Ready-To-Read Ser.). 32p. (J). (SPA.). pap. 3.99 (978-1-4169-1539-3(7) , Aladdin); lib. bdg. 11.89 (978-1-4169-1540-9(0) , Aladdin Library) Simon & Schuster Children's Publishing.

Neale, Cynthia. Hope in New York City: The Continuing Story of the Irish Dresser. 2007. (ENG.). 176p. (J). pap. 7.95 (***978-1-57249-387-2(9)*** , White Mane Kids) White Mane Publishing Co., Inc.

Nixon, Joan Lowery. Land of Promise. l.t. ed. 2001. (Ellis Island Stories Ser.). 169p. (J). (gr. 4 up). lib. bdg. 23.33 (978-0-8368-2812-2(7)) Stevens, Gareth Inc.

Nolan, Janet. The St. Patrick's Day Shillelagh. Stahl, Ben, illus. 2002. 32p. (J). (gr. 2-5). 16.95 (978-0-8075-7344-0(2)) Whitman, Albert & Co.

—The St. Patrick's Day Shillelagh. Stahl, Ben F., illus. 2002. 32p. (J). (gr. 2-5). pap. 6.95 (978-0-8075-7345-7(0)) Whitman, Albert & Co.

Schneider, Mical. Annie Quinn in America. (Adventures in Time Ser.). (J). 2003. (Illus.). 252p. (gr. 4-7). 15.95 (978-1-57505-510-7(4)); 2001. 6.95 (978-1-57505-535-0(X)) Lerner Publishing Group. (Carolrhoda Bks.).

Wargin, Kathy-Jo. The Legend of Thanksgiving. Papp, Robert, illus. 2008. (J). (978-0-310-71179-7(7)) Zonderkidz.

Whitney, Kim Ablon. See You down the Road: A Novel. 2004. 192p. (gr. 7). (J). lib. bdg. 17.99 (978-0-375-92467-5(1)); (YA). 15.95 (978-0-375-82467-8(7)) Random Hse. Children's Bks. (Knopf Bks. for Young Readers).

Wimmer, Mary. Reaching Shore. 2007. 280p. (YA). per. 14.95 (***978-1-59598-063-2(6)***) Goblin Fern Pr., Inc.

Yin. Brothers. Soentpiet, Chris, illus. 2006. 32p. (J). (gr. k). 16.99 (978-0-399-23406-4(3) , Philomel) Penguin Group (USA) Inc.

IRISH—UNITED STATES

see also Irish Americans

O'Hara, Megan. Irish Immigrants, 1840-1920. 2001. (Blue Earth Books). (Illus.). 32p. (J). (gr. 3-4). lib. bdg. 22.60 (978-0-7368-0795-1(0) , Bridgestone Bks.) Capstone Pr., Inc.

IRISH—UNITED STATES—FICTION

Lawson, Robert. The Great Wheel. 2004. (Illus.). 192p. (J). pap. 6.95 (978-0-8027-7705-8(8)) Walker & Co.

Loughrey, Eithne. Annie Moore: First in Line for America. 1999. (Illus.). 143p. (YA). (gr. 5-10). pap. 7.95 (978-1-85635-245-1(5)) Mercier Pr., Ltd., The IRL. *Dist:* Irish Bks. & Media, Inc.

O'Neill, Joan. Connie 2. 2007. 266p. pap. 10.95 (***978-0-340-91149-5(2)***) Hodder Children's Division GBR. *Dist:* Independent Pubs. Group.

—Dream Chaser. 2007. 272p. pap. 10.95 (***978-0-340-91148-8(4)***) Hodder Children's Division GBR. *Dist:* Independent Pubs. Group.

IRISH POETRY—COLLECTIONS

Emoe, Nicola, illus. A Child's Treasury of Irish Rhymes. 2000. 48p. (J). (ps-3). 15.95 (978-1-902283-18-0(X)) Barefoot Bks., Inc.

IRON

Blashfield, Jean F. Iron & the Trace Elements. 2001. (Sparks of Life Ser.). (Illus.). 64p. (J). (gr. 7-8). lib. bdg. 27.12 (978-0-7398-4359-8(1)) Raintree.

Capaccio, George. Iron. 2006. (Navigators Ser.). (J). pap. 42.00 (***978-1-4108-6237-2(2)***) Benchmark Education Co.

Franck, Irene M. & Brownstone, David M. Iron. 2003. (Illus.). 32p. (J). (978-0-7172-5717-1(7) , Grolier) Scholastic Library Publishing.

Harcourt School Publishers Staff. Iron Advanced Level: A Gift from the Earth. 3rd ed. 2002. (Trophies Reading Program Ser.). (Illus.). pap. 5.10 (978-0-15-323480-4(6)) Harcourt Schl. Pubs.

Hasan, Heather. Iron. 2005. (Interpreting the Periodic Table Ser.). (Illus.). 48p. (J). (gr. 5-8). lib. bdg. 26.50 (978-1-4042-0157-6(2)) Rosen Publishing Group, Inc., The.

Kassinger, Ruth. Iron & Steel: From Thor's Hammer to the Space Shuttle. 2003. (Material World Ser.). (Illus.). 80p. (gr. 6-8). lib. bdg. 25.90 (978-0-7613-2111-8(X) , Twenty-First Century Bks.) Lerner Publishing Group.

Morris, Neil. Iron. 2005. (Illus.). 32p. (J). (gr. 4 up). lib. bdg. 27.10 (978-1-58340-631-1(X)) Smart Apple Media.

Murray, Peter. Iron. 2001. (From the Earth Ser.). (Illus.). 24p. (J). 21.35 (978-1-58340-113-2(X)) Smart Apple Media.

Sparrow, Giles. Iron. 1998. (Elements Ser.). (Illus.). 32p. (J). (gr. 3-5). lib. bdg. 25.64 (978-0-7614-0880-2(0) , Benchmark Bks.) Cavendish, Marshall Corp.

Tocci, Salvatore. Iron. 2005. (True Bks.). (Illus.). (gr. 3-5). 47p. (J). pap. 6.95 (978-0-516-25571-2(1)); 48p. 25.00 (978-0-516-23695-7(4)) Scholastic Library Publishing. (Children's Pr.).

Zemlicka, Shannon. From Iron to Car. 2004. (Start to Finish Ser.). (Illus.). 24p. (J). 18.60 (978-0-8225-0943-1(1) , Lerner Pubns.) Lerner Publishing Group.

IRON CURTAIN COUNTRIES

see Communist Countries

IRVING, WASHINGTON, 1783-1859

Collins, David R. Washington Irving: Storyteller for a New Nation. 2004. (World Writers Ser.). (Illus.). 112p. (YA). (gr. 6-12). 23.95 (978-1-883846-50-3(1) , First Biographies) Reynolds, Morgan Inc.

ISABELLA I, QUEEN OF SPAIN, 1451-1504

Mann, Kenny. Isabel, Ferdinand & Fifteenth-Century Spain. 2001. (Rulers & Their Times Ser.). (Illus.). 80p. (J). (gr. 6 up). lib. bdg. 29.93 (978-0-7614-1030-0(9) , Benchmark Bks.) Cavendish, Marshall Corp.

Whitelaw, Nancy. Queen Isabella & the Unification of Spain. 2004. (World Leaders Ser.). (Illus.). 160p. (YA). (gr. 6-12). lib. bdg. 26.95 (978-1-931798-25-9(7)) Reynolds, Morgan Inc.

ISAIAH, THE PROPHET

PowerXpress Isaiah. 9.95 incl. audio compact disk (978-0-687-09796-8(7)) Abingdon Pr.

ISLAM

Here are entered works on the religion of which Muhammad is the prophet. Works on the community of believers in Islam are entered under Muslims.

see also Muslims

Ahmed, Aisha. Islam for the Junior. l.t. ed. 2000. 58p. (J). pap. 5.00 (978-1-879402-71-3(8)) Tahrike Tarsile Quran, Inc.

Al-Gailani, Noorah. Islamic Year: Surahs, Stories & Celebrations. 2003. (gr. 3-6). lib. bdg. 38.45 (978-0-613-80442-4(2)) Tandem Library Bks.

Al-Jibaly, Muhummad. Knowing Allah. l.t. ed. 1998. (Eemaan Made Easy Ser.). (Illus.). 63p. (J). (gr. 2). pap. 5.00 (978-1-891229-05-3(2)) Al-Kitaab & As-Sunnah Publishing.

—Knowing the Angels. l.t. ed. 1999. (Eemaan Made Easy Ser.: Vol. 2). (Illus.). 102p. (J). (gr. 2). pap. 7.00 (978-1-891229-06-0(0)) Al-Kitaab & As-Sunnah Publishing.

Alkouatli, Claire. Islam. 2006. (World Religions Ser.). (Illus.). 144p. (J). (gr. 8 up). lib. bdg. 39.93 (978-0-7614-2120-7(3)) Cavendish, Marshall Corp.

Allah in Person, Royall. The Center Page, Volume 1. 2003. (Illus.). 241p. 51.00 (978-0-9768502-0-5(6)) United Nation of Islam, The.

Allah's Best Friend. 2001. 16p. (J). pap. 1.00 (978-81-87570-76-9(8)) Goodword Bks. Pvt. Ltd. IND. *Dist:* Lodhia Ctr., The.

Amer, Fatmah. Islam. 2006. (QEB World of Faiths Ser.). (Illus.). 32p. (J). (gr. 3-6). lib. bdg. 27.10 (978-1-59566-208-8(1)) QEB Publishing Inc.

Aziz, Abdullah. Muhammad's Believe It or Else!, Bk. 3. 2001. 23p. (YA). mass mkt. 3.95 (978-1-931230-01-8(3) , Crescent Moon Pubns.) Christian Scholar's Pr.

Baig, Khalid. First Things First: For Inquiring Minds & Yearning Hearts. 2004. 432p. pap. 20.00 (978-0-9755157-0-9(5)) Open Mind Pr.

Barnes, Trevor. Islam: Worship, Festivals, & Ceremonies from Around the World. Kingfisher Editors, ed. 2005. (World Faiths Ser.). (Illus.). 40p. (J). (gr. 5-9). pap., pap. 6.95 (978-0-7534-5882-2(9) , Kingfisher) Houghton Mifflin Co. Trade & Reference Div.

Bodden, Valerie. Mosques. 2008. (***978-1-58341-562-7(9)*** , Creative Education) Creative Co., The.

The Brave Boy. l.t. ed. 2001. 16p. (J). pap. 1.00 (978-81-87570-74-5(1)) Goodword Bks. Pvt. Ltd. IND. *Dist:* Lodhia Ctr., The.

The Brave Boy: Quran Stories for Little Hearts. l.t. ed. 2001. 24p. (J). pap. 2.25 (978-81-87570-78-3(4)) Goodword Bks. Pvt. Ltd. IND. *Dist:* Lodhia Ctr., The.

Carr, Melissa S. Who Are the Muslims? 2003. (Introducing Islam Ser.). (Illus.). 112p. (J). lib. bdg. (978-1-59084-701-5(6)) Mason Crest Pubs.

Chaudhry, Saida. Call to Prophethood. (Illus.). (J). (gr. 2-5). pap. 4.00 (978-0-89259-046-9(7)) American Trust Pubns.

Clark, Charles. Islam. 2001. (Religions of the World Ser.). (Illus.). 104p. (YA). 29.95 (978-1-56006-986-7(4) , LML00902-178231, Lucent Bks.) Thomson Gale.

Conover, Sarah & Crane, Freda. Beautiful Signs/Ayat Jamilah: A Treasury of Islamic Wisdom for Children & Parents. Wahl, Valerie, illus. 2004. (Little Light of Mine Ser.). 208p. (J). pap. 19.95 (978-0-910055-94-9(7)) Eastern Washington Univ. Pr.

Corzine, Phyllis. The Islamic Empire. 2004. (World History Ser.). (Illus.). 112p. (J). (gr. 7-10). 32.45 (978-1-59018-371-7(1) , Lucent Bks.) Thomson Gale.

Daynes, Katie. Islam. 2007. (Young Reading Series 3 Gift Bks). 64p. (J). 8.99 (***978-0-7945-1865-3(6)*** , Usborne) EDC Publishing.

Delgado, Linda D. Saying Goodbye. 2006. (YA). per. (978-0-9767861-8-4(4)) Muslim Writers Publishing.

—Stories. 2006. (YA). per. (978-0-9767861-7-7(6)) Muslim Writers Publishing.

Doak, Robin S. Islamic Empire. 2004. (Great Empires of the Past Ser.). (Illus.). 128p. (J). (gr. 6-12). 35.00 (978-0-8160-5557-9(2)) Facts On File, Inc.

Dorling Kindersley Publishing Staff. Islam. 2005. (Eyewitness Bks.). (Illus.). 72p. (J). 15.99 (978-0-7566-1077-7(X) , 1241919) Dorling Kindersley Publishing, Inc.

Douglas, Susan. Ramadan. 2004. (gr. k-3). lib. bdg. 14.10 (978-0-613-79242-4(4)) Tandem Library Bks.

Douglass, Susan L. Ramadan. Reeves, Jeni, illus. 2004. (On My Own Holidays Ser.). 48p. (J). (gr. 2-4). lib. bdg. 25.26 (978-0-87614-932-4(8)) Lerner Publishing Group.

Douglass, Susan L. & Reeves. Ramadan. 2003. (On My Own Holidays Ser.). (Illus.). 48p. (J). (gr. k-3). 5.95 (978-1-57505-584-8(8)) Lerner Publishing Group.

Dudley, William. Islam (OPVP) 2004. (gr. 10-12). 36.20 (978-0-7377-2238-3(X)); 24.95 (978-0-7377-2239-0(8)) Thomson Gale. (Greenhaven Pr., Inc.).

Durkee, Noura. 12 Stories from the Quran, 6 Vols. 2001. (Illus.). 24p. (J). (978-1-900251-75-4(2)) Hood Hood Bks., Ltd.

Egan, Andrew. Islam. 2003. (Living Religions Ser.). (Illus.). 62p. (J). 28.56 (978-0-7398-6385-5(1)) Raintree.

Emerick, Yahiya. Color & Learn Salah Textbook & Coloring Book, Meehan, Patricia, illus. l.t. ed. 2000. 91p. (J). pap. 5.95 (978-1-933269-06-1(5)) Noorart, Inc.

—My First Book About Islam. Meehan, Patricia, illus. 2001. 292p. (J). (gr. 1-2). pap. 11.95 (978-1-889720-35-7(6)) Amirah Publishing.

—My First Book about Islam. l.t. ed. 2001. 292p. pap. 12.99 (978-1-933269-04-7(9)) Noorart, Inc.

Emerick, Yahiya, ed. Muslim Youth Speak: Voices of Todays Muslim Youth. 1998. 110p. (J). (gr. 6-9). pap. 7.95 (978-1-889720-21-0(6)) Amirah Publishing.

English Translation of the Meaning of the Quran. 2005. 14.95 (978-0-9773009-0-7(0)) Book of Signs Foundation.

Fadl, Khaled Abou el. Introducing Islam, 8 vols., Set. 2003. (Illus.). 112p. (YA). lib. bdg. (978-1-59084-696-4(6)) Mason Crest Pubs.

Fiqh, Tawhid & Akhlaq, A. A Guide for the Young Muslim, Bk. 2. 1998. (J). pap. 5.50 (978-1-871031-79-9(6)) Kazi Pubns., Inc.

The First Man: Quran Stories for Little Hearts. l.t. ed. 2001. 24p. (J). per. 4.25 (978-81-87570-93-6(8)) Goodword Bks. Pvt. Ltd. IND. *Dist:* Lodhia Ctr., The.

The First Man on the Earth. l.t. ed. 2001. 16p. (J). pap. 1.00 (978-81-87570-89-9(X)) Goodword Bks. Pvt. Ltd. IND. *Dist:* Lodhia Ctr., The.

Foreign Policy Research Institute Staff, ed. The Growth & Influence of Islam in the Nations of Asia & Central Asia, 17 vols., Set. 2006. (Illus.). 112,128p. (YA). lib. bdg. 441.15 (978-1-59084-832-6(2)) Mason Crest Pubs.

Friedman, Lauri S. Islam. 2006. 80-244*p. (gr. 7-10). 33.70 (978-0-7377-3460-7(4) , Greenhaven Pr., Inc.) Thomson Gale.

Ganeri, Anita. Hajj Stories. 2007. (J). (***978-1-84234-434-7(X)***) Cherrytree Pubns., Inc.

—Islam: Budi's Story. 2006. (This Is My Faith Bks.). (Illus.). 32p. (J). (gr. 1-4). 11.99 (978-0-7641-5966-4(6)); pap. 4.99 (978-0-7641-3475-3(2)) Barron's Educational Series, Inc.

—Muslim Festivals Through the Year. 2003. (Year of Festivals Ser.). 30p. (J). lib. bdg. 24.25 (978-1-58340-371-6(X)) Smart Apple Media.

—The Qur'an & Islam. Fennell, Tracy, illus. 2003. 30p. (J). lib. bdg. 24.25 (978-1-58340-241-2(1)) Smart Apple Media.

Garcha, Rajinder & Russell, Patricia Yates. The World of Islam in Literature for Youth: A Selective Annotated Bibliography for K-12. 2006. (Literature for Youth Ser.: Vol. 7). 242p. pap. 35.00 (978-0-8108-5488-8(0)) Scarecrow Pr., Inc.

Ghazi, A., ed. The First Ones: The Makkan Sahabah. Siddiqui, A. Sayeed, tr. 1999. (Stories of the Sahabah Ser.: Vol. II). (Illus.). 145p. (YA). (gr. 7-10). pap. 10.00 (978-1-56316-451-4(5)) IQRA International Educational Foundation.

—Those Promised Paradise. Siddiqui, M. Sayeed, tr. Siddiqui, M. Sayeed, illus. 1999. (Stories of the Sahabah Ser.: Vol. I). 256p. (YA). (gr. 7-10). pap. 10.00 (978-1-56316-374-6(8)) IQRA International Educational Foundation.

Ghazi, Suhaib Hamid. Ramadan. Rayyan, Omar, illus. 32p. (J). (gr. k-3). tchr. ed. 17.95 (978-0-8234-1254-9(7)) Holiday Hse., Inc.

Ghazi, Tasneema K. Let's Learn from the Holy Qur'an: An Activity Book for Children. Hagg, Sharelle Abdul, illus. l.t. ed. 1999. 56p. (J). (ps-1). ring bd., wbk. ed. 6.00 (978-1-56316-122-3(2)) IQRA International Educational Foundation.

Gnojewski, Carol. Ramadan: A Muslim Time of Fasting, Prayer, & Celebration. 2004. (Finding Out about Holidays Ser.). (Illus.). 48p. (J). (gr. 2-5). lib. bdg. 23.93 (978-0-7660-2275-1(7)) Enslow Pubs., Inc.

Gordon, Matthew S. Islam. 3rd ed. 2006. (World Religions Ser.). (Illus.). 128p. (YA). (gr. 6-12). 30.00 (978-0-8160-6612-4(4)) Facts On File, Inc.

Gulen, Fethullah. Questions & Answers about Faith, Vol. 1. 2005. Tr. of Asrin Getirdigi Tereddutler. 176p. reprint ed. pap. 12.95 (978-0-9521497-1-2(0) , Fountain, The) Light, Inc., The.

Habeeb, Mark. Islamic Fundamentalism. 2003. (Introducing Islam Ser.). (Illus.). 112p. (YA). lib. bdg. (978-1-59084-703-9(2)) Mason Crest Pubs.

Halman, Hugh Talat. Al-Khidr: The Green One. Qadi, Sidiqa, ed. Lipton, Abdallah, illus. 2001. 34p. (gr. 6-9). 10.00 (978-1-56316-500-9(7)) IQRA International Educational Foundation.

Haque, Muhammad S. Holy Quran with Modern English Translations & Anno Haque. 1998. 1000p. (J). 25.00 incl. audio (978-0-933057-05-0(9) , WOQHO002T) Namuk International, Inc.

Hartney, Chris, et al. Livewire Investigates Islam. 2004. (Livewires Ser.). (Illus.). 32p. pap. 4.10 (978-0-521-60113-9(4)) Cambridge Univ. Pr.

Hay, Jeff. Renaissance. 2001. (gr. 7-12). lib. bdg. 39.05 (978-0-613-73785-2(7)) Tandem Library Bks.

Hegedus, Umar. Muslim Mosque. (Keystones Ser.). (Illus.). 32p. (gr. 2-6). 2000. pap. 6.95 (978-0-7136-5344-1(2)); 1998. (J). 16.95 (978-0-7136-4335-0(8)) A & C Black GBR. *Dist:* Lubrecht & Cramer, Ltd.

Hipps, Amelia. Islam, Christianity, Judaism. 2003. (Introducing Islam Ser.). (Illus.). 112p. (J). lib. bdg. (978-1-59084-698-8(2)) Mason Crest Pubs.

Hodges, Rick. What Muslims Think, & How They Live. 2003. (Introducing Islam Ser.). (Illus.). 112p. (YA). lib. bdg. 24.95 (978-1-59084-702-2(4)) Mason Crest Pubs.

Hoyt-Goldsmith, Diane. Celebrating Ramadan. Migdale, Lawrence, illus. Migdale, Lawrence, photos by. 32p. (YA). (gr. 4-6). tchr. ed. 17.95 (978-0-8234-1581-6(3)) Holiday Hse., Inc.

—Celebrating Ramadan. Migdale, Lawrence, photos by. (Illus.). 32p. (J). (gr. 4-6). 6.95 (978-0-8234-1762-9(X)) Holiday Hse., Inc.

Hughes, Monica. My Id-Ul-Fitr. 2003. (Festivals Ser.). (Illus.). 24p. (J). pap. 5.50 (978-1-4109-0666-3(3)) Raintree.

—My Id-ul-Fitr. 2003. (Festivals Ser.). (Illus.). 24p. (J). lib. bdg. 18.56 (978-1-4109-0640-3(X)) Raintree.

Hussein, Musharraf, et al. Islam. 2006. (Illus.). 64p. (YA). pap., stu. ed. 21.00 (978-0-7487-9672-4(X)) Nelson Thornes Ltd. GBR. *Dist:* Trans-Atlantic Pubns., Inc.

Ibrahim, Muhammad & Ganeri, Anita. Muslim Prayer & Worship. 2007. (J). (***978-1-59771-090-9(3)***) Sea-To-Sea Pubns.

Interaction Publishers, Inc. Staff. Into Islam. 2004. (Illus.). (YA). (gr. 6-12). 48.00 (978-1-57336-401-0(0) , I3011) Interaction Pubs., Inc.

Jeffrey, Laura S. Celebrate Ramadan. 2007. (Celebrate Holidays Ser.). (Illus.). 112p. (J). lib. bdg. 31.93 (978-0-7660-2774-9(0)) Enslow Pubs., Inc.

Kemmetmueller, Donna Jean. My Muslim Friend: A Young Catholic Learns about Islam. Jacobsen, Laura, illus. 2006. 47p. (J). 15.95 (978-0-8198-4844-4(1)) Pauline Bks. & Media.

Khan, Aisha Karen. What You Will See Inside a Mosque. Pepis, Aaron, photos by. 2003. (Illus.). 32p. (978-2-89507-398-7(8)) Novalis Publishing.

—What You Will See Inside a Mosque. Pepis, Aaron, photos by. 2003. (What You Will See Inside- Ser.). (Illus.). 32p. (J). (gr. 1-5). 16.95 (978-1-893361-60-7(8)) Skylight Paths Publishing.

Khan, Farjana. Yippee! Ramadan's over, It's Eid. 2005. (ENG., Illus.). 28p. (J). per. (***978-1-4208-9412-7(9)***) AuthorHouse.

Khan, Rukhsana. Muslim Child: Understanding Islam Through Stories & Poems. Gallinger, Patty, illus. 2002. 104p. (J). (gr. 3-7). 15.95 (978-0-8075-5307-7(7)) Whitman, Albert & Co.

Khan, Saniyasnain. The Ark of Nuh. l.t. ed. 2001. 24p. pap. 4.25 (978-81-87570-82-0(2)) Goodword Bks. Pvt. Ltd. IND. *Dist:* Lodhia Ctr., The.

—The Ark of Nuh & the Animals Colouring Book: Quran Stories of Little Hearts. 2001. (Colour A Story Ser.). 24p. (J). pap. 2.25 (978-81-87570-84-4(9)) Goodword Bks. Pvt. Ltd. IND. *Dist:* Lodhia Ctr., The.

—The Ark of Nuh & the Great Flood Sticker Book: Quran Stories for Tiny Tots. l.t. ed. 2001. (Children's Stories from the Quran). 16p. (J). pap. 2.50 (978-81-87570-86-8(5)) Goodword Bks. Pvt. Ltd. IND. *Dist:* Lodhia Ctr., The.

—First Man. Anand, Achla, illus. l.t. ed. 2001. 24p. (J). pap. 2.25 (978-81-87570-94-3(6)) Goodword Bks. Pvt. Ltd. IND. *Dist:* Lodhia Ctr., The.

—Life Begins: Quran Stories for Little Hearts. l.t. ed. 2001. 24p. (J). pap. 2.25 (978-81-87570-80-6(6)) Goodword Bks. Pvt. Ltd. IND. *Dist:* Lodhia Ctr., The.

—Origin of Life (Colouring Book) l.t. ed. 2001. 16p. (J). pap. 1.00 (978-81-87570-81-3(4)) Goodword Bks. Pvt. Ltd. IND. *Dist:* Lodhia Ctr., The.

—Tell Me about the Prophet Musa: What Was the Mission of Musa, What Were His Miracles & What His Life Teaches Me. l.t. ed. 2001. (Tell Me About). (Illus.). 56p. per. 11.50 (978-81-87570-48-6(2)) Goodword Bks. Pvt. Ltd. IND. *Dist:* Lodhia Ctr., The.

—The Travels of Prophet Ibrahim: Quran Stories of Little Hearts. Anand, Achla, ed. l.t. ed. 2001. (Illus.). 24p. (J). pap. (978-81-7898-008-9(8)) Goodword Bks. Pvt. Ltd. IND. *Dist:* Lodhia Ctr., The.

Khan, Saniyasnain & Saniyasnain, Khan. Allah's Best Friend: Quran Stories for Little Hearts. Anand, Achla, illus. l.t. ed. 2001. 24p. (J). pap. 2.25 (978-81-87570-51-6(2)) Goodword Bks. Pvt. Ltd. IND. *Dist:* Lodhia Ctr., The.

Kheirabadi, Masoud. Islam. 2004. (Religions of the World Ser.). (Illus.). (gr. 9-13). 150p. 35.00 (978-0-7910-7859-4(0)); 120p. pap. (978-0-7910-8012-2(9)) Facts On File, Inc. (Chelsea Hse.).

Kidwai, Abdur Raheem. The Qur'an: Essential Teachings. 2001. 192p. pap. 18.50 (***978-0-86037-410-7(6)***) Islamic Foundation, Ltd. GBR. *Dist:* Kazi Pubns., Inc.

Knight, Khadijah. My Muslim Faith. (Illus.). 32p. (978-0-237-51898-1(8) , Evans Brothers, Limited); 2006. (J). (978-1-84234-391-3(2) , Cherrytree Books) Evans Publishing Group.

Landau, Elaine. Osama Bin Laden: A War Against the West. 2002. (Single Titles Ser.). (Illus.). 144p. (gr. 7 up). lib. bdg. 23.90 (978-0-7613-1709-8(0) , Twenty-First Century Bks.) Lerner Publishing Group.

Leadbeater, Tim. Islamic Empires, 600-1600. 2004. (Illus.). 48p. pap. 23.50 (***978-0-340-81200-6(1)*** , Hodder Murray) Hodder Education GBR. *Dist:* Trans-Atlantic Pubns., Inc.

Leadbeater, Tim & Clare, John. Islamic Empires, 600-1600. 2004. (Illus.). 48p. pap. 23.50 (***978-0-340-81199-3(4)*** , Hodder Murray) Hodder Education GBR. *Dist:* Trans-Atlantic Pubns., Inc.

Maqsood, Ruqaiyyah Waris. Islamic Mosques. 2005. (Let's Find Out about Ser.). (Illus.). 32p. (J). 25.36 (978-1-4034-7036-2(7)) Steck-Vaughn.

Marchant, Kerena. Id-Ul-Fitr. 1998. (Festivals Ser.). (Illus.). 32p. (gr. 2-4). lib. bdg. 22.90 (978-0-7613-0963-5(2) , Millbrook Pr.) Lerner Publishing Group.

—Muhammad & Islam. 2002. (Great Religious Leaders Ser.). (Illus.). 48p. (J). lib. bdg. 28.50 (978-1-58340-217-7(9)) Smart Apple Media.

—Muslim Festivals. Barber, Tina, illus. 2001. (Festival Tales Ser.). 32p. (J). (gr. 4-7). lib. bdg. 25.69 (978-0-7398-2735-2(9)) Raintree.

Marsh, Carole. What Is Islam? Who Are Muslims? 2002. (Here & Now Ser.). 32p. (YA). (gr. 2-8). pap. 9.95 (978-0-635-01080-3(1)) Gallopade International.

Marx, David F. Ramadan. 2002. (Rookie Read-About Holidays Ser.). (Illus.). 32p. (J). (gr. 1-2). 20.50 (978-0-516-22269-1(4)); pap. 5.95 (978-0-516-27377-8(9)) Scholastic Library Publishing. (Children's Pr.).

—Ramadan. 2002. (gr. k-3). lib. bdg. 14.10 (978-0-613-54317-0(3)) Tandem Library Bks.

Mazrui, Ali. Islam in Africa. 2006. (Africa Ser.). (Illus.). 112p. (YA). (gr. 9 up). lib. bdg. 24.95 (***978-1-59084-999-6(X)***) Mason Crest Pubs.

Muhaiyaddeen, M. R. Bawa. Why Can't I See the Angels? Children's Questions to a Sufi Saint. 2002. (Illus.). 220p. (J). 27.00 (978-0-914390-62-6(7)); pap. 22.00 (978-0-914390-63-3(5)) Fellowship Pr.

Najar, Qasim M. Allah Made the World. Emerick, Yahiya, ed. Meehan, Patricia, illus. l.t. ed. 2002. 36p. (J). (gr. k-2). pap. 6.95 (978-1-889720-32-6(1)) Amirah Publishing.

Naseem, Hina. Our Faith & Worship Workbook Vol. 2: Companion to the textbook of Islamic Aqa'id & Arkan. Abiva, Huseyn, ed. 1998. 100p. (J). (gr. 1-3). pap. 6.00 (978-1-56316-065-3(X)) IQRA International Educational Foundation.

Nason, Ruth. Visiting a Mosque. 2005. (Start up Religion Ser.). (Illus.). 24p. (J). (gr. 1-4). lib. bdg. (978-1-84234-344-9(0) , Cherrytree Books) Evans Publishing Group.

Oliver, Marilyn Tower. Muhammad. 2003. (Importance of Ser.). (Illus.). 112p. (J). (gr. 7-10). 32.45 (978-1-59018-232-1(4) , Lucent Bks.) Thomson Gale.

Overbeeke-Rippen, Francina van. Abraham & Ibrahim: The Bible & the Qur'an Told to Children. 2006. (J). pap. (978-1-57153-072-1(X) , Witherspoon Pr.) Curriculum Publishing, Presbyterian Church (U. S. A.).

Penney, Sue. Islam. (World Beliefs & Cultures Ser.). 48p. (J). 2000. (Illus.). (gr. 5-7). lib. bdg. 25.64 (978-1-57572-357-0(3)); 2nd ed. (gr. 6-9). 22.00 (***978-1-4329-0315-2(2)***) Heinemann Library.

Petrini, Catherine M. What Makes Me a Muslim? 2005. (What Makes Me A—? Ser.). (Illus.). 48p. (J). (ps-7). lib. bdg. 26.20 (978-0-7377-2265-9(7) , Greenhaven Pr., Inc.) Thomson Gale.

HI

Pickthall, Marmaduke William, tr. Juz' Four: Lantana Luah Birra: A Textbook for the Classroom. 1999. 9p. (YA). (gr. 10-12). pap. 6.00 (978-1-56316-121-6(4)) IQRA International Educational Foundation.

Pirotta, Saviour. Id-Ul-Fitr. 2007. (J). lib. bdg. (978-1-4042-3708-7(9) , PowerKids Pr.) Rosen Publishing Group, Inc., The.

Powell, Jillian. Id-Ul-Fitr. 2006. (J). (978-1-58340-943-5(2)) Smart Apple Media.

Qadi, Siddiga, et al, eds. Torchbearers of Islam, 5 vols. Siddigui, Abu Sayeed & Fadel, Muhammad, trs. from URD. 2000. (Stories of the Sahabah Ser.: Vol. 5). 160p. (YA). (gr. 6-9). pap. 10.00 (978-1-56316-454-5(X)) IQRA International Educational Foundation.

Quran Made Easy with Tajweed. 2004. 89p. (J). pap. 6.50 net. (978-0-9760681-0-5(9)) Quranic Educational Society.

Ries, Julien. The World of Islam. 2002. (Religions of Mankind Ser.). (Illus.). 32p. (YA). (gr. 5 up). 21.95 (978-0-7910-6627-0(4) , Chelsea Hse.) Facts On File, Inc.

Roper, Beryl C. Seekers after Truth. 1998. 90p. (YA). (gr. 9-11). pap. (978-1-885812-04-9(3)) Aquamarine Pubns.

Ross, Mandy. Mecca. 2003. (Holy Places Ser.). (Illus.). 32p. (J). lib. bdg. 24.28 (978-0-7398-6080-9(1)) Raintree.

Sabini, John. Islam, a Primer. 6th ed. 2001. (YA). pap. (978-0-913957-16-5(X)); pap. 11.50 (978-0-913957-17-2(8)) AMIDEAST.

Sadi, Shaikh Muslihuddin. Garden of Roses. Quraishi-Ahmed, Huda, ed. Ghazi, Abidullah & Ghazi, Tasneema K., trs. from PER. 1999. Tr. of Gulistan. (Illus.). 26p. (YA). (gr. 5-9). 7.00 (978-1-56316-303-6(9)) IQRA International Educational Foundation.

Saeed, Mahmud S. The Model of the Muslim Youth in the Story of Prophet Yusuf. (ARA.). 32p. (YA). pap. (978-1-882837-28-1(2)) WAMY International, Inc.

Saqr, Abdul B. How to Call People to Islam. Ahmad, Shakil, tr. 154p. (Orig.). (YA). pap. (978-1-882837-16-8(9)) WAMY International, Inc.

Sears, Evelyn. Muslims & the West. 2003. (Introducing Islam Ser.). (Illus.). 112p. (YA). lib. bdg. (978-1-59084-700-8(8)) Mason Crest Pubs.

Self, David. Islam. 2005. (Illus.). 48p. (J). pap. (978-0-8368-5874-7(3)); lib. bdg. 30.00 (978-0-8368-5868-6(9)) Stevens, Gareth Inc. (World Almanac Library).

Senker, Cath. My Muslim Year. 2007. (J). lib. bdg. (***978-1-4042-3728-5(3)*** , PowerKids Pr.) Rosen Publishing Group, Inc., The.

Shaikh, Khalid M. A Study of the Qur'an & Its Teachings. Liddle, Heidi et al, eds. 1999. Tr. of Ulum al-Qur'an. vii, 240p. (YA). (gr. 6-9). pap. 12.00 (978-1-56316-118-6(4)) IQRA International Educational Foundation.

Steer, Malcolm. A Christian's Evangelistic Pocket Guide to Islam. 2004. 80p. pap. (978-1-85792-915-7(2) , Christian Focus) Christian Focus Pubns.

The Story of Prophet Yusuf: Quran Stories for the Young People. 2001. 64p. (J). pap. 5.50 (978-81-7898-000-3(2)) Goodword Bks. Pvt. Ltd. IND. *Dist:* Lodhia Ctr., The.

Studies and Research Unit of Wamy Staff. Principles of Dialogue. (ARA.). 79p. (YA). pap. (978-1-882837-00-7(2)) WAMY International, Inc.

Syed, Ibrahim. Quranic Inspirations. 2007. 688p. (YA). per. 37.95 (***978-0-595-45003-9(2)***) iUniverse, Inc.

Tames, Richard. Muslim. (Illus.). 32p. (YA). (gr. 3 up). lib. bdg. 27.10 (978-1-932889-12-3(4)) Sea-To-Sea Pubns.

The Teachings of Islam. 2001. 46p. pap. 1.00 (978-81-85063-03-4(6)) Goodword Bks. Pvt. Ltd. IND. *Dist:* Lodhia Ctr., The.

Teece, Geoff. Islam. 2004. (Religion in Focus Ser.). (J). lib. bdg. (978-1-58340-467-6(8)) Smart Apple Media.

Thompson, Jan. Islam. (Illus.). 64p. (YA). (gr. 4 up). lib. bdg. 29.95 (978-1-59389-133-6(4)) Chrysalis Education.

Thompson, Joy. Islam. 2005. (World Religions Ser.). (Illus.). 58p. (J). (gr. 4-12). pap. 12.95 (978-1-55285-654-3(2) , Walrus Bks.) Whitecap Bks., Ltd. CAN. *Dist:* Firefly Bks., Ltd.

Tomljanovic, Tatiana. Ramadan. 2006. (J). (978-1-59036-461-1(9)); (978-1-59036-464-2(3)) Weigl Pubs., Inc.

The Travels of Prophet Ibrahim: Colouring Book. 2001. (Quran Stories for Tiny Tots). 16p. (J). pap. 1.00 (978-81-7898-007-2(X)) Goodword Bks. Pvt. Ltd. IND. *Dist:* Lodhia Ctr., The.

The Two Brothers: Quran Stories of Little Hearts. l.t. ed. 2001. 24p. pap. 4.25 (978-81-87570-41-7(5)) Goodword Bks. Pvt. Ltd. IND. *Dist:* Lodhia Ctr., The.

The Two Sons of Adam: Colouring Book. l.t. ed. 2001. 16p. pap. 1.00 (978-81-87570-92-9(X)) Goodword Bks. Pvt. Ltd. IND. *Dist:* Lodhia Ctr., The.

Wachal, Barbara S. The American Encounter with Islam. 2003. (Introducing Islam Ser.). (Illus.). 112p. (YA). lib. bdg. (978-1-59084-699-5(0)) Mason Crest Pubs.

The Way to Find God. 2001. 32p. pap. 0.65 (978-81-85063-02-7(8)) Goodword Bks. Pvt. Ltd. IND. *Dist:* Lodhia Ctr., The.

Whitehead, Kim. Islam: The Basics. 2003. (Introducing Islam Ser.). (Illus.). 112p. (YA). lib. bdg. (978-1-59084-697-1(4)) Mason Crest Pubs.

Wilkinson, Philip & Dorling Kindersley Publishing Staff. Islam. 2005. (Eyewitness Books). (Illus.). 72p. (J). (ps-7). lib. bdg. 19.99 (978-0-7566-1078-4(8) , 1241919) Dorling Kindersley Publishing, Inc.

Winchester, Faith. Muslim Holidays. 1999. (Ethnic Holidays Ser.). (Illus.). 24p. (J). (gr. 2-3). lib. bdg. 18.60 (978-1-56065-459-9(7) , Bridgestone Bks.) Capstone Pr., Inc.

Wood, Angela. Muslim Mosque. 1999. (Places of Worship Ser.). (Illus.). 32p. (J). (gr. 2 up). lib. bdg. 23.33 (978-0-8368-2609-8(4)) Stevens, Gareth Inc.

The Word of Our Little Friend, the Ants. l.t. ed. 2001. 32p. (J). pap. 1.74 (978-81-7898-010-2(X)) Goodword Bks. Pvt. Ltd. IND. *Dist:* Lodhia Ctr., The.

Wormser, Richard. American Islam: Growing up Muslim in America. 2002. (gr. 7-12). lib. bdg. 17.60 (978-0-613-75347-0(X)) Tandem Library Bks.

—American Islam: Growing up Muslim in America. 2002. (Illus.). 144p. (YA). pap. 8.95 (978-0-8027-7628-0(0)) Walker & Co.

ISLAM—FICTION

Abdel-Fattah, Randa. Does My Head Look Big in This? 2007. 368p. (J). (gr. 7 up). pap. 16.99 (***978-0-439-91947-0(9)*** , Orchard Bks.) Scholastic, Inc.

Aktar, Nasreen. Samira's Eid. Attard, Enebor, illus. 2004. 24p. (J). (ARA, BEN, GUJ, PER & ENG.). (978-1-85269-122-6(0)); (ARA, BEN, GUJ, PER & ENG.). (978-1-85269-131-8(X)); (ARA, BEN, GUJ, PER & ENG.). (978-1-85269-132-5(8)); (ARA, BEN, GUJ, PER & ENG.). (978-1-85269-133-2(6)); (ARA, BEN, GUJ, PER & ENG.). (978-1-85269-134-9(4)); (ARA, BEN, GUJ, PER & ENG.). (978-1-85269-135-6(2)); (ARA, BEN, GUJ, PER & ENG.). (978-1-85269-183-7(2)); (ARA, BEN, GUJ, PER & ENG.). (978-1-85269-502-6(1)); (ARA, BEN, GUJ, PER & ENG.). (978-1-85269-503-3(X)); (ARA, BEN, GUJ, PER & ENG.). (978-1-85269-572-9(2)); (URD, BEN & ENG.). (978-1-85269-538-5(2)); (URD, BEN & ENG.). (978-1-85269-539-2(0)); (URD, BEN & ENG.). (978-1-85269-540-8(4)) Mantra Publishing, Ltd.

Delgado, Linda D. The Visitors. 2006. 169p. (J). per. (978-0-9767861-1-5(7)) Muslim Writers Publishing.

Durkee, Noura. The Loyal Ansar. Quraishi-Ahmed, Huda et al, eds. Jaman, Sharon, illus. 1999. (Stories of the Sahabah Ser.: Vol. 3). 170p. (YA). (gr. 7-10). pap. 10.00 (978-1-56316-452-1(3)) IQRA International Educational Foundation.

Ganeri, Anita. Islamic Stories. Wallis, Rebecca, illus. 2006. 32p. (J). (gr. 4-6). 23.95 (978-1-4048-1313-7(6)) Picture Window Bks.

Katz, Karen. My First Ramadan. 2007. (Illus.). 32p. (J). (ps-k). 14.95 (***978-0-8050-7894-7(0)***) Holt, Henry & Co.

Lewis, Richard. The Flame Tree. 2004. (Illus.). 288p. (YA). 16.95 (978-0-689-86333-2(0)) Simon & Schuster Children's Publishing.

Matthews, Mary. Magid Fasts for Ramadan. Lewis, E. B., illus. 2000. 48p. (J). (gr. 4-6). 6.95 (978-0-618-04035-3(8) , Clarion Bks.) Houghton Mifflin Co. Trade & Reference Div.

Oppenheim, Shulamith Levey. The Hundredth Name. Hays, Michael, illus. 2003. 32p. (J). (gr. k-2). pap. 9.95 (978-1-56397-694-0(3)) Boyds Mills Pr.

Yamani, Muhammad Abdo. A Boy from Makkah, Vol. 1. Mohiuddin, Khadija & De Backer, Talha, eds. Lipton, Abdallah, illus. novel ed. 2002. 149p. (J). 10.00 (978-1-56316-057-8(9)) IQRA International Educational Foundation.

Zucker, Jonny. Fasting & Dates: A Ramadan & Eid-ul-Fitr Story. Cohen, Jan Barger, illus. 2004. (Festival Time! Ser.). 24p. (J). pap. 6.95 (978-0-7641-2671-0(7)) Barron's Educational Series, Inc.

ISLAM—HISTORY

Barr, Gary. History & Activities of the Islamic Empire. 2006. (Hands-On Ancient History Ser.). (Illus.). 32p. (J). (gr. 3-6). lib. bdg. 28.21 (978-1-4034-7926-6(7)) Heinemann Library.

Jessa, Azra, illus. Ramadhan & Eid-ul-Fitr. 2008. 16p. (J). 12.95 (***978-1-879402-23-2(8)***) Tahrike Tarsile Quran, Inc.

Martell, Hazel Mary. The World of Islam Before 1700. 1999. (Looking Back Ser.). (Illus.). 64p. (J). (gr. 6-9). 19.98 (978-0-8172-5430-8(7)) Raintree.

McAdam, Jessica & Aitchison, Kathleen. Symbols of Freedom. 2004. (Illus.). (J). (gr. 2-6). cd-rom 38.00 (978-1-57336-400-3(2) , I8025D) Interaction Pubs., Inc.

Rise & Spread of Islam DBA. 2002. spiral bd. 16.95 (978-1-56004-143-6(9)) Social Studies Schl. Service.

Roraback, Amanda. Islam in a Nutshell. 2nd exp. rev. ed. 2004. (Nutshell Notes). (Illus.). 60p. (YA). pap. 7.95 (978-0-9702908-8-5(8)) Enisen Publishing.

ISLAND ECOLOGY

Anderson, Sheila. Island. 2008. (First Step Nonfiction - Landforms Ser.). (J). lib. bdg. 18.60 (***978-0-8225-8594-7(4)*** , Lerner Pubns.) Lerner Publishing Group.

Frahm, Randy. Islands: Living Gems of the Sea. 2001. (Life on Earth Ser.). (Illus.). 32p. (J). lib. bdg. (978-1-58341-027-1(9) , Creative Education) Creative Co., The.

Hooper, Roseanne. Life in the Islands: Animals, People, Plants. 2000. (gr. 3-6). lib. bdg. 15.25 (978-0-613-43343-3(2)) Tandem Library Bks.

—Life on the Islands. 2001. (World Book Ecology Ser.). (Illus.). 32p. (J). (978-0-7166-5227-4(7)) World Bk., Inc.

Morris, Neil. Earth's Changing Islands. 2003. (Illus.). 32p. (J). 7.50 (978-1-4109-0344-0(3)); lib. bdg. 25.70 (978-1-4109-0177-4(7)) Raintree.

—Earth's Changing Islands. 2003. (gr. 3-6). lib. bdg. 15.90 (978-0-613-78237-1(2)) Tandem Library Bks.

—Living on Islands. 2004. (J). lib. bdg. 27.10 (978-1-58340-487-4(2)) Smart Apple Media.

Oxlade, Chris. Islands. 2003. (Science Files Ser.). (Illus.). 32p. (J). (gr. 3 up). lib. bdg. 24.67 (978-0-8368-3568-7(9)) Stevens, Gareth Inc.

Riley, Peter D. Survivor's Science on an Island. 2004. (Survivor's Science Ser.). (Illus.). 48p. (J). (gr. 6-8). lib. bdg. 28.56 (978-1-4109-0226-9(9)) Harcourt Schl. Pubs.

Silva Lee, Alfonso. My Island & I: The Nature of the Caribbean. Hayskar, Bonnie J., ed. Lago, Alexis, illus. 32p. (J). 2010. pap. 9.95 (978-1-929165-14-8(5)); 2002. (gr. 2-5). 15.95 (978-1-929165-15-5(3)) PANGAEA.

Winne, Joanne. Living on an Island. 2000. (Welcome Bks.). (Illus.). 24p. (J). (ps-2). 17.00 (978-0-516-23305-5(X) , Children's Pr.) Scholastic Library Publishing.

ISLANDS

see also Coral Reefs and Islands

also names of islands and groups of islands, e.g. Cuba

Anderson, Sheila. Island. 2008. (First Step Nonfiction - Landforms Ser.). (J). lib. bdg. 18.60 (***978-0-8225-8594-7(4)*** , Lerner Pubns.) Lerner Publishing Group.

Arita Vera. All Around the Islands. Moen Cabanting Ruth, illus. 2005. 24p. 12.95 (978-1-933067-09-4(8)) Mutual Publishing LLC.

Barber, Nicola. Island Home. 2007. (Homes Around the World Ser.). 32p. (J). (gr. 2-5). pap. (***978-0-7787-3555-7(9)***) Crabtree Publishing Co.

Beech, Sandy. Isle Be Seeing You. 2005. (Illus.). 179p. (J). (***978-1-4156-1539-3(X)*** , Aladdin) Simon & Schuster Children's Publishing.

—Weather's Here, Wish You Were Great. 2005. (Illus.). 186p. (J). (***978-1-4156-1165-4(3)*** , Aladdin) Simon & Schuster Children's Publishing.

—Worst Class Trip Ever. 2005. 173p. (J). (***978-1-4156-0619-3(6)*** , Aladdin) Simon & Schuster Children's Publishing.

Chambers, Catherine & Lapthorn, Nicholas. Islands. 2nd ed. 2007. (***978-1-4034-9690-4(0)***); pap. (***978-1-4034-9610-2(2)***) Heinemann.

Durban, Chris. Islands. 2004. (Geography First Ser.). (J). 23.70 (978-1-4103-0111-6(7) , Blackbirch Pr., Inc.) Thomson Gale.

Fowler, Allan. Let's Visit Some Islands. Rau, Dana, ed. 1998. (Rookie Read-About Science Ser.). (Illus.). 32p. (J). (gr. 1-2). pap. 4.95 (978-0-516-26366-3(8) , Children's Pr.) Scholastic Library Publishing.

—Let's Visit Some Islands. 1998. (Rookie Read-About Science Ser.). (Illus.). 32p. (J). (gr. 1-2). 20.50 (978-0-516-20807-7(1) , Children's Pr.) Scholastic Library Publishing.

Frahm, Randy. Islands: Living Gems of the Sea. 2001. (Life on Earth Ser.). (Illus.). 32p. (J). lib. bdg. (978-1-58341-027-1(9) , Creative Education) Creative Co., The.

French, Cathy. Haz una isla & Make an Island. 2005. spiral bd. 66.00 (***978-1-4108-5632-6(1)***) Benchmark Education Co.

Gibbons, Gail. Surrounded by Sea: Life on a New England Fishing Island. Gibbons, Gail, illus. (Illus.). 32p. (J). (ps-3). 2006. 6.95 (978-0-8234-2021-6(3)); 2005. 17.95 (978-0-8234-1941-8(X)) Holiday Hse., Inc.

Golden Books Staff. Air Power! 2007. (Color Plus Tattoos Ser.). (Illus.). 32p. (J). (gr. k-4). pap. 3.99 (978-0-375-84142-2(3) , Golden Bks.) Random Hse. Children's Bks.

Grant, Donald & Jeunesse, Gallimard. Atlas of Islands. 1999. (First Discovery Book Ser.). (Illus.). 24p. (J). (ps-2). 12.95 (978-0-439-04402-8(2)) Scholastic, Inc.

Hooper, Roseanne. Islands. 2004. (Life In... Ser.). (SPA., Illus.). (gr. 3-6). 32p. (J). pap. 6.95 (978-1-58728-568-4(1)); 31p. 12.95 (978-1-58728-553-0(3)) T&N Children's Publishing. (Two Can Publishing).

—Life on the Islands. 2001. (World Book Ecology Ser.). (Illus.). 32p. (J). (978-0-7166-5227-4(7)) World Bk., Inc.

Jennings, Terry. Coasts & Islands. (Restless Earth Ser.). (Illus.). 32p. (J). lib. bdg. 24.25 (978-1-931983-18-1(6)) Chrysalis Education.

Kehoe, Stasia Ward. I Live on an Island. 2000. (Kids in Their Communities Ser.). (Illus.). 24p. (J). (gr. 3). lib. bdg. 18.75 (978-0-8239-5439-1(0) , PowerKids Pr.) Rosen Publishing Group, Inc., The.

Llewellyn, Claire. Islands. 2000. (Heinemann First Library). (Illus.). 32p. (J). (gr. k-2). lib. bdg. 21.36 (978-1-57572-206-1(2)) Heinemann Library.

—Islands. 2002. (gr. k-3). lib. bdg. 15.25 (978-0-613-82109-4(2)) Tandem Library Bks.

Llewellyn, Claire, et al. Islands. 2002. (Geography Starts Ser.). (Illus.). 32p. (J). (gr. k-2). pap. 6.95 (978-1-58810-974-3(7) , 91457) Heinemann Library.

Mayer, Cassie. Islands. 2006. (Illus.). 24p. (J). (978-1-4034-8437-6(6)); pap. (978-1-4034-8443-7(0)) Heinemann Library.

Morris, Neil. Earth's Changing Islands. 2003. (Illus.). 32p. (J). 7.50 (978-1-4109-0344-0(3)); lib. bdg. 25.70 (978-1-4109-0177-4(7)) Raintree.

—Earth's Changing Islands. 2003. (gr. 3-6). lib. bdg. 15.90 (978-0-613-78237-1(2)) Tandem Library Bks.

Nadeau, Isaac. Islands. 2006. (Illus.). 24p. (J). lib. bdg. (978-1-4042-3126-9(X)) Rosen Publishing Group, Inc., The.

Niz, Xavier. Archipelagoes. 2005. (Illus.). 24p. (J). (ps-7). lib. bdg. 21.26 (978-0-7368-4306-5(X)) Capstone Pr., Inc.

Oxlade, Chris. Islands. 2003. (Science Files Ser.). (Illus.). 32p. (J). (gr. 3 up). lib. bdg. 24.67 (978-0-8368-3568-7(9)) Stevens, Gareth Inc.

Regan, Colm. People of the Islands. 1998. (Wide World Ser.). (Illus.). 48p. (J). (gr. 3-7). 18.98 (978-0-8172-5064-5(6)) Raintree.

Rigby Education Staff. Our Home on the Island. (Illus.). (J). bds. 3.95 (978-0-7635-6455-1(9) , 764559C99) Rigby Education.

Riley, Peter D. Survivor's Science on an Island. 2004. (Survivor's Science Ser.). (Illus.). 48p. (J). (gr. 6-8). lib. bdg. 28.56 (978-1-4109-0226-9(9)) Harcourt Schl. Pubs.

Royston, Angela. Islands. 2004. (J). 22.79 (978-1-4034-5590-1(2)) Heinemann Library.

Sheehan, Thomas F. Islands. 2008. (J). (***978-1-60044-545-3(4)***) Rourke Publishing, LLC.

Webster, Christine. Islands. 2005. (Illus.). 89p. (J). 21.26 (978-0-7368-3713-2(2)) Capstone Pr., Inc.

Winne, Joanne. Living on an Island. 2000. (Welcome Bks.). (Illus.). 24p. (J). (ps-2). 17.00 (978-0-516-23305-5(X) , Children's Pr.) Scholastic Library Publishing.

ISLANDS—FICTION

Abel's Island. 1999. (J). 9.95 (978-1-56137-345-1(1)) Novel Units, Inc.

Adshead, Paul S. Here We Go Round the Mulberry Bush. 2001. (Illus.). 16p. (J). 16.95 (978-0-85953-885-5(0)) Child's Play-International.

Agee, Jon. Terrific. Agee, Jon, illus. 2005. (Illus.). 32p. (J). (ps-17). (978-0-7868-5184-3(8) , Di Capua, Michael) Scholastic, Inc.

Alberto, Daisy. Barbie as the Island Princess. 2007. (Step into Reading Ser.). (Illus.). 32p. (J). (ps-2). 3.99 (***978-0-375-84353-2(1)***); lib. bdg. 11.99 (***978-0-375-94353-9(6)***) Random Hse. Children's Bks. (Random Hse. Bks. for Young Readers).

Alberto, Daisy & Wyss, Johann. Swiss Family Robinson. 2006. (Illus.). 112p. (J). (gr. 1-4). lib. bdg. 11.99 (978-0-375-97525-7(X) , Random Hse. Bks. for Young Readers) Random Hse. Children's Bks.

—Swiss Family Robinson. Hunt, Robert, illus. 2006. 112p. (J). (gr. 1-4). pap. 3.99 (978-0-375-87525-0(5) , Random Hse. Bks. for Young Readers) Random Hse. Children's Bks.

Anderson, Al. Pegasus: Adventures with Bingo Borden. Kurzyca, Krystyna Emilia, illus. 2006. 77p. (J). per. 19.50 (***978-1-887250-46-7(8)***) Agora Pubns., Inc.

Anderson, Kevin J. & Moesta, Rebecca. Crystal Doors, No. 1. 2006. 304p. (J). (gr. 7-17). 15.99 (978-0-316-01055-9(3)) Little Brown & Co.

Arrington, Aileen. Camp of the Angel. 2003. 154p. (YA). (gr. 5). 16.99 (978-0-399-23882-6(4) , Philomel) Penguin Group (USA) Inc.

Baglio, Ben M. Husky in a Hut. Baum, Ann, illus. 2005. 131p. (J). (ps-k). lib. bdg. 10.64 (978-0-606-33289-7(8)) Tandem Library Bks.

Bailey, Norman. Fight for Freedom. 2006. pap. (***978-1-84375-267-7(0)***) Universal Publishing Solutions Online, Limited (UPSO).

Ballantyne, Michael. Blown to Bits or the Lonely Man of Rakat. 2006. 36.99 (***978-1-4280-4221-6(0)***); pap. 30.99 (***978-1-4280-4226-1(1)***) IndyPublish.com.

Ballantyne, R. The Coral Island. 2006. pap. 14.95 (***978-1-55742-666-6(X)***) Wildside Pr.

Ballantyne, R. M. Blown to Bits; or, the Lonely Man of Rak. 2006. pap. (***978-1-4065-0515-3(3)***) Dodo Pr.

Bannerman, Helen. The Story of Little Black Mingo (Illustr. 2006. pap. (***978-1-4065-0770-6(9)***) Dodo Pr.

Bardwell, Harrison. The Mystery of Seal Islands. 2003. 223p. (J). pap. 13.95 (978-1-55753-337-1(7)) Purdue Univ. Pr.

Barlow, Galon L., Jr. The Adventures of Levi & Nathan at Bassett's Island. Guthrie, Adam, illus. l.t. ed. 1998. 78p. (gr. 6 up). pap. 7.95 (978-0-9666020-0-5(5) , 98-002) Farewell Pr.

Barry, Dave & Pearson, Ridley. Escape from the Carnivale: A Never Land Book. Call, Greg, illus. 2006. 144p. (gr. 3-17). 9.99 (978-0-7868-3789-2(6)) Hyperion Bks. for Children.

—Peter & the Secret of Rundoon. rev. ed. 2007. 496p. (YA). (gr. 7-17). 18.99 (***978-0-7868-3788-5(8)*** , Disney Editions) Disney Pr.

Barry, Dave & Pearson, Ridley. Peter & the Starcatchers. Call, Greg, illus. 2006. 480p. (gr. 5-17). reprint ed. pap. 7.99 (978-0-7868-4907-9(X) , Disney Editions) Disney Pr.

—Peter & the Starcatchers. 2004. 464p. (gr. 5-17). 17.99 (978-0-7868-5445-5(6)) Hyperion Bks. for Children.

Bartlett, Susan. Seal Island School. Bonnell, J., ed. Tusa, Tricia, illus. 2001. (Chapters Ser.). 80p. (J). (gr. 2-5). pap. 4.99 (978-0-14-131104-3(5) , Puffin) Penguin Group (USA) Inc.

—Seal Island School. Tusa, Tricia, illus. 1999. 80p. (J). (gr. 2-5). 15.99 (978-0-670-88349-3(2) , Viking Juvenile) Penguin Group (USA) Inc.

—Seal Island School. 2001. (gr. 3-6). lib. bdg. 13.00 (978-0-613-63991-0(X)) Tandem Library Bks.

Baum, L. Frank. The Enchanted Island of Yew. l.t. ed. 2005. 228p. pap. (978-1-84637-102-8(3)) Echo Library.

Baum, L. Frank. Sky Island (Being the Further Exciting A. 2006. pap. 45.99 (***978-1-4219-8094-2(0)***) IndyPublish.com.

Bell, Russell, illus. Herbert Hilligan's Tropical Adventure, Vol. 3. rev. ed. 1999. (Herbert Hilligan Ser.). 15.95 (978-1-57168-314-4(3)) Eakin Pr.

Bial, Raymond. Shadow Island: A Tale of Lake Superior. 2006. 176p. (J). (gr. 3-7). 18.95 (978-1-883953-37-9(5)); (gr. 4-7). pap. 12.95 (978-1-883953-36-2(7)) Midwest Traditions, Inc. (Blue Horse Bks.).

Blackstone, Stella. Una Isla Bajo el Sol. 2003. (SPA.). (gr. k-3). lib. bdg. 15.30 (978-0-613-67170-5(8)) Tandem Library Bks.

—Una Isla Bajo el Sol (An Island in the Sun) Ceccoli, Nicoletta, illus. 2003. (SPA.). 24p. (J). pap. 6.99 (978-1-84148-144-9(0)) Barefoot Bks., Inc.

—An Island in the Sun. Ceccoli, Nicoletta, illus. 2005. 24p. (J). pap. 6.99 (978-1-84148-079-4(7)); 15.99 (978-1-84148-193-7(9)) Barefoot Bks., Inc.

—Secret Seahorse. Beaton, Clare, illus. 24p. (J). 2005. pap. 6.99 (978-1-84148-937-7(9)); 2005. 15.99 (978-1-84148-704-5(X)); 2004. per. 6.99 (978-1-905236-15-2(8)) Barefoot Bks., Inc.

Blase, Dean. There's an Octopus under My Bed. Ross, D., illus. 2007. 32p. (J). 16.99 (***978-0-9777651-1-9(3)***) Shake It.

Boggs, Patdee. Island of Angels. 2006. 55p. pap. 12.95 (***978-1-4241-3758-9(6)***) PublishAmerica, Inc.

Bollinger/Papp, illus. King Kong: Journey to Skull Island. 2005. 32p. (J). lib. bdg. 13.85 (***978-1-4242-0614-8(6)***) Fitzgerald Bks.

Bond, A. Russell. Scientific American Boy. 2006. (Illus.). 320p. (J). (gr. 4-7). per. 19.95 (978-1-55709-185-7(4)) Applewood Bks.

Brown, Margaret. Al Gazira Al Sagheera: The Little Island. 2005. 48p. pap. 12.00 (978-977-6171-00-8(1) , 706-004) Al-Balsam Pubng. Hse. EGY. *Dist:* Bookworld Trade, Inc.

Brown, Margaret Wise. The Little Island. Weisgard, Leonard, illus. 2003. 48p. (J). (gr. k-3). 14.95 (978-0-385-74640-3(7)); lib. bdg. 16.99 (978-0-385-90872-6(5)) Random Hse. Children's Bks. (Doubleday Bks. for Young Readers).

Buchholz, Quint. El Coleccionista de Momentos. 2nd ed. 2003. (Rosa y Manzana Ser.). (SPA., Illus.). 48p. (J). (978-84-89804-16-6(8)) Loguez Ediciones ESP. *Dist:* Lectorum Pubns., Inc.

Bunting, Eve. Mouse Island. Catalano, Dominic, illus. 2008. (J). ***(*978-1-59078-447-1(2))*** Boyds Mills Pr.

Burger, Sharon. Five Amigos: The Mystery of Taboo Island. 2005. 48p. pap. 12.95 (978-1-4137-6300-3(6)) PublishAmerica, Inc.

Buzzeo, Toni. The Sea Chest. GrandPré, Mary, illus. 2002. 32p. (J). (gr. k up). 16.99 (978-0-8037-2703-8(8) , Dial) Penguin Group (USA) Inc.

Byrd, Sandra. Island Girl. 2005. (Friends for A Season Ser.). 240p. (J). reprint ed. pap. 10.99 (978-0-7642-0020-5(8)) Bethany Hse. Pubs.

Calu, John & Hart, Dave. The Treasure of Tucker's Island. 2003. 80p. (YA). pap. 8.95 (978-0-595-27953-1(8)) iUniverse, Inc.

Cann, Kate. Mediterranean Holiday. 2007. 336p. (J). pap. 5.99 ***(*978-0-06-115216-0(1)*** , HarperTeen) HarperCollins Pubs.

Cardosi, Calesse. The Gifts. 2007. 192p. (YA). 16.95 ***(*978-0-9776281-3-1(2))*** HPH Publishing.

Carey, Elizabeth Doyle. The Callahan Cousins: Summer Begins, 1. 2005. 208p. (J). pap. 7.99 (978-0-316-73696-1(1)) Little Brown & Co.

—The Callahan Cousins #2: Home Sweet Home. 2nd ed. 208p. (J). pap. 7.99 (978-0-316-73732-6(1)) Little Brown & Co.

—Home Sweet Home No. 2. 2nd ed. 2005. (Callahan Cousins Ser.: No. 2). (Illus.). 206p. (J). (gr. 3-7). 10.99 (978-0-316-73692-3(9)) Little Brown & Co.

—Keeping Cool. 3rd ed. 2006. (Callahan Cousins Ser.). (Illus.). 226p. (J). (gr. 3-7). 10.99 (978-0-316-73693-0(7)) Little Brown & Co.

—Summer Begins. 2005. (Callahan Cousins Ser.: No. 1). (Illus.). 274p. (J). (gr. 3-7). 10.99 (978-0-316-73690-9(2)) Little Brown & Co.

Carlton, Susan. Lobsterland. 2007. 224p. (YA). (gr. 9 up). 16.95 ***(*978-0-8050-8096-4(1))*** Holt, Henry & Co.

Cattell, Bob & Agard, John. Butter-Finger. Smy, Pam, illus. 2006. 128p. pap. 7.95 (978-1-84507-376-3(2)) Lincoln, Frances Ltd. GBR. *Dist:* Perseus Distribution.

Cattell, Bob & Agard, John. Calypso Boy. Smy, Pam, illus. 2007. 96p. (J). pap. 7.95 ***(*978-1-84507-626-9(5))*** Lincoln, Frances Ltd. GBR. *Dist:* Perseus Distribution.

Cattell, Bob, et al. Shine on Butterfinger. 2007. (Illus.). 96p. (J). 15.95 ***(*978-1-84507-773-0(3))*** Lincoln, Frances Ltd. GBR. *Dist:* Perseus Distribution.

Causton, Linda. Lester's Rainy Lake Pony. l.t. ed. 2004. (Illus.). 32p. (J). 12.00 (978-1-930374-09-6(7)) DeForest Pr.

Chapman, Tessie. Enchanted Island. 2005. 55p. pap. 12.95 (978-1-4137-5690-6(5)) PublishAmerica, Inc.

Cincotta, Wendy. Return to Evergreen. Cincotta, Eva, illus. 2002. (Adventures in Evergreen Ser.: Bk. 2). 120p. (J). (gr. 3-7). pap. 9.95 (978-0-9723010-1-5(1)) Evergreen Bks.

Cole, Bob. Power Reading: Comic Book/Treasure Island. Lee, Ioe, illus. 2005. 70p. (J). (gr. 4-6). vinyl bd. (978-1-883186-78-4(1) , PPCLC3) National Reading Styles Institute, Inc.

Collins, Pat L. The Fattening Hut. 2003. 192p. (YA). (gr. 7 up). tchr. ed. 15.00 (978-0-618-30955-9(1)) Houghton Mifflin Co. Trade & Reference Div.

Collins, Pat Lowery. The Fattening Hut. 2005. 192p. (YA). (gr. 7). pap. 7.99 (978-0-618-55209-2(X) , Graphia) Houghton Mifflin Co. Trade & Reference Div.

Connell, Richard. The Most Dangerous Game. 2006. pap. 9.99 (978-1-59986-969-8(1)) Filiquarian Publishing, LLC.

—Most Dangerous Game. 2006. pap. 15.95 ***(*978-1-4304-5151-8(3))*** Kessinger Publishing, LLC.

Connell, Richard. The Most Dangerous Game. 2004. reprint ed. pap. 15.95 (978-1-4191-7460-5(6)); pap. 1.99 (978-1-4192-7460-2(0)) Kessinger Publishing, LLC.

Copeland, Cynthia L. Elin's Island. 2003. (Single Titles Ser.: up). 144p. (gr. 6 up). lib. bdg. 22.90 (978-0-7613-2522-2(0) , Millbrook Pr.) Lerner Publishing Group.

Crossman, David A. The Secret of the Missing Grave. 1999. (Bean & Ab Mystery Ser.). 184p. (YA). (gr. 4-10). 16.95 (978-0-89272-456-7(0)) Down East Bks.

Croteau, Marie-Danielle. Gabby's School by the Sea. Casson, Sophie, illus. 2005. (Read-It! Readers Ser.). 32p. (J). (gr. k-3). 18.60 (978-1-4048-1072-3(2)) Picture Window Bks.

Crowe, Carole. Sharp Horns on the Moon. 2003. 128p. (YA). (gr. 4-6). 14.95 (978-1-56397-671-1(4)) Boyds Mills Pr.

Cue, Ian J. The Renewal: First Encounter. 2003. 192p. (YA). per. 9.95 (978-0-9741989-0-3(0)) Mill Creek Metro Publishing.

Davidson, Michele R. Stowaways to Smith Island: Hayden & Chloe's Enchanted Journey with the Nurses to Maryland's Mysterious Smith Island. Watjen, Laureen, illus. 2004. 128p. (J). pap. 8.95 (978-0-9754170-1-0(0)) Smith Island Foundation.

Decter, Ed. Expedition to Surf Island. Yuen Jr., Sammy, illus. 2009. (Outriders Ser.). 224p. (J). pap. 4.99 ***(*978-1-4169-1308-5(4)*** , Aladdin) Simon & Schuster Children's Publishing.

Defoe, Daniel. The Farther Adventures of Robinson Crusoe. (Illus.). (J). reprint ed. 32.50 (978-0-404-07912-3(1)) AMS Pr., Inc.

—Robinson Crusoe. Heller, Julek, illus. 1998. (Eyewitness Classics Ser.).Tr. of Robinson Crusoe. 64p. (J). (gr. 3-6). 14.95 (978-0-7894-3625-2(6)) Dorling Kindersley Publishing, Inc.

—Robinson Crusoe. 2001. (Modern Library Classics Ser.).Tr. of Robinson Crusoe. 320p. pap. 7.95 (978-0-375-75732-7(5) , Modern Library) Random House Publishing Group.

—Robinson Crusoe. Akib, Jamel, illus. 2006. (Classic Starts Ser.).Tr. of Robinson Crusoe. 160p. (J). 4.95 (978-1-4027-2664-4(3)) Sterling Publishing Co., Inc.

—Robinson Crusoe. 2000. (Coleccion "Clasicos Juveniles" Ser.).Tr. of Robinson Crusoe. (SPA., Illus.). 288p. (YA). (gr. 4-7). pap. 13.95 (978-1-58348-782-2(4)) iUniverse, Inc.

Defoe, Daniel, et al. Robinson Crusoe. (Classics Illustrated Ser.).Tr. of Robinson Crusoe. (Illus.). 52p. (YA). pap. 4.95 (978-1-57209-021-7(9)) Classics International Entertainment, Inc.

Dell, Scott O. L Isola Dei Delfini Blu. pap. 16.95 (978-88-09-02504-2(0)) Giunti, Gruppo Editoriale ITA. *Dist:* Distribooks, Inc.

Dixon, Franklin W. The Mystery of Cabin Island, No. 8. Rogers, Walter S., illus. 2004. (Hardy Boys Mystery Stories Ser.: No. 8). 210p. (J). (gr. 4-7). 17.95 (978-1-55709-266-3(4)) Applewood Bks.

Dixon, Franklin W. & Walker, Jeff. Typhoon Island, Vol. 180. 2003. (Hardy Boys Ser.). (Illus.). 160p. (J). pap. 4.99 (978-0-689-85884-0(1) , Aladdin) Simon & Schuster Children's Publishing.

Doherty, Berlie. Daughter of the Sea. 2000. (Illus.). (J). (978-0-606-18102-0(4)) Tandem Library Bks.

Dorros, Arthur. Isla. Kleven, Elisa, illus. 1999. Orig. Title: The Island. 40p. (J). (ps-1). pap. 6.99 (978-0-14-056505-8(1) , Puffin) Penguin Group (USA) Inc.

—Isla. 1999. Orig. Title: The Island. (J). 12.79 (978-0-606-16810-6(9)); (J). 13.79 (978-0-606-16811-3(7)); lib. bdg. 14.15 (978-0-613-14865-8(7)); (SPA.). lib. bdg. 15.30 (978-0-613-18258-4(8)) Tandem Library Bks.

—La Isla. ed. 2004. (SPA., Illus.). (J). (gr. k-3). spiral bd. (978-0-616-07275-2(9)) Canadian National Institute for the Blind/Institut National Canadien pour les Aveugles.

—La Isla. Kleven, Elisa, illus. 1999. (Picture Puffin Ser.). (SPA.). 40p. (J). (gr. k-3). pap. 6.99 (978-0-14-056541-6(8) , DT8806, Puffin) Penguin Group (USA) Inc.

Douglas, H. I. Voyage to the Stars: David's First Adventure. 2006. 156p. pap. 19.95 (978-1-4241-1176-3(5)) PublishAmerica, Inc.

Dowd, John. Hogsty Reef. 1999. 192p. (YA). (gr. 6-10). pap. 5.95 (978-1-56145-187-6(8) , Q19223) Peachtree Pubs., Ltd.

—Hogsty Reef. 1999. (gr. 7-12). lib. bdg. 14.10 (978-0-613-29258-0(8)) Tandem Library Bks.

Duckworth, Michael. Voodoo Island, Level 2. 2nd ed. 2000. (Bookworms Ser.). (Illus.). 6.50 (978-0-19-422989-0(0)) Oxford Univ. Pr., Inc.

Eden-Paul, Muriel Tuttle. A Day on Cumberland Island. 2001. (Illus.). 40p. (J). (gr. k-2). pap. 7.50 (978-1-888213-78-2(7)) Eastern National.

Edwards, Frank B. & Bianchi, John. Treasure Island with Lots of Dogs. 1999. (Dog Eared Classics Ser.). (Illus.). 32p. (J). (gr. 3-6). pap. 5.95 (978-1-894323-10-9(6)); lib. bdg. 15.95 (978-1-894323-11-6(4)) Pokeweed Pr. CAN. *Dist:* Fitzhenry & Whiteside, Ltd.

English, Karen. Neeny Coming, Neeny Going. 1998. (978-0-606-13656-3(8)) Tandem Library Bks.

Epner, Paul. Herbert Hilligan's Tropical Adventure. Kuon, Vuthy & Nguyen, Duke, illus. 2003. 32p. (J). 15.95 (978-0-9743335-2-6(2)) Imaginative Publishing, Ltd.

Erdrich, Louise. The Birchbark House. Erdrich, Louise, illus. 2002. (Illus.). 256p. (gr. 4-17). pap. 6.99 (978-0-7868-1454-1(3)) Hyperion Paperbacks for Children.

—The Birchbark House. 2002. (gr. 5-8). lib. bdg. 15.00 (978-0-613-59384-7(7)) Tandem Library Bks.

—The Game of Silence. 2005. (Illus.). 272p. (J). lib. bdg. 16.89 (978-0-06-029790-9(5)); 15.99 (978-0-06-029789-3(1)) HarperCollins Pubs.

—The Game of Silence. l.t. ed. 2000. 272p. (YA). (gr. 7-12). 20.95 (978-0-7862-2178-3(X)) Thorndike Pr.

Farber, Erica. Octopus Island. Mayer, Mercer, illus. 2006. (Critter Kids Adventure Ser.). 32p. (J). (gr. 2-5). pap. 4.95 (978-0-7696-4766-1(9) , Gingham Dog Pr.) School Specialty Publishing.

Farshtey, Greg. Prisoners of the Pit. 2007. (Bionicle Legends Ser.: No. 7). 144p. (J). pap. 4.99 ***(*978-0-439-89034-2(9))*** Scholastic, Inc.

Feinstein, Stephen. Robinson Crusoe. Hagerty, Carol, ed. 1998. (Classics Ser.: Set II). (Illus.). 77p. (YA). (gr. 5-12). pap. 7.95 (978-1-56254-272-6(9) , SP2729) Saddleback Educational Publishing.

Foster, Alan Dean. Hand of Dinotopia. 2002. (Dinotopia Ser.). (Illus.). 416p. (J). (gr. 5 up). pap. 7.99 (978-0-06-051851-6(0)) HarperCollins Pubs.

Francis, Marnie, et al. Green Isles of the Ocean. Evans, Fran et al, illus. 2005. 32p. pap. 12.95 (978-1-84323-421-0(1)) Beekman Bks., Inc.

Fuller, Harvey. Tommy & the Island. Fuller, Harvey, illus. 2007. (J). pap. 18.95 ***(*978-0-9773725-7-7(X))*** Flat Hammock Pr.

Garis, Howard Roger. The Curlytops on Star Island or Camping. 2006. 63.99 ***(*978-1-4280-0922-6(1));*** pap. 56.99 ***(*978-1-4280-0933-2(7))*** IndyPublish.com.

Gay, Marie-Louise. On My Island. Gay, Marie-Louise, illus. 2001. (Illus.). 36p. (J). (ps-4). 16.95 (978-0-88899-396-0(X)) Groundwood Bks. CAN. *Dist:* Perseus Distribution.

—Sur Mon Ile. ed. 2004. (FRE.). (J). (gr. k-3). spiral bd. (978-0-616-07261-5(9)) Canadian National Institute for the Blind/Institut National Canadien pour les Aveugles.

George, Jean Craighead. Tree Castle Island. 2003. 256p. (J). pap. 5.99 (978-0-06-000256-5(5) , Harper Trophy) HarperCollins Pubs.

—Tree Castle Island. 2003. (gr. 3-6). lib. bdg. 14.15 (978-0-613-67007-4(8)) Tandem Library Bks.

Gilleland, Rebecca. The Swiss Family Robinson Study Guide. 2003. stu. ed., ring bd. 14.99 (978-1-58609-194-1(8)) Progeny Pr.

Gisbert, Joan Manuel. El Misterio de la Isla Tokland. 1998. (SPA.). 288p. (J). 8.95 (978-84-395-0817-5(4)) Lectorum Pubns., Inc.

Godolphin, Mary. The Swiss Family Robinson Told in Words. 2004. reprint ed. pap. 15.95 (978-1-4191-8466-6(0)) Kessinger Publishing, LLC.

—The Swiss Family Robinson Told in Words of One Syllable. 2004. reprint ed. pap. 1.99 (978-1-4192-8466-3(5)) Kessinger Publishing, LLC.

Golding, William. Lord of the Flies. 50th anniv. ed. 2003. 336p. (gr. 12). 23.95 (978-0-399-52920-7(9) , Perigee Trade) Penguin Group (USA) Inc.

Goodale, Rebecca, illus. Island Dog. 1999. 38p. (J). (ps up). 17.95 (978-1-891090-03-5(8)) Two Dog Pr.

Greene, John McBride. Encounter at Ogre Island. Julich, Jenniffer, illus. 2006. 96p. pap. 9.50 (978-0-9772809-0-2(X)) Comprecom.

Gregory, Kristiana. Cabin Creek Mysteries #1 Secret of Robber's Cave. 2008. (Cabin Creek Mysteries Ser.). 192p. (J). pap. 4.99 ***(*978-0-439-92950-9(4)*** , Scholastic Paperbacks) Scholastic, Inc.

—Cabin Creek Mysteries #2 Clue at the Bottom Lake. 2008. (Cabin Creek Mysteries Ser.). 176p. (J). pap. 4.99 ***(*978-0-439-92951-6(2)*** , Scholastic Paperbacks) Scholastic, Inc.

Griffin, Adele. The Knaveheart's Curse: A Vampire Island Book: A Vampire Island Book. 2008. 128p. (J). (gr. 4-6). 14.99 ***(*978-0-399-25064-4(6)*** , Putnam Juvenile) Penguin Group (USA) Inc.

Guardiola, Pepa. Los Ojos de la Nereida. 2000. Tr. of Eyes of the Sea Nymph. (SPA.). 92p. (J). (gr. 3-5). 9.95 (978-84-236-5503-8(2)) Baker & Taylor Bks.

Gurney, James. Dinotopia: Journey to Chandara. 2007. (Illus.). 160p. 29.95 ***(*978-0-7407-6431-8(4))*** Andrews McMeel Publishing.

Halam, Ann. Dr. Franklin's Island. 2003. 272p. (gr. 7). mass mkt. 6.50 (978-0-440-23781-5(5) , Laurel Leaf) Random Hse. Children's Bks.

—Dr Franklin's Island. 2003. (gr. 7-12). lib. bdg. 13.55 (978-0-613-72267-4(1)) Tandem Library Bks.

Hamilton, Tisha. Pirate Island Storybook & Dress up Kit. 2006. (Storybook & Dress-up Kit Ser.). 24p. (J). pap. 18.99 (978-0-7944-1105-3(3)) Reader's Digest Assn., Inc., The.

Hammond, Jo. Home Before Dark. 2005. 144p. (YA). (gr. 7-12). pap. 7.95 (978-1-55143-340-0(0)) Orca Bk. Pubs. USA.

Hansen, Joyce. The Heart Calls Home. 1999. viii, 175p. (J). (gr. 7-12). 16.95 (978-0-8027-8636-4(7)) Walker & Co.

Hardy, Cindy & Masterman, Lorrine A. Egg Island Reader. 2003. (Math in A Cultural Context Ser.). (Illus.). 74p. pap. 14.95 (978-1-55059-246-7(7)) Temeron Bks., Inc.

Hawley, C. Mabel. Four Little Blossoms on Apple Tree Island. 2006. 24.99 ***(*978-1-4280-1723-8(2))*** IndyPublish.com.

Hawley, Mabel C. Four Little Blossoms on Apple Tree Island. 2004. reprint ed. pap. 1.99 (978-1-4192-2050-0(0)) Kessinger Publishing, LLC.

Hawthorne, Rachel. Island Girls & Boys. 2005. 336p. pap. 5.99 (978-0-06-075546-1(6)) HarperCollins Pubs.

Hazen, Lynn E. Mermaid Mary Margaret. 2004. (Illus.). 96p. (J). (gr. 2-5). 14.95 (978-1-58234-869-8(3) , Bloomsbury Children) Bloomsbury Publishing.

Headley, Lester "Zoom". Smiley B. 2006. (ENG., Illus.). 48p. per. 20.95 ***(*978-1-59800-548-6(0))*** Outskirts Press, Inc.

Hedderwick, Mairi. Katie Morag. 2003. (Katie Morag Ser.). (Illus.). 64p. (J). pap. 8.99 (978-0-09 943205 0(6)) Random Hse. GBR. *Dist:* Independent Pubs. Group.

—Katie Morag's Island World: Four More of Your Favourite Katie Morag Adventures. 2004. (Illus.). 112p. (J). pap. 14.99 (978-0-09-943303-3(6) , Red Fox) Random Hse. Children's Bks. GBR. *Dist:* Trafalgar Square Publishing.

Henty, G. A. The Stone Chest or the Secret of Cedar Island. 2004. reprint ed. pap. 15.95 (978-1-4191-8354-6(0)); pap. 1.99 (978-1-4192-8354-3(5)) Kessinger Publishing, LLC.

Hippely, Hilary Horder. Adventure on Klickitat Island. Upton, Barbara, illus. 2000. (J). (ps-ps). lib. bdg. 15.30 (978-0-613-24092-5(8)) Tandem Library Bks.

Hope, Laura Lee. The Bobbsey Twins on Blueberry Island, Vol. 10. 2004. (Bobbsey Twins Ser.: Vol. 10). (Illus.). 196p. (J). (gr. 3-8). 5.99 (978-0-448-43761-3(9) , Grosset & Dunlap) Penguin Group (USA) Inc.

Hortten, Jacqueline Faye. Pu Beach. l.t. ed. 2004. (Illus.). 27p. (J). pap. 14.95 (978-0-9728393-0-3(5)) Children's Bookshoppe Stop, The.

Horvath, Polly. The Corps of the Bare-Boned Plane. 2007. 272p. (J). (gr. 7 up). 17.00 ***(*978-0-374-31553-5(1)*** , Farrar, Straus & Giroux (BYR)) Farrar, Straus & Giroux.

Hyde, Dayton. Island of the Loons. 2002. (gr. 5-8). lib. bdg. 18.75 (978-0-613-57307-8(2)) Tandem Library Bks.

Ibbotson, Eva. Island of the Aunts. 2001. 304p. (YA). (gr. 4-7). pap. 5.99 (978-0-14-230049-7(7) , Puffin) Penguin Group (USA) Inc.

—Monster Mission. l.t. ed. 2006. pap. 16.95 (978-1-4056-6057-0(0)) BBC Audio GBR. *Dist:* BBC Audiobooks America.

—El Secreto Del Andén 13. 3rd ed. 2003. (SPA., Illus.). 190p. (978-84-7888-764-4(4) , 1952) Emece Editores.

Inches, Alison. Castaways! 2006. (Illus.). 24p. (J). lib. bdg. 9.00 ***(*978-1-4242-0950-7(1))*** Fitzgerald Bks.

Inkpen, Mick. Beachmoles & Bellvine. 2006. (Blue Nose Island Ser.: Bk. 2). (Illus.). (J). (ps). pap. 9.99 (978-0-340-87866-8(5) , Hodder & Stoughton) Hodder General Publishing Division GBR. *Dist:* Trafalgar Square Publishing.

—Bokobikes. 2006. (Blue Nose Island Ser.: Bk. 3). (Illus.). 34p. (J). (ps). 19.99 (978-0-340-70380-9(6) , Hodder & Stoughton) Hodder General Publishing Division GBR. *Dist:* Trafalgar Square Publishing.

—Ploo & the Terrible Gnobbler. 2006. (Blue Nose Island Ser.: Bk. 1). (Illus.). (J). (ps). pap. 11.95 (978-1-84032-988-9(2) , Hodder & Stoughton) Hodder General Publishing Division GBR. *Dist:* Trafalgar Square Publishing.

Islas Asombrosas 17: Leveled Books. 2001. (McGraw-Hill Lectura Ser.). (ENG & SPA.). (gr. 5 up). (978-0-02-188265-6(7)) Macmillan/McGraw-Hill Schl. Div.

Jamieson, Mark. Ico Island. 2007. (J). pap. 11.95 ***(*978-0-9792518-0-1(X))*** Gequalsa.

Jennings, Richard W. Ferret Island. 2007. 192p. (J). (gr. 4-6). 16.00 ***(*978-0-618-80632-4(6)*** , Walter Lorraine) Houghton Mifflin Co. Trade & Reference Div.

Johnson, Jan G. Orcas Island Mystery. 1999. 125p. (J). pap. 7.99 (978-0-8280-1314-7(4)) Review & Herald Publishing Assn.

Johnson, Sandi. Lost Island. Johnson, Britt, ed. Sturgeon, Bobbi, illus. l.t. ed. 2001. 22p. (J). (gr. k-5). spiral bd. 5.99 (978-1-929063-69-7(5) , 168) Moons & Stars Publishing For Children.

Jones, Chuck. The White Seal. Jones, Chuck, illus. 2006. (Illus.). 32p. (J). 8.95 (978-0-8249-6598-3(1) , Ideals Children's Bks.) Ideals Pubns.

Jones, Kimberly K. Sand Dollar Summer. 2006. 224p. (J). 15.95 (978-1-4169-0362-8(3) , McElderry, Margaret K.) Simon & Schuster Children's Publishing.

Keaney, Brian. The Hollow People. Ceccoli, Nicoletta, illus. 2007. (Promises of Dr. Sigmundus: Bk. 1). 240p. (YA). (gr. 7-12). lib. bdg. 19.99 ***(*978-0-375-94332-4(3)*** , Knopf Bks. for Young Readers) Random Hse. Children's Bks.

—The Hollow People. 2007. (Promises of Dr. Sigmundus: Bk. 1). (Illus.). 224p. (YA). (gr. 7-12). 16.99 ***(*978-0-375-84332-7(9)*** , Knopf Bks. for Young Readers) Random Hse. Children's Bks.

Kellogg, Elijah. The Ark of Elm Island. 2005. reprint ed. pap. 28.95 (978-1-4191-1833-3(1)) Kessinger Publishing, LLC.

Kelly, Theresa. Living on Nothing Atoll. 1999. (Aloha Cove Ser.: Vol. 1). (Illus.). 272p. (YA). (gr. 8-12). 5.99 (978-0-570-05483-2(4)) Concordia Publishing Hse.

—Living on Nothing Atoll. 1999. (gr. 7-12). lib. bdg. 14.15 (978-0-613-72659-7(6)) Tandem Library Bks.

—Tomorrow I'll Miss You, Vol. 3. 1999. (Aloha Cove Ser.: Vol. 3). (Illus.). 272p. (YA). (gr. 8-12). 5.99 (978-0-570-05485-6(0)) Concordia Publishing Hse.

—Tomorrow I'll Miss You. 1999. (gr. 7-12). lib. bdg. 14.15 (978-0-613-72575-0(1)) Tandem Library Bks.

Kenny, Kathryn & Koelsch, Michael. The Mystery on Cobbett's Island. Frame, Paul, illus. 2005. (Trixie Belden Ser.: Vol. 13). 272p. (J). (gr. 3-7). 6.99 (978-0-375-83053-2(7)); lib. bdg. 9.99 (978-0-375-93053-9(1)) Random Hse. Children's Bks. (Random Hse. Bks. for Young Readers).

Kimpton, Diana. Summer Vacation. Finlay, Lizzie, illus. 2007. 144p. (gr. 1-4). pap. 4.99 ***(*978-1-4231-0616-6(4))*** Hyperion Paperbacks for Children.

Lansing, Richard D., Jr. The Green Curly-Tailed Lizard. Lansing, Randy, illus. 1999. 48p. (J). (ps-4). mass mkt. 6.00 (978-0-9661844-4-0(0)) Purple Gorilla, LLC, The.

Larry, H. I. Zac Power #1: Poison Island. Oswald, Ash, illus. 2008. (Zac Power Ser.). 96p. (J). pap. 3.99 ***(*978-0-312-34659-1(X))*** Feiwel & Friends.

Lawrence, Iain. The Lightkeeper's Daughter. (YA). (gr. 9). 2004. 272p. pap. 7.95 (978-0-385-73127-0(2)); 2002. 256p. lib. bdg. 18.99 (978-0-385-90062-1(7)) Random Hse. Children's Bks. (Delacorte Bks. for Young Readers).

Laza, Aidan & Tipoti, Alick. Kuiyku Mabaigal: Waii & Sobai. 1998. (Illus.). 32p. pap. 14.95 (978-1-875641-40-6(8)) Magabala Bks. AUS. *Dist:* International Specialized Bk. Services.

Lee, Tanith. Return to Parrot Island. 2006. (Piratica Ser.: Vol. 2). 360p. (YA). (gr. 7 up). 17.99 (978-0-525-47769-3(1) , Dutton Juvenile) Penguin Group (USA) Inc.

Legend of the Island Horse. 2006. (J). (978-1-933343-22-8(2)) Stabenfeldt Inc.

Lehri, R. M. Cut & Make Festival Masks from India: 6 Full-Color Designs. 2001. (Illus.). 16p. (J). (gr. 3). pap. 5.95 (978-0-486-41667-0(4)) Dover Pubns., Inc.

Levert, Mireille. An Island in the Soup. 2001. (Illus.). 24p. (J). (ps-k). 15.95 (978-0-88899-403-5(6)) Groundwood Bks. CAN. *Dist:* Perseus Distribution.

Levin, Betty. Island Bound. 2000. (Illus.). 272p. (J). (gr. 3-7). pap. 4.95 (978-0-380-73174-9(6) , Harper Trophy) HarperCollins Pubs.

—Thorn. 2005. 176p. (J). (gr. 5). 16.95 (978-1-932425-46-8(2) , Lemniscaat) Boyds Mills Pr.

Libhart, Virginia B. Carrie's Dream. 2005. (978-0-9652963-7-3(7)) Harborseal Publishing Co.

Likins, Kim. Charlie's Perfect Day. Magalinska, Ingrid, illus. l.t. ed. 2003. 32p. (J). bds. (978-0-9729987-0-3(5)) Island Friends LLC.

Lloyd, Sam. Yummy Yummy! Food for My Tummy. Tickle, Jack, illus. 2004. 32p. (J). tchr. ed. 15.95 (978-1-58925-035-2(4) , tiger tales) ME Media LLC.

Lord of the Flies. 1998. 40p. (YA). 11.95 (978-1-56137-384-0(2) , NU3842SP) Novel Units, Inc.

H
I

Lucado, Max. Coming Home. 2007. (Illus.). 32p. (J). 15.99 (*978-1-58134-756-2(1)) Crossway Bks.

MacDonald, Golden. The Little Island. Weisgard, Leonard, illus. 2002. (J). 14.79 (978-0-7587-0034-6(2)) Book Wholesalers, Inc.

MacHado, Ana Maria. El Misterio de la Isla. 2004. Tr. of Mystery of the Island. (SPA., Illus.). 72p. (YA). 9.99 (978-84-241-8653-1(2)) Everest de Ediciones y Distribucion, S.L. ESP. *Dist:* Lectorum Pubns., Inc.

MacLachlan, Patricia. Two Novels: Baby/Journey. 2007. 224p. (J). (gr. 4-7). 16.99 (978-0-385-73423-3(9)) ; lib. bdg. 19.99 (978-0-385-90436-0(3)) Random Hse. Children's Bks. (Delacorte Bks. for Young Readers).

MacLachlan, Patricia & MacLachlan, Emily. Painting the Wind. Schneider, Katy, illus. 40p. (J). (ps-3). 2003. 15.99 (978-0-06-029798-5(0) , Cotler, Joanna Books); 2003. lib. bdg. 16.89 (978-0-06-029799-2(9) , Cotler, Joanna Books); 2006. reprint ed. pap. 6.99 (978-0-06-443825-4(2) , Harper Trophy) HarperCollins Pubs.

MacNeil, Stephen. Woolies & Worms. 2007. 192p. (J). (gr. 2-5). 16.95 (*978-0-8126-2751-0(2)) Cricket Bks.

MacPhail, Catherine. Underworld. 2005. 250p. (YA). (ps-7). 16.95 (978-1-58234-997-8(5) , Bloomsbury Children) Bloomsbury Publishing.

Majumdar, Anuradha. Island of Infinity: Marina's Dream. 2005. 300p. (J). (*978-0-14-333513-9(8) , Puffin) Penguin Group (USA) Inc.

Man-Kong, Mary. Barbie as the Island Princess. Tormey, Carlotta, illus. 2007. (Picture Book Ser.). 32p. (J). (ps-2). 8.99 (*978-0-375-84217-7(9) , Golden Bks.) Random Hse. Children's Bks.

—Barbie as the Island Princess: A Storybook. 2007. (Picturebacks(R) Ser.). (Illus.). 24p. (J). (ps-2). 3.99 (*978-0-375-84218-4(7) , Random Hse. Bks. for Young Readers) Random Hse. Children's Bks.

—Barbie as the Island Princess:MYOLG. 2007. (Make Your Own LGB Ser.). (Illus.). 16p. (J). (ps-2). 5.99 (*978-0-375-84219-1(5) , Golden Bks.) Random Hse. Children's Bks.

Mara, Sarah Robinson. A Snug Little Island, Hammond, Nancy Robinson, illus. 2005. 60p. (J). 18.50 (978-0-9766737-0-5(3)) Pink Granite Pr.

Marsh, Carole. The Secret of Eyesocket Island. 2007. 128p. (gr. 3-5). pap. 5.99 (*978-0-635-06236-9(4)); (gr. 7-14). 14.95 (*978-0-635-06240-6(2)) Gallopade International.

Marshall, Felicity. Sage's Ark. 2000. 32p. (J). (Illus.). pap. 12.95 (978-1-86368-253-4(8)); 21.95 (978-1-86368-290-9(2)) Fremantle Pr. AUS. *Dist:* International Specialized Bk. Services.

Martin, Jacqueline Briggs. On Sand Island. Johnson, David A., illus. 2003. 32p. (J). (gr. k-3). tchr. ed. 16.00 (978-0-618-23151-5(X)) Houghton Mifflin Co. Trade & Reference Div.

Martin, Nora. Flight of the Fisherbird. 2003. (Illus.). 200p. (J). 16.95 (978-1-58234-814-8(6) , Bloomsbury Children) Bloomsbury Publishing.

Martineck, Michael J. The Wrong Channel. 2005. 160p. (J). (gr. 4-8). 8.00 (978-0-9720978-1-9(3)) Our Little Secret Pr.

Mason, Jo-Anne. Paddy, the Goat That Saved Rainbow Island. 2003. 48p. (ps-3). 13.95 (978-0-333-97062-1(4)) Macmillan Caribbean GBR. *Dist:* Interlink Publishing Group, Inc.

McAllister, M. I. The Heir of Mistmantle. Rayyan, Omar, illus. 2007. (Mistmantle Chronicles Ser.: Bk. 3). 320p. (J). (gr. 3-7). 17.99 (*978-0-7868-5490-5(1)) Miramax Bks.

—Mistmantle Chronicles, the: Urchin & the Heartstone - Book #2. Rayyan, Omar, illus. 2nd rev. ed. 2007. 304p. (gr. 3-7). pap. 7.99 (*978-0-7868-5489-9(8)) Miramax Bks.

McAllister, M. I. Urchin of the Riding Stars. Ryann, Omar, illus. 2005. (Mistmantle Chronicles Ser.: Bk. 1). 288p. (gr. 3-7). 17.95 (978-0-7868-5486-8(3)) Miramax Bks.

McCullagh, Sheila. Pirate Gold. 2007. (Three Pirates Ser.). (Illus.). 48p. 15.95 (*978-1-84560-042-6(8)) Mercury Bks. Ltd. GBR. *Dist:* International Publishers Marketing.

—Shipwrecked. 2007. (Three Pirates Ser.). (Illus.). 48p. 15.95 (*978-1-84560-043-3(6)) Mercury Bks. Ltd. GBR. *Dist:* International Publishers Marketing.

McFadden, Patricia. Turtle Island. rev. ed. 2002. 240p. (J). per. 11.95 (978-0-9720198-0-4(4)) Green Turtle Pr.

McMullan, Kate. Revenge of the Dragon Lady. 2007. (Dragon Slayers' Academy Ser.: No. 2). 112p. (J). (gr. 1-6). 24.21 (*978-1-59961-378-9(6)) Spotlight.

—Sir Lancelot, Where Are You? 2007. (Dragon Slayers' Academy Ser.: No. 6). 112p. (J). (gr. 1-6). 24.21 (*978-1-59961-379-6(4)) Spotlight.

Meddaugh, Susan. Harry on the Rocks. 2007. (Illus.). 32p. (J). (gr. k-3). 6.95 (*978-0-618-84068-7(0) , Walter Lorraine) Houghton Mifflin Co. Trade & Reference Div.

—Harry on the Rocks. Meddaugh, Susan, illus. 2003. (Illus.). 32p. (J). (gr. k-3). tchr. ed. 15.00 (978-0-618-27603-5(3) , Walter Lorraine) Houghton Mifflin Co. Trade & Reference Div.

Meserve, Adria. No Room for Napoleon. 2006. (Illus.). 32p. (J). 16.00 (978-0-374-35536-4(3)) Farrar, Straus & Giroux.

Miller, Kyle Linda. Dillo: A Baby Armadillo's Adventure on Sanibel Island. Eddy, Randon, illus. l.t. ed. 2005. 64p. (J). per. 16.95 (978-0-9769332-0-5(9)) Jungle Hse. Pubns.

Miller, Wiley. The Extraordinary Adventures of Ordinary Basil Vol. 2: Island of the Volcano Monkeys. 2008. (Extraordinary Adventures of Ordinary Bas Ser.). 128p. (J). pap. 14.99 (*978-0-439-86132-8(2) , Blue Sky Pr., The) Scholastic, Inc.

Mongoose, Mongoose, Stop! Don't Run. 2004. (J). 8.99 (978-0-931548-65-9(9)) Island Heritage Publishing.

Montgomery, L. M. Anne of Avonlea. 2005. (Aladdin Classics Ser.). (Illus.). 398p. (J). (gr. 4-7). pap. 4.99 (978-1-4169-0328-4(3) , Aladdin) Simon & Schuster Children's Publishing.

—Anne of Avonlea. unabr. ed. 2002. (Dover Juvenile Classics Ser.). 272p. (J). (gr. 4-7). pap. 3.00 (978-0-486-42239-8(9)) Dover Pubns., Inc.

—Anne of Green Gables. l.t. ed. 2006. (ENG.). pap. (*978-1-4068-3174-0(3)) Echo Library.

—Anne of Green Gables. Rubio, Mary & Waterson, Elizabeth, eds. 2006. (Norton Critical Edition Ser.). (Illus.). 400p. (C). pap. 9.00 (978-0-393-92695-8(8)) Norton, W. W. & Co., Inc.

—Anne of Green Gables. 2006. (Scholastic Classics Ser.). (Illus.). viii, 272p. (J). (gr. 9-12). 25.00 (978-0-531-16980-3(4) , Watts, Franklin) Scholastic Library Publishing.

Montgomery, R. A. Return to Atlantis. 2005. (Illus.). 119p. (J). pap. (*978-0-7608-9706-5(9)) Sundance/Newbridge Educational Publishing.

Morgan, Clay. The Boy Who Spoke Dog. (J). (gr. 4-7). 2005. 176p. pap. 5.99 (978-0-14-240343-3(1) , Puffin); 2003. 192p. 15.99 (978-0-525-47159-2(6) , Dutton Juvenile) Penguin Group (USA) Inc.

Morgan, Clay. The Boy Who Spoke Dog: Return to Dog Island. 2007. 176p. (J). (gr. 4). 16.99 (*978-0-525-47401-2(3) , Dutton Juvenile) Penguin Group (USA) Inc.

Morpurgo, Michael. The Wreck of the Zanzibar. l.t. ed. 2003. (J). 16.95 (978-0-7540-7846-3(9) , Galaxy Children's Large Print) BBC Audiobooks America.

Morton-Shaw, Christine. The Riddles of Epsilon. 384p. 2006. (J). pap. 7.99 (978-0-06-072821-2(3)); Vol. 1. 2005. (gr. 7 up). 16.99 (978-0-06-072819-9(1)) HarperCollins Pubs.

My Time on Nantucket Coloring Book. 2005. (J). 3.95 (978-0-9755078-1-0(8)) Sweet Punkin Pr.

Nakagawa, Rieko. Guri & Gura's Seaside Adventure. Yamawaki, Yuriko, illus. 2003. (Guri & Gura Ser.). 32p. 10.95 (978-0-8048-3354-7(0)) Tuttle Publishing.

O'Dell, Scott. La Isla de los Delfines Azules. (SPA., Illus.). (YA). (gr. 5-8). (978-1-56137-541-7(1) , NU5722) Noguer y Caralt Editores, S. A. ESP. *Dist:* Lectorum Pubns., Inc.

—Island of the Blue Dolphins. 2002. (Illus.). (J). 15.00 (978-0-7587-0194-7(2)) Book Wholesalers, Inc.

—Island of the Blue Dolphins. 184p. (J). (gr. 3-5). pap. 5.99 (978-0-8072-8327-1(4)); 2004. (gr. 5-9). pap. 36.00 incl. audio (978-0-8072-8326-4(6) , YA163SP) Random Hse. Audio Publishing Group. (Listening Library).

Ormondroyd, Edward. Castaways on Long Ago. 2003. (Illus.). 188p. (gr. 5 up). 12.95 (978-0-9714612-8-4(7)) Green Mansion Pr. LLC.

Orr, Wendy. Nim's Island. Millard, Kerry, illus. (gr. 3-7). 2008. 144p. 5.50 (*978-0-385-73606-0(1)); 2002. 128p. 5.50 (978-0-440-41868-9(2)) Random Hse. Children's Bks. (Yearling).

—Nim's Island. 2002. (gr. 3-6). lib. bdg. 13.00 (978-0-613-46203-7(3)) Tandem Library Bks.

Osborne, Mary Pope. The Gray-Eyed Goddess. 2003. (Tales from the Odyssey Ser.: Bk. 4). (gr. 3-6). lib. bdg. 13.00 (978-0-613-68242-8(4)) Tandem Library Bks.

Pair, Regether. The Little Rock Island & a Little Rock Named Sam. 2007. 17.00 (*978-0-8059-8800-0(9)) Dorrance Publishing Co., Inc.

Panagopoulos, Janie Lynn. The Runes of Isle Royale: A Great Lakes Adventure in History & Mystery. 2000. (Illus.). 158p. (J). (gr. 3-7). pap. 8.95 (978-0-938682-63-9(6) , 982-63-6) River Road Pubns., Inc.

Papish, Ramiel. The Little Fox. 2006. (J). (978-1-889963-87-7(9)) Univ. of Alaska Pr.

Paulsen, Gary. The Island. 2006. 208p. (J). pap. 5.99 (978-0-439-78662-1(2) , Scholastic Paperbacks) Scholastic, Inc.

Peretti, Frank E. The Cooper Kids Adventure Series. 2004. (Cooper Kids Adventure Ser.). (J). (gr. 5-7). 23.96 (978-0-89107-901-9(7)) Crossway Bks.

—Escape from the Island of Aquarius, Vol. 2. 2005. (Cooper Kids Adventure Ser.: Vol. 2). 160p. pap. 5.99 (978-1-58134-619-0(0) , Crossway Bibles) Crossway Bks.

Ponti, Claude. DeZert Isle. Holliday, Mary Martin, tr. from FRE. Ponti, Claude, illus. 2003. (Illus.). 64p. (J). 16.95 (978-1-56792-237-0(6)) Godine, David R. Pub.

Pratchett, Terry. Jingo. 2000. (gr. 5-8). lib. bdg. 15.30 (978-0-613-57231-6(9)) Tandem Library Bks.

Rabley, Stephen. Tinker's Island. 2002. (Illus.). 16p. pap. (978-0-582-40284-3(0) , Putnam Juvenile) Penguin Group (USA) Inc.

Raven, Margot Theis. Circle Unbroken. Lewis, E.B., illus. 2007. 48p. (J). pap. 6.99 (*978-0-312-37603-1(0)) Square Fish.

Reynolds, Cynthia Furlong. Rascal Makes Mischief on Mackinac Island. Brege, Darrin, illus. 2006. (J). (ps-3). 17.95 (978-1-58726-312-5(2) , Mitten Pr.) Ann Arbor Media Group, LLC.

Rigby Education Staff. The Island of Wingo. (Sails Literacy Ser.). (Illus.). 16p. (gr. 2-3). 27.00 (978-0-7635-9946-1(8) , 699468C99) Rigby Education.

Robison, Dan. Death Chant: Kimo's Battle with the Shamanic Forces. 2006. 194p. (J). pap. (978-0-922993-52-9(1)) Marquette Bks., LLC.

Rockwell, Anne F. Ferryboat Ride! 1999. (Illus.). (J). (978-0-606-18088-7(5)) Tandem Library Bks.

Rohmann, Eric. Cinder-Eyed Cat. 2001. (gr. k-3). lib. bdg. 15.30 (978-0-613-36797-4(9)) Tandem Library Bks.

Roy, Ron. The Invisible Island. Gurney, John Steven, illus. 1999. (A to Z Mysteries Ser.: No. 9). 96p. (J). (gr. k-3). lib. bdg. 11.99 (978-0-679-99457-2(2)); pap. 3.99 (978-0-679-89457-5(8)) Random Hse. Children's Bks. (Random Hse. Bks. for Young Readers).

—The Invisible Island. Gurney, John Steven, illus. 1999. (A to Z Mysteries Ser.: No. 9). (gr. k-3). 90p. lib. bdg. 10.79 (978-0-606-17265-3(3)); (J). lib. bdg. 11.80 (978-0-613-21768-2(3)) Tandem Library Bks.

Rupp, Rebecca. The Dragon of Lonely Island. 2004. 160p. (J). (gr. 4-8). reprint ed. pap. (978-0-7567-7861-3(1)) DIANE Publishing Co.

—The Return of the Dragon. 2005. 160p. (J). (gr. 5-6). 15.99 (978-0-7636-2377-7(6)) Candlewick Pr.

Rushford, Patricia H. The Secret of Ghost Island. 2007. 128p. pap. 6.99 (*978-0-8024-6255-8(3)) Moody Pubs.

Rylant, Cynthia. The Islander. 1999. (Illus.). 112p. (J). (gr. 5-17). reprint ed. pap. 5.50 (978-0-440-41542-8(X) , Yearling) Random Hse. Children's Bks.

—The Islander. 1999. (gr. 5-8). lib. bdg. 13.00 (978-0-613-23002-5(7)) Tandem Library Bks.

Sachi. 2006. 26p. 10.05 (978-1-4116-7248-2(8)) Lulu.com.

Sage, Angie. Shark Island. (Illus.). 64p. (J). 7.95 (978-0-14-038120-7(1)) Penguin Bks., Ltd. GBR. *Dist:* Trafalgar Square Publishing.

Santa Takes A Vacation. 2005. (J). 5.95 (978-0-9769321-4-7(8)) Steingart, Nathan Publishing.

Schaefer, Lola M. An Island Grows. Felstead, Cathie, illus. 2006. 40p. (J). (gr. k-2). 16.99 (978-0-06-623930-9(3)); lib. bdg. 17.89 (978-0-06-623931-6(1)) HarperCollins Pubs.

The Secret Of Mystery Island, Set 3. 1998. (Comic Book Ser.). (Illus.). (J). (978-0-7652-0301-4(4)) Modern Curriculum Pr.

Shoup, Andrew J. Toko of Coco Oko. Shoup, Andrew J., illus. l.t. ed. 2002. (Illus.). 32p. (J). 16.95 (978-0-9720436-0-1(8) , SAN: 254-573X) TokoBooks.

Sims, Lesley. Island Adventures. 2004. (Puzzle Adventures Ser.). (Illus.). 48p. (J). pap. 4.95 (978-0-7945-0091-7(9) , Usborne) EDC Publishing.

Snedeker, Caroline. Downright Dencey. Barney, Maginel Wright, illus. 2003. (Young Adult Library). 274p. (YA). pap. 11.95 (978-1-883937-79-9(5)) Bethlehem Bks.

Sorrells, Walter. Static. 2006. 224p. (J). lib. bdg. 23.08 (*978-1-4242-2215-5(X)) Fitzgerald Bks.

Spalding, Andrea. An Island of My Own. 2007. 112p. (YA). pap. 11.99 (*978-1-55002-635-1(6) , Sandcastle Bks.) Dundurn Group, The CAN. *Dist:* Univ. of Toronto Pr.

Springer, Susan Woodward. Seldovia Sam & the Very Large Clam. Meissner, Amy, illus. 2005. (Seldovia Sam Ser.: Vol. 1). 64p. 6.95 (978-0-88240-570-4(5)) Graphic Arts Ctr. Publishing Co.

—Seldovia Sam & the Very Large Clam. 2003. (gr. 3-6). lib. bdg. 15.25 (978-0-613-77289-1(X)) Tandem Library Bks.

Sterns, Michael. Kokopelli & the Island of Change. Hageman, Erik, illus. 2nd ed. 2005. 64p. (J). 17.95 net. (978-0-615-12724-8(X)) Grasshopper Dream Productions.

Stevenson, James. The Castaway. Stevenson, James, illus. 2002. (Illus.). 32p. (J). (gr. 2 up). 15.95 (978-0-688-16965-7(1)) HarperCollins Pubs.

Stevenson, Robert Louis. Treasure Island. Date not set. (Nelson Readers Ser.). (J). pap. (978-0-17-556699-0(2)) Addison-Wesley Longman, Inc.

—Treasure Island. Hegarty, Carol, ed. 1998. (Classics Ser.: Set I). (Illus.). 79p. (YA). (gr. 5-12). pap. 6.95 (978-1-56254-281-8(8) , SP2818) Saddleback Educational Publishing.

—Treasure Island. Rebis, Greg, illus. 2007. (Graphic Revolve Ser.). 63p. (J). (gr. 4-6). lib. bdg. 22.60 (978-1-59889-050-1(6)) Stone Arch Bks.

Stilton, Geronimo. Lost Treasure of the Emerald Eye. Wolf, Matt, illus. 2004. (Geronimo Stilton Ser.: No. 1). 116p. (J). lib. bdg. 10.00 (*978-1-4242-0695-7(2)) Fitzgerald Bks.

—Lost Treasure of the Emerald Eye. 2007. (Geronimo Stilton Ser.: No. 1). 128p. (J). pap. 2.99 (*978-0-545-01032-0(2) , Scholastic Paperbacks) Scholastic, Inc.

—Lost Treasure of the Emerald Eye. Wolf, Matt & Keys, Larry, illus. 2004. (Geronimo Stilton Ser.: No. 1). 128p. (J). (gr. 2-5). pap. 6.99 (978-0-439-55963-8(4) , Scholastic Paperbacks) Scholastic, Inc.

—Shipwreck on the Pirate Islands. 2005. (Geronimo Stilton Ser.: No. 18). (Illus.). 128p. (J). 5.99 (978-0-439-69141-3(9) , Scholastic Paperbacks) Scholastic, Inc.

Stock, Catherine. Island Summer. 1999. (Illus.). 192p. (J). (gr. k-3). 16.00 (978-0-688-12780-0(0)) HarperCollins Pubs.

Strahinich, Helen, et al, trs. Tales from Gull Island. Reingold, Alan & Ning, Amy, illus. 2003. 60p. (978-0-7398-5176-0(4)) Steck-Vaughn.

Streib, Sally. Octopus Encounter. 2007. (J). (*978-0-8163-2210-7(4)) Pacific Pr. Publishing Assn.

Strickland, Brad. Guns of Tortuga. 2003. (gr. 3-6). lib. bdg. 13.00 (978-0-613-60418-5(0)) Tandem Library Bks.

Strickland, Brad, et al. The Storm: A Novelization. 2006. (Flight 29 down Ser.: Vol. 4). 224p. (J). (*978-1-4156-8721-5(8) , Grosset & Dunlap) Penguin Group (USA) Inc.

Strong, Louise. The Island Adventures of Frodo Mcadoo. 2005. (Illus.). 196p. (J). per. 12.95 (978-0-9770950-0-1(2)) Strong, Louise dev.

Suhay, Lisa. Our Fantasy Island. 2006. 30p. (J). pap. 8.00 (*978-0-9766628-0-8(9)) Fantasy Island Pr.

Summers, Kim. Senor Mundo & Me: A Happy Birthday Story. Mariscal, Javier, illus. 2004. 31p. (J). (gr. k-4). 20.00 (978-0-7567-7759-3(3)) DIANE Publishing Co.

Swift, Jonathan. Los Viajes de Gulliver. (SPA., Illus.). 144p. (YA). 14.95 (978-84-7281-080-8(1) , AF1080) Auriga, Ediciones S.A. ESP. *Dist:* Continental Bk. Co., Inc.

—Los Viajes de Gulliver. (Coleccion Clasicos de la Juventud). (SPA., Illus.). 204p. (J). 12.95 (978-84-7189-062-7(3) , ORT322) Ortells, Alfredo Editorial S.L. ESP. *Dist:* Continental Bk. Co., Inc.

Tait, Chris & Wyss, Johann David. The Swiss Family Robinson. Akib, Jamel, illus. 2007. 151p. (J). (*978-1-4287-4213-0(1)) Sterling Publishing Co., Inc.

Tate, Nikki. Tarragon Island. 2000. 184p. (J). (gr. 3-7). pap. 5.95 (978-1-55039-103-9(8)) Sono Nis Pr. CAN. *Dist:* Orca Bk. Pubs. USA.

—Tarragon Island. 1999. (gr. 3-6). lib. bdg. 12.95 (978-0-613-29357-0(6)) Tandem Library Bks.

Tentas, Jane Grant. Alice & the Bird Lady. Tentas, Jane Grant, illus. l.t. ed. 2002. 36p. per. 13.95 (978-0-9658983-6-2(9)) Book Nook Pr.

Tiffany, Grace. Ariel. 2005. 240p. (J). 16.99 (978-0-06-075327-6(7)); lib. bdg. 17.89 (978-0-06-075328-3(5)) HarperCollins Pubs.

Towles, LaRhonda. Ginger & Cocoa Island. Kirkpatrick, Philip, illus. 1998. i, 16p. (J). (ps-k). pap. 5.95 (978-0-9667894-0-9(7)) Towles, LaRhonda.

Townsend, John Rowe. The Islanders. 2006. (J). pap. 9.95 (978-1-932425-69-7(1) , Lemniscaat) Boyds Mills Pr.

Treasures of the Barrier Reef. 2005. (J). audio, cd-rom 24.95 (978-0-9771381-7-3(8)) Williams, Geoffrey T.

Trudeau, Scott & Holzbauer, David. A Treasure to Share: Adventures in Social Skills. Trudeau, Scott, illus. 2003. (Illus.). 68p. (J). (978-0-9743805-0-6(4)) Intellipop, LLC.

Unexpected Treasure, 6 vols. (Ragged Island Mysteriestm Ser.). 161p. (gr. 5-7). 42.50 (978-0-322-01650-7(9)) Wright Group, The.

Upton, Deborah. Scooby-Doo! Telephone Book. 2001. (Illus.). (J). 15.98 (978-0-7853-4755-2(0)) Publications International, Ltd.

Vachon, Mary Beth. Mac s Mackinac Island Adventure. Rusky, Ann G., illus. 2005. 216p. (J). pap. 17.95 (978-0-9766104-1-0(8)) Arbutus Pr.

Veneziano, Chuckie. My Time on Nantucket. 2005. (Illus.). 56p. (J). lib. bdg. 17.95 (978-0-9755078-0-3(X)) Sweet Punkin Pr.

Verne, Jules. La Isla Misteriosa. (SPA., Illus.). 192p. (YA). 11.95 (978-84-7281-105-8(0) , AF1105) Auriga, Ediciones S.A. ESP. *Dist:* Continental Bk. Co., Inc.

Vornholt, John. Dolphin Watch. 2002. (gr. 5-8). lib. bdg. 11.80 (978-0-613-70888-3(1)) Tandem Library Bks.

Wade, Judith. The Mermaid's Gift. 2004. 140p. (J). per. 5.99 (978-0-9728958-1-1(7) , 750) Riley Pr.

—The Secret of Mermaid Island. 2003. 136p. (J). mass mkt. 5.99 (978-0-9728958-0-4(9)) Riley Pr.

Walton, O. F. Saved at Sea: A Young Boy in a Dramatic Rescue. (Illus.). 144p. (J). mass mkt. 5.99 (978-1-85792-795-5(8) , Christian Heritage) Christian Focus Pubns. GBR. *Dist:* Riverside.

Weber, Susan. Seal Island School. 2001. (Puffin Chapters Ser.). (Illus.). (J). (978-0-606-21423-0(2)) Tandem Library Bks.

Werlin, Nancy. Locked Inside. 2001. 272p. (YA). (gr. 7). mass mkt. 5.99 (978-0-440-22829-5(8) , Laurel Leaf) Random Hse. Children's Bks.

Wheeler, Lisa. Castaway Cats. Goembel, Ponder, illus. 2006. 32p. (J). (ps-2). 16.95 (978-0-689-86232-8(6) , Atheneum) Simon & Schuster Children's Publishing.

Wigington, Patti. Summer's Ashes. 2007. 208p. (YA). pap. 15.00 (*978-0-9766805-9-8(9)) Keene Publishing.

Wiley. The Extraordinary Adventures of Ordinary Basil: Island of the Volcano Monkeys. 2007. (J). pap. (*978-0-439-86133-5(0)) Blue Sky Pr.

Wilkes, A. Treasure Island. (Young Reading Ser.: Vol. 2). 64p. (J). (gr. 2 up). lib. bdg. 13.95 (978-1-58086-796-2(0) , Usborne) EDC Publishing.

Willson, Sarah. Castaways: The Rugrats Meet the Wild Thornberrys. 2003. (gr. k-3). lib. bdg. 14.15 (978-0-613-66354-0(3)) Tandem Library Bks.

Winfield, Arthur M. The Rover Boys on Snowshoe Island or the Old Lumberman's. 2006. (ENG.). 332p. per. 30.95 (*978-1-4286-4114-3(9)) Kessinger Publishing, LLC.

Wisner, Helyn. Seaside Sleuths: The Bald Head Island G. 2006. pap. 11.50 (*978-1-4259-1097-6(1)) AuthorHouse.

Wooding, Chris. Storm Thief. 320p. 2007. (J). pap. 8.99 (*978-0-439-86514-2(X) , Scholastic Paperbacks); 2006. (YA). pap. 16.99 (978-0-439-86513-5(1) , Orchard Bks.) Scholastic, Inc.

Wyss, Johann. The Swiss Family Robinson. 2006. (Illus.). 61p. (J). lib. bdg. 30.77 (*978-1-4242-1334-4(7)) Fitzgerald Bks.

Wyss, Johann David. Classic Starts: the Swiss Family Robinson. Akib, Jamel, illus. 2007. (Classic Starts Ser.). 160p. (J). 4.95 (978-1-4027-3694-0(0)) Sterling Publishing Co., Inc.

—The Swiss Family Robinson. unabr. ed. 2001. (Dover Juvenile Classics Ser.). 336p. (J). (gr. 4-7). pap. 3.50 (978-0-486-41660-1(7)) Dover Pubns., Inc.

—The Swiss Family Robinson. McKowen, Scott, illus. 2006. (Unabridged Classics Ser.). 352p. 9.95 (978-1-4027-2602-6(3)) Sterling Publishing Co., Inc.

—Swiss Family Robinson: A Classic Story about Initiative. 2003. (Illus.). 32p. per. 3.95 (978-0-9747133-5-3(5) , Values to Live By Classic Stories) Thomas, Frederic Inc.

—The Swiss Family Robinson: Critical Reading Series. 2002. (Great Illustrated Classics Ser.). (Illus.). 240p. (J). (gr. 3-8). 21.35 (978-1-57765-801-6(9) , ABDO & Daughters) ABDO Publishing Co.

—The Swiss Family Robinson: Critical Reading Series. 1999. 336p. (J). (gr. 5-7). pap. 6.50 (978-0-440-41594-7(2) , Yearling) Random Hse. Children's Bks.

—Swiss Family Robinson: With a Discussion of Teamwork. Butterfield, Ned, illus. 2003. (Values in Action Illustrated Classics Ser.). 191p. (J). (978-1-59203-036-1(X)) Learning Challenge, Inc.

Wyss, Johann David, illus. The Swiss Family Robinson. 2004. reprint ed. pap. 30.95 (978-1-4191-5012-8(X)); pap. 1.99 (978-1-4192-5012-5(4)) Kessinger Publishing, LLC.

Wyss, Johann David & McGraw-Hill - Jamestown Education Staff. The Swiss Family Robinson: Critical Reading Series. unabr. ed. 1999. (Wordsworth Classics Ser.). (gr. 6-12). pap. 16.64 (978-0-89061-111-1(4) , 9780890611111) Jamestown.

ISLANDS OF THE PACIFIC

see also Borneo

Beales, R. A. James Cook: The Pacific Coast & Beyond. 2005. (In the Footsteps of Explorers Ser.). (Illus.). 32p. (J). (gr. 3-9). (978-0-7787-2415-5(8)); pap. (978-0-7787-2451-3(4)) Crabtree Publishing Co.

Broderick, Enid. Capt. James Cook. 2003. (Great Explorers Ser.). (Illus.). 48p. (J). (gr. 5 up). pap. 14.60 (978-0-8368-5174-8(9) , World Almanac Library) Stevens, Gareth Inc.

—Captain James Cook. 2001. (Great Explorers Ser.). (Illus.). 48p. (J). (gr. 5 up). lib. bdg. 30.00 (978-0-8368-5014-7(9) , World Almanac Library) Stevens, Gareth Inc.

Coffey, Maria & Pearson, Debora. Jungle Islands: My South Sea Adventure. Goering, Dag, photos by. 2000. (Travel Adventure Ser.). (Illus.). 88p. (J). (gr. 3 up). pap. 14.95 (978-1-55037-596-1(2)); lib. bdg. 26.95 (978-1-55037-597-8(0)) Annick Pr., Ltd. CAN. *Dist:* Firefly Bks., Ltd.

Currie, Stephen. Australia & the Pacific Islands. 2004. (J). (gr. 7-10). 29.95 (978-1-59018-496-7(3) , Lucent Bks.) Thomson Gale.

Dalal, Anita. Myths of Oceania. 2002. (Mythic World Ser.). (Illus.). 48p. (J). lib. bdg. 27.12 (978-0-7398-4978-1(6)) Raintree.

Darian-Smith, Kate. Australia, Antarctica, & the Pacific. (Continents of the World Ser.). 2006. (Illus.). 64p. (YA). (gr. 7-10). lib. bdg. 32.67 (978-0-8368-5912-6(X)); 2005. (J). (978-0-8368-5919-5(7)) Stevens, Gareth Inc. (World Almanac Library).

Franklin, Sharon, et al. Southwest Pacific: Understanding Geography & History Through Art. 1999. (Artisans Around the World Ser.). (Illus.). 48p. (J). (gr. 4-8). lib. bdg. 27.12 (978-0-7398-0120-8(1)) Raintree.

Kalman, Bobbie & Sjonger, Rebecca. Explora Australia y Oceania. 2007. (SPA.). 32p. (gr. 6-10). pap. (*978-0-7787-8298-8(0)) Crabtree Publishing Co.

—Explore Australia & Oceania. 2007. (Explore the Continents Ser.). (Illus.). 32p. (J). (gr. 1-7). (*978-0-7787-3073-6(5)); pap. (*978-0-7787-3087-3(5)) Crabtree Publishing Co.

Leppman, Elizabeth J. Australia & the Pacific. 2005. (Modern World Cultures Ser.). (Illus.). 128p. (J). (gr. 6-12). 30.00 (978-0-7910-8150-1(8) , Chelsea Hse.) Facts On File, Inc.

McClish, Bruce. Southeast Asia, Australia, & the Pacific Realm. 2007. (J). (*978-1-4034-9900-4(4)); pap. (*978-1-4034-9909-7(8)) Heinemann Library.

Petrie, Kristin. James Cook. 2004. (Explorers Set I Ser.). (Illus.). 32p. (J). (gr. k-6). lib. bdg. 22.78 (978-1-59197-596-0(4)) ABDO Publishing Co.

Proujan, Carl. Oceania & Antarctica. 2003. (World Cultures, People & Places Ser.). (Illus.). 64p. (J). (978-0-7922-4367-0(6)); (978-0-7922-4366-3(8)) National Geographic Society.

ISLANDS OF THE PACIFIC—FICTION

David, Christopher. Denholme & the Skeleton Mystery. 2006. 274p. pap. (*978-1-4120-8014-9(2)) Trafford Publishing.

Jackson, Dave. Sinking the Dayspring: John G. Paton. 2001. (gr. 3-6). lib. bdg. 14.15 (978-0-613-82919-9(0)) Tandem Library Bks.

Lawrence, Iain. The Cannibals. 2005. 240p. (J). (gr. 7-9). lib. bdg. 17.99 (978-0-385-90110-9(0) , Delacorte Bks. for Young Readers) Random Hse. Children's Bks.

—The Cannibals: The Curse of the Jolly Stone Trilogy. 2007. (Curse of the Jolly Stone Trilogy Ser.: Bk. II). 240p. (YA). (gr. 7 up). mass mkt. 6.50 (978-0-440-41933-4(6) , Laurel Leaf) Random Hse. Children's Bks.

Rosado, Maria. Family Face-off. 2000. (gr. 3-6). lib. bdg. 11.80 (978-0-613-25120-4(2)) Tandem Library Bks.

Wells, Helen. Cherry Ames, Chief Nurse. 2005. (YA). pap. (978-0-9771597-3-4(6)) Springer.

ISLANDS OF THE PACIFIC—HISTORY

Bingham, Jane. Captain Cook's Pacific Explorations. 2007. (J). (*978-1-4034-9756-7(7)) Heinemann Library.

Gaines, Ann Graham. Captain Cook Explores the Pacific in World History. 2002. (In World History Ser.). (Illus.). 128p. (J). (gr. 5-12). lib. bdg. 26.60 (978-0-7660-1823-5(7)) Enslow Pubs., Inc.

Greig, Charlotte. Oceania. 2002. (Cultures & Costumes Ser.). (Illus.). 64p. (J). (gr. 7 up). lib. bdg. (978-1-59084-432-8(7)) Mason Crest Pubs.

Harmon, Daniel E. Explorers of the South Pacific. 2002. (Exploration & Discovery Ser.). (Illus.). 64p. (YA). (gr. 5 up). lib. bdg. (978-1-59084-057-3(7)) Mason Crest Pubs.

Meltzer, Milton, et al. Captain James Cook: Three Times Around the World. 2001. (Great Explorations Ser.). (Illus.). 80p. (J). (gr. 4 up). lib. bdg. 28.50 (978-0-7614-1240-3(9) , Benchmark Bks.) Cavendish, Marshall Corp.

O'Brien, Patrick. The Mutiny on the Bounty. O'Brien, Patrick, illus. 2007. (Illus.). 40p. (J). (gr. 3-6). 17.95 (978-0-8027-9587-8(0)); 18.85 (978-0-8027-9588-5(9)) Walker & Co.

Shields, Charles J. James Cook & the Exploration of the Pacific. 2001. (Explorers of New Worlds Ser.). (Illus.). (J). 63p. pap. 25.00 (978-0-7910-6423-8(9)); 64p. 25.00 (978-0-7910-6422-1(0)) Facts On File, Inc. (Chelsea Hse.).

ISLE OF ECHOES (IMAGINARY PLACE)—FICTION

Roberts, Katherine. Crystal Mask. 2003. 272p. (J). (Echorium Sequence Ser.). 5.99 (978-0-439-44083-7(1) , Chicken Hse., The); Vol. 2. (Echorium Sequence Ser.: Vol. 2). pap. 4.99 (978-0-439-51147-6(X)) Scholastic, Inc.

—Crystal Mask, Vol. 2. Ontiveros, Martin & Down, Chris, illus. 2002. (Echorium Sequence Ser.: Vol. 2). 256p. (J). (gr. 4 up). pap. 15.95 (978-0-439-33864-6(6) , Chicken Hse., The) Scholastic, Inc.

—Crystal Mask. 2003. (gr. 3-6). lib. bdg. 13.00 (978-0-613-82493-4(8)) Tandem Library Bks.

—Dark Quetzal, Bk. 3. 2003. (Echorium Sequence Ser.: Vol. 3). 256p. (J). pap. 15.95 (978-0-439-45697-5(5) , Chicken Hse., The) Scholastic, Inc.

—Song Quest. (Illus.). (J). (gr. 5 up). 2000. 240p. pap. 5.95 (978-1-902618-94-4(7)); 1999. 236p. 16.95 (978-1-902618-28-9(9)) Element Children's Bks.

—Song Quest, Vol. 1. 2002. (Echorium Sequence Ser.: Vol. 1). 272p. (J). (gr. 4 up). pap. 5.99 (978-0-439-33892-9(1) , Chicken Hse., The) Scholastic, Inc.

ISRAEL

Aretha, David. Israel in the News: Past, Present, & Future. 2006. (Middle East Nations in the News Ser.). (Illus.). 128p. (J). lib. bdg. 33.27 (978-1-59845-028-6(X) , MyReportLinks.com Bks.) Enslow Pubs., Inc.

Bacon, Josephine. Cooking the Israeli Way. 2nd rev. exp. ed. 2002. (Easy Menu Ethnic Cookbooks). (Illus.). 72p. (J). (gr. 5-12). 25.26 (978-0-8225-4112-7(2) , Lerner Pubns.) Lerner Publishing Group.

Blumenthal, Scott. The Great Israel Scavenger Hunt. 2003. (Illus.). 96p. (J). 8.95 (978-0-87441-711-1(2)) Behrman Hse., Inc.

Boraas, Tracey. Israel. 2002. (Countries & Cultures Ser.). (Illus.). 64p. (J). (gr. 4). lib. bdg. 23.93 (978-0-7368-0938-2(4) , Bridgestone Bks.) Capstone Pr., Inc.

Burstein, Chaya M. A Kid's Catalog of Israel. Burstein, Chaya M., illus. rev. ed. 1998. (Jps Kids' Catalog Ser.). (Illus.). 288p. pap. 15.95 (978-0-8276-0651-7(6)) Jewish Pubn. Society.

Costain, Meredith & Collins, Paul, eds. Welcome to Israel. 2001. (Countries of the World Ser.). (Illus.). 32p. (J). 28.00 (978-0-7910-6876-2(5) , Chelsea Hse.) Facts On File, Inc.

Dietrick, Ellen. It's Israel's Birthday. Cohen, Tod, illus. 2008. (J). lib. bdg. (*978-0-8225-7668-6(6)) Kar-Ben Publishing.

Finkelstein, Norman H. Friends Indeed: The Special Relationship of Israel & the United States. 1998. (Single Titles Ser.: up). (Illus.). 176p. (gr. 7 up). lib. bdg. 24.90 (978-0-7613-0114-1(3) , Twenty-First Century Bks.) Lerner Publishing Group.

Fisher, Frederick. Israel. 1999. (Countries of the World Ser.). (Illus.). 96p. (J). (gr. 6 up). lib. bdg. 30.00 (978-0-8368-2319-6(2)) Stevens, Gareth Inc.

Fontes, Justine & Fontes, Ron. Israel. (to Z Ser.). (J). 2004. (gr. 2-4). pap. 6.95 (978-0-516-26811-8(2)); 2003. (Illus.). 40p. 24.50 (978-0-516-24560-7(0)) Scholastic Library Publishing. (Children's Pr.).

Garfinkle, Adam M. Israel. 2003. (Modern Middle East Nations & Their Strategic Place in the World Ser.). (Illus.). 112,128p. (YA). (gr. 7 up). lib. bdg. (978-1-59084-552-3(8)) Mason Crest Pubs.

Goldstein, Margaret J. Israel in Pictures. 80p. (YA). (gr. 5-12). 20.95 (978-1-58013-088-2(7)) Kar-Ben Publishing.

—Israel in Pictures. 2nd ed. 2004. (Visual Geography Series, Second Ser.). (Illus.). 80p. (J). (gr. 5-12). lib. bdg. 27.93 (978-0-8225-0935-6(0)) Lerner Publishing Group.

Gray, Susan Heinrichs. Israel. 2001. (First Reports). (Illus.). 48p. (J). (gr. 3 up). lib. bdg. 22.60 (978-0-7565-0129-7(6)) Compass Point Bks.

Green, Jen. Israel. 2001. (Nations of the World Ser.). (Illus.). 128p. (YA). (gr. 6-8). lib. bdg. 34.26 (978-0-7398-1286-0(6)) Raintree.

Gresko, Marcia S. Israel. 48p. 16.95 (978-0-929371-63-4(1)) Kar-Ben Publishing.

—Israel. (Ticket to Ser.). (Illus.). 48p. 2005. (gr. 2-4). 22.60 (978-1-57505-143-7(5)); 2000. (J). (gr. 3-5). lib. bdg. 22.60 (978-1-57505-118-5(4) , Carolrhoda Bks.) Lerner Publishing Group.

—A Ticket to Israel. 2003. (Illus.). 48p. (J). (gr. 1-2). 16.95 (978-1-58013-077-6(1)) Kar-Ben Publishing.

Grossman, Laurie. Children of Israel. Grossman, Laurie, photos by. 2003. (Illus.). 48p. (J). 17.95 (978-1-58013-072-1(0)) Kar-Ben Publishing.

—Children of Israel. 2000. (World's Children Ser.). (Illus.). 48p. (J). (gr. 3-6). (978-1-57505-448-3(5) , Carolrhoda Bks.) Lerner Publishing Group.

—Colors of Israel. Byers, Helen, illus. (Colors of the World Ser.). 24p. 2005. (gr. 3-6). lib. bdg. 19.93 (978-1-57505-382-0(9)); 2003. (J). (gr. 1-4). pap. 5.95 (978-1-57505-523-7(6)) Lerner Publishing Group.

—Colors of Israel. 2001. (gr. k-3). lib. bdg. 14.10 (978-0-613-79233-2(5)) Tandem Library Bks.

Harcourt School Publishers Staff. Place of Peace & Hope. 3rd ed. 2002. (Horizons Ser.). (Illus.). (J). pap. 7.30 (978-0-15-333626-3(9)) Harcourt Schl. Pubs.

Hintz, Martin. Israel. rev. ed. 2006. (Enchantment of the World, Second Ser.). (Illus.). 144p. (J). (gr. 5-9). 36.00 (978-0-516-24854-7(5) , Children's Pr.) Scholastic Library Publishing.

Hughes, Christopher. Israel. 2003. (Nations in Conflict Ser.). (Illus.). 48p. (J). 24.95 (978-1-56711-525-3(X) , Blackbirch Pr., Inc.) Thomson Gale.

Italia, Bob. Israel. 2001. (Countries Ser.). (Illus.). 40p. (J). (gr. k-6). lib. bdg. 22.78 (978-1-57765-497-1(8) , Checkerboard Library) ABDO Publishing Co.

Kalman, Bobbie. Israel: The People. 1999. (Lands, Peoples, & Cultures Ser.). (Illus.). (J). (978-0-606-18062-7(1)) Tandem Library Bks.

Landau, Elaine. Israel. 1999. (True Bks.). (Illus.). 48p. (J). (gr. 3-5). 25.00 (978-0-516-20983-8(3) , Children's Pr.) Scholastic Library Publishing.

—Israel. 1999. (gr. 3-6). lib. bdg. 15.25 (978-0-613-54582-2(6)) Tandem Library Bks.

Lenhart, Crystal. One Nation under God: A Family Study of Biblical Israel. 2003. (Illus.). 76p. (J). (gr. 5 up). pap. 12.00 (978-1-886987-16-6(5)) House of David.

Matray, James I., ed. Arbitrary Borders: Political Boundaries in World History. (Illus.). (gr. 9-13). lib. bdg. 242.55 (978-0-7910-8422-9(1) , Chelsea Hse.) Facts On File, Inc.

Mesenas, Geraldine & Fisher, Frederick. Welcome to Israel. 2001. (Welcome to My Country Ser.). (Illus.). 48p. (J). (gr. 2 up). lib. bdg. 26.00 (978-0-8368-2519-0(5)) Stevens, Gareth Inc.

Nations of the World: Includes: Brazil, Egypt, Germany, Israel, 4 bks., Set. 2001. (Illus.). (YA). (gr. 5-9). lib. bdg. 95.92 (978-0-7398-4289-8(7)) Raintree.

Park, Ted. Israel. 2000. (Taking Your Camera to Ser.). (Illus.). 32p. (J). (gr. 4-7). lib. bdg. 22.83 (978-0-7398-1801-5(5)) Raintree.

—Taking Your Camera To... Includes: Australia, Brazil, Canada, Egypt, France, Israel, Italy, Japan, Mexico, Panama, Russia, Spain, 12 bks., Set. 2000. (Taking Your Camera to Ser.). (Illus.). (J). (gr. 4-7). 273.96 (978-0-7398-3096-3(1)) Raintree.

—Taking Your Camera to Israel. 1999. (Illus.). pap. (978-0-7398-2154-1(7)) Steck-Vaughn.

Randall, Ronne. Israel. 1999. (Food & Festivals Ser.). 32p. (J). (gr. 1-4). lib. bdg. 25.69 (978-0-8172-5759-0(4)) Raintree.

—Israel. 1999. (Food & Festivals Ser.). (Illus.). 32p. (J). (gr. 2-5). pap. 6.95 (978-0-7398-0959-4(8)) Steck-Vaughn.

Richardson, Adele. Israel. 2006. (Illus.). 24p. (J). 15.95 (978-1-58341-447-7(9) , Creative Education) Creative Co., The.

Richardson, Adele D. Israel. 2000. (Let's Investigate Ser.). (Illus.). 32p. (J). (gr. 4-7). lib. bdg. (978-1-58341-033-2(3) , Creative Education) Creative Co., The.

Rivlin, Lilly & Gevirtz, Gila. Welcome to Israel! 2000. (Illus.). 128p. (J). (gr. 4-6). pap. 12.95 (978-0-87441-692-3(2)) Behrman Hse., Inc.

Roop, Peter & Roop, Connie. A Visit to Israel. (Visit To... Ser.). 32p. pap. 6.50 (978-1-4034-4149-2(9)) Heinemann Library.

Schemenauer, Elma. Welcome to Israel. 2007. (Welcome to the World Ser.). 32p. (J). (gr. 1-5). 27.07 (*978-1-59296-917-3(8)) Child's World, Inc.

Schroeder, Holly. Israel ABCs: A Book about the People & Places of Israel. Wolf, Claudia, illus. 2004. (Country ABCs Ser.). 32p. (J). (gr. k-5). 23.93 (978-1-4048-0179-0(0)) Picture Window Bks.

Sha'Ban, Mervet A., et al. If You Could Be My Friend: Letters of Mervet Akram Sha'Ban & Galit Fink. Ellbaz, Ariane & Khadige, Beatrice, trs. from FRE. 1998. (Illus.). 118p. (YA). (gr. 5-9). 16.99 (978-0-531-33113-2(X) , Orchard Bks.) Scholastic, Inc.

—If You Could Be My Friend: Letters of Mervet Akram Sha'Ban & Galit Fink. Elbaz, Ariane & Khadige, Beatrice, trs. from FRE. 1998. (Illus.). 118p. (YA). (gr. 5-9). pap. 15.95 (978-0-531-30113-5(3) , Orchard Bks.) Scholastic, Inc.

Smith, Debbie. Israel - The Culture. 1998. (Lands, Peoples & Cultures Ser.). (Illus.). 32p. (J). (gr. 4-5). (978-0-86505-231-4(X)); pap. (978-0-86505-311-3(1)) Crabtree Publishing Co.

—Israel - The Land. 1998. (Lands, Peoples & Cultures Ser.). (Illus.). 32p. (J). (gr. 4-5). (978-0-86505-229-1(8)); pap. (978-0-86505-309-0(X)) Crabtree Publishing Co.

—Israel - The People. 1998. (Lands, Peoples & Cultures Ser.). (Illus.). 32p. (J). (gr. 4-5). (978-0-86505-230-7(1)); pap. (978-0-86505-310-6(3)) Crabtree Publishing Co.

—Israel the Culture. 1999. (gr. 3-6). lib. bdg. 16.40 (978-0-613-11686-2(0)) Tandem Library Bks.

—Israel the Land. 1999. (gr. 3-6). lib. bdg. 16.40 (978-0-613-11687-9(9)) Tandem Library Bks.

—Israel the People. 1999. (gr. 3-6). lib. bdg. 16.40 (978-0-613-11688-6(7)) Tandem Library Bks.

Sofer, Barbara. Keeping Israel Safe: The Israel Defense Forces. 2008. (Israel Ser.). (J). lib. bdg. 16.95 (*978-0-8225-7221-3(4)) Kar-Ben Publishing.

Spengler, Kremena. Israel: A Question & Answer Book. 2005. (Fact Finders Ser.). (Illus.). 32p. (J). 22.60 (978-0-7368-3753-8(1)) Capstone Pr., Inc.

Stotksy, Sandra. Israel. 1999. (Major World Nations Ser.). (Illus.). 144p. (YA). (gr. 4-7). lib. bdg. 21.95 (978-0-7910-4742-2(3) , Chelsea Hse.) Facts On File, Inc.

Thoennes, Kristin. Israel. 1999. (Countries of the World Ser.). (Illus.). 126p. (J). (gr. 2-3). 18.60 (978-0-7368-0152-2(9) , Bridgestone Bks.) Capstone Pr., Inc.

Thomas. In the Land of Milk & Honey. 1999. 32p. (J). 15.95 (978-0-06-025383-7(5)); 15.89 (978-0-06-025384-4(3)) HarperCollins Pubs.

Waldman, Neil. Masada. Waldman, Neil, illus. 2003. (Illus.). 64p. (YA). (gr. 4-6). 18.95 (978-1-59078-063-3(9)) Boyds Mills Pr.

—Masada. Waldman, Neil, illus. 1998. (Illus.). 64p. (J). (gr. 5-9). 16.00 (978-0-688-14481-4(0)) HarperCollins Pubs.

—The Never-Ending Greenness: We Made Israel Bloom. Waldman, Neil, illus. 2003. (Illus.). 32p. (YA). (gr. k-2). 16.95 (978-1-59078-064-0(7)) Boyds Mills Pr.

Walsh, Kieran. Israel. 2003. (Countries in the News Ser.). (Illus.). 24p. (J). 25.64 (978-1-58952-679-2(1)) Rourke Publishing, LLC.

Webster, Matt. Inside Israel's Mossad: The Institute for Intelligence & Special Tasks. 2005. (Inside the World's Most Famous Intelligence Agencies Ser.). (Illus.). 64p. (YA). (gr. 7-12). lib. bdg. 26.50 (978-0-8239-3815-5(8)) Rosen Publishing Group, Inc., The.

Woolf, Alex. Focus on Israel. 2006. (Illus.). 64p. (J). pap. (*978-0-8368-6742-8(4)); (gr. 5-7). lib. bdg. 33.27 (*978-0-8368-6735-0(1)) Stevens, Gareth Inc. (World Almanac Library).

ISRAEL—ANTIQUITIES

Morley, Jacqueline & James, John. The Temple at Jerusalem. 2001. (Magnifications Ser.). (Illus.). 48p. (J). (gr. 3-8). 18.95 (978-0-87226-653-7(2) , Bedrick, Peter Bks.) School Specialty Publishing.

ISRAEL—FICTION

Abraham, Michelle Shapiro. My Cousin Tamar Lives in Israel. Koffsky, Ann D., illus. 2006. (J). (ps). pap. 6.95 (*978-0-8074-0989-3(8)) URJ Pr.

Carmi, Daniella. Samir & Yonatan. Lotan, Yael, tr. from HEB. 2002. 192p. (J). (gr. 3-7). pap. 4.99 (978-0-439-13523-8(0) , Scholastic Paperbacks) Scholastic, Inc.

—Samir & Yonatan. 2000. (gr. 3-6). lib. bdg. 13.00 (978-0-613-45824-5(9)) Tandem Library Bks.

—Samir & Yonatan. 2000. (Illus.). 192p. (J). (gr. 3-7). pap. 15.95 (978-0-439-13504-7(4) , Levine, Arthur A. Bks.) Scholastic, Inc.

Clinton, Cathryn. Stone in My Hand. Johnson, Peter, illus. 2002. 192p. (YA). (gr. 6-12). 15.99 (978-0-7636-1388-4(6)) Candlewick Pr.

Dillon, Sally Pierson. Exile of the Chosen: God's Heroes from Solomon to Malachi. 2003. 223p. (J). pap. 10.99 (978-0-8280-1703-9(4) , 58-710) Review & Herald Publishing Assn.

Elkeles, Simone. How to Ruin a Summer Vacation. 2006. 240p. (J). pap. 9.95 (978-0-7387-0961-1(1) , Flux) Llewellyn Pubns.

Kass, Pnina Moed. Real Time. 2006. 192p. (YA). (gr. 7). reprint ed. pap. 7.99 (978-0-618-69174-6(X)) Houghton Mifflin Co.

—Real Time. 2004. 192p. (YA). (gr. 7 up). 15.00 (978-0-618-44203-4(0) , Clarion Bks.) Houghton Mifflin Co. Trade & Reference Div.

Kir-on, Callanitte. The 3-D Files: Prisoner on the Loose. 2003. (Illus.). (J). 10.95 (978-1-931681-47-6(3)) Israel Bk. Shop.

Levine, Anna. Running on Eggs. 1999. 128p. (J). (gr. 5-9). 15.95 (978-0-8126-2875-3(6)) Cricket Bks.

Levitin, Sonia. Singing Mountain. 2000. (978-0-606-17938-6(0)) Tandem Library Bks.

McOmber, Rachel B., ed. McOmber Phonics Storybooks: Razz Visits Raz in Israel. rev. ed. (Illus.). (J). (978-0-944991-75-6(0)) Swift Learning Resources.

Oz, Amos. Soumchi. 2003. 53p. pap. 7.95 (978-1-59264-038-6(9)) Toby Pr.

Rahav, Sivan. Ha-Zeman Ha-tsa'ir. 2000. (HEB., Illus.). 224p. (978-965-448-879-2(5)) Miskal.

Ramsay, Elizabeth. The Burning Light. Katz, Avi, illus. 2005. 144p. (J). (gr. 4-9). 14.95 (978-1-930143-43-2(5)); pap. 9.95 (978-1-930143-44-9(3)) Pitspopany Pr. (Devora Publishing).

Rouss, Sylvia A. Sammy Spider's First Israel: A Book about the Five Senses. Kahn, Katherine Janus, illus. 2002. 32p. (J). (ps-3). pap. 7.95 (978-1-58013-035-6(6)) Kar-Ben Publishing.

—Sammy Spider's First Israel: A Book about the Five Senses. 2002. lib. bdg. 16.40 (978-0-613-81763-9(X)) Tandem Library Bks.

—Sammy Spider's Israel Fun Book. (Illus.). 24p. (J). (ps-3). pap. (978-1-58013-119-3(0)) Kar-Ben Publishing.

Sandell, Lisa Ann. The Weight of the Sky. 2006. 304p. (J). (gr. 7). 16.99 (978-0-670-06028-3(3) , Viking Juvenile) Penguin Group (USA) Inc.

Semel, Nava & Silveira, Carlos. Clases de Vuelo. Silveira, Carlos, tr. 2002. (Joven Coleccion Ser.). (SPA., Illus.). 206p. (978-84-89804-06-7(0)) Loguez Ediciones ESP. *Dist:* Lectorum Pubns., Inc.

Stein, Evaleen. Pepin: A Tale of Twelfth Night. Matsubara, T., illus. 2004. reprint ed. pap. 22.95 (978-1-4179-4325-8(4)) Kessinger Publishing, LLC.

Stein, Tammar. Light Years: A Novel. 2005. 272p. (J). (gr. 9). lib. bdg. 17.99 (978-0-375-93023-2(X) , Knopf Bks. for Young Readers) Random Hse. Children's Bks.

Zeyv, Sender. Aleph Shin: A Novel for the Sixth Millennium, Revised Edition. rev. ed. 2002. (Illus.). 480p. lib. bdg. 23.95 (978-0-9677044-4-9(8)) TMS Publishing Co.

ISRAEL—HISTORY

Bard, Mitchell G. The Founding of the State of Israel. 2003. (gr. 7-12). lib. bdg. 30.35 (978-0-613-73892-7(6)) Tandem Library Bks.

Claybourne, Anna. Golda Meir. 2003. (Leading Lives Ser.). (Illus.). 64p. (J). lib. bdg. 28.50 (978-1-4034-0835-8(1)) Heinemann Library.

Corona, Laurel. Israel. 2002. (Modern Nations of the World Ser.). (Illus.). 112p. (J). (gr. 7-10). 29.95 (978-1-59018-115-7(8) , Lucent Bks.) Thomson Gale.

Gallagher, Michael. Israel & Palestine. 2005. (Illus.). 44p. (J). (gr. 6-9). lib. bdg. 29.95 (978-1-58340-605-2(0)) Smart Apple Media.

Greenfeld, Howard. A Promise Fulfilled: Theodor Herzl, Chaim Weizmann, David Ben-Gurion, & the Creation of the State of Israel. 2005. (Illus.). 144p. (J). (gr. 7 up). 18.99 (978-0-06-051504-1(X)); 19.89 (978-0-06-051505-8(8)) HarperCollins Pubs.

Israel in Pictures. 2003. (Illus.). 64p. (J). 15.95 (978-1-58013-076-9(3)) Kar-Ben Publishing.

Kurtis, Arlene & Lerman, Jona. The Stone Pillow: The Life & Times of Jona Lerman. 1999. (YA). (gr. 7-12). per. 15.00 (978-0-9676869-0-5(3)) Globus Bks.

Lehman, Emil. Israel: Idea & Reality. (Illus.). (J). (gr. 8 up). 3.95 (978-0-8381-0205-3(0) , 10-205) United Synagogue of America Bk. Service.

Marsh, Carole. Golda Meir. 2002. (One Thousand Readers Ser.). (Illus.). 12p. (J). (gr. k-4). 2.95 (978-0-635-01513-6(7) , 15137) Gallopade International.

Roop, Peter & Roop, Connie. Israel. 2003. (Illus.). 32p. (J). (gr. k-2). lib. bdg. 14.75 (978-0-613-87164-8(2)) Tandem Library Bks.

Sherman, Josepha. Your Travel Guide to Ancient Israel. 80p. (J). (gr. 4-8). 19.95 (978-1-58013-093-6(3)) Kar-Ben Publishing.

—Your Travel Guide to Ancient Israel. 2005. (Passport to History Ser.). (Illus.). 96p. 26.60 (978-0-8225-3072-5(4)) Lerner Publishing Group.

Slavicek, Louise Chipley. Israel. 2002. (Creation of the Modern Middle East Ser.). (Illus.). 125p. (gr. 6-12). 35.00 (978-0-7910-6511-2(1) , Chelsea Hse.) Facts On File, Inc.

Smith, Debbie. Israel. 1999. (Culture Ser.). (978-0-606-18061-0(3)) Tandem Library Bks.

Wagner, Heather Lehr. Israel & the Arab World. 2002. (People at Odds Ser.). (Illus.). 112p. (J). (gr. 5 up). 30.00 (978-0-7910-6705-5(X) , Chelsea Hse.) Facts On File, Inc.

Worth, Richard. The Arab-Israeli Conflict. 2006. (Open for Debate Ser.). (Illus.). 127p. (J). (gr. 7 up). lib. bdg. 39.93 (978-0-7614-2295-2(1) , Benchmark Bks.) Cavendish, Marshall Corp.

Zeigler, Donald J. Israel. (Modern World Nations Ser.). (Illus.). (gr. 6-12). 2003. 200p. pap. 30.00 (978-0-7910-7177-9(4)); 2002. 150p. 30.00 (978-0-7910-7235-6(5)); 2nd rev. ed. 2006. 120p. (J). 30.00 (978-0-7910-9210-1(0)) Facts On File, Inc. (Chelsea Hse.).

ISRAEL—HISTORY—FICTION

Kaplan, Kathy Walden. The Dog of Knots. 2005. 139p. (J). pap. 7.50 (978-0-8028-5274-8(2)) Eerdmans, William B. Publishing Co.

Shapiro, David L. Sara's Journey. 2005. 293p. (YA). (gr. 7-12). pap. 12.95 (978-0-8276-0776-7(8)) Jewish Pubn. Society.

ISRAEL—POLITICS AND GOVERNMENT

Brackett, Virginia. Menachem Begin. 2002. (Major World Leaders Ser.). (Illus.). 112p. (gr. 6-12). 30.00 (978-0-7910-6946-2(X) , Chelsea Hse.) Facts On File, Inc.

Crompton, Samuel Willard. Ariel Sharon. 2nd rev. ed. 2007. (Modern World Leaders Ser.). 112p. (J). (gr. 6-12). 30.00 (***978-0-7910-9263-7(1)*** , Chelsea Hse.) Facts On File, Inc.

Ellis, Deborah. Three Wishes: Palestinian & Israeli Children Speak. 2006. (Illus.). 144p. (J). pap. 8.95 (978-0-88899-645-9(4)) Groundwood Bks. CAN. *Dist:* Perseus Distribution.

Ellis, Deborah, ed. Three Wishes: Palestinian & Israeli Children Speak. 2004. (YA). 16.95 (978-0-88899-608-4(X) , Libros Tigrillo) Groundwood Bks. CAN. *Dist:* Transition Vendor.

Sommers, Michael A. Ehud Olmert. 2007. (J). (***978-1-4042-1904-5(8)***) Rosen Publishing Group, Inc., The.

Worth, Richard. Ariel Sharon. 2003. (Major World Leaders Ser.). (Illus.). 112p. (gr. 6-12). 30.00 (978-0-7910-7653-8(9) , Chelsea Hse.) Facts On File, Inc.

ISRAEL-ARAB BORDER CONFLICTS

see Jewish-Arab Relations

ISRAEL-ARAB WAR, 1967

Baughan, Brian. Arab-Israeli Relations, 1950-1979. 2007. (J). (***978-1-4222-0171-8(6)***) Mason Crest Pubs.

Blohm, Craig E. The Israeli-Palestinian Conflict. 2006. (J). (978-1-59018-645-9(1) , Lucent Bks.) Thomson Gale.

Frank, Mitch. Understanding the Holy Land: Answering Questions about the Israeli-Palestinian Conflict. 2005. (Illus.). 160p. (YA). (gr. 6). 17.99 (978-0-670-06032-0(1) , Viking Juvenile) Penguin Group (USA) Inc.

Gunderson, Cory Gideon. The Israeli-Palestinian Conflict. 2004. (World in Conflict-the Middle East Ser.). (Illus.). 48p. (J). (gr. 4-8). lib. bdg. 25.65 (978-1-59197-416-1(X)) ABDO Publishing Co.

King, John. Israel & Palestine. 2005. (Middle East Ser.). (Illus.). 56p. (J). (978-1-4109-1621-1(9)); pap. (978-1-4109-1627-3(8)) Raintree.

Matray, James I., ed. Arbitrary Borders: Political Boundaries in World History. (Illus.). (gr. 9-13). lib. bdg. 242.55 (978-0-7910-8422-9(1) , Chelsea Hse.) Facts On File, Inc.

Miller, Debra A. The Arab-Israeli Conflict. 2004. (Lucent Library of Conflict in the Middle East). (Illus.). 112p. (J). (gr. 7-10). 29.95 (978-1-59018-491-2(2) , Lucent Bks.) Thomson Gale.

Pendergast, Tom, et al. The Middle East Conflict. 2005. (Middle East Conflict Reference Library). (Illus.). lxvii, 267p. (J). 67.00 (978-0-7876-9456-2(8) , UXL) Thomson Gale.

ISRAELITES

see Jews

ISTANBUL (TURKEY)

Bator, Robert. Daily Life in Ancient & Modern Istanbul. Rothero, Chris, illus. 2000. (Cities Through Time Ser.). 64p. (gr. 5-12). 25.26 (978-0-8225-3217-0(4)) Lerner Publishing Group.

Bowden, Rob. Istanbul. 2007. (Global Cities Ser.). (Illus.). 64p. (J). (gr. 5-8). 30.00 (978-0-7910-8850-0(2) , Chelsea Hse.) Facts On File, Inc.

McNeese, Tim. Constantinople. 2003. (Sieges That Changed the World Ser.). (Illus.). 112p. (gr. 6-12). pap. 13.25 (978-0-7910-7527-2(3) , Chelsea Hse.) Facts On File, Inc.

ISTANBUL (TURKEY)—FICTION

Taylor, Cora. Adventure in Istanbul No. 1: The Spy Who Wasn't There. 2005. (Juvenile Novel Ser.). (Illus.). 176p. (J). (gr. 4-6). pap. 7.95 (978-1-55050-315-9(4)) Coteau Bks. CAN. *Dist:* Fitzhenry & Whiteside, Ltd.

ISTANBUL (TURKEY)—HISTORY

Bator, Robert. Daily Life in Ancient & Modern Istanbul. Rothero, Chris, illus. 2000. (Cities Through Time Ser.). 64p. (gr. 5-12). 25.26 (978-0-8225-3217-0(4)) Lerner Publishing Group.

Donovan, Sue. Istanbul, Once Constantinople. 2007. (Shockwave: History & Politics Ser.). (Illus.). 36p. (J). (gr. 4-6). lib. bdg. 25.00 (***978-0-531-17755-6(6)*** , Children's Pr.) Scholastic Library Publishing.

Fall of Rome/Byzantium DBA. 2003. spiral bd. 16.95 (978-1-56004-155-9(2)) Social Studies Schl. Service.

Feldman, Ruth Tenzer. The Fall of Constantinople. 2007. (J). lib. bdg. (***978-0-8225-5918-4(8)***) Twenty First Century Bks.

Lace, William W. The Unholy Crusade: The Ransacking of Medieval Constantinople. 2006. (Lucent Library of Historical Eras). 112p. (YA). (gr. 5-9). lib. bdg. 32.45 (978-1-59018-846-0(2) , Lucent Bks.) Thomson Gale.

McNeese, Tim. Constantinople: April 6-May 29, 1453. 2003. (Sieges That Changed the World Ser.). (Illus.). 112p. (gr. 6-12). 30.00 (978-0-7910-7102-1(2) , Chelsea Hse.) Facts On File, Inc.

ITALIAN AMERICANS

Aldridge, Rebecca. Italian Americans. 2003. (Immigrants in America Ser.). (J). pap. 9.95 (978-0-7910-7509-8(5)); (Illus.). 112p. (gr. 6-12). 30.00 (978-0-7910-7129-8(4)) Facts On File, Inc. (Chelsea Hse.).

Anderson, Dale. Italian Americans. 2006. (World Almanac Library of American Immigration). 48p. (J). pap. (978-0-8368-7325-2(4)); lib. bdg. (978-0-8368-7312-2(2)) Stevens, Gareth Inc. (World Almanac Library).

Behnke, Alison. Italians in America. 2005. (In America Ser.). (Illus.). 80p. (J). (gr. 5-8). lib. bdg. 27.93 (978-0-8225-4696-2(5)) Lerner Publishing Group.

Bowen, Richard. The Italian Americans. 2002. (Welcome to America Ser.). (Illus.). 64p. (J). (gr. 5 up). lib. bdg. (978-1-59084-114-3(X)) Mason Crest Pubs.

Bryan, Nichol. Italian Americans. 2004. (One Nation Ser.). (Illus.). 32p. (J). (gr. k-6). lib. bdg. 22.78 (978-1-57765-985-3(6)) ABDO Publishing Co.

Burgan, Michael. Italian Immigrants. 2004. (Immigration to the United States Ser.). (Illus.). 96p. (J). (gr. 4-9). 35.00 (978-0-8160-5681-1(1)) Facts On File, Inc.

Deiters, Erika & Deiters, Jim. The Italian Community in America. 2003. (J). pap. (978-1-58417-091-4(3)); lib. bdg. (978-1-58417-028-0(X)) Lake Street Pubs.

Fahey, Kathleen. Italians. 2000. (gr. 3-6). lib. bdg. 17.60 (978-0-613-32696-4(2)) Tandem Library Bks.

Murphy, Jim. Pick-and-Shovel Poet: The Journeys of Pascal D'Angelo. 2000. (Illus.). 176p. (J). (gr. 5-9). tchr. ed. 20.00 (978-0-395-77610-0(4) , Clarion Bks.) Houghton Mifflin Co. Trade & Reference Div.

Nickles, Greg. The Italians. 2000. 15.75 (978-0-606-22837-4(3)) Tandem Library Bks.

—The Italians: We Came to North America. 2006. (Illus.). 32p. (J). (gr. 4-8). reprint ed. 19.00 (978-0-7567-9906-9(6)) DIANE Publishing Co.

Parker, Lewis K. Why Italian Immigrants Came to America. 2003. (Reading Power Ser.). (Illus.). 24p. (J). lib. bdg. 17.25 (978-0-8239-6460-4(4) , PowerKids Pr.) Rosen Publishing Group, Inc., The.

Petrini, Catherine M. The Italian-Americans. 2001. (Immigrants in America Ser.). (Illus.). 104p. (YA). (gr. 4-12). 29.95 (978-1-56006-882-2(5) , LML00902-178205, Lucent Bks.) Thomson Gale.

Spinelli, Jerry. Knots in My Yo-Yo String: The Autobiography. 1998. (Illus.). 160p. (J). (gr. 5-8). pap. 10.95 (978-0-679-88791-1(1) , Knopf Bks. for Young Readers) Random Hse. Children's Bks.

—Knots in My Yo-Yo String: The Autobiography of a Kid. 1998. (J). (978-0-606-13553-5(7)) Tandem Library Bks.

—Knots in My Yo-Yo String: The Autobiography of a Kid. l.t. ed. 2000. (Illus.). 187p. (J). (gr. 8-12). 21.95 (978-0-7862-2973-4(X)) Thorndike Pr.

Weinberger, Kimberly. Journey to a New Land: An Oral History. Meers, Tony, illus. 2000. 32p. (J). (978-1-57255-813-7(X)); pap. (978-1-57255-812-0(1)) Mondo Publishing.

Yoder, Carolyn. Italian Americans. (We Are America Ser.). (Illus.). 32p. (J). 2003. (gr. 2-4). lib. bdg. (978-1-4034-0166-3(7)); 2002. pap. 6.95 (978-1-4034-0421-3(6)) Heinemann Library.

ITALIAN AMERICANS—FICTION

Ayres, Katherine. Under Copp's Hill. 2000. (American Girl Collection). (Illus.). (J). (978-0-606-20963-2(8)) Tandem Library Bks.

Bunting, Eve. A Picnic in October. Carpenter, Nancy, illus. 2004. 32p. (J). (gr. 1-4). lib. bdg. 13.20 (978-0-606-30433-7(9)) Tandem Library Bks.

Creech, Sharon. Granny Torrelli Makes Soup. Raschka, Chris, illus. 160p. (J). 2003. (gr. 3-6). 15.99 (978-0-06-029290-4(3) , HarperChildren's Audio); 2003. (gr. 4-7). lib. bdg. 16.89 (978-0-06-029291-1(1) , Cotler, Joanna Books); 2005. reprint ed. pap. 5.99 (978-0-06-440960-5(0) , Harper Trophy) HarperCollins Pubs.

Holm, Jennifer L. Penny from Heaven. 2007. (Illus.). 272p. (J). (gr. 5-7). 6.99 (978-0-375-83689-3(6) , Yearling) Random Hse. Children's Bks.

Hoobler, Dorothy & Hoobler, Thomas. The Second Decade: Voyages. Hoffman, Robin, illus. 2000. (Century Kids Ser.). 160p. (gr. 5-8). lib. bdg. 22.90 (978-0-7613-1601-5(9) , Twenty-First Century Bks.) Lerner Publishing Group.

—The 1970's: Arguments. Hoffman, Robin, illus. 2002. (Century Kids Ser.). 160p. (gr. 5-8). lib. bdg. 22.90 (978-0-7613-1607-7(8) , Twenty-First Century Bks.) Lerner Publishing Group.

Kroll, Steven. Sweet America. 2004. 172p. (J). lib. bdg. 16.92 (***978-1-4242-0773-2(8)***) Fitzgerald Bks.

—Sweet America: An Immigrant's Story. 2004. (Jamestown's American Portraits Ser.). (Illus.). 176p. (J). (gr. 5-7). pap. 4.95 (978-0-7696-3423-4(0) , Waterbird Bks.) School Specialty Publishing.

Kroll, Steven. When I Dream of Heaven. 2004. 156p. (J). lib. bdg. 16.92 (***978-1-4242-0770-1(3)***) Fitzgerald Bks.

Lasky, Kathryn. Home at Last: Sofia's Immigrant Diary. 2003. (My America Ser.). (Illus.). 112p. (J). pap. 12.95 (978-0-439-44963-2(4)); (gr. 3-4). pap. 4.99 (978-0-439-20644-0(8)) Scholastic, Inc.

Little Italy (Italians) 76p. (YA). (gr. 6-12). pap. 9.95 (978-0-8224-3677-5(9)) Globe Fearon Educational Publishing.

Martino, Carmela. Rosa, Sola. 2005. 256p. (J). (gr. 4-7). 15.99 (978-0-7636-2395-1(4)) Candlewick Pr.

Nobisso, Josephine. En Ingles, por Supuesto. Ziborova, Dasha, illus. 2003. Orig. Title: In English, of Course. (SPA.). 32p. 16.95 (978-0-940112-14-8(0)) Gingerbread Hse.

—En ingles, por Supuesto. Ziborova, Dasha, illus. 2003. Orig. Title: In English, of Course. (SPA.). 32p. pap. 8.95 (978-0-940112-16-2(7)) Gingerbread Hse.

Schirripa, Steve & Fleming, Charles. Nicky Deuce: Welcome to the Family. 2006. 176p. (gr. 5-8). 5.99 (978-0-440-42053-8(9) , Yearling) Random Hse. Children's Bks.

Schirripa, Steven R. & Fleming, Charles. Nicky Deuce: Home for the Holidays. 2006. 208p. (J). (gr. 4-7). 15.95 (978-0-385-73258-1(9)); lib. bdg. 17.99 (978-0-385-90276-2(X)) Random Hse. Children's Bks. (Delacorte Bks. for Young Readers).

Sirof, Harriet. Because She's My Friend. 2000. (gr. 3-6). lib. bdg. 23.40 (978-0-613-81931-2(4)) Tandem Library Bks.

—Because She's My Friend. 2000. 196p. (YA). (gr. 4-7). pap. 13.95 (978-0-595-09241-3(1) , Backinprint.com) iUniverse, Inc.

Smith, D. James. The Boys of San Joaquin. 240p. (J). (gr. 3-7). 2006. pap. 5.99 (978-1-4169-1619-2(9) , Aladdin); 2005. (Illus.). 16.99 (978-0-689-87606-6(8) , Atheneum) Simon & Schuster Children's Publishing.

Testa, Maria. Becoming Joe Dimaggio. Hunt, Scott, illus. 2002. 64p. (J). (gr. 5-9). 14.99 (978-0-7636-1537-6(4)) Candlewick Pr.

—Becoming Joe DiMaggio. Hunt, Scott, illus. 2005. 64p. (J). (gr. 5-9). reprint ed. pap. 5.99 (978-0-7636-2444-6(6)) Candlewick Pr.

Winthrop, Elizabeth. Franklin Delano Roosevelt: Letters from a Mill Town Girl. 2001. (Dear Mr. President Ser.). (Illus.). 128p. (J). (gr. 4-6). 9.95 (978-1-890817-61-9(9)) Winslow Pr.

Woodruff, Elvira. Orphan of Ellis Island. 2000. (gr. 5-8). lib. bdg. 12.40 (978-0-613-30079-7(3)) Tandem Library Bks.

ITALIAN LANGUAGE

Amery, Heather. First Thousand Words in Italian. Cartwright, Stephen, illus. rev. ed. 2004. (First Thousand Words Ser.). (ITA & ENG.). 64p. (J). (ps-6). 12.99 (978-0-7945-0286-7(5) , Usborne) EDC Publishing.

Berlitz Publishing Staff. New Basic Italian. rev. ed. 2003. (Berlitz Kids Language Pack Ser.). (ITA & ENG., Illus.). 26.95 (978-981-246-367-8(4) , 463674) Berlitz Publishing.

Berlitz Publishing Staff, ed. Italian. Demarest, Chris L., illus. 2nd ed. 2004. (Berlitz Kids Ser.). (ITA & ENG.). 128p. (ps-4). pap. 12.95 (978-981-246-390-6(9) , 463909) Berlitz Publishing.

Bruzzone, Catherine & Martineau, Susan. Hide & Speak Italian. Comfort, Louise, illus. 2005. (Hide & Speak Ser.). (ENG & ITA.). 32p. (J). pap. 7.95 (978-0-7641-3151-6(6)) Barron's Educational Series, Inc.

Dai Zovi, Lonnie. Canti,Ritmi e Rime: Chants, Rhythms & Rhymes for the Italian Classroom. 2004. 30.50 (978-0-935301-87-8(9)) Vibrante Pr.

Davies, H. & Iannaco, G. Italian Dictionary for Beginners. 2004. (Beginner's Dictionaries Ser.). (ITA.). 128p. (J). pap. 12.95 (978-0-7945-0290-4(3) , Usborne); lib. bdg. 20.95 (978-1-58086-555-5(0)) EDC Publishing.

Goodman, Marlene. Let's Learn Italian Picture Dictionary. 2003. (ENG & ITA., Illus.). 80p. 10.95 (978-0-07-140826-4(6) , 9780071408264) McGraw-Hill Cos., The.

Graziano, Carlo. Dialoghi Simpatici. (ITA.). (J). (gr. 7-10). audio 15.00 (978-0-8442-8034-9(8) , National Textbook Co.) McGraw-Hill/Contemporary.

Hippocrene Books Staff. Hippocrene Children's Illustrated Italian Dictionary: Italian-English/English-Italian. 1999. (ITA & ENG., Illus.). 96p. (gr. k-5). 14.95 (978-0-7818-0771-5(9)) Hippocrene Bks., Inc.

Hochstatter, Daniel J. Italian. 2003. (ENG & ITA., Illus.). 96p. 11.95 (978-0-07-140830-1(4) , 9780071408301) McGraw-Hill Cos., The.

Hochstatter, Daniel J., illus. Italian. 2003. (Just Look 'n Learn Picture Dictionary Ser.). (ITA & ENG.). 96p. (J). (gr. 4-7). pap. 11.95 (978-0-8442-8057-8(7) , 80577) McGraw-Hill Trade.

Lipton, Gladys C. & Colaneri, John. Beginning Italian Bilingual Dictionary. 3rd rev. ed. 1998. (Beginning Dictionaries in Foreign Languages Ser.). (ENG & ITA., Illus.). 180p. (gr. 4-7). pap. 10.99 (978-0-7641-0282-0(6)) Barron's Educational Series, Inc.

Mio Primo Dizionario Illustrato de Italia. (ITA., Illus.). pap. 9.95 (978-88-8148-840-7(X)) European Language Institute ITA. *Dist:* Distribooks, Inc.

Mio Primo Dizionario Illustrato de Italiano. (ITA., Illus.). pap. 9.95 (978-88-8148-835-3(3)); pap. 9.95 (978-88-8148-830-8(2)); pap. 9.95 (978-88-8148-845-2(0)) European Language Institute ITA. *Dist:* Distribooks, Inc.

The Rosetta Stone Language Library: Italian Level 2. (J). (gr. 1 up). 2005. cd-rom 239.00 (978-1-883972-73-8(6)); 1999. cd-rom 239.00 (978-1-883972-65-3(5)) Fairfield Language Technologies.

Rossi, Sophia. Buon Natale: Learning Songs & Traditions in Italian. Kelleher, Kathie, illus. 2007. (ITA.). (J). lib. bdg. 19.95 (***978-1-59972-067-8(1)***) Teach Me Tapes, Inc.

Un Tuffo Nel Mistero. 2000. (ITA., Illus.). 70p. (YA). (gr. 8-10). pap. 11.95 (978-88-8148-334-1(3)) European Language Institute ITA. *Dist:* Distribooks, Inc., Midwest European Pubns.

ITALIAN LANGUAGE—CONVERSATION AND PHRASE BOOKS

Gorjanc, Adele A. Italian Conversation: A Practical Guide for Students & Travelers. (Illus.). 202p. (J). pap. 11.95 (978-0-8283-1670-5(8)) Branden Bks.

Mallozzi, Fernando, et al. Amici Vol. 1: A Text for Beginners in Italian. Mallozzi, Luciana, illus. 2nd rev. ed. 1999. 321p. (YA). (gr. 7-8). 34.00 (978-0-9637279-4-7(X)) MVM Pubs.

Sansone, Emma. Getting to Know Italy & Italian. Woolley, Kim, illus. 2005. 33p. (J). reprint ed. pap. 13.00 (978-0-7567-9579-5(6)) DIANE Publishing Co.

Wightwick, Jane. Way Cool Italian Phrasebook. 2005. 96p. audio compact disk 12.95 (978-0-07-144841-3(1) , 9780071448413); (ENG & ITA., Illus.). pap. 6.95 (978-0-07-144843-7(8) , 9780071448437) McGraw-Hill Cos., The.

ITALIAN LANGUAGE—READERS

Alla Ricerca Dell'amico Scomparso. 2000. (ITA., Illus.). 70p. (YA). (gr. 6-8). 11.95 (978-88-8148-324-2(6)) European Language Institute ITA. *Dist:* Distribooks, Inc., Midwest European Pubns.

Apicella, A. Gaston: Level 3. 2000. (FRE & ENG., Illus.). (J). pap., act. bk. ed. 7.95 (978-88-8148-349-5(1)) European Language Institute ITA. *Dist:* Distribooks, Inc., Midwest European Pubns.

Burke, David. Cinderella (English to Italian - Level 1) Learn ITALIAN Through Fairy Tales Ser.). 2007. (Learn Italian Through Fairy Tales Ser.). (ENG & ITA., Illus.). (J). per. 14.95 incl. audio compact disk (***978-1-891888-77-9(3)***) Slangman Publishing.

—Goldilocks (English to Italian - Level 2) Learn ITALIAN Through Fairy Tales. 2007. (Learn Italian Through Fairy Tales Ser.). (ENG & ITA., Illus.). (J). per. 14.95 incl. audio compact disk (***978-1-891888-82-3(X)***) Slangman Publishing.

Il Diario di Val. 2000. (ITA.). 70p. (YA). (gr. 7-9). pap. 11.95 (978-88-8148-329-7(7)) European Language Institute ITA. *Dist:* Distribooks, Inc., Midwest European Pubns.

Eva & Vincent. 2000. (ITA & ENG., Illus.). 80p. (J). pap. 12.95 (978-88-8148-180-4(4)) European Language Institute ITA. *Dist:* Distribooks, Inc., Midwest European Pubns.

Mistero Alle Olimpiadi Dell' Acqua. 2000. (ITA., Illus.). 70p. (YA). (gr. 6-8). pap. 11.95 (978-88-8148-457-7(9)) European Language Institute ITA. *Dist:* Distribooks, Inc., Midwest European Pubns.

Mistero en las Olimpiadas Acuaticas. 2000. (SPA., Illus.). 70p. (YA). (gr. 6-8). pap. 11.95 (978-88-8148-456-0(0)) European Language Institute ITA. *Dist:* Distribooks, Inc., Midwest European Pubns.

Il Mondo di Gu. 2000. (ITA & ENG., Illus.). 80p. (J). pap. 12.95 (978-88-8148-173-6(1)) European Language Institute ITA. *Dist:* Distribooks, Inc., Midwest European Pubns.

Il Segno Nella Roccia. 2000. (ITA., Illus.). 70p. (YA). (gr. 8-10). pap. 11.95 (978-88-8148-467-6(6)) European Language Institute ITA. *Dist:* Distribooks, Inc., Midwest European Pubns.

La Sirenetta: Family, The Weather, Gardens, Underwater Life. 2000. (ITA & ENG., Illus.). 24p. (J). (gr. k-5). pap. 7.95 (978-88-8148-364-8(5)) European Language Institute ITA. *Dist:* Distribooks, Inc., Midwest European Pubns.

Il Soldatino di Piombo: Toys, In Town, At the Market, Prepositions of Place. 2000. (ITA & ENG., Illus.). 24p. (J). (gr. k-5). pap. 7.95 (978-88-8148-294-8(0)) European Language Institute ITA. *Dist:* Distribooks, Inc., Midwest European Pubns.

Il Souvenir Egizio. 2000. (ITA., Illus.). 70p. (YA). (gr. 7-9). pap. 11.95 (978-88-8148-447-8(1)) European Language Institute ITA. *Dist:* Distribooks, Inc., Midwest European Pubns.

ITALIAN LANGUAGE—STUDY AND TEACHING

Pattis, Anne-Francoise. Italian Coloring Book. 2nd ed. 2001. (Let's Learn Ser.). (ITA., Illus.). 64p. (J). pap. 9.95 incl. audio (978-0-8442-9276-2(1)) McGraw-Hill/Contemporary.

Wightwick, Jane. Way Cool Italian Phrasebook. 2005. (ENG & ITA., Illus.). 96p. pap. 6.95 (978-0-07-144843-7(8) , 9780071448437) McGraw-Hill Cos., The.

ITALIAN POETRY—COLLECTIONS

Calcutt, David. Homer's Odyssey: 26 Speaking Parts. 1999. (Dramascripts Classic Texts Ser.). (J). (gr. 6-11). pap. 17.95 (978-0-17-432562-8(2)) Nelson Thornes Ltd. GBR. *Dist:* Trans-Atlantic Pubns., Inc.

ITALIANS—UNITED STATES

see also Italian Americans

Franchino, Vicky. Italian Americans. 2002. (Spirit of America: Our Cultural Heritage Ser.). (Illus.). 32p. (J). (gr. 2-6). 27.07 (978-1-56766-153-8(X)) Child's World, Inc.

Todd, Anne M. Italian Immigrants, 1880-1920. 2001. (Blue Earth Books). (Illus.). 32p. (J). (gr. 3-4). lib. bdg. 22.60 (978-0-7368-0796-8(9) , Bridgestone Bks.) Capstone Pr., Inc.

Ueda, Reed & Stotsky, Sandra, eds. Italian-American Answer Book. 1999. (Ethnic Answer Book Ser.). (Illus.). 136p. (YA). (gr. 5 up). lib. bdg. 8.95 (978-0-7910-4797-2(0) , Chelsea Hse.) Facts On File, Inc.

ITALY

Adams, Colleen. A Primary Source Guide to Italy. 2003. (Countries of the World, a Primary Source Journey Ser.). (Illus.). 24p. (J). pap. (978-0-8239-8077-2(4)); lib. bdg. 19.95 (978-0-8239-6593-9(7)) Rosen Publishing Group, Inc., The.

Arnold, Helen. Italy. 2000. (Postcards from...Ser.). (Illus.). 32p. (J). (gr. 2-4). pap. 6.95 (978-0-8172-6223-5(7)) Steck-Vaughn.

Austin Goes to Italy. 2nd ed. 2002. (Travels Ser.). (Illus.). 20p. (J). (gr. k-2). reprint ed. pap. 9.95 (978-0-9670001-6-9(5)) Austin Publishing.

Barter, James E. Renaissance Florence. 2002. (Traveler's Guide to Ser.). (Illus.). 112p. (YA). (gr. 5). 29.95 (978-1-59018-145-4(X) , Lucent Bks.) Thomson Gale.

Behnke, Alison. Italy in Pictures. 2nd rev. ed. 2003. (Visual Geography Ser.). (Illus.). 80p. (J). (gr. 5-12). 27.93 (978-0-8225-0368-2(9)) Lerner Publishing Group.

Bell, Rachael. Italy. 1999. (Visit to Ser.). 32p. (J). (gr. k-2). lib. bdg. 21.36 (978-1-57572-853-7(2)) Heinemann Library.

Berendes, Mary. Italy. 2007. (Welcome to the World Ser.). 32p. (J). (gr. 1-5). 27.07 (****978-1-59296-918-0(6)***) Child's World, Inc.

Boast, Clare. Italy. 1998. (Next Stop! Ser.). (Illus.). 32p. (J). lib. bdg. 19.92 (978-1-57572-567-3(3)) Heinemann Library.

Canizares, Susan. Italy. 1999. (ps-2). lib. bdg. 10.10 (978-0-613-21780-4(2)) Tandem Library Bks.

Cassidy, Picot. Italy. 2001. (Nations of the World Ser.). (Illus.). 128p. (YA). (gr. 6-8). lib. bdg. 34.26 (978-0-7398-1287-7(4)) Raintree.

Cooper, Sharon Katz. Italy ABCs: A Book about the People & Places of Italy. Eitzen, Allan, illus. 2006. (Country ABCs Ser.). 32p. (J). (gr. k-5). 23.93 (978-1-4048-1569-8(4)) Picture Window Bks.

Costain, Meredith & Collins, Paul. Welcome to Italy. 2001. (Countries of the World Ser.). (Illus.). 32p. (J). (gr. 4 up). 28.00 (978-0-7910-6550-1(2) , 010207, Chelsea Hse.) Facts On File, Inc.

Fontes, Justine & Fontes, Ron. Italy. (to Z Ser.). (J). 2004. (gr. 2-4). pap. 6.95 (978-0-516-26812-5(0)); 2003. (ENG & ITA., Illus.). 40p. 24.50 (978-0-516-24559-1(7)) Scholastic Library Publishing. (Children's Pr.).

Fournier, Christine. Canada. 2002. (Countries Ser.). (Illus.). 40p. (J). (gr. k-6). lib. bdg. 22.78 (978-1-57765-751-4(9) , Checkerboard Library) ABDO Publishing Co.

Furgang, Kathy. Mount Vesuvius: Europe's Mighty Volcano of Smoke & Ash. 2001. (Volcanoes of the World Ser.). (Illus.). 24p. (J). lib. bdg. 19.95 (978-0-8239-5658-6(X) , PowerKids Pr.) Rosen Publishing Group, Inc., The.

Garrington, Sally. Italy. 2004. (Countries of the World Ser.). (Illus.). 64p. (J). (gr. 6-12). 30.00 (978-0-8160-5502-9(5)) Facts On File, Inc.

Green, Jen. Focus on Italy. 2006. (Illus.). 64p. (J). pap. (978-0-8368-6743-5(2)); lib. bdg. (978-0-8368-6736-7(X)) Stevens, Gareth Inc. (World Almanac Library).

Gritzner, Charles, ed. Italy. 2004. (Modern World Nations Ser.). (Illus.). 200p. (gr. 6-12). pap. 30.00 (978-0-7910-7769-6(1) , Chelsea Hse.) Facts On File, Inc.

Harvey, Miles. Look What Came from Italy. 1999. (Look What Came from... Ser.). (Illus.). 32p. (J). (gr. 2-4). pap. 6.95 (978-0-531-15938-5(8) , Watts, Franklin) Scholastic Library Publishing.

Hausam, Josephine Sander. Italy. 1999. (Countries of the World Ser.). (Illus.). 96p. (J). (gr. 6 up). lib. bdg. 30.00 (978-0-8368-2310-3(9)) Stevens, Gareth Inc.

Italia, Bob. Italy. 2002. (Countries Ser.). (Illus.). 40p. (J). (gr. k-6). lib. bdg. 22.78 (978-1-57765-754-5(3) , Checkerboard Library) ABDO Publishing Co.

Italy, 6 vols. (gr. 2-5). 36.95 (978-0-7368-8397-9(5)) Red Brick Learning.

Levinson, Debra. Italy's Best with Kids: Extraordinary Places to Sleep, Eat & Play. 2003. (J). pap. 19.95 (978-0-9633577-4-8(3)) Max Pubn., Inc.

Malone, Margaret Gay. Italy. 2002. (Discovering Cultures Ser.). (Illus.). 48p. (J). 25.64 (978-0-7614-1176-5(3) , Benchmark Bks.) Cavendish, Marshall Corp.

Mason, Paul. Italy. (Illus.), 48p. (J). 2006. lib. bdg. (****978-1-4109-2461-2(0));*** 2005. lib. bdg. (978-1-4109-1864-2(5)) Steck-Vaughn.

Needham, Ed. Italy & the Italians. 2004. (Focus on Europe Ser.). (J). lib. bdg. 28.50 (978-1-932799-14-9(1)) Stargazer Bks.

Nickles, Greg. Italy: The Land. 2001. (gr. 3-6). lib. bdg. 16.40 (978-0-613-43457-7(9)) Tandem Library Bks.

—Italy - The Culture. 2001. (Lands, Peoples & Cultures Ser.). (Illus.). 32p. (J). (gr. 4-5). pap. (978-0-7787-9739-5(2)) Crabtree Publishing Co.

—Italy - The Land. (Lands, Peoples & Cultures Ser.). (Illus.). 32p. (J). (gr. 4-5). 2001. (978-0-7787-9369-4(9)); 2000. pap. (978-0-7787-9737-1(6)) Crabtree Publishing Co.

Olson, Nathan. Italy. 2005. (Fact Finders Ser.). (Illus.). 32p. 22.60 (978-0-7368-3754-5(X)) Capstone Pr., Inc.

Park, Ted. Italy. 2000. (Taking Your Camera to Ser.). (Illus.). 32p. (J). (gr. 4-7). lib. bdg. 22.83 (978-0-7398-1807-7(4)) Raintree.

—Taking Your Camera to Italy. 2001. (Illus.). pap. (978-0-7398-3328-5(6)) Steck-Vaughn.

Paul Mason. Italy. 2006. (Illus.). 48p. (J). pap. (****978-1-4109-2468-1(8)***) Steck-Vaughn.

Pavlovic, Zoran. Italy. 2003. (Modern World Nations Ser.). (Illus.). 150p. (gr. 6-12). 30.00 (978-0-7910-7608-8(3) , Chelsea Hse.) Facts On File, Inc.

Petersen, Christine & Petersen, David. Italy. (True Bks.). (Illus.). 48p. (J). (gr. 3-5). 2002. pap. 6.95 (978-0-516-27360-0(4)); 2001. 25.00 (978-0-516-22256-1(2)) Scholastic Library Publishing. (Children's Pr.).

Pirotta, Saviour. Italy. 1999. (Food & Festivals Ser.). (Illus.). 32p. (J). (gr. 2-5). pap. 6.95 (978-0-7398-0958-7(X)) Steck-Vaughn.

Popper, Garry. Mario in Italy. Johnson, Andi, illus. 2004. 36p. (ps-7). 4.00 (978-1-84161-059-7(3)) Ravette Publishing, Ltd. GBR. *Dist:* Parkwest Pubns., Inc.

Potter, Giselle. The Year I Didn't Go to School. Potter, Giselle, illus. 2002. (Illus.). 40p. (J). (ps-3). 16.95 (978-0-689-84730-1(0) , Atheneum/Anne Schwartz Bks.) Simon & Schuster Children's Publishing.

Powell, Jillian. Descubramos Italia. 2006. (ENG & SPA.). (J). pap. (****978-0-8368-7962-9(7));*** lib. bdg. (****978-0-8368-7955-1(4)***) Stevens, Gareth Inc.

—Looking at Italy. 2006. (Illus.). 32p. (J). pap. (****978-0-8368-7677-2(6));*** lib. bdg. (****978-0-8368-7670-3(9)***) Stevens, Gareth Inc.

Powell, Katherine. Italy. 1998. (Origins Ser.). (Illus.). 32p. (J). (gr. 5-8). 21.00 (978-0-531-14450-3(X) , Watts, Franklin) Scholastic Library Publishing.

Ruth, Angie. My Adventure in Italy. 2007. 44p. (J). 8.99 (978-1-59092-430-3(4) , Orchard Academy Pr.) Windstorm Creative.

Sansone, Emma. Getting to Know Italy & Italian. Woolley, Kim, illus. 2005. 33p. (J). reprint ed. pap. 13.00 (978-0-7567-9579-5(6)) DIANE Publishing Co.

Thoennes, Kristin. Italy. 1999. (Countries of the World Ser.). (Illus.). 126p. (J). (gr. 2-3). 18.60 (978-0-7368-0153-9(7) , Bridgestone Bks.) Capstone Pr., Inc.

Thomson, Ruth. Italy. Hampton, David, photos by. 2007. (Living In- Ser.). (Illus.). 32p. (J). (****978-1-59771-043-5(1)*** , 1268841) Sea-To-Sea Pubns.

Ueda, Reed & Stotsky, Sandra, eds. Italian-American Answer Book. 1999. (Ethnic Answer Book Ser.). (Illus.). 136p. (YA). (gr. 5 up). pap. 9.95 (978-0-7910-4798-9(9) , Chelsea Hse.) Facts On File, Inc.

Winter, Jane Kohen & Jermyn, Leslie. Italy. 2nd ed. 2003. (Illus.). 144p. (gr. 5 up). lib. bdg. 37.07 (978-0-7614-1500-8(9) , Cavendish, Marshall Reference Bks.) Cavendish, Marshall Corp.

ITALY—ANTIQUITIES

Armentrout, David & Armentrout, Patricia. Treasures from Italy. 2000. (Treasures from the Past Ser.). (Illus.). 48p. (J). (gr. 4-8). lib. bdg. 29.93 (978-1-55916-292-0(9)) Rourke Publishing, LLC.

Bradley, Pamela. Pompeii & Herculaneum. 2005. pap., stu. ed. 23.95 (978-0-521-60895-4(3)) Cambridge Univ. Pr.

ITALY—CIVILIZATION

Bloom, Harold. The Italian Renaissance. 2004. (Bloom's Period Studies Ser.). (Illus.), 350p. (J). (gr. 9-13). 45.00 (978-0-7910-7895-2(7) , Chelsea Hse.) Facts On File, Inc.

Boekhoff, P. M. & Kallen, Stuart A. The Italian Renaissance. 2003. (History of the World Ser.). (Illus.). 48p. (J). (gr. 3-5). 23.70 (978-0-7377-1036-6(5) , Kidhaven) Thomson Gale.

Hay, Jeff. Renaissance. 2001. (gr. 7-12). lib. bdg. 39.05 (978-0-613-73785-2(7)) Tandem Library Bks.

Nickles, Greg. Italy - The Culture. 2001. (Lands, Peoples & Cultures Ser.). (Illus.). 32p. (J). (gr. 4-5). (978-0-7787-9371-7(0)) Crabtree Publishing Co.

Schomp, Virginia. The Italian Renaissance. 2002. (Cultures of the Past Ser.). (Illus.). 80p. (J). (gr. 5). 29.93 (978-0-7614-1492-6(4) , Benchmark Bks.) Cavendish, Marshall Corp.

Waldman, Nomi J. The Italian Renaissance. 2004. (Daily Life Ser.). (Illus.). 48p. (J). 26.20 (978-0-7377-1398-5(4) , Greenhaven Pr., Inc.) Thomson Gale.

ITALY—FICTION

Allen, Jonathan. I'm Not Scared! 2007. 32p. (ps-k). 14.99 (****978-0-7868-3722-9(5)***) Hyperion Pr.

Avi. Magia de Medianoche. 2004. (SPA.). 194p. (YA). 10.99 (978-84-348-9112-8(3)) SM Ediciones ESP. *Dist:* Lectorum Pubns., Inc.

Balit, Christina. Escape from Pompeii. rev. ed. 2003. (Illus.). 32p. (J). 16.95 (978-0-8050-7324-9(8) , Holt, Henry & Co. Bks. For Young Readers) Holt, Henry & Co.

Balocco, Patrizia & Francia, Giada, eds. Alex & Penny Ballooning over Italy. 2007. (Illus.). 80p. (J). (gr. 2-5). 14.95 (978-88-544-0160-0(9) , White Star) Rizzoli International Pubns., Inc.

Banks, Kate. Friends of the Heart: Amici Del Cuore. 2005. 144p. (J). 16.00 (978-0-374-32455-1(7)) Farrar, Straus & Giroux.

Barrett, Tracy. On Etruscan Time. rev. ed. 2005. 176p. (J). 17.95 (978-0-8050-7569-4(0) , Holt, Henry & Co. Bks. For Young Readers) Holt, Henry & Co.

Bass, Anthony & Cherubini, Tiziano. Maxwell in Italy. 2002. (Illus.). 40p. (J). (SPA.). 17.00 (978-0-9724084-1-7(X) , 881757); (ITA., 17.00 (978-0-9724084-0-0(1) , 881757); (FRE., 17.00 (978-0-9724084-2-4(8) , 881757) Hopscotch, LLC.

Baxter, Linda. The Winter of the Stone Woman. Marks, Dea, illus. 1999. (Cover-to-Cover Novels Ser.). 75p. (J). (gr. 2-5). lib. bdg. 13.95 (978-0-7807-8965-4(2) , Covercraft); (gr. 4-8). pap. 5.60 (978-0-7891-2926-0(4)) Perfection Learning Corp.

Birch, Beverley & Shakespeare, William. Romeo & Juliet. 2007. (Illus.). 80p. 13.95 (****978-0-7502-4966-9(8)*** , Hodder Wayland) Hodder Children's Division GBR. *Dist:* Independent Pubs. Group.

Burg, Ann E. Rebekkah's Journey: A World War II Refugee Story. Iskowitz, Joel, illus. 2006. 48p. (J). (gr. 3-5). 17.95 (978-1-58536-275-2(1)) Sleeping Bear Pr.

Buzzati, Dino & Lobb, Frances. The Bears' Famous Invasion of Sicily. 2003. (New York Review Children's Collection). (Illus.). 152p. (J). 18.95 (978-1-59017-076-2(8) , NYR Children's Collection) New York Review of Bks., Inc., The.

Buzzati, Dino & Snicket, Lemony. The Bears' Famous Invasion of Sicily. Buzzati, Dino, illus. 2005. (Illus.). 192p. (J). pap. 5.99 (978-0-06-072608-9(3)) HarperCollins Pubs.

Collodi, Carlo. The Adventures of Pinocchio. Murray, M. A., tr. from ITA. Innocenti, Roberto, illus. rev. ed. 2005. (Creative Editions Ser.). 192p. (J). (gr. 4 up). 24.95 (978-1-56846-190-8(9)) Creative Co., The.

—Las Aventuras de Pinocho. (SPA., Illus.). 160p. (YA). 14.95 (978-84-7281-190-4(5) , AF1905) Auriga, Ediciones S.A. ESP. *Dist:* Continental Bk. Co., Inc.

—Las Aventuras de Pinocho. (Coleccion Cuentos Universales). (SPA.). (YA). (gr. 4 up). (978-84-261-3145-4(X) , JV30301) Juventud, Editorial ESP. *Dist:* Lectorum Pubns., Inc.

Creech, Sharon. The Castle Corona. Diaz, David, illus. 2007. 336p. (J). (gr. 3-7). lib. bdg. 19.89 (****978-0-06-084622-0(4));*** 18.99 (****978-0-06-084621-3(6)***) HarperCollins Pubs. (Cotler, Joanna Books).

Daly, Maureen. The Small War of Sergeant Donkey. Dennis, Wesley, illus. 2000. (Living History Library). 104p. (J). (gr. 5-9). reprint ed. pap. 11.95 (978-1-883937-47-8(7)) Bethlehem Bks.

D'Amicis, Edmundo. Corazon. 2001. Tr. of Heart. (SPA., Illus.). 288p. (978-84-206-3562-0(6)) Alianza Editorial, S. A.

de Paola, Tomie. Big Anthony: His Story. 3.70 (978-0-399-24873-3(0)); 22.25 (978-0-399-24925-9(7)); 22.25 (978-0-399-24926-6(5)) Penguin Group (USA) Inc.

—Big Anthony: His Story. de Paola, Tomie, illus. 1998. (Illus.). 32p. (J). (ps-3). 16.99 (978-0-399-23189-6(7) , Putnam Juvenile) Penguin Group (USA) Inc.

—Big Anthony: His Story. 2001. 12.79 (978-0-606-21064-5(4)) Tandem Library Bks.

—Days of the Blackbird: A Tale of Northern Italy. de Paola, Tomie, illus. 2005. (Illus.). 32p. (J). (ps-k). reprint ed. pap. 5.99 (978-0-14-240271-9(0) , Puffin) Penguin Group (USA) Inc.

Fienberg, Anna. The Witch in the Lake: A Novel. 2002. 220p. (J). (gr. 5-9). pap. 7.95 (978-1-55037-722-4(1)); lib. bdg. 18.95 (978-1-55037-723-1(X)) Annick Pr., Ltd. CAN. *Dist:* Firefly Bks., Ltd.

French, Simon. Change the Locks. 2006. 112p. (J). pap. 15.00 (978-0-14-330172-1(1) , Penguin Global) Penguin Group (USA) Inc.

Funke, Cornelia. Inkheart. 2008. (Inkheart Movie Ser.). 576p. (J). 9.99 (****978-0-545-04626-8(2)*** , Scholastic) Scholastic, Inc.

—Inkheart. Bell, Anthea, tr. 2005. (Illus.). 560p. (ps-7). pap. 8.99 (978-0-439-70910-1(5)) Scholastic, Inc.

—Inkheart. 2003. 544p. (J). 60.00 (978-0-439-61671-3(9) , Chicken Hse., The) Scholastic, Inc.

—Inkheart. Bell, Anthea, tr. from GER. 2003. (Illus.). 544p. (J). (gr. 3-6). pap. 19.95 (978-0-439-53164-1(0) , Chicken Hse., The) Scholastic, Inc.

—Inkheart. Bell, Anthea, tr. 2005. 550p. (J). (ps-7). lib. bdg. 15.04 (978-0-606-33803-5(9)) Tandem Library Bks.

—Inkheart. l.t. ed. 2006. 709p. (YA). pap. 10.95 (978-0-7862-8363-7(7)) Thorndike Pr.

—Inkheart. Bell, Anthea, tr. l.t. ed. 2005. (Illus.). 709p. (J). (gr. 3-7). 23.95 (978-0-7862-8041-4(7) , Large Print Pr.) Thorndike Pr.

—The Thief Lord. Latsch, Oliver, tr. from GER. Burmingham, Christian, illus. (J). 2002. 352p. (gr. 4-7). pap. 16.95 (978-0-439-40437-2(1)); 2003. 376p. (gr. 3-6). reprint ed. 6.99 (978-0-439-42089-1(X)) Scholastic, Inc. (Chicken Hse., The).

Gandolfi, Silvana & Schwartz, Lynne Sharon. Aldabra, or, the Tortoise Who Loved Shakespeare. 2004. 151p. (J). (978-0-439-49744-2(2) , Levine, Arthur A. Bks.) Scholastic, Inc.

Grant, Crystal. Warrior Boy. 2007. (ENG.). 92p. per. 14.95 (****978-1-4241-3978-1(3)***) PublishAmerica, Inc.

Gutman, Anne & Hallensleben, Georg. Gaspard on Vacation. 2001. (Illus.). 32p. (J). (ps-1). 9.95 (978-0-375-81115-9(X) , Knopf Bks. for Young Readers) Random Hse. Children's Bks.

Hamilton, Martha & Weiss, Mitch. Priceless Gifts: A Folktale from Italy. Kanzler, John, illus. 2007. 32p. (gr. k-3). 16.95 (978-0-87483-788-9(X)) August Hse. Pubs., Inc.

Harcourt School Publishers Staff. The Violin Man, Level D. 2001. (Collections Ser.). (Illus.). (J). 6.90 (978-0-15-314405-9(X)) Harcourt Schl. Pubs.

Hawes, Louise. The Vanishing Point: The Story of Lavinia Fontana. 2004. 240p. (YA). (gr. 5-9). 17.00 (978-0-618-43423-7(2)) Houghton Mifflin Co. Trade & Reference Div.

Heuston, Kimberley B. Dante's Daughter. 2004. 304p. (YA). 16.95 (978-1-886910-97-3(9) , Lemniscaat) Boyds Mills Pr.

Higson, Charlie. Blood Fever. 2006. 368p. (gr. 5-17). 16.95 (978-0-7868-3662-8(8)) Hyperion Bks. for Children.

—Blood Fever. 2nd rev. ed. 2007. (Young Bond Ser.). 368p. (gr. 7 up). pap. 7.99 (****978-1-4231-0029-4(8)***) Miramax Bks.

Hoffman, Mary. City of Stars. 2005. (Illus.). 457p. (J). (ps-7). per. 15.00 (978-0-606-33760-1(1)) Tandem Library Bks.

Hogan, Mary. Pretty Face. 2008. 224p. (J). 16.99 (****978-0-06-084111-9(7));*** lib. bdg. 17.89 (****978-0-06-084112-6(5)***) HarperCollins Pubs. (HarperTeen).

Hood, Ann. How I Saved My Father's Life (and Ruined Everything Else) 2008. 224p. (J). pap. 16.99 (****978-0-439-92819-9(2)*** , Scholastic Pr.) Scholastic, Inc.

Horowitz, Anthony. Scorpia. (Alex Rider Ser.: Bk. 5). (YA). (gr. 5). 2006. 400p. pap. 7.99 (978-0-14-240578-9(7) , Puffin); 2005. 320p. 17.99 (978-0-399-24151-2(5) , Philomel) Penguin Group (USA) Inc.

Langton, Jane. Saint Francis & the Wolf. Plume, Ilse, illus. 2007. 32p. (J). 16.95 (****978-1-56792-320-9(8)***) Godine, David R. Pub.

Lasky, Kathryn. The Last Girls of Pompeii. 2007. 160p. (J). (gr. 5 up). 15.99 (978-0-670-06196-9(4) , Viking Juvenile) Penguin Group (USA) Inc.

Lawrence, Caroline. Pirates of Pompeii, Vol. 3. 2004. (Roman Mysteries Ser.: No. 3). (Illus.). 176p. (J). (gr. 3). pap. 5.99 (978-0-14-240227-6(3) , Puffin) Penguin Group (USA) Inc.

—Secrets of Vesuvius. 2004. (Roman Mysteries Ser.: No. 2). (Illus.). 192p. (J). (gr. 3 up). pap. 5.99 (978-0-14-240118-7(8) , Puffin) Penguin Group (USA) Inc.

Levithan, David. Are We There Yet? 2007. 224p. (J). (gr. 7). pap. 8.99 (978-0-375-83956-6(9) , Knopf Bks. for Young Readers) Random Hse. Children's Bks.

Llorente, Pilar Molina. El Terrible Florentino. 8th ed. (SPA., Illus.). 109p. (YA). (gr. 5-8). (978-84-279-3147-3(6) , NG5362) Noguer y Caralt Editores, S. A. ESP. *Dist:* Lectorum Pubns., Inc.

—El Terrible Florentino. 2001. (SPA.). (gr. 7-12). lib. bdg. 17.60 (978-0-613-80649-7(2)) Tandem Library Bks.

Lollino, Jessica. Lily & the Big Italian Wedding. Lollino, Jessica, ed. 2006. (Little Lily Mays Ser.: vol. 2). (Illus.). 32p. (J). pap. 20.00 (978-0-9712383-2-9(4)) Culture Connection, The.

Mercer, Gary. Justin Flowers & the Orb of Time. 2003. 147p. pap. 16.95 (978-1-59286-530-7(5)) PublishAmerica, Inc.

Miss O, Harlie, Justine, and Isabella, with Devra Newberger Speregen, Juliette. Miss O & Friends: Picture Perfecto! 2006. (Miss O & Friends Ser.). (Illus.). 128p. (J). pap. 5.99 (978-0-8230-2949-5(2)) Watson-Guptill Pubns., Inc.

Morpurgo, Michael. Jo-Jo the Melon Donkey. Kerins, Tony, illus. 2002. (Yellow Bananas Ser.). 48p. (J). (gr. 3-4). pap. (978-0-7787-0988-6(4)); lib. bdg. (978-0-7787-0942-8(6)) Crabtree Publishing Co.

Napoli, Donna Jo. Fire in the Hills. 2006. 256p. (YA). (gr. 7). 16.99 (978-0-525-47751-8(9) , Dutton Juvenile) Penguin Group (USA) Inc.

—Three Days. 2003. (Illus.). 160p. (YA). pap. 5.99 (978-0-14-250025-5(9) , Puffin) Penguin Group (USA) Inc.

—Three Days. 2003. (gr. 3-6). lib. bdg. 14.15 (978-0-613-67041-8(8)) Tandem Library Bks.

Nitz, Kristin Wolden. Saving the Griffin. Jaeggi, Yoshiko, illus. 2007. 192p. (J). (gr. 3-6). 14.95 (978-1-56145-380-1(3) , Peachtree Junior) Peachtree Pubs., Ltd.

Nobisso, Josephine. In English, of Course. Ziborova, Dasha, illus. 2003. Tr. of En Ingles, Por Supuesto. 32p. (J). (SPA.). 16.95 (978-0-940112-07-0(8)); pap. 8.95 (978-0-940112-08-7(6)) Gingerbread Hse.

Osborne, Mary Pope. Vacation under the Volcano, Vol. 13. unabr. ed. 2004. (Magic Tree House Ser. : No. 13). 74p. (J). (gr. k-3). pap. 17.00 incl. audio (978-0-8072-0782-6(9) , LFTR 241 SP, Listening Library) Random Hse. Audio Publishing Group.

—Vacation under the Volcano. Murdocca, Sal, illus. 1998. (Magic Tree House Ser.: No. 13). (J). (gr. k-3). 96p. lib. bdg. 11.99 (978-0-679-99050-5(X)); 80p. mass mkt. 3.99 (978-0-679-89050-8(5)) Random Hse. Children's Bks. (Random Hse. Bks. for Young Readers).

—Vacation under the Volcano, nO. 13. Murdocca, Sal, illus. 1998. (Magic Tree House Ser. : No. 13). (J). (gr. k-3). (978-0-606-13972-4(9)) Tandem Library Bks.

Parkinson, Curtis. Domenic's War: A Story of the Battle of Monte Cassino. 2006. 200p. (J). (gr. 5-9). pap. 9.95 (978-0-88776-751-7(6)) Tundra Bks., Inc./Livres Toundra, Inc. CAN. *Dist:* Random Hse., Inc.

Pedersen, Janet. Pino & the Signora's Pasta. Pedersen, Janet, illus. 2005. (Illus.). 32p. (J). (ps-3). 16.99 (978-0-7636-2396-8(2)) Candlewick Pr.

Pinocho: The Human Body, Sea Life, the Bedroom. 1999. Tr. of Pinocchio. (SPA & ENG., Illus.). (J). (ps-5). pap. 7.95 (978-88-8148-253-5(3)) European Language Institute ITA. *Dist:* Distribooks, Inc., Midwest European Pubns.

Rosen, Michael & Shakespeare, William. Shakespeare's Romeo & Juliet. Ray, Jane, tr. Ray, Jane, illus. 2003. 80p. (J). (gr. 7). 17.99 (978-0-7636-2258-9(3)) Candlewick Pr.

Sabuda, Robert. Uh-Oh Leonardo! 2003. (Illus.). 48p. (J). 16.95 (978-0-689-81160-9(8) , Atheneum) Simon & Schuster Children's Publishing.

Scieszka, Jon. Da Wild, Da Crazy, Da Vinci. McCauley, Adam, illus. 2006. (Time Warp Trio Ser.: No. 14). 96p. (J). (gr. 2). pap. 4.99 (978-0-14-240465-2(9) , Puffin) Penguin Group (USA) Inc.

Shakespeare, William & Clayborne, Anna. Romeo & Juliet - Internet Referenced. 2006. 64p. (J). 8.99 (978-0-7945-1240-8(2) , Usborne) EDC Publishing.

Smith, Annie Laura. Saving da Vinci. 2005. (YA). mass mkt. 6.99 (****978-0-9753367-6-2(2)***) Onstage Publishing, LLC.

Weaver, Tess. Opera Cat. Wesson, Andrea, illus. 2002. 32p. (J). (gr. k-3). 15.00 (978-0-618-09635-0(3) , Clarion Bks.) Houghton Mifflin Co. Trade & Reference Div.

Weisleder, Stanley. Wings of the Panther. 2004. 224p. 15.00 (978-0-936783-38-3(9)) Merril Pr.

Weston, Carol. The Diary of Melanie Martin. 2001. (Illus.). 144p. (J). (ps-7). per. 13.00 (978-0-613-33751-9(4)) Tandem Library Bks.

Whytock, Cherry. My Saucy Stuffed Ravioli: The Life of Angelica Cookson Potts. Whytock, Cherry, illus. 2005. (Illus.). 176p. (YA). 14.95 (978-0-689-86550-3(3)) Simon & Schuster Children's Publishing.

Winterson, Jeanette. The King of Capri. Ray, Jane, illus. 2003. 32p. (J). 16.95 (978-1-58234-830-8(8) , Bloomsbury Children) Bloomsbury Publishing.

Woodbury, Mary. The International Polly McDoodle. 2004. (Polly Mcdoodle Mystery Ser.). 200p. (J). (gr. 4-7). pap. 7.95 (978-1-55050-293-0(X)) Coteau Bks. CAN. *Dist:* Fitzhenry & Whiteside, Ltd.

YKids Staff. Leonardo da Vinci. 2008. (Great Figures in History Ser.). 144p. (J). pap. 14.95 (*978-981-05-7555-7(6)*) Youngjin (Singapore) Pte Ltd. SGP. *Dist:* Independent Pubs. Group.

ITALY—HISTORY

Anderson, Dale. Italian Americans. 2006. (World Almanac Library of American Immigration). 48p. (J). pap. (978-0-8368-7325-2(4)); lib. bdg. (978-0-8368-7312-2(2)) Stevens, Gareth Inc. (World Almanac Library).

Ball, Karen. Pompeii. Cerisier, Emmanuel, illus. 2006. 64p. (J). 8.99 (978-0-7945-1270-5(4) , Usborne) EDC Publishing.

Ford, Nick. Niccolo Machiavelli: Florentine Statesman, Playwright, & Poet. 2004. (Rulers, Scholars, & Artists of Renaissance Europe Ser.). (J). lib. bdg. 31.95 (978-1-4042-0316-7(8)) Rosen Publishing Group, Inc., The.

Greenblatt, Miriam. Lorenzo de Medici & Renaissance Italy. 2002. (Rulers & Their Times Ser.). (Illus.). 80p. (J). (gr. 8-12). lib. bdg. 29.93 (978-0-7614-1490-2(8) , Benchmark Bks.) Cavendish, Marshall Corp.

Hancock, Lee. Lorenzo de' Medici: Florence's Great Leader & Patron of the Arts. 2004. (Rulers, Scholars, & Artists of Renaissance Europe Ser.). (Illus.). 112p. (J). lib. bdg. 31.95 (978-1-4042-0315-0(X)) Rosen Publishing Group, Inc., The.

Haugen, Brenda. Benito Mussolini: Fascist Italian Dictator. (Illus.). 112p. (J). 2007. pap. (*978-0-7565-1988-9(8));* 2006. (978-0-7565-1892-9(X)) Compass Point Bks.

Hay, Jeff. Renaissance. 2001. (gr. 7-12). lib. bdg. 39.05 (978-0-613-73785-2(7)) Tandem Library Bks.

Herold, Vickey. Discover the Renaissance in Italy. 2006. pap. 39.00 (**978-1-4108-6465-9(0)*) Benchmark Education Co.

—The Renaissance in Italy. 2006. pap. 39.00 (**978-1-4108-6462-8(6)*) Benchmark Education Co.

Holmes, Burton. Southern Italy. Schlesinger, Arthur M., Jr. & Isreal, Fred L., eds. 1999. (World 100 Years Ago Ser.). (Illus.). 144p. (YA). (gr. 4-7). lib. bdg. 29.95 (978-0-7910-4672-2(9) , Chelsea Hse.) Facts On File, Inc.

Kaplan, Sarah Pitt. Pompeii: City of Ashes. 2005. (Illus.). 48p. (J). (ps-7). 24.00 (978-0-516-25122-6(8)); (YA). (gr. 7-12). pap. 6.95 (978-0-516-25091-5(4)) Scholastic Library Publishing. (Children's Pr.).

Kelley, Gary. T is for Toscana. 2003. (Illus.). 40p. 17.95 (978-1-56846-177-9(1) , Creative Editions) Creative Co., The.

Knight, Patricia. Mussolini & Fascism. 2003. (Questions & Analysis in History Ser.). (Illus.). 144p. 90.00 (978-0-415-27921-5(6)); 20.95 (978-0-415-27922-2(4)) Routledge.

Lindeen, Mary. Ashes to Ashes: Uncovering Pompeii. 2007. (Shockwave: People & Communities Ser.). (Illus.). 36p. (J). (gr. 4-6). lib. bdg. 25.00 (**978-0-531-17745-7(9)* , Children's Pr.) Scholastic Library Publishing.

Marino, John A., ed. Early Modern Italy: 1550-1796. 2002. (Short Oxford History of Italy Ser.). (Illus.). 330p. 34.95 (978-0-19-870042-5(3)) Oxford Univ. Pr., Inc.

McKerley, Jennifer Guess. The Leaning Tower of Pisa. 2006. (Great Structures in History Ser.). (J). (978-0-7377-3151-4(6) , Greenhaven Pr., Inc.) Thomson Gale.

Parker, Victoria. Pompeii AD 79: A City Buried by a Volcanic Eruption. 2006. (When Disaster Struck Ser.). (Illus.). 56p. (J). (gr. 4-7). lib. bdg. 32.86 (978-1-4109-2276-2(6)) Raintree.

Roberts, Russell. Mt. Vesuvius & the Destruction of Pompei, A. D. 79. 2005. (Natural Disasters Ser.). (Illus.). 32p. (J). (gr. 1-4). lib. bdg. (978-1-58415-419-8(5)) Mitchell Lane Pubs., Inc.

Sadik, Ademola O. Italy. 2006. (European Union Ser.). (Illus.). 88p. (J). (gr. 5 up). lib. bdg. (978-1-4222-0052-0(3)) Mason Crest Pubs.

Schoell, William. Giuseppe Verdi & Italian Opera. 2007. (Illus.). 128p. (J). (gr. 9 up). lib. bdg. 27.95 (978-1-59935-041-7(6)) Reynolds, Morgan Inc.

Speaker-Yuan, Margaret. Benito Mussolini. 2005. (History's Villains Ser.). (J). (978-1-56711-899-5(2) , Blackbirch Pr., Inc.) Thomson Gale.

Tanaka, Shelley. The Buried City of Pompeii: What It Was Like When Vesuvius Exploded. Ruhl, Greg, illus. Christopher, Peter, photos by. 2003. 48p. (J). (gr. 4-9). reprint ed. 17.00 (978-0-7567-6722-8(9)) DIANE Publishing Co.

—The Buried City of Pompeii: What It Was Like When Vesuvius Exploded. 2001. (I Was There Bk.). (Illus.). (J). 14.79 (978-0-606-20584-9(5)) Tandem Library Bks.

Zelasco, Marco & Zelasco, Pierangelo. Florence in the 1440s. Ripamonti, Aldo, illus. 2001. (Journey to the Past Ser.). 56p. (J). (gr. 6-8). lib. bdg. 27.12 (978-0-7398-1957-9(7)) Raintree.

ITALY—HISTORY—FICTION

Alexander, Lloyd. The Rope Trick. 2002. 192p. (J). (gr. 3-6). 16.99 (978-0-525-47020-5(4) , Dutton Juvenile) Penguin Group (USA) Inc.

Alexander, Lloyd, contrib. by. The Rope Trick. 2004. 195p. (J). (gr. 5). lib. bdg. 13.64 (978-0-606-30794-9(X)) Tandem Library Bks.

Beaufrand, Mary Jane. Primavera. 2008. 256p. (YA). (gr. 7-17). 16.99 (**978-0-316-01644-5(6)*) Little Brown & Co.

Bradford, Emma. Kat & the Missing Notebooks. Sano, Kazuhiko, illus. 1999. (Stardust Classics: No. 4). 119p. (J). (gr. 2-5). 12.95 (978-1-889514-27-7(6)); pap. 5.95 (978-1-889514-28-4(4)) Dolls Corp.

Castaldo, Nancy F. Pizza for the Queen. Potter, Melisande, illus. 2005. 32p. (J). (ps-ps). 16.95 (978-0-8234-1865-7(0)) Holiday Hse., Inc.

Gavin, Jamila. The Blood Stone. 2005. (Illus.). 352p. (YA). (gr. 6-8). 18.00 (978-0-374-30846-9(2)) Farrar, Straus & Giroux.

Grey, Christopher Peter. Leonardo's Shadow: Or, My Astonishing Life as Leonardo da Vinci's Servant. 2006. 400p. (YA). 16.95 (978-1-4169-0543-1(X) , Atheneum) Simon & Schuster Children's Publishing.

Hawes, Louise. Vanishing Point. 2007. 240p. (YA). (gr. 5). pap. 7.99 (**978-0-618-74788-7(5)*) Houghton Mifflin Co. Trade & Reference Div.

Hoffman, Mary. The Falconer's Knot: A Story of Friars, Flirtation & Foul Play. 2007. (Illus.). 288p. (YA). (gr. 7 up). 16.95 (978-1-59990-056-8(4) , Bloomsbury Children) Bloomsbury Publishing.

Konigsburg, E. L. The Second Mrs. Giaconda. 3rd ed. (J). pap. 4.95 (978-0-13-800061-5(1)) Prentice Hall (Schl. Div.).

—The Second Mrs. Gioconda. 1998. 160p. (J). (gr. 5-9). pap. 5.99 (978-0-689-82121-9(2) , Aladdin) Simon & Schuster Children's Publishing.

—The Second Mrs. Gioconda. l.t. ed. 2006. 156p. 22.95 (978-0-7862-8286-9(X)) Thorndike Pr.

Meyer, Carolyn. Duchessina: A Novel of Catherine de' Medici. 2007. (Young Royals Ser.). (Illus.). 272p. (YA). 17.00 (978-0-15-205588-2(6)) Harcourt Children's Bks.

Napoli, Donna Jo. Daughter of Venice. 2003. 288p. (YA). (gr. 7). pap. 6.50 (978-0-440-22928-5(6) , Laurel Leaf) Random Hse. Children's Bks.

O'Dell, Scott. The Road to Damietta. 2004. 320p. (YA). (gr. 7). pap. 6.99 (978-0-618-49493-4(6) , Graphia) Houghton Mifflin Co. Trade & Reference Div.

Selfors, Suzanne. Saving Juliet. 2008. 256p. (YA). 16.95 (**978-0-8027-9740-7(7)*) Walker & Co.

Tetzner, Lisa. The Black Brothers. Binder, Hannes, illus. 2004. 146p. (YA). 16.95 (978-1-932425-04-8(7) , Lemniscaat) Boyds Mills Pr.

ITALY—HISTORY—1815-1915

Stiles, Andrina. The Unification of Italy, 1815-70. 2nd ed. 2001. (Illus.). 128p. pap. 13.99 (978-0-340-75386-6(2) , Hodder Murray) Hodder Education GBR. *Dist:* Trafalgar Square Publishing.

ITALY—HISTORY—1914-1946

De Angelis, Luciano. That One Peculiar Year. Noble, Cinzia Donatelli, tr. from ITA. 2006. (ENG.). 88p. per. (**978-88-95145-03-7(8)*) Italian Paths of Culture.

ITALY—SOCIAL LIFE AND CUSTOMS

Austin Goes to Italy. 2nd ed. 2002. (Travels Ser.). (Illus.). 20p. (J). (gr. k-2). reprint ed. pap. 9.95 (978-0-9670001-6-9(5)) Austin Publishing.

Bisignano, Alphonse. Cooking the Italian Way. 2nd rev. exp. ed. 2003. (Easy Menu Ethnic Cookbooks). (Illus.). 72p. (J). (gr. 5-12). pap. 7.95 (978-0-8225-4161-5(0)) Lerner Publishing Group.

—Cooking the Italian Way. Wolfe, Robert L., illus. 2nd rev. exp. ed. 2002. (Easy Menu Ethnic Cookbooks). 72p. (J). (gr. 5-12). 25.26 (978-0-8225-4113-4(0) , Lerner Pubns.) Lerner Publishing Group.

Borlenghi, Patricia & Wright, Rachel. Italy. 2005. (Illus.). 32p. (J). (gr. 4-7). lib. bdg. 27.10 (978-1-932889-93-2(0)) Sea-To-Sea Pubns.

Ferro, Jennifer. Italian Foods & Culture. 1999. (Festive Foods & Celebrations Ser.). (Illus.). 48p. (J). (gr. 3-6). lib. bdg. 27.93 (978-1-57103-302-4(5)) Rourke Publishing, LLC.

Hammond, Paula. Italy & Switzerland. 2002. (Cultures & Costumes Ser.). (Illus.). 64p. (J). (gr. 7 up). lib. bdg. (978-1-59084-438-0(6)) Mason Crest Pubs.

Lassieur, Allison. The Ancient Romans. (People of the Ancient World Ser.). (J). 2005. (Illus.). 112p. (gr. 6-8). pap. 9.95 (978-0-531-16742-7(9)); 2004. 30.50 (978-0-531-12338-6(3)) Scholastic Library Publishing. (Watts, Franklin).

Lynch, Emma. We're from Italy. 2005. (Heinemann First Library). (Illus.). 32p. (J). (978-1-4034-5805-6(7)); pap. (978-1-4034-5814-8(6)) Heinemann.

McCulloch, Julie. Italy. (Illus.). 48p. (J). 2002. (gr. 4-6). pap. (978-1-58810-388-8(9) , 91137); 2001. (gr. 3-5). lib. bdg. 25.64 (978-1-58810-086-3(3)) Heinemann Library.

—Italy. 2001. (Illus.). 48p. (J). (gr. 3-3). lib. bdg. 17.05 (978-0-613-89892-8(3)) Tandem Library Bks.

Mehta-Jones, Shilpa. Life in Ancient Rome. 2004. (Peoples of the Ancient World Ser.). (Illus.). 32p. (J). (978-0-7787-2034-8(9)); pap. (978-0-7787-2064-5(0)) Crabtree Publishing Co.

Nickles, Greg. Italy: The Culture. 2001. (gr. 3-6). lib. bdg. 16.40 (978-0-613-43456-0(0)) Tandem Library Bks.

—Italy: The People. 2001. (gr. 3-6). lib. bdg. 16.40 (978-0-613-43458-4(7)) Tandem Library Bks.

—Italy - The People. (Lands, Peoples & Cultures Ser.). (Illus.). 32p. (J). (gr. 4-5). 2001. (978-0-7787-9370-0(2)); 2000. pap. (978-0-7787-9738-8(4)) Crabtree Publishing Co.

Pirotta, Saviour. Italy. 1999. (Food & Festivals Ser.). (Illus.). 32p. (J). (gr. 1-4). lib. bdg. 25.69 (978-0-8172-5760-6(8)) Raintree.

Rossi, Sophia. Buon Natale: Learning Songs & Traditions in Italian. Kelleher, Kathie, illus. 2007. (ITA.). (J). lib. bdg. 19.95 (**978-1-59972-067-8(1)*) Teach Me Tapes, Inc.

Sheen, Barbara. Foods of Italy. 2005. (Taste of Culture Ser.). (Illus.). 64p. (J). (gr. 4-8). lib. bdg. 27.45 (978-0-7377-3034-0(X) , Greenhaven Pr., Inc.) Thomson Gale.

Tankard, Fiona. Italy. 2004. (Letters from Around the World Ser.). (J). lib. bdg. (978-1-84234-247-3(9) , Cherrytree Books) Evans Publishing Group.

Thoennes, Kristin. Christmas in Italy. 1998. (Christmas Around the World Ser.). (Illus.). 24p. (J). (gr. 2-3). 18.60 (978-0-7368-0090-7(5) , Bridgestone Bks.) Capstone Pr., Inc.

Thomson, Ruth. Italy. Hampton, David, photos by. 2007. (Living In- Ser.). (Illus.). 32p. (J). (**978-1-59771-043-5(1)* , 1268841) Sea-To-Sea Pubns.

Waldman, Nomi J. The Italian Renaissance. 2004. (Daily Life Ser.). (Illus.). 48p. (J). 26.20 (978-0-7377-1398-5(4) , Greenhaven Pr., Inc.) Thomson Gale.

Zelasco, Marco & Zelasco, Pierangelo. Florence in the 1440s. Ripamonti, Aldo, illus. 2001. (Journey to the Past Ser.). 56p. (J). (gr. 6-8). lib. bdg. 27.12 (978-0-7398-1957-9(7)) Raintree.

IVAN IV, CZAR OF RUSSIA, 1530-1584

Price, Sean. Ivan the Terrible: Tsar of Death. 2007. (Wicked Historytrade; Ser.). 128p. (J). spiral bd. 30.00 (**978-0-531-12597-7(1)* , Children's Pr.) Scholastic Library Publishing.

IVORY COAST

see Cote d'Ivoire

IWO JIMA, BATTLE OF, JAPAN, 1945

Bradley, James & Powers, Ron. Flags of Our Fathers: A Young People's Edition. 2005. (Illus.). 224p. (YA). (gr. 7). mass mkt. 5.99 (978-0-440-22920-9(0) , Laurel Leaf) Random Hse. Children's Bks.

—Flags of Our Fathers: Heroes of Iwo Jima. abr. ed. (Illus.). 224p. (YA). (gr. 7). 2001. lib. bdg. 17.99 (978-0-385-90009-6(0)); 2003. reprint ed. pap. 8.95 (978-0-385-73064-8(0)) Random Hse. Children's Bks. (Delacorte Bks. for Young Readers).

Hama, Larry. The Battle of Iwo Jima: Guerilla Warfare in the Pacific. 2007. (Graphic Battles of World War II Ser.). (Illus.). 48p. (**978-1-4042-7421-1(9)*); pap. (**978-1-4042-6030-6(7)*) Rosen Publishing Group, Inc., The.

—The Battle of Iwo Jima: Guerilla Warfare in the Pacific. Williams, Anthony, illus. 2007. (Graphic Battles of World War II Ser.). 48p. (YA). (gr. 5-8). lib. bdg. 29.25 (978-1-4042-0781-3(3)) Rosen Publishing Group, Inc., The.

McGowan, Tom. Battle of Iwo Jima. 1999. (gr. 3-6). lib. bdg. 14.10 (978-0-613-51985-4(X)) Tandem Library Bks.

Nelson, S. D. Quiet Hero: The Ira Hayes Story. Nelson, S. D., illus. 2006. (Illus.). (J). lib. bdg. 16.95 (978-1-58430-263-6(1)) Lee & Low Bks., Inc.

J

JACKSON, ANDREW, 1767-1845

Behrman, Carol H. Andrew Jackson. (History Maker Bios Ser.). (Illus.). (J). 2005. 48p. (gr. 3-5). 26.60 (978-0-8225-1543-2(1)); 2003. 112p. (gr. 6-12). lib. bdg. 29.27 (978-0-8225-0093-3(0)) Lerner Publishing Group.

Burke, Rick. Andrew Jackson. (American Lives Ser.). (Illus.). 32p. (J). 2003. (gr. 2-4). lib. bdg. (978-1-4034-0156-4(X)); 2002. pap. 6.95 (978-1-4034-0412-1(7)) Heinemann Library.

—Andrew Jackson. 2003. (gr. 3-6). lib. bdg. 15.25 (978-0-613-60848-0(8)) Tandem Library Bks.

Burton, Alma Holman. Four American Patriots: Patrick Henry, Alexander Hamilton, Andrew Jackson, Ulysses S. Grant: A Book for Young Americans. 2000. (Illus.). (J). (978-0-89526-204-2(5)) Regnery Publishing, Inc., An Eagle Publishing Co.

Feinstein, Stephen. Andrew Jackson: A MyReportLinks.com Book. 2002. (Presidents Ser.). (Illus.). 48p. (J). (gr. 4-10). lib. bdg. 25.26 (978-0-7660-5003-7(3) , MyReportLinks.com Bks.) Enslow Pubs., Inc.

Frost, J. Old Hickory. reprint ed. 150.00 (978-0-7222-8720-0(8)) Library Reprints, Inc.

Gaines, Ann Graham. Andrew Jackson: Our Seventh President. 2001. (Spirit of America: Our Presidents Ser.). (Illus.). 48p. (J). (gr. 2-6). 28.50 (978-1-56766-847-6(X)) Child's World, Inc.

Harmon, Daniel E. Andrew Jackson. 2003. (Childhoods of the Presidents Ser.). (Illus.). 48p. (J). (gr. 4 up). lib. bdg. (978-1-59084-274-4(X)) Mason Crest Pubs.

Marrin, Albert. Old Hickory: Andrew Jackson & the American People. 2004. 240p. (J). (gr. 7). 35.00 (978-0-525-47293-3(2) , Dutton Juvenile) Penguin Group (USA) Inc.

Mis, Melody S. How to Draw the Life & Times of Andrew Jackson. 2006. (Kid's Guide to Drawing the Presidents of the United States of America Ser.). (J). 25.25 (978-1-4042-2984-6(1) , PowerKids Pr.) Rosen Publishing Group, Inc., The.

Olson, Tod & Doherty, Kieran. Andrew Jackson. 2003. (Encyclopedia of Presidents Ser.). (Illus.). 110p. (J). 34.00 (978-0-516-22760-3(2) , Children's Pr.) Scholastic Library Publishing.

Rausch, Monica. Andrew Jackson. 2006. (J). (ENG & SPA.). pap. (**978-0-8368-7989-6(9)*); (ENG & SPA.). lib. bdg. (**978-0-8368-7982-7(1)*); (Illus.). 24p. pap. (**978-0-8368-7690-1(3)*); (Illus.). 24p. lib. bdg. (**978-0-8368-7683-3(0)*) Stevens, Gareth Inc. (Weekly Reader Early Learning Library).

Schlesinger, Arthur M., Sr., et al, eds. The Election of 1828. 2003. (Major Presidential Elections & the Administrations That Followed Ser.). (Illus.). 154p. (YA). (gr. 7 up). lib. bdg. (978-1-59084-353-6(3)) Mason Crest Pubs.

Somervill, Barbara A. Andrew Jackson. 2003. (Profiles of the Presidents Ser.). (Illus.). 64p. (J). (gr. 4 up). lib. bdg. 23.93 (978-0-7565-0255-3(1)) Compass Point Bks.

Stanley, George Edward. Andrew Jackson: Young Patriot. Henderson, Meryl, illus. 2003. (Childhood of Famous Americans Ser.). 192p. (J). pap. 5.99 (978-0-689-85744-7(6) , Aladdin) Simon & Schuster Children's Publishing.

—Andrew Jackson: Young Patriot. 2003. (gr. 3-6). lib. bdg. 13.00 (978-0-613-66478-3(7)) Tandem Library Bks.

Venezia, Mike. Andrew Jackson: Seventh President, 1829-1837. Venezia, Mike, illus. 2005. (Getting to Know the U. S. Presidents Ser.). (Illus.). 32p. (J). (gr. 3-4). pap. 7.95 (978-0-516-27481-2(3) , Children's Pr.) Scholastic Library Publishing.

Venezia, Mike, illus. Andrew Jackson. 2005. (Getting to Know the U. S. Presidents Ser.). 32p. (J). (gr. 3-4). 26.00 (978-0-516-22612-5(6) , Children's Pr.) Scholastic Library Publishing.

Welsbacher, Anne. Andrew Jackson. 1999. (United States Presidents Ser.). (Illus.). 32p. (J). (gr. k-6). lib. bdg. 22.78 (978-1-56239-811-8(3) , Checkerboard Library) ABDO Publishing Co.

Whitelaw, Nancy. Andrew Jackson: Frontier President. 2004. (Notable Americans Ser.). (Illus.). 128p. (J). (gr. 6-12). 23.95 (978-1-883846-67-1(6) , First Biographies) Reynolds, Morgan Inc.

JACKSON, ANDREW, 1767-1845—FICTION

Sargent, Dave & Sargent, Pat. Snow: (White) Be Truthful, 25, 53. Lenoir, Jane, illus. 2001. (Saddle Up Ser.: 53). 36p. (J). pap. 6.95 (978-1-56763-624-6(1)); lib. bdg. 22.60 (978-1-56763-623-9(3)) Ozark Publishing.

JACKSON, JESSE, 1941-

Gillis, Jennifer Blizin. Jesse Jackson. 2005. (Illus.). 32p. (J). (978-1-4034-6983-0(0)); pap. (978-1-4034-6990-8(3)) Heinemann Library.

Haskins, James. Jesse Jackson: Civil Rights Activist. 2000. (African-American Biographies Ser.). (Illus.). 128p. (YA). (gr. 6-12). lib. bdg. 26.60 (978-0-7660-1390-2(1)) Enslow Pubs., Inc.

Jakoubek, Robert. Jesse Jackson: Civil Rights Leader & Politician. (Black Americans of Achievement Ser.). (Illus.). 112p. (gr. 6-12). 2005. pap. 13.25 (978-0-7910-8334-5(9)); 2004. (J). 30.00 (978-0-7910-8160-0(5)) Facts On File, Inc. (Chelsea Hse.).

Simon, Charman. Jesse Jackson: I Am Somebody! 1998. (Community Builders Ser.). (Illus.). 48p. (J). (gr. 3-5). pap. 6.95 (978-0-516-26133-1(9) , Children's Pr.) Scholastic Library Publishing.

Woog, Dan. Jesse Jackson. 1999. (People in the News Ser.). (Illus.). 118p. (YA). (gr. 6-9). 32.45 (978-1-56006-631-6(8) , Lucent Bks.) Thomson Gale.

JACKSON, MAHALIA, 1911-1972

Dunham, Montrew. Mahalia Jackson: Gospel Singer & Civil Rights Champion, 7 vols. Underdown, Harold, ed. Morrison, Cathy, illus. 3rd rev. ed. 2003. (Young Patriots Ser.: Vol. 7). 120p. (J). pap. 9.95 (978-1-882859-39-9(1)); 15.95 (978-1-882859-38-2(3)) Patria Pr., Inc.

—Mahalia Jackson: Gospel Singer & Civil Rights Champion. 2003. (gr. 3-6). lib. bdg. 18.75 (978-0-613-80207-9(1)) Tandem Library Bks.

Kramer, Barbara. Mahalia Jackson: The Voice of Gospel & Civil Rights. 2003. (African-American Biographies Ser.). (Illus.). 128p. (J). lib. bdg. 26.60 (978-0-7660-2115-0(7)) Enslow Pubs., Inc.

JACKSON, STONEWALL, 1824-1863

Brager, Bruce L. There He Stands: The Story of Stonewall Jackson. 2005. (Civil War Leaders Ser.). (Illus.). 176p. (J). (gr. 6-12). 26.95 (978-1-931798-44-0(3)) Reynolds, Morgan Inc.

Doak, Robin S. Thomas "Stonewall" Jackson: Confederate General. 2005. (Signature Lives Ser.). (Illus.). 112p. (J). (gr. 5-7). (978-0-7565-0987-3(4)) Compass Point Bks.

Hale, Sarah Elder, ed. Stonewall Jackson: Spirit of the South. 2005. (Cobblestone the Civil War Ser.). (Illus.). 48p. (J). 17.95 (978-0-8126-7907-6(5)) Cobblestone Publishing Co.

Hewson, Martha S. Stonewall Jackson: Confederate General. (Famous Figures of the Civil War Era Ser.). (Illus.). 80p. (J). 2001. (gr. 8-12). 25.00 (978-0-7910-6002-5(0)); 2000. (gr. 4-7). pap. 25.00 (978-0-7910-6140-4(X)) Facts On File, Inc. (Chelsea Hse.).

Marsh, Carole. Thomas "Stonewall" Jackson. 2002. (One Thousand Readers Ser.). (Illus.). 12p. (J). (gr. k-4). 2.95 (978-0-635-01490-0(4) , 14904) Gallopade International.

—The Virginia Reader: Thomas "Stonewall" Jackson. 2001. (Virginia Experience! Ser.). (Illus.). 12p. (J). (gr. k-4). pap. 2.95 (978-0-635-00370-6(8)) Gallopade International.

McLeese, Don. Stonewall Jackson. 2006. (Civil War Military Leaders Ser.). (Illus.). 32p. (gr. 3-6). 19.95 (978-1-59515-477-4(9)) Rourke Publishing, LLC.

Mcleese, Don. Stonewall Jackson. 2005. 32p. pap. 6.45 (978-1-59515-791-1(3)) Rourke Publishing, LLC.

Robertson, James I. Standing Like a Stone Wall: The Life of General Thomas J. Jackson. 2001. (Illus.). 192p. (YA). (gr. 6 up). 22.00 (978-0-689-82419-7(X) , Atheneum) Simon & Schuster Children's Publishing.

JACKSON, STONEWALL, 1824-1863—FICTION

Gibboney, Douglas Lee. Stonewall Jackson at Gettysburg. 2002. (Illus.). 132p. pap. 12.95 (978-1-57249-317-9(8) , Burd Street Pr.) White Mane Publishing Co., Inc.

JACKSON, THOMAS JONATHAN, 1824-1863

see Jackson, Stonewall, 1824-1863

JACOB (BIBLICAL PATRIARCH)

Auld, Mary. Jacob & Esau. Mayo, Diana, illus. 2000. (Bible Stories Ser.). 32p. (J). (gr. 2-4). pap. 7.95 (978-0-531-15436-6(X) , Watts, Franklin) Scholastic Library Publishing.

—Jacob & Esau. 2000. (gr. 3-6). lib. bdg. 16.40 (978-0-613-62466-4(1)) Tandem Library Bks.

Nakhat, Shamim. The Story of Yaqub & Yusuf: Based on Qur'anic Facts. 2005. (Me & My Holy Qur'an Ser.). (Illus.). 24p. (J). (**978-81-7231-618-1(6)*) Islamic Bk. Service.

J K L

PowerXpress Jacob Unit. 2005. 115.00 (978-0-687-03920-3(7)) Abingdon Pr.

Racklin-Siegel, Alison, illus. Jacob's Travels. 2005. (ENG & HEB.). (J). per. 9.95 (978-0-939144-53-2(0)) EKS Publishing Co.

JAGUAR

Cole & Leeson. El Jaguar y el Leopardo. 2002. (Gatos Salvajes del Mundo Serie).Tr. of Wild Cats Of The World: The Jaguar And The Leopard. (SPA.). 24p. (J). (gr. 3-5). 24.94 (978-1-4103-0005-8(6) , Blackbirch Pr., Inc.) Thomson Gale.

Cole, Melissa S. Jaguars & Leopards. l.t. ed. 2001. (Wild Cats of the World Ser.). (Illus.). 23p. (J). (gr. 3-6). 22.45 (978-1-56711-447-8(4) , Blackbirch Pr., Inc.) Thomson Gale.

Cooper, Jason. Jaguars. 2002. (Illus.). 24p. (J). lib. bdg. 20.64 (978-1-58952-403-3(9)) Rourke Publishing, LLC.

Erdman, Roxanna. Elogio del Jaguar. 1998. (SPA.). (gr. 1-3). lib. bdg. 9.95 (978-968-19-0433-3(8)) Aguilar Editorial MEX. *Dist:* Libros Sin Fronteras, Santillana USA Publishing Co., Inc.

—Elogio del Tlacuache. 1998. (SPA.). (ps-3). lib. bdg. 9.95 (978-968-19-0432-6(X)) Aguilar Editorial MEX. *Dist:* Libros Sin Fronteras, Santillana USA Publishing Co., Inc.

Feinstein, Stephen. The Jaguar: Help Save This Endangered Species! 2008. (Saving Endangered Species Ser.). 128p. (J). (gr. 6 up). lib. bdg. 33.27 (***978-1-59845-065-1(4)*** , MyReportLinks.com Bks.) Enslow Pubs., Inc.

Frost, Helen. Jaguars. Saunders-Smith, Gail, ed. 2002. (Rain Forest Animals Ser.). (Illus.). 24p. (J). (gr. k-1). lib. bdg. 15.93 (978-0-7368-1193-4(1) , Pebble Bks.) Capstone Pr., Inc.

Grolier Educational Staff, contrib. by. Jaguars. 2001. (Nature's Children Ser.). (Illus.). 48p. (J). (978-0-7172-5539-9(5) , Grolier) Scholastic Library Publishing.

Huntrods, David. Jaguars. 2006. (Amazing Animals Ser.). (J). (978-1-59036-392-8(2)); (978-1-59036-398-0(1)) Weigl Pubs., Inc.

Lalley. Jaguars. 2001. (Animals of the Rain Forest Ser.). (SPA., Illus.). pap. (978-0-7398-3356-8(1)) Steck-Vaughn.

Lalley, Pat. Jaguars. 2000. (Animals of the Rain Forest Ser.). (Illus.). 32p. (J). (gr. 4-7). lib. bdg. 22.83 (978-0-7398-3102-1(X)) Raintree.

Lee Stacy. Jaguar. 2004. (Hot Cars Ser.). 32p. pap. 6.95 (978-1-59515-346-3(2)) Rourke Publishing, LLC.

Malaspina, Ann. The Jaguar. 2000. (Endangered Animals & Habitats Ser.). (Illus.). 96p. (YA). (gr. 4-12). 29.95 (978-1-56006-813-6(2) , Lucent Bks.) Thomson Gale.

Mezzanotte, Jim. The Story of Jaguar. 2005. (Classic Cars Ser.). (Illus.). 24p. (YA). lib. bdg. 22.00 (978-0-8368-4535-8(8)) Stevens, Gareth Inc.

Middleton, Don. Jaguars. 1999. (PowerKids Readers Ser.). (Illus.). 24p. (J). (gr. k-4). lib. bdg. 18.75 (978-0-8239-5210-6(X)) Rosen Publishing Group, Inc., The.

Murray, Julie. Jaguars. 2005. (Animal Kingdom Set Ii Ser.). (Illus.). 24p. (J). (gr. k-4). lib. bdg. 21.35 (978-1-59197-322-5(8)) ABDO Publishing Co.

Squire, Ann O. Jaguars. 2005. (True Bks.). (Illus.). (J). (gr. 3-5). 47p. pap. 6.95 (978-0-516-27933-6(5)); 48p. 25.00 (978-0-516-22793-1(9)) Scholastic Library Publishing. (Children's Pr.).

St. Pierre, Stephanie. Jaguars. 2002. (In the Wild Ser.). (Illus.). 24p. (J). (gr. k-2). pap. 6.95 (978-1-58810-381-9(1) , 91101) Heinemann Library.

Stacy, Lee. Jaguar. 2005. (Hot Cars Ser.). (Illus.). 32p. (gr. 4-8). 19.95 (978-1-59515-211-4(3)) Rourke Publishing, LLC.

Stephanie, St Pierre. Jaguars. 2001. (In the Wild Ser.). (Illus.). 24p. (J). (ps-3). lib. bdg. 21.36 (978-1-58810-108-2(8)) Heinemann Library.

Stille, Darlene R. Jaguars. 2001. (First Reports). (Illus.). 48p. (J). (gr. 3 up). lib. bdg. 21.26 (978-0-7565-0055-9(9)) Compass Point Bks.

Tourville, Amanda Doering. A Jaguar Grows Up. Denman, Michael & Huiett, William J., illus. 2006. (Wild Animals Ser.). 24p. (J). (gr. 1-3). 25.26 (978-1-4048-3159-9(2) , 1265741) Picture Window Bks.

Vogel, Elizabeth. Jaguars. 2002. (PowerKids Readers Ser.). (Illus.). 24p. (J). (gr. 1). lib. bdg. 16.00 (978-0-8239-6024-8(2) , PowerKids Pr.) Rosen Publishing Group, Inc., The.

Walker, Sally M. Jaguars. 2008. (Nature Watch Ser.). (J). lib. bdg. 26.60 (***978-0-8225-7510-8(8)*** , Lerner Pubns.) Lerner Publishing Group.

Welsbacher, Anne. Jaguars. 2000. (Wild Cats Ser.). (Illus.). 24p. (J). (gr. k-6). lib. bdg. 21.35 (978-1-57765-090-4(5) , Checkerboard Library) ABDO Publishing Co.

Zumbusch, Amelie von. Jaguars: World's Strongest Cats. 2007. (Dangerous Cats Ser.). (Illus.). 24p. (J). (gr. k-5). lib. bdg. 21.25 (978-1-4042-3628-8(7) , PowerKids Pr.) Rosen Publishing Group, Inc., The.

JAGUAR—FICTION

Ada, Alma Flor & Campoy, F. Isabel. Eyes of the Jaguar. Davalos, Felipe, illus. (Gateways to the Sun). 48p. (J). (gr. k-6). pap. 13.95 (978-1-58105-970-0(1)) Santillana USA Publishing Co., Inc.

Albert, Burton. Journey of the Nightly Jaguar: Spanish Paperback Edition. Roth, Robert, illus. 2000. (J). pap. 4.95 (978-0-689-80590-5(X) , Aladdin) Simon & Schuster Children's Publishing.

Armellada, Fray Cesareo. El Tigre y ll Rayo. 2001. Tr. of Jaguar & the Lightning. (Illus.). (J). (978-0-606-20650-1(7)) Tandem Library Bks.

Campoy, F. Isabel. Rosa Raposa. Aruego, Jose & Dewey, Ariane, illus. 2002. 32p. (J). (gr. k-2). 16.00 (978-0-15-202161-0(2) , Gulliver Bks.) Harcourt Children's Bks.

Cowcher, Helen. Jaguar. 2000. (SPA.). 32p. (J). pap. (978-980-257-248-9(9)) Ekare, Ediciones.

—Jaguar. (Illus.). 40p. (CHI, ENG, URD, TUR & VIE.). (J). 16.95 (978-1-84059-009-8(2)); 2001. (VIE, ENG, URD, TUR & CHI., (J). 16.95 (978-1-84059-014-2(9)); 2001. (BEN, ENG, URD, TUR & VIE., (YA). 16.95 (978-1-84059-008-1(4)); 2001. (GRE, ENG, URD, TUR & VIE., (YA). 16.95 (978-1-84059-010-4(6)); 2001. (GUJ, ENG, URD, TUR & VIE., (YA). 16.95 (978-1-84059-011-1(4)); 2001. (TUR, ENG, URD, VIE & CHI., (YA). 16.95 (978-1-84059-012-8(2)); 2001. (URD, ENG, TUR, VIE & CHI., (YA). 16.95 (978-1-84059-013-5(0)); 2001. (TUR., (YA). 16.95 (978-1-84059-015-9(7)) Milet Publishing.

—Jaguar. (J). (gr. 1-2). (978-0-590-36037-1(X)); (SPA., Illus.). (gr. 1-3). pap. 3.96 net. (978-0-590-87599-8(X) , SO30738, Scholastic Pr.); 2002. 32p. pap. 5.99 (978-0-439-39470-3(8)) Scholastic, Inc.

Gosse, Jim. Jimmy Jaguar: Collection of Stories. 2006. 17.00 (978-0-8059-9373-8(8)) Dorrance Publishing Co., Inc.

El Jaguar 11: Leveled Books. 2001. (McGraw-Hill. Lectura Ser.). (ENG & SPA.). (gr. 4 up). (978-0-02-188211-3(8)) Macmillan/McGraw-Hill Schl. Div.

Jaguar Attack! Individual Title, 6 Packs. (Bookweb Ser.). 32p. (gr. 5 up). 34.00 (978-0-7635-3787-6(X)) Rigby Education.

Jaguar's Jungleberry Jamboree. 2001. (ps-2). lib. bdg. 9.80 (978-0-613-32702-2(0)) Tandem Library Bks.

Mawhinney, Art, illus. Go, Baby Jaguar! 2007. (Go, Diego, Go! Ser.). 24p. (J). pap. 3.99 (978-1-4169-4065-4(0) , Simon Spotlight/Nickelodeon) Simon & Schuster Children's Publishing.

Rimes, Leann. Jag. Bernal, Richard, illus. 2003. 40p. (J). (gr. k-3). 15.99 (978-0-525-47155-4(3) , Dutton Juvenile) Penguin Group (USA) Inc.

Sargent, Pat L. The Jaguar, 8 vols. Lenoir, Jane, illus. 2007. (Barney the Bear Killer Ser.: 8). 164p. (YA). lib. bdg. 25.25 (***978-1-59381-424-3(0)***) Ozark Publishing.

Smith, Roland. Jaguar. 1999. 256p. (gr. 4-7). pap. 5.95 (978-0-7868-1312-4(1)) Disney Pr.

—Jaguar. unabr. ed. 1999. (YA). (gr. 5 up). pap., stu. ed. 52.50 incl. audio (978-0-7887-3848-7(8) , 41046X4) Recorded Bks., LLC.

JAILS

see Prisons

JAM

Zemlicka, Shannon. From Fruit to Jelly. 2004. (Start to Finish Ser.). (J). pap. 4.95 (978-0-8225-0748-2(X)); (Illus.). 24p. 18.60 (978-0-8225-0942-4(3) , Lerner Pubns.) Lerner Publishing Group.

JAMAICA

Bastyra, Judy. Jamaica. 2006. (Living In- Ser.). (Illus.). 32p. (J). (978-1-59771-047-3(4)) Sea-To-Sea Pubns.

Brownlie, Alison. Jamaica. Cunningham, Susan M., photos by. 2004. (Letters from Around the World Ser.). (Illus.). 32p. (J). (978-1-84234-251-0(7) , Cherrytree Books) Evans Publishing Group.

—Jamaica. 1999. (We Come from Ser.). (Illus.). 32p. (J). (gr. 1-4). lib. bdg. 25.69 (978-0-8172-5511-4(7)) Raintree.

Capek, Michael. Jamaica. 1999. (Ticket to Ser.). (Illus.). 48p. (gr. 2-4). 22.60 (978-1-57505-137-6(0)); (J). (gr. 3-5). lib. bdg. 22.60 (978-1-57505-112-3(5) , Carolrhoda Bks.) Lerner Publishing Group.

Crespi, Jess. Exploring Jamaica with the Five Themes of Geography. 2005. (Library of the Western Hemisphere). (Illus.). 24p. 19.95 (978-1-4042-2674-6(5) , PowerKids Pr.); pap. (978-0-8239-4646-4(0)); (Illus.). 24p. pap. (978-0-8239-4634-1(7)) Rosen Publishing Group, Inc., The.

Gritzner, Janet H. Jamaica. 2004. (Modern World Nations Ser.). (Illus.). 120p. (gr. 6-12). 30.00 (978-0-7910-7913-3(9) , Chelsea Hse.) Facts On File, Inc.

Hamilton, Janice. Jamaica in Pictures. 2005. (Visual Geography Series, Second Ser.). (Illus.). 80p. (J). (gr. 5-12). 27.93 (978-0-8225-2394-9(9)) Lerner Publishing Group.

Heinemann Staff. Jamaica. (World Focus Ser.). (Illus.). 31p. (J). (gr. 3-7). pap. 3.99 (978-0-431-07266-1(3)) Oxfam Publishing GBR. *Dist:* Stylus Publishing, LLC.

Heinrichs, Ann. Jamaica. 2003. (True Bks.). (Illus.). (J). 47p. (gr. 3-5). pap. 6.95 (978-0-516-27751-6(0)); 48p. 25.00 (978-0-516-22676-7(2)) Scholastic Library Publishing. (Children's Pr.).

—Jamaica. 2003. (gr. 3-6). lib. bdg. 15.25 (978-0-613-67970-1(9)) Tandem Library Bks.

Horst, Heather A. & Garner, Andrew. Jamaican Americans. 2007. (New Immigrants Ser.). (Illus.). 144p. (J). (gr. 6-12). 27.95 (978-0-7910-8790-9(5) , Chelsea Hse.) Facts On File, Inc.

Kwek, Karen. Welcome to Jamaica. 2005. 48p. (J). lib. bdg. 26.00 (978-0-8368-2564-0(0)) Stevens, Gareth Inc.

Morris, Kerry-Ann. Jamaica. 2003. (Countries of the World Ser.). (Illus.). 96p. (J). (gr. 6 up). lib. bdg. 30.00 (978-0-8368-2364-6(8)) Stevens, Gareth Inc.

Pluckrose, Henry Arthur. Jamaica. 1999. (Picture a Country Ser.). (Illus.). 32p. (J). (gr. k-2). pap. 6.95 (978-0-531-15374-1(6) , Watts, Franklin) Scholastic Library Publishing.

Roy, Jennifer Rozines & Roy, Gregory. Jamaica. 2004. (Discovering Cultures Ser.). (Illus.). 48p. (J). 25.64 (978-0-7614-1793-4(1) , Benchmark Bks.) Cavendish, Marshall Corp.

Sheehan, Sean. Jamaica. 2nd ed. 2004. (Cultures of the World Ser.). (Illus.). 144p. (J). 37.07 (978-0-7614-1785-9(0)) Cavendish, Marshall Corp.

Simpson, Joanne M. Why Heritage. collector's ed. 2002. (Illus.). 70p. per. 10.00 (978-976-610-480-1(8) , 991096) Creative Links JAM. *Dist:* BookMasters, Inc.

Wilkins, Frances. Jamaica. 1999. (Major World Nations Ser.). (Illus.). 144p. (YA). (gr. 4-7). lib. bdg. 21.95 (978-0-7910-4978-5(7) , Chelsea Hse.) Facts On File, Inc.

Williams, Colleen Madonna Flood. Jamaica. 2003. (Discovering the Caribbean Ser.). (Illus.). 64p. (J). (gr. 5 up). lib. bdg. (978-1-59084-294-2(4)) Mason Crest Pubs.

Wilson, Amber. Jamaica — the Culture. 2003. (Lands, Peoples, & Cultures Ser.). (Illus.). 32p. (J). (978-0-7787-9332-8(X)); pap. (978-0-7787-9700-5(7)) Crabtree Publishing Co.

—Jamaica - the Land. 2003. (Lands, Peoples, & Cultures Ser.). (Illus.). 32p. (J). (978-0-7787-9330-4(3)); pap. (978-0-7787-9698-5(1)) Crabtree Publishing Co.

—Jamaica - the People. 2003. (Lands, Peoples, & Cultures Ser.). (Illus.). 32p. (J). (978-0-7787-9331-1(1)); pap. (978-0-7787-9699-2(X)) Crabtree Publishing Co.

—Jamaica the Land. 2003. (gr. k-3). lib. bdg. 16.40 (978-0-613-82414-9(8)) Tandem Library Bks.

—Jamaica the People. 2003. (gr. 3-6). lib. bdg. 16.40 (978-0-613-84499-4(8)) Tandem Library Bks.

Zephaniah, Benjamin. J Is for Jamaica. Das, Prodeepta, photos by. 2006. (World Alphabets Ser.). (Illus.). 32p. (gr. k-2). 15.95 (978-1-84507-401-2(7)) Lincoln, Frances Ltd. GBR. *Dist:* Perseus Distribution.

JAMAICA—FICTION

Angelou, Maya. Cedric of Jamaica. Rockwell, Lizzy, illus. 2005. (Random House Pictureback Book Ser.). (J). (978-0-375-83269-7(6)); lib. bdg. (978-0-375-93269-4(0)) Random Hse., Inc.

Belafonte, Harry. Island in the Sun. 2001. (978-0-606-21254-0(X)) Tandem Library Bks.

Birch, Beverley. Julius Caesar. 2007. (Illus.). 80p. 13.95 (***978-0-7502-4962-1(5)*** , Hodder Wayland) Hodder Children's Division GBR. *Dist:* Independent Pubs. Group.

Browne, Diane, et al. The Cat Woman & the Spinning Wheel & Other Stories. Haynes-Peart, Andrea et al, illus. 2002. (Doctor Bird Reading Ser.). 64p. (J). pap. (978-976-637-092-3(3)) Randle, Ian Pubs.

—Sweet, Sweet Mango Tree & Other Stories. Brown, Clovis et al, illus. 2002. (Doctor Bird Reading Ser.). 32p. (J). pap. (978-976-637-090-9(7)) Randle, Ian Pubs.

Burford, Lorrimer. A Jamaican Storyteller's Tale. 2005. 197p. 7.99 (978-976-8184-84-9(1)) Penguin Group (USA) Inc.

Campbell, Peggy, et al. How Did We Get Here? & Other Stories. Brown, Clovis et al, illus. 2002. (Doctor Bird Reading Ser.). 39p. (J). pap. (978-976-637-093-0(1)) Randle, Ian Pubs.

D'Costa. Sprat Morrison. Date not set. (Illus.). 192p. pap. 26.00 (978-0-582-05207-9(6)) Addison-Wesley Longman, Ltd. GBR. *Dist:* Trans-Atlantic Pubns., Inc.

Hall, Rose. After the Storm. jazvic, Beryl, illus. 2005. (J). bds. 19.95 (978-0-9770503-0-7(0)) Institute For Behavior Change Incorporated The.

Hanson, Regina. A Season for Mangoes. Velasquez, Eric, illus. 2005. 40p. (J). (gr. k-3). 15.00 (978-0-618-15972-7(X) , Clarion Bks.) Houghton Mifflin Co. Trade & Reference Div.

Hausman, Gerald & Hinds, Uton. The Jacob Ladder. 2001. (Illus.). 128p. (J). (gr. 5-8). pap. 15.95 (978-0-531-30331-3(4) , Orchard Bks.) Scholastic, Inc.

Magnus, Kellie. Little Lion Goes to School. Robinson, Michael, illus. l.t. ed. 2003. 16p. (J). 9.99 (978-0-9744211-0-0(3)) Media Magic New York.

McKnight, Penny. Nix. 2006. (Illus.). 84p. (J). (978-1-59166-610-3(4)) Jones, Bob Univ. Pr.

Phillpotts, Karl, et al. In Jamaica Where I Live & Other Stories. Stennett, Errol et al, illus. 2002. (Doctor Bird Reading Ser.). 31p. (J). pap. (978-976-637-089-3(3)) Randle, Ian Pubs.

Rees, Celia. Pirates! 2003. 340p. (J). 16.95 (978-1-58234-816-2(2) , Bloomsbury Children) Bloomsbury Publishing.

Richmond, Beulah. Anancy & Friends: A Grandmother's Anancy Stories for Her Grandchildren. Brown, Clovis, illus. 2004. 52p. 5.99 (978-976-8184-48-1(5)) Penguin Group (USA) Inc.

Strickland, Brad. Mutiny! Fuller, Thomas E. & Saponaro, Dominick, illus. 2002. 208p. (J). (gr. 3-6). pap. 4.99 (978-0-689-85296-1(7) , Aladdin) Simon & Schuster Children's Publishing.

Temple, Frances. Tiger Soup: An Anansi Story from Jamaica. 1998. (J). (978-0-606-13850-5(1)) Tandem Library Bks.

Van West, Patricia E. The Crab Man. Lucas, Cedric, illus. 40p. (J). (ps-3). 2001. pap. 8.95 (978-1-890515-25-6(6)); 1998. 15.95 (978-1-890515-08-9(6)) Turtle Bks.

Winter, Jeanette. Angelina's Island. 2007. (Illus.). 32p. (J). (ps-3). 16.00 (978-0-374-30349-5(5) , Farrar, Straus & Giroux (BYR)) Farrar, Straus & Giroux.

Wohlt, Julia. Naughty Eddie Larue. Brown, Clovis, illus. 27p. (978-976-610-173-2(6)) Creative Links.

JAMAICAN AMERICANS

Caravantes, Peggy. Marcus Garvey: Black Nationalist. 2004. (Twentieth Century Leaders Ser.). (Illus.). 128p. (YA). (gr. 6-12). 23.95 (978-1-931798-14-3(1)) Reynolds, Morgan Inc.

Horst, Heather A. & Garner, Andrew. Jamaican Americans. 2007. (New Immigrants Ser.). (Illus.). 144p. (J). (gr. 6-12). 27.95 (978-0-7910-8790-9(5) , Chelsea Hse.) Facts On File, Inc.

Kallen, Stuart A. Marcus Garvey & the Back to Africa Movement. 2006. (Lucent Library of Black History). (Illus.). 112p. (J). (gr. 7-10). 32.45 (978-1-59018-838-5(1) , Lucent Bks.) Thomson Gale.

Mohamed, Paloma. A Man Called Garvey: The Life & Times of the Great Leader Marcus Garvey. Braithwaithe, Barrington, illus. l.t. ed. 2004. (Majority Press Inc., Wisdom for Children Ser.: No. 1). 32p. (J). 12.95 (978-0-912469-40-9(4)) Majority Pr., Inc., The.

JAMAICAN AMERICANS—FICTION

Gunning, Monica. A Shelter in Our Car. Pedlar, Elaine, tr. Pedlar, Elaine, illus. 2004. 32p. (J). 16.95 (978-0-89239-189-9(8)) Children's Bk. Pr.

Never So Good (Jamaicans) 76p. (YA). (gr. 6-12). pap. 9.95 (978-0-8224-3806-9(2)) Globe Fearon Educational Publishing.

Winter, Jeanette. Angelina's Island. 2007. (Illus.). 32p. (J). (ps-3). 16.00 (978-0-374-30349-5(5) , Farrar, Straus & Giroux (BYR)) Farrar, Straus & Giroux.

JAMES I, KING OF ENGLAND, 1566-1625

Marsh, Carole. King James, I. 2002. (One Thousand Readers Ser.). (Illus.). 12p. (J). (gr. k-4). 2.95 (978-0-635-01519-8(6) , 15196) Gallopade International.

JAMES, JESSE, 1847-1882

Bruns, Roger A. Jesse James: Legendary Outlaw. 1998. (Historical American Biographies Ser.). (Illus.). 128p. (YA). (gr. 6-12). lib. bdg. 26.60 (978-0-7660-1055-0(4)) Enslow Pubs., Inc.

Collins, Kathleen. Jesse James: Western Bank Robber. 2003. (Famous People in American History Ser.). (Illus.). 32p. (J). pap. (978-0-8239-4184-1(1)) Rosen Publishing Group, Inc., The.

Frisch, Aaron. Jesse James. 2005. (Illus.). 48p. (gr. 5-9). 21.95 (978-1-58341-338-8(3) , Creative Education) Creative Co., The.

Landau, Elaine. Jesse James: Wild West Train Robber. 2004. (Best of the West Biographies Ser.). (Illus.). 48p. (J). lib. bdg. 23.93 (978-0-7660-2208-9(0)) Enslow Pubs., Inc.

Miller, Steven G. The Legend of Jessie James. 2001. (History Channel History Guides Ser.). (Illus.). 40p. (J). pap. 9.99 (978-0-86730-845-7(1)) Lebhar-Friedman Bks.

Robinson, J. Dennis. Jesse James: Legendary Rebel & Outlaw. 2006. (J). (978-0-7565-1871-4(7)) Compass Point Bks.

Saffer, Barbara. Jesse James. 2001. (Famous Figures of the American Frontier Ser.). (Illus.). 64p. (J). (gr. 5 up). pap. 8.95 (978-0-7910-6500-6(6)); 25.00 (978-0-7910-6499-3(9)) Facts On File, Inc. (Chelsea Hse.).

JAMES, WILL, 1892-1942

James, Will. The Will James Cowboy Book, Vol. 1. rev. ed. (Illus.). 128p. (J). (gr. 4). 18.00 (978-0-87842-469-6(5) , 816) Mountain Pr. Publishing Co., Inc.

JAMESTOWN (VA.)—FICTION

Archambault, Jeanne. Larry the Lawnmower. Corey, Victoria, illus. 2004. 32p. (J). 14.95 (978-0-9763031-0-7(8)); per. 10.00 (978-0-9763031-1-4(6)) Jitterbug Bks.

Carbone, Elisa. Blood on the River: James Town 1607. 2007. 237p. (J). (gr. 4). per. 6.99 (***978-0-14-240932-9(4)*** , Puffin) Penguin Group (USA) Inc.

Hall, Lucy. From England to Jamestowne: A Journey to Find My Father. 2007. (J). (***978-0-9763706-5-9(4)***) Tendril Pr. LLC.

Hermes, Patricia. The Starving Time Bk. 2: Elizabeth's Jamestown Colony Diary. 2002. (My America Ser.: Bk. 2). (Illus.). 112p. (J). (gr. 2-5). pap. 4.99 (978-0-439-36902-2(9) , Scholastic Pr.) Scholastic, Inc.

Karwoski, Gail Langer. Surviving Jamestown: The Adventures of Young Sam Collier. Casale, Paul, illus. 2001. 192p. (J). (gr. 3-7). 14.95 (978-1-56145-239-2(4)); pap. 8.95 (978-1-56145-245-3(9)) Peachtree Pubs., Ltd.

—Surviving Jamestown: The Adventures of Young Sam Collier. 2001. (gr. 3-6). lib. bdg. 17.60 (978-0-613-51595-5(1)) Tandem Library Bks.

Lapallo, Connie. Dark Enough to See the Stars in a Jamestown Sky. 2006. (YA). (gr. 7 up). pap. 19.95 (***978-1-59526-421-3(3)***) Media Creations, Inc.

Massie, Elizabeth. 1609: Winter of the Dead: A Novel of the Founding of Jamestown. 2007. (Young Founders Ser.). 192p. (YA). 5.99 (978-0-7653-5604-8(X) , Tor Kids) Doherty, Tom Assocs., LLC.

Stone, Marie. On Their Own: A Journey to Jamestown. 2006. (J). (978-1-57249-385-8(2) , White Mane Kids) White Mane Publishing Co., Inc.

JAMESTOWN (VA.)—HISTORY

Becker, Sandra. Pocahontas. 2003. (Folk Heroes Ser.). (Illus.). 24p. (J). lib. bdg. 15.95 (978-1-59036-074-3(5)) Weigl Pubs., Inc.

Benge, Janet & Benge, Geoff. John Smith: A Foothold in the New World. 2006. (Illus.). 192p. (J). pap. (978-1-932096-36-1(1)) Emerald Bks.

Brannon, Barbara. Discover Jamestown. 2005. 39.00 (***978-1-4108-5142-0(7)***) Benchmark Education Co.

Braun, Eric. The Story of Jamestown. Erwin, Steve et al, illus. 2005. (Graphic History Ser.). 32p. (J). (gr. 2-5). lib. bdg. 25.26 (978-0-7368-4967-8(X)) Capstone Pr., Inc.

Bruchac, Joseph. Pocahontas. 2003. (Illus.). 192p. (J). (gr. 6-8). 17.00 (978-0-15-216737-0(4) , Silver Whistle) Harcourt Trade Pubs.

Cooper, Michael L. Jamestown, 1607. 2006. (Illus.). 112p. (J). (gr. 3-7). 18.95 (978-0-8234-1948-7(7)) Holiday Hse., Inc.

Doherty, Kieran. To Conquer Is to Live: The Life of Captain John Smith of Jamestown. 2001. (Single Titles Ser.). (Illus.). 144p. (J). (gr. 6-8). lib. bdg. 23.90 (978-0-7613-1820-0(8) ; Twenty-First Century Bks.) Lerner Publishing Group.

Early Jamestown (NCHS) (YA). (gr. 5-8). spiral bd., tchr.'s planning gde. ed. 11.50 (978-0-382-40928-8(0)) Cobblestone Publishing Co.

Edwards, Judith. Jamestown, John Smith, & Pocahontas in American History. 2002. (In American History Ser.). (Illus.). 128p. (YA). (gr. 5-12). lib. bdg. 26.60 (978-0-7660-1842-6(3)) Enslow Pubs., Inc.

Fradin, Dennis B. Jamestown, Virginia. 2006. (Turning Points in U. S. History Ser.). (Illus.). 48p. (J). (gr. 3-6). lib. bdg. 29.93 (978-0-7614-2122-1(X) , Benchmark Bks.) Cavendish, Marshall Corp.

Fritz, Jean. The Double Life of Pocahontas. 2004. 24.95 incl. audio (978-1-56008-189-0(9)) Weston Woods Studios, Inc.

—Who's Saying What in Jamestown, Thomas Savage? Comport, Sally Wern, illus. 2007. 64p. (J). (gr. 2 up). 18.99 (978-0-399-24644-9(4) , Putnam Juvenile) Penguin Group (USA) Inc.

Hall-Quest, Olga. Sterling Point Books: Jamestown: the Perilous Adventure. 2007. (Sterling Point Bks.). 192p. (J). pap. 6.95 (*978-1-4027-5122-6(2)) Sterling Publishing Co., Inc.

Harkins, Susan & Harkins, William H. Jamestown: The First English Colony. 2006. (Building America Ser.). (Illus.). 48p. (J). (gr. 4-8). lib. bdg. 20.95 (978-1-58415-458-7(6)) Mitchell Lane Pubs., Inc.

Jamestown: Scholastic Technology Activity Folder. 2001. (Instant Internet Activities Folder Ser.). (J). 3.95 (978-0-439-30954-7(9)) Scholastic, Inc.

Jenner, Caryn. The Story of Pocahontas, Vol. 2. Martin, Linda, ed. 2000. (Readers Ser.). (Illus.). 32p. (J). (gr. 1-3). pap. 3.99 (978-0-7894-6636-5(8)) Dorling Kindersley Publishing, Inc.

—The Story of Pocahontas. 2000. (Illus.). 32p. (J). (ps-ps). lib. bdg. 11.80 (978-0-613-33108-1(7)) Tandem Library Bks.

Jenner, Caryn & Dorling Kindersley Publishing Staff. The Story of Pocahontas. 2000. (Readers Ser.). (Illus.). 32p. (J). (gr. 1-3). 14.99 (978-0-7894-6637-2(6)) Dorling Kindersley Publishing, Inc.

Kells, Deanne. The Jamestown Community. 2005. 39.00 (*978-1-4108-4624-2(5)) Benchmark Education Co.

Kline, Trish. Captain John Smith. 2001. (Discover the Life of an Explorer Ser.). (Illus.). 24p. (J). (gr. 1-4). lib. bdg. 20.64 (978-1-58952-065-3(3)) Rourke Publishing, LLC.

Knowlton, MaryLee & Riehecky, Janet. The Settling of Jamestown. 2002. (Events That Shaped America Ser.). (Illus.). 32p. (J). (gr. 3 up). lib. bdg. 24.67 (978-0-8368-3225-9(6)) Stevens, Gareth Inc.

Landau, Elaine. Explore Colonial Jamestown with Elaine Landau. 2006. (Explore Colonial America with Elaine Landau Ser.). (Illus.). 48p. (J). (gr. 1-3). lib. bdg. 23.93 (978-0-7660-2554-7(3) , Enslow Elementary) Enslow Pubs., Inc.

Lange, Karen E. 1607: A New Look at Jamestown. Block, Ira, photos by. 2007. (Illus.). 48p. (J). (gr. 3-7). 17.95 (978-1-4263-0012-7(3)); lib. bdg. 27.90 (978-1-4263-0013-4(1)) National Geographic Society. (National Geographic Children's Bks.).

Loker, Aleck. Fearless Captain: The Adventures of John Smith. 2006. (Founders of the Republic Ser.). 176p. (J). lib. bdg. 26.95 (978-1-931798-83-9(4)) Reynolds, Morgan Inc.

Marcovitz, Hal. John Smith, Explorer & Colonial Leader. 2001. (Explorers of New Worlds Ser.). (Illus.). (J). 63p. pap. (978-0-7910-6433-7(6)); (gr. 4-6). 25.00 (978-0-7910-6432-0(8)) Facts On File, Inc. (Chelsea Hse.).

McCartney, Martha W. Jamestown: An American Legacy. 2002. per. 9.95 (978-1-888213-77-5(9)) Eastern National.

McNeese, Tim. Jamestown. 2007. (Colonial Settlements in America Ser.). (Illus.). 112p. (YA). (gr. 5-8). 30.00 (*978-0-7910-9335-1(2) , Chelsea Hse.) Facts On File, Inc.

Oney, Yannick. First American Colonies. 2004. (World Discovery History Readers Ser.). (Illus.). 32p. (J). pap. (978-0-439-66555-1(8)) Scholastic, Inc.

Petrie, Kristin. John Smith. 2007. (Illus.). 32p. (J). 22.78 (978-1-59679-751-2(7)) ABDO Publishing Co.

Pickett, Margaret F. Jamestown. 2004. (American Forts & Their Strategic Importance Ser.). (J). (978-1-59084-716-9(4)) Mason Crest Pubs.

Pierce, Alan. Jamestown Colony. 2005. (American Moments Ser.). (Illus.). 48p. (J). (gr. 4-8). lib. bdg. 25.65 (978-1-59197-733-9(9)) ABDO Publishing Co.

Riehecky, Janet. The Settling of Jamestown. 2002. (Landmark Events in American History Ser.). (Illus.). 48p. (J). (gr. 5 up). pap. 14.60 (978-0-8368-5355-1(5)); lib. bdg. 30.00 (978-0-8368-5341-4(5)) Stevens, Gareth Inc. (World Almanac Library).

Rossi, Anne. Bright Ideas: The Age of Invention in America 1870-1910. 2005. (Crossroads America Ser.). (Illus.). 40p. (J). (gr. 5-9). 12.95 (978-0-7922-8276-1(0) , National Geographic Children's Bks.) National Geographic Society.

Ruffin, Frances E. Jamestown. 2006. (Illus.). 23p. (J). pap. (978-0-8368-6417-5(4)); lib. bdg. 19.33 (978-0-8368-6410-6(7)) Stevens, Gareth Inc.

Schaefer, Lola M. Pocahontas. Saunders-Smith, Gail, ed. 2002. (First Biographies Ser.). (Illus.). 24p. (J). (gr. k-1). lib. bdg. 15.93 (978-0-7368-1175-0(3) , Pebble Bks.) Capstone Pr., Inc.

Schanzer, Rosalyn. John Smith Escapes Again! Schanzer, Rosalyn, illus. 2006. (Illus.). 64p. (J). (gr. 4-9). 16.95 (978-0-7922-5930-5(0)); lib. bdg. 25.90 (978-0-7922-5931-2(9)) National Geographic Society. (National Geographic Children's Bks.).

Sewall, Marcia. James Towne: Struggle for Survival. Sewall, Marcia, illus. 2001. (Illus.). 40p. (J). (gr. 3-5). 18.99 (978-0-689-81814-1(9) , Atheneum) Simon & Schuster Children's Publishing.

Sonneborn, Liz. Pocahontas 1595-1617. 2002. (American Indian Biographies Ser.). (Illus.). 32p. (J). (gr. 3-4). lib. bdg. 23.93 (978-0-7368-1214-6(8) , Blue Earth Bks.) Capstone Pr., Inc.

Trumbauer, Lisa. Pocahontas & the Early Colonies. 2007. (J). (*978-1-4034-9666-9(8)); pap. (*978-1-4034-9674-4(9)) Heinemann Library.

Worland, Gayle. The Jamestown Colony. 2004. (Let Freedom Ring Ser.). (Illus.). 48p. (J). 17.95 (978-0-7368-2462-0(6) , Bridgestone Bks.) Capstone Pr., Inc.

Zemlicka, Shannon. Pocahontas. Reeves, Jeni, illus. 2002. (On My Own Biographies Ser.). 47p. (J). lib. bdg. 23.93 (978-0-87614-598-2(5) , Carolrhoda Bks.) Lerner Publishing Group.

—Pocahontas. 2002. (gr. 3-6). lib. bdg. 14.10 (978-0-613-52481-0(0)) Tandem Library Bks.

JAMESTOWN (VA.)—HISTORY—FICTION

Carbone, Elisa. Blood on the River: James Town, 1607. 2006. (Illus.). 256p. (YA). (gr. 7-8). 16.99 (978-0-670-06060-3(7) , Viking Adult) Penguin Group (USA) Inc.

Hermes, Patricia. Our Strange New Land: Elizabeth's Jamestown Colony Diary, Bk. 1. 2002. (My America Ser.: Bk. 1). 112p. (J). (gr. 2-5). 4.99 (978-0-439-36898-8(7) , Scholastic Pr.) Scholastic, Inc.

—Our Strange New Land: Elizabeth's Jamestown Colony Diary. 2002. (gr. 3-6). lib. bdg. 13.00 (978-0-613-53849-7(8)) Tandem Library Bks.

—Season of Promise: Elizabeth's Jamestown Colony Diary. 2002. (My America Ser.: Bk. 3). (Illus.). 112p. (J). (gr. 2-5). pap. 10.95 (978-0-439-38898-6(8)); pap. 4.99 (978-0-439-27206-3(8)) Scholastic, Inc. (Scholastic Pr.).

—Season of Promise: Elizabeth's Jamestown Colony Diary. 2002. (gr. 3-6). lib. bdg. 13.00 (978-0-613-57130-2(4)) Tandem Library Bks.

Kudlinski, Kathleen V. My Lady, Pocahontas. 400th anniv. ed. 2006. 208p. (YA). (gr. 6-8). 16.95 (978-0-7614-5293-5(1)) Cavendish, Marshall Corp.

Lees, Stuart. The Lucky Sovereign. Lees, Stuart, illus. 2002. (Illus.). (J). (gr. 3-5). 15.95 (978-1-57091-488-1(5)) Charlesbridge Publishing, Inc.

Lees, Stuart, illus. The Lucky Sovereign. 2002. (J). pap. (978-1-57091-489-8(3)) Charlesbridge Publishing, Inc.

Lincoln Collier, James. The Corn Raid. 2004. 142p. (J). lib. bdg. 16.92 (*978-1-4242-0768-8(1)) Fitzgerald Bks.

Ransom, Candice F. Sam Collier & the Founding of Jamestown. Archambault, Matthew, illus. 2006. (On My Own History Ser.). 48p. (J). (gr. 1-2). 25.26 (978-1-57505-874-0(X) , Millbrook Pr.) Lerner Publishing Group.

Sam Collier & the Founding of Jamestown. 2007. (J). pap. 5.95 (*978-0-8225-6451-5(3) , First Avenue Editions) Lerner Publishing Group.

JANIE (FICTITIOUS CHARACTER : COONEY)—FICTION

Cooney, Caroline B. The Voice on the Radio. 1998. 224p. (YA). (gr. 7-12). mass mkt. 6.50 (978-0-440-21977-4(9) , Laurel Leaf) Random Hse. Children's Bks.

—The Voice on the Radio. 1998. (J). (978-0-606-13886-4(2)) Tandem Library Bks.

—What Janie Found. 2002. 192p. (YA). (gr. 7). pap. 6.50 (978-0-440-22772-4(0) , Laurel Leaf) Random Hse. Children's Bks.

—What Janie Found. 2002. (gr. 7-12). lib. bdg. 14.15 (978-0-613-64454-9(9)) Tandem Library Bks.

JANSEN, CAM (FICTITIOUS CHARACTER)—FICTION

Adler, David A. Cam Jansen & the Barking Treasure Mystery. Natti, Susanna, illus. 1999. (Cam Jansen Ser.: No. 19). 64p. (J). (gr. 2-5). 13.99 (978-0-670-88516-9(9) , Viking Juvenile) Penguin Group (USA) Inc.

—Cam Jansen & the Birthday Mystery. Natti, Susanna, illus. 2000. (Cam Jansen Ser.: No. 20). 64p. (J). (gr. 3-7). 13.99 (978-0-670-88877-1(X) , Viking Juvenile) Penguin Group (USA) Inc.

—Cam Jansen & the Catnapping Mystery. 1998. (Cam Jansen Ser.: No. 18). (Illus.). 64p. (J). (gr. 2-5). 13.99 (978-0-670-88044-7(2) , Viking Juvenile) Penguin Group (USA) Inc.

—Cam Jansen & the Catnapping Mystery. 2000. (Cam Jansen Ser.: No. 18). 10.79 (978-0-606-20353-1(2)); (J). (978-0-606-20227-5(7)) Tandem Library Bks.

—Cam Jansen & the First Day of School Mystery, Vol. 22. Natti, Susanna, illus. 2002. (Cam Jansen Ser.: No. 22). 80p. (J). 13.99 (978-0-670-03575-5(0) , Viking Juvenile) Penguin Group (USA) Inc.

—Cam Jansen & the Mystery of Flight 54. 1999. (Cam Jansen Ser.: No. 12). (Illus.). (J). lib. bdg. 5.30 (978-0-15-314312-0(6)) Harcourt Schl. Pubs.

—Cam Jansen & the Mystery of the Babe Ruth Baseball. Natti, Susanna, illus. 2004. (Cam Jansen Ser.: No. 6). 64p. (J). (gr. 2-4). pap. 3.99 (978-0-14-240015-9(7) , Puffin) Penguin Group (USA) Inc.

—Cam Jansen & the Mystery of the Babe Ruth Baseball. (Cam Jansen Ser.: No. 6). 57p. (J). (gr. 2-4). pap. 3.99 (978-0-8072-1347-6(0) , Listening Library) Random Hse. Audio Publishing Group.

—Cam Jansen & the Mystery of the Babe Ruth Baseball. 1998. (Cam Jansen Ser.: No. 6). (J). 3.50 (978-0-439-04442-4(1)) Scholastic, Inc.

—Cam Jansen & the Mystery of the Gold Coins. 2004. (Cam Jansen Ser.: No. 5). (Illus.). 64p. (YA). (gr. 2-4). 3.99 (978-0-14-240014-2(9) , Puffin) Penguin Group (USA) Inc.

—Cam Jansen & the Mystery of the Television Dog. 2004. (Cam Jansen Ser.: No. 4). (Illus.). 64p. (J). (gr. 2-4). pap. 3.99 (978-0-14-240013-5(0) , Puffin) Penguin Group (USA) Inc.

—Cam Jansen & the Mystery of the UFO. Natti, Susanna, illus. 2004. (Cam Jansen Ser.: No. 2). 64p. (J). (gr. 2-4). pap. 3.99 (978-0-14-240011-1(4) , Puffin) Penguin Group (USA) Inc.

—Cam Jansen & the Scary Snake Mystery. 1999. (Cam Jansen Ser.: No. 17). (J). 10.79 (978-0-606-17411-4(7)) Tandem Library Bks.

—Cam Jansen & the School Play Mystery. Natti, Susanna, illus. 2001. (Cam Jansen Ser.: No. 21). 64p. (J). (gr. 2-6). 14.99 (978-0-670-89280-8(7) , Viking Juvenile) Penguin Group (USA) Inc.

—Cam Jansen & the Secret Service Mystery. Natti, Susanna, illus. 2006. (Cam Jansen Ser.). 64p. (J). (gr. 2). 13.99 (978-0-670-06092-4(5) , Viking Juvenile) Penguin Group (USA) Inc.

—Cam Jansen & the Summer Camp Mysteries: A Super Special. Allen, Joy, illus. 2007. (Cam Jansen Ser.). 128p. (J). 4.99 (978-0-14-240742-4(9) , Puffin); 14.99 (978-0-670-06218-8(9) , Viking Adult) Penguin Group (USA) Inc.

—The Mystery at the Haunted House. Natti, Susanna, illus. 2004. (Cam Jansen Ser.: No. 13). 64p. (J). (gr. 2-4). pap. 3.99 (978-0-14-240210-8(9) , Puffin) Penguin Group (USA) Inc.

—The Mystery of the Carnival Prize. 2004. (Cam Jansen Ser.: No. 9). (Illus.). 64p. (J). (gr. 2-4). pap. 3.99 (978-0-14-240018-0(1) , Puffin) Penguin Group (USA) Inc.

—The Mystery of the Circus Clown. 2004. (Cam Jansen Ser.: No. 7). (Illus.). 64p. (J). (gr. 2-4). pap. 3.99 (978-0-14-240016-6(5) , Puffin) Penguin Group (USA) Inc.

—The Mystery of the Monkey House. Natti, Susanna, illus. 2004. (Cam Jansen Ser.: No. 10). 64p. (J). (gr. 2-4). pap. 3.99 (978-0-14-240019-7(X) , Puffin) Penguin Group (USA) Inc.

—The Mystery of the Monster Movie. 2004. (Cam Jansen Ser.: No. 8). (Illus.). 64p. (J). (gr. 2-4). pap. 3.99 (978-0-14-240017-3(3) , Puffin) Penguin Group (USA) Inc.

—The Mystery of the Stolen Diamonds. Natti, Susanna, illus. 2004. (Cam Jansen Ser.: No. 1). 64p. (J). (gr. 2-4). pap. 3.99 (978-0-14-240010-4(6) , Puffin) Penguin Group (USA) Inc.

—The Valentine Baby Mystery. Natti, Susanna, illus. (Cam Jansen Ser.: No. 25). 80p. (J). 2006. (gr. 2). pap. 3.99 (978-0-14-240694-6(5) , Puffin); 2005. (gr. 3-7). 13.99 (978-0-670-06009-2(7) , Viking Juvenile) Penguin Group (USA) Inc.

—Young Cam Jansen & the Baseball Mystery. Moore, Lisa, ed. Natti, Susanna, illus. 2001. (Young Cam Jansen Ser.: No. 5). 32p. (J). pap. 3.99 (978-0-14-131106-7(1) , Puffin) Penguin Group (USA) Inc.

—Young Cam Jansen & the Baseball Mystery. Natti, Susanna, illus. 1999. (Young Cam Jansen Ser.: No. 5). 32p. (J). (gr. k-3). 14.99 (978-0-670-88481-0(2) , Viking Juvenile) Penguin Group (USA) Inc.

—Young Cam Jansen & the Baseball Mystery. 2001. (Young Cam Jansen Ser.: No. 5). (gr. 3-6). lib. bdg. 11.80 (978-0-613-35625-1(X)); (Illus.). (J). (978-0-606-21540-4(9)) Tandem Library Bks.

—Young Cam Jansen & the Dinosaur Game. Natti, Susanna, illus. 1998. (Young Cam Jansen Ser.: No. 1). 32p. (J). (gr. k-3). pap. 3.99 (978-0-14-037779-8(4) , Puffin) Penguin Group (USA) Inc.

—Young Cam Jansen & the Dinosaur Game. 1998. (Young Cam Jansen Ser.: No. 1). (J). (978-0-606-13934-2(6)) Tandem Library Bks.

—Young Cam Jansen & the Double Beach Mystery. Natti, Susanna, illus. (Young Cam Jansen Ser.: No. 8). 32p. (J). (gr. k-2). 2003. pap. 3.99 (978-0-14-250079-8(8) , Puffin); 2002. 13.99 (978-0-670-03531-1(9) , Viking Juvenile) Penguin Group (USA) Inc.

—Young Cam Jansen & the Double Beach Mystery. Natti, Susanna, illus. 2003. (Young Cam Jansen Ser.: No. 8). 30p. (J). (ps). lib. bdg. 11.80 (978-0-613-67477-5(4)) Tandem Library Bks.

—Young Cam Jansen & the Library Mystery. Natti, Susanna, illus. (Young Cam Jansen Ser.: No. 7). 32p. (J). 2002. pap. 3.99 (978-0-14-230202-6(3) , Puffin); 2001. 14.99 (978-0-670-89281-5(5) , Viking Juvenile) Penguin Group (USA) Inc.

—Young Cam Jansen & the Lost Tooth. Natti, Susanna, illus. 1999. (Young Cam Jansen Ser.: No. 3). 32p. (J). (gr. k-3). pap. 3.99 (978-0-14-130273-7(9) , Puffin) Penguin Group (USA) Inc.

—Young Cam Jansen & the Missing Cookie. Natti, Susanna, illus. 1998. (Young Cam Jansen Ser.: No. 2). 32p. (J). (gr. k-3). pap. 3.99 (978-0-14-038050-7(7) , Puffin) Penguin Group (USA) Inc.

—Young Cam Jansen & the Missing Cookie. 1998. (Young Cam Jansen Ser.: No. 2). (J). (978-0-606-13935-9(4)) Tandem Library Bks.

—Young Cam Jansen & the New Girl Mystery. Natti, Susanna, illus. 32p. (J). 2005. pap. 3.99 (978-0-14-240353-2(9) , Puffin); Vol. 10. 2004. 13.99 (978-0-670-05915-7(3) , Viking Juvenile) Penguin Group (USA) Inc.

—Young Cam Jansen & the Pizza Shop Mystery. Natti, Susanna, illus. 2001. (Young Cam Jansen Ser.: No. 6). 32p. (J). pap. 3.99 (978-0-14-230020-6(9) , Puffin) Penguin Group (USA) Inc.

—Young Cam Jansen & the Zoo Note Mystery. Natti, Susanna, illus. 2003. (Young Cam Jansen Ser.). 32p. (J). (gr. k-3). 13.99 (978-0-670-03626-4(9) , Viking Juvenile) Penguin Group (USA) Inc.

Harcourt School Publishers Staff. Cam Jansen... Library Edition. 1999. (Collections Ser.). (Illus.). (J). lib. bdg. 5.30 (978-0-15-314326-7(6)) Harcourt Schl. Pubs.

Natti, Susanna, illus. Cam Jansen & the Snowy Day Mystery. 2004. (Cam Jansen Ser.: No. 24). 64p. (J). (gr. 3-7). 13.99 (978-0-670-05922-5(6) , Viking Juvenile) Penguin Group (USA) Inc.

JAPAN

Auch, Alison & Stewart, Joan. Welcome to Japan. 2002. (Spyglass Books). (Illus.). 24p. (J). (gr. 1 up). lib. bdg. 18.60 (978-0-7565-0368-0(X)) Compass Point Bks.

Boast, Clare. Japan. 1998. (Next Stop! Ser.). 32p. (J). lib. bdg. 19.92 (978-1-57572-568-0(1)) Heinemann Library.

Boraas, Tracey. Egypt. 2001. (Countries & Cultures Ser.). (Illus.). 64p. (J). (gr. 3-4). lib. bdg. 23.93 (978-0-7368-0768-5(3) , Bridgestone Bks.) Capstone Pr., Inc.

Burgan, Michael. Japan: A Question & Answer Book. 2004. (Fact Finders Ser.). (Illus.). 32p. (J). lib. bdg. 22.60 (978-0-7368-2478-1(2)) Capstone Pr., Inc.

Costain, Meredith & Collins, Paul. Welcome to Japan. 2001. (Countries of the World Ser.). (Illus.). 32p. (J). (gr. 4 up). 28.00 (978-0-7910-6541-9(3) , 010208, Chelsea Hse.) Facts On File, Inc.

Education for Global Involvement Staff, et al. Latin America & Japan: Crossing Borders & Making Connections. 2000. (Illus.). 163p. (YA). (gr. 6-12). pap. 19.95 (978-0-89994-405-0(1)) Social Science Education Consortium, Inc.

Fisher, Teresa. Japan. 1999. (We Come from Ser.). (Illus.). 32p. (J). (gr. 1-4). lib. bdg. 25.69 (978-0-8172-5217-5(7)) Raintree.

Frost, Helen. A Look at Japan. Saunders-Smith, Gail, ed. 2002. (Our World Ser.). (Illus.). 24p. (J). (gr. k-1). lib. bdg. 15.93 (978-0-7368-1168-2(0) , Pebble Bks.) Capstone Pr., Inc.

Green, Jen. Japan. 2000. (Nations of the World Ser.). (Illus.). 128p. (YA). (gr. 6-8). lib. bdg. 34.26 (978-0-8172-5783-5(7)) Raintree.

Green, Jen & Phillips, Charles. Japan. 2007. (National Geographic Countries of the World Ser.). (Illus.). 64p. (J). (gr. 3-5). lib. bdg. 27.90 (978-1-4263-0029-5(8) , National Geographic Children's Bks.) National Geographic Society.

Greene, Meg. Japan: A Primary Source Cultural Guide. 2005. (Primary Sources of World Cultures Ser.). (Illus.). 128p. (J). (gr. 4-8). lib. bdg. 34.60 (978-1-4042-2912-9(4)) Rosen Publishing Group, Inc., The.

Gritzner, Charles F. & Phillips, Douglas. Japan. 2003. (Modern World Nations Ser.). (Illus.). (gr. 6-12). 150p. 30.00 (978-0-7910-7239-4(8)); 200p. pap. 30.00 (978-0-7910-7504-3(4)) Facts On File, Inc. (Chelsea Hse.).

Harvey, Miles. Look What Came from Japan. 1999. (Look What Came from Ser.). (Illus.). 32p. (J). (gr. 2-4). pap. 6.95 (978-0-531-15966-8(3) , Watts, Franklin) Scholastic Library Publishing.

—Look What Came from Japan. 1999. (Illus.). 31p. (J). (ps-ps). lib. bdg. 15.25 (978-0-8085-8421-6(9)) Tandem Library Bks.

Heinrichs, Ann. Japan. rev. ed. 2006. (Enchantment of the World, Second Ser.). (Illus.). 144p. (J). (gr. 5-9). 36.00 (978-0-516-24851-6(0) , Children's Pr.) Scholastic Library Publishing.

Hiemen, Sara. Japan ABCs: A Book about the People & Places of Japan. Ouren, Todd, illus. 2004. (Country ABCs Ser.). 32p. (gr. k-5). 23.93 (978-1-4048-0021-2(2)) Picture Window Bks.

Ishii, Takayuki. One Thousand Paper Cranes: The Story of Sadako & the Children's Peace Statue. 2001. (Illus.). 112p. (J). (gr. 5 up). reprint ed. pap. 4.99 (978-0-440-22843-1(3) , Laurel Leaf) Random Hse. Children's Bks.

Japan—Land of Great Surprises (Children's Reading Book - 2001/02) 2001. (2001-2002 Children's Reading Book Ser.). 56p. (J). pap. 5.75 (978-0-8341-1877-5(7)) Beacon Hill Pr. of Kansas City.

Kalman, Bobbie. Japan: The Culture. 2001. (gr. 3-6). lib. bdg. 16.40 (978-0-613-32709-1(8)) Tandem Library Bks.

—Japan: The Land. 2001. (gr. 3-6). lib. bdg. 16.40 (978-0-613-32710-7(1)) Tandem Library Bks.

—Japan - The Culture. 2nd rev. ed. 2000. (Lands, Peoples & Cultures Ser.). (Illus.). 32p. (J). (gr. 4-5). (978-0-7787-9377-9(X)); pap. (978-0-7787-9745-6(7)) Crabtree Publishing Co.

—Japan - The Land. 2nd rev. ed. 2000. (Lands, Peoples & Cultures Ser.). (Illus.). 32p. (J). (gr. 4-5). (978-0-7787-9375-5(3)); pap. (978-0-7787-9743-2(0)) Crabtree Publishing Co.

—Japan - The People. 2nd rev. ed. 2000. (Lands, Peoples & Cultures Ser.). (Illus.). 32p. (J). (gr. 4-5). (978-0-7787-9376-2(1)); pap. (978-0-7787-9744-9(9)) Crabtree Publishing Co.

A Look at Japan, 6 vols. (gr. k-2). 28.95 (978-0-7368-9367-1(9)) Red Brick Learning.

March, Michael. Guide to Japan. 1998. (World Guides Ser.). (Illus.). 32p. (J). (gr. 2-6). lib. bdg. 21.27 (978-1-884756-49-8(2)) Davidson Titles, Inc.

—Japan. 2003. (Country Files Ser.). 32p. (J). lib. bdg. 24.25 (978-1-58340-237-5(3)) Smart Apple Media.

Marx, David F. Japan. 1999. (gr. k-3). lib. bdg. 14.10 (978-0-613-54588-4(5)) Tandem Library Bks.

Mathur-Kamat, Ambika. Miss Panda in Japan. Crawford, K. Michael, illus. 2001. (Miss Panda Ser.). 40p. (J). pap. 11.99 (978-1-59092-028-2(7) , Little Blue Works) Windstorm Creative.

Messager, Alexandre. We Live in Japan. Duffet, Sophie, illus. 2007. (Kids Around the World Ser.). 48p. (J). (gr. 3-7). 15.95 (*978-0-8109-1283-0(X) , Abrams Bks. for Young Readers) Abrams, Harry N., Inc.

Moreton, Daniel. Day in Japan. 1999. (J). pap. 2.50 (978-0-439-04571-1(1)) Scholastic, Inc.

Morrow, Robin. Japan. 2002. (Ask about Asia Ser.). (Illus.). 48p. (J). (gr. 4 up). lib. bdg. (978-1-59084-200-3(6)) Mason Crest Pubs.

Park, Ted. Japan. 2000. (Taking Your Camera to Ser.). (Illus.). 32p. (J). (gr. 4-7). lib. bdg. 22.83 (978-0-7398-1805-3(8)) Raintree.

—Taking Your Camera to Japan. 1999. (Illus.). pap. (978-0-7398-2155-8(5)) Steck-Vaughn.

Poisson, Barbara Aoki. The Ainu of Japan. 2002. (First Peoples Ser.). (Illus.). 48p. (J). (gr. 4-8). lib. bdg. 23.93 (978-0-8225-4176-9(9)) Lerner Publishing Group.

Popper, Garry. Keito in Japan. Johnson, Andi, illus. 2004. 36p. (ps-7). 4.00 (978-1-84161-058-0(5)) Ravette Publishing, Ltd. GBR. *Dist:* Parkwest Pubns., Inc.

Powell, Jillian. Looking at Japan. 2007. (J). pap. (*978-0-8368-8178-3(8)); 32p. (gr. 2-4). lib. bdg. 25.27 (*978-0-8368-8171-4(0)) Stevens, Gareth Inc.

J K L

Reiser, Robert. Japan. 2002. (Discovering Cultures Ser.). 48p. (J). 25.64 (978-0-7614-1177-2(1) , Benchmark Bks.) Cavendish, Marshall Corp.

Reynolds, Jeff E. Japan. (to Z Ser.). (Illus.). 40p. (J). 2005. (gr. 2-4). pap. 6.95 (978-0-516-25072-4(8)); 2004. 24.50 (978-0-516-23655-1(5)) Scholastic Library Publishing. (Children's Pr.).

Richardson, Adele D. Japan. 1998. (Let's Investigate Ser.). (Illus.). 32p. (J). (ps-3). lib. bdg. (978-0-88682-983-4(6) , Creative Education) Creative Co., The.

Roop, Peter & Roop, Connie. A Visit to Japan. (Visit to Ser.). 32p. pap. 6.50 (978-1-4034-4150-8(2)) Heinemann Library.

Ruth, Angie. My Adventure in Japan. 2007. 44p. (J). 8.99 (978-1-59092-431-0(2) , Orchard Academy Pr.) Windstorm Creative.

Scher, Linda & Oates-Johnson, Mary. The Culture Kit: Japan. 2000. 64p. (J). (gr. 1-4). pap. 16.95 (978-0-590-38159-8(8)) Scholastic, Inc.

Shelley, Rex, et al. Japan. 2nd ed. 2001. (Cultures of the World Ser.). (Illus.). 144p. (gr. 5 up). lib. bdg. 37.07 (978-0-7614-1356-1(1) , Benchmark Bks.) Cavendish, Marshall Corp.

Sherrow, Victoria. The Making of the Atom Bomb. 1999. (World History Ser.). (Illus.). 128p. (YA). (gr. 8-11). 27.45 (978-1-56006-585-2(0) , LML00902-177940, Lucent Bks.) Thomson Gale.

Sinnott, Susan. Japan. 2000. (First Reports). (Illus.). 48p. (J). (gr. 3 up). lib. bdg. 22.60 (978-0-7565-0030-6(3)) Compass Point Bks.

Stewart, Tobi Stanton. A Primary Source Guide to Japan. 2003. (Countries of the World : A Primary Source Journey Ser.). (Illus.). 24p. (J). pap. (978-0-8239-8078-9(2)); lib. bdg. 19.95 (978-0-8239-6594-6(5)) Rosen Publishing Group, Inc., The. (PowerKids Pr.).

Streissguth, Thomas. Japan. 2008. (Country Explorers Ser.). (J). lib. bdg. 27.93 (*978-0-8225-8659-3(2) , Lerner Pubns.) Lerner Publishing Group.

Tames, Richard. Japan. 2000. (Exploration Into... Ser.). (Illus.). 48p. (J). (gr. 4-7). 25.00 (978-0-7910-6023-0(3) , Chelsea Hse.) Facts On File, Inc.

Tames, Richard & Tames, Shelia. Japan. 2005. (Illus.). 32p. (J). (gr. 4-7). lib. bdg. 27.10 (978-1-932889-97-0(3)) Sea-To-Sea Pubns.

Thomas, Mark. The Akashi-Kaikyo Bridge: World's Longest Bridge. 2002. (Reading Power Ser.). (Illus.). 24p. (J). lib. bdg. 17.25 (978-0-8239-5990-7(2) , PowerKids Pr.) Rosen Publishing Group, Inc., The.

—The Seikan Railroad Tunnel: World's Longest Tunnel. 2002. (Reading Power Ser.). (Illus.). 24p. (J). (gr. 1). lib. bdg. 17.25 (978-0-8239-5991-4(0) , PowerKids Pr.) Rosen Publishing Group, Inc., The.

Tidmarsh, Celia. Focus on Japan/By Celia Tidmarsh. 2006. (Illus.). 64p. pap. (978-0-8368-6729-9(7)); lib. bdg. (978-0-8368-6722-0(X)) Stevens, Gareth Inc. (World Almanac Library).

Tull, Mary, et al. Northern Asia: Understanding Geography & History Through Art. 1999. (Artisans Around the World Ser.). (Illus.). 48p. (J). (gr. 4-8). lib. bdg. 27.12 (978-0-7398-0119-2(8)) Raintree.

Waugh, John C. Kansai International Airport: Airport in the Sea. 2004. (High Interest Bks.). (Illus.). 48p. (J). (gr. 7-12). pap. 6.95 (978-0-516-25909-3(1) , Children's Pr.) Scholastic Library Publishing.

Whyte, Harlinah. Japan. 1998. (Countries of the World Ser.). (Illus.). 96p. (J). (gr. 6 up). lib. bdg. 30.00 (978-0-8368-2126-0(2)) Stevens, Gareth Inc.

Whyte, Harlinah & Frank, Nicole. Welcome to Japan. 1999. (Welcome to My Country Ser.). (Illus.). 48p. (J). (gr. 2 up). lib. bdg. 26.00 (978-0-8368-2397-4(4)) Stevens, Gareth Inc.

Witherick, M. E. Japan. 2000. (Country Studies). (Illus.). 64p. (YA). (gr. 6-8). lib. bdg. 27.07 (978-1-57572-422-5(7)) Heinemann Library.

Zocchi, Judy. In Japan. Brodie, Neale, illus. 2005. (Global Adventures II Ser.). 32p. (J). per. 9.95 (978-1-59646-140-6(3)) Dingles & Co.

—In Japan/en Japon. Brodie, Neale, illus. 2005. (Global Adventures II Ser.).Tr. of En Japon. (ENG & SPA.). 32p. (J). per. 9.95 (978-1-59646-142-0(X)) Dingles & Co.

JAPAN—BIOGRAPHY

Bloom, Harold, intro. The Tale of Genji. 2003. (Bloom's Modern Critical Interpretations Ser.). (Illus.). 150p. (gr. 9-13). 45.00 (978-0-7910-7584-5(2) , Chelsea Hse.) Facts On File, Inc.

Blumberg, Rhoda. Shipwrecked! The True Adventures of A Japanese Boy. 2001. (gr. 3-6). lib. bdg. 16.45 (978-0-613-61458-0(5)) Tandem Library Bks.

Christopher, Matt. At the Plate with... Ichiro. 2003. (Illus.). 112p. (J). (gr. 5-8). pap. 4.99 (978-0-316-13679-2(4)) Little, Brown Bks. for Young Readers.

Duffield, Katy. Ken Kutaragi: Playstation Developer. 2007. (Innovators Ser.). (Illus.). 64p. (J). (gr. 4-8). 24.95 (*978-0-7377-3862-9(6) , Kidhaven) Thomson Gale.

Gold, Alison Leslie. A Special Fate: Chiune Sugihara: Hero of the Holocaust. 2000. (J). (978-0-590-39541-0(6)); (Illus.). 176p. (YA). (gr. 4-9). pap. 15.95 (978-0-590-39525-0(4) , Scholastic Reference) Scholastic, Inc.

Hoobler, Dorothy & Hoobler, Thomas. Japanese Portraits. Bruck, Victoria V., illus. 2000. 96p. (YA). (gr. 6-8). reprint ed. 20.00 (978-0-7881-9518-1(2)) DIANE Publishing Co.

Levin, Judith. Ichiro Suzuki. 2007. (Baseball Superstars Ser.). 144p. (J). (gr. 6-12). 30.00 (*978-0-7910-9440-2(5) , Chelsea Hse.) Facts On File, Inc.

McCully, Emily Arnold. Manjiro: The Boy Who Risked His Life for Two Countries. 2008. (J). (*978-0-374-34792-5(1)) Farrar, Straus & Giroux.

Mochizuki, Ken. Pasaje a la Libertad: La Historia de Chiune Sugihara. Sarfati, Esther, tr. Lee, Dom, illus. 1999. (SPA.). 32p. (J). (gr. 3-5). 12.76 net. (978-1-880000-81-6(4) , LW8823) Lee & Low Bks., Inc.

—Passage to Freedom: The Sugihara Story. ed. 2004. (Illus.). (J). (gr. k-3). spiral bd. (978-0-616-03098-1(3)) Canadian National Institute for the Blind/Institut National Canadien pour les Aveugles.

—Passage to Freedom: The Sugihara Story. Lee, Dom, illus. 1999. 32p. (J). (gr. 1 up). 15.95 (978-1-880000-49-6(0)) Lee & Low Bks., Inc.

—Passage to Freedom: The Sugihara Story. Lee, Dom, illus. 2000. (Live Oak Readalong Ser.). (J). (gr. 1-6). pap. 16.95 incl. audio (978-0-87499-630-2(9)) Live Oak Media.

—Passage to Freedom, Grades 1-6: The Sugihara Story. Lee, Dom, illus. 2000. (J). pap., tchr. ed. 33.95 incl. audio (978-0-87499-632-6(5)) Live Oak Media.

Savage, Jeff. Ichiro Suzuki. 2007. (J). pap. 5.95 (978-0-8225-7266-4(4) , Lerner Pubns.); 2005. (Illus.). 32p. (gr. 3-4). lib. bdg. 22.60 (978-0-8225-1344-5(7)) Lerner Publishing Group.

Stewart, Mark. Ichiro Suzuki: The Best in the West. 2002. (New Wave Ser.). (Illus.). 48p. (gr. 4 up). lib. bdg. 22.90 (978-0-7613-2616-8(2) , Millbrook Pr.) Lerner Publishing Group.

JAPAN—CIVILIZATION

Greene, Meg. The Technology of Ancient Japan. 2005. (Technology of the Ancient World Ser.). (Illus.). 48p. (J). (978-1-4042-0559-8(4)) Rosen Publishing Group, Inc., The.

Guile, Melanie. Japan. 2003. (Illus.). 32p. (J). lib. bdg. 25.70 (978-1-4109-0470-6(9)) Raintree.

Harvey, Miles. Look What Came from Japan. 1999. (J). (978-0-606-20146-9(7)) Tandem Library Bks.

Kalman, Bobbie. Japan: The People. 2001. (gr. 3-6). lib. bdg. 16.40 (978-0-613-32711-4(X)) Tandem Library Bks.

Khanduri, Kamini. Japanese Art & Culture. 2003. (World Art & Culture Ser.). (Illus.). 56p. (J). lib. bdg. 29.99 (978-0-7398-6609-2(5)) Raintree.

Morrow, Robin. Japan. 2002. (Ask about Asia Ser.). (Illus.). 48p. (J). (gr. 4 up). lib. bdg. (978-1-59084-200-3(6)) Mason Crest Pubs.

Richardson, Adele D. Japan. 2000. (Let's Investigate Ser.). (Illus.). 32p. (J). pap. 10.60 (978-0-89812-005-9(5) , Creative Paperbacks) Creative Co., The.

Schomp, Virginia. Japan in the Days of the Samurai. 1998. (Cultures of the Past Ser.). (Illus.). 80p. (J). (gr. 5 up). lib. bdg. 29.93 (978-0-7614-0304-3(3) , Benchmark Bks.) Cavendish, Marshall Corp.

Steele, Philip & MacDonald, Fiona. Swords & Samurai: The Ancient Warrior Culture of the East. 2004. (Illus.). 128p. pap. 17.99 (978-1-84215-954-5(2) , Southwater) Anness Publishing GBR. *Dist:* National Bk. Network.

Whyte, Harlinah. Japan. 1998. (Countries of the World Ser.). (Illus.). 96p. (J). (gr. 6 up). lib. bdg. 30.00 (978-0-8368-2126-0(2)) Stevens, Gareth Inc.

JAPAN—FICTION

Asai, Carrie. The Book of the Shadow, Vol. 5. l.t. ed. 2004. 288p. 20.95 (978-0-7862-6771-2(2) , Large Print Pr.) Thorndike Pr.

—The Book of the Sword Vol. 5: Samurai Girl, l.t. ed. 2004. 302p. 20.95 (978-0-7862-6684-5(8) , Large Print Pr.) Thorndike Pr.

Bauld, Jane Scoggins. Journey of the Third Seed. Darr, Cynthia G., illus. 2001. 40p. (J). (gr. k-2). 9.95 (978-1-57168-429-5(8)); 16.95 (978-1-57168-428-8(X)) Eakin Pr.

Bell, Lili. The Sea Maidens of Japan. Brammer, Erin McGonigle, illus. 2004. 28p. (J). (gr. k-4). reprint ed. (978-0-7567-7881-1(6)) DIANE Publishing Co.

—The Sea Maidens of Japan. Brammer, Erin McGonigle, illus. 2001. 32p. (J). (ps-3). 14.95 (978-0-8249-5426-0(2) , Ideals Children's Bks.) Ideals Pubns.

Betsy, Howie. Hi Hi Puffy Amiyumi Trifold with Pen. 2006. 80p. (J). pap. 9.99 (978-0-439-74665-6(5) , Scholastic Paperbacks) Scholastic, Inc.

Bidoli, Katie. Karate Adventures of Kisho, Hana, & Nobu: Karate Is for Everyone! 2006. (Illus.). 16p. (J). 10.00 (*978-1-60243-029-7(2)) Keen's Martial Arts Academy.

Blumberg, Rhoda. Commodore Perry in the Land of the Shogun. 2003. (Illus.). 144p. (J). (gr. 3 up). pap. 8.99 (978-0-06-008625-1(4) , Harper Trophy) HarperCollins Pubs.

Catalano, Dominic. Mr. Basset Plays. 2004. (Illus.). 32p. (YA). (gr. k-2). pap. 7.95 (978-1-59078-314-6(X)) Boyds Mills Pr.

Christian, Mary Blount. If Not for the Calico Cat. Serra, Sebastia, illus. 2007. 32p. (J). 16.99 (978-0-525-47779-2(9) , Dutton Juvenile) Penguin Group (USA) Inc.

Clamp. X/1999 Vol. 17: Suite. Clamp, illus. 2005. (X/1999 Ser.). (Illus.). 176p. (YA). pap. 9.95 (978-1-59116-682-5(9)) Viz Media.

Coatsworth, Elizabeth. Cat Who Went to Heaven. Craig, Daniel & Vitale, Raoul, illus. 2008. 96p. (J). pap. 4.99 (*978-1-4169-4973-2(9) , Aladdin) Simon & Schuster Children's Publishing.

Coatsworth, Elizabeth. Gata Que Se Fue Para el Cielo. (SPA.). (YA). 8.95 (978-958-04-1530-5(7) , NR4853) Norma S.A. COL. *Dist:* AIMS International Bks., Inc., Distribuidora Norma, Inc., Lectorum Pubns., Inc.

David, Peter, et al. Spy-School Confidential, Vol. 5. 2002. (SpyBoy Ser.). (Illus.). 96p. (YA). pap. 12.95 (978-1-56971-834-6(2)) Dark Horse Comics.

Davis, Dan, illus. Scooby-Doo & the Samurai Ghost. 2005. (Scooby-Doo Ser.). 24p. (J). 3.99 (978-0-439-69644-9(5)) Scholastic, Inc.

Duey, Kathleen. Samurai. 2007. (Illus.). 96p. (J). 24.21 (978-1-59961-229-4(1)) Spotlight.

Furuyama, Kan & Taniguchi, Jiro. Samurai Legend. Pannone, Frank, ed. Kobayashi, Mayumi, tr. from JPN. 2003. Orig. Title: Kaze No Sho. (Illus.). 240p. pap. 15.95 (978-1-58664-856-5(X) , CMX 63801G, CPM Manga) Central Park Media Corp.

Gerber, Linda. Now & Zen. Pilkington, Roger, ed. 2006. (S. A. S. S. (Students Across the Seven Seas) Ser.). 224p. (YA). (gr. 7). pap. 6.99 (978-0-14-240657-1(0) , Puffin) Penguin Group (USA) Inc.

Gerstein, Mordicai, illus. Three Samurai Cats: A Story from Japan. 2003. 32p. (J). (gr. k-3). 6.95 (978-0-8234-1877-0(4)) Holiday Hse., Inc.

—Three Samurai Cats: A Story from Japan. 2004. (J). (978-0-439-69256-4(3)) Scholastic, Inc.

Golden, Arthur. Memoirs of a Geisha. 1999. (gr. 7-12). lib. bdg. 24.55 (978-0-613-35817-0(1)) Tandem Library Bks.

Gollub, Matthew. Ten Oni Drummers. Stone, Kazuko G., illus. 2000. (JPN & ENG.). 32p. (J). (ps-3). 15.95 (978-1-58430-011-3(6)) Lee & Low Bks., Inc.

Goto, Scott. The Perfect Sword. 2008. (J). (*978-1-57091-697-7(7)) Charlesbridge Publishing, Inc.

Gratz, Alan. Samurai Shortstop. 2006. 288p. (J). (gr. 6 up). 17.99 (978-0-8037-3075-5(6) , Dial) Penguin Group (USA) Inc.

Gratz, Alan M. Samurai Shortstop. 2008. 288p. (YA). (gr. 6). pap. 7.99 (*978-0-14-241099-8(3) , Puffin) Penguin Group (USA) Inc.

Hamazaki, Tatsuya. . hack //Legend of the Twilight, Volume 1: Kaplan SAT/ACT Vocabulary-Building Manga. Izumi, Rei, illus. 2007. (Kaplan SAT/ACT Score-Raising Manga Ser.). 192p. pap. 9.99 (*978-1-4277-5497-4(7)) Kaplan Bks.

Hana's Year: Evaluation Guide. 2006. (J). (978-1-55942-408-0(7)) Marsh Media.

Harcourt School Publishers Staff. The Bird in the Plum Tree: On Level. 3rd ed. 2002. (Trophies Reading Program Ser.). (Illus.). pap. 5.10 (978-0-15-322999-2(3)) Harcourt Schl. Pubs.

—Side by Side 5-Pack, On Level. 3rd ed. 2002. (Trophies Reading Program Ser.). (Illus.). (gr. 1). pap. 20.10 (978-0-15-326844-1(1)) Harcourt Schl. Pubs.

—Trofeos On Level: Mi Abuelita/Yo. 3rd ed. 2002. (SPA., Illus.). (gr. 1). pap. 5.50 (978-0-15-323905-2(0)) Harcourt Schl. Pubs.

Haugaard, Erik C. The Boy & the Samurai. 2005. 240p. (YA). (gr. 5-9). pap. 6.95 (978-0-618-61511-7(3)) Houghton Mifflin Co. Trade & Reference Div.

—The Revenge of the Forty-Seven Samurai. 2005. 240p. (YA). (gr. 5-9). pap. 6.95 (978-0-618-54896-5(3)) Houghton Mifflin Co. Trade & Reference Div.

Haugaard, Erik Christian. The Samurai's Tale. 2005. 256p. (YA). (gr. 5-9). pap. 6.95 (978-0-618-61512-4(1)) Houghton Mifflin Co. Trade & Reference Div.

—The Samurai's Tale. 2001. (YA). 20.25 (978-0-8446-7175-8(4)) Smith, Peter Pub., Inc.

Hayashi, Fumino. Neon Genesis Evangelion: Angelic Days. 2006. 184p. (YA). (Angelic Days Ser.: Vol. 2). (Illus.). pap. (978-1-4139-0348-5(7)); pap. (978-1-4139-0344-7(4)) ADV Manga.

—Neon Genesis Evangelion Vol. 3: Angelic Days. 2006. (Illus.). 184p. (YA). pap. (978-1-4139-0350-8(9)) ADV Manga.

Hearn, Lian. Leyendas de los Otori I. (SPA.). 312p. (J). (gr. 8-12). pap. 13.95 (978-956-239-300-3(3)) Santillana USA Publishing Co., Inc.

Hiwatari, Saki. Please Save My Earth, Vol. 17. Hiwatari, Saki, illus. 2006. (Please Save My Earth Ser.). 208p. (YA). pap. 9.99 (978-1-4215-0550-3(9)) Viz Media.

—Please Save My Earth, Vol. 18. 2006. (Please Save My Earth Ser.). 208p. (YA). pap. 9.99 (978-1-4215-0551-0(7)) Viz Media.

Hoobler, Dorothy. The Ghost in the Tokaido Inn. 2001. (J). 12.64 (978-0-606-21212-0(4)) Tandem Library Bks.

Hoobler, Dorothy & Hoobler, Thomas. The Demon in the Teahouse. 2005. 192p. (J). (gr. 7). pap. 5.99 (978-0-14-240540-6(X) , Puffin) Penguin Group (USA) Inc.

—The Ghost in the Tokaido Inn. (J). 2005. 240p. (gr. 4). pap. 5.99 (978-0-14-240541-3(8) , Puffin); 1999. 1p. (gr. 5-9). 17.99 (978-0-399-23330-2(X) , Philomel) Penguin Group (USA) Inc.

—In Darkness, Death. 208p. 2005. (J). (gr. 5). pap. 6.99 (978-0-14-240366-2(0) , Puffin); 2004. (YA). (gr. 4). 16.99 (978-0-399-23767-6(4) , Philomel) Penguin Group (USA) Inc.

—A Samurai Never Fears Death. 2007. (Samurai Mystery Ser.). 224p. (YA). (gr. 5-9). 14.99 (978-0-399-24609-8(6) , Philomel) Penguin Group (USA) Inc.

—The Sword That Cut the Burning Grass. (J). (gr. 5). 2006. 224p. pap. 5.99 (978-0-14-240689-2(9) , Puffin); 2005. 212p. 10.99 (978-0-399-24272-4(4) , Philomel) Penguin Group (USA) Inc.

Hotta, Yumi. Hikaru No Go Vol. 4: Divine Illusions. Obata, Takeshi, illus. 2005. (Hikaru No Go Ser.). 200p. (YA). pap. 7.95 (978-1-59116-688-7(8)) Viz Media.

Iijima, Geneva Cobb. The Way We Do It in Japan. Billin-Frye, Paige, illus. 2002. 32p. (J). (gr. k-4). 15.95 (978-0-8075-7822-3(3)) Whitman, Albert & Co.

James, Grace. The Moon Maiden & Other Japanese Fairy Tales. Goble, Warwick, illus. 2005. 192p. (J). (gr. 3). pap. 9.95 (978-0-486-44392-8(2)) Dover Pubns., Inc.

Kalman, Maira. Sayonara, Mrs Kackleman. Kalman, Maira, illus. 2006. (Illus.). 30p. (J). (gr. k-4). reprint ed. 17.00 (978-0-7567-9840-6(X)) DIANE Publishing Co.

Kimmel, Eric A. Sword of the Samurai. 2000. (gr. 3-6). lib. bdg. 12.10 (978-0-613-33731-1(X)) Tandem Library Bks.

—Sword of the Samurai: Adventure Stories from Japan. Evans, Michael, illus. 2000. (Trophy Chapter Bks.). 112p. (J). (gr. 2-5). pap. 4.99 (978-0-06-442131-7(7) , Harper Trophy) HarperCollins Pubs.

—Sword of the Samurai: Adventure Stories from Japan. 2000. (J). (978-0-606-19999-5(3)) Tandem Library Bks.

Kishimoto, Masashi. Naruto Anime Profiles: Episodes 1-37. 2006. (Naruto Anime Profiles Ser.). (YA). pap. 14.99 (978-1-4215-0657-9(2)) Viz Media.

Kobayashi, Makoto. Club 9, Vol. 1. 2003. (Illus.). 192p. pap. 15.95 (978-1-56971-915-2(2)) Dark Horse Comics.

Lasky, Kathryn. Kazunomiya: Prisoner of Heaven, Japan, 1858. 2004. (Royal Diaries). (Illus.). 160p. (J). (gr. 4-7). pap. 10.95 (978-0-439-16485-6(0)) Scholastic, Inc.

Leibold, Jay. Secret of the Ninja No. 16: Choose Your Own Adventure #16. 2007. (Choose Your Own Adventure Ser.: Vol. 16). (Illus.). 144p. (J). mass mkt. 5.99 (978-1-933390-16-1(6)) Chooseco LLC.

Libster, Bernard. The Bonsai Bear. Cheung, Aries, illus. 2006. 31p. (J). (gr. k-4). reprint ed. 16.00 (*978-1-4223-5857-3(7)) DIANE Publishing Co.

—The Bonsai Bear. Cheung, Aries, illus. 1999. 32p. (ps-3). 15.95 (978-0-935699-15-9(5)) Illumination Arts Publishing Co., Inc.

London, Jonathan. Moshi Moshi. Yoshi, Miyake, illus. 1998. (Around the World Ser.). 32p. (gr. k-4). lib. bdg. 23.90 (978-0-7613-0110-3(0) , Millbrook Pr.) Lerner Publishing Group.

Manley, Ruth. The Plum-Rain Scroll. 2005. (UQP Children's Classics Ser.). 378p. (J). pap. 18.95 (978-0-7022-3505-4(9)) Univ. of Queensland Pr. AUS. *Dist:* International Specialized Bk. Services.

Manz, L. B. Noshi's Special Gift. Yoshikawa, Sachiko, illus. 2003. (J). (978-0-9710278-9-3(7)) All About Kids Publishing.

Marks, Graham. Missing in Tokyo. 2006. 256p. (YA). 16.95 (978-1-58234-907-7(X) , Bloomsbury Children) Bloomsbury Publishing.

Matsuno, Masako. A Pair of Red Clogs. Mizumura, Kazue, illus. 2002. 32p. (J). 16.95 (978-1-930900-20-2(1)) Purple Hse. Pr.

Mayer, Mercer. Shibumi & the Kitemaker. Mayer, Mercer, illus. 2005. (Illus.). 48p. (J). pap. 5.95 (978-0-7614-5145-7(5)) Cavendish, Marshall Corp.

—Shibumi & the Kitemaker. 1999. (Accelerated Reader Bks.). (Illus.). 48p. (YA). (ps-3). 18.95 (978-0-7614-5054-2(8) , Cavendish Children's Bks.) Cavendish, Marshall Corp.

—Shibumi & the Kitemaker. 2003. (gr. k-3). lib. bdg. 14.10 (978-0-613-87253-9(3)) Tandem Library Bks.

McCann, Jesse Leon. The Case of the Karate Kitty-Nappers. 2000. (Illus.). 57p. (J). (ps-3). pap. 3.99 (978-0-439-20654-9(5)) Scholastic, Inc.

—The Case of the Karate Kitty-Nappers. 2000. (Ace Ventura Chapter Bk.: Vol. 1). (J). 10.79 (978-0-606-19525-6(4)) Tandem Library Bks.

Miyazaki, Hayao. Princess Mononoke Film Comics, Vol. 1. 2006. (Princess Mononoke Film Comics Ser.). (YA). 9.99 (978-1-4215-0597-8(5)) Viz Media.

Mosel, Arlene. The Funny Little Woman. Lent, Blair, illus. 2002. (J). 13.19 (978-0-7587-0033-9(4)) Book Wholesalers, Inc.

Myers, Tim. Basho & the Fox. Han, Oki S., illus. 2000. 32p. (J). (gr. k-3). 15.95 (978-0-7614-5068-9(8) , Cavendish Children's Bks.) Cavendish, Marshall Corp.

—Basho & the River Stones. Han, Oki S., illus. 2004. 32p. (J). 16.95 (978-0-7614-5165-5(X)) Cavendish, Marshall Corp.

—The Furry-Legged Teapot: A Unique Retelling. McGuire, Robert, illus. 2007. (J). 16.99 (978-0-7614-5295-9(8)) Cavendish, Marshall Corp.

Nakagawa, Hirotaka. Sumo Boy. Hasegawa, Yoshifumi, illus. 2006. 40p. (J). (ps-k). 15.99 (978-0-7868-3635-2(0)) Hyperion Pr.

Nakajo, Hisaya. Hana-Kimi. 2007. (Hana-Kimi Ser.). 184p. (YA). Vol. 16. pap. 9.99 (978-1-4215-0991-4(1)); Vol. 17. pap. 9.99 (978-1-4215-0992-1(X)) Viz Media.

Namioka, Lensey. Coming of the Bear. 2005. 208p. pap. 7.95 (978-0-8048-3613-5(2)) Tuttle Publishing.

—Island of Ogres. 2005. 1p. pap. 7.95 (978-0-8048-3612-8(4)) Tuttle Publishing.

—Valley of the Broken Cherry Trees. 2005. 256p. pap. 7.95 (978-0-8048-3610-4(8)) Tuttle Publishing.

—Village of the Vampire Cat. 2005. (Zenta & Matsuzo Mystery Ser.). 224p. (J). pap. 7.95 (978-0-8048-3611-1(6)) Tuttle Publishing.

Newman, Leslea. Hachiko Waits. Kodaira, Machiyo, illus. rev. ed. 2004. 96p. (J). 16.95 (978-0-8050-7336-2(1) , Holt, Henry & Co. Bks. For Young Readers) Holt, Henry & Co.

Ohnogi, Hiroki. Raxephon Novel, Vol. 1. 2005. 200p. (YA). pap. 7.95 (978-1-59796-000-7(4)) DrMaster Pubns. Inc.

Ohnogi, Hiroshi. Rahxephon Novel. 2006. (Illus.). 200p. (YA). Vol. 4. pap. 7.95 (*978-1-59796-003-8(9)); Vol. 5. pap. 7.95 (*978-1-59796-004-5(7)) DrMaster Pubns. Inc.

Okei-san: The Girl from Wakamatsu. 2006. (J). pap. 11.95 (*978-0-9642112-8-5(9)) Barsotti Bks.

Oni Wa Soto, 6 vols. (Multicultural Programs Ser.). 16p. (gr. 1-6). 42.50 (978-0-7802-1478-1(1)) Wright Group, The.

Osborne, Mary Pope. Dragon of the Red Dawn. Murdocca, Sal, illus. 2007. (Magic Tree House Ser.: No. 37). 128p. (J). (gr. k-3). 11.99 (978-0-375-83727-2(2) , Random Hse. Bks. for Young Readers) Random Hse. Children's Bks.

—Dragon of the Red Dawn. Murdocca, Sal, illus. 2007. (Magic Tree House Ser.: No. 37). 108p. (J). (gr. k-3). pap. (978-0-375-83728-9(0)) Random Hse., Inc.

—La Noche de los Ninjas. 2004. (Coleccion la Casa Del Arbol the Magic Tree House Ser.).Tr. of Night of the Ninjas. (SPA., Illus.). (J). pap. 4.95 (978-1-930332-66-9(1)) Lectorum Pubns., Inc.

Otey Little, Mimi. Yoshiko & the Foreigner. Otey Little, Mimi, illus. 2004. (Illus.). 31p. (J). (gr. 4-8). reprint ed. 16.00 (978-0-7567-7510-0(8)) DIANE Publishing Co.

Paterson, Katherine. The Master Puppeteer. 3rd ed. (J). pap. 3.95 (978-0-13-800095-0(6)) Prentice Hall (Schl. Div.).
—El Signo del Crisantemo. 2003. (SPA., Illus.). 142p. (YA). (gr. 5-8). (978-84-348-6699-7(4) , SM30544) SM Ediciones ESP. *Dist:* Lectorum Pubns., Inc.

Pearce, Jacqueline. Manga Touch. 2007. (Orca Currents Ser.). 112p. (YA). (gr. 5 up). pap. (*978-1-55143-746-0(5)); lib. bdg. (*978-1-55143-748-4(1)) Orca Bk. Pubs.

Peers, Judi. Sayonara Sharks. 2001. (Sports Stories Ser.). (Illus.). 84p. (gr. 3-8). (J). (*978-1-55028-731-8(1)); 7.95 (978-1-55028-730-1(3)) Lorimer, James & Co., Ltd., Pubs. CAN. *Dist:* Casemate Pubs. & Bk. Distributors, LLC.

Perkins, Lucy Fitch. The Japanese Twins. 2005. 26.95 (978-1-4218-0369-2(0) , 1st World Library - Literary Society) 1st World Publishing, Inc.
—The Japanese Twins. 2004. reprint ed. pap. 15.95 (978-1-4191-6781-2(2)); pap. 1.99 (978-1-4192-6781-9(7)) Kessinger Publishing, LLC.

Perkins, Lucy Fitch. The Japanese Twins (Yesterday's Classics) 2006. (J). per. 9.95 (*978-1-59915-058-1(1)) Yesterday's Classics.

Pirotta, Saviour. Turtle Bay. Mistry, Nilesh, illus. 2005. 32p. (J). pap. 7.95 (978-1-84507-411-1(4)) Lincoln, Frances Ltd. GBR. *Dist:* Perseus Distribution.

Place, Francois. The Old Man Mad about Drawing: A Tale of Hokusai. Rodarmor, William, tr. from FRE. 2004. (Illus.). 108p. (J). 19.95 (978-1-56792-260-8(0)) Godine, David R. Pub.

Pray, Ralph. Jingu: The Hidden Princess. Li, Xiaojun, illus. 2002. 80p. (YA). 14.95 (978-1-885008-21-3(X) , 188500821x) Shen's Bks.

Puccini, Giacomo. Madame Butterfly. Fucíkova, Renata, illus. 2005. 40p. (J). 15.95 (978-1-933327-04-4(9)) Purple Bear Bks., Inc.
—Madame Butterfly. Fuc#0237;kov#0225;, Ren#0225;ta, illus. 2005. 40p. (J). 16.85 (978-1-933327-08-2(1)) Purple Bear Bks., Inc.

Reynolds, Betty. Japanese Celebrations: Cherry Blossoms, Lanterns & Stars! 2006. (Illus.). 48p. (J). 16.95 (978-0-8048-3658-6(2)) Tuttle Publishing.
—Tokyo Friends. 2006. (Illus.). 64p. pap. 12.95 (978-0-8048-3808-5(9) , PeriplusEdition) Tuttle Publishing.

Roman, Javier. Adventures of Tinturu & Kumachan the M. 2007. (Illus.). 48p. pap. 12.95 (*978-1-4241-1626-3(0)) PublishAmerica, Inc.

Sadamoto, Yoshiyuki. Neon Genesis Evangelion, Vol. 10. 2007. (Neon Genesis Evangelion Ser.). 200p. (YA). pap. 9.99 (978-1-4215-1160-3(6)) Viz Media.

Saijyo, Shinji. Iron Wok Jan!, 27 vols. (Illus.). Vol. 1. 2nd ed. 2002. 190p. (YA). pap. 9.95 (978-1-58899-256-7(X)); Vol. 4. 2003. 200p. (YA). (gr. 8 up). pap. 9.95 (978-1-58899-259-8(4)); Vol. 5. 2003. 200p. pap. 9.95 (978-1-58899-260-4(8)) ComicsOne Corp./Dr. Masters.
—Iron Wok Jan!, 27 vols., Vol. 6. Oyama, Keiko, ed. Kawahara, Sahe, tr. from JPN. 2003. (Illus.). 200p. (YA). 9.95 (978-1-58899-261-1(6)) ComicsOne Corp./Dr. Masters.

Say, Allen. The Ink-Keeper's Apprentice. 2006. 160p. (YA). (gr. 7). reprint ed. pap. 6.95 (978-0-618-21613-0(8) , Walter Lorraine) Houghton Mifflin Co. Trade & Reference Div.
—Kamishibai Man. 2005. (Illus.). 32p. (J). (gr. k-3). 17.00 (978-0-618-47954-2(6) , Walter Lorraine) Houghton Mifflin Co. Trade & Reference Div.
—Tea with Milk. Say, Allen, illus. 2002. (Illus.). (J). 24.36 (978-0-7587-3768-7(8)) Book Wholesalers, Inc.
—Tea with Milk. Say, Allen, illus. 1999. (Illus.). 32p. (J). (gr. k-3). tchr. ed. 17.00 (978-0-395-90495-4(1) , Walter Lorraine) Houghton Mifflin Co. Trade & Reference Div.
—Tree of Cranes. Say, Allen, illus. 2002. (Illus.). 25.28 (978-0-7587-3857-8(9)) Book Wholesalers, Inc.

Say, Allen, retold by. Under the Cherry Blossom Tree: An Old Japanese Tale. 2005. (Illus.). 32p. (J). (gr. k-3). 5.95 (978-0-618-55615-1(X) , Walter Lorraine) Houghton Mifflin Co. Trade & Reference Div.

Scieszka, Jon. Sam Samurai, Vol. 10. McCauley, Adam, illus. (Time Warp Trio Ser.: No. 10). (J). 2004. 112p. (gr. 2-6). pap. 4.99 (978-0-14-240088-3(2) , Puffin); 2001. 80p. (gr. 1-5). 14.99 (978-0-670-89915-9(1) , Viking Juvenile) Penguin Group (USA) Inc.

Shakespeare, William & Appignanesi, Richard. Romeo & Juliet. Leong, Sonia, illus. 2007. (Manga Shakespeare Ser.). 208p. (J). (gr. 2-8). pap. 9.95 (*978-0-8109-9325-9(2) , Abrams Bks. for Young Readers) Abrams, Harry N. , Inc.

So-Un, Kim. Tigers of the Kumgang Mountains. 2005. (Illus.). 32p. (J). 16.95 (978-0-8048-3653-1(1)) Tuttle Publishing.

Stokes, Katherine. The Motor Maids in Fair Japan. 2006. 78.99 (*978-1-4280-1270-7(2)); pap. 71.99 (*978-1-4280-1264-6(8)) IndyPublish.com.
—Motor Maids in Fair Japan. 2006. pap. (*978-1-4068-3090-3(9)) Echo Library.

Stutzman, D. J. The Promise Ring. 2007. (J). pap. 9.00 (*978-0-8059-7365-5(6)) Dorrance Publishing Co., Inc.

Takahashi, Rumiko. Inu Yasha Animanga. (Inuyasha Ser.). (YA). Vol. 15. 2006. 208p. pap. 11.99 (978-1-4215-0482-7(0)); Vol. 16. 2006. 208p. pap. 11.99 (978-1-4215-0483-4(9)); Vol. 19. 2007. 216p. pap. 11.99 (978-1-4215-0903-7(2)); Vol. 20. 2007. 216p. pap. 11.99 (978-1-4215-0904-4(0)) Viz Media.
—Inuyasha, Vol. 29. 2007. (Inuyasha Ser.). 192p. (YA). pap. 8.95 (978-1-4215-0900-6(8)) Viz Media.

Tamura, Yumi. Basara, Vol. 22. 2007. (Basara Ser.). 192p. (YA). pap. 9.99 (978-1-4215-0979-2(2)) Viz Media.

Toriyama, Akira. Dragon Ball 10. 2003. (gr. 3-6). lib. bdg. 16.40 (978-0-613-67401-0(4)) Tandem Library Bks.
—Dragon Ball 11. 2003. (gr. 3-6). lib. bdg. 16.40 (978-0-613-67400-3(6)) Tandem Library Bks.

Tung, Angela. Song of the Stranger. Artenstein, Michael, ed. 1999. (Roxbury Park Bks.). (J). 192p. (gr. 3-7). pap. 4.95 (978-1-56565-948-3(1) , 09481W); 96p. (gr. 5-8). 12.95 (978-1-56565-774-8(8) , 07748W) Lowell Hse. (Roxbury Park).

Turner, Pamela S. Hachiko: The True Story of a Loyal Dog. Nascimbene, Yan, illus. 2004. 32p. (J). (gr. k-3). tchr. ed. 15.00 (978-0-618-14094-7(8)) Houghton Mifflin Co. Trade & Reference Div.

Umezu, Kazuo. The Drifting Classroom, Vol. 8. Roman, Annette, ed. Umezu, Kazuo, illus. 2007. (Drifting Classroom Ser.). 192p. (YA). pap. 9.99 (*978-1-4215-0960-0(1)) Viz Media.

Uncle Markie. Piglette & BoBo Do Tokyo. l.t. ed. 2002. 28p. 9.95 (978-0-9633943-7-8(1)) Studio 403.

Watanabe, Taeko. Kaze Hikaru. (Kaze Hikaru Ser.). (YA). Vol. 2. 2006. 208p. pap. 8.99 (978-1-4215-0581-7(9)); Vol. 4. 2007. 200p. pap. 8.99 (978-1-4215-1017-0(0)) Viz Media.

Watsuki, Nobuhiro. Rurouni Kenshin, 3. Watsuki, Nobuhiro, illus. 2004. (Rurouni Kenshin Ser.). 200p. (YA). pap. 7.95 (978-1-59116-250-6(5) , Viz Comics) Viz Media.
—Rurouni Kenshin. 2004. (Rurouni Kenshin Ser.). (Illus.). (YA). Vol. 4. 208p. pap. 7.95 (978-1-59116-251-3(3)); Vol. 5. 200p. pap. 7.95 (978-1-59116-320-6(X)) Viz Media. (Viz Comics).
—Rurouni Kenshin: Meiji Swordsman Romantic Story, Vol. 1. Yagi, Kenichiro, tr. from JPN. Watsuki, Nobuhiro, illus. 2003. (Rurouni Kenshin Ser.). (Illus.). 208p. (YA). pap. 7.95 (978-1-59116-220-9(3)) Viz Media.
—Rurouni Kenshin: The Two Hitokiri, Vol. 2. 2003. (Rurouni Kenshin Ser.). (Illus.). 200p. (YA). pap. 7.95 (978-1-59116-249-0(1)) Viz Media.

Welles, Lee. Gaia Girls Way of Water. 2007. (Gaia Girls Ser.). 336p. (J). pap. 12.95 (*978-1-933609-03-4(6)) Daisyworld Pr.

West, Tracey. Hi Hi Puffy Amiyumi World Tour Sticker Storybook. 2006. 18p. (J). pap. 4.99 (978-0-439-79387-2(4) , Scholastic Paperbacks) Scholastic, Inc.

Whitesel, Cheryl Aylward. Blue Fingers: A Ninja's Tale. 2004. 256p. (YA). (gr. 5-9). tchr. ed. 15.00 (978-0-618-38139-5(2) , Clarion Bks.) Houghton Mifflin Co. Trade & Reference Div.

Williams, Laura E. The Long Silk Strand: A Grandmother's Legacy to Her Granddaughter. Bochak, Grayce, illus. 2003. 32p. (YA). (gr. 4-6). pap. 8.95 (978-1-56397-856-2(3)) Boyds Mills Pr.
—The Long Silk Strand: A Grandmother's Legacy to Her Granddaughter. 2000. (Illus.). (J). (978-0-606-18013-9(3)) Tandem Library Bks.

Williston, Teresa Pierce. The Bamboo Cutter & the Moon Maiden: A Japanese Folk Tale. Marsh, Dilleen, illus. 2006. 32p. (J). 16.95 (978-1-933317-39-7(6)) Silverleaf Pr.

Wilson, Mary. Paper Dragonfly. 2007. 32p. 15.95 (*978-0-9726614-3-0(3)) Shenanigan Bks.

Winnick, Karen B. The Night of the Fireflies. Ito, Yoriko, illus. 2004. 32p. (J). (ps up). 15.95 (978-1-56397-725-1(7)) Boyds Mills Pr.

Wisniewski, David. Sumo Mouse. Wisniewski, David, illus. 2002. (Illus.). 32p. (J). (ps-3). 16.95 (978-0-8118-3492-6(1)) Chronicle Bks. LLC.
—Sumo Mouse. Wisniewski, David, illus. 2004. (Illus.). 26p. (J). (gr. k-4). reprint ed. 17.00 (978-0-7567-8506-2(5)) DIANE Publishing Co.

Wood, Lena. Carpet of Bones. 2006. (Illus.). 192p. (J). pap. 6.99 (978-0-7847-1535-2(1)) Standard Publishing.

Yashima, Taro. Crow Boy. 2000. (J). pap. 19.97 incl. audio (978-0-7366-9208-3(8)) Books on Tape, Inc.
—Crow Boy. Yashima, Taro, illus. 2004. (Illus.). 34p. (J). (gr. k-3). reprint ed. pap. 14.00 (978-0-7567-7102-7(1)) DIANE Publishing Co.
—Crow Boy. Yashima, Taro, illus. (Illus.). 28.95 incl. audio compact disk (978-1-59112-802-1(1)); pap. 35.95 incl. audio compact disk (978-1-59112-803-8(X)) Live Oak Media.
—Crow Boy. 2005. (Illus.). (J). pap. 18.95 incl. audio compact disk (978-1-59112-801-4(3)) Live Oak Media.

Yoshida, Akimi. Banana Fish. 2007. (Banana Fish Ser.). 192p. (YA). Vol. 18. pap. 9.99 (978-1-4215-0876-4(1)); Vol. 19. pap. 9.99 (978-1-4215-0877-1(X)) Viz Media.

Yumoto, Kazumi. The Letters. 2003. 176p. (YA). (gr. 7). pap. 5.50 (978-0-440-23822-5(6) , Laurel Leaf) Random Hse. Children's Bks.

JAPAN—FOREIGN RELATIONS—UNITED STATES

Barr, Gary. Pearl Harbor. 2004. (Illus.). 56p. (J). pap. 8.95 (978-1-4034-4577-3(X)); lib. bdg. (978-1-4034-4569-8(9)) Heinemann Library.

Blumberg, Rhoda. Commodore Perry in the Land of the Shogun. 2003. (gr. 5-8). lib. bdg. 16.45 (978-0-613-60049-1(5)) Tandem Library Bks.

Crewe, Sabrina & Uschan, Michael V. The Bombing of Pearl Harbor. 2003. (Events That Shaped America Ser.). (Illus.). 32p. (J). (gr. 3 up). lib. bdg. 24.67 (978-0-8368-3392-8(9)) Stevens, Gareth Inc.

Gaines, Ann Graham. Commodore Perry Opens Japan to Trade in World History. 2000. (In World History Ser.). (Illus.). 128p. (YA). (gr. 5-12). lib. bdg. 26.60 (978-0-7660-1462-6(2)) Enslow Pubs., Inc.

Hasday, Judy L. Pearl Harbor. 2000. (Great Disasters, Reforms & Ramifications Ser.). (Illus.). 112p. (J). (gr. 4-7). 30.00 (978-0-7910-5271-6(0) , Chelsea Hse.) Facts On File, Inc.

McGowen, Tom. The Attack on Pearl Harbor. (Cornerstones of Freedomtrade;, Second Ser.). 48p. (J). 2007. pap. 5.95 (*978-0-531-18685-5(7)); 2002. (Illus.). (gr. 4-6). 26.00 (978-0-516-22586-9(3)) Scholastic Library Publishing. (Children's Pr.).

Richard Tames. Pearl Harbor. 2nd ed. 2006. (Point of Impact Ser.). (Illus.). 32p. (J). pap. (*978-1-4034-9151-0(8)) Heinemann Library.

Tames, Richard. Pearl Harbor: The U. S. Enters World War II. 2001. (Point of Impact Ser.). (Illus.). 32p. (J). (gr. 5-7). lib. bdg. 24.22 (978-1-57572-416-4(2)) Heinemann Library.
—Pearl Harbor: The U. S. Enters World War II. 2001. (gr. 5-8). lib. bdg. 15.90 (978-0-613-36122-4(9)) Tandem Library Bks.

Tames, Richard. Pearl Harbor: The U.S. Enters World War II. 2006. (Point of Impact Ser.). (Illus.). 32p. (YA). (gr. 5-8). lib. bdg. 29.29 (*978-1-4034-9142-8(9)) Heinemann Library.

Taylor, Theodore. Air Raid—Pearl Harbor! The Story of December 7, 1941. 2001. (Great Episodes Ser.). (Illus.). 208p. (YA). (gr. 5-9). pap. 6.00 (978-0-15-216421-8(9) , Gulliver Bks.) Harcourt Children's Bks.

JAPAN—HISTORY

Anderson, Dale. Japanese Americans. 2006. (World Almanac Library of American Immigration). (Illus.). 48p. (J). pap. (978-0-8368-7326-9(2)); lib. bdg. (978-0-8368-7313-9(0)) Stevens, Gareth Inc. (World Almanac Library).

Ball, Jacqueline A. Himeji Castle: Japan's Samurai Past. 2005. (Castles, Palaces, & Tombs Ser.). (J). lib. bdg. 25.27 (978-1-59716-001-8(6)) Bearport Publishing Co., Inc.

BBC Educational Publishing, prod. Japan 2000. (YA). cd-rom 149.95 (978-0-7365-4640-9(5)) Films Media Group.

Behnke, Alison. Japan in Pictures. 2nd rev. ed. 2003. (Visual Geography Ser.). (Illus.). 80p. (J). (gr. 5-12). 27.93 (978-0-8225-1956-0(9)) Lerner Publishing Group.

Blumberg, Rhoda. Shipwrecked! The True Adventures of a Japanese Boy. (Illus.). 80p. (J). (gr. 3 up). 2003. pap. 7.99 (978-0-688-17485-9(X)); 2001. 16.95 (978-0-688-17484-2(1)); 2001. 17.89 (978-0-06-029365-9(9)) HarperCollins Pubs.

Britton, Tamara L. Japan. 2000. (Countries Ser.). (Illus.). 40p. (J). (gr. k-6). lib. bdg. 22.78 (978-1-57765-387-5(4) , Checkerboard Library) ABDO Publishing Co.

DeAngelis, Gina. Japan. 2003. (Many Cultures, One World Ser.). (Illus.). 32p. (J). (gr. 2-3). lib. bdg. 23.93 (978-0-7368-1533-8(3) , Bridgestone Bks.) Capstone Pr., Inc.

Dower, John. Embracing Defeat: Japan in the Wake of World War II. 2000. (gr. 7-12). lib. bdg. 28.00 (978-0-613-28833-0(5)) Tandem Library Bks.

Harris, Nathaniel. Hiroshima. 2004. (Illus.). 56p. (J). 27.07 (978-1-4034-4872-9(8)); pap. (978-1-4034-6259-6(3)) Heinemann Library.

Haslam, Andrew. Japan. 2004. (Make It Work! History Ser.). (Illus.). 63p. (gr. 3-6). 14.95 (978-1-58728-311-6(5) , Two Can Publishing) T&N Children's Publishing.

Haslam, Andrew, contrib. by. Japan. 2004. (Make It Work! History Ser.). (Illus.). 64p. (J). (gr. 3-6). pap. 7.95 (978-1-58728-305-5(0) , Two Can Publishing) T&N Children's Publishing.

Haslam, Andrew & Doran, Clare. Old Japan. 2000. (Make-It-Work! Ser.). (Illus.). 64p. (YA). (gr. 4-9). 13.95 (978-0-7166-4607-5(2)) World Bk., Inc.

Hunt, Norman Bancroft. Living in Early China & Japan. 2007. (Living in the Ancient World Ser.). 96p. (gr. 6-12). 35.00 (978-0-8160-6342-0(7)) Facts On File, Inc.

Johnson, Darv. The Longest Bridge. 2002. (Extreme Places Ser.). (Illus.). 48p. (J). (gr. 3-5). 26.20 (978-0-7377-1416-6(6) , Kidhaven) Thomson Gale.

Klam, Julie. Pearl Harbor & the Rise of Japan. 2002. (Illus.). 48p. (J). lib. bdg. 28.50 (978-1-58340-188-0(1)) Smart Apple Media.

Kuroi, Hiromitsu. Secrets of the Ninja: Their Training, Tools, & Techniques. Cahill, Jennifer, ed. 2003. (Illus.). 96p. 19.95 (978-0-9723124-6-2(3)) DH Publishing, Inc.

Leavitt, Caroline. Samurai. 2006. (Edge Books, Warriors of History). (Illus.). 32p. (J). (gr. 4-7). lib. bdg. 23.93 (*978-0-7368-6433-6(4) , Edge Bks.) Capstone Pr., Inc.

Miocevich, Grant. Investigating Japan: Prehistory to Postwar. Cheng & Tsui, ed. 2005. (Illus.). 84p. (YA). (gr. 10-12). per. 24.99 (978-0-7339-0163-8(8)) Pearson Education Australia AUS. *Dist:* Cheng & Tsui Co.

Moore, Willamarie. StarFestival Grades 7-9 Tanabata Festival Team: Exploring Cultural Heritage. Miyagawa, Shigeru, ed. 2000. (Illus.). 47p. (YA). (gr. 7-11). pap., stu. ed., wbk. ed. 10.00 (978-1-929724-10-9(1)) Star-Festival, Inc.

Nishimura, Shigeo. An Illustrated History of Japan. Nishimura, Shigeo, illus. 2005. (Illus.). 61p. (J). (ps-7). 19.95 (978-0-8048-3670-8(1)) Tuttle Publishing.

Pilbeam, Mavis. Japan under the Shoguns, 1185-1868. 1999. (Looking Back Ser.). (Illus.). (gr. 6-9). 63p. (J). 19.98 (978-0-8172-5434-6(X)); 64p. (YA). 19.98 (978-0-8172-5431-5(5)) Raintree.

Richardson, Hazel. Life in Ancient Japan. 2005. (Peoples of the Ancient World Ser.). (Illus.). 32p. (J). (ps-9). pap. (978-0-7787-2071-3(3)); lib. bdg. (978-0-7787-2041-6(1)) Crabtree Publishing Co.

Roberson, John R. Japan Meets the World: The Birth of a Super Power. 1998. (Single Titles Ser.: up). (Illus.). 208p. (gr. 7-12). lib. bdg. 24.90 (978-0-7613-0407-4(X) , Millbrook Pr.) Lerner Publishing Group.

Roop, Peter. Japan. 2003. (gr. k-3). lib. bdg. 14.75 (978-0-613-82332-6(X)) Tandem Library Bks.

Shigeru, Kayano & Suzuki, David. The Ainu: History, Culture & Folktales. 2004. (Illus.). 32p. (gr. 3-6). 14.95 (978-0-8048-3511-4(X)) Tuttle Publishing.

Shogun Japan DBA. 2002. spiral bd. 16.95 (978-1-56004-142-9(0)) Social Studies Schl. Service.

Zocchi, Judy. In Japan. Brodie, Neale, illus. 2005. (Global Adventures I Ser.). 32p. (J). pap. 9.95 (978-1-59646-139-0(X)); lib. bdg. 20.65 (978-1-59646-004-1(0)) Dingles & Co.
—In Japan/en Japon. Brodie, Neale, illus. 2005. (Global Adventures I Ser.).Tr. of En Japon. (ENG & SPA.). 32p. (J). pap. 9.95 (978-1-59646-141-3(1)); lib. bdg. 20.65 (978-1-59646-005-8(9)) Dingles & Co.

Zurlo, Tony. The Japanese Americans. 2003. (Immigrants in America Ser.). (Illus.). 112p. (J). 29.95 (978-1-59018-001-3(1) , Lucent Bks.) Thomson Gale.

JAPAN—HISTORY—1868-1945

Bodden, Valerie. The Bombing of Hiroshima & Nagasaki. 2007. (J). (978-1-58341-545-0(9) , Creative Education) Creative Co., The.

Holmes, Burton. The Cities of Japan. Israel, Fred L. & Schlesinger, Arthur M., Jr., eds. 1998. (World 100 Years Ago Ser.). (Illus.). 132p. (YA). (gr. 5 up). pap. 19.95 (978-0-7910-4669-2(9) , Chelsea Hse.) Facts On File, Inc.
—The Cities of Japan. Schlesinger, Arthur M., Jr. & Isreal, Fred L., eds. 1999. (World 100 Years Ago Ser.). (Illus.). 144p. (YA). (ps-3). lib. bdg. 29.95 (978-0-7910-4668-5(0) , Chelsea Hse.) Facts On File, Inc.

JAPAN—SOCIAL LIFE AND CUSTOMS

Behnke, Alison. Japan in Pictures. 2nd rev. ed. 2003. (Visual Geography Ser.). (Illus.). 80p. (J). (gr. 5-12). 27.93 (978-0-8225-1956-0(9)) Lerner Publishing Group.

Brenner, Barbara & Takaya, Julia. Chibi: A True Story from Japan. Otani, June, illus. 1999. 63p. (J). (ps-ps). lib. bdg. 14.10 (978-0-613-17774-0(6)) Tandem Library Bks.

Brenner, Barbara, et al. Chibi: A True Story from Japan. Otani, June, illus. 1999. 64p. (J). (gr. k-3). pap. 7.95 (978-0-395-72088-2(5) , Clarion Bks.) Houghton Mifflin Co. Trade & Reference Div.

Brownlie, Alison. Japan. 2004. (Letters from Around the World Ser.). (J). (978-1-84234-256-5(8) , Cherrytree Books) Evans Publishing Group.

Byers, Helen. Japan. 2004. (National Geographic Reading Expeditions Ser.). (Illus.). 24p. (J). pap. (978-0-7922-4540-7(7)) National Geographic Society.

Donovan, Sandra. Teens in Japan. (Illus.). 96p. (J). 2007. (*978-0-7565-3193-5(4)); 2006. (gr. 5-7). 31.93 (*978-0-7565-2444-9(X)) Compass Point Bks.

Godden, Rumer. Miss Happiness & Miss Flower. 2002. (Illus.). 128p. (J). (gr. 3-7). 14.89 (978-0-06-029193-8(1)) HarperCollins Pubs.

Hammond, Paula. China & Japan. 2002. (Cultures & Costumes Ser.). (Illus.). 64p. (J). (gr. 7 up). lib. bdg. (978-1-59084-436-6(X)) Mason Crest Pubs.

Haslam, Andrew. Japan. 2001. (gr. 3-6). lib. bdg. 16.40 (978-0-613-43335-8(1)) Tandem Library Bks.

Krasno, Rena. Floating Lanterns & Golden Shrines. Sugita, Toru, illus. 2000. (Celebrating Japanese Festivals Ser.: Vol. 4). 48p. (J). (gr. 3-5). lib. bdg. 19.95 (978-1-881896-21-0(8) , Dragon Bks.) Pacific View Pr.

McCulloch, Julie. Japan. 2002. (Illus.). 48p. (J). (gr. 4-6). pap. (978-1-58810-389-5(7) , 91139) Heinemann Library.
—Japan. Davies, Nicholas Beresford, illus. 2001. (World of Recipes Ser.). 48p. (J). (gr. 3-5). lib. bdg. 25.64 (978-1-58810-087-0(1)) Heinemann Library.

Parker, Victoria. We're from Japan. 2005. (Illus.). 32p. (J). (978-1-4034-5786-8(7)); pap. (978-1-4034-5793-6(X)) Heinemann.

Raintree Steck-Vaughn Staff. Japan. 1999. (Food & Festivals Ser.). (Illus.). 32p. (J). (gr. 1-4). lib. bdg. 25.69 (978-0-7398-1407-9(9)) Raintree.

Takabayashi, Mari. I Live in Tokyo. (Illus.). 32p. (J). (gr. k-3). 2001. tchr. ed. 16.00 (978-0-618-07702-1(2)); 2004. reprint ed. pap. 6.95 (978-0-618-49484-2(7)) Houghton Mifflin Co. Trade & Reference Div.

Temko, Florence. Traditional Crafts from Japan. Gooch, Randall, illus. 2005. (Culture Crafts Ser.). 64p. (gr. 3-8). 23.93 (978-0-8225-2938-5(6)) Lerner Publishing Group.

Walsh, Kieran. Japan. 2005. (Countries in the News Ser.). (Illus.). 24p. (gr. 1-4). 17.95 (978-1-59515-289-3(X)) Rourke Publishing, LLC.

West, Patricia. East Meets West: Japan & America. 2005. (Illus.). 12p. (J). pap. (*978-0-328-13382-6(5) , Scott Foresman) Addison-Wesley Educational Pubs., Inc.

Weston, Reiko. Cooking the Japanese Way. 2nd rev. exp. ed. 2002. (Easy Menu Ethnic Cookbooks). (Illus.). 72p. (J). (gr. 5-12). 25.26 (978-0-8225-4114-1(9) , Lerner Pubns.) Lerner Publishing Group.

Zocchi, Judy. In Japan. Brodie, Neale, illus. 2005. (Global Adventures I Ser.). 32p. (J). pap. 9.95 (978-1-59646-139-0(X)); lib. bdg. 20.65 (978-1-59646-004-1(0)) Dingles & Co.
—In Japan/en Japon. Brodie, Neale, illus. 2005. (Global Adventures I Ser.).Tr. of En Japon. (ENG & SPA.). 32p. (J). lib. bdg. 20.65 (978-1-59646-005-8(9)) Dingles & Co.

JAPANESE—UNITED STATES

Aihara, Chris. Nikkei Donburi: A Japanese American Cultural Survival Guide. Iwasaki, Glen, illus. 2004. 124p. (J). (gr. 1-4). pap. 18.95 (978-1-879965-18-8(6)) Polychrome Publishing Corp.

Chin, Steven A. When Justice Failed: The Fred Korematsu Story. 2001. (Nonfiction Bookbag Ser.). (YA). (gr. 7-8). per. 8.45 (978-1-58830-211-3(3)) Metropolitan Teaching & Learning Co.

Motoyoshi, Michelle. The Japanese in California. 1999. (California Cultures Ser.). (Illus.). 64p. (J). (gr. 4-8). pap. 14.95 (978-1-884925-90-0(1)) Toucan Valley Pubns., Inc.

Nickles, Greg. The Japanese. 2001. (We Came to North America Ser.). (Illus.). 32p. (J). (gr. 4). (978-0-7787-0193-4(X)); pap. (978-0-7787-0207-8(3)) Crabtree Publishing Co.

Uchida, Yoshiko. Journey to Topaz. 2005. 160p. pap. 9.95 (978-1-890771-91-1(0)) Heyday Bks.

Wallner, Rosemary. Japanese Immigrants, 1850-1950. 2001. (Blue Earth Books). (Illus.). 32p. (J). (gr. 3-4). lib. bdg. 22.60 (978-0-7368-0797-5(7) , Bridgestone Bks.) Capstone Pr., Inc.

JAPANESE—UNITED STATES—FICTION

Berry, Eileen M. Haiku on Your Shoes. Regan, Dana, illus. 2005. 56p. (J). (ps-ps). pap. 7.49 (978-1-59166-374-4(1)) Jones, Bob Univ. Pr.

Bunting, Eve. So Far from the Sea. Soentpiet, Chris K., illus. 1998. 32p. (J). (gr. 4-6). tchr. ed. 16.00 (978-0-395-72095-0(8) , Clarion Bks.) Houghton Mifflin Co. Trade & Reference Div.

Claire, Elizabeth. Where Is Taro? Rosenthal, Marilyn, ed. Lustig, Loretta, illus. 2000. (J). pap., act. bk. ed., instr.'s gde. ed. 15.00 (978-0-937630-10-5(1)) Eardley Pubns.

Igus, Toyomi. Two Mrs Gibsons. 2001. (gr. k-3). lib. bdg. 16.40 (978-0-613-65372-5(6)) Tandem Library Bks.

McCoy, Karen Kawamoto. Bon Odori Dancer. Yao, Carolina, illus. 1998. 32p. (J). (gr. 1-4). pap. 14.95 (978-1-879965-16-4(X)) Polychrome Publishing Corp.

Okei-san: The Girl from Wakamatsu. 2006. (J). pap. 11.95 (***978-0-9642112-8-5(9))** Barsotti Bks.

Tung, Angela. Song of the Stranger. Artenstein, Michael, ed. 1999. (Roxbury Park Bks.). (J). 192p. (gr. 3-7). pap. 4.95 (978-1-56565-948-3(1) , 09481W); 96p. (gr. 5-8). 12.95 (978-1-56565-774-8(8) , 07748W) Lowell Hse. (Roxbury Park).

Uchida, Yoshiko. A Jar of Dreams. 1998. (J). pap. 3.95 (978-0-87628-469-8(1)) Ctr. for Applied Research in Education, The.

Yamate, Sandra S. Day of Remembrance. Date not set. (J). 12.95 (978-1-879965-12-6(7)) Polychrome Publishing Corp.

Yashima, Taro. Umbrella. unabr. ed. (J). (gr. k-3). 24.95 incl. audio (978-0-670-73864-9(6)) Live Oak Media.

JAPANESE AMERICANS

Anderson, Dale. Japanese Americans. 2006. (World Almanac Library of American Immigration). (Illus.). 48p. (J). pap. (978-0-8368-7326-9(2)); lib. bdg. (978-0-8368-7313-9(0)) Stevens, Gareth Inc. (World Almanac Library).

Aronson, Virginia. Konnichiwa Florida Moon: The Story of George Morikami, Pineapple Pioneer. 2002. (Illus.). 64p. (J). (gr. 3-7). 10.95 (978-1-56164-263-2(0)) Pineapple Pr., Inc.

Blumberg, Rhoda. Shipwrecked! The True Adventures of A Japanese Boy. 2001. (gr. 3-6). lib. bdg. 16.45 (978-0-613-61458-0(5)) Tandem Library Bks.

Bryan, Nichol. Japanese Americans. 2004. (One Nation Set Ii Ser.). (Illus.). 32p. (J). (gr. k-6). lib. bdg. 22.78 (978-1-59197-529-8(8)) ABDO Publishing Co.

Burgan, Michael. The Japanese American Internment: Civil Liberties Denied. 2006. (Snapshots in History Ser.). (Illus.). 96p. lib. bdg. **(*978-0-7565-2453-1(9))** Compass Point Bks.

Contino, Jennifer. The Japanese Americans. 2002. (Welcome to America Ser.). (Illus.). 64p. (J). (gr. 4-7). lib. bdg. (978-1-59084-106-8(9)) Mason Crest Pubs.

Cooper, Michael L. Fighting for Honor: Japanese Americans & World War II. 2000. (Illus.). 128p. (J). (gr. 5-9). tchr. ed. 18.00 (978-0-395-91375-8(6) , Clarion Bks.) Houghton Mifflin Co. Trade & Reference Div.

—Remembering Manzanar: Life in a Japanese Relocation Camp. 2002. (Illus.). 80p. (J). (gr. 4-6). tchr. ed. 15.00 (978-0-618-06778-7(7) , Clarion Bks.) Houghton Mifflin Co. Trade & Reference Div.

Donlan, Leni. How Did This Happen Here? Japanese Internment Camps. 2007. **(*978-1-4109-2701-9(6));** pap. **(*978-1-4109-2712-5(1))** Steck-Vaughn.

Goldstein, Margaret J. Japanese in America. 2006. (Illus.). 80p. (J). 27.93 (978-0-8225-3952-0(7) , Lerner Pubns.) Lerner Publishing Group.

Grapes, Bryan J. Japanese-American Internment Camps. 2000. (History Firsthand Ser.). (Illus.). 202p. (YA). (gr. 7-10). lib. bdg. 32.45 (978-0-7377-0413-6(6) , Greenhaven Pr., Inc.) Thomson Gale.

Ingram, Scott. Japanese Immigrants. 2004. (Immigration to the United States Ser.). (Illus.). 96p. (J). (gr. 4-9). 35.00 (978-0-8160-5688-0(9)) Facts On File, Inc.

Japanese-American Internment. 2004. (Historical Reader Ser.). (Illus.). 240p. (gr. 6-12). 13.32 (978-0-618-00365-5(7) , 2-00102) McDougal Littell Inc.

Japanese-American National Museum Staff. Regenerations Oral History Project Vol. 3: Rebuilding Japanese American Families, Communities & Civil Rights in the Resettlement Era. unabr. ed. 2000. (Illus.). 505p. (YA). (gr. 9-12). (978-1-881161-08-0(0)) Japanese American National Museum.

Japanese-American National Museum Staff & Chicago Japanese American Historical Society Staff. Regenerations Oral History Project Vol. 3: Rebuilding Japanese American Families, Communities & Civil Rights in the Resettlement Era. unabr. ed. 2000. (Illus.). 708p. (YA). (gr. 9-12). (978-1-881161-07-3(2)) Japanese American National Museum.

Japanese-American National Museum Staff & Japanese American Historical Society of San Diego Staff. Regenerations Oral History Project Vol. 3: Rebuilding Japanese American Families, Communities & Civil Rights in the Resettlement Era. unabr. ed. 2000. 386p. (YA). (gr. 9-12). (978-1-881161-09-7(9)) Japanese American National Museum.

Japanese-American National Museum Staff & Japanese American Resource Center-Museum Staff. Regenerations Oral History Project Vol. 3: Rebuilding Japanese American Families, Communities & Civil Rights in the Resettlement Era. unabr. ed. 2000. 727p. (YA). (gr. 9-12). (978-1-881161-10-3(2)) Japanese American National Museum.

Japanese-American National Museum Staff, et al. Regenerations Oral History Project Vol. 3: Rebuilding Japanese American Families, Communities & Civil Rights in the Resettlement Era. unabr. ed. 2000. (Illus.). 2326p. (YA). (gr. 9-12). (978-1-881161-06-6(4)) Japanese American National Museum.

Komatsu, Kimberly & Komatsu, Kaleigh. In America's Shadow. 2003. (Illus.). 96p. (gr. 3 up). 35.00 (978-0-9709829-0-2(9)) George, Thomas Bks.

Kops, Deborah. Racial Profiling. 2006. (Open for Debate Ser.). (Illus.). 127p. (YA). (gr. 6-9). lib. bdg. 39.93 (978-0-7614-2298-3(6) , Benchmark Bks.) Cavendish, Marshall Corp.

Mattern, Joanne. Japanese Americans. 2003. (Immigrants in America Ser.). (Illus.). 112p. (gr. 6-12). 30.00 (978-0-7910-7130-4(8)); pap. 13.25 (978-0-7910-7510-4(9)) Facts On File, Inc. (Chelsea Hse.).

McDaniel, Melissa. Japanese Americans. 2002. (Spirit of America: Our Cultural Heritage Ser.). (Illus.). 32p. (J). (gr. 2-6). 27.07 (978-1-56766-154-5(8)) Child's World, Inc.

Nickles, Greg. The Japanese. 2001. (We Came to North America Ser.). (Illus.). 32p. (J). (gr. 4). (978-0-7787-0193-4(X)); pap. (978-0-7787-0207-8(3)) Crabtree Publishing Co.

—Japanese. 2001. (gr. 3-6). lib. bdg. 17.60 (978-0-613-43459-1(5)) Tandem Library Bks.

—The Japanese: We Came to North America. 2006. (Illus.). 32p. (J). (gr. 4-8). reprint ed. 19.00 (978-0-7567-9908-3(2)) DIANE Publishing Co.

Oppenheim, Joanne. Dear Miss Breed: True Stories of the Japanese American Incarceration During World War II & a Librarian Who Made a Difference. 2006. (Illus.). 288p. (J). (gr. 7 up). pap. 22.99 (978-0-439-56992-7(3)) Scholastic, Inc.

Parker, Lewis K. Why Japanese Immigrants Came to America. 2003. (Reading Power Ser.). (Illus.). 24p. (J). lib. bdg. 17.25 (978-0-8239-6463-5(9) , PowerKids Pr.) Rosen Publishing Group, Inc., The.

Perl, Lila. Barbed Wire & Guard Towers: The Internment of Japanese Americans During World War II. 2002. (Great Journeys Ser.). (Illus.). 112p. (J). 32.79 (978-0-7614-1321-9(9) , Benchmark Bks.) Cavendish, Marshall Corp.

Peterson, Tiffany. Japanese Americans. 2004. (We Are America Ser.). (Illus.). 32p. (J). lib. bdg. 24.22 (978-1-4034-5022-7(6)) Heinemann Library.

Ruggiero, Adriane. World War II. 2002. (American Voices From Ser.). (Illus.). xxi, 117p. (J). 34.21 (978-0-7614-1206-9(9) , Benchmark Bks.) Cavendish, Marshall Corp.

Sakurai, Gail. Japanese American Internment Camps. (Cornerstones of Freedomtrade;, Second Ser.). 48p. (J). 2007. pap. 5.95 **(*978-0-531-18690-9(3));** 2002. (Illus.). (gr. 4-6). 26.00 (978-0-516-22276-9(7)) Scholastic Library Publishing. (Children's Pr.).

Slavicek, Louise Chipley. Daniel Inouye. 2007. (Asian Americans of Achievement Ser.). 128p. (YA). (gr. 6-10). lib. bdg. 30.00 (978-0-7910-9271-2(2) , Chelsea Hse.) Facts On File, Inc.

Tiger, Caroline & Noguchi, Isamu. Isamu Noguchi. 2007. (Asian Americans of Achievement Ser.). (Illus.). 112p. (J). (gr. 6-12). 30.00 (978-0-7910-9276-7(3) , Chelsea Hse.) Facts On File, Inc.

Welch, Catherine A. Children of the Relocation Camps. 2005. (Picture the American Past Ser.). (Illus.). 48p. (gr. 2-5). lib. bdg. 22.60 (978-1-57505-350-9(0)) Lerner Publishing Group.

West, Patricia. East Meets West: Japan & America. 2005. (Illus.). 12p. (J). pap. **(*978-0-328-13382-6(5)** , Scott Foresman) Addison-Wesley Educational Pubs., Inc.

Yancey, Diane. The Internment of the Japanese. 2002. (World History Ser.). (Illus.). 112p. (YA). (gr. 8-11). 32.45 (978-1-59018-013-6(5) , LML00902-180218, Lucent Bks.) Thomson Gale.

Zurlo, Tony. The Japanese Americans. 2003. (Immigrants in America Ser.). (Illus.). 112p. (J). 29.95 (978-1-59018-001-3(1) , Lucent Bks.) Thomson Gale.

JAPANESE AMERICANS—FICTION

Banks, Jacqueline Turner. A Day for Vincent Chin & Me. 128p. (J). (gr. 5-9). 2005. pap. 5.95 (978-0-618-54879-8(3)); 2001. (Illus.). 15.00 (978-0-618-13199-0(X)) Houghton Mifflin Co. Trade & Reference Div.

Boyd, Jones Veda. Laura's Victory: End of the Second World War. 2006. 144p. (J). pap. 4.97 (978-1-59789-103-5(7)) Barbour Publishing, Inc.

Cheaney, J. B. My Friend the Enemy. 2007. 272p. (J). (gr. 5-9). 6.50 **(*978-0-440-42102-3(0)** , Yearling) Random Hse. Children's Bks.

Ching, Tokie. Girl's Day in Hawaii with Yuki Chan. 2006. 40p. (J). 12.95 **(*978-1-56647-820-5(0))** Mutual Publishing LLC.

Crilley, Mark. Akiko Vol. 7: The Battle for Boach's Keep. 2004. (Illus.). 144p. pap. 14.95 (978-1-57989-064-3(4)) Sirius Entertainment, Inc.

—Akiko & the Alpha Centauri 5000. Crilley, Mark, illus. 2004. (Illus.). 176p. (gr. 3). pap. 5.50 (978-0-440-41892-4(5) , Yearling) Random Hse. Children's Bks.

—Akiko & the Great Wall of Trudd. 2002. (gr. 3-6). lib. bdg. 13.00 (978-0-613-50400-3(3)) Tandem Library Bks.

—Akiko & the Journey to Toog. Crilley, Mark, illus. (Illus.). (gr. 3 up). 2005. 192p. 5.50 (978-0-440-41893-1(3) , Yearling); 2003. 176p. 9.95 (978-0-385-73042-6(X) , Delacorte Bks. for Young Readers) Random Hse. Children's Bks.

—Akiko in the Castle of Alia Rellapor. 2002. (gr. 3-6). lib. bdg. 13.00 (978-0-613-49540-0(3)) Tandem Library Bks.

—Akiko in the Sprubly Islands. Crilley, Mark, illus. 2001. (Akiko Ser.: Vol. 2). (Illus.). 176p. (J). (gr. 3-3). pap. 5.50 (978-0-440-41651-7(5) , Yearling) Random Hse. Children's Bks.

—Akiko in the Sprubly Islands. 2001. (Illus.). 146p. (J). (gr. 4-7). lib. bdg. 13.00 (978-0-613-42696-1(7)) Tandem Library Bks.

—Akiko on the Planet Smoo. Crilley, Mark, illus. 2001. (Akiko Ser.: Vol. 1). (Illus.). 176p. (J). (gr. 3-3). pap. 5.50 (978-0-440-41648-7(5) , Yearling) Random Hse. Children's Bks.

—Akiko on the Planet Smoo. 2001. (gr. 3-6). lib. bdg. 13.00 (978-0-613-42697-8(5)) Tandem Library Bks.

—Akiko: Pieces of Gax. Crilley, Mark, illus. 2006. (Illus.). 224p. (J). (gr. 3). 9.95 (978-0-385-73044-0(6) , Delacorte Bks. for Young Readers) Random Hse. Children's Bks.

—Akiko Pocket-Size. 2004. (Illus.). 192p. pap. 11.95 (978-1-57989-067-4(9)) Sirius Entertainment, Inc.

—Akiko: The Training Master. Crilley, Mark, illus. 2006. (Illus.). 224p. (gr. 3). 5.50 (978-0-440-41894-8(1) , Yearling) Random Hse. Children's Bks.

—Flights of Fancy. exp. ed. 2007. (Illus.). 264p. pap. 24.95 **(*978-1-57989-088-9(1))** Sirius Entertainment, Inc.

Crilley, Mark. The Training Master. Crilley, Mark, illus. 2005. (Akiko Ser.). (Illus.). 224p. (J). (gr. 3). 9.95 (978-0-385-73043-3(8) , Delacorte Bks. for Young Readers) Random Hse. Children's Bks.

Easton, Kelly. Hiroshima Dreams. 2007. 192p. (YA). (gr. 7). 16.99 **(*978-0-525-47821-8(3)** , Dutton Juvenile) Penguin Group (USA) Inc.

Falwell, Cathryn. Butterflies for Kiri. Falwell, Cathryn, illus. 2003. (Illus.). 32p. (J). (978-1-58430-100-4(7)) Lee & Low Bks., Inc.

Hawes, Louise. Rosey in the Present Tense. 1999. (Illus.). (J). (978-0-606-20488-0(1)) Tandem Library Bks.

—Rosey in the Present Tense. l.t. ed. 2002. 186p. (J). 22.95 (978-0-7862-4418-8(6)) Thorndike Pr.

—Rosey in the Present Tense. 1999. 176p. (YA). (gr. 7). 16.95 (978-0-8027-8685-2(5)) Walker & Co.

Hennelly, Nilsson. Keeper of the River. 1999. (Rafters Ser.: Vol. 2). 144p. (J). (gr. 3-7). 12.95 (978-0-7373-0317-9(4) , 03174W); pap. 4.95 (978-0-7373-0299-8(2) , 02992W) Lowell Hse. (Roxbury Park).

Icenoggle, Jodi. America's Betrayal. 2001. (gr. 7-12). lib. bdg. 16.40 (978-0-613-83690-6(1)) Tandem Library Bks.

—America's Betrayal. 2001. 208p. (J). (gr. 7 up). 7.95 (978-1-57249-252-3(X) , White Mane Kids) White Mane Publishing Co., Inc.

Kadohata, Cynthia. Kira-Kira. 2004. (Illus.). 256p. 16.95 (978-0-689-85639-6(3) , Atheneum); 2006. 272p. (J). reprint ed. pap. 6.99 (978-0-689-85640-2(7) , Aladdin) Simon & Schuster Children's Publishing.

—Kira-Kira. l.t. ed. 2005. 201p. 23.95 (978-0-7862-7616-5(9) , Large Print Pr.) Thorndike Pr.

—Weedflower. 2006. (J). (978-0-689-04937-8(4)); (Illus.). 272p. (gr. 5 up). 16.95 (978-0-689-86574-9(0)) Simon & Schuster Children's Publishing. (Atheneum).

Lee-Tai, Amy. A Place Where Sunflowers Grow. Hoshino, Felicia, illus. 2006. (JPN.). 32p. (J). 16.95 (978-0-89239-215-5(0)) Children's Bk. Pr.

Mazer, Harry. A Boy No More. 2004. (Illus.). 144p. (J). 16.95 (978-0-689-85533-7(8)) Simon & Schuster Children's Publishing.

Mitsui Brown, Janet, illus. Oshogatsu with Obaachan. 2005. (J). (978-1-879965-24-9(0)) Polychrome Publishing Corp.

Mochizuki, Ken. Baseball Saved Us. Lee, Dom, illus. (Picture Book Readalong Ser.). 28.95 incl. audio compact disk (978-1-59112-916-5(8)); pap. 39.95 incl. audio compact disk (978-1-59112-917-2(6)); 2004. (J). audio 25.95 (978-1-59112-456-6(5)) Live Oak Media.

—Beacon Hill Boys. 208p. (J). 2004. (gr. 7 up). 5.99 (978-0-439-24906-5(6)); 2002. (gr. 9 up). pap. 16.95 (978-0-439-26749-6(8) , Scholastic Pr.) Scholastic, Inc.

Namioka, Lensey. Mismatch. 224p. (gr. 5-9). 2007. (YA). mass mkt. 6.50 (978-0-440-23879-9(X) , Laurel Leaf); 2006. (J). 15.95 (978-0-385-73183-6(3) , Delacorte Bks. for Young Readers) Random Hse. Children's Bks.

Noguchi, Rick & Jenks, Deneen. Flowers from Mariko. Kumata, Michelle Reiko, illus. 2001. 32p. (J). (gr. 1 up). 16.95 (978-1-58430-032-8(9)) Lee & Low Bks., Inc.

Okimoto, Jean Davies. Talent Night. 2000. (gr. 7-12). lib. bdg. 22.20 (978-0-613-83512-1(3)) Tandem Library Bks.

—Talent Night. 2000. 180p. (gr. 7-12). pap. 12.95 (978-0-595-00795-0(3) , Backinprint.com) iUniverse, Inc.

Parkhurst, Liz S. Under One Flag: A Year at Rohwer. Clifton, Tom, illus. 2005. 32p. (J). 16.95 (978-0-87483-759-9(6) , 1241971) August Hse. Pubs., Inc.

Patneaude, David. Thin Wood Walls. 2004. (Illus.). 240p. (YA). (gr. 5-9). tchr. ed. 16.00 (978-0-618-34290-7(7)) Houghton Mifflin Co. Trade & Reference Div.

Rue, Nancy N. The Stand. 2001. (Christian Heritage Ser.). 192p. (J). (gr. 3-8). pap. (978-1-56179-893-3(2)) Focus on the Family Publishing.

Salisbury, Graham. Eyes of the Emperor. (YA). (gr. 7-11). 2007. 256p. mass mkt. 6.50 (978-0-440-22956-8(1) , Laurel Leaf); 2005. 240p. 15.95 (978-0-385-72971-0(5) , Lamb, Wendy); 2005. 240p. lib. bdg. 17.99 (978-0-385-90874-0(1) , Lamb, Wendy) Random Hse. Children's Bks.

—House of the Red Fish. 2008. 304p. (YA). (gr. 7). mass mkt. 6.50 **(*978-0-440-23838-6(2)** , Laurel Leaf) Random Hse. Children's Bks.

Salisbury, Graham. Under the Blood-Red Sun. 2005. 272p. (YA). (gr. 7-10). pap. 6.50 (978-0-553-49487-7(2) , Laurel Leaf) Random Hse. Children's Bks.

Say, Allen. Home of the Brave. 2002. (Illus.). 32p. (J). (gr. k-3). 17.00 (978-0-618-21223-1(X) , Walter Lorraine) Houghton Mifflin Co. Trade & Reference Div.

—Music for Alice. 2004. (Illus.). 32p. (J). (gr. k-3). tchr. ed. 17.00 (978-0-618-31118-7(1) , Walter Lorraine) Houghton Mifflin Co. Trade & Reference Div.

—Tea with Milk. Say, Allen, illus. 2002. (Illus.). (J). 24.36 (978-0-7587-3768-7(8)) Book Wholesalers, Inc.

—Tea with Milk. Say, Allen, illus. 1999. (Illus.). 32p. (J). (gr. k-3). tchr. ed. 17.00 (978-0-395-90495-4(1) , Walter Lorraine) Houghton Mifflin Co. Trade & Reference Div.

Smith, Greg Leitich. Ninjas, Piranhas, & Galileo. 2005. 192p. (J). (gr. 5-8). pap. 6.99 (978-0-316-01181-5(9)) Little Brown & Co.

Terasaki, Stanley Todd. Ghosts for Breakfast. Shinjo, Shelly, illus. 2002. 32p. (J). (gr. k-4). 16.95 (978-1-58430-046-5(9)) Lee & Low Bks., Inc.

Trottier, Maxine. Flags. Morin, Paul, illus. l.t. ed. 1999. 27p. (ps-3). 16.95 (978-0-7737-3136-3(9)) Stoddart Kids CAN. *Dist:* Fitzhenry & Whiteside, Ltd.

Uchida, Yoshiko. Samurai of Gold Hill. Forberg, Ati, illus. 2005. 119p. (J). (gr. 2). pap. 8.95 (978-1-59714-015-7(5)) Heyday Bks.

Wahl, Jan. Candy Shop. Wong, Nicole E., illus. 2004. 32p. (J). 15.95 (978-1-57091-508-6(3)) Charlesbridge Publishing, Inc.

Walters, Eric. Caged Eagles. 2001. 256p. (J). (gr. 7-12). pap. 7.95 (978-1-55143-139-0(4)) Orca Bk. Pubs. USA.

—Caged Eagles. 2001. (gr. 7-12). lib. bdg. 16.40 (978-0-613-86415-2(8)) Tandem Library Bks.

Wells, Rosemary. Practice Makes Perfect. Wheeler, Jody, illus. 2002. (Yoko & Friends School Days Ser.: No. 10). 32p. (gr. k-2). 9.99 (978-0-7868-0725-3(3)) Disney Pr.

—Practice Makes Perfect. 2002. (gr. k-3). lib. bdg. 11.80 (978-0-613-74979-4(0)) Tandem Library Bks.

—Read Me a Story. Wheeler, Jody & Nez, John, illus. 2002. (Yoko & Friends School Days Ser.: Bk. 8). 32p. (gr. k-2). pap. 3.99 (978-0-7868-1533-3(7) , Volo) Hyperion Bks. for Children.

—When I Grow Up. Wheeler, Jody, illus. 2003. (Yoko & Friends School Days Ser.: Bk. 12). 32p. (gr. k-2). 9.99 (978-0-7868-0731-4(8) , Volo) Hyperion Bks. for Children.

—Yoko's Paper Cranes. Wells, Rosemary, illus. 2001. (Illus.). 32p. (ps-2). 15.99 (978-0-7868-0737-6(7)) Hyperion Bks. for Children.

JAPANESE LANGUAGE—CONVERSATION AND PHRASE BOOKS

Ace Academics, ed. Japanese: A Whole Course in a Box! 2007. (Exambusters Ser.). 384p. (gr. 7 up). 12.95 (978-1-881374-96-1(3) , Exambusters) Ace Academics, Inc.

Association for Japanese-Language Staff. Japanese for Young People Vol. I: Kana Workbook. 1998. (Japanese for Young People Ser.). (Illus.). 144p. (gr. 8-12). pap., wbk. ed. 19.00 (978-4-7700-2180-9(1)) Kodansha International JPN. *Dist:* Oxford Univ. Pr., Inc.

Association for Japanese Language, Teaching Staff. Japanese for Young People, Vol. 2. 1999. (Japanese for Young People Ser.). (Illus.). 224p. pap., stu. ed. 28.00 (978-4-7700-2332-2(4)) Kodansha International JPN. *Dist:* Oxford Univ. Pr., Inc.

Davis, Carla Norman. Japanese Made Fun. 1999. (J). Vol. 1, Bk. 1. (gr. 1-3). wbk. ed. 15.00 (978-1-930272-12-5(X)); Vol. 1, Bk. 2. (gr. 4-5). wbk. ed. 15.00 (978-1-930272-13-2(8)) Queen Enterprises, Inc.

Drew, David. What If? Harradine, Dona, tr. Falla, Dominique, illus. 1999. (Hello! Lote Ser.). (IND.). 17p. (J). pap. 5.99 (978-0-7339-0868-2(3)) Pearson Education Australia AUS. *Dist:* Cheng & Tsui Co.

—What If? Batt, Deleece, tr. Falla, Dominique, illus. 1999. (Hello! Lote Ser.). (JPN.). 17p. (J). pap. 5.99 (978-0-7339-0895-8(0)) Pearson Education Australia AUS. *Dist:* Cheng & Tsui Co.

Dumont, Deborah, intro. Hippocrene Children's Illustrated Japanese Dictionary: English-Japanese/Japanese-English. 2001. (Hippocrene Children's Illustrated Foreign Language Dictionaries Ser.). (JPN & ENG., Illus.). 94p. (gr. k-5). pap. 11.95 (978-0-7818-0849-1(9)) Hippocrene Bks., Inc.

Green, Yuko. Japanese Word Book. 2004. (JPN., Illus.). 112p. pap. 19.95 (978-1-57306-196-4(4)) Bess Pr., Inc.

—My First Hiragana. 2000. (Illus.). 48p. (J). (gr. k-5). pap., act. bk. ed. 4.95 (978-0-486-41336-5(5)) Dover Pubns., Inc.

Inui, Tazuko & Yoon, Selina. Sing 'n Learn Japanese Two: More Japanese Through Favorite Songs, Vol. 2. 1998. (Sing 'n Learn Ser.). (ENG & JPN., Illus.). 32p. (J). (ps-6). pap. 14.95 incl. audio (978-1-888194-23-4(5)) Master Communications, Inc.

—Sing 'n Learn Japanese Two Vol. 2: More Japanese Through Favorite Songs. 1998. (Sing 'n Learn Ser.). (ENG & JPN., Illus.). 32p. (J). (ps-6). pap. 17.95 incl. audio compact disk (978-1-888194-24-1(3)) Master Communications, Inc.

Japanese Language Association Staff. Japanese for Young People II: Kanji Workbook. 1999. (Japanese for Young People Ser.). 112p. pap., wbk. ed. 19.00 (978-4-7700-2333-9(2)) Kodansha International JPN. *Dist:* Oxford Univ. Pr., Inc.

Konda, Cynthia. Okasan & Me: Japanese American Educational Program. 2003. (JPN., Illus.). 26p. (J). (ps up). spiral bd. 19.99 (978-0-9743613-0-7(5)) Okasan & Me.

Lee, Margaret. Tsumiki. 2004. (JPN & ENG., Illus.). (gr. 7-9). 194p. pap., tchr. ed. 135.00 (978-0-17-010268-1(8)); 177p. pap., stu. ed. 34.95 (978-0-17-010267-4(X)); 129p. pap., wbk. ed. 21.95 (978-0-17-010270-4(X)) Cengage Learning Australia AUS. *Dist:* Cheng & Tsui Co.

Mahoney, Judy. Teach Me More... Japanese W/Cassette: A Musical Journey Through the Year. 2005. (Teach Me More...Ser.). (ENG & JPN., Illus.). 20p. (J). (ps-7). pap. 13.95 incl. audio (978-0-934633-20-8(7)) Teach Me Tapes, Inc.

Malm, Kiyoko. Irasshai Explorer Japanese in the Middle: A Multimedia Exploratory Course for Middle Schools. Rieken, Elizabeth & Duncan, Gregory, eds. Handley, Chris, illus. 1998. 144p. (gr. 6-8). pap., stu. ed. 24.95 incl. VHS (978-1-892720-02-3(7)) Georgia Public Broadcasting.

McBride, Helen, et al. Kimono, Level 3. 2000. (JPN.). 160p. (J). pap., wbk. ed. 21.95 (978-0-8219-1038-2(8) , 58653) EMC/Paradigm Publishing.

—Kimono, Level 3. Incl. Level 3. 2000. pap., wbk. ed. 21.95 (978-0-8219-1038-2(8) , 58653); Level 3. tchr. ed. 169.00 (978-0-8219-1049-8(3) , 58653); (J). (gr. k-5). (JPN.). 160p. 2000. Set stu. ed. 34.95 (978-0-8219-1037-5(X) , 58253) EMC/Paradigm Publishing.

Passport Books Staff, ed. Japanese Picture Dictionary: Elementary Through Junior High. Goodman, Marlene, illus. 2003. (Let's Learn... Picture Dictionary Ser.). (JPN.). 80p. (J). (gr. 4-7). pap. 11.95 (978-0-8442-8494-1(7) , 84947) McGraw-Hill Trade.

Peterson, Hiromi & Omizo, Naomi. Adventures in Japanese, Vol. 2. Muronaka, Michael & Kaylor, Emiko, illus. (JPN & ENG.). (gr. 7-10). 2004. 210p. pap., wbk. ed. 19.95 (978-0-88727-321-6(1)); 1999. 580p. (YA). pap. 39.95 (978-0-88727-320-9(3)) Cheng & Tsui Co.

—Adventures in Japanese: Field Test Edition. 2004. (JPN & ENG., Illus.). (gr. 9-12). 462p. pap. 45.00 (978-0-88727-416-9(1)); 116p. pap., wbk. ed. 21.95 (978-0-88727-417-6(X)) Cheng & Tsui Co.

School Zone Publishing Company Staff. Japanese - Make a Word Bingo Game. (Illus.). (J). 6.99 (978-0-88743-527-0(0)) School Zone Publishing Co.

JAPANESE LANGUAGE—GRAMMAR

Brenda, Stapleton. Grammar Keys: A Guide for Japanese Students. 3rd ed. 2005. pap. (978-0-9770443-0-6(0)) Top Shelf Publishing.

Evans, Meg & Masano, Yoko. Mirai Stage 1: Course Book, Stage 2. 2004. (JPN & ENG., Illus.). 108p. (gr. 7-10). per., act. bk. ed. 20.99 (978-0-7339-1213-9(3)) Pearson Education Australia AUS. *Dist:* Cheng & Tsui Co.

Evans, Meg, et al. Mirai: Japanese Activity Book, Stage 1. 2004. (JPN & ENG., Illus.). iv, 99p. (gr. 6-9). per., act. bk. ed. 18.95 (978-0-7339-0482-0(3)) Pearson Education Australia AUS. *Dist:* Cheng & Tsui Co.

—Mirai Stage 1: Course Book. 2004. (JPN & ENG., Stage 1. Illus.). 141p. (gr. 6-9). tchr. ed., per. 100.00 (978-0-7339-0504-9(8)); Stage 1. (Illus.). 191p. (gr. 6-9). stu. ed., per. 39.99 (978-0-7339-0425-7(4)); Stage 2. (gr. 7-10). per. 100.00 (978-0-7339-1214-6(1)); Stage 2. (Illus.). 158p. (gr. 7-10). tchr. ed., per. 100.00 (978-0-7339-1367-9(9)); Stage 2. (Illus.). 168p. (gr. 7-10). stu. ed., per. 37.99 (978-0-7339-0929-0(9)) Pearson Education Australia AUS. *Dist:* Cheng & Tsui Co.

Goodman, Marlene. Let's Learn Japanese Picture Dictionary. 2003. (JPN & ENG., Illus.). 80p. 11.95 (978-0-07-140827-1(4) , 9780071408271) McGraw-Hill Cos., The.

Green, Yuko. Japanese Word Book. 2004. (JPN., Illus.). 112p. pap. 19.95 (978-1-57306-196-4(4)) Bess Pr., Inc.

Inui, Tazuko & Yoon, Selina. Sing 'n Learn Japanese One Vol. 1: Introduce Japanese with Favorite Children's Songs. 1998. (Sing 'n Learn Ser.). (ENG & JPN., Illus.). 32p. (J). (ps-6). pap. 14.95 incl. audio (978-1-888194-21-0(9)); pap. 17.95 incl. audio compact disk (978-1-888194-22-7(7)) Master Communications, Inc.

Kardy, Glenn. Kana de Manga: A Fun, Easy Way to Learn the ABCs of Japanese. 2005. (Illus.). 144p. (YA). pap. (978-4-921205-01-0(9)) Japanime Co., Ltd.

School Zone Publishing Company Staff. Japanese - Alphabet Game. (Illus.). (J). 6.99 (978-0-88743-525-6(4)); 2.79 (978-0-88743-534-8(3)) School Zone Publishing Co.

—Japanese - Colors & Shapes. (Illus.). (J). 2.79 (978-0-88743-531-7(9)) School Zone Publishing Co.

—Japanese - Dominoes Game. (Illus.). (J). 6.99 (978-0-88743-528-7(9)) School Zone Publishing Co.

—Japanese - Three Letter Words. (Illus.). (J). 2.79 (978-0-88743-530-0(0)) School Zone Publishing Co.

—Japanese - Three Word Rhyme. (Illus.). (J). 2.79 (978-0-88743-529-4(7)) School Zone Publishing Co.

Takahashi, Peter X. Jimi's Book of Japanese: A Motivating Method to Learn Japanese (Kanji) Moto, Mikki, ed. Toka, Yumie, illus. 2006. (J). pap. 24.95 (978-0-9723247-5-5(5) , PB&J OmniMedia) Takahashi & Black.

—Jimi's Book of Japanese: A Motivating Method to Learn Japanese (Katakana) Moto, Mikki, ed. Toka, Yumie, illus. 2005. (JPN & ENG.). 76p. (J). pap. 18.95 (978-0-9723247-2-4(0) , PB&J OmniMedia) Takahashi & Black.

—Jimi's Sumo Stack: A Motivating Method to Memorize Japanese. Toka, Yumie, illus. 2006. pap. 19.95 (978-0-9723247-8-6(X) , PB&J OmniMedia) Takahashi & Black.

JAVA (INDONESIA)—FICTION

Lewis, Richard. The Flame Tree. 2004. (Illus.). 288p. (YA). 16.95 (978-0-689-86333-2(0)) Simon & Schuster Children's Publishing.

JAY, JOHN, 1745-1829

Miller, Chuck. John Jay. 2003. (America's Founders Ser.). (J). pap. (978-1-58417-083-9(2)); lib. bdg. (978-1-58417-020-4(4)) Lake Street Pubs.

Powell, Phelan. John Jay. 2000. (Revolutionary War Leaders Ser.). (Illus.). 80p. (J). (gr. 4-7). pap. 27.50 (978-0-7910-6137-4(X)); (gr. 8-12). 27.50 (978-0-7910-5979-1(0)) Facts On File, Inc. (Chelsea Hse.).

—John Jay: First Chief Justice of the Supreme Court. 2001. (gr. 5-8). lib. bdg. 17.60 (978-0-613-32726-8(8)) Tandem Library Bks.

White, Casey. John Jay. 2005. (Library of American Thinkers). (Illus.). 112p. (J). (978-1-4042-0507-9(1)) Rosen Publishing Group, Inc., The.

JAZZ

Armentrout, David & Armentrout, Patricia. Jazz & Blues. 1999. (Sounds of Music Ser.). (Illus.). 24p. (J). (gr. 1-4). lib. bdg. 19.27 (978-0-86593-533-4(5)) Rourke Publishing, LLC.

Bakay, Betty J. Razz Ma Tazz - Classical 'n Jazz Instruments. 1999. (Illus.). 24p. (YA). (gr. k-12). pap. (978-0-9677268-0-9(8)) CopyRite Printing.

Barron, Rachel Stiffler. John Coltrane: Jazz Revolutionary. 2004. (Masters of Music Ser.). (Illus.). 112p. (YA). (gr. 6-12). 23.95 (978-1-883846-57-2(9) , First Biographies) Reynolds, Morgan Inc.

Ben-Hur, Roni Amos, text. Talk Jazz: A Comprehensive Collection of Be Bop Studies for All Instrumentalists & Vocalists. Ben-Hur, Roni Amos, . 2003. 54p. (YA). pap. 19.00 net. (978-0-9744943-0-2(5) , (201 862-1692) Bohobza Music.

Bolden, Tonya. Take-Off! American All-Girl Bands During WW II. 2007. (Illus.). 80p. (J). (gr. 5-9). lib. bdg. 21.99 (978-0-375-92797-3(2) , Knopf Bks. for Young Readers) Random Hse. Children's Bks.

—Take-Off (Book & CD) American All-Girl Bands During World War II. 2007. (Illus.). 80p. (J). (gr. 5-9). 18.99 (978-0-375-82797-6(8) , Knopf Bks. for Young Readers) Random Hse. Children's Bks.

Coltrane, John, contrib. by. John Coltrane's Giant Steps. abr. ed. 2002. (Live Oak Readalong Ser.). (Illus.). (J). (ps-4). 25.95 incl. audio (978-0-87499-973-0(1)) Live Oak Media.

Gourse, Leslie. Blowing on the Changes: The Art of the Jazz Horn Players. 1998. (Art of Jazz Ser.). (Illus.). 144p. (J). (gr. 8-12). pap. 8.95 (978-0-531-15880-7(2) , Watts, Franklin) Scholastic Library Publishing.

—Blowing on the Changes: The Art of the Jazz Horn Players. 1998. (Illus.). 144p. (YA). (gr. 8-12). lib. bdg. 17.60 (978-0-613-29202-3(2)) Tandem Library Bks.

—Wynton Marsalis: Trumpet Genius. (Book Report Biographies Ser.). (Illus.). 112p. (YA). (gr. 6-8). 2000. pap. 6.95 (978-0-531-16407-5(1)); 1999. 18.95 (978-0-531-11673-9(5)) Scholastic Library Publishing. (Watts, Franklin).

Hal Leonard Corporation Staff, creator. Jazzy Opera Classix: For Clarinet. 2005. 36p. pap. 19.95 incl. audio compact disk (978-1-902455-29-7(0) , 1902455290) Schott Musik International GmbH & Co. KG DEU. *Dist:* Leonard, Hal Corp.

—Jazzy Opera Classix: For Violin. 2005. 36p. pap. 19.95 incl. audio compact disk (978-1-902455-32-7(0) , 1902455320) Schott Musik International GmbH & Co. KG DEU. *Dist:* Leonard, Hal Corp.

Hannah, Jonny. Hot Jazz Special. Hannah, Jonny, illus. 2005. (Illus.). 40p. (J). (gr. 1-5). 16.99 (978-0-7636-2308-1(3)) Candlewick Pr.

Harcourt School Publishers Staff. Jazz Advanced Level: America's Musical Heritage. 3rd ed. 2002. (Trophies Reading Program Ser.). (Illus.). pap. 5.10 (978-0-15-323389-0(3)) Harcourt Schl. Pubs.

Lee, Jeanne. Jam! The Story of Jazz Music. 1999. (Library of African American Arts & Culture). (Illus.). 64p. (YA). (gr. 7-12). lib. bdg. 26.50 (978-0-8239-1852-2(1) , AAJAZZ) Rosen Publishing Group, Inc., The.

Marin, Reva. Oscar: The Life & Music of Oscar Peterson. 2003. (Illus.). 144p. (J). (gr. 6 up). 16.95 (978-0-88899-537-7(7)) Groundwood Bks. CAN. *Dist:* Perseus Distribution.

McDonough, Yona Zeldis. Who Was Louis Armstrong? O'Brien, John & Harrison, Nancy, illus. 2004. (Who Was...? Ser.). 112p. (J). 13.89 (978-0-448-43560-2(8)); (gr. 3-7). pap. 4.99 (978-0-448-43368-4(0)) Penguin Group (USA) Inc. (Grosset & Dunlap).

Monroe, Judy. Duke Ellington. 2005. (Fact Finders Ser.). (Illus.). 32p. (J). 22.60 (978-0-7368-3741-5(8)) Capstone Pr., Inc.

Orgill, Roxane. If I Only Had a Horn: Young Louis Armstrong. Jenkins, Leonard, illus. 2002. 32p. (J). (gr. 4-6). pap. 5.95 (978-0-618-25076-9(X)) Houghton Mifflin Co. Trade & Reference Div.

—If I Only Had a Horn: Young Louis Armstrong. 2002. (gr. k-3). lib. bdg. 14.10 (978-0-613-70726-8(5)) Tandem Library Bks.

Parker, Robert Andrew. Piano Starts Here: The Young Art Tatum. 2008. (J). ***978-0-375-83965-8(8)*** , Schwartz & Wade Bks.) Random Hse. Children's Bks.

Pinkney, Andrea Davis. Ella Fitzgerald: The Tale of a Vocal Virtuosa. Pinkney, Brian, illus. 2007. 32p. (gr. k-4). pap. 5.99 (978-0-7868-1416-9(0)) Disney Pr.

—Ella Fitzgerald: The Tale of a Vocal Virtuosa. Pinkney, Brian, illus. 2002. 32p. (gr. k-4). 17.49 (978-0-7868-2493-9(X)); 16.99 (978-0-7868-0568-6(4)) Hyperion Bks. for Children. (Jump at the Sun).

Raschka, Chris. Charlie Parker Played Be Bop. Raschka, Chris, illus. 2000. (Live Oak Readalong Ser.). (Illus.). (J). pap. 18.95 incl. audio compact disk (978-1-59112-419-1(0)) Live Oak Media.

—Mysterious Thelonious. Raschka, Chris, illus. (Illus.). pap. 18.95 incl. audio compact disk (978-1-59112-421-4(2)); 2000. 28.95 incl. audio compact disk (978-1-59112-422-1(0)) Live Oak Media.

Ronkko, Kevin. My Adventure with Smooth Jazz: Advanced My Adventure. 2007. 44p. (J). pap. 8.99 (978-1-59092-469-3(X) , Orchard Academy Pr.) Windstorm Creative.

Schoeneberger, Megan. Ella Fitzgerald. 2005. (Fact Finders Ser.). (Illus.). 32p. (J). 22.60 (978-0-7368-3742-2(6)) Capstone Pr., Inc.

What Jazz & Blues Can I Play - Alto Sax. 20p. 6.95 (978-1-85909-426-6(0) , Warner Bros. Pubns.) Alfred Publishing Co., Inc.

What Jazz & Blues Can I Play - Flute. 20p. 6.95 (978-1-85909-422-8(8) , Warner Bros. Pubns.) Alfred Publishing Co., Inc.

What Jazz & Blues Can I Play - Trumpet. 20p. 6.95 (978-1-85909-425-9(2) , Warner Bros. Pubns.) Alfred Publishing Co., Inc.

What Jazz & Blues Can I Play - Violin. 24p. 6.95 (978-1-85909-424-2(4) , Warner Bros. Pubns.) Alfred Publishing Co., Inc.

What Jazz Blues Can I Play. 20p. 6.95 (978-1-85909-423-5(6) , Warner Bros. Pubns.) Alfred Publishing Co., Inc.

Willey, Rich. Home Cookin' [97] 24 Dixie Jazz Duets for C Treble Clef Instruments. 2002. 49p. (YA). 14.95 (978-0-9726185-7-1(0)) Boptism Music Publishing.

—Home Cookin' [97] 24 Dixie Jazz Duets for E-flat Instruments. 2002. 49p. (YA). 14.95 (978-0-9726185-6-4(2)) Boptism Music Publishing.

Winter, Jonah. Dizzy. Qualls, Sean, illus. 2006. (J). 16.99 (978-0-439-50736-3(7) , Levine, Arthur A. Bks.) Scholastic, Inc.

—Once upon a Time in Chicago. Winter, Jeanette, illus. 2000. 32p. (ps-3). 15.49 (978-0-7868-2404-5(2)) Hyperion Bks. for Children.

—Once upon a Time in Chicago: The Story of Benny Goodman. 2000. 32p. (J). 14.99 (978-0-7868-0733-8(4)) Disney Pr.

—Once upon a Time in Chicago: The Story of Benny Goodman. 2000. (J). mass mkt. 16.00 (978-0-689-80342-0(7) , Simon & Schuster Children's Publishing) Simon & Schuster Children's Publishing.

JAZZ—FICTION

Arrhenius, Peter. The Penguin Quartet. Peterson, Ingela, illus. 1998. (Picture Bks.). 28p. (J). (ps-3). 15.95 (978-1-57505-252-6(0) , Carolrhoda Bks.) Lerner Publishing Group.

Calmenson, Stephanie. Jazzmatazz! Degen, Bruce, illus. 2008. 32p. (J). 16.99 (***978-0-06-077289-5(1)***); lib. bdg. 17.89 (***978-0-06-077290-1(5)***) HarperCollins Pubs.

Carter, Don. Heaven's All-Star Jazz Band. Carter, Don, illus. 2002. (Illus.). 40p. (J). (gr. k-3). 15.95 (978-0-375-81571-3(6) , Knopf Bks. for Young Readers) Random Hse. Children's Bks.

Crow, Kristyn. Cool Daddy Rat. Lester, Mike, illus. 2008. 32p. (J). (ps). 16.99 (***978-0-399-24375-2(5)*** , Putnam Juvenile) Penguin Group (USA) Inc.

Daly, Niki. Ruby Sings the Blues. Daly, Niki, illus. 2007. (Illus.). 32p. (J). pap. 6.95 (978-1-59990-029-2(7) , Bloomsbury Children) Bloomsbury Publishing.

—Ruby Sings the Blues. 2005. (Illus.). 32p. (YA). 16.95 (978-1-58234-995-4(9)) Bloomsbury Publishing.

Davis, David. Jazz Cats. Galey, Chuck, illus. 2001. 32p. (J). (gr. 2-4). pap. 15.95 (978-1-56554-859-6(0)) Pelican Publishing Co., Inc.

Ehrhardt, Karen. This Jazz Man. Roth, Robert, illus. 2006. 32p. (J). (ps-2). 16.00 (978-0-15-205307-9(7)) Harcourt Trade Pubs.

Friedman, Carol. Nicky the Jazz Cat. 2004. (Illus.). 32p. (J). (ps-3). 16.95 (978-0-9726092-0-3(2)) Dominick Pictures.

—Nicky the Jazz Cat. Friedman, Carol, illus. 2005. (Illus.). 32p. (J). 16.95 (978-1-57687-248-2(3) , PowerHouse Kids) powerHouse Cultural Entertainment, Inc.

—Nicky's Jazz Christmas. 2006. (Illus.). 32p. (J). 16.95 (978-1-57687-341-0(2)) powerHouse Cultural Entertainment, Inc.

Hurwitz, Andy Blackman. Charlie Bird Count to the Beat: Baby Loves Jazz. Cunningham, Andrew, illus. 2006. 18p. (J). (ps-1). 7.99 (978-0-8431-2086-8(X) , Price Stern Sloan) Penguin Group (USA) Inc.

—Philly Joe Giraffe's Jungle Jazz: Baby Loves Jazz. Cunningham, Andrew, illus. 2007. 16p. (J). bds. 7.99 (978-0-8431-2193-3(9) , Price Stern Sloan) Penguin Group (USA) Inc.

Myers, Walter Dean. Jazz. Myers, Christopher, illus. 2006. 48p. (J). (gr. 4-8). 18.95 (978-0-8234-1545-8(7)) Holiday Hse., Inc.

Neftzger, Amy. All That the Dog Ever Wanted. 2005. (Illus.). 32p. (J). lib. bdg. 21.99 (978-0-9746296-1-2(8) , FOG104) Fields of Gold Publishing, Inc.

Norelli, Sallianne & O'Neil, Amy. The Jazz Jamboree. Yeagle, Barbara, illus. 2002. (Read-To-Me Ser.). 24p. (J). (978-0-7665-1210-8(X)) Abrams, Harry N. , Inc.

Panahi, H. L. The Bebop Express. Johnson, Steve & Fancher, Lou, illus. 2005. 32p. (J). (ps-3). 15.99 (978-0-06-057190-0(X)); lib. bdg. 16.89 (978-0-06-057191-7(8)) HarperCollins Pubs. (Geringer, Laura Book).

Pinkwater, Daniel M. Mush's Jazz Adventure. Pinkwater, Jill, illus. ed. 2005. 42p. (J). lib. bdg. 15.00 (978-1-59054-909-4(0)) Fitzgerald Bks.

Raschka, Chris. John Coltrane's Giant Steps. Raschka, Chris, illus. (Illus.). pap. 16.95 incl. audio (978-0-87499-972-3(3)); pap. incl. audio (978-0-87499-974-7(X)); pap. 18.95 incl. audio compact disk (978-1-59112-416-0(6)); pap. incl. audio compact disk (978-1-59112-603-4(7)) Live Oak Media.

—John Coltrane's Giant Steps. 2002. (Live Oak Readalong Ser.). (Illus.). (J). 28.95 incl. audio compact disk (978-1-59112-417-7(4)) Live Oak Media.

—John Coltrane's Giant Steps. 2002. (Illus.). 32p. (J). (ps-2). 17.99 (978-0-689-84598-7(7) , Atheneum/Richard Jackson Bks.) Simon & Schuster Children's Publishing.

Seeger, Pete & Jacobs, Paul DuBois. The Deaf Musicians. Christie, Gregory, illus. 2006. 32p. (J). (ps-3). 16.99 (978-0-399-24316-5(X)) Penguin Group (USA) Inc.

Shahan, Sherry. The Jazzy Alphabet. Thelen, Mary, illus. 2006. 30p. (J). (gr. k-4). reprint ed. 16.00 (978-1-4223-5730-9(9)) DIANE Publishing Co.

Taylor, Debbie. Sweet Music in Harlem. Morrison, Frank, tr. Morrison, Frank, illus. 2004. 32p. (J). 16.95 (978-1-58430-165-3(1)) Lee & Low Bks., Inc.

JAZZ—HISTORY AND CRITICISM

Asirvatham, Sandy. The History of Jazz. 2006. (Illus.). 108p. (J). (gr. 4-8). reprint ed. 25.00 (978-1-4223-5545-9(4)) DIANE Publishing Co.

—The History of Jazz. 2003. (American Mosaic Ser.). (Illus.). 108p. (J). (gr. k-17). pap. 30.00 (978-0-7910-7489-3(7) , Chelsea Hse.) Facts On File, Inc.

Brasch, Nicolas. Jazz & Blues. 2004. (J). lib. bdg. 27.10 (978-1-58340-548-2(8)) Smart Apple Media.

Gourse, Leslie. Fancy Fretwork: The Great Jazz Guitarists. 2000. (Art of Jazz Ser.). (Illus.). 144p. (YA). (gr. 8-12). pap. 8.95 (978-0-531-16404-4(7) , Watts, Franklin) Scholastic Library Publishing.

—Sophisticated Ladies: The Great Women of Jazz. French, Martin, illus. 2007. 64p. (J). 19.99 (978-0-525-47198-1(7) , Dutton Juvenile) Penguin Group (USA) Inc.

—Timekeepers: The Great Jazz Drummers. 2000. (Art of Jazz Ser.). (Illus.). 144p. (J). (gr. 8-12). pap. 8.95 (978-0-531-16405-1(5) , Watts, Franklin) Scholastic Library Publishing.

Handyside, Chris. A History of Jazz. 2006. (Illus.). 48p. (J). (978-1-4034-8149-8(0)) Heinemann Library.

—A History of Jazz. 2006. (J). (978-1-4109-1812-3(2)) Steck-Vaughn.

Kallen, Stuart A. The History of Jazz. 2002. (Illus.). 112p. (J). 32.45 (978-1-59018-125-6(5) , Lucent Bks.) Thomson Gale.

Kirgiss, Crystal. Jazz. 2000. (J). (978-1-58341-067-7(8)) Creative Co., The.

—Jazz. 2001. (World of Music Ser.). (Illus.). 32p. (J). (gr. 2-7). lib. bdg. 22.60 (978-1-58340-043-2(5)) Smart Apple Media.

Mour, Stanley I. American Jazz Musicians. 1998. (Collective Biographies Ser.). (Illus.). 128p. (YA). (gr. 6-12). lib. bdg. 26.60 (978-0-7660-1027-7(9)) Enslow Pubs., Inc.

Raschka, Chris. Charlie Parker Played Be Bop. 2004. 14p. (J). pap. 6.99 (978-0-439-57823-3(X)) Scholastic, Inc.

Riggs, Kate. Jazz Music. 2008. (J). (***978-1-58341-567-2(X)*** , Creative Education) Creative Co., The.

Shipton, Alyn. Jazz Makers: Vanguards of Sound. 2002. (Oxford Profiles Ser.). (Illus.). 272p. (YA). (gr. 9 up). 50.00 (978-0-19-512689-1(0)) Oxford Univ. Pr., Inc.

Winter, Jonah. Dizzy. Qualls, Sean, illus. 2006. 48p. (J). (gr. 3-8). pap. 16.99 (978-0-439-50737-0(5) , Levine, Arthur A. Bks.) Scholastic, Inc.

JEALOUSY

Berry, Joy Wilt. Let's Talk about Feeling Jealous: An Interpersonal Feelings Book. Fitzpatrick, Roey, illus. rev. ed. 1999. (Let's Talk about Ser.: Vol. 3). 36p. (J). (ps-2). pap. 3.95 (978-1-58634-042-1(5) , 01-0202-03) Goldstar Publishing, Inc.

—Let's Talk about Feeling Jealous: An Interpersonal Feelings Book. Smith, Maggie, illus. 2002. (J). (978-0-439-34156-1(6)) Scholastic, Inc.

Croft, Priscilla. Dealing with Jealousy. 1999. (Conflict Resolution Library). 24p. (gr. k-4). pap. 6.95 (978-1-56838-264-7(2)) Hazelden Publishing & Educational Services.

Dougherty, Karla. Jealousy: Triumphing over Rivalry & Envy. 2003. (Teen Issues Ser.). (Illus.). 64p. (J). lib. bdg. 22.60 (978-0-7660-1909-6(8)) Enslow Pubs., Inc.

Hewitt, Sally, et al. Teimlo'n Genfigennus. 2005. (WEL., Illus.). 32p. (978-0-86174-097-0(1)) Drake Educational Assocs. Ltd.

Kravetz, Jonathan. How to Deal with Jealousy. 2007. (Let's Work It Out Ser.). (Illus.). 24p. (J). (gr. 2-5). lib. bdg. 21.25 (***978-1-4042-3674-5(0)*** , PowerKids Pr.) Rosen Publishing Group, Inc., The.

Medina, Sarah. Jealous. Brooker, Jo, illus. 2007. (Feelings Ser.). 24p. (J). (ps-k). 5.99 (978-1-4034-9301-9(4)); lib. bdg. 21.36 (978-1-4034-9294-4(8)) Heinemann Library.

Tubbs, Janet. Jealousy. 2000. (Spud Packs Ser.). (Illus.). 16p. (J). (ps-4). pap. 19.95 (978-1-881185-19-2(2)) Arcadia Pr.

JEALOUSY—FICTION

Benton, Jim. Let's Pretend This Never Happened. Benton, Jim, illus. 2004. (Dear Dumb Diary Ser.: Bk. 1). (Illus.). 80p. (J). 4.99 (978-0-439-62904-1(7) , Scholastic Paperbacks) Scholastic, Inc.

Berenstain, Stan & Berenstain, Jan. The Berenstain Bears & the Big Date. 1998. (Berenstain Bears Big Chapter Bks.). (J). (gr. 2-6). (978-0-606-13951-9(6)) Tandem Library Bks.

—The Berenstain Bears & the Green-Eyed Monster. Berenstain, Stan & Berenstain, Jan, illus. 2002. (Berenstain Bears First Time Bks.). (Illus.). (J). 11.19 (978-0-7587-0946-2(3)) Book Wholesalers, Inc.

Borchard, Therese Johnson. Whitney Sews Joseph's Many-Colored Coat: And Learns a Lesson about Jealousy. 1999. (Emerald Bible Collection). (Illus.). 80p. (gr. 3-7). 5.95 (978-0-8091-6664-0(X) , 6664-x) Paulist Pr.

Brooks, Jillian. The Makeover. 2003. 157p. (J). (978-0-439-35494-3(3)) Scholastic, Inc.

Brouwer, Sigmund. Sewer Rats. 2006. 112p. (gr. 5-10). lib. bdg. 14.95 (978-1-55143-527-5(6)); (J). pap. 7.95 (978-1-55143-488-9(1)) Orca Bk. Pubs. USA.

Carlson, Melody. Deep Green: Color Me Jealous. 2004. 196p. (YA). pap. 12.99 (978-1-57683-530-2(8)) Nav-Press Publishing Group.

Carrer, Chiara. Que Celosa! 2002. (My First Book Soup Ser.). (SPA., Illus.). 12p. 11.95 (978-84-207-4351-6(8) , GS30697) Grupo Anaya, S.A. ESP. *Dist:* Distribooks, Inc., Lectorum Pubns., Inc.

Christopher, Matt. Head to Head. Koelsch, Michael, illus. 2005. 57p. (J). (ps-7). lib. bdg. 12.19 (978-0-606-33454-9(8)) Tandem Library Bks.

J K L

Clarke, Kathryn. The Breakable Vow. 2004. 480p. (YA). (gr. 7 up). 16.89 (978-0-06-051822-6(7)) HarperCollins Pubs.

Clarke, Kathryn Ann. The Breakable Vow. 2004. 480p. (J). (gr. 7 up). pap. 6.99 (978-0-06-051821-9(9)) HarperCollins Pubs.

Colon, Suzan. Smallville No.9: Temptation Book. 2004. (gr. 7-12). lib. bdg. 14.15 (978-0-613-71778-6(3)) Tandem Library Bks.

Cosby, Bill. Friends of a Feather: One of Life's Little Fables. Cosby, Erika, illus. 2003. 64p. (gr. k-3). 16.95 (978-0-06-009147-7(9) , Harper Entertainment) HarperCollins Pubs.

Danziger, Paula. Barfburger Baby, I Was Here First. Karas, G. Brian, tr. Karas, G. Brian, illus. 2004. 32p. (J). (ps-3). 16.99 (978-0-399-23204-6(4) , Putnam Juvenile) Penguin Group (USA) Inc.

—Barfburger Baby, I Was Here First. Karas, G. Brian, illus. 2007. 32p. (J). pap. 5.99 (978-0-14-240739-4(9) , Puffin) Penguin Group (USA) Inc.

DeFelice, Cynthia C. The Ghost & Mrs. Hobbs. 2001. (Ghost Mysteries Ser.). (Illus.). 192p. (J). (gr. 3-7). 16.00 (978-0-374-38046-5(5) , Farrar, Straus & Giroux (BYR)) Farrar, Straus & Giroux.

—The Ghost & Mrs. Hobbs. 2003. 192p. (J). pap. 5.99 (978-0-06-001172-7(6) , Harper Trophy) HarperCollins Pubs.

—The Ghost & Mrs. Hobbs. 2003. (gr. 3-6). lib. bdg. 14.15 (978-0-613-85155-8(2)) Tandem Library Bks.

Dierssen, A. & Sohr, D. Old Red Tractor. 2006. (Illus.). 32p. (J). 16.95 (978-0-7358-2088-3(0)) North-South Bks., Inc.

Egan, Tim. A Mile from Ellington Station. 2001. (Illus.). 32p. (J). (gr. k-3). tchr. ed. 15.00 (978-0-618-00393-8(2)) Houghton Mifflin Co. Trade & Reference Div.

Feiffer, Jules. The House Across the Street. Feiffer, Jules, illus. 2003. (Illus.). 28p. (J). (gr. 1-4). reprint ed. 16.00 (978-0-7567-6845-4(4)) DIANE Publishing Co.

—The House Across the Street. 2002. (Illus.). 32p. (J). (ps-17). (978-0-7868-0910-3(8)) Hyperion Bks. for Children.

Fox, Paula. Radiance Descending. 1999. (978-0-606-17838-9(4)) Tandem Library Bks.

Friedman, Rainey L. Jerome's Jam. 2002. (Illus.). (J). 15.95 (978-0-9666199-2-8(7)) DreamDog Pr.

Guest, Elissa Haden. Iris & Walter & the Substitute Teacher. Davenier, Christine, tr. Davenier, Christine, illus. 2004. (Iris & Walter Ser.). 44p. (J). 15.00 (978-0-15-205013-9(2) , Gulliver Bks.) Harcourt Children's Bks.

Hale, Bruce. Key Lardo: A Chet Gecko Mystery. Hale, Bruce, illus. 2007. (Chet Gecko Mystery Ser.: No. 12). (Illus.). 128p. (J). (gr. 3-7). pap. 4.95 (978-0-15-205235-5(6) , Harcourt Paperbacks) Harcourt Children's Bks.

—Key Lardo: A Chet Gecko Mystery. 2006. (Chet Gecko Mystery Ser.: No. 12). (Illus.). 128p. (J). (gr. 3-7). 14.00 (978-0-15-205074-0(4)) Harcourt Children's Bks.

Harper, Meg. My Mum & the Green Eyed Monster. 2006. (My Mum Ser.). 160p. (J). pap. 8.99 (*978-0-7459-4993-2(2)) Lion Hudson plc GBR. *Dist:* Independent Pubs. Group.

Hazen, Lynn E. Buzz Bumble to the Rescue. Newton, Jill, illus. 2005. 32p. (J). 15.95 (978-1-58234-932-9(0) , Bloomsbury Children) Bloomsbury Publishing.

Hooks, Gwendolyn. Three's a Crowd. Walker, Sylvia, illus. 2004. 32p. (J). lib. bdg. 15.00 (*978-1-4242-0240-9(X)) Fitzgerald Bks.

Howe, James. Pinky & Rex & the School Play. 2006. (J). (gr. 1-4). 24.21 (978-1-59961-078-8(7)) Spotlight.

Joosse, Barbara M. Nugget & Darling. 2001. (Illus.). (J). (978-0-606-21360-8(0)) Tandem Library Bks.

Khan, Rukshana. Silly Chicken. Kyong, Yunmee, illus. 2005. 32p. (J). (ps-3). 15.99 (978-0-670-05912-6(9) , Viking Juvenile) Penguin Group (USA) Inc.

Kindig, Tess Eileen. Double Whammy!, Vol. 8. 2001. (Slam Dunk Ser.: Vol. 8). 96p. (J). (gr. 1-4). 4.99 (978-0-570-07142-6(9)) Concordia Publishing Hse.

Kindig, Tess Eileen & Van Severen, Joe. Double Whammy!, Vol. 7. 2001. (Slam Dunk Ser.: Vol. 7). (Illus.). 96p. (J). (gr. 1-4). 4.99 (978-0-570-07143-3(7)) Concordia Publishing Hse.

Kline, Suzy. Molly Gets Mad. Bluthenthal, Diana Cain, illus. 2001. 1p. (J). (gr. 1-4). 14.99 (978-0-399-23408-8(X) , Putnam Juvenile) Penguin Group (USA) Inc.

Lamb, Charles & Lamb, Mary. Tales from Shakespeare: "Othello" Strang, Kay, ed. Andrews, Gary, illus. rev. ed. 2005. 40p. pap. 4.95 (978-0-9542905-4-2(2)) Capercaillie Bks., Ltd GBR. *Dist:* Wilson & Assocs.

Lewis, Beverly. Second-Best Friend. 2002. (Holly's Heart Ser.: Bk. 6). 160p. (YA). pap. 6.99 (978-0-7642-2505-5(7)) Bethany Hse. Pubs.

Lightle, Lugenia L. Ruguma: New to America. 2005. 135p. pap. 19.95 (978-1-4137-6723-0(0)) PublishAmerica, Inc.

Mackall, Dandi Daley. Upsetting Annie. 2007. (Faithgirlz!#8482; / Blog On! Ser.). 128p. (J). pap. 6.99 (978-0-310-71264-0(5)) Zonderkidz.

Madonna. The English Roses, Too Good to be True. 2006. (Illus.). 64p. (J). (ps-6). 19.95 (978-0-670-06147-1(6)) Callaway Editions, Inc.

—Las Rosas Inglesas. Fulvimari, Jeffrey, illus. 2003. Tr. of English Roses. (SPA.). 48p. (J). 19.95 (978-0-439-60978-4(X) , Scholastic en Espanol) Scholastic, Inc.

Martin, Patricia. Lulu Atlantis & the Quest for True Blue Love. 2008. (J). (*978-0-375-84016-6(8)); 240p. (gr. 2-6). lib. bdg. 17.99 (*978-0-375-94016-3(2)) Random Hse. Children's Bks. (Schwartz & Wade Bks.).

Mazer, Norma Fox. Ten Ways to Make My Sister Disappear. 2007. (J). (*978-0-439-83984-6(X)); 160p. (gr. 4-7). pap. 16.99 (*978-0-439-83983-9(1)) Scholastic, Inc. (Levine, Arthur A. Bks.).

Mccue, Mimi. The Accidental Cheerleader. 2007. (Candy Apple Ser.: No. 1). 176p. (J). pap. 4.99 (978-0-439-92928-8(8)) Scholastic, Inc.

McDonald, Megan. Judy Moody Gets Famous! Reynolds, Peter H., illus. (Judy Moody Ser.: No. 2). 144p. (J). (gr. 1-5). 2003. pap. 5.99 (978-0-7636-1931-2(0)); 2001. 15.99 (978-0-7636-0849-1(1)) Candlewick Pr.

—Judy Moody Gets Famous! 2003. (Judy Moody Ser.: No. 2). (gr. 3-6). lib. bdg. 14.15 (978-0-613-62107-6(7)) Tandem Library Bks.

McKeown, Adam & Shakespeare, William. Othello. Hundley, Sterling, illus. 2005. (Young Reader's Shakespeare Ser.). 80p. (J). 14.95 (978-1-4027-1115-2(8)) Sterling Publishing Co., Inc.

Middleton, Charlotte. Do You Still Love Me? Middleton, Charlotte, illus. 2003. (Illus.). 32p. (J). (gr. k-1). 15.99 (978-0-7636-2254-1(0)) Candlewick Pr.

Mooney, E. S. Snow-off. 2000. (gr. k-3). lib. bdg. 11.25 (978-0-613-33069-5(2)) Tandem Library Bks.

Morgan, Michaela. Silly Sausage & the Little Visitor. Shulman, Dee, illus. 2006. (Read-It! Chapter Books). (J). 21.26 (978-1-4048-2735-6(8)) Picture Window Bks.

Palatini, Margie. The Wonder Worm Wars. 1999. (978-0-606-16660-7(2)) Tandem Library Bks.

Ramirez, Linda M. & Salcines, Maria Luisa. Playtime for Molly: A Story about Filial Therapy: How a Parent & Child Play to Improve Their Relationship. 2001. (Illus.). 24p. pap. 8.95 (978-0-9713839-0-6(1)) MarLin Bks.

Ritchie, Madonna, ed. & illus. The English Roses. Ritchie, Madonna, illus. Fulvimari, Jeffrey, illus. 2003. 48p. (J). 19.95 (978-0-670-03678-3(1)) Callaway Editions, Inc.

—The English Roses. Ritchie, Madonna, illus. ed. 2006. 48p. (J). (ps-6). 9.95 (978-0-670-06180-8(8)) Callaway Editions, Inc.

Rosen, Michael. Howler. Layton, Neal, illus. 2004. 32p. (J). (ps-2). 15.95 (978-1-58234-851-3(0) , Bloomsbury Children) Bloomsbury Publishing.

Russo, Marisabina. The Trouble with Baby. Russo, Marisabina, illus. 2003. (Illus.). 32p. (J). (ps up). 16.89 (978-0-06-008925-2(3)) HarperCollins Pubs.

Sander, Sonia. Meet Blueberry Muffin. S. I. Artists Staff, illus. 2004. (Strawberry Shortcake Ser.). 32p. (J). (ps-2). pap. 3.99 (978-0-448-43570-1(5) , Grosset & Dunlap) Penguin Group (USA) Inc.

Scholastic, Inc. Staff & Hooks, Gwendolyn. Three's a Crowd. Walker, Sylvia, illus. 2004. (Just for You! Ser.). 32p. (gr. k-3). pap. 3.99 (978-0-439-56865-4(X) , Teaching Resources) Scholastic, Inc.

Schotter, Roni. The House of Joyful Living. Widener, Terry, illus. 2008. (J). (*978-0-374-33429-1(3)) Farrar, Straus & Giroux.

Selvadurai, Shyam. Swimming in the Monsoon Sea. 2007. 280p. (J). (gr. 8). pap. 9.95 (*978-0-88776-834-7(2)) Tundra Bks., Inc./Livres Toundra, Inc. CAN. *Dist:* Random Hse., Inc.

Simmons, Jane. Ebb & Flo & the New Friend. Simmons, Jane, illus. 2002. (Illus.). 32p. (J). (ps-2). 6.99 (978-0-689-84890-2(0) , Aladdin) Simon & Schuster Children's Publishing.

—Ebb & Flo & the New Friend. 2002. (ps-2). lib. bdg. 15.30 (978-0-613-50532-1(8)) Tandem Library Bks.

Smith, Stephen & Caldwell, Lise. Spiked. 2006. (Game on for Girls Ser.). 128p. (J). pap. 5.99 (978-0-7847-1731-8(1) , 42148) Standard Publishing.

Spelman, Cornelia Maude. When I Feel Jealous. Parkinson, Kathy, illus. (Way I Feel Bks.). 24p. (J). 2005. (gr. 3-6). pap. 6.95 (978-0-8075-8902-1(0)); 2003. (ps-1). 15.95 (978-0-8075-8886-4(5)) Whitman, Albert & Co.

Spinelli, Eileen. Lizzie Logan, Second Banana. 2000. (978-0-606-17827-3(9)) Tandem Library Bks.

Stein, David Ezra. Ned's New Friend. Stein, David Ezra, illus. 2007. (Cowboy Ned & Andy Ser.). 32p. (J). (ps-1). 14.99 (978-1-4169-2490-6(6) , Simon & Schuster Children's Publishing) Simon & Schuster Children's Publishing.

Swan, Bill. Corner Kick. 2004. (Sports Stories Ser.). 120p. (J). (gr. 3-8). 7.95 (978-1-55028-816-2(4)); (*978-1-55028-817-9(2)) Lorimer, James & Co., Ltd., Pubs. CAN. *Dist:* Casemate Pubs. & Bk. Distributors, LLC.

Waber, Bernard. Evie & Margie. Waber, Bernard, illus. 2003. (Illus.). 32p. (J). (gr. k-3). 15.00 (978-0-618-34124-5(2) , Walter Lorraine) Houghton Mifflin Co. Trade & Reference Div.

Walsh, Marissa, ed. Not Like I'm Jealous or Anything: The Jealousy Book. 2006. 208p. (J). (gr. 9). pap. 9.95 (978-0-385-73317-5(8)); pap., lib. bdg. 11.99 (978-0-385-90336-3(7)) Random Hse. Children's Bks. (Delacorte Bks. for Young Readers).

Wesley, Valerie Wilson. How to Fish for Trouble. Roos, Maryn, illus. 2004. 89p. (J). lib. bdg. 15.00 (*978-1-4242-0643-8(X)) Fitzgerald Bks.

JEEPS

see Automobiles; Trucks

JEFFERSON, THOMAS, 1743-1826

Adler, David A. A Picture Book of Thomas Jefferson. Wallner, John & Wallner, Alexandra, illus. 2003. (J). (ps-3). audio compact disk 18.95 (978-1-59112-769-7(6)) Live Oak Media.

—A Picture Book of Thomas Jefferson. Wallner, John, illus. 1999. 28.95 incl. audio compact disk (978-1-59112-770-3(X)); pap. 39.95 incl. audio compact disk (978-1-59112-771-0(8)) Live Oak Media.

—A Picture Book of Thomas Jefferson. Wallner, John & Wallner, Alexandra, illus. unabr. ed. 1999. (J). (gr. 1-6). pap. 16.95 incl. audio (978-0-87499-651-7(1)) Live Oak Media.

Aldridge, Rebecca. Thomas Jefferson. 2001. (Let Freedom Ring Ser.). (Illus.). 48p. (J). (gr. 3-4). lib. bdg. 22.60 (978-0-7368-1035-7(8) , Bridgestone Bks.) Capstone Pr., Inc.

Barrett, Marvin. Meet Thomas Jefferson. Fogarty, Pat, illus. 2001. 80p. (J). (gr. 1-5). pap. 4.99 (978-0-375-81211-8(3) , Random Hse. Bks. for Young Readers) Random Hse. Children's Bks.

—Meet Thomas Jefferson. 2001. (gr. k-3). lib. bdg. 12.40 (978-0-613-85715-4(1)) Tandem Library Bks.

Behrman, Carol H. Thomas Jefferson. 2004. (Presidential Leaders Ser.). (Illus.). 112p. (J). 29.27 (978-0-8225-0822-9(2) , Lerner Pubns.) Lerner Publishing Group.

Bernstein, Richard B. Thomas Jefferson: The Revolution of Ideas. 2004. (Oxford Portraits Ser.). (Illus.). 256p. (YA). 28.00 (978-0-19-514368-3(X)) Oxford Univ. Pr., Inc.

Bober, Natalie S. Thomas Jefferson: Draftsman of a Nation. 2007. 352p. (YA). (gr. 7 up). 22.95 (*978-0-8139-2632-2(7)) Univ. Pr. of Virginia.

Burke, Rick. Thomas Jefferson. (American Lives Ser.). (Illus.). 32p. (J). 2003. (gr. 2-4). lib. bdg. (978-1-4034-0160-1(8)); 2002. pap. 6.95 (978-1-4034-0416-9(X)) Heinemann Library.

Davis, Kenneth C. Don't Know Much about Thomas Jefferson, Vol. 5. Shepperson, Rob, illus. 2005. (Don't Know Much About Ser.). 128p. (J). (gr. 2-5). lib. bdg. 15.89 (978-0-06-028821-1(3)) HarperCollins Pubs.

Doeden, Matt. Thomas Jefferson: Great American. Purcell, Gordon & Beatty, Terry, illus. 2006. (Graphic Library). 32p. (J). (978-0-7368-5488-7(6)) Capstone Pr., Inc.

Emerson, Judy. Thomas Jefferson. Saunders-Smith, Gail, ed. 2003. (First Biographies Ser.). (Illus.). 24p. (J). (gr. k-1). lib. bdg. 15.93 (978-0-7368-2088-2(4) , Pebble Bks.) Capstone Pr., Inc.

Ferris, Jeri Chase. Thomas Jefferson: Father of Liberty. 1998. (Trailblazers Biographies Ser.). (Illus.). 112p. (J). (gr. 4-7). lib. bdg. (978-1-57505-009-6(9) , Carolrhoda Bks.) Lerner Publishing Group.

Ferry, Joseph. Thomas Jefferson. 2003. (Childhood of the Presidents Ser.). (Illus.). 48p. (J). (gr. 4 up). lib. bdg. (978-1-59084-271-3(5)) Mason Crest Pubs.

Ford, Carin T. Thomas Jefferson: The Third President. 2003. (Heroes of American History Ser.). (Illus.). 32p. (J). (gr. 1-4). lib. bdg. 22.60 (978-0-7660-1861-7(X)) Enslow Pubs., Inc.

Fradin, Dennis Brindell. Who Was Thomas Jefferson? O'Brien, John & Harrison, Nancy, illus. 2003. (Who Was...? Ser.). 112p. (J). (gr. 3-7). 13.89 (978-0-448-43236-6(6)); pap. 4.99 (978-0-448-43145-1(9)) Penguin Group (USA) Inc. (Grosset & Dunlap).

—Who Was Thomas Jefferson? 2003. (gr. 3-6). lib. bdg. 13.00 (978-0-613-63486-1(1)) Tandem Library Bks.

Furgang, Kathy. The Declaration of Independence & Thomas Jefferson of Virginia. 2002. (Framers of the Declaration of Independence Ser.). (Illus.). 24p. (J). (gr. 3). lib. bdg. 18.75 (978-0-8239-5589-3(3) , PowerKids Pr.) Rosen Publishing Group, Inc., The.

Gaines, Ann Graham. Thomas Jefferson. 2004. (Triangle History of the American Revolution Ser.). (Illus.). 104p. (J). 27.45 (978-1-56711-781-3(3) , Blackbirch Pr., Inc.) Thomson Gale.

Giblin James Cross. Thomas Jefferson: A Picture Book Biography. 2006. 48p. (J). pap. 5.99 (978-0-439-81067-8(1) , Scholastic Paperbacks) Scholastic, Inc.

Gomez, Rebecca. Thomas Jefferson. 2003. (First Biographies Ser.). (Illus.). 32p. (J). (gr. k-4). lib. bdg. 22.78 (978-1-57765-947-1(3)) ABDO Publishing Co.

Harness, Cheryl. Thomas Jefferson. (Illus.). 48p. (J). 2007. (gr. 3-7). pap. 7.95 (978-1-4263-0043-1(3)); 2004. (gr. 2). 17.95 (978-0-7922-6496-5(7)) National Geographic Society. (National Geographic Children's Bks.).

Heinrichs, Ann. Thomas Jefferson. 2002. (Profiles of the Presidents Ser.). (Illus.). 64p. (J). (gr. 4 up). lib. bdg. 23.93 (978-0-7565-0206-5(3)) Compass Point Bks.

Jones, Veda Boyd. Thomas Jefferson. (Revolutionary War Leaders Ser.). (Illus.). 80p. (gr. 3 up). 2000. (J). 27.50 (978-0-7910-5353-9(9)); 1999. (YA). pap. 8.95 (978-0-7910-5696-7(1)) Facts On File, Inc. (Chelsea Hse.).

Kallen, Stuart A. Thomas Jefferson. 2001. (Founding Fathers Ser.). (Illus.). 64p. (J). (gr. 3-8). lib. bdg. 25.65 (978-1-57765-014-0(X) , ABDO & Daughters) ABDO Publishing Co.

Kishel, Ann-Marie. Thomas Jefferson: A Life of Patriotism. 2006. (Pull Ahead Books). (Illus.). 32p. (J). 22.60 (978-0-8225-3480-8(0) , Lerner Pubns.) Lerner Publishing Group.

—Thomas Jefferson: Una Vida de Patriotismo. 2006. (Libros para Avanzar Ser.). (ENG & SPA.). 32p. (J). lib. bdg. 22.60 (978-0-8225-6238-2(3) , Ediciones Lerner) Lerner Publishing Group.

Landau, Elaine. The Louisiana Purchase: Would You Close the Deal? 2008. (What Would You Do? Ser.). (Illus.). 48p. (J). (gr. 3-4). lib. bdg. 23.93 (*978-0-7660-2902-6(6) , Enslow Elementary) Enslow Pubs., Inc.

Lanier, Shannon & Feldman, Jane. Jefferson's Children: The Story of One American Family. 2004. (Illus.). 144p. (J). (gr. 4-8). reprint ed. 20.00 (978-0-7567-7418-9(7)) DIANE Publishing Co.

—Jefferson's Children: The Story of One American Family. Feldman, Jane, photos by. 2002. 160p. (gr. 5). pap. 16.95 (978-0-375-82168-4(6) , Random Hse. Bks. for Young Readers) Random Hse. Children's Bks.

—Jefferson's Children: The Story of One American Family. Feldman, Jane, photos by. 2002. (Illus.). 160p. (J). (ps-7). lib. bdg. 24.55 (978-0-613-57230-9(0)) Tandem Library Bks.

Larkin, Tanya. What Was Cooking in Edith Roosevelt's White House? 2001. (Cooking Throughout American History Ser.). (Illus.). 24p. (J). (gr. 3). lib. bdg. 19.95 (978-0-8239-5610-4(5) , PowerKids Pr.) Rosen Publishing Group, Inc., The.

Lusted, Marcia Amidon. Revolution & the New Nation. 2007. (*978-1-59036-739-1(1)); (*978-1-59036-740-7(5)) Weigl Pubs., Inc.

Manolis, Kay. Thomas Jefferson: A Life of Patriotism. 2007. (Illus.). 24p. (J). lib. bdg. 19.95 (978-1-60014-093-8(9)) Bellwether Media.

Marsh, Carole. Thomas Jefferson. 2002. (One Thousand Readers Ser.). (Illus.). 12p. (J). (gr. k-4). 2.95 (978-0-635-01476-4(9) , 14769) Gallopade International.

—Thomas Jefferson: An Ohio Experience Reader. 2001. (J). (gr. k-5). pap. 1.95 (978-0-635-00451-2(8)) Gallopade International.

—The Virginia Reader: Thomas Jefferson. 2001. (Virginia Experience! Ser.). (Illus.). 12p. (J). (gr. k-5). pap. 2.95 (978-0-635-00360-7(0)) Gallopade International.

Mayer, Cassie. Thomas Jefferson. 2007. (J). (*978-1-4034-9969-1(1)); pap. (*978-1-4034-9978-3(0)) Heinemann Library.

McLeese, Don. Thomas Jefferson. (Heroes of the American Revolution Ser.). 32p. 2005. (Illus.). (gr. 2-5). 19.95 (978-1-59515-217-6(2)); 2004. pap. 5.95 (978-1-59515-318-0(7)) Rourke Publishing, LLC.

Mis, Melody S. How to Draw the Life & Times of Thomas Jefferson. 2006. (Kid's Guide to Drawing the Presidents of the United States of America Ser.). (J). 25.25 (978-1-4042-2980-8(9) , PowerKids Pr.) Rosen Publishing Group, Inc., The.

Monsell, Helen Albee. Thomas Jefferson: Third President of the United States. unabr. ed. 2001. (Childhood of Famous Americans Ser.). (J). (gr. 1-3). pap. 39.95 incl. audio Blackstone Audio, Inc.

Mullin, Rita Thievon. Thomas Jefferson: Architect of Freedom. 2007. (Sterling Biographies Ser.). (Illus.). 128p. (J). 12.95 (978-1-4027-4750-2(0)); pap. 5.95 (978-1-4027-3397-0(6)) Sterling Publishing Co., Inc.

Murphy, Frank. Thomas Jefferson's Feast. Walz, Richard, illus. 2003. 48p. (J). (gr. 2-4). pap. 3.99 (978-0-375-82289-6(5) , Random Hse. Bks. for Young Readers) Random Hse. Children's Bks.

—Thomas Jefferson's Feast. 2003. (gr. k-3). lib. bdg. 11.80 (978-0-613-86238-7(4)) Tandem Library Bks.

Nardo, Don. Thomas Jefferson. 2003. (Encyclopedia of Presidents Ser.: Vol. 3). (Illus.). 110p. (J). 34.00 (978-0-516-22768-9(8) , Children's Pr.) Scholastic Library Publishing.

Nelson, Sheila. Thomas Jefferson's America: The Louisiana Purchase (1800-1811) 2005. (How America Became America Ser.). (Illus.). 96p. (J). lib. bdg. (978-1-59084-904-0(3)) Mason Crest Pubs.

Pflueger, Lynda. Thomas Jefferson: Creating a Nation. 2004. (America's Founding Fathers Ser.). (Illus.). 128p. (J). lib. bdg. 26.60 (978-0-7660-2212-6(9)) Enslow Pubs., Inc.

Pingry, Patricia A. Meet Thomas Jefferson. Johnson, Meredith, ed. Johnson, Meredith, illus. 2003. 32p. (J). 9.95 (978-0-8249-5459-8(9)) Ideals Pubns.

Raabe, Emily. Thomas Jefferson & the Louisiana Purchase. 2003. (Reading Power Ser.). (Illus.). 24p. (J). lib. bdg. 17.25 (978-0-8239-6499-4(X) , PowerKids Pr.) Rosen Publishing Group, Inc., The.

Raatma, Lucia. Thomas Jefferson. 2001. (Compass Point Early Biographies Ser.). (Illus.). 32p. (J). (gr. 2 up). lib. bdg. 21.26 (978-0-7565-0070-2(2)) Compass Point Bks.

Rausch, Monica. Thomas Jefferson. 2006. (J). (ENG & SPA.). pap. (*978-0-8368-7990-2(2)); (ENG & SPA.). lib. bdg. (*978-0-8368-7983-4(X)); (Illus.). 24p. pap. (*978-0-8368-7691-8(1)); (Illus.). 24p. lib. bdg. (*978-0-8368-7684-0(9)) Stevens, Gareth Inc. (Weekly Reader Early Learning Library).

Reiter, Chris. Thomas Jefferson: A MyReportLinks.com Book. 2002. (Presidents Ser.). (Illus.). 48p. (J). (gr. 4-10). lib. bdg. 25.26 (978-0-7660-5071-6(8) , MyReportLinks.com Bks.) Enslow Pubs., Inc.

Ribke, Simone T. Thomas Jefferson. (Rookie Biographies Ser.). (Illus.). (J). 2004. 31p. (gr. 1-2). pap. 4.95 (978-0-516-27927-5(0)); 2003. 32p. 20.50 (978-0-516-25884-3(2)) Scholastic Library Publishing. (Children's Pr.).

Roberts, Russell. Thomas Jefferson. 2006. (Profiles in American History Ser.). (Illus.). 48p. (J). (gr. 4-8). lib. bdg. 20.95 (978-1-58415-439-6(X)) Mitchell Lane Pubs., Inc.

Ruffin, Frances E. Sally Hemings. 2002. (American Legends Ser.). (Illus.). 24p. (J). (gr. 3). lib. bdg. 18.75 (978-0-8239-5828-3(0) , PowerKids Pr.) Rosen Publishing Group, Inc., The.

Schaefer, Ted & Schaefer, Lola. The Thomas Jefferson Memorial. 2005. (Symbols of Freedom Ser.). (Illus.). 32p. (J). (gr. k-2). lib. bdg. 25.36 (978-1-4034-6660-0(2)) Heinemann Library.

Schaefer, Ted & Schaefer, Lola M. The Thomas Jefferson Memorial. 2005. (Symbols of Freedom Ser.). (Illus.). 32p. (J). pap. (978-1-4034-6669-3(6)) Heinemann Library.

Schlesinger, Arthur M., Sr., et al, eds. The Election of 1800. 2003. (Major Presidential Elections & the Administrations That Followed Ser.). (Illus.). 154p. (J). (gr. 7 up). lib. bdg. (978-1-59084-352-9(5)) Mason Crest Pubs.

Sherrow, Victoria. Thomas Jefferson. 2002. (History Maker Bios Ser.). (Illus.). 47p. (J). pap. 6.95 (978-0-8225-0382-8(4)); (gr. 2-4). 26.60 (978-0-8225-0197-8(X)) Lerner Publishing Group. (Lerner Pubns.).

Skarmeas, Nancy J., ed. Thomas Jefferson. 1998. (Great Americans Ser.). (Illus.). 96p. 17.95 (978-0-8249-4086-7(5)) Ideals Pubns.

The Story of Thomas Jefferson. 2003. (Illus.). 26p. (J). (ps-k). 6.95 (978-0-8249-6502-0(7)) Ideals Pubns.

Thomas Jefferson: A Life of Patriotism. 2006. (J). pap. 5.95 (978-0-8225-5695-4(2)) Lerner Publishing Group.

Thomas Jefferson: Architect, Inventor, President. 2005. (Discovery Readers Ser.). (Illus.). 32p. (J). (gr. 1-2). 3.95 (978-0-8249-5510-6(2)) Ideals Pubns.

Thomas Jefferson: Una vida de patriotismo (A Life of Patriotism) 2007. (J). pap. 5.95 (978-0-8225-6554-3(4) , Ediciones Lerner) Lerner Publishing Group.

J K L

Thomas Jefferson & the Louisiana Purchase: Individual Title Six-Packs. (On Deck Ser.: Vol. 2). 24p. (gr. 4-5). 35.00 (978-0-7578-5810-9(4)) Rigby Education.

Uschan, Michael V. Thomas Jefferson. 2002. (Raintree Biographies Ser.). (Illus.). 32p. (J). lib. bdg. 25.69 (978-0-7398-5676-5(6)) Raintree.

Venezia, Mike. Thomas Jefferson. Venezia, Mike, illus. 2005. (Getting to Know the U. S. Presidents Ser.). (Illus.). 32p. (J). (gr. 3-4). pap. 7.95 (978-0-516-27477-5(5) , Children's Pr.) Scholastic Library Publishing.

Venezia, Mike, illus. Thomas Jefferson. 2004. (Gtk Us Presidents Ser.). (J). 27.00 (978-0-516-22608-8(8) , Children's Pr.) Scholastic Library Publishing.

Viegas, Jennifer. The Declaration of Independence: A Primary Source Investigation into the Action of the Second Continental Congress. 2005. (Great American Political Documents Ser.). (Illus.). 112p. (YA). (gr. 7-12). lib. bdg. 26.50 (978-0-8239-3802-5(6)) Rosen Publishing Group, Inc., The.

Wagner, Heather Lehr. Thomas Jefferson. (Great American Presidents Ser.). (Illus.). (gr. 4-8). 2004. 112p. pap. 30.00 (978-0-7910-7788-7(8)); 2003. 100p. 30.00 (978-0-7910-7602-6(4)) Facts On File, Inc. (Chelsea Hse.).

Whitelaw, Nancy. Thomas Jefferson: Philospher & President. 2004. (Notable Americans Ser.). (Illus.). 144p. (YA). (gr. 6-12). 23.95 (978-1-883846-81-7(1) , First Biographies) Reynolds, Morgan Inc.

Young, Robert. A Personal Tour of Monticello. 1999. (How It Was Ser.). (Illus.). 64p. (J). (gr. 4-6). lib. bdg. (978-0-8225-3575-1(0) , Lerner Pubns.) Lerner Publishing Group.

JEFFERSON, THOMAS, 1743-1826—FICTION

Armstrong, Jennifer. Thomas Jefferson: Letters from a Philadelphia Bookworm. 2001. (Dear Mr. President Ser.: Vol. 2). (Illus.). 117p. (J). (gr. 5-7). 8.95 (978-1-890817-30-5(9)) Winslow Pr.

Fleming, Candace. Big Cheese for the White House: The True Tale of a Tremendous Cheddar. Schindler, S. D., illus. 2004. 32p. (J). (ps-ps). lib. bdg. 14.15 (978-0-606-30286-9(7)) Tandem Library Bks.

—A Big Cheese for the White House: The True Tale of a Tremendous Cheddar. Schindler, S. D., illus. 2004. 32p. (J). reprint ed. pap. 6.95 (978-0-374-40627-1(8) , Sunburst) Farrar, Straus & Giroux.

—The Hatmaker's Sign: A Story by Benjamin Franklin. Parker, Robert A., illus. 1998. 40p. (J). (gr. k-4). pap. 15.95 (978-0-531-30075-6(7) , Orchard Bks.) Scholastic, Inc.

—The Hatmaker's Sign: A Story by Benjamin Franklin. Parker, Robert, illus. 2000. (J). (978-0-606-19857-8(1)) Tandem Library Bks.

Goldsmith, Howard. Thomas Jefferson & the Ghostriders. 2008. (Ready-to-read COFA Ser.). 32p. (J). pap. 3.99 ***(978-1-4169-2692-4(5)** , Aladdin) Simon & Schuster Children's Publishing.

—Thomas Jefferson & the Ghostriders. Rose, Drew, illus. 2008. (Ready-to-read COFA Ser.). 32p. (J). lib. bdg. 13.89 ***(978-1-4169-2749-5(2)** , Aladdin) Simon & Schuster Children's Publishing.

Sargent, Dave & Sargent, Pat. Popcorn: (Blue Corn) Work Hard, 30, 47. Lenoir, Jane, illus. 2001. (Saddle Up Ser.). 36p. (J). lib. bdg. 22.60 (978-1-56763-659-8(4)); pap. 6.95 (978-1-56763-660-4(8)) Ozark Publishing.

Thomas Jefferson: Letters from a Philadelphia Bookworm. 2002. (Dear Mr. President Ser.). (J). (gr. 4-7). 25.95 incl. audio (978-0-87499-989-1(8)) Live Oak Media.

Turner, Ann Warren. When Mr. Jefferson Came to Philadelphia: What I Learned of Freedom 1776. Hess, Mark, illus. 2004. 32p. (J). (ps-3). 15.99 (978-0-06-027579-2(0)) HarperCollins Pubs.

Williams, Mark London. Trail of Bones. Koelsch, Michael, illus. 2005. (Danger Boy Ser.: No. 3). 320p. (J). (gr. 4-8). 12.99 (978-0-7636-2154-4(4)) Candlewick Pr.

JEKYLL, DOCTOR (FICTITIOUS CHARACTER)—FICTION

Dalmatian Press Staff, adapted by. Dr. Jekyll & Mr. Hyde. 2002. (YA). (gr. 9-12). stu. ed. (978-1-58130-785-6(3)) Novel Units, Inc.

—The Strange Case of Dr. Jekyll & Mr. Hyde. 2002. (Spot the Classics Ser.). (Illus.). 171p. (J). (gr. k-5). 4.99 (978-1-57759-552-6(1)) Dalmatian Pr.

Stevenson, Robert Louis. Dr. Jekyll & Mr. Hyde. (Classics Illustrated Ser.). (Illus.). 52p. (YA). pap. 4.95 (978-1-57209-008-8(1)) Classics International Entertainment, Inc.

—Dr. Jekyll & Mr. Hyde. (YA). (gr. 5-12). pap. 6.50 (978-0-8224-9255-9(5)) Globe Fearon Educational Publishing.

—Dr Jekyll & Mr Hyde. abr. ed. 1999. (gr. 7-12). lib. bdg. 15.25 (978-0-613-32488-5(9)) Tandem Library Bks.

—Dr. Jekyll & Mr. Hyde. Redondo, Nestor, illus. 2nd ed. 1998. (Illustrated Classic Book Ser.). 61p. (J). (gr. 3 up). reprint ed. pap. 4.95 (978-1-56767-237-4(X)) Educational Insights, Inc.

—The Strange Case of Dr. Jekyll & Mr. Hyde. 2002. (Great Illustrated Classics Ser.). (Illus.). 240p. (J). (gr. 3-8). 21.35 (978-1-57765-800-9(0) , ABDO & Daughters) ABDO Publishing Co.

—The Strange Case of Dr. Jekyll & Mr. Hyde. (Young Collector's Illustrated Classics Ser.). (Illus.). 192p. (J). (gr. 3-7). 9.95 (978-1-56156-460-6(5)) Kidsbooks, Inc.

JELLYFISHES

Allen, Catherine Judge, et al. Grzimek's Student Animal Resource: Sponges Corals Jellyfishes & Other Animals. 2005. (Grzimek's Student Animal Life Resource Ser.). (Illus.). 200p. (J). 67.00 (978-0-7876-9412-8(6) , UXL) Thomson Gale.

Brennan, Joseph K. Jellyfish & Other Stingers, Vol. 7. World Book, Inc. Staff, ed. 2001. (World Book's Animals of the World Ser.: Set 2). (Illus.). 64p. (J). (978-0-7166-1221-6(6)) World Bk., Inc.

Cheshire, Gerard. Jellyfish. (Scary Creatures Ser.). 32p. (J). 2008. pap. 8.95 ***(978-0-531-21005-5(7)** , Watts, Franklin); 2007. spiral bd. 26.00 ***(978-0-531-20446-7(4)** , Children's Pr.) Scholastic Library Publishing.

Coldiron, Deborah. Jellyfish. 2007. (Underwater World Ser.). (Illus.). 32p. (J). (gr. k-4). lib. bdg. 24.21 ***(978-1-59928-810-9(9)** , Buddy Bks.) ABDO Publishing Co.

Dornhoffer, Mary K. Jellyfish. 2004. (First Reports). (Illus.). 48p. (J). (gr. 3 up). lib. bdg. 22.60 (978-0-7565-0578-3(X)) Compass Point Bks.

Douglas, Lloyd G. Jellyfish. 2005. (Ocean Life Ser.). (Illus.). 24p. (J). (ps-2). pap. 4.95 (978-0-516-23738-1(1)); 18.00 (978-0-516-25025-0(6)) Scholastic Library Publishing. (Children's Pr.).

George, Twig C. Jellies: The Life of Jellyfish. (Illus.). 32p. (gr. k-3). 2001. 3. pap. 8.95 (978-0-7613-1485-1(7)); 2000. (All about Animals Ser.). lib. bdg. (978-0-7613-1659-6(0)) Lerner Publishing Group. (Millbrook Pr.).

—Jellies: The Life of Jellyfish. 2001. (gr. k-3). lib. bdg. 17.60 (978-0-613-91019-4(2)); (Illus.). (J). 15.75 (978-0-606-21262-5(0)) Tandem Library Bks.

Gross, Miriam J. The Jellyfish. 2006. (Illus.). 24p. (J). lib. bdg. (978-1-4042-3192-4(7) , PowerKids Pr.) Rosen Publishing Group, Inc., The.

Herriges, Ann. Jellyfish. 2006. (Blastoff! Readers Ser.). (Illus.). 24p. (J). (gr. k-3). lib. bdg. 16.95 (978-1-60014-018-1(1)) Bellwether Media.

Hirschmann, Kris. Jellyfish. 2004. (Illus.). 48p. (J). (gr. 4-7). 26.20 (978-0-7377-2342-7(4) , Greenhaven Pr., Inc.) Thomson Gale.

Jellyfish. (Under the Sea Ser.). 24p. (J). 6.95 (978-0-7368-5112-1(7)) Capstone Pr., Inc.

Jellyfish Oceans Alive. 2006. (Illus.). 24p. (J). (gr. k-2). 18.50 ***(978-0-531-17869-0(2))** Scholastic Library Publishing.

King, David C. Jellyfish. 2005. (Animals Animals Ser.). (Illus.). 48p. (J). (gr. 3-7). lib. bdg. (978-0-7614-1867-2(9) , Benchmark Bks.) Cavendish, Marshall Corp.

Landau, Elaine. Jellyfish. 1999. (True Bks.). (Illus.). 48p. (J). (gr. 3-5). pap. 6.95 (978-0-516-26494-3(X)); 25.00 (978-0-516-20676-9(1)) Scholastic Library Publishing. (Children's Pr.).

—Jellyfish. 1999. (gr. 3-6). lib. bdg. 15.25 (978-0-613-39507-6(7)) Tandem Library Bks.

Lindeen, Carol K. Jellyfish. 2004. (Under the Sea Ser.). 24p. (J). lib. bdg. 19.93 (978-0-7368-2600-6(9) , Pebble Bks.) Capstone Pr., Inc.

Logue, Mary. Sea Jellies. 2004. (Science Around Us Ser.). 32p. (J). (gr. 2-6). 27.07 (978-1-59296-272-3(6)) Child's World, Inc.

Lunis, Natalie. Gooey Jellyfish. 2008. (J). lib. bdg. 21.28 ***(978-1-59716-510-5(7))** Bearport Publishing Co., Inc.

Martin-James, Kathleen. Floating Jellyfish. (Pull Ahead Bks.). (Illus.). 32p. (J). (gr. k-2). 2003. pap. 5.95 (978-0-8225-3769-4(9)); 2001. lib. bdg. 22.60 (978-0-8225-3766-3(4) , Lerner Pubns.) Lerner Publishing Group.

—Floating Jellyfish. 2001. (gr. k-3). lib. bdg. 14.10 (978-0-613-58833-1(9)) Tandem Library Bks.

McFee, Shane. Jellyfish. 2007. (J). lib. bdg. ***(978-1-4042-3799-5(2)** , PowerKids Pr.) Rosen Publishing Group, Inc., The.

McKenzie, Michelle. Jellyfish Inside Out. 2003. (Illus.). 48p. (J). 14.95 (978-1-878244-43-7(4)) Monterey Bay Aquarium.

Parker, Steve. Sponges, Jellyfish & Other Simple Animals. 2006. (Animal Kingdom Classification Ser.). (Illus.). 48p. (J). (gr. 4-6). 26.60 (978-0-7565-1614-7(5)) Compass Point Bks.

Rustad, Marth E. Jellyfish. 2005. (Ocean Life Ser.). 24p. (YA). (gr. k-3). pap. (978-0-7368-3413-1(3) , Pebble Bks.) Capstone Pr., Inc.

Rustad, Martha E. H. Jellyfish. 2003. (Ocean Life Ser.). (Illus.). 24p. (J). (gr. k-1). lib. bdg. 15.93 (978-0-7368-1656-4(9) , Pebble Bks.) Capstone Pr., Inc.

Schaefer, Lola M. Jellyfish. 2002. (Ooey-Gooey Animals Ser.). (Illus.). 24p. (J). (ps-1). pap. 5.25 (978-1-58810-714-5(0) , 91367); lib. bdg. 17.08 (978-1-58810-505-9(9)) Heinemann Library.

—La Medusa. 2002. (Animales Resbalosos (Ooey-Gooey Animals) Ser.). (SPA.). 24p. (J). (ps-1). lib. bdg. 18.50 (978-1-58810-765-7(5)); (Illus.). pap. 5.25 (978-1-58810-809-8(0) , 91519) Heinemann Library.

Stone, Lynn M. Jellyfish. 2006. (Rourke Discovery Library). (Illus.). 24p. (gr. 1-4). 14.95 (978-1-59515-439-2(6)) Rourke Publishing, LLC.

Windsor, Jo. Jellyfish: Early Level Satellite Individual Title Six-Packs. (Sails Literacy Ser.). 16p. (gr. 1-2). 27.00 (978-0-7578-2927-7(9)) Rigby Education.

JEMISON, MARY, 1743-1833

Aller, Susan Bivin. Living with the Senecas: A Story about Mary Jemison. Harden, Laurie, illus. 2007. (Creative Minds Biographies Ser.). (J). spiral bd. 22.60 (978-0-8225-5989-4(7)) Lerner Publishing Group.

Jemison, Mary. The Diary of Mary Jemison: Captured by the Indians. Roop, Connie & Roop, Peter, eds. 2000. (In My Own Words Ser.). (Illus.). 64p. (J). (gr. 5 up). lib. bdg. 27.07 (978-0-7614-1010-2(4) , Benchmark Bks.) Cavendish, Marshall Corp.

JENGHIS KHAN, 1162-1227

see Genghis Khan, 1162-1227

JENNER, EDWARD, 1749-1823

Edward Jenner y la vacuna Antivariolica. 2000. (McGraw-Hill Ciencias Ser.). (ENG & SPA.). (gr. 3 up). (978-0-02-279631-0(2)) Macmillan/McGraw-Hill Schl. Div.

Marrin, Albert. Dr. Jenner & the Speckled Monster: The Search for the Smallpox Vaccine. 2002. (Illus.). 96p. (J). 19.99 (978-0-525-46922-3(2) , Dutton Juvenile) Penguin Group (USA) Inc.

Rodríguez, Ana María. Edward Jenner: Conqueror of Smallpox. 2006. (Great Minds of Science Ser.). (Illus.). 128p. (J). lib. bdg. 31.93 (978-0-7660-2504-2(7)) Enslow Pubs., Inc.

Underwood, Deborah. Has a Cow Saved Your Life? 2006. (Illus.). 32p. (J). (978-1-4109-2580-0(3)); pap. (978-1-4109-2609-8(5)) Steck-Vaughn.

JEREMIAH, THE PROPHET

PowerXpress Jeremiah Unit. 2006. 115.00 (978-0-687-03930-2(4)) Abingdon Pr.

JERUSALEM

Ashabranner, Brent. Gavriel & Jemal: Two Boys of Jerusalem. Conklin, Paul, photos by. 2005. (Illus.). 94p. (J). (gr. 4-10). reprint ed. 12.00 (978-0-7567-9758-4(6)) DIANE Publishing Co.

Bowden, Rob. Jerusalem. 2005. (Great Cities of the World Ser.). (Illus.). 48p. (J). pap. (978-0-8368-5211-0(7)); 30.00 (978-0-8368-5051-2(3)) Stevens, Gareth Inc. (World Almanac Library).

Burgdorf, Larry. Zerubbabel Rebuilds the Temple: Ezra 3-6 for Children. Eitzen, Allan, illus. 2006. (Arch Books). (ENG.). (J). 1.99 (978-0-7586-0870-3(5)) Concordia Publishing Hse.

Furstinger, Nancy. Jerusalem. 2005. (Cities Ser.). (Illus.). 32p. (J). (gr. k-6). lib. bdg. 22.78 (978-1-59197-860-2(2)) ABDO Publishing Co.

Gold, Yeshara. Hurry, Friday's a Short Day: One boy's erev Shabbat in Jerusalem's old City. 2000. 31p. 13.99 (978-1-57819-541-1(1) , HURH) Mesorah Pubns., Ltd.

Jerusalem 30 A. D. When Yeshua (Jesus) Walked. 2004. (YA). 0.00 net. (978-0-9748424-0-0(0)) Magee, Burke & Glenna.

Kent, Deborah. Jerusalem. 2002. (Cities of the World Ser.). (Illus.). 64p. (YA). (gr. 4-9). pap. 9.95 (978-0-516-25960-4(1) , Children's Pr.) Scholastic Library Publishing.

—Jerusalem. 2001. (gr. 5-8). lib. bdg. 18.75 (978-0-613-51498-9(X)) Tandem Library Bks.

Lusted, Marcia Amidon. The Holy City of Jerusalem. 2002. (Building History Ser.). (Illus.). 112p. (J). (gr. 6-9). 32.45 (978-1-59018-028-0(3) , Lucent Bks.) Thomson Gale.

Morley, Jacqueline & James, John. The Temple at Jerusalem. 2001. (Magnifications Ser.). (Illus.). 48p. (J). (gr. 3-8). 18.95 (978-0-87226-653-7(2) , Bedrick, Peter Bks.) School Specialty Publishing.

Podwal, Mark. Jerusalem Sky: Stars, Crosses & Crescents. Podwal, Mark, illus. 2005. (Illus.). 32p. (J). (gr. k-12). 15.95 (978-0-385-74689-2(X) , Doubleday Bks. for Young Readers) Random Hse. Children's Bks.

Ross. The Western Wall. 2003. (Holy Places Ser.). (Illus.). 32p. (J). pap. 6.95 (978-1-4109-0055-5(X)) Raintree.

Slavik, Diane. Daily Life in Ancient & Modern Jerusalem. Webb, Ray, illus. 2003. 64p. (J). 18.95 (978-1-58013-075-2(5)) Kar-Ben Publishing.

—Daily Life in Ancient & Modern Jerusalem. Webb, Ray, illus. 2005. (Cities Through Time Ser.). 64p. (gr. 5-12). 25.26 (978-0-8225-3218-7(2)) Lerner Publishing Group.

Waldman, Neil. The Golden City: Jerusalem's 3,000 Years. Waldman, Neil, illus. 2003. (Illus.). 32p. (YA). (gr. 2-4). 15.95 (978-1-56397-918-7(7)) Boyds Mills Pr.

Zakon, Miriam S. Sister in White: The Story of Schuester Selma. 1999. (Illus.). 118p. (YA). (gr. 3-10). 10.95 (978-1-56871-186-7(7)) Targum Pr., Inc.

JERUSALEM—FICTION

Bentley, Susan E. The Adventures of Twitcher & Solomon. 2005. 96p. (J). pap. 10.99 (978-1-4141-0467-6(7)) Pleasant Word.

Dennis, Jeanne Gowen & Seifert, Sheila. Escape! Hohn, David, tr. Hohn, David, illus. 2003. (Strive to Thrive Ser.). 96p. (J). pap., pap. 5.99 (978-0-7814-3895-7(0) , 0781438950) Cook, David C. Publishing Co.

Emmer, E. R. The Dolphin Project. 2005. (Going to Ser.). (Illus.). 202p. (gr. 4-8). pap. 6.95 (978-1-893577-12-1(0)) Four Corners Publishing Co., Inc.

Ganz, Yaffa. Savta Simcha & the Roundabout Journey to Jerusalem. Klineman, Harvey, illus. 2000. 128p. (J). 15.99 (978-1-58330-452-5(5)) Feldheim Pubs.

Haggard, H. Rider. Pearl-Maiden. Kou, Christopher D. & McHugh, Michael J., eds. 2003. 372p. (YA). pap. 9.95 (978-1-930367-89-0(9)) Christian Liberty Pr.

Hawse, Alberta. Encounter Christ Through the Dramatic Story of Vinegar Boy. 2002. (Wholesome Adventure & Positive Influence for Today's Youth Ser.). 224p. (YA). pap. 9.99 (978-0-8024-6588-7(9)) Moody Pubs.

Henty, G. A. For the Temple: A Tale of the Fall of Jerusalem. 1999. (gr. 3-6). lib. bdg. 26.85 (978-0-613-80291-8(8)) Tandem Library Bks.

Hyman, Frieda Clark. Victory on the Walls: A Story of Nehemiah. 2005. 182p. (J). pap. ***(978-1-883937-96-6(5))** Bethlehem Bks.

Jinks, Catherine. Pagan's Crusade. 2004. (Pagan Chronicles Ser.: Bk. 1). (Illus.). 256p. (YA). (gr. 7 up). reprint ed. pap. 6.99 (978-0-7636-2584-9(1)) Candlewick Pr.

Kelly, Clint. Escape Underground. 2001. (KidWitness Tales Ser.). 128p. (J). (gr. 3-8). pap. 5.99 (978-1-56179-964-0(5)) Bethany Hse. Pubs.

—Escape Underground. 2001. (gr. 5-8). lib. bdg. 14.15 (978-0-613-85882-3(4)) Tandem Library Bks.

Kelly, Clint & Ware, Jim. Escape Underground & the Prophet's Kid. 2001. (KidWitness Tales Ser.). 128p. (J). (gr. 3-8). pap. 5.99 (978-1-56179-965-7(3)) Bethany Hse. Pubs.

King, Bonnie. Left Behind: Marion's Story. 2005. 57p. pap. 12.95 (978-1-4137-9286-7(3)) PublishAmerica, Inc.

MacLean, Ruth. Jerusalem News. 2000. (Newsbox Ser.). (Illus.). 40p. (J). (ps-3). pap. (978-1-85792-372-8(3) , Christian Focus) Christian Focus Pubns.

Molina, Maria Isabel. De Victoria para Alejandro. (SPA., Illus.). 136p. (YA). (gr. 5-8). 8.95 (978-84-204-4861-9(3)) Alfaguara, Ediciones, S.A.- Grupo Santillana ESP. *Dist:* Lectorum Pubns., Inc.

—De Victoria para Alejandro. 2003. (SPA., Illus.). 135p. (J). (gr. 5-8). pap. 11.95 (978-968-19-0387-9(0)) Santillana USA Publishing Co., Inc.

Morgenstern, Susie. Mon Amour. 2002. (GER.). 124p. pap. 15.00 (978-1-4000-3959-3(2) , New Media German Language) Random House Foreign Language Publishing.

Morpurgo, Michael. On Angel Wings. 2007. 48p. 8.99 ***(978-0-7636-3466-7(2))** Candlewick Pr.

Nye, Naomi. Habibi. 1999. (gr. 7-12). lib. bdg. 14.15 (978-0-613-18312-3(6)) Tandem Library Bks.

Nye, Naomi Shihab. Habibi. unabr. ed. 2000. (YA). pap. 49.24 incl. audio (978-0-7887-3642-1(6) , 41008X4) Recorded Bks., LLC.

—Habibi. 1999. 272p. (YA). (gr. 5 up). pap. 5.99 (978-0-689-82523-1(4) , Simon Pulse) Simon & Schuster Children's Publishing.

—Habibi. 1999. (J). 12.64 (978-0-606-16320-0(4)) Tandem Library Bks.

Orlev, Uri. El Monstruo de la Oscuridad. (Barco de Vapor). (SPA.). 90p. (YA). (gr. 5-8). 7.50 (978-84-348-5327-0(2) , SM7480) SM Ediciones ESP. *Dist:* Lectorum Pubns., Inc.

Oz, Amos. Soumchi. 2003. 53p. pap. 7.95 (978-1-59264-038-6(9)) Toby Pr.

Rouss, Sylvia A. Tali's Jerusalem Scrapbook. Oppenheimer, Nancy, illus. 2003. 32p. (gr. 1-4). 14.95 (978-1-930143-68-5(0)); pap. 9.95 (978-1-930143-69-2(9)) Pitspopany Pr.

—Tali's Jerusalem Scrapbook. 2003. (gr. k-3). lib. bdg. 18.75 (978-0-613-81198-9(4)) Tandem Library Bks.

Smith, Chris. One City, Two Brothers: The Story of Jerusalem. Fronty, Aurélia, illus. 2007. 32p. (J). (ps-5). 16.99 ***(978-1-84686-042-3(3))** Barefoot Bks., Inc.

Solitaire, Jenna. Keeper of the Waters. 3rd rev. ed. 2006. (Guardian of the Boards Ser.). 256p. (YA). 6.99 (978-0-7653-5359-7(8) , Tor Teen) Doherty, Tom Assocs., LLC.

JESUS CHRIST

see also Christianity

Adams, Michelle Medlock. What Is Easter? Wummer, Amy, illus. 26p. (J). 2007. bds. 12.99 ***(978-0-8249-6691-1(0));*** 2006. bds. 6.95 (978-0-8249-6639-3(2) , Candy Cane Pr.) Ideals Pubns.

Ahmed, Shabbir. Jesus: Prophet of Islam. 2003. 35p. (YA). pap. 12.00 (978-1-879402-73-7(4)) Tahrike Tarsile Quran, Inc.

Allen, Raymond E. From Jesus to Santa Claus. Headings, Wade, photos by. 2000. 16p. (J). (ps-7). pap. 4.95 (978-0-9703697-0-3(0)) True To The Word, LLP.

Ammerman, Mark. Jesus Feeds the 5,000. Wheeler, Ron, illus. 1999. (Little Bible Bks.). 24p. (J). 1.99 (978-1-57748-658-9(7)) Barbour Publishing, Inc.

Arthur, Kay & Arndt, Janna. Jesus, to Eternity & Beyond. 2005. (Discover-4-Yourself for Kids Ser.). 143p. (J). pap. 8.99 (978-1-888655-90-2(9)) Precept Ministries.

Arthur, Kay & Shearer, Cyndy. Jesus in the Spotlight. (Discover-4-Yourself for Kids Ser.). 128p. (J). 2006. pap. 8.99 (978-1-888655-24-7(0)); 2004. pap. 8.99 (978-1-888655-73-5(9)) Precept Ministries.

Arthur, Kay, et al. Jesus, Awesome Power, Awesome Love. 2004. (Discover-4-Yourself for Kids Ser.). 138p. (J). pap. 8.99 (978-1-888655-75-9(5)) Precept Ministries.

Association of Christian Schools International Staff. Fifth Grade Bible: Christ & My Choices. 2000. (Elementary Bible Ser.). (Illus.). 176p. (gr. 5-6). pap., stu. ed. 14.90 (978-1-58331-112-7(2) , 7122) Assn. of Christian Schls. International.

Babcock, Bruce. The Life of Jesus. Babcock, Bruce, illus. unabr. ed. 1998. (Illus.). 15p. (J). (ps-6). pap. 5.95 (978-1-892161-01-7(X)) Babcock Publishing Co.

Bader, Joanne. He's Risen! He's Alive! Heroldt, Richard, illus. 2003. (Arch Bks.). (ENG.). 16p. (J). 1.99 (978-0-570-07583-7(1)) Concordia Publishing Hse.

Bagley, Val. My Little Book about Jesus. 2004. 9.95 (978-1-57734-665-4(3)) Covenant Communications, Inc.

Bagley, Val Chadwick, illus. I Will Trust in Heavenly Father & Jesus. 2006. (J). (978-1-59811-056-2(X)) Covenant Communications.

Balika, Susan. Jesus Is My Special Friend. Bolling, Vickey, illus. 2003. 24p. (J). 2.49 (978-0-7847-1270-2(0)) Standard Publishing.

Ballman, Swanee. Mary & Martha's Dinner Guest. Boddy, Joe, illus. 1998. (Arch Bks.). (ENG.). 16p. (J). (gr. k-4). 1.99 (978-0-570-07548-6(3)) Concordia Publishing Hse.

Beerman, Merlin. Seeds of Wisdom Christ's Object Lessons. 2000. (Bible Study Ser.). per. 6.95 (978-0-9668482-1-2(7)) Revelation Pubns.

Berger, Alison J. Where Is Jesus? 2001. 16p. (J). (gr. 3-7). pap. 2.00 (978-1-58595-146-8(3)) Twenty-Third Pubns./Bayard.

Better, Cathy Drinkwater. In His Footsteps. 2000. (Illus.). 32p. (J). (ps-2). 12.99 (978-0-570-07035-1(X)) Concordia Publishing Hse.

Bible Lessons for Juniors, Book 3: The Life of Christ. 2007. (J). ***(978-1-60178-014-0(1))** Reformation Heritage Bks.

The Birth of Jesus Bible Sticker Book. 2003. (Illus.). 16p. (J). 2.98 (978-1-4054-1559-0(2)) Parragon, Inc.

Bishop, Jennie. Jesus Must Be Really Special. Wummer, Amy, illus. (J). 2007. ***(978-0-7847-1988-6(8));*** 2006. 32p. 14.99 (978-0-7847-1379-2(0) , 04029) Standard Publishing.

Blundell, Trevor & Biblewise Staff. On the Way for 3 - 9's: Christmas & Jesus' Miracles, Vol. 2. 88-104p. (J). pap. 11.99 (978-1-85792-319-3(7) , Christian Focus) Christian Focus Pubns. GBR. *Dist:* Riverside.

Bostrom & Kucharik. Quien Es Jesus? (Who Is Jesus?) 2000. (Little Hearts Ser.). (SPA.). (J). 8.99 (978-0-7899-0856-8(5) , 497775) Editorial Unilit.

Bostrom, Kathleen Long & Kucharik, Elena. Who Is Jesus? 1999. (Little Blessings Ser.). (Illus.). 80p. (J). 9.99 (978-0-8423-5144-7(2)) Tyndale Hse. Pubs.

—Why Is There a Cross? 2005. (Little Blessings Ser.). (Illus.). 64p. (J). 9.99 (978-1-4143-0288-1(6)) Tyndale Hse. Pubs.

Bowler, Kathryn C. & Osborne, Rick. I Want to Know, Sam's Club: About God, Jesus, the Bible & Prayer. 2001. 168p. (J). 27.99 (978-0-310-70242-9(9)) Zonderkidz.

Bozzuti, Jones M. Jesus, the Word. 2005. (Illus.). 32p. (J). 16.99 (978-0-8066-5169-9(5) , Augsburg Bks.) Augsburg Fortress, Pubs.

Breems, Beau. The Promise. Breems, Beau, illus. 2006. (YA). 10.00 (978-0-9768680-9-5(1)); 20.00 (978-0-9768680-8-8(3)) Burning Bush Creation.

Breems, Beau A. La Gran Historia: The Illustrated Gospel from Creation to Resurrection. Breems, Beau A., illus. 2005. Tr. of His Story. (SPA.). (J). 10.99 (978-0-9768680-5-7(9)) Burning Bush Creation.

Breems, Beau Alan. His Story: The Illustrated Gospel from Creation to Resurrection. Breems, Beau Alan, illus. 2005. (J). per. 14.95 (978-0-9768680-2-6(4)) Burning Bush Creation.

Brighter Child Publishing Staff. The Beginners Bible: New Testament Favorites: Birth of Jesus & Story of Easter. 1999. (Beginner's Bible Ser.). (J). (ps-3). cd-rom 19.95 (978-1-57791-003-9(6)) Brighter Minds Children's Publishing.

Brown, Alan. Jesus & Christianity. 2002. (Great Religious Leaders Ser.). (Illus.). 48p. (J). lib. bdg. 28.50 (978-1-58340-221-4(7)) Smart Apple Media.

Bryant, Patricia White. Jesus, Is Your Daddy Mean? 112p. (J). 7.95 (978-1-56794-148-7(6) , C-2485) Star Bible & Tract Corp.

Buck, Deanna Draper. My First Articles of Faith Book. Harston, Jerry, illus. 2000. (J). 12.95 (978-1-57345-839-9(2)) Deseret Bk. Co.

Budensiek, Joy. Jesus, My Very Best Friend. 2003. (J). (978-0-9618730-8-0(6)) FEA Ministries.

Buehner, Caralyn. In the Garden. Dorman, Brandon, illus. 2007. (J). 18.95 (***978-1-59038-403-9(2)***) Deseret Bk. Co.

Busch, Melinda Kay. Jesus & the Woman at the Well. Clark, Bill, illus. 2005. (Arch Books). (ENG.). 16p. (J). 1.99 (978-0-7586-0675-4(3)) Concordia Publishing Hse.

Carter, Nancy & Julien, Terry, illus. Jesus Loves Me. 2006. 16p. (J). pap. 1.99 (978-0-7847-1804-9(0) , 04186) Standard Publishing.

CC Pastors Wives. Passion for Jesus. 1998. (Cross Training Ser.). 80p. (YA). (gr. 10-12). pap., tchr. ed. 15.00 incl. VHS (978-1-57405-248-0(9)) CharismaLife Pubs.

Choi, Young-Jin. Jesus Feeds Everybody! Kim, Jung-cho, illus. 2007. Tr. of Jesus' Breadbasket. (J). bds. 5.95 (***978-0-8198-3987-9(6)***) Pauline Bks. & Media.

—Mary's Big Surprise. Kim, Jung-cho, illus. 2007. Tr. of Mary, Crying & Laughing. (J). bds. 5.95 (***978-0-8198-4853-6(0)***) Pauline Bks. & Media.

Chronicles of Faith - Jesus. 2007. 224p. (J). pap. 4.97 (***978-1-59789-925-3(9)***) Barbour Publishing, Inc.

Concordia Publishing Staff, ed. Stories about Jesus for Little Ones. 1998. (Illus.). 35p. (J). (ps-1). 8.99 (978-0-570-05476-4(1)) Concordia Publishing Hse.

Consuegra, Claudio & Consuegra, Pamela. Making Jesus My Best Friend: Baptism Preparation for Younger Children (Ages 8-10) 2005. (Illus.). 95p. (J). (gr. 4-7). pap. 8.99 (978-0-8280-1836-4(7)) Review & Herald Publishing Assn.

Courtney, Claudia. Modest King: Palm Sunday. 2000. (ps-2). lib. bdg. 10.65 (978-0-613-72824-9(6)) Tandem Library Bks.

Dandi. Picture Me with My Friend Jesus: Boy Version. Strebel, Carol, illus. 1998. 10p. (J). (ps-3). bds. 4.99 (978-1-57151-541-4(0)) Playhouse Publishing.

—Picture Me with My Friend Jesus: Girl Version. Strebel, Carol, illus. 1998. 10p. (J) (ps-3). bds. 4.99 (978 1 57151-542-1(9)) Playhouse Publishing.

Dateno, Maria Grace. The Stations of the Cross for Children. Pompei, Maria Teresa, tr. Richards, Virginia Helen, illus. 2006. (SPA.). 24p. (J). 1.25 (978-0-8198-7095-7(1)) Pauline Bks. & Media.

David C. Cook. Cruisin' the Amazing Amazon: A Jungle Journey to Discover Jesus. 2003. (Very Exciting Bible School Ser.). 300p. (J). (gr. 3-4). spiral bd. 69.99 (978-0-7814-3635-9(4) , 0781436354) Cook, David C. Publishing Co.

Davidson, Alice Joyce. The J Is for Jesus: The Candy Cane Story. Anderson, Nancy Munger, illus. 1998. (Christmas Board Bks.). 14p. (J). (ps). bds. 3.99 (978-0-310-97553-3(0)) Zonderkidz.

Davis, Mary J. Five-Minute Sunday School Activities for Preschoolers: Jesus Shows Me. Galey, Chuck, illus. 2005. 96p. (J). pap. 11.95 (978-1-58411-047-7(3)) Rainbow Pubs. & Legacy Pr.

De Graaf, Anne. Jesus' Miracles. Montero, Jose Perez, illus. 2000. (Little Children's Bible Bks.). 38p. (J). (ps-1). 5.99 (978-0-8054-2178-1(5)) B&H Publishing Grp.

Dede, Vivian Hughes. Jesus' First Miracle. Dyrud, Chris Wold, illus. 2005. (ENG.). 16p. (J). 1.99 (978-0-7586-0865-9(9)) Concordia Publishing Hse.

Demi. Jesus: Based upon the King James Version of the Holy Bible. Demi, illus. 2005. (Illus.). 48p. (J). 19.95 (978-0-689-86905-1(3) , McElderry, Margaret K.) Simon & Schuster Children's Publishing.

dePaola, Tomie. The Miracles of Jesus. 2008. 32p. (J). (ps). pap. 6.99 (***978-0-14-241068-4(3)*** , Puffin) Penguin Group (USA) Inc.

Di Silvestro, Frank. Playing Ball with Jesus. 2001. 17p. (J). pap. (978-0-934591-06-5(7)) Songs & Stories Children Love.

Dorn, Patrick Rainville. Is Jesus Here? Van Fleet, Douglas, illus. 2002. 32p. (J). pap. 6.95 (978-0-8198-3685-4(0) , 332-138) Pauline Bks. & Media.

Dowley, Tim. My First Story of Jesus. 2007. (Illus.). 32p. 7.99 (978-0-8024-1776-3(0)) Moody Pubs.

Dowley, Tim & Wyatt, Peter. The Wise Men's Tale. Pierce, Martin, illus. 2002. 14p. (J). (gr. k-3). 5.99 (978-0-8254-7256-5(3)) Kregel Pubns.

Doyle, Christopher. The Story of Jesus. Chapman, Gillian, illus. 2005. (ENG.). 64p. (J). 9.99 (978-0-7586-0986-1(8)) Concordia Publishing Hse.

Dudley-Smith, Timothy, retold by. Stories of Jesus. (Illus.). 160p. (J). (gr. 2-5). pap. 8.95 (978-0-7459-4292-6(X) , Lion) Lion Hudson plc GBR. *Dist:* Trafalgar Square Publishing.

Earley, Catherine. Jesus Loves Me for Me. 2006. 28p. (J). per. 7.99 (***978-1-59886-726-8(1)***) Tate Publishing & Enterprises, L.L.C.

Esquinaldo, Virginia. What Did Baby Jesus Do? Esquinaldo, Virginia, illus. 2006. (Illus.). 14p. (J). bds. 6.95 (978-0-8198-8310-0(7)) Pauline Bks. & Media.

Fitzgerald, Josephine. Christ, Our Burden Bearer. Skorackiji, Olga et al, eds. 2003. 168p. (YA). pap. 8.95 (978-0-910487-55-9(3)) Royalty Publishing Co.

Flanagan, Anne. Miracles of Jesus Act/Col Bk. 24p. pap. 1.25 (978-0-8198-4836-9(0) , 332-225) Pauline Bks. & Media.

Fletcher, Sarah. Jesus & the Family Trip. Jones, Doug, illus. 1998. (Arch Bks.). (ENG.). 16p. (J). (gr. k-4). 1.99 (978-0-570-07547-9(5)) Concordia Publishing Hse.

Fogle, Robin. Itty-bitty Bible Activity Book, the Legend of the Candy Cane. 2007. (Illus.). 48p. (J). pap. 1.49 (***978-1-59317-212-1(5)***) Warner Pr. Pubs.

Frank, Penny. The First Easter. (Illus.). 24p. pap. 2.99 (978-0-7459-4123-3(0) , Lion) Lion Hudson plc GBR. *Dist:* Trafalgar Square Publishing.

—Jesus on Trial. (Illus.). 24p. 2.99 (978-0-7459-4122-6(2) , Lion) Lion Hudson plc GBR. *Dist:* Trafalgar Square Publishing.

—Jesus the King. 1999. (Illus.). 24p. (J). pap. 2.99 (978-0-7459-4121-9(4) , Lion) Lion Hudson plc GBR. *Dist:* Independent Pubs. Group.

Freed, Shirley & Moon, Louise. Help Me! Morelan, Bill, ed. Butler, Steven, illus. 2003. 8p. (J). (-k). pap. 3.99 (978-1-58938-097-4(5)) Concerned Communications.

Freed, Shirley Ann & Moon, Louise. Jesus Loves Me Anyway. Morelan, Bill, ed. Harrell, Rob, illus. l.t. ed. 2002. 16p. (J). (gr. 1-2). pap. 3.99 (978-1-58938-026-4(6)) Concerned Communications.

Frey, Daniel J., illus. Jacy's Coloring & Activity Book. 2006. 32p. (J). 3.00 (978-0-9755314-2-6(5)) Majestic Publishing, LLC.

Fryar, Jane L. Jesus Enters Jerusalem. Dorenkamp, Michelle, illus. 2004. (ENG.). 16p. (J). 1.99 (978-0-7586-0641-9(9)) Concordia Publishing Hse.

Galvin, Jennifer. Jesus Loves Me Pre-School Activity Book. Galvin, Jennifer, illus. 2006. (Illus.). 32p. (J). pap. 6.95 (978-0-8091-6734-0(4) , 6734-4) Paulist Pr.

Ganeri, Anita. The Easter Story. Phillips, Rachael, illus. 2003. (Festival Stories Ser.). 24p. (J). (978-0-237-52531-6(3)); pap. (978-0-237-52475-3(9)) Evans Publishing Group. (Evans Brothers, Limited).

—The Easter Story. Phillips, Rachael, tr. Phillips, Rachael, illus. 2004. 23p. (J). lib. bdg. (978-1-58340-488-1(0)) Smart Apple Media.

Gemmen, Heather & McNeil, Mary. How Did That Happen?, Level 4. Foote, Dan, tr. Foote, Dan, illus. 1999. (Rocket Readers Ser.). 32p. (J). (gr. 4 up). pap., pap. 4.99 (978-0-7814-3978-7(7) , 0781439787) Cook, David C. Publishing Co.

—Something New, Level 3. Johnson, Meredith, ed. Johnson, Meredith, tr. 1999. (Rocket Readers Ser.). 24p. (J). (gr. 3 up). pap., pap. 8.99 (978-0-7814-3986-2(8) , 0781439868) Cook, David C. Publishing Co.

Gillis, Bonnie, illus. The Theophany of Our Lord. 2002. (Twelve Great Feasts for Children Ser.). 24p. pap. 5.95 (978-1-888212-38-9(1) , 005673) Conciliar Pr.

Glavich, Mary Kathleen. A Child's Book of Miracles. 2004. (978-0-8294-1038-9(4)) Loyola Pr.

Goddard, Carrie Lou. Jesus Goes to School. 1999. (Illus.). 24p. (J). (gr. k-3). 13.00 (978-0-687-09015-0(6)) Abingdon Pr.

God's Gift: The Birth of Jesus. (Illus.). 16p. (J). pap. 1.50 (978-0-87162-855-8(4) , E4573) Warner Pr. Pubs.

Graham, Ruth Bell & Watson, Jeffrey. One Wintry Night. 2007. 72p. 12.99 (***978-0-8010-1306-5(2)***) Baker Bks.

Green, John. The Miracles of Jesus Stained Glass Coloring Book. 2007. 16p. (J). pap. 5.95 (***978-0-486-46226-4(9)***) Dover Pubns., Inc.

Greendyk, William, tr. from ENG. El Hijo de la Viuda. l.t. ed. 2004. Orig. Title: The Widow's Son. (SPA., Illus.). 92p. (J). pap. (978-1-932789-11-9(1)) Editorial Sendas Antiguas, LLC.

Grob, John-Marc. Nativity. 2000. (Bible Kingdom Ser.). (J). pap. 1.99 (978-0-8054-0981-9(5)) B&H Publishing Grp.

Groome, Thomas H., et al. Acerandote a Jesus (Coming to Jesus), Grade 2. 1998. (Acercandote a la Fe Ser.). (SPA & ENG., Illus.). 288p. (J). (gr. 2-3). pap. 12.36 net. (978-0-8215-4462-4(4)) Sadlier, William H. Inc.

Haidle, Helen & Spector, Joel. He Is Alive! Spector, Joel, illus. 2001. (Illus.). 40p. (J). 12.99 (978-0-310-70033-3(7)) Zonderkidz.

Hall, Sarah. Who Is Jesus? What Did He Do?: Why Do People Remember Him? Berkshire, Lisa, illus. 2003. 64p. (J). (gr. 1-2). pap. 10.95 (978-0-7459-4664-1(X) , Lion Children's) Lion Hudson plc GBR. *Dist:* Independent Pubs. Group.

Halpin, D. I Learn about Jesus Col/Act Bk. 32p. pap. 1.25 (978-0-8198-3686-1(9) , 332-139) Pauline Bks. & Media.

Hamilton, Eleanor P. The Narrow Gate: Where Jesus Walked, 1. Hamilton, Patrick H., illus. 2006. (J). spiral bd. 17.50 (978-0-9755173-4-5(1)) Autumn Light Pubns.

Handloser, Rick. Sneezy Neezy. Byous, Shawn, illus. 2006. 48p. pap. 19.97 (978-1-59800-291-1(0)) Outskirts Press, Inc.

Harman, Debbie G. Jesus Said- 2004. (Illus.). 17.95 (978-1-59156-091-3(8)) Covenant Communications, Inc.

Hartman, Sara. Mary Magdalene's Easter Story. Koehler, Ed, illus. 2005. (ENG.). 16p. (J). 1.99 (978-0-7586-0722-5(9)) Concordia Publishing Hse.

Hays Moore, Angela. Maggie Seeks the Kingdom of God. Kizer Kiel, Casey, illus. 2007. 32p. (J). 19.99 (***978-1-59879-323-9(3)***) Lifevest Publishing, Inc.

Henning. God Sent a Baby King. 2006. (Illus.). 32p. 14.00 (978-0-687-49498-9(2)) Abingdon Pr.

Here Comes Jesus! 2005. 16p. (J). per. 4.99 (978-1-59441-079-6(8) , CD-204006) Carson-Dellosa Publishing Co., Inc.

Hinkle, Cynthia. Star of Wonder. van der Sterre, Johanna, illus. 2005. (Arch Books). (ENG.). 16p. (J). 1.99 (978-0-7586-0724-9(5)) Concordia Publishing Hse.

Howick, E. Keith. The Life of Jesus the Messiah, 5 bks. 2003. 97.75 (978-1-886249-05-9(9)) WindRiver Publishing.

—The Second Coming of Jesus the Messiah. 2003. 304p. 21.95 (978-1-886249-04-2(0)) WindRiver Publishing.

Howie, Vicki. Someone Very Special. Bishop, Roma, illus. 2004. 24p. (ps-k). 6.99 (978-0-8066-4154-6(1) , Augsburg Bks.) Augsburg Fortress, Pubs.

Hudson, Angus. Localiza la Diferencia (Find the Difference) Parabolas Que Jesus Relato. (SPA.). (J). 1.89 (978-1-56063-965-7(2) , 497756) Editorial Unilit.

Hummel, Patti M. Jesus Loves Me: Bible Memory for Preschoolers. Simon, Gale L., illus. 2000. 64p. (J). (ps-3). pap. 6.99 (978-0-8024-4344-1(3)) Moody Pubs.

—Jesus Loves Me: Bible Memory for Toddlers. Simon, Gale L., illus. 2000. 64p. (J). (ps-k). pap. 6.99 (978-0-8024-4343-4(5)) Moody Pubs.

Hurst, Diane. Calming the Storm. Overstreet, Laura, illus. 2006. (Sing A Story Ser.). 20p. (J). bds. 4.99 (978-0-7847-1814-8(8) , 04136) Standard Publishing.

I Can Talk to You about Anything. 1999. 24p. (J). 10.99 (978-1-55513-622-2(2)) Cook, David C. Publishing Co.

I Wonder What Jesus Would Do: Fun to Color & Do. 2001. (978-0-7424-0020-7(4) , Instructional Fair) Schaffer, Frank Pubns.

Illustrated Christmas Story. 2007. 72p. pap. 14.95 (***978-0-8256-3550-2(0)*** , Amsco Music) Music Sales Corp.

Itty-Bitty Book: Jesus. 2006. (J). pap. 1.49 (***978-1-59317-164-3(1)***) Warner Pr. Pubs.

James, Ben, illus. Los Tres Reyes Magos, the Three Wise Men. 2006. (J). bds. (978-0-9786863-2-1(2)) ITRON Publishing.

James, Bethan. My First Picture Book about Jesus. Wickenden, Nadine, illus. 2007. (ENG.). 32p. (J). 14.99 (***978-0-7586-1330-1(X)***) Concordia Publishing Hse.

James, Betsy, illus. The Word & Picture Books Set 1: For Year B/C, 6 vols. Incl. Breakfast at the Lake. Wehreim, Carol. bds. 4.95 (978-0-8298-1186-5(9)); Come to Jesus. Wehreim, Carol, ed. bds. 4.95 (978-0-8298-1183-4(4)); First Church. Wehreim, Carol, ed. bds. 4.95 (978-0-8298-1188-9(5)); Jesus, a Special Baby. Wehreim, Carol, ed. bds. 4.95 (978-0-8298-1184-1(2)); Jesus Goes Fishing. Wehreim, Carol, ed. bds. 4.95 (978-0-8298-1185-8(0)); Loving Shepherd. Wehreim, Carol, ed. bds. 4.95 (978-0-8298-1187-2(7)); (Illus.). 12p. (J). (ps-4). 1997. (Word & Picture Bks.). 29.70 (978-0-8298-1189-6(3)) Pilgrim Pr., The/United Church Pr.

Jeffs, Stephanie. Where's Jesus. Laver, Sarah, 8th, illus. 2004. 32p. 13.95 (978-0-8294-1728-9(1)) Loyola Pr.

Jesus. 2004. 32p. (J). 0.99 (978-0-7647-1039-1(7) , In Celebration) Schaffer, Frank Pubns.

Jesus & His Disciples: Coloring Book. (Illus.). 16p. (J). pap. 1.50 (978-0-87162-856-5(2) , E6040) Warner Pr. Pubs.

Jesus Bendice a los Ninos, 6 vols. 2000. (Arch Bks.). (SPA.). 24p. (J). (ps-3). 2.49 (978-0-570-05174-9(6)) Concordia Publishing Hse.

The Jesus Files. 1998. (Cross Training Ser.: Vol. 7). 64p. (J). (gr. 7-9). pap., tchr. ed. 15.00 incl. VHS (978-1-57405-253-4(5)) CharismaLife Pubs.

Jesus Is Born. 2004. (978-0-8294-9909-4(1)) Loyola Pr.

Jesus Is Everything I Need: Challenging Bible Activities on Jesus & All He Is to Us! (Illus.). 16p. (J). pap. 1.50 (978-0-87162-818-3(X) , E4512) Warner Pr. Pubs.

Jesus Lives! 2004. (In Celebration Coloring & Activity Book Ser.). 32p. (J). (gr. k-2). pap. 1.99 (978-0-7647-1013-1(3) , In Celebration) Schaffer, Frank Pubns.

Jesus, our Righteousness. 2005. (YA). 14.00 (978-1-59872-121-8(6)) Instantpublisher.com.

John: Jesus in My Life. 1998. (Club 56 Ser.). (J). (gr. 5-6). 28p. pap., wbk. ed. 2.79 (978-1-57405-242-8(X)); 176p. tchr. ed., spiral bd. 29.99 (978-1-57405-241-1(1)) CharismaLife Pubs.

Johnson, Alice W. & Warner, Allison H. Believe & You're There at the Miracles of Jesus. Nelson, Holly, illus. 2007. 96p. (J). pap. 7.95 (***978-1-59038-722-1(8)***) Deseret Bk. Co.

—Believe & You're There When the Stone Was Rolled Away. Nelson, Holly, illus. 2007. 96p. (J). pap. 7.95 (***978-1-59038-723-8(6)***) Deseret Bk. Co.

—Believe & You're There When the White Dove Descended. Nelson, Holly, illus. 2007. 96p. (J). pap. 7.95 (***978-1-59038-721-4(X)***) Deseret Bk. Co.

Jones, Ron, ed. Jesus: Passages from the Gospel Records. 2003. (978-0-9747452-0-6(0)) Titus Institute of California.

Jones, Sally Lloyd. Lift-the-Flap Nativity. Moroney, Tracey, illus. 2006. 18p. (J). bds. 12.99 (978-0-7847-1280-1(8) , 03505) Standard Publishing.

Journey with Jesus. 2006. pap. 39.99 (978-0-8307-4273-8(5)) Gospel Light Pubns.

Keating, Susan K. Jesus Christ. 2002. (Great Names Ser.). (Illus.). 32p. (J). (gr. 3 up). lib. bdg. (978-1-59084-138-9(7)) Mason Crest Pubs.

Keelty, M. A Child's Life of Christ. 2005. (J). pap. 9.95 (978-0-911845-13-6(5)) Neumann Pr., The.

Kids in Service. 2002. ring bd. 69.99 (978-1-59185-155-4(6)) CharismaLife Pubs.

Kids in Service Transparencies. 2002. 29.99 (978-1-59185-147-9(5)) CharismaLife Pubs.

Kimethu, Susan. Kids, Let's Follow Christ. l.t. ed. 2002. (Illus.). 65p. per. 6.99 (978-0-9719328-1-4(6)) Dansu Pubs., LLC.

Klug, Ron & Klug, Lyn. Jesus Lives! The Story of Jesus for Children. Konsterlie, Paul, illus. 2004. 32p. (Orig.). (ps-3). 7.99 (978-0-8066-1952-1(X) , 10-3527, Augsburg Bks.) Augsburg Fortress, Pubs.

Konzen, Lisa. The Great Catch of Fish: Luke 5:1-11 for Children. Rooney, Ronnie, illus. 2006. (Arch Books). (ENG.). (J). 1.99 (978-0-7586-0871-0(3)) Concordia Publishing Hse.

Krenzer, Rolf. Jesus Is Risen. Maloney, Linda M., tr. from GER. Droop, Constanza, illus. 2005. 24p. (ps-3). 14.95 (978-0-8146-2764-8(1)) Liturgical Pr.

Lagerlof, Selma. The Emperor's Vision & Other Christ Legends. 2002. (Illus.). 224p. (J). pap. 14.95 (978-0-86315-381-5(X)) Floris Bks. GBR. *Dist:* SteinerBooks, Inc.

Land Fairer Than Day. 7.50 (978-0-8054-5937-1(5)) B&H Publishing Grp.

Lane, Leena. Come to the Party with Jesus. Saunderson, Chris, illus. 2007. (J). 5.99 (978-0-9789056-5-1(2)) New Day Publishing, Inc.

Langford, Norman F. King Nobody Wanted. 2007. 41.99 (***978-1-4280-5205-5(4)***); pap. 34.99 (***978-1-4280-5207-9(0)***) IndyPublish.com.

Larkin, Jean K., ed. Learning about Jesus: Activities for Junior High, 4 vols. 2002. (Ready Resources for Catholic Teens (For Junior High) Ser.). 32p. (YA). 14.95 (978-0-89837-223-6(2) , P2J2) Pflaum Publishing Group.

Larson, Beverly. El Cuento de la Ballena (The Whale's Tale) 2000. (Play along Ser.). (SPA.). (J). (ps-k). bds. 4.99 (978-0-7899-0820-9(4) , 493788) Editorial Unilit.

Later Life of Jesus: Pict O Graph. (Pict-O-Graph Ser.). (Illus.). (J). 10.99 (978-0-7847-1028-9(7) , 02228) Standard Publishing.

Lee, Witness. Christ in His Excellency. 2000. 70p. (J). (gr. 6). per. 6.00 (978-0-7363-0947-9(0) , 06-022-001) Living Stream Ministry.

—The Crucified Christ. 2002. 165p. per. 8.25 (978-0-7363-1485-5(7) , 07-964-001) Living Stream Ministry.

—The Wonderful Being of Christ. 2000. 51p. (J). (gr. 6). per. 5.50 (978-0-7363-0835-9(0) , 06-909-001) Living Stream Ministry.

Let's Shine Jesus' Light on Halloween. 2006. 16p. (J). pap. 1.99 (978-0-7847-1531-4(9) , 04360) Standard Publishing.

Lingo, Susan L. Discover-N-Do Object Talks That Teach about Jesus: 23 Messages That Teach Kids Ways to Investigate & Find Jesus. Becker, Linda, illus. 2006. 48p. (J). pap. 6.99 (978-0-7847-1372-3(3) , 02902) Standard Publishing.

—Edible Object Talks That Teach about Jesus. Becker, Paula, illus. 2000. (Edible Object Talks Ser.). 48p. (YA). pap. 6.99 (978-0-7847-1184-2(4) , 02825) Standard Publishing.

Lord, Jill Roman. If Jesus Came to Visit Me. Graef, Renee, illus. 2004. 28p. (J). bds. 6.95 (978-0-8249-6568-6(X)) Ideals Pubns.

—If Jesus Lived Inside My Heart. Wummer, Amy, illus. 2007. 26p. (J). (ps-k). bds. 6.99 (***978-0-8249-6686-7(4)*** , Candy Cane Pr.) Ideals Pubns.

Lord, Jill Roman. If Jesus Walked Beside Me. Graef, Renée, illus. 2006. 26p. (J). bds. 6.95 (978-0-8249-6638-6(4) , Candy Cane Pr.) Ideals Pubns.

Lottridge, Celia B. Stories from the Life of Jesus. Wolfsgruber, Linda, illus. 2007. 168p. (J). 10.00 (***978-0-88899-840-8(6)***) Groundwood Bks. CAN. *Dist:* Perseus Distribution.

Lounsbury, Pete. Jesus & the Blind Man. 2007. (J). per. 12.95 (***978-1-59879-408-3(6)***) Lifevest Publishing, Inc.

Mackall, Dandi Daley. This Is the Lunch That Jesus Served. Huang, Benrei, illus. 2006. 32p. (J). pap. 9.99 (978-0-8066-5118-7(0) , Augsburg Bks.) Augsburg Fortress, Pubs.

Mackenzie, Carine. God, the Ten Commandments, & Jesus. 2004. 40p. (J). pap. 12.99 (978-1-85792-850-1(4) , Christian Focus) Christian Focus Pubns. GBR. *Dist:* Riverside.

—The Names of Jesus. 64p. (J). pap., act. bk. ed. 11.99 (978-1-85792-650-7(1) , Christian Focus) Christian Focus Pubns. GBR. *Dist:* Riverside.

Madise, Muriel. My Little Christian Alphabet Book: The ABC's of Christianity. 2002. (Illus.). 32p. (J). 15.95 (978-0-9714994-0-9(3)) MiracleLand Publishers.

Maier, Paul L. The Very First Easter. 32p. (J). 9.99 (978-0-570-07195-2(X)) Concordia Publishing Hse.

—The Very First Easter. Ordaz, Francisco, illus. 2004. (ENG.). 32p. (J). pap. 6.99 (978-0-7586-0627-3(3)); 12.99 (978-0-570-07053-5(8)) Concordia Publishing Hse.

Marsh, Dilleen, tr. & illus. What Happens When People Die? Marsh, Dilleen, illus. 2003. (J). 12.95 (978-1-57008-954-1(X)) Deseret Bk. Co.

Mayhan, Benton. Peter & His Friend Jesus. 1998. (Illus.). 16p. (J). (ps-1). 3.95 (978-0-687-05338-4(2)) Abingdon Pr.

JKL

McGuire, George. God & Me. 2006. 36p. pap. 13.99 (978-1-4116-9218-3(7)) Lulu.com.

Mills, Charles. God & Me. 2001. 315p. (J). (978-0-8280-1560-8(0) , 073-260) Review & Herald Publishing Assn.

The Miracles of Jesus. 2006. (Illus.). 10p. (J). bds. 14.99 (978-0-7847-1201-6(8) , 04052) Standard Publishing.

Miracles of Jesus. (Pict-O-Graph Ser.). (Illus.). (J). 10.99 (978-0-7847-1026-5(0) , 02226) Standard Publishing.

Miracles of Jesus. (Illus.). 16p. (J). pap. 1.50 (978-0-87162-858-9(9) , E6039) Warner Pr. Pubs.

Mitchell, Stephen. Jesus: What He Really Said & Did. 2003. (gr. 7-12). lib. bdg. 15.30 (978-0-613-71515-7(2)) Tandem Library Bks.

Mooney, Belinda T. Christ the King, Lord of History. 2000. 200p. (YA). (gr. 9-12). pap., stu. ed., wbk. ed. 16.50 (978-0-89555-673-8(1) , 1754) TAN Bks. and Pubs., Inc.

Moore, Eva. Jesus Gives His Blessing. 2006. 32p. (J). pap. 3.99 (978-0-439-81508-6(8)) Scholastic, Inc.

—Jesus in Jerusalem. 2007. 32p. (J). pap. 3.99 (978-0-439-89038-0(1)) Scholastic, Inc.

Mortimer, F. L. More about Jesus. 288p. (J). pap. 7.99 (978-1-85792-592-0(0)) Christian Focus Pubns. GBR. *Dist:* Riverside.

Mummery, Sue. Why 2000. Mummery, Sue, illus. 1999. (Illus.). 32p. (J). (ps-3). pap. (978-1-85792-483-1(5)) Christian Focus Pubns.

Munger, Robert Boyd & Nystrom, Carolyn. My Heart - Christ's Home: Retold for Children. 2005. 5p. pap. 7.50 (978-0-8308-6549-9(7)) InterVarsity Pr.

Murphy, Elspeth Campbell. Happy Easter, God. Lewis, Jim, illus. 2001. (Prayer-Poems Ser.). 32p. (J). (ps-3). 7.99 (978-0-7642-2386-0(0)) Bethany Hse. Pubs.

My Book about Jesus. 2004. (Exploring Luther's Small Catechism Ser.). (ps-k). 2.99 (978-0-8066-6750-8(8)) Augsburg Fortress, Pubs.

My Life in Jesus. 30p. (gr. 5-6). stu. ed. 9.50 (978-0-570-00760-9(7) , 22-2874) Concordia Publishing Hse.

My Story of Jesus. 2006. (J). 16p. pap. 1.99 (978-0-7847-1715-8(X) , 04176); 32p. pap. 2.89 (978-0-7847-1281-8(6) , 22094); (Illus.). 24p. bds. 6.99 (978-0-7847-1397-6(9) , 04057) Standard Publishing.

Navpress Publishing Staff. Seguridad en Cristo. 2000. Tr. of Lessons on Assurance. (SPA.). 32p. (YA). pap. 1.50 (978-0-311-13666-7(4) , Editorial Mundo Hispano) Casa Bautista de Publicaciones.

Nederveld, Patricia L. A Father's Wish: The Story of Jesus & a Little Boy. 1998. (God Loves Me Ser.). (Illus.). 24p. (J). (ps-3). pap. 2.95 (978-1-56212-300-0(9) , 001231, Faith Alive Christian Resources) CRC Pubns.

—Follow Me! The Story of Twelve Helpers for Jesus. 1998. (God Loves Me Ser.). (Illus.). 24p. (J). (ps-3). pap. 2.95 (978-1-56212-298-0(3) , 001229, Faith Alive Christian Resources) CRC Pubns.

—Get up & Walk! The Story of Jesus & a Man Who Couldn't Walk. 1998. (God Loves Me Ser.). (Illus.). 24p. (J). (ps-3). pap. 2.95 (978-1-56212-302-4(5) , 001233, Faith Alive Christian Resources) CRC Pubns.

—I Love You, Jesus! The Story of Mary's Gift to Jesus. 1998. (God Loves Me Ser.). (Illus.). 24p. (J). (ps-3). pap. 2.95 (978-1-56212-311-6(4) , 001242, Faith Alive Christian Resources) CRC Pubns.

—A Little Lunch: The Story of Jesus & the Hungry Crowd. 1998. (God Loves Me Ser.). (Illus.). 24p. (J). (ps-3). pap. 2.95 (978-1-56212-303-1(3) , 001234, Faith Alive Christian Resources) CRC Pubns.

—A Scary Storm: The Story of Jesus & a Storm. 1998. (God Loves Me Ser.). (Illus.). 24p. (J). (ps-3). pap. 2.95 (978-1-56212-304-8(1) , 001235, Faith Alive Christian Resources) CRC Pubns.

—Thank You, Jesus! The Story of Jesus & One Thankful Man. 1998. (God Loves Me Ser.). (Illus.). 24p. (J). (ps-3). pap. 2.95 (978-1-56212-305-5(X) , 001236, Faith Alive Christian Resources) CRC Pubns.

—Who Is This Child? The Story of Jesus in the Temple. 1998. (God Loves Me Ser.). (Illus.). 24p. (J). (ps-3). pap. 2.95 (978-1-56212-297-3(5) , 001228, Faith Alive Christian Resources) CRC Pubns.

—A Wonderful Sight! The Story of Jesus & a Man Who Couldn't See. 1998. (God Loves Me Ser.). (Illus.). 24p. (J). (ps-3). pap. 2.95 (978-1-56212-306-2(8) , 001237, Faith Alive Christian Resources) CRC Pubns.

Neese, Amberly. Miracles of Jesus, Vol. 8. 2000. (Pulse Ser.). 96p. 14.99 (978-0-8307-2509-0(1) , Gospel Light) Gospel Light Pubns.

Neff, LaVonne. The Jesus Book: 40 Bible Stories. Goffe, Toni, illus. 2004. (Life of Christ for Children Ser.). 84p. (ps-k). 9.95 (978-0-8294-1373-1(1)) Loyola Pr.

Neitzel, Shirley & Anderson, David W. These Are the Friends of Jesus. Huang, Benrei, illus. 2005. 32p. (J). pap. 9.99 (978-0-8066-5119-4(9) , Augsburg Bks.) Augsburg Fortress, Pubs.

Niemann, Sibyl. The Centurion & the Songbird: Stories about the Gospels. 2003. (J). 32p. 5.00 (978-0-88489-629-6(3)); 128p. per. 6.95 (978-0-88489-628-9(5)) St. Mary's Pr.

Noble, Marty. The Life of Jesus Stained Glass Coloring Book. 2005. 16p. (J). (gr. 3). pap. 5.95 (978-0-486-44476-5(7)) Dover Pubns., Inc.

Nottingham, Sharon, illus. Sealing Love, Jr. 2002. 182p. (J). pap. 11.95 (978-0-9717734-1-7(6)) Sealing Touch End - Time Memory Fellowship.

Nyland, Richard. Jesus. 2005. 18.99 (978-1-59467-983-4(5)); per. 10.99 (978-1-59467-982-7(7)) Xulon Pr., Inc.

Oke, Janette. I Wonder... Did Jesus Have a Pet Lamb? Gauthier, Corbert, illus. 2004. 24p. 9.99 (978-0-7642-2901-5(X)) Bethany Hse. Pubs.

O'Neal, Debbie Trafton. J Is for Jesus: An Easter Alphabet & Activity Book. Bryan-Hunt, Jan, illus. 2005. 32p. (J). pap., act. bk. ed. 10.99 (978-0-8066-5123-1(7) , Augsburg Bks.) Augsburg Fortress, Pubs.

Osborne, Rick. I Want to Know about Jesus: Who Jesus Is, What He Did, & Why He Died for Me. 1998. (I Want to Know Ser.). (Illus.). 32p. (J). (gr. 2-5). 9.99 (978-0-310-22087-9(4)) Zondervan.

Padgett, Jim, illus. Jesus, God's Gift of Love. 1998. 16p. (J). (ps-3). 4.00 (978-0-687-08449-4(0)) Abingdon Pr.

Paprocki, Joseph. Jesus, Should I Follow You? Sawyer, Kieran, ed. 2003. (Developing Faith Ser.). (Illus.). 80p. (gr. 9-12). stu. ed. 6.95 (978-0-87793-557-5(2)) Ave Maria Pr.

Parker, Victoria & Dyson, Janet. Jesus on the Cross. 2003. (Bible Discoverers Ser.). (Illus.). 64p. (gr. 3-7). pap. 7.99 (978-1-84215-739-8(6) , Southwater) Anness Publishing GBR. *Dist:* National Bk. Network.

Parry, Linda. Jesus Calls His Disciples. Parry, Alan, illus. 1998. 12p. (J). pap. 2.99 (978-0-8054-1786-9(9)) B&H Publishing Grp.

—Jesus Makes Friends. Parry, Alan, illus. 1998. 12p. (J). pap. 2.99 (978-0-8054-1787-6(7)) B&H Publishing Grp.

Perez III, Librado. Thank You Jesus. l.t. ed. 2006. (Illus.). 36p. (J). 23.99 ***(978-1-59879-317-8(9))*** Lifevest Publishing, Inc.

—Thank You Jesus. Perez III, Librado, illus. l.t. ed. 2006. (Illus.). 36p. (J). per. 11.99 ***(978-1-59879-209-6(1))*** Lifevest Publishing, Inc.

Pingry, Patricia A. Bible Story Cards: The Story of Jesus. 2006. (Illus.). 10p. 7.95 (978-0-8249-1704-3(9)) Ideals Pubns.

—The Easter Story. 2006. (Illus.). 32p. pap. 3.95 (978-0-8249-5531-1(5) , Ideals Children's Bks.) Ideals Pubns.

—The Easter Story. Utt, Mary Ann, illus. 2003. 26p. (J). bds. 6.95 (978-0-8249-4231-1(0)) Ideals Pubns.

—Jesus in the Temple: Based on Luke 2:40/52. Munger, Nancy, illus. 2005. (Children of the Bible Ser.). 26p. (J). bds. 6.95 (978-0-8249-6569-3(8)) Ideals Pubns.

—The Story of Easter. Wells, Lorraine Schreiner, illus. 2002. (ENG & SPA.). 32p. (J). 3.95 (978-0-8249-4204-5(3)) Ideals Pubns.

—The Story of Loaves & Fishes. Venturi-Pickett, Stacy, illus. 2003. 26p. (J). bds. 6.95 (978-0-8249-6518-1(3)) Ideals Pubns.

Pipkin, Evelyn Ruth. The Pretty Little Red Bird. l.t. ed. 2004. 19p. (J). (gr. 1-3). 7.95 (978-0-9755789-0-2(1)) Two Seed Planters Inc.

Plante, Patty. Joy for Jesus: Friends with God, 1. 2nd ed. 2003. (Joy for Jesus Ser.: 1). Orig. Title: Joy for Jesus: Friends with God. 91p. (J). ring bd. 24.95 (978-1-889723-31-0(2)) Family Harvest Church.

—Joy for Jesus: Jesus in Me. 2003. (Joy for Jesus Ser.: 2). 78p. (J). ring bd. 24.95 (978-1-889723-40-2(1)) Family Harvest Church.

—Viviendo Como Jesus, Libro 1. Garcia de Ortiz, Lic. Rosalinda, tr. from ENG. 2003. (SPA.). 71p. (J). ring bd. 24.95 (978-1-889723-32-7(0)) Family Harvest Church.

Plekker, Robert J. Who Is Jesus Christ? & What Is Christianity? 1998. (Illus.). 284p. (Orig.). (J). (gr. 6 up). pap. 19.95 (978-0-9660565-1-8(5)) Joint Heirs Pubs.

Press, Running. The Story of Easter. 2007. 128p. (J). 4.95 (978-0-7624-2937-0(2) , Running Pr. Minature Editions) Running Pr. Bk. Pubs.

Puhalo, Lazar. Twelve Great Feast Days. Date not set. (Illus.). 45p. (J). pap. 5.00 (978-1-879038-43-1(9) , 9011) Synaxis Pr.

Pulley, Kelly, illus. Jesus & His Friends. 2007. (I Can Read!). 32p. (J). pap. 3.99 ***(978-0-310-71461-3(3))*** Zonderkidz.

—My First I Can Read! Jesus Saves the World. 2008. 32p. pap. ***(978-0-310-71553-5(9))*** Zonderkidz.

Redding, David Asbury. He Never Spoke Without a Parable: His Kingdom, Your Antagonist, It's up to You, 3 bks, 5 vols. l.t. ed. 2003. pap. 16.00 (978-0-9671701-3-8(3) , 0-9671701-3-3) Starborne Hse.

Reese, Kimberly Ingalls. Celebrate Jesus! At Christmas: Family Devotions for Advent Through Epiphany. 2000. (Illus.). 128p. (J). (gr. 1-5). 6.99 (978-0-570-07127-3(5)) Concordia Publishing Hse.

The Revolutionary Revelation on the Book of Revelation & its all about Jesus. 2005. (YA). per. (978-1-59872-168-3(2)) Instantpublisher.com.

Rhodes, Karen. Do You Know Jesus? 2005. (J). pap. 1.79 ***(978-1-59317-111-7(0))*** Warner Pr. Pubs.

Rhydderch, Gwyn, et al. Iesu'r Ffrind: 16 Sesiwn Yn Cyflwyno Bywyd Iesu Ar Gyfer Plant Cynradd Yn Seiliedig Ar Efengyl Luc. 2005. (WEL., Illus.). 63p. (978-1-85994-007-5(2)) Cyhoeddiadau'r Gair.

Rikkers, Doris. Little Jesus, Little Me. Stott, Dorothy, illus. 2000. 12p. (J). 5.99 (978-0-310-23205-6(8)) Zonderkidz.

—Little Jesus, Little Me. 2008. 14p. (J). bds. 4.99 ***(978-0-310-71651-8(9))*** Zondervan.

Risen Today. 7.50 (978-0-8054-5925-8(1)) B&H Publishing Grp.

Robinson, Hilary. E-Mail: Jesus@anytime. Lewis, Anthony, tr. Lewis, Anthony, illus. 2004. 32p. (J). 19.95 (978-0-340-85537-9(1)); pap. 8.95 (978-0-340-85538-6(X)) Hodder General Publishing Division GBR. (Hodder & Stoughton). *Dist:* Trafalgar Square Publishing.

Robinson, Timothy, illus. Good Things Jesus Did. 1999. (Missions & Me Ser.). 13p. (J). 7.99 (978-1-56309-285-5(9)) Woman's Missionary Union.

Robinson, Timothy M. Three Days Without Light. Madsen, Jim, illus. 2000. (J). 15.95 (978-1-57345-567-1(9)) Deseret Bk. Co.

Rock, Lois. Learning about Jesus. 2003. (Illus.). (J). (ps-3). 14.95 (978-0-316-60556-4(5)) Little, Brown Bks. for Young Readers.

Rock, Lois. Miracles of Jesus. 2007. (Illus.). 48p. (J). pap. 9.95 ***(978-0-7459-4946-8(0))*** Lion Hudson plc GBR. *Dist:* Independent Pubs. Group.

Rose, Drew, illus. God's Son, Jesus. 2005. (Bible Activity Bks.). 96p. (J). (ps-3). 2.99 (978-0-7814-4314-2(8) , 0781443148) Cook, David C. Publishing Co.

Rottmann, Erik. The Easter Victory: The Story of Easter: Matthew 26-28 for Children. Billin-Frye, Paige, illus. 2006. (ENG.). (J). 1.99 (978-0-7586-0869-7(1)) Concordia Publishing Hse.

—Jesus, My Good Shepherd. Miyake, Yoski, illus. 2005. (ENG.). 16p. (J). 1.99 (978-0-7586-0725-6(3)) Concordia Publishing Hse.

Sadlier Team Staff. Coming to Jesus, Catechist's Annotated Guide: Keystone Parish Edition. 1998. (Coming to Faith Program Ser.). (Illus.). 344p. (J). (gr. 2). pap. 32.76 net. (978-0-8215-4372-6(5)) Sadlier, William H. Inc.

Sanders, Nancy I. Jesus Walks on the Water. Swisher, Elizabeth, illus. 2005. (ENG.). 16p. (J). 1.99 (978-0-7586-0864-2(0)) Concordia Publishing Hse.

Sanna, Ellyn. The Miracles of Jesus. 2000. (Young Reader's Christian Library). (Illus.). 224p. (J). (gr. 3-7). pap. 1.39 (978-1-57748-723-4(0)) Barbour Publishing, Inc.

Sattgast, Linda J. I Want to Be Like Jesus. 2001. 96p. (J). pap. 7.99 (978-0-310-70102-6(3)) Zonderkidz.

Schlitt, D. Celebrate the Names of Jesus. 2004. 52p. 6.99 (978-0-8054-0825-6(8)) B&H Publishing Grp.

School Specialty Publishing. Story of Jesus. 2004. 10p. (J). 1.99 (978-0-7647-1047-6(8) , In Celebration) Schaffer, Frank Pubns.

Simon, Mary Manz. Donde Esta Jesus? Pascua de Resurreccion, 1. 1999. (Hear Me Read Bible Stories Ser.). (SPA., Illus.). 32p. (J). (ps-3). 2.75 (978-0-570-09928-4(5)) Concordia Publishing Hse.

—Jesus Is with Us. 2000. (Illus.). 96p. (J). (gr. 4-7). 6.99 (978-0-88486-269-7(0) , Arrowood Pr.) BBS Publishing Corp.

St. Clair, Barry. Jesus No Equal: A Passionate Encounter with the Son of God. Reeves, Dale & Durden, Leslie, eds. 1999. 176p. (gr. 7 up). pap. 10.99 (978-0-7847-1043-2(0) , 23319) Standard Publishing.

St. Pierre, Stephanie. Jesus, the Good Shepherd. Bolam, Emily, illus. 2003. 14p. (J). bds. 7.99 (978-0-7847-1272-6(7) , 04032) Standard Publishing.

Stanton, Sue. Child's Guide to the Stations of the Cross. Blake, Anne Catharine, illus. 2008. 32p. (J). (gr. k-4). 10.95 ***(978-0-8091-6739-5(5)*** , 6739-5) Paulist Pr.

Stayton, Claudia Grace. Day by Day the Jesus Way: What Jesus Has to Say about Life, Love, & the Way to God. 2003. 144p. per. 5.95 (978-0-9728900-0-7(9) , 888-899-3207) Good News Connections.

Stewart, Jennifer, ed. Jesus Is Born! Ebert, Len, illus. 1999. 48p. (J). (ps-2). pap. 2.49 (978-0-7847-0995-5(5) , 20065, Bean Sprouts) Standard Publishing.

Stiegemeyer, Julie. Things I See at Christmas. Mitter, Kathy, illus. 2005. (ENG.). 16p. (J). (ps-17). bds. 4.99 (978-0-7586-0809-3(8)) Concordia Publishing Hse.

Stohs, Anita Reith. Hush Little One. Kanzler, John, illus. 2006. (ENG.). 20p. (J). bds. 4.99 (978-0-7586-0861-1(6)) Concordia Publishing Hse.

—Hush, Little One: A Lullaby for God's Children. Kanzler, John, tr. Kanzler, John, illus. 2004. 32p. (J). 12.99 (978-0-570-07144-0(5)) Concordia Publishing Hse.

Stortz, Diane M. Jesus Loves You: A Read-The-Pictures Book. Trasler, Janee, illus. 2007. (J). (978-0-7847-1987-9(X)) Standard Publishing.

Story of Jesus. 2004. 16p. (J). act. bk. ed. 8.99 (978-0-570-07178-5(X)) Concordia Publishing Hse.

The Story of Jesus. 2001. (Illus.). 24p. (J). bds. 6.95 (978-0-8249-4129-1(2)) Ideals Pubns.

The Story of Jesus: La Historia de Jesus. 2002. (ENG & SPA., Illus.). 30p. (J). 3.95 (978-0-8249-5448-2(3)) Ideals Pubns.

Story of Jesus for Children. 2004. pap. 14.98 (978-0-7378-0584-0(6)) Brentwood Home Video.

Strang Communications Company Staff, ed. Ages 4-5 Activities: Spring 2002. 2002. (J). pap. 3.29 (978-1-57405-929-8(7)) CharismaLife Pubs.

—Ages 4-5 Activities: Summer 2002. 2002. (J). (ps-k). pap. 3.29 (978-1-57405-967-0(X)) CharismaLife Pubs.

Strobel, Lee. The Case for Christ for Kids. 2006. (Illus.). 96p. (J). pap. 7.99 (978-0-310-71147-6(9)) Zonderkidz.

Stuckey, Denise. Jesus, I Feel Close to You. Saroff, Phyllis, illus. 2005. 32p. (J). 10.95 (978-0-8091-6718-0(2) , 6718-2) Paulist Pr.

Student Activity Workbook for Breakthrough! the Bible for Young Catholics: Getting to Know Jesus. 2007. (J). pap. 6.95 ***(978-0-88489-978-5(0))*** St. Mary's Pr.

Tebo, Mary Elizabeth & Jablonski, Patricia E. The Very First Easter. Winek-Leliwa, Anna, illus. 2002. 32p. (J). pap. 6.95 (978-0-8198-8032-1(9) , 332-400) Pauline Bks. & Media.

Thorne, Rick. The Hidden Secrets of Jesus & Other Revelations. 2004. (Illus.). 268p. (YA). pap. 19.95 (978-0-937327-04-3(2)) Soul Pubns.

Tippett, James S. Jesus Lights the Sabbath Lamp: A Story of What Might Have Happened One Day When Jesus Was a Child. Fisher, Nell, illus. 1999. 24p. (J). (ps-3). 9.00 (978-0-687-09025-9(3)) Abingdon Pr.

True God, True Man. 2004. (Effective Dre Ser.). pap. (978-0-8294-1499-8(1)) Loyola Pr.

Turton, Karalynn Teresa. The Passion for Children: Bilingual (English & Spanish) Guide to the Passion of Christ, 1 bk. Ruiz, Jeanette, tr. Burnett, Anne, illus. 2005. (J). 3.00 (978-0-9765180-0-6(7)) Catholic World Mission.

Understanding Scripture: The Genesis Creation Story. 2004. (Our Catholic Tradition Handbooks Ser.). (978-0-8294-1044-0(9)) Loyola Pr.

Van Leeuwen, Wendy. Miracle Man Activity Book. 2007. (Illus.). 16p. (J). pap. 1.89 ***(978-1-59317-209-1(5))*** Warner Pr. Pubs.

Verbal, Pat. Topper's Very's Best Hat: A Special Gift for Jesus. 1998. (Illus.). 35p. (J). (ps-3). pap. 10.95 (978-0-921788-43-0(6)) Kindred Productions.

A Walk on the Waves. 2007. (Illus.). (J). bds. 5.95 ***(978-0-8198-8315-5(8))*** Pauline Bks. & Media.

Walker, Joni. Jesus Is with Me. Walker, Joni, illus. 2004. (ENG., Illus.). 20p. (J). bds. 4.99 (978-0-7586-0628-0(1)) Concordia Publishing Hse.

—Jesus Knows Me. Walker, Joni, illus. 2003. (ENG., Illus.). 14p. (J). (ps-k). bds. 4.99 (978-0-7586-0507-8(2)) Concordia Publishing Hse.

Warner, Anna Bartlett. Yes Jesus Loves Me. 2006. (Illus.). 36p. (J). 14.99 (978-0-7847-1512-3(2) , 04154) Standard Publishing.

Warner Press Staff. Jesus in My Heart Coloring Books Intermediate. 2005. 2.69 (978-0-87162-939-5(9)) Warner Pr. Pubs.

—Jesus Loves Me Coloring Book Pre-K. 2005. (J). pap. 2.69 (978-1-59317-017-2(3)) Warner Pr. Pubs.

Warnes, Tim, illus. Jesus Loves Me! 2006. 32p. (J). 12.95 (978-1-4169-0065-8(9)) Simon & Schuster Children's Publishing.

Warnes, Tim, illus. Jesus Loves Me. 2008. 26p. (J). bds. 7.99 ***(978-1-4169-5367-8(1)*** , Little Simon Inspirations) Simon & Schuster Children's Publishing.

Washington, Linda. Celebrate Jesus! Children's Journal: Come Meet the Most Awesome Person Ever! Kehney, Cindy & Kilgore, Jack, eds. 1999. (Celebrate Jesus! 2000 50-Day Spiritual Adventure Ser.). (Illus.). 64p. (J). 7.00 (978-1-57849-175-9(4)) Mainstay Church Resources.

Watson, Jane Werner & Golden Books Staff. The Story of Jesus. 2002. (Illus.). 24p. (J). (gr. k-k). 2.99 (978-0-307-96031-3(5) , Golden Bks.) Random Hse. Children's Bks.

Wertheim, Janie-Sue & Shapiro, Kathy. Walk with Y'shua Through the Jewish Year. Rosen, Ruth, ed. Clemons, Carol, illus. 1998. (YA). (gr. 5 up). pap. 6.00 (978-1-881022-40-4(4)) Purple Pomegranate Productions.

White, Joseph A. Miracles of Jesus: Bible 101 Series. 2001. 164p. per. 14.95 (978-0-9636278-6-5(4)) White DEI.

Who Is Jesus. 2004. pap. 5.95 (978-1-58516-138-6(1)) American Bible Society.

Wilber, Peggy M. Why Did Jesus Do That?, Level 4. Foote, Dan, tr. Foote, Dan, illus. 1999. (Rocket Readers Ser.). 32p. (J). (gr. 4 up). pap., pap. 4.99 (978-0-7814-3994-7(9) , 0781439949) Cook, David C. Publishing Co.

Wildsmith, Brian. The Easter Story. Wildsmith, Brian, illus. 2004. (Illus.). 24p. (ps-7). 18.00 (978-0-8028-5189-5(4)) Eerdmans, William B. Publishing Co.

—Jesus. Wildsmith, Brian, illus. 2004. (Illus.). 24p. (gr. 3-7). 20.00 (978-0-8028-5212-0(2)) Eerdmans, William B. Publishing Co.

Williams, Lynda Anne. This Is Why I Talk to Jesus. 2005. (J). act. bk. ed. 10.00 (978-0-9771015-0-4(9)) Let's Learn Library of Knowledge Series.

Wilson, Etta. A Child's Story of Easter. Utt, Mary Ann, illus. 2001. 32p. (J). 7.95 (978-0-8249-5365-2(7)) Ideals Pubns.

Wisconsin Evangelical Lutheran Synod Staff. Christ-Light 2 Bk. A: Student Lessons. 1998. (J). (gr. 5-6). 4.50 (978-0-8100-0635-5(9)) Northwestern Publishing Hse.

Wolcott, Carolyn M. Jesus Goes to the Marketplace: A Story of What Might Have Happened One Day When Jesus Was a Child. Fisher, Nell, illus. 1999. 32p. (J). (ps-3). 9.00 (978-0-687-09005-1(9)) Abingdon Pr.

Woolsey, Cheryl L. My Best Friend Jesus: 180 Devotions & Worship Activities for Preschoolers. 1998. (Illus.). (J). (ps). 12.99 (978-0-8280-1308-6(X)) Review & Herald Publishing Assn.

World Wide Publications Staff. Jesus Is My Friend. 1998. (Christian Growth Ser.). 26p. (J). (gr. k-5). mass mkt. 4.95 (978-0-89066-296-0(7) , 62967) World Wide Pubns.

Worship Him. 1998. (Cross Training Ser.: Vol. 7). 64p. (J). (gr. 7-9). pap., tchr. ed. 15.00 incl. VHS (978-1-57405-254-1(3)) CharismaLife Pubs.

You Are Always with Me. 1999. 24p. (J). 12.99 (978-1-55513-623-9(0)) Cook, David C. Publishing Co.

Zobel-Nolan, Allia. Amazing Life of Jesus. Cox, Steve, illus. 2005. 10p. (J). 10.99 (978-0-8254-5522-3(7)) Kregel Pubns.

Zoom Zone: Kidz Pack. 2004. (J). (gr. 2-6). 9.99 (978-0-8066-4984-9(4)); (ps-1). 9.99 (978-0-8066-4983-2(6)) Augsburg Fortress, Pubs.

JESUS CHRIST—ART

see also Bible—Pictorial Works; Christian Art and Symbolism

Daily, Eileen M. Beyond the Written Word: Exploring Faith Through Christian Art. 2005. (Illus.). 32p. (YA). pap. 85.00 (978-0-88489-849-8(0)) St. Mary's Pr.

Morris, Neil. The Life of Jesus. 2003. (Art Revelations Ser.). (Illus.). 32p. (J). (gr. 6-9). 18.95 (978-1-59270-002-8(0)) Enchanted Lion Bks., LLC.

Newton, Richard. The Life of Jesus Christ for the Young. 2004. reprint ed. pap. 22.95 (978-1-4191-6962-5(9)); pap. 1.99 (978-1-4192-6962-2(3)) Kessinger Publishing, LLC.

Olsen, Greg. Beautiful Savior. 2004. (Illus.). (J). (978-1-59156-553-6(7)) Covenant Communications.

JESUS CHRIST—BIOGRAPHY

see also Jesus Christ—Nativity

Anonymous. Good Shepherd A Life of Christ for Child. 2006. pap. 87.99 ***(978-1-4280-3918-6(X))*** IndyPublish.com.

Babcock, Bruce. The Life of Jesus. Babcock, Bruce, illus. unabr. ed. 1998. (Illus.). 15p. (J). (ps-6). pap. 5.95 (978-1-892161-01-7(X)) Babcock Publishing Co.

Beers, Gilbert. Tell Me the Story of Jesus. 2001. (Illus.). 128p. (J). (gr. k-3). 14.99 (978-0-8423-3868-4(3)) Tyndale Hse. Pubs.

Belec, Glynis. Jesus Washes Peter's Feet. 2001. (gr. k-3). lib. bdg. 9.85 (978-0-613-71025-1(8)) Tandem Library Bks.

Blanc-Rerat, Martine, illus. All about Jesus: The Life & Teachings of Jesus in the Bible's Own Words. 2004. 240p. (gr. 4-7). 15.95 (978-0-8294-1506-3(8)) Loyola Pr.

Brennan, Gerald T. The Man Who Never Died. 2005. (Illus.). viii, 87p. (J). pap. 11.95 (978-1-933184-09-8(4)) Sophia Institute Pr.

Brighter Vision Publishing Staff. Life of Jesus. pap. 2.25 (978-1-55254-025-1(1)) Brighter Vision Pubns.

Caldwell, Lise. The Life of Christ: Classic Bible Stories. 1998. (Happy Day Bks.). (Illus.). 24p. (J). (ps-2). pap. 2.49 (978-0-7847-0828-6(2) , 04258, Bean Sprouts) Standard Publishing.

Colvin, Adele B. Story of Jesus as Told in the Donkey's Tales. Carmichael, Peyton H., illus. 1998. 32p. (J). (ps-3). pap. 9.95 (978-1-57587-073-1(8)) Crane Hill Pubs.

Conn. Jesus Christ for Youth, 2 vols. 2006. (Illus.). 112p. pap., stu. ed. 6.00 (978-0-687-33286-1(9)); 128p. pap. 10.00 (978-0-687-33276-2(1)) Abingdon Pr.

Connolly, Sean. New Testament Miracles. 2003. (Art Revelations Ser.). (Illus.). 32p. (J). (gr. 6-9). 18.95 (978-1-59270-012-7(8)) Enchanted Lion Bks., LLC.

Daily, Eileen M. Beyond the Written Word: Exploring Faith Through Christian Art. 2005. (Illus.). 32p. (YA). pap. 85.00 (978-0-88489-849-8(0)) St. Mary's Pr.

Dalmatian Press Staff. The Life of Jesus: Big Best Book to Color. 2004. (Big Best Book to Color Ser.). (Illus.). 80p. (J). pap. 2.99 (978-1-4037-0758-1(8) , Spirit Pr.) Dalmatian Pr.

Daybell, Chad G. Through the Eyes of John. Murray, Rhett E., illus. 2004. 29p. (J). 19.95 (978-1-932898-16-3(6) , 98166) Spring Creek Bk. Co.

de Sturtz, Marie Ester. Manos a la Obra: La vida de Jesus - español (Hands to Work: the Life of Jesus - Spanish) 2006. 6.99 (***978-0-7586-1241-0(9)***) Concordia Publishing Hse.

Dean, Bessie. Let's Learn about Jesus: The Life of Christ Retold for Children. 1999. (Children's Inspirational Coloring Bks.). (Illus.). 72p. (J). (ps-6). reprint ed. pap. 6.98 (978-0-88290-669-0(0)) Horizon Pubs. & Distributors, Inc.

Dearmer, Mabel. A Child's Life of Christ. 2006. pap. 30.95 (***978-1-4286-0075-1(2)***) Kessinger Publishing, LLC.

Dumont, C. & Lacoursiere, Suzanne. Jesus: A Story of Love. Merola, Caroline, tr. from FRE. Merola, Caroline, illus. 2003. 32p. (J). mass mkt. 5.95 (978-0-8198-3977-0(9) , 332-153) Pauline Bks. & Media.

Evans, Peggy & Milton, Ralph. The Birth & Childhood Stories of Jesus: With Links to the Whole Church Family. 2000. (Family Story Bible Curriculum Modules Ser.). (Illus.). 32p. (J). 64.95 incl. VHS (978-1-55145-390-3(8)) Wood Lake Bks., Inc. CAN. *Dist:* Words Distributing Co.

Ferguson, Sinclair B. Big Book of Questions & Answers about Jesus: A Family Guide to Jesus' Life & Ministry. 2000. (Illus.). 96p. (J). (ps-3). pap. (978-1-85792-559-3(9) , Christian Focus) Christian Focus Pubns.

Foster, Charles. Story of the Gospel. 2004. reprint ed. pap. 33.95 (978-1-4191-1372-7(0)) Kessinger Publishing, LLC.

Haidle, Helen. Journey to the Cross. Haidle, David, illus. 2001. 256p. (J). (gr. 1-7). 14.99 (978-0-310-70023-4(X)) Zondervan.

Ham, Ken. The Mission of Jesus: Good News for Everyone. 2000. (Awesome Adventure Bible Stories Ser.). (Illus.). 33p. (J). (gr. k-3). pap. 5.99 (978-0-89051-326-2(0)) Master Bks.

Harik, Ramsay M. Jesus of Nazareth: Teacher & Prophet. 2001. (Book Report Biographies Ser.). (Illus.). 100p. (YA). (gr. 6-8). pap. 6.95 (978-0-531-15552-3(8) , Watts, Franklin) Scholastic Library Publishing.

Hemenway, Priya. The Little Book of Jesus. 2004. (Illus.). 152p. (978-0-7607-5447-4(0)) Barnes & Noble, Inc.

Heyer, Carol, illus. The First Easter. 2003. 32p. (J). 14.95 (978-0-8249-5463-5(7)) Ideals Pubns.

Hook, Richard & Hook, Frances, illus. Jesus, the Friend of Children. 6th ed. 2006. 112p. (J). 14.99 (978-0-7814-4390-6(3)) Cook, David C. Publishing Co.

Humble-Jackson, Sally. The Miracle Maker: The Greatest Story Ever Told. (Illus.). 48p. (J). pap. (978-0-340-74958-6(X) , Hodder & Stoughton) Hodder General Publishing Division.

Hunt, Marigold. A Life of Our Lord for Children. 2003. (Illus.). v, 189p. (J). 14.95 (978-1-928832-64-5(4)) Sophia Institute Pr.

James, Steven. Never the Same: Stories of Those Who Encountered Jesus. 2005. (Invert Ser.). 144p. (J). pap. 9.99 (978-0-310-25951-0(7)) Zondervan.

Jeffs, Stephanie. People Jesus Met. Tulip, Jenny, illus. 2004. (My First Find Out about Book Ser.). 24p. (ps up). pap. 3.95 (978-0-8294-1731-9(1)) Loyola Pr.

—Things Jesus Did. Tulip, Jenny, illus. 2004. 24p. (ps up). pap. 3.95 (978-0-8294-1734-0(6)) Loyola Pr.

Jeffs, Stephanie, et al. Bywyd Iesu. 2005. (WEL., Illus.). 92p. (978-1-85994-496-7(5)) Cyhoeddiadau'r Gair.

Jesus Christ - the Passion: And the Gospels of Matthew, Mark, Luke & John. 2004. mass mkt. 14.95 net. (978-0-9749755-4-2(0)) UniversityPress.Info.

Joslin, Mary. On That Easter Morning. Cann, Helen, illus. 2006. 0032p. (J). 16.00 (978-1-56148-517-8(9)) Good Bks.

Kunkel, Jeff. Jesus, This Is Your Life: Stories & Pictures by Kids. 2001. (Illus.). 48p. (gr. k-7). 12.99 (978-0-8066-4165-2(7) , Augsburg Bks.) Augsburg Fortress, Pubs.

Kuyper, Vicki J. Jesus Speaks to Teens: Not Your Ordinary Meditations on the Word of Jesus. 2004. (Jesus Speaks Ser.). (Illus.). 192p. (J). 14.99 (978-0-7642-2866-7(8)) Bethany Hse. Pubs.

Lane, Leena. Stories of Jesus. Bishop, Roma, illus. 2003. 32p. 8.00 (978-0-687-06537-0(2)) Abingdon Pr.

Laubach, Frank. The Story of Jesus: Part 1. Woodworth, Ralph, ed. Aldredge, Terry Beckham, illus. 2005. per. (978-0-9749168-6-6(2)) FEA Ministries.

—The Story of Jesus: Part 2. Woodworth, Ralph, ed. Aldredge, Terry Beckham, illus. 2005. per. (978-0-9749168-8-0(9)) FEA Ministries.

The Life of Christ. 1998. (Explore the Bible Ser.). (Illus.). (J). (gr. 3-8). 360p. stu. ed. 21.95 (978-1-892114-52-5(6)); 131p. pap., stu. ed., wbk. ed. 12.95 (978-1-892114-51-8(8)) Sky Media.

Lottridge, Celia B. Stories from the Life of Jesus. Wolfsgruber, Linda, tr. Wolfsgruber, Linda, illus. 2004. 128p. (J). 24.95 (978-0-88899-497-4(4)) Groundwood Bks. CAN. *Dist:* Perseus Distribution.

Mears, Henrietta C. What Jesus Is All About: Meet the Man Whose Life - & Death - Changed the Course of History. 2004. 140p. pap. 9.99 (978-0-8307-3332-3(9) , Gospel Light) Gospel Light Pubns.

Minett, Gail Ann. Jesus & His Friends. Oneill, Rachel, illus. 2002. 12p. (J). 10.99 (978-0-8254-7246-6(6)) Kregel Pubns.

Mitchell, Stephen. The Truth about Jesus: What He Really Said & Did. 2002. 176p. (J). (gr. 7 up). 15.95 (978-0-06-623836-4(6)) HarperCollins Pubs.

Moore, Christopher. Lamb. 2003. (gr. 7-12). lib. bdg. 23.40 (978-0-613-70985-9(3)) Tandem Library Bks.

Moore, Eva. Read & Learn: The Life of Jesus. 2007. 96p. (J). (ps-3). pap. 9.99 (***978-0-545-01162-4(0)***) Scholastic, Inc.

Morris, Neil. The Life of Jesus. 2003. (Art Revelations Ser.). (Illus.). 32p. (J). (gr. 6-9). 18.95 (978-1-59270-002-8(0)) Enchanted Lion Bks., LLC.

National Gallery of Art Staff. Jesus of Nazareth: The National Gallery of Art, Washington. (Illus.). 40p. (J). (gr. 1 up). 24.99 (978-0-7112-0871-1(9)) Lincoln, Frances Ltd. GBR. *Dist:* Antique Collectors' Club.

New Leaf Press Staff. Who is Jesus? Son of God, Son of Man. 2000. (Awsome Adventure Bible Stories Ser.). (Illus.). 40p. (J). (gr. 2-7). pap. 5.99 (978-0-89051-328-6(7)) Master Bks.

Newton, Richard. The Life of Jesus Christ for the Young. 2004. reprint ed. pap. 22.95 (978-1-4191-6962-5(9)); pap. 1.99 (978-1-4192-6962-2(3)) Kessinger Publishing, LLC.

Pappas, Barbara. God's Bubbly, Gurgly, Overwhelming, Overflowing Love. Boutzarelos, Irene, illus. 2000. 88p. (J). (gr. 1-7). 15.95 (978-0-9623721-6-2(1)) Amnos Pubns.

Paris, Pilar, et al. Jesus Grows Up. 2003. (Illus.). 64p. (978-2-89088-895-1(9)) Novalis Publishing.

Parker, Victoria. Jesus in Galilee: And Other New Testament Stories. 2000. (Discovering the Bible Ser.). (Illus.). 64p. (gr. 3-7). 12.95 (978-0-7548-0477-2(1) , Lorenz Bks.) Anness Publishing GBR. *Dist:* National Bk. Network.

Parry, Linda. Jesus Calls His Disciples. Parry, Alan, illus. 1998. 12p. (J). pap. 2.99 (978-0-8054-1786-9(9)) B&H Publishing Grp.

—Jesus Makes Friends. Parry, Alan, illus. 1998. 12p. (J). pap. 2.99 (978-0-8054-1787-6(7)) B&H Publishing Grp.

Parry, Linda & Parry, Alan. The Greatest Story Ever Told: A Pop-up Activity Book. 2004. 8p. act. bk. ed. 10.95 (978-0-8294-1701-2(X)) Loyola Pr.

Paterson, Katherine. Life of Jesus for Children. Roca, Francois, illus. 2008. (J). (***978-0-545-01173-0(6)***); 48p. pap. 17.99 (***978-0-545-01172-3(8)***) Scholastic, Inc. (Levine, Arthur A. Bks.).

Pelizzoli, Francesca, illus. Miracle Maker: A Life of Jesus, Retold & Remembered. 1998. 48p. (J). 19.99 (978-0-7459-3629-1(6) , Lion) Lion Hudson plc GBR. *Dist:* Independent Pubs. Group.

Pfeifer, Alice Ann. Jesus & the Gospels, 6 booklets. 1998. (Illus.). (YA). (gr. 9-13). pap., stu. ed. 7.45 (978-0-89837-157-4(0)) Pflaum Publishing Group.

Pingry, Patricia. Story of Jesus. 2006. (Illus.). 32p. (J). pap. 3.95 (978-0-8249-5545-8(5)) Ideals Pubns.

Rock, Lois. A Little Life of Jesus. 2004. (Illus.). 352p. (J). pap. 8.99 (978-0-7459-4878-2(2)) Lion Hudson plc GBR. *Dist:* Trafalgar Square Publishing.

—The Time of Jesus: Crafts that Recreate Everyday Life. 2003. (Illus.). 64p. (J). pap. 19.99 (978-0-7459-3881-3(7) , Lion) Lion Hudson plc GBR. *Dist:* Independent Pubs. Group.

—Who Is Jesus? 2007. Orig. Title: Tell Me about Jesus. (Illus.). 21p. (J). 12.95 (978-0-8198-8313-1(1)) Pauline Bks. & Media.

Skevington, Andrea. The Story of Jesus. 2008. (Illus.). 128p. (J). 16.95 (***978-0-7459-4982-6(7)***) Lion Hudson plc GBR. *Dist:* Independent Pubs. Group.

Smith, Allen Elwyn. Men Called Him Master. 2007. 95.99 (***978-1-4280-5222-2(4)***); pap. 89.99 (***978-1-4280-5239-0(9)***) IndyPublish.com.

St. John, P. Historias Que Jesus Conto (Stories That Jesus Told) (SPA.). 56p. (J). 9.99 (978-1-56063-589-5(4) , 498751) Editorial Unilit.

Standard Publishing Staff. Jesus & His Friends. Caldwell, Lise, ed. McCallum, Jodie, illus. 1998. (Happy Day Bks.). 24p. (J). (ps-2). 2.49 (978-0-7847-0830-9(4) , 04260, Bean Sprouts) Standard Publishing.

Stiegemeyer, Julie. Bright Easter Day. Spellman, Susan, illus. 2005. (ENG.). 32p. (J). 9.99 (978-0-7586-0818-5(7)) Concordia Publishing Hse.

Tolmasoff, Dale. This Is No Fairy Tale. Gauthier, Corbert, illus. 2005. 40p. (J). (ps-3). pap. 15.99 (978-1-58134-644-2(1) , Crossway Bibles) Crossway Bks.

Watson, Jane Werner. The Story of Jesus. Smath, Jerry, illus. 2007. 24p. (J). (gr. k-k). 2.99 (978-0-375-83941-2(0) , Golden Inspirational) Random Hse. Children's Bks.

White, Ellen G. Story of Jesus. 2003. (Review Kids Ser.). (Illus.). 142p. (J). 19.99 (978-0-8280-1765-7(4) , 196-010) Review & Herald Publishing Assn.

Wilder, John Watson. His Name Is Jesus. 2005. pap. 19.95 (978-1-4179-9157-0(7)) Kessinger Publishing, LLC.

Wilger, Jennifer R., ed. Jesus Appears to His Followers. 2004. (Bible Big Bks.). (Illus.). 8p. (ps). pap. 15.99 (978-1-55945-430-8(X) , Flagship Church Resources) Group Publishing, Inc.

Zoom Zone Passport: Learner Resource. 2004. (J). (gr. 2-6). 2.99 (978-0-8066-4980-1(1)) Augsburg Fortress, Pubs.

JESUS CHRIST—BIRTH

see Jesus Christ—Nativity

JESUS CHRIST—FICTION

Adams, Michelle Medlock. Little Colt's Palm Sunday. Parmenter, Wayne, illus. 2005. 28p. (J). 14.95 (978-0-8249-5503-8(X)) Ideals Pubns.

—Memories of the Manger. Ettlinger, Doris, illus. 2005. (J). (ps-4). 32p. 16.95 (978-0-8249-5476-5(9)); (978-0-8249-5484-0(X) , Ideals Pr.) Ideals Pubns.

—The Sparrow's Easter Song. Eldridge, Marion, illus. 2003. 32p. (J). 14.95 (978-0-8249-5470-3(X)) Ideals Pubns.

Alborghetti, Marci. The Miracle of the Myrrh. Blondon, Herve, illus. 2003. (J). 16.95 (978-0-87946-249-9(3) , 708) ACTA Pubns.

—The Miracle of the Myrrh. Blondon, Herve, illus. 2000. 40p. (J). (ps-3). 16.95 (978-1-890817-16-9(3)) Winslow Pr.

Alexander, Florence & Alexander, Stanley. Jesus Child Is Born: Dare to Be Great. l.t. ed. 2003. (Illus.). 32p. (YA). 7.99 net. (978-0-915960-85-9(0)) Ebon Research Systems Publishing, LLC.

Amery, Heather. Christmas Story. rev. ed. 2006. 16p. (J). pap. 4.99 (978-0-7945-1286-6(0) , Usborne) EDC Publishing.

—Story of Baby Jesus Board Bk. rev. ed. 2006. 10p. (J). bds. 7.99 (978-0-7945-1187-6(2) , Usborne) EDC Publishing.

—Story of Jesus. 2005. (Illus.). 100p. (J). 14.99 incl. audio compact disk (978-0-7945-0831-9(6) , Usborne) EDC Publishing.

Aoki, Hisako. Santa's Favorite Story: Santa Tells the Story of the First Christmas. Gantschev, Ivan, illus. 2007. 28p. (J). (ps-3). 9.99 (***978-1-4169-5029-5(X)***) Simon & Schuster Children's Publishing.

Arroyo, Madeline. What Matthias Found. Vavak, S. Dean, illus. 2005. 32p. (YA). (ps-7). 16.95 (978-0-9740061-1-6(4)) Stairway Pubns.

Arruda, Suzanne M. A Stocking for Jesus. Ogden, Betina, illus. 2005. (J). pap. 7.95 (978-0-8198-7076-6(5) , 332-372) Pauline Bks. & Media.

Ash, Jo Ann Clark. Yule, the Great Christmas Bear. 2000. (Illus.). 28p. (J). (ps-5). pap. 8.00 (978-0-9715835-0-4(1)) Clark, Jo Ann.

Auer, Chris. The Littlest Magi: A Christmas Tale. Eagle, Bruce, illus. 2004. 32p. (J). 15.99 (978-0-310-70663-2(7)) Zonderkidz.

—Molly & the Good Shepherd. Wummer, Amy, illus. 2005. 40p. (J). 12.99 (978-0-310-70826-1(5)) Zonderkidz.

Ayres, Honor, illus. Story of Jesus Boxed Set. 2006. 10p. bds. 14.99 (978-0-7847-1977-0(2)) Standard Publishing.

Bertola, Ann Marie, et al, contrib. by. Four in the Afternoon. 2003. 118p. pap. 11.99 (978-0-9743661-0-4(2)) Circle Pr.

The Best Thing about Christmas. 2006. 16p. (J). pap. 1.99 (978-0-7847-1546-8(7) , 04362) Standard Publishing.

The Best Thing about Easter. 2006. 16p. (J). pap. 1.99 (978-0-7847-1724-0(9) , 04185) Standard Publishing.

Black, Chuck. Kingdom's Reign, 4 bks. Black, Andrea & Black, Brittney, eds. Johnson, Marcella, illus. 2004. 160p. (YA). per. 9.95 (978-0-9679240-3-8(0)) Perfect Praise Publishing.

Bolme, Edward Sarah. Baby Bible Board Books Collection No. 1: Stories of Jesus, 4 vols. Gillette, Tim, illus. l.t. ed. 2003. 20p. (J). bds. 23.99 (978-0-9725546-4-0(5)) CREST Pubns.

—Jesus Feeds the People. Gillette, Tim, illus. l.t. ed. 2003. 20p. (J). bds. 6.99 (978-0-9725546-0-2(2)) CREST Pubns.

—Jesus Heals a Little Girl. Gillette, Tim, illus. l.t. ed. 2003. 20p. (J). bds. 6.99 (978-0-9725546-1-9(0)) CREST Pubns.

—Jesus Helps a Blind Man. Gillette, Tim, illus. l.t. ed. 2003. 20p. (J). bds. 6.99 (978-0-9725546-2-6(9)) CREST Pubns.

—Jesus Stops a Storm. Gillette, Tim, illus. l.t. ed. 2003. 20p. (J). bds. 6.99 (978-0-9725546-3-3(7)) CREST Pubns.

Bond, Katherine Grace. Sleepy-Time Dance. 2002. 12p. 5.99 (978-0-310-70252-8(6)) Zondervan.

Bowman, Crystal. J Is for Jesus: The Sweetest Story Ever Told. Gévry, Claudine, illus. 2005. 20p. (J). (ps). 6.99 (978-0-310-70891-9(5)) Zonderkidz.

—A Star for Jesus. Gévry, Claudine, illus. 2006. 14p. (J). 6.99 (978-0-310-71216-9(5)) Zonderkidz.

Brantley, Steven & Brantley, Judi. The Legend of Snowflake, the Messenger Deer. McDaniel-Clark, Carol, illus. l.t. ed. 2002. 40p. (J). 16.95 (978-1-892570-04-8(1)) Spring Hse. Bks.

Brindle, Susan A., et al. The Little Caterpillar That Finds Jesus (La Oruguita que Encuentra a Jesus) A Parable of the Eucharist (Una Parabola Acerca de la Eucaristia) Emmanuelli Klosterman, Carmen A., tr. Brindle, Susan A. et al, illus. 1999. (Seven Sacraments Ser.). (ENG & SPA.). 72p. (gr. k-10). pap. 9.95 (978-1-889733-08-1(3) , 01011) Precious Life Bks., Inc.

Brown, Margaret Wise. A Child Is Born: Picture Book. Cooper, Floyd, illus. 2000. 32p. (ps-ps). 16.99 (978-0-7868-0673-7(7)) Hyperion Bks. for Children.

Brown, Rachel W. N. Small Camel Follows the Star. Ferri, Giuliano, illus. 2007. 32p. (J). (gr. k-3). 16.95 (***978-0-8075-7453-9(8)***) Whitman, Albert & Co.

Butler, M. Christina. A Star So Bright: A Christmas Tale. Pedler, Caroline, illus. 2006. 21p. (J). (ps-2). 14.95 (978-1-56148-536-9(5)) Good Bks.

Carlson, Melody, et al. Benjamin's Box: A Resurrection Story. Stockman, Jack, illus. 2000. 40p. (J). (gr. k-5). 10.99 (978-0-310-70044-9(2)) Zonderkidz.

Chapman, Mary Beth & Chapman, Steven Curtis. Shaoey & Dot: A Christmas Miracle. Chapman, Jim, illus. 2005. 32p. (J). (ps-7). pap. 16.99 (978-1-4003-0691-6(4)) Nelson, Thomas Inc.

Chesterfield, Sadie. The Nativity Story: Children's Movie Storybook. 2006. 48p. (J). pap. 8.99 (978-0-06-128522-6(6) , Harper Entertainment) HarperCollins Pubs.

The Christmas Story. 2005. (Illus.). 32p. (J). 3.95 (978-0-8249-5512-0(9)) Ideals Pubns.

Clements, Andrew. Bright Christmas: An Angel Remembers. Kiesler, Kate A., illus. 2000. 32p. (J). (gr. k-3). 6.95 (978-0-618-05153-3(8) , Clarion Bks.) Houghton Mifflin Co. Trade & Reference Div.

—Bright Christmas: An Angel Remembers. 2000. (gr. k-3). lib. bdg. 14.10 (978-0-613-31024-6(1)) Tandem Library Bks.

Cotten, Cynthia S. This Is the Stable. Bettoli, Delana, illus. rev. ed. 2006. 32p. (J). (ps-3). 16.95 (978-0-8050-7556-4(9) , Holt, Henry & Co. Bks. For Young Readers) Holt, Henry & Co.

The Crippled Lamb. 2004. (Max Lucado Ser.). 32p. 19.99 incl. DVD (978-1-4003-0181-2(5)) Nelson, Thomas Inc.

Crisp, Marty. The Most Precious Gift. Cooper, Floyd, illus. 2006. 32p. (J). (gr. k). 16.99 (978-0-399-24296-0(1) , Philomel) Penguin Group (USA) Inc.

Dacey, Richard. Spinner McClock & the Christmas Visit. Gillett, Hallie, illus. 2004. 32p. (J). 13.95 (978-1-929039-24-1(7)) Ambassador Bks., Inc.

Dalmatian Press Staff. The Baby Jesus Pop-up Book. 2005. (Illus.). 9p. (J). 10.99 (978-1-4037-1504-3(1)) Dalmatian Pr.

—The Newborn King. (Illus.). (J). (ps-1). 2004. 14p. bds. 5.99 (978-1-57759-837-4(7)); 2001. 13p. bds. 7.99 (978-1-4037-1581-4(5)) Dalmatian Pr.

Daniewicz, Mark. When Jesus Was a Kid Like Me. 2005. 32p. (J). lib. bdg. 19.95 (978-1-59298-106-9(2)) Beaver's Pond Pr., Inc.

Davidson, Alice Joyce. The J Is for Jesus: The Candy Cane Story. Anderson, Nancy Munger, illus. 1998. (Christmas Board Bks.). 14p. (J). (ps). bds. 3.99 (978-0-310-97553-3(0)) Zonderkidz.

—My Day with Jesus. Clar, David Austin, illus. 2005. (Easter Board Bks.). 16p. (J). bds. 3.99 (978-0-310-70843-8(5)) Zonderkidz.

Davis, Holly & Tada, Eareckson J. My Birthday, Jesus' Birthday. Anderson, Nancy Munger, illus. 1998. (J). 5.99 (978-0-310-97420-8(8)) Zonderkidz.

DeBoer, Jesslyn. Countdown to Christmas. 2006. 14p. (J). 3.99 (978-0-310-70845-2(1)) Zondervan.

—Welcome, Baby Jesus. 2006. (Christmas Minis Ser.). 14p. (J). (gr. 4). 3.99 (978-0-310-70846-9(X)) Zondervan.

Delong, Nancy. Happy Birthday Jesus: The Very First Ho. 2005. 115p. pap. 16.95 (978-1-4137-7599-0(3)) PublishAmerica, Inc.

Edwards, Carol. Jacy Faces Evil: Jacy's Search for Jesus Book III. Frey, Daniel J., illus. 2008. 32p. (J). 15.95 (***978-0-9755314-3-3(3)***) Majestic Publishing, LLC.

Edwards, Carol. Jacy's Search for Jesus, Frey, Daniel J., illus. 2005. 32p. (J). 15.95 (978-0-9755314-0-2(9)) Majestic Publishing, LLC.

Elkins, Stephen. I've Just Seen Jesus: A Very Special Story for Children. Colton, Ellie, illus. 2003. (Dove Award Signature Ser.). 32p. (J). 14.99 incl. audio compact disk (978-0-8054-2665-6(5)) B&H Publishing Grp.

Falk, Karen. Tacianna & the Endless Ball of String. 2006. 83p. pap. 14.95 (978-1-4241-3287-4(8)) PublishAmerica, Inc.

Felton, Jerilyn E. The Master's Companion: A Christian Midrash. 2007. (YA). (***978-0-88489-936-5(5)***) St. Mary's Pr.

Fine, Edith Hope. Cricket at the Manger. Pels, Winslow, illus. 2005. 32p. (J). 15.95 (978-1-56397-993-4(4)) Boyds Mills Pr.

Fletcher, Susan. Alphabet of Dreams. 2008. 432p. (YA). mass mkt. 6.99 (***978-0-689-85152-0(9)*** , Simon Pulse) Simon & Schuster Children's Publishing.

Flinn, Lias. Unwrapping the Christmas Creche. 18.00 (978-0-687-05441-1(9)) Abingdon Pr.

Flinn, Lisa. Good News Travels Fast: An Easter Story. 2003. (gr. k-3). lib. bdg. 13.00 (978-0-613-73198-0(0)) Tandem Library Bks.

—Unwrapping the Christmas Creche. 2005. 32p. 15.00 (978-0-687-49783-6(3)) Abingdon Pr.

Flinn, Lisa & Younger, Barbara. The Christmas Garland. Corvino, Lucy, tr. Corvino, Lucy, illus. 2003. 32p. (J). 14.95 (978-0-8249-5460-4(2) , Ideals Children's Bks.) Ideals Pubns.

Fogle, Robin. The Legend of the Candy Cane. 2006. (J). pap. 1.79 (***978-1-59317-158-2(7)***) Warner Pr. Pubs.

Foreman, Michael. Cat in the Manger. rev. ed. 2001. (Illus.). 32p. (J). (ps-3). 17.95 (978-0-8050-6677-7(2) , Holt, Henry & Co. Bks. For Young Readers) Holt, Henry & Co.

Forlini, Victoria, ed. The Birth of Jesus. Mada Design Staff, illus. 2005. 22p. (J). (ps-ps). 9.99 (978-0-696-22827-8(0)) Meredith Bks.

Frank, Penny. Jesus Gives the People Food. 1999. (Illus.). 24p. (J). pap. 2.99 (978-0-7459-4118-9(4) , Lion) Lion Hudson plc GBR. *Dist:* Independent Pubs. Group.

J
K
L

—Jesus' Special Friends. 1999. (Illus.). 24p. (J). pap. 2.99 (978-0-7459-4116-5(8) , Lion) Lion Hudson plc GBR. *Dist:* Independent Pubs. Group.

Freed, Shirley Ann & Moon, Louise. Let the Children Come. Morelan, Bill, ed. Butler, Steven, illus. l.t. ed. 2002. 16p. (J). (gr. 6). pap. 3.99 (978-1-58938-028-8(2)) Concerned Communications.

Freeman, Emily. God Bless Your Way: A Christmas Journey. Burr, Dan, illus. 2007. 32p. (J). (ps-3). 19.95 incl. audio compact disk (*978-1-59038-806-8(2)) Deseret Bk. Co.

Gantschev, Ivan. The Rabbit & the Bear: A Christmas Tale. Gantschev, Ivan, illus. 2007. (Illus.). 32p. (J). (ps). 16.95 (*978-0-7358-2145-3(3)) North-South Bks., Inc.

Ginolfi, Art. The Tiny Star. 2005. 32p. (J). pap. 3.99 (978-1-4003-0683-1(3)) Nelson, Thomas Inc.

Grant, Cindy M. Itty-Bitty Jesus Is Born Christmas Storybook. 2005. (J). pap. 1.29 (978-1-59317-117-9(X)) Warner Pr. Pubs.

Gregory, Jeannette T. Letters to Jesus. 2002. per. 7.99 (978-0-9748056-9-6(6)) Chosen Word Publishing.

Hallinan, P. K. I Know Jesus Loves Me. Hallinan, P. K., illus. 2007. (Illus.). 28p. (J). (ps-3). 8.99 (*978-0-8249-5553-3(6) , Ideals Children's Bks.) Ideals Pubns.

Harrast, Tracy. Oh Holy Night. Corke, Estelle, illus. 2006. 12p. (J). 9.99 (978-0-7586-1129-1(3)) Concordia Publishing Hse.

Hartman, Bob. Granny Mae's Christmas Play. Cravath, Lynne W., illus. 2004. 40p. (gr. k-5). 16.99 (978-0-8066-4063-1(4) , Augsburg Bks.) Augsburg Fortress, Pubs.

—Who Frightened the Fishermen. (Illus.). 48p. pap. 6.99 (978-0-7459-4987-1(8)) Lion Hudson plc GBR. *Dist:* Trafalgar Square Publishing.

Hawse, Alberta. Encounter Christ Through the Dramatic Story of Vinegar Boy. 2002. (Wholesome Adventure & Positive Influence for Today's Youth Ser.). 224p. (YA). pap. 9.99 (978-0-8024-6588-7(9)) Moody Pubs.

Herman, John. One Winter's Night. Dillon, Leo & Dillon, Diane, illus. 2005. 32p. (J). pap. 5.99 (978-0-14-240458-4(6) , Puffin) Penguin Group (USA) Inc.

Heyer, Carol. Humphrey's First Christmas. 2007. (Illus.). 32p. (J). (ps-3). 14.99 (*978-0-8249-5559-5(5) , Ideals Children's Bks.) Ideals Pubns.

Hill, Karen. The Something Wonderful: A Christmas Story. Reagan, Susan, illus. 2005. 36p. (J). (ps-3). pap. 15.99 (978-1-58134-732-6(4) , Crossway Bibles) Crossway Bks.

Hillenbrand, Will. Asleep in the Stable. (Illus.). 32p. (J). (gr. k-3). tchr. ed. 16.95 (978-0-8234-1824-4(3)) Holiday Hse., Inc.

Hillenbrand, Will. Cock-a-Doodle Christmas! Hillenbrand, Will, illus. 2007. (Illus.). 32p. (J). (ps-2). 16.99 (*978-0-7614-5354-3(7)) Cavendish, Marshall Corp.

Hoffman, Mary. Three Wise Women. Russell, Lynne, illus. 2005. 32p. (J). pap. 7.95 (978-1-84507-447-0(5)) Lincoln, Frances Ltd. GBR. *Dist:* Perseus Distribution.

Holcomb, Nan. Leah's Night of Wonder. Yoder, Dot, illus. l.t. ed. 1998. 32p. (J). (ps-3). lib. bdg. 9.95 (978-0-944727-35-5(2)) Jason & Nordic Pubs.

Hood, Karen Jean Matsko. Jesus Loves the Little Children A Daily Journal Book. 2005. (J). 19.95 (978-1-59210-139-9(9)) Whispering Pine Pr., Inc.

Hooks, William H. The Legend of the Christmas Rose. 1999. (Illus.). 32p. (J). (gr. k-4). 14.95 (978-0-06-027102-2(7)) ; 14.89 (978-0-06-027103-9(5)) HarperCollins Pubs.

Horner, Susan. The Mission: An Angel's Most Important Assignment. Allen, Joe, illus. 2006. pap. 10.99 (978-1-59317-148-3(X)) Warner Pr. Pubs.

Howie, Vicki. The Easter Swallows. Grudina, Paola Bertolini, illus. 2007. 32p. (J). 10.95 (978-0-8198-2360-1(0)) Pauline Bks. & Media.

Hulme, Joy N. Stable in Bethlehem: A Christmas Counting Book. Andreasen, Dan, illus. 2007. 24p. (J). (ps-k). 9.95 (*978-1-4027-4121-0(9)) Sterling Publishing Co., Inc.

Hunt, Susan & Hunt, Richie. Discovering Jesus in Exodus, Vol. 2. 2005. (Illus.). 176p. pap. 16.99 (978-1-58134-453-0(8) , Crossway Bibles) Crossway Bks.

Ippolito, Eva Marie. The Donkey's Tale. Ippolito, Eva Marie, illus. 2003. (Illus.). Ill, 15p. (J). (ps-3). pap. 1.95 (978-0-9705350-3-0(1)) Ippolito, Eva Marie.

Jackson, Leona Novy. The Littlest Christmas Kitten. Dupre, Kelly, illus. 2005. 32p. (J). 16.00 (978-0-930643-18-8(6) , 1250560) Images Unlimited.

Jacob's Gift. 2004. (Max Lucado Ser.). 32p. 19.99 incl. DVD (978-1-4003-0182-9(3)) Nelson, Thomas Inc.

Jeffs, Stephanie. Christopher Bear's First Christmas. Thomas, Jacqui, illus. 2004. (Christopher Bear Ser.). 30p. 5.99 (978-0-8066-4349-6(8) , Augsburg Bks.) Augsburg Fortress, Pubs.

Jeffs, Stephanie, et al. Llygoden y Nadolig. 2005. (WEL., Illus.). 30p. (978-1-85994-497-4(3)) Cyhoeddiadau'r Gair.

Jenkins, Barbie. The Legend of Christmas Kiss. 2005. 32p. 13.99 (978-1-4165-3382-5(6) , Howard Bks.) Simon & Schuster.

The Jesus & the Children, Beginner's Biblereg; 2007. (Biblia para Principiantes Ser.). 24p. (J). 5.99 (978-0-8297-5011-9(8)) Vida Pubs.

Jesus Goes to a Wedding. 2001. (Favorite Stories about Jesus Bks.). (Illus.). 12p. (J). 0.99 (978-0-8254-7229-9(6)) Kregel Pubns.

Jesus Is My Special Friend. 2006. 16p. (J). pap. 1.99 (978-0-7847-1695-3(1) , 02997) Standard Publishing.

The Jesus Is Risen!, Beginner's Biblereg; 2007. (Biblia para Principiantes Ser.). 24p. (J). 5.99 (978-0-8297-5012-6(6)) Vida Pubs.

Jesus Loves the Little Children Adventures in Learning Book. 2005. (J). 15.95 (978-1-59210-350-8(2)) Whispering Pine Pr., Inc.

Jesus Loves the Little Children Christian Adventures. 2005. (J). 15.95 (978-1-59210-410-9(X)) Whispering Pine Pr., Inc.

Jesus Loves the Little Children Story Book. 2005. (J). 15.95 (978-1-59649-440-4(9)) Whispering Pine Pr., Inc.

Johnson, Lissa Halls. The Worst Wish. 2000. (Kidwitness Tales Ser.). (Illus.). 128p. (J). (gr. 3-7). pap. 5.99 (978-1-56179-882-7(7)) Bethany Hse. Pubs.

Kidd, Pennie. Sleepy Jesus. Poole, Susie, illus. 2002. 28p. (J). pap. 8.99 (978-0-7459-4792-1(1) , Lion) Lion Hudson plc GBR. *Dist:* Independent Pubs. Group.

Kinkade, Thomas, illus. Away in a Manger Board Book. 2007. 28p. (J). bds. 6.99 (*978-0-06-078735-6(X) , Harper Festival) HarperCollins Pubs.

Knott, Anthony & Kneen, Maggie. An Angel Came to Nazareth. Kneen, Maggie, illus. 2005. (Illus.). 24p. (J). (ps-3). 15.95 (978-0-8118-4798-8(5)) Chronicle Bks. LLC.

Lang, Gordon. Everyday Encounters: Face to Face with Jesus. 2003. 115p. per. 14.95 (978-1-932338-19-5(5)) Lifevest Publishing, Inc.

Lanier, W. Chandler. Yallid, Stable Boy of Bethlehem. 2000. 70p. (J). (gr. 3-9). pap. 7.99 (978-1-58158-011-2(8) , Parable Pubns.) McDougal Publishing Co.

Lewis, Anthony & Robinson, Hilary. Email Jesus@ Bethlehem. 2004. (Illus.). 32p. (J). pap. 10.99 (978-0-340-88463-8(0) , Hodder & Stoughton) Hodder General Publishing Division GBR. *Dist:* Trafalgar Square Publishing.

Little Fish Jesus Merchandiser. (J). 128.16 (978-0-8307-2907-4(0) , Gospel Light) Gospel Light Pubns.

Lloyd-Jones, Sally. The Jesus Bible Storybook: From Creation to Happily Ever After. Nguyen, Vincent & Jago, illus. 2007. 352p. (J). 16.99 (978-0-310-70825-4(7)) Zonderkidz.

Lloyd Jones, Sally. Little One, We Knew You'd Come. Morris, Jackie, illus. 2006. 40p. (J). (ps-3). 16.99 (978-0-316-52391-2(7)) Little Brown & Co.

Lockhart, Linda J. A Little Angel Dressed in Red. 2006. (J). pap. 8.00 (978-0-8059-6923-8(3)) Dorrance Publishing Co., Inc.

Loesch, Joe. He Is Risen: The True Meaning of Easter As Told by God's Animals. Hutchinson, Cheryl, ed. Cox, Brian T., illus. unabr. ed. 1999. (Bible Stories for Kids Ser.). 56p. (gr. k-5). reprint ed. 16.95 incl. audio compact disk (978-1-932332-09-4(X)) Toy Box Productions.

Lozano, Neal. Will You Bless Me? Hatke, Ben, illus. 2006. (J). lib. bdg. 14.95 (978-1-883551-32-2(3) , MCP-323, Maple Corners Press) Attic Studio Publishing Hse.

Lucado, Max. The Crippled Lamb. Bonham, Liz, illus. collector's ed. 2004. 30p. (J). (gr. k-4). reprint ed. 18.00 (978-0-7567-8021-0(7)) DIANE Publishing Co.

—The Crippled Lamb. Bonham, Liz, illus. (J). (ps-2). 2005. 20p. bds., bds. 15.99 (978-1-4003-0695-4(7)); 1999. 16p. bds. 6.99 (978-0-8499-7502-8(6)) Nelson, Thomas Inc.

—The Crippled Lamb. collector's ed. 2006. 32p. (J). 19.99 (978-1-4003-0877-4(1)) Nelson, Thomas Inc.

Maccabe, Catherine. Teddy Bear, Piglet, Kitten & Me. Scruton, Clive, illus. 2004. 28p. 11.99 (978-0-8066-4148-5(7) , Augsburg Bks.) Augsburg Fortress, Pubs.

Machle, Rick. Ester's Easter Tale: How the Easter Bunny Came to Be. Nervig, Sandy, illus. 1999. 36p. (J). pap. 7.99 (978-0-9670375-0-9(6)) Growing Ideas, L.L.C.

Mackall, Dandi Daley. The Light of Christmas. Walker, John, illus. 2007. 32p. (J). (ps-3). 14.99 (*978-0-7586-1270-0(2)) Concordia Publishing Hse.

—Little Lost Donkey. 2007. 26p. (J). bds. 6.99 (*978-1-4003-1009-8(1)) Nelson, Thomas Inc.

Mackall, Dandi Daley. The Shepherd's Christmas Story. Catalano, Dominic, illus. 2005. 32p. (J). (ps-k). 12.99 (978-0-7586-0904-5(3)) Concordia Publishing Hse.

Mackall, Dandi Daley, adapted by. El Pastorcito: Para ninos de 4-7 Anos.Tr. of Little Shepherd. (SPA.). 32p. 3.99 (978-0-7586-0362-3(2)) Concordia Publishing Hse.

Marsh, Carole. The Legend of the Candy Cane. 2003. 12p. (J). (gr. k-4). pap. 2.95 (978-0-635-02124-3(2)) Gallopade International.

The Mary & Little Jesus, Beginner's Biblereg; 2007. 24p. (J). 5.99 (978-0-8297-5010-2(X)) Vida Pubs.

Masterson, Rebecca. Jesus & the Great Garbage War. 2008. 120p. (YA). pap. 14.99 (978-1-59092-393-1(6) , Blue Works) Windstorm Creative.

Mayer, Mercer. The Little Drummer Mouse. 2006. (Illus.). 40p. (J). (ps). 16.99 (978-0-8037-3147-9(7) , Dial) Penguin Group (USA) Inc.

McAlister, Sharon. That First Christmas. 2005. 48p. pap. 19.95 (978-1-4137-6966-1(7)) PublishAmerica, Inc.

McCarthy, Margaret. The Cat Did Not Know. 2006. pap. 10.20 (978-1-85390-923-8(8)) Veritas Pubns. IRL. *Dist:* STL Distribution North America.

McCaughrean, Geraldine. Father & Son: A Nativity Story. Negrin, Fabian, illus. 2006. 40p. (ps-3). 16.99 (978-1-4231-0344-8(0)) Hyperion Pr.

—The Jesse Tree. Willey, Bee, illus. 2005. 93p. (J). (gr. k). 20.00 (978-0-8028-5288-5(2) , Eerdmans Bks For Young Readers) Eerdmans, William B. Publishing Co.

McElligott, Walter Lee. A Blessed Bethlehem Birth: As told by Abraham & Anna Mousenstern. Collier, Kevin Scott, illus. 2006. 28p. (J). E-Book 5.00 incl. cd-rom (*978-1-933090-21-4(9)) Guardian Angel Publishing, Inc.

McGee, Marni. A Song in Bethlehem. Cockcroft, Jason, illus. 2007. 40p. (J). (gr. k-3). 15.99 (*978-0-375-83447-9(8)); lib. bdg. 18.99 (*978-0-375-93447-6(2)) Random Hse. Children's Bks. (Knopf Bks. for Young Readers).

Meyers, David. The Illustrated Life of Jesus: Through the Gospels, Arranged Chronologically. 2005. (Illus.). 304p. (978-1-59258-125-2(0)) Hylas Publishing.

Milbourne, Anna. Very First Christmas. 2006. 24p. (J). 9.99 (978-0-7945-1474-7(X) , Usborne) EDC Publishing.

Montgomery Gibson, Jane. Jesus Is! Montgomery Gibson, Jane, illus. 2005. (J). bds. 8.99 (978-1-4183-0033-3(0)) Christ Inspired, Inc.

—Jesus Loves Me. Montgomery Gibson, Jane, illus. 2005. (J). bds. 8.99 (978-1-4183-0048-7(9)) Christ Inspired, Inc.

Morpurgo, Michael. On Angel Wings. 2007. 48p. 8.99 (*978-0-7636-3466-7(2)) Candlewick Pr.

Murphy, Paul. The 13th Apostle. 2004. 224p. pap. 11.99 (978-1-58169-142-9(4) , 3000, Evergreen Pr.) Genesis Communications, Inc.

Myers, Bill. Eli. 2000. (gr. 3-6). lib. bdg. 22.25 (978-0-613-51822-2(5)) Tandem Library Bks.

Napoli, Donna Jo. Song of the Magdalene: A Novel. 1998. (Illus.). 256p. (YA). (gr. 7-12). pap. 4.99 (978-0-590-93706-1(5) , Scholastic Paperbacks) Scholastic, Inc.

—Song of the Magdalene: A Novel. 2004. (Illus.). 256p. (YA). pap. 6.99 (978-0-689-87396-6(4) , Simon Pulse) Simon & Schuster Children's Publishing.

—Song of the Magdalene: A Novel. 1998. (J). (978-0-606-13789-8(0)) Tandem Library Bks.

Nazoa, Aquiles. A Small Nativity. Hazelton, Hugh, tr. from SPA. Caceres, Ana Palmero, illus. 2007. 44p. (J). (ps-3). 9.95 (*978-0-88899-839-2(2)) Groundwood Bks. CAN. *Dist:* Perseus Distribution.

Olson, Kris C. The Shepherd & the Wolf. 2006. 51p. pap. 12.95 (*978-1-4241-1655-3(4)) PublishAmerica, Inc.

One Baby Jesus. 2005. (Ideals Christmas Classic Ser.). (Illus.). 30p. (J). 3.95 (978-0-8249-5511-3(0)) Ideals Pubns.

Pantelides, Sherry. It's Red Like Me! A Story about the Blood of Jesus. Perez, Debi, illus. 2007. (J). lib. bdg. 12.99 (*978-0-9771076-0-5(4)) Lacey Productions.

Pasquali, Elena. Ituku's Christmas Journey. Kolanovic, Dubravka, illus. 2005. 32p. (J). (ps-3). 16.00 (978-1-56148-495-9(4)) Good Bks.

Passey, Marion. My Tiny Book of Christmas. Harston, Jerry, illus. 2006. (J). bds. 5.95 (978-1-886249-33-2(4) , Trumpet Media) WindRiver Publishing.

Petersen, Alicia. A Sparrow Alone. 2004. 154p. (YA). (978-1-59166-204-4(4)) Jones, Bob Univ. Pr.

Pierce, Chonda & Pierce, David. Tales from the Manger. LeBarre, Matt, illus. 2004. 96p. (J). pap. 9.99 (978-0-310-70849-0(4)) Zonderkidz.

Pigman, Shari. Little Frog Finds Jesus. 2005. 23p. (J). 12.67 (978-1-4116-5779-3(9)) Lulu.com.

Pingry, Patricia A. A Child's Easter. Britt, Stephanie McFetridge, illus. 2001. 32p. (J). (ps-3). 12.95 (978-0-8249-4197-0(7) , Ideals Children's Bks.) Ideals Pubns.

Quinlan, Janet, adapted by. Love: The Selfish Giant. 2005. (Illus.). (*978-1-4127-3758-6(3)) Publications International, Ltd.

Ramos, Peregrina. The Little Clay Jar = la Vasijita de Barro. Graham, Dennis, illus. 2006. Tr. of vasijita de Barro. (SPA & ENG.). (J). per. 15.95 (978-0-9788381-0-2(6)) Word Gift Pubns.

Rangel, Graciela. Anthony's Christmas Journey. 2006. pap. 9.95 (*978-1-59526-650-7(X) , Lumina Christian Bks.) Media Creations, Inc.

Robinson, Ella M. Happy Home Stories. 2005. 137p. per. 10.95 (978-1-57258-313-9(4)) TEACH Services, Inc.

Roche, Luane. The Proud Tree. Sharp, Chris, illus. 1999. 48p. (J). (gr. 1-5). pap. 11.95 (978-0-7648-0377-2(8)) Liguori Pubns.

Roesti, Delores. Mareena Maree Mulligan & the Flying Wheel Chair: Book 1: School Days. 2007. 81p. pap. 9.95 (*978-0-7414-4048-8(2)) Infinity Publishing.

Rowe, Kysha D. What Creatures Teach Us, 1. 2005. (Illus.). 112p. (J). per. (978-0-9769339-0-8(X)) Rowe, Kysha.

Rowlands, Avril. The Christmas Sheep: And Other Stories. Moran, Rosslyn, illus. 2001. 48p. (J). (ps-3). 16.00 (978-1-56148-336-5(2)) Good Bks.

Sample, Lempi. The Life of Jesus: As Seen Through the Eyes of a Shepherd Boy. Mikels, Leroy, illus. l.t. ed. 1999. 67p. (J). 9.95 (978-1-55967-234-4(X)) Triune Biblical Univ.

Sanchez, Elizabeth. Jesus, It's Me Nicholas! Gutierrez, Chris, illus. 2005. 12p. (J). per. 9.99 (978-1-59879-062-7(5)) Lifevest Publishing, Inc.

Saranpa, Rob. The Night Jesus Met Santa Claus. Hicks, John, illus. 2005. 32p. (J). pap. 19.99 incl. audio compact disk (978-1-4141-0554-3(1)) Pleasant Word.

Sellers, Amy C., ed. Finding Jesus: Contemporary Children's Story. Behan, Rachel A., illus. l.t. ed. 2006. 19p. (J). 24.95 (*978-1-934194-00-3(X)) Olmstead LLC.

Sieger, Ted. The Fourth King: The Story of the Other Wise Man. 2006. (Illus.). 48p. (J). (ps). 15.99 (978-0-7636-3121-5(3)) Candlewick Pr.

Skevington, Andrea. The Little Christmas Tree. Hussey, Lorna, illus. 2002. 32p. (J). (gr. k-2). pap. 8.99 (978-0-7459-4588-0(0) , Lion) Lion Hudson plc GBR. *Dist:* Independent Pubs. Group.

Slate, Joseph. What Star Is This? Jay, Alison, illus. 2005. 32p. (J). (ps-3). 15.99 (978-0-399-24014-0(4) , Putnam Juvenile) Penguin Group (USA) Inc.

Smith, Kathryn. Little Lamb's Christmas Story. Wood, Amanda, illus. 2002. (Snuffleheads Ser.). 14p. (J). (gr. k-3). 7.99 (978-1-85985-442-6(7)); 7.99 (978-0-8254-7253-4(9)) Kregel Pubns.

Speare, Elizabeth George. The Bronze Bow. 2002. (J). 14.74 (978-0-7587-0173-2(X)) Book Wholesalers, Inc.

—The Bronze Bow. 1999. (J). 9.95 (978-1-56137-726-8(0)) Novel Units, Inc.

Speirs, Gill & Speirs, John. The Donkey & the Golden Light: Peace, Goodwill & a New Beginning for All. 2004. (Illus.). 32p. (J). (ps-3). 16.95 (978-0-8109-4812-9(5)) Abrams, Harry N. , Inc.

Speirs, John. Little Boys Christmas Gift. 2001. (Illus.). 32p. (J). (ps-3). 16.95 (978-0-8109-4399-5(9)) Abrams, Harry N. , Inc.

Spellman, Rhonda J., as told by. When I Was a Little Boy, by Jesus: Written for Children, Illustrated by Children: Experience the Life Jesus Lived When Jesus Was a Little Boy. l.t. ed. 2003. (Illus.). 32p. (J). per. 19.95 (978-0-9741009-0-6(0)) Bound By Faith Publishing.

Spence, Eleanor. Me & Jeshua. Conroy, Shane, illus. 2000. (StarMaker Bks.). 165p. (YA). pap. 5.50 (978-0-88489-671-5(4)) St. Mary's Pr.

St. Paul, Mary. How Jesus Lived: Coloring Book. 2002. (Illus.). 24p. (J). pap. 6.00 (978-1-930873-65-0(4)) Neumann Pr., The.

Stockstill, Gloria McQueen. The Blind Man by the Road. Girouard, Patricia L., illus. 2003. (ENG.). 20p. (J). bds. 4.99 (978-0-7586-0144-5(1)) Concordia Publishing Hse.

Stohs, Reith Anita. Oh Come, Little Children. Huang, Benrei, illus. 2006. 32p. (J). 14.99 (978-0-7586-1215-1(X)) Concordia Publishing Hse.

Strasser, Myrna. Story of the Nativity. 2005. (J). (978-0-310-70890-2(7)) Zonderkidz.

Tafuri, Nancy. The Donkey's Christmas Song. Tafuri, Nancy, illus. 2002. (Illus.). 32p. (J). (ps-k). pap. 16.95 (978-0-439-27313-8(7) , Scholastic Pr.) Scholastic, Inc.

—The Donkey's Christmas Welcome. 2002. (Illus.). (J). pap. (978-0-439-27314-5(5)) Scholastic, Inc.

Tangvald, Christine Harder. The Best Thing about Easter. Nobens, Cheryl A., illus. 2006. 28p. (J). (ps-2). 7.99 (978-0-7847-1285-6(9) , 04039) Standard Publishing.

Tatum, Gwen. K. C.'s Light: I Was Born from a Light. 1999. (Illus.). 32p. (J). pap. 8.00 (978-0-8059-4728-1(0)) Dorrance Publishing Co., Inc.

—K. C.'s Light: I Was Born from a Light. Mallard-Howard, Sabrina, illus. 1998. 32p. (J). (gr. k-6). pap. 9.95 (978-0-9664727-0-7(5)) TNT Publishing.

Taylor, Shirley A. The Cross in the Egg. Hall, Wendell E., illus. 1999. 32p. (J). (ps-2). 15.95 (978-0-87483-549-6(6)) August Hse. Pubs., Inc.

That's What a Friend Is! 2003. 24p. (J). bds. 6.95 (978-0-8249-5468-0(8)) Ideals Pubns.

Thomas, Joan G. If Jesus Came to My House: Reillustrated. McElrath-Eslick, Lori, illus. 2005. (HarperBlessings Ser.). 40p. (J). pap. 5.99 (978-0-06-083944-4(9) , Harper Trophy) HarperCollins Pubs.

Thomas Nelson Publishing Staff. The Greatest Shepherd of All: A Really Woolly Christmas Story. 2006. (Illus.). 32p. (J). 7.99 (978-1-4003-0964-1(6)) Nelson, Thomas Inc.

Tolan, Stephanie S. Bartholomew's Blessing. Moore, Margie, illus. 2004. 32p. (J). (ps-3). lib. bdg. 16.89 (978-0-06-001198-7(X)) HarperCollins Pubs.

Underhill, Marjorie Fay. Jeremiah. Garrett, Caroline S., tr. Garrett, Caroline S., illus. 2003. (J). 12.00 (978-1-887905-75-6(8)) Parkway Pubs., Inc.

Van Dyke, Henry. The Other Wise Man. Barrett, Robert, illus. 2007. 32p. 8.99 (*978-0-8249-5565-6(X) , Ideals Children's Bks.) Ideals Pubns.

—The Other Wise Man. 2004. pap. 11.95 incl. audio compact disk (978-1-932226-34-8(X)) Wizard Academy Pr.

Villarreal, Carlos C. The Light Beneath the Shadow: Sharing God's Love with Your Child as You Read Together: A Bedtime Story Intended to Awaken Your Parental Christian Spirit. 2006. 48p. pap. 12.95 (978-1-4241-1247-0(8)) PublishAmerica, Inc.

Visconti, Guido. One Night in a Stable. Cimatoribus, Alessandra, illus. 2004. 32p. (J). 16.00 (978-0-8028-5279-3(3)) Eerdmans, William B. Publishing Co.

Vivas, Julie, illus. The Nativity. 2006. 36p. (J). pap. 7.00 (978-0-15-206085-5(5) , Voyager Bks./Libros Viajeros) Harcourt Children's Bks.

Waddell, Martin. Room for a Little One: A Christmas Tale. Cockcroft, Jason, illus. 2004. 32p. (J). 15.95 (978-0-689-86841-2(3) , McElderry, Margaret K.) Simon & Schuster Children's Publishing.

—Room for a Little One: A Christmas Tale. Cockcroft, Jason, illus. 2006. 32p. (J). 9.95 (978-1-4169-2518-7(X) , McElderry, Margaret K.) Simon & Schuster Children's Publishing.

Walburg, Lori. The Legend of the Easter Egg. 2004. (Illus.). 26p. (J). bds. 6.99 (978-0-310-70785-1(4)) Zonderkidz.

—The Legend of the Easter Egg. Bernardin, James, illus. 1999. 32p. (J). 15.99 (978-0-310-22447-1(0)) Zonderkidz.

Ward, Helen. The Animals' Christmas Carol. 2001. (Picture Books for Holidays). (Illus.). 40p. lib. bdg. 24.90 (978-0-7613-2408-9(9) , Millbrook Pr.) Lerner Publishing Group.

—The Animals Christmas Carol. 2001. (Illus.). 40p. (J). 16.95 (978-0-7613-1496-7(2) , Millbrook Pr.) Lerner Publishing Group.

Ware, Jim. Dangerous Dreams. 2001. (Kidwitness Tales Ser.). (Illus.). 128p. (J). (gr. 4-7). mass mkt. (978-1-56179-956-5(4)) Focus on the Family Publishing.

Wensell, Paloma. Christmas Star. Wensell, Ulises, illus. 2006. 16p. (J). 7.95 (978-0-8146-3155-3(X) , Liturgical Pr. Bks.) Liturgical Pr.

Wiersum, Gale. The Animals' Christmas Eve. 2007. (Illus.). 24p. (J). (gr. k-k). 2.99 (*978-0-375-83923-8(2) , Golden Inspirational) Random Hse. Children's Bks.

Wilhelm, Hans. The Christmas Angel. 2007. 32p. (J). (ps-k). pap. 3.99 (*978-0-545-00853-2(0)) Scholastic, Inc.

Wilson, Karma. Mortimer's Christmas Manger. Chapman, Jane, illus. 2005. 40p. (J). 15.95 (978-0-689-85511-5(7) , McElderry, Margaret K.) Simon & Schuster Children's Publishing.

Wormell, Christopher. Through the Animals' Eyes: A Story of the First Christmas. Wormell, Christopher, illus. 2006. (Illus.). 64p. (J). 18.95 (978-0-7624-2669-0(1)) Running Pr. Bk. Pubs.

Wright, Boyd. Donkey Tales. 2006. 74p. pap. 14.95 (978-1-4241-1900-4(6)) PublishAmerica, Inc.

Zemanick, Patty. A Walk with Papa. Hammack, Sandra, illus. 2006. pap. 14.95 (978-0-9788289-0-5(9)) Dragonfly Ministries.

Zobel-Nolan, Allia. Jesus & the Children. MacLean, Moira, illus. 2000. (Mini Handle Bks.:). 5p. (J). (ps). bds. 7.99 (978-1-57584-669-9(1)) Reader's Digest Children's Publishing, Inc.

JESUS CHRIST—ICONOGRAPHY

see Jesus Christ—Art

JESUS CHRIST—NATIVITY

see also Christmas

Adams, Michelle Medlock. What Is Christmas? Wummer, Amy, illus. 2006. 26p. (J). (ps). bds. 6.95 (978-0-8249-6668-3(6) , Candy Cane Pr.) Ideals Pubns.

Alexander, Florence & Alexander, Stanley. Jesus Christ Is Born. l.t. ed. 2003. (Dare to Be Great Ser.). (Illus.). 36p. (J). 7.99 (978-0-915960-02-6(8)) Ebon Research Systems Publishing, LLC.

Anderson, Raymond & Anderson, Georgene. The Jesse Tree: Stories & Symbols of Advent. 2004. (Illus.). 64p. (J). 5.99 (978-0-8066-2524-9(4) , 10-25244, Augsburg Bks.) Augsburg Fortress, Pubs.

Arensen, Shel. The First Christmas: Nativity Puzzle Book with 6 Play Pieces. 2003. (Illus.). 16p. (J). 10.99 (978-0-8254-5509-4(X)) Kregel Pubns.

Aston, Al. The Shepherds' Surprise. Hutchinson, Joy, illus. 2005. 16p. pap. 2.00 (978-1-84427-178-8(1)) Scripture Union GBR. *Dist:* STL Distribution North America.

Baby Jesus. 2002. (Little Pups Board Bks.). (Illus.). 11p. (J). (ps). bds. 2.99 (978-1-57759-996-8(9)) Dalmatian Pr.

Baby Jesus. 16p. (J). 1.89 (978-0-7847-1386-0(3)) Standard Publishing.

Baby Jesus Is Born: A Touch & Feel Book. 2003. (Illus.). 10p. (J). bds. 10.99 (978-0-8254-5507-0(3)) Kregel Pubns.

Baby's First Nativity. 2002. (J). spiral bd. (978-0-9720158-3-7(3)) Story Reader, Inc.

Bierhorst, John. El Nino Espiritu: Una Historia de la Navidad. Aramburu, Francisco Gonzalez, tr. Cooney, Barbara, illus. 2003. (SPA.). 26p. (J). (gr. 3-7). reprint ed. 20.00 (978-0-7567-6882-9(9)) DIANE Publishing Co.

Boadt, Lawrence. Stations of the Nativity. 2002. (Illus.). 32p. (J). 10.95 (978-0-8091-6699-2(2) , 6699-2) Paulist Pr.

Bowen, Cheryl & Keefer, Mikal. Jesus— Manger Miracle/ [author, Cheryl Bowen ; Editor, Mikal Keefer]. 2005. (BibleVenture Centers Ser.). (Illus.). 111p. pap. (978-0-7644-2809-8(8)) Group Publishing, Inc.

Brickey, Joseph, illus. When Jesus Was Born in Bethlehem. 2000. 30p. (J). 17.95 (978-1-57345-841-2(4)) Deseret Bk. Co.

Brooks, Felicity. Nativity Jigsaw Bk. 2006. 14p. (J). bds. 12.99 (978-0-7945-1188-3(0) , Usborne) EDC Publishing.

Buck, Nola. Christmas in the Manger. Bond, Felicia, illus. 1998. 16p. (J). (ps-k). bds. 6.99 (978-0-694-01227-5(0) , Harper Festival) HarperCollins Pubs.

Busch, Melinda Kay. Born on Christmas Morn. Hall, Melanie, illus. 2003. (Arch Bks.). (ENG.). 16p. (J). (gr. k-4). 1.99 (978-0-570-07584-4(X)) Concordia Publishing Hse.

Catholic Baby's Nativity. 2001. (Illus.). (J). 10.99 (978-0-88271-007-5(9)) Regina Pr., Malhame & Co.

Charette, Beverly. Story of Christmas for Children. 2004. pap. 3.95 (978-0-8249-5338-6(X)) Ideals Pubns.

Chocheli, Niko, illus. Prepare O Bethlehem: The Feast of the Nativity. 2000. 32p. (J). 18.00 (978-0-88141-208-6(2)) St. Vladimir's Seminary Pr.

Cooner, Donna D. Here Is Christmas. Jenkins, Debra Reid, illus. 2000. 32p. (J). (ps-2). 14.95 (978-1-57856-298-5(8) , WaterBrook Pr.) WaterBrook Pr.

Crossley-Holland, Kevin. How Many Miles to Bethlehem? Malone, Peter, illus. 2004. (J). (978-0-439-67643-4(6)); 32p. 16.95 (978-0-439-67642-7(8)) Scholastic, Inc. (Levine, Arthur A. Bks.).

Crump, Fred, Jr. Three Kings & a Star. 2005. 40p. (J). (ps-3). 12.95 (978-1-932715-52-1(5)) UMI (Urban Ministries, Inc.).

Davidson, Candy. The Little Lamb. 2000. (Illus.). 64p. (J). pap. 8.95 (978-1-892861-38-2(0)) Vision Publishing Group.

Dorling Kindersley Publishing Staff. The Christmas Story. 1999. 12p. (J). pap. 7.95 (978-0-7894-4740-1(1)) Dorling Kindersley Publishing, Inc.

Dowley, Tim. Follow the Star. Prole, Helen, illus. 2005. (J). pap. 6.99 (978-0-8254-7304-3(7)) Kregel Pubns.

Dowley, Tim & Wyart, Peter. The Shepherd's Tale. Pierce, Martin, illus. 2002. 14p. (J). (gr. k-3). 5.99 (978-0-8254-7257-2(1)) Kregel Pubns.

Ellis, Gwen. Christmas Angels: Read & Share. 2007. 32p. (J). 12.99 (***978-1-4003-0854-5(2)***) Nelson, Thomas Inc.

The First Christmas. 2003. (Illus.). (J). bds. 6.98 (978-1-4054-0967-4(3)) Parragon, Inc.

The First Christmas. (Illus.). 12p. (J). 4.95 (978-1-58989-102-9(3)) Thurman Hse., LLC.

The First Christmas. 2003. (Illus.). 30p. (J). 14.95 (978-0-8249-5469-7(6)) Ideals Pubns.

Fogle, Robin. A Christmas Story. 2006. (J). pap. 1.79 (***978-1-59317-159-9(5)***) Warner Pr. Pubs.

Follow That Star. (Hear Me Read Classroom Sets Ser.). 32.00 (978-0-570-07172-3(0)) Concordia Publishing Hse.

Forlini, Victoria, ed. The Birth of Jesus: Deluxe Sound Storybook. 2004. (ENG.). 22p. (J). 14.95 (978-0-696-22362-4(7)) Meredith Bks.

French, Fiona. Bethlehem: With Words from the King James Bible. 2001. (Illus.). 32p. (J). (gr. k-3). 15.95 (978-0-06-029623-0(2)) HarperCollins Pubs.

Ganeri, Anita. The Christmas Story. Phillips, Rachael, illus. 2003. (Festival Stories Ser.). 24p. (J). pap. (978-0-237-52468-5(6) , Evans Brothers, Limited) Evans Publishing Group.

—The Christmas Story. Phillips, Rachael, tr. Phillips, Rachael, illus. 2004. (J). lib. bdg. (978-1-58340-489-8(9)) Smart Apple Media.

Gemmen, Heather & McNeil, Mary. Jesus Loves Me: Level 2. Clar, David Austin, tr. Clar, David Austin, illus. 2004. (Rocket ReaderT2 Ser.). 40p. (J). (gr. 2 up). pap., pap. 8.99 (978-0-7814-4013-4(0) , 0781440130) Cook, David C. Publishing Co.

Gillis, Bonnie, illus. The Nativity of Our Lord. 2002. (Twelve Great Feasts for Children Ser.). 24p. pap. 5.95 (978-1-888212-36-5(5) , 005671) Conciliar Pr.

Gore, Leonid & Bunting, Eve. Who Was Born This Special Day? 2003. (Illus.). 32p. (J). pap. 6.99 (978-0-689-85955-7(4) , Aladdin) Simon & Schuster Children's Publishing.

Greene, Carol. My Turn Bible Stories about Colors. 1998. (My Turn Bible Stories Ser.). (Illus.). 32p. (J). (ps-1). 6.99 (978-0-570-05061-2(8)) Penguin Group (USA) Inc.

Greene, Rhonda Gowler. The Stable Where Jesus Was Born. Gaber, Susan, illus. (J). (ps-1). 2007. 32p. 9.99 (***978-1-4169-5048-6(6));*** 2002. 40p. 6.99 (978-0-689-85350-0(5) , Aladdin) Simon & Schuster Children's Publishing.

Grimes, Nikki. Voices of Christmas. 2006. (J). 15.99 (978-0-310-71192-6(4)) Zonderkidz.

Hansen, Janis. Jesus: The Birthday of the King, 5 vols. Francisco, Wendy, illus. (Bible Adventure Club). 2003. 36p. wbk. ed. 19.99 incl. audio, cd-rom (978-1-58134-331-1(0)); 2001. (J). (978-1-58134-334-2(5)) Crossway Bks.

Harmon, Ruth. The Christmas Story. Date not set. 4.95 (978-0-88271-132-4(6) , 1415) Regina Pr., Malhame & Co.

Hartman, Bob. Noisy Stable: And Other Christmas Stories. 2004. (Illus.). 64p. (J). pap. 6.99 (978-0-7459-4824-9(3) , Lion) Lion Hudson plc GBR. *Dist:* Independent Pubs. Group.

Hartman, Sara. When Jesus Was Born. Mitter, Kathy, illus. 2007. 16p. (J). (gr. k-4). 1.99 (***978-0-7586-1281-6(8)***) Concordia Publishing Hse.

Heaps, Kelly S. & Dunn, Susan. Miracle: The Story of the First Christmas. Lindgren, Renae, illus. 1999. (Holy Bear's Travel Ser.). 32p. (J). (gr. k-5). pap. 7.95 (978-1-885628-31-2(5)) Buckaroo Bks.

Henning, Heather. Christmas. Chapman, Gillian, illus. 2007. (ENG.). 16p. (J). pap. 9.99 (***978-0-7586-1383-7(0)***) Concordia Publishing Hse.

Herman, John. One Winter's Night. Dillon, Leo & Dillon, Diane, illus. 2003. 40p. (J). (ps-3). 16.99 (978-0-399-23418-7(7) , Philomel) Penguin Group (USA) Inc.

Heyer, Carol, illus. The Christmas Story. (J). 6.95 (978-0-8249-5347-8(9)) Ideals Pubns.

Hickman, Martha Whitmore. A Baby Born in Bethlehem. Ferri, Giuliano, illus. 32p. (J). (gr. k-4). 2004. pap. 6.95 (978-0-8075-5523-1(1)); 1999. 15.95 (978-0-8075-5522-4(3)) Whitman, Albert & Co.

Hoffman, Patricia. Bethlehem Town. Munger, Nancy, illus. 2006. (ENG.). 20p. (J). 5.99 (978-0-7586-1214-4(1)) Concordia Publishing Hse.

—Bethlehem Town: Where Jesus Was Born. Munger, Nancy, illus. 2003. 32p. (J). 8.99 (978-0-7586-0412-5(2)) Concordia Publishing Hse.

Howie, Vicky, et al. Cnoc, Cnoc! Pwy Sy 'na? Llyfr Fflapiau Stori'r Nadolig. 2005. (WEL., Illus.). 20p. (978-1-85994-498-1(1)) Cyhoeddiadau'r Gair.

Hudak, Michal. The Uproar at Bethlehem. 2005. (Illus.). 24p. (ps-4). 14.95 (978-0-8146-2774-7(9)) Liturgical Pr.

The Incarnation of Christ: Immanuel, l.t. ed. 2004. Tr. of Incarnation of Christ. (CHI., Illus.). 52p. (J). (978-0-9752775-0-8(2) , 0-9752775-0-2) Unitrust Design.

James, Steven. JawDroppers: 36 Shocking Stories for Students Based on the Sayings of Jesus. Reeves, Dale, ed. 2001. 160p. (gr. 7 up). 10.99 (978-0-7847-1264-1(6)) Standard Publishing.

Jeffs, Stephanie. Baby Jesus. Tulip, Jenny, illus. 2004. (My First Find Out about Book Ser.). 24p. (ps up). pap. 3.95 (978-0-8294-1730-2(3)) Loyola Pr.

Jesus' Birth. (Bulletin Board Jumbo Cutouts Ser.). (Illus.). 96p. (J). 9.99 (978-0-7847-0551-3(8) , 02588) Standard Publishing.

Johnson, Cathy Ann, illus. The Christmas Story. 2005. 24p. (J). (ps-k). bds. 6.99 (978-1-4003-0633-6(7)) Nelson, Thomas Inc.

Joslin, Mary. On That Christmas Night. Cann, Helen, illus. 2005. 32p. (J). (ps-3). 16.00 (978-1-56148-494-2(6)) Good Bks.

Kennedy, Anne Vittur. One Shining Star: A Christmas Counting Book. 2006. (Illus.). 22p. (J). 6.99 (978-0-310-71029-5(4)) Zonderkidz.

Kidd, Pennie. Sleepy Jesus. Poole, Susie, illus. 2003. 28p. 7.99 (978-0-8066-4499-8(0) , Augsburg Bks.) Augsburg Fortress, Pubs.

Kim, Magdalena & Jablonski, Patricia E. When Jesus Was Born: The Story of the Very First Christmas. 2001. (Illus.). 40p. (J). pap. 6.95 (978-0-8198-8297-4(6) , 332-407) Pauline Bks. & Media.

Kinkade, Thomas, illus. Away in a Manger. 2005. 32p. (J). lib. bdg. 17.89 (978-0-06-078733-2(3)) HarperCollins Pubs.

Knowlton, Laurie Lazzaro. The Nativity: Mary Remembers. Kubiak, Kasi, illus. 2003. 32p. (J). (gr. k-2). 14.95 (978-1-56397-714-5(1)) Boyds Mills Pr.

Lafortune, Claude. The Wonderful Story of Christmas. 2003. (Illus.). 48p. act. bk. ed. (978-2-89507-439-7(9)); 24p. (978-2-89507-438-0(0)) Novalis Publishing.

Lane, Leena & Chapman, Gillian. Step by Step Christmas Creche. 2005. (Illus.). 32p. (ps-1). pap. 6.50 (978-0-687-06257-7(8)) Abingdon Pr.

Lashbrook, Marilyn. No Tree for Christmas: The Story of Jesus' Birth. Britt, Stephanie McFetridge, illus. 2000. (Libros Yo Tambien! Ser.). (SPA.). 32p. (J). (ps-2). 5.95 (978-1-58170-042-8(3)) Standard Publishing.

—No Tree for Christmas: The Story of Jesus' Birth. 1998. (J). (ps-2). pap. 5.95 (978-0-933657-71-7(4)) Standard Publishing.

Lift the Flap Nativity. 2001. (Illus.). 18p. (J). 10.99 (978-0-88271-026-6(5)) Regina Pr., Malhame & Co.

Lindecker, Leslie. The First Christmas. Calvert-Weyant, Lynda, tr. Calvert-Weyant, Lynda, illus. 2002. (My First Treasury Ser.). 40p. (J). (978-0-7853-6878-6(7) , 7167800) Publications International, Ltd.

Lingo, Susan L. My Good Night Christmas: With Read & Sing-along CD. Parks, Kathy, illus. 2001. 32p. (J). 17.99 incl. audio compact disk (978-0-7847-1205-4(0)) Standard Publishing.

Maier, Paul L. The Very First Christmas. 32p. (J). 9.99 (978-0-570-07186-0(0)) Concordia Publishing Hse.

—The Very First Christmas. Ordaz, Francisco, illus. (J). 2004. 20p. (ps-k). bds. 6.99 (978-0-7586-0689-1(3)); 2003. 32p. (gr. 1-5). 6.99 (978-0-7586-0616-7(8)) Concordia Publishing Hse.

—The Very First Christmas. 1998. (Illus.). 32p. (J). (gr. k-5). 12.99 (978-0-570-05064-3(2)) Concordia Publishing Hse.

Martin, Oscar, Jr., creator. Birth of Jesus, l.t. ed. 2003. (Illus.). 25p. (J). E-Book 19.95 incl. cd-rom (978-0-9748416-4-9(1)) Build Your Story.

Mayer, Marianna. Young Jesus of Nazareth. 1999. (Illus.). 32p. (J). (ps-3). 16.00 (978-0-688-16727-1(6)); 15.89 (978-0-688-16728-8(4)) HarperCollins Pubs.

McDermott, Gerald. The Light of the World. McDermott, Gerald, illus. 2006. 32p. (J). 16.99 (978-0-525-47488-3(9) , Dutton Juvenile) Penguin Group (USA) Inc.

Milligan, Bryce. Brigid's Cloak: An Ancient Irish Story. Cann, Helen, illus. 2004. 32p. (J). (gr. k up). 16.00 (978-0-8028-5224-3(6)) Eerdmans, William B. Publishing Co.

Mills, Elise, illus. The Very First Christmas. 2002. (Sticker Stories Ser.). 16p. (J). 4.99 (978-0-448-42867-3(9) , Grosset & Dunlap) Penguin Group (USA) Inc.

Miralles, Jose & McTeigue, Jane, illus. Christmas Star: A Light-up Shadow-Box Book. 2005. 10p. (J). (gr. k-4). reprint ed. 10.00 (978-0-7567-9559-7(1)) DIANE Publishing Co.

Nason, Ruth. Gifts at Christmas. 2005. (Start up Religion Ser.). (Illus.). 24p. (J). (gr. 1-4). lib. bdg. (978-1-84234-340-1(8) , Cherrytree Books) Evans Publishing Group.

Navillus, Nelle. The True Story of Christmas. Eitzen, Allan, illus. 1998. 12.95 (978-1-58173-147-7(7)) Sweetwater Pr.

Nederveld, Patricia L. An Amazing Star! The Story of the Wise Men. 1998. (God Loves Me Ser.). (Illus.). 24p. (J). (ps-3). pap. 2.95 (978-1-56212-295-9(9) , 001226, Faith Alive Christian Resources) CRC Pubns.

—Good News! The Story of the Shepherds. 1998. (God Loves Me Ser.). (Illus.). 24p. (J). (ps-3). pap. 2.95 (978-1-56212-294-2(0) , 001225, Faith Alive Christian Resources) CRC Pubns.

—Jesus Is Born! The Story of Christmas. 1998. (God Loves Me Ser.). (Illus.). 24p. (J). (ps-3). pap. 2.95 (978-1-56212-293-5(2) , 001224, Faith Alive Christian Resources) CRC Pubns.

—Waiting, Waiting, Waiting! The Story of Simeon & Anna. 1998. (God Loves Me Ser.). (Illus.). 24p. (J). (ps-3). pap. 2.95 (978-1-56212-296-6(7) , 001227, Faith Alive Christian Resources) CRC Pubns.

Neff, Larry M. Ha Nacido Jesus (Vida de Cristo)Tr. of Jesus Is Born. (SPA.). 12p. (J). 5.99 (978-0-7899-0033-3(5) , 497759) Editorial Unilit.

Noble, Marty. Little Advent Calendar Sticker Activity Book. 2001. (Dover Little Activity Bks.). (Illus.). 4p. (J). (ps-5). 1.50 (978-0-486-41746-2(8)) Dover Pubns., Inc.

—Nativity Sticker Activity Book. 2001. (Illus.). 4p. (J). (ps-3). 1.50 (978-0-486-41745-5(X)) Dover Pubns., Inc.

Nye, Christopher. The Old Shepherd's Tale. 2004. (Illus.). 32p. (J). 16.95 (978-0-913098-85-1(X)) Orion Society, The.

One Baby Jesus: A New Twelve Days of Christmas. 2001. (Illus.). 24p. (J). bds. 6.95 (978-0-8249-4138-3(1)) Ideals Pubns.

O'Neal, Debbie Trafton. Go Tell It on the Mountain. King, Fiona, illus. 2004. 32p. 8.99 (978-0-8066-4559-9(8) , Augsburg Bks.) Augsburg Fortress, Pubs.

Parry, Alan & Parry, Linda. The Herald Angels. 2003. (Illus.). 16p. 9.99 (978-1-85608-253-2(9)) Hunt, John Publishing Ltd. GBR. *Dist:* STL Distribution North America.

Pawlitz, Gail. Sing Glory Glory! Jesus Is Born! Jung, Sehee, illus. 2007. 10p. (J). (ps). bds. 6.99 (***978-0-7586-1310-3(5)***) Concordia Publishing Hse.

Pingry, Patricia A. The Christmas Story. Edelson, Wendy, illus. 2004. 26p. (J). bds. 6.95 (978-0-8249-6549-5(3)) Ideals Pubns.

Pingry, Patricia A. & Venturi-Pickett, Stacy. The Story of Mary. 2000. (Illus.). 26p. (J). (ps-3). bds. 6.95 (978-0-8249-4183-3(7) , Ideals Children's Bks.) Ideals Pubns.

Pinkney, Debbie, illus. The First Christmas. 2004. (J). (***978-0-7853-1894-1(1)***) Publications International, Ltd.

Poole, Susie. A Christmas Journey. 48p. 11.99 (978-1-86024-273-1(1)) Authentic Media.

—A Christmas Journey. Poole, Susie, illus. 2006. (Illus.). 44p. (J). 14.99 (978-0-7847-1461-4(4) , 04087) Standard Publishing.

—Christmas Journey. 2002. 48p. 14.99 (978-1-86024-375-2(4)) Authentic Media.

Robinson, Timothy M. A Night Without Darkness. Madsen, Jim, illus. 1999. (J). 15.95 (978-1-57345-504-6(0)) Deseret Bk. Co.

Root, Phyllis. All for the Newborn Baby. Bayley, Nicola, illus. 2000. (J). 15.99 (978-0-7636-0735-7(5)) Candlewick Pr.

Round, Graham. Baby Jesus. 2001. (Bible Story Sticker Book Ser.). 16p. (J). (ps-5). pap. 4.99 (978-0-8254-7245-9(8)) Kregel Pubns.

Scholastic, Inc. Staff. Nativity Board Book. 2007. (J). bds. 5.99 (***978-0-545-00067-3(X)*** , Cartwheel Bks.) Scholastic, Inc.

Smath, Jerry, tr. & illus. Long Ago in Bethlehem. Smath, Jerry, illus. 2002. 4p. (J). 12.99 (978-0-7814-3893-3(4) , 0781438934) Cook, David C. Publishing Co.

Stanley, Mandy, illus. Lift & Look Nativity. 2005. 8p. (J). (ps-ps). per. 7.99 (978-0-7847-1750-9(8) , 04376) Standard Publishing.

Stevenson, Peter, illus. Catholic Baby's First Nativity. 2000. (First Bible Collection). (J). (ps-k). 10.99 (978-0-88271-689-3(1)) Regina Pr., Malhame & Co.

Stiegemeyer, Julie. Bethlehem Night. Capaldi, Gina, illus. 2005. 32p. (J). (ps-ps). 12.99 (978-0-7586-0907-6(8)) Concordia Publishing Hse.

Surman, Richard. Children's Nativity: The Christmas Story Through a Child's Eyes. 2000. (Illus.). 40p. (J). (gr. 1-5). 22.95 (978-0-00-628124-5(9)) Zondervan.

Tulip, Jenny, illus. Born in a Stable. 2001. (Giant Zig-Zag Book Ser.). 10p. (J). (ps-k). 4.99 (978-0-8254-7213-8(X)) Kregel Pubns.

Tyrrell, Frances, illus. The Huron Carol. 2004. 32p. 16.00 (978-0-8028-5263-2(7)) Eerdmans, William B. Publishing Co.

Vander Klipp, Michael A. Joy to the World. Anderson, Nancy Munger, illus. 1998. 14p. (J). (ps). bds. 3.99 (978-0-310-97660-8(X)) Zonderkidz.

Walker, Joni. Tell Me the Christmas Story. Walker, Joni, illus. 2003. (ENG., Illus.). 14p. (J). (ps-k). bds. 4.99 (978-0-7586-0508-5(0)) Concordia Publishing Hse.

Walsh, Mary C. Saint Francis Celebrates Christmas. Caswell, Helen Rayburn, illus. 1998. 32p. (ps-3). 15.95 (978-0-8294-1112-6(7)) Loyola Pr.

Wangerin, Walter, Jr. Angels & All Children: A Nativity Story in Words, Music, & Art. Ladwig, Tim, illus. 2004. 40p. (gr. 2-7). 18.99 incl. audio compact disk (978-0-8066-3712-9(9) , Augsburg Bks.) Augsburg Fortress, Pubs.

Wilkeshuis, Cornelis. The Gift for the Child: A Story. Verstegen, Jeska, illus. 28p. (J). 16.95 (978-0-86315-349-5(6)) Floris Bks. GBR. *Dist:* SteinerBooks, Inc.

Yamamoto, Makoto. O Holy Night: The First Christmas. Moritsu, Wakako, illus. 2005. 24p. (J). (ps-ps). pap. 16.95 (978-0-8198-5440-7(9)) Pauline Bks. & Media.

Youd, Pauline. Why Were the Shepherds Excited? A Christmas Story. Sandland, Reg, illus. 2000. 13p. (J). (gr. 1-4). 3.95 (978-0-8198-8298-1(4)) Pauline Bks. & Media.

Zobel-Nolan, Allia. Flap Nativity. 2001. (Lift-the-Flap Playbook Ser.). (Illus.). 18p. (J). bds. 10.99 (978-1-57584-831-0(7)) Reader's Digest Assn., Inc., The.

JESUS CHRIST—NATIVITY—DRAMA

Edwards, Emyr. O Achos y Mab Bychan: Casgliad o Ddramau I Blant Ar Gyfer y Nadolig. 2005. (WEL.). 149p. (978-0-86381-601-7(0)) Gwasg Carreg Gwalch.

Taylor, Damon. Baby Boy, Bundle of Joy: The Christmas Story. 2004. (Child Sockology Ser.). (Illus.). 10p. (J). bds. 6.99 (978-0-8254-3865-3(9)) Kregel Pubns.

JESUS CHRIST—NATIVITY—POETRY

Bunting, Eve. Who Was Born This Special Day? 2003. (ps-2). lib. bdg. 15.30 (978-0-613-88998-8(3)) Tandem Library Bks.

Maccarone, Grace. Ya Nacio el Nino. 2000. (SPA.). (ps-2). lib. bdg. 14.15 (978-0-613-33270-5(9)) Tandem Library Bks.

One Baby Jesus: A New Twelve Days of Christmas. 2001. (Illus.). 24p. (J). bds. 6.95 (978-0-8249-4138-3(1)) Ideals Pubns.

JESUS CHRIST—PARABLES

Allison, Diane W., illus. Jesus' Little Parables of the Kingdom. 1998. 32p. (J). (ps-2). 16.95 (978-0-87510-327-3(8)) Eddy, The Writings of Mary Baker.

Ancell, Carolyn D. Jesus' Parables: A Reproducible Activity Book. 2002. (Illus.). 32p. (YA). (gr. 5-8). pap. 9.95 (978-1-893757-30-1(7) , 30-7) Needer, E.T. Publishing.

Bess, C. W. From Sad to Glad: And Other Bible Lessons for Kids. 2001. (FaithBuilders for Kids Ser.: Vol. 8). 96p. (J). (ps-3). reprint ed. pap. 4.99 (978-0-8010-6372-5(8)) Baker Bks.

—Straight as a String. 2001. (Faithbuilders for Kids Ser.: No. 7). (Illus.). 96p. (J). pap. 4.99 (978-0-8010-6371-8(X)) Baker Bks.

Bess, C. W. & DeBrand, Roy E. Why Go to Church? And Other Bible Lessons for Kids. 2001. (FaithBuilders for Kids Ser.: Vol. 9). 96p. (J). (ps-3). reprint ed. pap. 4.99 (978-0-8010-6373-2(6) , Bible-Centered) Baker Bks.

Bessiere, Gerard. Jesus Sat down & Said... Marsh, Gwen, tr. from FRE. Adam, Christine & Beinfait, Andree, illus. 1998. (Tales of Heaven & Earth Ser.).Tr. of Alors Jesus S'Assit et Dit.... 32p. (J). (gr. 3-7). pap. 19.95 (978-0-88682-827-1(9) , Creative Education) Creative Co., The.

Bruinsma, Sheryl. Do Not Feed the Bears: And Other Bible Lessons for Kids. 2001. (FaithBuilders for Kids Ser.: Vol. 10). 96p. (J). (ps-3). reprint ed. pap. 4.99 (978-0-8010-6374-9(4)) Baker Bks.

Butcher, Sam. Precious Moments Bible Stories. 2000. (Illus.). (J). (978-0-8010-4447-2(2)) Baker Bks.

Carlson, Melody. The Other Brother. Bjorkman, Steve, illus. 2004. 40p. (ps-3). 9.99 (978-1-58134-122-5(9)) Crossway Bks.

—The Parable of Two Builders: A Retelling of the Bible Story. Bjorkman, Steve, illus. 2003. 40p. (J). 9.99 (978-0-310-70145-3(7)) Zonderkidz.

JKL

Christensen, James C. Parables. 1999. (Illus.). 72p. (J). 19.95 (978-1-57345-558-9(X) , Shadow Mountain) Deseret Bk. Co.

Courtney, Claudia. Bleat! The Parable of the Lost Sheep. Mitter, Kathy, illus. 1998. (Phonetic Bible Stories Ser.). (ENG.). 16p. (J). (ps-1). 2.99 (978-0-570-05092-6(8)) Concordia Publishing Hse.

—Stand Strong: The Parable of the Wise & Foolish Builders. Morris, Susan, illus. 2000. (Phonetic Bible Stories Ser.). (ENG.). 16p. (J). (ps-1). 2.99 (978-0-570-07089-4(9)) Concordia Publishing Hse.

Dean, Bessie. Stories Jesus Told: The Lord's Parables Retold for Children. rev. ed. 1999. (Childrens' Inspirational Coloring Books Ser.). (Illus.). 72p. (J). pap. 6.98 (978-0-88290-670-6(4)) Horizon Pubs. & Distributors, Inc.

Dreyer, Nicole E. The Parable of the Talents. Morris, Susan, illus. 2007. 16p. (J). (gr. k-4). 1.99 (***978-0-7586-1282-3(6)***) Concordia Publishing Hse.

Freed, Shirley & Moon, Louise. Ten Precious Coins. Morelan, Bill, ed. Butler, Steven, illus. 2003. 16p. (J). (gr. 1 up). pap. 3.99 (978-1-58938-112-4(2)) Concerned Communications.

—The Two Houses. Morelan, Bill, ed. Butler, Steven, illus. 2003. 16p. (J). (gr. 2 up). pap. 3.99 (978-1-58938-116-2(5)) Concerned Communications.

Froeb, Lori. A Child's Book of Parables. Mioroney, Tracy, illus. 2006. 28p. (J). 15.99 (978-0-7847-1278-8(6) , 04344) Standard Publishing.

Gemmen, Heather & McNeil, Mary. Time's Up, Pre-Level 1. Williams, Jenny, tr. Williams, Jenny, illus. 2004. (Rr2 Ser.). 40p. (J). (ps-1). pap., pap. 8.99 (978-0-7814-4009-7(2) , 0781440092) Cook, David C. Publishing Co.

Glavich, Mary Kathleen. A Child's Book of Parables. 2004. (978-0-8294-1039-6(2)) Loyola Pr.

The Good Samaritan. 2003. (Illus.). 12p. (J). bds. 6.99 (978-0-8254-5505-6(7)) Kregel Pubns.

Ham, Ken. The Parables of Jesus: The Teachings of Jesus. 2000. (Awesome Adventure Bible Stories Ser.). (Illus.). 33p. (J). (gr. 2-7). pap. 5.99 (978-0-89051-331-6(7)) Master Bks.

Hartman, Bob. Parables to Learn By: Based on Stories Told by Jesus. Julien, Terry, illus. 2001. 160p. (J). pap. 14.95 (978-0-8198-5933-4(8) , 332-280) Pauline Bks. & Media.

Heffernan, Eileen & Jablonski, Patricia E., eds. Jesus Is Good! Five Gospel-Based Stories for Little People. 2001. (J). pap. (978-0-8198-3973-2(6)) Daughters of St. Paul.

Higgs, Liz Curtis. Parable of the Lily. 1999. 7.99 (978-0-8499-5891-5(1)) Nelson, Thomas Inc.

James, Steven. JawDroppers: 36 Shocking Stories for Students Based on the Sayings of Jesus. Reeves, Dale, ed. 2001. 160p. (gr. 7 up). 10.99 (978-0-7847-1264-1(6)) Standard Publishing.

Jeffs, Stephanie. Stories Jesus Told. Tulip, Jenny, illus. 2004. (My First Find Out about Book Ser.). 24p. (ps up). pap. 3.95 (978-0-8294-1733-3(8)) Loyola Pr.

Lashbrook, Marilyn. Sowing & Growing: The Parable of the Sower & the Soils. 1998. (Me Too! Bks.). (J). (ps-2). 5.95 (978-0-933657-74-8(9) , 3000893) Standard Publishing.

Lee, Witness. Experience of Christ in Galatians, Ephesians, Philippians, & Colossians. 2001. 66p. (J). (gr. 6). per. 6.00 (978-0-7363-0850-2(4) , 07-082-001) Living Stream Ministry.

Littleton, Mark. Stories Jesus Told: Lift-the-Flap. Moroney, Trace, illus. 2004. 20p. (J). bds. 10.99 (978-0-8254-5519-3(7)) Kregel Pubns.

Lloyd-Jones, Sally. My Thankful Heart. 2004. (Sweet Hearts Ser.). (Illus.). 12p. (J). bds. 8.99 (978-1-4143-0064-1(6)) Tyndale Hse. Pubs.

Lois, Rock. Good Samaritan. Alex, Ayliffe, illus. 2007. 16p. bds. 5.99 (***978-1-56148-561-1(6)***) Good Bks.

Make Believe Ideas. The Good Samaritan. 2006. (Illus.). 32p. (J). (ps-3). 8.97 (978-1-59145-529-5(4)) Nelson, Thomas Inc.

—The Loaves & Fish. 2006. (Illus.). 32p. (J). (ps-3). 8.97 (978-1-59145-528-8(6)) Nelson, Thomas Inc.

On the Way for 3 - 9's: Parables, Easter & 2nd Coming. 88-104p. (J). pap. 11.99 (978-1-85792-403-9(7) , Christian Focus) Christian Focus Pubns. GBR. *Dist:* Riverside.

The Parables of Jesus. 2004. (Junior Bible Ser.: Vol. 12). 36p. pap. 5.95 (978-1-58516-140-9(3)) American Bible Society.

Parker, Victoria. Jesus in Galilee: And Other New Testament Stories. 2000. (Discovering the Bible Ser.). (Illus.). 64p. (gr. 3-7). 12.95 (978-0-7548-0477-2(1) , Lorenz Bks.) Anness Publishing GBR. *Dist:* National Bk. Network.

Pingry, Patricia A. The Story of the Good Samaritan. Venturi-Pickett, Stacy, illus. 2001. 26p. (J). (ps-3). bds. 6.95 (978-0-8249-4109-3(8)) Ideals Pubns.

Piper, Sophie & Archbold, Tim. The Good Bad Guy & Other Peculiar Parables. 2004. (Illus.). 64p. (J). pap. 6.99 (978-0-7459-4695-5(X) , Lion) Lion Hudson plc GBR. *Dist:* Independent Pubs. Group.

Rabbit. Parables That Jesus Told. (J). pap. 19.95 (978-0-689-80229-4(3) , Simon & Schuster Children's Publishing) Simon & Schuster Children's Publishing.

Runk, Wesley T. The Big Splash: And Other Bible Lessons for Kids. 2001. (FaithBuilders for Kids Ser.: Vol. 11). 96p. (J). (ps-3). pap. 4.99 (978-0-8010-6375-6(2)) Baker Bks.

Sanna, Ellyn. The Parables of Jesus. 2000. (Young Reader's Christian Library). (Illus.). 224p. (J). (gr. 3-7). pap. 1.39 (978-1-57748-724-1(9)) Barbour Publishing, Inc.

Schenck, Walter J., compiled by. Handbook of Jesus' Parables. 2001. (Illus.). 124p. (gr. 4-7). pap. 9.95 (978-0-595-16658-9(X)) iUniverse, Inc.

Sorvillo, Carmen R. & Moore, Helen H. Pop-Up Parables & Other Bible Stories. 1999. 48p. (gr. 1-3). tchr. ed. 9.99 (978-0-570-05353-8(6) , 12-3404GJ) Concordia Publishing Hse.

Stockstill, Gloria McQueen. Jesus Rose on Easter Morn: A Listen! Look! Book. Durrell, Julie, illus. 2004. (ENG.). 20p. (J). bds. 4.99 (978-0-7586-0143-8(3)) Concordia Publishing Hse.

Taylor, Damon. Francis Takes a Tumble: The Story of the Good Samaritan. 2003. (Child Sockology Ser.). (Illus.). 32p. (J). 10.99 (978-0-8254-3867-7(5)) Kregel Pubns.

Trull, Joe E. Look for the Hook: And Other Bible Lessons for Kids. 2001. (FaithBuilders for Kids Ser.: Vol. 12). 96p. (J). (ps-3). pap. 4.99 (978-0-8010-6376-3(0)) Baker Bks.

Wach, Randy-Lynne. A Child's Collection of Parables. Harston, Jerry, illus. 2007. 13.95 (***978-1-59038-724-5(4)***) Deseret Bk. Co.

Wilber, Peggy M. Why Did Jesus Say That?, Level 4. Julien, Terry, tr. Julien, Terry, illus. 1999. (Rocket Readers Ser.). 32p. (J). (gr. 4 up). pap., pap. 4.99 (978-0-7814-3995-4(7) , 0781439957) Cook, David C. Publishing Co.

Wilber, Peggy M., et al. God Can Help!, Level 3. Graham, Alastair, tr. Graham, Alastair, illus. 1999. (Rocket Readers Ser.). 48p. (J). (gr. 3 up). pap., pap. 8.99 (978-0-7814-3998-5(1) , 0781439981) Cook, David C. Publishing Co.

Zobel Nolan, Allia. Good Shepherd & the Little Lost Lamb. Mitchell, Melanie, illus. 2006. 10p. (J). bds. 12.99 (978-0-7847-1789-9(3) , 04296) Standard Publishing.

JESUS CHRIST—POETRY

Bunting, Eve. Who Was Born This Special Day? 2003. (ps-2). lib. bdg. 15.30 (978-0-613-88998-8(3)) Tandem Library Bks.

Jeffs, Stephanie. Share Out the Food with Jesus. Saunderson, Chris, illus. 2007. (J). 5.99 (978-0-9789056-1-3(X)) New Day Publishing, Inc.

Lane, Leena. Sail in the Boat with Jesus. Saunderson, Chris, illus. 2007. (J). 5.99 (978-0-9789056-0-6(1)) New Day Publishing, Inc.

—Stand up & Walk with Jesus. Saunderson, Chris, illus. 2007. (J). 5.99 (978-0-9789056-4-4(4)) New Day Publishing, Inc.

MacKall, Dandi Daley. A Tree for Christmas. Catalano, Dominic, illus. 2004. 32p. (J). (gr. 2 up). 12.99 (978-0-7586-0669-3(9)) Concordia Publishing Hse.

Stiegemeyer, Julie. Baby in a Manger. Wong, Nicole, illus. 2004. 32p. (J). (gr. k-4). 9.99 (978-0-7586-0726-3(1)) Concordia Publishing Hse.

Taylor, Jane. Twinkle, Twinkle Little Star. Harker, Lesley, illus. 2001. 24p. (J). (ps-2). 15.95 (978-0-439-29656-4(0) , Chicken Hse., The) Scholastic, Inc.

JESUS CHRIST—SERMON ON THE MOUNT

see Sermon on the Mount

JESUS CHRIST—TEACHINGS

Anonymous. The Wonderful Story of Jesus. Lee, Ella Dolbear, illus. 2004. reprint ed. pap. 20.95 (978-1-4179-3177-4(9)) Kessinger Publishing, LLC.

Bergt, Carolyn S. Who's the Greatest? Jesus Talks about Greatness: Mattew 18:1-9: 19:13-15; 20:17-28: John 13:12-17 for Children. Blanchette, Dave, illus. 2005. (J). (978-0-7586-0931-1(0)) Concordia Publishing Hse.

Bolanos, Roxana, creator. Miracles of Jesus. l.t. ed. 2002. (Illus.). 5p. (J). pap. 24.95 (978-0-9729001-5-7(2)) Quiltown.

Carmody, Michael A. Life with Jesus: Bible Study Workbook. 2003. 32p. (YA). pap. 10.00 (978-0-910487-54-2(5)) Royalty Publishing Co.

Conn. Jesus Christ for Youth, 2 vols. 2006. (Illus.). 112p. pap., stu. ed. 6.00 (978-0-687-33286-1(9)); 128p. pap. 10.00 (978-0-687-33276-2(1)) Abingdon Pr.

Fair, Barbara A. Children Following the Teachings of Jesus: An Activity Book for Kids. Date not set. (J). (gr. k-2). pap. (978-0-9621174-3-5(9)) Fair, Barbara A.

Ficocelli, Elizabeth. The Imitation of Christ for Children: A Guide to Following Jesus. Sabatino, Chris, illus. 2006. 64p. (J). pap. 8.95 (978-0-8091-6733-3(6) , 6733-6) Paulist Pr.

Flamini, Lorella, illus. Growing in Love: Virtues for Little Ones. 2006. Orig. Title: Giochiamo con Gesu. (J). 11.95 (978-0-8198-3105-7(0)) Pauline Bks. & Media.

Haidle, Helen. What Did Jesus Promise. Anderson, Nancy Munger, illus. 2001. 30p. (J). 5.99 (978-0-310-70036-4(1)) Zonderkidz.

Ham, Ken. Jesus Heals: The Faith That Heals. 2000. (Awesome Adventure Bible Stories Ser.). (Illus.). (J). (gr. 2-7). pap. 5.99 (978-0-89051-330-9(9)) Master Bks.

Hamilton, Eleanor P. Playtime at the Feet of Jesus: (Bound Version), 1. 2006. (J). 10.00 (978-0-9755173-3-8(3)) Autumn Light Pubns.

—Playtime at the Feet of Jesus: Scrapbook Version, 1. 2006. (J). pap. 9.00 (978-0-9755173-2-1(5)) Autumn Light Pubns.

Harik, Ramsay M. Jesus of Nazareth: Teacher & Prophet. 2001. (Book Report Biographies Ser.). (Illus.). 100p. (YA). (gr. 6-8). pap. 6.95 (978-0-531-15552-3(8) , Watts, Franklin) Scholastic Library Publishing.

McCallen, A. J. And Jesus Said. 2000. pap. 9.95 (978-0-8146-1795-3(6)) Liturgical Pr.

Moran, Mary Y. & Myers, Theresa F. Jesus Teaches Us. 77p. (J). (gr. 3). pap. 2.25 (978-0-8198-3925-1(6)) Pauline Bks. & Media.

Pingry, Patricia A. The Story of the Lord's Prayer. Garvin, Elaine, illus. 2004. 24p. (J). bds. 6.95 (978-0-8249-6519-8(1)) Ideals Pubns.

Runk, Wesley T. Jesus Is Your Wedge: And More Truths for Kids. 2001. (FaithBuilders for Kids Ser.: Vol. 6). Tr. of Fam039000. 96p. (J). (ps-3). reprint ed. pap. 4.99 (978-0-8010-6350-3(7) , Object Lessons) Baker Bks.

Schut, Jessie. Telling Your Friends about Jesus. (Friendship Ser.). stu. ed. 3.25 (978-1-56212-744-2(6) , 300550); 55p. mentor's hndbk. ed. 6.25 (978-1-56212-251-5(7) , 300555) CRC Pubns. (Faith Alive Christian Resources).

Teachings of Jesus. 2004. (In Celebration Coloring & Activity Book Ser.). 32p. (J). pap. 1.99 (978-0-7647-1021-6(4) , In Celebration) Schaffer, Frank Pubns.

Vitek, John. Living the Questions Jesus Asks: A Guide for Teens. 2003. 136p. (YA). per. 6.95 (978-0-88489-782-8(6)) St. Mary's Pr.

Wells, Elizabeth & Trout, Lisa. The Beatitudes: Practical Activities. 2001. (Illus.). 32p. (J). (gr. 9-12). pap. 9.95 (978-1-893757-26-4(9)) Needer, E.T. Publishing.

JESUS CHRIST IN ART

see Jesus Christ—Art

JET PLANES

Amato, William. Supersonic Jets. 2002. (Reading Power Ser.). (Illus.). 24p. (J). (gr. 2). lib. bdg. 17.25 (978-0-8239-6009-5(9) , PowerKids Pr.) Rosen Publishing Group, Inc., The.

Los Aviones Tienen Alas. 2003. (Enciclopedia Me Pregunto Por Que). (SPA., Illus.). 32p. (J). (gr. 3-5). (978-84-241-2169-3(4) , EV2031) Everest de Ediciones y Distribucion, S.L. ESP. *Dist:* Lectorum Pubns., Inc.

Baysura, Kelly. Jet Airliners. 2001. (Flying Machines Ser.). (Illus.). 24p. (J). (gr. 1-4). lib. bdg. 20.64 (978-1-58952-005-9(X)) Rourke Publishing, LLC.

Braulick, Carrie A. Jets. 2007. (Blazers—Horsepower Ser.). (Illus.). 32p. (J). 19.93 (978-0-7368-6451-0(2) , 1258927) Capstone Pr., Inc.

Burgan, Michael. The World's Fastest Military Airplanes. 2000. (Built for Speed Ser.). (Illus.). 48p. (J). (gr. 3-4). lib. bdg. 21.26 (978-0-7368-0568-1(0) , Capstone High-Interest Bks.) Capstone Pr., Inc.

Byers, Ann. The Crash of the Concorde: When Disaster Strikes! 2005. (When Disaster Strikes! Ser.). (Illus.). 48p. (YA). (gr. 5-8). lib. bdg. 23.95 (978-0-8239-3673-1(2)) Rosen Publishing Group, Inc., The.

David, Jack. F-16 Fighting Falcon. 2007. (Torque: Military Machines Ser.). (Illus.). 24p. (J). (gr. 3-7). lib. bdg. 20.00 (***978-0-531-18451-6(X)*** , Children's Pr.) Scholastic Library Publishing.

Doeden, Matt. Jets. 2007. 24p. (J). (978-0-7368-6719-1(8) , Pebble Bks.) Capstone Pr., Inc.

Fighter Jets. (Mighty MacHines Ser.). 16p. (J). (978-2-7643-0172-2(3)) Phidal Publishing, Inc./Editions Phidal, Inc.

Glassman, Bruce, ed. Boeing 747. 2003. (Super Structures of the World Ser.). (Illus.). 48p. (J). 24.95 (978-1-56711-864-3(X)); 11.20 (978-1-4103-0191-8(5)) Thomson Gale. (Blackbirch Pr., Inc.).

Green, Michael & Green, Gladys. Air Superiority Fighters: F/A-22 Raptors. 2003. (War Planes Ser.). (Illus.). 32p. (J). lib. bdg. 22.60 (978-0-7368-2148-3(1) , Capstone High/Low Bks.) Capstone Pr., Inc.

—Close Air Support Fighters: A-10 Thunderbolt II. 2003. (War Planes Ser.). (Illus.). 32p. (J). lib. bdg. 22.60 (978-0-7368-2150-6(3) , Capstone High/Low Bks.) Capstone Pr., Inc.

High Flying: Level P, 6 vols., Vol. 3. (Explorers Ser.). 32p. (gr. 3-6). 44.95 (978-0-7699-0619-5(2)) Shortland Pubns. (U. S. A.) Inc.

Hill, Lee Sullivan. Jets. 2005. (Pull Ahead Bks.). (Illus.). 32p. (J). (gr. k-2). lib. bdg. 22.60 (978-0-8225-1541-8(5)) Lerner Publishing Group.

Jay Jay the Jet Plane: High-Flying Adventures. (Illus.). (J). spiral bd. (978-1-58605-820-3(7)) LeapFrog Enterprises, Inc.

Jefferis. Jets, 6 bks., Set. 2003. mass mkt. 48.30 (978-1-4109-0275-7(7)) Raintree.

Jefferis, David. Jets. 2001. (Monster Machines Ser.). (Illus.). 32p. (J). (ps-3). lib. bdg. 25.69 (978-0-7398-2878-6(9)) Raintree.

—Jets. 2003. (gr. 3-6). lib. bdg. 16.40 (978-0-613-78220-3(8)) Tandem Library Bks.

Murdico, Suzanne J. Concorde. 2001. (gr. 7-12). lib. bdg. 15.25 (978-0-613-52010-2(6)) Tandem Library Bks.

Pallotta, Jerry. The Jet Alphabet Book. Bolster, Rob, illus. 1999. 32p. (J). (ps-3). 16.95 (978-0-88106-916-7(7)) Charlesbridge Publishing, Inc.

Petruccio, Steven James. Shiny Jet Planes Stickers. 2006. 2p. (J). pap. 1.50 (978-0-486-44925-8(4)) Dover Pubns., Inc.

Reavis, Tracey. Stealth Jet Fighter: The F-117A. 2000. (High-Tech Military Weapons Ser.). (Illus.). 48p. (YA). (gr. 7-12). 24.00 (978-0-516-23341-3(6) , Children's Pr.) Scholastic Library Publishing.

Roza, Greg. The Incredible Story of Jets. 2004. (Kid's Guide to Incredible Technology Ser.). (Illus.). 24p. (J). lib. bdg. 19.95 (978-0-8239-6713-1(1) , PowerKids Pr.) Rosen Publishing Group, Inc., The.

Schaefer, A. R. Jet Fighter Planes. 2004. (Wild Rides! Ser.). (Illus.). 32p. (J). lib. bdg. 22.60 (978-0-7368-2725-6(0)) Capstone Pr., Inc.

Stone, Lynn M. A-10 Thunderbolt II. 2005. (Fighting Forces Ser.). (Illus.). 32p. (J). (gr. 4-8). 19.95 (978-1-59515-178-0(8)) Rourke Publishing, LLC.

—F-16 Fighting Falcon. 2005. (Fighting Forces Ser.). (Illus.). 32p. (J). (gr. 4-8). 19.95 (978-1-59515-182-7(6)) Rourke Publishing, LLC.

Supersonic Jets: Individual Title Six-Packs. (On Deck Ser.). 24p. (gr. 4-5). 35.00 (978-0-7578-1059-6(4)) Rigby Education.

Sweetman, Bill. Jump Jets: The AV-8B Harriers. 2002. (War Planes Ser.). (Illus.). 32p. (J). (gr. 3-4). lib. bdg. 21.26 (978-0-7368-1068-5(4) , Capstone High-Interest Bks.) Capstone Pr., Inc.

JET PLANES—FICTION

Cook, Sherry & Johnson, Terri. Jazzy Jet, 26 vols. Kuhn, Jesse, illus. l.t. ed. 2006. (Quirkles—Exploring Phonics through Science Ser.: 10). 32p. (J). 7.99 (978-1-933815-09-1(4) , Quirkles, The) Creative 3, LLC.

JEWELRY

see also Gems

Baker, Diane. Jazzy Jewelry: Power Beads, Crystals, Chokers, Illusion & Tattoo Styles. 2000. (Kids Can Bks.). (Illus.). 144p. (J). (gr. 3-9). pap. 12.95 (978-1-885593-47-4(3) , Williamson Bks.) Ideals Pubns.

Balchin, Judy & Haines, Kristy. Funstation Jewelry Design, 5 vols., Set. 1998. (Funstations Ser.). (Illus.). 48p. (J). (gr. 3-7). 17.95 (978-1-57145-350-1(4) , Silver Dolphin Bks.) Advantage Pubs. Group.

Design your own Jewelry. 2004. (How 2 Kits Ser.). (Illus.). 48p. (J). (978-1-84229-927-2(1)) Top That! Publishing PLC.

Elton, Candice & Elton, Richard. Every Kid Needs Secret Jewelry. 2005. (Illus.). 48p. (J). spiral bd. 19.95 (978-1-58685-707-3(X)) Gibbs Smith, Publisher.

Ettinger, Roseann. Popular Jewelry, 1840-1940. 3rd rev. ed. 2002. (Illus.). 176p. (gr. 10-13). pap. 29.95 (978-0-7643-1582-4(X)) Schiffer Publishing, Ltd.

Johnson, Anne Akers. Pulseras Rusticas. 2004. (SPA., Illus.). 32p. (J). (gr. 1). spiral bd. 17.95 (978-968-5528-11-5(X)) Klutz Latino MEX. *Dist:* Independent Pubs. Group.

Kelley, Lyngerda & Schiffer, Nancy N. Costume Jewelry: The Great Pretenders. 4th rev. ed. 2002. (Illus.). 168p. (gr. 10-13). pap. 29.95 (978-0-7643-1573-2(0)) Schiffer Publishing, Ltd.

MacDonald, Fiona. Clothing & Jewelry. (Discovering World Cultures Ser.). (Illus.). 40p. (J). (gr. 4). 2001. pap. (978-0-7787-0246-7(4)); 2000. lib. bdg. (978-0-7787-0236-8(7)) Crabtree Publishing Co.

—Clothing & Jewelry. 2001. (gr. 3-6). lib. bdg. 17.60 (978-0-613-32413-7(7)) Tandem Library Bks.

McDonald, Fiona. Jewelry & Makeup Through History. 2006. (J). lib. bdg. (978-0-8368-6856-2(0)) Stevens, Gareth Inc.

Morrill, Penny Chittim & Berk, Carole A. Mexican Silver: 20th Century Handwrought Jewelry & Metalwork. 3rd rev. ed. 2001. (Illus.). 272p. (gr. 10-13). 59.95 (978-0-7643-1370-7(3)) Schiffer Publishing, Ltd.

Morrison, Mary. Christmas Jewelry. Morrison, James, photos by. 2nd rev. ed. 2002. (Illus.). 160p. (Orig.). (gr. 10-13). pap. 19.95 (978-0-7643-1531-2(5)) Schiffer Publishing, Ltd.

Reynolds, Helen. Jewelry & Accessories. 2003. (Fashionable History of Costume Ser.). (Illus.). 32p. (J). lib. bdg. 25.70 (978-1-4109-0029-6(0)) Raintree.

Schiffer, Nancy N. Rhinestones! A Collector's Handbook & Price Guide. 4th rev. ed. 2003. (Illus.). 160p. (gr. 10-13). pap. 16.95 (978-0-7643-1751-4(2)) Schiffer Publishing, Ltd.

—Silver Jewelry Treasures. 3rd rev. ed. 2003. (Schiffer Book for Collectors Ser.). (Illus.). 144p. (gr. 10-13). pap. 16.95 (978-0-7643-1852-8(7)) Schiffer Publishing, Ltd.

Stillerman, Robbie. Pretty Jewelry Sticker. 2004. (Illus.). 4p. (J). pap., act. bk. ed. 1.50 (978-0-486-43308-0(0)) Dover Pubns., Inc.

Torres, Laura & Johnson, Anne Akers. Brazaletes de la Amistad. 2004. (SPA., Illus.). 60p. (J). (gr. 3). spiral bd. 17.95 (978-968-5528-05-4(5)) Klutz Latino MEX. *Dist:* Independent Pubs. Group.

Ward, Charlotte, ed. Gem Care. Ward, Fred, photos by. 2nd ed. 2003. (Fred Ward Gem Book Ser.). (Illus.). 32p. pap. 9.95 (978-1-887651-07-3(1)) Gem Bk. Pubs.

JEWELRY MAKING

Baker, Diane. Jazzy Jewelry. 2001. (gr. 3-6). lib. bdg. 22.20 (978-0-613-57605-5(5)) Tandem Library Bks.

Boase, Petra & Beak, Nick Huckleberry. Crafty Badges. Freeman, John, photos by. 2000. (Crafty Kids Ser.). (Illus.). 64p. (J). (gr. 3 up). lib. bdg. 26.00 (978-0-8368-2500-8(4)) Stevens, Gareth Inc.

Brend, Dawn. Jazzy Jewelry: Recycle Materials to Make Cool Stuff. 2007. (EcoCrafts Ser.). (Illus.). 48p. (J). pap. 7.95 (***978-0-7534-5969-0(8)*** , Kingfisher) Houghton Mifflin Co. Trade & Reference Div.

Cartier. (Exploring the World Ser.). 48p. (YA). 8.95 (978-0-7565-1139-5(9)) Compass Point Bks.

Dena, Anael. Beaded Jewelry. 2001. (Educational Activity Kits Ser.). (Illus.). (J). (gr. 2-6). pap. 5.95 (978-0-7641-7462-9(2)) Barron's Educational Series, Inc.

DiSalle, Rachel & Warwick, Ellen. Junk Drawer Jewelry. Kurisu, Jane, illus. 2006. 40p. (978-1-55337-966-9(7)); (978-1-55337-965-2(9)) Kids Can Pr., Ltd.

Haab, Sherri. Picture Bracelets. 2003. (Illus.). 24p. (J). (gr. 3 up). spiral bd. 12.95 (978-1-57054-972-4(9)) Klutz.

Haab, Sherri & Haab, Michelle. Dangles & Bangles: 25 Funky Accessories to Make & Wear. Pollak, Barbara, illus. 2005. 96p. (J). pap. 9.95 (978-0-8230-0064-7(8)) Watson-Guptill Pubns., Inc.

Hufford, Deborah. Fashion Crafts: Create Your Own Style. 2005. (Snap Books Craft Ser.). (Illus.). 32p. (J). (gr. 3-5). lib. bdg. 22.60 (978-0-7368-4384-3(1)) Capstone Pr., Inc.

Johnson, Anne Akers. Spool Knit Jewelry: Make Beautiful Bracelets, Anklets & Rings. Klutz Press Staff, ed. 2004. (Illus.). 50p. (YA). spiral bd. 19.95 (978-1-57054-804-8(8)) Klutz.

Koontz, Robin Michal. Jewelry Making for Fun! 2007. (J). lib. bdg. (***978-0-7565-3273-4(6)***) Compass Point Bks.

Macfarlane, Katherine. The Jeweler's Art. 2007. (Eye on Art Ser.). 128p. (gr. 7-10). 31.20 (***978-1-59018-984-9(1)*** , Lucent Bks.) Thomson Gale.

Running Press Staff & Nicholson, Sue. Funky Jewelry: Fun Stuff to Unlock & Share. 2001. (Quarto Children's Book Ser.). (Illus.). 32p. (J). pap. 9.95 (978-0-7624-1062-0(0) , Running Pr. Kids) Running Pr. Bk. Pubs.

Sadler, Judy Ann. Beads.Tr. of Perles. (FRE., Illus.). (J). pap. 7.99 (978-0-590-24194-6(X)) Scholastic, Inc.

—Hemp Jewelry. Bradford, June, illus. 2005. (Kids Can Do It Ser.). 40p. (YA). (gr. 3 up). (978-1-55337-775-7(3)); (978-1-55337-774-0(5)) Kids Can Pr., Ltd.

Scheunemann, Pam. Cool Beaded Jewelry. 2005. (Cool Crafts Ser.). (Illus.). 32p. (J). (gr. k-6). lib. bdg. 22.78 (978-1-59197-739-1(8)) ABDO Publishing Co.

Souter, Gillian. Beads 'n' Badges. Watson, Clare, illus. Martin, Andre, photos by. 2001. (Handy Crafts Ser.). 48p. (J). (gr. 2 up). lib. bdg. 24.67 (978-0-8368-2819-1(4)) Stevens, Gareth Inc.

JEWELS

see Gems; Jewelry; Precious Stones

JEWISH-ARAB RELATIONS

Blohm, Craig E. The Israeli-Palestinian Conflict. 2006. (J). (978-1-59018-645-9(1) , Lucent Bks.) Thomson Gale.

Ellis, Deborah. Three Wishes: Palestinian & Israeli Children Speak. 2006. (Illus.). 144p. (J). pap. 8.95 (978-0-88899-645-9(4)) Groundwood Bks. CAN. *Dist:* Perseus Distribution.

Ellis, Deborah, ed. Three Wishes: Palestinian & Israeli Children Speak. 2004. (YA). 16.95 (978-0-88899-608-4(X) , Libros Tigrillo) Groundwood Bks. CAN. *Dist:* Transition Vendor.

Frank, Mitch. Understanding the Holy Land: Answering Questions about the Israeli-Palestinian Conflict. 2005. (Illus.). 160p. (YA). (gr. 6). 17.99 (978-0-670-06032-0(1) , Viking Juvenile) Penguin Group (USA) Inc.

Gottfried, Ted. The Israelis & Palestinians: Small Steps to Peace. 2000. (Headliners Ser.). (Illus.). 64p. (gr. 5-8). lib. bdg. 25.90 (978-0-7613-1859-0(3) , Millbrook Pr.) Lerner Publishing Group.

Hanel, Rachael. The Israeli-Palestinian Conflict. 2007. (J). (978-1-58341-548-1(3) , Creative Education) Creative Co., The.

Harris, Nathaniel. Israel & the Arab Nations in Conflict. 1999. (New Perspectives Ser.). (Illus.). 64p. (J). (gr. 4-7). lib. bdg. 28.54 (978-0-8172-5019-5(0)) Raintree.

Israel & Palestine: The Roots of Conflict; Fight for Peace, 2 cass.; set. 2003. (YA). (gr. 9-12). tchr. ed. 89.95 (978-1-58738-432-5(9)) Discovery Communications.

Katz, Samuel M. Jerusalem or Death: Palestinian Terrorism. 72p. (YA). (gr. 9 up). 19.95 (978-1-58013-208-4(1)) Kar-Ben Publishing.

—Jerusalem or Death: Palestinian Terrorism. 2003. (Terrorist Dossiers Ser.). (Illus.). 72p. (J). (gr. 6-12). 26.60 (978-0-8225-4033-5(9)) Lerner Publishing Group.

Luxenberg, Alan H. The Palestine Mandate & the Creation of Israel, 1920-1949. 2007. (J). ***978-1-4222-0170-1(8))*** Mason Crest Pubs.

Minnis, Ivan. The Arab-Israeli Conflict. 2002. (Troubled World Ser.). (Illus.). 64p. (J). (gr. 6 up). lib. bdg. 28.54 (978-0-7398-6340-4(1)) Raintree.

Ross, Stewart. The Arab-Israeli Conflict. 56p. (J). 2005. pap. 8.95 (978-1-4034-5524-6(4)); 2004. lib. bdg. 31.36 (978-1-4034-4871-2(X)) Heinemann Library.

Senker, Cath. The Arab-Israeli Conflict. 2004. (Questioning History Ser.). (J). lib. bdg. 28.50 (978-1-58340-441-6(4)) Smart Apple Media.

Sha'Ban, Mervet A., et al. If You Could Be My Friend: Letters of Mervet Akram Sha'Ban & Galit Fink. Ellbaz, Ariane & Khadige, Beatrice, trs. from FRE. 1998. (Illus.). 118p. (YA). (gr. 5-9). 16.99 (978-0-531-33113-2(X) , Orchard Bks.) Scholastic, Inc.

—If You Could Be My Friend: Letters of Mervet Akram Sha'Ban & Galit Fink. Elbaz, Ariane & Khadige, Beatrice, trs. from FRE. 1998. (Illus.). 118p. (YA). (gr. 5-9). pap. 15.95 (978-0-531-30113-5(3) , Orchard Bks.) Scholastic, Inc.

Slavicek, Louise Chipley. Israel. 2002. (Creation of the Modern Middle East Ser.). (Illus.). 125p. (gr. 6-12). 35.00 (978-0-7910-6511-2(1) , Chelsea Hse.) Facts On File, Inc.

Whiting, Jim. The Creation of Israel. 2007. (Monumental Milestones Ser.). (Illus.). 48p. (YA). lib. bdg. 29.95 ***(978-1-58415-538-6(8))*** Mitchell Lane Pubs., Inc.

JEWISH-ARAB RELATIONS—FICTION

Clinton, Cathryn. Stone in My Hand. Johnson, Peter, illus. 2002. 192p. (YA). (gr. 6-12). 15.99 (978-0-7636-1388-4(6)) Candlewick Pr.

—Stone in My Hand. 2004. (Illus.). 208p. (YA). (gr. 6 up). reprint ed. pap. 5.99 (978-0-7636-2561-0(2)) Candlewick Pr.

Levine, Anna. Running on Eggs. 1999. 128p. (J). (gr. 5-9). 15.95 (978-0-8126-2875-3(6)) Cricket Bks.

Nye, Naomi Shihab. Habibi. 1999. (J). 12.64 (978-0-606-16320-0(4)) Tandem Library Bks.

JEWISH HOLIDAYS

see Fasts and Feasts—Judaism

JEWISH LANGUAGE

see Hebrew Language

JEWISH LITERATURE

see also Bible; Hebrew Literature

Cahn, Yehuda. It's the Effort That Counts. Shiman, Hedy, illus. 2001. (J). pap. (978-0-9707757-0-2(9)) Torah Pubn. Fund.

Goldin, Barbara Diamond. One Hundred One Jewish Read-Aloud Stories: Ten Minute Readings from the World's Best-Loved Jewish Literature. 2002. (Illus.). 360p. (J). tchr. ed. 12.95 (978-1-57912-212-6(4) , 81212) Black Dog & Leventhal Pubs., Inc.

Karkowsky, Nancy. The Ten Commandments: Text. (J). (gr. 3-4). pap. act. bk. ed. 6.50 (978-0-87441-477-6(6)) Behrman Hse., Inc.

JEWISH RELIGION

see Judaism

JEWS

see also Discrimination

Bitton-Jackson, Livia. My Bridges of Hope. 2002. (gr. 7-12). lib. bdg. 13.00 (978-0-613-73376-2(2)) Tandem Library Bks.

Chait, Baruch. The Lost Treasure of Tikkun Hamiddos Island. Pollack, Gadi, illus. (Good Middos Ser.: Vol. 2). 62p. 25.99 (978-1-58330-478-5(9)) Feldheim Pubs.

Chwast, Seymour, illus. Had Gadya: A Passover Song. rev. ed. 2007. 32p. (J). pap. 7.95 ***(978-1-59643-298-7(5))*** Roaring Brook Pr.

Clark, Anne. My Jewish Faith. 1998. (My Faith Ser.). (Illus.). 32p. 7.99 (978-0-237-51897-4(X) , Evans Brothers, Limited) Evans Publishing Group GBR. *Dist:* Independent Pubs. Group.

Cone, Molly. Hello, Hello, Are You There, God? Kaye, Rosalind Charney, illus. rev. ed. 2004. viii, 55p. (gr. k-3). pap. 12.95 (978-0-8074-0648-9(1) , 102553) URJ Pr.

Dion, L. N. The Opposites of My Jewish Year. Olson, Julie, illus. 2005. 12p. (J). (ps-ps). per. 5.95 (978-1-58013-113-1(1)) Kar-Ben Publishing.

Gritter, Marissa. The Jewish Americans. 2002. (Welcome to America Ser.). (Illus.). 64p. (J). (gr. 5 up). lib. bdg. (978-1-59084-109-9(3)) Mason Crest Pubs.

Haberle, Susan E. Jewish Immigrants, 1880-1924. 2002. (Blue Earth Books). (Illus.). 32p. (J). (gr. 4). lib. bdg. 22.60 (978-0-7368-1207-8(5) , Bridgestone Bks.) Capstone Pr., Inc.

Horton, Casey. The Jews: We Came to North America. 2006. (Illus.). 32p. (J). (gr. 4-8). reprint ed. 19.00 (978-0-7567-9905-2(8)) DIANE Publishing Co.

Katz, Yoni, prod. Virtual l'Shana Tovah. 2003. (J). cd-rom 12.00 (978-1-932349-23-8(5) , 20,000) Jewish Educational Media.

Lehman-Wilzig, Tami. Keeping the Promise: A Torah's Journey. Orback, Craig, illus. 2004. 32p. (J). (gr. 1-5). 16.95 (978-1-58013-117-9(4)); pap. 6.95 (978-1-58013-118-6(2)) Kar-Ben Publishing.

Morris, Ann. Grandma Esther Remembers: A Jewish-American Family Story. Linenthal, Peter, illus. 2002. (What Was It Like, Grandma? Ser.). 32p. (gr. k-3). lib. bdg. 22.90 (978-0-7613-2318-1(X) , Millbrook Pr.) Lerner Publishing Group.

Poole, Josephine. Anne Frank. Barrett, Angela, illus. 2005. 40p. (J). (gr. 5 up). 17.95 (978-0-375-83242-0(4) , Knopf Bks. for Young Readers) Random Hse. Children's Bks.

Ruggiero, Adriane. The Jews. 2006. 80-244*p. (gr. 10-12). 34.95 (978-0-7377-2767-8(5) , Greenhaven Pr., Inc.) Thomson Gale.

Seidman, Laurence. What Makes Someone a Jew? 2007. (Illus.). 32p. (J). pap. 8.99 (978-1-58023-321-7(X)) Jewish Lights Publishing.

Skolnik, Fred & Berenbaum, Michael. Encyclopedia Judaica, 22 Vols., Set. 2nd rev. ed. 2006. (Illus.). 1995.00 (978-0-02-865928-2(7) , Macmillan Reference USA) Thomson Gale.

Thompson, Gare. Our New Life in America: The Marks Family Lives the American Dream. 2002. (Voices from America's Past Ser.). (Illus.). 40p. (J). (978-0-7922-8701-8(0)) National Geographic Society.

Ueda, Reed & Stotsky, Sandra, eds. Jewish-American Answer Book. 1999. (Ethnic Answer Book Ser.). (Illus.). 136p. (J). (gr. 5 up). lib. bdg. 19.75 (978-0-7910-4799-6(7) , Chelsea Hse.) Facts On File, Inc.

JEWS—BIOGRAPHY

see also Rabbis

Abramson, Ann. Who Was Anne Frank? Harrison, Nancy, illus. 2007. (Who Was... ? Ser.). 112p. (J). pap. 4.99 (978-0-448-44482-6(8) , Grosset & Dunlap) Penguin Group (USA) Inc.

Adler, David A. A Picture Book of Anne Frank. Ritz, Karen, illus. 2004. (J). (ps-3). audio compact disk 18.95 (978-1-59112-781-9(5)) Live Oak Media.

Antin, Mary. Promised Land. 2001. (gr. 7-12). lib. bdg. 19.90 (978-0-613-50135-4(7)) Tandem Library Bks.

Arem, T. Z. The Story of Reb Baruch Ber Lebowitz: The Kamenitzer Rosh Yeshiba - Rabbi Baruch Ber Leibowitz & His Successor, Rabbi Reuven Grozovsky. (ArtScroll Youth Ser.). (Illus.). 128p. (YA). (gr. 6-12). pap. 8.99 (978-0-89906-804-6(9) , RBBP) Mesorah Pubns., Ltd.

Ashby, Ruth. Anne Frank: Young Diarist. 2005. 186p. (J). lib. bdg. 18.46 ***(978-1-4242-2208-7(7))*** Fitzgerald Bks.

Avital, Moshe. Not to Forget, Impossible to Forgive: Poignant Reflections on the Holocaust. 2004. (Illus.). 339p. (YA). (978-965-90462-4-9(3)) Mazo Pubs.

Ayer, Eleanor H. In the Ghettos: Teens Who Survived the Ghettos of the Holocaust. 1999. (Teen Witnesses to the Holocaust Ser.). (Illus.). 64p. (YA). (gr. 7-12). lib. bdg. 26.50 (978-0-8239-2845-3(4) , TWGHET) Rosen Publishing Group, Inc., The.

Bankston, John. Edward Teller & the Development of the Hydrogen Bomb. l.t. ed. 2002. (Unlocking the Secrets of Science Ser.). (Illus.). 56p. (gr. 4-10). lib. bdg. 25.70 (978-1-58415-108-1(0)) Mitchell Lane Pubs., Inc.

Bayer, Linda N. Elie Wiesel: Spokesman for Remembrance. 2005. (Holocaust Biographies Ser.). (Illus.). 112p. (J). (gr. 7-12). lib. bdg. 26.50 (978-0-8239-3306-8(7) , HBWIES) Rosen Publishing Group, Inc., The.

Berkow, Ira. Hank Greenberg: Hall-of-Fame Slugger. Ellison, Mick, illus. 2000. 108p. pap. 9.95 (978-0-8276-0685-2(0)) Jewish Pubn. Society.

Bierman, Carol. Journey to Ellis Island. McGaw, Laurie, illus. 1998. 48p. (gr. 3-17). 17.95 (978-0-7868-0377-4(0)) Hyperion Bks. for Children.

—Journey to Ellis Island: How My Father Came to America. 1999. 48p. (J). pap. 8.95 (978-0-7868-1411-4(X)) Disney Pr.

Bierman, Carol & Hehner, Barbara. Journey to Ellis Island: How My Father Came to America. McGaw, Laurie, illus. 2003. 48p. (gr. 4-8). 18.00 (978-0-7567-6844-7(6)) DIANE Publishing Co.

Bitton-Jackson, Livia. I Have Lived a Thousand Years: Growing up in the Holocaust. 1999. (J). 11.64 (978-0-606-15948-7(7)); (gr. 7-12). lib. bdg. 13.00 (978-0-613-17811-2(4)) Tandem Library Bks.

—My Bridges of Hope: Searching for Life & Love after Auschwitz. 2001. (YA). (978-0-606-20815-4(1)) Tandem Library Bks.

Borden, Louise. The Journey That Saved Curious George: The True Wartime Escape of Margret & H. A. Rey. Drummond, Allan, illus. 2005. 80p. (J). (gr. 3-5). 17.00 (978-0-618-33924-2(8)) Houghton Mifflin Co. Trade & Reference Div.

Brown, Jonatha A. Anne Frank. 2004. (Gente Que Hay Que Conocer Ser.). (Illus.). 24p. (J). pap. (978-0-8368-4358-3(4)) Stevens, Gareth Inc.

Dunn, Joeming W. & Dunn, Ben. Anne Frank. Dunn, Joeming W. & Dunn, Ben, illus. 2007. (Bio-Graphics Ser.). (Illus.). 32p. (J). (gr. 3-6). lib. bdg. 27.07 ***(*978-1-60270-065-9(6)*** , Graphic Planet) Magic Wagon.

Eisenberg, Azriel. Fill a Blank Page: A Biography of Solomon Schechter. (Illus.). (J). (gr. 6-11). 3.75 (978-0-8381-0730-0(3) , 10-730) United Synagogue of America Bk. Service.

Finkelman, Shimon. The Story of Reb Yosef Chaim: The Life & Times of Rabbi Yosef Chaim Sonnefield, the Guardian of Jerusalem. Dershowitz, Yosef, illus. (ArtScroll Youth Ser.). 160p. (YA). (gr. 6-12). 11.99 (978-0-89906-779-7(4) , CHFH) Mesorah Pubns., Ltd.

Finkelstein, Norman H. Captain of Innocence: France & the Dreyfus Affair. 2000. (gr. 7-12). lib. bdg. 23.40 (978-0-613-81391-4(X)) Tandem Library Bks.

—Captain of Innocence: France & the Dreyfus Affair. 2001. (Illus.). 160p. (YA). (gr. 7-12). pap. 13.95 (978-0-595-15651-1(7) , Backinprint.com) iUniverse, Inc.

Frank, Anne. Anne Frank: The Diary of a Young Girl. adapted ed. pap., tchr. ed. 4.95 (978-0-8359-0138-3(6)) Globe Fearon Educational Publishing.

Gertner, Sheina Sachar. The Tree Stood Still. 2006. 96p. per. 9.95 ***(*978-1-58939-886-3(6))*** Virtualbookworm.com Publishing, Inc.

Goldman, David J. Jewish Sports Stars: Athletic Heroes Past & Present. 2006. (Illus.). 96p. (J). pap. 9.95 (978-1-58013-183-4(2)) Kar-Ben Publishing.

Harris, Samuel R. Sammy Child Survivor of the Holocaust. 2005. (Illus.). 128p. pap. 14.95 (978-0-9759253-0-0(X)) Harris, Samuel.

Hermann, Spring. Anne Frank: Hope in the Shadows of the Holocaust. 2005. (Holocaust Heroes & Nazi Criminals Ser.). (Illus.). 160p. (J). (gr. 6-12). lib. bdg. 27.93 (978-0-7660-2531-8(4)) Enslow Pubs., Inc.

Houghton, Sarah. Elie Wiesel: A Holocaust Survivor Cries Out for Peace. 2003. (High Five Reading Ser.). (Illus.). (J). 64p. lib. bdg. 22.60 (978-0-7368-2792-8(7)); 48p. pap. 8.75 (978-0-7368-2833-8(8)) Capstone Pr., Inc.

—Elie Wiesel: A Holocaust Survivor Cries Out for Peace, 6 vols. (gr. 4 up). 49.95 (978-0-7368-2843-7(5) , High Five) Red Brick Learning.

Kacer, Kathy. Hiding Edith. 2006. (Illus.). 120p. (J). pap. 10.95 (978-1-897187-06-7(8)) Second Story Pr. CAN. *Dist:* Orca Bk. Pubs. USA.

Kaplan, William & Tanaka, Shelley. One More Border: The True Story of One Family's Escape from War-Torn Europe. Taylor, Stephen, illus. 2004. 61p. (J). (gr. 3-6). pap. 9.95 (978-0-88899-638-1(1)) Groundwood Bks. CAN. *Dist:* Perseus Distribution.

Kurtis, Arlene & Lerman, Jona. The Stone Pillow: The Life & Times of Jona Lerman. 1999. (YA). (gr. 7-12). per. 15.00 (978-0-9676869-0-5(3)) Globus Bks.

Lee, Carol Ann. Anne Frank & the Children of the Holocaust. 2008. 256p. (J). (gr. 4). 6.99 ***(*978-0-14-241069-1(1)*** , Puffin) Penguin Group (USA) Inc.

Lewis, Brenda Ralph. Anne Frank Biography. 2001. (Eyewitness Readers Ser.). (Illus.). (J). (978-0-606-21469-8(0)) Tandem Library Bks.

Lobel, Anita. No Pretty Pictures: A Child of War. 2000. (Illus.). 208p. (J). (gr. 5 up). pap. 6.99 (978-0-380-73285-2(8)) HarperCollins Pubs.

—No Pretty Pictures: A Child of War. 2000. (978-0-606-17979-9(8)); (gr. 5-8). lib. bdg. 14.15 (978-0-613-28590-2(5)) Tandem Library Bks.

Maarsen, Jacqueline Van. A Friend Called Anne: One Girl's Story of War, Peace & a Unique Friendship with Anne Frank. 2005. (Illus.). 176p. (J). (gr. 3). 15.99 (978-0-670-05958-4(7) , Viking Juvenile) Penguin Group (USA) Inc.

Mara, Wil. Anne Frank. 2006. (Illus.). 31p. (978-0-516-29841-2(0)) Children's Pr., Ltd.

Matuz, Roger. Albert Kahn: Architect of Detroit. 2002. (Detroit Biography Series for Young Readers). (Illus.). 104p. (YA). (gr. 5 up). pap. 14.95 (978-0-8143-2957-3(8)) Wayne State Univ. Pr.

—Albert Kahn: Builder of Detroit. 2002. (Detroit Biography Series for Young Readers). (Illus.). 104p. (J). 27.95 (978-0-8143-2956-6(X) , Great Lakes Bks.) Wayne State Univ. Pr.

Metzger, Lois. Yours, Anne: The Life of Anne Frank. 2004. (Illus.). 97p. (J). (978-0-439-59099-0(X)) Scholastic, Inc.

Michelson, Richard. As Good as Anybody. 2008. 40p. (J). (gr. 1-5). lib. bdg. 19.99 ***(*978-0-375-93335-6(2)*** , Knopf Bks. for Young Readers) Random Hse. Children's Bks.

Millman, Isaac. Hidden Child. Millman, Isaac, illus. 2005. (Illus.). 80p. (J). (gr. 4-9). 18.00 (978-0-374-33071-2(9) , Farrar, Straus & Giroux (BYR)) Farrar, Straus & Giroux.

Perl, Lila. Four Perfect Pebbles. 1999. (gr. 5-8). lib. bdg. 14.15 (978-0-7857-1852-9(4)) Tandem Library Bks.

—Four Perfect Pebbles: A Holocaust Story. 1999. (Illus.). 144p. (J). (gr. 3 up). pap. 5.99 (978-0-380-73188-6(6) , Harper Trophy) HarperCollins Pubs.

—Four Perfect Pebbles: A Holocaust Story. 1999. (Illus.). (J). 12.64 (978-0-606-17971-3(2)) Tandem Library Bks.

Rabinovici, Schoschana. Thanks to My Mother. 2000. (978-0-606-18455-7(4)) Tandem Library Bks.

Rubin, Susan Goldman. Haym Salomon: American Patriot. Slonim, David, illus. 2007. 40p. (J). (ps-5). 16.95 (978-0-8109-1087-4(X) , Abrams Bks. for Young Readers) Abrams, Harry N. , Inc.

Rubin, Susan Goldman & Weissberger, Ela. The Cat with the Yellow Star: Coming of Age in Terezin. 2006. (Illus.). 40p. (J). (gr. 3-7). 16.95 (978-0-8234-1831-2(6)) Holiday Hse., Inc.

Russo, Marisabina. Always Remember Me: How One Family Survived World War II. Russo, Marisabina, illus. 2005. (Illus.). 48p. (J). (gr. 1-5). 17.99 (978-0-689-86920-4(7) , Atheneum) Simon & Schuster Children's Publishing.

Saunders, Nicholas. The Life of Anne Frank. 2006. (Stories from History Ser.). 48p. (J). 14.95 (978-0-7696-4714-2(6)); pap. 6.95 (978-0-7696-4695-4(6)) School Specialty Publishing.

Schanzer, Rosalyn. Escaping to America: A True Story. Schanzer, Rosalyn, illus. 2000. (Illus.). 32p. (J). (gr. 3-7). 15.89 (978-0-688-16990-9(2)); 15.95 (978-0-688-16989-3(9)) HarperCollins Pubs.

Schmittroth, Linda. People of the Holocaust. 1998. (J). 49.00 (978-0-7876-1744-8(X)); pap. 49.00 (978-0-7876-1745-5(8)) Thomson Gale. (UXL).

Schmittroth, Linda, ed. People of the Holocaust, 2 vols. 1998. (Holocaust Library). (Illus.). 416p. (YA). (gr. 4-7). lib. bdg. 120.00 (978-0-7876-1743-1(1) , GML00502-111144, UXL) Thomson Gale.

Schur, Maxine Rose. Hannah Szenes: A Song of Light. rev. ed. 1998. 106p. pap. 9.95 (978-0-8276-0628-9(1)) Jewish Pubn. Society.

Senker, Cath. Anne Frank: Voice of Hope. 2001. (Famous Lives Ser.). (Illus.). 48p. (J). (gr. 3-7). lib. bdg. 27.12 (978-0-8172-5719-4(5)) Raintree.

Siegal, Aranka. Grace in the Wilderness: After the Liberation, 1945-1948. 2003. (gr. 5-8). lib. bdg. 14.10 (978-0-613-59626-8(9)) Tandem Library Bks.

—Grace in the Wilderness: After the Liberation 1945-1948. unabr. ed. 1998. (YA). Class Set. 124.70 incl. audio (978-0-7887-2539-5(4) , 46709); Homework Set. (gr. 7). 58.24 incl. audio (978-0-7887-2234-9(4) , 40718) Recorded Bks., LLC.

Silverman, Erica. Sholom's Treasure: How Sholom Aleichem Became a Writer. Gerstein, Mordicai, illus. 2005. 40p. (J). 16.00 (978-0-374-38055-7(4) , Farrar, Straus & Giroux (BYR)) Farrar, Straus & Giroux.

Singer, Flora M. Flora - I Was but A Child. 2007. (J). pap. 15.95 ***(*978-0-9760739-8-7(6))*** Holocaust Survivors' Memoirs Project.

Speregen, Devra Newberger. Ilan Ramon: Jewish Star. 2004. (Illus.). 120p. pap. 9.95 (978-0-8276-0769-9(5)) Jewish Pubn. Society.

Spielman, Gloria. Janusz Korczak's Children. 2007. (Kar-Ben for Older Readers Ser.). (Illus.). (J). (gr. 2-5). 17.95 (978-1-58013-255-8(3)) Kar-Ben Publishing.

—Janusz Korczak's Children. Archambault, Matthew, illus. 2007. (Kar-Ben for Older Readers Ser.). (J). (gr. 2-5). pap. 7.95 ***(*978-0-8225-7050-9(5))*** Kar-Ben Publishing.

Tito, E. Tina. Liberation: Teens in the Concentration Camps & the Teen Soldiers Who Liberated Them. 1999. (Teen Witnesses to the Holocaust Ser.). (Illus.). 64p. (YA). (gr. 7-12). lib. bdg. 26.50 (978-0-8239-2846-0(2) , TWLIBE) Rosen Publishing Group, Inc., The.

van Maarsen, Jacqueline & Lee, Carol Ann. A Friend Called Anne. 2007. 176p. (J). (gr. 3). pap. 6.99 (978-0-14-240719-6(4) , Puffin) Penguin Group (USA) Inc.

Venable, Alan. The Story of Anne Frank. Ham, Jeff, illus. 2001. (J). (gr. 5-6). 65.00 incl. audio, cd-rom (978-1-58702-398-9(9)) Johnston, Don Inc.

Warren, Andrea. Surviving Hitler: A Boy in the Nazi Death Camps. 2002. (gr. 3-6). lib. bdg. 15.30 (978-0-613-56635-3(1)) Tandem Library Bks.

Watad, Mahmoud. Agnostic Reader. 2007. (Illus.). 220p. pap. 19.00 ***(*978-1-59102-535-1(4))*** Prometheus Bks., Pubs.

Woog, Adam. Anne Frank. 2004. (Heroes & Villains Ser.). (Illus.). 112p. (J). 29.95 (978-1-59018-349-6(5) , Lucent Bks.) Thomson Gale.

JEWS—CZECHOSLOVAKIA—FICTION

Kanefield, Teri. Rivka's Way. 2001. (Illus.). 144p. (J). (gr. 5-9). 15.95 (978-0-8126-2870-8(5)) Cricket Bks.

Winter, Kathryn. Katarina. 1999. (J). (978-0-606-17441-1(9)) Tandem Library Bks.

JEWS—FESTIVALS

see Fasts and Feasts—Judaism

JEWS—FICTION

Abraham, Michelle Shapiro. Good Morning, Boker Tov. Alko, Selina, illus. 2004. pap. 6.95 (978-0-8074-0783-7(6) , 101974) URJ Pr.

—Good Night, Lilah Tov. Alko, Selina, illus. 2004. pap. 6.95 (978-0-8074-0784-4(4) , 101975) URJ Pr.

Abraham, Michelle Shapiro. My Cousin Tamar Lives in Israel. Koffsky, Ann D., illus. 2006. (J). (ps). pap. 6.95 ***(*978-0-8074-0989-3(8))*** URJ Pr.

Ada, Alma Flor. Celebrate Hannukah with Bubbe's Tales. Epelbaum, Mariano, illus. 2006. 31p. (J). (978-1-59820-134-5(4)) Santillana USA Publishing Co., Inc.

J K L

Adelson, Leone. The Mystery Bear: A Purim Story. Howland, Naomi, illus. 2004. 32p. (J). (gr. k-3). tchr. ed. 15.00 (978-0-618-33725-5(3) , Clarion Bks.) Houghton Mifflin Co. Trade & Reference Div.

—The Mystery Bear: A Purim Story. Howland, Naomi, tr. Howland, Naomi, illus. 2004. 32p. (J). (ps-2). 15.00 (978-0-618-33727-9(X) , Clarion Bks.) Houghton Mifflin Co. Trade & Reference Div.

Adler, David A. One Yellow Daffodil: A Hanukkah Story. Bloom, Lloyd, illus. 1999. 32p. (J). (gr. 1-5). pap. 7.00 (978-0-15-202094-1(2) , Harcourt Paperbacks) Harcourt Children's Bks.

—One Yellow Daffodil: A Hanukkah Story. 1999. (gr. 3-6). lib. bdg. 14.15 (978-0-613-22137-5(0)) Tandem Library Bks.

Aleichem, Sholom. Holiday Tales of Sholem Aleichem. Shevrin, Aliza, ed. 2003. 128p. pap. 6.95 (978-0-486-42864-2(8)) Dover Pubns., Inc.

Asner, Anne-Marie. Klutzy Boy. Asner, Anne-Marie, illus. l.t. ed. 2007. (Illus.). 32p. (J). per. 6.95 (978-0-9753629-4-5(1)) Matzah Ball Bks.

Attema, Martha. Hero. 2003. (Orca Young Readers Ser.). (Illus.). 144p. (J). (gr. 3-6). pap. 5.95 (978-1-55143-251-9(X)) Orca Bk. Pubs. USA.

Barth-Grozinger, Inge. Something Remains. Bell, Anthea, tr. from GER. 2006. 400p. (gr. 5-9). 16.99 (978-0-7868-3880-6(9)) Hyperion Pr.

Bat-Ami, Miriam. Two Suns in the Sky. 1999. 208p. (YA). (gr. 7-12). 17.95 (978-0-8126-2900-2(0)) Cricket Bks.

—Two Suns in the Sky. 2001. 208p. (J). pap. 6.99 (978-0-14-230036-7(5) , Puffin) Penguin Group (USA) Inc.

—Two Suns in the Sky. 2001. (gr. 7-12). lib. bdg. 15.30 (978-0-613-44425-5(6)) Tandem Library Bks.

Bell, Mary Reeves. Secret of Mezuzah. 1999. (J). (978-0-606-18974-3(2)) Tandem Library Bks.

Benenfeld, Rikki. Let's Go to Shul. Benenfeld, Rikki, illus. 2002. (Illus.). 24p. (J). (ps-1). 10.95 (978-1-929628-08-7(0)) Hachai Publishing.

Benjamin, Ruth. Stranger to Her People. 207p. (YA). 14.95 (978-1-56062-210-9(5) , CFR129H); pap. 11.95 (978-1-56062-231-4(8) , CFR129S) CIS Communications, Inc.

Bennett, Cherie & Gottesfeld, Jeff. Anne Frank & Me. 2002. 291p. (YA). pap. 6.99 (978-0-698-11973-4(8) , Putnam Juvenile) Penguin Group (USA) Inc.

Biers-Ariel, Matt. The Seven Species. Goodman, Tama, illus. 2003. 48p. 19.95 (978-0-8074-0852-0(2) , 161902) URJ Pr.

—Solomon & the Trees. Silverberg-Kiss, Esti, illus. 2004. (J). (gr. k-3). 13.95 (978-0-8074-0749-3(6) , 101055) URJ Pr.

Blanc, Esther Silverstein & Eagle, Godeane. Long Johns for a Small Chicken. Dixon, Tennessee, illus. 2003. (J). 16.95 (978-1-884244-23-0(8)) Volcano Pr.

Blatt, Evelyn. More Precious Than Gold: A Story of Inquisition Spain in the 1490's. Gardner, Eve-Lynn J., ed. Toron, Eli, illus. 2002. 200p. (J). (gr. 2-5). pap. 8.95 (978-1-929628-10-0(2)) Hachai Publishing.

Blitz, Shmuel. Bedtime Stories of Jewish Holidays. 1998. 48p. 14.99 (978-1-57819-174-1(2) , BEDJH) Mesorah Pubns., Ltd.

—Bedtime Stories of Jewish Values. 1998. 48p. 14.99 (978-1-57819-195-6(5) , BEDV) Mesorah Pubns., Ltd.

—Bedtime Stories of Torah Values. 1999. 48p. 14.99 (978-1-57819-498-8(9) , BEDB) Mesorah Pubns., Ltd.

—Bedtime Stories to Make You Smile. 2003. 14.99 (978-1-57819-745-3(7) , BEDS) Mesorah Pubns., Ltd.

—My First Book of Jewish Stories. Katz, Tova, illus. 1999. (ArtScroll Youth Ser.). 48p. (J). 14.99 (978-1-57819-294-6(3) , MFJS) Mesorah Pubns., Ltd.

Brightwood, Laura, illus. Wise People of Helm. Brightwood, Laura, . 2006. (J). (978-0-9779290-4-7(3)) 3-C Institute for Social Development.

Buckvar, Felice. Dangerous Dream. Kemnitz, Myrna, ed. 1998. 123p. (YA). (gr. 5 up). 9.99 (978-0-88092-277-7(X) , 277X) Royal Fireworks Publishing Co.

Carney, Karen L. What Is the Meaning of Shiva. Carney, Karen L., illus. rev. ed. 2001. (Barklay & Eve Ser.: Bk. 3). Orig. Title: Barklay & Eve. (Illus.). (J). pap. 6.95 (978-0-9667820-2-8(X)) Dragonfly Publishing.

Chaikin, Miriam. Angel Secrets: Stories Based on Jewish Legend. Gore, Leonid, illus. 2005. 80p. (J). 18.95 (978-0-8050-7150-4(4) , Holt, Henry & Co. Bks. For Young Readers) Holt, Henry & Co.

Chotjewitz, David. Daniel Half Human. Orgel, Doris, tr. 2006. 336p. (YA). reprint ed. mass mkt. 5.99 (978-0-689-85748-5(9) , Simon Pulse) Simon & Schuster Children's Publishing.

Chwast, Seymour. The Miracle of Hanukkah. 2006. (Illus.). 28p. 14.95 (978-1-59354-157-6(0)) Blue Apple Bks.

Cleveland, Robert. Magic Apple. Hoffmire, Baird, illus. 2006. 32p. pap. 3.95 (978-0-87483-800-8(2)) August Hse. Pubs., Inc.

Cohen, Barbara. The Carp in the Bathtub. 48p. (J). (gr. 2-4). pap. 5.95 (978-0-8072-1332-2(2) , Listening Library) Random Hse. Audio Publishing Group.

Cohen, Deborah Bodin. The Seventh Day. Hall, Melanie, illus. 2005. 24p. (J). (ps-3). pap. 6.95 (978-1-58013-125-4(5)); 16.95 (978-0-929371-24-5(0)) Kar-Ben Publishing.

Cohen, Leslie, et al. Jewish Love Stories for Kids: An Anthology of Short Stories. 2005. (Jewish Stories for Kids Ser.). 232p. (J). 16.95 (978-1-930143-45-6(1) , 3451); pap. 12.95 (978-1-930143-46-3(X) , 346X) Pitspopany Pr. (Devora Publishing).

Cohen, R. G. The Place That I Love. Levitas, Alexander, illus. 2006. 30p. (J). 10.95 (978-1-929628-29-2(3)) Hachai Publishing.

Cohen, Shari. Alfie's Bark Mitzvah. 2006. (Illus.). (J). per. 18.00 net. (978-1-58985-055-2(6)) Five Star Pubns., Inc.

Collins, Alan. Boys from Bondi. 160p. pap. 11.95 (978-0-7022-2084-5(1)) Univ. of Queensland Pr. AUS. *Dist:* International Specialized Bk. Services.

Cooper, Alexandra. Spin the Dreidel! Gévry, Claudine, illus. 2004. 14p. (J). 7.99 (978-0-689-86430-8(2) , Little Simon) Simon & Schuster Children's Publishing.

Dell, Pamela. The Gold Coin: A Story about New York City's Lower East Side. 2002. (Scrapbooks of America Ser.). (Illus.). 48p. (J). (gr. 2-6). 28.50 (978-1-59187-017-3(8)) Child's World, Inc.

Dostis, Isaac & Haddad Ikonomopoulos, Marcia. Ten Gold Medals: Glory or Freedom. 2005. (Illus.). ii, 72p. (J). (978-0-8197-0770-3(8)) Bloch Publishing Co.

DuCharme, Dede Fox. The Treasure in the Tiny Blue Tin. 1998. (Chaparral Books for Young Readers). 144p. (J). (gr. 5-8). pap. 11.95 (978-0-87565-180-4(1)) Texas Christian Univ. Pr.

Edwards, Michelle. Misha the Minstrel. 2004. (Illus.). (gr. 3-7). 8.95 (978-0-930100-19-3(0)) Holy Cow! Pr.

Elmer, Robert. Promise of Zion, Vols. 1-6. 2002. (Promise of Zion Ser.). (Illus.). (J). pap. 35.99 (978-0-7642-8057-3(0)) Bethany Hse. Pubs.

Emerman, Ellen. Just Right: The Story of a Jewish Home. Rosenfeld, Dina, ed. Kranz, Sarah, illus. 1999. 32p. (J). (ps-1). 9.95 (978-0-922613-91-5(5)) Hachai Publishing.

Evans, Marion, Anna Baraitser. Home Number One. 2006. (Illus.). 63p. (YA). pap. (978-0-9529426-7-2(4)) Loki Books Ltd.

Feder, Harriet K. Death on Sacred Ground. 2003. (Young Adult Fiction Ser.). (Illus.). 192p. (J). (gr. 7 up). 14.95 (978-0-8225-0741-3(2) , Carolrhoda Bks.) Lerner Publishing Group.

Feldman, Eve B. Seymour, the Formerly Fearful. 2000. 164p. (J). (gr. 4-7). pap. 11.95 (978-0-595-00391-4(5) , Backinprint.com) iUniverse, Inc.

Finkelstein, Ruth. Big Like Me. Touson, Esther, illus. 2001. 32p. (J). 9.95 (978-1-929628-04-9(8)) Hachai Publishing.

Flam, Chanie. Erev Shabbos. (Goldie Gold Board Book Ser.: Vol. 2). (Illus.). (J). (ps-1). bds. 4.95 (978-1-58330-026-8(0)) Feldheim Pubs.

Fleischman, Sid. The Entertainer & the Dybbuk. 2007. 192p. (J). (gr. 4-9). 16.99 (***978-0-06-134445-9(1)**); lib. bdg. 17.89 (***978-0-06-134446-6(X)***) HarperCollins Pubs. (Greenwillow Bks.).

Fruchter, Yaakov. Best of Olomeinu - Series 2: Stories for All Year 'Round. 2003. 136p. 13.99 (978-1-57819-398-1(2) , BO1H); pap. 10.99 (978-1-57819-399-8(0) , BO1P) Mesorah Pubns., Ltd.

Gaberman, Judith. One-Way to Ansonia. 2001. 196p. pap. 12.95 (978-0-595-15830-0(7) , Backinprint.com) iUniverse, Inc.

Ganz, Yaffa. The Adventures of Jeremy & Heddy Levi. Katz, Avi, illus. 2005. 204p. (J). 16.95 (978-1-930143-50-0(8) , 3508); pap. 12.95 (978-1-930143-51-7(6) , 3516) Pitspopany Pr. (Devora Publishing).

—Savta Simcha & the Roundabout Journey to Jerusalem. Klineman, Harvey, illus. 2000. 128p. (J). 15.99 (978-1-58330-452-5(5)) Feldheim Pubs.

—The Travels & Tales of Dr. Emanuel J. Mitzva. 2003. (J). 15.99 (978-1-58330-581-2(5)) Feldheim Pubs.

Garren, Devorah-Leah. Shabbos Is Coming! We're Lost in the Zoo! Katz, Maya S., illus. 1999. 32p. (J). (ps-3). 12.95 (978-1-880582-32-9(5)) Judaica Pr., Inc., The.

Geller, Beverly Mach. The Mitzvah Girl. Perel, Rivka-Lisa, illus. 2000. 24p. (J). (ps-3). 12.95 (978-965-229-203-2(6)) Gefen Publishing Hse., Ltd ISR. *Dist:* Gefen Bks.

Geras, Adele & Moxley, Sheila. Rebecca's Passover. 2004. (Illus.). 32p. (J). (gr. k-4). pap. 7.95 (978-1-84507-155-4(7)) Lincoln, Frances Ltd. GBR. *Dist:* Perseus Distribution.

Glaser, Linda. Bridge to America: Based on a True Story. 2005. (Illus.). 208p. (J). (gr. 4-6). 16.00 (978-0-618-56301-2(6)) Houghton Mifflin Co. Trade & Reference Div.

—Mrs. Greenberg's Messy Hanukkah. Cote, Nancy, illus. 2004. 32p. (J). (gr. 1-3). 15.95 (978-0-8075-5297-1(6)) Whitman, Albert & Co.

Glasthal, Jacqueline B. Liberty on 23rd Street. Reingold, Alan, illus. 2006. (Adventures in America Ser.). (J). (978-1-893110-45-8(1)) Silver Moon Pr.

Glatshteyn, Yankev. Emil & Karl. Shandler, Jeffrey, tr. 2008. 208p. (YA). pap. 6.99 (***978-0-312-37387-0(2)***) Square Fish.

Gleitzman, Morris. Once. 2005. 160p. (J). pap. (***978-0-14-330195-0(0)*** , Puffin) Penguin Group (USA) Inc.

Gold-Vukson, Marji. The Numbers of My Jewish Year. 2006. (J). 5.95 (978-1-58013-148-3(4)) Kar-Ben Publishing.

Goldberg, Malky. What Else Do I Say? A Lift the Flap Book. Argoff, Patti, illus. 2007. (J). (ps-k). bds. 9.95 (***978-1-929628-34-6(X)***) Hachai Publishing.

Goldin, Barbara Diamond. While the Candles Burn: Eight Stories for Hanukkah. 1999. (978-0-606-17434-3(6)) Tandem Library Bks.

Goldstein, Andrew. My Jewish Home. Kreiswirth, Kinny, illus. 2000. 12p. (J). (ps up). 4.95 (978-1-58013-070-7(4)) Kar-Ben Publishing.

Greenberger, Tehilla. Gifts to Treasure. Toron, Eli, illus. 2007. (Fun to Read Book). 224p. (J). per. 10.95 (***978-1-929628-32-2(3)***) Hachai Publishing.

Greenburg, Dan. My Grandma, Major League Slugger. Davis, Jack E., illus. 2001. (Zack Files Ser.: No. 24). 64p. (J). (gr. 2-5). pap. 4.99 (978-0-448-42550-4(5) , Grosset & Dunlap) Penguin Group (USA) Inc.

—My Grandma, Major League Slugger. 2001. (gr. 3-6). lib. bdg. 13.00 (978-0-613-58376-3(0)) Tandem Library Bks.

Greene, Bette. Summer of My German Soldier. 2000. (J). (gr. 6 up). 20.50 (978-0-8446-7144-4(4)) Smith, Peter Pub., Inc.

—Summer of My German Soldier. 1999. (978-0-606-17432-9(X)) Tandem Library Bks.

Greene, Bette & Hunt, Robert, illus. Summer of My German Soldier. 2003. 256p. (J). (gr. 5). 18.99 (978-0-8037-2869-1(7) , Dial) Penguin Group (USA) Inc.

Greif, Jean-Jacques. The Fighter. 2006. 288p. (YA). (gr. 9 up). 16.95 (978-1-58234-891-9(X) , Bloomsbury Children) Bloomsbury Publishing.

Hamilton, Doris K. Daniel's Christmas Story. 2006. pap. 7.95 (978-0-533-15495-1(2)) Vantage Pr., Inc.

Hannigan, Lynne. Sam's Passover. 2004. (Illus.). 32p. pap. 5.95 (978-0-7136-4084-7(7) , 93342) A & C Black GBR. *Dist:* Consortium Bk. Sales & Distribution.

Hantman, Clea. Goddesses No.3: Muses on the Move. 2002. (gr. 5-8). lib. bdg. 13.00 (978-0-613-71476-1(8)) Tandem Library Bks.

Harcourt School Publishers Staff. Quiet Heroes Advanced Level. 3rd ed. 2002. (Trophies Reading Program Ser.). (Illus.). pap. 5.10 (978-0-15-323466-8(0)) Harcourt Schl. Pubs.

Hautzig, Esther. A Picture of Grandmother. Peck, Beth, illus. 2002. 80p. (J). (gr. 2-5). 15.00 (978-0-374-35920-1(2) , Farrar, Straus & Giroux (BYR)) Farrar, Straus & Giroux.

Hershenhorn, Esther. Chicken Soup by Heart. Litzinger, Rosanne, illus. 2002. 32p. (J). (gr. k-3). 16.95 (978-0-689-82665-8(6)) Simon & Schuster Children's Publishing.

Hesse, Karen. The Cats in Krasinski Square. Watson, Wendy, illus. 2004. 32p. (J). (gr. 2-5). pap. 16.95 (978-0-439-43540-6(4) , Scholastic Pr.) Scholastic, Inc.

Hest, Amy. Love You, Soldier. Lamut, Sonja, illus. 2000. 80p. (J). (gr. 3-7). 16.99 (978-0-7636-0943-6(9)) Candlewick Pr.

Hodes, Loren. Too Big, Too Little. . . Just Right! Hodes, Loren, illus. 2002. (Illus.). (J). 9.95 (978-1-880582-72-5(4) , TTTH) Judaica Pr., Inc., The.

Hoestlandt, Jo. Star of Fear, Star of Hope. 1998. Tr. of Grande Peur sous les Etoiles. (J). pap. 3.95 (978-0-439-04457-8(X)) Scholastic, Inc.

—Star of Fear, Star of Hope. 2000. Tr. of Grande Peur sous les Etoiles. (J). (978-0-606-20296-1(X)); (gr. 3-6). lib. bdg. 17.60 (978-0-613-29518-5(8)) Tandem Library Bks.

Hoffman, Allen. Big League Dreams. 1999. (Small Worlds Ser.). 296p. 12.95 (978-0-7892-0583-4(1)) Abbeville Pr., Inc.

Holland, Cheri. Maccabee Jamboree: A Hanukkah Countdown. Schanzer, Rosalyn, illus. 1998. 24p. (J). (ps-1). pap. 4.95 (978-1-58013-019-6(4)) Kar-Ben Publishing.

Hunt, Angela Elwell. The Deadly Chase. 2000. (Colonial Captives Ser.: Vol. 2). 192p. (gr. 4-7). pap. 12.95 (978-0-595-08997-0(6) , Backinprint.com) iUniverse, Inc.

Hurwitz, Johanna. Dear Emma. 2002. (Illus.). 160p. (J). 15.99 (978-0-06-029840-1(5)) HarperCollins Pubs.

—Faraway Summer. Azarian, Mary, illus. 1998. 160p. (J). (gr. 3-7). 14.95 (978-0-688-15334-2(8)) HarperCollins Pubs.

Ioannides, Mara W. Cohen. A Shout in the Sunshine. 2007. 120p. (J). pap. 12.95 (***978-0-8276-0838-2(1)***) Jewish Pubn. Society.

Jacobs, Laurie A. A Box of Candles. Ephraim, Shelly Ephraim, illus. 2005. 40p. (J). (ps-ps). 17.95 (978-1-59078-169-2(4)) Boyds Mills Pr.

Jessup, Jack. A Donkey Named Rico. 2001. 497p. lib. bdg. (978-0-7541-1539-7(9)) Minerva Pr.

Johnson, Lissa Halls. The Worst Wish. 2000. (Kidwitness Tales Ser.). (Illus.). 128p. (J). (gr. 3-7). pap. 5.99 (978-1-56179-882-7(7)) Bethany Hse. Pubs.

Johnston, Tony. The Harmonica. Mazellan, Ron, illus. 2004. 32p. (J). 15.95 (978-1-57091-547-5(4)) Charlesbridge Publishing, Inc.

Jules, Jacqueline. The Hardest Word: A Yom Kippur Story. Kahn, Katherine Janus, illus. 2001. 32p. (J). (ps-2). pap. 7.95 (978-1-58013-028-8(3)) Kar-Ben Publishing.

—The Hardest Word: A Yom Kippur Story. Kahn, Katherine Janus, illus. 2001. 32p. (J). (ps-2). 17.95 (978-1-58013-030-1(5) , Carolrhoda Bks.) Lerner Publishing Group.

—The Ziz And the Hanukkah Miracle. Kahn, Katherine, illus. 2006. 32p. (J). 17.95 (978-1-58013-160-5(3)) Kar-Ben Publishing.

Jungman, Ann. The Prince Who Thought He Was a Rooster. 2008. 96p. (J). 14.95 (***978-1-84507-793-8(8)***); (Illus.). pap. 7.95 (***978-1-84507-794-5(6)***) Lincoln, Frances Ltd. GBR. *Dist:* Perseus Distribution.

Kacer, Kathy. Clara's War. 2005. (Holocaust Remembrance Ser.). (Illus.). 196p. (YA). (gr. 5 up). pap. 5.95 (978-1-896764-42-9(8)) Second Story Pr. CAN. *Dist:* Orca Bk. Pubs. USA, Univ. of Toronto Pr., Univ. of Toronto Pr.

—Clara's War. 2001. (gr. 5-8). lib. bdg. 14.10 (978-0-613-51538-2(2)) Tandem Library Bks.

—Night Spies. 2003. (gr. 3-6). lib. bdg. 14.10 (978-0-613-85822-9(0)) Tandem Library Bks.

Kahrs, Tina & Gibbs, Noni Beth. Rahab's Promise: Young Jael Learns That Walls Can Be Broken, but God's Promises Cannot. 2007. (Illus.). 32p. (J). pap. 9.99 (***978-0-8127-0432-7(0)***) Autumn Hse. Publishing Co.

Kasnett, Yitzchak. The Studen't Guide to the Cohens of Tzefat. (J). pap. 3.99 (978-0-89906-849-7(9) , SGCO) Mesorah Pubns., Ltd.

Katies Choice. 2005. (YA). per. (978-1-59872-217-8(4)) Instantpublisher.com.

Kimmel, Eric A. Onions & Garlic: An Old Tale. Arnold, Katya, illus. 2005. 29p. (J). (gr. k-4). reprint ed. 16.00 (978-0-7567-9638-9(5)) DIANE Publishing Co.

—When Mindy Saved Hanukkah. McClintock, Barbara, illus. 1998. 32p. (J). (ps-2). pap. 15.95 (978-0-590-37136-0(3)) Scholastic, Inc.

—Zigazak! A Magical Hanukkah Night. Goodell, Jon, illus. 2001. 32p. (J). (ps-3). 15.95 (978-0-385-32652-0(1)); lib. bdg. 17.99 (978-0-385-90004-1(X)) Random Hse. Children's Bks. (Doubleday Bks. for Young Readers).

Kimmelman, Leslie. The Runaway Latkes. Yalowitz, Paul, illus. 2000. 32p. (J). (ps-2). 15.95 (978-0-8075-7176-7(8)) Whitman, Albert & Co.

—Sound the Shofar! A Story for Rosh Hashanah & Yom Kippur. Himmelman, John, illus. 1998. 32p. (J). (ps-1). 15.99 (978-0-06-027501-3(4)) HarperCollins Pubs.

Klein, Rachel. The Moth Diaries. 2002. 256p. (YA). (978-1-58243-205-2(8)) Counterpoint.

Koffsky, Ann D. I Can! Koffsky, Ann D., illus. 1999. (J). (ps-k). spiral bd. 5.99 (978-0-914080-31-2(8)) Shulsinger Sales, Inc.

Koons, Jon. A Confused Hanukkah: An Original Story of Chelm. Schindler, S. D., illus. 2004. 40p. (J). (gr. k). 16.99 (978-0-525-46969-8(9) , Dutton Juvenile) Penguin Group (USA) Inc.

Kositsky, Lynne. Candles. 1998. (Beloved Books). 102p. (YA). (gr. 5-9). pap. 6.95 (978-1-896184-44-9(8)) Roussan Pubs., Inc./Roussan Editeur, Inc. CAN. *Dist:* Orca Bk. Pubs. USA.

Kosofsky, Chaim. Much, Much Better. 2006. (Illus.). 32p. (J). (ps-3). 14.95 (978-1-929628-22-3(6)) Hachai Publishing.

Kranzler, Gershon. Chanan & His Violin & Other Stories. Waldman, Bryna, illus. 1999. 114p. (gr. 4-8). 13.95 (978-0-8266-0349-4(1)) Merkos L'Inyonei Chinuch.

—The Glass Blower of Venice & Other Stories. Waldman, Bryna, tr. (Illus.). 96p. (YA). reprint ed. 11.00 (978-0-8266-0348-7(3)) Merkos L'Inyonei Chinuch.

—Seder in Herlin: And Other Stories. Kotler, Arkady & Kotler, Elina, illus. 2003. 108p. (gr. 5-9). reprint ed. 13.95 (978-0-8266-0343-2(2)) Merkos L'Inyonei Chinuch.

Kubert, Joe. The Adventures of Yaakov & Isaac. 64p. 9.99 (978-1-58330-741-0(9)) Feldheim Pubs.

Kushner, Lawrence & Schmidt, Gary. In God's Hands. Baek, Matthew J., illus. 2005. 32p. (J). (gr. k-3). 16.99 (978-1-58023-224-1(8)) Jewish Lights Publishing.

Lakin, Patricia. Don't Forget. Rand, Ted, illus. 2000. 32p. (YA). (gr. k-3). pap. 5.95 (978-0-688-17522-1(8)) HarperCollins Pubs.

Lanton, Sandy. Daddy's Chair. Haas, Shelly O., illus. 2000. 32p. (J). (gr. k-2). 14.95 (978-0-9702482-0-6(2)); pap. 6.95 (978-0-9702482-1-3(0)) Lanton Haas Pr.

—Lots of Latkes: A Hanukkah Story. Redenbaugh, Vicki J., illus. 2003. 32p. (J). (ps-3). 14.95 (978-1-58013-091-2(7)) Kar-Ben Publishing.

Lasky, Kathryn. Broken Song. 2007. 160p. (J). pap. 6.99 (978-0-14-240741-7(0) , Puffin) Penguin Group (USA) Inc.

—Marven of the Great North Woods. Hawkes, Kevin, illus. 2002. 48p. (J). (gr. 1-4). pap. 7.00 (978-0-15-216826-1(5) , Voyager Bks./Libros Viajeros) Harcourt Children's Bks.

—The Night Journey. 2005. 160p. (J). (gr. 3-7). 15.99 (978-0-670-05963-8(3) , Viking Juvenile); (Illus.). (YA). pap. 5.99 (978-0-14-240322-8(9) , Puffin) Penguin Group (USA) Inc.

—The Night Journey. 2002. (J). (gr. 6 up). 20.25 (978-0-8446-7210-6(6)) Smith, Peter Pub., Inc.

Lawton, Wendy. Shadow of His Hand: A Story Based on the Life of Holocaust Survivor Anita Dittman. 2004. (Daughters of the Faith Ser.). 160p. (J). pap. 6.99 (978-0-8024-4074-7(6)) Moody Pubs.

Leeds, Constance & Bennett, Constance. The Silver Cup. 2007. 240p. (YA). (gr. 6-9). 16.99 (978-0-670-06157-0(3) , Viking Adult) Penguin Group (USA) Inc.

Lester, Julius. Pharaoh's Daughter: A Novel of Ancient Egypt. 2002. 192p. (J). (gr. 5 up). pap. 5.99 (978-0-06-440969-8(4) , Harper Trophy) HarperCollins Pubs.

—Pharaoh's Daughter: A Novel of Ancient Egypt. 2002. (gr. 5-8). lib. bdg. 14.15 (978-0-613-87835-7(3)) Tandem Library Bks.

Levine, Gail Carson. Dave at Night. 2001. (ps-7). 281p. (J). lib. bdg. 14.15 (978-0-613-34669-6(6)); 12.64 (978-0-606-21137-6(3)) Tandem Library Bks.

Levitin, Sonia. The Cure. 1999. 192p. (YA). (gr. 5 up). 16.00 (978-0-15-201827-6(1) , Silver Whistle) Harcourt Trade Pubs.

—The Cure. 2000. 272p. (J). (gr. 7 up). pap. 6.99 (978-0-380-73298-2(X) , Harper Trophy) HarperCollins Pubs.

—Cure. 2000. (gr. 5-8). lib. bdg. 14.15 (978-0-613-29918-3(3)) Tandem Library Bks.

—Singing Mountain. 2000. (978-0-606-17938-6(0)) Tandem Library Bks.

Lewin, Waldtraut. Freedom Beyond the Sea. 2003. (gr. 7-12). lib. bdg. 13.55 (978-0-613-72276-6(0)) Tandem Library Bks.

Lewin, Waldtraut & Crawford, Elizabeth. Freedom Beyond the Sea. 2003. 272p. (YA). (gr. 9-12). pap. 5.50 (978-0-440-22868-4(9) , Laurel Leaf) Random Hse. Children's Bks.

Littlesugar, Amy. Willy & Max: A Holocaust Story. Low, William, illus. 2006. 40p. (J). (ps). 15.99 (978-0-399-23483-5(7) , Philomel) Penguin Group (USA) Inc.

Littman, Sarah. Confessions of a Closet Catholic. McClelland, Charles E. & Scher, Steven P., eds. 2005. 176p. (J). (gr. 5-8). 15.99 (978-0-525-47365-7(3) , Dutton Juvenile) Penguin Group (USA) Inc.

Lowry, Lois. Compte les Etoiles. pap. 16.95 (978-2-211-03436-4(5)) Archimede Editions FRA. *Dist:* Distribooks, Inc.

—Number the Stars. 2004. 144p. (J). (gr. 5-9). pap. 29.00 incl. audio (978-1-4000-8637-5(X) , Listening Library) Random Hse. Audio Publishing Group.

—Number the Stars. 1998. 144p. (YA). (gr. 5-7). reprint ed. mass mkt. 6.50 (978-0-440-22753-3(4) , Laurel Leaf) Random Hse. Children's Bks.

—Number the Stars. 1998. (J). (978-0-606-13670-9(3)); (gr. 5-8). lib. bdg. 14.15 (978-0-613-72319-0(8)) Tandem Library Bks.

—Number the Stars - Musical. 1998. 33p. (J). pap. 6.95 (978-0-87129-834-8(1) , N03) Dramatic Publishing Co.

—Quien Cuenta las Estrellas. 5th ed. 1998. (SPA., Illus.). 152p. (J). 8.95 (978-84-239-8867-9(8)) Espasa Calpe, S.A. ESP. *Dist:* Continental Bk. Co., Inc.

Lutz, Norma Jean. Carrie's Courage: Battling the Powers of Bigotry. 2005. (Sisters in Time Ser.). 144p. (J). pap. 4.97 (978-1-59310-656-0(4)) Barbour Publishing, Inc.

Mack, Tracy. Birdland. 2003. 208p. (J). pap. 16.95 (978-0-439-53590-8(5)) Scholastic, Inc.

Mamet, David. Bar Mitzvah. Sultan, Donald, illus. 1999. 45p. (YA). reprint ed. 27.00 (978-0-7567-6490-6(4)) DIANE Publishing Co.

—Bar Mitzvah. 1999. (Illus.). 48p. (gr. 8). 26.95 (978-0-8212-2546-2(4)) Little Brown & Co.

Mark, Yudel. The Jewish Pope: A Yiddish Tale. Goodman, Ruth Fisher, tr. from YID. 2006. (Illus.). 128p. (YA). pap. 10.00 (978-1-56474-459-3(0)) Fithian Pr.

Matas, Carol. Rebecca. 2000. (Illus.). 160p. (J). pap. (978-0-439-98718-9(0)) Scholastic, Inc.

—Sparks Fly Upward. 2002. 192p. (YA). (gr. 5-9). 15.00 (978-0-618-15964-2(9) , Clarion Bks.) Houghton Mifflin Co. Trade & Reference Div.

Matas, Carol & Matas, Carol. Greater Than Angels. 1999. 177p. lib. bdg. 11.64 (978-0-606-17196-0(7)) Tandem Library Bks.

Mazer, Harry. The Last Mission. 192p. (YA). (gr. 7 up). pap. 4.99 (978-0-8072-1366-7(7) , Listening Library) Random Hse. Audio Publishing Group.

Mazer, Norma Fox. Good Night, Maman. 2001. (Illus.). (J). 12.64 (978-0-606-21217-5(5)) Tandem Library Bks.

McDonough, Yona Zeldis. The Doll with the Yellow Star. Root, Kimberly Bulcken, illus. 2005. 64p. (J). (gr. 3-5). 17.95 (978-0-8050-6337-0(4) , Holt, Henry & Co. Bks. For Young Readers) Holt, Henry & Co.

Medoff, Francine. The Mouse in the Matzah Factory. Bosch, Nicole in den, illus. 2003. 32p. (J). (ps-3). pap. 6.95 (978-1-58013-048-6(8)) Kar-Ben Publishing.

Meiseles, Shayna. The Bat Mitzvah Club: Debbie's Story. 2001. 244p. (J). (gr. 5-7). 15.95 (978-0-8266-0029-5(8)) Merkos L'Inyonei Chinuch.

Melmed, Laura Krauss. Moishe's Miracle: A Hanukkah Story. Slonim, David, illus. 2005. 32p. (J). (ps-3). pap. 6.95 (978-0-8118-5234-0(2)) Chronicle Bks. LLC.

—Moishe's Miracle: A Hanukkah Story. Slonim, David, illus. 2000. 32p. (J). (ps up). 15.95 (978-0-688-14682-5(1)); lib. bdg. 15.89 (978-0-688-14683-2(X)) HarperCollins Pubs.

Meltzer, Amy. A Mezuzah on the Door. Fried, Janice, illus. 2007. (Jewish Identity Ser.). 32p. (J). (ps-2). 17.95 (***978-1-58013-249-7(9));*** pap. 7.95 (***978-1-58013-251-0(0))*** Kar-Ben Publishing.

Miklowitz, Gloria D. The Enemy Has a Face. 2004. 143p. (YA). pap. 8.00 (978-0-8028-5261-8(0)) Eerdmans, William B. Publishing Co.

Miller, Deborah U. & Ostrove, Karen. Fins & Scales: A Kosher Tale. Ostrove, Karen, illus. 2004. (Israel Ser.). (Illus.). 32p. (J). (gr. 1-3). pap. 4.95 (978-0-929371-25-2(9)) Kar-Ben Publishing.

Mills, Steven L. Rafi's Search for the Torah Munching Monster. 2001. (Illus.). 48p. (J). 9.95 (978-1-881283-31-7(3)) Alef Design Group.

Morgan, Anna. Daughters of the Ark. 2005. (Illus.). 230p. (J). (gr. 5-9). pap. 7.95 (978-1-896764-92-4(4)) Second Story Pr. CAN. *Dist:* Orca Bk. Pubs. USA, Univ. of Toronto Pr.

Motoyama, Keiko & MacKall, Dandi Daley. Who'll Light the Chanukah Candles? 2003. (Illus.). 16p. (J). pap. 4.99 (978-0-689-85025-7(5) , Little Simon) Simon & Schuster Children's Publishing.

Naomi, Aunt. Jewish Fairy Tales & Legends. 2006. pap. 28.95 (***978-1-4254-9788-0(8))*** Kessinger Publishing, LLC.

Napoli, Donna Jo. The King of Mulberry Street. 2005. 256p. (J). (gr. 3-7). 15.95 (978-0-385-74653-3(9)); lib. bdg. 17.99 (978-0-385-90890-0(3)) Random Hse. Children's Bks. (Lamb, Wendy).

Narvaez, Concha Lopez. El Tiempo y la Promesa.Tr. of Time & the Promise. (SPA.). (YA). (gr. 5-8). 164p. (978-84-216-2558-3(6) , BU7323); 9th ed. (Illus.). 208p. (978-84-216-1538-6(6) , BU6188) Bruño, Editorial ESP. *Dist:* Lectorum Pubns., Inc.

Nattel, Lilian. River Midnight. 1999. (978-0-606-17451-0(6)) Tandem Library Bks.

Netzarel, Orly. Yellow, Yellow-Brown, Yellow-Brown & Black. 2001. 160p. pap. 11.95 (978-0-595-18742-3(0) , Writers Club Pr.) iUniverse, Inc.

Nislick, June Levitt. Zayda Was a Cowboy. 2005. 128p. (J). pap. 9.95 (978-0-8276-0817-7(9)) Jewish Pubn. Society.

Now I Am Thee. (Yoni Gold Board Book Ser.). (J). bds. 4.95 (978-1-58330-153-1(4)) Feldheim Pubs.

Nye, Naomi. Habibi. 1999. (gr. 7-12). lib. bdg. 14.15 (978-0-613-18312-3(6)) Tandem Library Bks.

Oberman, Sheldon. The Always Prayer Shawl. Lewin, Ted, illus. 2005. 40p. (J). (ps-17). pap. 10.95 (978-1-59078-332-0(8)) Boyds Mills Pr.

O'Connell, Rebecca. Penina Levine Is a Hard-Boiled Egg. Sue, Majella Lue, illus. 2007. 176p. (J). (gr. 4-6). 16.95 (978-1-59643-140-9(7)) Roaring Brook Pr.

Olswanger, Anna. Shlemiel Crooks. Koz, Paula Goodman, illus. 2005. 36p. (J). (ps-7). 15.95 (978-1-58838-165-1(X)) NewSouth, Inc.

Orgel, Doris. Devil in Vienna. 2004. 256p. (YA). (gr. 3-6). pap. 6.99 (978-0-14-240236-8(2) , Puffin) Penguin Group (USA) Inc.

Orlev, Ori. El Hombre del Otro Lado. (SPA., Illus.). 192p. (YA). (gr. 5-8). (978-84-348-6721-5(4) , SM30476) SM Ediciones ESP. *Dist:* Lectorum Pubns., Inc.

Ostow, Micol. Emily Goldberg Learns to Salsa. 2007. 288p. (J). (gr. 7). pap. 7.99 (***978-1-59514-144-6(8)*** , Razorbill) Penguin Group (USA) Inc.

Parrish, Shelley Berlin. Sharing Grandma's Gift. Petosa-Sigel, Kristi, illus. 2000. 40p. (J). 18.00 (978-0-89716-936-3(0)) Peanut Butter Publishing.

Pausewang, Gudrun. Final Journey. Crampton, Patricia, tr. 1998. 160p. (J). (gr. 7-12). pap. 6.99 (978-0-14-130104-4(X) , Puffin) Penguin Group (USA) Inc.

Pearl, Sydelle. Elijah's Tears: Stories for the Jewish Holidays. Skortcheva, Rossitza, illus. 2004. 80p. (YA). pap. 14.95 (978-1-58980-178-3(4)) Pelican Publishing Co., Inc.

Peretz, I. L. & Goldin, Barbara Diamond. The Magician's Visit: A Passover Tale. Parker, Robert Andrew, illus. 2006. 28p. (J). (gr. 4-8). reprint ed. 15.00 (978-1-4223-5408-7(3)); pap. 5.00 (978-1-4223-5400-1(8)) DIANE Publishing Co.

Perrin, Randy, et al. Time Like a River. 2004. 144p. (gr. 5 up). 14.95 (978-1-57143-061-8(X)) RDR Bks.

Petersen, Alicia. A Sparrow Alone. 2004. 154p. (YA). (978-1-59166-204-4(4)) Jones, Bob Univ. Pr.

Pfeiffer, Chaviva Krohn & Shvadron, Shalom Mordekhai. More Maggid Stories for Children. Nodel, Norman & Katz, Tova, illus. 2000. (ArtScroll Youth Ser.). 48p. (J). 14.99 (978-1-57819-497-1(0) , YMAG2) Mesorah Pubns., Ltd.

Polacco, Patricia. The Butterfly. Polacco, Patricia, illus. 2000. (Illus.). 48p. (J). (ps-3). 16.99 (978-0-399-23170-4(6) , Philomel) Penguin Group (USA) Inc.

—A Christmas Tapestry. Polacco, Patricia, illus. 2002. (Illus.). 48p. (J). (gr. k-3). 16.99 (978-0-399-23955-7(3) , Philomel) Penguin Group (USA) Inc.

—The Keeping Quilt. Polacco, Patricia, illus. 2002. (Illus.). (J). 26.17 (978-0-7587-2927-9(8)) Book Wholesalers, Inc.

—The Keeping Quilt. 2001. (J). (gr. k-3). 26.95 incl. audio (978-0-8045-6842-5(1) , 6842) Spoken Arts, Inc.

—The Keeping Quilt. 2001. (J). (978-0-606-20749-2(X)) Tandem Library Bks.

—Keeping Quilt. 2001. (gr. k-3). lib. bdg. 15.30 (978-0-613-37155-1(0)) Tandem Library Bks.

—The Keeping Quilt. 10th anniv. ed. 1998. (Illus.). 48p. (J). (ps-3). 17.95 (978-0-689-82090-8(9)) Simon & Schuster Children's Publishing.

—Mrs. Katz & Tush. Polacco, Patricia, illus. 2002. (Illus.). (J). 14.79 (978-0-7587-3191-3(4)) Book Wholesalers, Inc.

Polacco, Patricia, illus. The Keeping Quilt. 2001. 32p. (J). (ps-3). pap. 6.99 (978-0-689-84447-8(6) , Aladdin) Simon & Schuster Children's Publishing.

Pressler, Mirjam. Malka. Murdoch, Brian, tr. from GER. 2003. 288p. (YA). (gr. 5-12). 18.99 (978-0-399-23984-7(7) , Philomel) Penguin Group (USA) Inc.

Prins, Piet. Hideout in the Swamp. 2006. (Illus.). 136p. (J). pap. (978-1-894666-73-2(9)) Inheritance Pubns.

Propp, Vera W. When the Soldiers Were Gone. 2001. (gr. 3-6). lib. bdg. 13.00 (978-0-613-36028-9(1)); (Illus.). (J). (978-0-606-20989-2(1)) Tandem Library Bks.

—When the Soldiers Were Gone: A Novel. 2006. 101p. (J). (gr. 4-8). reprint ed. 15.00 (978-1-4223-5310-3(9)) DIANE Publishing Co.

Pushker, Gloria Teles. Toby Belfer & the High Holy Days. Hierstein, Judith, illus. 2001. 32p. 15.95 (978-1-56554-765-0(9)) Pelican Publishing Co., Inc.

Radding, Alan. Miracles: Stories for Jewish Children & Their Families. 2003. 135p. (J). pap. 12.95 (978-1-59113-309-4(2)) Booklocker.com, Inc.

Radin, Ruth Y. Escape to the Forest: Based on a True Story of the Holocaust. Hamlin, Janet, illus. 96p. (J). (gr. 4 up). 2001. pap. 4.25 (978-0-06-440822-6(1)); 2000. 13.89 (978-0-06-028521-0(4)) HarperCollins Pubs.

Rahlens, Holly-Jane. Prince William, Maximilian Minsky, & Me. (YA). (gr. 7-11). 2007. 320p. pap. 7.99 (***978-0-7636-3299-1(6));*** 2005. 160p. 16.99 (978-0-7636-2704-1(6)) Candlewick Pr.

Rappaport, Doreen. The Secret Seder. McCully, Emily Arnold, illus. 2005. 40p. (gr. k-4). 16.99 (978-0-7868-0777-2(6)) Hyperion Bks. for Children.

Revell, Cindy, illus. A Sack Full of Feathers. 2007. 32p. pap. (***978-1-55143-863-4(1))*** Orca Bk. Pubs.

Robinson, Ronnie D. Yankee Doodle Boychik. 2002. (gr. 7-12). lib. bdg. 24.00 (978-0-613-74651-9(1)) Tandem Library Bks.

Rocklin, Joanne. The Very Best Hanukkah Gift. 2001. (978-0-606-22400-0(9)) Tandem Library Bks.

Rogasky, Barbara. Gilgul. Brooker, Kyrsten, illus. 2002. (J). (978-0-8234-1619-6(4)) Holiday Hse., Inc.

Rogers, Kirby. Operation Dewey. 2002. (Illus.). ix, 100p. (J). pap. (978-1-877633-65-2(8)) Luthers.

Rose, Robert. Godintoxicated Becoming Paranoid. 2007. 260p. pap. 29.95 (***978-1-4327-0041-6(3))*** Outskirts Press, Inc.

Rosen, Michael J. Chanukah Lights Everywhere. Iwai, Melissa, illus. 2006. 32p. (J). pap. 6.00 (978-0-15-205675-9(0) , Voyager Bks./Libros Viajeros) Harcourt Children's Bks.

Rosen, Sybil. Speed of Light. 2001. (J). (978-0-606-20923-6(9)) Tandem Library Bks.

Rosenbaum, Andria Warmflash. A Grandma Like Yours: A Grandpa Like Yours. Bjornson, Barbara, illus. 2006. (J). 16.95 (978-1-58013-167-4(0)) Kar-Ben Publishing.

Rosenbloom, Fiona. You Are So Not Invited to My Bat Mitzvah! 2007. 208p. (gr. 7 up). pap. 8.99 (***978-0-7868-3891-2(4))*** Hyperion Pr.

Rosenfeld, Dina. Five Alive: My Yom Tov Five Senses. Leff, Tova, illus. 2002. 32p. (J). (ps-k). 9.95 (978-1-929628-09-4(9)) Hachai Publishing.

—Get Well Soon. Lyampe, Rina, illus. 2001. 32p. (J). (ps-k). 9.95 (978-1-929628-05-6(6)) Hachai Publishing.

Rossoff, Donald. The Perfect Prayer. Keiser, Tammy L., illus. 2003. (gr. k-3). 13.95 (978-0-8074-0853-7(0) , 164005) URJ Pr.

Roth, Matthue. Never Mind the Goldbergs. 2005. 368p. (J). pap. 16.95 (978-0-439-69188-8(5) , PUSH) Scholastic, Inc.

Roth, Philip. The Human Stain. 2001. (gr. 7-12). lib. bdg. 23.45 (978-0-613-45775-0(7)) Tandem Library Bks.

Rouss, Sylvia A. Aaron's Bar Mitzvah. Dubois, Liz Goulet, tr. Dubois, Liz Goulet, illus. 2003. (J). 14.95 (978-0-8246-0447-9(4)) David, Jonathan Publishers, Inc.

—The Littlest Candlesticks. Hannon, Holly, illus. 2005. (Littlest Ser.). 32p. (J). 14.95 (978-1-930143-48-7(6) , Devora Publishing) Pitspopany Pr.

—Lots of Latkes. Kahn, Katherine Janus, illus. 2003. 32p. (J). (ps-3). pap. 6.95 (978-1-58013-061-5(5)) Kar-Ben Publishing.

—My Baby Brother: What a Miracle! Dubois, Liz Goulet, illus. 2002. (J). 14.95 (978-0-8246-0445-5(8)) David, Jonathan Publishers, Inc.

—Sammy Spider's First Haggadah. Kahn, Katherine Janus, illus. 2007. 32p. (J). pap. 5.95 (***978-1-58013-230-5(8))*** Kar-Ben Publishing.

—Sammy Spider's First Purim. Kahn, Katherine Janus, illus. 2000. 32p. (J). (ps-3). pap. 7.95 (978-1-58013-062-2(3)) Kar-Ben Publishing.

—Sammy Spider's Hanukkah Fun Book. Kahn, Katherine Janus, illus. 2003. 24p. (J). (ps-3). pap. 4.95 (978-1-58013-032-5(1)) Kar-Ben Publishing.

Roy, Jennifer Rozines. Yellow Star. 2006. 256p. (YA). (gr. 5-9). 16.95 (978-0-7614-5277-5(X)) Cavendish, Marshall Corp.

Rubel, Nicole. It's Hot & Cold in Miami. 2006. (Illus.). 208p. (J). 17.00 (978-0-374-33611-0(3)) Farrar, Straus & Giroux.

Ruby, Lois. Shanghai Shadows. 2006. 256p. (J). (gr. 7 up). 16.95 (978-0-8234-1960-9(6)) Holiday Hse., Inc.

Rudolph, Lieba. The Best Call of All. Gerber, Pesach, illus. 1998. 32p. (J). 12.95 (978-0-8266-0025-7(5)) Merkos L'Inyonei Chinuch.

Safran, Faigy. Uncle Moishy Visits Torah Island. Snowden, Linda, illus. (J). pap. 5.99 (978-0-89906-806-0(5) , UM1P) Mesorah Pubns., Ltd.

Sandell, Lisa Ann. The Weight of the Sky. 2006. 304p. (J). (gr. 7). 16.99 (978-0-670-06028-3(3) , Viking Juvenile) Penguin Group (USA) Inc.

Sasson, Jean. Ester's Child. 2003. (gr. 7-12). lib. bdg. 22.20 (978-0-613-70913-2(6)) Tandem Library Bks.

Saturen, Myra. Journey to a New World. 2006. (J). pap. 9.99 (978-0-88092-494-8(2)) Royal Fireworks Publishing Co.

—Journey to a New World: Mystic River of the West. 2006. (J). pap. (***978-0-88092-495-5(0))*** Royal Fireworks Publishing Co.

Saturen, Myra. Julietta. (YA). pap. 9.99 (978-0-88092-538-9(8)) Royal Fireworks Publishing Co.

Schmidt, Gary. Mara's Stories: Glimmers in the Darkness. 2008. 128p. (J). pap. 6.99 (***978-0-312-37388-7(0))*** Square Fish.

Schnur, Steven. The Koufax Dilemma. Treatner, Meryl, illus. 2001. 196p. (YA). pap. 14.95 (978-0-595-19998-3(4) , Backinprint.com) iUniverse, Inc.

—Koufax Dilemma. 2001. (gr. 3-6). lib. bdg. 24.55 (978-0-613-85103-9(X)) Tandem Library Bks.

Schorr, Melissa. Goy Crazy: But Please Don't Tell My Jewish Grandmother! 2006. 352p. (gr. 7-17). 15.99 (978-0-7868-3852-3(3)) Hyperion Pr.

Schotter, Roni. Passover Magic. 1998. (J). (978-0-606-13696-9(7)); lib. bdg. 15.25 (978-0-613-71817-2(8)) Tandem Library Bks.

—Purim Play. Hafner, Marylin, illus. 1998. 32p. (J). (ps-3). 15.95 (978-0-316-77518-2(5)) Little Brown & Co.

Schraff, Anne. Darkness. 2000. 119p. (J). pap. (978-0-7891-5183-4(9)); (gr. 5-12). lib. bdg. 13.95 (978-0-7807-9367-5(6)) Perfection Learning Corp.

Schram, Peninnah. The Hungry Clothes & Other Jewish Folktales. DeConno, Gianni, illus. 2008. (Folktales of the World Ser.). 96p. (J). 14.95 (***978-1-4027-2651-4(1))*** Sterling Publishing Co., Inc.

—The Magic Pomegranate: A Jewish Folktale. Hall, Melanie, illus. 2007. (On My Own Folklore Ser.). 48p. (J). (gr. 2 5). lib. bdg. 25.26 (***978-0-8225-6742-4(3)*** , Millbrook Pr.) Lerner Publishing Group.

Schuman, Burt E. Chanukah on the Prairie. Kaye, Rosalind Charney, illus. 2004. (gr. k-3). 13.95 (978-0-8074-0814-8(X) , 381780) URJ Pr.

Schwartz, Ellen. Jesse's Star. 2000. (Young Reader Ser.). (J). 11.64 (978-0-606-19476-1(2)) Tandem Library Bks.

Schwartz, Howard. A Journey to Paradise: And Other Jewish Tales. Carmi, Giora, illus. 2005. (Jewish Storyteller Ser.). 48p. (J). (ps-4). pap. 9.95 (978-0-943706-16-0(5) , Devora Publishing) Pitspopany Pr.

Scott, Walter, Sr. Ivanhoe. Marcos, Pablo, illus. 2002. (Great Illustrated Classics Ser.). 240p. (J). (gr. 3-8). 21.35 (978-1-57765-811-5(6) , ABDO & Daughters) ABDO Publishing Co.

—Ivanhoe. (SPA., Illus.). 176p. (YA). 14.95 (978-84-7281-096-9(8) , AF1096) Auriga, Ediciones S.A. ESP. *Dist:* Continental Bk. Co., Inc.

—Ivanhoe. 2000. (gr. 7-12). lib. bdg. 17.65 (978-0-613-64293-4(7)) Tandem Library Bks.

Semel, Nava & Silveira, Carlos. Clases de Vuelo. Silveira, Carlos, tr. 2002. (Joven Coleccion Ser.). (SPA., Illus.). 206p. (978-84-89804-06-7(0)) Loguez Ediciones ESP. *Dist:* Lectorum Pubns., Inc.

Sharon, Lynn. Angelicum: Jewish Sci-Fi. 1999. pap. 9.95 (978-0-943706-63-4(7)) Pitspopany Pr.

Shemtov, Esther G. Mindy Gets Her Reward: And Other Stories for Children. Lieberman, Hendel, illus. 2000. 62p. (Orig.). (J). reprint ed. pap. 8.95 (978-0-8266-0366-1(1)) Merkos L'Inyonei Chinuch.

Shollar, Leah Pearl. Shadow Play: A True Story of Tefillah. Gerber, Pesach, illus. 2006. 32p. (J). 11.95 (978-1-929628-21-6(8)) Hachai Publishing.

Shulman, Lisa. The Matzo Ball Boy. Litzinger, Rosanne, illus. 32p. (J). 2007. pap. 5.99 (978-0-14-240769-1(0) , Puffin); 2005. 15.99 (978-0-525-47169-1(3) , Dutton Juvenile) Penguin Group (USA) Inc.

Sigal, Maxine Handelman. Shabbat Angels. Rothenberg, Joani, illus. 2003. (gr. k-3). 13.95 (978-0-8074-0865-0(4) , 164051) URJ Pr.

Silberman, Shoshana. A Family Haggadah II, Vol. 2. Kahn, Katherine Janus, illus. l.t. ed. 2003. 64p. (J). pap. 6.95 (978-1-58013-014-1(3)) Kar-Ben Publishing.

Silverman, Erica. When the Chickens Went on Strike. Trueman, Matthew, illus. 2005. 32p. (J). pap. 6.99 (978-0-14-240279-5(6) , Puffin) Penguin Group (USA) Inc.

Silverman, Manuel S. Rosie & the Mole: The Story of a Bris. 1999. (Illus.). 48p. (J). (gr. 1-4). 16.95 (978-0-943706-22-1(X) , Devora Publishing) Pitspopany Pr.

—Rosie & the Mole: The Story of a Bris. Kahn, Katherine Janus, illus. 1999. 48p. (J). (gr. 1-4). pap. 9.95 (978-0-943706-20-7(3) , Devora Publishing) Pitspopany Pr.

Simpson, Lesley. The Purim Surprise. Church, Peter, illus. 2004. (Purim Ser.). 32p. (J). (ps-3). pap. 6.95 (978-1-58013-090-5(9)) Kar-Ben Publishing.

—The Shabbat Box. Bosch, Nicole in den, illus. 2001. 32p. (J). (ps-1). pap. 6.95 (978-1-58013-027-1(5)) Kar-Ben Publishing.

Singer, Isaac Bashevis. Zlateh the Goat & Other Stories. Sendak, Maurice, illus. 2001. (Sendak Reissues Ser.). 104p. (gr. 4-7). 17.95 (978-0-06-028477-0(3)) HarperCollins Pubs.

Soci Et E de La Faune Et Des Parcs Du Qu Ebec. Sarah de Cordoba. Sanchez, Andres & Tagle, illus. 2003. (SPA.). 130p. (J). pap. 4.99 (978-968-16-7020-7(5)) Fondo de Cultura Economica USA.

Spinelli, Jerry. Milkweed. 2005. 240p. (YA). (gr. 7). pap. 6.99 (978-0-440-42005-7(9) , Laurel Leaf); 2003. (Illus.). 224p. (J). (gr. 5). 15.95 (978-0-375-81374-0(8) , Knopf Bks. for Young Readers); 2003. (Illus.). 224p. (J). (gr. 5). lib. bdg. 17.99 (978-0-375-91374-7(2) , Knopf Bks. for Young Readers) Random Hse. Children's Bks.

—Milkweed. l.t. ed. 2003. 279p. (YA). 23.95 (978-0-7862-6146-8(3) , Large Print Pr.) Thorndike Pr.

Spring, Debbie. The Righteous Smuggler: A Holocaust Remembrance Book for Young Readers. 2005. (Illus.). 160p. (YA). pap. 6.95 (978-1-896764-97-9(5)) Second Story Pr. CAN. *Dist:* Univ. of Toronto Pr.

Starting First Grade. (Tami & Moishy Ser.: Vol. 4). (J). bds. 6.95 (978-1-58330-968-1(3)) Feldheim Pubs.

Steiner, Lili. My Bubbe - My Grandmother. Epstein, Debby, illus. 1998. 24p. (J). pap. 14.95 (978-1-891397-02-8(8)) Steiner, Lili Pubns.

—My Zaidah - My Grandfather. Epstein, Debby, illus. 1998. (My Jewish Family Series with a Bissel Yiddish). 24p. (J). pap. 14.95 (978-1-891397-01-1(X)) Steiner, Lili Pubns.

Stillerman, Marci. Nine Spoons: A Chanukah Story. Rosenfeld, D. L., ed. Gerber, Perren, illus. 1998. 32p. (J). (gr. k-3). 11.95 (978-0-922613-84-7(2)) Hachai Publishing.

Stuchner, Joan Betty. The Kugel Valley Klezmer Band. Row, Richard, illus. 2005. 30p. (J). (gr. 2-6). reprint ed. 16.00 (978-0-7567-8605-2(3)) DIANE Publishing Co.

—The Kugel Valley Klezmer Band. Bow, Richard, illus. 2001. 32p. (J). (ps-3). 15.95 (978-1-56656-430-4(1) , Crocodile Bks.) Interlink Publishing Group, Inc.

Sugarman, Brynn Olenberg. Rebecca's Journey Home. Shapiro, Michelle, illus. 2006. 32p. (J). 17.95 (978-1-58013-157-5(3)) Kar-Ben Publishing.

Suzuki, Etsuo. Anne Frank. 2006. (Illus.). 160p. pap. 9.95 (978-1-56970-974-0(2)) Digital Manga Publishing.

Taback, Simms. Kibitzers & Fools: Tales My Zayda Told Me. 2005. (Illus.). 48p. (J). (gr. 1-6). 16.99 (978-0-670-05955-3(2) , Viking Juvenile) Penguin Group (USA) Inc.

Tal, Eve. Double Crossing: A Jewish Immigration Story. 2005. 216p. (gr. 3-7). 16.95 (978-0-938317-94-4(6)) Cinco Puntos Pr.

Taniuchi, Yutaka. The Miracle Visas. 2001. 176p. (J). (gr. 4-7). 16.95 (978-965-229-256-8(7)) Gefen Publishing Hse., Ltd ISR. *Dist:* Gefen Bks.

Tarbescu, Edith. Annushka's Voyage. Dabcovich, Lydia & Degen, Bruce, illus. 1998. 32p. (J). (gr. k-3). tchr. ed. 16.00 (978-0-395-64366-2(X) , Clarion Bks.) Houghton Mifflin Co. Trade & Reference Div.

Taylor, Marilyn. Faraway Home. 2003. 224p. (J). (gr. 5 up). pap. 7.95 (978-0-86278-643-4(6)) O'Brien Pr., Ltd., The IRL. *Dist:* Independent Pubs. Group.

Terwilliger, Kelly. Bubbe Isabella & the Sukkot Cake. Hornung, Phyllis, illus. 2005. 24p. (J). (ps-2). pap. 6.95 (978-1-58013-128-5(X)); 15.95 (978-1-58013-187-2(5)) Kar-Ben Publishing.

The Three Messengers. 2000. (J). 7.00 (978-0-930213-62-6(9)) Breslov Research Institute.

Ungar, Richard. Even Higher. Ungar, Richard, illus. 2007. 32p. (J). (gr. 2-5). 18.95 (***978-0-88776-758-6(3))*** Tundra Bks., Inc./Livres Toundra, Inc. CAN. *Dist:* Random Hse., Inc.

Ungar, Richard. Rachel's Library. 2004. 32p. (J). (gr. 2-5). 15.95 (978-0-88776-678-7(1)) Tundra Bks., Inc./Livres Toundra, Inc. CAN. *Dist:* Random Hse., Inc.

Vogiel, Eva. Facing the Music. 2003. 284p. 19.95 (978-1-880582-94-7(5)) Judaica Pr., Inc., The.

Vogiel, Eva & Steinberg, Ruth. A Light for Greytowers. 252p. 11.99 (978-0-87306-598-6(0)) Feldheim Pubs.

Vorst, Rochel Groner. The Sukkah That I Built. Victor-Elsby, Elizabeth, illus. 2002. 26p. (J). (ps-k). 9.95 (978-1-929628-07-0(2)) Hachai Publishing.

Wasserman, Mira. Too Much of a Good Thing. Carolan, Christine, illus. 2003. 32p. (J). (ps-3). 15.95 (978-1-58013-082-0(8)); pap. 6.95 (978-1-58013-066-0(6)) Kar-Ben Publishing.

J
K
L

—Too Much of a Good Thing. 2003. (gr. k-3). lib. bdg. 15.25 (978-0-613-81210-8(7)) Tandem Library Bks.

Watts, Irene. Remember Me: A Search for Refuge in Wartime Britain. 2000. (gr. 5-8). lib. bdg. 16.40 (978-0-613-45685-2(8)) Tandem Library Bks.

Watts, Irene N. Finding Sophie. 2002. (gr. 5-8). lib. bdg. 15.25 (978-0-613-62903-4(5)) Tandem Library Bks.

—Finding Sophie. 2002. 144p. (J). (gr. 5). pap. 6.95 (978-0-88776-613-8(7)) Tundra Bks., Inc./Livres Toundra, Inc. CAN. *Dist:* Random Hse., Inc.

—Goodbye Marianne. 1998. 48p. pap. 6.95 (978-1-896239-03-3(X)) Shillingford, J. Gordon Publishing CAN. *Dist:* Univ. of Toronto Pr.

—Remember Me: A Search for Refuge in Wartime Britain. 2000. 192p. (J). (gr. 5 up). pap. 7.95 (978-0-88776-519-3(X)) Tundra Bks., Inc./Livres Toundra, Inc. CAN. *Dist:* Random Hse., Inc.

—A Telling Time. Shoemaker, Kathryn E., illus. 32p. (J). 7.95 (978-1-896580-72-2(6)) Tradewind Bks. CAN. *Dist:* Orca Bk. Pubs. USA.

Weber, Ilse. Mendel Rosenbusch: Tales for Jewish Children. Fisher, Hans, tr. from GER. Burden, P. John, illus. 2006. Orig. Title: Mendel Rosenbusch: Geschichen Fur Jud Kinder. 128p. (J). pap. 18.00 (978-1-933480-05-3(X)) Bunim & Bannigan Ltd.

—Mendel Rosenbusch: Tales for Jewish Children. Fisher, Hans & Fisher, Ruth, trs. from GER. Burden, P. John, illus. 2006. Orig. Title: Mendel Rosenbusch: Geschichen Fur Jud Kinder. 128p. (J). lib. bdg. 20.00 (978-1-933480-04-6(1)) Bunim & Bannigan Ltd.

—Mendel Rosenbusch: Tales for Jewish Children. Fisher, Hans & Fisher, Ruth, trs. from GER. 2001. Orig. Title: Mendel Rosenbusch: Geschichen Fur Jud Kinder. 232p. (J). (gr. 3-7). 14.00 (978-1-928746-19-5(5)) Herodias.

Weil, Sylvie. My Guardian Angel. 2004. 208p. (J). (gr. 4-7). pap. 16.95 (978-0-439-57681-9(4) , Levine, Arthur A. Bks.) Scholastic, Inc.

Weissenberg, Fran. The Streets Are Paved with Gold. 2002. 156p. (Orig.). pap. 12.95 (978-0-595-21985-8(3) , Backinprint.com) iUniverse, Inc.

Werlin, Nancy. Are You Alone on Purpose? 2007. 208p. (YA). (gr. 7). pap. 7.99 (978-0-14-240777-6(1) , Puffin) Penguin Group (USA) Inc.

Willett, Fangette H. The Boy Who Found Hashem. Jacobs, Jody, illus. 1998. ii, 14p. (J). (gr. 1-5). pap. 4.95 (978-0-9642613-1-0(6)) KinderWord.

Wiseman, Eva. My Canary Yellow Star. 2002. (gr. 5-8). lib. bdg. 15.25 (978-0-613-62688-0(5)) Tandem Library Bks.

—My Canary Yellow Star. 2001. (Illus.). 240p. (J). (gr. 3-7). pap. 6.95 (978-0-88776-533-9(5)) Tundra Bks., Inc./Livres Toundra, Inc. CAN. *Dist:* Random Hse., Inc.

Wisniewski, David, illus. & retold by. Golem. Wisniewski, David, retold by. 2007. 32p. (J). (gr. 1-5). 6.95 (***978-0-618-89424-6(1)*** , Clarion Bks.) Houghton Mifflin Co. Trade & Reference Div.

Woodruff, Elvira. The Memory Coat. Dooling, Michael, illus. 1999. 32p. (J). (gr. 2-5). pap. 16.95 (978-0-590-67717-2(9)) Scholastic, Inc.

Wulf, Linda Press. The Night of the Burning: Devorah's Story. 2006. (Illus.). 224p. (J). (gr. 5-8). 16.00 (978-0-374-36419-9(2) , Farrar, Straus & Giroux (BYR)) Farrar, Straus & Giroux.

Yavin, T. S. All-Star Season. Orback, Craig, illus. 2007. 160p. (J). (gr. 4-6). spiral bd. 15.95 (978-1-58013-211-4(1)) Kar-Ben Publishing.

Yolen, Jane. The Devil's Arithmetic. 2002. (J). 13.19 (978-0-7587-9594-6(7)) Book Wholesalers, Inc.

—The Devil's Arithmetic. 2004. (Puffin Modern Classics Ser.). 176p. (gr. 3). pap. 6.99 (978-0-14-240109-5(9) , Puffin) Penguin Group (USA) Inc.

Yoon, Salina. My First Menorah. Yoon, Salina, illus. 2005. (Illus.). 20p. (J). (ps-2). 7.99 (978-0-689-87746-9(3) , Little Simon) Simon & Schuster Children's Publishing.

Yorinks, Arthur. The Flying Latke. ed. 2004. (Illus.). (J). (gr. k-3). spiral bd. (978-0-616-03066-0(5)) Canadian National Institute for the Blind/Institut National Canadien pour les Aveugles.

Zalben, Jane Breskin. The Fortuneteller in 5B. 2001. 160p. (gr. 4-7). pap. 11.95 (978-0-595-14657-4(0) , Backinprint.com) iUniverse, Inc.

Zeyv, Sender. Aleph Shin: A Novel for the Sixth Millennium, Revised Edition. rev. ed. 2002. (Illus.). 480p. lib. bdg. 23.95 (978-0-9677044-4-9(8)) TMS Publishing Co.

Zucker, Jonny. Four Special Questions: A Passover Story. Cohen, Jan Barger, illus. 2003. (Festival Time! Ser.). 24p. (J). (ps-2). pap. 6.95 (978-0-7641-2267-5(3)) Barron's Educational Series, Inc.

—It's Party Time! A Purim Story. Cohen, Jan Barger, illus. 2003. (Festival Time! Ser.). 24p. (J). (ps-2). pap. 6.95 (978-0-7641-2268-2(1)) Barron's Educational Series, Inc.

Zytman, Leah. The Bravest Fireman. Diskind, Leah M., illus. 1998. 32p. (J). (ps-1). 9.95 (978-0-922613-88-5(5)) Hachai Publishing.

JEWS—FOLKLORE

Here are entered works on post-Biblical Jewish folklore and Jews as a theme in folklore.

Bernstein, Robin. Terrible, Terrible! A Folktale Retold. Kawasaki, Shauna Mooney, illus. 1998. 32p. (J). (ps-5). 15.95 (978-1-58013-016-5(X)); pap. 6.95 (978-1-58013-017-2(8)) Kar-Ben Publishing.

Cope, Jane, illus. The Kingfisher Treasury of Jewish Stories. 2003. (Kingfisher Treasury of Stories Ser.). 160p. (J). (gr. k-3). pap. 6.95 (978-0-7534-5671-2(0) , Kingfisher) Houghton Mifflin Co. Trade & Reference Div.

Could Anything Be Worse? 2004. (J). pap. 14.95 incl. audio (978-1-56008-184-5(8)) Weston Woods Studios, Inc.

Demas, Corinne. Magic Apple. 2002. (gr. 3-6). lib. bdg. 11.80 (978-0-613-50218-4(3)) Tandem Library Bks.

Forest, Heather. A Big Quiet House: A Yiddish Folktale. 2000. (Illus.). (J). 13.75 (978-0-606-20570-2(5)) Tandem Library Bks.

Fowles, Shelley. The Bachelor & the Bean. 2007. (Illus.). 32p. (J). pap. 7.95 (***978-1-84507-020-5(8)***) Lincoln, Frances Ltd. GBR. *Dist:* Perseus Distribution.

Friedlander, Gerald. Jewish Fairy Tales. 2001. (Dover Juvenile Classics Ser.). 96p. (J). (gr. 4-7). pap. 2.00 (978-0-486-41982-4(7)) Dover Pubns., Inc.

Geras, Adele. My Grandmother's Stories: A Collection of Jewish Folk Tales. Lobel, Anita, illus. 2003. 96p. (J). (gr. 1-7). lib. bdg. 21.99 (978-0-375-92285-5(7) , Knopf Bks. for Young Readers) Random Hse. Children's Bks.

Gilman, Phoebe. Something from Nothing. (J). (gr. k-13). pap. (978-0-590-47281-4(X) , SO8818); (Illus.). 32p. pap. 5.99 (978-0-590-74557-4(3)) Scholastic, Inc.

Goldin, Barbara. The Family Book of Midrash: 52 Jewish Stories from the Sages. 2006. 128p. pap. 19.95 (978-0-7425-5285-2(3)) Rowman & Littlefield Pubs., Inc.

Goldreich, Gloria. Ten Traditional Jewish Children's Stories. 2000. (Illus.). 48p. (J). (ps-3). pap. 9.95 (978-0-943706-87-0(4)) Pitspopany Pr.

Jaffe, Nina. The Way Meat Loves Salt: A Cinderella Tale from the Jewish Tradition. August, Louise, illus. rev. ed. 1998. 32p. (J). (ps-4). 17.95 (978-0-8050-4384-6(5) , Holt, Henry & Co. Bks. For Young Readers) Holt, Henry & Co.

Joseph Had a Little Overcoat. 2004. 29.95 incl. cd-rom (978-1-55592-109-5(4)); 24.95 incl. audio (978-1-55592-083-8(7)); pap. 18.95 incl. audio compact disk (978-0-7882-0325-1(8)); pap. 32.75 incl. audio (978-0-7882-0326-8(6)); pap. 14.95 incl. audio (978-0-7882-0324-4(X)) Weston Woods Studios, Inc.

Kimmel, Eric A. Gershon's Monster: A Story for the Jewish New Year. Muth, Jon J., illus. 2000. (Gershon's Monster Ser.). 32p. (J). (gr. k-3). 17.99 (978-0-439-10839-3(X) , Scholastic Pr.) Scholastic, Inc.

Labensohn, Judy, et al. Jewish Sports Stories for Kids. 2005. (Illus.). 224p. (J). (gr. 3-7). 16.95 (978-1-930143-66-1(4)); pap. 12.95 (978-1-930143-67-8(2)) Pitspopany Pr. (Devora Publishing).

Lofin, Michael, illus. Coat for the Moon: And Other Jewish Tales. 2000. (Jps Young Adult Story Collections). 96p. (gr. 3 up). pap. 9.95 (978-0-8276-0736-1(9)) Jewish Pubn. Society.

Matov, G. Tales of Tzaddikim. Weinbach, Shaindel, tr. Bardugo, Miriam, illus. (J). pap. 56.99 (978-0-89906-842-8(1)); 1999. 1576p. 84.99 (978-0-89906-841-1(3) , TA6H) Mesorah Pubns., Ltd.

Mindel, Rabbi Nissan. The Storyteller Volume 5, Vol. 5. Smechov, Zeli, illus. 1998. 324p. (gr. 4-7). 17.95 (978-0-8266-1313-4(6)) Merkos L'Inyonei Chinuch.

Oberman, Sheldon. Solomon & the Ant: And Other Jewish Folktales. 168p. (J). 19.95 (978-1-59078-307-8(7)) Boyds Mills Pr.

Ouaknin, Marc-Alain & Rotnemer, Dory. I'll Tell You a Story. Matthews, Sarah, tr. from FRE. Baron, Nicole, illus. 1998. (Tales of Heaven & Earth Ser.).Tr. of Toi Je Donne Mes Histoires. 32p. (YA). (gr. 3-7). pap. 19.95 (978-0-88682-830-1(9) , Creative Education) Creative Co., The.

Pirotta, Saviour & Kelly, Anne M. Jewish Festivals. 2001. (Festival Tales Ser.). (Illus.). 32p. (J). (gr. 4-7). lib. bdg. 25.69 (978-0-7398-2733-8(2)) Raintree.

Prose, Francine. The Demons' Mistake: A Story from Chelm. Kaminskiy, Mark, illus. 2000. 32p. (J). (gr. 1). 15.95 (978-0-688-17565-8(1)) HarperCollins Pubs.

Rogasky, Barbara & Fisher, Leonard Everett. Dybbuk: A Version. 2005. (Illus.). 64p. (J). (gr. 5 up). 16.95 (978-0-8234-1616-5(X)) Holiday Hse., Inc.

Rosman, Steven M. Sidrah Stories: A Torah Companion. 120p. (J). (gr. 4-6). pap., tchr. ed., wbk. ed. 8.95 (978-0-8074-0429-4(2) , 121723) URJ Pr.

Schacht, Rebecca. Lights along the Path: Jewish Folklore Through the Grades for Children Age Four to Twelve. Morgan, Jacqui, illus. 1999. 194p. (J). (ps-7). 16.95 (978-0-9668448-0-1(7) , 1001) Chelsey Pr.

Schram, Peninnah. Ten Classic Jewish Children's Stories. Allon, Jeffrey, illus. 48p. (J). 2000. (ps-3). pap. 9.95 (978-0-943706-88-7(2)); 1998. (Jewish Storyteller Ser.: Vol. 3). (gr. 1-4). 16.95 (978-0-943706-96-2(3)) Pitspopany Pr.

Schwartz, Howard. Before You Were Born. Swarner, Kristina, illus. rev. ed. 2005. 32p. (J). 16.95 (978-1-59643-028-0(1)) Roaring Brook Pr.

—The Day the Rabbi Disappeared: Jewish Holiday Tales of Magic. Passicot, Monique, illus. 2003. (Young Adult Story Collections). 80p. pap. 9.95 (978-0-8276-0757-6(1)) Jewish Pubn. Society.

—Diamond Tree: Jewish Folktales from Around the World. 1998. (J). (978-0-606-12914-5(6)) Tandem Library Bks.

—Invisible Kingdoms: Jewish Tales of Angels, Spirits, & Demons. Fieser, Stephen, illus. 2002. 80p. (J). (gr. 3 up). 18.89 (978-0-06-027856-4(0)) HarperCollins Pubs.

—A Journey to Paradise: And Other Jewish Tales. Carmi, Giora, illus. 2005. (Jewish Storyteller Ser.). 48p. (J). (ps-3). 16.95 (978-0-943706-21-4(1) , Devora Publishing) Pitspopany Pr.

—Next Year in Jerusalem: 3000 Years of Jewish Stories. 1998. (J). (978-0-606-13659-4(2)) Tandem Library Bks.

Shollar, Leah P. A Thread of Kindness: A Tzedakah Story. Cohen, Yehudis, ed. Mekibel, Shoshana, illus. 2000. 32p. (J). (gr. k-3). 9.95 (978-1-929628-01-8(3)) Hachai Publishing.

Sperber, Daniel, et al. Ten Best Jewish Children's Stories. 2000. (Illus.). 48p. (J). (ps-3). pap. 9.95 (978-0-943706-86-3(6)) Pitspopany Pr.

Stampler, Ann Redisch. Shlemazel & the Remarkable Spoon of Pohost. Cohen, Jacqueline M., illus. 2006. 40p. (J). (gr. k-3). 16.00 (978-0-618-36959-1(7) , Clarion Bks.) Houghton Mifflin Co. Trade & Reference Div.

—Something for Nothing. Cohen, Jacqueline M., illus. 2003. 32p. (J). (gr. 3-5). tchr. ed. 15.00 (978-0-618-15982-6(7) , Clarion Bks.) Houghton Mifflin Co. Trade & Reference Div.

Steinberg, Sari. King Solomon Figures It Out. Taulo, Tuija, illus. 2005. 32p. (J). (gr. k-3). 9.95 (978-965-465-004-5(5) , Devora Publishing) Pitspopany Pr.

Story of Pnei Yehoshua. (J). 6.99 (978-0-89906-845-9(6) , PNYH) Mesorah Pubns., Ltd.

Taback, Simms. Joseph Had a Little Overcoat. Taback, Simms, illus. 2001. (Live Oak Readalong Ser.). (Illus.). (J). 28.95 incl. audio compact disk (978-1-59112-412-2(3)) Live Oak Media.

Ungar, Richard & Tenenbaum, Samuel. Rachel Captures the Moon. Ungar, Richard, illus. 2001. (Illus.). 32p. (J). (gr. 2-5). 16.95 (978-0-88776-505-6(X)) Tundra Bks., Inc./Livres Toundra, Inc. CAN. *Dist:* Random Hse., Inc.

Waldman, Debby. A Sack Full of Feathers. Revell, Cindy, illus. 2006. 32p. (J). 17.95 (978-1-55143-332-5(X)) Orca Bk. Pubs. USA.

JEWS—GERMANY

Ayer, Eleanor H. Parallel Journeys. 2000. (gr. 7-12). lib. bdg. 14.15 (978-0-613-28600-8(6)) Tandem Library Bks.

Hillman, Laura. I Will Plant You a Lilac Tree: A Memoir of a Schindler's List Survivor. 2005. (Illus.). 256p. (YA). 16.95 (978-0-689-86980-8(0) , Atheneum) Simon & Schuster Children's Publishing.

Russo, Marisabina. Always Remember Me: How One Family Survived World War II. Russo, Marisabina, illus. 2005. (Illus.). 48p. (J). (gr. 1-5). 17.99 (978-0-689-86920-4(7) , Atheneum) Simon & Schuster Children's Publishing.

JEWS—HISTORY

Aretha, David. Israel in the News: Past, Present, & Future. 2006. (Middle East Nations in the News Ser.). (Illus.). 128p. (J). lib. bdg. 33.27 (978-1-59845-028-6(X) , MyReportLinks.com Bks.) Enslow Pubs., Inc.

Bartoletti, Susan Campbell. Hitler Youth: Growing up in Hitler's Shadow. 2005. (Illus.). 176p. (J). pap. 19.95 (978-0-439-35379-3(3)) Scholastic, Inc.

Bauer, Yehuda. History of the Holocaust. 2001. (gr. 7-12). lib. bdg. 28.00 (978-0-613-50117-0(9)) Tandem Library Bks.

—A History of the Holocaust. rev. ed. 2002. (Single Titles-Adult Ser.). (YA). (gr. 9-12). pap. 17.95 (978-0-531-15576-9(5) , Watts, Franklin) Scholastic Library Publishing.

Bauer, Yehuda & Keren, Nili. A History of the Holocaust. rev. ed. 2001. (Single Titles Social Studies Ser.). (Illus.). 432p. (YA). (gr. 9-12). 37.50 (978-0-531-11884-9(3) , Watts, Franklin) Scholastic Library Publishing.

Behar, Yvonne. Out of Spain Vol. 1: Our Spanish Heritage. Brooks, Andree Aelion, ed. 2000. (Illus.). 36p. (J). (gr. 5-7). pap. 4.95 (978-0-9702700-0-9(3)) Brooks, Andree Aelion.

—Out of Spain Vol. 2: Off to Other Lands - Sephardi Jews from 1492 to the Present. Brooks, Andree Aelion, ed. 2000. (Illus.). 65p. (J). (gr. 5-7). pap. 4.95 (978-0-9702700-1-6(1)) Brooks, Andree Aelion.

—Out of Spain Vol. 3: Celebrating Sephardi Culture. Brooks, Andree Aelion, ed. (Illus.). 58p. (J). (gr. 5-7). pap. 4.95 (978-0-9702700-3-0(8)) Brooks, Andree Aelion.

Beker, Avi, ed. Jewish Communities of the World. 1998. (More History Reading Ser.). (Illus.). 256p. (YA). (gr. 7-12). pap. (978-0-8225-9822-0(1) , Lerner Pubns.) Lerner Publishing Group.

Broida, Marian. Ancient Israelites & Their Neighbors: An Activity Guide. 2003. (Illus.). 160p. (J). pap. 16.95 (978-1-55652-457-8(9)) Chicago Review Pr., Inc.

Brown, Jonatha A. Anne Frank. Acosta, Tatiana & Gutierrez, Guillermo, trs. 2004. (Gente Que Hay Que Conocer Ser.). (SPA., Illus.). 24p. (J). lib. bdg. 19.33 (978-0-8368-4351-4(7)) Stevens, Gareth Inc.

Charry, Elias & Segal, Abraham. The Eternal People. (Illus.). 448p. (J). (gr. 9-11). 7.50 (978-0-8381-0206-0(9) , 10-206) United Synagogue of America Bk. Service.

Diner, Hasia. Jews in America. 1998. (Religion in America Ser.). (Illus.). 160p. (YA). (gr. 6 up). 30.00 (978-0-19-510678-7(4)) Oxford Univ. Pr., Inc.

Draper, Allison Stark. Pastor Andre Trocme: Spiritual Leader of the French Village, Le Chambon. 2005. (Holocaust Biographies Ser.). (Illus.). 112p. (YA). (gr. 7-12). lib. bdg. 26.50 (978-0-8239-3378-5(4)) Rosen Publishing Group, Inc., The.

Eisenberg, Azriel. Fill a Blank Page: A Biography of Solomon Schechter. (Illus.). (J). (gr. 6-11). 3.75 (978-0-8381-0730-0(3) , 10-730) United Synagogue of America Bk. Service.

Finkelstein, Norman H. The Other 1492: Jewish Settlement in the New World. 2001. (Illus.). 116p. (YA). (gr. 7-12). pap. 9.95 (978-0-595-15279-7(1)) iUniverse, Inc.

—Other 1492: Jewish Settlement in the New World. 2001. (gr. 7-12). lib. bdg. 18.75 (978-0-613-81390-7(1)) Tandem Library Bks.

Haberle, Susan E. Jewish Immigrants, 1880-1924. 2002. (Blue Earth Books). (Illus.). 32p. (J). (gr. 4). lib. bdg. 22.60 (978-0-7368-1207-8(5) , Bridgestone Bks.) Capstone Pr., Inc.

Hans, Julia. Lamps, Scrolls, & Goatskin Bottles: A Handbook of Bible Customs for Kids. 2000. (Illus.). 144p. (YA). 16.99 (978-0-7847-1165-1(8) , 02271) Standard Publishing.

Jones, Graham. How They Lived in Bible Times. Deverell, Richard, illus. 2003. 48p. 6.49 (978-1-85999-435-1(0)) Scripture Union GBR. *Dist:* Gabriel Resources.

Jovinelly, Joann & Netelkos, Jason. The Crafts & Culture of the Ancient Hebrews. 2002. (Crafts of the Ancient World Ser.). (Illus.). 48p. (YA). (gr. 5-8). lib. bdg. 29.25 (978-0-8239-3511-6(6) , Rosen Central) Rosen Publishing Group, Inc., The.

Laurel Corona. Jewish Americans. 2004. (Immigrants in America Ser.). (Illus.). 112p. (J). 29.95 (978-1-59018-431-8(9)) Thomson Gale.

Leiman, Sondra. The Atlas of Great Jewish Communities: A Voyage Through History. 2004. (gr. 4-6). pap. 14.00 (978-0-8074-0801-8(8) , 123941) URJ Pr.

Levinger, Elma Ehrli. The Story of the Jew for Young People. 2005. pap. 30.95 (978-1-4191-5468-3(0)) Kessinger Publishing, LLC.

Mann, Kenny. The Ancient Hebrews. 1998. (Cultures of the Past Ser.). (Illus.). 80p. (YA). (gr. 5 up). lib. bdg. 29.93 (978-0-7614-0302-9(7) , Benchmark Bks.) Cavendish, Marshall Corp.

McNeese, Tim. Masada. 2003. (Sieges That Changed the World Ser.). (Illus.). 112p. (gr. 6-12). 30.00 (978-0-7910-7103-8(0) , Chelsea Hse.) Facts On File, Inc.

Reece, Katherine E. The Israelites: The Lawgivers. 2005. (Ancient Civilizations Ser.). (Illus.). 48p. (gr. 4-8). 20.95 (978-1-59515-239-8(3)) Rourke Publishing, LLC.

Robb, Andy. Hodgepodge Hebrews. 2004. (Holy Happenings Ser.). (Illus.). 128p. pap. 6.50 (978-0-687-02326-4(2)) Abingdon Pr.

Rosenfield, Geraldine. The Heroes of Masada. Sugarman, S. Allan, illus. 38p. (J). (gr. 6-10). pap. 1.50 (978-0-8381-0733-1(8) , 10-732) United Synagogue of America Bk. Service.

Schiffman, Lawrence H. Understanding Second Temple & Rabbinic Judaism. 2003. (YA). 29.50 (978-0-88125-813-4(X)) Ktav Publishing Hse., Inc.

Senker, Cath. Judaism Around the World. 2007. (J). (***978-1-59920-056-9(2)***) Smart Apple Media.

Sheehan, Sean. After the Holocaust. 2001. (Holocaust Ser.). (Illus.). 64p. (YA). (gr. 6-8). lib. bdg. 28.54 (978-0-7398-3259-2(X)) Raintree.

—Survival & Resistance. 2001. (Holocaust Ser.). (Illus.). 64p. (YA). (gr. 6-8). lib. bdg. 28.54 (978-0-7398-3260-8(3)) Raintree.

Shuter, Jane. Aftermath of the Holocaust. 2003. (Holocaust Ser.). 56p. (Illus.). (J). (gr. 6-8). lib. bdg. 28.50 (978-1-4034-0807-5(6)); pap. 8.95 (978-1-4034-3199-8(X)) Heinemann Library.

—Aftermath of the Holocaust. 2003. (Illus.). 56p. (J). (gr. 4-7). lib. bdg. 17.60 (978-0-613-60949-4(2)) Tandem Library Bks.

Stadtler, Bea. The Adventures of Gluckel of Hameln. (J). (gr. 6-10). 3.75 (978-0-8381-0731-7(1) , 10-731) United Synagogue of America Bk. Service.

Taylor, Peter Lane & Nicola, Christos. The Secret of Priest's Grotto: A Holocaust Survival Story. 2007. 64p. (YA). (gr. 5 up). pap. 8.95 (***978-1-58013-261-9(8)***) Kar-Ben Publishing.

Waldman, Neil. The Promised Land: The Birth of the Jewish People. Waldman, Neil, illus. 2003. (Illus.). 40p. (YA). (gr. 6-9). 21.95 (978-1-56397-332-1(4)) Boyds Mills Pr.

Weilerstein, Sadie Rose. Jewish Heroes, 2 bks. Cassel, Lili, illus. 208p. (J). (gr. 2-3). Bk. 1. 4.25 (978-0-8381-0180-3(1)); Bk. 2. 4.25 (978-0-8381-0177-3(1)) United Synagogue of America Bk. Service.

JEWS—HISTORY—FICTION

Adams, Anne Tyra. Songbird of the Nile: The Diary of Miriam's Best Friend, Egypt, 1527 B. C. -1526 B. C. 2004. (Promised Land Diaries). (Illus.). 192p. (J). 10.99 (978-0-8010-4525-7(8)) Baker Bks.

Benderly, Beryl Lieff. Jason's Miracle: A Hanukkah Story. 2004. 114p. (J). (gr. 4-8). reprint ed. (978-0-7567-7792-0(5)) DIANE Publishing Co.

—Jason's Miracle: A Hanukkah Story. 2000. (Illus.). 120p. (J). (gr. 4-8). 14.95 (978-0-8075-3781-7(0)) Whitman, Albert & Co.

Booth, Bradley. Plagues in the Palace. 2006. 159p. (J). (978-0-8163-2143-8(4)) Pacific Pr. Publishing Assn.

Cheng, Andrea. Marika. 1998. 148p. (YA). (gr. 5 up). 16.95 (978-1-886910-78-2(2) , Lemniscaat) Boyds Mills Pr.

Chotjewitz, David. Daniel, Half Human: And the Good Nazi. Orgel, Doris, tr. from GER. 2004. (Illus.). 304p. (YA). 17.95 (978-0-689-85747-8(0) , Atheneum) Simon & Schuster Children's Publishing.

Chotjewitz, David & Orgel, Doris. Daniel, Half Human: And the Good Nazi. 2004. 298p. (J). (978-3-551-58045-0(6)) Carlsen Verlag DEU. *Dist:* Distribooks, Inc.

Dennis, Jeanne Gowen & Seifert, Sheila. Attack! Hohn, David, tr. Hohn, David, illus. 2003. (Strive to Thrive Ser.). 96p. (J). pap., pap. 5.99 (978-0-7814-3894-0(2) , 0781438942) Cook, David C. Publishing Co.

—Deadly Expedition! Hohn, David, tr. Hohn, David, illus. 2003. (Survivor Ser.). 96p. (J). pap., pap. 5.99 (978-0-7814-3897-1(7) , 0781438977) Cook, David C. Publishing Co.

—Trapped! Hohn, David, tr. Hohn, David, illus. 2003. (Survivor Ser.). 96p. (J). pap., pap. 5.99 (978-0-7814-3898-8(5) , 0781438985) Cook, David C. Publishing Co.

Hernandez, David. Land of the Pharaohs. 2003. (Adventures of Toby Digz Ser.). (Illus.). 96p. (J). pap. 5.99 (978-1-4003-0195-9(5)) Nelson, Thomas Inc.

Jacqueline Jules Staff. The Ziz & the Hanukkah Miracle. 2006. (J). pap. 7.95 (978-1-58013-164-3(6)) Kar-Ben Publishing.

Kaplan, Kathy Walden. The Dog of Knots. 2005. 139p. (J). pap. 7.50 (978-0-8028-5274-8(2)) Eerdmans, William B. Publishing Co.

Kelly, Clint & Ware, Jim. Escape Underground & the Prophet's Kid. 2001. (KidWitness Tales Ser.). 128p. (J). (gr. 3-8). pap. 5.99 (978-1-56179-965-7(3)) Bethany Hse. Pubs.

Kerr, Judith. When Hitler Stole Pink Rabbit.Tr. of Cuando Hitler Robo el Conejo Rosa. (SPA.). 172p. (J). 11.95 (978-84-204-3201-4(6)) Santillana USA Publishing Co., Inc.

Lasky, Kathryn. Broken Song. 2005. 160p. (J). (gr. 7). 15.99 (978-0-670-05931-7(5) , Viking Juvenile) Penguin Group (USA) Inc.

Lawrence, Caroline. The Assassins of Rome, Vol. 4. 2005. (Illus.). 176p. (J). (gr. 3-7). pap. 5.99 (978-0-14-240214-6(1) , Puffin) Penguin Group (USA) Inc.

Lawton, Wendy. Shadow of His Hand: A Story Based on the Life of Holocaust Survivor Anita Dittman. 2004. (Daughters of the Faith Ser.). 160p. (J). pap. 6.99 (978-0-8024-4074-7(6)) Moody Pubs.

Lehmann, R' Marcus, contrib. by. The Family y Aguilar. 12.95 (978-0-87306-318-0(X)) Feldheim Pubs.

Maltz, Fran. Keeping Faith in the Dust. Spark, illus. 1999. 72p. (J). (gr. 4-7). pap. 7.95 (978-1-881283-25-6(9)) Alef Design Group.

Matas, Carol. Rosie in New York City: Gotcha! 2003. (Aladdin Historical Fiction Ser.). (Illus.). 128p. (J). (gr. 3-6). pap. 9.95 (978-0-689-85714-0(4) , Aladdin) Simon & Schuster Children's Publishing.

—Rosie in New York City: Gotcha! 2003. (gr. 5-8). lib. bdg. 13.00 (978-0-613-66469-1(8)) Tandem Library Bks.

Matas, Carol. Turned Away: The World War II Diary of Devorah Bernstein. 2005. (Dear Canada Ser.). (Illus.). 199p. (J). pap. (***978-0-439-96946-8(8)***) Scholastic Canada, Ltd.

McKay, Sharon E. Esther. 2004. 336p. (J). pap. (***978-0-14-331204-8(9)***) Penguin Group (Canada).

Michaelson, Richard. Across the Alley. Lewis, E. B., illus. 2006. 32p. (J). (ps-3). 16.99 (978-0-399-23970-0(7) , Putnam Juvenile) Penguin Group (USA) Inc.

Miklowitz, Gloria. Secrets in the House of Delgado. 2001. (gr. 5-8). lib. bdg. 15.30 (978-0-613-55662-0(3)) Tandem Library Bks.

Miklowitz, Gloria D. Masada: The Last Fortress. 2004. 198p. (YA). (gr. 4-7). 16.00 (978-0-8028-5165-9(7)) Eerdmans, William B. Publishing Co.

—Secrets in the House of Delgado. 2004. 192p. (J). (gr. 4 up). pap. 8.00 (978-0-8028-5210-6(6)) Eerdmans, William B. Publishing Co.

Napoli, Donna Jo. Daughter of Venice. 2003. 288p. (YA). (gr. 7). pap. 6.50 (978-0-440-22928-5(6) , Laurel Leaf) Random Hse. Children's Bks.

—Daughter of Venice. 2003. (gr. 7-12). lib. bdg. 13.55 (978-0-613-72327-5(9)) Tandem Library Bks.

Number the Stars. 2004. (Literature Connections Ser.). (gr. 6-12). (978-0-395-88457-7(8) , 2-70863) McDougal Littell Inc.

Orgad, Dorit & Silverston, Sondra. The Boy from Seville. 2007. (Kar-Ben for Older Readers Ser.). (J). (gr. 5-7). 16.95 (978-1-58013-253-4(7)) Kar-Ben Publishing.

Ray, Mary. Beyond the Desert Gate. 2nd ed. 2001. (Young Adult Historical Library). (Illus.). 190p. (YA). (gr. 3-9). 11.95 (978-1-883937-54-6(X) , 54-X) Bethlehem Bks.

Shapiro, David L. Sara's Journey. 2005. 293p. (YA). (gr. 7-12). pap. 12.95 (978-0-8276-0776-7(8)) Jewish Pubn. Society.

Shulevitz, Uri. The Travels of Benjamin of Tudela: Through Three Continents in the Twelfth Century. 2005. (Illus.). 48p. (J). 17.00 (978-0-374-37754-0(5) , Farrar, Straus & Giroux (BYR)) Farrar, Straus & Giroux.

Speare, Elizabeth George. The Bronze Bow. 2002. (J). 14.74 (978-0-7587-0173-2(X)) Book Wholesalers, Inc.

—The Bronze Bow. 1999. (J). 9.95 (978-1-56137-726-8(0)) Novel Units, Inc.

Stuchner, Joan Betty. Honey Cake. Nugent, Cynthia, illus. 2008. (J). (***978-0-375-85189-6(5));*** pap. (***978-0-375-85190-2(9));*** lib. bdg. (***978-0-375-95189-3(X)***) Random Hse., Inc.

Toksvig, Sandi. Hitler's Canary. 2007. 192p. (J). (gr. 6 up). 16.95 (978-1-59643-247-5(0)) Roaring Brook Pr.

Weil, Sylvie. My Guardian Angel. 2007. 208p. (J). pap. 5.99 (***978-0-439-57682-6(2)*** , Scholastic Paperbacks) Scholastic, Inc.

Zusak, Markus. The Book Thief. (YA). (gr. 7 up). 2007. 576p. pap. 11.99 (***978-0-375-84220-7(9));*** 2006. 560p. 16.95 (978-0-375-83100-3(2)); 2006. 560p. lib. bdg. 18.99 (978-0-375-93100-0(7)) Random Hse. Children's Bks. (Knopf Bks. for Young Readers).

JEWS—LANGUAGE

see Hebrew Language

JEWS—LITERATURE

see Hebrew Literature; Jewish Literature

JEWS—NETHERLANDS

Abramson, Ann. Who Was Anne Frank? Harrison, Nancy, illus. 2007. (Who Was... ? Ser.). 112p. (J). pap. 4.99 (978-0-448-44482-6(8) , Grosset & Dunlap) Penguin Group (USA) Inc.

Ashby, Ruth. Anne Frank: Young Diarist. 2005. 186p. (J). lib. bdg. 18.46 (***SPA-1-4242-2208-7(7)***) Fitzgerald Bks.

Brown, Jonatha A. Anne Frank. (People to Know Ser.). 2004. (J). pap. (978-0-8368-4316-3(9)); 2004. (Illus.). 24p. (YA). lib. bdg. 19.33 (978-0-8368-4309-5(6)); 2003. (Illus.). 48p. (J). (gr. 5 up). lib. bdg. 30.00 (978-0-8368-5090-1(4) , World Almanac Library); 2003. (Illus.). 48p. (J). (gr. 5 up). pap. 10.95 (978-0-8368-5250-9(8) , World Almanac Library) Stevens, Gareth Inc.

Denenberg, Barry. Portrait of Anne Frank & Her Family. 2005. (Shadow Life Ser.). (Illus.). 240p. (J). pap. 16.95 (978-0-439-41678-8(7)) Scholastic, Inc.

Dunn, Joeming W. & Dunn, Ben. Anne Frank. Dunn, Joeming W. & Dunn, Ben, illus. 2007. (Bio-Graphics Ser.). (Illus.). 32p. (J). (gr. 3-6). lib. bdg. 27.07 (***978-1-60270-065-9(6)*** , Graphic Planet) Magic Wagon.

Goff, Elizabeth Hudson & Brown, Jonatha A. Anne Frank. 2006. (Graphic Biographies (World Almanac Library (Firm))). (Illus.). (J). pap. (978-0-8368-6248-5(1)); 32p. lib. bdg. 26.00 (978-0-8368-6196-9(5)) Stevens, Gareth Inc. (World Almanac Library).

Heims, Neil. Reading the Diary of Anne Frank. 2005. (Engaged Reader Ser.). (Illus.). 81p. (J). (gr. 4-8). lib. bdg. 25.00 (978-0-7910-8829-6(4) , Chelsea Hse.) Facts On File, Inc.

Jacobsen, Ruth. Rescued Images: Memories of a Childhood in Hiding. 2001. (Illus.). 96p. (YA). (gr. 7). 19.95 (978-1-931414-00-5(9)) Mikaya Pr.

Johnson, Emma. Anne Frank. 2003. (Twentieth Century History Makers Ser.). (Illus.). 112p. (J). lib. bdg. 32.85 (978-0-7398-5261-3(2)) Raintree.

Koestler-Grack, Rachel A. The Story of Anne Frank. 2003. (Breakthrough Biographies Ser.). (Illus.). 32p. (gr. 3-5). 23.00 (978-0-7910-7311-7(4) , Chelsea Hse.) Facts On File, Inc.

Lee, Carol Ann. Anne Frank & the Children of the Holocaust. 2006. 256p. (YA). (gr. 4). 16.99 (978-0-670-06107-5(7) , Viking Juvenile) Penguin Group (USA) Inc.

Maarsen, Jacqueline Van. A Friend Called Anne: One Girl's Story of War, Peace & a Unique Friendship with Anne Frank. 2005. (Illus.). 176p. (J). (gr. 3). 15.99 (978-0-670-05958-4(7) , Viking Juvenile) Penguin Group (USA) Inc.

Mara, Wil. Anne Frank. 2006. (Illus.). 31p. (978-0-516-29841-2(0)) Children's Pr., Ltd.

Poole, Josephine. Anne Frank. Barrett, Angela, illus. 2005. 40p. (J). (gr. 5). lib. bdg. 19.99 (978-0-375-93242-7(9) , Knopf Bks. for Young Readers) Random Hse. Children's Bks.

Saunders, Nicholas. The Life of Anne Frank. 2006. (Stories from History Ser.). 48p. (J). 14.95 (978-0-7696-4714-2(6)); pap. 6.95 (978-0-7696-4695-4(6)) School Specialty Publishing.

Senker, Cath. Anne Frank: Voice of Hope. 2001. (Famous Lives Ser.). (Illus.). 48p. (J). (gr. 3-7). lib. bdg. 27.12 (978-0-8172-5719-4(5)) Raintree.

Whiting, Jim. Anne Frank. 2007. (What's So Great About... ? Ser.). (J). lib. bdg. 25.70 (***978-1-58415-581-2(7)***) Mitchell Lane Pubs., Inc.

JEWS—NEW YORK (STATE)—NEW YORK—FICTION

Baker, Sharon. A Nickel, a Trolley, a Treasure House. Peck, Beth, illus. 2007. 32p. (J). (gr. k-5). 16.99 (978-0-670-05982-9(X) , Viking Juvenile) Penguin Group (USA) Inc.

Hest, Amy. When Jessie Came Across the Sea. Lynch, P. J., illus. 2003. 40p. (J). (gr. 1-7). pap. 6.99 (978-0-7636-1274-0(X)) Candlewick Pr.

Lasky, Kathryn. Dreams in the Golden Country: The Diary of Zipporah Feldman, a Jewish Immigrant Girl, New York City, 1903. 1998. (Dear America Ser.). (Illus.). 192p. (J). (gr. 4-9). pap. 10.95 (978-0-590-02973-5(8)) Scholastic, Inc.

Levine, Gail Carson. Dave at Night. 2001. 304p. (J). (gr. 3-7). reprint ed. pap. 6.99 (978-0-06-440747-2(0) , Harper Trophy) HarperCollins Pubs.

—Dave at Night. unabr. ed. 2004. 278p. (J). (gr. 4-7). pap. 38.00 incl. audio (978-0-8072-8379-0(7) , YA174SP, Listening Library) Random Hse. Audio Publishing Group.

—Dave at Night. 1999. (YA). pap., stu. ed. 69.95 incl. audio (978-0-7887-3794-7(5) , 41038) Recorded Bks., LLC.

Schwabach, Karen. A Pickpocket's Tale. 240p. (J). (gr. 3-7). 2008. 5.99 (***978-0-375-83380-9(3)*** , Yearling); 2006. (Illus.). 15.95 (978-0-375-83379-3(X) , Random Hse. Bks. for Young Readers); 2006. (Illus.). lib. bdg. 17.99 (978-0-375-93379-0(4) , Random Hse. Bks. for Young Readers) Random Hse. Children's Bks.

JEWS—PALESTINE—HISTORY

Hall, John G. The Palestinian Authority. 2002. (Creation of the Modern Middle East Ser.). (Illus.). 125p. (gr. 6-12). 35.00 (978-0-7910-6515-0(4) , Chelsea Hse.) Facts On File, Inc.

Schur, Maxine Rose. Hannah Szenes: A Song of Light. rev. ed. 1998. 106p. pap. 9.95 (978-0-8276-0628-9(1)) Jewish Pubn. Society.

JEWS—PERSECUTIONS

Downing, David. Persecution & Emigration. 2005. (World Almanac Library of the Holocaust). (Illus.). 48p. (978-0-8368-5951-5(0)); (YA). (gr. 5 up). lib. bdg. 30.00 (978-0-8368-5944-7(8)) Stevens, Gareth Inc. (World Almanac Library).

Forest, James H. Silent As a Stone: Mother Maria of Paris & the Trash Can Rescue. Pancheshnaya, Dasha, illus. 2007. (J). 18.00 (***978-0-88141-314-4(3)***) St. Vladimir's Seminary Pr.

Mochizuki, Ken. Pasaje a la Libertad: La Historia de Chiune Sugihara. Sarfati, Esther, tr. Lee, Dom, illus. 1999. (SPA.). 32p. (J). (gr. 3-5). 12.76 net. (978-1-880000-81-6(4) , LW8823) Lee & Low Bks., Inc.

Russo, Marisabina. Always Remember Me: How One Family Survived World War II. Russo, Marisabina, illus. 2005. (Illus.). 48p. (J). (gr. 1-5). 17.99 (978-0-689-86920-4(7) , Atheneum) Simon & Schuster Children's Publishing.

Shuter, Jane. Life & Death in Hitler's Europe. 2003. (Holocaust Ser.). 56p. (Illus.). (J). lib. bdg. 28.50 (978-1-4034-0811-2(4)); pap. 8.95 (978-1-4034-3203-2(1)) Heinemann Library.

—Life & Death in Hitler's Europe. 2003. (gr. 5-8). lib. bdg. 17.60 (978-0-613-60969-2(7)) Tandem Library Bks.

—Prelude to the Holocaust. 2003. (Holocaust Ser.). (Illus.). 56p. (J). lib. bdg. 28.50 (978-1-4034-0813-6(0)); pap. 8.95 (978-1-4034-3205-6(8)) Heinemann Library.

Smith, Frank Dabba. My Secret Camera: Life in the Lodz Ghetto. 2000. (Illus.). 40p. (J). (gr. 4-7). lib. bdg. 27.12 (978-0-7398-2198-5(9)) Raintree.

Thornton, Jeremy. Religious Intolerance: Jewish Immigrants Come to America (1881-1914) 2004. (Primary Sources of Immigration & Migration in America Ser.). (Illus.). 24p. (J). lib. bdg. 19.95 (978-0-8239-6834-3(0)) Rosen Publishing Group, Inc., The.

—Religious Intolerance: Jewish Immigrants Come to America, 1890-1924. 2004. (Primary Sources of Immigration & Migration in America Ser.). (Illus.). 24p. (J). lib. bdg. (978-0-8239-8960-7(7)) Rosen Publishing Group, Inc., The.

Toll, Nelly. Behind the Secret Window: A Memoir of a Hidden Childhood During World War II. 2003. 176p. (J). (gr. 3-6). pap. 5.99 (978-0-14-230241-5(4) , Puffin) Penguin Group (USA) Inc.

Wukovits, John F. Anne Frank. 1998. (Importance of Ser.). (Illus.). 96p. (YA). (gr. 7-10). 32.45 (978-1-56006-353-7(X) , Lucent Bks.) Thomson Gale.

Ziemian, Joseph. The Cigarette Sellers of Three Crosses Square. 2005. (Library of Holocaust Testimonies). (Illus.). 168p. pap. 17.50 (978-0-85303-686-9(1)) Vallentine Mitchell Pubs. GBR. *Dist:* International Specialized Bk. Services.

JEWS—POLAND

Adler, David A. A Hero & the Holocaust: The Story of Janusz Korczak & His Children. Farnsworth, Bill, illus. 2002. 32p. (J). (gr. 4-6). tchr. ed. 16.95 (978-0-8234-1548-9(1)) Holiday Hse., Inc.

Beyer, Mark. Emmanuel Ringelblum: Historian of the Warsaw Ghetto. 2005. (Holocaust Biographies Ser.). (Illus.). 112p. (YA). (gr. 7-12). lib. bdg. 26.50 (978-0-8239-3375-4(X)) Rosen Publishing Group, Inc., The.

Opdyke, Irene Gut. In My Hands: Memories of a Holocaust Rescuer. 1999. (Illus.). 288p. (YA). (gr. 9-8). pap. 18.00 (978-0-679-89181-9(1) , Knopf Bks. for Young Readers) Random Hse. Children's Bks.

Opdyke, Irene Gut & Armstrong, Jennifer. In My Hands: Memories of a Holocaust Rescuer. unabr. ed. 2004. 248p. (J). (gr. 5 up). pap. 42.00 incl. audio (978-0-8072-0867-0(1) , LYA 150 SP, Listening Library) Random Hse. Audio Publishing Group.

Schanzer, Rosalyn. Escaping to America: A True Story. Schanzer, Rosalyn, illus. 2000. (Illus.). 32p. (J). (gr. 3-7). 15.95 (978-0-688-16989-3(9)) HarperCollins Pubs.

Smith, Frank Dabba. My Secret Camera: Life in the Lodz Ghetto. 2000. (Illus.). 40p. (J). (gr. 4-7). lib. bdg. 27.12 (978-0-7398-2198-5(9)) Raintree.

Warren, Andrea. Surviving Hitler: A Boy in the Nazi Death Camps. 2002. (gr. 3-6). lib. bdg. 15.30 (978-0-613-56635-3(1)) Tandem Library Bks.

Ziemian, Joseph. The Cigarette Sellers of Three Crosses Square. 2005. (Library of Holocaust Testimonies). (Illus.). 168p. pap. 17.50 (978-0-85303-686-9(1)) Vallentine Mitchell Pubs. GBR. *Dist:* International Specialized Bk. Services.

JEWS—RELIGION

see Judaism

JEWS—RITES AND CEREMONIES

Chanover, Hyman & Zusman, Evelyn. A Book of Prayer for Junior Congregations: Sabbath & Festivals. (ENG & HEB.). 256p. (J). (gr. 4-7). 4.50 (978-0-8381-0174-2(7) , 10-174) United Synagogue of America Bk. Service.

Eisenberg, Azriel & Robinson, Jessie B. My Jewish Holidays. 208p. (J). (gr. 5-6). 3.95 (978-0-8381-0176-6(3) , 10-176) United Synagogue of America Bk. Service.

Kurtz, Joan. Around & Around: Jewish Lifecycle Ceremonies. 1999. (Illus.). (J). pap. 8.00 (978-1-891877-03-2(8)) Sheron Enterprises, Inc.

Metter, Bertram. Bar Mitzvah, Bat Mitzvah: The Ceremony, the Party, & How the Day Came to Be. Reilly, Joan & Katz, Avi, illus. 2007. 80p. (J). (gr. 5-9). pap. 5.95 (***978-0-618-76773-1(8)*** , Clarion Bks.) Houghton Mifflin Co. Trade & Reference Div.

JEWS—SOVIET UNION

Siegal, Aranka. Upon the Head of the Goat: A Childhood in Hungary, 1939-1944. 2003. (gr. 5-8). lib. bdg. 14.10 (978-0-613-59754-8(0)) Tandem Library Bks.

Taybert, Efim. I Kedriy Tojze Plachyt. 2003. Tr. of And Cedars Also Cry. (RUS.). 254p. (YA). pap. (978-0-9728301-2-6(X)) Publishing Hse. Gelany.

JEWS—SOVIET UNION—FICTION

Blumberg, Margie. Avram's Gift. McGaw, Laurie, illus. 48p. 2005. (YA). pap. 7.95 (978-0-9624166-3-7(0)); 2003. (J). (gr. 3 up). (978-0-9624166-2-0(2)) MB Publishing, LLC.

Howland, Naomi. Latkes, Latkes, Good to Eat: A Chanukah Story. 2004. (Illus.). 32p. (J). (ps-3). pap. 5.95 (978-0-618-49295-4(X) , Clarion Bks.) Houghton Mifflin Co. Trade & Reference Div.

—Latkes, Latkes, Good to Eat: A Chanukah Story. Howland, Naomi, illus. 1999. (Illus.). 32p. (J). (gr. k-3). tchr. ed. 16.00 (978-0-395-89903-8(6) , Clarion Bks.) Houghton Mifflin Co. Trade & Reference Div.

Sandman, Rochel. Perfect Porridge: A Story about Kindness. Zakashansky-Zverev, Chana, illus. 2000. 32p. (J). (ps-2). 9.95 (978-0-922613-92-2(3)) Hachai Publishing.

JEWS—UNITED STATES

Brooks, Philip. Extraordinary Jewish Americans. 1998. (Extraordinary People Ser.). (Illus.). 288p. (YA). (gr. 6 up). pap. 16.95 (978-0-516-26350-2(1) , Children's Pr.) Scholastic Library Publishing.

Bryan, Nichol. Jewish Americans. 2004. (One Nation Ser.). (Illus.). 32p. (J). (gr. k-6). lib. bdg. 22.78 (978-1-57765-986-0(4)) ABDO Publishing Co.

Cohn, Janice. The Christmas Menorahs: How a Town Fought Hate. 2000. (J). 13.75 (978-0-606-19688-8(9)) Tandem Library Bks.

Diner, Hasia. Jews in America. 1998. (Religion in America Ser.). (Illus.). 160p. (YA). (gr. 6 up). 30.00 (978-0-19-510678-7(4)) Oxford Univ. Pr., Inc.

Finkelstein, Norman H. Forged in Freedom: Shaping the Jewish-American Experience. 2002. (Illus.). 192p. (gr. 6-12). 19.95 (978-0-8276-0748-4(2)) Jewish Pubn. Society.

Granfield, Linda. 97 Orchard Street, New York: Stories of Immigrant Life. 2001. (gr. 3-6). lib. bdg. 24.60 (978-0-613-56823-4(0)) Tandem Library Bks.

—97 Orchard Street, New York: Stories of Immigrant Life. Alda, Arlene, photos by. 2001. (Illus.). 56p. (J). (gr. 3-6). pap. 15.00 (978-0-88776-580-3(7)) Tundra Bks., Inc./Livres Toundra, Inc. CAN. *Dist:* Random Hse., Inc.

Haberle, Susan E. Jewish Immigrants, 1880-1924. 2002. (Blue Earth Books). (Illus.). 32p. (J). (gr. 4). lib. bdg. 22.60 (978-0-7368-1207-8(5) , Bridgestone Bks.) Capstone Pr., Inc.

Horton, Casey. Jews. 2000. (gr. 3-6). lib. bdg. 17.60 (978-0-613-27915-4(8)) Tandem Library Bks.

Laurel Corona. Jewish Americans. 2004. (Immigrants in America Ser.). (Illus.). 112p. (J). 29.95 (978-1-59018-431-8(9)) Thomson Gale.

Lewin, Rhoda. Reform Jews of Minneapolis. 2004. (Images of America Ser.). (Illus.). 128p. pap. 19.99 (978-0-7385-3217-2(7)) Arcadia Publishing.

Michelson, Richard. As Good as Anybody. 2008. 40p. (J). (gr. 1-5). lib. bdg. 19.99 (***978-0-375-93335-6(2)*** , Knopf Bks. for Young Readers) Random Hse. Children's Bks.

Rappaport, Doreen. In the Promised Land: Lives of Jewish Americans. Van Wright, Cornelius & Hu, Ying-Hwa, illus. 2005. 32p. (J). (gr. k-4). 15.99 (978-0-688-17150-6(8)) HarperCollins Pubs.

Rosenberg, Pam. Jewish Americans. 2004. (Our Cultural Heritage Ser.). 32p. (J). (gr. 2-6). 27.07 (978-1-59296-181-8(9)) Child's World, Inc.

Rubin, Susan Goldman. L' Chaim! To Jewish Life in America: Celebrating from 1654 until Today. 2004. (Illus.). 176p. (J). (gr. 5-17). 24.95 (978-0-8109-5035-1(9)) Abrams, Harry N. , Inc.

—Haym Salomon: American Patriot. Slonim, David, illus. 2007. 40p. (J). (ps-5). 16.95 (978-0-8109-1087-4(X) , Abrams Bks. for Young Readers) Abrams, Harry N. , Inc.

Schanzer, Rosalyn. Escaping to America: A True Story. Schanzer, Rosalyn, illus. 2000. (Illus.). 32p. (J). (gr. 3-7). 15.89 (978-0-688-16990-9(2)); 15.95 (978-0-688-16989-3(9)) HarperCollins Pubs.

Stein, Robert. Jewish Americans: Coming to America. 2006. (Illus.). 128p. (J). (gr. 4-8). reprint ed. 15.00 (978-1-4223-5576-3(4)) DIANE Publishing Co.

Stone, Amy. Jewish Americans. 2006. (World Almanac Library of American Immigration). (Illus.). 48p. (J). pap. (978-0-8368-7327-6(0)); lib. bdg. (978-0-8368-7314-6(9)) Stevens, Gareth Inc. (World Almanac Library).

Taylor, Peter Lane & Nicola, Christos. The Secret of Priest's Grotto: A Holocaust Survival Story. 2007. 64p. (J). (gr. 5 up). 18.95 (978-1-58013-260-2(X)) Kar-Ben Publishing.

Thornton, Jeremy. Religious Intolerance: Jewish Immigrants Come to America (1881-1914) 2004. (Primary Sources of Immigration & Migration in America Ser.). (Illus.). 24p. (J). lib. bdg. 19.95 (978-0-8239-6834-3(0)) Rosen Publishing Group, Inc., The.

—Religious Intolerance: Jewish Immigrants Come to America, 1890-1924. 2004. (Primary Sources of Immigration & Migration in America Ser.). (Illus.). 24p. (J). lib. bdg. (978-0-8239-8960-7(7)) Rosen Publishing Group, Inc., The.

Ueda, Reed & Stotsky, Sandra, eds. Jewish-American Answer Book. 1999. (Ethnic Answer Book Ser.). (Illus.). 136p. (gr. 5 up). (J). lib. bdg. 19.75 (978-0-7910-4799-6(7)); (YA). pap. 9.95 (978-0-7910-4800-9(4)) Facts On File, Inc. (Chelsea Hse.).

Wells, Rosemary, et al. Streets of Gold. Fogelman, Phyllis J., ed. Andreasen, Dan, illus. 1999. 40p. (J). (gr. k-3). 16.99 (978-0-8037-2149-4(8) , Dial) Penguin Group (USA) Inc.

JEWS—UNITED STATES—FICTION

Abelove, Joan. Saying It Out Loud. 2001. 144p. (YA). (gr. 7 up). pap. 5.99 (978-0-14-131227-9(0) , Puffin) Penguin Group (USA) Inc.

Adler, David A. One Yellow Daffodil: A Hanukkah Story. Bloom, Lloyd, illus. 1999. 32p. (J). (gr. 1-5). pap. 7.00 (978-0-15-202094-1(2) , Harcourt Paperbacks) Harcourt Children's Bks.

Altman, Linda Jacobs. The Legend of Freedom Hill. Van Wright, Cornelius, illus. 2003. 32p. (J). (978-1-58430-169-1(4)) Lee & Low Bks., Inc.

—The Legend of Freedom Hill. Van Wright, Cornelius & Hu, Ying-Hwa, illus. 2000. 32p. (J). (ps up). 15.95 (978-1-58430-003-8(5)) Lee & Low Bks., Inc.

—The Legend of Freedom Hill. Van Wright, Cornelius et al, illus. 2004. 32p. (J). (ps-k). lib. bdg. 13.75 (978-0-606-30127-5(5)) Tandem Library Bks.

Avrech, Robert J. The Hebrew Kid & the Apache Maiden. 2006. 228p. (J). pap. 11.95 (978-0-9754382-2-0(0)) Seraphic Pr.

Baer, Julie, illus. & text. I Only Like What I Like. Baer, Julie, text. 2003. 32p. (J). 15.99 (978-1-932188-00-4(2)) Bollix Bks.

Baskin, Nora Raleigh. The Truth about My Bat Mitzvah. 2008. 144p. (J). 15.99 (***978-1-4169-3558-2(4)*** , Simon & Schuster Children's Publishing) Simon & Schuster Children's Publishing.

Benjamin, Ruth. The Lost Treasure of Chelton. 2004. viii, 170p. (J). 13.95 (978-1-932443-02-8(9)) Judaica Pr., Inc., The.

Benjamin, Ruth. The Mysterious Lighthouse of Chelton. 2006. (ENG.). 160p. (J). 14.95 (***978-1-932443-57-8(6)***) Judaica Pr., Inc., The.

Center for Learning Network Staff & Potok, Chaim. Davita's Harp: Curriculum Unit. 1998. (Novel Ser.). 107p. (YA). (gr. 9-12). tchr. ed., spiral bd. 19.95 (978-1-56077-576-8(9)) Ctr. for Learning, The.

J K L

Chaikin, Miriam. Finders Weepers. Egielski, Richard, illus. 2001. 136p. (YA). pap. 11.95 (978-0-595-19878-8(3) , Backinprint.com) iUniverse, Inc.

—I Should Worry, I Should Care. 2000. (Illus.). 116p. (gr. 4-7). pap. 9.95 (978-0-595-09011-2(7) , Backinprint-.com) iUniverse, Inc.

Cohen, Barbara. Molly's Pilgrim. Duffy, Daniel M. & Deraney, Michael J., illus. rev. ed. 1998. 32p. (J). (ps-3). 16.99 (978-0-688-16279-5(7)) HarperCollins Pubs.

—Molly's Pilgrim. Duffy, Daniel Mark & Deraney, Michael J., illus. 97th rev. ed. 1998. 32p. (J). (gr. 1-4). pap. 3.99 (978-0-688-16280-1(0) , Harper Trophy) HarperCollins Pubs.

—Molly's Pilgrim. (Literature to Go Ser.). pap., tchr. ed. incl. VHS (978-0-7919-2685-7(0)) Phoenix Films & Video.

da Costa, Deborah. Hanukkah Moon. Mosz, Gosia, illus. 2007. (Hanukkah Ser.). (J). (gr. 1-5). pap. 7.95 (***978-1-58013-245-9(6)***) Kar-Ben Publishing.

Edwards, Michelle. Papa's Latkes. Gustavson, Adam & Schuett, Stacey, illus. 2004. 32p. (J). (gr. k-2). 15.99 (978-0-7636-0779-1(7)) Candlewick Pr.

Edwards, Michelle. Papa's Latkes. Schuett, Stacey, illus. 2007. 32p. (J). (gr. k-2). pap. 6.99 (***978-0-7636-3563-3(4)***) Candlewick Pr.

Faigen, Anne G. New World Waiting. 2006. iii, 188p. (J). pap. (978-0-9744715-5-6(0)) Local History Co., The.

Ferber, Brenda A. Julia's Kitchen. 2006. (Illus.). 160p. (J). 16.00 (978-0-374-39932-0(8)) Farrar, Straus & Giroux.

Fireside, Bryna J. Private Joel & the Sewell Mountain Seder. Costello, Shawn, illus. 2008. (Passover Ser.). (J). lib. bdg. 16.95 (***978-0-8225-7240-4(0)***) Kar-Ben Publishing.

Fuchs, Menucha. Hand in Hand: Stories about You & Me. Goldfield, Zelda, tr. from HEB. Gershtein, Yonathan, illus. 1999. (Children's Learning Ser.: Vol. 2). 48p. (J). (gr. 1-4). pap. 4.95 (978-1-880582-43-5(0)) Judaica Pr., Inc., The.

Fuks, Menuhah & Tager, Gavriella. Smile with Avigayil #1: Avigayil & the Little Student. Haas, Esti, illus. 2006. 64p. (J). 12.95 (***978-1-932443-60-8(6)***) Judaica Pr., Inc., The.

—Smile with Avigayil #2: Avigayil & the Black Cat. Haas, Esti, illus. 2006. (ENG.). 64p. (J). 12.95 (***978-1-932443-58-5(4)***) Judaica Pr., Inc., The.

Gadot, A. S. The First Gift. Lafrance, Marie, illus. 2006. 24p. (J). 15.95 (978-1-58013-146-9(8)) Kar-Ben Publishing.

Gardner, Sheldon. The Converso Legacy. 2005. 264p. (J). 18.95 (978-1-932687-18-7(1) , Devora Publishing) Pitspopany Pr.

Geras, Adele. Voyage. 2006. (Illus.). 117p. (J). pap. 6.95 (978-1-903015-00-1(6)) Barn Owl Bks, London GBR. *Dist:* Independent Pubs. Group.

Glaser, Linda. Mrs. Greenberg's Messy Hanukkah. Cote, Nancy, illus. 2006. 32p. (J). (gr. 1-3). 6.95 (978-0-8075-5298-8(4)) Whitman, Albert & Co.

Goldin, Barbara Diamond. The Best Hanukkah Ever. Katz, Avi, illus. 2007. 32p. (J). (gr. k-3). 16.99 (***978-0-7614-5355-0(5)***) Cavendish, Marshall Corp.

Goldin, Barbara Diamond. Night Lights: A Sukkot Story. Carmi, Giora, illus. 2004. (gr. k-3). 13.95 (978-0-8074-0803-2(4) , 142687) URJ Pr.

Greene, Bette. Summer of My German Soldier. 1999. (Illus.). 208p. (J). (gr. 5-9). pap. 6.99 (978-0-14-130636-0(X) , Puffin) Penguin Group (USA) Inc.

—Summer of My German Soldier. 2000. (J). (gr. 6 up). 20.50 (978-0-8446-7144-4(4)) Smith, Peter Pub., Inc.

—Summer of My German Soldier. 1999. (978-0-606-17432-9(X)) Tandem Library Bks.

—Summer of My German Soldier. 2006. (Puffin Modern Classics Ser.). 240p. (J). (gr. 5). pap. 6.99 (978-0-14-240651-9(1) , Puffin) Penguin Group (USA) Inc.

—Summer of My German Soldier. l.t. ed. 2000. (LRS Large Print Cornerstone Ser.). 305p. (YA). (gr. 6-12). lib. bdg. 29.95 (978-1-58118-059-6(4) , 23473) LRS.

Greene, Bette & Hunt, Robert, illus. Summer of My German Soldier. 2003. 256p. (J). (gr. 5). 18.99 (978-0-8037-2869-1(7) , Dial) Penguin Group (USA) Inc.

Griffis, Molly Levite. Simon Says. 2004. vi, 263p. (J). 22.95 (978-1-57168-836-1(6)); pap. (978-1-57168-847-7(1)) Eakin Pr. (Eakin Pr.).

Heller, Linda. The Castle on Hester Street. Kulikov, Boris, illus. 2007. 40p. (J). 15.99 (978-0-689-87434-5(0) , Simon & Schuster Children's Publishing) Simon & Schuster Children's Publishing.

Hesse, Karen & Hesse, Hermann. A Time for Angels. rev. ed. 2000. 288p. (gr. 5-9). 16.99 (978-0-7868-0621-8(4)); 17.49 (978-0-7868-2534-9(0)) Hyperion Pr.

Houston, Julian. New Boy. 288p. (J). (gr. 7). 2008. pap. 7.99 (***978-0-618-88405-6(X)***); 2005. 16.00 (978-0-618-43253-0(1)) Houghton Mifflin Co. Trade & Reference Div.

Hubner, Carol Korb. The Devora Doresh Mysteries 2. 2007. (Illus.). 280p. (J). 16.95 (***978-1-932443-68-4(1)***) Judaica Pr., Inc., The.

Kahn, Katherine Janus & Rouss, Sylvia A. Sammy Spider's First Sukkot. 2004. (Illus.). 32p. (J). (ps-3). (978-1-58013-142-1(5)); pap. (978-1-58013-083-7(6)) Kar-Ben Publishing.

Kornblatt, Marc. Understanding Buddy. l.t. ed. 2002. 100p. (J). 21.95 (978-0-7862-3712-8(0)) Thomson Gale.

Koss, Amy Goldman. How I Saved Hanukkah. 2000. (J). 11.64 (978-0-606-20239-8(0)) Tandem Library Bks.

Lakin, Patricia. Don't Forget. Rand, Ted, illus. 2000. 32p. (YA). (gr. k-3). pap. 5.95 (978-0-688-17522-1(8)) HarperCollins Pubs.

Levinson, Robin K. Shoshana & the Native Rose. Kehl, Drusilla, illus. 2006. 103p. (J). (gr. 3-5). per. 12.00 (978-0-9773673-2-0(0)) Gali Girls, Inc.

Levitin, Sonia. Singing Mountain. 2000. (978-0-606-17938-6(0)) Tandem Library Bks.

—Strange Relations. 2007. 304p. (gr. 7). (J). 15.99 (978-0-375-83751-7(5)); (YA). lib. bdg. 18.99 (978-0-375-93751-4(X)) Random Hse. Children's Bks. (Knopf Bks. for Young Readers).

Lieurance, Suzanne. The Locket: Surviving the Triangle Shirtwaist Fire. 2008. (Historical Fiction Adventures (HFA) Ser.). (Illus.). 160p. (J). (gr. 3-6). lib. bdg. 27.93 (***978-0-7660-2928-6(X)***) Enslow Pubs., Inc.

Littman, Sarah. Confessions of a Closet Catholic. 2006. 208p. (J). (gr. 5). reprint ed. pap. 5.99 (978-0-14-240597-0(3) , Puffin) Penguin Group (USA) Inc.

Manushkin, Fran. Sophie & the Shofar. Kaye, Rosalind Charney, illus. 2004. (J). (gr. k-3). 13.95 (978-0-8074-0751-6(8) , 101078) URJ Pr.

Matas, Carol. Rosie in Los Angeles: Action! 2004. (Illus.). 128p. (J). pap. 9.95 (978-0-689-85716-4(0) , Aladdin) Simon & Schuster Children's Publishing.

—Rosie in Los Angeles: Action! 2004. (gr. 3-6). lib. bdg. 13.00 (978-0-613-91044-6(3)) Tandem Library Bks.

—The War Within: A Novel of the Civil War. l.t. ed. 2003. (J). 22.95 (978-0-7862-5499-6(8)) Thorndike Pr.

Mazer, Norma Fox. Good Night, Maman. Mazer, Norma Fox, illus. 2001. (Harper Trophy Bks.). 192p. (J). (gr. 5 up). pap. 6.99 (978-0-06-440923-0(6) , Harper Trophy) HarperCollins Pubs.

—Good Night, Maman. 2001. (gr. 3-6). lib. bdg. 14.15 (978-0-613-35953-5(4)) Tandem Library Bks.

Mazer, Norma Fox. Good Night Maman: A Novel. 2006. 185p. (J). (gr. k-4). reprint ed. 16.00 (***978-1-4223-5862-7(3)***) DIANE Publishing Co.

Michelson, Richard. Grandpa's Gamble. Moser, Barry, illus. 1999. (Accelerated Reader Bks.). 32p. (YA). (ps up). 15.95 (978-0-7614-5034-4(3) , Cavendish Children's Bks.) Cavendish, Marshall Corp.

—Too Young for Yiddish. Waldman, Neil, illus. 2002. 32p. (J). (gr. k-4). 15.95 (978-0-88106-118-5(2)) Charlesbridge Publishing, Inc.

Millman, M. C. Cheery Bim Band No. 7: Stage Fright. Frank, Connie, illus. (Cheery Bim Band Ser.: Vol. 7). 143p. (J). (gr. 5-6). 13.95 (978-1-56062-272-7(5) , CJR148H) CIS Communications, Inc.

Morgenstern, Susie. Mon Amour. 2002. (GER.). 124p. pap. 15.00 (978-1-4000-3959-3(2) , New Media German Language) Random House Foreign Language Publishing.

Moss, Marissa. Hannah's Journal: The Story of an Immigrant Girl. 2002. (Young American Voices Ser.). (Illus.). 56p. (YA). (gr. 3-7). pap. 7.00 (978-0-15-216329-7(8) , Silver Whistle) Harcourt Trade Pubs.

—Hannah's Journal: The Story of an Immigrant Girl. 2002. (gr. 3-6). lib. bdg. 15.30 (978-0-613-53818-3(8)) Tandem Library Bks.

Napoli, Donna Jo. The King of Mulberry Street. 2007. 256p. (gr. 3-7). 6.50 (***978-0-553-49416-7(3)*** , Yearling) Random Hse. Children's Bks.

Nixon, Joan Lowery. Land of Hope. l.t. ed. 2001. (Ellis Island Stories Ser.). 171p. (J). (gr. 4 up). lib. bdg. 23.33 (978-0-8368-2811-5(9)) Stevens, Gareth Inc.

Old Ways, New Ways (Eastern European Jews) 76p. (YA). (gr. 6-12). pap. 9.95 (978-0-8224-3682-9(5)) Globe Fearon Educational Publishing.

Pinkham, Mark Amaru. Love Me Later. 2005. 202p. 14.95 (978-1-932188-02-8(9)) Adventures Unlimited Pr.

Polacco, Patricia. The Trees of the Dancing Goats. Polacco, Patricia, illus. 2002. (Illus.). (J). 25.11 (978-0-7587-3858-5(7)) Book Wholesalers, Inc.

—The Trees of the Dancing Goats. Polacco, Patricia, illus. 2000. (Illus.). 32p. (J). (gr. k-3). 7.99 (978-0-689-83857-6(3) , Aladdin) Simon & Schuster Children's Publishing.

—The Trees of the Dancing Goats. 2000. (J). (978-0-606-20094-3(0)) Tandem Library Bks.

—Trees of the Dancing Goats. 2000. (gr. k-3). lib. bdg. 15.30 (978-0-613-30164-0(1)) Tandem Library Bks.

Pushker, Gloria Teles. Toby Belfer Visits Ellis Island. Hierstein, Judith, illus. 2003. 32p. pap. 15.95 (978-1-58980-117-2(2)) Pelican Publishing Co., Inc.

Rael, Elsa Okon. Rivka's First Thanksgiving. Kovalski, Maryann, illus. 2004. 32p. (J). pap. 6.99 (978-0-689-84105-7(1) , Aladdin) Simon & Schuster Children's Publishing.

—What Zeesie Saw on Delancey Street. 2000. (978-0-606-17943-0(7)) Tandem Library Bks.

Rappaport, Doreen. The Year of the Paper Menorahs. Alcorn, Stephen, illus. 2000. 32p. (J). 15.99 (978-0-7868-0400-9(9)) Hyperion Bks. for Children.

Reinhardt, Dana. A Brief Chapter in My Impossible Life. (gr. 7). 2007. 256p. (YA). pap. 8.99 (***978-0-375-84691-5(3)***); 2006. 240p. (J). 15.95 (978-0-385-74698-4(9)); 2006. 240p. (J). lib. bdg. 17.99 (978-0-385-90940-2(3)) Random Hse. Children's Bks. (Lamb, Wendy).

Rinn, Miriam. The Saturday Secret. 1999. (Illus.). 144p. (J). (gr. 4-7). pap. 7.95 (978-1-881283-26-3(7)) Alef Design Group.

Rocklin, Joanne. Very Best Hanukkah Gift. 2001. (gr. 3-6). lib. bdg. 12.40 (978-0-613-85709-3(7)) Tandem Library Bks.

Rosen, Michael J. Chanukah Lights Everywhere. Iwai, Melissa, illus. 2000. (J). (978-0-15-201810-8(7)) Harcourt Trade Pubs.

Rosenthal, Betsy R. It's Not Worth Making a Tzimmes Over! Rivers, Ruth, illus. 2006. 32p. (J). 15.95 (978-0-8075-3677-3(6)) Whitman, Albert & Co.

Rosten, Carrie. Chloe Leiberman (Sometimes Wong) 2007. 224p. (YA). (gr. 7). pap. 8.99 (978-0-385-73248-2(1) , Delacorte Bks. for Young Readers) Random Hse. Children's Bks.

Roth, Matthue. Never Mind the Goldbergs. 2006. 368p. (J). pap. 7.99 (978-0-439-69189-5(3) , PUSH) Scholastic, Inc.

Rothenberg, Joan. Matzah Ball Soup. Rothenberg, Joan, illus. 2005. (Illus.). 29p. (J). (ps-2). reprint ed. 15.00 (978-0-7567-8930-5(3)) DIANE Publishing Co.

Ruby, Lois. Swindletop. 2000. (Illus.). 128p. (J). 15.95 (978-1-57168-393-9(3)) Eakin Pr.

Sachs, Marilyn. Lost in America. rev. ed. 2005. 160p. (J). 16.95 (978-1-59643-040-2(0)) Roaring Brook Pr.

Satten, Sandra C. In the Thirteenth Year. Spark, illus. 1999. 72p. (YA). (ps up). pap. 7.95 (978-1-881283-24-9(0)) Alef Design Group.

Summer of My German Soldier. 1999. (YA). 9.95 (978-1-56137-113-6(0)) Novel Units, Inc.

Vander Zee, Ruth & Sneider, Marian. Eli Remembers. Farnsworth, Bill, illus. 2007. 32p. (J). (gr. 3-7). 18.00 (***978-0-8028-5309-7(9)*** , Eerdmans Bks For Young Readers) Eerdmans, William B. Publishing Co.

Weber, Judith Eichler. Seeking Safety. Martin, John F., illus. 2006. (Adventures in America Ser.). (J). (978-1-893110-46-5(X)) Silver Moon Pr.

Yorinks, Arthur. The Flying Latke. Steig, William & Colin, Paul, illus. 2002. 32p. (J). pap. 6.99 (978-0-689-85348-7(3) , Aladdin) Simon & Schuster Children's Publishing.

—Flying Latke. 2002. (gr. k-3). lib. bdg. 15.30 (978-0-613-90793-4(0)) Tandem Library Bks.

Zalben, Jane Breskin. Beni's Family Treasury: Stories for the Jewish Holidays. Zalben, Jane Breskin, illus. rev. ed. 1998. (Illus.). 120p. (J). (ps-4). 18.95 (978-0-8050-5889-5(3) , Holt, Henry & Co. Bks. For Young Readers) Holt, Henry & Co.

—Pearl's Passover: A Family Celebration Through Stories, Recipes, Crafts, & Songs. Zalben, Jane Breskin, illus. 2002. (Illus.). 48p. (J). (gr. k-3). 16.00 (978-0-689-81487-7(9)) Simon & Schuster Children's Publishing.

Zolkower, Edie Stoltz. Too Many Cooks: A Passover Parable. 2000. (gr. k-3). lib. bdg. 14.10 (978-0-613-81767-7(2)) Tandem Library Bks.

JIUJITSU

see Judo

JOAN, OF ARC, SAINT, 1412-1431

Brooks, Polly Schoyer. Beyond the Myth: The Story of Joan of Arc. 1999. 192p. (J). (gr. 7-12). pap. 8.95 (978-0-395-98138-2(7)) Houghton Mifflin Co. Trade & Reference Div.

—Beyond the Myth: The Story of Joan of Arc. 1999. (gr. 7-12). lib. bdg. 17.60 (978-0-613-21209-0(6)) Tandem Library Bks.

Bull, Angela. Joan of Arc, Vol. 4. Bell, Mike, illus. 2000. (Readers Ser.). 48p. (J). (gr. 2-4). pap. 3.99 (978-0-7894-5719-6(9)) Dorling Kindersley Publishing, Inc.

—Joan of Arc. 2000. (gr. k-3). lib. bdg. 11.80 (978-0-613-32723-7(3)); (Illus.). (J). 10.79 (978-0-606-20743-0(0)) Tandem Library Bks.

Bull, Angela & Dorling Kindersley Publishing Staff. Joan of Arc. Bell, Mike, illus. 2000. (Readers Ser.). 48p. (J). (ps-3). 12.95 (978-0-7894-5718-9(0)) Dorling Kindersley Publishing, Inc.

Guiteras, Gregory. The Story of Joan of Arc. 2002. (Illus.). 32p. (J). pap. 3.95 (978-0-486-42385-2(9)) Dover Pubns., Inc.

Hilliam, David. Joan of Arc: Heroine of France. 2004. (Medieval Leaders in Ancient History Ser.). (Illus.). 112p. (J). lib. bdg. 31.95 (978-1-4042-0164-4(5)) Rosen Publishing Group, Inc., The.

Hodges, Margaret. Joan of Arc: The Lily Maid. Rayevsky, Robert, illus. 1999. 32p. (J). (gr. 4-6). tchr. ed. 16.95 (978-0-8234-1424-6(8)) Holiday Hse., Inc.

Kathleen, Kudlinski. Dk Biography Joan of Arc Hc. 2008. 128p. 14.99 (***978-0-7566-3527-5(6)***) Dorling Kindersley Publishing, Inc.

Kudlinski, Kathleen. Dk Biography Joan of Arc Pb. 2008. 128p. pap. 4.99 (***978-0-7566-3526-8(8)***) Dorling Kindersley Publishing, Inc.

Lace, William W. Joan of Arc & the Hundred Years' War in World History. 2003. (In World History Ser.). (Illus.). 128p. (J). (gr. 5-12). lib. bdg. 26.60 (978-0-7660-1938-6(1)) Enslow Pubs., Inc.

Pickels, Dwayne E. Joan of Arc. 2001. (Women of Achievement Ser.). (Illus.). 112p. (J). 30.00 (978-0-7910-6314-9(3) , Chelsea Hse.) Facts On File, Inc.

Roberts, Jeremy. Saint Joan of Arc. 2000. (Biography Ser.). (Illus.). 112p. (J). (gr. 6-12). lib. bdg. 25.26 (978-0-8225-4981-9(6) , Lerner Pubns.) Lerner Publishing Group.

Ross, Nancy W. Joan of Arc. 2003. (Landmark Bks.). 160p. (YA). (gr. 5-8). 5.99 (978-0-375-80232-4(0) , Random Hse. Bks. for Young Readers) Random Hse. Children's Bks.

—Joan of Arc. 1999. (Landmark Bks.). 160p. (J). lib. bdg. 11.99 (978-0-375-90232-1(5)) Random Hse., Inc.

Ross, Nancy Wilson. Joan of Arc. 2003. vii, 182p. pap. 29.00 (978-0-7581-5017-2(2)) Textbook Pubs.

Stanley, Diane. Joan of Arc. Stanley, Diane, illus. (Illus.). 48p. (J). 2002. (gr. 2 up). pap. 7.99 (978-0-06-443748-6(5) , Harper Trophy); 1998. (gr. 3 up). 16.89 (978-0-688-14330-5(X)) HarperCollins Pubs.

—Joan of Arc. 2002. (gr. 3-6). lib. bdg. 15.25 (978-0-613-44855-0(3)) Tandem Library Bks.

Thompson, Paul B. Joan of Arc: Warrior Saint of France. 2007. (Rulers of the Middle Ages Ser.). (Illus.). 160p. (YA). (gr. 7-9). lib. bdg. 34.60 (***978-0-7660-2716-9(3)***) Enslow Pubs., Inc.

Tompert, Ann. Joan of Arc: Heroine of France. Garland, Michael, illus. 2003. 32p. (YA). (gr. k-2). 15.95 (978-1-59078-009-1(4)) Boyds Mills Pr.

Wallace, Susan Helen. Saint Joan of Arc: God's Soldier. Morelli, Ray, illus. 2000. (Encounter the Saints Ser.: Vol. 7). 132p. (J). (gr. 5-9). pap. 5.95 (978-0-8198-7033-9(1) , 332-344) Pauline Bks. & Media.

Whiting, Jim. The Life & Times of Joan of Arc. 2005. (Biography from Ancient Civilizations Ser.). (Illus.). 48p. (J). (gr. 4-8). lib. bdg. 29.95 (978-1-58415-345-0(8)) Mitchell Lane Pubs., Inc.

Wilkinson, Philip. Joan of Arc: The Teenager Who Saved Her Nation. 2007. (World History Biographies Ser.). (Illus.). 64p. (J). (gr. 3-7). 17.95 (978-1-4263-0116-2(2)); lib. bdg. 27.90 (978-1-4263-0117-9(0)) National Geographic Society. (National Geographic Children's Bks.).

Williams, Jay. Joan of Arc: Warrior Saint. 2007. (Sterling Point Bks.). 144p. (YA). (gr. 7 up). pap. 6.95 (***978-1-4027-5120-2(6)***) Sterling Publishing Co., Inc.

JOAN, OF ARC, SAINT, 1412-1431—DRAMA

Shaw, George Bernard. Saint Joan. rev. ed. 2001. (gr. 7-12). lib. bdg. 18.80 (978-0-613-44251-0(2)) Tandem Library Bks.

JOAN, OF ARC, SAINT, 1412-1431—FICTION

Chandler, Pauline. Warrior Girl: A Novel of Joan of Arc. 2006. 368p. (J). 16.99 (978-0-06-084102-7(8)); lib. bdg. 17.89 (978-0-06-084103-4(6)) HarperCollins Pubs.

Everett-Green, Evelyn. A Heroine of France. 2007. 188p. pap. 14.99 (***978-1-4264-7060-8(6)***); 206p. pap. 15.99 (***978-1-4264-7136-0(X)***) BiblioBazaar.

Johnson, Vargie. Joan of Arc the Messenger: What Made Them Famous? 2006. 156p. (J). per. 15.00 (978-1-931195-95-9(1)) KiwE Publishing, Ltd.

Twain, Mark. Personal Recollections of Joan of Arc. 1999. reprint ed. pap. 28.00 (978-1-4047-1122-8(8)); pap. 28.00 (978-1-4047-1123-5(6)) Classic Textbooks.

JOB DISCRIMINATION

see Discrimination in Employment

JOB HUNTING

Applying for a Job. 1999. (SmartReader Ser.). Level 1. (J). pap., tchr. ed. 19.95 incl. audio (978-0-7887-1155-8(5) , 79416T3); Level 2. (YA). pap., tchr. ed. 19.95 incl. audio (978-0-7887-0553-3(9) , 79335T3) Recorded Bks., LLC.

Bolles, Richard Nelson & Christen, Carol. What Color Is Your Parachute? For Teens. 2006. (Parachute Library Ser.). (Illus.). 176p. (YA). pap. 14.95 (978-1-58008-713-1(2)) Ten Speed Pr.

Cambridge Educational, prod. Job Search Win Labpak. (YA). cd-rom 247.50 (978-0-7365-4351-4(1)) Films Media Group.

Coon, Nora E. Teen Dream Jobs: How to Find the Job You Really Want! 2004. (Illus.). 132p. (YA). (gr. 6-12). pap. (978-1-58270-093-9(1)) Beyond Words Publishing, Inc.

Corwen, Leonard. Successful Job Hunting. 2005. 99p. pap. 7.95 (978-1-56450-220-9(1)) Films Media Group.

Elliott, Jane, ed. 50 Cutting-Edge Jobs. (Illus.). 348p. (YA). pap. (978-0-89434-312-4(2) , Ferguson Publishing Co.) Facts On File, Inc.

Farr, Michael. Job Search Basics. 3rd ed. 2006. (Illus.). 240p. (YA). pap. 16.95 (978-1-59357-313-3(8) , J3138, JIST Works) JIST Publishing.

Farr, Michael J. Busqueda Rapida de Trabajo. 2002. (SPA.). (gr. 7-12). lib. bdg. 11.80 (978-0-613-49719-0(8)) Tandem Library Bks.

—Seven Steps to Getting a Job Fast. 2002. (gr. 7-12). lib. bdg. 17.60 (978-0-613-49775-6(9)) Tandem Library Bks.

Gabler, Laura R., ed. Career Exploration on the Internet: A Student's Guide to More Than 500 Web Sites. 2nd ed. (Illus.). 752p. (YA). pap. (978-0-89434-305-6(X) , Ferguson Publishing Co.) Facts On File, Inc.

Hall, Dan. A Guide to Summer & Part-Time Jobs: They're Not Just Jobs. 1998. (High School-to-Career Ser.). 232p. (YA). pap. 129.00 incl. VHS (978-1-56370-487-1(0) , JV4870) JIST Publishing.

Lambie, Brian, ed. Creative Job Search. 2002. spiral bd. 15.95 (978-0-9670505-4-6(5)) Minnesota Dept. Employment & Economic Development.

Marcom Group Ltd, prod. Moving on up Win Labpak. (YA). cd-rom 222.50 (978-0-7365-4359-0(7)) Films Media Group.

Morem, Susan. How to Get a Job & Keep It. 2002. 292p. (gr. 9). pap. 16.95 (978-0-89434-351-3(3) , Ferguson Publishing Co.) Facts On File, Inc.

O'Neill, Lucy. Job Smarts. 2002. (Smarts Ser.). (Illus.). 48p. (YA). (gr. 7-12). pap. 23.00 (978-0-516-23928-6(7) , Children's Pr.) Scholastic Library Publishing.

—Job Smarts. 2002. (gr. 7-12). lib. bdg. 15.25 (978-0-613-58703-7(0)) Tandem Library Bks.

Organize Your Job Search: The Key to Getting a Good Job Fast. 1998. (Job Search Ser.). (gr. 10 up). pap. 99.00 incl. VHS (978-0-942784-71-8(5) , C7-305A) JIST Publishing.

Schwartz, Stuart B. Finding Work. 1998. (Looking at Work Ser.). 32p. (J). lib. bdg. 19.00 (978-0-516-21300-2(8) , Children's Pr.) Scholastic Library Publishing.

Schwartz, Stuart B. & Conley, Craig. Considering a Job Offer. (Looking at Work Ser.). pap. 6.95 (978-0-7368-8521-8(8)); 1999. (Illus.). 32p. (J). (gr. 3-4). lib. bdg. 21.26 (978-0-7368-0178-2(2)) Capstone Pr., Inc. (LifeMatters Bks.).

—Finding Work. (Looking at Work Ser.). pap. 6.95 (978-0-7368-8023-7(2) , LifeMatters Bks.) Capstone Pr., Inc.

—Networking to Find a Job. 1999. (Looking at Work Ser.). (Illus.). 32p. (J). (gr. 2-3). lib. bdg. 21.26 (978-0-7368-0180-5(4) , LifeMatters Bks.) Capstone Pr., Inc.

Success in the World of Work: Succeeding on the Job. (Success in the World of Work Ser.). cd-rom 159.95 (978-1-56191-660-3(9)) Films Media Group.

A Teenager's Guide to the Workplace. 2001. 132p. per. 15.00 (978-0-9679861-1-1(7)) New Books Publishing.

Troutman, Kathryn K. Creating Your High School Resume: A Step-by-Step Guide to Preparing an Effective. 2003. (gr. 7-12). lib. bdg. 17.60 (978-0-613-78784-0(6)) Tandem Library Bks.

—Creating Your High School Resume: A Step-by-Step Guide to Preparing an Effective Resume for Jobs, College & Training Programs. 2nd ed. 2003. (Illus.). 160p. pap. 8.95 (978-1-56370-902-9(3) , JIST Works) JIST Publishing.

Vernon, Naomi. A Teen's Guide to Finding a Job. Caldwell, Candice J., illus. 2000. xviii, 149p. (YA). (gr. 9 up). pap. 19.95 (978-0-9676383-9-3(9) , SAN:253-0481) New Bee-ginnings.

The World of Work. 2005. (Illus.). (gr. 7-12). lib. bdg. 682.20 (978-0-8239-3909-1(X)) Rosen Publishing Group, Inc., The.

World of Work: Choose the Right Career for You!, 7 bks. Incl. Choosing a Career as a Paramedic. Giddens, Sandra & Giddens, Owen. 2005. lib. bdg. 25.25 (978-0-8239-3244-3(3) , WWPAME); Choosing a Career in Child Care. Weintraub, Aileen. 2005. lib. bdg. 25.25 (978-0-8239-3241-2(9) , WWCHCA); Choosing a Career in Computers. Weigant, Chris. 2005. lib. bdg. 25.25 (978-0-8239-3044-9(0) , WWCOMP); Choosing a Career in Hotels, Motels & Resorts. Rue, Nancy N. 1999. lib. bdg. 25.25 (978-0-8239-2999-3(X) , WWHOMO); Choosing a Career in Law Enforcement. Wirths, Claudine G. 2005. lib. bdg. 25.25 (978-0-8239-3282-5(6) , WWLAEN); Choosing a Career in the Restaurant Industry. Beal, Eileen J. 1999. lib. bdg. 25.25 (978-0-8239-3002-9(5) , WWREST); 64p. (YA). (gr. 7-12). (Illus.). Set lib. bdg. 167.65 (978-0-8239-9306-2(X)) Rosen Publishing Group, Inc., The.

World of Work: Exciting World of Careers, 7 bks. Incl. Choosing a Career as a Firefighter. Oleksy, Walter G. lib. bdg. 25.25 (978-0-8239-3245-0(1) , WWFIRE); Choosing a Career in Carpentry. Ross, Allison J. & Harrison, Scott. lib. bdg. 25.25 (978-0-8239-3294-8(X)); Choosing a Career in the Pulp & Paper Industry. Draper, Allison Stark. lib. bdg. 25.25 (978-0-8239-3333-4(4)); 64p. (YA). (gr. 7-12). 2005. (Illus.). Set lib. bdg. 167.65 (978-0-8239-9208-9(X)) Rosen Publishing Group, Inc., The.

The World of Work Set 1. 2005. (Illus.). (gr. 7-12). lib. bdg. 176.75 (978-0-8239-9727-5(8)) Rosen Publishing Group, Inc., The.

The World of Work Set 2. 2005. (Illus.). (gr. 7-12). lib. bdg. 202.00 (978-0-8239-9444-1(9)) Rosen Publishing Group, Inc., The.

The World of Work Set 3. 2005. (Illus.). (gr. 7-12). lib. bdg. 202.00 (978-0-8239-9443-4(0)) Rosen Publishing Group, Inc., The.

The World of Work Set 4. 2005. (Illus.). (gr. 7-12). lib. bdg. 202.00 (978-0-8239-9442-7(2)) Rosen Publishing Group, Inc., The.

The World of Work Set 5. 2005. (Illus.). (gr. 7-12). lib. bdg. 126.25 (978-0-8239-9716-9(2)) Rosen Publishing Group, Inc., The.

JOB HUNTING—FICTION

Durham, Kathryn. Mom, Can You Buy Me This? Richard Gets a Job, 2004. 115p. (YA). spiral bd. 11.95 (978-0-9703876-2-2(8)) Pen & Paper Publishing.

A Job for Little Elf. 2006. (J). (***978-1-932570-72-4(1)*)** Literacy Footprints Inc.

McElligott, Matthew. Backbeard: Pirate for Hire. McElligott, Matthew, illus. 2007. (Illus.). 32p. (J). 17.85 (***978-0-8027-9633-2(8)**);* 16.95 (***978-0-8027-9632-5(X)***) Walker & Co.

JOBS

see Occupations; Professions

JOGUES, ISAAC, SAINT, 1607-1646

Orfeo, Christine Virginia & Tebo, Mary Elizabeth. Saint Isaac Jogues: With Burning Heart. Kiwak, Barbara, illus. 2002. (Encounter the Saints Ser.). 132p. (J). pap. 5.95 (978-0-8198-7063-6(3) , 332-360) Pauline Bks. & Media.

JOHN, THE APOSTLE, SAINT

Daybell, Chad G. Through the Eyes of John. Murray, Rhett E., illus. 2004. 29p. (J). 19.95 (978-1-932898-16-3(6) , 98166) Spring Creek Bk. Co.

Saint John the Divine. The Revelation of St. John the Divine. 1999. (Classic Portables Ser.). 160p. (J). 10.95 (978-1-84068-016-4(4)) Creation Bks. GBR. *Dist:* Subterranean Co.

Woodman, Ros. Bible Detectives: John. 64p. (YA). pap., act. bk. ed. 7.99 (978-1-85792-759-7(1) , Christian Focus) Christian Focus Pubns. GBR. *Dist:* Riverside.

JOHN, THE BAPTIST, SAINT

Johnson, Alice W. & Warner, Allison H. Believe & You're There When the White Dove Descended. Nelson, Holly, illus. 2007. 96p. (J). pap. 7.95 (***978-1-59038-721-4(X)***) Deseret Bk. Co.

JOHN, THE BAPTIST, SAINT—FICTION

Hip Hip Hooray, It's Monsoon Day! 2007. (ENG & SPA.). (YA). pap. 15.95 (***978-1-886679-36-8(3)***) Arizona Sonora Desert Museum Pr.

JOHN, ELTON, 1947-

O'Mahony, John. Elton John. 2003. (World Musicmakers Ser.). (Illus.). 64p. (J). 26.20 (978-1-56711-972-5(7) , Blackbirch Pr., Inc.) Thomson Gale.

Schlesinger, Ethan. Elton John. 2008. (J). (***978-1-4222-0189-3(9)***) Mason Crest Pubs.

White, Katherine. Elton John. 2006. (Rock & Roll Hall of Famers Ser.). (Illus.). 112p. (YA). (gr. 5-8). lib. bdg. 29.25 (978-0-8239-3641-0(4)) Rosen Publishing Group, Inc., The.

JOHN HENRY (LEGENDARY CHARACTER)

Kessler, Brad. John Henry. Jackson, Barry, illus. 2005. (Rabbit Ears-A Classic Tale Ser.). 40p. (J). (gr. k-5). 25.65 (978-1-59197-764-3(9)) Spotlight.

Krensky, Stephen, adapted by. John Henry. 2007. (On My Own Folklore Ser.). (Illus.). 48p. (J). (gr. 2-5). lib. bdg. 25.26 (978-1-57505-887-0(1) , Millbrook Pr.) Lerner Publishing Group.

Lester, Julius. John Henry. Pinkney, Jerry, illus. 2002. (J). 14.04 (978-0-7587-0123-7(3)) Book Wholesalers, Inc.

—John Henry. Pinkney, Jerry, illus. 1999. 40p. (J). (ps-17). pap. 7.99 (978-0-14-056622-2(8) , Puffin) Penguin Group (USA) Inc.

—John Henry. 1999. (ps-2). lib. bdg. 16.45 (978-0-7857-1862-8(1)) Tandem Library Bks.

—John Henry. unabr. ed. 1998. (Illus.). (J). (ps-4). 24.95 incl. audio (978-0-7882-0682-5(6) , HRA377) Weston Woods Studios, Inc.

JOHNSON, ANDREW, 1808-1875

Alter, Judy. Andrew Johnson: A MyReportLinks.com Book. 2002. (Presidents Ser.). (Illus.). 48p. (J). (gr. 4-10). lib. bdg. 25.26 (978-0-7660-5007-5(6) , MyReportLinks.com Bks.) Enslow Pubs., Inc.

Burgan, Michael. Andrew Johnson. 2003. (Profiles of the Presidents Ser.). (Illus.). 64p. (J). (gr. 4 up). lib. bdg. 23.93 (978-0-7565-0264-5(0)) Compass Point Bks.

Harper, Judith E. Andrew Johnson: Our Seventeenth President. 2001. (Spirit of America: Our Presidents Ser.). (Illus.). 48p. (J). (gr. 2-6). 28.50 (978-1-56766-854-4(2)) Child's World, Inc.

Havelin, Kate. Andrew Johnson. 2005. (Presidential Leaders Ser.). (Illus.). 112p. (J). (gr. 6-12). lib. bdg. 29.27 (978-0-8225-1000-0(6)) Lerner Publishing Group.

Malone, Mary. Andrew Johnson. 1999. (United States Presidents Ser.). (Illus.). 128p. (YA). (gr. 5-12). lib. bdg. 26.60 (978-0-7660-1034-5(1)) Enslow Pubs., Inc.

Nardo, Don. Andrew Johnson. 2004. (Encyclopedia of Presidents Ser.). (Illus.). 110p. (J). 34.00 (978-0-516-24242-2(3) , Children's Pr.) Scholastic Library Publishing.

Randolph, Ryan P. How to Draw the Life & Times of Andrew Johnson. 2006. (Kid's Guide to Drawing the Presidents of the United States of America Ser.). (J). 25.25 (978-1-4042-2994-5(9) , PowerKids Pr.) Rosen Publishing Group, Inc., The.

Venezia, Mike. Andrew Johnson. Venezia, Mike, illus. 2006. (Illus.). 32p. (J). (gr. 3-4). pap. 7.95 (978-0-516-25484-5(7) , Children's Pr.) Scholastic Library Publishing.

—Andrew Johnson: Seventeenth President. Venezia, Mike, illus. 2005. (Illus.). 32p. (J). (ps-7). 27.00 (978-0-516-22622-4(3) , Children's Pr.) Scholastic Library Publishing.

Welsbacher, Anne. Andrew Johnson. 2000. (United States Presidents Ser.). (Illus.). 32p. (J). (gr. k-6). lib. bdg. 22.78 (978-1-57765-240-3(1) , Checkerboard Library) ABDO Publishing Co.

JOHNSON, JAMES WELDON, 1871-1938

Shull, Jodie A. Words of Promise: A Story about James Weldon Johnson. Stetz, Ken, illus. 2006. (Creative Minds Biography Ser.). 64p. (J). (gr. 4-7). 22.60 (978-1-57505-755-2(7) , Carolrhoda Bks.) Lerner Publishing Group.

JOHNSON, LADY BIRD, 1912-2007

Appelt, Kathi. Miss Lady Bird's Wildflowers: How a First Lady Changed America. Hein, Joy Fisher, illus. 2005. 40p. (J). 16.99 (978-0-06-001107-9(6)); lib. bdg. 17.89 (978-0-06-001108-6(4)) HarperCollins Pubs.

Mattern, Joanne. Lady Bird Johnson. 2007. (First Ladies Ser.). (Illus.). 32p. (J). (gr. k-6). lib. bdg. 24.21 (***978-1-59928-795-9(1)*** , Checkerboard Library) ABDO Publishing Co.

JOHNSON, LYNDON B. (LYNDON BAINES), 1908-1973

Burgan, Michael. Lyndon Baines Johnson. 2003. (Profiles of the Presidents Ser.). (Illus.). 64p. (J). (gr. 4 up). lib. bdg. 23.93 (978-0-7565-0280-5(2)) Compass Point Bks.

Colbert, Nancy A. Great Society: The Story of Lyndon Baines Johnson. 2004. (Notable Americans Ser.). (Illus.). 144p. (YA). (gr. 6-12). 23.95 (978-1-883846-84-8(6) , First Biographies) Reynolds, Morgan Inc.

Joseph, Paul. Lyndon B. Johnson. 2000. (United States Presidents Ser.). (Illus.). 32p. (J). (gr. k-6). lib. bdg. 22.78 (978-1-56239-814-9(8) , Checkerboard Library) ABDO Publishing Co.

Levy, Debbie. Lyndon B. Johnson. 2003. (Presidential Leaders Ser.). (Illus.). 112p. (J). 29.27 (978-0-8225-0097-1(3) , Lerner Pubns.) Lerner Publishing Group.

Mattern, Joanne. Lady Bird Johnson. 2007. (First Ladies Ser.). (Illus.). 32p. (J). (gr. k-6). lib. bdg. 24.21 (***978-1-59928-795-9(1)*** , Checkerboard Library) ABDO Publishing Co.

Mis, Melody S. How to Draw the Life & Times of Lyndon B. Johnson. 2007. (Kid's Guide to Drawing the Presidents of the United States of America Ser.). (Illus.). 32p. (J). 25.25 (978-1-4042-3012-5(2) , PowerKids Pr.) Rosen Publishing Group, Inc., The.

Schultz, Randy. Lyndon B. Johnson: A MyReportLinks.com Book. 2002. (Presidents Ser.). (Illus.). 48p. (J). (gr. 4-10). lib. bdg. 25.26 (978-0-7660-5011-2(4)) Enslow Pubs., Inc.

Schuman, Michael A. Lyndon B. Johnson. 1998. (United States Presidents Ser.). (Illus.). 128p. (YA). (gr. 5-12). lib. bdg. 26.60 (978-0-89490-938-2(X)) Enslow Pubs., Inc.

Venezia, Mike. Lyndon B. Johnson. Venezia, Mike, illus. 2007. (Getting to Know the U. S. Presidents Ser.). 32p. (J). 7.95 (***978-0-531-17948-2(6)**);* (Illus.). (gr. 3-4). 27.00 (978-0-516-22640-8(1)) Scholastic Library Publishing. (Children's Pr.).

Williams, Jean Kinney. Lyndon B. Johnson. 2005. (Encyc of Presidents, 2ND Ser.). (Illus.). 112p. (J). (gr. 6-8). 34.00 (978-0-516-22977-5(X) , Watts, Franklin) Scholastic Library Publishing.

JOHNSTOWN (PA.)—FLOOD, 1889

Gow, Mary. Johnstown Flood: The Day the Dam Burst. 2003. (American Disasters Ser.). (Illus.). 48p. (J). (gr. 4-10). lib. bdg. 23.93 (978-0-7660-2109-9(2)) Enslow Pubs., Inc.

Leathers, Dan. The Johnstown, Pennsylvania, Flood 1889. 2007. (Natural Disasters Ser.). (J). lib. bdg. 25.70 (***978-1-58415-570-6(1)***) Mitchell Lane Pubs., Inc.

JOKES

see Wit and Humor

JOLIET, LOUIS, 1645-1700

Binns, Tristan Boyer. Louis Jolliet. 2002. (Groundbreakers Ser.). (Illus.). 48p. (J). (gr. 5-7). lib. bdg. 27.07 (978-1-58810-597-4(0)) Heinemann Library.

Donaldson-Forbes, Jeff. Jacques Marquette & Louis Jolliet. 2002. (Famous Explorers Ser.). (Illus.). 24p. (J). (gr. 3). lib. bdg. 18.75 (978-0-8239-5835-1(3) , PowerKids Pr.) Rosen Publishing Group, Inc., The.

Harmon, Daniel E. Jolliet & Marquette: Explorers of the Mississippi River. 2001. (Explorers of New Worlds Ser.). (Illus.). (J). 63p. pap. 25.00 (978-0-7910-6427-6(1)); 64p. 25.00 (978-0-7910-6426-9(3)) Facts On File, Inc. (Chelsea Hse.).

—Jolliet & Marquette: Explorers of the Mississippi River. 2001. (Illus.). 63p. (J). (gr. 4-7). lib. bdg. 17.60 (978-0-613-65434-0(X)) Tandem Library Bks.

Petrie, Kristin. Marquette & Jolliet. 2007. (Illus.). 32p. (J). 22.78 (978-1-59679-745-1(2)) ABDO Publishing Co.

Zelenyi, Alexander. Marquette & Jolliet: Quest for the Mississippi. 2006. (In the Footsteps of Explorers Ser.). (Illus.). 32p. (J). (gr. 3-9). (978-0-7787-2431-5(X)); pap. (978-0-7787-2467-4(0)) Crabtree Publishing Co.

JONAH, THE PROPHET

Amery, H. Jonah & the Whale. 2004. (Bible Tales Readers Ser.). 16p. (J). lib. bdg. 12.95 (978-1-58086-632-3(8) , Usborne); (Illus.). pap. 4.95 (978-0-7945-0414-4(0)) EDC Publishing.

Ammerman, Mark. Jonah & the Big Fish. 2000. (Little Bible Bks.). (Illus.). 24p. (J). (ps-3). 1.99 (978-1-57748-684-8(6)) Barbour Publishing, Inc.

Arthur, Kay & Domeij, Scoti. Wrong Way Jonah. 2006. (Discover-4-Yourself for Kids Ser.). 93p. (J). pap. 8.99 (978-1-888655-21-6(6)) Precept Ministries.

Auld, Mary. The Story of Jonah. 2000. (Bible Stories Ser.). (Illus.). 32p. (J). (gr. 2-4). pap. 7.95 (978-0-531-15388-8(6) , Watts, Franklin) Scholastic Library Publishing.

—Story of Jonah. 1999. (gr. 3-6). lib. bdg. 16.40 (978-0-613-62489-3(0)) Tandem Library Bks.

Bishop, Jennie. Jonah & the Big Fish Coloring Book. 2007. (Illus.). 16p. (J). pap. 1.89 (***978-1-59317-206-0(0)***) Warner Pr. Pubs.

Chocheli, Niko, illus. The Book of Jonah: Illustrated for Children by Niko Chocheli. 2000. 32p. (J). 15.00 (978-0-88141-207-9(4)) St. Vladimir's Seminary Pr.

Dalmatian Press Staff. Jonah & the Big Fish Activity. rev. ed. 2004. 32p. pap. 49.00 (978-1-57759-890-9(3)) Dalmatian Pr.

Davidson, Alice Joyce. Jonah & the Big Fish. 2003. 12p. (J). bds. 6.99 (978-0-310-70852-0(4)) Zonderkidz.

—Jonas y el Gran Pez. 1998. (My Bible Friends Ser.).Tr. of Jonah & the Big Fish. (SPA.). 12p. (J). 3.99 (978-0-8297-2484-4(2)) Vida Pubs.

Frank, Penny. Jonah Runs Away. 1999. (Lion Story Bible Ser.). (Illus.). 24p. pap. 2.99 (978-0-7459-4114-1(1) , Lion) Lion Hudson plc GBR. *Dist:* Independent Pubs. Group.

Gressman, Carylee Anne. Draw & Write Through History: Creation Through Jonah. Wolf, Aaron D., ed. Dick, Peggy, illus. 2006. (J). per. 12.95 (978-0-9778597-0-2(3)) CPR Pubng.

Hansen, Janis. Jonah & His Amazing Voyage, 5 vols. Wendy, Francisco, illus. 2003. (Bible Adventure Club). 36p. wbk. ed. 19.99 incl. audio, cd-rom (978-1-58134-326-7(4)) Crossway Bks.

—Jonah & His Amazing Voyage. Francisco, Wendy, illus. 2001. (J). (978-1-58134-329-8(9)) Crossway Bks.

Harder Tangvald, Christine. Swish, Swish, Went the Giant Fish: And Other Bible Stories about Prayer. Griego, Tony, illus. 1999. (Read Aloud, Read Alone Ser.). 32p. (J). (978-0-7814-0929-2(2)) Cook, David C. Publishing Co.

Jonah & the Great Fish. 2004. 24.95 incl. audio (978-1-56008-042-8(6)) Weston Woods Studios, Inc.

Jonah Bible Sticker Book. 2003. (Illus.). 16p. (J). 2.98 (978-1-4054-1555-2(X)) Parragon, Inc.

Kenny, Cindy. Draw with Jonah & Friends. 2002. (Big Idea Books Ser.). (Illus.). 18p. (J). 6.99 (978-0-310-70463-8(4)) Zonderkidz.

Lashbrook, Marilyn. I Don't Want To: The Story of Jonah. 1998. (J). (ps-2). pap. 5.95 (978-0-933657-68-7(4)) Standard Publishing.

Lois, Rock. Jonah & Whale. Alex, Ayliffe, illus. 2007. 0016p. pap. 5.99 (***978-1-56148-558-1(6)***) Good Bks.

Lowry, Mark. Ol' Jonah's Tossed into the Ocean. 2001. (Illus.). 24p. (J). 12.99 (978-0-310-70188-0(0)) Zondervan.

Make Believe Ideas. Jonah the Moaner. 2006. (Illus.). 32p. (J). (ps-3). 8.97 (978-1-59145-527-1(8)) Nelson, Thomas Inc.

Pingry, Patricia A. Jonah & the Fish: Based on Jonah 1-3:3. 2005. (Stories from the Bible Ser.). (Illus.). 26p. (J). bds. 6.95 (978-0-8249-6626-3(0)) Ideals Pubns.

—The Story of Jonah. Venturi-Pickett, Stacy, illus. 1998. 26p. (J). (ps-k). bds. 6.95 (978-0-8249-4094-2(6) , Ideals Children's Bks.) Ideals Pubns.

Pulley, Kelly, illus. Jonah & the Big Fish. 2007. (I Can Read!). 32p. (J). pap. 3.99 (***978-0-310-71459-0(1)***) Zonderkidz.

School Specialty Publishing. Story of Jonah. 2004. 10p. (J). 1.99 (978-0-7647-1048-3(6) , In Celebration) Schaffer, Frank Pubns.

Simon, Mary Mans. Jonah & the Big Fish: Read & Learn the Bible. 2005. (Illus.). 24p. (J). pap. 2.99 (978-1-4037-1158-8(5) , Spirit Pr.) Dalmatian Pr.

Slater, Teddy. Jonah & the Big Fish. 2006. 32p. (J). pap. 3.99 (978-0-439-85878-6(X)) Scholastic, Inc.

Smart Kids Publishing Staff. Jonah & the Whale: All about Responsibility. 2006. 12p. (ps). bds. 14.95 (978-0-8249-6661-4(9) , Candy Cane Pr.) Ideals Pubns.

Taylor, Damon. Hide & Sink: The Story of Jonah. 2002. (Child Sockology Ser.). 32p. (J). 10.99 (978-0-8254-3855-4(1)) Kregel Pubns.

Taylor, Damon J. Escondido y Hundido: La Historia de Jonas. 2003. (Mis Calcetines Ser.).Tr. of Hide & Sink the Story of Jonah. (SPA., Illus.). 32p. (YA). 6.99 (978-0-8254-0751-2(6) , Editorial Portavoz) Kregel Pubns.

Wickenden, Nadine, illus. The Story of Jonah. 2006. 10p. (J). (gr. k-4). reprint ed. 8.00 (978-0-7567-9923-6(6)) DIANE Publishing Co.

Zondervan. Jonah & the Big Fish. DeVries, Catherine, ed. Pulley, Kelly, illus. 2005. (Beginner's Bible' Ser.). 22p. (J). (ps). 5.99 (978-0-310-71102-5(9)) Zonderkidz.

JONATHAN (BIBLICAL CHARACTER)

Dietrich, Julie. David & His Friend, Jonathan. Ramsey, Marcy, illus. 2005. (Arch Books). (ENG.). 16p. (J). 1.99 (978-0-7586-0723-2(7)) Concordia Publishing Hse.

JONES, HERCULEAH (FICTITIOUS CHARACTER)—FICTION

Byars, Betsy. The Black Tower. 2007. (Herculeah Jones Ser.). 144p. (J). (gr. 3). 6.99 (***978-0-14-240937-4(5)*** , Puffin) Penguin Group (USA) Inc.

—The Dark Stairs: A Herculeah Jones Mystery. (Herculeah Jones Mystery Ser.). 160p. (J). (gr. 3-5). pap. 4.99 (978-0-8072-1478-7(7) , Listening Library) Random Hse. Audio Publishing Group.

—Death's Door. 2006. (Herculeah Jones Mystery Ser.). 144p. (J). (gr. 3). pap. 5.99 (978-0-14-240565-9(5) , Puffin) Penguin Group (USA) Inc.

—Death's Door: A Herculeah Jones Mystery. 2000. (Illus.). (J). 12.64 (978-0-606-18400-7(7)) Tandem Library Bks.

—Disappearing Acts. 2006. (Herculeah Jones Mystery Ser.). 144p. (J). (gr. 3). pap. 5.99 (978-0-14-240566-6(3) , Puffin) Penguin Group (USA) Inc.

—Disappearing Acts. 1999. (Herculeah Jones Mystery Ser.). (Illus.). (J). 11.64 (978-0-606-18401-4(5)) Tandem Library Bks.

—King of Murder. 2007. (Herculeah Jones Mystery Ser.). 144p. (J). pap. 5.99 (978-0-14-240759-2(3) , Puffin) Penguin Group (USA) Inc.

JONES, INDIANA (FICTITIOUS CHARACTER)—FICTION

DK Publishing. Glow-in-the-Dark Indiana Jones. 2008. (Ultimate Sticker Bks.). 16p. (J). (ps-12). pap. 6.99 (***978-0-7566-3498-8(9)***) Dorling Kindersley Publishing, Inc.

—Indiana Jones. 2008. (Ultimate Sticker Bks.). 16p. (J). (ps-12). pap. 6.99 (***978-0-7566-3499-5(7)***) Dorling Kindersley Publishing, Inc.

—Indiana Jones: The Ultimate Guide. 2008. 144p. (J). 24.99 (***978-0-7566-3500-8(4)***) Dorling Kindersley Publishing, Inc.

Luceno, James. Movie Novelization. 2008. (Indiana Jones Ser.). 160p. (J). 6.99 (***978-0-545-00701-6(1)*** , Scholastic) Scholastic, Inc.

McCay, William. Young Indiana Jones & the Mask of the Madman. 1998. (Young Indiana Jones Ser.: No. 18). (J). (gr. 4-6). pap. 3.99 (978-0-679-87907-7(2) , Random Hse. Bks. for Young Readers) Random Hse. Children's Bks.

Stine, Megan & Stine, H. William. Young Indiana Jones & the Ring of Power. 1999. (Young Indiana Jones Ser.). (J). (gr. 4-6). pap. 3.99 (978-0-679-89049-2(1)); lib. bdg. 11.99 (978-0-679-99049-9(6)) Random Hse. Children's Bks. (Random Hse. Bks. for Young Readers).

Weyn, Suzanne. Indiana Jones: Temple of Doom Novelization: Temple of Doom Novelization. 2008. (Indiana Jones Ser.). 176p. (J). 6.99 (***978-0-545-04255-0(0)*** , Scholastic) Scholastic, Inc.

Windham, Ryder. Indiana Jones: Last Crusade Novelization: Last Crusade Novelization. 2008. (Indiana Jones Ser.). 176p. (J). 6.99 (***978-0-545-04256-7(9)*** , Scholastic) Scholastic, Inc.

—Indiana Jones: Raiders of the Lost Ark Novelizat: Raiders of the Lost Ark Novelizat. 2008. (Indiana Jones Ser.). 176p. (J). 6.99 (***978-0-545-00700-9(3)*** , Scholastic) Scholastic, Inc.

JONES, JIGSAW (FICTITIOUS CHARACTER)—FICTION

Preller, James. The Case of Hermie the Missing Hamster. Alley, R. W., illus. 2001. (Jigsaw Jones Mystery Ser.: No. 1). 80p. (J). (gr. 1-4). pap. 3.99 (978-0-590-69125-3(2)) Scholastic, Inc.

—The Case of the Bicycle Bandit. 2001. (Jigsaw Jones Mystery Ser.). (Illus.). (J). 10.79 (978-0-606-21268-7(X)) Tandem Library Bks.

—The Case of the Christmas Snowman. Alley, R. W., illus. 1998. (Jigsaw Jones Mystery Ser.: No. 2). 80p. (J). (gr. 1-4). pap. 3.99 (978-0-590-69126-0(0)) Scholastic, Inc.

—The Case of the Class Clown. 2001. (Jigsaw Jones Mystery Ser.: No. 12). (Illus.). 80p. (J). (gr. 1-4). pap. 3.99 (978-0-439-18474-8(6)) Scholastic, Inc.

—The Case of the Class Clown. 2001. (Jigsaw Jones Mystery Ser.). (Illus.). (J). 10.79 (978-0-606-20742-3(2)) Tandem Library Bks.

—The Case of the Disappearing Dinosaur. Smith, Jamie & Alley, R. W., illus. 2002. (Jigsaw Jones Mystery Ser.: No. 17). 96p. (J). pap. 3.99 (978-0-439-30639-3(6)) Scholastic, Inc.

—Case of the Ghost Writer. 2001. (Jigsaw Jones Mystery Ser.). (Illus.). (J). 10.79 (978-0-606-20740-9(6)) Tandem Library Bks.
—The Case of the Great Sled Race. 1999. (Jigsaw Jones Mystery Ser.: No. 8). (Illus.). (J). (gr. 1-4). 10.79 (978-0-606-18527-1(5)) Tandem Library Bks.
—The Case of the Marshmallow Monster. 2001. (Jigsaw Jones Mystery Ser.: No. 11). (Illus.). 80p. (J). (gr. 1-4). pap. 3.99 (978-0-439-18473-1(8)) Scholastic, Inc.
—The Case of the Marshmallow Monster. 2001. (Jigsaw Jones Mystery Ser.). (Illus.). (J). 10.79 (978-0-606-20741-6(4)) Tandem Library Bks.
—The Case of the Mummy Mystery. Alley, R. W., illus. 2001. (Jigsaw Jones Mystery Ser.: No. 6). 80p. (J). (gr. 1-4). pap. 3.99 (978-0-439-08094-1(0)) Scholastic, Inc.
—The Case of the Mummy Mystery. 2000. (Jigsaw Jones Mystery Ser.: No. 6). (Illus.). (J). (gr. 1-4). 10.79 (978-0-606-18528-8(3)) Tandem Library Bks.
—The Case of the Perfect Prank. 2004. (Jigsaw Jones Ser.). (Illus.). 80p. (J). pap. 3.99 (978-0-439-55996-6(0) , Scholastic Paperbacks) Scholastic, Inc.
—The Case of the Rainy Day Mystery. Smith, Jamie, illus. 2003. (Jigsaw Jones Mystery Ser.: No. 21). 80p. (J). mass mkt. 3.99 (978-0-439-42631-2(6) , Scholastic Paperbacks) Scholastic, Inc.
—The Case of the Runaway Dog. 1999. (Jigsaw Jones Mystery Ser.: No. 7). (Illus.). (J). (gr. 1-4). 10.79 (978-0-606-18529-5(1)) Tandem Library Bks.
—The Case of the Secret Valentine, No. 3. Alley, R. W. & Speirs, John, illus. 1999. (Jigsaw Jones Mystery Ser.: No. 3). 80p. (J). (gr. 1-4). 3.99 (978-0-590-69127-7(9)) Scholastic, Inc.
—The Case of the Secret Valentine. 1999. (Jigsaw Jones Mystery Ser.: No. 3). (J). (gr. 1-4). 10.79 (978-0-606-15986-9(X)) Tandem Library Bks.
—The Case of the Spooky Sleepover. Alley, R. W., illus. 2001. (Jigsaw Jones Mystery Ser.: No. 4). 80p. (J). (gr. 1-4). pap. 3.99 (978-0-590-69129-1(5)) Scholastic, Inc.
—The Case of the Spooky Sleepover. 1999. (Jigsaw Jones Mystery Ser.: No. 4). (Illus.). (J). (gr. 1-4). 10.79 (978-0-606-16586-0(X)) Tandem Library Bks.
—The Case of the Stolen Baseball Card. 1999. (Jigsaw Jones Mystery Ser.: No. 5). (J). (gr. 1-4). 10.79 (978-0-606-16933-2(4)) Tandem Library Bks.
—The Case of the Stolen Baseball Cards. Alley, R. W. & Speirs, John, illus. 2001. (Jigsaw Jones Mystery Ser.: No. 5). 80p. (J). (gr. 1-4). mass mkt. 3.99 (978-0-439-08083-5(5)) Scholastic, Inc.
—The Case of the Vanishing Painting. Smith, Jamie & Alley, R. W., illus. 2004. (Jigsaw Jones Ser.). 96p. (J). (gr. 2-4). pap. 3.99 (978-0-439-66165-2(X) , Scholastic Paperbacks) Scholastic, Inc.
—A Jigsaw Jones Mystery, Vol. 30. Alley, R. W. & Smith, Jamie, illus. 2006. (Jigsaw Jones Super Special Ser.). 112p. (J). pap. 4.99 (978-0-439-79396-4(3)) Scholastic, Inc.
—The Race Against Time. 2003. (Jigsaw Jones Mystery Ser.: No. 20). (Illus.). 96p. (J). pap. 3.99 (978-0-439-42630-5(8) , Scholastic Paperbacks) Scholastic, Inc.
Preller, James & Preller, Jimmy. The Great Sled Race. Alley, R. W., illus. 2001. (Jigsaw Jones Mystery Ser.: No. 8). 80p. (J). (gr. 1-4). pap. 3.99 (978-0-439-11427-1(6) , Scholastic Paperbacks) Scholastic, Inc.
Preller, James, et al. The Case of the Runaway Dog. Alley, R. W., illus. 2001. (Jigsaw Jones Mystery Ser.: No. 7). 80p. (J). (gr. 1-4). pap. 3.99 (978-0-439-11426-4(8)) Scholastic, Inc.
Preller, Jimmy. The Case of the Stinky Science Project. Alley, R. W., illus. 2001. (Jigsaw Jones Mystery Ser.: No. 9). 80p. (J). (gr. 1-4). pap. 3.99 (978-0-439-11428-8(4)) Scholastic, Inc.
—The Case of the Stinky Science Project. 2000. (Jigsaw Jones Mystery Ser.: No. 9). (Illus.). (J). (gr. 1-4). 10.79 (978-0-606-18530-1(5)) Tandem Library Bks.
—The Ease of the Ghostwriter. 2001. (Jigsaw Jones Mystery Ser.: No. 10). 80p. (J). (gr. 1-4). pap. 3.99 (978-0-439-11429-5(2)) Scholastic, Inc.

JONES, JOHN PAUL, 1747-1792

Alphin, Elaine Marie & Alphin, Arthur B. I Have Not Yet Begun to Fight: A Story about John Paul Jones. Casale, Paul, tr. Casale, Paul, illus. 2004. (Creative Minds Biography Ser.). 64p. (J). 22.60 (978-1-57505-601-2(1) , Carolrhoda Bks.) Lerner Publishing Group.
Bradford, James C. John Paul Jones: And the American Navy. 2005. (Library of American Lives & Times). (Illus.). 112p. (J). (gr. 4-8). lib. bdg. 31.95 (978-0-8239-5726-2(8)) Rosen Publishing Group, Inc., The.
Brager, Bruce L. John Paul Jones: America's Sailor. 2006. (Illus.). 160p. (J). lib. bdg. 26.95 (978-1-931798-84-6(2)) Reynolds, Morgan Inc.
Cooper, Michael. Hero of the High Seas: John Paul Jones & the American Revolution. 2006. (Illus.). 128p. (J). (gr. 5). 32.90 (978-0-7922-5548-2(8)); pap. 21.95 (978-0-7922-5547-5(X)) National Geographic Society. (National Geographic Children's Bks.).
Egan, Tracie. John Paul Jones. 2003. (Famous People in American History Ser.). (Illus.). 32p. (J). lib. bdg. 6.50 (978-0-8239-4185-8(X) , Rosen Central) Rosen Publishing Group, Inc., The.
—John Paul Jones: Heroe de la Marina Estadounidense. 2003. (ENG & SPA.). (J). pap. (978-0-8239-4231-2(7)) Rosen Publishing Group, Inc., The.
Harkins, Susan and William. The Life & Times of John Paul Jones. 2007. (Profiles in American History Ser.). (Illus.). 48p. (J). lib. bdg. 22.95 (***978-1-58415-529-4(9)***) Mitchell Lane Pubs., Inc.
Haugen, Brenda & Santella, Andrew. John Paul Jones: Father of the American Navy. 2004. (Signature Lives Ser.). (Illus.). 112p. (J). 30.60 (978-0-7565-0829-6(0)) Compass Point Bks.
Heinrichs, Ann. John Paul Jones. 2004. (Our People Ser.). (Illus.). 32p. (J). (gr. 2-6). 27.07 (978-1-59296-175-7(4)) Child's World, Inc.
Ingram, Scott. John Paul Jones. 2002. (Triangle History of the American Revolution Ser.). (Illus.). 104p. (J). 28.70 (978-1-56711-609-0(4) , Blackbirch Pr., Inc.) Thomson Gale.
Lutz, Norma Jean. John Paul Jones. 1999. (Revolutionary War Leaders Ser.). (Illus.). 80p. (gr. 3 up). (J). 31.00 (978-0-7910-5359-1(8)); (YA). pap. 27.50 (978-0-7910-5702-5(X)) Facts On File, Inc. (Chelsea Hse.).
Marsh, Carole. The Virginia Reader: John Paul Jones. 2001. (Virginia Experience! Ser.). (Illus.). 12p. (J). (gr. k-4). pap. 2.95 (978-0-635-00507-6(7)) Gallopade International.
Price Hossell, Karen. John Paul Jones. 2004. (American War Biographies Ser.). (J). pap. 8.50 (978-1-4034-5086-9(2)); lib. bdg. 29.93 (978-1-4034-5079-1(X)) Heinemann Library.
Sonneborn, Liz. John Paul Jones: American Naval Hero. 2005. (Leaders of the American Revolution Ser.). (Illus.). 123p. (J). (ps-8). lib. bdg. 30.00 (978-0-7910-8621-6(6) , Chelsea Hse.) Facts On File, Inc.
Sperry, Armstrong. John Paul Jones: The Pirate Patriot. 2006. (Sterling Point Bks.). (Illus.). 176p. (J). 12.95 (978-1-4027-3185-3(X)); pap. 6.95 (978-1-4027-3615-5(0)) Sterling Publishing Co., Inc.
Tibbitts, Alison Davis. John Paul Jones: Father of the American Navy. 2002. (Historical American Biographies Ser.). (Illus.). 128p. (J). (gr. 6-9). lib. bdg. 26.60 (978-0-7660-1448-0(7)) Enslow Pubs., Inc.

JONES, JULIET (FICTITIOUS CHARACTER)—FICTION

Morris, Gilbert. Too Smart Jones & the Cat's Secret: A Gilbert Morris Mystery. 2000. (Gilbert Morris Mysteries Ser.: Vol. 6). (Illus.). 124p. (J). (gr. 2-7). pap. 5.99 (978-0-8024-4030-3(4)) Moody Pubs.
—Too Smart Jones & the Disappearing Dogs: A Gilbert Morris Mystery. 2000. (Gilbert Morris Mysteries Ser.: Vol. 3). (Illus.). 128p. (J). (gr. 4-7). pap. 5.99 (978-0-8024-4027-3(4)) Moody Pubs.
—Too Smart Jones & the Pool Party Thief: A Gilbert Morris Mystery. 1999. (Gilbert Morris Mysteries Ser.: Vol. 1). (Illus.). 115p. (J). (gr. 2-7). pap. 5.99 (978-0-8024-4025-9(8)) Moody Pubs.
—Too Smart Jones & the Stolen Bicycle: A Gilbert Morris Mystery. 2000. (Gilbert Morris Mysteries Ser.: Vol. 9). (Illus.). 133p. (J). (gr. 4-7). pap. 5.99 (978-0-8024-4031-0(2)) Moody Pubs.

JONES, JUNIE B. (FICTITIOUS CHARACTER)—FICTION

Park, Barbara. Junie B. , First Grader (at Last!) Brunkus, Denise, illus. (Junie B. Jones Ser.: No. 18). 96p. (J). 2002. (gr. k-3). pap. 3.99 (978-0-375-81516-4(3)); 2001. (gr. k-3). 11.95 (978-0-375-80293-5(2)); 2001. (gr. 1-4). lib. bdg. 13.99 (978-0-375-90293-2(7)) Random Hse. Children's Bks. (Random Hse. Bks. for Young Readers).
—Junie B. , First Grader (at Last!) 2001. (Junie B. Jones Ser.: No. 18). (J). (gr. k-3). lib. bdg. 11.80 (978-0-613-57510-2(5)) Tandem Library Bks.
—Junie B., 1st Grader: Shipwrecked. Brunkus, Denise, illus. 2004. (Junie B. Jones Ser.: No. 23). 96p. (J). (gr. 1-4). 11.95 (978-0-375-82804-1(4) , Random Hse. Bks. for Young Readers) Random Hse. Children's Bks.
—Junie B., First Grader: Aloha-Ha-Ha! 2006. (Junie B. Jones Ser.: No. 26). (Illus.). 128p. (J). (gr. k-3). lib. bdg. 13.95 (978-0-375-93403-2(0)); (gr. 2-5). 11.95 (978-0-375-83403-5(6)) Random Hse. Children's Bks. (Random Hse. Bks. for Young Readers).
—Junie B., First Grader: Boo... & I Mean It! Brunkus, Denise, illus. (Junie B. Jones Ser.: No. 24). 96p. (J). (gr. k-3). 2005. pap. 3.99 (978-0-375-82807-2(9)); 2004. 11.95 (978-0-375-82806-5(0)); 2004. lib. bdg. 13.99 (978-0-375-92806-2(5)) Random Hse. Children's Bks. (Random Hse. Bks. for Young Readers).
—Junie B., First Grader: Boss of Lunch. Brunkus, Denise, illus. 2003. (Junie B. Jones Ser.: No. 19). 96p. (J). (gr. k-3). lib. bdg. 11.99 (978-0-375-90294-9(5) , Golden Bks.) Random Hse. Children's Bks.
—Junie B., First Grader: Boss of Lunch. 2002. (Junie B. Jones Ser.: No. 19). (J). (gr. k-3). lib. bdg. 11.80 (978-0-613-63168-6(4)) Tandem Library Bks.
—Junie B., First Grader: Cheater Pants. Brunkus, Denise, tr. Brunkus, Denise, illus. 2004. (Junie B. Jones Ser.: No. 21). 96p. (J). (gr. 1-4). pap. 3.99 (978-0-375-82302-2(6) , Random Hse. Bks. for Young Readers) Random Hse. Children's Bks.
—Junie B., First Grader: Cheater Pants. Brunkus, Denise, illus. 2003. (Junie B. Jones Ser.: No. 21). 96p. (J). (gr. k-3). lib. bdg. 13.99 (978-0-375-92301-2(2)); (gr. 1-4). 11.95 (978-0-375-82301-5(8)) Random Hse. Children's Bks. (Random Hse. Bks. for Young Readers).
—Junie B., First Grader: One-Man Band. Brunkus, Denise, illus. 2003. (Junie B. Jones Ser.: No. 22). 96p. (J). (gr. k-3). 11.95 (978-0-375-82522-4(3)); (gr. 1-4). lib. bdg. 13.99 (978-0-375-92522-1(8)) Random Hse. Children's Bks. (Random Hse. Bks. for Young Readers).
—Junie B., First Grader: Shipwrecked. Brunkus, Denise, illus. (Junie B. Jones Ser.: No. 23). 96p. (J). (gr. k-3). 2005. mass mkt. 3.99 (978-0-375-82805-8(2)); 2004. lib. bdg. 13.99 (978-0-375-92804-8(9)) Random Hse. Children's Bks. (Random Hse. Bks. for Young Readers).
—Junie B., First Grader: Toothless Wonder. Brunkus, Denise, illus. (Junie B. Jones Ser.: No. 20). 96p. (J). 2003. (gr. k-3). pap. 3.99 (978-0-375-82223-0(2)); 2002. (gr. 1-4). 11.95 (978-0-375-80295-9(9)) Random Hse. Children's Bks. (Random Hse. Bks. for Young Readers).
—Junie B., First Grader: Toothless Wonder. 2003. (Junie B. Jones Ser.: No. 20). (J). (gr. k-3). lib. bdg. 11.80 (978-0-613-71014-5(2)) Tandem Library Bks.
—Junie B. Jones & a Little Monkey Business, Vol. 2. unabr. ed. 2004. (Junie B. Jones Ser.: Vol. 2). 68p. (J). (gr. k-3). pap. 17.00 incl. audio (978-0-8072-0779-6(9) , LFTR 238 SP, Listening Library) Random Hse. Audio Publishing Group.
—Junie B. Jones & Her Big Fat Mouth. unabr. ed. 1999. (Junie B. Jones Ser.: No. 3). (J). (gr. k-3). pap., stu. ed. 24.24 incl. audio (978-0-7887-2982-9(9) , 40864) Recorded Bks., LLC.
—Junie B. Jones & Some Sneaky Peeky Spying. unabr. ed. 1999. (Junie B. Jones Ser.: No. 4). (J). (gr. k-3). pap., stu. ed. 23.24 incl. audio (978-0-7887-3169-3(6) , 40904X4) Recorded Bks., LLC.
—Junie B. Jones & the Mushy Gushy Valentime. unabr. ed. 2004. (Junie B. Jones Ser.: No. 14). 69p. (J). (gr. k-3). pap. 17.00 incl. audio (978-0-8072-0335-4(1) , Listening Library) Random Hse. Audio Publishing Group.
—Junie B. Jones & the Mushy Gushy Valentime. Brunkus, Denise, illus. 1999. (Junie B. Jones Ser.: No. 14). 80p. (J). (gr. k-3). pap. 3.99 (978-0-375-80039-9(5)); lib. bdg. 11.99 (978-0-375-90039-6(X)) Random Hse. Children's Bks. (Random Hse. Bks. for Young Readers).
—Junie B. Jones & the Mushy Gushy Valentime. Brunkus, Denise, illus. 1999. (Junie B. Jones Ser.: No. 14). 69p. (J). (gr. k-3). lib. bdg. 11.80 (978-0-613-21832-0(9)) Tandem Library Bks.
—Junie B. Jones & the Mushy Gushy Valentime. 1999. (Junie B. Jones Ser.: No. 14). (J). (gr. k-3). 10.79 (978-0-606-19516-4(5)) Tandem Library Bks.
—Junie B. Jones & the Stupid Smelly Bus. unabr. ed. 2004. (Junie B. Jones Ser.: Vol. 1). 69p. (J). (gr. k-3). pap. 17.00 incl. audio (978-0-8072-0778-9(0) , LFTR 237 SP, Listening Library) Random Hse. Audio Publishing Group.
—Junie B. Jones Collection, Bks. 17-20. abr. ed. 2002. (J). pap. 23.00 incl. audio (978-0-8072-0965-3(1) , Listening Library) Random Hse. Audio Publishing Group.
—Junie B. Jones Has a Monster under Her Bed. unabr. ed. 2004. (Junie B. Jones Ser.: No. 11). 69p. (J). (gr. k-3). pap. 17.00 incl. audio (978-0-8072-0644-7(X) , Listening Library) Random Hse. Audio Publishing Group.
—Junie B. Jones Has a Peep in Her Pocket. Brunkus, Denise, illus. 2000. (Junie B. Jones Ser.: No. 15). 80p. (J). (gr. k-3). lib. bdg. 11.99 (978-0-375-90040-2(3)); pap. 3.99 (978-0-375-80040-5(9)) Random Hse. Children's Bks. (Random Hse. Bks. for Young Readers).
—Junie B. Jones Has a Peep in Her Pocket. 2000. (Junie B. Jones Ser.: No. 15). (Illus.). (J). (gr. k-3). 10.79 (978-0-606-18499-1(6)) Tandem Library Bks.
—Junie B. Jones Is a Beauty Shop Guy. Brunkus, Denise & Silverpin Studio Staff, illus. 1998. (Junie B. Jones Ser.: No. 11). 80p. (J). (gr. k-3). lib. bdg. 11.99 (978-0-679-98931-8(5) , Random Hse. Bks. for Young Readers) Random Hse. Children's Bks.
—Junie B. Jones Is a Beauty Shop Guy. Brunkus, Denise, illus. 1998. (Junie B. Jones Ser.: No. 11). 80p. (J). (gr. 1-4). pap. 3.99 (978-0-679-88931-1(0) , Random Hse. Bks. for Young Readers) Random Hse. Children's Bks.
—Junie B. Jones Is a Beauty Shop Guy. Brunkus, Denise, illus. 1998. (Junie B. Jones Ser.: No. 11). (J). (gr. k-3). 10.79 (978-0-606-13963-2(X)) Tandem Library Bks.
—Junie B. Jones Is a Graduation Girl. Brunkus, Denise, illus. 2001. (Junie B. Jones Ser.: No. 17). 80p. (J). (gr. k-3). pap. 3.99 (978-0-375-80292-8(4) , Random Hse. Bks. for Young Readers) Random Hse. Children's Bks.
—Junie B. Jones Is a Graduation Girl. 2001. (Junie B. Jones Ser.: No. 17). (J). (gr. k-3). lib. bdg. 11.80 (978-0-613-33766-3(2)) Tandem Library Bks.
—Junie B. Jones Is (Almost) a Flower Girl. Brunkus, Denise, illus. 1999. (Junie B. Jones Ser.: No. 13). 80p. (J). (gr. 1-4). lib. bdg. 11.99 (978-0-375-90038-9(1)); (gr. k-3). pap. 3.99 (978-0-375-80038-2(7)) Random Hse. Children's Bks. (Random Hse. Bks. for Young Readers).
—Junie B. Jones Is (Almost) a Flower Girl. 1999. (Junie B. Jones Ser.: No. 13). (J). (gr. k-3). 10.79 (978-0-606-16840-3(0)) Tandem Library Bks.
—Junie B. Jones Is Captain Field Day. Brunkus, Denise, illus. 2001. (Junie B. Jones Ser.: No. 16). 80p. (J). (gr. k-3). pap. 3.99 (978-0-375-80291-1(6)); lib. bdg. 11.99 (978-0-375-90291-8(0)) Random Hse. Children's Bks. (Random Hse. Bks. for Young Readers).
—Junie B. Jones Is Captain Field Day. (Junie B. Jones Ser.: No. 16). (J). (gr. k-3). 2001. lib. bdg. 11.80 (978-0-613-33767-0(0)); 2000. 10.79 (978-0-606-19899-8(7)) Tandem Library Bks.
—Junie B. Jones Smells Something Fishy. Brunkus, Denise & Silverpin Studio Staff, illus. 1998. (Junie B. Jones Ser.: No. 12). 80p. (J). (gr. k-3). lib. bdg. 11.99 (978-0-679-99130-4(1) , Random Hse. Bks. for Young Readers) Random Hse. Children's Bks.
—Junie B. Jones Smells Something Fishy. Brunkus, Denise, illus. 1998. (Junie B. Jones Ser.: No. 12). 80p. (J). (gr. 1-4). pap. 3.99 (978-0-679-89130-7(7) , Random Hse. Bks. for Young Readers) Random Hse. Children's Bks.
—Junie B. Jones's First Boxed Set Ever!, 4 bks., Set. Brunkus, Denise, illus. 2001. (Junie B. Jones Ser.). (J). (gr. 1-4). pap. 15.96 (978-0-375-81361-0(6) , Random Hse. Bks. for Young Readers) Random Hse. Children's Bks.
—Junie B. Jones's Second Boxed Set Ever!, Bks. 5-8. 2002. (Illus.). (J). (gr. 1-4). pap. 15.96 (978-0-375-82265-0(8) , Random Hse. Bks. for Young Readers) Random Hse. Children's Bks.

JONES, MOTHER, 1830-1930

Altgeld, John P. & Jones, Mother. Autobiography of Mother Jones. 2003. (Labor Classics Ser.). (Illus.). 304p. (Orig.). reprint ed. 25.00 (978-0-88286-167-8(0)) Kerr, Charles H. Publishing Co.
Gay, Kathlyn. Mother Jones. 2006. (American Workers Ser.). (Illus.). 144p. (J). lib. bdg. 26.95 (978-1-59935-016-5(5)) Reynolds, Morgan Inc.
Jones, Mary H. & Kerr, Charles H. Autobiography of Mother Jones. 10th annot. ed. 2006. (Labor Classics Ser.). (Illus.). 160p. (Orig.). pap. 15.00 (978-0-88286-311-5(8)) Kerr, Charles H. Publishing Co.
Koestler-Grack, Rachel A. The Story of Mother Jones. 2004. (Breakthrough Biographies Ser.). (Illus.). 32p. (gr. 3-5). 23.00 (978-0-7910-7316-2(5) , Chelsea Hse.) Facts On File, Inc.
Kraft, Betsy Harvey. Mother Jones: One Woman's Fight for Labor. 2006. (Illus.). 116p. (YA). (gr. 6-10). reprint ed. 17.00 (978-1-4223-5443-8(1)) DIANE Publishing Co.
Miller, Connie Colwell. Mother Jones: Labor Leader. Erwin, Steve & Barnett, Charles, illus. 2007. (Graphic Library). 32p. (J). 25.26 (978-0-7368-5487-0(8)); (***978-0-7368-9662-7(7)***) Capstone Pr., Inc.

JORDAN

Carew-Miller, Anna. Jordan. 2003. (Modern Middle East Nations & Their Strategic Place in the World Ser.). (Illus.). 112,128p. (YA). (gr. 7 up). lib. bdg. (978-1-59084-507-3(2)) Mason Crest Pubs.
Jankowski, Susan. Jordan in the News: Past, Present, & Future. 2006. (Middle East Nations in the News Ser.). (Illus.). 128p. (J). lib. bdg. 33.27 (978-1-59845-030-9(1) , MyReportLinks.com Bks.) Enslow Pubs., Inc.
Kummer, Patricia K. Jordan. 2006. (Enchantment of the World, Second Ser.). (Illus.). 144p. (J). 36.00 (978-0-516-24870-7(7) , Children's Pr.) Scholastic Library Publishing.
Marcovitz, Hal. Jordan. 2002. (Creation of the Modern Middle East Ser.). (Illus.). 125p. (gr. 6-12). 35.00 (978-0-7910-6507-5(3) , Chelsea Hse.) Facts On File, Inc.
Pundyk, Grace. Welcome to Jordan. 2004. (Welcome to My Country Ser.). (J). lib. bdg. 26.00 (978-0-8368-2565-7(9)) Stevens, Gareth Inc.
Skinner, Patricia. Jordan. 2003. (Countries of the World Ser.). (Illus.). 96p. (J). (gr. 6 up). lib. bdg. 30.00 (978-0-8368-2365-3(6)) Stevens, Gareth Inc.
South, Coleman. Jordan. 2nd ed. 2007. (Cultures of the World Ser.). 144p. (J). lib. bdg. 39.93 (***978-0-7614-2080-4(0)*** , Benchmark Bks.) Cavendish, Marshall Corp.
Wagner, Heather Lehr. King Abdullah II: King of Jordan. Schlesinger, Arthur M., Jr., ed. 2005. (Major World Leaders Ser.). (Illus.). 112-144p. (J). (gr. 6-12). 30.00 (978-0-7910-8259-1(8) , Chelsea Hse.) Facts On File, Inc.
Whitehead, Susan. Jordan. 1999. (Major World Nations Ser.). (Illus.). 144p. (YA). (gr. 4-7). lib. bdg. 21.95 (978-0-7910-4980-8(9) , Chelsea Hse.) Facts On File, Inc.
Wills, Karen. Jordan. 2000. (Modern Nations of the World Ser.). (Illus.). 112p. (YA). (gr. 7-10). 29.95 (978-1-56006-822-8(1) , Lucent Bks.) Thomson Gale.

JORDAN, MICHAEL, 1963-

Brenner, Richard J. Michael Jordan. (J). 2000. 25.01 (978-0-688-16586-4(9)); 1999. (Illus.). 32p. pap. 3.95 (978-0-688-16587-1(7)) HarperCollins Pubs.
—Michael Jordan. 1999. (978-0-606-17077-2(4)) Tandem Library Bks.
Dougherty, Denis. Michael Jordan. 1999. (Jam Session Ser.). (Illus.). 32p. (J). (gr. 3-8). lib. bdg. 24.21 (978-1-57765-038-6(7) , ABDO & Daughters) ABDO Publishing Co.
Greenfield, Eloise. For the Love of the Game: Michael Jordan & Me. Gilchrist, Jan Spivey, illus. 1999. (Trophy Picture Bk.). 32p. (J). (ps-3). pap. 6.99 (978-0-06-443555-0(5) , Harper Trophy) HarperCollins Pubs.
—For the Love of the Game: Michael Jordan & Me. 1999. (gr. k-3). lib. bdg. 15.30 (978-0-613-17800-6(9)) Tandem Library Bks.
Gutman, Bill. Michael Jordan & Scottie Pippen. 1998. (Teammates Ser.). (Illus.). 112p. (gr. 4-6). lib. bdg. 23.90 (978-0-7613-0420-3(7) , Millbrook Pr.) Lerner Publishing Group.
Houghton, Sarah. Michael Jordan: The Best Ever. 2001. (Illus.). 64p. (J). pap. (978-0-7368-9502-6(7)) Capstone Pr., Inc.
—Michael Jordan: The Best Ever, 6 vols. (gr. 4 up). 49.95 (978-0-7368-9512-5(4) , High Five) Red Brick Learning.
Kirkpatrick, Rob, et al, contrib. by. Michael Jordan, Basketball Superstar: Rob Kirkpatrick. 2001. (Great Record Breakers in Sports Ser.). (Illus.). 24p. (J). lib. bdg. 18.75 (978-0-8239-5633-3(4) , PowerKids Pr.) Rosen Publishing Group, Inc., The.
Lovitt, Chip. Michael Jordan. (Scholastic Biography Ser.). (Illus.). (gr. 4-9). 2nd rev. ed. 1998. 213p. (YA). pap. 4.50 (978-0-590-59644-2(6)); 3rd rev. ed. 1999. 224p. (J). pap. 4.50 (978-0-439-12961-9(3)) Scholastic, Inc.
—Michael Jordan. 1999. (978-0-606-17877-8(5)) Tandem Library Bks.
McCormick, Lisa Wade. Michael Jordan. 2006. (Illus.). 31p. (J). (978-0-516-29843-6(7)) Children's Pr., Ltd.
Raber, Thomas R. Michael Jordan: Basketball Skywalker. 3rd rev. exp. ed. 1999. (Sports Achievers Biographies Ser.). (Illus.). 80p. (gr. 4-9). (978-0-8225-9846-6(9) , LernerSports) Lerner Publishing Group.

JOSEPH, NEZ PERCE CHIEF, 1840-1904

Chief Joseph of the Nez Perce. (Photo Illustrated Biographies Ser.). 24p. (J). 6.95 (978-0-7368-8426-6(2)) Capstone Pr., Inc.
Englar, Mary. Chief Joseph 1840-1904. 2004. (American Indian Biographies Ser.). (Illus.). 32p. (J). (gr. 3-4). lib. bdg. 23.93 (978-0-7368-2444-6(8) , Blue Earth Bks.) Capstone Pr., Inc.
Kiely Miller, Barbara. Chief Joseph. 2007. (J). pap. (***978-0-8368-8321-3(7)*** , Weekly Reader Early Learning Library) Stevens, Gareth Inc.
Klingel, Cynthia Fitterer & Noyed, Robert B. Chief Joseph: Chief of the Nez Perce. 2002. (Spirit of America: Our People Ser.). (Illus.). 32p. (J). (gr. 2-6). 27.07 (978-1-56766-165-1(3)) Child's World, Inc.

Koestler-Grack, Rachel A. Chief Joseph. 2004. (Illus.). 32p. (J). pap. 7.50 (978-1-4034-5008-1(0)); lib. bdg. 24.22 (978-1-4034-5001-2(3)) Heinemann Library.

McLeese, Don. Chief Joseph. 2003. (Native American Legends Ser.). (Illus.). 32p. (J). 28.50 (978-1-58952-726-3(7)) Rourke Publishing, LLC.

Miller, Barbara Kiely. Chief Joseph. 2007. (Great Americans Ser.). 24p. (J). (gr. 2-4). lib. bdg. 19.93 (***978-0-8368-8314-5(4)*** , Weekly Reader Early Learning Library) Stevens, Gareth Inc.

—Jefe Joseph. 2007. (Grandes Personajes (Great Americans) Ser.). (SPA.). 24p. (J). (gr. 2-4). lib. bdg. 19.93 (***978-0-8368-8331-2(4)*** , Weekly Reader Early Learning Library) Stevens, Gareth Inc.

—Jefe Joseph (Chief Joseph) 2007. (Grandes Personajes (Great Americans) Ser.). (SPA.). 24p. (J). (gr. 2-4). pap. 5.95 (***978-0-8368-8338-1(1)*** , Weekly Reader Early Learning Library) Stevens, Gareth Inc.

Sutcliffe, Jane. Chief Joseph. 2004. (History Maker Bios Ser.). (J). pap. 6.95 (978-0-8225-2068-9(0)) Lerner Publishing Group.

—Chief Joseph. Parlin, Tim, tr. Parlin, Tim, illus. 2004. (History Maker Bios Ser.). 48p. (J). (gr. 3-5). lib. bdg. 26.60 (978-0-8225-0696-6(3)) Lerner Publishing Group.

Troy, Don & Court, Rob. Art of Early Egypt. 2003. (Scribbles Institute : Art in Ancient Civilizations Ser.). 32p. (J). (gr. 1-5). 21.36 (978-1-56766-553-6(5)) Child's World, Inc.

JOSEPH, SAINT

Drake, Tim. From an Angel in a Dream, the Story of Saint Joseph, Marys Husband: De un Angel en un Sueño, la Historia de San José, Esposo de María. Alvarado, Tomas, tr. Webber, John & Cohee, Ron, illus. 2nd ed. 2003. (SPA.). (J). 5.00 (978-0-9747571-0-0(1)) Catholic World Mission.

Glen, Jo. Thirty Activity Days, Story of Mary & Joseph: The Story of Mary & Joseph. 1998. (Illus.). 24p. 9.99 (978-1-85608-367-6(5)) Hunt, John Publishing Ltd. GBR. *Dist:* APG Sales and Fulfillment.

—30 Days with Mary & Joseph. 2004. (Illus.). 30p. (ps-3). 11.95 (978-0-8294-1475-2(4)) Loyola Pr.

Lovasik, Lawrence G. El Buen San Jose. (SPA.). (J). 1.50 (978-0-89942-464-4(3)) Catholic Bk. Publishing Corp.

JOSEPH (SON OF JACOB)

Amery, H. Joseph & the Amazing Coat. 2004. (Bible Tales Readers Ser.). (SPA., Illus.). 16p. (J). pap. 4.95 (978-0-7945-0417-5(5)) EDC Publishing.

Auld, Mary. Joseph & His Brothers. 2000. (Bible Stories Ser.). (Illus.). 32p. (J). (gr. 2-4). pap. 7.95 (978-0-531-15386-4(X) , Watts, Franklin) Scholastic Library Publishing.

—Joseph & His Brothers. 1999. (gr. 3-6). lib. bdg. 16.40 (978-0-613-62467-1(X)) Tandem Library Bks.

Chronicles of Faith - Joseph. 2007. 224p. (J). pap. 4.97 (***978-1-59789-926-0(7))*** Barbour Publishing, Inc.

Davidson, Alice Joyce. Joseph & the Splendid Coat. Lyon, Tammie Speer, illus. 1998. (My Bible Friends Board Bks.). 12p. (J). 3.99 (978-0-310-97325-6(2)) Zondervan.

De Graaf, Anne. Joseph. Montero, Jose Perez, illus. 2000. (Little Children's Bible Bks.). 38p. (J). (ps-1). 5.99 (978-0-8054-2175-0(0)) B&H Publishing Grp.

Frank, Penny. Joseph & the King of Egypt. 1999. (Lion Story Bible Ser.). (Illus.). 24p. pap. 2.99 (978-0-7459-4106-6(0) , Lion) Lion Hudson plc GBR. *Dist:* Independent Pubs. Group.

—Joseph the Dreamer. 1999. (Lion Story Bible Ser.). (Illus.). 24p. pap. 2.99 (978-0-7459-4105-9(2) , Lion) Lion Hudson plc GBR. *Dist:* Independent Pubs. Group.

Harrast, Tracy. Joseph & the Big Dreams. 2000. (Peek-a-Bible Ser.). (Illus.). (J). 6.99 (978-0-310-97872-5(6)) Zondervan.

Joseph: A Bible Story to Color. (Illus.). 16p. (J). pap. 1.50 (978-0-87162-812-1(0) , E6026) Warner Pr. Pubs.

Joseph & the Colorful Coat: A Little Story in Color. (Illus.). 16p. (J). pap. 1.50 (978-0-87162-733-9(7) , E4313) Warner Pr. Pubs.

Joseph Bible Sticker Book. 2003. (Illus.). 16p. (J). 2.98 (978-1-4054-1556-9(8)) Parragon, Inc.

Koralek, Jenny. The Coat of Many Colors. Baynes, Pauline, illus. 2004. 32p. (J). 16.00 (978-0-8028-5277-9(7)) Eerdmans, William B. Publishing Co.

Mendenhall, Cheryl, illus. Joseph & His Coat of Many Colors. 2004. 24p. (J). 2.99 (978-1-4037-0966-0(1) , Spirit Pr.) Dalmatian Pr.

Murdock, Hy. Joseph. (Bible Stories Ser.: No. S846-4). (Illus.). (J). (ps-2). 3.95 (978-0-7214-5067-4(9) , Dutton Juvenile) Penguin Group (USA) Inc.

Nakhat, Shamim. The Story of Yaqub & Yusuf: Based on Qur'anic Facts. 2005. (Me & My Holy Qur'an Ser.). (Illus.). 24p. (J). (***978-81-7231-618-1(6))*** Islamic Bk. Service.

Nederveld, Patricia L. Plenty to Eat: The Story of Joseph & His Brothers. 1998. (God Loves Me Ser.). (Illus.). 24p. (J). (ps-3). pap. 2.95 (978-1-56212-279-9(7) , 001210, Faith Alive Christian Resources) CRC Pubns.

—Two Coats for Joseph: The Story of Young Joseph. 1998. (God Loves Me Ser.). (Illus.). 24p. (J). (ps-3). pap. 2.95 (978-1-56212-278-2(9) , 001209, Faith Alive Christian Resources) CRC Pubns.

Pennington, Jack & Tank, Darrel, illus. Joseph. 2004. 87p. (J). pap. (978-0-8280-1855-5(3)) Review & Herald Publishing Assn.

Pingry, Patricia A. Joseph & the Dream: Based on Genesis 37/46:7. 2005. (Stories from the Bible Ser.). (Illus.). 26p. (J). bds. 6.95 (978-0-8249-6625-6(2)) Ideals Pubns.

PowerXpress Joseph. 9.95 incl. audio compact disk (978-0-687-09598-8(0)) Abingdon Pr.

Taylor, Damon. Forgive & Forget: The Story of Joseph. 2002. (Child Sockology Ser.). (Illus.). 32p. (J). 10.99 (978-0-8254-3856-1(X)) Kregel Pubns.

JOURNALISM

Anderson, Catherine. Newspaper. 2004. (Field Trip! Ser.). (Illus.). 24p. (J). pap. 5.50 (978-1-4034-6169-8(4)); lib. bdg. 20.64 (978-1-4034-6163-6(5)) Heinemann Library.

Doyle, Alfreda C. News Crew: Story Rhyme Coloring Book. 1998. (Illus.). 24p. (J). (gr. 3-8). pap. 8.95 (978-1-56820-326-3(8)) Story Time Stories That Rhyme.

Emmer, Rae. School Newspaper. 2002. (Reading Power Ser.). (Illus.). 24p. (J). (gr. 1). lib. bdg. 17.25 (978-0-8239-5966-2(X) , PowerKids Pr.) Rosen Publishing Group, Inc., The.

Gish, Melissa. A Newspaper Publisher. 2003. 24p. (J). lib. bdg. 21.35 (978-1-58340-324-2(8)) Smart Apple Media.

Gourley, Catherine. Media Wizards: A Behind-the-Scenes Look at Media Manipulations. 1999. (Single Titles Ser.). (Illus.). 128p. (gr. 7 up). lib. bdg. 26.90 (978-0-7613-0967-3(5) , Twenty-First Century Bks.) Lerner Publishing Group.

Hall, Homer L. High School Journalism. rev. ed. 1998. 117p. (YA). pap., stu. ed., wbk. ed. 8.94 (978-0-8239-2857-6(8)) Rosen Publishing Group, Inc., The.

Hamilton, John. Real-Time Reporting. 2004. (War in Iraq Ser.). (Illus.). 48p. (J). (gr. 4-8). lib. bdg. 25.65 (978-1-59197-497-0(6)) ABDO Publishing Co.

Jordano, Kimberly & Adsit, Kim. Jumping into Journals: Guided Journaling for Beginning Readers & Writers. Cernek, Kim, ed. Weller, Linda, illus. 2006. 112p. pap. 15.99 (978-1-59198-227-2(8) , 2229) Creative Teaching Pr., Inc.

Kokino, Olga. Journalism: Student Activities Book. Matthews, Douglas L., ed. 2003. (Illus.). stu. ed., per., wbk. ed. (978-1-931680-16-5(7) , Expert Systems for Teachers) Teaching Point, Inc.

Levin, Mark. The Reporter's Notebook: Writing Tools for Student Journalists. 2000. 100p. (J). (gr. 3-8). pap. 10.00 (978-0-9676409-0-7(3)) Mind - Stretch.

McGraw-Hill Staff. Journalism Today, Workbook. 6th ed. 2001. pap. 29.32 (978-0-658-00407-0(7) , 9780658004070) Glencoe/McGraw-Hill.

Morrison, Taylor. Civil War Artist. 2004. (Illus.). 32p. (J). (gr. k-3). pap. 5.95 (978-0-618-49538-2(X) , Walter Lorraine) Houghton Mifflin Co. Trade & Reference Div.

Pelusey, Michael & Pelusey, Jane. Newspapers (Media) 2005. (Media Ser.). (Illus.). 32p. (J). (ps-8). lib. bdg. 21.95 (978-0-7910-8800-5(6) , Chelsea Hse.) Facts On File, Inc.

Saenger, Diana. Everyone Wants My Job! The ABCs of Entertainment Writing. Fife, Bruce, ed. unabr. ed. 2003. (Writing & Publishing Ser.). (Illus.). 159p. (YA). (gr. 8-12). pap. 15.00 (978-0-941599-53-5(1)) Piccadilly Bks., Ltd.

Stay, Byron L. Mass Media. 1999. (Opposing Viewpoints Ser.). (Illus.). 203p. (YA). (gr. 10-12). pap. 21.20 (978-0-7377-0054-1(8) , Greenhaven Pr., Inc.) Thomson Gale.

Sullivan, George. Journalists at Risk: Reporting America's Wars. 2006. (People's History Ser.). (Illus.). 128p. (J). (gr. 6-9). 29.27 (978-0-7613-2745-5(2) , Twenty-First Century Bks.) Lerner Publishing Group.

JOURNALISM—FICTION

Axelrod, Amy. The News Hounds Catch a Wave: A Geography Adventure. Bowers, Tim, illus. 2001. (J). 13.00 (978-0-689-82410-4(6) , Simon & Schuster Children's Publishing) Simon & Schuster Children's Publishing.

Brenner, Barbara. Good News. Duke, Kate, illus. 1999. (Bank Street Reader Collection). 48p. (J). (ps-2). lib. bdg. 22.60 (978-0-8368-1775-1(3)) Stevens, Gareth Inc.

Brown, Don. Kid Blink Beats the World. Brown, Don, illus. rev. ed. 2004. (Illus.). 32p. (J). 16.95 (978-1-59643-003-7(6)) Roaring Brook Pr.

Clarke, Nicole. Copycat. 2007. (Flirt Ser.: No. 9). 224p. (J). (gr. 7). pap. 6.99 (978-0-448-44561-8(1) , Grosset & Dunlap) Penguin Group (USA) Inc.

—French Twist. 2007. (Flirt Ser.: Vol. 8). 224p. (YA). pap. 6.99 (978-0-448-44463-5(1) , Grosset & Dunlap) Penguin Group (USA) Inc.

—Issues. 2006. (Flirt Ser.: No. 5). 224p. (J). (gr. 7). pap. 6.99 (978-0-448-44394-2(5) , Grosset & Dunlap) Penguin Group (USA) Inc.

Clement-Moore, Rosemary. Hell Week. 2008. 336p. (YA). 16.99 (***978-0-385-73414-1(X));*** lib. bdg. 19.99 (***978-0-385-90429-2(0))*** Dell Publishing. (Delacorte Pr.).

Clements, Andrew. The Landry News. Murdocca, Sal, illus. 2002. (J). 13.40 (978-0-7587-6519-2(3)) Book Wholesalers, Inc.

—The Landry News. Selznick, Brian, illus. 2000. 144p. (J). (gr. 3-7). pap. 5.99 (978-0-689-82868-3(3) , Aladdin) Simon & Schuster Children's Publishing.

—The Landry News. 1999. (J). (978-0-606-19720-5(6)) Tandem Library Bks.

—The Landry News. l.t. ed. 2000. (Juvenile Ser.). (Illus.). 138p. (J). (gr. 4-7). 21.95 (978-0-7862-2707-5(9)) Thorndike Pr.

Clements, Andrew & Murdocca, Salvatore. The Landry News. 1999. (Illus.). 128p. (J). (gr. 3-7). 15.95 (978-0-689-81817-2(3)) Simon & Schuster Children's Publishing.

Ellerbee, Linda. Ghoul Reporter Digs up Zombies! 2000. (Get Real Ser.: No. 5). 208p. (J). (gr. 3-7). 14.89 (978-0-06-028249-3(5)); No. 5. pap. 4.99 (978-0-06-440759-5(4) , Avon) HarperCollins Pubs.

—Girl Reporter Blows Lid off Town! 2000. (Get Real Ser.: No. 1). (Illus.). 208p. (J). (gr. 3-7). 14.89 (978-0-06-028245-5(2)) HarperCollins Pubs.

—Girl Reporter Blows Lid off Town! 2000. (Get Real Ser.: No. 1). (Illus.). (J). (978-0-606-18691-9(3)) Tandem Library Bks.

—Girl Reporter Bytes Back! 2001. (Get Real Ser.: No. 8). 176p. (J). (gr. 3-7). 14.89 (978-0-06-029258-4(X)) HarperCollins Pubs.

—Girl Reporter Gets the Skinny! 2001. (Get Real Ser.: No. 7). (Illus.). 192p. (J). (gr. 3-7). 14.89 (978-0-06-029257-7(1)) HarperCollins Pubs.

—Girl Reporter Gets the Skinny! 2001. (gr. 3-6). lib. bdg. 13.00 (978-0-613-31242-4(2)) Tandem Library Bks.

—Girl Reporter Rocks Polls! 2000. (Get Real Ser.: No. 6). 224p. (J). (gr. 3-7). 14.89 (978-0-06-028250-9(9)) HarperCollins Pubs.

—Girl Reporter Sinks School! 2000. (Get Real Ser.: No. 2). (Illus.). 176p. (J). (gr. 3-7). 14.89 (978-0-06-028246-2(0)) HarperCollins Pubs.

—Girl Reporter Sinks School! 2000. (gr. 3-6). lib. bdg. 12.40 (978-0-613-21600-5(8)); (Get Real Ser.: No. 2). (Illus.). (J). (978-0-606-18692-6(1)) Tandem Library Bks.

—Girl Reporter Snags Crush! 2000. (Get Real Ser.: No. 4). (Illus.). 229p. (J). (gr. 3-7). 14.89 (978-0-06-028248-6(7)) HarperCollins Pubs.

—Girl Reporter Snags Crush! 2000. (Get Real Ser.: No. 4). (Illus.). (J). (978-0-606-18902-6(5)) Tandem Library Bks.

—Girl Reporter Stuck in Jam! 2000. (Get Real Ser.: No. 3). (Illus.). 224p. (J). (gr. 3-7). 14.89 (978-0-06-028247-9(9)) HarperCollins Pubs.

—Girl Reporter Stuck in Jam! 2000. (gr. 3-6). lib. bdg. 12.40 (978-0-613-25334-5(5)); (Get Real Ser.: No. 3). (Illus.). (J). (978-0-606-18901-9(7)) Tandem Library Bks.

Feinstein, John. Last Shot: A Final Four Mystery. 2006. 272p. (J). (gr. 6-10). reprint ed. pap. 6.50 (978-0-553-49460-0(0) , Yearling) Random Hse. Children's Bks.

—Vanishing Act. 2008. 288p. (J). (gr. 5). 6.50 (***978-0-440-42125-2(X)*** , Yearling) Random Hse. Children's Bks.

—Vanishing Act: Mystery at the U. S. Open. 2006. 288p. (J). (gr. 5). lib. bdg. 18.99 (978-0-375-93592-3(4) , Knopf Bks. for Young Readers) Random Hse. Children's Bks.

—Vanishing Act: Mystery at the U.S. Open. 2006. 288p. (J). (gr. 5). 16.95 (978-0-375-83592-6(X) , Knopf Bks. for Young Readers) Random Hse. Children's Bks.

Frampton, David. Beastie ABC. Frampton, David, illus. Date not set. (Illus.). 32p. (J). (ps-1). pap. 5.99 (978-0-06-443653-5(5)) HarperCollins Pubs.

—My Beastie Book of ABC. Frampton, David, illus. 2002. (Illus.). 32p. (J). (ps-1). 15.89 (978-0-06-028824-2(8)) HarperCollins Pubs.

Gaberman, Judith. First the Good News. 2001. 164p. pap. 11.95 (978-0-595-15835-5(8) , Backinprint.com) iUniverse, Inc.

Garden, Nancy. The Year They Burned the Books. 1999. 256p. (YA). (gr. 7-12). 17.00 (978-0-374-38667-2(6) , Farrar, Straus & Giroux (BYR)) Farrar, Straus & Giroux.

Givner, Joan. Ellen Fremedon: Journalist. 2005. 192p. (ps-7). 15.95 (978-0-88899-668-8(3)) Groundwood Bks. CAN. *Dist:* Perseus Distribution.

Harcourt School Publishers Staff. Stop the Presses: Take-Home Book. 1999. (Collections Ser.). (Illus.). (J). (gr. 3). pap. 1.90 (978-0-15-317267-0(3)) Harcourt Schl. Pubs.

Hazen, Lynn E. Buzz Bumble to the Rescue. Newton, Jill, illus. 2005. 32p. (J). 15.95 (978-1-58234-932-9(0) , Bloomsbury Children) Bloomsbury Publishing.

Hogan, Mary. Susanna Hits Hollywood. 2008. (YA). (***978-0-385-73514-8(6));*** 256p. lib. bdg. (***978-0-385-90503-9(3))*** Dell Publishing. (Delacorte Pr.).

—Susanna Sees Stars. 2007. 256p. (YA). (gr. 7). pap. 7.99 (***978-0-385-73513-1(8));*** lib. bdg. 10.99 (***978-0-385-90502-2(5))*** Random Hse. Children's Bks. (Delacorte Bks. for Young Readers).

Hutchins, Hazel J. Robyn Makes the News. Cathcart, Yvonne, illus. 2003. (First Novel Ser.). 64p. (J). (gr. 1-5). 4.95 (978-0-88780-593-6(0)) Formac Publishing Co., Ltd. CAN. *Dist:* Casemate Pubs. & Bk. Distributors, LLC.

Mackall, Dandi Daley. Grace under Pressure. 2007. (Faithgirlz!#8482; / Blog On! Ser.). 128p. (J). pap. 6.99 (978-0-310-71263-3(7)) Zonderkidz.

Marsh, Carole. The Adventure Diaries of P. J., the Photo-Journalist! l.t. ed. 2002. (Illus.). 48p. (J). lib. bdg. 9.95 (978-0-635-01279-1(0)) Gallopade International.

Mazer, Anne. The Pen Is Mightier Than the Sword. Gesue, Monica, illus. 2001. (Amazing Days of Abby Hayes Ser.: No. 6). 128p. (J). (gr. 4-7). pap. 4.99 (978-0-439-17882-2(7)) Scholastic, Inc.

Messina, Lynn. Savvy Girl. 2008. (Illus.). 256p. (YA). pap. 7.95 (***978-0-15-206161-6(4)*** , Harcourt Paperbacks) Harcourt Children's Bks.

Pratchett, Terry. The Truth. 2001. (gr. 5-8). lib. bdg. 15.30 (978-0-613-57290-3(4)) Tandem Library Bks.

Stilton, Geronimo. All Because of a Cup of Coffee. 2004. (Geronimo Stilton Ser.: No. 10). (Illus.). 112p. (J). (gr. 2-5). lib. bdg. 13.94 (978-0-606-33273-6(1)) Tandem Library Bks.

—The Curse of the Cheese Pyramid. Wolf, Matt, illus. 2004. (Geronimo Stilton Ser.: No. 2). 113p. (J). lib. bdg. 10.00 (***978-1-4242-0696-4(0))*** Fitzgerald Bks.

—I'm Too Fond of My Fur! Wolf, Matt, illus. 2004. (Geronimo Stilton Ser.: No. 4). 116p. (J). lib. bdg. 10.00 (***978-1-4242-0698-8(7))*** Fitzgerald Bks.

—It's Halloween, You 'Fraidy Mouse! Wolf, Matt, illus. 2004. 113p. (J). lib. bdg. 10.00 (***978-1-4242-0280-5(9))*** Fitzgerald Bks.

—It's Halloween, You 'Fraidy Mouse! 2004. (Geronimo Stilton Ser.: No. 11). (Illus.). 113p. (J). (gr. 2-5). lib. bdg. 13.94 (978-0-606-33274-3(X)) Tandem Library Bks.

—Lost Treasure of the Emerald Eye. Wolf, Matt, illus. 2004. (Geronimo Stilton Ser.: No. 1). 116p. (J). lib. bdg. 10.00 (***978-1-4242-0695-7(2))*** Fitzgerald Bks.

—The Mona Mousa Code. Wolf, Matt, illus. 2005. (Geronimo Stilton Ser.: No. 15). 113p. (J). lib. bdg. 10.00 (***978-1-4242-0284-3(1))*** Fitzgerald Bks.

—The Mona Mousa Code. Wolf, Matt, illus. 2005. (Geronimo Stilton Ser.: No. 15). 113p. (J). (ps-k). lib. bdg. 13.54 (978-0-606-33278-1(2)) Tandem Library Bks.

—The Phantom of the Subway. Wolf, Matt, illus. 2004. (Geronimo Stilton Ser.: No. 13). 112p. (J). lib. bdg. 10.00 (***978-1-4242-0282-9(5))*** Fitzgerald Bks.

—The Phantom of the Subway. 2004. (Geronimo Stilton Ser.: No. 13). (Illus.). 112p. (J). (gr. 2-5). lib. bdg. 13.94 (978-0-606-33276-7(6)) Tandem Library Bks.

—Valentine's Day Disaster. Keys, Larry et al, illus. 2006. (Geronimo Stilton Ser.: No. 23). 122p. (J). lib. bdg. 18.46 (***978-1-4242-0292-8(2))*** Fitzgerald Bks.

—Watch Your Whiskers, Stilton! 2005. (Geronimo Stilton Ser.: No. 17). (Illus.). 111p. (J). (gr. 2-5). lib. bdg. 13.94 (978-0-606-33292-7(8)) Tandem Library Bks.

Stilton, Geronimo. The Wild, Wild West. Stilton, Geronimo et al, illus. 2005. (Geronimo Stilton Ser.: No. 21). 121p. (J). lib. bdg. 18.46 (***978-1-4242-0290-4(6))*** Fitzgerald Bks.

Stilton, Geronimo, text. A Cheese-Colored Camper. 2005. (Geronimo Stilton Ser.: No. 16). (Illus.). 111p. (J). (ps-k). lib. bdg. 12.64 (978-0-606-33281-1(2)) Tandem Library Bks.

Trembath, Don. Popsicle Journal. 2002. (gr. 7-12). lib. bdg. 15.25 (978-0-613-88505-8(8)) Tandem Library Bks.

Wallace, Rich. One Good Punch. 2007. 128p. (YA). (gr. 7). 15.99 (***978-0-375-81352-8(7));*** lib. bdg. 18.99 (***978-0-375-91352-5(1))*** Random Hse. Children's Bks. (Knopf Bks. for Young Readers).

Whybrow, Ian. Dear Little Wolf. Ross, Tony, illus. 2005. (Little Wolf Adventures Ser.). 64p. (gr. 3-6). pap., lib. bdg. 14.95 (978-0-87614-902-7(6)) Lerner Publishing Group.

Winerip, Michael. Adam Canfield of the Slash. 2005. (Adam Canfield of the Slash Ser.). 336p. (J). (gr. 3-7). 15.99 (978-0-7636-2340-1(7)) Candlewick Pr.

Winston, Sherri. Kayla Chronicles. 2008. 208p. (YA). (gr. 7-17). 16.99 (***978-0-316-11430-1(8))*** Little, Brown Bks. for Young Readers.

JOURNALISM—UNITED STATES

Bausum, Ann. Muckrakers: How Writers Exposed Scandal, Inspired Reform, & Invented Investigative Journalism. 2007. (Illus.). 112p. (YA). (gr. 5 up). 21.95 (***978-1-4263-0137-7(5));*** lib. bdg. 32.90 (***978-1-4263-0138-4(3))*** National Geographic Society. (National Geographic Children's Bks.).

Cohen, Daniel. Yellow Journalism: Scandal, Sensationalism, & Gossip in the Media. 2000. (Single Titles Ser.: up). (Illus.). 128p. (gr. 7 up). lib. bdg. (978-0-7613-1502-5(0) , Millbrook Pr.) Lerner Publishing Group.

Lange, Ellen. Writing Clearly: An Editing Guide. 2nd ed. 1999. (Illus.). 275p. (J). pap. 39.95 (978-0-8384-0949-7(0)) Thomson Heinle.

JOURNALISM—VOCATIONAL GUIDANCE

Alagna, Magdalena. War Correspondents: Life under Fire. 2005. (Extreme Careers Ser.). (Illus.). 64p. (YA). (gr. 5-8). 26.50 (978-0-8239-3798-1(4)) Rosen Publishing Group, Inc., The.

Bonnice, Sherry. Journalist. 2002. (Careers with Character Ser.). (Illus.). 96p. (YA). (gr. 7 up). (978-1-59084-316-1(9)) Mason Crest Pubs.

Ferguson. Careers in Focus: Newspapers. 2007. (Careers in Focus Ser.). 192p. (gr. 6-12). 29.95 (***978-0-8160-6573-8(X)*** , Ferguson Publishing Co.) Facts On File, Inc.

Heidrich, Delana S. Create a Magazine, Grades 5-8: A Complete Framework for Students to Use in Creating an Original Magazine. Armstrong, Beverly, illus. 1999. 88p. pap., tchr. ed. 11.99 (978-0-88160-310-1(4) , LW-379, Learning Works, The) Creative Teaching Pr., Inc.

Parks, Peggy J. News Media. 2002. (Careers for the Twenty-First Century Ser.). (Illus.). 104p. (J). 27.45 (978-1-59018-205-5(7) , LML00902-182128, Lucent Bks.) Thomson Gale.

Seidman, David L. Careers in Journalism. 2005. (Careers Ser.). (Illus.). 192p. (J). (gr. 7-12). lib. bdg. 26.50 (978-0-8239-3298-6(2) , CAJOUR) Rosen Publishing Group, Inc., The.

JOURNALISTIC PHOTOGRAPHY

see Photojournalism

JOURNALISTS

African-American Journalists. 2000. (My Ancestors—My Heroes Ser.: Vol. 17). (J). (gr. 3-4). (978-1-893091-16-0(3)) Parker Publishing Co.

Bowman-Kruhm, Mary & Wirths, Claudine G. A Day in the Life of a Newspaper Reporter. 1999. (Kids' Career Library). (Illus.). 24p. (J). (gr. 3). lib. bdg. 18.75 (978-0-8239-5306-6(8) , PowerKids Pr.) Rosen Publishing Group, Inc., The.

Christensen, Bonnie. The Daring Nellie Bly: America's Star Reporter. Christensen, Bonnie, illus. 2003. (Illus.). 32p. (J). (gr. 1-7). 16.95 (978-0-375-81568-3(6) , Knopf Bks. for Young Readers) Random Hse. Children's Bks.

—The Daring Nellie Bly: America's Star Reporter. 2003. (Illus.). 32p. (J). (gr. 1-7). lib. bdg. 18.99 (978-0-375-91568-0(0) , Knopf Bks. for Young Readers) Random Hse. Children's Bks.

Dublin, Anne. June Callwood: A Life of Action. 2006. (Illus.). 140p. pap. 12.95 (978-1-897187-14-2(9)) Second Story Pr. CAN. *Dist:* Orca Bk. Pubs. USA.

Fradin, Dennis Brindell & Fradin, Judith Bloom. Ida B. Wells: Mother of the Civil Rights Movement. 2000. (Illus.). 192p. (J). (gr. 5-9). tchr. ed. 19.00 (978-0-395-89898-7(6) , Clarion Bks.) Houghton Mifflin Co. Trade & Reference Div.

Gallop-Goodman, Gerda. Diane Sawyer. 2001. (Women of Achievement Ser.). (Illus.). (J). 108p. pap. 30.00 (978-0-7910-6317-0(8)); 112p. 30.00 (978-0-7910-6316-3(X)) Facts On File, Inc. (Chelsea Hse.).

—Diane Sawyer. 2002. (gr. 5-8). lib. bdg. 18.75 (978-0-613-50889-6(0)) Tandem Library Bks.

H G Wells, hombre del Futuro 10: Leveled Books. 2001. (McGraw-Hill. Lectura Ser.). (ENG & SPA.). (gr. 4 up). (978-0-02-188210-6(X)) Macmillan/McGraw-Hill Schl. Div.

Horner, Matina S., intro. Barbara Walters: Journalist. 1999. (Women of Achievement Ser.). (Illus.). 112p. (gr. 4-7). (J). pap. 9.95 (978-0-7910-4717-0(2)); (YA). 21.95 (978-0-7910-4716-3(4)) Facts On File, Inc. (Chelsea Hse.).

Lemieux, Carlotta & Hacker, Carlotta. E. Cora Hind. (Illus.). 64p. (J). (gr. 5 up). pap. (978-1-55041-834-7(3)) Fitzhenry & Whiteside, Ltd.

Moore, Heidi. Ida B. Wells-Barnett. 2004. (Illus.). 32p. (J). pap. 6.95 (978-1-4034-5706-6(9)); lib. bdg. (978-1-4034-4997-9(X)) Heinemann Library.

Pascal, Janet B. Jacob Riis: Reporter & Reformer. 2005. (Oxford Portraits Ser.). (Illus.). 176p. (YA). 28.00 (978-0-19-514527-4(5)) Oxford Univ. Pr., Inc.

Pingelton, Timothy J. A Student's Guide to Ernest Hemingway. 2005. (Understanding Literature Ser.). (Illus.). 160p. (YA). (gr. 7-13). lib. bdg. 27.93 (978-0-7660-2431-1(8)) Enslow Pubs., Inc.

Satter, James. Journalists Who Made History. 1998. (Profiles Ser.). (Illus.). 160p. (gr. 5 up). lib. bdg. 19.95 (978-1-881508-39-7(0)) Oliver Pr., Inc.

Saverwein, Stan. Ma Murray: The Story of Canada's Crusty Queen of Publishing. 2003. (Amazing Stories Ser.). (Illus.). 144p. pap. (978-1-55153-979-9(9)) Altitude Publishing Canada Ltd.

Skog, Jason. Yellow Journalism. 2006. (J). lib. bdg. (978-0-7565-2456-2(3)) Compass Point Bks.

Somervill, Barbara A. Ida Tarbell: Pioneer Investigative Reporter. 2004. (World Writers Ser.). (Illus.). 112p. (YA). (gr. 6-12). 23.95 (978-1-883846-87-9(0) , First Biographies) Reynolds, Morgan Inc.

Whitelaw, Nancy. Joseph Pulitzer & the New York World. rev. exp. ed. 2004. (Makers of the Media Ser.). (Illus.). 128p. (J). lib. bdg. 21.95 (978-1-931798-36-5(2)) Reynolds, Morgan Inc.

JOURNEYS

see Voyages and Travels; Voyages around the World

JUAREZ, BENITO, 1806-1872

Ada, Alma Flor & Campoy, F. Isabel, contrib. by. Sonrisas. (Literature Collection of Puertas Al Sol Ser.). (SPA.). 32p. (J). (gr. k-6). pap. 13.95 (978-1-59437-701-3(4)) Santillana USA Publishing Co., Inc.

Kaplan, Leslie. Cinco de Mayo. 2004. (Library of Holidays). (Illus.). 24p. (J). lib. bdg. 18.75 (978-0-8239-6662-2(3) , PowerKids Pr.) Rosen Publishing Group, Inc., The.

MacMillan, Dianne M. Mexican Independence Day & Cinco de Mayo. 2nd ed. 2008. (Best Holiday Books Ser.). 48p. (J). (gr. 3-4). lib. bdg. 23.93 ***(*978-0-7660-3044-2(X))*** Enslow Pubs., Inc.

Smiles: Pablo Picasso, Gabriela Mistral, Benito Juarez. 2001. (Gateways to the Sun Ser.). (Illus.). (J). (gr. k-1). pap. 10.95 (978-1-58105-570-2(6)) Santillana USA Publishing Co., Inc.

JUDAISM

see also Jews; Sabbath; Synagogues

Abraham, Michelle Shapiro. The Be a Mensch Campaign. 2004. (gr. 4-6). stu. ed. 5.95 (978-0-8074-0743-1(7) , 571206); pap., tchr. ed., tchr.'s training gde. ed. 12.00 (978-0-8074-0745-5(3) , 208056) URJ Pr.

Abrams, Judith Z. The Secret World of Kabbalah. 2006. (Illus.). 80p. (YA). (gr. 5-9). pap. 9.95 (978-1-58013-224-4(3)) Kar-Ben Publishing.

Adam Woog. Jew. 2004. (What Makes Me a — ? Ser.). (Illus.). 48p. (J). 26.20 (978-0-7377-2266-6(5) , Kidhaven) Thomson Gale.

Adelman, Penina, et al. The JGirl's Guide: The Young Jewish Woman's Handbook for Coming of Age. 2005. 240p. (J). pap. 14.99 (978-1-58023-215-9(9)) Jewish Lights Publishing.

Apelbaum, Shiffy. Moshe Mendel the Mitzva Maven & the Wonderful World of Berachos. 2000. (Illus.). (J). 16.99 (978-1-58330-453-2(3)) Feldheim Pubs.

Atkinson, Kenneth. Judaism. 2004. (Religions of the World Ser.). (Illus.). 150p. (gr. 9-13). 35.00 (978-0-7910-7860-0(4) , Chelsea Hse.) Facts On File, Inc.

Auerbach, Annie. Eight Chanukah Lights. Iwai, Melissa, illus. 2005. 18p. (J). 10.95 (978-1-58117-326-0(1) , Intervisual/Piggy Toes) Dalmatian Pr.

Bamberger, David & Bedor, Deborah. Judaism & the World's Religions. (J). (gr. 7-8). pap. 9.95 (978-0-87441-461-5(X)) Behrman Hse., Inc.

Barnes, Trevor. Judaism: Worship, Festivals, & Ceremonies from Around the World. Kingfisher Editors, ed. 2005. (World Faiths Ser.). (Illus.). 40p. (J). (gr. 5-9). pap., pap. 6.95 (978-0-7534-5883-9(7) , Kingfisher) Houghton Mifflin Co. Trade & Reference Div.

Barron, Sharon. Moses & Judaism. 2002. (Great Religious Leaders Ser.). (Illus.). 48p. (J). lib. bdg. 28.50 (978-1-58340-219-1(5)) Smart Apple Media.

Berg, Yehuda & Belmont, Louis. The Power of Kabbalah for Teens. 2005. (Illus.). 224p. pap. 13.95 (978-0-8065-2588-4(6) , Citadel Pr.) Kensington Publishing Corp.

Berkson, Marc & VanDusen, Susan. The Synagogue: House of the Jewish People. Collins, Matt, illus. 1999. 96p. (J). (gr. 3-5). pap. 5.95 (978-0-87441-664-0(7)) Behrman Hse., Inc.

Big Berel Outsmarts a Robber. 2000. (J). 7.00 (978-0-930213-69-5(6)) Breslov Research Institute.

Blitz, Shmuel & Katz, Tova. Hagadah Shel Pesaho: The ArtScroll Children's Haggadah. 2000. (ArtScroll Ser.). (Illus.). 96p. (J). 16.99 (978-1-57819-136-9(X) , HCHH); pap. 10.99 (978-1-57819-137-6(8) , HCHP) Mesorah Pubns., Ltd.

Bosch, Nicole in den, illus. Let's Ask Four Questions: "Why Is This Night Different?" 2000. 12p. (J). (ps up). 4.95 (978-1-58013-071-4(2)) Kar-Ben Publishing.

Cahn, Yehuda. It's the Effort That Counts. Shiman, Hedy, illus. 2001. (J). pap. (978-0-9707757-0-2(9)) Torah Pubn. Fund.

Cardin, Nina Beth & Blumenthal, Scott. The Time of Our Lives: A Teen Guide to the Jewish Life Cycle. 2002. (Illus.). 95p. (J). 8.95 (978-0-87441-718-0(X)) Behrman Hse., Inc.

Cato, Vivienne. The Torah & Judaism. 2003. 30p. (J). lib. bdg. 16.95 (978-1-58340-244-3(6)) Smart Apple Media.

Chaikin, Miriam. Angels Sweep the Desert Floor: Bible Legends about Moses in the Wilderness. Koshkin, Alexander, illus. 2002. 112p. (J). (gr. 3-5). 19.00 (978-0-395-97825-2(4) , Clarion Bks.) Houghton Mifflin Co. Trade & Reference Div.

—Menorahs, Mezuzas, & Other Jewish Symbols. Weihs, Erika, illus. 2003. 112p. (J). (gr. 5-6). pap. 5.95 (978-0-618-37835-7(9) , Clarion Bks.) Houghton Mifflin Co. Trade & Reference Div.

—Menorahs, Mezuzas, & Other Jewish Symbols. 2003. (gr. 3-6). lib. bdg. 14.10 (978-0-613-73018-1(6)) Tandem Library Bks.

Chait, Baruch. The Terrifying Trap of the Bad Middos Pirates, 2 vols. Pollack, Gadi, illus. (Good Middos Ser.). 96p. 25.99 (978-1-58330-664-2(1)) Feldheim Pubs.

Chwast, Seymour, illus. Had Gadya: A Passover Song. rev. ed. 2007. 32p. (J). pap. 7.95 ***(*978-1-59643-298-7(5))*** Roaring Brook Pr.

Cisner, Naftali. Get Ready for Shabbos with Mendel. Cisner, Naftali, illus. 2003. (Illus.). 10p. (J). bds. 5.95 (978-1-880582-03-9(1)) Judaica Pr., Inc., The.

Clark, Anne. My Jewish Faith. 2006. (World Faiths Ser.). (Illus.). 31p. (J). (978-1-84234-389-0(0) , Cherrytree Books) Evans Publishing Group.

—My Jewish Faith. 1998. (My Faith Ser.). (Illus.). 32p. 7.99 (978-0-237-51897-4(X) , Evans Brothers, Limited) Evans Publishing Group GBR. *Dist:* Independent Pubs. Group.

Clement, Janet. The Jewish Alphabet. Rodriguez, Albert G., illus. 2006. 32p. (J). 15.95 (978-1-58980-414-2(7)) Pelican Publishing Co., Inc.

Cohn, Janice. The Christmas Menorahs: How a Town Fought Hate. Farnsworth, Bill, illus. 2004. 40p. (J). (gr. 2-6). pap. 6.95 (978-0-8075-1153-4(6)) Whitman, Albert & Co.

Cone, Molly. Hello, Hello, Are You There, God? Kaye, Rosalind Charney, illus. rev. ed. 2004. viii, 55p. (gr. k-3). pap. 12.95 (978-0-8074-0648-9(1) , 102553) URJ Pr.

Cook, Esky. Jewish Artwork by Esky: Children, Borders, Hebrew Alphabets. (Illus.). 128p. (Orig.). (J). (gr. 1-8). pap. 19.95 (978-1-885143-02-0(8)) Preferred Enterprises.

—Jewish Artwork by Esky: Complete Set of Jewish Graphics. (Illus.). 384p. (Orig.). (J). (gr. 1-8). pap. 59.95 (978-1-885143-00-6(1)) Preferred Enterprises.

—Jewish Artwork by Esky: Mitzvot, Animals, Food & Brachot. Whitman, Jonathan, ed. (Illus.). 128p. (Orig.). (J). (gr. 1-8). pap. 19.95 (978-1-885143-03-7(6)) Preferred Enterprises.

Corona, Laurel. Judaism. 2003. (Religions of the World Ser.). (Illus.). 128p. (J). 29.95 (978-1-56006-987-4(2) , Lucent Bks.) Thomson Gale.

Danny Sees Double. 2000. (J). 7.00 (978-0-930213-73-2(4)) Breslov Research Institute.

Dick, Judy. The Seder Activity Book. Dick, Judy, illus. 2004. (Illus.). 39p. (gr. k-3). pap., act. bk. ed. 9.95 (978-0-8074-0728-8(3) , 101097) URJ Pr.

Diner, Hasia. Jews in America. 1998. (Religion in America Ser.). (Illus.). 160p. (YA). (gr. 6 up). 30.00 (978-0-19-510678-7(4)) Oxford Univ. Pr., Inc.

Dorling Kindersley Publishing Staff. Judaism. 2003. (Eyewitness Bks.). (Illus.). 64p. (J). (gr. 3). lib. bdg. 19.99 (978-0-7894-9548-8(1)) Dorling Kindersley Publishing, Inc.

—Shabbat. 2005. (Ultimate sticker Bks.). 16p. (J). pap. 6.99 (978-0-7566-0982-5(8)) Dorling Kindersley Publishing, Inc.

Dorling Kindersley Publishing Staff & Charing, Douglas. Judaism. 2003. (Eyewitness Bks.). (Illus.). 64p. (J). pap. 15.99 (978-0-7894-9240-1(7)) Dorling Kindersley Publishing, Inc.

Dowley, Tim. The Kregel Pictorial Guide to the Tabernacle. 2003. (Kregel Pictorial Guide Ser.). (Illus.). 32p. pap. 8.99 (978-0-8254-2468-7(2)) Kregel Pubns.

Feuerman, Simcha. The Family Sefer Hachinuch. 2002. (Illus.). (J). pap. 30.00 (978-0-7657-6181-1(5)) Rowman & Littlefield Pubs., Inc.

Fish, Dorothy & Cohen, Betty. Matzah's Favorite Thing. 1998. (Illus.). 20p. (J). (ps-3). spiral bd. 5.99 (978-0-914080-09-1(1)) Shulsinger Sales, Inc.

Friedman, Rachel. Al-Horishonim: Judaic History for Children. Weiner, Goldy, ed. Weiss, Jacob, illus. Wertzberger, C. N., photos by. unabr. ed. 1999. (YID.). 128p. (J). (gr. 7-9). 30.00 (978-0-9677313-0-8(5)); pap. 15.00 (978-0-9677313-1-5(3)) Friedman, Yuda.

Friedman, Rifka. The Yarmulke, Kippah, Coppel Book. Friedman, Rifka, illus. 1998. (Illus.). (J). (ps-k). 9.95 (978-0-922613-87-8(7)) Hachai Publishing.

Fritz Loses His Wits. 2000. (J). 7.00 (978-0-930213-45-9(9)) Breslov Research Institute.

Fuchs, Menucha. Middos: Stories for Children. Miri, illus. 2000. (Children's Learning Ser.: Vol. 14). (J). (ps-5). pap. 4.95 (978-1-880582-64-0(3)) Judaica Pr., Inc., The.

—Stories about Rosh Hashanah & Yom Kippur. Chana, illus. 2000. (Children's Learning Ser.: Vol. 12). 48p. (J). (ps-5). pap. 4.95 (978-1-880582-65-7(1)) Judaica Pr., Inc., The.

—Sukkos with the Cohen Family. Chana, illus. 2000. (Children's Learning Ser.: Vol. 13). 48p. (J). (ps-5). pap. 4.95 (978-1-880582-69-5(4)) Judaica Pr., Inc., The.

Ganeri, Anita. Jewish Stories. Phillips, Rachael, illus. 2001. (Storyteller Ser.). 30p. (YA). 22.00 (978-0-237-52033-5(8) , Evans Brothers, Limited) Evans Publishing Group GBR. *Dist:* Independent Pubs. Group.

—Judaism. 2006. (This Is My Faith Bks.). (Illus.). 32p. (J). (gr. 1-4). pap. 4.99 (978-0-7641-3476-0(0)); 11.99 (978-0-7641-5967-1(4)) Barron's Educational Series, Inc.

Ganz, Yaffa. Lag Ba'omer & Tu Bishvat with Bina, Benny, & Chaggai Hayonah. 1999. 27p. 9.99 (978-1-57819-155-0(6) , YTUB) Mesorah Pubns., Ltd.

Gevirtz, Gila. Count Me In: Jewish Wisdom in Action. 2005. (J). (978-0-87441-194-2(7)) Behrman Hse., Inc.

Ginsburgh, Judy. My Jewish World: Songs for Jewish Learning, Vol. 2. 2004. 288p. (gr. k-3). pap. 39.95 (978-0-8074-0822-3(0) , 993250) URJ Pr.

Glazer, Devorah. A Touch of the High Holidays: A Touch & Feel Book. Seva, illus. 2006. 16p. (J). bds. 7.95 (978-0-8266-0020-2(4)) Merkos L'Inyonei Chinuch.

Gold, Avie. Pirkei Avos, Vol. 2. Horen, Michael & Halasz, Andras, illus. (J). pap. 12.99 (978-0-89906-199-3(0) , PIYP) Mesorah Pubns., Ltd.

Gold-Vukson, Marji. The Colors of My Jewish Year. Wikler, Madeline, illus. 1998. 12p. (J). (ps-1). bds. (978-1-58013-011-0(9)) Kar-Ben Publishing.

Goldin, Barbara Diamond. The Hebrew Months Tell Their Story. 2000. (Doodle Family Ser.). (Illus.). 48p. (gr. k-5). 16.95 (978-1-930143-04-3(4)); pap. 9.95 (978-1-930143-05-0(2)) Pitspopany Pr.

Goldner, Harriet. Please, Don't Pass over the Seder Plate: A Haggadah for the Young & Young-at-Heart. 2006. (978-0-9779676-0-5(3)) Goldner, Harriet LLC.

Goldstein, Jessica, ed. Tower of Babel. Racklin-Siegel, Carol, illus. 2001. 32p. (J). per. 9.95 (978-0-939144-35-8(2)) EKS Publishing Co.

Gorsky, Jonathan & Ganeri, Anita. Jewish Prayer & Worship. 2007. (J). ***(*978-1-59771-092-3(X))*** Sea-To-Sea Pubns.

Graham, Ian. Judaism. (Illus.). 64p. (YA). (gr. 4 up). lib. bdg. 29.95 (978-1-59389-132-9(6)) Chrysalis Education.

—Judaism. 2005. (World Religions Ser.). (Illus.). 58p. (J). (gr. 4-12). pap. 12.95 (978-1-55285-656-7(9) , Walrus Bks.) Whitecap Bks., Ltd. CAN. *Dist:* Firefly Bks., Ltd.

Greenbaum, Iris & Radousky, Judith, eds. Siddur Shabat B'Yachad: A Child's First Siddur. Bearson, Lee, illus. 2001. 32p. (J). pap. 4.50 (978-0-939144-36-5(0)) EKS Publishing Co.

Greenbaum, Judith & Radousky, Judith, eds. Shabbat B'Yachad Leader's Guide. Bearson, Lee, illus. 2001. 40p. (J). pap. 13.95 incl. audio compact disk (978-0-939144-37-2(9)) EKS Publishing Co.

Greenberg, Sidney & Silverman, Morris. Siddurenu. (J). (gr. 3-7). 8.95 (978-0-87677-099-3(5)) Prayer Bk. Pr., Inc.

Groffman, Simcha. Simcha's Torah Stories: The Weekly Parashah with Chaim, Av & You! 2000. (Illus.). 207p. (J). (gr. 3-12). 17.99 (978-1-56871-119-5(0)) Targum Pr., Inc.

Groner, Judyth. Thank You, God! A Jewish Child's Book of Prayers. Wikler, Madeline, illus. 2003. 32p. (J). (ps-2). pap. 6.95 (978-1-58013-101-8(8)) Kar-Ben Publishing.

Groner, Judyth Saypol & Wikler, Madeline. Come, Let Us Welcome Shabbat: A Joyful Celebration for Families. Wikler, Madeline, illus. rev. ed. 2000. (HEB., Illus.). 32p. (J). (gr. 5-12). pap. 4.95 (978-1-58013-012-7(7)) Kar-Ben Publishing.

Halper, Sharon. To Learn Is to Do: A Tikkun Olam Road Map. Koffsky, Ann D., illus. 2004. vi, 56p. (gr. 4-6). pap. 8.95 (978-0-8074-0729-5(1) , 123935) URJ Pr.

Hartney, Chris, et al. Livewire Investigates Judaism. 2004. (Livewires Ser.). (Illus.). 32p. pap. 4.10 (978-0-521-60112-2(6)) Cambridge Univ. Pr.

Hipps, Amelia. Islam, Christianity, Judaism. 2003. (Introducing Islam Ser.). (Illus.). 112p. (J). lib. bdg. (978-1-59084-698-8(2)) Mason Crest Pubs.

Hoffman, Edward. My Bar/Bat Mitzvah: A Memory & Keepsake Journal. Wells, Leigh, illus. 2005. 114p. (gr. 7-9). spiral bd. 19.95 (978-0-8118-4594-6(X)) Chronicle Bks. LLC.

Horen, Michael, illus. My Blessings for Food. 2003. (ArtScroll Ser.). (ENG, ARC & HEB.). (J). 49.99 (978-0-89906-702-5(6) , TCH3) Mesorah Pubns., Ltd.

Howland, Naomi. The Matzah Man: A Passover Story. 2002. (Illus.). 32p. (J). (gr. k-3). 16.00 (978-0-618-11750-5(4) , Clarion Bks.) Houghton Mifflin Co. Trade & Reference Div.

Hughes, Monica. My Rosh Hashanah. 2003. (Festivals Ser.). (Illus.). 24p. (J). pap. 5.50 (978-1-4109-0667-0(1)) Raintree.

—My Rosh Hashanah. 2003. (ps-2). lib. bdg. 13.55 (978-0-613-78203-6(8)) Tandem Library Bks.

Kaplan, Nochem. Daily Halachos. 2002. (Halichos Yisroel Dinim Workbook Ser.: Pt. 1). (HEB.). (gr. 6 up). 12.00 (978-1-878895-13-4(3) , A105) Torah Umesorah Pubns.

—The Laws of Shabbos, Sefer Torah, Tefillin, Mezuzah & Mitzvos Bein Adam L'Chaveiroh, Vol. 2. 2002. (Halichos Yisroel Dinim Workbook Ser.: Pt. II). (HEB.). (gr. 6 up). 12.00 (978-1-878895-14-1(1) , A106) Torah Umesorah Pubns.

Karesh, Sara & Hurvitz, Mitchell. Encyclopedia of Judaism. 2008. (Encyclopedia of World Religions Ser.). 64p. (gr. 9). pap. 9.95 ***(*978-0-8160-7337-5(6)*** , Checkmark Bks.) Facts On File, Inc.

Katz, Karen A., et al. What Does Being Jewish Mean? Read-Aloud Responses to Questions Jewish Children Ask about History, Culture, & Religion. 2003. 160p. pap. 11.00 (978-0-7432-5413-7(9) , Fireside) Simon & Schuster.

Keene, Michael. Judaism. 2005. (Illus.). 48p. (J). pap. (978-0-8368-5875-4(1)); lib. bdg. 30.00 (978-0-8368-5869-3(7)) Stevens, Gareth Inc. (World Almanac Library).

Kimmel, Eric A. Bar Mitzvah: A Jewish Boy's Coming of Age. Weihs, Erika, illus. 2004. 143p. (J). (gr. 6-9). reprint ed. pap. 15.00 (978-0-7567-7261-1(3)) DIANE Publishing Co.

—Wonders & Miracles: A Passover Companion. 2004. (Wonders & Miracles Ser.). (Illus.). 144p. (J). pap. 18.95 (978-0-439-07175-8(5)) Scholastic, Inc.

Kimmelman, Leslie. Dance, Sing, Remember: A Celebration of Jewish Holidays. Eitan, Ora, illus. 2000. 48p. (J). (ps-3). 18.99 (978-0-06-027725-3(4)) HarperCollins Pubs.

Kripke, Dorothy Karp. Let's Talk about God. Tripp, Christine, tr. Tripp, Christine, illus. 2003. (J). 9.95 (978-1-881283-34-8(8)) Alef Design Group.

Kurtz, Joan. Around & Around: Jewish Lifecycle Ceremonies. 1999. (Illus.). (J). pap. 8.00 (978-1-891877-03-2(8)) Sheron Enterprises, Inc.

Laurel Corona. Jewish Americans. 2004. (Immigrants in America Ser.). (Illus.). 112p. (J). 29.95 (978-1-59018-431-8(9)) Thomson Gale.

Lehman-Wilzig, Tami. Keeping the Promise: A Torah's Journey. Orback, Craig, illus. 2004. 32p. (J). (gr. 1-5). 16.95 (978-1-58013-117-9(4)); pap. 6.95 (978-1-58013-118-6(2)) Kar-Ben Publishing.

Lieberman, M. Coloring Books on Events of the Jewish Months: Iyar, Sivan, Tamuz, Av, Elul. 2002. (Learn As You Color Series 2). 6.00 (978-0-914131-87-8(7)) Torah Umesorah Pubns.

—Coloring Books on the Parshas Hashavua: Bamidbar. 2002. (Learn As You Color Ser.). 6.00 (978-0-914131-82-3(6) , D703) Torah Umesorah Pubns.

Manushkin, Fran. Come, Let Us Be Joyful! The Story of Hava Nagila. Kaye, Rosalind Charney, illus. 2004. (gr. k-3). 13.95 (978-0-8074-0731-8(3) , 101073) URJ Pr.

The Merchant of Breslov. 2000. (J). 7.00 (978-0-930213-70-1(X)) Breslov Research Institute.

Metter, Bertram. Bar Mitzvah, Bat Mitzvah: The Ceremony, the Party, & How the Day Came to Be. Reilly, Joan, illus. 2007. 80p. (J). (gr. 5-9). 15.00 ***(*978-0-618-76772-4(X)*** , Clarion Bks.) Houghton Mifflin Co. Trade & Reference Div.

Michels, Dia L. Look What I See! Where Can I Be? at the Synagogue. Bowles, Michael J. N., photos by. 2003. (Look What I See! Where Can I Be? Ser.: Vol. 4). (Illus.). 32p. 16.95 (978-1-930775-16-9(4)); 2002. (J). pap. 9.95 (978-1-930775-14-5(8)) Platypus Media, L.L.C.

Morrison, Martha A. & Brown, Stephen F. Judaism. (World Religions Ser.). 144p. (J). (gr. 6-12). 2nd rev. ed. 2002. (Illus.). 30.00 (978-0-8160-4766-6(9)); 3rd rev. ed. 2006. 30.00 (978-0-8160-6613-1(2)) Facts On File, Inc.

Musleah, Rahel & Jarrett, Judy. Apples & Pomegranates: A Rosh Ha-Shanah Seder. 2004. (ENG & HEB., Illus.). 64p. (J). pap. 7.95 (978-1-58013-123-0(9)) Kar-Ben Publishing.

Nason, Ruth. The Jewish Faith. 2005. (Start up Religion Ser.). (Illus.). 24p. (J). (gr. 1-4). lib. bdg. (978-1-84234-341-8(6) , Cherrytree Books) Evans Publishing Group.

—Visiting a Synagogue. 2005. (Start up Religion Ser.). (Illus.). 24p. (J). (gr. 1-4). lib. bdg. (978-1-84234-343-2(2) , Cherrytree Books) Evans Publishing Group.

Ochs, Carol. Reaching Godward: Voices from Jewish Spiritual Guidance. Kofsky, Ann, illus. 2004. 250p. pap. 14.95 (978-0-8074-0866-7(2) , 142612) URJ Pr.

Pasachoff, Naomi E. Basic Judaism for Young People Vol. 3: God. (Basic Judaism Ser.). (J). (gr. 6-7). pap. 9.95 (978-0-87441-425-7(3)); pap., wbk. ed. 5.25 (978-0-87441-473-8(3)) Behrman Hse., Inc.

Penney, Sue. Judaism. 2nd ed. (World Beliefs & Cultures Ser.). 48p. (J). (gr. 6-9). 22.00 ***(*978-1-4329-0316-9(0))*** Heinemann Library.

Pfeiffer, Chaviva. Maggid Stories for Children. 1998. 48p. 14.99 (978-1-57819-295-3(1) , YMAG) Mesorah Pubns., Ltd.

Plaut, W. Gunther & Meyer, Michael. The Reform Judaism Reader: North American Documents. 2004. xi, 228p. (gr. 10-12). pap. 15.95 (978-0-8074-0732-5(1) , 386054) URJ Pr.

Podwal, Mark H. The Menorah Story. Podwal, Mark H., illus. 1998. (Illus.). 24p. (J). (ps-3). 15.00 (978-0-688-15758-6(0)) HarperCollins Pubs.

—A Sweet Year: A Taste of the Jewish Holidays. Podwal, Mark H., illus. 2003. (Illus.). 32p. (J). (ps-3). lib. bdg. 14.99 (978-0-385-90869-6(5) , Doubleday Bks. for Young Readers) Random Hse. Children's Bks.

Prenzlau, Sheryl. Deuteronomy: Jewish Children's Bible. Smekhov, Zely, illus. 1998. (Jewish Storyteller Ser.). 64p. (J). (gr. 2-5). 18.95 (978-0-943706-35-1(1)) Pitspopany Pr.

—Leviticus: The Jewish Children's Bible. Smekhov, Zely, illus. 1998. (Jewish Storyteller Ser.). 64p. (J). (gr. 2-5). 18.95 (978-0-943706-33-7(5)) Pitspopany Pr.

Ray, Eric. Sofer: The Story of a Torah Scroll. 1998. (Illus.). 32p. (Orig.). (J). (gr. 4). pap. 6.95 (978-0-933873-98-8(0)) Torah Aura Productions.

Reisman, Bernard. The New Jewish Experiential Book: The Quest for Jewish Identity. 2nd ed. 2001. xii, 439p. (gr. 6-12). pap. 45.00 (978-0-88125-709-0(5)) Ktav Publishing Hse., Inc.

Roper, Beryl C. Seekers after Truth. 1998. 90p. (YA). (gr. 9-11). pap. (978-1-885812-04-9(3)) Aquamarine Pubns.

Rose, Or. Abraham Joshua Heschel: Man of Spirit, Man of Action. 2003. (Illus.). 80p. pap. 9.95 (978-0-8276-0758-3(X)) Jewish Pubn. Society.

J K L

Roseman, Kenneth D. Until the Messiah Comes. 2004. (Do-It-Yourself Jewish Adventure Ser.). (Illus.). 145p. (gr. 4-6). pap. 11.95 (978-0-8074-0706-6(2) , 140073) URJ Pr.

Rosenberg, Amye. Mitzvot. (Illus.). 30p. (J). (gr. 1-5). pap. 4.95 (978-0-87441-387-8(7)) Behrman Hse., Inc.

Rosenberg, Larry. Jewish Synagogue. 2000. (gr. 3-6). lib. bdg. 14.10 (978-0-613-88866-0(9)) Tandem Library Bks.

Rossel, Seymour. The Storybook Haggadah. Zwebner, Janet, illus. 2006. 72p. (J). pap. 9.95 (978-1-932687-84-2(X)) Pitspopany Pr.

—When a Jew Prays, Vol. 1. Weihs, Erika, illus. 192p. (J). (gr. 4-5). pap. 9.50 (978-0-87441-093-8(2)) Behrman Hse., Inc.

Rossel, Seymour, et al. When a Jew Seeks Wisdom: The Sayings of the Fathers, Vol. 3. (Jewish Values Ser.). (J). (gr. 7). pap. 9.50 (978-0-87441-089-1(4)) Behrman Hse., Inc.

Rudin, Jacob P. & Abramson, Lillian S., eds. Haggadah for Children: Their Family & Friends. 1999. (Illus.). 46p. (J). pap. 3.95 (978-0-8197-0664-5(7)) Bloch Publishing Co.

Salkin, Jeffery K. For Kids - Putting God on Your Guest List: How to Claim the Spiritual Meaning of Your Bar or Bat Mitzvah. 2nd ed. 2007. 144p. pap. 15.99 ***978-1-58023-308-8(2)*** Jewish Lights Publishing.

Salkin, Jeffrey K. For Kids—Putting God on Your Guest List: How to Reclaim the Spiritual Meaning O. 1998. (gr. 3-6). lib. bdg. 24.55 (978-0-613-82288-6(9)) Tandem Library Bks.

Schecter, Ellen. The Family Haggadah. Waldman, Neil, illus. 1999. (ENG & HEB.). 80p. (J). (gr. 4-7). 13.99 (978-0-670-88341-7(7) , Viking Juvenile) Penguin Group (USA) Inc.

Schiffman, Lawrence H. Understanding Second Temple & Rabbinic Judaism. 2003. (YA). 29.50 (978-0-88125-813-4(X)) Ktav Publishing Hse., Inc.

Schneerson, Menachem M. My Pesukim: Children Saying Pesukim with the Rebbe. 2002. (ENG & HEB.). cd-rom 12.00 (978-1-931607-57-5(5)) Jewish Educational Media.

—My Pesukim, Hebrew: Children Saying Pesukim with the Rebbe. 2002. (ENG & HEB.). cd-rom 12.00 (978-1-931607-56-8(7)) Jewish Educational Media.

—The Rebbe Talks to Children. 1998. (YID.). (J). (gr. 4-10). Vol. 3. 204p. 16.95 (978-0-922613-94-6(X)); Vol. 4. 220p. 16.95 (978-0-922613-95-3(8)) Hachai Publishing. (Tzivos Hashem).

Schwarz, Rabbi Jacob D., ed. In the Land of Kings & Prophets. 2004. reprint ed. pap. 22.95 (978-1-4179-4135-3(9)) Kessinger Publishing, LLC.

Segal, Eliezer L. & Gordon-Lucas, Bonnie. Uncle Eli Repents: Rosh Hashanah & Yom Kippur Prayer Book. 2001. (J). pap. (978-1-886411-52-4(2)) No Starch Pr., Inc.

—Uncle Eli Repents: Rosh Hashanah & Yom Kippur Prayer Book - Maohazor Le-Rosh Ha-Shanah Ove-Yom Ha-Kipurim. 2001. (Illus.). (J). pap. (978-1-886411-51-7(4)) No Starch Pr., Inc.

—Uncle Eli's Passover Haggadah. 1999. (Illus.). 64p. 17.95 (978-1-886411-27-2(1)) No Starch Pr., Inc.

Segal, Eliezer Lorne. Uncle Eli's Special-for-Kids, Most Funever, under-the-Table Passover Haggadah. Gordon-Lucas, Bonnie, illus. 2004. 61p. (J). (gr. k-4). reprint ed. 13.00 (978-0-7567-8112-5(4)) DIANE Publishing Co.

Seidman, Laurence. What Makes Someone a Jew? 2007. (Illus.). 32p. (J). pap. 8.99 (978-1-58023-321-7(X)) Jewish Lights Publishing.

Senker, Cath. Judaism Around the World. 2007. (J). ***978-1-59920-056-9(2)*** Smart Apple Media.

Shazak Productions Inc. Staff, Shazak Productions. Miracle Lights: The Complete Story of Chanukah... Like You've Never Seen Before! 2004. (Illus.). 64p. (J). 15.95 (978-1-930925-06-9(9)) Torah Excel.

Siegel, Danny. Tikkun Olam Repairing the World Through Mitzvah: Repairing the World Through Mitzvah. 2002. (YA). pap. (978-0-88125-742-7(7)) Ktav Publishing Hse., Inc.

Siegel, Danny & Eisenberger, Naomi. Mitzvah Magic: Kids Can Do Mitzvahs. 2002. (Illus.). 64p. (J). (gr. 2 up). pap. 8.95 (978-1-58013-034-9(8)) Kar-Ben Publishing.

Simon, Solomon & Bial, Morrison D. The Rabbi's Bible Vol. 1: Torah, 2 pts. (J). (gr. 5-6). wbk. ed. 8.95 (978-0-87441-020-4(7)) Behrman Hse., Inc.

Simon, Solomon & Rothberg, Abraham. The Rabbi's Bible Vol. 3: Later Prophets. (J). (gr. 7-8). pap. 8.95 (978-0-87441-026-6(6)) Behrman Hse., Inc.

Singer, Howard. With Mind & Heart. (J). (gr. 8 up). 3.95 (978-0-8381-0203-9(4) , 10-203) United Synagogue of America Bk. Service.

Sirois, Celia. My Jewish Friend: A Young Catholic Learns about Judaism. Santillan, Mariano, illus. 2008. (J). 15.95 ***(978-0-8198-4857-4(3))*** Pauline Bks. & Media.

Sokoloff, David, illus. I Can Do a Mitzvah! 1998. 12p. (J). (ps-1). bds. 5.00 (978-1-889655-11-6(2)) Jewish Educational Toys.

Spector Siegel, Deborah. The Cross by Day, the Mezuzzah by Night. 2000. 213p. (gr. 7 up). pap. 12.95 (978-0-8276-0737-8(7)) Jewish Pubn. Society.

Stein, Larry. Josh Discovers Passover! Goodman, Marlene K., illus. l.t. ed. 2004. (Josh Discovers Ser.). 32p. (J). pap. 7.95 (978-0-9669910-1-7(X)) Ruach Publishing.

Steinbock, Steven E. Torah: The Growing Gift. 1998. (gr. 3-6). lib. bdg. 22.20 (978-0-613-90671-5(3)) Tandem Library Bks.

Stone, Amy. Jewish Americans. 2006. (World Almanac Library of American Immigration). (Illus.). 48p. (J). pap. (978-0-8368-7327-6(0)); lib. bdg. (978-0-8368-7314-6(9)) Stevens, Gareth Inc. (World Almanac Library).

Stoppleman, Monica. Jewish. (Illus.). 32p. (YA). (gr. 3 up). lib. bdg. 27.10 (978-1-932889-10-9(8)) Sea-To-Sea Pubns.

Sullivan, Lawrence Eugene. The Religious Tradition of Judaism. 2002. (Religions of Mankind Ser.). (Illus.). 32p. (YA). (gr. 5 up). 21.95 (978-0-7910-6630-0(4) , Chelsea Hse.) Facts On File, Inc.

Swarner, Kristina, illus. The Bedtime Sh'ma: A Good Night Book. 2007. (ENG & HEB.). 40p. (J). 17.95 ***(978-0-939144-55-6(7))***; pap. 10.95 ***(978-0-939144-54-9(9))*** EKS Publishing Co.

Tatz, Akiva. The Thinking Jewish Teenager's Guide to Life. 1999. 224p. 22.99 (978-1-56871-175-1(1)) Targum Pr., Inc.

Taylor, I. N. A. & Michelson, Jeremy. Judaism Pupil Book. 2006. (Illus.). 64p. (YA). pap. 21.00 (978-0-7487-9671-7(1)) Nelson Thornes Ltd. GBR. *Dist:* Trans-Atlantic Pubns., Inc.

Taylor, Ina. Judaism: Core Edition for Higher Ability Students. 2000. (Foundations in Religious Education Ser.). 88p. (YA). (gr. 6-9). pap. 19.95 (978-0-7487-5193-8(9)) Nelson Thornes Ltd. GBR. *Dist:* Trans-Atlantic Pubns., Inc.

—Judaism Essential Edition. 2000. (Foundations in Religious Education Ser.). 88p. (J). (gr. 6-9). pap. 19.95 (978-0-7487-5194-5(7)) Nelson Thornes Ltd. GBR. *Dist:* Trans-Atlantic Pubns., Inc.

Teece, Geoff. Judaism. 2004. (Religion in Focus Ser.). (Illus.). (J). lib. bdg. (978-1-58340-468-3(6)) Smart Apple Media.

Topek, Susan R. Shalom, Shabbat: A Book for Havdalah. Ephraim, Shelly S., illus. 1998. 12p. (J). (ps up). 5.95 (978-1-58013-010-3(0)) Kar-Ben Publishing.

Weiss, Bernard P. I Am Jewish. 2004. (Religions of the World Ser.). (Illus.). 24p. (J). lib. bdg. 18.75 (978-0-8239-6810-7(3) , PowerKids Pr.) Rosen Publishing Group, Inc., The.

Whitman, Jonathan, ed. Jewish Artwork by Esky: Shabbat & Jewish Holidays. (Illus.). (Orig.). (J). (gr. 1-8). pap. 19.95 (978-1-885143-01-3(X)) Preferred Enterprises.

Wood, Angela. Jewish Synagogue. 1999. (Places of Worship Ser.). (Illus.). 32p. (J). (gr. 2 up). lib. bdg. 23.33 (978-0-8368-2608-1(6)) Stevens, Gareth Inc.

Wood, Angela Gluck. Judaism. 2006. (QEB World of Faiths Ser.). (Illus.). 32p. (J). lib. bdg. 19.95 (978-1-59566-209-5(X)) QEB Publishing Inc.

Wood, Cavan. Judaism. 2003. (Living Religions Ser.). (Illus.). 62p. (J). 28.56 (978-0-7398-6386-2(X)) Raintree.

Zakon, Miriam S. The Queen of Bais Yaakov: The Story of Dr. Judith Grunfeld. 2002. 122p. (YA). 10.95 (978-1-56871-284-0(7)) Targum Pr., Inc.

JUDGES

see also Courts; Lawyers

Benson, Michael. William Howard Taft. 2005. (Presidential Leaders Ser.). (Illus.). 112p. (J). 29.27 (978-0-8225-0849-6(4) , Lerner Pubns.) Lerner Publishing Group.

Boerst, William J. Galileo Galilei & the Science of Motion. 2004. (Profiles in Science Ser.). (Illus.). 144p. (YA). (gr. 6-12). lib. bdg. 26.95 (978-1-931798-00-6(1)) Reynolds, Morgan Inc.

Collins, David R. Clarence Thomas: Fighter with Words. Lauve, Celia, illus. 2003. 32p. (J). 14.95 (978-1-56554-862-6(0)) Pelican Publishing Co., Inc.

DeJohn, Heather. The Chief Justice of the Supreme Court. 2002. (American Leaders Ser.). (Illus.). 32p. (J). 23.70 (978-1-56711-663-2(9) , Blackbirch Pr., Inc.) Thomson Gale.

Frost, Helen. Thurgood Marshall. Saunders-Smith, Gail, ed. 2003. (Famous Americans Ser.). (Illus.). 24p. (J). (gr. k-1). lib. bdg. 15.93 (978-0-7368-1643-4(7) , Pebble Bks.) Capstone Pr., Inc.

Gorman, Jacqueline Laks. Judge. 2005. (Illus.). 24p. (J). pap. (978-0-8368-4575-4(7)); lib. bdg. 19.33 (978-0-8368-4568-6(4)) Stevens, Gareth Inc.

Harris, Nancy. First Guide to Government: What's the State Judicial Branch? 2007. (J). ***(978-1-4034-9511-2(4));*** pap. ***(978-1-4034-9517-4(3))*** Heinemann Library.

Haskins, James & Poole, Cecil F. Cecil Poole: A Life in the Law. 2002. (Illus.). xii, 172p. (YA). 15.00 (978-0-9635086-2-1(8)) Ninth Judicial Circuit Historical Society.

Haugen, Brenda. Thurgood Marshall: Civil Rights Lawyer & Supreme Court Justice. 2006. (Illus.). 112p. (J). lib. bdg. ***(978-0-7565-1877-6(6))*** Compass Point Bks.

Hill, Mary. Sandra Day O'Connor. 2003. (Welcome Book Ser.). (Illus.). 24p. (J). 17.00 (978-0-516-25868-3(0) , Children's Pr.) Scholastic Library Publishing.

—Sandra Day O'Connor. 2003. (gr. k-3). lib. bdg. 12.95 (978-0-613-67763-9(3)) Tandem Library Bks.

Horn, Geoffrey M. Thurgood Marshall. 2004. (Trailblazers of the Modern World Ser.). (Illus.). 48p. (J). (gr. 5 up). pap. 11.95 (978-0-8368-5258-5(3)); lib. bdg. 30.00 (978-0-8368-5098-7(X)) Stevens, Gareth Inc. (World Almanac Library).

Howse, Jennifer. Sandra Day O'Connor. 2007. (J). ***(978-1-59036-647-9(6)); (978-1-59036-648-6(4))*** Weigl Pubs., Inc.

Jarrow, Gail. Robert H. Jackson: Voice of Justice. 2008. (J). ***(978-1-59078-511-9(8)*** , Calkins Creek) Boyds Mills Pr.

Kelly, Zachary A. Judges & Lawyers. (Law & Order Ser.). (J). 2000. (Illus.). 48p. (gr. 4-8). lib. bdg. 27.93 (978-0-86593-577-8(7)); 1998. lib. bdg. 16.95 (978-0-86625-661-2(X)) Rourke Publishing, LLC.

Littlefield, Sophie W. & Wiecek, William. Oliver Wendell Holmes Jr: The Supreme Court & American Legal Thought. 2005. (Library of American Lives & Times). (Illus.). 112p. (J). (gr. 5-8). lib. bdg. 31.95 (978-1-4042-2652-4(4) , PowerKids Pr.) Rosen Publishing Group, Inc., The.

Manaugh, Sara. Judges & Sentencing. 2001. (Crime, Justice & Punishment Ser.). (Illus.). 80p. (YA). (gr. 8 up). 30.00 (978-0-7910-4296-0(0) , Chelsea Hse.) Facts On File, Inc.

Mara, Wil. Thurgood Marshall: Champion for Civil Rights. 2004. (Great Life Stories Ser.). (Illus.). 125p. (J). 30.50 (978-0-531-12058-3(9) , Watts, Franklin) Scholastic Library Publishing.

Marsh, Carole. George Wythe. 2002. (One Thousand Readers Ser.). (Illus.). 12p. (J). (gr. k-4). 2.95 (978-0-635-01558-7(7) , 15587) Gallopade International.

—Lewis F. Powell, Jr. 2002. (One Thousand Readers Ser.). (Illus.). 12p. (J). (gr. k-4). 2.95 (978-0-635-01554-9(4) , 15544) Gallopade International.

Marshall, Thurgood. Thurgood Marshall: Supreme Court Justice. (Black Americans of Achievement Ser.). (Illus.). 112p. (J). (gr. 6-12). 2005. pap. 13.25 (978-0-7910-8337-6(3)); 2004. 30.00 (978-0-7910-8163-1(X)) Facts On File, Inc. (Chelsea Hse.).

McElroy, Lisa Tucker. John G. Roberts, Jr: Chief Justice. 2007. (Gateway Biography Ser.). (J). 23.93 (978-0-8225-6389-1(4) , Lerner Pubns.) Lerner Publishing Group.

—Meet My Grandmother: She's a Supreme Court Justice. 1999. (gr. 3-6). lib. bdg. 16.40 (978-0-613-26179-1(8)) Tandem Library Bks.

—Sandra Day O'Connor: Supreme Court Justice. 2003. (Gateway Biography Ser.). 48p. lib. bdg. 23.90 (978-0-7613-2502-4(6) , Millbrook Pr.) Lerner Publishing Group.

McLeese, Don & Marshall, Thurgood. Thurgood Marshall. 2003. (Rourke Discovery Library). (Illus.). 24p. (gr. 2-5). 14.95 (978-1-58952-303-6(2)) Rourke Publishing, LLC.

Morris, Roz. Hugo L. Black: Justice for All. 2001. (Alabama Roots Biography Ser.). (Illus.). 128p. (J). (978-1-878561-85-5(5)) Seacoast Publishing, Inc.

Pasternak, Ceel & Thornburg, Linda. Cool Careers for Girls in Law. 2001. (Illus.). (gr. 7). 128p. pap. 12.95 (978-1-57023-157-5(5)); 132p. (J). 19.95 (978-1-57023-160-5(5)) Impact Pubns.

—Cool Careers for Girls in Law. 2001. (YA). lib. bdg. 22.20 (978-0-613-79030-7(8)) Tandem Library Bks.

Powell, Phelan. John Jay: First Chief Justice of the Supreme Court. 2001. (gr. 5-8). lib. bdg. 17.60 (978-0-613-32726-8(8)) Tandem Library Bks.

Taylor-Butler, Christine. Thurgood Marshall. 2006. (Rookie Biographies Ser.). (Illus.). 32p. (J). (gr. 1-2). 20.50 (978-0-516-25015-1(9) , Children's Pr.) Scholastic Library Publishing.

Wetterer, Charles M. & Wetterer, Margaret K. Chief Justice. Walters, Kurt K. C., illus. 2005. 32p. (J). (978-1-59336-306-2(0)); pap. (978-1-59336-307-9(9)) Mondo Publishing.

Wheeler, Jill C. Thurgood Marshall. 2003. (Breaking Barriers Ser.). (Illus.). 64p. (J). (gr. 3-8). lib. bdg. 25.65 (978-1-57765-907-5(4)) ABDO Publishing Co.

White, Casey. John Jay. 2005. (Library of American Thinkers). (Illus.). 112p. (J). (978-1-4042-0507-9(1)) Rosen Publishing Group, Inc., The.

White, G. Edward. Oliver Wendell Holmes: Sage of the Supreme Court. 1999. (Portraits Ser.). (Illus.). 160p. (YA). (gr. 7 up). 28.00 (978-0-19-511667-0(4)) Oxford Univ. Pr., Inc.

Whitelaw, Nancy. Mr. Civil Rights: The Story of Thurgood Marshall. 2nd rev. exp. ed. 2004. (Notable Americans Ser.). (Illus.). 144p. (YA). (gr. 6-12). 23.95 (978-1-931798-02-0(8)) Reynolds, Morgan Inc.

Young, Evan A. Lone Star Justice: A Biography of Justice Tom C. Clark. 1998. (Illus.). 160p. (YA). (gr. 7 up). 12.95 (978-1-885777-11-9(6)) Hendrick-Long Publishing Co.

JUDO

see also Karate

Blackall, Bernie. Martial Arts. 1999. (Top Sport Ser.). 32p. (J). (gr. 4-6). lib. bdg. 21.36 (978-1-57572-705-9(6)) Heinemann Library.

Brousse, Michel & Matsumoto, David. A Century of Dedication, the History of Judo in America. 2003. (YA). pap. 25.00 (978-0-9729790-0-9(X)); pap. 30.00 (978-0-9729790-1-6(8)) United States Judo Federation, Inc.

Buckley, Thomas. Jujitsu & Judo. 2004. (Child's World of Sports). (Illus.). 32p. (J). (gr. 1-5). 25.64 (978-1-59296-030-9(8)) Child's World, Inc.

Chesterman, Barnaby. Judo. 2003. (Martial & Fighting Arts Ser.). (Illus.). 96p. (J). (gr. 7 up). lib. bdg. (978-1-59084-389-5(4)) Mason Crest Pubs.

Chesterman, Barnaby & Willingham, Bob. Judo. 2004. 32p. (YA). lib. bdg. 24.67 (978-0-8368-4192-3(1)) Stevens, Gareth Inc.

Collins, Paul. Judo. 2001. (Martial Arts Ser.). (Illus.). 32p. (J). (gr. 3 up). 28.00 (978-0-7910-6553-2(7) , 010251, Chelsea Hse.) Facts On File, Inc.

Craats, Rennay. Judo. 2001. (For the Love of Sports Ser.). (Illus.). 24p. (J). lib. bdg. 15.95 (978-1-930954-22-9(0)) Weigl Pubs., Inc.

Crossingham, John & Kalman, Bobbie. Judo in Action. Crabtree, Marc, photos by. 2005. (Sports in Action Ser.). (Illus.). 32p. (J). (978-0-7787-0342-6(8)) Crabtree Publishing Co.

—Judo in Action. 2005. (Sports in Action Ser.). (Illus.). 32p. (J). pap. (978-0-7787-0362-4(2)) Crabtree Publishing Co.

Johnson, Nathan. Jujutsu. 2002. (Martial & Fighting Arts Ser.). (Illus.). 96p. (J). (gr. 7 up). lib. bdg. (978-1-59084-390-1(8)) Mason Crest Pubs.

Lebell, Gene. Gene Lebell's Grappling & Self-Defense for the Young Adult. 2002. (gr. 7-12). lib. bdg. 22.20 (978-0-613-84440-6(8)) Tandem Library Bks.

Mason, Paul. A World-Class Judo Player. 2004. (Making of a Champion Ser.). (Illus.). 48p. (J). pap. 8.50 (978-1-4034-5534-5(1)); lib. bdg. (978-1-4034-4673-2(3)) Heinemann Library.

Morris, Neil. Judo. 2001. (Get Going! Ser.). (Illus.). 32p. (J). (gr. 4-6). lib. bdg. 22.79 (978-1-58810-038-2(3)) Heinemann Library.

Randall, Pamela. Jiu Jitsu. 1999. (Martial Arts Ser.). (Illus.). 24p. (J). lib. bdg. 18.75 (978-0-8239-5235-9(5) , PowerKids Pr.) Rosen Publishing Group, Inc., The.

—Judo. 1999. (Martial Arts Ser.). (Illus.). 24p. (J). lib. bdg. 18.75 (978-0-8239-5238-0(X) , PowerKids Pr.) Rosen Publishing Group, Inc., The.

Sander, Hedda & Deling, Bjorn. Judo: From White/Yellow Belt to Brown Belt. 2004. (Illus.). 184p. pap. 17.95 (978-1-84126-076-1(2)) Meyer & Meyer Sport, Ltd. GBR. *Dist:* Lewis International, Inc.

Santoro, Laura. Aikido for Kids. 1998. (Illus.). 96p. (J). (gr. 4-7). 14.95 (978-0-8069-9405-5(3)) Sterling Publishing Co., Inc.

JUDSON, ADONIRAM, 1788-1850

Hambrick, Sharon. Adoniram Judson: God's Man in Burma. 2001. (Illus.). 143p. (J). 6.49 (978-1-57924-625-9(7)) Jones, Bob Univ. Pr.

JUGGLERS AND JUGGLING

Beak, Nick Huckleberry & Boase, Petra. Crafty Juggling. Freeman, John, photos by. 2000. (Crafty Kids Ser.). (Illus.). 64p. (J). (gr. 3 up). lib. bdg. 26.00 (978-0-8368-2502-2(0)) Stevens, Gareth Inc.

Huckleberry, Bea. Awesome Juggling Tricks. 2001. (Fun Factory... Ser.). (Illus.). 64p. pap. 6.95 (978-1-84215-492-2(3) , Southwater) Anness Publishing GBR. *Dist:* National Bk. Network.

Jaffe, Elizabeth Dana. Juggling. 2002. (Games Around the World Ser.). (Illus.). 32p. (J). (gr. 3 up). lib. bdg. 21.26 (978-0-7565-0191-4(1)) Compass Point Bks.

Juggling. Date not set. 64p. (J). 5.98 (978-1-4054-0408-2(6)) Parragon, Inc.

Juggling Kid Kit. 2004. (Kid Kits Ser.). (Illus.). 32p. (J). 9.95 (978-1-58086-417-6(1)) EDC Publishing.

Juggling Skills. 2004. (Formula Fun Ser.). (Illus.). 48p. (J). (978-1-84229-588-5(8)) Top That! Publishing PLC.

Just Juggling. 2004. (Whizz Kits Ser.). (Illus.). 48p. (J). (978-1-84229-940-1(9)) Top That! Publishing PLC.

Mitchelson, Mitch. How to Be a Juggler. Shone, Rob & Harper, Peter, illus. 2006. (Most Excellent Book Of-Ser.). 32p. (J). (978-1-59604-127-1(7)) Stargazer Bks.

Top That Publishing Staff, ed. Boob Juggling. 2004. (Naughty Shenanigans Ser.). (Illus.). 48p. (978-1-84510-218-0(5)) Top That! Publishing PLC.

Whiter, Barbara. Juggling. 2002. 32p. mass mkt. 4.95 (978-0-689-02458-0(4)) Meadowbrook Pr.

JUNGLE ANIMALS

Burnard, Damon. I Spy in the Jungle. Cairns, Julia, illus. 2001. 28p. (J). (ps-k). bds. 6.95 (978-0-8118-2987-8(1)) Chronicle Bks. LLC.

Casado, Dami & Casado, Alicia. Bebes de la Selva. 2005. (SPA.). 12p. 7.99 (978-84-272-6061-0(X)) Molino, Editorial ESP. *Dist:* Santillana USA Publishing Co., Inc.

Dann, Geoff, photos by. Jungle Animals. 2001. (Touch & Feel Ser.). (Illus.). 12p. (J). bds. 6.99 (978-0-7894-7932-7(X)) Dorling Kindersley Publishing, Inc.

de Lambilly-Bresson, Elisabeth. Animals in the Jungle. 2007. (Animal Show & Tell Ser.). 16p. (J). (ps-2). lib. bdg. 17.27 ***(978-0-8368-8206-3(7))*** Stevens, Gareth Inc.

DK Publishing Staff. Jungle Babies. 2007. (Illus.). 12p. (J). bds. 12.99 (978-0-7566-2718-8(4)) Dorling Kindersley Publishing, Inc.

Jungle. 2002. (Fuzzy Felts Ser.). (J). 4.98 (978-0-7525-5233-0(3)) Parragon, Inc.

Jungle Animals. 2002. (Questions & Answers Ser.). 32p. (J). 7.95 (978-0-7525-7250-5(4)) Parragon, Inc.

Look Who's Popping Up: In the Jungle. 2003. (J). (ps-k). 4.98 (978-0-7525-8902-2(4)) Parragon, Inc.

Lynch, Emma. The Jungle. 2004. (Raintree Sprouts Ser.). (Illus.) 24p. (J). pap. 5.50 (978-1-4109-0871-1(2)); lib. bdg. 18.56 (978-1-4109-0866-7(6)) Raintree.

Lynn, Sara. Jungle Friends. (Illus.). (J). bds. (978-0-7636-0042-6(3)) Candlewick Pr.

Martín Larrañaga, Ana. Jungle Jamboree. 2000. (Ana's Animals Bks.). (Illus.). (J). (ps-k). 3.95 (978-1-58646-003-7(X)) Polka Dot Pr.

Paul, Tessa. In the Jungle. 1998. (Animal Trackers Ser.). (Illus.). 32p. (J). (gr. 2-3). pap. (978-0-86505-599-5(8)); lib. bdg. (978-0-86505-591-9(2)) Crabtree Publishing Co.

Pipe, Jim. Jungle Animals. 2007. (J). ***(978-1-59604-159-2(5))*** Stargazer Bks.

Priddy, Roger. Baby Gund Cloth Book Jungle Fun. 2006. 10p. 9.95 ***(978-0-312-49845-0(4)*** , Priddy Bks.) St. Martin's Pr.

Priddy, Roger. Pop-up Jungle IQ. 2007. 12p. (J). bds. 5.95 (978-0-312-49917-4(5) , Priddy Bks.) St. Martin's Pr.

Radley, Gail. Forests & Jungles. Sherlock, Jean, illus. (Vanishing from Ser.). 2005. 32p. (gr. 6-12). lib. bdg. 22.60 (978-1-57505-405-6(1)); 2003. 32p. (J). (gr. 3-5). 6.95 (978-1-57505-567-1(8)); 1998. (J). lib. bdg. (978-0-8225-1937-9(2)) Lerner Publishing Group.

—Forests & Jungles. Sherlock, Jean, illus. 2001. 32p. (J). (ps-7). lib. bdg. 15.25 (978-0-613-64497-6(2)) Tandem Library Bks.

Rettore, Kenny E. Jungle Friends. Ferri, Francesca, illus. 2004. 6p. (J). 12.95 (978-0-7641-2810-3(8)) Barron's Educational Series, Inc.

Wickings, Ruth. Animals in the Jungle. 2006. (First Fun Pop-ups Ser.). (Illus.). 12p. bds. 8.95 (978-1-84560-020-4(7)) Mercury Bks. Ltd. GBR. *Dist:* International Publishers Marketing.

J K L

JUNGLE ANIMALS—FICTION

Alborough, Jez. Tall. Alborough, Jez, illus. 2005. (Illus.). 40p. (J). (ps up). 15.99 (978-0-7636-2784-3(4)) Candlewick Pr.

—Tall. Alborough, Jez, illus. 2007. (Illus.). 34p. (J). (gr. k-ps). bds. 6.99 (978-0-7636-3328-8(3)) Candlewick Pr.

—Watch Out! Big Bro's Coming! Alborough, Jez, illus. 1998. (Illus.). 32p. (J). (ps-3). pap. 6.99 (978-0-7636-0584-1(0)) Candlewick Pr.

Alegria, Ciro. Sacha en el Reino de los Arboles. (SPA.). 96p. (YA). (gr. 5-8). (978-84-204-3693-7(3), AF1748) Alfaguara, Ediciones, S.A.- Grupo Santillana ESP. *Dist:* Lectorum Pubns., Inc.

—Sacha en el Reino de los Arboles. (SPA.). (YA). (gr. 5-8). (978-956-11-0965-0(4), UV6346) Universitaria, Editorial S.A.

Allen, Nancy Kelly. On the Banks of the Amazon/en las orillas del Amazonas. de la Vega, Eida, tr. Driessen, Elizabeth, illus. 2004. Tr. of En las orillas del Amazonas. (SPA & ENG.). 32p. (J). (gr. 4-6). 16.95 (978-0-9720192-7-9(8), 626099) Raven Tree Pr.

Anderson, Bob. Obo. Anderson, Bob, illus. 1999. (Illus.). 48p. (J). (ps-5). bds. 16.00 (978-1-57174-124-0(0)) Hampton Roads Publishing Co., Inc.

Andreae, Giles. The Lion Who Wanted to Love. Wojtowycz, David, illus. 1998. 32p. (J). (ps-2). 14.95 (978-1-888444-25-4(8), 21023) Little Tiger Pr.

Anholt, Laurence. Eco-Wolf & the Three Pigs. 2004. (Illus.). 64p. (C). (gr. 3-5). 13.26 (978-0-7565-0630-8(1)) Compass Point Bks.

Ashman, Linda. Starry Safari. Mack, Jeff, illus. 2005. 40p. (J). 16.00 (978-0-15-204766-5(2)) Harcourt Children's Bks.

Avilés Junco, Martha, illus. Jungle Stories: My First Treasury. 2004. 40p. (J). bds. (978-1-4127-0461-8(8), 7219800) Publications International, Ltd.

Baena, Gloria. Invitacion a la Fiesta del Gran Gorila. Osorno, Laura, illus. 2003. (SPA.). 32p. (J). 8.95 (978-958-04-7072-4(3)) Norma S.A. COL. *Dist:* Distribuidora Norma, Inc., Lectorum Pubns., Inc.

Baker, Keith. Quien es la Bestia? Ada, Alma Flor, tr. 2005. (SPA., Illus.). 28p. (J). bds. 6.95 (978-0-15-205596-7(7), Red Wagon Bks.) Harcourt Children's Bks.

—Who Is the Beast? 2003. (Illus.). 28p. (J). bds. 6.95 (978-0-15-204752-8(2), Red Wagon Bks.) Harcourt Children's Bks.

Base, Graeme. Jungle Drums. 2004. (Illus.). 40p. (J). (ps-3). 18.95 (978-0-8109-5044-3(8)) Abrams, Harry N., Inc.

Bentley, Dawn. Who's in the Jungle. Valderrama, Rosario, illus. 2001. (Sneak-A-Peek Board Book Ser.: Vol. 1). 10p. (ps-k). bds. 6.95 (978-1-58117-141-9(2), Intervisual/Piggy Toes) Dalmatian Pr.

The Big Game. 2007. (J). per. (*978-1-932570-68-7(3)) Literacy Footprints Inc.

Bilgrami, Shaheen. A Magic Color Book: Jungle Art Show. Girouard, Patrick, illus. 2002. (Pinwheel Ser.). 10p. (J). (ps-k). 5.95 (978-1-4027-0206-8(X)) Sterling Publishing Co., Inc.

Bright, Paul. Nobody Laughs at a Lion! Buckingham, Matt, illus. 2005. 28p. (J). 16.00 (978-1-56148-471-3(7)) Good Bks.

Brooks, David. You Can Count in the Jungle. 2005. (Illus.). 24p. (J). bds. (978-1-55971-931-5(1), NorthWord Bks. for Young Readers) T&N Children's Publishing.

Brown, J. A. Hurray for Elephant. 2003. (Funny Faces Ser.). (Illus.). (J). 3.95 (978-1-58925-717-7(0), tiger tales) ME Media LLC.

Burgess, W. Thornton. Whitefoot the Wood Mouse. 2006. 24.99 (*978-1-4280-4184-4(2)); pap. 18.99 (*978-1-4280-4180-6(X)) IndyPublish.com.

Campbell, Rod. Pop-Up Jungle. (Illus.). 24p. (J). bds. 9.99 (978-0-333-73350-9(9)) Pan Macmillan GBR. *Dist:* Trafalgar Square Publishing.

Carle, Eric. Slowly, Slowly Said the Sloth. Carle, Eric, illus. 2007. 32p. (J). (ps). pap. 7.99 (978-0-14-240847-6(6), Puffin) Penguin Group (USA) Inc.

Charles, Faustin. The Selfish Crocodile. Terry, Michael, illus. 1999. 32p. (J). (gr. k-2). 14.95 (978-1-888444-56-8(8)) Little Tiger Pr.

Cherry, Lynne. Great Kapok Tree. 2000. (gr. k-3). lib. bdg. 15.30 (978-0-613-28507-0(7)) Tandem Library Bks.

—Great Kapok Tree: A Tale of the Amazon Rain Forest. 2000. (Illus.). 33p. lib. bdg. 13.80 (978-0-606-17843-3(0)) Tandem Library Bks.

Child's Play, ed. Down in the Jungle. 2006. (Illus.). 16p. 19.99 (978-1-84643-009-1(7)) Child's Play-International.

Chukovskii, Kornei. Doctor Ouch. Seabaugh, Jan, tr. from RUS. Seabaugh, Jan, illus. 2004. (Children's International Ser.: 1). Orig. Title: Aibolit. 50p. (J). pap. 6.99 (978-0-9740551-0-7(7)) Smith, Viveca Publishing.

Cocca-Leffler, Maryann. Jungle Halloween. Cocca-Leffler, Maryann, illus. 2000. (Illus.). 32p. (J). (ps-1). pap. 6.95 (978-0-8075-4057-2(9)) Whitman, Albert & Co.

Cole, Babette. Tarzana. 2nd ed. 2003. (Babette Cole Ser.). (SPA., Illus.). 34p. (J). 12.95 (978-84-233-2274-9(2)) Ediciones Destino ESP. *Dist:* Planeta Publishing Corp.

Cole, Bob. Power Reading: Classics/Jungle Book. Connor, Robin, illus. 2004. 94p. (J). (gr. 4 up). vinyl bd. 39.95 (978-1-883186-61-6(7), PPCL2) National Reading Styles Institute, Inc.

Crowson, Andrew. Flip Flap Safari. Crowson, Andrew, illus. 2003. (Illus.). 12p. (J). bds. (978-1-85602-473-0(3)) Chrysalis Children's Bks.

Dahl, Roald. The Enormous Crocodile. 2003. (gr. k-3). lib. bdg. 16.45 (978-0-613-87826-5(4)) Tandem Library Bks.

DePrisco, Dorothea. Mini Whos in the Jungle. 2006. 10p. (J). 4.95 (978-1-58117-507-3(8), Intervisual/Piggy Toes) Dalmatian Pr.

Dodd, Lynley. Sniff-Snuff-Snap! Dodd, Lynley, illus. 2000. (Gold Star First Readers Ser.). (Illus.). 32p. (J). (gr. 1 up). lib. bdg. 22.00 (978-0-8368-2677-7(9)) Stevens, Gareth Inc.

Donaldson, Julia. Where's My Mom? Scheffler, Axel, illus. 2008. 32p. (J). (ps). 16.99 (*978-0-8037-3228-5(7), Dial) Penguin Group (USA) Inc.

Durant, Alan. If You Go Walking in Tiger Wood. Boon, Debbie, illus. 2005. 24p. (J). pap. 9.99 (978-0-00-710390-4(5), HarperSport) HarperCollins Pubs. Ltd. GBR. *Dist:* Trafalgar Square Publishing.

Edwards, Pamela Duncan. Roar! Cole, Henry, illus. Date not set. 32p. (J). (ps-2). pap. 5.99 (978-0-06-443572-7(5)) HarperCollins Pubs.

—Roar! A Noisy Counting Book. Cole, Henry, illus. 2000. 32p. (J). (ps-2). 16.99 (978-0-06-028384-1(X)); 15.89 (978-0-06-028385-8(8)) HarperCollins Pubs.

Emmett, Jonathan. Through the Heart of the Jungle. Gomez, Elena, illus. 2003. 32p. (J). tchr. ed. 15.95 (978-1-58925-029-1(X)); pap. 5.95 (978-1-58925-380-3(9)) ME Media LLC. (tiger tales).

—Through the Heart of the Jungle. 2003. (gr. k-3). lib. bdg. 14.10 (978-0-613-85249-4(4)) Tandem Library Bks.

Frampton, David. The Whole Night Through. Frampton, David, illus. Date not set. (Illus.). 32p. (J). (ps-1). pap. 5.99 (978-0-06-443652-6(7)) HarperCollins Pubs.

—The Whole Night Through: A Lullaby. Frampton, David, illus. 2004. (Illus.). 30p. (J). (gr. k-4). reprint ed. (978-0-7567-7723-4(2)) DIANE Publishing Co.

—The Whole Night Through: A Lullaby. Frampton, David, illus. 2001. (Illus.). 32p. (J). (ps-1). 15.89 (978-0-06-028826-6(4)); 15.95 (978-0-06-028825-9(6)) HarperCollins Pubs.

Freedman, Claire. Snuggle up, Sleepy Ones. Macnaughton, Tina, illus. 28p. (J). (ps). 2007. bds. 8.95 (*978-1-56148-562-8(4)); 2005. 16.00 (978-1-56148-475-1(X)) Good Bks.

Freedman, Claire & Cabban, Vanessa. Gooseberry Goose. 2003. (Illus.). 32p. (J). (ps-2). tchr. ed. 15.95 (978-1-58925-030-7(3), tiger tales) ME Media LLC.

Freeman, Claire. One Magical Morning. Ho, Louise, illus. 2005. 28p. (J). 16.00 (978-1-56148-472-0(5)) Good Bks.

Freeman, Mylo. Potty! 2004. (Illus.). 30p. (J). (ps). 13.95 (978-1-58246-070-3(1), Tricycle Pr.) Ten Speed Pr.

Friends for Lion. 2000. 16p. (J). bds. 7.95 (978-0-7525-4602-5(3)) Parragon, Inc.

Gibert, Bruno. The King Is Naked! 2004. (Illus.). 32p. (J). (gr. k-ps). 14.00 (978-0-618-41067-5(8), Clarion Bks.) Houghton Mifflin Co. Trade & Reference Div.

Gibson, Kari Smalley. Mooki & the Too-Proud Peacock. 2004. 32p. (J). pap. 6.99 (978-0-310-70922-0(9)) Zonderkidz.

—Mooki the Berry Bandit. 2004. 32p. (J). pap. 6.99 (978-0-310-70921-3(0)) Zonderkidz.

Greco, Francesca. Gideon. 2002. (Illus.). 40p. (J). 16.95 (978-1-932065-02-2(4)) Star Bright Bks., Inc.

Greene, Janice. Jungle Book. abr. ed. 2001. (gr. 7-12). lib. bdg. 15.25 (978-0-613-36449-2(X)) Tandem Library Bks.

Guettier, Benedicte. In the Jungle. 2002. (Illus.). 14p. (J). bds. 11.95 (978-1-929132-38-6(7)) Kane/Miller Bk. Pubs., Inc.

Guzman, Lila. Kichi in Jungle Jeopardy. Johnson, Regan, illus. (J). 2007. per. 8.95 (978-0-9769417-2-9(4)); 2006. 144p. 15.95 (978-0-9769417-1-2(6)) Blooming Tree Pr.

Halsey, Megan. Three Pandas Planting. 1999. mass mkt. 3.99 (978-0-689-83304-5(0), Aladdin) Simon & Schuster Children's Publishing.

Hamilton, Virginia. Jaguarundi. Cooper, Floyd, illus. 1998. 40p. (J). (ps-3). pap. 14.95 (978-0-590-47366-8(2), Blue Sky Pr., The) Scholastic, Inc.

Harvey, Damian. Just the Thing! Chapman, Lynne, illus. 2005. 32p. (J). (ps-ps). 15.95 (978-0-7696-4300-7(0), Gingham Dog Pr.) School Specialty Publishing.

Hewitt, Sally. Face to Face Safari: Dare You Face the Six Giant Pop-up Animals? Gilvan-Cartwright, Chris, illus. 2003. 12p. (J). (ps-1). 14.95 (978-0-8109-4261-5(5)) Abrams, Harry N., Inc.

I Can Swim, 6 Packs. (Sails Literacy Ser.). 16p. (gr. k up). 27.00 (978-0-7635-4399-0(3)) Rigby Education.

Isadora, Rachel. A South African Night. Isadora, Rachel, illus. 1998. (Illus.). (J). (ps-3). 32p. 16.99 (978-0-688-11389-6(3)); 24p. 14.89 (978-0-688-11390-2(7)) HarperCollins Pubs.

Jones, Sally Lloyd. Farmyard Boogie. Abel, Simone, illus. 2001. (Flip Flap Ser.). 10p. (J). bds. 8.95 (978-1-57145-547-5(7), Silver Dolphin Bks.) Advantage Pubs. Group.

Jones, Sally Lloyd & Abel, Simone, illus. Jungle Jive! 2001. (Flip Flap Ser.). 10p. (J). bds. 8.95 (978-1-57145-548-2(5), Silver Dolphin Bks.) Advantage Pubs. Group.

The Jungle: Individual Title Six-Packs. (Sails Literacy Ser.). 16p. (gr. k up). 27.00 (978-0-7635-4388-4(8)) Rigby Education.

Kipling, Rudyard. The Jungle Book. Alexander, Gregory, illus. 1999. (Classics Ser.).Tr. of 192. 160p. (J). 12.95 (978-0-7892-0558-2(0)); pap. 7.95 (978-0-7892-0548-3(3)) Abbeville Pr., Inc. (Abbeville Kids).

—The Jungle Book. 2000. (Dover Juvenile Classics Ser.).Tr. of 192. 160p. (J). (gr. 4-7). pap. 2.50 (978-0-486-41024-1(2)) Dover Pubns., Inc.

—The Jungle Book. 1998. (Children's Classics).Tr. of 192. (ENG., Illus.). 192p. (J). (gr. 4-7). pap. (978-1-85326-119-0(X), 119XWW) Wordsworth Editions, Ltd.

—The Jungle Book: A Classic Story about Uniqueness. 2003. (Illus.). 32p. per. 3.95 (978-0-9747133-1-1(7), Values to Live By Classic Stories) Thomas, Frederic Inc.

—The Jungle Book: Mowgli Knows Best, No. 4. Hale, Nathan, illus. 2007. (Easy Reader Classics Ser.). 32p. (J). pap. 3.95 (978-1-4027-4125-8(1)) Sterling Publishing Co., Inc.

—The Jungle Book Mowgli's Big Birthday, No. 3. Hale, Nathan, illus. 2007. (Easy Reader Classics Ser.). 32p. (J). pap. 3.95 (978-1-4027-4124-1(3)) Sterling Publishing Co., Inc.

Kipling, Rudyard & Hedge, Tricia. The Jungle Book, Level 2. 2nd abr. ed. 2000. (Bookworms Ser.).Tr. of 192. (Illus.). 64p. 6.50 (978-0-19-422977-7(7)) Oxford Univ. Pr., Inc.

Knutson, Kimberley. Jungle Jamboree. 1998. (Accelerated Reader Bks.). (Illus.). 32p. (J). (ps-3). 15.95 (978-0-7614-5032-0(7), Cavendish Children's Bks.) Cavendish, Marshall Corp.

Kroll, Steven. Jungle Bullies. Nguyen, Vincent, illus. 2006. 32p. (J). 16.99 (978-0-7614-5297-3(4)) Cavendish, Marshall Corp.

Laird, Elizabeth. Beautiful Bananas. Pichon, Liz, tr. Pichon, Liz, illus. 2004. 32p. (J). 15.95 (978-1-56145-305-4(6)) Peachtree Pubs., Ltd.

Laxman, Kamala. The Thama Stories. Laxman, R. K., illus. 120p. (J). pap. (978-0-14-037812-2(X), Puffin) Penguin Group (USA) Inc.

Lewis, Anthony, illus. Little Jungle Explorers. 14p. bds. 4.99 (*978-1-84643-036-7(4)) Child's Play International Ltd. GBR. *Dist:* Child's Play-International.

Lornsen, Boy. El Bosque en Peligro. (SPA.). 141p. (J). (gr. 3-5). (978-84-279-3451-1(3), NG0993) Noguer y Caralt Editores, S. A. ESP. *Dist:* Lectorum Pubns., Inc.

Maelor, Gwawr, et al. Tan Yn y Jyngl. 2005. (WEL., Illus.). 16p. (978-1-85644-842-0(8)) Univ. of Wales, Aberystwyth, Centre for Educational Studies.

Mahy, Margaret. Simply Delicious! Allen, Jonathan, illus. 1999. 32p. (J). (gr. k-4). pap. 15.95 (978-0-531-30181-4(8), Orchard Bks.) Scholastic, Inc.

Mangan, Anne. The Monkey Who Wanted the Moon. Walters, Catherine, illus. 2000. 32p. (J). (gr. k-3). 15.95 (978-1-56656-376-5(3)) Interlink Publishing Group, Inc.

Massey, Jane, illus. Jungle Animals. 2000. (Touch & Fit Ser.). 10p. (J). (ps-k). bds. 12.95 (978-1-57145-415-7(2), Silver Dolphin Bks.) Advantage Pubs. Group.

McDonnell, Flora. Splash! 2003. (Illus.). 26p. (J). (gr. k-k). bds. 6.99 (978-0-7636-2035-6(1)) Candlewick Pr.

—Splash! 2004. (TAM, VIE, SPA, GUJ & PER., Illus.). 25p. (J). (978-1-85269-487-6(4)); (978-1-85269-488-3(2)); (978-1-85269-489-0(0)); (978-1-85269-492-0(0)); (978-1-85269-486-9(6)) Mantra Publishing, Ltd.

McPhail, David M. Edward in the Jungle. McPhail, David M., illus. 2004. (Illus.). 28p. (J). (gr. k-4). reprint ed. lib. bdg. 16.00 (978-0-7567-8009-8(8)) DIANE Publishing Co.

Melmed, Laura Krauss. Jumbo's Lullaby. Sorensen, Henri, illus. 1999. 24p. (J). (ps-k). lib. bdg. 15.89 (978-0-688-16996-1(1)) HarperCollins Pubs.

Miserable Monkey. 2000. 14p. (J). bds. 7.95 (978-0-7525-4605-6(8)) Parragon, Inc.

Mitchell, Melanie. Mommy & Baby: Jungle. 2006. (Illus.). 8p. (J). bds. 6.95 (978-0-8027-8979-2(X)) Walker & Co.

Moss, Miriam & Andreae, Giles. The Pop-Up Rumble in the Jungle. Mockler, Joanna & Wojtowycz, David, illus. 2001. 12p. (J). (ps-1). 14.95 (978-1-58925-658-3(1), tiger tales) ME Media LLC.

Mouse Works Staff. Simba. 1999. (Disney's Friendly Tales Ser.). (Illus.). 10p. (J). (ps-k). 6.99 (978-0-7364-1011-3(2)) Mouse Works.

Murray, Andrew. The Very Sleepy Sloth. Tickle, Jack, tr. Tickle, Jack, illus. 2003. 32p. (J). tchr. ed. 15.95 (978-1-58925-033-8(8), tiger tales) ME Media LLC.

Nash, Sarah. The Snuggliest Snuggle in the World. Howarth, Daniel, illus. 2006. 10p. (J). bds. 12.95 (978-0-7696-4649-7(2), Gingham Dog Pr.) School Specialty Publishing.

Osborne, Mary Pope. Tigers at Twilight, Vol. 19. unabr. ed. 2004. (Magic Tree House Ser.: No. 19). 72p. (J). (gr. k-3). pap. 17.00 incl. audio (978-0-8072-0928-8(7), S FTR 251 SP, Listening Library) Random Hse. Audio Publishing Group.

—Tigers at Twilight. Murdocca, Sal, illus. 1999. (Magic Tree House Ser.: No. 19). 96p. (J). (gr. k-3). lib. bdg. 11.99 (978-0-679-99065-9(8)); mass mkt. 3.99 (978-0-679-89065-2(3)) Random Hse. Children's Bks. (Random Hse. Bks. for Young Readers).

—Tigers at Twilight. 1999. (Magic Tree House Ser.: No. 19). (J). (gr. k-3). (Illus.). 71p. lib. bdg. 10.79 (978-0-606-16957-8(1)); lib. bdg. 11.80 (978-0-613-16224-1(2)) Tandem Library Bks.

Paterson, Brian. Zigby & the Ants. 2004. (J). (978-0-06-053796-8(5)) HarperCollins Pubs.

Peck, Dale. Lost Cities: The Second Voyage. Terry, Michael, illus. 2007. 400p. (J). (gr. 5 up). 16.95 (978-1-58234-859-9(6)) Bloomsbury Publishing.

Post, Jim & Post, Janet. Jungle Beat. Vasconsellos, Daniel, illus. 2007. 32p. 15.99 (*978-1-57939-352-6(7)) Andrews McMeel Publishing.

Pritchett, Dylan. The First Music. Banks, Erin Bennett, illus. 2006. 32p. (ps-2). 16.95 (978-0-87483-776-6(6)) August Hse. Pubs., Inc.

Puckett, Mary. Moo-Moo's Jungle. 2004. (Illus.). 62p. (J). (ps-7). per. 14.95 (978-1-59453-126-2(9), 1861) Airleaf Publishing & Bookselling.

Rigby Education Staff. The Jungle Sun. (Sails Literacy Ser.). (Illus.). 16p. (gr. 2-3). 27.00 (978-0-7635-9941-6(7), 699417C99) Rigby Education.

Risk, Mary & Jansen, Jacqueline. I Want My Banana: English-French Version: Je Veux Ma Banane. De Wolf, Alex, illus. 1998. (I Can Read Bks.). (ENG & FRE.). (J). (ps up). pap. 9.95 incl. audio (978-0-7641-7190-1(9)) Barron's Educational Series, Inc.

Roddie, Shen. The Gossipy Parrot. Terry, Michael, tr. Terry, Michael, illus. 2004. 32p. (J). 20.00 (978-0-7475-6079-1(X)) Bloomsbury Publishing Plc GBR. *Dist:* Independent Pubs. Group.

Rose, Gerald. Horrible Melena. (SPA.). (J). 8.95 (978-958-04-7343-5(9)) Norma S.A. COL. *Dist:* Distribuidora Norma, Inc.

Squillace, Elisa, illus. Down in the Jungle. 2005. (Classic Books with Holes). 16p. (J). bds. 5.99 (978-1-904550-61-7(4)) Child's Play-International.

Sykes, Julie. I Don't Want to Go to Bed! Warnes, Tim, illus. 1998. 14p. (J). (ps-2). bds. 6.95 (978-1-888444-33-9(9), 21301) Little Tiger Pr.

—I Don't Want to Go to Bed! Warnes, Tim, illus. 2001. (J). 32p. 5.95 (978-1-58925-350-6(7)); 26p. tchr. ed. 14.95 (978-1-58925-001-7(X)) ME Media LLC. (tiger tales).

—I Don't Want to Go to Bed! Warnes, Tim, illus. 1998. (ENG, URD, SPA, VIE & CHI.). 32p. (J). (978-1-85430-535-0(2)); (978-1-85430-537-4(9)); (978-1-85430-539-8(5)); (978-1-85430-538-1(7)); (978-1-85430-536-7(0)) Magi Pubns.

—I Don't Want to Take a Bath! Warnes, Tim, illus. 1998. (J). (ps-2). 32p. pap. 5.95 (978-1-888444-36-0(3), 21036); 14p. bds. 6.95 (978-1-888444-34-6(7), 21300) Little Tiger Pr.

—Wait for Me, Little Tiger! Warnes, Tim, illus. 2001. 28p. (J). (ps-k). tchr. ed. 14.95 (978-1-58925-009-3(5), tiger tales) ME Media LLC.

Talbott, Hudson. Safari Journal. 2003. (Illus.). 64p. (J). 18.00 (978-0-15-216393-8(X)) Harcourt Children's Bks.

Tashiro, Chisato. Chameleon's Colors. Martens, Marianne, tr. from GER. 2003. (Illus.). 32p. (J). 15.95 (978-0-7358-1887-3(8)) North-South Bks., Inc.

—Chameleon's Colors bilingual L. 2007. (J). 16.50 (978-0-7358-2104-0(6)) North-South Bks., Inc.

—Chameleons Colors bilingual PB. 2007. (SPA.). (J). pap. 6.95 (978-0-7358-2105-7(4)) North-South Bks., Inc.

—Chameleons Colors PB. 2007. (Illus.). (J). pap. 6.95 (978-0-7358-2111-8(9)) North-South Bks., Inc.

Taylor, Thomas. The Loudest Roar. 2003. (Illus.). (J). pap. (978-0-439-50131-6(8), Levine, Arthur A. Bks.) Scholastic, Inc.

Taylor, Thomas, illus. The Loudest Roar. 2003. 32p. (J). 15.95 (978-0-439-50130-9(X), Levine, Arthur A. Bks.) Scholastic, Inc.

Weeks, Sarah. Piece of Jungle. Duranceau, Suzanne, illus. 1999. 32p. (J). (ps-3). 15.95 incl. audio (978-0-06-028409-1(9), Geringer, Laura Book) HarperCollins Pubs.

Willis, Jeanne. El Nino Que Perdio el Ombligo. Ross, Tony, illus. (SPA.). (J). 8.95 (978-958-04-5632-2(1)) Norma S.A. COL. *Dist:* Distribuidora Norma, Inc., Lectorum Pubns., Inc.

Wilson, Anna. The Foolish Turtle. Gordon, Mike, illus. 2005. 32p. (J). (gr. k-1). lib. bdg. 11.15 (978-0-606-33597-3(8)) Tandem Library Bks.

Wilson, Karma & Watts, Suzanne. Hilda Must Be Dancing. 2004. (Illus.). 32p. (J). 16.99 (978-0-689-84788-2(2), McElderry, Margaret K.) Simon & Schuster Children's Publishing.

Wyss, Tyan. African Dream. Immelman, Sarita, illus. 2006. 48p. (J). pap. 15.95 (*978-1-58939-915-0(3)) Virtualbookworm.com Publishing, Inc.

Yaccarino, Dan. Deep in the Jungle. Yaccario, Dan, illus. 2002. (J). 25.11 (978-0-7587-2371-0(7)) Book Wholesalers, Inc.

Ziefert, Harriet. Monkey's Noisy Jungle. Newton, Jill, illus. 2007. bds. 7.95 (978-1-59354-598-7(3)) Blue Apple Bks.

JUNGLES

DK Publishing. Jungle. 2008. 14p. (J). (gr. k-2). 12.99 (*978-0-7566-3364-6(8)) Dorling Kindersley Publishing, Inc.

Dorling Kindersley Publishing Staff. Jungle. 2004. (Dk Picture Stickers Ser.). 16p. (J). pap. 3.99 (978-0-7566-0248-2(3)) Dorling Kindersley Publishing, Inc.

Dorling Kindersley Publishing Staff, ed. Jungle. 2004. (Dk Eyewitness Books Ser.). (Illus.). 72p. (J). 15.99 (978-0-7566-0694-7(2)) Dorling Kindersley Publishing, Inc.

Dorling Kindersley Publishing Staff & Millard, Anne. In the Jungle. 2002. (Little Windows Ser.). (Illus.). 16p. (J). bds. 6.95 (978-0-7894-8570-0(2)) Dorling Kindersley Publishing, Inc.

Fitzgerald, Stephanie. Remote Jungles. 2007. (J). (*978-1-4329-0109-7(5)); pap. (*978-1-4329-0115-8(X)) Heinemann Library.

Harvey, Bob. Get Inside the Jungle. (Get Inside Ser.). (Illus.). 48p. (J). pap. 18.95 (978-1-904668-94-7(1)) Mercury Bks. Ltd. GBR. *Dist:* International Publishers Marketing.

Jolly Jungle Giant Sticker Shapes. 2002. (Sticker Shapes Ser.). 16p. (J). pap. 5.98 (978-0-7525-7928-3(2)) Parragon, Inc.

Jungle Fun. 2003. 32p. 12.98 (978-1-4054-2004-4(9)) Parragon, Inc.

Miller, Joe. If the Earth... Were a Few Feet in Diameter. McLean, Wilson, illus. 1999. 36p. (J). (ps-3). tchr. ed. 16.95 (978-0-86713-054-6(7), 85131) Greenwich Workshop Pr.

Raintree Steck-Vaughn Staff. True Tales from the Jungles. 1999. (Illus.). (J). pap. 13.00 (978-0-7398-0853-5(2)) Steck-Vaughn.

Robinson, Fay. In the Jungle. Lopez, Paul, illus. 2004. (Treasure Tree Ser.). 32p. (J). (978-0-7166-1604-7(1)) World Bk., Inc.

Ward, Beck & Bainbridge, Katie, eds. Life in the Jungle: Touch & Feel. 2004. (Magic Windows Ser.). (Illus.). 10p. (J). bds. 7.95 (978-0-7624-1843-5(5), Running Pr. Kids) Running Pr. Bk. Pubs.

J K L

JUNGLES—FICTION

Adams, Pam. Elephant. 2005. (Illus.). 8p. (J). (ps). bds. 5.99 (978-1-904550-27-3(4)) Child's Play-International.

—Tiger. 2005. (Illus.). 8p. (J). (ps). bds. 5.99 (978-1-904550-28-0(2)) Child's Play-International.

Alcott, Louisa May. The Louisa Alcott Reader: A Supplementar. 2006. pap. ***(978-1-4065-0590-0(0))** Dodo Pr.

Aristizabal, Nora. The Wonderful Jungle / la selva Maravillosa. 2005. 44p. pap. (978-958-30-1966-1(6)) Panamericana Editorial.

Baker, Liza. Harold & the Purple CrayonTM: Dinosaur Days. Chiang, Andy, illus. 2002. (Harold & the Purple Crayon Ser.). 40p. (J). (ps-1). 12.99 (978-0-06-000541-2(6)) HarperCollins Pubs.

Ballantyne, R. M. Gorilla Hunters A Tale of the Wilds of A. 2006. pap. 36.95 ***(978-1-4286-5952-0(8))** Kessinger Publishing, LLC.

Bannerman, Helen. The Boy & the Tigers. Petrone, Valeria, illus. 2004. (Little Golden Book Ser.). 24p. (J). (gr. k-k). 2.99 (978-0-375-82719-8(6) , Golden Bks.) Random Hse. Children's Bks.

Bares, Alice. It Happened in the Jungle. 2001. 32p. (J). pap. (978-0-9712134-0-1(2)) Second Helping Foundation, The.

Barlow, Steve & Skidmore, Steve. Tales of Dark Forest Trilogy. 3rd ed. 2003. (Tales of the Dark Forest Ser.). (Illus.). 192p. (J). pap. 10.99 (978-0-00-710865-7(6)) HarperCollins Pubs. Ltd. GBR. *Dist:* Independent Pubs. Group.

Bell, Michele Ashman. Rescue: A Jungle Adventure. 2006. 246p. (J). pap. (978-1-59811-093-7(4)) Covenant Communications.

The Big Game. 2007. (J). per. ***(978-1-932570-68-7(3))** Literacy Footprints Inc.

Bjerkvold, Belinda & Kipling, Rudyard. The Jungle Book. Larrea, Miguel & Andrada, Javier, illus. 2006. (J). lib. bdg. ***(978-0-8368-7663-5(6))** Stevens, Gareth Inc.

Bollinger/Papp, illus. King Kong: Meet Kong & Ann. 2005. 32p. (J). lib. bdg. 13.85 ***(978-1-4242-0615-5(4))** Fitzgerald Bks.

Bruna, Dick. Let's Learn: Boris in the Forest. 2004. (Illus.). 24p. pap. 4.99 (978-1-59226-174-1(4)) Big Tent Entertainment, Inc.

Bush, John & Geraghty, Paul. The Bungle in the Jungle. (Illus.). 32p. (J). 17.95 (978-0-09-174056-6(8)) Random Hse. GBR. *Dist:* Trafalgar Square Publishing.

Campoy, F. Isabel. Rosa Raposa. Aruego, Jose & Dewey, Ariane, illus. 2002. 32p. (J). (gr. k-2). 16.00 (978-0-15-202161-0(2) , Gulliver Bks.) Harcourt Children's Bks.

Child's Play, ed. Down in the Jungle. 2006. (Illus.). 16p. 19.99 (978-1-84643-009-1(7)) Child's Play-International.

Christie, Jean. Thunder in the Jungle. Chambers, Sally, illus. 2002. (Curious Creatures Bks.). 12p. (J). (ps-k). bds. 12.95 (978-1-4027-0209-9(4)) Sterling Publishing Co., Inc.

Cole, Bob. Power Reading: Classics/Jungle Book. Connor, Robin, illus. 2004. 94p. (J). (gr. 4 up). vinyl bd. 39.95 (978-1-883186-61-6(7) , PPCL2) National Reading Styles Institute, Inc.

—Power Reading: Comic Book/Jungle Book. Connor, Robin, illus. 2005. 62p. (J). (gr. 3 up). vinyl bd. 39.95 (978-1-883186-74-6(9) , PPCLC2) National Reading Styles Institute, Inc.

Connell, Richard. Most Dangerous Game. 2006. pap. 15.95 ***(978-1-4304-5151-8(3))** Kessinger Publishing, LLC.

Curtis, Jamie Lee. A Donde Van los Globos? Cornell, Laura, illus. (J). 2004. (SPA.). 28p. 21.99 (978-84-8488-056-1(7)); 2002. (CAT & SPA.). 16p. (978-84-8488-057-8(5)) Serres, Ediciones, S. L. ESP. *Dist:* Lectorum Pubns., Inc.

Dalmatian Press Staff. Jungle BK. 2007. 5p. 9.99 ***(978-1-4037-3605-5(7))** Dalmatian Pr.

—Jungle Book/Dinosaurs. 2007. 64p. pap. 4.99 ***(978-1-4037-3593-5(X))** Dalmatian Pr.

Dalmation Press. Jungle Book: Mowgli. 2007. 48p. 3.99 ***(978-1-4037-3604-8(9))** Dalmatian Pr.

de Beer, Hans. Jungle Adventure Coloring Storybook. 2004. (Little Polar Bear Story Ser.). (Illus.). 24p. (J). pap. 2.95 (978-1-4027-1286-9(3)) Sterling Publishing Co., Inc.

Disney Press Staff & Bergen, Lara Rice. Walt Disney's the Jungle Book. 2007. 96p. (ps-2). 12.99 ***(978-1-4231-0166-6(9))** Disney Pr.

Doder, Joshua. Grk & the Pelotti Brothers. 2006. 240p. (J). pap. (978-1-84270-527-8(X)) Andersen.

Drescher, Henrik. Hubert the Pudge: A Vegetarian Tale. Drescher, Henrik, illus. 2006. (Illus.). 40p. (J). (ps-3). 16.99 (978-0-7636-1992-3(2)) Candlewick Pr.

Dubuvoy, Silvia. Murmullos de la Selva. Tsuda, Efrain Rodriguez, illus. 2005. (SPA.). 53p. (J). (gr. 3-7). pap. 9.99 (978-84-241-8660-9(5)) Everest de Ediciones y Distribucion, S.L. ESP. *Dist:* Lectorum Pubns., Inc.

Dumortier, Marjorie. Zoe & her Zany Animals. 2006. (Illus.). 32p. (J). 14.99 (978-0-7145-3306-3(8)) Boyars, Marion Pubs., Inc.

DuQuette, Keith. Little Monkey Lost. DuQuette, Keith, illus. 2007. 32p. (J). (ps). 15.99 (978-0-399-24294-6(5) , Putnam Juvenile) Penguin Group (USA) Inc.

Edwards, Richard. Un Lugar Seguro para Pequeno Mono/ Little Monkey's One Safe Place. Sarfatti, Esther, tr. Winter, Susan, illus. 2006. (ENG & SPA.). 32p. (J). (ps-1). 15.95 (978-1-84507-736-5(9)) Lincoln, Frances Ltd. GBR. *Dist:* Perseus Distribution.

Elliott, David. Evangeline Mudd & the Golden-Haired Apes of the Ikkinasti Jungle. Wesson, Andrea, illus. 2007. 208p. (J). (gr. 2-5). 5.99 (978-0-7636-2614-3(7)) Candlewick Pr.

—Evangeline Mudd & the Golden-Haired Apes of the Ikkinasti Jungle. Wesson, Andrea, illus. 2004. 208p. pap. (978-0-7445-8379-3(9)) Walker Bks., Ltd.

Elsie Elephant's Jungle Shower. 2002. (My First Tab Story Ser.). (J). bds. 3.98 (978-0-7525-8955-8(5)) Parragon, Inc.

Fraser, Jess, illus. Jungle Jingles. 2007. (J). cd-rom 9.99 ***(978-0-9795190-8-6(X))** Color & Learn.

Gondek, Heather. Who's in the Jungle? Lift-the-Flap 'n' Learn. Gilvan-Cartwright, Chris, illus. 2005. (Fun with Animals Ser.). 10p. (J). 9.95 (978-1-58117-075-7(0) , Intervisual/Piggy Toes) Dalmatian Pr.

Greene, Janice. Jungle Book. abr. ed. 2001. (gr. 7-12). lib. bdg. 15.25 (978-0-613-36449-2(X)) Tandem Library Bks.

Grey, Zane. Ken Ward in the Jungle. l.t. ed. 1999. 272p. (J). pap. (978-0-7540-3608-1(1)) BBC Audiobooks America.

Gutman, Anne. Lisa in the Jungle. Hallensleben, Georg, illus. 2003. (Misadventures of Gaspard & Lisa Ser.). 32p. (J). (ps-3). 9.95 (978-0-375-82254-4(2) , Knopf Bks. for Young Readers) Random Hse. Children's Bks.

Harcourt School Publishers Staff. Hiding Places: Take-Home Book. 1999. (Collections Ser.). (Illus.). (J). pap. 1.90 (978-0-15-317222-9(3)) Harcourt Schl. Pubs.

Harper, Wilhelmina. The Gunniwolf. Upton, Barbara, illus. 2003. 32p. (J). (ps). 15.99 (978-0-525-46785-4(8) , Dutton Juvenile) Penguin Group (USA) Inc.

Harter, Debbie. The Animal Boogie. 2005. (Illus.). (J). pap. ***(978-1-905236-49-7(2))** Barefoot Bks., Inc.

—Cha-Cha-Cha en la Selva (The Animal Boogie) Harter, Debbie, illus. 2003. (SPA., Illus.). 32p. (J). pap. 9.99 (978-1-84148-913-1(1)) Barefoot Bks., Inc.

—De paseo por la selva (Walking through the Jungle) Ugalde, Raquel, tr. Harter, Debbie, illus. 2003. (SPA., Illus.). 32p. (J). 6.99 (978-1-84148-995-7(6)) Barefoot Bks., Inc.

Harter, Debbie, illus. De Paseo por la Selva (Walking through the Jungle) 2002. (SPA & ENG.). 32p. (J). (gr. k-2). 9.99 incl. audio compact disk (978-1-84148-912-4(3)) Barefoot Bks., Inc.

Hiebert, Elfrieda H. & Juel, Connie. Who's in the Jungle? (Little Book Practice Reader Ser.). (J). (978-0-8136-0885-3(6)) Modern Curriculum Pr.

Jenisch, Betty. Rennie. 2007. 9.00 ***(978-0-8059-8947-2(1))** Dorrance Publishing Co., Inc.

Jones, Allan Frewin. Legend of the Anaconda King. 2006. 186p. (J). pap. ***(978-0-439-85670-6(1))** Scholastic, Inc.

Jordan, Apple. The Bungle in the Jungle. 2005. (Madagascar Ser.). 32p. (J). 3.99 (978-0-439-69629-6(1)) Scholastic, Inc.

Jungle BK. 2007. 18p. bds. 11.99 ***(978-1-4037-3606-2(5))** Dalmatian Pr.

Jungle Book. 2000. (Illus.). 48p. (YA). stu. ed., per. 6.95 (978-1-56254-292-4(3) , SP2923) Saddleback Educational Publishing.

Jungle Law: MainSails Individual Title Six-Packs. (Sails Literacy Ser.). (gr. 5 up). 37.00 (978-0-7578-8049-0(5)) Rigby Education.

Jungle Tales. 2002. 232p. (J). 5.98 (978-0-7525-8910-7(5)) Parragon, Inc.

Kehret, Peg. The Secret Journey. 2000. (J). (978-0-606-19874-5(1)) Tandem Library Bks.

Kendrick, Robert. Treasure Quest: Journey to the Jungle. 2004. 46p. pap. 19.95 (978-1-4137-1467-8(6)) PublishAmerica, Inc.

Kipling, Rudyard. The Jungle Book. Pablo Marcos Studio Staff, illus. 2002. (Great Illustrated Classics Ser.).Tr. of 192. 240p. (J). (gr. 3-8). 21.35 (978-1-57765-812-2(4) , ABDO & Daughters) ABDO Publishing Co.

—The Jungle Book. Alexander, Gregory, illus. 1999. (Classics Ser.).Tr. of 192. 160p. (J). 12.95 (978-0-7892-0558-2(0)); pap. 7.95 (978-0-7892-0548-3(3)) Abbeville Pr., Inc. (Abbeville Kids).

—The Jungle Book. Alexander, Gregory, illus. 2000. Tr. of 192. 160p. (J). pap. 8.99 (978-1-85793-998-9(0) , Pavilion Bks., Ltd.) Anova Bks. GBR. *Dist:* Trafalgar Square Publishing.

—The Jungle Book. Alexander, Gregory, illus. 2003. (Chrysalis Children's Classics Ser.).Tr. of 192. 159p. (YA). pap. (978-1-84365-038-6(X)) Chrysalis Children's Bks.

—The Jungle Book. 2000. (Dover Juvenile Classics Ser.).Tr. of 192. 160p. (J). (gr. 4-7). pap. 2.50 (978-0-486-41024-1(2)) Dover Pubns., Inc.

—The Jungle Book. 2001. Tr. of 192. 168p. 8.95 (978-1-84232-943-6(X)) House of Stratus, Inc. GBR. *Dist:* Midpoint Trade Bks., Inc.

—The Jungle Book. Daily, Don, illus. 2003. Tr. of 192. 56p. (J). 9.98 (978-0-7624-1495-6(2) , Courage Bks.) Running Pr. Bk. Pubs.

—The Jungle Book. 2001. (Saddleback Classics).Tr. of 192. (Illus.). (J). 13.75 (978-0-606-21558-9(1)) Tandem Library Bks.

—The Jungle Book. 1998. (Children's Classics).Tr. of 192. (ENG., Illus.). 192p. (J). (gr. 4-7). pap. (978-1-85326-119-0(X) , 119XWW) Wordsworth Editions, Ltd.

—Jungle Book. 2007. 192p. (J). 19.95 ***(978-0-9545103-9-8(9))** Palazzo Editions, Ltd. GBR. *Dist:* Independent Pubs. Group.

—The Jungle Book. Corvino, Lucy, illus. 2008. (Classic Starts Ser.). 160p. (J). 5.95 ***(978-1-4027-4576-8(1))** Sterling Publishing Co., Inc.

—The Jungle Book: #1 Rikki-Tikki-Tavi Moves In. 2007. (Easy Reader Classics Ser.). 32p. (J). (ps-3). 21.35 ***(978-1-59961-336-9(0))** Spotlight.

—The Jungle Book: Mowgli's Story. Bayley, Nicola, illus. unabr. ed. 2005. 160p. (J). (gr. 4-7). 19.99 (978-0-7636-2317-3(2)) Candlewick Pr.

—The Jungle Book by Rudyard Kipling: Digital Classics. 2002. cd-rom 5.00 (978-1-931457-07-1(7)) Stargate Electronic Library, Inc.

—The Jungle Books. (Borders Classics Ser.). 276p. 7.95 (978-1-58726-165-7(0)) Ann Arbor Media Group, LLC.

—The Jungle Books. 2004. (Barnes & Noble Classics Ser.). (Illus.). 432p. pap. 5.95 (978-1-59308-109-6(X)) Barnes & Noble, Inc.

—The Jungle Books. 2005. 336p. (gr. 12). pap. 4.95 (978-0-451-52975-6(8) , Signet Classics) Penguin Group (USA) Inc.

—Rikki Tikki Tavi Moves In No. 1, No. 1. Madsen, Jim, illus. 2006. (Easy Reader Classics Ser.). 32p. (J). pap. 3.95 (978-1-4027-3289-8(9)) Sterling Publishing Co., Inc.

Kipling, Rudyard & Hedge, Tricia. The Jungle Book, Level 2. 2nd abr. ed. 2000. (Bookworms Ser.).Tr. of 192. (Illus.). 64p. 6.50 (978-0-19-422977-7(7)) Oxford Univ. Pr., Inc.

Landolf, Diane Wright. The Jungle Book. Rowe, John, illus. 2008. 112p. (J). ***(978-0-375-84276-4(4));** lib. bdg. ***(978-0-375-94062-0(6))** Random Hse., Inc.

Leaney, Cindy. Jungle Journey. Whitehouse, Patty, ed. King, Sue & Wilks, Peter, illus. 2004. (Friendly Phonics Ser.). 24p. (J). lib. bdg. 14.95 (978-1-59054-183-8(9)) Fitzgerald Bks.

LeapFrog Staff. Disney Lion King - U. K. 2003. (Illus.). spiral bd. 14.99 (978-1-59319-006-4(9)) LeapFrog Enterprises, Inc.

Lee, Evelyn. Mountain Mists: A Story of the Virungas. Kratter, Paul, illus. 1999. (Habitat Ser.: No. 14). 36p. (J). (gr. 1-4). 26.95 (978-1-56899-789-6(2)); (ps-3). 15.95 (978-1-56899-785-8(X)); (ps-3). pap. 5.95 (978-1-56899-786-5(8)) Soundprints.

—Mountain Mists: A Story of the Virungas. 1999. (gr. k-3). lib. bdg. 15.25 (978-0-613-56927-9(X)) Tandem Library Bks.

Lewis, Anthony, illus. Little Jungle Explorers. 14p. bds. 4.99 ***(978-1-84643-036-7(4))** Child's Play International Ltd. GBR. *Dist:* Child's Play-International.

Lornsen, Boy. El Bosque en Peligro. (SPA.). 141p. (J). (gr. 3-5). (978-84-279-3451-1(3) , NG0993) Noguer y Caralt Editores, S. A. ESP. *Dist:* Lectorum Pubns., Inc.

Lost in the Jungle. 2004. (J). (978-1-932570-27-4(6)) Literacy Footprints Inc.

Lost in the Woods CONNECT-IT. 2005. (J). per. 24.95 (978-0-9749412-2-6(0)) EDCO Publishing, Inc.

Ludy, Mark. Jujo: Of the Jungle. 2007. (Illus.). 32p. (J). 16.95 (978-0-9664276-5-3(3)) Green Pastures Publishing, Inc.

MacCracken, Joan. Trisba & Sula: A Miskitu Folktale from Nicaragua (Una Leyenda de los Miskitos de Nicaragua) Macdonald, Isabel et al, trs. Silva, Augusto Alves da, illus. 2005. (ENG & SPA.). 16.95 (978-0-9646018-2-6(6)) Tiffin Pr. of Maine.

Marsh, T. F. Quest for Forgiveness. Marsh, T. F., illus. 2006. (Amazing Travels of Wannabe Ser.). (Illus.). 32p. (J). 8.99 (978-0-7847-1803-2(2) , 04129) Standard Publishing.

Martin, Nicole. The Werewolf. 2006. 146p. pap. ***(978-1-4120-8802-2(X))** Trafford Publishing.

Maselli, Christopher P. N. Escape from Jungle Island. 1998. (Commander Kellie & the Superkids' Early Adventures Ser.). (J). pap. (978-1-57562-217-0(3)) Copeland, Kenneth Pubns.

Mason, Jane B. & Hines Stephens, Sarah. Jungle Book. 2004. 128p. (J). pap. 3.99 (978-0-439-57424-2(2) , Scholastic Paperbacks) Scholastic, Inc.

McKee, David. Elmer & the Kangaroo. McKee, David, illus. 2000. (Elmer Bks.). (Illus.). 32p. (J). (ps up). 15.99 (978-0-688-17951-9(7)) HarperCollins Pubs.

McMullan, Kate. A Wedding for Wiglaf? 2007. (Dragon Slayers' Academy Ser.: No. 4). 112p. (J). (gr. 1-6). 24.21 ***(978-1-59961-380-2(8))** Spotlight.

Merberg, Julie & Bober, Suzanne. Dreaming with Rousseau. 2007. (Illus.). 22p. (J). (ps). bds. 6.95 (978-0-8118-5712-3(3)) Chronicle Bks. LLC.

Montgomery, R. A. Lost on the Amazon. 1999. (Illus.). 114p. mass mkt. (978-0-553-23733-7(0)) Random Hse., Inc.

Moss, Miriam. Jungle Song. Kennaway, Adrienne, illus. 2004. 32p. (J). 15.95 (978-1-84507-039-7(9)) Lincoln, Frances Ltd. GBR. *Dist:* Perseus Distribution.

Mukerji, Dhan Gopal. Jungle Beasts & Men. Allen, J. E., illus. 2005. reprint ed. pap. 22.95 (978-0-7661-9403-8(5)) Kessinger Publishing, LLC.

Napoli, Donna Jo & Johnston, Shelagh. Hotel Jungle. Spengler, Kenneth, tr. Spengler, Kenneth, illus. 2004. 33p. (J). 15.95 (978-1-59336-002-3(9)); pap. (978-1-59336-003-0(7)) Mondo Publishing.

Nino, Jairo Anibal. Zoro. 2003. (SPA., Illus.). 97p. (J). (ps-7). pap. (978-958-30-0291-5(7) , PV4489) Panamericana Editorial COL. *Dist:* Lectorum Pubns., Inc.

Okorafor-Mbachu, Nnedi. Zahrah the Windseeker. Cooper, Stephanie & Hall, Amanda, illus. 2005. 320p. (YA). (gr. 5-7). 16.00 (978-0-618-34090-3(4)) Houghton Mifflin Co. Trade & Reference Div.

Parker, Jeff. King Liar. 2002. (Illus.). 64p. (J). per. 5.95 (978-1-59269-002-2(5)) Mcruffy Pr.

Parker, Jeff. Law of the Jungle. 2007. (Fantastic Four Set II Ser.). 24p. (J). (gr. 2-6). 21.35 ***(978-1-59961-390-1(5))** Spotlight.

Peretti, Frank. Deadly Curse of Toco Rey: Cooper Kids #6. Life Publishers International, tr. from ENG. 2005. (RUS., Illus.). 156p. (J). (978-0-7361-0347-3(3)) Life Pubs. International.

Pitcher, Caroline. Lord of the Forest. Morris, Jackie, illus. 2004. 32p. (J). 16.95 (978-1-84507-058-8(5)) Lincoln, Frances Ltd. GBR. *Dist:* Perseus Distribution.

Price, Sharon K. The Magic Seed. Artigas, Alexandra, illus. 2002. (Magic Jungle Ser.: Vol. 1). 32p. (J). (gr. 2-6). 17.95 (978-0-9720839-0-4(1)) PowerPartners, USA, Inc.

Richards, Kitty. Bird Who Cried Wolf. 2000. (gr. k-3). lib. bdg. 11.80 (978-0-613-24367-4(6)) Tandem Library Bks.

Richards, Lucy, illus. Jumping Jungle (W/Hang Tag) 2004. (Cuddly Cuffs Ser.: No. 7). 12p. (J). tchr. ed. 5.95 (978-1-58925-727-6(8) , tiger tales) ME Media LLC.

—Jumping Jungle (W/Header Card) 2004. (Cuddly Cuffs Ser.: 7). 6p. (J). tchr. ed. 5.95 (978-1-58925-731-3(6) , tiger tales) ME Media LLC.

Richardson, Dick. The Oglin: A Hero's Journey Across Africa... Towards the Tomorrows. Feek, Cathy, illus. 2004. 417p. (J). 24.95 (978-0-9759440-3-5(7)) Savanna Pr.

Rossell, Judith. The Lost Treasure of the Green Iguana: A Jungle Maze Adventure. 2007. (Illus.). 32p. (Orig.). (J). pap. 4.95 (978-1-57990-949-9(3)) Lark Bks.

Ruben's Jungle. 2003. Tr. of Selva de Ruben. (SPA., Illus.). 26p. bds. 16.95 (978-0-9706953-1-4(4)) Globo Libros.

San Souci, Robert D. Double-Dare to Be Scared: Another 13 Chilling Tales. Ouimet, David, illus. 2004. (Dare to Be Scared Ser.). 144p. (J). 16.95 (978-0-8126-2716-9(4)) Cricket Bks.

Schick, Joel, illus. The Jungle Book: A Story about Loyalty. 2006. (J). 6.99 (978-1-59939-023-9(X) , Reader's Digest Young Families, Inc.) Reader's Digest Children's Publishing, Inc.

The Show: Individual Title Six-Packs. (Sails Literacy Ser.). 16p. (gr. k up). 27.00 (978-0-7635-4413-3(2)) Rigby Education.

Smith, Roland. Cryptid Hunters. 2005. 352p. (J). (gr. 5-17). 15.99 (978-0-7868-5161-4(9)) Hyperion Bks. for Children.

—Cryptid Hunters. 2006. 352p. (gr. 5-17). pap. 5.99 (978-0-7868-5162-1(7)) Hyperion Pr.

Souci, Robert D. San & Burroughs, Edgar Rice. Tarzan. McCurdy, Michael, illus. 2004. 31p. (J). (gr. k-4). reprint ed. 16.00 (978-0-7567-7576-6(0)) DIANE Publishing Co.

Soundprints. Forest Adventures: Story-Time Treasury. 2005. (Smithsonian Institution Story-Time Treasures Ser.). (Illus.). 256p. (J). (ps-2). 14.95 (978-1-59069-227-1(6) , HT2001) Studio Mouse LLC.

Spann, Bill. The Agents of Little Woods. 2005. 116p. pap. 16.95 (978-1-4137-6574-8(2)) PublishAmerica, Inc.

Squillace, Elisa, illus. Down in the Jungle. 2005. (Classic Books with Holes). 16p. (J). bds. 5.99 (978-1-904550-61-7(4)) Child's Play-International.

Stewart, Paul & Riddell, Chris. Beyond the Deepwoods. 2004. (Edge Chronicles Ser.: Bk. 1). (Illus.). 288p. (J). (gr. 5-7). 12.95 (978-0-385-75068-4(4)); lib. bdg. 14.99 (978-0-385-75069-1(2)) Random Hse. Children's Bks. (Fickling, David Bks.).

Stilton, Geronimo. Four Mice Deep in the Jungle. Wolf, Matt & Keys, Larry, illus. 2004. (Geronimo Stilton Ser.: No. 5). 128p. (J). pap. 6.99 (978-0-439-55967-6(7) , Scholastic Paperbacks) Scholastic, Inc.

Storm, Rory. Jungle Guide. 2002. (Survivors Ser.). 128p. (J). (gr. 3-7). pap. 4.99 (978-0-439-32856-2(X)) Scholastic, Inc.

The Strange Shoe: Individual Title Six-Packs. 32p. (gr. 3 up). 37.00 (978-0-7635-9679-8(5)) Rigby Education.

Thompson, Lisa. On the Trail of the Golden Man. 2005. (Treasure Trackers Ser.). (Illus.). 80p. (gr. 5-9). 19.00 (978-0-7910-8875-3(8)) Facts On File, Inc.

Thornewell, Danielle. The Mems. 2007. (ENG.). 52p. per. 12.95 ***(978-1-4241-6106-5(1))** PublishAmerica, Inc.

Thottam, Meena, adapted by. Brothers of the Jungle. 2006. (J). 3.95 ***(978-0-9776917-4-6(8)** , Curcumin Bks.) Davlaw Press.

ToyBox Innovations, creator. Deep in the Jungle. abr. ed. 2006. (Disney's Read along Collection). (J). (ps-3). pap. 14.99 incl. audio compact disk (978-0-7634-2182-3(0)) Walt Disney Records.

Trimble, Irene. Jungle Friends. 2003. (gr. k-3). lib. bdg. 11.80 (978-0-613-65128-8(6)) Tandem Library Bks.

Tub Tales: The Jungle. 2003. (Illus.). 10p. (J). 6.00 (978-0-9713507-2-4(8) , 843) Panline U.S.A., Inc.

Turin, Adela. El Ovillo Blanco. 2001. (SPA.). 40p. (J). (gr. 3). (978-84-264-3558-3(0)) Editorial Lumen ESP. *Dist:* Lectorum Pubns., Inc.

Tyminski, Lori, illus. The Jungle Book 2. 2003. (J). 15.98 (978-0-7853-7968-3(1)) Publications International, Ltd.

Urdaneta, Josefina. Pequeno Zambo. 2000. 7.95 (978-980-6437-13-5(6)) Baker & Taylor Bks.

Uribe, Veronica. Buzz, Buzz, Buzz. Calderon, Gloria, illus. 2001. 32p. (J). (ps-k). 15.95 (978-0-88899-430-1(3)) Groundwood Bks. CAN. *Dist:* Perseus Distribution.

Wallace, Karen. Alice Goes to Hollywood. Dewar, Bob, illus. 2006. (Read-It! Chapter Books). 48p. (J). (gr. 2-4). 19.95 (978-1-4048-1678-7(X)) Picture Window Bks.

Weeks, Sarah. Piece of Jungle. Duranceau, Suzanne, illus. 1999. 32p. (J). (ps-3). 15.95 incl. audio (978-0-06-028409-1(9) , Geringer, Laura Book) HarperCollins Pubs.

Wildsmith, Brian. Jungle Party. Wildsmith, Brian, illus. 2006. (Illus.). 32p. (J). 16.95 (978-1-59572-052-8(9)); pap. 6.95 (978-1-59572-053-5(7)) Star Bright Bks., Inc.

Wilkes, Angela. Animales de la Selva Tropical. 2004. (Ladders Ser.).Tr. of Rain Forest Animals. (SPA., Illus.). 32p. (J). (ps-3). pap. 6.95 (978-1-58728-409-0(X) , Two Can Publishing) T&N Children's Publishing.

Williams, Anita. The Captain's Hat. Banks, Timothy, illus. 2000. 104p. (J). (gr. 1-5). pap. 7.95 (978-1-57924-330-2(4) , 119743) Jones, Bob Univ. Pr.

Wood, Francis Eugene. The Nipkins, Vol. II. Pickett, Elizabeth, ed. McDermott, Robert W., illus. Wood, Chris, photos by. rev. ed. 2002. 140p. (J). pap. 12.00 (978-0-9657047-8-6(5)) Tip-Of-The-Moon Publishing Co.

Youngberg, Norma R. Jungle Thorn. 2000. (Illus.). 112p. (J). reprint ed. per. 8.95 (978-1-57258-157-9(3) , 945-6024) TEACH Services, Inc.

JUNIOR HIGH SCHOOLS

Cassel, Katrina L. Junior High Survival Manual. 1998. (gr. 7-12). lib. bdg. 16.45 (978-0-613-72804-1(1)) Tandem Library Bks.

JUNK

see Waste Products

JUPITER (PLANET)

Adamson, Thomas K. Jupiter. (J). 2008. (***978-1-4296-0738-4(6)***); 2003. (Illus.). 24p. lib. bdg. 17.26 (978-0-7368-2112-4(0) , Pebble Bks.) Capstone Pr., Inc.

Adamson, Thomas K. Jupiter: Jupiter. 2006. (ENG & SPA., Illus.). 24p. (J). (978-0-7368-5879-3(2)) Capstone Pr., Inc.

Asimov, Isaac. The Solar System: Jupiter. 2004. (Illus.). 32p. 14.00 (978-1-59102-178-0(2)) Prometheus Bks., Pubs.

Asimov, Isaac & Hantula, Richard. Jupiter. Porras, Carlos & D'Andrea, Patricia, trs. 2003. (Isaac Asimov's Biblioteca del Universo del Siglo XXI). (SPA., Illus.). 32p. (J). (gr. 3 up). pap. 8.95 (978-0-8368-3867-1(X) , Weekly Reader Early Learning Library) Stevens, Gareth Inc.

—Jupiter. Porras, Carlos & D'Andrea, Patricia, trs. 2003. (Isaac Asimov's Biblioteca del Universo del Siglo XXI). (SPA., Illus.). 32p. (J). (gr. 3 up). lib. bdg. 24.67 (978-0-8368-3854-1(8)) Stevens, Gareth Inc.

—Jupiter. rev. ed. 2002. (Isaac Asimov's 21st Century Library of the Universe). (Illus.). 32p. (YA). (gr. 3 up). lib. bdg. 24.67 (978-0-8368-3235-8(3)) Stevens, Gareth Inc.

—Jupiter: The Spotted Giant. 2003. (Isaac Asimov's 21st Century Library of the Universe). (Illus.). 32p. (J). (gr. 3 up). pap. (978-0-8368-3939-5(0) , Weekly Reader Early Learning Library) Stevens, Gareth Inc.

Birch, Robin. Jupiter. 2004. (Solar System Ser.). (Illus.). 32p. (gr. 3-5). 23.00 (978-0-7910-7926-3(0) , Chelsea Hse.) Facts On File, Inc.

Feinstein, Stephen. Jupiter: A Myreportlinks. com Book. 2005. (Solar System Ser.). (Illus.). 48p. (J). (ps-10). lib. bdg. 25.26 (978-0-7660-5303-8(2) , MyReportLinks.com Bks.) Enslow Pubs., Inc.

Geiger, Beth. The Inside Story of Jupiter. 2006. (J). 7.80 (978-1-933798-07-3(6)) Sally Ride Science.

Goldstein, Margaret J. Jupiter. 2005. (Pull Ahead Bks.). (Illus.). 32p. (gr. 2-4). lib. bdg. 22.60 (978-0-8225-4652-8(3)) Lerner Publishing Group.

Goss, Tim. Jupiter. 2003. (Universe Ser.). (Illus.). 32p. (J). (gr. 3-5). lib. bdg. 22.79 (978-1-58810-911-8(9)); pap. 7.50 (978-1-4034-0612-5(X)) Heinemann Library.

Howard, Fran. Jupiter. 2007. (Planets Ser.). (ENG., Illus.). 32p. (J). (gr. k-4). lib. bdg. 24.21 (***978-1-59928-827-7(3)*** , Buddy Bks.) ABDO Publishing Co.

Jupiter. (Galaxy Ser.). 24p. (J). 6.95 (978-0-7368-8886-8(1)) Capstone Pr., Inc.

Landau, Elaine. Jupiter. (True Booktrade;: Space Ser.). 48p. (J). 2008. pap. 6.95 (***978-0-531-14789-4(4)***); 2007. (Illus.). (gr. 3-5). lib. bdg. 26.00 (***978-0-531-12559-5(9)***) Scholastic Library Publishing. (Children's Pr.).

Miller, Ron. Jupiter. 2002. (Worlds Beyond Ser.). (Illus.). 72p. (gr. 7 up). lib. bdg. (978-0-7613-2356-3(2) , Twenty-First Century Bks.) Lerner Publishing Group.

Orme, Helen & Orme, David. Let's Explore Jupiter. 2006. (J). pap. (***978-0-8368-8125-7(7)***); lib. bdg. (***978-0-8368-7940-7(6)***) Stevens, Gareth Inc.

Oxlade, Chris. Jupiter, Neptune, & the Outer Planets. 2007. lib. bdg. (***978-1-4042-3736-0(4)*** , Rosen Central) Rosen Publishing Group, Inc., The.

Potts, Steve. Jupiter: Our Solar System. 2001. (Illus.). 23p. (J). lib. bdg. 21.35 (978-1-58340-097-5(4)) Smart Apple Media.

Richardson, Adele. Jupiter. 2008. (***978-1-4296-0722-3(X)***) Capstone Pr., Inc.

Richardson, Adele D. Jupiter. 2005. (First Facts Ser.). (Illus.). 24p. (J). 21.26 (978-0-7368-3688-3(8)) Capstone Pr., Inc.

Ring, Susan. Jupiter. (Exploring Planets Ser.). (J). 2004. pap. (978-1-59036-230-3(6)); 2002. (Illus.). 24p. lib. bdg. 15.95 (978-1-59036-103-0(2)) Weigl Pubs., Inc.

Simon, Charnan. Jupiter. 2003. (Planets Ser.). (Illus.). 32p. (J). (gr. 2-6). 27.07 (978-1-59296-049-1(9)) Child's World, Inc.

Simon, Seymour. Destination Jupiter. 2000. 13.79 (978-0-606-20339-5(7)); (J). (978-0-606-20286-2(2)) Tandem Library Bks.

Slade, Suzanne. A Look at Jupiter. 2008. (J). lib. bdg. (***978-1-4042-3829-9(8)*** , PowerKids Pr.) Rosen Publishing Group, Inc., The.

Spangenburg, Ray. Look at Jupiter. 2001. (gr. 5-8). lib. bdg. 24.55 (978-0-613-54274-6(6)) Tandem Library Bks.

Sparrow, Giles. Jupiter. (Exploring the Solar System Ser.). (Illus.). 39p. (J). (gr. 4-7). 2002. pap. 7.95 (978-1-58810-960-6(7) , 91443); 2001. lib. bdg. 24.22 (978-1-57572-395-2(6)) Heinemann Library.

Taylor-Butler, Christine. Jupiter. (Scholastic News Nonfiction Readers: Space Science Ser.). 24p. (J). 2008. pap. 6.95 (***978-0-531-14761-0(4)***); 2007. (Illus.). (gr. 1-2). lib. bdg. 20.00 (***978-0-531-14696-5(0)***) Scholastic Library Publishing. (Children's Pr.).

Vogt, Gregory L. Jupiter. 6 vols. (gr. 2-5). 36.95 (978-0-7368-8968-1(X)) Red Brick Learning.

—Jupiter, Saturn, Uranus & Neptune. 2000. (Our Universe Ser.). (Illus.). 48p. (YA). (gr. 5-12). lib. bdg. 22.83 (978-0-7398-3109-0(7)) Raintree.

Wimmer, Teresa. Jupiter. 2007. (J). (978-1-58341-517-7(3) , Creative Education) Creative Co., The.

World Book, contrib. by. Jupiter, Ceres & the Asteroids. 2nd ed. 2006. (World Book's Solar System & Space Exploration Library). (Illus.). 64p. (J). (***978-0-7166-9515-8(4)***) World Bk., Inc.

World Book, Inc Staff, contrib. by. Jupiter. 2006. (World Book's Solar System & Space Exploration Library). (Illus.). 63p. (J). (978-0-7166-9505-9(7)) World Bk., Inc.

Young, Abby. Jupiter. 2006. (J). (***978-1-4042-1967-0(6)***) Rosen Publishing Group, Inc., The.

JURISPRUDENCE

see Law

JURISTS

see Lawyers

JURY

De Capua, Sarah. Serving on a Jury. 2002. (True Bks.). (Illus.). 48p. (J). (gr. 3-5). pap. 6.95 (978-0-516-27364-8(7)); 25.00 (978-0-516-22329-2(1)) Scholastic Library Publishing. (Children's Pr.).

Decapua, Sarah. Serving on a Jury. 2002. (gr. 3-6). lib. bdg. 15.25 (978-0-613-54355-2(6)) Tandem Library Bks.

DeGezelle, Terri. Serving on a Jury. 2005. (First Facts Ser.). (Illus.). 24p. (J). 21.26 (978-0-7368-3686-9(1)) Capstone Pr., Inc.

Smith, Rich. Seventh Amendment: The Right to a Trial by Jury. 2007. (Bill of Rights Ser.). (ENG., Illus.). 32p. (J). (gr. 4-8). lib. bdg. 25.65 (***978-1-59928-919-9(9)*** , ABDO & Daughters) ABDO Publishing Co.

—Sixth Amendment: The Right to a Fair Trial. 2007. (Bill of Rights Ser.). (ENG., Illus.). 32p. (J). (gr. 4-8). lib. bdg. 25.65 (***978-1-59928-918-2(0)*** , ABDO & Daughters) ABDO Publishing Co.

JUSTICE, ADMINISTRATION OF

see also Courts; Crime and Criminals

Berger, Leslie B. Grand Jury. 2000. (Crime, Justice & Punishment Ser.). (Illus.). 80p. (YA). (gr. 7-12). 30.00 (978-0-7910-4290-8(1) , Chelsea Hse.) Facts On File, Inc.

Cohen, Laura. The Gault Case & Young People's Rights: Debating Supreme Court Decisions. 2006. (Debating Supreme Court Decisions Ser.). (Illus.). 128p. (J). lib. bdg. 26.60 (978-0-7660-2476-2(8)) Enslow Pubs., Inc.

Crime, Justice, & Punishment. 2005. 80 - 120p. pap. 1140.00 (978-0-7910-8076-4(5) , Chelsea Hse.) Facts On File, Inc.

Davis, Mary L. Working in Law & Justice. 1999. (Exploring Careers Ser.). (Illus.). 112p. (YA). (gr. 6-9). lib. bdg. (978-0-8225-1766-5(3) , Lerner Pubns.) Lerner Publishing Group.

Dupont, Ellen. The United States Justice System. 2002. (Crime & Detection Ser.). (Illus.). 96p. (J). (gr. 7 up). lib. bdg. (978-1-59084-377-2(0)) Mason Crest Pubs.

Egendorf, Laura K. The Legal System. 2002. (Opposing Viewpoints Ser.). (Illus.). 200p. (J). (gr. 10-12). pap. 24.95 (978-0-7377-1231-5(7) , Greenhaven Pr., Inc.) Thomson Gale.

Emert, Phyllis Raybin. Attorneys General: Enforcing the Law. 2005. (Illus.). 176p. (J). (gr. 7 up). lib. bdg. 24.95 (978-1-881508-66-3(8)) Oliver Pr., Inc.

Fitzpatrick, Anne. The U. S. Government Judicial. 2003. (Let's Investigate Ser.). (Illus.). 32p. (J). lib. bdg. 18.95 (978-1-58341-263-3(8) , Creative Education) Creative Co., The.

Gold, Susan Dudley. In Re Gault: Do Minors Have the Same Rights As Adults? 2007. (Supreme Court Milestones Ser.). 144p. (YA). (gr. 9 up). lib. bdg. 39.93 (978-0-7614-2584-7(5) , Benchmark Bks.) Cavendish, Marshall Corp.

Hanrahan, Clare. Legal System. 2007. (Opposing Viewpoints Ser.). (Illus.). 240p. (gr. 10-12). 36.20 (***978-0-7377-3757-8(3)***); pap. 24.95 (***978-0-7377-3758-5(1)***) Thomson Gale. (Greenhaven Pr., Inc.).

Harris, Nancy. First Guide to Government: What's the State Judicial Branch? 2007. (J). (***978-1-4034-9511-2(4)***); pap. (***978-1-4034-9517-4(3)***) Heinemann Library.

Hermsen, Sarah, et al. American Reference Library. 2004. (Crime & Punishment in America Reference Library). 39p. (J). lib. bdg. 5.00 (978-0-7876-9174-5(7) , UXL) Thomson Gale.

Hile, Kevin. The Trial of Juveniles As Adults. 2003. (Point/Counterpoint Ser.). (Illus.). 112p. (gr. 9-13). pap. 15.95 (978-0-7910-7506-7(0) , Chelsea Hse.) Facts On File, Inc.

—The Trial of Juveniles as Adults. 2003. (Point/Counterpoint Ser.). (Illus.). 112p. (gr. 9-13). 32.95 (978-0-7910-7374-2(2) , Chelsea Hse.) Facts On File, Inc.

—Trial of Juveniles as Adults. 2003. (gr. 7-12). lib. bdg. 21.05 (978-0-613-83448-3(8)) Tandem Library Bks.

Hunter, David. Inequities of the Justice System. 2006. (Incarceration Issues Ser.). (Illus.). 112p. (YA). (gr. 7 up). (978-1-59084-995-8(7)) Mason Crest Pubs.

Jacobs, Thomas A. They Broke the Law - You Be the Judge: True Cases of Teen Crime. 2004. 224p. (YA). (gr. 7 up). pap. 15.95 (978-1-57542-134-6(8)) Free Spirit Publishing, Inc.

Johnson, Toni. Handcuff Blues: Helping Teens Stay Out of Trouble with the Law. Gross, Daerick, illus. 1999. 206p. (J). pap. 10.95 (978-1-885535-43-6(0)) Goofy Foot Pr.

Kelly, Zachary A. Laws. 1998. (Law & Order Ser.). (J). lib. bdg. 16.95 (978-0-86625-664-3(4)) Rourke Publishing, LLC.

Luthringer, Chelsea. So What Is Justice Anyway? (Students Guide to American Civics Ser.). 48p. (YA). 2000. lib. bdg. 23.95 (978-0-8239-3448-5(9)); 1999. (Illus.). (gr. 5-8). lib. bdg. 23.95 (978-0-8239-3096-8(3) , CVJUST) Rosen Publishing Group, Inc., The. (Rosen Central).

Mattern, Joanne. Attorney General. 2003. (America's Leaders Ser.). (Illus.). 32p. (J). 24.94 (978-1-56711-278-8(1) , Blackbirch Pr., Inc.) Thomson Gale.

Miller, Jake. Community Rules: Making & Changing Rules & Laws in Communities. 2005. (Communities at Work Ser.). (Illus.). 24p. (J). lib. bdg. 19.95 (978-1-4042-2782-8(2) , PowerKids Pr.) Rosen Publishing Group, Inc., The.

Peacock, Nancy. Great Prosecutions. 2001. (Crime, Justice & Punishment Ser.). (Illus.). 80p. (J). 30.00 (978-0-7910-4292-2(8) , Chelsea Hse.) Facts On File, Inc.

Smith, Roger & McIntosh, Marsha. Youth in Prison. 2006. (Incarceration Issues Ser.). (Illus.). 112p. (J). (gr. 7 up). (978-1-59084-990-3(6)) Mason Crest Pubs.

Thompson, Julian F. Hard Time. 2003. (Illus.). 256p. (YA). 16.95 (978-0-689-85424-8(2) , Atheneum) Simon & Schuster Children's Publishing.

Townsend, John. Lawmakers & the Police. 2005. (J). (978-1-4109-2052-2(6)); pap. (978-1-4109-2057-7(7)) Steck-Vaughn.

Wilker, Josh. Revenge & Retribution. 1999. (Crime, Justice & Punishment Ser.). (Illus.). 80p. (YA). (gr. 7-12). 30.00 (978-0-7910-4321-9(5) , Chelsea Hse.) Facts On File, Inc.

JUVENILE DELINQUENCY

see also Child Welfare

Barbour, Scott, ed. Teen Violence. 1998. (Opposing Viewpoints Digests Ser.). (Illus.). 144p. (YA). (gr. 6-9). lib. bdg. 31.20 (978-1-56510-865-3(5) , Greenhaven Pr., Inc.) Thomson Gale.

Biscontini, Tracey. Youth Violence. 2007. (History of Issues Ser.). (Illus.). 240p. (gr. 10-12). 36.20 (978-0-7377-2877-4(9) , Greenhaven Pr., Inc.) Thomson Gale.

Daniels, Peggy. Gangs. 2007. (Issues that Concern You Ser.). (Illus.). 144p. (gr. 7-10). 33.70 (***978-0-7377-3815-5(4)*** , Greenhaven Pr., Inc.) Thomson Gale.

Ford, Jean. Rural Crime & Poverty: Violence, Drugs, & Other Issues. 2008. (Youth in Rural North America Ser.). (J). (978-1-4222-0016-2(7)) Mason Crest Pubs.

Hile, Kevin. The Trial of Juveniles As Adults. 2003. (Point/Counterpoint Ser.). (Illus.). 112p. (gr. 9-13). pap. 15.95 (978-0-7910-7506-7(0) , Chelsea Hse.) Facts On File, Inc.

—The Trial of Juveniles as Adults. 2003. (Point/Counterpoint Ser.). (Illus.). 112p. (gr. 9-13). 32.95 (978-0-7910-7374-2(2) , Chelsea Hse.) Facts On File, Inc.

—Trial of Juveniles as Adults. 2003. (gr. 7-12). lib. bdg. 21.05 (978-0-613-83448-3(8)) Tandem Library Bks.

Jacobs, Thomas A. They Broke the Law — You Be the Judge: True Cases of Teen Crime. 2003. (gr. 7-12). lib. bdg. 25.70 (978-0-613-82794-2(5)) Tandem Library Bks.

—They Broke the Law - You Be the Judge: True Cases of Teen Crime. 2004. 224p. (YA). (gr. 7 up). pap. 15.95 (978-1-57542-134-6(8)) Free Spirit Publishing, Inc.

Lange, Donna. On the Edge of Disaster: Youth in the Juvenile Court System. 2004. (Youth with Special Needs Ser.). (Illus.). 128p. (J). lib. bdg. (978-1-59084-741-1(5)) Mason Crest Pubs.

Miller, Maryann. Coping with Weapons & Violence at School & on Your Streets. rev. ed. 1999. (Coping Ser.). (Illus.). 189p. (YA). (gr. 7-12). lib. bdg. 26.50 (978-0-8239-2968-9(X) , COWESC) Rosen Publishing Group, Inc., The.

Schmidt, April. Youth Violence. 2006. (Illus.). 244p. (gr. 10-12). 36.20 (978-0-7377-2490-5(0)); pap. 24.95 (978-0-7377-2491-2(9)) Thomson Gale. (Greenhaven Pr., Inc.).

Townsend, John. Fiendish Crimes & Punishing Times: Listen Up! 2006. (Raintree Freestyle Ser.). (Illus.). 48p. (J). (978-1-4109-1872-7(6)) Steck-Vaughn.

Webb, Margot. Coping with Street Gangs. rev. ed. 1999. (Coping Ser.). (Illus.). 168p. (YA). (gr. 7-12). lib. bdg. 26.50 (978-0-8239-2972-6(8) , COSTGA) Rosen Publishing Group, Inc., The.

Weill, Sabrina Solin. We're Not Monsters: Teens Speak Out about Teens in Trouble. 2002. (gr. 7-12). lib. bdg. 15.25 (978-0-613-71899-8(2)) Tandem Library Bks.

JUVENILE DELINQUENCY—FICTION

Baskin, Nora Raleigh. In the Company of Crazies. Raleigh, Henry P., illus. 2006. 176p. (J). 15.99 (978-0-06-059607-1(4)); lib. bdg. 16.89 (978-0-06-059608-8(2)) HarperCollins Pubs.

Bee, Clair. Hungry Hurler Vol. 23: The Homecoming. 2002. (Chip Hilton Sports Ser.: Vol. 23). (Illus.). 208p. (J). pap. 5.99 (978-0-8054-2125-5(4)) B&H Publishing Grp.

Carradice, Phil. Nat & the Havannah. 2000. 104p. pap. 12.95 (978-1-85902-719-6(9)) Beekman Bks., Inc.

Collinson, Roger. Manos largas (Sticky Fingers) Vinos, Maria, tr. Betteo, Patricio, illus. 2000. (la Orilla Del Viento Ser.). (SPA.). 120p. (J). 6.99 (978-968-16-6071-0(4) , 128) Fondo de Cultura Economica USA.

Fox, Paula. How Many Miles to Babylon? 2005. 104p. (J). pap. (978-1-932425-39-0(X) , Lemniscaat) Boyds Mills Pr.

Henry, April. Shock Point. 2006. 192p. (YA). (gr. 6). 16.99 (978-0-399-24385-1(2) , Putnam Juvenile) Penguin Group (USA) Inc.

McClintock, Norah. Bang. 2007. (Orca Soundings Ser.). 112p. (YA). (gr. 7 up). pap. (***978-1-55143-654-8(X)***); lib. bdg. (***978-1-55143-656-2(6)***) Orca Bk. Pubs.

—Down. 2007. (Orca Soundings Ser.). 112p. (YA). (gr. 7 up). pap. (***978-1-55143-766-8(X)***); lib. bdg. (***978-1-55143-768-2(6)***) Orca Bk. Pubs.

Mikaelsen, Ben. Touching Spirit Bear. 2001. 256p. (J). (gr. 5 up). 16.99 (978-0-380-97744-4(3)) HarperCollins Pubs.

—Touching Spirit Bear. l.t. ed. 2004. 305p. pap. 10.95 (978-0-7862-6351-6(2)) Thorndike Pr.

Rapp, Adam. The Buffalo Tree. (J). 2002. 192p. (gr. 5 up). pap. 6.95 (978-0-06-001226-7(9) , HarperTeen); 1998. 336p. (gr. 7 up). pap. 11.00 (978-0-06-440711-3(X) , Harper Trophy) HarperCollins Pubs.

Sachar, Louis. Buracos. pap. 29.95 (978-85-336-1280-8(X)) Livraria Martins Editora BRA. *Dist:* Distribooks, Inc.

—Holes. 1998. 240p. (J). (gr. 4-7). 17.00 (978-0-374-33265-5(7) , Farrar, Straus & Giroux (BYR)) Farrar, Straus & Giroux.

—Holes. 240p. (J). (gr. 4-6). pap. 5.99 (978-0-8072-8073-7(9) , Listening Library) Random Hse. Audio Publishing Group.

—Holes. 2000. (Newbery Ser.). (Illus.). 240p. (J). (gr. 5-6). reprint ed. pap. 6.50 (978-0-440-41480-3(6) , Yearling) Random Hse. Children's Bks.

—Holes. l.t. ed. 2003. 288p. pap. 10.95 (978-0-7862-6190-1(0)) Thorndike Pr.

—Small Steps. (YA). 2008. 288p. (gr. 7). pap. 8.99 (***978-0-385-73315-1(1)***); 2006. 272p. (gr. 5). 16.95 (978-0-385-73314-4(3)); 2006. 272p. (gr. 7). lib. bdg. 19.99 (978-0-385-90333-2(2)) Random Hse. Children's Bks. (Delacorte Bks. for Young Readers).

—Small Steps. rev. l.t. ed. 2006. 339p. 23.95 (978-0-7862-8297-5(5)) Thorndike Pr.

Spradlin, Michael P. Live & Let Shop. 2006. (Spy Goddess Ser.). (Illus.). 288p. (J). pap. 5.99 (978-0-06-059409-1(8)) HarperCollins Pubs.

Spradlin, Michael P., illus. & reader. Live & Let Shop. Spradlin, Michael P., reader. 2005. (Spy Goddess Ser.: Bk. 1). 224p. (gr. 7 up). 15.99 (978-0-06-059407-7(1)) HarperCollins Pubs.

Strasser, Todd. Boot Camp. 2007. 256p. (YA). (gr. 8 up). 15.99 (978-1-4169-0848-7(X)) Simon & Schuster Children's Publishing.

Trueman, Terry. Inside Out. 128p. (J). 2003. 15.99 (978-0-06-623962-0(1)); 2003. lib. bdg. 16.89 (978-0-06-623963-7(X)); 2004. reprint ed. pap. 6.99 (978-0-06-447376-7(7) , HarperTeen) HarperCollins Pubs.

Volponi, Paul. Black & White. 2005. 192p. (YA). (gr. 7). 15.99 (978-0-670-06006-1(2) , Viking Adult) Penguin Group (USA) Inc.

JUVENILE LITERATURE

see Children's Literature

K

KAFKA, FRANZ, 1883-1924

Bloom, Harold. Franz Kafka. 2004. (Bloom's BioCritiques Ser.). (Illus.). 112p. (YA). (gr. 9-13). 35.00 (978-0-7910-7871-6(X) , Chelsea Hse.) Facts On File, Inc.

—The Metamorphosis. 2007. (Bloom's Guides). 88p. (gr. 9). 30.00 (978-0-7910-9298-9(4) , Chelsea Hse.) Facts On File, Inc.

Gonzalez Férriz, Ramon. Franz Kafka -el miedo a la Vida. 2005. 96p. pap. (978-958-30-1360-7(9)) Panamericana Editorial.

KAHLO, FRIDA, 1910-1954

Frith, Margaret. Frida Kahlo: The Artist Who Painted Herself. 2003. (gr. k-3). lib. bdg. 14.15 (978-0-613-68237-4(8)) Tandem Library Bks.

Guzman, Lila & Guzman, Rick. Frida Kahlo: Painting Her Life. 2006. (Famous Latinos Ser.). (Illus.). 32p. (J). lib. bdg. 22.60 (978-0-7660-2643-8(4) , Enslow Elementary) Enslow Pubs., Inc.

Guzman, Lila & Guzman, Rick. Frida Kahlo: Pinto su Vida. 2007. (Latinos Famosos Ser.). (SPA., Illus.). 32p. (J). (gr. 3-4). lib. bdg. 22.60 (***978-0-7660-2678-0(7)*** , Enslow Elementary) Enslow Pubs., Inc.

Hillstrom, Laurie. Frida Kahlo. 2007. (Twentieth Century Most Influential Hispanics Ser.). (Illus.). 128p. (gr. 7-10). 31.20 (***978-1-4205-0019-6(8)*** , Lucent Bks.) Thomson Gale.

Holzhey, Magdalena. Frida Kahlo: The Artist in the Blue House. 2003. (Adventures in Art Ser.). (Illus.). 30p. (J). (gr. 5 up). 14.95 (978-3-7913-2863-8(8)) Prestel Publishing.

Johnston, Lissa Jones & Kahlo, Frida. Frida Kahlo: Painter of Strength. 2006. (Fact Finders Ser.). (Illus.). 32p. (J). 22.60 (978-0-7368-6417-6(2)) Capstone Pr., Inc.

Kent, Deborah. Frida Kahlo: An Artist Celebrates Life. 2004. (Proud Heritage: the Hispanic Library Ser.). 40p. (J). (gr. 3-7). 28.50 (978-1-59296-167-2(3)) Child's World, Inc.

Klein, Adam G. & Kahlo, Frida. Frida Kahlo. 2007. (Illus.). 32p. (J). 22.78 (978-1-59679-731-4(2)) ABDO Publishing Co.

Laidlaw, Jill. Frida Kahlo. Iribarren Berrade, Miguel, tr. 2006. (Los artistas en su mundo Ser.). (SPA., Illus.). 46p. (J). 19.95 (978-84-932442-4-8(4)) Blume ESP. *Dist:* Independent Pubs. Group.

Laidlaw, Jill A. Frida Kahlo. 2003. (Artists in Their Time Ser.). (Illus.). 48p. (J). 23.50 (978-0-531-12236-5(0)); (gr. 5-7). pap. 6.95 (978-0-531-16642-0(2)) Scholastic Library Publishing. (Watts, Franklin).

—Frida Kahlo. 2003. (gr. 5-8). lib. bdg. 15.25 (978-0-613-59483-7(5)) Tandem Library Bks.

Lenero, Carmen. Frida Kahlo. Mesquita, Camila, illus. 2004. (Niñez de...Ser.). 24p. pap. 6.95 (978-85-7416-216-4(7)) Callis Editora Ltda BRA. *Dist:* Independent Pubs. Group.

Morrison, John F. Frida Kahlo. 2003. (Great Hispanic Heritage Ser.). (Illus.). 112p. (J). (gr. 6-12). 30.00 (978-0-7910-7254-7(1)); pap. 30.00 (978-0-7910-7517-3(6)) Facts On File, Inc. (Chelsea Hse.).

Sabbeth, Carol. Frida Kahlo & Diego Rivera: Their Lives & Ideas, 24 Activities. 2005. (For Kids Ser.). (Illus.). 160p. (J). pap. 17.95 (978-1-55652-569-8(9) , 1241061) Chicago Review Pr., Inc.

Venezia, Mike. Frida Kahlo. 1999. (Getting to Know the World's Greatest Artists Ser.). (Illus.). 32p. (gr. 3-4). pap. 6.95 (978-0-516-26466-0(4)); (J). 27.00 (978-0-516-20975-3(2)) Scholastic Library Publishing. (Children's Pr.).

—Frida Kahlo. 1999. (gr. 3-6). lib. bdg. 15.25 (978-0-613-37352-4(9)) Tandem Library Bks.

Wooten, Sara McIntosh. Frida Kahlo: Her Life in Paintings. 2005. (Latino Biography Library). (Illus.). 128p. (J). (gr. 6-13). lib. bdg. 31.93 (978-0-7660-2487-8(3)) Enslow Pubs., Inc.

J
K
L

Woronoff, Kristen. Frida Kahlo: Mexican Painter. 2002. (Famous Women Juniors Ser.). (Illus.). 32p. (J). (gr. 3-5). 23.70 (978-1-56711-594-9(2) , Blackbirch Pr., Inc.) Thomson Gale.

KAIULANI, PRINCESS OF HAWAII, 1875-1899

Linnea, Sharon. Princess Ka'iulani: Hope of a Nation, Heart of a People. 1999. (Women of Spirit Ser.). (Illus.). 242p. (J). (gr. 5-9). 18.00 (978-0-8028-5145-1(2)) Eerdmans, William B. Publishing Co.

McDonnell, Peter. The Last Princess. 2005. (Illus.). 16p. ***(978-0-7367-2910-9(0))*** Zaner-Bloser, Inc.

Stanley, Fay. The Last Princess: The Story of Princess Ka'iulani of Hawai'i. Stanley, Diane, illus. rev. ed. 2001. 40p. (J). (gr. 2 up). 15.89 (978-0-06-029215-7(6)); 16.99 (978-0-688-18020-1(5)) HarperCollins Pubs.

KAKURO

Chisholm, Alastair. Kakuro for Kids Vol. 2: Samurai Edition. 2006. 144p. (J). pap. 5.95 (978-0-8027-9607-3(9)) Walker & Co.

—Kakuro Kids Vol. 1: Ninja Edition. 2006. 144p. (J). pap. 5.95 (978-0-8027-9606-6(0)) Walker & Co.

Hodder Children's Books. Kakuro for Beginners Blue Book. 2007. 160p. (J). mass mkt. ***(*978-0-340-93101-1(9))*** Hodder & Stoughton Canada.

—Kakuro for Beginners Red Book. 2007. 160p. (J). mass mkt. ***(*978-0-340-93100-4(0))*** Hodder & Stoughton Canada.

Moore, Gareth. The Kids' Book of Kakuro! Catlow, Nikalas, illus. 2006. 224p. (J). mass mkt. 5.99 (978-1-4169-2732-7(8) , Simon Scribbles) Simon & Schuster Children's Publishing.

Pazzelli, John. Kids' Kakuro. Zourelias, Diana, illus. 2006. 80p. (J). pap. 5.95 (978-0-486-45344-6(8)) Dover Pubns., Inc.

Poskitt, Kjartan. Kakuro & Other Fun Number Puzzles. 2006. (Illus.). 144p. (J). pap. 4.99 (978-0-439-88051-0(3) , Scholastic Paperbacks) Scholastic, Inc.

KALAHARI DESERT

Inserra, Rose & Powell, Susan. The Kalahari. 1998. (Ends of the Earth Ser.). (Illus.). 48p. (J). lib. bdg. 25.45 (978-0-431-06932-6(8)) Heinemann.

KANGAROOS

Anderson, Jill. Kangaroos. 2006. (Illus.). 24p. (J). 6.95 (978-1-55971-936-0(2)); 12.95 (978-1-55971-935-3(4)) T&N Children's Publishing. (NorthWord Bks. for Young Readers).

Burt, Denise. Kangaroos. McLeod, Neil, photos by. 2000. (Nature Watch Ser.). (Illus.). 48p. (J). (gr. 3-6). lib. bdg. 25.26 (978-1-57505-388-2(8) , Carolrhoda Bks.) Lerner Publishing Group.

Carle, Eric. Does a Kangaroo Have a Mother, Too? Carle, Eric, illus. 2000. (Illus.). 32p. (J). (ps-1). lib. bdg. 17.89 (978-0-06-028767-2(5)) HarperCollins Pubs.

Dolbear, Emily J. & Primm, E. Russell. Kangaroos Have Joeys. 2001. (Animals & Their Young Ser.). (Illus.). 24p. (J). (gr. 1 up). lib. bdg. 18.60 (978-0-7565-0061-0(3)) Compass Point Bks.

Eckart, Edana. Red Kangaroo. 2003. (Welcome Book Ser.). (Illus.). 24p. (J). 17.00 (978-0-516-24304-7(7)); pap. 4.95 (978-0-516-27896-4(7)) Scholastic Library Publishing. (Children's Pr.).

—Red Kangaroo. 2003. (gr. k-3). lib. bdg. 12.95 (978-0-613-67761-5(7)) Tandem Library Bks.

Fenton, Julie A. Kangaroos & Other Marsupials, Vol. 6. World Book, Inc. Staff, ed. 2002. (World Book's Animals of the World Ser.: Set 1). 64p. (J). (978-0-7166-1243-8(7)) World Bk., Inc.

Gareth Stevens Publishing Staff, contrib. by. Kangaroos. 2004. (All about Wild Animals Ser.). (Illus.). 32p. (J). (gr. 2 up). lib. bdg. 23.33 (978-0-8368-4119-0(0)) Stevens, Gareth Inc.

Gordon, Sharon. Guess Who Hops. 2004. (SPA & ENG., Illus.). 31p. (J). 21.36 (978-0-7614-1764-4(8) , Benchmark Bks.) Cavendish, Marshall Corp.

Gordon, Sharon. Guess Who Hops: Adivina Quién Salta. 2007. (SPA & ENG.). (J). ***(*978-0-7614-2884-8(4)); (*978-0-7614-2867-1(4))*** Cavendish, Marshall Bks., Ltd.

Harcourt School Publishers Staff. Does a Kangaroo Have a Mother Too? Big Book. 3rd ed. 2002. (Trophies Reading Program Ser.). (Illus.). pap. 55.10 (978-0-15-325445-1(9)) Harcourt Schl. Pubs.

Hewett, Joan. A Kangaroo Joey Grows Up. Hewett, Richard, photos by. (Baby Animals Ser.). (Illus.). 32p. (gr. k-3). 2005. lib. bdg. 21.27 (978-1-57505-165-9(6)); 2003. (J). pap. 6.95 (978-0-8225-0091-9(4)) Lerner Publishing Group.

—Kangaroo Joey Grows Up. 2002. (gr. k-3). lib. bdg. 15.25 (978-0-613-55728-3(X)) Tandem Library Bks.

Jango-Cohen, Judith. Kangaroos. 2005. (Animals Animals Ser.). (Illus.). 48p. (J). (gr. 3-7). lib. bdg. (978-0-7614-1869-6(5) , Benchmark Bks.) Cavendish, Marshall Corp.

Kangaroos Have Joeys. (Animals & Their Young Ser.). 24p. (J). 7.95 (978-0-7565-1243-9(3)) Compass Point Bks.

Lantier-Sampon, Patricia & Lehne, Judith Logan. The Wonder of Kangaroos. McGee, John F., illus. 2001. (Animal Wonders Ser.). 48p. (J). (gr. 1 up). lib. bdg. 26.00 (978-0-8368-2766-8(X)) Stevens, Gareth Inc.

Lehne, Judith Logan. Kangaroo Magic for Kids. McGee, John F., illus. 1999. (Animal Magic for Kids Ser.). 48p. (J). (gr. 3 up). lib. bdg. 26.00 (978-0-8368-2634-0(5)) Stevens, Gareth Inc.

Lever, E., et al. Kangaroos. Parish, Steve, photos by. 1999. (Animals Are Fun! Ser.). (Illus.). 16p. (J). (ps up). lib. bdg. 19.33 (978-0-8368-2614-2(0)) Stevens, Gareth Inc.

Levine, Michelle. Jumping Kangaroos. 2005. (Pull Ahead Bks.). (J). 22.60 (978-0-8225-2421-2(X) , Lerner Pubns.); 32p. pap. 5.95 (978-0-8225-2440-3(6)) Lerner Publishing Group.

The Life Cycle of a Kangaroo, Vol. 2. 2005. (Animals, Animals Ser.). (YA). (gr. k-3). (978-0-7368-3396-7(X) , Pebble Bks.) Capstone Pr., Inc.

Marsico, Katie. A Kangaroo Joey Grows Up. 2007. (Scholastic News Nonfiction Readers: Life Cycles Ser.). 24p. (J). 6.95 ***(*978-0-531-18695-4(4)*** , Children's Pr.) Scholastic Library Publishing.

McNeil, Niki, et al. HOCPP 1121 Kangaroos. 2006. spiral bd. 12.50 ***(*978-1-60308-121-4(6))*** In the Hands of a Child.

Miller, Chuck. Tree Kangaroos. 2002. (Animals of the Rain Forest Ser.). (Illus.). 32p. (YA). lib. bdg. 22.83 (978-0-7398-5532-4(8)) Raintree.

Miller-Schroeder, Patricia. Kangaroos. 2002. (Untamed World Ser.). (Illus.). 64p. (J). lib. bdg. 28.54 (978-0-7398-4972-9(7)) Raintree.

Montgomery, Sy. Quest for the Tree Kangaroo: An Expedition to the Cloud Forest of New Guinea. Bishop, Nic, photos by. 2006. (Scientists in the Field Ser.). (Illus.). 80p. (J). (gr. 4-6). 18.00 (978-0-618-49641-9(6)) Houghton Mifflin Co. Trade & Reference Div.

Murray, Julie. Kangaroos. 2005. (Animal Kingdom Set Ii Ser.). (Illus.). 24p. (J). (gr. k-4). lib. bdg. 21.35 (978-1-59197-338-6(4)) ABDO Publishing Co.

Murray, Peter. Kangaroos. 2005. (World of Mammals Ser.). 40p. (J). (gr. 2-6). 29.93 (978-1-59296-499-4(0)) Child's World, Inc.

Niz, Xavier. Kangaroos. 2005. (Illus.). 24p. (J). 21.26 (978-0-7368-3719-4(1)) Capstone Pr., Inc.

Noonan, Diana. The Kangaroo. 2002. (Life Cycle Ser.). (Illus.). 32p. (gr. k-2). 23.00 (978-0-7910-6968-4(0) , Chelsea Hse.) Facts On File, Inc.

Penny, Malcolm. Kangaroo. 2003. (Natural World Ser.). (Illus.). 48p. (J). lib. bdg. 28.56 (978-0-7398-6057-1(7)) Raintree.

—Kangaroos. 2002. (Secret World Of... Ser.). (Illus.). 48p. (J). lib. bdg. 27.12 (978-0-7398-4986-6(7)) Raintree.

Petty, Kate. Kangaroos. 2005. (Illus.). 24p. (J). (ps-3). lib. bdg. 22.80 (978-1-59604-036-6(X)) Stargazer Bks.

Pohl, Kathleen. Kangaroos. 2006. (Illus.). 24p. (J). pap. ***(*978-0-8368-7824-0(8));*** lib. bdg. ***(*978-0-8368-7817-2(5))*** Stevens, Gareth Inc. (Weekly Reader Early Learning Library).

—Kangaroos: Canguros. 2006. (ENG & SPA., Illus.). 24p. (J). pap. ***(*978-0-8368-8013-7(7));*** lib. bdg. ***(*978-0-8368-8006-9(4))*** Stevens, Gareth Inc. (Weekly Reader Early Learning Library).

Rebus, Anna. Kangaroos. 2006. (J). (978-1-59036-393-5(0)); (978-1-59036-399-7(X)) Weigl Pubs., Inc.

Reilly, Pauline. Kangaroo. Russell, Gayle, illus. (Picture Roo Bks.). 32p. (J). pap. (978-0-86417-538-0(8) , Kangaroo Pr.) Simon & Schuster Australia.

Rigby Education Staff. Kangaroo. (Illus.). (J). suppl. ed. 20.00 (978-0-7635-6461-2(3) , 764613C99) Rigby Education.

Ripple, William John. Kangaroos. 2005. (Desert Animals Ser.). (Illus.). 24p. (J). 15.93 (978-0-7368-3635-7(7) , Pebble Bks.) Capstone Pr., Inc.

Slater, Patrick. Australian Kangaroos & Wallabies. 2002. (Nature Kids Ser.). (Illus.). 52p. (J). (gr. 3 up). lib. bdg. (978-1-59084-217-1(0)) Mason Crest Pubs.

Spilsbury, Louise & Spilsbury, Richard. A Mob of Kangaroos. 2004. 32p. (J). pap. 6.95 (978-1-4034-5417-1(5)); (Illus.). lib. bdg. 24.22 (978-1-4034-4690-9(3)) Heinemann Library.

—Watching Kangaroos in Australia. 2006. (Heinemann First Library). (Illus.). 32p. (J). pap. (978-1-4034-7238-0(6)); lib. bdg. 25.36 (978-1-4034-7225-0(4)) Heinemann Library.

Swan, Erin Pembrey. Kangeroos & Koalas: What They Have in Common. 2000. (gr. 3-6). lib. bdg. 15.25 (978-0-613-34804-1(4)) Tandem Library Bks.

Swanson, Diane. Kangaroos. 2003. (Welcome to the Whole World Ser.). (Illus.). 32p. (J). (gr. k-2). pap. 5.95 (978-1-55285-471-6(X)) Whitecap Bks., Ltd. CAN. *Dist:* Firefly Bks., Ltd.

Tourville, Amanda Doering. A Kangaroo Grows Up. Denman, Michael, illus. 2006. 24p. (J). (978-1-4048-3160-5(6) , 1265742) Picture Window Bks.

Trumbauer, Lisa. The Life Cycle of a Kangaroo. 2002. (Life Cycles Ser.). (Illus.). 24p. (J). (gr. k-1). lib. bdg. 15.93 (978-0-7368-1452-2(3) , Pebble Bks.) Capstone Pr., Inc.

Twine, Alice. Kangaroos. 2008. (J). lib. bdg. ***(*978-1-4042-4145-9(0)*** , PowerKids Pr.) Rosen Publishing Group, Inc., The.

Whitehouse, Patricia. El Canguro. 2003. (Animales del Zoologico (Zoo Animals) Ser.). 24p. (ps-1). (J). lib. bdg. 17.08 (978-1-4034-0337-7(6)); (SPA., Illus.). pap. 5.25 (978-1-4034-0555-5(7)) Heinemann Library.

—Kangaroo. 2003. (Zoo Animals Ser.). (Illus.). 24p. (ps-1). (J). lib. bdg. 17.08 (978-1-58810-889-0(9)); pap. 5.25 (978-1-4034-0545-6(X)) Heinemann Library.

—Kangaroo. 2002. (ps-2). lib. bdg. 13.30 (978-0-613-81797-4(4)) Tandem Library Bks.

Wildlife Education, Ltd. Staff. Kangaroos. Millsap, Darrel, illus. (Zoobooks Ser.). (J). 2001. 24p. 15.95 (978-0-937934-80-7(1)); 1999. 18p. pap. 2.95 (978-0-937934-63-0(1)) Wildlife Education, Ltd.

Wilsdon, Christina. Kangaroos. 2006. (J). (978-1-59939-078-9(7) , Reader's Digest Young Families, Inc.) Reader's Digest Children's Publishing, Inc.

KANGAROOS—FICTION

Atkinson, Sally. The Tales of Tango Bk. II: The Sticky Situation. Metzel, Lee, illus. 1998. 32p. (J). (gr. k-4). 14.95 (978-0-9653034-1-5(1)) Tango's Grove Publishing.

Baker, David. The Roos, A home for Baby. 2005. 14p. 12.49 (978-1-4116-2290-6(1)) Lulu.com.

—The Roos, Baby's new Friend. 2006. 18p. 12.49 (978-1-4116-9123-0(7)) Lulu.com.

Beach, Don M. Sydney Kangaroo's Christmas. 1999. 22p. (J). 14.95 incl. audio (978-0-9671485-0-2(2)) Dot E. Pubs.

Benjamin, A. H. Baa! Moo! What Will We Do? Chapman, Jane, tr. Chapman, Jane, illus. 2003. 32p. (J). pap. 6.95 (978-1-58925-381-0(7) , tiger tales) ME Media LLC.

—Un Canguro en la Granja? Chapman, Jane, illus. 2002. (SPA.). (J). (gr. k-2). pap. 14.95 (978-84-488-0936-2(X) , BS30628) Beascoa, Ediciones S.A. ESP. *Dist:* Lectorum Pubns., Inc.

Berg, Dick. Padunkapoo: The Hawaiian Kangaroo. Berg, Gary, ed. l.t. ed. 2005. (Illus.). 28p. (J). per. 6.99 (978-0-9769985-1-8(3)) Grace Publishing.

Blackstone, Stella. Who Are You, Baby Kangaroo? Beaton, Clare, illus. 2004. 24p. (J). (ps-2). per. 6.99 (978-1-905236-19-0(0)) Barefoot Bks., Inc.

Bornemann, Elsa. Cuentos a Salto de Canguro. 2003. (SPA., Illus.). 97p. (J). (gr. 3-5). pap. 9.95 (978-950-511-245-6(9)) Alfaguara S.A. de Ediciones ARG. *Dist:* Santillana USA Publishing Co., Inc.

Bridges, Margaret Park. Will You Take Care of Me? Sweet, Melissa, illus. 1998. 32p. (J). (ps-k). 15.89 (978-0-688-15195-9(7)) HarperCollins Pubs.

Bruel, Nick. Boing! Bruel, Nick, illus. rev. ed. 2004. (Illus.). 32p. (J). 15.95 (978-1-59643-002-0(8)) Roaring Brook Pr.

Bump! KinderReaders Individual Title, 6 pack. (Kinderstarters Ser.). 8p. (ps-1). 21.00 (978-0-7635-8649-2(8)) Rigby Education.

Caddy, David. Smash. 2000. (Illus.). 128p. (J). pap. 10.95 (978-1-86368-271-8(6)) Fremantle Pr. AUS. *Dist:* International Specialized Bk. Services.

Carle, Eric. Hal Lil Kangar Aidan Un? Does a Kangaroo Have a Mother Too? 2005. 32p. pap. 12.00 (978-977-6171-05-3(2) , 706-003) Al-Balsam Pubng. Hse. EGY. *Dist:* Bookworld Trade, Inc.

Chichester-Clark, Emma. Happy Birthday to You, Blue Kangaroo. 2007. (Illus.). 32p. (J). (ps-k). 16.95 ***(*978-1-84270-518-6(0))*** Transworld Publishers Ltd. GBR. *Dist:* Independent Pubs. Group.

Clark, Emma Chichester. I Love You, Blue Kangaroo! Clark, Emma Chichester, illus. 2001. (Illus.). 32p. (J). (ps-3). pap. 6.99 (978-0-440-41549-7(7) , Dragonfly Bks.) Random Hse. Children's Bks.

—I Love You, Blue Kangaroo! 2001. (gr. k-3). lib. bdg. 15.30 (978-0-613-85711-6(9)); (Illus.). (J). 13.79 (978-0-606-20715-7(5)) Tandem Library Bks.

—Merry Christmas to You, Blue Kangaroo! Clark, Emma Chichester, illus. 2004. (Illus.). 32p. (J). (gr. k-k). lib. bdg. 17.99 (978-0-385-90918-1(7) , Doubleday Bks. for Young Readers) Random Hse. Children's Bks.

—Te Quiero Mucho Canguro Azul! 2002. Tr. of I Love You Blue Kangaroo!. (SPA.). 108p. (J). 14.95 (978-84-488-1211-9(5) , BS31491) Beascoa, Ediciones S.A. ESP. *Dist:* Lectorum Pubns., Inc.

—What Shall We Do, Blue Kang? 2002. (Illus.). 32p. (J). (978-1-84270-185-0(1)) Andersen GBR. *Dist:* Random Hse. of Canada, Ltd.

—Where Are You, Blue Kangaroo? 2002. (ps-2). lib. bdg. 15.30 (978-0-613-89781-5(1)) Tandem Library Bks.

Cook, Sherry & Johnson, Terri. Kitchen Chemistry Kal, 26 vols. Kuhn, Jesse, illus. l.t. ed. 2006. (Quirkles—Exploring Phonics through Science Ser.: 11). 32p. (J). 7.99 (978-1-933815-10-7(8) , Quirkles, The) Creative 3, LLC.

Cox, Robert & Robins, Jim. The Kangaroo Who Couldn't Hop. (Illus.). 32p. (J). (ps-ps). 2005. pap. (978-0-7344-0717-7(3)); 2002. (978-0-7344-0165-6(5)) Hachette Livre Australia. (Lothian Bks.).

deRubertis, Barbara. Rooney 'Roo. Cockrille, Eva V., illus. 1998. (Let's Read Together Ser.). 32p. (J). (ps-3). pap. 4.95 (978-1-57565-044-9(4)); pap. 8.95 incl. audio (978-1-57565-049-4(5)) Kane Pr., The.

Dolan, Heidi. The Kangaroo Conspiracy. 2000. (Illus.). 240p. (YA). (gr. 6-12). pap. 6.94 (978-0-9702565-0-8(7)) Smiletime Publishing.

Edwards, Pamela Duncan. Mcgillycuddy Could. Date not set. 32p. (J). (ps-1). pap. 5.99 (978-0-06-443688-5(8)) HarperCollins Pubs.

—McGillycuddy Could! Porter, Sue, illus. 2005. 32p. (J). (ps-1). 14.99 (978-0-06-029001-6(3)); lib. bdg. 15.89 (978-0-06-029002-3(1)) HarperCollins Pubs.

Eggleton, Jill. Kangaroo's Pouch: Emergent Level Satellite Individual Title Six-Packs. (Sails Literacy Ser.). (gr. k-1). 27.00 (978-0-7578-7918-0(7)) Rigby Education.

French, Jackie. Josephine Wants to Dance. Whatley, Bruce, illus. 2007. 32p. (J). (ps-1). 15.95 ***(*978-0-8109-9431-7(3)*** , Abrams Bks. for Young Readers) Abrams, Harry N. , Inc.

Glinski, Donita. Jeremy. Harris, Leslie, illus. 2006. 32p. 14.95 (978-1-57197-464-8(4) , Ivy House Publishing Group) Pentland Pr., Inc.

Goodhart, Pippa. Hoppy Birthday, Jo-Jo! Birkett, Georgie, illus. 2005. (Green Bananas Ser.). 48p. (J). (978-0-7787-1025-7(4)) Crabtree Publishing Co.

—Hoppy Birthday, Jo-Jo! 2005. (Green Bananas Ser.). (Illus.). 48p. (J). (ps). pap. (978-0-7787-1041-7(6)) Crabtree Publishing Co.

Hamilton, Elizabeth L. Katie Kangaroo's Leap of Courage. l.t. ed. 2005. (Character Critters Ser.: No. 9). (Illus.). 32p. (J). per. 5.95 (978-0-9754629-6-6(2) , Character-in-Action) Quiet Impact, Inc.

Hanson, Anders. Kangaroo Boxers. Nobens, C. A., illus. 2006. (Fact & Fiction Ser.). 24p. (J). 21.35 (978-1-59679-945-5(5) , SandCastle); pap. (978-1-59679-946-2(3)) ABDO Publishing Co.

Heller, Sarah. Joey the Kangaroo. 2001. (64 Zoo Lane Ser.). 24p. (J). pap. 7.99 (978-0-439-31795-5(9)) Scholastic, Inc.

Hiebert, Elfrieda H. & Juel, Connie. Kangaroo in the Kitchen. (Little Book Practice Reader Ser.). (J). 9.90 (978-0-8136-0742-9(6)) Modern Curriculum Pr.

Joyce, Rita. Wandawillie. 2005. (J). lib. bdg. 17.95 (978-1-59094-095-2(4)) Jawbone Publishing Corp.

Katz, Avner. The Little Pickpocket. Katz, Avner, illus. 1999. Tr. of Kayas Ha-Katan. (Illus.). 27p. (J). (ps-2). reprint ed. 15.00 (978-0-7881-6596-2(8)) DIANE Publishing Co.

Kimpton, Diana. The Lamb-A-Roo. Beardshaw, Rosalind, illus. 2006. 32p. (J). 15.95 (978-0-7696-4619-0(0) , Gingham Dog Pr.) School Specialty Publishing.

Kita, Suzanne. Willie's Wallabies. Davis, Lambert, illus. 2000. (J). 10.99 (978-0-89610-425-9(7)) Island Heritage Publishing.

Langeland, Deirdre. Kangaroo Island: A Story of an Australian Mallee Forest. 2005. (Soundprints' Wild Habitats Ser.). (Illus.). 32p. (J). (gr. 1-4). pap. 8.95 incl. reel tape (978-1-59249-095-0(6)) Soundprints.

Langeland, Deirdre, text. Be Careful, Kangaroo! 2005. (Soundprints' Read-and-Discover Ser.). (Illus.). 32p. (J). (ps-1). pap. 3.95 (978-1-59249-145-2(6) , S2010) Soundprints.

Law, Felicia. Joey's Day at Rumble's Cave Hotel. Pak, Yoon Mi, illus. 2006. (Read-It! Readers Ser.). 32p. (J). (gr. 2-4). 18.60 (978-1-4048-1339-7(X)) Picture Window Bks.

—Rumble Meets Keesha Kangaroo. 2005. (Read-It! Readers Ser.). (Illus.). 32p. (J). (ps-k). lib. bdg. 18.60 (978-1-4048-1290-1(3)) Picture Window Bks.

Lee, Brian. Bouncey the Elf & Friends - Bedtime St. 2005. (ENG., Illus.). 53p. pap. ***(*978-0-7552-1023-7(9))*** Authors OnLine, Ltd.

Lennon, Joan. There's a Kangaroo in My Soup! Rasmussen, Wendy, illus. 2000. 128p. (J). (gr. 1-4). 16.95 (978-0-8126-2898-2(5)) Cricket Bks.

Lewis, Edwina. Who Jumps? Parker, Ant, illus. 2003. (Who. . . Ser.). 16p. (YA). (978-1-85602-447-1(4)) Chrysalis Children's Bks.

Linklater, Eric. The Wind on the Moon. Bentley, Nicolas, illus. 2004. (New York Review Children's Collection). 376p. (J). 18.95 (978-1-59017-100-4(4) , NYR Children's Collection) New York Review of Bks., Inc., The.

Lithgow, John. Marsupial Sue. Davis, Jack E., illus. 2001. 40p. (J). (ps-3). 17.95 incl. audio compact disk (978-0-689-84394-5(1)) Simon & Schuster Children's Publishing.

Lithgow, John & Davis, Jack E. Marsupial Sue. 2004. (Illus.). 40p. (J). reprint ed. pap. 6.99 (978-0-689-87410-9(3) , Aladdin) Simon & Schuster Children's Publishing.

Maar, Paul. El Canguro Aprende a Volar (Kangaroo Learns to Fly) (SPA.). 56p. (J). (gr. 2). 7.95 (978-958-04-1490-2(4) , 10266271) Norma S.A. COL. *Dist:* Distribuidora Norma, Inc.

McBratney, Sam. I Love It When You Smile. Fuge, Charles, illus. 2006. 32p. (J). 15.99 (978-0-06-084245-1(8)) HarperCollins Pubs.

McKee, David. Elmer & the Kangaroo. McKee, David, illus. 2000. (Elmer Bks.). (Illus.). 32p. (J). (ps up). 15.99 (978-0-688-17951-9(7)) HarperCollins Pubs.

Moncure, Jane Belk. Word Bird's New Friend. 2002. (New Word Bird Library). (Illus.). 32p. (J). (ps-3). 22.79 (978-1-56766-844-5(5)) Child's World, Inc.

Most, Bernard. The Very Boastful Kangaroo. 2003. (Green Light Readers Level 2 Ser.). (Illus.). 24p. (J). 11.95 (978-0-15-204880-8(4)); pap. 3.95 (978-0-15-204840-2(5)) Harcourt Children's Bks. (Green Light Readers).

—Very Boastful Kangaroo. 1999. (Green Light Readers Ser.). (978-0-606-18193-8(8)); lib. bdg. 11.80 (978-0-613-63362-8(8)) Tandem Library Bks.

Parish, Steve, illus. The Kangaroos' Great Escape. 2005. 24p. (J). lib. bdg. 20.67 (978-0-8368-5971-3(5)) Stevens, Gareth Inc.

Payne, Emmy. Katy Bolsa. 1999. Tr. of No Tiene. (978-0-606-17498-5(2)) Tandem Library Bks.

Pedley, Ethel. Dot & the Kangaroo. 2006. pap. ***(*978-1-4250-0966-3(2))*** Assistedreadingbooks.com Inc.

Pedley, Ethel C. Dot & the Kangaroo. 2004. reprint ed. pap. 15.95 (978-1-4191-1659-9(2)); pap. 1.99 (978-1-4192-1659 6(7)) Kessinger Publishing, LLC.

Ratner, Susan. Kandoo Kangaroo: Hops into Homeschool. 2000. (Illus.). 20p. (J). (ps-3). pap. 6.99 (978-0-89051-290-6(6) , 303-052) Master Bks.

Rigby Education Staff. Baby Kangaroo. (Sails Literacy Ser.). (Illus.). 16p. (gr. k-1). 27.00 (978-0-7635-9879-2(8) , 698798C99) Rigby Education.

Sargent, Dave & Sargent, Pat. Kenny Kangaroo: Fighting, 56 vols., 49. Lenoir, Jane, illus. 2001. (Animal Pride Ser.: Vol. 49). 36p. (J). lib. bdg. 19.95 (978-1-56763-539-3(3)) Ozark Publishing.

Sargent, Dave, et al. Kenny Kangaroo: Fighting, 17, 49. 2000. (Animal Pride Ser.: 48). (Illus.). 42p. (J). pap. 6.95 (978-1-56763-540-9(7)) Ozark Publishing.

Simms, Mattie. Q. 2006. (J). pap. 2.99 ***(*978-0-9772077-1-8(4))*** Kanlearn, Inc.

Simon, Francesca. Pablo Diablo Y la Cangura Fantasma. Ross, Tony, illus. 2005. (Pablo Diablo Ser.).Tr. of Horrid Harry & the Kangaroo Ghost. (SPA.). (J). (gr. 2-3). pap. 8.95 (978-84-348-9684-0(2)) SM Ediciones ESP. *Dist:* Iaconi, Mariuccia Bk. Imports.

Thomas, Pam. Mamarswpial. 2005. (WEL., Illus.). 128p. pap. (978-0-86243-360-4(6)) Y Lolfa.

van Genechten, Guido. Kangaroo Christine. van Genechten, Guido, illus. 2006. (Illus.). 32p. (J). 6.95 (978-1-58925-396-4(5) , tiger tales) ME Media LLC.

van Holst Pellekaan, Karen. Coco Makes Music. De Backker, Vera, illus. 2000. (Coco the Koala Ser.). 29p. (J). (ps up). lib. bdg. 23.33 (978-0-8368-2730-9(9)) Stevens, Gareth Inc.

—Coco's Surprise. De Backker, Vera, illus. 2000. (Coco the Koala Ser.). 31p. (J). (ps up). lib. bdg. 23.33 (978-0-8368-2731-6(7)) Stevens, Gareth Inc.

Zoehfeld, Kathleen Weidner. Roo's New Babysitter. 1999. (My Very First Winnie the Pooh Ser.). (Illus.). 32p. (J). (ps-k). 11.99 (978-0-7868-3215-6(0)) Disney Pr.

KANSAS

Bjorklund, Ruth. Kansas. 2000. (Celebrate the States Ser.). (Illus.). 144p. (gr. 4-8). lib. bdg. 37.07 (978-0-7614-0646-4(8) , Benchmark Bks.) Cavendish, Marshall Corp.

Bograd, Larry. Uniquely Kansas. 2004. (Heinemann State Studies). (Illus.). 48p. (J). (gr. 3-7). pap. 9.00 (978-1-4034-4723-4(3)); 31.36 (978-1-4034-4654-1(7)) Heinemann Library.

Deady, Kathleen W. Kansas Facts & Symbols. (States & Their Symbols Ser.). 24p. (J). 2000. (Illus.). (gr. 2-3). lib. bdg. 18.60 (978-0-7368-0638-1(5) , Bridgestone Bks.); 2003. lib. bdg. 19.93 (978-0-7368-2246-6(1)) Capstone Pr., Inc.

Fredeen, Charles. Kansas. 2nd rev. exp. ed. (Hello U. S. A. Ser.). (Illus.). 84p. (J). (gr. 3-6). 2003. pap. 6.95 (978-0-8225-0780-2(3)); 2002. lib. bdg. 25.26 (978-0-8225-4082-3(7)) Lerner Publishing Group.

—Kansas. rev. ed. 2002. (gr. 3-6). lib. bdg. 15.25 (978-0-613-46083-5(9)) Tandem Library Bks.

Griekspoor, Phyllis & Tanner, Beccy. Kansas: The Prairie Spirit History People Stories. 2000. (Illus.). v, 310p. (J). (gr. 7-8). 27.10 (978-0-913205-26-6(5)) Sage Hill Pubs., LLC.

Heinrichs, Ann. Kansas. 2005. (Welcome to the USA Ser.). (Illus.). 40p. (J). (gr. 1-5). 27.07 (978-1-59296-443-7(5)) Child's World, Inc.

—Kansas. 2003. (This Land Is Your Land Ser.). (Illus.). 48p. (J). (gr. 3 up). lib. bdg. 22.60 (978-0-7565-0353-6(1)) Compass Point Bks.

Ingram, Scott. Kansas: The Sunflower State. 2002. (World Almanac Library of the States). (Illus.). 48p. (J). (gr. 5 up). lib. bdg. 30.00 (978-0-8368-5134-2(X) , World Almanac Library) Stevens, Gareth Inc.

—Kansas: The Sunflower State. 2003. (Illus.). 48p. (J). (gr. 4-7). lib. bdg. 38.05 (978-0-613-76808-5(6)) Tandem Library Bks.

Ingram, W. Scott. Kansas. 2003. (From Sea to Shining Sea Ser.: 2). (Illus.). 80p. (J). 30.50 (978-0-516-22395-7(X) , Children's Pr.) Scholastic Library Publishing.

—Kansas: The Sunflower State. 2002. (World Almanac Library of the States). (Illus.). 48p. (J). (gr. 5 up). pap. 14.95 (978-0-8368-5304-9(0) , World Almanac Library) Stevens, Gareth Inc.

Kansas. 2000. (Switched on Schoolhouse Ser.). (Illus.). (YA). (gr. 7-12). pap. 24.95 incl. cd-rom (978-0-7403-0268-8(X) , SOSKS) Alpha Omega Pubns., Inc.

Kavanagh, James. Kansas Birds. Leung, Raymond, illus. 2001. (Pocket Naturalist Ser.). 12p. pap. 5.95 (978-1-58355-047-2(X)) Waterford Pr., Ltd.

Kummer, Patricia K. Kansas. rev. ed. 2002. (One Nation Ser.). (Illus.). 48p. (J). (gr. 3-4). lib. bdg. 22.60 (978-0-7368-1240-5(7) , Bridgestone Bks.) Capstone Pr., Inc.

Labairon, Cassandra Sharri. Kansas. 2008. (J). (***978-1-58341-641-9(2)*** , Creative Education) Creative Co., The.

Marsh, Carole. Big Activity Book. 2001. (Kansas Experience! Ser.). per. 9.95 (978-0-635-00339-3(2)) Gallopade International.

—The Big Kansas Reproducible Activity Book. 2001. (Carole Marsh Kansas Bks.). (Illus.). 96p. (J). (gr. 2-6). pap., act. bk. ed. 9.95 (978-0-7933-9943-7(2)) Gallopade International.

—A Coloring Book. 2001. (Kansas Experience! Ser.). pap. 3.95 (978-0-635-00344-7(9)) Gallopade International.

—Kansas Classic Christmas Trivia. 2002. (Carole Marsh Kansas Bks.). (Illus.). 32p. pap. 14.95 (978-0-635-01399-6(1) , 13991, Marsh, Carole Bks.); lib. bdg. 21.95 (978-0-635-01400-9(9) , 14009) Gallopade International.

—Kansas Current Events Projects: 30 Cool, Activities, Crafts, Experiments & More for Kids to Do to Learn about Your State! 2003. (Kansas Experience Ser.). 32p. (gr. k-5). pap. 5.95 (978-0-635-02035-2(1) , Marsh, Carole Bks.) Gallopade International.

—The Kansas Experience Pocket Guide. 2001. (Carole Marsh Kansas Bks.). (Illus.). 96p. (J). (gr. 3-8). pap. 6.95 (978-0-7933-9914-7(9)) Gallopade International.

—Kansas Geography Projects: 30 Cool, Activities, Crafts, Experiments & More for Kids to Do to Learn about Your State! 2003. (Kansas Experience Ser.). 32p. (gr. k-5). pap. 5.95 (978-0-635-01835-9(7) , Marsh, Carole Bks.) Gallopade International.

—Kansas Government Projects: 30 Cool, Activities, Crafts, Experiments & More for Kids to Do to Learn about Your State! 2003. (Kansas Experience Ser.). 32p. (gr. k-5). pap. 5.95 (978-0-635-01935-6(3) , Marsh, Carole Bks.) Gallopade International.

—Kansas Jeopardy! Answers & Questions about Our State! 2004. (Carole Marsh Kansas Bks.). (Illus.). 32p. (J). (gr. 3-8). pap. 7.95 (978-0-7933-9798-3(7)) Gallopade International.

—Kansas "Jography" A Fun Run Thru Your State! 2004. 32p. (J). (gr. 3-8). pap. 7.95 (978-0-7933-9827-0(4)) Gallopade International.

—Kansas Millionaire: Game Book. 2001. (Carole Marsh Kansas Bks.). (Illus.). 32p. (J). (gr. 3-8). pap., act. bk. ed. 9.95 (978-0-635-00048-4(2)) Gallopade International.

—Kansas People Projects: 30 Cool, Activities, Crafts, Experiments & More for Kids to Do to Learn about Your State! 2003. (Kansas Experience Ser.). 32p. (gr. k-5). pap. 5.95 (978-0-635-01985-1(X) , Marsh, Carole Bks.) Gallopade International.

—Kansas Symbols & Facts Projects: 30 Cool, Activities, Crafts, Experiments & More for Kids to Do to Learn about Your State! 2003. (Kansas Experience Ser.). 32p. (gr. k-5). pap. 5.95 (978-0-635-01885-4(3) , Marsh, Carole Bks.) Gallopade International.

—My First Book: New Edition. 2001. (Kansas Experience! Ser.). pap. 7.95 (978-0-635-00346-1(5) , Marsh, Carole Bks.) Gallopade International.

—My First Book about Kansas. 2004. (Carole Marsh Kansas Bks.). (Illus.). 32p. (J). (gr. k-4). pap. 7.95 (978-0-7933-9885-0(1)) Gallopade International.

—The Survivor: A Class Challenge. 2001. (Carole Marsh Kansas Bks.). lib. bdg. 29.95 (978-0-635-00662-2(6) , Marsh, Carole Bks.) Gallopade International.

—Who Wants to Be a Millionaire? 2001. (Carole Marsh Kansas Bks.). lib. bdg. 29.95 (978-0-635-00049-1(0)) Gallopade International.

McNamara, Connie. Go Jayhawks: My First Kansas Words. 2004. (J). bds. 11.95 (978-0-9759703-1-7(3)) Shamrock Publishing, Inc.

McNeese, Tim. Brown V. Board of Education. 2006. (Great Supreme Court Decisions Ser.). 144p. (J). (gr. 5-8). 30.00 (978-0-7910-9238-5(0) , Chelsea Hse.) Facts On File, Inc.

Meyer, Diana Lambdin. A Kid's Guide to Kansas City. 3rd ed. 2005. 184p. (J). per. 14.95 (978-0-9763873-0-5(1)) Kansas City Guidebooks.

Murray, Julie. Kansas. 2006. (Buddy Book Ser.). (Illus.). 32p. (J). (gr. k-4). lib. bdg. 22.78 (978-1-59197-675-2(8) , Buddy Bks.) ABDO Publishing Co.

Nault, Jennifer. A Guide to Kansas. 2001. (American States Ser.). 32p. (J). (Illus.). (gr. 4-7). lib. bdg. 16.95 (978-1-930954-90-8(5)); per. 7.95 (978-1-930954-67-0(0)) Weigl Pubs., Inc.

Netzley, Patricia D. Kansas. 2002. (Seeds of a Nation Ser.). (Illus.). 48p. (J). (gr. 3-5). 23.70 (978-0-7377-1019-9(5) , Kidhaven) Thomson Gale.

Obregon, Jose M. Kansas. 2005. (Bilingual Library of the United States of America: Set 1). (ENG & SPA., Illus.). 32p. (J). (ps-k). lib. bdg. 22.50 (978-1-4042-3081-1(5) , Buenas Letra) Rosen Publishing Group, Inc., The.

Olien, Rebecca. Kansas. 2003. (Land of Liberty Ser.). (Illus.). 64p. (J). (gr. 3-4). lib. bdg. 23.93 (978-0-7368-1584-0(8) , Bridgestone Bks.) Capstone Pr., Inc.

Reed, Jennifer. Kansas: A MyReportLinks. Com Book. 2003. (States Ser.). (Illus.). 48p. (J). lib. bdg. 25.26 (978-0-7660-5140-9(4) , MyReportLinks.com Bks.) Enslow Pubs., Inc.

Scillian, Devin & Scillian, Corey. S Is for Sunflower: A Kansas Alphabet. Bowles, Doug, illus. 2004. (State Ser.). 40p. (J). 17.95 (978-1-58536-061-1(9) , 1235980) Sleeping Bear Pr.

Taylor-Butler, Christine. Kansas. 2006. 32p. (gr. 1-2). (YA). pap. 5.95 (978-0-516-26454-7(0)); (Illus.). (J). 20.50 (978-0-516-24966-7(5)) Scholastic Library Publishing. (Children's Pr.).

Thomas, William. Kansas. 2006. (Portraits of the States Ser.). (Illus.). 32p. (J). pap. 8.95 (978-0-8368-4684-3(2)); lib. bdg. 23.33 (978-0-8368-4665-2(6)) Stevens, Gareth Inc.

Zeinert, Karen. Tragic Prelude: Bleeding Kansas. 2001. (Illus.). xiv, 105p. (J). (gr. 6-9). pap. 25.00 (978-0-208-02446-6(8) , Linnet Bks.) Shoe String Pr., Inc.

KANSAS—FICTION

Adee, Donna & Adee, Ed. Jonathan Finds True Treasure. Rectenbaugh, Marci, illus. 2004. (Jonathan Ser.: Bk. 2). 344p. (J). per. 10.95 (978-0-9654272-5-8(0)) Harvest Pubns.

Baum, L. Frank. Mago di Oz. pap. 14.95 (978-88-451-2500-3(9)) Fabbri - RCS Libri ITA. *Dist:* Distribooks, Inc.

Boeve, Eunice. Maggie Rose & Sass. 2005. 144p. pap. 19.95 (978-1-4137-7964-6(6)) PublishAmerica, Inc.

—The Summer of the Crow. 2000. 224p. (J). pap. 12.95 (978-1-58597-059-9(X)) Leathers Publishing.

Boushell, Mike. Gridiron Hero. (J). pap. 9.99 (978-0-88092-601-0(5)) Royal Fireworks Publishing Co.

Cheaney, J. B. The Middle of Somewhere. 2007. (Illus.). 224p. (J). (gr. 4-6). 15.99 (978-0-375-83790-6(6)); lib. bdg. 18.99 (978-0-375-93790-3(0)) Random Hse. Children's Bks. (Knopf Bks. for Young Readers).

Durham, David. Gabriel's Story. 2002. (gr. 7-12). lib. bdg. 22.25 (978-0-613-49406-9(7)) Tandem Library Bks.

Duvall, Deborah L. Rabbit Goes to Kansas. 2007. (Illus.). 32p. (J). (gr. 1 up). 16.95 (***978-0-8263-4181-5(0)***) Univ. of New Mexico Pr.

Francis, Dorothy Brenner. The Jayhawk Horse Mystery. Ersland, William, illus. 2001. (Cover-to-Cover Novel Ser.). 80p. (J). pap. (978-0-7891-5349-4(1)); (gr. 2-5). lib. bdg. 13.95 (978-0-7807-9728-4(0)) Perfection Learning Corp.

Garretson, Jerri. Twister Twyla: The Kansas Cowgirl. Dollar, Diane A., illus. 2003. 32p. (J). 5.95 (978-0-9659712-5-6(2)) Ravenstone Pr.

Gregory, Kristiana. Journey of Faith. 2003. (gr. 3-6). lib. bdg. 13.00 (978-0-613-72119-6(5)) Tandem Library Bks.

—Winter Tidings. 2004. (Prairie River Ser.: No. 3). 192p. (J). (gr. 4-7). pap. 4.99 (978-0-439-44001-1(7) , Scholastic Paperbacks) Scholastic, Inc.

Gregory, Kristinana. Hope Springs Eternal. 2005. (Prairie River Ser.: No. 4). 176p. (J). pap. 4.99 (978-0-439-44003-5(3) , Scholastic Paperbacks) Scholastic, Inc.

Grigsby, Cynthia. Hollow Creek: A Haunted Beginning, 01. 2006. 163p. (J). 14.95 (978-0-9786840-0-6(1)) Grigsby, Cynthia.

Harcourt School Publishers Staff. A Big Day for Nicodemus: Take-Home Book. 2001. (Collections Ser.). (Illus.). (J). pap. 1.90 (978-0-15-319540-2(1)) Harcourt Schl. Pubs.

—Prairie Fire On Level. 3rd ed. 2002. (Trophies Reading Program Ser.). (Illus.). pap. 5.10 (978-0-15-323352-4(4)) Harcourt Schl. Pubs.

—Prairie Neighbors Advanced Level. 3rd ed. 2002. (Trophies Reading Program Ser.). (Illus.). pap. 5.10 (978-0-15-323307-4(9)) Harcourt Schl. Pubs.

—Sitting around the Campfire: Take-Home Book. 1999. (Collections Ser.). (Illus.). (J). pap. 1.90 (978-0-15-317234-2(7)) Harcourt Schl. Pubs.

Harkrader, L. D. Airball: My Life in Briefs. 2005. 208p. (J). (ps-7). 16.95 (978-1-59643-060-0(5)) Roaring Brook Pr.

—Airball: My Life in Briefs. 2008. 224p. (J). pap. 6.99 (***978-0-312-37382-5(1)***) Square Fish.

Hopkinson, Deborah. Our Kansas Home. Faricy, Patrick, illus. ed. 2005. 64p. (J). lib. bdg. 15.00 (978-1-59054-910-0(4)) Fitzgerald Bks.

—Prairie Skies: Cabin in the Snow. 2002. (gr. 3-6). lib. bdg. 11.80 (978-0-613-63224-9(9)) Tandem Library Bks.

—Prairie Skies: Our Kansas Home. 2003. (gr. 3-6). lib. bdg. 11.80 (978-0-613-61582-2(4)) Tandem Library Bks.

—Prairie Skies: Pioneer Summer. 2002. (gr. 3-6). lib. bdg. 11.80 (978-0-613-45093-5(0)) Tandem Library Bks.

Hopkinson, Deborah & Faricy, Patrick. Cabin in the Snow. 2002. (Prairie Skies Ser.). 80p. (J). pap. 3.99 (978-0-689-84351-8(8) , Aladdin) Simon & Schuster Children's Publishing.

Jennings, Richard W. The Great Whale of Kansas. 2001. (Illus.). 160p. (J). (gr. 5-9). tchr. ed. 15.00 (978-0-618-10228-0(0) , Walter Lorraine) Houghton Mifflin Co. Trade & Reference Div.

Klaassen, Mike. The Brute. 2005. 180p. (YA). pap. 14.99 (978-1-59092-225-5(5) , Blue Works) Windstorm Creative.

Kochenderfer, Lee. The Victory Garden. 2003. 176p. (J). (gr. 3-7). pap. 5.99 (978-0-440-41703-3(1) , Yearling) Random Hse. Children's Bks.

—The Victory Garden. 2003. (gr. 3-6). lib. bdg. 13.00 (978-0-613-85701-7(1)) Tandem Library Bks.

LeapFrog Staff, compiled by. The Wizard of Oz. 2001. (J). spiral bd. 14.99 (978-1-58605-044-3(3)) LeapFrog Enterprises, Inc.

Maclean, Christine. Mary Margaret Meets Her Match. 2007. 176p. (J). (gr. 3-5). 15.99 (978-0-525-47775-4(6) , Dutton Juvenile) Penguin Group (USA) Inc.

McAfee, Joan K. Riddle of the Lost Gold. 2002. (Illus.). 162p. (YA). pap. 9.95 (978-0-89745-262-5(3)) Sunflower Univ. Pr.

McMullan, Kate. For This Land Bk. 2: Meg's Prairie Diary. 2003. (My America Ser.). (Illus.). 112p. (J). pap. 10.95 (978-0-439-37059-2(0) , Scholastic Pr.) Scholastic, Inc.

Moss, Marissa. Rose's Journal: The Story of a Girl in the Great Depression. 2003. (Young American Voices Ser.). (Illus.). 56p. (J). pap. 7.00 (978-0-15-204605-7(4) , Silver Whistle) Harcourt Trade Pubs.

—Rose's Journal: The Story of a Girl in the Great Depression. Moss, Marissa, illus. 2001. (Young American Voices Ser.). (Illus.). 56p. (YA). (gr. 3-7). 15.00 (978-0-15-202423-9(9) , Silver Whistle) Harcourt Trade Pubs.

Osborne, Mary Pope. Twister on Tuesday, Vol. 23. 2004. (Magic Tree House Ser. : No. 23). 70p. (J). (gr. k-3). pap. 17.00 incl. audio (978-0-8072-9932-6(4) , Listening Library) Random Hse. Audio Publishing Group.

—Twister on Tuesday. Murdocca, Sal, illus. 2001. (Magic Tree House Ser.: No. 23). 96p. (J). (gr. k-3). 11.99 (978-0-679-99069-7(0)); 23. pap. 3.99 (978-0-679-89069-0(6)) Random Hse. Children's Bks. (Random Hse. Bks. for Young Readers).

—Twister on Tuesday. 2001. (Magic Tree House Ser. : No. 23). (J). (gr. k-3). lib. bdg. 11.80 (978-0-613-35706-7(X)); (Illus.). (978-0-606-21498-8(4)) Tandem Library Bks.

Peters, Julie Anne. Far from Xanadu. 2007. 288p. (YA). (gr. 7 up). pap. 7.99 (***978-0-316-15971-5(9)***) Little, Brown Bks. for Young Readers.

Prigger, Mary Skillings. Aunt Minnie & the Twister. Lewin, Betsy, illus. 2002. 40p. (J). (gr. k-3). 15.00 (978-0-618-11136-7(0) , Clarion Bks.) Houghton Mifflin Co. Trade & Reference Div.

Reiss, Kathryn. Riddle of the Prairie Bride. 2001. (American Girl Collection). (Illus.). (J). (978-0-606-21400-1(3)) Tandem Library Bks.

Richardson, Steve. Billy's Mountain. Leonhard, Herb, illus. 2007. 52p. 14.95 (***978-0-9786422-0-4(1)***) Impossible Dreams Publishing Co.

Ruby, Lois. Steal Away Home. 1999. 208p. (J). (gr. 3-7). pap. 5.99 (978-0-689-82435-7(1) , Aladdin) Simon & Schuster Children's Publishing.

—Steal Away Home. 1999. 192p. lib. bdg. 11.64 (978-0-606-15921-0(5)); (gr. 3-6). lib. bdg. 13.00 (978-0-613-12154-5(6)) Tandem Library Bks.

Sargent, Daina. Kansas: Conquer Fear. Lenoir, Jane, illus. l.t. ed. 2004. (Double Trouble Ser.). 48p. (J). pap. 6.95 (978-1-59381-125-9(X)); lib. bdg. 22.60 (978-1-59381-124-2(1)) Ozark Publishing.

Smith, Florence B. Painted Eagle's Dream. 2001. 220p. (J). pap. 8.00 (978-1-893463-41-7(9)) Prickly Pr.

Thomas, Carroll. Blue Creek Farm: A Matty Trescott Novel. 2000. (Illus.). 185p. (J). pap. 9.95 (978-1-57525-243-8(0)) Smith and Kraus Publishers, Incorporated.

—Blue Creek Farm: A Matty Trescott Novel. 2000. (gr. 3-6). lib. bdg. 18.75 (978-0-613-62668-2(0)) Tandem Library Bks.

—Riding by Starlight: A Matty Trescott Novel. 2002. (Illus.). ix, 173p. (J). 9.95 (978-1-57525-315-2(1)) Smith and Kraus Publishers, Incorporated.

Uhlig, Richard Allen. Last Dance at the Frosty Queen. 2007. 368p. (YA). (gr. 9). lib. bdg. 18.99 (***978-0-375-93967-9(9)***); 15.99 (***978-0-375-83967-2(4)***) Random Hse. Children's Bks. (Knopf Bks. for Young Readers).

Uncle Markie. Pigletté & Bobo in Kansas City. 2003. (YA). ring bd. 9.95 (978-1-933129-08-2(5)) Studio 403.

Waggoner, Sandra. Maggie's Treasure. 2005. (Gatlin Fields Ser.). 107p. (J). per. 6.99 (978-0-9766823-0-1(3)) Sable Creek Pr. LLC.

Walter, Dan. Hello, Willie! 2007. (J). 14.95 (***978-1-932888-52-2(7)***) Mascot Bks., Inc.

Wilder, Laura Ingalls. Little House on the Prairie. Williams, Garth, illus. (Little House Ser.). (J). 2004. 352p. pap. 8.99 (978-0-06-058181-7(6) , Harper Trophy); 2003. 272p. pap. 5.99 (978-0-06-052237-7(2)); 1999. 320p. (gr. 3-6). 29.95 (978-0-06-028244-8(4)) HarperCollins Pubs.

—Little House on the Prairie. Williams, Garth, illus. l.t. ed. 1999. (Little House Ser.). 420p. (J). (gr. 3-6). lib. bdg. 35.95 (978-1-58118-051-0(9) , 22771) LRS.

—Little House on the Prairie. 1999. (Little House Ser.). (J). (gr. 3-6). 11.95 (978-1-56137-834-0(8)) Novel Units, Inc.

—La Pequena Cuidad en la Pradera. (SPA., Illus.). 206p. (YA). (gr. 5-8). 8.95 (978-84-279-3235-7(9) , NG7786) Noguer y Caralt Editores, S. A. ESP. *Dist:* Lectorum Pubns., Inc.

Wilson, N. D. 100 Cupboards. 2007. (J). pap. (***978-0-375-83882-8(1)***); 304p. lib. bdg. (***978-0-375-93881-8(8)***); 304p. (gr. 3-7). 16.99 (***978-0-375-83881-1(3)***) Random Hse., Inc.

KANSAS—HISTORY

Good, Diane L. Brown vs. Board of Education: A Civil Rights Milestone. 2004. (Cornerstones of Freedom Ser.). (J). 26.00 (978-0-516-24225-5(3) , Children's Pr.) Scholastic Library Publishing.

Marsh, Carole. Jeopardy. (New York Experience! Ser.). 2004. 32p. (J). (gr. 3-8). pap. 7.95 (978-0-635-01061-0(6)); 2001. pap. 7.95 (978-0-635-00347-8(3)) Gallopade International.

—Jography. 2001. (Kansas Experience! Ser.). pap. 7.95 (978-0-635-00348-5(1) , Marsh, Carole Bks.) Gallopade International.

—Kansas History Projects: 30 Cool, Activities, Crafts, Experiments & More for Kids to Do to Learn about Your State! 2003. (Kansas Experience Ser.). 32p. (gr. k-5). pap. 5.95 (978-0-635-01785-7(7) , Marsh, Carole Bks.) Gallopade International.

—My First Pocket Guide Kansas. 2000. (Kansas Experience! Ser.). (Illus.). 96p. (J). (gr. 3-8). 12.95 (978-0-635-01306-4(1) , 13061) Gallopade International.

McArthur, Debra. The Kansas-Nebraska Act & Bleeding Kansas in American History. 2003. (In American History Ser.). (Illus.). 128p. (J). lib. bdg. 26.60 (978-0-7660-1988-1(8)) Enslow Pubs., Inc.

Miller, Jake. Brown vs. Board of Education of Topeka: Challenging School Segregation in the Supreme Court. 2004. (Library of the Civil Rights Movement Ser.). (Illus.). 24p. (J). lib. bdg. 19.95 (978-0-8239-6250-1(4)) Rosen Publishing Group, Inc., The.

Robertson, Theda Robinson. Journey to a Free Land: The Story of Nicodemus, the First All Black Town West of the Mississippi. 2006. (Illus.). (J). (978-0-9705721-6-5(6)) Written Images, Inc.

Saltman, Julie. Fort Leavenworth. 2004. (American Forts & Their Strategic Importance Ser.). (J). (978-1-59084-712-1(1)) Mason Crest Pubs.

Young, Jeff C. Bleeding Kansas & the Violent Clash over Slavery in the Heartland. 2006. (Wild History of the American West Ser.). (Illus.). 128p. (J). lib. bdg. 33.27 (978-1-59845-013-2(1) , MyReportLinks.com Bks.) Enslow Pubs., Inc.

KANSAS—HISTORY—FICTION

Breault, Christie Merriman. Logan West, Printer's Devil. Archembault, Matthew, illus. 2006. 142p. (J). pap. (978-1-59336-762-6(7)) Mondo Publishing.

Kimmel, Cody E. In the Eye of the Storm. Snow, Scott, illus. 2003. (Adventures of Young Buffalo Bill Ser.). 144p. (J). (gr. 3-7). 15.99 (978-0-06-029115-0(X)) HarperCollins Pubs.

Kimmel, E. Cody. In the Eye of the Storm. Snow, Scott, illus. 2003. (Adventures of Young Buffalo Bill Ser.). 144p. (J). (gr. 3-7). lib. bdg. 16.89 (978-0-06-029116-7(8)) HarperCollins Pubs.

Kimmel, Elizabeth Cody. One Sky above Us. Bernardin, James & Snow, Scott, illus. 2002. (Adventures of Young Buffalo Bill Ser.). 192p. (J). (gr. 3-6). 15.99 (978-0-06-029119-8(2)) HarperCollins Pubs.

—To the Frontier. Snow, Scott, illus. 2002. (Adventures of Young Buffalo Bill Ser.). 192p. (J). (gr. 4-7). 15.95 (978-0-06-029117-4(6)) HarperCollins Pubs.

McMullan, Kate. A Fine Start Bk. 3: Meg's Prairie Diary. 2003. (My America Ser.: No. 3). 112p. (J). pap. 12.95 (978-0-439-37061-5(2)) Scholastic, Inc.

—For This Land Bk. 2: Meg's Prairie Diary. 2003. (gr. 3-6). lib. bdg. 19.90 (978-0-613-63038-2(6)) Tandem Library Bks.

Thomas, Carroll. The Town on Rambling Creek: A Matty Trescott Novel. 2004. (Illus.). ix, 185p. (J). (978-1-57525-376-3(3)) Smith and Kraus Publishers, Incorporated.

KANSAS CITY CHIEFS (FOOTBALL TEAM)

Hawkes, Brian. The History of the Kansas City Chiefs. 2004. (NFL Today Ser.). (Illus.). 32p. 18.95 (978-1-58341-301-2(4) , Creative Education) Creative Co., The.

KARATE

Blackall, Bernie. Martial Arts. 1999. (Top Sport Ser.). 32p. (J). (gr. 4-6). lib. bdg. 21.36 (978-1-57572-705-9(6)) Heinemann Library.

Carlon, Roger. Super Karate for Kids. 2000. (Illus.). 90p. (J). (gr. 7-11). pap. 10.95 (978-0-86568-184-2(8)) Unique Pubns.

Collins, Paul. Karate. 2001. (Martial Arts Ser.). (Illus.). 32p. (J). (gr. 3 up). 28.00 (978-0-7910-6555-6(3) , 010252, Chelsea Hse.) Facts On File, Inc.

—Kung Fu. 2001. (Martial Arts Ser.). (Illus.). 32p. (J). (gr. 3 up). 28.00 (978-0-7910-6556-3(1) , 010253, Chelsea Hse.) Facts On File, Inc.

—Taek Won Do. 2001. (Martial Arts Ser.). (Illus.). 32p. (J). (gr. 3 up). 28.00 (978-0-7910-6554-9(5) , 010254, Chelsea Hse.) Facts On File, Inc.

Cook, Harry. Karate. 2004. 32p. (YA). lib. bdg. 24.67 (978-0-8368-4193-0(X)) Stevens, Gareth Inc.

Craats, Rennay. For the Love of Karate. Nault, Jennifer & Turner, Kara, eds. 2003. (For the Love of Sports Ser.). (Illus.). 24p. (J). pap. 6.95 (978-1-59036-071-2(0)) Weigl Pubs., Inc.

—Karate. 2001. (For the Love of Sports Ser.). (Illus.). 24p. (J). lib. bdg. 15.95 (978-1-930954-17-5(4)) Weigl Pubs., Inc.

Dillman, George A. & Thomas, Chris. Pressure Point Karate Made Easy: A Guide to the Dillman Pressure Point Method for Beginners & Younger Martial Artists. 1999. (Illus.). 144p. (gr. 6 up). pap. 14.95 (978-1-889267-02-9(3)) Dillman, George Karate International, Pubs.

Gaines, Ann Graham. The Composite Guide to Martial Arts. 2000. (Composite Guide Ser.). (Illus.). (J). (gr. 8-12). 18.65 (978-0-7910-5866-4(2) , Chelsea Hse.) Facts On File, Inc.

Gold Medal Kumite: The Making of Champions. 2nd l.t. ed. 2000. 150p. (YA). spiral bd. 25.00 (978-1-929364-04-6(0)) JIA Publishing.

Hughes, Morgan. Karate. 2005. (Junior Sports Ser.). (Illus.). 32p. (gr. 2-4). 19.95 (978-1-59515-193-3(1)) Rourke Publishing, LLC.

Jensen, Julie. Beginning Karate. King, Andy, illus. 1998. (Beginning Sports Ser.). 80p. (gr. 3-5). 22.60 (978-0-8225-3512-6(2)) Lerner Publishing Group.

Johnson, Nathan. Karate. 2002. (Martial & Fighting Arts Ser.). (Illus.). 96p. (J). (gr. 7 up). lib. bdg. (978-1-59084-388-8(6)) Mason Crest Pubs.

Kalman, Bobbie & MacAulay, Kelley. Karate in Action. 2005. (Sports in Action Ser.). (Illus.). 32p. (J). pap. (978-0-7787-0361-7(4)) Crabtree Publishing Co.

Karate: A Master's Secrets of Uechi-Ryu. 2003. (Illus.). 576p. (YA). pap. 49.95 (978-0-9746989-0-8(3)) Iron Arm International.

Lindeen, Carol K. Let's Do Karate! 2007. (Pebble Plus Ser.). (Illus.). 24p. (J). 19.93 (978-0-7368-6358-2(3) , Pebble Bks.) Capstone Pr., Inc.

MacAulay, Kelley & Kalman, Bobbie. Karate in Action. 2005. (Sports in Action Ser.). (Illus.). 32p. (J). (978-0-7787-0341-9(X)) Crabtree Publishing Co.

Macken, JoAnn Early. Karate. 2005. (Illus.). 24p. (J). pap. (978-0-8368-4521-1(8)); (YA). lib. bdg. 19.33 (978-0-8368-4514-3(5)) Stevens, Gareth Inc.

Morris, Neil. Karate. 2001. (Get Going! Ser.). (Illus.). 32p. (J). (gr. 4-6). lib. bdg. 22.79 (978-1-58810-039-9(1)) Heinemann Library.

—Kung Fu. 2001. (Get Going! Ser.). (Illus.). 32p. (J). (gr. 4-6). lib. bdg. 22.79 (978-1-58810-040-5(5)) Heinemann Library.

—Tae Kwan Do. 2001. (Illus.). 32p. (J). (gr. 4-6). lib. bdg. 22.79 (978-1-58810-041-2(3)) Heinemann Library.

Randall, Pamela. Aikido. 1999. (Martial Arts Ser.). (Illus.). 24p. (J). lib. bdg. 18.75 (978-0-8239-5234-2(7) , PowerKids Pr.) Rosen Publishing Group, Inc., The.

—Karate. 1999. (Martial Arts Ser.). (Illus.). 24p. (J). lib. bdg. 18.75 (978-0-8239-5236-6(3) , PowerKids Pr.) Rosen Publishing Group, Inc., The.

—Kung Fu. 1999. (Martial Arts Ser.). (Illus.). 24p. (J). lib. bdg. 18.75 (978-0-8239-5237-3(1) , PowerKids Pr.) Rosen Publishing Group, Inc., The.

—Tae Kwon Do. 1999. (Martial Arts Ser.). (Illus.). 24p. (J). lib. bdg. 18.75 (978-0-8239-5233-5(9) , PowerKids Pr.) Rosen Publishing Group, Inc., The.

Santoro, Laura & Corso, Jennifer. Aikido for Kids. 1998. 96p. (YA). (gr. 6-8). reprint ed. 15.00 (978-0-7567-6028-1(3)) DIANE Publishing Co.

Schwartz, Stuart B. & Conley, Craig. Karate Blocks. 1998. (Martial Arts Ser.). (Illus.). 48p. (J). (gr. 3-4). lib. bdg. 21.26 (978-0-7368-0008-2(5) , Capstone High-Interest Bks.) Capstone Pr., Inc.

—Karate Kicks. 1998. (Martial Arts Ser.). (Illus.). 48p. (J). (gr. 3-4). lib. bdg. 21.26 (978-0-7368-0009-9(3) , Capstone High-Interest Bks.) Capstone Pr., Inc.

—Karate Punches. 1998. (Martial Arts Ser.). (Illus.). 48p. (J). (gr. 3-4). lib. bdg. 21.26 (978-0-7368-0010-5(7) , Capstone High-Interest Bks.) Capstone Pr., Inc.

—Karate Strikes. 1998. (Martial Arts Ser.). (Illus.). 48p. (J). (gr. 3-4). lib. bdg. 21.26 (978-0-7368-0011-2(5) , Capstone High-Interest Bks.) Capstone Pr., Inc.

Webster-Doyle, Terrence. Facing the Double-Edged Sword: The Art of Karate for Young People. Cameron, Rod, illus. 1999. (Education for Peace Ser.). 96p. (gr. 3-9). 14.95 (978-0-8348-0465-4(4) , Weatherhill, Inc.) Shambhala Pubns., Inc.

KARATE—FICTION

Barnes, Dawn. Beware of the Haunted Eye. 2007. (Black Belt Club Ser.: No. 3). 128p. (J). pap. 4.99 (978-0-439-85657-7(4) , Blue Sky Pr., The) Scholastic, Inc.

—Night on the Mountain of Fear. Chang, Bernard, illus. 2006. (Black Belt Club Ser.: No. 2). 176p. (J). pap. 4.99 (978-0-439-63939-2(5)); (gr. 2-5). 16.99 (978-0-439-63937-8(9)) Scholastic, Inc. (Blue Sky Pr., The).

Barnes, Dawn. Seven Wheels of Power. 2007. (Black Belt Club Ser.: No. 1). 176p. (J). pap. 2.99 ***(978-0-545-01029-0(2))*** Scholastic, Inc.

—Seven Wheels of Power. Chang, Bernard, illus. 2005. (Black Belt Club Ser.: No. 1). 176p. (J). 4.99 (978-0-439-63936-1(0)); pap. 16.95 (978-0-439-63935-4(2)) Scholastic, Inc. (Blue Sky Pr., The).

Barnes, Susan. Kelly Karate: Discovers the Ice Princess. 2004. 138p. (J). (gr. 4-8). pap. 5.95 (978-0-9705777-3-3(7)) McBook Pubs., LLC.

Bass, L. G. The Outlaws of Moonshadow Marsh the Sign of Qin, Bk. 1. 2006. 400p. (gr. 5-17). reprint ed. pap. 7.99 (978-0-7868-5566-7(5)) Hyperion Pr.

Bidoli, Katie. Karate Adventures of Kisho, Hana, & Nobu: Karate Is for Everyone! 2006. (Illus.). 16p. (J). 10.00 ***(*978-1-60243-029-7(2))*** Keen's Martial Arts Academy.

Carey, Michael. Little Kathy Likes Karate. Connors, Jackie, ed. 2003. (Illus.). 30p. (J). spiral bd. 10.95 (978-0-9743679-1-0(5)) Reiki Blessings.

Chin, Oliver Clyde. Julie Black Belt: The Kung Fu Chronicles. Chua, Charlene, illus. 2007. 36p. (J). (ps-3). 15.95 ***(*978-1-59702-009-1(5))*** Immedium.

Christopher, Matt. Head to Head. Koelsch, Michael, illus. 2005. 57p. (J). (ps-7). lib. bdg. 12.19 (978-0-606-33454-9(8)) Tandem Library Bks.

DK Publishing. Kung Fu Panda: the Warrior's Guide: The Warrior's Guide. 2008. 48p. (J). (gr. 2-6). 12.99 ***(*978-0-7566-3825-2(9))*** Dorling Kindersley Publishing, Inc.

—Kung Fu Panda Ultimate Sticker Book. 2008. (Ultimate Sticker Bks.). 16p. (J). (gr. 2-6). pap. 6.99 ***(*978-0-7566-3824-5(0))*** Dorling Kindersley Publishing, Inc.

Krulik, Nancy E. Karate Katie, No. 18. John and Wendy Staff, illus. 2006. (Katie Kazoo, Switcheroo Ser.: No. 18). 80p. (J). (gr. 2-5). pap. 3.99 (978-0-448-43767-5(8) , Grosset & Dunlap) Penguin Group (USA) Inc.

Milky, Dj. Kung Fu Klutz & Karate Cool, Vol. 1. 2007. (Illus.). 192p. pap. 4.99 ***(*978-1-59816-052-9(4)*** , Tokyopop Kids) TOKYOPOP, Inc.

Nevius, Carol. Karate Hour. Thomson, Bill, illus. 2004. 32p. (J). 14.95 (978-0-7614-5169-3(2)) Cavendish, Marshall Corp.

Rockwell, Anne F. Chip & the Karate Kick. Meisel, Paul, illus. 2004. (Good Sports Ser.). 40p. (J). (ps-1). lib. bdg. 15.89 (978-0-06-028446-6(3)) HarperCollins Pubs.

Stone, Jeff. Crane. 2007. (Five Ancestors Ser.: Bk. 4). 256p. (J). (gr. 5-9). 15.99 (978-0-375-83077-8(4) , Random Hse. Bks. for Young Readers) Random Hse. Children's Bks.

Trembath, Don. Bachelors. 2002. (gr. 3-6). lib. bdg. 15.25 (978-0-613-85895-3(6)) Tandem Library Bks.

—The Big Show. 2003. (Black Belt Ser.). (Illus.). 144p. (J). (gr. 3-7). pap. 6.95 (978-1-55143-266-3(8)) Orca Bk. Pubs. USA.

—Big Show. 2003. (gr. 3-6). lib. bdg. 15.25 (978-0-613-83710-1(X)) Tandem Library Bks.

Walker, Pamela. In Gold & Jade, No. 2. 2006. (Kung Fu Princess Ser.). (Illus.). 224p. (J). (gr. 7). pap. 6.99 (978-0-448-44140-5(3) , Grosset & Dunlap) Penguin Group (USA) Inc.

Williams, Jacklyn. Happy Birthday, Gus! Cushman, Doug, illus. 2005. (Read-It! Readers Ser.). 32p. (J). (gr. k-3). 18.60 (978-1-4048-0957-4(0)) Picture Window Bks.

KARTS AND KARTING

Los Carritos: Individual Title Six-Packs. (Coleccion Pm Ser.: Vol. 1). Tr. of Go-carts. (SPA.). 16p. (gr. k-1). 26.00 (978-0-7578-0670-4(8)) Rigby Education.

David, Jack. Go Kart Racing. 2008. (Illus.). 24p. (J). lib. bdg. 19.95 (978-1-60014-123-2(4)) Bellwether Media.

David, Jack. Karts. 2008. (Illus.). 24p. (J). lib. bdg. 19.95 ***(*978-1-60014-149-2(8))*** Bellwether Media.

Doeden, Matt. Shifter Karts: High-Speed Go-Karts. 2005. (Blazers—Horsepower Ser.). (Illus.). 149p. (J). 19.33 (978-0-7368-3790-3(6)) Capstone Pr., Inc.

Herran, Joe & Thomas, Ron. Karting. 2003. (Action Sports Ser.). (Illus.). 32p. (J). (gr. 4-8). 28.00 (978-0-7910-7535-7(4) , Chelsea Hse.) Facts On File, Inc.

Icanberry, Mark, creator. Electric Lunch. 2000. (Look, Learn & Do Ser.). (Illus.). 48p. (J). 14.95 (978-1-893327-03-0(5)) Look, Learn & Do Pubns.

Nichols, John. Street Luge. 2001. (Extreme Sports Ser.). (Illus.). 48p. (J). (gr. 3-6). lib. bdg. 24.26 (978-0-7398-4692-6(2)) Raintree.

Savage, Jeff. Go-Karts. 2003. (Wild Rides! Ser.). (Illus.). 32p. (J). (gr. 3-4). lib. bdg. 21.26 (978-0-7368-1517-8(1) , Capstone High-Interest Bks.) Capstone Pr., Inc.

Smith, Graham. Karting. 2002. (Radical Sports Ser.). (Illus.). 32p. (J). (gr. 5-7). lib. bdg. 25.64 (978-1-58810-624-7(1)); pap. 7.50 (978-1-4034-0104-5(7) , 91652) Heinemann Library.

—Karting. 2003. (gr. 5-8). lib. bdg. 15.25 (978-0-613-45787-3(0)) Tandem Library Bks.

KARTS AND KARTING—FICTION

Maddox, Jake. Go-Kart Rush. Tiffany, Sean, illus. 2007. 63p. (J). pap. ***(*978-1-59889-415-8(3))*** Stone Arch Bks.

Midnight Lightning, 6 vols., Pack. (Bookweb Ser.). 32p. (gr. 5 up). 34.00 (978-0-7635-3790-6(X)) Rigby Education.

Montanari, Eva. Go-Cart Number 1. 2005. (Illus.). 31p. (J). lib. bdg. 24.67 (978-0-8368-4478-8(5)) Stevens, Gareth Inc.

KEATS, JOHN, 1795-1821

Kirkpatrick, Patricia. John Keats. Delessert, Etienne, illus. 2005. (Voices in Poetry Ser.). 48p. (gr. 5-9). 21.95 (978-1-58341-345-6(6) , Creative Education) Creative Co., The.

KELLER, HELEN, 1880-1968

Adams, Colleen. The Courage of Helen Keller. 2003. (Reading Room Collection). (Illus.). 24p. (J). lib. bdg. 18.75 (978-0-8239-3710-3(0)) Rosen Publishing Group, Inc., The.

Adler, David A. Helen Keller. Wallner, John, illus. 32p. (J). 4.95 (978-0-8234-2042-1(6)) Holiday Hse., Inc.

—Helen Keller. Wallner, John C., illus. 32p. (J). (gr. k-3). tchr. ed. 14.95 (978-0-8234-1606-6(2)) Holiday Hse., Inc.

Auster, Michael A. They Led the Way. 2005. (Yellow Umbrella Ser.). (J). (978-0-7368-5315-6(4)); (Illus.). 16p. (978-0-7368-5279-1(4)) Capstone Pr., Inc.

Benge, Janet and Geoff. Helen Keller Facing Her Challenges/Challenging the World Read-along, 1 bk. James, Kennon, illus. 2003. (Another Great Achiever Ser.). (J). lib. bdg. 23.95 incl. audio (978-1-57537-793-3(4)); lib. bdg. 23.95 incl. audio compact disk (978-1-57537-743-8(8)) Advance Publishing, Inc.

Benge, Janet Hazel & Benge, Geoffrey Francis. Helen Keller: Facing Her Challenges, Challenging the World. James, Kennon, illus. 2000. (Another Great Achiever Ser.). 48p. (J). (gr. 3-6). lib. bdg. 16.95 (978-1-57537-105-4(7)); 9.95 (978-1-57537-107-8(3)) Advance Publishing, Inc.

Butler, Darren J. The Miracle at the Pump: The Story of Helen Keller & Annie Sullivan. Lee, Linda Sanders, illus. 2000. 32p. (J). (gr. 1-7). pap. 4.99 (978-0-9700752-4-6(3)) Onstage Publishing, LLC.

Cline-Ransome, Lesa. Helen Keller: The World in Her Heart. Ransome, James, illus. 2008. 32p. (J). 16.99 ***(*978-0-06-057074-3(1))***; lib. bdg. 17.89 ***(*978-0-06-057075-0(X))*** HarperCollins Pubs. (Collins).

Dash, Joan. The World at Her Fingertips: The Story of Helen Keller. 2002. (World at Her Fingertips Ser.). (Illus.). 240p. (J). 4.99 (978-0-590-90716-3(6) , Scholastic Pr.) Scholastic, Inc.

Davidson, Margaret. Helen Keller. 1999. (Illus.). (J). (gr. 3-6). lib. bdg. 12.40 (978-0-8085-5141-6(8)) Tandem Library Bks.

Devillier, Christy. Helen Keller. 2004. (First Biographies Set Iv Ser.). (Illus.). 32p. (J). (gr. k-4). lib. bdg. 22.78 (978-1-59197-514-4(X)) ABDO Publishing Co.

Dolan, Sean. Helen Keller. 2006. 32p. (J). (gr. 1-2). pap. 4.95 (978-0-516-25481-4(2) , Children's Pr.) Scholastic Library Publishing.

Dolan, Sean J. Helen Keller. 2005. (Rookie Biographies(R) Ser.). (Illus.). 31p. (J). (ps-ps). 20.50 (978-0-516-25269-8(0) , Children's Pr.) Scholastic Library Publishing.

Dubois, Muriel L. Helen Keller. 2003. (Photo-Illustrated Biographies Ser.). (Illus.). 24p. (J). (gr. 2-3). lib. bdg. 18.60 (978-0-7368-1605-2(4) , Bridgestone Bks.) Capstone Pr., Inc.

—Helen Keller, 6 vols. (gr. 2-5). 36.95 (978-0-7368-4559-5(3)) Red Brick Learning.

Feinstein, Stephen. Read about Helen Keller. 2004. (I Like Biographies! Ser.). (Illus.). 24p. (J). lib. bdg. 21.26 (978-0-7660-2299-7(4)) Enslow Pubs., Inc.

Fetty, Margaret. Helen Keller: Break down the Walls! 2007. (Defining Moments Ser.). (Illus.). 32p. (J). lib. bdg. 25.27 (978-1-59716-271-5(X)) Bearport Publishing Co., Inc.

Ford, Carin T. Helen Keller: Lighting the Way for the Blind & Deaf. 2001. (People to Know Ser.). (Illus.). 112p. (J). (gr. 6-12). lib. bdg. 20.95 (978-0-7660-1530-2(0)) Enslow Pubs., Inc.

—Helen Keller: Meet a Woman of Courage. 2002. (Meeting Famous People Ser.). (Illus.). 32p. (J). (gr. 1-4). lib. bdg. 22.60 (978-0-7660-1856-3(3)) Enslow Pubs., Inc.

Garrett, Leslie. Helen Keller: A Photographic Story of a Life. 2004. (Biography Ser.). (Illus.). 128p. (J). 14.99 (978-0-7566-0488-2(5)); (gr. 8). pap. 4.99 (978-0-7566-0339-7(0)) Dorling Kindersley Publishing, Inc.

Ghiglieri, Carol. Easy Reader Biographies: Helen Keller: An Inspiring Life. 2007. 16p. pap. 2.99 ***(*978-0-439-77417-8(9)*** , Teaching Resources) Scholastic, Inc.

Helen Keller. (Photo Illustrated Biographies Ser.). 24p. (J). 6.95 (978-0-7368-3433-9(8)) Capstone Pr., Inc.

Helenthal, Janet. Helen Keller. 2005. (Illus.). 16p. (J). ***(*978-0-7367-2853-9(8))*** Zaner-Bloser, Inc.

Keller, Helen. To Love This Life: Quotations by Helen Keller. 2002. (Time to Love Ser.). 144p. (J). reprint ed. pap. 4.50 (978-0-439-31913-3(7)) Scholastic, Inc.

Kent, Deborah. Helen Keller: Author & Advocate for the Disabled. 2003. (Spirit of America). (Illus.). 32p. (J). (gr. 2-6). 27.07 (978-1-59296-005-7(7)) Child's World, Inc.

Klingel, Cynthia Fitterer & Noyed, Robert B. Helen Keller. 2001. (Wonder Books Level 2: Biographies Ser.). (Illus.). 24p. (J). (ps-3). 22.79 (978-1-56766-952-7(2)) Child's World, Inc.

Koestler-Grack, Rachel A. The Story of Helen Keller. 2003. (Breakthrough Biographies Ser.). (Illus.). 32p. (J). (gr. 3-5). 23.00 (978-0-7910-7315-5(7) , Chelsea Hse.) Facts On File, Inc.

Lakin, Patricia. Helen Keller & the Big Storm. Magnuson, Diana, illus. 2002. (Ready-to-Read Ser.: Level 2). 32p. (J). pap. 3.99 (978-0-689-84104-0(3) , Aladdin) Simon & Schuster Children's Publishing.

—Helen Keller & the Big Storm. 2002. (gr. k-3). lib. bdg. 11.80 (978-0-613-45056-0(6)) Tandem Library Bks.

Lawlor, Laurie. Helen Keller, Rebellious Spirit: The Life & Times of Helen Keller. 2001. (Illus.). 176p. (J). (gr. 4-6). tchr. ed. 22.95 (978-0-8234-1588-5(0)) Holiday Hse., Inc.

Leavitt, Amie. Helen Keller. 2007. (What's So Great About...? Ser.). (J). lib. bdg. 25.70 ***(*978-1-58415-583-6(3))*** Mitchell Lane Pubs., Inc.

Lundell, Margo. A Girl Named Helen Keller: Una Nina Llamada Helen Keller. Trivas, Irene, illus. 2003. (SPA.). 48p. (J). (ps-3). pap. 3.99 (978-0-439-46786-5(1) , Scholastic en Espanol) Scholastic, Inc.

Lynch, Emma. Helen Keller. 2005. (Lives & Times Ser.). 32p. (J). (Illus.). (gr. 2-4). lib. bdg. 24.21 (978-1-4034-6350-0(6)); pap. (978-1-4034-6364-7(6)) Heinemann Library.

MacLeod, Elizabeth. Helen Keller: A Determined Life. Krystoforski, Andrej, illus. 2007. 32p. pap. ***(*978-1-55453-000-7(8))*** Kids Can Pr., Ltd.

—Helen Keller: A Determined Life. 2004. (Snapshots Ser.). (Illus.). 32p. (J). (gr. 4-6). (978-1-55337-509-8(2)); (978-1-55337-508-1(4)) Kids Can Pr., Ltd.

Marsh, Carole. Helen Keller. 2002. (One Thousand Readers Ser.). (Illus.). 12p. (J). (gr. k-4). 2.95 (978-0-635-01478-8(5) , 14785) Gallopade International.

McLeese, Don. Helen Keller. 2002. (J). lib. bdg. 20.64 (978-1-58952-302-9(4)) Rourke Publishing, LLC.

Roop, Peter & Roop, Connie. Give Me a Sign, Helen Keller! 2004. (Scholastic Chapter Book Biography Ser.). (Illus.). 55p. (J). (978-0-439-55444-2(6)) Scholastic, Inc.

Sabin, Francene. Helen Keller: Una Chica Valiente. abr. ed. 2007. 64p. (J). pap. 3.99 ***(*978-0-439-87999-6(X)*** , Scholastic en Espanol) Scholastic, Inc.

Sabin, Francene & Mattern, Joanne. Helen Keller, Girl of Courage. Meyer, Jean, illus. 2006. 56p. (J). ***(*978-0-439-66043-3(2))*** Scholastic, Inc.

Shichtman, Sandra H. Helen Keller: Out of a Dark & Silent World. 2002. (Gateway Biography Ser.). (Illus.). 48p. (gr. 2-4). lib. bdg. 23.90 (978-0-7613-2550-5(6) , Millbrook Pr.) Lerner Publishing Group.

Steck-Vaughn Staff. Helen Keller: Triumph. 2003. pap. 4.10 (978-0-7398-7648-0(1)) Steck-Vaughn.

Sullivan, George. Helen Keller. 2000. (gr. 3-6). lib. bdg. 12.40 (978-0-613-36393-8(0)) Tandem Library Bks.

Sullivan, George. Her Life in Pictures. 2007. (Helen Keller Ser.). 80p. (J). (gr. 2-5). 17.99 ***(*978-0-439-91815-2(4)*** ; Scholastic Nonfiction) Scholastic, Inc.

Sullivan, George E. Helen Keller. 2002. (In Their Own Words Ser.). (Illus.). 128p. (J). (gr. 3-7). pap. 12.95 (978-0-439-14751-4(4)); (gr. 4-6). mass mkt. 4.99 (978-0-439-09555-6(7)) Scholastic, Inc.

—Helen Keller. 2001. (In Their Own Words Ser.). (Illus.). (J). 11.15 (978-0-606-20725-6(2)) Tandem Library Bks.

Sutcliffe, Jane. Helen Keller. Verstraete, Elaine, illus. 2002. (On My Own Biographies Ser.). 48p. (J). lib. bdg. 23.93 (978-0-87614-600-2(0) , Carolrhoda Bks.) Lerner Publishing Group.

—Helen Keller. 2002. (gr. 3-6). lib. bdg. 14.10 (978-0-613-52398-1(9)) Tandem Library Bks.

Thompson, Gare. Who Was Helen Keller? O'Brien, John & Harrison, Nancy, illus. 2003. (Who Was...? Ser.). 112p. (J). pap. 4.99 (978-0-448-43144-4(0) , Grosset & Dunlap) Penguin Group (USA) Inc.

—Who Was Helen Keller? 2003. (gr. 3-6). lib. bdg. 13.00 (978-0-613-63485-4(3)) Tandem Library Bks.

Walker, Pamela. Helen Keller. 2001. (Real People Ser.). (Illus.). 24p. (J). (ps-2). 18.00 (978-0-516-23434-2(X)); pap. 4.95 (978-0-516-23588-2(5)) Scholastic Library Publishing. (Children's Pr.).

—Helen Keller. 2001. (gr. k-3). lib. bdg. 12.95 (978-0-613-58837-9(1)) Tandem Library Bks.

Welvaert, Scott R. Helen Keller: Courageous Advocate. Martin, Cynthia & Tucker, Keith, illus. 2005. (Graphic Library). 32p. (J). (gr. 3-7). lib. bdg. 25.26 (978-0-7368-4964-7(5)) Capstone Pr., Inc.

Woodhouse, Jayne. Helen Keller. 2002. (Lives & Times Ser.). (Illus.). 24p. (J). (gr. k-3). pap. 6.50 (978-1-4034-0030-7(X) , 91474) Heinemann Library.

—Helen Keller. 2002. (gr. k-3). lib. bdg. 12.95 (978-0-613-88095-4(1)) Tandem Library Bks.

KELLER, HELEN, 1880-1968—FICTION

Lakin, Patricia. Helen Keller & the Big Storm. Magnuson, Diana, illus. ed. 2005. 32p. (J). lib. bdg. 15.00 (978-1-59054-945-2(7)) Fitzgerald Bks.

Miller, Sarah Elizabeth. Miss Spitfire: Reaching Helen Keller. 2007. 240p. (J). (gr. 5-9). 16.99 (978-1-4169-2542-2(2)) Simon & Schuster Children's Publishing.

KENNEDY, EDWARD MOORE, 1932-

Kennedy, Edward M. My Senator & Me: A Dog's Eye View of Washington, D. C. Small, David, illus. 2006. 56p. (J). (ps-3). pap. 16.99 (978-0-439-65077-9(1) , Scholastic) Scholastic, Inc.

Kennedy, Edward M. My Senator & Me: A Dog's-Eye View of Washington, D. C. Small, David, illus. 2007. 53p. (J). reprint ed. 17.00 ***(*978-1-4223-6791-9(6))*** DIANE Publishing Co.

Kennedy, Edward Moore. My Senator & Me: A Dog's Eye View of Washington, D.C. Small, David, illus. 2006. (J). ***(*978-1-4156-7168-9(0)); (*978-0-439-65078-6(X))*** Scholastic, Inc. (Scholastic Pr.).

KENNEDY, JOHN F. (JOHN FITZGERALD), 1917-1963

Abraham, Philip. John F. Kennedy & PT109. 2002. (Survivors Ser.). (Illus.). 48p. (YA). (gr. 7-12). 24.00 (978-0-516-23905-7(8) , Children's Pr.) Scholastic Library Publishing.

—John F. Kennedy & PT109. 2002. (gr. 7-12). lib. bdg. 15.25 (978-0-613-58779-2(0)) Tandem Library Bks.

Anderson, Catherine Corley. John F. Kennedy. 2004. (Presidential Leaders Ser.). (Illus.). 112p. (J). 29.27 (978-0-8225-0812-0(5) , Lerner Pubns.) Lerner Publishing Group.

Ashby, Ruth. John & Jacqueline Kennedy. 2004. (Illus.). 48p. (J). pap. (978-0-8368-5700-9(3)); lib. bdg. 30.00 (978-0-8368-5694-1(5)) Stevens, Gareth Inc. (World Almanac Library).

Brown, Jonatha A. John F. Kennedy. (People We Should Know Ser.). 2006. 24p. (J). pap. 5.95 (978-0-8368-4768-0(7)); 2006. 24p. (J). lib. bdg. 19.33 (978-0-8368-4761-1(X)); 2005. (J). pap. (978-0-8368-4754-3(7)); 2005. (Illus.). 24p. (YA). lib. bdg. 19.33 (978-0-8368-4747-5(4)) Stevens, Gareth Inc.

Burgan, Michael. John F. Kennedy. 2001. (Trailblazers of the Modern World Ser.). (Illus.). 48p. (J). (gr. 5 up). pap. 14.95 (978-0-8368-5225-7(7)); lib. bdg. 30.00 (978-0-8368-5065-9(3)) Stevens, Gareth Inc. (World Almanac Library).

Capstone Press Staff. John F. Kennedy. 1998. (Biografias Ser.). (Illus.). 24p. (J). (gr. k-3). lib. bdg. 14.00 (978-0-516-21379-8(2) , Children's Pr.) Scholastic Library Publishing.

Cooper, Ilene. Jack: The Early Years of John F. Kennedy. 2003. (Illus.). 160p. (J). (gr. 5-9). 22.99 (978-0-525-46923-0(0) , Dutton Juvenile) Penguin Group (USA) Inc.

Darraj, Susan Muaddi. John F. Kennedy. (Great American Presidents Ser.). (Illus.). (gr. 4-8). 2004. 112p. pap. 30.00 (978-0-7910-7786-3(1)); 2003. 100p. 30.00 (978-0-7910-7600-2(8)) Facts On File, Inc. (Chelsea Hse.).

J
K
L

Dohery, Kieran. John F. Kennedy. 2005. (Encyc of Presidents, 2ND Ser.). (Illus.). 112p. (J). (gr. 6-8). 34.00 (978-0-516-22976-8(1) , Watts, Franklin) Scholastic Library Publishing.

Downing, David. John F. Kennedy. (Illus.). 64p. 2003. pap. 8.95 (978-1-4034-3495-1(6)); 2001. (J). (gr. 5-7). lib. bdg. 27.86 (978-1-58810-164-8(9)) Heinemann Library.

Emerson, Judy. John F. Kennedy. Saunders-Smith, Gail, ed. 2004. (First Biographies Ser.). (Illus.). 24p. (J). (gr. k-1). lib. bdg. 15.93 (978-0-7368-2368-5(9) , Pebble Bks.) Capstone Pr., Inc.

Ford, Carin T. John F. Kennedy: The 35th President. 2006. (Heroes of American History Ser.). (Illus.). 32p. (J). lib. bdg. 22.60 (978-0-7660-2601-8(9) , Enslow Elementary) Enslow Pubs., Inc.

Franchino, Vicky. John F. Kennedy. 2001. (Compass Point Early Biographies Ser.). (Illus.). 32p. (J). (gr. 2 up). lib. bdg. 21.26 (978-0-7565-0113-6(X)) Compass Point Bks.

Frost, Helen. John F. Kennedy. Saunders-Smith, Gail, ed. 2003. (Famous Americans Ser.). (Illus.). 24p. (J). (gr. k-1). lib. bdg. 15.93 (978-0-7368-1642-7(9) , Pebble Bks.) Capstone Pr., Inc.

Goldsmith, Howard. John F. Kennedy & the Stormy Sea. Benoit, Renné, illus. 2006. 32p. (J). lib. bdg. 15.00 (***978-1-4242-0958-3(7)***) Fitzgerald Bks.

—John F. Kennedy & the Stormy Sea. Benoit, Renne, illus. 2006. (Ready-to-Read Cofa Ser.). 32p. (J). pap. 3.99 (978-0-689-86816-0(2) , Aladdin); lib. bdg. 11.89 (978-0-689-86817-7(0) , Aladdin Library) Simon & Schuster Children's Publishing.

Harper, Judith E. John F. Kennedy: Our Thirty-Fifth President. 2001. (Spirit of America: Our Presidents Ser.). (Illus.). 48p. (J). (gr. 2-6). 28.50 (978-1-56766-869-8(0)) Child's World, Inc.

Heiligman, Deborah. High Hopes: A Photobiography of John F. Kennedy. Feresten, Nancy, ed. 2003. (Illus.). 64p. (J). (gr. 5). 17.95 (978-0-7922-6141-4(0) , National Geographic Children's Bks.) National Geographic Society.

Hinman, Bonnie. John F. Kennedy, Jr. 2000. (They Died Too Young Ser.). (Illus.). 48p. (J). (gr. 4-7). 27.00 (978-0-7910-5857-2(3) , Chelsea Hse.) Facts On File, Inc.

Hodge, Marie. John F. Kennedy: Voice of Hope. 2007. (Sterling Biographies Ser.). (Illus.). 128p. (J). 12.95 (978-1-4027-4749-6(7)); pap. 5.95 (978-1-4027-3232-4(5)) Sterling Publishing Co., Inc.

John F Kennedy. (Famous Americans Ser.). 24p. (J). 5.95 (978-0-7368-3375-2(7)); 6.95 (978-0-7368-4469-7(4)) Capstone Pr., Inc.

John F Kennedy, 6 vols. (gr. 2-5). 36.95 (978-0-7368-4561-8(5)) Red Brick Learning.

Jones, Brenn. Learning about Public Service from the Life of John F. Kennedy, Jr. 2002. (Character Building Book Ser.). (Illus.). 24p. (J). (gr. 3). lib. bdg. 18.75 (978-0-8239-5776-7(4) , PowerKids Pr.) Rosen Publishing Group, Inc., The.

Jones, Veda Boyd. John F. Kennedy. 2006. 32p. (gr. 1-2). (YA). pap. 4.95 (978-0-516-29797-2(X)); (Illus.). (J). 20.50 (978-0-516-25038-0(8)) Scholastic Library Publishing. (Children's Pr.).

Joseph, Paul. John F. Kennedy. 2000. (United States Presidents Ser.). (Illus.). 32p. (J). (gr. k-6). lib. bdg. 22.78 (978-1-56239-745-6(1) , Checkerboard Library) ABDO Publishing Co.

Kaplan, Howard S. John F. Kennedy: A Photographic Story of a Life. 2004. (Biography Ser.). (Illus.). 128p. (J). 14.99 (978-0-7566-0489-9(3)); pap. 4.99 (978-0-7566-0340-3(4)) Dorling Kindersley Publishing, Inc.

Manolis, Kay. John F. Kennedy: A Life of Citizenship. 2007. (Illus.). 24p. (J). lib. bdg. 19.95 (978-1-60014-087-7(4)) Bellwether Media.

Marcovitz, Hal. John F. Kennedy. 2003. (Childhood of the Presidents Ser.). (Illus.). 48p. (J). (gr. 4 up). lib. bdg. (978-1-59084-272-0(3)) Mason Crest Pubs.

Margaret, Amy. John F. Kennedy Library & Museum. 2004. (Presidential Libraries Ser.). (Illus.). 24p. (J). lib. bdg. 18.75 (978-0-8239-6269-3(5) , PowerKids Pr.) Rosen Publishing Group, Inc., The.

Mattern, Joanne. Jacqueline Kennedy. 2007. (First Ladies Ser.). (Illus.). 32p. (J). (gr. k-6). lib. bdg. 24.21 (***978-1-59928-796-6(X)*** , Checkerboard Library) ABDO Publishing Co.

McDonough, Yona Zeldis. Who Was John F. Kennedy? Weber, Jill & Harrison, Nancy, illus. 2004. (Who Was— ? Ser.). 112p. (J). (gr. 2-6). 13.89 (978-0-448-43744-6(9)); pap. 4.99 (978-0-448-43743-9(0)) Penguin Group (USA) Inc. (Grosset & Dunlap).

—Who Was John F. Kennedy? Weber, Jill, illus. 2005. 106p. (J). (gr. 2-6). lib. bdg. 12.19 (978-0-606-33098-5(4)) Tandem Library Bks.

Olson, Nathan. John F. Kennedy: American Visionary. Bascle, Brian, illus. 2007. (J). (978-0-7368-6852-5(6)) Capstone Pr., Inc.

Potts, Steve. John F. Kennedy. Schon, Isabel, ed. Ferrer, Martín Luis Guzman, tr. from ENG. 1998. (Biografias Ilustradas con Fotografias Ser.). (SPA., Illus.). 24p. (J). (gr. 2-3). lib. bdg. 18.60 (978-1-56065-807-8(X) , CAP2790, Bridgestone Bks.) Capstone Pr., Inc.

Price Hossell, Karen. John F. Kennedy's Inaugural Speech. 2005. (Illus.). 48p. (J). (978-1-4034-6810-9(9)); pap. (978-1-4034-6815-4(X)) Heinemann Library.

Raatma, Lucia. John F. Kennedy. 2002. (Profiles of the Presidents Ser.). (Illus.). 64p. (J). (gr. 4 up). lib. bdg. 23.93 (978-0-7565-0205-8(5)) Compass Point Bks.

Schultz, Randy. John F. Kennedy: A MyReportLinks.com Book. 2002. (Presidents Ser.). (Illus.). 48p. (J). (gr. 4-10). lib. bdg. 25.26 (978-0-7660-5012-9(2)) Enslow Pubs., Inc.

Sommer, Shelley. John F. Kennedy: His Life & Legacy. 2005. (Illus.). 160p. (J). 16.99 (978-0-06-054135-4(0)); lib. bdg. 17.89 (978-0-06-054136-1(9)) HarperCollins Pubs.

Spies, Karen Bornemann. John F. Kennedy. 1999. (United States Presidents Ser.). (Illus.). 160p. (YA). (gr. 5-12). lib. bdg. 26.60 (978-0-7660-1039-0(2)) Enslow Pubs., Inc.

Sutcliffe, Jane. John F. Kennedy. (History Maker Bios Ser.). (J). 2005. (Illus.). 48p. 26.60 (978-0-8225-1546-3(6)); 2004. pap. (978-0-8225-2540-0(2)) Lerner Publishing Group. (Lerner Pubns.).

Upadhyay, Ritu. John F Kennedy the Making of a Leader. 2005. 44p. (J). lib. bdg. 15.00 (***978-1-4242-0851-7(3)***) Fitzgerald Bks.

Upadhyay, Ritu & Time for Kids Editors. John F. Kennedy: The Making of a Leader. 2005. (Time for Kids Ser.). (Illus.). 48p. (J). 14.99 (978-0-06-057603-5(0)); pap. 3.99 (978-0-06-057602-8(2)) HarperCollins Pubs.

Venezia, Mike. John F. Kennedy. Venezia, Mike, illus. 2007. (Getting to Know the U. S. Presidents Ser.). 32p. (J). 7.95 (***978-0-531-17947-5(8)***); (Illus.). (gr. 3-4). 27.00 (978-0-516-22639-2(8)) Scholastic Library Publishing. (Children's Pr.).

Zamora, Dulce. How to Draw the Life & Times of John Fitzgerald Kennedy. 2007. (Kid's Guide to Drawing the Presidents of the United States of America Ser.). (Illus.). 32p. (J). 25.25 (978-1-4042-3011-8(4) , PowerKids Pr.) Rosen Publishing Group, Inc., The.

KENNEDY, JOHN F. (JOHN FITZGERALD), 1917-1963—ASSASSINATION

Coates, Tim. The Shooting of John F. Kennedy 1963: The Warren Commission. 2003. (Moments of History Ser.). (Illus.). 320p. (978-1-84381-025-4(5)) Coates, Tim.

Gogerly, Liz. The Kennedy Assassination. 2002. (Days That Shook the World Ser.). (Illus.). 48p. (J). lib. bdg. 27.12 (978-0-7398-5235-4(3)) Raintree.

Hampton, Wilborn. Kennedy Assassinated! The World Mourns: A Reporter's Story. 2001. (Illus.). 96p. (J). (gr. 5-11). pap. 8.99 (978-0-7636-1564-2(1)) Candlewick Pr.

—Kennedy Assassinated! the World Mourns: A Reporter's Story. 2001. (gr. 5-8). lib. bdg. 17.60 (978-0-613-44397-5(7)) Tandem Library Bks.

Harkins, Susan and William. The Assassination of John F. Kennedy 1963. 2007. (Monumental Milestones Ser.).Tr. of 48. (Illus.). (J). lib. bdg. 29.95 (***978-1-58415-540-9(X)***) Mitchell Lane Pubs., Inc.

Hossell, Karen Price. Assassination of John F. Kennedy: Death of the New Frontier. 2003. (gr. 5-8). lib. bdg. 15.25 (978-0-613-58183-7(0)) Tandem Library Bks.

The JFK Assassination. 2003. (Eye on History Ser.). 32p. (gr. 5-12). 5.99 (978-0-7424-0253-9(3) , IF2679) School Specialty Publishing.

Kallen, Stuart A. The Kennedy Assassination. 2003. (Mystery Library). (Illus.). 104p. (J). 29.95 (978-1-59018-128-7(X)) Thomson Gale.

Price Hossell, Karen. The Assassination of John F. Kennedy: Death of the New Frontier. 2003. (Point of Impact Ser.). (Illus.). 32p. (J). (gr. 5-7). lib. bdg. 25.64 (978-1-58810-905-7(4)); pap. (978-1-4034-0533-3(6)) Heinemann Library.

Rivera, Sheila. The Assassination of John F. Kennedy. 2005. (American Moments Ser.). (Illus.). 48p. (J). (gr. 4-8). lib. bdg. 25.65 (978-1-59197-277-8(9)) ABDO Publishing Co.

Spencer, Lauren. The Assassination of John F. Kennedy. 2003. (Library of Political Assassinations). (Illus.). 64p. (YA). (gr. 7-12). lib. bdg. 26.50 (978-0-8239-3541-3(8)) Rosen Publishing Group, Inc., The.

Stockland, Patricia M. The Assassination of John F. Kennedy. 2007. (Essential Events Ser.). (ENG., Illus.). 112p. (YA). (gr. 8-12). lib. bdg. 32.79 (***978-1-59928-848-2(6)*** , Essential Library) ABDO Publishing Co.

Williams, Brian. The Assassination of President Kennedy. 2002. (Dates with History Ser.). (Illus.). 31p. (J). lib. bdg. 24.25 (978-1-58340-214-6(4)) Smart Apple Media.

KENNEDY, ROBERT F., 1925-1968

Aronson, Marc. Robert F. Kennedy: Crusader. 2007. (Up Close Ser.). (Illus.). 208p. (J). (gr. 6 up). 15.99 (978-0-670-06066-5(6) , Viking Juvenile) Penguin Group (USA) Inc.

Mills, Judie. Robert Kennedy: His Life. 1998. (Single Titles Ser.: up). (Illus.). 560p. (gr. 7 up). lib. bdg. 36.90 (978-1-56294-250-2(6) , Twenty-First Century Bks.) Lerner Publishing Group.

KENNEDY, ROBERT F., 1925-1968—ASSASSINATION

Ching, Juliet. The Assassination of Robert F. Kennedy. 2003. (Library of Political Assassinations). (Illus.). 64p. (YA). (gr. 7-12). lib. bdg. 26.50 (978-0-8239-3545-1(0) , Rosen Central) Rosen Publishing Group, Inc., The.

Koestler-Grack, Rachel A. The Assassination of Robert F. Kennedy. 2005. (American Moments Ser.). (J). (gr. 4-8). lib. bdg. 25.65 (978-1-59197-931-9(5)) ABDO Publishing Co.

KENNEDY FAMILY

Uschan, Michael V. The Kennedys. 2001. (History Makers Ser.). (Illus.). 112p. (J). (gr. 7-10). 28.70 (978-1-56006-875-4(2) , Lucent Bks.) Thomson Gale.

KENOBI, OBI-WAN (FICTITIOUS CHARACTER)—FICTION

Brooks, Terry. The Phantom Menace. 2000. (gr. 7-12). lib. bdg. 15.90 (978-0-613-70931-6(4)) Tandem Library Bks.

Davids, Paul & Davids, Hollace. Star Wars, 3 bks. l.t. ed. Incl. Prophets of the Dark Side. lib. bdg. 22.60 (978-0-8368-1994-6(2)); Queen of the Empire. lib. bdg. 22.60 (978-0-8368-1993-9(4)); Zorba the Hutt's Revenge. lib. bdg. 22.60 (978-0-8368-1991-5(8)); 112p. (J). (gr. 4 up). 1997. Set lib. bdg. 67.80 (978-0-8368-1988-5(8)) Stevens, Gareth Inc.

Watson, Jude. The Captive Temple. 2000. (Star Wars Ser.: Bk. 7). (J). (gr. 4-7). 11.64 (978-0-606-19619-2(6)) Tandem Library Bks.

—The Desperate Mission. 2005. (Star Wars Ser.: No. 1). 168p. (J). lib. bdg. 20.00 (***978-1-4242-0774-9(6)***) Fitzgerald Bks.

—The Desperate Mission. 2005. (Star Wars Ser.: No. 1). 168p. (J). (978-1-4155-9754-5(5)) Scholastic, Inc.

—The Fight for Truth. 2000. (Star Wars Ser.: Bk. 9). (J). (gr. 4-7). 11.64 (978-0-606-19621-5(8)) Tandem Library Bks.

—The Hidden Past. 1999. (Star Wars Ser.: Bk. 3). (J). (gr. 4-7). 11.64 (978-0-606-17040-6(5)) Tandem Library Bks.

—The Mark of the Crown. 1999. (Star Wars Ser.: Bk. 4). 144p. (J). (gr. 4-7). pap. 4.99 (978-0-590-51934-2(4)) Scholastic, Inc.

—The Mark of the Crown. 1999. (Star Wars Ser.: Bk. 4). (J). (gr. 4-7). (978-0-606-19617-8(X)) Tandem Library Bks.

—The Shattered Peace. Nielsen, Cliff, illus. 2000. (Star Wars Ser.: Bk. 10). 144p. (J). (gr. 3-7). pap. 4.99 (978-0-590-52084-3(9)) Scholastic, Inc.

—The Shattered Peace. 2000. (Star Wars Ser.: Bk. 10). (J). (gr. 4-7). (978-0-606-19615-4(3)) Tandem Library Bks.

—The Trail of the Jedi. 2002. (Star Wars Ser.: No. 2). (gr. 3-6). lib. bdg. 13.00 (978-0-613-50649-6(9)) Tandem Library Bks.

—The Uncertain Path. 2000. (Star Wars Ser.: Bk. 6). (Illus.). 144p. (J). (gr. 4-7). pap. 5.99 (978-0-590-51969-4(7)) Scholastic, Inc.

—The Uncertain Path. 2000. (Star Wars Ser.: Bk. 6). (J). (gr. 4-7). (978-0-606-19618-5(8)) Tandem Library Bks.

—The Way of the Apprentice. 2002. (Star Wars Ser.: No. 1). (gr. 3-6). lib. bdg. 13.00 (978-0-613-50655-7(3)) Tandem Library Bks.

Wolverton, Dave. The Rising Force. 1999. (Star Wars Ser.: Bk. 1). (J). (gr. 4-7). (978-0-606-16649-2(1)) Tandem Library Bks.

KENTUCKY

Aki, Michelle & Becker, Maki. Uniquely Kentucky. 2003. (State Studies). (Illus.). 48p. (J). 27.07 (978-1-4034-4491-2(9)); pap. 8.50 (978-1-4034-4506-3(0)) Heinemann Library.

Barrett, T. Kentucky. 1998. (Celebrate the States Ser.). (Illus.). 144p. (gr. 4-8). lib. bdg. 37.07 (978-0-7614-0657-0(3) , Benchmark Bks.) Cavendish, Marshall Corp.

Barrett, Tracy. Kentucky. 2nd ed. 2008. (Celebrate the States Ser.). (J). lib. bdg. 39.93 (***978-0-7614-2715-5(5)*** , Benchmark Bks.) Cavendish, Marshall Corp.

Blair, Eric. The Legend of Daniel Boone: A Retelling of the Classic Traditional Tale. Chambers-Goldbert, Micah, illus. 2005. (Read-It! Readers Ser.). 32p. (J). (gr. k-3). 18.60 (978-1-4048-0974-1(0)) Picture Window Bks.

—La Leyenda de Daniel Boone. Chambers-Goldberg, Micah, illus. 2006. (Read-It! Readers en Espanol Ser.).Tr. of Legend of Daniel Boone. (SPA.). 32p. (J). (ps-3). 19.95 (978-1-4048-1656-5(9)) Picture Window Bks.

Boraas, Tracey. Daniel Boone: Frontier Scout. 2002. (Let Freedom Ring Ser.). (Illus.). 48p. (J). (gr. 3-4). lib. bdg. 22.60 (978-0-7368-1347-1(0) , Bridgestone Bks.) Capstone Pr., Inc.

Brown, Dottie. Kentucky. (Hello U. S. A. Ser.). (Illus.). (J). (gr. 3-6). 2000. 72p. pap. 5.95 (978-0-8225-9687-5(3) , First Avenue Editions); 2nd rev. exp. ed. 2002. 84p. lib. bdg. 25.26 (978-0-8225-4083-0(5)) Lerner Publishing Group.

—Kentucky. rev. ed. 2002. (gr. 3-6). lib. bdg. 15.25 (978-0-613-46084-2(7)) Tandem Library Bks.

Brown, Vanessa. Kentucky. Brusca, Maria Cristina, tr. 2005. (Bilingual Library of the United States of America: Set 1). (ENG & SPA., Illus.). 32p. (J). (gr. 2-5). lib. bdg. 22.50 (978-1-4042-3082-8(3) , Buenas Letra) Rosen Publishing Group, Inc., The.

Burton, K. Melissa. Kentucky's Capitol. 2007. 32p. pap. 14.95 (***978-0-913383-96-4(1)***) McClanahan Publishing Hse., Inc.

Capek, Michael. A Personal Tour of a Shaker Village. 2001. (How It Was Ser.). (Illus.). 64p. (J). (gr. 4-6). lib. bdg. (978-0-8225-3584-3(X) , Lerner Pubns.) Lerner Publishing Group.

Deady, Kathleen W. Kentucky Facts & Symbols. (States & Their Symbols Ser.). 24p. (J). 2000. (Illus.). (gr. 2-3). lib. bdg. 18.60 (978-0-7368-0639-8(3) , Bridgestone Bks.); 2003. lib. bdg. 19.93 (978-0-7368-2247-3(X)) Capstone Pr., Inc.

Evdokimoff, Natasha. A Guide to Kentucky. 2001. (American States Ser.). (Illus.). 32p. (J). lib. bdg. 16.95 (978-1-59036-004-0(4)) Weigl Pubs., Inc.

Gaines, Ann Graham. Kentucky. 2003. (It's My State! Ser.). (Illus.). 80p. (J). 27.07 (978-0-7614-1525-1(4) , Benchmark Bks.) Cavendish, Marshall Corp.

Harcourt School Publishers Staff. At the Center of the Earth. 3rd ed. 2002. (Horizons Ser.). (Illus.). (J). pap. 5.50 (978-0-15-333407-8(X)) Harcourt Schl. Pubs.

Heinrichs, Ann. Kentucky. 2005. (Welcome to the USA Ser.). 40p. (J). (gr. 1-5). 27.07 (978-1-59296-375-1(7)) Child's World, Inc.

—Kentucky. 2003. (This Land Is Your Land Ser.). (Illus.). 48p. (J). (gr. 3 up). lib. bdg. 22.60 (978-0-7565-0322-2(1)) Compass Point Bks.

Ingram, Scott. Kentucky: The Blue Grass State. 2002. (World Almanac Library of the States). (Illus.). 48p. (J). (gr. 5 up). lib. bdg. 30.00 (978-0-8368-5135-9(8)); pap. 14.95 (978-0-8368-5305-6(9)) Stevens, Gareth Inc. (World Almanac Library).

Kelly Allen, Nancy. Daniel Boone: Trailblazer. Waites, Joan C., illus. 2005. 32p. (J). (gr. 2-4). 15.95 (978-1-58980-212-4(8)) Pelican Publishing Co., Inc.

Kentucky. 2000. (Switched on Schoolhouse Ser.). (Illus.). (YA). (gr. 7-12). pap. 24.95 incl. cd-rom (978-0-7403-0269-5(8) , SOSKY) Alpha Omega Pubns., Inc.

Kentucky - Fishing Map Guide: Lake Maps & Fishing Information for Kentucky Lakes Plus Ohio River Coverage. 2002. (Illus.). 224p. (YA). spiral bd. 21.95 (978-1-885010-60-5(5)) Sportsman's Connection.

Kramer, Sydelle. Who Was Daniel Boone? Ulrich, George, illus. 2006. (Who Was... ? Ser.). 112p. (J). (gr. 2-5). pap. 4.99 (978-0-448-43902-0(6) , Grosset & Dunlap) Penguin Group (USA) Inc.

Kummer, Patricia K. Kentucky. rev. ed. 2002. (One Nation Ser.). (Illus.). 48p. (J). (gr. 3-4). lib. bdg. 22.60 (978-0-7368-1241-2(5) , Bridgestone Bks.) Capstone Pr., Inc.

Labairon, Cassandra Sharri. Kentucky. 2008. (J). (***978-1-58341-642-6(0)*** , Creative Education) Creative Co., The.

Lantier, Patricia. Kentucky. 2006. (Portraits of the States Ser.). (Illus.). 32p. pap. (978-0-8368-4685-0(0)) Stevens, Gareth Inc.

Loeper, John J. Meet the Drakes on the Kentucky Frontier. 1998. (Early American Family Ser.). (Illus.). 64p. (J). (gr. 3 up). lib. bdg. 25.64 (978-0-7614-0845-1(2) , Benchmark Bks.) Cavendish, Marshall Corp.

Marsh, Carole. Kentucky Classic Christmas Trivia. 2002. (Carole Marsh Kentucky Bks.). (Illus.). 32p. pap. 6.95 (978-0-635-01401-6(7) , 14017); lib. bdg. 21.95 (978-0-635-01402-3(5) , 14025) Gallopade International. (Marsh, Carole Bks.).

—The Kentucky Coloring Book. 2004. (Kentucky Experience! Ser.). (Illus.). 32p. (J). (gr. k-2). pap. 3.95 (978-0-7933-9471-5(6)) Gallopade International.

—The Kentucky Experience Pocket Guide. 2004. (Kentucky Experience! Ser.). (Illus.). 96p. (J). (gr. 3-8). pap. 6.95 (978-0-7933-9451-7(1)) Gallopade International.

—Kentucky Geography Projects: 30 Cool, Activities, Crafts, Experiments & More for Kids to Do to Learn about Your State! 2003. (Kentucky Experience Ser.). 32p. (gr. k-5). pap. 5.95 (978-0-635-01836-6(5) , Marsh, Carole Bks.) Gallopade International.

—Kentucky Government Projects: 30 Cool, Activities, Crafts, Experiments & More for Kids to Do to Learn about Your State! 2003. (Kentucky Experience Ser.). 32p. (gr. k-5). pap. 5.95 (978-0-635-01936-3(1) , Marsh, Carole Bks.) Gallopade International.

—Kentucky Jeopardy! Answers & Questions about Our State! 2004. (Kentucky Experience! Ser.). (Illus.). 32p. (J). (gr. 3-8). pap. 7.95 (978-0-7933-9516-3(X)) Gallopade International.

—Kentucky "Jography" A Fun Run Thru Our State! 2004. (Kentucky Experience! Ser.). (Illus.). 32p. (J). (gr. 3-8). pap. 7.95 (978-0-7933-9517-0(8)) Gallopade International.

—Kentucky Millionaire: Game Book. 2001. (Carole Marsh Kentucky Bks.). (Illus.). 32p. (J). (gr. 3-8). pap., act. bk. ed. 9.95 (978-0-635-00050-7(4)) Gallopade International.

—Kentucky People Projects: 30 Cool, Activities, Crafts, Experiments & More for Kids to Do to Learn about Your State! 2003. (Kentucky Experience Ser.). 32p. (gr. k-5). pap. 5.95 (978-0-635-01986-8(8) , Marsh, Carole Bks.) Gallopade International.

—Kentucky Survivor: Game Book. 2001. (Carole Marsh Kentucky Bks.). (Illus.). 32p. (J). (gr. 3-8). pap., act. bk. ed. 9.95 (978-0-635-00538-0(7)) Gallopade International.

—Kentucky Symbols & Facts Projects: 30 Cool, Activities, Crafts, Experiments & More for Kids to Do to Learn about Your State! 2003. (Kentucky Experience Ser.). 32p. (gr. k-5). pap. 5.95 (978-0-635-01886-1(1) , Marsh, Carole Bks.) Gallopade International.

—My First Book about Kentucky. 2004. (Kentucky Experience! Ser.). (Illus.). 32p. (J). (gr. k-4). pap. 7.95 (978-0-7933-9515-6(1)) Gallopade International.

—The Survivor: A Class Challenge. 2001. (Carole Marsh Kentucky Bks.). lib. bdg. 29.95 (978-0-635-00663-9(4)) Gallopade International.

Murray, Julie. Kentucky. 2006. (J). (gr. k-4). 22.78 (978-1-59197-676-9(6) , Buddy Bks.) ABDO Publishing Co.

Nemerson, Roy. Daniel Boone. 2005. (Heroes of America Ser.). (Illus.). 240p. (J). (gr. 3-8). lib. bdg. 21.35 (978-1-59679-256-2(6)) ABDO Publishing Co.

Niz, Xavier. Kentucky. 2003. (Land of Liberty Ser.). (Illus.). 64p. (J). (gr. 3-4). 23.93 (978-0-7368-1585-7(6) , Bridgestone Bks.) Capstone Pr., Inc.

Petrie, Kristin. Daniel Boone. 2004. (Explorers Set I Ser.). (J). (gr. k-6). lib. bdg. 22.78 (978-1-59197-592-2(1)) ABDO Publishing Co.

Powell, Robert A. Kentucky's Covered Bridges. 2001. per. 7.90 (978-0-9651406-4-5(4)) Silverhawke Pubns.

Riehle, Mary Ann McCabe. B Is for Bluegrass: A Kentucky Alphabet. Burgiss, Wes, illus. 2002. 40p. (J). (ps-5). 17.95 (978-1-58536-056-7(2)) Sleeping Bear Pr.

Santella, Andrew. Kentucky. 2007. (America the Beautiful, Third Ser.). 144p. (J). spiral bd. 38.00 (***978-0-531-18574-2(5)*** , Children's Pr.) Scholastic Library Publishing.

Schaffer, David. Kentucky: A MyReportLinks. Com Book. 2003. (States Ser.). (Illus.). 48p. (J). (gr. 4-10). lib. bdg. 25.26 (978-0-7660-5126-3(9) , MyReportLinks.com Bks.) Enslow Pubs., Inc.

Stein, R. Conrad. Kentucky. 2nd ed. 1999. (America the Beautiful, Second Ser.). (Illus.). 144p. (YA). (gr. 5-8). 36.00 (978-0-516-20687-5(7) , Children's Pr.) Scholastic Library Publishing.

Valzania, Kimberly. Kentucky. 2003. (Rookie Read-About Geography Ser.). (Illus.). (J). (gr. 1-2). 31p. pap. 5.95 (978-0-516-27842-1(8)); 32p. 20.50 (978-0-516-22697-2(5)) Scholastic Library Publishing. (Children's Pr.).

—Kentucky. 2003. (gr. k-3). lib. bdg. 14.10 (978-0-613-67905-3(9)) Tandem Library Bks.

Williams, Suzanne Morgan. Kentucky. 2001. (From Sea to Shining Sea Ser.: 2). (Illus.). 80p. (J). (gr. 3-5). 30.50 (978-0-516-22310-0(0) , Children's Pr.) Scholastic Library Publishing.

Zronik, John Paul. Daniel Boone: Woodsman of Kentucky. 2006. (In the Footsteps of Explorers Ser.). (Illus.). 32p. (J). (gr. 3-9). pap. (978-0-7787-2464-3(6) , 1253442); (978-0-7787-2428-5(X) , 1253442) Crabtree Publishing Co.

KENTUCKY—FICTION

Altsheler, A. Joseph. Forest Runners A Story of the Great War. 2006. pap. 72.99 ***(*978-1-4280-3186-9(3))*** Indy-Publish.com.

Altsheler, Joseph A. The Forest Runners: A Story of the Great. 2006. pap. ***(*978-1-4065-0810-9(1))*** Dodo Pr.

Barkley, Roger C. Johnny Grasshopper. 2006. 52p. pap. 12.95 (978-1-4241-0221-1(9)) PublishAmerica, Inc.

Bell, Albert A., Jr. The Secret of the Lonely Grave. 2007. 160p. pap. 8.95 ***(*978-1-932158-79-3(0)*** , Claystone Bks.) Ingalls Publishing Group, Inc.

Birdseye, Tom. A Tough Nut to Crack. 2006. 128p. (J). (gr. 3-7). 16.95 (978-0-8234-1967-8(3)) Holiday Hse., Inc.

Borden, Louise. Just in Time for Christmas. 2000. (Illus.). (J). pap. 5.99 (978-0-590-45356-1(4)) Scholastic, Inc.

—Just in Time for Christmas. 2000. (J). 12.79 (978-0-606-19573-7(4)) Tandem Library Bks.

Brouwer, Sigmund. Cobra Threat: Football. 2007. (Orca Sports Ser.). 176p. (YA). (gr. 5 up). pap. ***(*978-1-55143-725-5(2))*** Orca Bk. Pubs.

Byars, Betsy. Keeper of the Doves. (J). 2002. 96p. (gr. 3-7). 14.99 (978-0-670-03576-2(9) , Viking Juvenile); 2004. (Illus.). 128p. reprint ed. pap. 5.99 (978-0-14-240063-0(7) , Puffin) Penguin Group (USA) Inc.

Campbell, Joanna. Melanie's Last Ride. 1998. (Thoroughbred Ser.: No. 29). 192p. (gr. 4-7). mass mkt. 4.99 (978-0-06-106531-6(5) , Harper Entertainment) Harper-Collins Pubs.

Caudill, Rebecca. Up & down the River. Merwin, Decie, illus. 2005. 143p. (J). (ps-17). pap. 11.95 (978-1-883937-81-2(7)) Bethlehem Bks.

Clevenger, Lee. IncrediBoy: Be Careful What You Wish. 2004. 267p. (J). pap. 12.95 (978-0-9764052-0-7(2)) Thomas Max Publishing.

Crum, Shutta. My Mountain Song. 2007. (Illus.). 32p. (J). 16.00 ***(*978-1-4223-6590-8(5))*** DIANE Publishing Co.

—My Mountain Song. Rand, Ted, tr. Rand, Ted, illus. 2004. 32p. (J). (gr. k-3). tchr. ed. 16.00 (978-0-618-15970-3(3) , Clarion Bks.) Houghton Mifflin Co. Trade & Reference Div.

—Spitting Image. 2003. 224p. (J). tchr. ed. 15.00 (978-0-618-23477-6(2) , Clarion Bks.) Houghton Mifflin Co. Trade & Reference Div.

Dadey, Debbie. Whistler's Hollow. 2002. 130p. (J). 14.95 (978-1-58234-789-9(1) , Bloomsbury Children) Bloomsbury Publishing.

Ernst, Kathleen. Midnight in Lonesome Hollow: A Kit Mystery. Tibbles, Jean-Paul, illus. 2007. 192p. (J). 10.95 ***(*978-1-59369-161-5(0));*** pap. 6.95 ***(*978-1-59369-160-8(2))*** American Girl Publishing, Inc. (American Girl).

Ferris, Jean. Underground. 2007. (Illus.). 176p. (J). (gr. 7 up). 16.00 ***(*978-0-374-37243-9(8)*** , Farrar, Straus & Giroux (BYR)) Farrar, Straus & Giroux.

Florence, Leigh Anne. Woody, the Kentucky Wiener: The Adoption. Asher, James, illus. 2003. 32p. (J). (gr. 1-3). pap. 12.95 (978-0-9741417-0-1(4)) HotDiggetyDog Pr.

—Woody, the Kentucky Wiener Welcomes a Dad, Vol. 2. Asher, James, illus. 2004. 32p. (J). (gr. 1-3). pap. 12.95 (978-0-9741417-1-8(2)) HotDiggetyDog Pr.

Godby, Ron. The King of Imperial Hill. 2006. 76p. pap. 14.95 (978-1-4241-1061-2(0)) PublishAmerica, Inc.

Hart, Alison. Gabriel's Horses. 2007. 224p. (J). (gr. 3-7). 14.95 ***(*978-1-56145-398-6(6)*** , Peachtree Junior) Peachtree Pubs., Ltd.

Hemphill, Helen. Runaround. 2007. 117p. (YA). (gr. 8 up). 16.95 (978-1-932425-83-3(7) , Front Street) Boyds Mills Pr.

Henson, Heather. Making the Run. 2002. 240p. (J). (gr. k-4). 15.89 (978-0-06-029797-8(2)); (gr. 10 up). 15.95 (978-0-06-029796-1(4)) HarperCollins Pubs. (HarperTeen).

—Making the Run: A Novel. 2003. (gr. 7-12). lib. bdg. 15.30 (978-0-613-65699-3(7)) Tandem Library Bks.

Hopka, Cathy. Dreamer: Inspired by a True Story. 2005. (Illus.). 136p. (J). (gr. 4-7). pap. 4.99 (978-0-439-77494-9(2)) Scholastic, Inc.

Johnson, Annie F. Two Little Knights of Kentucky: The Little Colonel's Neighbors. Barry, Etheldred B., illus. 2004. (Little Colonel Ser.). 128p. (J). (gr. 4-7). reprint ed. per. 9.95 (978-1-55709-316-5(4)) Applewood Bks.

Johnston, Annie Fell. The Little Colonel. 2005. reprint ed. pap. 21.95 (978-0-7661-9402-1(7)) Kessinger Publishing, LLC.

Johnston, Annie Fell. The Little Colonel (Illustrated Edition) 2006. pap. ***(*978-1-4065-1132-1(3))*** Dodo Pr.

Johnston, Annie Fellows. The Giant Scissors. Barry, Etheldred B., illus. 2005. reprint ed. pap. 22.95 (978-1-4179-0341-2(4)) Kessinger Publishing, LLC.

—In the Desert of Waiting the Legend of Camel Back Mountain. 2005. reprint ed. pap. 15.95 (978-1-4179-3370-9(4)) Kessinger Publishing, LLC.

—The Little Colonel. Barry, Etheldred B., illus. 2004. (Little Colonel Ser.). 128p. (J). (gr. 4-7). reprint ed. per. 12.95 (978-1-55709-315-8(6)) Applewood Bks.

—Mary Ware the Little Colonel's Chum. Barry, Etheldred B., illus. 2004. reprint ed. pap. 30.95 (978-1-4179-1704-4(0)) Kessinger Publishing, LLC.

Johnston, Fellows Annie. Little Colonel. 2006. pap. 18.99 ***(*978-1-4280-3283-5(5))*** IndyPublish.com.

Keehn, Sally M. Magpie Gabbard & the Quest for the Buried Moon. 2007. 208p. (YA). (gr. 5-8). 16.99 (978-0-399-24340-0(2) , Philomel) Penguin Group (USA) Inc.

Korbel, Wendy. Gus: Adventures on the Farm. 2007. 24p. (J). pap. 8.99 ***(*978-1-59886-999-6(X))*** Tate Publishing & Enterprises, L.L.C.

Marsh, Carole. The Mystery at the Kentucky Derby. 2001. 160p. (J). (gr. 2-8). 14.95 (978-0-635-02394-0(6)); pap. 5.95 (978-0-635-02393-3(8)) Gallopade International.

Mason, Bobbie. Shiloh & Other Stories. 2001. (gr. 7-12). lib. bdg. 21.05 (978-0-613-56842-5(7)) Tandem Library Bks.

Mitchell, Betsy. Journey to the Bottomless Pit: The Story of Stephen Bishop & Mammoth Cave. 2004. (Illus.). 128p. (J). (gr. 3-7). 15.99 (978-0-670-05908-9(0) , Viking Juvenile) Penguin Group (USA) Inc.

Pryor, Bonnie. Joseph: 1861 - A Rumble of War. Dodson, Bert, illus. 1999. (American Adventures Ser.). 176p. (J). (gr. 3-7). 14.95 (978-0-688-15671-8(1)) HarperCollins Pubs.

—Joseph: 1861 - A Rumble of War. 2000. (Illus.). (J). (978-0-606-17975-1(5)) Tandem Library Bks.

—Joseph: 1861—A Rumble of War. 2000. (American Adventures Ser.). (Illus.). 176p. (J). (gr. 3-7). pap. 4.50 (978-0-380-73103-9(7) , Harper Trophy) HarperCollins Pubs.

Rice, Alice Caldwell Hegan. Mrs. Wiggs of the Cabbage Patch. (Illus.). 153p. reprint ed. lib. bdg. 88.00 (978-0-7222-4934-5(9)) Library Reprints, Inc.

—Mrs. Wiggs of the Cabbage Patch. 2004. 168p. 14.95 (978-0-8131-9074-7(6)) Univ. Pr. of Kentucky.

Skinner, Constance Lindsay. Becky Landers: Frontier Warrior. 2006. (Living History Library). 200p. (J). pap. 13.95 (978-1-932350-06-7(3)) Bethlehem Bks.

Standish, Burt L. Frank Merriwell in Kentucky. Rudman, Jack, ed. 2003. (Frank Merriwell Ser.). 29.95 (978-0-8373-9363-6(9)); pap. 9.95 (978-0-8373-9063-5(X)) Merriwell, Frank Inc.

Wedekind, Annie. A Horse of Her Own. 2008. 288p. (J). 16.95 ***(*978-0-312-36927-9(1))*** Feiwel & Friends.

White, Herman H. Valley of the Flames. 2004. 96p. (J). 19.95 (978-1-932278-09-5(5)) Mayhaven Publishing.

White, Ruth. Tadpole. 2003. 208p. (J). (gr. 4-8). 16.00 (978-0-374-31002-8(5) , Farrar, Straus & Giroux (BYR)) Farrar, Straus & Giroux.

—Tadpole. 2004. 208p. (gr. 5). 5.99 (978-0-440-41979-2(4) , Yearling) Random Hse. Children's Bks.

—Tadpole. l.t. ed. 2003. 201p. (J). 24.95 (978-0-7862-5813-0(6)) Thorndike Pr.

Winston, Annie. Admiral Wright's Heroical Storicals: Daniel Boone & the Battle of Boonesborough. 3rd ed. 2007. (Illus.). 288p. (J). 12.99 ***(*978-0-9779535-4-7(8)*** , Sonship Pr.) 21st Century Pr.

Wyatt, Leslie J. Poor Is Just a Starting Place. 2005. 192p. (J). (gr. 6-17). 16.95 (978-0-8234-1884-8(7)) Holiday Hse., Inc.

KENTUCKY—HISTORY

Alter, Judy. Daniel Boone: Frontiersman. 2002. (Spirit of America: Our People Ser.). (Illus.). 32p. (J). (gr. 2-6). 27.07 (978-1-56766-162-0(9)) Child's World, Inc.

Appelt, Kathi & Schmitzer, Jeanne Cannella. Down Cut Shin Creek: The Pack Horse Librarians of Kentucky. 2001. (Illus.). 64p. (J). (gr. 3-7). 16.99 (978-0-06-029135-8(4)) HarperCollins Pubs.

Armentrout, David & Armentrout, Patricia. Daniel Boone. 2002. (People Who Made a Difference Ser.). (Illus.). 24p. (J). (gr. 2-5). 14.95 (978-1-58952-052-3(1)) Rourke Publishing, LLC.

—Daniel Boone. Sarfatti, Esther & de la Vega, Eida, trs. from ENG. 2001. (Personas que Cambiaron la Historia Ser.). (SPA., Illus.). 24p. (J). (gr. 1-4). lib. bdg. 19.27 (978-1-58952-166-7(8) , RK7295) Rourke Publishing, LLC.

Brown, John Mason. Sterling Point Books: Daniel Boone: the Opening of the Wilderness. 2007. (Sterling Point Bks.). 176p. (J). pap. 6.95 ***(*978-1-4027-5119-6(2))*** Sterling Publishing Co., Inc.

De Capua, Sarah. The Wilderness Road. 2006. (We the People Ser.). (Illus.). 48p. (J). (gr. 4-6). 23.93 (978-0-7565-1637-6(4)) Compass Point Bks.

Deinard, Jenny. How to Draw Kentuckys Sights & Symbols. 2002. (Kids Guide to Drawing America Ser.). 32p. (J). lib. bdg. 25.25 (978-0-8239-6073-6(0) , PowerKids Pr.) Rosen Publishing Group, Inc., The.

Grier, William F. The Five Lives of the Kentucky River, 2001. (Illus.). 221p. (YA). (978-0-945084-99-0(4)) Stuart, Jesse Foundation, The.

Louisville A to Z. 2005. (J). mass mkt. 12.95 (978-0-9770603-0-6(6)) Mayden Publishing Corp.

Marsh, Carole. Kentucky History Projects: 30 Cool, Activities, Crafts, Experiments & More for Kids to Do to Learn about Your State! 2003. (Kentucky Experience Ser.). 32p. (gr. k-5). pap. 5.95 (978-0-635-01786-4(5) , Marsh, Carole Bks.) Gallopade International.

—My First Pocket Guide Kentucky. 2000. (Kentucky Experience! Ser.). (Illus.). 96p. (J). (gr. 3-8). 12.95 (978-0-635-01307-1(X) , 1307X, Marsh, Carole Bks.) Gallopade International.

McCarthy, Pat. Daniel Boone: Frontier Legend. 2000. (Historical American Biographies Ser.). (Illus.). 128p. (YA). (gr. 6-12). lib. bdg. 26.60 (978-0-7660-1256-1(5)) Enslow Pubs., Inc.

Santella, Andrew. Daniel Boone & the Cumberland Gap. 2007. (Cornerstones of Freedomtrade;, Second Ser.). 48p. (J). 5.95 ***(*978-0-531-18687-9(3)*** , Children's Pr.) Scholastic Library Publishing.

Simon, Barbara Brooks. Escape to Freedom: The Underground Railroad Adventures of Callie & William. 2004. (I Am American Ser.). (Illus.). 40p. (J). (gr. 3-7). pap. 6.99 (978-0-7922-6551-1(3) , National Geographic Children's Bks.) National Geographic Society.

Walther, Peggy Roney. Kentucky: The Bluegrass State. 2001. (Illus.). ix, 278p. (J). (978-1-56733-050-2(9)) Clairmont Pr., Inc.

KENYA

Adamson, Joy. Born Free. 2000. (gr. 7-12). lib. bdg. 24.55 (978-0-613-36139-2(3)) Tandem Library Bks.

Alembi, Ezekiel. Jaramogi Oginga Odinga: People's Revolutionary. 2004. (Lion Books). (Illus.). x, 78p. (J). (978-9966-951-24-3(5)) Sasa Sema Publications Ltd.

Auch, Alison. Welcome to Kenya. 2002. (Spyglass Books). (Illus.). 24p. (J). (gr. 1 up). lib. bdg. 18.60 (978-0-7565-0369-7(8)) Compass Point Bks.

Barber, Nicola. Living in the African Savannah. 2007. (J). pap. ***(*978-1-4109-2823-8(3));*** lib. bdg. ***(*978-1-4109-2814-6(4))*** Steck-Vaughn.

Bentley, Joyce. Kenya: Our Lives, Our World. 2005. 32p. 18.95 (978-1-59389-225-8(X)) Chrysalis Education.

Boast, Clare. Kenya. 1998. (Next Stop! Ser.). (Illus.). 32p. (J). (ps-3). lib. bdg. (978-1-57572-677-9(7)) Heinemann.

Bowden, Rob. Kenya. 2003. (Countries of the World Ser.). (Illus.). 64p. (gr. 6-12). 30.00 (978-0-8160-5384-1(7)) Facts On File, Inc.

—Kenya. 2003. (Changing Face Of... Ser.). (Illus.). 48p. (J). lib. bdg. 28.56 (978-0-7398-5491-4(7)) Raintree.

Bowden, Rob & Sheehan, Sean. Kenya: Listen Up! 2006. (Destination Detectives Ser.). (Illus.). 48p. (J). pap. (978-1-4109-2341-7(X)); lib. bdg. (978-1-4109-2330-1(4)) Steck-Vaughn.

Bull, Schuyler. Through Tsavo: A Story of an East African Savanna. Kratter, Paul, illus. 1998. (Soundprints' Wild Habitats Ser.). 32p. (J). (gr. 1-4). pap. 6.95 (978-1-56899-553-3(9) , S7008) Soundprints.

Cantwell, Rebecca. Teens in Kenya. 2007. (Illus.). 96p. (J). pap. ***(*978-0-7565-3195-9(0))*** Compass Point Bks.

Cantwell, Rebecca & Compass Point Books Staff. Teens in Kenya. 2006. (Global Connections Ser.). (Illus.). 96p. (J). (gr. 5-7). 31.93 ***(*978-0-7565-2445-6(8))*** Compass Point Bks.

Corona, Laurel. Kenya. 1999. (Modern Nations of the World Ser.). (Illus.). 128p. (YA). (gr. 7-10). 27.45 (978-1-56006-590-6(7) , Lucent Bks.) Thomson Gale.

Corrigan, Jim. Kenya. 2004. (Africa Ser.). (Illus.). 79p. (J). lib. bdg. (978-1-59084-809-8(8)) Mason Crest Pubs.

Daley, Patrick. Kenya. 2002. (Steadwell Books World Tour). (Illus.). 48p. (J). lib. bdg. (978-0-7398-4712-1(0)) Raintree.

Derr, Victoria. Kenya. 1999. (Countries of the World Ser.). (Illus.). 96p. (J). (gr. 6 up). lib. bdg. 30.00 (978-0-8368-2311-0(7)) Stevens, Gareth Inc.

Ferguson, Amanda. The Attack Against the U. S. Embassies in Kenya & Tanzania. 2005. (Terrorist Attacks Ser.). (Illus.). 64p. (J). (gr. 7-12). lib. bdg. 26.50 (978-0-8239-3652-6(X)) Rosen Publishing Group, Inc., The.

Fontes, Justine & Fontes, Ron. Kenya. (to Z Ser.). (J). 2004. (gr. 2-4). pap. 6.95 (978-0-516-26813-2(9)); 2003. (Illus.). 40p. 24.50 (978-0-516-24566-9(X)) Scholastic Library Publishing. (Children's Pr.).

Frost, Helen. A Look at Kenya. 2005. (One World, Many Cultures Ser.). (Illus.). 24p. (J). (gr. k-3). pap. (978-0-7368-9420-3(9) , Pebble Bks.) Capstone Pr., Inc.

—A Look at Kenya. Saunders-Smith, Gail, ed. 2001. (Our World Ser.). (Illus.). 24p. (J). (gr. k-1). lib. bdg. 15.93 (978-0-7368-0984-9(8) , Pebble Bks.) Capstone Pr., Inc.

Giles, Bridget. Kenya. 2001. (Nations of the World Ser.). (Illus.). 128p. (YA). (gr. 6-8). lib. bdg. 34.26 (978-0-7398-1290-7(4)) Raintree.

Graham, Ian. Kenya. 2003. (Country Files Ser.). 32p. (J). lib. bdg. 24.25 (978-1-58340-238-2(1)) Smart Apple Media.

Grolier Educational Staff, contrib. by. Kenya. 2003. (Illus.). 32p. (J). (978-0-7172-5795-9(9) , Grolier) Scholastic Library Publishing.

Haskins, James & Benson, Kathleen. Count Your Way Through Kenya. Lévêque, Lyne, illus. 2007. (Count Your Way Ser.). 24p. (J). 19.93 (978-1-57505-884-9(7) , Millbrook Pr.) Lerner Publishing Group.

Hiemen, Sara. Kenya ABCs: A Book about the People & Places of Kenya. Avila, Antonio, illus. 2004. (Country ABCs Ser.). 32p. (J). (gr. k-5). 23.93 (978-1-4048-0022-9(0)) Picture Window Bks.

Italia, Bob. Kenya. 2000. (Countries Ser.). (Illus.). 40p. (J). (gr. k-6). lib. bdg. 22.78 (978-1-57765-389-9(0) , Checkerboard Library) ABDO Publishing Co.

Kairi, Wambui. Kenya. (We Come from Ser.). (Illus.). 32p. (J). (gr. 1-4). 2000. lib. bdg. 25.69 (978-0-8172-5512-1(5)); 1999. lib. bdg. 25.69 (978-0-7398-1373-7(0)) Raintree.

Levy, Janey. A Primary Source Guide to Kenya. 2003. (Countries of the World : A Primary Source Journey Ser.). (Illus.). 24p. (J). pap. (978-0-8239-8074-1(X)); lib. bdg. 19.95 (978-0-8239-6590-8(2)) Rosen Publishing Group, Inc., The. (PowerKids Pr.).

A Look at Kenya, 6 vols. (gr. k-2). 28.95 (978-0-7368-9421-0(7)) Red Brick Learning.

Lynch, Emma. We're from Kenya. 2005. (We're from Ser.). (Illus.). 32p. (J). pap. (978-1-4034-5815-5(4)); lib. bdg. (978-1-4034-5806-3(5)) Heinemann Library.

Marshall, David. Guide to Kenya. rev. ed. 1999. (World Guides Ser.). (Illus.). 32p. (gr. 2-6). lib. bdg. 21.27 (978-1-884756-50-4(6)) Davidson Titles, Inc.

—Kenya. 1998. (Worldfocus Ser.). (Illus.). 32p. (J). pap. (978-1-57572-030-2(2)) Heinemann Library.

Marshall, David & Sayer, Geoff. Kenya. (World Focus Ser.). (Illus.). 32p. (J). (gr. 3-7). pap. 3.99 (978-0-431-07255-5(8)) Oxfam Publishing GBR. *Dist:* Stylus Publishing, LLC.

McCollum, Sean. Kenya. (Country Explorers Ser.). 2008. (J). lib. bdg. 27.93 ***(*978-0-8225-8661-6(4)*** , Lerner Pubns.); 1999. (Illus.). 48p. (gr. 2-4). 22.60 (978-1-57505-130-7(3)); 1999. (Illus.). 48p. (J). (gr. 3-5). lib. bdg. 22.60 (978-1-57505-105-5(2) , Carolrhoda Bks.) Lerner Publishing Group.

McQuail, Lisa. The Masai of Africa. 2002. (First Peoples Ser.). (Illus.). 48p. (J). (gr. 4-8). 23.93 (978-0-8225-4855-3(0)) Lerner Publishing Group.

NgCheong-Lum, Roseline & Derr, Victoria. Welcome to Kenya. 2000. (Welcome to My Country Ser.). (Illus.). 48p. (J). (gr. 2 up). lib. bdg. 26.00 (978-0-8368-2511-4(X)) Stevens, Gareth Inc.

Nicolotti, Muriel. Kuntai: A Masai Child. 2005. (Children of the World Ser.). (Illus.). 24p. (J). (gr. k-3). 22.45 (978-1-4103-0290-8(3) , 1244126, Blackbirch Pr., Inc.) Thomson Gale.

Oppong, Joseph R. & Oppong, Esther D. Kenya. 2003. (Modern World Nations Ser.). (Illus.). 150p. (gr. 6-12). 30.00 (978-0-7910-7474-9(9) , Chelsea Hse.) Facts On File, Inc.

Raatma, Lucia. Kenya. 2002. (First Reports). (Illus.). 48p. (J). (gr. 3 up). lib. bdg. 22.60 (978-0-7565-0185-3(7)) Compass Point Bks.

Ryan, Patrick. Welcome to Kenya. 2007. (Welcome to the World Ser.). 32p. (J). (gr. 1-5). 27.07 ***(*978-1-59296-919-7(4))*** Child's World, Inc.

Saffer, Barbara. Kenya. 2001. (Countries & Cultures Ser.). (Illus.). 64p. (J). (gr. 3-4). lib. bdg. 23.93 (978-0-7368-0771-5(3) , Bridgestone Bks.) Capstone Pr., Inc.

Salas, Laura Purdie. Germany. 2001. (Countries & Cultures Ser.). (Illus.). 64p. (J). (gr. 3-4). lib. bdg. 23.93 (978-0-7368-0769-2(1) , Bridgestone Bks.) Capstone Pr., Inc.

Sammis, Fran. Colors of Kenya. Reeves, Jeni, illus. 1998. (Colors of the World Ser.). (ENG & SWA.). 24p. (J). (gr. 1-4). 5.95 (978-1-57505-282-3(2)); (gr. 3-6). lib. bdg. 19.93 (978-1-57505-280-9(6)) Lerner Publishing Group.

Sommers, Michael A. Kenya: A Primary Source Cultural Guide. 2005. (Primary Sources of World Cultures Ser.). (J). lib. bdg. (978-1-4042-0478-2(4)) Rosen Publishing Group, Inc., The.

Thomson, Ruth. Kenya. 2006. (Living In- Ser.). (Illus.). 32p. (J). (978-1-59771-044-2(X)) Sea-To-Sea Pubns.

Wilson-Max, Ken. Furaha Means Happy! A Book of Swahili Words. 2000. (J). (978-0-606-19448-8(7)) Tandem Library Bks.

KENYA—FICTION

Ahern, Carolyn L. Tino Turtle Travels to Nairobi, Kenya. 2008. (Illus.). (J). 17.95 incl. audio compact disk ***(*978-0-9793158-3-1(2))*** Tino Turtle Travels, LLC.

Allende, Isabel. El Bosque de los Pigmeos. 2005. Tr. of Forest of the Pygmies. (SPA.). 304p. pap. 7.99 (978-0-06-081619-3(8) , Rayo) HarperCollins Pubs.

—Forest of the Pygmies. Peden, Margaret Sayers, tr. from SPA. 2005. 304p. (J). (gr. 5 up). 19.99 (978-0-06-076196-7(2) , Rayo) HarperCollins Pubs.

—Forest of the Pygmies. l.t. ed. 2005. 304p. (J). (gr. 5 up). pap. 19.99 (978-0-06-076200-1(4) , Rayo) HarperCollins Pubs.

Arensen, Shel. The Carjackers, Vol. 2. 2003. (Rugendo Rhino Ser.). 128p. pap. 5.99 (978-0-8254-2042-9(3)) Kregel Pubns.

—Poachers Beware, Vol. 3. 2003. (Rugendo Rhino Ser.: Vol. 3). 128p. (J). pap. 5.99 (978-0-8254-2039-9(3)) Kregel Pubns.

—The Poison Arrow Tree. 2003. (Rugendo Rhino Ser.). (Illus.). 128p. (J). pap. 5.99 (978-0-8254-2041-2(5)) Kregel Pubns.

—The Secret Oath, Vol. 4. 2003. (Rugendo Rhino Ser.: Vol. 4). 112p. (J). pap. 5.99 (978-0-8254-2040-5(7)) Kregel Pubns.

Chamberlin, Richard & Chamberlin, Mary. Mama Panya's Pancakes: A Market Day in Kenya. Cairns, Julia, illus. 2005. 40p. (J). ***(*978-1-84148-160-9(2))*** Barefoot Bks., Inc.

Chamberlin, Richard & Chamberlin, Mary. Mama Panya's Pancakes: A Village Tale from Kenya. Cairns, Julia, illus. 2006. 40p. (J). (gr. k-2). pap. 6.99 (978-1-905236-64-0(6)) Barefoot Bks., Inc.

Conway, David & Daly, Jude. Lila & the Secret of Rain. 2008. (Illus.). 32p. (J). 16.95 ***(*978-1-84507-407-4(6))*** Lincoln, Frances Ltd. GBR. *Dist:* Perseus Distribution.

Cunnane, Kelly. For You Are a Kenyan Child. Juan, Ana, illus. 2006. 40p. (J). (ps-2). 16.95 (978-0-689-86194-9(X) , Atheneum) Simon & Schuster Children's Publishing.

Grey, Chelsea Gillian. Leperit the Zebra. Denman, Michael L. & Huiett, William J., illus. 2005. (Meet Africa's Animals Ser.). (J). (ps-2). 32p. 14.95 (978-1-59249-438-5(2) , H6505); 36p. pap. 6.95 (978-1-59249-439-2(0) , S6505) Soundprints.

—Leperit the Zebra: African Wildlife Foundation. Denman, Michael L. & Huiett, William J., illus. 2005. (Meet Africa's Animals Ser.). 36p. (J). (ps-2). 2.95 (978-1-59249-441-5(2) , S6555) Soundprints.

Kessler, Cristina. Our Secret Siri Aang. 2004. 240p. (YA). (gr. 5). 16.99 (978-0-399-23985-4(5) , Philomel) Penguin Group (USA) Inc.

Larkin, Jim & Rambo, Lee Elliot. Books for Oliver. Brown, Dan, illus. 2006. (J). (978-1-59336-336-9(2)); pap. (978-1-59336-337-6(0)) Mondo Publishing.

Malaika: Safari Adventure to Kenya. 2006. (J). 4.99 (978-0-9765982-0-6(5)) Simba Publishing Co.

Markham, Beryl. The Good Lion. 2005. (Illus.). 32p. (J). (gr. 3-5). 16.00 (978-0-618-56306-7(7)) Houghton Mifflin Co. Trade & Reference Div.

Mbuthia, Waithira. My Sister's Wedding: A Story of Kenya. Karanja, Geoffrey Gacheru, illus. 2005. (Make Friends Around the World Ser.). 32p. (J). (gr. k-3). 15.95 (978-1-56899-896-1(1) , B8006); pap. 6.95 (978-1-56899-897-8(X) , S8006) Soundprints.

—My Sister's Wedding: A Story of Kenya. 2002. (gr. k-3). lib. bdg. 14.10 (978-0-613-70813-5(X)) Tandem Library Bks.

My Sister's Wedding: A Story of Kenya. 2005. (Make Friends Around the World Ser.). (Illus.). 32p. (J). (gr. k-3). 8.95 incl. reel tape (978-1-56899-900-5(3) , SC8006) Soundprints.

J K L

Talbott, Hudson. Safari Journal. 2003. (Illus.). 64p. (J). 18.00 (978-0-15-216393-8(X)) Harcourt Children's Bks.

Tellem, Sundiata. Chaka Goes to Kenya. 2005. (Illus.). 24p. (J). per. 8.99 (978-1-932338-71-3(3)) Lifevest Publishing, Inc.

Tomaselli, Mela. The Magic Pot: Folk Tales & Legends of the Giriama of Kenya. 2004. (Illus.). 80p. (978-9966-21-950-3(1)) Paulines Pubns., Africa.

KEPLER, JOHANNES, 1571-1630

Gow, Mary. Johannes Kepler: Discovering the Laws of Planetary Motion. 2003. (Great Minds of Science Ser.). (Illus.). 128p. (J). lib. bdg. 26.60 (978-0-7660-2098-6(3)) Enslow Pubs., Inc.

Hasan, Heather. Kepler & the Laws of Planetary Motion. 2004. (Primary Sources of Revolutionary Scientific Discoveries & Theories Ser.). (Illus.). 64p. (J). lib. bdg. 29.25 (978-1-4042-0308-2(7)) Rosen Publishing Group, Inc., The.

Rodríguez, Ruiz & Jaime, Alejandro. Johannes Kepler -Del otro lado esta Dios. 2005. 124p. pap. (978-958-30-1647-9(0)) Panamericana Editorial.

KEROSENE

see Petroleum

KEY, FRANCIS SCOTT, 1779-1843

Bowdish, Lynea. Francis Scott Key & the "Star Spangled Banner" Burman, Harry, illus. 2002. 32p. (J). (gr. 1-5). 15.95 (978-1-59034-038-7(8)) Mondo Publishing.

—Francis Scott Key & "The Star Spangled Banner" 2002. (Illus.). 32p. (J). 15.95 (978-1-59034-195-7(3)) Mondo Publishing.

Crewe, Sabrina & Ingram, Scott. The Writing of "The Star-Spangled Banner" 2004. (Events That Shaped America Ser.). (Illus.). 32p. lib. bdg. 24.67 (978-0-8368-3409-3(7)) Stevens, Gareth Inc.

Dell, Pamela. The National Anthem. 2004. (Let's See Library). (Illus.). 24p. (J). (gr. 1 up). lib. bdg. 19.93 (978-0-7565-0619-3(0)) Compass Point Bks.

Firestone, Mary. Our National Anthem. Skeens, Matthew, illus. 2006. (J). 23.93 (978-1-4048-2215-3(1)) Picture Window Bks.

Gregson, Susan R. Francis Scott Key: Patriotic Poet. 2003. (Let Freedom Ring Ser.). (Illus.). 48p. (J). (gr. 3-4). lib. bdg. 22.60 (978-0-7368-1554-3(6) , Bridgestone Bks.) Capstone Pr., Inc.

Healy, Nick. The Star-Spangled Banner. 2003. (J). (978-1-58417-055-6(7)); pap. (978-1-58417-118-8(9)) Lake Street Pubs.

Ingram, Scott. The Writing of "The Star-Spangled Banner" 2004. (Landmark Events in American History Ser.). (Illus.). 48p. (J). (gr. 5 up). pap. 11.95 (978-0-8368-5418-3(7)); lib. bdg. 30.00 (978-0-8368-5390-2(3)) Stevens, Gareth Inc. (World Almanac Library).

Jacobson, Ryan. The Story of the Star-Spangled Banner. Martin, Cynthia, illus. 2006. (Graphic Library). 32p. (J). (978-0-7368-5493-1(2)) Capstone Pr., Inc.

Kjelle, Marylou Morano. Francis Scott Key. 2006. (What's So Great About... ? Ser.). (Illus.). 32p. (J). (gr. 1-4). lib. bdg. (978-1-58415-474-7(8)) Mitchell Lane Pubs., Inc.

Kroll, Steven. By the Dawn's Early Light: The Story of the Star Spangled Banner. Andreasen, Dan, illus. 2000. 40p. (J). (ps-3). pap. 5.99 (978-0-590-45055-3(7)) Scholastic, Inc.

—By the Dawn's Early Light: The Story of the Star-Spangled Banner. 2000. (Illus.). (J). 12.79 (978-0-606-18522-6(4)) Tandem Library Bks.

Kroll, Steven & Kroll, Steven. By the Dawn's Early Light: The Story of the Star-Spangled Banner. Andreasen, Dan, illus. 2000. 40p. (J). (ps-ps). lib. bdg. 14.15 (978-0-613-28433-2(X)) Tandem Library Bks.

Landau, Elaine. The National Anthem. (True Booktrade;: American History Ser.). 48p. (J). 2008. pap. 6.95 (*978-0-531-14783-2(5)); 2007. (Illus.). (gr. 3-5). lib. bdg. 26.00 (*978-0-531-12633-2(1)) Scholastic Library Publishing. (Children's Pr.).

Lilly, Melinda. The Star Spangled Banner. 2003. (Rourke Discovery Library). (Illus.). 24p. (gr. 1-4). 14.95 (978-1-58952-365-4(2)) Rourke Publishing, LLC.

Nobleman, Marc Tyler. The Star-Spangled Banner. 2003. (First Facts Ser.). (Illus.). 24p. (J). lib. bdg. 19.93 (978-0-7368-2293-0(3)) Capstone Pr., Inc.

Ouren, Todd, illus. The Star Spangled Banner. 2004. (Patriotic Songs Ser.). 24p. (J). (ps-4). 22.60 (978-1-4048-0175-2(8)) Picture Window Bks.

Pingry, Patricia. O Little Town of Bethlehem. 2005. (Illus.). 16p. (J). bds. 12.99 (978-0-8249-6566-2(3)) Ideals Pubns.

Sonneborn, Liz. The Star-Spangled Banner: The Story Behind Our National Anthem. 2003. (America in Words & Song Ser.). (Illus.). 32p. (J). (gr. 3-5). 23.00 (978-0-7910-7337-7(8) , Chelsea Hse.) Facts On File, Inc.

Welch, Catherine A. The Star-Spangled Banner. Warwick, Carrie, illus. 2005. (On My Own History Ser.). 48p. (J). 25.26 (978-1-57505-590-9(2)) Lerner Publishing Group.

KEY, FRANCIS SCOTT, 1779-1843—FICTION

Sargent, Dave & Sargent, Pat. Chet: (Chestnut) Be Optimistic. 25, 15. Lenoir, Jane, illus. 2001. (Saddle Up Ser.: 15). 36p. (J). pap. 6.95 (978-1-56763-610-9(1)); lib. bdg. 22.60 (978-1-56763-609-3(8)) Ozark Publishing.

The Star-Spangled Banner. 2003. (Illus.). 32p. (J). 16.95 (978-0-8249-5462-8(9)) Ideals Pubns.

KEYS

see Locks and Keys

KIDD, WILLIAM, D. 1701

Hamilton, Sue L. Captain Kidd. 2007. (Pirates! Ser.). (ENG., Illus.). 32p. (J). (gr. 3-6). 24.21 (*978-1-59928-759-1(5) , ABDO & Daughters) ABDO Publishing Co.

Weintraub, Aileen. Captain Kidd: 17th-Century Pirate of the Indian Ocean & African Coast. 2002. (Library of Pirates). (Illus.). 24p. (J). (gr. 3). lib. bdg. 18.75 (978-0-8239-5797-2(7) , PowerKids Pr.) Rosen Publishing Group, Inc., The.

KIDD, WILLIAM, D. 1701—FICTION

Lourie, Peter. The Lost Treasure of Captain Kidd. 2003. (Illus.). 96p. (YA). (gr. 4-6). pap. 9.95 (978-1-56397-851-7(2)) Boyds Mills Pr.

KIDNAPPING

Burns, Jan. Kidnapping. 2007. (Crime Scene Investigations Ser.). (Illus.). 128p. (gr. 7-10). 31.20 (*978-1-59018-989-4(2) , Lucent Bks.) Thomson Gale.

Howard, Amanda. Kidnapping File: The Graeme Thorne Case. 2008. (J). lib. bdg. (*978-1-59716-548-8(4)) Bearport Publishing Co., Inc.

Koopmans, Andy. The Leopold & Loeb Case. 2003. (Famous Trials Ser.). (Illus.). 112p. (J). 29.95 (978-1-59018-227-7(8) , Lucent Bks.) Thomson Gale.

Mayell, Mark. The Lindbergh Kidnapping. 2003. (Famous Trials Ser.). (Illus.). 112p. (J). 29.95 (978-1-59018-267-3(7) , Lucent Bks.) Thomson Gale.

—Saskatchewan. 2003. (Illus.). 128p. (J). 29.95 (978-1-59018-052-5(6) , Lucent Bks.) Thomson Gale.

Monroe, Judy. The Lindbergh Baby Kidnapping Trial: A Headline Court Case. 2000. (Headline Court Cases Ser.). (Illus.). 128p. (YA). (gr. 6-12). lib. bdg. 26.60 (978-0-7660-1389-6(8)) Enslow Pubs., Inc.

Raatma, Lucia. Safety Around Strangers. 1998. (Safety First! Ser.). (Illus.). 24p. (J). (gr. 1-2). lib. bdg. 18.60 (978-0-7368-0060-0(3) , Bridgestone Bks.) Capstone Pr., Inc.

—Safety Around Strangers. 2004. (Living Well Ser.). 32p. (J). (gr. 2-6). 27.07 (978-1-59296-244-0(0)) Child's World, Inc.

Spikes, James L. Taffey Pop Kids Presents the Adventures of Lemmon Head & Mudd Duck: What to Do if Someone Tries to Grab YOU!!! Spikes, Leon, Jr., illus. 2007. 32p. (J). 14.95 (978-0-9771438-0-1(5)) Taffey Pop Kids Publishing.

Townsend, John. Kidnappers & Assassins. 48p. (J). 2006. pap. 8.90 (978-1-4109-1432-3(1)); 2005. lib. bdg. 31.43 (978-1-4109-1426-2(7)) Raintree.

KIDNAPPING—FICTION

Ace Lacewing: Bug Detective. 2005. (Illus.). 40p. (J). (ps-k). 15.95 (978-1-57091-569-7(5)) Charlesbridge Publishing, Inc.

Alger, Horatio. Helping Himself. 2006. 180p. pap. 13.99 (978-1-4264-0881-6(1)); 168p. pap. 16.99 (978-1-4264-0862-5(5)) BiblioBazaar.

—Helping Himself. 2006. pap. (*978-1-4065-0709-6(1)) Dodo Pr.

—Helping Himself: Or, Grant Thornton's Ambition. unabr. ed. 2002. (Polyglot Press Alger Ser.). (Illus.). (J). pap. 17.95 (978-1-4115-0006-8(7)) Polyglot Pr., Inc.

—Jack's Ward. 2006. pap. (*978-1-4065-0711-9(3)) Dodo Pr.

—Jack's Ward: Or, The Boy Guardian. 2006. 176p. pap. 13.99 (978-1-4264-0882-3(X)); 168p. pap. 16.99 (978-1-4264-0863-2(3)) BiblioBazaar.

Alger, Horatio. Timothy Crump's Ward: A Story of American Life. 2006. pap. (*978-1-4250-3339-2(3)) Assistedreadingbooks.com Inc.

Allen, Jonathan. I'm Not Scared! 2007. 32p. (ps-k). 14.99 (*978-0-7868-3722-9(5)) Hyperion Pr.

Allen, Kathleen. Witch Hunter. 2005. 131p. pap. 19.95 (978-1-4137-7839-7(9)) PublishAmerica, Inc.

Antieau, Kim. Broken Moon. 2007. 192p. (YA). (gr. 9 up). 15.99 (978-1-4169-1767-0(5) , McElderry, Margaret K.) Simon & Schuster Children's Publishing.

Ardagh, Philip. The Green Men of Gressingham. Phillips, Mike, illus. 2006. 72;88p. (J). (gr. 2-3). lib. bdg. (978-1-59889-000-6(X)) Stone Arch Bks.

Arensen, Shel. The Secret Oath, Vol. 4. 2003. (Rugendo Rhino Ser.: Vol. 4). 112p. (J). pap. 5.99 (978-0-8254-2040-5(7)) Kregel Pubns.

Ariano, Tara. Untitled: A Bad Teen Novel. 2002. 154p. pap. 11.95 (978-0-595-22478-4(4) , Writers Club Pr.) iUniverse, Inc.

Arterburn, Stephen & Hunt, Angela Elwell. Paige. 2004. (Young Believer on Tour Ser.). (J). pap. 3.99 (978-0-8423-8338-7(7)) Tyndale Hse. Pubs.

Austin, M. O. Boy Named Joe. 2006. pap. 12.99 (*978-1-4259-6217-3(3)) AuthorHouse.

Awiakta, Marilou. Rising Fawn & the Fire Mystery. 96p. (J). per. 14.95 (978-1-55591-600-8(7)) Fulcrum Publishing.

Babbitt, Natalie. Tuck Everlasting. l.t. ed. 2003. 248p. (J). 16.95 (978-0-7540-7847-0(7) , Galaxy Children's Large Print) BBC Audiobooks America.

—Tuck Everlasting. Babbitt, Natalie, illus. 2002. (Illus.). (J). 14.43 (978-0-7587-6382-2(4)) Book Wholesalers, Inc.

—Tuck Everlasting. 139p. (J). (gr. 4-6). pap. 4.95 (978-0-8072-1385-8(3) , Listening Library) Random Hse. Audio Publishing Group.

—Tuck Everlasting. 2003. 152p. (J). 25.95 (978-0-7862-5181-0(6)) Thorndike Pr.

Bachman, Kathy. Silent Raiders. 2005. 60p. pap. 12.95 (978-1-4137-5802-3(9)) PublishAmerica, Inc.

Banscherus, Jurgen & Baron, Daniel C. The Night of the Blue Heads. Butschkow, Ralf, illus. 2008. (J). pap. (*978-1-59889-910-8(4)); lib. bdg. (*978-1-59889-874-3(4)) Stone Arch Bks.

Bateman, Colin. Running with the Reservoir Pups. 2005. 272p. (J). (gr. 5-9). lib. bdg. 17.99 (978-0-385-90268-7(9) , Delacorte Bks. for Young Readers) Random Hse. Children's Bks.

Bell, Julia. Dirty Work. 2007. 192p. (YA). 16.95 (*978-0-8027-9741-4(5)) Walker & Co.

Bennett, Holly. The Bonemender's Choice. 2007. 240p. (YA). (gr. 7 up). pap. (*978-1-55143-718-7(X)) Orca Bk. Pubs.

Biggar, Joan R. Trapped at Haunted Canyon. 1998. (Megan Parnell Mysteries Ser.: Vol. 4). 160p. (J). (gr. 5-9). 5.99 (978-0-570-05069-8(3) , 56-1893) Concordia Publishing Hse.

Bloor, Edward. Taken. 2007. (gr. 7). 256p. (J). lib. bdg. 19.99 (*978-0-375-93636-4(X)); 272p. (YA). 16.99 (*978-0-375-83636-7(5)) Random Hse. Children's Bks. (Knopf Bks. for Young Readers).

Blyton, Enid. The Sea of Adventure. 7th rev. ed. 2003. (Adventure Series [3] Ser.). 192p. (J). pap. 9.99 (978-0-330-30173-2(X)) Pan Macmillan GBR. *Dist:* Trafalgar Square Publishing.

Boatfield, Jonny. The Twilight Book. 2001. (Illus.). 32p. (J). (gr. 1-4). pap. 10.99 (978-0-7475-5083-9(2)) Bloomsbury Publishing Plc GBR. *Dist:* Independent Pubs. Group.

Bosch, Pseudonymous. The Name of This Book Is Secret. Ford, Gilbert, illus. rev. ed. 2007. 384p. (J). (gr. 3-7). 16.99 (*978-0-316-11366-3(2)) Little, Brown Bks. for Young Readers.

Bowler, Tim. Storm Catchers. 2003. (Illus.). 208p. (YA). 16.95 (978-0-689-84573-4(1) , McElderry, Margaret K.) Simon & Schuster Children's Publishing.

Brin, Susannah. Tough Guys. 2000. (gr. 7-12). lib. bdg. 11.80 (978-0-613-51058-5(5)) Tandem Library Bks.

Brook, Harry, retold by. Kidnapped. 2004. (Paperback Classics Ser.). 144p. (J). lib. bdg. 12.95 (978-1-58086-640-8(9) , Usborne) EDC Publishing.

Brown, Anne. The Dumari Chronicles: Year One: Year One. 2007. 376p. (YA). per. 20.95 (*978-0-595-45725-0(8)) iUniverse, Inc.

Bryant, Jennifer. The Trial. 2004. (Illus.). 176p. (J). (gr. 3-7). lib. bdg. 16.99 (978-0-375-92752-2(2) , Knopf Bks. for Young Readers) Random Hse. Children's Bks.

Bryant, Jennifer. The Trial: A Novel. 2005. (Illus.). 169p. (J). (*978-1-4156-3151-5(4) , Yearling) Random Hse. Children's Bks.

Bunting, Eve. Hideout. 1999. (J). (gr. 5-8). lib. bdg. 14.15 (978-0-7857-1473-6(1)) Tandem Library Bks.

—The Lambkins. Keegan, Jonathan, illus. 192p. (J). 2006. pap. 5.99 (978-0-06-059908-9(1) , Harper Trophy); 2005. (gr. 5 up). 15.99 (978-0-06-059906-5(5) , Cotler, Joanna Books) HarperCollins Pubs.

Cameron, Ann. Colibri. 2003. 240p. (J). (gr. 5-8). 17.00 (978-0-374-31519-1(1) , 53501559, Farrar, Straus & Giroux (BYR)) Farrar, Straus & Giroux.

—Colibri. 2005. 256p. (YA). (gr. 7). pap. 5.99 (978-0-440-42052-1(0) , Laurel Leaf) Random Hse. Children's Bks.

—Colibri. Rioja, Alberto Jimenez, tr. from ENG. 2005. (SPA., Illus.). 256p. (J). (gr. 6-9). pap. 14.99 (978-0-439-68314-2(9) , Scholastic en Espanol) Scholastic, Inc.

Cardosi, Calesse. The Gifts. 2007. 192p. (YA). 16.95 (*978-0-9776281-3-1(2)) HPH Publishing.

Carpentiere, Elizabeth. Kidnapped. 2004. 64p. (YA). per. 3.95 (978-1-56254-820-9(4) , SP8204) Saddleback Educational Publishing.

Castilla, Julia Mercedes. Luisa Viaja en Tren. 2003. (SPA.). 128p. (978-958-30-0795-8(1) , PV30463) Panamericana Editorial COL. *Dist:* Lectorum Pubns., Inc.

Chiu, Harry. Enve Lopt Unfolded. 2007. 268p. per. 17.95 (*978-0-595-44707-7(4)) iUniverse, Inc.

The Clamdollar Caper. 2002. (Rose Doolittle Mystery Ser.: 2). 260p. (J). per. 14.95 (978-0-9712971-1-1(8)) Creston Hall Pubns.

Clark, Mary Higgins. Deck the Halls. 2001. (gr. 7-12). lib. bdg. 16.45 (978-0-613-50293-1(0)) Tandem Library Bks.

Clark, Sherryl. The Littlest Pirate: Nicholas Nosh Is off to Sea! Jellett, Tom, illus. 2006. (Nibbles Ser.). 72p. (J). pap. 3.95 (978-0-7624-2654-6(3) , Running Pr. Kids) Running Pr. Bk. Pubs.

Coatsworth, Elizabeth Jane. The White Horse. Sewell, Helen, illus. 2005. 169p. (J). pap. 11.95 (978-1-883937-86-7(8)) Bethlehem Bks.

Colfer, Eoin. The Arctic Incident. l.t. ed. 2003. (Artemis Fowl Ser.: Bk. 2). 296p. (J). (gr. 3-6). 16.95 (978-0-7540-7839-5(6) , Galaxy Children's Large Print) BBC Audiobooks America.

—The Arctic Incident. (Artemis Fowl Ser.: Bk. 2). 288p. (ps-17). 2003. (J). pap. 7.99 (978-0-7868-1708-5(9)); 2002. 16.95 (978-0-7868-0855-7(1)) Hyperion Bks. for Children.

—The Arctic Incident. l.t. ed. 2003. (Artemis Fowl Ser.: Bk. 2). 313p. (J). (gr. 3-6). 25.95 (978-0-7862-4825-4(4)) Thorndike Pr.

—Artemis Fowl. (Artemis Fowl Ser.: Bk. 1). (FRE.). pap. 34.95 (978-2-07-054681-7(0)) Gallimard, Editions FRA. *Dist:* Distribooks, Inc.

—Artemis Fowl. 2003. (Artemis Fowl Ser.: Bk. 1). (Illus.). 416p. (ps-17). pap. 5.99 (978-0-7868-1787-0(9)) Hyperion Bks. for Children.

—Artemis Fowl. 2002. (Artemis Fowl Ser.: Bk. 1). 304p. (J). (ps-17). pap. 7.99 (978-0-7868-1707-8(0)) Hyperion Paperbacks for Children.

—Artemis Fowl. 2001. (Artemis Fowl Ser.: Bk. 1). 288p. (gr. 8-17). 16.95 (978-0-7868-0801-4(2)) Miramax Bks.

—Artemis Fowl. abr. ed. 2001. (Artemis Fowl Ser.: Bk. 1). (Illus.). 2p. (J). (gr. 3-6). cd-rom (978-0-14-180286-2(3) , Penguin AudioBooks) Penguin Group (USA) Inc.

—Artemis Fowl. (Artemis Fowl Ser.: Bk. 1). 2003. (gr. 7-12). lib. bdg. 14.15 (978-0-613-75035-6(7)); 2002. (gr. 5-8). lib. bdg. 16.15 (978-0-613-60637-0(X)) Tandem Library Bks.

—Artemis Fowl. l.t. ed. 2001. (Artemis Fowl Ser.: Bk. 1). 312p. (J). (gr. 3-6). 28.95 (978-1-58724-092-8(0) , Wheeler Publishing, Inc.) Thomson Gale.

—Artemis Fowl: The Graphic Novel. Rigano, Giovanni & Lamanna, Paolo, illus. 2007. (Artemis Fowl Ser.). 112p. (gr. 5 up). 18.99 (*978-0-7868-4881-2(2)) Miramax Bks.

—Artemis Fowl: The Graphic Novel. Lamanna, Paolo, illus. 2007. (Artemis Fowl Ser.). 112p. (gr. 5 up). pap. 9.99 (*978-0-7868-4882-9(0)) Miramax Bks.

—Artemis Fowl Encuentro en el Artico: Encuentro en el Artico. 2005. (SPA., Illus.). 320p. (J). pap. 13.95 (978-0-307-34310-9(3) , Montena) Random House Mondadori ESP. *Dist:* Random Hse., Inc.

—El Cubo B. 2005. (Artemis Fowl Ser.: No. 3). (SPA., Illus.). 352p. (J). pap. 13.95 (978-0-307-34311-6(1) , Montena) Random House Mondadori ESP. *Dist:* Random Hse., Inc.

—Encuentro en el Artico. 2002. (Artemis Fowl Ser.: Bk. 2). (SPA.). 320p. pap. (978-84-8441-173-4(7) , MO32015) Grijalbo Mondadori, S.A.-Montena.

—The Opal Deception. 2005. (Artemis Fowl Ser.: Bk. 4). 352p. (gr. 5-17). 16.95 (978-0-7868-5289-5(5)) Hyperion Bks. for Children.

—The Opal Deception. 2005. (Artemis Fowl Ser.: Bk. 4). (J). pap. 7.99 (978-0-7868-3640-6(7)) Miramax Bks.

Comer, O. B. Chile & Co. Mrs. Fable's Ghost & the Kidnappers. 1998. 105p. (J). (gr. 4-6). pap. 4.95 (978-0-9662064-9-4(5)) Paige Publishing.

Cooney, Caroline B. The Face on the Milk Carton. l.t. ed. 2006. 225p. (YA). 21.95 (978-0-7862-8504-4(4)) Thorndike Pr.

—Hit the Road. 2006. 192p. (gr. 7). (J). lib. bdg. 17.99 (978-0-385-90174-1(7)); (YA). 15.95 (978-0-385-72944-4(8)) Random Hse. Children's Bks. (Delacorte Bks. for Young Readers).

—The Voice on the Radio. 1998. 224p. (YA). (gr. 7-12). mass mkt. 6.50 (978-0-440-21977-4(9) , Laurel Leaf) Random Hse. Children's Bks.

—The Voice on the Radio. 1998. (J). (978-0-606-13886-4(2)) Tandem Library Bks.

Coppel, Chris. Far from Burden Dell. 2005. 286p. (J). pap. 4.95 (978-0-9746481-6-3(7)) Brown Barn Bks.

Corder, Zizou. Lionboy. (Lionboy Trilogy : Bk. 1). (Illus.). (gr. 3-6). 2003. 288p. (J). 15.99 (978-0-8037-2982-7(0) , Dial); 2004. 304p. (YA). reprint ed. pap. 7.99 (978-0-14-240226-9(5) , Puffin) Penguin Group (USA) Inc.

—Truth. 2006. (Lionboy Trilogy : Bk. 3). 240p. (J). (gr. 3). pap. 6.99 (978-0-14-240705-9(4) , Puffin) Penguin Group (USA) Inc.

Coté, Denis. La Machination du Scorpion Noir. 2004. (Mon Roman Ser.). (FRE.). 160p. (J). (gr. 2). pap. (978-2-89021-667-9(5)) Diffusion du livre Mirabel.

Cross, Gillian. The Nightmare Game. 2007. 272p. (J). (gr. 7). 18.99 (*978-0-525-47923-9(6) , Dutton Juvenile) Penguin Group (USA) Inc.

Davis, Susan Page. Feather. 2006. (Illus.). 213p. (J). (978-1-59166-668-4(6)) Jones, Bob Univ. Pr.

de Brunhoff, Jean. Babar & Zephir. de Brunhoff, Jean, illus. 2005. (Illus.). 38p. (J). (gr. k-4). reprint ed. 16.00 (978-0-7567-8935-0(4)) DIANE Publishing Co.

de Brunhoff, Laurent. Babar's Rescue. 2004. (Illus.). 32p. (J). (ps-3). 16.95 (978-0-8109-4839-6(7)) Abrams, Harry N. , Inc.

Deaver, Julie Reece. Night I Disappeared. 2002. 242p. (J). (ps-7). per. 14.15 (978-0-613-60586-1(1)) Tandem Library Bks.

DeMatteis, J.M. Stardust Kid. 2008. (Stardust Kind Ser. : Ser.). (Illus.). 128p. pap. 14.99 (*978-1-934506-04-2(4)) Boom! Studios.

Dixon, Franklin W. Kidnapped at the Casino. 2007. (Hardy Boys Undercover Brothers: Super Mystery Ser.). 240p. (J). pap. 5.99 (978-1-4169-3923-8(7) , Aladdin) Simon & Schuster Children's Publishing.

Ducharme, Huguette. Enquete Tres Speciale. Caron, Romi, illus. 2004. (Collection des 6 Ans : Vol. 32). (FRE.). 68p. (YA). 7.95 (978-2-922565-94-2(7)) Editions de la Paix CAN. *Dist:* World of Reading, Ltd.

Duey, Kathleen. Celou Sudden Shout: Idaho, 1826. 1998. (American Diaries Ser.: No. 9). (J). (gr. 3-7). (978-0-606-13121-6(3)) Tandem Library Bks.

Dunlop, Ed. Sherlock Jones: The Missing Diamond. 2004. 109p. (J). (978-1-59166-316-4(4)) Jones, Bob Univ. Pr.

Ehrenhaft, Daniel. Drawing a Blank: Or How I Tried to Solve a Mystery, End a Feud, & Land the Girl of My Dreams. Ristow, Trevor, illus. 2006. 336p. (J). 16.99 (978-0-06-075252-1(1)); lib. bdg. 16.89 (978-0-06-075253-8(X)) HarperCollins Pubs.

Erickson, John R. The Case of the Kidnapped Collie. Holmes, Gerald L., illus. 1998. (Hank the Cowdog Ser.: No. 26). 144p. (J). (gr. 2-5). 14.99 (978-0-670-88433-9(2) , Viking Juvenile); Vol. 26. pap. 4.99 (978-0-14-130402-1(2) , Puffin) Penguin Group (USA) Inc.

—The Case of the Kidnapped Collie. 1999. (Hank the Cowdog Ser.: No. 26). (gr. 3-6). lib. bdg. 13.00 (978-0-7857-9075-4(6)) Tandem Library Bks.

—The Case of the Kidnapped Collie. Holmes, Gerald L., illus. 1999. (Hank the Cowdog Ser.: No. 26). (J). (gr. 2-5). 11.64 (978-0-606-09375-0(3)) Tandem Library Bks.

Eustache, Harold. Shuswap Journey. 2004. 176p. pap. 15.95 (978-1-894778-15-2(4)) Theytus Bks., Ltd. CAN. *Dist:* Orca Bk. Pubs. USA.

Eyerly, Jeannette. The Seeing Summer. Ishiwata, Make, illus. 1999. 153p. (YA). (gr. 3 up). pap. 10.00 (978-1-885218-15-5(X)) National Federation of the Blind.

Feinstein, John. Vanishing Act. 2008. 288p. (J). (gr. 5). 6.50 (*978-0-440-42125-2(X) , Yearling) Random Hse. Children's Bks.

—Vanishing Act: Mystery at the U. S. Open. 2006. 288p. (J). (gr. 5). lib. bdg. 18.99 (978-0-375-93592-3(4) , Knopf Bks. for Young Readers) Random Hse. Children's Bks.

—Vanishing Act: Mystery at the U.S. Open. 2006. 288p. (J). (gr. 5). 16.95 (978-0-375-83592-6(X) , Knopf Bks. for Young Readers) Random Hse. Children's Bks.

Flanagan, John. The Icebound Land. 2008. (Ranger's Apprentice Ser.: Bk. 3). 288p. (J). (gr. 5). 7.99 (*978-0-14-241075-2(6) , Puffin) Penguin Group (USA) Inc.

Freeman, Martha. Who Stole Halloween? 224p. (J). (ps-7). 16.95 (978-0-8234-1962-3(2)) Holiday Hse., Inc.

Gelsey, James. Scooby-Doo! & the Hoopster Horror. 2005. (Illus.). 61p. (J). lib. bdg. 15.00 (*978-1-4242-0305-5(8)) Fitzgerald Bks.

Giff, Patricia Reilly. Kidnap at the Catfish Cafe. Cravath, Lynne W., illus. 2000. (Adventures of Minnie & Max Ser.: Vol. 1). 80p. (J). (gr. 2-6). pap. 4.99 (978-0-14-130821-0(4) , Puffin) Penguin Group (USA) Inc.

—Kidnap at the Catfish Cafe. Cravath, Lynne, illus. 1998. 80p. (J). (gr. 2-6). 13.99 (978-0-670-88180-2(5) , Viking Juvenile) Penguin Group (USA) Inc.

—Kidnap at the Catfish Cafe. 2000. (gr. 3-6). lib. bdg. 13.00 (978-0-613-25875-3(4)); (Illus.). (J). 11.79 (978-0-606-18384-0(1)) Tandem Library Bks.

Gilden, Mel. Britney Spears Is a Three-Headed Alien: The Inside Story. 2001. (gr. 7-12). lib. bdg. 18.80 (978-0-613-82444-6(X)) Tandem Library Bks.

Gioseffi, Anthony P. Mainframe. 2007. 144p. per. 11.95 (*978-0-595-44953-8(0)) iUniverse, Inc.

Gordon, Amy. Magic by Heart. Gustavson, Adam, illus. 2007. 128p. (J). (gr. 3-7). 16.95 (*978-0-8234-1995-1(9)) Holiday Hse., Inc.

Greene, Michele Dominguez. Chasing the Jaguar. 240p. (J). 2008. pap. 7.99 (*978-0-06-076355-8(8) , Rayo); 2006. 15.99 (978-0-06-076353-4(1)) HarperCollins Pubs.

—Chasing the Jaguar. Greene, Michele Dominguez, illus. 2006. 240p. (J). lib. bdg. 16.89 (978-0-06-076354-1(X)) HarperCollins Pubs.

Grimes, Martha. Biting the Moon. 2000. (gr. 7-12). lib. bdg. 22.25 (978-0-613-34018-2(3)) Tandem Library Bks.

Grover, Lorie Ann. Hold Me Tight. 2005. 352p. (J). 16.95 (978-0-689-85248-0(7) , McElderry, Margaret K.) Simon & Schuster Children's Publishing.

Haddix, Margaret Peterson. Escape from Memory. (YA). 2005. 288p. (gr. 7-12). mass mkt. 6.99 (978-1-4169-0338-3(0) , Simon Pulse); 2003. (Illus.). 224p. 16.95 (978-0-689-85421-7(8)) Simon & Schuster Children's Publishing.

Hassinger, Peter W. The Book of Alfar: A Tale of the Hudson Highlands. 2002. (Illus.). 272p. (J). (gr. 4 up). 15.89 (978-0-06-028470-1(6) , Geringer, Laura Book) HarperCollins Pubs.

Hata, Kenjiro. Hayate the Combat Butler, Volume 2. 2007. (Conversational Ser.). 200p. (YA). pap. 9.99 (978-1-4215-0852-8(4)) Viz Media.

Hautman, Pete. Snatched. 2007. 224p. (J). pap. 6.99 (978-0-14-240795-0(X) , Puffin) Penguin Group (USA) Inc.

Hautman, Pete & Logue, Mary. Snatched. 2006. (Bloodwater Ser.: No. 1). 176p. (YA). (gr. 4). 15.99 (978-0-399-24377-6(1) , Putnam Juvenile) Penguin Group (USA) Inc.

Hicks, John. Divided World. 2003. 192p. (YA). per. 6.50 (978-0-9742829-1-6(X)) Quiet Man Publishing.

Higgins, Jack & Richards, Justin. Sure Fire. 2007. 256p. (YA). (gr. 7). 16.99 (*978-0-399-24784-2(X) , Putnam Juvenile) Penguin Group (USA) Inc.

Hirsch, Odo. Bartlett & the City of Flames. McLean, Andrew, illus. 2003. 150p. (J). 15.95 (978-1-58234-831-5(6) , Bloomsbury Children) Bloomsbury Publishing.

Hofland. Little Manuel, the Captive Boy. 2003. 63p. 88.00 (978-0-7950-5545-4(5)) New Library Press.Net.

Hoosier, Wanda M. Princess Mandisa. McCabe, Pat, illus. 1999. 34p. (J). 15.00 (978-1-56469-070-8(9)) Harmony Hse. Pubs.

Horton, Randy. Great UFO Frame-up. 2000. (gr. 5-8). lib. bdg. 11.80 (978-0-613-51213-8(8)) Tandem Library Bks.

Ibbotson, Eva. Island of the Aunts. 2001. 304p. (YA). (gr. 4-7). pap. 5.99 (978-0-14-230049-7(5) , Puffin) Penguin Group (USA) Inc.

—Monster Mission. l.t. ed. 2006. pap. 16.95 (978-1-4056-6057-0(0)) BBC Audio GBR. *Dist:* BBC Audiobooks America.

Jacobson, Jack. No Ordinary Boy. 2003. 188p. (YA). pap. 13.95 (978-1-58736-165-4(5) , Starbound Bks.) Wheatmark.

Jacques, Brian. The Taggerung. (Redwall Ser.). 2003. (gr. 7-12). lib. bdg. 16.45 (978-0-613-71577-5(2)); 2002. (gr. 5-8). lib. bdg. 16.45 (978-0-613-50253-5(1)) Tandem Library Bks.

Johansen, K. V. The Drone War: A Cassandra Virus Novel. 2007. (Cassandra Virus Ser.). 150p. (YA). pap. 9.95 (*978-0-9739505-2-6(8)) Sybertooth Inc. CAN. *Dist:* Lightning Source, Inc.

Kaaberbol, Lene. The Shamer's Signet. 2nd rev. ed. 2007. (Shamer Chronicles Ser.). 320p. (YA). pap. 8.95 (*978-0-8050-8217-3(4) , Holt, Henry & Co. Bks. For Young Readers) Holt, Henry & Co.

Kay, Alan. Breaking the Rules. 2007. (Young Heroes of History: 7). (J). pap. 7.95 (*978-1-57249-389-6(5) , White Mane Kids) White Mane Publishing Co., Inc.

Keene, Carolyn. False Notes. ed. 2005. (Nancy Drew Ser.: 3). 154p. (J). lib. bdg. 15.00 (978-1-59054-810-3(8)) Fitzgerald Bks.

—Secret in the Stars. 2000. lib. bdg. 13.00 (978-0-613-63459-5(4)) Tandem Library Bks.

Kehret, Peg. Abduction! (J). 2006. 224p. (gr. 4). pap. 6.99 (978-0-14-240617-5(1) , Puffin); 2004. 192p. (gr. 5). reprint ed. 16.99 (978-0-525-47294-0(0) , Dutton Juvenile) Penguin Group (USA) Inc.

—Don't Tell Anyone. 2000. (Illus.). 144p. (YA). (gr. 5-9). 15.99 (978-0-525-46388-7(7) , Dutton Juvenile) Penguin Group (USA) Inc.

—Spy Cat. 2003. 192p. (J). (gr. 5-6). 15.99 (978-0-525-47046-5(8) , Dutton Juvenile) Penguin Group (USA) Inc.

Korman, Gordon. The Abduction. 2006. (Kidnapped Ser.). (J). 24.95 (978-0-439-89552-1(9)); 39.95 (978-0-439-89847-8(1)) Scholastic, Inc.

—The Rescue. 2006. (Kidnapped Ser.: No. 3). 160p. (J). pap. 4.99 (978-0-439-84779-7(6)) Scholastic, Inc.

—The Search. 2006. (Kidnapped Ser.: Bk. 2). 144p. (J). pap. 4.99 (978-0-439-84778-0(8) , Scholastic Paperbacks) Scholastic, Inc.

Lago-Weed, Melissa. The Hairys: Don't Talk to Strangers. 2004. 33p. pap. 17.95 (978-1-4137-3223-8(2)) PublishAmerica, Inc.

Lawrence, Caroline. The Colossus of Rhodes. 2006. (Roman Mysteries Ser.). (Illus.). 208p. (J). 16.95 (978-1-59643-082-2(6)) Roaring Brook Pr.

—Pirates of Pompeii, Vol. 3. 2004. (Roman Mysteries Ser.: No. 3). (Illus.). 176p. (J). (gr. 3). pap. 5.99 (978-0-14-240227-6(3) , Puffin) Penguin Group (USA) Inc.

Lee, Tanith. Wolf Star. 2002. (Claidi Journals: Bk. 2). (gr. 7-12). lib. bdg. 14.15 (978-0-613-53584-7(7)) Tandem Library Bks.

Littke, Lael. Searching for Selene. 2003. 203p. (J). pap. 13.95 (978-1-59038-179-3(3)) Deseret Bk. Co.

Lowachee, Karin. War Child. 2002. (gr. 3-6). lib. bdg. 15.30 (978-0-613-52925-9(1)) Tandem Library Bks.

Mangano, J. M. Crossing Cadogan Bay. 2002. 222p. pap. 14.95 (978-0-595-22370-1(2) , Writer's Showcase Pr.) iUniverse, Inc.

Mark, Yudel. The Jewish Pope: A Yiddish Tale. Goodman, Ruth Fisher, tr. from YID. 2006. (Illus.). 128p. (YA). pap. 10.00 (978-1-56474-459-3(0)) Fithian Pr.

Mason, Lynn. Disappeared. 2003. (Illus.). 208p. (YA). (gr. 7). mass mkt. 5.99 (978-0-553-49400-6(7) , Bantam Bks. for Young Readers) Random Hse. Children's Bks.

Mason, Tom. Take It to the Max. 2001. (gr. 3-6). lib. bdg. 11.80 (978-0-613-87080-1(8)) Tandem Library Bks.

Mazer, Norma Fox. The Missing Girl. 2008. 288p. (J). 16.99 (*978-0-06-623776-3(9)); lib. bdg. 17.89 (*978-0-06-623777-0(7)) HarperCollins Pubs. (HarperTeen).

McAllister, M. I. The Heir of Mistmantle. Rayyan, Omar, illus. 2007. (Mistmantle Chronicles Ser.: Bk. 3). 320p. (J). (gr. 3-7). 17.99 (*978-0-7868-5490-5(1)) Miramax Bks.

Mccabe, Jr. Planting the Wilderness or, the Pioneer Boys: a Story of Frontier Life. 2007. pap. 27.95 (*978-1-4304-8187-4(0)) Kessinger Publishing, LLC.

McNeece, Alexander. Sam Iver: Imminent Threat. 2007. 140p. per. 11.95 (*978-0-595-43260-8(3)) iUniverse, Inc.

Meissner, Susan. A Window to the World. 2005. 320p. pap. 11.99 (978-0-7369-1414-7(5)) Harvest Hse. Pubs.

Merialdo, Lee K. Kidnapped. 2006. 112p. pap. 10.95 (978-0-7414-3407-4(5)) Infinity Publishing.

Meyer, Louis A. & Nielsen, Cliff. In the Belly of the Bloodhound: Being an Account of a Particularly Peculiar Adventure in the Life of Jacky Faber. 2006. (Bloody Jack Adventures Ser.). (Illus.). 528p. (J). (gr. 8 up). 17.00 (978-0-15-205557-8(6)) Harcourt Children's Bks.

Millman, Selena. More Than a Hero. 2006. 92p. (YA). per. 11.37 (*978-1-4243-2351-7(7)) Independent Publisher Services.

Mills, Sam. The Viper Within. 2008. 304p. (J). (gr. 7). 16.99 (*978-0-375-84465-2(1)); lib. bdg. 19.99 (*978-0-375-94465-9(6)) Random Hse. Children's Bks. (Knopf Bks. for Young Readers).

Mitchelhill, Barbara. The Case of the Disappearing Daughter. Ross, Tony, illus. 2007. 72p. (J). (*978-1-59889-269-7(X)) Stone Arch Bks.

Mitchell, Chris. The Realm Legends. 2006. pap. 40.99 (*978-1-4208-9129-4(4)) AuthorHouse.

Mohr, L. C. Krumbuckets. 2008. (Illus.). 144p. (J). per. 8.95 (978-0-9769417-7-4(5)) Blooming Tree Pr.

—Krumbuckets. Musheno, Erica, illus. 2007. 144p. (J). (gr. 2-7). 13.95 (978-0-9769417-6-7(7)) Blooming Tree Pr.

Much Ado at the Zoo. 2001. (gr. k-3). lib. bdg. 11.80 (978-0-613-32851-7(5)) Tandem Library Bks.

Napoli, Donna Jo. Three Days. 2003. (Illus.). 160p. (YA). pap. 5.99 (978-0-14-250025-5(9) , Puffin) Penguin Group (USA) Inc.

—Three Days. 2003. (gr. 3-6). lib. bdg. 14.15 (978-0-613-67041-8(8)) Tandem Library Bks.

Neff, Henry H. The Hound of Rowan. 2007. (Tapestry Ser.: Bk. 1). (Illus.). 414p. (J). (gr. 3-7). 17.99 (978-0-375-83894-1(5) , Random Hse. Bks. for Young Readers) Random Hse. Children's Bks.

—The Hound of Rowan. Neff, Henry H., illus. 2007. (Tapestry Ser.: Bk. 1). (Illus.). 414p. (J). (gr. 3-7). lib. bdg. 20.99 (978-0-375-93894-8(X) , Random Hse. Bks. for Young Readers) Random Hse. Children's Bks.

—The Hound of Rowan. 2007. (J). pap. (978-0-375-83895-8(3)) Random Hse., Inc.

Nixon, Joan Lowery. The Kidnapping of Christina Lattimore. 2004. 320p. (YA). pap. 5.95 (978-0-15-205031-3(0) , Harcourt Paperbacks) Harcourt Children's Bks.

—Kidnapping of Christina Lattimore. 2004. (gr. 7-12). lib. bdg. 14.10 (978-0-613-71632-1(9)) Tandem Library Bks.

Norton, Mary. Borrowers Aloft: Plus the Short Tale, Poor Stainless. 2003. (gr. 3-6). lib. bdg. 14.10 (978-0-613-66944-3(4)) Tandem Library Bks.

Oram, Hiawyn. Princess Chamomile Gets Her Way. 2001. (Illus.). (J). (978-0-606-21386-8(4)) Tandem Library Bks.

Pascal, Francine. Run. 2000. 206p. pap. (978-0-671-03748-2(X) , Simon & Schuster Children's Publishing) Simon & Schuster Children's Publishing.

—Secuestrada. 2002. (Sweet Valley High Ser.).Tr. of Kidnapped. (SPA.). (YA). 7.95 (978-84-272-3883-1(5)) Molino, Editorial ESP. *Dist:* AIMS International Bks., Inc.

Pfeffer, Susan Beth. Twice Taken. 1999. 199p. (YA). (gr. 6-8). reprint ed. 15.00 (978-0-7881-6675-4(1)) DIANE Publishing Co.

Phillips, Grant R. Jay Walker & the Case of the Missing Action Figure. 2004. (J). pap. 10.95 (978-0-9749608-4-5(5)) Quiet Storm Publishing Group.

Poole, Richard. Jewel & Thorn. 2007. (Book of Lowmoor Ser.). (Illus.). 391p. (YA). (gr. 7 up). per. 11.95 (*978-0-689-87290-7(9)) Simon & Schuster, Ltd. GBR. *Dist:* Independent Pubs. Group.

Pow, Tom. Captives. 2007. 192p. (YA). 17.95 (*978-1-59643-201-7(2)) Roaring Brook Pr.

Prophet, John M. Body in the Salt Marsh Boatyard: A Casey Miller Mystery. 2004. 162p. (YA). pap. 13.95 (978-0-595-30991-7(7) , Mystery & Suspense Pr.) iUniverse, Inc.

Pullman, Philip. Der Goldene Kompass. (GER.). pap. 27.95 (978-3-453-13744-8(2)) Verlag Wilhelm Heyne DEU. *Dist:* Distribooks, Inc.

Pyle, Howard. The Story of Jack Ballister's Fortunes. 2007. (YA). (*978-0-486-45467-2(3)) Dover Pubns., Inc.

Rautenberg, Karen Rita. Lady Lucy's Gallant Knight. 2007. 156p. (J). pap. 7.95 (978-1-933255-22-4(6)) DNA Pr.

Rector, Rebecca Kraft. Tria & the Great Star Rescue. 2003. (gr. 3-6). lib. bdg. 13.00 (978-0-613-86232-5(5)) Tandem Library Bks.

Richards, Kitty. Yo Ho Ho & a Bottle of Milk. 2000. (gr. 3-6). lib. bdg. 11.80 (978-0-613-27654-2(X)) Tandem Library Bks.

Rika, Tanaka. Kilala Princess. 20th rev. ed. 2007. (Illus.). pap. 5.99 (*978-1-59816-768-9(5) , Tokyopop Kids) TOKYOPOP, Inc.

Rivera, Raquel. Orphan Ahwak. 2007. 144p. (J). (gr. 4-8). pap. (*978-1-55143-653-1(1)) Orca Bk. Pubs.

Roberts, Willo Davis. Hostage. 2001. 144p. (J). pap. 5.99 (978-0-689-84446-1(8) , Aladdin) Simon & Schuster Children's Publishing.

—Hostage. 2001. (J). 11.64 (978-0-606-21237-3(X)) Tandem Library Bks.

—The Kidnappers: A Mystery. 1999. (J). (978-0-606-16224-1(0)); (gr. 3-6). lib. bdg. 13.00 (978-0-613-23008-7(6)) Tandem Library Bks.

—The One Left Behind. (J). 2007. 139p. (gr. 3-7). per. 5.99 (978-0-689-85083-7(2)); 2006. (Illus.). 144p. 16.95 (978-0-689-85075-2(1) , Atheneum) Simon & Schuster Children's Publishing.

Rowley, B. J. Missing Children. 2000. (Light Traveler Adventure Ser.: Vol. 3). 252p. (YA). (gr. 6-12). pap. 13.95 (978-0-9700103-3-9(8)) Golden Wings Enterprises.

Roy, Ron. Kidnapped at the Capital. Woodruff, Liza & Bush, Timothy, illus. 2002. (Road to Reading Ser.: Vol. 2). 80p. (J). (gr. 2-5). pap. 3.99 (978-0-307-26514-2(5) , Random Hse. Bks. for Young Readers) Random Hse. Children's Bks.

—Kidnapped at the Capital. 2002. (gr. 3-6). lib. bdg. 11.80 (978-0-613-50212-2(4)) Tandem Library Bks.

—The Kidnapped King. Gurney, John Steven, illus. 2000. (A to Z Mysteries Ser.: No. 11). 96p. (J). (gr. k-3). lib. bdg. 11.99 (978-0-679-99459-6(9)); pap. 3.99 (978-0-679-89459-9(4)) Random Hse. Children's Bks. (Random Hse. Bks. for Young Readers).

—The Kidnapped King. Gurney, John Steven, illus. 2000. (A to Z Mysteries Ser.: No. 11). (J). (gr. k-3). lib. bdg. 11.80 (978-0-613-25876-0(2)); (978-0-606-18481-6(3)) Tandem Library Bks.

Schraff, Anne. The Case of the Watery Grave. 2002. (PageTurner Detective Ser.). 80p. (YA). per. 3.95 (978-1-56254-390-7(3) , SP 3903) Saddleback Educational Publishing.

Schulte, Elaine. Daniel Colton Kidnapped. 2003. (gr. 3-6). lib. bdg. 14.70 (978-0-613-85516-7(7)) Tandem Library Bks.

Seher, H. R. Virtual Law. 2005. 154p. pap. 19.95 (978-1-4137-5249-6(7)) PublishAmerica, Inc.

Shackelford, Mary. Cinnamon's Quest. 2005. 115p. pap. 16.95 (978-1-4137-6430-7(4)) PublishAmerica, Inc.

Sharmat, Marjorie Weinman. A Dog Star Is Born. 2000. (Illus.). (J). (978-0-606-18494-6(5)) Tandem Library Bks.

Shaw, Janet Beeler. Kaya's Escape. 2002. (gr. 3-6). lib. bdg. 14.10 (978-0-613-46223-5(8)) Tandem Library Bks.

—Kaya's Escape! A Survival Story, Bk. 2. Farnsworth, Bill & McAliley, Susan, illus. 2002. (American Girls Collection: Bk. 2). 88p. (gr. 2-7). (J). 12.95 (978-1-58485-426-5(X)); 6.95 (978-1-58485-425-8(1)) American Girl Publishing, Inc.

Sherrard, Valerie. Eyes of a Stalker. 2006. 180p. (YA). pap. 12.99 (*978-1-55002-643-6(7) , Boardwalk Bks.) Dundurn Group, The CAN. *Dist:* Univ. of Toronto Pr.

Smith, Roland. Jack's Run. 2007. 256p. (gr. 5-17). pap. 5.99 (*978-1-4231-0407-0(2)) Hyperion Pr.

Spirn, Michele & Strong, Jeremy. Missing. O'Connor, Niamh, illus. 2007. 112p. (J). (*978-1-59889-278-9(9)) Stone Arch Bks.

Springer, Nancy. The Case of the Left-Handed Lady: An Enola Holmes Mystery. 2008. 256p. (J). (gr. 4-8). pap. 6.99 (*978-0-14-241190-2(6) , Puffin); 2007. 224p. (YA). (gr. 5-9). 12.99 (978-0-399-24517-6(0) , Philomel) Penguin Group (USA) Inc.

Stevenson, Robert Louis. Kidnapped. Kennedy, Cam, illus. 2007. 64p. (J). (gr. 5). pap. 11.95 (*978-0-88776-843-9(1)) Tundra Bks., Inc./Livres Toundra, Inc. CAN. *Dist:* Random Hse., Inc.

Stevenson, Robert Louis. Secuestrado. 3rd ed. (Coleccion Clasicos en Accion). (SPA., Illus.). 80p. (YA). (gr. 5-8). 15.95 (978-84-241-5781-4(8) , EV1487) Everest de Ediciones y Distribucion, S.L. ESP. *Dist:* Lectorum Pubns., Inc.

—Secuestrado. 2002. (Clover Ser.). (SPA., Illus.). 156p. (YA). 11.50 (978-84-392-8006-4(8) , EV5548) Lectorum Pubns., Inc.

—Secuestrado. 1999. (SPA.). 360p. (978-950-03-7852-9(3) , 4000) Losada.

Stevenson, Robert Louis, intro. Kidnapped: Catriona. 2007. 480p. pap. 15.00 (*978-1-84697-033-7(4)) BirlinnPolygon GBR. *Dist:* Interlink Publishing Group, Inc.

Stratton, Allan. Chanda's Wars. 2008. 400p. (J). 17.99 (*978-0-06-087262-5(4)); lib. bdg. 18.89 (*978-0-06-087264-9(0)) HarperCollins Pubs.

Sweet, J.H. & Sierra, Holly. Spiderwort & the Princess of Haiku: The Fairy Chronicles. 2007. (Fairy Chronicles Ser.). (Illus.). 128p. (J). (gr. 2 up). pap. 6.99 (*978-1-4022-1025-9(6) , Sourcebooks Jabberwocky) Sourcebooks, Inc.

Thoene, Jake & Thoene, Luke. The Mystery of the Yellow Hands. 2006. (Baker Street Detectives Ser.). 144p. (J). 9.99 (978-1-4143-0370-3(X)) Tyndale Hse. Pubs.

Tosal, Oscar. Adios, Papa! 1998. (SPA.). (gr. 7-12). lib. bdg. 14.10 (978-0-613-80723-4(5)) Tandem Library Bks.

Trottier, Maxine. By the Standing Stone. 2001. (gr. 3-6). lib. bdg. 16.40 (978-0-613-51481-1(5)) Tandem Library Bks.

Uderzo, Albert & Goscinny, René. Asterix & the Vikings. 2007. (Illus.). 64p. 12.95 (978-0-7528-8590-2(1)) Orion Bks. Ltd. GBR. *Dist:* Sterling Publishing Co., Inc.

Van Meter, Jen. Hopeless Savages, 3 vols., Vol. 1. 2nd ed. 2003. (Illus.). 136p. (YA). (gr. 7 up). pap. 11.95 (978-1-929998-75-3(9)) Oni Pr., Inc.

Villeneuve, Marie-Paule & Audet, Patrice. Qui a Enleve Polka? 2004. (FRE., Illus.). 122p. (J). 8.95 (978-2-922565-81-2(5)) Editions de la Paix CAN. *Dist:* World of Reading, Ltd.

Walsh, Laurence & Walsh, Suella. In the Middle of the Night. 2006. (J). pap. (*978-0-88092-473-3(X)) Royal Fireworks Publishing Co.

Wenzell, Tim. Absent Children. 2000. 316p. (YA). pap. 15.95 (978-0-595-12142-7(X)) iUniverse, Inc.

West, Tracey. Yu-Gi-Oh Gx Reader #3 Rescue Duel. 2008. 32p. pap. 3.99 (*978-0-439-88840-0(9) , Scholastic) Scholastic, Inc.

White, Ellen Emerson. Long Live the Queen. 2008. (YA). pap. 8.99 (*978-0-312-37490-7(9)) Feiwel & Friends.

—Long May She Reign. 2007. 720p. (YA). (gr. 7 up). pap. 15.95 (*978-0-312-36767-1(8)) Feiwel & Friends.

Wicke, Ed. Mattie & the Highwaymen. Warne, Tom, illus. 2003. 232p. (J). per. 8.99 (978-0-9677652-1-1(8) , BlacknBlue Pr. UK) Blacknblue Pr.

Wilkins, Kim. Ghost Ship: Sunken Kingdom #1. Cornish, D. M., illus. 2008. 96p. (J). (gr. 4-7). pap. 5.99 (*978-0-375-84806-3(1) , Random Hse. Bks. for Young Readers) Random Hse. Children's Bks.

—Ghost Ship: Sunken Kingdom #1. Cornish, D. M., illus. 2008. 96p. (J). (gr. 4-7). lib. bdg. 11.99 (*978-0-375-94806-0(6) , Random Hse. Bks. for Young Readers) Random Hse. Children's Bks.

Wilson, Eric. Kootenay Kidnapper. 2001. (gr. 3-6). lib. bdg. 13.00 (978-0-613-54818-2(3)) Tandem Library Bks.

Windle, Jeanette. Captured in Colombia, Vol. 3. 2002. (Parker Twins Ser.: No. 3). 160p. (gr. 3-8). pap. 5.99 (978-0-8254-4147-9(1)) Kregel Pubns.

Wittlinger, Ellen. Long Night of Leo & Bree. 2003. (gr. 7-12). lib. bdg. 15.30 (978-0-613-73433-2(5)) Tandem Library Bks.

Yaccarino, Dan. Los Cuatro Vientos. (SPA.). (J). 7.95 (978-958-04-7606-1(3)) Norma S.A. COL. *Dist:* Distribuidora Norma, Inc.

KILLING, MERCY

see Euthanasia

KINDERGARTEN

Beck, Isabel L., et al. Trophies Kindergarten: The Party. 2003. (Trophies Ser.). (gr. k-6). 13.80 (978-0-15-329523-2(6)) Harcourt Schl. Pubs.

Burton, Marilee Robin. Kindergarten Enrichment. 2001. (Enrichment Wkbks.). (Illus.). 32p. (J). (gr. k). pap., wbk. ed. 2.49 (978-0-88743-455-6(X) , 02150) School Zone Publishing Co.

Guy, Ginger Foglesong. My School/Mi Escuela. Escriva, Vivi, illus. 2006. (ENG & SPA.). 24p. (J). lib. bdg. 13.89 (978-0-06-079102-5(0) , Harper Festival); 12.99 (978-0-06-079101-8(2) , Rayo) HarperCollins Pubs.

Harcourt School Publishers Staff. Look out Kindergarten, Here I Come! Library Book. 3rd ed. 2002. (Trophies Reading Program Ser.). (Illus.). pap. 13.50 (978-0-15-329251-4(2)) Harcourt Schl. Pubs.

Hays, Anna Jane. Ready, Set, Preschool! Stories, Poems & Picture Games with an Educational Guide for Parents. Kelley, True, illus. 2005. 40p. (J). (ps-1). 16.95 (978-0-375-82519-4(3) , Knopf Bks. for Young Readers) Random Hse. Children's Bks.

Hoffman, Joan. Kindergarten Basics. (J). 2004. 32p. pap. 2.49 (978-1-58947-436-9(8)); 2003. 64p. pap., wbk. ed. 3.79 (978-1-58947-036-1(2)) School Zone Publishing Co.

Hughes. My First, 4 vols., Set 1. 2003. (Illus.). (J). pap. 19.80 (978-1-4109-0668-7(X)) Raintree.

Kannenberg, Stacey. Let's Get Ready for Kindergarten! rev. ed. 2006. (Illus.). 30p. (J). (ps-1). per. 19.00 (978-1-933476-00-1(1)) Cedar Valley Publishing.

Kindergarten Skills. 2000. (Kelley Wingate Ser.). 80p. (J). (ps-1). pap. 9.99 (978-0-88724-593-0(5)) Carson-Dellosa Publishing Co., Inc.

Leatherdale, Mary Beth. My Class & Me: Kindergarten. Ritchie, Scot, illus. 2004. (Memory Scrapbks. for Kids). 32p. (J). (gr. k-3). (978-1-55337-129-8(1)) Kids Can Pr., Ltd.

Pfister, Marcus. Rainbow Fish Colors/Colores. Pfister, Marcus, illus. 2005. (ENG & SPA., Illus.). 24p. (J). bds. 4.99 (978-0-7358-1978-8(5)) North-South Bks., Inc.

Practice Power School Bus Book: Kindergarten. 2003. 24p. (J). spiral bd. (978-1-930355-42-2(4)) Greenbrier/Scentex.

Rigby. Let's Get Ready for Kindergarten. 2002. (J). pap. 16.99 (978-0-7578-2420-3(X)) Rigby Education.

Riley, Kathryn & Burton, Marilee R. Kindergarten Scholar: Grade K. Merer, Laura, illus. rev. ed. 2002. (Super-Deluxe Wkbks.). 128p. (J). pap. 7.99 (978-1-58947-006-4(0) , 02457) School Zone Publishing Co.

School Zone Interactive Staff. Kindergarten. (J). 2005. cd-rom 24.99 (978-1-58947-682-0(4)); 2002. 320p. 19.99 (978-1-58947-852-7(5)) School Zone Publishing Co.

Wells, Rosemary. My Kindergarten. 2004. (Illus.). 96p. (ps-1). 16.99 (978-0-7868-0833-5(0)) Hyperion Bks. for Children.

KINDERGARTEN—FICTION

Algeo, Kristie. When Daddy Goes Away. 2006. (ENG., Illus.). 36p. (J). per. 21.99 (978-1-4141-0643-4(2)) Pleasant Word.

Bieber, Hartmut. Busy Bear Goes to Kindergarten. 2004. (Illus.). 14p. (J). 5.99 (978-1-59384-049-5(7)) Parklane Publishing.

Bowie, C. W. Laboriosos deditos de las Manos. Canetti, Yanitzia, tr. Willingham, Fred, illus. 2004. Tr. of Busy Fingers. (SPA.). 32p. (J). pap. 7.95 (978-1-58089-043-4(1)) Charlesbridge Publishing, Inc.

—Laboriosos deditos de los Pies. Canetti, Yanitzia, tr. Willingham, Fred, illus. 2004. Tr. of Busy Toes. (SPA.). 32p. (J). pap. 7.95 (978-1-58089-098-4(9)) Charlesbridge Publishing, Inc.

Brillhart, Julie. Molly Rides the School Bus. 2002. (Illus.). 32p. (J). (ps-2). 15.95 (978-0-8075-5210-0(0)) Whitman, Albert & Co.

Carlson, Nancy. Henry's 100 Days of Kindergarten. Carlson, Nancy, illus. 32p. (J). 2007. pap. 5.99 (978-0-14-240758-5(5) , Puffin); 2004. (Illus.). 15.99 (978-0-670-05977-5(3) , Viking Juvenile) Penguin Group (USA) Inc.

—Henry's Show & Tell. Carlson, Nancy, illus. 2006. (Illus.). 32p. (J). (ps). reprint ed. pap. 5.99 (978-0-14-240639-7(2) , Puffin) Penguin Group (USA) Inc.

—Look Out Kindergarten, Here I Come! (Preparante, Kindergarten, Alla Voy!) Mlawer, Teresa, tr. Carlson, Nancy, illus. 2004. (ENG & SPA., Illus.). 32p. (J). (gr. k-3). 15.99 (978-0-670-03673-8(0) , Viking Juvenile) Penguin Group (USA) Inc.

—Look Out Kindergarten, Here I Come! (Preparante, Kindergarten, Alla Voy!) 1999. (Illus.). 32p. (J). (ps up). 15.99 (978-0-670-88378-3(6) , Viking Juvenile) Penguin Group (USA) Inc.

—Look Out Kindergarten, Here I Come! (Preparante, Kindergarten, Alla Voy!) 2001. (gr. k-3). lib. bdg. 14.15 (978-0-613-43847-6(7)) Tandem Library Bks.

Cleary, Beverly. Ramona the Pest. (Ramona Ser.). (J). (gr. 3-5). Dell Publishing.

—Ramona the Pest. Dockray, Tracy, illus. 2006. 211p. (J). lib. bdg. 20.00 (*978-1-4242-0410-6(0)) Fitzgerald Bks.

—Ramona the Pest. (Ramona Quimby Ser.). 192p. (J). (gr. 3-5). pap. 4.99 (978-0-8072-1438-1(8) , Listening Library) Random Hse. Audio Publishing Group.

Cooper, Ilene. Jake's Best Thumb. Muñoz, Claudio, illus. 2008. 32p. (J). (ps). 16.99 (*978-0-525-47788-4(8) , Dutton Juvenile) Penguin Group (USA) Inc.

Davis, Katie. Kindergarten Rocks! 2005. (Illus.). 32p. (J). 15.00 (978-0-15-204932-4(0)) Harcourt Trade Pubs.

DePaola, Tomie. Hide-and-Seek All Week. 2001. (Illus.). 32p. (J). (ps-3). lib. bdg. 11.80 (978-0-613-50319-8(8)) Tandem Library Bks.

dePaola, Tomie. Stagestruck. 2007. 32p. (J). (ps). pap. 6.99 (*978-0-14-240899-5(9) , Puffin) Penguin Group (USA) Inc.

Edwards, Pamela Duncan. Ms. Bitsy Bat's Kindergarten. Cole, Henry, illus. 2005. (J). (*978-1-4156-2782-2(7)) Hyperion Bks. for Children.

Elliott, Laura Malone. Hunter's Best Friend at School. Munsinger, Lynn, illus. 2002. 32p. (J). (ps-2). 16.99 (978-0-06-000230-5(1)); 17.89 (978-0-06-000231-2(X)) HarperCollins Pubs.

Gregory, Nan. Amber Waiting. Denton, Kady MacDonald, illus. 2004. (Northern Lights Books for Children). 32p. (J). (ps-1). 17.95 (978-0-88995-258-4(2)) Red Deer Pr. CAN. *Dist:* Fitzhenry & Whiteside, Ltd.

Hamilton, Richard. Let's Take over the Kindergarten. Heap, Sue, illus. 2007. 32p. (J). (ps-1). 15.95 (978-1-58234-707-3(7)) Bloomsbury Publishing.

Harper, Jessica. A Place Called Kindergarten. Karas, G. Brian, illus. 2006. 32p. (J). (ps-3). 15.99 (978-0-399-24226-7(0) , Putnam Juvenile) Penguin Group (USA) Inc.

Hays, Anna Jane. Kindergarten Countdown. Davick, Linda, illus. 2007. 24p. (J). (ps-1). lib. bdg. 11.99 (978-0-375-94252-5(1)); 8.99 (978-0-375-84252-8(7)) Random Hse. Children's Bks. (Knopf Bks. for Young Readers).

Himle, Lisa. Hands As Warm As Toast. Langton, Bruce, illus. 2006. 32p. (J). 17.95 (978-1-58726-298-2(3) , Mitten Pr.) Ann Arbor Media Group, LLC.

Houdek, Andi. Mice in My Tummy. 2006. (J). per. 16.95 (978-0-9771939-9-8(3) , 012) New World Publishing.

Huxman, Karin (K. D.). Dragon Talk. 2006. (Illus.). 24p. (J). lib. bdg. 24.95 (978-0-9778651-7-8(7)) Dragonfly Publishing, Inc.

Johnston, Tony. Off to Kindergarten. Sweet, Melissa, illus. 2007. 32p. (J). (ps-3). 7.99 (*978-0-439-73090-7(2) , Cartwheel Bks.) Scholastic, Inc.

Klein, Adria F. Max Goes to School. Gallagher-Cole, Mernie, illus. 2005. (Read-It! Readers Ser.). 24p. (J). (ps). lib. bdg. 18.60 (978-1-4048-1179-9(6)) Picture Window Bks.

Klingel, Cynthia Fitterer & Noyed, Robert B. Kaya's Kindergarten & the Letter K. 2003. (Alphaphonics Ser.). (Illus.). 24p. (J). (ps-2). 21.36 (978-1-59296-101-6(0)) Child's World, Inc.

—Sabina at School & the Letter S. 2003. (Alphaphonics Ser.). (Illus.). 24p. (J). (ps-2). 21.36 (978-1-59296-109-2(6)) Child's World, Inc.

MacDowell, Maureen. Tomorrow Is the First Day of School. Hergenrother, Max, illus. 2007. 32p. (J). 15.95 (*978-0-9791463-0-5(5)) Wading River Bks., LLC.

McGhee, Alison. Countdown to Kindergarten. Bliss, Harry, illus. 2006. 32p. (J). reprint ed. pap. 6.00 (978-0-15-205586-8(X) , Voyager Bks./Libros Viajeros) Harcourt Children's Bks.

—Countdown to Kindergarten. Bliss, Harry, illus. 2002. 32p. (J). (ps-2). 16.00 (978-0-15-202516-8(2) , Silver Whistle) Harcourt Trade Pubs.

—Countdown to Kindergarten. Bliss, Harry, illus. pap. 16.95 incl. audio (978-1-59112-467-2(0)); pap. incl. audio compact disk (978-1-59112-469-6(7)); pap. 18.95 incl. audio compact disk (978-1-59112-927-1(3)); pap. incl. audio (978-1-59112-929-5(X)) Live Oak Media.

Meredith, Carol. Jamie Anderson Wouldn't. . . Szekat, Lorrie, illus. 1998. 24p. (J). (ps-1). 15.95 (978-1-55037-457-5(5)) Annick Pr., Ltd. CAN. *Dist:* Firefly Bks., Ltd.

Park, Barbara. Junie B. Jones & a Little Monkey Business. Brunkus, Denise, illus. 2007. (Junie B. Jones Ser.: No. 2). 80p. (J). (gr. k-3). 9.99 (978-0-375-84157-6(1) , Random Hse. Bks. for Young Readers) Random Hse. Children's Bks.

—Junie B. Jones & the Stupid Smelly Bus. Brunkus, Denise, illus. 2007. (Junie B. Jones Ser.: No. 1). 80p. (J). (gr. k-3). 9.99 (978-0-375-84156-9(3) , Random Hse. Bks. for Young Readers) Random Hse. Children's Bks.

—Junie B. Jones Is a Beauty Shop Guy. Brunkus, Denise, illus. 2006. (Junie B. Jones Ser.: No. 11). (SPA.). 80p. (J). (gr. k-3). pap. 3.99 (978-0-439-66124-9(2) , Scholastic en Espanol) Scholastic, Inc.

—Junie B. Jones Is a Graduation Girl. Brunkus, Denise, illus. 2001. (Junie B. Jones Ser.: No. 17). 80p. (J). (gr. k-3). pap. 3.99 (978-0-375-80292-8(4)); lib. bdg. 11.99 (978-0-375-90292-5(9)) Random Hse. Children's Bks. (Random Hse. Bks. for Young Readers).

—Junie B. Jones Is a Graduation Girl. 2001. (Junie B. Jones Ser.: No. 17). (J). (gr. k-3). lib. bdg. 11.80 (978-0-613-33766-3(2)); (Illus.). 10.79 (978-0-606-21273-1(6)) Tandem Library Bks.

—Junie B. Jones Is Captain Field Day. Brunkus, Denise, illus. 2001. (Junie B. Jones Ser.: No. 16). 80p. (J). (gr. k-3). lib. bdg. 11.99 (978-0-375-90291-8(0) , Random Hse. Bks. for Young Readers) Random Hse. Children's Bks.

—Junie B. Jones y el Negocio del Mono. Brunkus, Denise, illus. 2005. (Junie B. Jones Ser.).Tr. of Junie B Jones Little Monkey Business. (SPA.). 80p. (J). pap. 3.99 (978-0-439-42514-8(X) , Scholastic en Espanol) Scholastic, Inc.

—Junie B. Jones y su Gran Bocota. Brunkus, Denise, illus. 2005. (Junie B. Jones Ser.).Tr. of Junie B. Jones Big Fat Mouth. (SPA.). 80p. (J). pap. 3.99 (978-0-439-42516-2(6) , Scholastic en Espanol) Scholastic, Inc.

—Junie B. Jones's Second Boxed Set Ever!, Bks. 5-8. 2002. (Illus.). (J). (gr. 1-4). pap. 15.96 (978-0-375-82265-0(8) , Random Hse. Bks. for Young Readers) Random Hse. Children's Bks.

Pattison, Darcy. 19 Girls & Me. Salerno, Steven, illus. 2006. 32p. (J). (ps). 16.99 (978-0-399-24336-3(4) , Philomel) Penguin Group (USA) Inc.

Penn, Audrey. Un Beso en Mi Mano. 2006. (SPA.). 32p. 16.95 (978-1-933718-01-9(3)) Tanglewood Pr.

—The Kissing Hand. 2007. 32p. (ps-3). 28.95 (*978-1-933718-07-1(2)) Tanglewood Pr.

—The Kissing Hand. Harper, Ruth E. & Leak, Nancy M., illus. 2006. 32p. 16.95 (978-1-933718-00-2(5)) Tanglewood Pr.

—The Kissing Hand. unabr. ed. 2007. 32p. (J). (ps-3). pap. 9.95 incl. audio compact disk (*978-1-933718-10-1(2)) Tanglewood Pr.

Plucker, Sheri. Me, Hailey. Fargo, Todd, illus. 2005. (Turtle Books). 32p. (J). (gr. k-3). pap. 9.95 (978-0-944727-49-2(2)); lib. bdg. 15.95 (978-0-944727-50-8(6) , Turtle Bks.) Jason & Nordic Pubs.

Robbins, Jacqui. The New Girl ... & Me. Phelan, Matt, illus. 2006. 32p. (J). (ps-2). 16.95 (978-0-689-86468-1(X) , Atheneum) Simon & Schuster Children's Publishing.

Rockwell, Anne. Welcome to Kindergarten. Rockwell, Anne, illus. 2004. (Illus.). 32p. (J). pap. 6.95 (978-0-8027-7664-8(7)); 15.95 (978-0-8027-8745-3(2)) Walker & Co.

Rogers, Jacqueline. Tiptoe into Kindergarten. Rogers, Jacqueline, illus. (Illus.). (J). (ps-1). 2003. 40p. pap. 6.99 (978-0-439-48592-0(4)); 1999. 32p. pap. 10.95 (978-0-590-46653-0(4)) Scholastic, Inc. (Cartwheel Bks.).

—Tiptoe into Kindergarten. 2003. (gr. k-3). lib. bdg. 14.15 (978-0-613-64686-4(X)) Tandem Library Bks.

Schwartz, Amy. Annabelle Swift, Kindergartener. Schwartz, Amy, illus. 2002. (Illus.). (J). 14.74 (978-0-7587-1954-6(X)) Book Wholesalers, Inc.

—Annabelle Swift, Kindergartner. 2000. (J). pap. 19.97 incl. audio (978-0-7366-9198-7(7)) Books on Tape, Inc.

Schwartz, Amy & Kaye, Randye. Annabelle Swift, Kindergartner. 2004. (Live Oak Readalong Ser.). (Illus.). (J). pap. 18.95 incl. audio compact disk (978-1-59112-687-4(8)) Live Oak Media.

Skarmeas, Nancy J. My First Day of School. Johnson, Meredith, illus. 2001. 32p. (J). (ps-3). 9.95 (978-0-8249-4198-7(5)) Ideals Pubns.

Slate, Joseph. Miss Bindergarten Celebrates the 100th Day of Kindergarten. 2002. (Miss Bindergarten Ser.). (Illus.). (YA). 15.53 (978-1-4046-2578-5(X)) Book Wholesalers, Inc.

—Miss Bindergarten Celebrates the 100th Day of Kindergarten. Wolff, Ashley, illus. (J). (gr. k-1). 2002. 40p. pap. 6.99 (978-0-14-250005-7(4) , Puffin); 1998. 32p. 16.99 (978-0-525-46000-8(4) , Dutton Juvenile) Penguin Group (USA) Inc.

—Miss Bindergarten Celebrates the 100th Day of Kindergarten. 2003. (gr. k-3). lib. bdg. 15.30 (978-0-613-58122-6(9)) Tandem Library Bks.

—Miss Bindergarten Celebrates the Last Day of Kindergarten. Wolff, Ashley, illus. 40p. (J). (ps). 2008. pap. 6.99 (*978-0-14-241060-8(8) , Puffin); 2006. 16.99 (978-0-525-47744-0(6) , Dutton Juvenile) Penguin Group (USA) Inc.

—Miss Bindergarten Gets Ready for Kindergarten. Wolff, Ashley, illus. 2001. 40p. (J). pap. 6.99 (978-0-14-056273-6(7) , Puffin) Penguin Group (USA) Inc.

—Miss Bindergarten Gets Ready for Kindergarten. 2001. (gr. k-3). lib. bdg. 15.30 (978-0-613-35982-5(8)); (Illus.). (J). (978-0-606-21333-2(3)) Tandem Library Bks.

—Miss Bindergarten Has a Wild Day in Kindergarten. Wolff, Ashley, illus. 2006. 40p. (J). (ps). reprint ed. pap. 6.99 (978-0-14-240709-7(7) , Puffin) Penguin Group (USA) Inc.

—Miss Bindergarten Plans a Circus with Kindergarten. Wolff, Ashley, illus. 2005. 36p. (J). (ps-ps). lib. bdg. 13.79 (978-0-606-33114-2(X)) Tandem Library Bks.

—Miss Bindergarten Stays Home from Kindergarten. Wolff, Ashley, illus. (J). (ps-2). 2000. 1p. 16.99 (978-0-525-46396-2(8) , Dutton Juvenile); 2004. 48p. reprint ed. pap. 6.99 (978-0-14-230127-2(2) , Puffin) Penguin Group (USA) Inc.

—Miss Bindergarten Takes a Field Trip with Kindergarten. Wolff, Ashley, illus. (J). (ps up). 2004. 40p. pap. 6.99 (978-0-14-240139-2(0) , Puffin); 2001. 32p. 16.99 (978-0-525-46710-6(6) , Dutton Juvenile) Penguin Group (USA) Inc.

Sturges, Philemon. I Love School! Halpern, Shari, illus. 2004. 32p. (J). (ps-1). 12.99 (978-0-06-009284-9(X)); lib. bdg. 14.89 (978-0-06-009285-6(8)) HarperCollins Pubs.

Wells, Rosemary. Mama, Don't Go! 2001. (Yoko & Friends School Days Ser.: No. 1). (Illus.). 32p. (gr. k-2). 9.99 (978-0-7868-0720-8(2) , Volo) Hyperion Bks. for Children.

—The School Play. Wheeler, Jody, illus. 2001. (Yoko & Friends School Days Ser.: No. 2). 32p. (gr. k-2). 9.99 (978-0-7868-0721-5(0)); pap. 3.99 (978-0-7868-1527-2(2)) Hyperion Bks. for Children. (Volo).

—The School Play. 2001. (J). (978-0-606-22547-2(1)) Tandem Library Bks.

—The World Around Us: Based on Timothy Goes to School & Other Stories. 2001. (Get Set for Kindergarten Ser.). (Illus.). (J). (978-0-606-21536-7(0)) Tandem Library Bks.

Wilson, Ritchie. Kinji Goes to Kindergarten. 2006. (Illus.). 28p. pap. 11.95 (978-1-59800-516-5(2)) Outskirts Press, Inc.

Winget, Susan. Tucker's Four-Carrot School Day. Winget, Susan, illus. 2005. (Illus.). 40p. (J). (ps-k). 12.99 (978-0-06-054642-7(5)); lib. bdg. 13.89 (978-0-06-054643-4(3)) HarperCollins Pubs.

Wolff, Ashley. Miss Bindergarten Plans a Circus with Kindergarten. Slate, Joseph & Wolff, Ashley, illus. 2002. 40p. (J). 16.99 (978-0-525-46884-4(6) , Dutton Juvenile) Penguin Group (USA) Inc.

Wolff, Ashley, illus. Miss Bindergarten Stays Home from Kindergarten. 2002. (Miss Bindergarten Ser.). (J). 25.45 (978-0-7587-3144-9(2)) Book Wholesalers, Inc.

KINDNESS—FICTION

Allred, Chris Ross. Sir E. Bobbo! 2004. 21p. pap. 14.95 (978-1-4137-2785-2(9)) PublishAmerica, Inc.

Anonymous. Theobald the Iron Hearted or Love to Ene. 2004. reprint ed. pap. 15.95 (978-1-4191-8941-8(7)) Kessinger Publishing, LLC.

—Theobald the Iron Hearted or Love to Enemies. 2004. reprint ed. pap. 1.99 (978-1-4192-8941-5(1)) Kessinger Publishing, LLC.

Aston, Dianna Hutts. Not So Tall for Six. Dormer, Frank W., illus. 2008. (J). (*978-1-57091-705-9(1)) Charlesbridge Publishing, Inc.

Banta, Sandra F. Fancy the Beautiful Little Dragon: Book Number Two Little One's Series. Hecker, Vera, illus. l.t. ed. 2006. 45p. per. 11.99 (978-1-59879-157-0(5)) Lifevest Publishing, Inc.

Brightwood, Laura, illus. Little Freddie & His Whistle. Brightwood, Laura, . 2007. (J). DVD (*978-1-934409-01-5(4)) 3-C Institute for Social Development.

Brimner, Larry Dane. New Kid. 2003. (gr. k-3). lib. bdg. 14.10 (978-0-613-67653-3(X)) Tandem Library Bks.

Brouwer, Sigmund. Strunk Soup. 2003. (Watch Out for Joel Ser.). (Illus.). 32p. (J). pap. 3.99 (978-0-7642-2585-7(5)) Bethany Hse. Pubs.

Butler, M. Christina. One Winter's Day. Macnaughton, Tina, illus. 2006. 28p. (J). 16.00 (978-1-56148-532-1(2)) Good Bks.

Clairmont, Patsy. Stinky. Oeltjenbruns, Joni, illus. 2006. (Tails from the Pantry Ser.). 32p. (J). 9.99 (978-1-4003-0803-3(8)) Nelson, Thomas Inc.

Colman. Pearl Story Book A Collection of Tales O. 2006. pap. 87.99 (*978-1-4280-4925-3(8)) IndyPublish.com.

Cuyler, Margery. Kindness Is Cooler, Mrs. Ruler. Yoshikawa, Sachiko, illus. 2007. 50p. (J). (gr. k-2). 16.99 (978-0-689-87344-7(1) , Simon & Schuster Children's Publishing) Simon & Schuster Children's Publishing.

Early, Kelly. Something for Nothing. Sherman, Shandel, illus. l.t. ed. 2006. 13p. (J). 14.95 (978-1-59879-131-0(1)); per. 8.95 (978-1-59879-100-6(1)) Lifevest Publishing, Inc.

Eddy, Ron. What's up with Lyle? A Story about Kindness. Eddy, Ron & Vann, Robert, illus. 2006. (VeggieTales Ser.). 16p. (J). 5.99 (978-1-4169-4061-6(8) , Little Simon Inspirations) Simon & Schuster Children's Publishing.

Freeman, Don. Fly High, Fly Low (50th Anniversary Ed.) Freeman, Don, illus. 2007. 64p. (J). (ps). pap. 7.99 (978-0-14-240817-9(4) , Puffin) Penguin Group (USA) Inc.

Friend, R. R. Friend - Hats off to Heroes. 2005. (Down on Friendly Acres Ser.: 3). (J). lib. bdg. (978-0-9743627-5-5(1)); (Illus.). 90p. per. (978-0-9743627-2-4(7)) Sunflower Seeds Pr.

Hall, S.C. Turns of Fortune & Other Tales. 2007. (ENG.). 116p. per. (*978-1-4065-1586-2(8)) Dodo Pr.

Hallinan, P. K. Let's Be Kind. 2003. (Illus.). 24p. (J). bds. 7.95 (978-0-8249-5477-2(7)) Ideals Pubns.

Hennessy, B. G. Because of You: A Book of Kindness. Nakata, Hiroe, illus. 2005. 24p. (J). (gr. k-2). 15.99 (978-0-7636-1926-8(4)) Candlewick Pr.

Hill, Karen. Ava, the One & Only. Roos, Maryn, illus. 2005. 24p. (J). 9.99 (978-1-4169-0511-0(1) , Little Simon) Simon & Schuster Children's Publishing.

Howell, Trisha Adelena. The Adventures of Melon & Turnip. Lopez, Paul, illus. 2004. 32p. 15.95 (978-1-931210-04-1(7)) Howell Canyon Pr.

Hyde, Catherine Ryan. Pay It Forward. 2000. (gr. 7-12). lib. bdg. 16.45 (978-0-613-33844-8(8)) Tandem Library Bks.

Johnson, Pete. The Kindness Bubble. 2004. 36p. (J). pap. 16.95 (978-1-932373-60-8(8)) Cedar Hill Publishing.

Jones, Julie. The Problem at Pepperpine Zoo. Jones, Julie, illus. l.t. ed. 2004. (Illus.). 24p. (J). pap. 7.95 (978-0-9745553-0-0(4)) Greenwood Street Publishing. GSP.

Lang, Andrew. The Queen & the Mouse: A Story about Friendship. Lohmann, Renate, illus. 2006. (J). (978-1-59939-081-9(7) , Reader's Digest Young Families, Inc.) Reader's Digest Children's Publishing, Inc.

Marsh, T. F. Quest for Kindness. Marsh, T. F., illus. 2006. (Amazing Travels of Wannabe Ser.). (Illus.). 32p. (J). 8.99 (978-0-7847-1802-5(4) , 04128) Standard Publishing.

Mims, Melanie. Neeko's Angel: A Story about Kindness. Floyd, John, Jr., illus. 2005. (J). pap. 6.95 (*978-0-9752860-7-4(2)) OurRainbow Pr., LLC.

Rice, David L. Because Brian Hugged His Mother. Thompson, K. Dyble, illus. 1999. (J). (ps-ps). lib. bdg. 16.40 (978-0-613-23140-4(6)) Tandem Library Bks.

Schieber, Barry J. An Open Heart: A Story about Moritz. 2006. (Illus.). 32p. (J). 17.00 (*978-0-9721457-2-5(9)) Silent Moon Bks.

Sewell, Anna. Black Beauty: And a Discussion of Kindness. Martin, Richard, illus. 2003. (Values in Action Illustrated Classics Ser.). 191p. (J). (978-1-59203-028-6(9)) Learning Challenge, Inc.

Simon, Mary Manz. Kitty Shows Kindness. Clearwater, Linda, illus. 2006. (First Virtues for Toddlers Ser.). 20p. (J). 5.99 (978-0-7847-1408-9(8) , 04036) Standard Publishing.

Stevens, Carla. Who's Knocking at the Door? Chapman, Lee, illus. 2004. 40p. (J). 16.95 (978-0-7614-5168-6(4)) Cavendish, Marshall Corp.

Stoutland, Allison. What Can I Do Today? 2005. 32p. 16.95 (978-0-9670941-3-7(5)) Inch By Inch Pubns., LLC.

Vincent, Victoria. The City of Kind Words: A Story by Tory. l.t. ed. 2006. (Illus.). 56p. (J). per. 19.95 (*978-0-9788950-0-6(2)) All Over Creation.

Wallace, Nancy Elizabeth. The Kindness Quilt. 2006. (Illus.). 48p. (J). (gr. k-2). 16.99 (978-0-7614-5313-0(X)) Cavendish, Marshall Corp.

Wert, Richard. The Boxer's Backyard. 2007. (J). pap. 8.99 (*978-1-60247-023-1(5)) Tate Publishing & Enterprises, L.L.C.

Wilson, Karen Collett. Pogonip Magic. Zerga, Susan A., illus. 2002. 40p. (J). (ps-3). 14.95 (978-0-9722570-0-8(4)) Snowbound Bks.

Xavier, Coco. A Little Kindness. Style Guide Staff & Riley, Kellee, illus. 2006. (Holly Hobbie & Friends Ser.). 96p. (J). act. bk. ed. 2.99 (978-1-4169-1849-3(3) , Simon Scribbles) Simon & Schuster Children's Publishing.

KINDNESS TO ANIMALS

see Animals—Treatment

KINETICS

see Dynamics; Motion

KING, BILLIE JEAN, 1943-

Lannin, Joanne. Billie Jean King: Tennis Trailblazer. 1999. (Lerner Biographies Ser.). (Illus.). 128p. (gr. 6-12). lib. bdg. 27.93 (978-0-8225-4959-8(X)) Lerner Publishing Group.

KING, CORETTA SCOTT, 1927-2006

Armentrout, David & Armentrout, Patricia. Coretta Scott King. 2004. (Discover the Life of an American Legend Ser.). (Illus.). 24p. (gr. 2-5). 20.64 (978-1-58952-659-4(7)) Rourke Publishing, LLC.

Gelfand, Dale Evva & Rhodes, Lisa Renee. Coretta Scott King: Civil Rights Activist. 2nd rev. ed. 2006. (Black Americans of Achievement, Legacy Edition Ser.). (Illus.). 144p. (J). (gr. 6-12). 30.00 (978-0-7910-9522-5(3) , Chelsea Hse.) Facts On File, Inc.

Mattern, Joanne. Coretta Scott King: Civil Rights Activist. 2003. (Reading Power Ser.). (Illus.). 24p. (J). lib. bdg. 17.25 (978-0-8239-6504-5(X) , PowerKids Pr.) Rosen Publishing Group, Inc., The.

—Coretta Scott King: Civil Rights Activist: Individual Title Six-Packs. (On Deck Ser.: Vol. 2). 24p. (gr. 4-5). 35.00 (978-0-7578-5841-3(4)) Rigby Education.

McPherson, Stephanie Sammartino. Coretta Scott King. 2007. (J). lib. bdg. (*978-0-8225-7156-8(0)) Twenty First Century Bks.

Medearis, Angela Shelf. Dare to Dream: Coretta Scott King & the Civil Rights Movement. Rich, Anna, illus. 1999. (Rainbow Biography Ser.). 64p. (J). (gr. 3-7). pap. 4.99 (978-0-14-130202-7(X) , Puffin) Penguin Group (USA) Inc.

J
K
L

—Dare to Dream: Coretta Scott King & the Civil Rights Movement. 1999. (gr. 3-6). lib. bdg. 13.00 (978-0-613-14663-0(8)) Tandem Library Bks.

Pingry, Patricia A. The Story of Coretta Scott King. Walker, Steven, illus. 2007. 26p. (J). (ps-k). bds. 6.99 (***978-0-8249-6717-8(8)***, Candy Cane Pr.) Ideals Pubns.

Press, Petra. Coretta Scott King: An Unauthorized Biography. 1999. (Profiles Ser.). (Illus.). 56p. (J). (gr. 4-6). lib. bdg. 24.22 (978-1-57572-496-6(0)) Heinemann Library.

Rhodes, Lisa Renee. Coretta Scott King: Civil Rights Activist. (Black Americans of Achievement Ser.). (Illus.). 112p. (J). (gr. 6-12). 2005. pap. 13.25 (978-0-7910-8371-0(3)); 2004. 30.00 (978-0-7910-8251-5(2)) Facts On File, Inc. (Chelsea Hse.).

—Coretta Scott King: Humanitarian. 1999. (Black Americans of Achievement Ser.). (Illus.). 144p. (YA). (gr. 4-7). 30.00 (978-0-7910-4690-6(7)) ; (gr. 5 up). pap. 6.65 (978-0-7910-4691-3(5)) Facts On File, Inc. (Chelsea Hse.).

Waxman, Laura Hamilton. Coretta Scott King. 2008. (History Maker Biographies Ser.). (J). lib. bdg. 26.60 (***978-0-8225-7168-1(4)***, Lerner Pubns.) Lerner Publishing Group.

KING, MARTIN LUTHER, JR., 1929-1968

Adler, David A. Dr. Martin Luther King, Jr. A Historical Perspective. Bootman, Colin, illus. 48p. (J). (gr. k-3). pap. 4.95 (978-0-8234-1803-9(0)) Holiday Hse., Inc.

—Dr. Martin Luther King, Jr. Level 2: A House House Reader. Bootman, Colin, illus. 2001. (Reader Ser.). 48p. (J). (gr. k-3). tchr. ed. 15.95 (978-0-8234-1572-4(4)) Holiday Hse., Inc.

—A Picture Book of Martin Luther King, Jr. Casilla, Robert, illus. 32p. (J). (gr. k-3). pap. 6.95 (978-0-8234-0847-4(7)); tchr. ed. 17.95 (978-0-8234-0770-5(5)) Holiday Hse., Inc.

—A Picture Book of Martin Luther King, Jr., , Mlawer, Teresa, tr. Casilla, Robert, illus. unabr. ed. 1999. (J). pap. 33.95 incl. audio (978-0-87499-569-5(8)) Live Oak Media.

Alexander, Florence. Dare to Be. . . Martin Luther King Jr. Whitmore, Yvette, illus. 2003. (ENG & SPA.). 17p. (J). 3.99 (978-0-915960-65-1(6)) Ebon Research Systems Publishing, LLC.

Ansary, Mir Tamim. El Día de Martin Luther King, Jr. 2003. Tr. of Martin Luther King, Jr. Day. (SPA., Illus.). 32p. (J). lib. bdg. 22.79 (978-1-4034-3004-5(7)) Heinemann Library.

—Martin Luther King, Jr. Day. (Illus.). 32p. (J). 2006. (***978-1-4034-8889-3(4));*** 2002. pap. 6.95 (978-1-58810-432-8(X) , 91160); 1999. lib. bdg. 21.36 (978-1-57572-873-5(7)) Heinemann Library.

Ansary, Mir Tamim. Martin Luther King Jr. Day. 2002. (Illus.). 32p. (J). (gr. k-3). lib. bdg. 14.75 (978-0-613-36108-8(3)) Tandem Library Bks.

Aretha, David. Selma & the Voting Rights ACT. 2007. (J). (***978-1-59935-056-1(4))*** Reynolds, Morgan Inc.

Armentrout, David & Armentrout, Patricia. Coretta Scott King. 2004. (Discover the Life of an American Legend Ser.). (Illus.). 24p. (gr. 2-5). 20.64 (978-1-58952-659-4(7)) Rourke Publishing, LLC.

Bader, Bonnie. Who Was Martin Luther King Jr. Harrison, Nancy & Wolf, Elizaabeth, illus. 2007. (Who Was... ? Ser.). 112p. (J). (gr. 2-5). 4.99 (***978-0-448-44723-0(1)***, Grosset & Dunlap) Penguin Group (USA) Inc.

Baker, Courtney. Let's Read about Martin Luther King, Jr. Hu, Ying-Hwa & Van Wright, Cornelius, illus. 2001. (First Biographies Ser.). (J). pap. (978-0-439-22112-2(9)) Scholastic, Inc.

Ball, Jacqueline A. Martin Luther King, Jr: I Have a Dream! 2005. (Defining Moments Ser.). (Illus.). 32p. (J). (gr. 3-7). lib. bdg. 25.27 (978-1-59716-077-3(6)) Bearport Publishing Co., Inc.

Bolden, Tonya. M. L. K. The Journey of a King. Adelman, Bob, ed. 2007. 128p. (J). (gr. 5-9). 19.95 (978-0-8109-5476-2(1) , Abrams Bks. for Young Readers) Abrams, Harry N. , Inc.

Boyd, Herb. Martin Luther King, Jr. Marcos, Pablo, illus. 2005. (Heroes of America Ser.). 240p. (J). (gr. 3-8). lib. bdg. 21.35 (978-1-59679-258-6(2)) ABDO Publishing Co.

Brown, Adele Q. Martin Luther King, Jr. 2003. (Trailblazers of the Modern World Ser.). (Illus.). 48p. (J). (gr. 5 up). lib. bdg. 30.00 (978-0-8368-5091-8(2)); pap. (978-0-8368-5251-6(6)) Stevens, Gareth Inc. (World Almanac Library).

Brown, Jonatha A. Martin Luther King, Jr. 2005. (Illus.). 24p. (ENG & SPA.). (J). pap. (978-0-8368-4590-7(0)); (J). lib. bdg. (978-0-8368-4474-0(2)); (ENG & SPA., (J). lib. bdg. 19.33 (978-0-8368-4583-9(8)); (YA). lib. bdg. 19.33 (978-0-8368-4467-2(X) , Weekly Reader Early Learning Library) Stevens, Gareth Inc.

Bull, Angela. Free at Last! The Story of Martin Luther King, Jr. 2000. (Readers Ser.). (Illus.). 48p. (J). (gr. 5-4). pap. 3.99 (978-0-7894-5717-2(2)) Dorling Kindersley Publishing, Inc.

—Free at Last! the Story of Martin Luther King, Jr. 2000. (gr. k-3). lib. bdg. 11.80 (978-0-613-32592-9(3)) Tandem Library Bks.

Bull, Angela & Dorling Kindersley Publishing Staff. Free at Last! The Story of Martin Luther King, Jr. 2000. (Readers Ser.). (Illus.). 48p. (gr. 2-4). 12.99 (978-0-7894-5716-5(4)) Dorling Kindersley Publishing, Inc.

Casilla, Robert, illus. A Picture Book of Martin Luther King, Jr. 2004. (J). pap. 18.95 incl. audio compact disk (978-1-59112-773-4(4)) Live Oak Media.

Ching, Jacqueline. The Assassination of Martin Luther King, Jr. 2003. (Library of Political Assassinations). (Illus.). 64p. (YA). (gr. 7-12). lib. bdg. 26.50 (978-0-8239-3543-7(4)) Rosen Publishing Group, Inc., The.

Claybourne, Anna. Martin Luther King, Jr. Civil Rights Hero. 2001. (Famous Lives Ser.). (Illus.). 48p. (J). (gr. 4-6). lib. bdg. 27.12 (978-0-7398-4433-5(4)) Raintree.

Colbert, Jan. Dear Dr. King: Letters from Today's Children to Dr. Martin Luther King, Jr. 2000. (Illus.). (J). (978-0-606-18256-0(X)) Tandem Library Bks.

Coleman, Wim & Perrin, Pat. Martin Luther King, Jr. National Historic Site: A MyReportLinks.com Book. 2005. (Virtual Field Trips Ser.). (Illus.). 48p. (J). (gr. 4-10). lib. bdg. 25.26 (978-0-7660-5225-3(7) , MyReportLinks.com Bks.) Enslow Pubs., Inc.

Darby, Jean. Martin Luther King, Jr. 2005. (Lighting Bolt Bios Ser.). (Illus.). 112p. (J). (gr. 6-12). 27.93 (978-0-8225-2471-7(6)) Lerner Publishing Group.

Davis, Kenneth C. Don't Know Much about Martin Luther King Jr., Vol. 6. Kodaira, Machiyo, illus. 2006. (Don't Know Much About Ser.). 144p. (J). (gr. 2-5). lib. bdg. 16.89 (978-0-06-028822-8(1)) HarperCollins Pubs.

The Day Martin Luther King Jr Died, 6 vols. (Multicultural Programs Ser.). 16p. (gr. 1-6). 31.95 (978-0-7802-8325-1(2)) Wright Group, The.

de Kay, James T. Meet Martin Luther King, Jr. 2001. (Landmark Bks.). (Illus.). 112p. (J). (gr. 4-7). 4.99 (978-0-375-80395-6(5) , Random Hse. Bks. for Young Readers) Random Hse. Children's Bks.

—Meet Martin Luther King, Jr. 2001. (Landmark Bks.). (Illus.). (J). (978-0-606-20793-5(7)) Tandem Library Bks.

—Meet Martin Luther King, Jr. 2001. (gr. 3-6). lib. bdg. 11.80 (978-0-613-44541-2(4)) Tandem Library Bks.

Dean, Sheri. Martin Luther King Day. 2006. (Illus.). 24p. (J). pap. (978-0-8368-6513-4(8)); lib. bdg. 19.33 (978-0-8368-6506-6(5)) Stevens, Gareth Inc.

—Martin Luther King Jr. Day/dia De Martin Luther King Jr. 2006. (ENG & SPA., Illus.). 24p. (J). pap. 5.95 (978-0-8368-6527-1(8)); lib. bdg. 19.33 (978-0-8368-6520-2(0)) Stevens, Gareth Inc.

Devillier, Christy. Martin Luther King, Jr. 2001. (First Biographies Ser.). (Illus.). 32p. (J). (gr. k-4). lib. bdg. 22.78 (978-1-57765-592-3(3) , Buddy Bks.) ABDO Publishing Co.

Doering, Amanda. Martin Luther King Jr. Day. 2006. (First Facts Ser.). (Illus.). 24p. (J). (978-0-7368-5391-0(X)) Capstone Pr., Inc.

Douglas, Lloyd G. Let's Get Ready for Martin Luther King, Jr. Day. 2003. (Wel-Celebrations Ser.). (Illus.). 24p. (J). 17.00 (978-0-516-24259-0(8)); pap. 4.95 (978-0-516-24351-1(9)) Scholastic Library Publishing. (Children's Pr.).

Downing, David. Martin Luther King, Jr. 2002. (Leading Lives Ser.). 64p. (J). (gr. 5-7). pap. 8.95 (978-1-4034-0123-6(3) , 91614); (Illus.). lib. bdg. 28.50 (978-1-58810-580-6(6)) Heinemann Library.

Fandel, Jennifer. Martin Luther King, Jr. 2005. (Genius Ser.). (Illus.). 48p. (gr. 5-9). 21.95 (978-1-58341-329-6(4) , Creative Education) Creative Co., The.

—Martin Luther King, Jr: Great Civil Rights Leader. 2007. (Graphic Library). (Illus.). 32p. (J). (978-0-7368-6498-5(9)) Capstone Pr., Inc.

Farris, Christine King. My Brother Martin: A Sister Remembers Growing up with the Rev. Dr. Martin Luther King Jr. Soentpiet, Chris K., illus. 2003. 40p. (J). 17.95 (978-0-689-84387-7(9)) Simon & Schuster Children's Publishing.

Feeney, Kathy. Martin Luther King, Jr. 2002. (Photo-Illustrated Biographies Ser.). (Illus.). 24p. (J). (gr. 2-3). lib. bdg. 18.60 (978-0-7368-1111-8(7) , Bridgestone Bks.) Capstone Pr., Inc.

—Martin Luther King, Jr. (Photo Illustrated Biographies Ser.). 24p. (J). pap. 6.95 (978-0-7368-3435-3(4)) Capstone Pr., Inc.

Feinstein, Stephen. Read about Martin Luther King, Jr. 2004. (I Like Biographies Ser.!). (Illus.). 24p. (J). lib. bdg. 24.95 (978-0-7660-2300-0(1)) Enslow Pubs., Inc.

Fine, Edith Hope. Martin Luther King, Jr: Champion of Civil Rights. 2006. (Heroes of American History Ser.). (Illus.). 32p. (J). lib. bdg. 22.60 (978-0-7660-2466-3(0) , Enslow Elementary) Enslow Pubs., Inc.

Fleming. Famous Americans Series: Martin Luther King. 2003. (Illus.). 32p. (J). pap. 9.95 (978-0-590-53545-8(5)) Scholastic, Inc.

Fleming, Alice Mulcahey. Martin Luther King, Jr. A Dream of Hope. 2008. (Sterling Biographies Ser.). (Illus.). 128p. (J). pap. 5.95 (***978-1-4027-4439-6(0))*** Sterling Publishing Co., Inc.

Foran, Jill. Martin Luther King Jr. Day. 2004. (American Holidays Ser.). (Illus.). 24p. (J). pap. 6.95 (978-1-59036-167-2(9)); lib. bdg. 17.10 (978-1-59036-107-8(5)) Weigl Pubs., Inc.

Franklin, V. P. Martin Luther King, Jr. 1998. (Biography Ser.). (Illus.). 192p. (J). 20.00 (978-0-517-20098-8(8)) Random Hse. Value Publishing.

Frost, Helen. Martin Luther King, Jr Day. (National Holidays Ser.). 24p. (J). pap. 5.95 (978-0-7368-8727-4(X)) Capstone Pr., Inc.

Ganeri, Anita. Martin Luther King, Jr. 2003. (Twentieth Century History Makers Ser.). (Illus.). 112p. (J). lib. bdg. 32.85 (978-0-7398-5257-6(4)) Raintree.

Gelfand, Dale Evva & Rhodes, Lisa Renee. Coretta Scott King: Civil Rights Activist. 2nd rev. ed. 2006. (Black Americans of Achievement, Legacy Edition Ser.). (Illus.). 144p. (J). (gr. 6-12). 30.00 (978-0-7910-9522-5(3) , Chelsea Hse.) Facts On File, Inc.

Gnojewski, Carol. Martin Luther King, Jr. , Day: Honoring a Man of Peace. 2002. (Finding Out about Holidays Ser.). (Illus.). 48p. (J). (gr. 1-4). lib. bdg. 23.93 (978-0-7660-1574-6(2)) Enslow Pubs., Inc.

Gogerly, Liz. The Dream of Martin Luther King. 2003. (Days That Shook the World Ser.). (Illus.). 47p. (J). lib. bdg. 28.56 (978-0-7398-6050-2(X)) Raintree.

Gotsch, Patrice. Martin Luther King, Jr: Changing Lives. Arreola, Gil, illus. 2005. 19p. (J). pap. (***978-1-55501-779-8(7))*** Ballard & Tighe Pubs.

Graves, Kerry A. I Have a Dream: The Story Behind Martin Luther King, Jr.'s Most Famous Speech. 2003. (America in Words & Song Ser.). (Illus.). 32p. (gr. 3-5). 23.00 (978-0-7910-7335-3(1) , Chelsea Hse.) Facts On File, Inc.

Harcourt School Publishers Staff. Martin Luther King, Jr. 3rd ed. 2002. (Horizons Ser.). (Illus.). (J). pap. 3.70 (978-0-15-333218-0(2)) Harcourt Schl. Pubs.

Hatt, Christine. Martin Luther King, Jr. 2004. (Judge for Yourself Ser.). (Illus.). 64p. (J). pap. (978-0-8368-5565-4(5)); (gr. 5 up). lib. bdg. 30.00 (978-0-8368-5562-3(0)) Stevens, Gareth Inc. (World Almanac Library).

Isaacs, Sally Senzell. America in the Time of Martin Luther King Jr. 1948 to 1976. (Illus.). 48p. (J). (gr. 4-7). 2002. pap. 8.50 (978-1-57572-939-8(3)); 1999. lib. bdg. (978-1-57572-780-6(3)) Heinemann Library.

Jackson, Garnet N. Martin Luther King, Jr. A Man of Peace. Ford, George Cephas, illus. 2001. (Hello Reader! Ser.). 48p. (J). (978-0-439-20643-3(X)) Scholastic, Inc.

Jakoubek, Robert E. Martin Luther King, Jr. Civil Rights Leader. (Black Americans of Achievement Ser.). (Illus.). 112p. (gr. 6-12). 2005. pap. 13.25 (978-0-7910-8335-2(7)); 2004. 30.00 (978-0-7910-8161-7(3)) Facts On File, Inc. (Chelsea Hse.).

January, Brendan. Martin Luther King, Jr. Minister & Civil Rights Activist. 2000. (Career Biographies Ser.). (Illus.). 128p. (J). (gr. 6-12). 25.00 (978-0-89434-342-1(4) , F405, Ferguson Publishing Co.) Facts On File, Inc.

Jeffrey, Gary. Martin Luther King, Jr: The Life of a Civil Rights Leader. Riley, Terry, illus. 2006. (Graphic Biographies Ser.). 48p. (J). lib. bdg. 29.95 (978-1-4042-0858-2(5)) Rosen Publishing Group, Inc., The.

—Martin Luther King Jr: The Life of a Civil Rights Leader. Forsey, Christopher, illus. 2006. 48p. (J). (978-1-4042-0920-6(4)); pap. (978-1-4042-0921-3(2)) Rosen Publishing Group, Inc., The.

Jeffrey, Laura S. Celebrate Martin Luther King, Jr. , Day. 2006. (Celebrate Holidays Ser.). (Illus.). 104p. (J). lib. bdg. 31.93 (978-0-7660-2492-2(X)) Enslow Pubs., Inc.

Jones, Rob Lloyd. Martin Luther King, Jr. 2006. (Illus.). 62p. (J). pap. (***978-0-439-02299-6(1))*** Scholastic, Inc.

Jones, Rob Lloyd. Martin Luther King, Jr. - Internet Referenced. Le, Rolland Leonard, illus. 2006. 64p. (J). 8.99 (978-0-7945-1260-6(7) , Usborne) EDC Publishing.

Judge for Yourself New Releases: Martin Luther King, Jr.; Mahatma Gandhi, 2 bks. 2004. (Illus.). (J). (gr. 5 up). lib. bdg. 58.53 (978-0-8368-5560-9(4) , World Almanac Library) Stevens, Gareth Inc.

Kaplan, Leslie C. Martin Luther King Jr. Day. 2004. (Library of Holidays). (Illus.). 24p. (J). lib. bdg. 18.75 (978-0-8239-6661-5(5) , PowerKids Pr.) Rosen Publishing Group, Inc., The.

King Farris, Christine. My Brother Martin: A Sister Remembers Growing up with the Rev. Dr. Martin Luther King Jr. Soentpiet, Chris, illus. 2005. 40p. (J). 7.99 (978-0-689-84388-4(7) , Aladdin) Simon & Schuster Children's Publishing.

King, Martin Luther, Jr. I Have a Dream. 2007. (Illus.). 40p. (J). pap. 6.99 (***978-0-590-20517-7(X)***, Scholastic Paperbacks) Scholastic, Inc.

King, Meet Martin Luther, Jr. Meet Martin Luther King Jr. 2004. 32p. (J). 7.95 (978-0-8249-5486-4(6)) Ideals Pubns.

Kupperstein, Joel. Celebrating Martin Luther King Jr Day: Dreaming of Change. 1999. (ps-2). lib. bdg. 10.65 (978-0-613-34121-9(X)) Tandem Library Bks.

—Celebrating Martin Luther King Jr. Day No. 4522: Dreaming of Change. Willingham, Fred, illus. 1999. (Learn to Read Read to Learn Holiday Ser.). 16p. (J). (ps-2). pap. 2.99 (978-1-57471-567-5(4)) Creative Teaching Pr., Inc.

Linney, Susan. Martin Luther King, Jr: With a Discussion of Responsibility. 2004. (Values in Action Ser.). (J). (978-1-59203-069-9(6)) Learning Challenge, Inc.

Lowery, Linda. Martin Luther King Jr Day. 2004. (gr. k-3). lib. bdg. 14.10 (978-0-613-79212-7(2)) Tandem Library Bks.

—Martin Luther King, Jr. Day. Mitchell, Hetty, illus. rev. ed. 2004. (On My Own Holidays Ser.). 48p. (J). (gr. 2-4). lib. bdg. 25.26 (978-1-57505-624-1(0)) Lerner Publishing Group.

Lynch, Emma, et al. Martin Luther King, Jr. 2005. (Illus.). 32p. (J). (978-1-4034-6351-7(4)); pap. (978-1-4034-6365-4(4)) Heinemann Library.

MacMillan, Dianne M. Martin Luther King, Jr. Day. 2nd ed. 2008. (Best Holiday Books Ser.). 48p. (J). (gr. 3-4). lib. bdg. 23.93 (***978-0-7660-3043-5(1))*** Enslow Pubs., Inc.

Malam, John. Martin Luther King. (Illus.). 24p. (978-0-237-51919-3(4) , Evans Brothers, Limited) Evans Publishing Group.

Manheimer, Ann S. Martin Luther King Jr: Dreaming of Equality. 2005. (Trailblazer Biography Ser.). (Illus.). 112p. (J). 30.60 (978-1-57505-627-2(5) , Carolrhoda Bks.) Lerner Publishing Group.

Mara, Wil. Martin Luther King, Jr. (Rookie Biographies Ser.). (Illus.). 32p. (J). (gr. 1-2). 2003. pap. 4.95 (978-0-516-27333-4(7)); 2002. 20.50 (978-0-516-22517-3(0)) Scholastic Library Publishing. (Children's Pr.).

—Martin Luther King, Jr. 2002. (gr. 3-6). lib. bdg. 12.95 (978-0-613-59518-6(1)) Tandem Library Bks.

Marsh, Carole. Martin Luther King, Jr. 2002. (One Thousand Readers Ser.). (Illus.). 12p. (J). (gr. k-4). 2.95 (978-0-635-01477-1(7) , 14777) Gallopade International.

—Martin Luther King, Jr. An Ohio Experience Reader. 2001. (J). (gr. k-5). pap. 1.95 (978-0-635-00439-0(9)) Gallopade International.

—The Virginia Reader: Martin Luther King, Jr. 2001. (Virginia Experience! Ser.). 12p. (J). (gr. k-5). pap. 2.95 (978-0-635-00364-5(3)) Gallopade International.

Martin Luther King, Jr. 2001. (Childhood of Famous Americans Ser.). (J). (gr. 1-3). pap. 39.95 incl. audio Blackstone Audio, Inc.

Martin Luther King, Jr. (Guided Reading Levels Ser.). (Illus.). 4.76 (978-0-7362-0962-5(X)) Hampton-Brown Bks.

Martin Luther King, Jr, Vol. 3. 2005. (First Biographies Ser.). (YA). (gr. k-3). (978-0-7368-8112-8(3) , Pebble Bks.) Capstone Pr., Inc.

Martin Luther King, Jr. (Compass Point Early Biographies Ser.). 32p. (J). 7.95 (978-0-7565-1177-7(1)) Compass Point Bks.

Martin Luther King, Jr, 6 vols. (gr. k-2). 28.95 (978-0-7368-8136-4(0)); (gr. 2-5). 36.95 (978-0-7368-4562-5(3)) Red Brick Learning.

Martin Luther King Jr. Una vida de determinacion (A Life of Determination) 2007. (J). pap. 5.95 (978-0-8225-6556-7(0) , Ediciones Lerner) Lerner Publishing Group.

Martin Luther King, Jr Day, 6 vols. (gr. k-2). 28.95 (978-0-7368-8751-9(2)) Red Brick Learning.

Martin Lutheran King Jr. 2002. (Illus.). (J). pap. (978-0-7398-5935-3(8)) Steck-Vaughn.

Martin's Big Words. 2004. pap. 38.75 incl. audio compact disk (978-1-55592-637-3(1)); pap. 32.75 incl. audio (978-1-55592-367-9(4)); pap. 14.95 incl. audio (978-1-55592-169-9(8)); (J). 29.95 incl. cd-rom (978-1-55592-133-0(7)); (J). 24.95 incl. audio (978-1-55592-092-0(6)) Weston Woods Studios, Inc.

Marx, David F. Martin Luther King, Jr. Day: Holidays. 2001. (Rookie Read-About Holidays Ser.). (Illus.). 32p. (J). (gr. 1-2). 19.50 (978-0-516-22211-0(2) , Children's Pr.) Scholastic Library Publishing.

Marzollo, Jean. Feliz Cumpleaños, Martin Luther King. Pinkney, J. Brian, illus. 2003. (SPA.). 32p. (J). (ps-2). pap. 5.99 (978-0-590-47507-5(X) , SO5483, Scholastic en Espanol) Scholastic, Inc.

—Happy Birthday, Martin Luther King. Pinkney, J., illus. 2006. 32p. (J). pap. 5.99 (978-0-439-78224-1(4) , Scholastic Paperbacks) Scholastic, Inc.

—Happy Birthday, Martin Luther King. Pinkney, J. Brian, illus. 2000. (J). (ps-3). reprint ed. pap. 5.99 (978-0-439-09942-4(0)) Scholastic, Inc.

Mattern, Joanne. Coretta Scott King: Civil Rights Activist. 2003. (Reading Power Ser.). (Illus.). 24p. (J). lib. bdg. 17.25 (978-0-8239-6504-5(X) , PowerKids Pr.) Rosen Publishing Group, Inc., The.

McKissack, Patricia C. & McKissack, Fredrick L. Martin Luther King, Jr. Man of Peace. rev. ed. 2001. (Great African Americans Ser.). (Illus.). 32p. (J). (gr. 1-4). lib. bdg. 18.60 (978-0-7660-1678-1(1)) Enslow Pubs., Inc.

McLeese, Don. Martin Luther King, Jr. 2002. (Illus.). 24p. (J). lib. bdg. 20.64 (978-1-58952-286-2(9)) Rourke Publishing, LLC.

McNeil, Niki, et al. HOCPP 1055 Martin Luther King Jr. 2006. spiral bd. 18.50 (***978-1-60308-055-2(4))*** In the Hands of a Child.

McPherson, Stephanie Sammartino. Coretta Scott King. 2007. (J). lib. bdg. (***978-0-8225-7156-8(0))*** Twenty First Century Bks.

Medearis, Angela Shelf. Dare to Dream: Coretta Scott King & the Civil Rights Movement. Rich, Anna, illus. 1999. (Rainbow Biography Ser.). 64p. (J). (gr. 3-7). pap. 4.99 (978-0-14-130202-7(X) , Puffin) Penguin Group (USA) Inc.

—Dare to Dream: Coretta Scott King & the Civil Rights Movement. 1999. (gr. 3-6). lib. bdg. 13.00 (978-0-613-14663-0(8)) Tandem Library Bks.

Michelson, Richard. As Good as Anybody. 2008. 40p. (J). (gr. 1-5). lib. bdg. 19.99 (***978-0-375-93335-6(2)***, Knopf Bks. for Young Readers) Random Hse. Children's Bks.

Mir Tamim Ansary. Martin Luther King Jr. Day. 2nd ed. 2006. (Illus.). 32p. (J). pap. (***978-1-4034-8902-9(5))*** Heinemann Library.

Murcia, Rebecca Thatcher. The Civil Rights Movement. 2005. (Monumental Milestones Ser.). (Illus.). 48p. (YA). (ps-7). lib. bdg. (978-1-58415-401-3(2)) Mitchell Lane Pubs., Inc.

Murray, Julie. Martin Luther King, Jr. Day. 2005. (Buddy Book Ser.). (Illus.). 24p. (J). (gr. k-4). lib. bdg. 21.35 (978-1-59197-589-2(1)) ABDO Publishing Co.

Myers, Walter Dean. I've Seen the Promised Land: The Life of Dr. Martin Luther King, Jr. Jenkins, Leonard, illus. 2004. 40p. (J). (gr. k-3). lib. bdg. 17.89 (978-0-06-027704-8(1)) HarperCollins Pubs.

—I've Seen the Promised Land: The Life of Dr. Martin Luther King, Jr. Jenkins, Leonard, tr. Jenkins, Leonard, illus. 2004. 40p. (J). (gr. k-3). 16.99 (978-0-06-027703-1(3)) HarperCollins Pubs.

Nelson, Robin. Martin Luther King, Jr. Day. 2003. (First Step Nonfiction Ser.). (Illus.). 24p. (J). (gr. k-2). lib. bdg. 18.60 (978-0-8225-1282-0(3)) Lerner Publishing Group.

Nettleton, Pamela Hill. Martin Luther King, Jr. Yesh, Jeff, illus. 2004. (Biographies Ser.). 24p. (C). (gr. k-3). 22.60 (978-1-4048-0188-2(X)) Picture Window Bks.

Nobleman, Marc Tyler. Martin Luther King, Jr. Day. 2004. (Let's See Ser.). (Illus.). 24p. (J). (gr. 1-3). lib. bdg. 19.93 (978-0-7565-0646-9(8)) Compass Point Bks.

Pastan, Amy. Martin Luther King, Jr. A Photographic Story of a Life. 2004. (Biography Ser.). (Illus.). 128p. (J). 14.99 (978-0-7566-0491-2(5)); (YA). (gr. 8). pap. 4.99 (978-0-7566-0342-7(0)) Dorling Kindersley Publishing, Inc.

Patrick, Denise Lewis. A Lesson for Martin Luther King, Jr. Pate, Rodney S., illus. 2003. (Ready-to-Read Ser.). 32p. (J). pap. 3.99 (978-0-689-85397-5(1) , Aladdin) Simon & Schuster Children's Publishing.

—Lesson for Martin Luther King Jr. 2003. (gr. k-3). lib. bdg. 11.80 (978-0-613-73360-1(6)) Tandem Library Bks.

Pettit, Jayne. Martin Luther King, Jr. A Man with a Dream. 2001. (Book Report Biographies Ser.). (Illus.). 100p. (J). (gr. 6-8). pap. 6.95 (978-0-531-15553-0(6) , Watts, Franklin) Scholastic Library Publishing.

J K L

—Martin Luther King, Jr: A Man with A Dream. 2001. (gr. 5-8). lib. bdg. 15.25 (978-0-613-34352-7(2)) Tandem Library Bks.

Picture Window Books, contrib. by. Martin Luther King Jr. (Biographies Ser.). 32p. (J). pap. 7.95 (978-1-4048-0461-6(7)) Picture Window Bks.

Pierce, Alan. Assasination of Martin Luther King, Jr. 2005. (American Moments Set Ii Ser.). (Illus.). 48p. (J). (gr. 4-8). lib. bdg. 25.65 (978-1-59197-727-8(4) , ABDO & Daughters) ABDO Publishing Co.

Pingry, Patricia A. The Story of Coretta Scott King. Walker, Steven, illus. 2007. 26p. (J). (ps-k). bds. 6.99 (***978-0-8249-6717-8(8)*** , Candy Cane Pr.) Ideals Pubns.

Press, Petra. Coretta Scott King: An Unauthorized Biography. 1999. (Profiles Ser.). (Illus.). 56p. (J). (gr. 4-6). lib. bdg. 24.22 (978-1-57572-496-6(0)) Heinemann Library.

Price Hossell, Karen. I Have a Dream. 2005. (Illus.). 48p. (J). (978-1-4034-6811-6(7)); pap. (978-1-4034-6816-1(8)) Heinemann Library.

Raatma, Lucia. Martin Luther King, Jr. 2001. (Compass Point Early Biographies Ser.). (Illus.). 32p. (J). (gr. 2 up). lib. bdg. 21.26 (978-0-7565-0114-3(8)) Compass Point Bks.

Rappaport, Doreen. Martin's Big Words: The Life of Dr. Martin Luther King Jr. Collier, Bryan, illus. 2001. 40p. (gr. k-4). 15.99 (978-0-7868-0714-7(8)) Hyperion Bks. for Children.

Rappaport, Doreen. Martin's Big Words: The Life of Dr. Martin Luther King Jr. Collier, Bryan, illus. rev. ed. 2007. 40p. (ps-17). pap. 6.99 (***978-1-4231-0635-7(0)*** , Jump at the Sun) Hyperion Bks. for Children.

Rau, Dana Meachen. Martin Luther King, Jr. Day. 2001. (True Holiday Bks.). (Illus.). 48p. (J). (gr. 3-5). 25.00 (978-0-516-22246-2(5) , Children's Pr.) Scholastic Library Publishing.

—Martin Luther King, Jr. Day. 2001. (gr. 3-6). lib. bdg. 15.25 (978-0-613-51661-7(3)) Tandem Library Bks.

Reverend Martin Luther King, Jr. 1999. (SmartReader Ser.). (J). Level 1. pap., tchr. ed. 19.95 incl. audio (978-0-7887-0760-5(4) , 79347T3); Level 2. pap., tchr. ed. 19.95 incl. audio (978-0-7887-0122-1(3) , 79310T3) Recorded Bks., LLC.

Ringgold, Faith. My Dream of Martin Luther King. Ringgold, Faith, illus. 1998. (Dragonfly Bks.). (Illus.). 32p. (J). (gr. k-3). pap. 7.99 (978-0-517-88577-2(8) , Dragonfly Bks.) Random Hse. Children's Bks.

—My Dream of Martin Luther King. Ringgold, Faith, illus. 1998. (Illus.). (J). (ps-ps). lib. bdg. 16.45 (978-0-613-11892-7(8)) Tandem Library Bks.

Riordan, James. The Story of Martin Luther King. 2001. (Illus.). 48p. (J). lib. bdg. 24.25 (978-1-930643-24-6(1)) Chrysalis Education.

Rivera, Sheila. Martin Luther King Jr. A Life of Determination. 2006. (Pull Ahead Books). (Illus.). 32p. (J). 22.60 (978-0-8225-3477-8(0) , Lerner Pubns.) Lerner Publishing Group.

—Martin Luther King, Jr: A Life of Determination. 2006. (Illus.). 32p. (J). pap. 5.95 (978-0-8225-5697-8(9)) Lerner Publishing Group.

Roop, Peter & Roop, Connie. Martin Luther King, Jr., Set 1. 2002. (Lives & Times Ser.). (Illus.). 24p. (J). (gr. k-3). pap. 6.50 (978-1-58810-346-8(3) , 91106) Heinemann Library.

Ruffin, Frances E. Martin Luther King & the March on Washington. Marchesi, Stephen, illus. 2000. (All Aboard Reading Ser.). 48p. (J). (gr. 1-3). pap. 3.99 (978-0-448-42421-7(5) , Grosset & Dunlap) Penguin Group (USA) Inc.

—Martin Luther King & the March on Washington. 2001. (gr. k-3). lib. bdg. 11.80 (978-0-613-31457-2(3)) Tandem Library Bks.

Rustad, Martha E. H. Martin Luther King, Jr: A Life of Fairness. 2007. (Illus.). 24p. (J). lib. bdg. 19.95 (978-1-60014-090-7(4)) Bellwether Media.

Santella, Andrew. Martin Luther King Jr. Civil Rights Leader & Nobel Prize Winner. 2003. (Journey to Freedom). (Illus.). 40p. (J). (gr. 3-7). 28.50 (978-1-56766-539-0(X)) Child's World, Inc.

Schaefer, Lola M. Martin Luther King, Jr. Saunders-Smith, Gail, ed. 1998. (Famous Americans Ser.). (Illus.). 24p. (J). (gr. k-1). lib. bdg. 15.93 (978-0-7368-0111-9(1) , Pebble Bks.) Capstone Pr., Inc.

Schraff, Anne E. Martin Luther King, JR: We Shall Overcome. 2005. (African-American Biography Library). (Illus.). 128p. (J). (gr. 6-13). lib. bdg. 31.93 (978-0-7660-1774-0(5)) Enslow Pubs., Inc.

Schuldt, Lori Meek. Martin Luther King, Jr: With Profiles of Mohandas K. Gandhi & Nelson Mandela. 2006. (Biographical Connections Ser.). (Illus.). 112p. (J). (978-0-7166-1822-5(2)) World Bk., Inc.

Schulke, Flip. Martin Luther King, Jr. A Documentary... Montgomery to Memphis. 1999. (Illus.). 224p. (gr. 8 up). pap. 17.95 (978-0-393-07492-5(7)) Norton, W. W. & Co., Inc.

Shah, Ruchir, ed. Martin Luther King, Jr. 2007. (YA). 6.95 (***978-0-9795887-0-9(7)***) EZ Comics.

Sweeney, Alyse. Easy Reader Biographies: Martin Luther King, Jr: A Man with a Dream. 2007. 16p. pap. 2.99 (***978-0-439-77419-2(5)*** , Teaching Resources) Scholastic, Inc.

Trailblazers of the Modern World: Louis Armstrong; Anne Frank; Martin Luther King, Jr.; Theodore Roosevelt; Gloria Steinem; The Wright Brothers, 6 bks. 2003. (Illus.). (J). (gr. 5 up). lib. bdg. 175.60 (978-0-8368-5088-8(2) , World Almanac Library) Stevens, Gareth Inc.

Trueit, Trudi Strain. Martin Luther King, Jr. Day. 2007. (Holidays, Festivals, & Celebrations Ser.). 32p. (J). (gr. k-4). 22.79 (***978-1-59296-814-5(7)***) Child's World, Inc.

—Martin Luther King Jr. Day. 2006. (Rookie Read-About Holidays Ser.). (Illus.). 31p. (J). (978-0-531-12459-8(2)) Children's Pr., Ltd.

—Martin Luther King Jr Day. rev. ed. 2006. (Rookie Read-About Holidays Ser.). (Illus.). 32p. (J). (gr. 1-2). pap. 5.95 (978-0-531-11840-5(1) , Children's Pr.) Scholastic Library Publishing.

Uschan, Michael V. Martin Luther King, Jr. 2003. (Heroes & Villains Ser.). (Illus.). 112p. (J). 29.95 (978-1-59018-257-4(X) , Lucent Bks.) Thomson Gale.

Valerie Schloredt & Pam Brown. Martin Luther King, Jr. Pionero de los derechos Civiles. 2005. (Pacificadores Mundiales Ser.). (gr. 5-7). 28.70 (978-1-4103-0506-0(6) , Blackbirch Pr., Inc.) Thomson Gale.

Vaughn, Wally G. & Davis, Mattie Campbell, eds. The Selma Campaign, 1963-1965: The Decisive Battle of the Civil Rights Movement. 2006. 261p. pap. 19.95 (978-0-912469-44-7(7)) Majority Pr., Inc., The.

Walker, Pamela. Martin Luther King, Jr. 2001. (Real People Ser.). (Illus.). 24p. (J). (ps-2). 17.00 (978-0-516-23436-6(6)); pap. 4.95 (978-0-516-23590-5(7)) Scholastic Library Publishing. (Children's Pr.).

—Martin Luther King, Jr. 2001. (gr. k-3). lib. bdg. 12.95 (978-0-613-58854-6(1)) Tandem Library Bks.

Waxman, Laura Hamilton. Coretta Scott King. 2008. (History Maker Biographies Ser.). (J). lib. bdg. 26.60 (***978-0-8225-7168-1(4)*** , Lerner Pubns.) Lerner Publishing Group.

Who Was Martin Luther King, Jr? (Guided Reading Levels Ser.). 28.56 (978-0-7362-1055-3(5)) Hampton-Brown Bks.

Winget, Mary. Martin Luther King, Jr. 2003. (History Maker Bios Ser.). (Illus.). 47p. (J). 26.60 (978-0-8225-4674-0(4) , Lerner Pubns.) Lerner Publishing Group.

—Martin Luther King, Jr. 2004. (History Maker Bios Ser.). (Illus.). 48p. (J). pap. (978-0-8225-4804-1(6) , Lerner Pubns.) Lerner Publishing Group.

KING PHILIP'S WAR, 1675-1676—FICTION

Jacobs, Paul S. James Printer: A Novel of King Philip's War. 2000. 224p. (J). (gr. 4-7). 4.50 (978-0-590-97541-4(2)) Scholastic, Inc.

KINGFISHERS

Adams, Pam. Kingfisher. 1999. (Pocket Pals Ser.). (Illus.). 12p. (J). (ps-1). bds. 1.99 (978-0-85953-863-3(X)) Child's Play-International.

KINGFISHERS—FICTION

Burns, Dal. The Kookaburra & Other Stories. 2007. (ENG.). 76p. per. 14.95 (***978-1-4241-1770-3(4)***) PublishAmerica, Inc.

KINGS, QUEENS, RULERS, ETC.

see also Dictators; Queens

also names of countries with the subdivision Kings and Rulers, e.g. Great Britain—Kings and Rulers; etc.; also names of individual kings and rulers, e.g. Elizabeth 2nd, Queen of Great Britain; etc.

African Kings & Queens. 2000. (My Ancestors—My Heroes Ser.: Vol. 1). (J). (gr. 3-4). (978-1-893091-00-9(7)) Parker Publishing Co.

Aller, Susan Bivin. Sitting Bull. 2004. (History Maker Bios Ser.). (J). pap. 6.95 (978-0-8225-2072-6(9)) Lerner Publishing Group.

—Sitting Bull. Parlin, Tim, tr. Parlin, Tim, illus. 2004. (History Maker Bios Ser.). 47p. (J). 26.60 (978-0-8225-0700-0(5) , Carolrhoda Bks.) Lerner Publishing Group.

Bankston, John. The Life & Times of Alexander the Great. 2004. (Biography of Ancient Civilizations Ser.). (Illus.). 48p. (J). lib. bdg. (978-1-58415-235-4(4)) Mitchell Lane Pubs., Inc.

Barth, Linda. Mohammed Reza Pahlavi. 2002. (Major World Leaders Ser.). (Illus.). 112p. (J). (gr. 6-12). 30.00 (978-0-7910-6948-6(6) , Chelsea Hse.) Facts On File, Inc.

Barton-Wood, Sara. Queen Elizabeth II: Monarch of Our Times. 2001. (Famous Lives Ser.). (Illus.). 48p. (J). (gr. 4-6). lib. bdg. 27.12 (978-0-7398-4430-4(X)) Raintree.

Behnke, Alison. The Conquests of Alexander the Great. 2007. (Pivotal Moments in History Ser.). 160p. (YA). (gr. 9-12). lib. bdg. 38.60 (978-0-8225-5920-7(X) , Twenty-First Century Bks.) Lerner Publishing Group.

Bhote, Themina. Charlemagne: Life & Times of an Early Medieval Emperor. 2004. (Medieval Leaders Ser.). (Illus.). 112p. (J). lib. bdg. 31.95 (978-1-4042-0161-3(0)) Rosen Publishing Group, Inc., The.

Briscoe, Diana. King Tut: Tales from the Tomb. 2002. (High Five Reading Ser.). (Illus.). 48p. (J). (gr. 3-4). lib. bdg. 22.60 (978-0-7368-9553-8(1) , Capstone High-Interest Bks.); pap. (978-0-7368-9531-6(0)) Capstone Pr., Inc.

Burleigh, Robert. Napoleon: The Story of the Little Corporal. 2007. (Illus.). 48p. (J). (gr. 4-7). 18.95 (978-0-8109-1378-3(X) , Abrams Bks. for Young Readers) Abrams, Harry N., Inc.

Can't You Make Them Behave, King George? 2002. (978-1-56137-402-1(4)) Novel Units, Inc.

Can't You Make Them Behave, King George? 2004. 24.95 incl. audio (978-1-56008-171-5(6)); 29.95 incl. cd-rom (978-1-55592-378-5(X)); (J). pap. 14.95 incl. audio (978-1-56008-172-2(4)); (J). pap. 18.95 incl. audio compact disk (978-1-55592-377-8(1)); (J). pap. 18.95 incl. audio compact disk (978-1-55592-380-8(1)); (J). pap. 38.75 incl. audio compact disk (978-1-55592-379-2(8)); (J). pap. 38.75 incl. audio compact disk (978-1-55592-381-5(X)); (J). pap. 32.75 incl. audio (978-1-55592-350-1(X)) Weston Woods Studios, Inc.

Chrisp, Peter, contrib. by. Alexander the Great. 2000. (Illus.). 48p. (YA). 14.95 (978-0-7894-6109-4(9)) Dorling Kindersley Publishing, Inc.

Clark, Connie. Who in the World Was the Unready King? The Story of Ethelred. Mickle, Jed, illus. 2005. 40p. (J). (gr. 2 up). pap. 9.50 (978-0-9728603-7-6(1) , BIO-ETH) Peace Hill Pr.

Collier, James Lincoln. The Tecumseh You Never Knew. Copeland, Greg, illus. 2004. (You Never Knew Ser.). (J). 25.50 (978-0-516-24426-6(4) , Children's Pr.) Scholastic Library Publishing.

Cotter, Charis. Kids Who Rule: The Remarkable Lives of Five Child Monarchs. 2007. (Illus.). 120p. (J). (gr. 4-6). 24.95 (***978-1-55451-062-7(7)***); pap. 14.95 (***978-1-55451-061-0(9)***) Annick Pr., Ltd. CAN. *Dist:* Firefly Bks., Ltd.

Daning, Tom. Roman Mythology: Romulus & Remus. 2007. (Jr. Graphic Mythologies Ser.). (Illus.). 24p. (J). (978-1-4042-2340-0(1)); pap. (978-1-4042-2150-5(6)); (gr. 2-6). lib. bdg. 21.25 (978-1-4042-3397-3(0)) Rosen Publishing Group, Inc., The. (PowerKids Pr.).

Darraj, Susan Muaddi. Queen Noor. 2004. (Women in Politics Ser.). (Illus.). 120p. 30.00 (978-0-7910-7736-8(5)); 116p. pap. 30.00 (978-0-7910-8002-3(1)) Facts On File, Inc. (Chelsea Hse.).

Davenport, John C. Saladin. 2003. (Ancient World Leaders Ser.). (Illus.). 112p. (gr. 6-12). 30.00 (978-0-7910-7223-3(1) , Chelsea Hse.) Facts On File, Inc.

Davis, Kenneth C. Don't Know Much about the Kings & Queens of England. Date not set. 48p. (J). (gr. 1-4). pap. 5.99 (978-0-06-446229-7(3)) HarperCollins Pubs.

—Don't Know Much about the Kings & Queens of England. Schindler, S. D., illus. 2002. (Don't Know Much About Ser.: No. 3). 48p. (J). (gr. 1-4). 15.89 (978-0-06-028612-5(1)) HarperCollins Pubs.

Diouf, Sylviane A. Kings & Queens of Central Africa. 2000. (Kings & Queens of Africa Ser.). (Illus.). 64p. (J). (gr. 5-7). 25.50 (978-0-531-20372-9(7) , Watts, Franklin) Scholastic Library Publishing.

—Kings & Queens of East Africa. (Watts Library). (Illus.). 64p. (J). (gr. 5-7). 2001. pap. 8.95 (978-0-531-16534-8(5)); 2000. 25.50 (978-0-531-20373-6(5)) Scholastic Library Publishing. (Watts, Franklin).

—Kings & Queens of Southern Africa. (Watts Library). (Illus.). 64p. (J). (gr. 5-7). 2001. pap. 8.95 (978-0-531-16535-5(3)); 2000. 25.50 (978-0-531-20374-3(3)) Scholastic Library Publishing. (Watts, Franklin).

—Kings & Queens of Southern Africa. 2000. (gr. 3-6). lib. bdg. 17.60 (978-0-613-54600-3(8)) Tandem Library Bks.

—Kings & Queens of West Africa. (Watts Library). (Illus.). 64p. (J). (gr. 5-7). 2001. pap. 8.95 (978-0-531-16536-2(1)); 2000. 25.50 (978-0-531-20375-0(1)) Scholastic Library Publishing. (Watts, Franklin).

Eastwood, Kay. Medieval Society. 2003. (Medieval World Ser.). (Illus.). 32p. (J). (gr. 5). (978-0-7787-1345-6(8)); pap. (978-0-7787-1377-7(6)) Crabtree Publishing Co.

Emperor Ashoka of India: What Makes a Ruler Legitimate? (NCHS) (YA). (gr. 6-9). spiral bd., tchr.'s planning gde. ed. 11.50 (978-0-382-44467-8(1)) Cobblestone Publishing Co.

Evento, Susan. Sitting Bull. 2005. (Rookie Biographies Ser.). (Illus.). 32p. (J). (gr. 1-2). pap. 4.95 (978-0-516-25829-4(X) , Children's Pr.) Scholastic Library Publishing.

Evento, Susan & Vargus, Nanci Reginelli. Sitting Bull. 2004. (Rookie Biographies Ser.). (J). 20.50 (978-0-516-21719-2(4) , Children's Pr.) Scholastic Library Publishing.

Fitterer, C. Ann. Tecumseh: Chief of the Shawnee. 2002. (Spirit of America: Our People Ser.). (Illus.). 32p. (J). (gr. 2-6). 27.07 (978-1-56766-168-2(8)) Child's World, Inc.

Ford, Nick. Henry VIII: The King, His Six Wives & His Court. 2004. (Leaders of the Middle Ages Ser.). (Illus.). 112p. (YA). lib. bdg. 31.95 (978-1-4042-0163-7(7)) Rosen Publishing Group, Inc., The.

Forsyth, Fiona. Augustus: The First Emperor. 2003. (Leaders of Ancient Rome Ser.). (Illus.). 112p. (YA). (gr. 5-8). lib. bdg. 31.95 (978-0-8239-3588-8(4) , Rosen Central) Rosen Publishing Group, Inc., The.

Gaines, Ann Graham. King George III. 2000. (Revolutionary War Leaders Ser.). (Illus.). 80p. (J). (gr. 4-7). pap. 27.50 (978-0-7910-6136-7(1) , Chelsea Hse.) Facts On File, Inc.

Greenblatt, Miriam. Augustus & Imperial Rome. 1999. (Rulers & Their Times Ser.). (Illus.). 80p. (J). (gr. 6 up). lib. bdg. 29.93 (978-0-7614-0912-0(2) , Benchmark Bks.) Cavendish, Marshall Corp.

—Napoleon Bonaparte & Imperial France. 2005. (Rulers & Their Times Ser.). (Illus.). 96p. (J). (gr. 3-7). lib. bdg. (978-0-7614-1837-5(7) , Benchmark Bks.) Cavendish, Marshall Corp.

—Rulers & Their Times - Group 1, 4 bks., Set. Incl. Alexander the Great & Ancient Greece. (YA). lib. bdg. 29.93 (978-0-7614-0913-7(0)); Augustus & Imperial Rome. (J). lib. bdg. 29.93 (978-0-7614-0912-0(2)); Hatshepsut & Ancient Egypt. (YA). lib. bdg. 29.93 (978-0-7614-0911-3(4)); Peter the Great & Tsarist Russia. (J). lib. bdg. 29.93 (978-0-7614-0914-4(9)); 80p. (gr. 6 up). 1999. (Illus.). 1999. Set lib. bdg. 119.71 (978-0-7614-0910-6(6) , Benchmark Bks.) Cavendish, Marshall Corp.

—Suleyman the Magnificent & the Ottoman Empire. 2002. (Rulers & Their Times Ser.). (Illus.). 80p. (J). (gr. 8-12). 29.93 (978-0-7614-1489-6(4) , Benchmark Bks.) Cavendish, Marshall Corp.

Havelin, Kate. Queen Elizabeth I. 2002. (Biography Ser.). (Illus.). 112p. (J). (gr. 6-12). lib. bdg. 27.93 (978-0-8225-0029-2(9) , Lerner Pubns.) Lerner Publishing Group.

Hayhurst, Chris. Toro Sentado: Jefe Sioux. 2003. (ENG & SPA.). (J). pap. (978-0-8239-4238-1(4)) Rosen Publishing Group, Inc., The.

Haywood, John. How We Lived: Leadership & Society. 2006. (Illus.). 64p. pap., pap. 8.99 (978-1-84476-082-4(0) , Southwater) Anness Publishing GBR. *Dist:* National Bk. Network.

Henderson, Harry. The Age of Napoleon. 1998. (Illus.). 112p. (YA). (gr. 4-12). 27.45 (978-1-56006-319-3(X) , LML00902-177711, Lucent Bks.) Thomson Gale.

Heyer, Carol, illus. & retold by. Excalibur. Heyer, Carol, retold by. (978-1-59093-022-9(3) , Eager Minds Pr.) Warehousing & Fulfillment Specialists, LLC (WFS, LLC).

Holub, Joan. Elizabeth & the Royal Pony: Based on a True Story of Elizabeth I of England. Aleshina, Nonna, illus. 2007. (Ready-To-Read Ser.). (J). (***978-1-4287-2005-3(7)*** , Aladdin) Simon & Schuster Children's Publishing.

Itzkowitz, Norman. Vlad the Impaler: The Real Count Dracula. 2007. (Wicked History Ser.). (Illus.). 128p. (YA). (gr. 8-12). lib. bdg. 30.00 (***978-0-531-12599-1(8)*** , Watts, Franklin) Scholastic Library Publishing.

Jeffrey, Gary & Petty, Kate. Sitting Bull: The Life of a Lakota Sioux Chief. 2005. (Graphic Nonfiction Ser.). (Illus.). 48p. (J). (gr. 4-6). lib. bdg. 26.50 (978-1-4042-0247-4(1)) Rosen Publishing Group, Inc., The.

Jiang, Cheng A. Empress of China Zhongguo De Nu Huangdi: Wu Ze Tian. Xu, De Y., illus. 1998. 32p. (J). (gr. 3-6). 14.95 (978-1-878217-32-5(1)); pap. 7.95 (978-1-878217-31-8(3)) Victory Pr.

Kings & Queens. 2002. (History Makers Ser.). 32p. (J). 9.95 (978-0-7525-7827-9(8)) Parragon, Inc.

Kings & Queens of Scotland. 2002. 192p. 3.95 (978-1-85534-915-5(9)) Geddes & Grosset, Ltd. GBR. *Dist:* CPG Publishing, Inc.

Knox, Barbara. Forbidden City: China's Imperial Palace. 2006. (Castles, Palaces, & Tombs Ser.). (Illus.). 32p. (J). lib. bdg. 25.27 (978-1-59716-070-4(9) , 1251394) Bearport Publishing Co., Inc.

Koestler-Grack, Rachel A. Chief John Ross. 2004. (Illus.). 32p. (J). pap. 7.50 (978-1-4034-5007-4(2)); lib. bdg. 24.22 (978-1-4034-5000-5(5)) Heinemann Library.

—Chief Joseph. 2004. (Illus.). 32p. (J). pap. 7.50 (978-1-4034-5008-1(0)); lib. bdg. 24.22 (978-1-4034-5001-2(3)) Heinemann Library.

—Tecumseh 1768-1813. 2002. (American Indian Biographies Ser.). (Illus.). 32p. (J). (gr. 3-4). lib. bdg. 23.93 (978-0-7368-1212-2(1) , Blue Earth Bks.) Capstone Pr., Inc.

Kramer, Ann. Eleanor of Aquitane: The Queen Who Rode off to Battle. 2006. (World History Biographies Ser.). (Illus.). 64p. (J). (gr. 3-7). 17.95 (978-0-7922-5895-7(9)); lib. bdg. 27.90 (978-0-7922-5896-4(7)) National Geographic Society. (National Geographic Children's Bks.).

Kucharczyk, Emily Rose. Wilma Mankiller: Native American Leader. 2002. (Famous Women Juniors Ser.). (Illus.). 32p. (J). (gr. 3-5). 23.70 (978-1-56711-593-2(4) , Blackbirch Pr., Inc.) Thomson Gale.

Kudalis, Eric. The Royal Mummies: Remains from Ancient Egypt. 2002. (Mummies Ser.). (Illus.). 32p. (J). (gr. 3-4). lib. bdg. 21.26 (978-0-7368-1308-2(X) , Capstone High-Interest Bks.) Capstone Pr., Inc.

Lace, William W. Elizabeth I & Her Court. 2002. (Lucent Library of Historical Eras. Elizabethan England Library). (Illus.). 112p. (J). 28.70 (978-1-59018-098-3(4) , Lucent Bks.) Thomson Gale.

Landon, Margaret. Anna & the King. 1999. (Illus.). (J). 11.60 (978-0-606-21838-2(6)); 2000. (gr. 3-6). lib. bdg. 12.95 (978-0-613-24213-4(0)) Tandem Library Bks.

Leaders of Ancient Rome, 6 bks. Incl. Augustus : The First Emperor. Forsyth, Fiona. lib. bdg. 31.95 (978-0-8239-3588-8(4)); Cicero : Defender of the Republic. Forsyth, Fiona. lib. bdg. 31.95 (978-0-8239-3590-1(6)); Constantine : Ruler of Christian Rome. Morgan, Julian. lib. bdg. 31.95 (978-0-8239-3592-5(2)); Hadrian : Consolidating the Empire. Morgan, Julian. lib. bdg. 31.95 (978-0-8239-3593-2(0)); Julius Caesar : Conqueror & Dictator. Thorne, James. lib. bdg. 31.95 (978-0-8239-3595-6(7)); Nero : Destroyer of Rome. Morgan, Julian. lib. bdg. 31.95 (978-0-8239-3596-3(5)); 112p. (YA). (gr. 5-8). 2003. (Illus.). 2002. Set lib. bdg. 191.70 (978-0-8239-3887-2(5) , Rosen Central) Rosen Publishing Group, Inc., The.

Locke, Ian. Magnificent Monarchs. Rowe, Alan, illus. 2003. 63p. (J). pap. 3.99 (978-0-330-37496-5(6) , Pan) Pan Macmillan GBR. *Dist:* Trafalgar Square Publishing.

Lunge-Larsen, Lise. Race of Birkebeiners. Azarian, Mary, illus. 2007. 32p. (J). (gr. k). 6.95 (***978-0-618-91599-6(0)***) Houghton Mifflin Co. Trade & Reference Div.

Madame M. Trauma Queens/Trauma Kings. l.t. ed. 2003. (Madame M Presents:). (Illus.). 68p. (YA). per. 15.95 (978-0-9704159-3-6(1) , 0970415931) Creepy Little Productions.

Marilyn Tower Oliver. Henry VIII. 2004. (Importance of Ser.). (Illus.). 112p. (J). 32.45 (978-1-59018-424-0(6)) Thomson Gale.

Mayer, Cassie. Tecumseh. 2007. (J). (***978-1-4034-9975-2(6)***); pap. (***978-1-4034-9984-4(5)***) Heinemann Library.

Meltzer, Milton. Ten Kings: And the Worlds They Rule. Andersen, Bethanne, illus. 2002. 144p. (J). (gr. 3-7). pap. 21.95 (978-0-439-31293-6(0) , Orchard Bks.) Scholastic, Inc.

—Ten Queens: Portraits of Women of Power. Andersen, Bethanne, illus. 2003. 144p. (J). (gr. 7-12). reprint ed. pap. 14.99 (978-0-525-47158-5(8) , Dutton Juvenile) Penguin Group (USA) Inc.

—Ten Queens: Portraits of Women of Power. 2004. (gr. 7-12). lib. bdg. 24.60 (978-0-613-72581-1(6)) Tandem Library Bks.

Monroe, Judy. Chief Red Cloud 1822-1909. 2004. (American Indian Biographies Ser.). (Illus.). 32p. (J). (gr. 3-4). lib. bdg. 23.93 (978-0-7368-2445-3(6) , Blue Earth Bks.) Capstone Pr., Inc.

Nardo, Don. King Arthur. 2002. (Heroes & Villains Ser.). (Illus.). 112p. (J). (gr. 6). 27.45 (978-1-56006-948-5(1) , Lucent Bks.) Thomson Gale.

—Women Leaders of Nations. 1998. (History Makers Ser.). (Illus.). 112p. (YA). (gr. 7-10). 27.45 (978-1-56006-397-1(1) , Lucent Bks.) Thomson Gale.

Pancella, Peggy. Alexander the Great. 2003. (Historical Biographies Ser.). (Illus.). 32p. (J). pap. 7.50 (978-1-4034-3707-5(6)); lib. bdg. 22.79 (978-1-4034-3699-3(1)) Heinemann Library.

—Mansa Musa. 2003. (Historical Biographies Ser.). (Illus.). 32p. (J). pap. 7.50 (978-1-4034-3711-2(4)); lib. bdg. 22.79 (978-1-4034-3703-7(3)) Heinemann Library.

—Qin Shi Huangdi. 2003. (Historical Biographies Ser.). (Illus.). 32p. (J). pap. 7.50 (978-1-4034-3712-9(2)); lib. bdg. 22.79 (978-1-4034-3704-4(1)) Heinemann Library.

Paparchontis, Kathleen. 100 Leaders Who Changed the World. 2003. (People Who Changed the World Ser.). (Illus.). 112p. (J). (gr. 5 up). lib. bdg. 30.00 (978-0-8368-5472-5(1) , World Almanac Library) Stevens, Gareth Inc.

Pfeffer, Wendy. Mysterious Spinners. Kim, Julie J., illus. 2005. 48p. (J). (978-1-59336-315-4(X)); pap. (978-1-59336-316-1(8)) Mondo Publishing.

Phillips, Larissa. Cochise: Jefe Apache. de la Vega, Eida, tr. from ENG. 2003. (Grandes Personajes en la Historia de Los Estados Unidos Ser.). (ENG & SPA., Illus.). 32p. (J). pap. (978-0-8239-4223-7(6)) Rosen Publishing Group, Inc., The.

Poulakidas, Georgene. Black Hawk's War. 2004. (Primary Sources of American Wars Ser.). (Illus.). 24p. (J). lib. bdg. (978-1-4042-2682-1(6)) Rosen Publishing Group, Inc., The.

Price-Groff, Claire. Queen Victoria & Nineteenth-Century England. 2003. (Rulers & Their Times Ser.). (Illus.). 96p. (YA). (gr. 8-12). 29.93 (978-0-7614-1488-9(6) , Benchmark Bks.) Cavendish, Marshall Corp.

Price, Sean. Ivan the Terrible: Tsar of Death. 2007. (Wicked Historytrade; Ser.). 128p. (J). spiral bd. 30.00 (***978-0-531-12597-7(1)*** , Children's Pr.) Scholastic Library Publishing.

Raatma, Lucia. Queen Noor: American-Born Queen of Jordan. 2006. (Signature Lives Ser.). (Illus.). 112p. (J). (gr. 5-7). 30.60 (978-0-7565-1595-9(5)) Compass Point Bks.

Reed, Jennifer. The Saudi Royal Family. 2nd rev. ed. 2007. (Modern World Leaders Ser.). (Illus.). 120p. (YA). (gr. 6-12). 30.00 (978-0-7910-9218-7(6) , Chelsea Hse.) Facts On File, Inc.

Reed, Jennifer Bond. The Saudi Royal Family. (Major World Leaders Ser.). (Illus.). (gr. 6-12). 2003. 144p. pap. 30.00 (978-0-7910-7187-8(1)); 2002. 112p. 30.00 (978-0-7910-7063-5(8)) Facts On File, Inc. (Chelsea Hse.).

Reid, Struan. Montezuma. 2002. (Historical Biographies Ser.). (Illus.). 32p. (J). (gr. 2-4). lib. bdg. 22.79 (978-1-58810-566-0(0)) Heinemann Library.

Robb, Andy. Catastrophic Kings. 2004. (Holy Happenings Ser.). (Illus.). 128p. pap. 6.50 (978-0-687-02306-6(8)) Abingdon Pr.

Roberts, Russell. Rulers of Ancient Egypt. 1998. (History Makers Ser.). (Illus.). 96p. (YA). (gr. 7-10). 28.70 (978-1-56006-438-1(2) , Lucent Bks.) Thomson Gale.

Roshell, Starshine. Real-Life Royalty. 2007. (Girls Rock! Ser.). 32p. (J). (gr. 1-5). 24.21 (***978-1-59296-869-5(4)***) Child's World, Inc.

Rulers & Their Times, 4 bks., Group 4. Incl. Eleanor of Aquitaine & the High Middle Ages. Plain, Nancy. 96p. lib. bdg. 29.93 (978-0-7614-1834-4(2)); Han Wu Di & Ancient China. Greenblatt, Miriam. 80p. lib. bdg. 29.93 (978-0-7614-1835-1(0)); Julius Caesar & the Roman Republic. Greenblatt, Miriam. 96p. lib. bdg. 29.93 (978-0-7614-1836-8(9)); Napoleon Bonaparte & Imperial France. Greenblatt, Miriam. 96p. lib. bdg. (978-0-7614-1837-5(7)); (Illus.). (J). (gr. 3-7). 2005. (978-0-7614-1833-7(4) , Benchmark Bks.) Cavendish, Marshall Corp.

Rulers, Scholars, & Artists of the Renaissance, 6 bk. set. 2005. (YA). (gr. 5-8). lib. bdg. 191.70 (978-1-4042-0370-9(2)) Rosen Publishing Group, Inc., The.

Schanzer, Rosalyn. George vs. George: The Revolutionary War as Seen by Both Sides. 2004. (Illus.). 64p. (J). (gr. 4-9). 16.95 (978-0-7922-7349-3(4) , National Geographic Children's Bks.) National Geographic Society.

Schiel, Katy. Monarchy: A Primary Source Analysis. 2003. (Primary Sources of Political Systems Ser.). (Illus.). 64p. (J). lib. bdg. 29.25 (978-0-8239-4520-7(0)) Rosen Publishing Group, Inc., The.

Serrano, Francisco. The Poet King of Tezcoco: A Great Leader of Ancient Mexico. Serrano, Pablo, illus. 2007. 48p. (J). 18.95 (978-0-88899-787-6(6)) Groundwood Bks. CAN. *Dist:* Perseus Distribution.

Stanley, George Edward. Crazy Horse: Young War Chief. Henderson, Meryl, illus. 2005. 199p. (J). (978-1-4156-2931-4(5) , Aladdin) Simon & Schuster Children's Publishing.

Sutcliffe, Jane. Chief Joseph. 2004. (History Maker Bios Ser.). (J). pap. 6.95 (978-0-8225-2068-9(0)) Lerner Publishing Group.

—Chief Joseph. Parlin, Tim, tr. Parlin, Tim, illus. 2004. (History Maker Bios Ser.). 48p. (J). (gr. 3-5). lib. bdg. 26.60 (978-0-8225-0696-6(3)) Lerner Publishing Group.

Tames, Richard. Monarchy. 2003. (Political & Economic Systems Ser.). (Illus.). 64p. (YA). (gr. 5-8). lib. bdg. 28.50 (978-1-4034-0320-9(1)) Heinemann Library.

Thomas, Susanna. Rameses II: Pharaoh of the New Kingdom. 2003. (Leaders of Ancient Egypt Ser.). (Illus.). 112p. (J). (gr. 5-8). lib. bdg. 31.95 (978-0-8239-3597-0(3) , Rosen Central) Rosen Publishing Group, Inc., The.

—Snefru: The Pyramid Builder. 2003. (Leaders of Ancient Egypt Ser.). (Illus.). 112p. (J). (gr. 5-8). lib. bdg. 31.95 (978-0-8239-3598-7(1) , Rosen Central) Rosen Publishing Group, Inc., The.

Todd, Anne M. Chief Tecumseh. 2004. (Illus.). 32p. (J). pap. 7.50 (978-1-4034-5009-8(9)); lib. bdg. 24.22 (978-1-4034-5002-9(1)) Heinemann Library.

—Crazy Horse 1842-1877. 2002. (American Indian Biographies Ser.). (Illus.). 32p. (J). (gr. 3-4). lib. bdg. 23.93 (978-0-7368-1210-8(5) , Blue Earth Bks.) Capstone Pr., Inc.

—Osceola. 2004. (Illus.). 32p. (J). pap. 7.50 (978-1-4034-5010-4(2)); lib. bdg. 24.22 (978-1-4034-5003-6(X)) Heinemann Library.

—Sitting Bull 1831-1890. 2002. (American Indian Biographies Ser.). (Illus.). 32p. (J). (gr. 3-4). lib. bdg. 23.93 (978-0-7368-1215-3(6) , Blue Earth Bks.) Capstone Pr., Inc.

Trumbauer, Lisa. King Ludwig's Castle: Germany's Neuschwanstein. 2005. (Castles, Palaces, & Tombs Ser.). (J). lib. bdg. 25.27 (978-1-59716-002-5(4)) Bearport Publishing Co., Inc.

Wagner, Heather Lehr. King Abdullah II: King of Jordan. Schlesinger, Arthur M., Jr., ed. 2005. (Major World Leaders Ser.). (Illus.). 112-144p. (J). (gr. 6-12). 30.00 (978-0-7910-8259-1(8) , Chelsea Hse.) Facts On File, Inc.

Whiting, Jim. The Life & Times of Augustus Caesar. 2005. (Biography from Ancient Civilizations Ser.). (Illus.). 48p. (J). (ps-7). lib. bdg. 29.95 (978-1-58415-336-8(9)) Mitchell Lane Pubs., Inc.

—The Life & Times of Nero. 2005. (Biography from Ancient Civilizations Ser.). (Illus.). 48p. (J). (gr. 5-8). lib. bdg. 29.95 (978-1-58415-349-8(0)) Mitchell Lane Pubs., Inc.

Wilkes, Angela. King Arthur. 2003. (gr. 3-6). lib. bdg. 14.10 (978-0-613-90430-8(3)) Tandem Library Bks.

Wolfson, Evelyn. King Arthur & His Knights in Mythology. Bock, William Sauts, illus. 2002. (Mythology Ser.). 128p. (YA). (gr. 6-12). lib. bdg. 26.60 (978-0-7660-1914-0(4)) Enslow Pubs., Inc.

KINGS, QUEENS, RULERS, ETC.—FICTION

Aarrestad, Thomas. The Potter Giselle. 2001. (Illus.). (J). (ps-3). 14.95 (978-0-8249-5403-1(3)) Ideals Pubns.

Abbott, Tony. The Riddle of Zorfendorf Castle. Merrell, David, illus. 2005. 124p. (J). (ps-k). lib. bdg. 10.79 (978-0-606-33298-9(7)) Tandem Library Bks.

—Riddle of Zorfendorf Castle. Merrell, David, illus. 2005. 124p. (J). lib. bdg. 15.38 (***978-1-4242-0310-9(4)***) Fitzgerald Bks.

Abbott, Tony. The Tower of the Elf King. 2000. (gr. 3-6). lib. bdg. 11.80 (978-0-613-33156-2(7)) Tandem Library Bks.

Abreu, Byron. The Ice Queen & the Sun King. 2005. 23.00 (978-0-8059-9726-2(1)) Dorrance Publishing Co., Inc.

Aiken, Joan. The Witch of Clatteringshaws. 2005. 144p. (J). (gr. 5). lib. bdg. 17.99 (978-0-385-90252-6(2) , Delacorte Bks. for Young Readers) Random Hse. Children's Bks.

—The Witch of Clatteringshaws. 2006. 160p. (gr. 4-7). 5.99 (978-0-440-42037-8(7) , Yearling) Random Hse. Children's Bks.

Alcantara, Ignacio, illus. Who's That Crying? 2005. 63p. (J). 17.00 (978-0-9659538-1-8(5)) Soul Vision Works Publishing.

Alexander, Lloyd. Dream-of-Jade: The Emperor's Cat. Burkett, D. Brent, illus. 2005. 48p. (J). 16.95 (978-0-8126-2736-7(9)) Cricket Bks.

—The Rope Trick. 2004. 208p. (J). (gr. 5 up). reprint ed. pap. 5.99 (978-0-14-240119-4(6) , Puffin) Penguin Group (USA) Inc.

Allan, Nicholas. The Queen's Knickers. 2000. (Illus.). 32p. (J). pap. 9.99 (978-0-09-941314-1(0)) Random Hse. GBR. *Dist:* Independent Pubs. Group.

Amery, H. & Cartwright, S. The Royal Broomstick. 2004. (First Stories Ser.). 16p. (J). lib. bdg. 12.95 (978-1-58086-572-2(0)) EDC Publishing.

Andersen, D. R. Why the Moon Changes in the Night Sky. 2005. 40.00 (***978-1-4108-4190-2(1)***) Benchmark Education Co.

Andersen, Hans Christian. The Emperor's New Clothes. Archipowa, Anastassija, illus. 1998. 32p. (J). (ps-4). 15.95 (978-1-56397-699-5(4)) Boyds Mills Pr.

—The Emperor's New Clothes. 2005. 12p. pap. (978-958-30-1782-7(5)) Panamericana Editorial.

—The Emperor's New Clothes. Burton, Virginia Lee, illus. 2004. 48p. (J). (gr. k-3). tchr. ed. 16.00 (978-0-618-34421-5(7)); pap. 6.95 (978-0-618-34420-8(9)) Houghton Mifflin Co. Trade & Reference Div.

—The Nightingale. Oleynikov, Igor, illus. 2007. Tr. of Nattergalen. 40p. (J). 16.50 (978-1-933327-31-0(6)); 15.95 (978-1-933327-30-3(8)) Purple Bear Bks., Inc.

—The Snow Queen. Tatarnikov, Pavel, illus. 2006. 48p. (J). 16.50 (978-1-933327-23-5(5)); 15.95 (978-1-933327-22-8(7)) Purple Bear Bks., Inc.

—El Traje Nuevo del Emperador. (SPA., Illus.). 48p. (J). (gr. 3-5). (978-84-241-5527-8(0) , EV0621); 4th ed. 2003. 32p. (978-84-241-5520-9(3) , EV0649) Everest de Ediciones y Distribucion, S.L. ESP. *Dist:* Lectorum Pubns., Inc.

—El Traje Nuevo del Emperador. (SPA.). 64p. (J). 9.50 (978-84-207-3349-4(0)) Grupo Anaya, S.A. ESP. *Dist:* AIMS International Bks., Inc.

Anderson, Ho Che. King. 2002. (gr. 7-12). lib. bdg. 21.05 (978-0-613-50952-7(8)) Tandem Library Bks.

Anna, Jennifer. Year of the Dragon. 2nd ed. 2007. (Illus.). 56p. (J). pap. 24.99 (***978-1-59092-155-5(0)*** , Blue Works) Windstorm Creative.

Anthony, David & David, Charles. Trek Through Tangleroot: Knightscares #5. 2004. (Illus.). 200p. (J). per. 5.99 (978-0-9728461-4-1(X)) Sigil Publishing.

Aptekar, Devan. Brain Swap. 2006. (Teen Titans Ser.). (Illus.). 32p. (J). pap. 3.99 (978-0-439-83009-6(5)) Scholastic, Inc.

Ashley, Mike, ed. Royal Whodunnits: Tales of Right Royal Murder & Mystery. 2004. 434p. reprint ed. pap. 12.00 (978-0-7567-8391-4(7)) DIANE Publishing Co.

Atwater-Rhodes, Amelia. Wolfcry. 2008. 208p. (YA). (gr. 9). pap. 7.99 (***978-0-440-23886-7(2)*** , Delacorte Bks. for Young Readers) Random Hse. Children's Bks.

Atwater-Rhodes, Amelia. Wolfcry Vol. 4: The Kiesha'ra. 2006. (Illus.). 208p. (YA). (gr. 7). 14.95 (978-0-385-73195-9(7)); lib. bdg. 16.99 (978-0-385-90354-7(5)) Random Hse. Children's Bks. (Delacorte Bks. for Young Readers).

Aubin, Henry T. Rise of the Golden Cobra. Taylor, Stephen, illus. 2007. 200p. (J). (gr. 6-12). 21.95 (***978-1-55451-060-3(0)***); pap. 11.95 (***978-1-55451-059-7(7)***) Annick Pr., Ltd. CAN. *Dist:* Firefly Bks., Ltd.

Babbitt, Natalie. Bub: Or the Very Best Thing. Babbitt, Natalie, illus. 1998. (Illus.). (J). (gr. k-3). pap., tchr. ed. 37.95 incl. audio (978-0-87499-467-4(5)); pap. 15.95 incl. audio (978-0-87499-465-0(9)) Live Oak Media.

Bacon, Joy. Oliver Bean Visits the Queen. DeVito, Pamela, illus. 1998. 48p. (J). (gr. k-5). pap. 8.95 (978-1-883650-45-2(3)) Windswept Hse. Pubs.

The Bad Luck of King Fred: Individual Title Six-Packs. (Action Packs Ser.). 104p. (gr. 3-5). 44.00 (978-0-7635-8408-5(8)) Rigby Education.

Badoe, Adwoa A. The Queen's New Shoes. Ageda, Belinda, illus. 1998. 24p. (J). (gr. 3-7). pap. 7.95 (978-0-88961-232-7(3)) Women's Pr. CAN. *Dist:* Univ. of Toronto Pr.

Bailey, Len. Clabbernappers. 2005. (Illus.). 224p. (J). 17.95 (978-0-7653-0981-5(5) , Tor Bks.) Doherty, Tom Assocs., LLC.

Barbalet, Margaret. Reggie Queen of the Street. McLean, Andrew, illus. 2005. 32p. (J). pap. 10.00 (978-0-14-350091-9(0) , Penguin Global) Penguin Group (USA) Inc.

Barrett, Tracy. Anna of Byzantium. 2000. (Illus.). 224p. (YA). (gr. 7-12). pap. 5.99 (978-0-440-41536-7(5) , Laurel Leaf) Random Hse. Children's Bks.

—Anna of Byzantium. 2000. (J). 11.64 (978-0-606-19742-7(7)); (gr. 7-12). lib. bdg. 12.40 (978-0-613-28364-9(3)) Tandem Library Bks.

Beddor, Frank. The Looking Glass Wars. 2007. (Looking Glass Wars Trilogy: Bk. 1). 400p. (J). (gr. 5 up). 8.99 (***978-0-14-240941-1(3)*** , Puffin) Penguin Group (USA) Inc.

—Seeing Redd. 2007. (Looking Glass Wars Trilogy: Bk. 2). 384p. (YA). (gr. 6 up). 17.99 (***978-0-8037-3155-4(8)*** , Dial) Penguin Group (USA) Inc.

Bell, Hilari. Shield of Stars. 2007. (Shield, Sword, & Crown Ser.). (Illus.). 272p. (J). 16.99 (978-1-4169-0594-3(4) , Simon & Schuster Children's Publishing) Simon & Schuster Children's Publishing.

Berenguer, Carmen. El Rey Mocho. Salvador, Carmen, illus. 2000. (SPA.). 24p. (J). (ps-3). pap. 6.95 (978-980-257-068-3(0)) Ekare, Ediciones VEN. *Dist:* Kane/Miller Bk. Pubs., Inc., Lectorum Pubns., Inc.

Besson, Luc. Arthur & the Forbidden City. (Illus.). 192p. (J). 2006. pap. 5.99 (978-0-06-059628-6(7) , Harper Trophy); 2005. 15.99 (978-0-06-059626-2(0)); 2005. lib. bdg. 16.89 (978-0-06-059627-9(9)) HarperCollins Pubs.

Birch, Beverley & Shakespeare, William. Macbeth. 2007. (Illus.). 80p. 13.95 (***978-0-7502-4965-2(X)*** , Hodder Wayland) Hodder Children's Division GBR. *Dist:* Independent Pubs. Group.

Blackaby, Susan. El Traje Nuevo del Emperador: Version del Cuento de los Hermanos Grimm. Delage, Charlene, illus. 2006. (Read-It! Readers en Espanol Ser.).Tr. of Emperor's New Clothes: A Retelling of the Grimm's Fairy Tale. (SPA.). 32p. (J). (ps-3). 19.95 (978-1-4048-1629-9(1)) Picture Window Bks.

Bober, Natalie S. Countdown to Independence. 2001. (Illus.). 368p. (YA). (gr. 7 up). 26.95 (978-0-689-81329-0(5) , Atheneum) Simon & Schuster Children's Publishing.

Bode, N. E. The Somebodies. 2006. (Illus.). 288p. (J). lib. bdg. 17.89 (978-0-06-079112-4(8)) HarperCollins Pubs.

—The Somebodies. Ferguson, Peter, illus. 2006. 288p. (J). 16.99 (978-0-06-079111-7(X) , HarperCollins) HarperCollins Pubs.

Bogumill, Mark P. KingMaker: The Swamp Crusade, 4 vols. 2003. 310p. (YA). bds. 25.00 (978-0-9744870-0-7(7)) KingMaker Bks. LLC.

Bolton, Michael. The Secret of the Lost Kingdom. Jermann, David, illus. 2004. 36p. (J). (gr. k-4). reprint ed. (978-0-7567-7849-1(2)) DIANE Publishing Co.

—The Secret of the Lost Kingdom. 2006. 44p. (J). 12.95 (978-1-59764-218-7(5)) New Line Bks.

—El Secreto del Reino Perdido. Jermann, David, illus. (Buenas Noches Coleccion). (SPA.). (J). (gr. 3). pap. 7.16 (978-958-04-4904-1(X)) Norma S.A. COL. *Dist:* Lectorum Pubns., Inc.

Bower, Tamara. How the Amazon Queen Fought the Prince of Egypt. Bower, Tamara, illus. 2005. (Illus.). 40p. (J). (gr. 2-6). 17.99 (978-0-689-84434-8(4) , Atheneum) Simon & Schuster Children's Publishing.

Bowman, Vicki. Julie Flies Back to the Past. 2005. 71p. pap. 14.95 (978-1-4137-7529-7(2)) PublishAmerica, Inc.

Boyce, Catherine & Boyce, Peter. Tea with the Queen. Sibert, Stephanie Grace, illus. 2006. 32p. (J). per. 16.95 net. incl. audio compact disk (978-0-9778420-0-1(2) , 10,000) Semper Studio.

Boyd, David. Hidden Message. Alward, Jeff, illus. 2007. 48p. (J). lib. bdg. 23.08 (***978-1-4242-1637-6(0)***) Fitzgerald Bks.

Brennan, Herbie. Fairy Nuff: A Tale of Bluebell Ball. Collins, Ross, illus. 2002. 128p. (J). (gr. 2-4). 13.95 (978-1-58234-770-7(0) , Bloomsbury Children) Bloomsbury Publishing.

Brenner, Peter. King for One Day. Wyss, Manspeter, illus. 36p. (J). (ps-3). 12.95 (978-0-87592-027-6(6)) Scroll Pr., Inc.

Brightwood, Laura, illus. Debate in Sign Language. Brightwood, Laura, . 2006. (J). (978-0-9779290-6-1(X)) 3-C Institute for Social Development.

—King's New Suit. Brightwood, Laura, . 2007. (J). DVD (***978-1-934409-05-3(7)***) 3-C Institute for Social Development.

Brightwood, Laura, illus. Wise People of Helm. Brightwood, Laura, . 2006. (J). (978-0-9779290-4-7(3)) 3-C Institute for Social Development.

Brooks, Felicity. King Arthur. rev. ed. 2007. 144p. (J). pap. 4.99 (***978-0-7945-1483-9(9)*** , Usborne) EDC Publishing.

Brooks, Felicity. Tales of King Arthur. 2002. (gr. 3-6). lib. bdg. 12.95 (978-0-613-75320-3(8)) Tandem Library Bks.

Broome, Errol. Gracie & the Emperor. 2005. 160p. (J). (gr. 5-9). 18.95 (978-1-55037-891-7(0)); pap. 7.95 (978-1-55037-890-0(2)) Annick Pr., Ltd. CAN. *Dist:* Firefly Bks., Ltd.

Brown, Gladys. The Adventures of King Flapjack. 2005. 36p. pap. 13.95 (978-1-4116-2694-2(X)) Lulu.com.

Bulla, Lynda. Freedom Rings: An American Parable. 2005. (Illus.). 32p. (J). lib. bdg. 14.99 (978-0-9724272-3-4(6)) Katydid Publishing LLC.

Burchett, Jan, et al. Exile. 2006. (Lady Grace Mysteries, from the Daybookes of Lady Grace Cavendish Ser.). 208p. (J). (gr. 3-7). 7.95 (978-0-385-73322-9(4)); lib. bdg. 9.99 (978-0-385-90341-7(3)) Random Hse. Children's Bks. (Delacorte Bks. for Young Readers).

Burns, Dal. The Adventures of Phoo. 2006. 148p. pap. 19.95 (978-1-4241-1773-4(9)) PublishAmerica, Inc.

Buzzati, Dino & Lobb, Frances. The Bears' Famous Invasion of Sicily. 2003. (New York Review Children's Collection). (Illus.). 152p. (J). 18.95 (978-1-59017-076-2(8) , NYR Children's Collection) New York Review of Bks., Inc., The.

Buzzati, Dino & Snicket, Lemony. The Bears' Famous Invasion of Sicily. Buzzati, Dino, illus. 2005. (Illus.). 192p. (J). pap. 5.99 (978-0-06-072608-9(3)) HarperCollins Pubs.

Cabot, Meg. The Princess Diaries Box Set Vols. I-III: Princess in Love; Princess in the Spotlight; The Princess Diaries. 2003. (Princess Diaries). 304p. (gr. 7 up). pap. 19.99 (978-0-06-058745-1(8)) HarperCollins Pubs.

Cadic, Oliver. Queen Margot. 2007. (Illus.). 52p. pap. 13.95 (***978-1-905460-19-9(8)***) CineBook GBR. *Dist:* Biblio Distribution.

Cadic, Olivier & Gheysens, Francois. Queen Margot: The Age of Innocence. Spear, Luke, tr. from FRE. Derenne, Juliette, illus. 2007. 48p. pap. 13.95 (***978-1-905460-10-6(4)***) CineBook GBR. *Dist:* Biblio Distribution.

Cadnum, Michael. The King's Arrow. 2008. 224p. (YA). (gr. 7). 16.99 (***978-0-670-06331-4(2)*** , Viking Juvenile) Penguin Group (USA) Inc.

Cameron-Anasti, Patsy, et al, contrib. by. Spider Riders Bk. 1: Shards of the Oracle. movie tie-in ed. 2005. (Illus.). 224p. (J). pap. 5.99 (978-1-55704-652-9(2)) Newmarket Pr.

Carey, Janet Lee. Dragon's Keep. (Illus.). 320p. (YA). 2008. pap. 7.95 (***978-0-15-206401-3(X)*** , Magic Carpet Bks.); 2007. (gr. 6-10). 17.00 (978-0-15-205926-2(1)) Harcourt Children's Bks.

—Dragon's Keep. 2007. 302p. (J). (***978-1-4287-3929-1(7)***) Harcourt Trade Pubs.

Casey, Dawn. The Great Race: The Story of the Chinese Zodiac. Wilson, Anne, illus. 2006. 32p. (J). 16.99 (978-1-905236-77-0(8)) Barefoot Bks., Inc.

Cassidy, Anne. The Crying Princess. Paine, Colin, illus. 2004. (Read-It! Readers Ser.). 32p. (C). (gr. k-3). 18.60 (978-1-4048-0053-3(0)) Picture Window Bks.

—The Queen's Dragon. Williamson, Gwyneth, illus. 2004. (Read-It! Readers Ser.). 32p. (C). (gr. k-3). 18.60 (978-1-4048-0553-8(2)) Picture Window Bks.

Cavendish, Grace. Conspiracy. 2005. (Lady Grace Mysteries, from the Daybookes of Lady Grace Cavendish Ser.). 208p. (J). (gr. 3-7). 6.95 (978-0-385-73153-9(1) , Delacorte Bks. for Young Readers) Random Hse. Children's Bks.

—The Lady Grace Mysteries: Assassin. l.t. ed. 2006. pap. 16.95 (978-1-4056-6068-6(6)) BBC Audio GBR. *Dist:* BBC Audiobooks America.

Cherubini. Pinocchio in Africa. 2006. (ENG.). 62.99 (***978-1-4280-1918-8(9)***) IndyPublish.com.

—Pinocchio in Africa. 2004. reprint ed. pap. 15.95 (978-1-4191-4166-9(X)); pap. 1.99 (978-1-4192-4166-6(4)) Kessinger Publishing, LLC.

Chester, Laura. Hiding Glory. Lippincott, Gary, illus. 2007. 160p. (J). 18.95 (***978-1-59543-616-0(2)***) Willow Creek Pr., Inc.

Climo, Shirley. Atlanta's Race: A Greek Myth. 2000. (J). 13.75 (978-0-606-19360-3(X)) Tandem Library Bks.

Clinton, J. Noel. The Prince of Warwood & the King's Key. 2005. (YA). per. 9.99 (978-0-9773115-1-4(1)) C2 (C squared) Publishing.

Coatsworth, Elizabeth Jane. The White Horse. Sewell, Helen, illus. 2005. 169p. (J). pap. 11.95 (978-1-883937-86-7(8)) Bethlehem Bks.

Cole, Babette. Princess Smartypants Rules. Cole, Babette, illus. 2005. (Illus.). 32p. (J). (ps-3). 15.99 (978-0-399-24349-3(6) , Putnam Juvenile) Penguin Group (USA) Inc.

Cole, Lucreta. The King of Amphiboly: A Fable. 2007. 78p. 18.95 (***978-0-533-15586-6(X)***) Vantage Pr., Inc.

Combel Editorial Staff. Como la Sal. 2004. (Caballo alado clasicos-Al Galope Ser.). (SPA., Illus.). 24p. 6.95 (978-84-7864-786-6(4)) Combel Editorial, S.A. ESP. *Dist:* Independent Pubs. Group.

Comrie, Margaret S. The Heroes of Castle Bretten. 2003. (Illus.). 229p. (J). (978-1-894666-65-7(8)) Inheritance Pubns.

Cooney, Caroline B. Enter Three Witches: A Story of Macbeth. 2007. 288p. (J). (gr. 7 up). pap. 16.99 (978-0-439-71156-2(8) , Scholastic Pr.) Scholastic, Inc.

Cordero, Silvia Jaeger. El Huevo Azul. Sunset Producciones Staff, illus. rev. ed. 2004. (Castillo de la Lectura Verde Ser.). (SPA.). 136p. (J). (gr. 4-6). pap. 7.95 (978-970-20-0127-0(7)) Castillo, Ediciones, S. A. de C. V. MEX. *Dist:* Macmillan.

Corvino, Lucy, illus. Arabian Nights: Retold from the Original. 2008. (Classic Starts Ser.). 160p. (J). 5.95 (***978-1-4027-4573-7(7)***) Sterling Publishing Co., Inc.

Cotes, Everard. The Story of Sonny Sahib. 2004. reprint ed. pap. 15.95 (978-1-4191-8402-4(4)); pap. 1.99 (978-1-4192-8402-1(9)) Kessinger Publishing, LLC.

Coville, Bruce & Shakespeare, William. William Shakespeare's the Winter's Tale. Pham, LeUyen, illus. 2007. 40p. (J). (gr. 3 up). 16.99 (***978-0-8037-2709-0(7)*** , Dial) Penguin Group (USA) Inc.

Crake, D. A. Edwy the Fair or the First Chronicle of. 2006. 79.99 (***978-1-4280-0132-9(8));*** pap. 73.99 (***978-1-4280-0131-2(X))*** IndyPublish.com.

Creech, Sharon. The Castle Corona. Diaz, David, illus. 2007. 336p. (J). (gr. 3-7). lib. bdg. 19.89 (***978-0-06-084622-0(4));*** 18.99 (***978-0-06-084621-3(6))*** HarperCollins Pubs. (Cotler, Joanna Books).

Crichton, Julie. The King & the Queen & the Jelly Bean. Swaim, illus. l.t. ed. 2005. (SPA.). 24p. (J). bds. 7.95 (978-0-9761990-0-7(9)) Bean Bk. Publishing.

—El rey y la reina y el frijolito de Goma. Swaim, Ramon, illus. l.t. ed. 2005. 24p. (J). bds. 7.95 (978-0-9761990-1-4(7)) Bean Bk. Publishing.

Cross, Frances. Mystery of the Green Elephant. 2007. (Blobber Trilogy Ser.). 96p. pap. 7.95 (***978-1-84167-559-6(8))*** Ransom Publishing Ltd. GBR. *Dist:* International Publishers Marketing.

Cullen, Lynn. Moi & Marie Antoinette. Young, Amy, illus. 2006. 32p. (J). 16.95 (978-1-58234-958-9(4)) Bloomsbury Publishing.

Danticat, Edwidge. Anacaona: Golden Flower, Haiti 1490. 2005. (Royal Diaries). (Illus.). 192p. (J). pap. 10.95 (978-0-439-49906-4(2)) Scholastic, Inc.

Darden, Amy. Yesterday Once Again: Guenevere's Quest. 2003. (J). pap. 11.00 (978-0-8059-9238-0(3) , RoseDog Bks.) Dorrance Publishing Co., Inc.

Dart-Thornton, Cecilia. Lady of the Sorrows. 2003. (gr. 7-12). lib. bdg. 15.30 (978-0-613-61841-0(6)) Tandem Library Bks.

Davidson, Susanna. Emperor's New Clothes. 2006. 24p. (J). 9.99 (978-0-7945-1350-4(6) , Usborne) EDC Publishing.

De Angeli, Marguerite. The Door in the Wall. 1998. (Illus.). 128p. (J). (gr. 5-9). reprint ed. pap. 4.99 (978-0-440-22779-3(8) , Laurel Leaf) Random Hse. Children's Bks.

—The Door in the Wall. 1998. 11.64 (978-0-606-13344-9(5)) Tandem Library Bks.

de Brunhoff, Jean, et al. Isabelle the Flower Girl. 2004. (Babar Ser.). (Illus.). 24p. (J). (ps-3). 9.95 (978-0-8109-5039-9(1)) Abrams, Harry N. , Inc.

de Brunhoff, Laurent. Babar the King. de Brunhoff, Laurent, illus. 2002. (Babar Ser.). (Illus.). (J). 23.36 (978-0-7587-2011-5(4)) Book Wholesalers, Inc.

de Brunhoff, Laurent & de Brunhoff, Jean. Babar Goes to School. 2003. (Illus.). 32p. (J). (ps-1). 9.95 (978-0-8109-4582-1(7)) Abrams, Harry N. , Inc.

Deedy, Carmen Agra. The Yellow Star: The Legend of King Christian X of Denmark. Sorensen, Henri, illus. 2000. 32p. (J). (gr. 3-7). 16.95 (978-1-56145-208-8(4) , Q24691) Peachtree Pubs., Ltd.

Delessert, Etienne. Humpty Dumpty. 2006. (Illus.). 32p. (J). (gr. k-3). 17.00 (978-0-618-56987-8(1)) Houghton Mifflin Co.

DeLuise, Dom. King Bob's New Clothes. 1999. (J). (978-0-606-18949-1(1)) Tandem Library Bks.

Demi. The Empty Pot. 2007. (Illus.). 32p. (J). pap. 23.95 (***978-0-8050-8227-2(1)*** , Holt, Henry & Co. Bks. For Young Readers) Holt, Henry & Co.

Demi. King Midas: The Golden Touch. Demi, illus. 2002. (Illus.). 48p. (J). (gr. 2-5). 21.99 (978-0-689-83297-0(4) , McElderry, Margaret K.) Simon & Schuster Children's Publishing.

Dickins, Rosie. Emperor & the Nightingale. Philpot, Graham, illus. 2007. (First Reading Level 4 Ser.). 48p. (J). 8.99 (***978-0-7945-1614-7(9)*** , Usborne) EDC Publishing.

—Monkey King. Ovani, Germano, illus. 2007. (Young Reading Series 1 Gift Bks). 48p. (J). 8.99 (***978-0-7945-1593-5(2)*** , Usborne) EDC Publishing.

Dieterle', Nathalie. I Am the King! American Edition. Dieterle', Nathalie, illus. 2001. (Illus.). 32p. (J). (ps-k). pap. 15.95 (978-0-531-30324-5(1) , Orchard Bks.) Scholastic, Inc.

DiMarco, Carol. Rumors of War. Huft, Maggie, illus. 2005. (Delimit Nonpariel Ser.). 88p. (YA). pap. 9.99 (978-1-59092-052-7(X) , Blue Works) Windstorm Creative.

DiMarco, Carol & Bowman, Sharon. The Tale of Two Kingdoms. 2007. 88p. (J). pap. 10.99 (978-1-59092-170-8(4) , Little Blue Works) Windstorm Creative.

Dines, Carol. The Queen's Soprano. 2007. (Illus.). 336p. (YA). pap. 6.95 (***978-0-15-206102-9(9)*** , Harcourt Paperbacks) Harcourt Children's Bks.

—The Queen's Soprano. 2006. (Illus.). 336p. (YA). 17.00 (978-0-15-205477-9(4)) Harcourt Trade Pubs.

Disney Press Staff, ed. Lion King. 2007. 48p. (gr. 1-3). pap. 3.99 (***978-1-4231-0369-1(6))*** Disney Pr.

Disney Publishing Staff & LeapFrog Staff, compiled by. Disney's the Lion King. 2002. spiral bd. 14.95 (978-1-58605-929-3(7)) LeapFrog Enterprises, Inc.

Do, Kim-Thu, tr. Tang Monk Disciples Monkey King: English/Vietnamese. Ma, Wenhai, illus. 2005. (Adventures of Monkey King Ser.: No. 3). (ENG & VIE.). 32p. (J). 16.95 (978-1-57227-087-9(X)) Pan Asia Pubns. (USA), Inc.

Dokey, Cameron. The Storyteller's Daughter: A Retelling of the Arabian Nights. 2007. (Once upon a Time Ser.). 240p. (YA). pap. 5.99 (978-1-4169-3776-0(5) , Simon Pulse) Simon & Schuster Children's Publishing.

Doyle, Malachy. King Donal's Secret. Watson, Richard, illus. 2005. 24p. (J). lib. bdg. 22.65 (***978-1-59646-740-8(1))*** Dingles & Co.

Duffy, Carol Ann. Queen Munch & Queen Nibble. 2007. (J). bds. 13.50 (***978-1-59692-238-9(9))*** MacAdam/Cage Publishing, Inc.

Dunbar, Joyce. Magic Lemonade. McCafferty, Jan, illus. 2001. (Blue Bananas Ser.). 48p. (J). (gr. 1-2). (978-0-7787-0839-1(X)); pap. (978-0-7787-0885-8(3)) Crabtree Publishing Co.

—Magic Lemonade. McCafferty, Jan, illus. 2001. 48p. (J). (ps-ps). lib. bdg. 12.95 (978-0-613-52875-7(1)) Tandem Library Bks.

Dunn, Carolyn. A Pie Went By. 32p. (J). (ps-1). Date not set. pap. 4.99 (978-0-06-443649-6(7)); 2000. (Illus.). 14.95 (978-0-06-028807-5(8)) HarperCollins Pubs.

—Real Kings Don't Do Ballet. 2001. (J). 15.95 (978-0-688-16176-7(6)); lib. bdg. 15.89 (978-0-688-16177-4(4)) HarperCollins Pubs.

Durkee, Noura. The King, the Prince & the Naughty Sheep. Durkee, Noura, illus. 1999. (Illus.). 24p. (J). (gr. 1-5). 16.00 (978-1-879402-58-4(0)) Tahrike Tarsile Quran, Inc.

Dutta, Arup Kumar. The Boy Who Became King. Arya, Viki, illus. 2004. 122p. (J). (***978-81-291-0405-2(9))*** Rupa & Co.

Edmiston, Jim, illus. The Emperor Who Forgot His Birthday. 1999. 32p. (J). (ps-3). 14.95 (978-1-84148-015-2(0)) Barefoot Bks., Inc.

—The Emperor Who Hated Yellow. 1999. 32p. (J). (ps-k). 14.95 (978-1-902283-39-5(2)) Barefoot Bks., Inc.

Ellis, Sarah. The Queen's Feet. Petricic, Dusan, illus. 2006. 32p. 17.95 (978-0-88995-320-8(1)) Red Deer Pr. CAN. *Dist:* F & W Pubns., Inc., Fitzhenry & Whiteside, Ltd.

The Emperor's New Groove. unabr. ed. 2000. (J). pap. 9.98 incl. audio (978-0-7634-0710-0(0)) Walt Disney Records.

En la Corte del Rey Blas. 2000. Tr. of In King Blas' Court. (SPA., Illus.). (J). 4.95 (978-84-246-1635-9(9)) La Galera, S.A. Editorial ESP. *Dist:* AIMS International Bks., Inc.

Engelbreit, Mary. Queen of the Class. Engelbreit, Mary, illus. 2004. (Ann Estelle Stories Ser.). (Illus.). 32p. (J). (ps-3). 15.99 (978-0-06-008178-2(3)) HarperCollins Pubs.

Engelbreit, Mary. Queen of the Class. Engelbreit, Mary, illus. 2007. (Ann Estelle Stories Ser.). 32p. (J). pap. 6.99 (***978-0-06-008180-5(5)*** , Harper Trophy) HarperCollins Pubs.

Everett-Green, Evelyn. The Secret Chamber at Chad. 2006. (ENG.). 140p. 77.99 (***978-1-4280-4786-0(7))*** IndyPublish.com.

Farah, Barbara. Parabola O Jednom Mostu: Parable of the Bridge. 2005. (CRO., Illus.). 36p. pap. 15.00 (978-0-9769346-0-8(4)) Farah, Barbara.

Farley, Carol. The King's Secret: The Legend of King Sejong. Cooper, Floyd, illus. 2001. 32p. (J). (gr. 1 up). 15.95 (978-0-688-12776-3(2)) HarperCollins Pubs.

Farmer, Nancy. Clever Ali. De Marcken, Gail, illus. 2006. 40p. (J). pap. 17.99 (978-0-439-37014-1(0) , Orchard Bks.) Scholastic, Inc.

Farooqi, Imran A. The Spell of the Witch-Queen. 2006. (Illus.). 60p. pap. (***978-1-84401-816-1(4))*** Athena Pr.

Faulkner, Keith. King Leo. Holmes, Stephen, illus. 2002. (Slot-to-Slot Model Ser.). 16p. (J). 9.95 (978-1-931411-01-1(8)) CPG Publishing, Inc.

Ferris, Jean. Once upon a Marigold. 2002. 272p. (YA). (gr. 5 up). 17.00 (978-0-15-216791-2(9)); 2004. 288p. (J). reprint ed. pap. 5.95 (978-0-15-205084-9(1) , Harcourt Paperbacks) Harcourt Children's Bks.

—Once upon a Marigold. 2004. (gr. 5-8). lib. bdg. 14.10 (978-0-613-71637-6(X)) Tandem Library Bks.

Fine, Judith & Bazilian, Barbara. Princess Lily. Bazilian, Barbara, illus. 1998. (Illus.). 32p. (J). (gr. 1-5). 15.95 (978-1-58089-006-9(7)) Charlesbridge Publishing, Inc.

Finney, Patricia & Cavendish, Grace. Assasin, No. 1. 2004. (Lady Grace Mysteries, from the Daybookes of Lady Grace Cavendish Ser.). 208p. (J). (gr. 3-7). lib. bdg. 12.99 (978-0-385-90189-5(5) , Delacorte Bks. for Young Readers) Random Hse. Children's Bks.

—Assassin, No. 1. 2004. (Lady Grace Mysteries, from the Daybookes of Lady Grace Cavendish Ser.). 208p. (J). (gr. 3-7). 9.95 (978-0-385-73151-5(5) , Delacorte Bks. for Young Readers) Random Hse. Children's Bks.

—Deception. 2005. (Lady Grace Mysteries, from the Daybookes of Lady Grace Cavendish Ser.). 224p. (J). (gr. 3-7). 7.95 (978-0-385-73321-2(6)); lib. bdg. 9.99 (978-0-385-90340-0(5)) Random Hse. Children's Bks. (Delacorte Bks. for Young Readers).

—Feud. 2006. (Lady Grace Mysteries, from the Daybookes of Lady Grace Cavendish Ser.). 192p. (J). (gr. 3-7). 7.95 (978-0-385-73323-6(2)); lib. bdg. 9.99 (978-0-385-90342-4(1)) Random Hse. Children's Bks. (Delacorte Bks. for Young Readers).

Fisscher, Tiny. RUBY & the LION. 2008. 48p. 11.95 (***978-1-60136-014-4(2))*** Mars Media Pubs.

French, Allen. The Lost Baron. Wyeth, Andrew, illus. 2001. 320p. (J). (gr. 5-12). reprint ed. pap. 14.95 (978-1-883937-53-9(1) , 53-1) Bethlehem Bks.

Furgang, Kathy. A Throne for the King. ed. 2003. (Early Connections Ser.). (J). pap. 33.00 (978-1-4108-1372-5(X)) Benchmark Education Co.

Furgang, Kathy. A un trono para el rey a Throne for the King. 2005. spiral bd. 66.00 (***978-1-4108-5657-9(7))*** Benchmark Education Co.

Gallego Garcia, Laura. The Legend of the Wandering King. 2005. (Illus.). 224p. (J). (gr. 7-17). pap. 16.95 (978-0-439-58556-9(2) , Levine, Arthur A. Bks.) Scholastic, Inc.

Gallego Garcia, Laura & Bellm, Dan. The Legend of the Wandering King. 2005. (J). (978-0-439-58557-6(0) , Levine, Arthur A. Bks.) Scholastic, Inc.

Galloway, Priscilla. Aleta y la Reina: Una Historia de la Antigua Grecia.Tr. of Aleta & the Queen: A Tale of Ancient Greece. (SPA.). (YA). (gr. 5-8). pap. (978-968-6582-27-7(4)) Samara, Ediciones, S. A. de C. V.

Gebler, Carlo. The Bull Raid. 2005. 416p. (J). (gr. 7-9). pap. 9.99 (978-1-4052-2464-2(9)) Egmont Bks., Ltd. GBR. *Dist:* Independent Pubs. Group.

Gerhardt, Barbara. I Am of Scram. 2007. (Illus.). pap. 12.95 (***978-1-934246-15-3(8))*** Peppertree Pr., The.

Gibert, Bruno. The King Is Naked! 2004. (Illus.). 32p. (J). (gr. k-ps). 14.00 (978-0-618-41067-5(8) , Clarion Bks.) Houghton Mifflin Co. Trade & Reference Div.

Gleitzman, Morris. Two Weeks with the Queen. l.t. ed. 2002. 192p. (J). 16.95 (978-0-7540-7816-6(7) , Galaxy Children's Large Print) BBC Audiobooks America.

Glynn, W. Celebrando a Diario con el Rey.Tr. of Daily with the King. (SPA.). 10.99 (978-958-9269-28-2(1) , 490190) Editorial Unilit.

Going, K. L. The Liberation of Gabriel King. 2005. 192p. (J). (gr. 3-6). 15.99 (978-0-399-23991-5(X) , Putnam Juvenile) Penguin Group (USA) Inc.

Golden Books Staff. Knight Quest. Saunders, Zina, illus. 2006. (Hologramatic Sticker Book Ser.). 32p. (J). (ps-2). pap. 3.99 (978-0-375-83473-8(7) , Golden Bks.) Random Hse. Children's Bks.

Goss, Leon. King for a Day. Nichols, Chris, illus. 2005. (J). pap. (978-1-933156-09-5(0)); per. (978-1-933156-01-9(5)) GSVQ Publishing. (VisionQuest Kids).

Graham, Baxter. Old King Stinky Toes. Martin, James R., illus. 2005. 32p. (J). 15.95 (978-0-9764791-0-9(9)) Drumstick Media.

Grant, K. M. How the Hangman Lost His Heart. 2007. 256p. (YA). (gr. 7 up). 16.95 (***978-0-8027-9672-1(9))*** Walker & Co.

The Greedy King: Individual Title Six-Pack Pouch - Level K. (Lighthouse Ser.). 16p. (gr. 2 up). 28.00 (978-0-7578-0861-6(1)) Rigby Education.

Gregory, Kristiana. Catherine: The Great Journey, Russia, 1743. 2005. (Royal Diaries). (Illus.). 176p. (J). (gr. 4-9). pap. 10.99 (978-0-439-25385-7(3)) Scholastic, Inc.

—Eleanor: Crown Jewel of Aquitaine: France 1136. 2002. (Royal Diaries Ser.). (Illus.). 192p. (gr. 4-9). pap. 10.95 (978-0-439-16484-9(2) , Scholastic Pr.) Scholastic, Inc.

Gross, J. J. Izzy Hagbah. Binus, Ari, illus. 2005. 37p. (J). (gr. 1-4). 16.95 (978-1-932687-38-5(6)); pap. 9.95 (978-1-932687-39-2(4)) Pitspopany Pr. (Devora Publishing).

Gruffudd, Elena & Owen, Carys Eurwen. Clustiau March. 2005. (WEL., Illus.). 34p. (978-0-86381-329-0(1)) Gwasg Carreg Gwalch.

Haan, Linda de & Nijland, Stern. King & King. 2004. (Illus.). 32p. 14.95 (978-1-58246-061-1(2) , Tricycle Pr.) Ten Speed Pr.

—King & King & Family. 2004. (Illus.). 32p. (J). 14.95 (978-1-58246-113-7(9) , Tricycle Pr.) Ten Speed Pr.

Harcourt School Publishers Staff. The Bird in the Plum Tree: On Level. 3rd ed. 2002. (Trophies Reading Program Ser.). (Illus.). pap. 5.10 (978-0-15-322999-2(3)) Harcourt Schl. Pubs.

—The Emperor & the Peasant Boy: Take-Home Book. 2001. (Collections Ser.). (Illus.). (J). pap. 1.90 (978-0-15-319500-6(2)) Harcourt Schl. Pubs.

—King Leo's Treasure: Take-Home Book. 1999. (Signatures Ser.). (Illus.). (J). pap. 1.90 (978-0-15-313958-1(7)) Harcourt Schl. Pubs.

Harrison, Emma. The Queen's Curse. 2005. (Charmed Ser.). 224p. (YA). pap. 5.99 (978-1-4169-0024-5(1) , Simon Spotlight Entertainment) Simon & Schuster.

Harvey, Damian. A Gift for the King. Remphry, Martin, illus. 2005. (Reading Corner Ser.). 24p. (J). (gr. k-3). lib. bdg. 22.80 (978-1-59771-013-8(X)) Sea-To-Sea Pubns.

—Make Way for the Queen! Brown, Jo, illus. 2005. (Reading Corner Ser.). 24p. (J). (gr. k-3). lib. bdg. 22.80 (978-1-59771-012-1(1)) Sea-To-Sea Pubns.

Hendry, Frances. Quest for a Queen: The Lark. 2006. pap. (***978-1-905665-04-4(0))*** Pollinger In Print.

Henley, Karyn. King for a Day. 2000. (Tails Ser.). (Illus.). 28p. (J). (ps-5). 9.99 (978-0-8054-2285-6(4)) B&H Publishing Grp.

Henty, G. A. The Dragon & the Raven: Or the Days of King Alfred. 2000. (Illus.). 238p. (J). pap. 14.99 (978-1-887159-31-9(2)) Preston-Speed Pubns.

Henty, G. A. A March on London: A Story of Wat Tyler's Insurrection. (ENG.). 2004. 98.99 (***978-1-4142-1634-8(3));*** 2003. 272p. pap. 14.99 (***978-1-4043-8185-8(6))*** IndyPublish.com.

—A March on London: A Story of Wat Tyler's Insurrection. 2004. reprint ed. pap. 27.95 (978-1-4191-0224-0(9)); pap. 1.99 (978-1-4192-0224-7(3)) Kessinger Publishing, LLC.

Hewins, Shirley, illus. Rainy Brown & the Seven Midgets. l.t. ed. 2006. (J). (gr. k-3). pap. 11.95 (978-1-884242-24-3(3) , RB1STED); 44p. lib. bdg. 19.95 (978-1-884242-25-0(1) , RB1STED) Multicultural Pubns.

Hicks, Linda & Ashman, Linda. What Could Be Better Than This? Wingerter, Linda S., illus. 2006. 32p. (J). (ps-2). 16.99 (978-0-525-46954-4(0) , Dutton Juvenile) Penguin Group (USA) Inc.

Hillard, Cecelia. The Rescuers. 2001. 60p. (J). pap. 9.00 (978-0-8059-5424-1(4)) Dorrance Publishing Co., Inc.

Hirsch, Odo. Bartlett & the Ice Voyage. McLean, Andrew, illus. 2003. 175p. (J). (gr. 3-9). 14.95 (978-1-58234-797-4(2) , Bloomsbury Children) Bloomsbury Publishing.

Hobbs, Leigh. Old Tom's Guide to Being Good. Hobbs, Leigh, illus. 2006. 96p. (gr. 1-3). pap. 3.99 (978-0-7868-5694-7(7)) Hyperion Pr.

Hockerman, Dennis, illus. The Little Seed: A Tale about Integrity. 2006. (J). (***978-1-59939-094-9(9)*** , Reader's Digest Young Families, Inc.) Reader's Digest Children's Publishing, Inc.

Hoffman, Alice. The Foretelling. (J). (gr. 8-17). 2005. 176p. 16.99 (978-0-316-01018-4(9)); 2006. 192p. reprint ed. pap. 7.99 (978-0-316-15409-3(1)) Little Brown & Co.

—The Foretelling. l.t. ed. 2006. 156p. 23.95 (978-0-7862-8285-2(1)) Thorndike Pr.

Holub, Joan. Lydia & the Island Kingdom: A Story Based on the Real Life of Princess Liliuokalani of Hawaii. Aleshina, Nonna, illus. 2007. (Young Princesses Around the World Ser.). 48p. (J). pap. 3.99 (***978-0-689-87199-3(6)*** , Aladdin) Simon & Schuster Children's Publishing.

Hoobler, Dorothy & Hoobler, Thomas. The Sword That Cut the Burning Grass. (J). (gr. 5). 2006. 224p. pap. 5.99 (978-0-14-240689-2(9) , Puffin); 2005. 212p. 10.99 (978-0-399-24272-4(4) , Philomel) Penguin Group (USA) Inc.

Hood, Douglas. The Stone Hat. Simonton, Tom, illus. 2005. 16p. (J). pap. 5.00 (978-1-57274-754-8(4) , 2784, Bks. for Young Learners) Owen, Richard C. Pubs., Inc.

Hoosier, Wanda M. Princess Mandisa. McCabe, Pat, illus. 1999. 34p. (J). 15.00 (978-1-56469-070-8(9)) Harmony Hse. Pubs.

Hotta, Yumi. Hikaru No Go, Vol. 7. 2006. (Hikaru No Go Ser.). 208p. (YA). pap. 7.95 (978-1-4215-0641-8(6)) Viz Media.

Houser, Shauna. The Goblin King. Gerl, Clara, ed. 1999. 117p. (YA). pap. 12.95 (978-0-9663820-6-8(4)) Gerl Publishing.

Howard, Annabelle. Hammurabi's Law & Order. 2005. 40.00 (***978-1-4108-4233-6(9))*** Benchmark Education Co.

Howell, Gill. Snow King. Cann, Helen, illus. 2005. 24p. (J). lib. bdg. 22.65 (***978-1-59646-742-2(8))*** Dingles & Co.

Hutchins, Hazel. The List. Van Lieshout, Maria, illus. 2007. 32p. (J). (ps-1). pap. 7.95 (***978-1-55451-063-4(5));*** lib. bdg. 19.95 (***978-1-55451-064-1(3))*** Annick Pr., Ltd. CAN. *Dist:* Firefly Bks., Ltd.

Ihimaera, Witi. The Whale Rider. 2003. Orig. Title: Te Kaieke Tohora. (YA). (gr. 3-6). 152p. 17.00 (978-0-15-205017-7(5)); 168p. pap. 8.00 (978-0-15-205016-0(7) , Harcourt Paperbacks) Harcourt Children's Bks.

—Whale Rider. 2003. (gr. 5-8). lib. bdg. 16.45 (978-0-613-70660-5(9)) Tandem Library Bks.

Jackson, Dave & Jackson, Neta. Exiled to the Red River: Chief Spokane Garry. 2003. (Trailblazer Bks.). (Illus.). 144p. (J). pap. 6.99 (978-0-7642-2235-1(X)) Bethany Hse. Pubs.

James, Ian. Why the Sky Is Far Away: A Take from Nigeria. 2006. 42.00 (***978-1-4108-6172-6(4))*** Benchmark Education Co.

Janer, Montserrat. El Rey Listo y el Rey Fuerte. (SPA.). (J). pap. (978-84-236-3342-5(X)) Edebé ESP. *Dist:* Lectorum Pubns., Inc.

Jinks, Catherine. Pagan in Exile. 2005. (Pagan Chronicles Ser.: Bk. 2). (Illus.). 336p. (J). (gr. 7 up). reprint ed. pap. 6.99 (978-0-7636-2691-4(0)) Candlewick Pr.

Johnson, Michael. The Most Special Person. Latta, Doug, illus. 1999. 24p. (J). (gr. k-6). 12.95 (978-1-893672-00-0(X)) Johnson, Michael Presentations.

Jones, Frewin. The Sorcerer King. 2008. (Faerie Path Ser.: Bk. 3). 336p. (J). 16.99 (***978-0-06-087108-6(3));*** lib. bdg. 17.89 (***978-0-06-087109-3(1))*** HarperCollins Pubs. (Eos).

Jones, Jasmine. Enchanted: The Junior Novelization. rev. ed. 2007. 160p. (gr. 3-7). pap. 4.99 (***978-1-4231-0471-1(4))*** Disney Pr.

Jones, Stephen M. Charlemagne Mack: Rise of the Queen, Personal Journal #1. 2007. 178p. (J). (gr. 4-7). per. 14.95 (***978-1-933002-41-5(7))*** PublishingWorks.

Joslin. Minstrel's Tale. (J). pap. 8.95 (978-0-7459-3966-7(X) , Lion) Lion Hudson plc GBR. *Dist:* Trafalgar Square Publishing.

Journey to see the King. 2006. (J). (***978-0-9791168-0-3(5))*** Lighthouse Bk. Publishing.

Kalkipsakis, Thalia. Go Girl! #7 - Dancing Queen. Oswald, Ash, illus. 2008. (Go Girl! Ser.). 96p. (J). pap. 3.99 (***978-0-312-34651-5(4))*** Feiwel & Friends.

Katz, Welwyn Wilton. Beowulf. Gal, Laszlo, illus. 2nd ed. 2007. 96p. (J). (gr. 5 up). 17.95 (978-0-88899-807-1(4)) Groundwood Bks. CAN. *Dist:* Perseus Distribution.

Keegan, Shannon. Legend of the Sea Fairies. 2006. (J). per. 14.99 (978-0-9773433-0-0(8)) Bixie Gate Publishing.

Keene, Carolyn. The Clue in the Jewel Box, Vol. 20. Tandy, Russell H., illus. 2005. (Nancy Drew Mystery Stories). 216p. (J). (gr. 5-9). 17.95 (978-1-55709-277-9(X)) Applewood Bks.

Kindl, Patrice. Goose Chase. 2001. 224p. (J). (gr. 5-9). tchr. ed. 16.00 (978-0-618-03377-5(7)) Houghton Mifflin Co. Trade & Reference Div.

—Goose Chase. 2002. 224p. (YA). pap. 5.99 (978-0-14-230208-8(2) , Puffin) Penguin Group (USA) Inc.

—Goose Chase. 2002. (gr. 5-8). lib. bdg. 14.15 (978-0-613-60805-3(4)) Tandem Library Bks.

King Midas & the Golden Touch: Individual Title Six-Packs. 16p. (gr. 2 up). 35.00 (978-0-7635-9382-7(6)) Rigby Education.

King of the Mountain. Date not set. 5.95 (978-0-89868-357-8(2)); lib. bdg. 10.95 (978-0-89868-356-1(4)) ARO Publishing Co.

King Robert the First. 2004. per. 26.00 (978-0-8059-9391-2(6)) Dorrance Publishing Co., Inc.

King-Smith, Dick. The Queen's Nose. l.t. ed. 2002. (Illus.). 152p. (J). 16.95 (978-0-7540-7832-6(9) , Galaxy Children's Large Print) BBC Audiobooks America.

The King's Ring: KinderReaders Individual Title Six-Packs. (Kinderstarters Ser.). 8p. (ps-1). 21.00 (978-0-7635-8656-0(0)) Rigby Education.

Kolosov, Jacqueline. The Red Queen's Daughter. rev. ed. 2007. 399p. (YA). (gr. 7 up). 16.99 (***978-1-4231-0797-2(7))*** Hyperion Pr.

Korczak, Janusz. King Matt the First. 2004. 352p. (J). pap. 13.95 (978-1-56512-442-4(1)) Algonquin Bks. of Chapel Hill.

Kostick, Conor. Saga. 2008. 368p. (YA). (gr. 7). 18.99 (*978-0-670-06280-5(4) , Viking Juvenile) Penguin Group (USA) Inc.

Krensky Stephen. Mike Fink. Reeves, Jeni, illus. 2007. (On My Own Folklore Ser.). (J). pap. 6.95 (*978-0-8225-6478-2(5) , First Avenue Editions) Lerner Publishing Group.

Lamplighter Staff. True Princess. 2004. pap. 14.00 (978-1-58474-051-3(5)) Cornerstone Family Ministries/ Lamplighter Publishing.

Lang, Andrew. The Queen & the Mouse: A Story about Friendship. Lohmann, Renate, illus. 2006. (J). (978-1-59939-081-9(7) , Reader's Digest Young Families, Inc.) Reader's Digest Children's Publishing, Inc.

Lasky, Kathryn. Guardians of Ga'Hoole #14 Exile. 2008. 224p. pap. 5.99 (*978-0-439-88808-0(5) , Scholastic Paperbacks) Scholastic, Inc.

—Marie Antoinette: Princess of Versailles, Austria-France, 1769. 2000. (Royal Diaries Ser.). (Illus.). 240p. (J). (gr. 4-8). pap. 10.95 (978-0-439-07666-1(8)) Scholastic, Inc.

—Mary, Queen of Scots: Queen Without a Country, France 1553. 2002. (Royal Diaries Ser.). (Illus.). 112p. (J). (gr. 4-8). pap. 10.95 (978-0-439-19404-4(0) , Scholastic Pr.) Scholastic, Inc.

—To Be a King. 2006. (Guardians of Ga'Hoole Ser.: Bk. 11). 224p. (J). (gr. 4-7). pap. 4.99 (978-0-439-79570-8(2) , Scholastic Paperbacks) Scholastic, Inc.

Lay, Kathryn. Crown Me! 2004. 208p. (J). (gr. 4-6). tchr. ed. 16.95 (978-0-8234-1845-9(6)) Holiday Hse., Inc.

Lendler, Ian. An Undone Fairy Tale. Martin, Whitney, illus. 2005. 32p. (J). (gr. 1-3). 15.95 (978-0-689-86677-7(1) , Simon & Schuster Children's Publishing) Simon & Schuster Children's Publishing.

Levine, Gail Carson. The Princess Test. Elliott, Mark, illus. 1999. (Princess Tales Ser.). 96p. (J). (gr. 2-7). 9.99 (978-0-06-028062-8(X)) HarperCollins Pubs.

Lieshout, Elle van & Os, Erik van. The Nothing King. Gerritsen, Paula, illus. 2004. 32p. (J). (gr. k-3). 15.95 (978-1-932425-14-7(4) , Lemniscaat) Boyds Mills Pr.

Lindgren, Astrid. Mio, My Son. Wikland, Ilon, illus. 2003. Tr. of Mio, Min Mio. 179p. (J). 17.95 (978-1-930900-23-3(6)) Purple Hse. Pr.

Luberto, Bradley. Clide & Druce: A Repulsive Tale of Trolls & Tax Money. 2006. (ENG.). 48p. per. 12.95 (*978-1-4241-5012-0(4)) PublishAmerica, Inc.

Lucado, Max. Just the Way You Are. Martinez, Sergio, illus. 1999. Orig. Title: Children of the King. 31p. (ps-5). reprint ed. 15.99 (978-1-58134-114-0(8) , Crossway Bibles) Crossway Bks.

—The Way Home: A Princess Story. Elwell, Tristan, illus. 2005. 48p. (J). 16.99 (978-1-4003-0554-4(3)) Nelson, Thomas Inc.

Lutes, Jason. Houdini: The Handcuff King. Bertozzi, Nick, illus. 2007. 96p. (gr. 5-17). 16.99 (*978-0-7868-3902-5(3)) Hyperion Pr.

Lyon, Justice. The King of Meat-Yuk-Land. 2002. 20p. (J). 4.95 (978-0-9716596-0-5(5)) 7 Heads Publishing.

Ma, Wenhai, illus. Tang Monk Disciples Monkey King. 2005. (Adventures of Monkey King Ser.: No. 3). 32p. (J). 16.95 (978-1-57227-084-8(5)) Pan Asia Pubns. (USA), Inc.

—Tang Monk Disciples Monkey King: English/Chinese. 2005. (Adventures of Monkey King Ser.: No. 3). (ENG & CHI.). 32p. (J). 16.95 (978-1-57227-086-2(1)) Pan Asia Pubns. (USA), Inc.

MacDonald, George. Light Princess Large Print. 2006. pap. (*978-1-84702-350-6(9)) Echo Library.

MacHado, Ana Maria. Un Buen Coro. (Torre de Papel Ser.). (SPA., Illus.). (J). 7.95 (978-958-04-4525-8(7) , NR30643) Norma S.A. COL. Dist: Distribuidora Norma, Inc., Lectorum Pubns., Inc.

—Del Otro Lado Hay Secretos. (SPA.). pap. 11.95 (978-950-07-2221-6(6)) Editorial Sudamericana S.A. ARG. Dist: Distribooks, Inc.

Maddern, Eric. The King with Horse's Ears. Hess, Paul, illus. (J). 2004. 32p. 15.95 (978-1-84507-240-7(5)); 2003. 36p. 14.95 (978-0-7112-1957-1(5)) Lincoln, Frances Ltd. GBR. Dist: Perseus Distribution, Transition Vendor.

The Magic King. 2003. (J). (978-1-4120-3345-9(4)) Black Dot Pubns.

Martel, Suzanne. King's Daughter. 1998. (gr. 5-9). 14.95 (978-0-88899-323-6(4) , Libros Tigrillo) Groundwood Bks. CAN. Dist: Transition Vendor.

—The King's Daughter. rev. ed. 1998. 232p. (J). (gr. 5-9). pap. 5.95 (978-0-88899-218-5(1) , Libros Tigrillo) Groundwood Bks. CAN. Dist: Perseus Distribution.

Martha Louise, Princess. Why Kings & Queens Don't Wear Crowns (with CD) Sevig-Fajardo, Mari Elise, tr. from NOR. Nyhus, Svein, illus. 2006. Orig. Title: Fvorfor de kongelige ikke har krone pa Hodet. 32p. (J). 19.95 incl. audio compact disk (978-1-57534-038-8(0) , CSC 100C) Skandisk, Inc.

Martin, Rafe. The Shark God. Shannon, David, illus. 2007. 32p. (J). (ps-3). pap. 5.99 (*978-0-590-39570-0(X)) Scholastic, Inc.

Mastromonaco, Pina. King Bartholomew & the Jesters Riddle. Martin, David, illus. 2005. 32p. (ps-7). 15.95 (978-0-9744307-1-3(4)) Merry Lane Pr.

Mathias, B. J. Jeffrey William & The Little Prince. 2002. 10.00 (978-0-9711320-9-2(7)) Electronic Publishing Services.

Matsuura, Richard & Matsuura, Ruth. King Who Wanted to See God. Chao, Linus, illus. (J). 8.95 (978-1-887916-00-4(8)) Orchid Isle Publishing Co.

Mayo, Frank, illus. King Midas & the Golden Touch: A Tale about Greed. 2006. (J). 6.99 (978-1-59939-022-2(1) , Reader's Digest Young Families, Inc.) Reader's Digest Children's Publishing, Inc.

McAllister, Angela. Digory & the Lost King. Beck, Ian, illus. 2007. 128p. (J). (gr. 3-5). 14.95 (*978-1-59990-088-9(2)); pap. 5.95 (*978-1-59990-089-6(0)) Bloomsbury Publishing.

McAllister, M. I. The Heir of Mistmantle. Rayyan, Omar, illus. 2007. (Mistmantle Chronicles Ser.: Bk. 3). 320p. (J). (gr. 3-7). 17.99 (*978-0-7868-5490-5(1)) Miramax Bks.

—Mistmantle Chronicles, the: the Urchin & the Heartstone - Book #2. Rayyan, Omar, illus. 2nd rev. ed. 2007. 304p. (gr. 3-7). pap. 7.99 (*978-0-7868-5489-9(8)) Miramax Bks.

McAllister, M. I. Urchin of the Riding Stars. Rayyan, Omar, illus. 2006. (Mistmantle Chronicles Ser.: Bk. 1). 288p. (gr. 3-7). pap. 7.99 (978-0-7868-5487-5(1)) Hyperion Bks. for Children.

McCaffrey, Laura Williams. Water Shaper. 2006. 224p. (J). (gr. 5-9). 16.00 (978-0-618-61489-9(3) , Clarion Bks.) Houghton Mifflin Co. Trade & Reference Div.

McCaughrean, Geraldine. Casting the Gods Adrift: A Tale of Ancient Egypt. Ludlow, Patricia D., illus. 2003. 112p. (J). (gr. 4-7). 15.95 (978-0-8126-2684-1(2)) Cricket Bks.

—Princess Stories. Sanders, Lizzie, illus. 2002. 92p. pap. 13.95 (978-0-552-54503-7(1) , Corgi) Transworld Publishers Ltd. GBR. Dist: Trafalgar Square Publishing.

McCloskey, Larry. Murder Fit for a King. 2008. 168p. (J). pap. 11.99 (*978-1-55002-669-6(0) , Sandcastle Bks.) Dundurn Group, The CAN. Dist: Univ. of Toronto Pr.

McEvoy, Greg. The Ice Cream King. McEvoy, Greg, illus. 1999. (Illus.). 28p. (J). (ps-3). 7.95 (978-0-7737-6024-0(5)) Stoddart Kids CAN. Dist: Fitzhenry & Whiteside, Ltd.

—The Ice Cream King. 1998. (Illus.). 32p. (J). (ps-3). 13.95 (978-0-7737-3069-4(9)) Stoddart Kids CAN. Dist: Fitzhenry & Whiteside, Ltd.

McKee, David. King Rollo & the New Stockings. 2001. (Illus.). 32p. (J). 19.99 (978-0-86264-953-1(6)) Andersen GBR. Dist: Independent Pubs. Group.

McKeown, Adam. Macbeth. 2005. pap. (978-1-4027-2476-3(4)) Sterling Publishing Co., Inc.

McKibben, Marion A. Pearl the Rodeo Queen. 2006. 24p. (J). per. 12.00 (978-1-59971-711-1(5)) Aardvark Global Publishing.

McKillip, Patricia A. The Changeling Sea. 2003. (Firebird Ser.). (Illus.). 144p. (YA). (gr. 7). pap. 5.99 (978-0-14-131262-0(9) , Puffin) Penguin Group (USA) Inc.

McKissack, Patricia C. Nzingha, Warrior Queen of Matamba - Angola 1595. 2000. (Royal Diaries Ser.). (Illus.). 144p. (J). (gr. 4-8). pap. 10.95 (978-0-439-11210-9(9)) Scholastic, Inc.

McMullan, Kate. Pig Latin—Not Just for Pigs! 2006. (Dragon Slayers' Academy Ser.: No. 14). (J). (gr. 1-6). 24.21 (978-1-59961-127-3(9)) Spotlight.

Mead, Richelle. Vampire Academy. 2007. 336p. (J). (gr. 7). pap. 8.99 (*978-1-59514-174-3(X) , Razorbill) Penguin Group (USA) Inc.

Meadows, Daisy. Lucy the Diamond Fairy. 2008. (Scholastic First Discovery Ser.: No. 7). 80p. (Orig.). (J). pap. 4.99 (*978-0-439-93534-0(2) , Scholastic Paperbacks) Scholastic, Inc.

Meidell, Sherry. The Devil with the Three Golden Hairs: The Classic Brothers Grimm Folktale. 2006. (Illus.). 32p. (J). 16.95 (978-1-933317-50-2(7)) Silverleaf Pr.

Melling, David. The Kiss That Missed. 32p. (J). (gr. k-2). 2007. pap. 7.99 (978-0-7641-3624-5(0)); 2002. (Illus.). 14.95 (978-0-7641-5451-5(6)) Barron's Educational Series, Inc.

Meredith Books Staff. Shrek the Third. Marshall, Paula, ed. 2007. (I Can Find It Ser.). 24p. (J). pap. 4.99 (*978-0-696-23729-4(6)) Meredith Bks.

Meyer, Carolyn. Anastasia: The Last Grand Duchess: Russia 1914. 2000. (Royal Diaries Ser.). (Illus.). 224p. (J). (gr. 4-8). pap. 10.95 (978-0-439-12908-4(7)) Scholastic, Inc.

—Doomed Queen Anne. (Young Royals Ser.). (Illus.). 2004. 256p. (J). pap. 5.95 (978-0-15-205086-3(8)); 2002. 240p. (YA). (gr. 7 up). 17.00 (978-0-15-216523-9(1)) Harcourt Children's Bks. (Gulliver Bks.).

—Duchessina: A Novel of Catherine de' Medici. 2007. (Young Royals Ser.). (Illus.). 272p. (YA). 17.00 (978-0-15-205588-2(6)) Harcourt Children's Bks.

—Isabel: Jewel of Castilla, Spain 1466. 2000. (Royal Diaries Ser.). (Illus.). 208p. (J). (gr. 4-8). pap. 10.95 (978-0-439-07805-4(9)) Scholastic, Inc.

—Kristina, the Girl King, Sweden 1638. 2003. (Royal Diaries Ser.). 176p. (J). pap. 10.95 (978-0-439-24976-8(7) , Scholastic Pr.) Scholastic, Inc.

—Patience, Princess Catherine. 2004. (Young Royals Ser.). (Illus.). 208p. (YA). 17.00 (978-0-15-216544-4(4) , Gulliver Bks.) Harcourt Children's Bks.

—Patience, Princess Catherine: A Young Royals Book. 2005. (Young Royals Ser.). 208p. (gr. 7-17). pap. 5.95 (978-0-15-205447-2(2) , Gulliver Bks.) Harcourt Children's Bks.

Millman, Selena. The Prince & Me. 2006. 146p. (YA). per. 11.20 (*978-1-4243-2353-1(3)) Independent Publisher Services.

Mini Cuentos: Rey de los Sapos, Sapatillas Rojas.Tr. of Mini Fairy Tales: King & His Shoes. (SPA.). (J). (gr. k-4). 4.98 (978-970-607-619-9(0)) Larousse, Ediciones, S. A. de C. V. MEX. Dist: Continental Bk. Co., Inc.

Mitchell, Mark S. The Curious Kingship of Sir George, 5 vols. 1998. (Chronicles of the House of Chax Ser.: Bk. 3). 89p. (J). (gr. 3-6). 9.99 (978-0-88092-355-2(5) , 3555) Royal Fireworks Publishing Co.

Moore, Beth. My Child, My Princess: A Parable about the King for Little Girls of All Ages. Warren, Beverly, illus. 2007. 32p. pap. 9.99 (978-0-8054-4455-1(6)) B&H Publishing Grp.

Moore, Raina. A Charming Princess Collection Book & Charm. 2005. (Charming Classics). 256p. (J). pap. 6.99 (978-0-06-059604-0(X) , Harper Festival) HarperCollins Pubs.

Morgan Creek Productions Staff. King & I. 1999. (Illus.). 31p. (J). pap. 3.50 (978-0-590-68064-6(1)) Scholastic, Inc.

—King & I: Deluxe Edition. 1999. (Illus.). 48p. pap. 5.99 (978-0-590-68066-0(8)) Scholastic, Inc.

Morpurgo, Michael. Jo-Jo the Melon Donkey. Kerins, Tony, illus. 2002. (Yellow Bananas Ser.). 48p. (J). (gr. 3-4). pap. (978-0-7787-0988-6(4)); lib. bdg. (978-0-7787-0942-8(6)) Crabtree Publishing Co.

Muhammad, Shahid. The Adventures of the Math Doctor: Book One: King Jafiz & the Evil Farmer Nimra. 2007. (J). per. 7.95 (*978-1-59872-778-4(8)) Instantpublisher-.com.

Nathan, Sarah. A Dream Come True. 2007. 32p. (gr. 1). pap. 3.99 (*978-1-4231-0909-9(0)) Disney Pr.

—Enchanted Storybook. rev. ed. 2007. 48p. (J). (gr. 2-7). 8.99 (*978-1-4231-0911-2(2)) Disney Pr.

Nelson, Brett Alan. The Magical Forest. Ueda, Kumiko, illus. 2003. 42p. (J). (978-0-9655078-7-5(4)) Windsong Publishing Co.

Nesbit, E. Lionel & the Book of Beasts. Hague, Michael, illus. 2006. 48p. (J). (gr. 2-4). lib. bdg. 17.89 (978-0-06-084272-7(5)); 16.99 (978-0-688-14006-9(8)) HarperCollins Pubs.

Newman, Marjorie. The King & the Cuddly. Bowman, Peter, illus. 2000. 32p. (J). (ps-1). 16.99 (978-0-09-176932-1(9)) Random Hse. GBR. Dist: Independent Pubs. Group.

Nix, Garth. Lady Friday. 2007. (Keys to the Kingdom Ser.: No. 5). 320p. (J). (gr. 4-7). pap. 17.99 (978-0-439-70088-7(4) , Scholastic Pr.) Scholastic, Inc.

Nobisso, Josephine. El Peso de Una Misa: Un Relato de fe. Szegedi, Katalin, illus. 2003. Orig. Title: The Weight of a Mass a Tale of Faith. (SPA.). 32p. 17.95 (978-0-940112-15-5(9)); pap. 9.95 (978-0-940112-17-9(5)) Gingerbread Hse.

—The Weight of a Mass: A Tale of Faith. Szegedi, Katalin, illus. 2002. (SPA.). 32p. (J). (gr. k-5). 17.95 (978-0-940112-09-4(4)); pap. 9.95 (978-0-940112-10-0(8)) Gingerbread Hse.

—Weight of a Mass: A Tale of Faith. 2003. (gr. k-3). lib. bdg. 18.75 (978-0-613-70732-9(X)) Tandem Library Bks.

La Noche en Que Casi Vimos a los Reyes Magos. (SPA.). (J). (978-0-9710860-9-8(5)) Libros, Encouraging Cultural Literacy.

Old King Cole: 6 Small Books. (gr. k-2). 23.00 (978-0-7635-8493-1(2)) Rigby Education.

O'Leary-Coggins, Annette C. Nanny Reilly. 2007. 116p. per. 10.95 (*978-0-595-44994-1(8)) iUniverse, Inc.

Olofsson, Helena-Adapt. The Little Jester. Board, Helena, tr. from SWE. Olofsson, Helena-Adapt, illus. 2002. (Illus.). 28p. (J). (gr. k-3). 16.00 (978-91-29-65499-8(8)) R & S Bks. SWE. Dist: Macmillan.

Olsen, Kent L. Tales of Kalindia. 2004. 356p. (YA). 30.95 (978-0-595-65998-2(5)); pap. 20.95 (978-0-595-29426-8(X)) iUniverse, Inc.

O'Neill, Katrina & Thompson, Lisa. In Search of the Egyptian Queen. Cantell, Brenda, illus. 2005. (Treasure Trackers Ser.). 80p. (gr. 5-9). 19.00 (978-0-7910-8874-6(X)) Facts On File, Inc.

Osborne, Mary Pope & Potter, Giselle. The Brave Little Seamstress. 2006. (Illus.). 40p. (J). (ps-3). reprint ed. pap. 6.99 (978-1-4169-1620-8(2) , Aladdin) Simon & Schuster Children's Publishing.

Osterbach, Batya Kirshenbaum. Pini the Pitcher: A Story for Hanukkah. Eisby, Lizzy, illus. 2005. 32p. (J). (gr. 1-4). 16.95 (978-1-932687-50-7(5) , Devora Publishing) Pitspopany Pr.

Osterlund, Anne. Aurelia. 2008. 288p. (YA). (gr. 7). pap. 8.99 (*978-0-14-240579-6(5) , Puffin) Penguin Group (USA) Inc.

Packard, Mary. I Am King! 2004. (My First Reader Ser.). 31p. (J). (gr. k-1). pap. 3.95 (978-0-516-24629-1(1) , Children's Pr.) Scholastic Library Publishing.

—I Am King! Gore, Leonid, illus. 2003. (My First Reader Ser.). 32p. (J). 18.50 (978-0-516-22927-0(3) , Children's Pr.) Scholastic Library Publishing.

Page, Nick & Page, Claire. The Summer Queen. 2006. (Read with Me (Make Believe Ideas) Ser.). (Illus.). 31p. (J). (gr. k-2). 3.95 (978-1-84610-170-0(0)) Make Believe Ideas GBR. Dist: Ingram Pub. Services.

Page, Nick & Claire. The King of Spring. 2006. (Read with Me (Make Believe Ideas) Ser.). (Illus.). 31p. (J). (gr. k-2). 3.95 (978-1-84610-169-4(7)) Make Believe Ideas GBR. Dist: Ingram Pub. Services.

Park, Linda Sue. Archer's Quest. 2006. (Illus.). 176p. (J). (gr. 5-9). 16.00 (978-0-618-59631-7(3) , Clarion Bks.) Houghton Mifflin Co. Trade & Reference Div.

Parragon Staff. Disney's the Lion King. Disney Staff, ed. 2007. 48p. (ps-2). 12.99 (*978-1-4231-0434-6(X)) Disney Pr.

Paterson, Katherine. The Wide-Awake Princess. Vagin, Vladimir Vasil'evich, illus. 2000. 48p. (J). (gr. k-3). tchr. ed. 15.00 (978-0-395-53777-0(0) , Clarion Bks.) Houghton Mifflin Co. Trade & Reference Div.

Paton Walsh, Jill. The Emperor's Winding Sheet. 2004. 256p. (YA). reprint ed. pap. 8.95 (978-1-886910-88-1(X) , Lemniscaat) Boyds Mills Pr.

Paulsen, Gary & Roberts, Esyllt Nest. Plygu Amser. 2005. (WEL.). 77p. (978-0-86381-683-3(5)) Gwasg Carreg Gwalch.

Penney, Shannon. Mariposa. 2008. (Barbie Fairytopia Ser.). 80p. (J). pap. 3.99 (*978-0-545-03590-3(2) , Scholastic Paperbacks) Scholastic, Inc.

Petty, Kate. Nightspinners. Smith, Mary Claire, illus. 2005. 32p. (J). 14.99 (978-1-85881-836-8(2)) Orion Children's Bks. GBR. Dist: Trafalgar Square Publishing.

Pfister, Marcus. How Leo Learned to Be King. 1998. (Illus.). 32p. (J). (ps-3). 15.95 (978-1-55858-913-1(9)) North-South Bks., Inc.

Pierce, Tamora. Emperor Mage. 2003. (Immortals Ser.: No. 3). (Illus.). 320p. (YA). 10.95 (978-0-689-85613-6(X) , Atheneum) Simon & Schuster Children's Publishing.

—Emperor Mage. 2002. (Immortals Ser.: No. 3). 20.50 (978-0-8446-7227-4(0)) Smith, Peter Pub., Inc.

—The Will of the Empress. (Circle Reforged Ser.: Bk. 1). 560p. (J). 2006. pap. 8.99 (978-0-439-44172-8(2)); 2005. (Illus.). (gr. 9-12). pap. 17.99 (978-0-439-44171-1(4) , Scholastic Pr.) Scholastic, Inc.

Pike, Christopher, pseud. The Yanti. 2006. (Alosha Trilogy: No. 3). 400p. (YA). (gr. 8 up). 18.95 (978-0-7653-1100-9(3) , Tor Bks.) Doherty, Tom Assocs., LLC.

Pikey, Mikey. The Diamond Tree, Episode III: the Beginning of the Rainbow. 2006. 153p. pap. 16.76 (*978-1-84728-099-2(4)) Lulu.com.

Pilegard, Virginia Walton. The Warlord's Messengers. Debon, Nicolas, illus. 2005. 32p. (J). (gr. 1-4). 15.95 (978-1-58980-271-1(3)) Pelican Publishing Co., Inc.

Pittar, Gill. Milly, Molly & What Was That? (book W/dolls) 2006. 28p. pap. (978-1-86972-105-3(5)) Milly Molly Bks.

Pohl, Linda P. The Grumpy Queen. Tezanos, Garrett, illus. 1998. 16p. (J). (ps-1). pap. 4.95 (978-0-9625453-3-7(3)) Pohl, Linda Perelman.

Pray, Ralph. Jingu: The Hidden Princess. Li, Xiaojun, illus. 2002. 80p. (YA). 14.95 (978-1-885008-21-3(X) , 188500821x) Shen's Bks.

Price, Robin. Die Clawdius, Vol. 3. 2007. (Spartapuss Tales Ser.). 192p. (J). pap. 14.95 (*978-0-9546576-8-0(3)) Mogzilla GBR. Dist: Independent Pubs. Group.

Price, Susan. The King's Head. l.t. ed. 2005. (Illus.). 264p. (J). pap. incl. audio (978-0-7540-7871-5(X) , CLP 452) BBC Audio.

Priest, Robert. The Old Pirate of Central Park. Priest, Robert, illus. 1999. (Illus.). 32p. (J). (gr. k-3). tchr. ed. 16.00 (978-0-395-90505-0(2)) Houghton Mifflin Co. Trade & Reference Div.

Pugliano-Martin, Carol. The el rey malo & Very Mean King. 2005. spiral bd. 66.00 (*978-1-4108-5648-7(8)) Benchmark Education Co.

Pugliano-Martin, Carol. The Very Mean King. ed. 2003. (Early Connections Ser.). (J). pap. 33.00 (978-1-4108-1365-7(7)) Benchmark Education Co.

Queen of Attolia Bound Galley. 2000. (J). (978-0-06-029062-7(5)) HarperCollins Pubs.

Queen of the Pool: Individual Chapter Book Title Six-Packs. Vol. 25. 32p. (gr. 3-4). 44.00 (978-0-7635-4473-7(6)) Rigby Education.

The Quest for Seven Castles. 2006. (J). per. 7.99 (978-0-9785523-1-2(8)) Dunlop, Edward.

Quin-Harkin, Janet. The King & I. novel ed. 1999. (Illus.). 73p. (J). pap. 3.99 (978-0-590-68065-3(X)) Scholastic, Inc.

Radunsky, Vladimir. The Mighty Asparagus. 2004. (Illus.). 34p. (J). 16.00 (978-0-15-216743-1(9) , Silver Whistle) Harcourt Trade Pubs.

Raintree Steck-Vaughn Staff. The Night Queen's Blue Velvet Dress. 1999. (J). pap. 35.60 (978-0-7398-0901-3(6)) Steck-Vaughn.

Ramirez, Gamaliel, illus. The Night We Almost Saw the Three Kings. 32p. (J). (gr. 1 up). 16.00 (978-0-9710860-8-1(7)) Libros, Encouraging Cultural Literacy.

Redbank, Tennant. Enchanted: A Storybook Life. 2nd rev. ed. 2007. 24p. (gr. 1). pap. 3.99 (*978-1-4231-1080-4(3)) Disney Pr.

—Enchanted: Before the Fall. 2007. 24p. (gr. 1). pap. 3.99 (*978-1-4231-1079-8(X)) Disney Pr.

Reed-Davis, Anita Paulette, et al. Zaine & the Cradle for the King. Gerber, Perren, illus. 1999. (J). (gr. 4-6). pap. 11.95 (978-0-9700812-0-9(0)) Two Peas in A Pod.

El Rey Sabio (The Wise King) 2000. (SPA.). (J). pap. 1.29 (978 1 56063 703 5(X) , 497734) Editorial Unilit.

Riddle, Sharon Kay & Sanders, Nancy/Ida. The King's Silverware. Lowe, Frank Allen, illus. 2007. 32p. (J). pap. 15.00 (*978-0-9761583-5-6(3)) Olive Leaf Pubns.

Rigby Education Staff. Queen of Hearts. (gr. k-2). 21.00 (978-0-7635-2406-7(9)) Rigby Education.

Riley, Lehman C. Meeting Dr. Martin Luther King. 2004. (Adventures of Papa Lemon's Little Wanderers Ser.: Bk. 1). 35p. (*978-0-9760523-0-2(X)) Matter of Africa America Time.

Rinaldi, Ann. Nine Days a Queen: The Short Life & Reign of Lady Jane Grey. (J). 2006. 240p. pap. 5.99 (978-0-06-054925-1(4) , Harper Trophy); 2005. 192p. (gr. 7 up). 15.99 (978-0-06-054923-7(8)); 2005. 192p. (gr. 7 up). lib. bdg. 16.89 (978-0-06-054924-4(6)) HarperCollins Pubs.

Rinaldi, Ann. The Redheaded Princess. 2008. 224p. (J). 15.99 (*978-0-06-073374-2(8)); lib. bdg. 16.89 (*978-0-06-073375-9(6)) HarperCollins Pubs.

Risso, Eduardo. Los misterios de la Luna Roja Vol. 1: Mysteries of the Red Moon. 2006. (SPA.). 48p. pap. 16.95 (978-1-59497-162-4(5)) Public Square Bks.

—Mysteries of the Red Moon, Vol. 3. 2006. (SPA.). 48p. pap. 16.95 (978-1-59497-163-1(3)) Public Square Bks.

Roberts, Katherine. I Am the Great Horse. 2006. (Illus.). 416p. (YA). pap. 16.99 (978-0-439-82163-6(0) , Chicken Hse., The) Scholastic, Inc.

Roderman, Anna Marie. Two Tales of Courage. 2004. 116p. (YA). pap. 7.95 (978-0-87714-318-5(8)) Denlingers Pubs., Ltd.

Rodgers, Frank. Little T & the Crown Jewels. 2007. (Read-It! Chapter Books). (J). 21.26 (978-1-4048-2726-4(9)) Picture Window Bks.

J
K
L

—Royal Roar. 2007. (Read-It! Chapter Books). (J). 21.26 (978-1-4048-2728-8(5)) Picture Window Bks.

Rodriguez, Artemio. The King of Things/el Rey de las Cosas. Rodriguez, Artemio, illus. 2006. (SPA & ENG., Illus.). 32p. 12.95 (978-0-938317-97-5(0)) Consortium Bk. Sales & Distribution.

Ron, Kare. The Adventures of Sir Noodlefish: The Cake Wars. McCracken, Ken, illus. 2000. 32p. (J). (gr. 1-3). pap. (978-1-931179-00-3(X)) Long Hill Productions, Inc.

Ross, Jillian. Alissa & the Castle Ghost. Backes, Nick, illus. 2nd ed. 1998. (Stardust Classics). (J). (gr. 2-6). 113p. 12.95 (978-1-889514-07-9(1)) ; 119p. pap. 5.95 (978-1-889514-08-6(X)) Dolls Corp.

Rovetch, Lissa & Whitman, Emily. Sir Henry, the Polite Knight. Barnard, Bryn, illus. 2006. (J). (*978-1-58987-204-2(5)) Kindermusik International.

Roy, Ron. The Yellow Yacht. Gurney, John Steven, illus. 2005. (A to Z Mysteries Ser.: No. 25). 85p. (J). (gr. k-3). lib. bdg. 11.19 (978-0-606-33237-8(5)) Tandem Library Bks.

The Royal Waker Upper. 2003. (J). 10.99 (978-0-89610-992-6(5)) Island Heritage Publishing.

Royde-Smith, N. G. Una and the Red Cross Knight & Other T. 2006. (Illus.). pap. 28.95 (*978-1-4254-8407-1(7)) Kessinger Publishing, LLC.

Rust, Patricia. King of Skittledeedoo. 1998. 32p. (J). (gr. k-3). 15.00 (978-0-9655890-5-5(6)) Markowitz Publishing.

—The King of Skittledeedoo. Chan, San Wei, illus. 2nd rev. ed. 2000. 32p. (J). (ps-3). lib. bdg. 12.95 (978-1-885848-00-0(5) , Power for Kids Pr.) Rust Foundation for Literacy, Inc., The.

Ryan, Brittney. The Legend of Holly Claus. Long, Laurel, illus. 2004. 544p. (J). (gr. 4 up). 16.99 (978-0-06-058511-2(0)); lib. bdg. 17.89 (978-0-06-058514-3(5)) HarperCollins Pubs. (Julie Andrews Collection).

—Legend of Holly Claus. Long, Laurel, illus. 2006. 544p. (J). pap. 7.99 (978-0-06-058515-0(3) , Julie Andrews Collection) HarperCollins Pubs.

Sanders, Roy E. Land of Pink: From thesNot So Far Ago Series. 2007. (J). 19.99 (*978-1-59879-327-7(6)) Lifevest Publishing, Inc.

Sanderson, Jeanette. Robin Hood Shoots for the Queen: A Legend from England. 2006. spiral bd. 42.00 (*978-1-4108-7167-1(3)) Benchmark Education Co.

Santillo, LuAnn. Dip & Sip. Santillo, LuAnn, ed. 2003. (Half-Pint Kids Readers Ser.). (Illus.). 7p. (J). (ps-1). pap. (978-1-59256-051-6(2)) Half-Pint Kids, Inc.

—The King. Santillo, LuAnn, ed. 2003. (Half-Pint Kids Readers Ser.). (Illus.). 7p. (J). (ps-1). pap. (978-1-59256-050-9(4)) Half-Pint Kids, Inc.

Sargent, Dave & Sargent, Pat. Whiskers: (Roan) Pride & Peace, 30, 59. Lenoir, Jane, illus. (Saddle Up Ser.: Vol. 59). 42p. (J). 2003. pap. 6.95 (978-1-56763-806-6(6)); 2002. lib. bdg. 22.60 (978-1-56763-805-9(8)) Ozark Publishing.

Scam, Busta. The Kingdom of Norne. 2006. (Illus.). 44p. pap. 12.95 (978-1-59663-516-6(9) , Castle Keep Pr.) Rock, James A. & Co. Pubs.

Schanback, Mindy. Princess from Another Planet. 2005. 254p. (J). (gr. 5-9). 16.95 (978-0-8234-1847-3(2)) Holiday Hse., Inc.

Scholastic, Inc. Staff. Battle for Morcia. 2006. (Knights' Kingdom Ser.). 4p. (J). bds. 9.99 (978-0-439-82814-7(7)) Scholastic, Inc.

—Isabel: Jewel of Castilla, Spain 1466. 2000. (Royal Diaries Ser.). (J). lthr. 9.95 (978-0-439-26656-7(4)) Scholastic, Inc.

—The King & I: Deluxe Storybook. 1999. (J). (978-0-606-16952-3(0)) Tandem Library Bks.

Scholastic, Inc. Staff. Nightingale/Ruisenor. 2007. (Bilingual Tales Ser.). (ENG & SPA.). 24p. (J). pap. 3.99 (*978-0-439-87970-5(1)) Scholastic, Inc.

Scieszka, Jon. Los Caballeros de la Mesa de la Cocina. Smith, Lane, illus. (SPA.). (J). (gr. 5-8). 7.95 (978-958-04-3400-9(X) , NR4516) Norma S.A. COL. Dist: Distribuidora Norma, Inc., Lectorum Pubns., Inc.

The Secret: Individual Chapter Book Title Six-Packs. Vol. 25. 32p. (gr. 3-4). 44.00 (978-0-7635-4470-6(1)) Rigby Education.

Sedgwick, Marcus. The Dark Flight Down. 240p. 2008. (YA). (gr. 7). pap. 7.99 (*978-0-553-48784-8(1)); 2005. (J). (gr. 5-7). 15.95 (978-0-385-74645-8(8)) Random Hse. Children's Bks. (Lamb, Wendy).

Seow, David. The Littlest Emperor. Polunin, Olga Marie, illus. 2004. 32p. (J). 15.95 (978-0-8048-3529-9(2)) Tuttle Publishing.

Shakespeare, William, et al. Hamlet. 2007. (Manga Shakespeare Ser.). 204p. (J). (gr. 2-8). pap. 9.95 (*978-0-8109-9324-2(4) , Abrams Bks. for Young Readers) Abrams, Harry N. , Inc.

Shinohara, Chie. Red River, Volume 17. 2007. (Red River Ser.). 192p. (YA). pap. 9.99 (978-1-4215-0997-6(0)) Viz Media.

Shulevitz, Uri. One Monday Morning. 2003. (Illus.). 48p. (J). reprint ed. pap. 6.95 (978-0-374-45648-1(8) , Sunburst) Farrar, Straus & Giroux.

—One Monday Morning. 2003. (ps-2). lib. bdg. 15.25 (978-0-613-71877-6(1)) Tandem Library Bks.

Simon, Les. The Secret of the Red Silk Pouch. 1998. 157p. (YA). (gr. 8-12). pap. 9.99 (978-0-88092-362-0(8) , 3628) Royal Fireworks Publishing Co.

Sims, Lesley. Snow Queen. 2005. 24p. (J). 9.95 (978-0-7945-1160-9(0) , Usborne) EDC Publishing.

Smith, Peggy. The Kingdom of Nod: A Sweet Tale about an Unlucky Young Queen, & the Men Who Try to Win Her Hand, for the Barton Reading & Spelling System. 2003. (J). pap. 7.95 (978-0-9744343-6-0(1) , SA-401) Bright Solutions for Dyslexia, LLC.

Snelson, Brian & Sellars, Rodney. Shaturanga: The Story of Onus. 2003. 244p. pap. 16.95 (978-0-595-29569-2(X)) iUniverse, Inc.

Sommer, Carl. The Great Royal Race. 2003. (Another Sommer-Time Story Ser.). (Illus.). 48p. (J). (gr. k-4). lib. bdg. 23.95 incl. audio compact disk (978-1-57537-708-7(X)); (gr. k-4). lib. bdg. 23.95 incl. audio (978-1-57537-758-2(6)); (gr. 1-4). 16.95 incl. audio (978-1-57537-557-1(5)); (gr. 1-4). 16.95 incl. audio compact disk (978-1-57537-508-3(7)) Advance Publishing, Inc.

Sorensen, Launa. The King's First Journey, Bk. 1. 2007. 280p. (YA). pap. 15.99 (978-1-59092-572-0(6) , Blue Works) Windstorm Creative.

Souci, Robert D. San. Well at the End of the World. Walsh, Rebecca, illus. 2004. 48p. (J). 16.95 (978-1-58717-212-0(7) , SeaStar Bks.) Chronicle Bks. LLC.

Souhami, Jessica. King Pom & the Fox. 2007. (Illus.). 36p. (J). (gr. k-3). 16.95 (*978-1-84507-478-4(5)) Lincoln, Frances Ltd. GBR. Dist: Perseus Distribution.

Souhami, Jessica. Rama & the Demon King: An Ancient Tale from India. 2006. (Illus.). 30p. (J). (gr. k-4). reprint ed. 15.00 (978-0-7567-9813-0(2)) DIANE Publishing Co.

Spongberg, Emily. Hannibal & the King. Spongberg, Tim, illus. l.t. ed. 1999. 32p. (J). (gr. k-4). 15.95 (978-1-893659-00-1(3)) Rainbow Hse. Publishing.

Springer, Nancy. Outlaw Princess of Sherwood. 2003. (Tales of Rowan Hood Ser.: No. 3). 128p. (J). (gr. 3-6). 16.99 (978-0-399-23721-8(6) , Philomel) Penguin Group (USA) Inc.

Sproul, R. C. The King Without a Shadow. Bonham, Liz, illus. 2000. 32p. (J). (ps-3). 16.99 (978-0-87552-700-0(0)) P & R Publishing.

Stanek, Robert. The Elf Queen & the King III. 2007. 232p. (YA). pap. 15.00 (978-1-57545-086-5(0)) Reagent Pr.

—The Elf Queen & the King IV. 2008. 238p. (YA). pap. 15.00 (978-1-57545-087-2(9)) Reagent Pr.

Stanley, Diane. Bella at Midnight. Ibatoulline, Ba, illus. 2008. 304p. (J). pap. 6.99 (*978-0-06-077575-9(0) , Harper Trophy) HarperCollins Pubs.

—Bella at Midnight. Ibatoulline, Bagram, illus. 2006. 288p. (J). (gr. 5-8). 16.99 (978-0-06-077573-5(4)); lib. bdg. 16.89 (978-0-06-077574-2(2)) HarperCollins Pubs.

Steck-Vaughn Staff. Dancing: The King who Loves Dancing. 1998. (Illus.). (J). pap. 11.50 (978-0-8172-8638-5(1)) Steck-Vaughn.

—The Night Queen's Blue Velvet Dress/The Universe. 1999. (Take Me Home Ser.). (J). (gr. 1-4). pap. 11.30 (978-0-7398-0941-9(5)) Steck-Vaughn.

Steptoe, John L. Las Bellas Hijas de Mufaro. Steptoe, John L., illus. 1998. Tr. of ghters. (Illus.). pap. 43.95 incl. audio compact disk (978-1-59519-139-7(9)); (SPA., (J). pap. 18.95 incl. audio compact disk (978-1-59519-138-0(0)) Live Oak Media.

Stevenson, Sucie, illus. & reader. The Emperor's New Clothes. Stevenson, Sucie, reader. 1998. (978-0-606-13367-8(4)) Tandem Library Bks.

Stewart, Mary. The Last Enchantment. 2003. (gr. 7-12). lib. bdg. 24.55 (978-0-613-66978-8(9)) Tandem Library Bks.

Stone, David Lee. The Ratastrophe Catastrophe. Lea, Bob, illus. 2004. (Illmoor Chronicles Ser.: Bk. 1). 288p. (gr. 5-9). 16.99 (978-0-7868-5128-7(7)) Hyperion Bks. for Children.

Strickler, Ashley. Once upon A Time. 2007. 212p. pap. 12.95 (*978-1-4327-0207-6(6)) Outskirts Press, Inc.

Sula, Sondra. Gopher World: The Sleazy Snakes. 2000. mass mkt. 8.95 (978-1-931179-14-0(X)) Long Hill Productions, Inc.

—Gopher World: The Sleazy Snakes. Johnson, Terri L., illus. 2000. 32p. (J). (gr. 1-3). pap. (978-0-9701450-7-9(1)) Long Hill Productions, Inc.

Sundberg, Norma J. An Odd Fable. Leiper, Esther M., illus. 2007. (ENG.). 32p. (J). pap. 13.95 (*978-0-9776958-5-0(9)) CyPress Pubns.

Sutcliff, Rosemary. The Mark of the Horse Lord. 2006. 256p. (YA). pap. 10.95 (978-1-932425-62-8(4) , Lemniscaat) Boyds Mills Pr.

The Sword, the Ring, & the Parchment. 2006. (J). per. 7.99 (978-0-9785523-0-5(X)) Dunlop, Edward.

Sypolt, Carl W. Adventures of David the Honeybee. 2003. 51p. pap. 9.95 (978-0-7414-1526-4(7)) Infinity Publishing.

Tamura, Yumi. Basara, Vol. 22. 2007. (Basara Ser.). 192p. (YA). pap. 9.99 (978-1-4215-0979-2(2)) Viz Media.

Teitelbaum, Michael. The Earth Kingdom Chronicles: the Tale of Azula. Spaziante, Patrick, illus. 2007. (Avatar Ser.). 96p. (J). pap. 5.99 (*978-1-4169-3608-4(4) , Simon Spotlight) Simon & Schuster Children's Publishing.

Terry, Will, illus. Little Rooster's Diamond Button. 2007. 32p. (J). (ps-2). 16.95 (978-0-8075-4644-4(5)) Whitman, Albert & Co.

Thal, Lilli. Mimus. Brownjohn, John, tr. from GER. 2005. 398p. (YA). (gr. 7-10). 19.95 (978-1-55037-925-9(9)) Annick Pr., Ltd. CAN. Dist: Firefly Bks., Ltd.

—Mimus. Brownjohn, John, tr. from GER. 2005. 398p. (YA). (gr. 7-10). pap. 9.95 (978-1-55037-924-2(0)) Annick Pr., Ltd. CAN. Dist: Firefly Bks., Ltd.

Thomas, Jane Resh. The Counterfeit Princess. 2005. (J). 208p. (gr. 5-9). 15.00 (978-0-395-93870-6(8)); 197p. (978-0-618-93780-6(3)) Houghton Mifflin Co. Trade & Reference Div. (Clarion Bks.).

Thompson, James. The Amarna Experiment. 2003. 128p. (YA). 21.95 (978-0-595-65753-7(2)); pap. 11.95 (978-0-595-28296-8(2)) iUniverse, Inc.

Tingle, Rebecca. The Edge on the Sword. (Sailing Mystery Ser.). 2003. 288p. (YA). (gr. 8-12). pap. 6.99 (978-0-14-250058-3(5) , Puffin); 2001. (Illus.). 1p. (J). (gr. 7 up). 18.99 (978-0-399-23580-1(9) , Putnam Juvenile) Penguin Group (USA) Inc.

—The Edge on the Sword. 2003. (gr. 5-8). lib. bdg. 15.30 (978-0-613-67451-5(0)) Tandem Library Bks.

—Far Traveler. 2006. 240p. (J). (gr. 4). pap. 6.99 (978-0-14-240630-4(9) , Puffin) Penguin Group (USA) Inc.

Trapani, Iza. I'm a Little Teapot. 1998. (Illus.). 32p. (J). (gr. 1-5). pap. 6.95 (978-1-58089-010-6(5)) Charlesbridge Publishing, Inc.

Troughton, Joanna, et al. A Friend for the King & Other Stories. 2002. (Illus.). 48p. pap. 0.40 (978-0-521-89006-9(3)) Cambridge Univ. Pr.

Trudel, Sylvain. Le Roi Qui Venait du Bout du Monde. Langlois, Suzane, illus. 2002. (Premier Roman Ser.). (FRE.). 64p. (J). (gr. 2-5). pap. (978-2-89021-279-4(3)) Diffusion du livre Mirabel.

—Le Royaume de Bruno. Langlois, Suzane, illus. 1998. (Premier Roman Ser.). (FRE.). 64p. (J). (gr. 2-5). pap. (978-2-89021-326-5(9)) Diffusion du livre Mirabel.

Turner, Megan Whalen. The King of Attolia. 400p. (J). 2007. (gr. 5 up). pap. 7.99 (*978-0-06-083579-8(6) , Eos); 2006. 16.99 (978-0-06-083577-4(X)); 2006. lib. bdg. 17.89 (978-0-06-083578-1(8)) HarperCollins Pubs.

Turner, Megan Whalen. The Queen of Attolia. (J). (gr. 5 up). 2001. 416p. pap. 7.99 (978-0-380-73304-0(8) , Harper Trophy); 2000. 288p. 15.95 (978-0-688-17423-1(X)) HarperCollins Pubs.

—The Queen of Attolia. 2001. (978-0-606-22313-3(4)) Tandem Library Bks.

El Valiente Gobernador (The Brave Ruler) 2000. (SPA.). (J). pap. 1.29 (978-1-56063-995-4(4) , 494020) Editorial Unilit.

Vivekanand, Jennifer. Zakkary Kay & the King of the Asparagus. 2004. 48p. pap. 12.95 (978-1-4137-2242-0(3)) PublishAmerica, Inc.

Voigt, Cynthia. Elske: A Novel of the Kingdom. Vermeer, Jan, illus. 2001. (Kingdom Ser.). 256p. (YA). pap. 10.00 (978-0-689-84444-7(1) , Simon Pulse) Simon & Schuster Children's Publishing.

Volpe, Theresa. The King's Mapmaker. 2006. (Early Explorers Ser.). (J). 36.00 (*978-1-4108-6129-0(5)) Benchmark Education Co.

Wallace, Karen. The Minestrone Mob. Brown, Judy, illus. 2007. (Read-It! Chapter Books). (J). (978-1-4048-2723-3(4)) Picture Window Bks.

—The Peanut Prankster. Brown, Judy, illus. 2007. (Read-It! Chapter Books). (J). 21.26 (978-1-4048-2724-0(2)) Picture Window Bks.

—Queen Carrion's Big Bear Hug. Flook, Helen, illus. 2007. (J). lib. bdg. (*978-1-4048-3709-6(4)) Picture Window Bks.

Wallace, Karen. Rollerblading Royals. (Illus.). mass mkt. 7.99 (978-0-340-72668-6(7) , Hodder & Stoughton) Hodder General Publishing Division GBR. Dist: Trafalgar Square Publishing.

Walt Disney Company Staff. King for a Day. 1998. (J). (ps-3). 2.99 (978-0-307-08726-3(3) , 08726, Golden Bks.) Random Hse. Children's Bks.

Wasserman, Mira. Too Much of a Good Thing. Carolan, Christine, illus. 2003. 32p. (J). (ps-3). 15.95 (978-1-58013-082-0(8)); pap. 6.95 (978-1-58013-066-0(6)) Kar-Ben Publishing.

—Too Much of a Good Thing. 2003. (gr. k-3). lib. bdg. 15.25 (978-0-613-81210-8(7)) Tandem Library Bks.

Watson, Jude. Queen Amidala. 1999. (gr. 3-6). lib. bdg. 14.15 (978-0-613-87068-9(9)) Tandem Library Bks.

Watts, Leander. Ten Thousand Charms. 2005. 240p. (YA). (gr. 5). 16.00 (978-0-618-44897-5(7)) Houghton Mifflin Co. Trade & Reference Div.

Weaver, Patricia. Ashaki, African Princess. 2001. 164p. (YA). pap. 12.95 (978-0-595-18283-1(6) , Writer's Showcase Pr.) iUniverse, Inc.

Webb, Beth. Fleabag Trilogy. 2005. 640p. (J). pap. 14.00 (978-0-7459-4977-2(0) , Lion) Lion Hudson plc GBR. Dist: Trafalgar Square Publishing.

Webb, Catherine. Mirror Wakes. 2005. 314p. (Orig.). (J). pap. 9.99 (978-1-904233-09-1(0) , Atom Books) Little, Brown Bk. Group Ltd. GBR. Dist: Trafalgar Square Publishing.

Wein, Elizabeth. The Empty Kingdom. 2008. (YA). (gr. 5). 16.99 (*978-0-670-06273-7(1) , Viking Juvenile) Penguin Group (USA) Inc.

Weiss, Ellen. Babar: Four Stories to Read & Share. Gibert, Jean Claude & Gray, J. M. L., illus. 2006. (J). (*978-0-8109-9308-2(2) , Abrams Bks. for Young Readers) Abrams, Harry N. , Inc.

Weiss, Ellen, et al. Babar & the Christmas House. 2003. (Illus.). 28p. (J). (ps-1). 9.95 (978-0-8109-4583-8(5) , 53604968) Abrams, Harry N. , Inc.

—Babar & the Scary Day. Gibert, Jean Claude, illus. 2004. 24p. (J). (ps-3). 9.95 (978-0-8109-5019-1(7)) Abrams, Harry N. , Inc.

Wend, Arran. The King & the Fire Chanter. 2007. (Illus.). 373p. (J). 15.95 (*978-0-9793284-0-4(3)) Antiquity Publishing.

Wilde, Oscar. The House of Pomegranates. 2005. (ENG.). 81p. pap. (*978-1-4065-0242-8(1)) Dodo Pr.

Wilkes, Angela & Rawson, Christopher. The Adventures of King Arthur. 2004. (Young Reading Ser.). (Illus.). 64p. (J). (gr. 2 up). pap. 5.99 (978-0-7945-0447-2(7) , Usborne) EDC Publishing.

Wilkins, Kim. Tide Stealers: Sunken Kingdom #2. Cornish, D. M., illus. 2008. 96p. (J). (gr. 4-7). pap. 5.99 (*978-0-375-84807-0(X)); lib. bdg. 11.99 (*978-0-375-94807-7(4)) Random Hse. Children's Bks. (Random Hse. Bks. for Young Readers).

Williams, Brenda. The Real Princess. 2006. (J). (978-1-905236-88-6(3)) Barefoot Bks., Inc.

Williams, Rozanne Lanczak. Fairy Tale Mail. Maio, Barbara, ed. Allen, Joy, illus. 2006. (Learn to Write Ser.). (J). 16p. pap. 2.99 (978-1-59198-301-9(0) , 6195); per. 6.99 (*978-1-59198-359-0(2)) Creative Teaching Pr., Inc.

Winterson, Jeanette. The King of Capri. Ray, Jane, illus. 2003. 32p. (J). 16.95 (978-1-58234-830-8(8) , Bloomsbury Children) Bloomsbury Publishing.

Wisniewski, David, retold by. Sundiata: Lion King of Mali. 1999. (Illus.). 32p. (J). (gr. k-3). 6.95 (978-0-395-76481-7(5) , Clarion Bks.) Houghton Mifflin Co. Trade & Reference Div.

Woo, Soo Jung. Legend Volume 3. 2007. (Illus.). 200p. (YA). pap. 10.95 (*978-89-527-4712-9(7)) ICE Kunion KOR. Dist: Diamond Bk. Distributors.

—Legend Volume 4. 2007. 200p. (YA). pap. 10.95 (*978-89-527-4871-3(9)) ICE Kunion KOR. Dist: Diamond Bk. Distributors.

—Legend Volume 5. 2007. 200p. (YA). pap. 10.95 (*978-89-527-4883-6(2)) ICE Kunion KOR. Dist: Diamond Bk. Distributors.

Wood, Audrey. King Bidgood's in the Bathtub. Wood, Don, illus. 2005. 32p. (J). (ps-ps). 17.95 (978-0-15-205578-3(9)) Harcourt Children's Bks.

Wrede, Patricia C. Calling on Dragons. 2003. (Enchanted Forest Chronicles: Bk. 3). (Illus.). 272p. (YA). pap. 5.95 (978-0-15-204692-7(5) , Magic Carpet Bks.) Harcourt Children's Bks.

—Calling on Dragons. unabr. ed. 2004. (Enchanted Forest Ser.: Vol 3). 244p. (J). (gr. 6 up). pap. 38.00 incl. audio (978-0-8072-0792-5(6) , LYA 347 SP, Listening Library) Random Hse. Audio Publishing Group.

—Calling on Dragons. 2003. (gr. 7-12). lib. bdg. 14.10 (978-0-613-59887-3(3)) Tandem Library Bks.

—Talking to Dragons. 2003. (Enchanted Forest Chronicles: Bk. 4). (Illus.). 272p. (YA). pap. 5.95 (978-0-15-204691-0(7) , Magic Carpet Bks.) Harcourt Children's Bks.

—Talking to Dragons. unabr. ed. 2004. (Enchanted Forest Chronicles Ser.). 255p. (J). (gr. 6 up). pap. 38.00 incl. audio (978-0-8072-0983-7(X) , S YA 385 SP, Listening Library) Random Hse. Audio Publishing Group.

—Talking to Dragons. 2003. (gr. 7-12). lib. bdg. 14.10 (978-0-613-59931-3(4)) Tandem Library Bks.

Wright, Randall. Hunchback. rev. ed. 2004. (Illus.). 256p. (J). 16.95 (978-0-8050-7232-7(2) , Holt, Henry & Co. Bks. For Young Readers) Holt, Henry & Co.

Wyss, Tyan. The Solitaire Prince. 2006. 168p. (YA). 12.95 (978-1-58939-907-5(2)); per. 12.95 (978-1-58939-906-8(4)) Virtualbookworm.com Publishing, Inc.

Yolen, Jane. The Emperor & the Kite. Young, Ed, illus. 1998. 32p. (J). (ps-ps). pap. 6.99 (978-0-698-11644-3(5) , Putnam Juvenile) Penguin Group (USA) Inc.

—The Emperor & the Kite. 1998. (J). (ps-3). 13.79 (978-0-606-13366-1(6)) Tandem Library Bks.

—The Queen's Own Fool. 2001. (978-0-606-22526-7(9)) Tandem Library Bks.

—Queen's Own Fool: A Novel of Mary Queen of Scots. 2001. (gr. 7-12). lib. bdg. 16.45 (978-0-613-44410-1(8)) Tandem Library Bks.

—Sword of the Rightful King: A Novel of King Arthur. 2004. (Illus.). 376p. (YA). reprint ed. pap. 6.95 (978-0-15-202533-5(2)) Harcourt Children's Bks.

Yolen, Jane & Harris, Robert J. Queen's Own Fool: A Novel of Mary Queen of Scots. 2001. (Illus.). 400p. (YA). pap. 7.99 (978-0-698-11918-5(5) , Putnam Juvenile) Penguin Group (USA) Inc.

Yonge, Charlotte. The Little Duke. 2006. pap. (*978-1-4250-2682-0(6)) Assistedreadingbooks.com Inc.

Yonge, Charlotte M. The Little Duke. 2005. 26.95 (978-1-4218-0318-0(6)); 164p. pap. 11.95 (978-1-4218-0418-7(2)) 1st World Publishing, Inc. (1st World Library - Literary Society).

—The Little Duke. 2004. reprint ed. pap. 15.95 (978-1-4179-9958-3(6)); pap. 1.99 (978-1-4179-9908-8(X)) Kessinger Publishing, LLC.

—Little Duke EasyRead Comfort Edition. 2006. pap. (*978-1-4250-0856-7(9)) Assistedreadingbooks.com Inc.

—Little Duke EasyRead Edition. 2006. pap. (*978-1-4250-0269-5(2)) Assistedreadingbooks.com Inc.

—Little Duke EasyRead Large Edition. 2006. pap. (*978-1-4250-1299-1(X)) Assistedreadingbooks.com Inc.

KINGS AND RULERS

see Kings, Queens, Rulers, etc.

KINGS CANYON NATIONAL PARK (CALIF.)

Dickmann, Nancy. Sequoia & Kings Canyon National Parks. 2006. (Symbols of Freedom Ser.). (Illus.). 32p. (J). (978-1-4034-7798-9(1)) Heinemann Library.

Nicholas, Jeff D. Sequoia & Kings Canyon. 2004. (Illus.). per. 4.95 (*978-1-58071-054-1(9) , Wish You Were Here) Sierra Pr.

O'Shei, Tim. Stranded! Amy Racina's Story of Survival. 2008. (J). (*978-1-4296-0088-0(8)) Capstone Pr., Inc.

KINGSLEY, MARY HENRIETTA, 1862-1900

Wagner, Heather Lehr. Mary Kingsley: Explorer of the Congo. 2004. (Women Explorers Ser.). 120p. 30.00 (978-0-7910-7714-6(4) , Chelsea Hse.) Facts On File, Inc.

KIPLING, RUDYARD, 1865-1936—FICTION

Blegvad, Lenore. Kitty & Mr. Kipling: Neighbors in Vermont. Blegvad, Erik, illus. 2005. 144p. (J). (gr. 3-5). 16.95 (978-0-689-87363-8(8) , McElderry, Margaret K.) Simon & Schuster Children's Publishing.

Spillebeen, Geert. Kipling's Choice. Edelstein, Terese, tr. 160p. (YA). (gr. 7 up). 2007. pap. 7.99 (*978-0-618-80035-3(2) , Graphia); 2005. 16.00 (978-0-618-43124-3(1)) Houghton Mifflin Co. Trade & Reference Div.

KIPPER (FICTITIOUS CHARACTER)—FICTION

Inkpen, Mick. A to Z: An Alphabet Adventure. 2001. (Kipper Ser.). (Illus.). 64p. (J). (ps-2). 16.95 (978-0-15-202594-6(4) , Red Wagon Bks.) Harcourt Children's Bks.

—Hissss! 2000. 11.75 (978-0-606-22337-9(1)); 1999. lib. bdg. 12.95 (978-0-613-25527-1(5)) Tandem Library Bks.

—Kipper. Inkpen, Mick, illus. 2002. (Illus.). (J). 13.15 (978-0-7587-6464-5(2)) Book Wholesalers, Inc.

—Kipper. (ENG & FRE., Illus.). 32p. (J). (978-1-85430-330-1(9) , 93450); (978-1-85430-333-2(3) , 93451) Magi Pubns.

—Kipper. 1999. (978-0-606-17487-9(7)) Tandem Library Bks.

—Kipper's Birthday. 2000. (Illus.). (J). (978-0-606-18181-5(4)) Tandem Library Bks.

—Kipper's Book of Numbers. Inkpen, Mick, illus. 2002. (Kipper Ser.). (Illus.). (J). 13.19 (978-0-7587-6465-2(0)) Book Wholesalers, Inc.

—Kipper's Book of Opposites. Inkpen, Mick, illus. 2002. (Kipper Ser.). (Illus.). (J). 13.19 (978-0-7587-6466-9(9)) Book Wholesalers, Inc.

—Kipper's Snowy Day. Inkpen, Mick, illus. 2002. (Kipper Ser.). (Illus.). (J). 13.15 (978-0-7587-2935-4(9)) Book Wholesalers, Inc.

—Kipper's Snowy Day. 1999. (978-0-606-17488-6(5)) Tandem Library Bks.

—Kipper's Toybox. Inkpen, Mick, illus. 2002. (Kipper Ser.). (Illus.). (J). 13.15 (978-0-7587-6467-6(7)) Book Wholesalers, Inc.

—Kipper's Toybox. (Illus.). 25p. (J). (CHI, ENG, URD, VIE & FRE.). (978-1-85430-350-9(3) , 93452); (ENG, FRE, URD, VIE & CHI., (978-1-85430-351-6(1) , 93453) Magi Pubns.

—Kipper's Toybox. 2000. (Illus.). (J). (978-0-606-18182-2(2)) Tandem Library Bks.

—Skates. 2001. (gr. k-3). lib. bdg. 12.95 (978-0-613-51326-5(6)) Tandem Library Bks.

KISSINGER, HENRY, 1923-

Wagner, Heather Lehr. Henry Kissinger: Ending the Vietnam War. 2007. (Modern Peacemakers Ser.). (Illus.). 120p. (YA). (gr. 9 up). 30.00 (978-0-7910-9222-4(4) , Chelsea Hse.) Facts On File, Inc.

KITCHEN GARDENS

see Vegetable Gardening

KITCHEN UTENSILS

see Household Equipment and Supplies

KITCHENS

Canizares, Susan & Chessen, Betsey. In the Kitchen. 2000. (My First Library). (Illus.). (J). (ps-k). 4.95 (978-0-439-15521-2(5)) Scholastic, Inc.

La Cocina: Individual Title Two-Packs. (Chiquilibros Ser.). (SPA.). (ps-1). 12.00 (978-0-7635-8560-0(2)) Rigby Education.

In the Kitchen, 6 Packs. (Bookweb Ser.). 32p. (gr. 3 up). 34.00 (978-0-7635-3951-1(1)) Rigby Education.

In the Kitchen. 2005. (J). (978-1-59564-720-7(1)) Steps To Literacy, LLC.

Pinkwater, Daniel M. Rainy Morning. Pinkwater, Jill, illus. 1999. (Pinkwater Ser.: Vol. 1). 32p. (J). (gr. k-3). 16.00 (978-0-689-81143-2(8) , Atheneum) Simon & Schuster Children's Publishing.

Solway, Andrew. What's Living in Your Kitchen? 2004. (Hidden Life Ser.). (Illus.). 32p. (J). pap. 7.50 (978-1-4034-5483-6(3)); lib. bdg. 25.64 (978-1-4034-4844-6(2)) Heinemann Library.

Tuxworth, Nicola & Lorenz Editors. Kitchen. 2003. (Illus.). 20p. 5.99 (978-0-7548-1198-5(0)) Anness Publishing GBR. *Dist:* National Bk. Network.

KITES

Amado, Elisa. Un Barrilete: Para el Dia de los Muertos. 1999. 13.75 (978-0-606-17570-8(9)) Tandem Library Bks.

Boyce, Jeremy. How to Make & Fly Stunt Kites. 2002. 64p. (J). pap. 9.98 (978-0-7525-4257-7(5)) Parragon, Inc.

Demi. Kites: Magic Wishes That Fly up to the Sky. 2000. (gr. k-3). lib. bdg. 15.30 (978-0-613-28339-7(2)) Tandem Library Bks.

Demi, Hitz. Kites: Magic Wishes That Fly up to the Sky. 2000. (J). (978-0-606-19772-4(9)) Tandem Library Bks.

Eden, Maxwell. The Magnificent Book of Kites. 2002. (Illus.). 464p. pap. 14.95 (978-1-4027-0094-1(6)) Sterling Publishing Co., Inc.

Greger, Margaret. Kites for Everyone. Greger, Del & Greger, Greg, illus. Greger, Greg, photos by. 3rd rev. ed. 2000. 128p. (YA). pap. 15.00 (978-0-9613680-1-2(2)) Greger, Margaret.

Harris, Elizabeth. Parafoil Stunt Kite. Parks, Kevin, illus. 2002. 24p. (J). pap. 7.95 (978-0-439-33875-2(1)) Scholastic, Inc.

Hosking, Wayne. Asian Kites. 2005. (Asian Arts & Crafts for Creative Kids Ser.). (Illus.). 64p. (J). 12.95 (978-0-8048-3545-9(4)) Tuttle Publishing.

The Kite. 2002. (J). 16.00 (978-0-9675413-6-5(0)) Libros, Encouraging Cultural Literacy.

Kites. (Early Intervention Levels Ser.). 21.30 (978-0-7362-0368-5(0)) Hampton-Brown Bks.

Kites: Individual Nonfiction Title Six-Packs. 24p. (gr. 3-4). 44.00 (978-0-7635-4488-1(4)) Rigby Education.

Loves, June. Balloons, Kites, Airships & Gliders. 2001. (Flight Ser.). (Illus.). (J). (gr. 5 up). 27.00 (978-0-7910-6563-1(4) , 010302, Chelsea Hse.) Facts On File, Inc.

Make a Kite: Individual Title Six-Packs. (Story Steps Ser.). (gr. k-2). 29.00 (978-0-7635-9588-3(8)) Rigby Education.

Mini Kites. 2004. (Formula Fun Ser.). (Illus.). 48p. (J). (978-1-84229-580-9(2)) Top That! Publishing PLC.

Murphy, Stuart J. Let's Fly a Kite: Symmetry. Floca, Brian, illus. 2000. (Mathstart Ser.). (J). (978-0-606-19985-8(3)) Tandem Library Bks.

Murray, Peter & Amparano, Julie. America's Latinos: Their Rich History, Culture, & Traditions. Dann, Penny, illus. 2003. (Proud Heritage-The Hispanic Library). 40p. (J). (gr. 3-7). 28.50 (978-1-56766-083-8(5)) Child's World, Inc.

Ostrovsky, Alexsandr. Paper Kite. Ostrovsky, Alexsandr, illus. (Childrens Ser.). (Illus.). (Orig.). (J). pap. 14.95 (978-0-934393-18-8(4)) Rector Pr., Ltd.

Packard, Mary. The Kite. Huang, Benrei, illus. 2003. (My First Reader Ser.). 32p. (J). 18.50 (978-0-516-22930-0(3) , Children's Pr.) Scholastic Library Publishing.

Pienkowski, Jan. The Red Kite. 2002. (Illus.). 300p. (978-0-85661-128-5(X) , Academic Pr.) Elsevier Science & Technology Bks.

Preszler, Eric. Kiteboarding. 2005. (X-Sports Ser.). (Illus.). 32p. (J). (ps). lib. bdg. 22.60 (978-0-7368-3783-5(3)) Capstone Pr., Inc.

Schmidt, Norman. Best Ever Paper Kites. 2003. (Illus.). 96p. pap. 7.95 (978-1-895569-53-7(2)) Tamos Bks., Inc. CAN. *Dist:* Sterling Publishing Co., Inc.

Stevens, Beth Dvergsten. Colorful Kites. 1999. (Cover-to-Cover Bks.). (Illus.). 56p. (J). (gr. 1-4). lib. bdg. 16.95 (978-0-7807-9002-5(2) , Covercraft); (gr. 3-5). 8.95 (978-0-7891-2843-0(8)) Perfection Learning Corp.

Torrijos, Eduardo & Garcia, Gretel. Papalotes: Tecnicas de Armado y Vuelo. Torrijos, Eduardo, illus. 2004. (SPA., Illus.). 157p. (J). pap. (978-970-643-734-1(7)) Selector, S.A. de C.V. MEX. *Dist:* Lectorum Pubns., Inc.

Williams, Deborah. My Kite. 2005. 8p. (Orig.). (J). pap. 4.25 (978-1-57874-082-6(7)) Kaeden Corp.

Windsor, Jo. Kitesurfing: Individual Title Six-Packs. (Sails Literacy Ser.). 20p. (gr. 2-3). 27.00 (978-0-7578-0716-9(X)) Rigby Education.

KITES—FICTION

Ada, Alma Flor. The Kite. (Stories the Year 'Round Ser.). (Illus.). 16p. (J). (gr. k-3). pap. 8.95 (978-1-58105-206-0(5)) Santillana USA Publishing Co., Inc.

Baumgart, Klaus. Laura's Secret. Waite, Judy, tr. from GER. 2003. Orig. Title: German. (Illus.). 32p. (J). (ps-2). tchr. ed. 16.95 (978-1-58925-031-4(1) , tiger tales) ME Media LLC.

Berenstain, Stan & Berenstain, Jan. The Berenstain Bears We Like Kites. 2004. (Berenstain Bears Ser.). (Illus.). 32p. (J). (ps-1). pap. 3.99 (978-0-679-89231-1(1) , Random Hse. Bks. for Young Readers) Random Hse. Children's Bks.

—The Berenstain Bears We Like Kites. 2004. (Berenstain Bears Ser.). (J). (ps-2). lib. bdg. 11.80 (978-0-613-87779-4(9)) Tandem Library Bks.

Bickel, Karla. The Kite Who Was Afraid to Fly. Bickel, Karla, illus. l.t. ed. 2004. (Illus.). 16p. (J). (ps-6). pap. 5.00 (978-1-891452-08-6(8) , 6) Heart Arbor Bks.

Bjorkman, Steve. The Flyaway Kite. Bjorkman, Steve, illus. 2000. (Illus.). 40p. (J). (ps-3). 9.99 (978-1-57856-264-0(3) , WaterBrook Pr.) WaterBrook Pr.

Blackaby, Susan. Riley Flies a Kite. Skeens, Matthew, illus. 2006. (Read-It! Readers Ser.). 24p. (J). (ps-3). 18.60 (978-1-4048-1586-5(4)) Picture Window Bks.

Blanco, Alberto. Angel's Kite (La Estrella de Angel) Bellm, Dan, tr. Morales, Rodolfo, illus. 1998. (ENG & SPA.). 32p. (J). (gr. 1-4). pap. 7.95 (978-0-89239-156-1(1)) Children's Bk. Pr.

—La Estrella de Angel. ed. 2004. Tr. of Angel's Kite. (ENG & SPA., Illus.). (J). (gr. k-3). spiral bd. (978-0-616-14604-0(3)) Canadian National Institute for the Blind/Institut National Canadien pour les Aveugles.

Burgess, Mark. Follow the Kite. 1998. (Illus.). 15p. (J). pap. 9.95 (978-0-00-136053-2(1)) Zondervan.

Chen, Jiang Hong. The Legend of the Kite: A Story of China. Chen, Jiang Hong, illus. 1999. (Multi-National Ser.). Orig. Title: La Legende du Cerf-Volant. (Illus.). 32p. (J). (gr. k-3). 15.95 (978-1-56899-810-7(4) , B8004); pap. 5.95 (978-1-56899-811-4(2) , S8004) Soundprints.

Danforth, Audrey & Kennedy, Jane. Kite Dance. Power, Kate Eason, illus. 2000. 8p. (J). (gr. k-2). pap. 3.75 (978-1-58323-003-9(3) , Seedling Pubns.) Continental Pr., Inc.

Demi, Hitz. Kites: Magic Wishes That Fly up to the Sky. Slattery, Joan, ed. Demi, Hitz, illus. 2000. (Illus.). 40p. (J). (gr. k-3). pap. 6.99 (978-0-375-81008-4(0) , Dragonfly Bks.) Random Hse. Children's Bks.

Deubreau, Sharon. Heather & Avery & the Magic Kite. Pileggi, Steve, illus. l.t. ed. 2006. 23p. (J). per. 11.99 (978-1-59879-143-3(5)) Lifevest Publishing, Inc.

Emmett, Jonathan. Someone Bigger. Reynolds, Adrian, illus. 2004. 32p. (J). (gr. k-3). 16.00 (978-0-618-44397-0(5) , Clarion Bks.) Houghton Mifflin Co. Trade & Reference Div.

Engelman, Beth. The Kite Race. 2007. 7p. 10.95 ***(978-1-58117-593-6(0)*** , Intervisual/Piggy Toes) Dalmatian Pr.

Fox, Paula. La Cometa Rota. (SPA., Illus.). 120p. (YA). (gr. 5-8). (978-84-279-3213-5(8) , NG7615) Noguer y Caralt Editores, S. A. ESP. *Dist:* Lectorum Pubns., Inc.

—La Cometa Rota. 2001. (SPA.). (gr. 3-6). lib. bdg. 18.20 (978-0-613-80658-9(1)) Tandem Library Bks.

Garay, Luis. The Kite. 2002. (Illus.). 32p. (J). (gr. 1-4). 14.95 (978-0-88776-503-2(3)) Tundra Bks., Inc./Livres Toundra, Inc. CAN. *Dist:* Random Hse., Inc.

Gruelle, Johnny. How Raggedy Ann Got Her Candy Heart. 2001. (ps-2). lib. bdg. 15.30 (978-0-613-90801-6(5)) Tandem Library Bks.

Hall, Bruce Edward. Henry & the Kite Dragon. Low, William, tr. Low, William, illus. 2004. 32p. (J). (gr. 1-5). 15.99 (978-0-399-23727-0(5) , Philomel) Penguin Group (USA) Inc.

Harcourt School Publishers Staff. Picture a Kite: Below Level. 3rd ed. 2002. (Trophies Reading Program Ser.). (Illus.). (J). (gr. 1). pap. 4.10 (978-0-15-322960-2(8)) Harcourt Schl. Pubs.

Harding, Kitchener L. Little Miss Priss: Flying Kites & Kisses Not for the Misses. Harding, Kitchener L., illus. l.t. ed. 1999. 10p. (J). (gr. 1-5). spiral bd. 4.95 (978-1-930503-00-7(8)) Office Max.

Head, Honor. Opposites. Stower, Adam, illus. 1998. (Ed Mouse Finds Out about Ser.). 32 p. (J). (ps-2). 19.98 (978-0-8172-5202-1(9)) Raintree.

Highway, Tomson. Dragonfly Kites: Kiweeginapiseek. ed. 2004. (Illus.). (J). (gr. k-3). spiral bd. (978-0-616-14619-4(1)) Canadian National Institute for the Blind/Institut National Canadien pour les Aveugles.

Hong, Chen Jian. La Leyenda De la Cometa. (SPA.). 32p. (978-84-95150-29-5(8)); (978-84-95150-39-4(5)) Corimbo, Editorial S.L.

Huntington, Amy, illus. Seagull Sam. 2007. 32p. (ps-2). 15.95 ***(978-0-89272-715-5(2))*** Down East Bks.

Ichikawa, Satomi. My Pig Amarillo: A Tale from Guatemala. Ichikawa, Satomi, illus. 2003. (Illus.). 32p. (J). (ps-3). 16.99 (978-0-399-23768-3(2) , Philomel) Penguin Group (USA) Inc.

Krensky, Stephen. Ben Franklin & His First Kite. Dodson, Bert, illus. ed. 2005. (Ready-to-Read Ser. Level 2). 32p. (J). lib. bdg. 15.00 (978-1-59054-941-4(4)) Fitzgerald Bks.

L'Heureux, Christine. Caillou, Ma Maman. braille ed. 2004. (FRE., Illus.). (J). (gr. 1). spiral bd. (978-0-616-03083-7(5)) Canadian National Institute for the Blind/Institut National Canadien pour les Aveugles.

—Caillou, Mon Papa. braille ed. 2004. (FRE., Illus.). (J). (gr. 1). bds. (978-0-616-03084-4(3)) Canadian National Institute for the Blind/Institut National Canadien pour les Aveugles.

Lin, Grace. Kite Flying. (Illus.). 32p. (J). (ps-3). 2004. pap. 6.99 (978-0-553-11254-2(6) , Dragonfly Bks.); 2002. 14.95 (978-0-375-81520-1(1) , Knopf Bks. for Young Readers) Random Hse. Children's Bks.

Little Blue Kite & Friends Activity Book. 2005. (YA). per. (978-1-59872-122-5(4)) Instantpublisher.com.

Little Boo Kite. 2005. (J). per. 9.25 (978-1-59872-032-7(5)) Instantpublisher.com.

MacDonald, Maryann. Rabbit's Birthday Kite. Munsinger, Lynn, illus. 1999. (Bank Street Reader Collection). 48p. (J). (gr. 1-3). lib. bdg. 22.60 (978-0-8368-1779-9(6)) Stevens, Gareth Inc.

Mayer, Mercer. Shibumi & the Kitemaker. Mayer, Mercer, illus. 2005. (Illus.). 48p. (J). pap. 5.95 (978-0-7614-5145-7(5)) Cavendish, Marshall Corp.

—Shibumi & the Kitemaker. 1999. (Accelerated Reader Bks.). (Illus.). 48p. (YA). (ps-3). 18.95 (978-0-7614-5054-2(8) , Cavendish Children's Bks.) Cavendish, Marshall Corp.

—Shibumi & the Kitemaker. 2003. (gr. k-3). lib. bdg. 14.10 (978-0-613-87253-9(3)) Tandem Library Bks.

—Tiger's Birthday. 2002. (Little Critter First Readers Ser.). (Illus.). 24p. (J). (gr. k-1). pap. 3.95 (978-1-57768-828-0(7)) School Specialty Publishing.

McCaughrean, Geraldine. The Kite Rider. 2003. (Illus.). 320p. (J). (gr. 7 up). pap. 6.99 (978-0-06-441091-5(9)) HarperCollins Pubs.

—The Kite Rider. 2002. (gr. 7-12). lib. bdg. 15.30 (978-0-613-68440-8(0)) Tandem Library Bks.

Mitchell, Robin. Windy. Mitchell, Robin & Steedman, Judith, illus. l.t. ed. 2002. 48p. (J). (ps-2). 14.95 (978-0-9688768-2-4(X)) Simply Read Bks. CAN. *Dist:* Perseus Distribution.

My Kite: KinderConcepts Individual Title Six-Packs. (Kinderstarters Ser.). 8p. (ps-1). 21.00 (978-0-7635-8715-4(X)) Rigby Education.

Okereke, Laurence. Barry Makes A Kite. 2007. (Illus.). 20p. (J). spiral bd. ***(978-0-9795739-2-7(0))*** Dion's Pubn.

Packard, Mary. The Kite. 2004. (My First Reader Ser.). (Illus.). 29p. (J). (gr. k-1). pap. 3.95 (978-0-516-24632-1(1) , Children's Pr.) Scholastic Library Publishing.

Palmer, Jan, illus. How Raggedy Ann Got Her Candy Heart. 2001. (My First Raggedy Ann Ser.). 32p. (J). pap. 6.99 (978-0-689-80887-6(9) , Aladdin) Simon & Schuster Children's Publishing.

Park, Linda Sue. The Kite Fighters. 2000. (Illus.). 144p. (J). (gr. 5-9). tchr. ed. 15.00 (978-0-395-94041-9(9) , Clarion Bks.) Houghton Mifflin Co. Trade & Reference Div.

—The Kite Fighters. 2002. (gr. 5-8). lib. bdg. 13.00 (978-0-613-57908-7(9)) Tandem Library Bks.

Perez, Monica, et al. Curious George & the Kite: Early Reader. 2007. (Illus.). 24p. (J). (gr. k-3). 3.99 (978-0-618-72396-6(X)) Houghton Mifflin Co.

Pilegard, Virginia Walton. The Warlord's Kites. Debon, Nicolas, illus. 2004. 432p. (J). pap. 15.95 (978-1-58980-180-6(6)) Pelican Publishing Co., Inc.

Reinheimer, Melinda T. Little Blue Kite Makes A Friend: Another Adventure of the Little Blue Kite. 2005. 24p. (J). per. 9.95 (978-1-59196-908-2(5)) Instantpublisher.com.

Rey, H. A. Curious George Flies a Kite. Rey, H. A., illus. 2002. (Curious George Picture Bks.). (Illus.). (J). 13.79 (978-0-7587-2314-7(8)) Book Wholesalers, Inc.

—Curious George Flies a Kite. ed. 2004. (J). (gr. k-3). spiral bd. (978-0-616-01770-8(7)); spiral bd. (978-0-616-01771-5(5)) Canadian National Institute for the Blind/Institut National Canadien pour les Aveugles.

Ricci, Christine. Dora & the Rainbow Kite Festival. Roper, Robert, illus. 2008. (Dora the Explorer Ser.). 24p. (J). pap. 3.99 ***(978-1-4169-4777-6(9)*** , Simon Spotlight/Nickelodeon) Simon & Schuster Children's Publishing.

Roche, Hannah. Corey's Kite. 1998. (My First Weather Bks.). (Illus.). 24p. (J). (ps-3). (978-1-84089-033-4(9) , Zero to Ten, Limited) Evans Publishing Group.

Rouillard, Wendy W. Barnaby's Kite Ride. Rouillard, Wendy W., illus. l.t. ed. 1998. (Illus.). 32p. (J). (gr. 1-3). 15.95 (978-0-9642836-6-4(2)) Barnaby & Co.

Ruiz-Flores, Lupe. Lupita's Papalote / el Papalote de Lupita. Ventura, Gabriela Baeza, tr. Rodriguez Howard, Pauline, illus. 32p. (J). (gr. k-2). 15.95 (978-1-55885-359-1(6) , Piñata Books) Arte Publico Pr.

Spalding, Andrea. The Most Beautiful Kite in the World. Watts, Leslie Elizabeth, illus. 32p. (J). (978-1-55041-716-6(9)) Fitzhenry & Whiteside, Ltd.

Torres, Leyla. El Festival de Cometas. Torres, Leyla, illus. 2004. (SPA., Illus.). 32p. (J). 16.00 (978-0-374-32299-1(6) , Frances Foster Bks.) Farrar, Straus & Giroux.

—The Kite Festival. Torres, Leyla, illus. 2004. (Illus.). 32p. (J). 16.00 (978-0-374-38054-0(6) , Farrar, Straus & Giroux (BYR)) Farrar, Straus & Giroux.

Ungerer, Tomi. No Kiss for Mother. 1998. (Illus.). 40p. (J). (ps-3). pap. 5.95 (978-1-57098-208-8(2)) Rinehart, Roberts Pubs.

Uribe, Veronica. Diego y la Gran Cometa Voladora. Coll, Ivar Da, illus. 2002. (Primeras Lecturas Coleccion). (SPA.). 32p. (J). pap. (978-980-257-132-1(6)) Ekare, Ediciones.

Wilcox, Michael. Colors Around Us. Barber, Julia, illus. 2004. 32p. (J). per. 19.95 (978-1-931780-32-2(3)) School of Color Publishing.

Williams Laura. Best Winds. 2006. (Illus.). 32p. (J). 16.95 (978-1-59078-274-3(7)) Boyds Mills Pr.

Wright, Cliff. Bear & Kite. 2005. (Illus.). 16p. (J). bds. 5.95 (978-0-8118-4820-6(5)) Chronicle Bks. LLC.

Wright, Sue. Davey & Goliath: The Kite. 2005. (Davey & Goliath Ser.). (Illus.). 40p. (J). pap. 3.99 (978-0-439-69831-3(6) , Scholastic Paperbacks) Scholastic, Inc.

Yolen, Jane. The Emperor & the Kite. Young, Ed, illus. 1998. 32p. (J). (ps-ps). pap. 6.99 (978-0-698-11644-3(5) , Putnam Juvenile) Penguin Group (USA) Inc.

—The Emperor & the Kite. 1998. (J). (ps-3). 13.79 (978-0-606-13366-1(6)) Tandem Library Bks.

KKK

see Ku Klux Klan (1915-)

KLEE, PAUL, 1879-1940

Connolly, Sean. Paul Klee. (Heinemann First Library). 32p. (J). 2006. (Illus.). lib. bdg. ***(978-1-4034-8496-3(1));*** 1999. lib. bdg. 21.36 (978-1-57572-952-7(0)) Heinemann Library.

Delpech, Sylvie & Leclerc, Caroline, eds. Paul Klee. 2006. (Sticker Art Shapes Ser.). (Illus.). 28p. 7.95 (978-1-84507-677-1(X)) Lincoln, Frances Ltd. GBR. *Dist:* Perseus Distribution.

Laidlaw, Jill A. Paul Klee. 2002. (Artists in Their Time Ser.). (J). (gr. 5-7). pap. 6.95 (978-0-531-16623-9(6)); (Illus.). 48p. pap. 23.50 (978-0-531-12230-3(1)) Scholastic Library Publishing. (Watts, Franklin).

Sean Connolly. Paul Klee. 2nd ed. 2006. (Heinemann First Library). (Illus.). 32p. (J). pap. ***(978-1-4034-8507-6(0))*** Heinemann Library.

KLONDIKE GOLD FIELDS

Berton, Pierre. The Golden Trail: The Story of the Klondike Rush. 2004. (Illus.). 144p. pap. (978-1-894856-04-1(X)) Fifth Hse. Pubs.

—The Great Klondike Gold Rush. 2007. (Illus.). 300p. (J). (gr. k). pap. 21.95 ***(978-1-897252-05-5(6))*** Fifth Hse. Pubs. CAN. *Dist:* Fitzhenry & Whiteside, Ltd.

—Sterling Point Books: Stampede for Gold: the Story of the Klondike Rush. 2007. (Sterling Point Bks.). 180p. (J). pap. 6.95 ***(978-1-4027-5121-9(4))*** Sterling Publishing Co., Inc.

Lourie, Peter. Yukon River: An Adventure to the Gold Fields of the Klondike. 2003. (Illus.). 48p. (YA). (gr. 4-6). pap. 9.95 (978-1-56397-878-4(4)) Boyds Mills Pr.

—Yukon River: An Adventure to the Gold Fields of the Klondike. 2000. (gr. 3-6). lib. bdg. 18.75 (978-0-613-49402-1(4)) Tandem Library Bks.

Nobleman, Marc Tyler. The Klondike Gold Rush. 2006. (We the People Ser.). (Illus.). 48p. (J). (gr. 4-6). 23.93 (978-0-7565-1630-7(7)) Compass Point Bks.

Shepherd, Donna Walsh. The Klondike Gold Rush. 1998. (Illus.). 64p. (J). (ps-6). lib. bdg. 15.25 (978-0-613-18841-8(1)) Tandem Library Bks.

KLONDIKE GOLD FIELDS—FICTION

Czuchna-Curl, Ardyce. Days of Gold. 2002. (Illus.). 128p. (J). pap. 12.95 (978-0-88196-012-9(8)) Oak Woods Media.

Dell, Pamela. Half-Breed: A Story of Two Boys During the Klondike Gold Rush. 2003. (Scrapbooks of America Ser.). (Illus.). 48p. (J). (gr. 2-6). 28.50 (978-1-59187-044-9(5)) Child's World, Inc.

Duncan, Sandy Frances. Gold Rush Orphan. 2005. (Illus.). 280p. (J). pap. 10.95 (978-1-55380-012-5(5)) Ronsdale Pr. CAN. *Dist:* Literary Pr. Group of Canada.

Greenwood, Barbara. Gold Rush Fever: A Story of the Klondike, 1898. Collins, Heather, illus. 2001. (History Comes Alive Ser.). 160p. (J). (gr. 4-6). (978-1-55074-850-5(5)); (978-1-55074-852-9(1)) Kids Can Pr., Ltd.

Hobbs, Will. Jason's Gold. 2000. (gr. 5-8). lib. bdg. 14.15 (978-0-613-29995-4(7)) Tandem Library Bks.

Hobbs, William. Jason's Gold. (Illus.). 240p. (J). (gr. 6 up). 2000. pap. 5.99 (978-0-380-72914-2(8)); 1999. 16.99 (978-0-688-15093-8(4)) HarperCollins Pubs.

Piotrowski, Robert. Gold Rush. Alward, Jeff, illus. 2007. 48p. (J). lib. bdg. 23.08 ***(978-1-4242-1628-4(1))*** Fitzgerald Bks.

KNIGHTHOOD

see Knights and Knighthood

KNIGHTS AND KNIGHTHOOD

see also Heraldry

Adam, Winky. Knights. 1998. (Illus.). 32p. (J). pap., act. bk. ed. 3.95 (978-0-486-40356-4(4)) Dover Pubns., Inc.

Adkins, Jan. What If You Met a Knight? Adkins, Jan, illus. 2006. (Illus.). 32p. (J). (gr. 4-8). 16.95 (978-1-59643-148-5(2)) Roaring Brook Pr.

J K L

Barter, James. A Medieval Knight. 2005. (Working Life Ser.). (Illus.). 112p. (YA). (gr. 7-10). lib. bdg. 29.95 (978-1-59018-580-3(3) , Lucent Bks.) Thomson Gale.

Brooks, Philip. Knights & Castles. Kingfisher Editors, ed. 2001. (Questions & Answers about... Ser.). 40p. (J). (gr. 4-6). pap. 7.95 (978-0-7534-5371-1(1) , Kingfisher) Houghton Mifflin Co. Trade & Reference Div.

Caviezel, Giovanni. Knights. 2007. (Little People Shape Bks.). 10p. (J). (ps-3). bds. 10.99 (*978-0-7641-6065-3(6)) Barron's Educational Series, Inc.

Chrisp, Peter. Warfare. 2004. (Medieval Realms Ser.). (J). (gr. 7-10). 29.95 (978-1-59018-537-7(4) , Lucent Bks.) Thomson Gale.

Coggins, Jack. The Illustrated Book of Knights. 2006. (Illus.). 112p. pap. 14.95 (978-0-486-45134-3(8)) Dover Pubns., Inc.

Colum, Padraic. The Story of King Arthur & Other Celtic Heroes. Jones, Wilfred, illus. 2005. 208p. pap. 9.95 (978-0-486-44061-3(3)) Dover Pubns., Inc.

Daly-Weir, Catherine. Knights. Crosby, Jeff, illus. 1998. (All Aboard Reading Ser.). 48p. (J). (gr. 1-3). pap. 3.99 (978-0-448-41857-5(6) , Grosset & Dunlap) Penguin Group (USA) Inc.

Dargie, Richard. Knights & Castles. 1998. (Age of Castles Ser.). (Illus.). 48 p. (J). (gr. 3-7). lib. bdg. 25.69 (978-0-8172-5122-2(7)) Raintree.

—Knights & Castles. 1998. (Age of Castles Ser.). (Illus.). 48p. (J). (gr. 4-8). pap. 7.95 (978-0-8172-8122-9(3)) Steck-Vaughn.

Dixon, Philip. Knights & Castles. 2007. (Insiders Ser.). 64p. (J). (gr. 3-7). 16.99 (*978-1-4169-3864-4(8)) Simon & Schuster Children's Publishing.

Dorling Kindersley Publishing Staff. Castle & Knight. 2005. (Ultimate sticker Bks.). 16p. (J). pap. 6.99 (978-0-7566-1455-3(4)) Dorling Kindersley Publishing, Inc.

Eastwood, Kay. The Life of a Knight. 2003. (Medieval World Ser.). (Illus.). 32p. (J). (gr. 5). (978-0-7787-1342-5(3)); pap. (978-0-7787-1374-6(1)) Crabtree Publishing Co.

English Heritage Staff. My Life as a Knight. 2005. (Illus.). 32p. pap. 19.95 (978-1-85074-985-1(X)) English Heritage GBR. *Dist:* Brown, David Bk. Co., The.

Farman, John. The Short & Bloody History of Knights. 2005. (Short & Bloody Histories Ser.). (Illus.). 96p. (gr. 6-12). lib. bdg. 19.93 (978-0-8225-0841-0(9)) Lerner Publishing Group.

—Short & Bloody History of Knights. 2002. (gr. 5-8). lib. bdg. 14.10 (978-0-613-52497-1(7)) Tandem Library Bks.

Firth, Rachel. Knights. 2004. (Discovery Program Ser.). (SPA., Illus.). 48p. (J). pap. 8.95 (978-0-7945-0385-7(3) , Usborne); lib. bdg. 16.95 (978-1-58086-509-8(7)) EDC Publishing.

—Knights. 2003. (gr. 3-6). lib. bdg. 17.60 (978-0-613-75424-8(7)) Tandem Library Bks.

—Knights & Armor - Internet Linked. 2006. (Illus.). 96p. (J). 17.99 (978-0-7945-1279-8(8) , Usborne) EDC Publishing.

Flynn, Benedict. King Arthur & the Knights of the Round Table. 2008. (Hear It Read It Ser.). 160p. (J). (gr. 2 up). 9.95 (*978-1-4022-1243-7(7) , Sourcebooks Jabberwocky) Sourcebooks, Inc.

Gibbons, Gail. Knights in Shining Armor. Gibbons, Gail, illus. 2002. (Illus.). (J). 13.15 (978-0-7587-2939-2(1)) Book Wholesalers, Inc.

—Knights in Shining Armor. 1998. (Illus.). 32p. (J). (ps-3). pap. 7.99 (978-0-316-30038-4(1)) Little Brown & Co.

Gilbert, Henry. King Arthur's Knights: The Tales Retold for Boys & Girls. 2004. reprint ed. pap. 27.95 (978-1-4191-2865-3(5)); pap. 1.99 (978-1-4192-2865-0(X)) Kessinger Publishing, LLC.

Gravett, Christopher. Knight. 2007. (DK Eyewitness Bks.). 72p. (J). (gr. 3-8). 15.99 incl. cd-rom (978-0-7566-3003-4(7)) Dorling Kindersley Publishing, Inc.

—Real Knights: Over 20 True Stories of Battle & Adventure. James, John, illus. 2005. 48p. (J). (gr. k-9). 15.95 (978-1-59270-034-9(9)) Enchanted Lion Bks., LLC.

Gravett, Christopher & Dorling Kindersley Publishing Staff. Knight. Dann, Geoff, photos by. 2004. (Eyewitness Books). (Illus.). 72p. (J). lib. bdg. 19.99 (978-0-7566-0695-4(0)) Dorling Kindersley Publishing, Inc.

Hamilton, John. Knights & Heroes. 2005. (Illus.). 32p. (J). (gr. 4-8). lib. bdg. 24.21 (978-1-59679-336-1(8) , ABDO & Daughters) ABDO Publishing Co.

Hanel, Rachael. Knights. 2007. (J). (978-1-58341-536-8(X) , Creative Education) Creative Co., The.

Hare, Christopher. Bayard the Good Knight Without Fear & Without Reproach. 2004. reprint ed. pap. 1.99 (978-1-4192-0906-2(X)) Kessinger Publishing, LLC.

Hart, Avery & Mantell, Paul. Knights & Castles: 50 Hands-On Activities to Experience the Middle Ages. 1998. (Kaleidoscope Kids Bks.: Vol. 2). (Illus.). 96p. (J). (gr. 2-8). pap. 12.95 (978-1-885593-17-7(1) , Williamson Bks.) Ideals Pubns.

Hindley, J. Knights & Castles. 2004. (Time Traveler Ser.). (Illus.). 32p. (J). lthr. 14.95 (978-1-58086-554-8(2)); pap. 6.95 (978-0-7945-0335-2(7)) EDC Publishing.

Hindley, Judy. Knights & Castles. 2003. (gr. 3-6). lib. bdg. 15.25 (978-0-613-75311-1(9)) Tandem Library Bks.

Knights Are Brave. 2002. (Little Friends Ser.). 32p. (J). 2.98 (978-1-84273-426-1(1) , Exclusive Editions) Parragon, Inc.

Lacey, Minna & Davidson, Susanna. Gladiators - Internet Referenced. 2006. 64p. (J). 8.99 (978-0-7945-1268-2(2) , Usborne) EDC Publishing.

Levin, Freddie. 1-2-3 Draw Knights, Castles & Dragons: A Step-by-Step Guide. 2001. (One-Two-Three Draw Ser.). (Illus.). 64p. (J). (gr. 1-7). pap. 8.99 (978-0-939217-43-4(0) , 32064) Peel Productions, Inc.

Lilly, Melinda. Knight. 2002. (Illus.). 32p. (J). lib. bdg. 26.60 (978-1-58952-227-5(3)) Rourke Publishing, LLC.

MacDonald, Fiona. Knights & Castles. 2005. (First Look at History Ser.). (Illus.). 24p. (J). lib. bdg. 22.00 (978-0-8368-4526-6(9)) Stevens, Gareth Inc.

—Knights, Castles, & Warfare in the Middle Ages. 2005. (World Almanac Library of the Middle Ages). (Illus.). 48p. (J). pap. (978-0-8368-5904-1(9)); lib. bdg. 30.00 (978-0-8368-5895-2(6)) Stevens, Gareth Inc. (World Almanac Library).

—You Wouldn't Want to Be a Medieval Knight! 2004. (You Wouldn't Want to Ser.). (Illus.). 32p. (J). (gr. 2-5). pap. 9.95 (978-0-531-16395-5(4) , Watts, Franklin) Scholastic Library Publishing.

MacDonald, Fiona & Bergin, Mark. How to Be a Medieval Knight. 2005. (How to Be Ser.). (Illus.). 32p. (J). (gr. 3-7). 14.95 (978-0-7922-3619-1(X) , National Geographic Children's Bks.) National Geographic Society.

MacDonald, Fiona & Salariya, David. You Wouldn't Want to Be a Medieval Knight! Armor You'd Rather Not Wear. Antram, David, illus. 2004. (You Wouldn't Want To Ser.). 32p. (J). 28.50 (978-0-531-12353-9(7) , Watts, Franklin) Scholastic Library Publishing.

Martin, Alex. Knights & Castles. 2004. (Picture That! Ser.). (Illus.). 64p. (gr. 3 up). 19.95 (978-1-58728-441-0(3) , Creative Publishing International) Quayside.

Martin, Michael. Knights. 2007. (Edge Books, Warriors of History). (Illus.). 32p. (J). (gr. 3-6). 23.93 (*978-0-7368-6431-2(8)) Capstone Pr., Inc.

Maynard, Christopher. Days of the Knights: A Tale of Castles & Battles. 1998. (Eyewitness Readers). (Illus.). 48p. (J). (gr. 2-4). pap. 3.99 (978-0-7894-2963-6(2) , 0-7894-4764-9) Dorling Kindersley Publishing, Inc.

McGovern, Ann. If You Lived in the Days of the Knights. Andreasen, Dan, illus. 2001. (If You Lived Ser.). 80p. (J). (gr. 2-5). pap. 5.99 (978-0-439-10565-1(X)) Scholastic, Inc.

—If You Lived in the Days of the Knights. 2001. (gr. 3-6). lib. bdg. 14.15 (978-0-613-32675-9(X)); 2000. (Illus.). (J). 12.79 (978-0-606-20718-8(X)) Tandem Library Bks.

Morpurgo, Michael. Sir Gawain & the Green Knight. Foreman, Michael, illus. 2004. 112p. (J). (gr. 3-7). 18.99 (978-0-7636-2519-1(1)) Candlewick Pr.

Murrell, Deborah. The Best Book of Knights & Castles. 2005. (Best Book of... Ser.). (Illus.). 32p. (J). (gr. k-3). 12.95 (978-0-7534-5935-5(3) , Kingfisher) Houghton Mifflin Co. Trade & Reference Div.

Nardo, Don. King Arthur. 2002. (Heroes & Villains Ser.). (Illus.). 112p. (J). (gr. 6). 27.45 (978-1-56006-948-5(1) , Lucent Bks.) Thomson Gale.

Nobleman, Marc Tyler. Gladiator. 2007. (J). (*978-1-4109-2976-1(0)); pap. (*978-1-4109-2997-6(3)) Steck-Vaughn.

—Knight. 2007. (J). (*978-1-4109-2971-6(X)); pap. (*978-1-4109-2992-1(2)) Steck-Vaughn.

Oakeshott, R. Ewart. A Knight & His Horse. 2nd rev. ed. 1999. (Illus.). 128p. (gr. 5-12). pap. 13.95 (978-0-8023-1297-6(7)) Dufour Editions, Inc.

Osborne, Mary Pope & Osborne, Will. Knights & Castles: A Nonfiction Companion to The Knight at Dawn. Murdocca, Sal, illus. 2000. (Magic Tree House Research Guide Ser.: No. 2). 128p. (J). (gr. k-3). lib. bdg. 11.99 (978-0-375-90297-0(X)); mass mkt. 4.99 (978-0-375-80297-3(5)) Random Hse. Children's Bks. (Random Hse. Bks. for Young Readers).

—Knights & Castles: A Nonfiction Companion to The Knight at Dawn. 2000. (Magic Tree House Research Guide Ser.: No. 2). (J). (gr. k-3). (978-0-606-18857-9(6)); lib. bdg. 13.00 (978-0-613-26101-2(1)) Tandem Library Bks.

Pratt, Leonie. Knights & Castles Things to Make & Do. Thompson, Josephine Et Al, illus. 2006. 32p. (J). pap. 6.99 (978-0-7945-1355-9(7) , Usborne) EDC Publishing.

Pyle, Howard. The Story of the Champions of the Round Table. 2004. reprint ed. pap. 28.95 (978-1-4191-8405-5(9)); pap. 1.99 (978-1-4192-8405-2(3)) Kessinger Publishing, LLC.

Reid, Struan. Lift the Lid on Knights: Explore a Medieval World of Chivalry & Adventure, & Build Your Own Knight! 2001. (Quarto Children's Book Ser.). (Illus.). 32p. (J). 22.95 (978-0-7624-1125-2(2) , Running Pr. Kids) Running Pr. Bk. Pubs.

Simon, Seymour. See More Knights & Castles. 2006. (Illus.). 40p. (J). 14.50 (978-0-8118-5408-5(6)); pap. 3.95 (978-0-8118-5409-2(4)) Chronicle Bks. LLC.

Smith, A. G. Knights in Armor Stained Glass Coloring Book. 2001. (Dover Little Activity Bks.). (Illus.). 8p. (J). (gr. k-5). pap. 1.50 (978-0-486-41615-1(1)) Dover Pubns., Inc.

Star, Fleur & Dorling Kindersley Publishing Staff. Castle & Knight. 2005. (Eye Wonder Ser.). (Illus.). 48p. (J). 9.99 (978-0-7566-1417-1(1)); lib. bdg. 17.99 (978-0-7566-1418-8(X)) Dorling Kindersley Publishing, Inc.

Steele, Philip. Knights. 1998. (Single Subject References Ser.). (Illus.). 64p. (J). (gr. 4-8). tchr. ed. 16.95 (978-0-7534-5154-0(9) , Kingfisher) Houghton Mifflin Co. Trade & Reference Div.

Steer, Dugald & De Lance, Geoffrey. Knight: A Noble Guide for Young Squires. Ceran, Milivoj et al, illus. 2006. 32p. (J). (gr. 1-4). 17.99 (978-0-7636-3062-1(4)) Candlewick Pr.

Taplin, Sam. Knight's Handbook. 2006. 80p. (J). 12.99 (978-0-7945-1136-4(8) , Usborne) EDC Publishing.

Weatherly, Myra. William Marshal: Medieval England's Greatest Knight. 2004. (British Heroes Ser.). (Illus.). 112p. (YA). (gr. 6-12). 23.95 (978-1-883846-48-0(X) , First Biographies) Reynolds, Morgan Inc.

Weintraub, Aileen. Knights: Warriors of the Middle Ages. 2005. (Way of the Warrior Ser.). (Illus.). 48p. (J). 24.00 (978-0-516-25117-2(1)); (gr. 7-12). pap. 6.95 (978-0-516-25086-1(8)) Scholastic Library Publishing. (Children's Pr.).

Wilkinson, Carole. A Knight's Journey. 2001. (Fact Meets Fiction Ser.). (Illus.). 96p. (J). (978-0-7608-8037-1(9)) Sundance/Newbridge Educational Publishing.

Williams, Colleen Madonna Flood. My Adventure with Knights. 2007. 44p. (J). 8.99 (978-1-59092-456-3(8) , Orchard Academy Pr.) Windstorm Creative.

Woog, Adam. A Medieval Knight. 2003. (Daily Life Ser.). (Illus.). 48p. (J). (gr. 4-6). 26.20 (978-0-7377-0992-6(8) , Kidhaven) Thomson Gale.

KNIGHTS AND KNIGHTHOOD—FICTION

Abbott, Tony. The Knights of Silversnow. 2002. (gr. 3-6). lib. bdg. 11.80 (978-0-613-50453-9(4)) Tandem Library Bks.

Aguirre-Sacasa, Roberto & Muniz, Jim. Marvel Holiday Special TPB, Vol. 2. 2005. (Fantastic Four Ser.). (Illus.). 120p. pap. 13.99 (978-0-7851-1472-7(6)) Marvel Enterprises, Inc.

Amery, H. & Cartwright, S. The Tournament. 2004. (First Stories Ser.). 16p. (J). pap. 4.95 (978-0-7945-0520-2(1)); lib. bdg. 12.95 (978-1-58086-571-5(2)) EDC Publishing.

Anthony, David & David, Charles. Voyage to Silvermight: Knightscares #4. 2004. (Illus.). 208p. (J). per. 5.99 (978-0-9728461-3-4(1)) Sigil Publishing.

Ardagh, Philip. The Green Men of Gressingham. Phillips, Mike, illus. 2006. 72;88p. (J). (gr. 2-3). lib. bdg. (978-1-59889-000-6(X)) Stone Arch Bks.

Armitage, Ronda. Small Knight & George. Robins, Arthur, illus. 2007. 32p. (J). (ps-2). 14.99 (*978-0-7641-6061-5(3)) Barron's Educational Series, Inc.

Banerjee, Anjali. The Silver Spell. Fiegenshuh, Emily, illus. 2005. (Knights of the Silver Dragon Ser.: Bk. 8). 174p. (J). (*978-1-4156-1645-1(0) , Mirrorstone) Wizards of the Coast.

Banks, Steven. Lost in Time. The Artifact Group, illus. 2006. 22p. (J). lib. bdg. 15.00 (*978-1-4242-0977-4(3)) Fitzgerald Bks.

—Lost in Time. 2007. 24p. (J). 21.35 (*978-1-59961-367-3(0)) Spotlight.

Barkan, Joanne. A Pup in King Arthur's Court. l.t. ed. 1999. (Adventures of Wishbone Ser.: No. 15). (Illus.). 164p. (J). (gr. 2-5). lib. bdg. 22.60 (978-0-8368-2593-0(4)) Stevens, Gareth Inc.

Barnes, Charles. Knight Light. 2006. 48p. pap. 12.95 (978-1-4241-3831-9(0)) PublishAmerica, Inc.

Baynton, Martin. Jane & the Magician. Baynton, Martin, illus. 2007. (Illus.). 32p. (J). (ps-3). pap. 4.99 (*978-0-7636-3571-8(5)) Candlewick Pr.

Beardsley, Martyn. Sir Gadabout 9. Ross, Tony, illus. 2007. (Sir Gadabout Ser.). 96p. (J). 6.95 (*978-1-84255-615-3(0)) Orion Publishing Group, Ltd. GBR. *Dist:* Independent Pubs. Group.

—Sir Gadabout & the Ghost. 2nd ed. 2007. (Sir Gadabout Ser.). (Illus.). 96p. (J). pap. 6.95 (*978-1-85881-072-0(8)) Orion Publishing Group, Ltd. GBR. *Dist:* Independent Pubs. Group.

—Sir Gadabout & the Little Horror. Ross, Tony, illus. 2007. (Sir Gadabout Ser.). 96p. (J). pap. 6.95 (*978-1-85881-893-1(1)) Orion Publishing Group, Ltd. GBR. *Dist:* Independent Pubs. Group.

—Sir Gadabout Goes Barking Mad, Vol. 7. Ross, Tony, illus. 2007. (Sir Gadabout Ser.). 96p. (J). pap. 6.95 (*978-1-84255-275-9(9)) Orion Publishing Group, Ltd. GBR. *Dist:* Independent Pubs. Group.

—Sir Gadabout Goes Overboard, Vol. 6. Ross, Tony, illus. 2007. (Sir Gadabout Ser.). 96p. (J). pap. 6.95 (*978-1-84255-274-2(0)) Orion Publishing Group, Ltd. GBR. *Dist:* Independent Pubs. Group.

Beekman, Kelley Lee. Sir Eli & the Halloween Dragon: The Legend of the Toasted Marshmallow. 2006. 55p. pap. 12.95 (*978-1-4241-4047-3(1)) PublishAmerica, Inc.

Bell, Hilari. The Goblin Wood. (Illus.). (J). 2003. 304p. (gr. 5 up). 17.99 (978-0-06-051371-9(3)); 2004. 384p. (gr. 7 up). reprint ed. pap. 6.99 (978-0-06-051373-3(X)) HarperCollins Pubs.

Bell, Hilari. The Last Knight. 2007. (Knight & Rogue Ser.). 368p. (YA). (gr. 7 up). 16.99 (*978-0-06-082503-4(0)); lib. bdg. 17.89 (*978-0-06-082504-1(9)) HarperCollins Pubs. (Eos).

Bulla, Clyde Robert. The Sword in the Tree. 2000. (gr. 3-6). lib. bdg. 12.10 (978-0-613-27147-9(5)) Tandem Library Bks.

Los Caballeros del Rey Arturo. (SPA., Illus.). (YA). 14.95 (978-84-7281-107-2(7) , AF1107) Auriga, Ediciones S.A. ESP. *Dist:* Continental Bk. Co., Inc.

Cadnum, Michael. Book of the Lion. 2001. (gr. 7-12). lib. bdg. 14.15 (978-0-613-44378-4(0)) Tandem Library Bks.

—The Dragon Throne. 2005. 224p. (YA). (gr. 7). 16.99 (978-0-670-03631-8(5) , Viking Juvenile) Penguin Group (USA) Inc.

—The Leopard Sword. 2002. 224p. (YA). (gr. 7 up). 15.99 (978-0-670-89908-1(9) , Viking Juvenile) Penguin Group (USA) Inc.

Cervantes Saavedra, Miguel de. Don Quixote. Marshall, Michael J., ed. abr. ed. 1999. (Core Classics Ser.: Vol. 6). (Illus.). 264p. (J). (gr. 4-6). pap. 7.95 (978-1-890517-10-6(0)) Core Knowledge Foundation.

—Don Quixote of the Mancha. 1999. (Everyman's Library Children's Classics). (Illus.). 256p. (gr. 8-12). 14.95 (978-0-375-40659-1(X) , Everyman's Library) Knopf Publishing Group.

Cervantes Saavedra, Miguel de & Brook, Henry. Don Quixote. 2005. (Illus.). 144p. (J). pap. 4.95 (978-0-7945-0955-2(X) , Usborne) EDC Publishing.

Ciencin, Scott. Return to Lost City. 2000. (Dinotopia Ser.). (Illus.). (J). (978-0-606-20466-8(0)) Tandem Library Bks.

Clamp. Magic Knight Rayearth. 39th rev. ed. 2000. (Magic Knight Rayearth Ser.: Vol. 3). (Illus.). 208p. (gr. 8-12). pap. 12.99 (978-1-892213-16-7(8) , Mixx Manga) Mixx Entertainment, Inc.

Comrie, Margaret S. The Heroes of Castle Bretten. 2003. (Illus.). 229p. (J). (978-1-894666-65-7(8)) Inheritance Pubns.

de Paola, Tomie. The Knight & the Dragon. de Paola, Tomie, illus. 2002. (Illus.). (J). 13.19 (978-0-7587-2938-5(3)) Book Wholesalers, Inc.

—The Knight & the Dragon. 1998. (Illus.). 32p. (J). (ps-3). pap. 5.99 (978-0-698-11623-8(2) , Putnam Juvenile) Penguin Group (USA) Inc.

de Troyes, Chretien. Perceval: King Arthur's Knight of the Holy Grail. Spirin, Gennadii, illus. 2007. 38p. (J). (gr. 4 up). 16.99 (978-0-7614-5339-0(3)) Cavendish, Marshall Corp.

Dixon, Andy. Los Caballeros del Rey Arturo. 2001. (SPA., Illus.). 32p. (YA). (gr. 3 up). lib. bdg. 16.95 (978-1-58086-318-6(3)) EDC Publishing.

Donnell, Annie Hamil. Three Young Knights. 2004. reprint ed. pap. 15.95 (978-1-4191-8994-4(8)) Kessinger Publishing, LLC.

Donnell, Annie Hamilton. Three Young Knights. 2004. reprint ed. pap. 1.99 (978-1-4192-8994-1(2)) Kessinger Publishing, LLC.

Downey, Glen. Gladiators. 2007. (Illus.). 48p. (J). lib. bdg. 23.08 (*978-1-4242-1627-7(3)) Fitzgerald Bks.

Driscoll, Laura. My Brother, the Knight. Smath, Jerry, illus. 2004. 32p. (J). lib. bdg. 20.00 (*978-1-4242-1109-8(3)) Fitzgerald Bks.

—My Brother, the Knight. Smath, Jerry, illus. 2004. (Social Studies Connects). 32p. (J). (gr. 1-3). pap. 4.99 (978-1-57565-140-8(8)) Kane Pr., The.

Ebers, Georg. The Greylock. 2004. reprint ed. pap. 15.95 (978-1-4191-6506-1(2)); pap. 1.99 (978-1-4192-6506-8(7)) Kessinger Publishing, LLC.

Edwards, Julie Andrews & Hamilton, Emma Walton. Dragon: Hound of Honor. 2004. 192p. (J). (gr. 4 up). 16.99 (978-0-06-057119-1(5) , Julie Andrews Collection) HarperCollins Pubs.

Feely, Jenny. Sir Andrew the Brave. 2001. (gr. k-3). lib. bdg. 11.65 (978-0-613-33431-0(0)) Tandem Library Bks.

Flanagan, John. The Icebound Land. 2008. (Ranger's Apprentice Ser.: Bk. 3). 288p. (J). (gr. 5). 7.99 (*978-0-14-241075-2(6) , Puffin) Penguin Group (USA) Inc.

French, Jackie. My Dad the Dragon. King, Stephen Michael, illus. 2007. (Funny Families Ser.). (J). (gr. 2-4). 107p. pap. 7.95 (*978-1-59889-436-3(6)); 112p. lib. bdg. 22.60 (*978-1-59889-343-4(2)) Stone Arch Bks.

Funke, Cornelia. Igraine the Brave. Bell, Anthea, tr. from GER. 2007. 224p. (J). (gr. 4-7). pap. 16.99 (*978-0-439-90379-0(3) , Chicken Hse., The) Scholastic, Inc.

Funke, Cornelia. The Princess Knight. Meyer, Kerstin, illus. 2004. 32p. (J). pap. 15.95 (978-0-439-53630-1(8) , Chicken Hse., The) Scholastic, Inc.

Gilman, Laura Anne. The Camelot Spell. 2006. (Grail Quest Trilogy Ser.: No. 1). 304p. (J). 10.99 (978-0-06-077279-6(4)); lib. bdg. 14.89 (978-0-06-077280-2(8)) HarperCollins Pubs.

—Morgain's Revenge. 2006. (Grail Quest Trilogy Ser.: No. 2). 288p. (J). lib. bdg. 14.89 (978-0-06-077283-3(2)) HarperCollins Pubs.

Gousseff, Catherine. The Perfect Knight. Negrin, Fabian, tr. from FRE. Negrin, Fabian, illus. 2004. (Books for Young Readers Ser.). 22p. 5.95 (978-0-89236-739-9(3)) Oxford Univ. Pr., Inc.

Graham, Denise R. Curse of the Lost Grove. 2005. (Knights of the Silver Dragon Ser.: Bk. 10). (Illus.). 177p. (J). (*978-1-4156-3841-5(1) , Mirrorstone) Wizards of the Coast.

Grant, K. M. Blaze of Silver. 2007. 272p. 16.95 (978-0-8027-9625-7(7)) Walker & Co.

—Blood Red Horse. 2006. 288p. (J). pap. 7.95 (978-0-8027-7734-8(1)) Walker & Co.

—Green Jasper. (J). 2007. 272p. pap. 7.95 (978-0-8027-9627-1(3)); 2006. 256p. 16.95 (978-0-8027-8073-7(3)) Walker & Co.

Gray, Margaret. The Lovesick Salesman. Cecil, Randy, illus. rev. ed. 2004. 192p. (J). 16.95 (978-0-8050-7558-8(5) , Holt, Henry & Co. Bks. For Young Readers) Holt, Henry & Co.

Grey, Patrick. Five Days till Dawn. 2002. (YA). pap. 15.00 (978-1-894869-51-5(6) , PO 00033) Zumaya Pubns. LLC.

Henty, G. A. A Knight of the White Cross: A Tale of the Siege of Rhodes. 1999. (gr. 3-6). lib. bdg. 26.85 (978-0-613-80289-5(6)) Tandem Library Bks.

Hightman, Jason. The Saint of Dragons. (gr. 7 up). 2004. (J). 16.99 (978-0-06-054011-1(7)); 2004. 304p. (J). lib. bdg. 17.89 (978-0-06-054012-8(5)); 2005. 340p. (YA). reprint ed. pap. 6.99 (978-0-06-054013-5(3)) HarperCollins Pubs.

—Samurai. 2006. 320p. (J). 15.99 (978-0-06-054014-2(1)); lib. bdg. 16.89 (978-0-06-054015-9(X)) HarperCollins Pubs.

Hoffman, Mary. Women of Camelot: Queens & Enchantresses at the Court of King Arthur. 2000. (Illus.). 72p. (J). 19.95 (978-0-7892-0646-6(3)) Abbeville Pr., Inc.

—Women of Camelot: Queens & Enchantresses at the Court of King Arthur. Balit, Christina, illus. 2006. 69p. (YA). (gr. 5-9). 20.00 (978-1-4223-5260-1(9)) DIANE Publishing Co.

Jinks, Catherine. Pagan's Crusade. 2003. (Pagan Chronicles Ser.: Bk. 1). (Illus.). 256p. (YA). 15.99 (978-0-7636-2019-6(X)) Candlewick Pr.

Johnson, Annie F. Two Little Knights of Kentucky: The Little Colonel's Neighbors. Barry, Etheldred B., illus. 2004. (Little Colonel Ser.). 128p. (J). (gr. 4-7). reprint ed. per. 9.95 (978-1-55709-316-5(4)) Applewood Bks.

Kimmel, Eric A. Don Quixote & the Windmills. Fisher, Leonard Everett, illus. 2004. 32p. (J). 16.00 (978-0-374-31825-3(5) , Farrar, Straus & Giroux (BYR)) Farrar, Straus & Giroux.

Kirkman, Robert. Marvel Knights 2099. 2005. (Marvel Heroes Ser.). (Illus.). 120p. (YA). pap. 13.99 (978-0-7851-1613-4(3)) Marvel Enterprises, Inc.

Knights. (Awesome Adventures Ser.). 16p. (J). (978-2-7643-0120-3(0)) Phidal Publishing, Inc./Editions Phidal, Inc.

Koller, Jackie Fre. Horace the Horrible: A Knight Meets His Match. Urbanovic, Jackie, illus. 2003. 32p. (J). 16.95 (978-0-7614-5150-1(1)) Cavendish, Marshall Corp.

Kurumada, Masami. Knights of the Zodiac. 2006. (Knights of the Zodiac Ser.). 208p. (YA). Vol. 14. pap. 7.95 (978-1-4215-0418-6(9)); Vol. 15. pap. 7.95 (978-1-4215-0656-2(4)); Vol. 16. pap. 7.95 (978-1-4215-0659-3(9)); Vol. 17. pap. 7.95 (978-1-4215-0660-9(2)) Viz Media.

Lang, Andrew & Ford, H. J. The Tale of the Cid: And Other Stories of Knights & Chivalry. Ford, H. J., illus. 2007. (Illus.). 208p. pap. 9.95 (*978-0-486-45470-2(3)) Dover Pubns., Inc.

Lassieur, Allison. Knights' Kingdom: Activity Book with Narrative. Mada Design Staff, illus. 2005. (Lego Knights' Kingdom Ser.). 32p. (J). pap. 5.99 (978-0-439-71828-8(7)) Scholastic, Inc.

—Welcome to the Kingdom of Morcia! A Knights Kingdom Sticker Book. Mada Design Staff, illus. 2005. (Lego Knights' Kingdom Ser.). 32p. (J). pap. 5.99 (978-0-439-70232-4(1)) Scholastic, Inc.

LeapFrog Staff, compiled by & des. Magic Tree House - Knights at Dawn. LeapFrog Staff, des. 2002. (J). spiral bd. 14.99 (978-1-58605-829-6(0)) LeapFrog Enterprises, Inc.

Limke, Jeff. King Arthur: Excalibur Unsheathed. Yeates, Thomas, illus. 2007. (Graphic Myths & Legends Ser.). 48p. (YA). (gr. 4-9). pap. 8.95 (*978-0-8225-6483-6(1)) Lerner Publishing Group.

Limke Jeff. El rey Arturo (King Arthur) La espada Excalibur desenvainada (Excalibur Unsheathed) Yeates, Thomas, illus. 2007. (Mitos y leyendas en viñetas (Graphic Myths & Legends) Ser.). (J). pap. 8.95 (*978-0-8225-7968-7(5) , Ediciones Lerner) Lerner Publishing Group.

Lipkowitz, Daniel. The Dark Fortress. Mada Design Staff, illus. 2005. 32p. (J). (ps-3). pap. 3.99 (978-0-439-74568-0(3)) Scholastic, Inc.

—Grand Tournament, No. 2. Mada Design Staff, illus. 2005. (Knights' Kingdom Reader Ser.: No. 2). 32p. (J). pap. 3.99 (978-0-439-70231-7(3)) Scholastic, Inc.

—The Lost Kingdom. Mada Design Staff, illus. 2005. (Knights' Kingdom Ser.: No. 1). 24p. (J). (ps-k). pap. 3.99 (978-0-439-74569-7(1)) Scholastic, Inc.

—Search for the King. 2005. (Lego Knights' Kingdom Ser.). (Illus.). 32p. (J). 3.99 (978-0-439-70230-0(5)) Scholastic, Inc.

Lorimer, Janet, told to. The Kula'I Street Knights: Set 1. 2002. 32p. (YA). (978-1-56254-409-6(8) , SP 4098) Saddleback Educational Publishing.

Lowenstein, Sallie, illus. Sir Kyle & Lady Madeline. Lowenstein, Sallie, . 2007. 32p. (J). 18.95 (978-0-9658486-6-4(3)) Lion Stone Bks.

Malory, Thomas & Lanier, Sidney. The Boy's King Arthur. Wyeth, N. C., illus. 2006. 352p. pap. 14.95 (978-0-486-44800-8(2)) Dover Pubns., Inc.

Marks, Alan, illus. The Stories of Knights. 2004. (Young Reading Series One Ser.). 48p. (J). (gr. 2 up). pap. 5.95 (978-0-7945-0755-8(7) , Usborne) EDC Publishing.

Matthews, John. Arthur of Albion: Marvellous Tales of the Round Table. Tatarnikau, Pavel, illus. 2007. (J). (*978-1-84686-049-2(0)) Barefoot Bks., Inc.

Matthews, John. The Barefoot Book of Knights. Manna, Giovanni, illus. 2002. 80p. (J). (gr. 4-7). 19.99 (978-1-84148-064-0(9)) Barefoot Bks., Inc.

Mayer, Marianna. Ivanhoe. Rush, John, illus. 2004. 56p. (J). 17.95 (978-1-58717-248-9(8)); 18.50 (978-1-58717-249-6(6)) Chronicle Bks. LLC. (SeaStar Bks.).

Mayer, Mercer. The Bravest Knight. 2007. (Illus.). 32p. (J). (gr. k-2). 16.99 (978-0-8037-3206-3(6) , Dial) Penguin Group (USA) Inc.

Mayher, Lauren. The Legend of Darien: A Hero Rises. 2007. pap. 12.95 (*978-0-9794545-0-9(6)) Blue Eyed Mayhem Publishing.

Mayhew, James. The Knight Who Took All Day. Mayhew, James, illus. 2005. (Illus.). 32p. (J). (ps-3). pap. 15.99 (978-0-439-74829-2(1) , Chicken Hse., The) Scholastic, Inc.

McAllister, Angela. Digory the Dragon Slayer. Beck, Ian, illus. 2006. 128p. (J). 14.95 (978-1-58234-722-6(0)); pap. 5.95 (978-1-58234-912-1(6)) Bloomsbury Publishing. (Bloomsbury Children).

McCaughrean, Geraldine & Marks, Alan. King Arthur. 2007. (Illus.). (J). pap. (*978-0-340-89437-8(7) , Hodder Children's Books) Hodder Children's Division.

McMullan, Kate. The Ghost of Sir Herbert Dungeonstone. 2006. (Dragon Slayers' Academy Ser.: No. 12). (J). (gr. 1-6). 24.21 (978-1-59961-124-2(4)) Spotlight.

—Help! It's Parent's Day at DSA. 2006. (Dragon Slayers' Academy Ser.: No. 10). (J). (gr. 1-6). 24.21 (978-1-59961-125-9(2)) Spotlight.

—Knight for a Day, Vol. 5. Basso, Bill, illus. 2003. (Dragon Slayers' Academy Ser.: No. 5). 112p. (gr. 2-5). mass mkt. 4.99 (978-0-448-43277-9(3) , Grosset & Dunlap) Penguin Group (USA) Inc.

—Knight for a Day. 2003. (Dragon Slayers' Academy Ser.: No. 5). (gr. 3-6). lib. bdg. 13.00 (978-0-613-72530-9(1)) Tandem Library Bks.

—Pig Latin—Not Just for Pigs! 2006. (Dragon Slayers' Academy Ser.: No. 14). (J). (gr. 1-6). 24.21 (978-1-59961-127-3(9)) Spotlight.

—Sir Lancelot, Where Are You? Basso, Bill, illus. 2003. (Dragon Slayers' Academy Ser.: No. 6). 112p. (gr. 3-7). pap. 4.99 (978-0-448-43278-6(1) , Grosset & Dunlap) Penguin Group (USA) Inc.

—Sir Lancelot, Where Are You? 2003. (Dragon Slayers' Academy Ser.: No. 6). (gr. 3-6). lib. bdg. 13.00 (978-0-613-72537-8(9)) Tandem Library Bks.

Melling, David. The Kiss That Missed. 2007. 32p. (J). (gr. k-2). pap. 7.99 (978-0-7641-3624-5(0)) Barron's Educational Series, Inc.

Milbourne, Anna. Stories of Knights & Castles. 2007. 96p. (J). 16.99 (978-0-7945-1466-2(9) , Usborne) EDC Publishing.

Morris, Gerald. The Ballad of Sir Dinadan. (Squire's Tales Ser.). 256p. (J). (gr. 5-9). 2005. pap. 5.95 (978-0-618-54894-1(7)); 2003. tchr. ed. 16.00 (978-0-618-19099-7(6)) Houghton Mifflin Co. Trade & Reference Div.

—The Lioness & Her Knight. 2005. (Squire's Tales Ser.). 352p. (J). (gr. 5-7). 16.00 (978-0-618-50772-6(8)) Houghton Mifflin Co. Trade & Reference Div.

—The Princess, the Crone, & the Dung-Cart Knight. (Squire's Tales Ser.). 320p. (YA). (gr. 5-9). 2006. pap. 6.95 (978-0-618-73748-2(0)); 2004. tchr. ed. 16.00 (978-0-618-37823-4(5)) Houghton Mifflin Co. Trade & Reference Div.

—The Quest of the Fair Unknown. 2006. 278p. (J). (gr. 5). 16.00 (978-0-618-63152-0(6)) Houghton Mifflin Co. Trade & Reference Div.

—The Savage Damsel & the Dwarf. (Squire's Tales Ser.). 224p. (gr. 5-9). 2004. (YA). pap. 5.95 (978-0-618-19681-4(1)); 2000. (J). tchr. ed. 16.00 (978-0-395-97126-0(8)) Houghton Mifflin Co. Trade & Reference Div.

—The Squire & His Knight. l.t. ed. 2001. (Illus.). 257p. (J). (gr. 4-7). 21.95 (978-0-7862-3039-6(8)) Thorndike Pr.

—The Squire, His Knight & His Lady. 2001. (Illus.). (J). (978-0-606-21454-4(2)) Tandem Library Bks.

—The Squire, His Knight, & His Lady. 1999. (Squire's Tales Ser.). 240p. (J). (gr. 5-9). tchr. ed. 16.00 (978-0-395-91211-9(3)) Houghton Mifflin Co. Trade & Reference Div.

—The Squire's Tale. 1998. (Squire's Tales Ser.). 224p. (J). (gr. 5-9). tchr. ed. 16.00 (978-0-395-86959-8(5)) Houghton Mifflin Co. Trade & Reference Div.

—Squire's Tale. 2000. (978-0-606-17839-6(2)) Tandem Library Bks.

Morrison, P. R. The Wind Tamer. 2006. 336p. (YA). 16.95 (978-1-58234-781-3(6)) Bloomsbury Publishing.

Morrison, P. R. Wind Tamer. 2007. 336p. (YA). pap. 7.95 (*978-1-59990-147-3(1) , Bloomsbury Children) Bloomsbury Publishing.

Moxilada, J. L. Jonty Jones Takes Guard. 2005. 242p. pap. 16.88 (978-1-4116-4126-6(4)) Lulu.com.

Muschla, Gary Robert. Crusader. 2006. (YA). pap. (978-0-88092-491-7(8)) Royal Fireworks Publishing Co.

Nash, Ogden. Custard the Dragon & the Wicked Knight. Munsinger, Lynn, illus. 1999. 32p. (J). (ps-3). pap. 6.99 (978-0-316-59905-4(0)) Little Brown & Co.

—Custard the Dragon & the Wicked Knight. 1999. (J). (gr. k up). pap., stu. ed. 25.20 incl. audio (978-0-7887-2986-7(1) , 40868); Class set. pap. 91.30 incl. audio (978-0-7887-3016-0(9) , 46833) Recorded Bks., LLC.

Neuschwander, Cindy. Sir Cumference & the Great Knight of Angleland. 2001. (gr. 3-6). lib. bdg. 16.40 (978-0-613-58135-6(0)) Tandem Library Bks.

Newman, Robert. Lost Treasures Bk. 5: Merlin's Mistake. 2001. 240p. (J). 13.49 (978-0-7868-2600-1(2)) Hyperion Pr.

Nunes, Rachel Ann. The Secret of the King. Ward, Jay Bryant, illus. 2005. 32p. (J). (ps-ps). 17.95 (978-1-59038-241-7(2) , Shadow Mountain) Deseret Bk. Co.

O'Brien, Patrick. The Making of a Knight: How Sir James Earned His Armor. 1998. (Illus.). 32p. (J). (gr. 1-4). 15.95 (978-0-88106-354-7(1)) Charlesbridge Publishing, Inc.

O'Connor, Jane. Sir Small & the Sea Monster. O'Brien, John, illus. 2005. (Step into Reading Ser.). 32p. (J). (gr. k-2). pap. 3.99 (978-0-375-82565-1(7) , Random Hse. Bks. for Young Readers) Random Hse. Children's Bks.

Osborn, Kelly. The Green Knight. 2006. 64p. pap. 12.95 (978-1-4241-1741-3(0)) PublishAmerica, Inc.

Osborne, Mary Pope. El Caballero del Alba. 2004. (Coleccion la Casa Del Arbol the Magic Tree House Ser.). (SPA.). (J). pap. 4.95 (978-1-930332-50-8(5)) Lectorum Pubns., Inc.

—The Knight at Dawn. unabr. ed. 2004. (Magic Tree House Ser. : No. 2). 66p. (J). (gr. k-3). pap. 17.00 incl. audio (978-0-8072-0331-6(9) , Listening Library) Random Hse. Audio Publishing Group.

Osborne, Mary Pope. The Knight at Dawn Book & CD. Murdocca, Sal, illus. 2008. (Stepping Stone Book(TM) Ser.). (J). (gr. k-3). 9.99 (*978-0-375-84406-5(6) , Random Hse. Bks. for Young Readers) Random Hse. Children's Bks.

Palacios, Argentina. Adventures of Don Quixote. abr. ed. 1999. (Dover Children's Thrift Classics Ser.). (Illus.). 64p. (J). (gr. 3-6). pap. 2.00 (978-0-486-40791-3(8)) Dover Pubns., Inc.

Peet, Bill. Cowardly Clyde. 1999. (Illus.). (J). (ps-2). lib. bdg. 17.60 (978-0-8085-3560-7(9)) Tandem Library Bks.

Peterson, Doug & Kenney, Cindy. The Spoon in the Stone: A Lesson in Serving Others. 2005. (VeggieTown Values Ser.: Bk. 1). (Illus.). 32p. pap. 3.99 (978-0-310-70626-7(2)) Zonderkidz.

Pierce, Tamora. Alanna: The First Adventure. Heyer, illus. 2002. (Song of the Lioness Ser.: Bk. 1). 240p. (YA). 11.95 (978-0-689-85323-4(8) , Atheneum) Simon & Schuster Children's Publishing.

—First Test. 2000. (Protector of the Small Ser.: No. 1). (Illus.). 256p. (YA). (gr. 7-11). mass mkt. 6.50 (978-0-679-88917-5(5) , Laurel Leaf) Random Hse. Children's Bks.

—First Test. 2000. (Protector of the Small Ser.: No. 1). (gr. 5-8). lib. bdg. 14.15 (978-0-613-25184-6(9)) Tandem Library Bks.

—Page. (Protector of the Small Ser.: No. 2). 2001. 288p. (YA). (gr. 7-11). mass mkt. 6.50 (978-0-679-88918-2(3) , Laurel Leaf); 2000. (Illus.). 272p. (gr. 5-9). lib. bdg. 17.99 (978-0-679-98915-8(3) , Random Hse. Bks. for Young Readers) Random Hse. Children's Bks.

—Page. 2001. (Protector of the Small Ser.: No. 2). (gr. 5-8). lib. bdg. 13.55 (978-0-613-50483-6(6)) Tandem Library Bks.

—Squire. 2002. (Protector of the Small Ser.: No. 3). 432p. (YA). (gr. 7-11). mass mkt. 6.50 (978-0-679-88919-9(1) , Laurel Leaf) Random Hse. Children's Bks.

—Squire. 2002. (Protector of the Small Ser.: No. 3). (gr. 5-8). lib. bdg. 14.15 (978-0-613-49349-9(4)) Tandem Library Bks.

Plummer, Rachel. Mystery of the Wizard's Tomb. 2006. (Knights of the Silver Dragon Ser.: Bk. 11). (Illus.). 192p. (J). pap. 5.99 (978-0-7869-3990-9(7) , Mirrorstone) Wizards of the Coast.

Prasadam, Smriti & Finn, Rebecca. My Knight's Castle: Through Play Books. 2008. (Illus.). 12p. (J). bds. 6.95 (*978-0-7475-8813-9(9)) Bloomsbury Publishing Plc GBR. *Dist:* Independent Pubs. Group.

Pringle, Eric. Big George & the Seventh Knight. Paine, Colin, illus. 2002. 208p. pap. 10.99 (978-0-7475-5539-1(7)) Bloomsbury Publishing Plc GBR. *Dist:* Independent Pubs. Group.

Pyle, Howard. Men of Iron. unabr. ed. 2003. (General Juvenile Ser.). 224p. (J). (gr. 5-8). pap. 8.95 (978-0-486-42841-3(9)) Dover Pubns., Inc.

—Men of Iron. l.t. ed. 2004. 329p. (J). 29.95 (978-0-7862-6775-0(5) , Large Print Pr.) Thorndike Pr.

—The Story of King Arthur & His Knights. McKowen, Scott, illus. 2005. (Unabridged Classics Ser.). 320p. (gr. 5-9). 9.95 (978-1-4027-2503-6(5) , 1252056) Sterling Publishing Co., Inc.

—The Story of Sir Lancelot & His Companions. 2004. reprint ed. pap. 27.95 (978-1-4179-5609-8(7)) Kessinger Publishing, LLC.

Ransom, Candice F. Key to the Griffon's Lair. Fiegenshuh, Emily, illus. 2005. (Knights of the Silver Dragon Ser.: Bk. 9). 182p. (J). (*978-1-4156-3032-7(1) , Mirrorstone) Wizards of the Coast.

Richards, Christopher, illus. King Arthur & the Knights of the Round Table. 2007. (Graphic Revolve Ser.). 63p. (J). (gr. 4-6). lib. bdg. 22.60 (978-1-59889-048-8(4)) Stone Arch Bks.

Roberts, Kerry Daniel. Mark of the Yuan-Ti, Bk. 12. 2006. (Knights of the Silver Dragon Ser.: Bk. 12). (Illus.). 192p. (J). pap. 5.99 (978-0-7869-4033-2(6) , Mirrorstone) Wizards of the Coast.

Ron, Kare. The Adventures of Sir Noodlefish: The Cake Wars. McCracken, Ken, illus. 2000. 32p. (J). (gr. 1-3). pap. (978-1-931179-00-3(X)) Long Hill Productions, Inc.

Rovetch, Lissa & Whitman, Emily. Sir Henry, the Polite Knight. Barnard, Bryn, illus. 2006. (J). (*978-1-58987-204-2(5)) Kindermusik International.

Royde-Smith, N. G. Una and the Red Cross Knight & Other T. 2006. (Illus.). pap. 28.95 (*978-1-4254-8407-1(7)) Kessinger Publishing, LLC.

Russell, Christopher. Dogboy. 2006. 272p. (J). 15.99 (978-0-06-084116-4(8)); lib. bdg. 16.89 (978-0-06-084117-1(6)) HarperCollins Pubs.

San Souci, Robert D. Young Lancelot. 1998. (J). (978-0-606-13937-3(0)) Tandem Library Bks.

Sandell, Lisa Ann. Song of the Sparrow. 2007. 416p. (YA). (gr. 7 up). pap. 16.99 (*978-0-439-91848-0(0) , Scholastic Pr.) Scholastic, Inc.

Scholastic, Inc. Staff. Battle for Morcia. 2006. (Knights' Kingdom Ser.). 4p. (J). bds. 9.99 (978-0-439-82814-7(7)) Scholastic, Inc.

Scholastic, Inc. Staff, creator. Knights' Kingdom Adventure Box. 2005. (Knights' Kingdom Ser.). (Illus.). 32p. (J). (ps-3). pap. 9.99 (978-0-439-78244-9(9)) Scholastic, Inc.

Scieszka, Jon. Knights of the Kitchen Table. Smith, Lane, illus. 2004. (Time Warp Trio Ser.: No. 1). 64p. (J). (gr. 2-6). pap. 4.99 (978-0-14-240043-2(2) , Puffin) Penguin Group (USA) Inc.

—Knights of the Kitchen Table. (Time Warp Trio Ser.: No. 1). 55p. (J). (gr. 2-4). pap. 3.99 (978-0-8072-1301-8(2)); 1998. pap. 17.00 incl. audio (978-0-8072-0391-0(2) , FTR193SP) Random Hse. Audio Publishing Group. (Listening Library).

Scott, Walter, Sr. Ivanhoe. Marcos, Pablo, illus. 2002. (Great Illustrated Classics Ser.). 240p. (J). (gr. 3-8). 21.35 (978-1-57765-811-5(6) , ABDO & Daughters) ABDO Publishing Co.

—Ivanhoe. (SPA., Illus.). 176p. (YA). 14.95 (978-84-7281-096-9(8) , AF1096) Auriga, Ediciones S.A. ESP. *Dist:* Continental Bk. Co., Inc.

—Ivanhoe. 2000. (gr. 7-12). lib. bdg. 17.65 (978-0-613-64293-4(7)) Tandem Library Bks.

Shire, Poppy. Brightheart the Knight's Pony. Berg, Ron, illus. 2007. (Magic Pony Carousel Ser.: No. 2). 96p. (J). pap. 3.99 (978-0-06-083782-2(9)); 14.99 (978-0-06-083780-8(2)) HarperCollins Pubs. (Harper Trophy).

Smith, Linda. Sir Cassie to the Rescue. Patkau, Karen, tr. Patkau, Karen, illus. 2003. 32p. (J). (ps-2). 16.95 (978-1-55143-243-4(9)) Orca Bk. Pubs. USA.

Spirin, Gennadii, illus. Perceval: King Arthur's Knight of the Holy Grail. 2007. 36p. (J). (*978-1-4287-3696-2(4) , Cavendish Children's Bks.) Cavendish, Marshall Corp.

Springer, Nancy. I Am Morgan le Fay: A Tale from Camelot. 2002. (Firebird Ser.). 240p. (YA). pap. 6.99 (978-0-698-11974-1(6) , Puffin) Penguin Group (USA) Inc.

—I Am Morgan le Fay: A Tale from Camelot. 2002. (gr. 7-12). lib. bdg. 14.15 (978-0-613-55214-1(8)) Tandem Library Bks.

Springett, Martin, illus. Jousting with Jesters: An ABC for the Younger Dragon. 2006. 32p. (J). 17.95 (978-1-55143-327-1(3)) Orca Bk. Pubs. USA.

Stanley, Diane. Bella at Midnight. Ibatoulline, Ba, illus. 2008. 304p. (J). pap. 6.99 (*978-0-06-077575-9(0) , Harper Trophy) HarperCollins Pubs.

—Bella at Midnight. Ibatoulline, Bagram, illus. 2006. 288p. (J). (gr. 5-8). 16.99 (978-0-06-077573-5(4)); lib. bdg. 16.89 (978-0-06-077574-2(2)) HarperCollins Pubs.

Steele, Michael Anthony. The Magic of the Tower. 2006. (Knights' Kingdom Ser.). 24p. (J). pap. 4.99 (978-0-439-82812-3(0)) Scholastic, Inc.

—Quest for the Tower. Schutz, Samantha, ed. 2006. (Knights' Kingdom Ser.). 24p. (J). pap. 3.99 (978-0-439-78801-4(3)) Scholastic, Inc.

Stewart, Paul. Joust of Honor. Riddell, Chris, illus. 2005. (Knight's Story Ser.: Bk. 2). 144p. (J). 9.95 (978-0-689-87240-2(2) , Atheneum) Simon & Schuster Children's Publishing.

Stewart, Paul & Riddell, Chris. Dragon's Hoard. 2005. (Knight's Story Ser.). (Illus.). 144p. (J). 9.95 (978-0-689-87241-9(0) , Atheneum) Simon & Schuster Children's Publishing.

Thomas, Shelley Moore. Get Well, Good Knight. Plecas, Jennifer, illus. 48p. (J). 2004. pap. 3.99 (978-0-14-240050-0(5) , Puffin); 2002. 13.99 (978-0-525-46914-8(1) , Dutton Juvenile) Penguin Group (USA) Inc.

—Good Night, Good Knight. Plecas, Jennifer, illus. 2002. 11.49 (978-1-4046-1571-7(7)) Book Wholesalers, Inc.

—Good Night, Good Knight. Plecas, Jennifer, illus. 2000. 48p. (J). (ps-2). 13.99 (978-0-525-46326-9(7) , Dutton Juvenile) Penguin Group (USA) Inc.

—Happy Birthday, Good Knight. Plecas, Jennifer, illus. 2006. 48p. (J). (ps). 13.99 (978-0-525-47184-4(7) , Dutton Juvenile) Penguin Group (USA) Inc.

—Take Care, Good Knight. Meisel, Paul, illus. 2006. 36p. (J). (ps). 15.99 (978-0-525-47695-5(4) , Dutton Juvenile) Penguin Group (USA) Inc.

Thomas, Shelley Moore & Plecas, Jennifer. Good Night, Good Knight. 2002. (Easy-to-Read Ser.). (Illus.). 48p. (J). pap. 3.99 (978-0-14-230201-9(5) , Puffin) Penguin Group (USA) Inc.

Thomson, Sarah L. Dragon's Egg. 2007. 272p. (J). (gr. 3-7). 16.99 (*978-0-06-128848-7(9)); lib. bdg. 17.89 (*978-0-06-128847-0(0)) HarperCollins Pubs. (Greenwillow Bks.).

Tolhurst, Marilyn. Knights: The Age of Adventure, to Unlock & Discover. 2001. (Treasure Chest Ser.). (Illus.). 32p. (J). (gr. 4-7). pap. 22.95 (978-1-56138-545-4(X) , Running Pr. Kids) Running Pr. Bk. Pubs.

Tompert, Ann. The Errant Knight. Keith, Doug, illus. 2003. 32p. 15.95 (978-0-9701907-6-5(X)) Illumination Arts Publishing Co., Inc.

Trumbauer, Lisa. The Hidden Dragon. Fiegenshuh, Emily, illus. 2005. (Knights of the Silver Dragon Ser.: Bk. 7). 178p. (J). (*978-1-4156-0424-3(X) , Mirrorstone) Wizards of the Coast.

Twain, Mark. A Connecticut Yankee in King Arthur's Court. 1999. reprint ed. pap. 28.00 (978-1-4047-1121-1(X)) Classic Textbooks.

Vande Velde, Vivian. The Book of Mordred. 2005. (Illus.). 352p. (YA). (gr. 7-7). 18.00 (978-0-618-50754-2(X)) Houghton Mifflin Co. Trade & Reference Div.

Velde, Vivian Vande. The Book of Mordred. 2007. 352p. (YA). (gr. 7). pap. 8.99 (*978-0-618-80916-5(3) , Graphia) Houghton Mifflin Co. Trade & Reference Div.

Vogler, Christopher. Ravenskull. 2006. (Illus.). 192p. pap. 10.99 (978-1-933164-14-4(X)) Seven Seas Entertainment, LLC.

Weyn, Suzanne. The Night Dance. 2005. 193p. (YA). (978-1-4156-4311-2(3) , Simon Pulse) Simon & Schuster Children's Publishing.

Wright, Joshua. Hapless, Hopeless, Horrible. 2004. (Illus.). 192p. (J). pap. 6.95 (978-1-74114-082-8(X)) Allen & Unwin AUS. *Dist:* Independent Pubs. Group.

—Plotless, Pointless, Pathetic. 2004. (Illus.). 180p. (J). pap. 6.95 (978-1-86508-785-6(8)) Allen & Unwin AUS. *Dist:* Independent Pubs. Group.

Wright, Mary J. The Brave Knight. 2005. 108p. pap. 16.95 (978-1-4137-8185-4(3)) PublishAmerica, Inc.

Wright, Rachel. Knights. (Illus.). 32p. (YA). (gr. 3 up). lib. bdg. 27.10 (978-1-932889-05-5(1)) Sea-To-Sea Pubns.

KNIGHTS OF THE ROUND TABLE

see Arthur, King

KNITTING

Aber, Linda Williams. Carrie Measures Up! Allen, Joy, illus. 2001. (Math Matters Ser.). 32p. (J). (gr. 1-3). pap. 4.95 (978-1-57565-100-2(9)) Kane Pr., The.

Bergman, Deborah. The Knitting Goddess: Finding the Heart & Soul of Knitting Through Instruction. 2002. (Illus.). 288p. pap. 12.95 (978-0-7868-8530-5(0)) Hyperion Pr.

Blanchette, Peg. Kids' Easy Knitting Projects. Nadel, Marc, illus. 2000. (Quick Starts for Kids! Ser.). 64p. (J). (gr. 3 up). pap. 8.95 (978-1-885593-48-1(1) , Williamson Bks.) Ideals Pubns.

—Kids' Easy Knitting Projects. 2001. (gr. 3-6). lib. bdg. 16.40 (978-0-613-57607-9(1)) Tandem Library Bks.

Blanchette, Peg & Thibault, Terri. 12 Easy Knitting Projects. 2006. (Quick Starts for Kids! Ser.). (Illus.). 64p. (J). 12.95 (978-0-8249-6784-0(4)); pap. 8.95 (978-0-8249-6785-7(2)) Ideals Pubns. (Williamson Bks.).

Bradberry, Sarah. Kids Knit! Simple Steps to Nifty Projects. 2006. (Illus.). 96p. (J). pap. 9.95 (978-1-4027-4057-2(3)) Sterling Publishing Co., Inc.

J
K
L

Clewer, Carolyn. Kids Can Knit: Fun & Easy Projects for Your Small Knitter. 2003. (Illus.). 128p. pap. 16.95 (978-0-7641-2718-2(7)) Barron's Educational Series, Inc.

Craig, Cindy. The Kids' Knitting Notebook. 2007. (Illus.). 112p. (J). 12.95 (978-1-60059-063-4(2)) Lark Bks.

Dorling Kindersley Publishing Staff. Knitting. 2007. (DK CREATE & MAKE Ser.). 48p. (J). 16.99 (978-0-7566-1775-2(8)) Dorling Kindersley Publishing, Inc.

Falick, Melanie. Kids Knitting. Nicholas, Kristin, illus. Hartlove, Chris, photos by. 2003. 128p. pap. 12.95 (978-1-57965-241-8(7)) Artisan.

For Fun! 2006. (J). (gr. 3-5). 565.00 (978-0-7565-1698-7(6)) Compass Point Bks.

Greco, Kathleen & Greco, Nick. Yummy Yarns Knits for Kids: 20 Easy-to-Knit Designs for Ages 2 to 8 Featuring Fun Novelty Yarns. VanDeHatert, Joe, photos by. 2005. (Illus.). 128p. (gr. 4-6). pap., pap. 19.95 (978-0-8230-5986-7(3)) Watson-Guptill Pubns., Inc.

Greco, Nick & Greco, Kathleen. Girl's Guide to Fun & Funky Knitting: Everything You Need to Be Successful. 2006. (Illus.). 96p. pap. 24.95 (978-1-57120-382-3(6), 1253728) C&T Publishing.

Guy, Lucinda & Hall, Francois. Kids Learn to Knit. 2006. (Illus.). 96p. pap. 14.95 (978-1-57076-335-9(6)) Trafalgar Square Bks.

Hansen, Robin. Sunny's Mittens: Learn to Knit, Lovikka Mittens. 2003. (Illus.). pap. 14.95 (978-0-89272-634-9(2)) Down East Bks.

Ivarsson, Anna-Stina Linden, et al. Second-Time Cool: The Art of Chopping up a Sweater. Lundin, Maria, tr. from SWE. 2005. (Illus.). 92p. (J). (gr. 5-12). pap. 12.95 (978-1-55037-910-5(0)) Annick Pr., Ltd. CAN. *Dist:* Firefly Bks., Ltd.

—Second-Time Cool: The Art of Chopping up a Sweater. Lundin, Maria, tr. from SWE. Guy, photos by. 2005. (Illus.). 92p. (J). (gr. 5-12). 24.95 (978-1-55037-911-2(9)) Annick Pr., Ltd. CAN. *Dist:* Firefly Bks., Ltd.

Johnson, Anne Akers. Knitting: Learn to Knit Six Great Projects. 2004. (Illus.). 96p. (J). 24.95 (978-1-57054-861-1(7)) Klutz.

Nelson, Robin. From Sheep to Sweater. 2003. (Start to Finish Ser.). (Illus.). 24p. (J). 18.60 (978-0-8225-0716-1(1), Lerner Pubns.) Lerner Publishing Group.

Okey, Shannon. Knitgrrl: Learn to Knit with 15 Fun & Funky Patterns. Jacques, Kathleen, illus. Fagan, Shannon et al, photos by. 2005. 96p. (YA). (gr. 4-6). pap., pap. 9.95 (978-0-8230-2618-0(3)) Watson-Guptill Pubns., Inc.

—KnitGrrl 2: Learn to Knit with 16 Alll-New Patterns. Jacques, Kathleen, illus. Fagan, Shannon, photos by. 2006. 96p. (YA). (gr. 7 up). pap. 9.95 (978-0-8230-2619-7(1)) Watson-Guptill Pubns., Inc.

Olson, Kay Melchisedech. Beginning Knitting: Stitches with Style. 2007. (Snap Books). (Illus.). 32p. (J). 25.26 (978-0-7368-6473-2(3)) Capstone Pr., Inc.

Percival, Kris. Speed Knitting. Stratton, Randy, illus. Giblin, Sheri, photos by. 2006. 132p. pap. 19.95 (978-0-8118-5245-6(8)) Chronicle Bks. LLC.

Sadler, Judy Ann. Knitting. Melo, Esperanca, illus. 2004. (Kids Can Do It Ser.). 40p. (J). (gr. 4-6). (978-1-55337-051-2(1)); (978-1-55337-050-5(3)) Kids Can Pr., Ltd.

—Quick Knits. Melo, Esperanca, illus. 2006. 40p. (978-1-55337-964-5(0)); (978-1-55337-963-8(2)) Kids Can Pr., Ltd.

Suzuki, Katsuno. Handknit Projects for All Kids of All Ages, 2 vols., Vol. 2. 2004. (Illus.). 48p. pap. 8.95 (978-0-89346-940-5(8)) Heian International Publishing, Inc.

Switzer, Chris. Projects for Alpaca & Llama. 2004. 16.00 (978-0-9642663-2-2(6)) Switzer Land Enterprises.

Thalacker, Karen & Dwyer, Mindy. Knitting with Gigi: Includes Step-By-Step Instructions & 8 Patterns. 2007. (J). pap. (***978-1-56477-799-7(5)***) Martingale & Co.

Warwick, Ellen. Fully Woolly. Lum, Bernice, illus. 2007. 80p. (YA). (gr. 5 up). (***978-1-55337-798-6(2)***) Kids Can Pr., Ltd.

Watt, Fiona & Harrison, Erica. How to Knit. 2007. (Art Ideas Ser.). 64p. (J). 14.99 (***978-0-7945-1577-5(0)***, Usborne) EDC Publishing.

Wenger, Jennifer, et al. Teen Knitting Club: Chill Out & Knit. 2004. (Illus.). 144p. (YA). 17.95 (978-1-57965-244-9(1)) Artisan.

KNIVES

Royston, Angela. Metal: Let's Look at a Knife & Fork. 2006. (Heinemann Read & Learn Ser.). (Illus.). 24p. (J). (978-1-4034-7675-3(6)); pap. (978-1-4034-7684-5(5)) Heinemann Library.

—Metal: Miremos un Cuchillo y un Tenedor. 2005. (Heinemann Lee y Aprende Ser.). (ENG & SPA., Illus.). 24p. (978-1-4034-7543-5(1)); pap. (978-1-4034-7552-7(0)) Heinemann Library.

Wright, Bill & Wright, Debbie. Theater-Made Military Knives of World War Two. 2001. (Schiffer Military History Book Ser.). (Illus.). 264p. (gr. 10-13). 59.95 (978-0-7643-1390-5(8)) Schiffer Publishing, Ltd.

KNOTS AND SPLICES

Adkins, Jan. Line: Tying It up, Tying It Down. 2004. 48p. (J). (978-0-937822-83-8(3)) WoodenBoat Pubns.

Bagai, Eric. Simple Knots for a Lifetime. Bagai, Eric, illus. 1998. (Illus.). 20p. (J). (gr. 4-12). 5.00 (978-0-943292-25-0(5), 602) Foreworks.

Groves. Knots & Knocks, Bk. 16. Date not set. (Illus.). 32p. (J). pap. 129.15 (978-0-582-18059-8(7)) Addison-Wesley Longman, Ltd. GBR. *Dist:* Trans-Atlantic Pubns., Inc.

Sadler, Judy Ann. Knotting. Gagnon, Céleste, illus. 2006. 40p. 6.95 (978-1-55337-834-1(2)) Kids Can Pr., Ltd. CAN. *Dist:* Wybel Marketing Group.

Smith, A. G. Celtic Knotwork Stained Glass Colouring Book. 2006. 16p. pap. 5.95 (978-0-486-44816-9(9)) Dover Pubns., Inc.

Stetson, Emily. 40 Knots to Know: Hitches, Loops, Bends & Bindings. Nadel, Marc, illus. 2002. (Quick Starts for Kids! Ser.). 64p. (J). pap. 8.95 (978-1-885593-70-2(8), Williamson Bks.) Ideals Pubns.

—40 Knots to Know: Hitches, Loops, Bends & Bindings. 2002. (gr. 3-6). lib. bdg. 17.60 (978-0-613-57048-0(0)) Tandem Library Bks.

KNOWLEDGE, SOCIOLOGY OF

The Big Book of Knowledge. 2003. 384p. (J). 9.98 (978-0-7525-8436-2(7)) Parragon, Inc.

KNOWLEDGE, THEORY OF

Here are entered works that treat the origin, nature, methods and limits of human knowledge.

see also Belief and Doubt; Intellect; Perception; Senses and Sensation

Carlson, Dale. The Teen Brain Book: Who & What Are You? Teasdale, Nancy, ed. Nicklaus, Carol, illus. 2004. 230p. (gr. 7-12). pap. 14.95 (978-1-884158-29-2(3)) Bick Publishing Hse.

Porchetta, Renato L. Universal Methodology: Semantics - the Mosaic Thinking. 2005. (Illus.). 300p. (YA). lib. bdg. 100.00 (978-0-9769931-0-0(4)) Ce Code Efficiency, Inc.

KNOX, HENRY, 1750-1806

Reit, Seymour V. Guns for General Washington: A Story of the American Revolution. 2001. (Great Episodes Ser.). 160p. (YA). (gr. 5-9). pap. 6.00 (978-0-15-216435-5(9), Gulliver Bks.) Harcourt Children's Bks.

Strum, Richard. Henry Knox: Washington's Artilleryman. 2006. (Forgotten Heroes of the American Revolution Ser.). (Illus.). 88p. (J). (gr. 5-11). lib. bdg. 23.95 (978-1-59556-013-1(0)) OTTN Publishing.

Strum, Richard M. Henry Knox: Washington's Artilleryman. 2006. (J). pap. (978-1-59556-018-6(1)) OTTN Publishing.

KOALA

Burt, Denise. Koalas. McLeod, Neil, photos by. 1999. (Nature Watch Ser.). (Illus.). 48p. (J). (gr. 3-6). lib. bdg. 25.26 (978-1-57505-380-6(2), Carolrhoda Bks.) Lerner Publishing Group.

Eckart, Edana. Koala. 2005. (Welcome Bks.). (Illus.). 24p. (ps-2). (J). pap. 4.95 (978-0-516-25164-6(3)); 18.00 (978-0-516-25053-3(1)) Scholastic Library Publishing. (Children's Pr.).

Ehrich, Joanne. Koalas: Zen in Fur, Hardcover Edition. 2007. (Illus.). 96p. 44.99 (***978-0-9764698-6-5(3)***) Koala Jo Publishing.

Feeney, Kathy. Koala Magic for Kids. McGee, John F., illus. 1999. (Animal Magic for Kids Ser.). 48p. (J). (gr. 3 up). lib. bdg. 26.00 (978-0-8368-2635-7(3)) Stevens, Gareth Inc.

—Koalas for Kids. 1999. (Wildlife for Kids Ser.). (Illus.). (J). (978-0-606-18080-1(X)) Tandem Library Bks.

Feeney, Kathy, et al. Wild Animals: Explore the Fascinating Worlds Of. . . McGee, John F., illus. 2000. 192p. (J). pap. (978-1-55971-741-0(6), NorthWord Bks. for Young Readers) T&N Children's Publishing.

Green, Carl R. The Koala: A MyReportLinks. Com Book. 2003. (Endangered & Threatened Animals Ser.). (Illus.). 48p. (J). (gr. 4-10). lib. bdg. 25.26 (978-0-7660-5058-7(0), MyReportLinks.com Bks.) Enslow Pubs., Inc.

Hanel, Rachael. Koalas. 2008. (J). (***978-1-58341-655-6(2)***, Creative Education) Creative Co., The.

Hewett, Richard, illus. & photos by. A Koala Joey Grows Up. Hewett, Richard, photos by. Hewett, Joan, photos by. 2004. (Baby Animals Ser.). 32p. (J). (gr. k-3). lib. bdg. 21.27 (978-1-57505-198-7(2)) Lerner Publishing Group.

Hoff, Mary King. Koalas: The Wild World of Animals. 2005. (Illus.). 32p. (J). (gr. 2-5). 18.95 (978-1-58341-351-7(0), Creative Education) Creative Co., The.

Inskipp, Carol. Koala. 2004. (Animals under Threat Ser.). (Illus.). 48p. (J). 29.93 (978-1-4034-5585-7(6)) Heinemann Library.

—The Koala. 2004. (Animals under Threat Ser.). (Illus.). 48p. (J). pap. 8.50 (978-1-4034-5692-2(5)) Heinemann Library.

Jacobs, Liza. Koalas. 2003. (Wild Wild World Ser.). (Illus.). 24p. (J). 23.70 (978-1-4103-0049-2(8), Blackbirch Pr., Inc.) Thomson Gale.

Johnson, Jinny. Koala. Ch'en-Ling, illus. 2001. (Busy Baby Animals Ser.). 16p. (J). (ps up). lib. bdg. 19.33 (978-0-8368-2925-9(5)) Stevens, Gareth Inc.

Kalman, Bobbie. The Life Cycle of a Koala. 2001. (Life Cycle Ser.). (Illus.). 32p. (J). (gr. 2-3). (978-0-7787-0655-7(9)); pap. (978-0-7787-0685-4(0)) Crabtree Publishing Co.

—Life Cycle of a Koala. 2002. (gr. 3-6). lib. bdg. 14.10 (978-0-613-52972-3(3)) Tandem Library Bks.

Kalman, Bobbie, et al. Les Koalas. 2005. (FRE., Illus.). 32p. (J). pap. (978-2-89579-033-4(7)) Crabtree Publishing Co.

Koala's Forest Adventures. 2002. (Animal's Around the World Mini Bks.). (Illus.). 32p. (J). (978-1-59069-166-3(0), H4002) Studio Mouse LLC.

Lantier-Sampon, Patricia & Feeney, Kathy. The Wonder of Koalas. McGee, John F., illus. 2001. (Animal Wonders Ser.). 48p. (J). (gr. 1 up). lib. bdg. 26.00 (978-0-8368-2767-5(8)) Stevens, Gareth Inc.

Leach, Michael. Koala: Habitats, Life Cycles, Food Chains, Threats. 2002. (Natural World Ser.). (Illus.). 48p. (J). lib. bdg. 27.12 (978-0-7398-5230-9(2)) Raintree.

Lee, Sandra. Koalas. 2006. (New Naturebooks). (Illus.). 32p. (J). (gr. 1-5). 27.07 (978-1-59296-641-7(1)) Child's World, Inc.

Lever, E., et al. Koalas. Parish, Steve, photos by. 1999. (Animals Are Fun! Ser.). (Illus.). 16p. (J). (ps up). lib. bdg. 19.33 (978-0-8368-2615-9(9)) Stevens, Gareth Inc.

Lynch, Wayne, photos by. Baby Koala. (Illus.). 36p. (J). 2004. pap. (978-1-55041-876-7(9)); 2003. (978-1-55041-874-3(2)) Fitzhenry & Whiteside, Ltd.

Malaspina, Ann. The Koala. 2001. (Endangered Animals & Habitats Ser.). (Illus.). 112p. (YA). (gr. 4-12). 28.70 (978-1-56006-876-1(0), Lucent Bks.) Thomson Gale.

Otfinoski, Steven. Koalas. 2007. (Animals Animals Ser.). (Illus.). 48p. (J). (gr. 4-7). lib. bdg. 28.50 (978-0-7614-2526-7(8), Benchmark Bks.) Cavendish, Marshall Corp.

Pingry, Patricia A. Baby Koala. 2003. (San Diego Zoo Animal Library: Vol. 3). (Illus.). 24p. (J). bds. 6.95 (978-0-8249-6528-0(0)) Ideals Pubns.

Pohl, Kathleen. Koalas: Koalas. 2006. (Illus.). 24p. (J). lib. bdg. (***978-0-8368-8007-6(2)***, Weekly Reader Early Learning Library) Stevens, Gareth Inc.

Riley, Joelle. Koalas. 2005. (Early Bird Nature Books). (Illus.). 48p. (J). (ps-7). lib. bdg. 25.26 (978-0-8225-2870-8(3), Lerner Pubns.) Lerner Publishing Group.

Saunders-Smith, Gail. Koalas. 1998. (J). pap. 13.25 (978-0-516-21233-3(8), Children's Pr.) Scholastic Library Publishing.

Swan, Erin Pembrey. Kangeroos & Koalas: What They Have in Common. 2000. (gr. 3-6). lib. bdg. 15.25 (978-0-613-34804-1(4)) Tandem Library Bks.

Theodorou, Rod. Koala. (Animals in Danger Ser.). (Illus.). 32p. (J). (gr. k-2). 2002. pap. 6.95 (978-1-58810-446-5(X), 91153); 2001. lib. bdg. 21.36 (978-1-57572-271-9(2)) Heinemann Library.

van Holst Pellekaan, Karen. Coco the Koala Series, 3 bks. De Backker, Vera, illus. Incl. Coco Makes Music. 29p. lib. bdg. 23.33 (978-0-8368-2730-9(9)); Coco the Koala. 29p. lib. bdg. 23.33 (978-0-8368-2729-3(5)); Coco's Surprise. 31p. lib. bdg. 23.33 (978-0-8368-2731-6(7)); (J). (ps up). (Illus.). 2000. Set lib. bdg. 69.99 (978-0-8368-2728-6(7)) Stevens, Gareth Inc.

KOALA—FICTION

Book Buddy: Koala with Story Book. Orig. Title: Child's Play. (Illus.). 10p. (J). (ps-4). reprint ed. (978-1-881469-43-8(3)) Safari, Ltd.

DALP. Koala Kid: Soft Spot Board Book. 2002. (Soft Spot Bks.). (Illus.). 10p. (J). bds. 3.99 (978-1-57759-627-1(7)) Dalmatian Pr.

Dennard, Deborah. Koala Country: A Story of an Australian Eucalyptus Forest. 2005. (Soundprints' Wild Habitats Ser.). (Illus.). 32p. (J). (gr. 1-4). 8.95 incl. audio (978-1-59249-106-3(5), SC7018) Soundprints.

Fox, Mem. Koala Lou. 2002. (Illus.). (J). 13.19 (978-0-7587-2941-5(3)) Book Wholesalers, Inc.

King, Jamie R. Kodi's Heroic Journey. Lemmon, David, illus. 1999. (Zoooo Stories Ser.). (J). (978-1-893993-01-3(9)) Medias & Co., Inc.

Koala Joey. 2002. (Baby Animals Ser.). (Illus.). (978-1-59069-056-7(7), 1-1003) Studio Mouse LLC.

Kroll, Virginia L. & Jones, Dawn L. Kingston's Flowering Forest. Maydak, Michael S., illus. 2001. (J). (978-0-9712840-5-0(9)) Boyds Collection Ltd., The.

Kylie's Concert: Evaluation Guide. 2006. (J). (978-1-55942-413-4(3)) Marsh Media.

Kylie's Song: Evaluation Guide. 2006. (J). (978-1-55942-414-1(1)) Marsh Media.

Parish, Steve, illus. Koala Commotion. 2005. 24p. (J). lib. bdg. 20.67 (978-0-8368-5972-0(3)) Stevens, Gareth Inc.

Ryan, Kate & Harvey, Roland. Belvedere in the City. 2004. (Illus.). 32p. pap. 6.99 (978-0-14-350044-5(9), Penguin Global) Penguin Group (USA) Inc.

Tabernik, John. Ricky the Picky Koala. Wise, Catlin, illus. 2005. (J). 14.95 (978-0-9773936-0-2(7)) Little Munchkin Bks.

van Holst Pellekaan, Karen. Coco Makes Music. De Backker, Vera, illus. 2000. (Coco the Koala Ser.). 29p. (J). (ps up). lib. bdg. 23.33 (978-0-8368-2730-9(9)) Stevens, Gareth Inc.

—Coco the Koala. De Backker, Vera, illus. 2000. (Coco the Koala Ser.). 29p. (J). (ps up). lib. bdg. 23.33 (978-0-8368-2729-3(5)) Stevens, Gareth Inc.

—Coco's Surprise. De Backker, Vera, illus. 2000. (Coco the Koala Ser.). 31p. (J). (ps up). lib. bdg. 23.33 (978-0-8368-2731-6(7)) Stevens, Gareth Inc.

KOBAYASHI, ISSA, 1762-1827

Gollub, Matthew. Cool Melons - Turn to Frogs! The Life & Poems of Issa. ed. 2004. (Illus.). (J). (gr. k-3). spiral bd. (978-0-616-03095-0(9)) Canadian National Institute for the Blind/Institut National Canadien pour les Aveugles.

—Cool Melons - Turn to Frogs! The Life & Poems of Issa. Stone, Kazuko G., illus. 1998. 40p. (J). (ps up). 16.95 (978-1-880000-71-7(7)) Lee & Low Bks., Inc.

KOCH, ROBERT, 1843-1910

Tracy, Kathleen. Robert Koch & the Study of Anthrax. 2004. (Uncharted, Unexplored, & Unexplained Ser.). (Illus.). 48p. (J). (gr. 4-8). lib. bdg. 29.95 (978-1-58415-261-3(3)) Mitchell Lane Pubs., Inc.

KOLBE, MAXIMILIAN, SAINT, 1894-1941

Jablonski, Patricia Edward. St. Maximilian Kolbe: Mary's Knight. Kelley, Patrick, illus. 2001. (Encounter the Saints Ser.: Vol. 10). 120p. (J). pap. 6.95 (978-0-8198-7045-2(5), 332-349) Pauline Bks. & Media.

Mohan, Claire J. St. Maximilian Kolbe: The Story of the Two Crowns. 1999. (Christian Hero Ser.). (Illus.). 72p. (J). pap. 8.95 (978-0-9621500-3-6(7)) Young Sparrow Pr., The.

KOREA

Anderson, Dale. Korean Americans. 2008. (J). (***978-1-60044-613-9(2)***) Rourke Publishing, LLC.

Behnke, Alison. Kim Jong Il's North Korea. 2007. (Dictatorships Ser.). (Illus.). 160p. (YA). (gr. 9-12). lib. bdg. 38.60 (***978-0-8225-7282-4(6)***, Twenty-First Century Bks.) Lerner Publishing Group.

Behnke, Alison. North Korea in Pictures. 2nd ed. 2005. (Visual Geography Ser.). (Illus.). 80p. (J). (gr. 5-12). 27.93 (978-0-8225-1908-9(9)) Lerner Publishing Group.

Benson, Sonia. Korean War: Almanac & Primary Sources. Raffaelle, Gerda-Ann, ed. 2001. (Korean War Reference Library). (Illus.). 200p. (YA). (gr. 6-10). 67.00 (978-0-7876-5691-1(7), GML00502-175533, UXL) Thomson Gale.

Boast, Clare. South Korea. 1998. (Next Stop! Ser.). 32p. (J). lib. bdg. 21.36 (978-1-57572-678-6(5)) Heinemann Library.

Bowden, Rob. South Korea. 2006. (Countries of the World Ser.). 64p. (gr. 6-12). 30.00 (978-0-8160-6013-9(4)) Facts On File, Inc.

Brimson, Samuel. Korea, North-Nicaragua, 8 vols. 2003. (Nations of the World Ser.: Vol. 5). (Illus.). 64p. (J). (gr. 5 up). lib. bdg. 30.00 (978-0-8368-5489-3(6), World Almanac Library) Stevens, Gareth Inc.

Britton, Tamara L. North Korea. 2004. (Countries Ser.). (J). (gr. k-6). lib. bdg. 22.78 (978-1-59197-295-2(7)) ABDO Publishing Co.

Burgan, Michael. The Korean War. 2003. (20th Century Perspectives Ser.). (J). 48p. pap. 7.95 (978-1-4034-3857-7(9)); pap. 114.50 (978-1-4034-3860-7(9)) Heinemann Library.

Choi, Anne Soon. Korean Americans. 2007. (New Immigrants Ser.). (Illus.). 136p. (J). (gr. 6-12). 27.95 (978-0-7910-8788-6(3), Chelsea Hse.) Facts On File, Inc.

De Capua, Sarah. Korea. 2004. (Discovering Cultures Ser.). (Illus.). 48p. (J). 25.64 (978-0-7614-1794-1(X), Benchmark Bks.) Cavendish, Marshall Corp.

Donovan, Sandra. Teens in South Korea. 2007. (J). lib. bdg. (***978-0-7565-3297-0(3)***) Compass Point Bks.

DuBois, Jill. Korea. 2nd ed. 2005. (Cultures of the World Ser.). (Illus.). 144p. (J). 37.07 (978-0-7614-1786-6(9), Benchmark Bks.) Cavendish, Marshall Corp.

Dudley, William. North & South Korea. 2002. (Opposing Viewpoints Ser.). (Illus.). 200p. (J). 36.20 (978-0-7377-1236-0(8)); (YA). (gr. 10-12). pap. 24.95 (978-0-7377-1235-3(X)) Thomson Gale. (Greenhaven Pr., Inc.).

Guile, Melanie. North & South Korea. 2003. 32p. (J). lib. bdg. 25.70 (978-1-4109-0472-0(5)) Raintree.

Haberle, Susan E. North Korea. 2005. (Fact Finders Ser.). (Illus.). 32p. (J). 22.60 (978-0-7368-3756-9(6)) Capstone Pr., Inc.

—South Korea. 2005. (Fact Finders Ser.). (Illus.). 32p. (J). 22.60 (978-0-7368-3761-3(2)) Capstone Pr., Inc.

Han, Suzanne C. Let's Color Korea-Traditional Lifestyles. 2001. 24p. (J). (gr. k-3). pap. 12.50 (978-0-930878-94-8(9)) Hollym International Corp.

Han, Suzanne Crowder. Let's Learn about Korea: Customs of Korea. (Illus.). 28p. (J). pap. (978-1-56591-000-3(1)) Hollym International Corp.

Harkrader, Lisa. South Korea: A MyReportLinks. com Book. 2004. (Top Ten Countries of Recent Immigrants Ser.). (Illus.). 48p. (YA). lib. bdg. 25.26 (978-0-7660-5181-2(1), MyReportLinks.com Bks.) Enslow Pubs., Inc.

Hill, Valerie. Korea. 2002. (Ask about Asia Ser.). (Illus.). 48p. (J). (gr. 4 up). lib. bdg. (978-1-59084-206-5(5)) Mason Crest Pubs.

Ho Siow Yen & Rabe, Monica. South Korea. 1998. (Festivals of the World Ser.). (Illus.). 32p. (J). (gr. 3 up). lib. bdg. 24.67 (978-0-8368-2019-5(3)) Stevens, Gareth Inc.

Hossell, Karen Price. The Korean War. 2003. (20th-Century Perspectives Ser.). (Illus.). 48p. (J). lib. bdg. 27.07 (978-1-4034-1144-0(1)) Heinemann Library.

Ingram, Scott. Kim il Sung. 2003. (History's Villains Ser.). (Illus.). 112p. (J). 28.70 (978-1-4103-0259-5(8), Blackbirch Pr., Inc.) Thomson Gale.

—Korean Americans. 2006. (World Almanac Library of American Immigration). (Illus.). 48p. (J). pap. (978-0-8368-7328-3(9)); lib. bdg. (978-0-8368-7315-3(7)) Stevens, Gareth Inc. (World Almanac Library).

Italia, Bob. South Korea. 2003. (Countries Ser.). (J). (gr. k-6). lib. bdg. 22.78 (978-1-57765-846-7(9)) ABDO Publishing Co.

Jackson, Tom. South Korea. 2007. (Countries of the World Ser.). (Illus.). 64p. (YA). (gr. 5 up). lib. bdg. 27.90 (***978-1-4263-0125-4(1)***, National Geographic Children's Bks.) National Geographic Society.

Kim, Kyoung-Mi. Living in South Korea. 2001. ("Living In" Ser.). (Illus.). 96p. pap. 9.95 (978-0-86647-131-2(6)) Pro Lingua Assocs., Inc.

Koestler-Grack, Rachel A. Kim il Sung & Kim Jong Il. 2003. (Major World Leaders Ser.). (Illus.). 112p. (J). (gr. 6-12). 30.00 (978-0-7910-7648-4(2), Chelsea Hse.) Facts On File, Inc.

Kummer, Patricia K. North Korea. 2007. (Enchantment of the World, Second Ser.). 144p. (J). spiral bd. 37.00 (***978-0-531-18485-1(4)***, Children's Pr.) Scholastic Library Publishing.

—South Korea. 2007. (Enchantment of the World, Second Ser.). 144p. (J). spiral bd. 37.00 (***978-0-531-18486-8(2)***, Children's Pr.) Scholastic Library Publishing.

Landau, Elaine. Korea. 1999. (gr. 3-6). lib. bdg. 15.25 (978-0-613-54603-4(2)) Tandem Library Bks.

March, Michael. Guide to South Korea. 1999. (World Guides Ser.). (Illus.). 32p. (J). (gr. 2-6). lib. bdg. 21.27 (978-1-884756-55-9(7)) Davidson Titles, Inc.

Martin, Jennifer C. The Korean Americans. 2005. (Immigrants in America Ser.). (Illus.). 112p. (YA). (gr. 7-10). lib. bdg. 29.95 (978-1-59018-079-2(8), Lucent Bks.) Thomson Gale.

Masse, Johanna. South Korea. 2002. (Countries of the World Ser.). (Illus.). 96p. (J). (gr. 6 up). lib. bdg. 30.00 (978-0-8368-2353-0(2)) Stevens, Gareth Inc.

Matray, James Irving. Korea Divided: The Thirty-Eighth Parallel & the Demilitarized Zone. 2004. (Arbitrary Borders Ser.). (Illus.). 112p. (gr. 9-13). 35.00 (978-0-7910-7829-7(9), Chelsea Hse.) Facts On File, Inc.

McMahon, Patricia. Chi-Hoon: A Korean Girl. 2003. (Illus.). 48p. (YA). (gr. 4-6). pap. 10.95 (978-1-56397-720-6(6)) Boyds Mills Pr.

Mueller, Mark. Let's Color Korea-Traditional Games. 2001. (Illus.). 24p. (J). (gr. k-3). pap. 12.50 (978-0-930878-95-5(7)) Hollym International Corp.

Nash, Amy K. North Korea. 1999. (Major World Nations Ser.). (Illus.). 144p. (YA). (gr. 4-7). lib. bdg. 21.95 (978-0-7910-4746-0(6) , Chelsea Hse.) Facts On File, Inc.

Olmstead, Mary. Korea. 2003. (World Tour Ser.). (Illus.). 48p. (J). lib. bdg. 25.70 (978-0-7398-6812-6(8)) Raintree.

Park, Frances & Park, Ginger. My Freedom Trip: A Child's Escape from South Korea. Jenkins, Debra Reid, illus. 2003. 32p. (J). (gr. k-2). 16.95 (978-1-56397-468-7(1)) Boyds Mills Pr.

Paymar, Michelle. Teens in South Korea. 2004. (Teens Around the World Ser.). (J). (978-1-59018-034-1(8) , Lucent Bks.) Thomson Gale.

Peterson, Mark. Brief History of Korea. 2008. (Brief History Ser.). 318p. (gr. 9). 45.00 (978-0-8160-5085-7(6)) Facts On File, Inc.

Piddock, Charles. North Korea. 2006. (Illus.). 48p. (J). pap. (978-0-8368-6716-9(5)); lib. bdg. (978-0-8368-6709-1(2)) Stevens, Gareth Inc. (World Almanac Library).

Pugliano-Martin, Carol. Discover Seoul. 2006. pap. 39.00 (***978-1-4108-6424-6(3)***) Benchmark Education Co.

—Seoul, Korea. 2006. pap. 39.00 (***978-1-4108-6421-5(9)***) Benchmark Education Co.

Ryan, Patrick. Welcome to South Korea. 2008. (Welcome to the World Ser.). 32p. (J). (gr. 1-5). 27.07 (***978-1-59296-978-4(X)***) Child's World, Inc.

Salter, Christopher. North Korea. 2003. (Modern World Nations Ser.). (Illus.). 150p. (gr. 6-12). 30.00 (978-0-7910-7233-2(9) , Chelsea Hse.) Facts On File, Inc.

Salter, Christopher L. South Korea. 2005. (Modern World Nations Ser.). 150p. (J). 30.00 (978-0-7910-8662-9(3) , Chelsea Hse.) Facts On File, Inc.

Salter, Kit & Salter, Christopher L. North Korea. 2nd rev. ed. 2007. (Modern World Nations Ser.). 128p. (gr. 6-12). 30.00 (***978-0-7910-9513-3(4)*** , Chelsea Hse.) Facts On File, Inc.

Schlesinger, Arthur M., Jr., ed. Kim Dae-Jung: South Korean President. 1999. (World Leaders Past & Present Ser.). (Illus.). 128p. (YA). (gr. 5-9). lib. bdg. 21.95 (978-0-7910-5215-0(X) , Chelsea Hse.) Facts On File, Inc.

Shalant, Phyllis. Look What We've Brought You from Korea: Crafts, Games, Recipes, Stories & Other Cultural Activities from Korean-Americans. Park, Soyoo H., illus. (J). (gr. 2 up). pap. 7.95 (978-0-382-24994-5(1)) Silver, Burdett & Ginn, Inc.

Shepheard, Patricia. South Korea. 1999. (Major World Nations Ser.). (Illus.). 144p. (YA). (gr. 4-7). lib. bdg. 21.95 (978-0-7910-4985-3(X) , Chelsea Hse.) Facts On File, Inc.

South Korea. (Countries of the World Ser.). 24p. (J). 6.95 (978-0-7368-8384-9(3)) Capstone Pr., Inc.

South Korea, 6 vols. (gr. 2-5). 36.95 (978-0-7368-8405-1(X)) Red Brick Learning.

Stickler, John & Stickler, Soma Han. Land of Morning Calm: Korean Culture Then & Now. Stickler, John & Stickler, Soma Han, illus. 2003. (Illus.). 32p. (YA). 16.95 (978-1-885008-22-0(8)) Shen's Bks.

Suyenaga, Ruth. Korean Children's Day. Kyong-Nan, Nani, illus. 2004. 23p. (J). (gr. 4-8). reprint ed. pap. 15.00 (978-0-7567-7068-6(8)) DIANE Publishing Co.

Suyenaga, Ruth, et al. Korean Children's Day. Kyong-Nan, Nani, illus. 2005. (Multicultural Celebrations Ser.). 32p. (J). 4.95 (978-1-59373-011-6(X)) Bunker Hill Publishing, Inc.

Tull, Mary, et al. Northern Asia: Understanding Geography & History Through Art. 1999. (Artisans Around the World Ser.). (Illus.). 48p. (J). (gr. 4-8). lib. bdg. 27.12 (978-0-7398-0119-2(8)) Raintree.

Walsh, Kieran. Korea. 2005. (Countries in the News Ser.). (Illus.). 24p. (gr. 1-4). 17.95 (978-1-59515-175-9(3)) Rourke Publishing, LLC.

Walters, Tara. North Korea. 2007. (True Booktrade;: Geography: Countries Ser.). 48p. (J). spiral bd. 26.00 (***978-0-531-16854-7(9)*** , Children's Pr.) Scholastic Library Publishing.

—South Korea. 2007. (True Booktrade;: Geography: Countries Ser.). 48p. (J). spiral bd. 26.00 (***978-0-531-16855-4(7)*** , Children's Pr.) Scholastic Library Publishing.

Weber, Valerie. I Come from South Korea. 2006. (Illus.). 24p. (J). pap. (978-0-8368-7244-6(4)); lib. bdg. (978-0-8368-7237-8(1)) Stevens, Gareth Inc. (Weekly Reader Early Learning Library).

Williams, Jean K. South Korea. 1998. (Illus.). 112p. (YA). (gr. 4-12). 27.45 (978-1-56006-446-6(3) , Lucent Bks.) Thomson Gale.

KOREA—FICTION

Choi, Sook Nyul. Echoes of White Giraffe. 2007. 144p. (YA). (gr. 7). pap. 6.95 (***978-0-618-80917-2(1)***) Houghton Mifflin Co. Trade & Reference Div.

Choi, Yangsook. Peach Heaven. 2005. (Illus.). 32p. (J). 16.00 (978-0-374-35761-0(7) , Farrar, Straus & Giroux (BYR)) Farrar, Straus & Giroux.

Clamp, creator. Legend of Chun Hyang, Vol. 1. 2004. (Illus.). 192p. (gr. 2-5). pap. 9.99 (978-1-59182-763-4(9) , Tokyopop Adult) TOKYOPOP, Inc.

Farley, Carol. The King's Secret: The Legend of King Sejong. Cooper, Floyd, illus. 2001. 32p. (J). (gr. 1 up). 15.95 (978-0-688-12776-3(2)) HarperCollins Pubs.

Groot, De. Clifton: Black Moon. Spear, Luke, tr. from FRE. Rodrigue, illus. 2007. 48p. pap. 9.99 (***978-1-905460-30-4(9)***) CineBook GBR. *Dist:* Biblio Distribution.

Lee, Marie Myung-Ok. Somebody's Daughter. 2006. 280p. pap. 14.00 (978-0-8070-8389-5(5)) Beacon Pr.

Lee, Tae-Joon. Waiting for Mama. Chun, Eun Hee, tr. Kim, Dong-Sung, illus. 2007. (KOR & ENG.). 32p. (J). (ps-2). 16.95 (***978-0-7358-2143-9(7)***) North-South Bks., Inc.

Lee, Uk-Bae. Sori's Harvest Moon Day: A Story of Korea. Lee, Uk-Bae, illus. 1999. (Make Friends Around the World Ser.). Orig. Title: Sori's Chu-Suk. (Illus.). 32p. (J). (gr. k-3). 15.95 (978-1-56899-687-5(X) , B8001); 5.95 (978-1-56899-688-2(8) , S8001) Soundprints.

Made in Korea: Sir's Six-Pack. (Greetings Ser.: Vol. 3). (gr. 3-5). 31.00 (978-0-7635-1824-0(7)) Rigby Education.

The Moneybag: a Tale from Korea: Small Versions of Big Books. (On Our Way to English Ser.). (gr. 3 up). 35.50 (978-0-7578-7247-1(6)) Rigby Education.

The Moneybag: a Tale from Korea: Third Grade Big Books. (On Our Way to English Ser.). (gr. 3 up). 29.95 (978-0-7578-4214-6(3)) Rigby Education.

Neilan, Eujin Kim, illus. The Rabbit & the Dragon King: Based on a Korean Folk Tale. 2003. 32p. (J). (gr. 2-4). 17.95 (978-1-56397-880-7(6)) Boyds Mills Pr.

Netcomics. Kingdom of the Winds, Vol. 1. 2007. (Kingdom of the Winds Ser.). (Illus.). 216p. per. 9.99 (***978-1-60009-251-0(9)***) Netcomics.

Park, Frances. Royal Bee. 2000. (gr. 3-6). lib. bdg. 17.60 (978-0-613-29043-2(7)) Tandem Library Bks.

Park, Frances & Park, Ginger. Where on Earth Is My Bagel? Lin, Grace, illus. 2001. 32p. (J). (ps-4). 16.00 (978-1-58430-033-5(7)) Lee & Low Bks., Inc.

Park, Linda Sue. Archer's Quest. 2006. (Illus.). 176p. (J). (gr. 5-9). 16.00 (978-0-618-59631-7(3) , Clarion Bks.) Houghton Mifflin Co. Trade & Reference Div.

—Bee-Bim Bop! Lee, Ho Baek, illus. 2005. 32p. (J). (gr. k-3). 15.00 (978-0-618-26511-4(2) , Clarion Bks.) Houghton Mifflin Co. Trade & Reference Div.

—The Firekeeper's Son. Downing, Julie, illus. 2004. 40p. (J). (gr. k-3). 16.00 (978-0-618-13337-6(2) , Clarion Bks.) Houghton Mifflin Co. Trade & Reference Div.

—The Kite Fighters. 2000. (Illus.). 144p. (J). (gr. 5-9). tchr. ed. 15.00 (978-0-395-94041-9(9) , Clarion Bks.) Houghton Mifflin Co. Trade & Reference Div.

—The Kite Fighters. 2002. (gr. 5-8). lib. bdg. 13.00 (978-0-613-57908-7(9)) Tandem Library Bks.

—Seesaw Girl. Tseng, Jean & Tseng, Mou-Sien, illus. 1999. 96p. (J). (gr. 4-6). tchr. ed. 14.00 (978-0-395-91514-1(7) , Clarion Bks.) Houghton Mifflin Co. Trade & Reference Div.

—Seesaw Girl. Tseng, Jean & Tseng, Mou-Sien, illus. 2001. 112p. (gr. 4-7). 5.50 (978-0-440-41672-2(8) , Yearling) Random Hse. Children's Bks.

—Seesaw Girl. Tseng, Jean & Tseng, Mou-Sien, illus. 2001. 96p. (J). (gr. 4-7). lib. bdg. 12.40 (978-0-613-35470-7(2)) Tandem Library Bks.

—Seesaw Girl. 1999. (Illus.). (J). (978-0-606-20902-1(6)) Tandem Library Bks.

—A Single Shard. braille ed. 2001. (gr. 2). spiral bd. (978-0-616-08848-7(5)) Canadian National Institute for the Blind/Institut National Canadien pour les Aveugles.

—A Single Shard. 2001. (Illus.). 160p. (J). (gr. 5-9). tchr. ed. 15.00 (978-0-395-97827-6(0) , Clarion Bks.) Houghton Mifflin Co. Trade & Reference Div.

—A Single Shard. 2002. (J). (gr. 5-6). stu. ed. (978-1-58130-771-9(3)) Novel Units, Inc.

—A Single Shard. unabr. ed. 2004. (Middle Grade Cassette Librariestm Ser.). (J). (gr. 5-9). pap. 36.00 incl. audio (978-0-8072-1760-3(3) , S YA 349 SP, Listening Library) Random Hse. Audio Publishing Group.

—A Single Shard. 2003. (gr. 5-8). lib. bdg. 14.15 (978-0-613-57327-6(7)) Tandem Library Bks.

—When My Name Was Keoko. 2002. 208p. (YA). (gr. 5-9). 16.00 (978-0-618-13335-2(6) , Clarion Bks.) Houghton Mifflin Co. Trade & Reference Div.

—When My Name Was Keoko. 2004. (Illus.). 208p. (J). (gr. 5). pap. 6.50 (978-0-440-41944-0(1) , Yearling) Random Hse. Children's Bks.

Wong, Janet S. The Trip Back Home. Jia, Bo, illus. 2000. 32p. (J). (ps-2). 17.00 (978-0-15-200784-3(9)) Harcourt Children's Bks.

Year of Impossible Goodbyes. 2002. (J). (gr. 5-6). stu. ed. (978-1-58130-799-3(3)) Novel Units, Inc.

KOREA, PEOPLE'S DEMOCRATIC REPUBLIC OF

Parks, Peggy J. North Korea. 2003. (Nations in Conflict Ser.). (Illus.). 48p. (J). 24.95 (978-1-4103-0077-5(3) , Blackbirch Pr., Inc.) Thomson Gale.

KOREA, REPUBLIC OF

Ho Siow Yen & Rabe, Monica. South Korea. 1998. (Festivals of the World Ser.). (Illus.). 32p. (J). (gr. 3 up). lib. bdg. 24.67 (978-0-8368-2019-5(3)) Stevens, Gareth Inc.

Kwek, Karen & Masse, Johanna. Welcome to South Korea. 2003. (Welcome to My Country Ser.). (Illus.). 48p. (J). (gr. 2 up). lib. bdg. 26.00 (978-0-8368-2553-4(5)) Stevens, Gareth Inc.

Salter, Christopher L. South Korea. 2003. (Modern World Nations Ser.). (Illus.). 200p. (J). (gr. 6-12). lib. bdg. 24.95 (978-0-7910-7050-5(6) , Chelsea Hse.) Facts On File, Inc.

KOREAN AMERICANS

Anderson, Dale. Korean Americans. 2008. (J). (***978-1-60044-613-9(2)***) Rourke Publishing, LLC.

Bryan, Nichol. Korean Americans. 2004. (One Nation Set Ii Ser.). (Illus.). 32p. (J). (gr. k-6). lib. bdg. 22.78 (978-1-59197-530-4(1)) ABDO Publishing Co.

Choi, Anne Soon. Korean Americans. 2007. (New Immigrants Ser.). (Illus.). 136p. (J). (gr. 6-12). 27.95 (978-0-7910-8788-6(3) , Chelsea Hse.) Facts On File, Inc.

Harkrader, Lisa. South Korea: A MyReportLinks. com Book. 2004. (Top Ten Countries of Recent Immigrants Ser.). (Illus.). 48p. (YA). lib. bdg. 25.26 (978-0-7660-5181-2(1) , MyReportLinks.com Bks.) Enslow Pubs., Inc.

Ingram, Scott. Korean Americans. 2006. (World Almanac Library of American Immigration). (Illus.). 48p. (J). pap. (978-0-8368-7328-3(9)); lib. bdg. (978-0-8368-7315-3(7)) Stevens, Gareth Inc. (World Almanac Library).

Klingel/Noyed. Korean Americans. 2003. (Spirit of America). (Illus.). 32p. (J). (gr. 2-6). 27.07 (978-1-59296-016-3(2)) Child's World, Inc.

Martin, Jennifer C. The Korean Americans. 2005. (Immigrants in America Ser.). (Illus.). 112p. (YA). (gr. 7-10). lib. bdg. 29.95 (978-1-59018-079-2(8) , Lucent Bks.) Thomson Gale.

Noonan, Sheila Smith. Korean Immigration. 2003. (Changing Face of North America Ser.). (Illus.). 112p. (YA). lib. bdg. (978-1-59084-693-3(1)) Mason Crest Pubs.

Orr, Tamra. The Korean Americans. 2002. (Welcome to America Ser.). (Illus.). 64p. (YA). (gr. 5 up). lib. bdg. (978-1-59084-110-5(7)) Mason Crest Pubs.

Peterson, Tiffany. Korean Americans. 2003. (We Are America Ser.). 32p. pap. 6.95 (978-1-4034-3136-3(1)); (Illus.). (J). lib. bdg. 24.22 (978-1-4034-0735-1(5)) Heinemann Library.

—Korean Americans. 2003. (gr. 3-6). lib. bdg. 15.25 (978-0-613-67419-5(7)) Tandem Library Bks.

Taus-Bolstad, Stacy. Koreans in America. 2005. (In America Ser.). (Illus.). 80p. (J). (ps-7). 27.93 (978-0-8225-4874-4(7) , Lerner Pubns.) Lerner Publishing Group.

Weber, Valerie. I Come from South Korea. 2006. (Illus.). 24p. (J). pap. (978-0-8368-7244-6(4)); lib. bdg. (978-0-8368-7237-8(1)) Stevens, Gareth Inc. (Weekly Reader Early Learning Library).

KOREAN AMERICANS—FICTION

An, Na. The Fold. 2008. 192p. (J). (gr. 5). 16.99 (***978-0-399-24276-2(7)*** , Putnam Juvenile) Penguin Group (USA) Inc.

Bonin, Liane. Pretty on the Outside: Fame Unlimited. 2007. 288p. (YA). pap. 9.99 (***978-0-451-22122-3(2)*** , N A L Trade) Penguin Group (USA) Inc.

Brandon, Anthony G. Moving Day. Yee, Wong Herbert, illus. 2005. (Green Light Readers Level 2 Ser.). 32p. (J). (ps-ps). 12.95 (978-0-15-205646-9(7)); pap. 3.95 (978-0-15-205652-0(1)) Harcourt Trade Pubs.

Choi, Yangsook. Behind the Mask. 2006. (Illus.). 40p. (J). 16.00 (978-0-374-30522-2(6) , Frances Foster Bks.) Farrar, Straus & Giroux.

Czech, Jan M. An American Face. 2000. (Illus.). 32p. (ps-3). pap. 8.95 (978-0-87868-718-3(1) , 7181, Child & Family Pr.) Child Welfare League of America, Inc.

—The Coffee Can Kid. Manning, Maurie, illus. 2002. 24p. pap. 8.95 (978-0-87868-821-0(8) , 8218, Child & Family Pr.) Child Welfare League of America, Inc.

—Coffee Can Kid. 2002. (gr. k-3). lib. bdg. 17.60 (978-0-613-53419-2(0)) Tandem Library Bks.

Kline, Suzy. Horrible Harry & the Dragon War. Remkiewicz, Frank, illus. 2002. 64p. (J). (gr. 1-3). 13.99 (978-0-670-03559-5(9) , Viking Juvenile) Penguin Group (USA) Inc.

—Horrible Harry & the Drop of Doom. (Horrible Harry Ser.: No. 9). (Illus.). 64p. (J). (gr. 2-4). 2000. pap. 3.99 (978-0-14-037256-4(3) , Puffin); 1998. 13.99 (978-0-670-85849-1(8) , Viking Juvenile) Penguin Group (USA) Inc.

—Horrible Harry & the Drop of Doom. 2000. (Illus.). (J). 10.79 (978-0-606-17861-7(9)) Tandem Library Bks.

Kline, Suzy & Kline, Suzy. Horrible Harry & the Dragon War. Remkiewicz, Frank, illus. 2003. 64p. (J). (ps-k). pap. 3.99 (978-0-14-250166-5(2) , Puffin) Penguin Group (USA) Inc.

—Horrible Harry & the Drop of Doom. Remkiewicz, Frank, illus. 2000. 57p. (J). (gr. 2-5). lib. bdg. 11.80 (978-0-613-28521-6(2)) Tandem Library Bks.

Lee, Marie G. F Is for Fabuloso. 1999. 192p. (J). (gr. 5-9). 15.95 (978-0-380-97648-5(X)) HarperCollins Pubs.

—Night of the Chupacabras. 1999. 128p. (gr. 3-7). pap. 3.99 (978-0-380-79773-8(9)) HarperCollins Pubs.

—Night of the Chupacabras. 1999. (978-0-606-17336-0(6)) Tandem Library Bks.

Lewis, Beverly. Better Than Best. 2000. (Girls Only (Go!) Ser.: Vol. 6). (Illus.). 128p. (J). (gr. 3-8). pap. 6.99 (978-1-55661-641-9(4)) Bethany Hse. Pubs.

Littleton, Mark. Sarah's Secret. 2001. (Ally OConnor Adventures Ser.: Vol. 2). 112p. (J). (gr. 4-7). pap. 5.99 (978-0-8010-4489-2(8)) Baker Bks.

Making Heaven (Koreans) 76p. (YA). (gr. 6-12). pap. 9.95 (978-0-8224-3801-4(1)) Globe Fearon Educational Publishing.

Na, An. A Step from Heaven. 2003. 160p. (YA). (gr. 7-11). pap. 7.99 (978-0-14-250027-9(5) , Puffin) Penguin Group (USA) Inc.

—A Step from Heaven. l.t. ed. 2002. 193p. (J). 22.95 (978-0-7862-4126-2(8)) Thomson Gale.

Na, An. Wait for Me. 2007. 192p. (YA). (gr. 7 up). 7.99 (***978-0-14-240918-3(9)*** , Puffin) Penguin Group (USA) Inc.

Oh, Jina, reader. A Step from Heaven. 2004. 160p. (J). (gr. 6 up). pap. 36.00 incl. audio (978-0-8072-2287-4(9) , Listening Library) Random Hse. Audio Publishing Group.

Pak, Soyung. Dear Juno. Hartung, Susan Kathleen, illus. 1999. 32p. (J). (ps-2). 17.99 (978-0-670-88252-6(6) , Viking Juvenile) Penguin Group (USA) Inc.

—Sumi's First Day of School Ever. Kim, Joung Un, illus. 2003. 32p. (J). (ps-3). 15.99 (978-0-670-03522-9(X) , Viking Juvenile) Penguin Group (USA) Inc.

Park, Frances & Park, Ginger. The Have a Good Day Café. Potter, Katherine, illus. 2005. 32p. (J). 16.95 (978-1-58430-171-4(6)) Lee & Low Bks., Inc.

Park, Linda Sue. Archer's Quest. 2006. (Illus.). 176p. (J). (gr. 5-9). 16.00 (978-0-618-59631-7(3) , Clarion Bks.) Houghton Mifflin Co. Trade & Reference Div.

—Project Mulberry. 2005. 240p. (J). (gr. 5-9). 16.00 (978-0-618-47786-9(1) , Clarion Bks.) Houghton Mifflin Co. Trade & Reference Div.

—Project Mulberry. 2007. 240p. (J). (gr. 4-7). pap. 6.50 (978-0-440-42163-4(2) , Yearling) Random Hse. Children's Bks.

Patz, Nancy & Roth, Susan L. Babies Can't Eat Kimchee! Patz, Nancy & Roth, Susan L., illus. 2006. (Illus.). 32p. (J). (ps-2). 16.95 (978-1-59990-017-9(3)) Bloomsbury Publishing.

Recorvits, Helen. My Name Is Yoon. Swiatkowska, Gabi, illus. 2003. 32p. (J). (gr. k-3). 16.00 (978-0-374-35114-4(7) , Farrar, Straus & Giroux (BYR)) Farrar, Straus & Giroux.

—Yoon & the Christmas Mitten. Swiatkowska, Gabi, illus. 2006. 32p. (J). 16.00 (978-0-374-38688-7(9)) Farrar, Straus & Giroux.

—Yoon & the Jade Bracelet. Swiatkowska, Gabriela, illus. 2008. (J). (978-0-374-38689-4(7)) Farrar, Straus & Giroux.

Remkiewicz, Frank, illus. Horrible Harry & the Drop of Doom. 2002. (Horrible Harry Ser.). (J). 11.49 (978-0-7587-0589-1(1)) Book Wholesalers, Inc.

Shin, Sun Yung. Cooper's Lesson. Cogan, Kim & Paek, Min, trs. from ENG. Cogan, Kim, illus. 2004. (ENG & KOR.). 32p. (J). 16.95 (978-0-89239-193-6(6)) Children's Bk. Pr.

Son, John. Finding My Hat. (First Person Fiction Ser.). 192p. (J). 2003. (gr. 6-10). pap. 16.95 (978-0-439-43538-3(2) , Orchard Bks.); 2005. reprint ed. pap. 6.99 (978-0-439-43539-0(0) , Scholastic Paperbacks) Scholastic, Inc.

Step from Heaven. 2002. (gr. 7-12). lib. bdg. 16.45 (978-0-613-60366-9(4)) Tandem Library Bks.

Yoo, David. Girls for Breakfast. 304p. (YA). (gr. 9). 2005. 15.95 (978-0-385-73192-8(2) , Delacorte Bks. for Young Readers); 2005. lib. bdg. 17.99 (978-0-385-90227-4(1) , Delacorte Bks. for Young Readers); 2006. reprint ed. pap. 5.99 (978-0-440-23883-6(8) , Laurel Leaf) Random Hse. Children's Bks.

Yoo, Paula. Good Enough. 2008. 336p. (J). 16.99 (***978-0-06-079085-1(7)***); lib. bdg. 17.89 (***978-0-06-079089-9(X)***) HarperCollins Pubs. (HarperTeen).

Yoo, Paula & Dereske, Jo. Good Enough. 2008. 272p. mass mkt. 6.99 (***978-0-06-079086-8(5)*** , HarperTeen) HarperCollins Pubs.

KOREAN LANGUAGE

Burke, David. GOLDILOCKS (Korean to English - Level 2) Learn ENGLISH Through Fairy Tales. 2007. (KOR & ENG.). (J). per. 14.95 incl. audio compact disk (***978-1-891888-10-6(2)***) Slangman Publishing.

Karapetian, Marjam. Bilingual Content Dictionary: English to Korean. 2004. (KOR & ENG.). 4.95 (978-0-9764829-7-0(5)); 4.95 (978-0-9764829-6-3(7)); 13.95 (978-0-9767958-0-3(9)); 9.95 (978-0-9764829-8-7(3)); 15.95 (978-0-9767958-1-0(7)) WizdomInc.

—Bilingual Content Dictionary: English to Korean: Social Studies - American History Through 1776. 2004. (KOR & ENG.). 14.95 (978-0-9764829-9-4(1)) WizdomInc.

Lee, Sungun, et al, creators. Korean Language I: Easy to Learn, 5 vols. 2nd ed. 2004. 152p. (C). pap. 15.00 (978-0-9762990-1-1(1)) Korean Culture Research, Inc.

Pihl, Marshall R. Korean Word Book. 2004. (KOR., Illus.). 112p. pap. 19.95 (978-1-57306-197-1(2)) Bess Pr., Inc.

The Rosetta Stone Language Library: Korean Level 1. 2005. (J). (gr. 1 up). cd-rom 209.00 (978-1-883972-78-3(7)) Fairfield Language Technologies.

KOREAN WAR, 1950-1953

Ashabranner, Brent. Remembering Korea: Korean War. Ashabranner, Jennifer, photos by. 2001. (Great American Memorials Ser.). (Illus.). 64p. (gr. 4-8). lib. bdg. 25.90 (978-0-7613-2156-9(X) , Twenty-First Century Bks.) Lerner Publishing Group.

Benson, Sonia. Korean War: Almanac & Primary Sources. Raffaelle, Gerda-Ann, ed. 2001. (Korean War Reference Library). (Illus.). 200p. (YA). (gr. 6-10). 67.00 (978-0-7876-5691-1(7) , GML00502-175533, UXL) Thomson Gale.

—Korean War: Biographies. 2001. (Korean War Reference Library). (Illus.). 200p. (YA). (gr. 6-10). 67.00 (978-0-7876-5692-8(5) , GML00502-175534, UXL) Thomson Gale.

Blohm, Craig E. Strategic Battles. 2003. (American War Library). (Illus.). 128p. (J). 29.95 (978-1-59018-261-1(8) , Lucent Bks.) Thomson Gale.

Burgan, Michael. The Korean War. 2003. (20th Century Perspectives Ser.). (J). 48p. pap. 7.95 (978-1-4034-3857-7(9)); pap. 114.50 (978-1-4034-3860-7(9)) Heinemann Library.

Conway, John Richard. Primary Source Accounts of the Korean War. 2006. (America's Wars Through Primary Sources Ser.). (Illus.). 128p. (J). lib. bdg. 33.27 (978-1-59845-003-3(4) , MyReportLinks.com Bks.) Enslow Pubs., Inc.

Cooper, Jason. Korean War Memorial. 2000. (Illus.). 24p. (J). (gr. 1-4). lib. bdg. 19.27 (978-1-55916-327-9(5)) Rourke Publishing, LLC.

Doak, Robin S. The Korean War. 2006. (Wars That Changed American History Ser.). (Illus.). 48p. (J). pap. (978-0-8368-7303-0(3)); lib. bdg. (978-0-8368-7294-1(0)) Stevens, Gareth Inc. (World Almanac Library).

Dolan, Edward F., Jr. America in the Korean War. 1998. (Illus.). 112p. (gr. 5-8). lib. bdg. 30.90 (978-0-7613-0361-9(8) , Millbrook Pr.) Lerner Publishing Group.

Edelman, Rob. The Korean War. 2005. (People at the Center of Ser.). (Illus.). 48p. (J). (ps-7). lib. bdg. 24.95 (978-1-56711-921-3(2) , Blackbirch Pr., Inc.) Thomson Gale.

Feldman, Ruth Tenzer. The Korean War. 2004. (Chronicle of America's Wars Ser.). (Illus.). 96p. (J). (gr. 5-12). 27.93 (978-0-8225-4716-7(3)) Lerner Publishing Group.

J K L

Fitzgerald, Brian. The Korean War: America's Forgotten War. 2006. (Snapshots in History Ser.). (Illus.). 96p. (J). (gr. 5-7). 30.60 (978-0-7565-1625-3(0)) Compass Point Bks.

Grant, Reg. The Korean War. 2004. (Atlas of Conflicts Ser.). (Illus.). 64p. (J). pap. 11.95 (978-0-8368-5673-6(2)); lib. bdg. 32.67 (978-0-8368-5666-8(X)) Stevens, Gareth Inc. (World Almanac Library).

Gruenberg, Leif A. The Korean War. 2004. (Defining Moments Ser.). (Illus.). xxii, 265p. (YA). lib. bdg. 49.00 (978-0-7808-0766-2(9)) Omnigraphics, Inc.

Hossell, Karen Price. The Korean War. 2003. (20th-Century Perspectives Ser.). (Illus.). 48p. (J). lib. bdg. 27.07 (978-1-4034-1144-0(1)) Heinemann Library.

Marquette, Scott. Korean Conflict. 2003. (America at War Ser.). (Illus.). 48p. (gr. 4-8). 20.95 (978-1-58952-390-6(3)) Rourke Publishing, LLC.

Martin, Michael. Life as a POW. 2003. (American War Library). (Illus.). 112p. (J). 29.95 (978-1-59018-260-4(X) , Lucent Bks.) Thomson Gale.

Nishi, Dennis. Korean War. 2003. (gr. 7-12). lib. bdg. 33.25 (978-0-613-73952-8(3)) Tandem Library Bks.

Rice, Earle. Korea 1950: From Pusan to Chosin. 2003. (Great Battles Through the Ages Ser.). (Illus.). 112p. (gr. 6-12). 30.00 (978-0-7910-7436-7(6) , Chelsea Hse.) Facts On File, Inc.

Rice, Earle, Jr. Korea 1950: Pusan to Chosin. 2004. (Great Battles Through the Ages Ser.). (Illus.). 112p. (gr. 6-12). pap. 13.25 (978-0-7910-7795-5(0) , Chelsea Hse.) Facts On File, Inc.

Santella, Andrew. Korean War. 2006. 48p. (J). (gr. 4-7). lib. bdg. (978-0-7565-2027-4(4)) Compass Point Bks.

Stein, R. Conrad. The Korean War: "The Forgotten War" 2000. (American War Ser.). (Illus.). 128p. (YA). (gr. 5-12). pap. 13.26 (978-0-7660-1729-0(X)) Enslow Pubs., Inc.

—The Korean War Veterans Memorial. 2002. (Cornerstones of Freedom: Vol. 2). (Illus.). 48p. (J). (gr. 4-6). 26.00 (978-0-516-22260-8(0) , Children's Pr.) Scholastic Library Publishing.

Strait, Sandy. What Was It Like in the Korean War? 1999. 371p. (YA). (gr. 9 up). pap. 14.99 (978-0-88092-398-9(9) , 3989, Kav Bks.) Royal Fireworks Publishing Co.

Young, Jeff C. The Korean War: A MyReportLinks. Com Book. 2003. (U.S. Wars Ser.). (Illus.). 48p. (J). lib. bdg. 25.26 (978-0-7660-5148-5(X) , MyReportLinks.com Bks.) Enslow Pubs., Inc.

KOREAN WAR, 1950-1953—FICTION

Balgassi, Haemi. Peacebound Trains. Soentpiet, Chris K., illus. 2000. 48p. (J). (gr. 4-6). 6.95 (978-0-618-04030-8(7) , Clarion Bks.) Houghton Mifflin Co. Trade & Reference Div.

Williams, Annie Morris. Marianne's Secret Cousins. Oldham, Cindi, illus. 2005. (Family History Adventures for Young Readers Ser.: 2). 240p. (J). per. 10.00 (978-0-9645272-8-7(6)) Field Stone Pubs.

KOREANS—UNITED STATES

Yoo, Paula. Sixteen Years in Sixteen Seconds: The Sammy Lee Story. Lee, Dom, illus. 2005. 32p. (J). (ps-k). 16.95 (978-1-58430-247-6(X)) Lee & Low Bks., Inc.

KOREANS—UNITED STATES—FICTION

Choi, Yangsook. The Name Jar. 2003. (gr. k-3). lib. bdg. 15.30 (978-0-613-82979-3(4)) Tandem Library Bks.

Kline, Suzy. Song Lee & the "I Hate You" Notes. Remkiewicz, Frank, illus. 1999. (Song Lee Ser.). 64p. (J). (gr. 2-5). 13.99 (978-0-670-87887-1(1) , Viking Juvenile) Penguin Group (USA) Inc.

—Song Lee in Room 2B. Remkiewicz, Frank, illus. 1999. (Song Lee Ser.). 64p. (J). (gr. 2-5). pap. 3.99 (978-0-14-130408-3(1) , Puffin) Penguin Group (USA) Inc.

Park, Frances & Park, Ginger. Good-Bye, 382 Shin Dang Dong. Choi, Yangsook, illus. 2002. 32p. (J). (ps-3). 16.95 (978-0-7922-7985-3(9) , National Geographic Children's Bks.) National Geographic Society.

Wong, Janet S. The Trip Back Home. Jia, Bo, illus. 2000. 32p. (J). (ps-2). 17.00 (978-0-15-200784-3(9)) Harcourt Children's Bks.

KOSCIUSZKO, TADEUSZ, 1746-1817

Greene, Meg. Thaddeus Kosciuszko. 2001. (Revolutionary War Leaders Ser.). (Illus.). 80p. (J). pap. 27.50 (978-0-7910-6399-6(2)); 27.50 (978-0-7910-6398-9(4)) Facts On File, Inc. (Chelsea Hse.).

—Thaddeus Kosciuszko: Polish General & Patriot. 2002. (gr. 5-8). lib. bdg. 17.60 (978-0-613-50838-4(6)) Tandem Library Bks.

KOUFAX, SANDY, 1935-

Doeden, Matt. Sandy Koufax. 2007. (Sports Heroes & Legends Ser.). (J). 27.93 (978-0-8225-5961-0(7) , Twenty-First Century Bks.) Lerner Publishing Group.

KU KLUX KLAN (1915-)

Heberlein, Regine I. White Supremacists. 2002. (Contemporary Issues Companion Ser.). 155p. (J). 36.20 (978-0-7377-0847-9(6) , Greenhaven Pr., Inc.) Thomson Gale.

Heinrichs, Ann. The Ku Klux Klan: A Hooded Brotherhood. 2002. (Journey to Freedom Ser.). (Illus.). 40p. (J). (gr. 3-7). 28.50 (978-1-56766-646-5(9)) Child's World, Inc.

KU KLUX KLAN (1915-)—FICTION

Blakeslee, Ann R. Summer Battles. 2000. (Illus.). 128p. (YA). (gr. 5-9). 14.95 (978-0-7614-5064-1(5) , Cavendish Children's Bks.) Cavendish, Marshall Corp.

Coleman, Evelyn. Circle of Fire. 2001. (American Girl Collection). (Illus.). (J). 12.60 (978-0-606-21249-6(3)) Tandem Library Bks.

Crawford, Ann Fears. Keechee: The Witch of the Woods. 2005. (J). (978-1-931823-21-0(9)) Halcyon Pr.

Hesse, Karen. Witness. 2004. 168p. (J). (gr. 5-9). pap. 29.00 incl. audio (978-0-8072-2094-8(9) , Listening Library) Random Hse. Audio Publishing Group.

—Witness. (J). (978-0-439-36634-2(8) , Scholastic Pr.); 2003. (Illus.). 176p. (YA). pap. 5.99 (978-0-439-27200-1(9) , Scholastic Paperbacks); 2001. (Illus.). 176p. (YA). (gr. 4-7). pap. 16.95 (978-0-439-27199-8(1)) Scholastic, Inc.

—Witness. 2001. (gr. 5-8). lib. bdg. 14.15 (978-0-613-62503-6(X)) Tandem Library Bks.

McMullan, Margaret. When I Crossed No-Bob. 2007. 224p. (J). (gr. 5-9). 16.00 (***978-0-618-71715-6(3)**) Houghton Mifflin Co. Trade & Reference Div.

Stauffacher, Sue. Bessie Smith & the Night Riders. Holyfield, John, illus. 2006. 32p. (J). (ps-3). 16.99 (978-0-399-24237-3(6) , Putnam Juvenile) Penguin Group (USA) Inc.

Vander Zee, Ruth. Mississippi Morning. Cooper, Floyd, illus. 2004. 32p. (J). 16.00 (978-0-8028-5211-3(4)) Eerdmans, William B. Publishing Co.

KUBLAI KHAN, 1216-1294—FICTION

McCaughrean, Geraldine. The Kite Rider. 2003. (Illus.). 320p. (J). (gr. 7 up). pap. 6.99 (978-0-06-441091-5(9)) HarperCollins Pubs.

—The Kite Rider. 2002. (gr. 7-12). lib. bdg. 15.30 (978-0-613-68440-8(0)) Tandem Library Bks.

KUWAIT

DiPiazza, Francesca. Kuwait in Pictures. 2nd ed. 2007. (Visual Geography Ser.). (Illus.). 80p. (J). (gr. 5-12). 27.93 (978-0-8225-6589-5(7) , Twenty-First Century Bks.) Lerner Publishing Group.

Foster, Leila Merrell. Kuwait. 1998. (Enchantment of the World, Second Ser.). (Illus.). 143p. (YA). (gr. 5-9). 36.00 (978-0-516-20604-2(4) , Children's Pr.) Scholastic Library Publishing.

Isiorho, Solomon A. Kuwait. 2002. (gr. 5-8). lib. bdg. 21.05 (978-0-613-50954-1(4)) Tandem Library Bks.

Korman, Susan. Kuwait. 2002. (Creation of the Modern Middle East Ser.). (Illus.). 125p. (gr. 6-12). 35.00 (978-0-7910-6512-9(X) , Chelsea Hse.) Facts On File, Inc.

Marcovitz, Hal. Kuwait. 2003. (Modern Middle East Nations & Their Strategic Place in the World Ser.). (Illus.). 112,128p. (YA). (gr. 5 up). lib. bdg. (978-1-59084-510-3(2)) Mason Crest Pubs.

Miller, Debra A. Kuwait. 2004. (Modern Nations of the World Ser.). (Illus.). 112p. (YA). (gr. 7-12). lib. bdg. 29.95 (978-1-59018-624-4(9) , Lucent Bks.) Thomson Gale.

O'Shea, Maria. Kuwait. 1999. (Cultures of the World Ser.). (Illus.). 128p. (gr. 5-12). lib. bdg. 37.07 (978-0-7614-0871-0(1) , Benchmark Bks.) Cavendish, Marshall Corp.

Willis, Terri. Kuwait. 2007. (Enchantment of the World, Second Ser.). (Illus.). 144p. (J). (gr. 5-9). 36.00 (978-0-516-24902-5(9) , Children's Pr.) Scholastic Library Publishing.

KWANZAA

Altman, Linda Jacobs. Celebrate Kwanzaa. 2008. (Celebrate Holidays Ser.). (Illus.). 104p. (J). (gr. 5 up). lib. bdg. 31.93 (***978-0-7660-2862-3(3)**) Enslow Pubs., Inc.

Chocolate, Deborah M. Newton. My First Kwanza Book. Massey, Cal, illus. 1999. 32p. (J). (ps-2). pap. 5.99 (978-0-439-12926-8(5)) Scholastic, Inc.

—My First Kwanzaa Book. 1999. (978-0-606-18580-6(1)); lib. bdg. 14.15 (978-0-613-22048-4(X)) Tandem Library Bks.

Cole, Harriette. Coming Together: Celebrations for African American Families. Pinderhughes, John, illus. 2003. 128p. 22.99 (978-0-7868-0753-6(9) , Jump at the Sun) Hyperion Bks. for Children.

Cooper, Jason. Kwanzaa. 2002. (Illus.). 24p. (J). lib. bdg. 20.64 (978-1-58952-220-6(6)) Rourke Publishing, LLC.

Cooper, Melrose. Kwanzaa. 1999. (Illus.). 24p. (J). (gr. 2-6). pap. 9.95 (978-1-58521-002-2(1)) Books for Black Children, Inc.

Cooper, Melrose. The SEVEN DAYS of KWANZAA. 2007. 24p. (J). pap. 4.99 (***978-0-439-56746-6(7)** , Cartwheel Bks.) Scholastic, Inc.

Corwin, Judith Hoffman. Kwanzaa Crafts: A Holiday Craft Book. 2004. (Illus.). 48p. (gr. k-4). reprint ed. pap. 6.00 (978-0-7567-7711-1(9)) DIANE Publishing Co.

Doering, Amanda. Kwanzaa. 2006. (First Facts Ser.). (Illus.). 24p. (J). (978-0-7368-5390-3(1)) Capstone Pr., Inc.

Freeman, Dorothy Rhodes & MacMillan, Dianne M. Kwanzaa. rev. ed. 2008. (Best Holiday Books Ser.). (Illus.). 48p. (J). (gr. 3-4). lib. bdg. 23.93 (***978-0-7660-3042-8(3)**) Enslow Pubs., Inc.

Gillis, Jennifer Blizin & Jordan, Denise M. Kwanzaa. 2002. (Fiestas Con Velas (Candle Time) Ser.). (SPA.). 24p. (J). (ps-1). lib. bdg. 18.50 (978-1-58810-783-1(3)); (Illus.). pap. 5.25 (978-1-58810-830-2(9) , 91591) Heinemann Library.

Gnojewski, Carol. Kwanzaa: Seven Days of African-American Pride. 2004. (Finding Out about Holidays Ser.). (Illus.). 48p. (J). lib. bdg. 23.93 (978-0-7660-2209-6(9)) Enslow Pubs., Inc.

—Kwanzaa Crafts. 2004. (Fun Holiday Crafts Kids Can Do Ser.). (Illus.). 32p. (J). lib. bdg. 22.60 (978-0-7660-2203-4(X)) Enslow Pubs., Inc.

Haven, Kendall F. New Year's to Kwanzaa: Original Stories of Celebration. 1999. 240p. (gr. 3-8). pap. 16.95 (978-1-55591-962-7(6)) Fulcrum Publishing.

Hoyt-Goldsmith, Diane. Celebrating Kwanzaa. Migdale, Lawrence, photos by. (Illus.). 32p. (J). (ps-7). pap. 6.95 (978-0-8234-1130-6(3)) Holiday Hse., Inc.

Hull, Bunny. Happy, Happy Kwanzaa: Kwanzaa for the World. Saint-James, Synthia, illus. 2003. 24p. (J). (gr. k-5). pap. 16.95 incl. audio compact disk (978-0-9721478-1-1(0) , KCC/HHKCD810, Kid's Creative Classics) BrassHeart Music.

James, Synthia Saint & Hull, Bunny. Happy, Happy Kwanzaa! Kwanzaa for the World with Book & Crayons. James, Synthia Saint, illus. 2000. (Illus.). 10.95 incl. audio (978-0-9673762-2-6(X)) BrassHeart Music.

Johnson, Dolores. The Children¿s Book of Kwanzaa: A Guide to Celebrating the Holiday. 2007. (Illus.). 159p. (J). pap. 7.00 (***978-1-4223-6600-4(6)**) DIANE Publishing Co.

Johnston, M. C. Kwanzaa. 2002. (Wonder Books Level 2: Holidays Ser.). (Illus.). 24p. (J). (ps-3). 22.79 (978-1-56766-025-8(8)) Child's World, Inc.

Jordan, Denise M. Kwanzaa. 2002. (Candle Time Ser.). 24p. (J). (ps-1). pap. 5.25 (978-1-58810-737-4(X)) Heinemann Library.

Kwanzaa, Vol. 2. 2005. (One World, Many Cultures Ser.). 24p. (YA). (gr. k-3). pap. (978-0-7368-9436-4(5) , Pebble Bks.) Capstone Pr., Inc.

Kwanzaa, 6 vols. (gr. k-2). 28.95 (978-0-7368-9437-1(3)) Red Brick Learning.

Kwanzaa, 6 vols. (Multicultural Programs Ser.). 16p. (gr. 1-3). 24.95 (978-0-7802-9208-6(1)) Wright Group, The.

A Kwanzaa Awakening: Lessons for the Children. 2000. (Illus.). 160p. (J). (gr. k-12). pap. 15.00 (978-0-9704644-0-8(1)) Imani Enterprises.

Lakeshore Learning Materials Staff, contrib. by. Kwanzaa Celebration Kit. 2000. (J). pap. 29.95 (978-1-929255-87-0(X)) Lakeshore Learning Materials.

Marsh, Carole. Kwanzaa: Activities, Crafts, Recipes & More! 2003. 32p. (J). (gr. 1-6). pap. 6.95 (978-0-635-02173-1(0)) Gallopade International.

Marx, David F. Kwanzaa. 2000. (Rookie Read-About Holidays Ser.). (Illus.). 32p. (J). (gr. 1-2). 19.50 (978-0-516-22207-3(4)); pap. 5.95 (978-0-516-27155-2(5)) Scholastic Library Publishing. (Children's Pr.).

McGee, Randel. Paper Crafts for Kwanzaa. 2008. (Paper Craft Fun for Holidays Ser.). (Illus.). 48p. (J). (gr. 3-4). lib. bdg. 23.93 (***978-0-7660-2949-1(2)** , Enslow Elementary) Enslow Pubs., Inc.

Murray, Julie. Kwanzaa. 2005. (Holidays Ser.). (Illus.). 24p. (J). (gr. k-4). lib. bdg. 21.35 (978-1-57765-955-6(4)) ABDO Publishing Co.

Nobleman, Marc Tyler. Kwanzaa. 2004. (Let's See Ser.). (Illus.). 24p. (J). (gr. 1 up). lib. bdg. 19.93 (978-0-7565-0647-6(6)) Compass Point Bks.

Raabe, Emily. A Kwanzaa Holiday Cookbook. 2002. (Festive Foods for the Holidays Ser.). (Illus.). 24p. (J). (gr. 2-5). lib. bdg. 19.95 (978-0-8239-5629-6(6) , PowerKids Pr.) Rosen Publishing Group, Inc., The.

Rau, Dana. Kwanzaa. 2000. (gr. 3-6). lib. bdg. 15.25 (978-0-613-51658-7(3)) Tandem Library Bks.

Rau, Dana Meachen. Kwanzaa. 2000. (True Bks.). (Illus.). 48p. (J). (gr. 3-5). 25.00 (978-0-516-21517-4(5) , Children's Pr.) Scholastic Library Publishing.

Robertson, Linda. Kwanzaa Fun: Great Things to Make & Do. 2003. (Holiday Fun Ser.). 32p. (J). (gr. 3-5). pap. 4.95 (978-0-7534-5685-9(0) , Kingfisher) Houghton Mifflin Co. Trade & Reference Div.

Ross, Kathy. All New Crafts for Kwanzaa. Holm, Sharon Lane, illus. 2006. 48p. (J). pap. 7.95 (978-0-8225-3435-8(5) , First Avenue Editions) Lerner Publishing Group.

Schaefer, Lola M. Kwanzaa. Saunders-Smith, Gail, ed. 2000. (Holidays & Celebrations Ser.). (Illus.). 24p. (J). (gr. k-1). lib. bdg. 15.93 (978-0-7368-0663-3(6) , Pebble Bks.) Capstone Pr., Inc.

Seven Candles for Kwanzaa. 2004. 29.95 incl. cd-rom (978-1-55592-739-4(4)); pap. 18.95 incl. audio compact disk (978-1-55592-746-2(7)); pap. 38.75 incl. audio compact disk (978-1-55592-753-0(X)); pap. 32.75 incl. audio (978-1-55592-307-5(0)); pap. 14.95 incl. audio (978-1-55592-046-3(2)) Weston Woods Studios, Inc.

Tokunbo, Dimitrea. The Sound of Kwanzaa. Cohen, Lisa, illus. 2008. (J). (***978-0-545-01865-4(X)** , Scholastic Pr.) Scholastic, Inc.

Trueit, Trudi Strain. Kwanzaa. 2006. (Rookie Read-About Holidays Ser.). (Illus.). (J). 31p. 20.50 (978-0-531-12458-1(4)); 32p. (gr. 1-2). pap. 5.95 (978-0-531-11839-9(8)) Scholastic Library Publishing. (Children's Pr.).

Walter, Mildred Pitts. Kwanzaa: A Family Affair. 2000. (Illus.). 95p. (YA). reprint ed. 17.00 (978-0-7881-6956-4(4)) DIANE Publishing Co.

Walton, Darwin M. Kwanzaa. 1999. (World of Holidays Ser.). (Illus.). 32p. (J). (gr. 2-5). lib. bdg. 25.69 (978-0-8172-5561-9(3)) Raintree.

—Kwanzaa. 1998. (World of Holidays Ser.). (Illus.). 31p. (J). (gr. 2-5). pap. 7.95 (978-0-8172-8107-6(X)) Steck-Vaughn.

Williams, Nancy. A Kwanzaa Celebration: Pop-up Book. Sabuda, Robert, illus. 2004. 14p. (J). reprint ed. 13.00 (978-0-7567-8229-0(5)) DIANE Publishing Co.

Wilson, Sule Greg C. Kwanzaa! Africa Lives in a New World Festival. 1999. (Library of African American Arts & Culture). (Illus.). 64p. (YA). (gr. 7-12). lib. bdg. 26.50 (978-0-8239-1857-7(2) , AAKWAN) Rosen Publishing Group, Inc., The.

Winne, Joanne. Let's Get Ready for Kwanzaa. 2001. (ps-2). lib. bdg. 12.95 (978-0-613-51085-1(2)) Tandem Library Bks.

Zocchi, Judy. On Kwanzaa. Wallis, Rebecca, illus. 2006. (Global Adventures I Ser.). (J). pap. 9.95 (978-1-59646-200-7(0)); 32p. lib. bdg. 20.65 (978-1-891997-49-5(1)); 32p. per. 9.95 (978-1-59646-201-4(9)) Dingles & Co.

—On Kwanzaa/la Kwanzaa. Wallis, Rebecca, illus. 2006. (Global Adventures I Ser.).Tr. of Kwanzaa. (ENG & SPA.). 32p. (J). pap. 9.95 (978-1-59646-202-1(7)); lib. bdg. 20.65 (978-1-891997-50-1(5)); per. 9.95 (978-1-59646-203-8(5)) Dingles & Co.

KWANZAA—FICTION

Ball, Lynda Anne. Kwanzaa Teddy, The Curious Bear. Johnson, Larry, illus. 2001. (Adventures of KT). 32p. (J). (ps-2). per. 6.95 (978-1-889383-11-8(2)) Angel Pubns.

Burden-Patmon, Denise. Imani's Gift at Kwanzaa. (J). 48.95 (978-0-8136-2248-4(4)) Modern Curriculum Pr.

Campoy, F. Isabel, et al. Celebra Kwanzaa con Botitas y Sus Gatitos. Docampo, Valeria, illus. 2006. (J). (978-1-59820-123-9(9)) Santillana USA Publishing Co., Inc.

—Celebrate Kwanzaa with Boots & Her Kittens. Docampo, Valeria, illus. 2006. 31p. (J). (978-1-59820-135-2(2)) Santillana USA Publishing Co., Inc.

Katz, Karen. My First Kwanzaa. Katz, Karen, illus. rev. ed. 2003. (Illus.). 32p. (J). 14.95 (978-0-8050-7077-4(X) , Holt, Henry & Co. Bks. For Young Readers) Holt, Henry & Co.

McKissack, Patricia C. & McKissack, Fredrick L. Messy Bessey's Holidays. Regan, Dana, illus. 1999. (Rookie Readers Ser.). 32p. (J). (gr. 1-2). 19.50 (978-0-516-20829-9(2) , Children's Pr.) Scholastic Library Publishing.

Medearis, Angela Shelf. Seven Spools of Thread: A Kwanzaa Story. Minter, Daniel, illus. 2000. 40p. (J). (gr. 2-5). 15.95 (978-0-8075-7315-0(9)); pap. 6.95 (978-0-8075-7316-7(7)) Whitman, Albert & Co.

—Too Many Holidays? Papp, Robert, illus. 2003. 149p. (J). (978-0-439-52327-1(3)) Scholastic, Inc.

Metzger, Steve. Dinofours, Our Holiday Show! Wilhelm, Hans, illus. 2002. (J). 3.50 (978-0-439-38218-2(1)) Scholastic, Inc.

Perry, Rex. It's Beginning to Look a Lot Like Kwanzaa! Perry, Rex, illus. 2004. (Illus.). 24p. (J). lib. bdg. 8.00 (***978-1-4242-0639-1(1)**) Fitzgerald Bks.

Rau, Dana Meachen. Holiday Time. 2004. (Compass Point Early Reader Ser.). (J). 18.60 (978-0-7565-0571-4(2)) Compass Point Bks.

Shahan, Sherry. Together for Kwanzaa. 2000. (Pictureback Ser.). (978-0-606-18504-2(6)) Tandem Library Bks.

L

LABOR (OBSTETRICS)

see Childbirth

LABOR AND LABORING CLASSES

see also Capitalism; Children—Employment; Communism; Labor Unions; Management—Employee Participation; Migrant Labor; Occupations; Peasantry; Socialism

also names of classes of laborers e.g. Agricultural Laborers; Miners; etc.; and names of countries, cities, etc. with the subdivisions Economic Conditions and Social Conditions, e.g. United States—Economic Conditions; United States—Social Conditions

Barbey, Dorine. People at Work. 2000. (Creative Discoveries Ser.). (Illus.). 75p. (J). (gr. 4 up). lib. bdg. 25.30 (978-0-88682-954-4(2) , Creative Education) Creative Co., The.

Barratt Brown, Michael. Young Person's Guide to the Global Crisis & the Alternative. 1999. (Illus.). 111p. (YA). pap. 26.50 (978-0-85124-620-8(6)) Spokesman Bks. GBR. *Dist:* Coronet Bks.

Career Guide to America's Top Industries. 2002. (gr. 7-12). lib. bdg. 22.20 (978-0-613-51108-7(5)) Tandem Library Bks.

Casil, Amy Sterling. The Department of Labor. 2005. (This Is Your Government Ser.). (Illus.). 64p. (J). lib. bdg. (978-1-4042-0210-8(2)) Rosen Publishing Group, Inc., The.

Greene, Jacqueline Dembar. The Triangle Shirtwaist Factory Fire. 2007. (Code Red Ser.). (Illus.). 32p. (J). (gr. 3-7). lib. bdg. 25.27 (978-1-59716-359-0(7)) Bearport Publishing Co., Inc.

MacDonald, Fiona. Work, Trade & Farming. 2001. (Through the Ages Ser.). (Illus.). 64p. (gr. 3-7). 12.95 (978-0-7548-0817-6(3)) Anness Publishing GBR. *Dist:* National Bk. Network.

Miller, Heather. Obrero de Construccion. 2003. (Esto es lo Que Quiero Ser (This Is What I Want to Be) Ser.). (SPA., Illus.). 24p. (J). (ps-1). lib. bdg. 18.50 (978-1-4034-0375-9(9)) Heinemann Library.

—Obrero de Construccion. 2002. (Esto es lo Que Quiero Ser (This Is What I Want to Be) Ser.). (SPA.). 24p. (J). pap. 5.25 (978-1-4034-0597-5(2)) Heinemann Library.

Pearce, Q. L. Given Kachepa. 2007. (Young Heroes Ser.). (Illus.). 64p. (J). (gr. 4-8). 27.45 (***978-0-7377-3668-7(2)** , Kidhaven) Thomson Gale.

Rau, Dana Meachen. Builders/Los Constructores. 2007. (Tools We Use/Instrumentos de Trabajo Ser.). (SPA & ENG.). 32p. (J). lib. bdg. 22.79 (***978-0-7614-2821-3(6)** , Benchmark Bks.) Cavendish, Marshall Corp.

Shuter, Jane. Life in an Egyptian Workers' Village. 2004. (Picture the Past Ser.). (Illus.). 32p. (J). 24.22 (978-1-4034-5832-2(4)) Heinemann Library.

Smith, Mike & Smith, Pam. The Reuther Brothers: Walter, Roy, & Victor. 2001. (Detroit Biography Series for Young Readers). (Illus.). 96p. (J). (gr. 5). 27.95 (978-0-8143-2994-8(2)); 14.95 (978-0-8143-2995-5(0)) Wayne State Univ. Pr. (Great Lakes Bks.).

Streissguth, Thomas. Legendary Labor Leaders. 1998. (Profiles Ser.). (Illus.). 160p. (gr. 5 up). lib. bdg. 19.95 (978-1-881508-44-1(7)) Oliver Pr., Inc.

Williams, Brian. Ancient Roman Jobs. (People in the Past Ser.). (Illus.). 48p. (J). 2003. (gr. 4-6). lib. bdg. 27.07 (978-1-58810-633-9(0)); 2002. pap. 8.50 (978-1-4034-0520-3(4)) Heinemann Library.

LABOR AND LABORING CLASSES—FICTION

Deitz Shea, Pegi. The Carpet Boy's Gift. Morin, Leane, illus. 2006. 32p. (J). pap. 7.95 (978-0-88448-249-9(9)) Tilbury Hse. Pubs.

Haddix, Margaret Peterson. Uprising. 2007. 352p. (YA). (gr. 7 up). 16.99 (***978-1-4169-1171-5(5))*** Simon & Schuster Children's Publishing.

Hampshire, David. Living & Working in Australia: A Survival Handbook. 3rd ed. 2005. (Illus.). 560p. pap. 24.95 (978-1-901130-80-5(0)) Survival Bks. GBR. *Dist:* National Bk. Network.

Jimenez, Francisco. Breaking Through. 2001. (gr. 7-12). lib. bdg. 15.25 (978-0-613-60762-9(7)) Tandem Library Bks.

Lanham, Edwin. Stricklands. 2002. (gr. 7-12). lib. bdg. 36.15 (978-0-613-62705-4(9)) Tandem Library Bks.

Loughrey, Eithne. Annie Moore: First in Line for America. 1999. (Illus.). 143p. (YA). (gr. 5-10). pap. 7.95 (978-1-85635-245-1(5)) Mercier Pr., Ltd., The IRL. *Dist:* Irish Bks. & Media, Inc.

Paterson, Katherine. Bread & Roses, Too. 2006. 288p. (J). (gr. 5-9). 16.00 (978-0-618-65479-6(8) , Clarion Bks.) Houghton Mifflin Co. Trade & Reference Div.

Pugliano-Martin, Carol. John Henry: An AMER Tall Tale. 2006. 42.00 (***978-1-4108-6170-2(8))*** Benchmark Education Co.

Sinclair, Upton, et al. The Jungle. (Classics Illustrated Ser.). (Illus.). 52p. (YA). pap. 4.95 (978-1-57209-025-5(1)) Classics International Entertainment, Inc.

Whitney, Phyllis A. A Long Time Coming. l.t. ed. 2002. (YA). lib. bdg. 27.95 (978-1-58547-184-3(4) , Premier) Center Point Large Print.

LABOR AND LABORING CLASSES—HOUSING

see Housing

LABOR AND LABORING CLASSES—UNITED STATES

American Worker, 6 bks., Set. Incl. Bread & Roses Strike of 1912. Baker, Julie. 144p. (YA). (gr. 6 up). 2007. lib. bdg. 27.95 (***978-1-59935-044-8(0));*** Cesar Chavez. Young, Jeff C. 160p. (YA). (gr. 5-8). 2007. lib. bdg. 27.95 (978-1-59935-036-3(X)); Homestead Steel Strike of 1892. Whitelaw, Nancy. (Illus.). 144p. (J). (gr. 5 up). 2006. lib. bdg. 26.95 (978-1-931798-88-4(5)); Ludlow Massacre of 1913-14. Laughlin, Rosemary. (Illus.). 144p. (J). (gr. 5 up). 2006. lib. bdg. 26.95 (978-1-931798-86-0(9)); Mother Jones. Gay, Kathlyn. (Illus.). 144p. (J). 2006. lib. bdg. 26.95 (978-1-59935-016-5(5)); Pullman Strike of 1894. Laughlin, Rosemary. (Illus.). 144p. (J). (gr. 4 up). 2006. lib. bdg. 26.95 (978-1-931798-89-1(3)); 2007. Set lib. bdg. 139.75 (***978-1-931798-98-3(2))*** Reynolds, Morgan Inc.

Casil, Amy Sterling. The Department of Labor. 2005. (This Is Your Government Ser.). (Illus.). 64p. (J). (gr. k-3). pap. 13.25 (978-1-4042-0663-2(9)) Rosen Publishing Group, Inc., The.

Crewe, Sabrina & Schaefer, Adam. The Triangle Shirtwaist Factory Fire. 2004. (Events That Shaped America Ser.). (Illus.). 32p. (J). (gr. 3 up). lib. bdg. 24.67 (978-0-8368-3402-4(X)) Stevens, Gareth Inc.

Gillis, Jennifer Blizin. Dolores Huerta. 2005. (Illus.). 32p. (J). (978-1-4034-6980-9(6)); pap. (978-1-4034-6987-8(3)) Heinemann Library.

Houle, Michelle M. Triangle Shirtwaist Factory Fire: Flames of Labor Reform. 2002. (American Disasters Ser.). (Illus.). 48p. (J). (gr. 4-10). lib. bdg. 23.93 (978-0-7660-1785-6(0)) Enslow Pubs., Inc.

McNeese, Tim. The Labor Movement: Unionizing America. 2007. (Reform Movements in American History Ser.). 160p. (gr. 6-12). 30.00 (***978-0-7910-9503-4(7)*** , Chelsea Hse.) Facts On File, Inc.

Sioux, Tracee. Immigrants, Migration, & the Industrial Revolution. 2004. (Primary Sources of Immigration & Migration in America Ser.). (Illus.). 24p. (J). lib. bdg. 19.95 (978-0-8239-6826-8(X) , PowerKids Pr.) Rosen Publishing Group, Inc., The.

Thomas, Mark. Work in Colonial America. 2002. (Welcome Colonial America Ser.). (Illus.). 24p. (J). (ps-2). 18.00 (978-0-516-23934-7(1)); pap. 4.95 (978-0-516-23495-3(1)) Scholastic Library Publishing. (Children's Pr.).

—Work in Colonial America. 2002. (gr. k-3). lib. bdg. 12.95 (978-0-613-58820-1(7)) Tandem Library Bks.

Thompson, E. L. Cesar Chavez, with Profiles of Terence V. Powderly & Dolores Huerta. 2006. (Biographical Connections Ser.). (Illus.). 112p. (J). (978-0-7166-1827-0(3)) World Bk., Inc.

Williams, Jean Kinney. Bridget "Biddy" Mason: From Slave to Businesswoman. 2005. (Signature Lives Ser.). (Illus.). 112p. (J). (gr. 5-7). (978-0-7565-1001-5(5)) Compass Point Bks.

LABOR DAY

Ansary, Mir Tamim. Labor Day. (Illus.). 32p. (J). 2006. (***978-1-4034-8888-6(6));*** 2002. pap. 6.95 (978-1-58810-431-1(1) , 91159); 1999. lib. bdg. 21.36 (978-1-57572-703-5(X)) Heinemann Library.

—Labor Day. 1999. (gr. k-3). lib. bdg. 14.75 (978-0-613-36105-7(9)) Tandem Library Bks.

Bredeson, Carmen. Labor Day. 2001. (Rookie Read-About Holidays Ser.). (Illus.). (J). (gr. 1-2). 31p. 19.50 (978-0-516-22378-0(X)); 32p. pap. 5.95 (978-0-516-26312-0(9)) Scholastic Library Publishing. (Children's Pr.).

—Labor Day. 2001. (gr. k-3). lib. bdg. 14.10 (978-0-613-54604-1(0)) Tandem Library Bks.

Hamilton, Lynn. Labor Day. 2004. (American Holidays Ser.). (J). pap. 6.95 (978-1-59036-166-5(0)); (Illus.). 24p. lib. bdg. 15.95 (978-1-59036-129-0(6)) Weigl Pubs., Inc.

Labor Day. 2001. (Illus.). (J). pap. 21.95 (978-1-58810-029-0(4)) Heinemann Library.

McNeil, Niki, et al. HOCPP 1104 Labor Day. 2006. spiral bd. 19.00 (***978-1-60308-104-7(6))*** In the Hands of a Child.

LABOR ORGANIZATIONS

see Guilds; Labor Unions

LABOR REPRESENTATION IN REGULATION OF INDUSTRY

see Management—Employee Participation

LABOR UNIONS

Ansary, Mir Tamim. Labor Day. 2002. (Holiday Histories Ser.). (Illus.). 32p. (J). (gr. k-2). pap. 6.95 (978-1-58810-431-1(1) , 91159) Heinemann Library.

Bredeson, Carmen. Labor Day. 2001. (Rookie Read-About Holidays Ser.). (Illus.). (J). (gr. 1-2). 31p. 19.50 (978-0-516-22378-0(X)); 32p. pap. 5.95 (978-0-516-26312-0(9)) Scholastic Library Publishing. (Children's Pr.).

—Labor Day. 2001. (gr. k-3). lib. bdg. 14.10 (978-0-613-54604-1(0)) Tandem Library Bks.

Brown, Jonatha A. Cesar Chavez. (People We Should Know Ser.). (J). 2006. 24p. pap. 5.95 (978-0-8368-4766-6(0)); 2006. 24p. lib. bdg. 19.33 (978-0-8368-4759-8(8)); 2005. (Illus.). 24p. pap. (978-0-8368-4752-9(0)); 2005. (Illus.). 24p. lib. bdg. 19.33 (978-0-8368-4745-1(8)); 2004. (Illus.). 48p. (gr. 5 up). pap. 11.95 (978-0-8368-5257-8(5) , World Almanac Library); 2004. (Illus.). 48p. (gr. 5 up). lib. bdg. 30.00 (978-0-8368-5097-0(1) , World Almanac Library) Stevens, Gareth Inc.

Collins, David R. Cesar Chavez. 2005. (Just the Facts Biographies Ser.). (Illus.). 112p. (J). (gr. 6-12). 27.93 (978-0-8225-2248-5(9)) Lerner Publishing Group.

Davis, Lucile. Cesar Chavez. Schon, Isabel, ed. Ferrer, Martín Luis Guzman, tr. from ENG. 1998. (Biografías Ilustradas con Fotografías Ser.). (SPA., Illus.). 24p. (J). (gr. 2-3). lib. bdg. 18.60 (978-1-56065-808-5(8) , CAP2791, Bridgestone Bks.) Capstone Pr., Inc.

del Castillo, Richard Griswold. César Chavez: La lucha por la Justicia. Colin, Jose Juan, tr. from ENG. Accardo, Anthony, illus. 2001. (Hispanic Civil Rights Ser.). (ENG & SPA.). 32p. (J). (ps-3). 15.95 (978-1-55885-324-9(3) , Piñata Books) Arte Publico Pr.

Ebon Research Systems Staff. Dare to Be... A Hero Vol. 3; Cesar Chavez. l.t. ed. 2003. Tr. of Atrevete Ser... Un Heroe Cesar Chavez. (ENG & SPA., Illus.). 16p. (J). 3.99 (978-0-9648313-6-0(8)) Ebon Research Systems Publishing, LLC.

Feinstein, Stephen. Read about Cesar Chavez. 2004. (I Like Biographies Ser.!). (Illus.). 24p. (J). lib. bdg. 21.26 (978-0-7660-2296-6(X)) Enslow Pubs., Inc.

Gaines, Ann Graham. Cesar E. Chavez: The Fight for Farm Workers' Rights. 2003. (Proud Heritage-The Hispanic Library). (Illus.). 40p. (J). (gr. 3-7). 28.50 (978-1-56766-209-2(9)) Child's World, Inc.

Gay, Kathlyn. Mother Jones. 2006. (American Workers Ser.). (Illus.). 144p. (J). lib. bdg. 26.95 (978-1-59935-016-5(5)) Reynolds, Morgan Inc.

Haugen, Brenda. Cesar Chavez: Crusader for Social Change. 2007. (J). lib. bdg. (***978-0-7565-3321-2(X))*** Compass Point Bks.

Krull, Kathleen. Cosechando Esperanza: La Historia de Cesar Chavez. Campoy, F. Isabel & Ada, Alma Flor, trs. Morales, Yuyi, illus. 2004. (SPA.). 48p. (J). pap. 7.00 (978-0-15-205169-3(4) , Voyager Bks./Libros Viajeros) Harcourt Children's Bks.

—Harvesting Hope: The Story of Cesar Chavez. Morales, Yuyi, illus. 2003. 48p. (J). (gr. 3-6). 17.00 (978-0-15-201437-7(3)) Harcourt Children's Bks.

Krull, Kathleen & Morales, Yuyi. Cosechando Esperanza: La Historia de Cesar Chavez. Ada, Alma Flor & Campoy, F. Isabel, trs. from ENG. Morales, Yuyi, illus. 2003. (SPA., Illus.). 48p. (J). 17.00 (978-0-15-204755-9(7) , Voyager Bks./Libros Viajeros) Harcourt Children's Bks.

Marcovitz, Hal. Cesar Chavez. 2003. (Great Hispanic Heritage Ser.). (Illus.). 112p. (gr. 6-12). 30.00 (978-0-7910-7253-0(3)); pap. 30.00 (978-0-7910-7515-9(X)) Facts On File, Inc. (Chelsea Hse.).

Matthews, J. L. & Rasinski, Timothy V. Cesar Chavez: Fighter in the Fields. 2002. (High Five Reading Ser.). (Illus.). 48p. (J). (gr. 2-3). lib. bdg. 22.60 (978-0-7368-9550-7(7) , Capstone High-Interest Bks.); pap. 16.95 (978-0-7368-9528-6(0)) Capstone Pr., Inc.

McLeese, Don. Cesar E. Chavez. 2003. (Rourke Discovery Library). (Illus.). 24p. (gr. 2-5). 14.95 (978-1-58952-285-5(0)) Rourke Publishing, LLC.

Miller, Calvin Craig. A. Philip Randolph & the African American Labor Movement. 2005. (Civil Rights Leaders Ser.). (Illus.). 160p. (YA). (gr. 6-12). 26.95 (978-1-931798-50-1(8)) Reynolds, Morgan Inc.

Miller, Connie Colwell. Mother Jones: Labor Leader. Erwin, Steve & Barnett, Charles, illus. 2007. (Graphic Library). 32p. (J). 25.26 (978-0-7368-5487-0(8)); (***978-0-7368-9662-7(7))*** Capstone Pr., Inc.

Roman, Michelle. Becoming Cesar Chavez. Ballis, George, photos by. 2002. (ENG & SPA., Illus.). 48p. (J). (gr. 1-6). pap. 8.95 (978-0-938911-21-0(X)) Individualized Education Systems/Poppy Lane Publishing.

Schaefer, Lola M. Cesar Chavez. Saunders-Smith, Gail, ed. 1998. (Famous Americans Ser.). (Illus.). 24p. (J). (gr. k-1). lib. bdg. 15.93 (978-0-7368-0109-6(X) , Pebble Bks.) Capstone Pr., Inc.

Seidman, David. Cesar Chavez: Labor Leader. 2004. (Great Life Stories Ser.). (Illus.). 127p. (J). 30.50 (978-0-531-12319-5(7) , Watts, Franklin) Scholastic Library Publishing.

Shea, Kitty. Cesar Chavez: Leader of Migrant Farm Workers. 2004. (Compass Point Early Biographies Ser.). (Illus.). 32p. (J). (gr. 1-3). lib. bdg. 21.26 (978-0-7565-0793-0(6)) Compass Point Bks.

Slade, Suzanne. Cesar Chavez: Champion & Voice of Farmworkers. Thompson, Jeffrey, illus. 2007. (J). lib. bdg. (***978-1-4048-3724-9(8))*** Picture Window Bks.

Smith, Mike & Smith, Pam. The Reuther Brothers: Walter, Roy, & Victor. 2001. (Detroit Biography Series for Young Readers). (Illus.). 96p. (J). (gr. 5). 27.95 (978-0-8143-2994-8(2)); 14.95 (978-0-8143-2995-5(0)) Wayne State Univ. Pr. (Great Lakes Bks.).

Soto, Gary. Cesar Chavez: A Hero for Everyone. Lohstoeter, Lori, illus. 2003. (Milestone Ser.). 80p. (J). pap. 3.99 (978-0-689-85922-9(8) , Aladdin) Simon & Schuster Children's Publishing.

—Cesar Chavez: A Hero for Everyone. 2003. (gr. 3-6). lib. bdg. 11.80 (978-0-613-90718-7(3)) Tandem Library Bks.

Wadsworth, Ginger. Cesar Chavez. Schroeder, Mark, illus. 2005. (Yo Solo - Biografías (on My Own - Biographies) Ser.). (SPA.). 48p. (J). (ps-ps). pap. 5.95 (978-0-8225-3125-8(9)) Lerner Publishing Group.

—Cesar Chavez. Schroder, Mark, illus. 2005. (Yo Solo (On My Own) Ser.). (SPA.). 48p. (J). (ps-7). lib. bdg. 23.93 (978-0-8225-3124-1(0) , Ediciones Lerner) Lerner Publishing Group.

—Cesar Chavez. 2005. (On My Own Biography Ser.). (Illus.). 48p. (J). 25.26 (978-1-57505-652-4(6) , Carolrhoda Bks.) Lerner Publishing Group.

—Cesar Chavez. Schroder, Mark, illus. 2005. 48p. (J). (gr. 1-3). pap. 5.95 (978-1-57505-826-9(X)) Lerner Publishing Group.

Wheeler, Jill C. Cesar Chavez. 2003. (Breaking Barriers Ser.). (Illus.). 64p. (J). (gr. 3-8). lib. bdg. 25.65 (978-1-57765-905-1(8)) ABDO Publishing Co.

Zannos, Susan. Cesar Chavez. 1998. (Real-Life Reader Biographies Ser.). (Illus.). 32p. (J). (gr. 4-7). lib. bdg. 15.95 (978-1-883845-71-1(8)) Mitchell Lane Pubs., Inc.

LABORATORY ANIMALS

Lubka, S. Ruth. Pupniks: The Story of Two Space Dogs. 2003. (Illus.). 32p. (J). 16.95 (978-0-7614-5137-2(4)) Cavendish, Marshall Corp.

Winiarskyj, Lesia, ed. Science & Conscience: The Animal Experimentation Controversy. 2000. 48p. (YA). 3.00 (978-0-941246-12-5(4)) National Assn. for Humane & Environmental Education.

LABORERS

see Labor and Laboring Classes

LABOURE, CATHERINE, SAINT, 1806-1876

Power-Waters, Alma. St. Catherine Labore & the Miraculous Medal. 2000. (Illus.). 138p. (J). pap. 9.95 (978-0-89870-765-6(X)) Ignatius Pr.

Roux, Marie-Geneviève & Charpy, Elisabeth. Saint Catherine Laboure: Mary's Messenger. Curreli, Augusta, illus. 2000. (Along the Paths of the Gospel Ser.). 74p. (J). (gr. 5-9). 6.95 (978-0-8198-7037-7(4) , 332-346) Pauline Bks. & Media.

LADYBIRDS

see Ladybugs

LADYBUGS

Allen, Judy. Are You a Ladybug? Humphries, Tudor, illus. 2003. (Backyard Bks.). 32p. (J). (ps-k). 5.95 (978-0-7534-5603-3(6) , Kingfisher) Houghton Mifflin Co. Trade & Reference Div.

Ashley, Susan. Ladybugs. 2004. (Weekly Reader Early Learning Library). (Illus.). 24p. (gr. 1 up). (J). pap. 5.95 (978-0-8368-4062-9(3)); (YA). lib. bdg. 19.33 (978-0-8368-4055-1(0)) Stevens, Gareth Inc. (Weekly Reader Early Learning Library).

Berger, Melvin & Berger, Gilda. Ladybugs. 2002. (Scholastic Readers Ser.). (Illus.). (J). (978-0-439-44541-2(8)) Scholastic, Inc.

Chrustowski, Rick. Bright Beetle. Chrustowski, Rick, illus. rev. ed. 2000. (Illus.). 32p. (J). (ps-3). 16.95 (978-0-8050-6058-4(8) , Holt, Henry & Co. Bks. For Young Readers) Holt, Henry & Co.

Cooper, Jason. Ladybugs. (Insects Ser.). 24p. (gr. k-2). 2006. (Illus.). 14.95 (978-1-59515-428-6(0)); 2005. pap. 5.45 (978-1-59515-742-3(5)) Rourke Publishing, LLC.

Coughlan, Cheryl. Ladybugs, Vol. 2. 2005. (Bugs, Bugs, Bugs Ser.). 24p. (YA). (gr. k-3). pap. (978-0-7368-8213-2(8) , Pebble Bks.) Capstone Pr., Inc.

Dahl, Michael. Lots of Ladybugs! Counting by Fives. Ouren, Todd, illus. 2004. (Know Your Numbers Ser.). 24p. (C). (gr. k-3). 22.60 (978-1-4048-0944-4(9)) Picture Window Bks.

Godkin, Celia. What about Ladybugs? Godkin, Celia, illus. 2001. (Illus.). 40p. (J). (ps-3). pap. 6.95 (978-0-87156-921-9(3)) Sierra Club Bks. for Children.

Hall, Margaret. Ladybugs. 2004. (Bugs, Bugs, Bugs! Ser.). (Illus.). 24p. (J). lib. bdg. 19.93 (978-0-7368-2589-4(4) , Pebble Bks.) Capstone Pr., Inc.

Hartley, Karen. Ladybug. 2002. (Bug Bks.). (Illus.). 32p. (J). (gr. k-2). pap. 6.95 (978-1-57572-458-4(8) , 90448) Heinemann Library.

—Ladybug. 2001. (Illus.). 32p. (J). (ps-3). lib. bdg. 15.25 (978-0-613-25911-8(4)) Tandem Library Bks.

Hartley, Karen & Macro, Chris. Ladybug. 2006. (Illus.). 32p. (J). (***978-1-4034-8299-0(3));*** 2nd ed. pap. (***978-1-4034-8312-6(4))*** Heinemann Library.

Heinrichs, Ann. Ladybugs. 2002. (Nature's Friends Ser.). (Illus.). 32p. (J). (gr. 2 up). lib. bdg. 21.26 (978-0-7565-0167-9(9)) Compass Point Bks.

Hughes, Monica. Ladybugs. 2003. (Raintree Sprouts Ser.). (Illus.). 24p. (J). pap. 5.50 (978-1-4109-0649-6(3)); lib. bdg. 18.56 (978-1-4109-0623-6(X)) Raintree.

—Ladybugs. 2003. (ps-2). lib. bdg. 13.55 (978-0-613-78258-6(5)) Tandem Library Bks.

Huliska-Beith, Laura, illus. Cinco Pequenas Mariquitas. 2005. Tr. of Five Little Ladybugs. (SPA.). 12p. (J). 4.95 (978-1-58117-333-8(4) , Intervisual/Piggy Toes) Dalmatian Pr.

Humphries, Tudor. Are You a Ladybug? 2003. (ps-2). lib. bdg. 12.95 (978-0-613-90173-4(8)) Tandem Library Bks.

Jacobs, Liza. Ladybugs. 2003. (Wild Wild World Ser.). (Illus.). 24p. (J). 22.45 (978-1-4103-0041-6(2) , Blackbirch Pr., Inc.) Thomson Gale.

Jango-Cohen, Judith. Hungry Ladybugs. 2003. (Pull Ahead Bks.). (Illus.). 32p. (J). 22.60 (978-0-8225-4667-2(1) , Lerner Pubns.) Lerner Publishing Group.

—Hungry Ladybugs. 2003. (gr. k-3). lib. bdg. 14.10 (978-0-613-58917-8(3)) Tandem Library Bks.

Ladybugs. (Bugs, Bugs, Bugs! Ser.). 24p. (J). 6.95 (978-0-7368-5097-1(X)) Capstone Pr., Inc.

Ladybugs. (Nature's Friends Ser.). 32p. (J). 7.95 (978-0-7565-1232-3(8)) Compass Point Bks.

Ladybugs, 6 vols. (gr. k-2). 28.95 (978-0-7368-8253-8(7)) Red Brick Learning.

Ladybugs: Red, Fiery, & Bright. 2007. 32p. (J). (gr. k-4). pap. 6.95 (***978-0-8225-6989-3(2)*** , First Avenue Editions) Lerner Publishing Group.

Lewellyn, Claire. Ladybug. Mendez, Simon, illus. 2004. (Starting Life Ser.). 24p. (ps-3). 16.95 (978-1-55971-892-9(7) , NorthWord Bks. for Young Readers) T&N Children's Publishing.

Llewellyn, Claire. Ladybugs. 2000. (gr. k-3). lib. bdg. 12.95 (978-0-613-54261-6(4)) Tandem Library Bks.

Llewellyn, Claire & Watts, Barrie. Ladybugs. 2002. (Minibeasts Ser.). (Illus.). 32p. (J). (gr. k-3). 22.00 (978-0-531-14654-5(5)); pap. 4.95 (978-0-531-14826-6(2)) Scholastic Library Publishing. (Watts, Franklin).

Loewen, Nancy. Spotted Beetles: Ladybugs in Your Backyard. Reibeling, Brandon, illus. 2004. (Backyard Bugs Ser.). 24p. (C). (gr. k-3). 22.60 (978-1-4048-0142-4(1)) Picture Window Bks.

Marie, Christian. Little Ladybugs. 2006. (Born to Be Wild Ser.). (Illus.). 23p. (J). lib. bdg. 22.00 (978-0-8368-6168-6(X)) Stevens, Gareth Inc.

Marsico, Katie. A Ladybug Larva Grows Up. 2007. (Scholastic News Nonfiction Readers: Life Cycles Ser.). 24p. (J). pap. 6.95 (***978-0-531-18697-8(0)*** , Children's Pr.) Scholastic Library Publishing.

McBee, M. C. Ladybugs. 2003. (Naturebooks: Creepy Crawlers Ser.). (Illus.). 32p. (J). (gr. 1-5). 25.64 (978-1-56766-979-4(4)) Child's World, Inc.

McLaughlin, Kari Massie. My Adventure with Ladybugs. 2007. 44p. (J). 8.99 (978-1-59092-457-0(6) , Orchard Academy Pr.) Windstorm Creative.

Meister, Cari. Ladybugs. 2001. (Insects Ser.). (Illus.). 24p. (J). (gr. k-6). lib. bdg. 21.35 (978-1-57765-463-6(3) , Checkerboard Library) ABDO Publishing Co.

Morgan, Sally. Ladybugs & Beetles. 2000. (Looking at Minibeasts Ser.). (Illus.). 32p. (J). (gr. 1-4). lib. bdg. 16.95 (978-1-929298-79-2(X)) Chrysalis Education.

Murray, Julie. Ladybugs. 2002. (Buddy Book Ser.). (Illus.). 24p. (J). (gr. k-4). lib. bdg. 21.35 (978-1-57765-721-7(7)) ABDO Publishing Co.

O'Brien, Joan. Lucky Ladybug Stickers. 2004. (Dover Little Activity Bks.). (Illus.). 4p. (J). pap. 1.50 (978-0-486-43008-9(1)) Dover Pubns., Inc.

Posada, Mia. Ladybugs: Red, Fiery & Bright. 2005. (Picture Bks.). (Illus.). 32p. (J). (gr. k-2). 15.95 (978-0-87614-334-6(6)) Lerner Publishing Group.

Pyers. Ladybugs, 6, Pack. 2004. (Minibeasts up Close Ser.). pap. 40.50 (978-1-4109-1544-3(1)) Harcourt Schl. Pubs.

Pyers, Greg. Ladybugs up Close. (Minibeasts up Close Ser.). (Illus.). 32p. (J). (ps-ps). 2005. lib. bdg. 27.50 (978-1-4109-1530-6(1)); 2004. pap. (978-1-4109-1537-5(9)) Harcourt Schl. Pubs.

Rau, Dana Meachen. Crawl, Ladybug, Crawl! 2007. (Go, Critter, Go! Ser.). (Illus.). 23p. (J). (ps-3). lib. bdg. 22.79 (***978-0-7614-2652-3(3)*** , Benchmark Bks.) Cavendish, Marshall Corp.

—Crawl, Ladybug, Crawl!/¡Trepa Mariquita, Trepa! 2007. (Go, Critter, Go!/¡Vamos Criaturita, Vamos! Ser.). (SPA & ENG.). 24p. (J). lib. bdg. 22.79 (***978-0-7614-2817-6(8)*** , Benchmark Bks.) Cavendish, Marshall Corp.

—¡Trepa, Mariquita, Trepa! 2007. (¡Vamos Criaturita, Vamos! Ser.). (SPA.). 24p. (J). lib. bdg. 22.79 (***978-0-7614-2793-3(7)*** , Benchmark Bks.) Cavendish, Marshall Corp.

Rizzati, Lorella. Ladybug. 1998. (Portable Pets Ser.). (Illus.). 12p. (J). (ps). bds. 6.95 (978-0-8109-5677-3(2)) Abrams, Harry N. , Inc.

Ross, Michael Elsohn. Ladybugology. Erickson, Darren, illus. Grogan, Brian, photos by. 2005. (Backyard Buddies Ser.). 48p. (gr. 3-6). 19.93 (978-1-57505-435-3(3)) Lerner Publishing Group.

Rustad, Martha E. H. Ladybugs. 2007. (Illus.). 24p. (J). lib. bdg. 19.95 (978-1-60014-077-8(7)) Bellwether Media.

Schwartz, David M. La Catarina. Kuhn, Dwight, photos by. 2001. (Springboards into Science Ser.). (SPA., Illus.). 24p. (J). (gr. 1 up). lib. bdg. 20.67 (978-0-8368-2992-1(1) , GHS31411) Stevens, Gareth Inc.

—Ladybug. Kuhn, Dwight, photos by. 2001. (Springboards into Science Ser.). (Illus.). 24p. (J). (gr. 1 up). lib. bdg. 20.67 (978-0-8368-2977-8(8)) Stevens, Gareth Inc.

Tracqui, Valerie. Face-to-Face with the Ladybug: Little Garden Monster. Lorne, Patrick, photos by. 2004. (Face-to-Face Ser.). (Illus.). 28p. (J). (ps-2). 9.95 (978-1-57091-453-9(2)) Charlesbridge Publishing, Inc.

LADYBUGS—FICTION

Anna, Jennifer. The Best Thing: An Almost True Story of Ladybugs & Sisters. 2007. (Illus.). 64p. (Orig.). (J). pap. 14.99 (***978-1-59092-154-8(2)*** , Blue Works) Windstorm Creative.

Beaulieu, Jeannine. Caillou' Ladybug. Verelst, Suana, illus. 2002. (Merry-go-Round Ser.). 24p. (J). pap. (978-2-89450-291-4(5)) Chouette Publishing.

Carle, Eric. Al Hashara Al Ghadiba: The Grouchy Ladybug. 2006. 24p. pap. 14.00 (978-977-6171-04-6(4) , 706-005) Al-Balsam Pubng. Hse. EGY. *Dist:* Bookworld Trade, Inc.

J
K
L

—The Grouchy Ladybug. Carle, Eric, illus. 1999. (Illus.). 44p. (J). (ps-k). bds. 7.99 (978-0-694-01320-3(X) , Harper Festival) HarperCollins Pubs.

Chapman, Mary Beth & Chapman, Steven Curtis. Shaoey & Dot: A Christmas Miracle. Chapman, Jim, illus. 2005. 32p. (J). (ps-7). pap. 16.99 (978-1-4003-0691-6(4)) Nelson, Thomas Inc.

—Shaoey & Dot: A Trip to Dr. Betterbee. 2005. 20p. (J). 6.99 (978-1-4003-0568-1(3)) Nelson, Thomas Inc.

—Shaoey & Dot: Thunder & Lightning Bugs. 2005. 20p. (J). 6.99 (978-1-4003-0570-4(5)) Nelson, Thomas Inc.

—Shoey & Dot: A Thunder & Lightning Bug Story. Chapman, Jim, illus. 2006. 32p. (J). 10.99 (978-1-4003-0743-2(0)) Nelson, Thomas Inc.

Chapman, Steven Curtis & Chapman, Mary Beth. Shaoey & Dot: Bug Meets Bundle. 2004. (Illus.). 32p. (J). 16.99 (978-1-4003-0482-0(2)) Nelson, Thomas Inc.

Crossley, David. Look Out Ladybug. 2001. (Follow the Trail Board Bks.). (Illus.). 10p. (J). bds. 5.95 (978-0-7641-5388-4(9)) Barron's Educational Series, Inc.

Cummins, Judi, creator. It's Raining Acorns & Ladybugs. 2005. (Illus.). 28p. (J). per. (978-0-9760377-4-3(2)) Cummins, Judi.

Devant, Jourdan. The Little Ladybug. 2006. (Illus.). 26p. (J). per. 10.99 (***978-1-59879-219-5(9)***) Lifevest Publishing, Inc.

Discovery Ladybug: A Play & Discover Book. 2002. (J). (978-1-931312-54-7(0)) SoftPlay, Inc.

Ernst, Lisa Campbell. Bubba & Trixie. 2000. (J). (978-0-606-20085-1(1)) Tandem Library Bks.

Finn, Isobel. The Very Lazy Ladybug. Tickle, Jack, illus. 2000. (J). (ps-3). 11.96 (978-1-888444-66-7(5)) Little Tiger Pr.

—The Very Lazy Ladybug. Tickle, Jack, illus. (J). 2005. 16p. bds. 6.95 (978-1-58925-758-0(8)); 2001. 28p. tchr. ed. 15.95 (978-1-58925-007-9(9)) ME Media LLC. (tiger tales).

Finn, Isobel & Tickle, Jack. The Very Lazy Ladybug. 2003. (Illus.). (J). 16p. tchr. ed. 15.95 (978-1-58925-714-6(6)); 32p. pap. 6.95 (978-1-58925-379-7(5)) ME Media LLC. (tiger tales).

Florie, Christine. Lara Ladybug. Dalby, Danny Brooks, illus. 2005. (Rookie Reader Skill Set Ser.). (J). (gr. k-2). 23p. pap. 4.95 (978-0-516-25281-0(X)); 24p. 17.00 (978-0-516-25137-0(6)) Scholastic Library Publishing. (Children's Pr.).

Garfield, Valerie. Harold & the Purple Crayon: The Giant Garden. 2002. (ps-2). lib. bdg. 11.80 (978-0-613-50439-3(9)) Tandem Library Bks.

Gerth, Melanie. Ten Little Ladybugs. Huliska-Beith, Laura, illus. 22p. (ps-k). 2005. (J). 10.95 (978-1-58117-091-7(2)); 2000. (YA). lp 12.95 (978-1-58117-122-8(6)) Dalmatian Pr. (Intervisual/Piggy Toes).

Greban, Quentin. Mommy, I Love You. Greban, Quentin, illus. 2005. (Illus.). 32p. (978-0-689-03922-5(0) , Milk & Cookies) ibooks, Inc.

Harcourt School Publishers Staff. Ladybugs Can Fly: Take-Home Book. 1999. (Collections Ser.). (Illus.). (J). pap. 1.90 (978-0-15-317225-0(8)) Harcourt Schl. Pubs.

Hooray for Boys & Girls! ed. 2006. (J). 15.95 (978-0-9776837-0-3(2)) West Woods Pr.

ImageBooks Staff. Finger Puppet Friends: Little Duck, Little Ladybug, Little Lamb, & Little Bee. 2007. (Illus.). 48p. (J). (ps). bds. 22.95 (978-0-8118-5805-2(7)) Chronicle Bks. LLC.

Kienzle, Patricia Taylor. Ladybug Hug. Coffey, Peg, illus. 2000. 24p. (J). (ps-2). pap. 4.00 (978-1-890798-12-3(6)) Kienzle, Patricia Taylor.

Ladybug, Ladybug: Individual Title Six-Pack. (Story Steps Ser.). (gr. k-2). 23.00 (978-0-7635-9802-0(X)) Rigby Education.

Ladybug's Winter Home. 2002. (Backyard Mini Bks.). (Illus.). 32p. (J). (978-1-59069-016-1(8) , H2005) Studio Mouse LLC.

Lenny's Lost Spots. 2005. (J). per. 8.95 (978-1-59566-131-9(X)) QEB Publishing Inc.

Martin, Anne E. There's A Ladybug in My House. Martin, Anne E., illus. l.t. ed. 2006. (Illus.). 45p. (J). per. 12.99 (978-1-59879-165-5(6)) Lifevest Publishing, Inc.

McCabe, Lauren A. How Many Spots Have I Got? Foulke, Nancy, illus. 2005. (J). 16.00 (978-1-893516-02-1(4)) Our Child Pr.

Metzger, Steve. Ladybug's Birthday. Williamson, James, illus. 2000. (Side-by-Side Ser.). (J). pap. 3.50 (978-0-590-02599-7(6)) Scholastic, Inc.

Morningforest, Chris & Raymond, Rebecca. Read along Ranch & Little Lacy Ladybug. 2006. 36p. (J). pap. 15.43 (978-1-4116-9804-8(5)) Lulu.com.

Morrow, John. Lilly Lightbug. 2006. (Illus.). 32p. (J). per. 15.95 (***978-0-9790832-0-4(6)***) Three Ring Circus Publishing Company.

Murawski, Kevin, illus. Harold & the Purple Crayon: The Giant Garden. 128p. (J). (978-0-06-059705-4(4)) HarperCollins Pubs.

O'Malley, Kevin. Little Buggy. 2002. (Gulliver Books). (Illus.). 32p. (J). (gr. k-2). 16.00 (978-0-15-216339-6(5) , Gulliver Bks.) Harcourt Children's Bks.

Otto, Carolyn B., et al. Big Box of Backyard Animals, 4 bks., Set. Sherrow, Victoria et al, illus. 2002. (Big Box of Board Bks.). 10p. (J). (ps-k). bds. (978-1-59069-177-9(6)) Studio Mouse LLC.

Pantelides, Sherry. It's Blue Like You! A Story about Loyalty. Perez, Debi, illus. 2007. 32p. (J). 12.99 (***978-0-9771076-1-2(2)***) Lacey Productions.

—It's Red Like Me! A Story about the Blood of Jesus. Perez, Debi, illus. 2007. (J). lib. bdg. 12.99 (***978-0-9771076-0-5(4)***) Lacey Productions.

—Make A Choice to Rejoice! A Story about Being Cheerful. Perez, Debi, illus. 2007. 32p. (J). 12.99 (***978-0-9771076-2-9(0)***) Lacey Productions.

Parrott, Darcie. Ladybug's Walk. 2007. 32p. (J). 10.95 (***978-0-9772692-8-0(0)***) Historical Pages Co.

Pedroni, Linda. The Lovely Little Ladybug. Pedroni, Linda, ed. Pedroni, Charmagne, illus. 2000. 59p. (J). per. 9.95 (978-0-9710011-0-7(3)) Pedroni, L T.

Puzzle Track Staff, ed. Hello Ladybug. 2007. (Puzzle Track Ser.). 20p. (J). bds. 18.95 (***978-0-7696-5629-8(3)***) School Specialty Publishing.

Rau, Dana Meachen. Look for Ladybugs. Schneider, Christine, illus. 2007. (Rookie Reader Ser.). 30p. (J). pap. (***978-0-531-12493-2(2)***) Children's Pr., Ltd.

—Look for Ladybugs. 2006. (Rookie Reader Skill Set Ser.). (Illus.). 32p. (J). (gr. k-2). 19.50 (978-0-531-12470-3(3) , Children's Pr.) Scholastic Library Publishing.

Rettore, A. S. Lucky Ladybug. 2004. 4p. (J). 7.99 (978-0-439-62770-2(2) , Cartwheel Bks.) Scholastic, Inc.

Schiller, Pam & Bartkowiak, Richele. Five Little Ladybugs. 2006. (Noodlebug Ser.). (Illus.). 16p. (J). (gr. k-k). 12.95 (978-0-7696-4277-2(2)) School Specialty Publishing.

School Specialty Publishing. My Very Best Coloring & Activity Book: Ladybug Picnic. 2002. 120p. (J). (gr. k-3). pap. 1.99 (978-0-7696-2786-1(2) , American Education Publishing) School Specialty Publishing.

Shaw, Nancy. Ladybug & Grasshopper. Adams Marks, Elizabeth, illus. 2002. (Two Can Read Ser.). 16p. (J). 2.99 (978-1-56472-664-3(9)) Edupress, Inc.

Sherrill, Carolyn. The Smiling Ladybugs. 2000. (Illus.). 16p. (J). pap. 9.95 (978-0-9674618-0-9(4)) Sherrill, Carolyn.

So-Lucky Ladybird. 2004. (Plush Pals Board Bks.). (Illus.). (J). (gr. k-1). bds. (978-0-7666-0562-6(0) , 39395) Modern Publishing.

Sweeney, Jacqueline. Meadow Magic. 2001. (We Can Read! Ser.). (Illus.). 32p. (J). (gr. 1-2). lib. bdg. 21.36 (978-0-7614-1124-6(0) , Benchmark Bks.) Cavendish, Marshall Corp.

Wert, Debra L. Eglin Long-Horn of Nightshade County: A Story about Tobacco Use & Choosing to Be Tobacco-Free. Wheeler, Penny et al, eds. 1998. (Illus.). 71p. (J). (gr. 4-6). pap. 12.95 (978-0-944576-25-0(7) , 420) Rocky River Pubs., LLC.

Young, Selina, illus. Ladybird, Ladybird. 2003. 32p. pap. 6.99 (978-1-84255-284-1(8)); (J). reprint ed. 6.95 (978-1-84255-055-7(1)) Orion Children's Bks. GBR. *Dist:* Trafalgar Square Publishing.

Zoehfeld, Kathleen Weidner. Ladybug at Orchard Avenue. Buchs, Thomas, illus. 2005. (Smithsonian's Backyard Ser.). 32p. (J). (ps-2). 6.95 (978-1-931465-42-7(8) , S5009) Soundprints.

LAFAYETTE, MARIE JOSEPH PAUL YVES ROCH GILBERT DU MOTIER, MARQUIS DE, 1757-1834

Collins, Kathleen. Marquis de Lafayette: French Hero of the American Revolution. 2003. (Primary Sources of Famous People in American History Ser.). (Illus.). 32p. (J). pap. (978-0-8239-4187-2(6)) Rosen Publishing Group, Inc., The.

Fritz, Jean. Why Not, Lafayette? Himler, Ronald, illus. 1999. 1p. (J). (gr. 5-9). 17.99 (978-0-399-23411-8(X) , Putnam Juvenile) Penguin Group (USA) Inc.

Grote, JoAnn A. Lafayette. 2000. (Revolutionary War Leaders Ser.). (Illus.). 80p. (J). pap. 27.50 (978-0-7910-6131-2(0)); (gr. 8-12). 27.50 (978-0-7910-5973-9(1)) Facts On File, Inc. (Chelsea Hse.).

Payan, Gregory. Marquis de Lafayette: French Hero of the American Revolution. 2005. (Library of American Lives & Times). (Illus.). 112p. (J). (gr. 4-8). lib. bdg. 31.95 (978-0-8239-5733-0(0)) Rosen Publishing Group, Inc., The.

LAFITTE, JEAN, 1782-1854

Weintraub, Aileen. Jean Lafitte: Pirate Hero of the War of 1812. 2002. (Library of Pirates). (Illus.). 24p. (J). (gr. 3). lib. bdg. 18.75 (978-0-8239-5796-5(9) , PowerKids Pr.) Rosen Publishing Group, Inc., The.

LAKE ERIE

see Erie, Lake

LAKE HURON (MICH. AND ONT.)

see Huron, Lake (Mich. and Ont.)

LAKE MICHIGAN

see Michigan, Lake

LAKE ONTARIO (N.Y. AND ONT.)

see Ontario, Lake (N.Y. and Ont.)

LAKE SUPERIOR

see Superior, Lake

LAKES

Barnes, Julia. 101 Facts about Lakes. 2003. (One Hundred One Facts about Our World Ser.). (Illus.). 32p. (J). (gr. 3 up). lib. bdg. 23.33 (978-0-8368-3707-0(X)) Stevens, Gareth Inc.

Beckett, Harry. Lake Erie. 1999. (Illus.). 32p. (J). (gr. 3-6). lib. bdg. 26.60 (978-0-86593-527-3(0)) Rourke Publishing, LLC.

—Lake Ontario. 1999. (Illus.). 32p. (J). (gr. 3-6). lib. bdg. 26.60 (978-0-86593-526-6(2)) Rourke Publishing, LLC.

Beckett, Harry, et al, contrib. by. Lake Huron. 1999. (Great Lakes of North America Ser.). (Illus.). 32p. (J). (gr. 3-6). lib. bdg. 26.60 (978-0-86593-525-9(4)) Rourke Publishing, LLC.

—Lake Michigan. 1999. (Great Lakes of North America Ser.). (Illus.). 32p. (J). (gr. 3-6). lib. bdg. 26.60 (978-0-86593-524-2(6)) Rourke Publishing, LLC.

Bedford, Kate. Geography. 2006. (Illus.). 32p. (J). (978-1-59604-100-4(5)) Stargazer Bks.

Braun. Rivers, Lakes & Ponds. 2001. (Biomes Ser.). (Illus.). (J). pap. (978-0-7398-4943-9(3)) Steck-Vaughn.

Braun, Eric & Donovan, Sandy. River, Lakes, & Ponds. 2001. (Illus.). 32p. (J). lib. bdg. 22.83 (978-0-7398-4757-2(0)) Raintree.

—Scientists of Rivers, Lakes, & Ponds. 2001. (Scientists of the Biomes Ser.). (Illus.). 48p. (J). lib. bdg. 24.26 (978-0-7398-4755-8(4)) Raintree.

Brooks, David. You Can Count at the Lake. 2005. (You Can Count Ser.). (Illus.). 24p. (J). (978-1-55971-909-4(5) , Two Can Publishing) T&N Children's Publishing.

Casado, Dami & Casado, Alicia. Los Ríos y Lagos. 2005. (SPA., Illus.). 14p. (J). per. 8.99 (978-84-272-7387-0(8)) Molino, Editorial ESP. *Dist:* Santillana USA Publishing Co., Inc.

Chambers, Catherine & Lapthorn, Nicholas. Lakes. 2nd ed. 2007. (J). (***978-1-4034-9601-0(3)***); pap. (***978-1-4034-9611-9(0)***) Heinemann.

Costain, Meredith. Caring for Our Pond. 2000. (gr. k-3). lib. bdg. 11.80 (978-0-613-30306-4(7)) Tandem Library Bks.

Cunningham, Alvin Robert. At the Lake. Daylight, Heather, illus. 2001. (Books for Young Learners). 16p. (J). pap. 5.00 (978-1-57274-244-4(5)) Owen, Richard C. Pubs., Inc.

Day, Trevor. Lakes & Rivers. Garratt, Richard, illus. 2006. (Biomes of the Earth Ser.). 272p. (J). (gr. 6-12). 39.50 (978-0-8160-5328-5(6)) Facts On File, Inc.

Declus, Jennifer. What Might I Find on a Pond. Kalasea, illus. 2004. (J). (978-0-9743690-2-0(0)) Britt Allcroft Productions.

Dorling Kindersley Publishing Staff. Pond Life. 2006. (Ultimate Sticker Bks.). 16p. (J). pap. 6.99 (978-0-7566-2100-1(3)) Dorling Kindersley Publishing, Inc.

—Rivers & Lakes. (Eye Wonder Ser.). (Illus.). 48p. (J). (gr. k-3). 2003. 9.99 (978-0-7894-9046-9(3)); 2002. lib. bdg. 17.99 (978-0-7894-9047-6(1)) Dorling Kindersley Publishing, Inc.

Frahm, Randy. Lakes. 2002. (LifeViews Ser.). (J). (978-0-89812-371-5(2) , Creative Paperbacks) Creative Co., The.

—Lakes: Timeless Reserviors. 2002. (LifeViews Ser.). (Illus.). 32p. (J). lib. bdg. (978-1-58341-244-2(1) , Creative Education) Creative Co., The.

Frisch, Aaron. Lakes. 2008. (J). (***978-1-58341-571-9(8)*** , Creative Education) Creative Co., The.

Gingold, Janet. My Adventure on a Lake: Advanced My Adventure. 2007. 44p. (J). pap. 8.99 (978-1-59092-442-6(8) , Orchard Academy Pr.) Windstorm Creative.

Green, Emily K. Lakes. 2006. (Blastoff! Readers Ser.). (Illus.). 24p. (J). lib. bdg. 16.95 (978-1-60014-037-2(8)) Bellwether Media.

Howard, Fran. Lakes & Ponds. 2007. (Habitats Ser.). (Illus.). 32p. (J). (gr. k-4). lib. bdg. 22.78 (978-1-59679-779-6(7)) ABDO Publishing Co.

Jackson, Kay. Lakes. 2006. (Earthforms Ser.). (Illus.). 24p. (J). (978-0-7368-5405-4(3) , 1252618) Capstone Pr., Inc.

—Life in a Freshwater Lake. 2005. (Ecosystems Ser.). (Illus.). 48p. (J). (gr. 4-8). 26.20 (978-0-7377-3145-3(1) , Kidhaven) Thomson Gale.

Jacobs, Robert P. & O'Connell, Eileen B. Fisheries Guide to Lakes & Ponds of Connecticut: Including the Connecticut River & Its Coves. 2002. (DEP Bulletin Ser.: 35). 368p. lib. bdg. 29.95 (978-0-942085-12-9(4)); (Illus.). pap. 19.95 (978-0-942085-11-2(6)) Connecticut Dept. of Environmental Protection, Environmental & Geographic Information Ctr.

Johnson, Rebecca L. A Journey into a Lake. Saroff, Phyllis V., illus. 2004. (Biomes of North America Ser.). (J). pap. 6.95 (978-0-8225-2043-6(5)); 48p. (gr. 3-6). lib. bdg. 23.93 (978-1-57505-594-7(5)) Lerner Publishing Group.

Kosek, Jane Kelly. What's Inside Lakes? 1999. (What's Inside Library). 24p. (J). (gr. k-4). lib. bdg. 18.75 (978-0-8239-5280-9(0) , PowerKids Pr.) Rosen Publishing Group, Inc., The.

Lakes Learning about the Earth. 2006. (Illus.). 24p. (J). (gr. k-2). 18.50 (***978-0-531-17889-8(7)***) Scholastic Library Publishing.

Macken, JoAnn Early. Lakes. (Illus.). 24p. (J). 2006. pap. (978-0-8368-6401-4(8)); 2006. lib. bdg. 19.33 (978-0-8368-6394-9(1)); 2005. (978-0-8368-4891-5(8)); 2005. lib. bdg. 19.33 (978-0-8368-4884-7(5)) Stevens, Gareth Inc.

—Lakes: Lagos. 2005. (SPA., Illus.). 24p. (J). (978-0-8368-6036-8(5)) Stevens, Gareth Inc.

—Lakes/Lagos. 2005. (SPA., Illus.). 24p. (J). (ps-17). lib. bdg. 19.33 (978-0-8368-6029-0(2)) Stevens, Gareth Inc.

Mayer, Cassie. Lagos y Estanques. 2007. (SPA & ENG.). (J). pap. (***978-1-4329-0388-6(8)***); lib. bdg. (***978-1-4329-0383-1(7)***) Heinemann Library.

—Lakes & Ponds. 2007. (J). (***978-1-4034-9365-1(0)***); pap. (***978-1-4034-9369-9(3)***) Heinemann Library.

Meister, Cari. Lake Victoria. 2002. (Rivers & Lakes Ser.). (Illus.). 24p. (J). (gr. k-6). lib. bdg. 21.35 (978-1-57765-105-5(7) , Checkerboard Library) ABDO Publishing Co.

Morris, Neil. Living by Lakes. 2004. (J). lib. bdg. (978-1-58340-485-0(6)) Smart Apple Media.

—Rivers & Lakes. 1998. (Wonders of Our World Ser.). (Illus.). 32p. (J). (gr. 3-4). (978-0-86505-834-7(2)); pap. (978-0-86505-846-0(6)) Crabtree Publishing Co.

Nadeau, Isaac. Water in Rivers & Lakes. 2003. (Water Cycle Ser.). (Illus.). 24p. (J). lib. bdg. 18.75 (978-0-8239-6266-2(0) , PowerKids Pr.) Rosen Publishing Group, Inc., The.

Ostopowich, Melanie. Oceans, Rivers, & Lakes. 2005. (Science Matters Ser.). (Illus.). 24p. (J). (ps-7). pap. 6.95 (978-1-59036-310-2(8)); lib. bdg. 24.45 (978-1-59036-304-1(3)) Weigl Pubs., Inc.

Owen, Andy, et al. Lakes. 2002. (Geography Starts Ser.). (Illus.). 32p. (J). (gr. k-2). pap. 6.95 (978-1-58810-975-0(5) , 91458) Heinemann Library.

Prevost, John F. Lake Superior. 2002. (Rivers & Lakes Ser.). (Illus.). 24p. (J). (gr. k-6). lib. bdg. 21.35 (978-1-57765-104-8(9) , Checkerboard Library) ABDO Publishing Co.

Rivers & Lakes, Set. Incl. Amazon River. Meister, Cari. lib. bdg. 21.35 (978-1-57765-101-7(4)); Lake Superior. Prevost, John F. lib. bdg. 21.35 (978-1-57765-104-8(9)); Lake Victoria. Meister, Cari. lib. bdg. 21.35 (978-1-57765-105-5(7)); Mississippi River. Prevost, John F. lib. bdg. 21.35 (978-1-57765-102-4(2)); Nile River. Meister, Cari. lib. bdg. 21.35 (978-1-57765-098-0(0)); Yangtze River. Meister, Cari. lib. bdg. 21.35 (978-1-57765-103-1(0)); 24p. (J). (gr. k-6). (Illus.). 2002. Set lib. bdg. 128.10 (978-1-57765-526-8(5) , Checkerboard Library) ABDO Publishing Co.

Royston, Angela. Lakes. 2004. (My World of Geography Ser.). (Illus.). 32p. (J). 22.79 (978-1-4034-5591-8(0)) Heinemann Library.

Ryan, William T. World of Water. 2003. (Science Links Ser.). (Illus.). 32p. (gr. 3-5). 23.00 (978-0-7910-7429-9(3) , Chelsea Hse.) Facts On File, Inc.

Schuh, Mari C. What Are Lakes? Saunders-Smith, Gail, ed. 2002. (Earth Features Ser.). (Illus.). 24p. (J). (gr. k-1). lib. bdg. 15.93 (978-0-7368-1170-5(2) , Pebble Bks.) Capstone Pr., Inc.

Tull, Mary. Rivers & Lakes. 2004. (National Geographic Reading Expeditions Ser.). (Illus.). 32p. (J). pap. (978-0-7922-4561-2(X)) National Geographic Society.

What Are Lakes?, 6 vols., Vol. 2. 2005. (Earth & Outer Space Ser.). (gr. k-2). 28.95 (978-0-7368-3276-2(9)) Red Brick Learning.

Zollman, Pam. Lake Tahoe. 2006. (Rookie Read-About Geography Ser.). (Illus.). 32p. (J). (gr. 1-2). 20.50 (978-0-516-25036-6(1) , Children's Pr.) Scholastic Library Publishing.

LAMPS—FICTION

Kay, Elizabeth. The Jinx on the Divide. 2007. 384p. (J). pap. 6.99 (***978-0-439-72456-2(2)***) Scholastic, Inc.

LANCASTER COUNTY (PA.)—FICTION

Brunstetter, Wanda E. Rachel Yoder: Back to School. 2007. (Rachel yoder Ser.). 160p. (J). pap. 4.97 (***978-1-59789-234-6(3)***) Barbour Publishing, Inc.

De Angeli, Marguerite. Henner's Lydia. 1998. (Illus.). 74p. (YA). (ps-3). 15.99 (978-0-8361-9093-9(9)) Herald Pr.

LAND

see Land Use

LAND SURVEYING

see Surveying

LAND USE

Here are entered general works which cover such topics as types of land, the utilization, distribution and development of land and the economic factors which affect the value of land. Works which treat only of ownership of land are entered under Real Estate.

see also Agriculture; Farms; Feudalism

Banting, Erinn. England — The Land. 2004. (Lands, Peoples, & Cultures Ser.). (Illus.). 32p. (J). (978-0-7787-9321-2(4)); pap. (978-0-7787-9689-3(2)) Crabtree Publishing Co.

Bauer, David. People Change the Land. 2003. (Illus.). 17p. (J). 15.93 (978-0-7368-2929-8(6)); pap. (978-0-7368-2888-8(5)) Yellow Umbrella Pr.

Casper, Julie Kerr. Lands: Taming the Wilds. 2007. (Natural Resources Ser.). 240p. (J). (gr. 6-12). 39.50 (***978-0-8160-6356-7(7)*** , Chelsea Hse.) Facts On File, Inc.

Dalgleish, Sharon. Managing the Land. 2003. (Our World - Our Future Ser.). (Illus.). 32p. (J). (gr. 4-8). 27.00 (978-0-7910-7020-8(4) , Chelsea Hse.) Facts On File, Inc.

Haswell, Arthur. Land. 2000. (Earth Strikes Back Ser.). (Illus.). 48p. (J). (gr. 2-6). lib. bdg. 16.95 (978-1-929298-59-4(5)) Chrysalis Education.

Holt, Rinehart and Winston Staff. Environmental Science Chptr. 14: Land. 4th ed. Date not set. pap. 11.20 (978-0-03-068074-8(3)) Holt, Rinehart & Winston.

Judging Land & Soil for Urban Use. 2002. (Illus.). 34p. (YA). stu. ed. 6.95 (978-1-56502-055-9(3) , 5018M) Ohio State Univ., Ohio Agricultural Education Curriculum Materials Service.

Ohio Urban Land Judging Scorecard. 2002. 2p. (YA). 0.59 (978-1-56502-056-6(1)) Ohio State Univ., Ohio Agricultural Education Curriculum Materials Service.

Shepard, Daniel. La Gente cambia la Tierra. 2005. Tr. of People Change the Land. (SPA., Illus.). 16p. (J). (gr. 1 up). lib. bdg. 15.93 (978-0-7368-4179-5(2)) Capstone Pr., Inc.

Ylvisaker, Anne. Land & Water: World Rivers. (Fact Finders Ser.). (Illus.). (J). (gr. 3-4). lib. bdg. 90.40 (978-0-7368-2559-7(2)) Capstone Pr., Inc.

LANDFORMS

see also Sand Dunes; Wetlands

Beers, Bonnie. Earth's Land & Water. 2000. (Yellow Umbrella Books). (Illus.). 16p. (J). (gr. 1). lib. bdg. 14.60 (978-0-7368-0737-1(3) , Pebble Bks.) Capstone Pr., Inc.

Benchmark Education Staff, compiled by. Landforms. 2006. spiral bd. 610.00 (***978-1-4108-6793-3(5)***) Benchmark Education Co.

Brimner, Larry Dane. Valleys & Canyons. 2000. (gr. 3-6). lib. bdg. 15.25 (978-0-613-54756-7(X)) Tandem Library Bks.

Burgan, Michael. Land & Water. 2004. (Discovery Channel School Science Ser.). (Illus.). 32p. (J). (gr. 5 up). lib. bdg. 24.67 (978-0-8368-3381-2(3)) Stevens, Gareth Inc.

Cox, Reg. The Seven Wonders of the Natural World. 2000. (Wonders of the World Ser.). (Illus.). 32p. (J). (gr. 4-7). 25.50 (978-0-7910-6049-0(7) , Chelsea Hse.) Facts On File, Inc.

Craats, Rennay. Natural Landmarks. 2004. (American Symbols Ser.). (J). pap. 6.95 (978-1-59036-177-1(6)); (Illus.). 24p. lib. bdg. 15.95 (978-1-59036-133-7(4)) Weigl Pubs., Inc.

Fredette, Nathalie & Lafleur, Claude. Our Planet Today. 2001. (Twenty-First Century Science Ser.). (Illus.). 64p. (J). (gr. 5 up). lib. bdg. 32.67 (978-0-8368-5003-1(3) , World Almanac Library) Stevens, Gareth Inc.

Gilbert, Miquel Angel. The Land. 2002. (Living Planet Ser.). (Illus.). 32p. (J). 23.70 (978-1-56711-668-7(X) , Blackbirch Pr., Inc.) Thomson Gale.

Harcourt School Publishers Staff. Formaciones Terrestres Advanced Level. 3rd ed. 2002. (Trofeos Ser.).Tr. of Terrestrial Formations. (SPA., Illus.). pap. 6.80 (978-0-15-324220-5(5)) Harcourt Schl. Pubs.

—Land Forms Advanced Level. 3rd ed. 2002. (Trophies Reading Program Ser.). (Illus.). pap. 5.10 (978-0-15-323310-4(9)) Harcourt Schl. Pubs.

Harris. Mountains & Highlands. 2003. (Biomes Atlas Ser.). (Illus.). 64p. pap. 9.50 (978-1-4109-0012-8(6)) Raintree.

—Mountains Highlands. 2003. (Biomes Atlas Ser.). pap. 48.30 (978-1-4109-0247-4(1)) Raintree.

How Water Got to the Plains: Individual Title Six-Packs. (gr. k-1). 23.00 (978-0-7635-8843-4(1)) Rigby Education.

Investigating Earth Systems Rocks & Landforms. 2002. stu. ed., bds. (978-1-58591-109-7(7)); 2001. stu. ed. (978-1-58591-079-3(1)) It's About Time, Herff Jones Education Diiv.

The Library of Landforms. (Illus.). (J). (gr. k-6). 127.50 (978-1-4042-3293-8(1)) Rosen Publishing Group, Inc., The.

Macken, JoAnn Early. Plains. 2006. (Illus.). 24p. (J). pap. (978-0-8368-6403-8(4)); lib. bdg. 19.33 (978-0-8368-6396-3(8)) Stevens, Gareth Inc.

Morris, Neil. Earth's Changing Continents. 2003. (Illus.). (J). pap. 7.50 (978-1-4109-0342-6(7)); 32p. lib. bdg. 25.70 (978-1-4109-0179-8(3)) Raintree.

—Earth's Changing Continents. 2003. (gr. 3-6). lib. bdg. 15.90 (978-0-613-78236-4(4)) Tandem Library Bks.

Nagel, Rob. UXL Encyclopedia of Landforms & Other Geologic Features, 3 vols. 2003. (Illus.). xxviii, 314p. (J). (978-0-7876-7670-4(5)); (978-0-7876-7671-1(3)); (978-0-7876-7672-8(1)) Thomson Gale. (UXL).

Nathan, Emma. Land. 2002. (Eyeopeners Ser.). (Illus.). 24p. (J). 22.45 (978-1-56711-651-9(5) , Blackbirch Pr., Inc.) Thomson Gale.

Nelson, Robin. Land. 2004. (First Step Nonfiction Ser.). (J). pap. (978-0-8225-5392-2(9)) Lerner Publishing Group.

Raintree Steck-Vaughn Staff. Wonders of the World. 2000. (Read All about It Ser.). (Illus.). (J). pap. 4.95 (978-0-8114-3790-5(6)) Steck-Vaughn.

Raum, Elizabeth. World's Wonders: Landforms. 2006. (Illus.). 32p. (J). (978-1-4109-2599-2(4)); pap. (978-1-4109-2628-9(1)) Steck-Vaughn.

Ring, Elizabeth. Grasslands. 2004. (Illus.). 48p. (J). (gr. 2-4). 24.95 (978-1-4103-0318-9(7) , Blackbirch Pr., Inc.) Thomson Gale.

Roza, Greg. On Flat Land: Learning the FL Sound. (PowerPhonics Ser.). (Illus.). (J). 2002. 24p. (gr. 1). lib. bdg. 18.50 (978-0-8239-5925-9(2)); 2001. 23p. pap. 26.40 (978-0-8239-8270-7(X)) Rosen Publishing Group, Inc., The. (PowerKids Pr.).

Science stories foss spanish landforms ea Cr05. 2005. (J). (978-1-59242-597-6(6)) Delta Education, LLC.

Steck-Vaughn Staff. Landforms. 2002. pap. (978-0-7398-6164-6(6)) Steck-Vaughn.

Taylor, Barbara. Understanding Landforms. 2007. (J). ***978-1-59920-049-1(X))** Smart Apple Media.

Waldron, Melanie. Coasts. 2007. (J). **(*978-1-4034-9615-7(3));** (Illus.). 32p. **(*978-0-431-10992-3(3))** Heinemann.

—Mapping Earthforms: Coasts Paperback. 2007. (Illus.). 32p. (J). **(*978-0-431-11002-8(6))** Heinemann.

Waldron, Melanie, et al. Valleys. 2nd ed. 2007. (J). **(*978-1-4034-9607-2(2));** pap. **(*978-1-4034-9617-1(X))** Heinemann.

Warhol, Tom. Tundra. 2006. (Earth's Biomes Ser.). (Illus.). 80p. (YA). (gr. 5-8). lib. bdg. 32.79 (978-0-7614-2193-1(9) , Benchmark Bks.) Cavendish, Marshall Corp.

LANDMARKS, PRESERVATION OF

see Natural Monuments

LANDSCAPE ARCHITECTURE

see also Cemeteries

Wishinsky, Frieda. The Man Who Made Parks: The Story of Parkbuilder Frederick Law Olmsted. Zhang, Song Nan, illus. 1999. 32p. (J). (gr. k-12). 15.95 (978-0-88776-435-6(5)) Tundra Bks., Inc./Livres Toundra, Inc. CAN. *Dist:* Random Hse., Inc.

LANDSCAPE PAINTING

Blizzard, Gladys S. Come Look with Me: Exploring Landscape Art with Children. 2006. (Come Look with Me Ser.). (Illus.). 32p. (YA). (gr. 1-8). 15.95 (978-0-934738-95-8(5)) Charlesbridge Publishing, Inc.

Thomson, Leo. Sense of Place: Landscapes. 2005. (Artventures Ser.). (Illus.). 32p. (J). (gr. 4-7). lib. bdg. 27.10 (978-1-58340-622-9(0) , 1247320) Smart Apple Media.

LANGUAGE AND LANGUAGES

Here are entered general works on the history, philosophy, origin, etc. of language. Comparative studies of languages are entered under Philology, Comparative.

see also Grammar; Phonetics; Rhetoric; Speech; Voice; Writing

also names of languages or groups of cognate languages, e.g. English Language; etc.; also classes of people with the subdivision Language, e.g. Children—Language; etc.

Aigner-Clark, Julie. La Guarderia de Idiomas (The Guarderia Language) 2004. (Baby Einstein Ser.). (SPA., Illus.). 16p. (J). bds. 5.95 (978-970-718-153-3(2) , Silver Dolphin en Español) Advanced Marketing, S. de R. L. de C. V. MEX. *Dist:* Perseus Distribution.

—Language Nursery. Zaidi, Nadeem, illus. 2001. (Baby Einstein Ser.). (ENG, SPA, FRE, HEB & JPN.). 16p. (J). (ps-ps). 5.99 (978-0-7868-0810-6(1)) Hyperion Bks. for Children.

Association, Japanese-Language For. Japanese for Young People. 1998. (gr. 7-12). lib. bdg. 29.25 (978-0-613-80456-1(2)) Tandem Library Bks.

—Japanese for Young People I: Student. 1998. (gr. 7-12). lib. bdg. 39.65 (978-0-613-80455-4(4)) Tandem Library Bks.

Barbe, Walter B., ed. Signposts Language Arts Activities for Grade 2. 2000. (Illus.). 64p. (J). (gr. 2-3). pap. 4.95 (978-1-56762-119-8(8)) Modern Learning Pr.

Bardakigian, K. D. & Thompson, Robert W. Western Armenian, 8 cass., Set. (ARM.). 319p. (YA). (gr. 10-12). pap. 185.00 incl. audio (978-0-88432-444-7(3) , AFAR15) Norton, Jeffrey Pubs., Inc.

Barfell, Judith A. Learn & Sign Funtime: Sign with God's Angels. 2005. (Beginnings Ser.). (J). per. 14.95 (978-0-9753717-0-1(3)) Learn and Sign Funtime Bks.

Beard, Adrian. Language Change. 2004. (Intertext Ser.). (Illus.). 128p. 19.95 (978-0-415-32056-6(9)); 71.95 (978-0-415-32055-9(0)) Routledge.

Benati, R., et al. Meine Freunde und ich - Student's Folder. 2005. pap. 10.95 (978-3-468-49503-8(X)) Langenscheidt Pubs Inc.

Berlitz Kids Staff, creator. 1,000 Palabras en Inglés. 2nd ed. 2005. (Berlitz 1,000 Words Ser.). (SPA & ENG., Illus.). 64p. (J). (ps-3). pap. 12.95 (978-981-246-533-7(2) , 465332) Berlitz Publishing.

Bluedorn, Johannah. Little Bitty Baby Learns Greek. Bluedorn, Johannah, illus. 2006. (GRE & ENG., Illus.). 30p. (J). bds. (978-1-933228-06-8(7)) Trivium Pursuit.

Bowers, Linda, et al. No Glamour Language & Reasoning. 2003. (J). per. 41.95 (978-0-7606-0500-4(9)) LinguiSystems, Inc.

Boyles, Peggy Palo. Realidades: Level 1, 2 vols. l.t. ed. 2004. 564p. (YA). (gr. 9-12). 282.00 (978-0-13-101687-3(3)) Prentice Hall Pr.

—Realidades: Level A. l.t. ed. 2004. (SPA.). 322p. (YA). (gr. 6-8). 161.00 (978-0-13-035966-7(1)) Prentice Hall Pr.

—Realidades: Level B, 2 vols. l.t. ed. 2004. (SPA.). 416p. (YA). (gr. 6-8). 208.00 (978-0-13-035967-4(X)) Prentice Hall Pr.

—Realidades Vol. 2: Level 2, 2 vols. l.t. ed. 2004. (SPA.). 508p. (YA). (gr. 9-12). 254.00 (978-0-13-035951-3(3)) Prentice Hall Pr.

Boyles, Peggy Palo, et al. Realidades Vol. 3: Level 3, 2 vols. l.t. ed. 2004. (SPA.). 614p. (YA). (gr. 9-12). 307.00 (978-0-13-035968-1(8)) Prentice Hall Pr.

Bravo! 2003. (YA). Vol. 1A. (gr. 6-8). wbk. ed. (978-0-8123-8970-8(0)); Vol. 1B. (-8). wbk. ed. (978-0-8123-9000-1(8)) McDougal Littell Inc.

Bridge to Communication Level C: Class Set. (Illus.). (J). (gr. 2-5). 275.00 (978-1-56014-777-0(6)) Santillana USA Publishing Co., Inc.

Bridge to Communication Level C: Student Language Book. (J). (gr. 2-5). 9.50 (978-1-56014-752-7(0)); (YA). (gr. 6-8). 9.50 (978-1-56014-755-8(5)) Santillana USA Publishing Co., Inc.

Bridge to Communication Level A: Student Language Book. (J). (gr. 2-5). 9.50 (978-1-56014-750-3(4)); (YA). (gr. 6-8). 9.50 (978-1-56014-753-4(9)) Santillana USA Publishing Co., Inc.

Bridge to Communication Level B: Student Language Book. (J). (gr. 2-5). 9.50 (978-1-56014-751-0(2)); (YA). (gr. 6-8). 9.50 (978-1-56014-754-1(7)) Santillana USA Publishing Co., Inc.

Burke, David. BEAUTY & the BEAST (English to Japanese - Level 3) Learn JAPANESE Through Fairy Tales. 2007. (ENG & JPN.). (J). per. 14.95 incl. audio compact disk **(*978-1-891888-90-8(0))** Slangman Publishing.

—CINDERELLA (English to Japanese - Level 1) Learn JAPANESE Through Fairy Tales. 2007. (ENG & JPN.). (J). per. 14.95 incl. audio compact disk **(*978-1-891888-78-6(1))** Slangman Publishing.

—GOLDILOCKS (English to Japanese - Level 2) Learn JAPANESE Through Fairy Tales. 2007. (ENG & JPN.). (J). per. 14.95 incl. audio compact disk **(*978-1-891888-84-7(6))** Slangman Publishing.

—GOLDILOCKS (Japanese to English - Level 2) Learn ENGLISH Through Fairy Tales. 2007. (JPN & ENG.). (J). per. 14.95 incl. audio compact disk **(*978-1-891888-04-5(8))** Slangman Publishing.

Burrill, Richard L. Somewhere Behind the Eyes: Language Treasures Aha! Date not set. (Illus.). 85p. (J). (gr. 4-12). 15.95 (978-1-878464-16-3(7)) Anthro Co., The.

Carole Marsh. Ah,So! Japanese for Kids. 2004. (Little Linguist Ser.). 32p. (gr. 2-6). pap. 5.95 (978-0-635-02434-3(9)) Gallopade International.

—It Really Is Greek to Me! 2004. (Little Linguist Ser.). 32p. 29.95 (978-0-635-02440-4(3)) Gallopade International.

—It Really Is Greek to Me! Greek for Kids. 2004. (Little Linguist Ser.). 32p. (gr. 2-6). pap. 5.95 (978-0-635-02432-9(2)) Gallopade International.

—Say What When You Sneeze? 2004. (Little Linguist Ser.). 32p. 29.95 (978-0-635-02439-8(X)) Gallopade International.

—Say What When You Sneeze? German for Kids. 2004. (Little Linguist Ser.). 32p. (gr. 2-6). pap. 5.95 (978-0-635-02431-2(4)) Gallopade International.

Chessen, Betsey & Berger, Samantha. Hello. 1999. (J). 2.50 (978-0-439-04560-5(6)) Scholastic, Inc.

—Hello. 1999. (ps-2). lib. bdg. 10.10 (978-0-613-21691-3(1)) Tandem Library Bks.

Classroom Literature Circles. 2003. 80p. (J). per. 9.99 (978-0-88724-944-0(2) , CD-0047) Carson-Dellosa Publishing Co., Inc.

Corbeil, Jean-Claude, et al. Milet Bilingual Visual Dictionary. 2001. (Milet Bilingual Visual Dictionary Ser.). (Illus.). 232p. (J). (gr. 1-3). (BEN & ENG.). 29.95 (978-1-84059-257-3(5)); (GUJ & ENG., 29.95 (978-1-84059-259-7(1)); (TUR & ENG., 29.95 (978-1-84059-260-3(5)) Milet Publishing.

Cutting, Joan. Pragmatics & Discourse: Resource Book for Students. 2002. (Routledge English Language Introductions Ser.). (Illus.). 200p. (YA). (gr. 13). 30.95 (978-0-415-25358-1(6)) Routledge.

DeCesare, Ruth. Songs for the German Class. (GER.). (J). 9.95 (978-0-8442-2262-2(3) , National Textbook Co.) McGraw-Hill/Contemporary.

Domínguez, Marcela, et al. Imagenes: Text. 2003. 381p. (YA). stu. ed. 109.16 incl. cd-rom, cd-rom (978-0-618-33149-9(2) , 385645) Houghton Mifflin College Div.

Dual Language Add-On Package. 2003. 170.50 (978-0-673-57714-6(7)) Celebration Pr.

Dual Language Classroom Library. 2003. 769.50 (978-0-673-77836-9(3)) Celebration Pr.

Erdogan, Fatih. Ece ve Efe ile Turkce. Hambleton, Laura, illus. 2007. (Abby & Zak Ser.). 48p. (J). pap. 16.95 **(*978-1-84059-493-5(4))** Milet Publishing.

Fremdwoerterbuch. (Duden-Schuelerduden Ser.). (GER.). 480p. (YA). 27.95 (978-3-411-05143-4(4)) Bibliographisches Institut & F. A. Brockhaus AG DEU. *Dist:* International Bk. Import Service, Inc.

Fuary, Margaret & Kessler, Deborah. Hao Ji Le! Activities for Beginners. Wright, Jessica, ed. 2002. (Illus.). 84p. (gr. 3-6). pap. 45.95 (978-1-86366-713-5(X)) Curriculum Corporation AUS. *Dist:* Cheng & Tsui Co.

FUNIX Book, Foreign Languages Made Fun. l.t. ed. 2001. 144p. spiral bd. 14.99 (978-0-929178-56-1(4)) Valley Forge Publishing.

Funston, James F., et al. Somos Asi En Sus Marcas A/B/ Level 1. 2002. (SPA., Illus.). (YA). (gr. 7-8). pap., act. bk. ed. 15.95 (978-0-8219-2318-4(8) , 70674); (gr. 8). pap. 24.95 (978-0-8219-2246-0(7) , 70897) EMC/ Paradigm Publishing.

Gigarjian, Ani & Avedikian, Linda. My Second Book of Armenian Words. 2nd ed. 2006. (J). 18.00 **(*978-0-9717799-1-4(0))** Gigarjian, Ani & Linda Avedikian.

Green, Joan. Signposts Language Arts Activities for Kindergarten, Bk. A. Barbe, Walter B., ed. 2000. (Illus.). 32p. (J). (gr. k-1). pap. 5.95 (978-1-56762-116-7(3)) Modern Learning Pr.

Greene, Jane Fell. Language! Student Mastery. 2nd rev. ed. 2000. Bk. I. 114p. stu. ed. 5.25 (978-1-57035-239-3(9) , 120 Bk I); Bk. C. 106p. stu. ed. 5.25 (978-1-57035-233-1(X) , 120 Bk C); Bk. D. 108p. stu. ed. 5.25 (978-1-57035-234-8(8) , 120 Bk D); Bk. B. 97p. stu. ed. 5.25 (978-1-57035-232-4(1) , 120 Bk B); Bk. E. 118p. stu. ed. 5.25 (978-1-57035-235-5(6) , 120 Bk E); Bk. F. 108p. stu. ed. 5.25 (978-1-57035-236-2(4) , 120 Bk F); Bk. G. 111p. stu. ed. 5.25 (978-1-57035-237-9(2) , 120 Bk G); Bk. H. 99p. stu. ed. 5.25 (978-1-57035-238-6(0) , 120 Bk H) Sopris West Educational Services.

Haskins, James & Benson, Kathleen. Count Your Way Through Afghanistan. Moore, Megan, illus. 2007. (Count Your Way Ser.). 24p. (J). 19.93 (978-1-57505-880-1(4) , Millbrook Pr.) Lerner Publishing Group.

—Count Your Way Through Egypt. Rama, Sue, illus. 2007. (Count Your Way Ser.). 24p. (J). 19.93 (978-1-57505-882-5(0) , Millbrook Pr.) Lerner Publishing Group.

—Count Your Way Through Kenya. Lévêque, Lyne, illus. 2007. (Count Your Way Ser.). 24p. (J). 19.93 (978-1-57505-884-9(7) , Millbrook Pr.) Lerner Publishing Group.

—Count Your Way Through South Africa. Neibert, Alissa, illus. 2007. (Count Your Way Ser.). 24p. (J). 19.93 (978-1-57505-883-2(9) , Millbrook Pr.) Lerner Publishing Group.

—Count Your Way Through Zimbabwe. Park, Janie Jaehyun, illus. 2007. (Count Your Way Ser.). 24p. (J). 19.93 (978-1-57505-885-6(5) , Millbrook Pr.) Lerner Publishing Group.

Haskins, James, et al. Count Your Way Through Iran. 2007. (Count Your Way Ser.). (Illus.). 24p. (J). 19.93 (978-1-57505-881-8(2) , Millbrook Pr.) Lerner Publishing Group.

Hindi Level One: The Rosetta Stone Language Library. 2005. (J). (gr. 1 up). cd-rom 209.00 (978-1-58022-043-9(6)) Fairfield Language Technologies.

Hippocrene Books, ed. Bengali Children's Picture Dictionary: English-Bengali/Bengali-English. 2006. 114p. 14.95 (978-0-7818-1128-6(7)) Hippocrene Bks., Inc.

Hippocrene Books Staff. Children's Illustrated Czech Dictionary. 1999. (Hippocrene Children's Illustrated Foreign Language Dictionaries Ser.). (CZE & ENG., Illus.). 96p. (J). (gr. k-5). 14.95 (978-0-7818-0732-6(8)) Hippocrene Bks., Inc.

—Children's Illustrated Czech Dictionary: English-Czech/ Czech-English. 2003. (Hippocrene Children's Illustrated Foreign Language Dictionaries Ser.). (Illus.). 96p. pap. 11.95 (978-0-7818-0987-0(8)) Hippocrene Bks., Inc.

—Hippocrene Children's Illustrated Dutch Dictionary: English-Dutch. 2001. Tr. of Dutch-English. (ENG & DUT.). (gr. 3-6). lib. bdg. 21.05 (978-0-613-74950-3(2)) Tandem Library Bks.

—Hippocrene Children's Illustrated Japanese Dictionary: English-Japanese. 2001. Tr. of Japanese. (ENG & JPN.). (gr. 3-6). lib. bdg. 21.05 (978-0-613-74946-6(4)) Tandem Library Bks.

Hippocrene Books Staff, ed. Children's Illustrated Irish Dictionary: English-Irish, Irish-English. 1998. (Children's Illustrated Foreign Language Dictionaries Ser.). (ENG & IRI., Illus.). 122p. (gr. k-5). 14.95 (978-0-7818-0713-5(1)) Hippocrene Bks., Inc.

Holt, Rinehart and Winston Staff. Alternate Assessment Guide. 1999. (Komm Mit! Ser.). pap. 20.00 (978-0-03-052924-5(7)) Holt, Rinehart & Winston.

—Elements of Language: Developing Language Skills. 4th ed. Date not set. (YA). (gr. 10). pap. 17.20 (978-0-03-070063-7(9)); (YA). (gr. 11). pap. 17.20 (978-0-03-070064-4(7)); (YA). (gr. 12). pap. 17.20 (978-0-03-070066-8(3)); (J). (gr. 6). pap. 17.20 (978-0-03-070058-3(2)); (YA). (gr. 7). pap. 17.20 (978-0-03-070059-0(0)); (YA). (gr. 8). pap. 17.20 (978-0-03-070061-3(2)); (YA). (gr. 9). pap. 17.20 (978-0-03-070062-0(0)) Holt, Rinehart & Winston.

—Elements of Language: Developing Language Skills Answer Key. 4th ed. Date not set. (J). (gr. 6). pap. 12.80 (978-0-03-070067-5(1)); (YA). (gr. 7). pap. 12.80 (978-0-03-070068-2(X)); (YA). (gr. 8). pap. 12.80 (978-0-03-070069-9(8)) Holt, Rinehart & Winston.

—Elements of Language: One-Stop Lesson Planner. 2003. (Elements of Language Ser.). 301.00 (978-0-03-057376-7(9)) Holt, Rinehart & Winston.

—Elements of Language 2004: Pennsylvania Annotated Edition. 4th ed. 2004. (YA). (gr. 12). 122.80 (978-0-03-073441-0(X)) Holt, Rinehart & Winston.

—Komm Mit! Level 2: Activities for Communication, Level 2. 1999. pap. 21.86 (978-0-03-052922-1(0)) Holt, Rinehart & Winston.

—Komm Mit! Level 3: Activities for Communication. 1999. (J). pap. 20.00 (978-0-03-053998-5(6)) Holt, Rinehart & Winston.

—Komm Mit! Level 3: Listening Activities. 1999. pap. 39.40 (978-0-03-053999-2(4)) Holt, Rinehart & Winston.

—Komm Mit! Level 3: Practice & Activities Book. 1999. (Komm Mit! Ser.). pap., tchr. ed. 28.13 (978-0-03-053997-8(8)) Holt, Rinehart & Winston.

Huddleston, Beth, et al. Sound Beginnings: Languages & Music of the World. 1998. (SPA, RUS & GER., Illus.). 16p. (J). pap. 19.95 incl. audio (978-1-885278-02-9(0)) Sound Beginnings.

Icelandic Sheepdog Christian Adventures in Learning Book. 2005. (J). 19.95 (978-1-59210-425-3(8)) Whispering Pine Pr., Inc.

Instructional Fair Staff, ed. Extra Help Math & Language Arts. 1998. (100+ Seriestm Ser.). (Illus.). 128p. (gr. 2 up). 12.99 (978-1-56822-491-6(5) , IF8775) School Specialty Publishing.

Jarvis. Student Lab Audio CDs: Used with ... Jarvis-? Como se Dice...? 8th ed. 2004. (YA). stu. ed., lab manual ed. 59.96 incl. cd-rom, cd-rom, audio compact disk (978-0-618-47151-5(0) , 328477) Houghton Mifflin College Div.

Kelley, Michelle. Different Places, Different Words. 2007. (World Around Me Ser.). (Illus.). 24p. (J). (gr. k-2). lib. bdg. 21.35 **(*978-1-59515-993-9(2))** Rourke Publishing, LLC.

Khare, Pratibha & Bekooy Khare, Catherine. Hindi Primer, Pt. 1. 2nd ed. 2004. (HIN & ENG.). 172p. spiral bd. (978-0-9663831-3-3(3)) Mukund Pubns.

Kiraz, George. The Syriac Alphabet for Children. 2004. (J). 25.00 (978-1-59333-113-9(4)); pap. 15.00 (978-1-59333-112-2(6)) Gorgias Pr., LLC.

Language Helper German. 2007. (J). 22.95 **(*978-0-9789152-0-9(8))** Chou-Chou Pr.

Lanza, Janet R., et al. Artic to Go. 2004. (J). per. 35.95 (978-0-7606-0540-0(8)) LinguiSystems, Inc.

Learn Bangla 2004. 2004. (J). cd-rom 29.95 (978-0-9748503-8-2(1)) Griha.

Level One - Supplemental Material. 2007. (J). pap. **(*978-0-932416-14-8(4))** Papaloizos Pubns., Inc.

Leventhal, Debra. What Is Your Language? 1998. (Picture Puffin Ser.). (J). (978-0-606-13901-4(X)) Tandem Library Bks.

Levine, Melvin D. Language Parts Catalog. Noon, Jennifer, ed. 1999. (Illus.). (YA). (gr. 7-10). pap., wbk. ed. 9.00 (978-0-8388-1980-7(X)) Educators Publishing Service, Inc.

LoGiudice, Carolyn & McConnell, Nancy. Room 28 a Social Language Program. 2004. (YA). per. 25.95 (978-0-7606-0530-1(0)) LinguiSystems, Inc.

Losada, Basilio. Isabel la Catolica. (SPA., Illus.). 192p. (YA). 11.95 (978-84-7281-122-5(0) , AF1122) Auriga, Ediciones S.A. ESP. *Dist:* Continental Bk. Co., Inc.

Mahnke. Audio Cd: Used with ... Butler-Grammar Links 1: A Theme-Based Course for Reference & Practice. 2nd ed. 2004. (YA). cd-rom 22.36 (978-0-618-35300-2(3) , 327296) Houghton Mifflin College Div.

Map Skills Grade 3. 2003. (Practice Makes Perfect Ser.). (Illus.). 48p. (J). (gr. 3). 4.99 (978-0-7439-3728-3(7)) Teacher Created Materials, Inc.

Mary Lu Muffoletto. Figures of Speech Grades 5-8. 2002. 64p. (J). pap. 8.94 (978-1-889369-49-5(7)) Teaching Ink, Inc.

McGraw-Hill Staff. Glencoe Literature, World Literature, Grammar & Language Workbook. 1999. pap. 20.64 (978-0-07-821537-7(4) , 9780078215377) Glencoe/ McGraw-Hill.

—Glencoe Literature World Literature Grammar Practice. 2000. pap., wbk. ed. 18.00 (978-0-07-824181-9(2) , 9780078241819) Glencoe/McGraw-Hill.

—Invitation to Languages. 2006. stu. ed. 46.00 (978-0-07-874249-1(8) , 9780078742491) Glencoe/McGraw-Hill.

Metropolitan Museum of Art Staff, contrib. by. Write Like an Ancient Egyptian! 2003. (Illus.). 69p. (J). (978-1-58839-036-3(5)) Metropolitan Museum of Art, The.

Morris, Paul. 101 Language Activities. 2004. (J). per. 35.95 (978-0-7606-0532-5(7)) LinguiSystems, Inc.

Moshi Moshi. 2004. (Yoroshiku Ser.: Stages 1 and 2). (JPN., Illus.). (gr. k-12). 152p. pap., tchr. ed. 32.95 (978-1-86366-143-0(3)); 148p. pap., stu. ed. 39.95 (978-1-86366-146-1(8)) Curriculum Corporation AUS. *Dist:* Cheng & Tsui Co.

Nannas, Anastasia. Let's Learn Greek Too!, Bk. 2. Un-Choi, Nicole, illus. 2002. (GRE.). 104p. (J). (gr. k-12). pap., stu. ed. 17.00 (978-0-918618-86-3(X)) Pella Publishing Co., Inc.

National Curriculum Development Centre Staff. Luo. 2004. Bk. 1. pap., pupil's gde. ed. (978-0-521-78936-3(2)); Bk. 2. pap., pupil's gde. ed. (978-0-521-78937-0(0)); Bk. 3. pap., pupil's gde. ed. (978-0-521-78938-7(9)); Bk. 4. pap., pupil's gde. ed. (978-0-521-78939-4(7)) Cambridge Univ. Pr.

National Japanese Curriculum Project Staff. Pera Pera. 2004. (Yoroshiku Ser.: Stages 3 and 4). (JPN.). 224p. (gr. k-12). pap., stu. ed. 45.95 (978-1-86366-147-8(6)) Curriculum Corporation AUS. *Dist:* Cheng & Tsui Co.

Nelson, Angela, creator. Lang-O-Learn: Everyday Object Cards. 2001. (SPA, FRE, GER, ITA & RUS.). (J). 19.95 (978-0-9668008-6-9(9)) Stages Learning Materials.

Nordstrom, Ursula. Secret Language. 167p. (J). (gr. 3-5). pap. 4.95 (978-0-8072-1425-1(6) , Listening Library) Random Hse. Audio Publishing Group.

Omary, Rachel, illus. Animals in Pashto. l.t. ed. 2003. 4p. (J). spiral bd. 10.95 (978-0-9740535-5-4(4)) Knight Publishing.

Palazzo-Craig, Janet. Language Development Variety Text. 2005. 48p. pap. 6.95 (978-1-4042-8562-0(8)); pap. 6.95 (978-1-4042-8567-5(9)) Rosen Publishing Group, Inc., The.

Papaloizos, Theodore C. Beginner's Elementary Conversation Greek. 2001. (GRE & ENG., Illus.). 106p. (J). pap. (978-0-932416-58-2(6)) Papaloizos Pubns., Inc.

—Elementary Conversation Greek, Book 2. 2001. (ENG & GRE., Illus.). 139p. pap. (978-0-932416-60-5(8)) Papaloizos Pubns., Inc.

—Elementary Conversation Greek, Book 3. 2000. (ENG & GRE., Illus.). 137p. (YA). pap. (978-0-932416-37-7(3)) Papaloizos Pubns., Inc.

—Learning Greek. 2003. (GRE & ENG., Illus.). 188p. (YA). pap., wbk. ed. (978-0-932416-44-5(6)) Papaloizos Pubns., Inc.

—This & That. 2001. (GRE & ENG., Illus.). 134p. (YA). pap. (978-0-932416-17-9(9)) Papaloizos Pubns., Inc.

—Workbook for Beginners' Elementary Conversation Greek. 2001. (GRE & ENG., Illus.). 77p. pap. (978-0-932416-59-9(4)) Papaloizos Pubns., Inc.

—Workbook for Elementary Conversation Greek. (GRE & ENG., Illus.). Bk. 2. 2001. 90p. pap. (978-0-932416-61-2(6)); Bk. 3. 2000. 92p. pap. (978-0-932416-55-1(1)) Papaloizos Pubns., Inc.

—Workbook for Learning Greek. 2003. (GRE & ENG.). 76p. (YA). pap. (978-0-932416-32-2(2)) Papaloizos Pubns., Inc.

—Workbook for This & That. 2001. (GRE & ENG.). 82p. (YA). pap. (978-0-932416-18-6(7)) Papaloizos Pubns., Inc.

Parker. Is It Hard or Soft?, 6 Packs. 2004. (Illus.). pap. 29.70 (978-1-4109-0775-2(9)) Raintree.

—Is It Rough or Smooth?, 6 Packs. 2004. (Illus.). pap. 29.70 (978-1-4109-0774-5(0)) Raintree.

—Is It Shiny or Dull?, 6 Packs. 2004. (Illus.). pap. 29.70 (978-1-4109-0776-9(7)) Raintree.

Pera Pera. 2004. (Yoroshiku Ser.: Stages 3 and 4). (JPN.). 136p. (gr. k-12). pap., tchr. ed., ldr.'s hndbk. ed. 45.95 (978-1-86366-141-6(7)) Curriculum Corporation AUS. *Dist:* Cheng & Tsui Co.

Realtime Associates and Mazer Corporation Staff & LeapFrog Staff, compiled by. Recognize Persuasive Language. 2002. (J). (gr. 3). 66.75 (978-1-58605-366-6(3)); (gr. 4). 66.75 (978-1-58605-422-9(8)); (gr. 5). 66.75 (978-1-58605-479-3(1)) LeapFrog Enterprises, Inc. (LeapFrog Schl. Hse.).

—Sensory Language/Imagery. 2002. (J). (gr. 4). 66.75 (978-1-58605-423-6(6) , LeapFrog Schl. Hse.) LeapFrog Enterprises, Inc.

El Recuerdo Egipcio. 2000. (SPA., Illus.). 70p. (YA). (gr. 7-9). pap. 11.95 (978-88-8148-446-1(3)) European Language Institute ITA. *Dist:* Distribooks, Inc., Midwest European Pubns.

Ristuccia, Christine. The Entire World of Attributes. 2003. (J). 29.99 (978-0-9723457-4-7(9)) Say It Right.

—The Entire World of R Screening Kit. 2000. (Illus.). (J). pap. 9.99 (978-0-9723457-3-6(6)) Say It Right.

Ristuccia, Christine & Ristuccia, James. The Entire World of S & Z Screening Kit. 2003. (Illus.). 20p. (J). pap. 9.99 (978-0-9723457-6-7(0)) Say It Right.

Romero, Victor Eclar. Learn Filipino: Book One, Book One. Francisco, Manny, illus. 2004. 384p. per. 29.95 (978-1-932956-41-2(7)) Magsimba Pr.

The Rosetta Stone Language Library: Dutch Level 2. 2005. (J). (gr. 1 up). cd-rom 239.00 (978-1-58022-046-0(0)) Fairfield Language Technologies.

The Rosetta Stone Language Library: German Level 2. 1999. (J). (gr. 1 up). cd-rom 239.00 (978-1-883972-59-2(0)) Fairfield Language Technologies.

The Rosetta Stone Language Library: Indonesian Level 1. 1999. (J). (gr. 1 up). cd-rom 209.00 (978-1-58022-031-6(2)) Fairfield Language Technologies.

The Rosetta Stone Language Library: Thai Level 1. 2005. (J). (gr. 1 up). cd-rom 209.00 (978-1-883972-75-2(2)) Fairfield Language Technologies.

Ruffenach, Jessie, ed. Baby Learns to Count. Thomas, Peter, tr. Blacksheep, Beverly, illus. l.t. ed. 2003. (NAV & ENG.). 16p. (J). bds. 7.95 (978-1-893354-47-0(4)) Salina Bookshelf.

School Specialty Publishing. The Best of Totline. 160p. (J). (gr. k-k). Vol. 3. 2003. pap. 16.99 (978-1-57029-461-7(5) , WPH99016); Vol. 4. 2004. pap. 16.99 (978-1-57029-496-9(8) , WPH99046) Schaffer, Frank Pubns. (Totline Pubns.).

Schwalm, Claudia. Being Bilingual Is Fun! Schwalm, Claudia, photos by. 1999. (Illus.). 32p. (J). (gr. k-6). 17.95 (978-1-57371-012-1(1)) Cultural Connections.

—Indonesian - English Mini-Book Set with Audio: Bahasa Indonesia. Schwalm, Claudia, illus. 2000. (Illus.). (J). (gr. k-9). pap. 21.95 (978-1-57371-040-4(7)) Cultural Connections.

—Tongan - English Mini-Book Set with Audio. Schwalm, Claudia, illus. 2001. (TON., Illus.). (Orig.). (J). (gr. k-8). pap. 21.95 (978-1-57371-037-4(7)) Cultural Connections.

Shah, Sapna Jaiswal. Sapna Aunty's Hindi Book of Colors: Rang. 2004. (HIN.). (J). 8.00 (978-0-9741686-0-9(2)) 3N Media Group.

Shooting Star Press. Word Play Spanish. Iosa, Ann W., illus. 2005. (Smart Kids Ser.). (SPA & ENG.). 13p. (J). (gr. 4-8). pap. 9.95 (978-1-59125-394-5(2) , Penton Kids) Penton Overseas, Inc.

Somos Latinos: A Unique Dual Language Series, 6 Bks, Set. 2004. (J). 120.00 (978-0-516-28547-4(5) , Children's Pr.) Scholastic Library Publishing.

Spaine Long, Sheri, et al. Nexos: Introductory Spanish. 2004. 504p. (YA). 113.56 incl. cd-rom (978-0-618-49609-9(2) , 334255) Houghton Mifflin College Div.

Stewart, Paul. Brown Eyes. 1998. (Penguin Readers Ser.). (Illus.). 31p. (J). pap. 7.33 (978-0-14-081582-5(1)) Longman Publishing Group.

Takarai, Saori & Kardy, Glenn. Manga Moods: Forty Faces + 80 Phrases. 2006. (Illus.). 96p. (YA). (978-4-921205-13-3(2)) Japanime Co., Ltd.

Thompson, Richard & Thompson, Ofa. Ko 'eku tohi 'oe fanga Manu. Slutz, Stephani, illus. 2004. (TON.). 16p. (J). (ps up). pap. 5.00 (978-0-9678979-2-9(0)) Friendly Isles Pr.

Trim, John & Kohl, Katrin M. Deutsch Direkt! Textbook. (J). (gr. 9-12). 16.95 (978-0-8219-0225-7(3) , 45290) EMC/Paradigm Publishing.

Verdick, Elizabeth. Words Are Not for Hurting. Heinlen, Marieka, illus. 2004. (Best Behavior Ser.). 40p. (J). (ps-2). pap. 11.95 (978-1-57542-156-8(9)) Free Spirit Publishing, Inc.

Winitz, Harris. The Learnables, Bk. 1. Baker, Sydney M., illus. 4th ed. 1999. (CZE, CHI, ENG, FRE & GER.). (YA). (gr. 7 up). pap. 45.00 incl. audio (978-1-887371-43-8(5)) International Linguistics Corp.

—The Learnables, 6 cassettes. 1999. (CHI, CZE, ENG, FRE & GER., Illus.). 51p. Bk. 2. 4th ed. (YA). (gr. 7 up). pap. 51.00 incl. audio (978-1-887371-44-5(3)); Bk. 3. 2nd ed. (J). pap. 45.00 incl. audio (978-0-939990-03-0(2)); Bk. 4. (YA). (gr. 7 up). pap. 45.00 incl. audio (978-1-887371-46-9(X)) International Linguistics Corp.

Workbook - My First Book. 2007. (J). pap. 20.00 (***978-0-932416-13-1(6)***) Papaloizos Pubns., Inc.

Yapese Alphabet. 2006. (Illus.). 56p. (J). bds. 4.95 (978-1-57306-260-2(X)) Bess Pr., Inc.

LANGUAGE AND LANGUAGES—VOCATIONAL GUIDANCE

Miller, Anne Meeker. Baby Sing & Sign: A Play-filled Language Development Program for Hearing Infants & Toddlers. 2004. (J). spiral bd. 14.95 (978-0-9749924-0-2(2)) Love Language Pubns.

LANGUAGE ARTS

see Communication; English Language; Reading; Speech

LAOS

Doeden, Matt. Laos in Pictures. 2007. (Visual Geography Ser.). (Illus.). 80p. (J). (gr. 5-12). 27.93 (978-0-8225-6590-1(0) , Twenty-First Century Bks.) Lerner Publishing Group.

Zickgraf, Ralph. Laos. 1999. (Major World Nations Ser.). (Illus.). 144p. (YA). (gr. 4-7). 29.95 (978-0-7910-4743-9(1) , Chelsea Hse.) Facts On File, Inc.

LAPLAND—FICTION

Penny, Anne. Scraper. 2006. (Illus.). 56p. pap. (***978-1-84401-921-2(7)***) Athena Pr.

LARGE TYPE BOOKS

Aardvark, D. The Congraduation Fish. Aardvark, D., illus. l.t. ed. 2005. (Illus.). 48p. (J). per. 12.95 (978-0-9755567-1-9(1)) Aardvark's Weedpatch Pr.

—Merry Kissmoose. Aardvark, D., illus. l.t. ed. 2005. (Illus.). 48p. (J). per. 12.95 (978-0-9755567-2-6(X)) Aardvark's Weedpatch Pr.

—Punkin's upside down Day. l.t. ed. 2004. (Illus.). 40p. (J). per. 10.95 (978-0-9755567-0-2(3)) Aardvark's Weedpatch Pr.

Aaron, Hugh. Suzy, Fair Suzy. Sproch, Lynnette, illus. l.t. ed. 1998. 32p. (J). (gr. k-4). pap. 8.95 (978-1-882521-07-4(2)) Stones Point Pr.

Abbatiello, Toya. What Will Alex Do? Gedeon, Gloria, illus. l.t. ed. 2000. 16p. (J). (gr. k-2). pap. 4.95 (978-1-57874-017-8(7) , Kaeden Bks.) Kaeden Corp.

Ackerman, Artur. Somewhere Below the Great White Clouds. l.t. ed. 2002. (Orig.). (J). pap. 12.95 (978-1-59232-053-0(8)) Seaburn Pubs.

Adams, Elizabeth. Me & My Shadows: Shadow Puppet Fun for Kids of All Ages. l.t. ed. 2002. (J). spiral bd. 16.96 (978-1-888725-78-0(8) , 1-888725-78-8, MacroPrintBooks) Science & Humanities Pr.

Adams, Emanuel F., Sr. Poor Butterfly: Untitled Memories. l.t. ed. 2002. 240p. (YA). bds. 16.00 (978-0-9644282-1-8(0)) Stick to The Word Publishing.

Adams, Mark Wayne. Miss Mary's Missing Book Bag. Adams, Mark Wayne, illus. l.t. ed. 2004. (Illus.). (J). (gr. k-6). pap. 8.95 (978-1-59616-000-2(4)) Caballo Bks.

Adler, Eric. Is the Sky Always Blue? Nakahodo, Neil, illus. l.t. ed. 2002. 32p. (J). 14.95 (978-0-9717080-0-6(2)) Kansas City Star Bks.

The Adventures of Chip Green the Forestry Kid, l.t. ed. 2005. (Illus.). 34p. (J). per. (978-0-9729753-8-4(1)) Really Big Coloring Bks., Inc.

The Adventures of Little Nina: Nina's First Trip. l.t. ed. 2005. (Illus.). 40p. (J). 16.95 (978-0-9769662-0-3(4)) Strategies Publishing Co.

The Adventures of Marc John Jefferies: The Missing Princess. l.t. ed. 2004. (Illus.). 110p. (YA). per. (978-0-9747218-3-5(2) , 100, Young Women Programming) Young Women Bks.

The Adventures of the Original Pumpkin Patch Pals. l.t. ed. 2005. (Illus.). 32p. (J). 15.00 (978-0-9770960-1-5(7)) 3 Pals Media, LLC.

Aesop. Aesop's Fables. Winter, Nilo, illus. l.t. ed. Date not set. (J). (gr. 1-12). lib. bdg. 22.95 (978-0-88411-991-3(2)) Amereon LTD.

Ahlberg, Allan. The Better Brown Stories. Wegner, Fritz, illus. l.t. ed. 1998. 272p. (J). pap. (978-0-7540-6006-2(3) , CLP 224) BBC Audio.

Ahmad, Iftikhar. World Cultures: A Global Mosaic, 8 vols. l.t. ed. 2004. 2467p. (YA). (gr. 6-9). 1236.00 (978-0-13-036895-9(4) , A-L00012-00) Prentice Hall Pr.

Ahmed, Aisha. Islam for the Junior. l.t. ed. 2000. 58p. (J). pap. 5.00 (978-1-879402-71-3(8)) Tahrike Tarsile Quran, Inc.

Aiken, Joan. Died on a Rainy Sunday. l.t. ed. 1999. (General Ser.). 192p. (YA). pap. 24.95 (978-0-7862-1962-9(9)); (978-0-7540-3811-5(4)) Thorndike Pr.

Al-Jibaly, Muhammad. Knowing Allah. l.t. ed. 1998. (Eemaan Made Easy Ser.). (Illus.). 63p. (J). (gr. 2). pap. 5.00 (978-1-891229-05-3(2)) Al-Kitaab & As-Sunnah Publishing.

—Knowing the Angels. l.t. ed. 1999. (Eemaan Made Easy Ser.: Vol. 2). (Illus.). 102p. (J). (gr. 2). pap. 7.00 (978-1-891229-06-0(0)) Al-Kitaab & As-Sunnah Publishing.

Albert, Toni Diana. Saving the Rain Forest with Cammie & Cooper. Bowles, Carol, illus. l.t. ed. 2003. 32p. (J). pap. 7.95 (978-1-929432-02-8(X) , 800-353-2791) Trickle Creek Bks.

Albright, Thomas B. Simple Spanish. 2nd l.t. ed. 2001. (Languages). (SPA.). 48p. (978-1-888264-16-6(0)) Twenty-First Century Co., The.

—Universal English: Second Language for All. unabr. l.t. ed. 2003. (Languages: Universal English for All). (ENM.). 128p. pap. 7.00 (978-1-888264-17-3(9)) Twenty-First Century Co., The.

Alex, N. L. Smile All the While. l.t. ed. 2005. (Illus.). 16p. (J). 4.99 (978-0-9766080-0-4(6)) Joe Girl Ink.

Alexander, Florence & Alexander, Stanley. Come with Me & See... African People. l.t. ed. 2003. (ENG & SPA., Illus.). 13p. (J). 3.99 (978-0-9648313-8-4(4)) Ebon Research Systems Publishing, LLC.

—Come with Me & See... Birds of the World. l.t. ed. 2003. (Illus.). 32p. (J). 7.99 net. (978-0-915960-95-8(8)) Ebon Research Systems Publishing, LLC.

—Come with Me & See... Children of the World. l.t. ed. 2003. (ENG & SPA., Illus.). 32p. (J). 9.99 (978-0-9648313-9-1(2)) Ebon Research Systems Publishing, LLC.

—Jesus Child Is Born: Dare to Be Great. l.t. ed. 2003. (Illus.). 32p. (YA). 7.99 net. (978-0-915960-85-9(0)) Ebon Research Systems Publishing, LLC.

Alexander, Geoff. Toothbugs!, Carole, Isaacs, illus. l.t. ed. 2005. 12p. (J). bds. 12.95 (978-0-9760944-0-1(1)) Alexander-Marcus Publishing.

Alexander, Ian. Big Book: Do You See a Dozen?, Vol. 2. l.t. ed. 2005. (Sadlier Phonics Reading Program). (Illus.). 8p. (YA). (ps-1). 22.50 (978-0-8215-7347-1(0)) Sadlier, William H. Inc.

Alexander, Lloyd. The Remarkable Journey of Prince Jen. l.t. ed. 2002. (LRS Large Print Cornerstone Ser.). (J). lib. bdg. 32.95 (978-1-58118-104-3(3) , 25787) LRS.

Alexie, Oscar & Berlin, James, Sr., trs. Maniar Angun. Sloat, Teri, illus. l.t. ed. 2000. 12p. (J). pap. 17.00 (978-1-58084-186-3(4)) Lower Kuskokwim Schl. District.

All Around the Busy Town. l.t. ed. 1999. (Illus.). 20p. (J). pap. 19.00 (978-1-893467-03-3(1)) Spedial Editions Pr.

Allen, Toi Lynn. Game Day/Test Day: Who's Keeping Score? l.t. ed. 2004. (Illus.). (YA). pap. 14.95 (978-0-9753787-0-0(8)) Allen, Toi Operations.

Allende, Isabel. City of the Beasts. l.t. ed. 2002. Tr. of Ciudad de las Bestias. 400p. (J). (gr. 5). pap. 19.99 (978-0-06-051195-1(8)) HarperCollins Pubs.

—Forest of the Pygmies. l.t. ed. 2005. 304p. (J). (gr. 5 up). pap. 19.99 (978-0-06-076200-1(4) , Rayo) HarperCollins Pubs.

Allgood, Jean. Come Follow Me Bk. 1: Understanding One's Worth: Color Orange. Smith, Sandra, illus. l.t. ed. 2004. 23p. (J). 14.95 (978-0-9741627-3-7(6)) Write Designs, Ltd.

Allison, Amy. Luis Alvarez & the Development of the Bubble Chamber. l.t. ed. 2002. (Unlocking the Secrets of Science Ser.). (Illus.). (J). (gr. 4-10). lib. bdg. 25.70 (978-1-58415-140-1(4)) Mitchell Lane Pubs., Inc.

Almond, David. Heaven Eyes. l.t. ed. 2001. 263p. (J). 24.95 (978-0-7862-3696-1(5)) Thorndike Pr.

—Kit's Wilderness. l.t. ed. 2000. 263p. (J). pap. 16.95 (978-0-7540-6115-1(9) , Galaxy Children's Large Print) BBC Audiobooks America.

—Kit's Wilderness. 2001. (Illus.). 256p. (YA). (gr. 7). mass mkt. 5.99 (978-0-440-41605-0(1) , Laurel Leaf) Random Hse. Children's Bks.

—Kit's Wilderness. l.t. ed. 2001. (Illus.). 272p. (J). (gr. 4-7). 22.95 (978-0-7862-2772-3(9)) Thorndike Pr.

—Skellig. 2000. (J). (978-0-606-19192-0(5)) Tandem Library Bks.

Alston, E. B. The Last Voyage of the Dan-D. Garrett, Toni, illus. l.t. ed. 2003. 47p. (J). per. 6.99 (978-0-9747735-0-6(6)) Righter Publishing Co., Inc.

Aminah, Ibrahim Ali. The Three Muslim Festivals. Ghazi, A., ed. Hadzic, Aldin, illus. l.t. ed. 1998. 68p. (J). (gr. 4-7). 9.00 (978-1-56316-308-1(X)) IQRA International Educational Foundation.

Andersen, Hans Christian, tr. Andersen's Fairy Tales. l.t. ed. 2004. (Large Print Ser.). 266p. 25.00 (978-1-58287-629-0(0)) North Bks.

—Andersen's Fairy Tales. l.t. ed. 2002. cd-rom 11.50 (978-0-9721271-0-3(0)) Woolf, Virginia M. Foundation.

Anderson, Laurie Halse. Fever 1793. l.t. ed. 2001. 22.95 (978-0-7862-3408-0(3)) Thorndike Pr.

—Speak. 1999. 208p. (YA). (gr. 8-12). 17.00 (978-0-374-37152-4(0) , Farrar, Straus & Giroux (BYR)) Farrar, Straus & Giroux.

—Speak. l.t. ed. 2000. 276p. (YA). (gr. 8-12). 20.95 (978-0-7862-2525-5(4)) Thorndike Pr.

Andrew, Alice, et al. Castun Neqliyarer. McCarr, Edith, illus. l.t. ed. 1999. Tr. of How to Prepare Fish. (ESK.). 8p. (J). (gr. k-3). pap. 6.00 (978-1-58084-115-3(5)) Lower Kuskokwim Schl. District.

—Cin'at (Roe) Sparck, Carole C., illus. l.t. ed. 1999. (ESK.). 8p. (J). (gr. k-3). pap. 6.00 (978-1-58084-153-5(8)) Lower Kuskokwim Schl. District.

—Hannairniaqtaa Iqaluum. McCarr, Edith, illus. l.t. ed. 1999. Tr. of How to Prepare Fish. (ESK.). 8p. (J). (gr. k-3). pap. 6.00 (978-1-58084-131-3(7)) Lower Kuskokwim Schl. District.

—How to Prepare Fish. McCarr, Edith, illus. l.t. ed. 1999. 8p. (J). (gr. k-3). pap. 6.00 (978-1-58084-052-1(3)) Lower Kuskokwim Schl. District.

—Iqaluum Sannaiyautaa. McCarr, Edith, illus. l.t. ed. 1999. Tr. of How to Prepare Fish. (ESK.). 8p. (J). (gr. k-3). pap. 6.00 (978-1-58084-124-5(4)) Lower Kuskokwim Schl. District.

—Meluk (Roe) Sparck, Carole C., illus. l.t. ed. 1999. (ESK.). 8p. (J). (gr. k-3). pap. 6.00 (978-1-58084-104-7(X)) Lower Kuskokwim Schl. District.

—Neqliuryaraq. McCarr, Edith, illus. l.t. ed. 1999. Tr. of How to Prepare Fish. (ESK.). 8p. (J). (gr. k-3). pap. 6.00 (978-1-58084-053-8(1)) Lower Kuskokwim Schl. District.

—Qanuq Itqanaiyarnagpat Qalut. McCarr, Edith, illus. l.t. ed. 1999. Tr. of How to Prepare Fishs. (ESK.). 8p. (J). (gr. k-3). pap. 6.00 (978-1-58084-139-9(2)) Lower Kuskokwim Schl. District.

—Roe. Sparck, Carole C., illus. l.t. ed. 1999. 8p. (J). (gr. k-3). pap. 6.00 (978-1-58084-103-0(1)) Lower Kuskokwim Schl. District.

Andrews-McKinney, Joyce. Jentle & Jewel Fix Things, Andrews-McKinney, Joyce, illus. l.t. ed. 2006. (Illus.). 17p. (J). im. lthr. 8.00 (978-0-9728975-4-9(2)) JA-M Pubs., LLC.

Anfuso, Dennis. Woodwin & Beckly Vol. 6: Book One in the Chronicles of Foress. Anfuso, Dennis, illus. collector's l.t. ed. 2002. (Illus.). 88p. (J). per. 9.95 (978-1-57433-001-4(2)) Interset Pr.

Anonymous. Las Doce Historias de la Tía Margarita. Greendyk, William, tr. from ENG. l.t. ed. 2004. Orig. Title: Aunt Margaret's Twelve Stories. (SPA.). 84p. (J). pap. 3.99 (978-1-932789-00-3(6) , X001N) Editorial Sendas Antiguas, LLC.

Appleby, Ellen. Les Trois Barbichu, Big Bk. l.t. ed. (FRE.). (J). bds. 29.99 (978-0-590-71769-4(3)) Scholastic, Inc.

Applegate, Katherine. Animorphs Boxed Set: The Separation; The Illusion; The Prophecy; The Proposal; The Mutation; The Weakness; The Arrival; The Hidden; The Other; The Familiar; The Journey, 12 bks. l.t. ed. Incl. Arrival. 148p. 2001. lib. bdg. 23.33 (978-0-8368-2771-2(6)); Conspiracy. 138p. 2000. lib. bdg. 23.33 (978-0-8368-2754-5(6)); Familiar. 143p. 2001. lib. bdg. 23.33 (978-0-8368-2774-3(0)); Hidden. 121p. 2001. lib. bdg. 23.33 (978-0-8368-2772-9(4)); Illusion. 156p. 2000. lib. bdg. 23.33 (978-0-8368-2755-2(4)); Journey. 139p. 2001. lib. bdg. 23.33 (978-0-8368-2775-0(9)); Mutation. 142p. 2000. lib. bdg. 23.33 (978-0-8368-2756-9(2)); Other. 130p. 2001. lib. bdg. 23.33 (978-0-8368-2773-6(2)); Prophecy. 141p. 2000. lib. bdg. 23.33 (978-0-8368-2757-6(0)); Proposal. 147p. 2000. lib. bdg. 23.33 (978-0-8368-2758-3(9)); Separation. 158p. 2000. lib. bdg. 23.33 (978-0-8368-2759-0(7)); Weakness. (Illus.). 129p. 2001. lib. bdg. 23.33 (978-0-8368-2770-5(8)); (J). (gr. 4 up). (Animorphs Ser.: Nos. 32-42). 2001. Set lib. bdg. 279.96 (978-0-8368-2862-7(3)) Stevens, Gareth Inc.

—The Arrival. l.t. ed. 2001. (Animorphs Ser.: No. 38). 148p. (J). (gr. 4 up). lib. bdg. 23.33 (978-0-8368-2771-2(6)) Stevens, Gareth Inc.

—The Conspiracy. l.t. ed. 2000. (Animorphs Ser.: No. 31). 138p. (J). (gr. 4 up). lib. bdg. 23.33 (978-0-8368-2754-5(6)) Stevens, Gareth Inc.

—The Familiar. l.t. ed. 2001. (Animorphs Ser.: No. 41). 143p. (J). (gr. 4 up). lib. bdg. 23.33 (978-0-8368-2774-3(0)) Stevens, Gareth Inc.

—The Hidden. l.t. ed. 2001. (Animorphs Ser.: No. 39). 121p. (J). (gr. 4 up). lib. bdg. 23.33 (978-0-8368-2772-9(4)) Stevens, Gareth Inc.

—The Illusion. l.t. ed. 2000. (Animorphs Ser.: No. 33). 156p. (J). (gr. 4 up). lib. bdg. 23.33 (978-0-8368-2755-2(4)) Stevens, Gareth Inc.

—The Journey. l.t. ed. 2001. (Animorphs Ser.: No. 42). 139p. (J). (gr. 4 up). lib. bdg. 23.33 (978-0-8368-2775-0(9)) Stevens, Gareth Inc.

—The Mutation. l.t. ed. 2000. (Animorphs Ser.: No. 36). 142p. (J). (gr. 4 up). lib. bdg. 23.33 (978-0-8368-2756-9(2)) Stevens, Gareth Inc.

—The Other. l.t. ed. 2001. (Animorphs Ser.: No. 40). 130p. (J). (gr. 4 up). lib. bdg. 23.33 (978-0-8368-2773-6(2)) Stevens, Gareth Inc.

—The Prophecy. l.t. ed. 2000. (Animorphs Ser.: No. 34). 141p. (J). (gr. 4 up). lib. bdg. 23.33 (978-0-8368-2757-6(0)) Stevens, Gareth Inc.

—The Proposal. l.t. ed. 2000. (Animorphs Ser.: No. 35). 147p. (J). (gr. 4 up). lib. bdg. 23.33 (978-0-8368-2758-3(9)) Stevens, Gareth Inc.

—The Separation. l.t. ed. 2000. (Animorphs Ser.: No. 32). 158p. (J). (gr. 4 up). lib. bdg. 23.33 (978-0-8368-2759-0(7)) Stevens, Gareth Inc.

—The Weakness. l.t. ed. 2001. (Animorphs Ser.: No. 37). (Illus.). 129p. (J). (gr. 4 up). lib. bdg. 23.33 (978-0-8368-2770-5(8)) Stevens, Gareth Inc.

Appleton, Victor. Tom Swift & His Airship. l.t. ed. 2000. (Tom Swift Original Ser.: Vol. 3). 186p. pap. 12.99 (978-1-57646-360-4(5)) Quiet Vision Publishing.

JKL

—Tom Swift & His Motor Boat. l.t. ed. 2000. (Tom Swift Original Ser.: Vol. 2). 182p. pap. 12.99 (978-1-57646-357-4(5)) Quiet Vision Publishing.

—Tom Swift & His Motor Cycle. l.t. ed. 2000. (Tom Swift Original Ser.: Vol. 1). 180p. pap. 12.99 (978-1-57646-354-3(0)) Quiet Vision Publishing.

Arciero, Susan. Nantucket 1, 2, 3. Arciero, Susan, illus. l.t. ed. 2000. (Illus.). (J). (ps). 7.95 (978-0-9677548-2-6(8)) Pigtail Publishing.

Ardagh, Philip. Awful End. Roberts, David, illus. l.t. ed. 2002. 184p. (J). 16.95 (978-0-7540-7826-5(4) , Galaxy Children's Large Print) BBC Audiobooks America.

Ardis, Marcia M. Sing Alongs: Helping Children Learn to Read. Johnson, Linda, illus. l.t. ed. 1999. 96p. (J). (ps-2). pap. 9.95 (978-0-9667936-0-4(9) , 122) Literacy Links.

Aresty, Reecy. Getting into College & Paying for It: Solutions for High School & College Families Guaranteed to Cut the Cost! l.t. ed. 2003. Tr. of Sueno Americano: Como Ingresar a la Universidad Y Pagar Los Mas Bajos Costos!. (SPA., Illus.). 258p. (YA). per. 27.95 (978-0-9760251-1-5(6)) College Assistance, Inc.

Arlene, Sonday. The Sonday System - Let's Play Learn: Shapes & Numbers Book. Cindy, Breckman, ed. l.t. ed. 2004. (Illus.). 29p. (J). per. (978-1-891602-12-2(8)) Winsor Learning, Inc.

Armstrong, Helen. The Road to Somewhere. Horse, Harry, illus. l.t. ed. 2005. (J). pap. (978-0-7540-7827-2(2) , CLP 417) BBC Audio.

Armstrong, Jennifer. Shattered: Stories of Children & War. l.t. ed. 2004. 201p. (J). 22.95 (978-0-7862-6508-4(6)) Thorndike Pr.

Armstrong, William H. Sounder. Barkley, James, illus. l.t. ed. 1999. (LRS Large Print Cornerstone Ser.). 230p. (YA). (gr. 6-12). lib. bdg. 27.95 (978-1-58118-054-1(3) , 22768) LRS.

Arnold, Bruce E. 1st Steps for a Beginning Guitarist: Chords & Chord Progressions. l.t. ed. 2001. (ENG.). 52p. (J). spiral bd. 23.99 (978-1-890944-90-2(4)) Muse Eek Publishing Co.

Arois, Marcia M. Family Literacy: Easy Ways for Families to Read & Write Together. Johnson, Linda, illus. l.t. ed. 1999. 96p. (J). (ps-3). pap. 9.95 (978-0-9667936-1-1(7) , 123) Literacy Links.

Asato, Dennis. A Dolphin Day in Hawaii. Asato, Dennis, illus. l.t. ed. 1999. (Illus.). 50p. (J). (ps-1). 12.00 (978-0-9653971-8-6(1)) Anoai Pr.

Ashepak, Agnes. Butterfly. Nevak, Caroline, illus. l.t. ed. 1999. 8p. (J). (gr. k-3). pap. 14.50 (978-1-58084-058-3(2)) Lower Kuskokwim Schl. District.

—Caqelngataq. Nevak, Caroline, illus. l.t. ed. 1999. Tr. of Butterfly. (ESK.). 8p. (J). (gr. k-3). pap. 14.50 (978-1-58084-059-0(0)); pap. 14.50 (978-1-58084-106-1(6)) Lower Kuskokwim Schl. District.

—Haqalikitaq. Nevak, Caroline, illus. l.t. ed. 1999. Tr. of Butterfly. (ESK.). 8p. (J). (gr. k-3). pap. 14.50 (978-1-58084-132-0(5)); pap. 14.50 (978-1-58084-140-5(6)) Lower Kuskokwim Schl. District.

—Saqaliqitaaq. Nevak, Caroline, illus. l.t. ed. 1999. Tr. of Butterfly. (ESK.). 8p. (J). (gr. k-3). pap. 14.50 (978-1-58084-125-2(2)) Lower Kuskokwim Schl. District.

Asimov, Janet & Asimov, Isaac. Norby & the Court Jester. l.t. ed. 1999. 168p. 24.95 (978-0-7838-8610-7(1)) Thorndike Pr.

Asner, Anne-Marie. Kvetchy Boy. Asner, Anne-Marie, illus. l.t. ed. 2006. (Illus.). 32p. (J). per. 6.95 (978-0-9753629-3-8(3)) Matzah Ball Bks.

—Noshy Boy. Asner, Anne-Marie, illus. l.t. ed. 2004. (Illus.). 32p. (J). per. 6.95 (978-0-9753629-1-4(7)) Matzah Ball Bks.

—Shmutzy Girl. Asner, Anne-Marie, illus. l.t. ed. 2004. (Illus.). 32p. (J). per. 6.95 (978-0-9753629-0-7(9)) Matzah Ball Bks.

Atinsky, Steve. Tyler on Prime Time. l.t. ed. 2002. 218p. (J). 23.95 (978-0-7862-4709-7(6)) Thorndike Pr.

Atseriak, Liz, et al. At the Beach. Curtis, Katie, illus. l.t. ed. 1999. 8p. (J). (gr. k-3). pap. 6.00 (978-1-58084-050-7(7)) Lower Kuskokwim Schl. District.

—Ceniami. Curtis, Katie, illus. l.t. ed. 1999. Tr. of At the Beach. (ESK.). 8p. (J). (gr. k-3). pap. 6.00 (978-1-58084-116-0(3)) Lower Kuskokwim Schl. District.

—Higyami (At the Beach) Curtis, Katie, illus. l.t. ed. 1999. (ESK.). 8p. (J). (gr. k-3). pap. 6.00 (978-1-58084-134-4(1)) Lower Kuskokwim Schl. District.

—Imarpiim Ceniini (At the Beach) Curtis, Katie, illus. l.t. ed. 1999. (ESK.). 8p. (J). (gr. k-3). pap. 6.00 (978-1-58084-051-4(5)) Lower Kuskokwim Schl. District.

—Sigyami (At the Beach) Curtis, Katie, illus. l.t. ed. 1999. (ESK.). 8p. (J). (gr. k-3). pap. 6.00 (978-1-58084-127-6(9)) Lower Kuskokwim Schl. District.

—Sirrami (At the Beach) Curtis, Katie, illus. l.t. ed. 1999. (ESK.). 8p. (J). (gr. k-3). pap. 6.00 (978-1-58084-141-2(4)) Lower Kuskokwim Schl. District.

—Tagium Sinaani (at the Beach) Curtis, Katie, illus. l.t. ed. 1999. (ESK.). 8p. (J). (gr. k-3). pap. 6.00 (978-1-58084-121-4(X)) Lower Kuskokwim Schl. District.

Atwater-Rhodes, Amelia. Midnight Predator. l.t. ed. 2004. 195p. 20.95 (978-0-7862-6576-3(0)) Thorndike Pr.

Auxier, Bryan. Where Have All the Dragons Gone? Daniels, Regina, illus. l.t. ed. 2002. 32p. (J). (gr. 3-7). pap. 7.95 (978-0-9719144-0-7(0)) Where? Pr., Inc.

—Where Have All the Unicorns Gone? Daniels, Regina, illus. l.t. ed. 2003. 16p. (J). 7.95 (978-0-9719144-1-4(9)) Where? Pr., Inc.

Avery, Terry. Moon Rabbit Builds a Fine House. l.t. ed. 2000. (Illus.). 32p. (J). (ps-3). 17.95 (978-1-929115-00-6(8)) Azro Pr., Inc.

Avi. The Good Dog. l.t. ed. 2003. 176p. (J). 23.95 (978-0-7862-5600-6(1)) Thorndike Pr.

Axelrod, Mitchell. Little Billy & Baseball Bob. Campbell, Ron, illus. l.t. ed. 2002. 32p. (J). per. 5.95 (978-0-9710591-2-2(8)) Wynn Publishing, Inc.

Ayers, Linda. Tiger Goes Collecting. Hunt, Jane, illus. l.t. ed. 2004. 55p. (J). per. 7.95 (978-0-9760505-2-0(8)) Blue Thistle Pr.

Ayers, Samuel J. Buddy Holly: A Legacy of Music. l.t. ed. 1999. (Illus.). 32p. (J). (gr. 3-8). pap. 8.00 (978-0-9667681-1-4(6)) Hermosa Creations.

—Ella Iles: Early Texas Teacher. Ayers, Samuel J., illus. l.t. ed. 1999. (Illus.). 32p. (J). (gr. 2-6). 13.00 (978-0-9667681-0-7(8)) Hermosa Creations.

—Roscoe Wilson: Champion of the Law, Education & Community Service. l.t. ed. 2000. (Illus.). 32p. (J). (gr. 3-8). 14.00 (978-0-9667681-2-1(4)) Hermosa Creations.

Ayres, Katherine. Stealing South: A Story of the Underground Railroad. l.t. ed. 2002. 231p. (J). 22.95 (978-0-7862-4422-5(4)) Thorndike Pr.

Azean, Evon, Sr. Aataq Maktuq. Beaver, Mary Lou, illus. l.t. ed. 1999. Tr. of Father Gets Up. (ESK.). 12p. (J). (gr. k-3). pap. 6.00 (978-1-58084-145-0(7)) Lower Kuskokwim Schl. District.

—At'a Maktur (Father Gets Up) Beaver, Mary Lou, illus. l.t. ed. 1999. (ESK.). 12p. (J). (gr. k-3). pap. 6.00 (978-1-58084-146-7(5)) Lower Kuskokwim Schl. District.

—Father Gets Up. Beaver, Mary Lou, illus. l.t. ed. 1999. 12p. (J). (gr. k-3). pap. 6.00 (978-1-58084-144-3(9)) Lower Kuskokwim Schl. District.

—Pissuryugtua. Mute, Frank, Jr., illus. l.t. ed. 2000. 8p. (J). pap. 14.50 (978-1-58084-189-4(9)) Lower Kuskokwim Schl. District.

Azinger, Marla. The Seaweed Christmas Tree. Azinger, Marla, illus. l.t. ed. 2000. (Illus.). 34p. (J). per. 14.95 (978-1-932373-01-1(2)) Cedar Hill Publishing.

Azordegan, Kambiz. The Ant & the Honey: Andy the Ant. Sajem, Johnny, illus. abr. l.t. ed. 1998. (Tootee's Magical Stories Ser.: Vol. 2). 40p. (J). 9.95 (978-1-890571-26-9(1)) Positive Children's Programming Corp.

—The Bear's Den: Bear's Family. Sajem, Johnny, illus. abr. l.t. ed. 1998. (Tootee's Magical Stories Ser.: Vol. 5). 40p. (J). 9.95 (978-1-890571-29-0(6)) Positive Children's Programming Corp.

—The Brave Donkey & the Cowardly Lion: Donkey, Lion & Fox. Sajem, Johnny, illus. abr. l.t. ed. 1998. (Tootee's Magical Stories Ser.: Vol. 6). 40p. (J). 9.95 (978-1-890571-30-6(X)) Positive Children's Programming Corp.

—Dukunoo Island: Anancy the Spider. Sajem, Johnny, illus. abr. l.t. ed. 1998. (Tootee's Magical Stories Ser.: Vol. 3). 34p. (J). 9.95 (978-1-890571-27-6(X)) Positive Children's Programming Corp.

—Mr. Rain: The Grate Rain. Sajem, Johnny, illus. abr. l.t. ed. 1998. (Tootee's Magical Stories Ser.: Vol. 4). 40p. (J). 9.95 (978-1-890571-28-3(8)) Positive Children's Programming Corp.

Azzopardi, Jeannie. Maricio & the Magic Suitcase. l.t. ed. 2004. (Illus.). 93p. (J). per. 14.00 incl. cd-rom (978-0-9744391-3-6(4) , MAR-BKCD-1st, Once Upon A Time in a Classroom) Interactive Media Publishing.

Babbitt, Natalie. Tuck Everlasting. 2003. 152p. (J). 25.95 (978-0-7862-5181-0(6)) Thorndike Pr.

Babcock, Jerry. Children's Keepsake Educational Coloring Book, Bk. 1. Babcock, Jerry, illus. l.t. unabr. ed. 1998. (Illus.). 44p. (J). (gr. k-4). pap. 4.99 (978-1-892161-05-5(2)) Babcock Publishing Co.

Babineaux, Jim. Cody Cottontail Makes a Wise Choice! Babineaux, Jim, illus. l.t. ed. 2005. (Illus.). 18p. (J). (978-0-9769769-0-5(0)) ALCAPS, LLC.

Baker, Carin Greenberg. Pride of the Green Mountains. Rabinowitz, Sandy & Keiffer, Christa, illus. l.t. ed. 1999. (Treasured Horses Collection). 128p. (J). (gr. 4 up). lib. bdg. 23.33 (978-0-8368-2279-3(X)) Stevens, Gareth Inc.

Baker, Frances Shands. From Mountain Man to Millionaire: The Story of Colonel Robert Campbell, 1804-1879 & Other Heroes in St. Louis, Missouri. Kunstmann, Sue, ed. Baker, Frances Shands & Fifth Grade Students, illus. l.t. ed. 2001. 64p. (J). (gr. 8 up). pap. 16.99 (978-0-9674867-7-2(7)) Campbell Hse. Museum.

Baldwin, Christy. Remembering Wilma. Barnes, Sarah, illus. l.t. ed. 2005. 22p. (J). per. 15.00 (978-0-9765072-0-8(X)) Tribute Bks.

Bankston, John. Albert Einstein & the Theory of Relativity. l.t. ed. 2002. (Unlocking the Secrets of Science Ser.). (Illus.). 56p. (gr. 4-10). lib. bdg. 25.70 (978-1-58415-137-1(4)) Mitchell Lane Pubs., Inc.

—Alexander Fleming & the Story of Penicillin. l.t. ed. 2002. (Unlocking the Secrets of Science Ser.). (Illus.). 56p. (gr. 4-10). lib. bdg. 25.70 (978-1-58415-106-7(4)) Mitchell Lane Pubs., Inc.

—Alicia Keys. l.t. ed. 2002. (Real Life Reader Biography Ser.). (Illus.). 32p. (J). (gr. 3-8). lib. bdg. 15.95 (978-1-58415-133-3(1)) Mitchell Lane Pubs., Inc.

—Ben Stiller. l.t. ed. 2002. (Real-Life Reader Biography Ser.). (Illus.). 32p. (J). (gr. 3-8). lib. bdg. 24.95 (978-1-58415-132-6(3)) Mitchell Lane Pubs., Inc.

—Edward Teller & the Development of the Hydrogen Bomb. l.t. ed. 2002. (Unlocking the Secrets of Science Ser.). (Illus.). 56p. (gr. 4-10). lib. bdg. 25.70 (978-1-58415-108-1(0)) Mitchell Lane Pubs., Inc.

—Julia Stiles. l.t. ed. 2002. (Real-Life Reader Biography Ser.). (Illus.). 32p. (J). (gr. 3-8). lib. bdg. 24.95 (978-1-58415-130-2(7)) Mitchell Lane Pubs., Inc.

—Michael J. Fox. l.t. ed. 2002. (Real Life Reader Biography Ser.). (Illus.). 32p. (J). (gr. 3-8). lib. bdg. 24.95 (978-1-58415-128-9(5)) Mitchell Lane Pubs., Inc.

—Robert Goddard & the Liguid Rocket Engine. l.t. ed. 2002. (Unlocking the Secrets of Science Ser.). (Illus.). 56p. (gr. 4-10). lib. bdg. 17.95 (978-1-58415-107-4(2)) Mitchell Lane Pubs., Inc.

Barkan, Joanne. A Pup in King Arthur's Court. l.t. ed. 1999. (Adventures of Wishbone Ser.: No. 15). (Illus.). 164p. (J). (gr. 2-5). lib. bdg. 22.60 (978-0-8368-2593-0(4)) Stevens, Gareth Inc.

—A Tale of Two Sitters. l.t. ed. 1999. (Adventures of Wishbone Ser.: No. 9). (Illus.). 144p. (J). (gr. 4 up). lib. bdg. 22.60 (978-0-8368-2305-9(2)) Stevens, Gareth Inc.

Barlow, Galon L., Jr. The Adventures of Levi & Nathan at Bassett's Island. Guthrie, Adam, illus. l.t. ed. 1998. 78p. (gr. 6 up). pap. 7.95 (978-0-9666020-0-5(5) , 98-002) Farewell Pr.

—The Adventures of Levi & Nathan from the Cape of Cod to the Outer Banks. Guthrie, Adam C., illus. l.t. ed. 1998. (YA). (gr. 6 up). mass mkt. 7.95 (978-0-9666020-2-9(1)) Farewell Pr.

Barlow, Steve L. & Skidmore, Steve. Mad Myths: A Touch of Wind! Ross, Tony, illus. l.t. ed. 2000. 95p. (J). pap. (978-0-7540-6116-8(7) , CLP 310) BBC Audio.

Barr, Mabel. Hamster Huey & the Gooey Kablooie: The Renowned Hero's Most Famous Adventure. l.t. ed. 2004. (Illus.). 8p. (J). 6.95 (978-0-9749090-0-4(9) , 214) Hamster Huey Pr.

Barrie, J. M. Peter Pan. l.t. ed. 2003. (Perennial Bestsellers Ser.). 269p. (J). 29.95 (978-0-7862-5263-3(4)) Thorndike Pr.

Barry, Margaret S. The Witch & the Holiday Club. Birch, Linda, illus. l.t. ed. 1998. 126p. (J). pap. 16.95 (978-0-7540-6035-2(7) , Galaxy Children's Large Print) BBC Audiobooks America.

Bass, L. G. Sign of the Qin. l.t. ed. 2004. 513p. 23.95 (978-0-7862-6772-9(0) , Large Print Pr.) Thorndike Pr.

Bastedo, Jaya. A Winter Walk with Haley. Macintosh, Tessa, illus. Macintosh, Tessa, photos by. l.t. ed. 1999. 24p. (J). (ps-5). pap. (978-1-894303-06-4(7)) Raven Rock Publishing.

Batchlor, Larry G. Juneteenth Story Activity & Coloring Book: From African Slaves to African Americans. Goings, Kenneth & La Rue, Linda, eds. Walker, Felix C., illus. l.t. ed. 2000. 60p. (J). (gr. 4-7). pap. 10.00 (978-0-9701357-0-4(X)) Jubilee Day/Juneteenth Celebration.

Baud, Jane Scroggins. The Girl Who Wanted to be a Horse. Darr, Cynthia G., illus. l.t. ed. 2001. 32p. (J). (gr. k-6). 17.95 (978-1-929701-04-9(7)) Under the Green Umbrella.

Bauer, Elizabeth. The Happy Forest: Animal Adventures in the Forest. Bauer, Elizabeth, illus. l.t. ed. 2001. 130p. (J). per. incl. cd-rom (978-0-9630409-7-8(9)) Galaxy Publishing Hse.

Bauer, Joan. Hope Was Here. l.t. ed. 2001. (YA). (gr. 8-12). 22.95 (978-0-7862-3258-1(7)) Thorndike Pr.

—Rules of the Road. 2000. (YA). (978-0-606-20252-7(8)) Tandem Library Bks.

Bauer, Susan Wise. Story of the World, Vol. 1. l.t. ed. 2002. (Story of the World: Vol. 1). (Illus.). 334p. (J). (gr. 1-7). pap. 21.95 (978-0-9714129-0-3(1) , SOTW1) Peace Hill Pr.

Baugher, Kristina, illus. & text. Death Turns Allie's Family Upside Down. Baugher, Kristina, text. l.t. ed. 1999. 27p. (J). pap. 8.00 (978-0-9635975-2-6(3)) Caring People Pr.

Bauld, Jane Scoggins. Never, Ever Shake a Baby. Romain, Trevor, illus. l.t. ed. 1999. 32p. (J). (gr. k-6). pap. (978-0-9651123-1-4(4)) Allen, Evelyn W.

—The Story of MotherTree. l.t. ed. 2000. (J). 12.95 (978-1-929701-03-2(9)) Under the Green Umbrella.

—Voyage of the Third Seed. Darr, Cynthia G., illus. l.t. ed. 2000. 32p. (J). 17.95 (978-1-929701-02-5(0)) Under the Green Umbrella.

Bauld, Jane Scoggins & Hefner, Kim. 101 Things to Cook. l.t. ed. 2000. 125p. (J). (ps-3). pap. 8.95 (978-1-929701-01-8(2)) Under the Green Umbrella.

Baum, L. Frank. Dorothy & the Wizard of Oz. l.t. ed. 2004. (Large Print Ser.). lib. bdg. 25.00 (978-1-58287-769-3(6)) North Bks.

—The Enchanted Island of Yew. l.t. ed. 2004. (Large Print Ser.). 207p. 25.00 (978-1-58287-737-2(8)) North Bks.

—Glinda of Oz. l.t. ed. 2004. (Large Print Ser.). 210p. 25.00 (978-1-58287-740-2(8)) North Bks.

—The Lost Princess of Oz. l.t. ed. 2004. (Large Print Ser.). 241p. 25.00 (978-1-58287-739-6(4)) North Bks.

—The Magic of Oz. l.t. ed. 2004. (Large Print Ser.). lib. bdg. 25.00 (978-1-58287-775-4(0)) North Bks.

—The Marvelous Land of Oz. l.t. ed. 2004. (Large Print Ser.). lib. bdg. 25.00 (978-1-58287-768-6(8)) North Bks.

—Ozma of Oz. l.t. ed. 2004. (Large Print Ser.). 210p. 25.00 (978-1-58287-736-5(X)) North Bks.

—Ozma of Oz. l.t. ed. 2003. (Perennial Bestsellers Ser.). 288p. (J). 29.95 (978-0-7862-5888-8(8)) Thorndike Pr.

—The Patchwork Girl of Oz. Neill, John R., illus. l.t. ed. 2005. (Thorndike Press Large Print Classics Ser.).Tr. of 220. 476p. (J). 20.95 (978-0-7862-8208-1(8)) Thorndike Pr.

—The Patchwork Girl of OZ. l.t. ed. 2004. (Large Print Ser.). lib. bdg. 25.00 (978-1-58287-771-6(8)) North Bks.

—Rinkitink in Oz. l.t. ed. 2004. (Large Print Ser.). lib. bdg. 25.00 (978-1-58287-774-7(2)) North Bks.

—The Road to Oz. l.t. ed. 2004. (Large Print Ser.). lib. bdg. 25.00 (978-1-58287-770-9(X)) North Bks.

—The Scarecrow of Oz. l.t. ed. 2004. (Large Print Ser.). lib. bdg. 25.00 (978-1-58287-773-0(4)) North Bks.

—Sky Island. l.t. ed. 2004. (Large Print Ser.). lib. bdg. 25.00 (978-1-58287-792-1(0)) North Bks.

—The Wonderful Wizard of Oz. l.t. unabr. ed. 2002. (Dover Large Print Classics Ser.). (Illus.). 256p. pap. 9.95 (978-0-486-42248-0(8)) Dover Pubns., Inc.

Beardsley, Martyn. Sir Gadabout Goes Overboard. l.t. ed. 2005. (J). pap. (978-1-4056-6010-5(4)) BBC Audio.

Beaton, Clare, illus. Animals: Los Animales. l.t. ed. 1998. (English-Spanish Bilingual First Bks.). (ENG & SPA.). 24p. (J). (ps up). lib. bdg. 14.45 (978-1-56674-247-4(1)) Forest Hse. Publishing Co., Inc.

—Clothes: La Ropa. l.t. ed. 1998. (English-Spanish Bilingual First Bks.). (ENG & SPA.). 24p. (J). (ps up). lib. bdg. 14.45 (978-1-56674-248-1(X)) Forest Hse. Publishing Co., Inc.

—Colors: Los Colores. l.t. ed. 1998. (English-Spanish Bilingual First Bks.). (ENG & SPA.). 24p. (J). (ps up). lib. bdg. 14.45 (978-1-56674-249-8(8)) Forest Hse. Publishing Co., Inc.

—Family: La Familia. l.t. ed. 1998. (English-Spanish Bilingual First Bks.). (ENG & SPA.). 24p. (J). (ps up). lib. bdg. 14.45 (978-1-56674-250-4(1)) Forest Hse. Publishing Co., Inc.

—Let's Pretend. l.t. ed. 1998. (Craft & Project Books for Children). 48p. (J). (ps-4). lib. bdg. 17.95 (978-1-56674-243-6(9)) Forest Hse. Publishing Co., Inc.

—Numbers/Los Numeros. l.t. ed. 1998. (English-Spanish Bilingual First Bks.). (ENG & SPA.). 24p. (J). (ps up). lib. bdg. 14.45 (978-1-56674-251-1(X)) Forest Hse. Publishing Co., Inc.

—Opposites: Los Contrarios. l.t. ed. 1998. (English-Spanish Bilingual First Bks.). (ENG & SPA.). 24p. (J). (ps up). lib. bdg. 14.45 (978-1-56674-252-8(8)) Forest Hse. Publishing Co., Inc.

Beck, Randy. Teen Quest. l.t. ed. 2004. 80p. (YA). per. 12.95 (978-1-59196-535-0(7)) Instantpublisher.com.

Beckler, Bruce. My Daddy Is A Deputy Sheriff. Finney, Simone, illus. l.t. ed. 2004. 14p. (J). per. 5.59 (978-0-9745210-4-6(3)) Myers Publishing Co.

—My Daddy Is A Fire Fighter: My Daddy Is A Fireman. Peek, Jeannette, illus. l.t. ed. 2004. 16p. (J). 5.59 (978-0-9745210-8-4(6)) Myers Publishing Co.

—My Daddy Is a Police Officer: My Daddy Wears a Star. Finney, Simone, illus. l.t. ed. 2004. 14p. (J). per. 5.59 (978-0-9745210-3-9(5)) Myers Publishing Co.

—My Daddy Is A Police Officer: Wears A Badge, 8 bks. Finney, Simone, illus. l.t. ed. 2004. 14p. (J). per. 5.59 (978-0-9745210-2-2(7)) Myers Publishing Co.

—My Mommy Is A Deputy Sheriff. Finney, Simone, illus. l.t. ed. 2004. 14p. (J). 5.59 (978-0-9745210-7-7(8)) Myers Publishing Co.

—My Mommy Is A Nurse. Peek, Jeannette, illus. l.t. ed. 2004. 20p. (J). 5.59 (978-0-9745210-9-1(4)) Myers Publishing Co.

—My Mommy Is A Police Officer: My Mommy Wears A Badge. Finney, Simone, illus. l.t. ed. 2004. 14p. (J). per. 5.59 (978-0-9745210-5-3(1)) Myers Publishing Co.

—My Mommy Is A Police Officer: My Mommy Wears A Star. Finney, Simone, illus. l.t. ed. 2004. 14p. (J). 5.59 (978-0-9745210-6-0(X)) Myers Publishing Co.

—The Secret Tunnels of Spring Mountain. l.t. ed. 2004. (Illus.). 220p. (J). per. 13.99 (978-0-9745210-0-8(0)) Myers Publishing Co.

—The Secrets of the Green Mansion. l.t. ed. 2004. (Illus.). 240p. (J). per. 13.99 (978-0-9745210-1-5(9)) Myers Publishing Co.

Becoming a Girl of Faith: According to God's Word. l.t. ed. 2004. 90p. (YA). 12.95 (978-0-9764304-2-1(8)) Girls of Faith.

Bee Smarter Starter Kit Grade 3. l.t. ed. 2002. (Illus.). 72p. (J). per. 14.99 (978-0-9717643-9-2(5) , Bee Smarter Study Kits) Verde Publishing, Inc.

Beere, Peter. At Gehenna's Door. l.t. ed. 2000. (Illus.). 304p. 18.99 (978-0-7089-9500-6(4)) Ulverscroft Large Print Bks. GBR. *Dist:* Ulverscroft Large Print Bks., Ltd.

Beeson, Lea Ann. A Leopard Is More Than His Spots. Popovich, Richard E., ed. Rockfield, Darryl, illus. l.t. ed. 2005. 51p. (J). lib. bdg. 19.95 (978-0-9604876-1-5(1)) REP Pubs.

Beets, Beans & Turnip Greens. l.t. ed. 2001. 19p. (978-1-893595-20-0(X)) Four Seasons Bks., Inc.

Beken, Robert A. Tijuana River Estuary & Border Field State Park: Land of diversity, land of Hope. l.t. ed. 2004. (Illus.). 260p. spiral bd. 34.95 (978-0-9761726-0-4(7)) Tritium Pr.

Belbin, David. Point Crime: Dying for You. l.t. ed. 2000. 217p. (J). pap. (978-0-7540-6119-9(1) , CLP 311) BBC Audio.

Belinsky, Ruth. We Are a Family. Hill, Linda W., ed. Harris, Rhonda, illus. l.t. ed. 2001. 30p. (J). (gr. k-5). pap. 9.95 (978-1-892614-37-5(5)) Briarwood Pubns.

Bell, N. Wayne. Childrens' Economics: A Book on Money & Finance. l.t. ed. 2004. (Illus.). 32p. (J). per. (978-0-9729753-5-3(7)) Really Big Coloring Bks., Inc.

—The Really Big Book of Zoo Animals. l.t. ed. 2004. (Illus.). 32p. (J). per. (978-0-9729753-6-0(5)) Really Big Coloring Bks., Inc.

Bell, Nasherrall, creator. Child Safety at Home, School & Play. l.t. ed. 2004. (Illus.). 32p. (J). pap. (978-0-9729753-3-9(0)) Really Big Coloring Bks., Inc.

Bell, William. Zack. l.t. ed. 2000. (LRS Large Print Cornerstone Ser.). 256p. (YA). (gr. 5-12). lib. bdg. 28.95 (978-1-58118-072-5(1) , 23656) LRS.

Benevenia, Rose. Dolly & Babe. Benevenia, Rose, illus. l.t. ed. 2004. (Illus.). 9p. (J). (gr. k-2). pap. 9.00 (978-0-9729044-0-7(9)) Cabbage Patch Pr.

Bennett, Cherie. Life in the Fat Lane. l.t. ed. 2000. 351p. (YA). (gr. 8-12). 21.95 (978-0-7862-2887-4(3)) Thorndike Pr.

Bennett, Jill. Playing Dead. l.t. ed. 2005. 320p. (J). pap. (978-0-7540-6138-0(8) , CLP 331) BBC Audio.

Benton, Imogene. Boxes. Berlin, James, tr. Strum, Beth & Brunk, Cara, illus. l.t. ed. 2001. 8p. (J). pap. 17.00 (978-1-58084-178-8(3)) Lower Kuskokwim Schl. District.

—Yaassit. Berlin, James, tr. Strum, Beth & Brunk, Cara, illus. l.t. ed. 2001. 8p. (J). pap. 17.00 (978-1-58084-179-5(1)) Lower Kuskokwim Schl. District.

—Yaassit. Kiokun, Dorothy & Berlin, James, trs. Strum, Beth & Brunk, Cara, illus. l.t. ed. 2001. 12p. (J). pap. 17.00 (978-1-58084-180-1(5)) Lower Kuskokwim Schl. District.

Berenstain, Stan & Berenstain, Jan. The Berenstain Bears & the Missing Watermelon Money. l.t. ed. 2001. (Berenstain Bears Ser.). (Illus.). 48p. (J). (gr. 1-3). pap. 3.99 (978-0-679-89230-4(3) , Random Hse. Bks. for Young Readers) Random Hse. Children's Bks.

—The Berenstain Bears' Easter Surprise. l.t. ed. 1998. (Berenstain Bears Ser.). (Illus.). 48p. (J). (ps-3). pap. 10.95 (978-0-590-94730-5(3)) Scholastic, Inc.

—The Berenstain Bears Play Ball. l.t. ed. 1998. (Berenstain Bears Ser.). (Illus.). 48p. (J). (ps-3). pap. 10.95 (978-0-590-94732-9(X)) Scholastic, Inc.

Berg, Dick. Padunkapoo: The Hawaiian Kangaroo. Berg, Gary, ed. l.t. ed. 2005. (Illus.). 28p. (J). per. 6.99 (978-0-9769985-1-8(3)) Grace Publishing.

Berggren, Jeff. Chicken Cherries. Hansen, Tammy A., ed. Berggren, Jeff, illus. l.t. ed. 2005. (Illus.). 32p. (J). per. 14.95 (978-0-9755033-0-0(8)) Deep Dish Design.

Bergsma, Jody Lynn. The Little Wizard. Bergsma, Jody Lynn, illus. l.t. ed. 2000. (Illus.). 32p. (J). (ps-7). 15.95 (978-0-935699-19-7(8)) Illumination Arts Publishing Co., Inc.

Beriot, Louis. L' Enfant Secret. l.t. ed. 2002. (French Ser.). (FRE., Illus.). 542p. 30.99 (978-2-84011-464-2(X)) Ulverscroft Large Print Bks. GBR. *Dist:* Ulverscroft Large Print Bks., Ltd.

Berlin, James, Sr. Cup'igtat Laanguarrutenka. Berlin, James & Nevak, Caroline, illus. l.t. ed. 1999. Tr. of My Yup'ik Eskimo Toys. (ESK.). 12p. (J). (gr. k-3). pap. 17.00 (978-1-58084-112-2(0)) Lower Kuskokwim Schl. District.

—My Yupik Eskimo Toys. Berlin, James & Nevak, Caroline, illus. l.t. ed. 1999. 12p. (J). (gr. k-3). pap. 17.00 (978-1-58084-074-3(4)) Lower Kuskokwim Schl. District.

—Yugtaat Naanguat. Berlin, James & Nevak, Caroline, illus. l.t. ed. 1999. Tr. of My Yup'ik Eskimo Toys. (ESK.). 12p. (J). (gr. k-3). pap. 17.00 (978-1-58084-075-0(2)) Lower Kuskokwim Schl. District.

Bernal, Mitchell. Skelanimals: Dead Animals Need Love Too, Bernal, Mitchell, illus. l.t. ed. 2005. (Illus.). 22p. (J). per. 12.95 (978-0-9766621-0-5(8) , 818 554-8965) Kreations.

Bernardini, Robert. The Crystal & the Keyhole: Santa's Magic Secret. Donato, Janice, illus. l.t. ed. 2001. 34p. (J). (ps-9). per. 14.95 (978-0-9703269-1-1(2)) P R I Publishing.

—Safety First Please & It Won't Make You Sneeze. Donato, Janice, illus. l.t. ed. 2001. 32p. (J). (ps-6). per. 14.95 (978-0-9703269-0-4(4) , 010) P R I Publishing.

Bernstein, Susan H. N. E. Pominonous Epstein & Change. l.t. ed. 2003. (E. Pominonous Epstein Ser.: No. 3). (Illus.). 20p. (Orig.). (J). (gr. k-3). pap. 8.95 (978-0-9706596-2-0(8)) Bernstein, Susan.

Berryhill, Judy. Chuckle & Giggle Vol. 2: Exploring the Natchez Trace. l.t. ed. 1998. (Illus.). 30p. (J). (ps-4). 14.00 (978-0-9653872-4-8(0)) Hartford Pubns.

Bersson, Robert & Shoup, Dolores. Stripes & Stars. Bersson, Robert & Trobaugh, Scott, illus. l.t. ed. 2003. 40p. (J). (gr. 1-4). per. 16.95 (978-0-9740585-0-4(5)) Legacy Group Productions, LLC.

Bevan, Jan Atchley. Corky the Bathtub Who Couldn't Swallow. Yovanovic, Christine, illus. l.t. ed. 2001. 48p. (J). pap. 12.95 (978-0-9653895-4-9(5)) Bookmark Publishing.

—Zachary Cooks up Some Fun. Garfinkel, Dana Kleiman, illus. l.t. ed. 2004. 32p. (J). 15.95 (978-0-9717641-6-3(6)) Ocean Publishing.

Bickel, Karla. The Animals' Debate. Bickel, Karla, illus. l.t. ed. 2004. (Illus.). 16p. (J). (ps-6). pap. 5.00 (978-1-891452-16-1(9) , 10) Heart Arbor Bks.

—Easter Lights. Bickel, Karla, illus. l.t. ed. 2004. (Illus.). 16p. (J). (ps-6). pap. 5.00 (978-1-891452-14-7(2) , 7) Heart Arbor Bks.

—Fishnet Valentine. Bickel, Karla, illus. l.t. ed. 2004. (Illus.). 16p. (J). (ps-5). pap. 5.00 (978-1-891452-13-0(4) , 4) Heart Arbor Bks.

—Handmade Necklace. Bickel, Karla, illus. l.t. ed. 2004. (Illus.). 16p. (J). (ps-6). pap. 5.00 (978-1-891452-11-6(8) , 1) Heart Arbor Bks.

—Heart Petals on the Hearth: A Collection of Children's Stories. Bickel, Karla, illus. 2004. (Illus.). 64p. (J). (ps-6). 20.00 (978-1-891452-00-0(2)) Heart Arbor Bks.

—The Kite Who Was Afraid to Fly. Bickel, Karla, illus. l.t. ed. 2004. (Illus.). 16p. (J). (ps-6). pap. 5.00 (978-1-891452-08-6(8) , 6) Heart Arbor Bks.

—Lilac Rose: A Flower's Lifetime. Bickel, Karla, illus. l.t. ed. 2004. (Illus.). 16p. (J). (ps-6). pap. 5.00 (978-1-891452-10-9(X) , 8) Heart Arbor Bks.

—The Reading Machine. Bickel, Karla, illus. l.t. ed. 2004. (Illus.). 16p. (J). (ps-6). pap. 5.00 (978-1-891452-15-4(0) , 9) Heart Arbor Bks.

—Surprise Christmas Birthday Party. Bickel, Karla, illus. l.t. ed. 2004. (Illus.). 16p. (J). (ps-6). pap. 5.00 (978-1-891452-12-3(6) , 3) Heart Arbor Bks.

—Teacher's Remarkable Secret. Bickel, Karla, illus. l.t. ed. 2004. (Illus.). 16p. (J). (ps-6). pap. 5.00 (978-1-891452-09-3(6) , 2) Heart Arbor Bks.

Bielma, Sherry. Rusty. Bielma, Sherry, illus. l.t. ed. 2002. (Illus.). 30p. (J). (ps-3). pap. 9.95 (978-1-892614-42-1(1) , 43) Briarwood Pubns.

Bijan, Nancy N. Let's Celebrate! Bijan, Nancy N., illus. l.t. ed. 1998. (Second Ser.). (Illus.). 22p. (J). (ps-6). pap. 6.95 (978-1-880710-19-7(6)) Monterey Pacific Pubs.

Billingsley, Franny. The Folk Keeper. l.t. ed. 2000. 224p. (YA). (gr. 5-9). 20.95 (978-0-7862-2461-6(4)) Thorndike Pr.

—Well Wished. l.t. ed. 2001. (Illus.). 197p. (J). (gr. 4-7). 21.95 (978-0-7862-3106-5(8)) Thorndike Pr.

Billiot, Wendy Wilson. Before the Saltwater Came. l.t. ed. 2005. (Illus.). 32p. (J). 19.95 (978-0-9762592-0-6(6)) Billiot, Wendy Wilson.

Billy, Molly L., et al. Inuqguaq. Sparck, Carole C., illus. l.t. ed. 2000. Tr. of Small Doll. (ESK.). 8p. (J). pap. 6.00 (978-1-58084-210-5(0)) Lower Kuskokwim Schl. District.

—A Small Doll. Sparck, Carole C., illus. l.t. ed. 2000. 8p. (J). (gr. k-3). pap. 6.00 (978-1-58084-209-9(7)) Lower Kuskokwim Schl. District.

—A Small Doll (Cup'ik) Sparck, Carole C., illus. l.t. ed. 2000. (ESK.). 8p. (J). (gr. k-3). pap. 6.00 (978-1-58084-211-2(9)) Lower Kuskokwim Schl. District.

Bingley, Margaret. A Dramatic Death. l.t. ed. 1998. 294p. (J). pap. 16.95 (978-0-7540-6019-2(5) , Galaxy Children's Large Print) BBC Audiobooks America.

Black, Jessica L. Dinosaurs Were We. Linke, Don, Jr., illus. l.t. ed. 2001. (Little Bks.). 8p. (J). (ps-1). pap. 10.95 (978-1-57332-188-4(5)); pap. 10.95 (978-1-57332-187-7(7)) HighReach Learning, Inc.

—I Like to Eat. Gray, Stacy A., illus. l.t. ed. 2001. (Cuddle Bks.). 7p. (J). (ps-1). pap. 10.95 (978-1-57332-211-9(3)) HighReach Learning, Inc.

—Just Imagine. Linke, Don, Jr., illus. l.t. ed. 2000. (Cuddle Bks.). 7p. (J). (ps-1). pap. 10.95 (978-1-57332-181-5(8)) HighReach Learning, Inc.

—My Toys. Bicking, Judith, illus. l.t. ed. 2001. (Cuddle Bks.). (J). (ps-1). pap. 10.95 (978-1-57332-219-5(9)) HighReach Learning, Inc.

—Teamwork. l.t. ed. 2003. (HRL Big Book Ser.). (Illus.). 8p. (Orig.). (J). (ps-k). pap. 10.95 (978-1-57332-261-4(X)) HighReach Learning, Inc.

—Teamwork. Crowell, Knox, illus. l.t. ed. 2003. (HRL Little Book Ser.). 8p. (Orig.). (J). (ps-k). pap. 10.95 (978-1-57332-262-1(8)) HighReach Learning, Inc.

Blackburn, C. Edward. The Stories of Christmas: As Told by a Little Lamb. Bishop, Megan, illus. l.t. ed. 2005. 24p. (J). 9.95 (978-0-9727440-3-4(7)) Redline Bks.

Blackman, Malorie. Dangerous Reality. l.t. ed. 2000. (Illus.). 208p. 18.99 (978-0-7089-9531-0(4)) Ulverscroft Large Print Bks. GBR. *Dist:* Ulverscroft Large Print Bks., Ltd.

—Whizziwig. Lee, Stephen, illus. l.t. ed. 1998. 120p. (J). pap. (978-0-7540-6026-0(8) , CLP 227) BBC Audio.

—Whizziwig Returns. l.t. ed. 2005. (Illus.). 160p. (J). pap. (978-0-7540-6128-1(0) , CLP 319) BBC Audio.

—Whizziwig Returns. unabr. l.t. ed. 2003. (Read-Along Ser.). 160p. (J). 24.95 incl. audio (978-0-7540-6234-9(1) , RA035, Galaxy Children's Large Print) BBC Audiobooks America.

Blackwood, Gary L. Spooky Spectres. 1999. (Secrets of the Unexplained Ser.). (Illus.). 80p. (J). (gr. 5-9). lib. bdg. 29.93 (978-0-7614-0746-1(4) , Benchmark Bks.) Cavendish, Marshall Corp.

Blair, Robert. Power-Glide Spanish Children's Course Upgrade, 2 bks. l.t. ed. 2001. (Illus.). 204p. (J). pap. 59.95 incl. audio compact disk (978-1-58204-210-7(1)) Power-Glide Foreign Language Courses.

Blair, Robert W. Power-Glide German Lower Elementary, 3 vols. l.t. ed. 2002. (Illus.). 355p. (J). pap. 119.95 incl. cd-rom, audio compact disk (978-1-58204-221-3(7)) Power-Glide Foreign Language Courses.

—Power-Glide Latin Lower Elementary, 2 vols. l.t. ed. (Illus.). 2002. 135p. (J). pap. 79.95 (978-1-58204-222-0(5)); 2000. 291p. (YA). pap. 149.95 incl. audio compact disk (978-1-58204-209-1(8)) Power-Glide Foreign Language Courses.

—Power-Glide Spanish Children's Course Workbook Upgrade, 2 bks. rev. ed. 2001. (SPA., Illus.). 204p. (J). pap., wbk. ed. 29.95 (978-1-58204-223-7(3)) Power-Glide Foreign Language Courses.

—Power-Glide Spanish Ultimate Adventure Course, 2. l.t. ed. 2002. (Illus.). 375p. (YA). pap. 149.95 incl. cd-rom, audio compact disk (978-1-58204-200-8(4)) Power-Glide Foreign Language Courses.

Bland, Caleb & Streit, Wendy. Skarskantuana. Bland, Caleb, illus. l.t. ed. 2002. (Great Lakes Ser.: Bk. 1). (Illus.). 26p. (YA). (gr. 3-9). spiral bd. 21.95 (978-0-9720790-0-6(9)) o-ho-lee-ab Publishing.

Bloess, Herman E., Jr. Winter Adventures of Danny Deermouse & Friends. Martinez, Mike Louis, illus. l.t. ed. 2001. 86p. (J). per. 17.95 (978-0-9716744-0-0(X)) Bloess, Herman E.

Blume, Judy. Are You There God? It's Me, Margaret. l.t. ed. 2002. (LRS Large Print Cornerstone Ser.). (J). lib. bdg. 28.95 (978-1-58118-088-6(8) , 24873) LRS.

—Superfudge. l.t. ed. 2000. (Fudge Ser.). 216p. (YA). (gr. 5-10). lib. bdg. 28.95 (978-1-58118-061-9(6) , 23475) LRS.

Blyton, Enid. Five Are Together Again. l.t. ed. 2000. 255p. (J). pap. (978-0-7540-6113-7(2) , CLP 308) BBC Audio.

—Five Go to Demon's Rocks. l.t. ed. 1999. (Illus.). 284p. (J). pap. (978-0-7540-6082-6(9) , CLP 281) BBC Audio.

—Five Have a Mystery to Solve. l.t. ed. 2000. (Famous Five Adventure Ser.). (Illus.). 263p. (J). pap. (978-0-7540-6094-9(2) , CLP 293) BBC Audio.

—Five on a Secret Trail. l.t. ed. 1998. (Illus.). 240p. (J). pap. 16.95 (978-0-7540-6024-6(1) , Galaxy Children's Large Print) BBC Audiobooks America.

—Secret Seven. l.t. ed. 2000. (Illus.). 121p. (J). pap. 16.95 (978-0-7540-6098-7(5) , Galaxy Children's Large Print) BBC Audiobooks America.

—Secret Seven Adventure. l.t. ed. 1998. (Illus.). 117p. (J). pap. (978-0-7540-6015-4(2) , CLP 218) BBC Audio.

—Secret Seven Fireworks. l.t. ed. 2000. 154p. (J). pap. (978-0-7540-6117-5(5) , CLP 312) BBC Audio.

—Secret Seven on the Trail. l.t. ed. 2005. 144p. (J). pap. (978-0-7540-7818-0(3) , CLP 408) BBC Audio.

—Well Done, Secret Seven. l.t. ed. 1998. (Illus.). 104p. (J). pap. 16.95 (978-0-7540-6027-7(6) , Galaxy Children's Large Print) BBC Audiobooks America.

Bock, Suzanne, illus. Meet the Angels, l.t. ed. 2004. 10p. (J). bds. 12.99 (978-0-9758709-4-5(7) , 13401) Journey Stone Creations, LLC.

Bograd, Larry & Hubbard, Coleen. Colorado Summer. Rabinowitz, Sandy & Keiffer, Christa, illus. l.t. ed. 1999. (Treasured Horses Collection). 128p. (J). (gr. 4 up). lib. bdg. 23.33 (978-0-8368-2277-9(3)) Stevens, Gareth Inc.

Boldt, Mark. Awareness Is Doing Something. l.t. ed. 1998. (U-Do Book Ser.). (Illus.). 32p. (J). (gr. k-8). pap. (978-0-9662556-2-1(3) , U-DO 03) Boldt.Entertainment.

—CC & the Cool Rule! l.t. ed. 2000. (U-Do Book Ser.). (Illus.). 32p. (J). (gr. k-8). (978-0-9662556-5-2(8) , U-Do, 06) Boldt.Entertainment.

—The Force B with U. l.t. ed. 1998. (U-Do Book Ser.). (Illus.). 92p. (J). (gr. k-8). pap. (978-0-9662556-3-8(1)) Boldt.Entertainment.

—It's a MADD House Here. l.t. ed. 1998. (U-Do Book Ser.). (Illus.). 24p. (J). (gr. k-6). pap. (978-0-9662556-1-4(5) , U-DO, 02) Boldt.Entertainment.

—Morning Matters. Boldt, Mark, ed. l.t. ed. 1999. (U-Do Book Ser.). (Illus.). 24p. (Orig.). (J). (gr. k-6). pap. (978-0-9662556-4-5(X) , U-DO, 05) Boldt.Entertainment.

Bolme, Edward Sarah. Baby Bible Board Books Collection No. 1: Stories of Jesus, 4 vols. Gillette, Tim, illus. l.t. ed. 2003. 20p. (J). bds. 23.99 (978-0-9725546-4-0(5)) CREST Pubns.

—Jesus Feeds the People. Gillette, Tim, illus. l.t. ed. 2003. 20p. (J). bds. 6.99 (978-0-9725546-0-2(2)) CREST Pubns.

—Jesus Heals a Little Girl. Gillette, Tim, illus. l.t. ed. 2003. 20p. (J). bds. 6.99 (978-0-9725546-1-9(0)) CREST Pubns.

—Jesus Helps a Blind Man. Gillette, Tim, illus. l.t. ed. 2003. 20p. (J). bds. 6.99 (978-0-9725546-2-6(9)) CREST Pubns.

—Jesus Stops a Storm. Gillette, Tim, illus. l.t. ed. 2003. 20p. (J). bds. 6.99 (978-0-9725546-3-3(7)) CREST Pubns.

Bond, Michael. The Tales of Olga da Polga. 2004. (J). 24.95 incl. audio (978-0-7540-6268-4(6) , Chivers Children's Audio Bks.) BBC Audiobooks America.

Boone, Melvin, Jr. JD Mc Doil What's up with Oil. l.t. ed. 2003. (Illus.). 32p. (J). 19.95 (978-0-9741750-0-3(5)) Never Stop Reading Never Stop Learning.

Booth-Cartwright, Karan. A Helping Hand: A Book of Short Stories for Children. l.t. ed. 2001. (Illus.). 65p. (J). (gr. k-8). pap. 12.95 (978-1-929819-50-8(1) , 01950) A+ Bk. Publishing.

Booth, Reed. Confessions of the Killer Bee Guy, 2nd l.t. ed. 2002. (Illus.). 84p. spiral bd. 20.00 (978-0-9722462-0-0(7)) Reed's Apiary.

Boritzer, Etan. What Is Right? l.t. ed. 2004. (What Is? Ser.). (Illus.). 32p. 6.95 (978-0-9762743-0-8(2)); 14.95 (978-0-9762743-1-5(0)) Lane, Veronica Bks.

Borntrager, Mary Christner. Andy. l.t. ed. 2002. 161p. 25.95 (978-0-7862-4029-6(6)) Thomson Gale.

—Daniel. l.t. ed. 2000. (Christian Fiction Ser.). 191p. 23.95 (978-0-7862-2859-1(8)) Thorndike Pr.

—Ellie. l.t. ed. 2001. (Christian Fiction Ser.). 208p. 23.95 (978-0-7862-3383-0(4)) Thorndike Pr.

—Mandy Bk. 9: Ellie's People. l.t. ed. 2002. (Christian Fiction Ser.). 25.95 (978-0-7862-4539-0(5)) Thorndike Pr.

—Polly. l.t. ed. 2002. 165p. (J). 25.95 (978-0-7862-4030-2(X)) Thomson Gale.

—Rachel. l.t. ed. 2001. (Thorndike Press Large Print Christian Fiction Ser.). 175p. (J). 23.95 (978-0-7862-3595-7(0)) Thorndike Pr.

—Rebecca. l.t. ed. 2001. (Thorndike Christian Fiction Ser.). 245p. 24.95 (978-0-7862-3252-9(8)) Thorndike Pr.

—Sarah. l.t. ed. 2002. (Christian Fiction Ser.). 177p. 25.95 (978-0-7862-4526-0(3)) Thorndike Pr.

Botts, Mary L., illus. Taylor's Halloween. l.t. ed. 1999. 16p. (J). (gr. k-6). pap. 3.99 (978-0-9668891-1-6(8)) Teach My Children Pubns.

Boueri, Marijean. Lebanon 1-2-3: A Counting Book in Three Languages. Badaji, Mona Trade, illus. 2005. (ENG, ARA & FRE.). 32p. (J). 16.95 (978-1-933002-03-3(4)) PublishingWorks.

Bouton, Warren Hussey. The Ghost of Ichabod Paddack: A Spooky Tale from Nantucket. Locke, Barbara K., illus. l.t. ed. 2002. 86p. (J). per. 5.95 (978-0-9700555-2-1(8)) Hither Creek Pr.

Bowen, Mary & Ruth, Monty. Estar a Salvo Durante un Terremoto y Otras Emergencias. Jepsen, Mark, illus. Reyes, Rico J., photos by. l.t. ed. 2000. (SPA.). 96p. (J). (gr. 4-7). 28.95 (978-0-9702765-1-3(6)) Global Vision, LLC.

Bowen, Mary, et al. To Be Safe During an Earthquake & Other Emergencies: With Lucy & Her Emergency Buddies. Jepsen, Ricki & Jepsen, Mark, illus. Reyes, Rico J., photos by. deluxe l.t. ed. 2000. (To Be Safe Ser.: Vol. 1). 9696p. (J). (ps-3). 28.95 (978-0-9702765-0-6(8)) Global Vision, LLC.

Bower, Gary. Wyatt's Wagon: Including Others. Velker, Kay, ed. Bower, Jan, illus. l.t. ed. 2001. (Thinking of Others: Vol. 2). 32p. (J). lib. bdg. 16.95 (978-0-9704621-1-4(5)) Storybook Meadow Publishing.

Bowler, Tim. River Boy. l.t. ed. 2001. 190p. (J). 22.95 (978-0-7862-3507-0(1)) Thorndike Pr.

Boye, B. D. Easy As 1, 2, 3. Boye, B. D., illus. l.t. ed. 2005. (Illus.). 22p. (J). per. 4.99 (978-0-9768078-0-3(7)) Innerchild Publishing, Inc.

—The Look Book. Boye, B. D., illus. l.t. ed. 2004. (Illus.). 20p. (J). per. 4.99 (978-0-9768078-1-0(5) , 100001) Innerchild Publishing, Inc.

—Our New Home. Boye, B. D., illus. l.t. ed. 2005. (Illus.). 18p. (J). per. 4.99 (978-0-9768078-2-7(3)) Innerchild Publishing, Inc.

Boyles, Peggy Palo. Realidades: Level 1, 2 vols. l.t. ed. 2004. 564p. (YA). (gr. 9-12). 282.00 (978-0-13-101687-3(3)) Prentice Hall Pr.

—Realidades: Level A. l.t. ed. 2004. (SPA.). 322p. (YA). (gr. 6-8). 161.00 (978-0-13-035966-7(1)) Prentice Hall Pr.

—Realidades: Level B, 2 vols. l.t. ed. 2004. (SPA.). 416p. (YA). (gr. 6-8). 208.00 (978-0-13-035967-4(X)) Prentice Hall Pr.

—Realidades Vol. 2: Level 2, 2 vols. l.t. ed. 2004. (SPA.). 508p. (YA). (gr. 9-12). 254.00 (978-0-13-035951-3(3)) Prentice Hall Pr.

Boyles, Peggy Palo, et al. Realidades Vol. 3: Level 3, 2 vols. l.t. ed. 2004. (SPA.). 614p. (YA). (gr. 9-12). 307.00 (978-0-13-035968-1(8)) Prentice Hall Pr.

Bradley, Kimberly Brubaker. Weaver's Daughter. l.t. ed. 2002. 173p. (J). 21.95 (978-0-7862-3763-0(5)) Thomson Gale.

Brady, Bill. A Charm for Jo. Brady, Laurie, illus. l.t. ed. 2005. (Turtle Books). 32p. (J). (gr. 2-5). lib. bdg. 15.95 (978-0-944727-48-5(4)) Jason & Nordic Pubs.

Brady, Karen. God Is Great: A Collection of 13 Story Book Poems, 1. l.t. ed. 2004. (Illus.). 20p. (J). 12.50 (978-0-9754169-0-7(1)) Bradybooks.biz.

Brand, Mona. Colors of Horses. Maizel, Karen, illus. l.t. ed. 2001. 12p. (J). (gr. k-1). pap. 4.95 (978-1-57874-024-6(X) , Kaeden Bks.) Kaeden Corp.

Brandon's Story. 2nd l.t. ed. 2001. 110p. (YA). spiral bd. 7.99 (978-0-9716330-0-1(2)) Deacon Denny Bks.

Brantley, Steven & Brantley, Judi. The Legend of Snowflake, the Messenger Deer. McDaniel-Clark, Carol, illus. l.t. ed. 2002. 40p. (J). 16.95 (978-1-892570-04-8(1)) Spring Hse. Bks.

—Molly's Christmas Mystery. McDaniel-Clark, Carol, illus. l.t. ed. 2001. 40p. (J). 16.95 (978-1-892570-06-2(8)) Spring Hse. Bks.

Brashares, Ann. The Sisterhood of the Traveling Pants. l.t. ed. 2002. (Sisterhood of Traveling Pants Ser. : Bk. 1). 344p. (YA). 24.95 (978-0-7862-3966-5(2)) Thomson Gale.

The Brave Boy. l.t. ed. 2001. 16p. (J). pap. 1.00 (978-81-87570-74-5(1)) Goodword Bks. Pvt. Ltd. IND. *Dist:* Lodhia Ctr., The.

The Brave Boy: Quran Stories for Little Hearts. l.t. ed. 2001. 24p. (J). pap. 2.25 (978-81-87570-78-3(4)) Goodword Bks. Pvt. Ltd. IND. *Dist:* Lodhia Ctr., The.

Bravo-Guzman, Pedro. Cantos del Alma. 1998th l.t. ed. 1998. (SPA.). 79p. per. 10.00 (978-0-922665-02-0(8)) Hispanic Publishing Works, Inc.

Bray, Libba. Rebel Angels. l.t. ed. 2006. (Thorndike Press Large Print the Literacy Bridge Ser.). 655p. (J). 23.95 (978-0-7862-8087-2(5)) Thorndike Pr.

Breakstone, Beth E. The 3 Little Pigs. Breakstone, Beth E., illus. l.t. ed. 2000. (Illus.). 20p. (J). 19.00 (978-1-893467-06-4(6)) Spedial Editions Pr.

Breems, Beau A. La Gran Historia: The Illustrated Gospel from Creation to Resurrection, Breems, Beau A., illus. l.t. ed. 2005. Tr. of His Story. (SPA., Illus.). 50p. (J). 19.95 (978-0-9768680-1-9(6) , 1000); per. 14.95 (978-0-9768680-3-3(2) , 3000) Burning Bush Creation.

—His Story: The Illustrated Gospel from Creation to Resurrection. Breems, Beau A., illus. l.t. ed. 2005. Tr. of Gran Historia. (Illus.). 50p. (J). 19.95 (978-0-9768680-0-2(8) , 0-9768680-0-8) Burning Bush Creation.

Brennan, Herbie. Faerie Wars. l.t. ed. 2004. 448p. 22.95 (978-0-7862-6831-3(X) , Large Print Pr.) Thorndike Pr.

Breslin, Theresa. Dream Master: Nightmare! unabr. l.t. ed. 2003. (Read-Along Ser.). 176p. (J). 29.95 incl. audio (978-0-7540-6236-3(8) , RA037, Galaxy Children's Large Print) BBC Audiobooks America.

—Dream Master Nightmare! l.t. ed. 2005. (Illus.). 216p. (J). pap. (978-0-7540-6144-1(2) , CLP 336) BBC Audio.

—Gladiator. 2004. (J). pap. 29.95 incl. audio (978-0-7540-6277-6(5) , Chivers Children's Audio Bks.) BBC Audiobooks America.

Brez, Lisa. Hickerdoodle Gets Lost. l.t. ed. 2003. (Illus.). 32p. (J). per. 6.99 (978-0-9743758-4-7(5)) Red Engine Pr.

—Hickerdoodle Gets the Hiccups. l.t. ed. 2003. (Illus.). 32p. (J). per. 6.99 (978-0-9743758-3-0(7)) Red Engine Pr.

—Hickerdoodle Meets a Chigger. l.t. ed. 2004. (Illus.). 40p. (J). per. 6.99 (978-0-9743758-5-4(3)) Red Engine Pr.

Brodland, Rita, ed. State Fair Time Warp. Freeman, Troy, illus. l.t. ed. 2002. (WeWrite Kids! Ser.). 64p. (J). (gr. k-3). pap. 8.95 (978-1-57635-059-1(2)) WeWrite LLC.

Brookes, Diane. How the Leopard Got Its Spots. Jonkisz, Barb, illus. l.t. ed. 1999. 24p. (J). (ps-3). pap. (978-1-894303-00-2(8)) Raven Rock Publishing.

—It Was a Lemon. Lewis, Stephen, illus. l.t. ed. 1999. 24p. (J). (ps-3). pap. (978-1-894303-03-3(2)) Raven Rock Publishing.

—Spring Blizzard. Wilcox, Betty M., illus. l.t. ed. 1999. 24p. (J). (ps-3). pap. (978-1-894303-04-0(0)) Raven Rock Publishing.

—The Story of Spot, the School Cat. Lewis, Stephen, illus. l.t. ed. 1999. 16p. (J). (ps-3). pap. (978-1-894303-02-6(4)) Raven Rock Publishing.

Brooks, John L., II. Balloons, Sea Creatures, Me. Spivey, Carlos, illus. l.t. ed. 1999. 20p. (J). (gr. k-3). pap. 7.00 (978-0-9661789-1-3(2)) Canis Lupus Productions.

Brown, Jane. Big Book: Who Has Four Feet? l.t. ed. 2005. (Sadlier Phonics Reading Program: Vol. 1). (Illus.). 8p. (YA). (ps-1). 22.50 (978-0-8215-7340-2(3)) Sadlier, William H. Inc.

Brown, Mark. Tommy Books: Faith, 10 vols. Mekis, Pete, illus. l.t. ed. 2005. 24p. (J). 12.99 (978-0-9762690-0-7(7)) Tommy Bks. Pubng.

J K L

—Tommy Books: Kings, 10 vols. Mekis, Pete, illus. l.t. ed. 2005. 24p. (J). 12.99 (978-0-9762690-4-5(X)) Tommy Bks. Pubng.

—Tommy Books Vol. 4: Praise, 10 vols. Mekis, Pete, illus. l.t. ed. 2005. 20p. (J). 12.99 (978-0-9762690-3-8(1)) Tommy Bks. Pubng.

Brown, Stephanie. Thea the Yellow Tomato. Brown, Stephanie, illus. l.t. ed. 1998. (Illus.). 32p. (J). (gr. k-4). 14.95 (978-0-9638152-6-2(1)) Freedom Publishing Co.

Bruce Woodcock's Business Network Writers Staff. The Great Universal Business Network: And How It Grew. Fisher, Suzanne, ed. Ritterbusch, Mark, illus. l.t. ed. 1999. (WeWrite Kids! Ser.: Vol. 43). 45p. (J). (gr. 3-8). pap. 3.95 (978-1-57635-051-5(7)) WeWrite LLC.

Brumett, Jonas O. The Legend of Kittyfish: A Learning Storybook. Johnson, Sandra L., illus. l.t. ed. 2002. 64p. (J). (ps-3). 16.95 (978-1-892812-01-8(0)) Froginhood & Friends, Inc.

—Peegus Learned to Bark: A Learning Storybook. Johnson, Sandra L., illus. l.t. ed. 2002. 64p. (J). (ps-3). 16.95 (978-1-892812-04-9(5)) Froginhood & Friends, Inc.

—A Real Fishing Experience: Froginhood & Friends. Johnson, Sandra L., illus. l.t. ed. 2002. 64p. (J). (ps-3). 16.95 (978-1-892812-00-1(2)) Froginhood & Friends, Inc.

Bryant, Louella. Two Tracks in the Snow. Fargo, Todd, illus. l.t. ed. 2004. (Turtle Bks.). 32p. (J). lib. bdg. 15.95 (978-0-944727-46-1(8) , Turtle Bks.) Jason & Nordic Pubs.

Brzycki, M. L. & Krueger, S. L. It Came from the Freezer ... or Was it the Drapes? l.t. ed. 2004. (Illus.). 110p. (YA). per. 13.00 (978-0-9747581-0-7(8)) StrangeDays Publishing.

Bucki, Jo Dee & O'Malley, John. Maya Visits a Hospital: Love Is the Best Medicine, 110 vols. Hicks, Mindy, ed. Matthews, Ashley, illus. l.t. ed. 2007. 32p. (J). per. 4.95 (978-0-9769069-0-2(2)) Maya Ventures & Publishing.

Buckler, Carol. Feathered Tales from the Barnyard. l.t. ed. 2004. (J). per. 5.95 (978-1-932496-20-8(3)) Penman Publishing, Inc.

Bucky Badger A Children's Story: Becky Gets a Brother, 4 vols. l.t. ed. 2005. (Illus.). (J). 9.99 (978-0-9765510-0-3(4)) Badgerland Bks. LLC.

Bunting, Eve. Blackwater. l.t. ed. 2000. 128p. (J). (gr. 8-12). 20.95 (978-0-7862-2753-2(2)) Thorndike Pr.

Burchett, Loni R. Bear & Katie in a Day at Nestlenook Farm. l.t. ed. 2004. (Illus.). 76p. (J). per. 11.95 (978-0-9742815-1-3(4)) Black Lab Publishing LLC.

—Bear & Katie in a Day with Friends, Vol. 3. l.t. ed. 2005. (Illus.). 68p. (J). per. 11.95 (978-0-9742815-2-0(2) , bk003) Black Lab Publishing LLC.

—Bear & Katie in the Great Searsport Caper. l.t. ed. 2004. (Illus.). 81p. (J). per. 12.95 (978-0-9742815-0-6(6)) Black Lab Publishing LLC.

Burge, Kenneth Dean. Lena's Star. Burge, Deborah Lynn, illus. l.t. ed. 2001. 36p. (J). per. 10.00 (978-0-9715953-0-9(5) , Verner Publishing) Verner Advertising, LLC.

Burnford, Sheila. The Incredible Journey. (J). (gr. 6-8). 18.95 (978-0-88411-099-6(0)) Amereon LTD.

Busic, Valerie. Jason's First Day. OI Foundation, ed. Meyers, Jeff, illus. l.t. ed. 2004. 48p. per. 8.50 (978-0-9642189-4-9(1)) Osteogenesis Imperfecta Foundation.

Butcher, H. Maxwell. I, Adam. Brookes, Shelley, illus. 2nd l.t. ed. 1999. 160p. (J). pap. (978-1-894303-08-8(3)) Raven Rock Publishing.

Butcher, Nancy. Dr. Jekyll & Mr. Dog. l.t. ed. 1999. (Adventures of Wishbone Ser.: No. 14). (Illus.). (J). (gr. 4 up). lib. bdg. 22.60 (978-0-8368-2592-3(6)) Stevens, Gareth Inc.

Buxton, Paul K., et al. Keeping Score. Adams, Alison, ed. 1999. (Early Connections Ser.). 16p. (J). (gr. k-2). pap. 4.50 (978-1-58344-068-1(2)) Benchmark Education Co.

Byars, Betsy. The Summer of the Swans. CoConis, Ted, illus. l.t. ed. 2000. (LRS Large Print Cornerstone Ser.). 176p. (YA). (gr. 5-12). lib. bdg. 27.95 (978-1-58118-060-2(8) , 23474) LRS.

—Trouble River. l.t. ed. 2004. (Beeler Mystery Ser.). 28.95 (978-1-58118-120-3(5)) LRS.

Byers, Carla Rae. Finding My Star Shoes: Rainbow Journeys. Kepler, Kit, ed. l.t. ed. 2000. Vol. 4. (Illus.). 18p. (gr. 1 up). spiral bd. 7.95 (978-0-9656124-9-4(X)) Heyokah Publishing Co.

—The Golden Word of My Way Vol. 3: The Adventures of Snowflake & Astar. l.t. ed. 2001. (gr. 3 up). 7.95 (978-1-930910-14-0(2)) Heyokah Publishing Co.

—Grandma's Gone to Heaven: Rinbow Butterfly Rose Shows the Way. l.t. ed. 2000. (Gateway to the Stars: Vol. 7). 25p. (gr. 3 up). 7.95 (978-1-930910-03-4(7)) Heyokah Publishing Co.

—Life Sucks! I'm Stuck! Vol. 9: The Stories of Isee. l.t. ed. 2000. (Illus.). 22p. (J). 7.95 (978-1-930910-06-5(1)) Heyokah Publishing Co.

—Lucky Little Duck Lessons! The Adventures of Snowflake & Astar. l.t. ed. 2000. Vol. 8. 18p. (gr. 1 up). 7.95 (978-1-930910-05-8(3)) Heyokah Publishing Co.

—Swiss Cheese Heart! The Adventures of Snowflake & Astar. Kepler, Kit, ed. l.t. ed. 2000. Vol. 3. 14p. (gr. 6 up). 7.95 (978-0-9656124-8-7(1)) Heyokah Publishing Co.

—What Color Are Your Bones? The Adventures of Snowflake & Astar. Kepler, Kit, ed. l.t. ed. 2000. Vol. 1. 19p. (gr. 1 up). 7.95 (978-0-9656124-5-6(7)) Heyokah Publishing Co.

Byrne, Susan K. Sierra Cloud: A True Story About a Horse with Courage. Stockbridge, Joan, ed. Byrne, Susan K., photos by. l.t. ed. 2002. (Illus.). 36p. (J). (gr. 3-7). spiral bd. 14.95 (978-0-9723652-0-8(6)) R&R Pubns.

Cabot, Meg. The Princess Diaries. l.t. ed. 2002. (Princess Diaries: Vol. I). 325p. (J). 24.95 (978-0-7862-4058-6(X)) Thomson Gale.

—Princess in Waiting. l.t. ed. 2003. (Princess Diaries: Vol. 4). 287p. (J). 25.95 (978-0-7862-5682-2(6)) Thorndike Pr.

Cabrera De Armida, Conception (Conchita). Before the Altar. rev. l.t. ed. 2000. 296p. (YA). per. 12.00 (978-968-7316-08-6(X)) CMJ Marian Pubs.

Cabrol, Lauent. L' Enfant de la Montagne Noire. l.t. ed. 2001. (French Ser.). (Illus.). 30.99 (978-2-84011-432-1(1)) Ulverscroft Large Print Bks. GBR. *Dist:* Ulverscroft Large Print Bks., Ltd.

California 2003-2004 Recall Election Calendar. l.t. ed. 2003. (Illus.). 40p. 14.95 (978-0-9745991-0-6(7)) Princess Ring, LLC.

Campaniello, Mickey. Mr. Mick Visits Our School. Fujitake, Dennis, illus. l.t. ed. 1999. 50p. (J). (ps-2). 12.95 (978-0-9673179-0-8(8)) Someone Special Foundation.

Campbell, Ellen Langas. Will Stephanie Get the Story? 2004. (Girls Know How Ser.: #1 - Journalism). (Illus.). 112p. (J). pap. 4.95 (978-0-9743604-0-9(6) , GIRLS KNOW HOW) NouSoma Communications, Inc.

Campbell, Judith. Let's Talk about It: Stories about Sensitive Issues, Dilemmas & Ethical Decision Making. Howard, Joanne, ed. Buckman, Frimma, illus. l.t. ed. 1998. 64p. (J). (gr. 2-6). pap. 10.00 (978-1-891180-51-4(7)) Campbell & Lockwood Pubs.

Candy, Wolf. The Tree, the House & the Hurricane. l.t. ed. 2005. (Illus.). 24p. (J). 7.00 (978-0-9762292-3-0(4)) New Global Publishing.

Caole, Francis & Michael, Veronica. Cameg Nertussia? Sparck, Amy, illus. l.t. ed. 1999. Tr. of What Do I Eat?. (ESK.). 8p. (J). (gr. k-3). pap. 6.00 (978-1-58084-149-8(X)) Lower Kuskokwim Schl. District.

—Canek Nerlarcia? Sparck, Amy, illus. l.t. ed. 1999. Tr. of What Do I Eat?. (ESK.). 8p. (J). (gr. k-3). pap. 6.00 (978-1-58084-094-1(9)) Lower Kuskokwim Schl. District.

—What Do I Eat? Sparck, Amy, illus. l.t. ed. 1999. 8p. (J). (gr. k-3). pap. 6.00 (978-1-58084-093-4(0)) Lower Kuskokwim Schl. District.

Capeci, Anne. Key to the Golden Dog. l.t. ed. 1999. (Wishbone Mysteries Ser.: No. 8). 144p. (J). (gr. 4 up). lib. bdg. 23.33 (978-0-8368-2389-9(3)) Stevens, Gareth Inc.

—The Maltese Dog. l.t. ed. 1999. (Wishbone Mysteries Ser.: No. 6). 144p. (J). (gr. 4 up). lib. bdg. 23.33 (978-0-8368-2387-5(7)) Stevens, Gareth Inc.

Capital Letters, Set. l.t. ed. Incl. Cities. Scheunemann, Pam. lib. bdg. 19.93 (978-1-57765-610-4(5)); Days. Scheunemann, Pam. lib. bdg. 19.93 (978-1-57765-611-1(3)); Months. Rondeau, Amanda. lib. bdg. 19.93 (978-1-57765-612-8(1)); Names. Scheunemann, Pam. lib. bdg. 19.93 (978-1-57765-608-1(3)); Places. Scheunemann, Pam. lib. bdg. 19.93 (978-1-57765-609-8(1)); States. Scheunemann, Pam. lib. bdg. 19.93 (978-1-57765-613-5(X)); 24p. (J). (ps-3). 2001. (Illus.). 2001. Set lib. bdg. 119.58 (978-1-57765-514-5(1) , SandCastle) ABDO Publishing Co.

Cappo, Nan Willard. Cheating Lessons. l.t. ed. 2003. 274p. (J). 24.95 (978-0-7862-5325-8(8)) Thorndike Pr.

Carlson, Dale P. Oscar the Orphaned Oyster. Harris, Fran D., ed. Caldwell, Don, illus. l.t. ed. 2000. 24p. (YA). pap. 10.00 (978-0-9664196-4-1(2)) De Day Publishing.

Carmine, Mary & Baynton, Martin. Daniel et Ses Dinosaures. l.t. ed. Tr. of Daniel et Ses Dinosaures. (FRE., Illus.). (J). bds. 29.99 (978-0-590-74124-8(1)) Scholastic, Inc.

Casey & the Amazing, Giant, Green Shirt: The Greatly Loved, Special, Brave, Smart, Kind, Fast, Patriotic American Kid! l.t. ed. 2001. (Kamaron Concept Book). 32p. 9.99 (978-0-9715713-0-3(9)) Kamaron Institute Pr.

Casey, Bert. Acoustic Guitar, Vol. 2, Bk. 2. l.t. ed. 2003. (Watch & Learn Ser.). (Illus.). 80p. pap. 14.95 (978-1-893907-43-0(0) , 256-535) Watch & Learn, Inc.

Cassidy, Anne. Patsy Kelly Investigates: A Family Affair. l.t. ed. 1998. 276p. (J). pap. (978-0-7540-6028-4(4) , CLP 231) BBC Audio.

Castillo, Carol. Me Too! Harrell, Rob, illus. l.t. ed. 2002. 16p. (J). (gr. 1-2). pap. 3.99 (978-1-58938-023-3(1)) Concerned Communications.

Causton, Linda. Lester's Rainy Lake Pony. l.t. ed. 2004. (Illus.). 32p. (J). 12.00 (978-1-930374-09-6(7)) DeForest Pr.

Chabon, Michael. Summerland. l.t. ed. 2003. 615p. (J). 25.95 (978-0-7862-5143-8(3)) Thorndike Pr.

Chaisson, Eric & McMillan, Steve. Astronomy Today. 2002. 688p. (YA). (gr. 9-12). stu. ed. (978-0-13-094334-7(7)) Prentice Hall Pr.

Chamberlain, Lyn. Quonby & the Tree Den. Weltner, Dave, illus. l.t. ed. 2004. 12p. (J). 7.95 (978-0-9706654-8-5(2)) Sprite Pr.

Chandler, Norman A. & Chandler, Roy F. The One Shot Brotherhood. Chandler, Roy F., illus. l.t. ed. 2001. (Illus.). 450p. (YA). (gr. 6 up). 65.00 (978-1-885633-20-0(3)) Iron Brigade Armory, Ltd.

Charles, Veronika Martenova. Stretch, Swallow & Stare. Charles, Veronika Martenova, illus. l.t. ed. 1999. (Illus.). 31p. (J). (ps-3). 16.95 (978-0-7737-3098-4(2)) Stoddart Kids CAN. *Dist:* Fitzhenry & Whiteside, Ltd.

Childs, Rob. Soccer Stars. l.t. ed. 2000. (Illus.). 112p. (978-0-7089-9523-5(3)) Ulverscroft Large Print Bks.

Ching, Jerry Yu & Onghai, Mike. The Greatest King. Ching, Jerry Yu, illus. 2nd l.t. ed. 2003. (Illus.). 52p. (978-0-9743215-0-9(8)) WebCartoons, LLC.

Christian, Reinar Carl, Sr. Nate: The New Bus on the Block! l.t. ed. 2005. (Illus.). 41p. (J). 16.99 (978-0-9769866-0-7(4)) Meritage Publishing.

The Christmas Chair. l.t. ed. 2004. (Illus.). 27p. (J). 12.95 (978-0-9763633-1-6(3)) Williams, Thomas.

Christoph, Renuka. JayCee Goes to the Park. Trice, Paul, illus. l.t. ed. 2001. (JayCee & Friends Ser.). 32p. (J). (ps-2). pap. 4.95 (978-0-9705468-0-7(7)) JayCee Productions.

Christopher, John. The City of Gold & Lead. l.t. ed. 2001. 205p. (J). (978-0-7540-4456-7(4) , Macmillan Reference USA) Thomson Gale.

—The City of Gold & Lead. l.t. ed. 2001. (Tripods Trilogy Ser.: Vol. 2). (Illus.). 205p. (J). 26.95 (978-0-7838-9290-0(X)) Thorndike Pr.

—The Pool of Fire. l.t. ed. 2001. (Tripods Trilogy Ser.). 205p. (J). 26.95 (978-0-7838-9289-4(6)) Thorndike Pr.

—The White Mountains: The Tripods Trilogy. l.t. ed. 2000. 168p. (J). 25.95 (978-0-7838-9170-5(9)) Thorndike Pr.

Chu, Godwin. After the Buffalo Jump Vol. 10: A Story of the Blackfoot Nation. Ham, Jeff, illus. 2001. (J). (gr. 5-6). 65.00 incl. audio, cd-rom (978-1-58702-684-3(8)) Johnston, Don Inc.

—After the Buffalo Jump Vol. 10: A Story of the Blackfoot Nation. Stemach, Jerry et al, eds. Ham, Jeff, illus. l.t. ed. 2001. (J). (gr. 5-6). 50.00 (978-1-58702-728-4(3)) Johnston, Don Inc.

Chu, Godwin, ed. After the Buffalo Jump Vol. 10: A Story of the Blackfoot Nation. Ham, Jeff, illus. l.t. ed. 2002. (J). (gr. 5-6). 150.00 (978-1-58702-046-9(7)) Johnston, Don Inc.

Chunko, Shelby E. & Madsen, Jane M. Hablemonos de la Tala Forestal: Un Libro de Silvicultura para Jovenes. De Banegas, Marianne N., tr. Smith, Heidi L., illus. l.t. unabr. ed. 1998. (SPA.). v, 32p. (J). (gr. 4-9). pap. 7.50 (978-0-9661896-2-9(0)) Pennsylvania Forestry Assn., The (PFA).

—Let's Talk about Clearcutting: A Forestry Book for Youth. Smith, Heidi L., illus. l.t. unabr. ed. 1998. v, 32p. (J). (gr. 4-9). pap. 7.50 (978-0-9661896-1-2(2)) Pennsylvania Forestry Assn., The (PFA).

Cintron, Carlos Juan, Sr., ed. Mis Primeros Pasos: Red de Niños. deluxe l.t. ed. 2005. (SPA., Illus.). 85p. (J). 12.00 (978-0-9765828-5-4(6)) Ed. Vida Abundante.

Cioffi, Dom, illus. Digby & the Lake Monster. l.t. ed. 2003. 36p. (J). per. (978-0-9745931-0-4(9)) Vermont Bookworks.

Claire, Elizabeth. Help Your Buddy Learn English, Bk. 1. Nichols, Dave, illus. l.t. ed. 2003. 64p. 15.00 (978-0-937630-04-4(7)) Eardley Pubns.

Clark, John T. & Clark, Nicole K. Adventures in Dreamtime. l.t. ed. 1998. (Illus.). 32p. (J). (gr. k-2). 15.95 (978-1-892176-12-7(2)) PremaNations Publishing.

—A Journey Through Your Heart. Clark, John T., illus. l.t. ed. 2000. (Illus.). 32p. (J). (ps-4). 17.95 (978-1-892176-14-1(9)) PremaNations Publishing.

Clark, Nicole K. & Clark, John T. The Oceans of Emotions-3D. Clark, John T., illus. l.t. ed. 1999. (Illus.). 32p. (J). (ps-4). 17.95 (978-1-892176-13-4(0)) PremaNations Publishing.

Clements, Andrew. Frindle. Selznick, Brian, illus. l.t. ed. 2000. (LRS Large Print Cornerstone Ser.). 116p. (YA). (gr. 4-10). lib. bdg. 24.95 (978-1-58118-062-6(4) , 23476) LRS.

—Jake Drake, Know-It-All. l.t. ed. 2002. (Juvenile Ser.). (Illus.). 76p. (J). 21.95 (978-0-7862-4139-2(X)) Thomson Gale.

—The Janitor's Boy. l.t. ed. 2000. 152p. (J). (gr. 4-7). 21.95 (978-0-7862-2903-1(9)) Thorndike Pr.

—The Landry News. l.t. ed. 2000. (Juvenile Ser.). (Illus.). 138p. (J). (gr. 4-7). 21.95 (978-0-7862-2707-5(9)) Thorndike Pr.

Clendenin, Priscilla. No Scare Science Fair: An Extra Out of the Ordinary Guide to Doing a Science Fair Project. Clendenin, Stephen P. & Uriz, Tony, illus. l.t. ed. 1998. Orig. Title: So You Have to Do a Science Fair Project.... 67p. (J). (gr. 1-8). pap. 15.95 (978-0-9679713-0-8(6)) Ribbitt Productions.

Clifton, Lisa. The Bunny Who Could Fly. Begley, Melinda, ed. Clifton, Paul, illus. l.t. ed. 1999. 36p. (J). (gr. k-6). 10.00 (978-1-886623-07-1(4)) Canal Side Pubs.

Clish, Marian L. Brice & Breezy: The Mall Adventure. Clish-Robinson, Lori, illus. unabr. l.t. ed. 2000. 41p. (J). (gr. k-3). per. 7.95 (978-1-928632-46-7(7)) Writers Marketplace:Consulting, Critiquing & Publishing.

—Brice & Breezy Set: The Mall Adventure. Robinson, Lori Clish, illus. 2000. (Brice & Breezy Ser.). 41p. (J). (gr. k-3). pap. 7.95 (978-1-928632-45-0(9)) Writers Marketplace:Consulting, Critiquing & Publishing.

—Don't Eat Ice Cream with Your Dirty Feet: Strange & Weird Poems for Kids. Robinson, Lori Clish, illus. unabr. ed. 2000. (J). (gr. k-5). 18.95 incl. audio (978-1-928632-42-9(4)); pap. 14.95 incl. audio compact disk (978-1-928632-40-5(8)); pap. 10.95 incl. audio (978-1-928632-39-9(4)); pap. 7.95 (978-1-928632-38-2(6)) Writers Marketplace:Consulting, Critiquing & Publishing.

—A Wolf's Tale. Anderson, Jan, illus. unabr. ed. 1999. (J). (gr. k-5). pap. 10.95 incl. audio (978-1-928632-00-9(9)) Writers Marketplace:Consulting, Critiquing & Publishing.

—You Choose the Way: A Book That Reads Like a Game - Mazash the Wizard. Anderson, Jan, illus. l.t. ed. 1999. 56p. (J). (gr. k-5). pap. 7.95 (978-1-928632-07-8(6)) Writers Marketplace:Consulting, Critiquing & Publishing.

Clo, David. You're in the Band Bk. 2: Unplugged. l.t. ed. 2001. 32p. (YA). (978-0-87718-085-2(7)) Willis Music Co.

Clyde, Addie M. Sophie the Sofa. l.t. ed. 2004. 40p. (J). per. (978-1-59196-744-6(9)) Instantpublisher.com.

Cofer, Amadeus. Friendship Rules: How to Make & Keep Friends, 1. l.t. ed. 2004. (Illus.). 36p. (J). 14.00 (978-1-932957-00-6(6)) Legacy Pubs.

—Mystery of the Golden Pearls: A Halloween Adventure in Clarkesville, 1. l.t. ed. 2004. (Illus.). 36p. (J). 14.00 (978-1-932957-02-0(2)) Legacy Pubs.

Cohen, Dennis. The Big Book of Space Discovery: A Fun-Filled Adventure into the Planets, Stars & Space Exploration. Fry, Sharon, ed. Estrine, Ron, illus. l.t. ed. 1999. 12p. (J). (gr. k-7). mass mkt. 12.00 (978-0-9674289-0-1(4)) Schmidt-Cannon International.

Cohen, Judith Love. You Can Be A Chemist. Katz, David A., illus. l.t. ed. 2005. Orig. Title: You Can Be A Woman Chemist. 40p. (J). per. 7.00 (978-1-880599-71-6(6)) Cascade Pass, Inc.

—You Can Be A Woman Chemist. Katz, David A., illus. l.t. ed. 2005. 40p. (J). 13.95 (978-1-880599-72-3(4)) Cascade Pass, Inc.

—You Can Be A Woman Video Game Producer. l.t. ed. 2005. (Illus.). 72p. (J). 17.95 (978-1-880599-74-7(0)); pap. 12.95 (978-1-880599-73-0(2)) Cascade Pass, Inc.

Cohen, Miriam. Eddy's Dream. Cohen, Adam, photos by. l.t. ed. 2000. (Illus.). 32p. (J). (gr. k-2). 16.95 (978-1-887734-57-8(0)) Star Bright Bks., Inc.

—Say Hi, Backpack Baby! Cohen, Miriam, illus. l.t. ed. 2001. (Backpack Baby Stories Ser.). (Illus.). 12p. (J). (ps). bds. 5.95 (978-1-887734-82-0(1)) Star Bright Bks., Inc.

—Wah! Wah! A Backpack Baby Story. l.t. ed. 2001. (Backpack Baby Stories Ser.). (Illus.). 12p. (J). (ps). bds. 5.95 (978-1-887734-81-3(3)) Star Bright Bks., Inc.

Cohen, Sonia. Gigi. l.t. ed. 2005. (Illus.). 34p. (J). 14.95 (978-0-615-12926-6(9)) Gigi Enterprises.

Cohen, Steve M. The Opening 8 (for You & Your Parents) 2nd l.t. ed. 2002. (Illus.). 359p. (J). 46.30 (978-0-9721087-1-3(8)) UPSCL (Unoffical Penisnula Scholastic Chess League, Inc.).

A Cold & Snowy Day. l.t. ed. 1999. (Illus.). 20p. (J). pap. 19.00 (978-1-893467-02-6(3)) Spedial Editions Pr.

Cole, Joanna. The Magic School Bus at the Waterworks. Degen, Bruce, illus. l.t. ed. (Magic School Bus Ser.). (FRE.). (J). (gr. 1-4). bds. 35.99 (978-0-590-73528-5(4)) Scholastic, Inc.

Coleman, Omer, Jr. ABC Land: Learning Is Great Fun. Coleman, Omer, Jr., ed. 2002. (Illus.). 32p. (J). (ps-1). pap. 10.00 (978-0-9720341-0-4(2)) Coleman, Omer.

Colfer, Eoin. The Arctic Incident. l.t. ed. 2003. (Artemis Fowl Ser.: Bk. 2). 296p. (J). (gr. 3-6). 16.95 (978-0-7540-7839-5(6) , Galaxy Children's Large Print) BBC Audiobooks America.

—The Arctic Incident. l.t. ed. 2003. (Artemis Fowl Ser.: Bk. 2). 313p. (J). (gr. 3-6). 25.95 (978-0-7862-4825-4(4)) Thorndike Pr.

—Artemis Fowl. l.t. ed. 2001. (Artemis Fowl Ser.: Bk. 1). 312p. (J). (gr. 3-6). 28.95 (978-1-58724-092-8(0) , Wheeler Publishing, Inc.) Thomson Gale.

—The Opal Deception. l.t. ed. 2005. (Artemis Fowl Ser.: Bk. 4). 421p. (J). 23.95 (978-0-7862-7754-4(8) , Large Print Pr.) Thorndike Pr.

Colledge, Anne. Northern Lights. 2000. (Illus.). (YA). 2nd l.t. ed. 94p. pap. (978-1-902628-81-3(0)); 3rd l.t. ed. 124p. per. (978-1-902628-83-7(7)) Pipers' Ash, Ltd.

Collodi, Carlo. The Adventures of Pinocchio. l.t. ed. 2004. (Large Print Ser.). 229p. 25.00 (978-1-58287-732-7(7)) North Bks.

Coman, Carolyn. Many Stones. l.t. ed. 2001. 24.95 (978-0-7862-3399-1(0)) Thorndike Pr.

Concepcion, Julio Antonio. Carlitos y Pescaito. Pontet, Daniel, illus. Diamond, Bobi, photos by. l.t. ed. 1998. Tr. of Carlitos & the Little Fish. (SPA.). 120p. pap. 10.00 (978-0-9659592-1-6(X)) Nadir Pubn.

Conner, Carol & Fabian, Melinda, illus. Follow & Find: Follow the Numbered Dots to Complete the Picture, Then Color the Picture! l.t. ed. 2000. (Nature Friend Fun Ser.: Vol. 3). 24p. (J). (gr. k-5). pap. 4.00 (978-1-890050-45-0(8)) Carlisle Pr.- Walnut Creek.

—Nature Mazes: Help Each Animal Find What It's Looking for in a Maze of Choices. There's Only One Right Path! l.t. ed. 2001. (Nature Friend Fun Ser.: No. 4). 24p. (J). (gr. 5-10). pap. 4.00 (978-1-890050-59-7(8)) Carlisle Pr.- Walnut Creek.

Connor, Elizabeth & Kinzler, Mary. Libby Saves Beauty's Colt. Garrett, Stephen, photos by. ltd. l.t. ed. 1999. (Illus.). 106p. (J). (gr. 2-6). 12.95 (978-0-9658468-1-3(4)) Adbeth Pr.

Conquistadore, H. Omni Presents the Universe. West, Jeremy, illus. l.t. ed. 2003. 51p. per. 8.99 (978-1-932338-14-0(4)) Lifevest Publishing, Inc.

The Constitution of the United States. l.t. ed. 1998. (Large Print Heritage Ser.). 103p. (YA). (gr. 7-12). lib. bdg. 19.95 (978-1-58118-037-4(3) , 22506) LRS.

Cook, Jean Thor. Los Amiguitos' Fiesta. Wilson, Lincoln, ed. Shade, Judith Donoho, illus. l.t. ed. 2001. Tr. of Little Friends' Fiesta. (SPA.). 28p. (J). (ps-3). 17.00 (978-0-9708940-0-7(7)) Gently Worded Bks., LLC.

Cooper, John. First Day. Roscetti, John, illus. l.t. ed. 2002. (Heroes Start As Kids!: Vol. 1). 97p. (J). (gr. 2-7). per. 5.95 (978-0-9711474-9-2(3)) A B C-123 Publishing.

Cooper-Pete, Beverly. Tootie Fruity Bear's Sing-A-Long Tunes. 4th l.t. ed. Tr. of Para que cantes junto con el oso Tootie Fruity. 32p. 2001. (SPA & ENG.). pap. (978-0-9714093-2-3(3)); 2000. (ENG & GER.). pap. (978-0-9714093-1-6(5)) Trey-Ish & Co.

Cooper, Susan. The Dark Is Rising. l.t. ed. 2001. (Dark Is Rising Sequence Ser.). 395p. (J). (gr. 4-7). 21.95 (978-0-7862-2920-8(9)) Thorndike Pr.

—Greenwitch. l.t. ed. 2001. (Dark Is Rising Sequence Ser.). 131p. (J). 21.95 (978-0-7862-2923-9(3)) Thorndike Pr.

—The Grey King. l.t. ed. 2002. (Dark Is Rising Sequence Ser.). 262p. (J). 21.95 (978-0-7862-2919-2(5)) Thomson Gale.

—King of Shadows. l.t. ed. 2000. (Thorndike Press Large Print Juvenile Ser.). (Illus.). 246p. (J). (gr. 8-12). 21.95 (978-0-7862-2706-8(0)) Thorndike Pr.

—Over Sea, under Stone. l.t. ed. 2000. (Dark Is Rising Sequence Ser.). 332p. (J). (gr. 4-7). 22.95 (978-0-7862-2918-5(7)) Thorndike Pr.

—Silver on the Tree. l.t. ed. 2002. (Dark Is Rising Sequence Ser.). (Illus.). 430p. (J). 23.95 (978-0-7862-2921-5(7)) Thomson Gale.

Cope-Robinson, Lyn. Cat Tails. Cope-Robinson, Lyn, illus. l.t. ed. 2003. (Illus.). 32p. (J). lib. bdg. (978-1-887774-14-7(9) , Wynden) Canmore Pr.

Cormier, Robert. Heroes. l.t. ed. 2000. 147p. (YA). (gr. 8-12). 21.95 (978-0-7862-2909-3(8)) Thorndike Pr.

—The Rag & Bone Shop. l.t. ed. 2002. 141p. (J). 24.95 (978-0-7862-3873-6(9)) Thomson Gale.

Cosley, Betty. The Story of Tiny McShane. Shepard, Brian, illus. l.t. ed. 1998. viii, 24p. (J). (ps-3). 14.95 (978-0-9664588-0-0(X)) Cosley Production.

Couloumbis, Audrey. Getting near to Baby. l.t. ed. 2000. (Juvenile Ser.). (Illus.). 215p. (J). (gr. 4-7). 22.95 (978-0-7862-2705-1(2)) Thorndike Pr.

Coulton, Mia. How Much Does This Hold? Graves, Dennis, illus. l.t. ed. 1998. 24p. (J). (gr. k-2). pap. 4.95 (978-1-57874-020-8(7)) Kaeden Corp.

Counce, Paula. A Journey Remembered. l.t. ed. 2004. (Illus.). 135p. (J). 19.95 (978-0-9762776-0-6(3)) Counce, Paula.

Coville, Bruce. There's an Alien in My Classroom! l.t. ed. 2000. (Illus.). 184p. (J). pap. 16.95 (978-0-7540-6108-3(6) , Galaxy Children's Large Print) BBC Audiobooks America.

A Cow Had a Wish. l.t. ed. Date not set. (Illus.). 32p. (J). (gr. 1-6). (978-0-9653327-1-2(3)) BF Publishing.

Craven, Lon Eric, illus. ABC Coloring Book: March of the Teddy Bears Kansas City 2002. l.t. ed. 2002. 32p. per. 5.95 (978-0-9717080-9-9(6)) Kansas City Star Bks.

Crawford, Ann Fears. Rosa: A German Woman on the Texas Frontier. Fain, Cheryl, illus. l.t. ed. 2003. 60p. (J). (gr. 3-8). 16.95 (978-1-931823-09-8(X)) Halcyon Pr.

Creech, Sharon. Heartbeat. l.t. ed. 2004. 160p. 23.95 (978-0-7862-6902-0(2) , Large Print Pr.) Thorndike Pr.

—Ruby Holler. l.t. ed. 2003. (Juvenile Ser.). 250p. (J). 22.95 (978-0-7862-5429-3(7)) Thorndike Pr.

—Walk Two Moons. l.t. ed. 2000. (Illus.). 287p. (J). 21.95 (978-0-7862-2773-0(7)) Thorndike Pr.

—The Wanderer. Diaz, David, illus. l.t. ed. 2002. 263p. (J). 24.95 (978-0-7862-4125-5(X)) Thorndike Pr.

Cress, Michelle H. Annie the Astronaut Meets Gussie the Green Man. l.t. ed. 1999. (LB Ser.). (Illus.). 8p. (J). (ps-1). pap. 10.95 (978-1-57332-153-2(2)) HighReach Learning, Inc.

—Annie the Astronaut Meets Gussie the Green Man. Cress, Michelle H., illus. l.t. ed. 1999. (BB Ser.). (Illus.). 8p. (J). (ps-1). pap. 10.95 (978-1-57332-152-5(4)) HighReach Learning, Inc.

Crichton, Julie. The King & the Queen & the Jelly Bean. Swaim, illus. l.t. ed. 2005. (SPA.). 24p. (J). bds. 7.95 (978-0-9761990-0-7(9)) Bean Bk. Publishing.

—El rey y la reina y el frijolito de Goma. Swaim, Ramon, illus. l.t. ed. 2005. 24p. (J). bds. 7.95 (978-0-9761990-1-4(7)) Bean Bk. Publishing.

Crider, Bill. Muttketeer! l.t. ed. 1999. (Adventures of Wishbone Ser.: No. 8). (Illus.). 144p. (J). (gr. 4 up). lib. bdg. 22.60 (978-0-8368-2304-2(4)) Stevens, Gareth Inc.

Cromwell, Patricia L. Marguerita & Sarabella's Glad Day. D. B. and Associates Design Group Staff & Butler, Dwayne, illus. l.t. ed. 2001. 16p. (J). (ps-6). pap. 6.95 (978-0-9664794-0-9(8) , 041998) Patty Cake Bks.

Crosby, Ruthann. Miracle in the Glass: To Save a Life Is to Save the World. Cook, Richard, illus. l.t. ed. 1998. 48p. (J). (gr. 3-6). pap. 14.95 (978-1-888125-26-9(8)) Publication Consultants.

Crosby, Vernon H. The Adventures of Scurry Little: Lost in my Dream. l.t. ed. 2004. 40p. (J). per. 10.95 (978-1-59196-819-1(4)) Instantpublisher.com.

Cross, Gillian. Gobbo the Great. l.t. ed. 2000. 192p. (J). pap. (978-0-7540-6123-6(X) , CLP 315) BBC Audio.

—Gobbo the Great. unabr. l.t. ed. 2003. (Read-Along Ser.). 176p. (J). 24.95 incl. audio (978-0-7540-6241-7(4) , RAO42, Galaxy Children's Large Print) BBC Audiobooks America.

Cross, Linda B. Lines from Linda. l.t. ed. 2003. 104p. (YA). per. 7.00 (978-0-9748591-2-5(5) , MSP) Main St Publishing, Inc.

Crump, Fred, Jr. Favorite Bible Stories: Retold & Illustrated by Fred Crump, Jr. Crump, Fred, Jr., illus. adapted l.t. ed. 2002. (Illus.). 50p. 16.95 (978-0-940955-75-2(X) , 0-69719, UMI) UMI (Urban Ministries, Inc.).

Cruzan, Patricia & Solly, Gloria, illus. Molly's Mischievous Dog. l.t. ed. 2004. 121p. (J). per. (978-0-9653543-3-2(4)) Clear Creek Pubs.

Cuentos de Siempre Oceano. l.t. ed. 2000. Tr. of Stories for All Time from Oceano. (SPA., Illus.). 96p. 28.00 (978-84-494-1307-0(9) , GML06502-176440) Oceano Grupo Editoria, S.A. ESP. *Dist:* Thomson Gale.

Cuentos Magicos. l.t. ed. 2002. Tr. of Magical Stories. (SPA., Illus.). 224p. 28.00 (978-84-494-2117-4(9) , GML07104-186002) Oceano Grupo Editoria, S.A. ESP. *Dist:* Thomson Gale.

Current, Sharon S. McQuillken Finds His Purpose. Holloway, Pam, illus. l.t. ed. 1998. 24p. (J). (gr. k-2). pap. 9.95 (978-0-9668072-0-2(0)) Sunshine Pr., LLC.

Curry, Casey. I Remember You Today: An Interactive Picturebook for Children Dealing with the Loss of a Sibling or Parent. 2003. (Illus.). 24p. (J). wbk. ed. (978-1-884878-15-2(6)) Annapolis Publishing Co.

Curry, Jane Louise. The Egyptian Box. l.t. ed. 2002. 216p. (J). 21.95 (978-0-7862-4896-4(3)) Thorndike Pr.

Curtin, Jeremiah, ed. Seneca Indian Myths. l.t. ed. 2001. (Illus.). 530p. pap. 16.95 (978-0-486-41602-1(X)) Dover Pubns., Inc.

Curtis, Christopher Paul. Bud, Not Buddy. l.t. ed. 2000. (Illus.). 279p. (J). (gr. 8-12). 22.95 (978-0-7862-2574-3(2)) Thorndike Pr.

Curtiss, A. B. The Little Chapel That Stood, Golino, Mirto, illus. l.t. ed. 2005. 36p. 18.95 (978-0-932529-77-0(1)) Oldcastle Publishing.

Cyr, Joe. Shawn the Hopping Christmas Tree. Cyr, Diane, ed. Henry, Diane, illus. l.t. ed. 2001. 32p. 5.95 (978-0-9713768-0-9(8)) Cyr, Joe.

—Two Tales of That Very First Christmas: An Angel Named Etoile & the Straw Girl, Owen, Ramon E., illus. l.t. ed. 2002. 24p. 5.95 (978-0-9713768-1-6(6)) Cyr, Joe.

D'Adamo, Francesco & Leonori, Ann. Iqbal Vol. 5: A Novel. l.t. ed. 2004. 138p. (J). 20.95 (978-0-7862-6385-1(7)) Thorndike Pr.

Dahlquist, Kathleen C. Tales of Erin: March 17th. Erickson, Beverly H., ed. Anthony, Ruth, illus. l.t. ed. 2000. 80p. (J). (gr. 1-5). pap. 15.00 (978-1-885527-20-2(9)) Feather Fables Publishing Company.

Daley, Jacque. Verses for Kids: For Fun & Learning. l.t. ed. 1998. (Illus.). (J). (gr. k-6). 10.00 (978-0-9667429-1-6(5)) Jacpak Bks.

Dalton, Annie. The Afterdark Princess. l.t. ed. 2005. (Illus.). 144p. (J). pap. (978-0-7540-7834-0(5) , CLP 425) BBC Audio.

—Tilly Beany Saves the World. Harker, Lesley, illus. l.t. ed. 2000. 206p. (J). pap. (978-0-7540-6106-9(X) , CLP 300) BBC Audio.

Damon - Beyond the Glory. l.t. ed. 2003. (Illus.). 152p. per. 14.95 (978-0-9724033-2-0(9)) Backroads Pr.

Dandridge, Derrick M. The Maple Kids Go to the Zoo. l.t. ed. 1999. (Maple Kids Ser.). (Illus.). 32p. (ps-2). pap. 5.00 (978-1-928694-01-4(2)) Modern Star Bks.

—The Original Maple Kids. l.t. ed. 1999. (Maple Kids Ser.). (Illus.). 28p. (ps-2). pap. 5.00 (978-1-928694-00-7(4)) Modern Star Bks.

Daniels, Lucy. Animal Ark: Dolphin in the Deep. unabr. l.t. ed. 2001. (Read-Along Ser.). 160p. (J). 29.95 incl. audio (978-0-7540-6243-1(0) , RAO44, Chivers Children's Audio Bks.) BBC Audiobooks America.

—Dolphin Diaries: Touching the Waves. Lawton, Judith, illus. l.t. ed. 2002. 216p. (J). 16.95 (978-0-7540-7822-7(1) , Galaxy Children's Large Print) BBC Audiobooks America.

—Hedgehogs in the Hall. l.t. ed. 2000. (Illus.). 214p. (J). pap. (978-0-7540-6109-0(4) , CLP 303) BBC Audio.

Dantzlerward, Walter, et al. This Is Virginia: The Virginia History & Social Science Standards of Learning Book Set, 2 vols. l.t. ed. 2002. 210p. lib. bdg. (978-0-9720535-0-1(6) , 0972053506) Academic Multimedia, Inc.

Danziger, Paula. This Place Has No Atmosphere. 2006. 176p. (J). (gr. 5). 5.99 (978-0-14-240680-9(5) , Puffin) Penguin Group (USA) Inc.

Das, Christina. Coo Coo Duckling. l.t. ed. 2005. (Illus.). 32p. (J). 15.95 (978-0-9763082-4-9(X) , A JuneOne Production) JuneOne Publishing Hub.

—Munchy Mouse. l.t. ed. 2005. (Illus.). 32p. (J). 15.95 (978-0-9763082-0-1(7) , A JuneOne Production) JuneOne Publishing Hub.

—Oomph-Pa-Pa at the Circus. l.t. ed. 2005. (Illus.). 32p. (J). 15.95 (978-0-9763082-2-5(3) , A JuneOne Production) JuneOne Publishing Hub.

—The Red Spotted Balloon. l.t. ed. 2005. (Illus.). 32p. (J). 15.95 (978-0-9763082-3-2(1) , A JuneOne Production) JuneOne Publishing Hub.

—Swinging under the Stars. l.t. ed. 2005. (Illus.). 32p. (J). 15.95 (978-0-9763082-1-8(5) , A JuneOne Production) JuneOne Publishing Hub.

Davids, Paul & Davids, Hollace. Star Wars, 3 bks. l.t. ed. Incl. Prophets of the Dark Side. lib. bdg. 22.60 (978-0-8368-1994-6(2)); Queen of the Empire. lib. bdg. 22.60 (978-0-8368-1993-9(4)); Zorba the Hutt's Revenge. lib. bdg. 22.60 (978-0-8368-1991-5(8)); 112p. (J). (gr. 4 up). 1997. Set lib. bdg. 67.80 (978-0-8368-1988-5(8)) Stevens, Gareth Inc.

Davis, Adda Leah. Caleb's Song. l.t. ed. 2003. (Illus.). 56p. (J). (978-0-9747904-0-4(0)) Golden Harvest Publishing Co.

Davis, Darren. Atlas - ABC's for Superheroes: ABC's for Superheroes. l.t. ed. 2004. (Illus.). 16p. (J). bds. 5.99 (978-1-59559-110-4(9) , Angel Gate) Left Field Ink.

Davis, Rebecca. ABC Fun. Blair, Bill, ed. Cagley, Diana, illus. l.t. ed. 2002. 62p. (J). (gr. k-3). spiral bd. 9.00 (978-0-9720881-0-7(5)) His Hands, Inc.

de Brunhoff, Laurent. Babar y Sus Amigos: Letras y Numeros. l.t. ed. 2000. (Babar Ser.).Tr. of Babar & His Friends: Letters & Numbers. (SPA., Illus.). 48p. (J). 15.95 (978-84-7546-912-6(4)) Beascoa, Ediciones S.A. ESP. *Dist:* Distribooks, Inc.

—Babar y Sus Amigos de Vacaciones. l.t. ed. 2000. (Babar Ser.).Tr. of Babar & His Friends on Vacation. (SPA., Illus.). 48p. (J). 15.95 (978-84-7546-535-7(8)) Beascoa, Ediciones S.A. ESP. *Dist:* Distribooks, Inc.

—Las Primeras Palabras de Babar. l.t. ed. 2000. (Babar Ser.).Tr. of Babar's First Words. (SPA., Illus.). 48p. (J). 15.95 (978-84-7546-828-0(4)) Beascoa, Ediciones S.A. ESP. *Dist:* Distribooks, Inc.

Dean, Jeffrey J. & Dean, Debra A. The Amazing Adventures of Abiola, Vol. 3. Ferguson, Dwayne, illus. l.t. ed. 1999. (Selected Children's Multicultural Stories). 32p. (J). (gr. 4-6). lib. bdg. 12.95 (978-1-56674-225-2(0)) Forest Hse. Publishing Co., Inc.

Deary, Terry. The Ghosts of Batwing Castle. l.t. ed. 2005. (Illus.). 88p. (J). pap. incl. audio (978-0-7540-7869-2(8) , CLP 451) BBC Audio.

—True Detective Stories. l.t. ed. 2005. (Illus.). 192p. (J). pap. (978-0-7540-6126-7(4) , CLP 320) BBC Audio.

—True Detective Stories. unabr. l.t. ed. 2003. (Read-Along Ser.). 176p. (J). 29.95 incl. audio (978-0-7540-6240-0(6) , RAO41, Galaxy Children's Large Print) BBC Audiobooks America.

—True Ghost Stories. Waytt, David, illus. l.t. ed. 1998. (J). pap. (978-0-7540-6022-2(5) , CLP 221) BBC Audio.

—True Horror Stories. Wyatt, David, illus. l.t. ed. 2000. 264p. (J). pap. (978-0-7540-6092-5(6) , CLP 290) BBC Audio.

—True Horror Stories. Wyatt, David, illus. unabr. l.t. ed. 2000. (Read-Along Ser.). 208p. (J). pap. 29.95 incl. audio (978-0-7540-6226-4(0) , RA027, Chivers Children's Audio Bks.) BBC Audiobooks America.

—True Mystery Stories. l.t. ed. 2005. (Illus.). 240p. (J). pap. (978-0-7540-7810-4(8) , CLP 420) BBC Audio.

Deedrick, Tami. Garbage Collectors. 1998. (Community Helpers Ser.). (Illus.). 24p. (J). (gr. k-3). pap. 14.00 (978-0-516-21259-3(1) , Children's Pr.) Scholastic Library Publishing.

DeFelice, Cynthia C. The Ghost of Fossil Glen. l.t. ed. 2000. (Juvenile Ser.). (Illus.). 185p. (J). (gr. 4-7). 21.95 (978-0-7862-2768-6(0)) Thorndike Pr.

—The Missing Manatee. l.t. ed. 2005. 183p. (J). 20.95 (978-0-7862-8178-7(2)) Thorndike Pr.

Demers, David & Demers, Lee Ann. My Grandpa Loves Trains: A Storybook for Preschoolers. Demers, David, photos by. l.t. ed. 2005. (Illus.). 76p. (J). per. 19.95 (978-0-922993-23-9(8)) Marquette Bks., LLC.

Denny, Joe. Triune: Jimmy's Escape. 2005. 80p. (J). pap. (978-0-9772240-0-5(7)) RS Publishing.

DeSantis, Debi. A Bunch of Giggles & Hugs. l.t. ed. 2005. (Illus.). 26p. (J). 12.95 (978-0-9770043-0-0(9)) New Global Publishing.

DeVos, Janie. Path Winds Home. Marsh, Nancy, illus. l.t. ed. 2005. 32p. 16.95 (978-0-9743758-0-9(2)) Red Engine Pr.

Diaz, Jamie, Studios Staff, illus. Batman. l.t. ed. 1998. (Look & Find Ser.: Vol. 19). 24p. (J). (gr. k-6). lib. bdg. 14.95 (978-1-56674-230-6(7) , HTS Bks.) Forest Hse. Publishing Co., Inc.

Diaz, T. Richard. Little Growler, Big Heart. l.t. ed. 2003. (Illus.). 12p. (J). lib. bdg. 11.95 (978-1-932338-21-8(7)) Lifevest Publishing, Inc.

DiCamillo, Kate. The Tale of Despereaux. Ering, Timothy B., illus. l.t. ed. 2004. 255p. 23.95 (978-0-7862-6578-7(7) , Large Print Pr.) Thorndike Pr.

Dickens, Charles. A Christmas Carol. l.t. ed. 1999. (Large Print Heritage Ser.). 140p. (YA). (gr. 7-12). lib. bdg. 24.95 (978-1-58118-041-1(1) , 22510) LRS.

—The Cricket on the Hearth. l.t. ed. 2005. 128p. pap. 17.95 (978-1-59688-048-1(1) , 1-59688-048-1) Large Print Bk. Co., The.

Dickman, Jean M. Santa in Space. l.t. ed. 2003. (Illus.). 32p. (J). per. 9.95 (978-0-9743718-0-1(7)) Tintagel Publications.

DiSunno, Rebecca, et al. Jeremy Goes to Camp Good Grief. l.t. ed. 2004. (Illus.). 48p. (J). per. 14.95 (978-0-9754932-0-5(5)) East End Hospice, Inc.

Dixon, Franklin W. The Test Case. l.t. ed. 2002. 169p. (J). 21.95 (978-0-7862-4657-1(X)) Thorndike Pr.

—Trouble in Warp Space. l.t. ed. 2002. 181p. (J). 21.95 (978-0-7862-4658-8(8)) Thorndike Pr.

Dixon, George. Pauses along the Trail. l.t. ed. 2002. (Illus.). 95p. pap. 9.95 (978-0-9721833-0-7(2)) Sleepy D Publishing.

The Dog & the Bone, Set 2. l.t. ed. 1999. (Illus.). 19p. (J). (gr. k-6). reprint ed. pap. 2.50 (978-1-893688-02-5(X)) Carroll Schl., The.

The Dog & the Wolf, Set 1. l.t. ed. 1999. (Illus.). 25p. (J). (gr. k-6). reprint ed. pap. 2.50 (978-1-893688-04-9(6)) Carroll Schl., The.

Doherty, Berlie. Famous Adventures of Jack. l.t. ed. 2005. (Illus.). 152p. (J). pap. (978-0-7540-6140-3(X) , CLP 332) BBC Audio.

—The Famous Adventures of Jack. unabr. l.t. ed. 2001. (Read-Along Ser.). 128p. (J). 24.95 incl. audio (978-0-7540-6237-0(6) , RAO38, Chivers Children's Audio Bks.) BBC Audiobooks America.

Dolphin Halloween & Elsie's Scrapbook. l.t. ed. 2004. (Illus.). 32p. (J). mass mkt. 4.99 (978-0-9760868-0-2(8)) Pluegl Bks.

Domoslai, Autumn. Grandmother Witch: Samhain at Grandmother's, 10 bks., Vol. 2. Price, Starr, ed. Domoslai, Autumn, illus. l.t. ed. 2005. (Illus.). 44p. (J). pap. 6.49 (978-0-9755403-7-4(8)) Spiral Publishing, Inc.

—Grandmother Witch Vol. I: Springtime. Domoslai, Autumn, illus. l.t. ed. 2004. (Illus.). 44p. (J). pap. 6.49 (978-0-9755403-5-0(1)) Spiral Publishing, Inc.

Donaldson, Julia. The Dinosaur's Diary. l.t. ed. 2005. (Illus.). 96p. (J). pap. (978-0-7540-7835-7(3) , CLP 426) BBC Audio.

Doolin, Jimmy. The Day the Circus Came to My Backyard. l.t. ed. 2003. 39p. lib. bdg. (978-0-9710432-4-4(8)) Children's Literacy Pubns.

The Dooples & the Shapes. l.t. ed. 2001. (Meet the Dooples). 32p. (J). lib. bdg. 19.95 (978-0-9656279-3-1(4)) Educational Media Enterprises, Inc.

Doucet, Sharon Arms. Fiddle Fever. 2000. (Illus.). 176p. (J). (gr. 5-9). tchr. ed. 15.00 (978-0-618-04324-8(1) , Clarion Bks.) Houghton Mifflin Co. Trade & Reference Div.

—Fiddle Fever. l.t. ed. 2001. 174p. (J). 20.95 (978-0-7862-3548-3(9)) Thomson Gale.

Doudna, Kelly. Aa: See It Say It Hear It. l.t. ed. 2000. (Alphabet Ser.). (Illus.). 24p. (J). (ps-3). lib. bdg. 19.93 (978-1-57765-394-3(7) , SandCastle) ABDO Publishing Co.

—Adjectives. l.t. ed. 2001. (Sentences Ser.). (Illus.). 24p. (J). (ps-3). lib. bdg. 19.93 (978-1-57765-617-3(2) , SandCastle) ABDO Publishing Co.

—Adverbs. l.t. ed. 2001. (Sentences Ser.). (Illus.). 24p. (J). (ps-3). lib. bdg. 19.93 (978-1-57765-616-6(4) , SandCastle) ABDO Publishing Co.

—A Bat Hangs from the Bat. l.t. ed. 2002. (Homonyms Ser.). (Illus.). 24p. (J). (ps-3). lib. bdg. 19.93 (978-1-57765-785-9(3) , SandCastle) ABDO Publishing Co.

—Cc: See It Say It Hear It. l.t. ed. 2000. (Alphabet Ser.). (Illus.). 24p. (J). (ps-3). lib. bdg. 19.93 (978-1-57765-396-7(3) , SandCastle) ABDO Publishing Co.

—Dd: See It Say It Hear It. l.t. ed. 2000. (Alphabet Ser.). (Illus.). 24p. (J). (ps-3). lib. bdg. 19.93 (978-1-57765-397-4(1) , SandCastle) ABDO Publishing Co.

—Do Not Squash the Squash. l.t. ed. 2002. (Homonyms Ser.). (Illus.). 24p. (J). (ps-3). lib. bdg. 19.93 (978-1-57765-791-0(8) , SandCastle) ABDO Publishing Co.

—An Ear Is Not an Ear. l.t. ed. 2002. (Homonyms Ser.). (Illus.). 24p. (J). (ps-3). lib. bdg. 19.93 (978-1-57765-788-0(8) , SandCastle) ABDO Publishing Co.

—Ee: See It Say It Hear It. l.t. ed. 2000. (Alphabet Ser.). (Illus.). 24p. (J). (ps-3). lib. bdg. 19.93 (978-1-57765-398-1(X) , SandCastle) ABDO Publishing Co.

—Ff: See It Say It Hear It. l.t. ed. 2000. (Alphabet Ser.). (Illus.). 24p. (J). (ps-3). lib. bdg. 19.93 (978-1-57765-399-8(8) , SandCastle) ABDO Publishing Co.

—A Fly Can Fly. l.t. ed. 2002. (Homonyms Ser.). (Illus.). 24p. (J). (ps-3). lib. bdg. 19.93 (978-1-57765-786-6(1) , SandCastle) ABDO Publishing Co.

—Gg: See It Say It Hear It. l.t. ed. 2000. (Alphabet Ser.). (Illus.). 24p. (J). (ps-3). lib. bdg. 19.93 (978-1-57765-400-1(5) , SandCastle) ABDO Publishing Co.

—Hh: See It Say It Hear It. l.t. ed. 2000. (Alphabet Ser.). (Illus.). 24p. (J). (ps-3). lib. bdg. 19.93 (978-1-57765-401-8(3) , SandCastle) ABDO Publishing Co.

—Homonyms, Set. l.t. ed. Incl. Bat Hangs from the Bat. lib. bdg. 19.93 (978-1-57765-785-9(3)); Do Not Squash the Squash. lib. bdg. 19.93 (978-1-57765-791-0(8)); Ear Is Not an Ear. lib. bdg. 19.93 (978-1-57765-788-0(8)); Fly Can Fly. lib. bdg. 19.93 (978-1-57765-786-6(1)); Line up on the Line. lib. bdg. 19.93 (978-1-57765-787-3(X)); Palm in My Palm. lib. bdg. 19.93 (978-1-57765-790-3(X)); Rose Rose from the Garden. lib. bdg. 19.93 (978-1-57765-789-7(6)); Top Is on Top. lib. bdg. 19.93 (978-1-57765-792-7(6)); 24p. (J). (ps-3). (Illus.). 2002. Set lib. bdg. 159.44 (978-1-57765-524-4(9) , SandCastle) ABDO Publishing Co.

—How Do You Feel?, Set. l.t. ed. Incl. I Feel Angry. lib. bdg. 19.93 (978-1-57765-187-1(1)); I Feel Brave. lib. bdg. 19.93 (978-1-57765-190-1(1)); I Feel Happy. lib. bdg. 19.93 (978-1-57765-188-8(X)); I Feel Sad. lib. bdg. 19.93 (978-1-57765-189-5(8)); I Feel Safe. lib. bdg. 19.93 (978-1-57765-191-8(X)); I Feel Scared. lib. bdg. 19.93 (978-1-57765-192-5(8)); 24p. (J). (ps-3). 1999. (Illus.). 1999. Set lib. bdg. 119.58 (978-1-57765-265-6(7) , SandCastle) ABDO Publishing Co.

—I Am Sorry. l.t. ed. 2001. (Good Manners Ser.). (Illus.). 24p. (J). (ps-3). lib. bdg. 19.93 (978-1-57765-573-2(7) , SandCastle) ABDO Publishing Co.

—I Feel Brave. l.t. ed. 1999. (How Do You Feel? Ser.). (Illus.). 24p. (J). (ps-3). lib. bdg. 19.93 (978-1-57765-190-1(1) , SandCastle) ABDO Publishing Co.

—Ii: See It Say It Hear It. l.t. ed. 2000. (Alphabet Ser.). (Illus.). 24p. (J). (ps-3). lib. bdg. 19.93 (978-1-57765-402-5(1) , SandCastle) ABDO Publishing Co.

—Jj: See It Say It Hear It. l.t. ed. 2000. (Alphabet Ser.). (Illus.). 24p. (J). (ps-3). lib. bdg. 19.93 (978-1-57765-403-2(X) , SandCastle) ABDO Publishing Co.

—Light & Dark. l.t. ed. 2000. (Opposites Ser.). (Illus.). 24p. (J). (ps-3). lib. bdg. 19.93 (978-1-57765-145-1(6) , SandCastle) ABDO Publishing Co.

—Line up on the Line. l.t. ed. 2002. (Homonyms Ser.). (Illus.). 24p. (J). (ps-3). lib. bdg. 19.93 (978-1-57765-787-3(X) , SandCastle) ABDO Publishing Co.

—Ll: See It Say It Hear It. l.t. ed. 2000. (Alphabet Ser.). (Illus.). 24p. (J). (ps-3). lib. bdg. 19.93 (978-1-57765-405-6(6) , SandCastle) ABDO Publishing Co.

—Nn: See It Say It Hear It. l.t. ed. 2001. (Alphabet Ser.). (Illus.). 24p. (J). (ps-3). lib. bdg. 19.93 (978-1-57765-434-6(X) , SandCastle) ABDO Publishing Co.

—Nouns. l.t. ed. 2001. (Sentences Ser.). (Illus.). 24p. (J). (ps-3). lib. bdg. 19.93 (978-1-57765-614-2(8) , SandCastle) ABDO Publishing Co.

—Opposites, Set. l.t. ed. Incl. Big & Small. lib. bdg. 19.93 (978-1-57765-144-4(8)); Light & Dark. lib. bdg. 19.93 (978-1-57765-145-1(6)); Long & Short. lib. bdg. 19.93 (978-1-57765-146-8(4)); Near & Far. lib. bdg. 19.93 (978-1-57765-147-5(2)); New & Old. lib. bdg. 19.93 (978-1-57765-148-2(0)); Wet & Dry. lib. bdg. 19.93 (978-1-57765-149-9(9)); (J). (ps-3). 2000. (Illus.). 24p. 2000. Set lib. bdg. 119.58 (978-1-57765-282-3(7) , SandCastle) ABDO Publishing Co.

—A Palm in My Palm. l.t. ed. 2002. (Homonyms Ser.). (Illus.). 24p. (J). (ps-3). lib. bdg. 19.93 (978-1-57765-790-3(X) , SandCastle) ABDO Publishing Co.

—Please. l.t. ed. 2001. (Good Manners Ser.). (Illus.). 24p. (J). (ps-3). lib. bdg. 19.93 (978-1-57765-570-1(2) , SandCastle) ABDO Publishing Co.

—Pronouns. l.t. ed. 2001. (Sentences Ser.). (Illus.). 24p. (J). (ps-3). lib. bdg. 19.93 (978-1-57765-619-7(9) , SandCastle) ABDO Publishing Co.

—Proper Nouns. l.t. ed. 2001. (Sentences Ser.). (Illus.). 24p. (J). (ps-3). lib. bdg. 19.93 (978-1-57765-618-0(0) , SandCastle) ABDO Publishing Co.

—The Rose Rose from the Garden. l.t. ed. 2002. (Homonyms Ser.). (Illus.). 24p. (J). (ps-3). lib. bdg. 19.93 (978-1-57765-789-7(6) , SandCastle) ABDO Publishing Co.

—Sentences, Set. l.t. ed. Incl. Adjectives. lib. bdg. 19.93 (978-1-57765-617-3(2)); Adverbs. lib. bdg. 19.93 (978-1-57765-616-6(4)); Nouns. lib. bdg. 19.93 (978-1-57765-614-2(8)); Pronouns. lib. bdg. 19.93 (978-1-57765-619-7(9)); Proper Nouns. lib. bdg. 19.93 (978-1-57765-618-0(0)); Verbs. lib. bdg. 19.93 (978-1-57765-615-9(6)); 24p. (J). (ps-3). (Illus.). 2001. Set lib. bdg. 119.58 (978-1-57765-513-8(3) , SandCastle) ABDO Publishing Co.

—Thank You. l.t. ed. 2001. (Good Manners Ser.). (Illus.). 24p. (J). (ps-3). lib. bdg. 19.93 (978-1-57765-571-8(0) , SandCastle) ABDO Publishing Co.

—The Top Is on Top. l.t. ed. 2002. (Homonyms Ser.). (Illus.). 24p. (J). (ps-3). lib. bdg. 19.93 (978-1-57765-792-7(6) , SandCastle) ABDO Publishing Co.

—Verbs. l.t. ed. 2001. (Sentences Ser.). (Illus.). 24p. (J). (ps-3). lib. bdg. 19.93 (978-1-57765-615-9(6) , SandCastle) ABDO Publishing Co.

Dowell, Andrea C. & Rokke, Kathi R. Miguel & Sarah: Close Friends & Cystic Fibrosis. Madden, Randi, illus. l.t. ed. 1999. 22p. (J). (gr. k-4). pap. 8.00 (978-0-9644972-1-4(2)) Children's Hospitals & Clinics.

Dowell, Frances O'Roark. Dovey Coe. l.t. ed. 2001. 171p. (J). 22.95 (978-0-7862-3590-2(X)) Thorndike Pr.

Dowling, James. Animal Ark Bk. 1: In the Beginning. Dowling, Brenda, ed. Ileana & Broderick, Michael, illus. 2nd l.t. ed. 1998. 48p. (J). (gr. 3-5). 19.95 (978-1-57087-381-2(X)) Professional Pr.

Doyle, Arthur Conan. The Adventure of the Speckled Band. Stemach, Jerry, ed. Letwenko, Michael, illus. l.t. ed. 2002. 104p. 150.00 (978-1-58702-041-4(6)) Johnston, Don Inc.

—The Return of Sherlock Holmes. l.t. ed. 1998. (Large Print Heritage Ser.). 278p. (YA). (gr. 7-12). lib. bdg. 29.95 (978-1-58118-038-1(1)) LRS.

Dozier, Kim. The Ear-Less Kingdom. Dozier, Ashlyn McCauley, illus. l.t. ed. 2003. (ENG.). 24p. (J). 7.50 (978-0-9745839-1-4(X) , Fun to Read Bks. with Royally Good Morals) MKADesigns.

—The Forgetful Princess. Dozier, Ashlyn McCauley, illus. 2nd l.t. ed. 2003. (ENG.). 24p. (J). 10.00 (978-0-9745839-0-7(1) , Fun to Read Bks. with Royally Good Morals) MKADesigns.

—Where's Dwight Dragon. Dozier, Ashlyn McCauley, illus. l.t. ed. 2004. (ENG.). 32p. (J). 10.00 (978-0-9745839-2-1(8) , Fun to Read Bks. with Royally Good Morals) MKADesigns.

Drachman, Eric. Leo the Lightning Bug. Muscarello, James, illus. l.t. ed. 2002. 32p. (J). (ps-2). 18.95 (978-0-9703809-0-6(9)) Kidwick Bks.

Duchene-Marshall, Michele A. Charley Finds A Family. Marshall, Alan David, ed. Ousley, Clayton Gerard, photos by. l.t. ed. 2004. Orig. Title: Charley finds a Home. (Illus.). 20p. (J). spiral bd. 10.00 (978-0-9761675-2-5(2)) Storybook Acres.

—Shirley's Red Satin Shoes. Marshall, Alan David, ed. Ousley, Clayton Gerard, photos by. l.t. ed. 2003. (Illus.). 17p. (J). spiral bd. 10.00 (978-0-9761675-1-8(4)) Storybook Acres.

Dunbar, Paula J. Ruby's Rainbow: A Story of Acadia National Park. l.t. ed. 2005. (Illus.). 32p. (J). (978-1-931207-59-1(3)) Dilligaf Publishing.

Dunn, Charles. Learning with Leonard & Friends: From A to Z. Ovange, Sheila & Groller, Scott, eds. Groller, Matt, illus. l.t. ed. 1998. 64p. (J). (ps-1). 17.95 (978-0-9663240-3-7(X)) Dunn, Charles Camaron.

Dunwoodie, Helen. Ghost on the Loose! l.t. ed. 2005. 176p. (J). pap. (978-0-7540-7830-2(2) , CLP 421) BBC Audio.

Durant, Alan. Creepe Hall Forever! l.t. ed. 2003. (Read-Along Ser.). 112p. (J). 24.95 (978-0-7540-6242-4(2) , RAO43, Galaxy Children's Large Print) BBC Audiobooks America.

—Leggs United: The Phantom Footballer. Smedley, Chris, illus. l.t. ed. 1999. 112p. (J). pap. (978-0-7540-6084-0(5) , CLP 282) BBC Audio.

Durin-Valois, Marc. Chamelle. l.t. ed. 2003. (French Ser.). (Illus.). 236p. 30.99 (978-2-84011-524-3(7)) Ulverscroft Large Print Bks. GBR. *Dist:* Ulverscroft Large Print Bks., Ltd.

Eagle, Golden. It's Good to Laugh at Yourself (Coyote Medicine. l.t. ed. 2004. (Illus.). 22p. (J). per. 9.95 (978-1-932338-36-2(5)) Lifevest Publishing, Inc.

—It's Good to Shed Your Skin (Snake Medicine) l.t. ed. 2004. (Illus.). 20p. (J). per. 9.95 (978-1-932338-38-6(1)) Lifevest Publishing, Inc.

—It's Okay to Cry (Frog Medicine) l.t. ed. 2004. (Illus.). 16p. (J). per. 9.95 (978-1-932338-37-9(3)) Lifevest Publishing, Inc.

—The Owl Who Lives in My House. l.t. ed. 2003. (Illus.). 24p. (J). per. 9.95 (978-1-932338-34-8(9)) Lifevest Publishing, Inc.

Eakle, Kit. In My Grandmother's Garden. Eakle, Laura Jean, illus. l.t. ed. 2001. 32p. (J). (gr. k-5). 21.95 (978-0-9713194-0-0(5) , MusicTales) MusicKit.COM.

Eastman, P. D. Are You My Mother? Eastman, P. D., illus. l.t. ed. 1998. (Bright & Early Board Bks.). (Illus.). 24p. (J). (gr. k-ps). bds. 4.99 (978-0-679-89047-8(5) , Random Hse. Bks. for Young Readers) Random Hse. Children's Bks.

Easton, Kelly. The Life History of a Star. l.t. ed. 2002. 200p. 22.95 (978-0-7862-4786-8(X)) Thorndike Pr.

Ebo, Runett Nia. Lord, Why Did You Make Me Black? l.t. ed. 2000. 10p. (YA). (ps up). pap. 9.99 (978-1-883753-21-4(X)) J.W.A.N.D. Enterprises.

Ebon Research Systems Staff. Dare to Be: Roberto Clemente. l.t. ed. 2003. Tr. of Atrevete a Ser un Heroe. . . Roberto Clemente. (ENG & SPA., Illus.). 22p. 3.99 (978-0-9648313-5-3(X)) Ebon Research Systems Publishing, LLC.

—Dare to Be Vol. 2: Lessons in the Life of Esperanza. l.t. ed. 2003. Tr. of Atrevete Ser... Un Heroe. (ENG & SPA., Illus.). 16p. (J). 3.99 (978-0-9648313-4-6(1)) Ebon Research Systems Publishing, LLC.

—Dare to Be... A Hero Vol. 3: Cesar Chavez. l.t. ed. 2003. Tr. of Atrevete Ser... Un Heroe Cesar Chavez. (ENG & SPA., Illus.). 16p. (J). 3.99 (978-0-9648313-6-0(8)) Ebon Research Systems Publishing, LLC.

Eckdahl, Judith & Eckdahl, Kathryn. A Collection of Street Games. O'Regan, Lucy, ed. Miranda, Pedro, illus. 2005. 42p. pupil's gde. ed. 13.95 (978-0-9767200-0-3(0)) Lesen Pub.

Edwards, Verne. The Museum Duck. Norman, Kimberly, illus. l.t. ed. 2000. 33p. (J). per. 8.00 (978-0-9705823-0-0(7)) Pearl Line Pr., Inc.

Efird, Carrie. Wiggly, Squiggly Bugs. Lent, Marion W., illus. l.t. ed. 1998. (Big Bks.). (J). (ps-k). pap. 10.95 (978-1-57332-117-4(6)) HighReach Learning, Inc.

Egoak, Julia K. The Story Knife. Egoak, Julia K. & Nevak, Caroline, illus. l.t. ed. 1999. 8p. (J). (gr. k-3). pap. 14.50 (978-1-58084-076-7(0)) Lower Kuskokwim Schl. District.

—Yaaruissun. Egoak, Julia K. & Nevak, Caroline, illus. l.t. ed. 1999. Tr. of Story Knife. (ESK.). 8p. (J). (gr. k-3). pap. 14.50 (978-1-58084-077-4(9)); pap. 14.50 (978-1-58084-118-4(X)) Lower Kuskokwim Schl. District.

Ehlin, Gina. Emma & Friends: Emma's Airport Adventure. Ayzenberg, Nina, illus. l.t. ed. 2005. 32p. (J). lib. bdg. 15.99 (978-1-59879-015-3(3)); per. 10.99 (978-1-59879-014-6(5)) Lifevest Publishing, Inc.

Elboz, Stephen. Temmi & Flying Bears. l.t. ed. 1999. (Illus.). 164p. (J). pap. (978-0-7540-6043-7(8) , CLP 245) BBC Audio.

Elizabeth, Ann. Little Annie Fountainhead. Larson, Karl, ed. Miskov, Kathy, illus. l.t. ed. 1999. 32p. (J). (gr. k-6). pap. 8.95 (978-0-9654436-5-4(5)) Honey Creek Publishing, Inc.

Elliott, Ruth & Elliott, David. The Richest Kid in the Poor House. Elliott, Ruth, illus. l.t. ed. 1999. (Illus.). 68p. (J). (ps-6). 19.95 (978-0-9668747-9-2(X)); pap. 14.95 (978-0-9668747-8-5(1)) Partnership Publishing.

Ellis, Marvie. Tacos Anyone? Bk. 2: An Autism Story Book. l.t. ed. 2005. Tr. of ¿Alguien quiere Tacos?. (SPA., Illus.). 32p. (J). per. 16.95 (978-1-933319-01-8(1)) Speech Kids Texas Pr.

Elms, Mae D. And Donna Makes Five. l.t. ed. 2000. (Adventure Ser.). 31p. (J). (gr. 1-6). pap. 22.95 (978-1-930002-30-2(0)) I & L Publishing.

—Travel into Adventure Land. l.t. ed. 2000. (Illus.). 150p. (J). (gr. 2-9). pap. 19.95 (978-1-930002-08-1(4)) I & L Publishing.

Emerick, Yahiya. Color & Learn Salah. Meehan, Patricia, illus. l.t. ed. 1999. 100p. (J). (gr. k-2). mass mkt. 6.00 (978-1-889720-31-9(3)) Amirah Publishing.

Emmanuel, Francois. La Chambre Voisine. l.t. ed. 2002. (French Ser.). (FRE., Illus.). 223p. 30.99 (978-2-84011-467-3(4)) Ulverscroft Large Print Bks. GBR. *Dist:* Ulverscroft Large Print Bks., Ltd.

English, D. N. Downtown Wanderings: Stories & Pictures of Downtown Jackson Tennessee. Galloway, Annette, ed. l.t. ed. 2002. (Illus.). 184p. per. 15.95 (978-0-9710470-0-6(6)) Main St Publishing, Inc.

—Miss Piglet of Steam Mill Ferry Road: Finds a New Home. Winbush, Danny, photos by. l.t. ed. 2002. (Illus.). 20p. 8.00 (978-0-9710470-9-9(X) , 75, MSP) Main St Publishing, Inc.

English, Karen. Francie. l.t. ed. 2002. 220p. (J). 21.95 (978-0-7862-3717-3(1)) Thomson Gale.

Ennis, Judith. Kalakala Comes Home: No Dream Is Too Big! McCoy, Lisa et al, eds. Ingram, Dean, tr. Wilburn, Kathy, photos by. l.t. ed. 2000. (Illus.). 50p. (J). 18.95 (978-0-9660092-7-9(4)) Puget Sound Pr.

Epstein, Brad, ed. Auburn University 101. l.t. ed. 2003. (My First Text Board Bks.). (Illus.). 20p. (J). bds. 9.95 (978-0-9727702-7-9(5)) Michaelson Entertainment.

—Cornell University 101: My First Text-Board-Book. l.t. ed. 2004. (101—My First Text-Board Books). (Illus.). 20p. (J). bds. 9.95 (978-1-932530-00-1(2)) Michaelson Entertainment.

—Dartmouth College 101. l.t. ed. 2003. (My First Text Board Bks.). (Illus.). 20p. (J). bds. 9.95 (978-0-9727702-5-5(9)) Michaelson Entertainment.

—Penn State University 101: My First Text-Board-Book. l.t. ed. 2004. (101—My First Text-Board Books). (Illus.). 20p. (J). bds. 9.95 (978-1-932530-04-9(5)) Michaelson Entertainment.

—Stanford University 101: My First Text-Board-Book. l.t. ed. 2003. (101—My First Text-Board Books). (Illus.). 20p. (J). bds. 9.95 (978-1-932530-05-6(3) , 101 Bk.) Michaelson Entertainment.

—University of Alabama 101. l.t. ed. 2003. (My First Text Board Bks.). (Illus.). 20p. (J). bds. 9.95 (978-0-9727702-6-2(7)) Michaelson Entertainment.

—University of Iowa 101: My First Text-Board-Book. l.t. ed. 2005. (101—My First Text-Board Books). (Illus.). 20p. (J). bds. 9.95 (978-1-932530-34-6(7)) Michaelson Entertainment.

—University of Michigan 101: My First Text-Board-Book. l.t. ed. 2003. (101—My First Text-Board Books). (Illus.). 20p. (J). bds. 9.95 (978-1-932530-02-5(9)) Michaelson Entertainment.

—University of Nebraska 101: My First Text-Board-Book. l.t. ed. 2003. (101—My First Text-Board Books). (Illus.). 20p. (J). bds. 9.95 (978-1-932530-03-2(7)) Michaelson Entertainment.

—University of Tennessee 101. l.t. ed. 2003. (My First Text Board Bks.). (Illus.). 20p. (J). bds. 9.95 (978-0-9727702-8-6(3)) Michaelson Entertainment.

—University of Washington 101. l.t. ed. 2003. (My First Text Board Bks.). (Illus.). 20p. (J). bds. 9.95 (978-0-9727702-9-3(1) , 101 Bk.) Michaelson Entertainment.

Epstein, Brad M. University of Michigan 123: My First Counting Book. l.t. ed. 2005. (Illus.). 30p. (J). 14.95 (978-1-932530-36-0(3)) Michaelson Entertainment.

—Usc 123: My First Counting Book. l.t. ed. 2005. (Illus.). 30p. (J). bds. 14.95 (978-1-932530-35-3(5)) Michaelson Entertainment.

Epstein, Brad M., ed. Arizona State University 101: My First Text-Board-Book. l.t. ed. 2003. (101—My First Text-Board Books). (Illus.). 20p. (J). bds. 9.95 (978-0-9727702-3-1(2) , 101 Bk.) Michaelson Entertainment.

—Clemson University 101: My First Text-Board-Book. l.t. ed. 2004. (101—My First Text-Board Books). (Illus.). 20p. (J). bds. 9.95 (978-1-932530-06-3(1)) Michaelson Entertainment.

—Florida State University 101: My First Text-Board-Book. l.t. ed. 2004. (My First Text Board Bks.). (Illus.). 20p. (J). bds. 9.95 (978-1-932530-07-0(X)) Michaelson Entertainment.

—Louisiana State University 101: My First Text-Board-Book. l.t. ed. 2004. (My First Text Board Bks.). (Illus.). 20p. (J). bds. 9.95 (978-1-932530-09-4(6)) Michaelson Entertainment.

—Michigan State University 101: My First Text-Board-Book. l.t. ed. 2004. (My First Text Board Bks.). (Illus.). 20p. (J). bds. 9.95 (978-1-932530-14-8(2)) Michaelson Entertainment.

—Purdue University 101: My First Text-Board-Book. l.t. ed. 2004. (101—My First Text-Board Books). (Illus.). 20p. (J). bds. 9.95 (978-1-932530-11-7(8)) Michaelson Entertainment.

—Texas A & M 101: My First Text. l.t. ed. 2003. (101—My First Text-Board Books). (Illus.). 20p. (J). bds. 9.95 (978-0-9727702-4-8(0)) Michaelson Entertainment.

—UCLA 101: My First Text-Board-Book. l.t. ed. 2004. (My First Text Board Bks.). (Illus.). 20p. (J). bds. 9.95 (978-1-932530-15-5(0)) Michaelson Entertainment.

—University of California, Berkeley 101: My First Text-Board-Book. l.t. ed. 2005. (101—My First Text-Board Books). (Illus.). 20p. (J). bds. 9.95 (978-1-932530-28-5(2)) Michaelson Entertainment.

—University of Florida 101: My First Text-Board-Book. l.t. ed. 2004. (101—My First Text-Board Books). (Illus.). 20p. (J). bds. 9.95 (978-1-932530-21-6(5)) Michaelson Entertainment.

—University of Georgia 101: My First Text-Board-Book. l.t. ed. 2004. (101—My First Text-Board Books). (Illus.). 20p. (J). bds. 9.95 (978-1-932530-08-7(8)) Michaelson Entertainment.

—University of Illinois 101: My First Text-Board-Book. l.t. ed. 2004. (101—My First Text-Board Books). (Illus.). 20p. (J). bds. 9.95 (978-1-932530-17-9(7)) Michaelson Entertainment.

—University of Mississippi 101: My First Text-Board-Book. l.t. ed. 2005. (101—My First Text-Board Books). (Illus.). 20p. (J). bds. 9.95 (978-1-932530-26-1(6)) Michaelson Entertainment.

—University of North Carolina 101: My First Text-Board-Book. l.t. ed. 2004. (My First Text Board Bks.). (Illus.). 20p. (J). bds. 9.95 (978-1-932530-12-4(6)) Michaelson Entertainment.

—University of Notre Dame 101: My First Text-Board-Book. l.t. ed. 2005. (101—My First Text-Board Books). (Illus.). 20p. (J). bds. 11.95 (978-1-932530-33-9(9)) Michaelson Entertainment.

—University of Texas at Austin 101: My First Text-Board-Book. l.t. ed. 2004. (101—My First Text-Board Books). (Illus.). 20p. (J). bds. 9.95 (978-1-932530-13-1(4)) Michaelson Entertainment.

—University of Wisconsin 101: My First Text-Board-Book. l.t. ed. 2004. (101—My First Text-Board Books). (Illus.). 20p. (J). bds. 9.95 (978-1-932530-18-6(5)) Michaelson Entertainment.

—USC 101: My First Text-Board-Book. l.t. ed. 2004. (101—My First Text-Board Books). (Illus.). 20p. (J). bds. 9.95 (978-0-9727702-0-0(8)) Michaelson Entertainment.

—Washington State University 101: My First Text-Board-Book. l.t. ed. 2005. (101—My First Text-Board Books). (Illus.). 20p. (J). bds. 9.95 (978-1-932530-25-4(8)) Michaelson Entertainment.

—Yale 101: My First Text. l.t. ed. 2003. (101—My First Text-Board Books). (Illus.). 20p. (J). bds. 9.95 (978-0-9727702-2-4(4)) Michaelson Entertainment.

Erdrich, Louise. The Game of Silence. l.t. ed. 2005. (Illus.). 319p. (J). (gr. 3-7). per. 22.95 (978-0-7862-7768-1(8) , Large Print Pr.); 2000. 272p. (YA). (gr. 7-12). 20.95 (978-0-7862-2178-3(X)) Thorndike Pr.

Erickson, Tim. Learning Mathematics with Graphing Calculator 1.3. 2001. 99p. act. bk. ed. 19.95 incl. cd-rom (978-0-9648496-1-7(5) , eeps media) Epistemological Engineering.

Evans, Mary. Big Book Vol. 2: Cats! Cats! Cats! Kovalcik, Terry, illus. l.t. ed. 2005. (Sadlier Phonics Reading Program). 8p. (YA). (ps-1). 22.50 (978-0-8215-7348-8(9)) Sadlier, William H. Inc.

—Big Book: Good Pets, Vol. 3. l.t. ed. 2005. (Sadlier Phonics Reading Program). (Illus.). 8p. (YA). (ps-1). 22.50 (978-0-8215-7350-1(0)) Sadlier, William H. Inc.

Evrard, Jackie. It's Great to Be Me! A Special Story & Activity Book. l.t. ed. 1998. (Illus.). 24p. (J). (gr. 1-5). pap. 11.95 (978-0-9666317-0-8(6)) Rainbow Write! Publishing.

Fabris, Judith. Money...Cool! Brolin, Carol, illus. l.t. ed. 2003. 155p. (YA). pap. 9.95 (978-1-893335-12-7(7)) Archipelago Pr.

Fabulas de Siempre. l.t. ed. Tr. of Traditional Fables. (SPA.). (J). 3.98 (978-84-7630-901-8(5)) Selector, S.A. de C.V. MEX. *Dist:* AIMS International Bks., Inc.

Falkner, John Meade. Moonfleet. l.t. ed. 2004. (Large Print Ser.). 370p. 26.00 (978-1-58287-658-0(4)) North Bks.

Famous Lives, 10 bks. l.t. ed. Incl. Story of Abraham Lincoln : President for the People. Weinberg, Larry. LaPadula, Tom, illus. 1997. lib. bdg. 22.60 (978-0-8368-1484-2(3)); Story of Alexander Graham Bell : Inventor of the Telephone. Davidson, Margaret. Marchesi, Stephen, illus. 1997. lib. bdg. 22.60 (978-0-8368-1483-5(5)); Story of Babe Ruth : Baseball's Greatest Legend. Eisenberg, Lisa. 1997. lib. bdg. 22.60 (978-0-8368-1486-6(X)); Story of Benjamin Franklin : Amazing American. Davidson, Margaret. Speirs, John, illus. 1997. lib. bdg. 22.60 (978-0-8368-1475-0(4)); Story of Christopher Columbus. Osborne, Mary Pope. Marchesi, Stephen, illus. 1997. lib. bdg. 22.60 (978-0-8368-1482-8(7)); Story of Davy Crockett : Frontier Hero. Retan, Walter. Petruccio, Steven James, illus. 1997. lib. bdg. 22.60 (978-0-8368-1485-9(1)); Story of George Bush : The Forty-First President of the United States. Sufrin, Mark. 1997. lib. bdg. 22.60 (978-0-8368-1478-1(9)); Story of Shirley Temple Black : Hollywood's Youngest Star. Fiori, Carlo. 1997. lib. bdg. 22.60 (978-0-8368-1481-1(9)); Story of Sitting Bull : Great Sioux Chief. Eisenberg, Lisa. Rickman, David, illus. 1996. lib. bdg. 22.60 (978-0-8368-1465-1(7)); Story of Walt Disney : Maker of Magical Worlds. Selden, Bernice. 1996. lib. bdg. 22.60 (978-0-8368-1468-2(1)); 100p. (J). (gr. 3 up). (Illus.). Set lib. bdg. 226.00 (978-0-8368-1998-4(5)) Stevens, Gareth Inc.

Farquhar-Claypool, Kris. Everglades Environmental Storybook: Upland & Inland Creatures. l.t. ed. 1999. (Voices of the Earth Ser.: Vol. II). (Illus.). 48p. (J). (gr. k-4). pap. 6.95 (978-0-9666720-0-8(3)) Earthwing Pubns.

Farrow, Stephanie, ed. Blue Wolf & Friends Storybook, 1 Vol., Units 1-4. l.t. ed. 2004. (Illus.). 93p. (978-0-9758759-2-6(2)) Progressive Language, Inc.

Faye, Joanne & Whaley, Stacey Lynn. Conversations with Kids Ages 3 to 6. l.t. ed. 2004. (Illus.). 24p. (J). 9.95 (978-0-9747375-0-8(X)) Joanne Faye Pr.

Felder, Deborah G. Changing Times, 14 bks., Set. Rabinowitz, Sandy & Keiffer, Christa, illus. l.t. ed. 1999. (Treasured Horses Collection). 128p. (J). (gr. 4 up). lib. bdg. 23.33 (978-0-8368-2276-2(5)) Stevens, Gareth Inc.

—Ride of Courage. Rabinowitz, Sandy & Keiffer, Christa, illus. l.t. ed. 1999. (Treasured Horses Collection). 128p. (J). (gr. 4 up). lib. bdg. 23.33 (978-0-8368-2280-9(3)) Stevens, Gareth Inc.

Fenton, Edward. Duffy's Rocks. l.t. ed. 1999. (Golden Triangle Bks.). 240p. (YA). (gr. 8-12). pap. 9.95 (978-0-8229-5706-5(X)) Univ. of Pittsburgh Pr.

Fetzer, Erin. The Sonday System Readers - 6a-10c, 1. Breckman, Cindy, ed. l.t. ed. 2004. (Illus.). 12p. (J). (978-1-891602-14-6(4)) Winsor Learning, Inc.

Fey, Sid & Vitello, Kathy. The Being Game: For the Love of Your Life. l.t. ed. 2004. (Illus.). 66p. per. 14.95 (978-0-9753530-5-9(5)) Fey, Sid Designs, Inc.

Feyh, Janelle. Does God Have a Remote Control? Feyh, Alexa & Deghand, Tim, illus. l.t. ed. 2003. 66p. (J). per. 11.95 (978-1-932344-26-4(8)) Thornton Publishing.

A Fifty Year Affair: Living with Light Planes. l.t. ed. 2004. (Illus.). 208p. (YA). pap. 18.95 (978-0-9746564-0-3(2)) Julson, D. K.

Fine, Anne. Crummy Mummy & Me. Douglass, Claire, illus. l.t. ed. 2002. 176p. (J). 16.95 (978-0-7540-7813-5(2) , Galaxy Children's Large Print) BBC Audiobooks America.

—Flour Babies. l.t. ed. 2000. 238p. (J). pap. 16.95 (978-0-7540-6110-6(8) , Galaxy Children's Large Print) BBC Audiobooks America.

Finley, Judith S. As the Waters Cover the Sea: A Visit to the Seashore. Fleet, Eric C., photos by. l.t. ed. 1998. (Caitlyn & Eryn Ser.: No. 1). (Illus.). 20p. (J). (gr. k-2). pap. 6.00 (978-0-9665424-0-0(1)) Master Design, The.

First Bank Community Writers Staff. Fir$t Kid$ Bank - $aving Is Fun. Freeman, Troy, illus. l.t. ed. 1998. (Kids! Ser.: No. 38). 70p. (J). (gr. 2-4). pap. 3.95 (978-1-57635-020-1(7)) WeWrite LLC.

The First Man: Quran Stories for Little Hearts. l.t. ed. 2001. 24p. (J). per. 4.25 (978-81-87570-93-6(8)) Goodword Bks. Pvt. Ltd. IND. *Dist:* Lodhia Ctr., The.

Fisher, Kathleen S. English for the Spanish Speaker, Vol. 4. l.t. ed. 1999. (ENG & SPA.). 110p. (gr. 7 up). wbk. ed. 12.95 (978-1-878253-18-7(2)) Fisher Hill.

Fisher, Phyllis Mae Richardson, illus. Chrissy (#1 in the 1989 Family Friends Paper Doll Set) l.t. ed. 2004. 24p. (J). 10.00 (978-0-9745615-5-4(X)) PJs Corner.

—Melly, #2 in the 1989 Family Friends Paper Doll Set, Vols. 3, Vol. 2. l.t. ed. 2004. 24p. (J). 10.00 (978-0-9745615-6-1(8)) PJs Corner.

Flake, Sharon G. The Skin I'm In. l.t. ed. 1999. 173p. (J). (gr. 7-12). 20.95 (978-0-7862-2179-0(8)) Thorndike Pr.

Fleming, David. Miss Mouse's House. Storms, Samantha Ivey, illus. l.t. ed. 2001. 36p. (J). 15.00 (978-0-9643003-2-3(X)) Country Place Bks.

Fletcher, Susan. Walk Across the Sea. l.t. ed. 2002. 218p. (J). 22.95 (978-0-7862-4439-3(9)) Thorndike Pr.

Fly Fishing the Flat Tops. 2nd l.t. ed. 2000. 62p. 14.00 (978-0-9715563-0-0(X)) Hidden Lakes Pr.

Foce, Natalia, tr. from ENG. Daniel, el Príncipe que Oraba, Apps, Fred, illus. l.t. ed. 2004. (SPA.). 36p. (J). 2.99 (978-1-932789-19-5(7)) Editorial Sendas Antiguas, LLC.

—David, el Luchador Valiente, Apps, Fred, illus. l.t. ed. 2004. (SPA.). 36p. (J). 2.99 (978-1-932789-18-8(9)) Editorial Sendas Antiguas, LLC.

—La Historia de Pablo — Viajes de Aventura, 1. Apps, Fred, illus. l.t. ed. 2004. Orig. Title: Journeys of Adventure — the Story of Paul. (SPA.). 36p. (J). 2.99 (978-1-932789-23-2(5)) Editorial Sendas Antiguas, LLC.

—Jesus el Milagroso. Anderson, Jeff, illus. l.t. ed. 2004. Orig. Title: Jesus the Miracle Worker. (SPA.). 24p. (J). 2.99 (978-1-932789-28-7(6)) Editorial Sendas Antiguas, LLC.

—Jesus Maestro. Anderson, Jeff, illus. l.t. ed. 2004. Orig. Title: Jesus the Teacher. (SPA.). 24p. (J). 2.99 (978-1-932789-26-3(X)) Editorial Sendas Antiguas, LLC.

—Jesus Narrador. Anderson, Jeff, illus. l.t. ed. 2004. Orig. Title: Jesus the Storyteller. (SPA.). 24p. (J). 2.99 (978-1-932789-25-6(1)) Editorial Sendas Antiguas, LLC.

—Jesus Niño. Anderson, Jeff, illus. l.t. ed. 2004. Orig. Title: Jesus the Child. (SPA.). 24p. (J). 2.99 (978-1-932789-24-9(3)) Editorial Sendas Antiguas, LLC.

—Jesus Salvador. Anderson, Jeff, illus. l.t. ed. 2004. Orig. Title: Jesus the Saviour. (SPA.). 24p. (J). 2.99 (978-1-932789-29-4(4)) Editorial Sendas Antiguas, LLC.

J
K
L

—Jesus Sanador. Anderson, Jeff, illus. l.t. ed. 2004. Orig. Title: Jesus the Healer. (SPA.). 24p. (J). 2.99 (978-1-932789-27-0(8)) Editorial Sendas Antiguas, LLC.

—El Nacimiento de Jesus: El Niño Prometido, 1. Apps, Fred, illus. l.t. ed. 2004. Orig. Title: The Birth of Jesus — the Promised Child. (SPA.). 36p. (J). 2.99 (978-1-932789-20-1(0)) Editorial Sendas Antiguas, LLC.

—El Plan de Rescate: La Historia de Noe, 1. Apps, Fred, illus. l.t. ed. 2004. Orig. Title: The Rescue Plan. (SPA.). 36p. (J). 2.99 (978-1-932789-15-7(4)) Editorial Sendas Antiguas, LLC.

—La Resurreccion: Jesus Esta Vivo, 1. Apps, Fred, illus. l.t. ed. 2004. Orig. Title: The Resurrection — Jesus Is Alive. (SPA.). 36p. (J). 2.99 (978-1-932789-21-8(9)) Editorial Sendas Antiguas, LLC.

—Samuel, el Niño que Escuchaba. Apps, Fred, illus. l.t. ed. 2004. (SPA.). 36p. (J). 2.99 (978-1-932789-17-1(0)) Editorial Sendas Antiguas, LLC.

—Saul — el Milagro en el Camino, 1. Apps, Fred, illus. l.t. ed. 2004. Orig. Title: Saul — the Miracle on the Road. (SPA.). 36p. (J). 2.99 (978-1-932789-22-5(7)) Editorial Sendas Antiguas, LLC.

—El Soñador de Dios: La Historia de José, Apps, Fred, illus. l.t. ed. 2004. (SPA.). 36p. (J). 2.99 (978-1-932789-16-4(2)) Editorial Sendas Antiguas, LLC.

Fontanez, Edwin. On This Beautiful Island. Fontanez, Edwin, illus. l.t. ed. 2004. (Illus.). 32p. (J). 16.95 (978-0-9640868-6-9(7) , 1241077) Exit Studio.

Forbes, Esther Hoskins. Johnny Tremain Set: Illustrated American Classics, 2 vols., l.t. ed. (J). reprint ed. (978-0-89064-029-6(7)) National Assn. for Visually Handicapped.

Formby, Caroline. Tristan's Bedtime Story. Formby, Caroline, illus. l.t. ed. 1998. (Children's Stories Published in Other Lands Ser.). (Illus.). 32p. (J). (gr. 2 up). lib. bdg. 12.95 (978-1-56674-269-6(2)) Forest Hse. Publishing Co., Inc.

—Tristan's Temper Tantrum. Formby, Caroline, illus. l.t. ed. 1998. (Children's Stories Published in Other Lands Ser.). (Illus.). 32p. (J). (gr. 2 up). lib. bdg. 12.95 (978-1-56674-224-5(2)) Forest Hse. Publishing Co., Inc.

Foster, Kathryn Joy. Always Room for One More. l.t. ed. 2004. (Illus.). 12p. (J). spiral bd. 13.00 (978-0-9728779-6-1(7) , TBK-21007) Read All Over Publishing.

—Pathway to Prosperity. l.t. ed. 2000. 59p. (YA). 15.00 (978-0-9728779-3-0(2) , TBK-21004) Read All Over Publishing.

—Press Toward the Mark: Mountain Moving Faith, 1. l.t. ed. 2000. 54p. (YA). 15.00 (978-0-9728779-2-3(4) , TBK-21003) Read All Over Publishing.

—Royal Seed. l.t. ed. 2000. 30p. (YA). spiral bd. 20.00 (978-0-9728779-4-7(0) , TBK-21005) Read All Over Publishing.

—What if Noah Rocked the Boat? l.t. ed. 2002. 32p. (J). spiral bd. 20.00 (978-0-9728779-5-4(9) , TBK-21006) Read All Over Publishing.

Fournier, Mark Edward. Rain: Attitude Is Everything. Kyle, Patricia Lynn, illus. 2nd l.t. ed. 2002. 50p. spiral bd. 17.99 (978-0-9725243-1-5(2)) Fournier Media.

The Fox & the Stork, Vol. 2. l.t. ed. 1999. (Illus.). 43p. (J). (gr. k-6). reprint ed. pap. 2.50 (978-1-893688-06-3(2)) Carroll Schl., The.

The Fox & the Thrush. l.t. ed. 1999. (Illus.). 15p. (J). (gr. k-6). reprint ed. pap. 2.50 (978-1-893688-03-2(8)) Carroll Schl., The.

Frazier, Jamine L. & Scott, James D., creators. Cosmic Kid & Tornado Kid Adventures. l.t. ed. 2001. 100p. (J). pap. 20.00 (978-1-877784-15-6(X)) Cardinal Publishing Group, The.

Frazier, Janet. The Case of the Theme Park Cry. l.t. ed. 2004. 90p. (J). per. (978-1-59196-737-8(6)) Instantpublisher.com.

Freed, Shirley Ann. Michael Never Gives Up. Morelan, Bill, ed. Harrell, Rob, illus. l.t. ed. 2002. 24p. (J). (gr. 1). pap. 3.99 (978-1-58938-041-7(X)) Concerned Communications.

Freed, Shirley Ann & Moon, Louise. Adam Named the Animals. Morelan, Bill, ed. Butler, Steven, illus. l.t. ed. 2002. 8p. (J). (ps-k). pap. 3.99 (978-1-58938-000-4(2)) Concerned Communications.

—Angels Care for Me. Morelan, Bill, ed. Harrell, Rob, illus. l.t. ed. 2002. 8p. (J). (ps-k). pap. 3.99 (978-1-58938-005-9(3)) Concerned Communications.

—Baby Is Sleeping. Morelan, Bill, ed. l.t. ed. 2002. (Illus.). 16p. (J). (gr. 5). pap. 3.99 (978-1-58938-006-6(1)) Concerned Communications.

—Baby Lamb. Morelan, Bill, ed. Butler, Steven, illus. l.t. ed. 2002. 8p. (J). (gr. 5). pap. 3.99 (978-1-58938-010-3(X)) Concerned Communications.

—A Big Big Lunch. Morelan, Bill, ed. Butler, Steven, illus. l.t. ed. 2002. 16p. (J). (gr. 1-2). pap. 3.99 (978-1-58938-030-1(4)) Concerned Communications.

—Blind, Blind Bart. Morelan, Bill, ed. Butler, Steven, illus. l.t. ed. 2002. 8p. (J). (gr. 3-4). pap. 3.99 (978-1-58938-020-2(7)) Concerned Communications.

—Creation. Morelan, Bill, ed. Butler, Steven, illus. l.t. ed. 2002. 16p. (J). (gr. 1-2). pap. 3.99 (978-1-58938-036-3(3)) Concerned Communications.

—Daniel & the Lions. Morelan, Bill, ed. Butler, Steven, illus. l.t. ed. 2002. 8p. (J). (gr. 5). pap. 3.99 (978-1-58938-011-0(8)) Concerned Communications.

—Daniel Prayed. Morelan, Bill, ed. Butler, Steven, illus. l.t. ed. 2002. 8p. (J). (gr. 6). pap. 3.99 (978-1-58938-012-7(6)) Concerned Communications.

—A Dark Dark Night. Morelan, Bill, ed. Butler, Steven, illus. l.t. ed. 2002. 8p. (J). (gr. 1-2). pap. 3.99 (978-1-58938-015-8(0)) Concerned Communications.

—Fishers of Men. Morelan, Bill, ed. Butler, Steven, illus. l.t. ed. 2002. 16p. (J). (gr. 6). pap. 3.99 (978-1-58938-029-5(0)) Concerned Communications.

—God Calls Samuel. Morelan, Bill, ed. Butler, Steven, illus. l.t. ed. 2002. 24p. (J). (gr. 6). pap. 3.99 Concerned Communications.

—God Makes the Sun Shine. Morelan, Bill, ed. Harrell, Rob, illus. l.t. ed. 2002. 8p. (J). (ps-k). pap. 3.99 (978-1-58938-013-4(4)) Concerned Communications.

—God's Promise. Morelan, Bill, ed. Butler, Steven, illus. l.t. ed. 2002. 16p. (J). (gr. 5). pap. 3.99 (978-1-58938-021-9(5)) Concerned Communications.

—How Far Is It? Morelan, Bill, ed. Butler, Steven, illus. l.t. ed. 2002. 16p. (J). (gr. 6). pap. 3.99 (978-1-58938-032-5(0)) Concerned Communications.

—Impossible! Impossible. Morelan, Bill, ed. Butler, Steven, illus. l.t. ed. 2002. 24p. (J). (gr. 3-4). pap. 3.99 (978-1-58938-046-2(0)) Concerned Communications.

—In Heaven I Will. Morelan, Bill, ed. Harrell, Rob, illus. l.t. ed. 2002. 16p. (J). (gr. 1-2). pap. 3.99 (978-1-58938-025-7(8)) Concerned Communications.

—The Jailer's Surprise. Morelan, Bill, ed. Butler, Steven, illus. l.t. ed. 2002. 24p. (J). (gr. 2). pap. 3.99 (978-1-58938-047-9(9)) Concerned Communications.

—Jericho March. Morelan, Bill, ed. Butler, Steven, illus. l.t. ed. 2002. 16p. (J). (gr. 6). pap. 3.99 (978-1-58938-017-2(7)) Concerned Communications.

—Jesus Helps His Dad. Morelan, Bill, ed. Butler, Steven, illus. l.t. ed. 2002. 16p. (J). (gr. 6). pap. 3.99 (978-1-58938-022-6(3)) Concerned Communications.

—Jesus Loves Me Anyway. Morelan, Bill, ed. Harrell, Rob, illus. l.t. ed. 2002. 16p. (J). (gr. 1-2). pap. 3.99 (978-1-58938-026-4(6)) Concerned Communications.

—Joseph, Egyptian Slave. Morelan, Bill, ed. Butler, Steven, illus. l.t. ed. 2002. 24p. (J). (gr. 7). pap. 3.99 (978-1-58938-042-4(8)) Concerned Communications.

—Joseph's Dream. Morelan, Bill, ed. Butler, Steven, illus. l.t. ed. 2002. 24p. (J). (gr. 7). pap. 3.99 (978-1-58938-043-1(6)) Concerned Communications.

—Joseph's New Coat. Morelan, Bill, ed. Butler, Steven, illus. l.t. ed. 2002. 8p. (J). (ps-k). pap. 3.99 (978-1-58938-008-0(8)) Concerned Communications.

—The Lame Man. Morelan, Bill, ed. Butler, Steven, illus. l.t. ed. 2002. 16p. (J). (gr. 2). pap. 3.99 (978-1-58938-044-8(4)) Concerned Communications.

—Let the Children Come. Morelan, Bill, ed. Butler, Steven, illus. l.t. ed. 2002. 16p. (J). (gr. 6). pap. 3.99 (978-1-58938-028-8(2)) Concerned Communications.

—Levi's Lunch. Morelan, Bill, ed. Butler, Steven, illus. l.t. ed. 2002. 16p. (J). (gr. 6). pap. 3.99 (978-1-58938-040-0(1)) Concerned Communications.

—Little Lamb & the Shepherd. Morelan, Bill, ed. Butler, Steven, illus. l.t. ed. 2002. 16p. (J). (gr. 6). pap. 3.99 (978-1-58938-033-2(9)) Concerned Communications.

—My Forever Friend. Morelan, Bill, ed. Harrell, Rob, illus. l.t. ed. 2002. 16p. (J). (gr. 1-2). pap. 3.99 (978-1-58938-034-9(7)) Concerned Communications.

—The Mysterious Star. Morelan, Bill, ed. Butler, Steven, illus. l.t. ed. 2002. 24p. (J). (gr. 3-4). pap. 3.99 (978-1-58938-037-0(1)) Concerned Communications.

—Naaman. Morelan, Bill, ed. Butler, Steven, illus. l.t. ed. 2002. 16p. (J). (gr. 1-2). pap. 3.99 (978-1-58938-027-1(4)) Concerned Communications.

—Noah's Ark. Morelan, Bill, ed. Butler, Steven, illus. l.t. ed. 2002. 16p. (J). (gr. 6). pap. 3.99 (978-1-58938-018-9(5)) Concerned Communications.

—The Prayed for Baby. Morelan, Bill, ed. Butler, Steven, illus. l.t. ed. 2002. 24p. (J). (gr. 6). pap. 3.99 (978-1-58938-039-4(8)) Concerned Communications.

—Rahab's Red Rope. Morelan, Bill, ed. Butler, Steven, illus. l.t. ed. 2002. 16p. (J). (gr. 2). pap. 3.99 (978-1-58938-045-5(2)) Concerned Communications.

—School Tools. Morelan, Bill, ed. Harrell, Rob, illus. l.t. ed. 2002. 8p. (J). (ps-k). pap. 3.99 (978-1-58938-003-5(7)) Concerned Communications.

—See Baby Jesus. Morelan, Bill, ed. Butler, Steven, illus. l.t. ed. 2002. 8p. (J). (gr. 5). pap. 3.99 (978-1-58938-004-2(5)) Concerned Communications.

—The Ten Lepers. Morelan, Bill, ed. Butler, Steven, illus. l.t. ed. 2002. 24p. (J). (gr. 7). pap. 3.99 (978-1-58938-038-7(X)) Concerned Communications.

—Water. Morelan, Bill, ed. Harrell, Rob, illus. l.t. ed. 2002. 8p. (J). (gr. 1-2). pap. 3.99 (978-1-58938-019-6(3)) Concerned Communications.

—Who Will Be in Heaven? Morelan, Bill, ed. Butler, Steven, illus. l.t. ed. 2002. 8p. (J). (gr. 5). pap. 3.99 (978-1-58938-009-7(6)) Concerned Communications.

Freed, Shirley Ann & Morelan, Bill. I Can Draw. Evans, Cassie & Harrell, Rob, illus. l.t. ed. 2002. 16p. (J). (gr. 5). pap. 3.99 (978-1-58938-014-1(2)) Concerned Communications.

Frels, Merry Hassell. Simmering Secrets of Weeping Mary: A Deuteronomy Devilrow Mystery. Morgan, Dana Duvall, illus. l.t. ed. 2005. 130p. (J). pap. 9.95 (978-0-9714358-9-6(8)) Longhorn Creek Pr.

French, Kathy J. Math & More Directed Activities: 1st Grade. Hollister, Michele, ed. l.t. ed. 2001. 200p. (J). (gr. 1). pap. (978-1-893632-06-6(7) , 300-109) Math Concepts, Inc.

—Math & More Directed Activities: 2nd Grade. Hollister, Michele, ed. l.t. ed. 2001. 200p. (J). (gr. 2). pap. (978-1-893632-07-3(5) , 300-110) Math Concepts, Inc.

—Math & More Directed Activities: 3rd Grade. Hollister, Michele, ed. l.t. ed. 2001. 200p. (J). (gr. 3). pap. (978-1-893632-08-0(3) , 300-111) Math Concepts, Inc.

—Math & More Directed Activities: 4th Grade. Hollister, Michele, ed. l.t. ed. 2001. 200p. (J). (gr. 4). pap. (978-1-893632-09-7(1) , 300-112) Math Concepts, Inc.

—Math & More Directed Activities: 5th Grade. Hollister, Michele, ed. l.t. ed. 2001. 200p. (J). (gr. 5). pap. (978-1-893632-10-3(5) , 300-113) Math Concepts, Inc.

—Math & More Directed Activities: Kindergarten. Hollister, Michele, ed. l.t. ed. 2001. 200p. (J). pap. (978-1-893632-05-9(9) , 300-108) Math Concepts, Inc.

—Mental Math: 1st Grade. Hollister, Michele, ed. l.t. ed. 1998. 150p. (J). (gr. 1). pap. 19.95 (978-1-893632-00-4(8) , 300-103) Math Concepts, Inc.

—Mental Math: 2nd Grade. Hollister, Michele, ed. l.t. ed. 1998. 140p. (J). (gr. 2). pap. 19.95 (978-1-893632-01-1(6) , 300-104) Math Concepts, Inc.

—Mental Math: 3rd Grade. Hollister, Michele, ed. l.t. ed. 1998. 150p. (J). (gr. 3). pap. 19.95 (978-1-893632-02-8(4) , 300-105) Math Concepts, Inc.

—Mental Math: 4th Grade. Hollister, Michele, ed. l.t. ed. 1998. 150p. (J). (gr. 4). pap. 19.95 (978-1-893632-03-5(2) , 300-106) Math Concepts, Inc.

—Mental Math: 5th Grade. Hollister, Michele, ed. l.t. ed. 1998. 150p. (J). (gr. 5). pap. 19.95 (978-1-893632-04-2(0) , 300-107) Math Concepts, Inc.

Freymann-Weyr, Garret. When I Was Older. l.t. ed. 2001. 159p. (J). 22.95 (978-0-7862-3546-9(2)) Thorndike Pr.

Friedman, Michael Jan. Hunchdog of Notre Dame. l.t. ed. 1999. (Adventures of Wishbone Ser.: No. 5). (Illus.). 139p. (J). (gr. 4 up). lib. bdg. 22.60 (978-0-8368-2301-1(X)) Stevens, Gareth Inc.

—The Stolen Trophy. l.t. ed. 1999. (Wishbone Mysteries Ser.: No. 5). 144p. (J). (gr. 4 up). lib. bdg. 23.33 (978-0-8368-2386-8(9)) Stevens, Gareth Inc.

Froberg, Dennis W. Anna Bristlecone. l.t. unabr. ed. 2000. (Illus.). 32p. (J). (gr. k-5). pap. 5.95 (978-1-928632-44-3(0)) Writers Marketplace:Consulting, Critiquing & Publishing.

Frontiera, Deborah K. Eric & the Enchanted Leaf: The First Adventure, Scott, Korey, illus. 2nd l.t. ed. 2004. 32p. (J). pap. 16.95 (978-0-9753410-0-1(6)) Jade Enterprises.

—Eric & the Enchanted Leaf / Eric y la Hoja Encantada: A Visit with Canis Lupis / una Visita con Canis Lupis. Santillan-Cruz, Silvia R., tr. Scott, Korey, illus. 2nd l.t. ed. 2005. (SPA & ENG.). 32p. (J). lib. bdg. 16.95 (978-0-9663629-8-5(5)) By Grace Enterprises.

Frost, Shelley & Troussieux, Ann. Throw Like a Girl: Discovering the Body, Mind & Spirit of the Athlete in You! l.t. ed. 2000. (Girls Know Best Ser.). (Illus.). 128p. (J). (gr. 3 up). lib. bdg. 23.33 (978-0-8368-2674-6(4)) Stevens, Gareth Inc.

Fulk, Dvon. Signs in the Earth: A Collection of Poems. Galloway, Annette, ed. Fulk, Dvon, photos by. l.t. ed. 2001. 154p. per. 14.00 (978-0-9710470-2-0(2)) Main St Publishing, Inc.

Fullwood, Millie F. Crow Joins the Choir. Srba, Lynne, illus. l.t. ed. 1998. 32p. (J). (ps-3). mass mkt. 9.95 (978-0-9667672-0-9(9) , 3468998-00) Fullwood Marketing Communications Co.

Funke, Cornelia. Inkheart. l.t. ed. 2006. 709p. (YA). pap. 10.95 (978-0-7862-8363-7(7)) Thorndike Pr.

—Inkheart. Bell, Anthea, tr. l.t. ed. 2005. (Illus.). 709p. (J). (gr. 3-7). 23.95 (978-0-7862-8041-4(7) , Large Print Pr.) Thorndike Pr.

Furbush, Helen. Lying Awake. McCroskey, Christine, illus. l.t. ed. 2004. 32p. (J). (gr. 1-6). 15.95 (978-0-9741787-0-7(5) , 1239134) Harbor Island Bks.

Furia, John. Collegiate Fitness. l.t. ed. 2003. 130p. (YA). per. 14.95 (978-1-59453-047-0(5) , 1825) Airleaf Publishing & Bookselling.

Fussell, Bonnie. More Than a Stove. Sadler, Dale, illus. l.t. ed. 2004. 32p. (J). pap. 7.99 (978-0-615-12702-6(9)) Blackberry Pubs.

Gaarder, Jostein. Hello? Is Anybody There? Gardner, Sally, illus. l.t. ed. 2002. 152p. (J). 16.95 (978-0-7540-7814-2(0) , Galaxy Children's Large Print) BBC Audiobooks America.

Gantos, Jack. Jack on the Tracks: Four Seasons of Fifth Grade. l.t. ed. 2002. 210p. (J). 22.95 (978-0-7862-4394-5(5)) Thorndike Pr.

—Joey Pigza Loses Control. l.t. ed. 2001. 196p. (J). 22.95 (978-0-7862-3425-7(3)) Thorndike Pr.

—Joey Pigza Swallowed the Key. l.t. ed. 2000. 174p. (J). 21.95 (978-0-7862-2912-3(8)) Thorndike Pr.

—What Would Joey Do? l.t. ed. 2003. (Juvenile Ser.). 264p. (J). 22.95 (978-0-7862-5468-2(8)) Thorndike Pr.

Garber, Linda. Don't Leave the Lawn! Garber, Linda, illus. l.t. ed. 1999. (Illus.). (J). (gr. 1-4). spiral bd. 9.95 (978-1-892218-04-9(6)) Murlin Pubns.

—My Balloon at the Zoo. Garber, Linda, illus. 2nd l.t. ed. 1999. (Illus.). 21p. (J). (gr. 1-4). spiral bd. 9.95 (978-1-892218-05-6(4)) Murlin Pubns.

—Sound Is Bound to Be Around. Garber, Linda, illus. l.t. ed. 1999. (Illus.). (J). (gr. 1-4). spiral bd. 9.95 (978-1-892218-06-3(2)) Murlin Pubns.

—Will This Tale Fly? Garber, Linda, illus. 2nd l.t. ed. 1999. (Illus.). 23p. (J). (gr. 1-4). spiral bd. 9.95 (978-1-892218-03-2(8)) Murlin Pubns.

Garcia-Alvarado, Belén & Venable, Alan. Border Crossing. Stotts, Bob, illus. l.t. ed. 2002. (J). (gr. 5-6). 150.00 (978-1-58702-032-2(7)) Johnston, Don Inc.

Gardner, Sally. The Boy Who Could Fly. Gardner, Sally, illus. l.t. ed. 2005. (Illus.). 86p. (J). pap. (978-0-7540-7815-9(9) , CLP 405) BBC Audio.

Garrick, Lainie. Losing Papou: One Child's Journey Towards Understanding & Accepting Death. Mandarino, Gene, illus. l.t. ed. 2003. 32p. (J). (978-0-9765725-0-3(8)) printONDEMANDpublisher.com.

Garside, Alice H. The Ant & the Duck, Set 2. l.t. ed. 1999. (Illus.). 29p. (Orig.). (J). (gr. k-6). reprint ed. pap. 2.50 (978-1-893688-05-6(4)) Carroll Schl., The.

—The Garside Readers, 6 vols., Set. l.t. ed. Incl. Fox & the Thrush. 15p. pap. 2.50 (978-1-893688-03-2(8)) ; Set 1. Dog & the Wolf. 25p. pap. 2.50 (978-1-893688-04-9(6)) ; Set 1. Man, the Fox & the Skunk. 19p. pap. 2.50 (978-1-893688-01-8(1)) ; Set 2. Ant & the Duck. 29p. pap. 2.50 (978-1-893688-05-6(4)) ; Set 2. Dog & the Bone. 19p. pap. 2.50 (978-1-893688-02-5(X)) ; Vol. 2. Fox & the Stork. 43p. pap. 2.50 (978-1-893688-06-3(2)) ; (J). (gr. k-6). reprint ed. (Illus.). 150p. 1999. reprint ed. Set pap. 15.00 (978-1-893688-00-1(3)) Carroll Schl., The.

—The Man, the Fox & the Skunk, Set 1. l.t. ed. 1999. (Illus.). 19p. (Orig.). (J). (gr. k-6). reprint ed. pap. 2.50 (978-1-893688-01-8(1)) Carroll Schl., The.

Gates, Susan. Cry Wolf. l.t. ed. 2000. 151p. (J). pap. (978-0-7540-6105-2(1) , CLP 301) BBC Audio.

Gebhart, Adalgiza. Gotta Have Hearts: Three Picture Stories for Preschoolers. Gebhart, Adalgiza, illus. l.t. ed. 2005. (Illus.). 76p. (J). 27.95 (978-0-922993-38-3(6)); per. 19.95 (978-0-922993-37-6(8)) Marquette Bks., LLC.

George, Jean Craighead. Julie of the Wolves. l.t. ed. 2004. (Beeler Mystery Ser.). 32.95 (978-1-58118-121-0(3)) LRS.

George, Marjorie. Doing the Right Thing. Brunk, Cara, illus. l.t. ed. 2000. 8p. (J). (gr. k-3). pap. 6.00 (978-1-58084-214-3(3)); 6.00 (978-1-58084-212-9(7)) Lower Kuskokwim Schl. District.

—Ellualriamek Cucukiyaraq. Brunk, Cara, illus. l.t. ed. 2000. Tr. of Doing the Right Thing. (ESK.). 8p. (J). (gr. k-3). pap. 6.00 (978-1-58084-213-6(5)) Lower Kuskokwim Schl. District.

Geringer, Lucy T. Rhymes & Times of Cleo-cat-tra. Kollock, Bernardita Cox, illus. l.t. ed. 2000. (Cleo-Cat-Tra Easy-to-Read Book Ser.). 28p. (J). (ps-2). pap. 7.95 (978-0-9760962-7-5(2)) Displays for Schls., Inc.

Gibbs, Dreene. Am I Pretty, Momma? 2nd l.t. ed. 2004. (Illus.). 32p. (J). bds. 12.95 (978-0-9741406-1-2(9) , 0138) Cranberry Quill Publishing Co.

Giff, Patricia Reilly. Lily's Crossing. l.t. ed. 2000. (Illus.). 200p. (J). (ps up). 22.95 (978-0-7862-2771-6(0)) Thorndike Pr.

—Nory Ryan's Song. l.t. ed. 2001. 176p. (J). 23.95 (978-0-7862-3459-2(8)) Thorndike Pr.

—Pictures of Hollis Woods. l.t. ed. 2003. 158p. (J). 23.95 (978-0-7862-5094-3(1)) Thorndike Pr.

Gill, Nancy Downs. One Christmas Night: For All Who Cherish a Christmas Memory. Shields, Noriko, illus. l.t. ed. 2000. 36p. (J). (ps-6). per. 7.95 (978-0-9675045-0-6(3)) Oak Hill Pr.

Gillen, Lisa P. Louie the Lifeguard. Gillen, Lisa P., illus. l.t. ed. 2000. (LB Ser.). (Illus.). (J). (ps-1). 6p. pap. 10.95 (978-1-57332-176-1(1)); 10p. pap. 10.95 (978-1-57332-175-4(3)) HighReach Learning, Inc.

Ginsberg, Martha. The Three Buddies in Hideaway Land. Loughran, Tony, illus. l.t. ed. 2003. 38p. (J). (ps-7). per. 9.95 (978-1-59453-054-8(8) , 1368) Airleaf Publishing & Bookselling.

Girls Know Best, 7 bks. l.t. ed. Incl. Boys Know It All : Wise Thoughts & Wacky Ideas from Guys Like You. Roehm, Michelle, compiled by. 167p. 1999. lib. bdg. 23.33 (978-0-8368-2455-1(5)); Girls Know Best Vol. 2 : Tips on Life & Fun Stuff to Do. Monson-Burton, Marianne, compiled by. 1999. lib. bdg. 23.33 (978-0-8368-2453-7(9)); Girls Know Best Vol. 3 : Your Words, Your World. Monson-Burton, Marianne, compiled by. 153p. 2000. lib. bdg. 23.33 (978-0-8368-2672-2(8)); Girls Knows Best : Advice for Girls from Girls on Just about Everything. Roehm, Michelle, compiled by. 160p. 1999. lib. bdg. 23.33 (978-0-8368-2452-0(0)); Girls Who Rocked the World : Heroines from Sacagawea to Sheryl Swoopes. Welden, Amelie. McCann, Jerry, illus. 117p. 1999. lib. bdg. 23.33 (978-0-8368-2454-4(7)); Girls Who Rocked the World Vol. 2 : Heroines from Harriet Tubman to Mia Hamm. Roehm, Michelle, compiled by. 152p. 2000. lib. bdg. 23.33 (978-0-8368-2673-9(6)); Throw Like a Girl : Discovering the Body, Mind & Spirit of the Athlete in You! Frost, Shelley & Troussieux, Ann. 128p. 2000. lib. bdg. 23.33 (978-0-8368-2674-6(4)); (J). (gr. 3 up). (Illus.). Set lib. bdg. 163.31 (978-0-8368-2741-5(4)) Stevens, Gareth Inc.

Giunta, Brian. The Seven Presidents. Chapin, Patrick O., illus. l.t. ed. 2003. 24p. (J). 8.95 (978-1-58597-172-5(3)) Leathers Publishing.

Gleitzman, Morris. Two Weeks with the Queen. l.t. ed. 2002. 192p. (J). 16.95 (978-0-7540-7816-6(7) , Galaxy Children's Large Print) BBC Audiobooks America.

—Worry Warts. l.t. ed. 2005. 160p. (J). pap. (978-0-7540-7881-4(7) , CLP 458) BBC Audio.

Gold Medal Kumite: The Making of Champions. 2nd l.t. ed. 2000. 150p. (YA). spiral bd. 25.00 (978-1-929364-04-6(0)) JIA Publishing.

Golden Eagle Productions Staff. Grandmother Moon & Sammy the Loon, 36 vols. l.t. ed. 2003. (Illus.). 24p. per. 9.95 (978-1-932338-24-9(1)) Lifevest Publishing, Inc.

Goldish, Meish. Big Book: How Many Are Here? Meyerhoff, Jill, illus. l.t. ed. 2005. (Sadlier Phonics Reading Program). 8p. (YA). (ps-1). 22.50 (978-0-8215-7344-0(6)) Sadlier, William H. Inc.

—Big Book: Zack Can Fix It!, Vol. 4. Scruton, Clive, illus. l.t. ed. 2005. (Sadlier Phonics Reading Program). 8p. (YA). (ps-1). 22.50 (978-0-8215-7359-4(4)) Sadlier, William H. Inc.

—Nice Vine, Quite Fine, Vol. 2. Sargent, Claudia Karabaic, illus. l.t. ed. 2005. (Little Books & Big Bks.: Vol. 7). 8p. (YA). (ps-3). 22.50 (978-0-8215-7516-1(3)) Sadlier, William H. Inc.

Gonzalez, David J. There Are No Space Aliens! 12 Biblical Points Disproving Space Aliens. l.t. ed. 2003. 48p. 9.95 (978-0-9741561-0-1(8)) Gonzalez, David J. Ministries.

Goodwin, Carol. Does This Belong Here? A Twiggyleaf Adventure. McDaniel, Thomas, illus. l.t. ed. 2003. 32p. (J). 14.95 (978-0-9741072-1-9(2)) CornerWind Media, L.L.C.

—The Great Acorn: A Twiggyleaf Adventure. McDaniel, Thomas, illus. l.t. ed. 2004. 32p. (J). 14.95 (978-0-9741072-2-6(0)) CornerWind Media, L.L.C.

—Tippy Needs A Home: A Twiggyleaf Adventure. McDaniel, Thomas, illus. l.t. ed. 2003. 32p. (J). per. 14.95 (978-0-09-741072-2(1)) CornerWind Media, L.L.C.

—What's the Hurry, Furry? A Twiggyleaf Adventure. McDaniel, Thomas, illus. l.t. ed. 2003. 32p. (J). 14.95 (978-0-9741072-0-2(4)) CornerWind Media, L.L.C.

Gordon, Karen. Selman Waksman & the Discovery of Streptomycin. l.t. ed. 2002. (Unlocking the Secrets of Science Ser.). (Illus.). 56p. (gr. 4-10). lib. bdg. 25.70 (978-1-58415-138-8(2)) Mitchell Lane Pubs., Inc.

Gorgas, Paula Blais. Little Lost Leprechaun. Taylor, Chet, illus. l.t. ed. 2005. 20p. (J). 17.99 (978-0-9755888-4-0(2)) Dragonfly Publishing, Inc.

Goswami, Hemesh. Boo-Boo Island: The Ghost-House & the Mystery of the Old Wooden House. l.t. ed. 2002. 108p. per. 4.95 (978-0-9718288-9-6(X)) Stylewriter Pubns.

Grace, Roz. Anthony's Surprise. Melvin, James, illus. l.t. ed. 1999. 32p. (J). (ps-3). 12.95 (978-0-9659181-2-1(2)) BMF Pr.

Graf, Rosanna. Beary Beary Quite Contrary. Lawson, Laura, illus. l.t. ed. 1998. 24p. (Orig.). (J). (gr. 2-5). pap. 7.50 (978-1-882788-02-6(8)) Vangar Pubs./Baltimore.

Graham, Wylie T. E. The Adventures of Sam & Hungry. Fallis, Margo & Kuehn, John, eds. Adle, Mary Ann, illus. l.t. ed. 2002. 37p. (J). (ps-4). pap. (978-0-9715665-0-7(X)) Schuerholz Graphics.

Grahame, Kenneth. The Wind in the Willows. l.t. ed. 2000. (LRS Large Print Heritage Ser.). 271p. (J). (gr. 3-8). lib. bdg. 29.95 (978-1-58118-066-4(7) , 23661) LRS.

Granger, Stacey. Colin Powell. l.t. ed. 2002. (Real-Life Reader Biography Ser.). (Illus.). 32p. (J). (gr. 3-8). lib. bdg. 15.95 (978-1-58415-144-9(7)) Mitchell Lane Pubs., Inc.

Graver, Elizabeth. Honey Thief. 2000. (gr. 7-12). lib. bdg. 22.25 (978-0-613-36404-1(X)) Tandem Library Bks.

Gray, Dianne E. Holding up the Earth. l.t. ed. 2002. 198p. (J). 22.95 (978-0-7862-3889-7(5)) Thomson Gale.

Graziani, Maria. The Adventures of Valeria Veterinarian: Las Aventuras de Valeria Veterinaria, 1. Elejalde, Eliana, illus. l.t. ed. 2004. (SPA.). 23p. (J). 7.00 (978-0-9762361-0-8(9)) Ed. Acespanish S.A.C.- Lima, Peru.

—A Black Cat on Halloween: Un Gato Negro en Dia de Brujas. Elejalde, Eliana, illus. l.t. ed. 2004. (SPA.). 23p. (J). 7.00 (978-0-9762361-1-5(7)) Ed. Acespanish S.A.C.- Lima, Peru.

Green, Bessie. Kiarnerualiyaraq. Nevak, Caroline, illus. l.t. ed. 1999. Tr. of How to Make Fish Strips. (ESK.). 12p. (J). (gr. k-3). pap. 17.00 (978-1-58084-073-6(6)) Lower Kuskokwim Schl. District.

—Neqliller Pinwaneg Iqallugneg (How to Make Fish Strips) Nevak, Caroline, illus. l.t. ed. 1999. (ESK.). 12p. (J). (gr. k-3). pap. 17.00 (978-1-58084-107-8(4)) Lower Kuskokwim Schl. District.

Greenberg, Martin H. & Waugh, Charles. Adoniram & Other Selections. l.t. ed. 2001. (Newbery Authors Collection: No. 6). 176p. (J). (gr. 4 up). lib. bdg. 23.33 (978-0-8368-2860-3(7)) Stevens, Gareth Inc.

—Dancing Tom & Other Selections. l.t. ed. 2001. (Newbery Authors Collection: No. 5). 160p. (J). (gr. 4 up). lib. bdg. 23.33 (978-0-8368-2859-7(3)) Stevens, Gareth Inc.

—For the Sake of Freedom & Other Selections. l.t. ed. 2001. (Newbery Authors Collection: No. 1). 176p. (J). (gr. 4 up). lib. bdg. 23.33 (978-0-8368-2855-9(0)) Stevens, Gareth Inc.

—The Highest Hit & Other Selections. l.t. ed. 2001. (Newbery Authors Collection: No. 2). 160p. (J). (gr. 4 up). lib. bdg. 23.33 (978-0-8368-2856-6(9)) Stevens, Gareth Inc.

—Lighthouse Island & Other Selections. l.t. ed. 2001. (Newbery Authors Collection: No. 4). 160p. (J). (gr. 4 up). lib. bdg. 23.33 (978-0-8368-2858-0(5)) Stevens, Gareth Inc.

Greenburg, Kay. Josh & Alisha Celebrate Chanukah. Correll, Cory, illus. l.t. ed. 1999. 40p. (J). (ps-6). 13.95 (978-0-9666903-0-9(3)) Stop & Smell the Roses, L.L.C.

Greendyk, William, tr. Los DOS Osos. l.t. ed. 2004. (SPA.). 152p. (J). pap. 5.99 (978-1-932789-02-7(2) , R009N) Editorial Sendas Antiguas, LLC.

—La Hierba Mala. l.t. ed. 2004. Tr. of Hierba Mala. (SPA.). 156p. (J). pap. 5.99 (978-1-932789-01-0(4) , X002N) Editorial Sendas Antiguas, LLC.

—El Hijo de la Viuda. l.t. ed. 2004. Orig. Title: The Widow's Son. (SPA., Illus.). 92p. (J). pap. (978-1-932789-11-9(1)) Editorial Sendas Antiguas, LLC.

—Los Niños de la Biblia. l.t. ed. 2004. (SPA.). 94p. (J). pap. 3.99 (978-1-932789-03-4(0) , X003N) Editorial Sendas Antiguas, LLC.

—Primeras Impresiones de Dios. l.t. ed. 2004. Tr. of Primeras Impresiones de Dios. (SPA.). 94p. (J). pap. 3.99 (978-1-932789-04-1(9) , W001N) Editorial Sendas Antiguas, LLC.

Greene, Bette. Summer of My German Soldier. l.t. ed. 2000. (LRS Large Print Cornerstone Ser.). 305p. (YA). (gr. 6-12). lib. bdg. 29.95 (978-1-58118-059-6(4) , 23473) LRS.

Greene, Susan. Consider It Golf: Golf Etiquette & Safety Tips for Children! Klavins, Dagne Angersbach, illus. l.t. ed. 2000. 40p. (J). (ps-4). 14.95 (978-0-9651100-7-5(9)) Excel Publishing.

Gremila, Elaine Demetri. Seasons of the Heart. l.t. ed. 2003. (Illus.). 140p. per. 11.95 (978-1-932338-16-4(0)) Lifevest Publishing, Inc.

Grey, Zane. Ken Ward in the Jungle. l.t. ed. 1999. 272p. (J). pap. (978-0-7540-3608-1(1)) BBC Audiobooks America.

Griffin, Adele. The Other Shepards. l.t. ed. 2000. (Illus.). 209p. (J). (gr. 4-7). 20.95 (978-0-7862-2914-7(4)) Thorndike Pr.

Griggs, Jermaine. The Secrets to Playing Piano by Ear. l.t. ed. 2001. (Illus.). 300p. (978-0-9744845-0-1(4)) Hear & Play Music.

Grimes, Brittney. Poetry for a Child - By a Child. l.t. ed. 1998. (Illus.). 40p. (J). pap. (978-1-889732-12-1(5) , Key-A-Teese Production) Word For Word Publishing Co.

Grimm, Jakob & Grimm, Wilhelm K. Grimm's Fairy Tales. l.t. ed. 2004. (Large Print Ser.). 477p. 26.00 (978-1-58287-627-6(4)) North Bks.

Grimsley-Fambro, Sonja. Santa Spent the Night with Me. Garfinkel, Dana, illus. l.t. ed. 2002. 30p. (J). per. 40.99 (978-1-893108-88-2(0)) Neighborhood Pr. Publishing.

—Santa Spent the Night with Me - Coloring Book. Garfinkel, Dana, illus. l.t. ed. 2002. 16p. (J). 4.99 (978-1-893108-89-9(9)) Neighborhood Pr. Publishing.

Grizzle, Charles R. Cats Mysterioso: True Tales Odd & Puzzling. l.t. ed. 2001. (Illus.). 140p. (J). pap. 9.95 (978-0-9644033-3-8(1)) Plateau Pubns.

Gross, Philip. Point Horror: Facetaker. l.t. ed. 2005. 176p. (J). pap. (978-0-7540-6130-4(2) , CLP 323) BBC Audio.

Gunnery, Sylvia. Menace & Mischief. l.t. ed. 1999. 104p. (J). (gr. 3-7). mass mkt. 5.95 (978-0-7736-7477-6(2)) Stoddart Kids CAN. *Dist:* Fitzhenry & Whiteside, Ltd.

Haas, Jessie. Unbroken. l.t. ed. 2000. (Juvenile Ser.). 248p. (J). (gr. 4-7). 21.95 (978-0-7862-2769-3(9)) Thorndike Pr.

Haddix, Margaret Peterson. Among the Hidden. l.t. ed. 2000. (Shadow Children Ser.). 185p. (YA). (gr. 5-8). 20.95 (978-0-7862-3051-8(7)) Thorndike Pr.

Haglund, Jill. Scrapbooking for Kids, Vol. 1. Arquette, Kerry, ed. Boshell, Kristine, illus. Booth, Herb, photos by. l.t. ed. 1999. 128p. (J). (gr. 1-5). pap. 19.95 (978-1-891898-01-3(9)) Tweety Jill Pubns.

Hairston, Angelica. Did Noah Have Whales on the Ark? Ferguson, Tamara, illus. l.t. ed. 2004. 44p. (J). (978-0-9716136-1-4(3)) Broadcast Quality Productions, Inc.

Hairston, Maya. My Oh Maya: The Writings of Maya Hairston. Miller, Edwin, Jr., illus. l.t. ed. 2002. 30p. (J). (gr. k-6). (978-0-9716136-0-7(5)) Broadcast Quality Productions, Inc.

Hajdusiewicz, Babs Bell. Peaceful Me: Poems & Activities to Help Children Resolve Conflicts Peacefully. l.t. ed. 2002. 32p. (J). (978-0-9665568-1-0(X)) Reading Realm.

Hale, Chaika P. Mama Is Hapai. Asato, Dennis, illus. l.t. ed. 1998. 32p. (J). (gr. 1-6). 14.00 (978-0-9653971-2-4(2)) Anoai Pr.

Hall / Waltz. Mortimer Jones: The Bubble Gum Nerd, 1. l.t. ed. 2003. (Illus.). 32p. 19.95 (978-0-9741774-2-7(3)) D. W. Publishing.

Hall, Henry R. The Little Airplane. l.t. ed. 2002. (Illus.). 36p. per. 9.95 (978-0-9723309-9-2(2)) Thornton Publishing.

Hall, Nancy R. My Grandparents Live in an RV, Hall, Nancy R., illus. l.t. ed. 2005. (Illus.). 32p. (J). 16.95 (978-0-9761759-0-2(8)) Jasnans Publishing Co.

Hamilton, Elizabeth L. Katie Kangaroo's Leap of Courage. l.t. ed. 2005. (Character Critters Ser.: No. 9). (Illus.). 32p. (J). per. 5.95 (978-0-9754629-6-6(2) , Character-in-Action) Quiet Impact, Inc.

—Ricky Raccoon's Trustworthiness Tree. l.t. ed. 2005. (Character Critters Ser.: No. 11). (Illus.). 32p. (J). per. 5.95 (978-0-9754629-8-0(9) , Character-in-Action) Quiet Impact, Inc.

Hamilton, Leo. Leo Hamilton Presents: Children's Dream Adventures, Larkin, Jessica, illus. l.t. ed. 2002. 40p. (J). (ps-5). pap. 8.99 (978-0-9671660-2-5(0)) Story Place, The.

—Leo Hamilton Presents: The Mighty Hill. Larkin, Jessica, illus. l.t. ed. 2002. 40p. (J). (gr. 1-9). pap. 9.99 (978-0-9671660-5-6(5)) Story Place, The.

—Leo Hamilton's Odd Collection of Animal & Insect Stories. Larkin, Jessica, illus. l.t. ed. (J). (ps-5). Vol. I. 2000. 36p. pap. 7.99 (978-0-9671660-0-1(4)); Vol. II. 2000. 40p. pap. 8.99 (978-0-9671660-1-8(2)); Vol. III. 2002. 24p. pap. 8.99 (978-0-9671660-3-2(9)) Story Place, The.

—Leo Hamilton's Odd Collection of Animal & Insect Stories Vol. I: No Crayons. l.t. ed. 2000. 36p. per. 5.99 net. (978-0-9671660-6-3(3)) Story Place, The.

Hamilton, Patricia Birdsong & Scripts Publishing Staff. What's Up: William Explains Ataxia to His New Friends. l.t. ed. 2005. (Ataxia: A Lifestyle Change). 44p. 18.95 (978-1-889826-90-5(1)) Scripts Publishing.

Hamilton, Virginia. M. C. Higgins, the Great. 2006. (Illus.). 288p. (J). pap. 5.99 (978-1-4169-1407-5(2) , Aladdin) Simon & Schuster Children's Publishing.

Hammerschlag, Carl A. The Go-Away Doll. Havill, Juanita, ed. Soasey, Beverly E., illus. l.t. ed. 1998. (Dr. H. Bks.). 32p. (J). (ps-12). 16.95 (978-1-889166-22-3(7) , 299-5425, Dr. H Bks.) Turtle Island Pr., Inc.

Hampton, Randall. A Christmas Kiss. l.t. ed. 2005. (Illus.). 48p. (J). per. 16.95 (978-1-59879-048-1(X)) Lifevest Publishing, Inc.

Hancock, Greg. My Hugger Is Empty. Morrison, Melody, illus. l.t. ed. 1999. 24p. (J). (ps-3). pap. (978-1-894303-14-9(8)) Raven Rock Publishing.

Hanna, James Milton, Sr. Once upon a Time in the South. l.t. ed. 2004. (Illus.). 235p. per. 12.95 (978-1-930052-15-4(4)) Cherokee Bks.

Hansen, T. Cory. The Last Little Pumpkin. Foldvary-Anderson, Carol, illus. l.t. ed. 2002. 38p. (J). cd-rom 11.95 (978-0-9706612-8-9(2)) JetKor.

Hanson, Paige & Hanson, Jon. Harry Spotter: The Incontinent Puppy, Sellers, Amy, illus. l.t. ed. 2005. 44p. (J). per. 20.00 (978-0-9721146-1-5(0)) Monroe Educational Media.

Happy Birthday to Me! l.t. ed. 1999. (Illus.). 22p. (J). pap. 19.00 (978-1-893467-04-0(X)) Spedial Editions Pr.

Harbo, Gary. The Northern Woods Adventure: Early Reader. Harbo, Gary, illus. l.t. ed. 2004. (If You Want to Succeed, You Need to Read! Ser.: 6). (Illus.). 33p. (J). 10.95 (978-1-884149-16-0(2)) Kutie Kari Bks., Inc.

Harding, Kitchener L. Clarence & Amous Become Famous. l.t. ed. 1999. (Illus.). 10p. (J). (gr. 1-5). spiral bd. 4.95 (978-1-930503-01-4(6)) Office Max.

—Little Miss Priss: Flying Kites & Kisses Not for the Misses. Harding, Kitchener L., illus. l.t. ed. 1999. 10p. (J). (gr. 1-5). spiral bd. 4.95 (978-1-930503-00-7(8)) Office Max.

Harkes, Willy. Little Dutch Girl in World War II. Blair, Jocelyn, illus. l.t. ed. 2004. 22p. (J). pap. 13.95 (978-0-9741627-1-3(X)) Write Designs, Ltd.

Harper, Stephan J. The Black Sheep. Beach, Mary FitzGerald, illus. l.t. ed. 2005. 32p. (J). lib. bdg. 16.95 (978-0-9741800-1-4(7)) Inspire Press, Inc.

Harris, Kandi. Princess, the Future Queen: A Mother's Guidance. Rippon, Jor-El, illus. l.t. ed. 2006. 32p. (J). bds. 12.99 (978-0-9770331-1-9(2)) Harris, K Publishing, Inc.

Hart, James W. Grandpa & the Computer. Kingsley, Steven, ed. Glasbergen, Randy, illus. l.t. ed. 2001. 84p. per. 12.95 (978-1-893798-18-2(6)) AIL Newmedia Publishing.

Hartland, Patricia. The Adventures of Captain Love & Dr. Smart, Vol. 1. Foster, Rollen, ed. l.t. ed. 1998. (Illus.). 32p. (J). (ps up). pap. 8.95 (978-1-891806-01-8(7)) LittleKid Pr.

—Jungle Bungle Vol. 2: The Adventures of Captain Love & Dr. Smart. Foster, Rollen, ed. l.t. ed. 1998. (Illus.). 32p. (J). (ps up). pap. 8.95 (978-1-891806-02-5(5)) LittleKid Pr.

Hartman, Jeff. The Red Coral House. Horton, Kate, illus. l.t. ed. 2002. 32p. 8.95 (978-0-9703490-1-9(7)) Hartman Publishing.

Haughom, Lisa, illus. & text. Jeux de Grammaire. Haughom, Lisa, text. l.t. ed. 2001. pap. 21.95 (978-0-9723849-8-8(7)) Languages For Kids.

Hawes, Louise. Rosey in the Present Tense. l.t. ed. 2002. 186p. (J). 22.95 (978-0-7862-4418-8(6)) Thorndike Pr.

Haworth, Margaret. Jarry, Garry Palas: Cat Tail Stories. Haworth, Margaret, photos by. l.t. ed. 2003. (Books That Help Ser.: Vol. 3). (Illus.). 34p. (J). (gr. 1-6). pap. 9.95 (978-0-9740313-5-4(6)) Haworth, Margaret.

Hawthorne, Nathaniel. The Scarlet Letter. l.t. ed. 2000. (LRS Large Print Heritage Ser.). 379p. (YA). (gr. 7-12). lib. bdg. 34.95 (978-1-58118-065-7(9) , 23660) LRS.

—A Wonder Book & Tanglewood Tales. l.t. ed. 2004. (Large Print Ser.). 563p. 26.00 (978-1-58287-673-3(8)) North Bks.

Hazelton, Jack W. Charlie Duck. Hazelton, Jack W., illus. l.t. ed. 2003. (Illus.). 24p. (J). 12.95 (978-1-928907-54-1(7)) Jack's Bookshelf, Inc.

—Grandma Claus' Rolling Pin. Hazelton, Jack W., illus. l.t. ed. 2002. (Illus.). 48p. (J). 14.95 (978-1-928907-53-4(9)) Jack's Bookshelf, Inc.

—Puddlefoot Pete. Hazelton, Jack W., illus. l.t. ed. 2002. (Illus.). 24p. cd-rom 9.95 (978-1-928907-51-0(2)) Jack's Bookshelf, Inc.

Hazelwood, Drema. The Apple Orchard Gang: Featuring Red Delicious. l.t. ed. 1999. (Illus.). 20p. (J). (ps-3). pap. 5.95 (978-1-891029-45-5(2)) Henderson Publishing.

Heaton, R. Scott. Opposite Land. Terrence, Chris, ed. Young, Sarah, illus. l.t. ed. 2000. 20p. (J). (ps-3). pap. 9.95 (978-0-9664880-2-9(4)) Green Mountain Publishing.

Hedrick, Georgia. Different Is Cool! A Skater Mouse Saga. Hedrick, Georgia, illus. l.t. ed. 2002. (Illus.). 34p. (J). cd-rom 11.95 (978-0-9706612-9-6(0)) JetKor.

—Share Me a Shadow. l.t. ed. 2002. 48p. (J). cd-rom 12.95 (978-0-9706612-7-2(4)) JetKor.

Hein, Connie L. Toliver in Time; for a Journey West: History in a Nutshell. Theobald, Denise, illus. l.t. ed. 2005. 28p. (J). lib. bdg. 17.95 (978-0-9740855-6-2(1)); per. 9.95 (978-0-9740855-7-9(X)) Still Water Publishing.

Heiner, Garth Farr. The Bully. Melander, Eric, illus. l.t. unabr. ed. 2001. (Fun-with-the-Law Ser.: No. 2). 32p. (J). (gr. k-7). pap. 5.95 (978-1-929905-02-7(5)) Fun With the Law, Inc.

—Finders Keepers. Melander, Eric, illus. l.t. unabr. ed. 2001. (Fun-with-the-Law Ser.: No. 4). 32p. (J). (gr. k-7). pap. 5.95 (978-1-929905-04-1(1)) Fun With the Law, Inc.

—Look Out Below. Melander, Eric, illus. l.t. unabr. ed. 2001. (Fun-with-the-Law Ser.: No. 6). 32p. (J). (gr. k-7). pap. 5.95 (978-1-929905-06-5(8)) Fun With the Law, Inc.

—Unwanted Muddy. Melander, Eric, illus. l.t. unabr. ed. 2001. (Fun-with-the-Law Ser.: No. 5). 32p. (J). (gr. k-7). pap. 5.95 (978-1-929905-05-8(X)) Fun With the Law, Inc.

Heinz, Brian J. The Alley Cat. Blair, June H., illus. l.t. ed. 2002. 32p. (J). 14.95 (978-0-936335-05-6(X)); pap. 6.95 (978-0-936335-06-3(8)) Ballyhoo BookWorks, Inc.

Heller, Andrew. No Bones about It. Rene, Perez, illus. l.t. ed. 2003. 12p. (J). 7.99 (978-0-9722038-5-2(0)) Mr Do It All, Inc.

Heller, Ruth. Nous Ne Sommes Pas Nes/Oeuf! l.t. ed. (FRE., Illus.). (J). bds. 29.99 (978-0-590-73029-7(0)) Scholastic, Inc.

Henderson, Tim. Butterflies & Magic Dreams. Hansen, Melissa, illus. l.t. ed. 2003. 28p. (J). (978-0-9728691-0-2(7)) Logan Bks.

Hendry, Diana. You Can't Kiss It Better. l.t. ed. 2005. (Illus.). 232p. (J). pap. incl. audio (978-0-7540-7872-2(8) , CLP 453) BBC Audio.

Henny, Rose. Teddy Finds His Way: A Teddy Tale. Henny, Rose, illus. l.t. ed. 2005. (Illus.). 22p. (J). per. 12.95 (978-0-9705458-7-9(8)) Royalty Bks. International.

Henry, Marguerite. King of the Wind. l.t. ed. 2001. (Illus.). 216p. (J). (gr. 4-7). 21.95 (978-0-7862-2848-5(2)) Thorndike Pr.

Hensley, Sarah M. Caillov Visits the Circus. Storch, Ellen N., illus. l.t. ed. 2005. (Hrl Board Book Ser.). (J). (ps-k). pap. 10.95 (978-1-57332-309-3(8)) HighReach Learning, Inc.

—A Day at the Beach. Smith, John, illus. l.t. ed. 2004. (HRL Board Book Ser.). 10p. (J). (ps-k). bds. 10.95 (978-1-57332-267-6(9)) HighReach Learning, Inc.

Henty, G. A. In the Reign of Terror: The Adventures of a Westminster Boy. l.t. ed. 2002. (Illus.). pap. 19.95 (978-1-4115-0618-3(9)) Polyglot Pr., Inc.

Here & There & Everywhere with Mother Goose & Friends. l.t. ed. 1999. (Illus.). 20p. (J). pap. 19.00 (978-1-893467-05-7(8)) Spedial Editions Pr.

Herron, Carolivia, photos by & adapted by. Little Georgia & the Apples: A Retelling of Aunt Georgia's First Catalpa Tale, Herron, Carolivia, adapted by. l.t. ed. 2004. (Illus.). 33p. (J). 10.00 (978-0-9760222-0-6(6) , Catalpa01) Epicenter Literary Software.

Heyman, Carly. My Extra Special Brother: How to Love, Understand, & Celebrate Your Sibling with Special Needs. Conley, Stephanie, illus. l.t. ed. 2003. 112p. pap. 12.95 (978-0-9727865-0-8(3) , 1003894) Fragile X Assn. of Georgia.

Hiaasen, Carl. Flush. l.t. ed. 2005. 335p. (YA). 23.95 (978-0-7862-7908-1(7)) Thorndike Pr.

Hicks, Ingrid M. E. Dare to Dream Ambrosia: The Adventures of Ambrosia Nittie. Hicks, Ingrid M. E., illus. 2nd rev. l.t. ed. 2002. (CHI.). 56p. (J). per. 14.95 (978-0-9678295-7-9(7)) NuVISIONS & Assocs., Inc.

Hill, Christopper T. If A Weren't for Apple. Hill, Christopper T., illus. l.t. ed. 1999. (Illus.). 90p. (YA). (gr. 2 up). pap. 12.95 (978-1-929136-00-1(5)) Topperhill Pubs.

Hill, Franklin. Wings of Change. Cheung, Aries, illus. l.t. ed. 2001. 32p. (J). (ps-3). 15.95 (978-0-935699-18-0(X) , 093569918x) Illumination Arts Publishing Co., Inc.

Hill, Grace Livingston. Cloudy Jewel. (J). reprint ed. lib. bdg. 24.95 (978-0-89190-037-5(3) , Rivercity Pr.) Amereon LTD.

Hill, Karen. One Bird. Hill, Karen, illus. l.t. ed. 2001. 28p. 8.00 (978-0-9714042-0-5(8)) Hill Publishing.

Hill-Ward, Robin. Global Healing: A Children's Book for All Ages. Hill-Ward, Robin, illus. l.t. ed. 2000. (Illus.). vii, 50p. (J). (gr. k-8). pap. 8.95 (978-0-9677955-6-0(7)) Hill-Ward, Robin.

Hinton, S. E. The Outsiders. l.t. ed. 2002. (LRS Large Print Cornerstone Ser.). (J). lib. bdg. 32.95 (978-1-58118-089-3(6) , 24874) LRS.

Hiris, Monica. Sleepy Polar Bear. Harston, Jerry, illus. l.t. ed. 2001. 24p. (J). (gr. k-1). pap. 4.95 (978-1-57874-072-7(X) , Kaeden Bks.) Kaeden Corp.

Hobbs, Valerie. Charlie's Run. 2000. (Illus.). 176p. (YA). (gr. 4-7). 16.00 (978-0-374-34994-3(0) , Farrar, Straus & Giroux (BYR)) Farrar, Straus & Giroux.

—Charlie's Run. l.t. ed. 2001. (Illus.). 166p. (J). (gr. 4-7). 21.95 (978-0-7862-3104-1(1)) Thorndike Pr.

Hock, Dan. The Birthday Bash 2 vols. An Iggy & Igor Mystery (#2) Hock, Dan, illus. l.t. ed. 2004. (Illus.). 51p. (J). per. 4.99 (978-0-9754046-1-4(X)) Anticipation Pr.

Hoelzel, Janet. Color Your Feelings: Get in Touch with Your Feelings, a Feelings Workbook. l.t. ed. 1998. (Illus.). 92p. (J). (gr. k-5). pap. 14.95 (978-1-892085-04-7(6) , 98-2) Arty Facts Pr.

Hoenecke, Karen. The Garden. Campbell, Jenny, illus. l.t. ed. 2000. 20p. (J). (gr. 1-2). pap. 4.95 (978-1-57874-007-9(X) , Kaeden Bks.) Kaeden Corp.

—Little Mouse. Gedeon, Gloria, illus. l.t. ed. 2001. 12p. (J). (gr. k-1). pap. 4.95 (978-1-57874-023-9(1)) Kaeden Corp.

—Snake Hunts for Lunch. Drzewiecki, Paul, illus. l.t. ed. 2001. 12p. (J). (gr. k-1). pap. 4.95 (978-1-57874-006-2(1) , Kaeden Bks.) Kaeden Corp.

Hoffman, Basia. The Bird & the Tadpole, Vol. 1. l.t. ed. 1998. (Tadpole Ser.: Series 1). (Illus.). 32p. (J). (gr. k-2). 15.95 (978-1-890582-03-6(4)) Creations by Basia.

—The Ocean & Pebbles. Solcyk, Phyllis, illus. l.t. ed. 1999. 32p. (J). (ps-2). pap. (978-1-890582-02-9(6)) Creations by Basia.

Hofmeister, Alan. The Creatures of Zoon, 10 vols. 2nd l.t. ed. 2001. (Fluency Builders Ser.: Bk. 4). 48p. (J). pap. (978-0-9709686-3-0(9)) Academic Success for All Learners.

—Instructor's Resource Manual. 2nd l.t. ed. 2001. (Fluency Builders Ser.: Bk. 10). 26p. (J). pap. (978-0-9709686-7-8(1)) Academic Success for All Learners.

—The Legend of Rudolfo. 2nd l.t. ed. 2001. (Fluency Builders Ser.: Bk. 5). 55p. (J). pap. (978-0-9709686-4-7(7)) Academic Success for All Learners.

Holcomb, Nan. Leah's Night of Wonder. Yoder, Dot, illus. l.t. ed. 1998. 32p. (J). (ps-3). lib. bdg. 9.95 (978-0-944727-35-5(2)) Jason & Nordic Pubs.

—Of Easter Eggs & Things. Yoder, Dot, illus. l.t. ed. 2000. 32p. (J). (ps-2). lib. bdg. 5.95 (978-0-944727-42-3(5)) Jason & Nordic Pubs.

Hollaway, David. Quigley Mccormick: And the Curse of the Polka Dotted Pig, 3 vols. l.t. ed. 2005. (Illus.). 156p. (J). per. 15.95 (978-1-933211-54-1(7)) Quackenworth Publishing.

Holm, Anne S. I Am David. l.t. ed. 2000. 208p. (J). pap. (978-0-7540-6121-2(3) , CLP 316) BBC Audio.

Holm, Jennifer L. Our Only May Amelia. l.t. ed. 2000. (Illus.). 261p. (J). (ps up). 21.95 (978-0-7862-2742-6(7)) Thorndike Pr.

Holofcener, Mark. Evan's Earthly Adventure. l.t. ed. 2003. (Illus.). 202p. (YA). mass mkt. 11.00 (978-0-9718626-1-6(3)) Holofcener, Mark.

Holt, Kimberly Willis. Keeper of the Night. l.t. ed. 2004. 336p. (J). 23.95 (978-0-7862-6431-5(4)) Thorndike Pr.

—When Zachary Beaver Came to Town. l.t. ed. 2000. 224p. (YA). 22.95 (978-0-7862-2515-6(7)) Thorndike Pr.

Homero Va a la Playa. l.t. ed. 2002. Tr. of Sam Goes to the Beach. (SPA.). 32p. lib. bdg. (978-1-59168-065-9(4)) Flying Rhinoceros, Inc.

Homophones, Set III. l.t. ed. Incl. Can You Hear Me from Here? Rondeau, Amanda. (ps-3). lib. bdg. 19.93 (978-1-57765-780-4(2)); Do We By, Buy, or Bye Tickets? Rondeau, Amanda. (ps-3). lib. bdg. 19.93 (978-1-57765-782-8(9)); They're There in Their Boat. Salzmann, Mary Elizabeth. (ps-3). lib. bdg. 19.93 (978-1-57765-

J
K
L

650-0(4)); Where Do I Wear Water Wings? Salzmann, Mary Elizabeth. (gr. 1-2). lib. bdg. 19.93 (978-1-57765-799-6(3)); Who's on Whose Spot? Salzmann, Mary Elizabeth. (ps-3). lib. bdg. 19.93 (978-1-57765-798-9(5)); You're on Your Phone. Salzmann, Mary Elizabeth. (ps-3). lib. bdg. 19.93 (978-1-57765-797-2(7)); 24p. (J). (Illus.). 2002. Set lib. bdg. 119.58 (978-1-57765-527-5(3) , SandCastle) ABDO Publishing Co.

Hood, Karen Jean Matsko. Washington State: Activity & Coloring Book. Parker, Michael, illus. l.t. ed. 2001. (Educational Activity & Coloring Book Ser.). 160p. (J). 9.95 (978-1-930948-56-3(5)) Whispering Pine Pr., Inc.

Hooker, Lou. The Year of the Fire. l.t. ed. 2004. (Illus.). 102p. (J). pap. 8.95 (978-0-9755106-0-5(6)) Hooker, Lou.

Hooper, Mary. Spook Summer. Hillard, Susan, illus. l.t. ed. 2005. 96p. (J). pap. (978-0-7540-7811-1(6) , CLP 397) BBC Audio.

Hoover, Marie, et al. Mikelngur Tenqmiar (Little Bird) (Cupig) Isaac, Cheri & Brunk, Cara, illus. l.t. ed. 1999. (ESK.). 8p. (J). (gr. k-3). pap. 6.00 (978-1-58084-165-8(1)) Lower Kuskokwim Schl. District.

—Nani Arnaq Iqvarta? Keene, Nellie & Brunk, Cara, illus. l.t. ed. 2000. Tr. of Where Is the Girl Picking Berries?. (ESK.). 8p. (J). (gr. k-3). pap. 6.00 (978-1-58084-201-3(1)) Lower Kuskokwim Schl. District.

—Where Is the Girl Picking Berries? Keene, Nellie & Brunk, Cara, illus. l.t. ed. 2000. 8p. (J). (gr. k-3). pap. 6.00 (978-1-58084-200-6(3)) Lower Kuskokwim Schl. District.

—Where Is the Girl Picking Berries? (Cup'ik) Keene, Nellie & Brunk, Cara, illus. l.t. ed. 2000. (ESK.). 8p. (J). (gr. k-3). pap. 6.00 (978-1-58084-202-0(X)) Lower Kuskokwim Schl. District.

—Yaquliyagaq. Isaac, Cheri & Brunk, Cara, illus. l.t. ed. 1999. (ESK.). 8p. (J). (gr. k-3). pap. 6.00 (978-1-58084-164-1(3)) Lower Kuskokwim Schl. District.

Hopkins, Lee Bennett. Mother Goose Through the Seasons: Theme 3. Fehlau, Dagmar et al, illus. l.t. ed. 1999. (Sadlier Phonics Reading Program). 16p. (YA). (ps-1). 29.85 (978-0-8215-0482-6(7)) Sadlier, William H. Inc.

Hopkins, Lee Bennett, selected by. Around the Neighborhood, Theme 3. l.t. ed. 1998. (Sadlier Phonics Reading Program). (Illus.). 16p. (YA). (gr. k-3). 29.85 (978-0-8215-0520-5(3)) Sadlier, William H. Inc.

—Around the Neighborhood: Theme Pack, Theme 3. l.t. ed. 1998. (Worlds of Poetry Ser.). (Illus.). 16p. (YA). (gr. k-3). 76.50 (978-0-8215-0527-4(0)) Sadlier, William H. Inc.

—Families, Families: Theme 2. l.t. ed. 1998. (Worlds of Poetry Ser.). (Illus.). 16p. (YA). (gr. k-3). 76.50 (978-0-8215-0517-5(3)) Sadlier, William H. Inc.

—Me, Myself & I! Theme 1. l.t. ed. 1998. (Sadlier Phonics Reading Program). (Illus.). 16p. (YA). (gr. k-3). 29.85 (978-0-8215-0500-7(9)) Sadlier, William H. Inc.

—Places to Visit, Places to See: Theme 4. l.t. ed. 1998. (Sadlier Phonics Reading Program). (Illus.). 16p. (YA). (gr. k-3). 29.85 (978-0-8215-0530-4(0)); 76.50 (978-0-8215-0537-3(8)) Sadlier, William H. Inc.

Horowitz, Alena Netia. The Tlytiettlym Tree. Horowitz, Alena Netia & De La Fuente, Mary, illus. l.t. ed. 2003. 64p. (J). per. 12.95 (978-0-923550-42-4(9)) Tetrahedron Publishing LLC.

Horowitz, Anthony. Groosham Grange. l.t. ed. 2005. 208p. (J). pap. (978-0-7540-7819-7(1) , CLP 409) BBC Audio.

Hortten, Jacqueline Faye. Pu Beach. l.t. ed. 2004. (Illus.). 27p. (J). pap. 14.95 (978-0-9728393-0-3(5)) Children's Bookshoppe Stop, The.

House, Darrell. Miller the Green Caterpillar. Argoff, Patti, illus. l.t. ed. 2005. 32p. 16.95 (978-0-9663276-9-4(1)) Red Engine Pr.

Howard, Pam. Be Kind to Others. l.t. ed. 2003. (HRL Little Book Ser.). (Illus.). 8p. (Orig.). (J). (ps-k). pap. 10.95 (978-1-57332-254-6(7)) HighReach Learning, Inc.

—Be Kind to Others. Middleton, Mikell, illus. l.t. ed. 2003. (HRL Big Book Ser.). 8p. (Orig.). (J). (ps-k). pap. 10.95 (978-1-57332-253-9(9)) HighReach Learning, Inc.

—Farmer Sam. Linke, Don, Jr., illus. l.t. ed. 2000. (Little Bks.). 8p. (J). (ps-k). pap. 10.95 (978-1-57332-149-5(4)); pap. 10.95 (978-1-57332-150-1(8)) HighReach Learning, Inc.

—Natalie Nurse. Linke, Don, Jr., illus. l.t. ed. 2000. (BB Ser.). 8p. (J). pap. 10.95 (978-1-57332-154-9(0)) HighReach Learning, Inc.

—See the Snow. Crowell, Knox, illus. l.t. ed. 2004. (HRL Board Book Ser.). 10p. (J). (ps-k). bds. 10.95 (978-1-57332-265-2(2)) HighReach Learning, Inc.

Howard, Pam & Crowell, Knox. A Flight to Polar Bay. l.t. ed. 2002. (Illus.). 8p. (J). (ps-1). pap. 10.95 (978-1-57332-220-1(2)); pap. 10.95 (978-1-57332-221-8(0)) HighReach Learning, Inc.

Howard-Parham, Pam. Caillou Finds Colors. Gillen, Lisa P., illus. l.t. ed. 2005. (Hrl Board Book Ser.). (J). (ps-k). bds. 10.95 (978-1-57332-313-0(6)) HighReach Learning, Inc.

—This Is Farmer Greg. Coates, Jennifer, illus. l.t. ed. 2005. (Hrl Board Book Ser.). (ps-k). pap. 10.95 (978-1-57332-305-5(5)) HighReach Learning, Inc.

Hubbard, Coleen. Christmas in Silver Lake, Rabinowitz, Sandy & Keiffer, Christa, illus. l.t. ed. 1999. (Treasured Horses Collection). 128p. (J). (gr. 4 up). lib. bdg. 23.33 (978-0-8368-2400-1(8)) Stevens, Gareth Inc.

—The Flying Angels. Rabinowitz, Sandy & Keiffer, Christa, illus. l.t. ed. 1999. (Treasured Horses Collection). 128p. (J). (gr. 4 up). lib. bdg. 23.33 (978-0-8368-2401-8(6)) Stevens, Gareth Inc.

—A Horse for Hannah. Rabinowitz, Sandy & Keiffer, Christa, illus. l.t. ed. 1999. (Treasured Horses Collection). 128p. (J). (gr. 4 up). lib. bdg. 23.33 (978-0-8368-2402-5(4)) Stevens, Gareth Inc.

—Louisiana Blue. Rabinowitz, Sandy & Keiffer, Christa, illus. l.t. ed. 1999. (Treasured Horses Collection). 128p. (J). (gr. 4 up). lib. bdg. 23.33 (978-0-8368-2403-2(2)) Stevens, Gareth Inc.

Hughes, Carol. Toots & Upside down House. l.t. ed. 1998. (Illus.). 184p. (J). pap. (978-0-7540-6037-6(3) , CLP 241) BBC Audio.

Hughes, Monica. Invitation to the Game. l.t. ed. 2001. 184p. (J). 26.95 (978-0-7838-9600-7(X) , Hall, G. K. & Co.) Thomson Gale.

—The Keeper of the Isis Light. l.t. ed. 2000. Orig. Title: Summerspell. (Illus.). 213p. (YA). 25.95 (978-0-7838-9295-5(0)) Thorndike Pr.

Hull, Donna L. Wally WaddleSnout & the Peppermint Race! Smith, Geoffrey P., illus. l.t. ed. 2001. 32p. (J). (ps-5). 13.95 (978-0-9710017-0-1(7)) TDH Bks.

The Hungry Mungry. l.t. ed. 2000. 36p. (J). (ps-2). pap. 9.95 (978-0-9701068-0-3(7)) Treetop Publishing.

Hunter, Alixander. The Handicapped Squirrel. l.t. ed. 1998. (Illus.). 32p. 19.95 (978-0-9665582-0-3(0)) Alixander Group.

Hunter, Julia, et al. A Puppy. Sparck, Carole C., illus. l.t. ed. 2000. 8p. (J). (gr. k-3). pap. 6.00 (978-1-58084-206-8(2)) Lower Kuskokwim Schl. District.

—A Puppy (Cup'ik) Sparck, Carole C., illus. l.t. ed. 2000. (ESK.). 8p. (J). (gr. k-3). pap. 6.00 (978-1-58084-208-2(9)) Lower Kuskokwim Schl. District.

—Qimugkauyar' Sparck, Carole C., illus. l.t. ed. 2000. Tr. of Puppy. (ESK.). 8p. (J). (gr. k-3). pap. 6.00 (978-1-58084-207-5(0)) Lower Kuskokwim Schl. District.

Hunter, Julius K. Absurd Alphabedtime Stories. Bauman, Todd, illus. 2nd rev. l.t. ed. 2004. 32p. (J). 16.95 (978-0-9761422-0-1(1)) J.K.H. Enterprises.

Hurcomb, Fran. One Lucky Fish. Schlagintweit, Kris, illus. l.t. ed. 1999. 32p. (J). (gr. k-5). pap. (978-1-894303-15-6(6)) Raven Rock Publishing.

Hyde, Philip, III. Defining Time: Lowering the Wacky Factor in Extending the Three Dimensions - A Linguistic Approach. l.t. ed. 2002. 121p. per. (978-0-9668013-2-3(6)) Groundwork Ideas Pr.

—The Football of Time: Why Globalization Isn't Working. Hyde, Philip, III, illus. l.t. ed. 2002. (Illus.). 116p. per. (978-0-9668013-1-6(8)) Groundwork Ideas Pr.

Ibbotson, Eva. Dial-a-Ghost. Hawkes, Kevin, illus. l.t. ed. 2002. 212p. (J). 22.95 (978-0-7862-3927-6(1)) Thomson Gale.

—The Secret of Platform 13. Porter, Sue, illus. l.t. ed. 2001. 250p. (J). (gr. 4-7). 22.95 (978-0-7862-3074-7(6)) Thorndike Pr.

—Which Witch? Large, Annabel, illus. 2000. 256p. (YA). (gr. 3-7). pap. 5.99 (978-0-14-130427-4(8) , Puffin); 1999. 224p. (J). (gr. 4-7). 15.99 (978-0-525-46164-7(7) , Dutton Juvenile) Penguin Group (USA) Inc.

—Which Witch? 2000. (J). (978-0-606-19882-0(2)) Tandem Library Bks.

Ilutsik, Paul. Neqsurtek. Slim, Zacharias & Horesh, David, illus. l.t. ed. 1999. Tr. of Two Subsistence Fishermen. (ESK.). 16p. (J). (gr. 3-5). pap. 6.00 (978-1-58084-173-3(2)) Lower Kuskokwim Schl. District.

The Incarnation of Christ: Immanuel, l.t. ed. 2004. Tr. of Incarnation of Christ. (CHI., Illus.). 52p. (J). (978-0-9752775-0-8(2) , 0-9752775-0-2) Unitrust Design.

Inspirational Press Staff. The Story of Christmas. l.t. gif. ed. 1998. (Arch Bks.). (Illus.). 80p. (J). (ps-3). 7.99 (978-0-88486-211-6(9) , Arrowood Pr.) BBS Publishing Corp.

Irvin, Christine M. Isaac the Frog. Less, Sally, illus. l.t. ed. 2002. 20p. (J). 3.95 (978-0-9706654-4-7(X)) Sprite Pr.

Jablonski, Carla. Homer Sweet Homer. Punchatz, Don, illus. l.t. ed. 1999. (Adventures of Wishbone Ser.: No. 13). (J). (gr. 4 up). lib. bdg. 22.60 (978-0-8368-2591-6(8)) Stevens, Gareth Inc.

Jackson, Bobby L. Little Red Ronnika. Mitchell, Rhonda, illus. l.t. ed. 1998. 32p. (J). (gr. 1-4). lib. bdg. 16.95 (978-1-884242-80-9(4)) Multicultural Pubns.

Jackson, Joan. Elim, the Determined Athlete: A Pups Journey to Be Part of the Team. l.t. ed. 1998. (Illus.). 32p. (gr. 3-6). 9.95 (978-1-888125-32-0(2)) Publication Consultants.

Jackson, Kamichi. You're Too Much, Reggie Brown. Goldberg, Jeff A., illus. l.t. ed. 2000. 110p. (J). (gr. 2-5). pap. 5.95 (978-0-615-11287-9(0)) Pen Poised Pr.

Jackson, Vicky, illus. Poepal's Purpose. l.t. ed. 2005. 20p. (J). 7.95 (978-0-9718741-0-7(7)) Tawa Productions.

Jacobs, Edwin. The Eve They Hi-Jacked Santa Claus. Simon, Mark & Barker, Aline, illus. l.t. ed. 2001. 47p. (J). 21.95 (978-0-9612948-5-4(X)) Lem Publishing & Production.

Jacques, Brian. Redwall. Chalk, Gary, illus. l.t. ed. 2002. (Redwall Ser.). (J). 25.95 (978-0-7862-3858-3(5)) Thomson Gale.

—The Taggerung. Standley, Peter, illus. l.t. ed. 2002. (Redwall Ser.). 683p. (J). 25.95 (978-0-7862-4014-2(8)) Thomson Gale.

—Triss. l.t. ed. 2004. (Redwall Ser.). 596p. (J). 23.95 (978-0-7862-6207-6(9)) Thorndike Pr.

Jansen, Marilyn. Amaryllis of Hawaii: Imaginations, Poetry, & Story. Jansen, Marilyn, illus. 5000th l.t. ed. 2004. (Illus.). 92p. (YA). 15.95 (978-0-9761070-0-2(7)) Jansen, Marilyn.

Jarman, Julia. The Time-Travelling Cat & the Tudor Treasure. l.t. ed. 2005. (J). pap. (978-1-4056-6005-1(8)) BBC Audio.

Jarrell, Pamela R. Animals, Animals. Crowell, Knox, illus. l.t. ed. 2000. (CB Ser.). 7p. (J). (ps-1). pap. 10.95 (978-1-57332-162-4(1)) HighReach Learning, Inc.

—Baby's Hands. Metzger, Jeanne, illus. l.t. ed. 2001. (Board Bk.). 12p. (J). (ps-1). 4.99 (978-1-57332-196-9(6)) HighReach Learning, Inc.

—Diving at the Reef. Ruminski, Jeff, illus. l.t. ed. 2002. (Little Bks.). 8p. (J). (ps-1). pap. 10.95 (978-1-57332-201-0(6)) HighReach Learning, Inc.

—Dr. Danny Checks My Teeth. Bicking, Judith, illus. l.t. ed. 2001. (Little Bks.). 8p. (J). (ps-1). pap. 10.95 (978-1-57332-218-8(0)) HighReach Learning, Inc.

—A Gift for Mother. Metzger, Jeanne, illus. l.t. ed. 1998. (Cuddle Bks.). 7p. (J). (ps-k). pap. 10.95 (978-1-57332-130-3(3)) HighReach Learning, Inc.

—Giving Gifts. Linke, Don, Jr., illus. l.t. ed. 1999. (CB Ser.). 7p. (J). (ps-1). pap. 10.95 (978-1-57332-156-3(7)) HighReach Learning, Inc.

—Going on Vacation. Gillen, Lisa P., illus. l.t. ed. 1999. (Cuddle Bks.). 7p. (J). (ps-k). pap. 10.95 (978-1-57332-138-9(9)) HighReach Learning, Inc.

—Good Manners. Metzger, Jeanne, illus. l.t. ed. 1999. (CB Ser.). 8p. (J). (ps-1). pap. 10.95 (978-1-57332-151-8(6)) HighReach Learning, Inc.

—I Can. Linke, Don, Jr., illus. l.t. ed. 1998. (Cuddle Bks.). 7p. (J). (ps-k). pap. 10.95 (978-1-57332-123-5(0)) HighReach Learning, Inc.

—I Like Fall. Middleton, Mikell, illus. l.t. ed. 2001. (Cuddle Bks.). 7p. (J). (ps-1). pap. 10.95 (978-1-57332-214-0(8)) HighReach Learning, Inc.

—In the Garden. Lent, Marion W., illus. l.t. ed. 1998. (Cuddle Bks.). 8p. (J). (ps-k). pap. 10.95 (978-1-57332-113-6(3)) HighReach Learning, Inc.

—Jennifer & Danny. Linke, Don, Jr., illus. l.t. ed. 1999. (Cuddle Bks.). 7p. (J). (ps-k). pap. 10.95 (978-1-57332-124-2(9)) HighReach Learning, Inc.

—Michael Monkey Pretends. Linke, Don, Jr., illus. l.t. ed. 1999. (Cuddle Bks.). 7p. (J). (ps-k). pap. 10.95 (978-1-57332-128-0(1)) HighReach Learning, Inc.

—Miss Tammy Is Cool! Gray, Stacy A., illus. l.t. ed. 2001. (Little Bks.). 6p. (J). (ps-1). pap. 10.95 (978-1-57332-210-2(5)) HighReach Learning, Inc.

—My Town. Linke, Don, Jr. & Carroll, Ken, Jr., illus. l.t. ed. 1998. (Big Bks.). 8p. (J). (ps-k). pap. 10.95 (978-1-57332-125-9(7)) HighReach Learning, Inc.

—My Town. Carroll, Ken, Jr. & Linke, Don, Jr., illus. l.t. ed. 1998. (Cuddle Bks.). 8p. (J). (ps-k). pap. 10.95 (978-1-57332-127-3(3)) HighReach Learning, Inc.

—See the Car. Carroll, Ken, Jr., illus. l.t. ed. 1998. (Cuddle Bks.). 6p. (J). (ps). pap. 10.95 (978-1-57332-105-1(2)) HighReach Learning, Inc.

—What Can It Be? Crowell, Knox, illus. l.t. ed. 2002. (Cuddle Bks.). 7p. (J). (ps-1). pap. 10.95 (978-1-57332-206-5(7)) HighReach Learning, Inc.

—What Do the Animals Say? Coales, Jennifer, illus. l.t. ed. 2001. (Board Bk.). 12p. (J). (ps-1). pap. 10.95 (978-1-57332-197-6(4)) HighReach Learning, Inc.

—Where Is the Teddy Bear? Metzger, Jeanne, illus. l.t. ed. 2001. (Board Bk.). 12p. (J). (ps-1). 4.99 (978-1-57332-191-4(5)) HighReach Learning, Inc.

—Who Does Bobby See? Gillen, Lisa P., illus. l.t. ed. 1999. (Cuddle Bks.). 7p. (J). (ps-k). pap. 10.95 (978-1-57332-133-4(8)) HighReach Learning, Inc.

Jarrell, Pamela R. & Gray, Stacy A. Carol Paints Everything. l.t. ed. 2001. (Big Bks.). (J). (ps-1). 10.95 (978-1-57332-212-6(1)) HighReach Learning, Inc.

Jauregui, Patricia. Sentimientos. Jauregui, Reginald, ed. Pineda, Jesus, illus. l.t. ed. 2004. (SPA.). 39p. (YA). pap. 19.95 (978-1-931481-41-0(5)) LiArt-Literature & Art.

Jax, T. L. Fraidy-Frieda's Light Show. Jax, T. L., illus. l.t. ed. 2004. (Illus.). 30p. (J). 9.95 (978-0-9743890-2-8(1)) Flaxenfluff Pr., LLC.

Jenkins, A. M. Damage. l.t. ed. 2002. 221p. (YA). 24.95 (978-0-7862-4749-3(5)) Thorndike Pr.

Jennings, Paul. Thirteen Unpredictable Tales. l.t. ed. 2005. (Illus.). 264p. (J). pap. (978-0-7540-6169-4(8) , CLP 362) BBC Audio.

—Unbearable! More Bizarre Stories. l.t. ed. 2005. (Illus.). 184p. (J). pap. incl. audio (978-0-7540-7856-2(6) , CLP 445) BBC Audio.

—Uncanny! Even More Surprising Stories. l.t. ed. 2000. 258p. (J). pap. (978-0-7540-6114-4(0) , CLP 309) BBC Audio.

—Undone! More Mad Endings. l.t. ed. 2005. (J). pap. (978-1-4056-6004-4(X)) BBC Audio.

Jenny Goes Swimming. l.t. ed. 2002. (Farmer Bob Ser.).Tr. of Juana Va a Nadar. (SPA.). 32p. (J). (gr. k-2). lib. bdg. (978-1-59168-060-4(3)) Flying Rhinoceros, Inc.

Jerrell, Pam & Mullican, Judy. Let's Take a Trip to Mexico. Linke, Don, Jr., illus. l.t. ed. 2000. (BB Ser.). 8p. (J). (ps-1). pap. 10.95 (978-1-57332-177-8(X)) HighReach Learning, Inc.

Joekay, Eliza, et al. Ayagciqiartukut (We Are Going) Sparck, Amy, illus. l.t. ed. 1999. (ESK.). 8p. (J). (gr. k-3). pap. 6.00 (978-1-58084-150-4(3)) Lower Kuskokwim Schl. District.

—Ayagtukut (We Are Going) Sparck, Amy, illus. l.t. ed. 1999. (ESK.). 8p. (gr. k-3). pap. 6.00 (978-1-58084-096-5(5)) Lower Kuskokwim Schl. District.

—Ellam Cai (Parts of the Sky) Joekay, Eliza, illus. l.t. ed. 1999. (ESK., Illus.). 12p. (J). (gr. k-3). pap. 6.00 (978-1-58084-098-9(1)) Lower Kuskokwim Schl. District.

—Illi Qilim (Parts of the Sky) Joekay, Eliza, illus. l.t. ed. 1999. (ESK., Illus.). 12p. (J). (gr. k-3). pap. 6.00 (978-1-58084-151-1(1)) Lower Kuskokwim Schl. District.

—Parts of the Sky. Joekay, Eliza, illus. l.t. ed. 1999. (Illus.). 12p. (J). (gr. k-3). pap. 6.00 (978-1-58084-097-2(3)) Lower Kuskokwim Schl. District.

—We Are Going. Sparck, Amy, illus. l.t. ed. 1999. 8p. (J). (gr. k-3). pap. 6.00 (978-1-58084-095-8(7)) Lower Kuskokwim Schl. District.

Johnson, Angela. Heaven. 1998. 144p. (YA). (gr. 7-12). 16.95 (978-0-689-82229-2(4)) Simon & Schuster Children's Publishing.

—Heaven. 2000. (Illus.). (YA). 11.64 (978-0-606-18799-2(5)) Tandem Library Bks.

—Heaven. l.t. ed. 2000. 157p. (J). (gr. 7-12). 20.95 (978-0-7862-2463-0(0)) Thorndike Pr.

Johnson, Angela & Palencar, John Jude. Heaven. 2000. (Illus.). 144p. (YA). (gr. 8-12). pap. 5.99 (978-0-689-82290-2(1) , Simon Pulse) Simon & Schuster Children's Publishing.

Johnson, Bob. The Castle of Gallimaufry Bk. 4: The Squatland Chronicles. l.t. ed. 2005. 56p. per. 11.00 (978-1-59453-510-9(8) , 2549) Airleaf Publishing & Bookselling.

Johnson, Brian. Ellie, the West Coast Eagle. Peet, Linda, illus. l.t. ed. 1999. 24p. (J). (ps-5). pap. (978-1-894303-25-5(3)) Raven Rock Publishing.

Johnson, Charisse, et al. Charisse & Leah's—Misunderstood: Coloring/Sticker Book (with Positive Messages) Chambers-Benjamin, Carol, ed. Johnson, Loren G., illus. l.t. ed. 1999. (Dreamers Ser.: No. 2C). 24p. (J). (ps-8). pap. 1.99 (978-1-889151-09-0(2)) Licensing by Loren, Inc.

Johnson, Janet L. The Ritz Carlton Cat. l.t. ed. 1999. (Illus.). 12p. pap. 18.95 (978-0-9673389-0-3(5)) Johnson, Janet L.

Johnson, Loren G., et al. Charisse & Leah's—Jesus & Me: Coloring/Sticker Book (with Positive Messages) Chambers-Benjamin, Carol, ed. l.t. ed. 1999. (Dreamers Ser.: No. 1C). (Illus.). 24p. (J). (ps-8). pap. 1.99 (978-1-889151-08-3(4)) Licensing by Loren, Inc.

Johnson, Michael. A Gift for Ida & Bell. l.t. ed. 2002. 32p. (J). 19.95 (978-1-893672-08-6(5)) Johnson, Michael Presentations.

Johnson, Nevlynn L., Sr. Faith, Courage & Wisdom: A Journey to Manhood. 3rd rev. l.t. ed. 2003. Orig. Title: Finding My Way: a Journey to Manhood. 240p. per. 14.95 (978-0-9741413-0-5(5)) In The Lead Publishing.

Johnson, Pete. Eyes of the Alien. l.t. ed. 2005. (Illus.). 200p. (J). pap. (978-0-7540-6127-4(2) , CLP 321) BBC Audio.

—Eyes of the Alien. unabr. l.t. ed. 2003. (Read-Along Ser.). 184p. (J). 24.95 incl. audio (978-0-7540-6239-4(2) , RAO40, Galaxy Children's Large Print) BBC Audiobooks America.

—Rescuing Dad. Nayler, Sarah, illus. l.t. ed. 2005. 256p. (J). pap. (978-0-7540-7809-8(4) , CLP 401) BBC Audio.

—Rescuing Dad. 2003. (Read-Along Ser.). (J). pap. 29.95 incl. audio (978-0-7540-6254-7(6) , Galaxy Children's Large Print) BBC Audiobooks America.

Johnson, Sandi & Fefie, Flora. Zemo to the Rescue: Dorp 7 Rock Band. l.t. ed. 2003. (Illus.). 15p. (J). (gr. k-5). spiral bd. 4.99 (978-1-929063-25-3(3) , 327) Moons & Stars Publishing For Children.

Johnston, Madeline. A Perfect Pet. Johnston, Madeline, illus. l.t. ed. 2000. 28p. (J). (ps-2). 9.95 (978-1-929115-03-7(2)) Azro Pr., Inc.

Jones, Ayaprun L. I Am. Brunk, Cara, illus. l.t. ed. 1999. 20p. (J). (gr. k-3). pap. 25.00 (978-1-58084-070-5(1)) Lower Kuskokwim Schl. District.

—Kui. Brunk, Cara, illus. l.t. ed. 1999. Tr. of I Am. (ESK.). 20p. (J). (gr. k-3). pap. 25.00 (978-1-58084-113-9(9)) Lower Kuskokwim Schl. District.

—Wiinga (I Am) Brunk, Cara, illus. l.t. ed. 1999. (ESK.). 20p. (J). (gr. k-3). pap. 25.00 (978-1-58084-071-2(X)) Lower Kuskokwim Schl. District.

Jones, David C. One Person to Another: Smoking, Chewing Tobacco & Young Peopole. l.t. ed. 2003. 20p. (YA). 4.00 (978-1-878400-17-8(7)) Dolphin Publishing.

Jones, Edward L. Mr. Moon Man Goes to Japan. Ingalls, Marjorie, illus. l.t. ed. 2001. 45p. (YA). (gr. 3-11). 14.95 (978-1-881533-00-9(X)) Jones, Edward-Lynne & Assocs.

Jones, Ivan. Ghost Hunter at Chillwood Castle. l.t. ed. 2005. 176p. (J). pap. (978-0-7540-6136-6(1) , CLP 329) BBC Audio.

Jones, Julie. The Problem at Pepperpine Zoo. Jones, Julie, illus. l.t. ed. 2004. (Illus.). 24p. (J). pap. 7.95 (978-0-9745553-0-0(4)) Greenwood Street Publishing. GSP.

Jossel, Joylynn M. When the Clock Strikes Eight. l.t. ed. 2002. (Illus.). 18p. (J). (ps-6). 8.95 (978-0-9706726-2-9(4)) End Of The Rainbow Projects.

Jougla, Frederic. Tricked on Halloween: Rina & Jax's Stories. Jougla, Karina, illus. l.t. ed. 2004. 36p. (J). bds. 14.99 (978-0-9754287-0-2(5)) Imagery Pr.

Joyce, Rita. Gozzy Goose's Christmas Gift. l.t. ed. 2002. (Illus.). 32p. (J). 7.95 (978-1-59094-015-0(6) , 0156) Jawbone Publishing Corp.

Juana Va a Nadar. l.t. ed. 2002. (Farmer Bob Ser.).Tr. of Jenny Goes Swimming. (SPA.). 32p. lib. bdg. (978-1-59168-061-1(1)) Flying Rhinoceros, Inc.

Juliana, M., et al, eds. Catholic Children's Treasure Box Vols. 11-20: Commonly Called Simply Treasure Box. Miki, illus. 2nd l.t. rev. ed. 1998. 32p. (J). (ps-3). pap. 35.00 (978-0-89555-582-3(4)) TAN Bks. and Pubs., Inc.

Justus, Adalu. Bipity Bop: From Grandmomi's Stories. Justus, Adalu, illus. l.t. ed. 1999. (Illus.). 8.50p. (J). (ps-3). spiral bd. 8.50 (978-0-937109-10-6(X) , 500) Ike, J. Bks.

Kairaiuak, Agnes, et al. Assikenqurraanka (My Favorite Things) Kairaiuak, Agnes et al, illus. l.t. ed. 1999. (ESK.). 8p. (J). (gr. k-3). pap. 6.00 (978-1-58084-161-0(9)) Lower Kuskokwim Schl. District.

—Makirallemni. Shantz, Joy, illus. l.t. ed. 2000. Tr. of When I Went on the Tundra. (ESK.). 8p. (J). (gr. k-3). pap. 6.00 (978-1-58084-195-5(3)) Lower Kuskokwim Schl. District.

—My Favorite Things. Kairaiuak, Agnes et al, illus. l.t. ed. 1999. 8p. (J). (gr. k-3). pap. 6.00 (978-1-58084-160-3(0)) Lower Kuskokwim Schl. District.

—Piniqapiaranka Cangssagqt (My Favorite Things) (Cupig) Kairaiuak, Agnes et al, illus. l.t. ed. 1999. (ESK.). 8p. (J). (gr. k-3). pap. 6.00 (978-1-58084-162-7(7)) Lower Kuskokwim Schl. District.

—When I Went on the Tundra. Shantz, Joy, illus. l.t. ed. 2000. 8p. (J). (gr. k-3). pap. 6.00 (978-1-58084-194-8(5)) Lower Kuskokwim Schl. District.

Kane, Tracy. Fairy Houses. Kane, Tracy, illus. 3rd ed. 2001. (Fairy Houses Ser.). (Illus.). 40p. (J). (ps-3). per., act. bk. ed. 15.95 (978-0-9708104-5-8(8)) Light-Beams Publishing.

—The Magic of Color. Kane, Tracy, illus. l.t. ed. 2005. (Illus.). 40p. (J). (gr. 1-3). 17.95 (978-0-9766289-0-3(2)) Light-Beams Publishing.

Kaposh, Mosh. The Moon, the Sun & a Hotdog Bun. Toron, Eli, illus. l.t. ed. 2002. (Experience Reading Ser.: Vol. 1). 32p. (J). (gr. k-5). 12.95 (978-0-9723488-0-5(8) , 651-695-9166) Nava Pubns.

Karl Marx & Christian Ethics. 2nd l.t. ed. 2000. 401p. (C). pap. 29.00 (978-0-9712616-0-0(1)) Arts Colony Pubs.

Kashino, Mark. The Journey of Mobius & Sidh: An Interactive Journey of Self Discovery. Kashino, Mark, illus. 2nd l.t. ed. 2001. 48p. 19.95 (978-0-9715709-0-0(6) , KEI Publishing) Kashino Enterprises, Inc.

Kasper, Joseph E. & Feller, Steven A. The Complete Book of Holograms: How They Work & How to Make Them. l.t. ed. 2001. (Illus.). 224p. pap. 11.95 (978-0-486-41580-2(5)) Dover Pubns., Inc.

Kassandra, ed. V antologia nuevo Milenio: Narracion (Cuentos) y Poesía. Ramírez, Antonio & Morrissey, Kay, photos by. l.t. ed. 2004. (SPA., Illus.). 100p. (YA). pap. 12.00 (978-1-931481-86-1(5)) LiArt-Literature & Art.

Katzakian, Norma. Naomi - A First Generation American. Chidester, Ardis & Folchi, Robert A., eds. Heggie, Dolores, illus. l.t. ed. 2000. (J). (gr. 4-7). pap. 12.95 (978-0-9662228-1-4(4)) Dab Publishing Co.

Keaster, Diane Wilmae. Goldie-the Wise, 25 vols. Page, Deb, illus. l.t. ed. 2004. (ZC Horses: 7). 76p. (J). (978-0-9721496-6-2(X)) ZC Horses Series of Children's Bks.

—Leroy-the Stallion, 25 bks. Page, Deb, illus. l.t. ed. 2003. (ZC Horses: 6). 76p. (J). 5.50 net. (978-0-9721496-5-5(1)) ZC Horses Series of Children's Bks.

Kehret, Peg. Escaping the Giant Wave. l.t. ed. 2003. 152p. (J). 21.95 (978-0-7862-5985-4(X)) Thorndike Pr.

—Terror at the Zoo. l.t. ed. 2002. (Juvenile Ser.). 164p. (J). 23.95 (978-0-7862-4511-6(5)) Thorndike Pr.

Keller, Rebecca. Real Science-4-Kids Chemistry Level I. l.t. ed. 2004. (Illus.). 72p. 24.95 (978-0-9749149-0-9(8)) Gravitas Pubns., Inc.

Kelley, Brooke H. Beach Fun. Lent, Marion W., illus. l.t. ed. 1998. (Cuddle Bks.). 6p. (J). (ps). pap. 10.95 (978-1-57332-118-1(4)) HighReach Learning, Inc.

Kendall, Gladys E. Why Pansies Have Faces. Klatt, Eileen, illus. l.t. ed. 1998. 15p. (J). (ps-5). pap. 10.95 (978-0-9659942-8-6(7) , 8-7) Erda Publishing Co.

Kerr, Judith. Mog's Christmas. l.t. ed. 2001. (Illus.). 32p. (J). (ps-2). 8.99 (978-0-00-664146-9(6)) Headline Bk. Publishing GBR. *Dist:* Trafalgar Square Publishing.

Ketchum, Ron, illus. Rochestrivia: 2,000 Amazing questions & answers all about Rochester NY, it's people & surrounding Towns. l.t. ed. 2005. 250p. per. 19.95 (978-0-930249-01-4(1)) Big Kids Productions (Publishing).

Key in Car: The Children's Reading Foundation Starter Books. l.t. ed. 2001. 28p. (J). cd-rom (978-0-9705383-0-7(8)) Sun Coast Communications, Inc.

Keyes, Eric, 3rd, et al. The Light in the Dark, 1. Marie, Paula Braxton, illus. l.t. ed. 2004. 40p. (J). per. 14.99 (978-0-9722795-5-0(5) , Precious Gems) EbonyEnergy Publishing.

Khan, Rukhsana. Dahling, If You Luv Me, Would You Please, Please Smile. l.t. ed. 1999. 196p. (YA). (gr. 7-9). pap. 8.95 (978-0-7737-6016-5(4)) Stoddart Kids CAN. *Dist:* Fitzhenry & Whiteside, Ltd.

Khan, Saniyasnain. The Ark of Nuh. l.t. ed. 2001. 24p. pap. 4.25 (978-81-87570-82-0(2)) Goodword Bks. Pvt. Ltd. IND. *Dist:* Lodhia Ctr., The.

—The Ark of Nuh & the Great Flood Sticker Book: Quran Stories for Tiny Tots. l.t. ed. 2001. (Children's Stories from the Quran). 16p. (J). pap. 2.50 (978-81-87570-86-8(5)) Goodword Bks. Pvt. Ltd. IND. *Dist:* Lodhia Ctr., The.

—First Man. Anand, Achla, illus. l.t. ed. 2001. 24p. (J). pap. 2.25 (978-81-87570-94-3(6)) Goodword Bks. Pvt. Ltd. IND. *Dist:* Lodhia Ctr., The.

—Life Begins: Quran Stories for Little Hearts. l.t. ed. 2001. 24p. (J). pap. 2.25 (978-81-87570-80-6(6)) Goodword Bks. Pvt. Ltd. IND. *Dist:* Lodhia Ctr., The.

—Origin of Life (Colouring Book) l.t. ed. 2001. 16p. (J). pap. 1.00 (978-81-87570-81-3(4)) Goodword Bks. Pvt. Ltd. IND. *Dist:* Lodhia Ctr., The.

—Tell Me about Hajj: What is the Hajj Is, Why It Is So Important, & What It Teaches Me. Ravindran, K.M., illus. 2nd l.t. ed. 2001. (Tell Me about Ser.). 40p. pap. 6.50 (978-81-87570-90-5(3)) Goodword Bks. Pvt. Ltd. IND. *Dist:* Lodhia Ctr., The.

—Tell Me about Hajj: What the Hajj Is,Why It's So Important & What It Teaches Me. 2nd l.t. ed. 2001. (Tell Me About). (Illus.). 40p. per. 9.75 (978-81-87570-00-4(8)) Goodword Bks. Pvt. Ltd. IND. *Dist:* Lodhia Ctr., The.

—Tell Me about the Prophet Musa: What Was the Mission of Musa, What Were His Miracles & What His Life Teaches Me. l.t. ed. 2001. (Tell Me About). (Illus.). 56p. per. 11.50 (978-81-87570-48-6(2)) Goodword Bks. Pvt. Ltd. IND. *Dist:* Lodhia Ctr., The.

Khan, Shahthureen. Thureen's Emotion: Poems. Khan, Shaima & Khan, Sabiha, eds. Khan, Shahnawaz, illus. Khan, Shahnawaz, photos by. l.t. ed. 1999. 20p. (YA). (gr. 5-12). spiral bd. 12.75 (978-1-928840-00-8(0)) DewDrop Arts & Technology.

Kimethu, Susan. Kids, Let's Follow Christ. l.t. ed. 2002. (Illus.). 65p. per. 6.99 (978-0-9719328-1-4(6)) Dansu Pubs., LLC.

Kimpel, Linda S. Charlie Chose a Champion; Shawn's Tiny Ship; Soldiers, Jeeps & Jelly Beans. Hunt, Courtney M., illus. l.t. ed. 1998. (Speech Creature Ser.). 24p. (J). (ps-3). pap. 24.95 (978-1-893240-00-1(2)) Chestleigh's Bks. Publishing Co.

King-Smith, Dick. The Crowstarver. l.t. ed. 2000. (Illus.). 243p. (J). pap. (978-0-7540-6095-6(0) , Galaxy Children's Large Print) BBC Audiobooks America.

—Saddlebottom. Bartelt, Robert, illus. l.t. ed. 2002. 152p. (J). 16.95 (978-0-7540-7817-3(5) , Galaxy Children's Large Print) BBC Audiobooks America.

—The Witch of Blackberry Bottom. unabr. l.t. ed. 2001. (Read-Along Ser.). 144p. (J). 29.95 incl. audio (978-0-7540-6238-7(4) , RAO39, Chivers Children's Audio Bks.) BBC Audiobooks America.

Kippling, Bozenka. Stories from the Inner World: Introducing My Best Friends. Sawatzky, Goranka, illus. l.t. ed. 2002. 48p. (J). per. (978-0-9689096-1-4(2)) Seed Children, Inc.

Kirkpatrick, June. Barn Kitty. Peterson, Lori, illus. l.t. ed. 1999. 32p. (J). (ps-3). pap. 10.95 (978-0-9660239-5-4(1)) Azro Pr., Inc.

Kirkpatrick, June & Brokaw, Michele. The Little Church Mouse of the Loretto Chapel. l.t. ed. 2000. (Illus.). 40p. (J). (gr. k-5). 16.50 (978-1-929115-02-0(4)) Azro Pr., Inc.

Kirwan, Debra Giampapa. Oh, Please Help Me Save the Tree! A Record-Your-Voice Book. Holodook, Joseph, illus. l.t. ed. 2002. (Adventures of Buford the Bull & Friends Ser.: Vol. 1). 16p. (J). 49.95 (978-0-9713153-7-2(X)) FunZone Co.

Kitze, Carrie A. We See the Moon. l.t. ed. 2003. (Illus.). 32p. (J). lib. bdg. 16.95 (978-0-9726244-0-4(6)) EMK Pr.

Kjelle, Marylou Morano. Raymond Damadian & the Development of the MRI. l.t. ed. 2002. (Unlocking the Secrets of Science Ser.). (Illus.). 56p. (gr. 4-10). lib. bdg. 25.70 (978-1-58415-141-8(2)) Mitchell Lane Pubs., Inc.

Kling, M. Terry & Ryan, Patricia K. The Holiday Miracle. Starbrook, Dirk, illus. l.t. ed. 2000. 73p. (J). (ps-5). 15.95 (978-0-9701849-0-0(5)) Citadel Entertainment Group.

Klug, Frances M. Stories from Heaven, Vol. XX. l.t. ed. 2000. (Illus.). 294p. (YA). (gr. 7 up). pap. 15.95 (978-1-892957-20-7(5)) City of God, St. Joseph's Hill of Hope.

Klug, Frances Marie. Stories from Heaven, Vol. XVII. l.t. ed. 2000. 371p. (YA). (gr. 7-13). pap. 15.95 (978-1-892957-17-7(5)) City of God, St. Joseph's Hill of Hope.

Knapp, Susan. Bells Goes to the Fair. l.t. ed. 2002. (Illus.). 44p. (J). 12.95 (978-1-888223-34-7(0)) McMillen Publishing.

Kneeland, Linda. Cookie. Fargo, Todd, illus. rev. l.t. ed. 1999. 32p. (J). (gr. k-3). lib. bdg. 14.95 (978-0-944727-39-3(5) , Turtle Bks.) Jason & Nordic Pubs.

Knight, Ernest C. Bean Head & the Imagination Machine. l.t. ed. 2002. (Illus.). 42p. per. 12.99 (978-0-9724680-7-7(2)) Lifevest Publishing, Inc.

Kochersperger, Jenny. Good Morning, Sun. l.t. ed. 2002. (Illus.). 32p. (J). (gr. k-4). 16.95 (978-0-9715884-0-0(6)) Beyond Borders Bks.

Kollmorgan, Loreen M. Animal Patrol. l.t. ed. 2005. (Illus.). 69p. (J). (ps-7). per. 12.95 (978-1-59453-169-9(2) , 1810) Airleaf Publishing & Bookselling.

Kondak, Margarida. The Wild Horses of Summer Bay. Kondak, Mary, illus. l.t. ed. 2002. 31p. 9.95 (978-1-890692-06-3(9)) Wizard Works.

Konigsburg, E. L. From the Mixed-Up Files of Mrs. Basil E. Frankweiler. l.t. ed. 2005. (Illus.). 205p. (J). 22.95 (978-0-7862-7297-6(X) , Large Print Pr.) Thorndike Pr.

—The Outcasts of 19 Schuyler Place. l.t. ed. 2004. (Thorndike Press Large Print the Literary Bridge Ser.). 346p. (J). 22.95 (978-0-7862-6483-4(7)) Thorndike Pr.

—Silent to the Bone. l.t. ed. 2001. 271p. (J). (gr. 4-7). 23.95 (978-0-7862-3169-0(6)) Thorndike Pr.

Kornblatt, Marc. Understanding Buddy. l.t. ed. 2002. 100p. (J). 21.95 (978-0-7862-3712-8(0)) Thomson Gale.

Koss, Amy Goldman. The Ashwater Experiment. l.t. ed. 2000. 188p. (YA). (gr. 8-12). 20.95 (978-0-7862-2686-3(2)) Thorndike Pr.

Kraemer, Katie. Aaron Carter. l.t. ed. 2002. (Real Life Reader Biographies Ser.). (Illus.). 32p. (J). (gr. 3-8). lib. bdg. 15.95 (978 1 58415 126 5(9)) Mitchell Lane Pubs., Inc.

Kurz, Ron. The Inner Music Experience. l.t. ed. 2003. 124p. (YA). 75.00 (978-0-939829-07-1(X) , Item#3) Kurz, Ron.

Lamperti, Noelle. Brown Like Me. 2nd l.t. ed. 1999. (Illus.). 32p. (J). (gr. 4-7). 12.95 (978-1-892281-03-6(1)) New Victoria Pubs., Inc.

Lang, Andrew, ed. Lilac Fairy Book. l.t. ed. 2004. (Large Print Ser.). lib. bdg. 26.00 (978-1-58287-778-5(5)) North Bks.

—Pink Fairy Book. l.t. ed. 2004. (Large Print Ser.). lib. bdg. 26.00 (978-1-58287-781-5(5)) North Bks.

Larousse Staff, ed. Larousse Student Dictionary: French-English / English-French. l.t. ed. 2003. (FRE & ENG., Illus.). 732p. (gr. 5). pap. 10.95 (978-2-03-542055-8(5)) Larousse, Editions FRA. *Dist:* Houghton Mifflin Co. Trade & Reference Div.

Larson, Eric. How Did Carpet Get in This House? Burns, William G., ed. l.t. ed. 2003. (Illus.). 62p. (YA). (gr. 4-7). pap. (978-0-9673696-2-4(2)) Caliber Pubns.

Larson, Helen C. Bird's Life. Larson, Helen C. & Shantz, Joy, illus. l.t. ed. 1999. 8p. (J). (gr. k-3). pap. 14.50 (978-1-58084-086-6(8)) Lower Kuskokwim Schl. District.

—Tengmiam Cullra. Larson, Helen C. & Shantz, Joy, illus. l.t. ed. 1999. Tr. of Bird's Life. (ESK.). 8p. (J). (gr. k-3). pap. 14.50 (978-1-58084-147-4(3)) Lower Kuskokwim Schl. District.

—Yaqulgem Angliurallra (Bird's Life) Larson, Helen C. & Shantz, Joy, illus. l.t. ed. 1999. (ESK.). 8p. (J). (gr. k-3). pap. 14.95 (978-1-58084-087-3(6)) Lower Kuskokwim Schl. District.

Lawrence, Ava. A Button for a Crown. Ford, Christina, illus. l.t. ed. 2003. 84p. (J). 14.95 (978-0-9651048-4-5(2)) Papillon Publishing.

Lawrence, Iain. The Buccaneers. 2001. (Illus.). 256p. (gr. 5-9). 16.95 (978-0-385-32736-7(6) , Delacorte Bks. for Young Readers) Random Hse. Children's Bks.

—The Buccaneers. l.t. ed. 2001. (Illus.). 320p. (J). 23.95 (978-0-7862-3464-6(4)) Thorndike Pr.

—The Smugglers. l.t. ed. 2001. (Illus.). 246p. (J). 22.95 (978-0-7862-3465-3(2)) Thorndike Pr.

Lawrence, Michael. The Killer Underpants. l.t. ed. 2003. (Illus.). 152p. (J). pap. 16.95 incl. audio (978-0-7540-7861-6(2) , Galaxy Children's Large Print) BBC Audiobooks America.

—The Poltergoose. l.t. ed. 2005. (Illus.). 168p. (J). pap. (978-0-7540-7836-4(1) , CLP 427) BBC Audio.

Layne, Carmela C. I See Many Colors Around My House: Los Colores que Veo Por Mi Casa. Layne, Carmela C., ed. Arevalo, Jose Daniel, illus. l.t. ed. 2005. (SPA.). 24p. (J). (ps-3). pap. 6.95 (978-0-9769538-0-7(3)) Pannycake Pubn.

Layos, Alexandra. An Almost True Horse Tale. Bauer, Dana, illus. l.t. ed. 2003. 20p. (J). (gr. 1-5). pap. 8.95 (978-0-9655501-3-0(3)) Saddle & Bridle, Inc.

Leavitt, Caroline. The Haunted Clubhouse. l.t. ed. 1999. (Wishbone Mysteries Ser.: No. 2). 144p. (J). (gr. 4 up). lib. bdg. 22.60 (978-0-8368-2383-7(4)) Stevens, Gareth Inc.

—Robinhound Crusoe. l.t. ed. 1999. (Adventures of Wishbone Ser.: No. 4). (Illus.). 144p. (J). (gr. 4 up). lib. bdg. 22.60 (978-0-8368-2300-4(1)) Stevens, Gareth Inc.

Lee, Betsy B. Whoa, Wiggle-Worm: A Little Lemon Book about an Overly Active Child, 1 bk. Varnedoe, Catharine E., illus. l.t. ed. 2003. 24p. (J). pap. 7.95 (978-0-9720267-3-4(8)) Learning Abilities Bks.

—10,000 White Horses 10,000 Caballos Blancos. Cruz-Torres, Natty, tr. Varnedoe, Catharine E., illus. l.t. ed. 2002. (SPA & ENG.). 24p. (J). pap. 5.95 (978-0-9720267-2-7(X)) Learning Abilities Bks.

Leedom, Tim C. The Light Side. l.t. ed. 2002. 80p. (J). per. 21.95 (978-0-9646885-1-3(4)) Manoa Valley Publishing Co., The.

Leeds, Elke, contrib. by. Toolbox of Hope: For When Your Body Doesn't Feel Good. l.t. ed. 2001. (Illus.). 132p. spiral bd. 24.95 (978-0-9716673-0-3(6)) Healing Heart Communications, Inc.

Leeson, Robert. Lucky Lad. l.t. ed. 1999. (Galaxy Children's Large Print Ser.). (Illus.). 100p. (J). pap. (978-0-7540-6042-0(X) , CLP 247) BBC Audio.

Legette, C. F. You'll Never Teach an Old Dog a New Trick. Legette, C. F., illus. l.t. ed. 2002. (Illus.). 36p. per. 14.95 (978-0-9722212-1-4(2)) CALs Ltd.

LeGrand, Hank, 3rd. Paddle Tail. Merrison, Stacy, illus. l.t. ed. 2004. 63p. (J). per. 7.95 (978-1-59466-020-7(4) , Growing Years) Port Town Publishing.

Leroux, Gaston. The Phantom of the Opera. l.t. ed. 1999. (Large Print Heritage Ser.). 420p. (J). (gr. 7-12). lib. bdg. 35.95 (978-1-58118-043-5(8) , 22512) LRS.

Levine, Gail Carson. Ella Enchanted. l.t. ed. 2000. (Juvenile Ser.). (Illus.). 294p. (J). (gr. 4-7). 21.95 (978-0-7862-2743-3(5)) Thorndike Pr.

—The Princess Tales, Vol. 1. Elliott, Mark, illus. l.t. ed. 2002. (Princess Tales Ser.). 240p. (J). (gr. 2-6). pap. 6.99 (978-0-06-051841-7(3)) HarperCollins Pubs.

Levy, Elizabeth. Seventh-Grade Tango. l.t. ed. 2001. (Illus.). 174p. (J). (gr. 3-7). 20.95 (978-0-7862-3105-8(X)) Thorndike Pr.

Lewin, Barbara D. Ono Mato Poeia. Lewin, Barbara D., illus. l.t. ed. 2001. (Illus.). 60p. (J). (gr. 1-3). pap. 7.95 (978-0-9707495-0-5(3)) M Pr. Publishing.

Lewis, C. S. The Horse & His Boy. Baynes, Pauline, illus. l.t. ed. 2000. (Chronicles of Narnia Ser.: Bk. 5). 253p. (J). (gr. 4-8). 21.95 (978-0-7862-2233-9(6)) Thorndike Pr.

—The Lion, the Witch & the Wardrobe. Baynes, Pauline, illus. l.t. ed. 2000. (Chronicles of Narnia Ser.: Bk.1). 208p. (J). (gr. 4-8). 21.95 (978-0-7862-2232-2(8)) Thorndike Pr.

—The Magician's Nephew. l.t. ed. 2000. (Chronicles of Narnia Ser.: Bk.6). 224p. (J). (gr. 4-8). 21.95 (978-0-7862-2231-5(X)) Thorndike Pr.

—Prince Caspian. Baynes, Pauline, illus. l.t. ed. 2000. (Chronicles of Narnia Ser.: Bk. 2). 262p. (J). (gr. 4-8). 21.95 (978-0-7862-2234-6(4)) Thorndike Pr.

Lewis, Carolyn. Hairy Beary Bk. 1: The Beginning, 3 vols. DeVince, James M., ed. Porcheron, Tammy, illus. l.t. ed. 2001. (Hairy Beary Ser.: 1). 40p. (J). pap. 9.95 (978-0-9712641-0-6(4)) J M D's Business Services.

Lewis, Omar. Myat & the Art Lesson, Vol. 3. Lewis, Omar, illus. l.t. ed. 2001. Tr. of Wonderful World of Myat. 36p. (J). 5.99 (978-1-886433-89-2(5)) A & B Distributors & Pubs. Group.

—The Wonderful World of Myat: Myat & Her Fear of the Dark, 6 vols. Lewis, Omar, illus. l.t. ed. 2001. 36p. (J). 5.99 (978-1-886433-87-8(9)) A & B Distributors & Pubs. Group.

Li, Deborah, illus. Tricia & the Blue Cap. l.t. ed. 2003. 28p. (J). 7.95 net. (978-0-9706654-5-4(8)) Sprite Pr.

Likins, Kim. Charlie's Perfect Day. Magalinska, Ingrid, illus. l.t. ed. 2003. 32p. (J). bds. (978-0-9729987-0-3(5)) Island Friends LLC.

Limb, Sue. You're Amazing, Mr. Jupiter. l.t. ed. 2005. (J). pap. (978-1-4056-6021-1(X)) BBC Audio.

Lincoln, Kelly J. Let's Go Storyknifing. Nevak, Caroline, illus. l.t. ed. 1999. 12p. (J). (gr. k-3). pap. 17.00 (978-1-58084-066-8(3)) Lower Kuskokwim Schl. District.

—Making a Grass Basket. Nevak, Caroline, illus. l.t. ed. 1999. 16p. (J). (gr. k-3). pap. 21.00 (978-1-58084-062-0(0)) Lower Kuskokwim Schl. District.

—Mingqiller Tapernarneg. Nevak, Caroline, illus. l.t. ed. 1999. Tr. of Making a Grass Basket. (ESK.). 16p. (J). (gr. k-3). pap. 21.00 (978-1-58084-063-7(9)) ; pap. 21.00 (978-1-58084-110-8(4)) Lower Kuskokwim Schl. District.

—Yaaruiyarciqukug. Nevak, Caroline, illus. l.t. ed. 1999. Tr. of Let's Go Story Knifing. (ESK.). 12p. (J). (gr. k-3). pap. 17.00 (978-1-58084-108-5(2)) Lower Kuskokwim Schl. District.

—Yaaruiyarluk. Nevak, Caroline, illus. l.t. ed. 1999. Tr. of Let's Go Story Knifing. (ESK.). 12p. (J). (gr. k-3). pap. 17.00 (978-1-58084-067-5(1)) Lower Kuskokwim Schl. District.

Lincoln, Rosalie. Arnat Castun Pillerkat Assigeskuneng. Lincoln, Rosalie & Nevak, Caroline, illus. l.t. ed. 1999. Tr. of What Girls Should Do When Eskimo Dancing. (ESK.). 16p. (J). (gr. k-3). pap. 21.00 (978-1-58084-111-5(2)) Lower Kuskokwim Schl. District.

—Nasaurluum Yurallra. Lincoln, Rosalie & Nevak, Caroline, illus. l.t. ed. 1999. Tr. of What Girls Should Do When Eskimo Dancing. (ESK.). 16p. (J). (gr. k-3). pap. 21.00 (978-1-58084-065-1(5)) Lower Kuskokwim Schl. District.

—What Girls Should Do When Eskimo Dancing. Lincoln, Rosalie & Nevak, Caroline, illus. l.t. ed. 1999. 16p. (J). (gr. k-3). pap. 20.00 (978-1-58084-064-4(7)) Lower Kuskokwim Schl. District.

Lisle, Janet Taylor. The Crying Rocks. l.t. ed. 2004. (Thorndike Press Large Print Literacy Bridge Ser.). 273p. (J). 22.95 (978-0-7862-6140-6(4)) Thorndike Pr.

—The Lost Flower Children. Ichikawa, Satomi, illus. 2001. 112p. (J). (ps-7). pap. 5.99 (978-0-698-11880-5(4) , Putnam Juvenile) Penguin Group (USA) Inc.

—The Lost Flower Children. l.t. ed. 2000. (Illus.). 188p. (J). 21.95 (978-0-7862-2890-4(3)) Thorndike Pr.

—Sirens & Spies. l.t. ed. 2003. 22.95 (978-0-7862-5378-4(9)) Thorndike Pr.

Litowinsky, Olga. The Pawloined Paper. l.t. ed. 1999. (Adventures of Wishbone Ser.: No. 11). (Illus.). (J). (gr. 4 up). lib. bdg. 22.60 (978-0-8368-2589-3(6)) Stevens, Gareth Inc.

The Little Entrepreneurs. l.t. ed. 2001. 65p. (J). 14.95 (978-0-9709119-2-6(0)) Limpid Butterfly Productions, The.

Lloyd, Paul R. Uh-Oh, Mommy Has the Flu. Zuk-Lloyd, Lynn, illus. l.t. ed. 2002. (J). cd-rom 16.95 (978-0-9723773-1-7(X)) PromiseGarden.com.

Long, Devata. Seeing Is Sometimes Believing. Garza, Amy Ammons, ed. Cain, Doreyl Ammons, illus. l.t. ed. 2001. 32p. (J). (gr. k-3). pap. 6.95 (978-0-9651232-8-0(6) , AC505, Catch the Spirit of Appalachia) Ammons Communications, Ltd.

Long, Laurie. Valuable Bible Characters - New Testament Math Puzzle Grade 1-2. Jackson, Cindy, illus. l.t. ed. 1999. 20p. (J). (gr. 1-2). pap. 4.50 (978-1-878669-75-9(3) , 3513) Creative Teaching Assocs.

—Valuable Bible Characters Math Puzzle Book. Jackson, Cindy, illus. l.t. ed. 1998. 20p. (J). (gr. 1-2). 4.50 (978-1-878669-72-8(9) , CRE3510) Creative Teaching Assocs.

Looper, Grace W. Molasses Making Time. l.t. ed. 2004. 152p. (YA). pap. 8.95 (978-0-9747685-5-7(3)) Bella Rosa Bks.

Loper, Kathleen. Angelina Katrina: Bugs in My Backyard. Waltz, Dan, illus. l.t. ed. 2004. 24p. (J). 17.95 (978-0-9741774-4-1(X)) D. W. Publishing.

—Angelina Katrina: Builds Troy Snowman. Waltz, Dan, illus. l.t. ed. 2004. 36p. (J). 17.95 (978-0-9741774-5-8(8)) D. W. Publishing.

Lorenz, Jinye. God's Mountain Not the Mountain God. Lorenz, Virginia O., ed. Lorenz, Jacob J., illus. l.t. ed. 1998. 120p. (YA). (gr. 6 up). pap. 12.95 (978-1-888350-09-8(1)) Lighted Lamp Pr.

Losty, Shelly Weiss. Dark Shadows A View of Collinsport. l.t. ed. 2002. 177p. 19.95 (978-0-9726299-0-4(4)) Bethany Pr., LLC.

Louthain, J. A. Ame the Elephant: Terrorized by Evil Mice. Eberbach, Andrea, illus. 2nd l.t. ed. 2003. 48p. (J). 12.97 (978-0-9679416-2-2(8) , 0-9679416-2-8) Alexie Bks.

Lowell, Melissa. Silver Blades, 10 bks. l.t. ed. Incl. Breaking the Ice. 144p. lib. bdg. 23.33 (978-0-8368-2063-8(0)) ; . Center Ice. 144p. lib. bdg. 23.33 (978-0-8368-2099-7(1)) ; Competition. lib. bdg. 23.33 (978-0-8368-2065-2(7)) ; Going for the Gold. 128p. lib. bdg. 23.33 (978-0-8368-2066-9(5)) ; Ice Princess. 144p. lib. bdg. 23.33 (978-0-8368-2096-6(7)) ; In the Spotlight. 128p. lib. bdg. 23.33 (978-0-8368-2064-5(9)) ; Perfect Pair. 96p. lib. bdg. 23.33 (978-0-8368-2067-6(3)) ; Rumors at the Rink. 144p. lib. bdg. 23.33 (978-0-8368-2097-3(5)) ; Skating Camp. 96p. lib. bdg. 23.33 (978-0-8368-2068-3(1)) ; Spring Break. 144p. lib. bdg. 23.33 (978-0-8368-2098-0(3)) ; (J). (gr. 4 up). 1998. Set lib. bdg. 233.30 (978-0-8368-2062-1(2)) Stevens, Gareth Inc.

Lowery, Rae. Case of the Lost Kid. l.t. ed. 2002. (Adventures of Charlie Ser.: No. 2). 111p. (YA). pap. 9.95 (978-1-891429-26-2(4) , 26-4) Armadillo Publishing Corp.

—Case of the Pack-Rat Park. l.t. ed. 2002. (Adventures of Charlie Ser.: No. 1). 87p. (YA). pap. 9.95 (978-1-891429-25-5(6) , 25-6) Armadillo Publishing Corp.

Lowes, Tom, illus. Casey's Four Holiday Celebrations. l.t. ed. 2003. 38p. (J). 16.95 (978-0-9722099-9-1(9) , C4HC) Caseys World Bks.

Lowry, Lois. Gathering Blue. l.t. ed. 2000. 256p. (J). (gr. 8-12). 22.95 (978-0-7862-3048-8(7)) Thorndike Pr.

Lucky the Goose. l.t. ed. 2002. 32p. lib. bdg. (978-1-59168-063-5(8)) Flying Rhinoceros, Inc.

Lumpkin, Susan. Look at Me! Carroll, Ken, Jr., illus. l.t. ed. 1999. (Cuddle Bks.). 7p. (J). (ps-k). pap. 10.95 (978-1-57332-145-7(1)) HighReach Learning, Inc.

Lunn, Janet. The Umbrella Party. 1998. (Illus.). (J). (ps-k). 14.95 (978-0-88899-298-7(X)) Groundwood Bks. CAN. *Dist:* Transition Vendor.

Luria, Paul. Magda Rose. l.t. ed. 1999. 150p. (J). (gr. 4-5). pap. 12.95 (978-0-943864-98-3(4)) Davenport, May Pubs.

Lyford, Cabot. Arthur the Moose. Lyford, Cabot, illus. l.t. ed. 2004. (Illus.). 32p. (J). lib. bdg. (978-0-9748145-0-6(4)) Castlebay, Inc.

Lyles, M. E. The Magic Stick. Garcia, Jopet & Stern, Ellen, illus. l.t. ed. 2000. 36p. (J). lib. bdg. 17.50 (978-1-887492-02-7(X)) Hi.I.Que Publishing.

Lynne, Rustyna. Bella's Birthday Manicure. Lynne, Rustyna, illus. l.t. ed. 2002. (Illus.). 14p. (J). (gr. k-2). spiral bd. 10.95 (978-0-9719657-6-8(5)) Red Carpet Publishing.

—Bella's Birthday Manicure: Special Needs Version. Lynne, Rustyna, illus. l.t. ed. 2002. (Illus.). 9p. (YA). (gr. 3-8). spiral bd. 10.95 (978-0-9719657-7-5(3)) Red Carpet Publishing.

—Derrick & Sierra Take Baths. Lawrence, Mary, illus. l.t. ed. 2002. 15p. (J). (gr. k-2). spiral bd. 11.95 (978-0-9719657-0-6(6)) Red Carpet Publishing.

—Derrick & Sierra Take Baths: Special Needs Version. Lawrence, Mary, illus. l.t. ed. 2002. 15p. (YA). (gr. 3-8). spiral bd. 11.95 (978-0-9719657-1-3(4)) Red Carpet Publishing.

—Giovanni's Pedicure. Lynne, Rustyna, illus. l.t. ed. 2002. (Illus.). 14p. (J). (gr. k-2). spiral bd. 10.95 (978-0-9719657-8-2(1)) Red Carpet Publishing.

—Giovanni's Pedicure: Special Needs Version. Lynne, Rustyna, illus. l.t. ed. 2002. (Illus.). 12p. (YA). (gr. 3-8). spiral bd. 10.95 (978-0-9719657-9-9(X)) Red Carpet Publishing.

—Tatiana's Shampoo. Lynne, Rustyna, illus. l.t. ed. 2002. (Illus.). 12p. (J). (gr. k-2). spiral bd. 10.95 (978-0-9719657-2-0(2)) Red Carpet Publishing.

—Tatiana's Shampoo: Special Needs Version. Lynne, Rustyna, illus. l.t. ed. 2002. (Illus.). 14p. (YA). (gr. 3-8). spiral bd. 10.95 (978-0-9719657-3-7(0)) Red Carpet Publishing.

—Tyler Brushes His Teeth. Lynne, Rustyna, illus. l.t. ed. 2002. (Illus.). 17p. (J). (gr. k-2). spiral bd. 10.95 (978-0-9719657-4-4(9)) Red Carpet Publishing.

—Tyler Brushes His Teeth: Special Needs Version. Lynne, Rustyna, illus. l.t. ed. 2002. 14p. (YA). (gr. 3-8). spiral bd. 10.95 (978-0-9719657-5-1(7)) Red Carpet Publishing.

MacCoon, Nancy. Backyard Wonders. Watkins, Courtney, illus. l.t. ed. 2003. 38p. (J). pap. 14.95 (978-0-9742495-0-6(5)) Vibatorium LLC.

Mackall, Debbie. Be Still! The Story of Little Bird & How He Found His Purpose. l.t. ed. 2005. (Illus.). 32p. (J). lib. bdg. 19.95 (978-0-9762273-0-4(4)) Dimensions in Media, Inc.

MacLachlan, Patricia. Sarah, Plain & Tall. l.t. ed. 1999. (LRS Large Print Cornerstone Ser.). 72p. (J). (gr. 3-8). lib. bdg. 19.95 (978-1-58118-049-7(7) , 22773) LRS.

MacLean, Alistair. Boondini. Bowser, Milton, illus. l.t. ed. 1998. 72p. (YA). 10.00 (978-0-940178-60-1(5) , BDNI) Sitare, Ltd.

Madame M. Trauma Queens/Trauma Kings. l.t. ed. 2003. (Madame M Presents:). (Illus.). 68p. (YA). per. 15.95 (978-0-9704159-3-6(1) , 0970415931) Creepy Little Productions.

Madame M's Creepy. l.t. ed. 2002. (Illus.). 60p. (J). per., act. bk. ed. 5.95 (978-0-9704159-2-9(3)) Creepy Little Productions.

Madison, Ron. Ned Learns to Say No: A Lesson about Drugs. l.t. ed. 2003. (Health & Safety Ser.). (Illus.). 24p. 4.95 (978-1-887206-23-5(X)) Ned's Head Productions.

Magi, Aria. The Lulilites: And the Star of Seven Rays. l.t. ed. 2005. (Illus.). 40p. (J). 19.95 (978-0-9759631-0-4(4)) Lulilite Productions.

Magnus, Kellie. Little Lion Goes to School. Robinson, Michael, illus. l.t. ed. 2003. 16p. (J). 9.99 (978-0-9744211-0-0(3)) Media Magic New York.

Maguire, Gregory. Four Stupid Cupids. l.t. ed. 2001. 225p. (J). 21.95 (978-0-7862-3547-6(0)) Thorndike Pr.

—Seven Spiders Spinning: Y Gregory Maguire. l.t. ed. 2002. (J). 21.95 (978-0-7862-4419-5(4)) Thorndike Pr.

—Six Haunted Hairdos. l.t. ed. 2002. 178p. (J). 21.95 (978-0-7862-4421-8(6)) Thorndike Pr.

Major, Devorah. Frederick Douglass: A Hero for All Times. Stemach, Jerry, ed. Nichols, Jack, illus. l.t. ed. 2000. (J). 50.00 (978-1-58702-451-1(9)) Johnston, Don Inc.

—Rosa Parks: Freedom Fighter. Stemach, Jerry, ed. Ham, Jeff, illus. l.t. ed. 2002. 150.00 (978-1-58702-027-8(0)); 2000. 50.00 (978-1-58702-448-1(9)) Johnston, Don Inc.

A Mal Tiempo, Buena Cara: El Humor en el Periodismo Puertorriqueno. l.t. ed. 2003. (SPA., Illus.). 48p. pap. (978-0-9743102-0-6(4)) Casa de Periodistas Editorial.

Malcolm, Jahnna N. Spirit of the West. Rabinowitz, Sandy & Keiffer, Christa, illus. l.t. ed. 1999. (Treasured Horses Collection). 122p. (J). (gr. 4 up). lib. bdg. 23.33 (978-0-8368-2282-3(X)) Stevens, Gareth Inc.

—The Stallion of Box Canyon. Rabinowitz, Sandy & Keiffer, Christa, illus. l.t. ed. 1999. (Treasured Horses Collection). 122p. (J). (gr. 4 up). lib. bdg. 23.33 (978-0-8368-2283-0(8)) Stevens, Gareth Inc.

Mandracchia, Charles, creator. A Wacky Wonder World. l.t. ed. 2005. (Illus.). 24p. (J). 13.95 (978-0-9721957-1-3(8)) Mandracchia, Charles.

Mankamyer, Laura. The Adventures of the Stonycreek Gang. Mankamyer, Laura, illus. l.t. ed. 2003. (Illus.). 84p. (J). 12.99 (978-0-9728431-4-0(0)) Mankamyer, Laura.

Marbury, Ja'Nitta. It's Okay to Be Me: Coloring the Self-Esteem of Children. Marbury, Ja'Nitta, illus. l.t. ed. 2001. Tr. of Esta Bien de Ser Como Yo!. (SPA., Illus.). 33p. (J). pap. 20.00 (978-0-9718307-1-4(1)) Shades of Me Publishing.

—Shades of Me: Coloring the Self-Esteem of African American Children. Marbury, Ja'Nitta, illus. l.t. ed. 2002. (Illus.). 22p. (J). pap. 20.00 (978-0-9718307-2-1(X)) Shades of Me Publishing.

Marceau-Chenkie, Brittany. Naya, the Inuit Cinderella. Brookes, Shelley, illus. l.t. ed. 1999. 24p. (J). (ps-3). pap. (978-1-894303-05-7(9)) Raven Rock Publishing.

Marek, Catherine. Sara's 1st Haircut, Sabrina, Adams, ed. Mitchell, Hazel, illus. l.t. ed. 2005. 30p. (J). per. 9.95 (978-0-9748251-3-7(1)) Zoe Life Publishing.

Marion the Magnet's First Mission. l.t. ed. 2001. 32p. 14.95 (978-0-9715345-1-3(9)) Hackleman, Sharon.

Marjorie, as told by. A Flower Unfolds: Inspirational Teachings in Verse from Kwan Yin, Bodhisattva of Mercy & Compassion. l.t. ed. 2003. (Illus.). 52p. 12.95 (978-0-9745712-0-1(2)) Sun Sprite Publishing.

Markarian, Marianne. The Pesky Bird, Wasielewski, Margaret M., illus. l.t. ed. 2005. 32p. (J). 16.00 (978-0-9767377-0-4(1)) Pomegranate Publishing.

Marks, Cindy. Another Summer: If Only There Was. Pickar, Steve, illus. l.t. ed. 1999. 56p. (J). (gr. 1-4). pap. 3.95 (978-0-9655425-0-0(5)) TiaraMoon Publishing.

Marlow, Herb. Cougar! l.t. ed. 1998. (Illus.). (J). (gr. k-8). 40p. lib. bdg. 16.95 (978-0-9666858-7-9(3)); 32p. pap. 5.95 (978-0-9666858-0-0(6) , C-1) Four Seasons Bks., Inc.

—Matt's Best Christmas Ever. Head, Pat, illus. l.t. ed. 2000. 44p. (J). (gr. k-7). lib. bdg. 21.95 (978-1-893595-05-7(6) , Matt-1) Four Seasons Bks., Inc.

—Matt's Best Christmas Ever Coloring Book. l.t. ed. 2002. (Illus.). 18p. spiral bd. 5.00 (978-1-893595-27-9(7)) Four Seasons Bks., Inc.

Marlow, Herb & Marlow, Lynn. Max the School House Mouse. Newberry, Loretta, illus. l.t. ed. 1998. (Max Ser.). 32p. (J). (gr. k-5). lib. bdg. 14.95 (978-0-9666858-5-5(7)) Four Seasons Bks., Inc.

Marlow, Herb & Marlowe, Lynn. Max the Rodeo Mouse. Newburry, Loretta, illus. l.t. ed. 2000. (Max Ser.). 32p. (J). (gr. k-6). lib. bdg. 14.95 (978-1-893595-07-1(2)) Four Seasons Bks., Inc.

Marrero, Rafelito. Amar sin decir Nada. 1000th l.t. ed. 2003. 137p. per. 14.95 net. (978-0-9747569-0-5(3)) Marrero, Rafael.

Marrs, Christie, creator. The Perfect Gift. l.t. ed. 2004. (Illus.). 57p. (J). mass mkt. 5.99 (978-1-928890-19-5(9)) I.B. Hoofinit Co.

—The Promise Keeper. l.t. ed. 2003. (Illus.). 53p. (J). mass mkt. 5.99 (978-1-928890-16-4(4)) I.B. Hoofinit Co.

Marsh, Carole. The Adventure Diaries of Brad, the U. S. Air Force Pilot! l.t. ed. 2002. (Illus.). 48p. (J). lib. bdg. 9.95 (978-0-635-01278-4(2)) Gallopade International.

—The Adventure Diaries of Dharma, the Dedicated Doctor! l.t. ed. 2002. (Illus.). 48p. (J). lib. bdg. 9.95 (978-0-635-01272-2(3)) Gallopade International.

—The Adventure Diaries of Felipe, the Fearless Firefighter! l.t. ed. 2002. (Illus.). 48p. lib. bdg. 9.95 (978-0-635-01270-8(7)) Gallopade International.

—The Adventure Diaries of Hannah, the Humanitarian Aid Worker! l.t. ed. 2002. (Illus.). 48p. (J). lib. bdg. (978-0-635-01275-3(8)) Gallopade International.

—The Adventure Diaries of Haz Matt, the Hazardous Materials Worker! l.t. ed. 2002. (Illus.). 48p. (J). lib. bdg. 9.95 (978-0-635-01280-7(4)) Gallopade International.

—The Adventure Diaries of Jack, the U. S. Army Special Forces Solider! l.t. ed. 2002. (Illus.). 48p. (J). lib. bdg. 9.95 (978-0-635-01273-9(1)) Gallopade International.

—The Adventure Diaries of Li, the Excellent EMT! l.t. ed. 2002. (Illus.). 48p. (J). lib. bdg. 9.95 (978-0-635-01276-0(6)) Gallopade International.

—The Adventure Diaries of Mike, the U. S. Marine! l.t. ed. 2002. (Illus.). 48p. (J). lib. bdg. 9.95 (978-0-635-01274-6(X)) Gallopade International.

—The Adventure Diaries of P. J., the Photo-Journalist! l.t. ed. 2002. (Illus.). 48p. (J). lib. bdg. 9.95 (978-0-635-01279-1(0)) Gallopade International.

—The Adventure Diaries of Riley, the Rescue Dog! l.t. ed. 2002. (Illus.). 48p. (J). lib. bdg. 9.95 (978-0-635-01277-7(4)) Gallopade International.

—The Adventure Diaries of the Perils of Pauline, the Police Officer! l.t. ed. 2002. (Illus.). 48p. (J). lib. bdg. 9.95 (978-0-635-01271-5(5)) Gallopade International.

—The Adventure Diaries of Vicki, the Volunteer! l.t. ed. 2002. (Illus.). 48p. (J). lib. bdg. 9.95 (978-0-635-01281-4(2)) Gallopade International.

Martin, Ann M. Gran Idea de Kristy. 2002. (Baby-Sitters Club Ser.).Tr. of Kristy's Great Idea. (SPA.). 168p. (J). 11.95 (978-84-272-3651-6(4)) Molino, Editorial ESP. *Dist:* AIMS International Bks., Inc.

Martin, Oscar, Jr., creator. Birth of Jesus. l.t. ed. 2003. (Illus.). 25p. (J). E-Book 19.95 incl. cd-rom (978-0-9748416-4-9(1)) Build Your Story.

—Civil Rights Leaders. l.t. ed. 2004. (Illus.). 25p. (J). E-Book 19.95 incl. cd-rom (978-0-9748416-9-4(2)) Build Your Story.

—The Creation Story. l.t. ed. 2003. (Illus.). 25p. (J). E-Book 19.95 incl. cd-rom (978-0-9748416-0-1(9)) Build Your Story.

—David & Goliath. l.t. ed. 2003. (Illus.). 25p. (J). E-Book 19.95 incl. cd-rom (978-0-9748416-3-2(3)) Build Your Story.

—Doctors. l.t. ed. 2003. (Illus.). 25p. (J). E-Book 19.95 incl. cd-rom (978-0-9748416-5-6(X)) Build Your Story.

—Famous Women. l.t. ed. 2003. (Illus.). 25p. (J). E-Book 19.95 incl. cd-rom (978-0-9748416-8-7(4)) Build Your Story.

—History of Music. l.t. ed. 2003. (Illus.). 25p. (J). E-Book 19.95 incl. cd-rom (978-0-9748416-7-0(6)) Build Your Story.

—Noah. l.t. ed. 2003. (Illus.). 25p. (J). E-Book 19.95 incl. cd-rom (978-0-9748416-1-8(7)) Build Your Story.

—Sports Legends. l.t. ed. 2003. (Illus.). 25p. (J). E-Book 19.95 incl. cd-rom (978-0-9748416-6-3(8)) Build Your Story.

—The Story of Moses. l.t. ed. 2003. (Illus.). 25p. (J). E-Book 19.95 incl. cd-rom (978-0-9748416-2-5(5)) Build Your Story.

Martin, Susan. The Combiners: Understanding Addition & Multiplication Word Problems. Martin, Susan, illus. l.t. ed. 1999. (Illus.). 80p. (J). (gr. 3-6). pap. 14.95 (978-0-941530-39-2(6)) Move It Math.

Martin, Tyler. Big Book: I Have a Question, Vol. 4. Williams, Toby, illus. l.t. ed. 2005. (Sadlier Phonics Reading Program). 8p. (YA). (ps-1). 22.50 (978-0-8215-7356-3(X)) Sadlier, William H. Inc.

Martinucci, Suzanne. At Space Camp, Vol. 2. l.t. ed. 2005. (Little Books & Big Bks.: Vol. 6). (Illus.). 8p. (YA). (ps-3). 22.50 (978-0-8215-7515-4(5)) Sadlier, William H. Inc.

Martivo, Kyalo. Herufi Zetu: African Traditional Writing Systems: Traditional Graphic Arts As Writing Systems. Leoni, Diana, illus. l.t. ed. 1999. 100p. (J). (gr. 5-8). pap. 8.95 (978-0-9642831-2-1(3)) Amenta Bks.

Massman-Wardzala, Joan. The Story of LittleMouse: LittleMouse Finds Tools for the Adventure of Life. Massman, Marjorie, ed. Wardzala, Phillip, illus. l.t. ed. 1999. (J). (gr. k-4). pap. 6.95 (978-0-9669902-0-1(X)) MassAward Publishing, Inc.

Mastorakis, Michael. We're off... to the Galapagos. Baker, Georgitti, ed. Mastorakis, Andreas, photos by. l.t. ed. 2000. (SPA & ENG., Illus.). (J). (gr. 1-8). lib. bdg. 18.95 (978-1-892306-02-9(6)) Cantemos-Bilingual Books and Music.

Matson, Laurie. Jaz-O & 'G' in Key West. Matson, Laurie, illus. l.t. ed. 2003. (Illus.). (J). 4.95 (978-0-9673704-5-3(0)) Seastory Pr.

Mattern, Joanne. Joseph E. Murray & the Story of the First Human Kidney Transplant. l.t. ed. 2002. (Unlocking the Secrets of Science Ser.). (Illus.). 56p. (gr. 4-10). lib. bdg. 25.70 (978-1-58415-136-4(6)) Mitchell Lane Pubs., Inc.

Matteson, Michael J. Legends of Christmas. Laskey, Robert, illus. l.t. ed. 1998. 144p. (J). (gr. 3-8). pap. 9.50 (978-1-890740-05-4(5)) Remnant Pr., The.

Matthews, Andrew. Point Horror: Darker. l.t. ed. 2000. 224p. (J). pap. (978-0-7540-6111-3(6) , CLP 305) BBC Audio.

Mayer, Mercer. Little Critter's the Picnic. l.t. ed. 1999. (Early Childhood First Bks.: No. 1). (Illus.). 20p. (J). (gr. k-1). lib. bdg. 13.95 (978-1-56674-219-1(6)) Forest Hse. Publishing Co., Inc.

Mazer, Norma Fox. After the Rain. l.t. ed. 2005. 359p. (YA). pap. 10.95 (978-0-7862-7913-5(3)) Thorndike Pr.

McCain, Steve. The Storybook Bear. l.t. ed. 2002. (Illus.). 40p. (J). per. 9.95 (978-1-932344-08-0(X)) Thornton Publishing.

McCarthy, Edward G. Farm Equipment: How Farmers Get All That Work Done. McCarthy, Edward G. & Sylvester, Carl, illus. 2nd l.t. ed. 1998. 48p. (J). (gr. 1-5). reprint ed. pap. 4.98 (978-0-9664138-0-9(6)) Ed D. Bear Enterprises.

McCaughrean, Geraldine. Daredevils & Desperadoes. l.t. ed. 2005. (J). pap. (978-0-7540-7845-6(0) , CLP 435) BBC Audio.

—Knights, Kings & Conquerors: 20 Stories from British History. Brassey, Richard, illus. l.t. ed. 2005. 216p. (J). pap. (978-0-7540-7820-3(5) , CLP 410) BBC Audio.

McCloskey, Robert. Homer Price. l.t. ed. (J). (gr. 4-6). reprint ed. 10.00 (978-0-89064-072-2(6)) National Assn. for Visually Handicapped.

McCottrell-Wade, Cheri C. If You Are Who You Say You Are... Line up with the Word. l.t. ed. 2002. 112p. (YA). per. 20.00 (978-0-9715945-3-1(8)) El-Shaddai Productions.

McCoy, Ellen R. The Bunny Run. 2nd l.t. ed. 2002. (Illus.). 144p. (J). per. 14.95 (978-0-9726065-0-9(5)) Paper Tale Pr.

McDalton, Magdalena. Carar Kuimarayarturtur (Cupik) Kiokun, Dorothy, tr. McDalton, Magdalena, illus. l.t. ed. 2000. 8p. (J). pap. 14.50 (978-1-58084-188-7(0)) Lower Kuskokwim Schl. District.

McDalton, Magdalena, et al. Aquiyaqatartua. Sparck, Carole C., illus. l.t. ed. 2001. 8p. (J). pap. 6.00 (978-1-58084-167-2(8)) Lower Kuskokwim Schl. District.

—Aquiyarciqiartua. Sparck, Carole C., illus. l.t. ed. 2001. 8p. (J). (gr. k-3). pap. 6.00 (978-1-58084-168-9(6)) Lower Kuskokwim Schl. District.

—I Want to Take It Home. Sparck, Carole C., illus. l.t. ed. 1999. 8p. (J). (gr. k-3). pap. 6.00 (978-1-58084-101-6(5)) Lower Kuskokwim Schl. District.

—Ut'rucugaqa. Sparck, Carole C., illus. l.t. ed. 1999. Tr. of I Want to Take It Home. (ESK.). 8p. (J). (gr. k-3). pap. 6.00 (978-1-58084-148-1(1)) Lower Kuskokwim Schl. District.

—Ut'rucugyaaqaqa. Sparck, Carole C., illus. l.t. ed. 1999. Tr. of I Want to Take It Home. (ESK.). 8p. (J). (gr. k-3). pap. 6.00 (978-1-58084-102-3(3)) Lower Kuskokwim Schl. District.

McDougal-Littell Staff, et al. Discovering French: Nouveau! Rouge, 2 vols. 3rd l.t. ed. 2004. 534p. (YA). (gr. 9-12). 267.00 (978-0-395-87486-8(6)) McDougal Littell Inc.

McElroy, Bonnie. Jagannath Coloring Book. McElroy, Bonnie, illus. l.t. ed. (Illus.). 48p. (J). pap. 4.95 (978-0-945475-29-3(2) , 1203) Mandala Publishing.

McGovern, Sheila. The Entire World of S & Z Book of Stories: 58 Targeted S & Z Pure Stories to Remediate Frontal & Lateral Lisps. l.t. ed. 2003. (Illus.). 148p. per. 34.99 (978-0-9723457-5-0(2)) Say It Right.

McGraw, Eloise Jarvis. The Moorchild. l.t. ed. 2002. 291p. (YA). 24.95 (978-0-7862-4787-5(8)) Thorndike Pr.

McGraw-Hill Staff & Johnson, Jack E. Glencoe Keyboarding with Computer Applications, Lessons 1-150. 2003. 596p. (gr. 9-12). stu. ed. 75.32 (978-0-07-860256-6(4) , 9780078602566) Glencoe/McGraw-Hill.

McGraw-Hill Staff & Spielvogel, Jackson J. Glencoe World History, 12 vols., Set. 2002. 3899p. (gr. 9-12). stu. ed. 93.72 (978-0-07-823993-9(1) , 9780078239939) Glencoe/McGraw-Hill.

McGraw, Nancy L. Simple Solutions Level 3. 2003. 280p. stu. ed., per. (978-0-9728730-0-0(7)) Bright Ideas Pr., LLC.

McHaney, Eric & McHaney, Mandy. Rich the Itch. Smith, Jordyn, illus. l.t. ed. 2005. 20p. (J). (978-0-9769086-0-9(3)) RTI Publishing, LLC.

McIntyre, Agnes, et al. Angliller (Growing Up) Curtis, Katie, illus. l.t. ed. 1999. (ESK.). 8p. (J). (gr. k-3). pap. 6.00 (978-1-58084-152-8(X)) Lower Kuskokwim Schl. District.

—Anglillra Ac'uruunam (Growing Up) Curtis, Katie, illus. l.t. ed. 1999. (ESK.). 8p. (J). (gr. k-3). pap. 6.00 (978-1-58084-100-9(7)) Lower Kuskokwim Schl. District.

—Growing Up. Curtis, Katie, illus. l.t. ed. 1999. 8p. (J). (gr. k-3). pap. 6.00 (978-1-58084-099-6(X)) Lower Kuskokwim Schl. District.

McKee, Ruby. The Land of Phonicia: An Enchanted Tale to Learn Phonics. Allen, Timothy, illus. l.t. ed. 2003. 52p. (J). per. 39.95 (978-0-9744944-0-1(2)) Jewel Publishing.

McKinley, Cynthia. One Smile. Byrne, Mary Gregg, illus. l.t. ed. 2002. 32p. (ps up). 15.95 (978-0-935699-23-4(6) , 0935699236) Illumination Arts Publishing Co., Inc.

McLaughlin, Marie. Those Toes. Rohr, Roni, illus. l.t. ed. 2000. 32p. (J). (ps-3). 15.95 (978-1-929115-01-3(6)) Azro Pr., Inc.

McNabb, Jeffrey G. Rule of Thumb Measuring System: Both English & Metric. Zimmerman, Pam & Kelley, Jim, illus. l.t. ed. 1999. (J). (gr. 4-8). pap. 5.00 (978-0-9669794-0-4(0)) Rule of Thumb Publishing.

McNicoll, Sylvia. Grave Secrets. l.t. ed. 1999. (Illus.). 176p. (J). (gr. 7-9). pap. 8.95 (978-0-7737-6015-8(6)) Stoddart Kids CAN. *Dist:* Fitzhenry & Whiteside, Ltd.

Mears, Richard Chase. Saint Nick & the Space Nicks. Westerfield, William Stephen, illus. l.t. ed. 2004. 32p. 16.95 (978-0-9754056-0-4(8)) Tuxedo Blue, LLC.

Mecham, Janeal A. Christmas Gifts. Mecham, Janeal A., illus. l.t. unabr. ed. 2003. (Illus.). 32p. (J). (gr. k-3). 12.95 (978-1-932280-16-6(2) , 80162) Granite Publishing & Distribution.

Meister, Cari. Basset Hounds. l.t. ed. 2001. (Dogs Ser.). (Illus.). 24p. (J). (gr. k-6). lib. bdg. 21.35 (978-1-57765-478-0(1) , Checkerboard Library) ABDO Publishing Co.

—Boxers. l.t. ed. 2001. (Dogs Ser.). (Illus.). 24p. (J). (gr. k-6). lib. bdg. 21.35 (978-1-57765-477-3(3) , Checkerboard Library) ABDO Publishing Co.

—Bulldogs. l.t. ed. 2001. (Dogs Ser.). (Illus.). 24p. (J). (gr. k-6). lib. bdg. 21.35 (978-1-57765-476-6(5) , Checkerboard Library) ABDO Publishing Co.

—Cavalier King Charles Spaniels. l.t. ed. 2001. (Dogs Ser.). (Illus.). 24p. (J). (gr. k-6). lib. bdg. 21.35 (978-1-57765-475-9(7) , Checkerboard Library) ABDO Publishing Co.

—Dogs - Set IV, 6 bks. l.t. ed. Incl. Basset Hounds. lib. bdg. 21.35 (978-1-57765-478-0(1)); Boxers. lib. bdg. 21.35 (978-1-57765-477-3(3)); Bulldogs. lib. bdg. 21.35 (978-1-57765-476-6(5)); Cavalier King Charles Spaniels. lib. bdg. 21.35 (978-1-57765-475-9(7)); Greyhounds. lib. bdg. 21.35 (978-1-57765-473-5(0)); Saint Bernards. lib. bdg. 21.35 (978-1-57765-474-2(9)); 24p. (J). (gr. k-6). 2001. (Illus.). 2001. Set lib. bdg. 128.10 (978-1-57765-501-5(X) , Checkerboard Library) ABDO Publishing Co.

—Greyhounds. l.t. ed. 2001. (Dogs Ser.). (Illus.). 24p. (J). (gr. k-6). lib. bdg. 21.35 (978-1-57765-473-5(0) , Checkerboard Library) ABDO Publishing Co.

—Saint Bernards. l.t. ed. 2001. (Dogs Ser.). (Illus.). 24p. (J). (gr. k-6). lib. bdg. 21.35 (978-1-57765-474-2(9) , Checkerboard Library) ABDO Publishing Co.

Mentink, Jarrett W. Alley the Cat. Carlson, Patrick W., illus. l.t. ed. 2002. 44p. (J). 14.95 (978-0-9723314-0-1(9)) Kids in the Clouds.

Messinger, Robert M. & Messinger, Laura M. Why Me? Why Did I Have to Get Diabetes? l.t. ed. 2004. (Illus.). 64p. 12.95 (978-1-893237-02-5(8)) Little Mai Pr.

Metzler, Rosemary M. Snooty the Fox & the Mysterious Black Box. Lahknau, Gaynel, illus. l.t. ed. 1998. 84p. (YA). (gr. 3 up). pap. 10.95 (978-0-88100-106-8(6)) National Writers Pr., The.

Meyer, Kay L. The Adventures of Billie & Annie—Baby Bison. Kirchoff, Arthur, illus. l.t. ed. 2004. 32p. (J). 6.00 (978-0-9744536-0-6(9) , 9780974453606) Meyer, Tjaden.

Meyers, Susan A. Callie & the Stepmother. Gauss, Rose, illus. l.t. ed. 2005. 64p. (J). pap. 6.95 (978-0-9718348-0-4(6)) Blooming Tree Pr.

Mi Cara Curiosa. 2002. (Wild Imagination Ser.).Tr. of My Fantastic Face. (SPA.). 24p. (J). lib. bdg. (978-1-59168-062-8(X)) Flying Rhinoceros, Inc.

Michael, Veronica & Caole, Frances. Ayuqucinka. Michael, Veronica & Shantz, Joy, illus. l.t. ed. 1999. Tr. of My Feelings. (ESK.). 8p. (J). (gr. k-3). pap. 6.00 (978-1-58084-055-2(8)); pap. 6.00 (978-1-58084-117-7(1)) Lower Kuskokwim Schl. District.

—Mihigimanitka. Michael, Veronica & Shantz, Joy, illus. l.t. ed. 1999. Tr. of My Feelings. (ESK.). 8p. (J). (gr. k-3). pap. 6.00 (978-1-58084-130-6(9)) Lower Kuskokwim Schl. District.

—My Feelings. Michael, Veronica & Shantz, Joy, illus. l.t. ed. 1999. 8p. (J). (gr. k-3). pap. 6.00 (978-1-58084-054-5(X)) Lower Kuskokwim Schl. District.

—Qanuqitipit. Shantz, Joy, illus. l.t. ed. 1999. Tr. of My Feelings. (ESK.). 8p. (J). (gr. k-3). pap. 6.00 (978-1-58084-123-8(6)) Lower Kuskokwim Schl. District.

—Qanuqitipit. Michael, Veronica & Shantz, Joy, illus. l.t. ed. 1999. Tr. of My Feelings. (ESK.). 8p. (J). (gr. k-3). pap. 6.00 (978-1-58084-138-2(4)) Lower Kuskokwim Schl. District.

Michaels, David. Bye-Bye, Katy, Vol. 3. Platt, Pierre, illus. l.t. ed. 2005. (Sadlier Phonics Reading Program). 8p. (YA). (ps-1). 22.50 (978-0-8215-7354-9(3)) Sadlier, William H. Inc.

Michels, Dia L. Look What I See! Where Can I Be? with My Animal Friends. Bowles, Michael J. N., photos by. l.t. ed. 2002. (Look What I See! Where Can I Be? Ser.: Vol. 3). (Illus.). 32p. 16.95 (978-1-930775-07-7(5)) Platypus Media, L.L.C.

Mike. Lemon Drop Rain: Poems & Drawings by Mr. Mike. Mike, illus. l.t. ed. 2003. (Illus.). 180p. (J). pap. 14.95 (978-0-9658365-6-2(8)) Beetle Bug Bks.

Milano, Jacque. Stay-at-Home Hank: The Little Hummingbird That Couldn't Fly. Milano, Jacque, illus. l.t. ed. 2003. (Illus.). 30p. (J). 9.95 (978-0-9728432-0-1(5)) Milano, Jacque & Assocs.

Miller, Brandy & Wittmaier, Jeffrey B., eds. Success: In Your Career & Personal Life, a How-to Guide. Leonard, David, illus. l.t. ed. 2002. 160p. (YA). per. 16.95 (978-0-9720961-0-2(8)) Miller, Larry.

Miller, Christian. The Champagne Sandwich. l.t. ed. 2003. (Isis Hardcover Ser.). (Illus.). 240p. (J). 32.50 (978-0-7531-6887-5(1)) ISIS Large Print Bks. GBR. *Dist:* Ulverscroft Large Print Bks., Ltd.

Miller, Kyle Linda. Dillo: A Baby Armadillo's Adventure on Sanibel Island. Eddy, Randon, illus. l.t. ed. 2005. 64p. (J). per. 16.95 (978-0-9769332-0-5(9)) Jungle Hse. Pubns.

Miller, Roger Carlton. The Ant & the Grasshopper, l.t. ed. 2003. Orig. Title: Same. (Illus.). 14p. (978-0-9712104-2-4(X)) Texas Woman's Univ. Pr.

Miller, S. K., illus. & creator. Jesse's Color Field. Miller, S. K., creator. l.t. ed. 2002. 68p. (J). (gr. k-5). pap. 16.95 (978-0-9714636-0-8(3)) Treehouse Treasures Corp.

Milord, Sonya. In One Day. Noland Anderson, illus. l.t. ed. 2002. 33p. (J). bds. 14.95 (978-0-9723826-1-8(5)) Tajiri Ventures LLC.

Miranda, Anne. The Best Place. l.t. ed. 2005. (Little Books & Big Bks.: Vol. 5). (Illus.). 8p. (YA). (ps-3). 22.50 (978-0-8215-7514-7(7)) Sadlier, William H. Inc.

—Big Book: Looking at Lizards, Vol. 2. l.t. ed. 2005. (Sadlier Phonics Reading Program). (Illus.). 8p. (YA). (ps-1). 22.50 (978-0-8215-7346-4(2)) Sadlier, William H. Inc.

—Big Book: Weather Wise, Vol. 3. l.t. ed. 2005. (Sadlier Phonics Reading Program). (Illus.). 8p. (YA). (ps-1). 22.50 (978-0-8215-7351-8(9)) Sadlier, William H. Inc.

—Peach Tree Street, Vol. 2. Lodge, Katherine, illus. l.t. ed. 2005. (Little Books & Big Bks.: Vol. 10). 8p. (YA). (ps-3). 22.50 (978-0-8215-7519-2(8)) Sadlier, William H. Inc.

Mishler, Donna. Historical People for Young Learners. Melvin, James, illus. l.t. ed. 1999. 32p. (J). (gr. k-5). pap., stu. ed. 5.95 (978-1-893709-03-4(5)) Suthernsky.

—Lighthouses of the Mid-Atlantic States. Melvin, James, illus. l.t. ed. 1999. 32p. (J). (gr. k-5). pap., stu. ed. 5.95 (978-1-893709-02-7(7)) Suthernsky.

—Travel Through Virginia. Melvin, James, illus. l.t. ed. 1999. 40p. (J). (gr. k-5). Bk. I. pap., stu. ed. 6.95 (978-1-893709-00-3(0)); Bk. II. pap., stu. ed. 5.95 (978-1-893709-01-0(9)) Suthernsky.

Mitchell, Robin. Windy. Mitchell, Robin & Steedman, Judith, illus. l.t. ed. 2002. 48p. (J). (ps-2). 14.95 (978-0-9688768-2-4(X)) Simply Read Bks. CAN. *Dist:* Perseus Distribution.

Modica, Cathy & Van Eyck, Laura. Niik & Bling: The Friendship Begins. Modica, Cathy, photos by. l.t. ed. 2005. (Illus.). 40p. (J). 19.95 (978-0-9762466-0-2(0)) Wholesome Puppy Tales.

Moeckel, Christine. Dick the Duck. Moeckel, Christine, illus. l.t. ed. 2004. (Illus.). 31p. (J). spiral bd. 9.98 (978-0-9720350-2-6(8)) Duckpond Publishing, Inc.

Moeri, Louise. The Devil in Ol' Rosie. l.t. ed. 2002. (Juvenile Ser.). 161p. (J). 21.95 (978-0-7862-3808-8(9)) Thomson Gale.

Mohr, Michale & Geer, Debi. Stephy Lynns' My Puppy. Archambault, A. J., illus. l.t. ed. 2002. 22p. per. 9.95 (978-0-9719597-8-1(1)) Thornton Publishing.

Moller, Jonathan R. Bath Time: Picture Book. l.t. ed. 2003. (Illus.). 71p. pap. 19.95 (978-0-9740169-0-0(X)) Lemonflavor Productions.

Molter, Carey. Bass Cannot Play Bass. l.t. ed. 2002. (Homographs Ser.). (Illus.). 24p. (J). (ps-3). lib. bdg. 19.93 (978-1-57765-793-4(4) , SandCastle) ABDO Publishing Co.

—Ck: See It Say It Hear It. l.t. ed. 2001. (More Blends Ser.). (Illus.). 24p. (J). (ps-3). lib. bdg. 19.93 (978-1-57765-447-6(1) , SandCastle) ABDO Publishing Co.

—The Five Senses. l.t. ed. 2001. (Senses Ser.). (Illus.). 24p. (J). (ps-3). lib. bdg. 19.93 (978-1-57765-631-9(8) , SandCastle) ABDO Publishing Co.

—Fruit Trees Produce Produce. l.t. ed. 2002. (Homographs Ser.). (Illus.). 24p. (J). (ps-3). lib. bdg. 19.93 (978-1-57765-794-1(2) , SandCastle) ABDO Publishing Co.

—Homographs, Set. l.t. ed. Incl. Bass Cannot Play Bass. lib. bdg. 19.93 (978-1-57765-793-4(4)); Fruit Trees Produce Produce. lib. bdg. 19.93 (978-1-57765-794-1(2)); Live Lions Live on Land. lib. bdg. 19.93 (978-1-57765-795-8(0)); Pete Presents the Presents. lib. bdg. 19.93 (978-1-57765-796-5(9)); 24p. (J). (ps-3). (Illus.). 2002. Set lib. bdg. 79.72 (978-1-57765-523-7(0) , SandCastle) ABDO Publishing Co.

—Live Lions Live on Land. l.t. ed. 2002. (Homographs Ser.). (Illus.). 24p. (J). (ps-3). lib. bdg. 19.93 (978-1-57765-795-8(0) , SandCastle) ABDO Publishing Co.

—Ng: See It Say It Hear It. l.t. ed. 2001. (More Blends Ser.). (Illus.). 24p. (J). (ps-3). lib. bdg. 19.93 (978-1-57765-450-6(1) , SandCastle) ABDO Publishing Co.

—Pete Presents the Presents. l.t. ed. 2002. (Homographs Ser.). (Illus.). 24p. (J). (ps-3). lib. bdg. 19.93 (978-1-57765-796-5(9) , SandCastle) ABDO Publishing Co.

—Ph: See It Say It Hear It. l.t. ed. 2001. (More Blends Ser.). (Illus.). 24p. (J). (ps-3). lib. bdg. 19.93 (978-1-57765-451-3(X) , SandCastle) ABDO Publishing Co.

—Sense of Hearing. l.t. ed. 2001. (Senses Ser.). (Illus.). 24p. (J). (ps-3). lib. bdg. 19.93 (978-1-57765-627-2(X) , SandCastle) ABDO Publishing Co.

—Sense of Sight. l.t. ed. 2001. (Senses Ser.). (Illus.). 24p. (J). (ps-3). lib. bdg. 19.93 (978-1-57765-626-5(1) , SandCastle) ABDO Publishing Co.

—Sense of Smell. l.t. ed. 2001. (Senses Ser.). (Illus.). 24p. (J). (ps-3). lib. bdg. 19.93 (978-1-57765-628-9(8) , SandCastle) ABDO Publishing Co.

—Sense of Taste. l.t. ed. 2001. (Senses Ser.). (Illus.). 24p. (J). (ps-3). lib. bdg. 19.93 (978-1-57765-629-6(6) , SandCastle) ABDO Publishing Co.

—Sense of Touch. l.t. ed. 2001. (Senses Ser.). (Illus.). 24p. (J). (ps-3). lib. bdg. 19.93 (978-1-57765-630-2(X) , SandCastle) ABDO Publishing Co.

—The Senses, Set. l.t. ed. Incl. Five Senses. lib. bdg. 19.93 (978-1-57765-631-9(8)); Sense of Hearing. lib. bdg. 19.93 (978-1-57765-627-2(X)); Sense of Sight. lib. bdg. 19.93 (978-1-57765-626-5(1)); Sense of Smell. lib. bdg. 19.93 (978-1-57765-628-9(8)); Sense of Taste. lib. bdg. 19.93 (978-1-57765-629-6(6)); Sense of Touch. lib. bdg. 19.93 (978-1-57765-630-2(X)); 24p. (J). (ps-3). 2001. (Illus.). 2001. Set lib. bdg. 119.58 (978-1-57765-515-2(X) , SandCastle) ABDO Publishing Co.

—Sh: See It Say It Hear It. l.t. ed. 2000. (Blends Ser.). (Illus.). 24p. (J). (ps-3). lib. bdg. 19.93 (978-1-57765-412-4(9) , SandCastle) ABDO Publishing Co.

—Tr: See It Say It Hear It. l.t. ed. 2000. (Blends Ser.). (Illus.). 24p. (J). (ps-3). lib. bdg. 19.93 (978-1-57765-411-7(0) , SandCastle) ABDO Publishing Co.

Moncus, Shane. Multiverse: By Shane Moncus - A Texas Street Poet. Galloway, Annette, ed. Moncus, Steve, illus. l.t. ed. 2001. (Multiverse). 72p. (C). per. 6.95 (978-0-9666676-8-4(9)) Main St Publishing, Inc.

Monsen, Annie. Friendly Fly. l.t. ed. 2005. (Illus.). 13p. (J). (ps-7). pap. 5.00 (978-1-59453-105-7(6) , 1909) Airleaf Publishing & Bookselling.

Monson-Burton, Marianne, compiled by. Girls Know Best Vol. 2: Tips on Life & Fun Stuff to Do. l.t. ed. 1999. (Girls Know Best Ser.). (Illus.). (J). (gr. 3 up). lib. bdg. 23.33 (978-0-8368-2453-7(9)) Stevens, Gareth Inc.

—Girls Know Best Vol. 3: Your Words, Your World. l.t. ed. 2000. (Girls Know Best Ser.). (Illus.). 153p. (J). (gr. 3 up). lib. bdg. 23.33 (978-0-8368-2672-2(8)) Stevens, Gareth Inc.

Montgomery, L. M. Anne of Avonlea. l.t. ed. 1998. (Avonlea Ser.: No. 2). 401p. (YA). (gr. 5-8). lib. bdg. 35.95 (978-1-58118-039-8(X) , 22507) LRS.

—Anne of Avonlea. l.t. ed. 2000. (Anne of Green Gables Ser.: Vol. 2). 366p. (gr. 5-8). pap. 21.99 (978-1-57646-306-2(0)) Quiet Vision Publishing.

—Anne of Green Gables. Stemach, Jerry, ed. Ham, Jeff, illus. l.t. ed. 2002. 150.00 (978-1-58702-021-6(1)); 2000. 50.00 (978-1-58702-502-0(7)) Johnston, Don Inc.

—Anne of Green Gables. l.t. ed. 2000. (Anne of Green Gables Ser.: Vol. 1). 294p. (gr. 5-8). pap. 17.95 (978-1-57646-302-4(8)) Quiet Vision Publishing.

—Anne of the Island. l.t. ed. 2006. (ENG.). pap. ***(*978-1-4068-3175-7(1))*** Echo Library.

—Anne of the Island. l.t. ed. 2004. 396p. 26.00 (978-1-58287-640-5(1)) North Bks.

—Anne of the Island. l.t. ed. 2000. (Anne of Green Gables Ser.: Vol. 3). 336p. (gr. 5-8). pap. 19.99 (978-1-57646-310-9(9)) Quiet Vision Publishing.

—Anne's House of Dreams. l.t. ed. 1999. (Avonlea Ser.: No. 5). 364p. (YA). (gr. 5-8). lib. bdg. 34.95 (978-1-58118-048-0(9) , 22517) LRS.

—Anne's House of Dreams. l.t. ed. 2000. (Anne of Green Gables Ser.: Vol. 5). 336p. (gr. 5-8). pap. 19.99 (978-1-57646-314-7(1)) Quiet Vision Publishing.

—The Golden Road. l.t. ed. 2000. (Sara Stanley of Avonlea Ser.: Vol. 2). 328p. 31.95 (978-1-57646-319-2(2)); pap. 19.99 (978-1-57646-318-5(4)) Quiet Vision Publishing.

—The Story Girl. l.t. ed. 2000. (Sara Stanley of Avonlea: Vol. 1). 370p. pap. 21.99 (978-1-57646-323-9(0)) Quiet Vision Publishing.

Montoya, Jerry. Do-It's Proof. Montoya, Jerry, illus. l.t. ed. 2002. (Illus.). 40p. (J). per. 6.95 (978-0-9722935-0-1(7)) Do-it's Proof Bks.

Moore, Clement C. The Night Before Christmas: A Trim-a-Tree Story. l.t. ed. 1999. (Illus.). 16p. (J). (ps-3). 6.99 (978-1-57866-076-6(9) , Galahad Bks.) BBS Publishing Corp.

Moore, Jim. The All Animal Band. Hall, Norris, illus. l.t. ed. 2004. 36p. (J). 16.00 (978-0-9752619-0-3(8)) Animal Band Productions, Inc., The.

Morina, Frances. Tiko at the Seashore. Morina, Frances, illus. Morina, Joseph A., photos by. l.t. ed. 1998. (Illus.). 24p. (J). (ps-2). pap. 3.95 (978-0-9664657-0-9(2) , Redbird Bks.) Redbird Enterprises.

Morpurgo, Michael. Kensuke's Kingdom. Foreman, Michael, illus. l.t. ed. 2000. 215p. (J). pap. (978-0-7540-6096-3(9) , CLP 295) BBC Audio.

Morris, Gerald. The Squire & His Knight. l.t. ed. 2001. (Illus.). 257p. (J). (gr. 4-7). 21.95 (978-0-7862-3039-6(8)) Thorndike Pr.

—The Squire's Tale. 1998. (Squire's Tales Ser.). 224p. (J). (gr. 5-9). tchr. ed. 16.00 (978-0-395-86959-8(5)) Houghton Mifflin Co. Trade & Reference Div.

Morris, Helen. Can You Do This? Chikoyak, Andrew J. & Nevak, Caroline, illus. l.t. ed. 1999. 8p. (J). (gr. k-3). pap. 14.50 (978-1-58084-154-2(6)) Lower Kuskokwim Schl. District.

—Enemni (My House) Conmy, Bet & Nevak, Caroline, illus. l.t. ed. 1999. (ESK.). 8p. (J). (gr. k-3). pap. 17.00 (978-1-58084-158-0(9)) Lower Kuskokwim Schl. District.

—Enka (My House) Conmy, Bet & Nevak, Caroline, illus. l.t. ed. 1999. (ESK.). 8p. (J). (gr. k-3). pap. 17.00 (978-1-58084-159-7(7)) Lower Kuskokwim Schl. District.

—Kuaten-qa Pituten? Chikoyak, Andrew J. & Nevak, Caroline, illus. l.t. ed. 1999. Tr. of Can you Do This?. (ESK.). 8p. (J). (gr. k-3). pap. (978-1-58084-156-6(2)) Lower Kuskokwim Schl. District.

—My House. Conmy, Bet & Nevak, Caroline, illus. l.t. ed. 1999. 8p. (J). (gr. k-3). pap. 17.00 (978-1-58084-157-3(0)) Lower Kuskokwim Schl. District.

—Waten-qaa Piyagngauten? (Can You Do This?) Chikoyak, Andrew J. & Nevak, Caroline, illus. l.t. ed. 1999. (ESK.). 8p. (J). (gr. k-3). pap. (978-1-58084-155-9(4)) Lower Kuskokwim Schl. District.

Morse, Christopher Hill. Ragged Mountain Revelry. l.t. ed. 2000. (Illus.). 74p. (YA). (gr. 1-12). pap. 25.00 (978-0-9678775-0-1(4)) Oculus Pr., The.

Moseley, James. The Ninth Jewel of the Mughal Crown: The Birbal Tales Vol. 1: From the Oral Traditions of India, 3 vols. Moseley, James, illus. l.t. ed. 2001. (Birbal Tales). (Illus.). 160p. (J). (gr. 3-6). 24.95 (978-0-9704447-1-4(0) , 1011092) Summerwind Marketing, Inc.

Mosher, Eunice D. Olympics, 2004? Ask Yia Yia & Pa Pou. Caso, Adolph, ed. Mosher, Eunice D. & Wenzel, Lauren M., illus. l.t. ed. 1998. 32p. (J). (ps-3). pap. 9.95 (978-0-8283-2033-7(0)) Branden Bks.

Mountain, Lee. Math Connections 1. 2001. 58p. (gr. 1). (J). pap., stu. ed. (978-1-58079-214-1(6)); pap., tchr. ed. (978-1-58079-217-2(0)) Barrett Kendall Publishing, Ltd.

—Math Connections 2. 2001. 58p. (gr. 2). (J). pap., stu. ed. (978-1-58079-216-5(2)); pap., tchr. ed. (978-1-58079-218-9(9)) Barrett Kendall Publishing, Ltd.

—Math Connections 3. 2001. 58p. (gr. 3). (J). pap., stu. ed. (978-1-58079-215-8(4)); pap., tchr. ed. (978-1-58079-219-6(7)) Barrett Kendall Publishing, Ltd.

Mouser, David B. Harry Potter's Muggles Guide to Magic. deluxe l.t. ed. 2001. 80p. (J). lib. bdg. 15.95 (978-1-929771-04-2(5)) H P Pubns., LTD.

Moyer, Bernadette A. But... We Are Twins. Moyer, Ariane M., illus. l.t. ed. 1998. 16p. (J). (ps-4). pap. 3.85 (978-0-9666183-8-9(6)) Two Bee-A-TwinBee Publishing, LLC.

Mracek, Ann. Friendship Flies the Sun: The Ancient Egyptian Legend of Scarab Beetle. l.t. ed. 2005. (DAN., Illus.). 32p. (J). per. 15.99 (978-0-9766488-0-2(6)) Mracek, Ann.

Mrs. Richardson's and Mrs. Doyle's 5th Grade Class. Prison - Not Me! Adeniyi, Olu-Jimi, illus. l.t. unabr. ed. 1998. (WeWrite Kids! Ser.: No. 39). 45p. (J). (gr. 3-5). pap. 3.95 (978-1-57635-021-8(5)) WeWrite LLC.

Mucha Aydlott, Julie A. My Favorite Time of Year. Mucha-Sullivan, Kalie A. & Mucha-Sullivan, Emily V., illus. l.t. ed. 2004. 22p. (J). 5.95 (978-0-9746093-2-4(3)) San Diego Business Accounting Solutions a Non CPA Firm.

Mullican, Judy. A Check up with Dr. Ling. Middleton, Mikell, illus. l.t. ed. 2001. (Big Bks.). 8p. (J). (ps-1). pap. 10.95 (978-1-57332-215-7(6)) HighReach Learning, Inc.

—Connie Cow's Friends. Metzger, Jeanne, illus. l.t. ed. 1999. (Cuddle Bks.). 6p. (J). (ps-k). pap. 10.95 (978-1-57332-137-2(0)) HighReach Learning, Inc.

—Dinosaurs Dinosaurs. Cress, Michelle H., illus. l.t. ed. 2000. (Cuddle Bks.). 6p. (J). (ps-1). pap. 10.95 (978-1-57332-184-6(2)) HighReach Learning, Inc.

—The Flowers. Meier, Kerry L., illus. l.t. ed. 2003. (HRL Big Book Ser.). 8p. (Orig.). (J). (ps-k). pap. 10.95 (978-1-57332-255-3(5)) HighReach Learning, Inc.

—Getting Dressed. Metzger, Jeanne, illus. l.t. ed. 2001. (Cuddle Bks.). 7p. (J). (ps-1). pap. 10.95 (978-1-57332-208-9(3)) HighReach Learning, Inc.

—Going to the Zoo. Gray, Stacy A., illus. l.t. ed. 2003. (HRL Big Book Ser.). 8p. (Orig.). (J). (ps-k). pap. 10.95 (978-1-57332-257-7(1)); pap. 10.95 (978-1-57332-258-4(X)) HighReach Learning, Inc.

—Horray for the U. S. A. Coates, Jennifer, illus. l.t. ed. 2000. (Big Bks.). (J). (ps-1). 10.95 (978-1-57332-183-9(4)) HighReach Learning, Inc.

—In the Desert. Linke, Don, Jr., illus. l.t. ed. 1998. (Cuddle Bks.). 10p. (J). (ps-k). pap. 10.95 (978-1-57332-119-8(2)) HighReach Learning, Inc.

—In the Forest. Cress, Michelle H., illus. l.t. ed. 1998. (Cuddle Bks.). 7p. (J). (ps-k). pap. 10.95 (978-1-57332-129-7(X)) HighReach Learning, Inc.

—In the Meadow. Coates, Jennifer, illus. l.t. ed. 2000. (CB Ser.). 7p. (J). (ps-1). pap. 10.95 (978-1-57332-142-6(7)) HighReach Learning, Inc.

—Inside the Big Red Barn. Metzger, Jeanne, illus. l.t. ed. 1999. (Children's Bks.). 8p. (J). (ps-k). pap. 10.95 (978-1-57332-136-5(2)); pap. 10.95 (978-1-57332-135-8(4)) HighReach Learning, Inc.

—It's a Bee! Ruminski, Jeff, illus. l.t. ed. 2003. (HRL Big Book Ser.). 8p. (Orig.). (J). (ps-k). pap. 10.95 (978-1-57332-259-1(8)); pap. 10.95 (978-1-57332-260-7(1)) HighReach Learning, Inc.

—Kenny & the Poison. Carroll, Ken, Jr., illus. l.t. ed. 1998. (Little Bks.). 8p. (Orig.). (J). (ps-k). pap. 10.95 (978-1-57332-088-7(9)) HighReach Learning, Inc.

—Like a Dinosaur. Gray, Stacy A., illus. l.t. ed. 2004. (HRL Board Book Ser.). 10p. (J). (ps-k). bds. 10.95 (978-1-57332-266-9(0)) HighReach Learning, Inc.

—Listen to the Animals. l.t. ed. 2001. (Cuddle Bks.). (Illus.). 8p. (J). (ps-1). pap. 10.95 (978-1-57332-192-1(3)) HighReach Learning, Inc.

—Looking for a Book. Coates, Jennifer, illus. l.t. ed. 2000. (BB Ser.). 8p. (J). (ps-1). pap. 10.95 (978-1-57332-165-5(6)); pap. 10.95 (978-1-57332-166-2(4)) HighReach Learning, Inc.

—Me! Me! Magnificent Me! Carroll, Ken, Jr., illus. l.t. ed. 1998. (Little Bks.). 8p. (J). (ps-k). pap. 10.95 (978-1-57332-108-2(7)); pap. 10.95 (978-1-57332-109-9(5)) HighReach Learning, Inc.

—Mr. Turkey. Carroll, Ken, Jr., illus. l.t. ed. 1998. (Cuddle Bks.). 7p. (J). (ps-k). pap. 10.95 (978-1-57332-126-6(5)) HighReach Learning, Inc.

—My Forest Friends. Carroll, Ken, Jr., illus. l.t. ed. 2000. (Little Bks.). 8p. (J). (ps-1). pap. 10.95 (978-1-57332-172-3(9)); pap. 10.95 (978-1-57332-180-8(X)) HighReach Learning, Inc.

—My Toys. Bicking, Judith, illus. l.t. ed. 2005. (Hrl Board Book Ser.). (J). (ps-k). pap. 10.95 (978-1-57332-307-9(1)) HighReach Learning, Inc.

—Patty Helps Out. Coates, Jennifer, illus. l.t. ed. 1999. (Cuddle Bks.). 8p. (J). (ps-k). pap. 10.95 (978-1-57332-140-2(0)); pap. 10.95 (978-1-57332-141-9(9)) HighReach Learning, Inc.

—People, People. Linke, Don, Jr. & Van Wagner, Holly, illus. l.t. ed. 2000. (CB Ser.). 6p. (J). (ps-1). pap. 10.95 (978-1-57332-159-4(1)) HighReach Learning, Inc.

—The Solar System Dance. Coates, Jennifer, illus. l.t. ed. 2001. (Little Bks.). (J). (ps-1). pap. 10.95 (978-1-57332-190-7(7)); 8p. pap. 10.95 (978-1-57332-189-1(3)) HighReach Learning, Inc.

—Something New at the Zoo. Ruminski, Jeff, illus. l.t. ed. 2002. (Little Bks.). 8p. (J). (ps-1). pap. 10.95 (978-1-57332-203-4(2)) HighReach Learning, Inc.

—Springtime on the Farm. Cress, Michelle H., illus. l.t. ed. 1998. (Big Bks.). 8p. (J). (ps-k). pap. 10.95 (978-1-57332-120-4(6)); pap. 10.95 (978-1-57332-121-1(4)) HighReach Learning, Inc.

—Story Time. Coates, Jennifer, illus. l.t. ed. 2000. (CB Ser.). 7p. (J). (ps-1). pap. 10.95 (978-1-57332-171-6(0)) HighReach Learning, Inc.

—Under the Sea. Carroll, Ken, Jr., illus. l.t. ed. 1998. (Little Bks.). 8p. (J). (ps-k). pap. 10.95 (978-1-57332-092-4(7)) HighReach Learning, Inc.

—What Can Li Zhang Cook? Coates, Jennifer, illus. l.t. ed. 2000. (BB Ser.). 8p. (J). (ps-1). pap. 10.95 (978-1-57332-160-0(5)); pap. 10.95 (978-1-57332-161-7(3)) HighReach Learning, Inc.

—What Pet Should I Get? Linke, Don, Jr., illus. l.t. ed. 1999. (Big Bks.). 8p. (J). (ps-k). pap. 10.95 (978-1-57332-132-7(X)); pap. 10.95 (978-1-57332-134-1(6)) HighReach Learning, Inc.

—What's in the Rain Forest? Metzger, Jeanne, illus. 2000. (Little Bks.). 8p. (J). (ps-1). pap. 10.95 (978-1-57332-186-0(9)) HighReach Learning, Inc.

Mullican, Judy & Carroll, Ken, Jr. Bedtime Stories. l.t. ed. 1999. (Cuddle Bks.). (Illus.). 6p. (J). (ps-k). pap. 10.95 (978-1-57332-147-1(8)) HighReach Learning, Inc.

Mullican, Judy & Coales, Jennifer. Time to Eat. l.t. ed. 2001. (Board Bk.). (Illus.). 12p. (J). (ps-1). 4.99 (978-1-57332-195-2(8)) HighReach Learning, Inc.

Mullican, Judy & Crowell, Knox. Caillou Finds Shapes. Gillen, Lisa P., illus. l.t. ed. 2005. (Hrl Board Book Ser.). (J). (ps-k). bds. 10.95 (978-1-57332-312-3(8)) HighReach Learning, Inc.

—A Firefighter in Class. l.t. ed. 1999. (Little Bks.). (Illus.). 8p. (J). (ps-k). pap. 10.95 (978-1-57332-148-8(6)); pap. 10.95 (978-1-57332-143-3(5)) HighReach Learning, Inc.

Mullican, Judy & Linke, Don, Jr. In the Fall. l.t. ed. 1999. (Cuddle Bks.). (Illus.). 6p. (J). (ps-k). pap. 10.95 (978-1-57332-146-4(X)) HighReach Learning, Inc.

Mumaugh, Lene. Touch of Christmas. Skrbic, Melissa, illus. l.t. ed. 2003. 28p. per. 9.95 (978-1-932344-19-6(5)) Thornton Publishing.

Murdock, Kita Helmetag & Helmetag, Patricia. Cecily Cicada, 2004th l.t. ed. 2004. (Illus.). 28p. (J). pap. 9.95 (978-0-615-12548-0(4)) Possum Products.

Myers, Walter Dean. Bad Boy: A Memoir. l.t. ed. 2005. (Thorndike Press Large Print the Literacy Bridge Ser.). 269p. (978-0-7862-7537-3(5)) Thorndike Pr.

—Shooter. l.t. ed. 2004. 213p. 22.95 (978-0-7862-6969-3(3) , Large Print Pr.) Thorndike Pr.

The Mysteries of Shapeville. l.t. ed. 2005. (Illus.). 48p. (J). 18.95 (978-0-9747509-1-0(3)) Del Gatto, Maria.

Na, An. A Step from Heaven. l.t. ed. 2002. 193p. (J). 22.95 (978-0-7862-4126-2(8)) Thomson Gale.

Nadimi, Suzan. The Hungry Cat, Downie, Christopher, illus. l.t. ed. 2005. (PER.). 32p. 5.95 net. (978-0-9764947-0-6(1)) Nur Pubns.

Najar, Qasim M. Allah Made the World. Emerick, Yahiya, ed. Meehan, Patricia, illus. l.t. ed. 2002. 36p. (J). (gr. k-2). pap. 6.95 (978-1-889720-32-6(1)) Amirah Publishing.

Naji, Jamilla. Musical Storyland: A Sing-A-Long Book with Musical Disc. l.t. ed. 2004. (Illus.). 32p. (J). per. 19.99 (978-0-9745568-0-2(7)) Worlds In Ink Publishing, Inc.

Napoli, Donna Jo. Crazy Jack. l.t. ed. 2000. 183p. (YA). (gr. 8-12). 20.95 (978-0-7862-3047-1(9)) Thorndike Pr.

Naylor, Phyllis Reynolds. Bernie Magruder & the Bats in the Belfry. l.t. ed. 2003. (Bernie Magruder Ser.). 139p. (J). 22.95 (978-0-7862-5739-3(3)) Thorndike Pr.

—Bernie Magruder & the Disappearing Bodies. l.t. ed. 2001. (Juvenile Ser.). 153p. (J). 20.95 (978-0-7862-3467-7(9)) Thorndike Pr.

—Bernie Magruder & the Haunted Hotel. l.t. ed. 2001. 127p. (J). 20.95 (978-0-7862-3600-8(0)) Thorndike Pr.

—The Boys Start the War. l.t. ed. 2002. (Thorndike Press Large Print Juvenile Ser.). 144p. (J). 22.95 (978-0-7862-4651-9(0)) Thorndike Pr.

—Jade Green: A Ghost Story. l.t. ed. 2000. 174p. (J). (gr. 4-7). 21.95 (978-0-7862-2886-7(5)) Thorndike Pr.

—Saving Shiloh. l.t. ed. 2002. 193p. (J). 22.95 (978-0-7862-3713-5(9)) Thorndike Pr.

—Shiloh. l.t. ed. 2000. (Shiloh Ser.: No. 1). 155p. (J). (gr. 4-7). lib. bdg. 27.95 (978-1-58118-058-9(6) , 23472) LRS.

Nelson, Esther. Blocks Are to Build. Hirsch, Davida, ed. Behr, Joyce, illus. l.t. ed. 1999. 28p. (Orig.). (J). (gr. k-1). pap. 7.95 (978-0-945110-15-6(4)) Granny Pr.

—Chairs Are to Sit. Hirsch, Davida, ed. Behr, Joyce, illus. l.t. ed. 1999. 28p. (Orig.). (J). (gr. k-1). pap. 7.95 (978-0-945110-14-9(6)) Granny Pr.

Nelson, Holly. Ig's Apples. l.t. ed. 2003. (Illus.). 15p. (J). per. 9.99 (978-1-932338-17-1(9)) Lifevest Publishing, Inc.

Nelson, Marilen. Bed Bear's Adventure to the Land of Lost Things. LeRoy, Doreene, illus. l.t. ed. 2002. 40p. (J). cd-rom 11.95 (978-1-59208-003-8(0) , 775-846-1185) JetKor.

Nettrour, Nelani. Banshees Bk. 2: Dragon Lands. Nettrour, Heather, illus. l.t. ed. 2003. 114p. (J). pap. 11.95 (978-1-932657-03-6(7)) Third Millennium Pubns.

—The Dragonlands Bk. 3: The Village. l.t. ed. 2004. (Illus.). 148p. (J). pap. 19.95 (978-1-932657-12-8(6)) Third Millennium Pubns.

—Jodi & the Seasons. Nettrour, Heather, illus. l.t. ed. 2004. 88p. pap. 11.95 (978-1-932657-16-6(9)) Third Millennium Pubns.

—Jodi's Bugs. Nettrour, Heather, illus. l.t. ed. 2003. 66p. (J). pap. 11.95 (978-1-932657-04-3(5)) Third Millennium Pubns.

New Mexico School for the Deaf Staff, 2nd Grade. Too Many Hands??? l.t. ed. 2004. (Illus.). 32p. (J). 16.95 (978-1-929115-10-5(5)) Azro Pr., Inc.

New Pet. l.t. ed. 2005. (Illus.). 32p. (J). lib. bdg. 14.95 (978-0-9658365-8-6(4)) Beetle Bug Bks.

Nicholas, Melissa. Big Book: Pumpkin Days, Vol. 3. l.t. ed. 2005. (Sadlier Phonics Reading Program). (Illus.). 8p. (YA). (ps-1). 22.50 (978-0-8215-7352-5(7)) Sadlier, William H. Inc.

—Big Book: Who Is My Mom? Cassels, Jean, illus. l.t. ed. 2005. (Sadlier Phonics Reading Program). 8p. (YA). (ps-1). 22.50 (978-0-8215-7341-9(1)) Sadlier, William H. Inc.

—Stop by a Pond. Gram, Patrick, illus. l.t. ed. 2005. (Little Books & Big Bks.: Vol. 3). 8p. (YA). (ps-3). 22.50 (978-0-8215-7512-3(0)) Sadlier, William H. Inc.

Nichole, Michelle. Love for Miraye. Nichole, Michelle, illus. l.t. ed. 2002. (Illus.). 26p. per. 16.50 (978-0-9705823-9-3(0)) Pearl Line Pr., Inc.

Nicholls, Stan. Fade to Black. l.t. ed. 1998. (Illus.). 274p. (J). pap. 16.95 (978-0-7540-6016-1(0) , Galaxy Children's Large Print) BBC Audiobooks America.

Nickerson, Margaret. Gathering Food. Nevak, Caroline, illus. l.t. ed. 1999. 8p. (J). (gr. k-3). pap. 14.50 (978-1-58084-060-6(4)) Lower Kuskokwim Schl. District.

—Katitchirugut Niqinik. Nevak, Caroline, illus. l.t. ed. 1999. Tr. of Gathering Food. (ESK.). 8p. (J). (gr. k-3). pap. 14.50 (978-1-58084-136-8(8)) Lower Kuskokwim Schl. District.

—Katitchiyuanni Niqinik. Nevak, Caroline, illus. l.t. ed. 1999. Tr. of Gathering Food. (ESK.). 8p. (J). (gr. k-3). pap. 14.50 (978-1-58084-126-9(0)) Lower Kuskokwim Schl. District.

—Neqengnaqler. Nevak, Caroline, illus. l.t. ed. 1999. Tr. of Gathering Food. (ESK.). 8p. (J). (gr. k-3). pap. 14.50 (978-1-58084-105-4(8)) Lower Kuskokwim Schl. District.

—Niginik Katittigaangapta. Nevak, Caroline, illus. l.t. ed. 1999. Tr. of Gathering Food. (ESK.). 8p. (J). (gr. k-3). pap. 14.50 (978-1-58084-133-7(3)) Lower Kuskokwim Schl. District.

—Quyurciyaraq Neqnek. Nevak, Caroline, illus. l.t. ed. 1999. Tr. of Gathering Food. (ESK.). 8p. (J). (gr. k-3). pap. 14.50 (978-1-58084-061-3(2)) Lower Kuskokwim Schl. District.

Nickles, Clay & Ayres, Ella. Ali's Treasure. l.t. ed. 2005. (Illus.). 38p. (J). per. 16.95 (978-1-59879-006-1(4)) Lifevest Publishing, Inc.

Nieves, David M. More Reptiles up Close. Nieves, David M., photos by. l.t. ed. 2002. (Illus.). 56p. (J). per. 11.95 (978-0-9673958-2-1(8)) Reptile Education & Research Publishing.

Nightingale, Kimberly, et al. A Book about Feeling Angry Vol. 2: Seemor's Flight to Freedom. Spaeth-Edwards, Heidi, illus. l.t. ed. 1998. 36p. (J). (ps-3). pap. 14.95 (978-0-9635127-1-0(4)) Emotional Management Education, Inc.

Nimmo, Jenny. Delilah Alone. l.t. ed. 1998. (Illus.). 156p. (J). pap. (978-0-7540-6014-7(4) , CLP 216) BBC Audio.

Nixon, Joan Lowery. Caught in the Act. l.t. ed. 1999. (Orphan Train Adventures Ser.: No. 2). 150p. (J). (gr. 4 up). lib. bdg. 23.33 (978-0-8368-2639-5(6)) Stevens, Gareth Inc.

—A Dangerous Promise. l.t. ed. 1999. (Orphan Train Adventures Ser.: No. 5). 148p. (J). (gr. 4 up). lib. bdg. 23.33 (978-0-8368-2642-5(6)) Stevens, Gareth Inc.

—A Family Apart. l.t. ed. 1999. (Orphan Train Adventures Ser.: No. 1). 162p. (J). (gr. 4 up). lib. bdg. 23.33 (978-0-8368-2638-8(8)) Stevens, Gareth Inc.

—In the Face of Danger. l.t. ed. 1999. (Orphan Train Adventures Ser.: No. 3). (J). (gr. 4 up). lib. bdg. 23.33 (978-0-8368-2640-1(X)) Stevens, Gareth Inc.

—Keeping Secrets. l.t. ed. 1999. (Orphan Train Adventures Ser.: No. 6). 163p. (J). (gr. 4 up). lib. bdg. 23.33 (978-0-8368-2643-2(4)) Stevens, Gareth Inc.

—Land of Dreams. l.t. ed. 2001. (Ellis Island Stories Ser.). 153p. (J). (gr. 4 up). lib. bdg. 23.33 (978-0-8368-2810-8(0)) Stevens, Gareth Inc.

—Land of Hope. l.t. ed. 2001. (Ellis Island Stories Ser.). 171p. (J). (gr. 4 up). lib. bdg. 23.33 (978-0-8368-2811-5(9)) Stevens, Gareth Inc.

—Land of Promise. l.t. ed. 2001. (Ellis Island Stories Ser.). 169p. (J). (gr. 4 up). lib. bdg. 23.33 (978-0-8368-2812-2(7)) Stevens, Gareth Inc.

—Nightmare. l.t. ed. 2004. 200p. 22.95 (978-0-7862-6911-2(1) , Large Print Pr.) Thorndike Pr.

—The Orphan Train Adventures, 6 bks. l.t. ed. Incl. Caught in the Act. 150p. lib. bdg. 23.33 (978-0-8368-2639-5(6)); Dangerous Promise. 148p. lib. bdg. 23.33 (978-0-8368-2642-5(6)); Family Apart. 162p. lib. bdg. 23.33 (978-0-8368-2638-8(8)); In the Face of Danger. lib. bdg. 23.33 (978-0-8368-2640-1(X)); Keeping Secrets. 163p. lib. bdg. 23.33 (978-0-8368-2643-2(4)); Place to Belong. lib. bdg. 23.33 (978-0-8368-2641-8(8)); (J). (gr. 4 up). 1999. Set lib. bdg. 139.98 (978-0-8368-2637-1(X)) Stevens, Gareth Inc.

—A Place to Belong. l.t. ed. 1999. (Orphan Train Adventures Ser.: No. 4). (J). (gr. 4 up). lib. bdg. 23.33 (978-0-8368-2641-8(8)) Stevens, Gareth Inc.

Nodelman, Perry. Behaving Bradley. l.t. ed. 2002. 272p. (J). 22.95 (978-0-7862-4779-0(7)) Thorndike Pr.

Nonan, Sammi. The Monkey That Could Fly. l.t. ed. 2001. 24p. (J). 2.99 (978-0-9704868-5-1(5)) Be-Mused Pubns.

Norman, Dayle. Tre's Surprise the Move. l.t. ed. 2005. 35p. (J). per. 8.00 (978-1-59196-896-2(8)) Instantpublisher.com.

Norriss, Andrew. Bernard's Watch. l.t. ed. 2000. 197p. (J). pap. (978-0-7540-6118-2(3) , CLP 313) BBC Audio.

Numeroff, Laura Joffe & Bond, Felicia. If You Give a Mouse a Cookie. l.t. ed. (FRE.). (J). bds. 29.99 (978-0-590-71930-8(0)) Scholastic, Inc.

Nye, Robert. Beowulf. l.t. ed. 2005. 168p. (J). pap. (978-0-7540-6125-0(6) , CLP 322) BBC Audio.

O'Brien, Robert C. Mrs. Frisby & the Rats of Nimh. Bernstein, Zena, illus. l.t. ed. 2000. (Rats of NIMH Ser.). 300p. (J). (gr. 4-7). lib. bdg. 29.95 (978-1-58118-056-5(X) , 23470) LRS.

Ocean, Suellen. The Acorn Mouse Vol. 1: A Children's Intro to Eating Acorns. Todd, Larry, illus. l.t. ed. 1999. 15p. (J). (gr. k-5). pap. 3.95 (978-0-9651140-4-2(X)) Ocean-Hose.

O'Connor, Barbara. Fame & Glory in Freedom, Georgia. l.t. ed. 2003. 126p. (J). 22.95 (978-0-7862-5994-6(9)) Thorndike Pr.

—Me & Rupert Goody. l.t. ed. 2000. (Illus.). 126p. (J). (gr. 8-12). 21.95 (978-0-7862-2767-9(2)) Thorndike Pr.

O'Keefe, M. Timothy. If I Were a Manatee: A Coloring & Activity Book. l.t. ed. 2002. 48p. (J). (ps-7). 4.95 (978-0-936513-50-8(0)) Larsen's Outdoor Publishing.

Oldfield, Jenny. El Dorado. l.t. ed. 2003. (Illus.). 208p. (J). 16.95 (978-0-7540-7840-1(X) , Galaxy Children's Large Print) BBC Audiobooks America.

Olick, Hilda. Kaviam Iqvaryallra. Olick, Hilda & Nevak, Caroline, illus. l.t. ed. 1999. (ESK.). 8p. (J). (gr. k-3). pap. 14.50 (978-1-58084-057-6(4)) Lower Kuskokwim Schl. District.

—Kavviar Paunerssuyallrim. Olick, Hilda & Nevak, Caroline, illus. l.t. ed. 1999. (ESK.). 8p. (J). (gr. k-3). pap. 14.50 (978-1-58084-114-6(7)) Lower Kuskokwim Schl. District.

—Kayuqtuq Aullaqsrugiaman. Olick, Hilda & Nevak, Caroline, illus. l.t. ed. 1999. (ESK.). 8p. (J). (gr. k-3). pap. 14.50 (978-1-58084-119-1(8)) Lower Kuskokwim Schl. District.

—Kayuqturuuq Ahiariarnirman. Nevak, Caroline, illus. l.t. ed. 1999. (ESK.). 8p. (J). (gr. k-3). pap. 14.50 (978-1-58084-142-9(2)) Lower Kuskokwim Schl. District.

—Pisukti Asianik Pukugiarami. Olick, Hilda & Nevak, Caroline, illus. l.t. ed. 1999. Tr. of When the Fox Went Berry Picking. (ESK.). 8p. (J). (gr. k-3). pap. 14.50 (978-1-58084-128-3(7)) Lower Kuskokwim Schl. District.

—Tiriganniaq Kablatariahuni Ahiariaqtuqhani. Olick, Hilda & Nevak, Caroline, illus. l.t. ed. 1999. Tr. of When the Fox Went Berry Picking. (ESK.). 8p. (J). (gr. k-3). pap. 14.50 (978-1-58084-135-1(X)) Lower Kuskokwim Schl. District.

—When the Fox Went Berry Picking. Olick, Hilda & Nevak, Caroline, illus. l.t. ed. 1999. 8p. (J). (gr. k-3). pap. 14.50 (978-1-58084-056-9(6)) Lower Kuskokwim Schl. District.

Olivares, Katie Lydon. ABC Book of Shadows. l.t. ed. 2005. (Illus.). 30p. (J). bds. 9.99 (978-0-9768573-0-3(8)) Itty Bitty Witch Works.

Oliver, Lin. Beezy's Big Boy. Dodge, Bill, illus. l.t. ed. 2000. 32p. (J). pap. 14.99 incl. audio (978-1-890647-61-2(6)); 14.95 (978-1-890647-60-5(8)) RC2 Corp.

—Journey of the Jupiter. Dodge, Bill, illus. l.t. ed. 2000. 32p. (J). pap. 14.99 incl. audio (978-1-890647-59-9(4)); 14.95 (978-1-890647-58-2(6)) RC2 Corp.

Oliver, Pamela. Weight Loss with Humor: Also Featuring over 100 Body Transformers Body Tips. Oliver, Tyler, illus. l.t. ed. 2001. 140p. per. 9.95 net. (978-0-9715488-0-0(3)) Brandworks Publishing.

Olivia, Cynthia. Big Book: In January & June, Vol. 4. l.t. ed. 2005. (Sadlier Phonics Reading Program: Vol. 16). (Illus.). 8p. (YA). (ps-1). 22.50 (978-0-8215-7355-6(1)) Sadlier, William H. Inc.

Olker, Constance. The Punctuation Pals Go Snow Skiing. l.t. ed. 2005. (Illus.). (J). per. 17.95 (978-0-9761289-7-7(7)) Nightengale Pr.

—The Punctuation Pals Go to the Baseball Park. l.t. ed. 2005. (Illus.). 22p. (J). per. 17.95 (978-0-9761289-8-4(5)) Nightengale Pr.

—The Punctuation Pals Go to the Beach. l.t. ed. 2005. (Illus.). 22p. (J). per. 17.95 (978-0-9761289-5-3(0)) Nightengale Pr.

—The Punctuation Pals Go to the Moon. l.t. ed. 2005. (Illus.). (J). per. 19.95 (978-0-9761289-6-0(9)) Nightengale Pr.

—The Punctuation Pals Meet at School. l.t. ed. 2005. (Illus.). 18p. (J). per. 16.95 (978-0-9761289-4-6(2)) Nightengale Pr.

Olkowski, Mary. The Twirling Dress. Olkowski, Mary, illus. l.t. ed. 2001. (Illus.). 36p. (J). bds. 10.95 (978-0-9709119-0-2(4) , 1011) Limpid Butterfly Productions, The.

Omary, Rachel, illus. Animals in Dari. l.t. ed. 2003. 4p. (J). spiral bd. 10.95 (978-0-9740535-3-0(8)) Knight Publishing.

—Animals in Farsi. l.t. ed. 2003. 4p. (J). spiral bd. 10.95 (978-0-9740535-4-7(6)) Knight Publishing.

—Animals in Pashto. l.t. ed. 2003. 4p. (J). spiral bd. 10.95 (978-0-9740535-5-4(4)) Knight Publishing.

—Shapes & Colors in Farsi. l.t. ed. 2004. 5p. (J). spiral bd. 14.95 (978-0-9740535-6-1(2)) Knight Publishing.

—Shapes & Colors in Pashto. l.t. ed. 2004. 5p. (J). spiral bd. 14.95 (978-0-9740535-8-5(9)) Knight Publishing.

Oppel, Kenneth. Firewing. l.t. ed. 2003. 459p. (J). 23.95 (978-0-7862-5986-1(8)) Thorndike Pr.

Oppenlander, Meredith. How to Make Snack Mix: Math B. Harston, Jerry, illus. l.t. ed. 1998. 16p. (J). (gr. k-2). pap. 4.95 (978-1-57874-004-8(5)) Kaeden Corp.

—In the Hen House. Gedeon, Gloria, illus. l.t. ed. 1998. 12p. (J). (gr. k-2). pap. 4.95 (978-1-57874-003-1(7)) Kaeden Corp.

Orgel, Joseph R. Families, Families: Theme 2. l.t. ed. 1998. (Sadlier Phonics Reading Program). (Illus.). 16p. (YA). (gr. k-3). 29.85 (978-0-8215-0510-6(6)) Sadlier, William H. Inc.

The Origin of Chinese, 1. l.t. ed. 2004. (CHI., Illus.). 60p. (J). (978-0-9752775-1-5(0) , 0-9752775-1-0) Unitrust Design.

Orthodox Woodriver District Baptist Association Staff. Treasured Talents in God's Time. Fisher, Suzanne, ed. Wesley, Robert B., illus. l.t. unabr. ed. 1999. (WeWrite Kids! Ser.: Vol. 42). 39p. (YA). (gr. 4-12). pap. 3.95 (978-1-57635-024-9(X)) WeWrite LLC.

Osborn, Shane & McConnell, Malcolm. Born to Fly: The Heroic Story of Downed U. S. Navy Pilot Lt. Shane Osborn. l.t. ed. 2002. 403p. 29.45 (978-0-7862-4101-9(2)) Thomson Gale.

Osen, Janet E. Mini Maestro Presents the Tic-Toc Clocks. Angermueller, Ivy & Boshart, Martha, illus. l.t. ed. 2000. 30p. (J). (ps-k). 16.95 incl. audio compact disk (978-0-9700489-0-5(4)) Little Fiddle Co., Inc., The.

Owens, Katherine. Tree Seasons Ball, 1 bk. l.t. ed. 2004. (Illus.). 40p. (J). per. 19.99 (978-0-9760419-0-0(1) , TREESEASONSBALL) ThatsMyLife Co.

Owhonda, John. Musa the Mouse. Stidom, Damon, illus. l.t. ed. 1999. 27p. (J). (gr. 1-4). 19.95 (978-0-9650505-3-1(X)) CGS Communications.

Ozaki, Yei Theodora, ed. Japanese Fairy Tales. l.t. ed. 2004. (Large Print Ser.). 335p. 26.00 (978-1-58287-750-1(5)) North Bks.

Paddington Bear. Childhood Memories. l.t. unabr. ed. 1999. 212p. (J). 21.95 (978-1-85089-456-8(6) , 894566) ISIS Large Print Bks. GBR. *Dist:* Transaction Pubs.

Padron, Mary E. Anna Victoria: With Doll. Pendergast, Patrice, illus. gif. collector's l.t. ed. 2002. 32p. (J). per. 25.95 (978-0-9648284-2-1(1)) Pink Hse. Pr.

Page, Deb, illus. Darby-the Cow Dog, 9 vols. l.t. ed. 2005. (ZC Horses: 9). 76p. (J). pap. 5.00 net. (978-0-9721496-8-6(6)) ZC Horses Series of Children's Bks.

Pallotta, Jerry. The Big Engine: Counting on the Big Engine. Butler, Paul, illus. l.t. ed. 2000. (Big Engine Ser.: No. 1). 12p. (J). (ps-k). 7.99 (978-0-9700383-0-2(5)) Great Train Stores, The.

Palmer, Catherine. Fatal Harvest. l.t. ed. 2004. (Matthew 25 Ser.). 496p. (YA). 28.95 (978-0-7862-6259-5(1)) Thorndike Pr.

Palmer, Edward G. Book of Edward Christian Mythology, 4 vols., Set. l.t. ed. 2005. (Illus.). 1306p. per. 123.80 (978-0-9768833-4-0(1) , 0976883341) JVED Publishing.

—Book of Edward Christian Mythology: Itching Christian Ears, 4 vols., Vol. 3. l.t. ed. 2005. (Illus.). 616p. per. 39.95 (978-0-9768833-2-6(5) , 0976883325) JVED Publishing.

—Book of Edward Christian Mythology Vol. II: God Does Not Change, 4 vols. l.t. ed. 2005. (Illus.). 356p. per. 27.95 (978-0-9768833-1-9(7) , 0976883317) JVED Publishing.

—Book of Edward Christian Mythology Vol. IV: Appendixes Reference, 4 vols. l.t. ed. 2005. (Illus.). 208p. per. 27.95 (978-0-9768833-3-3(3) , 0976883333) JVED Publishing.

Parente, Peter. Boomer to the Rescue. Ivanov, Aleksey, illus. l.t. ed. 2005. 28p. 15.95 (978-0-9745052-3-7(4) , Peeper & Friends) Tree Of Life Publishing.

—Peeper the Kinkajou. l.t. ed. 2004. (Peeper & Friends Ser.). (Illus.). 28p. 15.95 (978-0-9745052-0-6(X) , Peeper & Friends) Tree Of Life Publishing.

Parker, Sandy. What Day Is Today? Hofher, Cathy, illus. l.t. ed. 2003. 24p. (gr. k-1). 13.95 (978-0-9643462-3-9(0) , 10, Just Think Bks.) Canary Connect Pubns.

Pataki, Libby & Kimball, Wilson, texts. Madison in New York. l.t. ed. 2005. (Illus.). 32p. (J). 16.95 (978-1-893622-15-9(0) , VSP Bks.) Vacation Spot Publishing.

Paterson, Katherine. Bridge to Terabithia. Diamond, Donna, illus. l.t. ed. 1999. (LRS Large Print Cornerstone Ser.). 250p. (YA). (gr. 5-12). lib. bdg. 28.95 (978-1-58118-053-4(5) , 22769) LRS.

—The Great Gilly Hopkins. l.t. ed. 1999. (LRS Large Print Cornerstone Ser.). 300p. (YA). (gr. 5-12). lib. bdg. 29.95 (978-1-58118-052-7(7) , 22770) LRS.

—Jacob Have I Loved. l.t. ed. 2000. (LRS Large Print Cornerstone Ser.). 266p. (J). (gr. 5-12). lib. bdg. 29.95 (978-1-58118-073-2(X) , 23658) LRS.

—Lyddie. 2005. 192p. (J). (ps-7). pap. 3.99 (978-0-14-240438-6(1) , Puffin) Penguin Group (USA) Inc.

Paul, Karen. Kegginaqa. Cleary, Janice A., illus. l.t. ed. 2000. Tr. of My Face. (ESK.). 8p. (J). (gr. k-3). pap. 6.00 (978-1-58084-198-6(8)) Lower Kuskokwim Schl. District.

—My Face. Cleary, Janice A., illus. l.t. ed. 2000. 8p. (J). (gr. k-3). pap. 6.00 (978-1-58084-197-9(X)) Lower Kuskokwim Schl. District.

—My Face (Cup'ik) Cleary, Janice A., illus. l.t. ed. 2000. 8p. (J). (gr. k-3). pap. 6.00 (978-1-58084-199-3(6)) Lower Kuskokwim Schl. District.

Paul, Kate. Big Book: The Best Ride, Vol. 2. l.t. ed. 2005. (Sadlier Phonics Reading Program). (Illus.). 8p. (YA). (ps-1). 22.50 (978-0-8215-7345-7(4)) Sadlier, William H. Inc.

Paul, Paul A. Kia Una Pikau? Sparck, Carole C., illus. l.t. ed. 2000. Tr. of Whose Is This?. (ESK.). 8p. (J). (gr. k-3). pap. 6.00 (978-1-58084-204-4(6)) Lower Kuskokwim Schl. District.

—Whose Is This? Sparck, Carole C., illus. l.t. ed. 2000. 8p. (J). (gr. k-3). pap. 6.00 (978-1-58084-203-7(8)) Lower Kuskokwim Schl. District.

—Whose Is This? (Cup'ik) Sparck, Carole C., illus. l.t. ed. 2000. 8p. (J). (gr. k-3). pap. 6.00 (978-1-58084-205-1(4)) Lower Kuskokwim Schl. District.

Paulsen, Gary. Caught by the Sea. l.t. ed. 2002. 104p. (J). 22.95 (978-0-7862-4160-6(8)) Thomson Gale.

—Dogsong. l.t. ed. 2000. (Illus.). 184p. (J). (gr. 8-12). 21.95 (978-0-7862-2845-4(8)) Thorndike Pr.

—Foxman. l.t. ed. 2004. (YA). (gr. 6-12). 27.95 (978-1-58118-112-8(4)) LRS.

—Guts: The True Stories Behind Hatchet & the Brian Books. l.t. ed. 2001. (YA). 22.95 (978-0-7862-3407-3(5)) Thorndike Pr.

—Hatchet. l.t. ed. 2000. (LRS Large Print Cornerstone Ser.). 205p. (YA). (gr. 4-12). lib. bdg. 28.95 (978-1-58118-055-8(1) , 23469) LRS.

—My Life in Dog Years. Paulsen, Ruth Wright, illus. l.t. ed. 2000. (Juvenile Ser.). 176p. (J). (gr. 4-7). 21.95 (978-0-7862-2740-2(0)) Thorndike Pr.

—The Transall Saga. l.t. ed. 1999. 312p. (YA). (gr. 7-12). 21.95 (978-0-7862-2187-5(9)) Thorndike Pr.

Paulson, Michael W. The Baker Street Bunch No. 1: A Double Mystery Book. l.t. ed. 2004. (Illus.). 154p. (J). per. (978-0-9754241-0-0(6)) MiMar Publishing.

—The Baker Street Bunch & the Missing Pig Mystery. l.t. ed. 2004. (Illus.). 90p. (J). per. 3.95 (978-0-9754241-1-7(4)) MiMar Publishing.

Pearce, Philippa. A Dog So Small. Maitland, Anthony, illus. l.t. ed. 2005. 256p. (J). pap. (978-0-7540-7806-7(X) , CLP 402) BBC Audio.

—The Firework-Maker's Daughter. unabr. ed. 2003. (Read-Along Ser.). (J). (gr. 3-6). pap. 24.95 incl. audio (978-0-7540-6217-2(1) , Galaxy Children's Large Print) BBC Audiobooks America.

Peck, Richard. A Long Way from Chicago. l.t. ed. 2001. 188p. (J). (gr. 8-12). 22.95 (978-0-7862-3249-9(8)) Thorndike Pr.

—The Teacher's Funeral: A Comedy in Three Parts. 2006. 224p. (YA). (gr. 3). reprint ed. pap. 6.99 (978-0-14-240507-9(8) , Puffin) Penguin Group (USA) Inc.

—A Year down Yonder. l.t. ed. 2001. 160p. (J). 24.95 (978-0-7862-3282-6(X)) Thorndike Pr.

Penn, John I., Sr. About Caring & Healing: A Coloring & Activities Book about a Loving & Healing God. Rains, Wanda, illus. rev. l.t. ed. 2002. 36p. (J). 5.95 (978-0-9720785-0-4(9) , 821448) Penn, John.

Penn, Preston L. Rocky & Jamie. l.t. ed. 2000. (Illus.). 36p. (J). pap. 21.95 (978-0-9667210-1-0(2)) Lil Pee-Wee Publishing Co.

Percy, Graham, illus. La Bella Durmiente del Bosque. l.t. ed. 2001. (SPA.). 28p. (ps-3). incl. audio compact disk (978-84-8214-049-0(3) , 1620) Peralt Montagut.

—Caperucita Roja. l.t. ed. 2001. Tr. of Little Red Riding Hood. (SPA.). 28p. (J). (ps-3). 8.99 incl. audio (978-84-86154-06-6(5)) Peralt Montagut ESP. *Dist:* imaJen, Inc.

—Cinderella. l.t. ed. 2001. (SPA.). 28p. (ps-3). incl. audio compact disk (978-84-8214-091-9(4) , 1622) Peralt Montagut.

—Cinderella. l.t. ed. 2001. 28p. (J). (ps-2). 8.99 incl. audio (978-84-87650-25-3(2)) Peralt Montagut ESP. *Dist:* imaJen, Inc.

—The City Mouse & the Country Mouse. l.t. ed. 2001. (SPA.). 28p. (ps-3). incl. audio compact disk (978-84-8214-092-6(2) , 1622) Peralt Montagut.

—The City Mouse & the Country Mouse. l.t. ed. 2001. 28p. (J). (ps-3). 8.99 incl. audio (978-84-86154-62-2(6)) Peralt Montagut ESP. *Dist:* imaJen, Inc.

—The Gingerbread Man. l.t. ed. 2001. (SPA.). 28p. (ps-3). incl. audio compact disk (978-84-8214-094-0(9) , 1622) Peralt Montagut.

—The Gingerbread Man. l.t. ed. 2001. 28p. (J). (ps-3). 8.99 incl. audio (978-84-86154-40-0(5)) Peralt Montagut ESP. *Dist:* imaJen, Inc.

—Goldilocks & the Three Bears. l.t. ed. 2001. (SPA.). 28p. (ps-3). incl. audio compact disk (978-84-8214-087-2(6) , 1622) Peralt Montagut.

—Goldilocks & the Three Bears. l.t. ed. 2001. 28p. (J). (ps-3). 8.99 incl. audio (978-84-86154-91-2(X)) Peralt Montagut ESP. *Dist:* imaJen, Inc.

—Henny-Penny. l.t. ed. 2001. (SPA.). 28p. (ps-3). incl. audio compact disk (978-84-8214-084-1(1) , 1622) Peralt Montagut.

—Henny-Penny. l.t. ed. 2001. 28p. (J). (ps-3). 8.99 incl. audio (978-84-86154-39-4(1)) Peralt Montagut ESP. *Dist:* imaJen, Inc.

—Little Red Riding Hood. l.t. ed. 2001. (SPA.). 28p. (ps-3). incl. audio compact disk (978-84-8214-086-5(8) , 1622) Peralt Montagut.

—Little Red Riding Hood. l.t. ed. 2001. 28p. (J). (ps-3). 8.49 incl. audio (978-84-86154-90-5(1)) Peralt Montagut ESP. *Dist:* imaJen, Inc.

—The Nutcracker. l.t. ed. 2001. (SPA.). 28p. (ps-3). incl. audio (978-84-86154-60-8(X) , 1622) Peralt Montagut.

—The Nutcracker. l.t. ed. 2001. 28p. (J). (ps-3). 8.99 incl. audio compact disk (978-84-8214-089-6(2)) Peralt Montagut ESP. *Dist:* imaJen, Inc.

—The Pied Piper of Hamelin. l.t. ed. 2001. (SPA.). 28p. (ps-3). incl. audio compact disk (978-84-8214-085-8(X) , 1622) Peralt Montagut.

—The Pied Piper of Hamelin. l.t. ed. 2001. 28p. (J). (ps-3). 8.99 incl. audio (978-84-86154-38-7(3)) Peralt Montagut ESP. *Dist:* imaJen, Inc.

—Puss in Boots. l.t. ed. 2001. 28p. (J). (ps-3). 8.99 incl. audio compact disk (978-84-8214-090-2(6)); 8.99 incl. audio (978-84-87650-24-6(4)) Peralt Montagut ESP. *Dist:* imaJen, Inc.

—El Raton de Ciudad y el Raton de Campo. l.t. ed. 2001. Tr. of City Mouse & the Country Mouse. (SPA.). 28p. (J). (ps-3). incl. audio (978-84-86154-52-3(9)) Peralt Montagut.

—The Sleeping Beauty. l.t. ed. 2001. (SPA.). 28p. (ps-3). incl. audio compact disk (978-84-8214-071-1(X) , 1622) Peralt Montagut.

—The Sleeping Beauty. l.t. ed. 2001. 28p. (J). (ps-3). 8.99 incl. audio (978-84-87650-26-0(0)) Peralt Montagut ESP. *Dist:* imaJen, Inc.

—Snow White & the Seven Dwarfs. l.t. ed. 2001. (SPA.). 28p. (ps-3). incl. audio compact disk (978-84-8214-069-8(8) , 1622) Peralt Montagut.

—The Steadfast Tin Soldier. l.t. ed. 2001. (SPA.). 28p. (ps-3). incl. audio compact disk (978-84-8214-095-7(7) , 1622) Peralt Montagut.

—The Steadfast Tin Soldier. l.t. ed. 2001. 28p. (J). (ps-3). 8.99 incl. audio (978-84-86154-59-2(6)) Peralt Montagut ESP. *Dist:* imaJen, Inc.

—The Three Billy Goats Gruff. l.t. ed. 2001. (SPA.). 28p. (ps-3). incl. audio compact disk (978-84-8214-088-9(4) , 1622) Peralt Montagut.

—The Three Billy Goats Gruff. l.t. ed. 2001. 28p. (J). (ps-3). 8.99 incl. audio (978-84-86154-89-9(8)) Peralt Montagut ESP. *Dist:* imaJen, Inc.

—The Three Little Pigs. l.t. ed. 2001. (SPA.). 28p. (ps-3). incl. audio compact disk (978-84-8214-068-1(X) , 1622) Peralt Montagut.

—The Three Little Pigs. l.t. ed. 2001. 28p. (J). (ps-3). 8.49 incl. audio (978-84-87650-03-1(1)) Peralt Montagut ESP. *Dist:* imaJen, Inc.

—The Ugly Duckling. l.t. ed. 2001. (SPA.). 28p. (ps-3). incl. audio compact disk (978-84-8214-093-3(0) , 1622) Peralt Montagut.

—The Ugly Duckling. l.t. ed. 2001. 28p. (J). (ps-3). 8.99 incl. audio (978-84-87650-23-9(6)) Peralt Montagut ESP. *Dist:* imaJen, Inc.

—The Wolf & the Seven Little Kids. l.t. ed. 2001. (SPA.). 28p. (ps-3). incl. audio compact disk (978-84-8214-070-4(1) , 1622) Peralt Montagut.

—The Wolf & the Seven Little Kids. l.t. ed. 2001. 28p. (J). (ps-3). 8.99 incl. audio (978-84-86154-37-0(5)) Peralt Montagut ESP. *Dist:* imaJen, Inc.

Perez, Jaime O. Traditional Ceremonial Pathways: A Pilgrim's Journey. l.t. ed. 2003. (Illus.). 170p. per. 9.99 net. (978-0-9729612-0-2(8) , 44444) Sun Circle Pr.

Perkins, Lynne. Criss Cross. 2008. 368p. (J). pap. 6.99 (***978-0-06-009274-0(2)** , Greenwillow Bks.) HarperCollins Pubs.

Persinger, Eric. Plaid the Platypus. l.t. ed. 2004. (Illus.). 25p. (J). per. 8.99 (978-1-932338-54-6(3)) Lifevest Publishing, Inc.

Peters, Julie Anne. Define "Normal" l.t. ed. 2001. 250p. 22.95 (978-0-7862-3527-8(6)) Thorndike Pr.

Peters, Kathryn. A Pet for Elizabeth Rose. Peters, Kathryn, illus. l.t. ed. 2005. 42p. (J). 8.99 (978-0-9752647-9-9(6)) Proton Arts.

Petersen, Richard. Santa's Prayer. Vorlicek, Greta N., illus. l.t. ed. 2001. 32p. (YA). (gr. 2 up). pap. 10.00 (978-0-9632180-3-2(4)) Chinaberry Hse.

Peterson, Gerry, illus. Junior-Photo-Naturalist: My Trip to the Zoo. l.t. ed. 2001. 24p. (YA). (gr. 5 up). 6.97 (978-0-9702807-0-1(X)) Build-a-Bk.

Pettiford, Sherry Lynn. Don't Miss This End Time Move of God: From the Awakenings Series... Awakenings: the Cost. l.t. ed. 2001. 140p. per. (978-0-9715945-0-0(3)) El-Shaddai Productions.

Peyton, K. M. The Swallow Tale. l.t. ed. 2005. 216p. (J). pap. (978-0-7540-7837-1(X) , CLP 428) BBC Audio.

Pfeiffer, Joseph R. & Pfeiffer, Robert J. Billy's Unusual Adventure. Pfeiffer, Joseph R., illus. l.t. ed. 1998. (Illus.). 32p. (J). (gr. k-4). 11.95 (978-0-9659772-1-0(8)); pap. 5.95 (978-0-9659772-2-7(6)) Chessmore Publishing.

Phelan, Regina V. They Came Overland by Train, Vol. 6. Champy, Al, illus. l.t. ed. 1999. (History of California for the Young Reader Ser.). 63p. (J). lib. bdg. 15.00 (978-0-87062-295-3(1) , Clark, Arthur H. Co., The) Univ. of Oklahoma Pr.

Phillips, John A., Jr. Jahjep & Chip. Licon, Melissa, illus. l.t. ed. 2002. 28p. (978-0-9727968-0-4(0)) Jahjep Bks.

Phillips, Rachelle. Dinkey the Donkey. Randolph, Carolyn, illus. l.t. ed. 2004. 24p. (J). 7.50 (978-0-9748591-5-6(X) , MSP) Main St Publishing, Inc.

Pico Lost His Short Pants. l.t. ed. 2001. 32p. (J). 16.00 (978-0-9711901-0-8(0)) Sur Mar Publishing.

Pierce, Tamora. Page. 2000. (Protector of the Small Ser.: No. 2). (Illus.). 272p. (gr. 5-9). lib. bdg. 17.99 (978-0-679-98915-8(3) , Random Hse. Bks. for Young Readers) Random Hse. Children's Bks.

Pintozzi, Nick. Bentley & the Great Fire. Pintozzi, Nick et al, illus. l.t. ed. 2004. 120p. per. 17.95 (978-0-9749465-1-1(6)) BentDaiSha, LLC.

Pipkin, Evelyn Ruth. The Pretty Little Red Bird. l.t. ed. 2004. 19p. (J). (gr. 1-3). 7.95 (978-0-9755789-0-2(1)) Two Seed Planters Inc.

Piterski, Brahm & Piterski, Paul. Like a Fish on a Bike! l.t. ed. 1999. (Illus.). 32p. (J). (gr. 2-5). 14.95 (978-0-9658435-0-8(5)) Verdant Publishing, Inc.

Plum-Ucci, Carol. The Body of Christopher Creed. l.t. ed. 2001. 352p. (YA). 23.95 (978-0-7862-3509-4(8)) Thorndike Pr.

Poe, Edgar Allan. Edgar Allan Poe Collection. Stemach, Jerry, ed. Ham, Jeff, illus. l.t. ed. 2002. 104p. 150.00 (978-1-58702-015-5(7)) Johnston, Don Inc.

Pohrte, Kathysue, et al. In the Land of Liviaann. Pohrte, Kathysue, ed. Pohrte, Olivia & Pohrte, Juliann, illus. l.t. ed. 2003. 36p. (J). pap. 17.95 (978-0-9722296-0-9(4) , 872493) Pohrte, Dorey Publishing, Inc.

Porter, Eleanor H. Pollyanna. l.t. ed. 2000. (Large Print Heritage Ser.). 310p. (J). (gr. 7-12). lib. bdg. 29.95 (978-1-58118-069-5(1) , 23663) LRS.

—Pollyanna. l.t. ed. 2001. 267p. (J). 27.95 (978-0-7838-9602-1(6) , Hall, G. K. & Co.) Thomson Gale.

Portman, Michelle Eva. Compost, by Gosh! An Adventure with Vermicomposting. Portman, Michelle Eva, illus. l.t. ed. 2004. (Illus.). 42p. 16.95 (978-0-942256-16-1(6)) Flowerfield Enterprises.

Potok, Chaim. Zebra & Other Stories. l.t. ed. 2000. (Illus.). 200p. (J). (gr. 8-12). 20.95 (978-0-7862-2978-9(0)) Thorndike Pr.

Potts, Cheryl A. Another Sneeze, Louise! Gedeon, Gloria, illus. l.t. ed. 2001. 16p. (J). (gr. k-1). pap. 4.95 (978-1-57874-030-7(4) , Kaeden Bks.) Kaeden Corp.

Poussin, Nichol. Still Spins the Spider of Rennes-le-Chateau. l.t. ed. 2004. Tr. of arraignee tisse sa toile a Rennes-le-Chateaua. (Illus.). 347p. pap. (978-0-9541527-1-0(9) , http//www.keysofantiquity.com) DEK Publishing.

Powell, Randy. Tribute to Another Dead Rock Star. l.t. ed. 2000. 224p. (J). 21.95 (978-0-7862-2191-2(7)) Thorndike Pr.

Price, Olive. Three Golden Rivers. l.t. ed. 1999. (Golden Triangle Bks.). 272p. (YA). (gr. 4-7). pap. 9.95 (978-0-8229-5707-2(8)) Univ. of Pittsburgh Pr.

Price, Reynolds. A Perfect Friend. l.t. ed. 2001. 150p. (J). (gr. 4-7). 21.95 (978-0-7862-3589-6(6)) Thorndike Pr.

Price, Susan. The King's Head. l.t. ed. 2005. (Illus.). 264p. (J). pap. incl. audio (978-0-7540-7871-5(X) , CLP 452) BBC Audio.

Priest, Saira, photos by & des. If We Were... Priest, Saira, des. l.t. ed. 2003. 20p. 12.95 (978-0-9726628-7-1(1)) Native Nature.

Princess Aurora: A Special Day in Her Life. l.t. ed. 2005. (Illus.). 32p. (J). 5.95 (978-0-9766640-0-0(3) , 212-279-3492) Attitudes in Dressing, Inc.

Priscella the Monarch Butterfly. l.t. ed. 2000. 10p. (J). 5.95 (978-0-9716507-1-8(3)) Foglestories.

Pritchard, Herman S. The Nautical Road: A Straight Forward Approach to Learning the Navigation Rules. Helwig, Teresa L., ed. Sink, Cynthia, illus. 2nd rev. l.t. ed. 2004. 176p. (YA). 29.95 (978-0-9716479-3-0(3)) Selby Dean Ventures, Inc.

Progressive Langauge Staff, prod. Bluw Wolf & Friends, Units 1-4. l.t. ed. 2004. (Illus.). 53p. act. bk. ed. (978-0-9758759-3-3(0)) Progressive Language, Inc.

Pullman, Philip. The Amber Spyglass. l.t. ed. 2003. (His Dark Materials Ser.: Bk. 3). 686p. (YA). (gr. 7-12). 25.95 (978-0-7862-4122-4(5)) Thorndike Pr.

—The Golden Compass. l.t. ed. 2002. (His Dark Materials Ser.: Bk. 1). 550p. (YA). (gr. 7-12). 25.95 (978-0-7862-4123-1(3)) Thorndike Pr.

—I Was a Rat! Or the Scarlet Slippers. unabr. l.t. ed. 2001. (Read-Along Ser.). 224p. (J). 29.95 incl. audio (978-0-7540-6233-2(3) , RA034, Chivers Children's Audio Bks.) BBC Audiobooks America.

—The Subtle Knife. l.t. ed. 2002. (His Dark Materials Ser.: Bk. 2). 490p. (YA). (gr. 7-12). 25.95 (978-0-7862-4124-8(1)) Thorndike Pr.

Purcell, John. American City Flags Vols. 9&10: 146 Flags from Akron to Yonkers. l.t. ed. 2004. (Illus.). 400p. per. (978-0-9747728-0-6(1) , 48) North American Vexillological Assoc. (NAVA).

Pyle, Charles S., illus. The Daylight Limited: Lionel American Legend. l.t. ed. 1998. (Great Railway Adventures Ser.: Vol. 1). 30p. (J). 14.95 (978-1-890647-50-6(0)) RC2 Corp.

Pyle, Howard. Men of Iron. l.t. ed. 2004. 329p. (J). 29.95 (978-0-7862-6775-0(5) , Large Print Pr.) Thorndike Pr.

—The Merry Adventures of Robin Hood. l.t. ed. 2004. (Large Print Ser.). 518p. 26.00 (978-1-58287-684-9(3)) North Bks.

Rabinowitz, Sandy & Keiffer, Christa, illus. Treasured Horses Collection, 14 bks. l.t. ed. Incl. Christmas in Silver Lake. Hubbard, Coleen. 128p. lib. bdg. 23.33 (978-0-8368-2400-1(8)); Colorado Summer. Bograd, Larry & Hubbard, Coleen. 128p. lib. bdg. 23.33 (978-0-8368-2277-9(3)); Flying Angels. Hubbard, Coleen. 128p. lib. bdg. 23.33 (978-0-8368-2401-8(6)); Horse for Hannah. Hubbard, Coleen. 128p. lib. bdg. 23.33 (978-0-8368-2402-5(4)); Kate's Secret Plan. Saunders, Susan. 128p. lib. bdg. 23.33 (978-0-8368-2278-6(1)); Louisiana Blue. Hubbard, Coleen. 128p. lib. bdg. 23.33 (978-0-8368-2403-2(2)); Pretty Lady of Saratoga. Felder, Deborah G. 122p. lib. bdg. 23.33 (978-0-8368-2404-9(0)); Pride of the Green Mountains. Baker, Carin Greenberg. 128p. lib. bdg. 23.33 (978-0-8368-2279-3(X)); Ride of Courage. Felder, Deborah G. 128p. lib. bdg. 23.33 (978-0-8368-2280-9(3)); Riding School Rivals. Saunders, Susan. 128p. lib. bdg. 23.33 (978-0-8368-2281-6(1)); Rush for Gold. Hubbard, Coleen. 128p. lib. bdg. 23.33 (978-0-8368-2405-6(9)); Spirit of the West. Malcolm, Jahnna N. 122p. lib. bdg. 23.33 (978-0-8368-2282-3(X)); Stallion of Box Canyon. Malcolm, Jahnna N. 122p. lib. bdg. 23.33 (978-0-8368-2283-0(8)); Set. Changing Times. Felder, Deborah G. 128p. lib. bdg. 23.33 (978-0-8368-2276-2(5)); (J). (gr. 4 up). (Illus.). 1999. Set lib. bdg. 326.62 (978-0-8368-2471-1(7)) Stevens, Gareth Inc.

Rainville, Doris I., creator. The Girl Who Never Let Her Mother Brush Her Hair. l.t. ed. 2003. (Illus.). 24p. (J). per. 7.95 (978-0-9744879-0-8(2)) Magical Creations.

—The Power of Love. l.t. ed. 2003. (Illus.). 24p. (J). per. 7.95 (978-0-9744879-1-5(0)) Magical Creations.

Ramirez, Linda M. & Salcines, Maria Luisa. Maggie's Visit to the Playroom. Llendler, Christine, illus. l.t. ed. 2000. 16p. (Orig.). (J). pap. 6.95 (978-0-945199-22-9(8) , 956-668-1516) MarLin Bks.

Ramona Quimby, Age 8. 2005. (J). (978-1-59564-976-8(X)) Steps To Literacy, LLC.

Ratoff, Michael. Caspar & the Sun: An Adventure, 3 vols. Painter, Laurie, illus. l.t. ed. 2001. (Every Thing in an Empty Box Ser.). 56p. (J). (ps-3). lib. bdg. 9.95 (978-0-9627986-3-4(0)) Rebel Butterfly Pr.

—Every Thing in an Empty Box, Vol. 3. Painter, Laurie, illus. l.t. ed. 2001. 168p. (J). (ps-3). lib. bdg. 24.00 (978-0-9627986-5-8(7)) Rebel Butterfly Pr.

—Every Thing in an Empty Box, Vol. 3. Painter, Laurie, illus. l.t. ed. 2001. 168p. (J). lib. bdg. 24.00 (978-0-9627986-7-2(3)) Rebel Butterfly Pr.

—Silent Noisy Spring, 3 vols. Painter, Laurie, illus. l.t. ed. 2001. (Every Thing in an Empty Box Ser.). 56p. (J). (ps-3). lib. bdg. 9.95 (978-0-9627986-4-1(9)) Rebel Butterfly Pr.

—Silver & Shiny, 3 vols. Painter, Laurie, illus. 2nd l.t. ed. 2001. (Every Thing in an Empty Box Ser.). 56p. (J). (ps-3). lib. bdg. 9.95 (978-0-9627986-2-7(2)) Rebel Butterfly Pr.

Ratway, Michael J. & Ratway, Virginia K. Fractured Femur Fable. l.t. ed. 2003. (Illus.). 24p. (J). spiral bd. 10.00 (978-0-9724698-1-4(8)) Ratway, Michael.

Rawley, Phyllis Caves. Career Tips for Teens: What You Need to Know Before You Leave High School. l.t. ed. 2002. 200p. (YA). per 6.93 (978-0-9719057-0-2(3)) Brown Skin Girl Publishing.

Really Big Coloring Books Staff. ABC 123 Learn My Letters & Numbers. l.t. ed. 2003. Orig. Title: 123-ABC Learn My Letters & Numbers. (Illus.). 321p. (J). (978-0-9729753-1-5(4)) Really Big Coloring Bks., Inc.

Redding, David Asbury. He Never Spoke Without a Parable: His Kingdom, Your Antagonist, It's up to You, 3 bks, 5 vols. l.t. ed. 2003. pap. 16.00 (978-0-9671701-3-8(3) , 0-9671701-3-3) Starborne Hse.

—He Never Spoke Without a Parable: Your Father. l.t. ed. 2001. 64p. per. 6.00 (978-0-9671701-2-1(5)) Starborne Hse.

—He Never Spoke Without a Parable: Your Neighbor. rev. l.t. ed. 2000. 65p. pap. 10.00 (978-0-9671701-1-4(7) , 0-9671701-1-7) Starborne Hse.

Reece, Colleen L. Mysterious Monday. l.t. ed. 2001. (Christian Mystery Ser.). 192p. (J). 23.95 (978-0-7862-3068-6(1)) Thorndike Pr.

—Saturday Scare. l.t. ed. 2002. (Juli Scott, Super Sleuth Ser.). (Illus.). 211p. (J). 24.95 (978-0-7862-3195-9(5)) Thomson Gale.

—Thursday Trials. l.t. ed. 2001. (Juli Scott, Super Sleuth Ser.). (Illus.). 204p. (J). 23.95 (978-0-7862-3201-7(3)) Thorndike Pr.

—Trouble on Tuesday. l.t. ed. 2001. (Thorndike Christian Mystery Ser.). (Illus.). 192p. (J). 23.95 (978-0-7862-3178-2(5)) Thorndike Pr.

—Wednesday Witness. l.t. ed. 2001. (Juli Scott, Super Sleuth Ser.). (Illus.). 189p. (J). 23.95 (978-0-7862-3202-4(1)) Thorndike Pr.

Rees, Celia. Witch Child. l.t. ed. 2002. 284p. (J). 22.95 (978-0-7862-3896-5(8)) Thomson Gale.

Reilly, Dee Dee. Teaching Agnes to Dance. Walker, Betsy, illus. l.t. ed. 1999. 40p. (J). (ps-3). 14.95 (978-0-9669497-0-4(6)) Reilly Enterprises.

Renaud, Andrea. Sammy the Surfing Pelican Meets Steve the Surf Guru. l.t. ed. 2003. (Illus.). 32p. (J). per. (978-0-9717041-3-8(9)) A Happy Friend, Inc.

Renaud, Philip Francis. The Adventures of Sonny the Snow Snake. Wohlers, Lori, illus. l.t. ed. 2002. 22p. (J). bds. 10.95 (978-0-9711805-0-5(4)) Renaud & Co.

Richardson, Charisse K. The Real Slam Dunk. Richardson, Charisse K. & Palmer, Charly, illus. l.t. ed. 2002. 52p. (J). lib. bdg. 15.95 (978-0-9720689-0-1(2)) EnRich Communications.

Richmond, Marianne R., illus. Grand-O-Grams: Postcards to Keep in Touch with Your Grandkids All-year-round. l.t. ed. 2004. 44p. (J). pap. 9.95 (978-0-9753528-7-8(3)) Marianne Richmond Studios, Inc.

—Love-U-Grams: Postcards, Notes & Coupons to Connect with Your Kids. l.t. ed. 2005. 44p. (J). pap. 9.95 (978-0-9753528-9-2(X)) Marianne Richmond Studios, Inc.

Riddle, John & Whiting, Jim. Stephen Wozniak & the Story of Apple Computer. l.t. ed. 2002. (Unlocking the Secrets of Science Ser.). (Illus.). 56p. (gr. 4-10). lib. bdg. 17.95 (978-1-58415-109-8(9)) Mitchell Lane Pubs., Inc.

Riggott, Dean. Life on the Farm: A Pictorial Journey of Minnesota's Farmland & Its People. 100th l.t. ed. 2001. 124p. pap. 24.95 (978-0-9659875-2-3(3)) Riggott, Dean Photography.

Riker, Richard K. Scary Days Daze. l.t. ed. 2005. (Illus.). 224p. (J). 15.95 (978-0-9760416-1-0(8) , 3,000) Safe Harbor Pubns.

Riley, Barbara. Grow, Grow, Grow. Guggenheim, Jaenet, illus. l.t. ed. 2003. 40p. (J). 19.95 (978-1-929115-08-2(3)) Azro Pr., Inc.

Riley, John B. Benjamin Franklin: A Photo Biography. l.t. ed. 2004. (First Biographies Ser.). (Illus.). 24p. (YA). (gr. 5 up). 16.95 (978-1-883846-64-0(1) , First Biographies) Reynolds, Morgan Inc.

—George Washington Carver: A Photo Biography. l.t. ed. 2004. (First Biographies Ser.). (Illus.). 24p. (YA). (gr. 5 up). 16.95 (978-1-883846-62-6(5) , First Biographies) Reynolds, Morgan Inc.

—Jane Addams: A Photo Biography. l.t. ed. 2004. (First Biographies Ser.). (Illus.). 24p. (YA). (gr. 5 up). 16.95 (978-1-883846-61-9(7) , First Biographies) Reynolds, Morgan Inc.

—John Paul Jones: A Photo Biography. l.t. ed. 2004. (First Biographies Ser.). (Illus.). 24p. (YA). (gr. 5 up). 16.95 (978-1-883846-63-3(3) , First Biographies) Reynolds, Morgan Inc.

Rinaldi, Ann. A Ride into Morning: The Story of Tempe Wick. l.t. ed. 2005. 383p. (YA). 21.95 (978-0-7862-7957-9(5) , Large Print Pr.) Thorndike Pr.

Riordan, Rick. The Lightning Thief. 2006. (Percy Jackson & the Olympians Ser.: Bk. 1). 392p. (gr. 5 up). reprint ed. pap. 7.99 (978-0-7868-3865-3(5)) Miramax Bks.

Ristuccia, Christine. The Entire World of R Instructional Workbook: A Phonemic Approach to /R/ Remediation. l.t. ed. 2002. (Illus.). 200p. per. 34.99 (978-0-9723457-0-5(1)) Say It Right.

Ristuccia, Christine & Ristuccia, James. The Entire World of S & Z Instructional Workbook: A Comprehensive Approach to Remediate Frontal & Lateral Lisps. l.t. ed. 2003. (Illus.). 208p. (J). per. 34.99 (978-0-9723457-4-3(4)) Say It Right.

Roberts, Dannel. Me & Uncle Mike & Billy Goat Bob. Nichols, Brenda, illus. l.t. ed. 2002. (Me & Uncle Mike Children's Book Ser.: Bk. 3). 36p. (J). per. 14.95 (978-1-893459-02-1(0)) Lions & Tigers & Bears Publishing, Inc.

—Me & Uncle Mike & the 1-Eyed Croc. Stolte, F., illus. l.t. ed. 2002. (Me & Uncle Mike Children's Book Ser.: Bk. 4). 36p. per. 14.95 net. (978-1-893459-03-8(9)) Lions & Tigers & Bears Publishing, Inc.

—Me & Uncle Mike & the Pirate Ship. Stolte, F., illus. l.t. ed. 2001. (Me & Uncle Mike Children's Book Ser.: Bk. 2). 36p. (J). (ps-3). per. 14.95 (978-1-893459-01-4(2)) Lions & Tigers & Bears Publishing, Inc.

—Me & Uncle Mike & the Purple Gorilla, 5 bks, Bk. 5. l.t. ed. 2003. (Me & Uncle Mike Children's Book Ser.: Bk. 5). (Illus.). 32p. (J). per. 14.95 (978-1-893459-04-5(7)) Lions & Tigers & Bears Publishing, Inc.

Roberts, Mary Jane. Ambee. McAlpin, Theresa, ed. Stewart, Dean, illus. l.t. ed. 2000. 32p. (J). (gr. 1). pap. 4.99 (978-0-9675879-0-5(5)) Ambee Hse. Publishing.

Robinson, Kelley. The Magic of Lo: Book 1, lo Trilogy. l.t. ed. 2004. (Illus.). 160p. (YA). per. 9.95 (978-0-9745865-0-2(1) , SarahRose Children's Bks.) SarahRose Publishing.

Rock, Maria. MiMi's Garden, It's a Kid Thing! A Guide for Beginning Gardeners. l.t. ed. 2003. (Illus.). 45p. (J). 12.95 (978-0-9726979-0-3(X)) Rock Ink.

Rockwood, Joyce. To Spoil the Sun. l.t. ed. 2004. 259p. 20.95 (978-0-7862-6433-9(0)) Thorndike Pr.

Roddy, Lee. Cry of Courage. l.t. ed. 1999. (Paperback Ser.). 213p. (gr. 6-9). pap. 22.95 (978-0-7838-8611-4(X)) Thorndike Pr.

Roehm, Michelle, compiled by. Boys Know It All: Wise Thoughts & Wacky Ideas from Guys Like You. l.t. ed. 1999. (Girls Know Best Ser.). (Illus.). 167p. (J). (gr. 3 up). lib. bdg. 23.33 (978-0-8368-2455-1(5)) Stevens, Gareth Inc.

—Girls Knows Best: Advice for Girls from Girls on Just about Everything. 1999. (Girls Know Best Ser.). (Illus.). 160p. (J). (gr. 3 up). lib. bdg. 23.33 (978-0-8368-2452-0(0)) Stevens, Gareth Inc.

Rojas, Emilio. Mitos, Leyendas, Cuentos, Fabulas, Apologos y Parabolas, 3 vols, Vol. 2. Rojas, Emilio, ed. Farshchian, Mahmoud et al, illus. Arcos, Bernardo & Alcaraz, Lorena, photos by. l.t. ed. 2001. (SPA.). 224p. (J). (gr. 2 up). per. 15.95 (978-0-9706814-3-0(7)) EDITER'S Publishing Hse.

—Mitos, Leyendas, Cuentos, Fabulas, Apologos y Parabolas, 3 vols., Vol. 3. Rojas, Emilio, ed. Rojas, Lauyumi Michelle et al, illus. Alcaraz, Lorena & Arcos, Bernardo, photos by. 2nd rev. l.t. ed. 2002. (SPA.). 224p. (YA). (gr. 4 up). reprint ed. per. 15.95 (978-0-9706814-0-9(2)) EDITER'S Publishing Hse.

—Mitos, Leyendas, Cuentos, Fabulas, Apologos y Parabolas I, 3 vols. Rojas, Emilio, ed. Gonzalez, Elva Nitzchiani et al, illus. Alcaraz, Lorena & Arcos, Bernardo, photos by. l.t. ed. 2001. (SPA.). 224p. (YA). per. 15.95 (978-0-9706814-4-7(5)) EDITER'S Publishing Hse.

Rojas, Emilio, ed. El Cuento y las Corrientes Literarias. Minguer, Edgar, illus. Alcaraz, Lorena & Arcos, Bernardo, photos by. l.t. ed. 2002. (SPA.). 224p. (YA). (gr. 8 up). per. 15.95 (978-0-9706814-7-8(X)) EDITER'S Publishing Hse.

—En Busca de Si Mismo: Apologos y Parabolas. Minguer, Edgar, illus. Alcaraz, Lorena & Arcos, Bernardo, photos by. l.t. ed. 2002. (SPA.). 168p. (YA). per. 15.95 (978-0-9706814-9-2(6)) EDITER'S Publishing Hse.

—Libro Magico de la Fabula, el Cuento y la Leyenda. Farshchian, Mahmoud et al, illus. Arcos, Bernardo & Alcaraz, Lorena, photos by. l.t. ed. 2001. (SPA.). 224p. (J). per. 15.95 (978-0-9706814-5-4(3)) EDITER'S Publishing Hse.

Romano, Ralph & Burke, Joe. Elbo Elf: The Package Master of Christmas. l.t. ed. 2000. (Illus.). 29p. (J). (gr. 1-5). 19.95 (978-0-9704125-0-8(9)) Elbo Elf, Inc.

Rondeau, Amanda. Bella Blew Blue Bubbles. l.t. ed. 2002. (Homophones Ser.). (Illus.). 24p. (J). (ps-3). lib. bdg. 19.93 (978-1-57765-784-2(5) , SandCastle) ABDO Publishing Co.

—Can You Hear Me from Here? l.t. ed. 2002. (Homophones Ser.). (Illus.). 24p. (J). (ps-3). lib. bdg. 19.93 (978-1-57765-780-4(2) , SandCastle) ABDO Publishing Co.

—Do We By, Buy, or Bye Tickets? l.t. ed. 2002. (Homophones Ser.). (Illus.). 24p. (J). (ps-3). lib. bdg. 19.93 (978-1-57765-782-8(9) , SandCastle) ABDO Publishing Co.

—Months. l.t. ed. 2001. (Capital Letters Ser.). (Illus.). 24p. (J). (ps-3). lib. bdg. 19.93 (978-1-57765-612-8(1) , SandCastle) ABDO Publishing Co.

—The Prince Left His Prints. l.t. ed. 2002. (Homophones Ser.). (Illus.). 24p. (J). (ps-3). lib. bdg. 19.93 (978-1-57765-781-1(0) , SandCastle) ABDO Publishing Co.

—Sue Threw the Goop Through the Hoop. l.t. ed. 2002. (Homophones Ser.). (Illus.). 24p. (J). (ps-3). lib. bdg. 19.93 (978-1-57765-783-5(7) , SandCastle) ABDO Publishing Co.

—We Have a Wee Whale. l.t. ed. 2002. (Homophones Ser.). (Illus.). 24p. (J). (ps-3). lib. bdg. 19.93 (978-1-57765-779-8(9) , SandCastle) ABDO Publishing Co.

Roos, Stephen. The Gypsies Never Came. l.t. ed. 2001. (Juvenile Ser.). 116p. (J). 20.95 (978-0-7862-3469-1(5)) Thorndike Pr.

Rose, John N. Direct Approach: Maya 5. l.t. ed. 2003. (Illus.). 302p. per. 49.95 (978-0-9742948-0-3(2) , DA-Ma5) Platinum Rose Publishing.

Rose, Malcolm. The Alibi: The Perfect Murder... l.t. ed. 2000. (Illus.). 302p. (J). pap. (978-0-7540-6099-4(3) , CLP 297) BBC Audio.

—The Smoking Gun. l.t. ed. 1998. (Illus.). 228p. (J). pap. 16.95 (978-0-7540-6009-3(8) , Galaxy Children's Large Print) BBC Audiobooks America.

Ross, Andrea. To Touch the Sun. Davenport, May, ed. l.t. ed. 2000. 195p. (YA). (gr. 9-12). pap. 15.95 (978-0-943864-99-0(2)) Davenport, May Pubs.

Rothman, Cynthia Anne. Big Book. Alley, R. W., illus. l.t. ed. 2005. (Sadlier Phonics Reading Program). 8p. (YA). (ps-1). 22.50 (978-0-8215-7342-6(X)) Sadlier, William H. Inc.

—Big Book: A Party for Nine. l.t. ed. 2005. (Sadlier Phonics Reading Program). (Illus.). 8p. (YA). (gr. k-2). 22.50 (978-0-8215-7349-5(7)) Sadlier, William H. Inc.

—Big Book Vol. 3: I Love to Read. l.t. ed. 2005. (Sadlier Phonics Reading Program). (Illus.). 8p. (YA). (ps-1). 22.50 (978-0-8215-7353-2(5)) Sadlier, William H. Inc.

—Big Book: Violets & Vegetables, Vol. 4. l.t. ed. 2005. (Sadlier Phonics Reading Program). (Illus.). 8p. (YA). (ps-1). 22.50 (978-0-8215-7357-0(8)) Sadlier, William H. Inc.

—Big Book: Yes, You Can, Vol. 4. l.t. ed. 2005. (Sadlier Phonics Reading Program). (Illus.). 8p. (YA). (ps-1). 22.50 (978-0-8215-7358-7(6)) Sadlier, William H. Inc.

—Funny Bugs. Lester, Mike, illus. l.t. ed. 2005. (Little Books & Big Bks.: Vol. 4). 8p. (YA). (ps-3). 22.50 (978-0-8215-7513-0(9)) Sadlier, William H. Inc.

Rouillard, Wendy W. Barnaby's Kite Ride. Rouillard, Wendy W., illus. l.t. ed. 1998. (Illus.). 32p. (J). (gr. 1-3). 15.95 (978-0-9642836-6-4(2)) Barnaby & Co.

—A Penny for Barnaby. l.t. ed. 1998. (Illus.). 32p. (J). (gr. 1-3). 15.95 (978-0-9642836-7-1(0)) Barnaby & Co.

Rowles, Louis. Ida Claire Does Fabulous Hair. Brownlee, Sunny Dai, illus. l.t. ed. 2001. 25p. (J). (gr. 1-5). pap. 6.50 (978-0-9708748-0-1(4)) Rowles, Louis.

Rowling, J. K. Harry Potter & the Chamber of Secrets. GrandPré, Mary, illus. l.t. ed. 2000. (Harry Potter Ser.: Year 2). 464p. (gr. 3 up). 24.95 (978-0-7862-2273-5(5) , Large Print Pr.) Thorndike Pr.

—Harry Potter & the Deathly Hallows. l.t. ed. 2007. (Harry Potter Ser.: Year 7). (YA). 34.95 ***978-0-7862-9665-1(8))** Thorndike Pr.

—Harry Potter & the Goblet of Fire. GrandPré, Mary, illus. l.t. ed. 2000. (Harry Potter Ser.: Year 4). 936p. (gr. 3 up). 25.95 (978-0-7862-2927-7(6) , Large Print Pr.) Thorndike Pr.

—Harry Potter & the Half-Blood Prince. l.t. ed. 2005. (Harry Potter Ser.: Year 6). 832p. 29.95 (978-0-7862-7745-2(9) , Large Print Pr.) Thorndike Pr.

—Harry Potter & the Order of the Phoenix. l.t. ed. 2003. (Harry Potter Ser.: Year 5). 1093p. 29.95 (978-0-7862-5778-2(4) , Large Print Pr.) Thorndike Pr.

—Harry Potter & the Prisoner of Azkaban. GrandPré, Mary, illus. l.t. ed. 2000. (Harry Potter Ser.: Year 3). 592p. (gr. 3 up). 24.95 (978-0-7862-2274-2(3) , Large Print Pr.) Thorndike Pr.

—Harry Potter & the Sorcerer's Stone. GrandPré, Mary, illus. l.t. ed. 1999. (Harry Potter Ser.: Year 1). 422p. (gr. 3 up). 24.95 (978-0-7862-2272-8(7) , Large Print Pr.) Thorndike Pr.

Royster, D. A. Adoption Is... l.t. ed. 2005. (Illus.). 30p. (J). bds. 15.99 (978-0-9761538-0-1(7)) Unspeakable Joy Pr.

Rudner, Barry. Special Ed. Trabalka, Peggy, illus. l.t. ed. 2000. 28p. (J). (ps-3). 7.95 (978-0-9642206-6-9(0)) Windword Pr.

The Running of the Leaves. l.t. ed. 2001. 54p. (J). (gr. 4-6). spiral bd. 11.95 (978-0-9714293-0-7(8)) IBD Pr.

Rushford, Patricia H. Desperate Measures. l.t. ed. 2000. (Jennie McGrady Mysteries Ser.: No. 11). 333p. (J). (gr. 4-7). 23.95 (978-0-7862-2374-9(X)) Thorndike Pr.

Ruth, Annie. No! Not on the Pews. Ruth, Annie, illus. l.t. ed. 1999. (Illus.). 20p. (J). (gr. k-3). 2.50 (978-0-9656306-1-0(7)) Ruth, A. Creations.

Ruurs, Margriet. Emma & the Coyote. Spurll, Barbara, illus. l.t. ed. 2001. 24p. (J). (ps-3). 16.95 (978-0-7737-3140-0(7)) Stoddart Kids CAN. *Dist:* Fitzhenry & Whiteside, Ltd.

Sabol, Elizabeth, illus. Day Is Done: A Lullaby, l.t. ed. 2004. 26p. (J). pap. incl. audio compact disk (978-0-9747382-0-8(4)) LeDor Publishing.

Sager, Elizabeth R. Clif & Simmons: A Tale of Two Puppies. l.t. ed. 1999. (Illus.). 20p. (J). (gr. k-5). pap. 6.95 (978-0-9678386-0-1(6)) C.S. Publishing.

Salomon, Diana. Duke, the Babysitter. Salomon, Udo, photos by. l.t. ed. 2002. (Illus.). 16p. (J). 6.95 (978-0-9704581-1-7(8) , 1,000, Free Song) LeBlanc, Doreen.

Salzmann, Mary Elizabeth. Aa: See It Say It Hear It. l.t. ed. 2000. (Long Vowels Ser.). (Illus.). 24p. (J). (ps-3). lib. bdg. 19.93 (978-1-57765-413-1(7) , SandCastle) ABDO Publishing Co.

—Apostrophe. l.t. ed. 2001. (Punctuation Ser.). (Illus.). 24p. (J). (ps-3). lib. bdg. 19.93 (978-1-57765-625-8(3) , SandCastle) ABDO Publishing Co.

—Circles. l.t. ed. 1999. (What Shape Is It? Ser.). (Illus.). 24p. (J). (ps-3). lib. bdg. 19.93 (978-1-57765-163-5(4) , SandCastle) ABDO Publishing Co.

—Comma. l.t. ed. 2001. (Punctuation Ser.). (Illus.). 24p. (J). (ps-3). lib. bdg. 19.93 (978-1-57765-620-3(2) , SandCastle) ABDO Publishing Co.

—Do You Wonder?, , Set. l.t. ed. Incl. How? lib. bdg. 19.93 (978-1-57765-174-1(X)); What? lib. bdg. 19.93 (978-1-57765-170-3(7)); When? lib. bdg. 19.93 (978-1-57765-171-0(5)); Where? lib. bdg. 19.93 (978-1-57765-172-7(3)); Who? lib. bdg. 19.93 (978-1-57765-169-7(3)); Why? lib. bdg. 19.93 (978-1-57765-173-4(1)); 24p. (J). (ps-3). 2000. (Illus.). 2000. Set lib. bdg. 119.58 (978-1-57765-281-6(9) , SandCastle) ABDO Publishing Co.

—Exclamation Point. l.t. ed. 2001. (Punctuation Ser.). (Illus.). 24p. (J). (ps-3). lib. bdg. 19.93 (978-1-57765-621-0(0) , SandCastle) ABDO Publishing Co.

—How? l.t. ed. 2000. (Do You Wonder? Ser.). (Illus.). 24p. (J). (ps-3). lib. bdg. 19.93 (978-1-57765-174-1(X) , SandCastle) ABDO Publishing Co.

—II: See It Say It Hear It. l.t. ed. 2000. (Long Vowels Ser.). (Illus.). 24p. (J). (ps-3). lib. bdg. 19.93 (978-1-57765-415-5(3) , SandCastle) ABDO Publishing Co.

—The Knight Waits at Night. l.t. ed. 2002. (Homophones Ser.). (Illus.). 24p. (J). (ps-3). lib. bdg. 19.93 (978-1-57765-651-7(2) , SandCastle) ABDO Publishing Co.

—My Deer Is a Dear. l.t. ed. 2002. (Homophones Ser.). (Illus.). 24p. (J). (ps-3). lib. bdg. 19.93 (978-1-57765-652-4(0) , SandCastle) ABDO Publishing Co.

—Oa: See It Say It Hear It. l.t. ed. 2001. (Vowel Blends Ser.). (Illus.). 24p. (J). (ps-3). lib. bdg. 19.93 (978-1-57765-456-8(0) , SandCastle) ABDO Publishing Co.

—Ou: See It Say It Hear It. 2001. (Vowel Blends Ser.). (Illus.). 24p. (J). (ps-3). lib. bdg. 19.93 (978-1-57765-458-2(7) , SandCastle) ABDO Publishing Co.

—Ovals. l.t. ed. 1999. (What Shape Is It? Ser.). (Illus.). 24p. (J). (ps-3). lib. bdg. 19.93 (978-1-57765-168-0(5) , SandCastle) ABDO Publishing Co.

—Period. l.t. ed. 2001. (Punctuation Ser.). (Illus.). 24p. (J). (ps-3). lib. bdg. 19.93 (978-1-57765-622-7(9) , SandCastle) ABDO Publishing Co.

—Punctuation, Set. l.t. ed. Incl. Apostrophe. lib. bdg. 19.93 (978-1-57765-625-8(3)); Comma. lib. bdg. 19.93 (978-1-57765-620-3(2)); Exclamation Point. lib. bdg. 19.93 (978-1-57765-621-0(0)); Period. lib. bdg. 19.93 (978-1-57765-622-7(9)); Question Mark. lib. bdg. 19.93 (978-1-57765-623-4(7)); Quotation Marks. lib. bdg. 19.93 (978-1-57765-624-1(5)); 24p. (J). (ps-3). (Illus.). 2001. Set lib. bdg. 119.58 (978-1-57765-517-6(6) , SandCastle) ABDO Publishing Co.

—Question Mark. l.t. ed. 2001. (Punctuation Ser.). (Illus.). 24p. (J). (ps-3). lib. bdg. 19.93 (978-1-57765-623-4(7) , SandCastle) ABDO Publishing Co.

—Quotation Marks. l.t. ed. 2001. (Punctuation Ser.). (Illus.). 24p. (J). (ps-3). lib. bdg. 19.93 (978-1-57765-624-1(5) , SandCastle) ABDO Publishing Co.

—Sometimes Yy: See It Say It Hear It. l.t. ed. 2000. (Long Vowels Ser.). (Illus.). 24p. (J). (ps-3). lib. bdg. 19.93 (978-1-57765-418-6(8) , SandCastle) ABDO Publishing Co.

—Squares. l.t. ed. 1999. (What Shape Is It? Ser.). (Illus.). 24p. (J). (ps-3). lib. bdg. 19.93 (978-1-57765-164-2(2) , SandCastle) ABDO Publishing Co.

—They're There in Their Boat. l.t. ed. 2002. (Homophones Ser.). (Illus.). 24p. (J). (ps-3). lib. bdg. 19.93 (978-1-57765-650-0(4) , SandCastle) ABDO Publishing Co.

—Triangles. l.t. ed. 1999. (What Shape Is It? Ser.). (Illus.). 24p. (J). (ps-3). lib. bdg. 19.93 (978-1-57765-165-9(0) , SandCastle) ABDO Publishing Co.

—Uu: See It Say It Hear It. l.t. ed. 2000. (Long Vowels Ser.). (Illus.). 24p. (J). (ps-3). lib. bdg. 19.93 (978-1-57765-417-9(X) , SandCastle) ABDO Publishing Co.

—Vowel Blends, Set. l.t. ed. Incl. Ai : See It Say It Hear It. lib. bdg. 19.93 (978-1-57765-453-7(6)); Ea : See It Say It Hear It. lib. bdg. 19.93 (978-1-57765-454-4(4)); Ee : See It Say It Hear It. lib. bdg. 19.93 (978-1-57765-455-1(2)); Oa : See It Say It Hear It. lib. bdg. 19.93 (978-1-57765-456-8(0)); Oo : See It Say It Hear It. lib. bdg. 19.93 (978-1-57765-457-5(9)); Ou : See It Say It Hear It. lib. bdg. 19.93 (978-1-57765-458-2(7)); 24p. (J). (ps-3). 2001. (Illus.). 2001. Set lib. bdg. 119.58 (978-1-57765-299-1(1) , SandCastle) ABDO Publishing Co.

—What Color Is It?, Set. l.t. ed. Incl. Blue. lib. bdg. 19.93 (978-1-57765-161-1(8)); Green. lib. bdg. 19.93 (978-1-57765-162-8(6)); Orange. lib. bdg. 19.93 (978-1-57765-158-1(8)); Purple. lib. bdg. 19.93 (978-1-57765-160-4(X)); Red. lib. bdg. 19.93 (978-1-57765-159-8(6)); Yellow. lib. bdg. 19.93 (978-1-57765-157-4(X)); 24p. (J). (ps-3). 1999. Tr. of ¿de Qué Color Es?. (Illus.). 1999. Set lib. bdg. 119.58 (978-1-57765-264-9(9) , SandCastle) ABDO Publishing Co.

—When? l.t. ed. 2000. (Do You Wonder? Ser.). (Illus.). 24p. (J). (ps-3). lib. bdg. 19.93 (978-1-57765-171-0(5) , SandCastle) ABDO Publishing Co.

—Where Do I Wear Water Wings? l.t. ed. 2002. (Homophones Ser.). (Illus.). 24p. (J). (gr. 1-2). lib. bdg. 19.93 (978-1-57765-799-6(3) , SandCastle) ABDO Publishing Co.

—Who's on Whose Spot? l.t. ed. 2002. (Homophones Ser.). (Illus.). 24p. (J). (ps-3). lib. bdg. 19.93 (978-1-57765-798-9(5) , SandCastle) ABDO Publishing Co.

—Why? l.t. ed. 2000. (Do You Wonder? Ser.). (Illus.). 24p. (J). (ps-3). lib. bdg. 19.93 (978-1-57765-173-4(1) , SandCastle) ABDO Publishing Co.

—You're on Your Phone. l.t. ed. 2002. (Homophones Ser.). (Illus.). 24p. (J). (ps-3). lib. bdg. 19.93 (978-1-57765-797-2(7) , SandCastle) ABDO Publishing Co.

Sam Goes to the Beach. l.t. ed. 2002. (Farmer Bob Ser.). 32p. lib. bdg. (978-1-59168-064-2(6)) Flying Rhinoceros, Inc.

Sample, Lempi. The Life of Jesus: As Seen Through the Eyes of a Shepherd Boy. Mikels, Leroy, illus. l.t. ed. 1999. 67p. (J). 9.95 (978-1-55967-234-4(X)) Triune Biblical Univ.

Sanders, Stephanie. Q. T. Pie Meets Smart E. Pauling, Galen T., illus. l.t. ed. 2003. 36p. (J). mass mkt. 4.99 (978-0-9670875-4-2(6) , 313-533-7383) SanPaul Group, LLC, The.

Sandifer, Kevin W., ed. History of the United States, Beginning-Civil War Pt. 1: Its Beginning Through the Civil War. l.t. ed. 2004. (Illus.). 400p. lib. bdg. 19.95 (978-0-910653-60-2(7) , 8201T, Red River Pr.) Red River Pr.

—History of the United States, Reconstruction-Clinton Era Pt. 2. l.t. ed. 2007. (Illus.). 432p. lib. bdg. (978-0-910653-61-9(5) , 8202U, Red River Pr.) Red River Pr.

Sanroman, Susana. Senora Reganona: A Mexican Bedtime Story. Domi, illus. 1998. (SPA.). 24p. (J). (ps-k). 14.95 (978-0-88899-320-5(X)) Groundwood Bks. CAN. *Dist:* Perseus Distribution.

Sargent, Daina. Alaska: Be Brave, 4. Lenoir, Jane, illus. l.t. ed. 2004. (Double Trouble Ser.: 4). 48p. (J). pap. 9.95 (978-1-59381-121-1(7)); lib. bdg. 22.60 (978-1-59381-120-4(9)) Ozark Publishing.

—Arkansas: Dream Big. Lenoir, Jane, illus. l.t. ed. 2004. (Double Trouble Ser.). 48p. (J). pap. 6.95 (978-1-59381-123-5(3)); lib. bdg. 22.60 (978-1-59381-122-8(5)) Ozark Publishing.

—Colors & the Number 10, 11. Lenoir, Jane, illus. l.t. ed. 2004. (Learn to Read Ser.). 24p. (J). lib. bdg. 16.95 (978-1-59381-048-1(2)) Ozark Publishing.

—Colors & the Number 2, 11. Lenoir, Jane, illus. l.t. ed. 2004. (Learn to Read Ser.). 24p. (J). lib. bdg. 19.95 (978-1-59381-032-0(6)) Ozark Publishing.

—Colors & the Number 3, 11. Lenoir, Jane, illus. l.t. ed. 2004. (Learn to Read Ser.). 24p. (J). lib. bdg. 19.95 (978-1-59381-034-4(2)) Ozark Publishing.

—Colors & the Number 4, 11 vols. Lenoir, Jane, illus. l.t. ed. 2004. (Learn to Read Ser.). 24p. (J). lib. bdg. 19.95 (978-1-59381-036-8(9)) Ozark Publishing.

—Colors & the Number 5, 11. Lenoir, Jane, illus. l.t. ed. 2004. (Learn to Read Ser.). 24p. (J). lib. bdg. 19.95 (978-1-59381-038-2(5)) Ozark Publishing.

—Colors & the Number 6, 11. Lenoir, Jane, illus. l.t. ed. 2004. (Learn to Read Ser.). 24p. (J). lib. bdg. 19.95 (978-1-59381-040-5(7)) Ozark Publishing.

—Colors & the Number 7, 11. Lenoir, Jane, illus. l.t. ed. 2004. (Learn to Read Ser.). 24p. (J). lib. bdg. 19.95 (978-1-59381-042-9(3)) Ozark Publishing.

—Colors & the Number 8, 11. Lenoir, Jane, illus. l.t. ed. 2004. (Learn to Read Ser.). 24p. (J). lib. bdg. 19.95 (978-1-59381-044-3(X)) Ozark Publishing.

—Colors & the Number 9, 11. Lenoir, Jane, illus. l.t. ed. 2004. (Learn to Read Ser.). 24p. (J). lib. bdg. 19.95 (978-1-59381-046-7(6)) Ozark Publishing.

—Introduction to Colors & Numbers, 11 vols. Lenoir, Jane, illus. l.t. ed. 2004. (Learn to Read Ser.: 11). 24p. (J). lib. bdg. 19.95 (978-1-59381-050-4(4)) Ozark Publishing.

—Introduction to Colors & Numbers/Introduccion a los Colores Numeros, 11 vols. Lenoir, Jane, illus. l.t. ed. 2005. (Learn to Read Ser.: 11). (SPA & ENG.). 24p. (J). pap. 9.95 (978-1-59381-149-5(7)) Ozark Publishing.

—Kansas: Conquer Fear. Lenoir, Jane, illus. l.t. ed. 2004. (Double Trouble Ser.). 48p. (J). pap. 6.95 (978-1-59381-125-9(X)); lib. bdg. 22.60 (978-1-59381-124-2(1)) Ozark Publishing.

—Missouri: Teamwork. Lenoir, Jane, illus. l.t. ed. 2004. (Double Trouble Ser.). 48p. (J). pap. 6.95 (978-1-59381-127-3(6)); lib. bdg. 22.60 (978-1-59381-126-6(8)) Ozark Publishing.

Sargent, Dave & Sargent, Pat. The Colorado Blizzard: Be Determined, 10, 8. Lenoir, Jane, illus. l.t. ed. 2004. (Colorado Cowboys Ser.: 8). 32p. (J). (gr. 3-8). lib. bdg. 22.60 (978-1-59381-026-9(1)) Ozark Publishing.

—The Fire Vol. 10: Second Chance, 10 vols. Lenoir, Jane, illus. l.t. ed. 2005. (Colorado Cowboys Ser.: Vol. 10). 32p. (J). (gr. 3-8). lib. bdg. 22.60 (978-1-59381-104-4(7)) Ozark Publishing.

Sargent, Dave, et al. Berry Picking Time Vol. 3: (Apache) Be Brave, 20. Lenoir, Jane, illus. l.t. ed. 2003. (Story Keeper Ser.: 3). 42p. (J). Vol. 3. lib. bdg. 22.60 (978-1-56763-907-0(0)); vol. 3. pap. 6.95 (978-1-56763-908-7(9)) Ozark Publishing.

—The Bundle Keeper: (Pawnee) Be Responsible, 20, Vol. 18. Lenoir, Jane, illus. l.t. ed. 2004. (Story Keeper Ser.: 18). 48p. (J). pap. 6.95 (978-1-56763-938-4(0)) Ozark Publishing.

—Counting Coup Vol. 4: (Cheyenee) Be Proud, 20. Lenoir, Jane, illus. l.t. ed. 2003. (Story Keeper Ser.). 42p. (J). lib. bdg. 22.60 (978-1-56763-909-4(7)) Ozark Publishing.

—Counting Coup Vol. 4: (Cheyenne) Be Proud, 20. l.t. ed. 2003. (Story Keeper Ser.). (Illus.). 42p. (J). pap. 6.95 (978-1-56763-910-0(0)) Ozark Publishing.

—Dream Catcher Vol. 5: (Lakota Sioux) Be Strong, 20 vols., Vol. 5. Lenoir, Jane, illus. l.t. ed. 2003. (Story Keeper Ser.: 5). 42p. (J). pap. 6.95 (978-1-56763-912-4(7)) Ozark Publishing.

—Fields of Golden Corn Vol. 6: (Navajo) Be Energetic, 20 bks. Lenoir, Jane, illus. l.t. ed. 2003. (Story Keeper Ser.: 6). 42p. (J). lib. bdg. 22.60 (978-1-56763-913-1(5)) Ozark Publishing.

—Fierce Warriors Vol. 7: Learn Skills, 20 bks. Lenoir, Jane, illus. l.t. ed. 2004. (Story Keeper Ser.: 7). 48p. (J). lib. bdg. 22.60 (978-1-56763-915-5(1)) Ozark Publishing.

—A Hole in the Sun: (Choctaw) Be Independent, 20, Vol. 1. Lenoir, Jane, illus. l.t. ed. 2003. (Story Keeper Ser.: 1). 42p. (J). pap. 6.95 (978-1-56763-904-9(6)) Ozark Publishing.

—Keeping Ghosts Away Vol. 8: (Creek) Be Respectful, 20. Lenoir, Jane, illus. l.t. ed. 2003. (Story Keeper Ser.: Vol. 8). 42p. (J). pap. 6.95 (978-1-56763-918-6(6) , 1228135) Ozark Publishing.

—Knocking the Rice Vol. 9: (Chippewa) Be Powerful, 20. Lenoir, Jane, illus. l.t. ed. 2003. (Story Keeper Ser.: 9). 42p. (J). pap. 6.95 (978-1-56763-920-9(8)); lib. bdg. 22.60 (978-1-56763-919-3(4)) Ozark Publishing.

—Ladder at the Door Vol. 10: (Hopi) Be Curious, 20. Lenoir, Jane, illus. l.t. ed. 2004. (Story Keeper Ser.: 10). 48p. (J). pap. 6.95 (978-1-56763-922-3(4)); lib. bdg. 22.60 (978-1-56763-921-6(6)) Ozark Publishing.

—Land of the Sun Vol. 11: (Ute) Respect Elders, 20. Lenoir, Jane, illus. l.t. ed. 2004. (Story Keeper Ser.: Bk. 11). 48p. (J). 11. pap. 6.95 (978-1-56763-924-7(0)); Vol. 11. lib. bdg. 22.60 (978-1-56763-923-0(2)) Ozark Publishing.

—Little One Vol. 12: (Cherokee) Be Inventive, 20. Lenoir, Jane, illus. l.t. ed. 2003. (Story Keeper Ser.: Vol. 12). 42p. (J). pap. 6.95 (978-1-56763-926-1(7)) Ozark Publishing.

—On the Banks of the Wallowa River: (Nez Perce) Use Your Talent, 20, 13. Lenoir, Jane, illus. l.t. ed. 2004. (Story Keeper Ser.: 13). 48p. (J). pap. 6.95 (978-1-56763-928-5(3)); lib. bdg. 22.60 (978-1-56763-927-8(5)) Ozark Publishing.

—Rays of the Sun Vol. 15: (shoshone) Learn Lessons, 20 vols. Lenoir, Jane, illus. l.t. ed. 2004. (Story Keeper Ser.: 15). 48p. (J). pap. 6.95 (978-1-56763-932-2(1)) Ozark Publishing.

—Rays of the Sun Vol. 15: (Shoshone) Learn Lessons, 20 vols. Lenoir, Jane, illus. l.t. ed. 2004. (Story Keeper Ser.: 15). 48p. (J). lib. bdg. 22.60 (978-1-56763-931-5(3)) Ozark Publishing.

—A Strand of Wampum Vol. 2: Be Honest, 20. Lenoir, Sue, illus. l.t. ed. 2003. (Story Keeper Ser.: 2). 42p. (J). pap. 6.95 (978-1-56763-906-3(2)) Ozark Publishing.

—Summer Milky Way: (Blackfeet) Be Compassionate, 20, Vol. 16. Lenoir, Jane, illus. l.t. ed. 2004. (Story Keeper Ser.). 48p. (J). lib. bdg. 22.60 (978-1-56763-933-9(X)); pap. 6.95 (978-1-56763-934-6(8)) Ozark Publishing.

—Tattoos of Honor Vol. 17: (Osage) Be Gentle & Giving, 20 bks. Lenoir, Jane, illus. l.t. ed. 2004. (Story Keeper Ser.: Vol. 17). 42p. (J). pap. 6.95 (978-1-56763-936-0(4)); lib. bdg. 22.60 (978-1-56763-935-3(6)) Ozark Publishing.

—Truth, Power & Freedom Vol. 19: (Sioux) Show Respect, 20. Lenoir, Jane, illus. l.t. ed. 2004. (Story Keeper Ser.: 19). 42p. (J). 19. lib. bdg. 22.60 (978-1-56763-939-1(9)); Vol. 19. pap. 6.95 (978-1-56763-940-7(2)) Ozark Publishing.

—Valley Oaks Acorns Vol. 20: (Maidu) Be Helpful, 20. Lenoir, Jane, illus. l.t. ed. 2004. (Story Keeper Ser.: 20). 48p. (J). pap. 6.95 (978-1-56763-942-1(9)) Ozark Publishing.

Sargent, Pat L. The Cheetah, 6 vols, Vol. 6. Lenoir, Jane, illus. l.t. ed. 2004. (Barney the Bear Killer Ser.: No. 6). 146p. (YA). pap. 9.95 (978-1-56763-974-2(7)); lib. bdg. 25.25 (978-1-56763-973-5(9)) Ozark Publishing.

—The Grizzly, 8, Vol. 1. Lenoir, Jane, illus. l.t. ed. 2004. (Barney the Bear Killer Ser.: No. 1). 129p. (YA). lib. bdg. 25.25 (978-1-56763-963-6(1)) Ozark Publishing.

Sassy Wants to Be a Star Bk. 5: "The Audition" l.t. ed. 1999. (Illus.). 30p. (J). (ps-5). 6.00 (978-1-893727-02-1(5)) Mustafa, Malik.

Sathre, Vivian. Dog Overboard! l.t. ed. 1999. (Adventures of Wishbone Ser.: No. 12). (Illus.). (J). (gr. 4 up). lib. bdg. 22.60 (978-0-8368-2590-9(X)) Stevens, Gareth Inc.

Saunders, Kate. Spell of Witches. l.t. ed. 2005. (Illus.). 144p. (J). pap. (978-0-7540-6146-5(9) , CLP 339) BBC Audio.

Saunders, Susan. Riding School Rivals. Rabinowitz, Sandy & Keiffer, Christa, illus. l.t. ed. 1999. (Treasured Horses Collection). 128p. (J). (gr. 4 up). lib. bdg. 23.33 (978-0-8368-2281-6(1)) Stevens, Gareth Inc.

Scaglione, Joseph. My Lucky Penny. Szarko, Kathy, illus. deluxe l.t. ed. 1999. 64p. (J). (ps-4). pap. 24.95 incl. cd-rom (978-0-9675011-0-9(5)) New Day Enterprises, Ltd.

Scalpone, Joan Lundquist. "Cool" Capers: Children's Stories. l.t. ed. 2000. (Illus.). 32p. (J). pap. 12.00 (978-0-929198-21-7(2)) Mini DayTrip Bks.

Scalzo, Linda V. Carazona's Coloring Book. l.t. ed. 2004. (Illus.). 8p. (J). 2.99 (978-0-9753724-3-2(2)) Carazona Creations LLC.

—El circo llega al Pueblo: Version de Lectura Temprana. Torres, Marcela H., tr. Spalinski, Amanda, illus. l.t. ed. 2005. (SPA.). 24p. per. 9.99 (978-0-9753724-2-5(4)) Carazona Creations LLC.

—The Circus Is coming to Town: Early Reader Version. Spalinski, Amanda, illus. l.t. ed. 2005. 24p. (J). per. 9.99 (978-0-9753724-1-8(6)) Carazona Creations LLC.

—The Circus Is Coming to Town: Full-Length Version. l.t. ed. 2004. (Illus.). 32p. (J). 9.99 (978-0-9753724-0-1(8)) Carazona Creations LLC.

Schalk, Marian. A Great Miracle in a Small Mountain Village. VanBrugge, Marinus, tr. from DUT. Kramer, Jaap, illus. l.t. ed. 2002. 48p. (J). pap. 6.95 (978-0-9670728-9-0(1)) Early Foundations Pubs.

Scheber, Gregory. Earl Joins the Circus. Spicer, Bridgett, illus. l.t. ed. 2005. (Adventures of Earl the Squirrel Ser.). 32p. (J). (ps-3). 12.95 (978-1-878847-01-0(5)) Make Me A Story Pr.

—Earl the Squirrel. Spicer, Bridgett, illus. l.t. ed. 2005. (Adventures of Earl the Squirrel Ser.). 32p. (J). (ps-2). 12.95 (978-1-878847-00-3(7)) Make Me A Story Pr.

Scheunemann, Pam. Ch: See It Say It Hear It. l.t. ed. 2000. (Blends Ser.). (Illus.). 24p. (J). (ps-3). lib. bdg. 19.93 (978-1-57765-409-4(9) , SandCastle) ABDO Publishing Co.

—Cities. l.t. ed. 2001. (Capital Letters Ser.). (Illus.). 24p. (J). (ps-3). lib. bdg. 19.93 (978-1-57765-610-4(5) , SandCastle) ABDO Publishing Co.

—Days. l.t. ed. 2001. (Capital Letters Ser.). (Illus.). 24p. (J). (ps-3). lib. bdg. 19.93 (978-1-57765-611-1(3) , SandCastle) ABDO Publishing Co.

—Flour Does Not Flower. l.t. ed. 2002. (Homophones Ser.). (Illus.). 24p. (J). (ps-3). lib. bdg. 19.93 (978-1-57765-742-2(X) , SandCastle) ABDO Publishing Co.

—Fred Read the Red Book. l.t. ed. 2002. (Homophones Ser.). (Illus.). 24p. (J). (ps-3). lib. bdg. 19.93 (978-1-57765-745-3(4) , SandCastle) ABDO Publishing Co.

—Harry Is Not Hairy. l.t. ed. 2002. (Homophones Ser.). (Illus.). 24p. (J). (ps-3). lib. bdg. 19.93 (978-1-57765-743-9(8) , SandCastle) ABDO Publishing Co.

—Homophones, Set I. l.t. ed. Incl. Flour Does Not Flower. lib. bdg. 19.93 (978-1-57765-742-2(X)); Fred Read the Red Book. lib. bdg. 19.93 (978-1-57765-745-3(4)); Harry Is Not Hairy. lib. bdg. 19.93 (978-1-57765-743-9(8)); Moose Is in the Mousse. lib. bdg. 19.93 (978-1-57765-746-0(2)); Sam Has a Sundae on Sunday. lib. bdg. 19.93 (978-1-57765-744-6(6)); Two Kids Got to Go Too. lib. bdg. 19.93 (978-1-57765-747-7(0)); 24p. (J). (ps-3). (Illus.). 2002. Set lib. bdg. 119.58 (978-1-57765-518-3(4) , SandCastle) ABDO Publishing Co.

—The Moose Is in the Mousse. l.t. ed. 2002. (Homophones Ser.). (Illus.). 24p. (J). (ps-3). lib. bdg. 19.93 (978-1-57765-746-0(2) , SandCastle) ABDO Publishing Co.

—Names. l.t. ed. 2001. (Capital Letters Ser.). (Illus.). 24p. (J). (ps-3). lib. bdg. 19.93 (978-1-57765-608-1(3) , SandCastle) ABDO Publishing Co.

—Places. l.t. ed. 2001. (Capital Letters Ser.). (Illus.). 24p. (J). (ps-3). lib. bdg. 19.93 (978-1-57765-609-8(1) , SandCastle) ABDO Publishing Co.

—Sam Has a Sundae on Sunday. l.t. ed. 2002. (Homophones Ser.). (Illus.). 24p. (J). (ps-3). lib. bdg. 19.93 (978-1-57765-744-6(6) , SandCastle) ABDO Publishing Co.

—St: See It Say It Hear It. l.t. ed. 2000. (Blends Ser.). (Illus.). 24p. (J). (ps-3). lib. bdg. 19.93 (978-1-57765-407-0(2) , SandCastle) ABDO Publishing Co.

—States. l.t. ed. 2001. (Capital Letters Ser.). (Illus.). 24p. (J). (ps-3). lib. bdg. 19.93 (978-1-57765-613-5(X) , SandCastle) ABDO Publishing Co.

—Th: See It Say It Hear It. l.t. ed. 2000. (Blends Ser.). (Illus.). 24p. (J). (ps-3). lib. bdg. 19.93 (978-1-57765-408-7(0) , SandCastle) ABDO Publishing Co.

—Two Kids Got to Go Too. l.t. ed. 2002. (Homophones Ser.). (Illus.). 24p. (J). (ps-3). lib. bdg. 19.93 (978-1-57765-747-7(0) , SandCastle) ABDO Publishing Co.

Schirado, William C. Creatures, Vol. 1. Assenzo, Teresa M., illus. 18th l.t. ed. 1998. 128p. (J). (gr. k-6). 21.95 (978-0-9660166-1-1(0)) TW Publishing.

—Creatures Journey Through Life. l.t. ed. 2002. (Illus.). v, 27p. (J). (978-0-9660166-2-8(9)) TW Publishing.

Schlabach, Mary. Noah's Ark. l.t. ed. 2002. (Illus.). 24p. (J). 4.95 (978-0-9667622-0-4(7)) Schlabach Printers.

Schlessinger, Laura. Where's God? McFeeley, Daniel, illus. l.t. ed. 2003. 40p. (J). (ps-2). 16.99 (978-0-06-051909-4(6)) HarperCollins Pubs.

Schlusberg, Julian S. Who Paints the Sky? Berger, Ethel, illus. l.t. ed. 2002. 40p. (J). (ps-6). pap. (978-0-9720243-0-3(1)) Clover Pubns.

Schmidt, Sheila & Markham, Blake, illus. I Cried Too: Grief Recovery Book for Children. l.t. ed. 2001. 35p. lib. bdg. 12.99 (978-0-9716689-1-1(4)) Golden Faith Pubng.

Schneider, Stephen A. Color My Chess World. l.t. ed. 2004. (Illus.). 48p. (J). act. bk. ed. 19.50 incl. audio compact disk (978-0-9729456-9-1(5)) Championship Chess.

Schuepbach, Lynnette. Froggy Hollow. Schuepbach, Lynnette, illus. l.t. ed. 2004. (Illus.). 32p. (J). 7.00 net. (978-0-9759613-0-8(6)) Creative Sources.

—Shhhh!!! Schuepbach, Lynnette, illus. l.t. ed. 2004. (Illus.). 32p. (J). 7.00 net. (978-0-9759613-1-5(4)) Creative Sources.

Schumacher, Stef. Amazing Blue Animals, Vol. 2. l.t. ed. 2005. (Little Books & Big Bks.: Vol. 9). (Illus.). 8p. (YA). (ps-3). 22.50 (978-0-8215-7518-5(X)) Sadlier, William H. Inc.

Schwiebert, Pat & DeKlyen, Chuck. Tear Soup: A Recipe for Healing after Loss. Bills, Taylor, illus. 2nd rev. l.t. ed. 2004. 56p. reprint ed. 19.95 (978-0-9615197-6-6(2) , 798) Perinatal Loss.

Scogginsbauld, Jane. Texas in Bloom: A Wildflower Guide for Children. Waldrup, Gayle, photos by. l.t. ed. 1999. (Illus.). 24p. (J). (ps-3). pap. 14.95 (978-1-929701-00-1(4)) Under the Green Umbrella.

Scott, Kathleen. We are All Special... Babies are Very Special! l.t. ed. 2002. (Illus.). 40p. (J). 5.00 (978-0-9749177-4-0(5)) A New Day...A New Way!.

Scott, Susan Carlson. Fip's Magical World of Color, Vol. 14. Scott, Susan Carlson, illus. l.t. ed. 2002. (Illus.). 64p. (J). 15.95 (978-1-887932-94-3(1) , New Concord Pr.) Equine Graphics Publishing Group.

Scrapbook of Virtues Vol. 1: Building Character Through Virtues. l.t. ed. 2001. (Illus.). 82p. (J). 21.95 (978-0-9740504-0-9(7)) Virtuous Conquerors.

Seagreaves, Kelly E. The Best Pet. Zoller, Jayson D., illus. l.t. ed. 2004. 29p. (J). per. 8.99 (978-1-932338-53-9(5)) Lifevest Publishing, Inc.

Senn, J. A. & Skinner, Carol Ann. BK English: Communication Skills in the New Millennium. 2001. 1213p. (J). (gr. 6). stu. ed. (978-1-58079-107-6(7)); 648p. (gr. 7). tchr. ed. (978-1-58079-115-1(8)); 648p. (gr. 10). tchr. ed. (978-1-58079-118-2(2)); 648p. (gr. 11). tchr. ed. (978-1-58079-119-9(0)); 648p. (gr. 12). stu. ed. (978-1-58079-120-5(4)); 648p. (gr. 6). tchr. ed. (978-1-58079-114-4(X)); 648p. (gr. 8). tchr. ed. (978-1-58079-116-8(6)); 648p. (gr. 9). tchr. ed. (978-1-58079-117-5(4)); 1408p. (YA). (gr. 10). stu. ed. (978-1-58079-111-3(5)); 1472p. (YA). (gr. 11). stu. ed. (978-1-58079-112-0(3)); 1504p. (YA). (gr. 12). stu. ed. (978-1-58079-113-7(1)); 1336p. (YA). (gr. 7). stu. ed. (978-1-58079-108-3(5)); 1335p. (YA). (gr. 8). stu. ed. (978-1-58079-109-0(3)); 1471p. (YA). (gr. 9). stu. ed. (978-1-58079-110-6(7)) Barrett Kendall Publishing, Ltd.

Seuss, Dr. The Cat in the Hat. Seuss, Dr., illus. l.t. ed. 2007. (I Can Read It All by Myself). (Illus.). 72p. (J). (gr. k-3). 8.99 (978-0-394-80001-1(X) , Random Hse. Bks. for Young Readers) Random Hse. Children's Bks.

Sevaly, Karen & Sevaly, Richard. Word Wall Workbook - Contractions & Compound Words! Skill Based Worksheets & Reproducible Word Cards for Each Group of Words! Sevaly, Karen, illus. l.t. ed. 1999. (Illus.). 80p. (J). (gr. 1-3). pap., wbk. ed. 9.95 (978-1-57882-029-0(4) , TF-2431) Teacher's Friend Pubns., Inc.

Severs, Vesta-Nadine. Oswald Avery & the Story of DNA. l.t. ed. 2002. (Unlocking the Secrets of Science Ser.). (Illus.). 56p. (gr. 4-10). lib. bdg. 25.70 (978-1-58415-110-4(2)) Mitchell Lane Pubs., Inc.

Sewell, Anna. Black Beauty. Stemach, Jerry, ed. Ham, Jeff, illus. l.t. ed. (J). 2002. 150.00 (978-1-58702-023-0(8)); 2000. 50.00 (978-1-58702-508-2(6)) Johnston, Don Inc.

—Black Beauty. l.t. ed. 1999. (Large Print Heritage Ser.). 260p. (YA). (gr. 7-12). lib. bdg. 29.95 (978-1-58118-042-8(X) , 22511) LRS.

—Black Beauty, 2 vols., Set. l.t. ed. (YA). (gr. 8 up). reprint ed. 10.00 (978-0-89064-017-3(3)) National Assn. for Visually Handicapped.

—Black Beauty. l.t. ed. 2004. (Large Print Ser.). 268p. 25.00 (978-1-58287-619-1(3)) North Bks.

—Black Beauty. l.t. ed. 2001. 240p. (J). 28.95 (978-0-7838-9522-2(4)) Thorndike Pr.

Shaffert, Charles. Googus, the Toothless Alligator. Stringer, Margaret, illus. l.t. ed. 2003. 30p. (J). per. 7.95 (978-1-932338-27-0(6)) Lifevest Publishing, Inc.

Shams, K. The Pigle. Spears, Ashley E., illus. l.t. ed. 2004. 20p. (J). 9.99 (978-0-9728872-9-8(6)) Trent's Prints.

Shan, Darren, pseud. The Vampire's Assistant. l.t. ed. 2002. (Cirque du Freak: Bk. 2). 240p. (J). 24.95 (978-0-7862-3734-0(1)) Thomson Gale.

Shankman, Ed. I Went to the Party in Kalamazoo. Frank, Dave, illus. l.t. ed. 2002. 36p. per. 14.95 (978-0-615-12092-8(X)) KidStreet LLC.

Shapiro, Marc. J. K. Rowling: The Wizard Behind Harry Potter. l.t. ed. 2001. (J). (gr. 8-12). 23.95 (978-0-7862-3225-3(0)) Thorndike Pr.

Shaw, Mary. Brady Brady & the Puck on the Pond, 11 vols. Temple, Chuck, illus. l.t. ed. 2005. 32p. (J). per. (978-1-897169-07-0(8)) Brady Brady, Inc.

Sheehan, Irene. Mandy the Mama Mallard. Sheehan, Irene, illus. l.t. ed. 2002. (Illus.). 24p. (J). 7.95 (978-0-9711768-0-5(9)) Red Reef Publishing, Inc.

Shemin, Craig. Families Are Forever. McCoy, John, illus. l.t. ed. 2003. 34p. 9.95 (978-0-9728666-0-6(4) , 1) As Simple As That Publishing.

Shoup, Andrew J. Toko of Coco Oko. Shoup, Andrew J., illus. l.t. ed. 2002. (Illus.). 32p. (J). 16.95 (978-0-9720436-0-1(8) , SAN: 254-573X) TokoBooks.

Shusterman, Neal. Downsiders. l.t. ed. 2000. 336p. (YA). (gr. 6-12). lib. bdg. 29.95 (978-1-58118-071-8(3)) LRS.

—Full Tilt. l.t. ed. 2003. 243p. (J). 22.95 (978-0-7862-5886-4(1)) Thorndike Pr.

Sidle, Christian. Murphy Dog at the Circus. Lynn, Dianne, illus. l.t. ed. 2001. 80p. (J). (ps-3). per. 12.50 (978-0-9708053-6-2(5)) Authors & Artists Publishers of New York, Inc.

—Murphy Dog Bedtime Story. Lynn, Dianne, illus. l.t. ed. 2001. 48p. (J). (ps-3). per. 12.50 (978-0-9708053-3-1(0)) Authors & Artists Publishers of New York, Inc.

Silver, Karren L. Chi Chi in Cyberspace: The E-mailing Chihuahuas - Chichi@mcn.org. Phillips, Marc, illus. Isadore Press Staff, photos by. l.t. ed. 1999. (Growing up with Chihuahua Puppies Ser.: Vol. 1). 30p. (J). (gr. k-2). pap. 10.00 (978-0-9602600-3-4(X)) Isadore Pr.

Simon, Francesca. Horrid Henry Gets Rich Quick. Ross, Tony, illus. l.t. ed. 2002. (J). 16.95 (978-0-7540-7829-6(9) , Galaxy Children's Large Print) BBC Audiobooks America.

Simon, Gabriel. Og & His Frogs. Finch, Dianne, illus. l.t. ed. 1998. 32p. (J). (ps-3). lib. bdg. 12.95 (978-0-935343-72-4(5)) Peartree.

Simpson, Matt, creator. Happy Heart: English Book 1. l.t. ed. 2003. (Illus.). 44p. (J). per. (978-0-9727660-0-5(6)) Bks. by Matt.

Simundson-Olson, Marilyn. Kids Go-Rhyme. Tschudi, Dolores H., illus. l.t. ed. 2000. (Rhyme Time Ser.). (SPA.). 60p. (J). (gr. k-12). 23.95 incl. audio (978-1-888228-42-7(3)) Global Rhyme Time, Inc.

Sinclair, Carl R. The Way of the Eagle. 3rd l.t. rev. ed. 1998. Orig. Title: Elvis A. Eagle: A Magical Adventure. (Illus.). 220p. reprint ed. 17.95 (978-1-882833-01-6(5)) Scribe Pr.

Singer, Isaac Bashevis. Short Friday & Other Stories. l.t. ed. (YA). (gr. 10-12). reprint ed. 10.00 (978-0-89064-057-9(2)) National Assn. for Visually Handicapped.

Singleton, Linda Joy. Regeneration: The Search. l.t. ed. 2002. 240p. (J). 23.95 (978-0-7862-3868-2(2)) Thorndike Pr.

—Regeneration: The Truth. l.t. ed. 2002. 266p. (YA). 23.95 (978-0-7862-3869-9(0)) Thorndike Pr.

Sinke, Janet. Grandma's Christmas Tree. l.t. ed. 2004. (Illus.). 48p. (J). (978-0-9742732-1-1(X)) My Grandma & Me Pubs.

—Grandma's Treasure Chest. l.t. ed. 2005. (Illus.). 32p. (J). 16.95 (978-0-9742732-3-5(6)) My Grandma & Me Pubs.

Sitare Ltd. Staff. The Save Your Hair Wiz. MacLean, Alistair, ed. Milton, illus. l.t. ed. 2000. 100p. (YA). 10.00 (978-0-940178-66-3(4)) Sitare, Ltd.

Slamp, Kathy. Little House in the Arctic: An Adventure Story. l.t. ed. 2004. Orig. Title: Our Little House in the Arctic. (Illus.). 228p. pap. 17.95 (978-0-9713345-3-3(6)) Vessel Ministries.

Slim, Lillian. Casrar-am Neqai. Sparck, Carole C., illus. l.t. ed. 1999. Tr. of Mouse Food. (ESK.). 12p. (J). (gr. k-3). pap. 17.00 (978-1-58084-109-2(0)) Lower Kuskokwim Schl. District.

—Mouse Food. Sparck, Carole C., illus. l.t. ed. 1999. 12p. (J). (gr. k-3). pap. 17.00 (978-1-58084-068-2(X)) Lower Kuskokwim Schl. District.

—Uugnaraam Neqkai. Sparck, Carole C., illus. l.t. ed. 1999. Tr. of Mouse Food. (ESK.). 12p. (J). (gr. k-3). pap. 17.00 (978-1-58084-069-9(8)) Lower Kuskokwim Schl. District.

—Uuqnaraam Negkia. Sparck, Carole C., illus. l.t. ed. 1999. Tr. of Mouse Food. (ESK.). 12p. (J). (gr. k-3). pap. 17.00 (978-1-58084-122-1(8)) Lower Kuskokwim Schl. District.

—Uuqnaraam Negkia (Mouse Food) Sparck, Carole C., illus. l.t. ed. 1999. (ESK.). 12p. (J). (gr. k-3). pap. 17.00 (978-1-58084-129-0(5)); pap. 17.00 (978-1-58084-143-6(0)) Lower Kuskokwim Schl. District.

Small, David. Eulalie & the Hopping Head. Small, David, illus. l.t. ed. 2001. (Illus.). 32p. (J). pap. 5.95 (978-0-374-42202-8(8) , Sunburst) Farrar, Straus & Giroux.

Small, Pauline & Abalama, Katherine. At the Mountains (Cupik) Shantz, Joy, illus. l.t. ed. 2000. (ESK.). 8p. (J). (gr. k-3). pap. 6.00 (978-1-58084-196-2(1)) Lower Kuskokwim Schl. District.

Small, Pauline, et al. At the Mountains. Shantz, Joy, illus. l.t. ed. 2000. 8p. (J). (gr. k-3). pap. 6.00 (978-1-58084-191-7(0)) Lower Kuskokwim Schl. District.

—Ingrini. Shantz, Joy, illus. l.t. ed. 2000. Tr. of At the Mountains. (ESK.). 8p. (J). (gr. k-3). pap. 6.00 (978-1-58084-192-4(9)) Lower Kuskokwim Schl. District.

Smith, Beth. Red Bug. Coates, Jennifer, illus. l.t. ed. 2000. (Cardboard Bks.). 12p. (J). (ps-1). pap. 10.95 (978-1-57332-169-3(9)) HighReach Learning, Inc.

Smith, Beth Esh. Mike the Mail Carrier. Coates, Jennifer, illus. l.t. ed. 1999. (LB Ser.). 8p. (J). (ps-1). pap. 10.95 (978-1-57332-157-0(5)); pap. 10.95 (978-1-57332-144-0(3)) HighReach Learning, Inc.

—Off We Go! Linke, Don, Jr., illus. l.t. ed. 1998. (Little Bks.). (J). (ps-k). 10p. pap. 10.95 (978-1-57332-110-5(9)); 8p. pap. 10.95 (978-1-57332-111-2(7)) HighReach Learning, Inc.

—Phyllis the Forest Ranger. Crowell, Knox, illus. l.t. ed. 2000. (LB Ser.). 8p. (J). (ps-1). pap. 10.95 (978-1-57332-164-8(8)); pap. 10.95 (978-1-57332-163-1(X)) HighReach Learning, Inc.

Smith, Dianne M. Cyanne Rose & Sherbet Are Best Friends. l.t. ed. 2004. 22p. (YA). per. (978-1-59196-678-4(7)) Instantpublisher.com.

—Happy Birthday to You! l.t. ed. 2004. 24p. per. (978-1-59196-679-1(5)) Instantpublisher.com.

—I Don't Want To! l.t. ed. 2004. (YA). per. (978-1-59196-683-8(3)) Instantpublisher.com.

Smith, S. A. Saint Herman of Alaska. Smith, S. A., illus. l.t. ed. 2002. (Illus.). 32p. (J). per. 6.95 (978-0-9678400-1-7(5)) Christ the Saviour Brotherhood Publishing.

Smith, Sherri L. Lucy the Giant. l.t. ed. 2002. 236p. 23.95 (978-0-7862-4751-6(7)) Thorndike Pr.

Snicket, Lemony, pseud. The Bad Beginning. Helquist, Brett, illus. l.t. ed. 2002. (Series of Unfortunate Events Ser.: Bk. 1). 168p. (J). 16.95 (978-0-7540-7812-8(4) , Galaxy Children's Large Print) BBC Audiobooks America.

—The Reptile Room. Helquist, Brett, illus. l.t. ed. 2002. (Series of Unfortunate Events Ser.: Bk. 2). 184p. (J). pap. 16.95 (978-0-7540-7823-4(X) , Galaxy Children's Large Print) BBC Audiobooks America.

So You Want to Dig Dinosaurs: A Field Manual on the Practice, Principles & Politics of Vertebrate Paleontology. l.t. ed. 2001. 280p. (YA). 59.99 (978-0-9716206-0-5(1)) Dragons Claw Pr.

Solar, Kay. Where Do Babies Come From? Holden, Chanler, illus. Brignac, Candy, photos by. l.t. ed. 1998. 22p. (J). (ps-3). bds. 15.95 (978-0-9666945-0-5(3)) Solar, Kay.

Solice, Deborah. The Eye of the Undead: The Hidden Channel: an Adventure Series in Time. l.t. ed. 2005. (ENG., Illus.). 100p. (J). per. 7.59 (978-1-933300-01-6(9)) Wandering Sage Bookstore & More, LLC.

Sonday, Arlene. The Sonday System - Let's Play Learn: Alphabet Book. Breckman, Cindy, ed. l.t. ed. 2004. (Illus.). 53p. (J). per. (978-1-891602-11-5(X)) Winsor Learning, Inc.

Sonnenblick, Jordan. Drums, Girls & Dangerous Pie. l.t. ed. 2005. 314p. (YA). 21.95 (978-0-7862-8038-4(7)) Thorndike Pr.

Spalding, Robert, Jr. The Kingdom of Fu Fu. Lyle, Chris, illus. l.t. ed. 2001. 32p. (J). (ps-4). 15.95 (978-0-9711068-0-2(0) , FU001) Chattanooga FuFu Factory.

Spellman, Rhonda J., as told by. When I Was a Little Boy, by Jesus: Written for Children, Illustrated by Children: Experience the Life Jesus Lived When Jesus Was a Little Boy. l.t. ed. 2003. (Illus.). 32p. (J). per. 19.95 (978-0-9741009-0-6(0)) Bound By Faith Publishing.

Sperry, Armstrong. Call It Courage. Sperry, Armstrong, illus. l.t. ed. 2000. (LRS Large Print Cornerstone Ser.).Tr. of Newbery Summer. (Illus.). 114p. (YA). (gr. 5-12). lib. bdg. 24.95 (978-1-58118-063-3(2) , 23477) LRS.

Spietz, Heidi A. Natalie's New Home. Henderson, Frances, ed. l.t. ed. 1998. (Illus.). 27p. (J). (gr. 1-2). pap. 5.00 (978-0-929487-12-0(5)) American Montessori Consulting.

Spinelle, Nancy Louise. Moose's Loose Tooth. Gedeon, Gloria, illus. l.t. ed. 2001. 16p. (J). (gr. k-1). pap. 4.95 (978-1-57874-032-1(0) , Kaeden Bks.) Kaeden Corp.

—What's Missing. Campbell, Jenny, illus. l.t. ed. 2001. 16p. (J). (gr. k-1). pap. 4.95 (978-1-57874-013-0(4)) Kaeden Corp.

Spinelli, Jerry. Knots in My Yo-Yo String: The Autobiography of a Kid. l.t. ed. 2000. (Illus.). 187p. (J). (gr. 8-12). 21.95 (978-0-7862-2973-4(X)) Thorndike Pr.

—Stargirl. l.t. ed. 2001. 240p. (J). (gr. 8-12). 24.95 (978-0-7862-3218-5(8)) Thorndike Pr.

—Wringer. 1999. 15p. (J). pap., tchr.'s training gde. ed. 15.95 (978-1-58303-099-8(9)) Pathways Publishing.

—Wringer. l.t. ed. 2000. (Juvenile Ser.). 223p. (J). (gr. 4-7). 21.95 (978-0-7862-2774-7(5)) Thorndike Pr.

Spongberg, Emily. Hannibal & the King. Spongberg, Tim, illus. l.t. ed. 1999. 32p. (J). (gr. k-4). 15.95 (978-1-893659-00-1(3)) Rainbow Hse. Publishing.

Sportelli-Rehak, Angela. Moving Again Mom! Hinlicky, Gregg, illus. 2004. (Uncle Sam's Kids Ser.: Bk. 2). 40p. (J). (ps-7). pap. 7.95 (978-0-9714515-0-6(8)) Abidenme Bks.

Sprecher, John. Eric & the Angrrry Frog, Vol. 2. Forrest, James, illus. l.t. ed. Date not set. (Special Kids "Special Message" Book Ser.). 32p. (J). (gr. k-4). pap. 10.00 (978-1-892186-01-0(2)) Anythings Possible, Inc.

—Tori & Cassandra & the Pelican in Peril. Forrest, James, illus. l.t. ed. Date not set. (Special Kids "Special Message" Book Ser.: Vol. 3). 32p. (J). (gr. k-4). pap. 10.00 (978-1-892186-02-7(0)) Anythings Possible, Inc.

—Zoe & the Very Unmerry Bear. Forrest, James, illus. l.t. ed. Date not set. (Special Kids "Special Message" Book Ser.). 32p. (J). (gr. k-4). pap. 10.00 (978-1-892186-03-4(9) , SKPB4) Anythings Possible, Inc.

Spyri, Johanna. Heidi. l.t. ed. 2004. (Large Print Ser.). 433p. 26.00 (978-1-58287-666-5(5)) North Bks.

Squint Free Holy Bible for Kids. l.t. ed. 2000. (J). 1952p. (gr. 4-7). lthr. 17.99 (978-0-7852-5676-2(8)); 1728p. (gr. 8-12). lthr. 17.99 (978-0-7852-5674-8(1)) Nelson, Thomas Inc.

Squires, Mary L. Margaret Who Dared to Dream. l.t. ed. 2003. (Illus.). 45p. 12.95 (978-0-9631547-3-6(7)) Popular Truth, Inc.

Staffier, Jane Sarah. Casey & the Boston Freedom Trail. Staffier, Jane Sarah, illus. l.t. ed. 1999. (Beacon Hill Ser.: No. 2). (Illus.). 28p. (J). (gr. k-7). spiral bd. 9.95 (978-1-928895-01-5(8)) B.A.B., Ltd.

—Casey the Beacon Hill Cat Coloring Book Adventures, 4 vols., Set. Staffier, Jane Sarah, illus. l.t. ed. 2001. 130p. (J). (ps-7). pap. 32.95 (978-1-928895-04-6(2)) B.A.B., Ltd.

—Casey's Day at the Beach. Staffier, Jane Sarah, illus. l.t. ed. 1999. (Casey the Beacon Hill Cat Ser.). (Illus.). 28p. (gr. k-5). spiral bd. 9.95 (978-1-928895-00-8(X)) B.A.B., Ltd.

—Casey's History of the World: Or "Roots" Casey. l.t. ed. 1999. (Casey the Beacon Hill Cat Ser.: Vol. 4). 32p. (J). (gr. k-5). spiral bd. 9.95 (978-1-928895-03-9(4)) B.A.B., Ltd.

Staheli, Bee, ed. The Owl Who Couldn't Say Whoo. Clish, Lori, illus. l.t. ed. (J). (gr. k-5). pap. 7.95 (978-1-928632-50-4(5)) Writers Marketplace:Consulting, Critiquing & Publishing.

Staples, Suzanne Fisher. The Green Dog: A Mostly True Story. l.t. ed. 2004. 140p. (J). 21.95 (978-0-7862-6577-0(9)) Thorndike Pr.

StarKidz: I Am Who I Am. l.t. ed. 2003. (Illus.). 28p. (J). 16.95 (978-0-9743964-1-5(9)) World of Angels, A.

Steele, Alexander. Case of the Breaking Story. l.t. ed. 2000. (Wishbone Mysteries Ser.: No. 20). (Illus.). 144p. (J). (gr. 4 up). lib. bdg. 23.33 (978-0-8368-2703-3(1)) Stevens, Gareth Inc.

—Case of the On-Line Alien. l.t. ed. 1999. (Wishbone Mysteries Ser.: No. 9). 144p. (J). (gr. 4 up). lib. bdg. 23.33 (978-0-8368-2449-0(0)) Stevens, Gareth Inc.

—Moby Dog. l.t. ed. 1999. (Adventures of Wishbone Ser.: No. 10). (Illus.). 144p. (J). (gr. 4 up). lib. bdg. 22.60 (978-0-8368-2306-6(0)) Stevens, Gareth Inc.

—Tale of the Missing Mascot. l.t. ed. 1999. (Wishbone Mysteries Ser.: No. 4). 144p. (J). (gr. 4 up). lib. bdg. 23.33 (978-0-8368-2385-1(0)) Stevens, Gareth Inc.

Steele, D. Kelley. Fire in Her Hair: A Story of Friendship. James, Margaret Ray, illus. l.t. ed. 2002. 40p. (J). (gr. 1-6). 18.95 (978-0-9711534-0-0(X)) Hidden Path Pubn., Inc.

Steele, James M. Sadie Listens: An Inward Journey. l.t. ed. 2003. (Inward Journey Ser.: Vol. 1). (Illus.). iv, 48p. 17.95 (978-0-9716811-3-2(9)) Steele Studios.

Steele, Michael Anthony. Case of the Impounded Hounds. l.t. ed. 2000. (Wishbone Mysteries Ser.: No. 17). 138p. (J). (gr. 4 up). lib. bdg. 23.33 (978-0-8368-2700-2(7)) Stevens, Gareth Inc.

—Digging to the Center of the Earth. Punchatz, Don, illus. l.t. ed. 1999. (Adventures of Wishbone Ser.: No. 17). (J). (gr. 4 up). lib. bdg. 22.60 (978-0-8368-2595-4(0)) Stevens, Gareth Inc.

Steinbeck, John, et al. Of Mice & Men. 1999. (Literature Made Easy Ser.). (Illus.). 96p. pap. 6.99 (978-0-7641-0820-4(4)) Barron's Educational Series, Inc.

Stemach, Jerry. The Night of the Loch Ness Monster. Venable, Gail Portnuff, ed. Ham, Jeff, illus. l.t. ed. 2000. 124p. 50.00 (978-1-58702-457-3(8)); 65.00 incl. audio, cd-rom (978-1-893376-78-6(8)) Johnston, Don Inc.

Stephenson, Nancy. The Three Little Kittens. Faris, Eva, illus. l.t. ed. 2003. 30p. (J). per. 7.99 (978-1-932338-13-3(6)) Lifevest Publishing, Inc.

Stewart, Paul & Riddell, Chris. Blobheads. 2005. (Read-along Ser.). (Illus.). (J). audio (978-0-7540-6285-1(6)) BBC Audio.

Stien, Howard M. Stump House Stories. Hogue, Christina, illus. l.t. ed. 2000. 36p. (J). (ps-3). per. 10.00 (978-0-9707334-0-5(2)) Stump Hse. Bks.

Stimson, Judith A. Animal & Photography Adventures. Stimson, Judith A., photos by. 1999. (Illus.). 115p. (J). (gr. 3-5). wbk. ed. 25.00 (978-0-9669879-0-4(X)) ABConsulting.

Stokes, Anthony, ed. Voices on Violence: The Lives of Children in Their Own Words. l.t. ed. 2002. (Illus.). 80p. 10.00 (978-0-9724803-0-7(7)) Orange Boy Bks.

Stokes, N. L. Mystery of the Missing Teacup. l.t. ed. 2003. (Illus.). 48p. per. 19.95 (978-0-9729411-1-2(8)) Stylewriter Pubns.

Storie Tree Inc, Staff. A Pocket Pearl of Light: Twinkle & Shinmet Come Home. l.t. ed. 2003. (Illus.). 27p. pap. 6.00 (978-0-9679014-9-7(9)) Storie Tree, Inc., The.

J K L

Stormer, Kate. Casey's Unexpected Friend. Lowes, Tom, illus. l.t. ed. 2003. 38p. (J). 16.95 (978-0-9722099-7-7(2) , CUF) Caseys World Bks.

Stoutland, Allison. Take a Deep Breath: Little Lessons from Flowers for a Happier World. Hofher, Cathy, illus. l.t. ed. 2003. 32p. 14.95 (978-0-9670941-2-0(7)) Inch By Inch Pubns., LLC.

Strauss, Jess. The Adventures of Little Willie & Little Wilma: Stories to Be Read to Young Children with Love. l.t. ed. 2002. 171p. (J). per. 12.95 (978-1-931934-05-3(3)) Back Yard Pub.

Strelchun, Rory T. Writings & Stories by RTS: A Collection of Writings & Stories. l.t. ed. 2002. (YA). (gr. 6-8). mass mkt. 11.88 (978-0-9671942-3-3(7)) Top Tek Corp.

Strickland, Brad. Be a Wolf! l.t. ed. 1999. (Adventures of Wishbone Ser.: No. 1). (Illus.). 144p. (J). (gr. 4 up). lib. bdg. 22.60 (978-0-8368-2297-7(8)) Stevens, Gareth Inc.

—Salty Dog. l.t. ed. 1999. (Adventures of Wishbone Ser.: No. 2). (Illus.). 140p. (J). (gr. 4 up). lib. bdg. 22.60 (978-0-8368-2298-4(6)) Stevens, Gareth Inc.

Strickland, Brad & Fuller, Thomas E. The Disappearing Dinosaurs. l.t. ed. 1999. (Wishbone Mysteries Ser.: No. 10). 144p. (J). (gr. 4 up). lib. bdg. 23.33 (978-0-8368-2450-6(4)) Stevens, Gareth Inc.

—The Riddle of the Wayward Books. l.t. ed. 1999. (Wishbone Mysteries Ser.: No. 3). 144p. (J). (gr. 4 up). lib. bdg. 23.33 (978-0-8368-2384-4(2)) Stevens, Gareth Inc.

—The Treasure of Skeleton Reef. l.t. ed. 1999. (Wishbone Mysteries Ser.: No. 1). 144p. (J). (gr. 4 up). lib. bdg. 23.33 (978-0-8368-2382-0(6)) Stevens, Gareth Inc.

Strickland, Brad & Strickland, Barbara. Gullifur's Travels. l.t. ed. 1999. (Adventures of Wishbone Ser.: No. 18). (Illus.). (J). (gr. 4 up). lib. bdg. 22.60 (978-0-8368-2596-1(9)) Stevens, Gareth Inc.

Strickland, Brad, et al. Drive-In of Doom. l.t. ed. 1999. (Wishbone Mysteries Ser.: No. 7). 144p. (J). (gr. 4 up). lib. bdg. 23.33 (978-0-8368-2388-2(5)) Stevens, Gareth Inc.

Strong, Frances Dinkins. A Lucky Pair. Roscoe, Mattie Dinkins, illus. l.t. ed. 2002. 28p. pap. 6.49 (978-0-9720267-0-3(3)) Learning Abilities Bks.

Strong, Jeremy. Dinosaur Pox. l.t. ed. 2000. (Illus.). 112p. (J). pap. (978-0-7540-6122-9(1) , CLP 317) BBC Audio.

—I'm Telling You, They're Aliens! Sharratt, Nick, illus. l.t. ed. 2005. 144p. (J). pap. (978-0-7540-6150-2(7) , CLP 343) BBC Audio.

—Karate Princess in Monsta Trouble. Sharratt, Nick, illus. l.t. ed. 2005. 112p. (J). pap. (978-0-7540-6183-0(3) , CLP 375) BBC Audio.

—Krazy Kow Saves the World - Well, Almost. l.t. ed. 2003. (Illus.). 152p. (J). 16.95 (978-0-7540-7841-8(8) , Galaxy Children's Large Print) BBC Audiobooks America.

—My Mum's Going to Explode! Clifford, Rowan, illus. l.t. ed. 2005. 80p. (J). pap. (978-0-7540-7824-1(8) , CLP 414) BBC Audio.

—Pandemonium at School. l.t. ed. 2005. (Illus.). 104p. (J). pap. incl. audio (978-0-7540-7862-3(0) , CLP 448) BBC Audio.

—Pandemonium at School. 2004. (J). pap. 24.95 incl. audio (978-0-7540-6272-1(4) , Chivers Children's Audio Bks.) BBC Audiobooks America.

—Pirate Pandemonium. Sharratt, Nick, illus. l.t. ed. 2005. 152p. (J). pap. (978-0-7540-7807-4(8) , CLP 398) BBC Audio.

—Viking at School. Levers, John, illus. l.t. ed. 2000. 96p. (J). pap. (978-0-7540-6093-2(4) , CLP 291) BBC Audio.

Stuart, Matt. Who Can Run Fast? l.t. ed. 2005. (Little Books & Big Bks.: Vol. 1). (Illus.). 8p. (YA). (ps-3). 22.50 (978-0-8215-7510-9(4)) Sadlier, William H. Inc.

Stuck in the MUD. l.t. ed. 2004. (Illus.). 20p. (J). cd-rom 19.95 (978-0-9759370-0-6(6)) Brown&Matthews.

Students of Academy of Mastery and Excellence Staff. Phonics, 20 vols. 2000. 10p. (J). pap., wbk. ed. (978-0-9669902-1-8(8)) MassAward Publishing, Inc.

Su Chen Fang & Gui Fong Chang. Happy Birthday to You! l.t. ed. 1999. (Children's Stories Published in Other Lands Ser.). (Illus.). 32p. (J). (ps up). lib. bdg. 15.95 (978-1-56674-241-2(2)) Forest Hse. Publishing Co., Inc.

Sundberg, Peggy. Isabelle Lives a Dream. Wiles, Pat, illus. l.t. ed. 2003. 32p. (J). 15.95 (978-0-9721057-1-2(9)) Cowgirl Peg Enterprises LLC.

—Lonesome the Little Horse: His Mountain Adventure. l.t. ed. 2002. (Illus.). 32p. (J). 15.95 (978-0-9721057-0-5(0)) Cowgirl Peg Enterprises LLC.

Sutryn, Barbara M. Heartstrings: A Biography of Wilmos Csehy. l.t. ed. 2004. (Illus.). 160p. (YA). 21.00 (978-1-892135-33-9(7)) Lamp Post Publishing, Inc.

Sweet, Karen. The Adventures of Little AMP: The Sparrow Electric Car. Speckles, Jenny, illus. l.t. ed. 2002. 12p. (J). 8.95 (978-0-9714378-0-7(7)) Sweet Sommer Productions.

Swindells, Robert. World-Eater. l.t. ed. 2005. 200p. (J). pap. (978-0-7540-6192-2(2) , CLP 386) BBC Audio.

Szymanek, Susie. The Bumble Bee. Gedeon, Gloria, illus. l.t. ed. 2000. 16p. (J). (gr. k-2). pap. 4.95 (978-1-57874-028-4(2) , Kaeden Bks.) Kaeden Corp.

Tamaki, Donna, tr. How the Years Were Named. Kanazawa, Yuko, illus. l.t. ed. 1999. Tr. of Rainen Wa Nanidoshi. (ENG & JPN.). 12p. (J). (ps-12). 35.00 (978-1-893533-10-3(7) , 9) Kamishibai for Kids.

—Momotaro, the Peach Boy. Futamata, Eigoro, illus. l.t. ed. 1998. Tr. of Momotaro. (ENG & JPN.). 16p. (J). (ps-12). 35.00 (978-1-893533-08-0(5) , 1) Kamishibai for Kids.

—The Monkey & the Crab. Nishimaki, Kayako, illus. l.t. ed. 1998. Tr. of Saru to Kani. (ENG & JPN.). 16p. (J). (ps-12). 35.00 (978-1-893533-12-7(3) , 15) Kamishibai for Kids.

—The Old Man & the Mice. Kubo, Masao, illus. l.t. ed. 1999. Tr. of Nezumi Choja. (ENG & JPN.). 12p. (J). (ps-2). 35.00 (978-1-893533-13-4(1) , 19) Kamishibai for Kids.

Tan, Amy H. My Mommy's an Angel! Tan, Mariam, illus. l.t. ed. 2002. (Angel Ser.). 20p. (J). 18.95 incl. audio compact disk (978-0-9717299-0-2(5)) JeaMei Publishing.

Tanner, Dawn Leasman. A Kitty Named Indra/Una Gata Llamada Indra. Leasman, Nancy Packard, illus. l.t. ed. 2003. (SPA & ENG.). 36p. (J). per. 6.95 (978-0-9741725-0-7(2)) Leatherwood Publishing.

Tarazona, Oscar, illus. Volando con Alas Propias. l.t. ed. 2004. (SPA.). 116p. (YA). pap. 12.00 (978-1-931481-88-5(1)) LiArt-Literature & Art.

Tarver, Monroe S. Little Light Shine Bright. Tarver, Monroe S., illus. l.t. ed. 2004. (Illus.). 32p. (J). 6.99 (978-0-9743568-4-0(5)) Tarver, Monroe.

Tarver, S., 1st. Imaga & the Magic Pearls, 2nd l.t. ed. 2003. (Illus.). 20p. (J). 6.99 (978-0-9743568-0-8(8)) Tarver, Monroe.

Tate, Suzanne. Sandy Seal: A Tale of Sea Dogs. Melvin, James, illus. l.t. ed. 2004. (Suzanne Tate's Nature Ser.). 28p. (J). pap. 4.95 (978-1-878405-49-4(7)) Nags Head Art, Inc.

Taylor, Beth. Big Book: Tina's Toys. l.t. ed. 2005. (Sadlier Phonics Reading Program). (Illus.). 8p. (YA). (ps-1). 22.50 (978-0-8215-7343-3(8)) Sadlier, William H. Inc.

Taylor, Chet. Last, but Not Least. Taylor, Chet, illus. l.t. ed. 2004. (Illus.). 20p. (J). lib. bdg. 22.99 (978-0-9755888-1-9(8)) Dragonfly Publishing, Inc.

Taylor, Mildred D. Roll of Thunder, Hear My Cry. l.t. ed. 2000. (LRS Large Print Cornerstone Ser.). 348p. (YA). (gr. 5-12). lib. bdg. 32.95 (978-1-58118-057-2(8) , 23471) LRS.

Temperley, Alan. Huntress of the Sea. l.t. ed. 2000. (Illus.). 189p. (J). pap. (978-0-7540-6097-0(7) , CLP 298) BBC Audio.

—The Magician of Samarkand. 2004. (J). pap. 29.95 incl. audio (978-0-7540-6279-0(1) , Chivers Children's Audio Bks.) BBC Audiobooks America.

Temple, Bob. Chihuahuas. l.t. ed. 2000. (Dogs Ser.). (Illus.). 24p. (J). (gr. k-6). lib. bdg. 21.35 (978-1-57765-419-3(6) , Checkerboard Library) ABDO Publishing Co.

—Dogs - Set III, 6 bks. l.t. ed. Incl. Chihuahuas. lib. bdg. 21.35 (978-1-57765-419-3(6)); Jack Russell Terriers. lib. bdg. 21.35 (978-1-57765-424-7(2)); Pugs. lib. bdg. 21.35 (978-1-57765-422-3(6)); Scottish Terriers. lib. bdg. 21.35 (978-1-57765-421-6(8)); Shih Tzus. lib. bdg. 21.35 (978-1-57765-423-0(4)); Siberian Huskies. lib. bdg. 21.35 (978-1-57765-420-9(X)); 24p. (J). (gr. k-6). 2000. (Illus.). 2000. Set lib. bdg. 128.10 (978-1-57765-291-5(6) , Checkerboard Library) ABDO Publishing Co.

—Shih Tzus. l.t. ed. 2000. (Dogs Ser.). (Illus.). 24p. (J). (gr. k-6). lib. bdg. 21.35 (978-1-57765-423-0(4) , Checkerboard Library) ABDO Publishing Co.

—Siberian Huskies. l.t. ed. 2000. (Dogs Ser.). (Illus.). 24p. (J). (gr. k-6). lib. bdg. 21.35 (978-1-57765-420-9(X) , Checkerboard Library) ABDO Publishing Co.

Tennyson, Patrick & Bickford, Nicole. Tarantula Tracks: Rosie's Wild Adventure. l.t. ed. 2004. (Illus.). 32p. (J). 2.95 (978-0-9729000-1-0(2)) Butterfly Pavilion.

Tenorio-Coscarelli, Jane. The Ants. Coscarelli, Nicole, tr. l.t. ed. 1998. Tr. of Hormigas. (SPA & ENG.). 32p. (J). (gr. k-4). pap. 11.95 (978-0-9653422-2-3(0)) Quarter-Inch Publishing.

Tenorio-Coscarelli, Jane & Coscarelli, Nicole. The Tamale Quilt. l.t. ed. 1998. (Illus.). 48p. (J). (gr. k-6). 15.95 (978-0-9653422-3-0(9)) Quarter-Inch Publishing.

Tentas, Jane Grant. Alice & the Bird Lady. Tentas, Jane Grant, illus. l.t. ed. 2002. 26p. per. 13.95 (978-0-9658983-6-2(9)) Book Nook Pr.

Terhune, Albert Payson. Lad of Sunnybank. l.t. ed. 1999. (Perennial Ser.). 287p. (gr. 4-7). 26.95 (978-0-7838-8552-0(0)) Thorndike Pr.

—The Way of a Dog. l.t. ed. 1999. (Perennial Bestsellers Ser.). 337p. (YA). (gr. 5-9). 26.95 (978-0-7838-8743-2(4)) Thorndike Pr.

Thistle, Louise. Dramatizando la Gallinita Roja: Un Cuento para Contar y Actuar. Packer, Emily, illus. l.t. ed. 2003. Tr. of Dramatizing the Little Red Hen. (SPA.). 32p. (J). (gr. k-2). pap. 10.00 (978-0-9644186-4-6(9)) Literature Dramatization Pr.

—Dramatizing the Little Red Hen. Landes, William-Alan, ed. Packer, Emily, illus. l.t. ed. 2003. 32p. (J). (gr. k-2). pap. 10.00 (978-0-9644186-5-3(7)) Literature Dramatization Pr.

Thomas, Dina M. & Thomas, Andy, eds. The Artful Journey: The Artwork of Andy Thomas. Thomas, Tria M., photos by. l.t. ed. 2003. (Illus.). 122p. 50.00 (978-0-9742285-0-1(8)) Maze Creek Studio.

Thomas, Jeana. How Louie Became a Safety Swimmer: Water Safety. Triefenbach, Lisa, illus. l.t. ed. 2002. (Camp of Champs Ser.: Vol. 2). 24p. (J). (ps-3). pap. 6.95 (978-0-9701118-4-5(3) , 050-002) Charm Pubns., Inc.

Thryce, Marc & Robinson, Tim. Look at the Pictures. l.t. ed. 2005. (Little Books & Big Bks.: Vol. 2). (Illus.). 8p. (YA). (ps-3). 22.50 (978-0-8215-7511-6(2)) Sadlier, William H. Inc.

Tichenor, Richard. Tales from the Woods of Wisdom, Bk. 1. l.t. ed. 2001. 275p. (J). per. 24.95 (978-1-888725-50-6(8) , MacroPrintBooks) Science & Humanities Pr.

Tillman, Nancy. On the Night You Were Born, 1, l.t. ed. 2005. (Illus.). 32p. (J). 17.95 (978-0-9765761-0-5(4)) Darling Pr. LLC.

Tinkler, David. The Case of the Feeble Weeble. l.t. ed. 1998. (Illus.). 117p. (J). pap. 16.95 (978-0-7540-6025-3(X) , Galaxy Children's Large Print) BBC Audiobooks America.

—The Headmaster Went Splat! l.t. ed. 2000. (Illus.). 165p. (J). pap. (978-0-7540-6107-6(8) , CLP 302) BBC Audio.

—Revenge of the Dinner Ladies. l.t. ed. 2005. (J). pap. (978-0-7540-7804-3(3) , CLP 185) BBC Audio.

Titherington, Jeanne. Citrouille, Ma Citrouille. l.t. ed. Tr. of Citrouille, Ma Citrouille. (FRE.). (J). bds. 29.99 (978-0-590-73546-9(2)) Scholastic, Inc.

—Pumpkin Pumpkin. l.t. ed. 1999. (J). pap. 19.95 (978-0-590-72452-4(5)) Scholastic, Inc.

Todd, Cynthia & Ziemann, Debbie. ABC Rappin' Zebra/ Garden Party. Johnston, Cassie, illus. l.t. ed. 1999. (Sing Me a Song Ser.). 48p. (J). (ps-3). 15.95 (978-1-879056-12-1(7)) Alpenhorn Pr.

Toews, Rita Y. The Bully: A Discussion & Activity Story. Ljungberg, Jon, illus. l.t. ed. 2004. (ENG.). 40p. (J). (978-0-9736224-0-9(7)) Birds Hill Publishing.

Toledo, Leila J. Little Peter & Sela. Davis, Chad L., illus. l.t. ed. 2004. 17p. (J). pap. 8.95 (978-0-9753118-0-6(8)) Bimini Bks.

Tolkien, J. R. R., et al. Roverandom. Scull, Christina & Hammond, Wayne G., eds. 783rd l.t. ed. 1998. (Illus.). 191p. (J). 25.95 (978-0-7838-0299-2(4)) Thorndike Pr.

Tommy Books: Fear, 10 vols. l.t. ed. 2005. (Illus.). 24p. (J). 12.99 (978-0-9762690-5-2(8)) Tommy Bks. Pubng.

Tommy Books: Forgiveness, 10 vols. l.t. ed. 2005. (Illus.). 24p. (J). 12.99 (978-0-9762690-6-9(6)) Tommy Bks. Pubng.

Tommy Books: Grace & Mercy, 10 Vols. l.t. ed. 2005. (Illus.). 24p. (J). 12.99 (978-0-9762690-8-3(2)) Tommy Bks. Pubng.

Tommy Books: Thank You, 10 vols. l.t. ed. 2005. (Illus.). 24p. (J). 12.99 (978-0-9762690-9-0(0)) Tommy Bks. Pubng.

Tommy Books: Who Am I, 10 vols. l.t. ed. 2005. (Illus.). 24p. (J). 12.99 (978-0-9762690-7-6(4)) Tommy Bks. Pubng.

Tompkins, Robyn Lee. Miss Molly's Adventure in the Park: Another Great Adventure Brought to You by Miss Molly & Her Dog Reyburn, 10 vols. Carson, Shawn K., illus. l.t. ed. 2005. (ENG.). 60p. (J). per. (978-0-9741647-6-2(3)) NRG Pubns.

Torgerson, Scotty Delray. Jacob Goes to the Moon. 2nd l.t. ed. 2005. (Illus.). 32p. (J). 10.00 (978-0-9767116-0-5(5)) Torgerson Meadows Publishing.

Torrel, Wendy. Guardian of Dreams: A Bedtime Story, Klingbeil, Kendall, illus. l.t. ed. 2004. 32p. (J). 14.95 (978-0-9746890-0-5(9)); pap. 10.95 (978-0-9746890-1-2(7)) White Tulip Publishing.

Townson, Hazel. The One-Day Millionaires. l.t. ed. 1998. (Illus.). 79p. (J). pap. 16.95 (978-0-7540-6017-8(9) , Galaxy Children's Large Print) BBC Audiobooks America.

—The Vanishing Gran. Dupasquier, Philippe, illus. l.t. ed. 1998. 72p. (J). pap. (978-0-7540-6029-1(2) , CLP 232) BBC Audio.

Tracy, Kathleen. Barbara Mcclintock: Pioneering Geneticist. l.t. ed. 2002. (Unlocking the Secrets of Science Ser.). (Illus.). 56p. (gr. 4-10). lib. bdg. 25.70 (978-1-58415-111-1(0)) Mitchell Lane Pubs., Inc.

—Mary Kate & Ashley Olsen. l.t. ed. 2002. (Real-Life Reader Biography Ser.). (Illus.). 32p. (J). (gr. 3-8). lib. bdg. 15.95 (978-1-58415-124-1(2)) Mitchell Lane Pubs., Inc.

—Willem Kolff & the Invention of the Dialysis Machine. l.t. ed. 2002. (Unlocking the Secrets of Science Ser.). (Illus.). 56p. (gr. 4-10). lib. bdg. 25.70 (978-1-58415-135-7(8)) Mitchell Lane Pubs., Inc.

—William Hewlett: Pioneer of the Computer Age. l.t. ed. 2002. (Unlocking the Secrets of Science Ser.). (Illus.). 56p. (gr. 4-10). lib. bdg. 25.70 (978-1-58415-142-5(0)) Mitchell Lane Pubs., Inc.

Trogdon, Wendell. Who Killed Hoosier Hysteria? Sport Survives amid Fading Fervor. l.t. ed. 2004. (Illus.). 168p. (YA). pap. (978-0-9724033-3-7(7)) Backroads Pr.

Trottier, Maxine. Flags. Morin, Paul, illus. l.t. ed. 1999. 27p. (ps-3). 16.95 (978-0-7737-3136-3(9)) Stoddart Kids CAN. *Dist:* Fitzhenry & Whiteside, Ltd.

Tucker, Bethanie H. Mr. Base Ten Invents Mathematics. l.t. ed. 2002. (Illus.). 205p. (J). pap. 22.00 (978-1-929229-24-6(0)) aha! Process, Inc.

Tucker, Jennifer Herrick. Little Pumpkin. l.t. ed. 2001. 65p. (J). per. 9.95 (978-0-9715198-0-0(3)) PJN & Assocs.

Tunison, Dick. Marley & the Big Stone Castle. Carrel, Dolores W., illus. l.t. ed. 2001. 40p. (J). (gr. k-5). pap. 7.95 (978-0-9707015-0-3(0)) Emmaus Pr.

Turkovitz, Karen. What's So Special about Mitchell? Ryan, Linda et al, eds. Marshall, Ian, illus. l.t. ed. 2002. 26p. (J). (gr. k-4). pap. 6.95 (978-0-9679115-5-7(9)) Fivedegressbelowzero Pr.

Turman, Evelyn. J. B. 's Christmas Presents. Turman, Adam, illus. l.t. ed. 2004. 28p. (J). 15.95 (978-0-9753042-0-4(8)) Turman, E.

Turner, Barbara. A Day in San Francisco, Vol. 1. l.t. ed. 2003. (Illus.). 32p. (J). per. 14.95 (978-0-9747019-0-5(4)) Turner, Barbara.

Twain, Mark. The Prince & the Pauper. l.t. ed. 2000. (Large Print Heritage Ser.). 364p. (J). lib. bdg. 33.95 (978-1-58118-068-8(3) , 23662) LRS.

—The Prince & the Pauper. l.t. ed. 2000. (Perennial Bestsellers Ser.). 307p. (J). 26.95 (978-0-7838-9061-6(3)) Thorndike Pr.

'Twas the Night Before Testing. l.t. ed. 2001. 44p. (J). pap. 12.00 (978-0-9705117-0-6(1)) FUNdamentals in Education.

Ulmer, Louise. The Bible That Wouldn't Burn: How the Tyndale English Version of the Bible Came About. 2nd l.t. ed. 2003. (Illus.). 32p. 4.95 (978-0-941367-01-1(0)) Peach Blossom Pubns.

Umansky, Kaye. The Fwog Pwince: The Twuth! Williamson, Gwyneth, illus. l.t. ed. 1998. 88p. (J). pap. (978-0-7540-6030-7(6) , CLP 235) BBC Audio.

—Madness in the Mountains. 2004. (J). 24.95 incl. audio (978-0-7540-6271-4(6) , Chivers Children's Audio Bks.) BBC Audiobooks America.

—Wilma's Wicked Revenge. l.t. ed. 2000. (Illus.). 264p. (J). pap. (978-0-7540-6124-3(8) , CLP 318) BBC Audio.

—Wilma's Wicked Revenge. unabr. l.t. ed. 2003. (Read-Along Ser.). 256p. (J). 29.95 incl. audio (978-0-7540-6235-6(X) , RAO36, Galaxy Children's Large Print) BBC Audiobooks America.

Uncle Markie. Piglette & BoBo Do Tokyo. l.t. ed. 2002. 28p. 9.95 (978-0-9633943-7-8(1)) Studio 403.

—Piglette & BoBo See Hong Kong. l.t. ed. 2002. 46p. ring bd. 9.95 (978-0-9633943-8-5(X)) Studio 403.

—Piglette Goes Hawaiian. l.t. ed. 2001. 56p. ring bd. 9.95 (978-0-9633943-3-0(9)) Studio 403.

—Piglette Goes to Argentina. l.t. ed. 2001. 66p. ring bd. (978-0-9633943-1-6(2)) Studio 403.

—Piglette Goes to Northern California. l.t. ed. 2001. 36p. (978-0-9633943-2-3(0)) Studio 403.

—Piglette Takes the Concorde! l.t. ed. 2002. 56p. ring bd. 9.95 (978-0-9633943-4-7(7)) Studio 403.

Ure, Jean. Pumpkin Pie. l.t. ed. 2005. (J). pap. (978-0-7540-7886-9(8) , CLP 462) BBC Audio.

Van Scoyoc, Pam. Angel Wings. Telage, Susenne, illus. l.t. ed. 1998. 32p. (J). (ps-3). lib. bdg. 16.95 (978-0-9663629-1-6(8)) By Grace Enterprises.

Van Sickle, Lisa. Twin Stories: Shhhh... It's Bertha. McLaughlin, Wanda, ed. Hagle, Josh, illus. l.t. ed. 1998. 48p. (J). (gr. k-3). 16.95 (978-0-9659001-5-7(0)) Write Team, The.

Vanderdoes, Amanda & Ratcliffe, T. J., Jr. The Adventures of Makui. l.t. ed. 1999. (Illus.). (J). (gr. k-5). pap. 8.95 incl. audio (978-1-928632-18-4(1)) Writers Marketplace:Consulting, Critiquing & Publishing.

VanDerTuuk-Perkins, Jennifer E. Life with Gabriel. VanDerTuuk-Perkins, Jennifer E. & Perkins, Rodney R., illus. l.t. ed. 2004. 22p. (J). per. 9.95 (978-0-9749862-0-3(8)) Theragogy.com.

Vaterlaus, Stanford E. Time Breach. l.t. ed. 2001. 360p. (YA). (gr. 5-12). per. 14.00 (978-0-9707353-0-0(8)) SE-View Publishing.

Venable, Alan. The Story of Anne Frank. Stemach, Jerry, ed. Ham, Jeff, illus. l.t. ed. 2001. (J). (gr. 5-6). 50.00 (978-1-58702-520-4(5)) Johnston, Don Inc.

Verne, Jules. Around the World in 80 Days. l.t. ed. 1999. (Large Print Heritage Ser.). 325p. (gr. 7-12). lib. bdg. 32.95 (978-1-58118-040-4(3) , 22509) LRS.

Verses from the Quran: Illustrated by Children Around the World. l.t. ed. 2000. (Illus.). 110p. (YA). (gr. 2 up). pap. 12.00 (978-1-879402-79-9(3)) Tahrike Tarsile Quran, Inc.

Vincent, Mary. Follow the Leader: A Dog's-Eye View of Washington, D. C. 2nd l.t. ed. 2000. 117p. (gr. 5 up). per. 12.95 (978-0-9670911-0-5(1)); (YA). 19.95 (978-0-9670911-1-2(X)) Eastbank Publishing.

Vogel, Rob & Azarov, Max. Garry the Groundhog, l.t. ed. 2005. (Illus.). 10p. (J). spiral bd. 19.95 incl. DVD (978-0-9768455-0-8(4) , N/A) Vogel, Robert.

Voigt, Cynthia. Dicey's Song. l.t. ed. 2002. (Tillerman Cycle Ser.: Bk. 2). 370p. (YA). lib. bdg. 35.95 (978-1-58118-106-7(X) , 25790) LRS.

—A Solitary Blue. l.t. ed. 2005. (Tillerman Cycle Ser.: Bk. 3). 359p. (J). pap. 10.95 (978-0-7862-7912-8(5)) Thorndike Pr.

Vonthron, Satanta C. Caillov Visits the Farmer's Market. Meier, Kerry L., illus. l.t. ed. 2005. (Hrl Board Book Ser.). (J). (ps-k). pap. 10.95 (978-1-57332-310-9(1)) HighReach Learning, Inc.

—Down at the Shore. Storch, Ellen N., illus. l.t. ed. 2005. (Hrl Board Book Ser.). (J). (ps-k). pap. 10.95 (978-1-57332-306-2(3)) HighReach Learning, Inc.

Vorndran, Judith Clay. Mr. Bear Lives There. l.t. ed. 2005. (Illus.). 11p. (J). pap. 7.98 (978-0-9772439-0-7(7)) Vorndran, Judith Clay.

Vroom, Angela. Airplane Letters to God. l.t. ed. 2004. (Illus.). 24p. (J). pap. 8.50 (978-0-9762935-0-7(1)) Perkins Crawford.

Wade, Linda R. Condoleeza Rice. l.t. ed. 2002. (Real-Life Reader Biography Ser.). (Illus.). 32p. (gr. 3-8). lib. bdg. 15.95 (978-1-58415-145-6(5)) Mitchell Lane Pubs., Inc.

—Condoleezza Rice. 2004. (Illus.). 32p. (J). lib. bdg. (978-1-58415-332-0(6)) Mitchell Lane Pubs., Inc.

Wagner, Jeff. My Day... at the Zoo. Alvarado, Paulo, illus. 2004. 20p. (J). bds. (978-0-9754515-0-2(2)) Wagner Entertainment.

Waite, Elsie, et al. Following Rules. Sparck, Carole C., illus. l.t. ed. 2001. 8p. (J). pap. 6.00 (978-1-58084-169-6(4)) Lower Kuskokwim Schl. District.

—Maligtaqucaraq. Sparck, Carole C., illus. l.t. ed. 2001. 8p. (J). pap. 6.00 (978-1-58084-170-2(8)) Lower Kuskokwim Schl. District.

Wallace, Karen. Creakie Hall: Ace Ghosts. Ross, Tony, illus. l.t. ed. 1998. 72p. (J). pap. (978-0-7540-6034-5(9) , CLP 237) BBC Audio.

Walling, Sandy Seeley. A Day at the Beach. A Seaside Counting Book from One to Ten. Walling, Sandy Seeley, illus. l.t. ed. 2003. 28p. (J). 6.95 (978-0-9741940-0-4(X)) Abernathy Hse. Publishing.

Walling, Sandy Seeley, illus. & text. ABC's at the Zoo! The Fun Way to Teach Your Child the Relationship between Upper Case & Lower Case Letters, Walling, Sandy Seeley, text. l.t. ed. 2004. 36p. (J). per. 7.95 (978-0-9741940-1-1(8)) Abernathy Hse. Publishing.

Waltz, Dan. Kornstalkers: Corn Maze Massacre. Waltz, Dan, illus. l.t. ed. 2005. (Chilled to the Bone! Ser.: No. 1). (Illus.). 120p. (J). per. 6.99 (978-0-9741774-3-4(1)) D. W. Publishing.

Waltz, Dan Hall. Freckles the Frog: A Read-a-Long/Sing-a-Long Story Book. Waltz, Dan Hall, illus. l.t. ed. 2003. (Illus.). 24p. (J). 19.95 (978-0-9741774-0-3(7)) D. W. Publishing.

Warburton, Nick. The Strange Change of Flora Young. l.t. ed. 2005. 192p. (J). pap. (978-0-7540-7853-1(1) , CLP 443) BBC Audio.

Waring, Diana. Romans, Reformers, Revolutionaries Bk. B: A Digging Deeper Study Guide. 1998. 189p. (J). pap., stu. ed. 22.95 (978-1-930514-06-5(9)) Diana Waring Presents.

—Romans, Reformers, Revolutionaries Elementary Activity Book. Waring, Isaac, illus. 2nd l.t. ed. 2001. 96p. (J). per. 11.95 (978-1-930514-14-0(X) , RRA) Diana Waring Presents.

Watambe, Kyoko. The Mother Cat. Tamaki, Donna, tr. Watambe, Kyoko, illus. l.t. ed. 1998. Tr. of Neko No Okasan. (ENG & JPN., Illus.). 12p. (J). (ps-3). 35.00 (978-1-893533-09-7(3) , 18) Kamishibai for Kids.

Waters, Kim. Enchanted Tales: An ABC Fantasy. l.t. ed. 1999. (Illus.). 56p. (J). (gr. k-4). 15.95 (978-1-886069-08-4(5)) Mandala Publishing.

Watkins, Albert. The Brothers Three. l.t. ed. 2004. (Illus.). 48p. (J). pap. 22.95 (978-0-9629124-4-3(1)) Floppinfish Publishing Co., Ltd.

Watkins, Patricia. Boyd-Friend: His Yippie-Skippie Journey to a Forever Home. Watkins, Christopher, illus. l.t. ed. 2004. 44p. 10.95 (978-0-9753397-0-1(2)) Frayed Pages Publishing.

Watson, Don. The Legend of Red Leaf. Robbins, Ashley, illus. l.t. ed. 2005. 125p. (J). pap. 9.95 (978-0-9714358-6-5(3)) Longhorn Creek Pr.

Watson, Regal. The Ant That Can't, 1. l.t. ed. 2005. (Illus.). 50p. (J). per. 10.95 (978-0-9763686-0-1(9)) Rapha Publishing.

Watson, T. E. Mom, Can I Have a Dragon? Patterson, Dave, illus. 2nd l.t. ed. 2004. 32p. (J). (gr. 1-6). lib. bdg. 16.95 (978-1-58478-020-5(7) , Paw Prints Pr.) Heather & Highlands Publishing.

Watson, W. Hamp, Jr. Frederick Wilson Still Speaks - Big Words for Our Time. Watson, W. Hamp, Jr., ed. l.t. ed. 2004. (J). per. 12.95 (978-0-9746976-0-4(5)) Cambridge Way Publishing.

Waugh, Sylvia. Space Race. l.t. ed. 2001. 300p. (J). 20.95 (978-0-7862-3606-0(X)) Thorndike Pr.

Weaver, Will. Hard Ball: A Billy Baggs Novel. l.t. ed. 2000. (Illus.). 270p. (YA). (gr. 8-12). 20.95 (978-0-7862-2752-5(4)) Thorndike Pr.

Webber, Hiltrud M. Collecting Butterflies & Moths. l.t. ed. 1999. (Ozarkae Ser.: Vol. 2). (Illus.). 35p. (J). spiral bd. 10.95 (978-0-9652173-2-3(9)) HMW Pubns.

Weber, Elizabeth C. Lightning Phonics Program. abr. l.t. ed. 2000. 73p. (J). (ps-8). incl. cd-rom (978-0-9704777-0-5(8)) DEW Pubs.

Weddington, Carole. D+Anger I'm Mad! Anger Management Teen Style. l.t. ed. 2003. (YA). 28.00 (978-0-9638007-7-0(9)) JM Pubns.

Weeks, Timothy A. The Wise Mullet of Cook Bayou. l.t. ed. 2004. (Illus.). 48p. (J). per. (978-0-9713573-8-9(2)) Thomas Expressions, Inc.

Welden, Amelie. Girls Who Rocked the World: Heroines from Sacagawea to Sheryl Swoopes. McCann, Jerry, illus. l.t. ed. 1999. (Girls Know Best Ser.). 117p. (J). (gr. 3 up). lib. bdg. 23.33 (978-0-8368-2454-4(7)) Stevens, Gareth Inc.

Wengerd, Marvin, ed. Color & Discover: Color the Marked Areas, Out Jumps a Surprise Animal. Conner, Carol & Fabian, Melinda, illus. l.t. ed. 2000. (Nature Friend Fun Ser.: Vol. 2). 24p. (J). (gr. k-5). pap. 4.00 (978-1-890050-43-6(1)) Carlisle Pr.- Walnut Creek.

Werlin, Nancy. The Killer's Cousin. l.t. ed. 1999. 277p. (YA). (gr. 9-12). 21.95 (978-0-7862-2188-2(7)) Thorndike Pr.

Westenbroek, K. John. Blessly the Redemption Rabbit Easter Book & Coloring Book Attached. Escobar, Rudt & Nauta, Paul, illus. l.t. ed. 2002. 43p. (J). 14.99 (978-0-9716523-8-5(4)) Hope Harvest Publishing.

WeWrite Kids Staff. Let's All Have Fun! Swallow, Judy, illus. l.t. ed. 2000. (WeWrite Kids! Ser.). 50p. (J). (gr. 1-7). pap. 3.95 (978-1-57635-056-0(8)) WeWrite LLC.

—We're Moving! Fisher, Suzanne, ed. Freeman, Troy, illus. l.t. ed. 1999. (WeWrite Kids! Ser.: Vol. 44). 45p. (J). (gr. 2-6). pap. 3.95 (978-1-57635-052-2(5)) WeWrite LLC.

Wheeler, Karla. Heart-Shaped Pickles. Wheeler, Jenny Lee, illus. l.t. ed. 2003. 36p. (J). 4.95 (978-0-9675532-2-1(9)) Quality of Life Publishing Co.

—Timmy's Christmas Surprise. Wheeler, Jenny Lee, illus. l.t. ed. 2001. 24p. 4.95 (978-0-9675532-0-7(2)) Quality of Life Publishing Co.

Whelan, Gloria. Homeless Bird. l.t. ed. 2002. 147p. (J). 23.95 (978-0-7862-4060-9(1)) Thomson Gale.

White, E. B. Charlotte's Web. Williams, Garth, illus. l.t. ed. 1999. (LRS Large Print Cornerstone Ser.). 310p. (J). (gr. 2-8). lib. bdg. 29.95 (978-1-58118-050-3(0) , 22772) LRS.

—Stuart Little. Williams, Garth, illus. l.t. ed. 2000. (LRS Large Print Cornerstone Ser.). 175p. (J). (gr. 2-8). lib. bdg. 27.95 (978-1-58118-064-0(0) , 23655) LRS.

White, Russ. Cat Got Your Tongue? A Book of Idioms. Cornelison, Reuel, illus. l.t. ed. 2004. 44p. (J). per. (978-0-9742885-0-5(0) , 00) White, Russ.

White, Ruth. Belle Prater's Boy. l.t. ed. 2000. (Illus.). 221p. (YA). (gr. 4-7). 21.95 (978-0-7862-2885-0(7)) Thorndike Pr.

—Memories of Summer. 2000. 144p. (J). (gr. 7-10). 17.00 (978-0-374-34945-5(2) , Farrar, Straus & Giroux (BYR)) Farrar, Straus & Giroux.

White, T. H. The Sword in the Stone. l.t. ed. 2003. (Children's Large Print Ser.). 35.95 (978-1-58118-110-4(8)) LRS.

Whitedove, Michelle. My Invisible Friends: Guardian Angels. Poynter, Linda, illus. l.t. ed. 2005. 33p. (J). (ps-3). 18.95 (978-0-9714908-4-0(8)) Whitedove Pr.

Whiting, Jim. Charles Schulz. l.t. ed. 2002. (Real-Life Reader Biography Ser.). (Illus.). 32p. (gr. 3-8). lib. bdg. 15.95 (978-1-58415-131-9(5)) Mitchell Lane Pubs., Inc.

Whitman, John. Army of Terror. l.t. ed. 1998. (Star Wars Ser.: No. 6). 144p. (J). (gr. 4 up). lib. bdg. 22.60 (978-0-8368-2240-3(4)) Stevens, Gareth Inc.

—City of the Dead. l.t. ed. 1998. (Star Wars Ser.: No. 2). 144p. (J). (gr. 4 up). lib. bdg. 22.60 (978-0-8368-2236-6(6)) Stevens, Gareth Inc.

—Eaten Alive. l.t. ed. 1998. (Star Wars Ser.: No. 1). 144p. (J). (gr. 4 up). lib. bdg. 22.60 (978-0-8368-2235-9(8)) Stevens, Gareth Inc.

—Ghost of the Jedi. l.t. ed. 1998. (Star Wars Ser.: No. 5). 144p. (J). (gr. 4 up). lib. bdg. 22.60 (978-0-8368-2239-7(0)) Stevens, Gareth Inc.

—The Nightmare Machine. l.t. ed. 1998. (Star Wars Ser.: No. 4). 144p. (J). (gr. 4 up). lib. bdg. 22.60 (978-0-8368-2238-0(2)) Stevens, Gareth Inc.

—Planet Plague. l.t. ed. 1998. (Star Wars Ser.: No. 3). 144p. (J). (gr. 4 up). lib. bdg. 22.60 (978-0-8368-2237-3(4)) Stevens, Gareth Inc.

—Star Wars: Galaxy of Fear Boxed Set: Eaten Alive; City of the Dead; Planet Plague; The Nightmare Machine; Ghost of the Jedi; Army of Terror, 6 bks. l.t. ed. Incl. Army of Terror. lib. bdg. 22.60 (978-0-8368-2240-3(4)); City of the Dead. lib. bdg. 22.60 (978-0-8368-2236-6(6)); Eaten Alive. lib. bdg. 22.60 (978-0-8368-2235-9(8)); Ghost of the Jedi. lib. bdg. 22.60 (978-0-8368-2239-7(0)); Nightmare Machine. lib. bdg. 22.60 (978-0-8368-2238-0(2)); Planet Plague. lib. bdg. 22.60 (978-0-8368-2237-3(4)); 144p. (J). (gr. 4 up). 1998. (Star Wars Ser.: Nos. 1-6). Set lib. bdg. 135.60 (978-0-8368-2234-2(X)) Stevens, Gareth Inc.

Widder, Edith. The Bioluminescence Coloring Book. Baker, Charissa, illus. 2nd rev. l.t. ed. 2002. 25p. (J). 19.95 (978-0-9659686-6-9(9)) Harbor Branch Oceanographic Institution, Inc.

Widdifield, Lynn F. A Book about Me: A Place for You to Write about What Happens to You in Therapy. Widdifield, Lynn F., illus. l.t. ed. 1998. (Illus.). 50p. (J). (gr. 2-8). 21.00 (978-0-9668085-0-6(9) , 12160) Weathered Wise Publishing Co.

Wiggin, Kate Douglas. Rebecca of Sunnybrook Farm. l.t. ed. 1999. (Large Print Heritage Ser.). 340p. (YA). (gr. 7-12). lib. bdg. 33.95 (978-1-58118-045-9(4) , 22514) LRS.

—Rebecca of Sunnybrook Farm. l.t. ed. 2002. (Perennial Bestsellers Ser.). 374p. 29.95 (978-0-7862-4625-0(1)) Thorndike Pr.

Wilcox, John. Charlie the Chinook. Wiker, Betty, illus. l.t. ed. 1998. (J). (ps-3). pap. (978-0-9683640-7-9(1)) Raven Rock Publishing.

Wilde, Daxton. I'm a Super Hero. l.t. ed. 2001. (Illus.). 30p. (J). 2.95 net. (978-0-9749834-0-0(3)) Daxton Wilde Fnd.

Wilder, Laura Ingalls. Farmer Boy. Williams, Garth, illus. l.t. ed. 2000. (Little House Ser.). 400p. (J). (gr. 3-6). lib. bdg. 33.95 (978-1-58118-079-4(9) , 24071) LRS.

—The First Four Years. Williams, Garth, illus. l.t. ed. 2002. (LRS Large Print Cornerstone Ser.). (J). lib. bdg. 27.95 (978-1-58118-103-6(5) , 25535) LRS.

—Little House in the Big Woods. Williams, Garth, illus. l.t. ed. 2000. (Little House Ser.). 244p. (J). (gr. 3-6). lib. bdg. 28.95 (978-1-58118-078-7(0) , 24070) LRS.

—Little House on the Prairie. Williams, Garth, illus. l.t. ed. 1999. (Little House Ser.). 420p. (J). (gr. 3-6). lib. bdg. 35.95 (978-1-58118-051-0(9) , 22771) LRS.

—On the Banks of Plum Creek. l.t. ed. 2002. (LRS Large Print Cornerstone Ser.). (Illus.). (J). lib. bdg. 35.95 (978-1-58118-099-2(3) , 25531) LRS.

—These Happy Golden Years. l.t. ed. (J). (gr. 3-6). 35.95 (978-1-58118-102-9(7)) LRS.

Wildsmith, Brian. Brian Wildsmith's Opuestos. Fiol, Maria A., tr. Wildsmith, Brian, illus. l.t. ed. 1998. (SPA., Illus.). 16p. (J). (ps). bds. 4.95 (978-1-887734-18-9(X)) Star Bright Bks., Inc.

Wilhelm, Doug. Raising the Shades. l.t. ed. 2005. 182p. 20.95 (978-0-7862-7812-1(9) , Large Print Pr.) Thorndike Pr.

Wilkins, Jen. The Trucker That Saved the Day. l.t. ed. 2002. (Illus.). 16p. 3.95 (978-0-9651377-7-5(5)) Living Gold Pr.

Wilkinson, Dean. The Legend of Arthur King. l.t. ed. 2005. (J). pap. (978-1-4056-6022-8(8)) BBC Audio.

Williams, Deborah. Boys & Girls. Dragony, Barbara, illus. l.t. ed. 2000. 16p. (J). (gr. k-1). pap. 4.95 (978-1-57874-054-3(1) , Kaeden Bks.) Kaeden Corp.

Williams, Heather L. Deep in the Forest. Middleton, Mikell, illus. l.t. ed. 2003. (HRL Board Book Ser.). 10p. (J). (ps-k). bds. 10.95 (978-1-57332-264-5(4)) HighReach Learning, Inc.

Williams, Heather L. & Muench-Williams, Heather. Caillov Learns about Space. Storch, Ellen N., illus. l.t. ed. 2005. (Hrl Board Book Ser.). (J). (ps-k). bds. 10.95 (978-1-57332-308-6(X)) HighReach Learning, Inc.

Williams, Regina. What If... Keith, Doug, illus. l.t. ed. 2001. 32p. (J). (ps up). 15.95 (978-0-935699-22-7(8)) Illumination Arts Publishing Co., Inc.

Williams, Teresa A. J. Hugh Granville Tilley North Carolina House of Representatives 1887 And 1889, 1 book. l.t. ed. 2007. 17p. lib. bdg. 15.00 (978-0-9722724-3-8(7)) Blackfoot Burkino Cherokee Publishing.

Williams, Thomas. The Christmas Chair. l.t. ed. 2004. (Illus.). 27p. (J). audio compact disk 22.95 (978-0-9763633-0-9(5)) Williams, Thomas.

Wilson, David Henry. Can a Spider Learn to Fly? Scheffler, Axel, illus. l.t. ed. 2000. 143p. (J). pap. 16.95 (978-0-7540-6112-0(4) , Galaxy Children's Large Print) BBC Audiobooks America.

—Castle of Inside Out. Riddell, Chris, illus. l.t. ed. 2005. 216p. (J). pap. (978-0-7540-6193-9(0) , CLP 387) BBC Audio.

—Never Steal Wheels from a Dog. Scheffler, Axel, illus. l.t. ed. 2005. 168p. (J). pap. (978-0-7540-7821-0(3) , CLP 411) BBC Audio.

Wilson, Jacqueline. The Bed & Breakfast Star. Sharratt, Nick, illus. l.t. ed. 2000. 255p. (J). pap. (978-0-7540-6090-1(X) , CLP 292) BBC Audio.

—Cliffhanger. Sharratt, Nick, illus. l.t. ed. 2000. 86p. (J). pap. 16.95 (978-0-7540-6120-5(5) , Galaxy Children's Large Print) BBC Audiobooks America.

—Dustbin Baby. Sharratt, Nick, illus. l.t. ed. 2002. (J). 16.95 (978-0-7540-7828-9(0) , Galaxy Children's Large Print) BBC Audiobooks America.

—How to Survive Summer Camp. Heap, Sue, illus. l.t. ed. 2002. 256p. (J). 16.95 (978-0-7540-7808-1(6) , Galaxy Children's Large Print) BBC Audiobooks America.

—The Story of Tracy Beaker. Sharratt, Nick, illus. l.t. ed. 1998. 200p. (J). pap. 16.95 (978-0-7540-6021-5(7) , Galaxy Children's Large Print) BBC Audiobooks America.

Wilson, Rebekah. Grandmother's Hope Chest: Lucie's Snowflakes. l.t. ed. 2004. (Illus.). 80p. (J). 15.00 (978-1-59565-003-0(2)) Hope Chest Legacy, Inc.

—Grandmother's Hope Chest: The Running Rooster. l.t. ed. 2004. (Illus.). 52p. (J). 15.00 (978-1-59565-002-3(4)) Hope Chest Legacy, Inc.

Wilson, Wayne. Tony Blair. l.t. ed. 2002. (Real-Life Reader Biography Ser.). (Illus.). 32p. (J). (gr. 3-8). lib. bdg. 15.95 (978-1-58415-143-2(9)) Mitchell Lane Pubs., Inc.

Winter, Max. Did You Know?, Vol. 2. Rechin, Kevin, illus. l.t. ed. 2005. (Little Books & Big Bks.: Vol. 8). 8p. (YA). (ps-3). 22.50 (978-0-8215-7517-8(1)) Sadlier, William H. Inc.

The Wishbone Mysteries, 20 bks. l.t. ed. Incl. Case of the Breaking Story. Steele, Alexander. (Illus.). 144p. 2000. lib. bdg. 23.33 (978-0-8368-2703-3(1)); Case of the Cyber-Hacker. Capeci, Anne. (Illus.). 141p. 2000. lib. bdg. 23.33 (978-0-8368-2702-6(3)); Case of the Impounded Hounds. Steele, Michael Anthony. 138p. 2000. lib. bdg. 23.33 (978-0-8368-2700-2(7)); Case of the On-Line Alien. Steele, Alexander. 144p. 1999. lib. bdg. 23.33 (978-0-8368-2449-0(0)); Case of the Unsolved Case. Steele, Alexander. (Illus.). 139p. 2000. lib. bdg. 23.33 (978-0-8368-2696-8(5)); Disappearing Dinosaurs. Strickland, Brad & Fuller, Thomas E. 144p. 1999. lib. bdg. 23.33 (978-0-8368-2450-6(4)); Disoriented Express. Strickland, Brad. 167p. 2000. lib. bdg. 23.33 (978-0-8368-2697-5(3)); Drive-In of Doom. Strickland, Brad & Fuller, Thomas E. 144p. 1999. lib. bdg. 23.33 (978-0-8368-2388-2(5)); Forgotten Heroes. Steele, Michael Anthony. (Illus.). 139p. 2000. lib. bdg. 23.33 (978-0-8368-2695-1(7)); Haunted Clubhouse. Leavitt, Caroline. 144p. 1999. lib. bdg. 22.60 (978-0-8368-2383-7(4)); Key to the Golden Dog. Capeci, Anne. 144p. 1999. lib. bdg. 23.33 (978-0-8368-2389-9(3)); Lights! Camera! Action Dog! Butcher, Nancy. (Illus.). 139p. 2000. lib. bdg. 23.33 (978-0-8368-2694-4(9)); Maltese Dog. Capeci, Anne. 144p. 1999. lib. bdg. 23.33 (978-0-8368-2387-5(7)); Phantom of the Video Store. Gantt, Leticia. (Illus.). 141p. 2000. lib. bdg. 23.33 (978-0-8368-2701-9(5)); Riddle of the Wayward Books. Strickland, Brad & Fuller, Thomas E. 144p. 1999. lib. bdg. 23.33 (978-0-8368-2384-4(2)); Sirian Conspiracy. Friedman, Michael Jan. (Illus.) 141p. 2000. lib. bdg. 23.33 (978-0-8368-2699-9(X)); Stage Invader. Sathre, Vivian. (Illus.). 140p. 2000. lib. bdg. 23.33 (978-0-8368-2698-2(1)); Stolen Trophy. Friedman, Michael Jan. 144p. 1999. lib. bdg. 23.33 (978-0-8368-2386-8(9)); Tale of the Missing Mascot. Steele, Alexander. 144p. 1999. lib. bdg. 23.33 (978-0-8368-2385-1(0)); Treasure of Skeleton Reef. Strickland, Brad & Fuller, Thomas E. 144p. 1999. lib. bdg. 23.33 (978-0-8368-2382-0(6)); (J). (gr. 4 up). Set lib. bdg. 443.27 (978-0-8368-2752-1(X)) Stevens, Gareth Inc.

Witschen, Kay. Clinker Meets the Flying Squirrel. Luckemeyer, Norma, illus. l.t. ed. 2001. 28p. (YA). (gr. 1 up). pap. 5.95 (978-1-892740-00-7(1) , Park Pr.) J&J Collections.

Wittlinger, Ellen. Gracie's Girl. l.t. ed. 2002. 224p. (J). 22.95 (978-0-7862-3761-6(9)) Thomson Gale.

Wohlford, Martha Crikelair. Little Star's Big Day: A Children's Christmas Story. Schaefer, Heather Leigh, illus. l.t. ed. 2003. 36p. (J). (ps-7). per. 14.95 (978-1-59453-033-3(5) , 1) Airleaf Publishing & Bookselling.

Women in the Ancient Near East: Stories & Primary Sources from the Sumerians through the Early Israelites. l.t. ed. 1999. 94p. (YA). spiral bd. 16.95 net. (978-1-890380-07-6(5)) Women in World History Curriculum.

Wong, Benedict Norbert. Lo & Behold. Wong, Benedict Norbert, illus. l.t. ed. 2003. (Illus.). 38p. (gr. 1 up). 16.95 (978-0-9728192-0-6(7) , LOBE) Taiji Arts Publishing.

—Lo & Behold: Good Enough to Eat. Wong, Benedict Norbert, illus. l.t. ed. 2003. (Illus.). 40p. (J). (gr. 1-12). 16.95 (978-0-9728192-1-3(5) , 1002LB) Taiji Arts Publishing.

Wood, Debra. William Warrior Bear. Blake, Joshua Aaron, illus. l.t. ed. 2005. 30p. (J). per. 12.95 (978-1-59879-001-6(3)) Lifevest Publishing, Inc.

Wood, Frances M. Daughter of Madrugada. l.t. ed. 2004. 170p. 20.95 (978-0-7862-6142-0(0)) Thorndike Pr.

Wooding, Chris. Crashing. l.t. ed. 2001. (Illus.). 216p. 18.99 (978-0-7089-9539-6(X)) Ulverscroft Large Print Bks. GBR. *Dist:* Ulverscroft Large Print Bks., Ltd.

Wooding, Sharon. Mark Twain in Nevada, a History Coloring Book for Children. l.t. ed. 2003. (Illus.). 25p. (J). (SPA.). pap. 5.95 (978-0-9727757-1-7(4)); pap. 5.95 (978-0-9727757-0-0(6)) Susy & Livy Pubns.

Word, Reagan. The Windrider. l.t. ed. 2002. (Illus.). 32p. (J). 16.00 (978-0-9717629-0-9(2)) Color Cove Studio.

Wright, Mary H. Grandma Spoils Me. Megenhardt, Bill, illus. l.t. ed. 2005. 32p. (J). lib. bdg. 16.95 (978-0-9645493-4-0(4)) Bluebonnets, Boots & Bks.

Wrighton, Charlene, et al. Zoo-Phonics Reader Level B, Bk. 1. l.t. ed. 1999. (Readers Ser.). (Illus.). 50p. (Orig.). (J). (gr. 1). pap. 8.95 (978-0-9617342-3-7(X)) Zoo-phonics, Inc.

—Zoo-Phonics Reader Level B Bk. 1: Allie, Bubba, Catina. l.t. ed. 1999. (Readers Ser.). (Illus.). 48p. (J). (gr. 1). pap. 8.95 (978-0-9617342-2-0(1)) Zoo-phonics, Inc.

—Zoo-Phonics Reader Level C, Bk. 2. l.t. ed. 1999. (Readers Ser.). (Illus.). 50p. (J). (gr. 1). pap. 8.95 (978-0-9617342-4-4(8)) Zoo-phonics, Inc.

Wunderle, Steve L. & Wunderle, Sharon. Bucky Bear & the Surprise Fishing Trip. Wunderle, Steve L., photos by. l.t. ed. 1999. (Illus.). 28p. (J). (gr. k-4). pap. 5.95 (978-0-9611162-4-8(2)) Wunderle Outdoor Bks.

Wunderlich, Fran. How Does That Feel Stanley? l.t. ed. 1999. (Illus.). 25p. (J). (ps-4). pap. 10.95 (978-0-9649293-7-1(6)) Belle Terre Pr., Inc.

Wynne-Jones, Tim. The Boy in the Burning House. l.t. ed. 2002. 332p. (J). 23.95 (978-0-7862-4435-5(6)) Thorndike Pr.

Yamada, Debbie Leung. Striking It Rich: Treasures from Gold Mountain. Tang, You-shan, illus. l.t. ed. 2004. 128p. (J). (gr. 4-8). pap. 13.95 (978-1-879965-21-8(6)) Polychrome Publishing Corp.

Yoder, Karen L. Fire Kids! The Adventures of Hose Company. 2nd l.t. ed. 2002. 124p. (J). pap. 6.95 (978-0-9700487-3-8(4)) Stoney Creek Pr.

Young, Patricia A. The Holy Monks of Mt. Athos. Young, Patricia A., illus. l.t. ed. 2005. (Illus.). 28p. (J). 20.00 (978-0-913026-24-3(7)); 10.00 (978-0-913026-49-6(2)) St. Nectarios Pr.

Young Scribes Staff. Unlock the Secrets of Exeter: The Young Scribes of Exeter, NH. l.t. ed. 2004. (Illus.). 172p. (J). pap. 15.00 (978-0-9744803-9-8(8)) PublishingWorks.

Zabrosky, Joseph. Herbie Hanson, 1 vol., 4 bks. l.t. ed. 2005. (Illus.). 32p. (J). per. (978-0-9768831-0-4(4)) Elohim Bks.

—Rudy Cazootie, 3 vols., 4 bks. l.t. ed. 2005. (Illus.). 32p. (J). per. (978-0-9768831-2-8(0)) Elohim Bks.

—Sunny & Hunny, 2 vols., 4 bks. l.t. ed. 2005. (Illus.). 32p. (J). per. (978-0-9768831-1-1(2)) Elohim Bks.

Zabrosky, Joseph & Jacobs, Nathaniel. The Christmas Tree, 4 vols., 4bks. l.t. ed. 2005. (Illus.). 32p. (J). per. (978-0-9768831-3-5(9)) Elohim Bks.

Zannos, Susan. Chester Carlson & the Development of Xerography. l.t. ed. 2002. (Unlocking the Secrets of Science Ser.). (Illus.). 56p. (gr. 4-10). lib. bdg. 25.70 (978-1-58415-117-3(X)) Mitchell Lane Pubs., Inc.

—Edward Roberts & the Story of the Personal Computer. l.t. ed. 2002. (Unlocking the Secrets of Science Ser.). (Illus.). 56p. (gr. 4-10). lib. bdg. 25.70 (978-1-58415-118-0(8)) Mitchell Lane Pubs., Inc.

Zindel, Paul. The Scream Museum. l.t. ed. 2002. (Illus.). 175p. (J). 22.95 (978-0-7862-4473-7(9)) Thorndike Pr.

Zoller, Jayson D. The Laziest Duck. l.t. ed. 2004. (Illus.). 13p. (J). per. 7.99 (978-1-932338-52-2(7)) Lifevest Publishing, Inc.

Zuhdi, Darla L. Finding Your Dream. 2nd l.t. ed. 2001. (Cat Detectives Present Ser.). 88p. (J). (gr. 4-7). per. 6.99 (978-0-9706062-1-1(4)) Aloha Publications.

Zuk-Lloyd, Lynn. Christmas in North Woods: 10 Animated Stories for Children. Zuk-Lloyd, Lynn, illus. l.t. ed. 2002. (Illus.). (J). cd-rom 24.95 (978-0-9723773-0-0(1)) PromiseGarden.com.

LAS VEGAS (NEV.)

Abbey, Rita Deanin. Isaiah Stained-Glass Windows. Sanders, Laura, ed. Preston, Gregory, photos by. 2002. (ENG & HEB., Illus.). 40p. (J). pap. (978-0-9652870-1-2(7)) Gan Or.

Davis, Alan S. The Fun Seeker's Las Vegas: The Ultimate Guide to One of the World's Hottest Cities. 2nd rev. ed. 2006. (Illus.). 224p. pap. 19.95 (978-0-9759022-1-9(0)) Davis, A. S. Media Group.

Doyle, Julie. Springs in the Desert: A Kid's History of Las Vegas Activity Book. 2006. (Illus.). 48p. pap. 9.95 (978-1-932173-54-3(4)) Stephens Pr. LLC.

L'Engle, Madeleine. A Wrinkle in Time. l.t. ed. 1998. (Perennial Bestsellers Ser.). 208p. (J). (gr. 4-7). 24.95 (978-0-7838-8371-7(4)) Thorndike Pr.

Peters, Johnathan. Springs in the Desert: A Kid's History of Las Vegas. 2006. (Illus.). 228p. (J). 19.95 (978-1-932173-53-6(6)) Stephens Pr. LLC.

Rinella, Heidi Knapp. The Lobster Kids' Guide to Exploring Las Vegas. 2001. (Lobster Kids' City Explorers Ser.). (Illus.). 225p. (J). (ps-3). pap. 12.95 (978-1-894222-29-7(6)) Lobster Pr. CAN. *Dist:* Univ. of Toronto Pr.

LA SALLE, ROBERT CAVELIER, SIEUR DE, 1643-1687

Bergen, Lara Rice. The Travels of Sieur de la Salle. 1999. (Explorers & Exploration Ser.). (Illus.). 48p. (J). (gr. 4-7). lib. bdg. 22.83 (978-0-7398-1495-6(8)) Raintree.

Donaldson-Forbes, Jeff. La Salle. 2002. (Famous Explorers Ser.). (Illus.). 24p. (J). (gr. 3). lib. bdg. 18.75 (978-0-8239-5830-6(2) , PowerKids Pr.) Rosen Publishing Group, Inc., The.

Englar, Mary. Sieur de la Salle. 2004. (Fact Finders Ser.). (Illus.). 32p. (J). lib. bdg. 22.60 (978-0-7368-2666-2(1)) Capstone Pr., Inc.

Goodman, Joan Elizabeth. Despite All Obstacles: La Salle & the Conquest of the Mississippi. McNeely, Tom, illus. 2001. (Great Explorers Ser.). 48p. (J). (gr. 3-6). 19.95 (978-1-931414-01-2(7)) Mikaya Pr.

J K L

Harmon, Daniel E. LaSalle & the Exploration of the Mississippi. 2000. (Explorers of the New World Ser.). (Illus.). (J). 63p. (gr. 4-7). pap. 25.00 (978-0-7910-6162-6(0)); 64p. (gr. 8-12). 25.00 (978-0-7910-5952-4(9)) Facts On File, Inc. (Chelsea Hse.).

Heinrichs, Ann. La Salle: La Salle & the Mississippi River. 2002. (Exploring the World Ser.). (Illus.). 48p. (J). (gr. 4 up). lib. bdg. 22.60 (978-0-7565-0178-5(4)) Compass Point Bks.

Kline, Trish. Robert la Salle. 2002. (Discover the Life of an Explorer Ser.). (Illus.). 24p. (gr. 2-5). 14.95 (978-1-58952-069-1(6)) Rourke Publishing, LLC.

Marsh, Carole. Robert de La Salle: An Ohio Experience Reader. 2001. (J). (gr. k-5). pap. 1.95 (978-0-635-00430-7(5)) Gallopade International.

Mitchell, Mark. Raising la Belle. Mitchell, Mark, illus. (Professor Wigglestix & the Weather Ser.). (Illus.). 112p. 10.95 (978-1-57168-703-6(3)) Eakin Pr.

—Raising LaBelle. 2001. (Professor Wigglestix & the Weather Ser.). (Illus.). 112p. 16.95 (978-1-57168-535-3(9)) Eakin Pr.

Molzahn, Arlene Bourgeois. La Salle: Explorer of the Mississippi. 2004. (Explorers! Ser.). (Illus.). 48p. (J). lib. bdg. 23.93 (978-0-7660-2141-9(6)) Enslow Pubs., Inc.

Nardo, Don. Sieur de la Salle. 2001. (Exploration Ser.). (Illus.). 64p. (J). (gr. 5-7). 25.50 (978-0-531-11973-0(4), Watts, Franklin) Scholastic Library Publishing.

Petrie, Kristin. La Salle. 2007. (Illus.). 32p. (J). 22.78 (978-1-59679-750-5(9)) ABDO Publishing Co.

Santella, Andrew. Sieur de La Salle. 2002. (Groundbreakers Ser.). (Illus.). 48p. (J). (gr. 5-7). lib. bdg. 27.07 (978-1-58810-598-1(9)) Heinemann Library.

Zronik, John Paul. Sieur de La Salle: New World Adventurer. 2005. (In the Footsteps of Explorers Ser.). (Illus.). 32p. (J). (gr. 3-9). (978-0-7787-2413-1(1)); pap. (978-0-7787-2449-0(2)) Crabtree Publishing Co.

LASERS

Amazing Lasers: Fourth Grade Guided Comprehension Level K. (On Our Way to English Ser.). (gr. 4 up). 34.50 (978-0-7578-7148-1(8)) Rigby Education.

Gregory, Daniel. Solid State Lasers for the Laser Enthusiast - Pulse Edition, 1. American LaserTechnic, ed. 2003. (Illus.). 352p. (YA). per. 89.99 (978-0-9741805-0-2(5)) American LaserTechnic.

Hamilton, Gina L. The Science of Light: Spectrum, Lasers, & Optics. 2003. (J). lib. bdg. 27.14 (978-0-7398-6995-6(7)) Raintree.

Kallen, Stuart A. Lasers. 2001. (Kidhaven Science Library). (Illus.). 48p. (J). (gr. 3-5). 23.70 (978-0-7377-0944-5(8), LML00102-178530, Kidhaven) Thomson Gale.

El laser ilumina los Cielos. 2000. (McGraw-Hill Ciencias Ser.). (ENG & SPA.). (gr. 5 up). (978-0-02-279671-6(1)) Macmillan/McGraw-Hill Schl. Div.

Nardo, Don. Lasers. 2003. (Lucent Science & Technology Library). (Illus.). 112p. (J). 29.95 (978-1-59018-104-1(2), Lucent Bks.) Thomson Gale.

Parker, Steve. Lasers. 2002. (Tomorrow's Technology Ser.). (Illus.). 32p. (J). lib. bdg. 24.25 (978-1-931983-24-2(0)) Chrysalis Education.

Sarver, Amy. Science at the Grocery. 2004. (National Geographic Reading Expeditions Ser.). (Illus.). 24p. (J). pap. (978-0-7922-4567-4(9)) National Geographic Society.

Whyman, Kathryn. Light & Lasers. 2004. (J). lib. bdg. (978-1-932799-24-8(9)) Stargazer Bks.

Wyckoff, Edwin Brit. Laser Man: Theodore H. Maiman & His Brilliant Invention. 2007. (Genius at Work! Great Inventor Biographies Ser.). (Illus.). 32p. (J). (gr. 3-4). lib. bdg. 22.60 (***978-0-7660-2848-7(8)***, Enslow Elementary) Enslow Pubs., Inc.

LATCHKEY CHILDREN—FICTION

Christopher, Matt & #1 Sports Writer for Kids Staff. Mountain Bike Mania: Is Will Pedaling Out of Control? 1998. 160p. (J). (gr. 3-7). 15.95 (978-0-316-14355-4(3)) Little Brown & Co.

Hatton, Caroline K. Vero & Philippe. McDaniels, Preston, illus. 2001. 144p. (J). (gr. 3-7). 14.95 (978-0-8126-2940-8(X)) Cricket Bks.

Horowitz, Jeanine. Latch Key Kid. 2006. 75p. (YA). lib. bdg. 12.99 (***978-1-934190-10-4(1)***) Ocean Front Bk. Publishing, Inc.

Mantell, Paul. Mountain Bike Mania. 2007. 148p. (J). lib. bdg. (***978-1-59953-108-3(9)***) Norwood Hse. Pr.

Ocean Front Books. Coloring Book. l.t. ed. 2006. (J). lib. bdg. (***978-1-934190-02-9(0)***) Ocean Front Bk. Publishing, Inc.

LATIN AMERICA

see also South America

Ada, Alma Flor & Campoy, F. Isabel. Vuelo del Quetzal. (Gateway to the Sun Ser.). (SPA.). 48p. (J). (gr. k-6). pap. 13.95 (978-1-58105-811-6(X)) Santillana USA Publishing Co., Inc.

Ancona, George. Mis Fiestas. 32p. (J). 2006. (SPA.). (gr. 1-3). pap. 8.95 (978-0-516-25497-5(9)); 2005. (ENG & SPA.). 21.00 (978-0-516-25290-2(9)) Scholastic Library Publishing. (Children's Pr.).

Bingham, Caroline & Dorling Kindersley Publishing Staff. Pyramid. 2004. (Eye Wonder Ser.). (Illus.). 48p. (J). lib. bdg. 17.99 (978-0-7566-0286-4(6)) Dorling Kindersley Publishing, Inc.

Brimson, Samuel. Ecuador-Honduras, 8 vols. 2003. (Nations of the World Ser.: Vol. 3). (Illus.). 64p. (J). (gr. 5 up). lib. bdg. 30.00 (978-0-8368-5487-9(X), World Almanac Library) Stevens, Gareth Inc.

Delacre, Lulu. De Oro y Esmeraldas: Mitos, Leyendas y Cuentos Populares de Latinoamerica. Delacre, Lulu, illus. 1998. (SPA., Illus.). 80p. (J). pap. 6.99 (978-0-590-67684-7(9), SO8197, Scholastic en Espanol) Scholastic, Inc.

Education for Global Involvement Staff, et al. Latin America & Japan: Crossing Borders & Making Connections. 2000. (Illus.). 163p. (YA). (gr. 6-12). pap. 19.95 (978-0-89994-405-0(1)) Social Science Education Consortium, Inc.

Furlong, Arlene. Argentina. 1999. (Festivals of the World Ser.). (Illus.). 32p. (J). (gr. 3 up). lib. bdg. 24.67 (978-0-8368-2030-0(4)) Stevens, Gareth Inc.

Goring, Ruth. Dias Festivos y Celebraciones. Palacios, Argentina, tr. Date not set. (Vida Latina Ser.). (SPA., Illus.). 48p. (J). (gr. 4-8). lib. bdg. 18.95 (978-0-86625-564-6(8)) Rourke Publishing, LLC.

Gritzner, Charles F. Latin America. 2006. (Modern World Cultures Ser.). (Illus.). 128p. (J). (gr. 6-12). 30.00 (978-0-7910-8142-6(7), Chelsea Hse.) Facts On File, Inc.

MacHado, Ana Maria. Latin America. 2000. (Exploration Into... Ser.). (Illus.). 48p. (J). (gr. 4-7). 25.00 (978-0-7910-6024-7(1), Chelsea Hse.) Facts On File, Inc.

Merrill, Yvonne Y. Hands-On Latin America: Art Activities for All Ages. Simpson, Mary, illus. 1998. (Hands-on Ser.). 88p. (J). (gr. 3-7). pap. 20.00 (978-0-9643177-1-0(0)) KITS Publishing.

Orozco, Jose-Luis. Fiestas: A Year of Latin American Songs of Celebration. Kleven, Elisa, illus. 2002. (SPA.). 56p. (J). (ps-2). 17.99 (978-0-525-45937-8(5), Dutton Juvenile) Penguin Group (USA) Inc.

Schon, Isabel. The Best of Latino Heritage, 1996-2002: A Guide to the Best Juvenile Books about Latino People. 2003. (Illus.). 272p. 42.50 (978-0-8108-4669-2(1)) Scarecrow Pr., Inc.

Steele, Christy, et al. Fighting for American Values. 2007. (Latino-American History Ser.). 112p. (J). (gr. 5-8). 35.00 (978-0-8160-6444-1(X), Chelsea Hse.) Facts On File, Inc.

Stewart, Mark. Middle & South America. 2007. (J). (***978-1-4034-9897-7(0)***); pap. (***978-1-4034-9906-6(3)***) Heinemann Library.

Zaragoza, Gonzalo. America Latina: Epoca Colonial. (Biblioteca Iberoamericana Ser.). (SPA.). 96p. (YA). 16.50 (978-84-7525-445-6(4), ANY454) Grupo Anaya, S.A. ESP. *Dist:* Continental Bk. Co., Inc.

LATIN AMERICA—BIOGRAPHY

Duran, Gloria. Maria de Estrada: Gypsy Conquistadora. 1999. (Discoveries Ser.). 227p. (YA). (gr. 7 up). pap. 14.95 (978-1-891270-01-7(X)) Latin American Literary Review Pr.

Krohn Katherine. Shakira. 2007. (Biography Ser.). (J). 30.60 (***978-0-8225-7159-9(5)***, Twenty-First Century Bks.) Lerner Publishing Group.

Menard, Valerie. Ricky Martin. 1999. (Real Life Reader Biography Ser.). (Illus.). 32p. (gr. 3-8). lib. bdg. 15.95 (978-1-58415-059-6(9)) Mitchell Lane Pubs., Inc.

Thatcher Murcia, Rebecca. Shakira. 2007. (Blue Banner Biography Ser.). (Illus.). 32p. (J). (gr. 4-8). lib. bdg. 25.70 (***978-1-58415-609-3(0)***) Mitchell Lane Pubs., Inc.

Uschan, Michael B. Che Guevara, Firebrand Revolutionary. 2006. (Twentieth Century's Most Influential Hispanics Ser.). (Illus.). 112p. (J). (gr. 7-10). 32.45 (978-1-59018-970-2(1), Lucent Bks.) Thomson Gale.

Villegas, Jose Luis, illus. & photos by. Home Is Everything: The Latino Baseball Story: from the Barrio to the Major Leagues. Villegas, Jose Luis, photos by. 2003. Tr. of Homes Es Todo. (ENG & SPA.). 148p. (YA). pap. 25.95 (978-0-938317-70-8(9)) Cinco Puntos Pr.

LATIN AMERICA—FICTION

Alvarez, Julia. Finding Miracles. 2004. 272p. (gr. 7). (J). 15.95 (978-0-375-82760-0(9)); (YA). 17.99 (978-0-375-92760-7(3)) Random Hse. Children's Bks. (Knopf Bks. for Young Readers).

Delacre, Lulu. Salsa Stories. Delacre, Lulu, illus. 2000. (SPA., Illus.). 112p. (J). (gr. 2-6). pap. 15.95 (978-0-590-63118-1(7), Scholastic Reference) Scholastic, Inc.

Espana, Gonzalo. Historias de Amores y Desvarios en America. 2003. (SPA.). 180p. (978-958-30-0569-5(X), PV4378) Centro de Informacion y Desarrollo de la Comunicacion y la Literatura MEX. *Dist:* Lectorum Pubns., Inc.

Joseph, Lynn. The Color of My Words. 2002. 144p. (J). (gr. 5 up). pap. 5.99 (978-0-06-447204-3(3), Harper Trophy) HarperCollins Pubs.

LeapFrog Staff. Disney Princess Stories - Latin America. 2003. (Illus.). (J). spiral bd. 14.99 (978-1-59319-001-9(8)) LeapFrog Enterprises, Inc.

Reiser, Lynn W. Tortillas & Lullabies. Corazones, Valientes, illus. 1998. Tr. of Tortillas y Cancioncitas. (SPA & ENG.). 48p. (J). (ps-3). 16.99 (978-0-688-14628-3(7), Rayo) HarperCollins Pubs.

Skarmeta, Antonio. The Composition. Ruano, Alfonso, illus. 2003. 32p. (J). (gr. 3 up). pap. 5.95 (978-0-88899-550-6(4)) Groundwood Bks. CAN. *Dist:* Perseus Distribution.

—The Composition. Amado, Elisa, tr. from SPA. Ruano, Alfonso, illus. 2000. 32p. (J). (gr. 2-6). 16.95 (978-0-88899-390-8(0), Libros Tigrillo) Groundwood Bks. CAN. *Dist:* Perseus Distribution.

LATIN AMERICA—HISTORY

Benson, Sonia, et al, eds. UXL Hispanic American Chronology. 2nd ed. 2002. 200p. (J). 67.00 (978-0-7876-6600-2(9), UXL) Thomson Gale.

Coletti, Sharon. Everything You Need to Teach Latin America. 2005. (YA). ring bd. 149.95 (978-1-933558-03-5(2)) InspirEd Educators.

Harcourt School Publishers Staff. Social Studies: Canada/Latin America. 1999. (Harcourt Brace Social Studies). (Illus.). (gr. k-7). 16.60 (978-0-15-316093-6(4)) Harcourt Schl. Pubs.

Hirsch, E. D., ed. Independence for Latin America, Level 6. tchr. ed. 9.95 (978-0-7690-5090-4(5)); stu. ed. 49.95 (978-0-7690-2855-2(1)) Pearson Learning.

Miller, Calvin Craig. Che Guevara: In Search of Revolution. 2006. (World Leaders Ser.). (Illus.). 160p. (J). (gr. 6 up). lib. bdg. 26.95 (978-1-931798-93-8(1)) Reynolds, Morgan Inc.

Nickles, Greg. The Hispanics. 2000. (We Came to North America Ser.). (Illus.). 32p. (J). (gr. 4). (978-0-7787-0186-6(7)); pap. (978-0-7787-0200-9(6)) Crabtree Publishing Co.

Rice, Earle, Jr. A Brief Political & Geographic History of Latin America: Where Are Gran Colombia, la Plata, & Dutch Guiana? 2007. (Places in Time Ser.). (Illus.). 112p. (YA). (gr. 5-10). lib. bdg. 37.10 (***978-1-58415-626-0(0)***) Mitchell Lane Pubs., Inc.

Stein, R. Conrad. The Conquistadors: Building a Spanish Empire in the Americas. 2004. (Proud Heritage: the Hispanic Library Ser.). 40p. (J). (gr. 3-7). 28.50 (978-1-59296-144-3(4)) Child's World, Inc.

Vamos a Series, 4 bks., Set. Incl. Vamos a Colombia. Fox, Mary Virginia. 2001. lib. bdg. 21.36 (978-1-57572-382-2(4)); Vamos a Costa Rica. Fox, Mary Virginia. 2000. lib. bdg. 21.36 (978-1-57572-383-9(2)); Vamos a Cuba. Gillis, Jennifer & Schreier, Alta. 2001. lib. bdg. 21.36 (978-1-57572-384-6(0)); Vamos a Puerto Rico. Manning, Ruth. 2000. lib. bdg. 21.36 (978-1-57572-385-3(9)); (J). (gr. k-2). (SPA., Illus.). 32p. 2000. Set lib. bdg. 85.44 (978-1-58810-145-7(2)) Heinemann Library.

LATIN AMERICA—POLITICS AND GOVERNMENT

Blake, Charles H. Politics in Latin America: The Quests for Development, Liberty, & Governance. 2004. (Illus.). 400p. (YA). 61.16 (978-0-618-21552-2(2), 304680) Houghton Mifflin College Div.

Dunn, John M. Life in Castro's Cuba. 2004. (Way People Live Ser.). (Illus.). 112p. (J). (gr. 7-10). 29.95 (978-1-59018-464-6(5)) Thomson Gale.

Kingstone, Peter. Readings in Latin American Politics: Challenges to Democratization. 2005. (Illus.). 562p. (YA). 47.56 (978-0-618-37136-5(2), 329929) Houghton Mifflin College Div.

LATIN AMERICA—SOCIAL CONDITIONS

Dunn, John M. Life in Castro's Cuba. 2004. (Way People Live Ser.). (Illus.). 112p. (J). (gr. 7-10). 29.95 (978-1-59018-464-6(5)) Thomson Gale.

LATIN AMERICAN LITERATURE—HISTORY AND CRITICISM

Bloom, Harold, ed. Love in the Time of Cholera. 2005. (Illus.). 144-176p. (gr. 9-13). 45.00 (978-0-7910-8120-4(6), Chelsea Hse.) Facts On File, Inc.

LATIN AMERICANS

Here are entered works on citizens of Latin American countries. Works on citizens of Latin American countries in the United States are entered under Latin Americans—United States. Works on United States citizens of Latin American descent are entered under Hispanic Americans.

The Great Hispanic Heritage. 2005. (Illus.). 112p. (gr. 6-12). 180.00 (978-0-7910-7251-6(7), Chelsea Hse.) Facts On File, Inc.

Hovius, Christopher. Latino Migrant Workers: America's Harvesters. 2005. (Illus.). 112p. (J). (ps-7). lib. bdg. (978-1-59084-937-8(X)) Mason Crest Pubs.

Paths: Jose Marti, Frida Kahlo, Cesar Chavez. 2001. (Gateways to the Sun Ser.). (J). (gr. 3-4). lib. bdg. 14.95 (978-1-58105-573-3(0)) Santillana USA Publishing Co., Inc.

Schwartz, Eric. Job Diversity. 2005. (Illus.). 112p. lib. bdg. (978-1-59084-931-6(0)) Mason Crest Pubs.

LATIN AMERICANS—FICTION

Cuentos, Mitos y Leyendas para Ninos de America Latina (Stories, Myths & Legends for Latin American Children) (SPA., Illus.). 72p. (J). 9.95 (978-958-04-0957-1(9), NOR9609) Norma S.A. COL. *Dist:* Distribuidora Norma, Inc.

Madrigal, Antonio Hernandez. Erandi's Braids. 2001. (Illus.). (J). (978-0-606-21181-9(0)) Tandem Library Bks.

LATIN AMERICANS—UNITED STATES

Binns, Tristan Boyer. Mission San Juan Capistrano. 2002. (Visiting the Past Ser.). (Illus.). 32p. (J). (gr. 5-7). pap. 6.95 (978-1-58810-410-6(9), 91183) Heinemann Library.

—San Juan Capistrano. 2001. (Visiting the Past Ser.). (Illus.). 32p. (J). (gr. 5-7). lib. bdg. 24.22 (978-1-58810-272-0(6)) Heinemann Library.

—St. Augustine. (Visiting the Past Ser.). (Illus.). 32p. (J). (gr. 5-7). 2002. pap. 6.95 (978-1-58810-411-3(7), 91184); 2001. lib. bdg. 24.22 (978-1-58810-273-7(4)) Heinemann Library.

Muskat, Carrie. Moises Alou. 1999. (Latinos in Baseball Ser.). (Illus.). 72p. (gr. 4-10). lib. bdg. 18.95 (978-1-883845-86-5(6)) Mitchell Lane Pubs., Inc.

Winter, Jonah. Beisbol: Pioneros y Leyendas Del Beisbol Latino. 2002. (SPA., Illus.). (J). pap. 16.95 (978-1-58430-035-9(3)) Lee & Low Bks., Inc.

—Beisbol: Pioneros y Leyendas Del Beisbol Latino. Del Risco, Enrique, tr. 2002. (SPA., Illus.). 32p. (J). (gr. 1-5). pap. 6.95 (978-1-58430-036-6(1)) Lee & Low Bks., Inc.

LATIN LANGUAGE

Baddorf, Robert A. & Perrin, Christopher. Latin for Children, Primer A. 2006. 198p. pap., act. bk. ed. 16.95 (978-1-60051-005-2(1)) Classical Academic Pr.

Bolchazy, Marie Carducci. Quis Me Amat?/Who Loves Me? 2003. (I Am Reading Latin Ser.). (ENG & LAT., Illus.). 64p. (J). (gr. k-3). 12.00 (978-0-86516-541-0(6)) Bolchazy-Carducci Pubs.

Carole Marsh. Of All the Gaul! 2004. (Little Linguist Ser.). 32p. 29.95 (978-0-635-02437-4(3)) Gallopade International.

—Of All the Gaul! Latin for Kids. 2004. (Little Linguist Ser.). 32p. (gr. 2-6). pap. 5.95 (978-0-635-02429-9(2)) Gallopade International.

Craig, Karen. Matin Latin 1: Student, Vol. I. Blakey, Laura, illus. 1998. 144p. (J). (gr. 3-6). spiral bd. 28.00 (978-1-885767-46-2(3)) Canon Pr.

Craig, Karen L. Latin Grammar II: Student, Vol. 2. 1999. (Mars Hill Textbook Ser.). 244p. (YA). (gr. 7). stu. ed., spiral bd. 23.00 (978-1-885767-60-8(9)) Canon Pr.

—Latin Grammar II: Teacher's Guide: Answer Key, Vol. 2. 1999. (Mars Hill Textbook Ser.). 244p. (YA). stu. ed., spiral bd. 23.00 (978-1-885767-61-5(7)) Canon Pr.

—Matin Latin 2: Student, Vol. II. Blakey, Laura, illus. 1998. 204p. (J). (gr. 3-6). spiral bd. 33.00 (978-1-885767-48-6(X)) Canon Pr.

Garfield, Julie. Latin Primer, Vol. 2. 2000. (Latin Primer Ser.). 48p. (J). spiral bd. 15.00 (978-1-930443-07-5(2), C227) Logos Schl.

Latin Grammar. 2003. stu. ed., ring bd., wbk. ed. (978-1-931680-42-4(6)) Teaching Point, Inc.

Latin Words Sticker Book. 2006. 16p. (J). pap. 8.99 (978-0-7945-1145-6(7), Usborne) EDC Publishing.

Lowe, Leigh. Prima Latina Student Book: Introduction to Christian Latin. 2nd ed. 2003. 128p. (J). per. 14.00 (978-1-930953-51-2(8), 002) Memoria Pr.

Lundquist, Joegil K. & Lundquist, Jeanne L. English from the Roots Up: Help for Reading, Writing, Spelling, & S. A. T. Scores. 2003. 39.95 (978-1-885942-30-2(3)); II. (Illus.). 125p. 29.95 (978-1-885942-31-9(1)) Cune Pr., LLC.

Mcgraw-Hill-Glencoe Staff. Latin for Americans, Level 2. 9th ed. 2004. (C). stu. ed. 78.60 incl. cd-rom (978-0-07-861252-7(7), 9780078612527) Glencoe/McGraw-Hill.

McGraw-Hill Staff, et al. Latin for Americans: Level 2, 2 vols. 9th ed. 2003. 646p. (C). (gr. 9-12). stu. ed. 78.60 (978-0-07-828176-1(8), 9780078281761) Glencoe/McGraw-Hill.

Osburn, LeaAnn. Latin Verbs Rock! Exercise Book. 2007. spiral bd. 18.00 (***978-0-9760046-6-0(6)***) L & L Enterprises.

The Rosetta Stone Language Library: Latin Level 1. 2005. (J). (gr. 1 up). cd-rom 209.00 (978-1-58022-026-2(6)) Fairfield Language Technologies.

LATIN LANGUAGE—READERS

Baddorf, Robert & Perrin, Christopher. Latin for Children, Primer B. Baddorf, Robert, illus. 2005. (Illus.). pap., act. bk. ed. 16.95 (978-1-60051-011-3(6)) Classical Academic Pr.

—Latin for Children, Primer C. Baddorf, Robert, illus. 2006. (Illus.). pap., act. bk. ed. 16.95 (978-1-60051-017-5(5)) Classical Academic Pr.

Blair, Robert W. Power-Glide Latin Lower Elementary, 2 vols. l.t. ed. (Illus.). 2002. 135p. (J). pap. 79.95 (978-1-58204-222-0(5)); 2000. 291p. (YA). pap. 149.95 incl. audio compact disk (978-1-58204-209-1(8)) Power-Glide Foreign Language Courses.

Bolchazy, Marie Carducci. Quo Colore Est?/What Color Is It? 2003. (I Am Reading Latin Ser.). (ENG & LAT., Illus.). 64p. (J). (gr. k-3). 12.00 (978-0-86516-539-7(4)) Bolchazy-Carducci Pubs.

Church, Francis Pharcellus & O'Hanlon, Virginia. Yes Virginia, There Is a Santa Claus—In Latin! Vere Virginia, Sanctus Nicolaus Est! Kringe, Matthias, illus. 2001. (LAT.). 32p. (J). 12.00 (978-0-86516-506-9(8)) Bolchazy-Carducci Pubs.

Larsen, Aaron & Perrin, Christopher. Latin for Children, Primer B. 2004. pap. 24.95 (978-1-60051-006-9(X)) Classical Academic Pr.

—Latin for Children, Primer B Answer Key. 2004. pap. 9.95 (978-1-60051-007-6(8)) Classical Academic Pr.

—Latin for Children, Primer C. 2005. (Illus.). 310p. pap. 24.95 (978-1-60051-012-0(4)) Classical Academic Pr.

—Latin for Children, Primer C Answer Key. 2005. pap. 9.95 (978-1-60051-013-7(2)) Classical Academic Pr.

MacLaren, Dorothy H. Esopus Hodie, Aesop Today, Vol. 1. (ENG & LAT.). 64p. (YA). (gr. 9-12). 9.75 (978-0-939507-06-1(4), B20) American Classical League, The.

Moore, Karen. Latin for Children, Primer A History Reader: Libellus de Historia. 2005. (Illus.). 56p. pap. 9.95 (978-1-60051-004-5(3)) Classical Academic Pr.

Moore, Karen & Davis, Erin. Latin for Children, Primer B History Reader: Libellus de Historia. 2005. (Illus.). pap. 12.95 (978-1-60051-010-6(8)) Classical Academic Pr.

—Latin for Children, Primer C History Reader: Libellus de Historia. 2006. (Illus.). pap. 16.95 (978-1-60051-016-8(7)) Classical Academic Pr.

Pearcy, Lee T., et al. New First Steps in Latin. 2000. (Illus.). 1p. (YA). (gr. 6-12). pap., stu. ed. 19.95 (978-1-58510-008-8(0)) Focus Publishing/R. Pullins Co., Inc.

Seuss, Dr. Cattus Petasatus. Tunberg, Jennifer Morrish & Tunberg, Terence O., trs. from ENG. 2000. Tr. of Cat in the Hat. (LAT., Illus.). 80p. (YA). (ps-3). 20.00 (978-0-86516-472-7(X)); 26.00 (978-0-86516-471-0(1)) Bolchazy-Carducci Pubs.

Williams, Rose. The Young Romans. 2007. (LAT & ENG.). pap. (***978-0-86516-670-7(6)***) Bolchazy-Carducci Pubs.

LATTER-DAY SAINTS

see Mormons and Mormonism

LATVIA

Aizpuriete, Amanda. Latvia. Hartgers, Katarina, tr. Bultje, Jan Willem, photos by. 2006. (Looking at Europe Ser.). 48p. (YA). (gr. 5-8). 22.95 (978-1-881508-37-3(4)) Oliver Pr., Inc.

Barlas, Robert. Latvia. 2000. (Cultures of the World Ser.). (Illus.). 128p. (gr. 5-12). lib. bdg. 37.07 (978-0-7614-0977-9(7), Benchmark Bks.) Cavendish, Marshall Corp.

Docalavich, Heather. Latvia. 2006. (European Union Ser.). (Illus.). 88p. (J). (gr. 5 up). lib. bdg. (978-1-4222-0053-7(1)) Mason Crest Pubs.

LAVOISIER, ANTOINE LAURENT, 1743-1794

Yount, Lisa. Antoine Lavoisier: Founder of Modern Chemistry. 2008. (J). (***978-0-7660-3011-4(3));*** 2001. (Illus.). 128p. (YA). (gr. 4-10). pap. 13.26 (978-0-7660-1865-5(2)) Enslow Pubs., Inc.

LAW

see also Courts; Judges; Jury; Lawyers; Police

also special branches of law, e.g. International Law; For laws on special subjects see names of subjects with the subdivision Laws and Regulations, e.g. Automobiles—Laws and Regulations

Beel, Rory. The Second Informant. 2005. 65p. pap. 12.95 (978-1-4137-8359-9(7)) PublishAmerica, Inc.

Campbell, Andrea, et al. Rights of the Accused. 2000. (Crime, Justice & Punishment Ser.). (Illus.). 80p. (YA). 30.00 (978-0-7910-4303-5(7) , Chelsea Hse.) Facts On File, Inc.

Cooper, Corinne. The New Article 9. 2nd ed. 2000. 462p. pap. 39.95 (978-1-57073-831-9(9)) American Bar Assn.

De Capua, Sarah. Making a Law. 2004. (True Bks.). (Illus.). 48p. (J). (gr. 3-5). pap. 6.95 (978-0-516-27941-1(6) , Children's Pr.) Scholastic Library Publishing.

Fridell, Ron. Miranda Law: The Right to Remain Silent. 2005. (Supreme Court Milestones Ser.). (Illus.). 144p. (J). (978-0-7614-1942-6(X) , Benchmark Bks.) Cavendish, Marshall Corp.

Goldman. Study Guide: Used with ... Goldman-Business Law: Principles & Practices. 6th ed. 2003. (YA). stu. ed. 31.96 (978-0-618-30295-6(6) , 319043) Houghton Mifflin College Div.

Government & Law. 1999. (YA). (gr. 9-12). ring bd. 199.95 (978-0-8224-8035-8(2)) Globe Fearon Educational Publishing.

John, Peter Q. Watch Your Step: A Law Book for Teens. Crosby, Stanley, ed. Mallory, Linani, illus. 1998. 120p. (J). (gr. 6-12). pap. 12.50 (978-0-9667725-0-0(4)) Oktopus Publishing.

Kelly, Zachary A. Laws. 1998. (Law & Order Ser.). (J). lib. bdg. 16.95 (978-0-86625-664-3(4)) Rourke Publishing, LLC.

Kerrigan, Michael. The History of Punishment. 2002. (Crime & Detection Ser.). (Illus.). 96p. (J). (gr. 7 up). lib. bdg. (978-1-59084-386-4(X)) Mason Crest Pubs.

Kowalski, Kathiann M. Teen Rights: At Home, at School, Online. 2000. (Issues in Focus Ser.). (Illus.). 128p. (YA). (gr. 6-12). lib. bdg. 26.60 (978-0-7660-1242-4(5)) Enslow Pubs., Inc.

Landmark Supreme Court Cases, 35 bks., Set. (Illus.). (YA). (gr. 6-12). lib. bdg. 733.25 (978-0-89490-572-8(4)) Enslow Pubs., Inc.

Mabbutt, George C. Laws - 1. 2004. (Topic Bks.). (Illus.). 36p. bds. 5.00 (978-0-7188-1832-6(6)) Lutherworth Pr., The GBR. *Dist:* Parkwest Pubns., Inc.

—Laws - 2. 2004. (Topic Bks.). 36p. bds. 5.00 (978-0-7188-1833-3(4)) Lutherworth Pr., The GBR. *Dist:* Parkwest Pubns., Inc.

Marvis, B. & Worth, Richard. The Insanity Defense. 2001. (Crime, Justice & Punishment Ser.). (Illus.). 80p. (J). (gr. 9 up). 30.00 (978-0-7910-4294-6(4) , Chelsea Hse.) Facts On File, Inc.

Marzilli, Alan, ed. Point/Counterpoint. (Illus.). (J). 155.70 (978-0-7910-7368-1(8) , Chelsea Hse.) Facts On File, Inc.

Maybury, Richard J. Uncle Eric Talks about Personal, Career, & Financial Security. Williams, Jane A. & Daniels, Kathryn, eds. 2nd ed. 2004. ("Uncle Eric" Bk.). (Illus.). 187p. (YA). pap. 14.95 (978-0-942617-38-2(X)) Bluestocking Pr.

McGraw-Hill Staff. Street Law. 7th ed. 2004. stu. ed. 79.96 (978-0-07-860019-7(7) , 9780078600197) Glencoe/McGraw-Hill.

—Street Law, Student Workbook. 7th ed. 2004. (Illus.). viii, 102p. (C). pap. 19.96 (978-0-07-861208-4(X) , 9780078612084) Glencoe/McGraw-Hill.

Mothersole, Brenda. A-Level Law in Action. 2nd ed. 1999. (Law Masters Ser.). (Illus.). 560p. (C). pap. 37.95 (978-0-333-72780-5(0)) CENGAGE Learning.

Payno, Manuel. Los Bandidos de Rio Frio. Camacho, Ricardo, illus. 2003. (SPA.). 91p. (J). pap. (978-970-643-638-2(3)) Selector, S.A. de C.V. MEX. *Dist:* Lectorum Pubns., Inc.

Persico, Deborah A. Vernonia School District vs. Acton: Drug Testing in Schools. 1999. (Landmark Supreme Court Cases Ser.). (Illus.). 128p. (YA). (gr. 6-12). lib. bdg. 26.60 (978-0-7660-1087-1(2)) Enslow Pubs., Inc.

Schnapp, Eric Cesar, et al. Legally Clueless: A Law Guide for Young People. 2002. (YA). (gr. 9-12). per. 11.95 (978-0-9719337-2-9(3)) Elma Colletes & Sons.

Trembinski, Donna. Medieval Law & Punishment. 2005. (Medieval World Ser.). (Illus.). 32p. (J). (gr. 4-9). (978-0-7787-1360-9(1)); pap. (978-0-7787-1392-0(X)) Crabtree Publishing Co.

Trespacz, Karen L. Ferrell vs. Dallas I. S. D. Hairstyles in Schools. 1998. (Landmark Supreme Court Cases Ser.). (Illus.). 128p. (YA). (gr. 6-12). lib. bdg. 26.60 (978-0-7660-1054-3(6)) Enslow Pubs., Inc.

Upson, Eric B. & Upson, Greta Barclay. Everyday Law for Young Citizens: A Working Guide. Mitchell, Judy, ed. Gutierrez, Mark, illus. 2000. 160p. (YA). (gr. 5-9). pap., tchr. ed. 14.95 (978-1-57310-242-1(3)) Teaching & Learning Co.

Vinogradoff, Paul. Normas Sociales y Normas Juridicas. (Fondo 2000 Ser.). (SPA.). (J). 2.99 (978-968-16-5300-2(9)) Fondo de Cultura Economica USA.

Who Makes Our Laws? Set E, 6 vols. (Phonics Readers Ser.). (gr. k-2). 28.95 (978-0-7368-4073-6(7)) Red Brick Learning.

Zarate, Gustavo Azgad. Youth Law: A Practical Guide to Legal Issues That Affect Young Adults. 2nd ed. 2005. (YA). per. 25.00 (978-0-9763167-9-4(X)) Living Ministry, Inc.

LAW, CONSTITUTIONAL

see Constitutional Law

LAW, INTERNATIONAL

see International Law

LAW—UNITED STATES

Aaseng, Nathan. Plessy vs. Ferguson. 2003. (Famous Trials Ser.). (Illus.). 112p. (J). 29.95 (978-1-59018-268-0(5) , Lucent Bks.) Thomson Gale.

Axelrod-Contrada, Joan. Reno v. ACLU: Internet Censorship. 2006. (Supreme Court Milestones Ser.). (Illus.). 144p. (J). lib. bdg. 39.93 (978-0-7614-2144-3(0) , Benchmark Bks.) Cavendish, Marshall Corp.

Beier, Anne. The Supreme Court & the Judicial Branch. 2003. (Primary Source Library of American Citizenship). (Illus.). 32p. (J). pap. (978-1-4042-5092-5(1)) Rosen Publishing Group, Inc., The.

Benson, Edmund F. 10-20 Life. 2001. 60p. (J). pap. 3.95 (978-1-58614-300-8(X)) Arise Foundation.

Burgan, Michael. Miranda V. Arizona: The Rights of the Accused. 2006. (J). (978-0-7565-2008-3(8)) Compass Point Bks.

Burns, Kate. The Right to Die. 2007. (Hot Topics Ser.). 128p. (gr. 7-10). 31.20 (***978-1-59018-834-7(9)*** , Lucent Bks.) Thomson Gale.

Castle, Caroline. For Every Child: The UN Convention on the Rights of the Child in Words & Pictures. ed. 2004. (J). (gr. k-3). spiral bd. (978-0-616-14617-0(5)); spiral bd. (978-0-616-14618-7(3)) Canadian National Institute for the Blind/Institut National Canadien pour les Aveugles.

Cefrey, Holly. The Interstate Commerce ACT: The Government Takes Control of Trade Between the States. 2003. (America's Industrial Society in the Nineteenth Century Ser.). (Illus.). 32p. (J). pap. (978-0-8239-4282-4(1)) Rosen Publishing Group, Inc., The.

Cohen, Laura. The Gault Case & Young People's Rights: Debating Supreme Court Decisions. 2006. (Debating Supreme Court Decisions Ser.). (Illus.). 128p. (J). lib. bdg. 26.60 (978-0-7660-2476-2(8)) Enslow Pubs., Inc.

Crewe, Sabrina & Schaefer, Adam. The Triangle Shirtwaist Factory Fire. 2004. (Events That Shaped America Ser.). (Illus.). 32p. (J). (gr. 3 up). lib. bdg. 24.67 (978-0-8368-3402-4(X)) Stevens, Gareth Inc.

Crompton, Samuel Willard & McNeese, Tim. McCulloch V. Maryland: Implied Powers of the Federal Government. 2007. (Great Supreme Court Decisions Ser.). 136p. (J). (gr. 5-8). 30.00 (978-0-7910-9262-0(3) , Chelsea Hse.) Facts On File, Inc.

De Capua, Sarah. Making a Law. 2004. (True Bks.). (Illus.). 48p. (J). (gr. 3-5). pap. 6.95 (978-0-516-27941-1(6)); 25.00 (978-0-516-22801-3(3)) Scholastic Library Publishing. (Children's Pr.).

Donovan, Sandy. Making Laws: A Look at How a Bill Becomes a Law. 2004. (How Government Works Ser.). (Illus.). 56p. (J). (gr. 4-8). lib. bdg. 25.26 (978-0-8225-1346-9(3)) Lerner Publishing Group.

Egan, Tracie. How a Bill Becomes a Law. 2003. (Primary Source Library of American Citizenship). (J). pap. (978-1-4042-5085-7(9)) Rosen Publishing Group, Inc., The.

Fireside, Bryna J. Cruzan vs. Missouri: The Right to Die Case. 1999. (Landmark Supreme Court Cases Ser.). (Illus.). 128p. (YA). (gr. 6-12). lib. bdg. 20.95 (978-0-7660-1088-8(0)) Enslow Pubs., Inc.

Freedman, Jeri. Intellectual Property. 2008. (J). lib. bdg. (***978-1-4042-1348-7(1))*** Rosen Publishing Group, Inc., The.

Good, Diane L. Brown vs. Board of Education: A Civil Rights Milestone. 2004. (Cornerstones of Freedom Ser.). (J). 26.00 (978-0-516-24225-5(3) , Children's Pr.) Scholastic Library Publishing.

Hamilton, John. How a Bill Becomes a Law. 2005. (Government in Action! Ser.). (Illus.). 32p. (J). (gr. k-6). lib. bdg. 22.78 (978-1-59197-646-2(4)) ABDO Publishing Co.

Hanrahan, Clare. Legal System. 2007. (Opposing Viewpoints Ser.). (Illus.). 240p. (gr. 10-12). 36.20 (***978-0-7377-3757-8(3));*** pap. 24.95 (***978-0-7377-3758-5(1))*** Thomson Gale. (Greenhaven Pr., Inc.).

Hunter, David. Inequities of the Justice System. 2006. (Incarceration Issues Ser.). (Illus.). 112p. (YA). (gr. 7 up). (978-1-59084-995-8(7)) Mason Crest Pubs.

Kishel, Ann-Marie. Rules & Laws. 2007. (First Step Nonfiction Ser.). 24p. (J). (gr. k-2). 18.60 (978-0-8225-6396-9(7) , Lerner Pubns.) Lerner Publishing Group.

Koopmans, Andy. The Leopold & Loeb Case. 2003. (Famous Trials Ser.). (Illus.). 112p. (J). 29.95 (978-1-59018-227-7(8) , Lucent Bks.) Thomson Gale.

Lawrence, Katherine. Labor Legislation: The Struggle to Gain Rights for America's Workforce. 2004. (Progressive Movement, 1900-1920 Ser.). (Illus.). 32p. (J). lib. bdg. (978-1-4042-0191-0(2)) Rosen Publishing Group, Inc., The.

The Library of American Laws & Legal Principles. (Illus.). (YA). (gr. 5-8). 143.70 (978-1-4042-0621-2(3) , Rosen Central) Rosen Publishing Group, Inc., The.

Lieurance, Suzanne. The Triangle Shirtwaist Fire & Sweatshop Reform in American History. 2003. (In American History Ser.). (Illus.). 128p. (J). (gr. 5-12). lib. bdg. 26.60 (978-0-7660-1839-6(3)) Enslow Pubs., Inc.

Linz, Kathi. Chickens May Not Cross the Road: And Other Crazy but True Laws. Griego, Tony, illus. 2002. 32p. (J). (gr. 1-5). tchr. ed. 16.00 (978-0-618-11257-9(X)) Houghton Mifflin Co. Trade & Reference Div.

Marzilli, Alan, ed. Point/Counterpoint: Issues in Contemporary American Society. (Illus.). (gr. 9-13). pap. (978-0-7910-8046-7(3)); lib. bdg. 519.00 (978-0-7910-8468-7(X)) Facts On File, Inc. (Chelsea Hse.).

McKissack, Patricia C. & Zarembka, Arlene. To Establish Justice: Citizenship & the Constitution. 2004. (Illus.). 160p. (YA). (gr. 9-11). lib. bdg. 20.99 (978-0-679-99308-7(8) , Knopf Bks. for Young Readers) Random Hse. Children's Bks.

McKissack, Patricia C., et al. To Establish Justice: Citizenship & the Constitution. 2004. (Illus.). 160p. (YA). (gr. 9-11). 18.95 (978-0-679-89308-0(3) , Knopf Bks. for Young Readers) Random Hse. Children's Bks.

McLane, William. Furman vs. Georgia. 2001. (Famous Trials Ser.). (Illus.). 112p. (J). (gr. 7-10). lib. bdg. 29.95 (978-1-56006-470-1(6) , LML00902-177835, Lucent Bks.) Thomson Gale.

Miller, Jake. Brown vs. Board of Education of Topeka: Challenging School Segregation in the Supreme Court. 2004. (Library of the Civil Rights Movement Ser.). (Illus.). 24p. (J). lib. bdg. 19.95 (978-0-8239-6250-1(4)) Rosen Publishing Group, Inc., The.

—Community Rules: Making & Changing Rules & Laws in Communities. 2005. (Communities at Work Ser.). (Illus.). 24p. (J). lib. bdg. 19.95 (978-1-4042-2782-8(2) , PowerKids Pr.) Rosen Publishing Group, Inc., The.

Mitchell, Hayley R. The Death Penalty. 2000. (Contemporary Issues Companion Ser.). 154p. (YA). (gr. 9 up). lib. bdg. 36.20 (978-0-7377-0458-7(6)); (Illus.). (gr. 10 up). pap. 24.95 (978-0-7377-0457-0(8)) Thomson Gale. (Greenhaven Pr., Inc.).

New, David W. The Ten Commandments for Beginners. 2004. 60p. (YA). per. 4.95 (978-0-9721333-4-0(8)) Pocket Publication, A.

Pierce, Alan. Brown V. Board of Education. 2005. (American Moments Set Ii Ser.). (J). (gr. 4-8). lib. bdg. 25.65 (978-1-59197-725-4(8) , ABDO & Daughters) ABDO Publishing Co.

Point/Counterpoint Issues in Contemporary American Society. 2005. pap. 889.65 (978-0-7910-9185-2(6) , Chelsea Hse.) Facts On File, Inc.

Ramen, Fred. The Rights of the Accused. 2001. (Individual Rights & Civic Responsibility Ser.). (Illus.). 64p. (YA). (gr. 7-12). lib. bdg. 26.50 (978-0-8239-3238-2(9)) Rosen Publishing Group, Inc., The.

The Right to Due Process. 2005. (Bill of Rights Ser.). 138p. (YA). (gr. 10-13). lib. bdg. 33.70 (978-0-7377-1941-3(9) , Greenhaven Pr., Inc.) Thomson Gale.

Riley, Gail Blasser. And Justice for All. 2003. (Illus.). 60p. (J). (978-0-7398-5175-3(6)) Steck-Vaughn.

Roensch, Greg. Furman V. Georgia: Cruel & Unusual Punishment. 2007. (Great Supreme Court Decisions Ser.). 112p. (J). (gr. 5-8). 30.00 (978-0-7910-9382-5(4) , Chelsea Hse.) Facts On File, Inc.

Swain, Gwenyth. Dred & Harriet Scott: A Family's Struggle for Freedom. 2004. (Illus.). 102p. pap. 12.95 (978-0-87351-483-5(1) , Borealis Bk.) Minnesota Historical Society Pr.

Swann, Kristina. US Law - Student Text. 2005. (Illus.). 48p. (YA). 11.95 (978-1-58804-397-9(5)) PCI Educational Publishing.

Teichmann, Iris. Immigration & the Law. 2006. (Understanding Immigration Ser.). (Illus.). 44p. (J). (gr. 5-8). lib. bdg. 31.35 (978-1-58340-970-1(X)) Smart Apple Media.

Whelan, Elaine P., narrated by. My Mom's Making History: The Story of Computer Software, Copyrights & Creativity, 1. 2nd ed. 2003. 80p. (J). per. 12.99 (978-0-9726871-0-2(6)) Mainstreet Systems & Software Inc.

LAW—VOCATIONAL GUIDANCE

Cefrey, Holly. Choosing a Career As a Paralegal. 2005. (World of Work Ser.). (Illus.). 64p. (J). (gr. 7-12). lib. bdg. 25.25 (978-0-8239-3286-3(9)) Rosen Publishing Group, Inc., The.

Davis, Mary L. Working in Law & Justice. 1999. (Exploring Careers Ser.). (Illus.). 112p. (YA). (gr. 6-9). lib. bdg. (978-0-8225-1766-5(3) , Lerner Pubns.) Lerner Publishing Group.

J. G. Ferguson Publishing Company Staff, contrib. by. Careers in Focus: Law. 2nd ed. 2003. (Careers in Focus Ser.). 192p. (YA). (gr. 6-12). 22.95 (978-0-89434-476-3(5) , Ferguson Publishing Co.) Facts On File, Inc.

J. G. Ferguson Publishing Company Staff, ed. Careers in Focus: Law. 2001. (Careers in Focus Ser.). 188p. (YA). (gr. 7 up). lib. bdg. 22.95 (978-0-89434-331-5(9) , F709, Ferguson Publishing Co.) Facts On File, Inc.

Morgan, Marilyn. Careers in Criminology. 1998. (Careers in... Ser.). (Illus.). 224p. pap. 16.95 (978-0-7373-0272-1(0) , 9780737302721) McGraw-Hill Cos., The.

Parks, Peggy J. Lawyer. 2003. (Exploring Careers Ser.). (Illus.). 48p. (J). (gr. 3-5). 26.20 (978-0-7377-1485-2(9) , Kidhaven) Thomson Gale.

Pasternak, Ceel & Thornburg, Linda. Cool Careers for Girls in Law. 2001. (Illus.). (gr. 7). 128p. pap. 12.95 (978-1-57023-157-5(5)); 132p. (J). 19.95 (978-1-57023-160-5(5)) Impact Pubns.

Powell, Phelan & Wade, Linda R. Careers in Law & Politics. 2001. (Latinos at Work Ser.). (Illus.). 96p. (J). (gr. 5-12). lib. bdg. 22.95 (978-1-58415-080-0(7)) Mitchell Lane Pubs., Inc.

Quinlan, Kathryn A. Paralegal. 1998. (Careers Without College Ser.). (Illus.). 48p. (J). (gr. 3-7). pap. 19.00 (978-0-516-21285-2(0) , Children's Pr.) Scholastic Library Publishing.

Reeves, Diane Lindsey. Career Ideas for Teens in Law & Public Safety. 2005. (Career Ideas for Teens Ser.). (Illus.). 184p. (YA). (gr. 6-12). per. 40.00 (978-0-8160-5291-2(3) , Ferguson Publishing Co.) Facts On File, Inc.

Reeves, Diane Lindsey & Karlitz, Gail. Career Ideas for Teens in Law & Public Safety. (Career Ideas for Teens Ser.). 192p. (gr. 6-12). pap. 16.95 (978-0-8160-6922-4(0) , Checkmark Bks.) Facts On File, Inc.

LAW ENFORCEMENT

see also Police

Ashabranner, Brent. Badge of Valor: The National Law Enforcement Officers Memorial. Ashabranner, Jennifer, illus. 2000. (Great American Memorials Ser.). 64p. (gr. 4-8). lib. bdg. (978-0-7613-1522-3(5) , Twenty-First Century Bks.) Lerner Publishing Group.

Blashfield, Jean F. Interpol. 2003. (International Organizations Ser.). (Illus.). 48p. (J). (gr. 5 up). lib. bdg. 30.00 (978-0-8368-5520-3(5)); pap. 11.95 (978-0-8368-5529-6(9)) Stevens, Gareth Inc. (World Almanac Library).

Conrad, David. Law & Order. 2002. (Spyglass Books). (Illus.). 24p. (J). (gr. 1 up). lib. bdg. 18.60 (978-0-7565-0383-3(3)) Compass Point Bks.

Donkin, Andrew. Crime Busters. 2001. (Illus.). 48p. (J). (gr. 3-4). lib. bdg. 11.80 (978-0-613-43924-4(4)) Tandem Library Bks.

Emert, Phyllis Raybin. Attorneys General: Enforcing the Law. 2005. (Illus.). 176p. (J). (gr. 7 up). lib. bdg. 24.95 (978-1-881508-66-3(8)) Oliver Pr., Inc.

Grabowski, John F. The Ruby Ridge Scandal. 2005. (American Secrets & Scandals Ser.). (J). (978-1-59018-485-1(8) , Lucent Bks.) Thomson Gale.

Green, Michael. Law Enforcement, 8 bks. 1998. (Illus.). (gr. 3-7). pap. (978-0-531-19417-1(5) , Watts, Franklin) Scholastic Library Publishing.

—Law Enforcement, 7 bks. Incl. Bicycle Patrol Officers. 1999. lib. bdg. 21.26 (978-0-7368-0186-7(3)); Bomb Detection Squads. 2000. lib. bdg. 21.26 (978-1-56065-755-2(3)); Customs Service. 2000. lib. bdg. 21.26 (978-1-56065-756-9(1)); Motorcycle Police. 1999. lib. bdg. 21.26 (978-0-7368-0187-4(1)); Mounted Police. 2000. lib. bdg. 21.26 (978-1-56065-757-6(X)); Sheriffs & Deputy Sheriffs. 1999. lib. bdg. 21.26 (978-0-7368-0188-1(X)); United States Marshals Service. 1999. lib. bdg. 21.26 (978-0-7368-0189-8(8)); 48p. (J). (gr. 3-4). (Illus.). 2001. Set lib. bdg. 170.08 (978-0-7368-0461-5(7) , Capstone High-Interest Bks.) Capstone Pr., Inc.

—Mounted Police. 1998. (Law Enforcement Ser.). 48p. (J). lib. bdg. 19.00 (978-0-531-11560-2(7) , Watts, Franklin) Scholastic Library Publishing.

—SWAT Teams. 1998. (Law Enforcement Ser.). 48p. (J). lib. bdg. 19.00 (978-0-531-11561-9(5) , Watts, Franklin) Scholastic Library Publishing.

Holden, Henry M. Crime-Fighting Aircraft. 2002. (Aircraft Ser.). (Illus.). 48p. (J). (gr. 4-10). lib. bdg. 23.93 (978-0-7660-1718-4(4)) Enslow Pubs., Inc.

Jarvis, Ana & Lebredo, Raquel. Text: Basic Spanish for Law Enforcement. 2006. (ENG & SPA., Illus.). 288p. (YA). 57.96 (978-0-618-56785-0(2) , 328512) Houghton Mifflin College Div.

Jury Trials in the Classroom. 2001. (J). per. 22.95 (978-1-883055-44-8(X)) Dandy Lion Pubns.

Kelly, Zachary A. Law Enforcement. 1998. (Law & Order Ser.). (J). lib. bdg. (978-0-86625-663-6(6)) Rourke Publishing, LLC.

Schlesinger, Arthur M., Jr., ed. The Federal Bureau of Investigation. 2000. (Your Government Ser.). (Illus.). 64p. (YA). (gr. 3-9). 31.00 (978-0-7910-5530-4(2) , Chelsea Hse.) Facts On File, Inc.

Thomas, William. Working in Law Enforcement. 2005. (My Future Career Ser.). (J). lib. bdg. 26.00 (978-0-8368-4775-8(X)) Stevens, Gareth Inc.

Townsend, John. Lawmakers & the Police. 2005. (J). (978-1-4109-2052-2(6)); pap. (978-1-4109-2057-7(7)) Steck-Vaughn.

LAW ENFORCEMENT—VOCATIONAL GUIDANCE

Cassedy, Patrice. Law Enforcement. 2002. (Careers for the Twenty-First Century Ser.). (Illus.). 104p. (YA). 29.95 (978-1-56006-899-0(X) , LML00902-179322, Lucent Bks.) Thomson Gale.

Ferguson. What Can I Do Now: Safety & Security. 2nd rev. ed. 2007. (What Can I Do Now Ser.). 200p. (gr. 6-12). 29.95 (***978-0-8160-6030-6(4)*** , Ferguson Publishing Co.) Facts On File, Inc.

J. G. Ferguson Publishing Company Staff, contrib. by. Careers in Focus: Public Safety. 2nd ed. 2002. (Careers in Focus Ser.). 192p. (YA). (gr. 6-12). 22.95 (978-0-89434-442-8(0) , Ferguson Publishing Co.) Facts On File, Inc.

J. G. Ferguson Publishing Company Staff, ed. Careers in Focus: Public Safety. 2000. (Careers in Focus Ser.). 188p. (YA). (gr. 7 up). lib. bdg. 22.95 (978-0-89434-325-4(4) , F514, Ferguson Publishing Co.) Facts On File, Inc.

Karlitz, Gail. Virtual Apprentice: FBI Agent. 2008. (Virtual Apprentice Ser.). 64p. (J). (gr. 6-12). 29.95 (***978-0-8160-6758-9(9)*** , Ferguson Publishing Co.) Facts On File, Inc.

Meyer, Jared. Homeland Security Officers. 2006. (Extreme Careers Ser.). (Illus.). 64p. (J). (gr. 5-8). lib. bdg. 26.50 (978-1-4042-0945-9(X)) Rosen Publishing Group, Inc., The.

Miller, Heather. Police Officer. 2003. (This Is What I Want to Be Ser.). (Illus.). 24p. (J). (ps-1). lib. bdg. 18.50 (978-1-4034-0371-1(6)); pap. 5.25 (978-1-4034-0593-7(X)) Heinemann Library.

—Police Officer. 2003. (ps-2). lib. bdg. 13.30 (978-0-613-86439-8(5)) Tandem Library Bks.

Sanna, Ellyn. Homeland Security Officer. 2002. (Careers with Character Ser.). (Illus.). 96p. (YA). (gr. 7 up). lib. bdg. 22.95 (978-1-59084-315-4(0)) Mason Crest Pubs.

LAW OF NATIONS

see International Law

LAWN TENNIS

see Tennis

LAWRENCE, T. E. (THOMAS EDWARD), 1888-1935

MacLean, Alistair. Lawrence of Arabia. 2006. (Sterling Point Bks.). (Illus.). 176p. (J). pap. 6.95 (978-1-4027-3613-1(4)) Sterling Publishing Co., Inc.

LAWS

see Law

LAWYERS

see also Judges; Law—Vocational Guidance

African-American Lawyers. 2000. (My Ancestors—My Heroes Ser.: Vol. 14). (J). (gr. 3-4). (978-1-893091-13-9(9)) Parker Publishing Co.

Cooper, Ann Goode & Bowlin, William Harrison. Lawyer Will: The Story of an Appalachian Lawyer. Jessee, Diana, illus. 2004. 36p. (J). 12.95 (978-1-887905-90-9(1)) Parkway Pubs., Inc.

Crowe, Chris. Up Close: Thurgood Marshall: Thurgood Marshall. 2008. 208p. (YA). (gr. 6). 16.99 (***978-0-670-06228-7(6)***, Viking Juvenile) Penguin Group (USA) Inc.

Emert, Phyllis Raybin. Attorneys General: Enforcing the Law. 2005. (Illus.). 176p. (J). (gr. 7 up). lib. bdg. 24.95 (978-1-881508-66-3(8)) Oliver Pr., Inc.

Gold, Susan Dudley. Engel v. Vitale: Prayer in the Schools. 2005. (Supreme Court Milestones Ser.). (Illus.). 160p. (J). (978-0-7614-1940-2(3), Benchmark Bks.) Cavendish, Marshall Corp.

Harmon, Daniel E. Defense Lawyers. 2001. (Crime, Justice & Punishment Ser.). (Illus.). 80p. (J). (gr. 7-10). 30.00 (978-0-7910-4284-7(7), Chelsea Hse.) Facts On File, Inc.

Harris, Nancy. First Guide to Government: What's the State Judicial Branch? 2007. (J). (***978-1-4034-9511-2(4)***); pap. (***978-1-4034-9517-4(3)***) Heinemann Library.

Haskins, James & Poole, Cecil F. Cecil Poole: A Life in the Law. 2002. (Illus.). xii; 172p. (YA). 15.00 (978-0-9635086-2-1(8)) Ninth Judicial Circuit Historical Society.

Horn, Geoffrey M. Thurgood Marshall. 2004. (Trailblazers of the Modern World Ser.). (Illus.). 48p. (J). (gr. 5 up). pap. 11.95 (978-0-8368-5258-5(3)); lib. bdg. 30.00 (978-0-8368-5098-7(X)) Stevens, Gareth Inc. (World Almanac Library).

Kelly, Zachary A. Judges & Lawyers. (Law & Order Ser.). (J). 2000. (Illus.). 48p. (gr. 4-8). lib. bdg. 27.93 (978-0-86593-577-8(7)); 1998. lib. bdg. 16.95 (978-0-86625-661-2(X)) Rourke Publishing, LLC.

Kroll, Steven & Kroll, Steven. By the Dawn's Early Light: The Story of the Star-Spangled Banner. Andreasen, Dan, illus. 2000. 40p. (J). (ps-ps). lib. bdg. 14.15 (978-0-613-28433-2(X)) Tandem Library Bks.

Mara, Wil. Thurgood Marshall: Champion for Civil Rights. 2004. (Great Life Stories Ser.). (Illus.). 125p. (J). 30.50 (978-0-531-12058-3(9), Watts, Franklin) Scholastic Library Publishing.

McLeese, Don & Marshall, Thurgood. Thurgood Marshall. 2003. (Rourke Discovery Library). (Illus.). 24p. (gr. 2-5). 14.95 (978-1-58952-303-6(2)) Rourke Publishing, LLC.

Norgren, Jill. Belva Lockwood: The Woman Who Would Be President. 2007. (Illus.). 344p. 35.00 (***978-0-8147-5834-2(7)***) New York Univ. Pr.

Parks, Peggy J. Lawyer. 2003. (Exploring Careers Ser.). (Illus.). 48p. (J). (gr. 3-5). 26.20 (978-0-7377-1485-2(9), Kidhaven) Thomson Gale.

Pasternak, Ceel & Thornburg, Linda. Cool Careers for Girls in Law. 2001. (Illus.). (gr. 7). 128p. pap. 12.95 (978-1-57023-157-5(5)); 132p. (J). 19.95 (978-1-57023-160-5(5)) Impact Pubns.

—Cool Careers for Girls in Law. 2001. (YA). lib. bdg. 22.20 (978-0-613-79030-7(8)) Tandem Library Bks.

Schier, Mary Lahr. Strong-Minded Woman: The Story of Lavinia Goodell, Wisconsin's First Female Lawyer. 2001. (Illus.). 112p. (J). (gr. 5 up). 21.95 (978-0-9671787-3-8(8)) Midwest History Pr.

Sokoni, Opio Lumumba. I Want to Be a Lawyer When I Grow Up: A Strategic Children's Book. 1999. (Illus.). 48p. (YA). (gr. 3-12). pap. 10.00 (978-1-56411-194-4(6)) UBUS Communications Systems.

Wagner, Heather Lehr. Benjamin Hooks. 2003. (African American Leaders Ser.). (Illus.). 112p. (gr. 6-12). 30.00 (978-0-7910-7685-9(7), Chelsea Hse.) Facts On File, Inc.

Weatherford, Carole Boston. Great African-American Lawyers: Raising the Bar of Freedom. 2003. (Collective Biographies Ser.). (Illus.). 112p. (YA). (gr. 6-12). lib. bdg. 26.60 (978-0-7660-1837-2(7)) Enslow Pubs., Inc.

Wheeler, Jill C. Thurgood Marshall. 2003. (Breaking Barriers Ser.). (Illus.). 64p. (J). (gr. 3-8). lib. bdg. 25.65 (978-1-57765-907-5(4)) ABDO Publishing Co.

LAWYERS—FICTION

Bauer, Joan. Backwater. 2000. (978-0-606-20077-6(0)) Tandem Library Bks.

Clements, Bruce. What Erika Wants. 2005. 224p. (YA). (gr. 7-17). 16.00 (978-0-374-32304-2(6), Farrar, Straus & Giroux (BYR)) Farrar, Straus & Giroux.

Cormier, Robert. Rag & Bone Shop. 2003. lib. bdg. 14.15 (978-0-613-62220-2(0)) Tandem Library Bks.

Grippando, James. Leapholes. 2006. 176p. 15.95 (978-1-59031-666-5(5)) American Bar Assn.

Lethcoe, Jason. Wishing Well. Damkoehler, Katrina, illus. 2007. (Benjamin Bartholomew Piff Ser.: No. 3). 224p. (J). (gr. 3-7). 9.99 (***978-0-448-44498-7(4)***, Grosset & Dunlap) Penguin Group (USA) Inc.

Martini, Steve. Critical Mass. 1999. (gr. 7-12). lib. bdg. 16.45 (978-0-613-21386-8(6)) Tandem Library Bks.

RealBuzz Studios Staff. Hits & Misses, No. 3. 2007. 128p. (YA). pap. 4.97 (978-1-59789-571-2(7), Barbour Bks.) Barbour Publishing, Inc.

Schroder, Jack. The Nasty Affair at the Lake, 1 bk. 2004. 152p. (J). per. 9.95 (978-0-9745665-8-0(6)) Catalpa Pr.

Vaughan, Bridget & Moore, Larry. Grand Jury Connections. 2001. 264p. (YA). pap. 14.95 (978-0-9678436-0-5(X)) Gayle Publishing Co.

LAYOUT AND TYPOGRAPHY

see Printing

LEADERSHIP

Asgedom, Mawi. Win the Inner Battle: The Ultimate Teen Leadership Journal. Berger, Dave, ed. 2003. 96p. (YA). spiral bd. 14.00 (978-0-9743901-8-5(6)) Mawi, Incorporated.

Ball, Heather. Great Women Leaders. 2005. (Women's Hall of Fame Ser.). (Illus.). 100p. (YA). pap. 7.95 (978-1-896764-81-8(9)) Second Story Pr. CAN. *Dist:* Orca Bk. Pubs. USA, Univ. of Toronto Pr.

Carroll, Joan. Smile a Seven Step Journey Toward Self-Discovery & Leadership Empowerment. Glevicky, Greg, illus. 2000. 100p. (YA). pap. 9.95 (978-1-881223-18-4(3)) Zulema Enterprises.

Cefrey, Holly. Everything You Need to Know about the Art of Leadership: How to Be a Positive Influence in Your Home, School & Community. 2005. (Need to Know Library). (Illus.). 64p. (YA). (gr. 7-12). lib. bdg. 25.25 (978-0-8239-3217-7(6), NTLEAD) Rosen Publishing Group, Inc., The.

Gerety, Ed. Combinations: Opening the Door to Student Leadership. 2003. 160p. (YA). per. 14.95 (978-0-9725938-3-0(7)) Whaleback Publishing.

Gwartney, Becky, et al. Lead On: Destination Reality. 2003. (YA). pap. 14.99 (978-0-89265-968-5(8)) Randall Hse. Pubns.

Harcourt School Publishers Staff. Leaders for Peace. 3rd ed. 2003. (Horizons Ser.). (Illus.). (J). (gr. 3). pap. 5.50 (978-0-15-333278-4(6)) Harcourt Schl. Pubs.

Herbst, Jan. The Substitute Teacher's Organizer. Walter, LaDawn, ed. Hillam, Corbin, illus. 2001. 80p. (J). (gr. k-6). pap. 10.99 (978-1-57471-795-2(2), CTP 3359) Creative Teaching Pr., Inc.

Hirschmann, Kris. Leadership. 2003. (Illus.). 32p. (J). pap. 7.50 (978-1-4109-0325-9(7)); lib. bdg. 24.28 (978-0-7398-7006-8(8)) Raintree.

Islamic Guidance Society. Leadership & Unity in Islam: Proceedings of the IGS-ICOJ International Conference?Kobe 2001. 2002. 174p. pap. 14.95 (978-0-595-22559-0(4), Writers Club Pr.) iUniverse, Inc.

Kick, Fran. Kick It In: Developing the Self-Motivation to Take the Lead (Participant Book) 2002. 36p. 10.00 (978-1-59199-010-9(6)) Instruction & Design Concepts.

Kids in Leadership. 2002. pap. 69.99 (978-1-59185-156-1(4)) CharismaLife Pubs.

Kids in Leadership Cover. 2002. pap. 0.00 (978-1-59185-162-2(9)) CharismaLife Pubs.

Kids in Leadership Manual. 2002. pap. 10.00 (978-1-59185-148-6(3)) CharismaLife Pubs.

Kids in Leadership Transparencies. 2002. 29.99 (978-1-59185-150-9(5)) CharismaLife Pubs.

Kishel, Ann-Marie. Our Leaders. 2007. (First Step Nonfiction Ser.). 24p. (J). (gr. k-2). 18.60 (978-0-8225-6395-2(9), Lerner Pubns.) Lerner Publishing Group.

Leaders of the Middle Ages, 6 Bks, Set. 2004. (J). 191.70 (978-1-4042-0345-7(1)) Rosen Publishing Group, Inc., The.

Lewers, Rob & Murphy, Ed. The Hidden Hurt: How to Beat Bullying in Schools. 96p. pap. (978-1-876367-66-4(0)) Wizard Bks.

Linder, Nani Aki. All about Me Look at Me I'm a Star: Children's Workbook. 2003. 121p. pap. 97.00 (978-0-7414-1677-3(8)) Infinity Publishing.

Logan, Rochelle & Halverstadt, Julie. 100 Most Popular Business Leaders for Young Adults: Biographical Sketches & Professional Paths. 2002. (Profiles & Pathways Ser.). (Illus.). 419p. (gr. 6-12). 65.00 (978-1-56308-799-8(5), LU7995) Libraries Unlimited, Inc.

Marrin, Albert. Stalin. 2002. 244p. (J). 13.95 (978-1-893103-09-2(9)) Beautiful Feet Bks.

Maxwell, John C. Leading at School. 2001. (PowerPak Collection Ser.). 88p. (J). (gr. 5-9). pap. 3.99 (978-0-8499-7724-4(X)) Nelson, Thomas Inc.

—Liderazgo 101: Lo Que Todo Líder Necesita Saber. 2003. (SPA.). 112p. 8.99 (978-0-88113-758-3(8)) Grupo Nelson.

—Las 17 Cualidades Esenciales de un Jugador de Equipo. 2002. (SPA.). 176p. pap. 10.99 (978-0-88113-737-8(5)) Grupo Nelson.

Mayer, Cassie. Being a Leader. 2007. (J). (***978-1-4034-9486-3(X)***); pap. (***978-1-4034-9494-8(0)***) Heinemann Library.

Myers, Jeff. Secrets of Everyday Leaders. 2006. 112p. (YA). stu. ed. 17.99 (978-0-8054-6886-1(2)) B&H Publishing Grp.

—Secrets of Great Communicators. 2006. 192p. (YA). pap., stu. ed. 17.99 (978-0-8054-6880-9(3)) B&H Publishing Grp.

—Secrets of World Changers. 2006. 80p. (YA). pap., stu. ed. 12.99 (978-0-8054-6883-0(8)) B&H Publishing Grp.

Nelson, Robin. Being a Leader. (First Step Nonfiction Ser.). (Illus.). (J). (gr. k-2). 2003. 24p. lib. bdg. 18.60 (978-0-8225-1287-5(4)); 2002. 23p. pap. 3.95 (978-0-8225-1324-7(2)) Lerner Publishing Group.

Polston, Deborah. Eagle Child Series 4-6. 2007. (YA). per. 12.99 (***978-1-59886-381-9(9)***) Tate Publishing & Enterprises, L.L.C.

Raatma, Lucia. Leadership. 2002. (Character Education Ser.). (Illus.). 24p. (J). (gr. 1-2). lib. bdg. 18.60 (978-0-7368-1389-1(6), Bridgestone Bks.) Capstone Pr., Inc.

Rossiter, Diane E. Leadership Skills. 2nd ed. 2004. (Career Skills Library). (Illus.). 128p. (YA). (gr. 6-12). 21.95 (978-0-8160-5519-7(X), Ferguson Publishing Co.) Facts On File, Inc.

Sanders, Bruce. Bullying. 2005. (Let's Talk about Ser.). (Illus.). 32p. (J). (gr. 3-7). lib. bdg. 27.10 (978-1-59604-045-8(9)) Stargazer Bks.

Schwartz, Stuart B. & Conley, Craig. Being a Leader. (Job Skills Ser.). pap. 6.95 (978-0-7368-8517-1(X), Life-Matters Bks.) Capstone Pr., Inc.

Strack, Jay. Leadership Rocks: Becoming a Student of Influence. 2006. 128p. (YA). pap. 7.99 (978-1-4185-0593-6(5)) Nelson, Thomas Inc.

Strack, Jay & Edwards, David. Life: How to Get There from Here; Student Leadership University Study Guide Series. 2006. 128p. (YA). pap. 7.99 (978-1-4185-0599-8(4)) Nelson, Thomas Inc.

Strack, Jay & Land, Richard. Mercury Rising: 8 Issues That Are Too Hot to Handle: Student Leadership University Study Guide Series. 2006. 128p. (YA). pap. 7.99 (978-1-4185-0592-9(7)) Nelson, Thomas Inc.

Tibbs, Janet. Being A Leader, 8 vols., Vol. 7. 2004. (Illus.). (J). per. (978-1-932062-33-5(5)) Hability Solution Services, Inc.

Trahue, Jan & Trahue, Dwight. Kid Leaders: A Leadership Program for Elementary School Students. Deppenschmidt, Kurt, illus. 2001. (J). (gr. k-6). pap. 13.95 (978-1-57543-091-1(6)) MAR*CO Products, Inc.

United States, Army Junior ROTC Staff, et al, contrib. by. Army JROTC Leadership Education & Training. 2002. (Illus.). 416p. (J). (978-0-536-67808-9(1)) Pearson Custom Publishing.

WorldVenture Guide for Leaders of Grades 1-6. 2003. pap. 8.99 (978-1-56309-634-1(X)) Woman's Missionary Union.

Yancey, Diane. Leaders of the North & South. 1999. (American War Library). (Illus.). 128p. (YA). (gr. 4-12). 27.45 (978-1-56006-497-8(8), LML00902-177860, Lucent Bks.) Thomson Gale.

LEARNING, ART OF

see Study Skills

LEARNING AND SCHOLARSHIP

see also Culture; Education; Humanism; Research

Arnold, Ellen. Magnificent Mind Listens Mindfully. Farber, Deborah, illus. 2001. (MI Strategies for Kids Ser.). 32p. (J). (gr. 1-5). pap. 7.00 (978-1-56976-112-0(4), 1141, Zephyr Pr.) Chicago Review Pr., Inc.

Bain, John Aloysius & Mitchell, Robert Power. Checkmate! Ideas for Students. 2001. (Illus.). 72p. (YA). (gr. 2-12). wbk. ed. 3.95 (978-0-9639614-3-3(8)) Learning Plus, Inc.

Brighter Vision Publishing Staff. Fun with Friends. 2000. (Learning Adventures Grade 1 Ser.). (Illus.). (J). (gr. 1-2). pap. 2.25 (978-1-55254-062-6(6)) Brighter Vision Pubns.

Clayton, Lawrence & Morrison, Jaydene. Coping with a Learning Disability. rev. ed. 1999. (Coping Ser.). (Illus.). 121p. (YA). (gr. 7-12). lib. bdg. 26.50 (978-0-8239-2887-3(X), COLEDI) Rosen Publishing Group, Inc., The.

Early Learning. (My First Treasury Ser.). 40p. (J). bds. (978-0-7853-6336-1(X), 7158900) Publications International, Ltd.

Getting Ready for Kindergarten. (100+ Seriestm Ser.). 128p. (gr. k-6). 12.99 (978-1-56822-190-8(8), IF8781) School Specialty Publishing.

Howell, Dusti & Howell, Deanne, prods. Dr. Wiley Makes Sense. 2005. (YA). pap. 249.95 incl. cd-rom (978-0-9677328-9-3(1)) SolidA, Inc.

MacLachlan, Patricia. What You Know First. 1998. (Trophy Picture Bks.). (J). (978-0-606-13905-2(2)) Tandem Library Bks.

Miller, Sara Swan. Learn & Grow. Lacome, Susie, illus. 1999. 8p. (J). (ps-1). bds. 15.99 (978-1-57584-348-3(X), Reader's Digest Young Families, Inc.) Reader's Digest Children's Publishing, Inc.

Perry, William G., Jr. Learn to Love to Learn. Date not set. 300p. (YA). (gr. 8-12). pap. (978-1-887946-01-8(2)) Learning Net, The.

Schlemmer, Phil & Schlemmer, Dori. Challenging Projects for Creative Minds: 12 Self-Directed Enrichment Projects That Develop & Showcase Student Ability for Grades 1-5. 1998. (Illus.). 144p. (gr. 1-5). pap., tchr. ed. 29.95 (978-1-57542-048-6(1)) Free Spirit Publishing, Inc.

—Challenging Projects for Creative Minds: 20 Self-Directed Enrichment Projects That Develop & Showcase Student Ability for Grades 6 & Up. 1998. (Illus.). 168p. (gr. 6 up). pap., tchr. ed. 34.95 (978-1-57542-049-3(X)) Free Spirit Publishing, Inc.

Scott, John, text. How to Financially Fund Your College Education. 2004. (YA). 30.00 (978-1-879498-83-9(9)) SportAmerica.

Wesley, Sonya L. Game Plan Learning: A Discussion & Activity Tool. 2000. (Sport Ser.). (Illus.). (YA). spiral bd. 30.00 (978-1-931377-03-4(0)) Game Plan Pubns.

Word Fun. 2002. 192p. (J). pap. 3.98 (978-0-7525-7919-1(3)) Parragon, Inc.

LEARNING DISABILITIES

Allen, William H., creator. TEH Learns to Read: (13 Volume Set), 13 Volume Set. 2004. (Illus.). 40p. (J). 399.95 (978-0-9745938-0-7(X)) LD Coach, LLC.

Bowman-Kruhm, Mary & Wirths, Claudine G. Everything You Need to Know about Learning Disabilities. 1999. (Need to Know Library). (Illus.). 64p. (YA). (gr. 7-12). lib. bdg. 25.25 (978-0-8239-2956-6(6), NTLEDI) Rosen Publishing Group, Inc., The.

Brinkerhoff, Shirley. Why Can't I Learn Like Everyone Else? Youth with Learning Disabilities. 2004. (Youth with Special Needs Ser.). (Illus.). 128p. (J). (978-1-59084-730-5(X)) Mason Crest Pubs.

Clayton, Lawrence. Coping with a Learning Disability. 1999. (Coping Ser.). 128p. (YA). (gr. 6 up). pap. 6.95 (978-1-56838-291-3(X)) Hazelden Publishing & Educational Services.

Clayton, Lawrence & Morrison, Jaydene. Coping with a Learning Disability. rev. ed. 1999. (Coping Ser.). (Illus.). 121p. (YA). (gr. 7-12). lib. bdg. 26.50 (978-0-8239-2887-3(X), COLEDI) Rosen Publishing Group, Inc., The.

Conger, Mary. No-Glamour Literature. 1999. 295p. (YA). (gr. 5-12). spiral bd. 41.95 (978-0-7606-0301-7(4)) LinguiSystems, Inc.

Edwards, Nicola. My Friend Has Dyslexia. 2004. (J). lib. bdg. 27.10 (978-1-59389-167-1(9)) Chrysalis Education.

—My Friend Has Dyspraxia. 2004. (J). lib. bdg. 27.10 (978-1-59389-168-8(7)) Chrysalis Education.

Fisher, Gary L. The Survival Guide for Kids with LD (Learning Differences) 2002. lib. bdg. 18.00 (978-0-613-65002-1(6)) Tandem Library Bks.

Fisher, Gary L. & Cummings, Rhoda. Supera Tus Dificultades de Aprendizaje. 2005. (SPA., Illus.). 136p. (J). pap. 11.95 (978-968-860-453-3(4)) Editorial Pax MEX. *Dist:* Independent Pubs. Group.

Flynn, Margaret & Flynn, Peter. Having a Learning Disability. 1999. (Think about Ser.). (Illus.). 32p. (J). (gr. 2-5). lib. bdg. 16.95 (978-1-887068-86-4(4)) Smart Apple Media.

Gillen-Connell, Linda. Dumb Bunny. 2005. 67p. (J). (gr. 4-6). pap. 14.95 (978-1-4137-8454-1(2)) PublishAmerica, Inc.

Girod, Christina M. Learning Disabilities. 2001. (Diseases & Disorders Ser.). (Illus.). 120p. (J). (gr. 6-9). 27.45 (978-1-56006-844-0(2), GML12001-178175, Lucent Bks.) Thomson Gale.

Harris, Joseph. Living with Learning Disabilities. 2008. (Teen's Guides Ser.). 192p. (gr. 6-12). 34.95 (***978-0-8160-6485-4(7)***) Facts On File, Inc.

Kent, Susan. Let's Talk about Needing Extra Help in School. 2000. (Let's Talk Library). (Illus.). 24p. (J). (gr. 3). lib. bdg. 18.75 (978-0-8239-5422-3(6), PowerKids Pr.) Rosen Publishing Group, Inc., The.

Levete, Sarah. Learning Difficulties. 2006. (Let's Talk about Ser.). (Illus.). 32p. (J). (gr. 3-5). lib. bdg. 27.10 (978-1-59604-089-2(0)) Stargazer Bks.

Lewis, Nancy. Understanding Learning Differences: Recognizing Intellectual Individuality. Miller, Rosemary, illus. 2002. (YA). (gr. 4-12). spiral bd. (978-0-9716363-0-9(3)) Lewis, Nancy Erickson.

Libal, Autumn. My Name Isn't Slow: Youth with Mental Retardation. 2004. (Youth with Special Needs Ser.). (Illus.). 128p. (J). (978-1-59084-731-2(8)) Mason Crest Pubs.

McMurchie, Susan. Understanding My Learning Differences. 2003. 148p. (gr. 4-5). spiral bd. 29.00 incl. audio compact disk (978-1-57861-497-4(X), IEP RESOURCES) Attainment Co., Inc.

Paquette, Penny Hutc. Learning Disabilities: The Ultimate Teen Guide. 2006. (Illus.). 312p. pap. 17.95 (978-0-8108-5643-1(3)) Scarecrow Pr., Inc.

LEARNING DISABILITIES—FICTION

Butler, Dori Hillestad. Alexandra Hopewell, Labor Coach. 2005. 136p. (J). (gr. 3-6). 15.95 (978-0-8075-0242-6(1)) Whitman, Albert & Co.

Cutler, Jane. Spaceman. 1999. (978-0-606-16980-6(6)) Tandem Library Bks.

Gavalda, Anna. 95 Pounds of Hope. Rosner, Gill, tr. from FRE. 2003. (Illus.). 112p. (J). (gr. 3). 14.99 (978-0-670-03672-1(2), Viking Juvenile) Penguin Group (USA) Inc.

Hansen, Joyce. Yellow Bird & Me. 2005. 168p. (J). (gr. 5-9). pap. 6.95 (978-0-618-61116-4(9), Clarion Bks.) Houghton Mifflin Co. Trade & Reference Div.

Janover, Caroline D. Josh: A Boy with Dyslexia. 2004. 108p. (J). pap. 9.95 (978-0-595-31381-5(7), Backinprint.com) iUniverse, Inc.

Vision, David & Vision, Mutiya Sahar. If Only I Could! Alcantara, Ignacio, illus. 2005. 32p. (J). 17.00 (978-0-9659538-8-7(2)) Soul Vision Works Publishing.

Winkler, Henry & Oliver, Lin. The Curtain Went Up, My Pants Fell Down. Watson, Jesse Joshua, illus. 2007. (Hank Zipzer Ser.: No. 11). 160p. (J). 13.99 (978-0-448-44268-6(X)); pap. 4.99 (978-0-448-44267-9(1)) Penguin Group (USA) Inc. (Grosset & Dunlap).

—Holy Enchilada! Heyer, Carol & Watson, Jesse Joshua, illus. 2004. (Hank Zipzer Ser.: No. 6). 160p. (J). (gr. 3-8). pap. 4.99 (978-0-448-43353-0(2), Grosset & Dunlap) Penguin Group (USA) Inc.

—Holy Enchilada!, No. 6. Watson, Jesse Joshua, illus. 2004. (Hank Zipzer Ser.: No. 6). 160p. (J). (gr. 3-7). 13.99 (978-0-448-43554-1(3), Grosset & Dunlap) Penguin Group (USA) Inc.

—Holy Enchilada! 2006. (Hank Zipzer Ser.: No. 6). (J). (gr. 3-8). 24.21 (978-1-59961-105-1(8)) Spotlight.

—Holy Enchilada! 2003. (Hank Zipzer Ser.: No. 6). (gr. 3-6). lib. bdg. 13.00 (978-0-613-72546-0(8)) Tandem Library Bks.

—My Dog's a Scaredy-Cat: A Halloween Tail. Watson, Jesse Joshua, illus. 2006. (Hank Zipzer Ser.: No. 10). 160p. (J). 13.99 (978-0-448-43879-5(8), Grosset & Dunlap) Penguin Group (USA) Inc.

—My Dog's a Scaredy-Cat: A Halloween Tail. Heyer, Carol & Watson, Jesse Joshua, illus. 2006. (Hank Zipzer Ser.: No. 10). 160p. (J). (gr. 3-7). pap. 4.99 (978-0-448-43878-8(X), Grosset & Dunlap) Penguin Group (USA) Inc.

—Niagara Falls, or Does It? 2003. (Hank Zipzer Ser.: No. 1). (Illus.). 144p. (J). (gr. 2-5). pap. 4.99 (978-0-448-43162-8(9), Grosset & Dunlap) Penguin Group (USA) Inc.

—Niagara Falls, or Does It? Carol, Heyer, illus. 2003. (Hank Zipzer Ser.: No. 1). 144p. (J). (gr. 2-5). 12.99 (978-0-448-43232-8(3), Grosset & Dunlap) Penguin Group (USA) Inc.

—Niagara Falls, or Does It? 2004. (Hank Zipzer Ser.: No. 1). 128p. (J). (gr. 2-6). pap. 29.00 incl. audio (978-1-4000-9006-8(7), Listening Library) Random Hse. Audio Publishing Group.

—Niagara Falls, or Does It? 2006. (Hank Zipzer Ser.: No. 1). (J). (gr. 3-8). 24.21 (978-1-59961-108-2(2)) Spotlight.

—Niagara Falls, or Does It? 2003. (Hank Zipzer Ser.: No. 1). lib. bdg. 13.00 (978-0-613-63737-4(2)) Tandem Library Bks.

—Summer School! What Genius Thought That Up? 2006. (Hank Zipzer Ser.: No. 8). (J). (gr. 3-8). 24.21 (978-1-59961-107-5(4)) Spotlight.

—Summer School! What Genius Thought That Up? 2005. (Hank Zipzer Ser.: No. 8). (Illus.). 157p. (J). (ps-7). per. 11.64 (978-0-606-33097-8(6)) Tandem Library Bks.

—The Zippity Zinger. 2003. (Hank Zipzer Ser.: No. 4). (Illus.). 160p. (J). (gr. 3-8). mass mkt. 4.99 (978-0-448-43193-2(9) , Grosset & Dunlap) Penguin Group (USA) Inc.

—The Zippity Zinger. Heyer, Carol, illus. 2003. (Hank Zipzer Ser.: No. 4). 160p. (J). 13.99 (978-0-448-43287-8(0) , Grosset & Dunlap) Penguin Group (USA) Inc.

Wolff, Virginia Euwer. Probably Still Nick Swansen. 2002. 160p. (YA). pap. 7.99 (978-0-689-85226-8(6) , Simon Pulse) Simon & Schuster Children's Publishing.

Zemach, Kaethe. Ms. Mccaw Learns To Draw. (J). 2008. 32p. pap. 16.99 (978-0-439-82914-4(3)); 2006. (978-0-439-82915-1(1)) Scholastic, Inc. (Levine, Arthur A. Bks.).

LEATHERWORK

Fisher, Leonard Everett. The Tanners. 2000. (Colonial Craftsmen Ser.). (Illus.). 48p. (J). (gr. 4-8). lib. bdg. 24.21 (978-0-7614-1148-2(8) , Benchmark Bks.) Cavendish, Marshall Corp.

LEAVES

Blackaby, Susan. Catching Sunlight: A Book about Leaves. DeLage, Charlene, illus. 2004. (Growing Things Ser.). 24p. (C). (gr. k-2). 22.60 (978-1-4048-0111-0(1)) Picture Window Bks.

Bodach, Vijaya. Leaves. 2007. (Illus.). 24p. (J). 19.93 (978-0-7368-6344-5(3) , Pebble Bks.) Capstone Pr., Inc.

Burton, Jane & Taylor, Kim. The Nature & Science of Leaves. Bingxin, Wang et al, trs. 2000. (Nature & Science Ser.). (CHI & ENG., Illus.). 32p. (J). 8.95 (978-7-5600-1746-4(0)) Foreign Languages Teaching & Research Pr. CHN. *Dist:* Cheng & Tsui Co.

Capstone Press, contrib. by. Autumn Leaves, Vol. 3. 2005. (Our Seasons & Weather Ser.). 24p. (YA). (gr. k-3). pap. (978-1-56065-958-7(0) , Pebble Bks.) Capstone Pr., Inc.

Dorling Kindersley Publishing Staff. Trees & Leaves. 2006. (Ultimate Sticker Bks.). 16p. (J). pap. 6.99 (978-0-7566-2102-5(X)) Dorling Kindersley Publishing, Inc.

Edwards, Nicola. Leaves. 2007. (J). lib. bdg. (978-1-4042-3703-2(8) , PowerKids Pr.) Rosen Publishing Group, Inc., The.

Farndon, John. Leaves. 2005. (Illus.). 24p. (J). (gr. 2-4). 23.70 (978-1-4103-0422-3(1) , Blackbirch Pr., Inc.) Thomson Gale.

Figorito, Christine. How Leaves Change Color. 2002. (Reading Room Collection). (Illus.). 24p. (J). pap. (978-0-8239-8154-0(1)); lib. bdg. 18.75 (978-0-8239-3717-2(8)) Rosen Publishing Group, Inc., The.

Gerber, Carole. Leaf Jumpers. Evans, Leslie, illus. 32p. (J). 2006. pap. 6.95 (978-1-57091-498-0(2)); 2004. 15.95 (978-1-57091-497-3(4)) Charlesbridge Publishing, Inc.

Jacobs, Marian B. Why Do Leaves Change Color? 1999. (Library of Why). (Illus.). 24p. (J). (gr. k-4). lib. bdg. 18.75 (978-0-8239-5275-5(4) , PowerKids Pr.) Rosen Publishing Group, Inc., The.

Lake, Darlene A. Leaf Collecting & Preserving Made Easy. 2nd ed. 2003. (Illus.). 49p. (J). 12.00 (978-0-9747654-0-2(6) , Egap Gifa Bks.) Leafcollecting.com Publishing Co.

Lara, Enrique & Garcia, Luis. Leaves. 2004. (Illus.). (J). (978-81-89020-07-1(2)) Katha.

Leaves. 2006. 10.95 (978-1-933427-72-0(8)) teNeues Publishing Co.

Maestro, Betsy. Why Do Leaves Change Color? 2001. 24.75 (978-0-06-000333-3(2)) HarperCollins Pubs.

Marzollo, Jean. I Am a Leaf. Moffatt, Judith, illus. 1999. (Hello Reader! Science Ser.: Level 1). 32p. (J). (ps-1). pap. 3.99 (978-0-590-64120-3(4) , Cartwheel Bks.) Scholastic, Inc.

—I Am a Leaf. Moffatt, Judith, illus. 1999. (Hello Reader! Ser.). 32p. (J). (gr. k-2). lib. bdg. 10.79 (978-0-606-17544-9(X)) Tandem Library Bks.

—Soy una Hoja. Moffatt, Judith, illus. 2002. (Coleccion "Hola, Lector" Ser.).Tr. of I Am a Leaf. (SPA.). 32p. (J). (ps-1). pap. 3.99 (978-0-439-18307-9(3) , SO5268) Scholastic, Inc.

—Soy una Hoja. 2001. Tr. of I Am a Leaf. (SPA.). (gr. k-3). lib. bdg. 11.80 (978-0-613-84119-1(0)) Tandem Library Bks.

Moore, Johnny Ray. A Leaf. Rauchenstein, Kristin, illus. 1999. 8p. (J). (gr. k-2). pap. 3.75 (978-1-880612-90-3(9) , Seedling Pubns.) Continental Pr., Inc.

Morgan, Sally. Roots, Stems, & Leaves. 2002. (Looking at Plants Ser.). (Illus.). 32p. (J). lib. bdg. 24.25 (978-1-931983-11-2(9)) Chrysalis Education.

—Under a Leaf in Forests & Jungles. 2006. (Hidden Habitats Ser.). (J). (978-1-59389-284-5(5)) Chrysalis Education.

Pascoe, Elaine. Leaves & Trees. Kuhn, Dwight, photos by. 2001. (Nature Close-Up Ser.). (Illus.). 48p. (J). (gr. 4-8). 23.70 (978-1-56711-474-4(1) , Blackbirch Pr., Inc.) Thomson Gale.

Picture Window Books, contrib. by. Catching Sunlight. (Growing Things Ser.). 24p. (J). pap. 7.95 (978-1-4048-0387-9(4)) Picture Window Bks.

Roza, Greg. Lots of Leaves: Learning the L Sound. (Power-Phonics Ser.). (Illus.). (J). 2002. 24p. (gr. 1). lib. bdg. 18.50 (978-0-8239-5899-3(X)); 2001. 23p. lib. bdg. 26.40 (978-0-8239-8244-8(0)) Rosen Publishing Group, Inc., The. (PowerKids Pr.).

Rustad, Martha E. H. Leaves in Fall. 2008. (J). ***978-1-4296-0024-8(1))** Capstone Pr., Inc.

Saunders, Gail. Leaves. 1998. (Growing Flowers Ser.). 24p. (J). pap. 13.25 (978-0-516-21323-1(7) , Children's Pr.) Scholastic Library Publishing.

Stone, Lynn M. Leaves. 2008. (J). (***978-1-60044-553-8(5))** Rourke Publishing, LLC.

Ward, Kristin. Leaves. 2000. (PowerKids Readers Ser.). (Illus.). 24p. (J). (gr. 1). lib. bdg. 16.00 (978-0-8239-5533-6(8) , PKNALE, PowerKids Pr.) Rosen Publishing Group, Inc., The.

Warren, Jean. Leaves. Cubley, Kathleen, ed. 1998. (Sticker Book Ser.). (Illus.). 32p. (J). (ps). pap. 3.95 (978-1-57029-221-7(3) , WPH 3711, Totline Pubns.) Schaffer, Frank Pubns.

Whitehouse, Patricia. Las Hojas. (Plantas (Plants) Ser.). (SPA.). 24p. (J). (ps-1). 2003. lib. bdg. 17.08 (978-1-58810-777-0(9)); 2002. (Illus.). pap. 5.25 (978-1-58810-824-1(4) , 91647) Heinemann Library.

—Leaves. 2002. (Plants Ser.). (Illus.). 24p. (J). (ps-1). pap. 5.25 (978-1-58810-730-5(2) , 91404); lib. bdg. 17.08 (978-1-58810-521-9(0)) Heinemann Library.

Zoehfeld, Kathleen Weidner. Fall Leaves Change Color. (Science Readers Ser.). 32p. (J). 2002. (Illus.). pap. 3.99 (978-0-439-38195-6(9) , Scholastic Reference); 2001. (978-0-439-26986-5(5)) Scholastic, Inc.

—Fall Leaves Change Color. 2002. (gr. k-3). lib. bdg. 11.80 (978-0-613-57043-5(X)) Tandem Library Bks.

LEBANON

Amari, Suad. Cooking the Lebanese Way. 2nd rev. ed. 2003. (Easy Menu Ethnic Cookbooks). (Illus.). 72p. (J). 25.26 (978-0-8225-4116-5(5) , Lerner Pubns.) Lerner Publishing Group.

Aretha, David. Lebanon in the News: Past, Present, & Future. 2006. (Middle East Nations in the News Ser.). (Illus.). 128p. (J). lib. bdg. 33.27 (978-1-59845-023-1(9) , MyReportLinks.com Bks.) Enslow Pubs., Inc.

Boueri, Marijean. Lebanon 1-2-3: A Counting Book in Three Languages. Badaji, Mona Trade, illus. 2005. (ENG, ARA & FRE.). 32p. (J). 16.95 (978-1-933002-03-3(4)) PublishingWorks.

Boueri, Marijean, et al. Lebanon A to Z: A Middle Eastern Mosaic. Sabbagh, Tatianna, illus. 2006. (J). 25.00 (978-0-9744803-4-3(7)) PublishingWorks.

Cahill, Mary Jane. Lebanon. 1999. (Major World Nations Ser.). (Illus.). 144p. (YA). (gr. 4-7). 29.95 (978-0-7910-4981-5(7) , Chelsea Hse.) Facts On File, Inc.

Conley, Kate A. Lebanon. 2004. (Countries Ser.). (Illus.). 40p. (J). (gr. k-6). lib. bdg. 22.78 (978-1-59197-292-1(2)) ABDO Publishing Co.

Englar, Mary. Lebanon: A Question & Answer Book. 2007. 32p. (J). (***978-0-7368-6771-9(6))** Capstone Pr., Inc.

Hutchison, Linda. Lebanon. 2003. (Modern Nations of the World Ser.). (Illus.). 128p. (J). 29.95 (978-1-59018-116-4(6) , Lucent Bks.) Thomson Gale.

McDaniel, Jan. Lebanon. 2003. (Modern Middle East Nations & Their Strategic Place in the World Ser.). (Illus.). 112,128p. (J). (gr. 7 up). lib. bdg. (978-1-59084-511-0(0)) Mason Crest Pubs.

Sheehan, Sean & Latif, Zawiah Abdul. Lebanon. 2nd ed. 2007. (Cultures of the World Ser.). 144p. (J). lib. bdg. 39.93 (***978-0-7614-2081-1(9)** , Benchmark Bks.) Cavendish, Marshall Corp.

Stewart, James. Lebanon. 2008. (J). (***978-1-60044-617-7(5))** Rourke Publishing, LLC.

Willis, Terri. Lebanon. 2005. (Enchantment of the World, Second Ser.). (Illus.). 144p. (J). (gr. 5-9). 36.00 (978-0-516-23685-8(7) , Children's Pr.) Scholastic Library Publishing.

LEBANON—FICTION

St. John, Patricia. Nothing Else Matters. 2003. 176p. 6.49 (978-0-85421-972-8(2)) Scripture Union GBR. *Dist:* Gabriel Resources.

LEE, HENRY, 1756-1818

Bodie, Idella. Light-Horse Harry. 2004. (Illus.). 86p. (J). pap. 6.95 (978-0-87844-172-3(7)) Sandlapper Publishing Co., Inc.

LEE, ROBERT E. (ROBERT EDWARD), 1807-1870

Anderson, Paul Christopher. Robert E. Lee: Legendary Commander of the Confederacy. 2005. (Library of American Lives & Times). (Illus.). 112p. (YA). (gr. 4-8). lib. bdg. 31.95 (978-0-8239-5748-4(9)) Rosen Publishing Group, Inc., The.

Arnold, James R. & Wiener, Roberta. On to Richmond: The Civil War in the East, 1861-1862. 2005. (Civil War Ser.). (Illus.). 72p. (J). (gr. 5-12). lib. bdg. 25.26 (978-0-8225-2313-0(2)) Lerner Publishing Group.

Ashby, Ruth. Lee vs. Grant: The Major Battles. 2002. (Illus.). 48p. (J). lib. bdg. 28.50 (978-1-58340-184-2(9)) Smart Apple Media.

Bednarz, Robert, et al. TIME for Kids Readers: Robert E. Lee. 3rd ed. 2002. (Harcourt Horizons Ser.). (gr. k-7). pap. 38.10 (978-0-15-335279-5(5)) Harcourt Schl. Pubs.

Carter, E. J. Robert E. Lee. 2004. (American War Biographies Ser.). (Illus.). 48p. (J). pap. 8.50 (978-1-4034-5088-3(9)); lib. bdg. 27.07 (978-1-4034-5081-4(1)) Heinemann Library.

Gillis, Jennifer Blizin. Robert E. Lee: Confederate Commander. 2004. (Signature Lives Ser.). (Illus.). 112p. (J). 30.60 (978-0-7565-0821-0(5) , 1240144) Compass Point Bks.

Grabowski, Patricia A. Robert E. Lee: Confederate General. (Famous Figures of the Civil War Era Ser.). (Illus.). 80p. (J). (gr. 4-7). 2001. 25.00 (978-0-7910-6000-1(4)); 2000. pap. 25.00 (978-0-7910-6138-1(8)) Facts On File, Inc. (Chelsea Hse.).

Kantor, MacKinlay. Sterling Point Books: Lee & Grant at Appomattox. 2007. (Sterling Point Bks.). 144p. (J). pap. 6.95 (***978-1-4027-5124-0(9))** Sterling Publishing Co., Inc.

Marrin, Albert. Virginia's General: Robert E. Lee & the Civil War. 2003. (Illus.). 201p. (YA). pap. 14.95 (978-1-893103-14-6(5)) Beautiful Feet Bks.

Marsh, Carole. Robert E. Lee. 2002. (One Thousand Readers Ser.). (Illus.). 12p. (J). (gr. k-4). 2.95 (978-0-635-01493-1(9) , 14939) Gallopade International.

—The Virginia Reader: Robert E. Lee. 2001. (Virginia Experience! Ser.). (Illus.). 12p. (J). (gr. k-4). pap. 2.95 (978-0-635-00367-6(8)) Gallopade International.

McGowen, Tom. The Surrender at Appomattox. 2004. (Cornerstones of Freedom Ser.). (Illus.). 48p. (J). 26.00 (978-0-516-24231-6(8) , Children's Pr.) Scholastic Library Publishing.

McLeese, Don. Robert E. Lee. 2006. (Civil War Military Leaders Ser.). (Illus.). 32p. (J). (gr. 3-6). 19.95 (978-1-59515-476-7(0)) Rourke Publishing, LLC.

Mcleese, Don. Robert E Lee. 2005. 32p. pap. 6.45 (978-1-59515-790-4(5)) Rourke Publishing, LLC.

Monroe, Judy. Robert E. Lee. 2002. (Let Freedom Ring Ser.). (Illus.). 48p. (J). (gr. 3-4). lib. bdg. 22.60 (978-0-7368-1089-0(7) , Bridgestone Bks.) Capstone Pr., Inc.

Pingry, Patricia A. Meet Robert E. Lee. Johnson, Meredith, illus. 2004. (J). 9.95 (978-0-8249-5465-9(3) , Ideals Pr.) Ideals Pubns.

—The Story of Robert E. Lee. Johnson, Meredith, illus. 2004. 26p. (J). (ps-k). bds. 6.95 (978-0-8249-6501-3(9)) Ideals Pubns.

Ransom, Candice F. Robert E. Lee. 2005. (History Maker Bios Ser.). (Illus.). 48p. (J). 26.60 (978-0-8225-2437-3(6) , Lerner Pubns.) Lerner Publishing Group.

—Willie McLean & the Civil War Surrender. Reeves, Jeni, illus. 2005. (On My Own History Ser.). 48p. (J). 25.26 (978-1-57505-588-6(0)) Lerner Publishing Group.

Rice, Earle, Jr. Robert E. Lee: First Soldier of the Confederacy. 2005. (Civil War Leaders Ser.). (Illus.). 176p. (J). (gr. 6-12). 26.95 (978-1-931798-47-1(8)) Reynolds, Morgan Inc.

Robert E Lee. (Civil War Biographies Ser.). 48p. (YA). 7.95 (978-0-7368-4525-0(9)) Capstone Pr., Inc.

Robert E Lee, 6 vols. (gr. 2-5). 39.95 (978-0-7368-4605-9(0)) Red Brick Learning.

Robert E. Lee: The South's Faithful Servant. 2000. (Illus.). 32p. (YA). (gr. 5 up). pap. 5.00 (978-1-890541-22-4(2)) Americana Souvenirs & Gifts.

Robertson, James I., Jr. Robert E. Lee: Virginian Soldier, American Citizen. 2005. (Illus.). 176p. (YA). (gr. 7 up). 21.95 (978-0-689-85731-7(4) , Atheneum) Simon & Schuster Children's Publishing.

Schroeder, Patrick A. Thirty Myths about Lee's Surrender. 8th rev. ed. 2000. (Illus.). 32p. (YA). (gr. 7 up). pap. 4.00 (978-1-889246-05-5(0)) Schroeder Pubns.: Civil War Bks.

Smolinski, Diane. Soldiers of the Civil War. 2002. (Americans at War Ser.). (Illus.). 32p. (J). (gr. 4-6). lib. bdg. (978-1-58810-098-6(7)); pap. 6.95 (978-1-58810-392-5(7) , 91132) Heinemann Library.

Waryncia, Lou. Robert E. Lee: Duty & Honor. Hale, Sarah Elder, ed. 2005. (Civil War Ser.). (Illus.). 48p. (J). 17.95 (978-0-8126-7905-2(9)) Cobblestone Publishing Co.

LEEUWENHOEK, ANTONI VAN, 1632-1723

Yount, Lisa. Antoni Van Leeuwenhoek: First to See Microscopic Life. 2008. (J). (***978-0-7660-3012-1(1))** Enslow Pubs., Inc.

LEFT (POLITICAL SCIENCE)

see Right and Left (Political Science)

LEFT- AND RIGHT-HANDEDNESS—FICTION

Damon, Emma, illus. Milo in a Mess. 2006. (Read-It! Chapter Books). 48p. (J). (gr. 2-4). 19.95 (978-1-4048-1679-4(8)) Picture Window Bks.

Dougherty, Terri. Emily's Pictures. Rooney, Ronnie, illus. 2006. (Read-It! Readers Ser.). (J). 19.93 (978-1-4048-2409-6(X)) Picture Window Bks.

Ritter, John. Choosing up Sides. 2000. (gr. 5-8). lib. bdg. 14.15 (978-0-613-28444-8(5)) Tandem Library Bks.

Ritter, John H. Choosing up Sides. 2001. (J). 12.64 (978-0-606-20603-7(5)) Tandem Library Bks.

LEG

Brown, Jonatha A. Animal Feet & Legs. 2006. (Illus.). 24p. (J). pap. (978-0-8368-6865-4(X)); lib. bdg. (978-0-8368-6860-9(9)) Stevens, Gareth Inc.

Douglas, Lloyd G. My Legs & Feet. 2004. (Wel-My Body Ser.). (J). 18.00 (978-0-516-24064-0(1)); 24p. pap. 4.95 (978-0-516-22130-4(2)) Scholastic Library Publishing. (Children's Pr.).

Fowler, Allan. Arms & Legs & Other Limbs. 1999. (Rookie Read-About Science Ser.). (Illus.). 32p. (J). (gr. 1-2). 19.50 (978-0-516-20809-1(8) , Children's Pr.) Scholastic Library Publishing.

Hall, Peg. Whose Legs Are These? A Look at Animal Legs - Kicking, Running, & Hopping. Landmark, Ken, illus. 2004. (Whose Is It? Ser.). 24p. (C). (gr. k-2). 22.60 (978-1-4048-0007-6(7)) Picture Window Bks.

Leake, Diyan. Legs. 2007. (J). (***978-1-4329-0001-4(3))**; pap. (***978-1-4329-0006-9(4))** Heinemann Library.

Perkins, Wendy. Let's Look at Animal Legs. 2007. (J). (978-0-7368-6717-7(1)) Capstone Pr., Inc.

Schaefer, Lola M. Legs, Knees, Feet, & Toes. 2003. (It's My Body Ser.). (Illus.). 24p. (J). (ps-1). lib. bdg. 18.50 (978-1-4034-0890-7(4)); pap. 5.25 (978-1-4034-3482-1(4)) Heinemann Library.

Schaefer, Lola M. Some Kids Wear Leg Braces. 2008. (J). (***978-1-4296-0813-8(7))** Capstone Pr., Inc.

Viegas, Jennifer. The Lower Limbs: Learning How We Use Our Thighs, Knees, Legs, & Feet. 2002. (3-D Library of the Human Body). (Illus.). 48p. (YA). (gr. 5-8). lib. bdg. 26.50 (978-0-8239-3533-8(7) , Rosen Central) Rosen Publishing Group, Inc., The.

LEGAL HOLIDAYS

see Holidays

LEGAL PROFESSION

see Lawyers

LEGAL TENDER

see Paper Money

LEGENDS

see also Fables; Fairy Tales; Folklore; Mythology

Adil, Hajjah Amina & Sperling, Karima. My Little Lore of Light: A Child's Version of Lore of Light. 2005. (Illus.). x, 193p. (J). 22.00 (978-1-930409-35-4(4)) Islamic Supreme Council of America.

Attar, Farid Al-Din. Attar Stories for Young Adults. 2000. (Illus.). 202p. (J). (gr. 7-12). pap. 12.95 (978-1-930637-06-1(3) , A B C International Group, Inc.) Kazi Pubns., Inc.

Benge, Janet & Benge, Geoffrey Francis. Heroes of History, 5 vols. 2002. 34.95 (978-1-883002-89-3(3)) Emerald Bks.

Bingham, Jane. Classical Myth: A Treasury of Greek & Roman Legends, Art, & History. 2007. (World of Mythology Ser.). (Illus.). 96p. (YA). (gr. 6 up). 35.95 (***978-0-7656-8104-1(8))** Sharpe, M.E. Inc.

Brinkerhoff, Shirley. Contemporary Folklore. 2002. (North American Folklore Ser.). (Illus.). 112p. (YA). (gr. 7 up). lib. bdg. (978-1-59084-331-4(2)) Mason Crest Pubs.

Burtinshaw, Julie. Romantic Ghost Stories, Vol. 1. rev. ed. 2003. (Ghost Stories Ser.). (Illus.). 224p. (gr. 4). pap. (978-1-894877-28-2(4)) Lone Pine Publishing.

Coll Y Toste, Cayetano. Puerto Rican Tales: Legends of Spanish Colonial Times. 4th ed. 1999. (Illus.). 111p. reprint ed. pap. 9.95 (978-0-9601700-3-6(0)) Ediciones Libero.

Colum, Padraic. Myths of the World. Artzybasheff, Boris, illus. 2002. 328p. pap. 19.99 (978-0-86315-365-5(8)) Floris Bks. GBR. *Dist:* SteinerBooks, Inc.

Cooper, Gilly Cameron. How the World Began: Creation in Myths & Legends. 2006. (Illus.). 48p. pap., pap. 11.99 (978-1-84476-246-0(7) , Southwater) Anness Publishing GBR. *Dist:* National Bk. Network.

Daning, Tom. The Four Dragons: A Chinese Myth. 2007. (Graphic Myths (New York, N.Y.) Ser.). (Illus.). 24p. (J). (978-1-4042-2343-1(6)); pap. (978-1-4042-2153-6(0)); (gr. 2-6). lib. bdg. 21.25 (978-1-4042-3400-0(4)) Rosen Publishing Group, Inc., The. (PowerKids Pr.).

Jacq, Christian. Cuentos y Leyendas de la Epoca De Las Piramides. Corral, Mercedes, tr. from FRE. 6th ed. 2003. (Fables & Legends Ser.). (SPA., Illus.). 144p. (J). 9.95 (978-84-239-8893-8(7)) Espasa Calpe, S.A. ESP. *Dist:* Planeta Publishing Corp.

Johnston, Marianne. American Legends - Set 1, 6 bks. Incl. Casey Jones. lib. bdg. 18.75 (978-0-8239-5582-4(6)); Daniel Boone. lib. bdg. 18.75 (978-0-8239-5579-4(6)); Davy Crockett. lib. bdg. 18.75 (978-0-8239-5581-7(8)); Jim Bowie. lib. bdg. 18.75 (978-0-8239-5578-7(8)); Johnny Appleseed. lib. bdg. 18.75 (978-0-8239-5577-0(X)); Paul Bunyan. lib. bdg. 18.75 (978-0-8239-5580-0(X)); 24p. (J). (gr. 3). (Illus.). 2001. Set lib. bdg. 112.50 (978-0-8239-7059-9(0) , PowerKids Pr.) Rosen Publishing Group, Inc., The.

Lively, Penelope. In Search of a Homeland: The Story of the Aeneid. Andrew, Ian, illus. 2006. 128p. 19.95 (978-1-84507-685-6(0)) Lincoln, Frances Ltd. GBR. *Dist:* Perseus Distribution.

Mabie, Hamilton Wright. Legends That Every Child Should Know. 2004. reprint ed. pap. 22.95 (978-1-4191-2963-6(5)); pap. 1.99 (978-1-4192-2963-3(X)) Kessinger Publishing, LLC.

Mabie, Hamilton Wright. Legends That Every Child Should Know: A Selection of the Great Legends of All Times for Young People. 2006. 216p. pap. 12.99 (***978-1-4264-4960-4(7))**; 242p. pap. 15.99 (***978-1-4264-5261-1(6))** BiblioBazaar.

Mayer, Danuta, illus. The Brave Sister: A Story from the Arabian Nights. 2001. 25p. (J). 22.99 (978-0-7475-3904-9(9)) Bloomsbury Publishing Plc GBR. *Dist:* Trafalgar Square Publishing.

McCafferty, Catherine. The Legend of the Three Trees. 2001. (Illus.). 16p. (J). (ps-k). bds. 6.99 (978-0-8499-7618-6(9)) Nelson, Thomas Inc.

McCaughrean, Geraldine. Golden Book of Myths & Legends. (Illus.). 240p. (J). pap. 12.00 (978-1-85881-675-3(0)) Dolphin Paperbacks GBR. *Dist:* Trafalgar Square Publishing.

—Silver Myths. (Illus.). 240p. (J). pap. 12.00 (978-1-85881-676-0(9)) Dolphin Paperbacks GBR. *Dist:* Trafalgar Square Publishing.

Metaxas, Eric. King Midas & the Golden Touch. Prato, Rodica, illus. 2007. (J). 25.65 (978-1-59961-309-3(3)) ABDO Publishing Co.

Morgan, Robin. The Mer-Child: A Legend for Children & Other Adults. Zerner, Jesse S., illus. 2004. 64p. (gr. 1-9). pap. 10.95 (978-1-55861-054-5(5)) Feminist Pr. at The City Univ. of New York.

Myths & Legends. (Illus.). 40p. (YA). (gr. 5 up). lib. bdg. (978-1-59084-480-9(7)) Mason Crest Pubs.

Narvaez, Concha Lopez & Salmeron, Carmelo. La Leyenda del Viajero Que No Podia Detenerse. Lopez, Rafael Salmeron, illus. 2004. Tr. of Legend of the Traveler Who Couldn't Stop Walking. (SPA.). 96p. (YA). 9.99 (978-84-241-8754-5(7)) Everest de Ediciones y Distribucion, S.L. ESP. *Dist:* Lectorum Pubns., Inc.

Olson, Dennis L. Wisdom Warrior. 1999. (Illus.). 64p. 9.95 (978-1-55971-709-0(2) , NorthWord Bks. for Young Readers) T&N Children's Publishing.

Perry, Phyllis J. Ten Tall Tales: Origins, Activities & More. 2002. (Storytelling Ser.). (Illus.). 96p. (J). (gr. 3-8). pap. 15.95 (978-1-57950-069-6(2) , Upstart Bks.) Highsmith Inc.

Pilling, Ann. Kingfisher Treasury of Myths & Legends. 2003. (gr. 3-6). lib. bdg. 22.20 (978-0-613-67418-8(9)) Tandem Library Bks.

Priest, George E. The Great Winged Monster of the Piasa Valley: The Legend of the Piasa. 1998. (Illus.). 123p. (YA). (gr. 4-12). 17.00 (978-0-9678461-0-1(2)) ; pap. 15.00 (978-0-9678461-1-8(0)) Alton Museum of History & Art, Inc.

Reed, Natasha. Mythical Creatures. Kincaid, Angela, illus. 2005. 24p. (J). (ps-7). pap. (978-1-84510-119-0(7)) Top That! Publishing PLC.

Ross, Harriet, compiled by. Heroes & Heroines of Many Lands. 1999. 160p. (J). (gr. 3-9). reprint ed. lib. bdg. 13.95 (978-0-87460-214-2(9)) Lion Bks.

Ruffin, Frances E. American Legends - Set 2, 6 bks. Incl. Annie Oakley. lib. bdg. 18.75 (978-0-8239-5824-5(8)) ; Clara Barton. lib. bdg. 18.75 (978-0-8239-5825-2(6)) ; Molly Pitcher. lib. bdg. 18.75 (978-0-8239-5829-0(9)) ; Sally Hemings. lib. bdg. 18.75 (978-0-8239-5828-3(0)) ; Sojourner Truth. lib. bdg. 18.75 (978-0-8239-5826-9(4)) ; "Unsinkable" Molly Brown. lib. bdg. 18.75 (978-0-8239-5827-6(2)) ; 24p. (J). (gr. 3). 2002. (Illus.). 2001. Set lib. bdg. 112.50 (978-0-8239-7134-3(1) , PowerKids Pr.) Rosen Publishing Group, Inc., The.

Rumi, Jalal Al-Din. Kalilah & Dimnah Stories for Young Adults. 2000. (Illus.). 172p. (J). (gr. 7-12). pap. 12.95 (978-1-930637-07-8(1) , A B C International Group, Inc.) Kazi Pubns., Inc.

—Rumi Stories for Young Adults. 2000. (Illus.). 200p. (YA). (gr. 7-12). pap. 12.95 (978-1-930637-04-7(7) , A B C International Group, Inc.) Kazi Pubns., Inc.

San Souci, Robert D. Larger Than Life: The Adventures of American Legendary Heroes. Colon, Raul, illus. 2000. (978-0-15-200398-2(3)) Harcourt Trade Pubs.

Sanna, Ellyn. Folk Tales & Legends. 2002. (North American Folklore Ser.). (Illus.). 112p. (YA). (gr. 7 up). lib. bdg. (978-1-59084-346-8(0)) Mason Crest Pubs.

Steele, Phillip. Incredible Quests: Epic Journeys in Myth & Legend. 2006. (Illus.). 48p. pap., pap. 11.99 (978-1-84476-247-7(5) , Southwater) Anness Publishing GBR. *Dist:* National Bk. Network.

Stout, Steve. Legend of the Rock. Bednarik, Joelyn, illus. 1999. 32p. (J). (gr. k-6). pap. 5.95 (978-0-9609296-2-7(2)) Utica Hse. Publishing Co.

Teen People Magazine Editors. Celebrity Style Guide. rev. ed. 2006. (Teen People Ser.). (Illus.). 160p. pap. 16.95 (978-1-933405-35-3(X) , People Bks.) Time, Inc. Home Entertainment.

Townsend. Mysterious Urban Myths. 2004. (Out There Ser.). (Illus.). pap. 8.95 (978-1-4109-0968-8(9)) Raintree.

Townsend, John. Mysterious Urban Myths. 2004. (Illus.). 56p. (J). lib. bdg. 28.56 (978-1-4109-0567-3(5)) Raintree.

Trimble, Marcia. Serendipity Says to Know Me Is to Love Me. Grell, Susi, illus. 2000. 32p. (J). (ps-3). 15.95 (978-1-891577-77-2(8)) Images Pr.

Wargin, Kathy-Jo. The Legend of Mackinac Island. van Frankenhuyzen, Gijsbert, illus. rev. ed. 1999. (Great Lakes Legend Ser.). 46p. (J). (ps-3). 17.95 (978-1-886947-12-2(0)) Sleeping Bear Pr.

West, Colin. Long Tales, Short Tales & Tall Tales. 2000. (Illus.). 94p. (J). pap. 6.95 (978-0-552-52798-9(X)) Transworld Publishers Ltd. GBR. *Dist:* Trafalgar Square Publishing.

Whistler, Charles W. Havelok the Dane: A Legend of Old Grimsby & Lincoln. 2007. 248p. pap. 12.99 ***(978-1-4264-6429-4(0));*** 280p. pap. 16.99 ***(978-1-4264-6503-1(3))*** BiblioBazaar.

Williams, Rose. The Labors of Aeneas: What a Pain It Was to Found the Roman Race. 2003. (Illus.). (YA). 14.00 (978-0-86516-556-4(4)) Bolchazy-Carducci Pubs.

LEGENDS—AFRICA, WEST

Diakite, Baba Wague. The Hatseller & the Monkeys. Diakite, Baba Wague, illus. 1999. (Illus.). 32p. (J). (ps-2). pap. 16.95 (978-0-590-96069-4(5)) Scholastic, Inc.

LEGENDS, CELTIC

Chapple, G. Barton, illus. Celtic Myths & Legends. 2001. (World Book Myths & Legends Ser.). 64p. (J). (978-0-7166-2608-4(X)) World Bk., Inc.

Verniero, Joan C. One Hundred One Read-Aloud Celtic Myths & Legends: Ten-Minute Readings from the World's Best-Loved Literature. 2000. (Illus.). 384p. (J). (ps-3). tchr. ed. 12.95 (978-1-57912-098-6(9) , 81098) Black Dog & Leventhal Pubs., Inc.

LEGENDS—CHINA

Bouchard, David. The Dragon New Year: A Chinese Legend. Huang, Zhong-Yang, illus. 1999. (Chinese Legends Trilogy Ser.). 31p. (J). (gr. 1-5). 16.95 (978-1-56145-210-1(6) , Q30965) Peachtree Pubs., Ltd.

—The Dragon New Year: A Chinese Legend. Huang, Zhong-Yang, illus. 1999. 32p. 15.95 (978-1-55192-200-3(2)) Raincoast Bk. Distribution CAN. *Dist:* Transition Vendor.

—The Mermaid's Muse: The Legend of the Dragon Boats. 2002. (Chinese Legends Trilogy). (Illus.). 32p. (J). (gr. 3-6). 15.95 (978-1-55192-248-5(7)) Raincoast Bk. Distribution CAN. *Dist:* Perseus Distribution.

Casey, Dawn. The Great Race: The Story of the Chinese Zodiac. Wilson, Anne, illus. 2006. 32p. (J). 16.99 (978-1-905236-77-0(8)) Barefoot Bks., Inc.

Wilkinson, Philip. Chinese Myth: A Treasury of Legends, Art, & History. 2007. (World of Mythology Ser.). (Illus.). 96p. (YA). (gr. 6 up). 35.95 ***(978-0-7656-8103-4(X))*** Sharpe, M.E. Inc.

LEGENDS—EGYPT

Kramer, Ann. Egyptian Myth: A Treasury of Legends, Art, & History. 2007. (World of Mythology Ser.). (Illus.). 96p. (YA). (gr. 6 up). 35.95 ***(978-0-7656-8105-8(6))*** Sharpe, M.E. Inc.

Malam, John. Myths & Legends of the Desert. 2002. (Illus.). 32p. (J). (978-0-7534-0742-4(6) , Kingfisher) Houghton Mifflin Co. Trade & Reference Div.

Mayer, Danuta, illus. Ancient Egyptian Myths & Legends, 1 vols. 2001. (World Book Myths & Legends Ser.). 64p. (J). (978-0-7166-2606-0(3)) ; (978-0-7166-2607-7(1)) World Bk., Inc.

LEGENDS, ESKIMO

Dolitsky, Alexander B., ed. Tales & Legends of the Yupik Eskimos of Siberia. Michael, Henry N., tr. from RUS. unabr. ed. 2000. (Alaska-Siberia Research Center, Publication: No. 11). Orig. Title: Fairy Tales & Myths of the People of Chukotka & Kamchatka. (ENG., Illus.). 160p. (YA). (gr. 5-12). pap. 18.00 (978-0-9653891-3-6(8) , 94-3121266) Alaska-Siberia Research Ctr.

LEGENDS—HAWAII

Holokai, Ben W., Jr. Myths & Legends of Hawai'i Coloring Book. 2004. (Illus.). 32p. 5.95 (978-1-57306-212-1(X)) Bess Pr., Inc.

Varez, Dietrich. Lehua: A Legend Of Old Hawaii. l.t. ed. 2001. 40p. (J). 10.99 (978-0-89610-447-1(8)) Island Heritage Publishing.

LEGENDS—INDIA

Adhikary, Qiron. Feminist Folktales from India. 2003. (Illus.). 97p. (YA). per. 9.95 (978-0-9714127-3-6(1)) Masalai Pr.

Besant, Annie W. Legends & Tales Lotus Leaves for the Y. 2006. pap. 19.95 ***(978-1-4286-2494-8(5))*** Kessinger Publishing, LLC.

LEGENDS, INDIAN

see Indians of North America—Legends

LEGENDS—IRELAND

Lawrie, Robin, illus. Great Irish Legends for Children. 2005. 64p. pap. 19.95 (978-0-7171-3872-2(0)) Gill & MacMillan, Ltd. IRL. *Dist:* Irish Bks. & Media, Inc.

Leavy, Una. The O'Brien Book of Irish Fairy Tales & Legends. Field, Susan Anna, illus. 2002. 96p. (J). (gr. 3-6). 19.95 (978-0-86278-482-9(4)) O'Brien Pr., Ltd., The IRL. *Dist:* Independent Pubs. Group.

McCarthy, Bairbre. Favourite Irish Legends: A Dual Language Book. 1998. (ENG & IRI.). 61p. (J). pap. 7.95 (978-1-85635-186-7(6)) Irish Bks. & Media, Inc.

Milligan, Bryce. Brigid's Cloak: An Ancient Irish Story. Cann, Helen, illus. 2004. 32p. (J). (gr. k up). 16.00 (978-0-8028-5224-3(6)) Eerdmans, William B. Publishing Co.

LEGENDS, JEWISH

Ganeri, Anita. Jewish Stories. Phillips, Rachael, illus. 2006. 32p. (J). (gr. 4-6). 23.95 (978-1-4048-1310-6(1)) Picture Window Bks.

Gershator, Phillis. Wise & Not So Wise: Ten Tales from the Rabbis. Ginsburg, Alexa, illus. 2004. (New Children's Titles Ser.). 120p. (gr. 2-5). 15.95 (978-0-8276-0755-2(5)) Jewish Pubn. Society.

Goldin, Barbara. The Family Book of Midrash: 52 Jewish Stories from the Sages. 2006. 128p. pap. 19.95 (978-0-7425-5285-2(3)) Rowman & Littlefield Pubs., Inc.

Jaffe, Nina & Sutherland, Emily, illus. Tales for the Seventh Day: A Collection of Sabbath Stories. 2000. 73p. (J). pap. (978-0-590-12055-5(7)) Scholastic, Inc.

Philip, Neil. The Pirate Princess: And Other Fairy Tales. Weber, Mark, illus. 2005. 96p. (J). (ps-3). pap. 19.99 (978-0-590-10855-3(7) , Levine, Arthur A. Bks.) Scholastic, Inc.

Pinsker, Marlee. In the Days of Sand & Stars. Thisdale, Francois, illus. 2006. 88p. (J). (gr. 4-8). 22.95 (978-0-88776-724-1(9)) Tundra Bks., Inc./Livres Toundra, Inc. CAN. *Dist:* Random Hse., Inc.

LEGENDS—MEXICO

Fisher, Leonard Everett, illus. The Two Mountains: An Aztec Legend. 2000. 32p. (J). (gr. k-3). tchr. ed. 16.95 (978-0-8234-1504-5(X)) Holiday Hse., Inc.

LEGENDS—NORWAY

Lunge-Larsen, Lise. The Race of the Birkebeiners. Azarian, Mary, illus. 2001. 32p. (J). (gr. k-3). tchr. ed. 16.00 (978-0-618-10313-3(9)) Houghton Mifflin Co. Trade & Reference Div.

LEGENDS—SCANDINAVIA

May, Stephen, illus. Norse Myths & Legends. 2001. (World Book Myths & Legends Ser.). 64p. (J). (978-0-7166-2610-7(1)) World Bk., Inc.

Rayner, Olivia, illus. World Book Myths & Legends Series, 8 vols., Vol. 8. 2007. (World Book Myths & Legends Ser.). 64p. (gr. 4-8). 239.00 (978-0-7166-2613-8(6) , 31020) World Bk., Inc.

LEGENDS—SPAIN

Leyendas Espanolas. (SPA., Illus.). (YA). 11.95 (978-84-7281-212-3(X) , AF0099) Auriga, Ediciones S.A. ESP. *Dist:* Continental Bk. Co., Inc.

LEGENDS—UNITED STATES

Asfar, Dan. Ghost Stories of Old West, Vol. 1. rev. ed. 2003. (Ghost Stories Ser.). (Illus.). 216p. (gr. 4). pap. (978-1-894877-17-6(9)) Lone Pine Publishing.

—Ghost Stories of Michigan, Vol. 1. rev. ed. 2002. (Ghost Stories Ser.). (Illus.). 224p. (J). (gr. 4). pap. (978-1-894877-05-3(5)) Lone Pine Publishing.

—Ghost Stories of Pennsylvania, Vol. 1. rev. ed. 2002. (Ghost Stories Ser.). (Illus.). 208p. (gr. 4). pap. (978-1-894877-08-4(X)) Lone Pine Publishing.

Asfar, Dan & Thay, Edrick. Ghost Stories of America, 2 vols., Vol. 1. rev. ed. 2002. (Ghost Stories Ser.). (Illus.). 248p. (J). (gr. 4). pap. (978-1-894877-11-4(X)) Lone Pine Publishing.

Asfar, Dan, et al. Ghost Stories of America, 2 vols., Vol. 2. rev. ed. 2003. (Ghost Stories Ser.). (Illus.). 248p. (gr. 4). pap. (978-1-894877-31-2(4)) Lone Pine Publishing.

Delano, Marfe Ferguson. American Heroes. 2005. (National Geographic Ser.). (Illus.). 240p. (J). (gr. 5 up). 24.95 (978-0-7922-7208-3(0)); 45.90 (978-0-7922-7215-1(3)) National Geographic Society. (National Geographic Children's Bks.).

Drake, Samuel Adams. New England Legends & Folk Lore. 2001. 498p. (YA). reprint ed. (978-1-58218-443-2(7)); pap. (978-1-58218-442-5(9)) Digital Scanning, Inc.

Glass, Andrew, illus. The Legend of Strap Buckner: A Texas Tale. 2001. 32p. (J). (gr. k-3). tchr. ed. 16.95 (978-0-8234-1536-6(8)) Holiday Hse., Inc.

John Lennon. 2002. (Unseen Archives Ser.). 384p. (YA). 29.95 (978-0-7525-8514-7(2)) Parragon, Inc.

Mackall, Dandi Daley. The Legend of Ohio. LaFever, Greg, illus. 2005. (Legend Ser.). 40p. (J). (gr. k-5). 17.95 (978-1-58536-244-8(1)) Sleeping Bear Pr.

Smitten, Susan. Ghost Stories of New England, Vol. 1. Wangler, Chris, ed. rev. ed. 2003. (Ghost Stories Ser.). (Illus.). 224p. (J). (gr. 4). pap. (978-1-894877-12-1(8)) Lone Pine Publishing.

—Ghost Stories of Oregon, Vol. 1. rev. ed. 2002. (Ghost Stories Ser.). (Illus.). 216p. (J). (gr. 4). pap. (978-1-894877-13-8(6)) Lone Pine Publishing.

Sproul, Gloria. The Legend of the Grand Canyon. 2001. (Illus.). (J). (gr. 1-7). 16.00 (978-0-934372-02-2(0)) Mishe-Mokwa Pubns.

Teel, Gina. Ghost Stories of Minnesota, Vol. 1. Dykstra, Denise & Kubish, Shelagh, eds. rev. ed. 2002. (Ghost Stories Ser.). (Illus.). 208p. (J). (gr. 4). pap. (978-1-894877-07-7(1)) Lone Pine Publishing.

Thay, Edrick. Ghost Stories of Indiana, Vol. 1. rev. ed. 2002. (Ghost Stories Ser.). (Illus.). 200p. (J). (gr. 4). pap. (978-1-894877-06-0(3)) Lone Pine Publishing.

—Ghost Stories of Ohio, Vol. 1. rev. ed. 2002. (Ghost Stories Ser.). (Illus.). 192p. (J). (gr. 4). pap. (978-1-894877-09-1(8)) Lone Pine Publishing.

Vidal, Cesar. Gray Feather & the Big Dog. Torrecilla, Pablo, illus. 2002. (Legends of the Americas Ser.). 32p. (J). (gr. k-7). 18.95 (978-1-57768-973-7(9) , Bedrick, Peter Bks.) School Specialty Publishing.

LEGENDS—WALES

Jones, Gwyn E., ed. Welsh Legends & Folk Tales. 288p. (J). 3.99 (978-0-14-036770-6(5) , Puffin) Penguin Group (USA) Inc.

LEGENDS AND STORIES OF ANIMALS

see Animals—Fiction; Fables

LEGERDEMAIN

see Magic

LEGISLATORS

Boraas, Tracey. Sam Houston: Soldier & Statesman. 2002. (Let Freedom Ring Ser.). (Illus.). 48p. (J). (gr. 3-4). lib. bdg. 22.60 (978-0-7368-1350-1(0) , Bridgestone Bks.) Capstone Pr., Inc.

Espinosa, Rod. Patrick Henry. 2007. (Bio-Graphics Ser.). (Illus.). 32p. (J). (gr. 3-6). lib. bdg. 27.07 ***(978-1-60270-070-3(2)*** , Graphic Planet) Magic Wagon.

Firestone, Mary. The State Legislative Branch. 2004. (First Facts Ser.). (Illus.). 24p. (J). 15.95 (978-0-7368-2501-6(0)) Capstone Pr., Inc.

Gay, Oonagh & Leopold, Patricia, eds. Conduct Unbecoming? The Regulation of Parliamentary Behaviour. Gay, Oonagh & Leopold, Patricia, trs. 2004. 39.95 (978-1-84275-055-1(0)) Politico's Publishing Ltd. GBR. *Dist:* Consortium Bk. Sales & Distribution.

Gillis, Jennifer Blizin. Patrick Henry. 2004. (Illus.). 32p. (J). lib. bdg. 24.22 (978-1-4034-5960-2(6)) Heinemann Library.

Glaser, Jason & McDonnell, Peter. Patrick Henry: Muerte o Libertad. McDonnell, Peter, illus. 2007. (Graphic Library). (ENG & SPA.). (J). 25.26 (978-0-7368-6608-8(6)) Capstone Pr., Inc.

Kunstler, James Howard. Davy Crockett. Brodner, Steve, illus. 2005. (Rabbit Ears-A Classic Tale Ser.). 40p. (J). (gr. k-5). 25.65 (978-1-59197-762-9(2)) Spotlight.

Marcovitz, Hal. Nancy Pelosi. 2004. (Women in Politics Ser.). (Illus.). 120p. 30.00 (978-0-7910-7737-5(3)); 112p. pap. 30.00 (978-0-7910-8001-6(3)) Facts On File, Inc. (Chelsea Hse.).

Silate, Jennifer. The Calhoun-Randolph Debate on the Eve of the War of 1812: A Primary Source Investigation. 2004. (Great Historic Debates & Speeches Ser.). (Illus.). 64p. (YA). lib. bdg. 29.25 (978-1-4042-0150-7(5)) Rosen Publishing Group, Inc., The.

Slavicek, Louise Chipley. Daniel Inouye. 2007. (Asian Americans of Achievement Ser.). 128p. (YA). (gr. 6-10). lib. bdg. 30.00 (978-0-7910-9271-2(2) , Chelsea Hse.) Facts On File, Inc.

Wizner, Kira. John McCain: Profile of a Leading Republican. 2007. (J). ***(978-1-4042-1911-3(0))*** Rosen Publishing Group, Inc., The.

LEGISLATORS—UNITED STATES

see also United States—Congress

Adler, David A. A Picture Book of Patrick Henry. Wallner, John et al, illus. 2005. 32p. (J). (gr. k-3). pap. 6.95 (978-0-8234-1678-3(X)) Holiday Hse., Inc.

Allen, Charles F. David Crockett: Scout, Small Boy, Pilgrim, Mountaineer, Soldier, Bear-Hunter, & Congressman, Defender of the Alamo. (Illus.). 308p. reprint ed. lib. bdg. 98.00 (978-0-7222-4856-0(3)) Library Reprints, Inc.

—David Crockett, Scout: Small Boy, Pilgrim, Mountaineer, Soldier, Bear-Hunter & Congressman: Defender of the Alamo. McKernan, Frank, illus. 2000. (J). (978-0-89526-228-8(2)) Regnery Publishing, Inc., An Eagle Publishing Co.

Anderson, Dale. Elizabeth Dole. 2004. (Women in Politics Ser.). (Illus.). 120p. 30.00 (978-0-7910-7733-7(0)); 104p. pap. 30.00 (978-0-7910-7997-3(X)) Facts On File, Inc. (Chelsea Hse.).

Berger, Donna, illus. Davy Crockett. 2004. (Imagination Ser.). 32p. (J). (gr. 3 up). 22.60 (978-0-7565-0603-2(4)) Compass Point Bks.

Bonner, Mike. Stephen a Douglas: Champion of the Union. 2002. (gr. 5-8). lib. bdg. 17.60 (978-0-613-52728-6(3)) Tandem Library Bks.

Brager, Bruce L. John Kerry: Senator from Massachusetts. 2005. (Twentieth Century Leaders Ser.). (Illus.). 128p. (J). (gr. 6-12). lib. bdg. 23.95 (978-1-931798-64-8(8)) Reynolds, Morgan Inc.

Brill, Marlene Targ. Barack Obama. 2006. (J). pap. 6.95 (978-0-8225-6056-2(9) , First Avenue Editions) Lerner Publishing Group.

—Barack Obama: Working to Make a Difference. 2006. (Gateway Biographies Ser.). (Illus.). 48p. (J). 23.93 (978-0-8225-3417-4(7)) Lerner Publishing Group.

Burgan, Michael. Hillary Rodham Clinton: First Lady & Senator. 2005. (J). (978-0-7565-1588-1(2)) Compass Point Bks.

Caravantes, Peggy. American in Texas: The Story of Sam Houston. 2004. (Notable Americans Ser.). (Illus.). 144p. (YA). (gr. 6-12). 23.95 (978-1-931798-19-8(2)) Reynolds, Morgan Inc.

Collard, Sneed B., III. David Crockett: Fearless Frontiersman. 2006. (American Heroes Ser.). (Illus.). 48p. (J). lib. bdg. 28.50 (978-0-7614-2160-3(2) , Benchmark Bks.) Cavendish, Marshall Corp.

Crawford, Ann Fears. Barbara Jordan: Breaking the Barriers. 2002. (J). (978-1-57168-570-4(7) , Eakin Pr.) Eakin Pr.

—Barbara Jordan: Breaking the Barriers. 2003. (Illus.). 90p. (J). (gr. 7-9). lib. bdg. 19.95 (978-1-931823-11-1(1)) Halcyon Pr., Ltd.

Davis, William Michael. Barack Obama: The Politics of Hope. 2007. (Illus.). 168p. (YA). (gr. 10 up). lib. bdg. 25.95 ***(978-1-59556-024-7(6))*** OTTN Publishing.

Devaney, Sherri. Barack Obama. 2006. (Illus.). 112p. (J). (gr. 7-10). 32.45 (978-1-59018-937-5(X) , Lucent Bks.) Thomson Gale.

Driscoll, Laura. Hillary Clinton: An American Journey. Wood, Judith V., illus. 2007. (All Aboard Reading Ser.). 48p. (J). (gr. 1-3). pap. 3.99 ***(978-0-448-44787-2(8)*** , Grosset & Dunlap) Penguin Group (USA) Inc.

Dubois, Muriel L. The U. S. House of Representatives. 2003. (First Facts Ser.). (Illus.). 24p. (J). lib. bdg. 21.26 (978-0-7368-2288-6(7)) Capstone Pr., Inc.

—The U. S. Senate. 2003. (First Facts Ser.). (Illus.). 24p. (J). lib. bdg. 21.26 (978-0-7368-2290-9(9)) Capstone Pr., Inc.

Edwards, Roberta. Barack Obama: An American Story. Call, Ken, illus. 2007. (All Aboard Reading Ser.). 48p. (J). (gr. 1-3). pap. 3.99 ***(978-0-448-44799-5(1)*** , Grosset & Dunlap) Penguin Group (USA) Inc.

Egan, Tracie. How a Bill Becomes a Law. 2003. (Primary Source Library of American Citizenship). (J). pap. (978-1-4042-5085-7(9)) Rosen Publishing Group, Inc., The.

Feeney, Kathy. Davy Crockett. 2002. (Photo-Illustrated Biographies Ser.). (Illus.). 24p. (J). (gr. 2-3). lib. bdg. 18.60 (978-0-7368-1110-1(9) , Bridgestone Bks.) Capstone Pr., Inc.

Feinberg, Barbara Jane. John McCain: Serving His Country. 2000. (Gateway Biography Ser.). (Illus.). 48p. (J). (gr. 2-4). lib. bdg. 23.90 (978-0-7613-1974-0(3) , Millbrook Pr.) Lerner Publishing Group.

Fitzgerald, Brian. McCarthyism: The Red Scare. 2006. 96p. (YA). (gr. 7 up). lib. bdg. (978-0-7565-2007-6(X)) Compass Point Bks.

Flynn, Jean. Henry B. Gonzalez: Rebel with a Cause. 2003. (Illus.). v, 140p. (J). 16.95 (978-1-57168-780-7(7) , Eakin Pr.) Eakin Pr.

Freedman, Jeri. Hillary Rodham Clinton: Profile of a Leading Democrat. 2007. (J). ***(978-1-4042-1910-6(2))*** Rosen Publishing Group, Inc., The.

Gillis, Jennifer Blizin. Patrick Henry. 2004. (Illus.). 32p. (J). pap. 7.50 (978-1-4034-5968-8(1)) Heinemann Library.

Glaser, Jason. Patrick Henry: Liberty or Death. McDonnell, Peter, illus. 2005. (Graphic Library). 32p. (J). (gr. 3-7). lib. bdg. 25.26 (978-0-7368-4970-8(X)) Capstone Pr., Inc.

Gorman, Jacqueline Laks. Member of Congress. 2005. (Illus.). 24p. (J). pap. (978-0-8368-4577-8(3)); lib. bdg. 19.33 (978-0-8368-4570-9(6)) Stevens, Gareth Inc.

Green, Robert. John Glenn: Astronaut & U. S. Senator. 2000. (Career Biographies Ser.). (Illus.). 128p. (YA). (gr. 6-12). 25.00 (978-0-89434-341-4(6) , F403, Ferguson Publishing Co.) Facts On File, Inc.

Gregson, Susan R. Sam Houston: Texas Hero. 2005. (Signature Lives Ser.). (Illus.). 112p. (J). (gr. 5-7). (978-0-7565-1004-6(X)) Compass Point Bks.

Guernsey, JoAnn B. Hillary Rodham Clinton. 2005. (Biography ' Ser.). (Illus.). 112p. (J). 29.27 (978-0-8225-2372-7(8) , Lerner Pubns.); (gr. 6 up). pap. 7.95 (978-0-8225-9613-4(X)) Lerner Publishing Group.

Gullo, James. Hillary Rodham Clinton. 2003. (Importance of Ser.). (Illus.). 112p. (J). 32.45 (978-1-59018-310-6(X) , Lucent Bks.) Thomson Gale.

Haskins, Jim & Benson, Kathleen. John Lewis in the Lead: A Story of the Civil Rights Movement. Andrews, Benny, illus. 2006. 40p. (J). 17.95 (978-1-58430-250-6(X)) Lee & Low Bks., Inc.

Hilliard, Richard. Godspeed, John Glenn. 2006. (Illus.). (J). 16.95 (978-1-59078-384-9(0)) Boyds Mills Pr.

Holden, Henry M. Trailblazing Astronaut John Glenn: A MyReportLinks. com Book. 2004. (Space Flight Adventures & Disasters Ser.). (Illus.). 48p. (J). lib. bdg. 25.26 (978-0-7660-5166-9(8) , MyReportLinks.com Bks.) Enslow Pubs., Inc.

Jarnow, Jesse. Patrick Henry's Liberty or Death Speech: A Primary Source Investigation. 2004. (Great Historic Debates & Speeches Ser.). (Illus.). 64p. (J). lib. bdg. 29.25 (978-1-4042-0152-1(1)) Rosen Publishing Group, Inc., The.

Jordan, Denise M. Julian Bond: Civil Rights Activist & Chairman of the NAACP. 2001. (African-American Biographies Ser.). (Illus.). 128p. (J). (gr. 6-12). lib. bdg. 26.60 (978-0-7660-1549-4(1)) Enslow Pubs., Inc.

Kennedy, Edward M. My Senator & Me: A Dog's Eye View of Washington, D. C. Small, David, illus. 2006. 56p. (J). (ps-3). pap. 16.99 (978-0-439-65077-9(1) , Scholastic) Scholastic, Inc.

Kennedy, Edward M. My Senator & Me: A Dog;s-Eye View of Washington, D. C. Small, David, illus. 2007. 53p. (J). reprint ed. 17.00 ***(978-1-4223-6791-9(6))*** DIANE Publishing Co.

Kennedy, Edward Moore. My Senator & Me: A Dog's Eye View of Washington, D.C. Small, David, illus. 2006. (J). ***(978-1-4156-7168-9(0)); (978-0-439-65078-6(X))*** Scholastic, Inc. (Scholastic Pr.).

Kiely Miller, Barbara. Sam Houston. 2007. (J). pap. ***(978-0-8368-8323-7(3)*** , Weekly Reader Early Learning Library) Stevens, Gareth Inc.

Kunstler, James Howard. Davy Crockett. Brodner, Steve, illus. 2005. (Rabbit Ears-A Classic Tale Ser.). 40p. (J). (gr. k-5). 25.65 (978-1-59197-762-9(2)) Spotlight.

Leavitt, Amie. Nancy Pelosi. 2007. (Blue Banner Biography Ser.). (Illus.). 32p. (J). (gr. 4-8). lib. bdg. 25.70 ***(978-1-58415-613-0(9))*** Mitchell Lane Pubs., Inc.

Lutz, Norma Jean. J. C. Watts: Politician. 2000. (Black Americans of Achievement Ser.). (Illus.). 112p. (J). (gr. 4-7). 30.00 (978-0-7910-5338-6(5) , Chelsea Hse.) Facts On File, Inc.

Marcovitz, Hal. Nancy Pelosi. 2004. (Women in Politics Ser.). 120p. 30.00 (978-0-7910-7737-5(3)); 112p. pap. 30.00 (978-0-7910-8001-6(3)) Facts On File, Inc. (Chelsea Hse.).

Marsh, Carole. Harry Flood Byrd. 2002. (One Thousand Readers Ser.). (Illus.). 12p. (J). (gr. k-4). 2.95 (978-0-635-01538-9(2) , 15382) Gallopade International.

Mattern, Joanne. Hillary Rodham Clinton. 2007. (First Ladies Ser.). (Illus.). 32p. (J). (gr. k-6). lib. bdg. 24.21 ***(978-1-59928-792-8(7)*** , Checkerboard Library) ABDO Publishing Co.

McCain, John. Faith of Our Fathers. 2000. (gr. 7-12). lib. bdg. 23.45 (978-0-613-27819-5(4)) Tandem Library Bks.

McElroy Lisa Tucker. Nancy Pelosi: First Woman Speaker of the House. 2007. (Gateway Biographies Ser.). 48p. (J). (gr. 4-8). lib. bdg. 23.93 ***(978-0-8225-8685-2(1)*** , Lerner Pubns.) Lerner Publishing Group.

Melchiore, Susan McCarthy. Caesar Rodney. 2001. (gr. 3-6). lib. bdg. 17.60 (978-0-613-32357-4(2)) Tandem Library Bks.

Mendelsohn, James. Barbara Jordan: Getting Things Done. 2000. (Single Titles Ser.: up). (Illus.). 192p. (J). (gr. 7 up). lib. bdg. (978-0-7613-1467-7(9) , Twenty-First Century Bks.) Lerner Publishing Group.

Miller, Barbara Kiely. Sam Houston. 2007. (Great Americans Ser.). 24p. (J). (gr. 2-4). lib. bdg. 19.93 ***(978-0-8368-8316-9(0)*** , Weekly Reader Early Learning Library) Stevens, Gareth Inc.

Plourde, Lynn. What a President She Would Have Been: Margaret Chase Smith. 2008. (J). ***(978-1-58089-234-6(5))*** Charlesbridge Publishing, Inc.

Rau, Dana Meachen. Elizabeth Dole: Public Servant & Senator. 2005. (J). (978-0-7565-1583-6(1)) Compass Point Bks.

Raum, Elizabeth. John Glenn. 2005. (American Lives Ser.). (Illus.). 32p. (J). (978-1-4034-6940-3(7)); pap. (978-1-4034-6947-2(4)) Heinemann Library.

Renehan, Edward. The Clintons. 2005. (J). (978-0-7910-8526-4(0) , Chelsea Hse.) Facts On File, Inc.

Ryan, Bernard. Hillary Rodham Clinton: First Lady & Senator. 2004. (Ferguson Career Biographies Ser.). (Illus.). 160p. (J). (gr. 6-12). 25.00 (978-0-8160-5544-9(0) , Ferguson Publishing Co.) Facts On File, Inc.

Santella, Andrew. John Kerry. 2004. (Profiles of the Presidents Ser.). (J). (978-0-7565-0858-6(4)) Compass Point Bks.

Sapet, Kerrily. Barack Obama. 2007. (Political Profiles Ser.). (Illus.). 128p. (YA). (gr. 5 up). lib. bdg. 27.95 ***(978-1-59935-045-5(9))*** Reynolds, Morgan Inc.

Schuman, Michael. Barack Obama: We Are One People. 2008. (African-American Biography Library). (Illus.). 128p. (J). (gr. 6 up). lib. bdg. 31.93 ***(978-0-7660-2891-3(7))*** Enslow Pubs., Inc.

Seaver, Derrick. Kid in the House. 2002. 108p. (YA). pap. 9.95 (978-0-595-25053-0(X) , Writers Club Pr.) iUniverse, Inc.

Shichtman, Sandra H. Nancy Peolosi. 2007. (Political Profiles Ser.). (Illus.). 112p. (YA). (gr. 5 up). lib. bdg. 27.95 ***(978-1-59935-049-3(1))*** Reynolds, Morgan Inc.

Silate, Jennifer. The Calhoun-Randolph Debate on the Eve of the War of 1812: A Primary Source Investigation. 2004. (Great Historic Debates & Speeches Ser.). (Illus.). 64p. (YA). lib. bdg. 29.25 (978-1-4042-0150-7(5)) Rosen Publishing Group, Inc., The.

Tukan, Jaytoe Anthony, Sr. United States Senators from North Carolina 1954 - 2008. 2003. per. 12.95 (978-0-9665909-5-1(3)) Kalawantis Publishing Services, Inc.

Wagner, Heather Lehr. Hillary Rodham Clinton. 2004. (Women in Politics Ser.). (Illus.). 120p. 30.00 (978-0-7910-7735-1(7)); 110p. pap. 30.00 (978-0-7910-7999-7(6)) Facts On File, Inc. (Chelsea Hse.).

Watson, Marilyn Myrick. Barry Goldwater. 2007. (J). per. 6.95 ***(978-0-9790826-0-3(9))*** Acacia Publishing, Inc.

—Barry M. Goldwater. 2006. (J). ***(978-0-9788283-4-9(8))*** Acacia Publishing, Inc.

Welch, Catherine A. Patrick Henry. 2006. (History Maker Bios Ser.). (Illus.). 48p. (J). 26.60 (978-0-8225-5941-2(2) , Lerner Pubns.) Lerner Publishing Group.

Wheeler, Jill C. America's Leaders. 2002. (War on Terrorism Ser.). (Illus.). 64p. (J). (gr. 4-8). lib. bdg. 25.65 (978-1-57765-661-6(X) , ABDO & Daughters) ABDO Publishing Co.

—Hillary Rodham Clinton. 2003. (Breaking Barriers Ser.). (Illus.). 64p. (J). (gr. 3-8). lib. bdg. 25.65 (978-1-57765-741-5(1)) ABDO Publishing Co.

Winget, Mary. Gerald R. Ford. 2007. (Presidential Leaders Ser.). 112p. (J). (gr. 6-12). 29.27 (978-0-8225-1509-8(1) , Twenty-First Century Bks.) Lerner Publishing Group.

LEGUMES

Here are entered works on those plants belonging to the family Leguminosae, the pods or seeds of which are edible for man or domestic animals, e.g. peas, beans, lentils, etc. treated collectively.

Hughes, Meredith Sayles. Spill the Beans & Pass the Peanuts: Legumes. 1999. (Plants We Eat Ser.). (Illus.). 104p. (gr. 6-9). 26.60 (978-0-8225-2834-0(7)) Lerner Publishing Group.

Mitchell, Melanie S. Beans. (First Step Nonfiction Ser.). (Illus.). (gr. k-2). 2005. 24p. lib. bdg. 17.27 (978-0-8225-4608-5(6)); 2003. 23p. (J). pap. 5.95 (978-0-8225-4609-2(4) , Lerner Pubns.) Lerner Publishing Group.

Murray, Julie. Beans. 2007. (Life Cycles Ser.). 24p. (J). (gr. k-4). lib. bdg. 21.35 ***(978-1-59928-702-7(1)*** , Buddy Bks.) ABDO Publishing Co.

Royston, Angela. Bean. 2002. (Life Cycle of a... Ser.). (Illus.). 32p. (J). (gr. k-2). pap. 6.95 (978-1-58810-329-1(3) , 91059) Heinemann Library.

—Ciclo de Vida de el Frijol. 2003. Tr. of Bean. (SPA.). 32p. (J). pap. 6.95 (978-1-4034-3037-3(3)) Heinemann Library.

Schwartz, David M. Bean. Kuhn, Dwight, photos by. 2001. (Springboards into Science Ser.). (Illus.). 24p. (J). (gr. 1 up). lib. bdg. 20.67 (978-0-8368-2970-9(0)) Stevens, Gareth Inc.

Walker and Company Staff & Rockwell, Anne F. One Bean. Halsey, Megan, illus. 1999. 32p. (J). (ps-3). reprint ed. pap. 6.95 (978-0-8027-7572-6(1)) Walker & Co.

LEIA, PRINCESS (FICTITIOUS CHARACTER)—FICTION

Davids, Paul & Davids, Hollace. The Lost City of the Jedi. 1999. (Star Wars Ser.: Bk. 2). (Illus.). 94p. (J). (gr. 4-7). reprint ed. pap. 10.00 (978-0-7881-6480-4(5)) DIANE Publishing Co.

—Star Wars, 3 bks. l.t. ed. Incl. Prophets of the Dark Side. lib. bdg. 22.60 (978-0-8368-1994-6(2)); Queen of the Empire. lib. bdg. 22.60 (978-0-8368-1993-9(4)); Zorba the Hutt's Revenge. lib. bdg. 22.60 (978-0-8368-1991-5(8)); 112p. (J). (gr. 4 up). 1997. Set lib. bdg. 67.80 (978-0-8368-1988-5(8)) Stevens, Gareth Inc.

LEIF ERICSSON, D. CA. 1020

see Eriksson, Leif, d. ca. 1020

LEIGH-MALLORY, GEORGE HERBERT, 1886-1924

Salkeld, Audrey. Mystery on Everest: A Photobiography of George Mallory. 2000. (Illus.). 64p. (J). (gr. 5-8). 17.95 (978-0-7922-7222-9(6) , National Geographic Children's Bks.) National Geographic Society.

LEISURE

see also Hobbies; Recreation

Diwrnod i'r Brenin: Chwaraeon, Hamdden a Thwristiaeth Er 1900. 2005. (978-1-902346-01-4(7)) Addysg Y Cyfryngau Cymru.

Espeland, Pamela & Verdick, Elizabeth. Smart Ways to Spend Your Time: The Constructive Use of Time Assets. 2005. (Adding Assets Series for Kids). (Illus.). 80p. (J). (gr. 3-7). pap. 9.95 (978-1-57542-172-8(0) , 912) Free Spirit Publishing, Inc.

Nardo, Don. Arts. Leisure & Sport in Ancient Egypt. 2005. (Lucent Library of Historical Eras Ser.). (Illus.). 112p. (YA). (gr. 7-10). lib. bdg. 32.45 (978-1-59018-706-7(7) , Lucent Bks.) Thomson Gale.

—Leisure Life of the Ancient Greeks. 2004. (Lucent Library of Historical Eras). (Illus.). 112p. (J). (gr. 7-10). 32.45 (978-1-59018-528-5(5) , Lucent Bks.) Thomson Gale.

Non ap Emlyn. Hamddena - Llyfr 1 Lefel 3/4. 2005. (WEL & ENG., Illus.). 20p. (978-1-86085-600-6(4)) ICA Video.

—Hamddena - Llyfr 3 Lefel 5/6. 2005. (WEL & ENG., Illus.). 20p. (978-1-86085-602-0(0)) ICA Video.

—Hamddena - Llyfr 4 Lefel 6/7. 2005. (WEL & ENG., Illus.). 20p. (978-1-86085-603-7(9)) ICA Video.

Townsend, John. Weary Work & Lousy Leisure. 2006. (Raintree Freestyle Ser.). (Illus.). 48p. (J). (978-1-4109-1870-3(X)) Steck-Vaughn.

Trumbauer, Lisa. Our Favorite Things to Do. 2000. (Yellow Umbrella Books). (Illus.). 16p. (J). (gr. 1). lib. bdg. 14.60 (978-0-7368-0739-5(X) , Pebble Bks.) Capstone Pr., Inc.

Yates, Vicki. Having Fun. 2007. (J). ***(978-1-4034-9832-8(6)); pap. (978-1-4034-9840-3(7))*** Heinemann Library.

LEMMINGS

Souza, Dorothy M. What's a Lemming? 1998. (Creatures All Around Us Ser.). (Illus.). 40p. (J). (gr. 2-4). lib. bdg. (978-1-57505-088-1(9) , Carolrhoda Bks.) Lerner Publishing Group.

Squire, Ann. Lemmings. 2006. (True Book Ser.). (Illus.). 47p. (J). (978-0-516-25470-8(7)) Children's Pr., Ltd.

—Lemmings. 2006. (True Book Ser.). (Illus.). 47p. (J). (978-0-516-22823-5(4) , Children's Pr.) Scholastic Library Publishing.

LEMMINGS—FICTION

Thorpe, Kiki. Follow the Lemming. 2001. (gr. k-3). lib. bdg. 11.80 (978-0-613-35513-1(X)) Tandem Library Bks.

LEMON

Sloan, Peter. Making Lemonade. 1999. (gr. k-3). lib. bdg. 11.80 (978-0-613-30591-4(4)) Tandem Library Bks.

LEMURS

Baicker, Karen. Lemurs. 2007. (J). ***(978-1-59939-132-8(5)*** , Reader's Digest Young Families, Inc.) Reader's Digest Children's Publishing, Inc.

Butz, Christopher. Lemurs. 2002. (Animals of the Rain Forest Ser.). (Illus.). 32p. (YA). lib. bdg. 22.83 (978-0-7398-5528-7(X)) Raintree.

Darling, Kathy. Lemurs on Location. 1998. (On Location Ser.). (Illus.). 40p. (J). (gr. 1 up). 16.95 (978-0-688-12539-4(5)) HarperCollins Pubs.

Frost, Helen. Lemurs. Saunders-Smith, Gail, ed. 2002. (Rain Forest Animals Ser.). (Illus.). 24p. (J). (gr. k-1). lib. bdg. 15.93 (978-0-7368-1456-0(6) , Pebble Bks.) Capstone Pr., Inc.

Johnson, Jinny. Lemur. Ch'en-Ling, illus. Price, Susanna, photos by. 2001. (Busy Baby Animals Ser.). 16p. (J). (ps up). lib. bdg. 19.33 (978-0-8368-2926-6(3)) Stevens, Gareth Inc.

Jolly, Alison. Ny Aiay Ako: Ako the Aye-Aye. Rasamimanana, Hantanirina, tr. Ross, Deborah, illus. 2005. (MLA & ENG.). (J). 20.00 (978-0-9766009-0-9(0)) Lemur Conservation Foundation.

Kite, Lorien. Nature's Children, 21 vols., Set VI. 1999. (Nature's Children Ser.). (Illus.). (J). (gr. k-8). lib. bdg. 289.00 (978-0-7172-9351-3(3) , Grolier) Scholastic Library Publishing.

Land of the Lemurs. 2002. (Animal's Around the World Mini Bks.). (Illus.). 32p. (J). (978-1-59069-171-7(7) , H4007) Studio Mouse LLC.

Lemurs. 2002. pap. (978-0-7398-5813-4(0)) Steck-Vaughn.

Powzyk, Joyce. A Little Lemur Named Mew. 2003. (Illus.). 32p. lib. bdg. 22.90 (978-0-7613-2665-6(0) , Millbrook Pr.) Lerner Publishing Group.

Powzyk, Joyce A. In Search of Lemurs: My Days & Nights in a Madagascar Rain Forest. 1998. (Illus.). 48p. (J). (gr. 3-7). 17.95 (978-0-7922-7072-0(X) , T07072C, National Geographic Children's Bks.) National Geographic Society.

Shores, Erika L. Lemurs: Tree Dwellers. 2004. (Wild World of Animals Ser.). (Illus.). 24p. (J). lib. bdg. 21.26 (978-0-7368-2614-3(9) , Bridgestone Bks.) Capstone Pr., Inc.

LEMURS—FICTION

Cousins, Lucy. Jazzy in the Jungle. Cousins, Lucy, illus. 2002. (Illus.). 32p. (J). (gr. k-k). 14.99 (978-0-7636-1903-9(5)) Candlewick Pr.

David, Erica. Quiero Ser Libre. 2005. (Madagascar Ser.).Tr. of Born to Be Wild. (SPA., Illus.). 32p. (J). 3.99 (978-0-439-71575-1(X) , Scholastic en Espanol) Scholastic, Inc.

Dennard, Deborah. Lemur Landing: A Story of a Madagascan Dry Tropical Forest. Kest, Kristin, illus. 2001. (Wild Habitats Ser.). 36p. (J). (gr. 1-4). 26.95 (978-1-56899-982-1(8)) Soundprints.

Dennard, Deborah & Kest, Kristin. Lemur Landing: A Story of a Madagascan Dry Tropical Forest. 2005. (Wild Habitats Ser.). (Illus.). 32p. (J). (gr. 1-4). pap. 6.95 (978-1-56899-979-1(8) , S7019) Soundprints.

Jordan, Apple. Fearless Foursome. Dever, Bob & Morris, Michael, illus. 2005. (Madagascar Ser.). (SPA.). 64p. (J). (ps-ps). 2.99 (978-0-439-71307-8(2) , Scholastic en Espanol) Scholastic, Inc.

Lester, Helen. Something Might Happen. Munsinger, Lynn, illus. 2003. 32p. (J). (gr. k-3). tchr. ed. 16.00 (978-0-618-25406-4(4) , Walter Lorraine) Houghton Mifflin Co. Trade & Reference Div.

Ostrow, Kim. Darwin's Family Tree. 2001. (gr. k-3). lib. bdg. 11.80 (978-0-613-35602-2(0)) Tandem Library Bks.

Simpson, Fiona, ed. Madagascar: Play-Along. 2005. (Madagascar Ser.). 16p. (J). pap. 4.99 (978-0-439-69994-5(0)) Scholastic, Inc.

Steele, Michael Anthony. Esto es un Zoologico! 2005. (Madagascar Ser.).Tr. of Zoosters on the Loose. (SPA., Illus.). 24p. (J). 3.99 (978-0-439-71308-5(0)) Scholastic, Inc.

Walt Disney Company Staff, contrib. by. Walt Disney Pictures Presents Dinosaur. 2000. (Disney's Wonderful World of Reading Ser.). (Illus.). (J). (978-0-7172-6447-6(5) , Grolier) Scholastic Library Publishing.

—Walt Disney Pictures Presents Dinosaur. 2000. (Colorforms Books). (Illus.). (J). (978-1-57528-397-5(2)) University Games.

Zanimo & Brasset, Doris. I Am Funny. Zanimo & Brasset, Doris, illus. 2000. (Maki Ser.). (Illus.). 14p. (J). (ps up). bds. (978-1-894363-05-1(1)) Dominique & Friends.

LENIN, VLADIMIR ILICH, 1870-1924

Downing, David. Vladimir Ilyich Lenin. 2002. (Leading Lives Ser.). 64p. (J). (gr. 5-7). (Illus.). lib. bdg. 28.50 (978-1-58810-582-0(2)); pap. 8.95 (978-1-4034-0137-3(3) , 91616) Heinemann Library.

Edwards, Judith. Lenin & the Russian Revolution in World History. 2001. (In World History Ser.). (Illus.). 128p. (J). (gr. 5-12). lib. bdg. 26.60 (978-0-7660-1464-0(9)) Enslow Pubs., Inc.

Goldstein, Margaret J. V. I. Lenin. 2007. (Biography Ser.). 112p. (J). (gr. 6-12). 29.27 (978-0-8225-5977-1(3) , Twenty-First Century Bks.) Lerner Publishing Group.

Joihnson, Robert, compiled by. Lenin, Stalin & Communist Russia: The Myth & Reality of Communism. 2003. (Studymates Ser.). (Illus.). 132p. (C). pap. 27.50 (978-1-84285-039-8(3)) Studymates Ltd. GBR. *Dist:* Trans-Atlantic Pubns., Inc.

Naden, Corinne J. & Blue, Rose. Lenin. 2003. (Importance of Ser.). (Illus.). 112p. (J). 32.45 (978-1-59018-233-8(2) , Lucent Bks.) Thomson Gale.

LENINGRAD (RUSSIA)

see Saint Petersburg (Russia)

LENSES

Allman, Toney. From Octopus Eyes to Powerful Lenses. 2006. 32p. (J). (gr. 3-6). 24.95 (978-0-7377-3631-1(3) , Kidhaven) Thomson Gale.

I Spy! Individual Title Six-Packs. (Bookweb Ser.). 32p. (gr. 3 up). 34.00 (978-0-7635-3948-1(1)) Rigby Education.

Tocci, Salvatore. Experiments with a Hand Lens. 2002. (True Bks.). (J). (Illus.). 48p. (gr. 3-5). pap. 6.95 (978-0-516-26994-8(1) , Children's Pr.); (978-0-531-12155-9(0) , Watts, Franklin); (Illus.). 48p. (gr. 3-5). 25.00 (978-0-516-22506-7(5) , Children's Pr.) Scholastic Library Publishing.

LEONARDO, DA VINCI, 1452-1519

Anderson, Maxine. Amazing Leonardo da Vinci: Inventions You Can Build Yourself. 2006. (Build It Yourself Ser.). (Illus.). 128p. (J). pap. 14.95 (978-0-9749344-2-6(9)) Nomad Pr.

Byrd, Robert. Leonardo, the Beautiful Dreamer. Byrd, Robert, illus. 2003. (Illus.). 40p. (J). (gr. 2-5). 17.99 (978-0-525-47033-5(6) , Dutton Juvenile) Penguin Group (USA) Inc.

Connolly, Sean. Leonardo Da Vinci. (Heinemann First Library). (Illus.). 32p. (J). 2006. lib. bdg. ***(978-1-4034-8492-5(9));*** Set 1. 2002. pap. 6.50 (978-1-58810-283-6(1) , 91053) Heinemann Library.

Connolly, Sean, contrib. by. Leonardo Da Vinci. 1999. (Life & Work of. . . Ser.). (Illus.). 32p. (J). (gr. k-2). lib. bdg. 21.36 (978-1-57572-954-1(7)) Heinemann Library.

David, T. Leonardo Da Vinci: Mona Lisa. 2002. (Coleccion Joven Arte).Tr. of Leonardo Da Vinci: Mona Lisa. (SPA., Illus.). 120p. (YA). 11.96 (978-84-89804-08-1(7)) Loguez Ediciones ESP. *Dist:* Lectorum Pubns., Inc.

Dickins, Rosie & Ball, Karen. Leonardo Da Vinci - Internet Referenced. 2007. (Famous Lives Gift Bks). 64p. (J). 8.99 ***(978-0-7945-1594-2(0)*** , Usborne) EDC Publishing.

Fritz, Jean. Leonardo's Horse. Talbott, Hudson, illus. 2001. 48p. (J). (gr. 1-6). 18.99 (978-0-399-23576-4(0) , Putnam Juvenile) Penguin Group (USA) Inc.

Hall, Margaret. Leonardo Da Vinci. 2007. (Essential Lives Ser.). (ENG., Illus.). 112p. (J). (gr. 6-8). lib. bdg. 32.79 ***(978-1-59928-844-4(3)*** , Essential Library) ABDO Publishing Co.

Hart, Tony. Leonardo da Vinci. Hellard, Susan, illus. 2002. (Ninos Famosos Ser.). (SPA & ENG.). 24p. (gr. 1-5). pap. 6.95 (978-85-7416-167-9(5)) Callis Editora Ltda BRA. *Dist:* Independent Pubs. Group.

Herbert, Janis. Leonardo da Vinci for Kids: His Life & Ideas. 1998. (gr. 3-6). lib. bdg. 19.70 (978-0-613-70602-5(1)) Tandem Library Bks.

Hodge, Susie. The Life of Leonardo Da Vinci. 2006. (Stories from History Ser.). 48p. (J). 14.95 ***(978-0-7696-4718-0(9));*** pap. 6.95 ***(978-0-7696-4698-5(0))*** School Specialty Publishing.

Jusseaux, Patrick & Prunier, James. Leonardo da Vinci. Gonzalez Batlle, Jorge, tr. 2007. (Tras los pasos de ... Ser.). (SPA., Illus.). 128p. (J). pap. 14.95 (978-84-95939-83-8(5)) Blume ESP. *Dist:* Independent Pubs. Group.

Kaehue, Heinz. Leonardo Da Vinci: Dreams, Schemes & Flying Machines. 1999. (Adventures in Art Ser.). (Illus.). 30p. (gr. 4-7). 14.95 (978-3-7913-2166-0(8)) Prestel Publishing.

Kalz, Jill. The Mona Lisa. 2004. (What in the World? Ser.). (Illus.). 48p. 19.95 (978-1-58341-272-5(7) , Creative Education) Creative Co., The.

Koestler-Grack, Rachel A. Leonardo Da Vinci: Artist, Inventor, & Renaissance Man. 2005. (Makers of the Middle Ages & Renaissance Ser.). (Illus.). 146p. (J). (gr. 4-8). lib. bdg. 30.00 (978-0-7910-8626-1(7) , Chelsea Hse.) Facts On File, Inc.

Krull, Kathleen. Leonardo Da Vinci: Giants of Science 1. Kulikov, Boris, illus. 2005. 128p. (J). (gr. 3-7). 15.99 (978-0-670-05920-1(X) , Viking Juvenile) Penguin Group (USA) Inc.

Langley, Andrew. Da Vinci & His Times. 2006. (DK Eyewitness Bks.). (Illus.). 72p. (J). 15.99 (978-0-7566-1768-4(5)); lib. bdg. 19.99 (978-0-7566-1767-7(7)) Dorling Kindersley Publishing, Inc.

Lassieur, Allison. Leonardo da Vinci & the Renaissance in World History. 2000. (In World History Ser.). (Illus.). 128p. (YA). (gr. 5-12). lib. bdg. 26.60 (978-0-7660-1401-5(0)) Enslow Pubs., Inc.

Lebscky, Ibi. Leonardo. Cardoni, Paolo, illus. (Coleccion Seran Famosos).Tr. of Little Leonardo de Vinci. (SPA., Illus.). 28p. (J). (gr. 2-4). 10.36 (978-84-233-1399-0(9)) Ediciones Destino ESP. *Dist:* Lectorum Pubns., Inc.

Leonardo's "Quotebook" Thoughts by & about Leonardo Da Vinci. 2006. 104p. (J). pap. (978-0-935047-57-8(3)) Americas Group, The.

Leoni, Maria Teresa Zanobini. Leonardo Da Vinci. 2005. (Great Artists Ser.). (Illus.). 40p. (J). (gr. 5). pap. 7.95 (978-1-59270-048-6(9)) Enchanted Lion Bks., LLC.

The Life & Contributions of Leonardo Da Vinci. 2006. 58p. (J). pap. (978-0-935047-60-8(3)) Americas Group, The.

MacDonald, Fiona. Leonardo Da Vinci. 2000. (World in the Time of... Ser.). (Illus.). 48p. (J). (gr. 4-7). 22.95 (978-0-7910-6032-2(2) , Chelsea Hse.) Facts On File, Inc.

Malam, John. Leonardo Da Vinci. 1999. (Tell Me about Ser.). (Illus.). 24p. (gr. 2-5). lib. bdg. 19.93 (978-1-57505-367-7(5)) Lerner Publishing Group.

Mason, Antony & da Vinci, Leonardo. Leonardo da Vinci. 2004. (Lives of the Artists Ser.). (Illus.). 48p. (J). (gr. 5 up). pap. 29.26 (978-0-8368-5604-0(X)); lib. bdg. 30.00 (978-0-8368-5599-9(X)) Stevens, Gareth Inc. (World Almanac Library).

Mattern, Joanne. Leonardo Da Vinci. 2005. (Checkerboard Biography Library). (Illus.). 32p. (J). (gr. k-6). lib. bdg. 22.78 (978-1-59197-842-8(4)) ABDO Publishing Co.

Nichols, Catherine. Leonardo Da Vinci. 2006. (Primary Source Library of Famous Artists). (Illus.). 32p. (J). 21.95 (978-1-4042-2762-0(8) , PowerKids Pr.) Rosen Publishing Group, Inc., The.

Noble, Marty & da Vinci, Leonardo. Leonardo da Vinci Stained Glass Coloring Book. 2006. 16p. pap. 5.95 (978-0-486-45059-9(7)) Dover Pubns., Inc.

O'Connor, Barbara. Leonardo Da Vinci: Renaissance Genuis. 2005. (Trailblazer Biographies Ser.). (Illus.). 112p. (gr. 5-9). 27.93 (978-0-87614-467-1(9)) Lerner Publishing Group.

Plain, Nancy. Leonardo Da Vinci. 1999. (J). (978-0-7614-0790-4(1) , Benchmark Bks.) Cavendish, Marshall Corp.

Reed, Jennifer. Leonardo da Vinci: Genius of Art & Science. 2005. (Great Minds of Science Ser.). (Illus.). 128p. (J). lib. bdg. 26.60 (978-0-7660-2500-4(4)) Enslow Pubs., Inc.

Rinaldo, Denise. Leonardo Da Vinci: With a Discussion of Imagination. 2003. (Values in Action Ser.). (J). (978-1-59203-066-8(1)) Learning Challenge, Inc.

Romeo, Francesca. Leonardo Da Vinci. 2008. (YA). lib. bdg. 24.95 net. (***978-1-934545-00-3(7)***) Oliver Pr., Inc.

Ross, Stewart. Leonardo Da Vinci. 2002. (Scientists Who Made History Ser.). (Illus.). 48p. (J). lib. bdg. 27.12 (978-0-7398-5223-1(X)) Raintree.

Stanley, Diane. Leonardo Da Vinci. 2000. (gr. 3-6). lib. bdg. 15.30 (978-0-613-30003-2(3)) Tandem Library Bks.

Stanley, George E. Leonardo da Vinci: Young Artist, Writer, & Inventor. 2005. (Childhood of World Figures Ser.). 176p. (J). pap. 5.99 (978-1-4169-0570-7(7) , Aladdin) Simon & Schuster Children's Publishing.

Stanley, George Edward. Leonardo Da Vinci: Young Artist, Writer, & Inventor. 2005. (Childhood of World Figures Ser.). 166p. (J). (978-1-4156-3039-6(9) , Aladdin) Simon & Schuster Children's Publishing.

Strom, Laura Layton. Leonardo da Vinci: Artist & Scientist. 2007. (Shockwave: Life Stories Ser.). 36p. (J). (gr. 3-5). pap. 6.95 (***978-0-531-18798-2(5)*** , Children's Pr.) Scholastic Library Publishing.

Strom, Laura Layton & Leonardo. Leonardo Da Vinci: Artist & Scientist. 2007. (Shockwave: Life Stories Ser.). (Illus.). 36p. (J). (gr. 4-6). lib. bdg. 25.00 (***978-0-531-17771-6(8)*** , Children's Pr.) Scholastic Library Publishing.

Tello, Antonio. My Name Is Leonardo da Vinci. Boccardo, Johanna A., illus. 2006. (My Name Is ... Ser.). 64p. (J). pap. 7.99 (978-0-7641-3392-3(6)) Barron's Educational Series, Inc.

Visconti, Guido. The Genius of Leonardo. Roberts, Mark, tr. from ITA. Landmann, Bimba, illus. 2000. 40p. (J). (gr. 2-7). 16.99 (978-1-84148-301-6(X)) Barefoot Bks., Inc.

Whitteman, Barbara. Leonardo da Vinci. (Masterpieces Ser.). (Illus.). 32p. (J). pap. 6.95 (978-0-7368-3407-0(9)) Capstone Pr., Inc.

Williams, Colleen Madonna Flood. My Adventure with Leonardo da Vinci. 2007. 44p. (J). 8.99 (978-1-59092-458-7(4) , Orchard Academy Pr.) Windstorm Creative.

Witteman, Barbara. Leonardo Da Vinci. 2003. (Masterpieces, Artists & Their Works). (Illus.). 24p. (J). lib. bdg. 19.93 (978-0-7368-2228-2(3) , Bridgestone Bks.) Capstone Pr., Inc.

Zanobini Leoni, Maria Teresa. Leonardo Da Vinci. 2003. (Great Artists Ser.). (Illus.). 40p. (J). 15.95 (978-1-59270-007-3(1)) Enchanted Lion Bks., LLC.

LEONARDO, DA VINCI, 1452-1519—FICTION

Anholt, Laurence. Leonardo & the Flying Boy. 2007. (Anholt's Artists Books for Children Ser.). 32p. (J). (ps-3). pap. 7.99 (***978-0-7641-3851-5(0)***) Barron's Educational Series, Inc.

Anholt, Laurence. Leonardo & the Flying Boy: A Story about Leonardo da Vinci. 2000. (Illus.). 32p. (J). (ps-2). 15.99 (978-0-7641-5225-2(4)) Barron's Educational Series, Inc.

Bradford, Emma. Kat & the Missing Notebooks. Sano, Kazuhiko, illus. 1999. (Stardust Classics: No. 4). 119p. (J). (gr. 2-5). 12.95 (978-1-889514-27-7(6)); pap. 5.95 (978-1-889514-28-4(4)) Dolls Corp.

Dyer, K. C. Secret of Light. 2004. 200p. pap. 8.99 (978-1-55002-477-7(9)) Dundurn Group, The CAN. *Dist:* Univ. of Toronto Pr.

Grey, Christopher Peter. Leonardo's Shadow: Or, My Astonishing Life as Leonardo da Vinci's Servant. 2006. 400p. (YA). 16.95 (978-1-4169-0543-1(X) , Atheneum) Simon & Schuster Children's Publishing.

Konigsburg, E. L. The Second Mrs. Giaconda. 3rd ed. (J). pap. 4.95 (978-0-13-800061-5(1)) Prentice Hall (Schl. Div.).

—The Second Mrs. Gioconda. 1998. 160p. (J). (gr. 5-9). pap. 5.99 (978-0-689-82121-9(2) , Aladdin) Simon & Schuster Children's Publishing.

—The Second Mrs. Gioconda. l.t. ed. 2006. 156p. 22.95 (978-0-7862-8286-9(X)) Thorndike Pr.

Lewis, J. Patrick. The Stolen Smile. Kelley, Gary, illus. 2004. 40p. 17.95 (978-1-56846-192-2(5) , Creative Editions) Creative Co., The.

McCarthy, Meghan. Steal Back the Mona Lisa! 2006. (Illus.). 40p. (J). 16.00 (978-0-15-205368-0(9)) Harcourt Trade Pubs.

Osborne, Mary Pope. Monday with a Mad Genius. Murdocca, Sal, illus. 2007. (Stepping Stone Bks.). 128p. (J). (gr. 2-6). 11.99 (***978-0-375-83729-6(9)***); lib. bdg. 14.99 (***978-0-375-93729-3(3)***) Random Hse. Children's Bks. (Random Hse. Bks. for Young Readers).

—Monday with a Mad Genius. Murdocca, Sal, illus. 2007. (J). pap. (***978-0-375-83730-2(2)***) Random Hse., Inc.

Resnick, Mike. Lady with an Alien: An Encounter with Leonardo da Vinci. 2005. (Art Encounterstm Series- Ser.). 244p. pap. 6.99 (978-0-8230-0419-5(8)) Watson-Guptill Pubns., Inc.

—Lady with an Alien: An Encounter with Leonardo Da Vinci. 2005. (Art Encounters Ser.). (Illus.). 176p. (YA). (gr. 3-7). 15.95 (978-0-8230-0323-5(X)) Watson-Guptill Pubns., Inc.

Sabuda, Robert. Uh-Oh Leonardo! 2003. (Illus.). 48p. (J). 16.95 (978-0-689-81160-9(8) , Atheneum) Simon & Schuster Children's Publishing.

Scieszka, Jon. Da Wild, Da Crazy, Da Vinci. McCauley, Adam, illus. (Time Warp Trio Ser.: No. 14). (J). (gr. 2). 2006. 96p. pap. 4.99 (978-0-14-240465-2(9) , Puffin); 2004. 80p. 14.99 (978-0-670-05926-3(9) , Viking Juvenile) Penguin Group (USA) Inc.

YKids Staff. Leonardo da Vinci. 2008. (Great Figures in History Ser.). 144p. (J). pap. 14.95 (***978-981-05-7555-7(6)***) Youngjin (Singapore) Pte Ltd. SGP. *Dist:* Independent Pubs. Group.

LEONOWENS, ANNA HARRIETTE, 1834-1914

Landon, Margaret. Anna & the King. 1999. (Illus.). (J). 11.60 (978-0-606-21838-2(6)); 2000. (gr. 3-6). lib. bdg. 12.95 (978-0-613-24213-4(0)) Tandem Library Bks.

LEOPARDS

Chottin, Ariane. Little Leopards. 2005. (Born to Be Wild Ser.). (Illus.). 23p. (J). lib. bdg. 22.00 (978-0-8368-4438-2(6)) Stevens, Gareth Inc.

Cole & Leeson. El Jaguar y el Leopardo. 2002. (Gatos Salvajes del Mundo Serie).Tr. of Wild Cats Of The World: The Jaguar And The Leopard. (SPA.). 24p. (J). (gr. 3-5). 24.94 (978-1-4103-0005-8(6) , Blackbirch Pr., Inc.) Thomson Gale.

Cole, Melissa S. Jaguars & Leopards. l.t. ed. 2001. (Wild Cats of the World Ser.). (Illus.). 23p. (J). (gr. 3-6). 22.45 (978-1-56711-447-8(4) , Blackbirch Pr., Inc.) Thomson Gale.

Cooper, Jason. Leopards. 2002. (Eye to Eye with Big Cats Ser.). (Illus.). 24p. (J). lib. bdg. 20.64 (978-1-58952-404-0(7)) Rourke Publishing, LLC.

Corrigan, Patricia, et al. Big Cats! Exploring the Fascinating Worlds of Cougars, Leopards, Lions, & Tigers. McGee, John F., illus. 2002. (Our Wild World Ser.). 192p. (J). (gr. 2-5). 16.95 (978-1-55971-798-4(X) , NorthWord Bks. for Young Readers) T&N Children's Publishing.

Craft, Sarah S. Mother Snow Leopards & Their Babies. 1999. (Zoo Life Book Ser.). 24p. (J). (gr. k-4). lib. bdg. 18.75 (978-0-8239-5317-2(3) , PowerKids Pr.) Rosen Publishing Group, Inc., The.

Feeney, Kathy. Leopards. McGee, John F., illus. 2004. (Our Wild World Ser.). 48p. (J). (gr. 2-5). ring bd. 10.95 (978-1-55971-809-7(9)); pap. 7.95 (978-1-55971-796-0(3)) T&N Children's Publishing. (NorthWord Bks. for Young Readers).

Feeny, Kathy. Leopards. 2002. (gr. 3-6). lib. bdg. 16.40 (978-0-613-55861-7(8)) Tandem Library Bks.

Fletcher, Marty & Scherer, Glenn. The Snow Leopard: Help Save This Endangered Species! 2007. (Saving Endangered Species Ser.). (Illus.). 128p. (J). (gr. 5). lib. bdg. 33.27 (978-1-59845-040-8(9) , MyReportLinks.com Bks.) Enslow Pubs., Inc.

Gamble, Cyndi & Griffiths, Rodney. Leopards. 2004. (World-Life Library). (Illus.). 48p. pap. 17.95 (978-0-89658-656-7(1)) Voyageur Pr., Inc.

Gareth Stevens Publishing Staff, contrib. by. Leopards. 2004. (All about Wild Animals Ser.). (J). lib. bdg. (978-0-8368-4120-6(4)) Stevens, Gareth Inc.

Gentle, Victor & Perry, Janet. Leopards. 2002. (Big Cats Ser.). (Illus.). 24p. (J). (gr. 2 up). lib. bdg. 22.00 (978-0-8368-3026-2(1)) Stevens, Gareth Inc.

Greenberg, Daniel A. Leopards. 2002. (Animals, Animals Ser.). (Illus.). 45p. (J). 25.64 (978-0-7614-1448-3(7) , Benchmark Bks.) Cavendish, Marshall Corp.

Group/McGraw-Hill, Wright. Leopard Level: Adventure Journal Set. (Wildcatstm Ser.). (gr. 2-8). 31.95 (978-0-322-05792-0(2)) Wright Group, The.

—Leopard Level: Wildcats Leopard Complete Kit. (Wildcatstm Ser.). (gr. 2-8). 599.95 (978-0-322-06485-0(6)) Wright Group, The.

Johnson, Jinny. Leopard. Ch'en-Ling, illus. Price, Susanna, photos by. 2001. (Busy Baby Animals Ser.). 16p. (J). (ps up). lib. bdg. 19.33 (978-0-8368-2927-3(1)) Stevens, Gareth Inc.

Jordan, Bill. Leopard: Habitats, Life Cycles, Food Chains, Threats. 2001. (Illus.). 48p. (J). lib. bdg. 27.12 (978-0-7398-4436-6(9)) Raintree.

Kendell, Patricia. Leopards. 2003. (In the Wild Ser.). (Illus.). 32p. (J). lib. bdg. 25.70 (978-0-7398-5496-9(8)) Raintree.

Povey, Karen D. The Leopard. 2002. (Endangered Animals & Habitats Ser.). (Illus.). 128p. (J). 29.95 (978-1-56006-921-8(X) , Lucent Bks.) Thomson Gale.

Prebeg, Rick. Night Cat. Prebeg, Rick, photos by. 2005. (J). (978-1-933248-15-8(7)) World Quest Learning.

Schaefer, Lola M. Leopards: Spotted Hunters. 2001. (Wild World of Animals Ser.). (Illus.). 24p. (J). (gr. 1-2). lib. bdg. 18.60 (978-0-7368-0966-5(X) , Bridgestone Bks.) Capstone Pr., Inc.

Scott, Jonathan. The Leopard Family Book. 1999. (J). (978-0-606-17399-5(4)) Tandem Library Bks.

Squire, Ann O. Leopards. 2005. (True Bks.). (Illus.). (J). (gr. 3-5). 47p. pap. 6.95 (978-0-516-27934-3(3)); 48p. 25.00 (978-0-516-22794-8(7)) Scholastic Library Publishing. (Children's Pr.).

St. Pierre, Stephanie. Leopards. 2002. (In the Wild Ser.). (Illus.). 24p. (J). (gr. k-2). pap. 6.95 (978-1-58810-382-6(X) , 91102) Heinemann Library.

Stephanie, St Pierre. Leopards. 2001. (In the Wild Ser.). (Illus.). 24p. (J). (ps-3). lib. bdg. 21.36 (978-1-58810-105-1(3)) Heinemann Library.

Vogel, Elizabeth. Leopards. 2002. (PowerKids Readers Ser.). (Illus.). 24p. (J). (gr. 1). lib. bdg. 16.00 (978-0-8239-6019-4(6) , PowerKids Pr.) Rosen Publishing Group, Inc., The.

Welsbacher, Anne. Leopards. 2000. (Wild Cats Ser.). (Illus.). 24p. (J). (gr. k-6). lib. bdg. 21.35 (978-1-57765-088-1(3) , Checkerboard Library) ABDO Publishing Co.

Zumbusch, Amelie von. Leopards: Silent Stalkers. 2007. (Dangerous Cats Ser.). (Illus.). 24p. (J). (gr. k-5). lib. bdg. 21.25 (978-1-4042-3633-2(3) , PowerKids Pr.) Rosen Publishing Group, Inc., The.

LEOPARDS—FICTION

Anderson, Airlie, illus. A Very Spotty Flap Book. 2004. 10p. (J). bds. 5.95 (978-1-58925-703-0(0) , tiger tales) ME Media LLC.

Beeson, Lea Ann. A Leopard Is More Than His Spots. Popovich, Richard E., ed. Rockfield, Darryl, illus. l.t. ed. 2005. 51p. (J). lib. bdg. 19.95 (978-0-9604876-1-5(1)) REP Pubs.

Bond, Ruskin. Leopard on the Mountain. 1998. (Cambridge Reading Ser.). (Illus.). 64p. (gr. 2-6). pap. 12.00 (978-0-521-47704-8(2)) Cambridge Univ. Pr.

Brookes, Diane. How the Leopard Got Its Spots. Jonkisz, Barb, illus. l.t. ed. 1999. 24p. (J). (ps-3). pap. (978-1-894303-00-2(8)) Raven Rock Publishing.

Brooks, Erik, illus. Slow Days, Fast Friends. 2005. 32p. (J). (ps-ps). 16.95 (978-0-8075-7437-9(6)) Whitman, Albert & Co.

Carr, Jon & Carr, Debra. Lisa the Leopard in a Lesson on Obedience. 2000. 13p. 6.00 (978-1-885072-38-2(4)) Creflo Dollar Ministries Pubns.

Frampton, David. The Whole Night Through. Frampton, David, illus. Date not set. (Illus.). 32p. (J). (ps-1). pap. 5.99 (978-0-06-443652-6(7)) HarperCollins Pubs.

—The Whole Night Through: A Lullaby. Frampton, David, illus. 2004. (Illus.). 30p. (J). (gr. k-4). reprint ed. (978-0-7567-7723-4(2)) DIANE Publishing Co.

—The Whole Night Through: A Lullaby. Frampton, David, illus. 2001. (Illus.). 32p. (J). (ps-1). 15.89 (978-0-06-028826-6(4)); 15.95 (978-0-06-028825-9(6)) HarperCollins Pubs.

Kipling, Rudyard. How the Leopard Got His Spots. Lohstoeter, Lori, illus. 2006. (J). (gr. 2-6). 25.65 (978-1-59679-344-6(9)) Spotlight.

Knutson, Barbara. Sungura & Leopard: A Swahili Trickster Tale. 2007. (Illus.). 32p. (J). (gr. k-5). pap. 6.95 (978-0-8225-6801-8(2) , First Avenue Editions) Lerner Publishing Group.

Lama, Tenzing Norbu. Secret of the Snow Leopard. 2004. (Illus.). 40p. (J). 16.95 (978-0-88899-544-5(X)) Groundwood Bks. CAN. *Dist:* Perseus Distribution.

Mead, Katherine, retold by. Why the Leopard has Spots. 1998. (Illus.). 24p. (ps-3). pap. 4.95 (978-0-8172-7980-6(6)) Steck-Vaughn.

Montgomery, Rutherford G. Yellow Eyes. 2004. (Classic Ser.). (Illus.). 358p. (gr. 4-7). pap. 15.95 (978-0-87004-417-5(6)) Caxton Pr.

Morris, Jackie. The Snow Leopard. 2007. (Illus.). 32p. (J). (ps-3). 16.95 (***978-1-84507-600-9(1)***) Lincoln, Frances Ltd. GBR. *Dist:* Perseus Distribution.

Mudibo-Piwang, Catherine & Frascino, Edward. A Visit from the Leopard: Memories of a Ugandan Childhood. Roberts, James, illus. 2000. 64p. (J). (gr. 2-6). 15.95 (978-0-945912-27-9(7)) Pippin Pr.

Nagda, Ann Whitehead. World above the Clouds: A Story of A Himalayan Ecosystem. 2000. (gr. 3-6). lib. bdg. 14.10 (978-0-613-56876-0(1)) Tandem Library Bks.

Nash, Sarah. The Snuggliest Snuggle in the World. Howarth, Daniel, illus. 2006. 10p. (J). bds. 12.95 (978-0-7696-4649-7(2) , Gingham Dog Pr.) School Specialty Publishing.

Nussbaum, Ben & Wenzell, Gregory. Loli Leopard. 2005. (Illus.). (J). (ps-2). 32p. 9.95 (978-1-59249-516-0(8) , PS6556); 32p. 8.95 incl. cd-rom (978-1-59249-514-6(1) , SD6506); 32p. 14.95 incl. cd-rom (978-1-59249-512-2(5) , H6506); 32p. pap. 6.95 (978-1-59249-513-9(3) , S6506); 36p. pap. 2.95 (978-1-59249-515-3(X) , S6556) Soundprints.

Papineau, Lucie. Gilda the Giraffe & Lucky the Leopard. Sarrazin, Marisol, illus. 2005. (Gilda the Giraffe Ser.). 32p. (J). 22.60 (978-1-4048-1295-6(4)) Picture Window Bks.

Poppenhager, N. & Gantschev. Snow Leopards. 2006. (Illus.). 32p. (J). 15.95 (978-0-7358-2087-6(2)) North-South Bks., Inc.

Raintree Steck-Vaughn Staff. The Mystery of the Missing Leopard. 1999. (J). pap. 35.60 (978-0-7398-0915-0(6)) Steck-Vaughn.

Rockwell, Barry, illus. Why the Leopard has Spots. 1998. (Easy to Read Folktales Ser.). 32p. (J). (gr. 1-6). 19.97 (978-0-8172-5156-7(1)) Raintree.

Rundstrom, T. S. I Love to Leap! Miller, Bryan & Marshall, H. Keene, illus. 2002. 40p. (J). per. 16.00 (978-1-932062-14-4(9)) Hability Solution Services, Inc.

Sargent, Dave & Sargent, Pat. Lennie Leopard: Making New Friends, 56 vols., 50. Lenoir, Jane, illus. 2001. (Animal Pride Ser.: Vol. 50). 36p. (J). lib. bdg. 19.95 (978-1-56763-543-0(1)) Ozark Publishing.

Sargent, Dave, et al. Lennie Leopard: Making New Friends, 17, 50. 2000. (Animal Pride Ser.). (Illus.). 42p. (J). pap. 6.95 (978-1-56763-544-7(X)) Ozark Publishing.

Sargent, Pat. The Black Panther, 6, 2. Lenoir, Jane, illus. 2003. (Barney the Bear Killer Ser.: Vol. 2). 137p. (J). pap. 9.95 (978-1-56763-966-7(6)) Ozark Publishing.

Snow Leopard Mountain. 2002. (Animal's Around the World Mini Bks.). (Illus.). 32p. (J). (978-1-59069-170-0(9) , H4006) Studio Mouse LLC.

Souhami, Jessica. Leopard's Drum: An Asante Tale from West Africa. 2006. (Illus.). 32p. (J). pap. 7.95 (978-1-84507-385-5(1)); pap. 7.95 (978-1-84507-418-0(1)); pap. 7.95 (978-1-84507-419-7(X)); pap. 7.95 (978-1-84507-420-3(3)) Lincoln, Frances Ltd. GBR. *Dist:* Perseus Distribution.

Thorpe, Kiki. Snowbound. 2000. (gr. k-3). lib. bdg. 11.80 (978-0-613-31727-6(0)) Tandem Library Bks.

Uncool!, 6 Packs. (Bookweb Ser.). 32p. (gr. 6 up). 34.00 (978-0-7578-0901-9(4)) Rigby Education.

Wax, Wendy. Hippo Rules: A Tale of Good Manners. Terry, Michael, illus. 2007. 12p. (J). 12.99 (***978-0-7944-1289-0(0)***) Reader's Digest Assn., Inc., The.

Wax, Wendy. Where Is Leopard? A Tale of Cooperation. 2006. (Puppet & Story Book Ser.). (Illus.). 12p. (J). bds. 12.99 (978-0-7944-1128-2(2)) Reader's Digest Assn., Inc., The.

LEPIDOPTERA

see Butterflies; Moths

LEPROSY

Donnelly, Karen J. Leprosy: Hansen's Disease. 2002. (Epidemics Ser.). (Illus.). 64p. (YA). (gr. 7-12). lib. bdg. 26.50 (978-0-8239-3498-0(5)) Rosen Publishing Group, Inc., The.

Lynette, Rachel. Leprosy. 2005. (Understanding Diseases & Disorders Ser.). (Illus.). 48p. (J). (gr. 4-8). 26.20 (978-0-7377-3172-9(9) , Greenhaven Pr., Inc.) Thomson Gale.

LEPROSY—FICTION

Cindrich, Lisa. In the Shadow of the Pali: A Story of the Hawaiian Leper Colony. 2002. 240p. (YA). 18.99 (978-0-399-23855-0(7) , Putnam Juvenile) Penguin Group (USA) Inc.

Hostetter, Joyce. Healing Water. 2008. (YA). (***978-1-59078-514-0(2)*** , Calkins Creek) Boyds Mills Pr.

LETTER WRITING

see also Business Letters

Ashley, Susan. I Can Write a Letter. 2004. (Illus.). (J). 23p. pap. (978-0-8368-4335-4(5)); 24p. lib. bdg. 19.33 (978-0-8368-4328-6(2)) Stevens, Gareth Inc.

Evans, Lezlie. Can You Greet the Whole Wide World? 12 Common Phrases in 12 Different Languages. Roche, Denis, illus. 2006. 40p. (J). (gr. k-3). 16.00 (978-0-618-56327-2(X)) Houghton Mifflin Co.

Jarnow, Jill. Writing to Correspond. 2006. (Write Now Ser.). (J). 17.25 (978-1-4042-2831-3(4) , PowerKids Pr.) Rosen Publishing Group, Inc., The.

Nobleman, Marc Tyler. Extraordinary E-mails, Letters, & Resumes. 2006. 128p. (YA). (gr. 8-12). pap. 9.95 (978-0-531-17575-0(8) , Watts, Franklin) Scholastic Library Publishing.

—Extraordinary E-Mails, Letters, & Resumes. 2005. (F.W. Prep Ser.). (Illus.). 128p. (YA). (gr. 8-13). 30.50 (978-0-531-16759-5(3) , Watts, Franklin) Scholastic Library Publishing.

Parker, Shirley Ann. What Shall I Write? Personal Letters for All Occasions. 2002. (Illus.). 112p. pap. 9.95 incl. cd-rom (978-0-9720805-0-7(3)) Topaz Cove Creations.

Practice Power Bilingual Practice Book: Cursive Letters. 2003. (Illus.). 16p. (J). (gr. k-2). spiral bd. (978-1-930355-46-0(7)) Greenbrier/Scentex.

Practice Power Bilingual Practice Book: Manuscript Letters. 2003. (Illus.). 16p. (J). (ps-1). spiral bd. (978-1-930355-45-3(9)) Greenbrier/Scentex.

Spizman, Ali Lauren. The Thank You Book for Kids: Hundreds of Creative, Cool, & Clever Ways to Say Thank You! 2002. (Illus.). 160p. (gr. 4-7). 12.95 (978-1-56352-640-4(9)) Active Parenting Pubs.

Summers, Jean. The Kids' Guide to Writing Great Thank-You Notes. 2005. (Illus.). 38p. (J). per. 11.95 (978-1-59411-125-9(1)) Writers' Collective, The.

Top That Publishing Staff, ed. Fairy Princess Letter Writing. 2004. (Letter Writing Kits Ser.). (Illus.). 24p. (J). pap. (978-1-84229-874-9(7)) Top That! Publishing PLC.

—Magical Horses Letter Writing. 2004. (Letter Writing Kits Ser.). (Illus.). 24p. (J). pap. (978-1-84510-015-5(8)) Top That! Publishing PLC.

—Princess Letter Writing. 2005. (Illus.). 24p. pap. (978-1-84510-762-8(4)) Top That! Publishing PLC.

1,001 Essential Letters, 2002. cd-rom 4.99 (978-1-59150-098-8(2)) TOPICS Entertainment.

LETTER WRITING—FICTION

Bonners, Susan. Edwina Victorious. Bonners, Susan, illus. (Illus.). 144p. (J). 2007. pap. 5.95 (978-0-374-41960-8(4) , Sunburst); 2000. (gr. 2-5). 16.00 (978-0-374-31968-7(5) , Farrar, Straus & Giroux (BYR)) Farrar, Straus & Giroux.

Borden, Louise. Across the Blue Pacific: A World War II Story. Parker, Robert Andrew, illus. 2006. 48p. (J). (gr. k-3). 17.00 (978-0-618-33922-8(1)) Houghton Mifflin Co.

Bunting, Eve. Dear Wish Fairy. Bjhorkman, Steve, illus. 2000. (Hello Reader! Ser.). (J). (978-0-439-20634-1(0)) Scholastic, Inc.

Cardenas, Teresa. Cartas a Mi Mama. Unger, David, tr. 2006. (SPA.). 96p. (J). pap. 6.95 (978-0-88899-723-4(X)) Groundwood Bks. CAN. *Dist:* Perseus Distribution.

Croteau, Marie-Danielle. Fred & the Mysterious Letter. St-Aubin, Bruno, illus. 2005. 61p. (J). lib. bdg. 12.00 (***978-1-4242-1199-9(9)***) Fitzgerald Bks.

Croteau, Marie-Danielle. Lettre a Madeleine. 2002. (Roman Plus Ser.). (FRE., Illus.). 160p. (YA). (gr. 8 up). pap. (978-2-89021-364-7(1)) Diffusion du livre Mirabel.

Danziger, Paula & Martin, Ann M. P. S. Longer Letter Later: A Novel in Letters. 240p. (J). (gr. 3-5). pap. 4.99 (978-0-8072-1537-1(6) , Listening Library) Random Hse. Audio Publishing Group.

—P. S. Longer Letter Later: A Novel in Letters. 240p. 1999. (gr. 3-7). 6.99 (978-0-590-21311-0(3)); 1998. (J). (gr. 5-8). pap. 16.95 (978-0-590-21310-3(5)) Scholastic, Inc.

D'Lacey, Chris. From E to You. 2001. (gr. 7-12). lib. bdg. 13.00 (978-0-613-85076-6(9)) Tandem Library Bks.

D'Lacey, Chris & Newbery, Linda. From E to You. 2001. 208p. (YA). (gr. 7 up). mass mkt. 4.99 (978-0-7434-2285-7(6) , Simon Pulse) Simon & Schuster Children's Publishing.

Dunbar, Joyce. The Secret Friend. Craig, Helen, illus. 1998. (Panda & Gander Stories Ser.). (J). pap. (978-0-7636-0719-7(3)) Candlewick Pr.

JKL

Freeman, Don & Inches, Alison. Corduroy Writes a Letter. Eitzen, Allan, illus. 2004. (Easy-to-Read, Puffin Ser.). 32p. (J). (gr. k-3). pap. 3.99 (978-0-14-240130-9(7) , Puffin) Penguin Group (USA) Inc.

Gonzalez, Julie. Imaginary Enemy. 2008. 256p. (J). (gr. 7). 15.99 (***978-0-385-73552-0(9)*** , Delacorte Bks. for Young Readers) Random Hse. Children's Bks.

Hagerup, Klaus. Markus & Diana. Chace, Tara, tr. from NOR. 2006. 192p. (J). 17.95 (978-1-932425-59-8(4) , Front Street) Boyds Mills Pr.

Hoban, Lillian. Arthur's Pen Pal. Hoban, Lillian, illus. 2002. (Arthur the Chimpanzee Ser.). (Illus.). (J). 12.34 (978-0-7587-5989-4(4)) Book Wholesalers, Inc.

Inches, Alison. Corduroy Writes a Letter, Level 2. Eitzen, Allan, illus. 2002. (Easy-to-read, Viking Children's Ser.). 32p. (J). (gr. k-3). 13.99 (978-0-670-03548-9(3) , Viking Juvenile) Penguin Group (USA) Inc.

Ives, David. Scrib. 2005. 208p. (J). (gr. 5 up). 16.99 (978-0-06-059841-9(7)); lib. bdg. 17.89 (978-0-06-059842-6(5)) HarperCollins Pubs.

Johnson, Emily Rhoads. Write Me If You Dare! 2000. (Illus.). 176p. (J). (gr. 3-6). 15.95 (978-0-8126-2944-6(2)) Cricket Bks.

Jones, Christianne C. La Carta de Paula. Trover, Zachary, illus. 2006. (Read-It! Readers en Espanol Ser.).Tr. of Paula's Letter. (SPA.). 32p. (J). (ps-3). 19.95 (978-1-4048-1687-9(9)) Picture Window Bks.

—Paula's Letter. Trover, Zachary, illus. 2005. (Read-It! Readers Ser.). 32p. (J). (gr. k-3). 18.60 (978-1-4048-1183-6(4)) Picture Window Bks.

Klise, Kate. Regarding the Fountain. Klise, M. Sarah, illus. 1999. 144p. (J). (gr. 3-7). pap. 5.99 (978-0-380-79347-1(4) , Harper Trophy) HarperCollins Pubs.

—Regarding the Fountain: A Tale, in Letters, of Liars & Leaks. Klise, M. Sarah, illus. 1998. 144p. (J). (gr. 4-7). 16.99 (978-0-380-97538-9(6)) HarperCollins Pubs.

—Regarding the Fountain: A Tale, in Letters, of Liars & Leaks. 1999. (978-0-606-16342-2(5)) Tandem Library Bks.

Koutsky, Jan Dale. My Grandma, My Pen Pal. Koutsky, Jan Dale, illus. 2003. (Illus.). 32p. (J). (gr. k-2). 15.95 (978-1-56397-118-1(6)) Boyds Mills Pr.

Lewis, Beverly. Mystery Letters. 2003. (Holly's Heart Ser.: Bk. 12). (Illus.). 160p. (YA). reprint ed. pap. 6.99 (978-0-7642-2619-9(3)) Bethany Hse. Pubs.

Morpurgo, Michael. Farm Boy. Foreman, Michael, illus. 1999. 74p. (YA). pap. 16.99 (978-1-86205-192-8(5) , Pavilion Bks., Ltd.) Anova Bks. GBR. *Dist:* Trafalgar Square Publishing.

Nichol, Barbara. Beethoven Lives Upstairs. Cameron, Scott, illus. 1999. 48p. (J). (gr. k-3). pap. 5.95 (978-0-531-07118-2(9) , Orchard Bks.) Scholastic, Inc.

—Beethoven Lives Upstairs. 1999. (J). 12.75 (978-0-606-17185-4(1)) Tandem Library Bks.

—Beethoven Vive Arriba. 2003. (SPA., Illus.). 48p. (J). (gr. 3-5). 10.95 (978-1-56014-619-3(2) , SAN619) Santillana USA Publishing Co., Inc.

Stewart, Sarah. The Gardener. Small, David, illus. 2002. (J). 15.49 (978-0-7587-2567-7(1)) Book Wholesalers, Inc.

—The Gardener. Small, David, illus. 2000. (J). pap. 19.97 incl. audio (978-0-7366-9203-8(7)) Books on Tape, Inc.

—The Gardener. Small, David, illus. 1999. (J). (gr. k-3). pap. 16.95 incl. audio (978-0-87499-431-5(4)); pap., tchr. ed. 37.95 incl. audio (978-0-87499-432-2(2)) Live Oak Media.

—The Gardener. 2000. 13.75 (978-0-606-17840-2(6)) Tandem Library Bks.

Townson, Hazel. Deathwood Letters. 2003. (Illus.). 112p. (YA). 8.99 (978-1-84270-228-4(9)) Andersen GBR. *Dist:* Independent Pubs. Group.

LETTERING

Balchin, Judy. Creative Lettering. 2001. (Step-by-Step Ser.). (Illus.). 32p. (J). (ps-3). lib. bdg. 24.22 (978-1-57572-331-0(X)) Heinemann Library.

—Creative Lettering. 2001. (Step-By-Step Children's Crafts Ser.). (Illus.). 32p. pap. 7.95 (978-0-85532-907-5(6) , 9076) Search Pr., Ltd. GBR. *Dist:* Independent Pubs. Group.

—Creative Lettering. 2002. (gr. 3-6). lib. bdg. 16.40 (978-0-613-85900-4(6)) Tandem Library Bks.

Bukiet, Suzanne. Scripts of the World. 2nd ed. (Illus.). 91p. (YA). reprint ed. 19.95 (978-0-9656274-1-2(1)) Another Language Pr.

Campbell, Fiona. Calligraphy. 2005. (Illus.). 32p. (J). (gr. 3-6). lib. bdg. 27.10 (978-1-932889-83-3(3) , 1247649) Sea-To-Sea Pubns.

Higgins, Becky. Letter Art. 2001. (American Girl Library). (Illus.). 80p. (gr. 3 up). 7.95 (978-1-58485-287-2(9)) American Girl Publishing, Inc.

Mappin, Jennifer, text. The Lettering Book: A Totally Fun Approach to Lettering! 2004. (Illus.). 100p. (J). (978-1-74124-129-7(4)) Five Mile Pr. Pty Ltd. The.

Oxlade, Chris. Writing & Printing. (Illus.). 32p. (YA). (gr. 3 up). lib. bdg. 27.10 (978-1-932889-08-6(6)) Sea-To-Sea Pubns.

Phillips, Karen. Klutz Lettering. Date not set. 60p. (J). spiral bd. 16.95 (978-1-57054-428-6(X)) Klutz.

Sanders, Nancy I. Adventures with Letters. 1998. (Archy's Activity Bks.). (Illus.). 16p. (J). (ps-2). pap. 3.99 (978-0-570-05080-3(4)) Concordia Publishing Hse.

Scheuer, Lauren, et al. Letter Art 2: Cool & Colorful Letter Designs to Draw. 2006. 64p. (J). pap. 7.95 (978-1-58485-980-2(6)) American Girl Publishing, Inc.

Top That Publishing Staff, ed. Create Your Own Lettering. 2005. (Illus.). 48p. (978-1-84510-304-0(1)) Top That! Publishing PLC.

Top That! Team Staff, contrib. by. Create Your Own Lettering. 2002. (Art Tricks Ser.). (Illus.). 47p. (J). (978-0-439-40001-5(5)) Scholastic, Inc.

—I [Love] Dogs & Puppies. 2002. (Art Rom Ser.). (Illus.). 48p. (J). (978-0-439-53072-9(5)) Scholastic, Inc.

LETTERS

Amazing Grace: Letters Alone My Journey. 2004. 160p. pap. 14.95 net. (978-0-9747983-0-1(4)) Lewis-Thornton, Rae.

Atkins, Nancy L. Christmas Through Their Eyes: Letters to Santa. 2001. (Illus.). 48p. (J). (gr. 2-4). pap. 12.95 (978-0-9705747-0-1(3)) EarthSpring Publishing.

Babinat, Sally K. Letters of a Lifetime. 1999. iii, 235p. 38.50 (978-0-9672966-0-9(9)) Babblins.

Colbert, Jan. Dear Dr. King: Letters from Today's Children to Dr. Martin Luther King, Jr. 2000. (Illus.). (J). (978-0-606-18256-0(X)) Tandem Library Bks.

D'Amato-Neff, Adam L. Creative Learning: Letters, Numbers, & Colors. 2002. 122p. (J). pap. 10.95 (978-0-595-23162-1(4) , Writers Club Pr.) iUniverse, Inc.

Enea, Paul J. Letters to My Granddaughter. 2007. 64p. per. 9.95 (***978-0-595-43781-8(8)***) iUniverse, Inc.

Franson, Leanne, illus. Children's Letters to God. 1999. (J). 9.95 (978-0-7611-1604-2(4)) Workman Publishing Co., Inc.

Gudel, Helen. Dear Alexandra: A Story of Switzerland. Gudel, Helen, illus. 1999. (Make Friends Around the World Ser.). Orig. Title: Leiber Alex. (Illus.). 32p. (J). (gr. k-3). 15.95 (978-1-56899-739-1(6) , B8002); pap. 5.95 (978-1-56899-740-7(X) , S8002) Soundprints.

Jakobsen, Kathy. My New York. Jakobsen, Kathy, illus. anniv. rev. ed. 2005. (Illus.). 54p. (J). (gr. k-4). 19.00 (978-0-7567-8588-8(X)) DIANE Publishing Co.

—My New York. Jakobsen, Kathy, illus. anniv. ed. 2003. (Illus.). 48p. (J). (ps-17). 18.95 (978-0-316-92711-6(2)) Little Brown & Co.

—My Washington D. C. Jakobsen, Kathy, illus. 2000. (Illus.). 32p. (J). (978-0-316-45622-7(5)) Little Brown & Co.

Nolen, Jerdine. Plantzilla. Catrow, David, illus. 2002. 32p. (J). (gr. k-3). 16.00 (978-0-15-202412-3(3) , Silver Whistle) Harcourt Trade Pubs.

Pak, Soyung. Dear Juno. Hartung, Susan Kathleen, illus. 1999. 32p. (J). (ps-2). 17.99 (978-0-670-88252-6(6) , Viking Juvenile) Penguin Group (USA) Inc.

Practice Power Practice Book Manuscript Letters. 2000. (Illus.). 16p. (J). (ps-2). spiral bd., wbk. ed. (978-1-930355-05-7(X)) Greenbrier/Scentex.

Practice Power Workbook Manuscript Letters. 1999. (Illus.). 16p. (J). (ps-1). wbk. ed. (978-1-930355-14-9(9)) Greenbrier/Scentex.

Woodruff, Elvira. Dear Levi: Letters from the Overland Trail. 1998. (J). 11.64 (978-0-606-12910-7(3)) Tandem Library Bks.

LETTERS—FICTION

Ahlberg, Allan. The Jolly Postman: Or, Other People's Letters. Ahlberg, Janet, illus. 2006. 28p. (J). (gr. k-3). 19.99 (978-0-316-01776-3(0)) Little Brown & Co.

Alger Jr. Horatio Staff. Andy Grants Pluck. rev. ed. 2006. 312p. 29.95 (978-1-4218-1762-0(4)); pap. 14.95 (978-1-4218-1862-7(0)) 1st World Publishing, Inc. (1st World Library - Literary Society).

Andracki, Zenon. Dear Ashley: A Middle Grade Novel. 2006. (ENG.). 84p. per. 14.95 (***978-1-4241-6168-3(1)***) PublishAmerica, Inc.

Armstrong, Bill. Letters from Ozo, 1. 2005. (Illus.). 190p. (J). per. (978-0-9771676-0-9(7)) Rubicon Bks.

Banks, Steven. Dear SpongeBob . . . A Funny Fill-Ins Book. Style Guide Staff, illus. 2003. (SpongeBob SquarePants Ser.). 48p. (J). pap. 2.99 (978-0-689-85997-7(X) , Simon Spotlight) Simon & Schuster Children's Publishing.

Baxter, Linda. The Winter of the Stone Woman. Marks, Dea, illus. 1999. (Cover-to-Cover Novels Ser.). 75p. (J). (gr. 2-5). lib. bdg. 13.95 (978-0-7807-8965-4(2) , Covercraft); (gr. 4-8). pap. 5.60 (978-0-7891-2926-0(4)) Perfection Learning Corp.

Bennett, Evelyn & Benson, Jenny, creators. Life Letters: Kid's Stuff. 2003. (J). 19.95 (978-0-9746022-2-6(1)) Life Letters Publishing.

Bryant, Annie. Letters from the Heart. 2004. (Beacon Street Girls Ser.). 224p. (J). 7.99 (978-0-9746587-8-0(2) , Beacon Street Girls) B*tween Productions, Inc.

Cassels, Jean. Br'er Rabbit Captured! A Dr. David Harleyson Adventure. Cassels, Jean, illus. 2007. (Illus.). 32p. (J). 18.85 (***978-0-8027-9557-1(9)***); 17.95 (***978-0-8027-9556-4(0)***) Walker & Co.

Cassels, Jean. The Mysterious Collection of Dr. David Harleyson. Cassels, Jean, illus. 2004. (Illus.). 32p. (J). 17.95 (978-0-8027-8916-7(1)) Walker & Co.

Christie, Agatha. Misterio del Guia. 2000. (gr. 7-12). lib. bdg. 17.60 (978-0-613-63631-5(7)) Tandem Library Bks.

Cole, Barbara. Anna & Natalie. Himler, Ronald, illus. 2007. 32p. (J). 16.95 (***978-1-59572-105-1(3)***) Star Bright Bks., Inc.

Cook, Danielle, illus. Letters from Pyggles, 1. 2003. 24p. 9.00 (978-0-9729914-0-7(9)) Oden, Rachel.

Coyle, Carmela LaVigna. Thank You, Aunt Tallulah. MacPherson, Bruce, illus. 2006. 32p. 15.95 (978-0-87358-891-1(6) , Rising Moon Bks. for Young Readers) Northland Publishing.

Curtis, Philip. Pen Friend from Another Planet. Ross, Tony, illus. 2000. 148p. (J). (gr. 3). pap. 9.99 (978-0-86264-970-8(6)) Andersen GBR. *Dist:* Independent Pubs. Group.

Danneberg, Julie. First Year Letters. 2003. (gr. k-3). lib. bdg. 15.25 (978-0-613-62443-5(2)) Tandem Library Bks.

Danziger, Paula. P. S. Longer Letter Later: A Novel in Letters. 1999. (gr. 5-8). lib. bdg. 13.00 (978-0-613-18271-3(5)) Tandem Library Bks.

—Snail Mail No More. 2000. (gr. 3-6). lib. bdg. 13.00 (978-0-613-35753-1(1)) Tandem Library Bks.

Danziger, Paula & Martin, Ann M. P. S. Longer Letter Later: A Novel in Letters. 2006. 240p. (J). pap. 5.99 (978-0-439-83884-9(3) , Scholastic Paperbacks) Scholastic, Inc.

Dear Santa- 2005. (Illus.). 24p. (J). (ps-1). bds. 6.95 (978-0-8249-6618-8(X)) Ideals Pubns.

Decker, Timothy. The Letter Home. 2005. (Illus.). 32p. (J). (ps). 16.95 (978-1-932425-50-5(0) , Lemniscaat) Boyds Mills Pr.

Denslow, Sharon Phillips. All Their Names Were Courage. 2003. 144p. (J). (gr. 2 up). 15.99 (978-0-06-623810-4(2)) HarperCollins Pubs.

Durant, Alan. Dear Santa Claus. Cabban, Vanessa, illus. 2005. 32p. (J). (ps-2). 14.99 (978-0-7636-2829-1(8)) Candlewick Pr.

—Dear Santa Claus: Mini Edition. Cabban, Vanessa, illus. 2007. 32p. (J). (ps-2). 6.99 (***978-0-7636-3465-0(4)***) Candlewick Pr.

Durant, Alan. Dear Tooth Fairy. Cabban, Vanessa, illus. 2004. 32p. (J). (ps-2). 14.99 (978-0-7636-2175-9(7)) Candlewick Pr.

Edwards, Pamela Duncan. Dear Tooth Fairy. Fitzpatrick, Marie-Louise, illus. 2003. 32p. (J). (ps-2). 15.99 (978-0-06-623972-9(9) , Tegen, Katherine Bks) HarperCollins Pubs.

Eurpsville U. S. A. Inc. Staff. Alphabet Eurps on Parade. 1999. (Concept Bks.). (J). 7.95 (978-1-892522-01-6(2)) Eurpsville USA, Inc.

—Alphabet Eurps Visit the Zoo. 1999. (Concept Bks.). (J). 7.95 (978-1-892522-00-9(4)) Eurpsville USA, Inc.

Eurpsville U. S. A. Inc. Staff, ed. The Alphabet Eurps & the Birthday Surprise. 1999. (Illus.). (J). 19.95 (978-1-892522-13-9(6)) Eurpsville USA, Inc.

—The Alphabet Eurps on Parade. 1999. (Illus.). (J). 19.95 (978-1-892522-12-2(8)) Eurpsville USA, Inc.

—The Alphabet Eurps Visit the Zoo. 1999. (Illus.). (J). 19.95 (978-1-892522-11-5(X)) Eurpsville USA, Inc.

Fine, Anne. A Pack of Liars. unabr. ed. 1998. (J). pap. 29.95 incl. audio (978-0-7540-6204-2(X)) BBC Audiobooks America.

Fishbone, Greg. The Penguins of Doom. 2007. (From the Desk of Septina Nash Ser.). (Illus.). 192p. (J). (gr. 3-9). 13.95 (***978-1-933831-03-9(0)***) Blooming Tree Pr.

Fogelin, Adrian. The Sorta Sisters. 2007. 240p. (J). (gr. 3-7). 14.95 (***978-1-56145-424-2(9)*** , Peachtree Junior) Peachtree Pubs., Ltd.

Frank, Hillary. I Can't Tell You. 2004. 208p. (YA). (gr. 7). 16.00 (978-0-618-41202-0(6)); pap. 7.99 (978-0-618-49491-0(X) , Graphia) Houghton Mifflin Co. Trade & Reference Div.

Freeman, Don & Inches, Alison. Corduroy Writes a Letter. Eitzen, Allan, illus. 2004. (Easy-to-Read, Puffin Ser.). 32p. (J). (gr. k-3). pap. 3.99 (978-0-14-240130-9(7) , Puffin) Penguin Group (USA) Inc.

Gray, Dianne. Holding up the Earth. 2006. 224p. (J). (gr. 5-9). pap. 6.95 (978-0-618-73747-5(2)) Houghton Mifflin Co. Trade & Reference Div.

Gregory, Jeannette T. Letters to Jesus. 2002. per. 7.99 (978-0-9748056-9-6(6)) Chosen Word Publishing.

Grindley, Sally. Bravo, Max! Ross, Tony, illus. 2007. 160p. (J). (gr. 1-4). 15.99 (978-1-4169-0393-2(3) , McElderry, Margaret K.); pap. 4.99 (978-1-4169-3645-9(9) , Aladdin) Simon & Schuster Children's Publishing.

—Dear Max. Ross, Tony, illus. 144p. (J). 2007. pap. 4.99 (978-1-4169-3443-1(X) , Aladdin); 2006. (gr. 1-4). 14.95 (978-1-4169-0392-5(5) , McElderry, Margaret K.) Simon & Schuster Children's Publishing.

Haddad, Charles. Calliope Day Falls... in Love? 2003. (Illus.). 160p. (gr. 3-7). lib. bdg. 16.99 (978-0-385-90100-0(3) , Delacorte Bks. for Young Readers) Random Hse. Children's Bks.

Halpern, Julie. Get Well Soon. 2007. 208p. (YA). (gr. 7 up). 16.95 (***978-0-312-36795-4(3)***) Feiwel & Friends.

Harcourt School Publishers Staff. Beethoven Is Upstairs Level D: Library Edition. 2001. (Collections Ser.). (Illus.). (J). (gr. 5). 5.90 (978-0-15-314403-5(3)) Harcourt Schl. Pubs.

—Cyber-Stuffing. 3rd ed. 2002. (Trophies English Language Learners Ser.). (Illus.). pap. 51.00 (978-0-15-327898-3(6)) Harcourt Schl. Pubs.

—Dear Berta. 3rd ed. 2002. (Trophies English Language Learners Ser.). (Illus.). (gr. 4). pap. 5.10 (978-0-15-327750-4(5)) Harcourt Schl. Pubs.

—Dear Friend On Level. 3rd ed. 2002. (Trophies Reading Program Ser.). (Illus.). pap. 5.10 (978-0-15-323092-9(4)) Harcourt Schl. Pubs.

—Dear Grandma. 3rd ed. 2002. (Trophies English Language Learners Ser.). (Illus.). pap. 5.10 (978-0-15-327820-4(X)) Harcourt Schl. Pubs.

—Dear Grandma: Take-Home Book. 2001. (Collections Ser.). (Illus.). (J). pap. 1.90 (978-0-15-319516-7(9)) Harcourt Schl. Pubs.

—Dear Grandma Below Level. 3rd ed. 2002. (Trophies Reading Program Ser.). (Illus.). pap. 5.10 (978-0-15-323314-2(1)) Harcourt Schl. Pubs.

—Letters from Lila Advanced Level. 3rd ed. 2002. (Trophies Reading Program Ser.). (Illus.). pap. 5.10 (978-0-15-323105-6(X)) Harcourt Schl. Pubs.

—The Most Amazing Place Advanced Level. 3rd ed. 2002. (Trophies Reading Program Ser.). (Illus.). pap. 5.10 (978-0-15-323206-0(4)) Harcourt Schl. Pubs.

—A Most Surprising Thing Advanced Level. 3rd ed. 2002. (Trophies Reading Program Ser.). (Illus.). pap. 5.10 (978-0-15-323461-3(X)) Harcourt Schl. Pubs.

Harley, Bill. Dear Santa: The Letters of James B. Dobbins. Alley, R. W., illus. 2005. 32p. (J). 15.99 (978-0-06-623778-7(5)); lib. bdg. 16.89 (978-0-06-623779-4(3)) HarperCollins Pubs.

Harris, Christine. The Silver Path. (Illus.). (J). (CHI & ENG.). 32p. (978-1-85430-323-3(6) , 93425); (ENG & VIE., 26p. (978-1-85430-327-1(9) , 93381) Magi Pubns.

Hedstrom-Page, Deborah. From Log Cabin to White House with Abraham Lincoln. Martinez, Sergio, illus. 2007. 80p. (J). (gr. 3-9). 9.99 (978-0-8054-3269-5(8)) B&H Publishing Grp.

Helmore, Jim. Letterbox Lil. (Illus.). 32p. (978-0-19-279202-0) Oxford Univ. Pr., Inc.

Helmore, Jim & Wall, Karen. Letterbox Lil. (Illus.). 32p. (J). (ps-1). 10.99 (978-0-19-279201-3(6)) Oxford Univ. Pr., Inc.

Hensley, Sarah M. Caillou's Trip to the Harbor. Gillen, Lisa P., illus. l.t. ed. 2004. (Hrl Board Book Ser.). (J). (ps-1). pap. 10.95 (978-1-57332-290-4(3)) HighReach Learning, Inc.

—Helping Farmer Joe. Crowell, Knox, illus. l.t. ed. 2004. (Hrl Little Book Ser.). (J). (ps). pap. 10.95 (978-1-57332-296-6(2)); pap. 10.95 (978-1-57332-295-9(4)) HighReach Learning, Inc.

Holabird, Katharine. Angelina's Invitation to the Ballet. Craig, Helen, illus. 2007. 32p. (J). (ps). 16.99 (***978-0-670-06201-0(4)*** , Viking Juvenile) Penguin Group (USA) Inc.

Holmes, Sarah. Letters from Rapunzel. 2007. 192p. (J). (gr. 5-8). 15.99 (978-0-06-078073-9(8)); lib. bdg. 16.89 (978-0-06-078074-6(6)) HarperCollins Pubs.

Home Technology: Individual Title Six-Packs. (Bookweb Ser.). 32p. (gr. 3 up). 34.00 (978-0-7635-3950-4(3)) Rigby Education.

Horse, Harry, illus. The Last Polar Bears. 2007. 76p. (J). (gr. 1-5). 12.95 (***978-1-56145-379-5(X)*** , Peachtree Junior) Peachtree Pubs., Ltd.

Howard-Parham, Pam. Caillou Waits for Dinner. Crowell, Knox, illus. l.t. ed. 2004. (Hrl Board Book Ser.). (J). (ps-1). pap. 10.95 (978-1-57332-289-8(X)) HighReach Learning, Inc.

—The Dinosaur Surprise. Neveu, Fred, illus. l.t. ed. 2004. (Hrl Little Book Ser.). (J). (ps-1). pap. 10.95 (978-1-57332-294-2(6)); pap. 10.95 (978-1-57332-293-5(8)) HighReach Learning, Inc.

—Loving Our Country. Teeple, Jackie, illus. l.t. ed. 2004. (Hrl Little Book Ser.). (J). (ps-1). pap. 10.95 (978-1-57332-302-4(0)); pap. 10.95 (978-1-57332-301-7(2)) HighReach Learning, Inc.

Jarrell, Pamela R. Flitter, Flutter Butterfly. Middleton, Mikell, illus. l.t. ed. 2005. (Hrl Board Book Ser.). 12p. (J). (ps-1). pap. 10.95 (978-1-57332-286-7(5)) HighReach Learning, Inc.

Jones, Christianne C. La Carta de Paula. Trover, Zachary, illus. 2006. (Read-It! Readers en Espanol Ser.).Tr. of Paula's Letter. (SPA.). 32p. (J). (ps-3). 19.95 (978-1-4048-1687-9(9)) Picture Window Bks.

—Paula's Letter. Trover, Zachary, illus. 2005. (Read-It! Readers Ser.). 32p. (J). (gr. k-3). 18.60 (978-1-4048-1183-6(4)) Picture Window Bks.

Kehret, Peg. My Brother Made Me Do It: A Sister Remembers Growing up with the Rev. Dr. Martin Luther King Jr. 2001. (978-0-606-22136-8(0)) Tandem Library Bks.

Kelley, True. School Lunch. Kelley, True, illus. 2005. (Illus.). 32p. (J). (ps-ps). 16.95 (978-0-8234-1894-7(4)) Holiday Hse., Inc.

Kelly, Irene. A Small Dog's Big Life: Around the World with Owney. 2005. (Illus.). 32p. (J). 16.95 (978-0-8234-1863-3(4)) Holiday Hse., Inc.

Kephart, Beth. Undercover. 2007. 288p. (gr. 7 up). (J). 16.99 (***978-0-06-123893-2(7)***); (YA). lib. bdg. 17.89 (***978-0-06-123894-9(5)***) HarperCollins Pubs. (HarperTeen).

Kieper, Rienhold Richard. Ten Letters for Our Children. 2004. 26p. (J). pap. 10.00 (978-0-9719284-1-1(X)) Blue Thunder One, Inc.

Klise, Kate. Regarding the Fountain: A Tale, in Letters, of Liars & Leaks. 1999. (gr. 3-6). lib. bdg. 14.15 (978-0-613-17849-5(1)) Tandem Library Bks.

—Regarding the Sink: Where, Oh Where, Did Waters Go? Klise, M. Sarah, illus. 2006. (Regarding The ... Ser.). 144p. (J). pap. 5.95 (978-0-15-205544-8(4) , Harcourt Paperbacks) Harcourt Children's Bks.

Klise, Kate & Klise, M. Sarah. Regarding the Trees: A Splintered Saga Rooted in Secrets. 2007. (Regarding The ... Ser.). (Illus.). 160p. (J). pap. 5.95 (***978-0-15-206090-9(1)*** , Harcourt Paperbacks) Harcourt Children's Bks.

Klise, Kate & Klise, M. Sarah, illus. Regarding the Bees: A Lesson, in Letters, on Honey, Dating, & Other Sticky Subjects. 2007. (Regarding The ... Ser.). 144p. (YA). (gr. 3-7). 15.00 (978-0-15-205711-4(0)) Harcourt Trade Pubs.

Knaus, Patricia. Letters from Space. The Mousekins Staff, illus. 2004. 112p. (J). (gr. 3-4). pap. 8.50 (978-0-9758742-0-2(9) , 10704) KnausWorks.

LeSourd, Nancy. Liberty Letters: The Personal Correspondence of Emma Edmonds & Mollie Turner, Civil War Spies, 1862. 2004. (Liberty Letters Ser.). 224p. (J). 9.99 (978-0-310-70352-5(2)) Zonderkidz.

—The Personal Correspondence of Catherine Clark & Meredith Lyons: Pearl Harbor, 1941. 2004. (Liberty Letters Ser.). (Illus.). 240p. (J). (gr. 5 up). 9.99 (978-0-310-70353-2(0)) Zonderkidz.

Lyons, Mary E. Letters from a Slave Boy: The Story of Joseph Jacobs. 2007. 208p. (YA). (gr. 4-8). 15.99 (978-0-689-87867-1(2) , Atheneum) Simon & Schuster Children's Publishing.

—Letters from a Slave Girl: The Story of Harriet Jacobs. 2007. 192p. (YA). pap. 5.99 (978-1-4169-3637-4(8) , Simon Pulse) Simon & Schuster Children's Publishing.

Maxwell, Katie. The Year My Life Went down the Loo. 2003. (YA). pap. 5.99 (978-0-8439-5313-8(6)) Dorchester Publishing Co., Inc.

McCormack, Ann. Letters to Lucy from Kizzy. 2004. pap. 8.95 (978-0-533-14693-2(3)) Vantage Pr., Inc.

McDonald, Megan. Stink & the Incredible Super-Galactic Jawbreaker. Reynolds, Peter H., illus. 2007. (Stink Ser.). 144p. (J). (gr. k-3). pap. 4.99 (978-0-7636-3236-6(8)) Candlewick Pr.

—Stink & the Incredible Super-Galactic Jawbreaker. Reynolds, Peter, illus. 2006. 128p. (J). (gr. k-3). 12.99 (978-0-7636-2158-2(7)) Candlewick Pr.

McElroy, Lisa Tucker. Love, Lizzie: Letters to a Military Mom. Paterson, Diane, illus. 2005. 32p. (J). (gr. k-3). lib. bdg. 15.95 (978-0-8075-4777-9(8)) Whitman, Albert & Co.

Moranville, Sharelle Byars. The Snows. rev. ed. 2007. 240p. (YA). (gr. 8 up). 16.95 (978-0-8050-7469-7(4) , Holt, Henry & Co. Bks. For Young Readers) Holt, Henry & Co.

Moriarty, Jaclyn. The Year of Secret Assignments. (Illus.). 352p. 2004. (J). pap. 16.95 (978-0-439-49881-4(3) , Levine, Arthur A. Bks.); 2005. reprint ed. pap. 7.99 (978-0-439-49882-1(1) , Scholastic Paperbacks) Scholastic, Inc.

Mullican, Judy. May We Go to the Zoo? Gray, Stacey A., illus. l.t. ed. 2004. (Hrl Little Book Ser.). (J). (ps-1). pap. 10.95 (978-1-57332-304-8(7)); pap. 10.95 (978-1-57332-303-1(9)) HighReach Learning, Inc.

—Pretend. Meler, Kerry L., illus. l.t. ed. 2005. (Hrl Board Book Ser.). 10p. (J). (ps-1). pap. 10.95 (978-1-57332-283-6(0)) HighReach Learning, Inc.

Murray, Anna. Sarah's Page. 1998. (Illus.). 144p. (J). (gr. 4-7). 14.00 (978-1-886947-58-0(9)) Sleeping Bear Pr.

Napoli, Donna Jo. Pink Magic. Cameron, Chad, illus. 2005. 32p. (J). (gr. k-3). 15.00 (978-0-618-15985-7(1) , Clarion Bks.) Houghton Mifflin Co. Trade & Reference Div.

Nolen, Jerdine & Keliher, Brian. Plantzilla. Catrow, David, illus. 2005. 32p. (J). (ps-up). reprint ed. pap., pap. 7.00 (978-0-15-205392-5(1) , Voyager Bks./Libros Viajeros) Harcourt Children's Bks.

O'Kelley, Jeff. Sharing Our Stories. 2006. (Early Explorers Ser.). (J). 36.00 (*978-1-4108-6127-6(9)) Benchmark Education Co.

Olive the Octopus's Day of Juggling. 2001. (ps-2). lib. bdg. 9.80 (978-0-613-32908-8(2)) Tandem Library Bks.

Olsen, Mary-Kate. Sealed with a Kiss. 2001. (gr. 3-6). lib. bdg. 13.00 (978-0-613-43956-5(2)) Tandem Library Bks.

Onish, Liane. The Alphabet Eurps & the 4 Seasons. 1999. (Eurps Concept Bks.). (Illus.). (J). 7.95 (978-1-892522-08-5(X)) Eurpsville USA, Inc.

—The Alphabet Eurps Build Eurpsville. 1999. (Eurps Concept Bks.). (Illus.). (J). 7.95 (978-1-892522-05-4(5)) Eurpsville USA, Inc.

—Alphabet Eurps Meet Bipple. 1999. (Eurps Concept Bks.). (Illus.). (J). 7.95 (978-1-892522-03-0(9)) Eurpsville USA, Inc.

—The Alphabet Eurps on the Farm. 1999. (Illus.). (J). 7.95 (978-1-892522-07-8(1)) Eurpsville USA, Inc.

—The Alphabet Eurps Ride a Rainbow. 1999. (Eurps Concept Bks.). (Illus.). (J). 7.95 (978-1-892522-06-1(3)) Eurpsville USA, Inc.

—The Alphabet Eurps Visit School. 1999. (Eurps Concept Bks.). (Illus.). (J). 7.95 (978-1-892522-04-7(7)) Eurpsville USA, Inc.

Orloff, Karen Kaufman. I Wanna Iguana. Catrow, David, illus. 2004. 32p. (J). (ps-3). 16.99 (978-0-399-23717-1(8) , Putnam Juvenile) Penguin Group (USA) Inc.

Parham, Pam H. When I Take a Bath. Gillen, Lisa P., illus. l.t. ed. 2005. (Hrl Board Book Ser.). 12p. (J). (ps-1). pap. 10.95 (978-1-57332-284-3(9)) HighReach Learning, Inc.

Pattison, Darcy. Searching for Oliver K. Woodman. Cepeda, Joe, illus. 2005. 56p. (J). 16.00 (978-0-15-205184-6(8)) Harcourt Children's Bks.

PeachMoon Publishing. The Lizard in the Mailbox. 2007. (J). pap. 9.95 (*978-0-9795831-0-0(1)) PeachMoon Publishing.

Peake, Mervyn. Letters from a Lost Uncle. 2004. (Illus.). 19.95 (978-0-413-74590-3(2)) Methuen Publishing Ltd. GBR. *Dist:* Consortium Bk. Sales & Distribution.

Pennypacker, Sara. Clementine's Letter. Frazee, Marla, illus. rev. ed. 2008. 160p. (J). (gr. 2-7). 14.99 (*978-0-7868-3884-4(1)) Hyperion Pr.

PS, I Love You, Gramps: Individual Title, 6 packs. (Action Packs Ser.). 120p. (gr. 3-5). 44.00 (978-0-7635-8389-7(8)) Rigby Education.

Radzinski, Kandy. What Cats Want for Christmas. rev. ed. 2007. (Holiday Ser.). 32p. (J). 16.95 (*978-1-58536-340-7(5)) Sleeping Bear Pr.

Rakusin, Sudie. Dear Calla Roo. . . Love, Savannah Blue: A Letter to a Pen Pal. Rakusin, Sudie, illus. 2000. (Illus.). 36p. (J). (ps-4). 16.95 (978-0-9664805-1-1(1)) Winged Willow Pr.

—Dear Calla Roo... Love, Savannah Blue No. 2: A Letter about Getting Sick & Feeling Better. Rakusin, Sudie, illus. 2003. (Illus.). 32p. (J). (ps-4). 16.95 (978-0-9664805-3-5(8)) Winged Willow Pr.

Random House Staff. Keep in Touch: Letters, Notes, & More from the Sisterhood of the Traveling Pants. 2005. 144p. (J). (gr. 7). lib. bdg. 9.99 (978-0-385-90943-3(8) , Delacorte Bks. for Young Readers) Random Hse. Children's Bks.

Rissman, Angelica. Julius & the Lost Letter to Santa. 2003. (J). 7.99 (978-1-59384-019-8(5)) Parklane Publishing.

Robleda, Margarita. Mis Letras Favoritas. Gurovich, Natalia, illus. 2003. (SPA.). 32p. (J). 12.95 (978-970-690-808-7(0)) Planeta Mexicana Editorial S. A. de C. V. MEX. *Dist:* Lectorum Pubns., Inc.

Saksena, Kate. Hang on in There, Shelley. 2003. 219p. (J). 16.95 (978-1-58234-822-3(7) , Bloomsbury Children) Bloomsbury Publishing.

Sappey, Maureen. Letters from Vinnie. 2007. 248p. (J). (gr. 4-6). pap. 10.95 (*978-1-59078-538-6(X)) Boyds Mills Pr.

Scholastic, Inc. Staff. Dear Mrs. Larue. 2005. (J). pap. 550.00 (978-0-439-70787-9(0) , Sidekicks TM) Scholastic, Inc.

Schumacher, Julie. The Chain Letter. 2005. 208p. (J). (gr. 5-9). lib. bdg. 17.99 (978-0-385-90205-2(0) , Delacorte Bks. for Young Readers) Random Hse. Children's Bks.

Seal's Silly Sandwich. 2001. (ps-2). lib. bdg. 9.80 (978-0-613-33039-8(0)) Tandem Library Bks.

Skolsky, Mindy Warshaw. Love, from Your Friend Hannah. 1999. (gr. 3-6). lib. bdg. 14.15 (978-0-613-22801-5(4)) Tandem Library Bks.

Snicket, Lemony, pseud. The Beatrice Letters. Helquist, Brett, illus. 2006. (Series of Unfortunate Events Ser.). 72p. (J). 19.99 (978-0-06-058658-4(3)) HarperCollins Pubs.

Spinelli, Jerry. Love, Stargirl. 2007. (J). 192p. (gr. 5-8). lib. bdg. 19.99 (*978-0-375-91375-4(0)); 288p. (gr. 7-8). 16.99 (*978-0-375-81375-7(6)) Random Hse. Children's Bks. (Knopf Bks. for Young Readers).

Steffensmeier, Alexander. Millie Waits for the Mail. Steffensmeier, Alexander, illus. 2007. (Illus.). 32p. (J). (gr. k-2). 16.95 (*978-0-8027-9662-2(1)); 17.85 (*978-0-8027-9663-9(X)) Walker & Co.

Stewart, Sarah. The Gardener. Small, David, illus. 2007. 40p. (J). pap. 6.95 (*978-0-312-36749-7(X)) Square Fish.

Stewart, Sarah. Gardener. 2000. (gr. k-3). lib. bdg. 15.25 (978-0-613-29173-6(5)) Tandem Library Bks.

Teague, Mark. Detective LaRue: Letters from the Investigation. Teague, Mark, illus. 2004. (Detective Larue Ser.). (Illus.). 32p. (J). (ps-3). pap. 15.95 (978-0-439-45868-9(4) , Scholastic Pr.) Scholastic, Inc.

—Larue para Alcalde: Cartas de la Campana: Cartas de la Campana. 2008. (Larue for Mayor Ser.). 32p. (J). pap. 4.99 (*978-0-545-02214-9(2) , Scholastic en Espanol) Scholastic, Inc.

—The Letters from the Campaign. 2008. (Larue for Mayor Ser.). 32p. (J). pap. 16.99 (*978-0-439-78315-6(1) , Blue Sky Pr., The) Scholastic, Inc.

Thomas Jefferson: Letters from a Philadelphia Bookworm. 2002. (Dear Mr. President Ser.). (J). (gr. 4-7). 25.95 incl. audio (978-0-87499-989-1(8)) Live Oak Media.

Tolkien, J. R. R. Letters from Father Christmas. Tolkien, Baillie, ed. 2004. (Illus.). 112p. pap. 15.00 (978-0-618-51265-2(9)) Houghton Mifflin Co. Trade & Reference Div.

Van Straaten, Harmen. For Me. 2008. 32p. (J). (ps). 16.95 (*978-0-7358-2163-7(1)) North-South Bks., Inc.

Vonthron, Satanta C. Caillou's Dinosaur Day. Neveu, Fred, illus. l.t. ed. 2004. (Hrl Board Book Ser.). (J). (ps-1). pap. 10.95 (978-1-57332-288-1(1)) HighReach Learning, Inc.

Wallace, Bill. Pick of the Litter. 2005. 160p. (J). (ps-7). 16.95 (978-0-8234-1921-0(5)) Holiday Hse., Inc.

—Pick of the Litter. 2006. 176p. (J). pap. 4.99 (978-1-4169-2511-8(2) , Aladdin) Simon & Schuster Children's Publishing.

Ware-Holmes, Barbara. Letters to Julia. 1999. (J). (978-0-606-17466-4(4)) Tandem Library Bks.

Wells, Rosemary. Bunny Mail. 2004. (Max & Ruby Ser.). (Illus.). 32p. (J). (ps-3). 15.99 (978-0-670-03630-1(7) , Viking Juvenile) Penguin Group (USA) Inc.

Wells, Sheila Rae. Waiting for a Letter. 2004. 37p. (J). pap. 7.97 (978-1-4116-0908-2(5)) Lulu.com.

Whybrow, Ian. Little Wolf, Terror of the Shivery Sea. Ross, Tony, illus. 2005. (Middle Grade Fiction Ser.). 144p. (J). (gr. 3-6). 14.95 (978-1-57505-629-6(1)) Lerner Publishing Group.

—Little Wolf's Diary of Daring Deeds. Ross, Tony, illus. (Middle Grade Fiction Ser.). 132p. (gr. 3-6). 2005. 14.95 (978-1-57505-411-7(6)); 2003. (J). pap. 6.95 (978-0-87614-536-4(5) , Carolrhoda Bks.) Lerner Publishing Group.

—Little Wolf's Diary of Daring Deeds. 2000. (gr. 3-6). lib. bdg. 15.25 (978-0-613-68105-6(3)) Tandem Library Bks.

Whybrow, Ian. Lobito Aprende a Ser Malo (Little Wolf's Book of Badness) Azaola, Miguel, tr. Ross, Tony, illus. 2007. (Ediciones Lerner Single Titles Ser.). (SPA.). (J). (gr. 3-7). pap. 6.95 (*978-0-8225-8644-9(4) , Ediciones Lerner) Lerner Publishing Group.

Wigersma, Tanneke. Baby Brother. Talsma, Nynke Mare, illus. 2005. 32p. (J). (ps-ps). 16.95 (978-1-932425-55-0(1) , Lemniscaat) Boyds Mills Pr.

Wildner, Martina & Skofield, James. Shooting Stars Everywhere. 2006. 192p. (J). (gr. 7). 15.95 (978-0-385-73250-5(3) , Delacorte Bks. for Young Readers) Random Hse. Children's Bks.

Williams, Heather L. Caillou's Castle. Meler, Kerry L., illus. l.t. ed. 2005. (Hrl Board Book Ser.). (J). (ps-1). pap. 10.95 (978-1-57332-291-1(1)) HighReach Learning, Inc.

Winthrop, Elizabeth. Dear Mr. President - Franklin Delano Roosevelt: Letters from a Mill Town Girl. Winthrop, Elizabeth, illus. unabr. ed. 2003. (Illus.). (J). (gr. 4-7). 25.95 incl. audio (978-1-59112-213-5(9)) Live Oak Media.

Wittlinger, Ellen. Heart on My Sleeve. 2005. (Illus.). 240p. (YA). reprint ed. pap. 6.99 (978-0-689-84999-2(0) , Simon Pulse) Simon & Schuster Children's Publishing.

Woodruff, Elvira. Dear Austin: Letters from the Underground Railroad. 2000. (gr. 5-8). lib. bdg. 13.00 (978-0-613-28463-9(1)) Tandem Library Bks.

Wrede, Patricia C. & Stevermer, Caroline. The Mislaid Magician or Ten Years After: Being the Private Correspondence Between Two Prominent Families Regarding a Scandal Touching the Highest Levels of Government & the Security of the Realm. 2006. (Illus.). 336p. (J). (gr. 8 up). 17.00 (978-0-15-205548-6(7)) Harcourt Trade Pubs.

—Sorcery & Cecelia or the Enchanted Chocolate Pot: Being the Correspondence of Two Young Ladies of Quality Regarding Various Magical Scandals in London & the Country. 2003. (Illus.). 336p. (YA). 17.00 (978-0-15-204615-6(1)) Harcourt Children's Bks.

Yee, Lisa. So Totally Emily Ebers. 2008. 304p. (J). 5.99 (978-0-439-83848-1(7) , Levine, Arthur A. Bks.) Scholastic, Inc.

—So Totally Emily Embers. 2007. 304p. (J). (gr. 4-7). pap. 16.99 (978-0-439-83847-4(9) , Levine, Arthur A. Bks.) Scholastic, Inc.

Ylvisaker, Anne. Dear Papa. 2007. (Illus.). 192p. (J). (gr. 4). pap. 5.99 (*978-0-7636-3402-5(6)) Candlewick Pr.

Zweibel, Alan. Our Tree Named Steve. Catrow, David, illus. 2005. 32p. (J). (ps-3). 15.99 (978-0-399-23722-5(4) , Putnam Juvenile) Penguin Group (USA) Inc.

—Our Tree Named Steve. Catrow, David, illus. 2007. 32p. (J). pap. 5.99 (978-0-14-240743-1(7) , Puffin) Penguin Group (USA) Inc.

LETTERS OF CREDIT

see Credit

LETTERS OF THE ALPHABET

see Alphabet

LEUKEMIA

Abramovitz, Melissa. Leukemia. 2002. (Diseases & Disorders Ser.). (Illus.). 144p. (J). (gr. 6-9). 32.45 (978-1-56006-863-1(9) , Lucent Bks.) Thomson Gale.

Coerr, Eleanor. Sadako. Young, Ed, illus. 2002. (J). 24.55 (978-0-7587-3544-7(8)) Book Wholesalers, Inc.

—Sadako & the Thousand Paper Cranes. Himler, Ronald, illus. 2004. 80p. (gr. 8). pap. 5.99 (978-0-14-240113-2(7) , Puffin) Penguin Group (USA) Inc.

—Sadako & the Thousand Paper Cranes. Himler, Ronald, illus. 1999. 79p. (J). (ps-ps). lib. bdg. 13.00 (978-0-613-23029-2(9)) Tandem Library Bks.

—Sadako & the Thousand Paper Cranes. 1999. (978-0-606-17425-1(7)) Tandem Library Bks.

Himler, Ronald, illus. Sadako & the Thousand Paper Cranes. 2005. 80p. (J). pap. 3.99 (978-0-14-240440-9(3) , Puffin) Penguin Group (USA) Inc.

Klosterman, Lorrie. Leukemia. 2005. (Health Alert Ser.). (J). (978-0-7614-1916-7(0) , Benchmark Bks.) Cavendish, Marshall Corp.

Peacock, Judith. Leukemia. 1999. (Perspectives on Disease & Illness Ser.). (Illus.). 64p. (J). (gr. 4-6). lib. bdg. 23.93 (978-0-7368-0282-6(7) , LifeMatters Bks.) Capstone Pr., Inc.

Sadako & the Thousand Paper Cranes. 1999. (J). 9.95 (978-1-56137-178-5(5)); 11.95 (978-1-56137-631-5(0)) Novel Units, Inc.

Silverstein, Alvin, et al. Leukemia. 2000. (Diseases & People Ser.). (Illus.). 128p. (YA). (gr. 6-12). lib. bdg. 26.60 (978-0-7660-1310-0(3)) Enslow Pubs., Inc.

Vander Hook, Sue. Leukemia. 2000. (Understanding Illness Ser.). (Illus.). 32p. (J). lib. bdg. 16.95 (978-1-58340-027-2(3)) Smart Apple Media.

LEUKEMIA—FICTION

Banks, Kate. Lenny's Space. 2007. 160p. (J). (gr. 3-7). 16.00 (*978-0-374-34575-4(9) , Farrar, Straus & Giroux (BYR)) Farrar, Straus & Giroux.

Downham, Jenny. Before I Die. 2007. 326p. (YA). (gr. 9-12). 15.99 (*978-0-385-75155-1(9) , Fickling, David Bks.) Random Hse. Children's Bks.

O'Brien, Frances. Sheer Bliss. 2006. (ENG.). 144p. per. (*978-1-905886-32-6(2)) Troubador Publishing Ltd.

Rushford, Patricia H. Secrets of Ghost Island. 2007. (J). (*978-88-02-46255-4(0)) Moody Pubs.

Sonnenblick, Jordan. Drums, Girls & Dangerous Pie. (J). 2006. 29.95 (978-0-439-89550-7(2)); 2005. 288p. pap. 16.99 (978-0-439-75519-1(0) , Scholastic Pr.); 2006. 304p. reprint ed. pap. 6.99 (978-0-439-75520-7(4) , Scholastic Paperbacks) Scholastic, Inc.

—Drums, Girls & Dangerous Pie. l.t. ed. 2005. 314p. (YA). 21.95 (978-0-7862-8038-4(7)) Thorndike Pr.

Stirnkorb, Patricia. All about Me! Regular Version. 2005. (Illus.). 12p. (J). bds. 12.99 (978-0-9758709-8-3(X) , A.W.A. Gang) Journey Stone Creations, LLC.

LEVANT

see Middle East

LEWIS, C. S. (CLIVE STAPLES), 1898-1963

Benge, Janet & Benge, Geoff. C. S. Lewis: Master Storyteller. 2007. (Christian Heroes: Then & Now Ser.). 191p. (J). (gr. 3-7). per. (*978-1-57658-385-2(6)) YWAM Publishing.

Coren, Michael. C S Lewis: The Man Who Created Narnia. 2006. 160p. 14.95 (978-1-58617-109-4(7)) Ignatius Pr.

Davenport, John. C. S. Lewis. 2003. (Who Wrote That? Ser.). (Illus.). 112p. (gr. 6-12). 30.00 (978-0-7910-7620-0(2) , Chelsea Hse.) Facts On File, Inc.

Gifford, Clive. So You Think You Know Narnia? 2006. (YA). (gr. 4-7). pap. 8.95 (978-0-340-89392-0(3)) Hodder General Publishing Division GBR. *Dist:* Independent Pubs. Group.

Gormley, Beatrice. C. S. Lewis: The Man Behind Narnia. 2nd ed. 2005. (Illus.). 180p. (YA). (gr. 8-12). pap. 12.00 (978-0-8028-5301-1(3) , Eerdmans Bks For Young Readers) Eerdmans, William B. Publishing Co.

Lappi, Megan. C. S. Lewis. 2005. (My Favorite Writer Ser.). (Illus.). 32p. (J). (gr. k-7). lib. bdg. 26.00 (978-1-59036-285-3(3)); pap. 7.95 (978-1-59036-291-4(8)) Weigl Pubs., Inc.

Parker, Victoria. C.S. Lewis. 2006. (Illus.). 48p. (J). pap. (978-1-4034-7339-4(0)); lib. bdg. (978-1-4034-7336-3(6)) Heinemann Library.

Stone, Elaine Murray. C. S. Lewis: Creator of Narnia. Kelley, Patrick, illus. 2001. 144p. (gr. 4-9). 8.95 (978-0-8091-6672-5(0) , 6672-0) Paulist Pr.

Wade, Mary Dodson. C. S. Lewis: The Chronicler of Narnia. 2005. (Authors Teens Love Ser.). (Illus.). 112p. (J). (gr. 7-12). lib. bdg. 26.60 (978-0-7660-2446-5(6)) Enslow Pubs., Inc.

Wellman, Sam. C. S. Lewis: Author of Mere Christianity. 1999. (Heroes of the Faith Ser.). (Illus.). 208p. (YA). (gr. 4-7). lib. bdg. 17.95 (978-0-7910-5032-3(7) , Chelsea Hse.) Facts On File, Inc.

LEWIS, MERIWETHER, 1774-1809

Adler, David A. A Picture Book of Lewis & Clark. Himler, Ronald, illus. 2003. 32p. (J). (gr. k-3). tchr. ed. 16.95 (978-0-8234-1735-3(2)) Holiday Hse., Inc.

Benge, Janet Hazel & Benge, Geoffrey Francis. Meriwether Lewis: Off the Edge of the Map. 2001. 232p. pap. 8.99 (978-1-883002-80-0(X)) Emerald Bks.

Carter, E. J. The Lewis & Clark Journals. 2003. (Heinemann Know It Ser.). (Illus.). 48p. (J). pap. 8.50 (978-1-4034-3433-3(6)); lib. bdg. 27.07 (978-1-4034-0805-1(X)) Heinemann Library.

Devillier, Christy. Lewis & Clark. 2001. (First Biographies Ser.). (Illus.). 32p. (J). (gr. k-4). lib. bdg. 22.78 (978-1-57765-595-4(8) , Buddy Bks.) ABDO Publishing Co.

Ditchfield, Christin. The Lewis & Clark Expedition. 2006. (True Book - Westward Expansion Ser.). (Illus.). 48p. (J). (gr. 3-5). 25.00 (978-0-516-22835-8(8) , Children's Pr.) Scholastic Library Publishing.

Espinosa, Rod. Lewis & Clark. 2007. (Bio-Graphics Ser.). (Illus.). 32p. (J). (gr. 3-6). lib. bdg. 27.07 (*978-1-60270-069-7(9) , Graphic Planet) Magic Wagon.

Glaser, Jason. Lewis & Clark. 2004. (Fact Finders Ser.). (Illus.). 32p. (J). lib. bdg. 22.60 (978-0-7368-2665-5(3)) Capstone Pr., Inc.

Gunderson, Jessica Sarah. The Lewis & Clark Expedition. 2007. (Graphic Library). (Illus.). 32p. (J). 25.26 (978-0-7368-6493-0(8)) Capstone Pr., Inc.

Hamilton, John. The Corps of Discovery. 2003. (Lewis & Clark Expedition Ser.). (Illus.). 32p. (J). (gr. 3-8). lib. bdg. 24.21 (978-1-57765-761-3(6)) ABDO Publishing Co.

Kline, Trish. Lewis & Clark. 2002. (Discover the Life of an Explorer Ser.). (Illus.). 24p. (gr. 2-5). 14.95 (978-1-58952-067-7(X)) Rourke Publishing, LLC.

Klingel, Cynthia Fitterer & Noyed, Robert B. Lewis & Clark: Explorers. 2002. (Spirit of America: Our People Ser.). (Illus.). 32p. (J). (gr. 2-6). 27.07 (978-1-56766-164-4(5)) Child's World, Inc.

Kozar, Richard. Lewis & Clark: Explorers of the Louisiana Purchase. 2000. (Explorers of the New World Ser.). (Illus.). 64p. (J). (gr. 4 up). 25.00 (978-0-7910-5513-7(2) , Chelsea Hse.) Facts On File, Inc.

Lilly, Melinda. Sacagawea, Lewis, & Clark. 2003. (Rourke Discovery Library). (Illus.). 24p. (gr. 1-4). 14.95 (978-1-58952-362-3(8)) Rourke Publishing, LLC.

MacGregor, Carol Lynn. Lewis & Clark's Bittersweet Crossing. Hoopes, Gaye, tr. Hoopes, Gaye, illus. 2004. 32p. (J). 16.95 (978-0-87004-437-3(0) , 043700) Caxton Pr.

McCormick, Lisa Wade. Lewis & Clark. 2006. (Rookie Biographies Ser.). (Illus.). 32p. (J). (gr. 1-2). 20.50 (978-0-516-25039-7(6) , Children's Pr.) Scholastic Library Publishing.

Meloche, Renee. Meriwether Lewis: Courage on the Trail. 2005. (Illus.). 32p. (J). 6.99 (978-1-932096-27-9(2)) Emerald Bks.

Molzahn, Arlene Bourgeois. Lewis & Clark: American Explorers. 2003. (Explorers! Ser.). (Illus.). 48p. (J). (gr. 1-4). lib. bdg. 23.93 (978-0-7660-2067-2(3)) Enslow Pubs., Inc.

Petrie, Kristin. Lewis & Clark. 2007. (Illus.). 32p. (J). 22.78 (978-1-59679-743-7(6)) ABDO Publishing Co.

Ransom, Candice F. Lewis & Clark. (History Maker Bios Ser.). (J). 2003. (Illus.). 48p. (gr. 2-4). 26.60 (978-0-8225-0394-1(8) , Lerner Pubns.); 2002. pap. 6.95 (978-0-8225-1562-3(8)) Lerner Publishing Group.

Raum, Elizabeth. Lewis & Clark's Continental Journey. 2007. (J). (*978-1-4034-9757-4(5)) Heinemann Library.

Raum, Elizabeth. Meriwether Lewis. 2003. (Illus.). 32p. (J). pap. 6.95 (978-1-4034-4201-7(0)); lib. bdg. 24.22 (978-1-4034-4193-5(6)) Heinemann Library.

—Meriwether Lewis. 2003. (gr. k-3). lib. bdg. 15.25 (978-0-613-86556-2(1)) Tandem Library Bks.

Rodger, Ellen. Lewis & Clark: Opening the American West. 2005. (In the Footsteps of Explorers Ser.). (Illus.). 32p. (J). (ps-9). (978-0-7787-2410-0(7)); pap. (978-0-7787-2446-9(8)) Crabtree Publishing Co.

Santella, Andrew. Lewis & Clark. 2001. (Exploration Library). (Illus.). 64p. (J). (gr. 5-7). 25.50 (978-0-531-20323-1(9) , Watts, Franklin) Scholastic Library Publishing.

Sapp, Richard. Lewis & Clark on Their Journey to the Pacific. 2006. (In the Footsteps of American Heroes Ser.). (Illus.). 64p. (J). pap. (978-0-8368-6434-2(4)); lib. bdg. 32.67 (978-0-8368-6429-8(8)) Stevens, Gareth Inc. (World Almanac Library).

Scheuerman, Richard D., et al. The Expeditions of Lewis & Clark & Zebulon Pike: North American Journeys of Discovery Travelogue. 2nd ed. 2001. (Illus.). (J). (978-1-885360-24-3(X)) Demco, Inc.

Stout, Mary. Lewis & Clark. 2002. (Raintree Biographies Ser.). (Illus.). 32p. (J). lib. bdg. 25.69 (978-0-7398-5677-2(4)) Raintree.

Streissguth, Thomas. Lewis & Clark: Explorers of the Northwest. 1998. (Historical American Biographies Ser.). (Illus.). 128p. (YA). (gr. 6-12). lib. bdg. 26.60 (978-0-7660-1016-1(3)) Enslow Pubs., Inc.

Sullivan, George E. Lewis & Clark. 2000. (In Their Own Words Ser.). (Illus.). 128p. (J). (gr. 4-7). pap. 4.99 (978-0-439-09553-2(0)) Scholastic, Inc.

—Lewis & Clark. 2000. (J). 11.64 (978-0-606-19924-7(1)) Tandem Library Bks.

LEWIS AND CLARK EXPEDITION (1804-1806)

Adler, David A. A Picture Book of Sacagawea. Brown, Dan, illus. 32p. (J). (gr. k-3). 2005. 6.95 (978-0-8234-1665-3(8)); 2000. tchr. ed. 16.95 (978-0-8234-1485-7(X)) Holiday Hse., Inc.

Alter, Judy. Sacagawea: Native American Interpreter. 2002. (Spirit of America: Our People Ser.). (Illus.). 32p. (J). (gr. 2-6). 27.07 (978-1-56766-166-8(1)) Child's World, Inc.

Benge, Janet Hazel & Benge, Geoffrey Francis. Meriwether Lewis: Off the Edge of the Map. 2001. 232p. pap. 8.99 (978-1-883002-80-0(X)) Emerald Bks.

Bergen, Lara Rice. The Travels of Lewis & Clark. 2000. (Explorers & Exploration Ser.). (Illus.). 48p. (J). (gr. 4-7). lib. bdg. 22.83 (978-0-7398-1486-4(9)) Raintree.

Birchfield, D. L. Sacagawea. 2002. (Raintree Biographies Ser.). (Illus.). 32p. (J). lib. bdg. 25.69 (978-0-7398-5680-2(4)) Raintree.

Bloom Fradin, Judith & Brindell Fradin, Dennis. Who Was Sacagawea? Taylor, Van Paul & Harrison, Nancy, illus. 2002. (Who Was...? Ser.). 112p. (J). pap. 4.99 (978-0-448-42485-9(1) , Grosset & Dunlap) Penguin Group (USA) Inc.

Blumberg, Rhoda. The Incredible Journey of Lewis & Clark. 1999. 29.75 (978-0-8446-7030-0(8)) Smith, Peter Pub., Inc.

—York's Adventures with Lewis & Clark: An African-American's Part in the Great Expedition. 96p. (J). 2007. pap. 7.99 (978-0-06-009113-2(4)); 2004. (Illus.). (gr. 3 up). 17.99 (978-0-06-009111-8(8)) HarperCollins Pubs.

—York's Adventures with Lewis & Clark: An African-American's Part in the Great Expedition. Blumberg, Rhoda, illus. 2004. (Illus.). 96p. (J). (gr. 3 up). lib. bdg. 18.89 (978-0-06-009112-5(6)) HarperCollins Pubs.

Bruchac, Joseph. Sacajawea. 2001. (978-0-606-21405-6(4)) Tandem Library Bks.

Burger, James P. Lewis & Clark's Voyage of Discovery. 2002. (Library of the Westward Expansion). (Illus.). 24p. (J). (gr. 3). lib. bdg. 19.95 (978-0-8239-5848-1(5) , PowerKids Pr.) Rosen Publishing Group, Inc., The.

—The Library of the Westward Expansion, 6 bks. Incl. Lewis & Clark's Voyage of Discovery. lib. bdg. 19.95 (978-0-8239-5848-1(5)); Mountain Men of the West. lib. bdg. 19.95 (978-0-8239-5853-5(1)); Oregon Trail. lib. bdg. 19.95 (978-0-8239-5850-4(7)); Quest for California's Gold. lib. bdg. 19.95 (978-0-8239-5849-8(3)); Rocky Mountain Fur Trade. lib. bdg. 19.95 (978-0-8239-5851-1(5)); Transcontinental Railroad. lib. bdg. 19.95 (978-0-8239-5852-8(3)); 24p. (J). (gr. 3). 2002. (Illus.). 2001. Set lib. bdg. 117.00 (978-0-8239-7131-2(7) , PowerKids Pr.) Rosen Publishing Group, Inc., The.

Bursell, Susan. The Lewis & Clark Expedition. 2002. (Let Freedom Ring Ser.). (Illus.). 48p. (J). (gr. 3-4). lib. bdg. 22.60 (978-0-7368-1099-9(4) , Bridgestone Bks.) Capstone Pr., Inc.

Capstone Press, contrib. by. Lewis & Clark Expedition. (Exploring the West Ser.). 48p. (YA). pap. 7.95 (978-0-7368-4506-9(2)) Capstone Pr., Inc.

Carter, E. J. The Lewis & Clark Journals. 2003. (Heinemann Know It Ser.). (Illus.). 48p. (J). pap. 8.50 (978-1-4034-3433-3(6)); lib. bdg. 27.07 (978-1-4034-0805-1(X)) Heinemann Library.

Clifton, Chuck & Clifton, Joyce. A Daily Walk with Lewis & Clark - 1804. 2003. 308p. (J). spiral bd. 14.95 (978-0-9669760-3-8(7)) Maple Canyon Co.

—A Daily Walk with Lewis & Clark - 1805. 2003. 390p. (J). spiral bd. 14.95 (978-0-9669760-4-5(5)) Maple Canyon Co.

—A Daily Walk with Lewis & Clark - 1806. 2003. 292p. (J). spiral bd. 14.95 (978-0-9669760-5-2(3)) Maple Canyon Co.

Collard, Sneed B., III. Sacagawea: Brave Shoshone Girl. 2006. (American Heroes Ser.). (Illus.). 48p. (J). (gr. 3-5). lib. bdg. 28.50 (978-0-7614-2166-5(1) , Benchmark Bks.) Cavendish, Marshall Corp.

Conant, Susan Sens. Lewis & Clark's Journey of Discovery: A Guide for Young Explorers. Lynn, Rick, illus. 2004. 48p. (J). pap. (***978-0-9725584-1-9(1)***) Little Blue Pr.

Cooper, Terry, ed. Lewis & Clark: Instant Internet Activities Folder. 2001. 6p. 3.95 (978-0-439-30950-9(6)) Scholastic, Inc.

Crosby, Michael T. Sacagawea: Lewis & Clark's Pathfinder. 2007. 144p. (J). 25.95 (***978-1-59556-026-1(2)***) OTTN Publishing.

Daugherty, James. Of Courage Undaunted: Across the Continent with Lewis & Clark. 1999. (Illus.). 168p. (YA). (gr. 6-12). reprint ed. pap. 16.95 (978-1-893103-02-3(1)) Beautiful Feet Bks.

DeKeyser, Stacy. Sacagawea. 2004. (Watts Library). (Illus.). 64p. (J). 25.50 (978-0-531-12290-7(5) , Watts, Franklin) Scholastic Library Publishing.

Devillier, Christy. Lewis & Clark. 2001. (First Biographies Ser.). (Illus.). 32p. (J). (gr. k-4). lib. bdg. 22.78 (978-1-57765-595-4(8) , Buddy Bks.) ABDO Publishing Co.

Ditchfield, Christin. The Lewis & Clark Expedition. 2006. 48p. (gr. 3-5). (YA). pap. 6.95 (978-0-516-25222-3(4)); (Illus.). (J). 25.00 (978-0-516-22835-8(8)) Scholastic Library Publishing. (Children's Pr.).

Edwards, Judith. Lewis & Clark's Journey of Discovery in American History. 1999. (In American History Ser.). (Illus.). 128p. (YA). (gr. 5-12). lib. bdg. 26.60 (978-0-7660-1127-4(5)) Enslow Pubs., Inc.

Edwards, Judith & Comport, Sally Wern. The Great Expedition of Lewis & Clark: By Private Reubin Field, Member of the Corps of Discovery. Comport, Sally Wern, illus. 2003. (Illus.). 40p. (J). 17.00 (978-0-374-38039-7(2) , Farrar, Straus & Giroux (BYR)) Farrar, Straus & Giroux.

Eisenberg, Jana. Lewis & Clark: Path to the Pacific. 2005. (Trailblazers of the West Ser.). (Illus.). 48p. (J). (ps-7). 24.00 (978-0-516-25126-4(0)); (gr. 7-12). pap. 6.95 (978-0-516-25096-0(5)) Scholastic Library Publishing. (Children's Pr.).

Erdrich, Lise. Sacagawea. 2005. (Libros Ilustrados (Picture Bks.)). (SPA & ENG., Illus.). 40p. (J). (ps-6). 16.95 (978-0-8225-3191-3(7) , Ediciones Lerner) Lerner Publishing Group.

—Sacagawea. Buffalohead, Julie, illus. 2003. 40p. (J). (gr. 3-6). 16.95 (978-0-87614-646-0(9) , Carolrhoda Bks.) Lerner Publishing Group.

Espinosa, Rod. Lewis & Clark. 2007. (Bio-Graphics Ser.). (Illus.). 32p. (J). (gr. 3-6). lib. bdg. 27.07 (***978-1-60270-069-7(9)*** , Graphic Planet) Magic Wagon.

Faber, Harold, et al. Lewis & Clark: From Ocean to Ocean. 2001. (Great Explorations Ser.). (Illus.). 80p. (J). (gr. 4 up). lib. bdg. 29.93 (978-0-7614-1241-0(7) , Benchmark Bks.) Cavendish, Marshall Corp.

Feinstein, Stephen. Lee sobre Sacagawea/Read about Sacagawea. 2006. (I Like Biographies! Bilingual Ser.). (ENG & SPA., Illus.). 24p. (J). (gr. 1-3). lib. bdg. 21.26 (978-0-7660-2674-2(4) , Enslow Elementary) Enslow Pubs., Inc.

—Read about Sacagawea. 2004. (I Like Biographies Ser.!). (Illus.). 24p. (J). lib. bdg. 21.26 (978-0-7660-2297-3(8)) Enslow Pubs., Inc.

Fifer, Barbara. Going along with Lewis & Clark. 2004. (Illus.). 48p. (YA). (gr. 7 up). pap. 11.95 (978-1-56037-151-9(X)) Farcountry Pr.

—Going along with Lewis & Clark. 2000. (gr. 3-6). lib. bdg. 21.05 (978-0-613-70809-8(1)) Tandem Library Bks.

Ford, Carin T. Sacagawea: Meet an American Legend. 2003. (Meeting Famous People Ser.). (Illus.). 32p. (J). lib. bdg. 22.60 (978-0-7660-2004-7(5)) Enslow Pubs., Inc.

Fradin, Dennis Brindell. Who Was Sacagawea? 2002. (gr. 3-6). lib. bdg. 13.00 (978-0-613-43655-7(5)) Tandem Library Bks.

Fradin, Judith Bloom & Fradin, Dennis B. The Lewis & Clark Expedition. 2007. (Turning Points in U. S. History Ser.). (J). lib. bdg. (***978-0-7614-2044-6(4)*** , Benchmark Bks.) Cavendish, Marshall Corp.

Franklin, Virgil. The Story of Sacagawea. 2002. (Reading Room Collection). (Illus.). 24p. (J). pap. (978-0-8239-8162-5(2)); lib. bdg. 18.75 (978-0-8239-3725-7(9)) Rosen Publishing Group, Inc., The.

Frazier, Neta Lohnes. Path to the Pacific: The Story of Sacagawea. 2007. (Sterling Point Bks.). (Illus.). 177p. (J). (***978-1-4287-2899-8(6)***) Sterling Publishing Co., Inc.

—Path to the Pacific: The Story of Sacajawea. 2007. (Sterling Point Bks.). (Illus.). 192p. (J). pap. 6.95 (978-1-4027-4138-8(3)) Sterling Publishing Co., Inc.

—Sterling Point Books: Path to the Pacific: The Story of Sacajawea. 2007. (Sterling Point Bks.). (Illus.). 192p. (J). 12.95 (978-1-4027-4518-8(4)) Sterling Publishing Co., Inc.

Glaser, Jason. Lewis & Clark. 2004. (Fact Finders Ser.). (Illus.). 32p. (J). lib. bdg. 22.60 (978-0-7368-2665-5(3)) Capstone Pr., Inc.

Group/McGraw-Hill, Wright. Lewis & Clark: Mapping the West, 6 vols. (Book2WebTM Ser.). (gr. 4-8). 36.50 (978-0-322-04460-9(X)) Wright Group, The.

Gunderson, Jessica Sarah. Sacagawea: Journey into the West. Martin, Cynthia & Schultz, Barbara, illus. 2007. (Graphic Library). 32p. (J). 25.26 (978-0-7368-6499-2(7)) Capstone Pr., Inc.

Gunderson, Mary. Cooking on the Lewis & Clark Expedition. 2000. (Blue Earth Books). (Illus.). 32p. (J). (gr. 3-4). lib. bdg. 22.60 (978-0-7368-0354-0(8) , Bridgestone Bks.) Capstone Pr., Inc.

—Cooking on the Lewis & Clark Expedition. 1999. (Exploring History Through Simple Recipes Ser.). (Illus.). 32p. (J). (gr. 2-7). pap. 14.60 (978-0-516-21865-6(4) , Children's Pr.) Scholastic Library Publishing.

Hamilton, John. The Corps of Discovery. 2003. (Lewis & Clark Expedition Ser.). (Illus.). 32p. (J). (gr. 3-8). lib. bdg. 24.21 (978-1-57765-761-3(6)) ABDO Publishing Co.

—The Journey Home. 2003. (Lewis & Clark Expedition Ser.). (Illus.). 32p. (J). (gr. 3-8). lib. bdg. 24.21 (978-1-57765-766-8(7)) ABDO Publishing Co.

—The Missouri River. 2003. (Lewis & Clark Expedition Ser.). (Illus.). 32p. (J). (gr. 3-8). lib. bdg. 24.21 (978-1-57765-762-0(4)) ABDO Publishing Co.

—The Mountains. 2003. (Lewis & Clark Expedition Ser.). (Illus.). 32p. (J). (gr. 3-8). lib. bdg. 24.21 (978-1-57765-764-4(0)) ABDO Publishing Co.

—To the Pacific. 2003. (Lewis & Clark Expedition Ser.). (Illus.). 32p. (J). (gr. 3-8). lib. bdg. 24.21 (978-1-57765-765 1(9)) ABDO Publishing Co.

—Uncharted Lands. 2003. (Lewis & Clark Expedition Ser.). (Illus.). 32p. (J). (gr. 3-8). lib. bdg. 24.21 (978-1-57765-763-7(2)) ABDO Publishing Co.

Harcourt School Publishers Staff. Lewis & Clark. 3rd ed. 2002. (Horizons Ser.). (Illus.). (J). pap. 5.50 (978-0-15-333314-9(6)) Harcourt Schl. Pubs.

Hargrove, Julia. The Lewis & Clark Memorial: Fort Clatsop. Mitchell, Judy, ed. Mohrman, Gary, illus. 2001. (Historic Monuments Ser.). 32p. (J). (gr. 4-8). pap. 5.95 (978-1-57310-283-4(0)) Teaching & Learning Co.

Herbert, Janis. Lewis & Clark for Kids. 2003. (gr. 5-8). lib. bdg. 24.55 (978-0-613-70597-4(1)) Tandem Library Bks.

—Lewis & Clark for Kids: Their Journey of Discovery with 21 Activities. 2000. (For Kids Ser.). (Illus.). 144p. (J). (ps up). pap. 16.95 (978-1-55652-374-8(2)) Chicago Review Pr., Inc.

Hill, William E. & Hill, Jan C. West with Lewis & Clark: The Story of the Corps of Discovery. 2001. (Illus.). 40p. (J). (gr. 3-6). pap. 3.95 (978-0-9636071-4-0(6)) HillHouse Publishing.

Isaacs, Sally Senzell. America in the Time of Lewis & Clark: 1801 to 1850. 2001. (Illus.). 48p. (J). (gr. 4-7). lib. bdg. 17.05 (978-0-613-83687-6(1)) Tandem Library Bks.

—The Lewis & Clark Expedition. 2003. (Illus.). 32p. (J). pap. 7.50 (978-1-4034-4774-6(8)); lib. bdg. 25.64 (978-1-4034-2503-4(5)) Heinemann Library.

Isserman, Maurice. Across America: The Lewis & Clark Expedition. 2004. (Discovery & Exploration Ser.). (Illus.). 192p. (J). (gr. 6-12). 40.00 (978-0-8160-5256-1(5)) Facts On File, Inc.

Jenkinson, Clay S. Lewis & Clark in Iowa. 2004. (Illus.). 70p. per. 2.00 (978-0-9753751-0-5(5)) Humanities Iowa.

Johmann, Carol A. The Lewis & Clark Expedition: Join the Corps of Discovery to Explore Uncharted. Kline, Michael, illus. 2002. 112p. (J). (ps-7). lib. bdg. 22.20 (978-0-613-58156-1(3)) Tandem Library Bks.

—The Lewis & Clark Expedition: Join the Corps of Discovery to Explore Uncharted Territory. 2004. (Kaleidoscope Kids Bks.). (Illus.). 112p. (YA). (gr. 4-6). pap. 12.95 (978-1-885593-73-3(2) , Williamson Bks.) Ideals Pubns.

KIDs: Discover the Lewis & Clark Expedition. 2001. 16p. (J). pap. (978-1-888631-17-3(1)) Watercourse, The.

Kimmel, Elizabeth Cody. As Far As the Eye Can Reach: Lewis & Clark's Westward Quest. 2004. (Landmark Bks.). (Illus.). 128p. (J). (gr. 4). 5.99 (978-0-375-82728-0(5) , Random Hse. Bks. for Young Readers) Random Hse. Children's Bks.

—As Far as the Eye Can Reach: Lewis & Clark's Westward Quest. 2005. (Illus.). 119p. (YA). (gr. 4-8). reprint ed. 5.00 (978-0-7567-9660-0(1)) DIANE Publishing Co.

Kline, Trish. Lewis & Clark. 2002. (Discover the Life of an Explorer Ser.). (Illus.). 24p. (gr. 2-5). 14.95 (978-1-58952-067-7(X)) Rourke Publishing, LLC.

Klingel, Cynthia Fitterer & Noyed, Robert B. Lewis & Clark: Explorers. 2002. (Spirit of America: Our People Ser.). (Illus.). 32p. (J). (gr. 2-6). 27.07 (978-1-56766-164-4(5)) Child's World, Inc.

Koestler-Grack, Rachel A. Sacagawea. 2004. (Illus.). 32p. (J). pap. 7.50 (978-1-4034-5011-1(0)); lib. bdg. 24.22 (978-1-4034-5004-3(8)) Heinemann Library.

Kozar, Richard. Lewis & Clark: Explorers of the Louisiana Purchase. 2000. (Explorers of the New World Ser.). (Illus.). 64p. (J). (gr. 4 up). 25.00 (978-0-7910-5513-7(2) , Chelsea Hse.) Facts On File, Inc.

The Lewis & Clark Expedition, 6 vols. (gr. 2-5). 39.95 (978-0-7368-4589-2(5)) Red Brick Learning.

Lewis & Clark Expedition, Set. 2002. (J). (gr. 3-8). lib. bdg. 145.26 (978-1-57765-521-3(4)) ABDO Publishing Co.

Lewis & Clark Hands on Art And. 2004. pap. 12.95 (978-0-9715970-5-1(7)) Visual Manna.

Lilly, Melinda. Sacagawea, Lewis, & Clark. 2003. (Rourke Discovery Library). (Illus.). 24p. (gr. 1-4). 14.95 (978-1-58952-362-3(8)) Rourke Publishing, LLC.

Lourie, Peter. On the Trail of Lewis & Clark: A Journey up the Missouri River. 2004. (Exploration Ser.). (Illus.). 48p. (YA). (gr. 4-6). pap. 11.95 (978-1-59078-268-2(2)) Boyds Mills Pr.

—On the Trail of Lewis & Clark: A Journey up the Missouri River. Lourie, Peter, photos by. 2003. (Exploration Ser.). (Illus.). 48p. (YA). (gr. 4-6). 19.95 (978-1-56397-936-1(5)) Boyds Mills Pr.

—On the Trail of Sacagawea. 2003. (Exploration Ser.). (Illus.). 48p. (J). (gr. 4-6). 18.95 (978-1-56397-840-1(7)) Boyds Mills Pr.

MacGregor, Carol Lynn. Lewis & Clark's Bittersweet Crossing. Hoopes, Gaye, tr. Hoopes, Gaye, illus. 2004. 32p. (J). 16.95 (978-0-87004-437-3(0) , 043700) Caxton Pr.

Marcovitz, Hal. Fort Clatsop. 2004. (American Forts & Their Strategic Importance Ser.). (J). (978-1-59084-706-0(7)) Mason Crest Pubs.

—Sacagawea: Guide for the Lewis & Clark Expedition. 2000. (Explorers of the New World Ser.). (Illus.). (J). 63p. (gr. 4-7). pap. 25.00 (978-0-7910-6169-5(8)); 64p. (gr. 8-12). 25.00 (978-0-7910-5959-3(6)) Facts On File, Inc. (Chelsea Hse.).

—Sacagawea: Guide for the Lewis & Clark Expedition. 2001. (gr. 3-6). lib. bdg. 17.60 (978-0-613-33014-5(5)) Tandem Library Bks.

Marsh, Carole. Lewis & Clark Go on a Hike. 2003. 32p. (J). (gr. 3-8). pap. 5.95 (978-0-635-02122-9(6)) Gallopade International.

Maynard, Charles W. Fort Clatsop. 2002. (Famous Forts Throughout American History Ser.). (Illus.). 24p. (J). (gr. 3). lib. bdg. 18.75 (978-0-8239-5837-5(X) , PowerKids Pr.) Rosen Publishing Group, Inc., The.

McCormick, Lisa Wade. Lewis & Clark. 2006. 32p. (gr. 1-2). (YA). pap. 4.95 (978-0-516-21443-6(8)); (Illus.). (J). 20.50 (978-0-516-25039-7(6)) Scholastic Library Publishing. (Children's Pr.)

McGrath, Patrick. The Lewis & Clark Expedition. 2001. (Crossing America Ser.). 48p. (J). (gr. 5-8). pap. 6.99 (978-0-7424-0108-2(1) , IF6024) School Specialty Publishing.

McLeese, Don. Sacagawea. 2003. (Native American Legends Ser.). (Illus.). 32p. (J). 28.50 (978-1-58952-729-4(1)) Rourke Publishing, LLC.

Meinke, Amanda & Stegmann, Lisa. Lewis & Clark Famous Faces. Adams Marks, Elizabeth, illus. 2003. 2p. (J). pap. 2.99 (978-1-56472-289-8(9)) Edupress, Inc.

Milton, Joyce. Sacajawea. Hehenberger, Shelly, illus. 2001. (All Aboard Reading Ser.). 48p. (J). (gr. 1-3). pap. 3.99 (978-0-448-42539-9(4) , Grosset & Dunlap) Penguin Group (USA) Inc.

Molzahn, Arlene Bourgeois. Lewis & Clark: American Explorers. 2003. (Explorers! Ser.). (Illus.). 48p. (J). (gr. 1-4). lib. bdg. 23.93 (978-0-7660-2067-2(3)) Enslow Pubs., Inc.

Moran, Margaret. Lewis & Clark. 2004. (Navigators Ser.). (J). pap. 42.00 (978-1-4108-0432-7(1)) Benchmark Education Co.

Moran, Margaret. Lewis y Clark & Lewis & Clark. 2005. spiral bd. 84.00 (***978-1-4108-5712-5(3)***) Benchmark Education Co.

Murphy, Claire Rudolf. I Am Sacagawea, I Am York: Our Journey West with Lewis & Clark. Bond, Higgins, illus. 2005. 32p. (J). (gr. 3-5). 17.85 (978-0-8027-8921-1(8)); 16.95 (978-0-8027-8919-8(6)) Walker & Co.

On the Trail of Lewis & Clark Poster Map. 2004. (J). (978-0-9759433-1-1(6)) Maps For Kids Inc.

On the Trail of Lewis & Clark Timeline/Fact Poster. 2004. (J). (978-0-9759433-2-8(4)) Maps For Kids Inc.

Patent, Dorothy Hinshaw. Animals on the Trail with Lewis & Clark. Munoz, William, illus. 2002. 128p. (J). (gr. 4-6). 18.00 (978-0-395-91415-1(9) , Clarion Bks.) Houghton Mifflin Co. Trade & Reference Div.

—The Lewis & Clark Trail: Then & Now. Munoz, William, illus. 2002. 64p. (J). (gr. 4-8). 19.99 (978-0-525-46912-4(5) , Dutton Juvenile) Penguin Group (USA) Inc.

—Plants on the Trail with Lewis & Clark. Munoz, William, photos by. 2003. (Illus.). 112p. (J). (gr. 4-6). tchr. ed. 18.00 (978-0-618-06776-3(0) , Clarion Bks.) Houghton Mifflin Co. Trade & Reference Div.

Patzman, Barbara J. Would You Have Gone with Lewis & Clark? The Story of the Corps of Discovery for Young People. Albers, Everett C., ed. 2000. (Illus.). ii, 37p. (J). (gr. 4 up). pap. 6.95 (978-0-9674002-2-8(8)) United Printing.

Petrie, Kristin. Lewis & Clark. 2007. (Illus.). 32p. (J). 22.78 (978-1-59679-743-7(6)) ABDO Publishing Co.

—Sacagawea. 2007. (Illus.). 32p. (J). 22.78 (978-1-59679-749-9(5)) ABDO Publishing Co.

Pringle, Laurence P. American Slave, American Hero: York of the Lewis & Clark Expedition. Van Wright, Cornelius & Hu, Ying-Hwa, illus. 2006. 40p. (J). (gr. 3-5). 17.95 (978-1-59078-282-8(8)) Boyds Mills Pr.

—Dog of Discovery: A Newfoundland's Adventures with Lewis & Clark. 2004. (Illus.). 152p. (YA). (gr. 6-9). pap. 10.95 (978-1-59078-267-5(4)) Boyds Mills Pr.

—Dog of Discovery: A Newfoundland's Adventures with Lewis & Clark. Henderson, Meryl, illus. 2003. 152p. (YA). (gr. 6-9). 17.95 (978-1-59078-028-2(0)) Boyds Mills Pr.

Quiri, Patricia Ryon. The Lewis & Clark Expedition. 2000. (We the People Ser.). (Illus.). 48p. (J). (gr. 4 up). lib. bdg. 22.60 (978-0-7565-0044-3(3)) Compass Point Bks.

Ransom, Candice F. Lewis & Clark. (History Maker Bios Ser.). (J). 2003. (Illus.). 48p. (gr. 2-4). 26.60 (978-0-8225-0394-1(8) , Lerner Pubns.); 2002. pap. 6.95 (978-0-8225-1562-3(8)) Lerner Publishing Group.

Raum, Elizabeth. Lewis & Clark's Continental Journey. 2007. (J). (***978-1-4034-9757-4(5)***) Heinemann Library.

Raum, Elizabeth. William Clark. 2003. (Illus.). 32p. (J). pap. 6.95 (978-1-4034-4202-4(9)); lib. bdg. 24.22 (978-1-4034-4194-2(4)) Heinemann Library.

—William Clark. 2003. (gr. k-3). lib. bdg. 15.25 (978-0-613-87667-4(9)) Tandem Library Bks.

Rausch, Monica. Sacagawea. 2006. (Illus.). 24p. (J). pap. (***978-0-8368-7692-5(X)***); lib. bdg. (***978-0-8368-7685-7(7)***) Stevens, Gareth Inc. (Weekly Reader Early Learning Library).

Redmond, Shirley-Raye. Lewis & Clark: A Prairie Dog for the President. Manders, John, illus. 2003. (Step into Reading Ser.: No. 3). 48p. (J). (gr. k-2). pap. 3.99 (978-0-375-81120-3(6) , Random Hse. Bks. for Young Readers) Random Hse. Children's Bks.

Rodger, Ellen. Lewis & Clark: Opening the American West. 2005. (In the Footsteps of Explorers Ser.). (Illus.). 32p. (J). (ps-9). (978-0-7787-2410-0(7)); pap. (978-0-7787-2446-9(8)) Crabtree Publishing Co.

Roop, Peter & Roop, Connie. Off the Map: The Journals of Lewis & Clark. Tanner, Tim, illus. rev. ed. 1998. 44p. (J). (gr. 4-6). pap. 8.95 (978-0-8027-7546-7(2)) Walker & Co.

Roop, Peter & Roop, Connie, eds. Off the Map: The Journals of Lewis & Clark. Tanner, Tim, illus. 1998. 44p. (J). (ps-6). lib. bdg. 17.60 (978-0-613-08471-0(3)) Tandem Library Bks.

Ruffing, Faith Elizabeth. Lewis & Clark Bicentennial Corps of Discovery Journal & Record Book. 2003. (Illus.). 162p. spiral bd. 29.95 (978-0-9763970-0-7(5)) Lewis & Clark Bicentennial Corps of Discovery Arch.

Sachatello-Sawyer, Bonnie. Lewis & Clark: Background Information, Skill-Building Activities, & a Colorful Learning Poster. 2nd ed. 2004. (Illus.). 64p. pap., tchr. ed. 10.99 (978-0-439-51367-8(7)) Scholastic, Inc.

Santella, Andrew. Lewis & Clark. 2001. (gr. 3-6). lib. bdg. 17.60 (978-0-613-51659-4(1)) Tandem Library Bks.

Sapp, Richard. Lewis & Clark on Their Journey to the Pacific. 2006. (In the Footsteps of American Heroes Ser.). (Illus.). 64p. (J). pap. (978-0-8368-6434-2(4)); lib. bdg. 32.67 (978-0-8368-6429-8(8)) Stevens, Gareth Inc. (World Almanac Library).

Schanzer, Rosalyn. How We Crossed the West: The Adventures of Lewis & Clark. 2002. (Illus.). 48p. (J). (gr. 3-7). pap. 7.95 (978-0-7922-6726-3(5) , National Geographic Children's Bks.) National Geographic Society.

—How We Crossed the West: The Adventures of Lewis & Clark. 2002. (gr. 3-6). lib. bdg. 16.40 (978-0-613-58118-9(0)) Tandem Library Bks.

Sheely, Tiffany, illus. Captain William Clark's Great Montana Adventure. 2003. 32p. (J). mass mkt. 3.95 (978-0-9711667-0-7(6)) Outlook Publishing, Inc.

Spotlight on America: The Lewis & Clark Expedition & the Louisiana Purchase. 2003. (Illus.). 48p. (J). (gr. 4-8). 8.99 (978-0-7439-3233-2(1)) Teacher Created Materials, Inc.

Staeger, Rob. The Journey of Lewis & Clark. 2002. (Exploration & Discovery Ser.). (Illus.). 64p. (YA). (gr. 5 up). lib. bdg. (978-1-59084-056-6(9)) Mason Crest Pubs.

Stein, R. Conrad. Lewis & Clark. 1998. (Cornerstones of Freedom Ser.). (Illus.). 32p. (J). (gr. 4-6). pap. 5.95 (978-0-516-26228-4(9) , Children's Pr.) Scholastic Library Publishing.

Streissguth, Thomas. Lewis & Clark: Explorers of the Northwest. 1998. (Historical American Biographies Ser.). (Illus.). 128p. (YA). (gr. 6-12). lib. bdg. 26.60 (978-0-7660-1016-1(3)) Enslow Pubs., Inc.

Sullivan, George. Lewis & Clark. 2003. (Illus.). 128p. (J). (ps-7). per. 12.40 (978-0-613-25992-7(0)) Tandem Library Bks.

J K L

Sullivan, George E. Lewis & Clark. 2000. (In Their Own Words Ser.). (Illus.). 128p. (J). (gr. 4-7). pap. 4.99 (978-0-439-09553-2(0)); pap. 12.95 (978-0-439-14749-1(2)) Scholastic, Inc.

—Lewis & Clark. 2000. (J). 11.64 (978-0-606-19924-7(1)) Tandem Library Bks.

Sundling, Charles W. Explorers of the Frontier. 2000. (Frontier Land Ser.). (Illus.). 32p. (J). (gr. 3-8). lib. bdg. 24.21 (978-1-57765-044-7(1) , ABDO & Daughters) ABDO Publishing Co.

Wallner, Rosemary. Sacagawea 1788-1812. 2002. (American Indian Biographies Ser.). (Illus.). 32p. (J). (gr. 3-4). lib. bdg. 23.93 (978-0-7368-1213-9(X) , Blue Earth Bks.) Capstone Pr., Inc.

Ward, Gail. Lewis & Clark Activity Books Set, 3 books. 2002. (Illus.). 32p. 15.95 (978-1-886609-33-4(0)) Tamarack Bks., Inc.

—Native Americans along the Lewis & Clark Trail. 2002. 32p. (978-1-886609-31-0(4)) Tamarack Bks., Inc.

Webster, Christine. The Lewis & Clark Expedition. (Cornerstones of Freedomtrade;, Second Ser.). 48p. (J). 2007. pap. 5.95 (***978-0-531-18689-3(X));** 2003. (Illus.). (gr. 4-6). 26.00 (978-0-516-22678-1(9)) Scholastic Library Publishing. (Children's Pr.).

Witteman, Barbara. Sacagawea. 2002. (Photo-Illustrated Biographies Ser.). (Illus.). 24p. (J). (gr. 2-3). lib. bdg. 18.60 (978-0-7368-1112-5(5) , Bridgestone Bks.) Capstone Pr., Inc.

LEWIS AND CLARK EXPEDITION (1804-1806)—FICTION

Albers, Everett C. Lewis & Clark Meet the American Indians: As Told by Seaman the Dog. Eslinger, Kimberly, illus. 1999. 32p. (J). (ps-11). pap. 3.95 (978-0-9674002-0-4(1)) United Printing.

Ambrose, Stephen E. This Vast Land: A Young Man's Journal of the Lewis & Clark Expedition. l.t. ed. 2004. 265p. (J). 22.95 (978-0-7862-6139-0(0)) Thorndike Pr.

Bohner, Charles H. Bold Journey: West with Lewis & Clark. 2004. 192p. (J). (gr. 5-9). pap. 6.95 (978-0-618-43718-4(5)) Houghton Mifflin Co. Trade & Reference Div.

Brown, Duncan. Seaman's Adventures with Lewis & Clark. 2002. (Illus.). 40p. (J). pap. 7.95 (978-1-57960-093-8(X)) History Compass, LLC.

Eubank, Patricia Reeder. Seaman's Journal. Barrett, Robert, illus. 2002. 32p. (J). 15.95 (978-0-8249-5442-0(4)) Ideals Pubns.

Karwoski, Gail Langer. Seaman: The Dog Who Explored the West with Lewis & Clark. 1999. (978-0-606-17742-9(6)); (gr. 3-6). lib. bdg. 17.60 (978-0-613-23470-2(7)) Tandem Library Bks.

—SeaMan: The Dog Who Explored the West with Lewis & Clark. Watling, James, illus. 2003. 192p. (J). 14.95 (978-1-56145-276-7(9) , Q20194); (gr. 3-7). pap. 8.95 (978-1-56145-190-6(8) , Q20194) Peachtree Pubs., Ltd.

LaMear, Arline. Lewis & Clark, the Astoria Cats. Goza, Benjamin, illus. 2002. 32p. (J). (gr. 3-7). pap. 9.95 (978-0-9720394-0-6(6)) Lucky Cat Publishing.

Lasky, Kathryn. The Journal of Augustus Pelletier: The Lewis & Clark Expedition, 1804. 2000. (My Name Is America Ser.). (Illus.). 192p. (J). (gr. 4-8). pap. 10.95 (978-0-590-68489-7(2)) Scholastic, Inc.

McMullan, Kate. My Travels with Capts. Lewis & Clark, by George Shannon. Yorinks, Adrienne, illus. 2006. 288p. (J). pap. 6.99 (978-0-06-008101-0(5) , Harper Trophy) HarperCollins Pubs.

Nansel, Judy & Faircloth, Julie. A Bear's Tale of the Lewis & Clark Expedition. Nansel, Judy, illus. 2005. (Illus.). 60p. (YA). pap. 6.95 (978-1-892784-19-3(X) , 1512) HOPS Pr., LLC.

Olsen, Lauri. Pacific Bound: The Adventures of Lewis & Clark. Toonz Animation, ed. 2005. (Illus.). 44p. (J). 18.95 (978-0-9742502-5-0(2)) Gossamer Bks., LLC.

—Pacific Bound: The Adventures of Lewis & Clark. 2004. (Illus.). 46p. (J). per. 15.95 (978-0-9742502-4-3(4)) Gossamer Bks., LLC.

Sargent, Dave & Sargent, Pat. Mack: (Medicine Hat Paint) Be a Leader, 30, 39. Lenoir, Jane, illus. 2003. (Saddle Up Ser.: Vol. 39). 42p. (J). pap. 6.95 (978-1-56763-700-7(0)); lib. bdg. 22.60 (978-1-56763-699-4(3)) Ozark Publishing.

Scieszka, Jon. Lewis & Clark... & Jodie, Freddi, & Samantha. 2006. (Time Warp Trio: No. 2). 80p. (J). pap. 4.99 (978-0-06-111638-4(6) , Harper Trophy) HarperCollins Pubs.

Smith, Roland. The Captain's Dog: My Journey with the Lewis & Clark Tribe. 2000. (Great Episodes Ser.). (Illus.). 304p. (YA). (gr. 4-7). pap. 6.00 (978-0-15-202696-7(7) , Harcourt Paperbacks) Harcourt Children's Bks.

—The Captain's Dog: My Journey with the Lewis & Clark Tribe. 2000. (J). 12.65 (978-0-606-19000-8(7)); (gr. 3-6). lib. bdg. 14.15 (978-0-613-29900-8(0)) Tandem Library Bks.

Sneve, Virginia Driving Hawk. Bad River Boys. Farnsworth, Bill, illus. 2005. 32p. (YA). 16.95 (978-0-8234-1856-5(1)) Holiday Hse., Inc.

Van Steenwyk, Elizabeth. My Name Is York. Farnsworth, Bill, illus. 2000. 32p. (J). (ps-3). 7.95 (978-0-87358-758-7(8) , Rising Moon Bks. for Young Readers) Northland Publishing.

Williams, Mark London. Trail of Bones. Koelsch, Michael, illus. 2005. (Danger Boy Ser.: No. 3). 320p. (J). (gr. 4-8). 12.99 (978-0-7636-2154-4(4)) Candlewick Pr.

Wolf, Allan. New Found Land: Lewis & Clark's Voyage of Discovery. 2007. (Illus.). 512p. (YA). (gr. 7). pap. 8.99 (***978-0-7636-3288-5(0))** Candlewick Pr.

—New Found Land: Lewis & Clark's Voyage of Discovery. Wolf, Allan, illus. 2004. (Illus.). 512p. (J). (gr. 5 up). 18.99 (978-0-7636-2113-1(7)) Candlewick Pr.

LEXINGTON, BATTLE OF, 1775

Anderson, Dale. Lexington & Concord: April 19, 1775. 2004. (American Battlefields Ser.). (Illus.). 32p. (J). 14.95 (978-1-59270-027-1(6)) Enchanted Lion Bks., LLC.

Battles of Lexington & Concord. (American Revolution Ser.). 32p. (YA). 7.95 (978-0-7368-4491-8(0)) Capstone Pr., Inc.

Branse, J. L. A Day in the Life of a Colonial Soldier. 2002. (Library of Living & Working in Colonial Times). (Illus.). 24p. (J). (gr. 3). lib. bdg. 18.75 (978-0-8239-5819-1(1) , PowerKids Pr.) Rosen Publishing Group, Inc., The.

Crewe, Sabrina & Uschan, Michael V. Lexington & Concord. 2004. (Events That Shaped America Ser.). (Illus.). 32p. (J). (gr. 3 up). lib. bdg. 24.67 (978-0-8368-3398-0(8)) Stevens, Gareth Inc.

Fradin, Dennis Brindell. Let It Begin Here! Lexington & Concord: First Battles of the American Revolution. Day, Larry, illus. 2005. 32p. (J). 17.85 (978-0-8027-8946-4(3)); 16.95 (978-0-8027-8945-7(5)) Walker & Co.

Kent, Deborah. Lexington & Concord. 1998. (Cornerstones of Freedom Ser.). (Illus.). 32p. (J). (gr. 4-6). pap. 5.95 (978-0-516-26229-1(7) , Children's Pr.) Scholastic Library Publishing.

Kimmel, Heidi. Battles of Lexington & Concord. 2006. (Cornerstones of Freedom Ser.). (Illus.). 48p. (J). (978-0-516-23627-8(X)) Children's Pr., Ltd.

Kimmel, Heidi. The Battles of Lexington & Concord. 2007. (Cornerstones of Freedomtrade;, Second Ser.). 48p. (J). pap. 5.95 (***978-0-531-18763-0(2)** , Children's Pr.) Scholastic Library Publishing.

Niz, Xavier. Paul Revere's Ride. Bascle, Brian, illus. 2005. (Graphic Library). 32p. (J). (gr. 3-7). lib. bdg. 25.26 (978-0-7368-4965-4(3)) Capstone Pr., Inc.

Peacock, Judith. The Battles of Lexington & Concord. 2002. (Let Freedom Ring Ser.). (Illus.). 48p. (J). (gr. 3-4). lib. bdg. 22.60 (978-0-7368-1096-8(X) , Bridgestone Bks.) Capstone Pr., Inc.

Raatma, Lucia. The Battles of Lexington & Concord. 2003. (We the People Ser.). (Illus.). 48p. (J). (gr. 4 up). lib. bdg. 22.60 (978-0-7565-0490-8(2)) Compass Point Bks.

Randolph, Ryan P. & Randolph, Joanne. Paul Revere & the Minutemen of the American Revolution. 2005. (Library of American Lives & Times). (Illus.). 112p. (J). (gr. 4-8). lib. bdg. 31.95 (978-0-8239-5727-9(6)) Rosen Publishing Group, Inc., The.

Uschan, Michael V. Lexington & Concord. 2003. (Landmark Events in American History Ser.). (Illus.). 48p. (J). (gr. 5 up). lib. bdg. 30.00 (978-0-8368-5379-7(2)); pap. 11.95 (978-0-8368-5407-7(1)) Stevens, Gareth Inc. (World Almanac Library).

Waldman, Scott P. The Battle of Lexington & Concord. 2003. (Atlas of Famous Battles of the American Revolution Ser.). (Illus.). 24p. (J). lib. bdg. 21.25 (978-0-8239-6328-7(4) , PowerKids Pr.) Rosen Publishing Group, Inc., The.

Whitelaw, Nancy. The Shot Heard Round the World: The Battles of Lexington & Concord. 2004. (First Battles Ser.). (Illus.). 112p. (J). (gr. 6-12). 23.95 (978-1-883846-75-6(7) , First Biographies) Reynolds, Morgan Inc.

LIBERIA

Baughan, Brian. Liberia. 2007. (J). (978-1-4222-0088-9(4)) Mason Crest Pubs.

Debra A. Miller. Liberia. 2004. (Modern Nations of the World Ser.). (Illus.). 112p. (J). 29.95 (978-1-59018-540-7(4)) Thomson Gale.

Dubois, Muriel L. Liberia. 2005. (Fact Finders Ser.). (Illus.). 32p. (J). 22.60 (978-0-7368-3755-2(8)) Capstone Pr., Inc.

Levy, Patricia. Liberia. 1998. (Cultures of the World Ser.). (Illus.). 128p. (gr. 5-12). lib. bdg. 37.07 (978-0-7614-0810-9(X) , Benchmark Bks.) Cavendish, Marshall Corp.

Ng, Yumi. Welcome to Liberia. 2004. (Welcome to My Country Ser.). (Illus.). 48p. (J). lib. bdg. 26.00 (978-0-8368-2566-4(7)) Stevens, Gareth Inc.

Reef, Catherine. This Our Dark Country: The American Settlers of Liberia. 2002. (Illus.). 144p. (J). (gr. 5-9). tchr. ed. 17.00 (978-0-618-14785-4(3) , Clarion Bks.) Houghton Mifflin Co. Trade & Reference Div.

Rozario, Paul. Liberia. 2003. (Countries of the World Ser.). (Illus.). 96p. (J). (gr. 6 up). lib. bdg. 30.00 (978-0-8368-2366-0(4)) Stevens, Gareth Inc.

Streissguth, Thomas. Liberia in Pictures. 2006. (Visual Geography Series, Second Ser.). (Illus.). 80p. (J). 27.93 (978-0-8225-2465-6(1) , Twenty-First Century Bks.) Lerner Publishing Group.

LIBERIA—FICTION

Allen, C. William. The African Interior Mission. Lee, Xiongpao, illus. 2006. 232p. (J). pap. 20.00 (978-0-9653308-5-5(0)) Africana Homestead Legacy Pubs.

Wilson, Heather Gemmen. Lydia Barnes & the Blood Diamond Treasure. 2007. (J). (***978-0-89827-350-2(1))** Wesleyan Publishing Hse.

Zemser, Amy Bronwen. Beyond the Mango Tree. 1998. (Illus.). 156p. (YA). (gr. 5 up). 14.95 (978-0-688-16005-0(0)) HarperCollins Pubs.

—Beyond the Mango Tree. 2000. (978-0-606-17879-2(1)) Tandem Library Bks.

LIBERTY

see also Assembly, Right of; Civil Rights; Equality; Freedom of Religion

Beveridge, Amy. Let's Thank God for Freedom. 2006. 24p. (J). bds. 6.99 (978-0-7847-1505-5(X) , 04384) Standard Publishing.

Binns, Tristan Boyer. Symbols of Freedom, 6 bks., Set 1. 2001. (Illus.). (J). (gr. k-2). lib. bdg. 128.16 (978-1-58810-025-2(1)) Heinemann Library.

Bradley, Catherine. Freedom of Movement. 1998. (What Do We Mean by Human Rights? Ser.). (Illus.). 48p. (J). (gr. 4-8). 23.00 (978-0-531-14447-3(X) , Watts, Franklin) Scholastic Library Publishing.

—Freedom of Movement. 2005. (What Do We Mean by Human Rights? Ser.). (Illus.). 46p. (J). (gr. 5-9). lib. bdg. 29.95 (978-1-932889-64-2(7)) Sea-To-Sea Pubns.

Brown, Geoffrey, compiled by. Liberty, New York Memories. 2002. (Illus.). cd-rom 15.00 (978-0-9727403-0-2(9)) Between the Lakes Group, LLC.

Buckley, Susan & Leacock, Elspeth. Journeys for Freedom: A New Look at America's Story. Prato, Rodica, illus. 2006. 48p. (J). (gr. 4-6). 17.00 (978-0-618-22323-7(1)) Houghton Mifflin Co.

Harcourt School Publishers Staff. Celebrating Freedom. 3rd ed. 2002. (Horizons Ser.). (Illus.). (J). pap. 3.70 (978-0-15-333176-3(3)) Harcourt Schl. Pubs.

—Trofeos Advanced Level: Libertad. 3rd ed. 2002. (SPA., Illus.). pap. 6.80 (978-0-15-324128-4(4)) Harcourt Schl. Pubs.

Hess, Karl. Capitalism for Kids: Growing up to Be Your Own Boss. rev. ed. 2006. 196p. (J). pap. 8.95 (978-0-942617-35-1(5)) Bluestocking Pr.

King, Wilma. Children of the Emancipation. 2005. (Picture the American Past Ser.). (Illus.). 48p. (gr. 2-5). 22.60 (978-1-57505-396-7(9)) Lerner Publishing Group.

Let's Thank God for Freedom. 2006. 16p. (J). pap. 1.99 (978-0-7847-1723-3(0) , 04184); pap. 1.99 (978-0-7847-1538-3(6) , 22142) Standard Publishing.

Lewison, Wendy Cheyette. L Is for Liberty. Hines, Laura Freeman, illus. 2003. (Reading Railroad Bks.). 32p. (J). (ps-4). pap. 3.49 (978-0-448-43228-1(5) , Grosset & Dunlap) Penguin Group (USA) Inc.

Monk, Linda R. The Words We Live By: Your Annotated Guide to the Constitution. annot. ed. 2004. (Illus.). 288p. pap. 14.95 (978-0-7868-8620-3(X)) Hyperion Pr.

Neitzel, Shirley. Liberty & Justice for All. 2002. 32p. tchr. ed. 8.95 (978-0-938682-71-4(7) , 682-71-7) River Road Pubns., Inc.

Parker, Regina F. Let Freedom Ring. 2004. pap. 14.95 (978-0-9754131-0-4(4)) Kids Donate, Inc.

Rees, Peter. Liberty: Blessing or Burden? 2007. (Shockwave: the Human Experience Ser.). (Illus.). 36p. (J). (gr. 4-6). lib. bdg. 25.00 (***978-0-531-17760-0(2)** , Children's Pr.) Scholastic Library Publishing.

Rondeau, Amanda. Freedom. 2003. (United We Stand Ser.). (Illus.). 24p. (J). (ps-3). lib. bdg. 19.93 (978-1-57765-878-8(7)) ABDO Publishing Co.

Stephens, Edna Cucksey. Rock U. S. A. & the American Way: A Freedom Handbook. Herrick, Mark J., illus. 2002. 64p. (J). 22.95 (978-0-9712692-7-9(0)) EDCO Publishing, Inc.

To Be Free. 2003. (Illus.). pap. 5.60 (978-0-7398-7507-0(8)) Steck-Vaughn.

Veciana-Suarez, Ana. Flight to Freedom. 2004. (First Person Fiction Ser.). (SPA.). 240p. (J). (gr. 7 up). pap. 4.99 (978-0-439-66358-8(X) , Scholastic Paperbacks) Scholastic, Inc.

—Flight to Freedom. 2004. 215p. (YA). (gr. 8-12). lib. bdg. 15.30 (978-0-613-72054-0(7)) Tandem Library Bks.

LIBERTY BELL

Ashley, Susan. The Liberty Bell. 2004. (Weekly Reader Early Learning Library). (Illus.). 24p. (J). (gr. 2 up). pap. 5.95 (978-0-8368-4148-0(4)); lib. bdg. 19.33 (978-0-8368-4141-1(7)) Stevens, Gareth Inc. (Weekly Reader Early Learning Library).

Binns, Tristan Boyer. The Liberty Bell. (Symbols of Freedom Ser.). (Illus.). 32p. (J). (gr. k-2). 2002. pap. 6.95 (978-1-58810-403-8(6) , 91145); 2001. lib. bdg. 21.36 (978-1-58810-119-8(3)) Heinemann Library.

Douglas, Lloyd G. The Liberty Bell. 2003. (Welcome Book Ser.). (Illus.). 24p. (J). 18.00 (978-0-516-25852-2(4)); pap. 4.95 (978-0-516-27875-9(4)) Scholastic Library Publishing. (Children's Pr.).

—Liberty Bell. 2003. (gr. k-3). lib. bdg. 12.95 (978-0-613-67738-7(2)) Tandem Library Bks.

Figley, Marty Rhodes. Salvar a la Campana de la Libertad. Lepp, Kevin, illus. 2005. (Yo Solo - Historia (on My Own - History) Ser.). (SPA.). 48p. (J). (gr. 3-7). lib. bdg. 25.26 (978-0-8225-3094-7(5) , Ediciones Lerner) Lerner Publishing Group.

—Saving the Liberty Bell. Lepp, Kevin, tr. Lepp, Kevin, illus. 2005. (On My Own History Ser.). 48p. (J). 25.26 (978-1-57505-589-3(9)) Lerner Publishing Group.

—Saving the Liberty Bell. Lepp, Kevin, illus. 2004. 48p. (J). (ps-ps). lib. bdg. 12.75 (978-0-606-30522-8(X)) Tandem Library Bks.

Firestone, Mary. The Liberty Bell. Skeens, Matthew, illus. 2006. 24p. (J). lib. bdg. (***978-1-4048-3101-8(0))** Picture Window Bks.

Harris, Nancy. The Liberty Bell. 2007. (J). (***978-1-4034-9381-1(2));** pap. (***978-1-4034-9388-0(X))** Heinemann Library.

Healy, Nick. The Liberty Bell. 2003. (J). pap. (978-1-58417-119-5(7)); lib. bdg. (978-1-58417-057-0(3)) Lake Street Pubs.

Hicks, Terry Allan. Symbols of America Group 2, 6 bks., Set. Incl. Bald Eagle. lib. bdg. 28.50 (978-0-7614-2133-7(5)); Capitol. lib. bdg. 28.50 (978-0-7614-2132-0(7)); Declaration of Independence. lib. bdg. 28.50 (978-0-7614-2135-1(1)); Ellis Island. lib. bdg. 28.50 (978-0-7614-2134-4(3)); Pledge of Allegiance. lib. bdg. 28.50 (978-0-7614-2136-8(X)); Uncle Sam. lib. bdg. 28.50 (978-0-7614-2137-5(8)); (Illus.). 40p. (J). 2006. 2007. Set lib. bdg. 171.00 (***978-0-7614-2130-6(0)** , Benchmark Bks.) Cavendish, Marshall Corp.

James, Lincoln. Making History: The Liberty Bell. 2006. (Tony Stead Nonfiction Independent Reading Collection). (J). pap. (978-1-4042-5587-6(7)) Rosen Publishing Group, Inc., The.

Jango-Cohen, Judith. The Liberty Bell. (Pull Ahead Bks.). 32p. (J). (gr. k-3). 2004. (Illus.). lib. bdg. 22.60 (978-0-8225-3803-5(2)); 2003. pap. 5.95 (978-0-8225-3754-0(0)) Lerner Publishing Group.

—Liberty Bell. 2004. (ps-2). lib. bdg. 14.10 (978-0-613-81868-1(7)) Tandem Library Bks.

The Liberty Bell. 2001. (Illus.). 32p. (YA). (gr. 5 up). pap. 5.00 (978-1-890541-76-7(1)) Americana Souvenirs & Gifts.

Magaziner, Henry Jonas. Our Liberty Bell. O'Brien, John, illus. 2007. 32p. (J). (gr. 1-5). 15.95 (978-0-8234-1892-3(8)); 5.95 (***978-0-8234-2081-0(7))** Holiday Hse., Inc.

Marcovitz, Hal. The Liberty Bell. 2002. (American Symbols & Their Meanings Ser.). (Illus.). 48p. (YA). (gr. 4 up). lib. bdg. (978-1-59084-025-2(9)) Mason Crest Pubs.

McDonald, Megan. Saving the Liberty Bell. Carrington, Marsha Gray, illus. 2005. 32p. (J). 16.95 (978-0-689-85167-4(7) , Atheneum) Simon & Schuster Children's Publishing.

Murray, Julie. Liberty Bell. 2005. (Buddy Book Ser.). (Illus.). 24p. (J). (gr. k-4). lib. bdg. 21.35 (978-1-59197-507-6(7)) ABDO Publishing Co.

Nobleman, Marc Tyler. The Liberty Bell. 2004. (Let's See Library). (Illus.). 24p. (J). (gr. 1 up). lib. bdg. 19.93 (978-0-7565-0617-9(4)) Compass Point Bks.

Silate, Jennifer. The Liberty Bell. 2004. (Illus.). 24p. (J). lib. bdg. (978-1-4042-2687-6(7)) Rosen Publishing Group, Inc., The.

Yanuck, Debbie L. The Liberty Bell. 2003. (American Symbols Ser.). (Illus.). 24p. (J). (gr. 1-2). lib. bdg. 18.60 (978-0-7368-1630-4(5) , Bridgestone Bks.) Capstone Pr., Inc.

LIBERTY OF SPEECH

see Freedom of Speech

LIBRARIANS

Flanagan, Alice K. Librarians. 2001. (Community Workers Ser.). (Illus.). 32p. (J). (gr. 1 up). lib. bdg. 21.26 (978-0-7565-0063-4(X)) Compass Point Bks.

Forbes, Dina E. Laura Bush: Teacher, Librarian, & First Lady. 2005. (Ferguson Career Biographies Ser.). (Illus.). 144p. (J). (gr. 6-12). 25.00 (978-0-8160-5886-0(5) , Ferguson Publishing Co.) Facts On File, Inc.

Gorman, Jacqueline Laks. Librarian. Andersen, Gregg, photos by. 2002. (People in My Community Ser.). (Illus.). 24p. (J). (ps up). lib. bdg. 19.33 (978-0-8368-3296-9(5) , Weekly Reader Early Learning Library) Stevens, Gareth Inc.

—Librarian/El Bibliotecario. Acosta, Tatiana & Gutiérrez, Guillermo, trs. 2002. (Weekly Reader Early Learning Library). (ENG & SPA., Illus.). 24p. (J). (ps up). lib. bdg. 19.33 (978-0-8368-3310-2(4) , Weekly Reader Early Learning Library) Stevens, Gareth Inc.

Gorman, Jacqueline Laks & Macken, JoAnn Early. Librarian. Andersen, Gregg, photos by. 2002. (Weekly Reader Early Learning Library). (Illus.). 24p. (J). (ps up). pap. 7.93 (978-0-8368-3303-4(1) , Weekly Reader Early Learning Library) Stevens, Gareth Inc.

—Librarian/El Bibliotecario. Coffey, Colleen & Carrillo, Consuelo, trs. from ENG. Andersen, Gregg, photos by. 2002. (Weekly Reader Early Learning Library). (ENG & SPA., Illus.). 24p. (J). (ps up). pap. 7.93 (978-0-8368-3344-7(9) , Weekly Reader Early Learning Library) Stevens, Gareth Inc.

Hunter, Rebecca. Librarian. 2006. (People Who Help Us Ser.). (Illus.). 32p. (J). 22.95 (***978-1-84234-301-2(7)** , Evans Brothers, Limited) Evans Publishing Group GBR. *Dist:* Independent Pubs. Group.

Jango-Cohen, Judith. Librarians. (Pull Ahead Bks.). (J). 2005. (Illus.). 32p. lib. bdg. 22.60 (978-0-8225-1691-0(8)); 2004. pap. (978-0-8225-2533-2(X) , Lerner Pubns.) Lerner Publishing Group.

Kottke, Jan. A Day with a Librarian. 2000. (Welcome Bks.). (Illus.). 24p. (J). (ps-2). pap. 4.95 (978-0-516-23014-6(X)); 17.00 (978-0-516-23089-4(1)) Scholastic Library Publishing. (Children's Pr.).

—Day with a Librarian. 2000. (gr. k-3). lib. bdg. 12.95 (978-0-613-58760-0(X)) Tandem Library Bks.

Librarians. (Community Helpers Ser.). 24p. (J). 6.95 (978-0-7368-8456-3(4)) Capstone Pr., Inc.

Librarians. (Community Workers Ser.). 32p. (J). 7.95 (978-0-7565-1192-0(5)) Compass Point Bks.

Librarians, 6 vols. (gr. 2-5). 36.95 (978-0-7368-8471-6(8)) Red Brick Learning.

Liebman, Daniel. I Want to Be a Librarian. 2003. (I Want to Be Ser.). (Illus.). 24p. (J). (ps-2). pap. 3.99 (978-1-55297-689-0(0)); lib. bdg. 14.95 (978-1-55297-691-3(2)) Firefly Bks., Ltd.

—Quiero Ser Bibliotecario. 2003. (Quincy Rumpel Ser.). (SPA., Illus.). 24p. (J). (ps-2). pap. 5.99 (978-1-55297-726-2(9)) Firefly Bks., Ltd.

Miller, Heather. Librarian. 2003. (This Is What I Want to Be Ser.). (Illus.). 24p. (ps-1). (J). lib. bdg. 18.50 (978-1-4034-0369-8(4)); pap. 5.25 (978-1-4034-0591-3(3)) Heinemann Library.

Monroe, Judy. A Day in the Life of a Librarian. 2004. (First Facts Ser.). (Illus.). 24p. (J). (gr. k-3). lib. bdg. 21.26 (978-0-7368-2630-3(0)) Capstone Pr., Inc.

Oliver-Miles, Zelda. Amelia Gayle Gorgas: First Woman of Position. 2005. (Alabama Roots Biography Ser.). (Illus.). 100p. (J). (***978-1-59421-017-4(9))** Seacoast Publishing, Inc.

Rau, Dana Meachen. Librarian. 2007. (J). (***978-0-7614-2621-9(3))** Cavendish, Marshall Bks., Ltd.

—Librarians. 2007. (Tools We Use Ser.). 32p. (J). lib. bdg. 22.79 (***978-0-7614-2662-2(0)** , Benchmark Bks.) Cavendish, Marshall Corp.

Simon, Charnan. Lewis the Librarian. Thornburgh, Rebecca McKillip, illus. 2006. (Magic Door to Learning Ser.). 24p. (J). (gr. k-2). 21.36 (978-1-59296-624-0(1)) Child's World, Inc.

—Librarians. 2003. (Wonder Books Level 3: Careers Ser.). (Illus.). 32p. (J). (ps-2). 22.79 (978-1-56766-464-5(4)) Child's World, Inc.

Stamaty, Mark A. Muhimat Al Sayyda Alia: Inkaz Kuttub Al Iraq. 2005. 32p. pap. 12.00 (978-977-6171-01-5(X) , 706-001) Al-Balsam Pubng. Hse. EGY. *Dist:* Bookworld Trade, Inc.

Stamaty, Mark Alan. Alia's Mission: Saving the Books of Iraq. 2004. (Illus.). 32p. (J). (gr. 1). 12.95 (978-0-375-83217-8(3)); lib. bdg. 14.99 (978-0-375-93217-5(8)) Random Hse. Children's Bks. (Knopf Bks. for Young Readers).

Sweeney, Alyse. Welcome to the Library. 2007. (Scholastic News Nonfiction Readers Ser.). (Illus.). 24p. (J). (gr. k-2). 19.00 (978-0-531-16841-7(7) , Watts, Franklin) Scholastic Library Publishing.

Underwood, Deborah. Librarian. 2004. 26.20 (978-0-7377-2610-7(5) , Greenhaven Pr., Inc.) Thomson Gale.

Vogel, Elizabeth. Meet the Librarian. 2002. (PowerKids Readers Ser.). (Illus.). 24p. (J). (gr. 1). lib. bdg. 16.00 (978-0-8239-6031-6(5) , PowerKids Pr.) Rosen Publishing Group, Inc., The.

We Need Librarians, 6 vols. (gr. k-2). 28.95 (978-0-7368-8739-7(3)) Red Brick Learning.

Winter, Jeanette. The Librarian of Basra: A True Story from Iraq. 2005. (Illus.). 32p. (J). (gr. 2-4). 16.00 (978-0-15-205445-8(6)) Harcourt Children's Bks.

LIBRARIANS—FICTION

As Orange As Marmalade: Tan naranja como Mermelada. 2007. (ENG & SPA.). (J). per. 10.00 (***978-0-9749876-8-2(9)***) Doggie In The Window Pubns.

Barr, Terri. Lillian: The Librarain. Power, Kate Eason, illus. 1999. 16p. (J). (ps-2). pap. 3.75 (978-1-880612-86-6(0) , Seedling Pubns.) Continental Pr., Inc.

Berg, Brook. What Marion Taught Willis. Alberg, Nathan, illus. 2005. (J). 16.95 (978-1-932146-31-8(8) , 1242215) Highsmith Inc.

Condon, Bill. Miss Wolf & the Porkers: These Little Porkers Are in for a Shock! Magerl, Caroline, illus. 2006. (Bites Ser.). 96p. (J). pap. 3.95 (978-0-7624-2649-2(7) , Running Pr. Kids) Running Pr. Bk. Pubs.

Dahl, Michael. Attack of the Paperbats. Garvey, Brann, illus. 2007. (J). 40p. (***978-1-59889-325-0(4)***); 33p. pap. (***978-1-59889-420-2(X)***) Stone Arch Bks.

—The Beast Beneath the Stairs. Garvey, Brann, illus. 2007. (J). 40p. (***978-1-59889-323-6(8)***); 33p. pap. (***978-1-59889-418-9(8)***) Stone Arch Bks.

—The Book That Dripped Blood. Kendall, Bradford, illus. 2007. (J). 40p. (***978-1-59889-324-3(6)***); 33p. pap. (***978-1-59889-419-6(6)***) Stone Arch Bks.

—The Eye in the Graveyard. Garvey, Brann, illus. 2007. (J). 40p. (***978-1-59889-328-1(9)***); 33p. pap. (***978-1-59889-423-3(4)***) Stone Arch Bks.

—Poison Pages. Garvey, Brann, illus. 2007. (J). 40p. (***978-1-59889-327-4(0)***); 33p. pap. (***978-1-59889-422-6(6)***) Stone Arch Bks.

—The Smashing Scroll. Kendall, Bradford, illus. 2007. (J). 40p. (***978-1-59889-326-7(2)***); 33p. pap. (***978-1-59889-421-9(8)***) Stone Arch Bks.

Darden, Amy. Yesterday Once Again: Guenevere's Quest. 2003. (J). pap. 11.00 (978-0-8059-9238-0(3) , RoseDog Bks.) Dorrance Publishing Co., Inc.

Ernst, Lisa Campbell. Stella Louella's Runaway Book. Ernst, Lisa Campbell, illus. (Illus.). 40p. (J). 2001. pap. 7.99 (978-0-689-84460-7(3) , Aladdin); 1998. 16.95 (978-0-689-81883-7(1)) Simon & Schuster Children's Publishing.

—Stella Louella's Runaway Book. 2001. (ps-2). lib. bdg. 15.30 (978-0-613-52296-0(6)) Tandem Library Bks.

Henson, Heather. That Bookwoman. Small, David, illus. 2008. (J). (***978-1-4169-0812-8(9)***) Simon & Schuster Children's Publishing.

Mann, Pamela. The Frog Princess? (Illus.). (J). 2002. (TUR & ENG.). 24p. 15.95 (978-1-85269-324-4(X)); 2000. (BEN & ENG., 24p. 19.95 (978-1-85269-317-6(7)); 2000. (GUJ & ENG., 25p. 19.95 (978-1-85269-322-0(3)); 2000. (PAN & ENG., 24p. 17.95 (978-1-85269-323-7(1)); 2000. (SOM & ENG., 24p. 15.95 (978-1-85269-319-0(3)); 2000. (URD & ENG., 24p. 17.95 (978-1-85269-321-3(5)) Mantra Publishing, Ltd. GBR. *Dist:* AIMS International Bks., Inc.

McQuinn, Anna. Lola at the Library. Beardshaw, Rosalind, illus. 2006. 32p. (J). 15.95 (978-1-58089-113-4(6)); pap. 6.95 (978-1-58089-142-4(X)) Charlesbridge Publishing, Inc.

Monfredo, Miriam G. The Stalking Horse. 1999. (978-0-606-16386-6(7)) Tandem Library Bks.

Morris, Carla D. The Boy Who Was Raised by Librarians. Sneed, Brad, illus. 2007. 32p. (J). (gr. k-3). 16.95 (***978-1-56145-391-7(9)*** , Peachtree Junior) Peachtree Pubs., Ltd.

Peck, Richard. Here Lies the Librarian. 160p. (J). (gr. 5 up). 2007. 6.99 (***978-0-14-240908-4(1)*** , Puffin); 2006. 16.99 (978-0-8037-3080-9(2) , Dial) Penguin Group (USA) Inc.

—Here Lies the Librarian. rev. ed. 175p. 23.95 (***978-0-7862-9183-0(4)***) Thorndike Pr.

Ruurs, Margriet & Gooderham, Andrew. Ms. Bee's magical bookcase. 2004. (Illus.). 32p. (J). pap. 8.95 (978-1-894601-10-8(6)) Chestnut Publishing Group CAN. *Dist:* Hushion Hse. Publishing, Ltd.

Sanderson, Brandon. Alcatraz Versus the Evil Librarians. 2007. (Alcatraz Versus the Evil Librarians Ser.). 320p. (J). pap. 16.99 (***978-0-439-92550-1(9)*** , Scholastic Pr.) Scholastic, Inc.

Spanyol, Jessica. Carlo & the Really Nice Librarian. Spanyol, Jessica, illus. 2004. (Illus.). 32p. (J). (gr. k-k). 15.99 (978-0-7636-2526-9(4)) Candlewick Pr.

Štadler, Alexander. Beverly Billingsly Borrows a Book. 2006. (Illus.). 32p. (J). reprint ed. pap. 6.00 (978-0-15-205803-6(6) , Voyager Bks./Libros Viajeros) Harcourt Children's Bks.

—Beverly Billingsly Borrows a Book. 2002. (Illus.). 32p. (J). (ps-2). 16.00 (978-0-15-202510-6(3) , Silver Whistle) Harcourt Trade Pubs.

Stine, R. L. The Girl Who Cried Monster. 2005. 137p. (J). (ps-7). 12.04 (978-0-606-33299-6(5)) Tandem Library Bks.

Thaler, Mike. The Librarian from the Black Lagoon. Lee, Jared D., illus. unabr. ed. 2007. (J). (gr. k-2). pap. 18.95 incl. audio compact disk (***978-0-439-02774-8(8)***); pap. 14.95 incl. audio (***978-0-439-02773-1(X)***) Scholastic, Inc.

LIBRARIANSHIP

see Library Science

LIBRARIES

see also School Libraries

Anderson, Sheila. Library. 2008. (J). pap. (***978-0-8225-8839-9(0)***) Lerner Publishing Group.

Bauld, Jane Scoggins. We Need Librarians. Saunders-Smith, Gail, ed. 2000. (Helpers in Our School Ser.). (Illus.). 24p. (J). (gr. k-1). lib. bdg. 15.93 (978-0-7368-0531-5(1) , Pebble Bks.) Capstone Pr., Inc.

Burby, Liza N. A Day in the Life of a Librarian. 1999. (Kids' Career Library). (Illus.). 24p. (J). (gr. 3). lib. bdg. 18.75 (978-0-8239-5304-2(1) , PowerKids Pr.) Rosen Publishing Group, Inc., The.

Cummins, Julie. The Inside-Outside Book of Libraries. 2008. 48p. (J). (gr. 2-5). pap. 7.99 (***978-0-375-84451-5(1)*** , Dragonfly Bks.) Random Hse. Children's Bks.

DeGezelle, Terri. Manners at the Library. 2004. (First Facts Ser.). (Illus.). 24p. (J). (gr. k-2). lib. bdg. 21.26 (978-0-7368-2645-7(9) , First Facts) Capstone Pr., Inc.

En la Biblioteca, 6 Pks. (Coleccion Pm Ser.: Vol. 2). Tr. of At the library. (SPA.). 16p. (gr. k-1). 26.00 (978-0-7578-0686-5(4)) Rigby Education.

Finn, Carrie. Manners in the Library. 2007. (Way to Be! Ser.). (Illus.). 24p. (***978-1-4048-3557-3(1)*** , 1265722) Picture Window Bks.

Flanagan, Alice K. Exploring the Library. 2001. (Illus.). 48p. (J). (gr. 3 up). lib. bdg. 24.67 (978-0-8368-2955-6(7)) Stevens, Gareth Inc.

Flanagan, Alice K. & Dolbear, Emily J. Discovering Today's Library. 2006. (Illus.). 56p. (J). pap. (978-0-8368-7427-3(7)); lib. bdg. (978-0-8368-7426-6(9)) Stevens, Gareth Inc.

Frisch, Joy. Libraries. 2002. (Illus.). 24p. (J). lib. bdg. 21.35 (978-1-58340-146-0(6)) Smart Apple Media.

Getting to Know the Library, Bk. A. (J). (gr. 1-2). suppl. ed. (978-0-590-06374-6(X)) Scholastic, Inc.

Goldman, Phyllis, ed. Monkeyshines on the Library: For Your Information. 2003. (Illus.). 112p. (YA). per. 32.95 (978-1-888325-28-7(3)) Allosaurus Pubs.

Gorman, Jacqueline Laks. La Biblioteca. 2006. (I Like to Visit Ser.).Tr. of THE LIBRARY. (ENG & SPA.). (J). (gr. 1-2). 4.76 (978-0-8368-4603-4(6) , GHS33395) Stevens, Gareth Inc.

—Librarian. Andersen, Gregg, photos by. 2002. (People in My Community Ser.). (Illus.). 24p. (J). (ps up). lib. bdg. 19.33 (978-0-8368-3296-9(5) , Weekly Reader Early Learning Library) Stevens, Gareth Inc.

—The Library. 2005. (I Like to Visit Ser.). (Illus.). 24p. (J). pap. (978-0-8368-4459-7(9)); (YA). lib. bdg. 19.93 (978-0-8368-4452-8(1)) Stevens, Gareth Inc.

—The Library/La Biblioteca. Acosta, Tatiana & Gutiérrez, Guillermo, trs. 2005. (I Like to Visit/Me Gusta Visitar Ser.). (ENG & SPA., Illus.). 24p. (J). lib. bdg. 19.33 (978-0-8368-4596-9(X)) Stevens, Gareth Inc.

Gorman, Jacqueline Laks & Macken, JoAnn Early. Librarian. Andersen, Gregg, photos by. 2002. (Weekly Reader Early Learning Library). (Illus.). 24p. (J). (ps up). pap. 7.93 (978-0-8368-3303-4(1) , Weekly Reader Early Learning Library) Stevens, Gareth Inc.

Hamilton, John. Libraries & Reference Materials. 2005. (Straight to the Source Ser.). (Illus.). 32p. (J). (gr. k-6). lib. bdg. 22.78 (978-1-59197-545-8(X)) ABDO Publishing Co.

Harcourt School Publishers Staff. What Do You Find in the Library? 3rd ed. 2002. (Trophies English Language Learners Ser.). (Illus.). (J). pap. 3.20 (978-0-15-327576-0(6)) Harcourt Schl. Pubs.

Hoena, B. A. A Visit to the Public Library. 2004. (Pebble Plus, Let's Visit Ser.). (Illus.). 24p. (J). 17.26 (978-0-7368-2394-4(8) , Pebble Bks.) Capstone Pr., Inc.

Instructional Fair. Library Learning Cards. 1999. (Learning Cards Ser.). (J). (gr. k-5). 7.99 (978-0-7424-0650-6(4) , TSD23844) School Specialty Publishing.

Jackson, Candace. My Very Own Library Treasure Hunt. Greenwood, Richard & Erickson, Susan, eds. Jackson, Candace, illus. 1998. (Dewee & Libby Literacy Ser.: Vol. II). (Illus.). 44p. (J). (gr. k-7). pap. 4.45 (978-1-892240-01-9(7)) Museum Mania.

Jango-Cohen, Judith. Librarians. (Pull Ahead Bks.). (J). 2005. (Illus.). 32p. lib. bdg. 22.60 (978-0-8225-1691-0(8)); 2004. pap. (978-0-8225-2533-2(X) , Lerner Pubns.) Lerner Publishing Group.

Johnston, Marianne. Let's Visit the Library. 2000. (Our Community Ser.). (Illus.). 24p. (J). (gr. 3). lib. bdg. 18.75 (978-0-8239-5431-5(5) , PowerKids Pr.) Rosen Publishing Group, Inc., The.

Kottke, Jan. Day with a Librarian. 2000. (gr. k-3). lib. bdg. 12.95 (978-0-613-58760-0(X)) Tandem Library Bks.

Leone, Laura. Choosing a Career in Information Science. 2005. (World of Work Ser.). (Illus.). 64p. (YA). (gr. 7-12). lib. bdg. 25.25 (978-0-8239-3569-7(8)) Rosen Publishing Group, Inc., The.

Libeary Skills. 125p. (gr. k-3). 11.99 (978-0-513-02043-6(8) , TSD20438) Denison, T. S. & Co., Inc.

Malam, John. Library: From Ancient Scrolls to the World-wide Web: A Building Works Book. Malam, John, illus. 2006. (Illus.). 32p. (J). (gr. 4 up). reprint ed. 17.00 (978-1-4223-5173-4(4)) DIANE Publishing Co.

Mercier, Johanne. Caillou at the Library. rev. ed. 2005. (Out & About Ser.). (Illus.). 24p. (J). (ps-1). pap. 3.95 (978-2-89450-499-4(3)) Chouette Publishing CAN. *Dist:* Independent Pubs. Group.

My First Library. Date not set. (Illus.). (J). bds. 7.98 (978-0-7525-8724-0(2)) Parragon, Inc.

Prieto, Anita C. B Is for Bookworm: A Library Alphabet. Graef, Renee, illus. 2005. (National Alphabet Bks.). 40p. (J). (gr. k-5). 16.95 (978-1-58536-145-8(3)) Sleeping Bear Pr.

Prieto, Anita C. A Library Alphabet. 2007. 40p. pap. 7.95 (***978-1-58536-326-1(X)***) Sleeping Bear Pr.

Raatma, Lucia. Libraries. 1998. (True Bks.). (Illus.). 48p. (J). (gr. 3-5). 25.00 (978-0-516-20672-1(9) , Children's Pr.) Scholastic Library Publishing.

Radabaugh, Melinda Beth. Going to the Library. 2003. (First Time Ser.). (Illus.). 24p. (ps-1). (J). lib. bdg. 18.50 (978-1-4034-0230-1(2)); pap. 5.25 (978-1-4034-0469-5(0)) Heinemann Library.

—Going to the Library. 2003. (ps-2). lib. bdg. 13.30 (978-0-613-60881-7(X)) Tandem Library Bks.

Rau, Dana Meachen. Librarian. 2007. (J). (***978-0-7614-2621-9(3)***) Cavendish, Marshall Bks., Ltd.

—Librarians. 2007. (Tools We Use Ser.). 32p. (J). lib. bdg. 22.79 (***978-0-7614-2662-2(0)*** , Benchmark Bks.) Cavendish, Marshall Corp.

Sawa, Maureen. The Library Book: From Camels to Computers. Slavin, Bill, illus. 2006. 72p. (J). (gr. 6). 18.95 (978-0-88776-698-5(6)) Tundra Bks., Inc./Livres Toundra, Inc. CAN. *Dist:* Random Hse., Inc.

Schaefer, Lola M. Library. 2001. (Who Works Here? Ser.). (Illus.). 32p. (J). (gr. 1-3). lib. bdg. 21.36 (978-1-58810-127-3(4)) Heinemann Library.

Shea, Kitty. Out & about at the Public Library. Trover, Zachary, illus. 2005. (Field Trips Ser.). 24p. (J). (ps). lib. bdg. 23.93 (978-1-4048-1150-8(8)) Picture Window Bks.

Simon, Charnan. Lewis the Librarian. Thornburgh, Rebecca McKillip, illus. 2006. (Magic Door to Learning Ser.). 24p. (J). (gr. k-2). 21.36 (978-1-59296-624-0(1)) Child's World, Inc.

Sloan, Peter. At the Library. 2000. (ps-2). lib. bdg. 11.65 (978-0-613-37621-1(8)) Tandem Library Bks.

Somervill, Barbara A. The History of the Library. 2006. (Timeline Library Ser.). (Illus.). 32p. (J). (gr. 2-6). 27.07 (978-1-59296-438-3(9)) Child's World, Inc.

Stamaty, Mark A. Muhimat Al Sayyda Alia: Inkaz Kuttub Al Iraq. 2005. 32p. pap. 12.00 (978-977-6171-01-5(X) , 706-001) Al-Balsam Pubng. Hse. EGY. *Dist:* Bookworld Trade, Inc.

Stamaty, Mark Alan. Alia's Mission: Saving the Books of Iraq. 2004. (Illus.). 32p. (J). (gr. 1). 12.95 (978-0-375-83217-8(3)); lib. bdg. 14.99 (978-0-375-93217-5(8)) Random Hse. Children's Bks. (Knopf Bks. for Young Readers).

Sweeney, Alyse. Welcome to the Library. 2007. (Scholastic News Nonfiction Readers Ser.). (Illus.). 24p. (J). (gr. k-2). 19.00 (978-0-531-16841-7(7) , Watts, Franklin) Scholastic Library Publishing.

Toronto Public Library Staff. Research Ate My Brain: The Panic-Proof Guide to Surviving Homework. Newbigging, Martha, illus. 2005. 96p. (J). (gr. 5-12). 19.95 (978-1-55037-939-6(9)); pap. 8.95 (978-1-55037-938-9(0)) Annick Pr., Ltd. CAN. *Dist:* Firefly Bks., Ltd.

Underwood, Deborah. Librarian. 2004. 26.20 (978-0-7377-2610-7(5) , Greenhaven Pr., Inc.) Thomson Gale.

Vogel, Elizabeth. Meet the Librarian. 2002. (PowerKids Readers Ser.). (Illus.). 24p. (J). (gr. 1). lib. bdg. 16.00 (978-0-8239-6031-6(5) , PowerKids Pr.) Rosen Publishing Group, Inc., The.

Vogel, Jennifer. A Library Story: Building a New Central Library. 2006. (Exceptional Social Studies Titles for Intermediate Grades). (Illus.). 64p. (J). (gr. 4-7). lib. bdg. 26.60 (978-0-8225-5916-0(1) , Millbrook Pr.) Lerner Publishing Group.

Wallace, Karen & Lock, Deborah. A Trip to the Zoo/A Trip to the Library. 2006. (Read & Listen Bks.). 64p. (J). 9.99 (978-0-7566-1830-8(4)) Dorling Kindersley Publishing, Inc.

Winter, Jeanette. The Librarian of Basra: A True Story from Iraq. 2005. (Illus.). 32p. (J). (gr. 2-4). 16.00 (978-0-15-205445-8(6)) Harcourt Children's Bks.

Wu, Dana Ying-Hui. Our Libraries. 2001. (I Know America Ser.). (Illus.). 48p. (J). (gr. 2-4). lib. bdg. 24.90 (978-0-7613-1856-9(9) , Millbrook Pr.) Lerner Publishing Group.

LIBRARIES, CHILDREN'S

see also Children—Books and Reading; Children's Literature

Holt, Rinehart and Winston Staff. High School Library Box. 2000. (YA). pap. 221.80 (978-0-03-064479-5(8)) Holt, Rinehart & Winston.

Lock, Deborah & Dorling Kindersley Publishing Staff. A Trip to the Doctor. 2004. (Dk Readers Ser.). (Illus.). 32p. (J). 12.99 (978-0-7566-0278-9(5)) Dorling Kindersley Publishing, Inc.

Sasman, Irene D. H. The Millennium Children's Library, Set. 1999. (Illus.). (J). (gr. 2-3). pap. 99.95 (978-1-56831-989-6(4)) Learning Connection, The.

—The Millennium Children's Library Set. 1999. (Illus.). (J). (ps-2). pap. 99.95 (978-1-56831-987-2(8)); Set. (gr. 4-8). pap. 99.95 (978-1-56831-990-2(8)) Learning Connection, The.

Wallace, Karen & Dorling Kindersley Publishing Staff. A Trip to the Library. 2004. (Dk Readers Ser.). (Illus.). 32p. (J). pap. 3.99 (978-0-7566-0277-2(7)) Dorling Kindersley Publishing, Inc.

Waxman, Sydell. Believing in Books: The Story of Lillian Smith. Gallinger, Patty & Milkau, Liz, illus. 2004. (Stories of Canada Ser.). 83p. (J). (gr. 4-7). 14.95 (978-0-929141-77-0(6)) Napoleon Publishing/Rendezvous Pr. CAN. *Dist:* AtlasBooks Distribution.

LIBRARIES—FICTION

Adler, David A. Young Cam Jansen & the Library Mystery. Natti, Susanna, illus. 2002. (Young Cam Jansen Ser.: No. 7). 32p. (J). pap. 3.99 (978-0-14-230202-6(3) , Puffin) Penguin Group (USA) Inc.

Alexander, Lloyd. The Jedera Adventure. 2001. (Vesper Holly Ser.). (J). (gr. 3-6). lib. bdg. 14.15 (978-0-613-43837-7(X)) Tandem Library Bks.

Baggette, Susan K. Jonathan Goes to the Library. Moriarty, William J., photos by. 1998. (Jonathan Adventures Ser.). (Illus.). 16p. (J). (ps-k). bds. 5.95 (978-0-9660172-3-6(4)) Brookfield Reader, Inc., The.

Binaohan, Simon & Tacang, Brian. The Misadventures of Millicent Madding No. 1: Bully-Be-Gone. 2006. (Illus.). 224p. (J). lib. bdg. 17.89 (978-0-06-073912-6(6)) HarperCollins Pubs.

—The Misadventures of Millicent Madding Vol. 1: Bully-Be-Gone. 2006. (Illus.). 224p. (J). 16.99 (978-0-06-073911-9(8)) HarperCollins Pubs.

Bloor, Edward. Story Time. 2002. (J). 17.95 (978-0-439-26686-4(6)) Scholastic, Inc.

Bonners, Susan. Silver Balloon. 1999. (978-0-606-17355-1(2)); (gr. 3-6). lib. bdg. 12.95 (978-0-613-22775-9(1)) Tandem Library Bks.

Brown, Marc. D W 's Library Card. 2003. (D. W. Ser.). (ps-2). lib. bdg. 14.15 (978-0-613-71812-7(7)) Tandem Library Bks.

—D. W. y el Carne de Biblioteca. 2003. Tr. of D.W.'s Library Card. (SPA., Illus.). (gr. k-3). lib. bdg. 15.25 (978-0-613-89871-3(0)) Tandem Library Bks.

—D. W.'s Library Card. Brown, Marc, illus. 2002. (D. W. Ser.). (Illus.). (YA). 20.60 (978-0-7587-9783-4(4)) Book Wholesalers, Inc.

—D. W.'s Library Card. Brown, Marc, illus. (D. W. Ser.). (Illus.). 24p. (J). (ps-1). 2003. pap. 5.99 (978-0-316-73820-0(4)); 2001. 14.95 (978-0-316-11013-6(2)) Little, Brown Bks. for Young Readers.

Brown, Marc & Sarfatti, Esther. D. W. y el Carne de Biblioteca. 2004. Tr. of D.W.'s Library Card. (ENG & SPA., Illus.). (J). pap. 6.95 (978-1-930332-47-8(5)) Lectorum Pubns., Inc.

Bruss, Deborah. Book! Book! Book! Beeke, Tiphanie, illus. 2001. (J). (ps-1). 40p. pap. 16.95 (978-0-439-13525-2(7)); pap. (978-0-439-13526-9(5)) Scholastic, Inc.

Bunting, Eve. Our Library. Smith, Maggie, illus. 2007. 32p. (J). 21.00 (978-0-618-49458-3(8) , Clarion Bks.) Houghton Mifflin Co. Trade & Reference Div.

Carle, Eric. My Very First Library. Carle, Eric, illus. 2006. 20p. (J). (ps-k). bds. 23.99 (978-0-399-24666-1(5) , Philomel) Penguin Group (USA) Inc.

Child, Lauren. But, Excuse Me, That Is My Book. 2006. (Illus.). 32p. (J). (ps). 16.99 (978-0-8037-3096-0(9) , Dial) Penguin Group (USA) Inc.

Christie, Agatha. The Body in the Library. 2001. (Illus.). (J). 12.64 (978-0-606-21077-5(6)) Tandem Library Bks.

Clifford, Eth. Help! I'm a Prisoner in the Library. Hughes, George, illus. 2004. (Jo-Beth & Mary Rose Mystery Ser.). 112p. (J). (gr. 3-5). pap. 5.95 (978-0-618-49482-8(0)) Houghton Mifflin Co. Trade & Reference Div.

Colfer, Eoin. The Legend of Spud Murphy. McCoy, Glenn, illus. 112p. (gr. 2-6). 2005. reprint ed. pap. 4.99 (978-0-7868-5504-9(5)); Bk. 1. 2004. (J). 12.95 (978-0-7868-5501-8(0)) Miramax Bks.

—The Legend of the Worst Boy in the World, Bk. 3. McCoy, Glenn, illus. 3rd rev. ed. 2007. 112p. (J). (gr. 2-6). 12.95 (978-0-7868-5503-2(7)) Hyperion Pr.

Collins, Anthony. Rip Power: Reading gave him the strength to fight Back! 2006. 178p. per. 12.99 (978-1-59886-469-4(6)) Tate Publishing & Enterprises, L.L.C.

Cousins, Lucy. Maisy Goes to the Library. Cousins, Lucy, illus. 2005. (Illus.). 32p. (J). (gr. k-k). 12.99 (978-0-7636-2669-3(4)) Candlewick Pr.

Cowell, Cressida. Little Bo Peep's Library Book. Cowell, Cressida, illus. 1999. (Illus.). 32p. (J). (ps-2). pap. 14.95 (978-0-531-30179-1(6) , Orchard Bks.) Scholastic, Inc.

De Smet, Marian. Anna's Tight Squeeze. Meijer, Marja, illus. 2003. Orig. Title: Op Slot. 32p. (J). pap. 5.95 (978-1-58925-378-0(7) , tiger tales) ME Media LLC.

—Anna's Tight Squeeze. 2003. Orig. Title: Op Slot. (gr. k-3). lib. bdg. 14.10 (978-0-613-84707-0(5)) Tandem Library Bks.

Fraser, Mary Ann. I. Q. Goes to the Library. Fraser, Mary Ann, illus. 2003. (Illus.). 32p. (J). (gr. k-3). 15.95 (978-0-8027-8877-1(7)) Walker & Co.

Freeman, Don. Quiet! There's a Canary in the Library. Freeman, Don, illus. 2007. 48p. (J). (ps). 15.99 (***978-0-670-06230-0(8)*** , Viking Juvenile) Penguin Group (USA) Inc.

Gomez Cerda, Alfredo. El Monstruo y la Bibliotecaria. 4th ed. (SPA., Illus.). 62p. (J). (gr. 3-5). (978-84-279-3456-6(4) , NG1580) Noguer y Caralt Editores, S. A. ESP. *Dist:* Lectorum Pubns., Inc.

Greenwald, Sheila. The Mariah Delany Lending Library Disaster. 2000. (978-0-606-20450-7(4)) Tandem Library Bks.

Harcourt School Publishers Staff. I Took My Frog To... Library Book. 1999. (Collections Ser.). (Illus.). pap. 14.90 (978-0-15-313407-4(0)) Harcourt Schl. Pubs.

Hennessy, B. G. & Freeman, Don. Corduroy Goes to the Library. 2005. 20p. (J). (gr. 1). 11.99 (978-0-670-05991-1(9) , Viking Juvenile) Penguin Group (USA) Inc.

Herman, Gail. Sam's First Library Card. 2003. (gr. k-3). lib. bdg. 11.25 (978-0-613-67583-3(5)) Tandem Library Bks.

Hill, Susan. Stuart at the Library. 2001. (gr. k-3). lib. bdg. 11.80 (978-0-613-35576-6(8)) ; (Illus.). (J). (978-0-606-21471-1(2)) Tandem Library Bks.

Hoffman, Mary. Special Powers. 200p. pap. (978-0-340-62670-2(4) , Hodder & Stoughton) Hodder General Publishing Division.

Hopkins, Jackie Mims. Picture Book & Library Lessons. Thornburgh, Rebecca, illus. 2004. 32p. (ps-2). 16.95 (978-1-932146-27-1(X) , K67-39703, Upstart Bks.) Highsmith Inc.

Hurwitz, Johanna. A Llama in the Library. Graham, Mark, illus. 1999. 144p. (J). (gr. 2-5). 15.00 (978-0-688-16138-5(3)) HarperCollins Pubs.

Joosse, Barbara M. Hot City. Gauch, Patricia Lee, ed. Christie, Gregory R., illus. 2004. 32p. (J). (ps-3). 16.99 (978-0-399-23640-2(6) , Philomel) Penguin Group (USA) Inc.

Just Mrs. Goose. 2004. (Illus.). 152p. 12.95 (978-0-9746457-0-4(2)) Green Mansion Pr. LLC.

Kirk, Daniel. Library Mouse. 2007. (Illus.). 32p. (J). (ps-3). 15.95 (***978-0-8109-9346-4(5)*** , Abrams Bks. for Young Readers) Abrams, Harry N. , Inc.

Klein, Adria F. Max Goes to the Library. Gallagher-Cole, Mernie, illus. 2005. (Read-It! Readers Ser.). 24p. (J). (ps). lib. bdg. 18.60 (978-1-4048-1182-9(6)) Picture Window Bks.

Klingel, Cynthia Fitterer & Noyed, Robert B. The Amazing Letter L. 2003. (Alphaphonics Ser.). (Illus.). 24p. (J). (ps-2). 21.36 (978-1-59296-102-3(9)) Child's World, Inc.

Knudsen, Michelle. Library Lion. Hawkes, Kevin, illus. 2006. 48p. (J). (ps-2). 16.99 (978-0-7636-2262-6(1)) Candlewick Pr.

Krensky, Stephen. Locked in the Library! Krensky, Stephen, illus. 1998. (Arthur Chapter Bks. : Bk. 6). (Illus.). 64p. (J). (gr. 2-4). pap. 4.25 (978-0-316-11558-2(4)) Little, Brown Bks. for Young Readers.

—Locked in the Library! unabr. ed. 1998. (Arthur Chapter Bks.: Bk. 6). 58p. (J). (gr. 2-4). pap. 17.00 incl. audio (978-0-8072-0388-0(2) , FTR192SP, Listening Library) Random Hse. Audio Publishing Group.

Lakin, Patricia. Clarence the Copy Cat. Manders, John, illus. 2007. 32p. (J). (ps-3). pap. 6.99 (978-0-440-41725-5(2) , Dragonfly Bks.) Random Hse. Children's Bks.

Lock, Deborah. A Trip to the Library. 2004. (Illus.). 32p. (J). (ps-ps). lib. bdg. 10.79 (978-0-606-30871-7(7)) Tandem Library Bks.

Mayr, Diane. Littlebat's Halloween Story. Kendall, Gideon, illus. 2001. 32p. (J). (ps-2). 15.95 (978-0-8075-7629-8(8)) Whitman, Albert & Co.

McDonald, Megan. When the Library Lights Go Out. Tillotson, Katherine, tr. Tillotson, Katherine, illus. 2005. 40p. (J). 16.95 (978-0-689-86170-3(2) , Atheneum/Richard Jackson Bks.) Simon & Schuster Children's Publishing.

McGee, Marni. Winston the Book Wolf. Beck, Ian, illus. 2006. 32p. (J). 16.95 (978-0-8027-9569-4(2)) Walker & Co.

Meister, Cari. Tiny Goes to the Library. Davis, Rich, illus. 2000. (Easy-to-Read Ser.). 32p. (J). (ps-2). pap. 3.99 (978-0-14-130488-5(X) , Puffin) ; 13.89 (978-0-670-88556-5(8) , Viking Juvenile) Penguin Group (USA) Inc.

—Tiny Goes to the Library. 2000. (Puffin Easy-to-Read Ser.). (978-0-606-18458-8(9)) Tandem Library Bks.

Miller, William. Richard Wright & the Library Card. Christie, Gregory R., illus. 1999. 32p. (J). (gr. k up). 6.95 (978-1-880000-88-5(1)) Lee & Low Bks., Inc.

—Richard Wright y el Carne de Biblioteca. Christie, Gregory R., illus. 2003. (SPA.). (J). 32p. 16.95 (978-1-58430-180-6(5)); pap. 6.95 (978-1-58430-181-3(3)) Lee & Low Bks., Inc.

Montoya, Martha, creator. No, no a la Biblioteca! Take-Home. 2005. (Los Kitos Ser.). (SPA.). (YA). (gr. 1-3). 15.00 (978-0-8215-8812-3(5)) Sadlier, William H. Inc.

Mora, Pat. Una Biblioteca para Juana. Vidal, Beatriz, illus. 2002. (SPA.). 40p. (J). (gr. k-3). pap. 6.99 (978-0-440-41765-1(1)); lib. bdg. 17.99 (978-0-385-90863-4(6)) Random Hse. Children's Bks. (Dragonfly Bks.).

—Tomas & the Library Lady. Colon, Raul, illus. 2000. 40p. (J). (gr. k-3). pap. 6.99 (978-0-375-80349-9(1) , Dragonfly Bks.) Random Hse. Children's Bks.

—Tomas & the Library Lady. 2000. (978-0-606-18093-1(1)); lib. bdg. 15.30 (978-0-613-28362-5(7)) Tandem Library Bks.

—Tomas y la Senora de la Biblioteca. ed. 2004. (SPA., Illus.). (J). (gr. k-3). spiral bd. (978-0-616-03092-9(4)) Canadian National Institute for the Blind/Institut National Canadien pour les Aveugles.

Morpurgo, Michael. I Believe in Unicorns. Blythe, Gary, illus. 2006. 80p. (J). (gr. 1-4). 12.99 (978-0-7636-3050-8(0)) Candlewick Pr.

Morris, Carla D. The Boy Who Was Raised by Librarians. Sneed, Brad, illus. 2007. 32p. (J). (gr. k-3). 16.95 (***978-1-56145-391-7(9)*** , Peachtree Junior) Peachtree Pubs., Ltd.

Nickerson, Sara. How to Disappear Completely & Never Be Found. Comport, Sally Wern, illus. 288p. (J). (gr. 5 up). 2003. pap. 5.99 (978-0-06-441027-4(7)); 2002. 16.99 (978-0-06-029771-8(9)); 2002. lib. bdg. 17.89 (978-0-06-029772-5(7)) HarperCollins Pubs.

—How to Disappear Completely & Never Be Found. 2003. (gr. 7-12). lib. bdg. 14.15 (978-0-613-62207-3(3)) Tandem Library Bks.

Numeroff, Laura Joffe. Beatrice Doesn't Want To. Munsinger, Lynn, illus. ed. 2004. 32p. (J). (ps-k). 15.99 (978-0-7636-1160-6(3)) Candlewick Pr.

Paratore, Coleen. The Cupid Chronicles. 2006. (Wedding Planner's Daughter Ser.). 224p. (J). 15.95 (978-1-4169-0867-8(6) , Simon & Schuster Children's Publishing) Simon & Schuster Children's Publishing.

Paratore, Coleen Murtagh. The Cupid Chronicles. 2008. (Wedding Planner's Daughter Ser.). 224p. (J). pap. 5.99 (***978-1-4169-5484-2(8)*** , Aladdin) Simon & Schuster Children's Publishing.

Parish, Herman. Amelia Bedelia, Bookworm. Sweat, Lynn, illus. 2005. 64p. (J). lib. bdg. 13.85 (***978-1-4242-0518-9(2))*** Fitzgerald Bks.

—Amelia Bedelia, Bookworm. Sweat, Lynn, illus. 2003. 64p. (J). (gr. k-3). 16.99 (978-0-06-051890-5(1)); lib. bdg. 16.89 (978-0-06-051891-2(X)) HarperCollins Pubs.

—Amelia Bedelia Bookworm. Sweat, Lynn, illus. 2005. (I Can Read Bks.). 64p. (J). pap. 3.99 (978-0-06-051892-9(8) , Harper Trophy) HarperCollins Pubs.

Pearson, Mary E. I Can Do It All: Level B. Shelly, Jeff, illus. 2002. (Rookie Readers Ser.). 32p. (J). (gr. 1-2). 19.50 (978-0-516-22240-0(6) , Children's Pr.) Scholastic Library Publishing.

Porte, Barbara Ann. Harry in Trouble. 2002. (I Can Read Bks.). (Illus.). 48p. (J). (gr. k-3). pap. 15.95 (978-0-06-001153-6(X)) HarperCollins Pubs.

—Harry in Trouble. 2002. (gr. k-3). lib. bdg. 11.80 (978-0-613-62174-8(3)) Tandem Library Bks.

Rey, H. A. Curious George Visits the Library. 2003. (gr. k-3). lib. bdg. 11.80 (978-0-613-90204-5(1)) Tandem Library Bks.

Rey, H. A. & Rey, Margret. Curious George Visits the Library. Weston, Martha, illus. 2003. (Curious George Ser.). 24p. (J). (gr. k-3). pap. 3.95 (978-0-618-06568-4(7)) Houghton Mifflin Co.

—Curious George Visits the Library. Weston, Martha, illus. 2003. 24p. (J). (gr. k-3). 12.95 (978-0-618-06565-3(2)) Houghton Mifflin Co. Trade & Reference Div.

Rosado, Maria. Book 'Em Tommy. 2000. (Rugrats Chapter Bks.). (Illus.). (J). 10.79 (978-0-606-20577-1(2)) Tandem Library Bks.

Salem, Lynn & Stewart, Josie. Off to the Library. Frye, Lorna, illus. 1998. 8p. (J). (gr. k-2). pap. 3.75 (978-1-880612-73-6(9) , Seedling Pubns.) Continental Pr., Inc.

Sierra, Judy. Mind Your Manners, B. B. Wolf. Seibold, J. Otto, illus. 2007. 40p. (J). (ps-3). 16.99 (978-0-375-83532-2(6)); lib. bdg. 19.99 (978-0-375-93532-9(0)) Random Hse. Children's Bks. (Knopf Bks. for Young Readers).

—Wild about Books. Brown, Marc, tr. Brown, Marc, illus. 2004. 40p. (J). (ps-3). 16.95 (978-0-375-82538-5(X)); lib. bdg. 18.99 (978-0-375-92538-2(4)) Random Hse. Children's Bks. (Knopf Bks. for Young Readers).

Spanyol, Jessica. Carlo & the Really Nice Librarian. Spanyol, Jessica, illus. 2004. (Illus.). 32p. (J). (gr. k-k). 15.99 (978-0-7636-2526-9(4)) Candlewick Pr.

Stadler, Alexander. Beverly Billingsly Borrows a Book. 2006. (Illus.). 32p. (J). reprint ed. pap. 6.00 (978-0-15-205803-6(6) , Voyager Bks./Libros Viajeros) Harcourt Children's Bks.

—Beverly Billingsly Borrows a Book. 2002. (Illus.). 32p. (J). (ps-2). 16.00 (978-0-15-202510-6(3) , Silver Whistle) Harcourt Trade Pubs.

Terry, Sonya. "L" Is for Library. Wong, Nicole, illus. 2006. (J). 16.95 (978-1-932146-44-8(X) , Upstart Bks.) Highsmith Inc.

Thompson, Carol L. Mr. Wiggle Looks for Answers. 2003. (Mr. Wiggle Ser.). (Illus.). 32p. (J). 9.95 (978-1-57768-615-6(2) , Waterbird Bks.) School Specialty Publishing.

—Mr. Wiggle's Library. 2003. (Mr. Wiggle Ser.). (Illus.). 32p. (J). 9.95 (978-1-57768-613-2(6) , Waterbird Bks.) School Specialty Publishing.

Willis, Jeanne. Delilah D. at the Library. Reeve, Rosie, illus. 2007. 32p. (J). (gr. k-3). 16.00 (978-0-618-78195-9(1) , Clarion Bks.) Houghton Mifflin Co. Trade & Reference Div.

Willson, Sarah. Dora's Backpack. 2006. (Dora the Explorer Ser.). (Illus.). (J). (ps-2). 21.35 (978-1-59961-070-2(1)) Spotlight.

—La Mochila de Dora. Roper, Robert, illus. 2003. (Dora the Explorer Ser.).Tr. of Dora's Backpack. (SPA.). 24p. (J). pap. 3.99 (978-0-689-86306-6(3) , Libros Para Ninos) Simon & Schuster Children's Publishing.

Yoo, Tae-Eun. The Little Red Fish. 2007. (Illus.). (J). (***978-1-4287-3601-6(8)*** , Dial) Penguin Group (USA) Inc.

LIBRARIES—POETRY

Lewis, J. Patrick. Please Bury Me in the Library. Stone, Kyle M., illus. 2005. 32p. (J). 16.00 (978-0-15-216387-7(5) , Gulliver Bks.) Harcourt Children's Bks.

LIBRARIES, SCHOOL

see School Libraries

LIBRARY OF CONGRESS

see United States—Library of Congress

LIBRARY ORIENTATION

Here are entered works dealing with the instruction of readers in library use. .

Shea, Kitty. Out & about at the Public Library. Trover, Zachary, illus. 2005. (Field Trips Ser.). 24p. (J). (ps). lib. bdg. 23.93 (978-1-4048-1150-8(8)) Picture Window Bks.

Turrell, Linda. Complete Library Skills, Grade 5. rev. ed. 2004. (Illus.). 128p. (J). (gr. 5-5). pap. 13.99 (978-0-7424-1955-1(X) , IFG99136, Instructional Fair) Schaffer, Frank Pubns.

LIBRARY SCIENCE

Here are entered general works on the organization and administration of libraries. Works about services offered by libraries to patrons are entered under Library Service.

Adams, Anne. New Kids Reference Library, 4 vols. 1999. (J). 24.95 (978-0-8010-4455-7(3)) Baker Bks.

Apel, Melanie Ann. The Let's Talk Library, Set 10: Issues & Emotions, 6 bks. Incl. Let's Talk about Feeling Confused. lib. bdg. 18.75 (978-0-8239-5623-4(7)); Let's Talk about Feeling Embarrassed. lib. bdg. 18.75 (978-0-8239-5618-0(0)); Let's Talk about Feeling Lonely. lib. bdg. 18.75 (978-0-8239-5620-3(2)); Let's Talk about Feeling Worried. lib. bdg. 18.75 (978-0-8239-5622-7(9)); Let's Talk about Living with a Parent with Multiple Sclerosis. lib. bdg. 18.75 (978-0-8239-5621-0(0)); Let's Talk about Living with Your Single Dad. lib. bdg. 18.75 (978-0-8239-5619-7(9)); 24p. (J). (gr. 3). (Illus.). 2001. Set lib. bdg. 103.50 (978-0-8239-7070-4(1) , PowerKids Pr.) Rosen Publishing Group, Inc., The.

Harcourt School Publishers Staff. Library, Library. 3rd ed. 2002. (Trophies English Language Learners Ser.). (Illus.). pap. 5.10 (978-0-15-327833-4(1)) Harcourt Schl. Pubs.

Heiligman, Deborah. The New York Public Library Kid's Guide to Research. 1998. (Illus.). 134p. (YA). (gr. 4-9). pap. 14.95 (978-0-590-30715-4(0) , Scholastic Reference) Scholastic, Inc.

Jango-Cohen, Judith. Librarians. (Pull Ahead Bks.). (J). 2005. (Illus.). 32p. lib. bdg. 22.60 (978-0-8225-1691-0(8)); 2004. pap. (978-0-8225-2533-2(X) , Lerner Pubns.) Lerner Publishing Group.

School Specialty Publishing. Complete Library Skills. rev. ed. 2004. 128p. (J). (gr. k-2). pap. 13.99 (978-0-7424-1952-0(5) , IFG99138); (gr. 3-3). pap. 13.99 (978-0-7424-1953-7(3) , IFG99134); (gr. 4 up). pap. 13.99 (978-0-7424-1954-4(1) , IFG99135); (gr. 6 up). pap. 13.99 (978-0-7424-1956-8(8) , IFG99137) School Specialty Publishing.

Stewart-Brown, Sarah. The Library. 1999. (J). (978-0-606-17222-6(X)) Tandem Library Bks.

Suid, Murray. Research Start-Ups. 1999. (Illus.). 96p. (J). pap. 11.95 (978-1-57612-116-0(X)) Monday Morning Bks., Inc.

Underwood, Deborah. Librarian. 2004. 26.20 (978-0-7377-2610-7(5) , Greenhaven Pr., Inc.) Thomson Gale.

Upchurch, Sharon. Libary Skills. 1999. (Illus.). 80p. (YA). (gr. 5). pap. 9.95 (978-1-58037-098-1(5)) Twain, Mark Media, Inc. Pubs.

LIBRARY SCIENCE—VOCATIONAL GUIDANCE

Burby, Liza N. A Day in the Life of a Librarian. 1999. (Kids' Career Library). (Illus.). 24p. (J). (gr. 3). lib. bdg. 18.75 (978-0-8239-5304-2(1) , PowerKids Pr.) Rosen Publishing Group, Inc., The.

Flanagan, Alice K. Librarians. 2001. (Community Workers Ser.). (Illus.). 32p. (J). (gr. 1 up). lib. bdg. 21.26 (978-0-7565-0063-4(X)) Compass Point Bks.

Leone, Laura. Choosing a Career in Information Science. 2005. (World of Work Ser.). (Illus.). 64p. (YA). (gr. 7-12). lib. bdg. 25.25 (978-0-8239-3569-7(8)) Rosen Publishing Group, Inc., The.

Miller, Heather. Bibliotecario. Prieto, Carlos, tr. from ENG. 2003. (Esto es lo Que Quiero Ser (This Is What I Want to Be) Ser.). (SPA., Illus.). 24p. (J). (ps-1). lib. bdg. 18.50 (978-1-4034-0379-7(1)); pap. 5.25 (978-1-4034-0601-9(4)) Heinemann Library.

—Librarian. 2003. (This Is What I Want to Be Ser.). (Illus.). 24p. (ps-1). (J). lib. bdg. 18.50 (978-1-4034-0369-8(4)); pap. 5.25 (978-1-4034-0591-3(3)) Heinemann Library.

LIBRARY SERVICE

see Library Orientation

LIBYA

Di Piazza, Francesca. Libya in Pictures. 2006. (Visual Geography Series, Second Ser.). (Illus.). 80p. (J). (gr. 4-7). lib. bdg. 27.93 (978-0-8225-2549-3(6)) Lerner Publishing Group.

Harmon, Daniel E. Libya. 2003. (Modern Middle East Nations & Their Strategic Place in the World Ser.). (Illus.). 112,128p. (YA). (gr. 7 up). lib. bdg. (978-1-59084-512-7(9)) Mason Crest Pubs.

Hasday, Judy L. Libya. 2007. (J). (***978-1-4222-0083-4(3))*** Mason Crest Pubs.

Lange, Brenda. Muammar Qaddafi: President of Libya. Schlesinger, Arthur M., Jr., ed. 2005. (Major World Leaders Ser.). (Illus.). 112-144p. (J). (gr. 6-12). 30.00 (978-0-7910-8258-4(X) , Chelsea Hse.) Facts On File, Inc.

Miller, Debra A. Libya. 2005. (Modern Nations of the World Ser.). (Illus.). 112p. (YA). (gr. 7-10). lib. bdg. 29.95 (978-1-59018-443-1(2) , Lucent Bks.) Thomson Gale.

Naden, Corinne J. & Blue, Rose. Muammar Qaddafi. 2004. (Heroes & Villains Ser.). (Illus.). 96p. (J). (gr. 7-10). 29.95 (978-1-59018-555-1(2) , Lucent Bks.) Thomson Gale.

Rozario, Paul. Libya. 2004. (Countries of the World Ser.). (Illus.). 96p. (J). (gr. 6 up). lib. bdg. 30.00 (978-0-8368-3111-5(X)) Stevens, Gareth Inc.

Tan, Ronald. Welcome to Libya. 2005. (Welcome to My Country Ser.). (Illus.). 48p. (J). lib. bdg. 26.00 (978-0-8368-3129-0(2)) Stevens, Gareth Inc.

Willis, Terri. Libya. 1999. (Enchantment of the World, Second Ser.). (Illus.). 144p. (J). (gr. 5-9). 36.00 (978-0-516-21008-7(4) , Children's Pr.) Scholastic Library Publishing.

LIBYA—FICTION

Stolz, Joelle. The Shadows of Ghadames. 128p. (gr. 3-7). 2006. 5.99 (978-0-440-41949-5(2) , Yearling); 2004. (J). 15.95 (978-0-385-73104-1(3) , Delacorte Bks. for Young Readers) Random Hse. Children's Bks.

LIFE

Cardin, Nina Beth & Blumenthal, Scott. The Time of Our Lives: A Teen Guide to the Jewish Life Cycle. 2002. (Illus.). 95p. (J). 8.95 (978-0-87441-718-0(X)) Behrman Hse., Inc.

Ench, J. R. Life & Consciousness. rev. ed. 2000. 185p. (J). 19.95 (978-0-9672814-0-7(7)) Life Engineering Foundation.

Living World. 2000. 40p. (YA). 8.33 (978-0-7525-4528-8(0)) Parragon, Inc.

Parker. Life As..., 4 vols., Set 1. 2003. (Illus.). 74.24 (978-1-4109-0626-7(4)); pap. 19.80 (978-1-4109-0652-6(3)) Raintree.

Prentice-Hall Staff. Parade of Life: Animals. 2nd ed. (J). pap., act. bk. ed. (978-0-13-400458-7(2)) Prentice Hall (Schl. Div.).

Steck-Vaughn Staff. Life on the Tallest Tree. 2003. pap. 4.10 (978-0-7398-7636-7(8)) Steck-Vaughn.

Thornhill, Jan. I Found a Dead Bird: The Kids' Guide to the Cycle of Life & Death. 2006. (Illus.). 64p. 21.95 (978-1-897066-70-6(8)); pap. 9.95 (978-1-897066-71-3(6)) Maple Tree Pr. CAN. *Dist:* Perseus Distribution.

LIFE (BIOLOGY)

see also Biology; Genetics; Old Age; Reproduction

Agnew, Kate, ed. Classic Collections of Poetry & Prose Life & Death. 2007. 208p. pap. 8.95 (***978-1-84046-567-9(0))*** Totem Bks. GBR. *Dist:* National Bk. Network.

Banquieri, Eduardo. Life on Earth. 2005. (Our Planet Ser.). (Illus.). 32p. (J). (gr. 4-8). lib. bdg. 28.00 (978-0-7910-9010-7(8) , Chelsea Clubhouse) Facts On File, Inc.

Benchmark Education Staff, compiled by. Life Science. 2006. spiral bd. 255.00 (***978-1-4108-6947-0(4));*** 2006. spiral bd. 475.00 (***978-1-4108-6943-2(1));*** 2006. spiral bd. 75.00 (***978-1-4108-6928-9(8));*** 2006. spiral bd. 215.00 (***978-1-4108-6926-5(1));*** 2005. spiral bd. 165.00 (***978-1-4108-3853-7(6));*** 2005. spiral bd. 260.00 (***978-1-4108-3860-5(9));*** 2005. spiral bd. 145.00 (***978-1-4108-3861-2(7));*** 2005. spiral bd. 75.00 (***978-1-4108-3867-4(6));*** 2005. spiral bd. 50.00 (***978-1-4108-3868-1(4));*** 2005. spiral bd. 75.00 (***978-1-4108-3875-9(7));*** 2005. spiral bd. 360.00 (***978-1-4108-3852-0(8));*** 2005. spiral bd. 680.00 (***978-1-4108-4514-6(1));*** 2005. spiral bd. 950.00 (***978-1-4108-5433-9(7));*** 2005. spiral bd. 395.00 (***978-1-4108-5434-6(5));*** 2005. spiral bd. 550.00 (***978-1-4108-5846-7(4));*** 2005. spiral bd. 295.00 (***978-1-4108-5847-4(2));*** 2005. spiral bd. 305.00 (***978-1-4108-3831-5(5));*** 2005. spiral bd. 320.00 (***978-1-4108-3830-8(7));*** 2005. spiral bd. 35.00 (***978-1-4108-3876-6(5))*** Benchmark Education Co.

Bender, Lionel. Miracle of Life: Science Facts. 1999. (Illus.). 108p. (YA). reprint ed. 25.00 (978-0-7881-6832-1(0)) DIANE Publishing Co.

Breidahl, Harry. Dark Secrets: Life Without Sunlight. 2001. (Life in Strange Places Ser.). (Illus.). 32p. (J). (gr. 4 up). 28.00 (978-0-7910-6614-0(2) , 011001, Chelsea Hse.) Facts On File, Inc.

—Itty Gritty Critters: Life Between Grains of Sand. 2001. (Life in Strange Places Ser.). (Illus.). 32p. (J). (gr. 4 up). 28.00 (978-0-7910-6615-7(0) , 011005, Chelsea Hse.) Facts On File, Inc.

—Life in Strange Places, 6 bks. Incl. Dark Secrets : Life Without Sunlight. 28.00 (978-0-7910-6614-0(2) , 011001); Diminutive Drifters : Microscopic Aquatic Life. 28.00 (978-0-7910-6618-8(5) , 011002); Extraterrestrial Life : Life Beyond Earth? 28.00 (978-0-7910-6616-4(9) , 011003); Extremophiles : Life in Extreme Environments. 28.00 (978-0-7910-6617-1(7) , 011004); Itty Gritty Critters : Life Between Grains of Sand. 28.00 (978-0-7910-6615-7(0) , 011005); Zoo on You : Life on Human Skin. 28.00 (978-0-7910-6619-5(3) , 011006); (J). (gr. 4 up). 2001. (Illus.). 32p. 2005. Set pap. 168.00 (978-0-7910-6613-3(4) , 01100S, Chelsea Hse.) Facts On File, Inc.

Burnie, David & Dorling Kindersley Publishing Staff. Life. 2000. (Eyewitness Bks.). (Illus.). 64p. (J). (gr. 4-7). lib. bdg. 19.99 (978-0-7894-6718-8(6)) Dorling Kindersley Publishing, Inc.

DK Publishing. Where Do Babies Come From? 2008. 40p. (J). 8.99 (***978-0-7566-3368-4(0))*** Dorling Kindersley Publishing, Inc.

Dorling Kindersley Publishing Staff & Burnie, David. Life. 1999. (Eyewitness Bks.). (Illus.). 64p. (J). (gr. 4-7). 15.99 (978-0-7894-4884-2(X)) Dorling Kindersley Publishing, Inc.

Evans, David & Williams, Claudette. Living Things. (Let's Explore Science Ser.). (Illus.). (J). 12.95 (978-0-590-74945-9(5)) Scholastic, Inc.

Feely, Jenny. Living & Nonliving. 1999. (ps-2). lib. bdg. 11.45 (978-0-613-30560-0(4)) Tandem Library Bks.

Fleisher, Paul. Life Cycles of a Dozen Diverse Creatures. 1998. (Single Titles Ser.: 6). (Illus.). 80p. (gr. 3-7). pap. 9.95 (978-0-7613-0349-7(9) , Millbrook Pr.) Lerner Publishing Group.

Hewitt, Sally. Living Things. 2006. (Science Starters Ser.). (Illus.). 32p. (J). (978-1-59604-082-3(3)) Stargazer Bks.

Hibbert, Clare. Life Cycles. 2004. (Illus.). Set 1. pap. 40.50 (978-1-4109-0928-2(X)); Set 2. (J). 154.20 (978-1-4109-0547-5(0)) Raintree.

Hil, Mcgraw. Trfpaswak Clssfyng Lvng T. 2000. (McGraw-Hill Science Ser.). (gr. 4 up). (978-0-02-277636-7(2)) Macmillan/McGraw-Hill Schl. Div.

Holland, Gini. Alive & Not Alive: Vivo y No Vivo. 2007. (SPA & ENG.). (J). pap. (***978-0-8368-8308-4(X)*** , Weekly Reader Early Learning Library) Stevens, Gareth Inc.

—Alive & Not Alive/Vivo y No Vivo. 2007. (I Know Opposites/Conceptos Contrarios Ser.). (SPA & ENG.). 24p. (J). (gr. k-2). lib. bdg. 17.27 (***978-0-8368-8303-9(9)*** , Weekly Reader Early Learning Library) Stevens, Gareth Inc.

Holt, Rinehart and Winston Staff. Biology: History of Life: Resources for Chapter 12. 4th ed. 2004. (Illus.). pap. 9.20 (978-0-03-069942-9(8)) Holt, Rinehart & Winston.

—Holt Science & Technology. 4th ed. 2004. (Illus.). 75.80 (978-0-03-073164-8(X)) Holt, Rinehart & Winston.

—Holt Science & Technology: Life Science: Online Edition Upgrade. 4th ed. 2004. 7.93 (978-0-03-037212-4(7)) Holt, Rinehart & Winston.

—Holt Science & Technology: Life Sciences: Online Edition Upgrade. 4th ed. 2004. 31.93 (978-0-03-037169-1(4)) Holt, Rinehart & Winston.

—Holt Science & Technology Chptr. 2: Living Things: Chapter Resources - Tennessee Edition. 3rd ed. 2003. (J). pap. 11.40 (978-0-03-069107-2(9)) Holt, Rinehart & Winston.

Kalman, Bobbie. I Am a Living Thing. 2007. (Introducing Living Things Ser.). (Illus.). 24p. (J). (gr. 1-4). pap. ***978-0-7787-3253-2(3)*** Crabtree Publishing Co.

—Is It a Living Thing? 2007. (Introducing Living Things Ser.). (Illus.). 24p. (J). (gr. 1-4). pap. ***978-0-7787-3254-9(1)*** Crabtree Publishing Co.

—Living Things Need Water. 2007. (Introducing Living Things Ser.). (Illus.). 24p. (J). (gr. 1-4). pap. ***978-0-7787-3256-3(8)*** Crabtree Publishing Co.

—What is a Bat, 32 bks. Incl. How Do Animals Adapt? Langille, Jacqueline. 2000. (978-0-86505-980-1(2)); How Do Animals Find Food? 2001. (978-0-86505-986-3(1)); How Do Animals Move? Walker, Niki. 2000. (978-0-86505-981-8(0)); What Are Camouflage & Mimicry? 2001. (978-0-86505-985-6(3)); What Are Food Chains & Webs? 1997. (978-0-86505-876-7(8)); What Are Wetlands? 2002. (978-0-86505-993-1(4)); What Is a Bat? 1999. (978-0-86505-883-5(0)); What Is a Bear? Crossingham, John. 2001. (978-0-86505-983-2(7)); What Is a Biome? 1999. (978-0-86505-875-0(X)); What Is a Bird? 1999. (978-0-86505-880-4(6)); What Is a Cat? 2002. (978-0-86505-990-0(X)); What Is a Dinosaur? 1999. (978-0-86505-921-4(7)); What Is a Dog? Sotzek, Hannelore. 2000. (978-0-86505-979-5(9)); What Is a Fish? 1999. (978-0-86505-882-8(2)); What Is a Forest? Smithyman, Kathryn. 2002. (978-0-86505-992-4(6)); What Is a Horse? Levigne, Heather. 2001. (978-0-86505-984-9(5)); What Is a Life Cycle? 1997. (978-0-86505-874-3(1)); What Is a Living Thing? 1999. (978-0-86505-879-8(2)); What Is a Mammal? 1999. (978-0-86505-878-1(4)); What Is a Marine Mammal? Langille, Jacqueline. 1999. (978-0-86505-936-8(5)); What Is a Marsupial? Levigne, Heather. 2000. (978-0-86505-978-8(0)); What Is a Plant? Walker, Niki. 2000. (978-0-86505-982-5(9)); What Is a Primate? 1999. (978-0-86505-922-1(5)); What Is a Reptile? 1999. (978-0-86505-881-1(4)); What Is a Rodent? Langille, Jacqueline. 1999. (978-0-86505-923-8(3)); What Is a Whale? Levigne, Heather. 1999. (978-0-86505-935-1(7)); What Is an Amphibian? Langille, Jacqueline. 1999. (978-0-86505-934-4(9)); What Is an Arthropod? 2002. (978-0-86505-991-7(8)); What Is an Elephant? Crossingham, John. 2001. (978-0-86505-989-4(6)); What Is Hibernation? Crossingham, John. 2001. (978-0-86505-987-0(X)); What Is Migration? Crossingham, John. 2001. (978-0-86505-988-7(8)); What Is the Animal Kingdom? 1999. (978-0-86505-877-4(6)); 32p. (J). (gr. 2-3). (Illus.). o.p. (978-0-86505-996-2(9)); Set pap. (978-0-86505-974-0(8)) Crabtree Publishing Co.

—What Is a Living Thing? 1999. (Science of Living Things Ser.). (Illus.). 32p. (J). (gr. 2-3). (978-0-86505-879-8(2)) Crabtree Publishing Co.

—What Is a Living Thing? 1999. (gr. 3-6). lib. bdg. 14.10 (978-0-613-12335-8(2)) Tandem Library Bks.

Kids Publishing Science Staff. It's Alive! All about the Living World. 1999. (J). (gr. 2-6). pap. 6.95 (978-1-891418-20-4(3)) Science Kids.

Knight, Tim. Incredible Life Cycles. 2003. (Amazing Nature Ser.). (Illus.). 32p. (J). (gr. 2-4). lib. bdg. 24.22 (978-1-4034-1148-8(4)); pap. 6.95 (978-1-4034-3258-2(9)) Heinemann Library.

Lakeshore Learning Materials Staff, contrib. by. Caterpillar to Butterfly Learning Kit. 2000. (J). pap. 13.95 (978-1-929255-75-7(6)) Lakeshore Learning Materials.

Leber, Nancy. What Plants & Animals Need. 2003. (Compass Point Phonics Readers Ser.). (Illus.). 16p. (J). (gr. 1 up). 13.26 (978-0-7565-0529-5(1)) Compass Point Bks.

Lindeen, Carol. Living & Nonliving. 2008. (J). (***978-1-4296-0000-2(4)*** , Pebble Bks.) Capstone Pr., Inc.

Mason, Adrienne & Hodge, Deborah. Living Things. Boudreau, Ray, photos by. unabr. ed. 1998. (Starting with Science Ser.). (Illus.). 32p. (J). (gr. k 3). (978-1-55074-343-2(0)) Kids Can Pr., Ltd.

McCormick, Carol. Your Special Gift: A Child's Guide to the Facts of Life. 1999. 32p. (J). (gr. 4-8). pap. 5.98 (978-0-9675368-0-4(4)) Celestial Pr.

Noonan, Diana. Life Cycles Series, 6 vols., Set. 2005. (Illus.). 32p. (J). (gr. 2-4). pap. 138.00 (978-0-7910-7054-3(9) , Chelsea Hse.) Facts On File, Inc.

Power, Jules. How Life Begins. 2001. (J). 4.95 (978-0-671-32495-7(0) , Simon & Schuster Children's Publishing) Simon & Schuster Children's Publishing.

Riley, Peter D. Life Cycles. Moller, Ray, photos by. 2003. (Everyday Science Ser.). (Illus.). 32p. (J). (gr. 1 up). lib. bdg. 23.33 (978-0-8368-3716-2(9)) Stevens, Gareth Inc.

Rivera, Sheila. I Know It Is Living. 2006. (First Step Nonfiction Ser.). (Illus.). 8p. (J). pap. (978-0-8225-5687-9(1) , Lerner Pubns.) Lerner Publishing Group.

—I Know It Is Nonliving. 2006. (First Step Nonfiction Ser.). (Illus.). 8p. (J). pap. (978-0-8225-5685-5(5) , Lerner Pubns.) Lerner Publishing Group.

—Is It Living or Nonliving? 2006. (First Step Nonfiction Ser.). (Illus.). 8p. (J). pap. (978-0-8225-5686-2(3) , Lerner Pubns.) Lerner Publishing Group.

Ross, Michael. Life Cycles. Moore, Gustav, illus. 2003. 32p. (J). (gr. 2-5). pap. 7.95 (978-0-7613-1975-7(1) , First Avenue Editions) Lerner Publishing Group.

Royston, Angela. Living & Non-Living. 2003. (My World of Science Ser.). (Illus.). 32p. (J). (gr. k-2). lib. bdg. 22.79 (978-1-4034-0854-9(8)) Heinemann Library.

—Living & Nonliving. 2003. (Illus.). 32p. pap. 6.50 (978-1-4034-3167-7(1)) Heinemann Library.

Royston, Angela. Looking at Life Cycles: How Do Plants & Animals Change? 2008. (Looking at Science: How Things Change Ser.). 32p. (J). (gr. 1-3). lib. bdg. 22.60 (***978-0-7660-3091-6(1)*** Enslow Pubs., Inc.

Schwartz, David M. Life Cycles, 12 bks. Kuhn, Dwight, photos by. Incl. Bean. lib. bdg. 20.67 (978-0-8368-2970-9(0)); Chicken. lib. bdg. 20.67 (978-0-8368-2971-6(9)); Fighting Fish. lib. bdg. 20.67 (978-0-8368-2972-3(7)); Green Snake. lib. bdg. 20.67 (978-0-8368-2973-0(5)); Horse. lib. bdg. 20.67 (978-0-8368-2974-7(3)); Hummingbird. lib. bdg. 20.67 (978-0-8368-2975-4(1)); Jumping Spider. lib. bdg. 20.67 (978-0-8368-2976-1(X)); Ladybug. lib. bdg. 20.67 (978-0-8368-2977-8(8)); Maple Tree. lib. bdg. 20.67 (978-0-8368-2978-5(6)); Monarch Butterfly. lib. bdg. 20.67 (978-0-8368-2979-2(4)); Sunflower. lib. bdg. 20.67 (978-0-8368-2980-8(8)); Wood Frog. lib. bdg. 20.67 (978-0-8368-2981-5(6)); 24p. (J). (gr. 1 up). 2001. (Springboards into Science Ser.). (Illus.). Set lib. bdg. 248.04 (978-0-8368-2969-3(7)) Stevens, Gareth Inc.

Science Stories Foss Spanish Structures of Life EA CR05. 2005. (J). (978-1-59242-589-1(5)) Delta Education, LLC.

Silverstein, Alvin & Silverstein, Virginia. Metamorphosis: Nature's Magical Transformations. unabr. ed. 2003. (Science for Children Ser.). (Illus.). 80p. (J). (gr. 5-8). pap. 5.95 (978-0-486-42396-8(4)) Dover Pubns., Inc.

Stefoff, Rebecca. Living Things, 2 bks., Set, Group 4. Incl. Flytrap. lib. bdg. 22.79 (978-0-7614-0445-3(7)); Spider. lib. bdg. 22.79 (978-0-7614-0442-2(2)); (J). (gr. 1-12). (Illus.). 32p. 1999. Set lib. bdg. 45.57 (978-0-7614-0448-4(1) , Benchmark Bks.) Cavendish, Marshall Corp.

Stewart, Melissa. Life Without Light: A Journey to Earth's Dark Ecosystems. 1999. (Venture Bks.). (Illus.). 128p. (YA). (gr. 8-12). 24.00 (978-0-531-11529-9(1) , Watts, Franklin) Scholastic Library Publishing.

Trumbauer, Lisa. Life Cycles, 14 bks. Incl. Life Cycle of a Bee. 2002. lib. bdg. 15.95 (978-0-7368-1450-8(7)); Life Cycle of a Butterfly. 2002. lib. bdg. 15.93 (978-0-7368-1181-1(8)); Life Cycle of a Cat. 2002. lib. bdg. 15.93 (978-0-7368-1182-8(6)); Life Cycle of a Chicken. 2002. lib. bdg. 15.93 (978-0-7368-1183-5(4)); Life Cycle of a Cow. 2002. lib. bdg. 15.93 (978-0-7368-1451-5(5)); Life Cycle of a Dog. 2002. lib. bdg. 15.93 (978-0-7368-1184-2(2)); Life Cycle of a Frog. 2002. lib. bdg. 15.93 (978-0-7368-1185-9(0)); Life Cycle of a Grasshopper. 2003. lib. bdg. 15.93 (978-0-7368-2089-9(2)); Life Cycle of a Kangaroo. 2002. lib. bdg. 15.93 (978-0-7368-1452-2(3)); Life Cycle of a Penguin. 2003. lib. bdg. 15.93 (978-0-7368-2090-5(6)); Life Cycle of a Rabbit. 2003. lib. bdg. 15.93 (978-0-7368-2091-2(4)); Life Cycle of a Salmon. 2002. lib. bdg. 15.93 (978-0-7368-1453-9(1)); Life Cycle of a Turtle. 2003. lib. bdg. 15.93 (978-0-7368-2092-9(2)); Life Cycle of a Whale. 2002. lib. bdg. 15.93 (978-0-7368-1186-6(9)); 24p. (J). (gr. k-1). (Illus.). Set lib. bdg. 223.02 (978-0-7368-2322-7(0) , Pebble Bks.) Capstone Pr., Inc.

Vogt, Gregory L. The Biosphere: Realm of Life. 2007. (Earth's Spheres Ser.). (Illus.). 80p. (J). (gr. 6-8). 29.27 (978-0-7613-2840-7(8) , Twenty-First Century Bks.) Lerner Publishing Group.

Zoehfeld, Kathleen Weidner. What's Alive? 2001. 24.75 (978-0-06-000306-7(5)) HarperCollins Pubns.

LIFE, CHRISTIAN

see Christian Life

LIFE, FUTURE

see Future Life

LIFE—ORIGIN

Ackroyd, Peter. Escape from Earth. 2004. (Voyages Through Time Ser.). (Illus.). 144p. (J). 19.99 (978-0-7566-0171-3(1)) Dorling Kindersley Publishing, Inc.

—In the Beginning. 2003. (Voyages Through Time Ser.). (Illus.). 144p. (J). 19.99 (978-0-7894-9836-6(7)) Dorling Kindersley Publishing, Inc.

Bailey, Jacqui. The Dawn of Life, 4 vols. Lilly, Matthew, illus. 2001. (Cartoon History of the Earth Ser.). 32p. (J). (gr. 4-6). No. 2. (978-1-55337-081-9(3)); Vol. 2. (978-1-55337 072-7(4)) Kids Can Pr., Ltd.

Barron's Educational Editorial Staff. Searching for Human Origins. 1998. (Megascope Ser.). (Illus.). 64p. (J). (gr. 3-7). 6.95 (978-0-7641-5092-0(8)) Barron's Educational Series, Inc.

Gallant, Roy A. The Origins of Life. 2000. (Story of Science Ser.). (Illus.). 80p. (J). (gr. 5 up). lib. bdg. 29.93 (978-0-7614-1151-2(8) , Benchmark Bks.) Cavendish, Marshall Corp.

The Living Earth Series, 8 vols., Set. 2002. (YA). (gr. 7-12). 440.00 (978-0-8160-5017-8(1)) Facts On File, Inc.

Morgan, Jennifer. From Lava to Life: The Universe Tells Our Earth Story. Andersen, Dana Lynne, illus. (Sharing Nature with Children Book Ser.: Vol. 2). (YA). 2004. 48p. 19.95 (978-1-58469-043-6(7)); 2003. 47p. pap. 9.95 (978-1-58469-042-9(9)) Dawn Pubns.

—From Lava to Life: The Universe Tells Our Earth Story. 2003. (gr. 3-6). lib. bdg. 18.75 (978-0-613-79612-5(8)) Tandem Library Bks.

Stewart, Melissa. Life Without Light: A Journey to Earth's Dark Ecosystems. 1999. (Venture Bks.). (Illus.). 128p. (YA). (gr. 8-12). 24.00 (978-0-531-11529-9(1) , Watts, Franklin) Scholastic Library Publishing.

LIFE—POETRY

Fernandez-Maldonado, Ana Maria. Amar y Otros Verbos. 2002. (SPA., Illus.). 64p. (978-84-241-8650-0(8)) Everest de Ediciones y Distribucion, S.L. ESP. *Dist:* Lectorum Pubns., Inc.

The Greatest Work of Make-Believe. l.t. ed. 2002. (Illus.). 94p. pap. 12.00 (978-0-9702833-0-6(X) , BI000) Vinestreet Pr.

LIFE, SPIRITUAL

see Spiritual Life

LIFE AFTER DEATH

see Future Life

LIFE ON OTHER PLANETS

see also Interstellar Communication

Ackroyd, Peter. Escape from Earth. 2004. (Voyages Through Time Ser.). (Illus.). 144p. (J). 19.99 (978-0-7566-0171-3(1)) Dorling Kindersley Publishing, Inc.

Asimov, Isaac & Hantula, Richard. Is There Life in Outer Space? 2004. (Isaac Asimov's 21st Century Library of the Universe). (Illus.). 32p. (J). lib. bdg. 24.67 (978-0-8368-3950-0(1)) Stevens, Gareth Inc.

Baddiel, Ivor & Blezard, Tracey. Extraterrestrials: Investigations into the Unexplained. 1999. (Mysterious World Bks.). (Illus.). 32p. (YA). (gr. 5 up). pap. 6.95 (978-0-7641-0907-2(3)) Barron's Educational Series, Inc.

Bortz, Alfred B. Astrobiology. 2007. (Cool Science Ser.). 48p. (J). (gr. 4-8). lib. bdg. 26.60 (***978-0-8225-6771-4(7)*** , Lerner Pubns.) Lerner Publishing Group.

Branley, Franklyn M. Is There Life in Outer Space? Miller, Edward, illus. 1999. (Let's-Read-and-Find-Out Science Ser.). 40p. (J). (ps-1). 15.89 (978-0-06-028145-8(6)) HarperCollins Pubs.

—Is There Life in Outer Space. 1999. (Let's-Read-and-Find-Out Science Ser.). (Illus.). 40p. (J). (ps-1). 15.95 (978-0-06-028146-5(4)) HarperCollins Pubs.

—Is There Life in Outer Space? Miller, Edward, illus. rev. ed. 1999. (Let's-Read-and-Find-Out Science Ser.). 40p. (J). (ps-1). pap. 5.99 (978-0-06-445192-5(5) , Harper Trophy) HarperCollins Pubs.

Branley, Franklyn Mansfield. Is There Life in Outer Space? Miller, Edward, illus. 1999. 31p. (J). (ps-ps). lib. bdg. 13.00 (978-0-613-22877-0(4)) Tandem Library Bks.

Breidahl, Harry. Extraterrestrial Life: Life Beyond Earth? 2001. (Life in Strange Places Ser.). (Illus.). 32p. (J). (gr. 4 up). 28.00 (978-0-7910-6616-4(9) , 011003, Chelsea Hse.) Facts On File, Inc.

Coville, Bruce, compiled by. Bruce Coville's Alien Visitors. 1999. (Bruce Coville's Alien Adventures Ser.). (Illus.). 208p. (J). (gr. 3-7). pap. 4.99 (978-0-380-80254-8(6)) HarperCollins Pubs.

Donald, Rhonda Lucas. Life on Other Planets. (Watts Library). (J). 2004. (gr. 5-7). pap. 8.95 (978-0-531-16374-0(1)); 2003. (Illus.). 64p. 25.50 (978-0-531-12280-8(8)) Scholastic Library Publishing. (Watts, Franklin).

Evans, Hilary. Ancient Worlds, Ancient Mysteries. 2000. (Unexplained Ser.: Vo. 1). (Illus.). (J). (gr. 7-12). 17.95 (978-0-7910-6077-3(2) , Chelsea Hse.) Facts On File, Inc.

—Coming from the Skies. 2000. (Unexplained Ser.: Vol. 6). (Illus.). 45p. (J). (gr. 7-12). 11.95 (978-0-7910-6081-0(0) , Chelsea Hse.) Facts On File, Inc.

—Historic Realms of Marvels & Miracles. 2000. (Unexplained Ser.: Vol. 1). (Illus.). (J). (gr. 7-12). 11.95 (978-0-7910-6076-6(4) , Chelsea Hse.) Facts On File, Inc.

—Imagining Other Worlds. 2000. (Unexplained Ser.: Vol. 5). (Illus.). 43p. (J). (gr. 7-12). 11.95 (978-0-7910-6080-3(2) , Chelsea Hse.) Facts On File, Inc.

—Lost Words & Forgotten Secrets. 2000. (Unexplained Ser.: Vol. 3). (Illus.). 45p. (J). (gr. 7-12). 17.95 (978-0-7910-6078-0(0) , Chelsea Hse.) Facts On File, Inc.

—Making Contact. 2000. (Unexplained Ser.: Vol. 7). (Illus.). 44p. (J). (gr. 7-12). 17.95 (978-0-7910-6082-7(9) , Chelsea Hse.) Facts On File, Inc.

—Unexplained/From Other Worlds, 7 vols., Set. 2000. (J). 125.65 (978-0-7910-6075-9(6) , Chelsea Hse.) Facts On File, Inc.

—We Are Not Alone. 2000. (Unexplained Ser.: Vol. 4). (Illus.). 45p. (J). (gr. 7-12). 11.95 (978-0-7910-6079-7(9) , Chelsea Hse.) Facts On File, Inc.

Firestone, Mary. SETI Science. 2005. (Weird Careers in Science Ser.). (Illus.). 81p. (J). (gr. 4-8). lib. bdg. 25.00 (978-0-7910-8701-5(8) , Chelsea Hse.) Facts On File, Inc.

Getz, David. Life on Mars. McCarty, Peter, illus. rev. ed. 2004. 64p. (J). 14.95 (978-0-8050-7729-2(4) , Holt, Henry & Co. Bks. For Young Readers) Holt, Henry & Co.

Gifford, Clive. How to Live on Mars. Anderson, Scoular, illus. 2001. (How to Ser.). 96p. (J). (gr. 5-7). 16.00 (978-0-531-14647-7(2) , Watts, Franklin) Scholastic Library Publishing.

—How to Meet Aliens. Anderson, Scoular, illus. 2001. (How to Ser.). 96p. (J). (gr. 5-7). 16.00 (978-0-531-14642-2(1)); pap. 4.95 (978-0-531-14820-4(3)) Scholastic Library Publishing. (Watts, Franklin).

—How to Meet Aliens. 2001. (gr. 5-8). lib. bdg. 12.95 (978-0-613-54551-8(6)) Tandem Library Bks.

Gonzalez, David J. There Are No Space Aliens! 12 Biblical Points Disproving Space Aliens. l.t. ed. 2003. 48p. 9.95 (978-0-9741561-0-1(8)) Gonzalez, David J. Ministries.

Hamilton, John. Aliens. 2007. (World of Science Fiction Ser.). (Illus.). 32p. (J). (gr. 4-6). lib. bdg. 24.21 (978-1-59679-986-8(2)) ABDO Publishing Co.

Herbst, Judith. Aliens. (Unexplained Ser.). (Illus.). 48p. (J). 2005. (gr. 5-12). lib. bdg. 26.60 (978-0-8225-0960-8(1)); 2004. pap. 7.95 (978-0-8225-2402-1(3) , Lerner Pubns.) Lerner Publishing Group.

Innes, Brian. Alien Visitors & Abductions. 1998. (Unsolved Mysteries Ser.). (Illus.). 48p. (J). (gr. 3-7). pap. 8.05 (978-0-8172-4275-6(9)) Steck-Vaughn.

Jackson, Ellen B. Looking for Life in the Universe: The Search for Extraterrestrial Intelligence. Bishop, Nic, illus. Bishop, Nic, photos by. 2002. (Scientists in the Field Ser.). 64p. (J). (gr. 3-5). tchr. ed. 16.00 (978-0-618-12894-5(8)) Houghton Mifflin Co. Trade & Reference Div.

—Looking for Life in the Universe: The Search for Extraterrestrial Intelligence. Bishop, Nic, photos by. 2005. (Scientists in the Field Ser.). (Illus.). 64p. (J). (gr. 4-6). pap. 6.95 (978-0-618-54886-6(6)) Houghton Mifflin Co. Trade & Reference Div.

Jedicke, Peter. Seti. 2003. (Hot Science Ser.). (Illus.). pap. 28.50 (978-1-58340-369-3(8)) Smart Apple Media.

Jefferis, David. Alien Lifesearch: Quest for Extraterrestrial Organisms. 1999. (Megatech Ser.). (Illus.). 32p. (J). (gr. 4-5). pap. (978-0-7787-0059-3(3)); lib. bdg. (978-0-7787-0049-4(6)) Crabtree Publishing Co.

Krull, Kathleen. What Really Happened in Roswell? Just the Facts. 2003. (gr. 3-6). lib. bdg. 12.10 (978-0-613-66747-0(6)) Tandem Library Bks.

Martin, Michael. Alien Abductions. 2006. (Edge Books, the Unexplained). 32p. (J). (978-0-7368-4380-5(9)) Capstone Pr., Inc.

McDonald. Life in Outer Space. 1999. (Illus.). (J). pap. (978-0-7398-2498-6(8)) Steck-Vaughn.

Mist, Rosalind. Is There Life on Other Planets? The Planets of Our Solar System. 2006. (Stargazers Guides Ser.). (Illus.). 48p. (J). (978-1-4034-7708-8(6)); pap. (978-1-4034-7715-6(9)) Heinemann Library.

Nardo, Don. The Search for Extraterrestrial Life. 2006. (Lucent Library of Science & Technology). (Illus.). 112p. (J). (gr. 7-10). 29.95 (978-1-59018-832-3(2) , Lucent Bks.) Thomson Gale.

Netzley, Patricia D. The Curse of King Tut. 2000. (Mystery Library). (Illus.). 96p. (YA). (gr. 4-12). 27.45 (978-1-56006-684-2(9) , Lucent Bks.) Thomson Gale.

Nobleman, Marc Tyler. Aliens & UFOs. 2006. (Illus.). 32p. (J). pap. 7.99 (978-1-4109-2514-5(5)); lib. bdg. (978-1-4109-2509-1(9)) Steck-Vaughn.

Oxlade, Chris. The Mystery of Life on Other Planets. 2002. (Can Science Solve? Ser.). 32p. (Illus.). (J). (gr. 4-7). lib. bdg. 22.79 (978-1-58810-666-7(7)); pap. 7.50 (978-1-58810-929-3(1) , 91564) Heinemann Library.

—The Mystery of Life on Other Planets. 2002. (Illus.). 32p. (J). (gr. 4-7). lib. bdg. 15.90 (978-0-613-45802-3(8)) Tandem Library Bks.

Parker. Space Aliens. 2003. (Space Busters Ser.). (Illus.). 32p. (J). pap. 7.95 (978-1-4109-0072-2(X)) Raintree.

Parker, Steve. Space Aliens. 2002. (Young Library - Space Busters Ser.). 32p. (J). lib. bdg. 25.69 (978-0-7398-4849-4(6)) Raintree.

Pipe, Jim. Aliens. 2006. (Illus.). 32p. (J), lib. bdg. 25.27 (978-1-59716-202-9(7)) Bearport Publishing Co., Inc.

Roleff, Tamara L. Alien Abductions. 2003. (gr. 7-12). lib. bdg. 30.35 (978-0-613-73927-6(2)) Tandem Library Bks.

Roleff, Tamara L., ed. Alien Abductions. 2003. (Illus.). 160p. (J). lib. bdg. 32.45 (978-0-7377-1589-7(8) , Greenhaven Pr., Inc.) Thomson Gale.

Royston, Angela. Alien Neighbors? 2005. (Illus.). 32p. (J). lib. bdg. (978-1-4109-1931-1(5)) Steck-Vaughn.

—Alien Neighbors? The Solar System. 2005. (Illus.). 32p. (J). (gr. 3-5). 7.85 (978-1-4109-1962-5(5)) Steck-Vaughn.

Sautter, Aaron. How to Draw Disgusting Aliens. Lentz, Bob, illus. 2008. (J). (***978-1-4296-0075-0(6)***) Capstone Pr., Inc.

Skurzynski, Gloria. Are We Alone? Scientists Search for Life in Space. 2004. (Illus.). 96p. (J). (gr. 5 up). 28.90 (978-0-7922-6967-0(5)); 18.95 (978-0-7922-6567-2(X)) National Geographic Society. (National Geographic Children's Bks.).

Spangenburg, Ray. Life on Other Worlds. 2002. (gr. 7-12). lib. bdg. 24.55 (978-0-613-53828-2(5)) Tandem Library Bks.

Turner, Pamela S. At Life's Edge. 2008. (J). lib. bdg. (***978-1-58089-133-2(0)***) Charlesbridge Publishing, Inc.

Twist, Clint. The Search for Life in Space. 2005. (Science Quest Ser.). (Illus.). 32p. (J). lib. bdg. 24.67 (978-0-8368-4557-0(9)) Stevens, Gareth Inc.

Wingate, Philippa. Alien Abduction. 1998. (Paranormal Guides Ser.). (SPA.). 48p. (J). (gr. 4 up). lib. bdg. 13.95 (978-1-58086-011-6(7)); (Illus.). pap. 5.95 (978-0-7460-3054-7(1)) EDC Publishing.

LIFE ON OTHER PLANETS—FICTION

Appleton, Victor. Tom Swift & the Visitor from Planet X. 2006. pap. (***978-1-4068-0728-8(1)***) Echo Library.

Blundell, Judy. Star Wars: The Last of the Jedi #9. 2008. 160p. pap. 5 99 (***978-0-439-68142-1(1)***) Scholastic, Inc.

Broderick, Damien. Time Zones. 2000. (gr. 7-12). lib. bdg. 12.10 (978-0-613-29108-8(5)) Tandem Library Bks.

Calero, Dennis. You're Not the Captain of Me! 2006. 272p. pap. 9.95 (978-1-59687-375-9(2)) ibooks, Inc.

Cave, K. Henry Hobbs & the Lost Planet. 2002. (Illus.). 95p. (J). pap. 7.99 (978-0-340-80580-0(3) , Hodder & Stoughton) Hodder General Publishing Division GBR. *Dist:* Trafalgar Square Publishing.

Chatten, Vicky. Bonding. 2004. 173p. pap. 19.95 (978-1-4137-5348-6(5)) PublishAmerica, Inc.

Chester, Deborah. The Crystal Eye. 1999. (Lucasfilm's Alien Chronicles: Bk. 3). (J). (978-0-606-16276-0(3)) Tandem Library Bks.

Coville, Bruce. My Teacher Fried My Brains. 2005. (Illus.). 136p. (J). (***978-1-4156-1080-0(0)*** , Aladdin) Simon & Schuster Children's Publishing.

—My Teacher Glows in the Dark. 2005. (Illus.). 137p. (J). (***978-1-4156-1081-7(9)*** , Aladdin) Simon & Schuster Children's Publishing.

—My Teacher Is an Alien. 2005. (Illus.). 123p. (J). (***978-1-4156-1082-4(7)*** , Aladdin) Simon & Schuster Children's Publishing.

Crilley, Mark. Akiko & the Great Wall of Trudd. 2002. (gr. 3-6). lib. bdg. 13.00 (978-0-613-50400-3(3)) Tandem Library Bks.

—Bornstone's Elixir. 2001. (gr. 3-6). lib. bdg. 22.20 (978-0-613-50412-6(7)) Tandem Library Bks.

Delhohne, Jean-Philippe. Visit to Another Planet. 2004. (Illus.). 31p. (J). (gr. k-4). reprint ed. (978-0-7567-7768-5(2)) DIANE Publishing Co.

Etra, Jonathan. Aliens Dinner. Bjorkman, Steve, illus. 2002. (J). 11.91 (978-0-7587-5971-9(1)) Book Wholesalers, Inc.

—Aliens for Lunch. Bjorkman, Steve, illus. 2002. 11.91 (978-0-7587-5972-6(X)) Book Wholesalers, Inc.

Gentry, Stephen. Journey to the Stars & Back. 2005. 52p. (J). pap. 16.49 (978-1-4116-5985-8(6)) Lulu.com.

Gilden, Mel. Britney Spears Is a Three-Headed Alien: The Inside Story. 2001. (gr. 7-12). lib. bdg. 18.80 (978-0-613-82444-6(X)) Tandem Library Bks.

Glover, Sandra. E-T Mail. 2002. (Illus.). 80p. (YA). pap. 8.99 (978-1-84270-095-2(2)) Andersen GBR. *Dist:* Independent Pubs. Group.

Greenwood, Kerry. Alien Invasions. 2000. (gr. 7-12). lib. bdg. 12.10 (978-0-613-28728-9(2)) Tandem Library Bks.

Herman, Gail. Friend for E T. 2002. (gr. k-3). lib. bdg. 11.25 (978-0-613-87767-1(5)) Tandem Library Bks.

Homzie, H. B. & Phillips, Matthew. The Baby-Sitters Wore Diapers, No. 3. 2003. (Alien Clones from Outer Space Ser.). 80p. (J). pap. 3.99 (978-0-689-82344-2(4) , Aladdin) Simon & Schuster Children's Publishing.

Hood, Robert. Gadgets & Gizmos. 2005. (Thrillogy Ser.). (Illus.). 48p. (gr. 4-8). 17.50 (978-0-7910-8866-1(9)) Facts On File, Inc.

—Gadgets & Gizmos. 2000. (gr. 7-12). lib. bdg. 12.10 (978-0-613-28848-4(3)) Tandem Library Bks.

Johse, Jill Taylor. Wanted a Friend, Got an Alien. 2003. 58p. pap. 8.95 (978-0-595-30459-2(1)) iUniverse, Inc.

King, Stephen. Dreamcatcher. 2001. (gr. 7-12). lib. bdg. 16.45 (978-0-613-50299-3(X)) Tandem Library Bks.

Korman, Gordon. Invasion of the Nose Pickers. 2001. (gr. 3-6). lib. bdg. 13.00 (978-0-613-31362-9(3)) Tandem Library Bks.

Kulling, Monica. Go, Stitch, Go. 2002. (ps-2). lib. bdg. 11.80 (978-0-613-50612-0(X)) Tandem Library Bks.

Lavoie, Rejean. Des Legumes Pour Frank Einstein. Begin, Jean-Guy, illus. 2004. (Des 9 Ans. Ser.: Vol. 44). (FRE.). 120p. (J). 8.95 (978-2-89599-006-2(9)) Editions de la Paix CAN. *Dist:* World of Reading, Ltd.

Lowachee, Karin. War Child. 2002. (gr. 3-6). lib. bdg. 15.30 (978-0-613-52925-9(1)) Tandem Library Bks.

Magrs, Paul. Sick Building. 2007. 256p. ***978-1-84607-269-7(7))** Random Hse.

McCaffrey, Anne. The Masterharper of Pern. 1999. (Pern Ser.). (gr. 7-12). lib. bdg. 15.30 (978-0-613-37699-0(4)) Tandem Library Bks.

—The Skies of Pern. 2002. (Pern Ser.). (gr. 7-12). lib. bdg. 16.45 (978-0-613-62648-4(6)) Tandem Library Bks.

McCliggott, Timothy M. A Report on Quibnoida. McCliggott, Timothy M., illus. 2007. (Illus.). 52p. (YA). pap. 17.00 ***978-0-8059-7289-4(7))** Dorrance Publishing Co., Inc.

Metzger, Joanna. The Space Program. Elizalde, Marcelo, illus. 2006. 142p. (J). (978-1-59336-695-7(7)) Mondo Publishing.

Michalowski, Mark. Wetworld. 2007. 256p. ***978-1-84607-271-0(9))** Random Hse.

Mills, Judith. The Book of the Sage. 3rd rev. ed. 2004. (Goodfellow Chronicles Ser.). (Illus.). 304p. (J). pap. 9.95 ***978-1-55263-559-9(7))** Key Porter Bks. CAN. *Dist:* Perseus Distribution.

Mordenga, Michael P. Spirit Box. 2007. 280p. per. 17.95 ***978-0-595-43785-6(0))** iUniverse, Inc.

Pilkey, Dav. El Capitan Calzoncillos y la Invastion de las Horribles Camareras. 2002. (Captain Underpants Ser.). (SPA.). (gr. 3-6). lib. bdg. 13.00 (978-0-613-50415-7(1)) Tandem Library Bks.

Pocket Books Staff. Intruder. 2000. (gr. 7-12). lib. bdg. 14.15 (978-0-613-73179-9(4)) Tandem Library Bks.

Pringle, Eric. Big George & the Seventh Knight. Paine, Colin, illus. 2002. 208p. pap. 10.99 (978-0-7475-5539-1(7)) Bloomsbury Publishing Plc GBR. *Dist:* Independent Pubs. Group.

—Big George & the Winter King. Paine, Colin, illus. 2004. 208p. pap. 12.99 (978-0-7475-6341-9(1)) Bloomsbury Publishing Plc GBR. *Dist:* Independent Pubs. Group.

Ryan, Kevin. Nightscape. 2003. (gr. 7-12). lib. bdg. 14.15 (978-0-613-66528-5(7)) Tandem Library Bks.

Smith, Dean Wesley & Rusch, Kristine Kathryn. Little Green Men. 2002. (Roswell Ser.: Vol. 3). 208p. (YA). pap. 6.99 (978-0-7434-1836-2(0) , Simon Pulse) Simon & Schuster Children's Publishing.

Stewart, Paul & Riddell, Chris. Blobheads. 2005. (Read-along Ser.). (Illus.). (J). audio (978-0-7540-6285-1(6)) BBC Audio.

Strasser, Dirk. Lost in Space. 2005. (Thrillogy Ser.). (Illus.). 48p. (gr. 4-8). 17.50 (978-0-7910-8868-5(5)) Facts On File, Inc.

Strauss, Elizabeth. Message on a Rocket. 2000. (gr. k-3). lib. bdg. 11.80 (978-0-613-29696-0(6)) Tandem Library Bks.

Thorpe, Kiki. Lilo & Stitch: The Junior Novelization. 2002. (ps-2). lib. bdg. 13.00 (978-0-613-50630-4(8)) Tandem Library Bks.

Victor, Pamela. Baj & the Word Launcher: Space Age Asperger Adventures in Communication. Shadoian, Chris, illus. 2006. 112p. (J). pap. (978-1-84310-830-6(5)) Kingsley, Jessica Ltd.

Watson, Jude. Death on Naboo. 2006. (Star Wars Ser.: No. 4). 135p. (J). lib. bdg. 13.00 ***978-1-4242-0777-0(0))** Fitzgerald Bks.

—The Desperate Mission. 2005. (Star Wars Ser.: No. 1). 168p. (J). lib. bdg. 20.00 ***978-1-4242-0774-9(6))** Fitzgerald Bks.

—The Desperate Mission. 2005. (Star Wars Ser.: No. 1). 168p. (J). (978-1-4155-9754-5(X)) Scholastic, Inc.

Watson, Jude. Underworld. 2005. (Star Wars Ser.: No. 3). 137p. (J). lib. bdg. 20.00 ***978-1-4242-0776-3(2))** Fitzgerald Bks.

Waugh, Sylvia. Carrera Espacial. (SPA.). (YA). 8.95 (978-958-04-6028-2(0)) Norma S.A. COL. *Dist:* Distribuidora Norma, Inc.

Weiss, Bobbi J. G. & Weiss, David Cody. Brain Power. Mateu, Francesc, illus. 2003. (Dexter's Laboratory Ser.: No. 2). 24p. (J). pap. 3.50 (978-0-439-44942-7(1) , Scholastic Paperbacks) Scholastic, Inc.

Wells, H. G. The War of the Worlds. 2005. (Aladdin Classics Ser.). xv, 308p. (J). ***978-1-4155-9579-4(8)** , Aladdin) Simon & Schuster Children's Publishing.

Willis, Jeanne & Ross, Tony. Dr Xargle's Book of Earth Mobiles. 2004. (Illus.). 32p. (J). pap. 8.99 (978-1-84270-369-4(2)) Andersen GBR. *Dist:* Independent Pubs. Group.

—Dr. Xargle's Book of Earth Relations. (Illus.). 32p. (J). pap. 9.99 (978-1-84270-307-6(2)) Andersen GBR. *Dist:* Trafalgar Square Publishing.

—Dr. Xargle's Book of Earth Tiggers. 2001. (Illus.). 32p. (J). pap. 9.99 (978-1-84270-054-9(5)) Andersen GBR. *Dist:* Independent Pubs. Group.

—Dr. Xargles Book of Earthlets. 2003. (Illus.). 32p. (J). pap. 9.99 (978-1-84270-067-9(7)) Andersen GBR. *Dist:* Trafalgar Square Publishing.

Wrede, Patricia C. Attack of the Clones. 2002. (gr. 3-6). lib. bdg. 14.15 (978-0-613-50588-8(3)) Tandem Library Bks.

LIFE SKILLS

Here are entered works that discuss a combination of the skills needed by an individual to exist in modern society, including skills related to education, employment, finance, health, housing, psychology, etc.

see also Conduct of Life

Adler, Mia Sharon. Essential Proteen: A Life Skills Program for Helping Teens Succeed: Student Journal. 2006. viii, 39p. (YA). pap. 14.95 (978-0-87822-582-8(X) , 5284) Research Pr.

Alimonti, Frederick & Tedesco, Ann. Not Everyone Is Nice: Helping Children Learn Caution with Strangers. DePrince, Erik & Volinski, Jessica, illus. 2003. (Let's Talk Ser.). 48p. (J). pap. 8.95 (978-0-88282-233-4(0)) New Horizon Pr. Pubs., Inc.

Archbold, Tim, illus. Making Good Choices, 4 bks. Incl. Joe's Car : A Book about Friendship. Dixon, Annabelle. (J). 22.60 (978-1-4048-0662-9(8)) ; Sandbox : A Book about Fairness. Rowe, Don. (C). 22.60 (978-1-4048-0665-8(2)) ; Scary Video : A Book about Using Good Judgment. Rose, Gill. (C). 22.60 (978-1-4048-0663-4(6)) ; William & the Guinea-Pig : A Book about Responsibility. Rose, Gill. (C). 22.60 (978-1-4048-0664-1(4)) ; 24p. (gr. k-3). (Illus.). 2004. 90.40 (978-1-4048-0666-5(0)) Picture Window Bks.

Ask a Master: 100 More of Life's Questions Answered. 2001. (Ask A Master, Volume 2: Vol. 2). 96p. (C). pap. 6.00 (978-1-884864-18-6(X)) American Success Institute, Inc.

Asquith, Ros. The Teenage Worrier's Guide to Life. 2000. (Teenage Worrier Ser.). (Illus.). 336p. mass mkt. 9.99 (978-0-552-14534-3(3) , Corgi) Transworld Publishers Ltd. GBR. *Dist:* Trafalgar Square Publishing.

Barsa International Publishers, Inc. Staff. Claves para la Vida: Libro de Autorrealizacion. 2000. (SPA., Illus.). 448p. (YA). (978-1-56409-042-3(6)) EBP Latin America Group, Inc.

Becker, Helaine. Like A Pro: 101 Simple Ways to Do Really Important Stuff. Davila, Claudia, illus. 2006. 160p. (J). pap. 9.95 (978-1-897066-54-6(6)) Maple Tree Pr. CAN. *Dist:* Perseus Distribution.

Benson, Edmund F. Only Joking? 2001. 32p. (J). pap. 2.95 (978-1-58614-279-7(8)) Arise Foundation.

Benson, Edmund F. & Benson, Susan. ABC's of School Bus Safety. 2000. 16p. (J). pap. 1.95 (978-1-58614-179-0(1)) Arise Foundation.

—A Day in a Life Behind Bars. 2000. 16p. (J). pap. 1.95 (978-1-58614-176-9(7)) Arise Foundation.

—Excuse Me! 2000. 16p. (J). pap. 1.95 (978-1-58614-175-2(9)) Arise Foundation.

—Hacia una Mentalidad Mas Dinamica: Cuaderno de Pruebas. 1999. (SPA., Illus.). 28p. (J). (gr. 3-4). pap. 7.49 (978-1-58614-085-4(X)) Arise Foundation.

—Roots of Violence. 2000. 16p. (J). pap. 1.95 (978-1-58614-174-5(0)) Arise Foundation.

—Temper, Temper: 20 Tips for Managing Anger. 2000. 16p. (J). pap. 1.95 (978-1-58614-184-4(8)) Arise Foundation.

—20 Tips for Coping with Depression. 2000. 16p. (J). pap. 1.95 (978-1-58614-185-1(6)) Arise Foundation.

Berry, Joy. Get over it! Set. 6 vols. 2005. (Winning Skills Ser.). (Illus.). 48p. (J). 19.95 (978-1-57687-292-5(0) , PowerHouse Kids) powerHouse Cultural Entertainment, Inc.

Berry, Joy, contrib. by. Go for it! Set. 2005. (Winning skills series, go for It! Ser.). (Illus.). 288p. (J). pap. 19.95 (978-1-57687-294-9(7) , PowerHouse Kids) powerHouse Cultural Entertainment, Inc.

Berry, Joy Wilt. Earning an Allowance: A Kid's Money Book About. Bartholomew & Pace, Don, illus. rev. ed. 2000. (Living Skills Ser.: Vol. 1). 48p. (J). (gr. 1-7). pap. 4.95 (978-1-58634-140-4(5)) Goldstar Publishing, Inc.

—Tough Situations: Get over It! Bartholomew, illus. rev. ed. 2000. (Winning Skills Ser.: Vol. 5). 48p. (YA). (gr. 4-7). pap. 2.95 (978-1-58634-164-0(2)) Goldstar Publishing, Inc.

Biren, Richard L. I Can I Will I Did It: A Manual for Managing Change & Building Resiliency. Norcross, Harry, illus. 2001. 143p. (J). (gr. 3-6). pap. 13.95 (978-1-57543-090-4(8)) MAR*CO Products, Inc.

Bizos, Erato-Nadia, et al. Life Skills Matters: Grade 3. 2003. (XHO & AFR.). 40p. pap., tchr. ed., wbk. ed. 2.05 (978-0-521-53898-5(X)) Cambridge Univ. Pr.

—Life Skills Matters Grade 1. 2003. (AFR.). 32p. pap., wbk. ed. 1.85 (978-0-521-53886-2(6)) Cambridge Univ. Pr.

—Life Skills Matters Grade 1 Sesotho Translation. 2003. (AFR.). 32p. pap., wbk. ed. 1.85 (978-0-521-53884-8(X)) Cambridge Univ. Pr.

—Life Skills Matters Grade 1 Xitsonga Translation. 2003. (AFR.). 32p. pap., wbk. ed. 1.85 (978-0-521-53885-5(8)) Cambridge Univ. Pr.

—Life Skills Matters Grade 2 isXhosa Translation. 2003. (XHO & AFR.). 32p. pap., tchr. ed., wbk. ed. 1.85 (978-0-521-53892-3(0)) Cambridge Univ. Pr.

—Life Skills Matters Grade 2 Sesotho Translation. 2003. (AFR.). 32p. pap., wbk. ed. 1.85 (978-0-521-53890-9(4)) Cambridge Univ. Pr.

—Life Skills Matters Grade 2 Xitsonga Translation. 2003. (AFR.). 32p. pap., wbk. ed. 1.85 (978-0-521-53891-6(2)) Cambridge Univ. Pr.

—Life Skills Matters Grade 3 Workbook Sesotho Translation. 2003. (AFR.). 40p. pap. 2.05 (978-0-521-53896-1(3)) Cambridge Univ. Pr.

—Life Skills Matters Grade 3 Workbook Xitsonga Translation. 2003. (AFR.). 40p. pap. 2.05 (978-0-521-53897-8(1)) Cambridge Univ. Pr.

Blatt, Jessica. The Teen Girl's Gotta-Have-It Guide to Boys: From Getting Them to Getting over Them! Frenette, Cynthia, illus. 2007. (Teen Girl's Gotta-Have-It Guides). 96p. (YA). (gr. 7 up). pap. 8.95 (978-0-8230-1725-6(7)) Watson-Guptill Pubns., Inc.

Borcherding, Gwyn. The Good That I Should: Romans 7 for Kids. Nguyen, Vincent, illus. 2004. (ENG.). 32p. (J). 11.99 (978-0-7586-0392-0(4)) Concordia Publishing Hse.

Bostick, Nan. Consumer Spending. 2003. (Saddleback Lifeskills Ser.). (Illus.). 48p. wbk. ed. 8.95 (978-1-56254-568-0(X) , SP 568X) Saddleback Educational Publishing.

—Managing Money. 2003. (Saddleback Lifeskills Ser.). (Illus.). 48p. wbk. ed. 8.95 (978-1-56254-567-3(1) , SP 5671) Saddleback Educational Publishing.

Bowman, Margaret. The Commandments & Beatitudes: Guiding Our Lives. 1999. (Illus.). (YA). (gr. 9-13). pap., stu. ed. 7.45 (978-0-89837-167-3(8)) Pflaum Publishing Group.

Boyd, Ervin D., Sr. Help for the Hurting: Getting Beyond This Veil of Tears! 2003. (Illus.). 200p. (YA). spiral bd. 22.00 (978-0-9744024-0-6(0)) Anointed Word Pubns.

Brother 2 Brother, Vol. 1. 2001. 112p. (J). per. (978-0-9715205-0-9(X)) Coleman, Kenneth.

Brown, Cherie. Love Doesn't Hurt: Life Lessons for Young Women. 2003. (YA). (978-0-9743676-0-6(5)) Avantgarde Publishing Co.

Building a Culture of Life Leader's Manual. 2nd ed. 2004. (YA). per. 19.95 (978-0-9764572-0-6(2)) Together, Inc.

Building a Culture of Life Study Guide. 2004. (YA). per. 17.95 (978-0-9764572-1-3(0)) Together, Inc.

Candell, Arianna. Mind Your Manners: At Parties. Curto, Rosa M., illus. 2005. (Mind Your Manners Ser.). (ENG & SPA.). 36p. (J). pap. 6.95 (978-0-7641-3167-7(2)) Barron's Educational Series, Inc.

—Mind Your Manners: At the Park. Curto, Rosa M., illus. 2005. (Mind Your Manners Ser.). 36p. (J). pap. 6.95 (978-0-7641-3168-4(0)) Barron's Educational Series, Inc.

—Mind Your Manners: In School. Curto, Rosa M., illus. 2005. (Mind Your Manners Ser.). 36p. (J). pap. 6.95 (978-0-7641-3166-0(4)) Barron's Educational Series, Inc.

Carle, Gilda. Teen Talk with Dr. Gilda: A Girl's Guide to Dating. 2003. 304p. pap. 12.95 (978-0-06-095871-8(5)) HarperCollins Pubs.

Cherry Lake Publishing, compiled by. LIfe Skills Biographics. 2008. lib. bdg. ***978-1-60279-110-7(4))** Cherry Lake Publishing.

Chronicle Books LLC Staff. 101 Things to Do While You Wait. (J). 15.95 (978-0-8118-3922-8(2)) Chronicle Bks. LLC.

Coping. 2005. 192p. (gr. 7-12). lib. bdg. 1735.65 (978-0-8239-3906-0(5)) Rosen Publishing Group, Inc., The.

Coping: A Resource for Curious Young Minds, 7 bks. Incl. Coping When You Are the Survivor of a Violent Crime. Moe, Barbara. 134p. (gr. 7-12). 1999. lib. bdg. 26.50 (978-0-8239-2873-6(X) , COSUVI); Coping with Braces & Other Orthodontic Work. Lee, Jordan. 95p. (gr. 7-12). 1998. lib. bdg. 26.50 (978-0-8239-2721-0(0) , COBROR); Coping with Drugs & Sports. Nelson, Elizabeth Ann. 118p. (gr. 7-12). 1999. lib. bdg. 26.50 (978-0-8239-2864-4(0) , CODRSP); Coping with Eating Disorders. Moe, Barbara. 149p. (gr. 7-12). 1999. lib. bdg. 26.50 (978-0-8239-2974-0(4) , COEADI); Coping with Peer Pressure. Kaplan, Leslie S., ed. 215p. 1999. lib. bdg. 26.50 (978-0-8239-2975-7(2) , COPEPR); Coping with Street Gangs. Webb, Margot. 168p. (gr. 7-12). 1999. lib. bdg. 26.50 (978-0-8239-2972-6(8) , COSTGA); Coping with Weapons & Violence at School & on Your Streets. Miller, Maryann. 189p. (gr. 7-12). 1999. lib. bdg. 26.50 (978-0-8239-2968-9(X) , COWESC); (YA). (Illus.). 1999. Set lib. bdg. 185.50 (978-0-8239-9298-0(5)) Rosen Publishing Group, Inc., The.

Coping: A Specialized Title for Everyone, 6 bks. Incl. Coping : Now You've Got Your Period. Mahoney, Ellen Voelckers. Rosen, Roger, ed. 192p. 1993. lib. bdg. 26.50 (978-0-8239-1662-7(6) , COPERI); Coping When a Parent Has Multiple Sclerosis. Cristall, Barbara. Rosen, Ruth C., ed. 192p. 1992. lib. bdg. 26.50 (978-0-8239-1406-7(2) , COPAMS); Coping When a Parent Is Gay. Miller, Deborah. Rosen, Ruth C., ed. 140p. 1992. lib. bdg. 26.50 (978-0-8239-1404-3(6) , COPAGA); Coping with a Physically Challenged Brother or Sister. Ratto, Linda Lee. Rosen, Ruth C., ed. 139p. 1992. lib. bdg. 26.50 (978-0-8239-1492-0(5) , COPHBR); Coping with an Immigrant Parent. Reynolds, Moira D. Rosen, Ruth C., ed. 192p. 1992. lib. bdg. 26.50 (978-0-8239-1462-3(3) , COIMPA); Coping with Special Needs Classmates. McCarthy-Tucker, Sherri N. 115p. 1993. lib. bdg. 25.25 (978-0-8239-1598-9(0) , COSPNE); (YA). (gr. 7-12). (Illus.). Set lib. bdg. 151.50 (978-0-8239-9303-1(5)) Rosen Publishing Group, Inc., The.

Coping: Complex Issues Tackled, 7 bks. Incl. Coping in a Dysfunctional Family. Jamiolkowski, Raymond M. 192p. 1998. lib. bdg. 26.50 (978-0-8239-2715-9(6) , CODYFA); Coping When You or a Friend Is HIV-Positive. Kelly, Pat. 192p. 1998. lib. bdg. 26.50 (978-0-8239-2626-8(5) , COHIPO); Coping with Birth Control. Benson, Michael D. Benson, Roger, ed. 192p. 1998. lib. bdg. 26.50 (978-0-8239-2620-6(6) , COBICO); Coping with Discrimination & Prejudice. Bowman-Kruhm, Mary & Wirths, Claudine G. 192p. 2005. lib. bdg. 26.50 (978-0-8239-3299-3(0) , CODIPR); Coping with PMS. Moe, Barbara. 152p. 1998. lib. bdg. 25.25 (978-0-8239-2716-6(4) , COPMS); Coping with Sexual Harassment & Gender Bias. Shaw, Victoria. 192p. 2005. lib. bdg. 26.50 (978-0-8239-3267-2(2) , COSEHA); Coping with the Dangers of Tattooing, Body Piercing & Branding. Wilkinson, Beth. 192p. 1998. lib. bdg. 26.50 (978-0-8239-2717-3(2) , COTABO); (YA). (gr. 7-12). (Illus.). 2005. Set lib. bdg. 185.50 (978-0-8239-9299-7(3)) Rosen Publishing Group, Inc., The.

Coping: Guidance to Cope with an Ever-Changing World, 7 bks. Incl. Coping in a Blended Family. Hurwitz, Jane. 192p. 1997. lib. bdg. 26.50 (978-0-8239-2077-8(1) , COBLFA); Coping Through Conflict Resolution & Peer Mediation. Simpson, Carolyn. 192p. 1998. lib. bdg. 26.50 (978-0-8239-2076-1(3) , COCORE); Coping with Confrontations & Encounters with the Police. Wirths, Claudine G. & Bowman-Kruhm, Mary. 192p. 1998. lib. bdg. 26.50 (978-0-8239-2431-8(9) , COENPO); Coping with Drinking & Driving. Grosshandler, Janet. 192p. 1997. lib. bdg. 26.50 (978-0-8239-2447-9(5) , CODRDR); Coping with Interracial Dating. Nichols, Renea D. 192p. 1997. lib. bdg. 26.50 (978-0-8239-2446-2(7) , COINDA); Coping with Satanism : Rumor, Reality & Controversy. Ottens, Allen & Myer, Rick. 192p. 1998. lib. bdg. 26.50 (978-0-8239-2711-1(3) , COSATA); Coping with Teenage Motherhood. Simpson, Carolyn. v, 127p. 1998. lib. bdg. 26.50 (978-0-8239-2569-8(2) , COTEMO); (YA). (gr. 7-12). (Illus.). 2005. Set lib. bdg. 159.00 (978-0-8239-9300-0(0)) Rosen Publishing Group, Inc., The.

Coping: Keeping Teens One Step Ahead, 7 bks. Incl. Coping with a Learning Disability. Clayton, Lawrence & Morrison, Jaydene. 121p. lib. bdg. 26.50 (978-0-8239-2887-3(X) , COLEDI); Coping with an Unplanned Pregnancy. Simpson, Carolyn. 174p. lib. bdg. 26.50 (978-0-8239-2867-5(5) , COUNPR); Coping with Asthma. Simpson, Carolyn. 140p. lib. bdg. 26.50 (978-0-8239-2969-6(8) , COASTH); Coping with Date Rape & Acquaintance Rape. Parrot, Andrea. 173p. lib. bdg. 26.50 (978-0-8239-2861-3(6) , CODARA); Coping with Scoliosis. Eisenpreis, Bettijane. 164p. lib. bdg. 26.50 (978-0-8239-2557-5(9) , COSCBA); Coping with Self-Mutilation : A Helping Book for Teens Who Hurt Themselves. Simpson, Carolyn & Clarke, Alicia. 104p. lib. bdg. 26.50 (978-0-8239-2559-9(5) , COSEMU); Coping with Teen Parenting. Beyer, Kay. 209p. lib. bdg. 26.50 (978-0-8239-3035-7(1) , COTEPA); (YA). (gr. 7-12). (Illus.). 1999. Set lib. bdg. 185.50 (978-0-8239-9297-3(7)) Rosen Publishing Group, Inc., The.

Coping: Learning to Deal with Life's Problems, 8 bks. Incl. Coping : A Young Woman's Guide to Breast Cancer Prevention. Eisenpreis, Bettijane. 192p. 2005. lib. bdg. 26.50 (978-0-8239-2967-2(1) , COBRCA); Coping with ADD/ADHD (Attention Deficit Disorder/Attention Deficity Hyperactivity Disorder) Morrison, Jaydene. 192p. 2005. lib. bdg. 26.50 (978-0-8239-3196-5(X) , COADDA); Coping with Cancer. Cefrey, Holly. 128p. 2000. lib. bdg. 26.50 (978-0-8239-2849-1(7) , COCANC); Coping with Dyslexia. Donnelly, Karen J. 192p. 2005. lib. bdg. 26.50 (978-0-8239-2850-7(0) , CODYSL); Coping with Grieving & Loss. Giddens, Sandra & Giddens, Owen. 122p. 2000. lib. bdg. 25.25 (978-0-8239-2894-1(2) , COGRLO); Coping with Stress. Packard, Gwen K. 192p. 2005. lib. bdg. 26.50 (978-0-8239-3042-5(4) , COSTRE); (YA). (gr. 7-12). (Illus.). 2000. Set lib. bdg. 202.00 (978-0-8239-9415-1(5)) Rosen Publishing Group, Inc., The.

Coping: Perplexing Problems & Situations Explained, 6 bks. Incl. Coping with Changing Roles for Young Men & Women. Hanan, Jessica. 192p. 2005. lib. bdg. 26.50 (978-0-8239-2880-4(2) , COGERO); Coping with Depression & Other Mood Disorders. Gelman, Amy. 192p. 2005. lib. bdg. 26.50 (978-0-8239-2973-3(6) , CODEMO); Coping with Stuttering. Apel, Melanie Ann. 192p. 2005. lib. bdg. 26.50 (978-0-8239-2970-2(1) , COSTUT); Coping with the Beauty Myth : A Guide for Real Girls. Weiss, Stefanie Iris. 112p. 2000. lib. bdg. 25.25 (978-0-8239-3033-3(5) , COBEAU); Coping with Tourette's Syndrome & Other Tic Disorders. Moe, Barbara. 128p. 2000. lib. bdg. 26.50 (978-0-8239-2976-4(0) , COTICS); Coping with Ulcers, Heartburn & Stress-Related Stomach Disorders. Monroe, Judy. 192p. 2005. lib. bdg. 26.50 (978-0-8239-2971-9(X) , COULCE); (YA). (gr. 7-12). (Illus.). 2000. Set lib. bdg. 151.50 (978-0-8239-9295-9(0)) Rosen Publishing Group, Inc., The.

Coping: Positive Intervention for Your Teens in Crisis, 6 bks. Incl. Coping on a Tight Budget. Clark, Betty. 137p. 1990. lib. bdg. 25.25 (978-0-8239-1184-4(5) , COTIBU); Coping with Academic Anxiety. Ottens, Allen J. 192p. 1991. lib. bdg. 26.50 (978-0-8239-1337-4(6) , COACAN); Coping with an Illiterate Parent. Rue, Nancy N. Rosen, Roger, ed. 192p. 1990. lib. bdg. 26.50 (978-0-8239-1070-0(9) , COILPA); Coping with Choosing a College. Buckalew, Walker. Rosen, Roger, ed. 192p. 1990. lib. bdg. 26.50 (978-0-8239-1079-3(2) , COCHCO); Coping with Chronic Illness. Moe, Barbara.

JKL

Rosen, Ruth C., ed. 1992. lib. bdg. 25.25 (978-0-8239-1464-7(X) , COCHIL); Coping with Parents Who Are Activists. Webb, Margot. Rosen, Ruth C., ed. 192p. 1992. lib. bdg. 26.50 (978-0-8239-1416-6(X) , COPAAC); (YA). (gr. 7-12). (Illus.). 2005. Set lib. bdg. 106.00 (978-0-8239-9416-8(3)) Rosen Publishing Group, Inc., The.

Coping: Problems Facing Today's Teens, 6 bks. Incl. Coping with Aggression. Emanuele, Patricia. lib. bdg. 26.50 (978-0-8239-3360-0(1)); Coping with an Abusive Relationship. Cobb, Carlene. lib. bdg. 26.50 (978-0-8239-2822-4(5)); Coping with Bipolar Disorder & Manic-Depressive Illness. Jovinelly, Joann. lib. bdg. 26.50 (978-0-8239-3193-4(5)); Coping with Media Violence. Cefrey, Holly. lib. bdg. 26.50 (978-0-8239-2893-4(4)); Coping with Rejection. Moe, Barbara. lib. bdg. 26.50 (978-0-8239-3362-4(8)); Coping with Social Anxiety. Moehn, Heather. lib. bdg. 26.50 (978-0-8239-3363-1(6)); 192p. (YA). (gr. 7-12). 2005. (Illus.). 2000. Set lib. bdg. 151.50 (978-0-8239-9414-4(7)) Rosen Publishing Group, Inc., The.

Coping: Working Against the Odds, 8 bks. Incl. Coping When a Brother or Sister Is Autistic. Rosenberg, Marsha Sarah. lib. bdg. 26.50 (978-0-8239-3194-1(3)); Coping When Someone in Your Family Has Cancer. Rocha, Toni L. lib. bdg. 26.50 (978-0-8239-3195-8(1)); Coping with Dangers on the Internet. Rothman, Kevin F. lib. bdg. 26.50 (978-0-8239-3201-6(X)); Coping with Leukemia. Apel, Melanie Ann. lib. bdg. 26.50 (978-0-8239-3200-9(1)); Coping with Lyme Disease. Donnelly, Karen J. lib. bdg. 26.50 (978-0-8239-3199-6(4)); Coping with Mental Illness. Moe, Barbara. lib. bdg. 26.50 (978-0-8239-3205-4(2)); Coping with Schizophrenia. Kelly, Pat. lib. bdg. 26.50 (978-0-8239-2853-8(5)); Coping with Vision Disorders. Stanley, Debbie. lib. bdg. 26.50 (978-0-8239-3198-9(6)); 192p. (YA). (gr. 7-12). 2005. (Illus.). Set lib. bdg. 202.00 (978-0-8239-9206-5(3)) Rosen Publishing Group, Inc., The.

Coping Set 10. 2005. (gr. 7-12). lib. bdg. 132.50 (978-0-8239-3946-6(4)) Rosen Publishing Group, Inc., The.

Coping Set 11. 2005. (gr. 7-12). lib. bdg. 159.00 (978-0-8239-3945-9(6)) Rosen Publishing Group, Inc., The.

Coping Set 12. 2005. (gr. 7-12). lib. bdg. 212.00 (978-0-8239-3944-2(8)) Rosen Publishing Group, Inc., The.

Coping Set 13. 2005. (gr. 7-12). lib. bdg. 291.50 (978-1-4042-0226-9(9)) Rosen Publishing Group, Inc., The.

Coping Set 14. 2005. (gr. 7-12). lib. bdg. 238.50 (978-1-4042-0224-5(2)) Rosen Publishing Group, Inc., The.

Coping Set 2. 2005. (gr. 7-12). lib. bdg. 79.50 (978-0-8239-4097-4(7)) Rosen Publishing Group, Inc., The.

Coping Set 4. 2005. (gr. 7-12). lib. bdg. 79.50 (978-0-8239-4096-7(9)) Rosen Publishing Group, Inc., The.

Courtney, Vicki. BeTween: A Preteen Girl's Guide to Life. 2006. (Illus.). 160p. (J). pap. 14.99 (978-0-8054-4193-2(X)) B&H Publishing Grp.

Covey, Sean. Los 7 Habitos de los Adolescentes Altamente Efectivos. 2003. (SPA., Illus.). 288p. pap. 16.95 (978-1-4000-5926-3(7)) Grijalbo Mondadori, S.A.-Junior ESP. *Dist:* Random Hse., Inc.

Critical Thinking, Cause & Effect, Inferences. 20p. (gr. 4-6). 5.99 (978-0-7682-0591-6(3) , FS1702) Schaffer, Frank Pubns.

Critical Thinking, Self-Awareness. 2002. (100+ Seriestm Ser.). 128p. (gr. k-1). 12.99 (978-0-88012-846-9(1) , IF8701) School Specialty Publishing.

Critical Thinking Skills. 20p. (gr. 1 up). 5.99 (978-0-7682-0582-4(4) , FS8490); (gr. 2-3). 5.99 (978-0-7682-0589-3(1) , FS8670) Schaffer, Frank Pubns.

Crow, Gary & Crow, Marissa. The Yes Bank. 2003. (Illus.). 73p. (J). pap. 9.95 (978-0-9718758-7-6(1)) Koenisha Pubns.

DePino, Catherine S. Hi God, It's Me! E-Prayers for Teenage Boys. 2002. (gr. 7-12). lib. bdg. 22.20 (978-0-613-79632-3(2)) Tandem Library Bks.

—Hi God, It's Me! E-Prayers for Teenage Girls. 2002. (gr. 7-12). lib. bdg. 22.20 (978-0-613-79634-7(9)) Tandem Library Bks.

Dewey D's Life Skills Curriculum. (J). ring bd. 95.00 (978-1-56230-706-6(1)) Syndistar, Inc.

Do I Have To? (Kids Talk Ser.). 32p. (J). 8.95 (978-1-4048-0363-3(7)) Picture Window Bks.

Do You Have What It Takes. 2007. (YA). per. 35.00 (***978-0-9661256-9-6(X)***) Youth Communication - New York Center.

Douglas, Vincent. My Little Heavenly Helper Assortment. 2003. (My Little Heavenly Helper of... Ser.). (Illus.). 64p. (C). pap. 167.52 (978-0-7696-3242-1(4) , American Education Publishing) School Specialty Publishing.

Earnhardt, Crystal. Race to Victory Lane. 2003. 75p. (YA). pap. 2.49 (978-0-8280-1775-6(1)) Review & Herald Publishing Assn.

Erlbach, Arlene. The Middle School Survival Guide: How to Survive from the Day Elementary School Ends until the Second High School Begins. Flook, Helen, illus. 2003. 160p. (J). 16.95 (978-0-8027-8852-8(1)); pap. 8.95 (978-0-8027-7657-0(4)) Walker & Co.

Espeland, Pamela. Life Lists for Teens: Tips, Steps, Hints, & How-tos for Growing up, Getting Al. 2003. (gr. 7-12). lib. bdg. 21.05 (978-0-613-63048-1(3)) Tandem Library Bks.

—Life Lists for Teens: Tips, Steps, Hints, & How-Tos for Growing up, Getting along, Learning, & Having Fun. 2004. 272p. (YA). (gr. 5 up). pap. 11.95 (978-1-57542-125-4(9) , 785) Free Spirit Publishing, Inc.

Everly, Nita. Early Social Behavior Books Can You Be a Helper? 2007. (J). spiral bd. 11.95 (***978-0-7606-0741-1(9)***) LinguiSystems, Inc.

Fairness. (Character Education Classroom Helpers Ser.). 24p. (gr. k up). 3.99 (978-0-7682-2630-0(9) , FS99072); (gr. 1 up). 3.99 (978-0-7682-2631-7(7) , FS99073); (gr. 2 up). 3.99 (978-0-7682-2632-4(5) , FS99074); (gr. 3 up). 3.99 (978-0-7682-2633-1(3) , FS99075) Schaffer, Frank Pubns.

Falk, Emily. 78 Things they Didn't Teach You in School: But You Do Need to Know. 2004. (Illus.). 123p. (YA). pap. 10.95 (978-1-58786-016-4(3) , Rabbit's Foot Pr.) Blue Mountain Arts Inc.

Fear Not My Child, I Am Here: Emerging from the Spiral of Fear the Practical Mystic's Guide for Embracing Your Heart's Desire. 2003rd ed. 2003. 240p. per. 15.95 (978-0-9742213-0-4(9)) Community Works!.

Feet First: The Kidskills America Training Series. 2001. (Kidskills America Training Ser.). 70p. (J). spiral bd. 12.95 (978-0-9710641-1-9(3) , Kidskills America) Kidskills International.

Fey, Sid & Vitello, Kathy. The Being Game: For the Love of Your Life. l.t. ed. 2004. (Illus.). 66p. per. 14.95 (978-0-9753530-5-9(5)) Fey, Sid Designs, Inc.

Follow Directions Carefully. 20p. (gr. k-1). 5.99 (978-0-7682-0577-0(8) , FS8451); (gr. 1-2). 5.99 (978-0-7682-0578-7(6) , FS8452); (gr. 2-3). 5.99 (978-0-7682-0579-4(4) , FS8453) Schaffer, Frank Pubns.

Following Directions. (Classroom Helpers Ser.). 24p. (gr. k up). 3.99 (978-0-7682-0809-2(2) , FS194108); (gr. 1 up). 3.99 (978-0-7682-0817-7(3) , FS194116) Schaffer, Frank Pubns.

Forgiveness: Where the Divine & the Human Meet. 2001. 29p. 4.75 (978-0-9679622-3-8(4) , Desert Waters Publishing) Cheadle Bks.

Forrest, Jan. Coming Home to Ourselves: A Woman's Journey to Wholeness. 2nd rev. ed. 1999. (Illus.). 172p. (Orig.). pap. 13.95 (978-0-9663602-1-9(4)) Heart to Heart Pr.

Foster, John. Llinynnau. 2005. (WEL., Illus.). 78p. (978-1-85644-327-2(2)) Univ. of Wales, Aberystwyth, Centre for Educational Studies.

Foster, John & Stewart, Peter. Llinynnau. 2005. (WEL., Illus.). 71p. (978-1-85644-328-9(0)) Univ. of Wales, Aberystwyth, Centre for Educational Studies.

Fry, Eva. Be a Winner in Life: How to Overcome the Trials & Tempatations of Life to Find. 2002. (gr. 7-12). lib. bdg. 24.00 (978-0-613-78039-1(6)) Tandem Library Bks.

Game Plan Learning Journal for Student Athletes. 2000. (Illus.). (YA). spiral bd. (978-1-931377-18-8(9)) Game Plan Pubns.

Giddens, Sandra & Giddens, Owen. Coping with Grieving & Loss. 2003. (Coping Ser.). 124p. (YA). (gr. 7-12). lib. bdg. 26.50 (978-0-8239-3758-5(5)) Rosen Publishing Group, Inc., The.

Girls Know Best, 7 bks. l.t. ed. Incl. Boys Know It All : Wise Thoughts & Wacky Ideas from Guys Like You. Roehm, Michelle, compiled by. 167p. 1999. lib. bdg. 23.33 (978-0-8368-2455-1(5)); Girls Know Best Vol. 2 : Tips on Life & Fun Stuff to Do. Monson-Burton, Marianne, compiled by. 1999. lib. bdg. 23.33 (978-0-8368-2453-7(9)); Girls Know Best Vol. 3 : Your Words, Your World. Monson-Burton, Marianne, compiled by. 153p. 2000. lib. bdg. 23.33 (978-0-8368-2672-2(8)); Girls Knows Best : Advice for Girls from Girls on Just about Everything. Roehm, Michelle, compiled by. 160p. 1999. lib. bdg. 23.33 (978-0-8368-2452-0(0)); Girls Who Rocked the World : Heroines from Sacagawea to Sheryl Swoopes. Welden, Amelie. McCann, Jerry, illus. 117p. 1999. lib. bdg. 23.33 (978-0-8368-2454-4(7)); Girls Who Rocked the World Vol. 2 : Heroines from Harriet Tubman to Mia Hamm. Roehm, Michelle, compiled by. 152p. 2000. lib. bdg. 23.33 (978-0-8368-2673-9(6)); Throw Like a Girl : Discovering the Body, Mind & Spirit of the Athlete in You! Frost, Shelley & Troussieux, Ann. 128p. 2000. lib. bdg. 23.33 (978-0-8368-2674-6(4)); (J); (gr. 3 up). (Illus.). Set lib. bdg. 163.31 (978-0-8368-2741-5(4)) Stevens, Gareth Inc.

Girls' Life Magazine Editors. The Girls' Life Guide to Growing Up. 2000. (J). (978-0-606-19485-3(1)) Tandem Library Bks.

Girls' Life Magazine Editors, ed. Girls' Life Guide to Growing Up. 2000. (gr. 5-8). lib. bdg. 21.05 (978-0-613-27853-9(4)) Tandem Library Bks.

Glencoe McGraw-Hill Staff. Discovering Life Skills (Formerly Young Living) 9th ed. 2003. (C). stu. ed. 53.32 (978-0-07-829847-9(4) , 9780078298479) Glencoe/ McGraw-Hill.

Going Through Tough Times. 2004. (Faith 4 Life Ser.). 48p. 14.99 (978-0-7644-2469-4(6) , Flagship Church Resources) Group Publishing, Inc.

Gomez Seitz, M. Stella. The Master Cookie-Maker: A True Life Story for Children. 2003. 133p. (J). pap. 13.95 (978-0-595-26314-1(3) , Writers Club Pr.) iUniverse, Inc.

Goode, Ben. Some Things Are Worse Than Being Older Than Dirt. Mecham, David, illus. 2001. 89p. (YA). per. 6.95 (978-1-885027-11-5(7)) Apricot Pr.

Gottesman, Gregg & Baer, Daniel, eds. High School Survival. 1999. (Illus.). 256p. (YA). (gr. 8-12). pap. 10.95 (978-0-02-863250-6(8)) Peterson's.

Halliburton, Calvin W. Stop & Think with the Evaporating Cloud. Halliburton, Calvin W., illus. 2002. (Illus.). 32p. 5.95 (978-0-9723421-0-0(9)) THINK?! Publishing.

Harcourt School Publishers Staff. Year by Year. 3rd ed. 2002. (Trophies English Language Learners Ser.). (Illus.). pap. 5.10 (978-0-15-327640-8(1)) Harcourt Schl. Pubs.

Harper, Kimberly. Unmasking Your Grief: Leader's Guide to a Workbook for Teens on Death, Grief & Loss. Steatton, David L., ed. 2000. 34p. (J). (gr. 12 up). spiral bd. 10.00 (978-0-9703035-3-0(X)) United Medical Ctr.

Harper, Kimberly & Rubeck, Sherri. Unmasking Your Grief: A Workbook for Teens on Death, Grief & Loss, 2 vols., set. Stratton, David L., ed. 2000. 21p. (J). (gr. 12 up). spiral bd. 8.50 (978-0-9703035-2-3(1)) United Medical Ctr.

HarperCollins Staff. Eric Carle Spinner Signage. 1999. (J). pap. (978-0-694-01353-1(6)) HarperCollins Pubs.

Harris-Johnson, Debrah. African-American Teenagers Guide to Personal Growth, Health, Saftey, Sex An. 2001. (gr. 7-12). lib. bdg. 30.35 (978-0-613-90283-0(1)) Tandem Library Bks.

Hawran, Mary. How to Be A Recycling Hero. 2004. (Illus.). 64p. (J). 6.95 (978-0-9753758-0-8(6)) Stourbridge Distributors, Inc.

Hollis, Randy. Meet Sneazle, 1. Rahn, Jess, illus. 2004. 20p. (J). 6.95 (978-0-9758815-0-7(7)) SNZ Publishing.

Holt, Rinehart and Winston Staff. A Lifetime of Health: Life Skills. 4th ed. Date not set. pap., wbk. ed. 11.20 (978-0-03-068117-2(0)) Holt, Rinehart & Winston.

Holyoke, Nancy. Yikes! A Smart Girl's Guide to Surviving Tricky, Sticky, Icky Situations. 2002. (gr. 3-6). lib. bdg. 17.60 (978-0-613-61138-1(1)) Tandem Library Bks.

Hutchinson, Emily. Car & Driver. 2003. (Saddleback Lifeskills Ser.). (Illus.). 48p. wbk. ed. 8.95 (978-1-56254-573-4(6) , SP 5736) Saddleback Educational Publishing.

—Everyday Household Tasks. 2003. (Saddleback Lifeskills Ser.). (Illus.). 48p. wbk. ed. 8.95 (978-1-56254-565-9(5) , SP 5655) Saddleback Educational Publishing.

—Moving Out on Your Own. 2003. (Saddleback Lifeskills Ser.). (Illus.). 48p. wbk. ed. 8.95 (978-1-56254-564-2(7) , SP 5647) Saddleback Educational Publishing.

Invading the Lost World, Grades 7-9. 1998. 64p. pap., tchr. ed. 15.00 incl. VHS (978-1-57405-312-8(4)) CharismaLife Pubs.

Johnson, Alice W. Candlelights for the High School Student's World: Transforming the World Through Deeds of Kindness. Mederos-Blanco, Ana, ed. 2002. 285p. (YA). (gr. 6-12). pap. 10.00 (978-0-9715031-1-3(7)) Mal-Jonal Productions, Inc.

Johnson, Leona. Strengthening Family & Self: Teaching Package Teacher's Annotated Edition. annot. ed. 845p. (gr. 9-12). tchr. ed. 69.00 (978-1-59070-123-2(2)) Goodheart-Willcox Pub.

—Strengthening Family & Self: Teaching Package Teacher's Resource Guide. 424p. (gr. 9-12). tchr. ed. 64.00 (978-1-59070-125-6(9)) Goodheart-Willcox Pub.

—Strengthening Family & Self: Teaching Package Teacher's Resource Portfolio. 460p. (gr. 9-12). tchr. ed. 136.00 (978-1-59070-126-3(7)) Goodheart-Willcox Pub.

Jones, Steven. Journey to Excellence: An Introduction to E4. 2003. 75p. (YA). per. 19.99 (978-0-9729798-0-1(8)) Keytochange Publishing, Inc.

Kaufman, Gershen. Stick up for Yourself! Every Kid's Guide to Personal Power & Positive Self-Es. 1999. (gr. 5-8). lib. bdg. 21.05 (978-0-613-65000-7(X)) Tandem Library Bks.

Keyishan, Elizabeth. El Cigarrillo. 2002. (Todo lo Que Necesitas Saber Ser.). (SPA & ENG., Illus.). 64p. (YA). lib. bdg. 26.50 (978-0-8239-3581-9(7) , Buenas Letra) Rosen Publishing Group, Inc., The.

King, Emily. Mrs. Twiggenbotham Goes to a Party. 2003. (Illus.). 32p. (J). 12.99 (978-0-8254-3065-7(8)) Kregel Pubns.

Kirberger, Kimberly. Teen Love, on Relationships: A Book for Teenagers. 1999. (Teen Love Ser.). (Illus.). 300p. (YA). (gr. 8-12). pap. 14.95 (978-1-55874-734-0(6)) Health Communications, Inc.

Kirberger, Kimberly & Mortensen, Colin. On Friendship. 2000. (Teen Love Ser.). (Illus.). 400p. (YA). (gr. 7-12). pap. 12.95 (978-1-55874-815-6(6)) Health Communications, Inc.

Kramer, Ann G. Life Puzzles for Teens. Zimmerman, Martin, illus. 2001. 77p. (J). (gr. 6-9). pap. 11.99 (978-0-9659426-1-4(9)) Good 4U, Inc.

Kuehn, Eileen. Divorce: Finding a Place. 2001. (Grief & Loss Ser.). (Illus.). 64p. (J). (gr. 4-6). lib. bdg. 23.93 (978-0-7368-0747-0(0) , LifeMatters Bks.) Capstone Pr., Inc.

Lakeshore Learning Materials Staff, contrib. by. Harvey Crumbaker Complete Skills for Living Library, 4 vols., Set. 2000. (J). pap. 110.00 (978-1-929255-93-1(4)) Lakeshore Learning Materials.

—Skills for Living No. 1: Filling Out Forms & Following Directions. 2000. (J). pap. 29.95 (978-1-929255-94-8(2)) Lakeshore Learning Materials.

Lee, James L. & Pulvino, Charles J. Self-Exploration Inventories: 16 Reproducible Self-Scoring Instruments. 3rd ed. 2002. 32p. (J). pap. 12.95 (978-1-930572-15-7(8)) Educational Media Corp.

The Letter Dd: Things I Can Do, 6 vols. (gr. k-2). 17.50 (978-0-7368-4103-0(2)) Red Brick Learning.

Lewellen, Judie. The Teen Body Book: A Guide to Your Changing Body. 1999. (Your Body, Your Self Bks.). (Illus.). 144p. (YA). (gr. 4-9). pap. 11.95 (978-0-7373-0165-6(1) , 01651W) McGraw-Hill/Contemporary.

Life Balance. 2004. (Illus.). 156.00 (978-0-531-19326-6(8)) Scholastic Library Publishing.

Lifeskills for Telling Time by the 1/2 Hour. 2001. 12p. (J). per. 4.95 (978-1-58532-105-6(2)) Basic Educational Materials, Pubs.

Lifeskills for Telling Time by the 1/4 Hour. 2001. 12p. (J). per., wbk. ed. 4.93 (978-1-58532-106-3(0)) Basic Educational Materials, Pubs.

Lifeskills for Telling Time by the Hour. 2001. 12p. (J). per., wbk. ed. 4.95 (978-1-58532-104-9(4)) Basic Educational Materials, Pubs.

Llewellyn, Claire. The Kid's Survival Guide. 2002. (Illus.). 96p. (J). pap. 9.95 (978-0-439-35325-0(4)) Scholastic, Inc.

Madison, Lynda. The Feelings Book: The Care & Keeping of Your Emotions. Bendell, Norm, illus. 2002. (American Girl Library). 104p. (J). (gr. 3-8). pap. 8.95 (978-1-58485-528-6(2)) American Girl Publishing, Inc.

Magness, Valerie. A Special Book about Me! 2004. 40p. spiral bd. 10.00 (978-1-4116-2500-6(5)) Lulu.com.

Mahler, Deena E. 204 Fold & Say Social Skills. DeShong, Molly et al, eds. 2001. (Illus.). (J). (ps-4). spiral bd. 29.95 (978-1-58650-208-9(5)) Super Duper Pubns.

Maltbie, Karen. I Am the Leader of My Own Parade. Shubeck, Patricia K., illus. 2000. 36p. (J). (gr. k-5). 15.00 (978-0-9670934-1-3(4)) Magic Shoes Pr.

McGraw-Hill Staff. Creative Living. 7th ed. 1999. 384p. (C). stu. ed. 64.64 (978-0-02-648144-1(8) , 9780026481441) Glencoe/McGraw-Hill.

McGraw, Jay. Life Strategies for Teens. 2000. (Illus.). 240p. (YA). (gr. 8-12). pap. 14.95 (978-0-7432-1546-6(X) , Fireside) Simon & Schuster.

McTavish, Sandra. Life Skills: 225 Ready-to-Use Health Activities for Success & Well-Being (Grades 6-12) 2003. (Illus.). 288p. pap. 29.95 (978-0-7879-6959-2(1)) Wiley, John & Sons, Inc.

Mitchell, Jason. Class Is in Session: And So Is Life. 2001. (gr. 7-12). lib. bdg. 22.20 (978-0-613-85095-7(5)) Tandem Library Bks.

Monson-Burton, Marianne. Girls Know Best Vol. 3: Your Words, Your World. 1999. (gr. 3-6). lib. bdg. 17.60 (978-0-613-33368-9(3)) Tandem Library Bks.

Monson-Burton, Marianne, compiled by. Girls Know Best Vol. 3: Your Words, Your World. l.t. ed. 2000. (Girls Know Best Ser.). (Illus.). 153p. (J). (gr. 3 up). lib. bdg. 23.33 (978-0-8368-2672-2(8)) Stevens, Gareth Inc.

Mosatche, Harriet S. Too Old for This, Too Young for That: Your Survival Guide for the Middle-School. 2000. (gr. 5-8). lib. bdg. 24.55 (978-0-613-89619-1(X)) Tandem Library Bks.

Moss, Marissa. Amelia's Bully Survival Guide. 2030. (Amelia's Notebooks). (Illus.). (J). pap. 5.99 (978-1-4169-1288-0(6) , Aladdin) Simon & Schuster Children's Publishing.

Mulcahy, Lisa, et al. Bye Bye Boredom! The Girl's Life Big Book of Fun. 2003. (Illus.). 124p. (J). (978-0-439-44976-2(6)) Scholastic, Inc.

Mumford, Sally & Mackinnon, Debbie. What If. 2000. (Illus.). 192p. pap. 13.99 (978-0-09-185609-0(4)) Random Hse. GBR. *Dist:* Independent Pubs. Group.

National Crime Prevention Council (U.S.) Staff, contrib. by. McGruff & Scruff's Stories & Activities for Children of Promise. 2004. (Illus.). 24p. (J). (978-1-59686-001-8(4)) National Crime Prevention Council.

Navarra, Tova. The Kids' Guidebook: Great Advice to Help Kids Cope. Kerr, Tom, illus. 2nd ed. 2002. 128p. (J). (gr. 2-7). pap. 10.95 (978-0-7641-2066-4(2)) Barron's Educational Series, Inc.

—Young People. 2002. Tr. of Tough Problems. (gr. 5-8). lib. bdg. 15.25 (978-0-613-83481-0(X)) Tandem Library Bks.

The Need to Know Library: Dealing with Life's Issues, 7 vols. Incl. Everything You Need to Know about Being a Babysitter : A Teen's Guide to Responsible Child Care. Weintraub, Aileen. (J). (gr. 4-6). 2000. lib. bdg. 25.25 (978-0-8239-3085-2(8) , NTBASI); Everything You Need to Know about Cerebral Palsy. Pincus, Dion. (YA). (gr. 7-12). 2005. lib. bdg. 25.25 (978-0-8239-2960-3(4) , NTCEPA); Everything You Need to Know about Getting a Job. Frisch, Carlienne A. (YA). (gr. 7-12). 2005. lib. bdg. 25.25 (978-0-8239-2961-0(2) , NTGEJO); Everything You Need to Know about Living on Your Own. Krohn, Katherine E. (YA). (gr. 7-12). 2005. lib. bdg. 25.25 (978-0-8239-3088-3(2) , NTLIOW); Everything You Need to Know about the Art of Leadership : How to Be a Positive Influence in Your Home, School & Community. Cefrey, Holly. (YA). (gr. 7-12). 2005. lib. bdg. 25.25 (978-0-8239-3217-7(6) , NTLEAD); Everything You Need to Know about the Dangers of Overachieving : A Guide for Relieving Pressure & Anxiety. Giacobello, John. (YA). (gr. 7-12). 2005. lib. bdg. 25.25 (978-0-8239-3107-1(2) , NTOVAC); Everything You Need to Know about Virginity. Sommers, Michael A. & Sommers, Annie Leah. (YA). (gr. 7-12). 2005. lib. bdg. 25.25 (978 0-8239-3115-6(3) , NTVIRG); Everything You Need to Know When a Brother or Sister Is Autistic. Rosenberg, Marsha Sarah. (YA). (gr. 7-12). 2005. lib. bdg. 25.25 (978-0-8239-3123-1(4) , NTAUTI); 64p. (Illus.). 2000. Set lib. bdg. 202.00 (978-0-8239-9281-2(0)) Rosen Publishing Group, Inc., The.

The Need to Know Library: Learning to Deal with Problems Facing Every Teen, 9 bks. Incl. Everything You Need to Know about Cancer. Massari, Francesca. (YA). (gr. 7-12). 2005. lib. bdg. 25.25 (978-0-8239-3164-4(1) , NTCANC); Everything You Need to Know about Dealing with Stalking. Wright, Cynthia. (YA). (gr. 7-12). 2005. lib. bdg. 25.25 (978-0-8239-2841-5(1) , NTSTAL); Everything You Need to Know about Drug Abuse. Herscovitch, Arthur. (YA). (gr. 7-12). 2005. lib. bdg. 25.25 (978-0-8239-3036-4(X) , NTGUGU); Everything You Need to Know about Eating Smart. Weintraub, Aileen. (YA). (gr. 7-12). 2005. lib. bdg. 25.25 (978-0-8239-3082-1(3) , NTEASM); Everything You Need to Know about Looking & Feeling Your Best : A Guide for Girls. Sommers, Annie Leah. (YA). (gr. 7-12). 2005. lib. bdg. 25.25 (978-0-8239-3079-1(3) , NTGUWO); Everything You Need to Know about Looking & Feeling Your Best : A Guide for Guys. Sommers, Michael A. (YA). (gr. 7-12). 2005. lib. bdg. 25.25 (978-0-8239-3080-7(7) , NTGUGU); Everything You Need to Know about Mehndi, Temporary Tattoos & Other Body Arts. Weiss, Stefanie Iris. (J). (gr. 4-6). 2000. lib. bdg. 25.25 (978-0-8239-3086-9(6) , NTMEND); Everything You Need to Know about Public Speaking. Blumstein, Rachel. (YA). (gr. 7-12). 2005. lib. bdg. 25.25 (978-0-8239-3087-6(4) , NTPUSP); Ev-

JKL

erything You Need to Know about Weapons in School & at Home. Schleifer, Jay. (YA). (gr. 7-12). 2005. lib. bdg. 25.25 (978-0-8239-3315-0(6)); 64p. (Illus.). Set lib. bdg. 227.25 (978-0-8239-9283-6(7)) Rosen Publishing Group, Inc., The.

The Need to Know Library: Overcoming Life's Obstacles, 8 bks. Incl. Everything You Need to Know about Bias Incidents. 2nd rev. ed. Osborn, Kevin. (gr. 7-12). 1997. lib. bdg. 25.25 (978-0-8239-2600-8(1) , NTBIIN); Everything You Need to Know about Getting Your Period. Rue, Nancy N. (gr. 7-12). 1995. lib. bdg. 25.25 (978-0-8239-1870-6(X) , NTGEPE); Everything You Need to Know about Grieving. rev. ed. Spies, Karen Bornemann. (gr. 4-6). 1997. lib. bdg. 25.25 (978-0-8239-2623-7(0) , NTGRIE); Everything You Need to Know about Incest. rev. ed. Spies, Karen Bornemann. (gr. 4-6). 1997. lib. bdg. 25.25 (978-0-8239-2607-7(9) , NTINCE); Everything You Need to Know about Teen Marriage. rev. ed. Ayer, Eleanor H. (gr. 4-6). 1997. lib. bdg. 25.25 (978-0-8239-2502-5(1) , NTTEMA); Everything You Need to Know about the Dangers of Hazing. Schleifer, Jay. (gr. 4-6). 1996. lib. bdg. 25.25 (978-0-8239-2217-8(0) , NTHAZI); Everything You Need to Know about Your Parent's Divorce. rev. ed. Johnson, Linda Carlson. (gr. 7-12). 1998. lib. bdg. 25.25 (978-0-8239-2876-7(4) , NTPDIV); Everything You Need to Know When a Parent Is Out of Work. rev. ed. St. Pierre, Stephanie. (gr. 7-12). 1997. lib. bdg. 25.25 (978-0-8239-2608-4(7) , NTPAOU); 64p. (YA). (Illus.). Set lib. bdg. 202.00 (978-0-8239-9441-0(4)) Rosen Publishing Group, Inc., The.

The Need to Know Library: Solutions to Complicated Problems, 8 bks. Incl. Everything You Need to Know about an Addictive Personality. Bridgers, Jay. 1998. lib. bdg. 25.25 (978-0-8239-2777-7(6) , NTADPE); Everything You Need to Know about Asthma. Simpson, Carolyn. 1998. lib. bdg. 25.25 (978-0-8239-2567-4(6) , NTASTH); Everything You Need to Know about Dealing with Losses. Weiss, Stefanie Iris. 2000. lib. bdg. 25.25 (978-0-8239-3302-0(4)); Everything You Need to Know about Mononucleosis. Smart, Paul. 1998. lib. bdg. 25.25 (978-0-8239-2550-6(1) , NTMONO); Everything You Need to Know about Protecting Yourself & Others from Abduction. Wiloch, Thomas. 1998. lib. bdg. 25.25 (978-0-8239-2553-7(6) , NTABPR); Everything You Need to Know about Teen Fatherhood. Ayer, Eleanor H. 1998. lib. bdg. 25.25 (978-0-8239-2842-2(X) , NTTEFA); Everything You Need to Know about Your Legal Rights. Fox, Ken. 1998. lib. bdg. 25.25 (978-0-8239-2872-9(1) , NTLERI); Everything You Need to Know When Someone You Know Has Been Killed. Schleifer, Jay. 1998. lib. bdg. 25.25 (978-0-8239-2779-1(2) , NTKILL); 64p. (YA). (gr. 4-6). (Illus.). Set lib. bdg. 202.00 (978-0-8239-9287-4(X)) Rosen Publishing Group, Inc., The.

Neusom, Sherman. Big Fat Hunka Cheese's Quest Restored Svelte. 2003. (J). per. 799.00 (978-0-9742811-6-2(6)) Milligan Bks., Inc.

Nip It in the Bud. 2003. (Humble Heart Ser.). (J). spiral bd. (978-0-9746148-3-0(1)) Common Courtesy.

Njuguna, Isaac. Teenage Life Strategies - the Joy of Building on a Firm Foundation. 2007. 96p. per. (***978-1-84685-526-9(8)*** , Exposure Publishing) Meadow Bks.

Parnell, Frances Baynor. Skills for Living: Student Activity Guide. 2001. 172p. (J). pap., stu. ed. 11.96 (978-1-56637-776-8(5)) Goodheart-Willcox Pub.

Piven, Joshua & Borgenicht, David. The Worst-Case Scenario Survival Handbook. 1999. (Illus.). 176p. (gr. 7-12). per. 24.55 (978-0-613-33989-6(4)) Tandem Library Bks.

Pritchard, M. Ann. Phil the Pill & Friends: Making Positive Choices. 2005. (Illus.). 75p. (J). per. 11.99 (978-0-9772210-0-4(8)) MAMP Creations.

Raine, Alison. Ultimate You! 365 Days to a More Daring, Deep, & Adorable You. 2001. (gr. 7-12). lib. bdg. 13.00 (978-0-613-33175-3(3)) Tandem Library Bks.

Raintree Steck-Vaughn Staff. You Are Not Alone: Arkansas Edition, 18 bks., Set. 2003. (Illus.). (J). 491.82 (978-1-4109-0158-3(0)) Raintree.

Reybold, Laura. Los Peligros del Tatuaje y el Body Piercing. 2002. (Todo lo Que Necesitas Saber Ser.). (ENG & SPA., Illus.). 64p. (YA). lib. bdg. 26.50 (978-0-8239-3579-6(5)) Rosen Publishing Group, Inc., The.

Riso, Walter. Ama y no Sufras. (SPA.). (J). 12.99 (978-958-04-7529-3(6)) Norma S.A. COL. *Dist:* Distribuidora Norma, Inc.

Roca, Nuria. Mind Your Manners: On Vacation. Curto, Rosa M., illus. 2005. (Mind Your Manners Ser.). 36p. (J). pap. 6.95 (978-0-7641-3169-1(9)) Barron's Educational Series, Inc.

Rodell, Joysanna. Picture Story Cards Teaching Positive Life Lessons to Children. Martin, Roger, illus. 2000. (Fun Fables for Kids Ser.). (J). (ps-3). 26.95 (978-0-9702267-0-9(5)) Mountain Meadow Pr.

Roehm, Michelle, compiled by. Boys Know It All: Wise Thoughts & Wacky Ideas from Guys Like You. l.t. ed. 1999. (Girls Know Best Ser.). (Illus.). 167p. (J). (gr. 3 up). lib. bdg. 23.33 (978-0-8368-2455-1(5)) Stevens, Gareth Inc.

Roehm, Michelle, ed. Girls Know Best: Advice for Girls on Just about Everything. Roth, Marci Doane, illus. 1999. 160p. (J). (gr. 4-7). 6.98 (978-1-56731-313-0(2) , MJF Bks.) Fine Communications.

Rubin, Emily & Laurent, Amy, creators. The Feelings Book. 2002. (J). 29.00 (978-0-9749343-0-3(5)) Communication Crossroads.

Rush, Ryan. Home on Time: Life Management by the Book. 2003. 192p. per. 10.99 (978-0-9728899-0-2(6)) 21st Century Pr.

Salas, Laura Purdie. Taking the Plunge. 2004. (Illus.). 250p. (J). pap. 12.95 (978-1-58760-012-8(9) , 10129, Child & Family Pr.) Child Welfare League of America, Inc.

Saul, "Aunt" Laya. You Don't Have to Learn Everything the Hard Way: What I Wish Someone Had Told Me. 2004. 214p. (YA). per. 14.95 net. (978-0-9723229-4-2(9)) Kadima Pr.

Schleifer, Jay. Cuando Alguien a Quien Conoces Ha Muerto. 2002. (Todo lo Que Necesitas Saber Ser.). (ENG & SPA., Illus.). 64p. (YA). lib. bdg. 26.50 (978-0-8239-3583-3(3) , Buenas Letra) Rosen Publishing Group, Inc., The.

School Specialty Publishing. Fairness. 2003. (Character Education Classroom Helpers Ser.). 24p. (J). (gr. 4 up). pap. 3.99 (978-0-7682-2634-8(1) , FS99076); (gr. 5 up). pap. 3.99 (978-0-7682-2635-5(X) , FS99077) Schaffer, Frank Pubns.

Schwartz, Stuart B. Finding an Apartment. 1998. (Life Skills Ser.). (J). lib. bdg. (978-0-516-21462-7(4) , Children's Pr.) Scholastic Library Publishing.

—Living on Your Own. 1998. (Life Skills Ser.). (J). lib. bdg. (978-0-516-21294-4(X) , Children's Pr.) Scholastic Library Publishing.

—Setting Career Goals. 1998. (J). lib. bdg. (978-0-516-21297-5(4) , Children's Pr.) Scholastic Library Publishing.

Schwartz, Stuart B. & Conley, Craig. Finding an Apartment. (Life Skills-Career Bks.). 48p. pap. 6.95 (978-0-7368-8508-9(0) , LifeMatters Bks.) Capstone Pr., Inc.

Smithee, Allan. Crazy Days. 2002. (J). 14.95 (978-1-58728-449-6(9)); pap. 7.95 (978-1-58728-509-7(6)) T&N Children's Publishing. (Two Can Publishing).

Sonya, Wesley. Game Plan Career/Entrepreneur Journal for Student Athletes: A Discussion & Activity Tool. 2000. (Sport Ser.). (YA). spiral bd. (978-1-931377-26-3(X)) Game Plan Pubns.

—Game Plan Education/Socialization Journal for Student Athletes. 2000. (Sport Ser.). (YA). spiral bd. (978-1-931377-21-8(9)) Game Plan Pubns.

Staudacher, Carol. Getting Ahead at Work. 2003. (Saddleback Lifeskills Ser.). (Illus.). 48p. wbk. ed. 8.95 (978-1-56254-570-3(1) , SP 5701) Saddleback Educational Publishing.

—Job Search. 2003. (Saddleback Lifeskills Ser.). (Illus.). 48p. wbk. ed. 8.95 (978-1-56254-569-7(8) , SP 5698) Saddleback Educational Publishing.

Stewart, Bridgett. No Matter What. 2002. per. 12.99 (978-0-9652827-1-0(6)) Blue-Black Pr.

Stewart, Jan. Stars Knowing Yourself. 2004. (Illus.). 32p. (J). pap. 9.95 (978-0-89793-311-7(7)) Hunter Hse., Inc.

Storeby, Jordan. A Boy's Book of Daily Thoughts: For Ages 8 To 12. 2004. 374p. (J). pap. 12.95 (978-0-929636-20-7(1)) Syren Bk. Co.

Sullivan, James Kevin, illus. What Went RIght Today? Journal: WWRT Journal. 2007. 72p. (J). spiral bd. 12.95 (***978-0-9766990-1-9(X)***) Buz-Land Presentations, Inc.

Suter, Joanne. Community Resources. 2003. (Saddleback Lifeskills Ser.). (Illus.). 48p. wbk. ed. 8.95 (978-1-56254-571-0(X) , SP 571X) Saddleback Educational Publishing.

—Health & Safety. 2003. (Saddleback Lifeskills Ser.). (Illus.). 48p. wbk. ed. 8.95 (978-1-56254-566-6(3) , SP 5663) Saddleback Educational Publishing.

—Public Transportation & Travel. 2003. (Saddleback Lifeskills Ser.). (Illus.). 48p. wbk. ed. 8.95 (978-1-56254-572-7(8) , SP 5728) Saddleback Educational Publishing.

Swain, Claudia. What's a Girl to Do? 2004. 128p. pap. 6.99 (978-1-56309-440-8(1)) New Hope Pubs.

Swain, Gwenyth. Get Dressed! 2003. (Illus.). 24p. (J). (ps-2). pap. 6.95 (978-1-57505-159-8(1)) Lerner Publishing Group.

—Get Dressed! 2002. (gr. k-3). lib. bdg. 15.25 (978-0-613-46071-2(5)) Tandem Library Bks.

Taylor, Sally. On My Own: The Ultimate How-to Guide for Young Adults. (YA). 2002. cd-rom 19.95 (978-0-9711500-2-7(8)); 2nd ed. 2004. (Illus.). 640p. (gr. 11-12). reprint ed. per. 34.95 incl. cd-rom (978-0-9711500-0-3(1)) Silly Goose Productions, LLC.

Teen Magazine Editorial Staff, contrib. by. Secret Life of Guys. 2001. 128p. (J). (gr. 7-12). pap. 4.99 (978-0-439-11468-4(3)) Scholastic, Inc.

Timmons, Bonnie, illus. Yikes! A Smart Girl's Guide to Surviving Tricky, Sticky, Icky Situations. 2002. (American Girl Library). 88p. (gr. 3 up). pap. 8.95 (978-1-58485-530-9(4)) American Girl Publishing, Inc.

Understanding Catechesis. 2004. (Effective Dre Ser.). pap. (978-0-8294-1054-9(6)) Loyola Pr.

Underwood, Stacy L. Challenges & Choices: A Teen's Personal Guide for a Successful Progression Into Adulthood. 2001. (Illus.). 136p. (gr. 7-12). pap. 14.95 (978-0-595-16266-6(5)) iUniverse, Inc.

Vargas, Daraciela, adapted by. Refranero Popular de Puerto Rico. 2003. lib. bdg. 10.99 (978-0-9702021-5-4(6)) Conexion Educativa.

Veillette, Sally M. Coming to Your Senses: Soaring with Your Soul. 2005. (Illus.). 251p. pap. 19.95 (978-0-9741854-1-5(8)) Pop the Cork Publishing.

Wandberg, Robert. Life Skills - Contemporary Issues, 12 bks. Incl. Change : Making the Best of It. (J). lib. bdg. 23.93 (978-0-7368-0700-5(4)); Communication : Creating Understanding. (J). lib. bdg. 23.93 (978-0-7368-0693-0(8)); Conflict Resolution : Communication, Cooperation, Compromise. (J). lib. bdg. 23.93 (978-0-7368-0695-4(4)); Creative Problem Solving : What's a Better Way? (J). lib. bdg. 23.93 (978-0-7368-0694-7(6)); Ethics : Doing the Right Thing. (J). lib. bdg. 23.93 (978-0-7368-0699-2(7)); Making Tough Decisions : Working Through Hard Choices. (J). lib. bdg. 23.93 (978-0-7368-0697-8(0)); Peer Mediation : Agreeing on Solutions. (J). lib. bdg. 23.93 (978-0-7368-1023-4(4)); Resilience : Bouncing off, Bouncing Back. (J). lib. bdg. 23.93 (978-0-7368-0698-5(9)); Self-Acceptance : Building Confidence. Kaufman, Roberta Brack & Shepich, Millie. (YA). lib. bdg. 23.93 (978-0-7368-1024-1(2)); Self-Direction : Taking Positive Risks, Following Your Dreams. (J). lib. bdg. 23.93 (978-0-7368-0696-1(2)); Tolerance : Celebrating Differences. (J). lib. bdg. 23.93 (978-0-7368-1021-0(8)); Volunteering : Giving Back. (YA). lib. bdg. 23.93 (978-0-7368-1022-7(6)); 64p. (gr. 4-6). 2000. (Illus.). 2001. Set lib. bdg. 287.16 (978-0-7368-1037-1(4) , LifeMatters Bks.) Capstone Pr., Inc.

Warfield, Barbara J. Basic Christian Life Skills for Teens Vol. 1: Light It up - Living as Children of Light. Jones, Stephanie, illus. 1999. 40p. (YA). (gr. 6-12). stu. ed. 2.00 (978-1-929127-02-3(2)) N His Will Ministries.

Webster, Jeanne. If You Could Be Anything What Would You Be? A Teen's Guide to Mapping Out the Future. Nelson, Dianne, ed. 2004. (Illus.). 137p. (J). (gr. 5 up). pap. 19.95 (978-0-9749199-0-4(X)) Dupuis North Publishing.

Weierbach, Jane & Phillips-Hershey, Elizabeth. Mind over Basketball: Coach Yourself to Handle Stress. Beyl, Charles, illus. 2007. 48p. (J). (gr. 3-7). 14.95 (***978-1-4338-0135-8(3)*** , 4418006); pap. 8.95 (***978-1-4338-0136-5(1)*** , 4418007) American Psychological Assn. (Magination Pr.).

Wesley, Sonya L. Confidence Life-Skills, Life-Style Journal for Student Athletes: A Discussion & Activity Tool. 2000. (Sport Ser.). spiral bd. (978-0-9706421-3-4(X)) Game Plan Pubns.

—Game Plan Career Entrepreneur: A Discussion & Activity Tool. 2000. (Illus.). (YA). spiral bd. (978-1-931377-10-2(3)) Game Plan Pubns.

—Game Plan Conflict Resolution: A Discussion & Activity Tool. 2000. (Sport Ser.). (Illus.). (YA). spiral bd. (978-1-931377-07-2(3)) Game Plan Pubns.

—Game Plan Conflict Resolution Journal for Student Athletes: A Discussion & Activity Tool. 2000. (Sport Ser.). (YA). spiral bd. (978-1-931377-23-2(5)) Game Plan Pubns.

—Game Plan Curriculum for Student Athletes: A Discussion & Activity Tool. 2000. (Sport Ser.). (Illus.). (YA). spiral bd. (978-0-9706421-2-7(1)) Game Plan Pubns.

—Game Plan Education/Socialization: A Discussion & Activity Program. 2000. (Sports Ser.). (Illus.). (YA). spiral bd. (978-1-931377-11-9(1)) Game Plan Pubns.

—Game Plan Ethical Decision Making: A Discussion & Activity Tool. 2000. (Illus.). (YA). spiral bd. (978-1-931377-08-9(1)) Game Plan Pubns.

—Game Plan Ethical Decision Making Journal for Student Athletes: A Discussion & Activity Tool. 2000. (Sport Ser.). (YA). spiral bd. (978-1-931377-24-9(3)) Game Plan Pubns.

—Game Plan Individual Learning Styles: A Discussion & Activity Tool. 2000. (Sport Ser.). (Illus.). spiral bd. (978-1-931377-04-1(9)) Game Plan Pubns.

—Game Plan Mind/Body Training & Conditioning: A Discussion & Activity Program. 2000. (Sport Ser.). (Illus.). (YA). spiral bd. (978-1-931377-05-8(7)) Game Plan Pubns.

—Game Plan Mind/Body Training Journal for Student Athletes. 2000. (YA). spiral bd. (978-1-931377-20-1(0)) Game Plan Pubns.

—Game Plan Offensive/Defensive Living: A Discussion & Activity Tool. 2000. (Sport Ser.). (Illus.). (YA). spiral bd. (978-1-931377-06-5(5)) Game Plan Pubns.

—Game Plan Offensive/Defensive Living Journal for Student Athletes: A Discussion & Activity Tool. 2000. (Sport Ser.). (YA). spiral bd. (978-1-931377-22-5(7)) Game Plan Pubns.

—Game Plan Personality Styles: A Discussion & Activity Tool. 2000. (Illus.). (YA). spiral bd. (978-1-931377-01-0(4)) Game Plan Pubns.

—Game Plan Personality Styles Journal for Student Athletes. 2000. (Sport Ser.). (Illus.). (YA). spiral bd. (978-1-931377-16-4(2)) Game Plan Pubns.

—Game Plan Team/Individuality: A Discussion & Active Learning Tool. 2000. (Sport Ser.). (Illus.). (YA). spiral bd. 30.00 (978-1-931377-02-7(2)) Game Plan Pubns.

—Game Plan Team/Individuality Journal for Student Athletes: A Discussion & Activity Tool. 2000. (Sport Ser.). (Illus.). (YA). spiral bd. (978-1-931377-17-1(0)) Game Plan Pubns.

—Game Plan World of Sports: A Discussion & Activity Tool. 2000. (Sport Ser.). (Illus.). (YA). spiral bd. (978-1-931377-09-6(X)) Game Plan Pubns.

—Game Plan World of Sports Journal for Student Athletes: A Discussion & Activity Tool. 2000. (Sport Ser.). (YA). spiral bd. (978-1-931377-25-6(1)) Game Plan Pubns.

Wesley, Wesley. Game Plan Individual Learning Styles Journal for Student Athletes. 2000. (Sport Ser.). (Illus.). (YA). spiral bd. (978-1-931377-19-5(7)) Game Plan Pubns.

West, Patricia E. The Common Sense Book of Change. 3rd rev. ed. 2000. Orig. Title: Aquarium Book of Change. 190p. (YA). (gr. 5 up). pap. 7.50 (978-0-9670063-1-4(7)) +A Positive Action Pr.

Weston, Carol. For Teens Only: Quotes, Notes, & Advice You Can Use. 2002. (gr. 7-12). lib. bdg. 17.60 (978-0-613-82532-0(2)) Tandem Library Bks.

Whitney, Brooks. How to Survive Almost Anything. 2004. (Illus.). 80p. (J). pap. (***978-0-439-57900-1(7)***) Scholastic, Inc.

Wilde, Gary, et al. Handling Conflict. 2003. (Faith 4 Life Ser.). (Illus.). 48p. 14.99 (978-0-7644-2494-6(7) , Flagship Church Resources) Group Publishing, Inc.

Williams, Anna Graf, et al. The Family Guide to the American Workplace. Williams, Anna Graf, ed. 2003. (Illus.). 272p. per. 31.00 (978-0-9705790-4-1(7) , 866/332-5905) Learnovation, LLC.

World Book, Inc. Staff, contrib. by. Eating for Health, 5 vols., Vol. 3. 2002. (Illus.). (J). (978-0-7166-6703-2(7)) World Bk., Inc.

—Looking Your Best, 5 vols., Vol. 2. 2002. (Illus.). (J). (978-0-7166-6702-5(9)) World Bk., Inc.

—Recognizing Your Emotions, 5 vols., Vol. 5. 2002. (Illus.). (J). (978-0-7166-6705-6(3)) World Bk., Inc.

—Stayin in Shape, 5 vols., Vol. 1. 2002. (Illus.). (J). (978-0-7166-6701-8(0)) World Bk., Inc.

—Understanding Sexuality, 5 vols., Vol. 4. 2002. (Illus.). (J). (978-0-7166-6704-9(5)) World Bk., Inc.

Youngs, Bettie. Taste Berries for Teens: Inspirational Short Stories & Encouragement on Life. 1999. (gr. 7-12). lib. bdg. 22.20 (978-0-613-17746-7(0)) Tandem Library Bks.

Zellmann, Anton Josef. I Read Minds: And So Do You! l.t. ed. 2005. (Illus.). 264p. 35.00 (978-0-9763325-0-3(7)) Zellmann Publishing, LLC.

Zientek, Joan A. Mrs. Ruby's Life Lessons for Kids: Essential Skills for Increasing Emotional Quotient. Norcross, Harry, illus. 2001. 143p. (J). (gr. 3-5). pap. 19.95 (978-1-57543-094-2(0)) MAR*CO Products, Inc.

LIFE SUPPORT SYSTEMS (SPACE ENVIRONMENT)

see also Astronauts—Clothing; Project Apollo

Bredeson, Carmen. Nave Espacial. 2004. (Rookie Readers - Spanish Ser.). (J). 19.50 (978-0-516-25101-1(5) , Watts, Franklin) Scholastic Library Publishing.

Hayden, Kate. Astronaut: Living in Space. 2000. (Eyewitness Readers Ser.). (J). 10.79 (978-0-606-19376-4(6)) Tandem Library Bks.

—Astronaut Living in Space. 2000. (gr. k-3). lib. bdg. 11.80 (978-0-613-24252-3(1)) Tandem Library Bks.

Royston, Angela. Space. (Extreme Survival Ser.). (Illus.). 32p. (J). 2004. pap. 7.95 (978-1-4109-0363-1(X)); 2003. lib. bdg. 25.70 (978-1-4109-0004-3(5)) Raintree.

Whitehouse, Patricia. Living in Space. 2004. (J). 24.21 (978-1-4034-5151-4(6)); pap. 6.95 (978-1-4034-5655-7(0)) Heinemann Library.

LIFESAVING

Clements, Andrew. Brave Norman: A True Story. 2002. (ps-2). lib. bdg. 11.80 (978-0-613-57568-3(7)) Tandem Library Bks.

Murray, Kirsty. What Kids Are Made Of: True Stores of Young Rescuers, Rulers & Rebels. 2000. (gr. 3-6). lib. bdg. 16.40 (978-0-613-56688-9(2)) Tandem Library Bks.

—What Kids Are Made Of: True Stories of Young Rescuers, Rulers & Rebels. 2000. (Illus.). 160p. (J). (gr. 1-6). pap. 7.95 (978-1-55652-414-1(5)) Chicago Review Pr., Inc.

Weatherford, Carole Boston. Sink or Swim: African-American Lifesavers of the Outer Banks. 1999. (Illus.). xi, 81p. (J). (gr. 8 up). 15.95 (978-1-928556-01-5(9)); pap. 12.95 (978-1-928556-03-9(5)) Coastal Carolina Pr.

Weintraub, Aileen. First Response by Sea. 2006. (Natural Disasters Ser.). (Illus.). 48p. (J). (978-0-531-12434-5(7) , Children's Pr.) Scholastic Library Publishing.

Windsor, Jo. Life Savers: Early Level Satellite Individual Title Six-Packs. (Sails Literacy Ser.). 16p. (gr. 1-2). 27.00 (978-0-7578-2940-6(6)) Rigby Education.

LIFTS

see Elevators; Hoisting Machinery

LIGHT

see also Color; Lasers; Optics; Radiation; Radioactivity; X-Rays

Bang, Molly Garrett. My Light. Bang, Molly Garrett, illus. 2004. (Illus.). 40p. (J). pap. 16.95 (978-0-439-48961-4(X)) Scholastic, Inc.

Bauer, David. Luz y Sombra. 2005. Tr. of Light & Shadow. (SPA., Illus.). 16p. (J). (gr. 1 up). lib. bdg. 15.93 (978-0-7368-4137-5(7)) Capstone Pr., Inc.

Benchmark Education Staff, compiled by. Light & Sound. 2006. spiral bd. 199.00 (***978-1-4108-7121-3(5)***) Benchmark Education Co.

Berger, Samantha. Light. 1999. (J). pap. 2.50 (978-0-439-08120-7(3)) Scholastic, Inc.

Binns, Tristan Boyer. What Colour Is an Orange? 2006. (Illus.). 32p. (J). pap. (978-1-4109-2619-7(2)); lib. bdg. (978-1-4109-2590-9(0)) Steck-Vaughn.

Boulter, Carol & Wadsworth, Pamela. Golau. 2005. (WEL., Illus.). 24p. pap. (978-1-85596-231-6(4)) Dref Wen.

—Rhagor Am Olau. 2005. (WEL., Illus.). 24p. pap. (978-1-85596-232-3(2)) Dref Wen.

Branley, Franklyn M. Day Light, Night Light: Where Light Comes From. Schuett, Stacey, illus. rev. ed. 1998. (Let's Read-and-Find-Out Ser.). 32p. (J). (gr. k-4). 14.95 (978-0-06-027294-4(5)); 16.89 (978-0-06-027295-1(3)); pap. 5.99 (978-0-06-445171-0(2) , Harper Trophy) HarperCollins Pubs.

—Day Light, Night Light: Where Light Comes From, Stage 2. 1998. (Let's-Read-and-Find-Out Ser.). (J). 11.79 (978-0-606-12909-1(X)) Tandem Library Bks.

The Bridgestone Science Library: Our Physical World, 4 bks. Incl. Electricity. Olien, Rebecca. lib. bdg. 18.60 (978-0-7368-1404-1(3)); Light. Olien, Rebecca. lib. bdg. 18.60 (978-0-7368-1405-8(1)); Magnets. Olien, Rebecca. lib. bdg. 18.60 (978-0-7368-1406-5(X)); Sound. Olien, Becky. lib. bdg. 18.60 (978-0-7368-1407-2(8)); 24p. (J). (gr. 1-2). 2002. (Illus.). 2002. Set lib. bdg. 74.40 (978-0-7368-1408-9(6) , Bridgestone Bks.) Capstone Pr., Inc.

Brudnak, Karen, ed. Investigating Science - Energy, Light, & Sound. 2000. 48p. 9.95 (978-1-56234-429-0(3) , Mailbox Bks., The) Education Ctr., Inc.

Bryant-Mole, Karen & Ansary, Mir Tamim. Sound & Light. 2002. (Science All Around Me Ser.). (Illus.). 24p. (J). (gr. 1-3). pap. 6.95 (978-1-4034-0055-0(5) , 91499) Heinemann Library.

Building Blocks of Science: Light Teacher's Guide. 2007. (Illus.). ring bd. (***978-0-89278-339-7(7)***) Carolina Biological Supply Co.

Burnie, David & Dorling Kindersley Publishing Staff. Light. 2000. (Eyewitness Bks.). (Illus.). 64p. (J). (gr. 4-7). lib. bdg. 19.99 (978-0-7894-6709-6(7)) Dorling Kindersley Publishing, Inc.

J K L

Cheshire, Gerard. Light & Colors. 2006. (Illus.). 48p. (J). (978-1-58340-996-1(3) , 1262675) Smart Apple Media.

Clemmet, Mike. Light & Sound. 1998. (Fact Finders Ser.). (Illus.). 48p. (J). (gr. 3-7). pap. (978-0-563-37505-0(1)) BBC Worldwide.

Cooper, Christopher. Light: From Sun to Bulbs. 2003. (Science Answers Ser.). (Illus.). 32p. (J). pap. 7.50 (978-1-4034-3550-7(2)); lib. bdg. 24.22 (978-1-4034-0953-9(6)) Heinemann Library.

Cooper, Jason. Light. 2003. (Science Secrets Discovery Library). (Illus.). 24p. (gr. 1-4). 14.95 (978-1-58952-411-8(X)) Rourke Publishing, LLC.

Dalton, Cindy Devine. Light. 2001. (How Can I Experiment With? Ser.). (Illus.). 32p. (J). (gr. 1-4). lib. bdg. 28.50 (978-1-58952-014-1(9)) Rourke Publishing, LLC.

Dixon, Malcolm & Smith, Karen. Light & Color. 1998. (Young Scientists Ser.). (Illus.). 32p. (J). (ps-3). lib. bdg. 16.95 (978-1-887068-70-3(8)) Smart Apple Media.

Dorling Kindersley Publishing Staff. Light. 2006. (Eye Know Ser.). (Illus.). 24p. (J). 8.99 (978-0-7566-2225-1(5)) Dorling Kindersley Publishing, Inc.

Dorling Kindersley Publishing Staff & Burnie, David. Light. 1999. (Eyewitness Bks.). (Illus.). 64p. (J). (gr. 3-7). 15.99 (978-0-7894-4885-9(8)) Dorling Kindersley Publishing, Inc.

La energia de la luz y el sonido: Cuaderno de Evaluacion: Unit 3: la energia de la luz y el sonido (the Energy of Sound & Light) 2000. (McGraw-Hill Ciencias Ser.). (ENG & SPA.). (gr. 5 up). (978-0-02-278673-1(2)) Macmillan/McGraw-Hill Schl. Div.

La energia de la luz y el sonido: Recursos para el maestro con clave de Respuestas: Unit 3: la energia de la luz y el sonido (the Energy of Sound & Light) 2000. (McGraw-Hill Ciencias Ser.). (ENG & SPA.). (gr. 5 up). (978-0-02-278709-7(7)) Macmillan/McGraw-Hill Schl. Div.

Farndon, John. From Newton's Rainbow to Frozen Light: Discovering Light. 2007. (Illus.). 64p. (J). lib. bdg. ***978-1-4034-9556-3(4))** Heinemann Library.

Farndon, John. Light & Optics. 2000. (Science Experiments Ser.). (Illus.). 32p. (J). (gr. 3-5). lib. bdg. 25.64 (978-0-7614-1090-4(2) , Benchmark Bks.) Cavendish, Marshall Corp.

Fleisher, Paul. Waves: Principles of Light, Electricity, & Magnetism. 2005. (Secrets of the Universe Ser.). (Illus.). 80p. (gr. 6-12). 25.26 (978-0-8225-2987-3(4)) Lerner Publishing Group.

Frenkel, Karen A. Light & Sound Technology. 2006. (Navigators Ser.). (J). pap. 42.00 **(*978-1-4108-6228-0(3))** Benchmark Education Co.

—Looking at Light. 2006. (Navigators Ser.). (J). pap. 42.00 **(*978-1-4108-6226-6(7))** Benchmark Education Co.

Fullick, Ann. Seeing Things: Light. 2005. (Illus.). 56p. (J). pap. (978-1-4034-6422-4(7)); (gr. 6-8). lib. bdg. 32.86 (978-1-4034-4816-3(7)) Heinemann Library.

Gareth Stevens Publishing Staff, contrib. by. Light. 2003. (Discovery Channel School Science Ser.). (Illus.). 32p. (J). (gr. 5 up). lib. bdg. 24.67 (978-0-8368-3359-1(7)) Stevens, Gareth Inc.

Gish, Melissa. Light. 2005. (My First Look at Science Ser.). (Illus.). 24p. (gr. k-3). 15.95 (978-1-58341-373-9(1) , Creative Education) Creative Co., The.

Gold-Dworkin, Heidi. Exploring Light & Color. 2000. (gr. 3-6). lib. bdg. 22.20 (978-0-613-27811-9(9)) Tandem Library Bks.

Gold-Dworkin, Heidi, et al. Exploring Light & Color. 1999. (Little Scientists Ser.). (Illus.). 58p. (J). (gr. k-3). pap. 12.95 (978-0-07-134821-8(2) , 9780071348218) McGraw-Hill Cos., The.

Goldsmith, Mike. Light & Sound. 2007. (Kingfisher Young Knowledge Ser.). (Illus.). 48p. (J). (gr. k-3). 9.95 (978-0-7534-6036-8(X)) Houghton Mifflin Co.

Group/McGraw-Hill, Wright. Set 2: La Luz, 6 vols., Vol. 2. (First Explorers. Primeros Exploradores Nonfiction Sets Ser.). (SPA.). (gr. 1-2). 34.95 (978-0-7699-1485-5(3)) Shortland Pubns. (U. S. A.) Inc.

Halpern, Monica. Science Chapters: All about Light. 2006. (National Geographic Science Chapters Ser.). (Illus.). 48p. (gr. 1-4). 17.90 (978-0-7922-5942-8(4) , National Geographic Children's Bks.) National Geographic Society.

Hamilton, Gina L. The Science of Light: Spectrum, Lasers, & Optics. 2003. (J). lib. bdg. 27.14 (978-0-7398-6995-6(7)) Raintree.

Herold, Vickey. Discover Light. 2006. pap. 39.00 **(*978-1-4108-6491-8(X))** Benchmark Education Co.

—Light & Color. 2006. pap. 42.00 **(*978-1-4108-6488-8(X))** Benchmark Education Co.

Hewitt, Sally. Amazing Light. 2007. (J). 32p. pap. **(*978-0-7787-3626-4(1)); (*978-0-7787-3612-7(1))** Crabtree Publishing Co.

—Light & Dark. 1999. (It's Science! Ser.). (Illus.). 32p. (J). (gr. k-3). pap. 6.95 (978-0-516-26340-3(4) , Children's Pr.) Scholastic Library Publishing.

—Light & Dark. Moller, Ray, illus. 1998. (It's Science! Ser.). 32p. (J). (gr. k-3). 23.50 (978-0-516-20842-8(X) , Children's Pr.) Scholastic Library Publishing.

—Slide down a Rainbow: (Light) 2002. (Why Can't I Ser.). (Illus.). 32p. (J). lib. bdg. 24.25 (978-1-930643-70-3(5)) Chrysalis Education.

Hidalgo, Maria. Light. 2002. (Let's Investigate Ser.). (Illus.). 32p. (J). lib. bdg. (978-1-58341-230-5(1) , Creative Education) Creative Co., The.

Holt, Rinehart and Winston Staff. Holt Science & Technology: Sound & Light, Pt. O. 3rd ed. 2003. (SPA.). 18.60 (978-0-03-069363-2(2)) Holt, Rinehart & Winston.

—Holt Science & Technology Chapter 22: Physical Science: The Nature of Light. 5th ed. 2004. (Illus.). pap. 12.86 (978-0-03-030439-2(3)) Holt, Rinehart & Winston.

—Holt Science & Technology Chapter 23: Physical Science: Light & Our World. 5th ed. 2004. (Illus.). pap. 12.86 (978-0-03-030441-5(5)) Holt, Rinehart & Winston.

—Holt Science & Technology Chptr. 17: The Nature of Light: Chapter Resources - Tennessee Edition. 3rd ed. 2003. (J). pap. 11.40 (978-0-03-069126-3(5)) Holt, Rinehart & Winston.

—Holt Science & Technology Chptr. 18: Light & the World: Chapter Resources - Tennessee Edition. 3rd ed. 2003. (J). pap. 11.40 (978-0-03-069127-0(3)) Holt, Rinehart & Winston.

—Holt Science & Technology 2002 Pt. O: Sound & Light. 2nd ed. 2002. 18.60 (978-0-03-064807-6(6)); 46.66 (978-0-03-064808-3(4)) Holt, Rinehart & Winston.

Hunter, Rebecca. The Facts about Light. 2004. (Science the Facts Ser.). (Illus.). 32p. (J). lib. bdg. (978-1-58340-452-2(X)) Smart Apple Media.

Hunter, Rebecca M. Light & Dark. 2000. (Discovering Science Ser.). (Illus.). 32p. (J). (gr. 3-5). lib. bdg. 25.69 (978-0-7398-2973-8(4)) Raintree.

—Light & Dark. 2000. (Discovering Science Ser.). (Illus.). 32p. (J). (gr. 3-5). pap. 8.95 (978-0-7398-3017-8(1)) Steck-Vaughn.

Johnson, Rebecca L. The Magic of Light & Sound. 2003. (National Geographic Reading Expeditions Ser.). (Illus.). 32p. (J). pap. (978-0-7922-8886-2(6)) National Geographic Society.

—Peering into Darkness. 2003. (National Geographic Reading Expeditions Ser.). (Illus.). 32p. (J). (978-0-7922-8451-2(8)) National Geographic Society.

Juettner, Bonnie. Light. 2003. (Kidhaven Science Library). (Illus.). 48p. (J). 26.20 (978-0-7377-2074-7(3) , Greenhaven Pr., Inc.) Thomson Gale.

Kelly, Lynne. Simple Concepts in Physics: Sound & Light. (Illus.). 88p. (J). (gr. 5-6). pap. (978-1-875739-69-1(6)) Wizard Bks.

Kids Publishing Science Staff. Catch a Wave: The Story of Sound & Light. 1999. (J). (gr. 2-6). pap. 6.95 (978-1-891418-16-7(5)) Science Kids.

Light. (Jump Ser.). (Illus.). 32p. (J). (gr. 2-7). pap. (978-1-882210-28-2(X)) Action Publishing, Inc.

Llewellyn, Claire. Light & Dark. 2005. (Illus.). 24p. (J). (gr. 1-4). lib. bdg. (978-1-84234-333-3(5) , Cherrytree Books) Evans Publishing Group.

Madgwick, Wendy. Light & Dark. 1999. (Science Starters Ser.). (Illus.). 32p. (gr. k-4). pap. 7.95 (978-0-8172-5882-5(5)) Steck-Vaughn.

Mahaney, Ian F. Light. 2007. 24p. (J). pap. (978-1-4042-2185-7(9)); (Illus.). (gr. 4-6). lib. bdg. 21.25 (978-1-4042-3476-5(4)) Rosen Publishing Group, Inc., The. (PowerKids Pr.).

Miller-Schroeder, Patricia. The Science of Light & Color. 2000. (Living Science Ser.). (Illus.). 32p. (J). (gr. 2 up). lib. bdg. 24.67 (978-0-8368-2679-1(5)) Stevens, Gareth Inc.

Mondello, Cindy, ed. Investigating Science - Light & Sound. 2000. 48p. 9.95 (978-1-56234-437-5(4) , Mailbox Bks., The) Education Ctr., Inc.

Murray, Julie. Light & Dark. 2007. (Illus.). 24p. (J). 21.35 (978-1-59679-826-7(2)) ABDO Publishing Co.

Nankivell-Aston, Sally. Science Experiments with Light. 2000. (Science Experiments Ser.). (Illus.). 32p. (J). (gr. 3-5). pap. 6.95 (978-0-531-15429-8(7) , Watts, Franklin) Scholastic Library Publishing.

Nankivell-Aston, Sally & Jackson, Dorothy M. Science Experiments with Light. 2000. (Science Experiments Ser.). (Illus.). 32p. (J). (gr. 3-6). 22.00 (978-0-531-14577-7(8) , Watts, Franklin) Scholastic Library Publishing.

Nobleman, Marc Tyler. The Light Bulb. 2003. (Fact Finders Ser.). (Illus.). 32p. (J). lib. bdg. 22.60 (978-0-7368-2216-9(X)) Capstone Pr., Inc.

Olien, Rebecca. Light. 2002. (Bridgestone Science Library). (Illus.). 24p. (J). (gr. 1-2). lib. bdg. 18.60 (978-0-7368-1405-8(1) , Bridgestone Bks.) Capstone Pr., Inc.

Parker, Steve. Light. 2004. (Science View Ser.). (Illus.). 32p. (J). (gr. 4-8). 28.00 (978-0-7910-8209-6(1) , Chelsea Hse.) Facts On File, Inc.

—Light & Sound. 2000. (Science Fact Files Ser.). (Illus.). 48p. (J). (gr. 4-7). lib. bdg. 27.12 (978-0-7398-1011 8(1)) Raintree.

Parker, Victoria. Light. 2006. (Illus.). 24p. (J). (978-1-4034-7886-3(4)); pap. (978-1-4034-7892-4(9)) Steck-Vaughn.

Pipe, Jim. Light: What Is a Shadow? 2005. (Science Starters Ser.). (Illus.). 32p. (J). (gr. 3-7). lib. bdg. 27.10 (978-1-59604-017-5(3)) Stargazer Bks.

—Light & Dark. 2006. (Science Starters Ser.). (Illus.). 32p. (J). (978-1-59604-079-3(3)) Stargazer Bks.

Prentice-Hall Staff. Sound & Light. 2nd ed. (J). stu. ed. 7.97 (978-0-13-400565-2(1)); pap., act. bk. ed. (978-0-13-400581-2(3)) Prentice Hall (Schl. Div.).

Randolph, Joanne. Light in My World. 2006. (My World of Science Ser.). (J). 16.00 (978-1-4042-3286-0(9) , PowerKids Pr.) Rosen Publishing Group, Inc., The.

—Light in My World: La Luz en Mi Mundo. 2006. (My World of Science/ Mi mundo y la Ciencia Ser.). (ENG & SPA.). (J). 16.00 (978-1-4042-3317-1(2) , PowerKids Pr.) Rosen Publishing Group, Inc., The.

Rau, Dana Meachen. Hot & Bright: A Book about the Sun. Shea, Denise, illus. 2005. (Amazing Science Ser.). 24p. (J). (ps-k). lib. bdg. 22.60 (978-1-4048-1135-5(4)) Picture Window Bks.

Rea, Thelma. I Wonder Why the Sky Is Blue. 2002. (Reading Room Collection). (Illus.). 24p. (J). lib. bdg. 18.75 (978-0-8239-3724-0(0)) Rosen Publishing Group, Inc., The.

Richardson, Adele. Light: A Question & Answer Book. 2006. (Fact Finders Ser.). (Illus.). 32p. (J). (978-0-7368-5446-7(0)) Capstone Pr., Inc.

Riley, Peter D. Light & Dark. Moller, Ray, photos by. 2002. (Everyday Science Ser.). (Illus.). 32p. (J). (gr. 1 up). lib. bdg. 23.33 (978-0-8368-3249-5(3)) Stevens, Gareth Inc.

Riley, Peter D. Light & Seeing. 2007. (J). **(*978-1-59920-028-6(7))** Smart Apple Media.

Ring, Susan. Light & Shadow. 2003. (Yellow Umbrella Books). (Illus.). 16p. (J). (gr. 1). lib. bdg. 14.60 (978-0-7368-2020-2(5) , Pebble Bks.) Capstone Pr., Inc.

—Light & Shadow. 2003. (J). (978-0-7368-1712-7(3)) Yellow Umbrella Pr.

Rogers, K. Light, Sound & Electricity. 2004. (Library of Science Ser.). 64p. (J). lib. bdg. 17.95 (978-1-58086-376-6(0)) EDC Publishing.

Rosinsky, Natalie M. Light: Shadows, Mirrors, & Rainbows. Boyd, Sheree, illus. 2004. (Amazing Science Ser.). 24p. (C). (gr. k-4). 22.60 (978-1-4048-0013-7(1)) Picture Window Bks.

Roth, Susan L. The Story of Light. 2000. (Illus.). 14p. (J). (gr. 1-3). reprint ed. 20.00 (978-0-7881-9063-6(6)) DIANE Publishing Co.

Royston, Angela. Light & Dark. (My World of Science Ser.). (Illus.). 32p. (J). (gr. k-2). 2002. pap. 6.95 (978-1-4034-0041-3(5) , 91485); 2001. lib. bdg. 21.36 (978-1-58810-242-3(4)) Heinemann Library.

Sadler, Wendy. Light: Look Out! 2005. (Raintree Perspectives Ser.). (Illus.). 32p. (J). (978-1-4109-1551-1(4)); pap. (978-1-4109-1559-7(X)) Steck-Vaughn.

School Specialty Publishing. Light. 2004. (On-File Ser.). 4p. (J). (gr. 5-7). ring bd. 4.99 (978-0-7424-2921-5(0) , Instructional Fair) Schaffer, Frank Pubns.

Schuh, Mari. Light. 2007. (Illus.). 24p. (J). lib. bdg. 19.95 (978-1-60014-097-6(1)) Bellwether Media.

Shaw, Gina. Shadows Everywhere. Holub, Joan, illus. 1999. (Hello Reader! Science Ser.). (J). 20.01 (978-0-590-52296-0(5)) Scholastic, Inc.

Smuskiewicz, Alfred J. Light. 2007. (J). **(*978-1-4034-9929-5(2));** pap. **(*978-1-4034-9937-0(3))** Heinemann Library.

Snedden, Robert. Light & Sound. 1999. (Smart Science Ser.). (Illus.). 32p. (J). (gr. 3-5). lib. bdg. 22.79 (978-1-57572-870-4(2)) Heinemann Library.

Sohn, Emily. The Illuminating World of Light with Max Axiom, Super Scientist. Derington, Nick, illus. 2008. (J). **(*978-1-4296-0140-5(X))** Capstone Pr., Inc.

Solway, Andrew. Voyage of a Light Beam: Light. 2005. (Illus.). 32p. (J). (978-1-4109-1974-8(9)); lib. bdg. (978-1-4109-1943-4(9)) Steck-Vaughn.

Spilsbury, Richard & Spilsbury, Louise. What Is Light? Exploring Science with Hands-On Activities. 2008. (In Touch with Basic Science Ser.). 32p. (J). (gr. 3-4). lib. bdg. 22.60 **(*978-0-7660-3097-8(0))** Enslow Pubs., Inc.

Steck-Vaughn Staff. Light & Sound: Classroom Edition. 1999. (Illus.). (J). pap. (978-0-7398-1925-8(9)) Steck-Vaughn.

—Light & Sound: Ontario MOE Hybrid Version. 1999. (Illus.). (J). pap. 9.33 incl. cd-rom (978-0-7398-1271-6(8)) Raintree.

Stewart, Melissa. Fun with the Sun. 2004. (Investigate Science Ser.). (Illus.). 32p. (J). (gr. 1 up). lib. bdg. 21.26 (978-0-7565-0593-6(3)) Compass Point Bks.

Stille, Darlene R. Manipulating Light: Reflection, Refraction, & Absorption. 2005. (Exploring Science Ser.). (Illus.). 48p. (J). (gr. 5-7). (978-0-7565-1258-3(1)) Compass Point Bks.

Swinburne, Stephen R. Guess Whose Shadow? 2003. (Illus.). 32p. (YA). (gr. k-2). 15.95 (978-1-56397-724-4(9)) Boyds Mills Pr.

Taylor, Barbara. Light, Color & Art Activities. 2002. (gr. 3-6). lib. bdg. 17.60 (978-0-613-52871-9(9)) Tandem Library Bks.

Taylor, Barbara, text. Light, Color & Art Activities. 2002. (Arty Facts Ser.). (Illus.). 48p. (J). (gr. 3-4). pap. (978-0-7787-1142-1(0)); lib. bdg. (978-0-7787-1114-8(5)) Crabtree Publishing Co.

Taylor, Kim. Light. (Illus.). 32p. (YA). (gr. 3 up). lib. bdg. 27.10 (978-1-931983-75-4(5)) Chrysalis Education.

Tocci, Salvatore. Experiments with Light. 2001. (gr. 3-6). lib. bdg. 15.25 (978-0-613-54209-8(6)) Tandem Library Bks.

Top That Publishing Staff, ed. Light Science. 2004. (Top That! Labs Ser.). (Illus.). 24p. (J). (978-1-84510-153-4(7)) Top That! Publishing PLC.

Trumbauer, Lisa. All about Light. 2004. (Rookie Read-About Science Ser.). 32p. (J). (gr. 1-2). pap. 4.95 (978-0-516-25842-3(7) , Children's Pr.) Scholastic Library Publishing.

Upgrade kit dsm-3 Color&light. (J). 2004. (978-1-59242-527-3(5)); 2003. (978-1-59242-410-8(4)) Delta Education, LLC.

Wadsworth, Pamela. Golwg Gyntaf Ar Olau. 2005. (WEL., Illus.). 24p. pap. (978-1-85596-249-1(7)) Dref Wen.

Walker, Sally M. Light. 2006. (Early Bird Energy Ser.). (Illus.). 48p. (J). (gr. 3-7). 25.26 (978-0-8225-2925-5(4) , Lerner Pubns.) Lerner Publishing Group.

Walker, Sally M. La Luz (Light) 2007. (Libros de Energía para madrugadores (Early Bird Energy) Ser.). (SPA.). 48p. (J). (gr. 2-5). lib. bdg. 26.60 **(*978-0-8225-7719-5(4)** , Ediciones Lerner) Lerner Publishing Group.

Waters, Jennifer. Bright Lights & Shadowy Shapes. 2002. (Spyglass Books). (Illus.). 24p. (J). (gr. 1 up). 18.60 (978-0-7565-0227-0(6)) Compass Point Bks.

Whitfield, David. Northern Lights. 2006. (Science Matters Ser.). (J). (978-1-59036-413-0(9)); pap. (978-1-59036-419-2(8)) Weigl Pubs., Inc.

Whyman, Kathryn. Light & Lasers. 2004. (J). lib. bdg. (978-1-932799-24-8(9)) Stargazer Bks.

Wolfe, Gillian. Look: Seeing the Light in Art. 2006. (Look! Ser.). (Illus.). 40p. (J). (gr. 1-5). 16.95 **(*978-1-84507-467-8(X))** Lincoln, Frances Ltd. GBR. *Dist:* Perseus Distribution.

Wood, Robert W. Light Fundamentals. 1999. (Funtastic Science Activities for Kids Ser.). (Illus.). xii, 140p. (J). (gr. 4-7). 16.95 (978-0-7910-4843-6(8) , Chelsea Hse.) Facts On File, Inc.

Woodford, Chris. Light & Radiation. 2004. (Routes of Science Ser.). (Illus.). 40p. (J). pap. 11.20 (978-1-4103-0296-0(2)); (gr. 4-7). 24.95 (978-1-4103-0297-7(0)) Thomson Gale. (Blackbirch Pr., Inc.).

LIGHT—EXPERIMENTS

Caes, Charles J. How Do We Know the Speed of Light? 2001. (Great Scientific Questions & the Scientists Who Answered Them Ser.). (Illus.). 112p. (YA). (gr. 4-6). lib. bdg. 26.50 (978-0-8239-3387-7(3)) Rosen Publishing Group, Inc., The.

Challoner, Jack & Angliss, Sarah. Sound & Light. Le Jars, David, illus. 2001. (Hands-On Science Ser.). 40p. (J). (gr. 3-5). pap. 6.95 (978-0-7534-5347-6(9) , Kingfisher) Houghton Mifflin Co. Trade & Reference Div.

Clark, John Owen Edward. Light & Sound. 2006. (Real World Science Ser.). (Illus.). 32p. (J). 24.67 (978-0-8368-6306-2(2)) Stevens, Gareth Inc.

Cobb, Allan B. Super Science Projects about Light & Optics. 2005. (Psyched for Science Ser.). (Illus.). 48p. (YA). (gr. 5-8). lib. bdg. 23.95 (978-0-8239-3177-4(3) , SCLIOP) Rosen Publishing Group, Inc., The.

Dalton, Cindy Devine. Light. 2001. (How Can I Experiment With? Ser.). (Illus.). 32p. (J). (gr. 1-4). lib. bdg. 28.50 (978-1-58952-014-1(9)) Rourke Publishing, LLC.

DiSpezio, Michael A. Awesome Experiments in Light & Sound. 2006. (Illus.). 160p. (J). pap. 6.95 (978-1-4027-2372-8(5)) Sterling Publishing Co., Inc.

Dixon, Malcolm & Smith, Karen. Light & Color. 1998. (Young Scientists Ser.). (Illus.). 32p. (J). (ps-3). lib. bdg. 16.95 (978-1-887068-70-3(8)) Smart Apple Media.

Gardner, Robert. Dazzling Science Projects with Light & Color. LaBaff, Tom, illus. 2006. (Fantastic Physical Science Experiments Ser.). 48p. (J). lib. bdg. 23.93 (978-0-7660-2587-5(X) , Enslow Elementary) Enslow Pubs., Inc.

—Light, Sound, & Waves Science Fair Projects Using Sunglasses, Guitars, & Other Stuff. 2004. (Physics! Best Science Projects Ser.). (Illus.). 128p. (J). lib. bdg. 26.60 (978-0-7660-2126-6(2)) Enslow Pubs., Inc.

Glover, David. Color & Light. 2001. (Experiments in Science Ser.). (Illus.). (J). (978-0-7894-7464-3(6)) Dorling Kindersley Publishing, Inc.

—Sound & Light: Science Facts & Experiments. 2002. (Young Discoverers Ser.). (Illus.). 32p. (J). (gr. k-3). pap. 7.95 (978-0-7534-5512-8(9) , Kingfisher) Houghton Mifflin Co. Trade & Reference Div.

Lauw, Darlene. Light. 2002. (gr. 3-6). lib. bdg. 16.40 (978-0-613-52870-2(0)) Tandem Library Bks.

Lauw, Darlene & Puay, Lim Cheng. Light. 2002. (Science Alive! Ser.). (Illus.). 32p. (J). (gr. 4-5). lib. bdg. (978-0-7787-0560-4(9)); pap. (978-0-7787-0606-9(0)) Crabtree Publishing Co.

Lilly, Melinda. Me & My Shadow. 2006. (Rourke Discovery Library). (Illus.). 24p. (gr. 1-4). 14.95 (978-1-59515-403-3(5) , 1244274) Rourke Publishing, LLC.

Madgwick, Wendy. Light & Dark. 1999. (Science Starters Ser.). (Illus.). 32p. (J). (gr. k-4). 22.83 (978-0-8172-5556-5(7)) Raintree.

Meiani, Antonella. Light. 2003. (Experimenting with Science Ser.). (Illus.). 40p. (J). (gr. 4-8). lib. bdg. 23.93 (978-0-8225-0084-1(1)) Lerner Publishing Group.

Merrill, Amy French. Everyday Physical Science Experiments with Light. 2006. (Tony Stead Nonfiction Independent Reading Collection). pap. (978-1-4042-5679-8(2)) Rosen Publishing Group, Inc., The.

—Everyday Physical Science Experiments with Light & Sound. 2002. (Science Surprises Ser.). (Illus.). 24p. (J). lib. bdg. 19.95 (978-0-8239-5804-7(3) , PowerKids Pr.) Rosen Publishing Group, Inc., The.

Murphy, Brian. Light. 2004. (Experiment with Ser.). (SPA., Illus.). 32p. (gr. 2-5). (J). pap. 5.95 (978-1-58728-114-3(7)); 9.95 (978-1-58728-246-1(1)) T&N Children's Publishing. (Two Can Publishing).

Parker, Steve. The Science of Light: Projects & Experiments with Light & Color. 2005. (Illus.). (J). 32p. (gr. 4-6). lib. bdg. 29.29 (978-1-4034-7284-7(X)); 31p. (ps-6). pap. 7.95 (978-1-4034-7291-5(2)) Heinemann Library.

Richards, Jon. Light & Sight. 2008. (J). lib. bdg. **(*978-1-4042-3904-3(9)** , PowerKids Pr.) Rosen Publishing Group, Inc., The.

Riley, Peter D. Light & Color. 2005. (Illus.). 32p. (J). (gr. 4-7). lib. bdg. 27.10 (978-1-58340-715-8(4)) Smart Apple Media.

Zubrowski, Bernie. Mirrors: Finding Out about the Properties of Light. 2001. 59p. spiral bd. 9.00 (978-1-58651-903-2(4)) Pitsco/Pitsco LEGO Dacta.

LIGHT AMPLIFICATION BY STIMULATED EMISSION OF RADIATION

see Lasers

LIGHT AND SHADE

see Shadows

LIGHT SHIPS

see Lightships

LIGHTHOUSES

see also Lightships

Arrigo, Joseph A. Historic Great Lakes Lighthouses: Coloring Book. 2002. (Illus.). 32p. (J). (gr. 4-7). 3.95 (978-1-55709-537-4(X)) Applewood Bks.

—Historic Northern Lighthouses, 6 vols, Pack. 2005. (Illus.). 32p. (J). (gr. 4-7). pap. 23.70 (978-1-55709-910-5(3)) Applewood Bks.

—Historic Pacific Coast Lighthouses: Coloring Book. 2002. (Illus.). 32p. (J). (ps-3). 4.95 (978-1-55709-536-7(1)) Applewood Bks.

—Northern Lighthouses Coloring Book. 2002. (Illus.). 32p. (J). (gr. 4-7). per. 3.95 (978-1-55709-538-1(8)) Applewood Bks.

J K L

Batchelor, John. Lighthouses of the World. 2004. (Illus.). 32p. (J). pap. 3.95 (978-0-486-43685-2(3)) Dover Pubns., Inc.

Campbell, Loraine, illus. A Pocketful of Passage. 2007. (Great Lakes Books). xi, 77p. (J). pap. (***978-0-8143-3341-9(9)**) Wayne State Univ. Pr.

Clifford, Mary Louise & Clifford, J. Candace. Mind the Light, Katie: The History of Thirty-Three Female Lighthouse Keepers. 2006. (YA). per. 12.95 (978-0-9636412-7-4(1)) Cypress Communications.

The Colors of the Lighthouse: A Children's History of Absecon Lighthouse. ed. 2006. (J). 8.95 (***978-0-9779988-0-7(0)**) Absecon Lighthouse.

DeWire, Elinor. Florida Lighthouses for Kids. 2004. (Illus.). 64p. (J). pap. 8.95 (978-1-56164-323-3(8)) Pineapple Pr., Inc.

Giambarba, Paul. Cape Cod Light: The Lighthouse at Dangerfield. Giambarba, Paul, illus. 2000. (J). per. 9.95 (978-0-9653283-3-3(3)) On Cape Pubns.

Glupker, Dianne & Delsi, Dawna. Great Lights of Michigan. Delsi, Dawna, illus. 2005. (Illus.). (J). per. 9.95 (978-0-9769846-0-3(1) , 318924) Harambee Pr.

House, Katherine L. Lighthouses for Kids: History, Science, & Lore with 21 Activities. 2008. (For Kids Ser.). 144p. (J). (gr. 4-7). pap. 14.95 (***978-1-55652-720-3(9)**) Chicago Review Pr., Inc.

Keep the Lights Burning. 9.95 (978-1-59112-293-7(7)) Live Oak Media.

Krebs, Laurie. A Day in the Life of a Colonial Lighthouse Keeper. 2004. (Library of Living & Working in Colonial Times). (Illus.). 24p. (J). lib. bdg. 18.75 (978-0-8239-6226-6(1) , PowerKids Pr.) Rosen Publishing Group, Inc., The.

Lighthouse: Add-to Pack. (gr. k-2). 338.00 (978-0-7578-3307-6(1)) Rigby Education.

Lighthouse: Complete Package. (gr. k-2). 1819.00 (978-0-7578-3306-9(3)) Rigby Education.

Lighthouse: Levels B-D Package. (gr. k-2). 545.00 (978-0-7578-3260-4(1)) Rigby Education.

Lighthouse: Levels E-I Package. (gr. k-2). 543.00 (978-0-7578-3261-1(X)) Rigby Education.

Lighthouse: Levels J-M Package. (gr. k-2). 827.00 (978-0-7578-3262-8(8)) Rigby Education.

Lighthouse: Nonfiction Add-to Pack. (gr. k-2). 87.00 (978-0-7578-3308-3(X)) Rigby Education.

Lighthouses: Beacons of the Past. 2005. (Book Treks Ser.). (J). (gr. 3 up). stu. ed. 34.95 (978-0-673-62841-1(8)) Celebration Pr.

Mishler, Donna. Lighthouses of the Mid-Atlantic States. Melvin, James, illus. l.t. ed. 1999. 32p. (J). (gr. k-5). pap., stu. ed. 5.95 (978-1-893709-02-7(7)) Suthernsky.

National Geographic Society Staff. Lighthouses: Beacons of the Sea. 1999. (Cultural & Geographical Exploration Ser.). (Illus.). 144p. (YA). (gr. 7-12). 21.95 (978-0-7910-5444-4(6) , Chelsea Hse.) Facts On File, Inc.

O'Hara, Megan. Lighthouse: Living in a Great Lakes Lighthouse, 1910 to 1940. 1998. 32p. (J). pap. 21.00 (978-0-516-21252-4(4) , Children's Pr.) Scholastic Library Publishing.

Plisson, Philip. Lighthouses. 2005. (Illus.). 78p. (J). (gr. 2-7). 18.95 (978-0-8109-5958-3(5) , Abrams Bks. for Young Readers) Abrams, Harry N. , Inc.

Running Press Staff. Lighthouses. 2006. (Illus.). 96p. 9.98 (978-0-7624-2640-9(3) , Courage Bks.) Running Pr. Bk. Pubs.

Ruth, Angie. My Adventure at a Lighthouse. 2006. 44p. (J). 8.99 (978-1-59092-316-0(2) , Orchard Academy Pr.) Windstorm Creative.

Trumbauer, Lisa. Lighthouses of North America! Kline, Michael, illus. 2007. 96p. (J). (gr. 3-9). 16.99 (***978-0-8249-6791-8(7)**); pap. 12.99 (***978-0-8249-6790-1(9)**) Ideals Pubns. (Williamson Bks.).

Van Rynbach, Iris. Safely to Shore: America's Lighthouses. Van Rynbach, Iris, illus. 2004. (Illus.). 32p. (J). 16.95 (978-1-57091-434-8(6)) Charlesbridge Publishing, Inc.

—Safely to Shore: America's Lighthouses. 2004. (Illus.). 32p. (J). pap. 6.95 (978-1-57091-435-5(4)) Charlesbridge Publishing, Inc.

—Safely to Shore: America's Lighthouses. 2003. (gr. 3-6). lib. bdg. 15.25 (978-0-613-88750-2(6)) Tandem Library Bks.

Weintraub, Aileen. Alcatraz Island Light: The West Coast's First Lighthouse. 2003. (Great Lighthouses of North America Ser.). (Illus.). 24p. (J). pap. 18.75 (978-0-8239-6171-9(0) , PowerKids Pr.) Rosen Publishing Group, Inc., The.

—Boston Light: The First Lighthouse in North America. 2003. (Great Lighthouses of North America Ser.). (Illus.). 24p. (J). pap. 18.75 (978-0-8239-6170-2(2) , PowerKids Pr.) Rosen Publishing Group, Inc., The.

—Cape Disappointment Light: The First Lighthouse in the Pacific Northwest. 2003. (Great Lighthouses of North America Ser.). (Illus.). 24p. (J). pap. 18.75 (978-0-8239-6172-6(9) , PowerKids Pr.) Rosen Publishing Group, Inc., The.

—Navesink Twin Lights: The First U. S. Lighthouse to Use a Fresnel Lens. 2003. (Great Lighthouses of North America Ser.). (Illus.). 24p. (J). pap. 18.75 (978-0-8239-6169-6(9) , PowerKids Pr.) Rosen Publishing Group, Inc., The.

—Point Pianos Light: The West Coast's Oldest Continuously Active Lighthouse. 2003. (Great Lighthouses of North America Ser.). (Illus.). 24p. (J). pap. 18.75 (978-0-8239-6173-3(7) , PowerKids Pr.) Rosen Publishing Group, Inc., The.

Weintraub, Aileen, tr. Cape Hatteras Light: The Tallest Lighthouse in the United States. 2003. (Great Lighthouses of North America Ser.). (Illus.). 24p. (J). pap. 18.75 (978-0-8239-6168-9(0) , PowerKids Pr.) Rosen Publishing Group, Inc., The.

LIGHTHOUSES—FICTION

Ardizzone, Edward. Tim to the Lighthouse. 2006. (Little Tim Ser.). (Illus.). 48p. (J). 16.95 (978-1-84507-562-0(5)) Lincoln, Frances Ltd. GBR. *Dist:* Perseus Distribution.

Armitage, Ronda. Lighthouse Keeper. Date not set. (Illus.). 32p. (J). pap. (978-0-05-004387-5(0)) Addison-Wesley Longman, Inc.

Baldwin, Gloria. Lighthouse Lindy. 2007. 0.00 (***978-0-9790469-6-4(3)**) Arbor Bks.

Buchanan, Paul. Return to Terror Cove. 2001. (Heebie Jeebies Ser.: Vol. 10). 138p. (J). (gr. 3-7). pap. 5.99 (978-0-8054-2333-4(8)) B&H Publishing Grp.

Buzzeo, Toni. The Sea Chest. GrandPré, Mary, illus. 2002. 32p. (J). (gr. k up). 16.99 (978-0-8037-2703-8(8) , Dial) Penguin Group (USA) Inc.

Chase, Diana. The Light House Kids. 2003. (Illus.). 256p. (J). pap. 13.50 (978-1-86368-346-3(1)) Fremantle Pr. AUS. *Dist:* International Specialized Bk. Services.

Clark, Joyce. Katie. 2006. 196p. (***978-1-4122-0067-7(9)**) Trafford Publishing.

Collins, Anne. The Leopard & the Lighthouse. abr. ed. 2002. (Illus.). 16p. pap. (978-0-582-35287-2(8) , Putnam Juvenile) Penguin Group (USA) Inc.

Coons, Susan. The Lighthouse Mouse. 2006. 19.99 (***978-0-9721410-1-7(4)**) Vinland Pr.

Copeland, Cynthia L. Elin's Island. 2003. (Single Titles Ser.: up). 144p. (gr. 6 up). lib. bdg. 22.90 (978-0-7613-2522-2(0) , Millbrook Pr.) Lerner Publishing Group.

Doyle, Patrick H. T. Edgar Font's Hunt for a House to Haunt: Adventure One: the Castle Tower Lighthouse. 2006. (Illus.). 232p. (J). per. 6.99 (978-0-9786132-0-4(1)) Armadillo Bks.

Farren, Rick. Eliza's Wish. 2005. (J). per. 14.95 (***978-0-9794863-8-8(6)**) Summerland Publishing.

—The Secret of the Lighthouse. 2004. (J). per. 12.95 (978-0-9748087-3-4(3)) Journey Pubns., LLC.

—The Secret of the Lighthouse. 2004. (J). per. 12.95 (***978-0-9794863-7-1(8)**) Summerland Publishing.

Fletcher, Susan. Walk Across the Sea. Jakesevic, Nenad, illus. 224p. (J). 2003. pap. 11.95 (978-0-689-85707-2(1) , Aladdin); 2001. (gr. 5-9). 16.95 (978-0-689-84133-0(7) , Atheneum) Simon & Schuster Children's Publishing.

—Walk Across the Sea. 2003. (gr. 3-6). lib. bdg. 13.00 (978-0-613-62227-1(8)) Tandem Library Bks.

—Walk Across the Sea. l.t. ed. 2002. 218p. (J). 22.95 (978-0-7862-4439-3(9)) Thorndike Pr.

Fripp, Jon, et al. Kinnakeet & the Lighthouse. Moussa, Karen M., illus. 2000. 33p. (J). 5.50 (978-0-9638258-4-1(4)) Bicast, Inc.

Henderson, Holly E. Lighthouse Legend. 2001. (gr. 7-12). lib. bdg. 14.15 (978-0-613-74203-0(6)) Tandem Library Bks.

Hernandez, Ruben. Elisa Escuchaba el Canto de Las Ballenas. Corichi, Yadhira, illus. rev. ed. 2003. (Castillo de la Lectura Blanca Ser.). (SPA.). 48p. (J). (gr. 1-3). pap. 6.95 (978-970-20-0141-6(2)) Castillo, Ediciones, S. A. de C. V. MEX. *Dist:* Macmillan.

Hoff, Syd. The Lighthouse Children. Hoff, Syd, illus. 2002. (Illus.). (J). 12.34 (978-0-7587-6180-4(5)) Book Wholesalers, Inc.

Hopkinson, Deborah. Birdie's Lighthouse. Root, Kimberly B., illus. 2000. 32p. (J). (ps-3). 6.99 (978-0-689-83529-2(9) , Aladdin) Simon & Schuster Children's Publishing.

—Birdie's Lighthouse. 2000. (gr. 3-6). lib. bdg. 14.15 (978-0-613-28424-0(0)); (Illus.). (J). (978-0-606-17913-3(5)) Tandem Library Bks.

Janis, Tim. Shine Like a Lighthouse. Steve, Lavigne, illus. 2nd ed. 2007. (J). 12.95 (***978-0-9773335-1-6(5)**) Janis, Tim Ensemble, Inc.

Kinkade, Thomas. Katherine's Story. 2004. (Girls of Lighthouse Lane Ser.). 176p. (J). (gr. 5 up). 13.89 (978-0-06-054342-6(6)) HarperCollins Pubs.

Kinkade, Thomas & Tamar, Erika. Rose's Story. 2004. (Girls of Lighthouse Lane Ser.: No. 2). (Illus.). 192p. (J). (gr. 5 up). 12.99 (978-0-06-054344-0(2)) HarperCollins Pubs.

Lachenmeyer, Nathaniel. The Decoy. Slade, Christian, illus. 2007. 32p. (J). 17.95 (***978-1-58726-319-4(X)** , Mitten Pr.) Ann Arbor Media Group, LLC.

Lobel, Anita. One Lighthouse, One Moon. Lobel, Anita, illus. (Illus.). 48p. (J). 2002. pap. 6.99 (978-0-06-000537-5(8) , Harper Trophy); 2000. 16.99 (978-0-688-15539-1(1)) HarperCollins Pubs.

—One Lighthouse, One Moon. 2002. (gr. k-3). lib. bdg. 15.25 (978-0-613-84613-4(3)) Tandem Library Bks.

Love, Pamela. Lighthouse Seeds. Warner, Linda, illus. 2004. 32p. 15.95 (978-0-89272-541-0(9)) Down East Bks.

Mason, Jane B. & Stephens, Sarah Hines. Bella Baxter & the Lighthouse Mystery. Shelley, John, illus. 2006. (Bella Baxter Ser.). 80p. (J). pap. 3.99 (978-0-689-86282-3(2) , Aladdin) Simon & Schuster Children's Publishing.

McKinty, Adrian. The Lighthouse Land. 2006. (Illus.). 200p. (YA). (gr. 6-10). 16.95 (978-0-8109-5480-9(X)) Abrams, Harry N. , Inc.

Messer, Celeste M. The Ghost of Piper's Landing. Hoeffner, Deb, illus. 2004. 82-92p. 4.95 (978-0-9702171-7-2(X)) AshleyAlan Enterprises.

Munsch, Robert. Lighthouse: A Story of Remembrance. Wilson, Janet, illus. 2004. 28p. (J). pap. 5.95 (978-0-439-49032-0(4)) Scholastic, Inc.

Noel, Jeffrey. Rocky the Lighthouse Makes A Difference. 2006. pap. 34.00 (***978-1-4259-3566-5(4)**) AuthorHouse.

Panagopoulos, Janie Lynn. A Castle at the Straits. Evans, Laura, illus. 2003. 48p. (J). (gr. 1-6). (978-0-911872-83-5(3)) Mackinac State Historic Parks.

Parsons, Carol. Mystery at Eagle Harbor Lighthouse. 2006. (J). pap. 9.95 (978-1-59705-985-5(4)) Wings ePress, Inc.

Perdew, Suzanne, et al. The Mystery of the Abandoned Lighthouse. 2001. (Shoebox Kids Ser.: Bk. 12). (Illus.). 93p. (J). (978-0-8163-1819-3(0)) Pacific Pr. Publishing Assn.

Perrow, Angeli. Captain's Castaway. Harris, Emily, illus. 1998. 32p. (J). (ps-3). 15.95 (978-0-89272-419-2(6)) Down East Bks.

Prior, Natalie Jane. Lily Quench & the Lighthouse of Skellig Mor, Vol. 4. 2004. (Illus.). 160p. (J). (gr. 3-7). pap. 4.99 (978-0-14-240059-3(9) , Puffin) Penguin Group (USA) Inc.

Rowinski, Kate. Cats in the Dark. Bishop, Bonnie, illus. 1998. 32p. (J). (ps-3). 14.95 (978-0-89272-427-7(7)) Down East Bks.

Roy, James. Ichabod Hart & the Lighthouse Mystery. 2003. (Steampunk Ser.). (Illus.). 392p. pap. 15.50 (978-0-7022-3364-7(1)) Univ. of Queensland Pr. AUS. *Dist:* International Specialized Bk. Services.

Rylant, Cynthia. The Eagle. McDaniels, Preston, illus. 2004. (Lighthouse Family Ser.). 64p. (J). 14.95 (978-0-689-86243-4(1)) Simon & Schuster Children's Publishing.

—The Octopus. McDaniels, Preston, illus. 2005. (Lighthouse Family Ser.). 64p. (J). 15.99 (978-0-689-86246-5(6)) Simon & Schuster Children's Publishing.

—The Turtle. McDaniels, Preston, illus. 2005. (Lighthouse Family Ser.). 48p. (J). 14.95 (978-0-689-86244-1(X) , Simon & Schuster Children's Publishing) Simon & Schuster Children's Publishing.

Schneider, Richard H. The Lighthouse Boy: A Story of Courage. Petrov, Anton, illus. 2007. 32p. (J). (ps-3). pap. 8.99 (***978-0-8249-5557-1(9)** , Guideposts) Ideals Pubns.

Smith, Lauren E. Ashley Enright Investigations. 2006. 48p. pap. 12.95 (978-1-4241-2963-8(X)) PublishAmerica, Inc.

Smucker, Anna Egan. To Keep the South Manitou Light. 2004. (J). pap. 19.95 (978-0-8143-3236-8(6)); (Illus.). 144p. 23.95 (978-0-8143-3235-1(8) , Painted Turtle) Wayne State Univ. Pr.

Snowman, Sally R. Sammy the Boston Lighthouse Dog. 2005. (J). (gr. 3-5). 15.00 (978-0-9674666-2-0(8)) Snowman Learning Center, The.

Sollie, Andre. Hello, Sailor. Godon, Ingrid, illus. 2004. 32p. (J). 18.00 (978-0-333-98735-3(7)) Macmillan Publishers Ltd. GBR. *Dist:* Independent Pubs. Group.

—Hello, Sailor. Godon, Ingrid, illus. 2004. 32p. (J). pap. 8.99 (978-0-333-99290-6(3)) Macmillan Publishers Ltd. GBR. *Dist:* Independent Pubs. Group.

Stainton, Sue. The Lighthouse Cat. Mortimer, Anne, illus. 2004. 32p. (J). (ps-2). 15.99 (978-0-06-009604-5(7)) HarperCollins Pubs.

Stonehouse, Frederick. My Summer at the Lighthouse: A Boy's Journal. 2003. (Illus.). 32p. (J). (gr. 3-9). (978-1-892384-18-8(3)) Avery Color Studios, Inc.

Swift, Hildegarde H. Little Red Lighthouse & the Great Gray Bridge. 2002. (gr. k-3). lib. bdg. 16.45 (978-0-613-59908-5(X)) Tandem Library Bks.

—The Little Red Lighthouse & the Great Gray Bridge. Ward, Lynd, illus. anniv. ed. 2002. 64p. (J). (gr. k-3). 16.00 (978-0-15-204571-5(6)) Harcourt Children's Bks.

—The Little Red Lighthouse & the Great Gray Bridge: Restored Edition. Ward, Lynd, illus. 2003. 64p. (J). pap. 8.00 (978-0-15-204573-9(2) , Voyager Bks./Libros Viajeros) Harcourt Children's Bks.

Thiele, Colin. The Hammerhead Light. (Illus.). 196p. pap. (978-0-7344-0401-5(8) , Lothian Bks.) Hachette Livre Australia.

Valentine, Sally. The Ghost of the Charlotte Lighthouse. 2006. (J). (***978-1-59531-013-2(4)**) North Country Bks., Inc.

Vaughan, Marcia. Abbie Against the Storm: The True Story of a Young Heroine & a Lighthouse. Farnsworth, Bill, illus. 1999. 30p. (J). (gr. 1-3). 15.95 (978-1-58270-007-6(9)) Beyond Words Publishing, Inc.

Walls, Eric. The Harbor Light. 2006. (Illus.). 32p. (J). 11.99 (978-0-8254-4155-4(2)) Kregel Pubns.

Walton, O. F. Saved at Sea: A Young Boy in a Dramatic Rescue. (Illus.). 144p. (J). mass mkt. 5.99 (978-1-85792-795-5(8) , Christian Heritage) Christian Focus Pubns. GBR. *Dist:* Riverside.

—Saved at Sea A Lighthouse Story. 2004. reprint ed. pap. 15.95 (978-1-4191-4623-7(8)); pap. 1.99 (978-1-4192-4623-4(2)) Kessinger Publishing, LLC.

Wingate, Philippa. Hide & Seek in the Lighthouse. Rutherford, Peter, illus. 2005. (Hide & Seek Ser.). 16p. (J). (ps-k). 7.95 (978-1-904613-60-2(8) , Buster Bks.) O'Mara, Michael Bks., Ltd. GBR. *Dist:* Independent Pubs. Group.

Woodruff, Elvira. Fearless. 2008. 240p. (J). 16.99 (978-0-439-67703-5(3) , Scholastic Pr.) Scholastic, Inc.

LIGHTING

see also Candles

Evans, Neville. The Science of a Light Bulb. 1999. (Science World Ser.). (Illus.). 32p. (J). (gr. 2-4). lib. bdg. 25.69 (978-0-7398-1325-6(0)) Raintree.

Herriges, Ann. Lightning. 2006. (Blastoff! Readers Ser.). (Illus.). 24p. (J). lib. bdg. 16.95 (978-1-60014-025-9(4)) Bellwether Media.

Inventing the Electric Light. 2007. (Illus.). 32p. (J). (gr. 3-9). (***978-0-7787-2818-4(8)**); pap. (***978-0-7787-2840-5(4)**) Crabtree Publishing Co.

Mayer, Cassie. Thunder & Lightning. 2006. (Illus.). 24p. (J). (978-1-4034-8413-0(9)) Heinemann Library.

Tolhurst, Marilyn. Lights & Candles. Date not set. (Sense of History Ser.). (Illus.). 24p. pap. 27.69 (978-0-582-04026-7(4)) Addison-Wesley Longman, Ltd. GBR. *Dist:* Trans-Atlantic Pubns., Inc.

LIGHTNING

Branley, Franklyn M. Flash, Crash, Rumble, & Roll. Kelley, True, illus. 1999. (Let's-Read-and-Find-Out Science Ser.). 32p. (J). (gr. k-4). 15.89 (978-0-06-027859-5(5)); pap. 5.99 (978-0-06-445179-6(8) , Harper Trophy) HarperCollins Pubs.

Bryan, Ashley. Story of Lightning & Thunder. 1999. (978-0-606-16282-1(8)) Tandem Library Bks.

Burby, Liza N. Electrical Storms. 1999. (Extreme Weather Ser.). 24p. (J). (gr. k-4). lib. bdg. 18.75 (978-0-8239-5294-6(0) , PowerKids Pr.) Rosen Publishing Group, Inc., The.

Capstone Press, contrib. by. Lightning. 2005. (Our Seasons & Weather Ser.). 24p. (YA). (gr. k-3). pap. (978-1-56065-842-9(8) , Pebble Bks.) Capstone Pr., Inc.

Dussling, Jennifer. Lightning: It's Electrifying. Osiecki, Lori, illus. 2002. (All Aboard Science Reader Ser.). 48p. (J). pap. 3.99 (978-0-448-42860-4(1) , Grosset & Dunlap) Penguin Group (USA) Inc.

—Lightning: It's Electrifying. 2002. (gr. k-3). lib. bdg. 11.80 (978-0-613-64414-3(X)) Tandem Library Bks.

Egan, Lorraine Hopping. Lightning! Wheeler, Jody, illus. 1999. (Hello Reader! Science Ser.). 48p. (J). (gr. 2-4). pap. 3.99 (978-0-590-52285-4(X)) Scholastic, Inc.

—Wild Weather: Lightning! 1999. (Hello Reader! Ser.). (978-0-606-16937-0(7)) Tandem Library Bks.

Flanagan, Alice K. Lightning. 2003. (Wonder Books Level 1: Weather Ser.). (Illus.). 24p. (J). (ps-2). 22.79 (978-1-56766-451-5(2)) Child's World, Inc.

French, Cathy. Chasquea, cruje y fluye & Snap, Crackle, & Flow. 2005. spiral bd. 84.00 (***978-1-4108-5697-5(6)**) Benchmark Education Co.

Galiano, Dean. Thunderstorms & Lightning. (Weather Watchers' Library). (Illus.). 48p. (gr. 5-8). 2003. (YA). lib. bdg. 23.95 (978-0-8239-3093-7(9) , WETHLI, Rosen Central); 2005. lib. bdg. 23.95 (978-0-8239-3772-1(0)) Rosen Publishing Group, Inc., The.

Hamilton, John. Lightning. 2006. (Illus.). 32p. (J). (gr. 3-8). lib. bdg. 24.21 (978-1-59679-332-3(5) , ABDO & Daughters) ABDO Publishing Co.

Hidalgo, Maria. Lightning. 2006. (My First Look at Weather Ser.). (Illus.). 24p. (J). 15.95 (***978-1-58341-450-7(9)** , Creative Education) Creative Co., The.

Hopping, Lorraine Jean. Wild Weather: Lightning! Salas, Macarena A., tr. Wheeler, Jody, illus. 2002. (Hello Reader! Science Ser.). (SPA.). 48p. (J). (gr. 2-4). pap. 3.99 (978-0-439-16165-7(7) , SO0343, Scholastic en Espanol) Scholastic, Inc.

Howerton, Roger. What's So Striking about Lightning? Ask Max! 2002. (Illus.). 24p. (J). pap. 5.99 (978-0-89051-363-7(5) , 303-093) Master Bks.

Kalz, Jill. Lightning. 2002. (Illus.). 23p. (J). lib. bdg. 21.35 (978-1-58340-154-5(7)) Smart Apple Media.

Koontz, Dean. Lightning. 2003. (gr. 7-12). lib. bdg. 16.45 (978-0-613-70706-0(0)) Tandem Library Bks.

Lightning, 6 vols. (gr. k-2). 28.95 (978-0-7368-8010-7(0)) Red Brick Learning.

Lightning Weather. 2006. (Illus.). 24p. (J). (gr. k-2). 18.50 (***978-0-531-17877-5(3)**) Scholastic Library Publishing.

Mayer, Cassie. Thunder & Lightning. 2006. (Illus.). 24p. (J). pap. 5.99 (978-1-4034-8421-5(X)) Heinemann Library.

—Truenos y Relampagos. 2006. (ENG & SPA.). (J). (***978-1-4034-8654-7(9)**) Heinemann Library.

—Truenos y Relampagos (Thunder & Lightning) 2006. (ENG & SPA.). 24p. (J). pap. (***978-1-4034-8662-2(X)**) Heinemann Library.

Miles, Elizabeth. Thunder & Lightning. 2004. 32p. (J). (gr. k-2). (Illus.). lib. bdg. 24.21 (978-1-4034-5579-6(1)); pap. 7.60 (978-1-4034-5677-9(1)) Heinemann Library.

Pfeffer, Wendy. Thunder & Lightning. (Science Readers Ser.). 32p. (J). 2003. mass mkt. 3.99 (978-0-439-42504-9(2)); 2002. (Illus.). pap. (978-0-439-26988-9(1)) Scholastic, Inc. (Scholastic Reference).

Picture Window Books, contrib. by. Nature's Fireworks. (Amazing Science Ser.). 24p. (J). pap. 7.95 (978-1-4048-0337-4(8)) Picture Window Bks.

Preszler, June. Where Does Lightning Come From? A Book about Weather. 2007. 24p. (J). (978-0-7368-6754-2(6)) Capstone Pr., Inc.

Riley, Gail Blasser. Benjamin Franklin & Electricity. 2004. (Cornerstones of Freedom Ser.). (Illus.). 48p. (J). 26.00 (978-0-516-24240-8(7) , Children's Pr.) Scholastic Library Publishing.

Saunders-Smith, Gail. Lightning. 1998. (Weather Ser.). (Illus.). 24p. (J). (ps-2). pap. 13.25 (978-0-516-21332-3(6) , Children's Pr.) Scholastic Library Publishing.

—Los Relampagos (Lightning) 2003. (Weather Bilingual Ser.). (ENG & SPA., Illus.). 24p. (J). lib. bdg. 15.93 (978-0-7368-2308-1(5)) Capstone Pr., Inc.

Sherman, Joseph. Nature's Fireworks: A Book about Lightning. Wesley, Omarr, illus. 2004. (Amazing Science Ser.). 24p. (C). (gr. k-3). 22.60 (978-1-4048-0093-9(X)) Picture Window Bks.

Simon, Seymour. Lightning. 32p. (J). 2006. 16.99 (978-0-06-088438-3(X)); 2006. (Illus.). pap. 6.99 (978-0-06-088435-2(5)); 1999. (Illus.). pap. 6.99 (978-0-688-16706-6(3) , Harper Trophy) HarperCollins Pubs.

—Lightning. 1999. (Illus.). 32p. lib. bdg. 14.19 (978-0-606-16761-1(7)) Tandem Library Bks.

Watt, Fiona. Thunder & Lightning. (Information Ser.). (Illus.). 32p. (J). 3.50 (978-0-7214-1749-3(3) , Dutton Juvenile) Penguin Group (USA) Inc.

Weather Wise: Striking Lightning! 2001. (J). pap. 5.95 (978-1-56911-729-3(2)) Learning Resources, Inc.

Williams, Brian. Lightning. 2005. (What on Earth? Ser.). (Illus.). 32p. (J). 25.50 (978-0-516-25322-0(0) , Children's Pr.) Scholastic Library Publishing.

LIGHTSHIPS

Floca, Brian. Lightship. Floca, Brian, illus. 2007. (Illus.). 48p. (J). (ps-2). 16.99 (978-1-4169-2436-4(1), Atheneum/Richard Jackson Bks.) Simon & Schuster Children's Publishing.

LIMERICKS

see also Nonsense Verses

Brenner, Barbara. The Plant That Kept on Growing. Sweet, Melissa, illus. 1999. (Bank Street Reader Collection). 48p. (J). (ps-2). lib. bdg. (978-0-8368-1776-8(1)) Stevens, Gareth Inc.

Bumbalough, Jerry. Purple pup girls are grape Jelly. Bennett, Harry, Jr., illus. 2007. 16p. (J). 8.95 ***(978-0-9797960-0-5(8))*** Thirsty Sponge Publishing Co.

Bunny Days. (Happy Days Ser.). 48p. 5.99 (978-1-57029-271-2(X), WPH28007, Totline Pubns.) Schaffer, Frank Pubns.

Foster, John L. Loopy Limericks. 2001. (Illus.). 91p. (J). pap. 7.99 (978-0-00-711181-7(9)) HarperCollins Pubs. Ltd. GBR. *Dist:* Independent Pubs. Group.

Hubbell, Patricia. Boo! Halloween Poems & Limericks. Spackman, Jeff, illus. 40p. 2005. (YA). pap. 5.95 (978-0-7614-5151-8(X)); 1998. (J). 15.95 (978-0-7614-5023-8(8), Cavendish Children's Bks.) Cavendish, Marshall Corp.

Lear, Edward. Edward Lear. Mendelson, Edward, ed. Huliska-Beith, Laura, illus. 2001. (Poetry for Young People Ser.). 48p. 14.95 (978-0-8069-3077-0(2)) Sterling Publishing Co., Inc.

Monreal, Violeta. Susto en la Playa. 2004. (Coleccion Pictogramas Pictograms Ser.). (SPA.). 16p. (J). 8.50 (978-84-241-8103-1(4)) Everest de Ediciones y Distribucion, S.L. ESP. *Dist:* Lectorum Pubns., Inc.

Poffo, Lanny. Limericks from the Heart (and Lungs!) 2004. (Illus.). 180p. (J). pap. 14.00 (978-1-888580-29-7(1)) White-Boucke Publishing.

Smith, Elwood, illus. Jump Rope Rhymes. 1998. 48p. (YA). (gr. 4-7). spiral bd. 10.95 (978-1-57054-166-7(3)) Klutz.

Suarez, Maribel, illus. Kiss Away My Boo-Boo. (Rowing Frog's Rhymes Ser.). 16p. (J). (gr. k-3). 7.95 (978-1-59437-841-6(X)) Santillana USA Publishing Co., Inc.

LIMITATION OF ARMAMENT

see Disarmament

LIN, MAYA YING, 1959-

Lashnits, Tom. Maya Lin. 2007. (Asian Americans of Achievement Ser.). 128p. (YA). (gr. 6-10). lib. bdg. 30.00 (978-0-7910-9268-2(2), Chelsea Hse.) Facts On File, Inc.

Stone. Maya Lin. 2003. (Raintree Biographies Ser.). (Illus.). 32p. pap. 7.50 (978-1-4109-0069-2(X)) Raintree.

Stone, Amy. Maya Lin. 2003. (Raintree Biographies Ser.). (Illus.). 32p. (J). lib. bdg. 25.70 (978-0-7398-6863-8(2)) Raintree.

—Maya Lin. 2003. (gr. 3-6). lib. bdg. 15.90 (978-0-613-78165-7(1)) Tandem Library Bks.

LINCOLN, ABRAHAM, 1809-1865

Abnett, Dan. Abraham Lincoln & the Civil War. 2007. (Jr. Graphic Biographies Ser.). (Illus.). 24p. (J). (978-1-4042-2335-6(5)); pap. (978-1-4042-2145-1(X)); (gr. 2-6). lib. bdg. 21.25 (978-1-4042-3392-8(X)) Rosen Publishing Group, Inc., The. (PowerKids Pr.).

—Jr. Graphic Biographies, 6 bks., Set. Incl. Abraham Lincoln & the Civil War. lib. bdg. 21.25 (978-1-4042-3392-8(X)); Christopher Columbus & the Voyage of 1492. Q2A, illus. lib. bdg. 21.25 (978-1-4042-3390-4(3)); George Washington & the American Revolution. lib. bdg. 21.25 (978-1-4042-3395-9(4)); Harriet Tubman & the Underground Railroad. lib. bdg. 21.25 (978-1-4042-3393-5(8)); Hernan Cortes & the Fall of the Aztec Empire. lib. bdg. 21.25 (978-1-4042-3391-1(1)); Sitting Bull & the Battle of the Little Bighorn. lib. bdg. 21.25 (978-1-4042-3394-2(6)); (Illus.). 24p. (J). (gr. 2-6). 2007., PowerKids Pr. 2006. Set lib. bdg. 127.50 (978-1-4042-3550-2(7)) Rosen Publishing Group, Inc., The.

Abraham Lincoln. (Photo Illustrated Biographies Ser.). 24p. (J). 6.95 (978-0-7368-4462-8(7)); Vol. 3. 2005. (YA). (978-0-7368-8109-8(3), Pebble Bks.) Capstone Pr., Inc.

Abraham Lincoln. (Biographies Ser.). 24p. (J). 7.95 (978-1-4048-0458-6(7)) Picture Window Bks.

Abraham Lincoln, 6 vols. (gr. k-2). 28.95 (978-0-7368-8133-3(6)); (gr. 2-5). 36.95 (978-0-7368-4554-0(2)); (gr. 2-5). 39.95 (978-0-7368-4602-8(6)) Red Brick Learning.

Abraham Lincoln: A Life of Respect. 2006. (J). pap. 5.95 (978-0-8225-5700-5(2)) Lerner Publishing Group.

Abraham Lincoln: Letters from a Slave Girl. 2002. (J). (gr. 4-7). 25.95 incl. audio (978-0-87499-983-9(9)) Live Oak Media.

Abraham Lincoln: Una vida de respeto (A Life of Respect) 2007. (J). pap. 5.95 (978-0-8225-6559-8(5), Ediciones Lerner) Lerner Publishing Group.

Abraham Lincoln & Slavery. 95p. (YA). (gr. 8-12). pap. 14.50 (978-0-382-40942-4(6)); spiral bd., tchr.'s planning gde. ed. 13.00 (978-0-382-40941-7(8)) Cobblestone Publishing Co.

Adler, David A. A Picture Book of Abraham Lincoln. (Picture Book Biography Ser.). (Illus.). 32p. (J). (gr. k-3). lib. bdg., tchr. ed. 17.95 (978-0-8234-0731-6(4)) Holiday Hse., Inc.

—A Picture Book of Abraham Lincoln. Wallner, John & Wallner, Alexandra, illus. (Picture Book Biography Ser.). 32p. (J). (gr. k-3). pap. 6.95 (978-0-8234-0801-6(9)) Holiday Hse., Inc.

—A Picture Book of Abraham Lincoln. Wallner, John & Wallner, Alexandra, illus. 2004. (J). (ps-3). audio compact disk 18.95 (978-1-59112-777-2(7)) Live Oak Media.

Alter, Judy. Abraham Lincoln: A MyReportLinks.com Book. 2002. (Presidents Ser.). (Illus.). 48p. (J). (gr. 4-10). lib. bdg. 25.26 (978-0-7660-5005-1(X), MyReportLinks.com Bks.) Enslow Pubs., Inc.

Armentrout, David & Armentrout, Patricia. Abraham Lincoln. 2002. (People Who Made a Difference Ser.). (Illus.). 24p. (gr. 2-5). 14.95 (978-1-58952-051-6(3)) Rourke Publishing, LLC.

—Abraham Lincoln. Sarfatti, Esther & de la Vega, Eida, trs. (Personas que Cambiaron la Historia (People Who Made a Difference) Ser.). (SPA., Illus.). 24p. 2002. mass mkt. 5.95 (978-1-58952-248-0(6), RK31464); 2001. (J). (gr. 1-4). lib. bdg. 19.27 (978-1-58952-167-4(6), RK7298) Rourke Publishing, LLC.

—The Emancipation Proclamation. (Documents that Shaped the Nation Ser.). 48p. 2005. (Illus.). (gr. 4-6). 20.95 (978-1-59515-233-6(4)); 2004. pap. 7.95 (978-1-59515-332-6(2)) Rourke Publishing, LLC.

—La Proclama de Emancipacion. 2005. (SPA.). (J). (978-1-59515-645-7(3)) Rourke Publishing, LLC.

Armentrout, David, et al. El Discurso de Gettysburg. 2005. (SPA.). (J). (978-1-59515-647-1(X)) Rourke Publishing, LLC.

—The Gettysburg Address. 2005. (Documents that Shaped the Nation Ser.). (Illus.). 48p. (gr. 4-6). 20.95 (978-1-59515-232-9(6)) Rourke Publishing, LLC.

Armstrong, Jennifer. A Three-Minute Speech: Lincoln's Remarks at Gettysburg. 2003. (gr. 3-6). lib. bdg. 11.80 (978-0-613-66549-0(X)) Tandem Library Bks.

Arnold, James R. & Wiener, Roberta. On to Richmond: The Civil War in the East, 1861-1862. 2005. (Civil War Ser.). (Illus.). 72p. (J). (gr. 5-12). lib. bdg. 25.26 (978-0-8225-2313-0(2)) Lerner Publishing Group.

Aronson, Billy. Abraham Lincoln. 2008. (J). ***(978-0-7614-2839-8(9))*** Cavendish, Marshall Bks., Ltd.

Ashabranner, Jennifer & Ashabranner, Brent. No Better Hope: What the Lincoln Memorial Means to America. 2001. (Great American Memorials Ser.). (Illus.). 64p. (J). (gr. 4-8). lib. bdg. 25.90 (978-0-7613-1523-0(3), Twenty-First Century Bks.) Lerner Publishing Group.

Ashby, Ruth. Abraham & Mary Todd Lincoln. 2004. (Illus.). 48p. (J). pap. 11.95 (978-0-8368-5701-6(1)); lib. bdg. 30.00 (978-0-8368-5695-8(3)) Stevens, Gareth Inc. (World Almanac Library).

—Lincoln at War. 2002. (Illus.). 48p. (J). lib. bdg. 28.50 (978-1-58340-183-5(0)) Smart Apple Media.

Baldwin, James. Four Great Americans. 2006. pap. ***(978-1-4065-0509-2(9))*** Dodo Pr.

Baldwin, James. Four Great Americans: Washington, Franklin, Webster, Lincoln: A Book for Young Americans. 2000. (Illus.). (J). (978-0-89526-203-5(7)) Regnery Publishing, Inc., An Eagle Publishing Co.

Benge, Janet. Abraham Lincoln: A New Birth of Freedom. 2001. (gr. 3-6). lib. bdg. 15.30 (978-0-613-83101-7(2)) Tandem Library Bks.

Benge, Janet Hazel & Benge, Geoffrey Francis. Abraham Lincoln: A New Birth of Freedom. 2001. (Illus.). 224p. pap. 8.99 (978-1-883002-79-4(6)) Emerald Bks.

Bial, Raymond. Where Lincoln Walked. 1998. (Illus.). 48p. (J). (gr. 2-5). lib. bdg. 17.85 (978-0-8027-8631-9(6)) Walker & Co.

Black, Sonia W. Abraham Lincoln. 2002. (Primeras Biografias de Scholastic Ser.). (SPA., Illus.). 32p. (J). (gr. 2-4). pap. 3.99 (978-0-439-37481-1(2), SO31317, Scholastic en Espanol) Scholastic, Inc.

—Let's Read about Abraham Lincoln. Heyer, Carol, illus. 2002. (Scholastic First Biographies Ser.). 29p. (J). pap. 3.99 (978-0-439-29545-1(9)) Scholastic, Inc.

Blashfield, Jean F. Abraham Lincoln. 2000. (Illus.). 32p. (YA). (gr. 5 up). pap. 5.00 (978-1-890541-23-1(0)) Americana Souvenirs & Gifts.

—Abraham Lincoln. 2002. (Profiles of the Presidents Ser.). (Illus.). 64p. (J). (gr. 4 up). lib. bdg. 23.93 (978-0-7565-0202-7(0)) Compass Point Bks.

Bowers, John. The Life of Abraham Lincoln. 2006. (ENG.). 68p. per. 16.95 ***(978-1-4286-2279-1(9))*** Kessinger Publishing, LLC.

Bracken, Thomas. Abraham Lincoln: U. S. President. 1999. (Overcoming Adversity Ser.). (Illus.). 128p. (YA). (gr. 5 up). pap. 30.00 (978-0-7910-4705-7(9), Chelsea Hse.) Facts On File, Inc.

Burgan, Michael. The Gettysburg Address. 2005. (We the People Ser.). (Illus.). 48p. (J). (gr. 4-6). (978-0-7565-1271-2(9), 1244089) Compass Point Bks.

—The Lincoln-Douglas Debates. 2006. (Illus.). 48p. (J). (gr. 4-6). 23.93 (978-0-7565-1632-1(3)) Compass Point Bks.

Burke, Rick. Abraham Lincoln. (American Lives Ser.). (Illus.). 32p. (J). 2003. (gr. 2-4). lib. bdg. (978-1-4034-0155-7(1)); 2002. pap. 6.95 (978-1-4034-0411-4(9)) Heinemann Library.

Burleigh, Robert. Lincoln's Last Ride. rev. ed. Date not set. 32p. (J). 18.95 (978-0-8050-7529-8(1), Holt, Henry & Co. Bks. For Young Readers) Holt, Henry & Co.

Capstone Press, contrib. by. Abraham Lincoln. (Civil War Biographies Ser.). 48p. (YA). pap. 7.95 (978-0-7368-4522-9(4)) Capstone Pr., Inc.

Cary, Barbara. Meet Abraham Lincoln. Marchesi, Stephen, illus. 2001. (Landmark Bks.). 80p. (J). (gr. 2-5). 4.99 (978-0-375-80396-3(3), Random Hse. Bks. for Young Readers) Random Hse. Children's Bks.

—Meet Abraham Lincoln. 2001. (gr. 3-6). lib. bdg. 11.80 (978-0-613-84581-6(1)); (Illus.). (J). (978-0-606-20791-1(0)) Tandem Library Bks.

Cohn, Amy & Schmidt, Suzy. Abraham Lincoln. Johnson, David A., illus. 2002. 40p. (J). (gr. 2-6). pap. 16.95 (978-0-590-93566-1(6), Scholastic Pr.) Scholastic, Inc.

Collard, Sneed B. Abraham Lincoln: A Courageous Leader. 2006. (American Heroes Ser.). (Illus.). 48p. (J). (gr. 3-5). lib. bdg. 28.50 (978-0-7614-2162-7(9), Benchmark Bks.) Cavendish, Marshall Corp.

Collier, James Lincoln. The Abraham Lincoln You Never Knew. 2003. (You Never Knew Ser.). (Illus.). 80p. (J). 25.50 (978-0-516-24348-1(9), Children's Pr.) Scholastic Library Publishing.

Compass Point Books, contrib. by. Abraham Lincoln. (Compass Point Early Biographies Ser.). 24p. (J). pap. 7.95 (978-0-7565-1163-0(1)) Compass Point Bks.

D'Aulaire, Ingri & D'Aulaire, Edgar Parin. Abraham Lincoln. D'Aulaire, Ingri, illus. 2002. (Illus.). (J). 18.57 (978-0-7587-0030-8(X)) Book Wholesalers, Inc.

Davis, Kenneth C. Don't Know Much about Abraham Lincoln Abraham Lincoln, Vol. 4. Shepperson, Rob, illus. 2004. (Don't Know Much About Ser.). 144p. (J). (gr. 2-5). 15.89 (978-0-06-028820-4(5)) HarperCollins Pubs.

Dean, Sheri. Presidents Day/dia De Los Presidentes. 2006. (Illus.). 24p. (J). pap. (978-0-8368-6515-8(4)); (SPA., pap. 5.95 (978-0-8368-6529-5(4)); lib. bdg. 19.33 (978-0-8368-6508-0(1)); (SPA., lib. bdg. 19.33 (978-0-8368-6522-6(7)) Stevens, Gareth Inc.

Devillier, Christy. Abraham Lincoln. 2001. (First Biographies Ser.). (Illus.). 32p. (J). (gr. k-4). lib. bdg. 22.78 (978-1-57765-591-6(5), Buddy Bks.) ABDO Publishing Co.

DK Publishing Staff. Abraham Lincoln & the Civil War. 2006. 16p. (J). pap. 6.99 (978-0-7566-2662-4(5)) Dorling Kindersley Publishing, Inc.

Dunn, Joeming W. Abraham Lincoln. Espinosa, Rod, illus. 2007. (Bio-Graphics Ser.). 32p. (J). (gr. 3-6). lib. bdg. 27.07 ***(978-1-60270-064-2(8)***, Graphic Planet) Magic Wagon.

Emancipation Proclamation: Hope of Freedom for the Slaves. (Civil War Ser.). 48p. (YA). 7.95 (978-0-7368-4517-5(8)) Capstone Pr., Inc.

Feinstein, Stephen. Lee sobre Abraham Lincoln/Read about Abraham Lincoln. 2006. (I Like Biographies Ser.!). (ENG & SPA., Illus.). 24p. (J). (gr. 1-3). lib. bdg. 21.26 (978-0-7660-2672-8(8), Enslow Elementary) Enslow Pubs., Inc.

Findley, Violet. Easy Reader Biographies: Abraham Lincoln: A Great President, A Great American. 2007. 16p. pap. 2.99 ***(978-0-439-77418-5(7)***, Teaching Resources) Scholastic, Inc.

Fireside, Bryna J. The Mary Surratt "Lincoln Assassination" Trial: A Headline Court Case. 2001. (Headline Court Cases Ser.). (Illus.). 128p. (J). (gr. 6-12). lib. bdg. 26.60 (978-0-7660-1481-7(9)) Enslow Pubs., Inc.

FitzGerald, Dawn. Vinnie & Abraham. Stock, Catherine, illus. 2007. 48p. (J). (gr. k-3). 15.95 (978-1-57091-658-8(6)) Charlesbridge Publishing, Inc.

Fontes, Justine & Fontes, Ron. Abraham Lincoln: Abogado, Lider, Leyenda. 2006. (Dk Readers Ser.). 48p. (J). 14.99 (978-0-7566-2130-8(5)); pap. 3.99 (978-0-7566-2129-2(1)) Dorling Kindersley Publishing, Inc.

Fontes, Justine, et al. Abraham Lincoln: Lawyer, Leader, Legend. 2001. (Readers Ser.). (Illus.). 32p. (J). (gr. 5-3). pap. 3.99 (978-0-7894-7375-2(5)) Dorling Kindersley Publishing, Inc.

Fontes, Ron. Abraham Lincoln: Lawyer, Leader, Legend. 2001. (Eyewitness Readers Ser.). (Illus.). (J). 10.79 (978-0-606-20530-6(6)) Tandem Library Bks.

Fontes, Ron, et al. Abraham Lincoln: Lawyer, Leader, Legend. 2001. (Readers Ser.). (Illus.). 48p. (J). (ps-3). 14.99 (978-0-7894-7376-9(3)) Dorling Kindersley Publishing, Inc.

Ford, Carin T. Abraham Lincoln: The 16th President. 2003. (Heroes of American History Ser.). (Illus.). 32p. (J). (gr. 1-4). lib. bdg. 22.60 (978-0-7660-2000-9(2)) Enslow Pubs., Inc.

—The Battle of Gettysburg & Lincoln's Gettysburg Address. 2004. (Civil War Library Ser.). (Illus.). 48p. (J). lib. bdg. 23.93 (978-0-7660-2253-9(6)) Enslow Pubs., Inc.

—Lincoln, Slavery, & the Emancipation Proclamation. 2004. (Civil War Library Ser.). (Illus.). 48p. (J). lib. bdg. 23.93 (978-0-7660-2252-2(8)) Enslow Pubs., Inc.

Fradin, Dennis B. The Emancipation Proclamation. 2007. (Turning Points in U. S. History Ser.). (J). lib. bdg. (978-0-7614-2038-5(X), Benchmark Bks.) Cavendish, Marshall Corp.

Grabowski, John. Abraham Lincoln. 2001. (gr. 5-8). lib. bdg. 17.60 (978-0-613-32238-6(X)) Tandem Library Bks.

Grabowski, John F. Abraham Lincoln: Civil War President. (Famous Figures of the Civil War Era Ser.). (Illus.). 80p. (J). 2001. (gr. 8-12). 25.00 (978-0-7910-6004-9(7)), 2000. (gr. 4-7). pap. 25.00 (978-0-7910-6142-8(6)) Facts On File, Inc. (Chelsea Hse.).

—Abraham Lincoln: Civil War President. 2001. (Famous Figures of the Civil War Era Ser.). (Illus.). (J). 15.75 (978-0-606-20529-0(2)) Tandem Library Bks.

Group/McGraw-Hill, Wright. Abraham Lincoln: The Civil War President, 6 vols. (Book2WebTM Ser.). (gr. 4-8). 36.50 (978-0-322-04462-3(6)) Wright Group, The.

Hamilton, Lynn. Presidents Day. 2004. (American Holidays Ser.). (Illus.). 24p. (J). lib. bdg. 17.10 (978-1-59036-108-5(3)) Weigl Pubs., Inc.

—Presidents' Day. 2004. (American Holidays Ser.). (Illus.). 24p. (J). pap. 6.95 (978-1-59036-169-6(5)) Weigl Pubs., Inc.

Harcourt School Publishers Staff. Abraham Lincoln. 3rd ed. 2002. (Trophies English Language Learners Ser.). (Illus.). pap. 5.10 (978-0-15-327659-0(2)) Harcourt Schl. Pubs.

Harness, Cheryl. Abe Lincoln Goes to Washington 1837-1865. 2003. (Illus.). 48p. (J). (gr. 3-7). pap. 7.95 (978-0-7922-6906-9(3), National Geographic Children's Bks.) National Geographic Society.

—Abe Lincoln Goes to Washington 1837-1865. 2003. (gr. 3-6). lib. bdg. 16.40 (978-0-613-70986-6(1)) Tandem Library Bks.

—Young Abe Lincoln: The Frontier Days, 1809 -1837. 2003. 32p. (J). (gr. 3-7). pap. 7.95 (978-0-7922-6904-5(7), National Geographic Children's Bks.) National Geographic Society.

—Young Abe Lincoln: The Frontier Days, 1809-1837. 1998. (Illus.). 32p. (J). (gr. 3-7). 15.95 (978-0-7922-2713-7(1), National Geographic Children's Bks.) National Geographic Society.

—Young Abe Lincoln: The Frontier Days, 1809-1837. 2002. (gr. k-3). lib. bdg. 16.40 (978-0-613-65396-1(3)) Tandem Library Bks.

Haugen, Brenda. Abraham Lincoln: Great American President. 2005. (Illus.). 112p. (J). (gr. 5-7). (978-0-7565-0986-6(6), 1244078) Compass Point Bks.

Heinrichs, Ann. The Emancipation Proclamation. 2002. (We the People Ser.). (Illus.). 48p. (J). (gr. 4 up). lib. bdg. 22.60 (978-0-7565-0209-6(8)) Compass Point Bks.

Herbert, Janis. Abraham Lincoln for Kids: His Life & Times with 21 Activities. 2007. (For Kids Ser.). 160p. (J). pap. 14.95 ***(978-1-55652-656-5(3))*** Chicago Review Pr., Inc.

Hines, Gary. Thanksgiving in the White House. Wallner, Alexandra, illus. rev. ed. 2003. 32p. (J). 15.95 (978-0-8050-6530-5(X), Holt, Henry & Co. Bks. For Young Readers) Holt, Henry & Co.

Holford, David M. Lincoln & the Emancipation Proclamation in American History. 2002. (In American History Ser.). (Illus.). 128p. (YA). (gr. 5-12). lib. bdg. 26.60 (978-0-7660-1456-5(8)) Enslow Pubs., Inc.

Isaacs, Sally Senzell. America in the Time of Abraham Lincoln: 1815 to 1869. 2002. (America in the Time of... Ser.). (Illus.). 48p. (J). (gr. 4-7). pap. 8.50 (978-1-57572-937-4(7)) Heinemann Library.

January, Brendan. The Lincoln-Douglas Debates. 1998. (Illus.). 32p. (J). (gr. 4-7). lib. bdg. 14.10 (978-0-613-37439-2(8)) Tandem Library Bks.

Jeffery, Gary & Petty, Kate. Abraham Lincoln: The Life of America's Sixteenth President. Lacey, Mike, illus. 2005. 48p. (YA). pap. 9.95 (978-1-4042-5164-9(2)) Rosen Publishing Group, Inc., The.

Jones, Lynda. Abe Lincoln. Bolognese, Don, illus. 1999. (Hello Reader! Ser.). (J). 3.99 (978-0-590-87581-3(7)) Scholastic, Inc.

Judson, Clara Ingram. Abraham Lincoln: Friend of the People. 2007. (Sterling Point Bks.). 208p. (YA). (gr. 7 up). pap. 6.95 ***(978-1-4027-5117-2(6))*** Sterling Publishing Co., Inc.

Judson, Karen. Abraham Lincoln. 1998. (United States Presidents Ser.). (Illus.). 128p. (YA). (gr. 5-12). lib. bdg. 26.60 (978-0-89490-939-9(8)) Enslow Pubs., Inc.

Judson, Karen. Abraham Lincoln: "This Nation Shall Have a New Birth of Freedom" 2008. (Americans-the Spirit of a Nation Ser.). (Illus.). 128p. (J). (gr. 5 up). lib. bdg. 31.93 ***(978-0-7660-3170-8(5))*** Enslow Pubs., Inc.

Just a Few Words, Mr Lincoln. 2004. pap. 18.95 incl. audio compact disk (978-1-55592-437-9(9)); pap. 38.75 incl. audio compact disk (978-1-55592-438-6(7)) Weston Woods Studios, Inc.

Just a Few Words Mr Lincoln. 2004. pap. 32.75 incl. audio (978-1-55592-352-5(6)); pap. 14.95 incl. audio (978-1-55592-045-6(4)) Weston Woods Studios, Inc.

Knox, Barbara. Abraham Lincoln. Saunders-Smith, Gail, ed. 2004. (First Biographies Ser.). (Illus.). 24p. (J). (gr. k-1). lib. bdg. 15.93 (978-0-7368-2086-8(8), Pebble Bks.) Capstone Pr., Inc.

Korman, Justine. Abraham Lincoln: Lawyer, Leader, Legend. 2001. (gr. k-3). lib. bdg. 11.80 (978-0-613-35057-0(X)) Tandem Library Bks.

Krensky, Stephen. Abe Lincoln & the Muddy Pig. 2002. (gr. k-3). lib. bdg. 11.80 (978-0-613-44998-4(3)) Tandem Library Bks.

—Abraham Lincoln & the Muddy Pig. Griffith, Gershom, illus. 2002. (Ready-to-Read Ser.: Level 2). 32p. (J). pap. 3.99 (978-0-689-84103-3(5), Aladdin) Simon & Schuster Children's Publishing.

Landau, Elaine. The Emancipation Proclamation: Would You Do What Lincoln Did? 2008. (What Would You Do? Ser.). (Illus.). 48p. (J). (gr. 3-4). lib. bdg. 23.93 ***(978-0-7660-2899-9(2)***, Enslow Elementary) Enslow Pubs., Inc.

Lincoln, Abraham. The Gettysburg Address. McCurdy, Michael, illus. 1998. 32p. (J). (gr. k-3). pap. 6.95 (978-0-395-88397-6(0)) Houghton Mifflin Co. Trade & Reference Div.

Lincoln's Cabinet / Sumter Crisis. 2001. spiral bd. 14.95 (978-1-56004-108-5(0)) Social Studies Schl. Service.

MacDonald, Fiona. Abraham Lincoln. 2000. (World in the Time of... Ser.). (Illus.). 48p. (J). (gr. 4-7). 22.95 (978-0-7910-6028-5(4), Chelsea Hse.) Facts On File, Inc.

Magoon, Kekla. Abraham Lincoln. 2007. (Essential Lives Ser.). (ENG., Illus.). 112p. (YA). (gr. 8-12). lib. bdg. 32.79 ***(978-1-59928-839-0(7)***, Essential Library) ABDO Publishing Co.

Manolis, Kay. Abraham Lincoln: A Life of Honesty. 2007. (Illus.). 24p. (J). lib. bdg. 19.95 (978-1-60014-091-4(2)) Bellwether Media.

Mara, Wil. Abraham Lincoln. (Rookie Biographies Ser.). (Illus.). 32p. (J). (gr. 1-2). 2003. pap. 4.95 (978-0-516-27334-1(5)); 2002. 20.50 (978-0-516-22518-0(9)) Scholastic Library Publishing. (Children's Pr.).

—Abraham Lincoln. 2002. (gr. k-3). lib. bdg. 12.95 (978-0-613-59443-1(6)) Tandem Library Bks.

Margaret, Amy. Presidents' Day. 2002. (Library of Holidays). (Illus.). 24p. (J). lib. bdg. 18.75 (978-0-8239-5786-6(1), PowerKids Pr.) Rosen Publishing Group, Inc., The.

Marrin, Albert. Commander in Chief: Abraham Lincoln & the Civil War. 2003. (Illus.). 256p. (J). (gr. 7). pap. 14.99 (978-0-525-47069-4(7), Dutton Juvenile) Penguin Group (USA) Inc.

—Commander in Chief Abraham Lincoln & the Civil War. 2003. (Illus.). 246p. (YA). (gr. 8-12). lib. bdg. 24.60 (978-0-613-59800-2(8)) Tandem Library Bks.

Marsh, Carole. Abraham Lincoln. 2002. (One Thousand Readers Ser.). (Illus.). 12p. (J). (gr. k-4). 2.95 (978-0-635-01474-0(2), 14742) Gallopade International.

—Abraham Lincoln: An Ohio Experience Reader. 2001. (Illus.). (J). (gr. k-5). pap. 1.95 (978-0-635-00428-4(3)) Gallopade International.

J K L

—The Virginia Reader: Abraham Lincoln. 2001. (Virginia Experience! Ser.). 12p. (J). (gr. k-5). pap. 2.95 (978-0-635-00375-1(9)) Gallopade International.

Martin, Michael J. Emancipation Proclamation: Hope of Freedom for the Slaves. 2002. (Let Freedom Ring Ser.). (Illus.). 48p. (J). (gr. 3-4). lib. bdg. 22.60 (978-0-7368-1339-6(X) , Bridgestone Bks.) Capstone Pr., Inc.

Marx, David F. Presidents' Day. 2002. (Rookie Read-About Holidays Ser.). (Illus.). 32p. (J). (gr. 1-2). 20.50 (978-0-516-22268-4(6)); pap. 5.95 (978-0-516-27376-1(0)) Scholastic Library Publishing. (Children's Pr.).

Mattern, Joanne. Mary Todd Lincoln. 2007. (First Ladies Ser.). (Illus.). 32p. (J). (gr. k-6). lib. bdg. 24.21 (***978-1-59928-797-3(8)*** , Checkerboard Library) ABDO Publishing Co.

Mayer, Cassie. Abraham Lincoln. 2007. (J). (***978-1-4034-9968-4(3));*** pap. (***978-1-4034-9977-6(2))*** Heinemann Library.

Murphy, Jim. The Long Road to Gettysburg. 2000. (Illus.). 128p. (J). (gr. 4-6). pap. 8.95 (978-0-618-05157-1(0) , Clarion Bks.) Houghton Mifflin Co. Trade & Reference Div.

Nettleton, Pamela Hill. Abraham Lincoln. Yesh, Jeff, illus. 2004. (Biographies Ser.). 24p. (C). (gr. k-3). 22.60 (978-1-4048-0185-1(5)) Picture Window Bks.

Nicolay, Helen. The Boys Life of Abraham Lincoln. 2005. 26.95 (978-1-4218-0834-5(X)); 2004. 192p. pap. 11.95 (978-1-59540-434-3(1)) 1st World Publishing, Inc. (1st World Library - Literary Society).

Nobleman, Marc Tyler. The Lincoln Memorial. 2004. (Let's See Library). (Illus.). 24p. (J). (gr. 1 up). lib. bdg. 19.93 (978-0-7565-0618-6(2)) Compass Point Bks.

Oberle, Lora Polack. Abraham Lincoln. 2002. (Let Freedom Ring Ser.). (Illus.). 48p. (J). (gr. 3-4). lib. bdg. 22.60 (978-0-7368-1086-9(2) , Bridgestone Bks.) Capstone Pr., Inc.

Olson, Kay Melchisedech. The Assassination of Abraham Lincoln. 2005. (Graphic Library). (Illus.). 32p. (J). 22.60 (978-0-7368-3831-3(7)) Capstone Pr., Inc.

Olson, Steven P. Lincoln's Gettysburg Address: A Primary Source Investigation. 2004. (Great Historic Debates & Speeches Ser.). (Illus.). 64p. (J). lib. bdg. 29.25 (978-1-4042-0151-4(3)) Rosen Publishing Group, Inc., The.

Otfinoski, Steven. Abraham Lincoln. 2004. (Encyc of Presidents, 2ND Ser.). (Illus.). 110p. (J). 34.00 (978-0-516-22887-7(0) , Watts, Franklin) Scholastic Library Publishing.

Owens, L. L. Abraham Lincoln: A Great American Life. 2000. (Cover-to-Cover Bks.). (Illus.). (J). 55p. pap. (978-0-7891-5162-9(6)); 56p. (gr. 1-4). lib. bdg. 16.95 (978-0-7807-9307-1(2)) Perfection Learning Corp.

Parin D'Aulaire, Ingri & Parin D'Aulaire, Edgar. Abraham Lincoln. unabr. ed. 2001. (J). (gr. 3-5). pap. 20.00 incl. audio (978-0-8045-6719-0(0) , 6512G/6) Spoken Arts, Inc.

Patrick, Bethanne Kelly. Abraham Lincoln. 2003. (Childhoods of the Presidents Ser.). (Illus.). 48p. (J). (gr. 4 up). lib. bdg. (978-1-59084-275-1(8)) Mason Crest Pubs.

Petty, Kate. Abraham Lincoln: The Life of America's Sixteenth President. 2005. (Graphic Nonfiction Ser.). (Illus.). 48p. (J). (gr. 4-6). lib. bdg. 26.50 (978-1-4042-0237-5(4)) Rosen Publishing Group, Inc., The.

Phillips, Ellen Blue. Sterling Biographies: Abraham Lincoln: From Pioneer to President. 2007. (Sterling Biographies Ser.). (Illus.). 128p. (J). 12.95 (978-1-4027-4745-8(4)) Sterling Publishing Co., Inc.

Pingry, Patricia A. Meet Abraham Lincoln. Britt, Stephanie M., illus. 2001. (Meet Ser.). 32p. (J). 9.95 (978-0-8249-4132-1(2)) Ideals Pubns.

Pollard, Josephine. A Child's History of the Life of Lincoln. 1999. (Child's American History Ser.). (Illus.). 152p. (J). reprint ed. 15.00 (978-1-889128-59-7(7)) Mantle Ministries.

Porterfield, Jason. The Lincoln-Douglas Senatorial Debates of 1858: A Primary Source Investigation. 2004. (Great Historic Debates & Speeches Ser.). (Illus.). 64p. (YA). lib. bdg. 29.25 (978-1-4042-0153-8(X)) Rosen Publishing Group, Inc., The.

Price Hossell, Karen. The Emancipation Proclamation. 2005. (Illus.). 48p. (J). (978-1-4034-6813-0(3)); pap. (978-1-4034-6818-5(4)) Heinemann Library.

—The Gettysburg Address. 2005. (Illus.). 48p. (J). (978-1-4034-6812-3(5)); pap. (978-1-4034-6817-8(6)) Heinemann Library.

Raatma, Lucia. Abraham Lincoln. 2000. (Compass Point Early Biographies Ser.). (Illus.). 32p. (J). (gr. 2 up). lib. bdg. 21.26 (978-0-7565-0012-2(5)) Compass Point Bks.

Riehecky, Janet. The Emancipation Proclamation: The Abolition of Slavery. 2002. (Point of Impact Ser.). (Illus.). 32p. (J). (gr. 5-7). lib. bdg. 25.64 (978-1-58810-556-1(3)) Heinemann Library.

—The Emancipation Proclamation Set: The Abolition of Slavery. 2002. (Point of Impact Ser.). (Illus.). 32p. (J). (gr. 5-7). pap. (978-1-4034-0071-0(7) , 91552) Heinemann Library.

Rivera, Sheila. Abraham Lincoln: A Life of Respect. 2006. (Pull Ahead Books). (Illus.). 32p. (J). 22.60 (978-0-8225-3473-0(8) , Lerner Pubns.) Lerner Publishing Group.

—Abraham Lincoln: Una Vida de Respeto. 2006. (Libros para Avanzar Ser.). (ENG & SPA.). 32p. (J). lib. bdg. 22.60 (978-0-8225-6236-8(7)) Lerner Publishing Group.

Roberts, Jeremy. Abraham Lincoln. 2004. (Presidential Leaders Ser.). (Illus.). 112p. (J). (gr. 6-12). lib. bdg. 29.27 (978-0-8225-0817-5(6)) Lerner Publishing Group.

Rosinsky, Natalie M. Presidents' Day. 2004. (Let's See Ser.). (Illus.). 24p. (J). (gr. 1 up). lib. bdg. 19.93 (978-0-7565-0773-2(1)) Compass Point Bks.

Ruffin, Frances & Phillips, Ellen Blue. Abraham Lincoln: From Pioneer to President. 2007. (Sterling Biographies Ser.). (Illus.). 128p. (J). pap. 5.95 (978-1-4027-3396-3(8)) Sterling Publishing Co., Inc.

Ruffin, Frances E. The Lincoln Memorial. 2006. (Illus.). 24p. (J). pap. (978-0-8368-6418-2(2)); lib. bdg. 19.33 (978-0-8368-6411-3(5)) Stevens, Gareth Inc.

Schaefer, Lola M. Abraham Lincoln. Saunders-Smith, Gail, ed. 1998. (Famous Americans Ser.). (Illus.). 24p. (J). (gr. k-1). lib. bdg. 15.93 (978-0-7368-0108-9(1) , Pebble Bks.) Capstone Pr., Inc.

Schmidt, Roderic. How to Draw the Life & Times of Abraham Lincoln. 2006. (Kid's Guide to Drawing the Presidents of the United States of America Ser.). (J). 25.25 (978-1-4042-2993-8(0) , PowerKids Pr.) Rosen Publishing Group, Inc., The.

Schott, Jane A. Abraham Lincoln. (History Maker Bios Ser.). (Illus.). 48p. (J). 2003. (gr. 3-5). lib. bdg. 26.60 (978-0-8225-0196-1(1)); 2002. pap. 6.95 (978-0-8225-0381-1(6) , Lerner Pubns.) Lerner Publishing Group.

Slavicek, Louise Chipley. Abraham Lincoln. (Great American Presidents Ser.). (Illus.). (gr. 4-8). 2004. 112p. pap. 30.00 (978-0-7910-7780-1(2)); 2003. 100p. 30.00 (978-0-7910-7605-7(9)) Facts On File, Inc. (Chelsea Hse.).

—Abraham Lincoln. 2004. (gr. 3-6). lib. bdg. 17.60 (978-0-613-84047-7(X)) Tandem Library Bks.

Smolinski, Diane. The Home Front in the North. 2001. (Americans at War Ser.). (Illus.). 32p. (J). (gr. 4-6). lib. bdg. (978-1-58810-099-3(5)) Heinemann Library.

St. George, Judith. Stand Tall, Abe Lincoln. Faulkner, Matt, illus. 2008. 48p. (J). (ps). 16.99 (978-0-399-24174-1(4) , Philomel) Penguin Group (USA) Inc.

Stevenson, Augusta. Abraham Lincoln & George Washington. 2003. (gr. 3-6). lib. bdg. 15.30 (978-0-613-61599-0(9)) Tandem Library Bks.

Stone, Tanya Lee. Abraham Lincoln: A Photographic Story of a Life. Dorling Kindersley Publishing Staff, ed. 2005. (Biography Ser.). (Illus.). 128p. (J). 14.99 (978-0-7566-0833-0(3)); (gr. 8). pap. 4.99 (978-0-7566-0834-7(1)) Dorling Kindersley Publishing, Inc.

The Story of Abraham Lincoln. 2001. (Illus.). 24p. (J). (ps-k). 6.95 (978-0-8249-4107-9(1)) Ideals Pubns.

Sullivan, George. Abraham Lincoln. 2000. (gr. 3-6). lib. bdg. 12.40 (978-0-613-32239-3(8)) Tandem Library Bks.

Sullivan, George E. Abraham Lincoln. 2001. (In Their Own Words Ser.). (Illus.). 128p. (J). pap. 12.95 (978-0-439-14750-7(6)); (gr. 4-6). 4.99 (978-0-439-09554-9(9)) Scholastic, Inc.

—Abraham Lincoln. 2001. (In Their Own Words Ser.). (Illus.). (J). 11.64 (978-0-606-20724-9(4)) Tandem Library Bks.

—Picturing Lincoln: Famous Photographs That Popularized the President. 2000. (Illus.). 96p. (J). (gr. k-3). tchr. ed. 16.00 (978-0-395-91682-7(8) , Clarion Bks.) Houghton Mifflin Co. Trade & Reference Div.

Tiwari, Saral. Abraham Lincoln: The Civil War President. Turner, Ginger, illus. 2004. 48p. (J). pap. 17.95 (978-0-9742502-1-2(X)) Gossamer Bks., LLC.

Tiwari, Saral, illus. Abraham Lincoln: The Civil War President. 2004. 48p. (J). 15.95 (978-0-9742502-0-5(1)) Gossamer Bks., LLC.

Trumbauer, Lisa. Life in the Time of Abraham Lincoln & the Civil War. 2007. (J). (***978-1-4034-9668-3(4));*** pap. (***978-1-4034-9676-8(5))*** Heinemann Library.

Turner, Ann. Abe Lincoln Remembers. Minor, Wendell, illus. 2003. 32p. (J). (gr. 1-4). pap. 6.99 (978-0-06-051107-4(9) , Harper Trophy) HarperCollins Pubs.

—Abe Lincoln Remembers. 2003. (gr. k-3). lib. bdg. 14.15 (978-0-613-87326-0(2)) Tandem Library Bks.

Turner, Ann Warren. Abe Lincoln Remembers. Minor, Wendell, illus. 2001. 32p. (J). (gr. 1-4). 16.99 (978-0-06-027577-8(4)) HarperCollins Pubs.

Uglow, Loyd. Abraham Lincoln Will You Ever Give up? Read-along. James, Kennon, illus. 2003. (Another Great Achiever Ser.). (J). lib. bdg. 23.95 incl. audio compact disk (978-1-57537-740-7(3)); lib. bdg. 23.95 incl. audio (978-1-57537-790-2(X)) Advance Publishing, Inc.

Uschan, Michael V. Abraham Lincoln. 2002. (Beginning Biographies Ser.). (Illus.). 32p. (J). lib. bdg. 25.69 (978-0-7398-5678-9(2)) Raintree.

Usel, T. M. Abraham Lincoln. 1998. (Biografias Ilustradas con Fotografias Ser.). (SPA., Illus.). 24p. (J). (gr. 2-3). lib. bdg. 18.60 (978-1-56065-806-1(1) , CAP2789, Bridgestone Bks.) Capstone Pr., Inc.

Venezia, Mike. Abraham Lincoln. Venezia, Mike, illus. 2006. (Illus.). 32p. (J). (gr. 3-4). pap. 7.95 (978-0-516-25483-8(9) , Children's Pr.) Scholastic Library Publishing.

—Abraham Lincoln: Sixteenth President. Venezia, Mike, illus. 2005. (Illus.). 32p. (J). (ps-7). 27.00 (978-0-516-22621-7(5) , Children's Pr.) Scholastic Library Publishing.

Vierow, Wendy. The 1864 Presidential Election: A War-Weary Nation Reelects President Abraham Lincoln. 2004. (Headlines from History Ser.). (Illus.). 24p. (J). lib. bdg. 19.95 (978-0-8239-6224-2(5)) Rosen Publishing Group, Inc., The.

Walker, Pamela. Abraham Lincoln. 2001. (Real People Ser.). (Illus.). 24p. (J). (ps-2). 17.00 (978-0-516-23432-8(3)); pap. 4.95 (978-0-516-23586-8(9)) Scholastic Library Publishing. (Children's Pr.).

—Abraham Lincoln. 2001. (Illus.). 24p. (J). (ps-3). lib. bdg. 12.95 (978-0-613-58822-5(3)) Tandem Library Bks.

Welsbacher, Anne. Abraham Lincoln. 2001. (United States Presidents Ser.). (Illus.). 32p. (J). (gr. k-6). lib. bdg. 22.78 (978-1-56239-740-1(0) , Checkerboard Library) ABDO Publishing Co.

Winters, Kay. Abe Lincoln: The Boy Who Loved Books. Carpenter, Nancy, illus. 2004. 38p. (J). (ps-3). reprint ed. 17.00 (978-0-7567-7969-6(3)) DIANE Publishing Co.

—Abe Lincoln: The Boy Who Loved Books. Carpenter, Nancy, illus. 2006. 40p. (J). reprint ed. pap. 6.99 (978-1-4169-1268-2(1) , Aladdin) Simon & Schuster Children's Publishing.

Winters, Kay & Carpenter, Nancy. Abe Lincoln: The Boy Who Loved Books. 2003. (Illus.). 40p. (J). (gr. k-3). 16.95 (978-0-689-82554-5(4)) Simon & Schuster Children's Publishing.

LINCOLN, ABRAHAM, 1809-1865—ADDRESSES AND ESSAYS

Armentrout, David & Armentrout, Patricia. The Gettysburg Address. 2004. (Documents That Shaped the Nation Ser.). 48p. pap. 7.95 (978-1-59515-333-3(0)) Rourke Publishing, LLC.

Armstrong, Jennifer. A Three-Minute Speech. Lorenz, Albert, illus. 2003. (Milestone Ser.). 96p. (J). pap. 3.99 (978-0-689-85622-8(9) , Aladdin) Simon & Schuster Children's Publishing.

Feinberg, Barbara Silberdick. Abraham Lincoln's Gettysburg Address: Four Score & More— 2000. (Single Titles Ser.: 8). (Illus.). 80p. (J). (gr. 7 up). lib. bdg. (978-0-7613-1610-7(8) , Millbrook Pr.) Lerner Publishing Group.

Harness, Cheryl. Young Abe Lincoln: The Frontier Days, 1809 -1837. 2003. 32p. (J). (gr. 3-7). pap. 7.95 (978-0-7922-6904-5(7) , National Geographic Children's Bks.) National Geographic Society.

—Young Abe Lincoln: The Frontier Days, 1809-1837. 1998. (Illus.). 32p. (J). (gr. 3-7). 15.95 (978-0-7922-2713-7(1) , National Geographic Children's Bks.) National Geographic Society.

—Young Abe Lincoln: The Frontier Days, 1809-1837. 2002. (gr. k-3). lib. bdg. 16.40 (978-0-613-65396-1(3)) Tandem Library Bks.

Holzer, Harold, ed. & compiled by. Abraham Lincoln, the Writer: A Treasury of His Greatest Speeches & Letters. Holzer, Harold, compiled by. 2003. (Illus.). 96p. (YA). (gr. 4-6). 16.95 (978-1-56397-772-5(9)) Boyds Mills Pr.

Murphy, Jim. The Long Road to Gettysburg. 2000. (J). (978-0-606-19362-7(6)) Tandem Library Bks.

Rivera, Sheila. The Gettysburg Address. 2005. (American Moments Ser.). (Illus.). 48p. (J). (gr. 4-8). lib. bdg. 25.65 (978-1-59197-285-3(X)) ABDO Publishing Co.

Warrick, Karen Clemens. Gettysburg National Military Park: A MyReportLinks.com Book. 2005. (Virtual Field Trips Ser.). (Illus.). 48p. (J). (gr. 4-10). lib. bdg. 25.26 (978-0-7660-5223-9(0) , MyReportLinks.com Bks.) Enslow Pubs., Inc.

LINCOLN, ABRAHAM, 1809-1865—ANECDOTES

Collier, James Lincoln. Abraham Lincoln You Never Knew. 2004. (You Never Knew Ser.). (J). (gr. 4-6). pap. 6.95 (978-0-516-25835-5(4) , Children's Pr.) Scholastic Library Publishing.

Roop, Peter & Roop, Connie. Grace's Letter to Lincoln. 1998. (Chapters Ser.). (Illus.). 64p. (gr. 3-4). pap. 3.95 (978-0-7868-1296-7(6)) Hyperion Bks. for Children.

LINCOLN, ABRAHAM, 1809-1865—ASSASSINATION

Burgan, Michael. The Assassination of Abraham Lincoln. 2004. (Illus.). 48p. (J). (gr. 4 up). lib. bdg. 22.60 (978-0-7565-0678-0(0)) Compass Point Bks.

Fradin, Dennis B. The Assassination of Abraham Lincoln. 2006. (Turning Points in U. S. History Ser.). (Illus.). 48p. (J). lib. bdg. 29.93 (978-0-7614-2123-8(8) , Benchmark Bks.) Cavendish, Marshall Corp.

Giblin, James Cross. Good Brother, Bad Brother: The Story of Edwin Booth & John Wilkes Booth. 2005. (Illus.). 256p. (YA). (gr. 5-9). 22.00 (978-0-618-09642-8(6) , Clarion Bks.) Houghton Mifflin Co. Trade & Reference Div.

Holzer, Harold. The President Is Shot! The Assassination of Abraham Lincoln. 2004. (Illus.). 184p. (YA). (gr. 4-6). 17.95 (978-1-56397-985-9(3)) Boyds Mills Pr.

Jones, Rebecca C. The Mystery of Mary Surratt: The Plot to Kill President Lincoln. 2004. (Illus.). 96p. (J). pap. 9.95 (978-0-87033-560-0(X) , Tidewater Pubs.) Cornell Maritime Pr., Inc.

Marinelli, Deborah A. The Assassination of Abraham Lincoln. 2003. (Library of Political Assassinations). (Illus.). 64p. (J). (gr. 4-6). lib. bdg. 26.50 (978-0-8239-3539-0(6)) Rosen Publishing Group, Inc., The.

Naden, Corinne J. & Blue, Rose. Civil War Ends: Assassination, Reconstruction & the Aftermath. 1999. (House Divided Ser.). (Illus.). 112p. (J). (gr. 5-10). lib. bdg. 31.40 (978-0-8172-5583-1(4)) Raintree.

Olson, Kay Melchisedech. El Asesinato de Abraham Lincoln. Murtoff, Jessica, tr. Lohse, Otha Zackariah Edward, illus. 2006. (Historia Grafica en Espanol Ser.). (ENG & SPA.). 32p. (J). lib. bdg. 18.95 (978-0-7368-6055-0(X)) Capstone Pr., Inc.

—The Assassination of Abraham Lincoln. (Graphic History Ser.). 32p. (YA). pap. 7.95 (978-0-7368-5241-8(7)) Capstone Pr., Inc.

Somerlott, Robert. The Lincoln Assassination in American History. 1998. (In American History Ser.). (Illus.). 128p. (YA). (gr. 5-12). lib. bdg. 26.60 (978-0-89490-886-6(3)) Enslow Pubs., Inc.

Zeinert, Karen. The Lincoln Murder Plot. 1999. (Illus.). xvii, 113p. (YA). (gr. 6 up). 22.50 (978-0-208-02451-0(4) , Linnet Bks.) Shoe String Pr., Inc.

LINCOLN, ABRAHAM, 1809-1865—ASSASSINATION—FICTION

Rinaldi, Ann. An Acquaintance with Darkness. 2005. (Great Episodes Ser.). 384p. (YA). pap. 6.95 (978-0-15-205387-1(5) , Gulliver Bks.) Harcourt Children's Bks.

—An Acquaintance with Darkness. 1999. (J). 12.65 (978-0-606-16525-9(8)) Tandem Library Bks.

LINCOLN, ABRAHAM, 1809-1865—FICTION

Biros, Florence W. Love & Loyalty: The Traits That Made Lincoln Great. Ceremuga, Ashley, illus. McCoy, W. L., photos by. 2003. 328p. (YA). per. 14.95 (978-0-936369-92-1(2)) Son-Rise Pubns. & Distribution Co.

Blackwood, Gary. Second Sight. 2007. 288p. (J). pap. 6.99 (978-0-14-240747-9(X) , Puffin) Penguin Group (USA) Inc.

Borden, Louise. A. Lincoln & Me. 2000. (J). 12.79 (978-0-606-19625-3(0)) Tandem Library Bks.

—A Lincoln & Me. 2001. (gr. k-3). lib. bdg. 14.15 (978-0-613-33661-1(5)) Tandem Library Bks.

Borden, Louise W. A. Lincoln & Me. Lewin, Ted, illus. 2001. 32p. (J). (gr. 4). pap. 5.99 (978-0-590-45715-6(2)) Scholastic, Inc.

Brewer, Caroline. Kara & Friends Meet Abraham Lincoln. 2004. (Illus.). 40p. (J). 17.95 (978-0-9717790-4-4(X)) Unchained Spirit Enterprises.

Carr, Richard Wallace. Dolly & Ike at the Willard Hotel: Abraham Lincoln's Slippers. Parrish, Mary, illus. 2005. (J). 15.95 (978-0-933165-08-3(0)) Dicmar Publishing Co.

Caseley, Judith. Praying to A. L. 2000. 64p. (J). (gr. 5 up). 15.95 (978-0-688-15934-4(6)) HarperCollins Pubs.

Hedstrom-Page, Deborah. From Log Cabin to White House with Abraham Lincoln. Martinez, Sergio, illus. 2007. 80p. (J). (gr. 3-9). 9.99 (978-0-8054-3269-5(8)) B&H Publishing Grp.

Lewis, Catherine. Postcards to Father Abraham. Yeomans, Jane, illus. 2000. 304p. (YA). (gr. 7-12). 17.95 (978-0-689-82852-2(7) , Atheneum) Simon & Schuster Children's Publishing.

Myers, Anna. Assassin. 2007. 224p. (YA). pap. 6.95 (***978-0-8027-9643-1(5));*** 2005. (J). (978-0-8027-8989-1(7)) Walker & Co.

Osborne, Mary Pope. After the Rain Bk. 2: Virginia's Civil War Diary. 2002. (My America Ser.). 112p. (J). (gr. 2-5). pap. 10.95 (978-0-439-20138-4(1)); (Illus.). pap. 4.99 (978-0-439-36904-6(5)) Scholastic, Inc. (Scholastic Pr.).

Pinkney, Andrea Davis. Abraham Lincoln: Letters from a Young Slave Girl. 2001. (Dear Mr. President Ser.). (Illus.). 136p. (J). (gr. 4-7). 8.95 (978-1-890817-60-2(0)) Winslow Pr.

Sappey, Maureen. Letters from Vinnie. 2007. 248p. (J). (gr. 4-6). pap. 10.95 (***978-1-59078-538-6(X))*** Boyds Mills Pr.

Sargent, Dave & Sargent, Pat. Cassidy: (Dark Bucksin) Equal Rights for All, 30, 11. Lenoir, Jane, illus. 2001. (Saddle Up Ser.: 11). 36p. (J). lib. bdg. 22.60 (978-1-56763-669-7(1)) Ozark Publishing.

Tarbell, Ida M. Father Abraham. Campbell, Blendon, illus. 2004. reprint ed. pap. 15.95 (978-1-4179-0070-1(9)) Kessinger Publishing, LLC.

Williams, Maiya. The Hour of the Outlaw. 2007. 360p. (YA). (gr. 4-9). 16.95 (***978-0-8109-9355-6(4))*** Abrams, Harry N., Inc.

Winnick, Karen B. Mr. Lincoln's Whiskers. Winnick, Karen B., illus. 2003. (Illus.). 32p. (J). (gr. k-2). 16.95 (978-1-56397-485-4(1)); pap. 8.95 (978-1-56397-805-0(9)) Boyds Mills Pr.

—Mr. Lincoln's Whiskers. 1999. (gr. k-3). lib. bdg. 17.60 (978-0-613-78891-5(5)) Tandem Library Bks.

LINCOLN, ABRAHAM, 1809-1865—MONUMENTS, ETC.

Abraham Lincoln Birthplace National Historic Site Junior Ranger Program. 2001. (Illus.). 12p. (J). 4.50 (978-1-888213-74-4(4)) Eastern National.

Binns, Tristan Boyer. Lincoln Memorial. 2001. (gr. 3-6). lib. bdg. 15.25 (978-0-613-43349-5(1)) Tandem Library Bks.

Deady, Kathleen W. The Lincoln Memorial. 2002. (National Landmarks Ser.). (Illus.). 24p. (J). (gr. 2-3). lib. bdg. 18.60 (978-0-7368-1114-9(1) , Bridgestone Bks.) Capstone Pr., Inc.

Firestone, Mary. The Lincoln Memorial. Skeens, Matthew, illus. 2007. (J). lib. bdg. (***978-1-4048-3718-8(3))*** Picture Window Bks.

Nelson, Kristin L. The Lincoln Memorial. 2004. (Pull Ahead Bks.). (Illus.). 32p. (J). (gr. k-3). lib. bdg. 22.60 (978-0-8225-3690-1(0)) Lerner Publishing Group.

LINCOLN, MARY TODD, 1818-1882

Ashby, Ruth. Abraham & Mary Todd Lincoln. 2004. (Illus.). 48p. (J). pap. 11.95 (978-0-8368-5701-6(1)); lib. bdg. 30.00 (978-0-8368-5695-8(3)) Stevens, Gareth Inc. (World Almanac Library).

Bracken, Thomas. Abraham Lincoln: U. S. President. 1999. (Overcoming Adversity Ser.). (Illus.). 128p. (YA). (gr. 5 up). pap. 30.00 (978-0-7910-4705-7(9) , Chelsea Hse.) Facts On File, Inc.

Hull, Mary E. Mary Todd Lincoln: Tragic First Lady of the Civil War. 2000. (Historical American Biographies Ser.). (Illus.). 128p. (YA). (gr. 6-12). lib. bdg. 26.60 (978-0-7660-1252-3(2)) Enslow Pubs., Inc.

Larkin, Tanya. What Was Cooking in Mary Todd Lincoln's White House? 2001. (Cooking Throughout American History Ser.). (Illus.). 24p. (J). (gr. 3). lib. bdg. 19.95 (978-0-8239-5609-8(1) , PowerKids Pr.) Rosen Publishing Group, Inc., The.

Mattern, Joanne. Mary Todd Lincoln. 2007. (First Ladies Ser.). (Illus.). 32p. (J). (gr. k-6). lib. bdg. 24.21 (***978-1-59928-797-3(8)*** , Checkerboard Library) ABDO Publishing Co.

LINCOLN, MARY TODD, 1818-1882—FICTION

Rinaldi, Ann. An Unlikely Friendship: A Novel of Mary Todd Lincoln & Elizabeth Keckley. 2007. (Harcourt Great Episodes Ser.). (Illus.). 256p. (YA). (gr. 6-9). 17.00 (978-0-15-205597-4(5)) Harcourt Children's Bks.

LINCOLN, NANCY HANKS, 1784-1818—FICTION

Le Sueur, Meridel. Nancy Hanks of Wilderness Road: A Story of Abraham Lincoln's Mother. 2004. 80p. (gr. 5-7). pap. 7.95 (978-0-930100-73-5(5)) Holy Cow! Pr.

LINCOLN, THOMAS, 1853-1871

Hines, Gary. Thanksgiving in the White House. Wallner, Alexandra, illus. rev. ed. 2003. 32p. (J). 15.95 (978-0-8050-6530-5(X) , Holt, Henry & Co. Bks. For Young Readers) Holt, Henry & Co.

LINCOLN-DOUGLAS DEBATES, 1858

Burgan, Michael. The Lincoln-Douglas Debates. 2006. (Illus.). 48p. (J). (gr. 4-6). 23.93 (978-0-7565-1632-1(3)) Compass Point Bks.

January, Brendan. The Lincoln-Douglas Debates. 1998. (Illus.). 32p. (J). (gr. 4-7). lib. bdg. 14.10 (978-0-613-37439-2(8)) Tandem Library Bks.

LINCOLN MEMORIAL (WASHINGTON, D.C.)

Binns, Tristan Boyer. Lincoln Memorial. 2001. (gr. 3-6). lib. bdg. 15.25 (978-0-613-43349-5(1)) Tandem Library Bks.

Deady, Kathleen W. The Lincoln Memorial. 2002. (National Landmarks Ser.). (Illus.). 24p. (J). (gr. 2-3). lib. bdg. 18.60 (978-0-7368-1114-9(1) , Bridgestone Bks.) Capstone Pr., Inc.

DeGezelle, Terri. The Lincoln Memorial. 2004. (Fact Finders Ser.). (Illus.). 24p. (J). 15.95 (978-0-7368-2529-0(0)) Capstone Pr., Inc.

Firestone, Mary. The Lincoln Memorial. Skeens, Matthew, illus. 2007. (J). lib. bdg. (***978-1-4048-3718-8(3)***) Picture Window Bks.

Hargrove, Julia. Lincoln Memorial. Mitchell, Judy, ed. Mohrman, Gary, illus. 2001. (Historic Monuments Ser.). 48p. (J). (gr. 4-8). pap. 6.95 (978-1-57310-311-4(X)) Teaching & Learning Co.

Hopkinson, Deborah. Sweet Land of Liberty. Jenkins, Leonard, illus. 2007. 32p. (J). (gr. 1-5). 16.95 (978-1-56145-395-5(1) , Peachtree Junior) Peachtree Pubs., Ltd.

Murray, Julie. Lincoln Memorial. 2005. (Buddy Book Ser.). (Illus.). 24p. (J). (gr. k-4). lib. bdg. 21.35 (978-1-57765-670-8(9)) ABDO Publishing Co.

Nelson, Kristin L. The Lincoln Memorial. 2004. (Pull Ahead Bks.). (Illus.). 32p. (J). (gr. k-3). lib. bdg. 22.60 (978-0-8225-3690-1(0)) Lerner Publishing Group.

Nobleman, Marc Tyler. The Lincoln Memorial. 2004. (Let's See Library). (Illus.). 24p. (J). (gr. 1 up). lib. bdg. 19.93 (978-0-7565-0618-6(2)) Compass Point Bks.

LINDBERGH, CHARLES A. (CHARLES AUGUSTUS), 1902-1974

Charles Lindbergh. (Compass Point Early Biographies Ser.). 32p. (J). 7.95 (978-0-7565-1016-9(3)) Compass Point Bks.

Davis, Lucile. Charles Lindbergh. 1999. (Photo-Illustrated Biographies Ser.). (Illus.). 24p. (J). (gr. 2-3). lib. bdg. 18.60 (978-0-7368-0204-8(5) , Bridgestone Bks.) Capstone Pr., Inc.

—Charles Lindbergh. (Photo Illustrated Biographies Ser.). 24p. (J). pap. 6.95 (978-0-7368-3430-8(3)) Capstone Pr., Inc.

Edwards, Judith. The Lindbergh Baby Kidnapping in American History. 2000. (In American History Ser.). (Illus.). 128p. (YA). (gr. 5-12). lib. bdg. 26.60 (978-0-7660-1299-8(9)) Enslow Pubs., Inc.

Kent, Zachary. Charles Lindbergh & the Spirit of St. Louis in American History. 2001. (In American History Ser.). (Illus.). 128p. (YA). (gr. 5-12). lib. bdg. 26.60 (978-0-7660-1683-5(8)) Enslow Pubs., Inc.

Koestler-Grack, Rachel A. Spirit of St. Louis. 2005. (American Moments Ser.). (Illus.). 48p. (J). (gr. 4-8). lib. bdg. 25.65 (978-1-59197-940-1(4)) ABDO Publishing Co.

Koopmans, Andy. Charles Lindbergh. 2002. (Importance of Ser.). (Illus.). 112p. (J). (gr. 7-10). 32.45 (978-1-59018-245-1(6) , Lucent Bks.) Thomson Gale.

Kramer, Sydelle A. Night Flight. Charles Lindbergh's Incredible Adventure. Andreasen, Dan, illus. 2002. (All Aboard Reading Ser.). 48p. (J). pap. 3.99 (978-0-448-42634-1(X) , Grosset & Dunlap) Penguin Group (USA) Inc.

—Night Flight: Charles Lindbergh's Incredible Adventure. 2002. (gr. k-3). lib. bdg. 11.80 (978-0-613-43635-9(0)) Tandem Library Bks.

Lindbergh, Charles A., Jr. The Spirit of St Louis. 2003. 562p. pap. 29.00 (978-0-7581-3991-7(8)) Textbook Pubs.

Lucia, Raatma. Charles Lindbergh: Pilot. 2000. (Career Biographies Ser.). (Illus.). 128p. (J). (gr. 6-12). 25.00 (978-0-89434-340-7(8) , F401, Ferguson Publishing Co.) Facts On File, Inc.

Meachum, Virginia. Charles Lindbergh: American Hero of Flight. 2002. (People to Know Ser.). (Illus.). 128p. (YA). (gr. 6-12). lib. bdg. 26.60 (978-0-7660-1535-7(1)) Enslow Pubs., Inc.

Monroe, Judy. The Lindbergh Baby Kidnapping Trial: A Headline Court Case. 2000. (Headline Court Cases Ser.). (Illus.). 128p. (YA). (gr. 6-12). lib. bdg. 26.60 (978-0-7660-1389-6(8)) Enslow Pubs., Inc.

O'Hara, Megan, ed. The Boyhood Diary of Charles Lindbergh, 1913-1916: Early Adventures of the Famous Aviator. 2000. (Blue Earth Books). (Illus.). 32p. (J). (gr. 3-4). lib. bdg. 22.60 (978-0-7368-0600-8(8) , Bridgestone Bks.) Capstone Pr., Inc.

Raatma, Lucia. Charles Lindbergh. 2000. (Compass Point Early Biographies Ser.). (Illus.). 32p. (J). (gr. 2 up). lib. bdg. 21.26 (978-0-7565-0013-9(3)) Compass Point Bks.

Schwabacher, Martin. Charles Lindbergh: King of the Sky. 2001. (Book Report Biographies Ser.). (Illus.). (J). (978-0-531-11690-6(5) , Watts, Franklin) Scholastic Library Publishing.

Wagner, Heather Lehr. Charles Lindbergh. 2003. (Famous Flyers Ser.). (Illus.). 112p. (gr. 6-12). 30.00 (978-0-7910-7212-7(6)); pap. 30.00 (978-0-7910-7497-8(8)) Facts On File, Inc. (Chelsea Hse.).

LINGUISTICS

see Language and Languages

LINNE, CARL VON, 1707-1778

Anderson, Margaret J. Carl Linnaeus: Father of Classification. 2001. (Great Minds of Science Ser.). (Illus.). 128p. (YA). (gr. 4-10). pap. 13.26 (978-0-7660-1867-9(9)) Enslow Pubs., Inc.

Stephens, Catherine. Classification Clues. 2004. (National Geographic Reading Expeditions Ser.). (Illus.). 32p. (J). pap. (978-0-7922-4576-6(8)) National Geographic Society.

LIONS

Adamson, Joy. Born Free. 2000. (gr. 7-12). lib. bdg. 24.55 (978-0-613-36139-2(3)) Tandem Library Bks.

Albee, Sarah. Lions. 2006. (J). 7.99 (978-1-59939-035-2(3) , Reader's Digest Young Families, Inc.) Reader's Digest Children's Publishing, Inc.

Anderson, Jill. Lions. 2006. (Illus.). 24p. (J). 6.95 (978-1-55971-953-7(2)); 12.95 (978-1-55971-952-0(4)) T&N Children's Publishing. (NorthWord Bks. for Young Readers).

Animal Lives: Lions. 2006. pap. 4.99 (978-1-4206-8152-9(4)) Teacher Created Materials, Inc.

Barnes, Julia. 101 Facts about Lions. 2004. (One Hundred One Facts about Predators Ser.). (Illus.). 32p. (J). (gr. 3 up). lib. bdg. 23.33 (978-0-8368-4037-7(2)) Stevens, Gareth Inc.

Big Cats. 2004. (Explorasaws Ser.). (Illus.). 48p. (J). pap. (978-1-84229-758-2(9)) Top That! Publishing PLC.

Bocknek, Jonathan. Lions. 2001. (Untamed World Ser.). (Illus.). 64p. (J). lib. bdg. 28.54 (978-0-8172-4577-1(4)) Raintree.

Books Are Fun 8 Title Animal Lives Set: Lions. 2006. (J). (978-1-59566-311-5(8)) QEB Publishing Inc.

Bredeson, Carmen. Lions up Close. 2008. (Zoom in on Animals! Ser.). (Illus.). 24p. (J). (gr. 1-3). lib. bdg. 21.26 (***978-0-7660-3080-0(6)***) Enslow Pubs., Inc.

Browne, Philippa-Alys. "Lion roars" (African Animals ABC) (Illus.). 14.99 (978-1-84148-752-6(X)) Barefoot Bks., Inc.

Cole, Melissa S. Lions. 2001. (Wild Cats of the World Ser.). (Illus.). 24p. (J). (gr. 3-6). 22.45 (978-1-56711-448-5(2) , Blackbirch Pr., Inc.) Thomson Gale.

Cooper, Jason. Lions. 2002. (Illus.). 24p. (J). lib. bdg. 20.64 (978-1-58952-405-7(5)) Rourke Publishing, LLC.

Corrigan, Patricia, et al. Big Cats! Exploring the Fascinating Worlds of Cougars, Leopards, Lions, & Tigers. McGee, John F., illus. 2002. (Our Wild World Ser.). 192p. (J). (gr. 2-5). 16.95 (978-1-55971-798-4(X) , NorthWord Bks. for Young Readers) T&N Children's Publishing.

Darling, Kathy. Lions. Darling-Lyon, Tara, photos by. 2000. (Nature Watch Ser.). (Illus.). 48p. (J). (gr. 3-6). lib. bdg. 25.26 (978-1-57505-404-9(3) , Carolrhoda Bks.) Lerner Publishing Group.

Denis-Huot, Christine. The Lion, King of the Beasts. 2000. (Animal Close-Ups Ser.). (J). (978-0-606-19330-6(8)); (gr. 3-6). lib. bdg. 15.25 (978-0-613-35170-6(3)) Tandem Library Bks.

Denis-Huot, Christine & Denis-Huot, Michel. The Lion, King of the Beasts. 2000. (Animal Close-Ups Ser.). (Illus.). 28p. (J). (ps-3). pap. 6.95 (978-1-57091-426-3(5)) Charlesbridge Publishing, Inc.

Dineen, Jacqueline. Lions. 2003. (Amazing Animals Ser.). (Illus.). 24p. (J). lib. bdg. 21.35 (978-1-58340-230-6(6)) Weigl Pubs., Inc.

Fitzgerald, Patrick J., contrib. by. Lion Attacks. 2000. (J). (978-0-531-12103-0(8)); (978-0-531-17603-0(7)) Scholastic Library Publishing. (Watts, Franklin).

Frisch, Aaron. Lions. 2006. (Wild World of Animals Ser.). (Illus.). 32p. 18.95 (978-1-58341-433-0(9) , Creative Education) Creative Co., The.

Gareth Stevens Publishing Staff, contrib. by. Lions. 2004. (All about Wild Animals Ser.). (Illus.). 32p. (J). lib. bdg. 23.33 (978-0-8368-4185-5(9)) Stevens, Gareth Inc.

Gentle, Victor & Perry, Janet. Lions. 2002. (Big Cats Ser.). (Illus.). 24p. (J). (gr. 2 up). lib. bdg. 22.00 (978-0-8368-3027-9(X)) Stevens, Gareth Inc.

Gordon, Sharon. Adivina Quién Ruge. 2006. (Bookworms Ser.). (SPA & ENG., Illus.). 32p. (J). lib. bdg. 22.79 (978-0-7614-2386-7(9)) Cavendish, Marshall Corp.

—Guess Who Roars (Adivina Quién Ruge) 2006. (Bookworms Ser.). (SPA & ENG., Illus.). 32p. (J). lib. bdg. 22.79 (978-0-7614-2466-6(0)) Cavendish, Marshall Corp.

Group/McGraw-Hill, Wright. Lion Level: Adventure Journal Set. (Wildcats Ser.). (gr. 2-8). 31.95 (978-0-322-05789-0(2)) Wright Group, The.

—Lion Level: Wildcats Lion Complete Kit. (Wildcats Ser.). (gr. 2-8). 599.95 (978-0-322-06482-9(1)) Wright Group, The.

Hanel, Rachael. Lions. 2008. (J). (***978-1-58341-656-3(0)*** , Creative Education) Creative Co., The.

Hansen, Sarah. When Mountain Lions Attack! 2006. (When Wild Animals Attack! Ser.). (Illus.). 48p. (J). (gr. 4-10). lib. bdg. 23.93 (978-0-7660-2668-1(X)) Enslow Pubs., Inc.

Harcourt School Publishers Staff. Lions Advanced Level. 3rd ed. 2002. (Trophies Reading Program Ser.). (Illus.). pap. 5.10 (978-0-15-323025-7(8)) Harcourt Schl. Pubs.

—Trofeos Advanced Level: Los Leones. 3rd ed. 2002. (SPA., Illus.). (gr. 1). pap. 6.80 (978-0-15-323936-6(0)) Harcourt Schl. Pubs.

Head, Honor. What's It Like to Be a Baby Lion? Nichols, Matthew, illus. 1998. (Baby Animals Ser.). 32p. (gr. k-3). lib. bdg. 20.90 (978-0-7613-1254-3(4) , Millbrook Pr.) Lerner Publishing Group.

Holmes, Kevin J. Lions. 1998. (Animals Ser.). (Illus.). 24p. (J). (gr. 2-3). lib. bdg. 18.60 (978-0-7368-0065-5(4) , Bridgestone Bks.) Capstone Pr., Inc.

Horak, Steven A. Lions & Other Wild Cats. World Book, Inc. Staff, ed. 2002. (World Book's Animals of the World Ser.: Set 3). (Illus.). 64p. (J). (978-0-7166-1226-1(7)) World Bk., Inc.

Hugo, Pierre de. Lions. Hugo, Pierre de, illus. 2000. (First Discovery Book Ser.). (Illus.). 30p. (J). (ps-3). 12.95 (978-0-439-14825-2(1)) Scholastic, Inc.

Jacobs, Liza. Lions. 2003. (Wild Wild World Ser.). (Illus.). 24p. (J). 22.45 (978-1-4103-0043-0(9) , Blackbirch Pr., Inc.) Thomson Gale.

Johnson, Jinny. Lion. Woods, Michael, illus. 2006. 32p. (J). (978-1-58340-899-5(1)) Smart Apple Media.

Jordan, Bill. Lion. 1999. (Natural World Ser.). (Illus.). 48p. (J). (gr. 4-7). pap. 7.95 (978-0-7398-0948-8(2)) Steck-Vaughn.

—Lion: Habitats, Life Cycles, Food Chains, Threats. 1999. (Natural World Ser.). (Illus.). 48p. (J). (gr. 3-7). lib. bdg. 27.12 (978-0-7398-1057-6(X)) Raintree.

Kalman, Bobbie. The Life Cycle of a Lion. 2002. (Life Cycle Ser.). (Illus.). 32p. (J). (gr. 2-3). (978-0-7787-0656-4(7)); pap. (978-0-7787-0686-1(9)) Crabtree Publishing Co.

Kalman, Bobbie & Bishop, Amanda. El Ciclo de Vida del Leon. 2005. (Serie Ciclos de Vida Ser.). (SPA., Illus.). 32p. (J). (ps-ps). pap. (978-0-7787-8710-5(9)) Crabtree Publishing Co.

—El Ciclo de Vida Del Leon. 2005. (Serie Ciclos de Vida Ser.). (SPA., Illus.). 32p. (J). (978-0-7787-8664-1(1)) Crabtree Publishing Co.

—Les Lions. 2005. (FRE., Illus.). 32p. (J). pap. (978-2-89579-024-2(8)) Crabtree Publishing Co.

Kendell, Patricia. Lions. 2002. (In the Wild Ser.). (Illus.). 32p. (J). lib. bdg. 25.69 (978-0-7398-4907-1(7)) Raintree.

Landau, Elaine. Fierce Cats. 2003. (Fearsome, Scary, & Creepy Animals Ser.). (Illus.). 48p. (J). (gr. 1-4). lib. bdg. 23.93 (978-0-7660-2062-7(2)) Enslow Pubs., Inc.

Lang, Aubrey. Baby Lion. Lynch, Wayne, photos by. (Nature Babies Ser.). (Illus.). 36p. (J). (gr. k-3). 2003. pap. (978-1-55041-713-5(4)); 2002. (978-1-55041-711-1(8)) Fitzhenry & Whiteside, Ltd.

Latta, Jan. Leonor la Leona. 2006. (ENG & SPA., Illus.). 24p. (J). pap. (***978-0-8368-7976-6(7)***); lib. bdg. (***978-0-8368-7969-8(4)***) Stevens, Gareth Inc.

—Lisa the Lion. 2006. (Illus.). 24p. (J). pap. (***978-0-8368-7777-9(2)***); lib. bdg. (***978-0-8368-7770-0(5)***) Stevens, Gareth Inc.

Los Leones (Lions) 2006. (J). pap. 7.95 (978-0-8225-6628-1(1)); (SPA.). 40p. lib. bdg. 25.26 (978-0-8225-6491-1(2)) Lerner Publishing Group. (Ediciones Lerner).

Lions, 6 bks. 2005. (Animal Predators Ser.). (Illus.). 40p. (J). (gr. 3-6). pap. 46.95 (978-0-8225-5491-2(7)) Lerner Publishing Group.

Lions, 6 vols. (gr. 2-5). 36.95 (978-0-7368-8415-0(7)) Red Brick Learning.

Lions & Tigers. 2007. 24p. pap. 2.99 (***978-1-4037-3433-4(X)***) Dalmatian Pr.

Lockwood, Sophie. Lions. 2008. (World of Mammals Ser.). 40p. (J). (gr. 2-6). 29.93 (***978-1-59296-933-3(X)***) Child's World, Inc.

Macken, JoAnn Early. Lions. 2002. (Weekly Reader Early Learning Library). (Illus.). 24p. (J). (ps up). pap. (978-0-8368-3284-6(1)); lib. bdg. 19.33 (978-0-8368-3271-6(X)) Stevens, Gareth Inc. (Weekly Reader Early Learning Library).

Markle, Sandra. Lions. 2005. (Animal Predators Ser.). (Illus.). 40p. (J). (gr. 4-6). pap. 7.95 (978-1-57505-744-6(1)); (gr. 3-6). lib. bdg. 25.26 (978-1-57505-727-9(1)) Lerner Publishing Group.

Middleton, Don. Lions. 1999. (PowerKids Readers Ser.). 24p. (J). (gr. k-4). lib. bdg. 18.75 (978-0-8239-5208-3(8) , PowerKids Pr.) Rosen Publishing Group, Inc., The.

Morgan. Lions: Young Library Predators. 2003. (Predators Ser.). (Illus.). 32p. (J). lib. bdg. 25.70 (978-0-7398-6602-3(8)) Raintree.

Morgan, Paul & Drewett, Jim. Lions. 2005. (Illus.). 224p. 25.00 (978-1-905326-04-4(1)) Penguin Group (USA) Inc.

Murray, Julie. Lions. 2002. (Animal Kingdom Ser.). (Illus.). 24p. (J). (gr. k-4). lib. bdg. 21.35 (978-1-57765-647-0(4)) ABDO Publishing Co.

Orme, Helen. Lions in Danger. 2007. (Wildlife Survival Ser.). (Illus.). 32p. (J). (gr. 2-4). lib. bdg. 25.27 (978-1-59716-262-3(0)) Bearport Publishing Co., Inc.

Petty, Kate. Lions. 2004. (J). lib. bdg. (978-1-932799-43-9(5)) Stargazer Bks.

Pingry, Patricia. Cheetah. San Diego Zoo Staff, photos by. 2005. (San Diego Zoo Library Ser.: Vol. 12). (Illus.). 24p. (J). bds. 6.95 (978-0-8249-6579-2(5) , 1242115) Ideals Pubns.

Prebeg, Rick. Looking for Lions. Prebeg, Rick, photos by. 2005. (J). (978-1-933248-12-7(2)) World Quest Learning.

Prudom, Sharla. Jambo! Lions. Prudom, Sharla, photos by. 2002. (Jambo! Ser.). (SWA & ENG., Illus.). 11p. (J). cd-rom 12.50 (978-1-931792-24-0(0)) E-Digital Bks., LLC.

Rennert, Violette. Little Lions. 2005. (Born to Be Wild Ser.). (Illus.). 24p. (J). (ps). lib. bdg. 22.00 (978-0-8368-4737-6(7)) Stevens, Gareth Inc.

Richardson, Adele D. Lions: Life in the Pride. 2001. (Wild World of Animals Ser.). (Illus.). 24p. (J). (gr. 1-2). lib. bdg. 18.60 (978-0-7368-0964-1(3) , Bridgestone Bks.) Capstone Pr., Inc.

Riley Joelle. African Lions. 2007. (Pull Ahead Books-Animals Ser.). (J). 22.60 (***978-0-8225-6703-5(2)*** , Lerner Pubns.); pap. 6.95 (***978-0-8225-6707-3(5)*** , First Avenue Editions) Lerner Publishing Group.

Robinson, Claire. Lions. (In the Wild Ser.). (Illus.). 24p. (J). (gr. k-2). 2002. pap. 6.95 (978-1-57572-467-6(7) , 90457); 1998. lib. bdg. 21.36 (978-1-57572-132-3(5)) Heinemann Library.

Roitman, Tanya, illus. I'm Going to New York to Visit the Lions. 2005. 30p. (J). (ps-ps). lib. bdg. 10.75 (978-0-606-33872-1(1)) Tandem Library Bks.

Ryan, Marla Felkins & Corwin, Jeff. Into Wild India 2. 2004. (Jeff Corwin Experience Ser.). (Illus.). 48p. (J). 11.20 (978-1-4103-0234-2(2)); (gr. 4-7). 24.95 (978-1-4103-0233-5(4)) Thomson Gale. (Blackbirch Pr., Inc.).

Schafer, Susan. Lions. 2000. (Animals Animals Ser.). (Illus.). 48p. (J). (gr. 3-5). lib. bdg. 25.64 (978-0-7614-1166-6(6) , Benchmark Bks.) Cavendish, Marshall Corp.

Solway, Andrew. Lions & Other Mammals. 2006. (Illus.). 48p. (J). (978-1-4034-8220-4(9)); pap. (978-1-4034-8227-3(6)) Heinemann Library.

Spilsbury, Louise & Spilsbury, Richard. A Pride of Lions. 2003. (Animal Groups Ser.). (Illus.). 32p. pap. 6.95 (978-1-4034-3287-2(2)); (J). lib. bdg. 24.22 (978-1-4034-0745-0(2)) Heinemann Library.

—Watching Lions in Africa. 2006. (Heinemann First Library). (Illus.). 32p. (J). 25.36 (978-1-4034-7222-9(X)); pap. (978-1-4034-7235-9(1)) Heinemann Library.

Squire, Ann O. Lions. 2005. (True Bks.). (Illus.). (J). (gr. 3-5). 47p. pap. 6.95 (978-0-516-27936-7(X)); 48p. 25.00 (978-0-516-22795-5(5)) Scholastic Library Publishing. (Children's Pr.).

Stefoff, Rebecca. Lions. 2005. (Animalways Ser.). (Illus.). 112p. (J). (gr. 3-7). lib. bdg. (978-0-7614-1746-0(X) , Benchmark Bks.) Cavendish, Marshall Corp.

Suen, Anastasia. A Lion Grows Up. Denman, Michael L. & Huiett, William J., illus. 2005. (Wild Animals Ser.). 24p. (J). (ps). lib. bdg. 23.93 (978-1-4048-0985-7(6)) Picture Window Bks.

Swanson, Diane. Wild Cats. 1998. (Welcome to the World of Animals Ser.). (Illus.). 32p. (J). (gr. 3 up). lib. bdg. 23.33 (978-0-8368-2217-5(X)) Stevens, Gareth Inc.

There's a Lion in God's Jungle! 1999. (Peek-In Board Book Ser.). (Illus.). 10p. (J). (ps-k). bds. 4.99 (978-0-7847-1082-1(1) , 04288, Bean Sprouts) Standard Publishing.

Thomas, Isabel. Lion vs. Tiger. 2006. (Illus.). 32p. (J). (978-1-4109-2391-2(6)); pap. (978-1-4109-2398-1(3)) Steck-Vaughn.

Twinn, Michael. Lion. Adams, Pam, illus. 2000. (Pocket Pals Ser.). 12p. (J). (ps-1). bds. 1.99 (978-0-85953-870-1(2)) Child's Play-International.

Vogel, Elizabeth. Lions. 2002. (PowerKids Readers Ser.). (Illus.). 24p. (J). (gr. 1). lib. bdg. 16.00 (978-0-8239-6021-7(8) , PowerKids Pr.) Rosen Publishing Group, Inc., The.

Welsbacher, Anne. Lions. 2000. (Wild Cats Ser.). (Illus.). 24p. (J). (gr. k-6). lib. bdg. 21.35 (978-1-57765-086-7(7) , Checkerboard Library) ABDO Publishing Co.

Welvaert, Scott R. Lions. 2005. (Illus.). 24p. (J). 21.26 (978-0-7368-3720-0(5)) Capstone Pr., Inc.

Wildlife Education, Ltd. Staff, et al. Lions. Orr, Richard, illus. (Zoobooks Ser.). (J). 2001. 24p. 15.95 (978-0-937934-81-4(X)); 1998. 18p. pap. 2.95 (978-0-937934-42-5(9)) Wildlife Education, Ltd.

Winner, Cherie. Lions. 2004. (Our Wild World Ser.). (Illus.). 48p. (J). (gr. 2-5). ring bd. 10.95 (978-1-55971-806-6(4) , NorthWord Bks. for Young Readers) T&N Children's Publishing.

—Lions. McGee, John F., illus. 2004. (Our Wild World Ser.). 48p. (J). (gr. 2-5). pap. 7.95 (978-1-55971-787-8(4) , NorthWord Bks. for Young Readers) T&N Children's Publishing.

—Lions. 2001. (gr. 3-6). lib. bdg. 16.40 (978-0-613-55866-2(9)) Tandem Library Bks.

Zumbusch, Amelie von. Lions. 2007. (Safari Animals Ser.). (Illus.). 24p. (J). (gr. k-3). lib. bdg. 21.25 (978-1-4042-3612-7(0) , PowerKids Pr.) Rosen Publishing Group, Inc., The.

—Lions: King of the Beasts. 2007. (Dangerous Cats Ser.). (Illus.). 24p. (J). (gr. k-5). lib. bdg. 21.25 (978-1-4042-3631-8(7)) Rosen Publishing Group, Inc., The.

LIONS—FICTION

Aardema, Verna. The Lonely Lioness & the Ostrich Chicks. Heo, Yumi, illus. 2001. 30p. (J). (gr. 4-6). 17.00 (978-0-7567-5004-6(0)) DIANE Publishing Co.

Abercrombie, Barbara. The Show-and-Tell Lion. Cravath, Lynne Avril, illus. 2006. 32p. (J). (ps-2). 16.95 (978-0-689-86408-7(6) , McElderry, Margaret K.) Simon & Schuster Children's Publishing.

Adiccabandhu & Padmasri. The Lion & the Jackal. Adiccabandhu, illus. 2004. (Illus.). 32p. (gr. k-3). pap. 10.95 (978-1-899579-13-6(3)) Windhorse Pubns. GBR. *Dist:* Consortium Bk. Sales & Distribution.

Aesop. Lion & the Mouse PB. 2007. (Illus.). (J). pap. 6.95 (978-0-7358-2129-3(1)) North-South Bks., Inc.

Alvin, John & Alvin, Andrea, illus. Simba's Pride. 1998. (Classic Storybook Ser.). 96p. (J). (ps-3). 7.99 (978-1-57082-876-8(8)) Mouse Works.

Anderson, C. W. Blaze & the Mountain Lion. 1999. (J). (gr. 1-4). 21.75 (978-0-8446-6999-1(7)) Smith, Peter Pub., Inc.

Andreae, Giles. The Lion Who Wanted to Love. Wojtowycz, David, illus. 1998. 32p. (J). (ps-2). 14.95 (978-1-888444-25-4(8) , 21023) Little Tiger Pr.

Androcles & the Lion: Individual Title Six-Packs. 32p. (gr. 3 up). 37.00 (978-0-7635-9677-4(9)) Rigby Education.

Andy & the Lion. 2004. (J). 24.95 incl. audio (978-0-89719-698-7(8)) Weston Woods Studios, Inc.

Aryal, Aimee. Hello Nittany Lion! Ramondelli, Livio, illus. 2004. (J). 19.95 (978-0-9743442-9-4(X)) Mascot Bks., Inc.

J K L

Axtell, David. We're Going on A Lion Hunt. 2007. (Illus.). 32p. (J). pap. 7.95 (***978-0-8050-8219-7(0)*** , Holt, Henry & Co. Bks. For Young Readers) Holt, Henry & Co.

Azordegan, Kambiz. The Brave Donkey & the Cowardly Lion: Donkey, Lion & Fox. Sajem, Johnny, illus. abr. l.t. ed. 1998. (Tootee's Magical Stories Ser.: Vol. 6). 40p. (J). 9.95 (978-1-890571-30-6(X)) Positive Children's Programming Corp.

Balague, Lin & Long, Robert. La Dama y el Leon. 2000. (Cuentos y Leyendas Bilingues Ser.).Tr. of Princess & the Lion. (ENG & SPA., Illus.). (J). pap. (978-0-658-01015-6(8)) McGraw-Hill/Contemporary.

Barkow, Henriette & Finlay, Lizzie, illus. Buri & the Maroow: An Indian Folk Tale: Un Conte Traditionnel Indien = Buri et la Courge. 2004. (TAM, VIE, SPA, GUJ & PER.). 24p. (J). pap. (978-1-85269-583-5(8)) Mantra Publishing, Ltd.

Bates, Sheree. Megan's One Wish. 2006. 124p. (YA). pap. 12.99 (978-1-4141-0555-0(X)) Pleasant Word.

Baum, Roger S. The Oz Odyssey. Seitzinger, Victoria, illus. 2006. 176p. (J). 19.95 (978-1-57072-299-8(4)) Overmountain Pr.

Beaton, Clare. How Loud Is a Lion? 2002. (Illus.). 24p. (J). (gr. k-2). 14.99 (978-1-84148-896-7(8)) Barefoot Bks., Inc.

Beeke, Joel & Kleyn, Diana. How God Used a Snowdrift. Anderson, Jeff, illus. (Building on the Rock Ser.). 176p. (J). pap. (978-1-85792-817-4(2) , Christian Focus) Christian Focus Pubns. GBR. *Dist:* Riverside.

Berlin, Faith Frances. The Lion Next Door. 2002. 117p. pap. 16.95 (978-1-59129-910-3(1)) PublishAmerica, Inc.

Bishop, Dorothy S., et al. Leonardo el Leon y Ramon el Raton. 2001. Tr. of Lion & the Mouse. (SPA & ENG., Illus.). 64p. (J). 6.95 (978-0-8442-7445-4(3) , NT268) McGraw-Hill/Contemporary.

Blair, Eric. El Asno Vestido de Leon: Version de la Fabula de Esopo. Silverman, Dianne, illus. 2006. (Read-It! Readers en Espanol Ser.).Tr. of Donkey in the Lion's Skin: A Retelling of Aesop's Fable. (SPA.). 24p. (J). (ps-3). 19.95 (978-1-4048-1620-6(8)) Picture Window Bks.

—El Cascabel del Gato: Version de la Fabula de Esopo. Silverman, Dianne, illus. 2006. (Read-It! Readers en Espanol Ser.).Tr. of Belling the Cat: A Retelling of Aesop's Fable. (SPA.). 32p. (J). (ps-3). 19.95 (978-1-4048-1615-2(1)) Picture Window Bks.

Bolam, Emily, illus. Chunky Safari Lion. 2001. (Chunky Farm Ser.). 14p. (J). (ps). bds. 5.99 (978-0-7641-5330-3(7)) Barron's Educational Series, Inc.

Boulden, Jim & Boulden, Joan. The Lion Roars. Kennedy, Kari, ed. Prudhomme, Suzanne, illus. 1999. 24p. (J). (gr. 4-7). pap. 5.95 (978-1-892421-09-8(7) , 09-7AB) Boulden Publishing.

Brenner, Barbara & Hooks, William H. Lion & Lamb Step Out. Degen, Bruce, illus. 1998. (Bank Street Reader Collection). 48p. (J). (gr. 2-4). lib. bdg. 22.60 (978-0-8368-1772-0(9)) Stevens, Gareth Inc.

—Ups & Downs with Lion & Lamb. Degen, Bruce, illus. 1999. (Bank Street Reader Collection). 48p. (J). (gr. 2-4). lib. bdg. (978-0-8368-1783-6(4)) Stevens, Gareth Inc.

Brenner, Barbara, et al. Lion & Lamb. 1999. (Bank Street Reader Collection). (Illus.). (J). (gr. 2-4). lib. bdg. 22.60 (978-0-8368-2421-6(0)) Stevens, Gareth Inc.

Brett, Jan. Honey... Honey... Lion! Brett, Jan, illus. 2005. (Illus.). 36p. (J). (ps-3). 16.99 (978-0-399-24463-6(8) , Putnam Juvenile) Penguin Group (USA) Inc.

Bright, Paul. Nobody Laughs at a Lion! Buckingham, Matt, illus. 2005. 28p. (J). 16.00 (978-1-56148-471-3(7)) Good Bks.

Brightwood, Laura, illus. Lion & Mousie. Brightwood, Laura, . 2007. (J). DVD (***978-1-934409-00-8(6)*** 3-C Institute for Social Development.

Brown, J. A. Lion's Mane. Knight, Paula, illus. 2003. (Funny Faces Ser.). 10p. (J). 3.95 (978-1-58925-718-4(9) , tiger tales) ME Media LLC.

Brown, Ruth. Lion in the Long Grass. Brown, Ken, illus. 2004. 32p. (J). pap. 11.99 (978-1-84270-339-7(0)) Andersen GBR. *Dist:* Independent Pubs. Group.

Burroughs, Scott & Burroughs, Chrysti. The Super Short Amazing Story of Daniel in the Lions' Den. 2005. (J). 10.99 (978-0-8254-2299-7(X)) Kregel Pubns.

Bushar, Carol. Robby the Lion Doesn't Eat Meat. 2006. 30p. 12.96 (978-1-4116-9113-1(X)) Lulu.com.

Butterfield, Moira. Do Lions Like Lettuce? Canals, Sonia, illus. 2007. (Animal Flappers Bks.). 16p. (J). (gr. k-k). 7.99 (978-0-7641-6026-4(5)) Barron's Educational Series, Inc.

Cadnum, Michael. The Book of the Lion. 2001. (Illus.). 208p. (YA). pap. 6.99 (978-0-14-230034-3(9) , Puffin) Penguin Group (USA) Inc.

Charbonnet, Gabrielle. The Lion King: Just Can't Wait to Be King. 1998. (Disney Chapters Ser.). (Illus.). 64p. (J). (gr. 2-4). pap. 3.95 (978-0-7868-4178-3(8)) Disney Pr.

Chen, Zhiyuan, illus. Artie & Julie. 2007. (J). (***978-0-9787550-3-4(0)*** Heryin Publishing Corp.

Chesterfield, Sadie. Lion, the Witch, & the Wardrobe. Marderosian, Mark, illus. movie tie-in ed. 2005. (Narnia Ser.). 32p. (J). pap., act. bk. ed. 4.99 (978-0-06-076557-6(7)) Zonderkidz.

Chinatsu, Hagino, illus. Ahchoo! Lion's Got the Flu. 2006. 48p. (J). 16.50 (978-1-933327-27-3(8)); 15.95 (978-1-933327-26-6(X)) Purple Bear Bks., Inc.

Christie, Jean. Lester the Lazy Lion. 2000. (Felt Lift the Flap Bks.). (Illus.). (J). (ps-k). 4.95 (978-1-58646-007-5(2)) Polka Dot Pr.

Cohen, Caron Lee. Martin & the Giant Lions. Sayles, Elizabeth, illus. 2002. 32p. (J). (gr. k-3). 15.00 (978-0-618-04908-0(8) , Clarion Bks.) Houghton Mifflin Co. Trade & Reference Div.

Combel Editorial Staff. El Leon y el Raton. 2004. (Caballo alado clasicos-Al Galope Ser.). (SPA., Illus.). 24p. 6.95 (978-84-7864-784-2(8)) Combel Editorial, S.A. ESP. *Dist:* Independent Pubs. Group.

Conover, Chris. The Lion's Share. Conover, Chris, illus. 2003. (Illus.). 40p. (J). pap. 6.95 (978-0-374-44481-5(1) , Sunburst) Farrar, Straus & Giroux.

—Lion's Share. 2003. (gr. k-3). lib. bdg. 15.25 (978-0-613-71866-0(6)) Tandem Library Bks.

—Un Tesoro para Compartir. 2002. (SPA., Illus.). 246p. (J). (gr. k-2). 15.95 (978-84-261-3164-5(6) , JV30155) Juventud, Editorial ESP. *Dist:* Lectorum Pubns., Inc.

Corder, Zizou. Lionboy. (Lionboy Trilogy : Bk. 1). (Illus.). (gr. 3-6). 2003. 288p. (J). 15.99 (978-0-8037-2982-7(0) , Dial); 2004. 304p. (YA). reprint ed. pap. 7.99 (978-0-14-240226-9(5) , Puffin) Penguin Group (USA) Inc.

—Truth. (Lionboy Trilogy : Bk. 3). 240p. (J). 2006. (gr. 3). pap. 6.99 (978-0-14-240705-9(4) , Puffin); 2005. (Illus.). (gr. 5). 16.99 (978-0-8037-2985-8(5) , Dial) Penguin Group (USA) Inc.

Costello, Emily. The Bad Luck Lion. Day, Larry, illus. 1999. (Animal Emergency Ser.: No. 3). 128p. (J). (gr. 3-7). pap. 3.99 (978-0-380-79755-4(0)) HarperCollins Pubs.

Coxon, Michele. Look Out, Lion Cub! Coxon, Michele, illus. 1998. (Lift-the-Flap Bks.). (Illus.). 20p. (J). (ps-k). pap. 5.95 (978-1-887734-39-4(2)) Star Bright Bks., Inc.

Curry, Kenneth. Mandu & Minka. 2007. (Illus.). 22p. (J). 10.95 (***978-0-9798364-7-3(6)*** Curry Brothers Publishing.

Dalmatian Press Staff, ed. Lion King. 2006. 24p. (J). pap. 3.50 (978-1-4037-2888-3(7)) Dalmatian Pr.

Danby, Aaron. Jazzmin's Jamboree. Martin, M. J., illus. 2005. 40p. 13.95 (978-0-9730583-3-8(1)) Lion & Mouse Tales, Inc. CAN. *Dist:* Hushion Hse. Publishing, Ltd.

Dann, Colin. Lion Country. 2001. 114p. (J). pap. 8.99 (978-0-09-940777-5(9)) Random Hse. GBR. *Dist:* Independent Pubs. Group.

—Pride of the Plains. 2002. 128p. (J). pap. 8.99 (978-0-09-941126-0(1)) Random Hse. GBR. *Dist:* Independent Pubs. Group.

Daugherty, James. Andy & the Lion. Daugherty, James, illus. 2002. (Illus.). (J). 13.19 (978-0-7587-0091-9(1)) Book Wholesalers, Inc.

Disney Press Staff, ed. Lion King. 2007. 48p. (gr. 1-3). pap. 3.99 (***978-1-4231-0369-1(6)*** Disney Pr.

Disney Publishing Staff & LeapFrog Staff, compiled by. Disney's the Lion King. 2002. spiral bd. 14.95 (978-1-58605-929-3(7)) LeapFrog Enterprises, Inc.

DK Publishing. Hush Little Lion. 2008. 10p. (J). (ps-k). bds. 7.99 (***978-0-7566-3812-2(7)*** Dorling Kindersley Publishing, Inc.

Douglas, Babette. The Lyon Bear. 2004. (Illus.). (J). 9.99 (978-1-890343-18-7(8)) Kiss A Me Productions, Inc.

Douglas, Vincent. The Lion King - Cave Secret. 2002. (Disney Parent & Child Read Together Ser.). (Illus.). 40p. (ps-k). 4.99 (978-1-57768-735-1(3)) School Specialty Publishing.

Duey, Kathleen. Leo the Lion - Book & Dvd. Gurin, Laura, illus. 2007. 32p. 14.99 (***978-0-8249-6724-6(0)*** , Ideals Children's Bks.) Ideals Pubns.

Edwards, Pamela Duncan. Roar! Cole, Henry, illus. Date not set. 32p. (J). (ps-2). pap. 5.99 (978-0-06-443572-7(5)) HarperCollins Pubs.

—Roar! A Noisy Counting Book. Cole, Henry, illus. 2000. 32p. (J). (ps-2). 16.99 (978-0-06-028384-1(X)); 15.89 (978-0-06-028385-8(8)) HarperCollins Pubs.

Ehrlich, Fred. Does a Lion Brush? Bolam, Emily, illus. 2005. 32p. (J). (ps-k). pap. 5.95 (978-1-59354-125-5(2)) Blue Apple Bks.

Elgar, Rebecca. One Lonely Lion. (Illus.). (J). (ps-k). bds. 7.99 (978-0-590-24918-8(5)) Scholastic, Inc.

Evans, Robert J. Dorothy's Mystical Adventures in Oz. 2004. reprint ed. pap. 1.99 (978-1-4192-1658-9(9)) Kessinger Publishing, LLC.

Fatio, Louise. The Happy Lion. Duvoisin, Roger, illus. 2004. 40p. (J). (ps-3). 14.95 (978-0-375-82759-4(5)); lib. bdg. 16.99 (978-0-375-92759-1(X)) Random Hse. Children's Bks. (Knopf Bks. for Young Readers).

—The Happy Lion Roars. Duvoisin, Roger, illus. 2006. 40p. (J). (ps-3). 15.95 (978-0-375-83887-3(2)); lib. bdg. 17.99 (978-0-375-93887-0(7)) Random Hse. Children's Bks. (Knopf Bks. for Young Readers).

Fisher, Barbara. Nobody's Lion. Huismann, Duane, illus. 2004. (J). per. 16.95 (978-1-59571-049-9(3)) Word Association Pubs.

Fisscher, Tiny. RUBY & the LION. 2008. 48p. 11.95 (***978-1-60136-014-4(2)*** Mars Media Pubs.

Flexer, Michael. Lucy's Adventure: The Search for Aslan. Baynes, Pauline, illus. 2006. (Narnia Ser.). 96p. (J). 14.99 (978-0-06-085234-4(8)); pap. 3.99 (978-0-06-085233-7(X) , Harper Trophy) HarperCollins Pubs.

Fontes, Justine & Korman, Justine. The Lion King. 2003. (Illus.). 24p. (J). (gr. k-k). 2.99 (978-0-7364-2095-2(9) , Golden/Disney) Random Hse. Children's Bks.

Ford, Miela. Watch Us Play. 1998. (Illus.). 24p. (J). (ps-3). 15.00 (978-0-688-15606-0(1)) HarperCollins Pubs.

Friends for Lion. 2000. 16p. (J). bds. 7.95 (978-0-7525-4602-5(3)) Parragon, Inc.

Fuerst, Jeff. Lion & Rabbit: A Fable from India. 2006. spiral bd. 23.00 (***978-1-4108-7156-5(8)*** Benchmark Education Co.

Galvin, Laura Gates. Norman the Lion. Leeper, Christopher, illus. 2005. (African Wildlife Foundation(R) Ser.). (J). (ps-2). 36p. 8.95 incl. cd-rom (978-1-59249-208-4(8) , SD6503); 32p. 2.95 incl. cd-rom (978-1-59249-191-9(X) , S6553); 32p. 9.95 (978-1-59249-192-6(8) , PS6553) Soundprints.

—Norman the Lion. Leeper, Christopher J., tr. Leeper, Christopher J., illus. 2005. (African Wildlife Foundation(R) Ser.). 36p. (J). (ps-2). pap. 6.95 (978-1-59249-190-2(1) , S6503) Soundprints.

Gibert, Bruno. The King Is Naked! 2004. (Illus.). 32p. (J). (gr. k-ps). 14.00 (978-0-618-41067-5(8) , Clarion Bks.) Houghton Mifflin Co. Trade & Reference Div.

Giff, Patricia Reilly. Leones Perezosos, Corderos Afortunados. 2000. (SPA.). (YA). (gr. 1 up). 3.95 (978-0-922852-47-5(2)) AIMS International Bks., Inc.

Gold, Bernice. My Four Lions. Stanbridge, Joanne, illus. 1999. 24p. (J). (ps-1). lib. bdg. 17.95 (978-1-55037-603-6(9)) Annick Pr., Ltd. CAN. *Dist:* Firefly Bks., Ltd.

—My Four Lions. 1999. (978-0-606-18141-9(5)) Tandem Library Bks.

Golden Books Staff. Tawny Scrawny Lion. 2001. (Little Golden Bks.). (Illus.). 24p. (J). (gr. k-k). 2.99 (978-0-307-02168-7(8) , 98093, Golden Bks.) Random Hse. Children's Bks.

Green, George & Brooke, Amy/ J. George Green's, the Lion Who Couldn't Roar. 2007. (J). per. 17.99 (***978-1-933156-14-9(7)*** , Visikid Bks.) GSVQ Publishing.

Greenburg, Dan. Claws. 2007. 208p. (YA). (gr. 3-7). 5.99 (978-0-375-83411-0(7) , Yearling) Random Hse. Children's Bks.

Guidoux, Valerie, et al, illus. The Lion. 2000. (Abbeville Ser.). 32p. (J). (ps-1). pap. 6.95 (978-0-7892-0663-3(3) , Abbeville Kids) Abbeville Pr., Inc.

Guillaume, Robert, narrated by. Lion King: Read Along. 2001. (Illus.). 32p. (J). pap. 9.98 incl. audio compact disk (978-0-7634-0735-3(6)) Walt Disney Records.

Guillot, Rene. Sirga. Coudert, Agnes, illus. (Barril Sin Fondo Ser.). (SPA.). (J). (gr. 3-5). pap. (978-968-6465-64-8(2)) Casa de Estudios de Literatura y Talleres Artisticos Amaquemecan A.C. MEX. *Dist:* Lectorum Pubns., Inc.

Harry, Rebecca, illus. Little Lion. 2007. (Noisy Jungle Babies Ser.). 8p. (J). bds. 5.99 (978-0-7641-6036-3(2)) Barron's Educational Series, Inc.

Herman, Gail. The Lion & the Mouse. McCue, Lisa, illus. 1998. 28p. lib. bdg. 10.79 (978-0-606-15973-9(8)) Tandem Library Bks.

Herman, Gail & Aesop. The Lion & the Mouse. McCue, Lisa, illus. 1998. (Step into Reading Ser.). 32p. (J). (ps-k). lib. bdg. 11.99 (978-0-679-98674-4(X) , Random Hse. Bks. for Young Readers) Random Hse. Children's Bks.

Hiebert, Elfrieda H. & Juel, Connie. The Lion Roars. (Little Book Practice Reader Ser.). (J). (978-0-8136-0895-2(3)) Modern Curriculum Pr.

Hockerman, Dennis, illus. The Lion & the Mouse: A Tale about Being Helpful. 2006. (J). 6.99 (978-1-59939-007-9(8)) Reader's Digest Young Families, Inc.

Holt, Rinehart and Winston Staff. Where the Red Fern Grows: With Connections. 1998. pap., stu. ed. 13.20 (978-0-03-054053-0(4)) Holt, Rinehart & Winston.

Hurd, Clement, illus. Johnny Lion's Bad Day. 2002. (Johnny Lion Ser.). (J). 12.34 (978-0-7587-5039-6(0)) Book Wholesalers, Inc.

—Johnny Lion's Book. 2002. (Johnny Lion Ser.). (J). 12.34 (978-0-7587-4936-9(8)) Book Wholesalers, Inc.

—Johnny Lion's Rubber Boots. 2002. (Johnny Lion Ser.). (J). 12.34 (978-0-7587-5040-2(4)) Book Wholesalers, Inc.

Hurd, Edith Thacher. Johnny Lion's Bad Day. Hurd, Clement, illus. 2000. (I Can Read Bks.). 64p. (J). (gr. k-3). 14.95 (978-0-06-029335-2(7)) HarperCollins Pubs.

—Johnny Lion's Bad Day. Hurd, Clement, illus. 2001. (I Can Read Bks.). (J). 10.79 (978-0-606-20744-7(9)) Tandem Library Bks.

—Johnny Lion's Book. Hurd, Clement, illus. (I Can Read Bks.). 64p. (J). (gr. k-3). 2001. pap. 3.99 (978-0-06-444297-8(7) , Harper Trophy); 2000. 14.95 (978-0-06-029333-8(0)) HarperCollins Pubs.

—Johnny Lion's Book. 2001. (I Can Read Bks.). (Illus.). (J). 10.79 (978-0-606-20745-4(7)) Tandem Library Bks.

—Johnny Lion's Book. Hurd, Clement, illus. 2001. 63p. (J). (ps-ps). lib. bdg. 11.80 (978-0-613-33707-6(7)) Tandem Library Bks.

—Johnny Lion's Rubber Boots. Hurd, Clement, illus. 2000. (I Can Read Bks.). 64p. (J). (gr. k-3). 14.95 (978-0-06-029337-6(3)) HarperCollins Pubs.

—Johnny Lion's Rubber Boots. Hurd, Clement, illus. 2001. (I Can Read Bks.). (J). (978-0-606-20746-1(5)) Tandem Library Bks.

Hurwitz, Andy Blackman. Louis Lion Sings Good Night: Baby Loves Jazz. Cunningham, Andrew, illus. 2007. 16p. (J). 7.99 (978-0-8431-2192-6(0) , Price Stern Sloan) Penguin Group (USA) Inc.

Ingoglia, Gina, adapted by. The Lion King. 1998. (Disney's Junior Novel Ser.). (Illus.). 64p. (J). (gr. 3-7). pap. 3.25 (978-0-7868-4219-3(9)) Disney Pr.

Jackson, Kathryn. Tawney Scrawny Lion. Tenggren, Gustaf, illus. deluxe ed. Date not set. (J). (ps-2). reprint ed. (978-1-929566-61-7(1)) Cronies.

—Tawny Scrawny Lion: Classic Edition. Tenggren, Gustaf, illus. Date not set. 23p. (J). (ps-1). reprint ed. (978-1-929566-55-6(7)) Cronies.

Jenkins, Amanda. The Lion & the Mouse Shoot Hoops. 2006. spiral bd. 42.00 (***978-1-4108-7173-2(8)*** Benchmark Education Co.

Johnson, Crockett. Ellen's Lion: Twelve Stories by Crockett Johnson. 2003. (Illus.). 64p. (J). (gr. 1-5). 12.95 (978-0-375-82288-9(7)); lib. bdg. 14.99 (978-0-375-92288-6(1)) Random Hse. Children's Bks. (Knopf Bks. for Young Readers).

Johnson, Sandi. The Peaceful Lion. Johnson, Britt, ed. Kraft, Lauri, illus. l.t. ed. 2003. 28p. (J). (gr. k-5). spiral bd. 8.99 (978-1-929063-95-6(4) , 325) Moons & Stars Publishing For Children.

Jordan, Apple. Bug Stew! 2003. (gr. k-3). lib. bdg. 11.80 (978-0-613-73701-2(6)) Tandem Library Bks.

Kasza, Keiko. The Mightiest. 2003. (Picture Puffin Ser.). (Illus.). 32p. (J). pap. 5.99 (978-0-14-250185-6(9) , Puffin) Penguin Group (USA) Inc.

—The Mightiest. Kasza, Keiko, illus. 2001. (Illus.). 32p. (J). 16.99 (978-0-399-23586-3(8) , Putnam Juvenile) Penguin Group (USA) Inc.

—Mightiest. 2003. (ps-2). lib. bdg. 14.15 (978-0-613-89797-6(8)) Tandem Library Bks.

Kellogg, Elijah. Lion Ben of Elm Island. 2005. pap. 27.95 (978-1-4179-9427-4(4)) Kessinger Publishing, LLC.

Kilimo, R. Donkey Who Wanted to Be a Lion. 2004. (Illus.). 11p. 13.95 (978-9966-25-169-5(3)) Heinemann Kenya, Limited (East African Educational Publishers Ltd E.A.E.P.) KEN. *Dist:* Michigan State Univ. Pr.

Kinney, Kendall. Tiger Tails. 2004. 68p. (J). per. 10.95 (978-1-932196-21-4(8)) WordWright.biz, Inc.

Knudsen, Michelle. Library Lion. Hawkes, Kevin, illus. 2006. 48p. (J). (ps-2). 16.99 (978-0-7636-2262-6(1)) Candlewick Pr.

Kompelien, Tracy. Lion Manes. Nobens, C. A., illus. 2006. (Fact & Fiction Ser.). 24p. (J). 21.35 (978-1-59679-949-3(8) , SandCastle); pap. (978-1-59679-950-9(1)) ABDO Publishing Co.

La Fontaine, Jean De. El Leon y el Raton. (Coleccion Pequenos Clasicos). (SPA.). 24p. (J). (gr. k-3). (978-84-246-2533-7(1) , GL7988) La Galera, S.A. Editorial ESP. *Dist:* Lectorum Pubns., Inc.

LeapFrog Staff. Disney Lion King - U. K. 2003. (Illus.). spiral bd. 14.99 (978-1-59319-006-4(9)) LeapFrog Enterprises, Inc.

Leo the Lion. 1999. (Illus.). 6p. (J). 12.98 (978-1-58048-093-2(4)) Sandvik Publishing.

El Leon. 2002. Tr. of Lion. (SPA., Illus.). 22p. (J). 6.50 (978-84-246-1736-3(3)) La Galera, S.A. Editorial ESP. *Dist:* AIMS International Bks., Inc.

El leon y el Conejo: Individual Title Six-Packs. (Coleccion Pm Ser.).Tr. of Lion & the Rabbit. (SPA.). 16p. (gr. 1 up). 26.00 (978-0-7578-3007-5(2)) Rigby Education.

El leon y el Raton: Individual Title Six-Packs. (Coleccion Pm Ser.).Tr. of Lion & the Mouse. (SPA.). 16p. (gr. 1 up). 26.00 (978-0-7578-3019-8(6)) Rigby Education.

Lester the Lion Set 1. 2002. (J). (978-1-58453-191-3(6)) Pioneer Valley Educational Pr., Inc.

Lester's Haircut. 2002. (J). (978-1-58453-197-5(5)) Pioneer Valley Educational Pr., Inc.

Lester's Song. 2002. (J). (978-1-58453-196-8(7)) Pioneer Valley Educational Pr., Inc.

Lewis, C. S. Chronicles of Narnia: The Lion, the Witch & the Wardrobe Chapter Book. 2006. (Narnia Ser.). 384p. (J). pap. 14.99 (978-0-06-117453-7(X)) HarperCollins Pubs.

—The Lion, the Witch & the Wardrobe: Read-Aloud Edition. Baynes, Pauline, illus. 2005. (Chronicles of Narnia Ser.). 208p. (J). 14.99 (978-0-06-084524-7(4)) HarperCollins Pubs.

The Lion & the Mouse, Vol. 2. 2005. (Fluent Library). (YA). (ps-3). 29.34 (978-0-8215-8968-7(7)) Sadlier, William H. Inc.

Lion Country. 2003. (J). per. (978-1-884907-38-8(5)); per. (978-1-884907-39-5(3)) Paradise Pr., Inc.

The Lion King. 2003. (Illus.). 12.99 (978-0-7868-3478-5(1)) Disney Pr.

The Lion King. (Look & Find Ser.). 24p. (J). (978-0-7853-9532-4(6) , 3065710) Publications International, Ltd.

Lion King: Far from the Pridelands. (Read-Along Ser.). (J). 7.99 incl. audio (978-1-55723-673-9(9)) Walt Disney Records.

The Lion of Ain Jaloot: Fun Pack. 2000. (J). 29.99 incl. audio, VHS (978-0-9716826-5-8(8)) Fine Media Group.

The Lion Who Lost His Roar: A Story about Facing Your Fears. 2000. (Early Prevention Ser.). 53p. (J). pap. 11.50 (978-1-58815-004-2(6)) Childswork/Childsplay.

Lion's Lunch: Individual Title Six-Pack Pouch - Level H. (Lighthouse Ser.). 16p. (gr. 1 up). 26.00 (978-0-7578-0849-4(2)) Rigby Education.

Lion's Mane. Date not set. (Touch & Feel Ser.). (J). 4.98 (978-0-7525-9569-6(5)) Parragon, Inc.

The Little Lion. (Early Intervention Levels Ser.). 21.30 (978-0-7362-0367-8(2)) Hampton-Brown Bks.

Loesch, Joe. Lions, Lions Everywhere: The Story of Daniel as told by God's Animals. Hutchinson, Cheryl, ed. Cox, Brain T., illus. 2004. (Bible Stories for Kids Ser.). (J). bds. 16.95 incl. audio compact disk (978-1-932332-24-7(3)) Toy Box Productions.

Lofting, Hugh. The Story of Doctor Dolittle No. 4: Doctor Dolittle's Magical Cure. Kanzler, John, illus. 2007. (Easy Reader Classics Ser.). 32p. (J). pap. 3.95 (978-1-4027-4123-4(5)) Sterling Publishing Co., Inc.

Mackall, Dandi Daley. Don't Cry, Lion! 2007. 26p. (J). bds. 6.99 (***978-1-4003-1008-1(3)*** Nelson, Thomas Inc.

Markham, Beryl. The Good Lion. 2005. (Illus.). 32p. (J). (gr. 3-5). 16.00 (978-0-618-56306-7(7)) Houghton Mifflin Co. Trade & Reference Div.

Matteren, Joanne. The Old Lion & the Fox. 2005. 22.00 (***978-1-4108-4206-0(1)*** Benchmark Education Co.

May, Kara. Joe Lion's Big Boots. Allen, Jonathan, illus. 2005. (I Am Reading Ser.). 48p. (J). (gr. k-3). pap. 3.95 (978-0-7534-5856-3(X) , Kingfisher) Houghton Mifflin Co. Trade & Reference Div.

McAllister, Angela. Jasmine's Lion. (Illus.). 32p. (J). (ps-k). 2007. pap. 8.99 (***978-0-552-54878-6(2)*** , Corgi); 2005. 20.00 (978-0-385-60505-2(6) , Eden Project Books) Transworld Publishers Ltd. GBR. *Dist:* Independent Pubs. Group.

McKendry, Sam. Are You Ticklish? A Touch & Tickle Book. Mitchell, Melanie, illus. 2005. 12p. (J). (ps up). 10.95 (978-1-58117-376-5(8) , Intervisual/Piggy Toes) Dalmatian Pr.

McOmber, Rachel B., ed. McOmber Phonics Storybooks: Chatsworth. rev. ed. (Illus.). (J). (978-0-944991-74-9(2)) Swift Learning Resources.

Mollel, Tololwa M. Subira Subira. Saport, Linda, illus. ed. 2006. 32p. (J). (gr. k-3). pap. 5.95 (978-0-618-68926-2(5) , Clarion Bks.) Houghton Mifflin Co. Trade & Reference Div.

Montgomery, Rutherford G. Yellow Eyes. 2004. (Classic Ser.). (Illus.). 358p. (gr. 4-7). pap. 15.95 (978-0-87004-417-5(6)) Caxton Pr.

Mopurgo, Michael. El Leon Mariposa.Tr. of Butterfly Lion. (SPA., Illus.). 96p. (YA). (gr. 5-8). (978-84-241-3276-7(9) , EV1036) Everest de Ediciones y Distribucion, S.L. ESP. *Dist:* Lectorum Pubns., Inc.

—El Leon Mariposa. 2000. Tr. of Butterfly Lion. (SPA.). (gr. 5-8). lib. bdg. 17.60 (978-0-613-80622-0(0)) Tandem Library Bks.

Moran, Colette. Disney's the Lion King. 1999. (Illus.). (J). (978-0-7853-4148-2(X)) Publications International, Ltd.

Morgan, Nicola. Pride of Lions. 2000. (Illus.). 30p. (J). pap. (978-1-55041-077-8(6)) Fitzhenry & Whiteside, Ltd.

Morpurgo, Michael. The Butterfly Lion. 2000. (Illus.). (J). pap. 4.99 (978-0-14-038550-2(9) , Puffin) Penguin Group (USA) Inc.

Mouse Works Staff. Lion King. 1998. (Disney's the Lion King Simba's Pride Ser.). (Illus.). 24p. (J). (gr. k-3). 3.99 (978-1-57082-938-3(1)) Mouse Works.

—Simba. 1999. (Disney's Friendly Tales Ser.). (Illus.). 10p. (J). (ps-k). 6.99 (978-0-7364-1011-3(2)) Mouse Works.

—Simba Faces Danger. 1998. (Disney's the Lion King II, Simba's Pride Ser.). (Illus.). 18p. (J). 2.99 (978-1-57082-993-2(4)) Mouse Works.

Nayer, Judy. Androcles & the Lion: An Aesop's Fable. 2006. 42.00 (***978-1-4108-6165-8(1)***) Benchmark Education Co.

Ogburn, Jacqueline K. The Lady & the Lion. 2003. (Illus.). 32p. (J). (gr. k). 16.99 (978-0-8037-2651-2(1) , Dial) Penguin Group (USA) Inc.

Orlev, Uri. A Lion for Michael. Gleich, Jacky, illus. 2000. 32p. (J). (gr. k-4). 15.95 (978-1-58653-172-0(7)) Mondo Publishing.

Osborn School Students. Paw-Sing for Positive Daily Affirmations: Lion Pride. Rosa, M. Nina & Perrien, Vicki, eds. 2003. (J). pap. 16.99 (978-0-9740267-0-1(0)) Mz. Rosa Notions.

Osborne, Mary Pope. Lions at Lunchtime, Vol. 11. unabr. ed. 2004. (Magic Tree House Ser. : No. 11). 70p. (J). (gr. k-3). pap. 17.00 incl. audio (978-0-8072-0536-5(2) , Listening Library) Random Hse. Audio Publishing Group.

Osei-Agyemang, Andrew Nana. Before the Lion Became King: Law 202 the First Amendment Law of the Animal Kingdom. 2002. 32p. (J). pap. 10.00 (978-0-8059-5435-7(X)) Dorrance Publishing Co., Inc.

Papineau, Lucie. Gilda the Giraffe & Leonardo the Lion Cub. Sarrazin, Marisol, illus. 2005. (Gilda the Giraffe Ser.). 32p. (J). (ps-3). lib. bdg. 22.60 (978-1-4048-1294-9(6)) Picture Window Bks.

—Leonardo le Lionceau. ed. 2004. (FRE., Illus.). (J). (gr. k-3). spiral bd. (978-0-616-07264-6(3)) Canadian National Institute for the Blind/Institut National Canadien pour les Aveugles.

Papineau, Lucie, et al. Leonardo the Lion Cub. 2000. (Adventures of Gilda Ser.). (Illus.). 29p. (J). (ps-3). pap. (978-1-894363-44-0(2)) Dominique & Friends.

Parragon Staff. Disney's the Lion King. Disney Staff, ed. 2007. 48p. (ps-2). 12.99 (***978-1-4231-0434-6(X)***) Disney Pr.

Pfister, Marcus. How Leo Learned to Be King. 1998. (Illus.). 32p. (J). (ps-3). 15.95 (978-1-55858-913-1(9)) North-South Bks., Inc.

Pickup, Michael. The Adventures of Bhakta Musika & the Lion. 1998. (Illus.). 40p. (J). (ps-5). pap. 4.95 (978-81-87216-03-2(4)) Torchlight Publishing.

Pierce, Tamora. Lioness Rampant. unabr. ed. 2004. (Song of the Lioness Ser.: Bk. 4). 308p. (J). (gr. 6 up). pap. 38.00 incl. audio (978-0-8072-0985-1(6) , S YA 388 SP, Listening Library) Random Hse. Audio Publishing Group.

—Lioness Rampant. (Song of the Lioness Ser.: Bk. 4). (YA). 2005. 400p. mass mkt. 6.99 (978-0-689 87857 2(5) , Simon Pulse); 2003. (Illus.). 320p. 11.99 (978-0-689-85430-9(7) , Atheneum) Simon & Schuster Children's Publishing.

Pogo the Clown. A Brave Little Lion: Harley's Great Adventures. Miller, Richard D., illus. 2005. (J). 12.95 (978-0-9755253-5-7(2)) Chiliric Pubns.

Powell, Richard. Leo Lion. Rhodes, Katie, illus. 2004. (Fuzzy Friends Ser.). 10p. (J). 7.95 (978-1-58925-719-1(7) , tiger tales) ME Media LLC.

Powers, John. The Lion Who Couldn't Roar. Colavecchio, Alan, illus. 2002. 32p. (J). 13.95 (978-1-929039-10-4(7)) Ambassador Bks., Inc.

Pugliano-Martin, Carol. Little Lion. 2003. (Early Connections Ser.). (J). pap. 33.00 (978-1-4108-1092-2(5)) Benchmark Education Co.

Pulley, Kelly. The Beginner's Bible Lion's Big Sleepover Daniel's Scary Night. 2007. (Beginner's Bible' Ser.). 20p. (J). 6.99 (978-0-310-71387-6(0)) Zondervan.

Random House Disney Staff. Lion King. 2003. (gr. k-3). lib. bdg. 10.95 (978-0-613-73722-7(9)) Tandem Library Bks.

Rau, Dana Meachen. The Lion in the Grass. 2006. (Nature Ser.). (Illus.). 24p. (J). lib. bdg. 22.79 (978-0-7614-2305-8(2) , Benchmark Bks.) Cavendish, Marshall Corp.

Ready Reader Staff. Glenda the Lion, 6 bks., set, Level 6, Bk. 25. 2003. (J). (ps-3). pap. 33.50 (978-0-8136-2051-0(1)) Modern Curriculum Pr.

Redbank, Tennant. Walk, Don't Walk. Mathieu, Joe, illus. 1999. (Between the Lions Ser.). (J). (ps-k). lib. bdg. 11.99 (978-0-307-36507-1(7) , Golden Bks.) Random Hse. Children's Bks.

Reeves, Jeni, illus. Lion & Rabbit. 2008. (On My Own Folklore Ser.). (J). lib. bdg. (***978-0-8225-7546-7(9)*** , Millbrook Pr.) Lerner Publishing Group.

Rempel, Jennifer, illus. Lavi the Lion Finds His Pride. 2005. (J). 15.95 (978-0-9744715-2-5(6) , Towers Maguire Publishing) Local History Co., The.

Rose, Gerald. Horrible Melena. (SPA.). (J). 8.95 (978-958-04-7343-5(9)) Norma S.A. COL. *Dist:* Distribuidora Norma, Inc.

—The Lion & the Mouse. 2002. (Illus.). 16p. pap. 0.40 (978-0-521-01515-8(4)) Cambridge Univ. Pr.

—The Lion & the Mouse ELT Edition. 2001. (Cambridge Storybooks Ser.). (Illus.). 16p. pap. 5.00 (978-0-521-00724-5(0)) Cambridge Univ. Pr.

Rundstrom, T. S. & Waldron, Drue K. Lonely Lion Follows His Lunch. Waldron, Drue K. & Stevens, Amber R., illus. 2002. 32p. (J). per. 16.00 (978-1-932062-16-8(5)) Hability Solution Services, Inc.

Rundstrom, Teressa. Lonely Lion Follows His Lunch. Waldron, Drue, illus. 2002. 35p. (J). per. (978-1-932062-37-3(8)) Hability Solution Services, Inc.

Safari Press Staff, ed. Book Buddy - Lion with Story Book. (Illus.). 10p. (J). (ps-3). pap. (978-1-881469-84-1(0)) Safari, Ltd.

Sales, Gemma. Cuentame Una Historia Triste. (SPA.). 32p. (J). (gr. 1-3). (978-84-236-5769-8(8)) Edebé ESP. *Dist:* Lectorum Pubns., Inc.

Sargent, Dave & Sargent, Pat. Leo Lion: Responsibility, 56 vols., 51. Lenoir, Jane, illus. 2001. (Animal Pride Ser.: Vol. 51). 36p. (J). lib. bdg. 19.95 (978-1-56763-541-6(5)) Ozark Publishing.

Sargent, Dave, et al. Leo Lion: Responsibility, 17, 51. 2000. (Animal Pride Ser.: 51). (Illus.). 42p. (J). pap. 6.95 (978-1-56763-542-3(3)) Ozark Publishing.

Scheffler, Ursel. Be Brave, Little Lion! 2001. (gr. k-3). lib. bdg. 14.10 (978-0-613-34603-0(3)) Tandem Library Bks.

—Be Brave, Little Lion. 2001. (Illus.). (J). (978-0-606-21765-1(7)) Tandem Library Bks.

Silver Dolphin en Español Editors. Caritas felices: Simba: Happy Faces: Simba, Spanish-Language Edition. 2007. (Illus.). 8p. (J). bds. 7.95 (***978-970-718-392-6(6)*** , Silver Dolphin en Español) Advanced Marketing, S. de R. L. de C. V. MEX. *Dist:* Perseus Distribution.

Silverstein, Shel. Lafcadio, el Leon Que Devolvio el Disparo. 1998. (SPA., Illus.). 112p. (J). (gr. 3-5). (978-84-264-3663-4(3) , LM4642) Editorial Lumen ESP. *Dist:* Lectorum Pubns., Inc.

Simba's Pride Read-Along. 1998. (J). 6.98 incl. audio (978-0-7634-0479-6(9)) Walt Disney Home Video.

Simon-Kerr, Julia. The Lion, the Witch, & the Wardrobe: Coloring & Activity Book & Magnets. Redondo, Jesus, illus. movie tie-in ed. 2005. (Narnia Ser.). 32p. (J). pap., act. bk. ed. 4.99 (978-0-06-076558-3(5)) Zonderkidz.

Simon, Mary Manz. Lion Can Share. Harris, Phyllis & Clearwater, Linda, illus. 2006. (First Virtuestm for Toddlers Ser.). 20p. (J). 5.99 (978-0-7847-1576-5(9) , 04070) Standard Publishing.

Sleepytime Lion. 2005. (J). (978-0-9767179-5-9(6)) ABC Development, Inc.

Smalley, Roger, adapted by. The Big-Hearted Monkey & the Lion. 2005. (J). (978-1-933248-02-8(5)) World Quest Learning.

Smith, Alexander McCall. Akimbo & the Lions. Pham, LeUyen, illus. (Akimbo Ser.). 80p. (J). 2007. pap. 4.95 (978-1-59990-032-2(7) , Bloomsbury Children); 2005. 9.95 (978-1-58234-687-8(9)) Bloomsbury Publishing.

Sommer, Carl. I Am a Lion! 2003. (Another Sommer-Time Story Ser.). (Illus.). 48p. (J). (gr. k-4). lib. bdg. 23.95 incl. audio compact disk (978-1-57537-709-4(8)); (gr. k-4). lib. bdg. 23.95 incl. audio (978-1-57537-759-9(4)); (gr. 1-4). 16.95 incl. audio (978-1-57537-558-8(3)); (gr. 1-4). 16.95 incl. audio compact disk (978-1-57537-509-0(5)) Advance Publishing, Inc.

—I Am a Lion! Budwine, Greg, illus. 1999. (Another Sommer-Time Story Ser.). 48p. (J). (gr. k-4). 9.95 (978-1-57537-009-5(3)); lib. bdg. 16.95 (978-1-57537-059-0(X)) Advance Publishing, Inc.

Stein, Kristen. The Vegetarian Lion. 2006. 36p. (J). pap. 13.28 (978-1-4116-6459-3(0)) Lulu.com.

Stimson, Joan. Leon Valiente, Leon Miedoso. Rubio, Esther, tr. Rutherford, Meg, illus. Tr. of Brave Lion, Scared Lion. (SPA.). (J). (gr. k-1). pap. 2.80 net. (978-0-590-67520-8(6) , SO2849, Scholastic en Espanol) Scholastic, Inc.

—Leon Valiente, Leon Miedoso. 2000. Tr. of Brave Lion, Scared Lion. (SPA.). (ps-2). lib. bdg. 10.45 (978-0-613-88324-5(1)) Tandem Library Bks.

Stratten, Lou. Hello, I'm Sir Frettirick! Let's Say Hello to Our New Friends! Bennett, Judy, ed. Stratten, Lou & Denaro, Sal, illus. 2006. (J). 6.95 (978-0-9747173-1-9(2)) Stratten, Lou.

Trotter, Stuart, illus. Do You Know about Lions? 2002. (Softy Tops Ser.). 18p. (J). bds. 3.95 (978-0-7641-5579-6(2)) Barron's Educational Series, Inc.

Vere, Ed. Everyone's Noisy. 2001. (Illus.). 12p. (J). (ps). 6.95 (978-0-531-30335-1(7) , Orchard Bks.) Scholastic, Inc.

Waber, Bernard. A Lion Named Shirley Williamson. 2000. (Illus.). 40p. (J). (gr. k-3). pap. 6.95 (978-0-618-05580-7(0) , Walter Lorraine) Houghton Mifflin Co. Trade & Reference Div.

—A Lion Named Shirley Williamson. 2000. (Illus.). (J). (978-0-606-18212-6(8)) Tandem Library Bks.

—Lion Named Shirley Williamson. 2000. (gr. k-3). lib. bdg. 15.25 (978-0-613-28554-4(9)) Tandem Library Bks.

Walsh, Melanie. Do Lions Live on Lily Pads? 2006. (Illus.). 32p. (J). (gr. k-ps). 15.00 (978-0-618-47300-7(9)) Houghton Mifflin Co.

Walsh, Sheila. Will, God's Mighty Warrior. 2006. (Will, God's Mighty Warrior Ser.). (Illus.). 32p. (J). 12.99 (978-1-4003-0805-7(4)) Nelson, Thomas Inc.

Walt Disney Records Staff. The Lion King: The Lion King/ The Lion King II Simba's Pride/The Lion King the Brightest Star. unabr. ed. 2005. (Disney's Read along Collection Ser.). (J). audio compact disk 14.99 (978-0-7634-1149-7(3)) Walt Disney Records.

Walt Disney's The Lion King. 2002. (J). spiral bd. (978-0-9720651-4-6(8)) Story Reader, Inc.

Watt, F. & Wells, R. Este No Es Mi Leon. 2004. (Touchy-Feely Board Bks.).Tr. of That's Not My Lion. (SPA., Illus.). 10p. (J). (ps up). 7.95 (978-0-7460-5078-1(X)) EDC Publishing.

—That's Not My Lion. 2004. (Touchy-Feely Board Bks.). (SPA.). 10p. (J). 7.99 (978-0-7945-0047-4(1) , Usborne) EDC Publishing.

Wein, Elizabeth E. The Lion Hunter. 2007. (Mark of Solomon Ser.: Bk. 1). 208p. (YA). (gr. 7 up). 16.99 (978-0-670-06163-1(8) , Viking Juvenile) Penguin Group (USA) Inc.

Weiss, Ellen. Not So Fast! Cuddy, Robbin, illus. 2000. (My Very First Simba Stories Ser.). 32p. (ps-2). 12.99 (978-0-7868-3266-8(5)) Disney Pr.

—Simba's Moon. Cuddy, Robin, illus. Date not set. 32p. (J). (ps-2). 12.99 (978-0-7868-3267-5(3)) Disney Pr.

White, Mark. El Leon y el Raton: Version de la Fabula de Esopo. Rojo, Sara, illus. 2006. (Read-It! Readers en Espanol Ser.).Tr. of Lion & the Mouse: A Retelling of Aesop's Fable. (SPA.). 32p. (J). (ps-3). 19.95 (978-1-4048-1623-7(2)) Picture Window Bks.

Wolf, Gita. Very Hungry Lion. Roy, Indrapramit, illus. 2006. 24p. 20.95 (978-81-86211-02-1(0)) Tara Publishing IND. *Dist:* Consortium Bk. Sales & Distribution.

World of Lions. 2003. (J). per. (978-1-884907-55-5(5)) Paradise Pr., Inc.

Xiong, Kim. The Little Stone Lion. 2006. (Illus.). 40p. (J). 15.95 (978-0-9762056-1-6(0)) Heryin Publishing Corp.

Yaccarino, Dan. Deep in the Jungle. Yaccarino, Dan, illus. 2002. (J). 25.11 (978-0-7587-2371-0(7)) Book Wholesalers, Inc.

Yang, Huan. Artie & Julie. Chen, Zhiyuan & Huang, Hsiao-Yen, illus. 2007. 32p. (J). 15.95 (978-0-9787550-0-3(6)) Heryin Publishing Corp.

LIONS—HABITS AND BEHAVIOR

Arnosky, Jim. Little Lions. 1998. (Illus.). 1p. (J). (ps-1). 17.99 (978-0-399-22944-2(2) , Putnam Juvenile) Penguin Group (USA) Inc.

Kalman, Bobbie. Life Cycle of a Lion. 2002. (gr. 3-6). lib. bdg. 14.10 (978-0-613-52973-0(1)) Tandem Library Bks.

LIONS—POETRY

Andreae, Giles. Larry Lion's Rumbly Rhymes. Wojtowycz, David, illus. 2001. (J). (ps-k). bds. 5.95 (978-1-58925-651-4(4) , tiger tales) ME Media LLC.

Andreae, Giles & Wojtowycz, David. Larry Lion's Rumbly Rhymes. Andreae, Giles & Wojtowycz, David, illus. 2000. (Illus.). (J). (ps-k). bds. 6.95 (978-1-888444-68-1(1)) Little Tiger Pr.

LIQUID FUEL

see Gasoline; Petroleum As Fuel

LIQUIDS

Bentley, Joyce. Wet. 2006. (Things Around Us Ser.). (J). (978-1-59389-279-1(9)) Chrysalis Education.

Boothroyd, Jennifer. What Is a Liquid? 2007. (First Step Nonfiction Ser.). 24p. (J). (gr. k-3). 18.60 (978-0-8225-6838-4(1) , Lerner Pubns.) Lerner Publishing Group.

Brannon, Barbara. Discover Liquids. 2005. 39.00 (***978-1-4108-5118-5(4)***) Benchmark Education Co.

Brown, Mark. Solids, Liquids, & Gases. 2005. (J). per. 14.99 (978-1-59441-699-6(0) , K04027) Carson-Dellosa Publishing Co., Inc.

Doudna, Kelly. Let's be Kids & Measure Liquids. 2007. (Illus.). 24p. (J). 19.93 (978-1-59928-610-5(6) , Sand-Castle) ABDO Publishing Co.

—Let's Be Kids & Measure Liquids! 2006. (Illus.). 24p. (J). pap. (978-1-59928-611-2(4)) ABDO Publishing Co.

Fleisher, Paul. Liquids & Gases: Principles of Fluid Mechanics. 2005. (Secrets of the Universe Ser.). (Illus.). 80p. (gr. 6-12). 25.26 (978-0-8225-2988-0(2)) Lerner Publishing Group.

Frank, Marjorie Slavick, et al. Science Instant Readers Bk. 9: Solids, Liquids, & Gases. 1999. (Harcourt Science Ser.). (gr. 2 up). pap. 15.50 (978-0-15-316219-0(8)) Harcourt Schl. Pubs.

Glover, David. Solids & Liquids. 2002. (Young Discoverers Ser.). (Illus.). 32p. (J). (gr. k-3). pap. 7.95 (978-0-7534-5513-5(7) , Kingfisher) Houghton Mifflin Co. Trade & Reference Div.

Goodstein, Madeline. Fish Tank Physics Projects. 2002. (Science Fair Success Ser.). (Illus.). 128p. (YA). (gr. 6-12). lib. bdg. 26.60 (978-0-7660-1624-8(2)) Enslow Pubs., Inc.

Kjelle, Marylou Morano. The Properties of Liquids. 2007. (Library of Physical Science). (Illus.). 24p. (J). (978-1-4042-2359-2(2)); pap. (978-1-4042-2169-7(7)); lib. bdg. (978-1-4042-3422-2(5)) Rosen Publishing Group, Inc., The. (PowerKids Pr.).

McLuskey, Krista. The Science of Liquids & Solids. 2001. (Living Science Ser.). (Illus.). 32p. (J). (gr. 2 up). lib. bdg. 24.67 (978-0-8368-2789-7(9)) Stevens, Gareth Inc.

Merrill, Amy French. Everyday Physical Science Experiments with Liquids. 2002. (Science Surprises Ser.). (Illus.). 24p. (J). lib. bdg. 19.95 (978-0-8239-5801-6(9) , PowerKids Pr.) Rosen Publishing Group, Inc., The.

Mezzanotte, Jim. Líquidos. 2006. (ENG & SPA.). (J). pap. (978-0-8368-7409-9(9)); lib. bdg. (978-0-8368-7404-4(8)) Stevens, Gareth Inc. (Weekly Reader Early Learning Library).

Murphy, Stuart J. Room for Ripley. Wickstrom, Sylvie K., illus. 1999. (MathStart Ser.). 40p. (J). (gr. 2 up). pap. 5.99 (978-0-06-446724-7(4) , Harper Trophy); 15.95 (978-0-06-027620-1(7)) HarperCollins Pubs.

—Room for Ripley. 1999. (Math Start Ser.). (978-0-606-18716-9(2)); lib. bdg. 13.00 (978-0-613-22281-5(4)) Tandem Library Bks.

Nelson, Robin. Freezing & Melting. 2003. (First Step Nonfiction Ser.). (Illus.). 24p. (J). (gr. k-2). lib. bdg. 18.60 (978-0-8225-4590-3(X)) Lerner Publishing Group.

O'Daley, Anne. Liquids. 2003. (Illus.). 24p. (J). 22.45 (978-1-4103-0084-3(6) , Blackbirch Pr., Inc.) Thomson Gale.

Parker, Janice. The Science of Liquids & Solids. 2003. (Living Science Ser.). (Illus.). 32p. (J). (gr. 1-3). pap. 7.95 (978-1-930954-11-3(5)) Weigl Pubs., Inc.

Randolph, Joanne. Liquids in My World. 2006. (My World of Science Ser.). (J). 16.00 (978-1-4042-3285-3(0) , PowerKids Pr.) Rosen Publishing Group, Inc., The.

—Liquids in My World: Los Líquidos en Mi Mundo. 2006. (My World of Science/ Mi mundo y la Ciencia Ser.). (ENG & SPA.). (J). 16.00 (978-1-4042-3316-4(4) , PowerKids Pr.) Rosen Publishing Group, Inc., The.

Riley, Peter D. Solids & Liquids. 2007. (J). (***978-1-59920-029-3(5)***) Smart Apple Media.

Ryback, Carol. Liquids. 2006. (States of Matter Ser.). (J). pap. (978-0-8368-6804-3(8)); lib. bdg. (978-0-8368-6799-2(8)) Stevens, Gareth Inc.

Sullivan, Erin Ash. Liquids & Gases. 2005. (Navigators Ser.). (J). pap. 38.00 (***978-1-4108-5071-3(4)***) Benchmark Education Co.

Tocci, Salvatore. Experiments with Solids, Liquids, & Gases. 2002. 13.75 (978-0-606-22879-4(9)) Tandem Library Bks.

Water, Ice, & Steam. (Rosen Real Readers Big Bookstm Ser.). 12p. (J). (gr. 1-2). 31.95 (978-1-4042-6215-7(6)) Rosen Publishing Group, Inc., The.

Williams, Zella. Experiments with Solids, Liquids, & Gases. 2007. (Do-It-Yourself Science Ser.). (Illus.). 24p. (J). (gr. 2-5). lib. bdg. 23.95 (978-1-4042-3658-5(9) , PowerKids Pr.) Rosen Publishing Group, Inc., The.

LISTER, JOSEPH, BARON, 1827-1912

Bankston, John. Joseph Lister & the Story of Antiseptics. 2004. (Uncharted, Unexplored, & Unexplained Ser.). (Illus.). 48p. (J). (gr. 4-8). lib. bdg. 29.95 (978-1-58415-262-0(1)) Mitchell Lane Pubs., Inc.

Parks, Peggy J. Joseph Lister: Father of Antiseptics. 2005. (Giants of Science Ser.). 64p. (J). (gr. 5-7). 26.20 (978-1-4103-0322-6(5) , Blackbirch Pr., Inc.) Thomson Gale.

LISZT, FRANZ, 1811-1886

Corder, Frederick. Ferencz Liszt. 2001. 178p. (YA). reprint ed. 88.00 (978-0-7222-5447-9(4)) Library Reprints, Inc.

De Beaufort, Raphael L. The Abbe Liszt: The Story of His Life. 2001. 309p. (YA). reprint ed. 98.00 (978-0-7222-5446-2(6)) Library Reprints, Inc.

Hervey, Arthur. Franz Liszt & His Music. 2001. 176p. (YA). reprint ed. 88.00 (978-0-7222-5448-6(2)) Library Reprints, Inc.

Huneker, James. Franz Liszt. 2001. 458p. (YA). reprint ed. 98.00 (978-0-7222-5450-9(4)) Library Reprints, Inc.

Liszt, Franz. Letters, 2 vols., set. 2001. (YA). reprint ed. 250.00 (978-0-7222-5444-8(X)) Library Reprints, Inc.

Ramann, Lina. Franz Liszt: Artist & Man, 1811-1840, 2 vols., set. 2001. (YA). reprint ed. 250.00 (978-0-7222-5452-3(0)) Library Reprints, Inc.

Wagner, Richard. Correspondence of Wagner & Liszt, 2 vols., set. 2001. (YA). reprint ed. 250.00 (978-0-7222-5445-5(8)) Library Reprints, Inc.

Whiting, Jim. The Life & Times of Franz Liszt. 2004. (Masters of Music Ser.). (Illus.). 48p. (gr. 4-8). lib. bdg. 20.95 (978-1-58415-280-4(X)) Mitchell Lane Pubs., Inc.

LITERACY

Ferreiro, Emilia. Past & Present of the Verbs to Read & to Write: Essays on Literacy. Fried, Mark, tr. from SPA. 2003. (Illus.). 128p. 22.95 (978-0-88899-556-8(3)) Groundwood Bks. CAN. *Dist:* Perseus Distribution.

McGill-Franzen, Anne. Kindergarten Literacy: Matching Assessment & Instruction in Kindergarten. 2006. (Teaching Resources Ser.). (Illus.). 288p. pap. 25.99 (978-0-439-80034-1(X) , Theory & Practice) Scholastic, Inc.

Sasman, Irene D. H. Literacy Partners Books & Hands-On Library, Set. 1998. (Illus.). (J). (gr. k-3). pap. 99.95 (978-1-56831-533-1(3)); (gr. 3-4). pap. 99.95 (978-1-56831-536-2(8)); (ps-1). pap. 99.95 (978-1-56831-532-4(5)) Learning Connection, The.

Skidmore, Sharon, et al. Balanced Literacy. 2008. per. 34.00 (***978-1-879097-34-6(6)***) Kagan Publishing.

LITERACY—FICTION

Battle-Lavert, Gwendolyn. Papa's Mark. Bootman, Colin, illus. 2003. 32p. (J). (gr. k-3). tchr. ed. 16.95 (978-0-8234-1650-9(X)) Holiday Hse., Inc.

Bloom, Becky. Wolf. Biet, Pascal, illus. 1999. 32p. (J). (ps-3). pap. 16.95 (978-0-531-30155-5(9) , Orchard Bks.) Scholastic, Inc.

Bogart, Jo Ellen. Jeremiah Learns to Read. Fernandez, Laura & Jacobson, Rick, illus. 1999. 32p. (J). (gr. k-4). 15.95 (978-0-531-30190-6(7) , Orchard Bks.) Scholastic, Inc.

Bogart, JoEllen. Jeremiah Learns to Read. Jacobson, Rick & Fernandez, Laura, illus. 1999. 32p. (J). (gr. k-4). lib. bdg. 16.99 (978-0-531-33190-3(3) , Orchard Bks.) Scholastic, Inc.

Breault, Christie Merriman. Logan West, Printer's Devil. Archembault, Matthew, illus. 2006. 142p. (J). pap. (978-1-59336-762-6(7)) Mondo Publishing.

Conover, Chris. The Lion's Share. Conover, Chris, illus. 2003. (Illus.). 40p. (J). pap. 6.95 (978-0-374-44481-5(1) , Sunburst) Farrar, Straus & Giroux.

J
K
L

Gordon, Maria & Gordon, Mike, illus. Cats Can't Count, 4 vols. 2000. (Kids Corner Literacy Stories: Vol. 4). (J). (978-0-7608-4270-6(1)) Sundance/Newbridge Educational Publishing.

—Dogs Can't Read, 4 vols. 2000. (Kids Corner Literacy Stories: Vol. 1). (J). (978-0-7608-4271-3(X)) Sundance/ Newbridge Educational Publishing.

—Mice Can't Write, 4 vols. 2000. (Kids Corner Literacy Stories: Vol. 2). (J). (978-0-7608-4272-0(8)) Sundance/ Newbridge Educational Publishing.

—Spiders Can't Spell, 4 vols. 2000. (Kids Corner Literacy Stories: Vol. 3). (J). (978-0-7608-4273-7(6)) Sundance/ Newbridge Educational Publishing.

Gruber, Wilhelm. Upside-down Reader. 2000. (gr. 3-6). lib. bdg. 14.10 (978-0-613-28688-6(X)) Tandem Library Bks.

Haseley, Dennis. A Story for Bear. LaMarche, Jim, illus. 2002. 32p. (J). (gr. k-3). 16.00 (978-0-15-200239-8(1) , Silver Whistle) Harcourt Trade Pubs.

Hesse, Karen. Just Juice. Parker, Robert Andrew, illus. 1999. 144p. (J). (gr. 3-5). pap. 4.99 (978-0-590-03383-1(2) , Scholastic Paperbacks) Scholastic, Inc.

—Just Juice. 1999. (gr. 3-6). lib. bdg. 13.00 (978-0-613-23005-6(1)) Tandem Library Bks.

Hest, Amy. Mr. George Baker. Muth, Jon J., illus. 2004. 32p. (J). (gr. k-3). 16.99 (978-0-7636-1233-7(2)) Candlewick Pr.

—Mr. George Baker. Muth, Jon J., illus. 2007. 32p. (J). (gr. k-3). pap. 6.99 (978-0-7636-3308-0(9)) Candlewick Pr.

Jackson, Kamichi. You're Too Much, Reggie Brown. Goldberg, Jeff A., illus. l.t. ed. 2000. 110p. (J). (gr. 2-5). pap. 5.95 (978-0-615-11287-9(0)) Pen Poised Pr.

Kinsey-Warnock, Natalie. Lumber Camp Library. Bernardin, James, illus. 2003. 96p. (J). pap. 4.99 (978-0-06-444292-3(6)) HarperCollins Pubs.

—Lumber Camp Library. 2002. (gr. 3-6). lib. bdg. 13.00 (978-0-613-68447-7(8)) Tandem Library Bks.

Lowry, Lois. Zooman Sam. deGroat, Diane, illus. 1999. 160p. (J). (gr. 4-6). tchr. ed. 16.00 (978-0-395-97393-6(7) , Walter Lorraine) Houghton Mifflin Co. Trade & Reference Div.

—Zooman Sam. deGroat, Diane, illus. 2001. 160p. (gr. 4-7). 5.50 (978-0-440-41676-0(0) , Yearling) Random Hse. Children's Bks.

McKissack, Patricia C. A Picture of Freedom: The Diary of Clotee, a Slave Girl, Belmont Plantation, Virginia, 1859. 1999. (Dear America Ser.). (J). 9.95 (978-0-439-15599-1(1)) Scholastic, Inc.

Owens, Tom. Free to Learn. Pollema-Cahill, Phyllis, illus. 2000. (Cover-to-Cover Bks.). (J). 55p. pap. (978-0-7891-5164-3(2)); 56p. (gr. 1-4). lib. bdg. 16.95 (978-0-7807-9314-9(5)) Perfection Learning Corp.

Polacco, Patricia. Aunt Chip & the Great Triple Creek Dam Affair. Polacco, Patricia, illus. 2002. (Illus.). (J). 23.64 (978-0-7587-1998-0(1)) Book Wholesalers, Inc.

Rahaman, Vashanti. Read for Me, Mama. McElrath-Eslick, Lori, illus. 2003. 32p. (J). (gr. 2-4). 15.95 (978-1-56397-313-0(8)) Boyds Mills Pr.

Rue, Nancy N. The Ally. 1998. (Christian Heritage Ser.). 192p. (J). (gr. 3-7). pap. (978-1-56179-561-1(5)) Focus on the Family Publishing.

Stanley, Diane. Raising Sweetness. Karas, G. Brian, illus. 2002. 14.04 (978-1-4046-1758-2(2)) Book Wholesalers, Inc.

—Raising Sweetness. 2003. (Illus.). (J). 25.95 incl. audio (978-1-59112-266-1(X)); 28.95 incl. audio compact disk (978-1-59112-516-7(2)) Live Oak Media.

—Raising Sweetness, 4 bks. Stanley, Diane, illus. 2003. (Illus.). (J). pap. 37.95 incl. audio (978-1-59112-267-8(8)) Live Oak Media.

—Raising Sweetness, 4 bks. 2003. (Illus.). (J). pap. 39.95 incl. audio compact disk (978-1-59112-524-2(3)) Live Oak Media.

—Raising Sweetness. Karas, G. Brian, illus. (J). 2002. 32p. pap. 6.99 (978-0-698-11962-8(2)); 1999. 1p. 16.99 (978-0-399-23225-1(7)) Penguin Group (USA) Inc. (Putnam Juvenile).

—Raising Sweetness. 2002. lib. bdg. 15.30 (978-0-613-60831-2(3)) Tandem Library Bks.

Stolz, Joelle. The Shadows of Ghadames. 128p. (gr. 3-7). 2006. 5.99 (978-0-440-41949-5(2) , Yearling); 2004. (J). 15.95 (978-0-385-73104-1(3) , Delacorte Bks. for Young Readers) Random Hse. Children's Bks.

Wells, Rosemary. Read Me a Story. Wheeler, Jody & Nez, John, illus. 2002. (Yoko & Friends School Days Ser.: Bk. 8). 32p. (gr. k-2). pap. 3.99 (978-0-7868-1533-3(7) , Volo) Hyperion Bks. for Children.

LITERARY CHARACTERS

see Characters and Characteristics in Literature

LITERARY CRITICISM

see Criticism; Literature—History and Criticism

LITERATURE—BIO-BIBLIOGRAPHY

see also Authors

Drew, Bernard A. 100 More Popular Young Adult Authors: Biographical Sketches & Bibliographies. 2002. (Popular Authors Ser.). (Illus.). 500p. 65.00 (978-1-56308-920-6(3) , LU9203) Libraries Unlimited, Inc.

Literary Lifelines, 10 vols., Set. 1998. (Illus.). (YA). (gr. 6). lib. bdg. 335.00 (978-0-7172-9211-0(8) , Grolier) Scholastic Library Publishing.

Primm, E. Russell, III. Barbara Park to Seymour Simon, Vol. 5. 2002. (Favorite Children's Authors & Illustrators Ser.). (Illus.). (J). (gr. 3-8). lib. bdg. (978-1-59187-022-7(4)) Tradition Publishing Co.

—Carmen Lomas Garza to Ursula K. Le Guin, Vol. 3. 2002. (Favorite Children's Authors & Illustrators Ser.). (Illus.). (J). lib. bdg. (978-1-59187-020-3(8)) Tradition Publishing Co.

—Edward Lear to Helen Oxenbury, Vol. 4. 2002. (Favorite Children's Authors & Illustrators Ser.). (Illus.). (J). lib. bdg. (978-1-59187-021-0(6)) Tradition Publishing Co.

—Joanna Cole to Jack Gantos, Vol. 2. 2002. (Favorite Children's Authors & Illustrators Ser.). (Illus.). (J). lib. bdg. (978-1-59187-019-7(4)) Tradition Publishing Co.

—Peter Sis to Gene Zion, Vol. 6. 2002. (Favorite Children's Authors & Illustrators Ser.). (Illus.). (J). (gr. 3-8). lib. bdg. (978-1-59187-023-4(2)) Tradition Publishing Co.

—Verna Aardema to Brock Cole, Vol. 1. 2002. (Favorite Children's Authors & Illustrators Ser.). (Illus.). (J). lib. bdg. (978-1-59187-018-0(6)) Tradition Publishing Co.

Silvey, Anita. 500 Great Books for Teens. 2006. 416p. 26.00 (978-0-618-61296-3(3)) Houghton Mifflin Co.

LITERATURE—BIOGRAPHY

see Authors

LITERATURE—CRITICISM

see Literature—History and Criticism

LITERATURE—DICTIONARIES

Grolier Educational Staff. Lives & Works: Young Adult Authors, 8 vols. 1999. (YA). lib. bdg. 265.00 (978-0-7172-9227-1(4) , Grolier) Scholastic Library Publishing.

LITERATURE—EVALUATION

see Books and Reading; Criticism; Literature—History and Criticism

LITERATURE—HISTORY AND CRITICISM

see also Authors; Criticism

Animerica Magazine Staff. Best of Animerica Anime & Manga Monthly: The Year's Best Articles. 2003. (gr. 7-12). lib. bdg. 22.20 (978-0-613-79044-4(8)) Tandem Library Bks.

Barbour, Scott. American Modernism. 2000. (gr. 7-12). lib. bdg. 34.70 (978-0-613-64244-6(9)) Tandem Library Bks.

—American Modernism. 2000. (Literary Movements & Genres Ser.). (Illus.). 208p. (YA). (gr. 10 up). pap. (978-0-7377-0200-2(1) , Greenhaven Pr., Inc.) Thomson Gale.

Beacham's Guide to Literature for Young Adults, Vol. 16. 2003. 550p. 110.00 (978-0-7876-5836-6(7) , UXL) Thomson Gale.

Beacham's Literature for Young Adults, 14 vol., Set. 2002. (YA). 110.00 (978-0-7876-5182-4(6)) Thomson Gale.

The Bean Trees. 1998. 44p. (YA). 11.95 (978-1-56137-891-3(7) , NU8917SP) Novel Units, Inc.

Beers. Elements of Literature. 5th ed. 2003. (Illus.). 78.60 (978-0-03-068373-2(4)); tchr. ed. 134.46 (978-0-03-068382-4(3)) Holt, Rinehart & Winston.

—Elements of Literature: Online Upgrade Package (1 Year) 5th ed. 2004. (gr. 10). 7.93 (978-0-03-037291-9(7)) Holt, Rinehart & Winston.

Beetz, Kirk H. & Niemeyer, Suzanne, contrib. by. Beacham's Guide to Literature for Young Adults, Vol. 10. 2000. (Beacham's Guide to Literature for Young Adults Ser.: Vol. 10). (Illus.). 567p. (YA). 110.00 (978-0-7876-4978-4(3) , GML00502-115120, UXL) Thomson Gale.

Bloom, Harold. Bloom's Modern Critical Views. Henry, W. & Berg, Albert A., eds. (J). 455.40 (978-0-7910-7394-0(7) , Chelsea Hse.) Facts On File, Inc.

Bloom, Harold, ed. Anton Chekhov. 1999. (Bloom's Modern Critical Views Ser.). 200p. (YA). (gr. 8-12). 45.00 (978-0-7910-4783-5(0) , Chelsea Hse.) Facts On File, Inc.

—Bloom's Literary Places. (Illus.). (gr. 9-13). pap. 41.85 (978-0-7910-8391-8(8)); lib. bdg. 95.85 (978-0-7910-7835-8(3)) Facts On File, Inc. (Chelsea Hse.).

—Bloom's Modern Critical Interpretations. (Illus.). (gr. 9-13). lib. bdg. 113.85 (978-0-7910-8484-7(1) , Chelsea Hse.) Facts On File, Inc.

—Bloom's Modern Critical Views. (Illus.). (gr. 9-13). pap. 39.90 (978-0-7910-8479-3(5)); lib. bdg. 189.75 (978-0-7910-8487-8(6)) Facts On File, Inc. (Chelsea Hse.).

—Bloom's Period Studies. (Illus.). (gr. 9-13). lib. bdg. 379.50 (978-0-7910-7893-8(0)); lib. bdg. (978-0-7910-8069-6(2)) Facts On File, Inc. (Chelsea Hse.).

—Modern Critical Views. (Illus.). 144-300p. (J). 279.60 (978-0-7910-5220-4(6) , Chelsea Hse.) Facts On File, Inc.

—Rome. 2005. (Bloom's Literary Places Ser.). (Illus.). 150p. (gr. 9-13). pap. (978-0-7910-8383-3(7) , Chelsea Hse.) Facts On File, Inc.

Bloom, Harold, ed. & intro. Modern Critical Interpretations. Bloom, Harold, intro. 1999. (Illus.). 144-176p. (J). 419.40 (978-0-7910-5221-1(4) , Chelsea Hse.) Facts On File, Inc.

Bloom's Guides. 2005. 840.00 (978-0-7910-8718-3(2) , Chelsea Hse.) Facts On File, Inc.

Bloom's Literary Places. 2005. 150p. pap. 240.00 (978-0-7910-8719-0(0) , Chelsea Hse.) Facts On File, Inc.

Bloom's Major Literary Characters. 2005. 180p. pap. 640.00 (978-0-7910-8475-5(2) , Chelsea Hse.) Facts On File, Inc.

Bloom's Modern Critical Views. 2005. pap. 5355.00 (978-0-7910-9138-8(4) , Chelsea Hse.) Facts On File, Inc.

Bloom's Notes. 2005. pap. 870.00 (978-0-7910-9137-1(6) , Chelsea Hse.) Facts On File, Inc.

Bloom's Period Studies. 2005. 350p. pap. 630.00 (978-0-7910-8488-5(4) , Chelsea Hse.) Facts On File, Inc.

Blume, Judy. Freckle Juice. 1999. (YA). 11.95 (978-1-56137-822-7(4)); (J). 9.95 (978-1-56137-008-5(8)) Novel Units, Inc.

Bridges to Literature. 2002. (gr. 6-12). Vol. 2. stu. ed. (978-0-618-08734-1(6) , 2-03997); Vol. 3. stu. ed. (978-0-618-08735-8(4) , 2-03998) McDougal Littell Inc.

The Call of the Wild. 2004. (Classic Retelling Ser.). (gr. 6-12). (978-0-618-00373-0(8) , 2-00110) McDougal Littell Inc.

Campbell, Patty. Robert Cormier: Daring to Disturb the Universe. 2006. 304p. (YA). (gr. 7). pap. 14.95 (978-0-385-73046-4(2) , Delacorte Bks. for Young Readers) Random Hse. Children's Bks.

Center for Learning Network Staff. World Literature 1: A Thematic Approach — Curriculum Unit — Teacher Guide. rev. ed. 2001. (English Ser.). 230p. (YA). tchr. ed., spiral bd. 39.95 (978-1-56077-687-1(0)) Ctr. for Learning, The.

Charlotte's Web. 1998. 40p. (J). 11.95 (978-1-56137-630-8(2) , NU6302SP) Novel Units, Inc.

Chin, Mei & Bloom, Harold. One Hundred Years of Solitude. 2006. (Bloom's Guides Ser.). 136p. (gr. 9). 30.00 (978-0-7910-8578-3(3) , Chelsea Hse.) Facts On File, Inc.

Elson, H. William. Elson Grammer School Literature, Book Fo. 2006. 31.99 (***978-1-4219-7647-1(1)***); pap. 25.99 (***978-1-4219-7635-8(8)***) IndyPublish.com.

EMC-Paradigm Publishing Staff. World Literature & Multimedia Guide. 2002. (YA). (gr. 6-12). (978-0-8219-1880-7(X)) EMC/Paradigm Publishing.

The Engaged Reader. 2005. (Illus.). 64p. (gr. 4-8). pap. 150.00 (978-0-7910-9066-4(3) , Chelsea Hse.) Facts On File, Inc.

Factor, Judith, ed. Mosdos Press Literature Series: Gold Companion Workbook. 2001. (YA). (gr. 8 up). pap. 15.00 (978-0-9671009-7-5(6)) Mosdos Pr.

—Mosdos Press Literature Series: Gold Student Edition. 2001. (YA). (gr. 8 up). 50.00 (978-0-9671009-2-0(5)) Mosdos Pr.

—Mosdos Press Literature Series: Pearl Companion Workbook. 2003. (YA). (gr. 6 up). pap. 15.00 (978-0-9671009-8-2(4)) Mosdos Pr.

Finn, Perdita. Literature Circle Guide: From the Mixed-up Files of Mrs. Basil E. Frankweiler. 2001. 32p. pap. 5.95 (978-0-439-16360-6(9)) Scholastic, Inc.

Foster, Brett & Marcovitz, Hal. Rome. 2005. (Bloom's Literary Places Ser.). (Illus.). 197p. (YA). (gr. 9-13). per. 40.00 (978-0-7910-7839-6(6) , Chelsea Hse.) Facts On File, Inc.

Fuentes, Carlos & Bloom, Harold. The Death of Artemio Cruz. 2006. (Bloom's Modern Critical Interpretations Ser.).Tr. of Muerte de Artemio Cruz. 224p. (gr. 9). 45.00 (978-0-7910-8587-5(2) , Chelsea Hse.) Facts On File, Inc.

Gross, Ila Lane. Classic Literature Around the World. 2001. (Global Understanding - Cultural Literacy Ser.). (Illus.). 120p. (YA). (gr. 5-12). pap. 5.95 (978-0-9713649-3-6(1)) L.E.A.P. (Learning through an Expanded Arts Program, Inc).

Hacht, Anne Marie. Literary Themes for Students, 2 vols., Vol. 12. 2006. (Literary Themes for Students Ser.). (Illus.). 1200p. 190.00 (978-1-4144-0271-0(6)) Thomson Gale.

Harper, Amelia. Literary Lessons from The Lord of the Rings. Howe, John, illus. 2004. 622p. (YA). (gr. 7-12). stu. ed., spiral bd. 50.00 (978-0-9754934-1-0(8) , Literary Lessons) HomeScholar Bks.

Herron, Paul, ed. & contrib. by. A Cafe in Space: The Anais Nin Literary Journal, 2 vols., Vol. 2. Herron, Paul, contrib. by. 2004. (Illus.). 160p. (YA). pap. 15.00 (978-0-9652364-9-2(8)) Sky Blue Pr.

Holt, Rinehart and Winston Staff. Elements of Literature. 3rd annot. ed. 2003. (YA). (gr. 9). tchr. ed. 127.40 (978-0-03-071857-1(0)) Holt, Rinehart & Winston.

—Elements of Literature: Family Involvement Activities. 5th ed. 2003. (SPA & ENG., Illus.). pap. 38.80 (978-0-03-073853-1(9)) Holt, Rinehart & Winston.

—Elements of Literature: Florida Edition with Enhanced Online Edition. 3rd ed. 2003. (YA). (gr. 10). pap. 84.00 (978-0-03-070971-5(7)); (YA). (gr. 11). pap. 86.20 (978-0-03-070972-2(5)); (YA). (gr. 12). pap. 86.20 (978-0-03-070973-9(3)); (gr. 6). pap. 80.00 (978-0-03-070966-1(0)); (gr. 7). pap. 80.00 (978-0-03-070967-8(9)); (gr. 8). pap. 80.00 (978-0-03-070968-5(7)); (YA). (gr. 9). pap. 84.00 (978-0-03-070969-2(5)) Holt, Rinehart & Winston.

—Elements of Literature: Holt Adapted Reader Answer Key. 2003. 3rd ed. pap. 73.20 (978-0-03-073389-5(8)); 5th ed. pap. 23.20 (978-0-03-035911-8(2)); 5th ed. pap. 23.20 (978-0-03-035909-5(0)) Holt, Rinehart & Winston.

—Elements of Literature: Holt Reader. 2003. (Illus.). 4th ed. (gr. 10). pap. 13.20 (978-0-03-068394-7(7)); 5th ed. (gr. 11). pap. 13.20 (978-0-03-068396-1(3)); 5th ed. (gr. 12). pap. 13.20 (978-0-03-068397-8(1)); 5th ed. (gr. 7). 13.20 (978-0-03-068391-6(2)); 5th ed. (gr. 8). pap. 13.20 (978-0-03-068392-3(0)); 5th ed. (gr. 9). pap. 13.20 (978-0-03-068393-0(9)) Holt, Rinehart & Winston.

—Elements of Literature: Holt Reader: Interactive Worktext - Georgia Edition. 3rd ed. 2003. (gr. 6). pap. 11.00 (978-0-03-070197-9(X)); (gr. 7). pap. 11.00 (978-0-03-070198-6(8)); (gr. 8). pap. 11.00 (978-0-03-070199-3(6)) Holt, Rinehart & Winston.

—Elements of Literature: Holt Reader: Interactive Worktext - Mississippi Edition. 3rd ed. 2003. (gr. 10). pap., tchr. ed. 21.80 (978-0-03-072187-8(3)); (YA). (gr. 10). pap. 11.00 (978-0-03-071196-1(7)); (gr. 11). pap., tchr. ed. 21.80 (978-0-03-072188-5(1)); (YA). (gr. 11). pap. 11.00 (978-0-03-071197-8(5)); (gr. 12). pap., tchr. ed. 21.80 (978-0-03-072189-2(X)); (YA). (gr. 12). pap. 11.00 (978-0-03-071198-5(3)); (J). (gr. 6). pap. 11.00 (978-0-03-071191-6(6)); (gr. 6). pap., tchr. ed. 21.74 (978-0-03-072182-3(2)); (gr. 7). pap. 11.00 (978-0-03-071192-3(4)); (gr. 7). pap., tchr. ed. 21.80 (978-0-03-072183-0(0)); (gr. 8). pap. 11.00 (978-0-03-071193-0(2)); (gr. 8). pap., tchr. ed. 21.80 (978-0-03-072184-7(9)); (gr. 9). pap., tchr. ed. 21.80 (978-0-03-072186-1(5)); (YA). (gr. 9). pap. 11.00 (978-0-03-071194-7(0)) Holt, Rinehart & Winston.

—Elements of Literature: Mississippi Edition. 3rd annot. ed. 2003. (gr. 10). tchr. ed. 127.40 (978-0-03-071858-8(9)); (gr. 11). tchr. ed. 137.60 (978-0-03-071859-5(7)); (gr. 12). tchr. ed. 137.60 (978-0-03-071874-8(0)); (gr. 6). tchr. ed. 121.60 (978-0-03-071797-0(3)); (gr. 7). tchr. ed. 121.60 (978-0-03-071814-4(7)); (gr. 8). tchr. ed. 121.60 (978-0-03-071818-2(X)) Holt, Rinehart & Winston.

—Elements of Literature: New Mexico Edition. 3rd ed. 2003. (J). pap. 12.20 (978-0-03-071972-1(0)) Holt, Rinehart & Winston.

Hunsicker, Ranelda Mack. Hans Brinker. 2001. (Classics for Young Readers Ser.). (Illus.). 64p. (J). (gr. 3-6). pap., stu. ed., instr.'s gde. ed. 6.99 (978-0-87552-731-4(0)) P & R Publishing.

—Sir Gibbie: A Guide for Teachers & Students. 2001. (Classics for Young Readers Ser.). 62p. (J). (gr. 3-6). pap., stu. ed. 6.99 (978-0-87552-730-7(2)) P & R Publishing.

I Was a Teenage Fairy Reading Group Guide. 2000. (J). pap. (978-0-06-449252-2(4) , Harper Trophy) HarperCollins Pubs.

Jamieson, Jean. Bunnicula. 1999. 44p. (J). stu. ed. 11.95 (978-1-56137-712-1(0)) Novel Units, Inc.

Jones, Diana Wynne. Year of the Griffin Reading Group Guide. 2000. (J). (978-0-06-029311-6(X)) HarperCollins Pubs.

Klar, Elizabeth. Skinnybones. 1999. (J). 11.95 (978-1-58130-605-7(9)); 9.95 (978-1-58130-604-0(0)) Novel Units, Inc.

Kurian, George Thomas. Timetables of World Literature. 2003. 464p. (gr. 9 up). 75.00 (978-0-8160-4197-8(0)) Facts On File, Inc.

Levine, Gloria. Frankenstein. 1999. 44p. (YA). 11.95 (978-1-56137-751-0(1)) Novel Units, Inc.

Literary Movements Set. 2005. (Literary Movements Ser.). 432p. (gr. 9). 320.00 (978-0-8160-6528-8(4)); 255.00 (978-0-8160-6322-2(2)) Facts On File, Inc.

Literature. 2003. (Illus.). 40p. (YA). (gr. 5 up). lib. bdg. (978-1-59084-478-6(5)) Mason Crest Pubs.

Literature: Timeless Voices, Timeless Themes. 2001. (gr. 10). pap., tchr.'s training gde. ed. 5.47 (978-0-13-053407-1(2)); 2001. (YA). (gr. 10). 20.47 (978-0-13-053414-9(5)); 2001. (YA). (gr. 10). stu. ed. 55.97 (978-0-13-050836-2(5)); 2001. (YA). (gr. 10). pap. 8.47 (978-0-13-052966-4(4)); 2001. (YA). (gr. 10). pap. 7.47 (978-0-13-052965-7(6)); 2001. (YA). (gr. 10). pap. 7.47 (978-0-13-053412-5(9)); 2001. (YA). (gr. 10). pap., stu. ed., wbk. ed. 7.47 (978-0-13-053416-3(1)); 2001. (YA). (gr. 10). pap., stu. ed., wbk. ed. 7.47 (978-0-13-053411-8(0)); 2001. (YA). (gr. 10). trans. 134.97 (978-0-13-053413-2(7)); 2001. (YA). (gr. 10). cd-rom 199.97 (978-0-13-050820-1(9)); Copper Level. 2001. (J). (gr. 6). pap. 13.97 (978-0-13-052393-8(3)); Copper Level 2001. (J). (gr. 6). trans. 114.47 (978-0-13-052357-0(7)); Gold Level 2001. (YA). (gr. 9). pap. 5.47 (978-0-13-051431-8(4)); Platinum Level 2000. (YA). (gr. 10). pap. 7.47 (978-0-13-434643-4(2)); Platinum Level 2000. (YA). (gr. 10). trans. 160.97 (978-0-13-435109-4(6)); Platinum Level 2000. (YA). (gr. 10). trans. 33.47 (978-0-13-051235-2(4)) Prentice Hall PTR.

Lord of the Flies. 1998. 40p. (YA). 11.95 (978-1-56137-384-0(2) , NU3842SP) Novel Units, Inc.

Mass, Wendy. Great Authors of Children's Literature. 1999. (History Makers Ser.). (Illus.). 112p. (YA). (gr. 7-10). 28.70 (978-1-56006-589-0(3) , Lucent Bks.) Thomson Gale.

Mirande, Jaqueline. Arturo y los Caballeros de la Tabla Redonda. 2003. (Advanced Reading Ser.). (SPA., Illus.). 134p. (J). 11.95 (978-84-239-7072-8(8)) Espasa Calpe, S.A. ESP. *Dist:* Libros Sin Fronteras, Planeta Publishing Corp.

Modern Critical Interpretations. 2005. pap. 3465.00 (978-0-7910-9133-3(3) , Chelsea Hse.) Facts On File, Inc.

Modern Critical Interpretations, 2002-2003, 6 vols., Set. Incl. Cat on a Hot Tin Roof. Bloom, Harold, ed. & intro. 2001. 45.00 (978-0-7910-6342-2(9) , 054913); Cat-s Cradle - Kurt Vonnegut. Bloom, Harold. 2002. 45.00 (978-0-7910-6337-8(2) , 054912); Jungle - Upton Sinclair. Bloom, Harold, ed. & intro. 2001. 45.00 (978-0-7910-6341-5(0) , 054915); One Flew over the Cuckoo's Nest. Kesey, Ken. Bloom, Harold, ed. 2001. 45.00 (978-0-7910-6339-2(9) , 054916); Ragtime - F. L. Doctorow. Bloom, Harold, ed. 2001. 45.00 (978-0-7910-6343-9(7) , 054919); Sophie's Choice - William Styron. Bloom, Harold, ed. & intro. 2001. 45.00 (978-0-7910-6340-8(2) , 054917); Things Fall Apart - Chinua Achebe. Bloom, Harold, ed. & intro. 2001. 45.00 (978-0-7910-6336-1(4) , 054918); 150p. (YA). (gr. 8 up). Set lib. bdg. 227.70 (978-0-7910-7196-0(0) , 021847S, Chelsea Hse.) Facts On File, Inc.

Modern Critical Views 2003, 10 vols., Set. Incl. African-American Poets : Phillis Wheatley Through Countee Cullen. Bloom, Harold. 2002. 45.00 (978-0-7910-6332-3(1) , 054929); Agatha Christie. Bloom, Harold, ed. 2001. 45.00 (978-0-7910-5921-0(9) , 054928); American & Canadian Women Poets 1930-Present. Bloom, Harold, ed. & intro. 2002. 45.00 (978-0-7910-6331-6(3) , 054930); American Women Poets, 1650-1950. Bloom, Harold, ed. & intro. 2002. 45.00 (978-0-7910-6330-9(5) , 054931); Cormac McCarthy. Bloom, Harold, ed. & intro. 2001. 45.00 (978-0-7910-6333-0(X) , 054932); E. L. Doctorow. Bloom, Harold, ed. & intro. 2001. 45.00 (978-0-7910-6451-1(4) , 201889); Elizabeth Barrett Browning. Bloom, Harold, ed. & intro. 2001. 45.00 (978-0-7910-6450-4(6) , 054935); Moliere. Bloom, Harold, ed. & intro. 2001. 45.00 (978-0-7910-6335-4(6) , 054933); Octavio Paz. Bloom, Harold, ed. & intro. 2001. 45.00 (978-0-7910-6334-7(8) , 054934); 200p. (YA). (gr. 8 up). Set lib. bdg. 227.70 (978-0-7910-7194-6(4) , 021846S, Chelsea Hse.) Facts On File, Inc.

Moran, Karen. Literature Online: Reading & Internet Activities for Libraries & Schools. 1999. 94p. (J). (gr. 4-8). pap. 17.95 (978-1-57950-032-0(3) , Upstart Bks.) Highsmith Inc.

Moratín, Leandro Fernandez de. El Si de la Ninas. annot. ed. (SPA., Illus.). 176p. (J). 15.95 (978-84-207-2634-2(6) , ANY008) Grupo Anaya, S.A. ESP. *Dist:* Continental Bk. Co., Inc.

Night. 1998. 36p. (YA). 11.95 (978-1-56137-805-0(4) , NU8054SP) Novel Units, Inc.

Novel Units, Inc. Staff. Anne of Green Gables. 1999. (Avonlea Ser.: No. 1). 44p. (YA). (gr. 5-8). 9.95 (978-1-56137-341-3(9)) Novel Units, Inc.

—Banner in the Sky. 1999. (J). 9.95 (978-1-56137-481-6(4)) Novel Units, Inc.

—Great Expectations. 1998. 44p. (YA). 11.95 (978-1-56137-515-8(2) , NU5152SP) Novel Units, Inc.

—Hiroshima. 1999. 21p. (YA). (gr. 7-12). 9.95 (978-1-56137-136-5(X) , BK8279) Novel Units, Inc.

Novel Units, Inc. Staff, ed. A Tale of Two Cities. 1998. 44p. (YA). 11.95 (978-1-56137-433-5(4) , NU4334SP) Novel Units, Inc.

The Old Man & the Sea. 1998. 36p. (YA). 11.95 (978-1-56137-404-5(0) , NU4040SP) Novel Units, Inc.

Persky, Stan. The Short Version: An ABC Book. 2005. 352p. pap. 19.00 (978-1-55420-016-0(4) , Transmontanus) New Star Bks., Ltd. CAN. *Dist:* SPD-Small Pr. Distribution.

Prentice-Hall Staff, contrib. by. Authors in Depth: Platinum Level. 5th ed. 1999. (Prentice Hall Literature Library). 199p. (J). (gr. 10). (978-0-13-050403-6(3)) Prentice Hall PTR.

Raskin, Ellen. The Westing Game. 1998. (Assessment Packs Ser.). 15p. (J). pap., tchr.'s training gde. ed. 15.95 (978-1-58303-069-1(7)) Pathways Publishing.

Responding to Literature. 912p. (YA). (gr. 8). 52.95 (978-0-8219-1364-2(6) , 35456) EMC/Paradigm Publishing.

Roso, Calvin. The Great Gatsby. 1998. 86p. (YA). (gr. 9-12). stu. ed., ring bd. 14.99 (978-1-58609-167-5(0)) Progeny Pr.

—The Old Man & the Sea. 2000. 60p. (YA). (gr. 9-12). stu. ed., ring bd. 14.99 (978-1-58609-172-9(7)) Progeny Pr.

The Scarlet Letter. 2004. (Classic Retelling Ser.). (gr. 6-12). (978-0-395-98667-7(2) , 2-99911) McDougal Littell Inc.

The Scarlet Letter. 2000. (Illus.). (YA). 48p. stu. ed., per. 17.95 (978-1-56254-276-4(1) , SP2761); 80p. per. 6.95 (978-1-56254-274-0(5) , SP2745) Saddleback Educational Publishing.

Sperry, Armstrong. Call It Courage. 1999. Tr. of Newbery Summer. (YA). 11.95 (978-1-56137-492-2(X)); 9.95 (978-1-56137-245-4(5)) Novel Units, Inc.

Steinbeck, John, et al. Of Mice & Men. 1999. (Literature Made Easy Ser.). (Illus.). 96p. pap. 6.99 (978-0-7641-0820-4(4)) Barron's Educational Series, Inc.

Stobaugh, James. World Literature Student. 2005. (Broadman & Holman Literature Ser.). 272p. stu. ed. 24.99 (978-0-8054-5892-3(1)) B&H Publishing Grp.

Story Studio Vol. 2: Transmitting Stories Across the Curriculum. 2005. spiral bd. 39.95 (978-1-56820-173-3(7)) Story Time Stories That Rhyme.

Sylvester & the Magic Pebble. 1999. (J). 9.95 (978-1-56137-019-1(3)) Novel Units, Inc.

Taming of the Shrew. 1999. (YA). 9.95 (978-1-56137-768-8(6)) Novel Units, Inc.

Taylor, Mildred D. Roll of Thunder, Hear My Cry. 2000. (Novel Vocabulary Ser.). (J). 40p. pap., stu. ed., tchr.'s training gde. ed. 21.95 (978-1-58303-108-7(1)); 15p. pap., tchr.'s training gde. ed. 15.95 (978-1-58303-100-1(6)) Pathways Publishing.

—Roll of Thunder, Hear My Cry. Scholastic, Inc. Staff, ed. 1999. (Literature Guide Ser.). (Illus.). 16p. (J). pap. 3.95 (978-0-590-38927-3(0)) Scholastic, Inc.

Things Fall Apart. 1998. 40p. (YA). 11.95 (978-1-56137-813-5(5) , NU8135SP) Novel Units, Inc.

Thomson Gale Staff. Beacham's Guide to Literature for Young Adults. 1999. (Beacham's Guide to Literature for Young Adults Ser.). 5000p. (YA). 895.00 (978-0-7876-4979-1(1) , GML00502-115121) Thomson Gale.

Timeless Voices, Timeless Themes: Bronze, Literary Focus & Reading. 2001. (YA). (gr. 7). trans. 109.97 (978-0-13-052359-4(3)) Prentice Hall PTR.

Timeless Voices, Timeless Themes: Bronze, Selecciones Literarias. 2001. (YA). (gr. 7). pap. 13.97 (978-0-13-052394-5(1)) Prentice Hall PTR.

Timeless Voices, Timeless Themes: Copper, Literary Analysis Activity Book. 2001. (J). (gr. 6). pap. 6.97 (978-0-13-052365-5(8)) Prentice Hall PTR.

Timeless Voices, Timeless Themes: Gold, Literary Focus & Reading. 2001. (YA). (gr. 9). trans. 109.97 (978-0-13-051270-3(2)) Prentice Hall PTR.

Timeless Voices, Timeless Themes: Platinum, Assessment Success Planning Guide. 2001. (YA). (gr. 10). pap. 4.97 (978-0-13-051093-8(9)) Prentice Hall PTR.

Timeless Voices, Timeless Themes: Platinum, Lesson Planner. 2001. (YA). (gr. 10). pap. 9.97 (978-0-13-050908-6(6)) Prentice Hall PTR.

Timeless Voices, Timeless Themes: Platinum, Literary Focus & Reading. 2001. (YA). (gr. 10). trans. 109.97 (978-0-13-051281-9(8)) Prentice Hall PTR.

Timeless Voices, Timeless Themes: Silver, Literary Analysis Activity Book. 2001. (YA). (gr. 8). pap. 6.97 (978-0-13-052368-6(2)) Prentice Hall PTR.

Timeless Voices, Timeless Themes: Silver, Literary Focus & Reading. 2001. (YA). (gr. 8). trans. 109.97 (978-0-13-052350-1(X)) Prentice Hall PTR.

Timeless Voices, Timeless Themes: Silver, Selecciones Literarias. 2001. (YA). (gr. 8). pap. 14.47 (978-0-13-052395-2(X)) Prentice Hall PTR.

Timeless Voices Timeless Themes: Standardized Prentice Hll Literaturized Practice Test Grade 9. 5th ed. 1999. (J). (gr. 9). (978-0-13-437467-3(3)) Prentice Hall PTR.

Timeless Voices, Timeless Themes: World Literature, Assessment Success Planning Guide. 2001. (YA). (gr. 10). pap. 4.97 (978-0-13-053417-0(X)) Prentice Hall PTR.

Timeless Voices, Timeless Themes: World Literature, Literary Focus & Reading. 2001. (YA). (gr. 10). trans. 109.97 (978-0-13-053409-5(9)) Prentice Hall PTR.

Timeless Voices, Timeless Themes: World Literature, Strategies for Succeeding on Standardized Tests. 2001. (YA). (gr. 10). 23.47 (978-0-13-053418-7(8)) Prentice Hall PTR.

Voigt, Cynthia. Dicey's Song. 1998. (Tillerman Cycle Ser.: Bk. 2). 15p. (YA). (gr. 9-12). pap., tchr.'s training gde. ed. 15.95 (978-1-58303-042-4(5)) Pathways Publishing.

Welsch, Gabriel. The Great Gatsby. 2006. (Bloom's Guides Ser.). 144p. 30.00 (978-0-7910-8580-6(5) , Chelsea Hse.) Facts On File, Inc.

Wills, Adele. Texts Through History. 2004. (Routledge a Level English Guides Ser.). (Illus.). 96p. 19.95 (978-0-415-31910-2(2)); 71.95 (978-0-415-31909-6(9)) Routledge.

Zebrowski, Debra. World Literature. Matthews, Douglas L., ed. 2003. (Illus.). stu. ed., per., wbk. ed. (978-1-931680-53-0(1) , Expert Systems for Teachers) Teaching Point, Inc.

LITERATURE, MEDIEVAL

Kline, Daniel T., ed. Medieval Literature for Children. 2003. (Illus.). 352p. 120.00 (978-0-8153-3312-8(9)) Routledge.

LITERATURE—STORIES, PLOTS, ETC.

Beck, Isabel L., et al. Big Books & Big Book Collection: From Head to Toe. 1999. (Trophies Ser.). (gr. 1 up). pap. 58.90 (978-0-15-313373-2(2)) Harcourt Schl. Pubs.

—Big Books & Big Book Collection: I Swam with a Seal. 1999. (Trophies Ser.). (gr. 1 up). pap. 61.60 (978-0-15-313378-7(3)) Harcourt Schl. Pubs.

—Big Books & Big Book Collection: Let's Go Visiting. 1999. (Trophies Ser.). (gr. 1 up). pap. 58.90 (978-0-15-313369-5(4)) Harcourt Schl. Pubs.

—Big Books & Big Book Collection: Little White Dog. 1999. (Trophies Ser.). (gr. 1 up). pap. 58.90 (978-0-15-313374-9(0)) Harcourt Schl. Pubs.

—Big Books & Big Book Collection: On a Hot, Hot Day. 1999. (Trophies Ser.). (gr. 1 up). pap. 58.90 (978-0-15-313375-6(9)) Harcourt Schl. Pubs.

—Big Books & Big Book Collection: Sometimes. 99th ed. 1999. (Trophies Ser.). (gr. 1 up). pap. 56.40 (978-0-15-310806-8(1)) Harcourt Schl. Pubs.

—Big Books & Big Book Collection: Ten Dogs in the Window. 1999. (Trophies Ser.). (gr. 1 up). pap. 58.90 (978-0-15-313370-1(8)) Harcourt Schl. Pubs.

—Big Books & Big Book Collection: To Market, to Market. 1999. (Trophies Ser.). (gr. 1 up). pap. 61.60 (978-0-15-313377-0(5)) Harcourt Schl. Pubs.

—Big Books & Big Book Collection: Where Does the Brown Bear Go? 1999. (Trophies Ser.). (gr. 1 up). pap. 58.90 (978-0-15-313372-5(4)) Harcourt Schl. Pubs.

—Julian's Glorious Summer. 2003. (Trophies Ser.). (gr. 3 up). 50.40 (978-0-15-319277-7(1)) Harcourt Schl. Pubs.

Danny Stories & Other Tales. 2002. (Illus.). 216p. (YA). 23.50 (978-0-9722584-3-2(4)) Rolling Fork Publishing.

Gilbert, Yvonne, illus. Children's Classics to Read Aloud. 2003. (Classic Collections). 256p. (J). (gr. 2-5). pap. 8.95 (978-0-7534-5686-6(9) , Kingfisher) Houghton Mifflin Co. Trade & Reference Div.

Golding, William. Lord of the Flies. 1998. (Assessment Packs Ser.). 15p. (YA). (gr. 9-12). pap., tchr.'s training gde. ed. 15.95 (978-1-58303-048-6(4)) Pathways Publishing.

Golding, William, et al. Lord of the Flies. 1999. (Literature Made Easy Ser.). (Illus.). 96p. pap. 6.99 (978-0-7641-0821-1(2)) Barron's Educational Series, Inc.

Holt, Rinehart and Winston Staff. Elements of Literature: Adapted Reader. 5th ed. 2003. (Illus.). pap. 13.20 (978-0-03-035459-5(5)); pap. 13.20 (978-0-03-035461-8(7)); pap. 13.20 (978-0-03-035458-8(7)); pap. 13.20 (978-0-03-035454-0(4)) Holt, Rinehart & Winston.

—Elements of Literature: Holt Adapted Reader. 2003. 3rd ed. pap. 12.40 (978-0-03-067864-6(1)); 5th ed. (Illus.). pap. 13.20 (978-0-03-035712-1(8)); 5th ed. pap. 13.20 (978-0-03-035711-4(X)); 5th ed. (Illus.). (J). pap. 13.20 (978-0-03-035709-1(8)) Holt, Rinehart & Winston.

—Holt Adapted Reader: Elemental Literature. 3rd ed. 2003. pap. 12.40 (978-0-03-067866-0(8)); pap. 12.40 (978-0-03-067867-7(6)); pap. 12.40 (978-0-03-067862-2(5)); pap. 12.40 (978-0-03-067869-1(2)) Holt, Rinehart & Winston.

Jaffe, Charlotte & Roberts, Barbara. A Day No Pigs Would Die: L-I-T Guide. Date not set. (J). (gr. 4-10). pap. 8.95 (978-1-56644-005-9(X) , 005-XAP) Educational Impressions.

Killing Mr. Griffin. 1998. 40p. (YA). 11.95 (978-1-56137-343-7(5) , NU3435SP) Novel Units, Inc.

Lee, Harper & Hartley, Mary M. To Kill a Mockingbird: Notes. 1999. (Literature Made Easy Ser.). (Illus.). 96p. pap. 6.99 (978-0-7641-0822-8(0)) Barron's Educational Series, Inc.

Read Magazine Editorial Staff. Read for Your Life: Tales of Survival. 1998. (Best of READ Ser.). 160p. (gr. 5 up). lib. bdg. 24.90 (978-0-7613-0362-6(6) , Millbrook Pr.) Lerner Publishing Group.

Remarkable Farkle Newsletter Kit. 2000. (J). per. (978-0-689-01657-8(3) , Simon & Schuster Children's Publishing) Simon & Schuster Children's Publishing.

Scott, James. The Adventures of Huckleberry Finn: Activity Pack. 2002. 167p. (YA). (gr. 7-12). pap., act. bk. ed. 34.95 (978-1-58049-615-5(6) , PA0111) Prestwick Hse., Inc.

—Alice's Adventures in Wonderland: A Student Response Journal. 2002. (YA). (gr. 7-12). wbk. ed. 19.95 (978-1-58049-973-6(2) , RJ49) Prestwick Hse., Inc.

—Animal Farm: A Student Response Journal. 2002. 28p. (YA). (gr. 7-12). wbk. ed. 19.95 (978-1-58049-929-3(5) , RJ55) Prestwick Hse., Inc.

—Black Boy: Reproducible Teaching Unit. 2002. 67p. (YA). (gr. 7-12). ring bd. 29.50 (978-1-58049-401-4(3) , TU185) Prestwick Hse., Inc.

—Cannery Row: Reproducible Teaching Unit. 2002. 55p. (YA). (gr. 7-12). ring bd. 29.50 (978-1-58049-294-2(0) , TU179) Prestwick Hse., Inc.

—The Catcher in the Rye: Activity Pack. 2002. 108p. (YA). (gr. 7-12). pap., act. bk. ed. 34.95 (978-1-58049-614-8(8) , PA0108) Prestwick Hse., Inc.

—A Connecticut Yankee in King Arthur's Court: Reproducible Teaching Unit. 2002. 87p. (YA). (gr. 7-12). ring bd. 29.50 (978-1-58049-406-9(4) , TU189) Prestwick Hse., Inc.

—Dracula: A Student Response Journal. 2002. 36p. (YA). (gr. 7-12). wbk. ed. 19.95 (978-1-58049-925-5(2) , RJ51) Prestwick Hse., Inc.

—The Great Gatsby: Activity Pack. 2002. 145p. (YA). (gr. 7-12). pap., act. bk. ed. 34.95 (978-1-58049-612-4(1) , PA0105) Prestwick Hse., Inc.

—Hard Times: Reproducible Teaching Unit. 2002. 91p. (YA). (gr. 7-12). ring bd. 29.50 (978-1-58049-297-3(5) , TU182) Prestwick Hse., Inc.

—My Antonia: A Student Response Journal. 2002. 24p. (YA). (gr. 7-12). pap., wbk. ed. 19.95 (978-1-58049-974-3(0) , RJ50) Prestwick Hse., Inc.

—The Scarlet Letter: Activity Pack. 2002. 111p. (YA). (gr. 7-12). pap., act. bk. ed. 34.95 (978-1-58049-611-7(3) , PA0112) Prestwick Hse., Inc.

Spiegel, Richard A., et al, eds. Streams, No. 15. 2001. (Illus.). 150p. (YA). (gr. 7-12). pap. 10.00 (978-0-934830-68-3(1)) Ten Penny Players, Inc.

LITERATURE AS A PROFESSION

see Authors; Authorship; Journalism; Journalists

LITHUANIA

Bultje, Jan Willem. Lithuania. Hoving, Wilma, tr. 2006. (Looking at Europe Ser.). 48p. (YA). (gr. 5-8). 22.95 (978-1-881508-43-4(9)) Oliver Pr., Inc.

Docalavich, Heather. Lithuania. 2006. (European Union Ser.). (Illus.). 88p. (YA). (gr. 5 up). lib. bdg. (978-1-4222-0054-4(X)) Mason Crest Pubs.

Kagda, Sakina & Latif, Zawiah Abdul. Lithuania. 2nd ed. 2007. (Cultures of the World Ser.). 144p. (J). lib. bdg. 39.93 (***978-0-7614-2087-3(8)*** , Benchmark Bks.) Cavendish, Marshall Corp.

LITHUANIANS—UNITED STATES—FICTION

Ruby, Lois. Swindletop. 2000. (Illus.). 128p. (J). 15.95 (978-1-57168-393-9(3)) Eakin Pr.

LITTERING

see Refuse and Refuse Disposal

LITTLE, MALCOLM, 1925-1965

see X, Malcolm, 1925-1965

LITTLE, STUART (FICTITIOUS CHARACTER)—FICTION

Downes, Alice. Soccer Season. 2002. (ps-2). lib. bdg. 10.95 (978-0-613-50501-7(8)) Tandem Library Bks.

Driscoll, Laura. Stuart Little Bk. 2: Think Big, Vote Little! Perkins, Thomas, illus. 2003. (Festival Reader Ser.). 32p. (J). (ps-2). pap. 3.99 (978-0-06-000748-5(6) , Harper Festival) HarperCollins Pubs.

HarperCollins Staff, ed. Stuart's New Brother. 2000. (gr. k-3). lib. bdg. 11.80 (978-0-613-31764-1(5)) Tandem Library Bks.

Hill, Susan. The Stuart Little I Can Read Library Box Set: Stuart Hides Out; Stuart at the Library; Stuart at the Fun House. Halverson, Lydia, illus. 2003. (I Can Read Bks.). (J). (gr. k-3). pap. 11.99 (978-0-06-053915-3(1) , Harper Trophy) HarperCollins Pubs.

Rubin, Bruce Joel & Michaels, Julie. Stuart Little 2 Vol. 2: El Libro de la Película. 2003. (SPA., Illus.). 60p. (J). (gr. 3-5). 14.95 (978-84-204-6503-6(8)) Santillana USA Publishing Co., Inc.

Runnells, Treesha, des. Stuart Little 2: A Little Pop-up Adventure! 2002. (Media Favorites!! Ser.). 10p. (J). 9.95 (978-1-58117-179-2(X) , Intervisual/Piggy Toes) Dalmatian Pr.

White, E. B. Le Avventure di Stuart Little.Tr. of Stuart Little. (ITA.). pap. 17.95 (978-88-451-2736-6(2)); 2000. (J). pap. 15.95 (978-88-452-3861-1(X)) Fabbri - RCS Libri ITA. *Dist:* Distribooks, Inc.

—Stuart Little. Date not set. 141p. 18.95 (978-0-8488-2602-4(7)) Amereon LTD.

—Stuart Little. Williams, Garth, illus. 2001. (SPA.). 144p. (gr. 3-5). 22.90 (978-84-204-4669-1(6)) Harcourt Schl. Pubs.

—Stuart Little. Williams, Garth & Wells, Rosemary, illus. 60th anniv. ed. 2001. (Stuart-Little Ser.). 144p. (J). (gr. 5 up). pap. 8.99 (978-0-06-441092-2(7)) HarperCollins Pubs.

—Stuart Little. Williams, Garth, illus. 60th collector's anniv. ed. 1999. (Stuart-Little Ser.). 144p. (J). (gr. 4-7). 24.95 (978-0-06-028297-4(5)) HarperCollins Pubs.

—Stuart Little. Williams, Garth, illus. l.t. ed. 2000. (LRS Large Print Cornerstone Ser.). 175p. (J). (gr. 2-8). lib. bdg. 27.95 (978-1-58118-064-0(0) , 23655) LRS.

—Stuart Little. 131p. (J). pap. 5.95 (978-0-8072-8333-2(9)); 2004. (gr. 3-7). pap. 29.00 incl. audio (978-0-8072-8332-5(0) , YA165SP) Random Hse. Audio Publishing Group. (Listening Library).

—Stuart Little. 2001. (gr. 3-6). lib. bdg. 17.60 (978-0-613-83865-8(3)) Tandem Library Bks.

—Stuart Little: Read-Aloud Edition. Williams, Garth, illus. 1999. (Stuart-Little Ser.). 144p. (J). (gr. 7 up). 19.95 (978-0-06-028334-6(3)) HarperCollins Pubs.

LITTLE BEAR (FICTITIOUS CHARACTER : MINARIK)—FICTION

Little Bear. 2003. (Goodnight Mr. Moon Ser.). (Illus.). (J). bds. 2.98 (978-0-7525-4740-4(2)) Paragon, Inc.

Little Bear. 1999. (I Can Read Bks.). (J). (ps-1). pap. 1.95 (978-0-590-31967-6(1)) Scholastic, Inc.

Minarik, Else Holmelund. The Adventures of Little Bear. 1998. (Illus.). (J). 12.95 (978-0-06-028044-4(1)) HarperCollins Pubs.

—Un Beso para Osito. Sendak, Maurice, illus. 2003. (SPA.). 36p. (J). (gr. k-3). 11.95 (978-84-204-3050-8(1) , AF1633) Alfaguara, Ediciones, S.A.- Grupo Santillana ESP. *Dist:* Lectorum Pubns., Inc., Santillana USA Publishing Co., Inc.

—Un Beso para Osito. Sendak, Maurice, tr. Sendak, Maurice, illus. (SPA.). 34p. (J). (gr. k-3). pap. 8.95 (978-84-204-4827-5(3)) Santillana USA Publishing Co., Inc.

—Little Bear & the Missing Pie. 2002. (gr. k-3). lib. bdg. 11.80 (978-0-613-62523-4(4)) Tandem Library Bks.

—Little Bear's Friends - Los Amigos de Osito. (SPA.). 64p. (J). 7.95 (978-84-204-3049-2(8)) Santillana USA Publishing Co., Inc.

—Little Bear's Visit. Sendak, Maurice, illus. (J). pap. 12.95 incl. audio Weston Woods Studios, Inc.

—Osito. Sendak, Maurice, illus. 2003. (SPA.). 60p. (J). (gr. k-3). pap. 8.95 (978-84-204-3044-7(7) , AF1346) Santillana USA Publishing Co., Inc.

—Papa Oso Vuele a Casa. 2003. (Osito Ser.). (SPA., Illus.). (J). (ps-3). pap. (978-84-204-3048-5(X) , AF1359) Alfaguara, Ediciones, S.A.- Grupo Santillana ESP. *Dist:* Santillana USA Publishing Co., Inc.

—La Visita de Osito. Sendak, Maurice, illus. 2003. (Osito Ser.). (SPA.). 64p. (J). (gr. k-3). pap. 11.95 (978-968-19-0623-8(3) , AF1060) Santillana USA Publishing Co., Inc.

Sendak, Maurice, illus. Father Bear Comes Home. 2002. (Little Bear Ser.). (J). 12.34 (978-0-7587-6089-0(2)) Book Wholesalers, Inc.

—A Kiss for Little Bear. 2002. (Little Bear Ser.). (J). 12.34 (978-0-7587-6175-0(9)) Book Wholesalers, Inc.

—Little Bear's Friend. 2002. (Little Bear Ser.). (J). 12.34 (978-0-7587-6185-9(6)) Book Wholesalers, Inc.

LITTLE BEAR (FICTITIOUS CHARACTER : WADDELL)—FICTION

Waddell, Martin. Can't You Sleep, Little Bear? (CHI & ENG., Illus.). 32p. (J). (978-1-85430-315-8(5) , 93445) Magi Pubns.

—Let's Go Home, Little Bear. ed. 2004. (Illus.). (J). (gr. k-3). spiral bd. (978-0-616-01804-0(5)); spiral bd. (978-0-616-01805-7(3)) Canadian National Institute for the Blind/Institut National Canadien pour les Aveugles.

—You & Me, Little Bear. ed. 2004. (Illus.). (J). (ps-2). spiral bd. (978-0-616-01802-6(9)); spiral bd. (978-0-616-01803-3(7)) Canadian National Institute for the Blind/Institut National Canadien pour les Aveugles.

LITTLE BIGHORN, BATTLE OF THE, MONT., 1876

Abnett, Dan. Sitting Bull & the Battle of the Little Bighorn. 2007. (Jr. Graphic Biographies Ser.). (Illus.). 24p. (J). (978-1-4042-2337-0(1)); pap. (978-1-4042-2147-5(6)); (gr. 2-6). lib. bdg. 21.25 (978-1-4042-3394-2(6)) Rosen Publishing Group, Inc., The. (PowerKids Pr.).

Aller, Susan Bivin. Sitting Bull. 2004. (History Maker Bios Ser.). (J). pap. 6.95 (978-0-8225-2072-6(9)) Lerner Publishing Group.

—Sitting Bull. Parlin, Tim, tr. Parlin, Tim, illus. 2004. (History Maker Bios Ser.). 47p. (J). 26.60 (978-0-8225-0700-0(5) , Carolrhoda Bks.) Lerner Publishing Group.

Beck, John D. W. That Day at Greasy Grass: The Battle at Little Big Horn. 2001. (Illus.). 60p. (J). 18.95 (978-0-9714805-0-6(8)) Beck, John D.

Bednarz, Robert, et al. TIME for Kids Readers: What Happened at Little Bighorn? 3rd ed. 2002. (Harcourt Horizons Ser.). (gr. k-7). pap. 38.10 (978-0-15-335281-2(7)) Harcourt Schl. Pubs.

Cooper, Jason. Little Bighorn Battlefield. 2000. (Historic Landmarks Ser.). (Illus.). 24p. (J). (gr. 1-4). lib. bdg. 20.64 (978-1-55916-325-5(9)) Rourke Publishing, LLC.

Dolan, Edward F., Jr. The Battle of the Little Bighorn. 2002. (Kaleidoscope - American History Ser.). (Illus.). 48p. (J). 25.64 (978-0-7614-1457-5(6) , Benchmark Bks.) Cavendish, Marshall Corp.

Evento, Susan. Sitting Bull. 2005. (Rookie Biographies Ser.). (Illus.). 32p. (J). (gr. 1-2). pap. 4.95 (978-0-516-25829-4(X) , Children's Pr.) Scholastic Library Publishing.

Evento, Susan & Vargus, Nanci Reginelli. Sitting Bull. 2004. (Rookie Biographies Ser.). (J). 20.50 (978-0-516-21719-2(4) , Children's Pr.) Scholastic Library Publishing.

Fradin, Dennis B. Custer's Last Stand. 2006. (Turning Points in U. S. History Ser.). (Illus.). 48p. (J). lib. bdg. 29.93 (978-0-7614-2124-5(6) , Benchmark Bks.) Cavendish, Marshall Corp.

Green, Carl R. Custer's Stunning Defeat by American Indians at the Little Bighorn. 2006. (Wild History of the American West Ser.). (Illus.). 128p. (J). lib. bdg. 33.27 (978-1-59845-020-0(4) , MyReportLinks.com Bks.) Enslow Pubs., Inc.

January, Brendan. Little Bighorn: June 25, 1876. 2004. (American Battlefields Ser.). (Illus.). 32p. (J). 14.95 (978-1-59270-028-8(4)) Enchanted Lion Bks., LLC.

Jeffrey, Gary & Petty, Kate. Sitting Bull: The Life of a Lakota Sioux Chief. 2005. (Graphic Nonfiction Ser.). (Illus.). 48p. (J). (gr. 4-6). lib. bdg. 26.50 (978-1-4042-0247-4(1)) Rosen Publishing Group, Inc., The.

Knowlton, MaryLee & Uschan, Michael V. The Battle of the Little Bighorn. 2002. (Events That Shaped America Ser.). (Illus.). 32p. (J). (gr. 3 up). lib. bdg. 24.67 (978-0-8368-3222-8(1)) Stevens, Gareth Inc.

Maruca, Mary. A Kid's Guide to Exploring Little Bighorn Battlefield National Monument. 2001. 12p. (J). pap. 4.95 (978-1-58369-011-6(5)) Western National Parks Assn.

Nobleman, Marc Tyler. The Battle of the Little Bighorn. 2001. (We the People Ser.). (Illus.). 48p. (J). (gr. 4 up). lib. bdg. 22.60 (978-0-7565-0150-1(4)) Compass Point Bks.

Rau, Dana Meachen. George Armstrong Custer. 2003. (Compass Point Early Biographies Ser.). (Illus.). 32p. (J). (gr. 2 up). lib. bdg. 21.26 (978-0-7565-0419-9(8)) Compass Point Bks.

Snelson, Bob. Riding into Glory: An Introduction to the Battle of the Little Bighorn. 2004. (Illus.). 170p. (YA). per. 12.00 (978-0-9723935-4-6(4)) Snelsonbks.com.

Stanley, George Edward. Crazy Horse: Young War Chief. Henderson, Meryl, illus. 2005. 199p. (J). (978-1-4156-2931-4(5) , Aladdin) Simon & Schuster Children's Publishing.

Streissguth, Thomas. Custer's Last Stand. 2002. (Illus.). 142p. (YA). (gr. 8-12). lib. bdg. 28.90 (978-0-613-57353-5(6)) Tandem Library Bks.

—Custer's Last Stand. 2002. (At Issue in History Ser.). (Illus.). 128p. (YA). (gr. 7-10). pap. 23.70 (978-0-7377-1359-6(3)); lib. bdg. 33.70 (978-0-7377-1358-9(5)) Thomson Gale. (Greenhaven Pr., Inc.).

Theunissen, Steve. The Battle of the Little Bighorn. 2002. (History of the Old West Ser.). (Illus.). 64p. (J). (gr. 5 up). lib. bdg. (978-1-59084-065-8(8)) Mason Crest Pubs.

Uschan, Michael V. The Battle of Little Bighorn. 2002. (Landmark Events in American History Ser.). (Illus.). 48p. (J). (gr. 5 up). lib. bdg. 30.00 (978-0-8368-5338-4(5)); pap. 14.60 (978-0-8368-5352-0(0)) Stevens, Gareth Inc. (World Almanac Library).

Walker, Paul Robert. Remember Little Bighorn: Indians, Soldiers, & Scouts Tell Their Stories. 2006. (Illus.). 64p. (J). (gr. 4-8). 17.95 (978-0-7922-5521-5(6)); lib. bdg. 27.90 (978-0-7922-5522-2(4)) National Geographic Society. (National Geographic Children's Bks.).

LITTLE BIGHORN, BATTLE OF THE, MONT., 1876—FICTION

Kretzer-Malvehy, Terry. Passage to Little Bighorn. 1999. (978-0-606-18313-0(2)) Tandem Library Bks.

Sargent, Dave & Sargent, Pat. Comanche: (Red Bay) Perseverance, 25, 19. Lenoir, Jane, illus. 2001. (Saddle Up Ser.: 19). 36p. (J). pap. 6.95 (978-1-56763-648-2(9)); lib. bdg. 22.60 (978-1-56763-647-5(0)) Ozark Publishing.

LITTLE LEAGUE BASEBALL

Gola, Mark & Gallagher, Dave. The Little League Hitter's Journal. 2005. (Little League Baseball Guide Ser.). (Illus.). 160p. pap. 12.95 (978-0-07-144726-3(1) , 9780071447263) McGraw-Hill Cos., The.

Monteleone, John J. & Gola, Mark. Little League Baseball Guide to Correcting the 25 Most Common Mistakes: Recognizing & Repairing the Mistakes Young Playaers Make. 2003. (Little League Baseball Guides Ser.). (Illus.). 144p. pap. 14.95 (978-0-07-140887-5(8) , 9780071408875) McGraw-Hill Cos., The.

LITTLE LEAGUE BASEBALL—FICTION

Day, Karen. No Cream Puffs. 2008. 160p. (J). (gr. 5). 15.99 ***(978-0-375-83775-3(2));*** lib. bdg. 18.99 ***(978-0-375-93775-0(7))*** Random Hse. Children's Bks. (Lamb, Wendy).

Lupica, Mike. Heat. 2007. 240p. (J). pap. 6.99 (978-0-14-240757-8(7) , Puffin); 2006. 220p. (YA). (gr. 5). 16.99 (978-0-399-24301-1(1) , Philomel) Penguin Group (USA) Inc.

Preller, James. Six Innings: A Game in the Life. 2008. 160p. (J). 16.95 ***(978-0-312-36763-3(5))*** Feiwel & Friends.

Weatherford, Carole Boston. Champions on the Bench: The Cannon Street YMCA All-Stars. Jenkins, Leonard, illus. 2007. 32p. (J). (gr. 1-4). 16.99 (978-0-8037-2987-2(1) , Dial) Penguin Group (USA) Inc.

LITTLE WHISTLE (FICTITIOUS CHARACTER)—FICTION

Rylant, Cynthia. Little Whistle's Christmas. Bowers, Tim, illus. 2003. (Little Whistle Ser.). 32p. (J). 16.00 (978-0-15-204590-6(2)) Harcourt Children's Bks.

—Little Whistle's Dinner Party. Bowers, Tim, illus. 2004. 32p. (J). pap. 6.00 (978-0-15-205062-7(0) , Voyager Bks./Libros Viajeros) Harcourt Children's Bks.

—Little Whistle's Medicine. Bowers, Tim, illus. 2002. (Little Whistle Ser.). 32p. (J). (ps-2). 15.00 (978-0-15-201086-7(6)) Harcourt Children's Bks.

LIVERPOOL (ENGLAND)—FICTION

Gray, Keith. The Runner. 2005. (Illus.). 96p. (J). (gr. 2-4). pap. 7.99 (978-0-440-86656-5(1) , Corgi) Transworld Publishers Ltd. GBR. *Dist:* Trafalgar Square Publishing.

Heneghan, James. The Grave. 2000. (Illus.). (J). (gr. 7-10). pap. 7.95 (978-0-88899-414-1(1)) Groundwood Bks. CAN. *Dist:* Transition Vendor.

LIVESTOCK

see also Cattle; Cows; Dairying; Domestic Animals; Donkeys; Feeding and Feeds; Horses; Sheep; Veterinary Medicine

Barker, C. Penny. The Farm. 2004. 56p. spiral bd. 25.00 (978-1-4116-2501-3(3)) Lulu.com.

Farm Animals. 2002. (Tab Board Books Ser.). 12p. (J). bds. 4.95 (978-0-7894-8476-5(5)) Dorling Kindersley Publishing, Inc.

James, Diane. En la Granja. 2004. (Descubre los Animales Ser.).Tr. of On the Farm. (SPA., Illus.). 24p. (J). (ps-2). 9.95 (978-1-58728-489-2(8) , Two Can Publishing) T&N Children's Publishing.

Kallen, Stuart A. Is Factory Farming Harming America? 2006. (Illus.). 128p. (gr. 10-12). 21.20 (978-0-7377-3438-6(8)); pap. 29.95 (978-0-7377-3437-9(X)) Thomson Gale. (Greenhaven Pr., Inc.).

King-Smith, Dick. Chewing the Cud: An Extraordinary Life Remembered by the Author of Babe: the Gallant Pig. Horse, Harry, illus. 2002. 208p. (J). (gr. 5 up). 16.95 (978-0-375-81459-4(0) , Knopf Bks. for Young Readers) Random Hse. Children's Bks.

Knight, K. R. Farm Friends: Cuddly Pups Board Book. rev. ed. 2003. (Cuddly Pups Board Bks.). (Illus.). 20p. (J). bds. 4.99 (978-1-4037-0187-9(3)) Dalmatian Pr.

Peterson, Cris. Amazing Grazing. Upitis, Alvis, photos by. 2003. (Illus.). 32p. (J). (gr. k-2). 16.95 (978-1-56397-942-2(X)) Boyds Mills Pr.

Poole, Susie. God Hears the Farm Animals. 2004. (Illus.). 18p. (J). 6.99 (978-0-310-70864-3(8)) Zonderkidz.

Radtke, Becky. Invisible Farm Animals Magic Picture Book. 2000. (Illus.). 16p. (J). (ps-2). pap. 1.50 (978-0-486-41289-4(X)) Dover Pubns., Inc.

Scott, Janine. Farm Friends. 2002. (Spyglass Books). (Illus.). 24p. (J). (gr. 1 up). lib. bdg. 18.60 (978-0-7565-0232-4(2)) Compass Point Bks.

Stanos, Dimi. Taking Care of Farm Animals. 2002. (Windows on Literacy Ser.). (Illus.). 12p. (J). (978-0-7922-8482-6(8)) National Geographic Society.

Stone, Lynn M. Farm Animals. 2001. (Life on the Farm Ser.). (Illus.). 24p. (J). (gr. 1-4). lib. bdg. 20.64 (978-1-58952-090-5(4)) Rourke Publishing, LLC.

Thomas, Heather Smith. Your Calf: A Kid's Guide to Raising & Showing Beef & Dairy Calves. 2003. (Illus.). 186p. (J). (gr. 4-7). pap. 14.95 (978-0-88266-947-2(8) , 66947) Storey Publishing, LLC.

Watt, Fiona & Wells, Rachel. Anifeiliaid y Fferm. 2005. (WEL., Illus.). 8p. (978-1-84512-000-9(0)) Cymdeithas Lyfrau Ceredigion.

LIVING FOSSILS

see also names of specific fossils, e.g Platypus

Walker, Sally M. Fossil Fish Found Alive: Discovering the Coelacanth. 2005. (Photo Bks.). (Illus.). 64p. (gr. 5-12). 17.95 (978-1-57505-536-7(8)) Lerner Publishing Group.

LIVINGSTONE, DAVID, 1813-1873

Alex, Ben. David Livingstone. Rava, Giuseppe, illus. 1998. (Heroes of Faith & Courage Ser.). 50p. (gr. 3-12). reprint ed. pap. 7.99 (978-1-884543-21-0(9)) Authentic Media.

Freedman, Frances. David Livingstone. (Great Explorers Ser.). (Illus.). 48p. (J). (gr. 5 up). 2002. pap. 14.60 (978-0-8368-5175-5(7)); 2001. lib. bdg. 30.00 (978-0-8368-5015-4(7)) Stevens, Gareth Inc. (World Almanac Library).

Horne, C. Silvester. David Livingstone: Man of Prayer & Action. 1999. (Illus.). 152p. (YA). (gr. 9 up). pap. 6.00 (978-1-930092-11-2(3) , CLP29590) Christian Liberty Pr.

Mattews, Basil. Livingstone: The Pathfinder. 2003. 112p. (YA). pap. 8.95 (978-0-923309-86-2(1)) Hartland Pubns.

Otfinoski, Steven. David Livingstone: Deep in the Heart of Africa. 2006. (Great Explorations Ser.). (Illus.). 80p. (YA). (gr. 5-9). lib. bdg. 32.79 (978-0-7614-2226-6(9) , Benchmark Bks.) Cavendish, Marshall Corp.

Wellman, Sam. David Livingstone: Missionary & Explorer. 1999. (Heroes of the Faith Ser.). (Illus.). 208p. (YA). (gr. 4-7). 14.95 (978-0-7910-5038-5(6) , Chelsea Hse.) Facts On File, Inc.

Worth, Richard. Stanley & Livingstone & the Exploration of Africa in World History. 2000. (In World History Ser.). (Illus.). 128p. (YA). (gr. 5-12). lib. bdg. 26.60 (978-0-7660-1400-8(2)) Enslow Pubs., Inc.

LIZARDS

Allman, Toney. From Gecko Feet to Sticky Tape. 2006. (Imitating Nature Ser.). (Illus.). 32p. (J). (gr. 3-6). 24.95 (978-0-7377-3487-4(6) , Greenhaven Pr., Inc.) Thomson Gale.

Animals & the Environment: Incl. Lizards (4 bks.), Sharks (4 bks.), Snakes (12 bks.), 20 bks. (Illus.). (J). (gr. 3-4). lib. bdg. (978-1-56065-810-8(X) , Capstone High-Interest Bks.) Capstone Pr., Inc.

Arnosky, Jim. All about Lizards. 2004. (All About Ser.). 32p. (J). (ps-3). pap. 5.99 (978-0-590-48146-5(0) , Scholastic Paperbacks) Scholastic, Inc.

—All about Lizards: Y Jim Arnosky. 2004. (J). 15.95 (978-0-590-48145-8(2)) Scholastic, Inc.

Barron's Educational Editorial Staff. Keeping Lizards. 2000. (Unusual Pets Ser.). (Illus.). 64p. (J). (gr. 3-7). pap. 5.95 (978-0-7641-1281-2(3)) Barron's Educational Series, Inc.

Bredeson, Carmen. Fun Facts about Lizards! 2007. (I Like Reptiles & Amphibians! Ser.). (Illus.). 24p. (J). (gr. 1-3). lib. bdg. 21.26 (978-0-7660-2789-3(9) , Enslow Elementary) Enslow Pubs., Inc.

Burns, Diane L. Snakes, Salamanders & Lizards. Garrow, Linda, illus. 1998. 47p. (J). (gr. 2-5). lib. bdg. 16.40 (978-0-613-26969-8(1)) Tandem Library Bks.

Catala, Ellen. Snakes & Lizards. 2003. (J). 15.93 (978-0-7368-2940-3(7)); pap. (978-0-7368-2899-4(0)) Yellow Umbrella Pr.

Cheshire, Gerard. Lizards. (Scary Creatures Ser.). 32p. (J). 2008. pap. 8.95 ***(978-0-531-21007-9(3)*** , Watts, Franklin); 2007. spiral bd. 26.00 ***(978-0-531-20448-1(0)*** , Children's Pr.) Scholastic Library Publishing.

Clarke, Ginjer L. Giant Lizards: All Aboard Science Reader Station Stop 2. Rothman, Michael, illus. 2005. (All Aboard Science Reader Ser.). 48p. (J). (gr. 1-3). 13.99 (978-0-448-43828-3(3)); pap. 3.99 (978-0-448-43120-8(3)) Penguin Group (USA) Inc. (Grosset & Dunlap).

Claybourne, Anna. Lizards. 2003. (Secret World Of... Ser.). (Illus.). 48p. (J). lib. bdg. 27.14 (978-0-7398-7023-5(8)) Raintree.

Cummings, Pat, illus. & retold by. Ananse & the Lizard: A West African Tale. Cummings, Pat, retold by. rev. ed. 2002. 40p. (J). (ps-3). 16.95 (978-0-8050-6476-6(1) , Holt, Henry & Co. Bks. For Young Readers) Holt, Henry & Co.

Dahl, Michael. Monster Fish: The Adventure of the Ichthyosaurs. Yesh, Jeff, illus. 2004. (Dinosaur World Ser.). 24p. (C). (gr. k-3). 22.60 (978-1-4048-0941-3(4)) Picture Window Bks.

Dennard, Deborah. Lizards. Dewey, Jennifer Owings, illus. 2004. (Our Wild World Ser.). 48p. (J). (gr. 2-5). ring bd. 10.95 (978-1-55971-858-5(7)); pap. 7.95 (978-1-55971-857-8(9)) T&N Children's Publishing. (NorthWord Bks. for Young Readers).

Donovan. Iguanas. 2002. pap. (978-0-7398-5811-0(4)) Steck-Vaughn.

Eckart, Edana. Komodo Dragon. 2003. (Animals of the World Ser.). (Illus.). 24p. (J). 18.00 (978-0-516-24295-8(4)); pap. 4.95 (978-0-516-27893-3(2)) Scholastic Library Publishing. (Children's Pr.).

Engfer, Leeanne. My Pet Lizards. King, Andy, photos by. 1999. (All about Pets Ser.). (Illus.). 64p. (gr. 2-6). lib. bdg. 22.60 (978-0-8225-2263-8(2)) Lerner Publishing Group.

Everything Changes: Individual Title Six-Packs. (Discovery World Ser.). 16p. (gr. 1-2). 28.00 (978-0-7635-8461-0(4)) Rigby Education.

Flynn, James. From Egg to Lizard. 2003. (Grow up! Ser.). (J). (978-1-58417-173-7(1)); pap. (978-1-58417-179-9(0)) Lake Street Pubs.

Glaser, Jason. Gila Monsters. 2006. (World of Reptiles Ser.). (Illus.). 24p. (J). (978-0-7368-5424-5(X)) Capstone Pr., Inc.

—Horned Lizards. 2006. (World of Reptiles Ser.). (Illus.). 24p. (J). (978-0-7368-5421-4(5)) Capstone Pr., Inc.

—Komodo Dragons. 2006. (Illus.). 24p. (J). (978-0-7368-5422-1(3)) Capstone Pr., Inc.

Grolier Educational Staff, contrib. by. Iguanas. 2001. (Nature's Children Ser.). (Illus.). 48p. (J). (978-0-7172-5538-2(7) , Grolier) Scholastic Library Publishing.

Halfmann, Janet. Lizards. 2004. 26.20 (978-0-7377-1887-4(0) , Kidhaven) Thomson Gale.

Hanson, Anders. Lively Lizards. Nobens, C. A., illus. 2007. (Perfect Pets Ser.). 24p. (J). (gr. k-3). lib. bdg. 19.93 ***(978-1-59928-752-2(8)*** , SandCastle) ABDO Publishing Co.

Heathcote, Peter. Lizards. 2004. (Keeping Unusual Pets Ser.). (Illus.). 48p. (J). (978-1-4034-0827-3(0)) Heinemann Library.

Jacobs, Liza. Lizards. 2003. (Wild Wild World Ser.). (Illus.). 24p. (J). 22.45 (978-1-4103-0052-2(8) , Blackbirch Pr., Inc.) Thomson Gale.

Kalman, Bobbie. Endangered Komodo Dragons. 2004. (Earth's Endangered Animals Ser.). (Illus.). 32p. (J). (978-0-7787-1857-4(3)); pap. (978-0-7787-1903-8(0)) Crabtree Publishing Co.

Landau, Elaine. Your Pet Iguana. 2006. (True Book Ser.). (Illus.). 47p. (J). (978-0-531-16790-8(9)) Children's Pr., Ltd.

Lizards. (Eyes on Nature Ser.). 32p. (J). (gr. 1). pap. (978-1-882210-60-2(3)) Action Publishing, Inc.

Lizards: Individual Title Six-Packs. (Sails Literacy Ser.). (gr. 1-2). 36.00 (978-0-7578-6737-8(5)) Rigby Education.

Lizards: Level N, 6 vols. (Wonder Worldtm Ser.). 48p. 34.95 (978-0-7802-4583-9(0)) Wright Group, The.

Lizards Know It Alls. 2001. (Illus.). 24p. (J). (ps). pap. 2.79 (978-0-7681-0233-8(2) , 57090) Learning Horizons, Inc.

Lockwood, Sophie. Gila Monsters. 2006. (World of Reptiles Ser.). (Illus.). 40p. (J). (gr. 2-6). 29.93 (978-1-59296-547-2(4)) Child's World, Inc.

—Iguanas. 2006. (World of Reptiles Ser.). (Illus.). 40p. (J). (gr. 2-6). 29.93 (978-1-59296-548-9(2)) Child's World, Inc.

Looking at Lizards. 2005. (Book Treks Ser.). (J). (gr. 3 up). stu. ed. 34.95 (978-0-673-62835-0(3)) Celebration Pr.

Louise, Sara. Giant Lizards. 2001. (Animal Adventures Ser.). (Illus.). (J). 54p. pap. (978-0-7891-5304-3(1)); 56p. (gr. 1-4). lib. bdg. 16.95 (978-0-7807-9660-7(8)) Perfection Learning Corp.

Macken, JoAnn Early. Gila Monsters. 2005. (Illus.). 24p. (J). pap. (978-0-8368-4834-2(9)); lib. bdg. 19.33 (978-0-8368-4827-4(6)) Stevens, Gareth Inc.

Marsico, Katie. A Komodo Dragon Hatchling Grows Up. 2007. (Scholastic News Nonfiction Readers Ser.). (Illus.). 24p. (J). (gr. 1-2). 19.00 (978-0-531-17477-7(8) , Children's Pr.) Scholastic Library Publishing.

Mattern, Joanne. Lizards. 2001. (Animals Animals Ser.). (Illus.). 48p. (J). (gr. 3-5). lib. bdg. 25.64 (978-0-7614-1259-5(X)) Cavendish, Marshall Corp.

McNab, Chris & Lewis, Brenda Ralph. Lizards. 2006. (Nature's Monsters Ser.). (Illus.). 32p. (J). 23.33 (978-0-8368-6173-0(6)) Stevens, Gareth Inc.

Miller, Jake. The Bearded Dragon. 2003. (Lizard Library). (Illus.). 24p. (J). lib. bdg. 18.75 (978-0-8239-6412-3(4) , PowerKids Pr.) Rosen Publishing Group, Inc., The.

—The Gila Monster. 2003. (Lizard Library). (Illus.). 24p. (J). lib. bdg. 18.75 (978-0-8239-6414-7(0) , PowerKids Pr.) Rosen Publishing Group, Inc., The.

—The Green Iguana. 2003. (Lizard Library). (Illus.). 24p. (J). lib. bdg. 18.75 (978-0-8239-6415-4(9) , PowerKids Pr.) Rosen Publishing Group, Inc., The.

—The Komodo Dragon. 2003. (Lizard Library). (Illus.). 24p. (J). lib. bdg. 18.75 (978-0-8239-6416-1(7) , PowerKids Pr.) Rosen Publishing Group, Inc., The.

—The Leopard Gecko. 2003. (Lizard Library). (Illus.). 24p. (J). lib. bdg. 18.75 (978-0-8239-6413-0(2) , PowerKids Pr.) Rosen Publishing Group, Inc., The.

Miller, Janet K., illus. Efrain of the Sonoran Desert: A Lizard's Life among the Seri Indians. 2001. 32p. (J). (gr. 3-5). 15.95 (978-0-938317-55-5(5)) Cinco Puntos Pr.

Miller, Sara Swan. Snakes & Lizards: What They Have in Common. 2000. (Animals in Order Ser.). (Illus.). 48p. (J). (gr. 4-6). 26.50 (978-0-531-11594-7(1) , Watts, Franklin) Scholastic Library Publishing.

—Snakes & Lizards: What They Have in Common. 2000. (gr. 3-6). lib. bdg. 15.25 (978-0-613-37542-9(4)) Tandem Library Bks.

Moreton, Daniel & Chanko, Pamela. Snakes & Lizards. annual 1998. (Science Emergent Readers Ser.). (J). 3.25 (978-0-590-63900-2(5)) Scholastic, Inc.

—Snakes & Lizards: Serpientes y Lagartos. 2002. (Science Emergent Readers Ser.). (ENG & SPA., Illus.). (J). pap. (978-0-439-41163-9(7)) Scholastic, Inc.

Murray, Julie. Iguanas. 2002. (Animal Kingdom Ser.). (Illus.). 24p. (J). (gr. k-4). lib. bdg. 21.35 (978-1-57765-727-9(6)) ABDO Publishing Co.

—Lizards. 2005. (Animal Kingdom Set Ii Ser.). (Illus.). 24p. (J). (gr. k-4). lib. bdg. 21.35 (978-1-59197-325-6(2)) ABDO Publishing Co.

Myers, Jack. On the Trail of the Komodo Dragon: And Other Explorations of Science in Action. Rice, John, illus. 2004. 64p. (YA). (gr. 4-6). pap. 9.95 (978-1-59078-279-8(8)) Boyds Mills Pr.

O'Donnell, Kerri. Komodo Dragons. 2006. (Illus.). 24p. (J). lib. bdg. (978-1-4042-3530-4(2)) Rosen Publishing Group, Inc., The.

O'Shea, Mark & Arnold, Nicholas. Lizards. 2003. (Nature Watch Ser.). (Illus.). 64p. (gr. 3-7). 14.99 (978-0-7548-1218-0(9)) Anness Publishing GBR. *Dist:* National Bk. Network.

Ring, Susan. Serpientes y Lagartos. 2005. Tr. of Snakes & Lizards. (SPA., Illus.). 16p. (J). (gr. 1 up). lib. bdg. 15.93 (978-0-7368-4166-5(0)) Capstone Pr., Inc.

Robinson, Fay. Amazing Lizards! 1999. (Hello Reader! Ser.). (J). 10.79 (978-0-606-16936-3(9)) Tandem Library Bks.

Schaefer, Lola M. Lizards. 2004. (J). pap. (978-1-4034-5735-6(2)); lib. bdg. (978-1-4034-5047-0(1)) Heinemann Library.

Schafer, Susan. Lizards. 2000. (Perfect Pets Ser.). (Illus.). 32p. (J). (gr. 3-5). lib. bdg. 25.64 (978-0-7614-1103-1(8) , Benchmark Bks.) Cavendish, Marshall Corp.

Sovak, Jan. Lizards Coloring Book. 2006. 32p. (J). pap. 3.95 (978-0-486-44820-6(7)) Dover Pubns., Inc.

—Lizards Stained Glass Coloring Book. 2006. 16p. (J). pap. 5.95 (978-0-486-44817-6(7)) Dover Pubns., Inc.

Stevenson, Katherine. Iguanas. 2007. (New Naturebooks Ser.). 32p. (J). (gr. 1-5). 27.07 ***(978-1-59296-848-0(1))*** Child's World, Inc.

Stewart, Melissa. How Do Chameleons Change Color? 2008. (J). ***(978-0-7614-2922-7(0))*** Cavendish, Marshall Bks., Ltd.

Storad, Conrad J. Gila Monsters. 2008. (Early Bird Nature Books Ser.). (J). lib. bdg. 26.60 ***(978-0-8225-7888-8(3)*** , Lerner Pubns.) Lerner Publishing Group.

Taylor, Barbara. Dinosaur Legacy. 2005. (Illus.). 128p. pap. 17.99 (978-1-84476-081-7(2) , Southwater) Anness Publishing GBR. *Dist:* National Bk. Network.

Townsend, Emily Rose. Lizards. Saunders-Smith, Gail, ed. 2003. (Desert Animals Ser.). (Illus.). 24p. (J). (gr. k-1). lib. bdg. 15.93 (978-0-7368-2077-6(9) , Pebble Bks.) Capstone Pr., Inc.

Trueit, Trudi Strain. Lizards. 2003. (True Bks.). (gr. 3-5). pap. 6.95 (978-0-516-29351-6(6)); (Illus.). 48p. (J). 25.00 (978-0-516-22651-4(7)) Scholastic Library Publishing. (Children's Pr.).

—Lizards. 2003. (gr. 3-6). lib. bdg. 15.25 (978-0-613-68446-0(X)) Tandem Library Bks.

Velthaus, Sally. Geckos. 2005. (Bridgestone Books World of Reptiles). (Illus.). 24p. (J). (ps-7). lib. bdg. 21.26 (978-0-7368-4328-7(0)) Capstone Pr., Inc.

—Green Iguanas. 2006. (Bridgestone Books World of Reptiles). (Illus.). 24p. (J). (ps-7). lib. bdg. 21.26 (978-0-7368-4329-4(9)) Capstone Pr., Inc.

Waters, Jo. The Wild Side of Pet Lizards. 2004. (Raintree Perspectives Ser.). (Illus.). 32p. (J). 26.36 (978-1-4109-1022-6(9)); pap. 7.50 (978-1-4109-1162-9(4)) Harcourt Schl. Pubs.

Welsbacher, Anne. Komodo Dragons. 2002. (Predators in the Wild Ser.). (Illus.). 32p. (J). (gr. 3-4). lib. bdg. 21.26 (978-0-7368-1066-1(8) , Capstone High-Interest Bks.) Capstone Pr., Inc.

World Book, Inc. Staff, contrib. by. Iguanas & Other Lizards. 2005. (World Book's Animals of the World Ser.). (Illus.). 64p. (J). (978-0-7166-1268-1(2)) World Bk., Inc.

LIZARDS—FICTION

Ada, Alma Flor. The Lizard & the Sun. Davalos, Felipe, illus. 1999. 48p. (gr. k-3). pap. 6.99 (978-0-440-41531-2(4) , Dragonfly Bks.) Random Hse. Children's Bks.

Becker, Bonny. Holbrook, a Lizard's Tale. Carter, Abby, illus. 2006. 128p. (J). (gr. 3-5). 15.00 (978-0-618-71458-2(8) , Clarion Bks.) Houghton Mifflin Co. Trade & Reference Div.

Benevelli, Alberto. The Colors of the Chameleon. Serofilli, Loretta, illus. 2002. 32p. (J). (gr. k up). lib. bdg. 24.67 (978-0-8368-3042-2(3)) Stevens, Gareth Inc.

Bennett, Steven. The Adventures of Super Dad: Colossal Encounters (Book #1) 2005. 98p. pap. 10.49 (978-1-4116-5947-6(3)) Lulu.com.

Bentley, Dawn. Icky Sticky Chameleon. Mack, Jeff, illus. 2005. 18p. (J). 9.95 (978-1-58117-086-3(6) , Intervisual/Piggy Toes) Dalmatian Pr.

Berry, Virginia B. Iggie's Big Adventure Coloring Book: A True Story of Faith. Berry, Virginia B., ed. King, Garry W., illus. ed. 2002. 16p. (J). (gr. k-6). pap. 1.00 (978-0-9726091-1-1(3)) Berry Enterprises.

Bowler, Ann Martin & Sukanada, I. Gusti Made. Gecko's Complaint: A Balinese Folktale. 2003. (Illus.). 32p. 12.95 (978-0-7946-0165-2(0)) Tuttle Publishing.

Bush, Don. Magic Smith the Chameleon. 62p. (J). (gr. 3). 6.50 (978-0-943978-02-4(5)) Rolling Hills Pr.

Carle, Eric. The Mixed-up Chameleon. Carle, Eric, illus. 1998. (Illus.). 32p. (J). (ps up). 7.99 (978-0-694-01147-6(9) , Harper Festival) HarperCollins Pubs.

Carter, Aubrey Smith. The Enchanted Lizard: La Lagartijita Magica. Nelson, Esther Whitt, ed. Branton, Molly, illus. 2006. (ENG & SPA.). 96p. (J). 18.95 (978-1-893271-38-8(2)) Maverick Publishing Co.

La cola de Lagartija: Individual Title Six-Packs. (Coleccion Pm Ser.).Tr. of Lizard lost his tail. (SPA.). 16p. (gr. 1 up). 26.00 (978-0-7578-2969-7(4)) Rigby Education.

Cook, Sherry & Johnson, Terri. Inquisitive Inman, 26 vols. Kuhn, Jesse, illus. l.t. ed. 2006. (Quirkles—Exploring Phonics through Science Ser.: 9). 32p. (J). 7.99 (978-1-933815-08-4(6) , Quirkles, The) Creative 3, LLC.

Cummings, Pat. Harvey Moon Museum Boy. Cummings, Pat, illus. 2008. (Illus.). 32p. (J). 16.99 (978-0-688-17889-5(8)) HarperCollins Pubs.

—Harvey Moon Museum Boy. 2008. (Illus.). 32p. (J). lib. bdg. 17.89 (978-0-06-057861-9(0)) HarperCollins Pubs.

Cyr, Lynne G. Drako's ABC Adventures as an Iguana. ed. 2006. (Illus.). 37p. (J). spiral bd. 21.95 (978-0-9774543-0-3(4)) Cyr Design Publishing.

Dadey, Debbie. Swamp Monster in Third Grade 2: Lizards in the Lunch Line. 2004. (Little Apple Ser.). (Illus.). 96p. (J). (gr. 2-5). pap. 3.99 (978-0-439-63161-7(0) , Scholastic Paperbacks) Scholastic, Inc.

DeSica, Melissa. Gecko & Mosquito. Desica, Melissa, illus. 2007. (J). 14.95 (***978-0-9790647-6-0(7)*** Watermark Publishing, LLC.

Las Dos Iguanas.Tr. of Two Iguanas. (SPA.). (J). 9.95 (978-968-6044-78-2(7)) Corunda, Ediciones, S.A. de C.V. MEX. *Dist:* AIMS International Bks., Inc.

Eagle, Golden. Father Sun & Luis the Lizard. l.t. ed. 2005. (Illus.). 22p. (J). per. 9.99 (978-1-59879-026-9(9)) Lifevest Publishing, Inc.

Egner, Susan. Woodfin's Colors: The Prequel. Dewey, A. J., illus. 2002. 32p. (J). lib. bdg. 16.95 (978-0-9711711-2-1(2)) Egner, Inc.

Fienberg, Anna. Minton Goes Driving. Gamble, Kim, illus. 2001. (Minton Ser.). 32p. (J). (ps-1). pap. 6.95 (978-1-86448-594-3(9)) Allen & Unwin AUS. *Dist:* Independent Pubs. Group.

—Minton Goes Flying. Gamble, Kim, illus. 2001. (Minton Ser.). 32p. (J). (ps-1). mass mkt. 6.95 (978-1-86448-593-6(0)) Allen & Unwin AUS. *Dist:* Independent Pubs. Group.

—Minton Goes Sailing. Gamble, Kim, illus. 2001. (Minton Ser.). 32p. (J). (ps-1). pap. 6.95 (978-1-86448-592-9(2)) Allen & Unwin AUS. *Dist:* Independent Pubs. Group.

—Minton Goes Trucking. Gamble, Kim, illus. 2001. (Minton Ser.). 32p. (J). (ps-1). pap. 6.95 (978-1-86448-595-0(7)) Allen & Unwin AUS. *Dist:* Independent Pubs. Group.

Fontenot, Mary Alice & Landry, Julie Fontenot. Clovis Crawfish & the Twin Sister. 2007. 32p. (J). 15.95 (***978-1-58980-467-8(8)***) Pelican Publishing Co., Inc.

Frederick, Mary. Peeka, Pooka, & the Dinosaur. Williams, Allen, illus. 2000. 108p. (ps-3). pap. 9.95 (978-0-595-12812-9(2)) iUniverse, Inc.

Gecko Gathering. 2005. (Soundprints' Amazing Animal Adventures! Ser.). (Illus.). 36p. (J). (ps-2). 8.95 incl. reel tape (978-1-59249-322-7(X) , SC7107) Soundprints.

Giancamilli, Vanessa. Gecko Gathering. 2005. (Soundprints' Amazing Animal Adventures! Ser.). (Illus.). 32p. (J). (ps-2). 19.95 incl. audio (978-1-59249-321-0(1) , BC7107) Soundprints.

Goldie & the Three Geckos. 2000. pap. 8.99 (978-0-89610-357-3(9)) Island Heritage Publishing.

Goodyear-Brown, Paris. Gabby the Gecko. 2003. per. (978-1-932203-54-7(0)) Sundog, Ltd.

Gorman, Carol. Lizard Flanagan, Supermodel. 1998. 224p. (J). (gr. 7 up). 14.95 (978-0-06-024868-0(8)) HarperCollins Pubs.

Grace, Phillip. The Lizard of Cupcake Lake. 2006. (J). pap. 15.95 (***978-0-9601454-3-0(5)*** , 06-2129LIZ) Stelucan Pr.

Granados, Antonio. Este Era un Lapiz. Valderrama, Rosario, illus. 2002. (SPA.). 31p. (J). pap. 3.99 (978-968-16-6596-8(1)) Fondo de Cultura Economica USA.

Greene, Stephanie. Owen Foote, Mighty Scientist. Smith, Catharine Bowman, illus. 2004. 96p. (J). (gr. k-3). tchr. ed. 15.00 (978-0-618-43016-1(4) , Clarion Bks.) Houghton Mifflin Co. Trade & Reference Div.

Hale, Bruce. The Adventures of Space Gecko. (Illus.). (J). 8.95 (978-0-9621280-2-8(3)) Words & Pictures Publishing, Inc.

—The Chameleon Wore Chartreuse: A Chet Gecko Mystery. 2001. (Chet Gecko Mystery Ser.: No. 1). (J). (gr. 3-6). lib. bdg. 12.95 (978-0-613-35450-9(8)) Tandem Library Bks.

—The Mystery of Mr. Nice. 2000. (Chet Gecko Mystery Ser.: No. 2). (Illus.). 112p. (J). (gr. 3-7). 14.00 (978-0-15-202271-6(6)) Harcourt Children's Bks.

—The Mystery of Mr. Nice. 2001. (Chet Gecko Mystery Ser.: No. 2). (J). (gr. 3-7). lib. bdg. 12.95 (978-0-613-35466-0(4)) Tandem Library Bks.

—This Gum for Hire: A Chet Gecko Mystery. (Chet Gecko Mystery Ser.: No. 6). (Illus.). (J). (gr. 3-7). 2003. 144p. pap. 4.95 (978-0-15-202497-0(2) , Harcourt Paperbacks); 2002. 136p. 15.00 (978-0-15-202491-8(3)) Harcourt Children's Bks.

—This Gum for Hire: A Chet Gecko Mystery. 2003. (Chet Gecko Mystery Ser.: No. 6). (J). (gr. 3-6). lib. bdg. 12.95 (978-0-613-59895-8(4)) Tandem Library Bks.

Halfmann, Janet. Little Skink's Tail. Allen Klein, Laurie, illus. 2007. 32p. (J). (ps-3). 15.95 (978-0-9768823-8-1(8)) Sylvan Dell Pubng.

Hambleton, Laura. Welcome to Lizard Lounge. 2004. (Illus.). 28p. (J). pap. 7.95 (978-1-84059-390-7(3)) Milet Publishing.

Haneberg, Janet. Alamander, the Orange Salamander. 2006. 37p. (J). pap. 14.99 (978-1-4116-6678-8(X)) Lulu.com.

Harcourt School Publishers Staff. Pet Lizard On Level. 3rd ed. 2002. (Trophies Reading Program Ser.). (Illus.). 16p. pap. 5.10 (978-0-15-323274-9(9)) Harcourt Schl. Pubs.

Hollemann, Monika. Chameleon's Clever Trick: Runyangore-Rukiga Version. Bahemuka, Gaetano & Kagoro, Stephen, trs. 2000. (Cambridge African Language Library Ser.). (Illus.). pap. 3.65 (978-0-521-63772-5(4)) Cambridge Univ. Pr.

Johnson, Regan. Hold on to Your Tail: Letters from Camp Lizard. Johnson, Regan, illus. 2007. (Letters From Camp Lizard Ser.). (Illus.). 100p. (J). (gr. 2-7). per. (***978-1-933831-04-6(9)*** , Ready Blade) Blooming Tree Pr.

Karre, Nancy. On Herman's Pond. 2005. 8.00 (978-1-933281-00-1(6) , 2267) Battle Creek Area Mathematics & Science Ctr.

Kline, Trish. Lizard's Escape. Smith, Fred, illus. (Read-and-Discover - Great Plains Ser.). 48p. (J). 2005. (ps-1). 3.95 (978-1-56899-917-3(8) , S2005); 2002. (gr. 1-3). 7.95 (978-1-56899-916-6(X) , B2005) Soundprints.

—Lizard's Escape! 2002. (gr. k-3). lib. bdg. 11.80 (978-0-613-70878-4(4)) Tandem Library Bks.

—Lizard's Escape: Including 10" Toy. Smith, Fred, illus. 2005. (Read-and-Discover - Great Plains Ser.). 48p. (J). (ps-1). 12.95 (978-1-56899-918-0(6) , PS2055) Soundprints.

Kraatz, David. La Cancion del Geco. Luengas, Mauricio, illus. (SPA.). 16p. (J). (gr. 3-5). pap. 11.95 (978-1-56014-579-0(X)) Santillana USA Publishing Co., Inc.

Krailing, Tessa. Where's Iggy? Lewis, Jan & Eastwood, John, illus. 1999. (Petsitters Club Ser.: No. 8). 96p. (J). (gr. 1-4). pap. 3.95 (978-0-7641-0693-4(7)) Barron's Educational Series, Inc.

Laden, Nina. Private I Guana: The Case of the Missing Chameleon. 1999. (gr. k-3). lib. bdg. 15.25 (978-0-613-89998-7(9)) Tandem Library Bks.

The Last Coqui. 2002. (J). 16.00 (978-0-9675413-4-1(4)) Libros, Encouraging Cultural Literacy.

Law, Felicia. Rumble Meets Lucas Lizard. Pak, Yoon Mi, illus. 2006. (Read-It! Readers Ser.). 32p. (J). (gr. 2-4). 18.60 (978-1-4048-1334-2(9)) Picture Window Bks.

Lingenfelser, Lynda L. The Adventures of Lizah Lizard: The Laughing, Lovable Lizard. 2006. 46p. (J). per. 15.99 (978-0-615-13290-7(1)) Lingenfelser, Lynda L.

Little, Jean. Emma's Strange Pet. Plecas, Jennifer, illus. (I Can Read Bks.). 64p. (J). (gr. k-3). 2004. pap. 3.99 (978-0-06-444259-6(4) , Harper Trophy); 2003. 15.99 (978-0-06-028350-6(5)) HarperCollins Pubs.

A Look at Lizards. (Rigby Infoquest Ser.). (gr. 3 up). 30.00 (978-0-7578-3900-9(2)) Rigby Education.

Moeller, Kathleen H. La Historia de Geco. Romo, Alberto, tr. Veno, Joe, illus. 1999. (Books for Young Learners).Tr. of Gecko's Story. (SPA.). 12p. (J). (gr. k-2). pap. 5.00 (978-1-57274-293-2(3)) Owen, Richard C. Pubs., Inc.

Moon, Alice. Lucky's Special Thanksgiving. 2007. (Illus.). (J). pap. 9.95 (***978-0-9795831-2-4(8)***) PeachMoon Publishing.

Murray, I. P. C. Liz Looks for a Home. 1998. (Magic School Bus Ser.). (Illus.). 24p. (J). (gr. 1-4). pap. 3.50 (978-0-590-81839-1(2)) Scholastic, Inc.

My Special Place: Individual Title Six-Packs. (ps-2). 23.00 (978-0-7635-8811-3(3)) Rigby Education.

PeachMoon Publishing. The Lizard in the Mailbox. 2007. (J). pap. 9.95 (***978-0-9795831-0-0(1)***) PeachMoon Publishing.

—Lucky Goes to School. 2007. (J). pap. 9.95 (***978-0-9795831-1-7(X)***) PeachMoon Publishing.

Pickering, Jill. A Lizard Got into the Paint Pots. Wright, Petrina, illus. 2003. 64p. (J). (ps-3). 14.95 (978-0-333-98858-9(2)) Macmillan Caribbean GBR. *Dist:* Interlink Publishing Group, Inc.

Profiri, Charline. Counting Little Geckos. Rogers, Sheryl, illus. 2004. (J). bds. (978-1-891795-14-5(7)) RGU Group, The.

Puttock, Simon. "Here I Am!" Said Smedley. Chatterton, Martin & Chatterton, Ann, illus. 2001. (Blue Bananas Ser.). 48p. (J). (gr. 1-2). (978-0-7787-0838-4(1)); pap. (978-0-7787-0884-1(5)) Crabtree Publishing Co.

Quantz, Daniel. Face-to-Face with the Lizard! 2006. (Illus.). (J). (gr. 2-6). 21.35 (978-1-59961-014-6(0)) Spotlight.

Reich, Ashley. Izzy Lizzy. Reich, Ashley, illus. 2005. (Illus.). 32p. (J). per. 16.00 (978-0-9754298-3-9(3) , Ithaca Pr.) Authors & Artists Publishers of New York, Inc.

Riva, Renee. Izzy the Lizzy. Bjorkman, Steve, illus. 2005. 40p. (J). 9.99 (978-1-4000-7059-6(7) , WaterBrook Pr.) WaterBrook Pr.

Robertson, Elysia Hill. Dottie Goes to School. Robertson, Elysia Hill, illus. 2005. (Illus.). 30p. (J). per. 6.95 (978-0-9764444-8-0(8)) E. J. Publishing.

Salzmann, Mary Elizabeth. Leaping Lizards. Chawla, Neena, illus. (Fact & Fiction Ser.). 24p. (J). 2007. 21.35 (978-1-59928-450-7(2)); 2006. (978-1-59928-451-4(0)) ABDO Publishing Co.

Sanford, Christi. Legare the Lowcountry Lizard & His Sturdy New Tail. 2001. 24p. (J). pap. 11.95 (978-0-9675841-1-9(6)) Lowcountry Literature.

Santillo, LuAnn. Liz. Santillo, LuAnn, ed. 2003. (Half-Pint Kids Readers Ser.). (Illus.). 7p. (J). (ps-1). pap. (978-1-59256-083-7(0)) Half-Pint Kids, Inc.

Schafer, Susan. Where's My Tail? Cushman, Doug, illus. 2005. 32p. (J). 16.95 (978-0-7614-5170-9(6)) Cavendish, Marshall Corp.

Scott, C. Anne. Lizard Meets Ivana the Terrible. 2001. (gr. 3-6). lib. bdg. 11.80 (978-0-613-81946-6(2)) Tandem Library Bks.

Scott, C. Anne & Roth, Stephanie. Lizard Meets Ivana the Terrible. 2001. 128p. (J). pap. 3.99 (978-0-439-21999-0(X) , Scholastic Paperbacks) Scholastic, Inc.

Senisi, Ellen B. All Kinds of Friends, Even Green! 2002. (Illus.). 28p. (J). (gr. k-4). 15.95 (978-1-890627-35-5(6)) Woodbine Hse.

Shannon, George. La Cancion del Lagarto. Aruego, Jose & Dewey, Ariane, illus. unabr. ed. 2005. (SPA.). (J). (gr. 2-4). pap. 16.95 incl. audio (978-0-87499-349-3(0) , LK6492) Live Oak Media.

—Lizard's Home. Aruego, Jose & Dewey, Ariane, illus. 1999. 32p. (J). (ps-3). 15.89 (978-0-688-16003-6(4)) HarperCollins Pubs.

Shulman, Mark. Not Another Tea Party. Nguyen, Vincent, illus. 2006. 32p. (J). 14.95 (978-1-4027-3304-8(6)) Sterling Publishing Co., Inc.

Sis, Peter. Komodo! 1999. (Illus.). 40p. (ps-3). pap. 5.95 (978-0-688-16695-3(4)) HarperCollins Pubs.

So-Lazy Lizard. 2004. (Plush Pals Board Bks.). (Illus.). (J). (gr. k-1). bds. (978-0-7666-0561-9(2) , 39395) Modern Publishing.

Somerville, Kirra. The Lizard Gang. Fielding, Grace, illus. 2006. 28p. (J). pap. 17.95 (978-1-875641-89-5(0)) Magabala Bks. AUS. *Dist:* International Specialized Bk. Services.

Spinner, Stephanie. We're off to See the Lizard. 1998. (Weebie Zone Ser.). (J). (978-0-606-13066-0(7)) Tandem Library Bks.

Storad, Conrad J. Lizards for Lunch: A Roadrunner's Tale. 1999. (Sonoran Desert Tails Ser.). (Illus.). 32p. (J). (gr. k-4). 6.95 (978-1-891795-00-8(7)) RGU Group, The.

Strunk, Peter, illus. & creator. Two Inch Hero: The Adventures of Lorenzo Lizard. Strunk, Peter, creator. 2006. (J). 17.95 (***978-0-9785961-0-1(2)***) Smile Time Publishing.

Sydor, Colleen. Camilla Chameleon. Constantin, Pascale, illus. 2005. 32p. (J). (gr. 1-4). (978-1-55337-482-4(7)) Kids Can Pr., Ltd.

Twinem, Neecy. Baby Gecko's Colors. 2004. (New Board Book Ser.).Tr. of Los colores de Bebe Geco. (Illus.). 12p. (J). bds. 5.95 (978-0-87358-851-5(7) , Rising Moon Bks. for Young Readers) Northland Publishing.

Watson, T. E. I Wanna Iguana. Raptis, John, illus. 3rd l.t. ed. 2001. 32p. (J). 16.95 (978-1-58478-009-0(6) , Paw Prints Pr.) Heather & Highlands Publishing.

West, Tracey. Liz Busca un Hogar. 1999. (Coleccion Liz). (SPA., Illus.). 24p. (J). (gr. k-3). pap. 3.50 (978-0-590-68935-9(5) , SO6032, Scholastic en Espanol) Scholastic, Inc.

—Liz on the Move. Ostrom, Bob, illus. 1999. (Magic School Bus Ser.). 24p. (J). (gr. 1-4). pap. 3.50 (978-0-590-66236-9(8)) Scholastic, Inc.

—Liz Pone Orden. 1999. (Coleccion Liz). (SPA., Illus.). 24p. (J). (gr. k-3). pap. 3.50 (978-0-439-05869-8(4) , SO3476, Scholastic en Espanol) Scholastic, Inc.

—Liz Sorts It Out. Bracken, Caroline, illus. 1998. (Magic School Bus Ser.). 24p. (J). (gr. 1-4). pap. 3.50 (978-0-590-81838-4(4)) Scholastic, Inc.

Winter, Barbara. Chameleon Capers. 2004. (Amazing Dictionary Ser.). (Illus.). 64p. pap. 4.95 (978-0-921156-97-0(9)) Rubicon Publishing, Inc. CAN. *Dist:* International Publishers Marketing.

Yates, Gene, illus. The Chameleon Colors Book. 2006. (J). (***978-1-58865-361-1(7)***) Kidsbooks, Inc.

LLAMAS

Barnes, Julia. Camels & Llamas at Work. 2006. (Illus.). 32p. (J). 23.33 (978-0-8368-6222-5(8)) Stevens, Gareth Inc.

Frisch, Aaron: Llamas. 2002. (Let's Investigate Ser.). (Illus.). 32p. (J). lib. bdg. 18.95 (978-1-58341-242-8(5) , Creative Education) Creative Co., The.

Harman, Amanda. Llamas. 2004. (Nature's Children Ser.). (Illus.). 48p. (J). (978-0-7172-5968-7(4) , Grolier) Scholastic Library Publishing.

Hudak, Heather C. Llamas. 2006. (J). (978-1-59036-427-7(9)); (978-1-59036-434-5(1)) Weigl Pubs., Inc.

Murray, Julie. Llamas. 2002. (Animal Kingdom Ser.). (Illus.). 24p. (J). (gr. k-4). lib. bdg. 21.35 (978-1-57765-724-8(1)) ABDO Publishing Co.

Patent, Dorothy Hinshaw. Llamas. Munoz, William, illus. Munoz, William, photos by. 2001. (Early Bird Nature Bks.). 48p. (J). (gr. 2-4). lib. bdg. 25.26 (978-0-8225-0067-4(1) , Lerner Pubns.) Lerner Publishing Group.

LLAMAS—FICTION

Bent, Ruth. Llama Hiking with Katie. 2000. 28p. (J). (gr. 1-3). pap. 8.00 (978-0-615-11191-9(2)) Sijama Publishing.

Bonder, Dianna. Eleven Lazy Llamas. Bonder, Dianna, illus. 2005. (Illus.). 32p. (J). (ps-2). 16.95 (978-1-55285-609-3(7)) Whitecap Bks., Ltd. CAN. *Dist:* Firefly Bks., Ltd.

Chiappini, Lydia. A Llama's Tale: Freesia's Little Llama Farm. 2003. (Illus.). 64p. pap. 10.00 (978-0-9669355-9-2(4)) Chiappini, Lydia .

Crum, Anna-Maria & Fielder, John, illus. Maria's Mysterious Mission. Fielder, John, photos by. 2007. (J). 12.95 (***978-1-56579-588-4(1)***) Westcliffe Pubs.

Dewdney, Anna. Llama Llama Mad at Mama. Dewdney, Anna, illus. 2007. (Illus.). 40p. (J). (ps-k). 15.99 (***978-0-670-06240-9(5)*** , Viking Juvenile) Penguin Group (USA) Inc.

Dewdney, Anna. Llama, Llama Red Pajama. Dewdney, Anna, illus. 2005. (Illus.). 40p. (J). 16.99 (978-0-670-05983-6(8) , Viking Juvenile) Penguin Group (USA) Inc.

The Emperor's New Groove. unabr. ed. 2000. (J). pap. 9.98 incl. audio (978-0-7634-0710-0(0)) Walt Disney Records.

Fraggolosch, Audrey. Land of the Wild Llama: A Story of the Patagonian Andes. 2005. (Soundprints' Wild Habitats Ser.). (Illus.). 32p. (J). (gr. 1-4). 8.95 incl. audio (978-1-59249-110-0(3) , SC7022) Soundprints.

Guarino, Deborah. Is Your Mama a Llama? Kellogg, Steven, illus. 2002. (J). 13.83 (978-0-7587-2867-8(0)) Book Wholesalers, Inc.

—Is Your Mama a Llama? Kellogg, Steven, illus. (Scholastic Bookshelf Ser.). (J). 2004. 32p. 6.99 (978-0-439-59842-2(7) , Scholastic Paperbacks); 2006. 9.95 (978-0-439-87588-2(9)) Scholastic, Inc.

—Is Your Mama A Llama Read along Library. 2006. (J). 18.95 (978-0-439-87594-3(3)) Scholastic, Inc.

Guarino, Deborah & Kellogg, Steven. Ta Maman Est-Elle un Lama? (FRE., Illus.). (J). pap. 7.99 (978-0-590-74555-0(7)) Scholastic, Inc.

Hernandez, Elaine. Welcome to Humming Meadow Ranch. Hernandez, Stacy, illus. 2005. 28p. (J). lib. bdg. 16.95 (978-0-9766431-0-4(3)) Humming Meadow Ranch.

Hurwitz, Johanna. A Llama in the Library. Graham, Mark, illus. 1999. 144p. (J). (gr. 2-5). 15.00 (978-0-688-16138-5(3)) HarperCollins Pubs.

Livingstone, Star. Harley. Bang, Molly, illus. 2003. 64p. (J). (gr. 1-4). pap. 5.95 (978-1-58717-150-5(3) , SeaStar Bks.) Chronicle Bks. LLC.

—Harley. 2003. (gr. k-3). lib. bdg. 12.95 (978-0-613-65127-1(8)) Tandem Library Bks.

Llama on the Lam. 2001. (LLAMA ON THE LAM). 96p. (J). 22.00 (978-0-9649083-4-5(4)) Black River Trading Co.

Morris, Jennifer. Come, Llamas. 2006. 208p. (gr. 3-7). 5.99 (978-0-440-42024-8(5) , Yearling) Random Hse. Children's Bks.

Palacios, Argentina. El Secreto de la Llama - The Llama's Secret: Una Leyenda Peruana. 97th ed. 2003. (Leyendas del Mundo Ser.). (SPA., Illus.). 32p. (gr. 2-5). pap. 12.90 (978-0-8167-3072-8(5)) Harcourt Schl. Pubs.

Pearson, Georgene. Larry the Llama. 2005. 48p. per. 12.95 (978-1-933148-35-9(7)) Tate Publishing & Enterprises, L.L.C.

Slater, Teddy. Llamas in Pajamas. Kindert, Jennifer, illus. 2006. 32p. (J). (ps-ps). 6.95 (978-1-4027-2021-5(1)) Sterling Publishing Co., Inc.

Voss, Gisela. Picnics of New England: Recipes to Inspire & Paintings to Enchant. 1998. (Illus.). 72p. (J). (ps-3). 14.95 (978-0-87846-408-1(5)) Museum of Fine Arts, Boston.

Zarley, Jacqualynn R. Adventures with Lucy the Llama Book Two: Shung the Trickster. 2006. 54p. pap. 12.95 (978-1-4137-5996-9(3)) PublishAmerica, Inc.

LOAN FUNDS, STUDENT

see Student Loan Funds

LOCKHART, SALLY (FICTITIOUS CHARACTER)—FICTION

Pullman, Philip. The Ruby in the Smoke. 2003. (Sally Lockhart Trilogy: Bk. 1). (Illus.). (YA). pap. 9.95 (978-0-375-82545-3(2) , Knopf Bks. for Young Readers) Random Hse. Children's Bks.

—The Ruby in the Smoke. 2002. (Sally Lockhart Trilogy: Bk. 1). 22.00 (978-0-8446-7230-4(0)) Smith, Peter Pub., Inc.

—Sally y el Tigre en el Pozo. Miquel, Isabel de, tr. 2004. (SPA.). 512p. (978-84-95618-49-8(4) , Umbriel) Ediciones Urano S. A.

—Sally y la Sombra del Norte. Miguel, Isabel de, tr. 2002. Tr. of Shadow in the North. (SPA.). 347p. (J). pap. (978-84-95618-46-7(X) , Umbriel) Ediciones Urano S. A.

—The Shadow in the North. 2003. (Illus.). (J). pap. 9.95 (978-0-375-82546-0(0) , Knopf Bks. for Young Readers) Random Hse. Children's Bks.

—The Tiger in the Well. 2003. (Illus.). (J). pap. 9.95 (978-0-375-82547-7(9)) Random Hse. Children's Bks.

LOBBYING

see also Political Corruption

Horn, Geoffrey M. Political Parties, Interest Groups & the Media. 2003. (World Almanac Library of American Government). (Illus.). 48p. (J). (gr. 5 up). pap. 14.95 (978-0-8368-5483-1(7)); lib. bdg. 30.00 (978-0-8368-5478-7(0)) Stevens, Gareth Inc. (World Almanac Library).

LOBSTER FISHERIES

Volovar, Vivian. Lobster Lady. 2007. (Illus.). 32p. (J). pap. 14.95 (***978-0-9773725-8-4(8)***) Flat Hammock Pr.

LOBSTERS

Gilpin, Daniel. Lobsters, Crabs & Other Crustaceans. 2006. (Animal Kingdom Classification Ser.). (Illus.). 48p. (J). (gr. 4-6). 26.60 (978-0-7565-1612-3(9)) Compass Point Bks.

Gordon, Sharon. Guess Who Snaps. 2004. (SPA & ENG., Illus.). 31p. (J). 21.36 (978-0-7614-1765-1(6) , Benchmark Bks.) Cavendish, Marshall Corp.

Gordon, Sharon. Guess Who Snaps: Adivina Quién Tritura. 2007. (SPA & ENG.). (J). (***978-0-7614-2886-2(0) ; 978-0-7614-2870-1(4)***) Cavendish, Marshall Bks., Ltd.

Hirschmann, Kris. Lobsters. 2004. (Illus.). 48p. (J). (gr. 4-7). 26.20 (978-0-7377-2343-4(2) , Kidhaven) Thomson Gale.

Kalman, Bobbie & Sjonger, Rebecca. The Life Cycle of a Crayfish. 2006. (Life Cycle Ser.). (Illus.). 32p. (J). (gr. 2-3). lib. bdg. (978-0-7787-0629-8(X)) Crabtree Publishing Co.

Marsico, Katie. A Baby Lobster Grows Up. 2007. (Scholastic News Nonfiction Readers: Life Cycles Ser.). 24p. (J). pap. 6.95 (***978-0-531-18694-7(6)*** , Children's Pr.) Scholastic Library Publishing.

Rake, Jody Sullivan. Lobsters. 2006. (Under the Sea Ser.). (Illus.). 24p. (J). (gr. k-2). lib. bdg. 19.93 (978-0-7368-6363-6(X) , Pebble Bks.) Capstone Pr., Inc.

Rustad, Martha E. H. Lobsters. 2007. (Illus.). 24p. (J). lib. bdg. 19.95 (978-1-60014-082-2(3)) Bellwether Media.

J K L

Schaefer, Lola M. La Langosta. 2002. (Animales Acorazados (Musty-Crusty Animals) Ser.). (SPA.). 24p. (J). (ps-1). lib. bdg. 18.50 (978-1-58810-857-9(0)); (Illus.). pap. 5.25 (978-1-58810-819-7(8) , 91562) Heinemann Library.

—Lobsters. 2002. (Musty-Crusty Animals Ser.). (Illus.). 24p. (J). (ps-1). pap. 5.25 (978-1-58810-725-1(6) , 91378); lib. bdg. 17.08 (978-1-58810-516-5(4)) Heinemann Library.

Soundprints Staff, ed. Oceanic Collection III: Beluga Whale, Harp Seal, Walrus & Lobster Books, 4 micro bks. (Smithsonian Oceanic Collection). (Illus.). 128p. (J). (ps-2). 18.95 (978-1-56899-633-2(0)) Soundprints.

Souza, Dorothy M. Sea Creatures with Many Arms. 1998. (Creatures All Around Us Ser.). (Illus.). 40p. (J). (gr. 2-4). lib. bdg. (978-1-57505-262-5(8) , Carolrhoda Bks.) Lerner Publishing Group.

Stone, Tanya Lee. Lobsters. 2003. (Wild Wild World Ser.). 24p. (YA). 24.94 (978-1-56711-816-2(X) , Blackbirch Pr., Inc.) Thomson Gale.

World Book, Inc. Staff, contrib. by. Lobsters & Other Crustaceans. 2005. (World Book's Animals of the World Ser.). (Illus.). 64p. (J). (978-0-7166-1270-4(4)) World Bk., Inc.

LOBSTERS—FICTION

Chiu, Esther. The Lobster & the Sea. Takahashi, Mika, illus. 1998. 32p. (J). (gr. 2-5). pap. 14.95 (978-1-879965-14-0(3)) Polychrome Publishing Corp.

Debbie & the Baby Lobster. 2000. 22p. (J). 7.95 (978-1-931015-00-4(7)) Distant Waters Publishing & Designs.

Flemming, Paul & Goode, Jon. Lucy Lobster & Her Clacky Claws. 1999. (Snappy Fun Bks.: Vol. 7). (Illus.). 12p. (J). (gr. k-3). bds. 4.99 (978-1-57584-249-3(1) , Reader's Digest Children's Bks.) Reader's Digest Children's Publishing, Inc.

Kessler, Deirdre. Lobster in My Pocket. Jones, Brenda, illus. 2002. pap. 7.95 (978-1-55109-423-6(1)) Nimbus Publishing, Ltd. CAN. *Dist:* National Bk. Network.

Kidd, Richard. Lobsters in Love: A Whirlpool Romance. Kidd, Lindsey, illus. 2004. 32p. (J). pap. 7.95 (978-1-84507-154-7(9)) Lincoln, Frances Ltd. GBR. *Dist:* Perseus Distribution.

Kidd, Richard & Kidd, Lindsey. Monsieur Thermidor: A Fantastic Fishy Tale. 2001. (Illus.). 32p. (J). (ps-3). pap. 7.99 (978-0-7112-1224-4(4)) Lincoln, Frances Ltd. GBR. *Dist:* Antique Collectors' Club.

Schwarz, Viviane. Shark & Lobster's Amazing Undersea Adventure. Stewart, Joel, illus. 2006. 34p. (J). ***978-1-4156-8140-4(6))** Candlewick Pr.

Verrier, Suzy. Titus Tidewater. 2005. (J). 15.95 (978-0-9763231-1-2(7)) Islandport Pr., Inc.

Ziefert, Harriet. Bob & Shirley: A Tale of Two Lobsters. 1999. (Puffin Easy-to-Read Ser.). (J). (978-0-606-16820-5(6)) Tandem Library Bks.

LOCAL GOVERNMENT

see also Cities and Towns; Public Administration

Benchmark Education Staff. Local & State GOVT. 2005. 2.00 (***978-1-4108-4639-6(3))** Benchmark Education Co.

Benchmark Education Staff, compiled by. Social Studies Theme: GOVT & Citizenship. 2005. spiral bd. 115.00 (***978-1-4108-5331-8(4))** Benchmark Education Co.

Brannon, Barbara. Discover Local & State GOVT. 2005. 39.00 (***978-1-4108-5145-1(1))** Benchmark Education Co.

Johnson, Etta. Local & State GOVT. 2005. 39.00 (***978-1-4108-4591-7(5))** Benchmark Education Co.

Miller, Jake. Who's Who in an Urban Community. 2005. (Communities at Work Ser.). 19.95 (978-1-4042-2790-3(3) , PowerKids Pr.) Rosen Publishing Group, Inc., The.

LOCH NESS (SCOTLAND)

see Ness, Loch (Scotland)

LOCH NESS MONSTER

see also Ness, Loch (Scotland)

Delrio, Martin. The Loch Ness Monster. 2005. (Unsolved Mysteries Ser.). (Illus.). 48p. (YA). (gr. 5-8). lib. bdg. 25.25 (978-0-8239-3564-2(7)) Rosen Publishing Group, Inc., The.

DeMolay, Jack. The Loch Ness Monster: Scotland's Mystery Beast. 2007. (Jr. Graphic Mysteries Ser.). (Illus.). 24p. (J). (gr. 2-6). lib. bdg. 21.25 (978-1-4042-3406-2(3)) Rosen Publishing Group, Inc., The.

Flaherty, Alice. The Luck of the Loch Ness Monster: A Tale of Picky Eating. Magoon, Scott, illus. 2007. 40p. (J). (gr. 3-5). 16.00 (***978-0-618-55644-1(3))** Houghton Mifflin Co.

Gorman, Jacqueline Laks. The Loch Ness Monster. 2002. (X Science Ser.). (Illus.). 24p. (YA). (gr. 2 up). lib. bdg. 22.00 (978-0-8368-3200-6(0)) Stevens, Gareth Inc.

Hoffman, Mary Ann. Loch Ness Monster. 2006. (Tony Stead Independent Reading Collection). (J). pap. (978-1-4042-5673-6(3)) Rosen Publishing Group, Inc., The.

Holly Wallace. The Mystery of the Loch Ness Monster. 2nd ed. 2006. (Can Science Solve? Ser.). (Illus.). 32p. (J). pap. (***978-1-4034-8346-1(9))** Heinemann Library.

Jeffrey, Gary. The Loch Ness Monster & Other Lake Mysteries. Spender, Nik & Moulder, Bob, illus. 2005. (Graphic Mysteries Ser.). 48p. (J). (gr. 5-8). lib. bdg. 29.95 (978-1-4042-0796-7(1)) Rosen Publishing Group, Inc., The.

—The Loch Ness Monster, the Lake Erie Monster, & Champ of Lake Champlain. Spender, Nik, illus. 2005. (Graphic Mysteries Ser.). (J). (978-1-4042-0820-9(8)) Rosen Publishing Group, Inc., The.

—The Loch Ness Monster, the Lake Erie Monster, & Champ of Lake Champlain. Spender, Nik & Moulder, Bob, illus. 2005. (Graphic Mysteries Ser.). 48p. (J). pap. (978-1-4042-0807-0(0)) Rosen Publishing Group, Inc., The.

Parks, Peggy J. The Loch Ness Monster. (Mysterious Encounters Ser.). 48p. (J). (gr. 4-8). 2006. 26.20 (978-0-7377-3519-2(8) , Kidhaven); 2005. (Illus.). 26.20 (978-0-7377-3166-8(4) , Greenhaven Pr., Inc.) Thomson Gale.

Sievert, Terri. The Loch Ness Monster. 2004. (Edge Books, the Unexplained). (Illus.). 32p. (J). lib. bdg. 22.60 (978-0-7368-2716-4(1)) Capstone Pr., Inc.

Streissguth, Thomas. The Loch Ness Monster. 2002. (Mystery Library). (Illus.). 112p. (J). (gr. 4-12). 27.45 (978-1-56006-772-6(1) , Lucent Bks.) Thomson Gale.

Wallace, Holly. The Mystery of the Loch Ness Monster. (Can Science Solve? Ser.). 32p. (J). 2006. (Illus.). (***978-1-4034-8337-9(X));** 1999. (gr. 4-7). lib. bdg. 22.79 (978-1-57572-805-6(2)) Heinemann Library.

Yorke, Malcolm & Davis, Lee. Beastly Tales: Big Foot, Yeti & the Loch Ness Monster. 1998. (Eyewitness Readers). (Illus.). 48p. (J). (gr. 2-3). pap. 3.99 (978-0-7894-2962-9(4) , 0-7894-4754-1) Dorling Kindersley Publishing, Inc.

LOCKS AND KEYS

Cruz-Martinez, George. The Wonder of Keys for Kids. Sturgeon, Brad, illus. 2006. 43p. (J). (978-1-55452-013-8(4)) Essence Publishing.

LOCKWOOD, BELVA ANN, 1830-1917

Norgren, Jill. Belva Lockwood: The Woman Who Would Be President. 2007. (Illus.). 344p. 35.00 (***978-0-8147-5834-2(7))** New York Univ. Pr.

LOCOMOTION

see Aeronautics; Automobiles; Boats and Boating; Flight; Navigation; Transportation; Walking

LOCOMOTIVES

Barron's Educational Editorial Staff. Railways. 1998. (History Ser.). (Illus.). 32p. (J). (gr. 5). pap. 5.95 (978-0-7641-0538-8(8)) Barron's Educational Series, Inc.

Chant, Christopher. Railway Locomotives. Moore, John, ed. 2000. (World's Railroads Ser.). (Illus.). 64p. (J). (gr. 5 up). 27.50 (978-0-7910-5560-1(4) , Chelsea Hse.) Facts On File, Inc.

Dorling Kindersley Publishing Staff. The Big Book of Trains. 1998. (Illus.). 32p. (J). (gr. k-3). 14.99 (978-0-7894-3436-4(9)) Dorling Kindersley Publishing, Inc.

Farrington, Karen & Constable, Nick. Build Your Own Steam Locomotive: A Complete, Easy-to-Assemble Model. Osborne, Graham, illus. 2004. 34p. (J). (gr. 4-8). reprint ed. pap. 17.00 (978-0-7567-8261-0(9)) DIANE Publishing Co.

Hannon, Robert A. J. L. Cowen's Postwar Lionel Trains: O-Gauge Reference Manual II, Motorized Units, Rolling Stock & Accessories. 2003. (Illus.). 160p. per. 29.95 (978-0-9710225-2-2(6) , 0-9710225-2-6) CrowsNest Publishing.

Isaacs, Sally Senzell. The First Railroads. 2004. (Illus.). 32p. (J). pap. 7.50 (978-1-4034-4791-3(8)); lib. bdg. (978-1-4034-2506-5(X)) Heinemann Library.

Johnston, Marianne. Casey Jones. 2001. (American Legends Ser.). (Illus.). 24p. (J). (gr. 3). lib. bdg. 18.75 (978-0-8239-5582-4(6) , PowerKids Pr.) Rosen Publishing Group, Inc., The.

Mravec, James. You Can Draw Planes, Trains & Boats. 2005. (Illus.). 96p. spiral bd. (978-0-7853-8303-1(4) , 3460900) Publications International, Ltd.

O'Brien, Patrick. Steam, Smoke & Steel: Back in Time with Trains. 2000. (gr. k-3). lib. bdg. 15.25 (978-0-613-35240-6(8)) Tandem Library Bks.

—Steam, Smoke, & Steel: Back in Time with Trains. O'Brien, Patrick, illus. 2000. (Illus.). 32p. (J). (ps-3). pap. 16.95 (978-0-88106-969-3(8)); pap. 6.95 (978-0-88106-972-3(8)) Charlesbridge Publishing, Inc.

Sloan, Peter. Old & New Trains. 1999. (gr. k-3). lib. bdg. 11.80 (978-0-613-30642-3(2)) Tandem Library Bks.

Strickland, Paul. On the Move: Boats; Cars; Planes; Trains, 4 bks. Strickland, Paul, illus. 2002. (Illus.). (J). (ps up). pap. (978-0-8368-3333-1(3) , Weekly Reader Early Learning Library) Stevens, Gareth Inc.

Turnbull, S. Trains. 2004. (Discovery Program Ser.). (SPA., Illus.). 48p. (J). (gr. 3 up). lib. bdg. 16.95 (978-1-58086-410-7(4)) EDC Publishing.

Weitzman, David L. The John Bull: A British Locomotive Comes to America. Weitzman, David L., illus. 2004. (Illus.). 40p. (J). 16.00 (978-0-374-38037-3(6) , Farrar, Straus & Giroux (BYR)) Farrar, Straus & Giroux.

LOCOMOTIVES—FICTION

Awdry, Wilbert V. The Cranky Day & Other Thomas the Tank Engine Stories. 2000. (Random House Picturebacks Ser.). (Illus.). 24p. (J). (gr. k-3). pap. 3.25 (978-0-375-80246-1(0) , Random Hse. Bks. for Young Readers) Random Hse. Children's Bks.

—Para, Trencito, Para! Un Cuento de Thomas the Tank Engine. Marquez, Desirée, tr. 2001. (SPA., Illus.). 24p. (gr. k-ps). bds. 4.99 (978-0-375-81502-7(3) , RH Para Ninos) Random Hse. Children's Bks.

Bryant, Megan E. Little Engine That Could & the Fire Rescue: Based on Original Story by Watty Piper. Ong, Cristina & Lustig, Loretta, illus. 2003. (Reading Railroad Bks.). 32p. (J). pap. 3.49 (978-0-448-43279-3(X) , Grosset & Dunlap) Penguin Group (USA) Inc.

Carroll, Michelle T. The Invisible Train. Sanders, Terry, illus. 2000. (J). cd-rom 9.95 (978-1-58338-375-9(1)) CrossroadsPub.com.

Choo Choo Charlie Train Book (Thai) 2000. (THA.). (J). (978-1-58805-118-9(8)) DS-Max USA, Inc.

Gibbons, Faye. Full Steam Ahead. Meidell, Sherry, illus. 2003. 32p. (J). (gr. k-2). 15.95 (978-1-56397-858-6(X)) Boyds Mills Pr.

Kornfeld, Joanne. The Chocolate Train. Rast, Barbara Mason, illus. 2002. 24p. (J). (ps-4). 12.95 (978-0-9704629-3-0(X)) Earthkids Publishing.

Lippman, Peter. Mini Express. (J). 119.40 (978-0-7611-2876-2(X) , 22876); 2002. (Illus.). 20p. bds. 9.95 (978-0-7611-2852-6(2) , 12852) Workman Publishing Co., Inc.

Mysak, Mary. Little Train! Stickley, Kelly, illus. 2004. 16p. (J). 7.50 (978-0-9762274-0-3(1)) Helping Hands Children's Bks.

Ong, Christina. Little Engine That Could ABC Time. 2000. (ps-2). lib. bdg. 11.25 (978-0-613-26024-4(9)) Tandem Library Bks.

Ong, Cristina & Piper, Watty. The Little Engine That Could ABC. 1999. (Wee Pudgy Board Bks.). (Illus.). 20p. (J). (ps-k). 1.99 (978-0-448-41970-1(X) , Grosset & Dunlap) Penguin Group (USA) Inc.

Peters, Andrew Fusek. Animals Aboard! Coplestone, Jim, illus. 2007. 24p. (J). 16.95 (***978-1-84507-582-8(X))** Lincoln, Frances Ltd. GBR. *Dist:* Perseus Distribution.

Piper, Watty. The Little Engine That Could. Long, Loren, illus. 2005. 48p. (J). (ps-3). 17.99 (978-0-399-24467-4(0) , Philomel) Penguin Group (USA) Inc.

—The Little Engine That Could: Giant signed Edition. Long, Loren, illus. 2007. 48p. (J). (ps). 250.00 (***978-0-399-25084-2(0)** , Philomel) Penguin Group (USA) Inc.

—The Little Engine That Could ABC Time. Ong, Cristina, illus. 2000. (Reading Railroad Bks.). 32p. (J). (ps-3). pap. 3.99 (978-0-448-42166-7(6) , Grosset & Dunlap) Penguin Group (USA) Inc.

—The Little Engine That Could & the Snowy, Blowy Christmas. Ong, Cristina, illus. 1998. (All Aboard Bks.). 24p. (J). (ps-4). pap. 3.99 (978-0-448-41850-6(9) , Grosset & Dunlap) Penguin Group (USA) Inc.

—Little Engine That Could Helps Out. Ong, Cristina, illus. 1999. (All Aboard Reading Ser.). 32p. (J). (ps-1). pap. 3.99 (978-0-448-41973-2(4) , Grosset & Dunlap) Penguin Group (USA) Inc.

—Meet the Little Engine That Could. 2001. (First Friends, First Readers Ser.). (Illus.). (J). (978-0-606-21324-0(4)) Tandem Library Bks.

Read & Roll Train (English) 2000. (J). (978-1-58805-109-7(9)) DS-Max USA, Inc.

Riley, Lehman C. Meeting Dr. Martin Luther King. 2004. (Adventures of Papa Lemon's Little Wanderers Ser.: Bk. 1). 35p. (***978-0-9760523-0-2(X))** Matter of Africa America Time.

Stephens, Monique. The Little Engine That Could's Valentine's Day Surprise. Ong, Cristina, illus. 2003. (Reading Railroad Bks.). 32p. (J). (ps-4). pap. 3.99 (978-0-448-43280-9(3) , Grosset & Dunlap) Penguin Group (USA) Inc.

Wilcoxen, Chuck. Niccolini's Song. Buehner, Mark, illus. 2004. 40p. (J). (ps). 16.99 (978-0-525-46805-9(6) , Dutton Juvenile) Penguin Group (USA) Inc.

Wilson-Max, Ken, illus. Big Blue Engine. ed. 2000. 14p. (J). (ps-k). bds. 7.95 (978-0-439-13655-6(5) , Cartwheel Bks.) Scholastic, Inc.

LOCUSTS

Allen, Judy. Are You a Grasshopper? Humphries, Tudor, illus. 2002. (Backyard Bks.). 32p. (J). (gr. k-3). tchr. ed. 9.95 (978-0-7534-5366-7(5) , Kingfisher) Houghton Mifflin Co. Trade & Reference Div.

—Are You a Grasshopper? Humphries, Tudor, illus. 2004. (Backyard Bks.). 32p. (J). (ps up). 5.95 (978-0-7534-5806-8(3) , Kingfisher) Houghton Mifflin Co. Trade & Reference Div.

Ashley, Susan. Grasshoppers. 2004. (Weekly Reader Early Learning Library). (Illus.). 24p. (gr. 1 up). (J). pap. 5.95 (978-0-8368-4061-2(5)); (YA). lib. bdg. 19.33 (978-0-8368-4054-4(2)) Stevens, Gareth Inc. (Weekly Reader Early Learning Library).

Bodden, Valerie. Grasshoppers. 2007. (BugBooks). (J). (978-1-58341-544-3(0) , Creative Education) Creative Co., The.

Brennan, Patricia. Grasshoppers & Their Relatives, Vol. 5. World Book, Inc. Staff, ed. 2001. (World Book's Animals of the World Ser.: Set 2). (Illus.). 64p. (J). (978-0-7166-1219-3(4)) World Bk., Inc.

Cooper, Jason. Katydids. (Insects Discovery Library Ser.). 24p. (gr. k-2). 2006. (Illus.). 14.95 (978-1-59515-427-9(2)); 2005. pap. 5.45 (978-1-59515-741-6(7)) Rourke Publishing, LLC.

—Saltamontes. 2005. (Biblioteca del Descubrimiento de los Insectos Ser.). (SPA.). 24p. pap. 5.45 (978-1-59515-697-6(6)) Rourke Publishing, LLC.

Coughlan, Cheryl. Grasshoppers, 6 vols. (gr. k-2). 28.95 (978-0-7368-8252-1(9)) Red Brick Learning.

Grasshoppers. (Bugs, Bugs, Bugs! Ser.). 24p. (J). 6.95 (978-0-7368-5096-4(1)); Vol. 2. 2005. (YA). (978-0-7368-8212-5(X) , Pebble Bks.) Capstone Pr., Inc.

Grasshoppers. (Nature's Friends Ser.). 32p. (J). 7.95 (978-0-7565-1231-6(X)) Compass Point Bks.

Green, Emily K. Grasshoppers. 2006. (Blastoff! Readers Ser.). (Illus.). 24p. (J). lib. bdg. 16.95 (978-1-60014-014-3(9)) Bellwether Media.

—Grasshoppers. 2006. (Blastoff! Readers Ser.). (Illus.). 24p. (J). (gr. k-2). 18.50 (***978-0-531-17864-5(1))** Scholastic Library Publishing.

Grolier Educational Staff, contrib. by. Grasshoppers. 2001. (Nature's Children Ser.). (Illus.). 48p. (J). (978-0-7172-5537-5(9) , Grolier) Scholastic Library Publishing.

Halfmann, Janet. Grasshoppers. 1998. (Bugs Ser.). (Illus.). 32p. (YA). (gr. 3-12). lib. bdg. 16.95 (978-1-887068-34-5(1)) Smart Apple Media.

Hall, Margaret. Grasshoppers. 2004. (Pebble Plus: Bugs, Bugs, Bugs! Ser.). (Illus.). 24p. (J). lib. bdg. 19.93 (978-0-7368-2588-7(6) , Pebble Bks.) Capstone Pr., Inc.

Hartley, Karen, et al. Grasshopper. 2006. (Illus.). 32p. (J). (***978-1-4034-8297-6(7));** 2nd ed. pap. (***978-1-4034-8310-2(8))** Heinemann Library.

Hartley, Karen, et al. El Saltamontes. 2003. (Los Insectos Ser.). (SPA.). 32p. (J). pap. 6.95 (978-1-4034-3035-9(7)) Heinemann Library.

Hayward, Tim & Greenaway, Theresa. Grasshoppers & Crickets. 1999. (Minipets Ser.). (Illus.). 32p. (J). (gr. 1-5). lib. bdg. 25.69 (978-0-8172-5590-9(7)) Raintree.

—Grasshoppers & Crickets. 1999. (Minipets Ser.). (Illus.). 32p. (J). (gr. 1-5). pap. 5.95 (978-0-7398-1385-0(4)) Steck-Vaughn.

Heinrichs, Ann. Grasshoppers. 2002. (Nature's Friends Ser.). (Illus.). 32p. (J). (gr. 2 up). lib. bdg. 21.26 (978-0-7565-0166-2(0)) Compass Point Bks.

Hibbert, Clare. Life Cycles: The Life of a Grasshopper. 2004. (Illus.). pap. 7.50 (978-1-4109-0925-1(5)) Raintree.

—Life of a Grasshopper. 2004. (Raintree Perspectives Ser.). (Illus.). 32p. (J). lib. bdg. 25.70 (978-1-4109-0537-6(3)) Raintree.

Hovanec, Erin M. I Wonder What It's Like to Be a Grasshopper. 2000. (Life Science Wonder Bks.). (Illus.). 24p. (J). (gr. k-4). lib. bdg. 18.75 (978-0-8239-5452-0(8) , PowerKids Pr.) Rosen Publishing Group, Inc., The.

Hungry Hopper. (Backyard Bugs Ser.). 24p. (J). 7.95 (978-1-4048-0448-7(X)) Picture Window Bks.

Jacobs, Liza. Grasshoppers. 2003. (Wild Wild World Ser.). (Illus.). 24p. (J). 22.45 (978-1-4103-0051-5(X) , Blackbirch Pr., Inc.) Thomson Gale.

Kravetz, Jonathan. Locusts. 2006. (Gross Bugs Ser.). (Illus.). 24p. (J). lib. bdg. (978-1-4042-3042-2(4) , PowerKids Pr.) Rosen Publishing Group, Inc., The.

Lockwood, Sophie. Grasshoppers. 2007. (World of Insects Ser.). 40p. (J). (gr. 2-6). 29.93 (***978-1-59296-823-7(6))** Child's World, Inc.

Locust. 2001. (Zoology Ser.). (J). vinyl bd. 4.95 (978-1-58845-158-3(5)) School Specialty Publishing.

Loewen, Nancy. Hungry Hoppers: Grasshoppers in Your Backyard. Reibeling, Brandon, illus. 2004. (Backyard Bugs Ser.). 24p. (C). (gr. k-3). 22.60 (978-1-4048-0146-2(4)) Picture Window Bks.

Markle, Sandra. Locusts: Insects on the Move. 2008. (Insect World Ser.). (J). lib. bdg. 27.93 (***978-0-8225-7298-5(2)** , Lerner Pubns.) Lerner Publishing Group.

McDonald, Mary Ann. Grasshoppers. 2006. (New Naturebooks). (Illus.). 32p. (J). (gr. 1-5). 27.07 (978-1-59296-639-4(X)) Child's World, Inc.

Miller, Connie Colwell. Grasshoppers. 2005. (Illus.). 24p. (J). 21.26 (978-0-7368-3708-8(6)) Capstone Pr., Inc.

Miller, Sara Swan. Grasshoppers & Crickets of North America. (Animals in Order Ser.). (Illus.). (J). 2003. 48p. (gr. 4-6). pap. 6.95 (978-0-531-16376-4(8)); 2002. 47p. pap. 26.50 (978-0-531-12170-2(4)) Scholastic Library Publishing. (Watts, Franklin).

—Grasshoppers & Crickets of North America. 2002. (gr. 3-6). lib. bdg. 15.25 (978-0-613-59493-6(2)) Tandem Library Bks.

Morris, Neil & Morris, Ting. Grasshopper. 2003. (Illus.). 32p. (J). lib. bdg. 27.10 (978-1-58340-381-5(7)) Smart Apple Media.

Murray, Julie. Grasshoppers. 2005. (Animal Kingdom Set Ii Ser.). (Illus.). 24p. (J). (gr. k-4). lib. bdg. 21.35 (978-1-59197-317-1(1)) ABDO Publishing Co.

Pascoe, Elaine. Crickets & Grasshoppers. Kuhn, Dwight, photos by. 1998. (Nature Close-Up Ser.). (Illus.). 48p. (J). (gr. 4-8). 23.70 (978-1-56711-176-7(9) , Blackbirch Pr., Inc.) Thomson Gale.

Pyers. Grasshoppers 6-Pack. 2004. (Minibeasts up Close Ser.). pap. 40.50 (978-1-4109-1543-6(3)) Harcourt Schl. Pubs.

Pyers, Greg. Grasshoppers up Close. (Minibeasts up Close Ser.). (Illus.). 32p. (J). (ps-ps). 2005. lib. bdg. 27.50 (978-1-4109-1529-0(8)); 2004. pap. (978-1-4109-1536-8(0)) Harcourt Schl. Pubs.

Scholl, Elizabeth J. Grasshopper. 2004. (Bugs Ser.). (Illus.). 32p. (J). (gr. 4-7). 24.95 (978-0-7377-1771-6(8) , Greenhaven Pr., Inc.) Thomson Gale.

Squire, Ann O. Crickets & Grasshoppers. (True Bks.). (J). 2004. (gr. 3-5). pap. 6.95 (978-0-516-29357-8(5)); 2003. (Illus.). 47p. 25.00 (978-0-516-22657-6(6)) Scholastic Library Publishing. (Children's Pr.).

Taylor, Philip. Grasshopper. (Bug Bks.). 32p. pap. 6.95 (978-1-4034-3326-8(7)) Heinemann Library.

Trumbauer, Lisa. The Life Cycle of a Grasshopper. 2003. (Life Cycles Ser.). (Illus.). 24p. (J). (gr. k-1). lib. bdg. 15.93 (978-0-7368-2089-9(2) , Pebble Bks.) Capstone Pr., Inc.

Whitehouse, Patricia. El Saltamontes. Abello, Patricia, tr. 2003. (Los Insectos Ser.). (SPA & ENG., Illus.). 32p. (J). lib. bdg. 23.40 (978-1-4034-3012-0(8)) Heinemann Library.

Zuchora-Walske, Christine. Leaping Grasshoppers. 2000. (Pull Ahead Bks.). (Illus.). 32p. (J). (gr. k-2). lib. bdg. 22.60 (978-0-8225-3634-5(X) , Lerner Pubns.) Lerner Publishing Group.

LOCUSTS—FICTION

Abrams, Harry N., Staff, contrib. by. Grasshopper. 2001. (Portable Pets Ser.). (Illus.). 12p. (J). (ps-ps). bds. 6.95 (978-0-8109-5670-4(5)) Abrams, Harry N. , Inc.

Aesop. The Grasshopper & the Ant: A Tale about Planning. Hockerman, Dennis, illus. 2006. (J). (978-1-59939-082-6(5) , Reader's Digest Young Families, Inc.) Reader's Digest Children's Publishing, Inc.

Barkley, Roger C. Johnny Grasshopper. 2006. 52p. pap. 12.95 (978-1-4241-0221-1(9)) PublishAmerica, Inc.

Erdman & Perez. Mitos y Leyendas Indigenas. 2005. (SPA.). 72p. 13.99 (978-84-241-8013-3(5)) Everest de Ediciones y Distribucion, S.L. ESP. *Dist:* Lectorum Pubns., Inc.

Fleischman, Sid. La Maravillosa Granja de McBroom. Blake, Quentin, illus. 13th ed. 2003. (SPA.). 96p. (J). (gr. 3-5). 7.95 (978-84-204-4885-5(0)) Alfaguara, Ediciones, S.A.- Grupo Santillana ESP. *Dist:* Santillana USA Publishing Co., Inc.

—La Maravillosa Granja de McBroom. Blake, Quentin, illus. (SPA.). 90p. (J). (gr. 3-5). pap. 7.95 (978-968-19-0786-0(8)) Santillana USA Publishing Co., Inc.

Giovanni, Nikki. Jimmy Grasshopper Versus the Ants. Raschka, Christopher, illus. 2007. (J). ***(978-0-7636-3021-8(7))*** Candlewick Pr.

Heiner, Garth Farr. Arty Puts the Bite on Hopper. Melander, Eric, illus. unabr. ed. 2001. (Fun-with-the-Law Ser.: No. 1). 32p. (J). (gr. k-7). pap. 5.95 (978-1-929905-01-0(7)) Fun With the Law, Inc.

—Finders Keepers. Melander, Eric, illus. l.t. unabr. ed. 2001. (Fun-with-the-Law Ser.: No. 4). 32p. (J). (gr. k-7). pap. 5.95 (978-1-929905-04-1(1)) Fun With the Law, Inc.

—Unwanted Muddy. Melander, Eric, illus. l.t. unabr. ed. 2001. (Fun-with-the-Law Ser.: No. 5). 32p. (J). (gr. k-7). pap. 5.95 (978-1-929905-05-8(X)) Fun With the Law, Inc.

Kurtzman, Harvey. The Grasshopper & the Ant. 2002. (Illus.). (YA). (gr. 10 up). 25.00 (978-0-9710080-7-0(0)) Kitchen, Denis Publishing Co.

Quinlan, Janet, adapted by. Hard Work: The Ant & the Grasshopper. 2005. (Illus.). ***(978-1-4127-3761-6(3))*** Publications International, Ltd.

Shaw, Nancy. Ladybug & Grasshopper. Adams Marks, Elizabeth, illus. 2002. (Two Can Read Ser.). 16p. (J). 2.99 (978-1-56472-664-3(9)) Edupress, Inc.

Stone, Forrest. The Ant & Grasshopper Show. 2006. 42.00 ***(978-1-4108-6183-2(X))*** Benchmark Education Co.

White, Mark. La Cigarra y la Hormiga: Version de la Fabula de Esopo. Rojo, Sara, illus. 2006. (Read-It! Readers en Espanol Ser.).Tr. of Ant & the Grasshopper: A Retelling of Aesop's Fable. (SPA.). 32p. (J). (ps-3). 19.95 (978-1-4048-1614-5(3)) Picture Window Bks.

LODGING HOUSES

see Hotels, Motels, etc.

LOG CABINS

Rau, Dana Meachen. Bookworms: The Inside Story, 6 bks., Set. Incl. Castle. 32p. lib. bdg. 22.79 (978-0-7614-2272-3(2)); Igloo. 24p. lib. bdg. 22.79 (978-0-7614-2273-0(0)); Log Cabin. 24p. lib. bdg. 22.79 ***(978-0-7614-2274-7(9));*** Pyramid. 32p. lib. bdg. 22.79 ***(978-0-7614-2275-4(7));*** Skyscraper. 32p. lib. bdg. 22.79 (978-0-7614-2276-1(5)); Tepee. 32p. lib. bdg. 22.79 (978-0-7614-2277-8(3)); (Illus.). (J). (gr. k-2). 2006. 2006. Set lib. bdg. 136.71 ***(978-0-7614-2271-6(4)*** , Benchmark Bks.) Cavendish, Marshall Corp.

—Log Cabin. 2006. (Bookworms Ser.). (Illus.). 24p. (J). (gr. k-2). lib. bdg. 22.79 ***(978-0-7614-2274-7(9)*** , Benchmark Bks.) Cavendish, Marshall Corp.

Skinner, Tina. Log & Timber Frame Homes. 2003. (Schiffer Design Book Ser.). (Illus.). 224p. (gr. 10-13). 44.95 (978-0-7643-1754-5(7)) Schiffer Publishing, Ltd.

LOGGING

see Lumber and Lumbering

LOGIC

see also Knowledge, Theory of; Probabilities; Reasoning; Thought and Thinking

Berry, Joy Wilt. Saying No. Smith, Maggie, illus. 2001. (J). (978-0-439-34150-9(7)) Scholastic, Inc.

Brainy Baby Vertical Right/Left Tab Book. 2005. (Brainy Baby Ser.). (978-1-59394-450-6(0)) Bendon Publishing International.

Doudna, Kelly. I Can Predict, I Won't be Tricked. 2007. (Illus.). 24p. (J). 19.93 (978-1-59928-582-5(7) , Sand-Castle) ABDO Publishing Co.

How Would the Story End? 2000. 62p. spiral bd. 26.00 (978-1-886143-48-7(X)) Great Ideas for Teaching, Inc.

Hubbard, L. Ron. The Thinking Book. 2002. (Illus.). 380p. (YA). (gr. 5-9). pap. 29.50 (978-0-89739-011-8(3)) Heron Bks.

Kofman, Victoria. Guni-Pi Academy, Math & Logic: Hands-On Textbook for 4 - 7 Year Olds. 2006. spiral bd. (978-0-9777171-0-1(0)) VK Publishing, Inc.

—Guni-Pi Academy, Math & Logic: Hands-on Textbook for 4 - 7 Year Olds - Non-Laminated. 2006. spiral bd. (978-0-9777171-2-5(7)) VK Publishing, Inc.

Kreeft, Peter. Socratic Logic: A Logic Text Using Socratic Method, Platonic Questions, & Aristotelian Principles. 2004. (Illus.). x, 397p. (YA). 40.00 (978-1-890318-89-5(2)) St. Augustine's Pr., Inc.

Logic & Critical Thinking. 2003. (Mathematical Mind Ser.). 48p. (gr. 6-8). 5.99 (978-0-7424-0086-3(7) , IF2906) School Specialty Publishing.

Logic Fun. 2003. (Middle School Mastery Ser.). 64p. (gr. 5-8). 3.99 (978-1-56822-467-1(2) , IF2730) School Specialty Publishing.

Nance, James B. Intermediate Logic: Student. 2nd ed. 2006. 228p. (YA). per. 27.00 (978-1-59128-035-4(4)) Canon Pr.

—Intermediate Logic: Student- Old Cover. Marston, Paula, illus. 2002. 164p. (YA). (gr. 9). spiral bd. 25.00 (978-1-885767-13-4(7)) Canon Pr.

Nance, James B. & Wilson, Douglas. Introductory Logic: Student. 4th ed. 2005. 272p. (J). per. 29.00 (978-1-59128-033-0(8)) Canon Pr.

Pederson, Bridget. I Can Predict, I Won't Be Tricked! 2006. (Illus.). 24p. (J). (978-1-59928-583-2(5)) ABDO Publishing Co.

Schoenfield, Mark & Rosenblatt, Jeannette. Adventures with Logic. 2001. 64p. (J). (gr. 5-7). pap. 9.99 (978-0-8224-0285-5(8) , FE0285) Schaffer, Frank Pubns.

—Discovering Logic. 2001. 64p. (J). (gr. 4-6). pap. 9.99 (978-0-8224-1915-0(7) , FE1915) Schaffer, Frank Pubns.

—Playing with Logic. 2001. 64p. (J). (gr. 3-5). pap. 9.99 (978-0-8224-5310-9(X) , FE5310) Schaffer, Frank Pubns.

Schultz-Ferrell, Karren, et al. Introduction to Reasoning & Proof: Grades 3-5. 2007. (Math Process Standards Ser.). (Illus.). 160p. (C). pap. 25.00 ***(978-0-325-01033-5(1)*** , E01033) Heinemann.

Schulz, Charles M. The Peanuts Guide to the Seasons: A Jumbo Activity Book. Bennett, Elizabeth, illus. 2003. (Peanuts Club with Charlie Brown & Friends Ser.). 144p. (J). (978-0-439-46826-8(4)) Scholastic, Inc.

Schulz, Charles M. & Bennett, Elizabeth. The Peanuts Guide to Sports: A Jumbo Activity Book. 2003. (Peanuts Club with Charlie Brown & Friends Ser.). (Illus.). 144p. (J). (978-0-439-46824-4(8)) Scholastic, Inc.

Sherard, Wade H., III. Logic Decimal Problems. 1999. 64p. (gr. 4-11). pap. 10.95 (978-0-7690-0082-4(7)) Seymour, Dale Pubns.

LOMBARDI, VINCE, 1913-1970

Roensch, Greg. Vince Lombardi. 2003. (Football Hall of Famers Ser.). (Illus.). 112p. (YA). (gr. 5-8). lib. bdg. 29.25 (978-0-8239-3610-6(4) , Rosen Central) Rosen Publishing Group, Inc., The.

LONDON, JACK, 1876-1916

Bankston, John. Jack London. 2004. (Classic Storytellers Ser.). (Illus.). 48p. (J). (gr. 4-8). lib. bdg. 20.95 (978-1-58415-263-7(X)) Mitchell Lane Pubs., Inc.

Buckwalter, Stephanie. A Student's Guide to Jack London. 2007. (Understanding Literature Ser.). (Illus.). 160p. (YA). (gr. 6). lib. bdg. 27.93 ***(978-0-7660-2707-7(4))*** Enslow Pubs., Inc.

DeKoster, Katie, ed. The Call of the Wild. 1998. (Literary Companion to American Literature Ser.). (Illus.). 224p. (YA). (gr. 9-12). lib. bdg. (978-1-56510-830-1(2) , Greenhaven Pr., Inc.) Thomson Gale.

Dyer, Daniel. Jack London: A Biography. 2002. 240p. (J). pap. 5.99 (978-0-590-22217-4(1)) Scholastic, Inc.

Loewen, Nancy. Jack London. 1998. (Notebooks Ser.). 48p. 17.95 (978-1-56846-157-1(7) , Creative Education) Creative Co., The.

Stefoff, Rebecca. Jack London: An American Original. 2002. (Portraits Ser.). (Illus.). 128p. (YA). 28.00 (978-0-19-512223-7(2)) Oxford Univ. Pr., Inc.

Streissguth, Thomas. Jack London. 2005. (Biography Ser.). (Illus.). 112p. (gr. 6-12). lib. bdg. 27.93 (978-0-8225-4987-1(5)) Lerner Publishing Group.

LONDON (ENGLAND)

Gifford, Clive. So You Think You Know London? 2004. 160p. (J). pap. 8.95 (978-0-340-88189-7(5) , Hodder & Stoughton) Hodder General Publishing Division GBR. *Dist:* Trafalgar Square Publishing.

Hatt, Christine. London. 2000. (World Cities Ser.). (Illus.). 48p. (J). (gr. 2-6). lib. bdg. 16.95 (978-1-929298-29-7(3)) Chrysalis Education.

MacGowan, Shane & O'Callaghan, Deirdre. Hide That Can: A Photographic Diary of the Men of Arlington House. 2002. (Illus.). 192p. 39.95 (978-0-9542079-8-4(X)) Trolley GBR. *Dist:* D.A.P./Distributed Art Pubs.

Mason, Paul. London. Bowden, Rob, photos by. 2006. (Global Cities Ser.). 64p. (J). (gr. 5-8). 30.00 (978-0-7910-8852-4(9) , Chelsea Hse.) Facts On File, Inc.

McLaren, Chris. Rats, Bags, & Frogs of London. 2004. (Illus.). 96p. 8.99 (978-1-904153-05-4(4)) Watling St., Ltd. GBR. *Dist:* Trafalgar Square Publishing.

Nicholson, Louise & Cox, Paul. Look Out London! A Child's Own Guide. 2nd ed. 2000. (Illus.). 48p. (J). (gr. 4). pap. 9.95 (978-0-09-940327-2(7)) Random Hse. GBR. *Dist:* Trafalgar Square Publishing.

Riley, Gail Blasser. Tower of London: England's Ghostly Castle. 2006. (Illus.). 32p. (J). lib. bdg. 25.27 (978-1-59716-249-4(3)) Bearport Publishing Co., Inc.

Sasek, Miroslav. This Is London. 2004. (This Is ... Ser.). (Illus.). 64p. (J). (gr. k). 17.95 (978-0-7893-1062-0(7)) Universe Publishing.

Stacey, Gill. London. 2003. (Great Cities of the World Ser.). (Illus.). 48p. (J). (gr. 5 up). pap. 11.95 (978-0-8368-5182-3(X)); lib. bdg. 30.00 (978-0-8368-5022-2(X)) Stevens, Gareth Inc. (World Almanac Library).

LONDON (ENGLAND)—FICTION

Abbott, Candy. Gavin Goodfellow: The Lure of Burnt Swamp. 2007. 368p. pap. 14.95 ***(978-1-886068-03-2(8))*** Fruitbearer Publishing.

Abel, Heather & McKnight, Gillian. To Catch a Prince. 2005. 192p. (YA). 14.95 (978-0-689-87733-9(1)) Simon & Schuster Children's Publishing.

Abela, Deborah. Mission: Spy Force Revealed. O'Connor, George, illus. (Spy Force Ser.). 288p. (J). 2006. pap. 5.99 (978-1-4169-4024-1(3) , Aladdin); 2005. (gr. 4-7). 9.95 (978-0-689-87358-4(1) , Simon & Schuster Children's Publishing) Simon & Schuster Children's Publishing.

Adone, Claudio. My Grandfather Jack the Ripper. 2000. Tr. of Mio Nonno Jack Lo Squartatore. (Illus.). 304p. (J). (gr. 7-10). 19.00 (978-1-928746-16-4(0)) Herodias.

Ahern, Carolyn L. Tino Turtle Travels to London, England. Burt Sullivan, Neallia, illus. 2007. 36p. (J). 17.95 incl. audio compact disk ***(978-0-9793158-0-0(8))*** Tino Turtle Travels, LLC.

—Tino Turtle Travels to London, England Book & Singalong PlushToy Bundle. 2007. (J). 29.95 incl. audio compact disk ***(978-0-9793158-5-5(9))*** Tino Turtle Travels, LLC.

Ashcroft, Eagle. Nibs Goes to London. 2007. 104p. pap. 11.00 ***(978-1-60047-075-2(0))*** Wasteland Pr.

Ashley, Bernard. Little Soldier: A Novel. 2002. (Illus.). 240p. (J). (gr. 9 up). pap. 16.95 (978-0-439-22424-6(1) , Scholastic Pr.) Scholastic, Inc.

Atkinson, Sally. The Tales of Tango Bk. II: The Sticky Situation. Metzel, Lee, illus. 1998. 32p. (J). (gr. k-4). 14.95 (978-0-9653034-1-5(1)) Tango's Grove Publishing.

Barrie, J. M. Peter Pan. (SPA.). 191p. 15.95 (978-84-206-3689-4(4)) Alianza Editorial, S. A. ESP. *Dist:* Distribooks, Inc.

—Peter Pan: Peter & Wendy & Peter Pan in Kensington Gardens. 2004. (Illus.). 272p. (gr. 12). pap. 9.00 (978-0-14-243793-3(X) , Penguin Classics) Penguin Group (USA) Inc.

Barrie, J. M. Peter Pan in Kensington Gardens. 2006. pap. ***(978-1-4065-0950-2(7))*** Dodo Pr.

Becker, Tom. Darkside Book 1 Don't Turn Out the Light. 2008. 304p. (J). pap. 16.99 ***(978-0-545-03739-6(5)*** , Orchard Bks.) Scholastic, Inc.

Bemelmans, Ludwig. Madeline in London. Bemelmans, Ludwig, illus. 2002. (Madeline Ser.). (Illus.). (J). 14.04 (978-0-7587-5002-0(1)) Book Wholesalers, Inc.

—Madeline in London. Bemelmans, Ludwig, illus. deluxe ed. 2000. (Madeline Ser.). (Illus.). 64p. (J). (ps-3). pap. 7.99 (978-0-14-056649-9(X) , Viking Juvenile) Penguin Group (USA) Inc.

—Madeline in London. 2000. (gr. k-3). lib. bdg. 15.30 (978-0-8085-2353-6(8)) Tandem Library Bks.

—Madeline in London. Bemelmans, Ludwig, illus. 2000. (Madeline Ser.). (Illus.). (J). (ps-3). (978-0-606-18429-8(5)) Tandem Library Bks.

Blacker, Terence. The Angel Factory. (Illus.). 224p. 2003. (J). (gr. k-17). pap. 5.99 (978-0-689-86413-1(2) , Aladdin); 2002. (YA). (gr. 6-9). 16.95 (978-0-689-85171-1(5)) Simon & Schuster Children's Publishing.

Bloor, Edward. London Calling. 2006. 304p. (gr. 5). (J). lib. bdg. 18.99 (978-0-375-93635-7(1)); (YA). 16.95 (978-0-375-83635-0(7)) Random Hse. Children's Bks. (Knopf Bks. for Young Readers).

Borlenghi, Patricia. Chaucer the Cat & the Animal Pilgrims. Greenfield, Giles, illus. 2001. 77p. (J). (gr. 3-6). 22.99 (978-0-7475-4491-3(3)) Bloomsbury Publishing Plc GBR. *Dist:* Trafalgar Square Publishing.

Brooke, Samantha. Portraits from the Pipes. Simpson, Fiona, ed. 2006. (Flushed Away Ser.). 32p. (J). pap. 3.99 (978-0-439-90080-5(8)) Scholastic, Inc.

Brooks, Kevin. Candy. 2006. 384p. (J). pap. 7.99 (978-0-439-68328-9(9) , PUSH); 2005. 368p. pap. 16.95 (978-0-439-68327-2(0) , Chicken Hse., The) Scholastic, Inc.

Brundige, Patricia. Traveling with Aunt Patty: Aunt Patty Visits London. Wright, Cindy, ed. Hanlon, Leslie, illus. Date not set. (J). (gr. 1-4). 12.95 (978-0-9659668-0-1(1)) Aunt Patty's Travels-London.

Buckley-Archer, Linda. The Time Thief. 2007. (Gideon Trilogy Ser.). 512p. (J). (gr. 5 up). 17.99 ***(978-1-4169-1527-0(3))*** Simon & Schuster Children's Publishing.

Burnett, Frances Hodgson. A Little Princess. Corvino, Lucy, illus. 2005. (Classic Starts Ser.). 160p. 4.95 (978-1-4027-1275-3(8)) Sterling Publishing Co., Inc.

—A Little Princess. Marcos, Pablo, illus. 2005. (Great Illustrated Classics Ser.). 239p. (J). (gr. 3-8). 21.35 (978-1-59679-246-3(9) , ABDO & Daughters) ABDO Publishing Co.

—A Little Princess: The Story of Sara Crewe. (J). 16.95 (978-0-8488-1253-9(0)) Amereon LTD.

—A Little Princess: The Story of Sara Crewe. Warren, Eliza, ed. Marcos, Pablo, illus. 2006. 239p. (YA). reprint ed. 10.00 (978-0-7567-9835-2(3)) DIANE Publishing Co.

—A Little Princess: The Story of Sara Crewe. unabr. ed. 2000. (Dover Juvenile Classics Ser.). (Illus.). 240p. (J). (gr. 4-7). pap. 2.00 (978-0-486-41446-1(9)) Dover Pubns., Inc.

—A Little Princess: The Story of Sara Crewe. Rust, Graham, illus. 2000. 192p. (YA). (gr. 4-7). reprint ed. 18.95 (978-0-87923-784-4(8)) Godine, David R. Pub.

—A Little Princess: The Story of Sara Crewe. Collier, Mary & McClintock, Barbara, illus. 2000. 32p. (J). (ps-3). 18.99 (978-0-06-027891-5(9)) HarperCollins Pubs.

—A Little Princess: The Story of Sara Crewe. 2000. (Illus.). 32p. (J). (ps-3). 16.89 (978-0-06-029010-8(2)) HarperCollins Pubs.

—A Little Princess: The Story of Sara Crewe. Tudor, Tasha, illus. 1999. 336p. (J). (gr. 4 up). 17.99 (978-0-397-30693-0(8)) HarperCollins Pubs.

—A Little Princess: The Story of Sara Crewe. Lindskoog, Kathryn, ed. Chitouras, Barbara, illus. 2002. (Classics for Young Readers Ser.). 208p. (J). pap. 7.99 (978-0-87552-727-7(2)) P & R Publishing.

—A Little Princess: The Story of Sara Crewe. 2002. (Classics Ser.). (Illus.). 272p. pap. 10.00 (978-0-14-243701-8(8) , Penguin Classics) Penguin Group (USA) Inc.

—A Little Princess: The Story of Sara Crewe. 2006. (Scholastic Classics Ser.). v, 178p. (J). (gr. 9-12). 25.00 (978-0-531-16991-9(X) , Watts, Franklin) Scholastic Library Publishing.

—A Little Princess: The Story of Sara Crewe. Rust, Graham, illus. (J). pap. 22.95 (978-0-590-24079-6(X)) Scholastic, Inc.

—A Little Princess: The Story of Sara Crewe. 2001. (gr. 3-6). lib. bdg. 11.80 (978-0-613-63210-2(9)) Tandem Library Bks.

—A Little Princess: The Story of Sara Crewe. l.t. ed. 2003. 342p. (J). 29.95 (978-0-7862-5842-0(X)) Thorndike Pr.

—A Little Princess: With a Discussion of Generosity. Gribbon, Sean & Jael, illus. Gribbon, Sean & Jael, trs. 2003. (Values in Action Illustrated Classics Ser.). (J). (978-1-59203-050-7(5)) Learning Challenge, Inc.

—A Little Princess Book & Charm. Tudor, Tasha, illus. 1999. (Charming Classics). 336p. (J). (gr. 4 up). pap. 6.99 (978-0-694-01236-7(X) , Harper Festival) HarperCollins Pubs.

—Sara Crewe. l.t. ed. 2006. 92p. pap. (978-1-84637-263-6(1)) Echo Library.

—Sara Crewe or What Happened at Miss Minc. 2005. pap. 20.95 (978-0-7661-9708-4(5)) Kessinger Publishing, LLC.

—Sara Crewe or What Happened at Miss Minchin's. 2006. (ENG.). 88p. per. 9.45 (978-1-59462-359-2(7) , 395, Book Jungle) Standard Pubns., Inc.

—Sara Crewe or What Happened at Miss Minchin's - 1903. 2006. (ENG.). 88p. per. 9.45 (978-1-59462-360-8(0) , 396, Book Jungle) Standard Pubns., Inc.

Center for Learning Network Staff. Oliver Twist: Curriculum Unit —Novel Series. 2001. (Novel Ser.). 65p. (YA). tchr. ed., spiral bd. 19.95 (978-1-56077-684-0(6)) Ctr. for Learning, The.

Chitty, Joan E. Charlie Macaffee: Search for the Genie's Body. 2005. 267p. pap. 21.95 (978-1-4241-0007-1(0)) PublishAmerica, Inc.

Chris Wooding. The Haunting of Alaizabel Cray. l.t. ed. 2006. 463p. (YA). 22.95 (978-0-7862-8739-0(X)) Thorndike Pr.

Christen, Dennis H. Lundon's Bridge & the Three Keys. 2005. (YA). lib. bdg., act. bk. ed. 24.95 (978-0-9718151-3-1(5)); 2006. (ENG.). (J). per. 12.95 (978-0-9718151-2-4(7)) CG Star, L.L.C.

Chronicle Books LLC Staff. Charlotte in London. 2008. (J). 16.95 (978-0-8118-5635-5(6)) Chronicle Bks. LLC.

Chute, Marchette. The Wonderful Winter. 2002. 256p. 12.95 (978-0-9714612-1-5(X)) Green Mansion Pr. LLC.

Clarke, Nicole. London Calling. 2007. (Flirt Ser.: No. 8). 224p. (J). pap. 6.99 (978-0-448-44464-2(X) , Grosset & Dunlap) Penguin Group (USA) Inc.

Cooney, Caroline B. Terrorist. 1999. (978-0-606-17447-3(8)) Tandem Library Bks.

Cooper, Patrick. Tell Me Lies. 2007. (YA). (gr. 9). 304p. 15.99 (978-0-385-73270-3(8)); 288p. lib. bdg. 18.99 (978-0-385-90287-8(5)) Random Hse. Children's Bks. (Delacorte Bks. for Young Readers).

Cooper, Susan. King of Shadows. Clapp, John, illus. 192p. (J). (gr. 5-9). 2001. mass mkt. 5.99 (978-0-689-84445-4(X) , Aladdin); 1999. 16.00 (978-0-689-82817-1(9) , McElderry, Margaret K.) Simon & Schuster Children's Publishing.

—King of Shadows. l.t. ed. 2000. (Thorndike Press Large Print Juvenile Ser.). (Illus.). 246p. (J). (gr. 8-12). 21.95 (978-0-7862-2706-8(0)) Thorndike Pr.

Coppel, Chris. Far from Burden Dell. 2005. 286p. (J). pap. 4.95 (978-0-9746481-6-3(7)) Brown Barn Bks.

Craig, Joe. Jimmy Coates: Assassin? 2005. 224p. (J). (gr. 5 up). 15.99 (978-0-06-077263-5(8)) HarperCollins Pubs.

—Jimmy Coates: Assassin? 2006. 224p. (J). pap. 5.99 (978-0-06-077265-9(4) , Harper Trophy) HarperCollins Pubs.

Cutler, Lynn W. Baggage to London. Ohi, Ruth, illus. 2003. (Annikins Ser.: Vol. 13). 12p. (Orig.). (J). (ps-2). pap. 0.99 (978-1-55037-345-5(5)) Annick Pr., Ltd. CAN. *Dist:* Firefly Bks., Ltd.

Dalmatian Press Staff. Where Dreams Begin: Coloring & Activity Book with Stickers. 2004. (Disney Princess Ser.). (Illus.). 64p. (J). pap. 1.69 (978-1-4037-0861-8(4)) Dalmatian Pr.

Danziger, Paula. Thames Doesn't Rhyme with James. 1999. (Illus.). 160p. (J). (gr. 5-9). pap. 3.99 (978-0-698-11788-4(3) , Putnam Juvenile) Penguin Group (USA) Inc.

—Thames Doesn't Rhyme with James. 153p. (J). pap. 3.99 (978-0-8072-1473-2(6) , Listening Library) Random Hse. Audio Publishing Group.

—Thames Doesn't Rhyme with James. 1999. (gr. 3-6). lib. bdg. 13.00 (978-0-613-09469-6(7)) Tandem Library Bks.

—You Can't Eat Your Chicken Pox, Amber Brown. (Amber Brown Ser.: No. 2). 101p. (J). (gr. 3-6). pap. 3.50 (978-0-8072-1290-5(3) , Listening Library) Random Hse. Audio Publishing Group.

—You Can't Eat Your Chicken Pox, Amber Brown. Ross, Tony, illus. 2006. (Amber Brown Ser.). 112p. (J). (gr. 2). pap. 4.99 (978-0-14-240629-8(5) , Puffin) Penguin Group (USA) Inc.

David, Erica. Plumbing Problems. Simpson, Fiona, ed. 2006. (Flushed Away Ser.). 32p. (J). pap. 3.99 (978-0-439-90077-5(8)) Scholastic, Inc.

Davoll, Barbara. To London to See the Queen. Hockerman, Dennis, illus. 1999. (New Christopher Churchmouse Adventures Ser.: Vol. 4). 24p. (J). (ps-3). 9.99 (978-0-8024-5399-0(6)) Moody Pubs.

de Oliveira, Eddie. Johnny Hazzard. 2005. 352p. (J). (gr. 7-12). pap. 16.95 (978-0-439-67361-7(5) , PUSH) Scholastic, Inc.

Deekster, Deek. Ozzie Rozzie. 2005. 41p. (YA). pap. 7.85 (978-1-4116-6420-3(5)) Lulu.com.

Dick Whittington: Individual Title, 6 packs. 32p. (gr. 3 up). 37.00 (978-0-7635-9681-1(7)) Rigby Education.

Dickens, Charles. A Christmas Carol. l.t. ed. 1999. (Large Print Heritage Ser.). 140p. (YA). (gr. 7-12). lib. bdg. 24.95 (978-1-58118-041-1(1) , 22510) LRS.

—Oliver Twist. Andrew, Ian, illus. 2006. (Read & Listen Bks.). 64p. (J). 9.99 (978-0-7566-1835-3(5)) Dorling Kindersley Publishing, Inc.

—Oliver Twist. 2002. (Classics for Young Readers Ser.). (SPA.). (YA). 14.95 (978-84-392-0919-5(3) , EV30603) Gaviota Ediciones ESP. *Dist:* Lectorum Pubns., Inc.

—Oliver Twist. 2007. (Enriched Classics Ser.). 672p. pap. 4.95 ***(978-1-4165-3475-4(X)*** , Pocket) Simon & Schuster.

—Oliver Twist. 2000. (SPA.). 288p. (YA). (gr. 4-7). pap. 14.95 (978-0-595-13258-4(8)) iUniverse, Inc.

—Oliver Twist. Andreasen, Dan, illus. 2006. (Classic Starts Ser.). 160p. 4.95 (978-1-4027-2665-1(1)) Sterling Publishing Co., Inc.

—Oliver Twist. Gelev, Penko, illus. 2006. (Graphic Classics Ser.). 48p. (J). (gr. 4-8). 15.99 (978-0-7641-5975-6(5)); pap. 8.99 (978-0-7641-3490-6(6)) Barron's Educational Series, Inc.

—Oliver Twist. abr. ed. Date not set. (Nelson Readers Ser.). (J). pap. (978-0-17-557020-1(5)) Addison-Wesley Longman, Inc.

—Oliver Twist. abr. ed. (J). 9.95 (978-1-56156-372-2(2)) Kidsbooks, Inc.

—Oliver Twist. 2nd abr. ed. 2000. (Green Apple). 96p. (YA). pap. (978-1-57159-008-4(0)) Los Andes Publishing Co.

—Oliver Twist: With a Discussion of Honesty. 2003. (Values in Action Illustrated Classics Ser.). (J). (978-1-59203-051-4(3)) Learning Challenge, Inc.

Dixon, Franklin W. The London Deception. 1999. (Hardy Boys Mystery Stories Ser.: No. 158). (J). (gr. 3-6). (978-0-606-19052-7(X)) Tandem Library Bks.

Dowd, Siobhan. The London Eye Mystery. 2008. 336p. (J). ***(978-0-375-84976-3(9));*** lib. bdg. ***(978-0-375-94976-0(3))*** Random Hse. Children's Bks. (Fickling, David Bks.).

Downey, Glen. Rebel Prince. Okum, David, illus. 2007. 48p. (J). lib. bdg. 23.08 ***(978-1-4242-1642-0(7))*** Fitzgerald Bks.

Enthoven, Sam. The Black Tattoo. 2006. 512p. (J). (gr. 5-12). 19.99 (978-1-59514-114-9(6) , Razorbill) Penguin Group (USA) Inc.

Eschberger, Beverly. The Elephants Visit London: An Elephant Family Adventure. Gower, Jim, illus. l.t. ed. 2007. 96p. (J). per. 3.99 (978-1-932926-30-9(5) , Kinkajou Pr.) Artemesia Publishing, LLC.

Estrada, Ric, illus. Oliver Twist. 2002. (Great Illustrated Classics Ser.). 240p. (J). (gr. 3-8). 21.35 (978-1-57765-697-5(0) , ABDO & Daughters) ABDO Publishing Co.

Fearnley, Jan. Colin & the Curly Claw. Fearnley, Jan, illus. 2001. (Blue Bananas Ser.). (Illus.). 48p. (J). (gr. 1-2). (978-0-7787-0840-7(3)); pap. (978-0-7787-0886-5(1)) Crabtree Publishing Co.

—Colin & the Curly Claw. 2002. (gr. k-3). lib. bdg. 12.95 (978-0-613-52821-4(2)) Tandem Library Bks.

Fletcher, Charlie. Stoneheart. 2007. (Stoneheart Trilogy Ser.: Bk. 1). 464p. (gr. 5-9). 16.99 ***(978-1-4231-0175-8(8))*** Hyperion Pr.

Francis, Pauline & Dickens, Charles. Oliver Twist. 2000. (Fast Track Classics Ser.). (Illus.). 48p. (YA). pap. 9.99 (978-0-237-52537-8(2) , Evans Brothers, Limited) Evans Publishing Group GBR. *Dist:* Independent Pubs. Group.

Godden, Rumer. An Episode of Sparrows. 2004. (New York Review Children's Collection). 256p. (J). reprint ed. 16.95 (978-1-59017-124-0(1) , NYR Children's Collection) New York Review of Books, Inc., The.

Gordon, Roderick. Tunnels. 2008. 480p. (J). pap. 17.99 ***(978-0-439-87177-8(8)*** , Chicken Hse., The) Scholastic, Inc.

Griffiths, Robert. Adventures of Clive. 2005. 45p. (J). pap. 10.01 (978-1-4116-5332-0(7)); 89p. pap. 8.81 (978-1-4116-5191-3(X)) Lulu.com.

Hall, Margaret & Jones, Dawn L. Sebastian at the Tower of London. Wenzel, David, illus. 2001. (Suitcase Bear Adventures Ser.). (J). (978-0-9713174-1-3(0) , Bear & Co.) Bear & Co.

Halsey, Jacqueline. Peggy's Letter. 2005. (Orca Young Readers Ser.). (Illus.). 144p. (J). (gr. 3-6). pap. 5.95 (978-1-55143-363-9(X)) Orca Bk. Pubs. USA.

Hattersley, Ray. Buster's Diaries: The True Story of A Dog & His Man. 2001. (gr. 3-6). lib. bdg. 21.05 (978-0-613-51806-2(3)) Tandem Library Bks.

Hendry, Frances. Quest for a Queen: The Jackdaw. 2006. pap. ***(978-1-905665-05-1(9))*** Pollinger In Print.

Henty, G. A. When London Burned: A Story of Restoration Times & the Great Fire. l.t. ed. 2005. 724p. pap. (978-1-84637-212-4(7)) Echo Library.

Horowitz, Anthony. The Devil & His Boy. 2007. 192p. (J). 6.99 (978-0-14-240797-4(6) , Puffin); 2000. 1p. (YA). (gr. 5-9). 17.99 (978-0-399-23432-3(2) , Philomel) Penguin Group (USA) Inc.

—The Devil & His Boy. 2001. (978-0-606-22508-3(0)); (gr. 5-8). lib. bdg. 14.15 (978-0-613-44387-6(X)) Tandem Library Bks.

—Public Enemy Number Two. 2004. (Diamond Brothers Ser.). 208p. (J). (gr. 5). 16.99 (978-0-399-24154-3(X) , Philomel) ; pap. 6.99 (978-0-14-240218-4(4) , Puffin) Penguin Group (USA) Inc.

—Scorpia. (Alex Rider Ser.: Bk. 5). (YA). (gr. 5). 2006. 400p. pap. 7.99 (978-0-14-240578-9(7) , Puffin); 2005. 320p. 17.99 (978-0-399-24151-2(5) , Philomel) Penguin Group (USA) Inc.

—South by Southeast. 2005. (Diamond Brothers Ser.). 160p. (YA). (gr. 5-9). 16.99 (978-0-399-24155-0(8) , Philomel) Penguin Group (USA) Inc.

—Three of Diamonds. 2005. (Diamond Brothers Ser.). 240p. (J). (gr. 5). pap. 6.99 (978-0-14-240298-6(2) , Puffin); (YA). (gr. 4). 16.99 (978-0-399-24157-4(4) , Philomel) Penguin Group (USA) Inc.

Hoving, Isabel. The Dream Merchant. Velmans, Hester, tr. from DUT. 2005. 640p. (YA). (gr. 7 up). 19.99 (978-0-7636-2880-2(8)) Candlewick Pr.

Hunt, Elizabeth Singer. The Caper of the Crowned Jewels. 2008. (Secret Agent Jack Stalwart Ser.). 128p. (J). (gr. 1-4). pap. 4.99 ***(978-1-60286-013-1(0))*** Weinstein Bks.

Hutchinson, Emily. Oliver Twist. abr. ed. 2001. (gr. 7-12). lib. bdg. 15.25 (978-0-613-36566-6(6)) Tandem Library Bks.

Imbernon, Maite & Dickens, Charles. Oliver Twist. 2003. (Timeless Classics Ser.). (SPA., Illus.). 92p. (J). pap. 10.95 (978-84-204-5750-5(7)) Santillana USA Publishing Co., Inc.

Jarvis, Robin & Jarvis, Robert M. The Alchemist's Cat. 2004. 320p. (YA). 17.95 (978-1-58717-257-1(7) , SeaStar Bks.) Chronicle Bks. LLC.

Johnson, Gillian. Thora & the Green Sea-Unicorn: Another Half-Mermaid Tale. Johnson, Gillian, illus. 2007. 288p. (J). (gr. 4-6). 15.99 ***(978-0-06-074381-9(6));*** lib. bdg. 16.89 ***(978-0-06-074382-6(4))*** HarperCollins Pubs. (Tegen, Katherine Bks).

Johnston, Antony. Three Days in Europe, Vol. 1. 2003. (Illus.). 144p. pap. 14.95 (978-1-929998-72-2(4)) Oni Pr., Inc.

Keene, Carolyn. Dangerous Plays. 2006. 146p. (J). (978-1-4156-5040-0(3) , Aladdin) Simon & Schuster Children's Publishing.

Keep, Linda Lowery. Peace, Love, & Rock 'n' Roll. Field, Ann, illus. 2005. 144p. (J). 9.95 (978-0-307-10519-6(9) , Golden Bks.) Random Hse. Children's Bks.

Kenney, Cindy. The Star of Christmas: A Very Veggie Christmas Story. Bredow, Dennis, illus. 2002. 40p. (gr. k-3). 14.99 (978-0-310-70504-8(5)) Zonderkidz.

Kerr, P. B. The Akhenaten Adventure. 2004. (Children of the Lamp Ser.: Bk. 1). 368p. (J). (gr. 4-7). pap. 16.95 (978-0-439-67019-7(5) , Orchard Bks.) Scholastic, Inc.

Klearman-Cooper, Mel. The Dirty Little Orphan Girl. 2005. 50p. pap. 12.95 (978-1-4137-5891-7(6)) PublishAmerica, Inc.

Lane, Leonie. Tom Turner & the Dream Box. 2006. 119p. pap. ***(978-1-84685-460-6(1)*** , Exposure Publishing) Meadow Bks.

LeFaucheur, Sandi. The Secret Shelter. 2005. (Illus.). 144p. (J). pap. 12.95 (978-0-9746481-4-9(0)) Brown Barn Bks.

Levine, Phyllis. At the Skylight: With Matilda. 2003. pap. 12.95 (978-1-891429-45-3(0)) Armadillo Publishing Corp.

—At the Skylight with Matilda. 2007. 156p. pap. 12.95 ***(978-1-60047-089-9(0))*** Wasteland Pr.

—Matilda. 2007. 108p. pap. 12.95 ***(978-1-60047-079-0(3))*** Wasteland Pr.

Madonna. Goodbye, Grace? Fulvimari, Jeffrey, illus. 2007. (English Roses Ser.). 124p. (J). (gr. 3-7). 9.99 ***(978-0-14-240883-4(2)*** , Puffin) Penguin Group (USA) Inc.

—The New Girl. Fulvimari, Jeffrey, illus. 2007. (English Roses Ser.). 123p. (J). (gr. 2). 9.99 ***(978-0-14-240884-1(0)*** , Puffin) Penguin Group (USA) Inc.

Madonna & Madonna. Friends for Life!, No. 1. Fulvimari, Jeffrey, illus. 2007. (English Roses Ser.). 83p. (J). (gr. 3-7). 9.99 ***(978-0-14-241114-8(0)*** , Puffin) Penguin Group (USA) Inc.

Manning, Sarra. Pretty Things. 2006. 272p. (YA). (gr. 9). pap. 6.99 (978-0-14-240539-0(6) , Puffin) Penguin Group (USA) Inc.

Mark, Jan. Eyes Wide Open. 2003. (ENG., Illus.). 105p. ***(978-0-7136-7648-8(5))*** A & C Black.

Marks, Graham. Omega Place. 2007. 256p. (YA). (gr. 7 up). 16.95 ***(978-1-59990-127-5(7)*** , Bloomsbury Children) Bloomsbury Publishing.

Marsh, Carole. The Mystery at Big Ben: London, England. 2005. (Carole Marsh Mysteries Ser.). (Illus.). 144p. (J). (gr. 3-5). 14.95 (978-0-635-03472-4(7)); pap. 5.95 (978-0-635-03469-4(7)) Gallopade International.

Mayhew, James. Carlota Visita Londres. 2004. (SPA., Illus.). 36p. 16.99 (978-84-8488-089-9(3)) Serres, Ediciones, S. L. ESP. *Dist:* Lectorum Pubns., Inc.

McCaughrean, Geraldine. Dog Days. 2005. (Illus.). pap. 24.95 incl. audio (978-0-7540-6290-5(2) , Chivers Children's Audio Bks.) BBC Audiobooks America.

McKnight, Gillian. To Catch a Prince. 2006. 240p. (YA). mass mkt. 5.99 (978-0-689-87734-6(X) , Simon Pulse) Simon & Schuster Children's Publishing.

Mechling, Lauren & Moser, Laura. Foreign Exposure: The Social Climber Abroad. 2007. 320p. (YA). (gr. 7 up). pap. 8.99 ***(978-0-618-66379-8(7)*** , Graphia) Houghton Mifflin Co. Trade & Reference Div.

Moss, Alexandra. Sophie's Flight of Fancy, No. 4. 2005. (Royal Ballet School Diaries: No. 4). 144p. (gr. 3-5). mass mkt. 4.99 (978-0-448-43770-5(8) , Grosset & Dunlap) Penguin Group (USA) Inc.

Naidoo, Beverley. The Other Side of Truth. 2001. 272p. (J). (gr. 5 up). 17.99 (978-0-06-029628-5(3)) HarperCollins Pubs.

—The Other Side of Truth. 2000. 240p. (J). pap. (978-0-14-130476-2(6) , Putnam Juvenile) Penguin Group (USA) Inc.

Oliver & Company. (Read-Along Ser.). (J). 7.99 incl. audio (978-1-55723-024-9(2)) Walt Disney Records.

Paine, Penelope C. Time for Horatio. Maeno, Itoko, illus. 2001. 48p. (J). per. 17.95 (978-0-9707944-7-5(9)) Paper Posie.

Peacock, Shane. Eye of the Crow: The Boy Sherlock Holmes, His First Case. 2007. (Boy Sherlock Holmes Ser.). 260p. (J). (gr. 5-9). 19.95 ***(978-0-88776-850-7(4))*** Tundra Bks., Inc./Livres Toundra, Inc. CAN. *Dist:* Random Hse., Inc.

Penn, Audrey. Blackbeard & the Gift of Silence. 2007. 355p. (gr. 3-7). 15.95 ***(978-1-933718-11-8(0))*** Tanglewood Pr.

Peter Pan II: Return to Neverland. 2002. (Illus.). (J). 15.95 (978-0-7853-6003-2(4)) Publications International, Ltd.

Peters, Andrew Fusek & Player, Stephen. Ed & the River of the Damned. 2005. (Illus.). (J). pap. 9.99 (978-0-340-86637-5(3) , Hodder & Stoughton) Hodder General Publishing Division GBR. *Dist:* Trafalgar Square Publishing.

Poulsen, David A. The Book of Vampire. 4th rev. ed. 2007. (Salt & Pepper Chronicles). 160p. (gr. 3-7). pap. 6.95 ***(978-1-55263-805-7(7))*** Key Porter Bks. CAN. *Dist:* Perseus Distribution.

Priestley, Chris. Death & the Arrow. 2007. (Tom Marlowe Serie Ser.). (Illus.). 230p. (J). (gr. 4-6). 9.99 ***(978-0-552-55475-6(8)*** , Corgi) Transworld Publishers Ltd. GBR. *Dist:* Independent Pubs. Group.

—Redwulf's Curse. 2008. (Illus.). 272p. (YA). pap. 9.95 ***(978-0-552-55483-1(9))*** Transworld Publishers Ltd. GBR. *Dist:* Independent Pubs. Group.

—The White Rider. 2006. (Tom Marlowe Ser.). (Illus.). 256p. (J). (gr. 4-6). 9.99 ***(978-0-552-55474-9(X)*** , Corgi) Transworld Publishers Ltd. GBR. *Dist:* Independent Pubs. Group.

Prince, Maggie. The House on Hound Hill. 256p. (YA). 2003. (gr. 5). pap. 6.95 (978-0-618-33124-6(7)); 1998. (gr. 7-9). tchr. ed. 16.00 (978-0-395-90702-3(0)) Houghton Mifflin Co. Trade & Reference Div.

Pullman, Philip. I Was a Rat! 2000. (Illus.). 176p. (gr. 3-5). 15.95 (978-0-375-80176-1(6) , Knopf Bks. for Young Readers) Random Hse. Children's Bks.

—I Was a Rat! Or the Scarlet Slippers. l.t. ed. 2005. 256p. (J). pap. (978-0-7540-6132-8(9) , CLP 326) BBC Audio.

—I Was a Rat! Or the Scarlet Slippers. unabr. l.t. ed. 2001. (Read-Along Ser.). 224p. (J). 29.95 incl. audio (978-0-7540-6233-2(3) , RA034, Chivers Children's Audio Bks.) BBC Audiobooks America.

—I Was a Rat! Or the Scarlet Slippers. 2002. (gr. 7-12). lib. bdg. 13.00 (978-0-613-64439-6(5)) Tandem Library Bks.

—The Ruby in the Smoke. 2004. 230p. (J). (gr. 7 up). pap. 38.00 incl. audio (978-1-4000-9015-0(6) , Listening Library) Random Hse. Audio Publishing Group.

—Shadow in the North. 2006. 21.75 (978-0-8446-7289-2(0)) Smith, Peter Pub., Inc.

—Spring-Heeled Jack. Mostyn, David, illus. 2004. 112p. (gr. 3-7). 5.99 (978-0-440-41881-8(X) , Yearling) Random Hse. Children's Bks.

Radford, Michelle. Almost Fabulous. 2008. 256p. (J). pap. 8.99 ***(978-0-06-125235-8(2)*** , HarperTeen) HarperCollins Pubs.

Ravel, Edeet. The Secret Journey of Pauline Siddhartha. 2007. 224p. pap. 9.95 ***(978-1-55192-974-3(0))*** Raincoast Bk. Distribution CAN. *Dist:* Perseus Distribution.

Rayban, Chloe. Hollywood Bliss: My Life Starring Mum. 2007. 304p. (J). pap. 7.95 ***(978-1-59990-097-1(1)*** , Bloomsbury Children) Bloomsbury Publishing.

Rayban, Chloe. My Life Starring Mum. 2006. 250p. (J). 16.95 (978-1-58234-713-4(1) , Bloomsbury Children) Bloomsbury Publishing.

Regan, Peter. Riverside: The London Trip. 1998. (Illus.). 112p. (YA). (gr. 3 up). pap. 7.95 (978-1-901737-16-5(0)) Anvil Bks., Ltd. IRL. *Dist:* Dufour Editions, Inc.

Richards, Justin. The Death Collector. 336p. (YA). 2007. (gr. 7 up). pap. 7.95 ***(978-1-59990-148-0(X));*** 2006. 16.95 (978-1-58234-721-9(2)) Bloomsbury Publishing. (Bloomsbury Children).

Richards, Justin. The Invisible Detective: Ghost Soldiers. 2006. 160p. (J). (gr. 4). 11.99 (978-0-399-24500-8(6) , Putnam Juvenile) Penguin Group (USA) Inc.

Richardson, Nigel. The Wrong Hands. 272p. (YA). (gr. 7). 2008. mass mkt. 6.50 ***(978-0-553-49500-3(3)*** , Laurel Leaf); 2006. 15.95 (978-0-375-83459-2(1) , Knopf Bks. for Young Readers); 2006. lib. bdg. 17.99 (978-0-375-93459-9(6) , Knopf Bks. for Young Readers) Random Hse. Children's Bks.

Rosoff, Meg. How I Live Now. 2004. 208p. (YA). (gr. 7). 16.95 (978-0-385-74677-9(6) , Lamb, Wendy) Random Hse. Children's Bks.

Ross, Diane. The Little Red Engine Goes to Town. Wood, Leslie, illus. 2005. (Little Red Engine Ser.). 32p. (J). pap. 8.99 (978-0-233-00151-7(4)) Andre Deutsch GBR. *Dist:* Independent Pubs. Group.

Ross, N. J. Mick & Megan Visit London. 2000. (J). incl. audio (978-1-930303-09-6(2)) Angelic Enterprises.

Saksena, Kate. Hang on in There, Shelley. 2003. 219p. (J). 16.95 (978-1-58234-822-3(7) , Bloomsbury Children) Bloomsbury Publishing.

Sheldon, Dyan. I Conquer Britain. 2007. (Illus.). 208p. (YA). (gr. 7). 15.99 ***(978-0-7636-3300-4(3))*** Candlewick Pr.

Simmons, Steven J. Percy to the Rescue. Howard, Kim, illus. 1998. 32p. (J). (ps-3). 15.95 (978-0-88106-390-5(8)) Charlesbridge Publishing, Inc.

Spirn, Michele Sobel. The Bridges in London. 2000. (Going to Ser.). (Illus.). 121p. pap. 6.95 (978-1-893577-00-8(7)) Four Corners Publishing Co., Inc.

St. John, Patricia. Rainbow Garden. 2002. (gr. 3-6). lib. bdg. 15.30 (978-0-613-88836-3(7)) Tandem Library Bks.

Stanley, George Edward. The Spy Who Barked. Francis, Guy, illus. 2002. (Adam Sharp Ser.: No. 1). 48p. (J). (gr. 2-4). pap. 3.99 (978-0-307-26412-1(2) , Random Hse. Bks. for Young Readers) Random Hse. Children's Bks.

Stevenson, Robert Louis. Dr. Jekyll & Mr. Hyde. (YA). (gr. 5-12). pap. 6.50 (978-0-8224-9255-9(5)) Globe Fearon Educational Publishing.

—Dr Jekyll & Mr Hyde. abr. ed. 1999. (gr. 7-12). lib. bdg. 15.25 (978-0-613-32488-5(9)) Tandem Library Bks.

Stine, R. L. A Night in Terror Tower. 2004. (Goosebumps Ser.). 144p. (J). 4.99 (978-0-439-67111-8(6) , Scholastic Paperbacks) Scholastic, Inc.

Stockwell, Peter. The Market. 2005. 54p. pap. 12.95 (978-1-4137-6087-3(2)) PublishAmerica, Inc.

Stretton, Hesba. Jessica's First Prayer. 2004. reprint ed. pap. 15.95 (978-1-4191-2751-9(9)); pap. 1.99 (978-1-4192-2751-6(3)) Kessinger Publishing, LLC.

—Little Meg's Children. 2000. (Golden Inheritance Ser.: Vol. 5). (Illus.). 88p. (J). pap. (978-0-921100-92-8(2)) Inheritance Pubns.

—Little Meg's Children. (Early Children's Bks.). (J). reprint ed. 15.00 (978-0-384-56160-1(8)) Johnson Reprint Corp.

Stroud, Jonathan. The Amulet of Samarkand. 2003. (Bartimaeus Trilogy Ser.: Bk. 1). (Illus.). 464p. (gr. 5-17). 17.95 (978-0-7868-1859-4(X)) Hyperion Bks. for Children.

—The Golem's Eye. 2nd rev. ed. (Bartimaeus Trilogy Ser.: Bk. 2). 576p. (gr. 5-17). 2006. reprint ed. pap. 7.99 (978-0-7868-3654-3(7)); 2004. 17.95 (978-0-7868-1860-0(3)) Miramax Bks.

—Ptolemy's Gate. 3rd rev. ed. 2006. (Bartimaeus Trilogy Ser.: Bk. 3). 512p. (gr. 5-17). 17.95 (978-0-7868-1861-7(1)) Miramax Bks.

Swindells, Robert. Blitzed. 2008. 176p. (YA). pap. 9.95 ***(978-0-552-55589-0(4))*** Transworld Publishers Ltd. GBR. *Dist:* Independent Pubs. Group.

A Tale of Two Cities: Abridged. (ARA., Illus.). 48p. (J). 12.00 (978-0-86685-627-0(7)) International Bk. Ctr., Inc.

Taylor, G. P. Tersias. 2005. (Illus.). 336p. (J). ***(978-0-571-22152-3(1));*** pap. ***(978-0-571-22979-6(4))*** Faber & Faber, Ltd.

Taylor, G. P. Tersias the Oracle. 2006. 262p. (YA). (gr. 5). 17.99 (978-0-399-24258-8(9) , Putnam Juvenile) Penguin Group (USA) Inc.

Thoene, Jake & Thoene, Luke. The Giant Rat of Sumatra. 1998. (Baker Street Mysteries Ser.: Vol. 2). 168p. (J). (gr. 4-7). pap. 5.99 (978-0-7852-7079-9(5)) Nelson, Thomas Inc.

—The Giant Rat of Sumatra. 2006. (Tyndale Kids Ser.). 144p. (J). 9.99 (978-1-4143-0367-3(X)) Tyndale Hse. Pubs.

—The Mystery of the Yellow Hands. 2006. (Baker Street Detectives Ser.). 144p. (J). 9.99 (978-1-4143-0370-3(X)) Tyndale Hse. Pubs.

Thoene, Luke & Thoene, Jake. The Thundering Underground. 2006. (Baker Street Detectives Ser.). 128p. (J). 9.99 (978-1-4143-0369-7(6) , Tyndale Kids) Tyndale Hse. Pubs.

Thompson, Lisa. Lookout London. Jurevicius, Nathan, illus. 2006. (Read-It! Chapter Books). 80p. (J). (gr. 2-4). 19.95 (978-1-4048-1672-5(0)) Picture Window Bks.

Thomson, Sarah L. The Secret of the Rose. 2006. 304p. (J). 16.99 (978-0-06-087250-2(0)); lib. bdg. 17.89 (978-0-06-087251-9(9)) HarperCollins Pubs.

Updale, Eleanor. Montmorency: Thief, Liar, Gentleman. 2004. (Montmorency Ser.). 240p. (J). pap. 16.95 (978-0-439-58035-9(8) , Orchard Bks.) Scholastic, Inc.

—Montmorency on the Rocks: Doctor, Aristocrat, Murderer? 2006. 368p. (J). pap. 6.99 (978-0-439-60677-6(2) , Scholastic Paperbacks) Scholastic, Inc.

—Montmorency on the Rocks: Doctor, Aristocrat, Murderer? Hardcastle, Nick, illus. 2005. (Montmorency Ser.). 368p. (J). pap. 16.95 (978-0-439-60676-9(4) , Orchard Bks.) Scholastic, Inc.

—Montmorency's Revenge. 2007. (Montmorency Ser.: Vol. 4). 304p. (J). (gr. 7 up). pap. 16.99 (978-0-439-81373-0(5) , Orchard Bks.) Scholastic, Inc.

—Montmorency's Revenge Book 4. 2008. (Montmorency's Revenge Ser.). 304p. (J). pap. 6.99 ***(978-0-439-81374-7(3)*** , Scholastic Paperbacks) Scholastic, Inc.

Updale, Eleanor. Thief, Liar, Gentleman? 2005. (Montmorency Ser.). 240p. (J). reprint ed. pap. 6.99 (978-0-439-58036-6(6) , Scholastic Paperbacks) Scholastic, Inc.

Valentine, Jenny. Me, the Missing, & the Dead. 2008. 208p. (J). 16.99 ***(978-0-06-085068-5(X));*** lib. bdg. 17.89 ***(978-0-06-085069-2(8))*** HarperCollins Pubs.

Vernon, Louise A. A Heart Strangely Warmed. Eitzen, Allan, illus. 2002. (Louise A. Vernon's Religious Heritage Ser.). 126p. (YA). (gr. 4-9). 7.99 (978-0-8361-1769-1(7)) Herald Pr.

Walker, Peter Lancaster. Space Travelers Land at Buckingham Palace. Dixit, Rama, illus. 2007. (YA). per. 19.95 ***(978-1-934138-12-0(6))*** Bouncing Ball Bks., Inc.

Warner, Gertrude Chandler, creator. The Mystery of the Queen's Jewels, Vol. 11. 1998. (Boxcar Children Special Ser.: No. 11). (Illus.). 144p. (J). (gr. 2-5). 14.95 (978-0-8075-5450-0(2)); pap. 4.50 (978-0-8075-5451-7(0)) Whitman, Albert & Co.

Watson, Sally. Linnet. 2004. (YA). pap. 12.95 (978-1-59511-002-2(X) , 800-691-7779) Image Cascade Publishing.

—Mistress Malapert. 2002. (J). pap. 12.95 (978-1-930009-64-6(X) , 800-691-7779) Image Cascade Publishing.

Wells, H. G. The Magic Shop. Roca, Francois, illus. 2005. 32p. (J). (gr. 1-4). lib. bdg. 16.85 (978-1-933327-06-8(5)) Purple Bear Bks., Inc.

Wells, H. G. & Roca, Francois. The Magic Shop. ed. 2005. (Illus.). 32p. (J). 15.95 (978-1-933327-02-0(2)) Purple Bear Bks., Inc.

Whelan, Gloria. Farewell to the Island. 208p. (gr. 4 up). 1999. (Illus.). (YA). pap. 5.99 (978-0-06-440821-9(3) , Harper Trophy); 1998. (J). 16.95 (978-0-06-027751-2(3)) HarperCollins Pubs.

—Farewell to the Island. 1999. (J). (978-0-606-17462-6(1)) Tandem Library Bks.

—Farewell to the Island. 2004. 200p. (J). (ps-7). pap. 7.95 (978-1-882376-92-6(7)) Thunder Bay Pr.

Whytock, Cherry. My Scrumptious Scottish Dumplings: The Life of Angelica Cookson Potts. Whytock, Cherry, illus. 2006. 192p. (YA). mass mkt. 5.99 (978-0-689-86552-7(X) , Simon Pulse) Simon & Schuster Children's Publishing.

Whytock, Cherry, illus. My Scrumptious Scottish Dumplings: The Life of Angelica Cookson Potts. 2004. 176p. (YA). 14.95 (978-0-689-86549-7(X)) Simon & Schuster Children's Publishing.

Wicke, Ed. Akayzia Adams & the Masterdragon's Secret. Warne, Tom, illus. 2003. 280p. (J). pap. 9.99 (978-0-9677652-3-5(4) , BlacknBlue Pr. UK) Blacknblue Pr.

Wilkins, Rose. So Super-Starry. 2004. 208p. (J). pap. (978-0-330-42086-0(0) , Macmillan Children's Bks.) Pan Macmillan.

—So Super Starry. 2006. 230p. (YA). ***(978-1-4156-6975-4(9)*** , Puffin) Penguin Group (USA) Inc.

Wilkins, Rose. So Super Stylish. 2006. 288p. (J). (gr. 6). 16.99 (978-0-8037-3064-9(0) , Dial) Penguin Group (USA) Inc.

Wilson, Jacqueline. Girls Out Late. 2003. 224p. (YA). (gr. 7). mass mkt. 5.50 (978-0-440-22959-9(6) , Laurel Leaf) Random Hse. Children's Bks.

—Girls Out Late. Sharratt, Nick, illus. 2003. 192p. (YA). mass mkt. (978-0-552-54523-5(6) , Corgi) Transworld Publishers Ltd. GBR. *Dist:* Random Hse. of Canada, Ltd.

Wooding, Chris. The Haunting of Alaizabel Cray. 2004. 304p. (J). pap. 16.95 (978-0-439-54656-0(7)) Scholastic, Inc.

J K L

Woodruff, Elvira. The Christmas Doll. McClintock, Barbara, illus. 2002. 160p. (J). pap. 4.99 (978-0-590-31879-2(9) , Scholastic Paperbacks) Scholastic, Inc.

Wrede, Patricia C. & Stevermer, Caroline. Sorcery & Cecelia or the Enchanted Chocolate Pot: Being the Correspondence of Two Young Ladies of Quality Regarding Various Magical Scandals in London & the Country. 2003. (Illus.). 336p. (YA). 17.00 (978-0-15-204615-6(1)) Harcourt Children's Bks.

Wyre, Yvonne. The Adventures of Cuthbert the Coal Lorry. 2005. 160p. pap. (*978-1-84401-500-9(9)) Athena Pr.

Zephaniah, Benjamin. Refugee Boy. 2004. 296p. (J). (gr. 5-12). reprint ed. pap. 7.95 (978-1-58234-908-4(8) , Bloomsbury Children) Bloomsbury Publishing.

LONDON (ENGLAND)—HISTORY

Bailey, Jacqui. Royal London. Lilly, Matthew, illus. 2002. 48p. pap. 8.95 (978-0-7136-6261-0(1)) A & C Black GBR. *Dist:* Consortium Bk. Sales & Distribution.

Ball, Jacqueline A. Windsor Castle: England's Royal Fortress. 2005. (Castles, Palaces, & Tombs Ser.). (Illus.). 32p. (J). lib. bdg. 25.27 (978-1-59716-005-6(9)) Bearport Publishing Co., Inc.

Barter, James. Shakespeare's London. 2002. (Traveler's Guide to Ser.). (Illus.). 112p. (J). 29.95 (978-1-59018-146-1(8) , Lucent Bks.) Thomson Gale.

Bloom, Harold. London. 2005. (Bloom's Literary Places Ser.). (Illus.). 150p. (gr. 9-13). 40.00 (978-0-7910-7841-9(8) , Chelsea Hse.) Facts On File, Inc.

Bloom, Harold, ed. London. 2005. (Bloom's Literary Places Ser.). (Illus.). 150p. (gr. 9-13). pap. 40.00 (978-0-7910-8360-4(8) , Chelsea Hse.) Facts On File, Inc.

Brook, Henry. True Stories of the Blitz - Internet Referenced. Mcnee, Ian, illus. 2006. 160p. (J). pap. 4.99 (978-0-7945-1245-3(3) , Usborne) EDC Publishing.

Cottrell, Robert. London: Walled City to New Towns. 2006. (Arbitrary Borders Ser.). (Illus.). 144p. (J). (gr. 9-12). 35.00 (978-0-7910-8684-1(4) , Chelsea Hse.) Facts On File, Inc.

Dickins, Rosie. London Sticker Bk. Constantine, Adam, illus. 2006. 16p. (J). pap. 8.99 (978-0-7945-1284-2(4) , Usborne) EDC Publishing.

Doder, Joshua. Time Traveler's Guide to Shakespeare's London. 2004. (Timetraveller's Guides). (Illus.). 96p. (J). pap. 8.99 (978-1-904153-10-8(0)) Watling St., Ltd. GBR. *Dist:* Independent Pubs. Group.

—The Timetraveller's Guide to Saxon & Viking London. 2004. (Timetraveller's Guides). (Illus.). 96p. (J). (ps-7). pap. 8.99 (978-1-904153-07-8(0)) Watling St., Ltd. GBR. *Dist:* Independent Pubs. Group.

Elborough, Travis. Dungeons, Gallows, & Severed Heads of London. 2004. (Illus.). 96p. 8.99 (978-1-904153-03-0(8)) Watling St., Ltd. GBR. *Dist:* Trafalgar Square Publishing.

—Ghosts, Ghouls, & Phantoms of London. 2004. (Illus.). 96p. 8.99 (978-1-904153-02-3(X)) Watling St., Ltd. GBR. *Dist:* Trafalgar Square Publishing.

—Highwayman, Outlaws & Bandits of London. 2004. (. . . of London Ser.). (Illus.). 96p. 8.99 (978-1-904153-13-9(5)) Watling St., Ltd. GBR. *Dist:* Trafalgar Square Publishing.

—Rebels, Traitors & Turncoats of London. 2004. (. . . of London Ser.). (Illus.). 96p. 8.99 (978-1-904153-15-3(1)) Watling St., Ltd. GBR. *Dist:* Trafalgar Square Publishing.

Goodrich, Olivia. Timetraveler's Guide to Roman London. 2004. (Timetraveller's Guides). (Illus.). 96p. (J). pap. 7.95 (978-1-904153-06-1(2)) Watling St., Ltd. GBR. *Dist:* Independent Pubs. Group.

Holmes, Burton. London. Schlesinger, Arthur M., Jr., ed. 1999. (World 100 Years Ago Ser.). (Illus.). 144p. (YA). (ps-3). 29.95 (978-0-7910-4660-9(5) , Chelsea Hse.) Facts On File, Inc.

Israel, Fred L. & Schlesinger, Arthur M., Jr., eds. London. 1999. (World 100 Years Ago Ser.). (Illus.). 144p. (YA). (gr. 5-13). pap. 19.95 (978-0-7910-4661-6(3) , Chelsea Hse.) Facts On File, Inc.

Jocelyn, Marthe. A Home for Foundlings. 2005. (Lord Museum Book Ser.). (Illus.). 120p. (J). pap. 16.95 (978-0-88776-709-8(5)) Tundra Bks., Inc./Livres Toundra, Inc. CAN. *Dist:* Random Hse., Inc.

Kidney, Christine. Time Traveler's Guide to Medieval London. 2004. (Timetraveller's Guides). (Illus.). 96p. (J). pap. 8.99 (978-1-904153-08-5(9)) Watling St., Ltd. GBR. *Dist:* Independent Pubs. Group.

Marchant, Ian. Crypts, Caves, & Tunnels of London. 2004. (. . . of London Ser.). (Illus.). 96p. 8.99 (978-1-904153-04-7(6)) Watling St., Ltd. GBR. *Dist:* Trafalgar Square Publishing.

Morris, Neil. London. 2003. (Great Cities Through the Ages Ser.). (Illus.). 44p. (J). 18.95 (978-1-59270-013-4(6)) Enchanted Lion Bks., LLC.

Narayan, Natasha. Black Death & Other Putrid Plagues of London. 2004. (. . . of London Ser.). (Illus.). 96p. 8.99 (978-1-904153-01-6(1)) Watling St., Ltd. GBR. *Dist:* Trafalgar Square Publishing.

—Spies, Secret Agents & Spooks of London. 2004. (Illus.). 96p. 8.99 (978-1-904153-14-6(3)) Watling St., Ltd. GBR. *Dist:* Trafalgar Square Publishing.

—Time Traveler's Guide to Tudor London. 2004. (Timetraveller's Guides). (Illus.). 96p. (J). pap. 8.99 (978-1-904153-09-2(7)) Watling St., Ltd. GBR. *Dist:* Independent Pubs. Group.

—Time Traveler's Guide to Victorian London. 2004. (Timetraveller's Guides). (Illus.). 96p. (J). pap. 8.99 (978-1-904153-11-5(9)) Watling St., Ltd. GBR. *Dist:* Independent Pubs. Group.

—Witches, Wizards & Warlocks of London. 2004. (. . . of London Ser.). (Illus.). 96p. 8.99 (978-1-904153-12-2(7)) Watling St., Ltd. GBR. *Dist:* Trafalgar Square Publishing.

Robson, Pam. The Great Fire of London 1666. Marwood, Dez, illus. 2nd ed. 2003. 48p. pap. (978-0-7500-1935-4(2) , Hodder Wayland) Hodder Children's Division.

Shields, Charles J. The Great Plague & Fire of London. 2001. (Great Disasters, Reforms & Ramifications Ser.). (Illus.). 120p. (YA). (gr. 6-10). 21.95 (978-0-7910-6324-8(0) , Chelsea Hse.) Facts On File, Inc.

Smith, Helen. Pirates, Swashbucklers & Buccaneers of London. 2004. (. . . of London Ser.). (Illus.). 96p. 8.99 (978-1-904153-17-7(8)) Watling St., Ltd. GBR. *Dist:* Trafalgar Square Publishing.

LONDON (ENGLAND)—HISTORY—FICTION

Avi. The Traitors' Gate. Raude, Karina, illus. 2007. 368p. (J). (gr. 6-9). 17.99 (978-0-689-85335-7(1) , Atheneum/Richard Jackson Bks.) Simon & Schuster Children's Publishing.

Bajoria, Paul. The God of Mischief. Bertholf, Bret, illus. 2007. 400p. (J). (gr. 3-7). pap. 6.99 (*978-0-316-01628-5(4)) Little, Brown Bks. for Young Readers.

Bajoria, Paul. The Printer's Devil. 2007. 400p. (J). (gr. 4-8). pap. 6.99 (978-0-316-10678-8(X)) Little Brown & Co.

Bloor, Edward. London Calling. 2008. 304p. (YA). (gr. 5). pap. 8.99 (*978-0-375-84363-1(9) , Knopf Bks. for Young Readers) Random Hse. Children's Bks.

Burgess, Melvin. The Copper Treasure. Williams, Richard, illus. rev. ed. 2000. 112p. (YA). (gr. 4-7). 15.95 (978-0-8050-6381-3(1) , Holt, Henry & Co. Bks. For Young Readers) Holt, Henry & Co.

Curry, Jane Louise. The Black Canary. 2005. (Illus.). 288p. (J). (gr. 5 up). 17.99 (978-0-689-86478-0(7) , McElderry, Margaret K.) Simon & Schuster Children's Publishing.

Gardner, Sally. I, Coriander. 2007. 288p. (J). (gr. 5 up). pap. 6.99 (978-0-14-240763-9(1) , Puffin) Penguin Group (USA) Inc.

Garfield, Leon. Smith. 2000. (J). (978-0-606-21674-6(X)); (gr. 7-12). lib. bdg. 15.25 (978-0-613-30742-0(9)) Tandem Library Bks.

Hayner, Linda K. Ellanor's Exchange. 2005. 195p. (YA). (978-1-59166-462-8(4)) Jones, Bob Univ. Pr.

Hendry, Frances. Quest for a Queen: The Jackdaw. 2006. pap. (*978-1-905665-05-1(9)) Pollinger In Print.

Hooper, Mary. At the Sign of the Sugared Plum. (J). 2005. 176p. (gr. 4-7). pap. 6.95 (978-1-58234-695-3(X)); 2003. 200p. 16.95 (978-1-58234-849-0(9)) Bloomsbury Publishing. (Bloomsbury Children).

—Petals in the Ashes. 2004. 200p. (J). (gr. 5 up). 16.95 (978-1-58234-936-7(3) , Bloomsbury Children) Bloomsbury Publishing.

Jarvis, Robin. The Alchemist's Cat. 2006. 304p. (YA). pap. 6.95 (978-0-8118-5450-4(7)) Chronicle Bks. LLC.

Lawrence, Iain. The Convicts. 2005. 208p. (gr. 7-9). (J). lib. bdg. 17.99 (978-0-385-90109-3(7)); (YA). 15.95 (978-0-385-73087-7(X)) Random Hse. Children's Bks. (Delacorte Bks. for Young Readers).

—The Convicts. l.t. ed. 2005. 292p. (YA). 22.95 (978-0-7862-7911-1(7) , Large Print Pr.) Thorndike Pr.

Munch, Donna. Dark Tales of the Tower. 2005. (J). pap. 9.95 (978-1-932196-71-9(4)) WordWright.biz, Inc.

Nesbit, E. Phoenix & the Carpet. 2006. pap. (*978-1-4068-3504-5(8)) Echo Library.

Orme, David. Blitz. 2004. (Shades Ser.). 54p. (J). pap. 8.99 (978-0-237-52624-5(7) , Evans Brothers, Limited) Evans Publishing Group GBR. *Dist:* Independent Pubs. Group.

Priestley, Chris. The White Rider. l.t. ed. 2005. 248p. (J). pap. (978-0-7540-7927-9(9) , CLP 481) BBC Audio.

—The White Rider. 2005. (Illus.). 192p. (J). pap. 8.99 (978-0-440-86608-4(1) , Corgi) Transworld Publishers Ltd. GBR. *Dist:* Trafalgar Square Publishing.

Pullman, Philip. The Ruby in the Smoke. 2002. (Sally Lockhart Trilogy: Bk. 1). 22.00 (978-0-8446-7230-4(0)) Smith, Peter Pub., Inc.

Springer, Nancy. The Case of the Bizarre Bouquets: An Enola Holmes Mystery. 2008. 192p. (YA). (gr. 4). 14.99 (*978-0-399-24518-3(9) , Philomel) Penguin Group (USA) Inc.

—The Case of the Left-Handed Lady: An Enola Holmes Mystery. 2008. 256p. (J). (gr. 4-8). pap. 6.99 (*978-0-14-241190-2(6) , Puffin); 2007. 224p. (YA). (gr. 5-9). 12.99 (978-0-399-24517-6(0) , Philomel) Penguin Group (USA) Inc.

Springer, Nancy. The Case of the Missing Marquess: An Enola Holmes Mystery. (J). 2007. 224p. (gr. 3). 6.99 (*978-0-14-240933-6(2) , Puffin); 2006. 208p. (gr. 4). 10.99 (978-0-399-24304-2(6) , Philomel) Penguin Group (USA) Inc.

Stretton, Hesba. Lost Gip. 2003. (Golden Inheritance Ser.: Vol. 7). (Illus.). 121p. (J). (978-0-921100-93-5(0)) Inheritance Pubns.

Sturtevant, Katherine. At the Sign of the Star. 144p. (YA). 2002. pap. 6.95 (978-0-374-40458-1(5) , Sunburst); 2000. (gr. 5 up). 16.00 (978-0-374-30449-2(1) , Farrar, Straus & Giroux (BYR)) Farrar, Straus & Giroux.

—At the Sign of the Star. 2002. (gr. 3-6). lib. bdg. 14.10 (978-0-613-71732-8(5)) Tandem Library Bks.

—A True & Faithful Narrative. 2006. 256p. (YA). 17.00 (978-0-374-37809-7(6)) Farrar, Straus & Giroux.

—A True & Faithful Narrative. l.t. ed. 2006. 289p. (YA). 21.95 (978-0-7862-9081-9(1)) Thorndike Pr.

Thoene, Jake & Thoene, Luke. The Jeweled Peacock of Persia. 2006. (Baker Street Detectives Ser.). 144p. (J). 9.99 (978-1-4143-0368-0(8)) Tyndale Hse. Pubs.

Turnbull, Ann. Forged in the Fire. 2007. 320p. (YA). (gr. 7). 16.99 (978-0-7636-3144-4(2)) Candlewick Pr.

Updale, Eleanor. Montmorency & the Assassins, Bk. 3. 2007. (Montmorency & the Assassins Ser.). 416p. (J). pap. 6.99 (*978-0-439-68344-9(0)) Scholastic, Inc.

—Montmorency & the Assassins: Master, Criminal, Spy. 2006. 416p. (J). (gr. 4-7). pap. 16.99 (978-0-439-68343-2(2) , Orchard Bks.) Scholastic, Inc.

—Montmorency's Revenge. 2007. 289p. (J). (*978-1-4287-3312-1(4) , Orchard Bks.) Scholastic, Inc.

Updale, Eleanor. Thief, Liar, Gentleman? l.t. ed. 2006. 261p. 23.95 (978-0-7862-8643-0(1)) Thorndike Pr.

Wallace, Karen. The Unrivalled Spangles. 2006. 224p. (YA). 16.95 (978-1-4169-1503-4(6)) Simon & Schuster Children's Publishing.

—Wendy. 2003. 320p. (J). (978-0-689-83747-0(X) , Simon & Schuster Children's Publishing) Simon & Schuster Children's Publishing.

Wallace, Karen & Barrie, J. M. Wendy. 2005. 307p. (J). (*978-1-4156-1690-1(6) , Simon Pulse) Simon & Schuster Children's Publishing.

Wallace, Karen & Frost, Michael. Wendy. 2003. 320p. (J). 16.95 (978-0-689-86769-9(7)) Simon & Schuster Children's Publishing.

Walters, Jennie. House of Secrets. 2007. (Swallowcliffe Hall Ser.: Bk. 1). 224p. (J). pap. 9.99 (*978-0-689-87526-7(6) , Pocket Bks.) Simon & Schuster, Ltd. GBR. *Dist:* Independent Pubs. Group.

Wooding, Chris. The Haunting of Alaizabel Cray. 2005. 304p. (YA). (gr. 7-17). reprint ed. pap. 7.99 (978-0-439-59851-4(6)) Scholastic, Inc.

Woodruff, Elvira. Escape from the Tower of London. 2005. 240p. (J). pap. 4.99 (978-0-439-28134-8(2) , Scholastic Paperbacks) Scholastic, Inc.

—The Ravenmaster's Secret. 2003. (Illus.). 240p. (J). pap. 15.95 (978-0-439-28133-1(4)) Scholastic, Inc.

Zucker, Jonny. The Bombed House. Savage, Paul, illus. 2007. (Keystone Books). 33p. (J). (gr. 5-8). lib. bdg. 19.93 (978-1-59889-092-1(1)) Stone Arch Bks.

LONDON (ENGLAND)—TOWER OF LONDON

see Tower of London (London, England)

LONELINESS

Apel, Melanie Ann. Let's Talk about Feeling Lonely. 2001. (Let's Talk Library). (Illus.). 24p. (J). (gr. 3). lib. bdg. 18.75 (978-0-8239-5620-3(2) , PowerKids Pr.) Rosen Publishing Group, Inc., The.

Levete, Sarah. Making Friends. 2007. (J). (*978-1-59604-152-3(8)) Stargazer Bks.

Medina, Sarah. Lonely. Brooker, Jo, illus. 2007. (J). (*978-1-4034-9794-9(X)); pap. (*978-1-4034-9801-4(6)) Heinemann Library.

Moses, Brian. I Feel Lonely. 1999. (gr. k-3). lib. bdg. 14.45 (978-0-613-30495-5(0)) Tandem Library Bks.

LONELINESS—FICTION

Anderson, Jodi Lynn. May Bird & the Ever After, Bk. 1. Gore, Leonid, illus. 2006. 352p. (J). (gr. 5-9). reprint ed. pap. 5.99 (978-1-4169-0607-0(X) , Aladdin) Simon & Schuster Children's Publishing.

Brodkin, Adele M. The Lonely Only Dog. Di Fiori, Lawrence, illus. 1998. (Hello Reader! Ser.). 32p. (J). (gr. 1-3). pap. 3.99 (978-0-590-52280-9(9)) Scholastic, Inc.

Card, Orson Scott, ed. Future on Ice. rev. ed. 1998. 432p. (YA). (gr. 7 up). 24.95 (978-0-312-86694-5(1) , Tor Bks.) Doherty, Tom Assocs., LLC.

Carle, Eric. The Very Lonely Firefly. 1999. (Illus.). 32p. (J). (ps-k). 11.99 (978-0-399-23427-9(6) , Philomel) Penguin Group (USA) Inc.

Clark, Emma Chichester. Melrose & Croc: A Christmas to Remember. Clark, Emma Chichester, illus. 2006. (Illus.). 32p. (J). 16.95 (978-0-8027-9597-7(8)) Walker & Co.

Conner, Wendy Simpson. Princess of the Moon. (Illus.). (J). 16.95 (978-1-889599-20-5(4)) Interstellar Publishing Co.

Dalrymple, Farel. Pop Gun War. 2003. (Illus.). 136p. (gr. 11 up). pap. 13.95 (978-1-56971-934-3(9)) Dark Horse Comics.

Davidson, Betsy. Twyla Tulip & Her Talking Toes: A Friendship Story. Norcross, Harry, illus. 2000. 16p. (J). (gr. 1-3). pap. 6.95 (978-1-57543-080-5(0)) MAR*CO Products, Inc.

Dower, Laura. From the Files of Madison Finn: Only the Lonely. 2001. (gr. 3-6). lib. bdg. 13.00 (978-0-613-44497-2(3)) Tandem Library Bks.

Everson, Chance. Beginnings Vol. 2: Tales of the Mandrasaurs, Volume the Second. Geary, Steve, illus. 2004. cd-rom 9.95 (978-0-9760303-1-7(4)) R.A.R.E. TALES.

Floyd, Madeleine. Cold Paws, Warm Heart. 2005. (Illus.). 32p. (J). (ps-3). 15.99 (978-0-7636-2761-4(5)) Candlewick Pr.

Fogg, K. L. Serpent Tide. 2006. 16.95 (978-1-59156-861-2(7)) Covenant Communications, Inc.

Fritz, Jean. Homesick: My Own Story. Tomes, Margot, illus. 1999. 192p. (J). (gr. 3-7). pap. 5.99 (978-0-698-11782-2(4) , Putnam Juvenile) Penguin Group (USA) Inc.

—Homesick: My Own Story. 1999. (J). 12.64 (978-0-606-16799-4(4)) Tandem Library Bks.

Fuqua, Jonathon Scott. Catie & Josephine. Parke, Steven, illus. 2003. 72p. (J). (gr. 3-5). 16.00 (978-0-618-39403-6(6)) Houghton Mifflin Co. Trade & Reference Div.

Gil, Carmen. Un Fantasma con Asma. Webster, Sarah, illus. 2004. (Libros para Sonar Ser.). (SPA.). 40p. (J). 15.99 (978-84-8464-186-5(4)) Kalandraka Editora, S.L. ESP. *Dist:* Lectorum Pubns., Inc.

Gonzalez, Rigoberto. Soledad Sigh-Sighs / Soledad Suspiros. Ibarra, Rosa, illus. 2003. Tr. of Soledad Suspiros. (ENG & SPA.). 32p. (J). 16.95 (978-0-89239-180-6(4)) Children's Bk. Pr.

Grealish, Maureen M. Just Plain Worm. 25p. (J). (gr. k-2). (978-0-9667780-0-7(6)) Ballenwyck Publishing Corp.

Hanson, Anders. Lone Shark. Haberstroh, Anne, illus. (Fact & Fiction Ser.). 24p. (J). 2007. 21.35 (978-1-59928-452-1(9)); 2006. (978-1-59928-453-8(7)) ABDO Publishing Co.

Hartnett, Sonya. What the Birds See. 208p. (YA). (gr. 9). 2007. (Illus.). pap. 7.99 (*978-0-7636-3680-7(0)); 2003. 15.99 (978-0-7636-2092-9(0)) Candlewick Pr.

Henkes, Kevin. All Alone. Henkes, Kevin, illus. 2003. (Illus.). 40p. (J). 15.99 (978-0-06-054115-6(6)); lib. bdg. 16.89 (978-0-06-054116-3(4)) HarperCollins Pubs.

Hest, Amy. The Dog Who Belonged to No One. 2008. (J). (*978-0-8109-9483-6(6) , Abrams Bks. for Young Readers) Abrams, Harry N. , Inc.

Jahn-Clough, Lisa. On the Hill. 2004. (Illus.). 32p. (J). (gr. k-3). tchr. ed. 15.00 (978-0-618-40741-5(3) , Walter Lorraine) Houghton Mifflin Co. Trade & Reference Div.

Judd, Christopher M. Bearable Moments. 2005. (J). 18.95 (978-0-9766666-1-5(8)) Arcadian Hse.

Kadono, Eiko. Grandpa's Soup. Ichikawa, Satomi, illus. 2004. 32p. (J). (ps-3). 16.00 (978-0-8028-5195-6(9)) Eerdmans, William B. Publishing Co.

Keats, Ezra Jack. The Trip. Keats, Ezra Jack, illus. 2002. (Illus.). (J). 13.56 (978-0-7587-4943-7(0)) Book Wholesalers, Inc.

Kerr, Judith. The Other Goose. (Illus.). 32p. (J). 2002. pap. 8.99 (978-0-00-712735-1(9)); 2001. 15.99 (978-0-00-712119-9(9)) HarperCollins Pubs. Ltd. GBR. *Dist:* Independent Pubs. Group.

Klingel, Cynthia Fitterer & Noyed, Robert B. The Amazing Letter O. 2003. (Alphaphonics Ser.). (Illus.). 24p. (J). (ps-2). 21.36 (978-1-59296-105-4(3)) Child's World, Inc.

Lamar, Gail Renfroe. Moon of the Wishing Night. Mask, Cynthia, illus. 2004. 32p. (J). 17.95 (978-1-57966-047-5(9) , River City Kids) River City Publishing.

LaReau, Kara. Ugly Fish. Magoon, Scott, illus. 2006. 40p. (J). (ps-2). 16.00 (978-0-15-205082-5(5)) Harcourt Trade Pubs.

Linden, Dianne. Peacekeepers. (J). 82p. stu. ed. 9.95 (978-1-55050-297-8(2)); 2004. (Illus.). 220p. (gr. 4-7). pap. 7.95 (978-1-55050-271-8(9)) Coteau Bks. CAN. *Dist:* Fitzhenry & Whiteside, Ltd.

Lohans, Alison. The Raspberry Room. Newland, Gillian, illus. 2006. 64p. (gr. 2-3). pap. 4.99 (978-1-55143-353-0(2)) Orca Bk. Pubs. USA.

MacDonald, Amy. Little Beaver & the Echo. Fox-Davies, Sarah, illus. 1998. 32p. (J). (ps-3). pap. 6.99 (978-0-698-11628-3(3) , Putnam Juvenile) Penguin Group (USA) Inc.

Montijo, Rhode. Nino Nube. Mlawer, Teresa, tr. from ENG. 2006. (SPA & ENG., Illus.). 32p. (J). 12.99 (978-1-933032-06-1(5)) Lectorum Pubns., Inc.

Morison, Toby. Little Louie Takes Off. Morison, Toby, illus. 2007. (Illus.). 32p. (J). (ps-2). 16.95 (*978-0-8027-9645-5(1)) Walker & Co.

Parpan, Justin. Gwango's Lonesome Trail. Parpan, Justin, illus. 2006. (Illus.). 32p. (J). 15.95 (978-1-60108-004-2(2)) Red Cygnet Pr.

Perry, Sarah. Clara¿s Road. 2005. 64p. (J). per. (978-1-55306-945-4(5) , Epic Pr.) Essence Publishing.

Pugliano Martin, Carol. Lonely Pluto. 2005. 40.00 (*978-1-4108-4194-0(4)) Benchmark Education Co.

Ross, Bakthi. Millipede Curl. 2007. 17.00 (*978-0-8059-8820-8(3)) Dorrance Publishing Co., Inc.

Rylant, Cynthia. The Islander. 1999. (Illus.). 112p. (J). (gr. 5-17). reprint ed. pap. 5.50 (978-0-440-41542-8(X) , Yearling) Random Hse. Children's Bks.

—The Islander. 1999. (gr. 5-8). lib. bdg. 13.00 (978-0-613-23002-5(7)) Tandem Library Bks.

Seton, Ernest Thompson. Biography of A Grizzly. 2007. pap. 87.99 (*978-1-4280-5279-6(8)) IndyPublish.com.

Stren, Patti. Hug Me. (Illus.). (J). Date not set. 40p. pap. 5.99 (978-0-06-443754-7(X)); 2001. 32p. 14.95 (978-0-06-029317-8(9)) HarperCollins Pubs.

Taylor, Theodore. The Boy Who Could Fly Without a Motor. (Illus.). 2004. 168p. (J). pap. 5.95 (978-0-15-204767-2(0) , Harcourt Paperbacks); 2002. 144p. (YA). (gr. 3-6). 15.00 (978-0-15-216529-1(0)) Harcourt Children's Bks.

Teevin, Toni. What to Do? What to Do? Pedersen, Janet, illus. 2006. 32p. (J). (gr. k-3). 16.00 (978-0-618-44632-2(X) , Clarion Bks.) Houghton Mifflin Co. Trade & Reference Div.

Thomas, Charolette. Franklin Finds a Friend. 2006. (ENG.). 40p. per. 16.99 (*978-1-4259-6209-8(2)) AuthorHouse.

Van Lieshout, Elle & Van Os, Erik. The Wish. Gerritsen, Paula, illus. 2007. 32p. (J). (gr. 1-3). 15.95 (978-1-932425-91-8(8) , Lemniscaat) Boyds Mills Pr.

Viorst, Judith. Nobody Here but Me. Davenier, Christine, illus. 2008. (J). (*978-0-374-35540-1(1)) Farrar, Straus & Giroux.

Waechter, Philip. Me! Franceschelli, Christopher, tr. from GER. 2005. (Illus.). 64p. (J). (gr. k-3). 9.95 (978-1-59354-087-6(6)) Handprint Bks.

Wallace, Karen. Climbing a Monkey Puzzle Tree. 2004. 208p. (YA). (gr. 7-9). pap. 9.99 (978-0-689-83763-0(1)) Simon & Schuster, Ltd. GBR. *Dist:* Independent Pubs. Group.

Webster, Frank V. The Boys of Bellwood School. 2004. reprint ed. pap. 20.95 (978-1-4191-5509-3(1)); pap. 1.99 (978-1-4192-5509-0(6)) Kessinger Publishing, LLC.

Wells, Rosemary. The Small World of Binky Braverman. Egielski, Richard, illus. 40p. (J). (ps-3). 2003. 15.99 (978-0-670-03636-3(6) , Viking Juvenile); 2006. reprint ed. pap. 6.99 (978-0-14-240380-8(6) , Puffin) Penguin Group (USA) Inc.

White, Amanda. Sand Sister. Morales, Yuyi, illus. 2004. 32p. (J). 16.99 (978-1-84148-617-8(5)) Barefoot Bks., Inc.

Wormell, Christopher. The Big Ugly Monster & the Little Stone Rabbit. 2004. (Illus.). 32p. (J). (gr. k-3). 15.95 (978-0-375-82891-1(5) , Knopf Bks. for Young Readers) Random Hse. Children's Bks.

Wright, Dare. The Lonely Doll. 1998. (Illus.). 64p. (J). (gr. k-3). tchr. ed. 16.00 (978-0-395-89926-7(5)); pap. 6.95 (978-0-395-90112-0(X)) Houghton Mifflin Co. Trade & Reference Div.

JKL

Wyss, Thelma Hatch. Ten Miles from Winnemucca. 2002. 144p. (J). (gr. 7 up). 15.95 (978-0-06-029783-1(2)) HarperCollins Pubs.

Zolotow, Charlotte. The Bunny Who Found Easter. Craig, Helen, illus. 2001. (J). (ps-3). lib. bdg. 14.10 (978-0-613-35493-6(1)) Tandem Library Bks.

LONG ISLAND (N.Y.)—FICTION

Blume, Judy. Then Again, Maybe I Won't. (J). 125p. pap. 3.99 (978-0-8072-1445-9(0)); 2004. 164p. (gr. 5-9). pap. 29.00 incl. audio (978-0-8072-0796-3(9) , LYA 354 SP) Random Hse. Audio Publishing Group. (Listening Library).

Corbett, Sue. 12 Again. 2007. 240p. (J). (gr. 5 up). pap. 5.99 (978-0-14-240729-5(1) , Puffin) Penguin Group (USA) Inc.

Falk, Elizabeth Sullivan. Freedom's Fire. Wang, Qi Z., illus. 2004. (J). (978-1-59336-321-5(4)); pap. (978-1-59336-322-2(2)) Mondo Publishing.

Fitzhugh, Louise. The Long Secret. 2001. (Illus.). 288p. (J). (gr. 5 up). 15.95 (978-0-385-32784-8(6) , Delacorte Bks. for Young Readers) Random Hse. Children's Bks.

Kristina Learns about Fishing. 2007. (J). (*978-0-9792728-0-6(7)) Tracepaper Bks. Inc.

Newman, Leslea. Jailbait. 256p. (YA). (gr. 9). 2006. pap. 8.95 (978-0-385-73405-9(0)); 2005. lib. bdg. 17.99 (978-0-385-90230-4(1)) Random Hse. Children's Bks. (Delacorte Bks. for Young Readers).

Schmidt, Gary D. The Wednesday Wars. 2007. 272p. (J). (gr. 5-9). 16.00 (978-0-618-72483-3(4) , Clarion Bks.) Houghton Mifflin Co. Trade & Reference Div.

Thimble Islands Storybook. 2005. (J). (978-1-59872-094-5(5)) Instantpublisher.com.

LONG ISLAND (N.Y.)—HISTORY

Castrovilla, Selene. By the Sword: A Young Man Meets War. 2007. (Illus.). 40p. (J). (gr. 4-6). 17.95 (978-1-59078-427-3(8)) Boyds Mills Pr.

Shodell, Elly, ed. Particles of the Past: Sandmining on Long Island, 1870s-1980s. 2nd ed. (Illus.). 43p. (YA). (gr. 9-12). reprint ed. pap. 8.95 (978-0-9615059-0-5(7)) Port Washington Public Library.

LONG ISLAND (N.Y.), BATTLE OF, 1776

Castrovilla, Selene. By the Sword: A Young Man Meets War. 2007. (Illus.). 40p. (J). (gr. 4-6). 17.95 (978-1-59078-427-3(8)) Boyds Mills Pr.

LONGEVITY

see Old Age

LONGFELLOW, HENRY WADSWORTH, 1807-1882

Longfellow, Henry Wadsworth. Henry Wadsworth Longfellow. Schoonmaker, Frances, ed. Wallace, Chad, illus. 1998. (Poetry for Young People Ser.). 48p. (gr. 4-7). 14.95 (978-0-8069-9417-8(7)) Sterling Publishing Co., Inc.

LONGSTOCKING, PIPPI (FICTITIOUS CHARACTER)—FICTION

Lindgren, Astrid. Pippa Mediaslargas. (Pippi Longstocking Ser.).Tr. of Pippi Longstocking. (SPA.). (J). (gr. 3-5). pap. 9.95 (978-84-261-2304-6(X) , JV304X) Juventud, Editorial ESP. *Dist:* Continental Bk. Co., Inc., Lectorum Pubns., Inc.

—Pippi Goes on Board. (Pippi Longstocking Ser.). 140p. (J). (gr. 3-5). pap. 3.99 (978-0-8072-1401-5(9) , Listening Library) Random Hse. Audio Publishing Group.

—Pippi Goes to School. 1999. (Pippi Longstocking Storybooks). (Illus.). 64p. (J). (gr. k-2). pap. 5.99 (978-0-14-130236-2(4) , Puffin) Penguin Group (USA) Inc.

—Pippi Goes to School. 1999. (Pippi Longstocking Storybooks). (J). (gr. k-2). (978-0-606-18446-5(5)) Tandem Library Bks.

—Pippi Goes to the Circus. Chesworth, Michael, illus. 2000. (Pippi Longstocking Storybooks). 32p. (J). (gr. k-2). pap. 6.99 (978-0-14-130243-0(7) , Puffin) Penguin Group (USA) Inc.

—Pippi Goes to the Circus. 2000. (Pippi Longstocking Storybooks). (J). (gr. k-2). (978-0-606-18843-2(6)) Tandem Library Bks.

—Pippi in the South Seas. (Pippi Longstocking Ser.). 125p. (J). (gr. 3-5). pap. 3.99 (978-0-8072-1392-6(6) , Listening Library) Random Hse. Audio Publishing Group.

—Pippi Longstocking. Nunally, Tina, tr. from SWE. 2007. 208p. (J). (gr. k). 25.00 (*978-0-670-06276-8(6) , Viking Juvenile) Penguin Group (USA) Inc.

—Pippi Longstocking. Lamborn, Florence, tr. from SWE. Glanzman, Louis S., illus. 2005. (Puffin Modern Classics Ser.). 160p. (J). (gr. 3-7). pap. 5.99 (978-0-14-240249-8(4) , Puffin) Penguin Group (USA) Inc.

—Pippi Longstocking. Glanzman, Louis S., illus. 2005. (Puffin Modern Classics Ser.). 160p. (J). (*978-1-4155-8329-6(3) , Puffin) Penguin Group (USA) Inc.

—Pippi Longstocking. (Pippi Longstocking Ser.). 160p. (J). (gr. 3-5). pap. 4.99 (978-0-8072-1431-2(0) , Listening Library) Random Hse. Audio Publishing Group.

—Pippi's Extraordinary Ordinary Day. Chesworth, Michael, illus. 2001. (Pippi Longstocking Storybooks). 32p. (J). (gr. k-2). pap. 5.99 (978-0-14-056841-7(7) , Puffin) Penguin Group (USA) Inc.

—Pippi's Extraordinary Ordinary Day. 1999. (Pippi Longstocking Storybooks). (Illus.). 64p. (J). (gr. k-2). 14.99 (978-0-670-88073-7(6) , Viking Juvenile) Penguin Group (USA) Inc.

LOOKING GLASSES

see Mirrors

LOONS

Boring, Mel. Flamingos, Loons, & Pelicans. Recher, Andrew, illus. 2006. (Take-Along Guide Ser.). 48p. (J). 7.95 (978-1-55971-943-8(5)); 11.95 (978-1-55971-942-1(7)) T&N Children's Publishing. (NorthWord Bks. for Young Readers).

Kalz, Jill. Loons. 2003. (Birds Ser.). (Illus.). 24p. (J). lib. bdg. 21.35 (978-1-58340-133-0(4)) Smart Apple Media.

Love, Donna. Loons: Diving Birds of the North, Vol. 1. Turley, Joyce Mihran, tr. Turley, Joyce Mihran, illus. rev. ed. 64p. (gr. 4). pap. 12.00 (978-0-87842-482-5(2) , 340) Mountain Pr. Publishing Co., Inc.

—Loons: Diving Birds of the North. 2003. (gr. 3-6). lib. bdg. 21.10 (978-0-613-84998-2(1)) Tandem Library Bks.

Ring, Elizabeth. Loon at Northwood Lake. (Smith Sonian's Backyard Ser.). (Illus.). 32p. (J). (ps-2). pap. 6.95 (978-1-59249-482-8(X) , S5017) Soundprints.

LOONS—FICTION

Aston, Dianna Hutts. Loony Little. Murphy, Kelly, illus. 2007. 40p. (J). (ps-3). pap. 6.99 (*978-0-7636-3562-6(6)) Candlewick Pr.

Buzzeo, Toni. Little Loon & Papa. Spengler, Margaret, tr. Spengler, Margaret, illus. 2004. 32p. (J). (ps). 16.99 (978-0-8037-2958-2(8) , Dial) Penguin Group (USA) Inc.

Hyde, Dayton O. Island of the Loons. 2003. 176p. (YA). (gr. 4-6). pap. 9.95 (978-1-56397-681-0(1)) Boyds Mills Pr.

Lloyd, Jennifer. Looking for Loons. Wakelin, Kirsti, illus. 2007. 32p. (J). (ps-2). 16.95 (*978-1-894965-54-5(X)) Simply Read Bks. CAN. *Dist:* Perseus Distribution.

Love, Pamela. A Loon Alone. Sycks, Shannon, illus. 2002. 30p. pap. 9.95 (978-0-89272-526-7(5) , 1078); 29p. 14.95 (978-0-89272-571-7(0)) Down East Bks.

Trotter, Maxine. Loon Rock. Sylliboy, Helen, tr. Christmas, Dozay, illus. 22p. (J). (gr. k-2). pap. (978-0-920336-84-7(1)) Cape Breton Univ. Pr.

Wargin, Kathy-Jo. The Legend of the Loon. van Frankenhuyzen, Gijsbert, illus. (Great Lakes Legend Ser.). 48p. (J). (ps-3). 2000. 17.95 (978-1-886947-97-9(X)); 2003. pap. 7.95 (978-1-58536-167-0(4)) Sleeping Bear Pr.

LORD'S DAY

see Sabbath

LORD'S PRAYER

Beck, Ingrid. The Lord Is My Shepherd: From Psalm 23. 1999. (J). pap. (978-1-85608-400-0(0)) Hunt, John Publishing Ltd.

Bus, Sabrina. Our Father. Deneux, Xavier, illus. 2nd ed. 2006. 12p. (J). bds. 8.00 (978-0-8028-5313-4(7) , Eerdmans Bks For Young Readers) Eerdmans, William B. Publishing Co.

Church House Staff. Lord's Prayer Cube. 2006. 12.00 (*978-0-7151-4997-3(0)) Church Hse. Pubng. GBR. *Dist:* Church Publishing, Inc.

Holder, Heidi. The Lord's Prayer. 2004. (Illus.). 32p. (J). 16.95 (978-1-932425-03-1(9) , Lemniscaat) Boyds Mills Pr.

Ladwig, Tim, illus. The Lord's Prayer. 2004. 32p. pap. 8.50 (978-0-8028-5238-0(6)); (J). 17.00 (978-0-8028-5180-2(0)) Eerdmans, William B. Publishing Co.

The Lord's Prayer. 2004. (Exploring Luther's Small Catechism Ser.). (gr. 1-2). 2.99 (978-0-8066-6782-9(6)) Augsburg Fortress, Pubs.

Mackall, Dandi Daley. I Can Talk to God by Praying Jesus' Way. Gevry, Claudine, illus. 2005. 36p. (J). (ps-ps). 9.99 (978-0-7847-1654-0(4) , 04088) Standard Publishing.

Pastore, Vicki, illus. The Hail Mary/the Lord's Prayer. 2002. 32p. 7.95 (978-0-8091-6704-3(2) , 6704-2) Paulist Pr.

Pingry, Patricia A. The Story of the Lord's Prayer. Garvin, Elaine, illus. 2007. 28p. pap. 3.99 (*978-0-8249-5555-7(2) , Ideals Children's Bks.); 2004. 24p. (J). bds. 6.95 (978-0-8249-6519-8(1)) Ideals Pubns.

Reed. What Is the Lord's Prayer? 2006. 32p. pap. 2.00 (978-0-687-49347-0(1)) Abingdon Pr.

Rock, Lois. The Lord's Prayer & Ten Commandments Bible Words to Know & to Treasure. 2008. (Illus.). 64p. (J). 5.95 (*978-0-7459-4941-3(X)) Lion Hudson plc GBR. *Dist:* Independent Pubs. Group.

—Lords Prayer for Children. 1999. (Illus.). 32p. (J). (ps-3). 7.99 (978-0-88486-232-1(1) , Arrowood Pr.) BBS Publishing Corp.

—Our Father in Heaven: The Lord's Prayer for Children. Rivers, Ruth, illus. 2004. 32p. (J). pap. 11.00 (978-0-7459-4644-3(5) , Lion) Lion Hudson plc GBR. *Dist:* Independent Pubs. Group.

Swanson, Maggie. Lord's Prayer. 1999. (Maggie Swanson Board Books). (J). (ps-3). 3.95 (978-0-88271-711-1(1)) Regina Pr., Malhame & Co.

Teaching Your Child to Pray. 12.00 (978-0-687-08906-2(9)) Abingdon Pr.

Walker, Joni. Follow & Do Books: The Lord's Prayer. Walker, Joni, illus. 2004. (Follow & Do Ser.). (Illus.). 32p. (J). 6.99 (978-0-7586-0678-5(8)) Concordia Publishing Hse.

Wilson, Anne, illus. The Lord's Prayer. 2000. 32p. (J). (gr. 1-5). 12.99 (978-0-570-07132-7(1)) Concordia Publishing Hse.

Zobel-Nolan, Allia. The Lord's Prayer. Maclean, illus. 2003. (J). bds. 8.99 (978-0-7944-0044-6(2)) Reader's Digest Children's Publishing, Inc.

LOS ANGELES (CALIF.)

Andrade, Mary J. Uarhiri sapirhatiecheri Jukambekua: La velacion de los Angelitos. Murguia, Jose J., illus. Andrade, Mary J., photos by. 2005. Orig. Title: The Vigil of the Little Angels. 40p. (J). (gr. 3-6). pap. 9.95 (978-0-9665876-8-5(5)) La Oferta Publishing Co.

Barber, Nicola. Los Angeles. 2007. (Global Cities Ser.). 64p. (J). (gr. 5-8). 30.00 (978-0-7910-8847-0(2) , Chelsea Hse.) Facts On File, Inc.

Crewe, Sabrina. Los Angeles. 2004. (Great Cities of the World Ser.). (Illus.). 48p. (J). (gr. 5 up). 30.00 (978-0-8368-5029-1(7)); pap. 11.95 (978-0-8368-5189-2(7)) Stevens, Gareth Inc. (World Almanac Library).

Jaskol, Julie & Lewis, Brian. City of Angels: In & Around Los Angeles. Kleven, Elisa, illus. 1999. 48p. (J). (ps-3). 16.99 (978-0-525-46214-9(7) , Dutton Juvenile) Penguin Group (USA) Inc.

MacMillan, Dianne. Missions of the Los Angeles Area: San Gabriel Arcangel, San Fernando Rey de Espana, San Buenaventura. 1999. (California Missions Ser.). (Illus.). 80p. (gr. 4-7). pap. , lib. bdg. 23.93 (978-0-8225-9834-3(5)) Lerner Publishing Group.

MacMillan, Dianne M. Los Angeles Area Missions. 2007. (Exploring California Missions Ser.). (J). 27.93 (*978-0-8225-0898-4(2) , Lerner Pubns.) Lerner Publishing Group.

Marsak, Nathan & Cox, Nigel. Los Angeles Neon. 2002. (Illus.). 160p. (gr. 10-13). pap. 29.95 (978-0-7643-1542-8(0)) Schiffer Publishing, Ltd.

Stein, R. Conrad. Los Angeles. 2001. (Cities of the World Ser.). (Illus.). 64p. (YA). (gr. 4-9). pap. 9.95 (978-0-516-27283-2(7) , Children's Pr.) Scholastic Library Publishing.

Sweet-Carter, Bettye. Growing up L. A. Style: Byron: Was Zimmerman & Carter Publishing. 2000. 127p. (YA). reprint ed. pap. 11.95 (978-0-9705929-0-3(6) , 0970592906) Carter Publishing Co.

When Los Angeles Was Very Young 1849-1866. 2005. (YA). (978-1-59872-140-9(2)) Instantpublisher.com.

LOS ANGELES (CALIF.)—FICTION

The adventures of officer Byrd. 2007. (J). 16.99 (*978-0-9787322-0-2(0)) Officer Byrd Publishing Co.

Anderson, Dwayne. Partially Human. 2006. (YA). per. 12.00 (*978-0-9788612-0-9(5)) Capri Publishing.

Bencastro, Mario. A Promise to Keep. Giersbach-Rascon, Susan, tr. from SPA. 2005. 134p. (J). (gr. 3-7). pap. 9.95 (978-1-55885-457-4(6) , Piñata Books) Arte Publico Pr.

Blank, Jessica. Almost Home. rev. ed. 2007. 256p. (YA). (gr. 7 up). 15.99 (*978-1-4231-0642-5(3)) Hyperion Pr.

Block, Francesca Lia. Dangerous Angels. 1998. (Weetzie Bat Ser.). 496p. (J). (gr. 7-12). pap. 11.99 (978-0-06-440697-0(0) , Harper Trophy) HarperCollins Pubs.

—I Was a Teenage Fairy. 192p. (gr. 7 up). 1998. (J). 14.89 (978-0-06-027748-2(3)); 1998. (YA). 14.95 (978-0-06-027747-5(5) , Cotler, Joanna Books); 2000. (J). reprint ed. pap. 7.99 (978-0-06-440862-2(0) , Cotler, Joanna Books) HarperCollins Pubs.

—I Was a Teenage Fairy. 2000. (gr. 7-12). lib. bdg. 16.45 (978-0-613-28529-2(8)); (Illus.). (J). 14.64 (978-0-606-18903-3(3)) Tandem Library Bks.

—Violet & Claire. 2000. (J). (978-0-606-20003-5(7)) Tandem Library Bks.

—Wasteland. 2003. 160p. (J). 15.99 (978-0-06-028644-6(X)); (Illus.). 16.89 (978-0-06-028645-3(8)) HarperCollins Pubs. (Cotler, Joanna Books).

—Weetzie Bat. (Weetzie Bat Ser.). 128p. 2004. (J). pap. 7.99 (978-0-06-073625-5(9) , Harper Trophy); 10th anniv. ed. 1999. (J). (gr. 5 up). pap. 7.99 (978-0-06-440818-9(3) , Harper Trophy); 10th anniv. ed. 1999. (YA). (gr. 7-k). 14.95 (978-0-06-020534-8(2)) HarperCollins Pubs.

Bloom, Susan & Bertram, Debbie. City Hall: The Heart of Los Angeles. Leijten, Aileen, illus. 2003. 32p. (J). 9.95 (978-1-931290-24-1(5) , Smallfellow Pr.) Tallfellow Pr.

Brian, Kate. The Princess & the Pauper. 2004. 272p. (YA). reprint ed. mass mkt. 6.99 (978-0-689-87042-2(6) , Simon Pulse) Simon & Schuster Children's Publishing.

—The Princess & the Pauper. l.t. ed. 2003. 345p. (J). 22.95 (978-0-7862-6101-7(3) , Large Print Pr.) Thorndike Pr.

Brightwood, Laura, illus. Growing up in East L. A. Brightwood, Laura, . 2006. (J). (978-0-9779290-8-5(6)) 3-C Institute for Social Development.

Bunting, Eve. Noche de Humo. Andujar, Gloria de Aragon, tr. Diaz, David, illus. 1999. (SPA.). 36p. (J). (gr. 2-4). pap. 7.00 (978-0-15-201946-4(4) , Voyager Bks./Libros Viajeros) Harcourt Children's Bks.

—Noche de Humo. 1999. (978-0-606-16516-7(9)); (SPA.). lib. bdg. 14.15 (978-0-613-16782-6(1)) Tandem Library Bks.

—Smoky Night. 2002. (Illus.). (J). 13.19 (978-0-7587-0073-5(3)) Book Wholesalers, Inc.

—Smoky Night. Diaz, David, illus. 1999. 36p. (J). (ps-3). pap. 7.00 (978-0-15-201884-9(0) , Harcourt Paperbacks) Harcourt Children's Bks.

—Smoky Night. 1999. (978-0-606-16515-0(0)); lib. bdg. 14.15 (978-0-613-18279-9(0)) Tandem Library Bks.

Byng, Georgia. Molly Moon Stops the World. 2004. (Illus.). 384p. (J). 16.99 (978-0-06-051410-5(8)); lib. bdg. 17.89 (978-0-06-051413-6(2)) HarperCollins Pubs.

Castellucci, Cecil. Beige. 2007. (Illus.). 304p. (YA). (gr. 9 up). 16.99 (*978-0-7636-3066-9(7)) Candlewick Pr.

—Boy Proof. 208p. (YA). (gr. 9 up). 2005. 15.99 (978-0-7636-2333-3(4)); 2006. reprint ed. pap. 7.99 (978-0-7636-2796-6(8)) Candlewick Pr.

Castellucci, Cecil. The Queen of Cool. 2007. (Illus.). 176p. (YA). (gr. 9 up). pap. 7.99 (*978-0-7636-3413-1(1)) Candlewick Pr.

Chato & the Party Animals. 2004. 29.95 incl. audio compact disk (978-1-55592-703-5(3)); 24.95 incl. audio (978-1-55592-693-9(2)); pap. 14.95 incl. audio (978-1-55592-687-8(8)) Weston Woods Studios, Inc.

Chato's Kitchen. 2004. (J). 24.95 incl. audio (978-0-7882-0696-2(6)); pap. 18.95 incl. audio compact disk (978-1-55592-386-0(0)); pap. 18.95 incl. audio compact disk (978-1-55592-389-1(5)); pap. 38.75 incl. audio compact disk (978-1-55592-388-4(7)); pap. 38.75 incl. audio compact disk (978-1-55592-390-7(9)); pap. 32.75 incl. audio (978-1-55592-202-3(3)); pap. 32.75 incl. audio (978-1-55592-203-0(1)); (SPA.). pap. 14.95 incl. audio (978-0-7882-0134-9(4)); pap. 14.95 incl. audio (978-0-7882-0697-9(4)) Weston Woods Studios, Inc.

Cohn, Diana & Delgado, Francisco. Si, Se Puede! . 2005. Tr. of Yes, We Can!. (SPA.). 32p. pap. 7.95 (978-0-938317-89-0(X)) Cinco Puntos Pr.

Currier, Katrina Saltonstall. Kai's Journey to Gold Mountain: An Angel Island Story. 2004. 40p. 16.95 (978-0-9667352-7-7(7)); (Illus.). 44p. (J). pap. 10.95 (978-0-9667352-4-6(2)) Angel Island Assoc.

Cushman, Karen. The Loud Silence of Francine Green. 2006. 240p. (J). (gr. 5-9). 16.00 (978-0-618-50455-8(9) , Clarion Bks.) Houghton Mifflin Co. Trade & Reference Div.

Daughters Mo13 & Ewing, Lynne. Final Eclipse. 13th rev. ed. 2007. 288p. (YA). (gr. 7 up). 9.99 (*978-1-4231-0843-6(4)) Hyperion Bks. for Children.

de La Pena, Matt. Ball Don't Lie. 2005. 288p. (YA). (gr. 8-12). lib. bdg. 18.99 (978-0-385-90258-8(1)); (gr. 9-12). 16.95 (978-0-385-73232-1(5)) Random Hse. Children's Bks. (Delacorte Bks. for Young Readers).

de la Pena, Matt. Ball Don't Lie. 2007. 288p. (YA). (gr. 9). pap. 7.99 (978-0-385-73425-7(5) , Delacorte Bks. for Young Readers) Random Hse. Children's Bks.

Dean, Zoey. The A-List: A Novel. 2003. (A-List Ser.: Bk. 1). (YA). lib. bdg. 17.60 (978-0-613-70574-5(2)) Tandem Library Bks.

—Back in Black. 2005. (A-List Ser.: No. 5). 304p. (YA). (gr. 9-17). pap. 9.99 (978-0-316-01092-4(8) , Poppy) Little, Brown Bks. for Young Readers.

—Blonde Ambition. 2004. (A-List Ser.: No. 3). 233p. (YA). (gr. 8-12). per. 16.64 (978-0-606-33461-7(0)) Tandem Library Bks.

—Girls on Film. 2004. 250p. (YA). (gr. 8-12). per. 16.64 (978-0-606-33460-0(2)) Tandem Library Bks.

—Some Like It Hot. 6th ed. 2006. (A-List Ser.: No. 6). 320p. (J). (gr. 9-17). pap. 9.99 (978-0-316-01093-1(6) , Poppy) Little, Brown Bks. for Young Readers.

—Tall Cool One, No. 4. 2005. (A-List Ser.: No. 4). 304p. (YA). (gr. 9-17). pap. 9.99 (978-0-316-73508-7(6) , Poppy) Little, Brown Bks. for Young Readers.

—Tall Cool One. 2005. (A-List Ser.: No. 4). 295p. (YA). (gr. 7-17). per. 16.64 (978-0-606-33462-4(9)) Tandem Library Bks.

Dixon, Franklin W. Top Ten Ways to Die. 2006. 169p. (J). lib. bdg. 16.92 (*978-1-4242-0390-1(2)) Fitzgerald Bks.

Dumas Lachtman, Ofelia. Looking for la Unica. 2004. (ENG & SPA., Illus.). 190p. (J). pap. 9.95 (978-1-55885-412-3(6) , Piñata Books) Arte Publico Pr.

Espenson, Jane. Haunted. 2002. (Buffy the Vampire Slayer Ser.). (Illus.). 96p. (YA). pap. 12.95 (978-1-56971-737-0(0)) Dark Horse Comics.

Ewing, Lynne. Barbarian. 2004. (Sons of the Dark Ser.: Bk. 1). 272p. (gr. 7-17). 9.99 (978-0-7868-1811-2(5) , Volo) Hyperion Bks. for Children.

—The Becoming. rev. ed. 2004. (Daughters of the Moon Ser.: No. 12). 288p. (J). (gr. 7-17). 9.99 (978-0-7868-1892-1(1) , Volo) Hyperion Bks. for Children.

—Choice. 9th rev. ed. 2003. (Daughters of the Moon Ser.: No. 9). 288p. (gr. 7-17). 9.99 (978-0-7868-0851-9(9) , Volo) Hyperion Bks. for Children.

—Daughters of the Moon. 2000. 160p. (YA). pap. 4.99 (978-0-7868-1409-1(8)); Vol. 2. pap. 4.99 (978-0-7868-1410-7(1)) Disney Pr.

—Escape. rev. ed. 2004. (Sons of the Dark Ser.: Vol. 2). 270p. (J). (gr. 7-17). 9.99 (978-0-7868-1812-9(3) , Volo) Hyperion Bks. for Children.

—Goddess of the Night. 2000. (Daughters of the Moon Ser.: Vol. 1). 304p. (J). (gr. 7-17). 9.99 (978-0-7868-0653-9(2)) Disney Pr.

—Into the Cold Fire. 2nd rev. ed. 2000. (Daughters of the Moon Ser.: Vol. 2). (Illus.). 272p. (gr. 7-17). 9.99 (978-0-7868-0654-6(0)) Hyperion Bks. for Children.

—The Lost One. 2001. (Daughters of the Moon Ser.: No. 6). 288p. (J). (gr. 7-17). 9.99 (978-0-7868-0707-9(5) , Volo) Hyperion Bks. for Children.

—Moon Demon, Bk. 7. rev. ed. 2002. (Daughters of the Moon Ser.: No. 7). 289p. (J). (gr. 7-17). 9.99 (978-0-7868-0849-6(7) , Volo) Hyperion Bks. for Children.

—Night Shade. 2001. (Daughters of the Moon Ser.: Vol. 3). 288p. (J). (gr. 7-17). 9.99 (978-0-7868-0708-6(3) , Volo) Hyperion Bks. for Children.

—Party Girl. 1999. 128p. (YA). (gr. 9-11). pap. 5.50 (978-0-375-80210-2(X) , Laurel Leaf) Random Hse. Children's Bks.

—Party Girl. 1999. (978-0-606-17373-5(0)); (gr. 7-12). lib. bdg. 13.00 (978-0-613-23023-0(X)) Tandem Library Bks.

—The Prophecy. rev. ed. 2004. (Daughters of the Moon Ser.: No. 11). 288p. (J). (gr. 7-17). 9.99 (978-0-7868-1891-4(3) , Volo) Hyperion Bks. for Children.

—The Sacrifice. Scalora, Suza, illus. 5th rev. ed. 2001. (Daughters of the Moon Ser.: Bk. 5). 288p. (gr. 7-17). 9.99 (978-0-7868-0706-2(7) , Volo) Hyperion Bks. for Children.

—The Secret Scroll. 2001. (Daughters of the Moon Ser.: Vol. 4). 268p. (J). (gr. 7-17). reprint ed. 9.99 (978-0-7868-0709-3(1) , Volo) Hyperion Bks. for Children.

Fleischman, Paul. Breakout. 2003. 160p. 15.95 (978-0-8126-2696-4(6)) Cricket Bks.

—Breakout. 2005. 144p. (YA). reprint ed. pap. 6.99 (978-0-689-87189-4(9) , Simon Pulse) Simon & Schuster Children's Publishing.

—Breakout. 2005. (Illus.). 137p. (YA). (gr. 7-12). lib. bdg. 15.60 (978-1-4176-6932-5(2)) Tandem Library Bks.

Fleischman, Sid. Disappearing Act. 2003. (Illus.). 144p. (J). (gr. 3 up). 15.99 (978-0-06-051962-9(2)); lib. bdg. 16.89 (978-0-06-051963-6(0)) HarperCollins Pubs.

Gamble, Adam. Good Night Los Angeles. Kelly, Cooper, illus. 2007. (Good Night Our World Ser.). 20p. (J). bds. 9.95 (*978-1-60219-009-2(7)) Our World of Books.

Garfinkle, D. L. Stuck in the 70's. 2007. 192p. (YA). (gr. 7 up). 16.99 (978-0-399-24663-0(0) , Putnam Juvenile) Penguin Group (USA) Inc.

Greene, Michele Dominguez. Chasing the Jaguar. 240p. (J). 2008. pap. 7.99 (*978-0-06-076355-8(8) , Rayo); 2006. 15.99 (978-0-06-076353-4(1)) HarperCollins Pubs.

J K L

—Chasing the Jaguar. Greene, Michele Dominguez, illus. 2006. 240p. (J). lib. bdg. 16.89 (978-0-06-076354-1(X)) HarperCollins Pubs.

Harcourt School Publishers Staff. Everything on Olvera Street On Level. 3rd ed. 2002. (Trophies Reading Program Ser.). (Illus.). pap. 5.10 (978-0-15-323095-0(9)) Harcourt Schl. Pubs.

Haugaard, Kay. No Place. Peterson-Albandoz, Michelle, illus. 1999. 175p. (J). (gr. 3-8). 15.95 (978-1-57131-616-5(7)) Milkweed Editions.

—No Place. 2nd ed. 2007. (Illus.). 140p. pap. 6.95 ***(978-1-57131-675-2(2))*** Milkweed Editions.

—No Place. 1999. (J). (978-0-606-19034-3(1)) Tandem Library Bks.

Holder, Nancy. Not Forgotten. 2000. (Angel Ser.: No. 2). 256p. (YA). (gr. 7 up). pap. 5.99 (978-0-671-04145-8(2) , Simon Pulse) Simon & Schuster Children's Publishing.

—Not Forgotten. 2000. (gr. 7-12). lib. bdg. 14.15 (978-0-613-28001-3(6)) Tandem Library Bks.

Johnston, Tony. Angel City. Byard, Carole M., illus. 2006. 40p. (J). (ps). 15.99 (978-0-399-23405-7(5) , Philomel) Penguin Group (USA) Inc.

—Any Small Goodness: A Novel of the Barrio. Colon, Raul, illus. 128p. (J). (gr. 4 up). 2003. pap. 4.99 (978-0-439-23384-2(4) , Scholastic Paperbacks); 2001. 16.95 (978-0-439-18936-1(5) , Blue Sky Pr., The) Scholastic, Inc.

—Any Small Goodness: A Novel of the Barrio. 2002. (gr. 3-6). lib. bdg. 13.00 (978-0-613-67479-9(0)) Tandem Library Bks.

Koertge, Ronald. Margaux with an X. 176p. (YA). (gr. 9 up). 2004. 15.99 (978-0-7636-2401-9(2)); 2006. reprint ed. pap. 6.99 (978-0-7636-2679-2(1)) Candlewick Pr.

Kogler, Jennifer Anne. Ruby Tuesday. 2005. 320p. (J). (gr. 7 up). 15.99 (978-0-06-073956-0(8)) HarperCollins Pubs.

Lachtman, Ofelia Dumas. The Summer of El Pintor. 2001. (Illus.). 240p. (J). (gr. 11 up). pap. 9.95 (978-1-55885-327-0(8) , Piñata Books) Arte Publico Pr.

—Summer of el Pintor. 2001. (gr. 5-8). lib. bdg. 18.75 (978-0-613-59023-5(6)) Tandem Library Bks.

Mariotte, Jeff. Haunted. 2002. (Angel Ser.: Vol. 11). (Illus.). 336p. (YA). pap. 5.99 (978-0-7434-2748-7(3) , Simon Pulse) Simon & Schuster Children's Publishing.

—Haunted. 2002. (gr. 7-12). lib. bdg. 14.15 (978-0-613-63200-3(1)) Tandem Library Bks.

—Stranger to the Sun. 2002. (gr. 7-12). lib. bdg. 14.15 (978-0-613-63236-2(2)) Tandem Library Bks.

Markel, Michelle. Dream Town. Reese, Rick, illus. 2006. (J). 15.95 (978-1-59714-022-5(8)) Heyday Bks.

Matas, Carol. Rosie in Los Angeles: Action! 2004. (Illus.). 128p. (J). pap. 9.95 (978-0-689-85716-4(0) , Aladdin) Simon & Schuster Children's Publishing.

—Rosie in Los Angeles: Action! 2004. (gr. 3-6). lib. bdg. 13.00 (978-0-613-91044-6(3)) Tandem Library Bks.

Miklowitz, Gloria D. The Enemy Has a Face. 2004. 143p. (YA). pap. 8.00 (978-0-8028-5261-8(0)) Eerdmans, William B. Publishing Co.

Odom, Mel. Image. 2002. (Angel Ser.: Bk. 12). (Illus.). 240p. (YA). pap. 5.99 (978-0-7434-2750-0(5) , Simon Pulse) Simon & Schuster Children's Publishing.

Palmer, Robin. Cindy Ella. 2008. 304p. (YA). (gr. 7). 7.99 ***(978-0-14-240392-1(X)*** , Puffin) Penguin Group (USA) Inc.

Pinkwater, Daniel M. The Neddiad: How Neddie Took the Train, Went to Hollywood, & Saved Civilization. 2007. 320p. (J). (gr. 5). 16.00 ***(978-0-618-59444-3(2))*** Houghton Mifflin Co. Trade & Reference Div.

Purtill, C. Leigh. Love, Meg. 2007. 304p. (YA). 16.99 (978-1-59514-116-3(2) , Razorbill) Penguin Group (USA) Inc.

Rabin, Staton. Black Powder. 2005. 256p. (J). (gr. 6-9). 16.95 (978-0-689-86876-4(6) , McElderry, Margaret K.) Simon & Schuster Children's Publishing.

Riefe, Barbara. Amelia Dale Archer Story. 1998. 304p. (YA). (gr. 8 up). 22.95 (978-0-312-86077-6(3) , Forge Bks.) Doherty, Tom Assocs., LLC.

Rigby, Robert & Random House U. K. Ltd. Staff. Goal! The Dream Begins. 2006. (Illus.). 240p. (YA). pap. 6.95 (978-0-15-205798-5(6) , Harcourt Paperbacks) Harcourt Children's Bks.

Skolnick, Eliot. Viper. 2007. (YA). per. 8.99 ***(978-1-934360-01-9(5))*** Raider Publishing International.

Smith, Sherri L. Hot, Sour, Salty, Sweet. 2008. 176p. (J). ***(978-0-385-73417-2(4));*** lib. bdg. ***(978-0-385-90431-5(2))*** Dell Publishing. (Delacorte Pr.).

Sones, Sonya. One of Those Hideous Books Where the Mother Dies. 272p. (YA). 2004. (Illus.). 16.95 (978-0-689-85820-8(5)); 2005. (gr. 7-12). reprint ed. pap. 6.99 (978-1-4169-0788-6(2) , Simon Pulse) Simon & Schuster Children's Publishing.

Soto, Gary. Chato & the Party Animals. Guevara, Susan, illus. 25.95 incl. audio (978-1-59112-460-3(3)); 28.95 incl. audio compact disk (978-1-59112-920-2(6)); pap. 37.95 incl. audio (978-1-59112-461-0(1)); pap. 39.95 incl. audio compact disk (978-1-59112-921-9(4)) Live Oak Media.

—Chato & the Party Animals. Guevara, Susan, illus. 2000. (SPA.). 32p. (J). (ps-3). 16.99 (978-0-399-23159-9(5) , Putnam Juvenile) Penguin Group (USA) Inc.

—Chato & the Party Animals. 2004. (gr. k-3). lib. bdg. 15.30 (978-0-613-89799-0(4)) Tandem Library Bks.

—Chato & the Party Animals. Guevara, Susan, illus. 2004. (J). (ps-ps). lib. bdg. 13.79 (978-0-606-29661-8(1)) Tandem Library Bks.

—Chato & the Party Animals. Guevara, Susan, illus. 2004. 32p. (J). (gr. k-3). reprint ed. pap. 6.99 (978-0-14-240032-6(7) , Puffin) Penguin Group (USA) Inc.

—Chato y los Amigos Pachangueros. Guevara, Susan, illus. 2004. Tr. of Chato & the Party Animals. (SPA.). 32p. (J). (gr. k-3). reprint ed. pap. 7.99 (978-0-14-240033-3(5) , Puffin) Penguin Group (USA) Inc.

—Chato's Kitchen. 2002. (Live Oak Readalong Ser.). (Illus.). (J). pap. 16.95 incl. audio (978-1-59112-205-0(8)); pap. 18.95 incl. audio compact disk (978-1-59112-336-1(4)) Live Oak Media.

—Chato's Kitchen. Guevara, Susan, illus. 2002. 25.95 incl. audio (978-1-59112-206-7(6)); 28.95 incl. audio compact disk (978-1-59112-528-0(6)); pap. 37.95 incl. audio (978-1-59112-207-4(4)); pap. 39.95 incl. audio compact disk (978-1-59112-527-3(8)) Live Oak Media.

—Chato's Kitchen; Chato Y Su Cena. Guevara, Susan, illus. 2002. pap. 33.95 incl. audio (978-1-59112-208-1(2)) Live Oak Media.

Summers, Gillian. The Tree Shepherd's Daughter: The Faire Folk Trilogy. 2007. 336p. (J). (gr. 4-7). pap. 9.95 ***(978-0-7387-1081-5(4)*** , Flux) Llewellyn Pubns.

Trine, Greg. The Curse of the Bologna Sandwich. Montijo, Rhode, illus. 2006. (Melvin Beederman, Superhero Ser.). 144p. (J). 15.95 (978-0-8050-7928-9(9)); pap. 5.99 (978-0-8050-7836-7(3)) Holt, Henry & Co.

—The Fake Cape Caper. Montijo, Rhode, illus. 5th rev. ed. 2007. (Melvin Beederman, Superhero Ser.). 144p. (J). pap. 5.99 ***(978-0-8050-8159-6(3));*** (gr. 2 up). 16.95 ***(978-0-8050-8158-9(5))*** Holt, Henry & Co. (Holt, Henry & Co. Bks. For Young Readers).

—The Grateful Fred. Montijo, Rhode, illus. 3rd rev. ed. 2006. (Melvin Beederman, Superhero Ser.). 144p. (J). 15.95 (978-0-8050-7921-0(1)) Holt, Henry & Co.

—The Grateful Fred. Montijo, Rhode, illus. 3rd rev. ed. 2006. (Melvin Beederman, Superhero Ser.). 144p. (J). pap. 5.99 (978-0-8050-7922-7(X)) Holt, Henry & Co.

—Terror in Tights. Montijo, Rhode, illus. 4th rev. ed. 2007. (Melvin Beederman, Superhero Ser.). 144p. (J). (gr. 2-4). 16.95 (978-0-8050-7923-4(8)); pap. 5.99 (978-0-8050-7924-1(6)) Holt, Henry & Co.

Valdes-Rodriguez, Alisa. Haters. 2006. 368p. (J). (gr. 7-17). 16.99 (978-0-316-01307-9(2)) Little Brown & Co.

Woods, Brenda. Emako Blue. 128p. (YA). 2005. (gr. 6). pap. 5.99 (978-0-14-240418-8(7) , Puffin); 2004. (gr. 5-12). 15.99 (978-0-399-24006-5(3) , Putnam Juvenile) Penguin Group (USA) Inc.

—The Red Rose Box. 2002. 160p. (YA). (gr. 4-6). 16.99 (978-0-399-23702-7(X) , Putnam Juvenile) Penguin Group (USA) Inc.

—The Red Rose Box. 2003. (gr. 5-8). lib. bdg. 14.15 (978-0-613-87822-7(1)) Tandem Library Bks.

LOS ANGELES (CALIF.)—RACE RELATIONS

Cole, Michael D. The L. A. Riots: Rage in the City of Angels. 1999. (American Disasters Ser.). (Illus.). 48p. (YA). (gr. 4-10). lib. bdg. 23.93 (978-0-7660-1219-6(0)) Enslow Pubs., Inc.

LOS ANGELES DODGERS (BASEBALL TEAM)

Aretha, David. Dodger Blue[97]the Los Angeles Dodgers. 2007. (Sensational Sports Teams Ser.). (Illus.). 128p. (J). lib. bdg. 33.27 (978-1-59845-045-3(X) , MyReportLinks.com Bks.) Enslow Pubs., Inc.

Daddy's Heroes. Daddy's Heroes: Gibby's Homer. 2007. (1988 World Ser.). (Illus.). 32p. (J). 8.95 ***(978-0-9792111-0-2(7))*** Daddy's Heroes, Inc.

Epstein, Brad M. Los Angeles Dodgers 101: My first Team-board-book. 1.t. ed. 2007. (101—My First Text-Board Books). (Illus.). 22p. (J). bds. 10.95 ***(978-1-932530-80-3(0)*** , 101 Bk.) Michaelson Entertainment.

Friedman, Nick. Mike Piazza. 2007. (Baseball Superstars Ser.). 136p. (gr. 6-12). 30.00 ***(978-0-7910-9493-8(6))*** Facts On File, Inc.

Goodman, Michael E. Los Angeles Dodgers. 1998. (Baseball, the Great American Game Ser.). (Illus.). 32p. (YA). (gr. 3-12). pap. 21.30 (978-0-88682-912-4(7) , Creative Education) Creative Co., The.

Nichols, John. The Story of the Los Angeles Dodgers. 2007. (J). ***(978-1-58341-491-0(6)*** , Creative Education) Creative Co., The.

Pietrusza, David. The Los Angeles Dodgers Baseball Team. 1999. (Great Sports Teams Ser.). (Illus.). 48p. (YA). (gr. 4-10). lib. bdg. 23.93 (978-0-7660-1097-0(X)) Enslow Pubs., Inc.

Stewart, Mark. The Los Angeles Dodgers. 2007. (Team Spirit Ser.). (Illus.). 48p. (J). lib. bdg. 25.27 ***(978-1-59953-095-6(3))*** Norwood Hse. Pr.

Stewart, Wayne. Los Angeles Dodgers. 2002. 32p. (J). pap. 5.95 (978-0-89812-346-3(1) , Creative Paperbacks); (Illus.). (978-1-58341-212-1(3) , Creative Education) Creative Co., The.

LOTUS 1-2-3 (COMPUTER PROGRAM)

Bauld, Jane Scoggins. Journey of the Third Seed. Darr, Cynthia G., illus. 2001. 40p. (J). (gr. k-2). 9.95 (978-1-57168-429-5(8)); 16.95 (978-1-57168-428-8(X)) Eakin Pr.

Lotus 1-2-3 Millennium Intermediate. 1999. (Illus.). 220p. (YA). pap. (978-0-7423-0356-0(X) , LOT123M02LG) ComputerPREP, Inc.

Lotus 1-2-3 Millennium Introduction. 1999. (Illus.). (YA). pap. (978-0-7423-0355-3(1) , LOT123M01LG) ComputerPREP, Inc.

LOUIS XIV, KING OF FRANCE, 1638-1715

Barter, James E. The Palace of Versailles. 1998. (Building History Ser.). (Illus.). 112p. (YA). (gr. 6-9). 27.45 (978-1-56006-433-6(1) , Lucent Bks.) Thomson Gale.

Mason, Anthony. Versailles. 2005. (Places in History Ser.). (Illus.). 48p. (J). pap. (978-0-8368-5822-8(0)); lib. bdg. 30.00 (978-0-8368-5815-0(8)) Stevens, Gareth Inc. (World Almanac Library).

Tagliaferro, Linda. Palace of Versailles: France's Royal Jewel. 2005. (Castles, Palaces, & Tombs Ser.). (J). lib. bdg. 25.27 (978-1-59716-003-2(2)) Bearport Publishing Co., Inc.

Wilkinson, Richard. Louis XIV: France & Europe, 1661-1715. 2nd ed. 2002. (Illus.). 144p. pap. 17.95 (978-0-340-84688-9(7) , Hodder Murray) Hodder Education GBR. *Dist:* Trafalgar Square Publishing.

LOUISIANA

Bjorklund, Ruth & Santoro, Christopher. Louisiana. 2005. (It's My State! Ser.). (Illus.). 80p. (J). 27.07 (978-0-7614-1863-4(6) , Benchmark Bks.) Cavendish, Marshall Corp.

Brown, Vanessa. Louisiana/Luisiana. 2005. (Bilingual Library of the United States of America: Set 1). (ENG & SPA., Illus.). 32p. (J). (gr. 2-5). lib. bdg. 22.50 (978-1-4042-3083-5(1) , Buenas Letra) Rosen Publishing Group, Inc., The.

Capstone Press Staff, contrib. by. Louisiana. rev. ed. 2002. (One Nation Ser.). (Illus.). 48p. (J). (gr. 3-4). lib. bdg. 22.60 (978-0-7368-1242-9(3) , Bridgestone Bks.) Capstone Pr., Inc.

Cassels, Jean. The Twelve Days of Christmas in Louisiana. Cravath, Lynne Avril, illus. 2007. 32p. (J). (gr. k up). 9.95 ***(978-1-4027-3814-2(5))*** Sterling Publishing Co., Inc.

Corwin, Jeff. Into Wild Louisiana. Pascoe, Elaine, ed. 2003. (Jeff Corwin Experience Ser.). (Illus.). 48p. (J). 24.95 (978-1-4103-0060-7(9)); 11.20 (978-1-4103-0181-9(8)) Thomson Gale. (Blackbirch Pr., Inc.).

Culbertson, Manie. Louisiana: The Land & Its People Student Skillbuilder. 2nd ed. 1999. (Illus.). 128p. (J). (gr. 4-7). pap. 9.95 (978-1-56554-625-7(3)) Pelican Publishing Co., Inc.

Dartez, Cecilia Casrill. L Is for Louisiana. 2002. (Illus.). 32p. (J). (gr. k-3). pap. 7.95 (978-1-58980-022-9(2)) Pelican Publishing Co., Inc.

—L Is for Louisiana. 2002. (gr. k-3). lib. bdg. 16.40 (978-0-613-71062-6(2)) Tandem Library Bks.

Gildart, Leslie S. Louisiana: The Pelican State. 2002. (World Almanac Library of the States). (Illus.). 48p. (J). (gr. 5 up). lib. bdg. 30.00 (978-0-8368-5136-6(6)); pap. 14.95 (978-0-8368-5306-3(7)) Stevens, Gareth Inc. (World Almanac Library).

—Louisiana: The Pelican State. 2003. (gr. 3-6). lib. bdg. 38.05 (978-0-613-76809-2(4)) Tandem Library Bks.

Glaser, Jason. Louisiana. 2003. (Land of Liberty Ser.). (Illus.). 64p. (J). (gr. 3-4). lib. bdg. 23.93 (978-0-7368-1586-4(4) , Bridgestone Bks.) Capstone Pr., Inc.

Gravelle, Karen & Diouf, Sylviane A. Growing up in Crawfish Country: A Cajun Childhood. 1998. (Growing Up in America Ser.). (Illus.). 64p. (J). (gr. 3-6). 24.00 (978-0-531-11535-0(6) , Watts, Franklin) Scholastic Library Publishing.

Heinrichs, Ann. Louisiana. 2005. (Welcome to the USA Ser.). 40p. (J). (gr. 1-5). 27.07 (978-1-59296-376-8(5)) Child's World, Inc.

—Louisiana. 2003. (This Land Is Your Land Ser.). (Illus.). 48p. (J). (gr. 3 up). lib. bdg. 22.60 (978-0-7565-0354-3(X)) Compass Point Bks.

Hirshberg, Jackie. Nicky the Swamp Dog: A True Story. Guillory, D. Ray, photos by. 2000. (Illus.). 40p. (J). (gr. 3-5). 14.95 (978-0-925417-36-7(X)) Acadian Hse. Publishing.

Hyde, Judith Jensen. Louisiana. 2007. (Rookie Read-about' Geography: States Ser.). 32p. (J). pap. 5.95 ***(978-0-516-21747-5(X));*** (Illus.). (gr. 1-2). 20.50 (978-0-516-21848-9(4)) Scholastic Library Publishing. (Children's Pr.).

Johnstone, Robb. A Guide to Louisiana. 2000. (American States Ser.). (Illus.). 32p. (J). (gr. 3-7). lib. bdg. 16.95 (978-1-930954-55-7(7)) Weigl Pubs., Inc.

LaDoux, Rita C. Louisiana. (Hello U. S. A. Ser.). (gr. 3-6). 2001. 84p. (J). pap. 6.95 (978-0-8225-4229-2(3) , First Avenue Editions); 1999. (Illus.). 72p. pap. 5.95 (978-0-8225-9786-5(1)); 2nd exp. rev. ed. 2002. (Illus.). 84p. (J). lib. bdg. 25.26 (978-0-8225-4065-6(7)); 2nd rev. exp. ed. 2003. (Illus.). 84p. (J). pap. 6.95 (978-0-8225-4145-5(9)) Lerner Publishing Group.

—Louisiana. 2001. (gr. 3-6). lib. bdg. 15.25 (978-0-613-84027-9(5)) Tandem Library Bks.

Lantier, Patricia. Louisiana. 2006. (Portraits of the States Ser.). (Illus.). 32p. (J). pap. 8.95 (978 0 8368-4686-7(9)); lib. bdg. 23.33 (978-0-8368-4667-6(2)) Stevens, Gareth Inc.

Lassieur, Allison. Louisiana. 2007. (America the Beautiful, Third Ser.). (Illus.). 144p. (YA). (gr. 5-8). lib. bdg. 38.00 ***(978-0-531-18560-5(5)*** , Children's Pr.) Scholastic Library Publishing.

LeVert, Suzanne. Louisiana. 2nd ed. 2006. (Celebrate the States Ser.). (Illus.). 144p. (J). (978-0-7614-2032-3(0)); (978-0-7614-2021-7(5)) Cavendish, Marshall Corp. (Benchmark Bks.).

Loughran, Donna. Uniquely Louisiana. 2003. (Heinemann State Studies). (Illus.). 48p. (J). 27.07 (978-1-4034-4492-9(7)); pap. 8.50 (978-1-4034-4507-0(9)) Heinemann Library.

—Uniquely Louisiana. 2003. (gr. 3-6). lib. bdg. 38.60 (978-0-613-90274-8(2)) Tandem Library Bks.

Louisiana. 2000. (Switched on Schoolhouse Ser.). (Illus.). (YA). (gr. 7-12). pap. 24.95 incl. cd-rom (978-0-7403-0270-1(1) , SOSLA) Alpha Omega Pubns., Inc.

Macaulay, Ellen. Louisiana. 2003. (From Sea to Shining Sea Ser.: 2). (Illus.). 80p. (J). 30.50 (978-0-516-22399-5(2) , Children's Pr.) Scholastic Library Publishing.

Marsh, Carole. Louisiana Classic Christmas Trivia. 2002. (Carole Marsh Louisiana Bks.). (Illus.). 32p. pap. 6.95 (978-0-635-01403-0(3) , 14033, Marsh, Carole Bks.); lib. bdg. 21.95 (978-0-635-01404-7(1) , 14041) Gallopade International.

—Louisiana Current Events Projects: 30 Cool, Activities, Crafts, Experiments & More for Kids to Do to Learn about Your State! 2003. (Louisiana Experience Ser.). 32p. (gr. k-8). pap. 5.95 (978-0-635-02037-6(8) , Marsh, Carole Bks.) Gallopade International.

—The Louisiana Experience Pocket Guide. 2004. (Louisiana Experience! Ser.). (Illus.). 96p. (J). (gr. 3-8). pap. 6.95 (978-0-7933-9546-0(1)) Gallopade International.

—Louisiana Geography Projects: 30 Cool, Activities, Crafts, Experiments & More for Kids to Do to Learn about Your State! 2003. (Louisiana Experience Ser.). 32p. (gr. k-5). pap. 5.95 (978-0-635-01837-3(3) , Marsh, Carole Bks.) Gallopade International.

—Louisiana Government Projects: 30 Cool, Activities, Crafts, Experiments & More for Kids to Do to Learn about Your State! 2003. (Louisiana Experience Ser.). 32p. (gr. k-5). pap. 5.95 (978-0-635-01937-0(X) , Marsh, Carole Bks.) Gallopade International.

—Louisiana Jeopardy. 2004. (Louisiana Experience! Ser.). (Illus.). 32p. (J). (gr. 3-8). pap. 7.95 (978-0-7933-9548-4(8)) Gallopade International.

—Louisiana Jography. 2004. (Louisiana Experience! Ser.). (Illus.). 32p. (J). (gr. 3-8). pap. 7.95 (978-0-7933-9549-1(6)) Gallopade International.

—Louisiana Millionaire: Game Book. 2001. (Carole Marsh Louisiana Bks.). (Illus.). 32p. (J). (gr. 3-8). pap., act. bk. ed. 9.95 (978-0-635-00052-1(0)) Gallopade International.

—Louisiana People Projects: 30 Cool, Activities, Crafts, Experiments & More for Kids to Do to Learn about Your State! 2003. (Louisiana Experience Ser.). 32p. (gr. k-5). pap. 5.95 (978-0-635-01987-5(6) , Marsh, Carole Bks.) Gallopade International.

—Louisiana Survivor: Game Book. 2001. (Carole Marsh Louisiana Bks.). (Illus.). 32p. (J). (gr. 3-8). pap., act. bk. ed. 9.95 (978-0-635-00539-7(5)) Gallopade International.

—Louisiana Symbols & Facts Projects: 30 Cool, Activities, Crafts, Experiments & More for Kids to Do to Learn about Your State! 2003. (Louisiana Experience Ser.). 32p. (gr. k-5). pap. 5.95 (978-0-635-01887-8(X) , Marsh, Carole Bks.) Gallopade International.

—Louisiana's Big Activity Book. 2004. (Louisiana Experience! Ser.). (Illus.). 96p. (J). (gr. 2-6). pap. 9.95 (978-0-7933-9550-7(X)) Gallopade International.

—My First Book about Louisiana. 2004. (Louisiana Experience! Ser.). (Illus.). 32p. (J). (gr. k-4). pap. 7.95 (978-0-7933-9547-7(X)) Gallopade International.

—The Survivor: A Class Challenge. 2001. (Carole Marsh Louisiana Bks.). lib. bdg. 29.95 (978-0-635-00664-6(2)) Gallopade International.

—Who Wants to Be a Millionaire? 2001. (Carole Marsh Louisiana Bks.). lib. bdg. 29.95 (978-0-635-00053-8(9)) Gallopade International.

McAuliffe, Emily. Louisiana Facts & Symbols. (States & Their Symbols Ser.). 24p. (J). 1998. (Illus.). (gr. 2-3). lib. bdg. 18.60 (978-0-7368-0081-5(6) , Bridgestone Bks.); 2003. lib. bdg. 19.93 (978-0-7368-2248-0(8)) Capstone Pr., Inc.

Murray, Julie. Louisiana. 2006. (Illus.). 32p. (J). (gr. k-4). lib. bdg. 22.78 (978-1-59197-677-6(4) , Buddy Bks.) ABDO Publishing Co.

O'Neill, Elizabeth. Alfred Visits Louisiana. 2007. 24p. (J). pap. 12.00 ***(978-0-9790240-8-5(0))*** Funny Bone Bks.

Parker, Laurie. Louisiana Alphabet, 3 vols. Parker, Laurie, illus. 2001. (State Alphabet Ser.). (Illus.). 32p. 15.95 (978-1-893062-31-3(7)) Quail Ridge Pr., Inc.

Prieto, Anita C. P Is for Pelican: A Louisiana Alphabet. Knorr, Laura, illus. 2004. 40p. (J). 17.95 (978-1-58536-137-3(2)) Sleeping Bear Pr.

Reed, Jennifer. Louisiana: A MyReportLinks. Com Book. 2003. (States Ser.). (Illus.). 48p. (J). lib. bdg. 25.26 (978-0-7660-5141-6(2) , MyReportLinks.com Bks.) Enslow Pubs., Inc.

Shofner, Shawndra. Louisiana. 2008. (J). ***(978-1-58341-643-3(9)*** , Creative Education) Creative Co., The.

Weber, Valerie & Lewis, Geneva. Home Life in Grandma's Day. 1999. (In Grandma's Day Ser.). (Illus.). 32p. (J). (gr. 2-4). lib. bdg. 21.27 (978-1-57505-329-5(2) , Carolrhoda Bks.) Lerner Publishing Group.

LOUISIANA—FICTION

The Autobiography of Miss Jane Pittman: SourceBook. 2004. (Literature Connections Ser.). (Illus.). (gr. 6-12). (978-0-395-87490-5(4) , 2-70849) McDougal Littell Inc.

Ball, Marcia. Christmas Fais Do-Do. 2006. (Illus.). 36p. (J). per. 14.95 ***(978-1-58939-972-3(2))*** Virtualbookworm.com Publishing, Inc.

Brodt, Burton P. Four Little Old Men: A (Mostly) True Tale from a Small Cajun Town. Melanson, Luc, illus. 2005. 32p. (J). 14.95 (978-1-4027-2006-2(8)) Sterling Publishing Co., Inc.

Brown, Marc. Buster & the Great Swamp. 8th ed. 2005. (Postcards from Buster Ser.). (Illus.). 32p. (J). (gr. 1-4). pap. 14.99 (978-0-316-15912-8(3)); pap. 3.99 (978-0-316-00125-0(2)) Little Brown & Co.

Brunner, Celeste Walker. Louisiana Lessie. 2001. (Illus.). 40p. (J). pap. 11.00 (978-1-57921-333-6(2)) WinePress Publishing.

Carter, Joey. The Great Airboat Ride! A Cantor Kids! Book. 2006. 72p. pap. 9.95 (978-1-59800-523-3(5)) Outskirts Press, Inc.

Carville, James & McKissack, Patricia C. Lu & the Swamp Ghost. Catrow, David, tr. Catrow, David, illus. 2004. 40p. (J). 17.95 (978-0-689-86560-2(0) , Atheneum) Simon & Schuster Children's Publishing.

Cochran, Thomas. Running the Dogs. 2007. 160p. (J). (gr. 3-7). 16.00 ***(978-0-374-36360-4(9))*** Farrar, Straus & Giroux.

Collins, Sheila Hebert. Jolie Blonde & the Three Herberts: A Cajun Twist to an Old Tale. 1999. 32p. (J). (gr. k-3). pap. 15.95 (978-1-56554-324-9(6)) Pelican Publishing Co., Inc.

Couvillon, Jacques. The Chicken Dance. 2007. 336p. (YA). (gr. 5 up). 16.95 ***(978-1-59990-043-8(2)*** , Bloomsbury Children) Bloomsbury Publishing.

Davis, David. Jazz Cats. Galey, Chuck, illus. 2001. 32p. (J). (gr. 2-4). pap. 15.95 (978-1-56554-859-6(0)) Pelican Publishing Co., Inc.

J K L

Doucet, Sharon Arms. Fiddle Fever. 176p. (J). (gr. 5-9). 2007. pap. 6.95 (978-0-618-77682-5(6)); 2000. (Illus.). tchr. ed. 15.00 (978-0-618-04324-8(1)) Houghton Mifflin Co. Trade & Reference Div. (Clarion Bks.).

—Fiddle Fever. l.t. ed. 2001. 174p. (J). 20.95 (978-0-7862-3548-3(9)) Thomson Gale.

Downing, Johnette. Today Is Monday in Louisiana. Kadair, Deborah Ousley, illus. 2006. 32p. (J). 15.95 (978-1-58980-406-7(6)) Pelican Publishing Co., Inc.

Downing, Johnette & Kadair, Deborah Ousley. Down in Louisiana. 2007. 32p. (J). 15.95 (978-1-58980-451-7(1)) Pelican Publishing Co., Inc.

Duey, Kathleen. Louisiana Hurricane, 1860. 2000. (Illus.). (J). (978-0-606-18802-9(9)) Tandem Library Bks.

—Swamp: Bayou Teche, Louisiana 1850. 1999. (gr. 3-6). lib. bdg. 12.40 (978-0-613-15997-5(7)) Tandem Library Bks.

Duey, Kathleen & Bale, Karen. Swamp, Bayou Teche, Louisiana, 1851. 1999. (Survival! Ser.: No. 11). (978-0-606-16302-6(6)) Tandem Library Bks.

Duey, Kathleen & Bale, Karen A. Swamp: Bayou Teche, Louisiana 1851. Dodge, Bill, illus. 1999. (Survival! Ser.: No. 11). 160p. (J). (gr. 4-7). pap. 4.50 (978-0-689-82929-1(9) , 076714004504, Aladdin) Simon & Schuster Children's Publishing.

Dunham, Terri Hoover. The Legend of Papa Noël: A Cajun Christmas Story. Knorr, Laura, illus. 2006. 32p. (J). (gr. k-5). 17.95 (978-1-58536-256-1(5)) Sleeping Bear Pr.

Finley, Martha. Elsie's True Love. 224p. Bk. 5. 2000. (Elsie Dinsmore: Bk. 5). (YA). (gr. 5-9). 12.99 (978-1-928749-05-9(4)); Vol. 5. 2006. (Life of Faith': Elsie Dinsmore Ser.). (J). pap. 7.99 (978-1-928749-84-4(4)) Zonderkidz.

Fontenot, Mary Alice. Clovis Crawfish & Echo Gecko. Buckner, Julie Dupre, illus. 2003. 32p. (J). 15.95 (978-1-56554-708-7(X)) Pelican Publishing Co., Inc.

—Clovis Crawfish & Raoul Raccoon. Landry, Cat, illus. 1999. (Clovis Crawfish Ser.). 32p. (J). (gr. k-3). 15.95 (978-1-56554-369-0(6)) Pelican Publishing Co., Inc.

—Clovis Crawfish & Silvie Sulphur. Buckner, Julie Dupre, illus. 2004. (ENG & FRE.). 32p. (J). pap. 15.95 (978-1-56554-864-0(7)) Pelican Publishing Co., Inc.

Fontenot, Mary Alice & Landry, Julie Fontenot. Clovis Crawfish & the Twin Sister. 2007. 32p. (J). 15.95 (***978-1-58980-467-8(8)***) Pelican Publishing Co., Inc.

Garrett, Ann. El Guardian del Pantano. Chandler, Karen, illus. 2001. (SPA.). 40p. (J). (gr. 3-5). 8.95 (978-1-890515-28-7(0) , TK30971) Turtle Bks.

—El Guardian del Pantano. Gutiérrez, Guillermo, tr. Chandler, Karen, illus. 1998. (SPA.). 40p. (J). (gr. 3-5). 16.95 (978-1-890515-13-3(2) , TK2991) Turtle Bks.

—Guardian Del Pantano. 1999. (SPA.). (gr. 3-6). lib. bdg. 17.60 (978-0-613-35955-9(0)) Tandem Library Bks.

—Keeper of the Swamp. 1999. (gr. 3-6). lib. bdg. 17.60 (978-0-613-50211-5(6)) Tandem Library Bks.

—Keeper of the Swamp. Chandler, Karen, illus. 40p. (J). 2001. (ps-3). pap. 8.95 (978-1-890515-27-0(2)); 1998. (SPA.). (gr. 1-4). 16.95 (978-1-890515-12-6(4)) Turtle Bks.

Gates, Susan. Cry Wolf. l.t. ed. 2000. 151p. (J). pap. (978-0-7540-6105-2(1) , CLP 301) BBC Audio.

Harcourt School Publishers Staff. Bon Temps Advanced Level. 3rd ed. 2002. (Trophies Reading Program Ser.). (Illus.). pap. 5.10 (978-0-15-323305-0(2)); (SPA., pap. 6.80 (978-0-15-324215-1(9)) Harcourt Schl. Pubs.

Hebert-Collins, Sheila. Jean-Paul Hebert Was There. Bergeron, John W., illus. 2004. Tr. of Jean-Paul Hebert Etait La. (ENG & FRE.). 32p. (J). pap. 15.95 (978-1-56554-928-9(7)) Pelican Publishing Co., Inc.

Holt, Kimberly Willis. Mister & Me. 2000. (gr. 3-6). lib. bdg. 13.00 (978-0-613-33713-7(1)) Tandem Library Bks.

—My Louisiana Sky. rev. ed. 1998. 176p. (J). (gr. 4-7). 17.95 (978-0-8050-5251-0(8) , Holt, Henry & Co. Bks. For Young Readers) Holt, Henry & Co.

—My Louisiana Sky. 208p. (gr. 5 up). (YA). 4.99 (978-0-8072-8291-5(X)); 2004. (J). pap. 36.00 incl. audio (978-0-8072-8290-8(1) , YA152SP) Random Hse. Audio Publishing Group. (Listening Library).

—My Louisiana Sky. 2000. 208p. (J). (gr. 5-9). pap. 6.50 (978-0-440-41570-1(5) , Yearling) Random Hse. Children's Bks.

—My Louisiana Sky. 2000. (978-0-606-17562-3(8)) Tandem Library Bks.

—Part of Me: Stories of a Louisiana Family. 2006. 224p. (J). 16.95 (978-0-8050-6360-8(9) , Holt, Henry & Co. Bks. For Young Readers) Holt, Henry & Co.

Jackson, Brian. Walking Through Mirrors. 1999. (gr. 7-12). lib. bdg. 23.45 (978-0-613-24002-4(2)) Tandem Library Bks.

LaFaye, A. The Year of the Sawdust Man. 1999. (978-0-606-17947-8(X)) Tandem Library Bks.

Les Becquets, Diane. Love, Cajun Style. 2007. (Illus.). 304p. (YA). pap. 7.95 (978-1-59990-030-8(0) , Bloomsbury Children) Bloomsbury Publishing.

Literature Connections English: The Autobiography of Miss Jane Pittman. 2004. (gr. 6-12). (978-0-395-86993-2(5) , 2-70829) McDougal Littell Inc.

Lovett, Darrell F. Darrell's Lake Franklin. 2007. 13.00 (***978-0-8059-8807-9(6)***) Dorrance Publishing Co., Inc.

MacBride, Roger Lea. On the Banks of the Bayou. Andreasen, Dan, illus. 1998. (Little House Ser.: Vol. 1). 240p. (J). (gr. 3-7). 15.95 (978-0-06-024973-1(0)) HarperCollins Pubs.

Marcum, Lance. The Cottonmouth Club. 2005. 336p. (J). 18.00 (978-0-374-31562-7(0) , Farrar, Straus & Giroux (BYR)) Farrar, Straus & Giroux.

Martin, Jacqueline Briggs. Chicken Joy on Redbean Road: A Bayou Country Romp. Sweet, Melissa, illus. 2007. 32p. (J). (gr. 3-5). 17.00 (978-0-618-50759-7(0)) Houghton Mifflin Co.

Miranda, Hialeah. One Fun Summer's Day. 2004. 48p. pap. 12.95 (978-1-4137-1858-4(2)) PublishAmerica, Inc.

Nixon, Joan Lowery. The Haunting. Horowitz, Beverly, ed. 2000. 192p. (YA). (gr. 7-12). mass mkt. 5.99 (978-0-440-22008-4(4) , Laurel Leaf) Random Hse. Children's Bks.

—The Haunting. 2000. (YA). 11.64 (978-0-606-19191-3(7)) Tandem Library Bks.

Pockets Learning Staff. Samantha's Louisiana Adventure. 1998. (Illus.). 2p. (YA). (ps-1). 15.00 (978-1-888074-92-5(2)) Pockets of Learning.

Poole-Carter, Rosemary. Juliette Ascending. 2007. (YA). pap. 14.00 (***978-1-929976-41-6(0)*** , TOP) Top Pubns., Ltd.

Preble, Laura. Lica's Angel. 2003. 142p. (YA). 21.95 (978-0-595-74914-0(3)); pap. 11.95 (978-0-595-28253-1(9)) iUniverse, Inc.

Raphael, Morris. Ti-Nute, the Angel of Devil's Pond. Ferry, Kate, illus. 2000. 47p. (J). (978-0-8187-0332-4(6)) Harlo Pr.

Reneaux, J. J. Why Alligator Hates Dog: A Cajun Folktale. 2001. (ps-2). lib. bdg. 15.25 (978-0-613-49793-0(7)) Tandem Library Bks.

Rice, James. Gaston Goes to Mardi Gras Coloring Book. 2000. (Illus.). 32p. (J). (ps-3). pap. 3.25 (978-1-56554-773-5(X)) Pelican Publishing Co., Inc.

Salley, Coleen. Epossumondas Saves the Day. Stevens, Janet, illus. 2006. 48p. (J). 16.00 (978-0-15-205701-5(3)) Harcourt Trade Pubs.

Scallan, Dee. Moby Pincher's Wonderful Christmas Present/ Dee Scallan. 2004. (J). pap. 9.95 (978-1-59453-542-0(6)) Airleaf Publishing & Bookselling.

Schmitt, Nannette Toups. Remember Last Island. Gorman, Carolyn Portier, ed. Schmitt, Nannette Toups & Endres, Sharlene Duggan, illus. 2003. 206p. (YA). pap. 19.95 (978-0-9740901-0-8(7) , 11-May) Orage Publishing.

Shaik, Fatima. Melitte. 2000. (978-0-606-18432-8(5)) Tandem Library Bks.

Sinykin, Sheri Cooper. Giving up the Ghost. 2007. 224p. (J). (gr. 4-7). 14.95 (***978-1-56145-423-5(0)*** , Peachtree Junior) Peachtree Pubs., Ltd.

Smith, Debra West. Yankees on the Doorstep: The Story of Sarah Morgan. 2001. (Illus.). 176p. (J). (gr. 3-7). pap. 10.95 (978-1-56554-872-5(8)) Pelican Publishing Co., Inc.

Smith, George Harmon. Bayou Boy. 2000. 196p. (gr. 7-12). pap. 11.95 (978-0-595-00755-4(4) , Writer's Showcase Pr) iUniverse, Inc.

Stonecipher, Philip. Boudreau of de Bayou. Perez Sanchez, Delia, tr. from ENG. 1999. (SPA & ENG., Illus.). ii, 22p. (J). (gr. 2-3). 6.95 (978-0-943864-92-1(5)) Davenport, May Pubs.

Thomas, Wes. Down the Crawfish Hole. Thomas, Wes, illus. 2004. (Illus.). 32p. (J). 15.95 (978-1-58980-163-9(6)) Pelican Publishing Co., Inc.

Thomassie, Tynia. Cajun Through & Through. Glass, Andrew, illus. 2000. 32p. (J). (ps-3). 14.95 (978-0-316-84189-4(7)) Little Brown & Co.

—Feliciana Feydra LeRoux: A Cajun Tall Tale. 1998. (J). (978-0-606-13380-7(1)) Tandem Library Bks.

—Feliciana Feydra LeRoux Meets d'Loup Garou: A Cajun Tall Tale. Smith, Cat Bowman, illus. 1998. 32p. (J). (ps-3). 15.95 (978-0-316-84133-7(1)) Little Brown & Co.

Woods, Brenda. The Red Rose Box. 2002. 160p. (YA). (gr. 4-6). 16.99 (978-0-399-23702-7(X) , Putnam Juvenile) Penguin Group (USA) Inc.

—The Red Rose Box. 2003. (gr. 5-8). lib. bdg. 14.15 (978-0-613-87822-7(1)) Tandem Library Bks.

LOUISIANA—HISTORY

Bridges, Ruby. Through My Eyes. 1999. (Illus.). 64p. (J). (gr. 3-7). pap. 16.95 (978-0-590-18923-1(9)) Scholastic, Inc.

Culbertson, Manie & Long, Martha. Louisiana: The Land & Its People. 5th ed. 2007. 560p. 35.00 (978-1-58980-303-9(5)) Pelican Publishing Co., Inc.

Deinard, Jenny. How to Draw Louisianas Sights & Symbols. 2002. (Kids Guide to Drawing America Ser.). 32p. (J). lib. bdg. 25.25 (978-0-8239-6074-3(9) , PowerKids Pr.) Rosen Publishing Group, Inc., The.

Duey, Kathleen. Amelina Carrett: Thibodeau, Louisiana 1870. 1999. (American Diaries Ser.: No. 12). (J). (gr. 3-7). 10.64 (978-0-606-16281-4(X)) Tandem Library Bks.

Faucheux, Guy N. & Faucheux, Wallace P. Cajun Comiques Historic Louisiana: An Illustrated History for Kids of All Ages. 2004. (Illus.). 56p. (YA). lib. bdg. 16.95 (978-0-9718433-1-8(7)) St. Roux Pr.

Gayarre, Charles. History of Louisiana Volume IV: The American Dominiation, Vol. 4. 5th ed. 1999. 693p. (J). (ps-3). 45.00 (978-1-56554-750-6(0)) Pelican Publishing Co., Inc.

Gayarre, Charles E. History of Louisiana. 1999. (J). Vol. 1. 604p. 45.00 (978-1-56554-747-6(0)); Vol. 3. 666p. 45.00 (978-1-56554-749-0(7)) Pelican Publishing Co., Inc.

Knudsen, Anders. Antoine de la Mothe Cadillac: French Settlements at Detroit & Louisiana. 2006. (In the Footsteps of Explorers Ser.). (Illus.). 32p. (J). (gr. 3-9). (978-0-7787-2429-2(8)); pap. (978-0-7787-2465-0(4)) Crabtree Publishing Co.

Koestler-Grack, Rachel A. Daily Life in a Southern Trading Town: New Orleans. 2003. (J). (978-1-58417-013-6(1)); pap. (978-1-58417-076-1(X)) Lake Street Pubs.

Marsh, Carole. Louisiana History Projects: 30 Cool, Activities, Crafts, Experiments & More for Kids to Do to Learn about Your State! 2003. (Louisiana Experience Ser.). 32p. (gr. k-5). pap. 5.95 (978-0-635-01787-1(3) , Marsh, Carole Bks.) Gallopade International.

—My First Pocket Guide Louisiana. 2000. (Louisiana Experience! Ser.). (Illus.). 96p. (J). (gr. 3-8). 12.95 (978-0-635-01308-8(8) , 13088) Gallopade International.

Worth, Richard. Louisiana, 1682-1803. 2006. (Voices from Colonial America Ser.). (Illus.). 112p. (J). (gr. 5-9). 21.95 (978-0-7922-6544-3(0)); 32.90 (978-0-7922-6850-5(4)) National Geographic Society. (National Geographic Children's Bks.).

LOUISIANA PURCHASE

Alagna, Magdalena. The Louisiana Purchase: Expanding America's Boundaries. 2003. (Life in the New American Nation Ser.). (Illus.). 32p. (YA). pap. 6.50 (978-0-8239-4257-2(0)) Rosen Publishing Group, Inc., The.

Burgan, Michael. The Louisiana Purchase. 2002. (We the People Ser.). (Illus.). 48p. (J). (gr. 4 up). lib. bdg. 22.60 (978-0-7565-0210-2(1)) Compass Point Bks.

—The Louisiana Purchase. 2006. (Making a New Nation Ser.). (Illus.). 48p. (J). (978-1-4034-7828-3(7)); pap. (978-1-4034-7835-1(X)) Heinemann Library.

Chase, John. Louisiana Purchase. 2002. (gr. 3-6). lib. bdg. 22.20 (978-0-613-56807-4(9)) Tandem Library Bks.

Chase, John Churchill. The Louisiana Purchase: An American Story. 5th ed. 2003. (Illus.). 96p. reprint ed. pap. 12.95 (978-1-58980-084-7(2)) Pelican Publishing Co., Inc.

Gaines, Ann Graham. The Louisiana Purchase in American History. 2000. (In American History Ser.). (Illus.). 128p. (YA). (gr. 5-12). lib. bdg. 26.60 (978-0-7660-1301-8(4)) Enslow Pubs., Inc.

Jaffe, Elizabeth Dana. The Louisiana Purchase. 2002. (Let Freedom Ring Ser.). (Illus.). 48p. (J). (gr. 3-4). lib. bdg. 22.60 (978-0-7368-1100-2(1) , Bridgestone Bks.) Capstone Pr., Inc.

Landau, Elaine. The Louisiana Purchase: Would You Close the Deal? 2008. (What Would You Do? Ser.). (Illus.). 48p. (J). (gr. 3-4). lib. bdg. 23.93 (***978-0-7660-2902-6(6)*** , Enslow Elementary) Enslow Pubs., Inc.

The Louisiana Purchase. 2002. (History in the Headlines Ser.). 32p. (gr. 6-8). 6.99 (978-0-7682-0224-3(8) , GA13024) School Specialty Publishing.

Louisiana Purchase. (Exploring the West Ser.). 48p. (YA). 7.95 (978-0-7368-4507-6(0)) Capstone Pr., Inc.

Marsh, Carole. What a Deal! The Louisiana Purchase. 2003. 32p. (J). (gr. 3-8). pap. 5.95 (978-0-635-02123-6(4)) Gallopade International.

Nelson, Sheila. Thomas Jefferson's America: The Louisiana Purchase (1800-1811) 2005. (How America Became America Ser.). (Illus.). 96p. (J). lib. bdg. (978-1-59084-904-0(3)) Mason Crest Pubs.

Pierce, Alan. Louisiana Purchase. 2005. (American Moments Ser.). (Illus.). (J). (gr. 4-8). lib. bdg. 25.65 (978-1-59197-287-7(6) , ABDO & Daughters) ABDO Publishing Co.

Raabe, Emily. Thomas Jefferson & the Louisiana Purchase. 2003. (Reading Power Ser.). (Illus.). 24p. (J). lib. bdg. 17.25 (978-0-8239-6499-4(X) , PowerKids Pr.) Rosen Publishing Group, Inc., The.

Roop, Peter & Roop, Connie. Louisiana Purchase. Comport, Sally Wern, illus. 2004. 84p. (J). lib. bdg. 15.00 (***978-1-4242-0908-8(0)***) Fitzgerald Bks.

Sakurai, Gail. The Louisiana Purchase. January, Brendan, ed. 1998. (Cornerstones of Freedom Ser.). (Illus.). 32p. (J). (gr. 4-6). pap. 5.95 (978-0-516-26336-6(6) , Children's Pr.) Scholastic Library Publishing.

—The Louisiana Purchase. 1998. (Illus.). 30p. (J). (gr. 4-6). lib. bdg. 14.10 (978-0-613-37442-2(8)) Tandem Library Bks.

Schaffer, David. The Louisiana Purchase—the Deal of the Century That Doubled the Nation. 2006. (Wild History of the American West Ser.). (Illus.). 128p. (J). lib. bdg. 33.27 (978-1-59845-018-7(2) , MyReportLinks.com Bks.) Enslow Pubs., Inc.

Schlaepfer, Gloria G. The Louisiana Purchase. 2005. (Watts Library). (Illus.). 63p. (J). (gr. 5-8). 25.50 (978-0-531-12300-3(6) , Watts, Franklin) Scholastic Library Publishing.

Spotlight on America: The Lewis & Clark Expedition & the Louisiana Purchase. 2003. (Illus.). 48p. (J). (gr. 4-8). 8.99 (978-0-7439-3233-2(1)) Teacher Created Materials, Inc.

Steele, Christy. The Louisiana Purchase. 2005. (Illus.). 48p. (J). pap. (978-0-8368-5796-2(8)); lib. bdg. 30.00 (978-0-8368-5789-4(5)) Stevens, Gareth Inc. (World Almanac Library).

Thompson, Linda. La Compra de Louisiana. 2005. (ENG & SPA., Illus.). 48p. (J). (978-1-59515-662-4(3)) Rourke Publishing, LLC.

—The Louisiana Purchase. 2006. (Expansion of America II Ser.). (Illus.). 48p. (J). (gr. 4-8). 20.95 (978-1-59515-513-9(9)) Rourke Publishing, LLC.

—Louisiana Purchase. 2005. 48p. pap. 7.45 (978-1-59515-827-7(8)) Rourke Publishing, LLC.

Zurn, Jon. The Louisiana Purchase. 2007. (Essential Events Ser.). (ENG., Illus.). 112p. (YA). (gr. 8-12). lib. bdg. 32.79 (***978-1-59928-853-6(2)*** , Essential Library) ABDO Publishing Co.

LOVE, NAT, 1854-1921

Hominick, Judy & Spreier, Jeanne. Best Cowboy in the West: The Story of Nat Love. 2001. (Heroes to Remember Ser.). (Illus.). 60p. (J). 14.95 (978-1-893110-25-0(7)) Silver Moon Pr.

Penn, Sarah. Nat Love: African American Cowboy. 2003. (Famous People in American History Ser.). (Illus.). 32p. (J). pap. (978-0-8239-4188-9(4)) Rosen Publishing Group, Inc., The.

Underwood, Deborah. Nat Love. 2008. (History Maker Biographies Ser.). (J). lib. bdg. 26.60 (***978-0-8225-7171-1(4)*** , Lerner Pubns.) Lerner Publishing Group.

LOVE

see also Dating (Social Customs); Friendship; Marriage

Anderson, Joel. Tell Me about Love. Anderson, Joel & Smith, Kristi Carter, illus. 2005. 32p. (J). (ps-7). 9.99 (978-1-4003-0616-9(7)) Nelson, Thomas Inc.

Anthony, Carol K. Love, an Inner Connection: Based on Principles Drawn from the I Ching. 2nd rev. ed. 2002. 176p. per. 14.95 (978-1-890764-01-2(9)) Anthony Publishing Co.

Banks, Pat & Davidson, Carolyn. Where Grandma Lives, Love Is Forever. 1998. (Illus.). 34p. (J). (gr. 3-6). 7.50 (978-1-56469-033-3(4)) Harmony Hse. Pubs.

Benton, Jim. Love Bites. 2005. (It's Happy Bunny Ser.: No. 1). (Illus.). 72p. (J). 7.99 (978-0-439-69345-5(4)) Scholastic, Inc.

Bode, Janet. Heartbreak & Roses: Real Life Stories of Troubled Love. 2000. (YA). (978-0-606-19403-7(7)) Tandem Library Bks.

—Heartbreak & Roses: Real Life Stories of Young Love. Mack, Stanely, illus. rev. ed. 2000. (Single Titles Ser.). 144p. (J). (gr. 8-12). 24.00 (978-0-531-11776-7(6) , Watts, Franklin) Scholastic Library Publishing.

Boritzer, Etan. What Is Love? 2001. (Love & Feeling for Kids Ser.). (Illus.). 36p. (J). lib. bdg. 15.95 (978-1-56674-293-1(5)) Forest Hse. Publishing Co., Inc.

Bower, Gary. Tessa's Treasures: Cherishing Others. Bower, Jan, illus. 2000. (Thinking of Others: Vol. 1). 32p. (J). (ps-3). lib. bdg. 16.95 (978-0-9704621-0-7(7)) Storybook Meadow Publishing.

Chidvilasananda. Good Night, Sweet Dreams, I Love You! 2004. (Illus.). (J). (978-1-930939-01-1(9)) SYDA Foundation.

Clark, Chap. Next Time I Fall in Love: How to Handle Sex, Intimacy, & Feelings in Dating Relationships. 2004. 144p. pap. 18.00 (978-1-59244-684-1(1) , Wipf and Stock) Wipf & Stock Pubs.

Clibbon, Meg. Lots of Love. Clibbon, Lucy, illus. 2007. 24p. 5.95 (***978-1-84089-376-2(1)*** , Zero to Ten, Limited) Evans Publishing Group GBR. *Dist:* Independent Pubs. Group.

Conley, Erin. Psst - Crush: A Girl's Guide to Being Crazy in Love. 2007. (PSST! Ser.). (Illus.). 128p. (J). pap. 9.95 (***978-0-9772660-0-5(1)*** , Zest Bks.) Orange Avenue Publishing.

Dee, Catherine. Girls' Book of Love: Cool Quotes, Super Stories, Awesome Advice, & More. 2002. (gr. 3-6). lib. bdg. 18.75 (978-0-613-71776-2(7)) Tandem Library Bks.

Draper, Dar & Helser, Sarah Dawn. What is Love? Questions a Child Asks. 2004. (Illus.). 32p. 14.95 (978-0-9740880-4-4(8)) Lifebridge Bks.

Duksta, Laura. I Love You More. Keesler, Karen, illus. 2001. 33p. (J). (gr. k-2). 15.95 (978-0-9714403-0-2(1)) I Shine, Inc.

Garth, Lakita. The Naked Truth: About Sex, Love & Relationships. 2007. (Illus.). 164p. 14.99 (978-0-8307-4328-5(6) , Regal Bks.) Gospel Light Pubns.

Gelber, Carol. Love & Marriage Around World. 1998. (Illus.). 72p. (gr. 4-6). lib. bdg. 23.90 (978-0-7613-0102-8(X) , Millbrook Pr.) Lerner Publishing Group.

Graham, Terry L. Listening Is a Way of Loving. 1998. (Illus.). 140p. (J). (ps-3). pap. 18.95 (978-0-89334-156-5(8)) Humanics Publishing Group.

Halperin, Wendy Anderson. Love Is ... ed. 2005. (Illus.). 32p. (J). 8.95 (978-0-689-87618-9(1)) Simon & Schuster Children's Publishing.

Harris, Robie H. Es Alucinante! Emberley, Michael, illus. 2000. Tr. of It's So Amazing!. (J). (CAT.). 80p. (gr. k-2). pap. 17.95 (978-84-95040-33-6(6)); (SPA.). 84p. (gr. 3-5). 17.95 (978-84-95040-32-9(8) , RR4476) Serres, Ediciones, S. L. ESP. *Dist:* Lectorum Pubns., Inc.

Hawkins Harris, Jennifer. Love: The Book of Love for Kids. Gray Mayo, Jo Ann, illus. 2003. 20p. (J). per. 7.00 (978-0-9705458-2-4(7)) Royalty Bks. International.

Hickey, Elizabeth & Romney, S. P. I Love You: Affirmations Inspired by Nature. Campbell, Susan, illus. 2002. 32p. 24.99 (978-1-884862-14-4(4)) Family Connections Publishing Co.

Hoggarth, Janet. Sweet Hearts: A Whole Hearted Fun Guide to Love. Symonds, Sarah, illus. 2002. 160p. (J). (gr. 3-7). pap. 4.99 (978-0-439-28325-0(6) , Chicken Hse., The) Scholastic, Inc.

Hotchner, Beverly. Do I Really Love You? 1999. (Illus.). 62p. (YA). (gr. 8-12). pap. 12.95 (978-0-9677406-0-7(6)) Selwyn & Ross Pubs.

Hudson, Sue. I Love You. Watanabe, Kaori, illus. 2004. (My First Taggies Book Ser.). 3p. (J). 12.95 (978-0-439-64947-6(1) , Cartwheel Bks.) Scholastic, Inc.

I Love You Because You're. 2004. (J). pap. 6.99 (978-0-439-57711-3(X)) Scholastic, Inc.

Image of Love. 1999. (YA). (978-0-7814-0068-8(6)) Cook, David C. Publishing Co.

Kid, Penelope. Teach Me to Love. Goffe, Toni, illus. 2004. (Teach Me Ser.). 24p. (ps-2). 6.95 (978-0-8294-1369-4(3)) Loyola Pr.

Krulik, Nancy E. Who Do You Love? 2001. (gr. 5-8). lib. bdg. 11.80 (978-0-613-73318-2(5)) Tandem Library Bks.

LeJeune, Shonda. Love Is... 2003. (Illus.). 30p. (gr. 2 up). 14.50 (978-0-87516-691-9(1)); (ps-3). pap. 11.50 (978-0-87516-690-2(3)) DeVorss & Co.

Loving. 2002. (Precious Moments Ser.). (Illus.). 11p. (J). (ps). bds. 4.99 (978-1-57759-380-5(4)) Dalmatian Pr.

Marsh, Carole. Someone I Love Went off to War. 2003. 24p. (gr. 1-8). pap. 5.95 (978-0-635-02092-5(0)) Gallopade International.

Mattox, Brenda Sneathen. Famous Lovers from Literature. 2005. (Illus.). 32p. (gr. 5). pap. 3.95 (978-0-486-44464-2(3)) Dover Pubns., Inc.

Mayo, Jeanne. Uncensored: Dating, Relationship, & Sex. 2007. 224p. pap. 14.99 (978-1-57794-821-6(1)) Harrison Hse., Inc.

Radziszewicz, Tina. Ready or Not: A Girl's Guide to Making Her Own Decisions about Dating, Love, & Sex. 2006. (Illus.). 288p. (YA). (gr. 7 up). 16.95 (978-0-8027-9613-4(3)); pap. 9.95 (978-0-8027-9612-7(5)) Walker & Co.

Rasmussen, Klayne, et al. The FrogBuster: A Girl's Guide for Survival in the Dating Swamp. 2002. 214p. (YA). per. 16.95 (978-0-9703102-0-0(X)) Intralife Systems Publishing.

Roy, Jennifer Rozines. Romantic Breakup: It's Not the End of the World. 2000. (Teen Issues Ser.). (Illus.). 64p. (J). (gr. 6-12). lib. bdg. 22.60 (978-0-7660-1361-2(8)) Enslow Pubs., Inc.

Seventeen Magazine. True Love. 2007. 128p. (J). pap. 4.95 (978-1-58816-629-6(5)) Hearst Communications, Inc.

Shumway, Lindsey. I Chose You. 2005. (Illus.). 31p. (J). 15.99 (978-1-55517-861-1(8)) Cedar Fort, Inc./CFI Distribution.

Solomon, Iris L. & Solomon, Ron. Friendz Pakz: Love. 2003. (YA). (gr. 3 up). 4.99 (978-1-930680-07-4(4) , SSP-08LV) Swingset Pr., LLC.

Spencer, Lauren. Everything You Need to Know about Falling in Love. 2001. (Need to Know Library). (Illus.). 64p. (YA). (gr. 4-6). lib. bdg. 25.25 (978-0-8239-3395-2(4)) Rosen Publishing Group, Inc., The.

Stalfelt, Pernilla. The Love Book. Lundin, Maria, tr. from SWE. 2002. (Illus.). (J). 15.95 (978-0-88899-455-4(9)) Groundwood Bks. CAN. *Dist:* Transition Vendor.

Stewart, Arlene Hamilton, et al. The Love & Romance Teen Quiz Book. 2001. 240p. pap. 9.95 (978-0-7407-1988-2(2)) Andrews McMeel Publishing.

Stewart, Elizabeth. An Angel Named Love. 2005. 17.00 (978-0-8059-9815-3(2)) Dorrance Publishing Co., Inc.

Strong, Jennifer, ed. Love Stories: How Love Conquers All. 2001. (Teen People Ser.). 160p. (YA). (gr. 7 up). pap. 6.95 (978-0-06-447320-0(1) , Avon) HarperCollins Pubs.

Sullivan, Michelle. Check Him Out! Your Ultimate Guide to Guys. 2001. (Among Teens Ser.). (Illus.). 111p. (J). (978-0-439-27216-2(5)) Scholastic, Inc.

The True Love Waits Youth Bible. 2004. (Illus.). 1294p. pap. 19.99 (978-1-55819-621-6(8)) B&H Publishing Grp.

Vivekananda, Swami. Way of the Saint: Swami Vivekananda on Universal Love. 2005. (Illus.). 404p. per. (978-0-9728051-3-1(3)) Temple Universal Publishing.

von Konigslow, Andrea Wayne. Me Querrias Tu? von Konigslow, Andrea Wayne, illus. 2003. (Hablemos Ser.). (SPA., Illus.). 32p. (J). (gr. k). pap. 5.95 (978-1-55037-449-0(4)) Annick Pr., Ltd. CAN. *Dist:* Firefly Bks., Ltd.

Weedn, Flavia M. & Weedn, Lisa. I Love You Very. Weedn, Flavia M., illus. 2000. (Illus.). 26p. (ps-k). pap. 7.95 (978-0-7683-2157-9(3)) CEDCO Publishing.

Welch, Ariel & Welch, Ashley. Waiting. 2003. 122p. (YA). pap. 13.95 (978-0-595-27087-3(5)) iUniverse, Inc.

What Is... Love. (Illus.). 16p. (J). pap. 1.50 (978-0-87162-827-5(9) , E6019) Warner Pr. Pubs.

LOVE—FICTION

A. B. Publishing Staff. Nobody Loves Me. 1998. (J). (gr. 4-7). pap. 6.95 (978-1-881545-83-5(0)) A B Publishing.

Abbaszadeh, Paul. One Love: A True Love Story. 2003. 466p. (YA). pap. 28.95 (978-0-595-28878-6(2)) iUniverse, Inc.

Abbot, Hailey. After Summer. 2006. (Summer Boys Ser.). 224p. (J). pap. 8.99 (978-0-439-86367-4(8) , Scholastic Paperbacks) Scholastic, Inc.

Abbott, Hailey. The Bridesmaid. 2005. 272p. (YA). (gr. 7). pap. 7.95 (978-0-385-73220-8(1)); lib. bdg. 17.99 (978-0-385-90249-6(2)) Random Hse. Children's Bks. (Delacorte Bks. for Young Readers).

Abbott, Hailey. Last Summer. 2007. 240p. (J). pap. 8.99 ***(978-0-439-86725-2(8))*** Scholastic, Inc.

Abbott, Hailey, et al. Mistletoe. 2006. 240p. (J). pap. 8.99 (978-0-439-86368-1(6) , Scholastic) Scholastic, Inc.

Abel, Heather & McKnight, Gillian. To Catch a Prince. 2005. 192p. (YA). 14.95 (978-0-689-87733-9(1)) Simon & Schuster Children's Publishing.

Adams, Kendall. Lose Yourself No. 3. 2007. (Hook up or Break Up Ser.: No. 3). 256p. (J). pap. 8.99 (978-0-06-088565-6(3) , HarperTeen) HarperCollins Pubs.

Adams, Kevin. A Stegosaurus Named Sam. Adams, Kevin & Price, Michael, illus. 2004. (J). per. 12.50 (978-0-9740683-4-3(9)) Authors & Artists Publishers of New York, Inc.

Adams, Kylie. Bling Addiction. 2006. (Fast Girls, Hot Boys Ser.: No. 2). 240p. pap. 9.95 (978-1-4165-2041-2(4) , MTV) Simon & Schuster.

Adams, L. Happy Memories: A Continuing Family Saga for Young Adults. 2003. 516p. pap. 26.95 (978-0-595-29210-3(0)) iUniverse, Inc.

Adams, L. Dawn. Happy Memories: A Continuing Family Saga for Young Adults. 2003. (gr. 7-12). lib. bdg. 38.45 (978-0-613-85675-1(9)) Tandem Library Bks.

Adkins, Jan. A Storm Without Rain: A Novel in Time. 2004. 179p. 14.95 (978-0-937822-80-7(9)) WoodenBoat Pubns.

Albee, Sarah. Elmo Loves You. Swanson, Maggie, illus. 2002. (Big Bird's Favorites Board Bks.). 24p. (J). (gr. k-ps). bds. 4.99 (978-0-375-81208-8(3) , Random Hse. Bks. for Young Readers) Random Hse. Children's Bks.

—Elmo Loves You! Swanson, Maggie, illus. rev. ed. 2005. 24p. (J). (ps). pap. 3.50 (978-1-4037-1694-1(3)) Dalmatian Pr.

Alberts, Katharine O. Boo on the Loose. 2006. (J). 14.00 (978-0-8059-7071-5(1)) Dorrance Publishing Co., Inc.

Alcott, Louisa May. The Inheritance. 1998. (Classics Ser.). 208p. pap. 14.00 (978-0-14-043666-2(9) , Penguin Classics) Penguin Group (USA) Inc.

Allen, Tina. What Is Beautiful? Allen, Tina, illus. 2005. 48p. (J). pap. 25.25 (978-1-4208-0666-3(1)) AuthorHouse.

Amelio-Ortiz, Osvaldo Pastor. He Loves Me, He Loves Me Not: Margarita's Story. Ballester, Juan P., tr. 2006. (Magical Stories Ser.). (Illus.). 28p. (J). 16.95 (978-9974-7896-9-2(9)) Hardenville SA URY. *Dist:* Independent Pubs. Group.

Andreae, Giles. Heaven Is Having You. Cabban, Vanessa, illus. (J). (ps-k). 2007. 24p. bds. 7.95 ***(978-1-58925-820-4(7));*** 2002. 32p. tchr. ed. 15.95 (978-1-58925-016-1(8)) ME Media LLC. (tiger tales).

—Keep Love in Your Heart, Little One. Vulliamy, Clara, illus. 2007. 32p. (J). (ps-2). 15.95 ***(978-1-58925-066-6(4)*** , tiger tales) ME Media LLC.

Andreae, Giles. Love Is a Handful of Honey. Cabban, Vanessa, illus. 1999. 32p. (J). (ps-2). 14.95 (978-1-888444-58-2(4)) Little Tiger Pr.

—Love Is a Handful of Honey. Cabban, Vanessa, illus. 2004. 32p. (J). (ps-k). 5.95 (978-1-58925-353-7(1) , tiger tales) ME Media LLC.

—Love Is a Handful of Honey. 2001. (ps-2). lib. bdg. 14.10 (978-0-613-57645-1(4)) Tandem Library Bks.

Andronik, Catherine M. Wildly Romantic: The English Romantic Poets: The Mad, the Bad, & the Dangerous. 2007. (Illus.). 272p. (J). (gr. 9 up). 16.95 (978-0-8050-7783-4(9)) Holt, Henry & Co.

Anonuevo, Rechelle. The Moonlight Serenade. 2003. 140p. (YA). pap. 11.95 (978-0-595-30627-5(6)) iUniverse, Inc.

Anonymous. Theobald the Iron Hearted or Love to Ene. 2004. reprint ed. pap. 15.95 (978-1-4191-8941-8(7)) Kessinger Publishing, LLC.

—Theobald the Iron Hearted or Love to Enemies. 2004. reprint ed. pap. 1.99 (978-1-4192-8941-5(1)) Kessinger Publishing, LLC.

Appelt, Kathi. Oh My Baby, Little One. Dyer, Jane, illus. 2006. 32p. (J). pap. 3.99 (978-0-15-206031-2(6) , Voyager Bks./Libros Viajeros) Harcourt Children's Bks.

Applegate, Katherine. Forces of Nature. 2001. (True Love Ser.: No. 5). 224p. (YA). pap. 4.99 (978-1-931497-38-1(9)) 17th Street Productions, An Alloy Online Inc. Co.

—Heat. 2001. (Making Waves Ser.: No. 5). 272p. mass mkt. 4.99 (978-1-931497-16-9(8)) 17th Street Productions, An Alloy Online Inc. Co.

—Kate Finds Love. 1999. (Making Out Ser.: No. 19). 176p. (YA). (gr. 7-12). pap. 3.99 (978-0-380-81121-2(9)) HarperCollins Pubs.

—Lara Gets Lucky. 2000. (Making Out Ser.: No. 23). 176p. (YA). (gr. 7-12). pap. 3.99 (978-0-380-81527-2(3)) HarperCollins Pubs.

—Making Waves. 2001. (Making Waves Ser.: No. 1). 320p. (YA). mass mkt. 4.99 (978-1-931497-12-1(5)) 17th Street Productions, An Alloy Online Inc. Co.

—Second Chance. 2001. (True Love Ser.: No. 7). 208p. (YA). pap. 4.99 (978-1-931497-40-4(0)) 17th Street Productions, An Alloy Online Inc. Co.

—Sharing Sam. 2004. 160p. (YA). (gr. 7). pap. 8.95 (978-0-385-73135-5(3) , Delacorte Bks. for Young Readers) Random Hse. Children's Bks.

—Sharing Sam. 2004. (gr. 7-12). lib. bdg. 17.60 (978-0-613-81953-4(5)) Tandem Library Bks.

—Tease. 2001. (Making Waves Ser.: No. 2). 288p. (YA). mass mkt. 4.99 (978-1-931497-13-8(3)) 17th Street Productions, An Alloy Online Inc. Co.

—Two-Timing Aisha. 1999. (Making Out Ser.: No. 17). 176p. (YA). (gr. 7-12). pap. 3.99 (978-0-380-81119-9(7)) HarperCollins Pubs.

—Worlds Apart. 2001. (True Love Ser.: No. 8). 208p. (YA). pap. 4.99 (978-1-931497-41-1(9)) 17th Street Productions, An Alloy Online Inc. Co.

—Zoey Fools Around. 1998. (gr. 7-12). lib. bdg. 11.80 (978-0-613-71898-1(4)) Tandem Library Bks.

—Zoey's Broken Heart. 2000. (Making Out Ser.: No. 26). 176p. (YA). (gr. 7 up). pap. 3.99 (978-0-380-81530-2(3)) HarperCollins Pubs.

Arguello, Tito. A Dog in Love. 2005. 114p. (J). pap. 8.95 (978-1-4116-2287-6(1)) Lulu.com.

Argueta, Jorge. El Zipitio. Calderon, Gloria, illus. 2003. (SPA.). 32p. (J). 16.95 (978-0-88899-539-1(3)) Groundwood Bks. CAN. *Dist:* Perseus Distribution.

Arno, Iris H. I Love You, Dad. 1998. (978-0-606-13507-8(3)) Tandem Library Bks.

—I Love You, Mom. 1998. (978-0-606-13508-5(1)) Tandem Library Bks.

Ashley, Catherine C. N. Butterfly Girl. 2006. (J). per. 9.95 (978-0-9672699-3-1(8) , Papillon Children's Bks.) Ashcafe Publishing.

Ausbun, Nellie M. Skip & Meow. 2001. 22p. (J). per. 8.95 (978-0-7414-0613-2(6)) Infinity Publishing.

Austin, Lynn. Hidden Places. 2001. (gr. 5-8). lib. bdg. 22.25 (978-0-613-55604-0(6)) Tandem Library Bks.

Babbitt, Natalie. The Eyes of the Amaryllis. 2007. 144p. (J). pap. 6.99 ***(978-0-312-37008-4(3))*** Square Fish.

Bader, Amanda. Havana Nights. 2004. (gr. 7-12). lib. bdg. 14.15 (978-0-613-71571-3(3)) Tandem Library Bks.

Baek, Hye-Kyung. Bring It On, Vol. 2. 2006. (Illus.). 200p. (YA). pap. 10.95 ***(978-89-527-4471-5(3))*** ICE Kunion KOR. *Dist:* Diamond Bk. Distributors.

Bagdasarian, Adam. First French Kiss. 2005. 144p. (YA). (gr. 9). pap. 5.95 (978-0-374-42323-0(7) , Farrar, Straus & Giroux (BYR)) Farrar, Straus & Giroux.

Bailey, Erroll J. Mr. Dream Merchant. 2000. 288p. (YA). (gr. 7-12). 15.95 (978-1-902618-30-2(0)) Element Children's Bks.

Baker, Jennifer. Eternally Yours. 1999. (Enchanted Hearts Ser.: No. 2). 176p. (YA). (gr. 7-12). pap. 4.50 (978-0-380-80073-5(X)) HarperCollins Pubs.

—Eternally Yours No. 2: Enchanted Hearts. 1999. (J). (978-0-606-16363-7(8)) Tandem Library Bks.

Baker, Kage. The Life of the World to Come. rev. ed. 2005. (Company Ser.). 416p. mass mkt. 6.99 (978-0-7653-5432-7(2) , Tor Bks.) Doherty, Tom Assocs., LLC.

Baker, Liza. I Love You Because You're You. 2008. (Scooby-Doo Ser.). 24p. (J). bds. 8.99 ***(978-0-545-02931-5(7)*** , Cartwheel Bks.) Scholastic, Inc.

—I Love You Because You're You. McPhail, David M., illus. 2001. 32p. (J). (ps-k). pap. 9.95 (978-0-439-20638-9(3) , Cartwheel Bks.) Scholastic, Inc.

Balaban, Mariah, ed. What I Love Best. 2007. (Care Bears Ser.). 24p. (J). pap. 3.99 (978-0-439-89459-3(X)) Scholastic, Inc.

Banks, Steven. King of the Creeps. 2006. 176p. (YA). (gr. 7). 15.95 (978-0-375-83291-8(2)); lib. bdg. 17.99 (978-0-375-93291-5(7)) Random Hse. Children's Bks. (Knopf Bks. for Young Readers).

—Love Potion. Sasic, Natasha, illus. 2003. (Jimmy Neutron Boy Genius Ser.). 24p. (J). pap. 3.99 (978-0-689-86317-2(9) , Simon Spotlight/Nickelodeon) Simon & Schuster Children's Publishing.

Barklage, Sam. Full of Love. 2001. (Illus.). 16p. (J). pap. 10.00 (978-0-9716456-0-8(4)) Myers, Joy.

Barkley, Brad & Hepler, Heather. Dream Factory. 2007. 224p. (YA). (gr. 8 up). 16.99 (978-0-525-47802-7(7) , Dutton Juvenile) Penguin Group (USA) Inc.

—Scrambled Eggs at Midnight. 2007. 288p. (J). (gr. 7 up). pap. 7.99 (978-0-14-240867-4(0) , Puffin); 2006. 272p. (YA). (gr. 6). 16.99 (978-0-525-47760-0(8) , Dutton Juvenile) Penguin Group (USA) Inc.

Barnes, Derrick. The Making of Dr. Truelove. 2006. 240p. (YA). (gr. 11 up). pap. 7.99 (978-1-4169-1439-6(0) , Simon Pulse) Simon & Schuster Children's Publishing.

Barnholdt, Lauren. Two-Way Street. 2007. 304p. (YA). pap. 8.99 (978-1-4169-1318-4(1) , Simon Pulse) Simon & Schuster Children's Publishing.

Baronian, Jean-Baptiste. Con Todo Mi Corazon. 2000. (SPA., Illus.). 12p. (J). 16.95 (978-84-488-0686-6(7) , BS8814) Beascoa, Ediciones S.A. ESP. *Dist:* Lectorum Pubns., Inc.

Baskerville, Elizabeth. David's Kiss. Jamieson, Perry, illus. 1999. 24p. (J). (ps-3). 14.95 (978-1-890493-75-2(9) , Binnacle Kids) Binnacle Publishing Group.

Bauer, Joan. Thwonk. 2005. 224p. (YA). (gr. 7). pap. 7.99 (978-0-14-240429-4(2) , Puffin); 2001. 208p. (J). 16.99 (978-0-399-23751-5(8) , Putnam Juvenile) Penguin Group (USA) Inc.

—Thwonk. 2001. (978-0-606-22535-9(8)) Tandem Library Bks.

Beach, Rex. Heart of the Sunset. 2004. reprint ed. pap. 1.99 (978-1-4192-2303-7(8)) Kessinger Publishing, LLC.

Beach, Rex E. Heart of the Sunset. 2004. reprint ed. pap. 33.95 (978-1-4179-3787-5(4)) Kessinger Publishing, LLC.

Bedford, David. The Way I Love You. James, Ann, illus. 2004. 32p. (J). 12.95 (978-0-689-87625-7(4)) Simon & Schuster Children's Publishing.

Behm, Barbara J. Tears of Joy. Anderson, Ellen, illus. unabr. ed. 1999. 32p. (J). (gr. 1 up). lib. bdg. 16.95 (978-0-9669647-0-7(5)) WayWord Publishing.

La Bella y la Bestia. 2001. (978-84-305-7587-9(1)) Lectorum Pubns., Inc.

Bennet-Boltinghouse, JoAnn. A Pooch Finds Her Purpose. Julich, Jennifer, illus. 2006. (YolandaBaby Ser.). 32p. (J). 16.00 (978-0-9785151-0-2(2)) Ginger Pr., The.

Bennett, Cherie. The Haunted Heart. 1999. (J). (978-0-606-16362-0(X)) Tandem Library Bks.

—Love Him Forever. 1999. (Illus.). (YA). (978-0-606-17968-3(2)) Tandem Library Bks.

—Searching for David's Heart. 1998. 176p. (gr. 3-7). pap. 4.50 (978-0-590-30673-7(1)) Scholastic, Inc.

Berenstain, Stan & Berenstain, Jan. The Berenstain Bears & the Love Match. 1998. (Berenstain Bears Big Chapter Bks.). (J). (gr. 2-6). (978-0-606-13952-6(4)) Tandem Library Bks.

Bickel, Karla. Heart Petals on the Hearth: A Collection of Children's Stories. Bickel, Karla, illus. 2004. (Illus.). 64p. (J). (ps-6). 20.00 (978-1-891452-00-0(2)) Heart Arbor Bks.

—Heart Petals on the Hearth: A Collection of Children's Stories. 2004. (Illus.). 64p. (J). (ps-6). pap. 16.00 (978-1-891452-01-7(0)) Heart Arbor Bks.

—Heart Petals on the Hearth II: A Collection of Children's Stories. 2004. (Illus.). 80p. (J). (ps-6). 25.00 (978-1-891452-04-8(5)); pap. 20.00 (978-1-891452-05-5(3)) Heart Arbor Bks.

Big & Little. 2003. (J). pap. 12.95 (978-0-590-40698-7(1)) Scholastic, Inc.

Birch, Beverley & Shakespeare, William. Romeo & Juliet. 2007. (Illus.). 80p. 13.95 ***(978-0-7502-4966-9(8)*** , Hodder Wayland) Hodder Children's Division GBR. *Dist:* Independent Pubs. Group.

Bishop, Jennie. The Garden Wall. 2006. (J). 12.99 ***(978-1-59317-168-1(4))*** Warner Pr. Pubs.

Bjorkman, Steve. Good Night, Little One. Bjorkman, Steve, illus. 1999. (Illus.). 40p. (J). (ps-3). 9.99 (978-1-57856-275-6(9) , WaterBrook Pr.) WaterBrook Pr.

Blackman, Malorie. Black & White. 2007. 512p. (YA). (gr. 9 up). pap. 7.99 (978-1-4169-0017-7(9) , Simon Pulse) Simon & Schuster Children's Publishing.

—Naughts & Crosses. 2005. (Illus.). 400p. (YA). (gr. 9 up). 15.95 (978-1-4169-0016-0(0)) Simon & Schuster Children's Publishing.

Blackmore, Richard D. Lorna Doone, Level 4. 2nd abr. ed. 2000. (Bookworms Ser.). (Illus.). 96p. pap. 6.50 (978-0-19-423038-4(4)) Oxford Univ. Pr., Inc.

Bley, Anette. And What Comes after a Thousand? Bley, Anette, illus. 2007. (Illus.). 32p. (J). (gr. 1-5). 15.95 (978-1-933605-27-2(8) , 05272) Kane/Miller Bk. Pubs., Inc.

Blume, Judy. Forever... 2007. 208p. pap. 14.00 ***(978-1-4169-5391-3(4));*** 224p. mass mkt. 7.99 ***(978-1-4169-4738-7(8))*** Simon & Schuster. (Simon Spotlight Entertainment).

Blume, Judy. The Pain & the Great One. Trivas, Irene, illus. 2002. (J). 14.79 (978-0-7587-3361-0(5)) Book Wholesalers, Inc.

—The Pain & the Great One. 2002. 32p. (J). 17.95 (978-0-689-85507-8(9) , Atheneum/Richard Jackson Bks.) Simon & Schuster Children's Publishing.

Bode, N. E. Nobodies. Ferguson, Peter, illus. 2005. 304p. (J). 16.99 (978-0-06-055738-6(9)); lib. bdg. 17.89 (978-0-06-055739-3(7)) HarperCollins Pubs.

Bodett, Tom. Norman Tuttle on the Last Frontier. 208p. (YA). (gr. 7). 2006. mass mkt. 5.99 (978-0-553-49493-8(7) , Laurel Leaf); 2004. 15.95 (978-0-679-89031-7(9) , Knopf Bks. for Young Readers) Random Hse. Children's Bks.

—Norman Tuttle on the Last Frontier: A Novel in Stories. 2004. 208p. (J). (gr. 7). lib. bdg. 17.99 (978-0-679-99031-4(3) , Knopf Bks. for Young Readers) Random Hse. Children's Bks.

Bonnell, Kris. We Love Pets. 2007. (J). 3.95 ***(978-1-933727-56-1(X))*** Reading Reading Bks., LLC.

Boock, Paula. Dare Truth or Promise. 1999. 176p. (YA). (gr. 7-12). tchr. ed. 15.00 (978-0-395-97117-8(9)) Houghton Mifflin Co. Trade & Reference Div.

Bourgeois, Paulette. Franklin Dice "Te Quiero" Varela, Alejandra Lopez, tr. Clark, Brenda, illus. (SPA.). (J). (gr. k-2). pap. 5.95 (978-1-930332-23-2(8) , LC0736); ring bd. 10.95 (978-1-930332-24-9(6) , LC0862) Lectorum Pubns., Inc.

—Franklin Dice "Te Quiero" 2002. (SPA.). lib. bdg. 14.10 (978-0-613-64498-3(0)) Tandem Library Bks.

—Un Nouvel Ami pour Benjamin. ed. 2004. Tr. of Franklin's New Friend. (FRE., Illus.). (J). (ps-2). spiral bd. (978-0-616-01828-6(2)) Canadian National Institute for the Blind/Institut National Canadien pour les Aveugles.

Boyd, Lizi. I Love Daddy. Boyd, Lizi, illus. 2004. (Super Sturdy Picture Bookstm Ser.). (Illus.). 24p. (J). (gr. k-ps). 8.99 (978-0-7636-2217-6(5)) Candlewick Pr.

—I Love Mommy. Boyd, Lizi, illus. 2004. (Super Sturdy Picture Bookstm Ser.). (Illus.). 24p. (J). (gr. k-ps). 8.99 (978-0-7636-2216-9(8)) Candlewick Pr.

Boyle, Amanda N. The Dream. 2007. 59p. per. 8.95 ***(978-1-59824-506-6(6))*** E-BookTime LLC.

Boynton, Sandra. Consider Love: Its Moods & Many Ways. Boynton, Sandra, illus. (Illus.). 32p. (J). 2003. 12.95 (978-0-689-85908-3(2)); 2004. 7.99 (978-0-689-87814-5(1)) Simon & Schuster Children's Publishing. (Little Simon).

—Snuggle Puppy! A Love Song. 2003. (Illus.). 24p. (J). bds. 6.95 (978-0-7611-3067-3(5) , 13067) Workman Publishing Co., Inc.

Brady, Jenifer. Buddy Check. 2002. (gr. 7-12). lib. bdg. 32.65 (978-0-613-77905-0(3)) Tandem Library Bks.

Bratton, Howard R. No Statue on the Courthouse Lawn: The Old Graybeards of Past Years Hadn't Cottoned to Such Vanities. 2002. 416p. (YA). pap. 20.95 (978-0-595-22405-0(9) , Writers Club Pr.) iUniverse, Inc.

Brian, Kate. Lucky T. 304p. (YA). (gr. 9 up). 2007. pap. 8.99 (978-1-4169-3545-2(2) , Simon Pulse); 2005. 14.95 (978-0-689-87351-5(4)) Simon & Schuster Children's Publishing.

—The Princess & the Pauper. 2005. 272p. (YA). mass mkt. 3.99 (978-1-4169-0520-2(0) , Simon Pulse) Simon & Schuster Children's Publishing.

—Sweet 16. 2006. 272p. (YA). 15.99 (978-1-4169-0032-0(2)) Simon & Schuster Children's Publishing.

Brian, Kate & Frost, Michael. The Virginity Club. 2005. 336p. (YA). reprint ed. pap. 5.99 (978-1-4169-0346-8(1) , Simon Pulse) Simon & Schuster Children's Publishing.

Bright, J. E. The Trouble with Twins. 2006. (Follow Your Heart Ser.: No. 2). 240p. (J). pap. 8.99 (978-0-439-79141-0(3) , Scholastic Paperbacks) Scholastic, Inc.

Brodsky, Richard M. Jodi the Greatest Love Story Ever Told. Garbo, Irene, ed. 2002. (Illus.). 254p. (YA). 21.95 (978-0-9715423-0-3(9)) Trebloon Pubns.

Bronte, Charlotte. Jane Eyre. Harvey, Bob, illus. 2004. (Paperback Classics Ser.). 144p. (J). pap. 4.95 (978-0-7945-0658-2(5) , Usborne) EDC Publishing.

—Jane Eyre. 1999. (Saddleback Classics). (Illus.). (J). 13.75 (978-0-606-21557-2(3)) Tandem Library Bks.

—Jane Eyre. 2003. (Illus.). 48p. (978-0-7502-3668-3(X) , Hodder Wayland) Hodder Children's Division.

—Jane Eyre. Olimar, N., illus. 2nd ed. 1998. (Illustrated Classic Book Ser.). 61p. (J). (gr. 3 up). reprint ed. pap. 4.95 (978-1-56767-267-1(1)) Educational Insights, Inc.

—Jane Eyre. adapted ed. (YA). (gr. 5-12). pap. 8.50 (978-0-8359-0215-1(3)) Globe Fearon Educational Publishing.

—Jane Eyre. unabr. ed. 1998. (Wordsworth Classics Ser.). (YA). (gr. 6-12). 5.27 (978-0-89061-020-6(7) , R0207WW) Jamestown.

—Jane Eyre, Level 6. 2nd abr. ed. 2000. (Bookworms Ser.). (Illus.). 128p. 6.50 (978-0-19-423088-9(0)) Oxford Univ. Pr., Inc.

Brooke, Lauren. Love Is a Gift. 2004. (Heartland Ser.). 176p. mass mkt. 4.99 (978-0-439-42510-0(7) , Scholastic Paperbacks) Scholastic, Inc.

Brooks, Kevin. Candy. 2006. 384p. (J). pap. 7.99 (978-0-439-68328-9(9) , PUSH); 2005. 368p. pap. 16.95 (978-0-439-68327-2(0) , Chicken Hse., The) Scholastic, Inc.

Brown, Marc. Who's in Love with Arthur? 10th ed. 1998. (Arthur Chapter Bks. : Bk. 10). (Illus.). 64p. (J). (gr. 2-4). pap. 4.25 (978-0-316-11540-7(1)) Little, Brown Bks. for Young Readers.

—Who's in Love with Arthur?, Vol. 10. unabr. ed. 2004. (Arthur Chapter Bks.: Bk. 10). (Illus.). 57p. (J). (gr. 2-4). pap. 17.00 incl. audio (978-0-8072-0407-8(2) , Listening Library) Random Hse. Audio Publishing Group.

J
K
L

Brown, Marc, et al. Arthur & the Lost Diary. 9th ed. 1998. (Arthur Chapter Bks. : Bk. 9). (Illus.). 64p. (J). (gr. 2-4). 14.95 (978-0-316-11573-5(8)) Little, Brown Bks. for Young Readers.

Bruna, Dick. Miffy Says, I Love You! 2004. (Illus.). 12p. bds. 5.99 (978-1-59226-187-1(6)) Big Tent Entertainment, Inc.

Bunting, Eve. I Love You, Too! Sweet, Melissa, illus. 2004. 32p. (J). pap. 8.95 (978-0-439-45086-7(1) , Cartwheel Bks.) Scholastic, Inc.

—Two Different Girls. 2001. 32p. (YA). (gr. 6-12). pap. (978-0-8224-3535-8(7)) Globe Fearon Educational Publishing.

Bunting, Eve. You Were Loved Before You Were Born. Barbour, Karen, illus. 2008. (J). 32p. pap. 16.99 ***(*978-0-439-04061-7(2));*** pap. ***(*978-0-439-04062-4(0))*** Scholastic, Inc. (Blue Sky Pr., The).

Burg, Sarah, illus. The Secret of Love. 2006. 56p. (J). (ps). 11.00 (978-0-698-40050-4(X) , Minedition) Penguin Group (USA) Inc.

Burnham, Niki. Do-over. 2006. (Romantic Comedies Ser.). 240p. (YA). mass mkt. 5.99 (978-0-689-87620-2(3) , Simon Pulse) Simon & Schuster Children's Publishing.

—Royally Jacked. 2004. (gr. 7-12). lib. bdg. 14.15 (978-0-613-73454-7(8)) Tandem Library Bks.

—Scary Beautiful. 2005. (Romantic Comedies Ser.). 272p. (YA). pap. 6.99 (978-0-689-87619-6(X) , Simon Pulse) Simon & Schuster Children's Publishing.

Burnham, Niki & Saidens, Amy. Royally Jacked. 2003. (Romantic Comedies Ser.). 208p. (YA). pap. 6.99 (978-0-689-86668-5(2) , Simon Pulse) Simon & Schuster Children's Publishing.

—Spin Control. 2004. (Romantic Comedies Ser.). 256p. (YA). pap. 6.99 (978-0-689-86669-2(0) , Simon Pulse) Simon & Schuster Children's Publishing.

Burnham, Niki, et al. Fireworks: Four Summer Stories. 2007. (Fireworks Ser.). (Illus.). 240p. (YA). (gr. 7 up). pap. 8.99 (978-0-439-90300-4(9) , Scholastic Paperbacks) Scholastic, Inc.

Burton, Margie, et al. Life in the City. Adams, Alison, ed. 1999. (Early Connections Ser.). 16p. (J). (gr. k-2). pap. 4.50 (978-1-58344-069-8(0)) Benchmark Education Co.

Butterworth, MyLinda. The Monster Run. Day, Linda S., ed. Mercer, Matthew, illus. l.t. ed. 2004. 32p. (J). (ps-3). 14.95 (978-1-890905-23-1(2)) Day to Day Enterprises.

Byars, Betsy. A Blossom Promise. (Blossom Ser.). (J). (gr. 4-6). 145p. pap. 4.50 (978-0-8072-1444-2(2)); Set. 2000. pap. 29.00 incl. audio (978-0-8072-7322-7(8) , YA826SP) Random Hse. Audio Publishing Group. (Listening Library).

Cabot, Meg. In Love. (Princess Diaries: Vol. 3). (YA). 2003. 288p. (gr. 6 up). pap. 6.99 (978-0-06-447280-7(9)); 2002. 272p. (gr. 7 up). mass mkt. 5.99 (978-0-06-052568-2(1)); 2002. 240p. (gr. 7 up). 16.99 (978-0-06-029467-0(1)) HarperCollins Pubs.

—In Love, Vol. 3. 2004. (Princess Diaries: Vol. 3). 288p. (J). (gr. 7 up). pap. 38.00 incl. audio (978-0-8072-2284-3(4) , Listening Library) Random Hse. Audio Publishing Group.

—In Love. 2002. (Princess Diaries: Vol. 3). (gr. 7-12). lib. bdg. 15.30 (978-0-613-57919-3(4)) Tandem Library Bks.

—In Love. 2003. (Princess Diaries: Vol. 3). (YA). 24.95 (978-0-7862-4844-5(0)) Thorndike Pr.

Caffrey-Kira, Albina. The Bear Who Loves Apples. 2006. 25.00 (978-0-8059-9128-4(X)) Dorrance Publishing Co., Inc.

Calderone-Stewart, Lisa-Marie & Kunzman, Ed. Straight from the Heart & Other Stories. 2003. (Stories for Teens Ser.: Vol. 4). 72p. (YA). (gr. 7-12). pap. 4.95 (978-0-88489-592-3(0)) St. Mary's Pr.

—That First Kiss & Other Stories. 2003. (Catechism Connection for Teens Ser.). 96p. (YA). (gr. 7-12). pap. 4.95 (978-0-88489-589-3(0)) St. Mary's Pr.

Caletti, Deb. Honey, Baby, Sweetheart. 320p. (YA). 2005. pap. 7.99 (978-0-689-86474-2(4) , Simon Pulse); 2004. 15.95 (978-0-689-86765-1(4)) Simon & Schuster Children's Publishing.

—Honey, Baby, Sweetheart. l.t. ed. 2005. 367p. 22.95 (978-0-7862-7308-9(9) , Large Print Pr.) Thorndike Pr.

—Wild Roses. (YA). (gr. 7 up). 2006. 320p. pap. 6.99 (978-0-689-86475-9(2) , Simon Pulse); 2005. 304p. 15.95 (978-0-689-86766-8(2)) Simon & Schuster Children's Publishing.

Calkhoven, Laurie. Just My Luck. novel movie tie-in ed. 2006. (Illus.). 152p. (J). pap. 4.99 (978-0-439-83137-6(7)) Scholastic, Inc.

Callaghan-Joseph, Bernadette. Petals of Love. 2004. (J). pap. 16.00 (978-0-8059-6262-8(X)) Dorrance Publishing Co., Inc.

Campbell, Margaret. Shadow Across the Sun. 2002. 160p. (YA). pap. (978-0-7344-0262-2(7) , Lothian Bks.) Hachette Livre Australia.

Candlewick Press Staff. Ghmily Ams Ed. 2002. (J). bds. 12.99 (978-0-7636-1820-9(9)) Candlewick Pr.

Cann, Kate. Diving In. 2007. 304p. (J). pap. 5.99 (978-0-06-088601-1(3) , HarperTeen) HarperCollins Pubs.

—Diving In. 2000. (Livewire Ser.). 238p. (J). (gr. 7-11). pap. 9.99 (978-0-7043-4937-7(X)) Women's Pr., Ltd., The GBR. *Dist:* Independent Pubs. Group.

—Go! 2001. (Love Trilogy). 240p. (YA). (gr. 7 up). pap. (978-0-06-440868-4(X) , HarperTeen) HarperCollins Pubs.

—In the Deep End. 2007. 304p. (J). pap. 5.99 ***(*978-0-06-088602-8(1)*** , HarperTeen) HarperCollins Pubs.

—Ready? 2001. (Love Trilogy). 256p. (YA). (gr. 9 up). pap. (978-0-06-440869-1(8) , HarperTeen) HarperCollins Pubs.

—Sex. 2001. (Love Trilogy). 240p. (YA). (gr. 7 up). pap. (978-0-06-440870-7(1) , HarperTeen) HarperCollins Pubs.

Cann, Kate. Sink or Swim. 2007. 320p. (J). (gr. 9 up). pap. 5.99 ***(*978-0-06-088603-5(X)*** , HarperTeen) HarperCollins Pubs.

Card, Orson Scott, ed. Future on Ice. rev. ed. 1998. 432p. (YA). (gr. 7 up). 24.95 (978-0-312-86694-5(1) , Tor Bks.) Doherty, Tom Assocs., LLC.

Carlson, Melody. My Happy Heart. Osborn, Jim, illus. 2001. 32p. (J). (ps-5). 12.99 (978-0-8054-2382-2(6)) B&H Publishing Grp.

Carson, Diana Pastora. All the Muchos in the World: A Special Story about Love. Pruitt, Ginny, illus. 2006. 32p. (J). pap. 8.95 (978-0-8198-0779-3(6)) Pauline Bks. & Media.

Centeio, Tara Jaye. Mommy Loves Her Baby. Date not set. 32p. (J). (ps-1). pap. 5.99 (978-0-06-443715-8(9)) HarperCollins Pubs.

Chandler, Elizabeth. The Back Door of Midnight. 2004. (Dark Secrets Ser.). 224p. (YA). mass mkt. 5.99 (978-0-689-86642-5(9) , Simon Pulse) Simon & Schuster Children's Publishing.

Cheng, Cynthia. Aspirations. 2007. 150p. pap. 9.95 ***(*978-0-9739097-9-1(X))*** Burman Books, Inc. CAN. *Dist:* Independent Pubs. Group.

Cherrington, Sharnett Felicia. Bitter Sweet. 2005. (YA). per. 12.95 (978-1-933570-70-9(9)) Aardvark Global Publishing.

Cheshire, Simon. Kissing Vanessa. 2004. 144p. (YA). (gr. 7). 15.95 (978-0-385-73212-3(0) , Delacorte Bks. for Young Readers) Random Hse. Children's Bks.

Chetwin, Grace. Beauty & the Beast: A Personalized Modern Retelling. Roberts, Claire, illus. 1998. 71p. (J). pap. 25.00 (978-0-9649349-6-2(5) , Rivet Bks.) Feral Pr., Inc.

Chick, Sandra. I Never Told Her I Loved Her. 1998. (Livewire Ser.). 128p. (Orig.). (J). (gr. 6-9). 8.95 (978-0-7043-4947-6(7)) Women's Pr., Ltd., The GBR. *Dist:* Trafalgar Square Publishing.

Chris, Jerry. Beau, the Story of a Horse. 2003. 317p. (J). pap. 9.99 (978-0-88092-482-5(9)) Royal Fireworks Publishing Co.

Churchill & Fuge. Butterfly Kiss. (Illus.). 28p. (J). pap. (978-0-340-68614-0(6) , Hodder & Stoughton) Hodder General Publishing Division.

Clark, Catherine. The Alison Rules. 2005. 272p. (YA). reprint ed. pap. 6.99 (978-0-06-055982-3(9) , HarperTeen) HarperCollins Pubs.

Clark, Clara. Nellie Bishop. Shine, Andrea, illus. 2003. 128p. (YA). (gr. 4-6). pap. 12.95 (978-1-56397-642-1(0)) Boyds Mills Pr.

Clark, Emma Chichester. Te Quiero Mucho Canguro Azul! 2002. Tr. of I Love You Blue Kangaroo!. (SPA.). 108p. (J). 14.95 (978-84-488-1211-9(5) , BS31491) Beascoa, Ediciones S.A. ESP. *Dist:* Lectorum Pubns., Inc.

Clement-Davies, David. The Sight. 2002. (gr. 7-12). lib. bdg. 16.45 (978-0-613-68285-5(8)) Tandem Library Bks.

Coburn, Jake. LoveSick. 2005. 240p. (YA). (gr. 8-12). 16.99 (978-0-525-47383-1(1) , Dutton Juvenile) Penguin Group (USA) Inc.

Cohn, Rachel & Levithan, David. Nick & Norah's Infinite Playlist. (YA). (gr. 9 up). 2007. 200p. pap. 8.99 ***(*978-0-375-83533-9(4));*** 2006. 192p. 16.95 (978-0-375-83531-5(8)); 2006. 192p. lib. bdg. 18.99 (978-0-375-93531-2(2)) Random Hse. Children's Bks. (Knopf Bks. for Young Readers).

Colasanti, Susane. Take Me There. 2008. 304p. (YA). (gr. 7). 17.99 ***(*978-0-670-06333-8(9)*** , Viking Juvenile) Penguin Group (USA) Inc.

Colebank, Susan. Black Tuesday. 2007. 208p. (YA). 16.99 (978-0-525-47766-2(7) , Dutton Juvenile) Penguin Group (USA) Inc.

Collins, Jenny. Puppy Love. 2007. (First Kisses Ser.: No. 3). 192p. (J). pap. 5.99 ***(*978-0-06-114312-0(X)*** , HarperTeen) HarperCollins Pubs.

Colman. Pearl Story Book A Collection of Tales O. 2006. pap. 87.99 ***(*978-1-4280-4925-3(8))*** IndyPublish.com.

Colon, Suzan. Buried Secrets. 2003. (gr. 5-8). lib. bdg. 14.15 (978-0-613-64658-1(4)) Tandem Library Bks.

Come & Meet Lola: A Very Special Chicken That Will Capture the Hearts of Children of All Ages! (Englishspanish Story Book Ser.).Tr. of Ven a Conocer a Lola.... (ENG & SPA.). 32p. (J). 13.95 (978-1-931398-51-0(8)) Me+Mi Publishing.

Comino, Sandra. La Casita Azul. Zeller, Beatriz, tr. (SPA.). 128p. (J). 2004. pap. 6.95 (978-0-88899-540-7(7)); 2003. (Illus.). 15.95 (978-0-88899-504-9(0)) Groundwood Bks. CAN. *Dist:* Perseus Distribution.

—The Little Blue House. Zeller, Beatriz, tr. from SPA. 2004. 128p. (J). pap. 6.95 (978-0-88899-541-4(5) , Libros Tigrillo) Groundwood Bks. CAN. *Dist:* Perseus Distribution.

—The Little Blue House. Zeller, Beatriz & Wald, Susana, trs. from SPA. 2003. (Illus.). 128p. (J). (gr. 4-7). 15.95 (978-0-88899-503-2(2)) Groundwood Bks. CAN. *Dist:* Perseus Distribution.

Conford, Ellen. Crush. 1999. (J). 11.60 (978-0-606-15853-4(7)) Tandem Library Bks.

Connor, Joynce. Micheal & Mr. B. 2006. 48p. (J). (gr. k-3). 19.95 (978-0-9765469-1-7(4)) Diamond Cutter Pr., LLC.

Conway, David. The Most Important Gift of All. Littlewood, Karin, illus. 2006. 32p. (J). 15.95 (978-0-7696-4618-3(2) , Gingham Dog Pr.) School Specialty Publishing.

Cooney, Caroline B. The Girl Who Invented Romance. 2004. 192p. (J). (gr. 5). reprint ed. pap. 8.95 (978-0-385-73239-0(2) , Delacorte Bks. for Young Readers) Random Hse. Children's Bks.

Cooper, Ilene. I'll See You in My Dreams. 2000. 160p. (J). pap. 4.99 (978-0-14-037716-3(6) , Puffin) Penguin Group (USA) Inc.

Cooper, Mimi. Me Versus Cooties. 2006. 17p. 9.99 (978-1-4116-8256-6(4)) Lulu.com.

Cooper, Patrick. Tell Me Lies. 2007. (YA). (gr. 9). 304p. 15.99 (978-0-385-73270-3(8)); 288p. lib. bdg. 18.99 (978-0-385-90287-8(5)) Random Hse. Children's Bks. (Delacorte Bks. for Young Readers).

Cormier, Robert. Tenderness. 2004. 240p. (YA). (gr. 9). pap. 7.95 (978-0-385-73133-1(7) , Delacorte Bks. for Young Readers) Random Hse. Children's Bks.

Cousins, Lucy. Maisy Loves You: Book & Toy Gift Set. 2004. (Illus.). 1p. (J). 12.99 (978-0-7636-2564-1(7)) Candlewick Pr.

Coville, Bruce. Juliet Dove, Queen of Love. DiTerlizzi, Tony, illus. 2003. (Magic Shop Bks.). 208p. (J). (gr. 3-6). 17.00 (978-0-15-204561-6(9)) Harcourt Children's Bks.

Covington, Jean. Nanny Planted Love. 2005. (J). lib. bdg. 19.95 ***(*978-0-9754728-9-7(5)*** , Bear Hug Bks.) MidAmerica Publishing Co.

A Crab Called Mouse. 2006. (J). pap. 9.50 ***(*978-0-9787995-2-6(6))*** High-Pitched Hum Inc.

Crilley, Mark. Autumn. Crilley, Mark, illus. 2007. (Miki Falls Ser.). 176p. (J). (gr. 7 up). pap. 7.99 ***(*978-0-06-084618-3(6)*** , HarperTeen) HarperCollins Pubs.

Crites, Susan E. I Love You More Than Rainbows. Jarman, Rosemary & Jarman, Mark, illus. 2008. 32p. (J). 14.99 ***(*978-1-4003-1089-0(X))*** Nelson, Thomas Inc.

Croteau, Marie-Danielle. Fred & the Mysterious Letter. Cummins, Sarah, tr. from FRE. St-Aubin, Bruno, illus. 2005. (First Novel Ser.). 64p. (J). (gr. 2-5). ***(*978-0-88780-689-6(9));*** 4.95 (978-0-88780-688-9(0)) Formac Publishing Co., Ltd. CAN. *Dist:* Casemate Pubs. & Bk. Distributors, LLC.

Crystal, Billy. I Already Know I Love You. Sayles, Elizabeth, illus. 2004. 40p. (J). lib. bdg. 17.89 (978-0-06-059392-6(X)); 16.99 (978-0-06-059391-9(1)) HarperCollins Pubs.

Curtis, Jamie Lee. Tell Me Again about the Night I Was Born. ed. 2004. (Illus.). (J). (gr. k-3). spiral bd. (978-0-616-01623-7(9)) Canadian National Institute for the Blind/Institut National Canadien pour les Aveugles.

—Tell Me Again about the Night I Was Born. ed. 2004. (Illus.). (J). (gr. k-3). spiral bd. (978-0-616-01624-4(7)) Canadian National Institute for the Blind/Institut National Canadien pour les Aveugles.

—Tell Me Again about the Night I Was Born. Cornell, Laura, illus. 2000. 40p. (J). (gr. k-3). pap. 6.99 (978-0-06-443581-9(4) , Cotler, Joanna Books) HarperCollins Pubs.

—Tell Me Again about the Night I Was Born. 2000. (ps-2). lib. bdg. 14.15 (978-0-613-30152-7(8)) Tandem Library Bks.

Daley Mackall, Dandi. I Love You Daddy. Lee Schmidt, Karen, illus. 2006. (I Love You Ser.). 20p. (J). bds. 7.99 (978-0-7847-1816-2(4) , 04138) Standard Publishing.

—I Love You Mommy. Lee Schmidt, Karen, illus. 2005. (I Love You Ser.). 20p. (J). bds. 7.99 (978-0-7847-1815-5(6) , 04137) Standard Publishing.

Dalmatian Press Staff. Where Dreams Begin: Coloring & Activity Book with Stickers. 2004. (Disney Princess Ser.). (Illus.). 64p. (J). pap. 1.69 (978-1-4037-0861-8(4)) Dalmatian Pr.

Daly, Maureen. Seventeenth Summer. 2002. 320p. (YA). 17.95 (978-0-689-85383-8(1)) Simon & Schuster Children's Publishing.

Daly-Weir, Catherine. Love Is All You Need. 2000. (gr. k-3). lib. bdg. 14.15 (978-0-613-21934-1(1)) Tandem Library Bks.

Darwin, Florence Hen. The Lovers' Tasks. 2004. reprint ed. pap. 15.95 (978-1-4191-7098-0(8)) Kessinger Publishing, LLC.

Darwin, Florence Henrietta. The Lovers' Tasks. 2004. reprint ed. pap. 1.99 (978-1-4192-7098-7(2)) Kessinger Publishing, LLC.

Dautremer, Rébecca & Letmann, Mona, contrib. by. Enamorados. 2004. (SPA., Illus.). (J). 22.99 (978-84-88342-47-8(0)) S.A. Kokinos ESP. *Dist:* Lectorum Pubns., Inc.

Davenier, Christine. Leon & Albertine. Barth, Dominic, tr. 1998. (Illus.). 32p. (J). (ps-1). pap. 15.95 (978-0-531-30072-5(2) , Orchard Bks.) Scholastic, Inc.

David C. Cook. God Made Everything with Love, Set. 2007. (Land of Milk & Honey Ser.). (J). (ps). bds. 9.99 ***(*978-1-4347-0007-0(0))*** Cook, David C. Publishing Co.

Davidson, Dana. Played. 2005. 240p. (gr. 7-12). 16.99 (978-0-7868-3690-1(3) , Jump at the Sun) Hyperion Bks. for Children.

Davis, Caitlyn. What's Hot. 2007. (I Heart Bikinis Ser.: No. 3). 208p. (YA). (gr. 7 up). pap. 5.99 ***(*978-0-439-91852-7(9))*** Scholastic, Inc.

Davis, Gene. Dromedarius & Camela. 2006. lib. bdg. 18.95 (978-1-59094-115-7(2)) Jawbone Publishing Corp.

Davis, Stephie. Boyfriend Trick. 2007. (First Kisses Ser.: No. 2). 192p. (J). pap. 5.99 (978-0-06-114309-0(X) , HarperTeen) HarperCollins Pubs.

—Putting Boys on the Ledge. 2004. (YA). mass mkt. 5.99 (978-0-8439-5328-2(4)) Dorchester Publishing Co., Inc.

—Who Needs Boys? 2005. (YA). (gr. 7-12). mass mkt. 5.99 (978-0-8439-5397-8(7)) Dorchester Publishing Co., Inc.

de la Cruz, Melissa. The Au Pairs. 2004. (Au Pairs Ser.: Bk. 1). 304p. (YA). 14.95 (978-0-689-87066-8(3)) Simon & Schuster Children's Publishing.

De Montano, Marty K. Coyote in Love with a Star. Coffin, Tom, illus. 1998. (Tales of the People Ser.). 30p. (ps up). 14.95 (978-0-7892-0162-1(3)) Abbeville Pr., Inc.

Dean, Zoey. A-List, the: the Second Collection. 2007. (J). (gr. 10-17). pap. 29.99 ***(*978-0-316-06691-4(5)*** , Poppy) Little, Brown Bks. for Young Readers.

—Beautiful Stranger. 2007. (A-List Ser.: No. 9). 304p. (J). (gr. 9-17). pap. 9.99 ***(*978-0-316-11352-6(2)*** , Poppy) Little, Brown Bks. for Young Readers.

Decary, Marie. Amour Reglisse et Chocolat. 2002. (Roman Jeunesse Ser.). (FRE.). 96p. (YA). (gr. 4-7). pap. (978-2-89021-051-6(0)) Diffusion du livre Mirabel.

Delgado, M. E. The First Sandcastle. 2003. 359p. pap. 18.95 (978-0-595-25331-9(8) , Writers Club Pr.) iUniverse, Inc.

Denega, Danielle. I Love You Even If. 2007. 12p. 10.95 ***(*978-1-58117-557-8(4))*** Dalmatian Pr.

Denega, Danielle. Love & Friendship. 2007. (Littlest Pet Shop Ser.). 56p. (J). pap. 6.99 (978-0-439-89751-8(3)) Scholastic, Inc.

Desrosiers, Sylvie. Qui Veut Entrer dans la Legende? Sylvestre, Daniel, illus. 2003. (Roman Jeunesse Ser.). (FRE.). 96p. (YA). (gr. 4-7). pap. (978-2-89021-269-5(6)) Diffusion du livre Mirabel.

DiCamillo, Kate. The Miraculous Journey of Edward Tulane. Ibatoulline, Bagram, illus. 2006. 228p. (J). (gr. 2). 18.99 (978-0-7636-2589-4(2)) Candlewick Pr.

Dines, Carol. Talk to Me: Stories & a Novella. 1999. (978-0-606-16451-1(0)) Tandem Library Bks.

Dippold, Jane, illus. I Love My Baby. 1999. (Leap Frog Lift-a-Flap Ser.). (J). (978-0-7853-3367-8(3)) Publications International, Ltd.

Disney Staff. The Princess Collection Friendship Box: Cinderella; The Little Mermaid; Sleeping Beauty; Snow White & the Seven Dwarfs. 2001. (Illus.). 48p. (J). (ps-3). bds. 9.99 (978-0-7364-1138-7(0) , RH/Disney) Random Hse. Children's Bks.

Dixon, Thomas. The Victim: A Romance of the Real Jefferson Davis. Marchand, J. N., illus. 2004. reprint ed. pap. 41.95 (978-1-4179-1462-3(9)) Kessinger Publishing, LLC.

Dokey, Cameron. Beauty Sleep: A Retelling of Sleeping Beauty. 2006. (Once upon a Time Ser.). 208p. (YA). pap. 5.99 (978-1-4169-4014-2(6) , Simon Pulse) Simon & Schuster Children's Publishing.

—Lost & Found. 1999. (Enchanted Hearts Ser.: No. 3). 208p. (YA). (gr. 7-12). pap. 4.50 (978-0-380-80083-4(7)) HarperCollins Pubs.

—Lost & Found. 1999. (Enchanted Hearts Ser.). (Illus.). (YA). (978-0-606-17965-2(8)) Tandem Library Bks.

Dokey, Cameron & McClatchy, Lisa. Before Midnight: A Retelling of Cinderella. Lyon, Tammie, illus. 2007. (Once upon a Time Ser.). 208p. (YA). (gr. 6-10). pap. 5.99 (978-1-4169-3471-4(5) , Simon Pulse) Simon & Schuster Children's Publishing.

Dorfman, Ariel & Dorfman, Joaquin. The Burning City. 2005. 272p. (J). (gr. 5-9). lib. bdg. 17.95 (978-0-375-93203-8(8) , Random Hse. Bks. for Young Readers) Random Hse. Children's Bks.

—Burning City. (YA). mass mkt. (978-0-375-83205-5(X)); 2006. 288p. (J). (gr. 5-9). reprint ed. pap. 7.95 (978-0-375-83204-8(1) , Random Hse. Bks. for Young Readers) Random Hse. Children's Bks.

Dorling Kindersley Publishing Staff, contrib. by. Love & Kisses. 2005. (Glitter Stickers Ser.). (Illus.). 16p. (J). (ps-3). pap. 6.99 (978-0-7566-1413-3(9)) Dorling Kindersley Publishing, Inc.

Douglas, Ann. Freddy & Flossy Flutterby. Douglas, Ann, illus. 2002. (Illus.). 40p. (J). 16.95 (978-0-9723184-0-2(2)) Betta Place, Inc.

Douglas, Babette. Kiss a Me: A Little Whale Watching. 2004. (J). 9.99 (978-1-890343-08-8(0)) Kiss A Me Productions, Inc.

Douglas, Lola. More Confessions of a Hollywood Starlet. 2006. 224p. (YA). (gr. 7-12). 16.99 (978-1-59514-051-7(4) , Razorbill) Penguin Group (USA) Inc.

Downing, Erin. Prom Crashers. 2007. (Romantic Comedies Ser.). 256p. (YA). pap. 6.99 (978-1-4169-3559-9(2) , Simon Pulse) Simon & Schuster Children's Publishing.

Doyon, Stephanie. Taking Chances. 1999. (On the Road Ser.: No. 3). (978-0-606-18899-9(1)) Tandem Library Bks.

Draper, Sharon M. Romiette & Julio. 2001. (Illus.). (J). (978-0-606-20415-6(6)) Tandem Library Bks.

Du Jardin, Rosamond. A Man for Marcy. 2003. (YA). pap. 12.95 (978-1-930009-76-9(3) , 800-691-7779) Image Cascade Publishing.

Duffie, Charles. The Mole & the Owl: A Romantic Fable about Braving the Wide World for Love. 1998. (Illus.). 120p. 18.95 (978-1-57174-082-3(1)) Hampton Roads Publishing Co., Inc.

DuJardin, Rosamond. Boy Trouble. 2003. (YA). pap. 12.95 (978-1-930009-70-7(4) , 800-691-7779) Image Cascade Publishing.

—The Real Thing. 2003. (YA). pap. 12.95 (978-1-930009-71-4(2) , 800-691-7779) Image Cascade Publishing.

—Someone to Count On. 2003. (YA). pap. 12.95 (978-1-930009-78-3(X) , 800-691-7779) Image Cascade Publishing.

Duksta, Laura. I Love You More. Keesler, Karen, illus. 2007. 34p. (J). (gr. 4-7). 16.99 ***(*978-1-4022-1126-3(0)*** , Sourcebooks Jabberwocky) Sourcebooks, Inc.

Dumas, Alexandre. La Dama de las Camelias. (SPA.). (J). 9.00 (978-958-04-7139-4(8)) Norma S.A. COL. *Dist:* Distribuidora Norma, Inc.

Dumas, Alexandre. The Son of Clemenceau. 2006. 78.99 ***(*978-1-4280-1224-0(9))*** IndyPublish.com.

Edelmann, Heinz. Yellow Submarine. Andreanelli, Fiona, illus. 2004. 40p. (J). (gr. k). 17.99 (978-0-7636-2440-8(3)) Candlewick Pr.

Edwards, Jo. Go Figure. 2007. 288p. (YA). (gr. 9 up). pap. 8.99 ***(*978-1-4169-2492-0(2)*** , Simon Pulse) Simon & Schuster Children's Publishing.

Edwards, Johanna. Love Undercover. 2006. (Romantic Comedies Ser.). 288p. (YA). mass mkt. 5.99 (978-1-4169-2465-4(5) , Simon Pulse) Simon & Schuster Children's Publishing.

Edwards, Verne. The Museum Duck. Norman, Kimberly, illus. l.t. ed. 2000. 33p. (J). per. 8.00 (978-0-9705823-0-0(7)) Pearl Line Pr., Inc.

Emery, Anne. Dinny Gordon Senior. 2004. (J). per. 9.95 (978-1-59511-000-8(3)) Image Cascade Publishing.

Emmett, Jonathan. I Love You Always & Forever. Howarth, Daniel, illus. 2007. 32p. (J). (ps-3). pap. 14.99 (978-0-439-91654-7(2)) Scholastic, Inc.

Enderle, Dottie. Granny Gert & the Bunion Brothers. Kulka, Joe, illus. 2006. 32p. (J). (gr. k-3). 15.95 (978-1-58980-373-2(6)) Pelican Publishing Co., Inc.

Erickson, Timothy Ronald. Death's Whisper Recoil, 2. Erickson, Timothy Ronald, illus. 2003. (YA). pap. 14.95 (978-1-59492-001-1(X)) Erickson, Tim.

Espana, Gonzalo. Historias de Amores y Desvarios en America. 2003. (SPA.). 180p. (978-958-30-0569-5(X), PV4378) Centro de Informacion y Desarrollo de la Comunicacion y la Literatura MEX. *Dist:* Lectorum Pubns., Inc.

Esparza-Harris, Mechelle. The Love Note. 2004. 56p. pap. 12.95 (978-1-4137-5031-7(1)) PublishAmerica, Inc.

Evans, Edie. I Love You, Daddy. Fletcher, Rusty, illus. 2001. (Little Golden Bks.). 16p. (J). (gr. k-k). 2.99 (978-0-307-99508-7(9), Golden Bks.) Random Hse. Children's Bks.

—I Love You, Mommy. Fletcher, Rusty, illus. 1999. (Little Golden Bks.). 16p. (J). (gr. k-k). 2.99 (978-0-307-99507-0(0), Golden Bks.) Random Hse. Children's Bks.

Evans, Lauralee. The King's Heir. 2006. (YA). (****978-1-55517-865-9(0)***, Bonneville Bks.) Cedar Fort, Inc./CFI Distribution.

Evans, Nicholas. The Loop. 1999. (gr. 7-12). lib. bdg. 16.45 (978-0-613-21928-0(7)) Tandem Library Bks.

Exclaim Entertainment Staff. I Love My Family. 2007. (BOZ#8482; Ser.). 14p. (J). 4.99 (****978-0-310-71404-0(4)***) Zonderkidz.

Faith, Susan. Purple Love. Sasaki, Goro, illus. 2001. 32p. (J). (ps-7). 17.95 (978-0-9707793-5-9(6)) Purple People, Inc.

Farhadi, Hamid. Ghooch-Ali & the Story of Love. 2004. pap. 14.95 (978-0-533-14217-0(2)) Vantage Pr., Inc.

Fatio, Louise. The Happy Lion Roars. Duvoisin, Roger, illus. 2006. 40p. (J). (ps-3). 15.95 (978-0-375-83887-3(2), Knopf Bks. for Young Readers) Random Hse. Children's Bks.

Fevens, Irene. New Time New Place. 2000. 252p. (YA). mass mkt. (978-0-9686720-0-6(0)) Editions Odyssey.

Fiedler, Lisa. Romeo's Ex: Rosalind's Story. rev. ed. 2006. 256p. (YA). 16.95 (978-0-8050-7500-7(3), Holt, Henry & Co. Bks. For Young Readers) Holt, Henry & Co.

Fields, Alberta. To the Ends of the Earth. 2002. 129p. (gr. 8-12). pap. 17.95 (978-1-59129-333-0(2)) PublishAmerica, Inc.

Finley, Martha. Mildred & Elsie, Vol. 3. (Mildred Classics Ser.: Vol. 3). 288p. pap. 6.95 (978-1-58182-229-8(4)) Cumberland Hse. Publishing.

—Mildred at Roselands, Vol. 2. (Mildred Classics Ser.: Vol. 2). 288p. pap. 6.95 (978-1-58182-228-1(6)) Cumberland Hse. Publishing.

Fisher, Robert & Kelly, Beth. El Buho Que No Podia Ulular. 2nd ed. 2004. Tr. of Owl Who Didn't Give a Hoot. (SPA., Illus.). 99p. (J). (978-84-7720-685-9(6), OB10849) Obelisco, Ediciones S.A.

Fontaine, Catherine Silliman. Have a Not for Christmas ... & Always. 2006. (Illus.). 44p. (J). 11.95 (978-0-9776958-0-5(8)) CyPress Pubns.

Forester, MaMa Eagle. Young Eagle, Pretty Flower. Spears, Ashley E., illus. 2004. 16p. (J). 7.95 (978-0-9762389-4-2(2)) Trent's Prints.

Fowler, Doug. Never Let Me Go. 2002. (ENG.). 136p. 20.95 (****978-0-595-65129-0(1)***); 134p. (YA). pap. 10.95 (978-0-595-25371-5(7)) iUniverse, Inc. (Writers Club Pr.).

Fox, Peter. April. 2004. 192p. (YA). per. (978-0-9734848-2-3(9)) Coscom Entertainment.

Frank, Lucy. Will You Be My Brussels Sprout? 1998. (J). (978-0-606-13918-2(4)) Tandem Library Bks.

Frankel, Valerie. Fringe Girl in Love. 2007. 256p. (YA). pap. 9.99 (978-0-451-22046-2(3), N A L Trade) Penguin Group (USA) Inc.

Franklin, Emily. Lessons in Love: The Principles of Love. 2008. 272p. (gr. 12). pap. 9.99 (****978-0-451-22309-8(8)***, N A L Trade) Penguin Group (USA) Inc.

Frechette, Carole. Carmen. Ouriou, Susan, tr. 2005. (Illus.). 112p. (YA). 12.95 (978-0-88995-322-2(8)) Red Deer Pr. CAN. *Dist:* Fitzhenry & Whiteside, Ltd.

Fredericks, Mariah. Love. Watkins, Liselotte, illus. 2007. (In the Cards Ser.: No. 1). 288p. (J). (gr. 4-8). pap. 5.99 (****978-0-689-87655-4(6)***) Kaplan Bks.

French, Vivian. Pig in Love, Level 3. Archbold, Tim, illus. 2005. (Lightning Readers Ser.). 32p. (J). (gr. 1-2). pap., pap. 3.95 (978-0-7696-4221-5(7), Gingham Dog Pr.) School Specialty Publishing.

French/Archbold, Vivian/Tim. Pig in Love. 2005. (Illus.). 32p. (J). lib. bdg. 9.00 (****978-1-4242-0889-0(0)***) Fitzgerald Bks.

Friedman, Aimee. A Novel Idea. 2005. (Romantic Comedies Ser.). (Illus.). 256p. (YA). pap. 6.99 (978-1-4169-0785-5(8), Simon Pulse) Simon & Schuster Children's Publishing.

Friedman, Laurie. Love, Ruby Valentine. Cravath, Lynne Avril, illus. 2006. 32p. (J). 15.95 (978-1-57505-899-3(5), Carolrhoda Bks.) Lerner Publishing Group.

Fuchs, A. P. Magic Man. 2005. 50p. per. (978-0-9734848-7-8(X)) Coscom Entertainment.

Fuenmayor, Morella, illus. El Conde Olinos. 2000. (SPA.). 24p. (J). (ps-1). pap. 6.99 (978-980-257-241-0(1), EK7598) Ekare, Ediciones VEN. *Dist:* Kane/Miller Bk. Pubs., Inc., Lectorum Pubns., Inc.

Fujishima, Kosuke. Oh My Goddess! Mara Strikes Back. 2000. (gr. 7-12). lib. bdg. 24.55 (978-0-613-55175-5(3)) Tandem Library Bks.

Gabel, Claudia. In or Out. 2007. 256p. (YA). (gr. 7 up). pap. 8.99 (****978-0-439-91853-4(7)***) Scholastic, Inc.

—In or Out #2 Loves Me, Loves Me Not. 2007. 256p. pap. 8.99 (****978-0-439-91854-1(5)***) Scholastic, Inc.

—Sweet & Vicious. 2008. (In or Out Ser.). 256p. (J). pap. 8.99 (****978-0-439-91856-5(1)***, Scholastic Paperbacks) Scholastic, Inc.

Gallen, Tim. Love, Loss, & Algebra Equations. 2001. (gr. 7-12). lib. bdg. 24.55 (978-0-613-85093-3(9)) Tandem Library Bks.

—Love, Loss, & Algebra Equations. 2001. 244p. pap. 14.95 (978-0-595-17973-2(8), Writers Club Pr.) iUniverse, Inc.

Garcia, Mary. Play with Me: Togetherness Time for Your Preschooler & You. ed. (J). 2007. 16.95 (****978-0-9790931-2-8(0)***); 2006. 16.95 (****978-0-9790931-0-4(4)***) SMARTseeds Co., LLC, The.

—Play with Me: Togetherness Time for Your Preschooler & You: St. Valentine's Day. ed. 2007. (J). (****978-0-9790931-1-1(2)***) SMARTseeds Co., LLC, The.

Gardner, Sheldon. The Converso Legacy. 2005. 264p. (J). 18.95 (978-1-932687-18-7(1), Devora Publishing) Pitspopany Pr.

Garfinkle, Debra. The Band: Finding Love. 2007. 256p. (gr. 12 up). 9.99 (****978-0-425-21736-8(1)***, Berkley Trade) Penguin Group (USA) Inc.

Garris, Bekah J. Maybe Later: One girl's struggle with time & her lack of control over It. 2004. 170p. pap. 19.95 (978-1-4137-3821-6(4)) PublishAmerica, Inc.

Garza, Amy Ammons. Sterlen: And a Mosaic of Mountain Women. Ammons, David F. & Ammons, Sherilyn, eds. Cain, Doreyl Ammons, illus. 2005. 308p. (YA). per. 16.00 (978-0-9753023-2-3(9), Catch the Spirit of Appalachia) Ammons Communications, Ltd.

Gauthier, Bertrand. La Course a l'Amour. 2001. (Roman Plus Ser.). (FRE., Illus.). 160p. (YA). (gr. 8 up). pap. (978-2-89021-113-1(4)) Diffusion du livre Mirabel.

Gauthier, Gilles. L' Etrange Amour d'Edgar. 2001. (Roman Jeunesse Ser.). (FRE.). 96p. (YA). (gr. 4-7). pap. (978-2-89021-185-8(1)) Diffusion du livre Mirabel.

—Ma Babouche pour Toujours. 2002. (Premier Roman Ser.). (FRE.). 64p. (J). (gr. 2-5). pap. (978-2-89021-128-5(2)) Diffusion du livre Mirabel.

—Sauvez Ma Babouche! 2001. (Premier Roman Ser.). (FRE.). 64p. (J). (gr. 2-5). pap. (978-2-89021-110-0(X)) Diffusion du livre Mirabel.

Gauthier, Gilles & Derome, Pierre-Andre. Mon Cher Chausson. 2000. (Premier Roman Ser.). (FRE.). 64p. (J). (gr. 2-5). pap. (978-2-89021-416-3(8)) Diffusion du livre Mirabel.

George, Michele. The Rainbow of Love. 2004. (J). 5.00 (978-0-9672049-1-8(7)) Grace & Mercy Publishing.

Geras, Adele. The Tower Room. 2005. (Egerton Hall Novels: Vol. 1). 204p. (YA). (gr. 7-17). pap. 6.95 (978-0-15-205537-0(1), Harcourt Paperbacks) Harcourt Children's Bks.

Gillmor, Don. Yuck, a Love Story. Gay, Marie-Louise, illus. ed. 2004. (J). (gr. k-3). spiral bd. (978-0-616-07238-7(4)); spiral bd. (978-0-616-08494-6(3)) Canadian National Institute for the Blind/Institut National Canadien pour les Aveugles.

Gilmour, H. B. My Fantasy Dream Date With... 1999. 128p. (J). (gr. 4-7). pap. 4.99 (978-0-590-40894-3(1)) Scholastic, Inc.

Gliori, Debi. No Matter What. (Illus.). (J). 2008. 24p. bds. 6.95 (****978-0-15-206343-6(9)***, Red Wagon Bks.); 1999. 32p. 16.00 (978-0-15-202061-3(6)) Harcourt Children's Bks.

Globe-Fearon Staff, ed. Jane Eyre, Grades 5-12. pap., tchr. ed. 4.95 (978-0-8359-0109-3(2)) Globe Fearon Educational Publishing.

Godbersen, Anna. The Luxe. 2007. (Luxe Ser.). 448p. (J). lib. bdg. 18.89 (****978-0-06-134567-8(9)***); (YA). (gr. 9 up). 17.99 (****978-0-06-134566-1(0)***) HarperCollins Pubs. (HarperTeen).

Golden Books Staff. My Angel. 2004. (Little Nugget Ser.). (Illus.). 16p. (J). (gr. k-ps). bds. 3.99 (978-0-375-82991-8(1), Golden Bks.) Random Hse. Children's Bks.

—Share Your Love. 2006. (Illus.). 32p. (J). (ps-2). pap. 4.99 (978-0-375-83648-0(9), Golden Inspirational) Random Hse. Children's Bks.

Gonzales Bertrand, Diane, et al. Close to the Heart. 2002. (Illus.). 176p. (J). pap. 9.95 (978-1-55885-319-5(7), Piñata Books) Arte Publico Pr.

Goode, Caroline. Cupidity. 2005. (Romantic Comedies Ser.). 288p. (YA). mass mkt. 3.99 (978-1-4169-1147-0(2), Simon Pulse) Simon & Schuster Children's Publishing.

Goode, Caroline & Saidens, Amy. Cupidity. 2004. (Romantic Comedies Ser.). 288p. (YA). pap. 6.99 (978-0-689-87228-0(3), Simon Pulse) Simon & Schuster Children's Publishing.

Graham, Georgia. The Strongest Man This Side of Cremona. Graham, Georgia, illus. 1998. (Illus.). 32p. (J). (ps-3). pap. 15.95 (978-0-88995-182-2(9)) Red Deer Pr. CAN. *Dist:* Fitzhenry & Whiteside, Ltd.

Greene, Bette. Morning Is a Long Time Coming. l.t. ed. 2004. (Beeler Mystery Ser.). 35.95 (978-1-58118-122-7(1)) LRS.

—Philip Hall Likes Me, I Reckon Maybe. l.t. ed. 2003. (Children's Large Print Ser.). (J). 28.95 (978-1-58118-107-4(8)) LRS.

—Philip Hall Likes Me, I Reckon Maybe. Lilly, Charles, illus. 1999. (Puffin Newbery Library). 144p. (J). (gr. 3-7). pap. 5.99 (978-0-14-130312-3(3), Puffin) Penguin Group (USA) Inc.

—Philip Hall Likes Me, I Reckon Maybe. 1999. (gr. 3-6). lib. bdg. 14.15 (978-0-8085-3871-4(3)) Tandem Library Bks.

Greene, Janice. Jane Eyre. Hagerty, Carol, ed. 1998. (Classics Ser.: Set II). (Illus.). 77p. (YA). (gr. 5-12). pap. 7.95 (978-1-56254-268-9(0), SP2680) Saddleback Educational Publishing.

Gregory, Valiska. Shirley's Wonderful Baby. Degen, Bruce, illus. 1999. 32p. pap. 5.95 (978-0-06-443513-0(X)) HarperCollins Pubs.

Grey, Mini. The Adventures of the Dish & the Spoon. 2006. (Illus.). 32p. (J). (gr. 1). 16.95 (978-0-375-83691-6(8), Knopf Bks. for Young Readers) Random Hse. Children's Bks.

Gunn, Robin Jones. Take My Hand. 1999. (Sierra Jensen Ser.: Bk. 12). 144p. (YA). (gr. 7-11). pap. 6.99 (978-1-56179-736-3(7)) Bethany Hse. Pubs.

Gurley, Nan. Twice Yours: A Parable of God's Gift. Farnsworth, Bill, illus. 2004. 32p. (J). pap. 6.99 (978-0-310-70920-6(2)) Zonderkidz.

Gutman, Dan. Mr. Louie Is Screwy! Paillot, Jim, illus. 2007. (My Weird School Ser.: No. 20). 112p. (J). lib. bdg. 15.89 (****978-0-06-123480-4(X)***); pap. 3.99 (****978-0-06-123479-8(6)***, Harper Trophy) HarperCollins Pubs.

Haber, Karen. Crossing Infinity. 2006. 239p. pap. 9.95 (978-1-59687-411-4(2)) ibooks, Inc.

Haft, Erin. Pool Boys. 2006. 240p. (J). pap. 8.99 (978-0-439-83523-7(2), Scholastic Paperbacks) Scholastic, Inc.

Hall, S.C. Turns of Fortune & Other Tales. 2007. (ENG.). 116p. per. (****978-1-4065-1586-2(8)***) Dodo Pr.

Hallinan, P. K. ABC I Love You. 2003. (Illus.). 26p. (J). bds. 7.95 (978-0-8249-5458-1(0)) Ideals Pubns.

—How Do I Love You? (J). 24p. pap. 5.95 (978-0-8249-5360-7(6), Ideals); 2006. (Illus.). 32p. pap. 3.95 (978-0-8249-5518-2(8), Ideals Children's Bks.) Ideals Pubns.

—How Do I Love You/Como Te Amo. 2003. (SPA & ENG., Illus.). 32p. (J). 3.95 (978-0-8249-5471-0(8)) Ideals Pubns.

Hallinan, P. K. I Know Jesus Loves Me. Hallinan, P. K., illus. 2007. (Illus.). 28p. (J). (ps-3). 8.99 (****978-0-8249-5553-3(6)***, Ideals Children's Bks.) Ideals Pubns.

Hallinan, P. K., illus. How Do I Love You? 2002. 26p. (J). 6.95 (978-0-8249-4147-5(0)) Ideals Pubns.

Hammomnd, John & Hutchison, Gary. The Live & Loves of Adam Carter. 2005. 203p. (YA). pap. 13.99 (978-1-885631-98-5(7)) Hutchison, G.F. Pr.

Hannah, Martha. The Ghost of Hampton Court. Dowell, Larry, illus. 2006. 32p. (J). 17.95 (978-0-9779808-0-2(4)) CicadaSun.

Hansen, Lynne. The Change: Heritage of Horror Series. 2004. (Heritage of Horror Ser.: 2). 108p. (YA). pap. 9.00 (978-0-7599-4491-6(1)) Hard Shell Word Factory.

Hansen, Sara J. Sand Mermaids. 2004. 122p. pap. 17.95 (978-1-4137-1799-0(3)) PublishAmerica, Inc.

Hargrove, Jason. Looking Good, Cody Greer. 2006. 188p. pap. 19.95 (****978-1-4241-4013-8(7)***) PublishAmerica, Inc.

Harper, Meg. My Mum & the Hound from Hell. 2003. (My Mum Ser.). 160p. (J). pap. 9.99 (978-0-7459-4799-0(9), Lion) Lion Hudson plc GBR. *Dist:* Independent Pubs. Group.

Harrison, Emma, et al. Slipping Away. 2005. 163p. (YA). (978-1-4155-8181-0(9), Simon Spotlight) Simon & Schuster Children's Publishing.

Hart, Lavinia. Love n Kisses. 2000. (Illus.). 24p. (J). (gr. 3 up). pap. 8.95 (978-1-902618-91-3(2)) Element Children's Bks.

Hartinger, Brent. The Last Chance Texaco. 2005. 240p. (J). reprint ed. pap. 7.99 (978-0-06-050914-9(7), Harper-Teen) HarperCollins Pubs.

Harvey, Ken. Life in the Fridge: When Chocolate Milk Moved In. Hermes, Mary Sue, illus. 2002. 32p. (J). (ps-k). 12.95 (978-1-930093-16-4(0)) Brookfield Reader, Inc., The.

Harward, Barnaby, ed. Romeo & Juliet: Interfact Shakespeare. 2006. 144p. (YA). (gr. 6-10). reprint ed. pap. 25.00 (978-1-4223-5004-1(5)) DIANE Publishing Co.

Hasse, John Edward. I Love You When... Obligado, Lilian, illus. 2001. (Pictureback Shape Ser.). 24p. (J). (gr. k-3). pap. 3.25 (978-0-375-81063-3(3), Random Hse. Bks. for Young Readers) Random Hse. Children's Bks.

Hata, Kenjiro. Hayate the Combat Butler, Volume 2. 2007. (Conversational Ser.). 200p. (YA). pap. 9.99 (978-1-4215-0852-8(4)) Viz Media.

Hauman, Carrie. Zoe the Magic Love Dog. 2003. (Illus.). 32p. (J). 16.00 (978-0-9746333-8-1(0)) Alma Pr.

Hawley, Richard. Paul & Juliana: A Novel. 2003. 188p. (YA). 19.95 (978-1-890862-33-6(9)) Bancroft Pr.

Hawthorne, Rachel. Island Girls & Boys. 2005. 336p. pap. 5.99 (978-0-06-075546-1(6)) HarperCollins Pubs.

—Love on the Lifts. 2005. 320p. (J). pap. 5.99 (978-0-06-081536-3(1)) HarperCollins Pubs.

—Trust Me. 2007. (First Kisses Ser.: No. 1). 192p. (J). pap. 5.99 (978-0-06-114308-3(1), HarperTeen) HarperCollins Pubs.

Hayashi, Fumino. Neon Genesis Evangelion: Angelic Days. 2006. 184p. (YA). pap. (978-1-4139-0344-7(4)) ADV Manga.

Hayes, Joe & Castro Leal, Antonio. Pajaro Verde. 2005. (SPA.). 40p. pap. 8.95 (978-0-938317-90-6(3)) Cinco Puntos Pr.

Heath, Lorraine. Avon True Romance: An Amelia & the Outlaw. 2003. (gr. 7-12). lib. bdg. 13.00 (978-0-613-71381-8(8)) Tandem Library Bks.

Hébert, Marie-Francine. Le Coeur en Bataille. 2001. (Roman + — Special Editions Ser.). (FRE.). 160p. (YA). (gr. 8). pap. (978-2-89021-448-4(6)) Diffusion du livre Mirabel.

—Je T'Aime, Je Te Hais... 2001. (Roman + — Special Editions Ser.). (FRE.). 160p. (YA). (gr. 8). pap. (978-2-89021-449-1(4)) Diffusion du livre Mirabel.

—Sauve Qui Peut l'Amour. 2001. (Roman + — Special Editions Ser.). (FRE.). 160p. (YA). (gr. 8). pap. (978-2-89021-450-7(8)) Diffusion du livre Mirabel.

Heitritter, Laura. I Love You Just Because. Villim, Jim, illus. Date not set. 16p. (Orig.). (J). (ps up). pap. 6.95 (978-1-885964-01-4(3)) P2 Educational Services, Inc.

Heller, Andrew. Turn Your Heart On. Burgos, Javier Gonzalez, illus. 2005. (ENG.). 40p. (J). (ps-3). per. 23.00 (978-1-4208-1866-6(X)) AuthorHouse.

Heller, Sarah E. Disney's Princess Storybook Collection: Love & Friendship Stories. 1999. (Disneys Ser.). (Illus.). 304p. (J). (gr. k-5). 15.99 (978-0-7868-3247-7(9), Disney Editions) Disney Pr.

Hemphill, Helen. Runaround. 2007. 117p. (YA). (gr. 8 up). 16.95 (978-1-932425-83-3(7), Front Street) Boyds Mills Pr.

Henson, Heather. Making the Run. 2002. 240p. (J). (gr. k-4). 15.89 (978-0-06-029797-8(2)); (gr. 10 up). 15.95 (978-0-06-029796-1(4)) HarperCollins Pubs. (HarperTeen).

—Making the Run: A Novel. 2003. (gr. 7-12). lib. bdg. 15.30 (978-0-613-65699-3(7)) Tandem Library Bks.

Hermstad, Melanie. Bird, I Love You. Date not set. (978-0-517-58561-0(8)) Random Hse. Value Publishing.

Herrick, Ann. The Perfect Guy. 2005. 120p. (YA). pap. 9.95 (978-0-7599-3522-8(X)) Hard Shell Word Factory.

—Summer Replacement. 2004. (ENG.). 100p. (YA). per. 9.00 (978-0-7599-4168-7(8)) Hard Shell Word Factory.

Hesser, Terry Spencer. Kissing Doornobs. 1999. 160p. (YA). (gr. 7-12). reprint ed. pap. 5.99 (978-0-440-41314-1(1), Laurel Leaf) Random Hse. Children's Bks.

Hickey, Elizabeth & Cohen, James. I Love You More Than... Brown, Lynda Smart, illus. 1998. 32p. (J). 16.95 (978-1-884862-04-5(7)) Family Connections Publishing Co.

Hirschman, Jessica Elin & Cole, Jennifer Elin. I Love You All the Time. Bright, Bonnie, illus. 2000. 16p. (J). (ps-2). bds. 5.95 (978-0971555-0-8(4)) Cookie Bear Pr., Inc.

Hodges, Lynn & Buchanan, Sue. I Love You This Much. Bendall-Brunello, John, illus. 2006. (Song of God's Love Ser.). 16p. (J). 6.99 (978-0-310-70961-9(X)) Zonderkidz.

Hodges, Lynn, et al. I Love You This Much. Bendall-Brunello, John, illus. 2001. (Song of God's Love Ser.). 36p. (J). 14.99 incl. audio compact disk (978-0-310-23268-1(6)) Zonderkidz.

Hoffman, Mary. The Falconer's Knot: A Story of Friars, Flirtation & Foul Play. 2007. (Illus.). 288p. (YA). (gr. 7 up). 16.95 (978-1-59990-056-8(4), Bloomsbury Children) Bloomsbury Publishing.

Holder, Nancy. Smallville: Hauntings. 2003. (gr. 7-12). lib. bdg. 14.15 (978-0-613-72304-6(X)) Tandem Library Bks.

Holeman, Linda. Toxic Love. 2003. (gr. 5-8). lib. bdg. 17.60 (978-0-613-77315-7(2)) Tandem Library Bks.

—Toxic Love. 2003. 184p. (J). (gr. 6-9). pap. 8.95 (978-0-88776-647-3(1)) Tundra Bks., Inc./Livres Toundra, Inc. CAN. *Dist:* Random Hse., Inc.

Holly, Cate. You + Me = Heart Symbol. 2001. (Illus.). 80p. 5.99 (978-0-7407-1450-4(3)) Andrews McMeel Publishing.

Holm, Jennifer L. Boston Jane. unabr. ed. 2004. (Middle Grade Cassette Librariestm Ser.). 288p. (J). (gr. 5-9). pap. 38.00 incl. audio (978-0-8072-0787-1(X), S YA 307 SP, Listening Library) Random Hse. Audio Publishing Group.

Hopkins, Cathy. Mates, Dates & Diamond Destiny. 2006. (Mates, Dates Ser.). (Illus.). 272p. (YA). mass mkt. 6.99 (978-0-689-87697-4(1), Simon Pulse) Simon & Schuster Children's Publishing.

—Mates, Dates & Great Escapes. 2005. (Mates, Dates Ser.). 224p. (YA). (gr. 7-12). pap. 5.99 (978-0-689-87695-0(5), Simon Pulse) Simon & Schuster Children's Publishing.

—Mates, Dates & Mad Mistakes. 2004. (Mates, Dates Ser.). 224p. (YA). mass mkt. 5.99 (978-0-689-86722-4(0), Simon Pulse) Simon & Schuster Children's Publishing.

—Mates, Dates, & Sequin Smiles. 2004. (Mates, Dates Ser.). 208p. (YA). pap. 5.99 (978-0-689-86723-1(9), Simon Pulse) Simon & Schuster Children's Publishing.

—Mates, Dates & Sole Survivors. 2003. (Mates, Dates Ser.). 224p. (YA) mass mkt. 6.99 (978-0-689-85992-2(9), Simon Pulse) Simon & Schuster Children's Publishing.

—Mates, Dates & Sole Survivors. 2004. (Mates, Dates Ser.). (YA). (gr. 7-12). lib. bdg. 13.00 (978-0-613-73408-0(4)) Tandem Library Bks.

—Mates, Dates & Tempting Trouble. 2005. (Mates, Dates Ser.). 256p. (YA). mass mkt. 5.99 (978-0-689-87062-0(0), Simon Pulse) Simon & Schuster Children's Publishing.

—Mates, Dates Simply Fabulous Bks. 1-4, Set: Mates, Dates, & Inflatable Bras; Mates, Dates, & Cosmic Kisses; Mates, Dates, & Portobello Princesses; Mates, Dates, & Sleepover Secrets. 2006. (Mates, Dates Ser.: Bks. 1-4). 736p. (YA). pap. 10.99 (978-1-4169-1829-5(9)) Simon & Schuster Children's Publishing.

—The Princess of Pop. 2004. (Truth or Dare Ser.: No. 2). 224p. (YA). mass mkt. 5.99 (978-0-689-87002-6(7), Simon Pulse) Simon & Schuster Children's Publishing.

—Teen Queens & Has-Beens. 2004. (Truth or Dare Ser.: No. 3). 192p. (YA). pap. 5.99 (978-0-689-87129-0(5), Simon Pulse) Simon & Schuster Children's Publishing.

—White Lies & Barefaced Truths. 2005. (Truth or Dare Ser.: No. 1). 176p. (YA). mass mkt. 3.99 (978-1-4169-1152-4(9), Simon Pulse) Simon & Schuster Children's Publishing.

Horning, Sandra. The Giant Hug. Gorbachev, Valeri, illus. 2005. 40p. (J). (ps-3). 15.95 (978-0-375-82477-7(4), Knopf Bks. for Young Readers) Random Hse. Children's Bks.

Houde, Monique. Blinded by Love. 2004. (YA). pap. 14.95 (978-0-9748689-0-5(6)) Choices For Tomorrow.

How Do I Love You? 2005. (Illus.). 24p. (J). 7.95 (978-0-8249-5359-1(2)) Ideals Pubns.

Howat, Irene. Adoniram Judson: Danger on the Streets of Gold. 160p. (J). mass mkt. 5.99 (978-1-85792-660-6(9), Christian Focus) Christian Focus Pubns. GBR. *Dist:* Riverside.

J K L

Hughes, Lynn Gordon. To Live a Truer Life: A Story of the Hopedale Community. Lindro, illus. 2003. 32p. (J). 20.00 (978-0-9725017-2-9(X)) Blackstone Editions.

Hughes, Mark Peter. I Am the Wallpaper. 2007. 256p. (YA). (gr. 7-11). pap. 7.99 (978-0-440-42046-0(6)); 2005. 240p. (J). (gr. 5). 15.95 (978-0-385-73241-3(4)); 2005. 240p. (J). (gr. 5). lib. bdg. 17.99 (978-0-385-90265-6(4)) Random Hse. Children's Bks. (Delacorte Bks. for Young Readers).

Humphrey, T. Lewis. The Price of Love. 2003. 332p. (YA). pap. 18.95 (978-0-595-27260-0(6)) iUniverse, Inc.

Huskins, Suzanne Hallier, illus. No Matter What! 2004. (J). (978-1-887905-93-0(6)) Parkway Pubs., Inc.

I Met a Boy I Used to Know. 2000. (Katie Rose/Stacy Belford Ser.). (YA). pap. 12.95 (978-1-930009-13-4(5)) Image Cascade Publishing.

Ikumi, Mia. Tokyo Mew Mew (en Español), Vol. 5. 2006. (SPA., Illus.). 184p. reprint ed. pap. 10.95 (978-1-59497-173-0(0)) Public Square Bks.

Imes, Jarod. Age Ain't Nothing but a Number. 2007. 148p. (YA). pap. 10.99 (***978-1-934195-04-8(9)***) Abednego's Free.

Imes, Jarold. Ain't No Punk Christian. 2007. (YA). per. 10.99 (***978-1-934195-07-9(3)***) Abednego's Free.

Imes, Jarold, adapted by. U Can't Break Me. 2007. 148p. (YA). pap. 10.99 (***978-1-934195-03-1(0)***) Abednego's Free.

Inoue, Kazurou. Midori Days. 2006. (Midori Days Ser.). 208p. (YA). Vol. 6. pap. 9.99 (978-1-4215-0495-7(2)); Vol. 7. pap. 9.99 (978-1-4215-0496-4(0)) Viz Media.

Island, John. World of the Heart. Redford, Jim L., illus. 48p. (J). (ps-6). 14.95 (978-0-9637712-0-9(5)) Island Flowers, Inc.

Jabar, Cynthia. Wow! It Sure Is Good to Be You! Jabar, Cynthia, illus. 2006. (Illus.). 32p. (J). (gr. k-3). 9.95 (978-0-618-58132-0(4)) Houghton Mifflin Co.

Jacobs, Julie. My Heart Is a Magic House. Pons, Bernadette, illus. 2007. 32p. (J). (ps-1). 15.95 (978-0-8075-5335-0(2)) Whitman, Albert & Co.

Jacobson, Jennifer Richard. Stained. l.t. ed. 2006. 201p. (YA). 21.95 (978-0-7862-8283-8(5)) Thorndike Pr.

James, Brian. Perfect World. 2005. 304p. (J). pap. 7.99 (978-0-439-67365-5(8) , PUSH) Scholastic, Inc.

Jaysree. Drama. 2004. 134p. (YA). pap. 11.95 (978-0-595-29662-0(9)) iUniverse, Inc.

Jeffs, Stephanie. A Bad Day for Christopher Bear. Thomas, Jacqui, illus. 2004. (Christopher Bear Ser.). 30p. 5.99 (978-0-8066-4367-0(6) , Augsburg Bks.) Augsburg Fortress, Pubs.

—I Love You, Christopher Bear. Thomas, Jacqui, illus. 2004. (Christopher Bear Ser.). 32p. 5.99 (978-0-8066-4366-3(8) , Augsburg Bks.) Augsburg Fortress, Pubs.

Jenisch, Betty. Rennie. 2007. 9.00 (***978-0-8059-8947-2(1)***) Dorrance Publishing Co., Inc.

Jenkins, Emily. Love You When You Whine. Ruzzier, Sergio, illus. 2006. 32p. (J). 15.00 (978-0-374-34652-2(6)) Farrar, Straus & Giroux.

Johnson, Dolores, illus. Grandma's Hands. 1998. (Accelerated Reader Bks.). 32p. (J). (gr. 1-4). 15.95 (978-0-7614-5025-2(4) , Cavendish Children's Bks.) Cavendish, Marshall Corp.

Jones, Carrie. Love (and Other Uses for Duct Tape) 2008. 264p. (J). 16.95 (***978-0-7387-1257-4(4)*** , Flux) Llewellyn Pubns.

Jones, Jasmine. Enchanted: The Junior Novelization. rev. ed. 2007. 160p. (gr. 3-7). pap. 4.99 (***978-1-4231-0471-1(4)***) Disney Pr.

—Head over Heels. 2004. 152p. (J). lib. bdg. 16.92 (***978-1-4242-0677-3(4)***) Fitzgerald Bks.

Jones, Lara. I Love Hugs. Jones, Lara, illus. 2002. (Illus.). 16p. (J). bds. 6.95 (978-0-439-36767-7(0) , Cartwheel Bks.) Scholastic, Inc.

Jones, Terry. The Lady & the Squire. Foreman, Michael, illus. 2000. 304p. (J). (gr. 4-7). 22.99 (978-1-86205-417-2(7) , Pavilion Bks., Ltd.) Anova Bks. GBR. *Dist:* Independent Pubs. Group.

Joosse, Barbara M. Mama Do You Love Me? Lavallee, Barbara, illus. 1998. 24p. (J). (ps). bds. 6.95 (978-0-8118-2131-5(5)) Chronicle Bks. LLC.

—Me Quieres, Mama? Lasconi, Diego, tr. from SPA. Lavallee, Barbara, illus. 1998. (SPA.). 32p. (J). (ps-1). 15.95 (978-0-8118-2076-9(9) , CB0769) Chronicle Bks. LLC.

Joosse, Barbara M. & Lavallee, Barbara. Papa Do You Love Me? Lavallee, Barbara, illus. 2005. (Illus.). 36p. (J). 15.95 (978-0-8118-4265-5(7)) Chronicle Bks. LLC.

Jordan, Apple. Barbie: Love Is in the Air. Wolcott, Karen, illus. 2006. (Step into Reading Ser.). 32p. (J). (ps-1). 3.99 (978-0-375-83517-9(2)); lib. bdg. 11.99 (978-0-375-93517-6(7)) Random Hse. Children's Bks. (Random Hse. Bks. for Young Readers).

—Stuck on You! 2006. (Illus.). 24p. (J). (gr. 1-5). pap. 5.99 (978-0-7364-2431-8(8) , RH/Disney) Random Hse. Children's Bks.

Jordan, Deloris & Jordan, Roslyn. Did I Tell You I Love You Today? Evans, Shane, tr. Evans, Shane, illus. 2004. 32p. (J). 16.95 (978-0-689-85271-8(1)) Simon & Schuster Children's Publishing.

Jordan, Sabrina. First Kisses 4: It Had to Be You: It Had to Be You. 2007. (First Kisses Ser.: No. 4). 256p. (J). pap. 5.99 (***978-0-06-114313-7(8)*** , HarperTeen) HarperCollins Pubs.

Jung, Reinhardt. Bambert's Book of Missing Stories. 2006. 128p. (J). (gr. 4-7). pap. 5.50 (978-0-440-42045-3(8) , Yearling) Random Hse. Children's Bks.

Kamio, Yoko. Boys over Flowers. 2006. (Boys over Flowers Ser.).Tr. of Hana Yori Dango. 208p. (YA). Vol. 18. pap. 9.99 (978-1-4215-0532-9(0)); Vol. 19. pap. 9.99 (978-1-4215-0533-6(9)) Viz Media.

Karas, Phyllis. Spellbound. 1999. (Enchanted Hearts Ser.). (Illus.). (J). (978-0-606-17967-6(4)) Tandem Library Bks.

Karst, Patrice. The Invisible String. Stevenson, Geoff, illus. 2003. 36p. (J). 15.95 (978-0-87516-734-3(9) , Devorss Pubns.) DeVorss & Co.

Kasza, Keiko. A Mother for Choco. 2003. 32p. (J). (ps-1). bds. 6.99 (978-0-399-24191-8(4) , Putnam Juvenile) Penguin Group (USA) Inc.

Katschke, Judy. Facts about Flirting. 2003. (gr. 3-6). lib. bdg. 13.00 (978-0-613-66355-7(1)) Tandem Library Bks.

—The Facts about Flirting. 2003. (Two of a Kind Ser.: Vol. 27). (Illus.). 112p. mass mkt. 4.99 (978-0-06-009323-5(4) , Harper Entertainment) HarperCollins Pubs.

Katz, Karen. Daddy Hugs. Katz, Karen, illus. 2007. (Classic Board Bks.). 32p. (J). 7.99 (978-1-4169-4120-0(7) , Little Simon) Simon & Schuster Children's Publishing.

—Mommy Hugs. Katz, Karen, illus. 2006. (Illus.). 32p. (J). (ps-k). 12.99 (978-0-689-87772-8(2) , McElderry, Margaret K.) Simon & Schuster Children's Publishing.

Kaye, Amy. Unscripted. 2004. (Real Deal Ser.). (YA). mass mkt. 5.99 (978-0-8439-5315-2(2)) Dorchester Publishing Co., Inc.

Keene, Carolyn. Space Case. Jones, Jan Naimo, illus. 2004. 68p. (J). (ps-ps). lib. bdg. 12.00 (978-1-4176-3564-1(9)) Tandem Library Bks.

Keeshan, Robert. She Loves Me... She Loves Me Not... Sendak, Maurice, illus. 2003. (Sendak Reissues Ser.). 32p. 12.95 (978-0-06-028791-7(8)) HarperCollins Pubs.

Kehret, Peg. Wally Amos Presents Chip & Cookie - The First Adventure: No More Chocolate Chips. 2002. (Illus.). 40p. (J). (ps-3). 14.95 (978-1-58497-018-7(9)) Addax Publishing Group, Inc.

Kelman, Marcy. How We Became the Little Einstein. Song, Aram, illus. 2007. 16p. (J). (ps-k). pap. 5.99 (***978-1-4231-0212-0(6)***) Disney Pr.

Kemp, Kristen. How to Create the Boy of Your Dreams. 2002. (Genny in a Bottle Ser.: Vol. 4). (Illus.). 128p. (J). (gr. 4-6). pap. 4.50 (978-0-439-21181-9(6)) Scholastic, Inc.

Kennedy, Patricia Moran. The Loving Tree A Story of Love, Loss, & Transformation for All Ages. 2004. (Illus.). 64p. (YA). (gr. 5 up). per. 14.95 (978-0-9749848-0-3(9)) Dancer's Publishing.

Kennedy, Richard. Crazy in Love. Date not set. 48p. (J). (ps-3). 14.99 (978-0-06-027213-5(9)); lib. bdg. 15.89 (978-0-06-027214-2(7)) HarperCollins Pubs. (Geringer, Laura Book).

Kephart, Beth. Undercover. 2007. 288p. (gr. 7 up). (J). 16.99 (***978-0-06-123893-2(7)***); (YA). lib. bdg. 17.89 (***978-0-06-123894-9(5)***) HarperCollins Pubs. (HarperTeen).

Kern, Noris. I Love You with All My Heart. 2002. (Illus.). 26p. (J). bds. 6.95 (978-0-8118-3622-7(3)) Chronicle Bks. LLC.

Kern, Noris & Baronian, Jean-Baptiste. I Love You with All My Heart. 1998. (Illus.). 32p. (J). (ps-1). 15.95 (978-0-8118-2031-8(9)) Chronicle Bks. LLC.

Khan, Rukhsana. Dahling, If You Luv Me, Would You Please, Please Smile. l.t. ed. 1999. 196p. (YA). (gr. 7-9). pap. 8.95 (978-0-7737-6016-5(4)) Stoddart Kids CAN. *Dist:* Fitzhenry & Whiteside, Ltd.

Kidd, Richard. Lobsters in Love: A Whirlpool Romance. Kidd, Lindsey, illus. 2004. 32p. (J). pap. 7.95 (978-1-84507-154-7(9)) Lincoln, Frances Ltd. GBR. *Dist:* Perseus Distribution.

Kimmelman, Leslie. How Do I Love You? McCue, Lisa, illus. 2005. 32p. (J). 14.99 (978-0-06-001200-7(5)); lib. bdg. 16.89 (978-0-06-001201-4(3)) HarperCollins Pubs.

Kinski, Klaus. Yo Necesito Amor. (SPA.). 416p. (978-84-7223-916-6(0) , 6130) Tusquets Editores.

Kirwan, Anna. Of Flowers & Shadows. 2005. (Portraits Ser.: No. 2). 160p. (J). (gr. 4-7). pap. 9.99 (978-0-439-71010-7(3) , Scholastic Paperbacks) Scholastic, Inc.

Klause, Annette Curtis. Blood & Chocolate. 1999. (gr. 7-12). lib. bdg. 13.55 (978-0-613-22836-7(7)) Tandem Library Bks.

Kline, Suzy. Horrible Harry's Secret. Remkiewicz, Frank, illus. 1998. (Horrible Harry Ser.: No. 4). 64p. (J). (gr. 2-4). pap. 3.99 (978-0-14-130093-1(0) , Puffin) Penguin Group (USA) Inc.

Kollar, J. P. Three Tomato Brand. 2005. 127p. per. 12.95 (978-1-59879-076-4(5)) Lifevest Publishing, Inc.

Koops, Sheena. Voice of the Valley. 2006. 208p. (J). pap. 8.95 (978-1-55143-514-5(4)) Orca Bk. Pubs. USA.

Krulik, Nancy E. Love & SK8. 2004. 320p. (YA). pap. 5.99 (978-0-689-87076-7(0) , Simon Pulse) Simon & Schuster Children's Publishing.

—Ripped at the Seams. 2004. (Romantic Comedies Ser.). 336p. (YA). mass mkt. 6.99 (978-0-689-86771-2(9) , Simon Pulse) Simon & Schuster Children's Publishing.

Lambert, Janet. High Hurdles: A Dria Meredith Book. 2002. (J). per. 9.95 (978-1-930009-55-4(0)) Image Cascade Publishing.

—Whoa, Matilda. 2001. (Candy Kane Ser.: Vol. 2). (YA). pap. 12.95 (978-1-930009-46-2(1)) Image Cascade Publishing.

Lane, Dakota. Orpheus Obsession. 2005. (Illus.). 288p. (J). 16.99 (978-0-06-074173-0(2) , Tegen, Katherine Bks); lib. bdg. 17.89 (978-0-06-074174-7(0) , HarperTeen) HarperCollins Pubs.

Lane, Ronald. Avina's Song: A Children's Story. 2007. (ENG.). 48p. per. 12.95 (***978-1-4241-6252-9(1)***) PublishAmerica, Inc.

Lantz, Francess L. Heart Breakers. 2004. (gr. 5-8). lib. bdg. 13.00 (978-0-613-71465-5(2)) Tandem Library Bks.

—Someone to Love. 1998. (gr. 8-12). pap. 3.99 (978-0-380-77590-3(5)) HarperCollins Pubs.

—Someone to Love. 1998. (978-0-606-13787-4(4)) Tandem Library Bks.

Laurens, Jennifer. Falling for Romeo. 2007. (YA). per. 12.95 (***978-1-933963-94-5(8)***) Grove Creek Publishing, LLC.

Laurens, Jennifer. Magic Hands. 2007. (YA). per. 12.95 (978-1-933963-97-6(2)) Grove Creek Publishing, LLC.

Lawler, Janet. If Kisses Were Colors. Jay, Alison, illus. 2003. 32p. (J). (ps). 15.99 (978-0-8037-2617-8(1) , Dial) Penguin Group (USA) Inc.

Le Ny, Jeanine. Island Summer. 2007. (I Heart Bikinis Ser.: No. 2). 192p. (J). pap. 5.99 (***978-0-439-91851-0(0)*** , Scholastic Paperbacks) Scholastic, Inc.

Leavitt, Martine. Keturah & Lord Death. 2006. 216p. (YA). (gr. 7 up). 16.95 (978-1-932425-29-1(2) , Front Street) Boyds Mills Pr.

Lee, Chinlun. Good Dog, Paw! Lee, Chinlun, illus. 2004. (Illus.). 40p. (J). (ps-1). 15.99 (978-0-7636-2178-0(1)) Candlewick Pr.

Lefall, Kathy. Stargaze. 2003. 346p. (YA). pap. 18.95 (978-0-595-26878-8(1)) iUniverse, Inc.

L'Engle, Madeleine. The Joys of Love. 2008. 272p. (YA). 16.95 (***978-0-374-33870-1(1)***) Farrar, Straus & Giroux.

LeRoye, Dee. Crossfire. 2003. 137p. (YA). per. 5.99 (978-0-9727056-0-8(0)) Dakota Rose.

Les Becquets, Diane. Love, Cajun Style. 2005. 400p. (J). 16.95 (978-1-58234-674-8(7) , Bloomsbury Children) Bloomsbury Publishing.

Lester, Julius. Cupid: A Tale of Love & Desire. 2007. 208p. (YA). (gr. 7 up). 17.00 (978-0-15-202056-9(X) , Silver Whistle) Harcourt Trade Pubs.

—This Strange New Feeling: Three Love Stories from Black History. 2006. 208p. (YA). 16.99 (978-0-8037-3172-1(8) , Dial) Penguin Group (USA) Inc.

Letts, Billie. The Honk & Holler Opening Soon. 1999. (gr. 7-12). lib. bdg. 23.40 (978-0-613-17283-7(3)) Tandem Library Bks.

Leung, Helen. Toni. 2006. 251p. pap. 21.95 (978-1-4137-8990-4(0)) PublishAmerica, Inc.

Levithan, David. How They Met, & Other Stories. 2008. (YA). (***978-0-375-84886-5(X)***); lib. bdg. (***978-0-375-94886-2(4)***) Knopf, Alfred A. Inc.

Levithan, David. Marly's Ghost. Selznick, Brian, illus. 176p. 2007. (YA). (gr. 7). 6.99 (***978-0-14-240912-1(X)*** , Puffin); 2005. (J). 14.99 (978-0-8037-3063-2(2) , Dial) Penguin Group (USA) Inc.

Levy, Marc. If Only It Were True. 2000. 224p. mass mkt. 6.99 (978-0-7434-1717-4(8) , Pocket) Simon & Schuster.

Lewis, Anthony, illus. So Much to Love. 1999. (Leap Frog Lift-a-Flap Ser.). (J). (978-0-7853-3368-5(1)) Publications International, Ltd.

Light, Pamela D. New Life. 2002. (gr. 7-12). lib. bdg. 24.00 (978-0-613-78041-4(8)) Tandem Library Bks.

Limb, Sue. Girl, Going on 17: Pants on Fire. (Girl, 15 Ser.). (gr. 5 up). 2007. 256p. (YA). pap. 8.99 (***978-0-385-73219-2(8)***); 2006. 240p. (J). 14.95 (978-0-385-73218-5(X)); 2006. 240p. (YA). lib. bdg. 17.99 (978-0-385-90246-5(8)) Random Hse. Children's Bks. (Delacorte Bks. for Young Readers).

Linamen, Karen Scalf. Princess Madison & the Paisley Puppy. 2007. (Princess Madison Trilogy Ser.). (Illus.). 32p. (J). 12.99 (978-0-8007-1841-1(0)) Revell.

—Princess Madison & the Whispering Woods. 2006. (Princess Madison Trilogy Ser.). (Illus.). 32p. 12.99 (978-0-8007-1842-8(9)) Revell.

Little Golden Books Staff. Cinderella. 1999. (J). (ps-2). bds. 2.99 (978-0-307-01035-3(X) , Golden Bks.) Random Hse. Children's Bks.

Livingston, Sara J. Picture on the Wall: The Ultimate Love Story. 2007. 248p. (YA). per. 12.99 (***978-1-59886-476-2(9)***) Tate Publishing & Enterprises, L.L.C.

Lloyd-Jones, Sally. My Happy Heart. 2004. (Sweet Hearts Ser.). (Illus.). 12p. (J). bds. 8.99 (978-1-4143-0063-4(8)) Tyndale Hse. Pubs.

Lo, Jim. Showing Love to Other. Lo, Jim, illus. 2000. (Illus.). 30p. (J). (gr. 1-3). pap. 6.99 (978-0-89827-208-6(4)) Wesleyan Publishing Hse.

Lodge, Yvette. Love You Lots! A Heart-Shaped Pop-up Book. 2009. (Care Bears Ser.). (Illus.). 10p. (J). pap. 13.95 (***978-1-57791-302-3(7)***) Brighter Minds Children's Publishing.

Lorbiecki, Marybeth. Paul Bunyan's Sweetheart. Graef, Renee, illus. rev. ed. 2007. 32p. (J). (gr. 1-4). 16.95 (***978-1-58536-289-9(1)***) Sleeping Bear Pr.

The Lost Valentine's. 2005. (J). (978-1-58453-293-4(9)) Pioneer Valley Educational Pr., Inc.

Love & Sex: Ten Stories of Truth. 2003. 225p. (YA). (gr. 8-12). per. 16.45 (978-0-613-60696-7(5)) Tandem Library Bks.

Love in Bloom. 64p. (YA). (gr. 6-12). pap. (978-0-8224-2380-5(4)) Globe Fearon Educational Publishing.

Love Library: Guess How Much I Love You, Hug, Love & Kisses, 3 vols. Incl. Guess How Much I Love You. 10th anniv. ed. McBratney, Sam. Jeram, Anita, illus. 20p. 1996. reprint ed. bds. 6.99 (978-0-7636-0013-6(X)); Hug. Alborough, Jez. Alborough, Jez, illus. 32p. 2001. bds. 6.99 (978-0-7636-1576-5(5)); Love & Kisses. Wilson, Sarah & Wilson, Sarah. Sweet, Melissa & Sweet, Melissa, illus. 22p. 2001. bds. 6.99 (978-0-7636-1049-4(6)); (J). (gr. k-ps). 96p. 2002. 15.99 (978-0-7636-1670-0(2)) Candlewick Pr.

Lurie, April. Brothers, Boyfriends & Other Criminal Minds. 2007. 304p. (YA). (gr. 7). lib. bdg. 18.99 (978-0-385-90152-9(6) , Delacorte Bks. for Young Readers) Random Hse. Children's Bks.

Lynn, Tracy. Snow: A Retelling of Snow White & the Seven Dwarfs. 2006. (Once upon a Time Ser.). 272p. (YA). pap. 5.99 (978-1-4169-4015-9(4) , Simon Pulse) Simon & Schuster Children's Publishing.

Ma, Jyoti. Sparkling Together: Starbright & His Earthling Friends. Devi, Chandra, illus. 2004. 96p. pap. 19.95 (978-0-932040-54-1(3)) Integral Yoga Pubns.

Mac, Carrie. Crush. 2006. 112p. (gr. 3-6). lib. bdg. 14.95 (978-1-55143-521-3(7)); (gr. 7-12). pap. 7.95 (978-1-55143-526-8(8)) Orca Bk. Pubs. USA.

MacBride, Roger Lea. Bachelor Girl. Gilleece, David, illus. 1999. (Little House). 256p. (J). (gr. 3-6). 15.89 (978-0-06-028434-3(X)) HarperCollins Pubs.

—Bachelor Girl. Andreasen, Dan, illus. 1999. (Little House Ser.). 256p. (J). (gr. 3-6). 15.95 (978-0-06-027755-0(6)); (gr. 5 up). pap. 6.99 (978-0-06-440691-8(1) , Harper Trophy) HarperCollins Pubs.

—Bachelor Girl. 1999. (gr. 3-6). lib. bdg. 14.15 (978-0-613-21154-3(5)); (Illus.). (J). 12.64 (978-0-606-18676-6(X)) Tandem Library Bks.

MacKall, Dandi Daley. Crazy in Love. 2007. 192p. (J). (gr. 8 up). 16.99 (978-0-525-47780-8(2) , Dutton Juvenile) Penguin Group (USA) Inc.

Mackall, Dandi Daley. Crazy in Love. 2008. 240p. (YA). (gr. 7). pap. 6.99 (***978-0-14-241157-5(4)*** , Puffin) Penguin Group (USA) Inc.

MacKenzie, Catherine. The Lonely Grey Dog at No. 6: Tammy & Jake Learn about Love & Loyalty. 2005. (Illus.). 157p. (J). mass mkt. (978-1-84550-103-7(9) , Christian Focus) Christian Focus Pubns.

MacLachlan, Patricia. Who Loves Me? Shepherd, Amanda, illus. 2005. 40p. (J). (ps-3). lib. bdg. 15.89 (978-0-06-027977-6(X)); 14.99 (978-0-06-027976-9(1)) HarperCollins Pubs. (Cotler, Joanna Books).

Magsamen, Sandra. Messages from the Heart: Baby Love-:Huggable, Lovable, Snuggable Books. 2nd ed. 2006. (Message from the Heart Ser.). (Illus.). 10p. (J). (ps-17). 10.99 (978-0-316-16633-1(2)) Little Brown & Co.

Maguire, Gregory. Four Stupid Cupids. Clayton, Elaine, illus. 2001. 192p. (J). (gr. 4-6). tchr. ed. 16.00 (978-0-395-83895-2(9) , Clarion Bks.) Houghton Mifflin Co. Trade & Reference Div.

—Four Stupid Cupids. 2002. (gr. 3-6). lib. bdg. 12.95 (978-0-613-43035-7(2)) Tandem Library Bks.

—Four Stupid Cupids. l.t. ed. 2001. 225p. (J). 21.95 (978-0-7862-3547-6(0)) Thorndike Pr.

Mahy, Margaret. The Catalogue of the Universe. Hopes, illus. 2002. 192p. (YA). pap. 7.99 (978-0-689-85353-1(X) , Simon Pulse) Simon & Schuster Children's Publishing.

—The Catalogue of the Universe. 2002. (gr. 7-12). lib. bdg. 16.45 (978-0-613-57621-5(7)) Tandem Library Bks.

Malcolm, Jahnna N. Message in a Bottle. 2005. (Love Letters Ser.). 176p. (YA). pap. 5.99 (978-0-689-87224-2(0) , Simon Pulse) Simon & Schuster Children's Publishing.

—Mixed Messages. 2004. (Love Letters Ser.). 208p. (YA). pap. 5.99 (978-0-689-87222-8(4) , Simon Pulse) Simon & Schuster Children's Publishing.

—Perfect Strangers. (Love Letters Ser.). 224p. (YA). 2005. mass mkt. 3.99 (978-1-4169-1143-2(X)); 2004. mass mkt. 5.99 (978-0-689-87221-1(6)) Simon & Schuster Children's Publishing. (Simon Pulse).

—The Write Stuff. 2005. (Love Letters Ser.). 192p. (YA). mass mkt. 5.99 (978-0-689-87223-5(2)); 175p. (978-1-4155-7728-8(5)) Simon & Schuster Children's Publishing. (Simon Pulse).

Malkin, Nina. 6x: The Uncensored Confessions. 2005. (6x Ser.). 224p. (YA). (gr. 7-12). 8.99 (978-0-439-72421-0(X) , Scholastic Paperbacks) Scholastic, Inc.

Mancusi, Mari. Sk8er Boy. 2005. (YA). (gr. 8-12). mass mkt. 5.99 (978-0-8439-5604-7(6) , SMOOCH) Dorchester Publishing Co., Inc.

Manners, Tyler. Continental Change of Heart. 2006. 65p. pap. 12.95 (978-1-4137-9483-0(1)) PublishAmerica, Inc.

Manning, Sarra. French Kiss. 2006. 224p. (YA). (gr. 9). pap. 6.99 (978-0-14-240632-8(5) , Puffin) Penguin Group (USA) Inc.

—Guitar Girl. 2005. 240p. (YA). (gr. 9-12). reprint ed. pap. 6.99 (978-0-14-240318-1(0) , Puffin) Penguin Group (USA) Inc.

Marineau, Michele. Lean Mean Machines. Ouriou, Susan, tr. from FRE. 2004. (Northern Lights Books for Children Ser.). (Illus.). 128p. (YA). (gr. 4-9). pap. 7.95 (978-0-88995-230-0(2)) Red Deer Pr. CAN. *Dist:* Fitzhenry & Whiteside, Ltd.

—Lean Mean Machines. 2001. (gr. 7-12). lib. bdg. 16.40 (978-0-613-82356-2(7)) Tandem Library Bks.

Marshall, Catherine. Midnight Rescue/the Proposal/Christy's Choice. 2005. (Christy Juvenile Ser.). 384p. (J). pap. 9.99 (978-1-4003-0773-9(2)) Nelson, Thomas Inc.

—The Princess Club/Family Secrets/Mountain Madness. 2005. (Christy Juvenile Ser.). 368p. (J). pap. 9.99 (978-1-4003-0774-6(0)) Nelson, Thomas Inc.

Marsoli, Lisa Ann & Random House Disney Staff. Getting to Know You. 2004. (Random House Pictureback Book Ser.). (Illus.). 24p. (J). (ps-2). pap. 3.99 (978-0-7364-2258-1(7) , RH/Disney) Random Hse. Children's Bks.

Martin, LaJoyce. The Silver Ghost. 2004. (Illus.). 161p. (J). pap. 9.99 (978-1-56722-643-0(4)) Word Aflame Pr.

Mason, Jane. Flintstones in Viva Rock Vegas: Flintstones Movie Storybook. 2000. (Illus.). 32p. (J). (ps-3). pap. 5.99 (978-0-439-17304-9(3)) Scholastic, Inc.

Masters, William. Love & Sex. Cart, Michael, ed. 2003. 240p. (YA). pap. 13.95 (978-0-689-85668-6(7) , Simon Pulse) Simon & Schuster Children's Publishing.

Mauceri, Carman. Games of Love. 2001. 108p. pap. 14.95 (978-1-59286-500-0(3)) PublishAmerica, Inc.

Maxwell, Katie. Life, Love, & the Pursuit of Hotties. 2005. 196p. (YA). (gr. 8-12). mass mkt. 5.99 (978-0-8439-5549-1(X)) Dorchester Publishing Co., Inc.

Mazer, Norma Fox. Girlhearts. (J). (gr. 5 up). 2002. 320p. pap. 6.99 (978-0-380-72290-7(9)); 2001. 224p. lib. bdg. 16.89 (978-0-688-06866-0(9)) HarperCollins Pubs.

—Girlhearts. l.t. ed. 2003. 230p. 22.95 (978-0-7862-4843-8(2)) Thomson Gale.

McBratney, Sam. Guess How Much I Love You. 2002. (Illus.). (J). 23.40 (978-0-7587-2668-1(6)) Book Wholesalers, Inc.
—Guess How Much I Love You. Jeram, Anita, illus. 2005. 34p. (J). bds. 19.95 (978-0-9769313-1-7(1)) BrailleInk.
—Guess How Much I Love You. Jeram, Anita, illus. 10th anniv. ed. 32p. (J). 2004. 20.00 (978-0-7636-2435-4(7)); 2003. 12.00 (978-0-7636-2240-4(0)) Candlewick Pr.
—Guess How Much I Love You. Jeram, Anita, illus. 1999. 24p. (J). (ps). bds. 6.99 (978-0-8499-5971-4(3)) Nelson, Thomas Inc.
—Guess How Much I Love You & Story Time DVD. Jeram, Anita, illus. 2006. 32p. (J). (ps-3). 15.99 incl. DVD (978-0-7636-3503-9(0)) Candlewick Pr.
McBride, Martha J. And You Love Me. 2003. 346p. (YA). per. 5.99 (978-1-59196-391-2(5)) Instantpublisher.com.
McCafferty, Catherine. A Moment to Remember. Random House Disney Staff, illus. 2005. 24p. (J). (ps-2). pap. 3.99 (978-0-7364-2289-5(7) , RH/Disney) Random Hse. Children's Bks.
McCaughrean, Geraldine. Cyrano. 2006. (Illus.). 128p. (J). (gr. 7 up). 16.00 (978-0-15-205805-0(2)) Harcourt Children's Bks.
McCaughrean, Geraldine & Ray, Jane. Cuentos de Amor y Amistad. 2003. (FRE., Illus.). 110p. 24.95 (978-84-95939-09-8(6)) Blume ESP. *Dist:* Independent Pubs. Group.
McClymer, Kelly. Getting to Third Date. 2006. (Romantic Comedies Ser.). (Illus.). 304p. (YA). (gr. 9 up). pap. 5.99 (978-1-4169-1479-2(X) , Simon Pulse) Simon & Schuster Children's Publishing.
McCourt, Lisa. Love You Until... Haines, William, illus. 1999. 32p. (ps-3). 16.95 (978-0-8091-6658-9(5) , 6658-5) Paulist Pr.
McDaniel, Lurlene. As Long as We Both Shall Live: Two Novels. 2003. 416p. (YA). (gr. 7). mass mkt. 7.50 (978-0-553-57108-0(7) , Laurel Leaf) Random Hse. Children's Bks.
—How Do I Love Thee: Three Stories. 272p. (YA). (gr. 7). 2002. pap. 5.50 (978-0-553-57107-3(9) , Laurel Leaf); 2001. 9.95 (978-0-553-57154-7(0) , Starfire) Random Hse. Children's Bks.
—How Do I Love Thee: Three Stories. 2002. (gr. 5-8). lib. bdg. 13.55 (978-0-613-57906-3(2)) Tandem Library Bks.
—Kathleen's Story. 2006. (Angels in Pink Ser.). 256p. (YA). mass mkt. 6.50 (978-0-440-23865-2(X) , Laurel Leaf) Random Hse. Children's Bks.
—My Secret Boyfriend. 2005. (Illus.). 128p. (gr. 6-12). pap. 4.99 (978-1-58196-008-2(5)) Lerner Publishing Group.
—Until Angels Close My Eyes. 1998. (Angels Trilogy: No. 3). 256p. (YA). (gr. 7-12). pap. 5.50 (978-0-553-57115-8(X) , Laurel Leaf) Random Hse. Children's Bks.
—Until Angels Close My Eyes. 1998. (Angels Trilogy: No. 3). (978-0-606-13884-0(6)) Tandem Library Bks.
McDonald, Brenda. How Do You Love A Big Dog? 2007. 18.00 (*978-0-8059-7314-3(1)) Dorrance Publishing Co., Inc.
McGhee, Alison. All Rivers Flow to the Sea. 176p. (YA). (gr. 9 up). 2007. (Illus.). pap. 7.99 (*978-0-7636-3372-1(0)); 2005. 15.99 (978-0-7636-2591-7(4)) Candlewick Pr.
McGrath, Liz & Quick, Barbara. Even More/Todavía Mas. de la Vega, Eida, tr. McGrath, Liz, illus. 2004. Tr. of Todavía Mas. (SPA & ENG., Illus.). 34p. (J). (gr. k-3). 16.95 (978-0-9720192-8-6(6) , 626999) Raven Tree Pr.
McKnight, Gillian. The Frog Prince. 2006. 240p. (J). mass mkt. 5.99 (978-0-689-87735-3(8) , Simon Pulse) Simon & Schuster Children's Publishing.
—To Catch a Prince. 2006. 240p. (YA). mass mkt. 5.99 (978-0-689-87734-6(X) , Simon Pulse) Simon & Schuster Children's Publishing.
McMahon, Kara. Elmo's World: Love! Nelson, Mary Beth, illus. 2004. (Elmo's World Ser.). 12p. (J). (gr. k-ps). bds. 4.99 (978-0-375-82843-0(5) , Random Hse. Bks. for Young Readers) Random Hse. Children's Bks.
Meadows, Barbara. Road to Tomorrow. 2001. (gr. 7-12). lib. bdg. 31.55 (978-0-613-77561-8(9)) Tandem Library Bks.
Michot, Fabienne. Maki, I Love to Kiss You. braille ed. 2004. (J). (gr. 1). spiral bd., bds. (978-0-616-07268-4(6)) Canadian National Institute for the Blind/Institut National Canadien pour les Aveugles.
Michot, Fabienne, et al. I Love to Kiss You. Michot, Fabienne & Brasset, Doris, illus. 2000. (Maki Ser.). 14p. (J). (ps up). bds. (978-1-894363-24-2(8)) Dominique & Friends.
Milord, Susan. Love That Baby! 2005. (Illus.). 16p. (J). (gr. k-ps). pap. 7.95 (978-0-618-56323-4(7)) Houghton Mifflin Co. Trade & Reference Div.
Minne. I Love... Fortier, Nathalie, illus. 2005. 128p. (J). pap. 11.95 (978-1-929132-75-1(1)) Kane/Miller Bk. Pubs., Inc.
Minters, Frances. Sleepless Beauty. 1999. (978-0-606-17431-2(1)) Tandem Library Bks.
Miyasaka, Kaho. Kare First Love. (Kare First Love Ser.). Vol. 6. 2005. (Illus.). 200p. pap. 9.99 (978-1-4215-0139-0(2)); Vol. 7. 2006. 208p. (YA). pap. 9.99 (978-1-4215-0325-7(5)); Vol. 8. 2006. 208p. (YA). pap. 9.99 (978-1-4215-0546-6(0)); Vol. 9. 2006. 208p. (YA). pap. 9.99 (978-1-4215-0547-3(9)) Viz Media.
Moeyaert, Bart. It's Love We Don't Understand. Boeke, Wanda, tr. from DUT. 1998. 142p. (YA). (gr. 7 up). 15.95 (978-1-886910-71-3(5) , Lemniscaat) Boyds Mills Pr.
Montgomery, L. M. The Blue Castle. Date not set. (J). 22.95 (978-0-8488-2370-2(2)) Amereon LTD.
Moore, A. C. Always Room for Dessert. 2nd ed. 2004. 304p. (YA). per. 13.95 (978-0-9744060-0-8(7)) Moore, Ammanuel.
Moore, Alan. Alan Moore's Another Suburban Romance. 2003. (Illus.). 64p. (gr. 12 up). pap. 7.95 (978-1-59291-007-6(6)) Avatar Pr., Inc.
—Another Suburban Romance. 2003. (Illus.). 64p. 17.95 (978-1-59291-008-3(4)) Avatar Pr., Inc.
Morgenstern, Susie. Mon Amour. 2002. (GER.). 124p. pap. 15.00 (978-1-4000-3959-3(2) , New Media German Language) Random House Foreign Language Publishing.
Morris, Karen. Perils from the Seven Seas, Vol. 2. 2005. 127p. pap. 17.95 (978-1-4137-4663-1(2)) PublishAmerica, Inc.
Morrow, Tara Jaye. Mommy Loves Her Baby/Daddy Loves His Baby. Beeke, Tiphanie, illus. 2003. 32p. (J). (ps-1). 15.99 (978-0-06-029077-1(3)); lib. bdg. 16.89 (978-0-06-029078-8(1)) HarperCollins Pubs.
Mosher, Richard. Zazoo. (YA). (gr. 7 up). 2001. 256p. tchr. ed. 16.00 (978-0-618-13534-9(0) , Clarion Bks.); 2004. 272p. reprint ed. pap. 6.99 (978-0-618-43904-1(8) , Graphia) Houghton Mifflin Co. Trade & Reference Div.
Moulton, Mark Kimball. Caleb's Lighthouse. Sherwood, Stewart, illus. 2000. 48p. (J). (gr. k-3). 22.00 (978-0-7412-0736-4(2)) Lang Graphics, Ltd.
Mouse Works Staff. Beauty & the Beast & The Aristocats, 2 vols. 75th anniv. ed. 1998. (Illus.). (ps-3). (978-0-7364-0092-3(3)) Mouse Works.
—La Bella y la Bestia: Read Aloud Storybook Classic. 1999. (SPA., Illus.). 64p. (J). 6.99 (978-0-7364-0141-8(5)) Disney Pr.
—Sleeping Beauty/The Little Mermaid, 2 vols. 75th anniv. ed. 1998. (Illus.). (ps-3). 9.99 (978-0-7364-0091-6(5)) Mouse Works.
Ms. G. Mommy, Why Can't I Be Rich? Dade, Raheem, illus. 2005. 20p. (J). 7.00 (978-0-9724621-1-2(2)) ShaGru Entertainment, LLC.
Muller, Max. Memories A Story of German Love. 2006. 77.99 (*978-1-4280-2598-1(7)) IndyPublish.com.
Munsch, Robert. Love You Forever. McGraw, Sheila, illus. gif. ed. 2000. 32p. (J). (ps-1). 19.95 (978-1-55209-109-8(0)) Firefly Bks., Ltd.
—Siempre Te Querre. ed. 2004. (SPA., Illus.). (J). (gr. k-3). spiral bd. (978-0-616-14608-8(6)) Canadian National Institute for the Blind/Institut National Canadien pour les Aveugles.
Murakami, Maki. Gravitation, 12 vols., Vol. 2. rev. ed. 2003. (Illus.). 192p. pap. 9.99 (978-1-59182-334-6(X) , Tokyopop Adult) TOKYOPOP, Inc.
—Gravitation, 12 vols. Murakami, Maki, illus. rev. ed. (Illus.). (gr. 8 up). Vol. 3. 2003. 192p. pap. 9.99 (978-1-59182-335-3(8)); Vol. 4. 2004. 208p. pap. 9.99 (978-1-59182-336-0(6)); Vol. 5. 2004. 208p. pap. 9.99 (978-1-59182-337-7(4)) TOKYOPOP, Inc. (Tokyopop Adult).
—Gravitation, 12 vols. Yoshimoto, Ray, tr. from JPN. rev. ed. 2004. (Illus.). 208p. Vol. 6. pap. 9.99 (978-1-59182-338-4(2)); Vol. 7. pap. 9.99 (978-1-59182-339-1(0)) TOKYOPOP, Inc. (Tokyopop Adult).
—Gravitation: Volume 1, 12 vols. 2003. (Gravitation Ser.). (Illus.). 192p. pap. 9.99 (978-1-59182-333-9(1) , Tokyopop Adult) TOKYOPOP, Inc.
Murakami, Maki, creator. Gravitation. rev. ed. 2004. (Illus.). Vol. 8. 224p. pap. 9.99 (978-1-59182-340-7(4)); Vol. 9. 192p. pap. 9.99 (978-1-59182-341-4(2)) TOKYOPOP, Inc. (Tokyopop Adult).
My Antonia. 1999. (YA). 11.95 (978-1-56137-759-6(7)) Novel Units, Inc.
Myers, Jason. Exit Here. 2007. 464p. (YA). (gr. 11 up). pap. 7.99 (978-1-4169-1748-9(9) , Simon Pulse) Simon & Schuster Children's Publishing.
Myers, Walter Dean. Street Love. (J). 2007. 160p. pap. 7.99 (*978-0-06-440732-8(2)); 2006. 144p. 15.99 (978-0-06-028079-6(4)); 2006. 144p. (gr. 8 up). lib. bdg. 16.89 (978-0-06-028080-2(8)) HarperCollins Pubs. (Amistad).
—What They Found: Love on 145th Street. 2007. 256p. (YA). (gr. 9 up). 15.99 (*978-0-385-32138-9(4)); lib. bdg. 18.99 (*978-0-375-93709-5(9)) Random Hse. Children's Bks. (Lamb, Wendy).
Na, An. Wait for Me. 2006. 240p. (YA). (gr. 4). 15.99 (978-0-399-24275-5(9) , Putnam Juvenile) Penguin Group (USA) Inc.
Nanette. Tootie the Green Kitten. 2004. (Life on Granny's Farm Ser.). (J). 12.95 (978-0-9741269-7-5(7)) St. Bernard Publishing, LLC.
Napoli, Donna Jo. For the Love of Venice. 2000. (Illus.). (J). (978-0-606-17998-0(4)) Tandem Library Bks.
Nathan, Sarah. A Dream Come True. 2007. 32p. (gr. 1). pap. 3.99 (*978-1-4231-0909-9(0)) Disney Pr.
—Enchanted Storybook. rev. ed. 2007. 48p. (J). (gr. 2-7). 8.99 (*978-1-4231-0911-2(2)) Disney Pr.
—True Love's Kiss. rev. ed. 2007. 32p. (gr. 1). pap. 3.99 (*978-1-4231-0910-5(4)) Disney Pr.
Naylor, Phyllis Reynolds. Achingly Alice. 2003. (Alice Ser.). (Illus.). 160p. (YA). mass mkt. 5.99 (978-0-689-86396-7(9) , Simon Pulse) Simon & Schuster Children's Publishing.
Naylor, Phyllis Reynolds & Naylor, Magdelena R. Achingly Alice. 1999. (Alice Ser.). (YA). (gr. 5-9). 11.64 (978-0-606-16332-3(8)) Tandem Library Bks.
Neenan, Colin. Idiot! 2005. (Illus.). 160p. (YA). pap. 8.95 (978-0-9746481-1-8(6)) Brown Barn Bks.
Neighbour, Leona. Fairly Ballerina Princess. 2003. 26p. per. 10.95 (978-1-932344-42-4(X)) Thornton Publishing.
Nelson, Suzanne Johnson. Heart & Salsa. 2006. (S. A. S. S. (Students Across the Seven Seas) Ser.). 224p. (YA). (gr. 7). pap. 6.99 (978-0-14-240647-2(3) , Puffin) Penguin Group (USA) Inc.
Nesbit, E. In Homespun. 2006. pap. (*978-1-4068-3502-1(1)) Echo Library.
—The Incomplete Amorist. 2006. 65.99 (*978-1-4280-2983-5(4)) IndyPublish.com.
Newman, Marjorie. Mole & the Baby Bird. Benson, Patrick, illus. 2002. 32p. (J). (gr. k-3). 16.95 (978-1-58234-784-4(0) , Bloomsbury Children) Bloomsbury Publishing.
Nikola-Lisa, W. La Alegria de Ser Tu y Yo. Canetti, Yanitzia, tr. from ENG. Bryant, Michael, illus. unabr. ed. 1999. (SPA.). (J). (gr. k-3). pap. 16.95 incl. audio (978-0-87499-549-7(3)) BBC Audiobooks America.
—La Alegria de Ser Tu y Yo. Bryant, Michael, illus. 1999. (SPA.). (J). pap. 18.95 incl. audio compact disk (978-1-59519-124-3(0)) Live Oak Media.
—La Alegria de Ser Tu y Yo. Canetti, Yanitzia, tr. from ENG. Bryant, Michael, illus. unabr. ed. 1999. (SPA.). (J). (gr. k-3). 25.95 incl. audio (978-0-87499-550-3(7)) Live Oak Media.
Nilsson, Per. Heart's Delight. Chace, Tara, tr. from SWE. 2005. 192p. (YA). reprint ed. pap. 6.99 (978-0-689-87677-6(7) , Simon Pulse) Simon & Schuster Children's Publishing.
—Heart's Desire. Chace, Tara, tr. from SWE. 2004. 160p. (YA). 16.95 (978-1-886910-92-8(8) , Lemniscaat) Boyds Mills Pr.
Noonan, Rosalind. Sarah: Don't Say You Love Me. 1998. (gr. 7-12). lib. bdg. 12.40 (978-0-613-73055-6(0)) Tandem Library Bks.
Norac, Carl. I Love You So Much. Dubois, Claude K., illus. (J). (gr. k-ps). 2003. 20p. bds. 5.99 (978-0-385-74627-4(X) , Doubleday Bks. for Young Readers); 2002. 32p. pap. 5.99 (978-0-440-41744-6(9) , Dragonfly Bks.) Random Hse. Children's Bks.
—Las Palabras Dulces. 2003. (SPA., Illus.). 32p. (J). (978-84-95150-05-9(0) , COR1690) Corimbo, Editorial S.L. ESP. *Dist:* Lectorum Pubns., Inc.
Nunes, Lygia Bojunga. El Sofa Estampado. (SPA.). 184p. (YA). (gr. 5-8). (978-84-239-2748-7(2) , EC2752) Espasa Calpe, S.A. ESP. *Dist:* Lectorum Pubns., Inc.
O'Connell, Tyne. True Love, the Sphinx, & Other Unsolvable Riddles: A Comedy in Four Voices. 2007. 256p. (YA). (gr. 7 up). 16.95 (*978-1-59990-050-6(5)) Bloomsbury Publishing.
Odgers, Sally. A Bird, a Bloke, & a Boyfriend. 2005. (YA). mass mkt. 5.99 (978-0-8439-5465-4(5)) Dorchester Publishing Co., Inc.
Oke, Janette. Love Comes Softly, 4 vols. rev. ed. 2003. (Love Comes Softly Ser.: Vols. 1-4). 960p. pap. 51.99 (978-0-7642-9095-4(9)) Bethany Hse. Pubs.
Olkowski, Mary. From the Garden of My Soul. Olkowski, Mary, illus. unabr. ed. 1998. (Illus.). 50p. 12.99 (978-0-9668781-0-3(8) , 1001) Limpid Butterfly Productions, The.
Olsen, Ashley. Love Factor. 2003. (gr. 5-8). lib. bdg. 13.00 (978-0-613-64744-1(0)) Tandem Library Bks.
Olsen, Mary-Kate. Cross Our Hearts. 2003. (gr. 5-8). lib. bdg. 13.00 (978-0-613-64703-8(3)) Tandem Library Bks.
—Sealed with a Kiss. 2001. (gr. 3-6). lib. bdg. 13.00 (978-0-613-43956-5(2)) Tandem Library Bks.
—Secret Crush. 2002. (gr. 5-8). lib. bdg. 13.00 (978-0-613-64768-7(8)) Tandem Library Bks.
Olsen, Mary-Kate & Olsen, Ashley. So Little Time No.13: Love Is in the Air. 2004. (gr. k-3). lib. bdg. 13.00 (978-0-613-71468-6(7)) Tandem Library Bks.
—Two of a Kind No. 33: Heart to Heart. 2004. (gr. 3-6). lib. bdg. 13.00 (978-0-613-71364-1(8)) Tandem Library Bks.
Ostow, Micol. Crush du Jour. 2007. (Romantic Comedies Ser.). 224p. (YA). mass mkt. 6.99 (*978-1-4169-5027-1(3) , Simon Pulse) Simon & Schuster Children's Publishing.
Overend, Jenni. Welcome with Love. Vivas, Julie, illus. 2000. 36p. (J). (ps-4). 15.95 (978-0-916291-96-9(0)) Kane/Miller Bk. Pubs., Inc.
Oxenbury, Helen. All Fall Down. Oxenbury, Helen, illus. 1999. (Oxenbury Board Bks.). (Illus.). 10p. (J). (ps-k). bds. 6.99 (978-0-689-81985-8(4) , Little Simon) Simon & Schuster Children's Publishing.
Page, Nick & Claire. Snow White. 2006. (Read with Me (Make Believe Ideas) Ser.). (Illus.). 32p. (J). (gr. k-2). 3.95 (978-1-84610-163-2(8)) Make Believe Ideas GBR. *Dist:* Ingram Pub. Services.
Pandell, Karen. Te Amo Sol, Te Amo Luna/I Love You Sun, I Love You Moon. de Paola, Tomie, illus. 2003. (SPA & ENG.). 18p. (J). (ps-1). bds. 6.99 (978-0-399-24165-9(5) , Putnam Juvenile) Penguin Group (USA) Inc.
Park, Eun Ah. Sweet & Sensitive, Vol. 1. 2004. 200p. pap. (978-1-4139-0074-3(7)) ADV Manga.
Parker, Jade. To Catch A Pirate. 2007. 320p. (J). pap. 6.99 (*978-0-439-02694-9(6)) Scholastic, Inc.
Parker, Jeff, et al. Marvel Romance Redux: Another Kind of Love. 2007. (Illus.). 168p. pap. 13.99 (978-0-7851-2090-2(4)) Marvel Enterprises, Inc.
Parry, Glyn. Scooter Boy. 1998. pap. 12.95 (978-0-7022-2990-9(3)) Univ. of Queensland Pr. AUS. *Dist:* International Specialized Bk. Services.
Pascal, Francine. Dangerous Love. 1999. mass mkt. (978-0-553-23938-6(4)) Random Hse., Inc.
—Double Love. 1999. mass mkt. (978-0-553-23969-0(4)) Random Hse., Inc.
—My First Love & Other Disasters. 2005. 240p. (YA). mass mkt. 3.99 (978-1-4169-1145-6(6) , Simon Pulse) Simon & Schuster Children's Publishing.
—My First Love & Other Disasters. 2003. (Victoria Martin Trilogy: No. 2). (gr. 7-12). lib. bdg. 13.00 (978-0-613-66463-9(9)) Tandem Library Bks.
—One 2 Many. 1999. (Sweet Valley Jr. High Ser.: No. 27). (gr. 3-6). lib. bdg. 12.40 (978-0-613-16173-2(4)) Tandem Library Bks.
—Racing Hearts. 1999. mass mkt. (978-0-553-24131-0(1)) Random Hse., Inc.
Paterson, Judy. Tamlane. Collins, Sally J., illus. 1999. 32p. (J). (gr. k-4). pap. (978-1-871512-62-5(X)) Glowworm Bks., Ltd.
Pearson, Mary E. Scribbler of Dreams. 2002. 240p. (YA). (gr. 7 up). pap. 5.95 (978-0-15-204569-2(4) , Harcourt Paperbacks) Harcourt Children's Bks.
—Scribbler of Dreams. (gr. 7-12). 2005. 223p. (YA). per. 12.60 (978-0-606-25453-3(6)); 2001. lib. bdg. 14.10 (978-0-613-69084-3(2)) Tandem Library Bks.
Pearson, Susan. Slugs in Love. O'Malley, Kevin, illus. 2006. 32p. (J). (ps-3). 16.99 (978-0-7614-5311-6(3)) Cavendish, Marshall Corp.
Pechero-Loewen, Mariella. I Want to Know How You Found Me. 2004. 39p. pap. 17.95 (978-1-4137-2955-9(X)) PublishAmerica, Inc.
Peck, Richard. Amanda/Miranda. 2001. (gr. 7-12). lib. bdg. 14.15 (978-0-613-36046-3(X)) Tandem Library Bks.
Peckham, Lori, ed. Guide's Greatest Animal Stories. 2006. 144p. (YA). pap. 10.99 (*978-0-8280-1944-6(4)) Review & Herald Publishing Assn.
Penguin Books Staff. The Flintstones in Viva Rock Vegas, Level 2. 2001. (Illus.). 32p. (C). pap. 9.00 (978-0-582-45190-2(6)) Longman Publishing Group.
Penn, Audrey. A Pocket Full of Kisses. Gibson, Barbara Leonard, illus. 2004. (New Child & Family Press Titles Ser.). 32p. (ps-1). 16.95 (978-0-87868-894-4(3) , 8943, Child & Family Pr.) Child Welfare League of America, Inc.
—A Pocket Full of Kisses. Gibson, Barbara, illus. 2006. 32p. 16.95 (978-1-933718-02-6(1)) Tanglewood Pr.
Pennypacker, Sara. Pierre in Love. Mathers, Petra, illus. 2007. 40p. (J). pap. 16.99 (978-0-439-51740-9(0) , Orchard Bks.) Scholastic, Inc.
Perry Moore, Stephanie. Surrendered Heart: Living for God Is Challenging. 2002. (Payton Skky Ser.: Vol. 5). 192p. (YA). pap. 6.99 (978-0-8024-4240-6(4)) Moody Pubs.
Petty, Kate. Holly. 2000. 155p. (J). pap. 7.50 (978-1-85881-800-9(1)) Orion Children's Bks. GBR. *Dist:* Independent Pubs. Group.
—Josie. 2000. 167p. (J). pap. 7.99 (978-1-85881-801-6(X)) Orion Children's Bks. GBR. *Dist:* Independent Pubs. Group.
Petty, Kate. Summer Heat. 2004. (Summer Ser.). 536p. (J). per. 13.95 (*978-1-84255-162-2(0)) Orion Publishing Group, Ltd. GBR. *Dist:* Independent Pubs. Group.
Phipps, Alisha. Growing up with Allie: The Dance. 2005. 58p. pap. 12.95 (978-1-4137-9713-8(X)) PublishAmerica, Inc.
Piper, Noel. Most of All Jesus Loves You. Anderson, Debby, illus. 2005. 24p. (J). 9.99 (978-1-58134-630-5(1) , Crossway Bibles) Crossway Bks.
Pisano, Maryann. The Decision. 2003. 66p. (YA). pap. 8.95 (978-0-595-29262-2(3)) iUniverse, Inc.
Plank, Alex & Plank, Lisa. How Bad Could It Be? 2007. (ENG.). 64p. per. 12.95 (*978-1-4241-6217-8(3)) PublishAmerica, Inc.
Plummer, Louise. Finding Daddy. 2007. 176p. (YA). (gr. 7). 15.99 (978-0-385-73092-1(6) , Delacorte Bks. for Young Readers) Random Hse. Children's Bks.
Podmore, Ron. A Sign to Remember. 2002. (YA). per. 9.95 (978-0-9723537-0-0(4)) Puget Sound Pubns.
Pope, Paul. Escapo: A Life Affirming Romance Set in a Fin-de-Siecle Circus. 1999. (Illus.). 112p. (YA). pap. 9.95 (978-1-882402-14-4(6)) NBM Publishing Co.
Porter-Gaylord, Laurel. I Love My Mommy Because... Wolff, Ashley, illus. 2004. 24p. (J). (ps). bds. 6.99 (978-0-525-47247-6(9) , Dutton Juvenile) Penguin Group (USA) Inc.
Powers, Christine. Love Is a Rainbow. 1999. (Leap Frog Lift-A-Flap Ser.). (Illus.). (J). (978-0-7853-3370-8(3)) Publications International, Ltd.
Preble, Laura. Queen Geeks in Love. 2007. 304p. (gr. 12 up). 9.99 (*978-0-425-21717-7(5) , Berkley Trade) Penguin Group (USA) Inc.
Pride & Prejudice. 2002. (Illus.). (YA). 48p. stu. ed., per. 17.95 (978-1-56254-530-7(2) , SP5302); 80p. per. 6.95 (978-1-56254-529-1(9) , SP5299) Saddleback Educational Publishing.
Pride, Felicia, et al. Hallway Diaries: How to Be down Double Act the Summer She Learned to Dance. 2007. 400p. pap. 9.99 (*978-0-373-83084-8(X)) Harlequin Enterprises, Ltd. CAN. *Dist:* Simon & Schuster, Inc.
Quin-Harkin, Janet. Love Potion. 1999. (Enchanted Hearts Ser.: No. 4). (Illus.). 192p. (YA). (gr. 7 up). pap. 4.50 (978-0-380-80122-0(1)) HarperCollins Pubs.
—Love Potion. 1999. (Enchanted Hearts Ser.). (Illus.). (J). (978-0-606-17966-9(6)) Tandem Library Bks.
Quinlan, Janet, adapted by. Love: The Selfish Giant. 2005. (Illus.). (*978-1-4127-3758-6(3)) Publications International, Ltd.
Rallison, Janette. Life, Love, & the Pursuit of Free Throws. 2006. 192p. (J). pap. 6.95 (978-0-8027-8898-6(X)) Walker & Co.
Ramagos, Tonya. Disaster Strikes. 2001. (gr. 7-12). lib. bdg. 26.85 (978-0-613-84712-4(1)) Tandem Library Bks.
Ramos, Maria Cristina. Del Amor Nacen Los Rios. (SPA.). pap. 9.95 (978-950-07-1351-1(9)) Editorial Sudamericana S.A. ARG. *Dist:* Distribooks, Inc.
Random House Disney Staff. Belle's Secret. Harchy, Atelier Philippe, illus. 2005. (Disney Princess Ser.). 32p. (J). (ps-2). 4.99 (978-0-7364-2327-4(3) , RH/Disney) Random Hse. Children's Bks.
—Love at First Beep. 2008. (Step into Reading Ser.). 32p. (J). (ps-1). pap. 3.99 (*978-0-7364-2514-8(4) , RH/Disney) Random Hse. Children's Bks.
—Two Hearts. McCafferty, Catherine, illus. 2005. (Disney Princess Ser.). 24p. (J). (ps-2). pap. 3.99 (978-0-7364-2345-8(1) , RH/Disney) Random Hse. Children's Bks.
—Wall-E. 2008. (Read-Aloud Storybook Ser.). 72p. (J). (ps-3). 8.99 (*978-0-7364-2528-5(4) , RH/Disney) Random Hse. Children's Bks.
—1, 2, 3, Cook. 2007. (Illus.). 10p. (J). (gr. k-k). bds. 4.99 (*978-0-7364-2485-1(7) , RH/Disney) Random Hse. Children's Bks.

J K L

Random House Disney Staff & Berrios, Frank. Princess Vol. II, Vol. II. 2004. (Disney Princess Ser.). (Illus.). 72p. (J). (ps-3). 8.99 (978-0-7364-2241-3(2) , RH/Disney) Random Hse. Children's Bks.

Razzell, Mary. Snow Apples. 2006. 216p. (J). pap. 6.95 (978-0-88899-728-9(0)) Groundwood Bks. CAN. *Dist:* Perseus Distribution.

RealBuzz Studios Staff. Let There Be Lighten Up! 2007. (Goofyfoot Gurl Ser.: No. 1). 96p. (YA). pap. 4.97 (978-1-59789-573-6(3) , Barbour Bks.) Barbour Publishing, Inc.

Reber, Deborah. Blue's Valentines Day. Pontillo, Jenine, illus. 2000. (Blue's Clues Ser.). 16p. (J). (ps-k). pap. 3.99 (978-0-689-83062-4(9) , Simon Spotlight/Nickelodeon) Simon & Schuster Children's Publishing.

Redbank, Tennant. Enchanted: A Storybook Life. 2nd rev. ed. 2007. 24p. (gr. 1). pap. 3.99 (*978-1-4231-1080-4(3)) Disney Pr.

Reider, Katja. Rosalie & Truffle; A Story of Love. Bucker, Jutta, illus. 2005. (ENG & GER.). 64p. (ps-3). 9.95 (978-0-8109-5984-2(4)) Abrams, Harry N. , Inc.

Reilly, Tina. The Onion Girl. 2001. 520p. pap. (978-1-84223-013-8(1)) Poolbeg Pr. IRL. *Dist:* Dufour Editions, Inc.

Reimer, Charlotte. Problems with Pies. 2006. 68p. (YA). pap. 10.00 (978-1-4116-7646-6(7)) Lulu.com.

Reisfeld, Randi. All You Need Is a Love Spell. 1998. (gr. 7-12). lib. bdg. 13.00 (978-0-613-73088-4(7)) Tandem Library Bks.

The Reluctant Heart: A Penny Parrish Story. 2001. (Penny Parrish Story). 192p. (YA). pap. 12.95 (978-1-930009-31-8(3)) Image Cascade Publishing.

Rennison, Louise. Love Is a Many Trousered Thing. 2007. (Confessions of Georgia Nicolson Ser.). (J). 288p. lib. bdg. 17.89 (*978-0-06-085388-4(3)); 256p. (gr. 7 up). 16.99 (*978-0-06-085387-7(5)) HarperCollins Pubs. (HarperTeen).

Rettig, Liz. My Desperate Love Diary. 2007. 314p. (YA). (gr. 9 up). 16.95 (978-0-8234-2033-9(7)) Holiday Hse., Inc.

Rider, Harlan. The Dragon Must Win, 1. 2002. (Illus.). 64p. (J). 5.95 (978-0-9747151-0-0(7)) I M Printing.

Rinaldi, Ann. Brooklyn Rose. 240p. (YA). 2005. 17.00 (978-0-15-205117-4(1)); 2006. (Illus.). reprint ed. pap. 6.95 (978-0-15-205538-7(X) , Harcourt Paperbacks) Harcourt Children's Bks.

Rinaldi, Ann & Farnsworth, Bill. Sarah's Ground. 2005. (Illus.). 192p. (YA). mass mkt. 5.99 (978-0-689-85925-0(2) , Simon Pulse) Simon & Schuster Children's Publishing.

Ripslinger, Jon. Last Kiss. 2007. 288p. (J). (gr. 4-7). pap. 9.95 (*978-0-7387-1072-3(5)) Llewellyn Pubns.

Rivera, Jeff. Forever My Lady: A Novel. 2004. per. 12.95 (978-0-9762838-0-5(8)) JoAnne/Horatio Bks.

—Forever My Lady: Young Adult. 2005. (YA). per. 12.95 (978-0-9762838-1-2(6)) JoAnne/Horatio Bks.

Roberts, Dina. Thirty Cats. 2003. 162p. (YA). pap. 12.95 (978-0-595-29775-7(7)) iUniverse, Inc.

Roberts, Laura Peyton. Heart & Soul. 1998. (Clearwater Crossing Ser.: No. 3). (YA). (gr. 5-8). (978-0-606-13280-0(5)) Tandem Library Bks.

—Promises, Promises. 1998. (Clearwater Crossing Ser.: No. 4). (YA). (gr. 5-8). (978-0-606-13281-7(3)) Tandem Library Bks.

Robins, Eleanor. The Best Week Ever. 2003. (Illus.). 48p. (YA). per. 3.95 (978-1-56254-677-9(5) , SP6775) Saddleback Educational Publishing.

Roeder, Mark. The Summer of My Discontent: A Better Place II. 2003. 294p. (YA). pap. 18.95 (978-0-595-29806-8(0)) iUniverse, Inc.

Rogers, Kayron Upton. Oh Little Speck of Love, So Deep in My Heart. 2000. 36p. (J). pap. 7.95 (978-1-57921-321-3(9)) WinePress Publishing.

Rojas, Fernando de. La Celestina Level 6. 1998. (SPA.). (gr. 7-12). lib. bdg. 15.25 (978-0-613-80670-1(0)) Tandem Library Bks.

Romeo & Juliet. 2002. (Illus.). 48p. (YA). per. 17.95 (978-1-56254-626-7(0) , SP6260) Saddleback Educational Publishing.

Rose, Sherrie. A Girl, A Guy & A Ghost. 2003. (YA). mass mkt. 5.99 (978-0-8439-5276-6(8)) Dorchester Publishing Co., Inc.

—Girl, a Guy & a Ghost. 2003. (gr. 7-12). lib. bdg. 14.15 (978-0-613-76907-5(4)) Tandem Library Bks.

Rosenberg, Liz. Carousel. 1998. (978-0-606-13244-2(9)) Tandem Library Bks.

Ross, Dave. A Book of Hugs. Rader, Laura, illus. 2001. 30p. (J). 6.99 (978-0-06-000273-2(5) , Harper Festival) HarperCollins Pubs.

—A Book of Hugs. 1999. (J). (978-0-606-20284-8(6)) Tandem Library Bks.

—Book of Hugs. 1999. (ps-2). lib. bdg. 14.10 (978-0-613-31015-4(2)) Tandem Library Bks.

—A Book of Kisses. Rader, Laura, illus. 2001. 16p. (J). 6.99 (978-0-06-000274-9(3) , Harper Festival) HarperCollins Pubs.

—A Book of Kisses. 2000. 40p. (J). pap. 4.95 (978-0-06-443524-6(5)) HarperCollins Pubs.

Ross, Leanna. Julie Simone. 2004. 194p. (YA). pap. 14.95 (978-0-595-30376-2(5)) iUniverse, Inc.

Rostand, Edmond, as told by. Cyrano de Bergerac. Rostand, Edmond, .'8.97 (978-0-673-58340-6(6)) Addison-Wesley Longman, Inc.

—Cyrano de Bergerac. Rostand, Edmond, . 1999. (J). 11.95 (978-1-56137-622-3(1)) Novel Units, Inc.

Roth, Susan L. Mi Amor Por Ti/My Love for You. 2003. (ENG & SPA., Illus.). 24p. (J). (ps). bds. 5.99 (978-0-8037-2944-5(8) , Dial) Penguin Group (USA) Inc.

—My Love for You. Serlin, Andra, ed. Roth, Susan L., illus. 1999. (Illus.). 24p. (J). (ps). bds. 5.99 (978-0-8037-2352-8(0) , Dial) Penguin Group (USA) Inc.

Ruckdeschel, Liz & James, Sara. What If ... All the Boys Wanted You. 2006. 288p. (YA). (gr. 7-10). 10.99 (978-0-385-90318-9(9) , Delacorte Bks. for Young Readers) Random Hse. Children's Bks.

Ruditis, Paul. Love, Hollywood Style. 2008. (Romantic Comedies Ser.). 272p. (YA). mass mkt. 6.99 (*978-1-4169-5138-4(5) , Simon Pulse) Simon & Schuster Children's Publishing.

Rusackas, Francesca. Daddy All Day Long. Burris, Priscilla, tr. Burris, Priscilla, illus. 2004. 32p. (J). (ps-k). lib. bdg. 13.89 (978-0-06-050285-0(1)) HarperCollins Pubs.

Rushton, Rosie. The Dashwood Sisters' Secrets of Love. 2005. 336p. (gr. 7-17). 15.99 (978-0-7868-5136-2(8)) Hyperion Bks. for Children.

—The Dashwood Sisters' Secrets of Love. 2006. 336p. (gr. 7-17). reprint ed. pap. 8.99 (978-0-7868-5137-9(6)) Hyperion Pr.

—What a Week to Fall in Love. (Illus.). 144p. (J). 7.95 (978-0-14-038760-5(9)) Penguin Bks., Ltd. GBR. *Dist:* Trafalgar Square Publishing.

Ryan, Pam Muñoz. Nacho y Lolita. Rueda, Claudia, illus. 2005. (SPA.). 40p. (J). (ps-3). pap. 5.99 (978-0-439-76418-6(1) , Scholastic en Espanol) Scholastic, Inc.

Ryan, Sara. Empress of the World. 2003. (gr. 7-12). lib. bdg. 16.45 (978-0-613-67491-1(X)) Tandem Library Bks.

Ryder, Joanne. Won't You Be My Hugaroo? Sweet, Melissa, illus. 2006. 40p. (J). 16.00 (978-0-15-205778-7(1)) Harcourt Trade Pubs.

—Won't You Be My Kissaroo? Sweet, Melissa, illus. 2004. 32p. (J). 16.00 (978-0-15-202641-7(X) , Gulliver Bks.) Harcourt Children's Bks.

Ryder, Joanne & Sweet, Melissa. Won't You Be My Hugaroo? 2008. (Illus.). 30p. (J). (ps). bds. 6.95 (*978-0-15-206298-9(X) , Red Wagon Bks.) Harcourt Children's Bks.

—Won't You Be My Kissaroo? 2008. (Illus.). 30p. (J). (ps). bds. 6.95 (*978-0-15-206060-2(X) , Red Wagon Bks.) Harcourt Children's Bks.

Saenz, Benjamin Alire. Sammy & Juliana in Hollywood. 2004. 240p. (YA). 19.95 (978-0-938317-81-4(4)) Cinco Puntos Pr.

Saijyo, Shinji. Iron Wok Jan, Vol. 13. 2005. (Illus.). 208p. (YA). pap. 9.95 (978-1-59796-031-1(4)) DrMaster Pubns. Inc.

Sainsbury, Adam. The Coin. 2005. 84p. (YA). pap. 9.96 (978-1-4116-5358-0(0)) Lulu.com.

Sama, Kent. Fruit of the Spirit - Love. Moody, Julie, illus. 2005. (J). bds. 9.99 (978-1-4183-0060-9(8)) Christ Inspired, Inc.

Sandberg, Rasemary. Great Boy Girl Stories. 2000. (J). (978-5-550-03094-3(2)) Chambers Harrap Pubs., Ltd.

Sargent, Dave. Say You Love Me. Bowen, Debbie, ed. Lenoir, Jane, illus. 1998. 31p. (J). (gr. k-6). lib. bdg. 6.00 (978-1-56763-130-2(4)) Ozark Publishing.

Scaperrotta, Kirstyn. I Lost My Cracker to the Big Cheese: A Collection of Voices. 2003. 126p. (YA). pap. 10.95 (978-0-595-26478-0(6) , Writers Club Pr.) iUniverse, Inc.

Schertle, Alice. When the Moon Is High. 2003. (Illus.). 32p. (J). 16.89 (978-0-688-15144-7(2)) HarperCollins Pubs.

Schimel, Lawrence. Camelot Fantastic. 1998. (978-0-606-13242-8(2)) Tandem Library Bks.

Schlessinger, Laura. Why Do You Love Me? 2001. (gr. k-3). lib. bdg. 14.10 (978-0-613-36029-6(X)) Tandem Library Bks.

Schlessinger, Laura & Lambert, Martha. Why Do You Love Me? McFeeley, Daniel, illus. 2001. 40p. (J). (ps-2). pap. 6.99 (978-0-06-443654-0(3) , Harper Trophy) HarperCollins Pubs.

Schlessinger, Laura & Lambert, Martha L. Why Do You Love Me? Meisel, Paul & McFeeley, Daniel, illus. 1999. 40p. (J). (ps-2). 15.95 (978-0-06-027866-3(8)) HarperCollins Pubs.

Scholastic, Inc. Staff. Cars & Trucks. 2008. (Littlest Pet Shop Ser.). (SPA.). 24p. (J). pap. 3.99 (*978-0-545-02728-1(4) , Scholastic en Espanol) Scholastic, Inc.

—Summer Boys. 2003. (gr. 7-12). lib. bdg. 17.60 (978-0-613-72220-9(5)) Tandem Library Bks.

—10 Things I Hate about You. 1999. 170p. (gr. 6-11). pap. 4.99 (978-0-439-08730-8(9)) Scholastic, Inc.

Schott, Kenneth. The (Mis)Adventures of Captain Crazy. 2005. 124p. pap. 17.95 (978-1-4137-8190-8(X)) PublishAmerica, Inc.

Schraff, Anne. Lost & Found. 2007. (Bluford Ser.: No. 1). 144p. (J). pap. 3.99 (978-0-439-89839-3(0)) Scholastic, Inc.

—A Matter of Trust. 2007. (Bluford Ser.: No. 2). 144p. (J). pap. 3.99 (978-0-439-86547-0(6)) Scholastic, Inc.

Schreiber, Ellen. Teenage Mermaid. 2003. 160p. (J). (gr. 4 up). lib. bdg. 16.89 (978-0-06-008205-5(4)) HarperCollins Pubs.

Schroeder, Lisa. I Heart You, You Haunt Me. 2008. 240p. (YA). pap. 7.99 (*978-1-4169-5520-7(8) , Simon Pulse) Simon & Schuster Children's Publishing.

Schwarz, Laurence & KOL (AOL Kids) Staff. Sweet Nothings: As Seen on Cartoon Network. 6th ed. 2007. (Princess Natasha Ser.: No. 6). (Illus.). 80p. (J). (gr. 3-7). pap. 3.99 (978-0-316-15511-3(X)) Little Brown & Co.

Scott, Elizabeth. Bloom. 2007. 240p. (YA). (gr. 7 up). pap. 8.99 (978-1-4169-2683-2(6) , Simon Pulse) Simon & Schuster Children's Publishing.

Scott, James. My Antonia: Reproducible Teaching Unit. 1999. 54p. (YA). (gr. 7-12). ring bd. 29.50 (978-1-58049-144-0(8) , TU65) Prestwick Hse., Inc.

Scull, Robert. Happy Valentine's Day! 2002. (gr. k-3). lib. bdg. 14.15 (978-0-613-50443-0(7)) Tandem Library Bks.

Second Look. 64p. (YA). (gr. 6-12). pap. (978-0-8224-2385-0(5)) Globe Fearon Educational Publishing.

Selvadurai, Shyam. Swimming in the Monsoon Sea. 280p. (J). 2007. (gr. 8). pap. 9.95 (*978-0-88776-834-7(2)); 2005. 18.95 (978-0-88776-735-7(4)) Tundra Bks., Inc./Livres Toundra, Inc. CAN. *Dist:* Random Hse., Inc.

Shakespeare, William & Clayborne, Anna. Romeo & Juliet - Internet Referenced. 2006. 64p. (J). 8.99 (978-0-7945-1240-8(2) , Usborne) EDC Publishing.

Shakespeare, William & Unzner, C. Romeo & Juliet. 2006. (Illus.). 36p. (J). 17.95 (978-0-7358-2090-6(2)) North-South Bks., Inc.

Shalhout, Ahlam. For the Love of My Dreams, 1. 2004. 95p. per. 14.95 (978-0-9668179-2-8(3)) Expressions Woven.

Shaver, Brianna. A Diamond in the Rough. 2005. 160p. pap. 19.95 (978-1-4137-6601-1(3)) PublishAmerica, Inc.

Shay, Kathryn. Promises to Keep. 1999. 140p. (J). (gr. 5-8). pap. 5.99 (978-0-9673794-1-8(5)) Small Miracles Pr.

Sheldon, Georgie. True Loves Reward A Sequel to Mona. 2006. 79.99 (*978-1-4280-2545-5(6)) IndyPublish.com.

Shepard, Sara. Flawless. 2007. (Pretty Little Liars Ser.: Bk. 2). 352p. (gr. 9 up). (J). lib. bdg. 17.89 (978-0-06-088734-6(6)); (YA). 16.99 (978-0-06-088733-9(8)) HarperCollins Pubs. (HarperTeen).

—Pretty Little Liars. 2006. (Pretty Little Liars Ser.: Bk. 1). 304p. (J). 16.99 (978-0-06-088730-8(3)); No. 1. lib. bdg. 17.89 (978-0-06-088731-5(1)) HarperCollins Pubs. (HarperTeen).

Sher, Abby. Kissing Snowflakes. 2007. 256p. (YA). (gr. 7 up). pap. 8.99 (*978-0-545-00010-9(6)) Scholastic, Inc.

Shifflett, Stephen. Josie Unlimited. 2007. 136p. (YA). per. 11.95 (*978-0-595-43013-0(9)) iUniverse, Inc.

Shipley, Jocelyn. Seraphina's Circle: A Young Adult Novel. 2006. 144p. (YA). (gr. 6-9). pap. 9.95 (978-1-894549-51-6(1)) Sumach Pr. CAN. *Dist:* Orca Bk. Pubs. USA.

Shulman, Polly. Enthusiasm. 2006. 212p. (YA). (gr. 6). 15.99 (978-0-399-24389-9(5) , Putnam Juvenile) Penguin Group (USA) Inc.

Silverstein, Shel. The Giving Tree. Silverstein, Shel, illus. gif. ed. 2007. 64p. 16.99 (*978-0-06-124001-0(X)) HarperCollins Pubs.

Simendinger, Ted. 12 Miles to Paradise: A People Story about Horses & Horseracing. 2nd ed. 2004. 364p. per. 12.95 (978-0-9702405-4-5(6)) Airplane Reader Publishing.

Simmons, Jane. Come along, Daisy! Simmons, Jane, illus. 2003. (Illus.). 32p. (J). (ps-1). pap. 6.99 (978-0-316-16878-6(5)) Little, Brown Bks. for Young Readers.

Simon, Mary Manz. Bunny Loves Others. Stott, Dorothy, illus. 2006. (First Virtues for Toddlers Ser.). 20p. (J). 5.99 (978-0-7847-1409-6(6) , 04037) Standard Publishing.

Skillchecks for Romance. 2005. (Double Fastback Ser.). (J). (gr. 6-12). 64p. pap. 5.95 (978-0-13-024474-1(0)); 32p. pap. 5.95 (978-0-13-024457-4(0)) Globe Fearon Educational Publishing.

Slater, Teddy. Beauty & the Beast. Dias, Ron & Gonzaelz, Ric, illus. 2004. (Little Golden Book Ser.). 24p. (J). (gr. k-k). 2.99 (978-0-7364-2197-3(1) , Golden/Disney) Random Hse. Children's Bks.

Slott, Dan. She-Hulk Volume 4: Laws of Attraction TPB: Laws of Attraction TPB. 2007. (Illus.). 192p. pap. 19.99 (978-0-7851-2218-0(4)) Marvel Enterprises, Inc.

Smith Annie, Laura. Whispers in the Wind. 2006. 144p. pap. 12.95 (978-1-59113-914-0(7)) Booklocker.com, Inc.

Smith, Betty. Joy in the Morning. 2000. (gr. 7-12). lib. bdg. 22.25 (978-0-8085-1474-9(1)) Tandem Library Bks.

Sones, Sonya. What My Mother Doesn't Know. 2003. (Illus.). 272p. (YA). pap. 6.99 (978-0-689-85553-5(2) , Simon Pulse) Simon & Schuster Children's Publishing.

—What My Mother Doesn't Know. Harper, Charise Mericle, illus. 2001. 272p. (YA). (gr. 6-8). 17.00 (978-0-689-84114-9(0)) Simon & Schuster Children's Publishing.

Soto, Gary. Accidental Love. 192p. (YA). 2008. pap. 6.95 (*978-0-15-206113-5(4) , Harcourt Paperbacks); 2006. 16.00 (978-0-15-205497-7(9)) Harcourt Children's Bks.

Sparks, Beatrice. Treacherous Love: The Diary of an Anonymous Teenager. 2000. (978-0-606-17982-9(8)); (gr. 7-12). lib. bdg. 14.15 (978-0-613-27318-3(4)) Tandem Library Bks.

Sparks, Beatrice, ed. Treacherous Love: The Diary of an Anonymous Teenager. 2000. 176p. (YA). (gr. 7 up). pap. 5.99 (978-0-380-80862-5(5)) HarperCollins Pubs.

Spinelli, Jerry. Love, Stargirl. 2007. (J). 192p. (gr. 5-8). lib. bdg. 19.99 (*978-0-375-91375-4(0)); 288p. (gr. 7-8). 16.99 (*978-0-375-81375-7(6)) Random Hse. Children's Bks. (Knopf Bks. for Young Readers).

Stacy, Lori Moore. Beautiful You. 2000. (All about You Ser.). (Illus.). 112p. (J). (gr. 4-7). pap. 4.50 (978-0-439-15531-1(2)) Scholastic, Inc.

Stamaty, Mark Alan. Who Needs Donuts? 2003. (Illus.). 40p. (J). 16.95 (978-0-375-82550-7(9) , Knopf Bks. for Young Readers) Random Hse. Children's Bks.

Stampler, Ann Redisch. Shlemazel & the Remarkable Spoon of Pohost. Cohen, Jacqueline M., illus. 2006. 40p. (J). (gr. k-3). 16.00 (978-0-618-36959-1(7) , Clarion Bks.) Houghton Mifflin Co. Trade & Reference Div.

Stanley, Mandy. Who Do You Love? Stanley, Mandy, illus. 2007. 24p. (J). (ps). bds. 8.99 (*978-1-4169-3929-0(6) , Little Simon) Simon & Schuster Children's Publishing.

Steele, Julia. The Taker. 2006. 352p. (gr. 6-9). 15.99 (978-0-7868-4930-7(4)) Hyperion Pr.

Steig, William. Made for Each Other. 2000. (Illus.). 48p. (J). (gr. 9 up). 13.95 (978-0-06-028512-8(5) , Cotler, Joanna Books) HarperCollins Pubs.

Stewart, Melanie. First Crush. 2000. (gr. 3-6). lib. bdg. 11.80 (978-0-613-27826-3(7)) Tandem Library Bks.

Stilton, Geronimo. All Because of a Cup of Coffee. 2004. (Geronimo Stilton Ser.: No. 10). (Illus.). 128p. (J). mass mkt. 6.99 (978-0-439-55972-0(3) , Scholastic Paperbacks) Scholastic, Inc.

Stine, R. L. The New Girl. 2006. (Fear Street Ser.). 176p. (YA). pap. 5.99 (978-1-4169-1810-3(8) , Simon Pulse) Simon & Schuster Children's Publishing.

Stoehr, Shelley. Tomorrow Wendy: A Love Story. 2003. lib. bdg. 24.55 (978-0-613-87785-5(3)) Tandem Library Bks.

—Tomorrow Wendy: A Love Story. 2003. 176p. (YA). pap. 14.95 (978-0-595-26954-9(0) , Backinprint.com) iUniverse, Inc.

Stone, Amy Wingrove. I Love You Every Minute. Lennhoff, Andrew, illus. 2006. pap. 18.00 (978-0-8059-9119-2(0) , RoseDog Bks.) Dorrance Publishing Co., Inc.

Strachan, Linda. What Color Is Love? Wojtowycz, David, illus. 2004. 32p. (J). pap. 6.95 (978-1-58234-941-1(X) , Bloomsbury Children) Bloomsbury Publishing.

Strasser, Todd. For Money & Love. 2007. (Mob Princess Ser.). 208p. (YA). (gr. 9 up). pap. 8.99 (*978-1-4169-3533-9(9) , Simon Pulse) Simon & Schuster Children's Publishing.

Stutson, Caroline. Mama Loves You. Segal, John, illus. 2005. 32p. (J). pap. 6.99 (978-0-439-57842-4(6)) Scholastic, Inc.

Summers, Tamara. He's with Me. 2007. (I Heart Bikinis Ser.: No. 1). 224p. (J). pap. 5.99 (*978-0-439-91850-3(2) , Scholastic Paperbacks) Scholastic, Inc.

Sunderland, Margot & Hancock, Nicky. The Day the Sea Went Out & Never Came Back: A Story for Children Who Have Lost Someone They Love, 2 vols. Armstrong, Nicky, tr. Armstrong, Nicky, illus. 32p. pap. (978-0-86388-463-4(6) , 002-5147) Speechmark Publishing Ltd.

—The Frog Who Longed for the Moon to Smile: A Story for Children Who Yearn for Someone They Love, 2 vols. Armstrong, Nicky, tr. Armstrong, Nicky, illus. 28p. pap. (978-0-86388-495-5(4) , 002-5066) Speechmark Publishing Ltd.

Surace, Joan. The Story of Lucia. Rockford, Nancy, illus. 2006. (YA). pap. 8.00 (*978-0-8059-7062-3(2)) Dorrance Publishing Co., Inc.

Tafuri, Nancy. You Are Special, Little One. 2005. 15p. (J). bds. 7.99 (978-0-439-68613-6(X)) Scholastic, Inc.

Takahashi, Rumiko. Inuyasha, Vol. 29. 2007. (Inuyasha Ser.). 192p. (YA). pap. 8.95 (978-1-4215-0900-6(8)) Viz Media.

Take a Hike, Romeo. (Full House Ser.). 96p. (J). (gr. 4-6). pap. 3.95 (978-0-938753-75-9(4) , PP4) Parachute Publishing, LLC.

Talbott, Shawn M. Springtime Robins. 2006. (J). lib. bdg. 19.95 (*978-1-933732-05-3(9) , Bear Hug Bks.) MidAmerica Publishing Co.

Taniguchi, Tomoko. Let's Stay Together Forever. Pannone, Frank, ed. Rose, Julia, tr. from JPN. Taniguchi, Tomoko, illus. 2003. (Illus.). 192p. pap. 15.95 (978-1-58664-881-7(0) , CMX 62701G, CPM Manga) Central Park Media Corp.

Teis, Kyra, adapted by. The Magic Flute. 2006. 32p. (J). 17.95 (978-1-59572-058-0(8)) Star Bright Bks., Inc.

Thacker, Nola. LB (Laguna Beach) 2005. (Summer Share Ser.). 224p. (YA). pap. 8.99 (978-1-4169-0515-8(4) , Simon Pulse) Simon & Schuster Children's Publishing.

Thompson, Kelly. Lasting. 2005. 120p. pap. 17.95 (978-1-4137-9653-7(2)) PublishAmerica, Inc.

Thomson, Celia. The Stolen. 2004. (Nine Lives of Chloe King Ser.: No. 2). 288p. (YA). pap. 6.99 (978-0-689-86659-3(3) , Simon Pulse) Simon & Schuster Children's Publishing.

Toliver, Wendy. The Secret Life of a Teenage Siren. 2007. (Romantic Comedies Ser.). 304p. (YA). mass mkt. 6.99 (*978-1-4169-5065-3(6) , Simon Pulse) Simon & Schuster Children's Publishing.

Tremblay, Carole. Romeo, le Rat Romantique. ed. 2004. (FRE., Illus.). (J). (ps-3). spiral bd. (978-0-616-07266-0(X)) Canadian National Institute for the Blind/Institut National Canadien pour les Aveugles.

Tulloch, Richard. Weird Stuff. Nagle, Shane, illus. 2007. 224p. (J). pap. 6.95 (978-0-8027-9626-4(5)) Walker & Co.

Turner, Ann Warren. In the Heart. Mavor, Salley, illus. 2001. 32p. (J). (ps-3). 14.95 (978-0-06-023730-1(9)) HarperCollins Pubs.

Twomey, Cathleen. Beachmont Letters. 2003. (Illus.). 224p. (YA). (gr. 6-9). 16.95 (978-1-59078-050-3(7)) Boyds Mills Pr.

Tyrrell, Melissa. Beauty & the Beast. McMullen, Nigel, illus. 2005. (Fairytale Friends Ser.). 12p. (J). bds. 5.95 (978-1-58117-153-2(6) , Intervisual/Piggy Toes) Dalmatian Pr.

Ueda, Miwa. Change of Heart, 7 vols. Ueda, Miwa, illus. 4th rev. ed. 2003. (Illus.). 184p. pap. 9.99 (978-1-59182-197-7(5) , Tokyopop Adult) TOKYOPOP, Inc.

—Change of Heart, 11 , 8. Yoshimoto, Ray, tr. rev. ed. 2004. (Illus.). 192p. pap. 9.99 (978-1-59182-497-8(4) , Tokyopop Adult) TOKYOPOP, Inc.

—Change of Heart, 11, 9. rev. ed. 2004. (Illus.). 192p. pap. 9.99 (978-1-59182-498-5(2) , Tokyopop Adult) TOKYOPOP, Inc.

—Change of Heart, 7 vols., Vol. 5. Ueda, Miwa, illus. rev. ed. 2003. (Illus.). 184p. pap. 9.99 (978-1-59182-198-4(3) , Tokyopop Adult) TOKYOPOP, Inc.

—Change of Heart, 11 vols., Vol. 7. rev. ed. 2004. (Illus.). 192p. pap. 9.99 (978-1-59182-496-1(6) , Tokyopop Adult) TOKYOPOP, Inc.

—Peach Girl. 2002. Vol. 3. 3rd rev. ed. 184p. (gr. 8-12). pap. 9.99 (978-1-931514-13-2(5)); Vol. 4. 4th rev. ed. 184p. (gr. 8-12). pap. 9.99 (978-1-931514-14-9(3)); Vol. 5. 5th rev. ed. 184p. pap. 9.99 (978-1-931514-15-6(1)); Vol. 6. 6th rev. ed. 176p. pap. 9.99 (978-1-931514-16-3(X)); Vol. 7. 7th rev. ed. 184p. pap. 9.99 (978-1-931514-17-0(8)) TOKYOPOP, Inc.

Ueda, Miwa, creator. Peach Girl: Limited Collector's Edition, 2 Vols., Vol. 5-8. collector's ltd. ed. 2004. (Illus.). 768p. pap. 39.99 (978-1-59532-170-1(5) , Tokyopop Adult) TOKYOPOP, Inc.

Ueda, Rinko. Tail of the Moon, Volume 4. 2007. (Tail of the Moon Ser.). 200p. (YA). pap. 8.99 (978-1-4215-0816-0(8)) Viz Media.

—Trail of the Moon, Volume 3. 2007. (Tail of the Moon Ser.). 200p. (YA). pap. 8.99 (978-1-4215-0814-6(1)) Viz Media.

Umansky, Kaye. The Romantic Giant. Weir, Doffy, illus. 2006. 32p. (J). pap. 6.95 (978-1-903015-25-4(1)) Barn Owl Bks, London GBR. *Dist:* Independent Pubs. Group.

Ure, Jean. The Secret Life of Sally Tomato. l.t. ed. 2006. pap. 16.95 (978-1-4056-6018-1(X)) BBC Audio GBR. *Dist:* BBC Audiobooks America.

Vail, Rachel. Ever After. 2005. 192p. (J). (gr. 7-12). pap. 7.99 (978-0-06-058748-2(2) , Harper Trophy) HarperCollins Pubs.

Valera, Juan. Pepita Jimenez. 2000. (SPA.). (gr. 7-12). lib. bdg. 17.60 (978-0-613-80726-5(X)) Tandem Library Bks.

Van der Meer, Ron. Give Me a Kiss. 1999. (Illus.). 6p. (J). 12.95 (978-90-76048-21-5(5)) Van Der Meer Tennis Univ.

van Diepen, Allison. Snitch. 2007. 304p. (YA). pap. 6.99 (***978-1-4169-5030-1(3)*** , Simon Pulse) Simon & Schuster Children's Publishing.

Van Draanen, Wendelin. Confessions of a Serial Kisser. 2008. 272p. (J). (gr. 7). 15.99 (***978-0-375-84248-1(9)***); lib. bdg. 18.99 (***978-0-375-94248-8(3)***) Random Hse. Children's Bks. (Knopf Bks. for Young Readers).

Van Draanen, Wendelin. Flipped. 2003. (gr. 5-8). lib. bdg. 17.60 (978-0-613-62948-5(5)) Tandem Library Bks.

Van Lieshout, Maria. Bloom! A Little Book about Finding Love. 2007. (Illus.). 48p. (J). 12.95 (***978-0-312-36913-2(1)***) Feiwel & Friends.

Vaval, Fisepe. The Blueprint. Bubsy, Nancy, ed. 2003. 270p. (YA). pap. 15.00 (978-0-9743207-0-0(6)) Tayes Bks.

Velthuijs, Max & Bell, Anthea. Frog in Love. Farrell, Kate, ed. rev. ed. 2005. (Illus.). 32p. (J). 5.99 (978-0-8050-7654-7(9) , Holt, Henry & Co. Bks. For Young Readers) Holt, Henry & Co.

Viguie, Debbie. Midnight Pearls: A Retelling of the Little Mermaid. 2006. (Once upon a Time Ser.). 208p. (YA). pap. 5.99 (978-1-4169-4016-6(2) , Simon Pulse) Simon & Schuster Children's Publishing.

Villeneuve, Mireille. A Clown in Love. Villeneuve, Anne, illus. 2005. (Read-It! Readers Ser.). 32p. (C). (gr. k-3). 18.60 (978-1-4048-1069-3(2)) Picture Window Bks.

Vin, Lee, illus. Crazy Love Story. 2005. Vol. 3. rev. ed. 208p. pap. 9.99 (978-1-59182-949-2(6)); Vol. 4. 4th rev. ed. 192p. pap. 9.99 (978-1-59182-950-8(X)) TOKYOPOP, Inc. (Tokyopop Kids).

Viselman, Kenn. I Love You Bunches. 2004. (Illus.). 28p. 14.98 (978-0-9722361-0-2(4)) Viselman, Kenn Presents...

Vision, David & Vision, Mutiya Sahar, illus. Daddy Loves His Baby Girl. 2005. 32p. (J). 16.00 (978-0-9659538-7-0(4)) Soul Vision Works Publishing.

von Konigslow, Andrea Wayne. Would You Love Me? von Konigslow, Andrea Wayne, illus. (Illus.). (J). (ps-k). 2003. 32p. pap. 5.95 (978-1-55037-430-8(3)); 2003. 32p. lib. bdg. 15.95 (978-1-55037-431-5(1)); 2000. 24p. pap. 1.25 (978-1-55037-639-5(X)) Annick Pr., Ltd. CAN. *Dist:* Firefly Bks., Ltd.

von Ziegesar, Cecily. It Had to Be You: The Gossip Girl Prequel. 2007. 300p. 16.99 (***978-0-316-02065-7(6)*** , Tingley, Megan Bks.) Little, Brown Bks. for Young Readers.

Voss, Dawn. Avenging Aja. 2007. 50p. pap. 15.00 (***978-0-615-15324-7(0)***) Voss, Dawn L.

Voyer, Kelly. For Love of Rock. Voyer, Kelly, illus. 2003. (Annikins Ser.: Vol. 13). (Illus.). 11p. (Orig.). (J). (ps-2). pap. 0.99 (978-1-55037-349-3(8)) Annick Pr., Ltd. CAN. *Dist:* Firefly Bks., Ltd.

Waddell, Martin. Who Do You Love. Ashforth, Camilla, illus. 2004. 24p. (J). (gr. k-ps). bds. 6.99 (978-0-7636-2565-8(5)) Candlewick Pr.

Wagner, Paul. Just One Mo. 2003. 130p. (YA). pap. 10.95 (978-0-595-27223-5(1)) iUniverse, Inc.

Walker, Glenda & Adriana, Leah. Lovelet Kingdom. Chalifour, Ryan, illus. 1999. 45p. (J). (gr. 5-7). pap. 7.95 (978-0-7392-0039-1(9) , PO2808) Morris Publishing.

Wallin, Luke. In the Shadow of the Wind. 2001. 216p. (YA). pap. 15.95 (978-0-595-19243-4(2)) iUniverse, Inc.

Wang, Dorothea DePrisco & Imperato, Teresa. All the Ways I Love You. Downing, Julie, illus. 2005. 10p. (J). 8.95 (978-1-58117-190-7(0) , Intervisual/Piggy Toes) Dalmatian Pr.

Warburton, Carol. Edge of Night: A Novel. 2004. (Illus.). 278p. pap. 14.95 (978-1-59156-013-5(6)) Covenant Communications, Inc.

Ward, Heather P. I Promise I'll Find You. McGraw, Sheila, illus. 2005. 32p. (J). (ps-2). pap. 5.95 (978-1-55209-094-7(9)) Firefly Bks., Ltd.

Ward, Nick. The Ice Child. Bailey, Peter, tr. Bailey, Peter, illus. 2003. 32p. (YA). (978-1-84365-004-1(5) , Pavilion Children's Bks.) Chrysalis Children's Bks.

Waricha, Jean. Who Will Be My Valentine? 2004. (Full House Ser.: No. 3). (Illus.). 96p. mass mkt. 4.99 (978-0-06-054085-2(0) , Harper Entertainment) HarperCollins Pubs.

Wasserman, Robin. Unfabulous: Meltdown. 2006. (Teenick Ser.). 128p. (J). pap. 4.99 (978-0-439-84873-2(3)) Scholastic, Inc.

Watase, Yuu. Absolute Boyfriend, Vol. 3. 2007. (Absolute Boyfriend Ser.). (Illus.). 200p. (YA). pap. 8.99 (978-1-4215-1003-3(0)) Viz Media.

Watson, Willian. The Legend of the Rose Swan. 2002. (Illus.). 34p. (YA). (gr. 6 up). 15.95 (978-0-9727770-0-1(8)) From the Lillypad Productions.

Wax, Wendy. For Love or Money. Piluso, Piero, illus. 2006. 32p. (J). lib. bdg. 9.00 (***978-1-4242-0955-2(2)***) Fitzgerald Bks.

Weber, Lou, ed. I Love You So Much. 2005. 24p. (J). bds. 10.98 (978-1-4127-3440-0(1) , 9524102) Publications International, Ltd.

Webster, Jean. Daddy Long Legs. 2004. reprint ed. pap. 19.95 (978-1-4191-1490-8(5)) ; pap. 1.99 (978-1-4192-1490-5(X)) Kessinger Publishing, LLC.

Weimer, Heidi R. Love from My Heart: To a Snuggly Cuddly Little Boy (Parent Love Letters) Sharp, Chris, illus. 2005. 14p. (J). bds. 12.99 (978-0-8249-6654-6(6)) Ideals Pubns.

—Love from My Heart: To a Precious Sweet Little Girl (Parent Love Letters) Sharp, Chris, illus. 2005. 14p. (J). bds. 12.99 (978-0-8249-6655-3(4)) Ideals Pubns.

Welford, Sue. Secret Love Large Print. 2006. pap. (***978-1-905665-10-5(5)***) Pollinger In Print.

Wells, Carolyn. Patty at Home. 2007. (ENG.). 204p. per. 12.95 (***978-1-4218-3321-7(2)***) 1st World Publishing, Inc.

Westaway, Jane. Love & Other Excuses. 1999. 212p. (YA). (gr. 8 up). pap. 13.00 (978-1-877135-28-6(3)) Longacre Pr. NZL. *Dist:* Pacific Island Bks.

Weston, Carol. With Love from Spain, Melanie Martin. Roth, Marci, illus. 2005. 256p. (J). (gr. 3-7). 5.50 (978-0-440-41972-3(7) , Yearling) Random Hse. Children's Bks.

Weyn, Suzanne. The Night Dance. 2005. 193p. (YA). (978-1-4156-4311-2(3) , Simon Pulse) Simon & Schuster Children's Publishing.

Weyn, Suzanne. Reincarnation. 2008. 416p. (J). pap. 17.99 (***978-0-545-01323-9(2)*** , Scholastic Pr.) Scholastic, Inc.

Weyn, Suzanne & Gonzalez, Diana. South Beach Sizzle. 2005. 249p. (YA). (978-1-4155-7724-0(2) , Simon Pulse) Simon & Schuster Children's Publishing.

Weyn, Suzanne & Gonzalez, Diana. South Beach Sizzle. 2005. (Romantic Comedies Ser.). 272p. (YA). mass mkt. 5.99 (978-1-4169-0011-5(X) , Simon Pulse) Simon & Schuster Children's Publishing.

—South Beach Sizzle. 2005. 249p. (YA). (gr. 9-12). per. 14.45 (978-1-4176-6059-9(7)) Tandem Library Bks.

Wharton, Edith. Ethan Frome & Summer. 2001. (gr. 7-12). lib. bdg. 16.40 (978-0-613-50128-6(4)) Tandem Library Bks.

Wilhelm, Hans. Yo Siempre te Quierre. (SPA.). 296p. (J). 13.95 (978-84-261-2404-3(6)) Juventud, Editorial ESP. *Dist:* AIMS International Bks., Inc.

Willard, Nancy. Beauty & the Beast. 1999. (J). pap. 7.00 (978-0-15-201549-7(3)) Harcourt Children's Bks.

Willett, Edward. The Dark Unicorn. 18th ed. 1998. 158p. (YA). (gr. 6 up). 9.99 (978-0-88092-414-6(4) , 4144) Royal Fireworks Publishing Co.

Willey, Margaret. If Not for You. 2002. 164p. (YA). pap. 13.95 (978-0-595-25572-6(8) , Backinprint.com) iUniverse, Inc.

Williams, Jeanne. To Buy a Dream. 2001. 164p. (YA). pap. 11.95 (978-0-595-16527-8(3) , Backinprint.com) iUniverse, Inc.

Williams, Quan. The Leopard Man. 2005. 183p. pap. 19.95 (978-1-4137-5214-4(4)) PublishAmerica, Inc.

Williams, Sam. That's Love. Moriuchi, Mique, illus. 2007. 32p. (J). 16.95 (978-0-8234-2028-5(0)) Holiday Hse., Inc.

Willis, Jeanne. Never Too Little to Love. Fearnley, Jan, illus. 2004. 32p. (J). (ps up). 10.99 (978-0-7636-2267-1(2)) Candlewick Pr.

The Willow Tree. 2001. 336p. (J). pap. 14.95 (978-0-9678340-0-9(7)) B G & J Pubs.

Willson, Sarah. Rugrats' Easter Surprise. 2002. (gr. k-3). lib. bdg. 14.15 (978-0-613-51321-0(5)) Tandem Library Bks.

Wilson, Jacqueline. Girls in Love. 2002. 192p. (YA). (gr. 7). pap. 5.50 (978-0-440-22957-5(X) , Laurel Leaf) Random Hse. Children's Bks.

—Girls in Love. 2002. (gr. 7-12). lib. bdg. 13.00 (978-0-613-72336-7(8)) Tandem Library Bks.

—Girls in Love. (Illus.). (J). 2003. 160p. mass mkt. (978-0-552-54521-1(X) , Corgi); 2000. (Girlfriends Trilogy Ser.: No. 1). 156p. 17.95 (978-0-385-40804-2(8)) Transworld Publishers Ltd. GBR. *Dist:* Random Hse. of Canada, Ltd., Trafalgar Square Publishing.

Wilson, Sarah. Love & Kisses. Sweet, Melissa, illus. (J). (gr. k-ps). 2001. 22p. bds. 6.99 (978-0-7636-1049-4(6)); 2005. 32p. reprint ed. pap. 3.99 (978-0-7636-2011-0(4)) Candlewick Pr.

Wittlinger, Ellen. Lombardo's Law. 2003. 144p. (YA). (gr. 5-9). pap. 5.95 (978-0-618-31108-8(4)) Houghton Mifflin Co. Trade & Reference Div.

—Long Night of Leo & Bree. 2003. (gr. 7-12). lib. bdg. 15.30 (978-0-613-73433-2(5)) Tandem Library Bks.

—Razzle. 2003. 256p. (YA). pap. 7.99 (978-0-689-85600-6(8) , Simon Pulse) Simon & Schuster Children's Publishing.

Wolf, Ema. 18 Cuentos de Amor.Tr. of Eighteen Short Love Stories. (SPA.). (J). pap. (978-950-07-1107-4(9)) Editorial Sudamericana S.A.

Wolf, Erica. I Love You Just the Same. Wolf, Erica, illus. rev. ed. 2003. (Illus.). 32p. (J). 16.95 (978-0-8050-7128-3(8) , Holt, Henry & Co. Bks. For Young Readers) Holt, Henry & Co.

Woltz, Nicole. Simply Love. 2005. 101p. pap. 14.95 (978-1-4137-4011-0(1)) PublishAmerica, Inc.

Wood, Maryrose. Sex Kittens & Horn Dawgs Fall in Love. 256p. (YA). (gr. 7). 2007. pap. 8.99 (***978-0-385-73277-2(5)***); 2006. 15.95 (978-0-385-73276-5(7)); 2006. lib. bdg. 17.99 (978-0-385-90296-0(4)) Random Hse. Children's Bks. (Delacorte Bks. for Young Readers).

Would You Love Me? I Feel Orange Today, Foo, 100 bks., Set. 2000. (Annikins Ser.: No. 16). (Illus.). (J). pap. 125.00 (978-1-55037-642-5(X)) Annick Pr., Ltd. CAN. *Dist:* Firefly Bks., Ltd.

Yeo, Ho-Kyung. Honey Mustard, Vol. 4. 4th rev. ed. 2006. (Illus.). pap. 9.99 (978-1-59816-208-0(X) , Tokyopop Adult) TOKYOPOP, Inc.

Yezerski, Thomas F. Together in Pinecone Patch. Date not set. (J). pap. (978-0-374-47579-6(2) , Farrar, Straus & Giroux (BYR)) Farrar, Straus & Giroux.

—Together in Pinecone Patch. Yezerski, Thomas F., illus. 1998. (Illus.). 32p. (J). (gr. k-3). 16.00 (978-0-374-37647-5(6) , Farrar, Straus & Giroux (BYR)) Farrar, Straus & Giroux.

Yuki, Kaori. Angel Sancturary, Volume 18. 2007. (Angel Sanctuary Ser.). 200p. (YA). pap. 9.99 (978-1-4215-0976-1(8)) Viz Media.

Zimmerman, Zoe. Johnny. 2000. (gr. 7-12). lib. bdg. 12.40 (978-0-613-25817-3(7)) Tandem Library Bks.

Zindel, Paul. My Darling, My Hamburger. 1999. mass mkt. (978-0-553-24396-3(9)) ; (YA). mass mkt. (978-0-553-20759-0(8)) Random Hse., Inc.

Zola, Emile. A Love Episode. 2006. pap. 74.99 (***978-1-4280-1323-0(7)***) IndyPublish.com.

Zolotow, Charlotte & Vitale, Stefano. If You Listen. 2002. (Illus.). 32p. (J). (ps-3). reprint ed. 15.95 (978-0-7624-1335-5(2) , Running Pr. Kids) Running Pr. Bk. Pubs.

Zuckerman, Linda. I Will Hold You 'til You Sleep. Muth, Jon J., illus. 2006. (J). (978-0-439-43421-8(1)) ; 32p. pap. 16.99 (978-0-439-43420-1(3)) Scholastic, Inc. (Levine, Arthur A. Bks.).

LOVE (THEOLOGY)

Warner Press Staff. Love. 2000. (Lion Cub Upside-Down Books Ser.). (Illus.). (J). (ps-3). pap. 5.95 (978-0-87162-826-8(0)) Warner Pr. Pubs.

LOVE POETRY

Berry, George B. The Compassionate Side of a Common Man: Love Poems from the Heart, Vol. 3. unabr. ed. 2004. 120p. (YA). pap. 12.99 (978-0-9720308-6-1(7)) Mindfull Publishing Co.

Grimes, Nikki. Hopscotch Love: A Family Treasury of Love Poems. Rosales, Melodye Benson, illus. 1999. 40p. (J). (gr. 3 up). 17.99 (978-0-688-15667-1(3)) HarperCollins Pubs.

Martin, Susana. Mi Joven y Romantico Corazon (My Young Romantic Heart) Merino, Vladimiro, illus. 2000. (SPA.). 72p. (YA). pap. (978-950-11-1509-3(7)) Sigmar.

McNaughton, Tina, illus. My First Valentine's Day Book. 2006. (First Holiday Bks.). 12p. (J). (ps-k). bds., bds. 7.95 (978-0-7534-5930-0(2) , Kingfisher) Houghton Mifflin Co. Trade & Reference Div.

Niño, Jairo Aníbal. La Alegria De Querer. 2003. (SPA.). 72p. (978-958-30-0293-9(3) , PV30142) Centro de Informacion y Desarrollo de la Comunicacion y la Literatura MEX. *Dist:* Lectorum Pubns., Inc.

Smith, William J. Here Is My Heart: Love Poems. Dyer, Jane, illus. 1999. 64p. (J). (gr. k-3). 12.95 (978-0-316-19765-6(3)) Little Brown & Co.

Sones, Sonya. What My Mother Doesn't Know. 2003. (gr. 7-12). lib. bdg. 15.30 (978-0-613-61828-1(9)) Tandem Library Bks.

Turner, Ann Warren. A Lion's Hunger: Poems of First Love. Jimenez, Maria, illus. 1999. 48p. (YA). (gr. 7-12). 15.95 (978-0-7614-5035-1(1) , Cavendish Children's Bks.) Cavendish, Marshall Corp.

Weeks, Sarah. Be Mine, Be Mine, Sweet Valentine. Kosaka, Fumi, illus. 2005. 20p. (J). (ps-k). 9.99 (978-0-694-01514-6(8) , Geringer, Laura Book) HarperCollins Pubs.

LOVE POETRY—COLLECTIONS

Hopkins, Lee Bennett. Valentine Hearts: Holiday Poetry. Adinolfi, JoAnn, illus. 2004. (I Can Read Bks.). 32p. (J). (gr. k-3). lib. bdg. 16.89 (978-0-06-008058-7(2)) HarperCollins Pubs.

LOW, JULIETTE GORDON, 1860-1927

Aller, Susan Bivin. Juliette Low. 2007. (History Maker Biographies Ser.). (J). 26.60 (978-0-8225-6580-2(3) , Lerner Pubns.) Lerner Publishing Group.

Brown, Fern. Daisy & the Girl Scouts: The Story of Juliette Gordon Low. Dejohn, Marie, illus. 2005. 111p. (J). (gr. 3-6). lib. bdg. 15.90 (978-0-606-33708-3(3)) Tandem Library Bks.

Kent, Deborah. Juliette Gordon Lowe: Founder of the Girl Scouts of America. 2003. (Spirit of America). (Illus.). 32p. (J). (gr. 2-6). 27.07 (978-1-59296-006-4(5)) Child's World, Inc.

LOW TEMPERATURES

Hunter, Rebecca M. Hot & Cold. 2000. (Discovering Science Ser.). (Illus.). 32p. (J). (gr. 3-5). lib. bdg. 25.69 (978-0-7398-2972-1(6)) Raintree.

—Hot & Cold. 2000. (Discovering Science Ser.). (Illus.). 32p. (J). (gr. 3-5). pap. 8.95 (978-0-7398-3016-1(3)) Steck-Vaughn.

Martin, Elena. Hot or Cold? 2003. (Yellow Umbrella Books). (Illus.). 16p. (J). (gr. 1). lib. bdg. 14.60 (978-0-7368-2012-7(4) , Pebble Bks.) Capstone Pr., Inc.

—Hot or Cold? 2003. (Math Ser.). (J). (978-0-7368-1698-4(4)) Yellow Umbrella Pr.

Royston, Angela. Hot & Cold. (My World of Science Ser.). (Illus.). 32p. (J). (gr. k-2). 2002. pap. 6.95 (978-1-4034-0040-6(7) , 91484); 2001. lib. bdg. 21.36 (978-1-58810-241-6(6)) Heinemann Library.

—Hot & Cold. 2002. (gr. k-3). lib. bdg. 14.75 (978-0-613-86991-1(5)) Tandem Library Bks.

Strazzabosco, John. Extreme Temperatures: Learning about Positive & Negative Numbers. 2004. (PowerMath Ser.). (Illus.). 32p. (J). lib. bdg. (978-0-8239-8927-0(5)); lib. bdg. 22.50 (978-0-8239-8997-3(6)) Rosen Publishing Group, Inc., The. (PowerKids Pr.).

LOYALTY

Klingel, Cynthia Fitterer. Loyalty. 2007. (Learn about Values Ser.). 24p. (J). 21.36 (978-1-59296-672-1(1)) Child's World, Inc.

Raatma, Lucia. Loyalty. 2002. (Character Education Ser.). (Illus.). 24p. (J). (gr. 1-2). lib. bdg. 18.60 (978-0-7368-1390-7(X) , Bridgestone Bks.) Capstone Pr., Inc.

LOYALTY—FICTION

Blenkhorn, Les. The Adventures of Tracker. 2006. 26.99 (***978-1-4259-6605-8(5)***); pap. 16.99 (***978-1-4259-6604-1(7)***) AuthorHouse.

Buckman, Carole Duncan. Neighbors & Traitors. 2000. (StarMaker Bks.). 81p. (J). (gr. 6-9). pap. 5.50 (978-0-88489-548-0(3)) St. Mary's Pr.

Choyce, Lesley. Sudden Impact. 2005. (Orca Currents Ser.). 112p. (J). (gr. 4-10). pap. 7.95 (978-1-55143-476-6(8)) Orca Bk. Pubs. USA.

Cleveland, Rob. The Bear, the Bat & the Dove: Three Stories from Aesop. 2006. (Illus.). 32p. (J). pap. 3.95 (978-0-87483-810-7(X)) August Hse. Pubs., Inc.

Dickens, Charles. A Tale of Two Cities. Lynch, Brendan, illus. 2002. (Great Illustrated Classics Ser.). 240p. (J). (gr. 3-8). 21.35 (978-1-57765-802-3(7) , ABDO & Daughters) ABDO Publishing Co.

Dickerson, Julie G. Patrick Loves Peaches: A Story to Help Children Understand Peer Pressure & Loyalty. Brant, Patricia, illus. 1998. (Helping Children Understand Ser.). 32p. (Orig.). (J). (gr. k-6). pap. 11.95 (978-0-9646576-7-0(8)) Cherubic Pr.

Gardner, Sally. Boolar's Big Day Out. 2003. (Tales from the Box Ser.: Vol. 2). (Illus.). 128p. (J). 14.95 (978-1-58234-833-9(2) , Bloomsbury Children) Bloomsbury Publishing.

Golden Books Staff. Royal & Loyal. Harchy, Atelier Philippe, illus. 2004. (Disney Princess Ser.). 32p. (J). (ps-2). pap. 2.99 (978-0-375-82654-2(8) , Golden/Disney) Random Hse. Children's Bks.

Golding, Sally. Foley & Jem. Mark, Oliver, illus. 2004. 32p. (J). 14.95 (978-1-4027-1364-4(9)) Sterling Publishing Co., Inc.

Gunnery, Sylvia. Out of Bounds. 2004. (Sports Stories Ser.). 104p. (J). (gr. 3-8). 7.95 (978-1-55028-826-1(1)); (***978-1-55028-827-8(X)***) Lorimer, James & Co., Ltd., Pubs. CAN. *Dist:* Casemate Pubs. & Bk. Distributors, LLC.

Kroeger, Mary Kay. Paperboy. 2001. (gr. k-3). lib. bdg. 15.25 (978-0-613-34023-6(X)) Tandem Library Bks.

Lavender, William. Just Jane: A Daughter of England Caught in the Struggle of the American Revolution. (Great Episodes Ser.). (YA). 2005. 336p. pap. 6.95 (978-0-15-205472-4(3)); 2002. 288p. 17.00 (978-0-15-202587-8(1)) Harcourt Children's Bks. (Gulliver Bks.).

MacKenzie, Catherine. The Lonely Grey Dog at No. 6: Tammy & Jake Learn about Love & Loyalty. 2005. (Illus.). 157p. (J). mass mkt. (978-1-84550-103-7(9) , Christian Focus) Christian Focus Pubns.

Miklowitz, Gloria D. Camouflage. 1998. 166p. (YA). (gr. 7-12). 16.00 (978-0-15-201467-4(5)) Harcourt Trade Pubs.

Pantelides, Sherry. It's Blue Like You! A Story about Loyalty. Perez, Debi, illus. 2007. 32p. (J). 12.99 (***978-0-9771076-1-2(2)***) Lacey Productions.

Sargent, Dave & Sargent, Pat. Dan: (Dappled Mahogany Bay) Determination, 25, 21. Lenoir, Jane, illus. 2001. (Saddle Up Ser.: 21). 36p. (J). pap. 6.95 (978-1-56763-652-9(7)); lib. bdg. 22.60 (978-1-56763-651-2(9)) Ozark Publishing.

Schick, Joel, illus. The Jungle Book: A Story about Loyalty. 2006. (J). 6.99 (978-1-59939-023-9(X) , Reader's Digest Young Families, Inc.) Reader's Digest Children's Publishing, Inc.

Soto, Gary. Chato Goes Cruisin' Guevara, Susan, illus. 2007. 32p. (J). (ps). pap. 6.99 (978-0-14-240810-0(7) , Puffin) Penguin Group (USA) Inc.

Standish, Burt L. Frank Merriwell's Faith. Rudman, Jack, ed. 2003. (Frank Merriwell Ser.). 29.95 (978-0-8373-9360-5(4)); pap. 9.95 (978-0-8373-9060-4(5)) Merriwell, Frank Inc.

Turner, Megan Whalen. The King of Attolia. 400p. (J). 2007. (gr. 5 up). pap. 7.99 (***978-0-06-083579-8(6)*** , Eos); 2006. 16.99 (978-0-06-083577-4(X)); 2006. lib. bdg. 17.89 (978-0-06-083578-1(8)) HarperCollins Pubs.

LSD (DRUG)

Connolly, Sean. LSD. 2000. (Just the Facts Ser.). (Illus.). 56p. (YA). (gr. 6-8). lib. bdg. 24.22 (978-1-57572-258-0(5)) Heinemann Library.

Drew-Edwards, Suzanna. LSD & Other Hallucinogens. 2005. (What's the Deal? Ser.). (Illus.). 56p. (J). (978-1-4034-7029-4(4)) Heinemann Library.

LeVert, Suzanne. The Facts about LSD. 2005. (Drugs Ser.). (Illus.). 96p. (J). (978-0-7614-1974-7(8) , Benchmark Bks.) Cavendish, Marshall Corp.

Littell, Mary Ann. LSD. 2001. (Drug Library). (Illus.). 112p. (YA). (gr. 6-12). pap. 13.26 (978-0-7660-1924-9(1)) Enslow Pubs., Inc.

Petechuk, David. LSD. 2004. (Drug Education Library). (Illus.). 112p. (J). (gr. 7-10). 32.45 (978-1-59018-417-2(3)) Thomson Gale.

LULLABIES

Bang, Molly Garrett. Ten, Nine, Eight. Bang, Molly Garrett, illus. 2002. (Illus.). (J). 14.43 (978-0-7587-4590-3(7)) Book Wholesalers, Inc.

Banks, Kate. Si la Luna Pudiera Hablar. Hallensleben, Georg, illus. 2000. Tr. of And If the Moon Could Talk. (SPA.). (J). (gr. k-2). pap. 17.95 (978-84-261-3131-7(X) , JV0378) Juventud, Editorial ESP. *Dist:* Distribooks, Inc., Lectorum Pubns., Inc.

Beaton, Clare, illus. Mrs. Moon: Lullabies for Bedtime. 2003. 48p. (J). 19.99 incl. audio compact disk (978-1-84148-176-0(9)) Barefoot Bks., Inc.

J K L

Bleck, Linda, illus. A Children's Treasury of Lullabies. 2006. 24p. (J). bds. 12.95 (978-1-4027-2979-9(0)) Sterling Publishing Co., Inc.

Blomgren, Jennifer. Where Do I Sleep? A Pacific Northwest Lullaby. Gabriel, Andrea, illus. 2002. 32p. (J). (ps-1). 16.95 (978-1-57061-258-9(7)) Sasquatch Bks.

Boelts, Maribeth. Lullaby Lullabook. 2002. (Growing Tree Ser.). (Illus.). 8p. (J). (-k). 5.95 (978-0-694-01593-1(8), Harper Festival) HarperCollins Pubs.

Bookworks. Sleepy Time Lullabies: Stories & Songs. 2005. 20p. (J). bds. 14.99 (978-1-4003-0583-4(7)) Nelson, Thomas Inc.

Bourély, Antoinette & Caviezel, Giovanni. Lullabies under the Moon. Pledger, M., illus. 2006. 12p. (J). 6.99 (978-1-4169-1359-7(9), Little Simon) Simon & Schuster Children's Publishing.

Briggs, Kelly Paul. Lighthouse Lullaby. 2001. (Illus.). 32p. (ps-3). 15.95 (978-0-89272-486-4(2)) Down East Bks.

Brown, Margaret Wise. Sleepy Bunnies: The Lost Lullabies of Margaret Wise Brown. 2008. 32p. 15.99 (978-0-7868-0371-2(1)) Hyperion Bks. for Children.

—Sleepy Bunnies: The Lost Lullabies of Margaret Wise Brown. 2020. 32p. (J). pap. 5.99 (978-0-7868-1257-8(5)) Hyperion Paperbacks for Children.

Brown, Petra, illus. Hush, Little Baby. 2007. 24p. (J). 8.95 (*978-1-58925-819-8(3)*, tiger tales) ME Media LLC.

Card, Michael. Sleep Sound in Jesus: Gentle Lullabies for Little Ones & Inspirational Devotions for Parents. 2nd ed. 2003. (Illus.). 36p. wbk. ed. 15.99 (978-0-7369-1219-8(3)) Harvest Hse. Pubs.

Delacre, Lulu, illus. & compiled by. Arrorro Mi Nino: Latino Lullabies & Gentle Games. Delacre, Lulu, compiled by. 2004. (ENG & SPA.). 32p. (J). 16.95 (978-1-58430-159-2(7)) Lee & Low Bks., Inc.

Dodd, Emma. Amazing Baby: Rock-a-Bye Baby! 2007. (Amazing Baby Ser.). (Illus.). 12p. (J). bds. 12.95 (*978-1-59223-724-1(X)*, Silver Dolphin Bks.) Advantage Pubs. Group.

Dorling Kindersley Publishing Staff, ed. Hush Little Baby, Don't Say a Word. 2004. (Baby Fun Ser.). 12p. (J). pap. 5.99 (978-0-7566-0763-0(9)) Dorling Kindersley Publishing, Inc.

Dorrian, James G., contrib. by. Lullabys for Starry Nights. (J). pap. 10.98 (978-0-9647786-1-0(0), 3001-4) Baby Music Boom, Inc.

Feierabend, John M. The Book of Lullabies. 2000. (First Steps in Music Ser.). (Illus.). 112p. (J). (ps). pap. 12.95 (978-1-57999-056-5(8)) GIA Pubns., Inc.

Freedman, Claire. A Kiss Goodnight: A Collection of Lullabies. Williams, Sophy et al, illus. 2007. 28p. (J). (ps-1). 16.95 (*978-1-56148-564-2(0)*) Good Bks.

Garborg's Inc. Staff, compiled by. Royal Doulton: Bunnykins Lullaby & Goodnight Gift Book. 1999. (Illus.). 32p. (J). (ps-k). 6.99 (978-1-58375-651-5(5)) Garborg's, Inc.

Geras, Adele. From Lullaby to Lullaby. 1998. (J). 14.00 (978-0-671-89828-1(0), Simon & Schuster Children's Publishing) Simon & Schuster Children's Publishing.

Gerber, Carole. Hush! A Gaelic Lullaby. 2001. (ps-2). lib. bdg. 15.25 (978-0-613-85269-2(9)) Tandem Library Bks.

—Hush! A Gaelic Lullaby. Husted, Marty, illus. 2001. 32p. (J). (ps-2). pap. 6.95 (978-1-58089-026-7(1)) Charlesbridge Publishing, Inc.

—Hush! a Gaelic Lullaby. 2001. (gr. k-3). lib. bdg. 15.25 (978-0-613-35148-5(7)) Tandem Library Bks.

God Is with You in Sleep. Date not set. 44p. (J). (ps-5). 16.99 incl. audio compact disk (978-0-9702219-0-2(8)) Bowden Music Co.

Gosset, Adelaide L. J. Lullabies of the Four Nations: A Coronal of Song with Renderings from the Welsh & the Gaelic. 2001. 278p. (YA). reprint ed. 98.00 (978-0-7222-6147-7(0)) Library Reprints, Inc.

Greene, Ellin & Levi, Paul Alan. Mother's Song: An English Lullaby. Sayles, Elizabeth & McCully, Emily Arnold, illus. 2008. 34p. (J). 17.00 (978-0-395-71527-7(X), Clarion Bks.) Houghton Mifflin Co. Trade & Reference Div.

Gutmann, Bessie P. Nursery Songs & Lullabies. 2007. 32p. (J). (ps-3). 6.99 (978-0-448-44502-1(6), Grosset & Dunlap) Penguin Group (USA) Inc.

Halpern, Shari, illus. Hush Little Baby. 2007. 0024p. pap. 6.95 (*978-0-7358-2167-5(4)*) North-South Bks., Inc.

Heath, Beverly C. A Bedtime Lullaby. Floyd, John, Jr., illus. 2005. (J). bds. 5.95 (*978-0-9752860-1-2(3)*) OurRainbow Pr., LLC.

Ho, Minfong. Hush! A Thai Lullaby. ed. 2004. (Illus.). (J). (ps-1). spiral bd. (978-0-616-08497-7(8)) Canadian National Institute for the Blind/Institut National Canadien pour les Aveugles.

—Hush! A Thai Lullaby. Meade, Holly, illus. 2000. (ps-ps). lib. bdg. 15.30 (978-0-613-72622-1(7)) Tandem Library Bks.

—Hush! A Thai Lullaby. 2000. 13.75 (978-0-606-17855-6(4)) Tandem Library Bks.

Ho, Mingfong. Hush! A Thai Lullaby. Meade, Holly, illus. 2000. 32p. (J). (ps-k). pap. 6.99 (978-0-531-07166-3(9), Orchard Bks.) Scholastic, Inc.

—Hush! A Thai Lullaby. Meade, Holly, illus. ed. 2004. (J). (ps-1). spiral bd. (978-0-616-07255-4(4)) Canadian National Institute for the Blind/Institut National Canadien pour les Aveugles.

Hughes, Shirley. Rhymes for Annie Rose. Hughes, Shirley, illus. 2006. (Illus.). 48p. (J). (ps-2). reprint ed. 16.99 (978-0-7636-2940-3(5)) Candlewick Pr.

Hush Little Baby. 2004. pap. 14.95 incl. audio (978-0-7882-0622-1(2)) Weston Woods Studios, Inc.

Kiesler, Kate A. Fishing for a Dream: Ocean Lullabies & Night Verses. 1999. (Illus.). 32p. (J). (gr. k-ps). tchr. ed. 16.00 (978-0-395-94149-2(0), Clarion Bks.) Houghton Mifflin Co. Trade & Reference Div.

Lamont, Priscilla. Ring O'Roses: Nursery Rhymes, Action Rhymes & Lullabies. 1999. (Illus.). 72p. (J). (ps-1). pap. 10.99 (978-0-7112-1245-9(7)) Lincoln, Frances Ltd. GBR. *Dist:* Transition Vendor.

Long, Sylvia. Hush Little Baby. 2002. (Illus.). 26p. (J). bds. 6.95 (978-0-8118-2290-9(7)) Chronicle Bks. LLC.

Lou Weber. Strawberry Shortcake Musical Lullaby Treasury. 40p. 12.98 (978-1-4127-6085-0(2), PIL Kids) Publications International, Ltd.

McGill, Alice. In the Hollow of Your Hand: Slave Lullabies. Cummings, Michael, illus. 2000. 40p. (J). (gr. k-3). 18.00 (978-0-618-10445-1(3)); tchr. ed. 18.00 (978-0-395-85755-7(4)) Houghton Mifflin Co. Trade & Reference Div.

Melmed, Laura Krauss. Jumbo's Lullaby. Sorensen, Henri, illus. 1999. 24p. (J). (ps-k). lib. bdg. 15.89 (978-0-688-16996-1(1)) HarperCollins Pubs.

Millen, C. M. Blue Bowl Down: An Appalachian Rhyme. Meade, Holly, illus. 2004. 32p. (J). (gr. k-k). 16.99 (978-0-7636-1817-9(9)) Candlewick Pr.

Mitzo Thompson, Kim. Children's Lullaby Songs. 2006. (Read, Sing, & Play Along! Ser.). 320p. (J). pap. 24.95 (978-0-7696-4316-8(7)) School Specialty Publishing.

Olson-Brown, Ellen. Hush, Little Digger. White, Lee, illus. 2006. 28p. (J). 12.95 (978-1-58246-160-1(0), Tricycle Pr.) Ten Speed Pr.

Parmenter, Wayne, illus. Mother Goose Bedtime Rhymes. 2002. 40p. (J). bds. 12.98 (978-0-7853-7818-1(9), 7176200) Publications International, Ltd.

Pearson, Susan, ed. The Drowsy Hours: Poems for Bedtime. Malone, Peter, illus. 2002. 40p. (J). (ps up). 16.95 (978-0-688-16603-8(2)) HarperCollins Pubs.

Philip, Neil, ed. Weave Little Stars into My Sleep: Native American Lullabies. Curtis, Edward S., photos by. 2001. (Illus.). 32p. (J). (gr. k-3). 16.00 (978-0-618-08856-0(3), Clarion Bks.) Houghton Mifflin Co. Trade & Reference Div.

Potter, Beatrix. Lullabies. 2004. (Illus.). 12p. (J). (ps). pap. 5.99 (978-0-7232-4995-5(4), Warne) Penguin Group (USA) Inc.

Priddy, Roger. Lullaby 1. 2002. bds. 7.95 (978-0-312-49076-8(3), Priddy Bks.) St. Martin's Pr.

—Lullaby 2. 2002. bds. 7.95 (978-0-312-49077-5(1), Priddy Bks.) St. Martin's Pr.

Root, Phyllis. All for the Newborn Baby. Bayley, Nicola, illus. 2000. (J). 15.99 (978-0-7636-0735-7(5)) Candlewick Pr.

Roth, Susan L. Hanukkah, Oh Hanukkah. 2004. (Illus.). 24p. (J). (ps). 10.99 (978-0-8037-2843-1(3), Dial) Penguin Group (USA) Inc.

Saport, Linda. All the Pretty Little Horses: A Traditional Lullaby. Saport, Linda, illus. 2005. (Illus.). 32p. (J). (gr. k-ps). 5.95 (978-0-618-55162-0(X), Clarion Bks.) Houghton Mifflin Co. Trade & Reference Div.

Scholastic, Inc. Staff. Twinkle, Twinkle, Little Star. Berg, Michelle, illus. 2004. 8p. (J). 12.95 (978-0-439-61667-6(0), Cartwheel Bks.) Scholastic, Inc.

Seeger, Pete. One Grain of Sand: A Lullaby. Wingerter, Linda, illus. 2005. 30p. (J). (ps-4). reprint ed. 16.00 (978-0-7567-8586-4(3)) DIANE Publishing Co.

—One Grain of Sand: A Lullaby. Wingerter, Linda, illus. 2003. 32p. (J). (ps-1). 15.95 (978-0-316-78140-4(1), Tingley, Megan Bks.) Little, Brown Bks. for Young Readers.

Seuling, Barbara. Winter Lullaby. Newbold, Greg, illus. 2002. 32p. (J). (gr. k-2). pap. 6.00 (978-0-15-216808-7(7), Harcourt Paperbacks) Harcourt Children's Bks.

Stohs, Anita Reith. Hush Little One. Kanzler, John, illus. 2006. (ENG.). 20p. (J). bds. 4.99 (978-0-7586-0861-1(6)) Concordia Publishing Hse.

—Hush, Little One: A Lullaby for God's Children. Kanzler, John, tr. Kanzler, John, illus. 2004. 32p. (J). 12.99 (978-0-570-07144-0(5)) Concordia Publishing Hse.

Stringer, Roland & Lacoursiere, Patr. Dodo la Planete Do (Dream Songs Night Songs) Bourbonnière, Sylvie, illus. 2006. 36p. (J). 16.95 incl. audio compact disk (978-2-923163-06-2(0)) La Montagne Secrete CAN. *Dist:* National Bk. Network.

Stuart, Kelly. Cancion de Cuna de la Virgen de Guadalupe. Caban, Carlos, tr. Caban, Carlos, illus. 2003. (SPA.). 28p. (978-1-931721-18-9(1)) Bright Sky Pr.

Studio Mouse. Mother Goose Lullabies: Book & CD. rev. ed. 2007. 24p. 4.99 (*978-1-59069-559-3(3)*) Studio Mouse LLC.

Thomas, Joyce Carol. Hush Songs. 2000. (Illus.). 48p. (ps-k). 16.49 (978-0-7868-2488-5(3), Jump at the Sun) Hyperion Bks. for Children.

—Hush Songs. Joysmith, Brenda, illus. 2000. 48p. (ps-k). 15.99 (978-0-7868-0562-4(5), Jump at the Sun) Hyperion Bks. for Children.

Thompson, Kim Mitzo & Mitzo Hilderbrand, Karen. I Thank God for You. Schwartz, Carol, illus. 2005. (Read & Sing along Board Books with CDs Ser.). 18p. (J). (ps-k). bds., bds. 7.49 incl. audio compact disk (978-0-7696-4456-1(2)) School Specialty Publishing.

Tiger Tales Staff, ed. Twinkle, Twinkle Little Star: And Other Favorite Bedtime Rhymes. Rescek, Sanja, illus. 2006. 22p. (J). bds. 7.95 (978-1-58925-787-0(1), tiger tales) ME Media LLC.

Tunseth, Scott & Tunseth, Kathy Donaln. Tomorrow Begins at Bedtime. 2004. (Illus.). 48p. (ps-3). 13.99 (978-0-8066-4569-8(5), Augsburg Bks.) Augsburg Fortress, Pubs.

Walty, Margaret T., illus. Rock-a-Bye Baby: Lullabies for Bedtime. 1998. (Barefoot Poetry Collection). 40p. (J). (ps-k). 14.95 (978-1-902283-03-6(1)) Barefoot Bks., Inc.

Waters, J. Sleepy City. Flaherty, Katherine M. et al, illus. 2002. 16p. (J). (gr. 1-5). pap. (978-1-57579-252-1(4)) Pine Hill Pr., Inc.

Weber, Lou. Goodnight Elmo Musical Lullaby Treasury. 2005. 40p. 12.98 (978-1-4127-3781-4(8), PIL Kids) Publications International, Ltd.

Withrow, Sarah. Se un Bebé. Monroy, Manuel, illus. 2007. (SPA.). 32p. (J). 17.95 (*978-0-88899-788-3(4)*) Groundwood Bks. CAN. *Dist:* Perseus Distribution.

Yolen, Jane. Sleep Rhymes Around the World. 2000. (gr. k-3). lib. bdg. 18.75 (978-0-613-78915-8(6)) Tandem Library Bks.

Yolen, Jane, ed. Sleep Rhymes Around the World. 2003. (Illus.). 40p. (J). (gr. k-2). pap. 9.95 (978-1-56397-923-1(3)) Boyds Mills Pr.

LUMBER AND LUMBERING

see also Forest Products; Forests and Forestry; Trees; Wood

Appelbaum, Diana. Giants in the Land. McCurdy, Michael, illus. 2000. 32p. (J). (gr. 4-6). pap. 6.95 (978-0-618-03305-8(X)) Houghton Mifflin Co. Trade & Reference Div.

Cowan, Mary Morton. Timberrr! A History of Logging in New England. 2003. (Women at War Ser.). (Illus.). 128p. (gr. 5 up). lib. bdg. 25.90 (978-0-7613-1866-8(6), Twenty-First Century Bks.) Lerner Publishing Group.

Fischer, Maureen M. Nineteenth-Century Lumber Camp Cooking. 2000. (Blue Earth Books). (Illus.). 32p. (J). (gr. 3-4). lib. bdg. 22.60 (978-0-7368-0604-6(0), Bridgestone Bks.) Capstone Pr., Inc.

Fitzgerald, Dawn. Julia Butterfly Hill: Saving the Redwoods. 2002. (Gateway Greens Ser.). (Illus.). 48p. (gr. 2-4). lib. bdg. 23.90 (978-0-7613-2654-0(5), Millbrook Pr.) Lerner Publishing Group.

Hill, Julia Butterfly. Legacy of Luna: The Story of A Tree, A Woman & the Struggle to Save the Redwoo. 2001. (gr. 7-12). lib. bdg. 23.45 (978-0-613-50118-7(7)) Tandem Library Bks.

Llewellyn, Claire. Wood. 2002. (Material World Ser.). (Illus.). 32p. (J). (gr. 2-4). pap. 24.00 (978-0-531-14633-0(2), Watts, Franklin) Scholastic Library Publishing.

LUMBER AND LUMBERING—FICTION

Brooks, Walter R. & Slayton-Mitchell, Joyce. Knuckleboom Loaders Load Logs: A Trip to the Sawmill. Wiese, Kurt, illus. 2003. 40p. (J). 15.95 (978-1-58567-368-1(4)) Overlook Pr., The.

Honeycutt, Natalie. Twilight in Grace Falls. 1999. 192p. (J). (gr. 3-7). pap. 4.50 (978-0-380-73128-2(2)) HarperCollins Pubs.

—Twilight in Grace Falls. 1999. (978-0-606-15928-9(2)) Tandem Library Bks.

Horne, Constance. The Tenth Pupil. 2005. 160p. (J). (gr. 3-9). pap., tchr. ed. 8.95 (978-0-921870-86-9(8)) Ronsdale Pr. CAN. *Dist:* Literary Pr. Group of Canada.

Lasky, Kathryn. Marven of the Great North Woods. Hawkes, Kevin, illus. 2002. 48p. (J). (gr. 1-4). pap. 7.00 (978-0-15-216826-1(5), Voyager Bks./Libros Viajeros) Harcourt Children's Bks.

Lawrie, Robin & Lawrie, Christine, illus. Cheat Challenge. 2007. 32p. (J). pap. (*978-1-59889-442-4(0)*) Stone Arch Bks.

Petrie, Lettie A. Let Me Tell You About "Minnie the Mule & the Erie Canal" Petrie, Beth L., illus. 2001. (Erie Canal Ser.). (YA). (gr. 5-10). pap. 9.95 (978-0-9711638-0-5(4)) Petrie Pr.

Stanley, George Edward. Adam Sharp No. 5: Moose Master. 2004. (gr. k-3). lib. bdg. 11.80 (978-0-613-86694-1(0)) Tandem Library Bks.

Stone Arch Books (Firm : Afton, Minn.) Staff. Cheat Challenge. Lawrie, Robin & Lawrie, Christine, illus. 2007. (Ridge Riders Ser.). 40p. (J). (gr. 2-6). lib. bdg. 21.26 (*978-1-59889-347-2(5)*) Stone Arch Bks.

LUMINESCENCE, ANIMAL

see Bioluminescence

LUNAR EXPEDITIONS

see Space Flight to the Moon

LUNAR EXPLORATION

see Moon—Exploration

LUNAR PROBES

see also names of space projects, e.g. Mariner Project; etc.

Cole, Michael D. Moon Base: First Colony in Space. 1999. (Countdown to Space Ser.). (Illus.). 48p. (YA). (gr. 4-10). lib. bdg. 23.93 (978-0-7660-1118-2(6)) Enslow Pubs., Inc.

LUNCH ROOMS

see Restaurants

LUNCHEONS

Aunt Louisa Is coming for Lunch: Individual Title Six-Packs. (gr. 1-2). 25.00 (978-0-7635-9128-1(9)) Rigby Education.

Kalman, Bobbie. Lunch Munch: Step-by-Step Recipes. 2003. (Kid Power Ser.). (Illus.). 32p. (J). (gr. 3). (978-0-7787-1251-0(6)); pap. (978-0-7787-1273-2(7)) Crabtree Publishing Co.

Midday Meals around the World. (Meals Around the World Ser.). 24p. (J). 7.95 (978-1-4048-1131-7(1)) Picture Window Bks.

Pare, Jean. Company's Coming for Kids: Lunches. 1998. 142p. (J). (gr. 5-12). pap. (978-1-896891-36-1(5)) Company's Coming Publishing, Ltd.

Zurakowski, Michele. Midday Meals Around the World. Yesh, Jeff, illus. 2004. (Meals Around the World Ser.). 24p. (J). (gr. k-4). 22.60 (978-1-4048-0281-0(9), 1229526) Picture Window Bks.

LUTHER, MARTIN, 1483-1546

Alex, Ben. Martin Luther. Rava, Giuseppe, illus. 1998. (Heroes of Faith & Courage Ser.). 50p. (gr. 3-12). reprint ed. 7.99 (978-1-884543-13-5(8)) Authentic Media.

Booth, Edwin P. Martin Luther: The Great Reformer. 1999. (Heroes of the Faith Ser.). 208p. (J). (ps up). 14.95 (978-0-7910-5037-8(8), Chelsea Hse.) Facts On File, Inc.

Crompton, Samuel Willard. Martin Luther. 2003. (Spiritual Leaders & Thinkers Ser.). (Illus.). 120p. (gr. 9-13). 30.00 (978-0-7910-7863-1(9), Chelsea Hse.) Facts On File, Inc.

Luther, Servant of God: Student Guide. 80p. stu. ed. 10.95 (978-0-7586-0465-1(3)) Concordia Publishing Hse.

Martin Luther. (J). (gr. 3-4). stu. ed., wbk. ed. 3.00 (978-0-570-00637-4(6), 22-2802); (J). (gr. 5-6). stu. ed., wbk. ed. 3.00 (978-0-570-00639-8(2), 22-2804); (YA). (gr. 7-8). stu. ed., wbk. ed. 3.00 (978-0-570-00641-1(4), 22-2806); (Illus.). (J). (gr. k-2). stu. ed. 3.00 (978-0-570-00635-0(X), 22-2800) Concordia Publishing Hse.

Meet Martin Luther. 2004. (Exploring Luther's Small Catechism Ser.). (gr. 3-4). 2.99 (978-0-8066-6784-3(2)) Augsburg Fortress, Pubs.

Nohl, Frederick. Martin Luther: Hero of Faith. Hook, Richard, illus. 2003. 160p. (YA). pap. 9.99 (978-0-7586-0592-4(7)) Concordia Publishing Hse.

Rijswijk, Cor van. Martin Shows the Way. 2004. (Illus.). 43p. (J). (978-1-894666-80-0(1)) Inheritance Pubns.

Somervill, Barbara A. Martin Luther: Father of the Reformation. 2006. (Signature Lives Ser.). (Illus.). 112p. (J). (gr. 5-7). 30.60 (978-0-7565-1593-5(9)) Compass Point Bks.

LUXEMBOURG

Sheehan, Patricia & Dhilawala, Sakina. Luxembourg. 2nd ed. 2007. (Cultures of the World Ser.). 144p. (J). lib. bdg. 39.93 (*978-0-7614-2088-0(6)*, Benchmark Bks.) Cavendish, Marshall Corp.

Simons, Rae. Luxembourg. 2006. (European Union Ser.). (Illus.). 88p. (J). (gr. 5 up). lib. bdg. (978-1-4222-0055-1(8)) Mason Crest Pubs.

LYING

see Truthfulness and Falsehood

LYLE THE CROCODILE (FICTITIOUS CHARACTER)—FICTION

Waber, Bernard. Funny, Funny Lyle. Waber, Bernard, illus. 2002. (Lyle the Crocodile Ser.). (Illus.). (J). 14.74 (978-0-7587-2559-2(0)) Book Wholesalers, Inc.

—Lovable Lyle. Waber, Bernard, illus. 2002. (Lyle the Crocodile Ser.). (Illus.). (J). 14.74 (978-0-7587-3043-5(8)) Book Wholesalers, Inc.

—Lyle at Christmas. Waber, Bernard, illus. 2002. (Lyle the Crocodile Ser.). (Illus.). (J). 23.40 (978-0-7587-3058-9(6)) Book Wholesalers, Inc.

—Lyle at Christmas. 2003. (Lyle the Crocodile Ser.). (Illus.). 48p. (J). (gr. k-3). pap. 5.95 (978-0-618-38002-2(7), Walter Lorraine) Houghton Mifflin Co. Trade & Reference Div.

—Lyle at Christmas. Waber, Bernard, illus. 1998. (Lyle the Crocodile Ser.). (Illus.). 48p. (J). (gr. k-3). tchr. ed. 16.00 (978-0-395-91304-8(7), Walter Lorraine) Houghton Mifflin Co. Trade & Reference Div.

—Lyle at the Office. Waber, Bernard, illus. 2002. (Lyle the Crocodile Ser.). (Illus.). (J). 13.79 (978-0-7587-3059-6(4)) Book Wholesalers, Inc.

—Lyle Finds His Mother. Waber, Bernard, illus. 2002. (Lyle the Crocodile Ser.). (Illus.). (J). 14.74 (978-0-7587-3060-2(8)) Book Wholesalers, Inc.

—Lyle, Lyle, Crocodile. Waber, Bernard, illus. 2002. (Lyle the Crocodile Ser.). (Illus.). (J). 14.74 (978-0-7587-3061-9(6)) Book Wholesalers, Inc.

—Lyle, Lyle, Crocodile. 1999. (Lyle the Crocodile Ser.). (J). (ps-3). 9.95 (978-1-56137-327-7(3)) Novel Units, Inc.

Waber, Bernard & Waber, Bernard. Lyle at Christmas. Waber, Bernard, illus. 2003. (Lyle the Crocodile Ser.). (Illus.). 48p. (J). (ps-3). lib. bdg. 14.10 (978-0-613-88087-9(0)) Tandem Library Bks.

LYME DISEASE

Donnelly, Karen J. Coping with Lyme Disease. 2005. (Coping Ser.). (Illus.). 192p. (YA). (gr. 7-12). lib. bdg. 26.50 (978-0-8239-3199-6(4)) Rosen Publishing Group, Inc., The.

—Everything You Need to Know about Lyme Disease. 2005. (Need to Know Library). (Illus.). 64p. (YA). (gr. 7-12). 25.25 (978-0-8239-3216-0(8), NTLYDI) Rosen Publishing Group, Inc., The.

Monroe, Judy. Lyme Disease. 2001. (Perspectives on Disease & Illness Ser.). (Illus.). 64p. (J). (gr. 4-6). lib. bdg. 23.93 (978-0-7368-0751-7(9), LifeMatters Bks.) Capstone Pr., Inc.

Silverstein, Alvin. Lyme Disease. 2000. (gr. 5-8). lib. bdg. 17.60 (978-0-613-34342-8(5)) Tandem Library Bks.

Silverstein, Alvin, et al. Lyme Disease. 2002. (My Health Ser.). (Illus.). 48p. (J). (gr. 3-5). pap. 6.95 (978-0-531-16562-1(0), Watts, Franklin) Scholastic Library Publishing.

—Lyme Disease. Stromoski, Rick, illus. 2001. (My Health Ser.). 48p. (J). (gr. 3-5). 25.50 (978-0-531-11638-8(7), Watts, Franklin) Scholastic Library Publishing.

—Lyme Disease. 2000. (Library Ser.). (Illus.). 64p. (J). (gr. 5-7). 25.50 (978-0-531-11751-4(0), Watts, Franklin) Scholastic Library Publishing.

Veggeberg, Scott. Lyme Disease. 1998. (Diseases & People Ser.). (Illus.). 104p. (YA). (gr. 6-12). lib. bdg. 20.95 (978-0-7660-1052-9(X)) Enslow Pubs., Inc.

Yannielli, Len. Lyme Disease. 2003. (Deadly Diseases & Epidemics Ser.). (Illus.). 112p. (gr. 9-13). 31.95 (978-0-7910-7463-3(3), Chelsea Hse.) Facts On File, Inc.

LYNX

Barret & Allen. El Lynx. 2002. (Gatos Salvajes Serie).Tr. of Wild Cats: The Lynx. (SPA.). 24p. (J). (gr. 3-5). 22.45 (978-1-4103-0011-9(0), Blackbirch Pr., Inc.) Thomson Gale.

Barrett, Jalma. Lynx. Allan, Larry, photos by. 1998. (Wildcats of North America Ser.). (Illus.). 24p. (J). (gr. 3-6). 22.45 (978-1-56711-259-7(5) , Blackbirch Pr., Inc.) Thomson Gale.

Blackbirch. Lynx. 2001. lib. bdg. 17.60 (978-0-613-84278-5(2)) Tandem Library Bks.

Gentle, Victor & Perry, Janet. Lynxes. 2002. (Big Cats Ser.). (Illus.). 24p. (J). (gr. 2 up). lib. bdg. 22.00 (978-0-8368-3028-6(8)) Stevens, Gareth Inc.

Parker, Barbara Keevil & Parker, Duane F. Lynxes. 2006. (Early Bird Nature Books). (Illus.). 48p. (J). (ps-7). 25.26 (978-0-8225-2871-5(1) , Lerner Pubns.) Lerner Publishing Group.

St. Pierre, Stephanie. Lynx. 2002. (In the Wild Ser.). (Illus.). 24p. (J). (gr. k-2). pap. 6.95 (978-1-58810-383-3(8) , 91103) Heinemann Library.

Stephanie, St Pierre. Lynx. 2001. (In the Wild Ser.). (Illus.). 24p. (J). (ps-3). lib. bdg. 21.36 (978-1-58810-109-9(6)) Heinemann Library.

Swinburne, Stephen R. Bobcat: North America's Cat. 2003. (Illus.). 32p. (YA). (gr. 4-6). 15.95 (978-1-56397-843-2(1)) Boyds Mills Pr.

LYNX—FICTION

Denson, Robert & Jefferies, Marc John. The Lynx. 2006. 120p. (J). pap. 12.95 (***978-0-9770050-8-6(9)***) Big Smile, Inc.

Fox, L. B. The Adventures of Marky, Slash & Levy. 2006. (ENG.). 184p. per. 19.95 (***978-1-4241-4992-6(4)***) PublishAmerica, Inc.

Lynx Twins Together. 2002. (Wild Heritage Collection Mini Bks.). (Illus.). 32p. (J). (978-1-59069-240-0(3) , H3011) Studio Mouse LLC.

Smith, Stephanie. Lynx Twins Grow Up. Hynes, Robert, illus. 2nd ed. 2005. (Soundprints' Read-and-Discover Ser.). (J). (gr. 1-3). 48p. 7.95 (978-1-931465-20-5(7) , B2002); 32p. pap. 3.95 (978-1-931465-19-9(3) , S2002) Soundprints.

—Lynx Twins Grow Up. 2002. (gr. k-3). lib. bdg. 11.80 (978-0-613-70879-1(2)) Tandem Library Bks.

LYSERGIC ACID DIETHYLAMIDE

see LSD (Drug)

M

MACARTHUR, DOUGLAS, 1880-1964

Benge, Janet & Benge, Geoff. Douglas MacArthur: What Greater Honor. 2005. (Illus.). 205p. (J). 6.99 (978-1-932096-15-6(9)) Emerald Bks.

Finkelstein, Norman H. The Emperor General: A Biography of Douglas MacArthur. 2001. (Illus.). 136p. (YA). pap. 9.95 (978-0-595-15280-3(5)) iUniverse, Inc.

Fox, Mary Virginia. Douglas MacArthur. 1999. (Importance of Ser.). (Illus.). 96p. (YA). (gr. 7-10). 27.45 (978-1-56006-545-6(1) , Lucent Bks.) Thomson Gale.

Gaines, Ann Graham. Douglas MacArthur: Brilliant General, Controversial Leader. 2001. (Historical American Biographies Ser.). (Illus.). 128p. (YA). (gr. 6-12). lib. bdg. 26.60 (978-0-7660-1445-9(2)) Enslow Pubs., Inc.

Haugen, Brenda. Douglas MacArthur: America's General. 2005. (Illus.). 112p. (J). (gr. 5-7). (978-0-7565-0994-1(7)) Compass Point Bks.

McPherson, Stephanie Sammartino. Douglas MacArthur. 2005. (History Maker Bios Ser.). (Illus.). 48p. (J). 26.60 (978-0-8225-2434-2(1)) Lerner Publishing Group.

Rice, Earle. MacArthur, General of the Army. 2003. (Great Military Leaders of the Twentieth Century Ser.). (Illus.). 112p. (gr. 6-12). 30.00 (978-0-7910-7402-2(1) , Chelsea Hse.) Facts On File, Inc.

MCCARTHY, JOSEPH, 1908-1957

Brooks, Philip. The McCarthy Hearings. 2003. (20th Century Perspectives Ser.). (Illus.). 48p. (J). pap. (978-1-4034-4178-2(2)); lib. bdg. 27.07 (978-1-4034-3808-9(0)) Heinemann Library.

Fitzgerald, Brian. McCarthyism: The Red Scare. 2006. 96p. (YA). (gr. 7 up). lib. bdg. (978-0-7565-2007-6(X)) Compass Point Bks.

Levine, Ellen. Catch a Tiger by the Toe: Voices from the McCarthy Era. 2005. 176p. (J). (gr. 1-6). 15.99 (978-0-670-88461-2(8) , Viking Adult) Penguin Group (USA) Inc.

Zeinert, Karen. McCarthy & the Fear of Communism in American History. 1998. (In American History Ser.). (Illus.). 128p. (YA). (gr. 5-12). lib. bdg. 26.60 (978-0-89490-987-0(8)) Enslow Pubs., Inc.

MCCLELLAN, GEORGE BRINTON, 1826-1885

Arnold, James R. & Wiener, Roberta. On to Richmond: The Civil War in the East, 1861-1862. 2005. (Civil War Ser.). (Illus.). 72p. (J). (gr. 5-12). lib. bdg. 25.26 (978-0-8225-2313-0(2)) Lerner Publishing Group.

Kelley, Brent P. George McClellan. 2001. (Famous Figures of the Civil War Era Ser.). (Illus.). 80p. (J). pap. (978-0-7910-6405-4(0) , Chelsea Hse.) Facts On File, Inc.

—George McClellan: Union General. 2001. (Famous Figures of the Civil War Era Ser.). (Illus.). 80p. (YA). (gr. 5-8). 25.00 (978-0-7910-6404-7(2) , Chelsea Hse.) Facts On File, Inc.

MCCORMICK, CYRUS HALL, 1809-1884

Aldrich, Lisa J. Cyrus McCormick: And the Mechanical Reaper. 2004. (American Business Leaders Ser.). (Illus.). 112p. (YA). (gr. 6-12). 23.95 (978-1-883846-91-6(9) , First Biographies) Reynolds, Morgan Inc.

Welch, Catherine A. Rise of the Reaper: A Story about Cyrus Hall McCormick. Jones, Jan Naimo, illus. 2007. (Creative Minds Biography Ser.). (J). spiral bd. 22.60 (978-0-8225-5988-7(9)) Lerner Publishing Group.

MACDOWELL, EDWARD ALEXANDER, 1861-1908

Gilman, Lawrence. Edward Macdowell. 2001. 190p. (YA). reprint ed. 88.00 (978-0-7222-5455-4(5)) Library Reprints, Inc.

MacDowell, Edward. Macdowell. 2001. (YA). reprint ed. 150.00 (978-0-7222-5456-1(3)) Library Reprints, Inc.

Porte, John F. Edward Macdowell: A Great American Tone Poet, His Life & Music. 2001. 180p. (YA). reprint ed. 88.00 (978-0-7222-5457-8(1)) Library Reprints, Inc.

MCDUCK, SCROOGE (FICTITIOUS CHARACTER)—FICTION

Barks, Carl, et al. Uncle Scrooge #371. 2007. 64p. pap. 7.99 (***978-1-60360-001-9(9)***) Gemstone Publishing, Inc.

Salvagnini, Rudy, et al. Uncle Scrooge #370. 2007. 64p. pap. 7.99 (***978-1-60360-000-2(0)***) Gemstone Publishing, Inc.

MCGRADY, JENNIE (FICTITIOUS CHARACTER)—FICTION

Rushford, Patricia H. Desperate Measures. l.t. ed. 2000. (Jennie McGrady Mysteries Ser.: No. 11). 333p. (J). (gr. 4-7). 23.95 (978-0-7862-2374-9(X)) Thorndike Pr.

MCGUIRE, LIZZIE (FICTITIOUS CHARACTER)—FICTION

Alfonsi, Alice. Lizzie for President. 2004. 149p. (J). lib. bdg. 16.92 (***978-1-4242-0681-0(2)***) Fitzgerald Bks.

Alfonsi, Alice, adapted by. 'Rents: Lizzie Mcguire. 2005. 134p. (J). lib. bdg. 16.92 (***978-1-4242-0689-6(8)***) Fitzgerald Bks.

Banim, Lisa. Hands off My Crush-Boy! 2004. 125p. (J). lib. bdg. 16.92 (***978-1-4242-0684-1(7)***) Fitzgerald Bks.

—In the Doghouse. 2005. 124p. (J). lib. bdg. 16.92 (***978-1-4242-0685-8(5)***) Fitzgerald Bks.

Banim, Lisa & Minsky, Terri. The Case of the Kate Haters. 2005. (Illus.). 124p. (J). (***978-1-4156-3927-6(2)***) Disney Pr.

Disney Staff, prod. Gordo & the Girl & You're a Good Man. 2004. (Lizzie McGuire Ser.: Vol. 8). (Illus.). 96p. pap. 7.99 (978-1-59532-279-1(5) , Tokyopop Kids) TOKYOPOP, Inc.

Jones, Jasmine. Mirror,Mirror. 2004. 151p. (J). lib. bdg. 16.92 (***978-1-4242-0675-9(8)***) Fitzgerald Bks.

Jones, Jasmine, adapted by. All over It: Lizzie Mcguire. 2005. 138p. (J). lib. bdg. 16.92 (***978-1-4242-0690-2(1)***) Fitzgerald Bks.

—The Importance of Being Gordo. 2005. (Illus.). 138p. (J). (***978-1-4155-7362-4(X)***) Disney Pr.

—Importance of Being Gordo. 2005. 138p. (J). lib. bdg. 16.92 (***978-1-4242-0688-9(X)***) Fitzgerald Bks.

—Oh, Brother! 2005. 146p. (J). lib. bdg. 16.92 (***978-1-4242-0682-7(0)***) Fitzgerald Bks.

Maridan, Samantha. A Totally Hottie Summer: Junior Novel. 2nd rev. ed. 2006. (Lizzie McGuire Super Special Ser.). (Illus.). 272p. (gr. 3-7). pap. 6.99 (978-0-7868-3842-4(6)) Disney Pr.

Minsky, Terri. All over It! 2005. (Illus.). 138p. (J). (***978-1-4156-0271-3(9)***) Disney Pr.

—The Lizzie McGuire Movie. 2004. (Illus.). 96p. pap. 7.99 (978-1-59182-832-7(5) , Tokyopop Kids) TOKYOPOP, Inc.

—Mom's Best Friend & Movin' on Up, 7 vols. (Lizzie McGuire Ser.). (Illus.). 96p. Vol. 6. 2004. pap. 7.99 (978-1-59182-572-2(5)); Vol. 7. 2004. pap. 7.99 (978-1-59182-573-9(3)); Vol. 10. 2005. pap. 7.99 (978-1-59532-281-4(7)) TOKYOPOP, Inc. (Tokyopop Kids).

Minsky, Terri, creator. I Do, I Don't & Come Fly with Me, 4 vols. 2003. (Lizzie McGuire Ser.: Vol. 4). (Illus.). 192p. pap. 7.99 (978-1-59182-246-2(7) , Tokyopop Kids) TOKYOPOP, Inc.

—Lizzie McGuire: Pool Party; Picture Day, 7 vols., Vol 1. 2003. (Lizzie McGuire Ser.: Vol. 1). (Illus.). 96p. (gr. 2 up). pap. 7.99 (978-1-59182-147-2(9) , Tokyopop Kids) TOKYOPOP, Inc.

—Rumors & I've Got Rhythmic, 7 vols. , Vol. 2. 2003. (Lizzie McGuire Ser.: Vol. 2). (Illus.). 96p. (gr. 2 up). pap. 7.99 (978-1-59182-148-9(7) , Tokyopop Kids) TOKYOPOP, Inc.

—When Moms Attack & Misadventures in Babysitt, 4 vols., Vol. 3. 2003. (Lizzie McGuire Ser.: Vol. 3). (Illus.). 192p. pap. 7.99 (978-1-59182-245-5(9) , Tokyopop Kids) TOKYOPOP, Inc.

My Crush Tacular Book of Valentines: Decorate Your Own Cards - Lizzie Style! 2003. (Lizzie McGuire Ser.). (Illus.). 32p. (ps-17). pap. 5.99 (978-0-7868-4613-9(5) , Disney Editions) Disney Pr.

Papademetriou, Lisa. On the Job. 2005. (Illus.). 32p. (gr. 3-5). pap. 138.00 (978-0-7910-7408-4(0) , Chelsea Hse.) Facts On File, Inc.

Thorpe, Kiki. Totally Crushed: Junior Novel. 2nd rev. ed. 2002. (Lizzie McGuire Ser.). 128p. (gr. 3-7). pap. 4.99 (978-0-7868-4539-2(2)) Disney Pr.

Tuber, Douglas & Maile, Tim. Lizzie's Nightmare; Sibling Bonds, 7 vols., Vol. 5. 2004. (Lizzie McGuire Ser.: Vol. 5). (Illus.). 96p. pap. 7.99 (978-1-59182-571-5(7) , Tokyopop Kids) TOKYOPOP, Inc.

MCGWIRE, MARK, 1963-

Brenner, Richard J. Mark McGwire. 1999. (Illus.). 32p. (YA). (gr. 1 up). pap. 4.50 (978-0-688-17085-1(4) , Harper Trophy) HarperCollins Pubs.

—Mark McGwire. 1999. (J). (978-0-606-17075-8(8)) Tandem Library Bks.

Christopher, Matt. At the Plate with... Mark McGwire. 1999. 11.64 (978-0-606-17501-2(6)) Tandem Library Bks.

Dougherty, Terri. Mark McGwire. 1999. (Jam Session Ser.). (Illus.). 32p. (J). (gr. 3-8). lib. bdg. 24.21 (978-1-57765-349-3(1) , ABDO & Daughters) ABDO Publishing Co.

Gallagher, Jim. Mark McGwire. 1999. (Real-Life Reader Biography Ser.). (Illus.). 32p. (gr. 3-8). lib. bdg. 15.95 (978-1-58415-017-6(3)) Mitchell Lane Pubs., Inc.

Kirkpatrick, Rob. Mark McGwire. 2001. (Great Record Breakers in Sports Ser.). (Illus.). 24p. (J). lib. bdg. 18.75 (978-0-8239-5630-2(X) , PowerKids Pr.) Rosen Publishing Group, Inc., The.

—Mark McGwire: Record Breaker. 2000. (Reading Power Ser.). (Illus.). 24p. (J). (gr. 1). lib. bdg. 17.25 (978-0-8239-5535-0(4) , PowerKids Pr.) Rosen Publishing Group, Inc., The.

—Mark Mcgwire: Record Breaker. 2002. (Deportistas de Poder Ser.). (SPA.). 24p. (J). lib. bdg. 17.25 (978-0-8239-6115-3(X) , Buenas Letra) Rosen Publishing Group, Inc., The.

—Mark McGwire, Rompe Records. 2002. (Coleccion Power Kids). (SPA & ENG., Illus.). 24p. (J). (gr. k-2). lib. bdg. 17.25 (978-0-8239-6133-7(8) , RN31304, Buenas Letra) Rosen Publishing Group, Inc., The.

Mark Mcgwire, 6 vols. (gr. 4 up). 39.95 (978-0-7368-9274-2(5)) Red Brick Learning.

Mark Mcgwrie. (Sports Heroes Ser.). 48p. (YA). 7.95 (978-0-7368-9180-6(3)) Capstone Pr., Inc.

Muskat, Carrie. Mark McGwire. 1999. (Baseball Legends Ser.). (Illus.). 64p. (gr. 4-7). pap. 7.95 (978-0-7910-5491-8(8) , Chelsea Hse.) Facts On File, Inc.

—Mark McGwire. 1999. (Baseball Legends Ser.). (978-0-606-18036-8(2)); (gr. 5-8). lib. bdg. 16.40 (978-0-613-26135-7(6)) Tandem Library Bks.

Powell, Phelan. Mark McGwire. 2000. (Sports Heroes Ser.). (Illus.). 48p. (J). (gr. 3-4). lib. bdg. 21.26 (978-0-7368-0578-0(8) , Capstone High-Interest Bks.) Capstone Pr., Inc.

Preller, James. McGwire & Sosa: A Season to Remember. 1998. (Illus.). 32p. (J). (ps up). pap. 5.99 (978-0-689-82871-3(3) , Simon Pulse) Simon & Schuster Children's Publishing.

Rains, Rob. Mark McGwire: "Mac Attack!" 1998. (Superstar Ser.). (Illus.). 100p. (YA). (gr. 7-10). per. 5.95 (978-1-58261-004-7(5)) Sports Publishing, LLC.

—Mark McGwire: Slugger! Sporting News Staff, ed. 1998. (Illus.). 50p. (J). (gr. 1-6). 15.95 (978-1-58261-005-4(3)) Sports Publishing, LLC.

Savage, Jeff. Mark McGwire: Home Run King. (Sports Achievers Biographies Ser.). (Illus.). (YA). (gr. 4-9). 2003. 64p. pap. 5.95 (978-0-8225-9845-9(0) , Carolrhoda Bks.); 1999. 80p. lib. bdg. 22.60 (978-0-8225-3675-8(7) , LernerSports) Lerner Publishing Group.

Stewart, Mark Alan. Mark McGwire: Home Run King. 1999. (Sports Stars Ser.). 48p. (gr. 3-4). pap. 5.95 (978-0-516-26512-4(1) , Children's Pr.) Scholastic Library Publishing.

Thornley, Stew. Mark McGwire: Star Home Run Hitter. 1999. (Sports Reports). (Illus.). 104p. (YA). (gr. 4-10). lib. bdg. 20.95 (978-0-7660-1329-2(4)) Enslow Pubs., Inc.

Weber, Bruce & LaPadula, Tom. Mark McGwire: The Home-run King. 1999. (J). 3.99 (978-0-439-09905-9(6)) Scholastic, Inc.

MACHINERY

see also Agricultural Machinery; Engines; Inventions; Locomotives; Mechanical Drawing; Mechanics; Steam-Engines

Abramson, Andra Serlin. Heavy Equipment up Close. 2008. (Illus.). 28p. (J). 9.95 (***978-1-4027-4799-1(3)***) Sterling Publishing Co., Inc.

Adkins, Jan. Moving Heavy Things. 2004. 48p. (J). (978-0-937822-82-1(5)) WoodenBoat Pubns.

Alinas, Marv. Diggers. 2008. (Machines at Work Ser.). 24p. (J). 22.79 (***978-1-59296-948-7(8)***) Child's World, Inc.

Amazing Machines. 2004. (Sticker Timelines Ser.). (Illus.). 12p. (J). pap. (978-1-84229-844-2(5)) Top That! Publishing PLC.

Ardagh, Philip. A Hole in the Road. (Illus.). 32p. (J). lib. bdg. 24.25 (978-1-931983-02-0(X)) Chrysalis Education.

Armentrout, David & Armentrout, Patricia. Una Palanca. 2002. (Como Podemos Utilizar Maquinas Simples? Ser.). (SPA.). (J). 26.60 (978-1-58952-435-4(7)) Rourke Publishing, LLC.

—Una Polea. 2002. (Como Podemos Utilizar Maquinas Simples? Ser.). (SPA.). (J). 26.60 (978-1-58952-436-1(5)) Rourke Publishing, LLC.

Auch, Alison. Cool Tools. 2002. (Spyglass Books). (Illus.). 24p. (J). (gr. 1 up). lib. bdg. 18.60 (978-0-7565-0230-0(6)) Compass Point Bks.

Backhoes. (Mighty MacHines Ser.). 24p. (J). 6.95 (978-0-7368-5130-5(5)) Capstone Pr., Inc.

Backhoes Mighty Machines. 2006. (Illus.). 24p. (J). (gr. k-2). 18.50 (***978-0-531-17894-2(3)***) Scholastic Library Publishing.

Bailey, Gerry. Underwater Machines. Boulter, Steve & Smith, Jan, illus. 2005. (Crafty Inventions Ser.). 48p. (C). (gr. 4-6). 26.60 (978-1-4048-1045-7(5)) Picture Window Bks.

Baker, Wendy. Experimenta - Maquinas. (SPA.). 52p. (J). 17.50 (978-84-348-3997-7(0)) SM Ediciones ESP. *Dist:* AIMS International Bks., Inc.

Bender, Lionel. Diggers & Tractors. 2006. (J). (978-1-59389-267-8(5)) Chrysalis Education.

Berendes, Mary. Machines/Las M¿quinas. 2007. (WordBooks/Libros de Palabras Ser.). 24p. (J). 19.93 (***978-1-59296-799-5(X)***) Child's World, Inc.

Bridges, Sarah. I Drive a Backhoe. Muehlenhardt, Amy Bailey, illus. 2006. 24p. (J). (ps-2). 22.60 (978-1-4048-1604-6(8)) Picture Window Bks.

—I Drive a Dump Truck. Alderman, Derrick & Shea, Denise, illus. 2004. (Working Wheels Ser.). 24p. (C). (gr. k-2). 22.60 (978-1-4048-0614-6(8)) Picture Window Bks.

—I Drive a Street Sweeper. Muehlenhardt, Amy Bailey, illus. 2006. 24p. (J). (ps-2). 22.60 (978-1-4048-1608-4(9)) Picture Window Bks.

Brooks, Felicity. Diggers Lift-and-Look. 2005. (Illus.). 12p. (J). per. 9.95 (978-0-7945-1067-1(1) , Usborne) EDC Publishing.

Brooks, Felicity. Excavadoras. 2007. 12p. (J). bds. 9.99 (***978-0-7460-8347-5(5)*** , Usborne) EDC Publishing.

Bryant-Mole, Karen. Dot-to-Dot Machines. Round, Graham, illus. rev. ed. 2003. 24p. (J). pap. 3.99 (978-0-7945-1495-2(2) , Usborne) EDC Publishing.

Butterfield, Moira. Bulldozers & Other Construction Machines. Lyon, Chris & Biggin, Gary, illus. (J). mass mkt. 8.99 (978-0-590-24556-2(2)) Scholastic, Inc.

Canizares, Susan. Simple Machines. 1999. (J). 2.50 (978-0-439-08126-9(2)) Scholastic, Inc.

Carey, Craig Robert. Driving Force: Power Lifting. 2006. (Tonka Ser.: No. 8). (Illus.). 24p. (J). pap. 3.50 (978-0-439-83012-6(5)) Scholastic, Inc.

Castor, H. & Young, C. The Usborne Book of Machines that Work. 2004. (Young MacHines Ser.). 96p. (J). lib. bdg. 22.95 (978-1-58086-031-4(1) , Usborne) EDC Publishing.

Caterpillar Inc. Staff, contrib. by. Trucks & Diggers from One to Ten. 2003. (Illus.). 20p. (J). bds. 6.95 (978-0-8118-4029-3(8)) Chronicle Bks. LLC.

Caterpillar Tractor Company Staff, contrib. by. Big Yellow Trucks & Diggers: Colors. 2003. (Illus.). 20p. (J). bds. 6.95 (978-0-8118-4030-9(1)) Chronicle Bks. LLC.

The Clean Machine: Individual Title Six-Packs. (gr. k-1). 23.00 (978-0-7635-9077-2(0)) Rigby Education.

Concrete Mixers Mighty Machine. 2006. (Illus.). 24p. (J). (gr. k-2). 18.50 (***978-0-531-17896-6(X)***) Scholastic Library Publishing.

Cranes Might Machines. 2006. (Illus.). 24p. (J). (gr. k-2). 18.50 (***978-0-531-17897-3(8)***) Scholastic Library Publishing.

Dahl, Michael. Cut, Chop, & Stop: A Book about Wedges. Shea, Denise, illus. 2006. (Amazing Science Ser.). 24p. (J). (gr. k-4). 22.60 (978-1-4048-1307-6(1) , 1253207) Picture Window Bks.

—Pull, Lift, & Lower: A Book about Pulleys. Shea, Denise, illus. 2006. (Amazing Science Ser.). 24p. (J). (gr. k-4). 22.60 (978-1-4048-1305-2(5) , 1253208) Picture Window Bks.

—Scoop, Seesaw, & Raise: A Book about Levers. Shea, Denise, illus. 2006. (Amazing Science Ser.). 24p. (J). (gr. k-4). 22.60 (978-1-4048-1303-8(9)) Picture Window Bks.

—Simple Machines, 4 bks. Incl. Inclined Planes. lib. bdg. 18.60 (978-1-56065-447-6(3)); Levers. lib. bdg. 18.60 (978-1-56065-444-5(9)); Pulleys. lib. bdg. 18.60 (978-1-56065-445-2(7)); Wheels & Axles. lib. bdg. 18.60 (978-1-56065-446-9(5)); 24p. (J). (gr. 1-2). 1996. (Illus.). Set lib. bdg. 74.40 (978-1-56065-634-0(4) , Bridgestone Bks.) Capstone Pr., Inc.

—Twist, Dig, & Drill: A Book about Screws. Shea, Denise, illus. 2006. (Amazing Science Ser.). 24p. (J). (gr. k-4). 22.60 (978-1-4048-1306-9(3) , 1253212) Picture Window Bks.

Dahl, Michael & Shea, Denise. Levanta y Abre: Un Libro Sobre Palancas. Shea, Denise, illus. 2007. (ENG & SPA.). (J). lib. bdg. (***978-1-4048-3228-2(9)***) Picture Window Bks.

—Sube y Baja: Un Libro Sobre Poleas. Shea, Denise, illus. 2007. (ENG & SPA.). (J). lib. bdg. (***978-1-4048-3224-4(6)***) Picture Window Bks.

DK Publishing, creator. My Terrific Digger Book. 2007. (Illus.). 12p. (J). (ps-2). 12.99 (***978 0-7566-3100-0(9)***) Dorling Kindersley Publishing, Inc.

DK Publishing Staff. Trucks & Diggers. 2007. (Let's Look Ser.). (Illus.). 36p. (J). 4.99 (978-0-7566-2595-5(5)) Dorling Kindersley Publishing, Inc.

—Word. 2007. 12p. (J). (ps-1). bds. 8.99 (978-0-7566-2587-0(4)) Dorling Kindersley Publishing, Inc.

Dollin, Laura. Digger Power. 2003. (Tough Stuff Ser.).Tr. of Excavadora Superfuerte. (Illus.). 10p. (ps-17). 5.99 (978-0-7868-1980-5(4)) Hyperion Bks. for Children.

—Excavadora Superfuerte. 2003. (Tough Stuff Ser.). (SPA.). 10p. (ps-17). 5.99 (978-0-7868-1976-8(6)) Hyperion Bks. for Children.

Domnauer, Teresa. Extreme Machines, Level 2. 2007. (Extreme Readers Ser.). 32p. (J). (gr. k-1). pap. 3.95 (***978-0-7696-6540-5(3)***) School Specialty Publishing.

Dorling Kindersley Publishing Staff. Big Building Site. 2006. (Illus.). 12p. (J). (ps-1). bds. 8.99 (978-0-7566-2328-9(6)) Dorling Kindersley Publishing, Inc.

—Digger. 2006. (Machines at Work Ser.). 32p. (J). pap. 6.99 (978-0-7566-1907-7(6)) Dorling Kindersley Publishing, Inc.

—Excavadores y Volquetas/Diggers & Dumpers. 2004. (Things That Go Board Books Ser.). (ENG & SPA.). 10p. (J). bds. 3.99 (978-0-7566-0443-1(5)) Dorling Kindersley Publishing, Inc.

—Loader. 2006. (Illus.). 12p. (J). pap. 6.99 (978-0-7566-2330-2(8)) Dorling Kindersley Publishing, Inc.

—Maquinas Grandes. 2003. (DK Readers Ser.). (SPA., Illus.). 48p. (J). pap. 3.99 (978-0-7894-9518-1(X)) Dorling Kindersley Publishing, Inc.

—Maquinas Rescate / Rescue Machines. 2004. (My 1ST Board Books Ser.). 22p. (J). bds. 3.99 (978-0-7566-0445-5(1)) Dorling Kindersley Publishing, Inc.

—Maqunias Rapidas / Speedy Machines. 2004. (My 1ST Board Books Ser.). 24p. (J). bds. 3.99 (978-0-7566-0446-2(X)) Dorling Kindersley Publishing, Inc.

M N O

Douglas, Lloyd G. Simple Machines, 6 vols., Set. 2004. (Illus.). 24p. (J). (ps-2). 87.00 (978-0-516-29311-0(7)) Scholastic Library Publishing.

—What Is a Lever? 2002. (Welcome Bks.). (Illus.). 24p. (J). (ps-2). pap. 4.95 (978-0-516-24022-0(6) , Children's Pr.) Scholastic Library Publishing.

—What Is a Lever? 2002. (gr. k-3). lib. bdg. 12.95 (978-0-613-58881-2(9)) Tandem Library Bks.

—What Is a Plane? 2002. (gr. k-3). lib. bdg. 12.95 (978-0-613-58882-9(7)) Tandem Library Bks.

—What Is a Pulley? 2002. (gr. k-3). lib. bdg. 12.95 (978-0-613-58883-6(5)) Tandem Library Bks.

—What Is a Screw? 2002. (gr. k-3). lib. bdg. 12.95 (978-0-613-58884-3(3)) Tandem Library Bks.

—What Is a Wedge? 2002. (Wel-Simple MacHines Ser.). (Illus.). 24p. (J). (ps-2). 18.00 (978-0-516-23965-1(1)); pap. 4.95 (978-0-516-24026-8(9)) Scholastic Library Publishing. (Children's Pr.).

—What Is a Wedge? 2002. (gr. k-3). lib. bdg. 12.95 (978-0-613-58885-0(1)) Tandem Library Bks.

Dump Trucks Mighty Machines. 2006. (Illus.). 24p. (J). (gr. k-2). 18.50 (***978-0-531-17898-0(6)**) Scholastic Library Publishing.

Earth Movers. (Mighty MacHines Ser.). 24p. (J). 6.95 (978-0-7368-5135-0(6)) Capstone Pr., Inc.

Earth Movers Might Machines. 2006. (Illus.). 24p. (J). (gr. k-2). 18.50 (***978-0-531-17899-7(4)**) Scholastic Library Publishing.

Eggleton, Jill. The Amazing Machine. Kieley, Rob, illus. (Sails Literacy Ser.). 24p. (gr. 3 up). 27.00 (978-0-7578-6979-2(3)); Pack. 57.00 (978-0-7578-6995-2(5)) Rigby Education.

—The Amazing Machine: 6 Small Books. Kieley, Rob, illus. (Sails Literacy Ser.). 24p. (gr. 3 up). 25.00 (978-0-7578-6987-7(4)) Rigby Education.

Eick, Jean. Concrete Mixers. 2007. (Machines at Work Ser.). 24p. (J). 22.79 (978-1-59296-829-9(5)) Child's World, Inc.

—Diggers. 1998. (Machines at Work Ser.). (Illus.). 24p. (J). (ps-3). 21.36 (978-1-56766-529-1(2)) Child's World, Inc.

—Forklifts. 1998. (Machines at Work Ser.). (Illus.). 24p. (J). (ps-3). 21.36 (978-1-56766-530-7(6)) Child's World, Inc.

Everyday Machines, 6 Packs. (Rigby Focus Ser.). 16p. (gr. 1 up). 30.00 (978-0-7578-5559-7(8)); 28.00 (978-0-7578-5327-2(7)) Rigby Education.

Fowler, Allan. Simple Machines. 2001. (Rookie Read-About Science Ser.). (Illus.). 32p. (J). (gr. 1-2). pap. 4.95 (978-0-516-27310-5(8) , Children's Pr.) Scholastic Library Publishing.

—Simple Machines. 2001. (gr. k-3). lib. bdg. 12.95 (978-0-613-54661-4(X)) Tandem Library Bks.

French, Cathy. Del hacha al Cierre: Las maquinas simples & from Axes to Zippers: Simple Machines. 2005. spiral bd. 77.00 (***978-1-4108-5672-2(0)**) Benchmark Education Co.

French, Kathy. From Axes to Zippers: Simple Machines. 2004. (Navigators Ser.). (J). pap. 38.00 (978-1-4108-0413-6(5)) Benchmark Education Co.

Frost, Helen. Looking at Simple Machines, 6 bks. Saunders-Smith, Gail, ed. Incl. What Are Inclined Planes? lib. bdg. 15.93 (978-0-7368-0845-3(0)); What Are Levers? lib. bdg. 15.93 (978-0-7368-0846-0(9)); What Are Pulleys? lib. bdg. 15.93 (978-0-7368-0847-7(7)); What Are Screws? lib. bdg. 15.93 (978-0-7368-0848-4(5)); What Are Wedges? lib. bdg. 15.93 (978-0-7368-0849-1(3)); What Are Wheels & Axles? lib. bdg. 15.93 (978-0-7368-0850-7(7)); 24p. (J). (gr. k-1). 2001. (Illus.). 2000. Set lib. bdg. 95.58 (978-0-7368-0886-6(8) , Pebble Bks.) Capstone Pr., Inc.

—What Are Levers? Saunders-Smith, Gail, ed. 2001. (Looking at Simple Machines Ser.). (Illus.). 24p. (J). (gr. k-1). lib. bdg. 15.93 (978-0-7368-0846-0(9) , Pebble Bks.) Capstone Pr., Inc.

—What Are Pulleys? Saunders-Smith, Gail, ed. 2001. (Looking at Simple Machines Ser.). (Illus.). 24p. (J). (gr. k-1). lib. bdg. 15.93 (978-0-7368-0847-7(7) , Pebble Bks.) Capstone Pr., Inc.

Gardner, Robert. Sensational Science Projects with Simple Machines. LaBaff, Tom, illus. 2006. (Fantastic Physical Science Experiments Ser.). 48p. (J). lib. bdg. 23.93 (978-0-7660-2585-1(3) , Enslow Elementary) Enslow Pubs., Inc.

Glover, David. Pulleys & Gears. (Illus.). 24p. (J). 2006. (978-1-4034-8564-9(X)); 2002. (gr. 2-4). pap. 6.50 (978-1-4034-0057-4(1) , 91501) Heinemann Library.

—Ramps & Wedges. 2006. (Illus.). 24p. (J). (978-1-4034-8565-6(8)) Heinemann Library.

—Springs. 2002. (Simple Machines Ser.). (Illus.). 24p. (J). (gr. 2-4). pap. 6.50 (978-1-4034-0060-4(1) , 91504) Heinemann Library.

Glover, David & Barnes, Jon. Machines. (Make It Work! Ser.). (Illus.). 48p. (J). pap. 7.95 (978-0-590-24401-5(9)) Scholastic, Inc.

Glover, David & Glover, Penny. Diggers. 2005. (Big Machines Ser.). (Illus.). 30p. (J). (gr. 2-5). lib. bdg. 27.10 (978-1-58340-701-1(4)) Smart Apple Media.

Goldsack, Gabby. Trucks & Earthmovers. 2003. (Busy Books). (Illus.). 32p. (J). 9.95 (978-1-57768-901-0(1) , Waterbird Bks.) School Specialty Publishing.

Good, Keith. Gear Up! Marvelous Machine Projects. 1999. (Design It! Ser.). (Illus.). 30p. (gr. 4-8). lib. bdg. 21.27 (978-0-8225-3566-9(1)) Lerner Publishing Group.

Gore, Gordon R. Experimenting with Simple Machines: Hands-on Science Activities. 2000. (Experimenting With— Ser.). (Illus.). 48p. (J). pap. (978-1-55244-038-4(9)) Trifolium Bks., Inc.

Graham, Ian. In the Water. 2006. (QEB Machines at Work Ser.). (Illus.). 36p. (J). lib. bdg. 16.95 (978-1-59566-190-6(5)) QEB Publishing Inc.

—Trucks & Earthmovers. 2005. (World's Greatest Ser.). (Illus.). 32p. (978-1-4109-2088-1(7)); pap. (978-1-4109-2095-9(X)) Steck-Vaughn.

Grolier Educational Staff, contrib. by. Inside A—, 16 vols. 2000. (Illus.). 512p. (J). (gr. 5-8). 299.00 (978-0-7172-9521-0(4) , Grolier) Scholastic Library Publishing.

Gunn, Richard. Monster Movers. 2006. (Cool Wheels Ser.). (Illus.). 32p. (J). lib. bdg. (978-0-8368-6827-2(7)) Stevens, Gareth Inc.

Hankin, Rosie. Cut & Paste Trucks, Trains, & Big Machines. 2006. (Illus.). 32p. lib. bdg. (***978-0-8368-7721-2(7)**) Stevens, Gareth Inc.

Harris, Nicholas. How Things Work. 2006. (First Library of Knowledge). 32p. (gr. 2-4). 23.70 (978-1-4103-0346-2(2) , Blackbirch Pr., Inc.) Thomson Gale.

Hewitt, Sally. Springs: How Far Does It Stretch? 2005. (Science Starters Ser.). (Illus.). 32p. (J). (gr. 3-7). lib. bdg. 27.10 (978-1-59604-019-9(X)) Stargazer Bks.

Hill, Lee Sullivan. Earth Movers. 2003. (gr. k-3). lib. bdg. 14.10 (978-0-613-52364-6(4)) Tandem Library Bks.

—Earthmovers. 2003. (Pull Ahead Bks.). (Illus.). 32p. (J). (gr. k-2). lib. bdg. 22.60 (978-0-8225-0689-8(0)) Lerner Publishing Group.

—Palas Mecanicas (Earthmovers) 2006. (Libros para Avanzar Ser.). (ENG & SPA.). (J). 22.60 (978-0-8225-6230-6(8) , Ediciones Lerner) Lerner Publishing Group.

Hirst, Mike. Monster Machines. Veres, Laszlo, illus. 2005. (Twenty4Sevens Ser.). 48p. (J). pap. (978-0-439-78529-7(4)) Scholastic, Inc.

Holt, Rinehart and Winston Staff. Holt Science & Technology Chptr. 18: Work & Machines: Chapter Resources - Tennessee Edition. 3rd ed. 2003. (YA). pap. 11.40 (978-0-03-069179-9(6)) Holt, Rinehart & Winston.

Home, Jane. Diggers & Dumpers. 2006. (Rough & Tough Ser.). (Illus.). 10p. (ps). per., bds. 6.95 (978-1-84610-277-6(4)) Make Believe Ideas GBR. *Dist:* Ingram Pub. Services.

How Machines Help, 6 vols. (Sunshinetm Science Ser.). 24p. (gr. 1-2). 31.50 (978-0-7802-0301-3(1)); 36.95 (978-0-7802-0552-9(9)) Wright Group, The.

Jefferis, David. Extreme Structures. 2006. (Science Frontiers Ser.). (Illus.). 32p. (J). (gr. 3-9). pap. (978-0-7787-2872-6(2)) Crabtree Publishing Co.

—Machines & Inventions. 2002. (Young Library). (Illus.). 32p. (J). lib. bdg. 25.69 (978-0-7398-6323-7(1)) Raintree.

—Micro Machines. 2006. (Science Frontiers Ser.). (Illus.). 32p. (J). (gr. 3-9). pap. (978-0-7787-2873-3(0)) Crabtree Publishing Co.

—Young Library - Monster Machines, 5 bks., Set. Incl. Jets. lib. bdg. 25.69 (978-0-7398-2878-6(9)); Racing Cars. lib. bdg. 25.69 (978-0-7398-2880-9(0)); Spacecraft. lib. bdg. 25.69 (978-0-7398-2881-6(9)); Super Bikes. lib. bdg. 25.69 (978-0-7398-2882-3(7)); Trucks. lib. bdg. 25.69 (978-0-7398-2879-3(7)); 32p. (J). (ps-3). 2001. (Illus.). 2001. Set lib. bdg. 128.45 (978-0-7398-2883-0(5)) Raintree.

Jeffries, David. Monster Machines, 5 bks., Set. 2003. (C). pap. (978-1-4109-0149-1(1)) Raintree.

Jones, Melanie Davis. Big Machines. Gay-Kassel, Doreen, illus. 2003. (Rookie Reader Espanol Ser.). (J). (gr. k-2). pap. 4.95 (978-0-516-27829-2(0)); 24p. 19.50 (978-0-516-22845-7(5)) Scholastic Library Publishing. (Children's Pr.).

—Big Machines. 2003. (gr. k-3). lib. bdg. 12.95 (978-0-613-67600-7(9)) Tandem Library Bks.

—Grandes Maquinas. Gay-Kassel, Doreen, illus. 2003. (Rookie Reader Espanol Ser.). (SPA.). (J). 19.50 (978-0-516-25887-4(7) , Children's Pr.) Scholastic Library Publishing.

Kirk, Ellen. My Big Machine Book. 2007. (Illus.). 16p. (J). 5.99 (***978-0-06-089969-1(7)**) HarperCollins Pubs.

Kravetz, Jonathan. Learning about Simple Machines with Graphic Organizers. 2007. (Graphic Organizers in Science Ser.). (Illus.). 24p. (978-1-4042-2396-7(7)); pap. (978-1-4042-2206-9(5)) Rosen Publishing Group, Inc., The.

Lancaster, Juliana. PBIS- Building Big Things. 2005. pap., stu. ed. 8.00 (978-1-58591-565-1(3)) It's About Time, Herff Jones Education Diiv.

Lawrence, Debbie & Lawrence, Richard. Machines & Motion: God's Design for the Physical World. 2005. (Illus.). 160p. per. (978-0-9725365-9-2(0)) R & D Educational Ctr.

Levine, Shar & Johnstone, Leslie. First Science Experiments: Mighty Machines. 2006. (Illus.). 48p. (J). pap. 4.95 (978-1-4027-4051-0(4)) Sterling Publishing Co., Inc.

—First Science Experiments with Nature, Senses, Weather & Machines. Harpster, Steve, illus. 2005. 192p. (978-1-4027-2922-5(7)) Sterling Publishing Co., Inc.

—Mighty Machines. 2004. (Illus.). 48p. (J). 12.95 (978-1-4027-0900-5(5)) Sterling Publishing Co., Inc.

Lindeen, Mary. Graders. 2007. (Illus.). 24p. (J). lib. bdg. 19.95 (978-1-60014-118-8(8)) Bellwether Media.

Lindeen, Mary. Mighty Machines, Level 1, 6 bks., Set. Incl. Airplanes. 18.50 (***978-0-531-17556-9(1)**); Fire Trucks. 18.50 (***978-0-531-17557-6(X)**); Ships. 18.50 (***978-0-531-17558-3(8)**); Tractors. 18.50 (***978-0-531-17559-0(6)**); Trains. 18.50 (***978-0-531-17560-6(X)**); Trucks. 18.50 (***978-0-531-17561-3(8)**); 24p. (J). (gr. k-2). (Blastoff! Readers Ser.). 2007. 111.00 (***978-0-531-17741-9(6)** , Children's Pr.) Scholastic Library Publishing.

Litchfield, Jo & Brooks, Felicity. Diggers. 2004. (Chunky Board Bks.). (Illus.). 10p. (J). 4.95 (978-0-7945-0350-5(0) , Usborne) EDC Publishing.

Looking at Simple Machines Set. (gr. k-2). 172.95 (978-0-7368-9227-8(3)) Red Brick Learning.

MacAulay, Kelley & Kalman, Bobbie. Cool Construction Vehicles. 2007. (Vehicles on the Move Ser.). (Illus.). 32p. (J). (gr. 1-5). (***978-0-7787-3042-2(5)**); pap. (***978-0-7787-3056-9(5)**) Crabtree Publishing Co.

Machines. (Make it Work Ser.). 42p. (J). (gr. 4-8). pap. (978-1-882210-48-0(4)) Action Publishing, Inc.

Machines. 2002. (Questions & Answers Ser.). 32p. (J). 7.95 (978-0-7525-7242-0(3)) Parragon, Inc.

Machines: Big Book: Level E. 8p. 20.95 (978-0-322-00344-6(X)) Wright Group, The.

Machines in the Home: Individual Title Six-Packs. (gr. k-1). 23.00 (978-0-7635-9075-8(4)) Rigby Education.

Machines That Work. 2002. (Illus.). (J). pap. 5.43 (978-0-7398-5922-3(6)) Steck-Vaughn.

Martin, M. T. Earth Movers. 2006. (Blastoff! Readers Ser.). (Illus.). 24p. (J). lib. bdg. 16.95 (978-1-60014-047-1(5)) Bellwether Media.

Mason, Adrienne & Hodge, Deborah. Simple Machines. Boudreau, Ray, photos by. unabr. ed. 1998. (Starting with Science Ser.). (Illus.). 32p. (J). (gr. k-3). (978-1-55074-311-1(2)) Kids Can Pr., Ltd.

Mason, Paul. Wackiest Machines Ever: Forms of Energy. 2005. (Illus.). 32p. (J). (978-1-4109-1946-5(3)) Steck-Vaughn.

—Wackiest Machines Ever! Forms of Energy. 2005. (Illus.). 32p. (J). (gr. 3-5). lib. bdg. 28.21 (978-1-4109-1915-1(3)) Steck-Vaughn.

Matthews, Stuart. Levers & Pulleys. 2001. (How Does It Work? Ser.). (Illus.). 24p. (J). (gr. 2-7). lib. bdg. 21.30 (978-1-58340-068-5(0)) Smart Apple Media.

Maynard, Christopher. Extreme Machines, Vol. 4. 2000. (Eyewitness Readers). (Illus.). 48p. (J). (gr. 2-4). pap. 3.99 (978-0-7894-5417-1(3)) Dorling Kindersley Publishing, Inc.

—Extreme Machines. 2000. (Illus.). 48p. lib. bdg. 10.79 (978-0-606-18117-4(2)); lib. bdg. 11.80 (978-0-613-25102-0(4)) Tandem Library Bks.

Maynard, Christopher & Dorling Kindersley Publishing Staff. Extreme Machines. 2000. (Eyewitness Readers). (Illus.). 48p. (J). (gr. 2-4). 12.95 (978-0-7894-5418-8(1)) Dorling Kindersley Publishing, Inc.

McBride, Carol. Making Magnificent Machines: Fun with Math, Science & Engineering. 1999. (Illus.). 128p. (J). (gr. k-8). pap. 24.95 (978-1-56976-102-1(7) , 1104, Zephyr Pr.) Chicago Review Pr., Inc.

McClellan, Ray. Backhoes. 2006. (Blastoff! Readers Ser.). (Illus.). 24p. (J). lib. bdg. 16.95 (978-1-60014-042-6(4)) Bellwether Media.

—Concrete Mixers. 2006. (Blastoff! Readers Ser.). (Illus.). 24p. (J). lib. bdg. 16.95 (978-1-60014-044-0(0)) Bellwether Media.

Mega Machines. 2004. (Illus.). 64p. (J). pap. (978-2-7643-0202-6(9)) Phidal Publishing, Inc./Editions Phidal, Inc.

Mezzanotte, Jim. Cargadores. 2006. (Vehiculos Gigantes (Giant Vehicles) Ser.). (SPA.). 24p. (J). pap. 5.95 (978-0-8368-5994-2(4)); lib. bdg. 22.00 (978-0-8368-5987-4(1)) Stevens, Gareth Inc.

—Excavadoras. 2006. (Vehiculos Gigantes (Giant Vehicles) Ser.). (SPA.). 24p. (J). pap. 5.95 (978-0-8368-5995-9(2)); lib. bdg. 22.00 (978-0-8368-5988-1(X)) Stevens, Gareth Inc.

—Giant Diggers. 2005. (Illus.). 24p. (J). pap. (978-0-8368-4918-9(3)); lib. bdg. 22.00 (978-0-8368-4911-0(6)) Stevens, Gareth Inc.

—Giant Loaders. 2005. (Illus.). 24p. (J). pap. (978-0-8368-4920-2(5)); lib. bdg. 22.00 (978-0-8368-4913-4(2)) Stevens, Gareth Inc.

—Giant Scrapers. 2005. (Illus.). 24p. (J). (978-0-8368-4921-9(3)); lib. bdg. 22.00 (978-0-8368-4914-1(0)) Stevens, Gareth Inc.

—How Levers Work. 2006. (Illus.). 24p. (J). pap. (978-0-8368-7352-8(1)); lib. bdg. (978-0-8368-7347-4(5)) Stevens, Gareth Inc.

—How Pulleys Work. 2006. (Illus.). 24p. (J). pap. (978-0-8368-7353-5(X)); lib. bdg. (978-0-8368-7348-1(3)) Stevens, Gareth Inc.

—How Ramps, Wedges, & Screws Work. 2006. (Illus.). 24p. (J). pap. (978-0-8368-7354-2(8)); lib. bdg. (978-0-8368-7349-8(1)) Stevens, Gareth Inc.

—Raspadores. 2006. (Vehiculos Gigantes (Giant Vehicles) Ser.). (SPA.). 24p. (J). pap. 5.95 (978-0-8368-5997-3(9)); lib. bdg. 22.00 (978-0-8368-5990-4(1)) Stevens, Gareth Inc.

Mighty Machines, 6 vols., Set. 2006. (Blastoff! Readers Ser.). (Illus.). (J). (gr. k-2). 111.00 (***978-0-531-16881-3(6)**) Scholastic Library Publishing.

Mighty Movers. 2005. (J). (gr. k-4). lib. bdg. 128.10 (978-1-59197-824-4(6)) ABDO Publishing Co.

Mitton, Tony. Flashing Fire Engines. Parker, Ant, illus. 2000. (Amazing Machines Ser.). 24p. (J). (ps-k). pap. 3.95 (978-0-7534-5307-0(X) , Kingfisher) Houghton Mifflin Co. Trade & Reference Div.

—Flashing Fire Engines. 2000. (ps-2). lib. bdg. 11.80 (978-0-613-90366-0(8)) Tandem Library Bks.

—Roaring Rockets. Parker, Ant, illus. 2000. (Amazing Machines Ser.). 24p. (J). (ps-k). pap. 3.95 (978-0-7534-5305-6(3) , Kingfisher) Houghton Mifflin Co. Trade & Reference Div.

—Roaring Rockets. 2000. (ps-2). lib. bdg. 11.80 (978-0-613-88857-8(X)) Tandem Library Bks.

Monster Machines Stencil Book. 2007. (Illus.). 24p. (J). (gr. 3-7). bds. 12.95 (***978-1-59125-792-9(1)** , Penton Kids) Penton Overseas, Inc.

Moor, Jo Ellen & Norris, Jill. Simple Machines. Evans, Marilyn, ed. Robison, Don & Davis, Cindy, illus. 1998. (ScienceWorks for Kids Ser.: Vol. 8). 80p. (J). (gr. 1-3). pap., tchr. ed. 9.95 (978-1-55799-689-3(X) , EMC 860) Evan-Moor Educational Pubs.

Moore, Elaine. See You Later, Excavator. 2001. (Planet Reader Ser.). (Illus.). (J). (978-0-606-20901-4(8)) Tandem Library Bks.

El Mundo de las Maquinas. (Coleccion Lo Sabias?). (SPA., Illus.). 44p. (J). 12.95 (978-950-11-0939-9(9) , SGM9399) Sigmar ARG. *Dist:* Continental Bk. Co., Inc.

My Digger. 2002. (Chunky Vehicle Shaped Boards Ser.). (J). bds. 1.98 (978-0-7525-7049-5(8)); bds. 4.98 (978-0-7525-4773-2(9)) Parragon, Inc.

My First Book of Questions & Answers about Wings & Wheels. 2001. 128p. (J). 15.95 (978-0-7525-5848-6(X)) Parragon, Inc.

Nankivell-Aston, Sally. Science Experiments with Simple Machines. 2000. (J). (978-0-606-19792-2(3)) Tandem Library Bks.

O'Daley, Anne. Motion. 2003. (Illus.). 24p. (J). 22.45 (978-1-4103-0082-9(X) , Blackbirch Pr., Inc.) Thomson Gale.

O'Shei, Tim. The World's Most Dangerous Machines. 2007. (Edge Books, the World's Top Tens). (Illus.). 32p. 23.93 (978-0-7368-6439-8(3)) Capstone Pr., Inc.

Oxlade, Chris. All about Machines: Amazing Inventions That Made Life Easier. 2003. (Illus.). 64p. pap. 7.99 (978-1-84215-694-0(2) , Southwater) Anness Publishing GBR. *Dist:* National Bk. Network.

—Levers. 2003. (Useful Machines Ser.). (Illus.). 32p. (J). pap. 6.95 (978-1-4034-3677-1(0)); lib. bdg. 22.79 (978-1-4034-3662-7(2)) Heinemann Library.

—Levers. 2007. (J). (***978-1-59920-083-5(X)**) Smart Apple Media.

—Machines. Hawken, Nick, illus. 836th ed. 1998. (Young Scientist Concepts & Projects Ser.). 68p. (J). (gr. 4 up). lib. bdg. 27.33 (978-0-8368-2163-5(7)) Stevens, Gareth Inc.

—Machines: Fantastic Facts. 2000. (Fantastic Facts Ser.). (Illus.). 64p. (gr. 2-7). pap. 6.95 (978-1-84215-085-6(5) , Southwater) Anness Publishing GBR. *Dist:* National Bk. Network.

—Pulleys. 2003. (Useful Machines Ser.). (Illus.). 32p. (J). pap. 6.95 (978-1-4034-3678-8(9)); lib. bdg. 22.79 (978-1-4034-3663-4(0)) Heinemann Library.

—Pulleys. 2007. (J). (***978-1-59920-084-2(8)**) Smart Apple Media.

—Ramps & Wedges. 2003. (Useful Machines Ser.). (Illus.). 32p. (J). pap. (978-1-4034-3803-4(X)); lib. bdg. 22.79 (978-1-4034-3802-7(1)) Heinemann Library.

—Screws. 2007. (J). (***978-1-59920-085-9(6)**) Smart Apple Media.

—This Is My Digger. 2007. (***978-1-59771-104-3(7)**) Sea-To-Sea Pubns.

—This Is My Dump Truck. 2007. (***978-1-59771-105-0(5)**) Sea-To-Sea Pubns.

—Wedges & Ramps. 2007. (J). (***978-1-59920-086-6(4)**) Smart Apple Media.

Paes, Rob, illus. Mighty Machines. 2003. 12p. (J). (gr. k-3). 20.00 (978-0-7567-6652-8(4)) DIANE Publishing Co.

Palas Mecanicas (Earthmovers) 2006. (J). pap. 5.95 (978-0-8225-6644-1(3) , Ediciones Lerner) Lerner Publishing Group.

Parsont, Meg. Bulldozer. Curti, Anna, illus. 1999. (Go Bks.). 12p. (ps-k). 5.95 (978-0-7892-0543-8(2)) Abbeville Pr., Inc.

Pearson, Debora. Load 'Em up Trucks. McLeod, Chum, illus. 1999. (Mighty Wheels Ser.). 24p. (J). (gr. k-ps). lib. bdg. 15.95 (978-1-55037-593-0(8)) Annick Pr., Ltd. CAN. *Dist:* Firefly Bks., Ltd.

Pipe, Jim. Diggers. 2006. (Illus.). 24p. (J). (978-1-59604-115-8(3)) Stargazer Bks.

—Machines. 2006. (Science Starters Ser.). (Illus.). 32p. (978-1-59604-078-6(5)) Stargazer Bks.

Pluckrose, Henry Arthur. On the Move. 1999. (Machines at Work Ser.). (Illus.). 32p. (J). (gr. k-2). pap. 6.95 (978-0-531-15354-3(1) , Watts, Franklin) Scholastic Library Publishing.

—Under the Ground. 1999. (Illus.). (J). (978-0-606-18156-3(3)) Tandem Library Bks.

Priddy, Roger. First 100 Machines. 2006. (Illus.). 14p. (J). bds., bds. 8.95 (978-0-312-49806-1(3) , Priddy Bks.) St. Martin's Pr.

—Monster Machines. rev. ed. 2005. (Priddy Books Big Ideas for Little People). (Illus.). 32p. (J). bds. 6.95 (978-0-312-49538-1(2) , Priddy Bks.) St. Martin's Pr.

Randolph, Joanne. Concrete Mixers. 2002. (PowerKids Readers Ser.). (Illus.). 24p. (J). (gr. 1). lib. bdg. 16.00 (978-0-8239-6039-2(0) , PowerKids Pr.) Rosen Publishing Group, Inc., The.

—Road Machines, 6 bks. Incl. Concrete Mixers. lib. bdg. 16.00 (978-0-8239-6039-2(0)); Road Milling Machines. lib. bdg. 16.00 (978-0-8239-6041-5(2)); Road Pavers. lib. bdg. 16.00 (978-0-8239-6040-8(4)); Road Rollers. lib. bdg. 16.00 (978-0-8239-6037-8(4)); Road Scrapers. lib. bdg. 16.00 (978-0-8239-6042-2(0)); Snowplows. lib. bdg. 16.00 (978-0-8239-6038-5(2)); 24p. (J). (gr. 1). 2002. (Illus.). Set lib. bdg. 88.50 (978-0-8239-7115-2(5) , PowerKids Pr.) Rosen Publishing Group, Inc., The.

—Road Pavers. 2002. (PowerKids Readers Ser.). (Illus.). 24p. (J). (gr. 1). lib. bdg. 16.00 (978-0-8239-6040-8(4) , PowerKids Pr.) Rosen Publishing Group, Inc., The.

—Road Rollers. 2002. (PowerKids Readers Ser.). (Illus.). 24p. (J). (gr. 1). lib. bdg. 16.00 (978-0-8239-6037-8(4) , PowerKids Pr.) Rosen Publishing Group, Inc., The.

—Road Scrapers. 2002. (PowerKids Readers Ser.). (Illus.). 24p. (J). (gr. 1). lib. bdg. 16.00 (978-0-8239-6042-2(0) , PowerKids Pr.) Rosen Publishing Group, Inc., The.

—Snowplows. 2002. (PowerKids Readers Ser.). (Illus.). 24p. (J). (gr. 1). lib. bdg. 16.00 (978-0-8239-6038-5(2) , PowerKids Pr.) Rosen Publishing Group, Inc., The.

—Wheels & Axles in My World. 2006. (My World of Science Ser.). (Illus.). 24p. (J). 16.00 (978-1-4042-3313-3(X) , PowerKids Pr.) Rosen Publishing Group, Inc., The.

—Wheels & Axles in My World: Ejes y Ruedas en Mi Mundo. 2006. (My World of Science/ Mi mundo y la Ciencia Ser.). (ENG & SPA.). (J). 16.00 (978-1-4042-3325-6(3) , Buenas Letra) Rosen Publishing Group, Inc., The.

Richards, Jon. Forces & Simple Machines. 2008. (J). lib. bdg. (****978-1-4042-3908-1(1)***) Rosen Publishing Group, Inc., The.

Rigby Education Staff. Machines Around Your Home. (Illus.). 8p. (J). bds. 3.95 (978-0-7635-6491-9(5) , 764915C99) Rigby Education.

Rinkel, Ken, illus. Giant Machines. 2003. 12p. (J). (gr. k-3). 20.00 (978-0-7567-6653-5(2)) DIANE Publishing Co.

Rockwell, Anne F. Big Wheels. 2003. (Illus.). 24p. (J). (ps-1). 14.95 (978-0-8027-8882-5(3)) Walker & Co.

Rogers, Hal. Cherry Pickers. 2007. (Machines at Work Ser.). 24p. (J). 22.79 (978-1-59296-828-2(7)) Child's World, Inc.

—Graders. 2008. (Machines at Work Ser.). 24p. (J). 22.79 (****978-1-59296-951-7(8)***) Child's World, Inc.

Rogers, Hal. Snowplows. 2000. (Machines at Work Ser.). (Illus.). 24p. (J). (ps-3). 21.36 (978-1-56766-756-1(2)) Child's World, Inc.

Royston, Angela. Levers. (Machines in Action Ser.). 32p. pap. 7.50 (978-1-4034-4084-6(0)); 2000. (Illus.). (J). (gr. 3-5). lib. bdg. 22.79 (978-1-57572-319-8(0)) Heinemann Library.

—Ramps & Wedges. (Machines in Action Ser.). 32p. pap. 7.50 (978-1-4034-4086-0(7)); 2000. (Illus.). (J). (gr. 3-5). lib. bdg. 22.79 (978-1-57572-321-1(2)) Heinemann Library.

—Screws. (Machines in Action Ser.). 32p. pap. 7.50 (978-1-4034-4087-7(5)); 2000. (Illus.). (J). (gr. 3-5). lib. bdg. 22.79 (978-1-57572-322-8(0)) Heinemann Library.

—Springs. (Machines in Action Ser.). 32p. pap. 7.50 (978-1-4034-4088-4(3)); 2000. (Illus.). (J). (gr. 3-5). lib. bdg. 22.79 (978-1-57572-323-5(9)) Heinemann Library.

Rushby, Pamela. Science Chapters: Mysteries of the Fossil Dig. 2006. (Illus.). 48p. 17.90 (978-0-7922-5953-4(X) , National Geographic Children's Bks.) National Geographic Society.

Sadler, Wendy. Using Levers. 2005. (Machines Inside Machines Ser.). (Illus.). 32p. (J). (gr. 3-5). 19.25 (978-1-4109-1442-2(9)) Raintree.

—Using Levers, 6 vols. 2005. (Raintree Perspectives Ser.). (Illus.). (978-1-4109-1449-1(6)); (978-1-4109-1452-1(6)); (978-1-4109-1454-5(2)); (978-1-4109-1450-7(X)); (978-1-4109-1453-8(4)); (978-1-4109-1451-4(8)) Steck-Vaughn.

—Using Pulleys & Gears. 2005. (Raintree Perspectives Ser.). (Illus.). 32p. (978-1-4109-1445-3(3)) Steck-Vaughn.

—Using Ramps & Wedges. 2005. (Raintree Perspectives Ser.). (Illus.). 32p. (978-1-4109-1447-7(X)) Steck-Vaughn.

—Using Screws. 2005. (Raintree Perspectives Ser.). (Illus.). 32p. (978-1-4109-1443-9(7)) Steck-Vaughn.

—Using Springs. 2005. (Raintree Perspectives Ser.). (Illus.). 32p. (978-1-4109-1446-0(1)) Steck-Vaughn.

—Using Wheels & Axles. 2005. (Raintree Perspectives Ser.). (Illus.). 32p. (978-1-4109-1444-6(5)) Steck-Vaughn.

Saunders-Smith, Gail, ed. Mighty Machines. 2005. (Pebble Plus Ser.). (Illus.). (J). (gr. k-1). lib. bdg. 279.02 (978-0-7368-3804-7(X)) Capstone Pr., Inc.

Schaefer, Lola M. Push & Pull. Saunders-Smith, Gail, ed. 1999. (Way Things Move Ser.). (Illus.). 24p. (J). (gr. k-1). lib. bdg. 15.93 (978-0-7368-0396-0(3) , Pebble Bks.) Capstone Pr., Inc.

—Push & Pull. 1999. pap. 13.25 (978-0-516-21923-3(5) , Children's Pr.) Scholastic Library Publishing.

Schaefer, Ted. Machines Large & Small. 2007. (ENG & SPA.). (J). (978-1-59515-953-3(3)) Rourke Publishing, LLC.

Scholastic Clubs US Machines at Work Set #1: Machines at Work. 2006. (J). 39.80 (978-1-59566-321-4(5)) QEB Publishing Inc.

Scholastic Clubs US Machines at Worlk Set #2: Machines at Work. 2006. 39.80 (978-1-59566-322-1(3)) QEB Publishing Inc.

Secrets of the Fun Park, 6 Packs. (gr. k-1). 23.00 (978-0-7635-9080-2(0)) Rigby Education.

Shuter. War Machines. 2004. (Technology Through Time Ser.). (Illus.). pap. 7.50 (978-1-4109-0982-4(4)) Raintree.

Simon, Seymour. Giant Machines. 2002. (See More Readers Ser.). (Illus.). 32p. (J). (gr. k-4). pap. 3.95 (978-1-58717-127-7(9) , SeaStar Bks.) Chronicle Bks. LLC.

—Giant Machines. 2002. (gr. 3-6). lib. bdg. 11.80 (978-0-613-58411-1(2)) Tandem Library Bks.

Simple Machines. 2004. (Illus.). lib. bdg. 7.95 (978-0-8225-3352-8(9)); Set. 2006. (J). (gr. 2-4). 46.95 (****978-0-8225-3353-5(7)***) Lerner Publishing Group.

Simple Machines. (Rosen Real Readers Big Bookstm Ser.). 16p. (J). (gr. 2-3). 38.75 (978-1-4042-6220-1(2)) Rosen Publishing Group, Inc., The.

Simple Machines. 2001. (Inquiry Science Ser.). 32p. (gr. 2-3). 4.99 (978-1-56822-947-8(X) , IF20854) School Specialty Publishing.

Sloan, Peter. Big Machines. 1999. (gr. k-3). lib. bdg. 11.80 (978-0-613-30272-2(9)) Tandem Library Bks.

—Using Machines. 1999. (gr. k-3). lib. bdg. 11.80 (978-0-613-30832-8(8)) Tandem Library Bks.

Small Machines Sets: 1 Each of 3 Big Books. (Sunshinetm Science Ser.). (gr. 1-2). 93.95 (978-0-7802-0531-4(6)) Wright Group, The.

Small Machines Sets: 1 Each of 3 Student Books. (Sunshinetm Science Ser.). (gr. 1-2). 17.95 (978-0-7802-0272-6(4)) Wright Group, The.

Sobey, Edwin J. C. What's That? A Field Guide to Technology. 2004. (Watts Reference Ser.). (J). lib. bdg. 39.50 (978-0-531-12221-1(2) , Watts, Franklin) Scholastic Library Publishing.

Solway, Andrew. Castle under Siege! 2005. (Illus.). 32p. (J). (gr. 3-5). lib. bdg. 28.21 (978-1-4109-1918-2(8)) Steck-Vaughn.

—Castle under Siege! Simple Machines. 2005. (Illus.). 32p. (J). (gr. 4-6). 7.85 (978-1-4109-1949-6(8)) Steck-Vaughn.

Speed Machines Sticker Book. Date not set. (Illus.). 12p. (J). 3.98 (978-1-4054-0499-0(X)) Parragon, Inc.

Stone, Tanya Lee. P Is for Passover. Lucas, Margeaux, illus. 2003. (Holiday Alphabet Bks.). 24p. (J). (ps-1). pap. 4.99 (978-0-8431-0238-3(1) , Price Stern Sloan) Penguin Group (USA) Inc.

Stringer, John. Machines, Transportation & Art Activities. (Arty Facts Ser.). (Illus.). 48p. (J). (gr. 3-4). 2003. lib. bdg. (978-0-7787-1116-2(1)); 2002. pap. (978-0-7787-1144-5(7)) Crabtree Publishing Co.

—Machines, Transportation & Art Activities. 2002. (gr. 3-6). lib. bdg. 17.60 (978-0-613-52874-0(3)) Tandem Library Bks.

Sundance, ed. What Has an Engine? 2000. (ps-2). lib. bdg. 11.65 (978-0-613-37636-5(6)) Tandem Library Bks.

Targ Brill, Marlene. Concrete Mixers. 2006. (Illus.). 32p. (J). pap. 5.95 (978-0-8225-5899-6(8) , First Avenue Editions) Lerner Publishing Group.

Thales, Sharon. Inclined Planes to the Rescue. 2007. (First Facts Ser.). (Illus.). 24p. (J). (978-0-7368-6752-8(X) , 1264897) Capstone Pr., Inc.

—Levers to the Rescue. 2007. (First Facts Ser.). (Illus.). 24p. (J). (978-0-7368-6747-4(3) , 1264898) Capstone Pr., Inc.

—Pulleys to the Rescue. 2007. (First Facts Ser.). (Illus.). 24p. (J). (gr. 2-3). lib. bdg. 21.26 (978-0-7368-6748-1(1) , 1264899) Capstone Pr., Inc.

—Screws to the Rescue. 2007. (First Facts Ser.). (Illus.). 24p. (J). (gr. 2-3). lib. bdg. 21.26 (978-0-7368-6749-8(X) , 1264900) Capstone Pr., Inc.

—Wedges to the Rescue. 2007. (First Facts Ser.). (Illus.). 24p. (J). (gr. 2-3). lib. bdg. 21.26 (978-0-7368-6750-4(3) , 1264901) Capstone Pr., Inc.

Thompson, Gare. Science Chapters: Lever, Screw, & Inclined Plane: The Power of Simple Machines. 2006. (Illus.). 48p. (J). (gr. 1-4). 17.90 (978-0-7922-5949-7(1) , National Geographic Children's Bks.) National Geographic Society.

Tieck, Sarah. Earthmovers. 2005. (Buddy Book Ser.). (Illus.). 24p. (J). (gr. k-4). lib. bdg. 21.35 (978-1-59197-826-8(2)) ABDO Publishing Co.

—Inclined Planes. 2007. (Simple Machines Ser.). (Illus.). 24p. (J). (gr. k-4). lib. bdg. 21.35 (978-1-59679-818-2(1)) ABDO Publishing Co.

—Levers. 2007. (Simple Machines Ser.). (Illus.). 24p. (J). (gr. k-4). lib. bdg. 21.35 (978-1-59679-814-4(9)) ABDO Publishing Co.

—Pulleys. 2007. (Simple Machines Ser.). (Illus.). 24p. (J). (gr. k-4). lib. bdg. 21.35 (978-1-59679-815-1(7)) ABDO Publishing Co.

—Simple Machines, 6 vols., Set. Incl. Inclined Planes. lib. bdg. 21.35 (978-1-59679-818-2(1)); Levers. lib. bdg. 21.35 (978-1-59679-814-4(9)); Pulleys. lib. bdg. 21.35 (978-1-59679-815-1(7)); Screws. lib. bdg. 21.35 (978-1-59679-817-5(3)); Wedges. lib. bdg. 21.35 (978-1-59679-816-8(5)); Wheels & Axles. lib. bdg. 21.35 (978-1-59679-819-9(X)); (Illus.). 24p. (J). (gr. k-4). 2007. Set lib. bdg. 128.10 (978-1-59679-813-7(0) , Buddy Bks.) ABDO Publishing Co.

—Wedges. 2007. (Simple Machines Ser.). (Illus.). 24p. (J). (gr. k-4). lib. bdg. 21.35 (978-1-59679-816-8(5)) ABDO Publishing Co.

Tiner, John Hudson. Inclined Planes. 2002. (Illus.). 23p. (J). lib. bdg. 21.35 (978-1-58340-138-5(5)) Smart Apple Media.

—Levers. 2003. (Simple Machines Ser.). (Illus.). 24p. (J). lib. bdg. 21.35 (978-1-58340-135-4(0)) Smart Apple Media.

—Pulleys. 2003. (Simple Machines Ser.). (Illus.). 23p. (J). lib. bdg. 21.35 (978-1-58340-136-1(9)) Smart Apple Media.

Tocci, Salvatore. Experiments with Simple Machines. 2003. (True Bks.). (gr. 3-5). pap. 6.95 (978-0-516-27468-3(6) , Children's Pr.) Scholastic Library Publishing.

—Experiments with Simple Machines. 2003. (gr. 3-6). lib. bdg. 15.25 (978-0-613-67890-2(7)) Tandem Library Bks.

Tonka Coloring & Activity Books. 2004. (J). act. bk. ed. (978-0-7666-0813-9(1) , 99520); act. bk. ed. (978-0-7666-0814-6(X) , 99520); act. bk. ed. (978-0-7666-0815-3(8) , 99520); act. bk. ed. (978-0-7666-0816-0(6) , 99520) Modern Publishing.

Top That Publishing Staff, ed. Real Spies. 2004. (I-Quest Ser.). (Illus.). 48p. (J). per. (978-1-84510-134-3(0)) Top That! Publishing PLC.

Tuxworth, Nicola. Diggers & Dumpers. (Illus.). (ps). 2005. 12p. bds. 6.99 (978-0-7548-1336-1(3) , Lorenz Bks.); 2001. 20p. 5.95 (978-0-7548-0940-1(4)) Anness Publishing GBR. *Dist:* National Bk. Network.

—Machines at Work: A Very First Picture Book. 1999. (Pictures & Words Ser.). (Illus.). 24p. (J). (ps up). lib. bdg. 22.00 (978-0-8368-2432-2(6)) Stevens, Gareth Inc.

Walker, Sally M. & Feldmann, Roseann. Inclined Planes & Wedges. King, Andy, photos by. 2002. (Illus.). 48p. (YA). pap. (978-0-8225-2215-7(2) , Lerner Pubns.) Lerner Publishing Group.

—Levers. 2005. (Early Bird Physics Ser.). (Illus.). 48p. (gr. 3-6). lib. bdg. 25.26 (978-0-8225-2218-8(7)) Lerner Publishing Group.

—Levers. King, Andy, photos by. 2002. (Illus.). 48p. (YA). (978-0-8225-2212-6(8) , Lerner Pubns.) Lerner Publishing Group.

—Palancas. 2005. (Libros de Fisica para Madrugadores (Early Bird Physics) Ser.). (SPA & ENG., Illus.). 48p. (gr. 3-6). lib. bdg. 25.26 (978-0-8225-2972-9(6) , Ediciones Lerner) Lerner Publishing Group.

—Poleas. 2005. (Libros de Fisica para Madrugadores (Early Bird Physics) Ser.). (SPA & ENG., Illus.). 48p. (J). (gr. 3-7). lib. bdg. 25.26 (978-0-8225-2980-4(7) , Ediciones Lerner) Lerner Publishing Group.

—Pulleys. 2005. (Early Bird Physics Ser.). (Illus.). 48p. (gr. 3-6). lib. bdg. 25.26 (978-0-8225-2220-1(9)) Lerner Publishing Group.

—Pulleys. King, Andy, photos by. 2002. (Illus.). 48p. (YA). (978-0-8225-2214-0(4) , Lerner Pubns.) Lerner Publishing Group.

—Trabajo. 2005. (Libros de Fisica para Madrugadores (Early Bird Physics) Ser.). (SPA & ENG., Illus.). 48p. (J). (gr. 3-7). lib. bdg. 25.26 (978-0-8225-2984-2(X) , Ediciones Lerner) Lerner Publishing Group.

—Work. King, Andy, photos by. 2002. (Illus.). 48p. (978-0-8225-2211-9(X) , Lerner Pubns.) Lerner Publishing Group.

Walker, Sally M., et al. Inclined Planes & Wedges. 2005. (Early Bird Physics Ser.). (Illus.). 48p. (gr. 3-6). lib. bdg. 25.26 (978-0-8225-2221-8(7)) Lerner Publishing Group.

—Screws. (Early Bird Physics Ser.). (Illus.). 2005. 40p. (gr. 3-6). lib. bdg. 25.26 (978-0-8225-2222-5(5)); 2002. 48p. (YA). (978-0-8225-2216-4(0) , Lerner Pubns.) Lerner Publishing Group.

—Work. 2005. (Early Bird Physics Ser.). (Illus.). 48p. (gr. 3-6). lib. bdg. 25.26 (978-0-8225-2217-1(9)) Lerner Publishing Group.

Wallace, Karen. Big Machines. 2000. (Readers Ser.). (Illus.). 32p. (J). (ps-1). pap. 3.99 (978-0-7894-5411-9(4)) Dorling Kindersley Publishing, Inc.

—Big Machines. 2000. (gr. k-3). lib. bdg. 11.80 (978-0-613-24358-2(7)); (Illus.). (J). 10.79 (978-0-606-18114-3(8)) Tandem Library Bks.

—Gigantes de Hierro. 2003. (SPA.). (gr. k-3). lib. bdg. 11.80 (978-0-613-75200-8(7)) Tandem Library Bks.

Wallace, Karen & Dorling Kindersley Publishing Staff. Big Machines. 2000. (Eyewitness Readers). (Illus.). 32p. (J). (ps-1). 12.99 (978-0-7894-5412-6(2)) Dorling Kindersley Publishing, Inc.

Watt, Fiona & Wells, Rachel. Diggers. 2004. (Ultimate Touchy-Feely Ser.). (Illus.). 10p. (J). 15.95 (978-0-7945-0340-6(3) , Usborne) EDC Publishing.

Watts, Claire & Nicholson, Robert. Mega Machines. 2000. (Info Adventure Ser.). (Illus.). 32p. (J). (gr. 3-6). pap. 3.95 (978-1-58728-110-5(4) , Two Can Publishing) T&N Children's Publishing.

Welsbacher, Anne. Inclined Planes. 2000. (Bridgestone Science Library). (Illus.). 24p. (J). (gr. 1-2). lib. bdg. 18.60 (978-0-7368-0610-7(5) , Bridgestone Bks.) Capstone Pr., Inc.

—Wedges. 2000. (Bridgestone Science Library). (Illus.). 24p. (J). (gr. 1-2). lib. bdg. 18.60 (978-0-7368-0614-5(8) , Bridgestone Bks.) Capstone Pr., Inc.

Werther, Scott P. Extreme Machines, 6 bks. Incl. Big Rigs. lib. bdg. 17.25 (978-0-8239-5956-3(2)); Dragsters. lib. bdg. 17.25 (978-0-8239-5953-2(8)); Long Limousines. lib. bdg. 17.25 (978-0-8239-5958-7(9)); Low Riders. lib. bdg. 17.25 (978-0-8239-5954-9(6)); Monster Trucks. lib. bdg. 17.25 (978-0-8239-5955-6(4)); Powerboats. lib. bdg. 17.25 (978-0-8239-5957-0(0)); 24p. (J). (gr. 1). 2002. (Illus.). Set lib. bdg. 96.00 (978-0-8239-7118-3(X) , PowerKids Pr.) Rosen Publishing Group, Inc., The.

Whitehouse, Patricia. Loud Sounds, Soft Sounds. 2007. (J). (978-1-60044-191-2(2)) Rourke Publishing, LLC.

—Machines & Work. 2007. (J). (****978-1-4034-7916-7(X)***) Heinemann Library.

—Moving Machines. 2007. (J). (978-1-60044-192-9(0)) Rourke Publishing, LLC.

—Pushes & Pulls. 2007. (J). 6.00 (978-1-60044-193-6(9)) Rourke Publishing, LLC.

—What Can Dig? 2003. (Heinemann Read & Learn Ser.). (Illus.). 24p. (J). lib. bdg. 18.50 (978-1-4034-4369-4(6)) Heinemann Library.

—What Can Dig? 2003. (ps-2). lib. bdg. 28.65 (978-0-613-86883-9(8)) Tandem Library Bks.

Whiting, Sue & Book Company Staff. Speed Machines. Paes, Rob, illus. 2002. (Pop-up Bks.). 14p. (J). 12.95 (978-1-74047-133-6(4)) Book Co. Publishing Pty, Ltd., The AUS. *Dist:* Penton Overseas, Inc.

Williams, John. Water Projects. 1998. (Design & Create Ser.). (Illus.). 32p. (J). (gr. 2-5). lib. bdg. 17.98 (978-0-8172-4890-1(0)) Raintree.

Williams, Linda D. Concrete Mixers. 2004. (Pebble Plus: Mighty Machines Ser.). (Illus.). 24p. (J). lib. bdg. 19.93 (978-0-7368-2594-8(0) , Pebble Bks.) Capstone Pr., Inc.

—Concrete Mixers. (Mighty MacHines Ser.). 24p. (J). pap. 6.95 (978-0-7368-5132-9(1)) Capstone Pr., Inc.

—Dump Trucks. 2004. (Pebble Plus: Mighty Machines Ser.). (Illus.). 24p. (J). lib. bdg. 19.93 (978-0-7368-2596-2(7) , Pebble Bks.) Capstone Pr., Inc.

—Earthmovers. 2004. (Pebble Plus: Mighty Machines Ser.). (Illus.). 24p. (J). lib. bdg. 19.93 (978-0-7368-2597-9(5) , Pebble Bks.) Capstone Pr., Inc.

—Removedoras de Tierra: Earthmovers. 2006. (Pebble Plus Ser.). (ENG & SPA.). (978-0-7368-5871-7(7)) Capstone Pr., Inc.

Woods, Bob. Massive Machines. 2007. (Boys Rock! Ser.). 32p. (J). (gr. 1-5). 24.21 (****978-1-59296-858-9(9)***) Child's World, Inc.

Wright, Nicola. Diggers. 2006. (Illus.). 24p. (YA). (gr. 1 up). lib. bdg. 22.80 (978-1-931983-57-0(7)) Chrysalis Education.

MACHINERY, AUTOMATIC

see Automation

MACHINERY—HISTORY

The History of Machines: Individual Title Six-Packs. (gr. k-1). 23.00 (978-0-7635-9079-6(7)) Rigby Education.

Oxlade, Chris. Inventions & Machines: The Changing World. 2005. (Illus.). 128p. pap. 17.99 (978-1-84476-059-6(6) , Southwater) Anness Publishing GBR. *Dist:* National Bk. Network.

—Machines: A Story of Technology from Simple Screws, Gears & Levers, to High-Tech Gadgets. 2001. (Illus.). 64p. (gr. 3-7). 14.95 (978-0-7548-0652-3(9) , Lorenz Bks.) Anness Publishing GBR. *Dist:* National Bk. Network.

Woods, Michael & Woods, Mary B. Ancient Machines: From Wedges to Waterwheels. 2005. (Ancient Technology Ser.). (Illus.). 96p. (gr. 6-12). 25.26 (978-0-8225-2994-1(7)) Lerner Publishing Group.

MACHINES

see Machinery

MACINTOSH (COMPUTER)

Cochran, David W. Hyperstudio Express 3.1 For Windows Macintosh. 1999. (J). pap. (978-0-02-654033-9(9)) Glencoe/McGraw-Hill.

Read & Write for Mac. 2002. (YA). cd-rom 605.00 (978-1-932625-02-8(X)) Texthelp Systems, Inc.

Read & Write for Mac K-12. 2002. (YA). cd-rom (978-1-932625-10-3(0)) Texthelp Systems, Inc.

MACK, ALEX (FICTITIOUS CHARACTER)—FICTION

Stern, D. A. Alex Mack, Vol. 35. (Illus.). (J). mass mkt. (978-0-671-02523-6(6) , Aladdin) Simon & Schuster Children's Publishing.

MACKENZIE, ALEXANDER, SIR, 1763-1820

Manson, Ainslie. Alexander MacKenzie: From Canada by Land. 2003. (Illus.). (J). pap. (978-0-88899-483-7(4)) Douglas & McIntyre, Ltd.

MACKENZIE RIVER (N.W.T.)

Harris, Tim. The Mackenzie River. 2003. (Rivers of North America Ser.). (Illus.). 32p. (J). (gr. 3 up). lib. bdg. 24.67 (978-0-8368-3756-8(8)) Stevens, Gareth Inc.

MACKINAC ISLAND (MICH.)—FICTION

Hahn, Cathe. Step Up! Artley, Bob, illus. 2005. 32p. (J). 15.95 (978-1-58980-214-8(4)) Pelican Publishing Co., Inc.

Panagopoulos, Janie Lynn. A Castle at the Straits. Evans, Laura, illus. 2003. 48p. (J). (gr. 1-6). (978-0-911872-83-5(3)) Mackinac State Historic Parks.

Whelan, Gloria. Farewell to the Island. 1998. 208p. (J). (gr. 4 up). 16.95 (978-0-06-027751-2(3)) HarperCollins Pubs.

—Return to the Island. 192p. (J). (gr. 4-7). 2002. pap. 5.95 (978-0-06-440761-8(6)); 2000. 15.89 (978-0-06-028254-7(1)) HarperCollins Pubs.

MCKINLEY, WILLIAM, 1843-1901

Doak, Robin S. William McKinley. 2003. (Profiles of the Presidents Ser.). (Illus.). 64p. (J). (gr. 4 up). lib. bdg. 23.93 (978-0-7565-0271-3(3)) Compass Point Bks.

Edge, Laura Bufano. William McKinley. 2007. (Presidential Leaders Ser.). 112p. (J). (gr. 6-12). 29.27 (978-0-8225-1508-1(3) , Twenty-First Century Bks.) Lerner Publishing Group.

Feinstein, Stephen. William McKinley: A MyReportLinks.com Book. 2002. (Presidents Ser.). (Illus.). 48p. (J). (gr. 4-10). lib. bdg. 25.26 (978-0-7660-5004-4(1) , MyReportLinks.com Bks.) Enslow Pubs., Inc.

Marsh, Carole. William McKinley: An Ohio Experience Reader. 2001. (J). (gr. k-5). pap. 1.95 (978-0-635-00446-8(1)) Gallopade International.

Parker, Lewis K. How to Draw the Life & Times of William McKinley. 2007. (Kid's Guide to Drawing the Presidents of the United States of America Ser.). (Illus.). 32p. (J). 25.25 (978-1-4042-3001-9(7) , PowerKids Pr.) Rosen Publishing Group, Inc., The.

Riehecky, Janet. William McKinley. 2004. (Encyclopedia of Presidents Ser.). (Illus.). 110p. (J). 34.00 (978-0-516-22966-9(4) , Children's Pr.) Scholastic Library Publishing.

Schlesinger, Arthur M., Sr., et al, eds. The Election of 1896 & the Administration of William McKinley. 2002. (Major Presidential Elections & the Administrations That Followed Ser.). (Illus.). 154p. (YA). (gr. 7 up). lib. bdg. (978-1-59084-357-4(6)) Mason Crest Pubs.

Venezia, Mike. William Mckinley. 2006. (Illus.). 32p. (YA). (gr. 3-4). pap. 7.95 (978-0-516-25405-0(7) , Children's Pr.) Scholastic Library Publishing.

Venezia, Mike, illus. William McKinley. 2006. (Getting to Know the U. S. Presidents Ser.). 32p. (J). (gr. 3-4). 27.00 (978-0-516-22629-3(0) , Children's Pr.) Scholastic Library Publishing.

Wilson, Antoine. The Assassination of William McKinley. 2003. (Library of Political Assassinations). (Illus.). 64p. (YA). (gr. 7-12). lib. bdg. 26.50 (978-0-8239-3546-8(9)) Rosen Publishing Group, Inc., The.

MCKINLEY, MOUNT (ALASKA)

Establishment of Mount McKinley Park. (Shorey Historical Ser.). (Illus.). 32p. (J). reprint ed. pap. 10.00 (978-0-8466-0015-2(3) , S15) Shorey's Bookstore.

Gill, Shelley. Up on Denali: Alaska's Wild Mountain. Cartwright, Shannon, illus. 2006. 32p. (J). 16.95 (978-1-57061-366-1(4)); pap. 10.95 (978-1-57061-365-4(6)) Sasquatch Bks.

MCLAUGHLIN, KEN (FICTITIOUS CHARACTER)—FICTION

O'Hara, Mary. My Friend Flicka. 1999. (Illus.). 320p. (YA). (gr. 4-7). reprint ed. 37.95 (978-1-56849-725-9(3)) Buccaneer Bks., Inc.

—My Friend Flicka. 2003. (Charming Classics). (Illus.). 352p. (J). 6.99 (978-0-06-052429-6(4)) HarperCollins Pubs.

MACRAME

Johnson, Anne Akers. Pulseras Rusticas. 2004. (SPA., Illus.). 32p. (J). (gr. 1). spiral bd. 17.95 (978-968-5528-11-5(X)) Klutz Latino MEX. *Dist:* Independent Pubs. Group.

South, Lianne & Robins, Deri. Creative Bracelets. Hall, Mary, illus. 2000. 24p. (J). (978-0-439-24962-1(7)) Scholastic, Inc.

Torres, Laura & Johnson, Anne Akers. Brazaletes de la Amistad. 2004. (SPA., Illus.). 60p. (J). (gr. 3). spiral bd. 17.95 (978-968-5528-05-4(5)) Klutz Latino MEX. *Dist:* Independent Pubs. Group.

MACY, ANNE SULLIVAN, 1866-1936

see Sullivan, Annie, 1866-1936

MADAGASCAR

Bishop, Nic. Digging for Bird Dinosaurs: An Expedition to Madagascar. 2000. (Scientists in the Field Ser.). (Illus.). 48p. (J). (gr. 4-6). tchr. ed. 16.00 (978-0-395-96056-1(8)) Houghton Mifflin Co. Trade & Reference Div.

Blauer, Ettagale & Laure, Jason. Madagascar. 2000. (Enchantment of the World, Second Ser.). (Illus.). 144p. (YA). (gr. 5-9). 36.00 (978-0-516-21634-8(1) , Children's Pr.) Scholastic Library Publishing.

Corwin, Jeff. Into Wild Madagascar. Pascoe, Elaine, ed. 2003. (Jeff Corwin Experience Ser.). (Illus.). 48p. (J). 24.95 (978-1-56711-855-1(0)); 11.20 (978-1-4103-0174-1(5)) Thomson Gale. (Blackbirch Pr., Inc.).

Ellis, Royston & Jones, John R. Madagascar. 1999. (Festivals of the World Ser.). (Illus.). 32p. (J). (gr. 3 up). lib. bdg. 24.67 (978-0-8368-2023-2(1)) Stevens, Gareth Inc.

Junor, Amy. Madagascar. 2005. (Ultimate sticker Bks.). 16p. (J). pap. 6.99 (978-0-7566-1176-7(8)) Dorling Kindersley Publishing, Inc.

Kabana, Joni. Torina's World: A Child's Life in Madagascar. 2007. (Illus.). 52p. 14.95 (*978-0-9794771-4-0(X)) Arnica Publishing, Inc.

Oluonye, Mary N. Madagascar. (Ticket to Ser.). (Illus.). 48p. 2005. (gr. 2-4). 22.60 (978-1-57505-145-1(1)); 2000. (J). (gr. 3-5). lib. bdg. 22.60 (978-1-57505-120-8(6) , Carolrhoda Bks.) Lerner Publishing Group.

Powzyk, Joyce A. In Search of Lemurs: My Days & Nights in a Madagascar Rain Forest. 1998. (Illus.). 48p. (J). (gr. 3-7). 17.95 (978-0-7922-7072-0(X) , T07072C, National Geographic Children's Bks.) National Geographic Society.

MADAGASCAR—FICTION

Aboff, Marcie. Alex & Marty Run Wild. 2005. (Madagascar Ser.). 32p. (J). pap. 3.99 (978-0-439-69631-9(3)) Scholastic, Inc.

—Smile & Wave. 2005. (Madagascar Ser.: No. 3). 32p. (J). 3.99 (978-0-439-69630-2(5)) Scholastic, Inc.

Cunningham, Elaine. Missing in Madagascar. 2006. 32p. 4.50 (978-0-8341-2230-7(8)) Beacon Hill Pr. of Kansas City.

David, Erica. Quiero Ser Libre. 2005. (Madagascar Ser.).Tr. of Born to Be Wild. (SPA., Illus.). 32p. (J). 3.99 (978-0-439-71575-1(X) , Scholastic en Espanol) Scholastic, Inc.

Dennard, Deborah. Lemur Landing: A Story of a Madagascan Dry Tropical Forest. Kest, Kristin, illus. 2001. (Wild Habitats Ser.). 36p. (J). (gr. 1-4). 26.95 (978-1-56899-982-1(8)) Soundprints.

Dennard, Deborah & Kest, Kristin. Lemur Landing: A Story of a Madagascan Dry Tropical Forest. 2005. (Wild Habitats Ser.). (Illus.). 32p. (J). (gr. 1-4). pap. 6.95 (978-1-56899-979-1(8) , S7019) Soundprints.

Jordan, Apple. The Bungle in the Jungle. 2005. (Madagascar Ser.). 32p. (J). 3.99 (978-0-439-69629-6(1)) Scholastic, Inc.

—Fearless Foursome. Dever, Bob & Morris, Michael, illus. 2005. (Madagascar Ser.). (SPA.). 64p. (J). (ps-ps). 2.99 (978-0-439-71307-8(2) , Scholastic en Espanol) Scholastic, Inc.

—Madagascar: Fearless Foursome. 2005. (Madagascar Ser.). 64p. (J). 3.99 (978-0-439-69628-9(3)) Scholastic, Inc.

Lumry, Amanda & Hurwitz, Laura. Adventures of Riley: Mission to Madagascar. McIntyre, Sarah, illus. 2005. 36p. (gr. 2-3). 15.95 (978-0-9748411-2-0(9)) Eaglemont Pr.

McCaughrean, Geraldine. Pirate's Son. 1999. (978-0-606-17039-0(1)) Tandem Library Bks.

Meredith Books Staff, ed. Madagascar Activity Book & Floor Puzzle. 10p. (J). bds. 12.95 (978-0-696-22701-1(0)) Meredith Bks.

—Madagascar Stencil Activity Book with Stickers. 22p. (J). bds. 12.95 (978-0-696-22702-8(9)) Meredith Bks.

Richards, Kitty. Thornberry Thanksgiving. 2001. (gr. k-3). lib. bdg. 14.15 (978-0-613-43963-3(5)) Tandem Library Bks.

Simpson, Fiona, ed. Madagascar: Play-Along. 2005. (Madagascar Ser.). 16p. (J). pap. 4.99 (978-0-439-69994-5(0)) Scholastic, Inc.

Steele, Michael Anthony. Esto es un Zoologico! 2005. (Madagascar Ser.).Tr. of Zoosters on the Loose. (SPA., Illus.). 24p. (J). 3.99 (978-0-439-71308-5(0)) Scholastic, Inc.

—It's a Zoo in Here! 2005. (Illus.). (J). (*978-0-439-78585-3(5)) Scholastic, Inc.

Steele, Michael Anthony. MadagascarTM: It's a Zoo in Here! 2005. (Madagascar Ser.). (Illus.). 24p. (J). pap. 3.99 (978-0-439-69626-5(7)) Scholastic, Inc.

MADELINE (FICTITIOUS CHARACTER)—FICTION

Bemelmans, Ludwig. Mad about Madeline: The Complete Tales. Bemelmans, Ludwig, illus. 2001. (Madeline Ser.). (Illus.). 352p. (J). (ps-3). 35.00 (978-0-670-88816-0(8) , Viking Juvenile) Penguin Group (USA) Inc.

—Madeline. 2007. (Puffin Storytime Ser.). 48p. (J). (ps). pap. 9.99 (978-0-14-240871-1(9) , Puffin) Penguin Group (USA) Inc.

—Madeline. Bemelmans, Ludwig, illus. 2000. (Illus.). (J). (ps-ps). lib. bdg. 15.30 (978-0-8085-2322-2(8)) Tandem Library Bks.

—Madeline & the Bad Hat. Bemelmans, Ludwig, illus. 2002. (Madeline Ser.). (Illus.). (J). 14.04 (978-0-7587-4084-7(0)) Book Wholesalers, Inc.

—Madeline & the Bad Hat. Bemelmans, Ludwig, illus. 2000. (Madeline Ser.). (Illus.). 64p. (J). (ps-3). pap. 7.99 (978-0-14-056648-2(1) , Viking Juvenile) Penguin Group (USA) Inc.

—Madeline & the Bad Hat. Bemelmans, Ludwig, illus. 2000. (Madeline Ser.). (Illus.). (J). (ps-3). (978-0-606-18427-4(9)) Tandem Library Bks.

—Madeline & the Gypsies. Bemelmans, Ludwig, illus. 2000. (Madeline Ser.). (Illus.). 64p. (J). (ps-3). pap. 7.99 (978-0-14-056647-5(3) , Viking Juvenile) Penguin Group (USA) Inc.

—Madeline & the Gypsies. 2000. (gr. k-3). lib. bdg. 15.30 (978-0-8085-2352-9(X)) Tandem Library Bks.

—Madeline & the Gypsies. Bemelmans, Ludwig, illus. 2000. (Madeline Ser.). (Illus.). (J). (ps-3). (978-0-606-18428-1(7)) Tandem Library Bks.

—Madeline in America & Other Holiday Tales. Bemelmans, Ludwig, illus. 2002. (Madeline Ser.). (Illus.). (J). 18.68 (978-0-7587-4186-8(3)) Book Wholesalers, Inc.

—Madeline in America & Other Holiday Tales. Marciano, John Bemelmans, illus. 1999. (Madeline Ser.). (J). (ps-3). 112p. pap. 19.95 (978-0-590-03910-9(5) , Levine, Arthur A. Bks.); pap. 125.00 (978-0-439-09633-1(2)) Scholastic, Inc.

—Madeline in London. Bemelmans, Ludwig, illus. 2002. (Madeline Ser.). (Illus.). (J). 14.04 (978-0-7587-5002-0(1)) Book Wholesalers, Inc.

—Madeline in London. Bemelmans, Ludwig, illus. deluxe ed. 2000. (Madeline Ser.). (Illus.). 64p. (J). (ps-3). pap. 7.99 (978-0-14-056649-9(X) , Viking Juvenile) Penguin Group (USA) Inc.

—Madeline in London. 2000. (gr. k-3). lib. bdg. 15.30 (978-0-8085-2353-6(8)) Tandem Library Bks.

—Madeline in London. Bemelmans, Ludwig, illus. 2000. (Madeline Ser.). (Illus.). (J). (ps-3). (978-0-606-18429-8(5)) Tandem Library Bks.

—Madeline's Christmas. Bemelmans, Ludwig, illus. 2002. (Madeline Ser.). (Illus.). (J). 14.04 (978-0-7587-5650-3(X)) Book Wholesalers, Inc.

—Madeline's Christmas. Bemelmans, Ludwig, illus. deluxe ed. 2000. (Madeline Ser.). (Illus.). 32p. (J). (ps-3). pap. 7.99 (978-0-14-056650-5(3) , Viking Juvenile) Penguin Group (USA) Inc.

—Madeline's Christmas. 1999. (ps-2). lib. bdg. 15.30 (978-0-613-30014-8(9)) Tandem Library Bks.

—Madeline's Rescue. Bemelmans, Ludwig, illus. 2002. (Madeline Ser.). (Illus.). (J). 14.04 (978-0-7587-4085-4(9)) Book Wholesalers, Inc.

—Madeline's Rescue. Bemelmans, Ludwig, illus. 2000. (Madeline Ser.). (Illus.). 64p. (J). (ps-3). pap. 7.99 (978-0-14-056651-2(1) , Viking Juvenile) Penguin Group (USA) Inc.

—Madeline's Rescue. Bemelmans, Ludwig, illus. 2000. (Madeline Ser.). (J). (ps-3). (978-0-606-17822-8(8)) Tandem Library Bks.

Bemelmans, Ludwig & Barrett, Judi. Madeline's Rescue. 2000. (Madeline Ser.). (J). (ps-3). pap. 19.97 incl. audio (978-0-7366-9205-2(3)) Books on Tape, Inc.

Bemelmans, Ludwig & Wheeler, Jody. Madeline's Birthday. 1999. (Madeline Ser.). (Illus.). 16p. (J). (ps-3). act. bk. ed. 7.99 (978-0-670-88767-5(6) , Viking Juvenile) Penguin Group (USA) Inc.

Marciano, John Bemelmans. Madeline Says Merci: The Always Be Polite Book. Marciano, John Bemelmans, illus. 2001. (Madeline Ser.). (Illus.). 48p. (J). (ps-3). 12.99 (978-0-670-03505-2(X) , Viking Juvenile) Penguin Group (USA) Inc.

MADISON, DOLLEY, 1768-1849

Ashby, Ruth. James & Dolley Madison. 2005. (Illus.). 48p. (J). pap. (978-0-8368-5763-4(1)); lib. bdg. 30.00 (978-0-8368-5757-3(7)) Stevens, Gareth Inc. (World Almanac Library).

Brown, Don. Dolley Madison Saves George Washington. 2007. 32p. (J). (gr. k-3). 16.00 (978-0-618-41199-3(2)) Houghton Mifflin Co.

Figley, Marty Rhodes. Washington Is Burning. Orback, Craig, illus. 2006. (On My Own History Ser.). 48p. (J). 25.26 (978-1-57505-875-7(8)) Lerner Publishing Group.

Klingel, Cynthia Fitterer & Noyed, Robert B. Dolley Madison: First Lady. 2002. (Spirit of America: Our People Ser.). (Illus.). 32p. (J). (gr. 2-6). 27.07 (978-1-56766-170-5(X)) Child's World, Inc.

Larkin, Tanya. What Was Cooking in Dolly Madison's White House? 2001. (Cooking Throughout American History Ser.). (Illus.). 24p. (J). (gr. 3). lib. bdg. 19.95 (978-0-8239-5608-1(3) , PowerKids Pr.) Rosen Publishing Group, Inc., The.

Leininger, Tracy M. Unfading Beauty: The Story of Dolley Madison. Pulley, Kelly & Reed, Lisa, illus. 2000. 64p. (J). 16.00 (978-1-929241-20-0(8)) Vision Forum, Inc., The.

Mader, Jan. Dolley Madison. 2007. (J). (978-0-7368-6701-6(5) , Pebble Bks.) Capstone Pr., Inc.

Mattern, Joanne. Dolley Madison. 2007. (First Ladies Ser.). (Illus.). 32p. (J). (gr. k-6). lib. bdg. 24.21 (*978-1-59928-798-0(6) , Checkerboard Library) ABDO Publishing Co.

Patrick, Jean L. S. Dolley Madison. 2002. (History Maker Bios Ser.). (Illus.). (J). 47p. pap. 6.95 (978-0-8225-0379-8(4) , Lerner Pubns.); 48p. (gr. 3-5). lib. bdg. 26.60 (978-0-8225-0194-7(5)) Lerner Publishing Group.

Pflueger, Lynda. Dolley Madison: Courageous First Lady. 1999. (Historical American Biographies Ser.). (Illus.). 128p. (YA). (gr. 6-12). lib. bdg. 26.60 (978-0-7660-1092-5(9)) Enslow Pubs., Inc.

Shulman, Holly Cowan & Mattern, David B. Dolley Madison: Her Life, Letters, & Legacy. 2005. (Library of American Lives & Times). (Illus.). 112p. (YA). (gr. 4-8). lib. bdg. 31.95 (978-0-8239-5749-1(7)) Rosen Publishing Group, Inc., The.

Smalley, Roger. Dolley Madison Saves History. Cool, Anna-Maria et al, illus. 2005. (Graphic Library). 32p. (J). (gr. 3-7). lib. bdg. 25.26 (978-0-7368-4972-2(6)) Capstone Pr., Inc.

Washington Is Burning. 2007. (J). pap. 5.95 (*978-0-8225-6050-0(X) , First Avenue Editions) Lerner Publishing Group.

Weatherly, Myra. Dolley Madison: America's First Lady. 2004. (Notable Americans Ser.). (Illus.). 128p. (YA). (gr. 6-12). 23.95 (978-1-883846-95-4(1) , First Biographies) Reynolds, Morgan Inc.

Witteman, Barbara. Dolley Madison: First Lady. 2003. (Let Freedom Ring Ser.). (Illus.). 48p. (J). (gr. 3-4). lib. bdg. 22.60 (978-0-7368-1551-2(1) , Bridgestone Bks.) Capstone Pr., Inc.

MADISON, JAMES, 1751-1836

Ashby, Ruth. James & Dolley Madison. 2005. (Illus.). 48p. (J). pap. (978-0-8368-5763-4(1)); lib. bdg. 30.00 (978-0-8368-5757-3(7)) Stevens, Gareth Inc. (World Almanac Library).

Bramwell, Neil D. James Madison: A MyReportLinks. Com Book. 2003. (Presidents Ser.). (Illus.). 48p. (J). (gr. 4-10). lib. bdg. 25.26 (978-0-7660-5129-4(3) , MyReportLinks.com Bks.) Enslow Pubs., Inc.

Elish, Dan. James Madison. 2007. (Presidents & Their Times Ser.). 96p. (J). lib. bdg. 32.79 (*978-0-7614-2432-1(6) , Benchmark Bks.) Cavendish, Marshall Corp.

Fritz, Jean. The Great Little Madison. 1998. (Illus.). 160p. (J). (gr. 5-9). pap. 6.99 (978-0-698-11621-4(6) , Putnam Juvenile) Penguin Group (USA) Inc.

January, Brendan. James Madison. 2003. (Encyclopedia of Presidents Ser.: Vol. 4). (Illus.). 110p. (J). 34.00 (978-0-516-24210-1(5) , Children's Pr.) Scholastic Library Publishing.

Kallen, Stuart A. James Madison. 2001. (Founding Fathers Ser.). (Illus.). 64p. (J). (gr. 3-8). lib. bdg. 25.65 (978-1-57765-015-7(8) , ABDO & Daughters) ABDO Publishing Co.

Kelley, Brent P. James Madison. 2000. (Revolutionary War Leaders Ser.). (Illus.). 80p. (J). pap. 27.50 (978-0-7910-6130-5(2)); (gr. 8-12). 27.50 (978-0-7910-5972-2(3)) Facts On File, Inc. (Chelsea Hse.).

—James Madison: Father of the Constitution. 2001. (gr. 5-8). lib. bdg. 17.60 (978-0-613-32704-6(7)) Tandem Library Bks.

Kent, Zachary. James Madison: Creating a Nation. 2004. (America's Founding Fathers Ser.). (Illus.). 128p. (J). lib. bdg. 26.60 (978-0-7660-2180-8(7)) Enslow Pubs., Inc.

Kozleski, Lisa. James Madison. 2003. (Childhoods of the Presidents Ser.). (Illus.). 48p. (J). (gr. 4 up). lib. bdg. (978-1-59084-269-0(3)) Mason Crest Pubs.

Lusted, Marcia Amidon. Revolution & the New Nation. 2007. (*978-1-59036-739-1(1)); (*978-1-59036-740-7(5)) Weigl Pubs., Inc.

Marsh, Carole. James Madison. 2002. (One Thousand Readers Ser.). (Illus.). 12p. (J). (gr. k-4). 2.95 (978-0-635-01492-4(0) , 14920) Gallopade International.

—James Madison: An Ohio Experience Reader. 2001. (J). (gr. k-5). pap. 1.95 (978-0-635-00452-9(6)) Gallopade International.

—The Virginia Reader: James Madison. 2001. (Virginia Experience! Ser.). (Illus.). 12p. (J). (gr. k-4). pap. 2.95 (978-0-635-00358-4(9)) Gallopade International.

Mitchell, Barbara. Father of the Constitution: A Story about James Madison. Tavoularis, Alex, illus. 2004. (Creative Minds Biographies Ser.). 64p. (J). pap. 6.95 (978-1-57505-607-4(0)); 22.60 (978-1-57505-182-6(6) , Carolrhoda Bks.) Lerner Publishing Group.

Naden, Corinne J. & Blue, Rose. Marbury V. Madison: The Court's Foundation. 2004. (Supreme Court Milestones Ser.). (Illus.). 128p. (J). 37.07 (978-0-7614-1840-5(7) , Benchmark Bks.) Cavendish, Marshall Corp.

Pflueger, Lynda. Dolley Madison: Courageous First Lady. 1999. (Historical American Biographies Ser.). (Illus.). 128p. (YA). (gr. 6-12). lib. bdg. 26.60 (978-0-7660-1092-5(9)) Enslow Pubs., Inc.

Roberts, Jeremy. James Madison. 2004. (Presidential Leaders Ser.). (Illus.). 112p. (J). (gr. 6-12). lib. bdg. 29.27 (978-0-8225-0823-6(0)) Lerner Publishing Group.

Santella, Andrew. James Madison. 2002. (Profiles of the Presidents Ser.). (Illus.). 64p. (J). (gr. 4 up). lib. bdg. 23.93 (978-0-7565-0252-2(7)) Compass Point Bks.

Schmidt, Roderic. How to Draw the Life & Times of James Madison. 2006. (Kid's Guide to Drawing the Presidents of the United States of America Ser.). (J). 25.25 (978-1-4042-2981-5(7) , PowerKids Pr.) Rosen Publishing Group, Inc., The.

Somervill, Barbara. The Life & Times of James Madison. 2007. (J). lib. bdg. (*978-1-58415-530-0(2)) Mitchell Lane Pubs., Inc.

Venezia, Mike. James Madison. Venezia, Mike, illus. 2005. (Getting to Know the U. S. Presidents Ser.). (Illus.). 32p. (J). (gr. 3-4). pap. 7.95 (978-0-516-27478-2(3) , Children's Pr.) Scholastic Library Publishing.

Venezia, Mike, tr. & illus. James Madison. Venezia, Mike, illus. 2004. (Gtk Us Presidents Ser.). (J). 27.00 (978-0-516-22609-5(6) , Children's Pr.) Scholastic Library Publishing.

Welsbacher, Anne. James Madison. 1999. (United States Presidents Ser.). (Illus.). 32p. (J). (gr. k-6). lib. bdg. 22.78 (978-1-56239-739-5(7) , Checkerboard Library) ABDO Publishing Co.

MADONNA

see Mary, Blessed Virgin, Saint

MAFIA

Stockdale, Tom. Al Capone. 1999. (Life & Times of Ser.). (Illus.). 48p. (YA). (gr. 5 up). lib. bdg. 18.65 (978-0-7910-4638-8(9) , Chelsea Hse.) Facts On File, Inc.

MAFIA—FICTION

Colfer, Eoin. Encuentro en el Artico. 2002. (Artemis Fowl Ser.: Bk. 2). (SPA.). 320p. pap. (978-84-8441-173-4(7) , MO32015) Grijalbo Mondadori, S.A.-Montena.

Coté, Denis. La Machination du Scorpion Noir. 2004. (Mon Roman Ser.). (FRE.). 160p. (J). (gr. 2). pap. (978-2-89021-667-9(5)) Diffusion du livre Mirabel.

Korman, Gordon. Son of the Mob. 2002. 262p. (J). 16.49 (978-0-7868-2616-2(9)) Hyperion Bks. for Children.

Lurie, April. Brothers, Boyfriends & Other Criminal Minds. 2007. 304p. (YA). (gr. 7). lib. bdg. 18.99 (978-0-385-90152-9(6) , Delacorte Bks. for Young Readers) Random Hse. Children's Bks.

Shakespeare, William & Appignanesi, Richard. Romeo & Juliet. Leong, Sonia, illus. 2007. (Manga Shakespeare Ser.). 208p. (J). (gr. 2-8). pap. 9.95 (*978-0-8109-9325-9(2) , Abrams Bks. for Young Readers) Abrams, Harry N. , Inc.

MAGALHAES, FERNAO DE, D. 1521

Anthony, Laurence. Ferdinand Magellan. 2001. (Great Explorers Ser.). (Illus.). 48p. (J). (gr. 5 up). lib. bdg. 30.00 (978-0-8368-5016-1(5) , World Almanac Library) Stevens, Gareth Inc.

Bastable, Tony. Ferdinand Magellan. 2003. (Great Explorers Ser.). (Illus.). 48p. (J). (gr. 5 up). pap. 14.60 (978-0-8368-5176-2(5) , World Almanac Library) Stevens, Gareth Inc.

Burgan, Michael. Magellan: Ferdinand Magellan & the First Trip Around the World. 2001. (Exploring the World Ser.). (Illus.). 48p. (J). (gr. 4 up). lib. bdg. 22.60 (978-0-7565-0125-9(3)) Compass Point Bks.

Crompton, Samuel Willard. Ferdinand Magellan: And the Quest to Circle the Globe. Goetzmann, William H., ed. 2005. (Explorers of New Lands Ser.). (Illus.). 144p. (J). (ps-8). lib. bdg. 30.00 (978-0-7910-8608-7(9) , Chelsea Hse.) Facts On File, Inc.

Fandel, Jennifer. Ferdinand Magellan. 2003. (Explorers of the Unknown Ser.). (J). (978-1-58417-036-5(0)); pap. (978-1-58417-099-0(9)) Lake Street Pubs.

Gallagher, Jim. Ferdinand Magellan & the First Voyage Around the World. 1999. (Explorers of the New World Ser.). (Illus.). 63p. (YA). (gr. 4 up). 31.00 (978-0-7910-5508-3(6) , Chelsea Hse.) Facts On File, Inc.

Ganeri, Anita. Ferdinand Magellan. 1999. (What Would You Ask...? Ser.). (Illus.). 32p. (J). (gr. 2-6). lib. bdg. 16.95 (978-1-929298-02-0(1)) Chrysalis Education.

Great Explorers: Captain James Cook; Christopher Columbus; Ferdinand Magellan; John Cabot, 4 bks. 2002. (Illus.). (J). (gr. 5 up). pap. (978-0-8368-5179-3(X)); lib. bdg. 117.06 (978-0-8368-5019-2(X)) Stevens, Gareth Inc. (World Almanac Library).

Harcourt School Publishers Staff. The First Voyage Around the World. 3rd ed. 2002. (Horizons Ser.). (Illus.). (J). pap. 7.30 (978-0-15-333559-4(9)) Harcourt Schl. Pubs.

Hurwicz, Claude. Ferdinand Magellan. 2001. (Famous Explorers Ser.). (Illus.). 24p. (J). (gr. 3). lib. bdg. 18.75 (978-0-8239-5562-6(1) , PowerKids Pr.) Rosen Publishing Group, Inc., The.

Kaufman, Mervyn D. Ferdinand Magellan. 2004. (Fact Finders Ser.). (Illus.). 32p. (J). 16.95 (978-0-7368-2487-3(1)) Capstone Pr., Inc.

Kramer, S. A. Who Was Ferdinand Magellan? Wolf, Elizabeth & Harrison, Nancy, illus. 2004. (Who Was...? Ser.). 112p. (J). (gr. 3-7). pap. 4.99 (978-0-448-43105-5(X) , Grosset & Dunlap) Penguin Group (USA) Inc.

Landau, Elaine. Ferdinand Magellan. 2006. (History Maker Bios Ser.). (Illus.). 48p. (J). (gr. 3-7). 26.60 (978-0-8225-2942-2(4) , Lerner Pubns.) Lerner Publishing Group.

Levinson, Nancy Smiler. Magellan: And the First Voyage Around the World. 2001. (Illus.). 144p. (J). (gr. 5-9). tchr. ed. 19.00 (978-0-395-98773-5(3) , Clarion Bks.) Houghton Mifflin Co. Trade & Reference Div.

Magellan. (Exploring the World Ser.). 48p. (YA). 8.95 (978-0-7565-1146-3(1)) Compass Point Bks.

Mattern, Joanne. The Travels of Ferdinand Magellan. 2000. (Explorers & Exploration Ser.). (Illus.). 48p. (J). (gr. 4-7). lib. bdg. 22.83 (978-0-7398-1484-0(2)) Raintree.

Meltzer, Milton, et al. Ferdinand Magellan: First to Sail Around the World. 2001. (Great Explorations Ser.: Vol. 1). (Illus.). 80p. (J). (gr. 4 up). lib. bdg. 29.93 (978-0-7614-1238-0(7) , Benchmark Bks.) Cavendish, Marshall Corp.

Molzahn, Arlene Bourgeois. Ferdinand Magellan: First Explorer Around the World. 2003. (Illus.). 48p. (J). (gr. 1-4). lib. bdg. 23.93 (978-0-7660-2068-9(1)) Enslow Pubs., Inc.

Petrie, Kristin. Ferdinand Magellan. 2007. (Illus.). 32p. (J). 22.78 (978-1-59679-744-4(4)) ABDO Publishing Co.

Reid, Struan. Ferdinand Magellan. (Groundbreakers Ser.). (Illus.). 48p. (J). (gr. 5-7). 2002. pap. 8.50 (978-1-58810-369-7(2) , 91091); 2001. lib. bdg. 25.64 (978-1-58810-045-0(6)) Heinemann Library.

Senker, Cath. Magellan's Voyage Around the World. 2007. (J). (*978-1-4034-9754-3(0)) Heinemann Library.

Waldman, Stuart. Magellan's World. Manchess, Gregory, illus. 2007. (Great Explorers Ser.). 48p. (J). (gr. 4-8). 22.95 (*978-1-931414-19-7(X)) Mikaya Pr.

White, David. The First Voyage Around the World. 2002. (Exploration & Discovery Ser.). (Illus.). 64p. (J). (gr. 5 up). lib. bdg. (978-1-59084-054-2(2)) Mason Crest Pubs.

Whiting, Jim. Ferdinand Magellan. 2006. (What's So Great About... ? Ser.). (Illus.). 32p. (J). (gr. 1-4). lib. bdg. (978-1-58415-480-8(2)) Mitchell Lane Pubs., Inc.

MAGALHAES, FERNAO DE, D. 1521—FICTION

Johnson, Vargie. Ferdinand Magellan the Explorer: What Made Them Famous? 2006. 156p. (J). per. 15.00 (978-1-931195-92-8(7)) KiwE Publishing, Ltd.

Torrey, Michele. To the Edge of the World. 240p. (YA). (gr. 7). 2004. pap. 5.99 (978-0-440-23793-8(9) , Laurel Leaf); 2003. (Illus.). 15.95 (978-0-375-82338-1(7) , Knopf Bks. for Young Readers) Random Hse. Children's Bks.

MAGAZINES

see Periodicals

MAGELLAN, FERDINAND, D. 1521

see Magalhaes, Fernao de, d. 1521

MAGIC

Here are entered works on the use of charms, spells, etc., believed to have supernatural power to produce or prevent a particular result considered unobtainable by natural means. Works on performance of sleight of hand or tricks involving various types of illusion for purposes of entertainment are entered under Magic Tricks.

see also Card Tricks; Occultism

Andrews, Ted. Faerie Charms. 2001. (Young Person's School of Magic & Mystery Ser.: Vol. 6). (Illus.). 256p. (J). (gr. 7 up). 18.95 (978-1-888767-42-1(1)) Dragonhawk Publishing.

—Magic of Believing. Alexander-Harding, Pagyn & Haugen, Diane, eds. 2000. (Young Person's School of Magic & Mystery Ser.). (Illus.). 256p. (J). 18.95 (978-1-888767-43-8(X)) Dragonhawk Publishing.

Beahm, George & Goldin, Stan, eds. The Whimsic Alley Book of Spells: Mythical Incantations for Magicians of All Ages. 2007. (Illus.). 192p. (J). pap. 14.95 (***978-1-57174-535-4(1)***) Hampton Roads Publishing Co., Inc.

Beak, Nick Huckleberry & Boase, Petra. Crafty Magic. Freeman, John, photos by. 1999. (Crafty Kids Ser.). (Illus.). 64p. (J). (gr. 3 up). lib. bdg. 25.26 (978-0-8368-2481-0(4)) Stevens, Gareth Inc.

Blackstone, Gay. Around the House Magic. (Illus.). (J). (978-1-59093-000-7(2) , Eager Minds Pr.) Warehousing & Fulfillment Specialists, LLC (WFS, LLC).

Blum, Raymond. Mathemania. Sinclair, Jeff, illus. 2002. 96p. (gr. 3-7). pap. 6.95 (978-1-4027-0125-2(X)) Sterling Publishing Co., Inc.

Bruce, Marie. Everyday Spells for a Teenage Witch. 2002. (Illus.). 160p. 14.95 (978-0-572-02770-4(2)) Foulsham, W. Co., Ltd. GBR. *Dist:* APG Sales and Fulfillment.

Bryant, Page. Star Magic. Haugen, Diane, ed. 2001. (Young Person's School of Magic & Mystery Ser.: Vol. 4). (Illus.). 256p. (YA). (gr. 7 up). 18.95 (978-1-888767-44-5(8)) Dragonhawk Publishing.

Bulfinch, Thomas. Classic Treasury of Bulfinch's Mythology. 2003. (978-0-7624-1900-5(8)) Running Pr. Bk. Pubs.

Colbert, David. Magical Worlds of Harry Potter: A Treasury of Myths, Legends, & Fascinating Facts. 2001. (Illus.). 223p. (YA). (gr. 5 up). 14.95 (978-0-9708442-0-0(4)) Lumina Pr. LLC.

Denne, Ben. Magia Para Todos. 2005. (Titles in Spanish Ser.). (SPA.). 32p. (J). pap. 8.95 (978-0-7460-6394-1(6) , Usborne) EDC Publishing.

Empty Generic 6-Copy Voodoo Display. 2004. pap. (978-0-7624-1761-2(7)) Running Pr. Bk. Pubs.

Funston, Sylvia. Magic. Weissman, Joe, illus. 2003. (Strange Science Ser.). 40p. (J). (gr. 3-7). pap. 9.95 (978-1-894379-34-2(9)) Maple Tree Pr. CAN. *Dist:* Firefly Bks., Ltd.

Greenhaven Staff. Black Magic & Witches. 2002. (gr. 7-12). lib. bdg. 30.35 (978-0-613-73885-9(3)) Tandem Library Bks.

Hale, Nathan. The Devil You Know. Hale, Nathan, illus. 2005. (Illus.). 32p. (J). (ps-3). 17.85 (978-0-8027-8983-9(8)) Walker & Co.

Hamilton, John. Magic Rings & Other Magical Things. 2005. (Illus.). 32p. (J). (gr. 4-8). lib. bdg. 24.21 (978-1-59679-337-8(6) , ABDO & Daughters) ABDO Publishing Co.

Hamilton, John. Witches. 2007. (ENG., Illus.). 32p. (J). lib. bdg. 24.21 (***978-1-59928-776-8(5)*** , ABDO & Daughters) ABDO Publishing Co.

Jacklin, Karl. It's Magic. (Illus.). (J). (gr. 3-6). pap. (978-1-876367-03-9(2)) Wizard Bks.

Keable, Ian. The Big Book of Magic Fun. 2005. (Illus.). 192p. (J). (gr. 4). pap. 14.99 (978-0-7641-3222-3(9)) Barron's Educational Series, Inc.

Kilby, Janice Eaton, et al. The Book of Wizard Craft: In Which the Apprentice Finds Spells, Potions, Fantastic Tales & 50 Enchanting Things to Make. Burnett, Lindy, illus. deluxe ed. 2001. 144p. (J). (gr. 4-6). 7.95 (978-1-57990-206-3(5)) Lark Bks.

Kiraithe, Jackie. Magic Links: Manual. Gonzales, Linda, ed. 200p. (J). 48.00 (978-0-942787-95-5(1)) Binet International.

Kronzek, Allan Zola & Kronzek, Elizabeth. Diccionario del Mago. Paula Vicens, Ines Belasategui, tr. 2005. (Escritura desatada Ser.). (SPA.). 368p. (J). 17.95 (978-970-710-056-5(7)) Ediciones B ESP. *Dist:* Independent Pubs. Group.

Learn - Magic. 2001. 64p. (YA). per. 6.95 (978-0-9707797-0-0(4)) Crowl, Tom & the Mrs.

Marsh, Carole. Good Magic, Spells, Potions & More from History, Literature & Make-Believe. 2001. (Here & Now Series!). (Illus.). 48p. (J). (gr. 2-8). pap. 7.95 (978-0-635-00267-9(1)) Gallopade International.

Masessa, Ed. The Wandmaker's Guidebook. Araujo, Paige Krul, ed. Jankowski, Dan, illus. 2006. 18p. (J). 22.99 (978-0-439-86265-3(5) , Tangerine Pr.) Scholastic, Inc.

Mason, Tom & Danko, Dan. The Book of Appearing & Disappearing. 2001. (Illus.). 74p. (J). (978-0-439-32704-6(0)) Scholastic, Inc.

—The Book of Ghostly Magic. 2002. (Illus.). 74p. (J). (978-0-439-32709-1(1)) Scholastic, Inc.

Master Merlin & Steer, Dugald. Wizardology Handbook: A Course for Apprentices. Gilbert, Anne Young et al, illus. 2007. (Ologies Ser.). 80p. (J). (gr. 3 up). 12.99 (***978-0-7636-3401-8(8)***) Candlewick Pr.

McMaster, Shawn. 60 Super Simple More Magic Tricks. Abbett, Leo, illus. 1999. 80p. (J). (gr. 2-6). pap. 6.95 (978-0-7373-0155-7(4) , 01554W) McGraw-Hill/ Contemporary.

Merlin, Master. Wizardology: A Guide to the Wizards of the World. Steer, Dugald A., ed. 2007. (Ologies Ser.). (Illus.). 40p. (J). (gr. 3-7). 14.99 (***978-0-7636-3710-1(6)***) Candlewick Pr.

Muten, Burleigh. Goddesses: A World of Myth & Magic. Guay, Rebecca, illus. 2003. 80p. (J). 19.99 (978-1-84148-075-6(4)) Barefoot Bks., Inc.

Puzzle House Staff. Magic. Teviotdale, Stuart, illus. 2001. 128p. (J). (gr. 3-8). pap. 7.95 (978-0-439-22010-1(6)) Scholastic, Inc.

Roleff, Tamara L., ed. Black Magic & Witches. 2003. (Illus.). 127p. (J). pap. 18.70 (978-0-7377-1319-0(4)); lib. bdg. 32.45 (978-0-7377-1318-3(6)) Thomson Gale. (Greenhaven Pr., Inc.).

Rumstuckle, Cornelius. The Book of Wizardry: The Apprentice's Guide to the Secrets of the Wizards' Guild. 2003. (Illus.). 336p. pap. 12.95 (978-0-7387-0165-3(3)) Llewellyn Pubns.

Savage, Candace. Wizards: An Amazing Journey Through the Last Great Age of Magic. 2003. (Illus.). 80p. (J). (gr. 4-7). 17.95 (978-1-55054-943-0(X)) Douglas & McIntyre, Ltd. CAN. *Dist:* Transition Vendor.

Schwartz, David M. & Whitin, David. The Magic of a Million Activity Book: Great Classroom Activities & Reproducibles to Explore a Million & Other Big Numbers. 1998. 80p. (J). 10.95 (978-0-590-70133-4(9)) Scholastic, Inc.

Spelling, Phoebe. Hocus Pocus: A Whole Book of Magical Fun! 2001. (Illus.). 160p. (J). pap. 4.99 (978-0-439-29652-6(8)) Scholastic, Inc.

A Starter Kit for Wizards. 2002. 64p. (J). pap. 9.98 (978-0-7525-6298-8(3)) Parragon, Inc.

Tocci, Salvatore. Experiments with Magic. (True Bks.). (J). 2004. 47p. (gr. 3-5). pap. 6.95 (978-0-516-27808-7(8)); 2003. (Illus.). 48p. 25.00 (978-0-516-22788-7(2)) Scholastic Library Publishing. (Children's Pr.).

Vazquez-Vigo, Carmen. Por Arte de Magia. 2001. Tr. of Strange Man. (SPA.). 96p. (J). 6.50 (978-84-348-1776-0(4)) SM Ediciones ESP. *Dist:* AIMS International Bks., Inc.

Walton, Rick & Walton, Ann. Magical Mischief: Jokes That Shock & Amaze. Gable, Brian, illus. 2005. (Make Me Laugh! Ser.). 32p. (J). (gr. k-3). lib. bdg. 19.93 (978-1-57505-664-7(X)) Lerner Publishing Group.

Wickings, Ruth. Wizards. 2007. (Enchanted World Ser.). (Illus.). 12p. (J). (ps-3). 9.95 (***978-1-84560-033-4(9)***) Mercury Bks. Ltd. GBR. *Dist:* International Publishers Marketing.

Wizards are Magic. 2002. (Little Friends Ser.). (J). 2.98 (978-1-84273-425-4(3) , Exclusive Editions) Parragon, Inc.

Wood, Jamie. The Enchanted Diary: A Teen's Guide to Magick & Life. 2005. (Illus.). 193p. pap. 12.95 (978-1-58761-245-9(3) , Celestial Arts Publishing Company) Ten Speed Pr.

—The Teen Spell Book: Magick for Young Witches. 2004. (Illus.). 304p. 12.95 (978-1-58761-115-5(5) , Celestial Arts Publishing Company) Ten Speed Pr.

MAGIC—FICTION

Abarca, Jesse, Jr. Who's Dodie. Abarca, Jesse, Jr., ed. 2001. (Las Aventuras de Dodie el Pajaro Dodo y sus amigos). (Illus.). 8p. (Orig.). (J). pap. 4.95 (978-0-9704850-0-7(X)) Dodo Bks.

Abbott, Tony. Chariot of Queen Zara. Merrell, David, illus. 2006. 124p. (J). lib. bdg. 15.38 (***978-1-4242-0308-6(2)***) Fitzgerald Bks.

—The Coiled Viper. Jessell, Tim, illus. 2003. (Secrets of Droon Ser.: Vol. 19). 128p. (J). (gr. 2-5). pap. 4.99 (978-0-439-42080-8(6)) Scholastic, Inc.

—Dream Thief. Merrell, David, illus. 2003. (Secrets of Droon Ser.: No. 17). 128p. (J). (gr. 2-5). pap. 4.99 (978-0-439-42078-5(4) , Scholastic Paperbacks) Scholastic, Inc.

—Hidden Stairs & the Magic Carpet. 1999. (gr. 3-6). lib. bdg. 11.80 (978-0-613-16947-9(6)) Tandem Library Bks.

—Into the Land of the Lost. 2000. (gr. 3-6). lib. bdg. 11.80 (978-0-613-32690-2(3)) Tandem Library Bks.

—The Isle of Mists. Merrell, David, illus. 2004. 121p. (J). lib. bdg. 15.38 (***978-1-4242-0313-0(9)***) Fitzgerald Bks.

—The Knights of Silversnow. Jessell, Tim, illus. 2002. (Secrets of Droon Ser.: no. 16). 128p. (J). pap. 4.99 (978-0-439-30609-6(4) , Scholastic Paperbacks) Scholastic, Inc.

—The Knights of Silversnow. 2002. (gr. 3-6). lib. bdg. 11.80 (978-0-613-50453-9(4)) Tandem Library Bks.

—The Magic Escapes. ed. 2002. (Secrets of Droon Ser.: Bk. 1). (Illus.). 176p. (J). pap. 5.99 (978-0-439-42077-8(6) , Scholastic Paperbacks) Scholastic, Inc.

—The Magic Escapes. 2002. (gr. 3-6). lib. bdg. 13.00 (978-0-613-58158-5(X)) Tandem Library Bks.

—The Mask of Maliban. 2001. (gr. 3-6). lib. bdg. 11.80 (978-0-613-35785-2(X)) Tandem Library Bks.

—The Moon Dragon. Merrell, David, illus. 2006. (Little Apple Ser.). 121p. (J). (978-1-4156-4703-5(8)) Scholastic, Inc.

—Moon Dragon. Merrell, David, illus. 2006. 121p. (J). lib. bdg. 15.38 (***978-1-4242-0309-3(0)***) Fitzgerald Bks.

—Queen of Shadowthorn. 2007. (Secrets of Droon Ser.). 128p. (J). pap. 4.99 (***978-0-439-90252-6(5)*** , Scholastic Paperbacks) Scholastic, Inc.

—The Riddle of Zorfendorf Castle. Merrell, David, illus. 2005. 124p. (J). (ps-k). lib. bdg. 10.79 (978-0-606-33298-9(7)) Tandem Library Bks.

—Riddle of Zorfendorf Castle. Merrell, David, illus. 2005. 124p. (J). lib. bdg. 15.38 (***978-1-4242-0310-9(4)***) Fitzgerald Bks.

—Search for the Dragon Ship. Jessell, Tim, illus. 2003. (Secrets of Droon Ser.: Vol. 18). 128p. (gr. 2-5). pap. 3.99 (978-0-439-42079-2(2) , Scholastic Paperbacks) Scholastic, Inc.

—Search for the Dragon Ship. 2003. (gr. 3-6). lib. bdg. 11.80 (978-0-613-66379-3(9)) Tandem Library Bks.

—Sorcerer. 2006. (Illus.). 112p. (J). pap. 3.99 (978-0-439-67175-0(2) , Scholastic Paperbacks) Scholastic, Inc.

—The Tower of the Elf King. Merrell, David, illus. 2000. (Secrets of Droon Ser.: No. 9). 112p. (J). (gr. 2-5). pap. 3.99 (978-0-439-20772-0(X)) Scholastic, Inc.

Abbott, Tony & Gelsey, James. Escape from Jabar-Loo. 2007. (Secrets of Droon Ser.: No. 30). 128p. (J). pap. 3.99 (***978-0-439-90251-9(7)*** , Scholastic Paperbacks) Scholastic, Inc.

Abouzeid, Chris. Anatopsis. 2006. 336p. (J). (gr. 5). 16.99 (978-0-525-47583-5(4) , Dutton Juvenile) Penguin Group (USA) Inc.

Abrahamson, Jean. Manners Are Magic. 2005. (Illus.). 48p. 6.99 (978-1-57860-231-5(9)) Emmis Bks.

Abromovitz, Jaime. Zazzy-Q Ding-A-Ling: Ding-A-Lings: the Magic Wand. 2004. (Illus.). (J). per. 9.95 (978-0-9762587-2-8(2)) StoryGirl Productions, LLC.

Abshire, Lisa D. Sam's Magical Day. 2006. 48p. pap. 12.95 (978-1-4241-1484-9(5)) PublishAmerica, Inc.

Agee, Jon. Milo's Hat Trick. 2001. (Illus.). 32p. (J). (ps-17). (978-0-7868-0902-8(7)) Hyperion Bks. for Children.

Ahour, Paravish. All Children of the World Smile in the Same Language: Iran; the Cradle of Civilization. 2006. 103p. (J). per. 16.95 (978-1-60002-015-5(1) , 3593, Airleaf Publishing) Airleaf Publishing & Bookselling.

Alcantara, Ricardo. Mauro Ojos Brillantes. 9th ed. 2003. (SPA., Illus.). 48p. (978-84-236-2865-0(5) , ED6279) Edebé ESP. *Dist:* Lectorum Pubns., Inc.

Alcantara, Ricardo. Tomas y el Lapiz Magico. Gusti, illus. 2004. (SPA.). (J). pap. 10.50 (978-84-263-4829-6(7)) Vives, Luis Editorial (Edelvives) ESP. *Dist:* Lectorum Pubns., Inc.

Alexander, Alma. Gift of the Unmage. 2007. (Worldweavers Ser.: Bk. 1). 400p. (YA). (gr. 7 up). 16.99 (978-0-06-083955-0(4)); lib. bdg. 17.89 (978-0-06-083956-7(2)) HarperCollins Pubs.

—Spellspam. 2008. (Worldweavers Ser.). 448p. (J). 17.99 (***978-0-06-083958-1(9)***); lib. bdg. 18.89 (***978-0-06-083959-8(7)***) HarperCollins Pubs. (Eos).

—Worldweavers: Gift of the Unmage. 2008. (Worldweavers Ser.). 416p. (J). pap. 7.99 (***978-0-06-083957-4(0)*** , Eos) HarperCollins Pubs.

Alexander-Harding, Pagyn. Dreamtime Magic. Haugen, Diane, ed. 2001. (Young Person's School of Magic & Mystery Ser.: Vol. 2). (Illus.). 256p. (J). (gr. 7 up). 18.95 (978-1-888767-38-4(3)) Dragonhawk Publishing.

Alexander, Jason. Dad, Are You the Tooth Fairy? Spears, Ron, illus. 2005. 32p. (J). pap. 16.95 (978-0-439-66745-6(3)) Scholastic, Inc.

Alexander, Lee. Arnie Hackett. Hooper, Kevin T., illus. l.t. ed. 2002. 127p. (J). pap. 8.95 (978-0-9714782-5-1(2)) Crossroads Pr.

Alexander, Lloyd. The Cat Who Wished to Be a Man. 2000. 107p. (J). (ps-7). per. 13.00 (978-0-613-12359-4(X)) Tandem Library Bks.

—The Rope Trick. 2004. 208p. (J). (gr. 5 up). reprint ed. pap. 5.99 (978-0-14-240119-4(6) , Puffin) Penguin Group (USA) Inc.

Alexander, Michael. Until Wishes Are Fulfilled. 2007. (ENG.). 160p. per. (***978-1-84426-408-7(4)***) Upfront Publishing Ltd.

Alfonsi, Alice. Farewell to Love. 23rd novel rev. ed. 2007. (W. I. T. C. H. Ser.: Bk. 23). 144p. (gr. 3-7). pap. 4.99 (978-1-4231-0267-0(3)) Hyperion Pr.

Alfonsi, Alice. Trust Your Heart. novel rev. ed. 2007. (W. I. T. C. H. Ser.: Bk. 24). 144p. (gr. 3-7). pap. 4.99 (***978-1-4231-0288-5(6)***) Hyperion Pr.

Alton, Steve. The Firehills. 2005. 192p. (J). (gr. 7-13). 15.95 (978-1-57505-798-9(0) , Carolrhoda Bks.) Lerner Publishing Group.

—The Malifex. 2003. (Middle Readers Ser.). (Illus.). 182p. (J). (gr. 3-7). 14.95 (978-0-8225-0959-2(8)) Lerner Publishing Group.

Amades, Joan. El Molinillo Magico (The Magic Grinder) Valverde, Mikel, illus. 2001. (SPA.). 24p. (J). (gr. 1-3). (978-84-246-1986-2(2)) La Galera, S.A. Editorial.

Amano, Shiro. Kingdom Hearts: Chain of Memories, Vol. 2. 2nd rev. ed. 2007. 232p. (gr. 4-7). pap. 9.99 (978-1-59816-638-5(7) , Tokyopop Kids) TOKYOPOP, Inc.

Amato, Mary. The Word Eater. 2005. (Illus.). 151p. (YA). (gr. 4-6). tchr. ed. 15.95 (978-0-8234-1468-0(X)) Holiday Hse., Inc.

—The Word Eater. Ryniak, Christopher, illus. 2005. 151p. (J). reprint ed. pap. 6.95 (978-0-8234-1940-1(1)) Holiday Hse., Inc.

Amis, Yana. The Adventurers of Crystal Lake. 1998. (978-0-921252-85-6(4)) LEGAS.

Amodeo, John, et al. The Impossible Butterfly. 2004. (Zenda Ser.: 5). 144p. (J). (gr. 12-12). pap. 4.99 (978-0-448-43257-1(9) , Grosset & Dunlap) Penguin Group (USA) Inc.

Anacker, John. The Raven's Ring Pin. Hill, Connie, ed. 2004. (Illus.). 336p. pap. 12.95 (978-0-7387-0433-3(4)) Llewellyn Pubns.

Ander, illus. Me & My Bike. 2008. 68p. (J). 16.95 (***978-0-9787550-2-7(2)***) Heryin Publishing Corp.

Anderson, Al. Pegasus: Adventures with Bingo Borden. Kurzyca, Krystyna Emilia, illus. 2006. 77p. (J). per. 19.50 (***978-1-887250-46-7(8)***) Agora Pubns., Inc.

Anfuso, Dennis. Woodwin & Beckly Vol. 6: Book One in the Chronicles of Foress. Anfuso, Dennis, illus. collector's l.t. ed. 2002. (Illus.). 88p. (J). per. 9.95 (978-1-57433-001-4(2)) Interset Pr.

Anjelae, Samara. Wonder Windows: My Guardian Angel, My Fairy Godmother, My Magical Mermaid. 2002. 42.95 (978-0-9708754-0-2(1) , BelleTress Bks.) Red Wheel/Weiser.

Applegate, Katherine. The Escape. 1998. (Animorphs Ser.: No. 15). 170p. (J). (gr. 3-7). pap. 4.99 (978-0-590-49424-3(4)) Scholastic, Inc.

—Mystify the Magician. 2001. (EverWorld Ser.: No. 11). 208p. (J). (gr. 4-7). pap. 4.99 (978-0-590-87988-0(X)) Scholastic, Inc.

Arbuthnott, Gill. The Chaos Clock. 2003. (Kelpies Ser.). 160p. pap. 10.00 (978-0-86315-422-5(0)) Floris Bks. GBR. *Dist:* SteinerBooks, Inc.

Arengo, Sue. The Magic Cooking Pot. 2001. (Illus.). 24p. 5.50 (978-0-19-422074-3(5)) Oxford Univ. Pr., Inc.

Arevalo, Luis Paquime. Juan & the Magic Shoes. 2005. (J). per. 3.99 (978-0-9748598-1-1(8)) L. A. Eng Bks.

Arias, Carlos Ballesteros. The Magic Forest. 2006. (J). pap. 8.00 (***978-0-8059-7022-7(3)***) Dorrance Publishing Co., Inc.

Arkin, Alan. Cosmo: A Cautionary Tale. Richards, Jon, illus. 2005. 40p. (J). 19.95 (978-1-929115-12-9(1)) Azro Pr., Inc.

Armenteros, Sarah. Emma & the Mashed Potato Monster. 2007. 44p. (J). 16.99 (978-1-59092-384-9(7) , Little Blue Works) Windstorm Creative.

Arraras, Maria Celeste. Dogs. 2007. 32p. (J). pap. 16.99 (***978-0-545-01912-5(5)***) Scholastic, Inc.

Atwater-Rhodes, Amelia. Wolfcry. 2008. 208p. (YA). (gr. 9). pap. 7.99 (***978-0-440-23886-7(2)*** , Delacorte Bks. for Young Readers) Random Hse. Children's Bks.

Atwater-Rhodes, Amelia. Wolfcry Vol. 4: The Kiesha'ra. 2006. (Illus.). 208p. (YA). (gr. 7). 14.95 (978-0-385-73195-9(7)); lib. bdg. 16.99 (978-0-385-90354-7(5)) Random Hse. Children's Bks. (Delacorte Bks. for Young Readers).

Austin, M. O. Boy Named Joe. 2006. pap. 12.99 (***978-1-4259-6217-3(3)***) AuthorHouse.

Autin, Tony. My Curious Uncle Dudley. Yourgrau, Barry, illus. 2004. 224p. (J). (gr. 4-7). 15.99 (978-0-7636-1935-0(3)) Candlewick Pr.

Avi. The Book Without Words: A Fable of Medieval Magic. 2006. 224p. (gr. 5-9). reprint ed. pap. 5.99 (978-0-7868-1659-0(7)) Hyperion Pr.

—The Book Without Words: A Fable of Medieval Magic. l.t. ed. 2005. 220p. (YA). 23.95 (978-0-7862-7940-1(0)) Thorndike Pr.

—Midnight Magic. 2004. 256p. (J). (gr. 3-6). pap. 5.99 (978-0-439-24219-6(3) , Scholastic Paperbacks) Scholastic, Inc.

Azasu, Kwakuvi. Sweet Justice. 2000. pap. (978-9964-978-74-7(X)) Woeli Publishing Services.

Babbitt, Natalie. Elsie Times Eight. 2001. (Illus.). 32p. (J). (ps-17). (978-0-7868-0901-1(9)) Hyperion Bks. for Children.

—Elsie Times Eight. Babbitt, Natalie, illus. 2005. (Illus.). 26p. (J). (gr. k-4). reprint ed. 16.00 (978-0-7567-9640-2(7)) DIANE Publishing Co.

Bach, Richard & Gardner, Sally. La nina mas pequena del Mundo. Tapia, Sonia, tr. 2005. (Ninos Magicos Ser.). (SPA., Illus.). 128p. (J). pap. 7.95 (978-84-666-1339-2(0)) Ediciones B ESP. *Dist:* Independent Pubs. Group.

Bacon, Thomas. Of monsters, magik & Nano-technology! 2007. 114p. pap. 17.95 (978-0-533-15467-8(7)) Vantage Pr., Inc.

Bader, Bonnie & West, Tracey. The 100th Day of School. Molnar, Albert, illus. 2001. (Spooky School Ser.). 26p. (J). (978-0-439-21554-1(4)) Scholastic, Inc.

Baggott, Julianna & Bode, N. E. The Amazing Compendium. 2007. (Mr. Magorium's Wonder Emporium Ser.). 160p. (J). pap. 4.99 (***978-0-439-91636-3(4)***) Scholastic, Inc.

Bagley, Conor. Ziggy McFinster's Nantucket Adventure. Westcott, Nadine Bernard, illus. 2008. 40p. (***978-1-56625-315-4(2)*** , Volt Pr.) Bonus Bks., Inc.

Baker, E. D. Dragon's Breath. 2003. 250p. (J). 15.95 (978-1-58234-858-2(8) , Bloomsbury Children) Bloomsbury Publishing.

—Dragon's Breath: Read-Along/Homework Pack. unabr. ed. 2005. (YA). (gr. 5-8). 92.70 incl. audio (978-1-4193-3563-1(4) , 42041) Recorded Bks., LLC.

—No Place for Magic: The Fourth Tale of the Frog Princess. 2006. (Tales of the Frog Princess Ser.). 250p. (YA). 15.95 (978-1-58234-654-0(2)) Bloomsbury Publishing.

—Once upon a Curse: More Tales of the Frog Princess. 2004. (Illus.). 225p. (J). 15.95 (978-1-58234-892-6(8) , Bloomsbury Children) Bloomsbury Publishing.

—Once upon a Curse: The Sequel to the Frog Princess & Dragon's Breath. 2006. (Tales of the Frog Princess Ser.). (Illus.). 256p. (J). pap. 6.95 (978-1-58234-911-4(8) , Bloomsbury Children) Bloomsbury Publishing.

Baker, Keith. On the Go with Mr. & Mrs. Green. 2007. (Mr. & Mrs. Green Ser.). (Illus.). 72p. (J). pap. 5.95 (978-0-15-205867-8(2) , Harcourt Paperbacks) Harcourt Children's Bks.

—On the Go with Mr. & Mrs. Green. 2006. (Mr. & Mrs. Green Ser.). (Illus.). 72p. (J). 16.00 (978-0-15-205762-6(5)) Harcourt Trade Pubs.

—On the Go with Mr. & Mrs. Green. 2007. (Mr. & Mrs. Green Ser.). 72p. (J). (gr. 2-4). 27.07 (***978-1-59961-303-1(4)***) Spotlight.

Balfour, Melissa, et al. Yr Olion Traed Hud. 2005. (WEL., Illus.). 47p. (978-1-85596-677-2(8)) Dref Wen.

Balian, Lorna. The Sweet Touch. Balian, Lorna & Balian, Lecia, illus. 2005. 40p. (J). 16.95 (978-1-59572-017-7(0)) Star Bright Bks., Inc.

Ballerina Magic Shoes. 2003. (Illus.). 32p. (J). 5.98 (978-1-4054-1144-8(9)) Parragon, Inc.

Banks, Lynne Reid. The Farthest-Away Mountain. 2004. 160p. (gr. 4-7). pap. 4.99 (978-0-440-41926-6(3) , Yearling) Random Hse. Children's Bks.

—The Indian in the Cupboard. (Indian in the Cupboard Ser.: No. 1). 44p. (J). (gr. 4-7). 1999. 9.95 (978-1-56137-225-6(0)); 1998. 11.95 (978-1-56137-693-3(0) , NU6930SP) Novel Units, Inc.

—The Key to the Indian. 1999. (gr. 3-6). lib. bdg. 13.00 (978-0-613-23006-3(X)) Tandem Library Bks.

—El Secreto del Indio. 1998. Tr. of Secret of the Indian. (SPA., Illus.). 167p. (YA). (gr. 5-8). pap. 8.95 (978-84-241-5312-0(X) , EV0519) Lectorum Pubns., Inc.

Banner, Catherine. The Eyes of a King. 2008. 480p. (J). lib. bdg. 19.99 (*978-0-375-93875-7(3)); (gr. 7-11). 16.99 (*978-0-375-83875-0(9)) Random Hse. Children's Bks. (Random Hse. Bks. for Young Readers).

BareBones Publishing. The Legend of CaseyRock. 2007. (Illus.). 40p. (J). per. 12.00 (*978-0-9779601-2-5(9)) BareBones Publishing.

Barker, Cicely Mary. Candytuft's Enchanting Treats. 2007. 80p. (J). pap. 3.99 (978-0-7232-5904-6(6) , Warne) Penguin Group (USA) Inc.

—Magical Moonlight Feast. 2007. (Flower Fairies Ser.). (Illus.). 24p. (J). pap. 14.99 (978-0-7232-5784-4(1) , Warne) Penguin Group (USA) Inc.

Barker, Cicely Mary & Le Quesne, Pippa. Buttercup & the Fairy Gold. 2007. (Flower Fairies Ser.: Bk. 5). 80p. (J). 3.99 (978-0-7232-5840-7(6) , Warne) Penguin Group (USA) Inc.

—Zinnia's Magical Adventure: A Flower Fairy Chapter Book. 2006. 80p. (J). (gr. 7). 3.99 (978-0-7232-5774-5(4) , Warne) Penguin Group (USA) Inc.

Barker, Cicely Mary & Swain-Smith, Justine. Return to Fairyopolis. 2008. 24p. (J). (gr. k). 19.99 (*978-0-7232-5996-1(8) , Warne) Penguin Group (USA) Inc.

Barlow, Steve & Skidmore, Steve. Whizzard. 2002. (Tales of the Dark Forest Ser.). (Illus.). 256p. pap. 11.00 (978-0-00-710864-0(8)) HarperCollins Pubs. Ltd. GBR. *Dist:* Independent Pubs. Group.

Barron, T. A. Child of the Dark Prophecy. 2004. (Great Tree of Avalon Trilogy: Bk. 1). 432p. (YA). (gr. 5-6). 19.99 (978-0-399-23763-8(1) , Philomel) Penguin Group (USA) Inc.

—The Eternal Flame. 2006. (Great Tree of Avalon Trilogy: Bk. 3). (Illus.). 400p. (YA). (gr. 5). 19.99 (978-0-399-24213-7(9) , Philomel) Penguin Group (USA) Inc.

—The Seven Songs of Merlin. 2000. (Lost Years of Merlin Ser.: Vol. 2). (Illus.). 1p. (gr. 5-9). reprint ed. mass mkt. 6.99 (978-0-441-00701-1(5) , Ace Bks.) Penguin Group (USA) Inc.

—Shadows on the Stars. (Great Tree of Avalon Trilogy: Bk. 2). 2006. 384p. (gr. 12). mass mkt. 7.99 (978-0-441-01447-7(X) , Ace Bks.); 2005. (Illus.). 432p. (YA). (gr. 5 up). 19.99 (978-0-399-23764-5(X) , Philomel) Penguin Group (USA) Inc.

Barry, Dave & Pearson, Ridley. Peter & the Shadow Thieves. Call, Greg, illus. 2006. 576p. (gr. 5-17). 18.99 (978-0-7868-3787-8(X)) Hyperion Bks. for Children.

—Peter & the Starcatchers. Call, Greg, illus. 2006. 480p. (gr. 5-17). reprint ed. pap. 7.99 (978-0-7868-4907-9(X) , Disney Editions) Disney Pr.

—Peter & the Starcatchers. 2004. 464p. (gr. 5-17). 17.99 (978-0-7868-5445-5(6)) Hyperion Bks. for Children.

Barwin, Gary. The Magic Mustache. Jorisch, Stephane, illus. 1999. 32p. (J). (ps-2). lib. bdg. 17.95 (978-1-55037-607-4(1)) Annick Pr., Ltd. CAN. *Dist:* Firefly Bks., Ltd.

—Magic Mustache. 1999. lib. bdg. 15.25 (978-0-613-26096-1(1)) Tandem Library Bks.

Barwin, Gary & Jorisch, Stephane. The Magic Mustache. 1999. (Illus.). 32p. (J). (ps-2). pap. 6.95 (978-1-55037-606-7(3)) Annick Pr., Ltd. CAN. *Dist:* Firefly Bks., Ltd.

Base, Graeme. Jungle Drums. 2004. (Illus.). 40p. (J). (ps-3). 18.95 (978-0-8109-5044-3(8)) Abrams, Harry N. , Inc.

Bateman, Teresa. Hamster Camp: How Harry Got Fit. Cote, Nancy, illus. 2005. 32p. (J). (gr. k-4). 15.95 (978-0-8075-3139-6(1)) Whitman, Albert & Co.

Bates, Martine. Taker's Key. 1998. (gr. 3-6). lib. bdg. 17.60 (978-0-613-83388-2(0)) Tandem Library Bks.

Bateson-Hill, Margaret. Chanda & the Mirror of Moonlight. Littlewood, Karin, illus. 2003. (Folk Tales Series Ser.). 32p. (J). (gr. 3-4). (978-1-84089-217-8(X) , Zero to Ten, Limited) Evans Publishing Group.

Bauer, A. C. E. No Castles Here. 2007. 288p. (J). (gr. 4-8). 15.99 (978-0-375-83921-4(6)); lib. bdg. 18.99 (978-0-375-93921-1(0)) Random Hse. Children's Bks. (Random Hse. Bks. for Young Readers).

Baum, L. Frank. Magic of Oz. 2006. pap. 12.99 (*978-1-4280-2747-3(5)) IndyPublish.com.

Baum, L. Frank. Sky Island. 2004. (Twelve-Point Ser.). lib. bdg. 24.00 (978-1-58287-280-3(5)); lib. bdg. 25.00 (978-1-58287-792-1(0)) North Bks.

Baum, Roger S. The Wizard of Oz & The Magic Merry-Go-Round. Seitzinger, Victoria, illus. 2002. 32p. (J). 14.95 (978-1-57072-245-5(5)) Overmountain Pr.

Beamish, Diane. Grandma's Magic Button Necklace. 2006. 25p. 12.16 (978-1-4116-5487-7(0)) Lulu.com.

Begamudre, Ven. Phantom Queen. 2003. (gr. 7-12). lib. bdg. 19.90 (978-0-613-78476-4(6)) Tandem Library Bks.

Bell, Frank. Ma Jong & the Magic Carpet. Seaman, Paul, illus. 2004. 24p. pap. 7.00 (978-1-84161-070-2(4)) Ravette Publishing, Ltd. GBR. *Dist:* Parkwest Pubns., Inc.

Bell, Gillian. The Princess of Veryan. 2005. 263p. pap. 21.95 (978-1-4137-7982-0(4)) PublishAmerica, Inc.

Bell, Hilari. Fall of a Kingdom. 2005. (Farsala Trilogy Ser.). 448p. (YA). pap. 6.99 (978-0-689-85414-9(5) , Simon Pulse) Simon & Schuster Children's Publishing.

—The Goblin Wood. (Illus.). (J). 2003. 304p. (gr. 5 up). 17.99 (978-0-06-051371-9(3)); 2004. 384p. (gr. 7 up). reprint ed. pap. 6.99 (978-0-06-051373-3(X)) HarperCollins Pubs.

Bell, Hilari. The Prophecy. 208p. (J). 2007. pap. 6.50 (*978-0-06-059945-4(6) , Eos); 2006. lib. bdg. 16.89 (978-0-06-059944-7(8)); 2006. (Illus.). 15.99 (978-0-06-059943-0(X)) HarperCollins Pubs.

Bell, Russell, illus. Herbert Hilligan's Tropical Adventure, Vol. 3. rev. ed. 1999. (Herbert Hilligan Ser.). 15.95 (978-1-57168-314-4(3)) Eakin Pr.

Bellairs, John. The Chessmen of Doom. Gorey, Edward, illus. 2000. (John Bellairs Ser.). 160p. (J). (gr. 3-7). pap. 5.99 (978-0-14-130697-1(1) , Puffin) Penguin Group (USA) Inc.

—The Chessmen of Doom. Gorey, Edward, illus. 2000. 155p. (J). (ps-7). per. 14.15 (978-0-8335-6637-9(7)) Tandem Library Bks.

—The Figure in the Shadows. Mayer, Mercer, illus. 2004. (Lewis Barnavelt Ser.). 160p. (J). pap. 5.99 (978-0-14-240260-3(5) , Puffin) Penguin Group (USA) Inc.

—The Figure in the Shadows. 1999. (J). (gr. 3 up). 21.75 (978-0-8446-7009-6(X)) Smith, Peter Pub., Inc.

—The House with a Clock in Its Walls. Gorey, Edward, illus. 2004. (Lewis Barnavelt Ser.). 192p. (J). pap. 5.99 (978-0-14-240257-3(5) , Puffin) Penguin Group (USA) Inc.

—The House with a Clock in Its Walls. 179p. (J). (gr. 4-6). pap. 4.50 (978-0-8072-1423-7(X) , Listening Library) Random Hse. Audio Publishing Group.

—The House with a Clock in Its Walls. Gorey, Edward, illus. 2004. 179p. (J). (gr. 3-7). per. 13.04 (978-0-606-33073-2(9)) Tandem Library Bks.

—The Spell of Sorcerer's Skull. Gorey, Edward, illus. 2004. (Johnny Dixon Ser.). 176p. (J). pap. 5.99 (978-0-14-240265-8(6) , Puffin) Penguin Group (USA) Inc.

Bentley, Dawn. Lucky Leprechaun. Berg, Michelle, illus. 2003. 10p. (J). (ps-1). bds. 5.99 (978-0-8431-4587-8(0) , Price Stern Sloan) Penguin Group (USA) Inc.

Benz, Derek & Lewis, J. S. The Fall of the Templar. 2008. (Grey Griffins Ser.). 304p. (J). 12.99 (*978-0-439-83776-7(6) , Orchard Bks.) Scholastic, Inc.

—The Revenge of the Shadow King. 2006. (J). 384p. (gr. 4-7). pap. 10.99 (978-0-439-79574-6(5) , Orchard Bks.); 39.95 (978-0-439-87592-9(7) , Scholastic) Scholastic, Inc.

—The Rise of the Black Wolf. 2007. (Grey Griffins Ser.: No. 2). 320p. (J). (gr. 4-7). pap. 12.99 (978-0-439-83774-3(X) , Orchard Bks.) Scholastic, Inc.

Beobi & the Magic Coloring Book ABC First Words. 2005. (J). cd-rom 15.99 (978-0-9743847-8-8(X)) Cohn, Tricia.

Beobi & the Magic Coloring Book at the Horse Stables. 2006. (J). 3.99 (978-0-9743847-5-7(5)) Cohn, Tricia.

Beobi & the Magic Coloring Book Funland. 2006. (Illus.). 24p. (J). 3.99 (978-0-9743847-7-1(1)) Cohn, Tricia.

Beobi & the Magic Coloring Book in the Universe. 2006. (J). 3.99 (978-0-9743847-4-0(7)) Cohn, Tricia.

BEOBI & the Magic Coloring Book Our First Adventure. 2005. (J). cd-rom 15.99 (978-0-9743847-9-5(8)) Cohn, Tricia.

Beobi & the Magic Coloring Book Our First Adventure. 2005. (J). 3.99 (978-0-9743847-2-6(0)) Cohn, Tricia.

Bergman, Ingmar. Linterna Magica. (SPA.). 820p. (978-84-7223-895-4(4) , 6130) Tusquets Editores.

Bergsma, Jody Lynn. The Little Wizard. Bergsma, Jody Lynn, illus. l.t. ed. 2000. (Illus.). 32p. (J). (ps-7). 15.95 (978-0-935699-19-7(8)) Illumination Arts Publishing Co., Inc.

Bergstrom, William. The Magic Telescope. 2006. 9.95 (978-0-9787648-0-7(3)) Bergstrom Bks.

Bernardini, Robert. The Crystal & the Keyhole: Santa's Magic Secret. Donato, Janice, illus. l.t. ed. 2001. 34p. (J). (ps-9). per. 14.95 (978-0-9703269-1-2(2)) P R I Publishing.

Bernasconi, Pablo. The Wizard, the Ugly, & the Book of Shame. Bernasconi, Pablo, illus. 2005. (Illus.). 32p. (J). (ps-3). 16.95 (978-1-58234-673-1(9)) Bloomsbury Publishing.

Bernstein, Nina. Magic by the Book. Kulikov, Boris, illus. 2005. 240p. (J). 17.00 (978-0-374-34718-5(2) , Farrar, Straus & Giroux (BYR)) Farrar, Straus & Giroux.

—Magic by the Book. unabr. ed. 2005. (J). 63.75 incl. audio (978-1-4193-3607-2(X) , 42048) Recorded Bks., LLC.

—Magic by the Book. l.t. ed. 2006. 248p. (J). 22.95 (978-0-7862-8382-8(3)) Thorndike Pr.

Berryhill, Shane. Chance Fortune & the Outlaws. 2006. (Adventures of Chance Fortune Ser.). 272p. (J). (gr. 5-8). 17.95 (978-0-7653-1468-0(1) , Starscape) Doherty, Tom Assocs., LLC.

Bessen, Luc. Arthur & the Minimoys. Sowchek, Ellen, tr. from FRE. 2005. 240p. (J). 15.99 (978-0-06-059623-1(6)) HarperCollins Pubs.

Besson, Luc. Arthur & the Forbidden City. (Illus.). 192p. (J). 2006. pap. 5.99 (978-0-06-059628-6(7) , Harper Trophy); 2005. 15.99 (978-0-06-059626-2(0)); 2005. lib. bdg. 16.89 (978-0-06-059627-9(9)) HarperCollins Pubs.

—Arthur & the Invisibles. movie tie-in ed. 2006. 416p. (J). pap. 7.99 (978-0-06-122726-4(9)) HarperCollins Pubs.

—Arthur & the Minimoys. (Illus.). (J). 2006. 256p. pap. 6.99 (978-0-06-059625-5(2) , Harper Trophy); 2005. 240p. lib. bdg. 16.89 (978-0-06-059624-8(4)) HarperCollins Pubs.

Betancourt, Jeanne. Magic Pony. Bachem, Paul, illus. 2002. (Pony Pals Ser.: No. 35). 96p. (J). (gr. 2-5). mass mkt. 3.99 (978-0-439-30645-4(0)) Scholastic, Inc.

Billingsley, Franny. Well Wished. Gore, Leonid, illus. 2000. 176p. (J). (gr. 3-7). pap. 9.95 (978-0-689-83255-0(9) , Aladdin) Simon & Schuster Children's Publishing.

—Well Wished. 2000. (978-0-606-17941-6(0)); (gr. 3-6). lib. bdg. 13.00 (978-0-613-28693-0(6)) Tandem Library Bks.

—Well Wished. l.t. ed. 2001. (Illus.). 197p. (J). (gr. 4-7). 21.95 (978-0-7862-3106-5(8)) Thorndike Pr.

Bird, Sheila & Bird, Sheila M. Dr. Witch's Animal Hospital. Parrish, Emma, illus. 2007. (I Am Reading Ser.). 48p. (J). (ps-3). pap. 3.95 (*978-0-7534-5977-5(9) , Kingfisher) Houghton Mifflin Co. Trade & Reference Div.

Black, Holly. Ironside: A Modern Faery's Tale. 2007. 336p. (YA). (gr. 4-7). 16.99 (978-0-689-86820-7(0) , McElderry, Margaret K.) Simon & Schuster Children's Publishing.

—Tithe: A Modern Faerie Tale. (YA). 2002. 320p. (gr. 7 up). 17.99 (978-0-689-84924-4(9)); 2004. 336p. reprint ed. pap. 6.99 (978-0-689-86704-0(2) , Simon Pulse) Simon & Schuster Children's Publishing.

—Tithe: A Modern Faerie Tale. 2004. (gr. 7-12). lib. bdg. 15.30 (978-0-613-73456-1(4)); 331p. (YA). per. 13.64 (978-0-606-30074-2(0)) Tandem Library Bks.

—Valiant: A Modern Tale of Faerie. 2006. 320p. (YA). pap. 7.99 (978-0-689-86823-8(5) , Simon Pulse) Simon & Schuster Children's Publishing.

—Valiant: A Modern Tale of Faerie. rev. l.t. ed. 353p. 21.95 (978-0-7862-8226-5(6)) Thorndike Pr.

Black, Holly & DiTerlizzi, Tony. Spiderwick Chronicles Set: The Field Guide, the Seeing Stone, Lucinda's Secret, the Ironwood Tree, the Wrath of Mulgarath. DiTerlizzi, Tony, illus. movie tie-in ed. 2008. (Spiderwick Chronicles). 672p. (J). 49.99 (*978-1-4169-5016-5(8)) Simon & Schuster Children's Publishing.

Blacker, Terence & Ross, Tony. Estrella de la Tele. 2003. (Serafina the Little Witch Ser.). (SPA.). 80p. (J). 7.95 (978-84-8453-066-4(3)) Ediciones del Bronce ESP. *Dist:* Planeta Publishing Corp.

—Fuera de Control. 2003. (Serafina the Little Witch Ser.). (SPA., Illus.). 72p. (J). 7.95 (978-84-8453-049-7(3)) Ediciones del Bronce ESP. *Dist:* Planeta Publishing Corp.

—Una Intrusa en el Hospital. 2003. (Serafina the Little Witch Ser.). (SPA., Illus.). 72p. (J). 7.95 (978-84-8453-010-7(8)) Ediciones del Bronce ESP. *Dist:* Planeta Publishing Corp.

—Un Mundo de Problemas. 2003. (Serafina the Little Witch Ser.). (SPA.). 80p. (J). 7.95 (978-84-8453-009-1(4)) Ediciones del Bronce ESP. *Dist:* Planeta Publishing Corp.

Blackford, Ami. Quest for the Dragon Stone: A Duncan Family Adventure. Blackford, Ami, illus. 2006. (Illus.). 48p. (J). (gr. 3-7). 16.95 (978-1-60108-008-0(5)) Red Cygnet Pr.

Blackford, Ami. Quest for the Elfin Elixir: A Duncan Family Adventure. Blackford, Ami, illus. 2007. 80p. (J). (gr. 3-7). 16.95 (*978-1-60108-021-9(2)) Red Cygnet Pr.

Blair, Eric. Rumpelstiskin: Version del Cuento de los Hermanos Grimm. Shaw, David, illus. 2006. (Read-It! Readers en Espanol Ser.).Tr. of Rumpelstiltskin: A Retelling of the Grimm's Fairy Tale. (SPA.). 32p. (J). (ps-3). 19.95 (978-1-4048-1637-4(2)) Picture Window Bks.

Bliss, Bob, illus. The Hardest Lessons: The Lost Babies Series #3. 2007. 118p. (J). per. 5.99 (*978-0-9792499-2-1(9)) Howell, M Kay.

—The Ruby Hind: The Lost Babies Series #1. 2007. 116p. (J). per. 5.99 (*978-0-9792499-0-7(2)) Howell, M Kay.

—Too Many Parents: The Lost Babies Series #2. 2007. 109p. (J). per. 5.99 (*978-0-9792499-1-4(0)) Howell, M Kay.

Blumer, J. Michael. The Book of Second Chances, Bk. 1. 2006. 380p. pap. 14.99 (978-1-59092-317-0(0) , Blue Works) Windstorm Creative.

Blyton, Enid. The Goblin Aeroplane. (Illus.). 140p. (J). (gr. k-6). pap. 5.95 (978-0-09-973590-8(3)) Random Hse. GBR. *Dist:* Trafalgar Square Publishing.

Bode, N. E. The Anybodies. Ferguson, Peter, illus. 288p. (J). 2004. 16.99 (978-0-06-055735-5(4)); 2004. lib. bdg. 17.89 (978-0-06-055736-2(2)); 2005. reprint ed. pap. 6.99 (978-0-06-055737-9(0)) HarperCollins Pubs.

—Nobodies. Ferguson, Peter, illus. 2005. 304p. (J). 16.99 (978-0-06-055738-6(9)); lib. bdg. 17.89 (978-0-06-055739-3(7)) HarperCollins Pubs.

—The Somebodies. 2006. (Illus.). 288p. (J). lib. bdg. 17.89 (978-0-06-079112-4(8)) HarperCollins Pubs.

—The Somebodies. Ferguson, Peter, illus. 2006. 288p. (J). 16.99 (978-0-06-079111-7(X) , HarperCollins) HarperCollins Pubs.

Book Company Staff. Pick a Pixie. 2002. (Sparkle Bks.). 10p. (J). bds. 8.95 (978-1-74047-154-1(7)) Book Co. Publishing Pty, Ltd., The AUS. *Dist:* Penton Overseas, Inc.

Booth, Martin. Doctor Illuminatus. 2006. (Alchemist's Son Ser.: Pt. 1). 192p. (J). (gr. 4-9). pap. 6.99 (978-0-316-01285-0(8)) Little Brown & Co.

—Soul Stealer. 2006. (Alchemist's Son Ser.: Pt. 2). 256p. (J). (gr. 5-9). pap. 6.99 (978-0-316-05993-0(5)) Little Brown & Co.

Boston, L. M. The Stones of Green Knowe. Boston, Peter, illus. 2006. (Green Knowe Ser.). 144p. (J). 17.00 (978-0-15-205560-8(6)); pap. 5.95 (978-0-15-205566-0(5)) Harcourt Trade Pubs.

Bottner, Barbara. Pish & Posh. Bottner, Barbara, illus. 2005. (I Can Read Bks.). 48p. (J). pap. 3.99 (978-0-06-051418-1(3) , Harper Trophy) HarperCollins Pubs.

Bottner, Barbara. Pish & Posh Wish for Fairy Wings. Bottner, Barbara, illus. 2007. (I Can Read Bks.). 48p. (J). pap. 3.99 (*978-0-06-051421-1(3) , Harper Trophy) HarperCollins Pubs.

Bottner, Barbara & Kruglik, Gerald. Pish & Posh. Bottner, Barbara, illus. 2004. (I Can Read Bks.). 48p. (J). (gr. k-3). pap. 15.99 (978-0-06-051416-7(7)) HarperCollins Pubs.

—Pish & Posh Wish for Fairy Wings. Bottner, Barbara, illus. 2006. (I Can Read Bks.). (Illus.). 48p. (J). lib. bdg. 16.89 (978-0-06-051420-4(5)) HarperCollins Pubs.

Bottner/Kruglik. Pish & Posh. Bottner, Barbara, illus. 2004. 48p. (J). lib. bdg. 13.85 (*978-1-4242-0513-4(1)) Fitzgerald Bks.

Bourgeois, Paulette. Franklin & the Magic Show. 2002. (gr. k-3). lib. bdg. 11.80 (978-0-613-50558-1(1)) Tandem Library Bks.

Bova, Louise. Harry Potter & the Sorcerer's Stone: Stationery Kit. 2000. (Illus.). (J). (gr. 1-5). 10.95 (978-0-439-23658-4(4)) Scholastic, Inc.

Bow, Patricia. The Bone Flute. 2004. 144p. (J). (gr. 5-12). pap. 6.95 (978-1-55143-301-1(X)) Orca Bk. Pubs. USA.

The Boy Who Went to the North Wind: Individual Title Six-Packs. (Literatura 2000 Ser.). (gr. 2-3). 33.00 (978-0-7635-0217-1(0)) Rigby Education.

Bradley, Rachel Victoria. Dillon & Daisy: Magical Mayhem & Other Stories. 2006. 9.00 (978-0-8059-9000-3(3)) Dorrance Publishing Co., Inc.

Bramscher, Cynthia. Night of the Corn Maiden. 2003. 211p. pap. 19.95 (978-1-59286-704-2(9)) PublishAmerica, Inc.

Bray, Libba. A Great & Terrible Beauty. (YA). (gr. 7). 2003. 416p. 16.95 (978-0-385-73028-0(4)); 2005. 432p. reprint ed. pap. 8.95 (978-0-385-73231-4(7)) Random Hse. Children's Bks. (Delacorte Bks. for Young Readers).

—A Great & Terrible Beauty. 2005. 403p. (YA). (gr. 8-12). per. 15.60 (978-0-606-33978-0(7)) Tandem Library Bks.

—A Great & Terrible Beauty. l.t. ed. 2005. 512p. (YA). (gr. 8-12). pap. 10.95 (978-0-7862-8082-7(4)); 2004. 507p. 23.95 (978-0-7862-6504-6(3) , Large Print Pr.) Thorndike Pr.

—Rebel Angels. (gr. 7). 2006. 592p. (YA). pap. 9.99 (978-0-385-73341-0(0)); 2005. 560p. (J). lib. bdg. 18.99 (978-0-385-90257-1(3)); 2005. 560p. (YA). 16.95 (978-0-385-73029-7(2)) Random Hse. Children's Bks. (Delacorte Bks. for Young Readers).

—Rebel Angels. l.t. ed. 2006. (Thorndike Press Large Print the Literacy Bridge Ser.). 655p. (J). 23.95 (978-0-7862-8087-2(5)) Thorndike Pr.

Bray, Libba. The Sweet Far Thing. 2007. 448p. (YA). (gr. 7). 17.99 (*978-0-385-73030-3(6)); lib. bdg. 20.99 (*978-0-385-90295-3(6)) Random Hse. Children's Bks. (Delacorte Bks. for Young Readers).

Breed, Kristine. The Mystery of Black Magic. 2004. 48p. pap. 12.95 (978-1-4137-4240-4(8)) PublishAmerica, Inc.

Brennan, Herbie. The Purple Emperor: Faerie Wars II. 2004. 400p. (J). 17.95 (978-1-58234-880-3(4) , Bloomsbury Children) Bloomsbury Publishing.

Bridges, Mitzi Pool. The Magic Star Book III: The Delaney Family Mysteries. 2001. 112p. pap. 9.95 (978-0-595-19145-1(2) , Writers Club Pr.) iUniverse, Inc.

Brignole, Giancarla, tr. El Pulpo Campanero. Meconni, Beppe, illus. (Fabulas De Familia Ser.). (SPA.). 32p. (978-970-20-0262-8(1)) Castillo, Ediciones, S. A. de C. V.

Brin, Susannah. Rabbit Tattoo. 2001. (gr. 5-8). lib. bdg. 11.80 (978-0-613-57864-6(3)) Tandem Library Bks.

Brooks, Bruce. Throwing Smoke. 2000. (Illus.). 144p. (J). (gr. 5 up). 15.95 (978-0-06-028972-0(4) , Geringer, Laura Book) HarperCollins Pubs.

—Throwing Smoke. 2002. (gr. 3-6). lib. bdg. 14.10 (978-0-613-68470-5(2)) Tandem Library Bks.

Brown, Jeff. Stanley & the Magic Lamp. Nash, Scott, illus. 2003. (Stanley Lambchop Adventure Ser.). 112p. (J). pap. 4.99 (978-0-06-009793-6(0) , Harper Trophy) HarperCollins Pubs.

—Stanley & the Magic Lamp. 2003. (gr. k-3). lib. bdg. 13.00 (978-0-613-68465-1(6)) Tandem Library Bks.

Brown, Marc. D. W. the Big Boss. 2005. (Arthur's 8 x 8 Bks.). (Illus.). 24p. (J). (ps-3). pap. 3.99 (978-0-316-73395-3(4)) Little Brown & Co.

Browne, N. M. Silverboy. 2007. (Illus.). 240p. (YA). 16.95 (978-1-58234-780-6(8) , Bloomsbury Children) Bloomsbury Publishing.

—The Story of Stone. 2005. 336p. (YA). (gr. 8-12). 17.95 (978-1-58234-655-7(0) , Bloomsbury Children) Bloomsbury Publishing.

—Warriors of Alavna. (J). 2004. 312p. (gr. 5-10). pap. 7.95 (978-1-58234-916-9(9)); 2002. 319p. 16.95 (978-1-58234-775-2(1)) Bloomsbury Publishing. (Bloomsbury Children).

—Warriors of Camlann. 2003. (Illus.). 275p. (J). 16.95 (978-1-58234-817-9(0) , Bloomsbury Children) Bloomsbury Publishing.

Brownlow, Brooke. The Magic of Old Oak Hill. 2005. 48p. pap. 12.95 (978-1-4241-0223-5(5)) PublishAmerica, Inc.

Bruchac, Joseph. Heroes & Heroines, Monsters & Magic: Native American Legends & Folktales. Burgevin, Daniel, illus. 2004. 200p. (gr. 3-7). reprint ed. pap. 12.95 (978-0-89594-995-0(4) , Crossing Pr., Inc.) Ten Speed Pr.

Bryant, Jennifer. Into Enchanted Woods. Browne, James, illus. 2001. (Winterthur Book for Children Ser.). (J). (978-0-912724-59-1(5)) Winterthur, Henry Francis du-Pont Museum, Inc.

Buchanan, Johnny & Conway, Beth. Rachel & the Magic Beads. Bosak, Virginia, illus. 2007. 16p. (YA). pap. 7.99 (*978-0-9768772-9-5(5)) Wise Guides, Inc.

Buckley, Michael. Magic & Other Misdemeanors. Ferguson, Peter, illus. 2007. (Sisters Grimm Ser.: Bk. 5). 304p. (YA). (gr. 3-7). 14.95 (*978-0-8109-9358-7(9) , Amulet Bks.) Abrams, Harry N. , Inc.

Burchell, Graham. Wumpleberries & Gronglenuts. 2005. 242p. pap. 11.99 (978-1-4116-5399-3(8)) Lulu.com.

Burgess, Melvin. Lady: My Life As A Bitch. 2002. (gr. 7-12). lib. bdg. 15.30 (978-0-613-68355-5(2)) Tandem Library Bks.

Burke, Ellinor Rozecki. Susana Worrywart & the Magical Teddy Bear Balloon. Perciopelo, illus. 2003. 32p. (J). 17.99 (978-0-9741586-3-1(1)) Comfort Tales, LLC.

M
N
O

—Susana Worrywart & the Magical Teddy Bear Balloon: With CD for Relaxation. Perciopelo, illus. 2003. 32p. (J). 27.00 incl. audio compact disk (978-0-9741586-0-0(7)) Comfort Tales, LLC.

Burningham, John. The Magic Bed. Burningham, John, illus. 2003. (Illus.). 48p. (J). (ps-3). 16.95 (978-0-375-82423-4(5) , Knopf Bks. for Young Readers) Random Hse. Children's Bks.

Burns, Laura J. Inherit the Witch. 2004. (Charmed Ser.). 224p. (YA). mass mkt. 6.99 (978-0-689-86708-8(5) , Simon Spotlight Entertainment) Simon & Schuster.

Burns, Laura J. & Metz, Melinda. Apocalypse Memories. 2004. (Buffy the Vampire Slayer Ser.). 256p. (YA). pap. 6.99 (978-0-689-86700-2(X) , Simon Spotlight Entertainment) Simon & Schuster.

Byers, Carla Rae. How Was My Soul Born! The Magic of Believing, Vol. 1. Kepler, Kit, ed. 2000. Vol. 2. (Illus.). 12p. (gr. 1 up). 7.95 (978-0-9656124-7-0(3)) Heyokah Publishing Co.

Byng, Georgia. Molly Moon Detiene el Mundo. 2004. (SPA.). 358p. (gr. 5-8). 18.99 (978-84-348-9610-9(9)) SM Ediciones ESP. *Dist:* Lectorum Pubns., Inc.

—Molly Moon Stops the World. 2005. 416p. (J). (ps-7). reprint ed. pap. 7.99 (978-0-06-051415-0(9) , Harper Trophy) HarperCollins Pubs.

Byrne, John William. Jonnie & the Magic Whistle. 2007. 172p. per. (***978-1-84685-675-4(2)*** , Exposure Publishing) Meadow Bks.

Calhoun, Dia. Avielle of Rhia. 2006. 400p. (J). 16.99 (978-0-7614-5320-8(2)) Cavendish, Marshall Corp.

Calmenson, Stephanie. The Frog Principal. Brunkus, Denise, illus. 2006. 32p. (J). pap. 5.99 (978-0-439-81217-7(8) , Scholastic Paperbacks) Scholastic, Inc.

Cardwell, Helen. Amber Janusson: Protector of the Magic Lands. 2003. 136p. pap. 11.95 (978-0-595-29436-7(7)) iUniverse, Inc.

Carman, Patrick. Beyond the Valley of Thorns. 2005. (Land of Elyon Ser.: Bk. 2). (Illus.). 240p. (J). (ps-7). pap. 11.99 (978-0-439-70094-8(9) , Orchard Bks.) Scholastic, Inc.

—The Dark Hills Divide. (Land of Elyon Ser.: Bk. 1). (J). 2006. 288p. pap. 6.99 (978-0-439-79175-5(8)); 2005. (Illus.). 272p. pap. 11.95 (978-0-439-70093-1(0) , Orchard Bks.); 2005. (Illus.). 253p. (978-0-439-75843-7(2) , Orchard Bks.) Scholastic, Inc.

—The Dark Hills Divide. l.t. ed. 2005. (Land of Elyon Ser.: Bk. 1). 356p. 23.95 (978-0-7862-7752-0(1) , Large Print Pr.) Thorndike Pr.

—Into the Mist. 2007. 304p. (J). (gr. 4-7). pap. 11.99 (***978-0-439-89952-9(4)*** , Orchard Bks.) Scholastic, Inc.

Carman, Patrick. The Tenth City. 2006. (Land of Elyon Ser.: Bk. 3). 208p. (J). pap. 11.99 (978-0-439-70095-5(7) , Orchard Bks.) Scholastic, Inc.

—The Tenth City. l.t. ed. 2006. (Land of Elyon Ser.: Bk. 3). 225p. (J). 23.95 (978-0-7862-7789-6(0)) Thorndike Pr.

Carmody, Isobelle. The Legend Begins. 2006. (Illus.). 208p. (J). (gr. 1-7). 12.95 (978-0-375-83854-5(6)); (gr. 3-7). lib. bdg. 14.99 (978-0-375-93854-2(0)) Random Hse. Children's Bks. (Random Hse. Bks. for Young Readers).

—Little Fur: The Legend Begins. 2006. (Illus.). 272p. (J). (978-0-375-83855-2(4)) Random Hse., Inc.

—Magic Night. Lee, Declan, illus. 2007. (Picture Book Ser.). 40p. (J). (ps-1). 16.99 (***978-0-375-83918-4(6));*** lib. bdg. 19.99 (***978-0-375-93918-1(0))*** Random Hse. Children's Bks. (Random Hse. Bks. for Young Readers).

—A Mystery of Wolves: Little Fur #3. 2008. (J). pap. (***978-0-375-83859-0(7));*** (Little Fur: 3). 12.99 (***978-0-375-83858-3(9));*** (Little Fur: 3). lib. bdg. 15.99 (***978-0-375-93858-0(3))*** Random Hse., Inc.

—Night Gate. 2006. 272p. (gr. 4-7). 6.50 (978-0-375-83017-4(0) , Yearling) Random Hse. Children's Bks.

—Winter Door. (Gateway Trilogy Ser.). 336p. (J). (gr. 3-5). 2007. 5.99 (978-0-375-83019-8(7) , Yearling); 2006. 16.95 (978-0-375-83018-1(9) , Random Hse. Bks. for Young Readers); 2006. lib. bdg. 18.99 (978-0-375-93018-8(3) , Random Hse. Bks. for Young Readers) Random Hse. Children's Bks.

Carothers, Daniella. Over the Valley. 2007. 148p. pap. 17.95 (***978-1-59299-291-1(9))*** Inkwater Pr.

Carr, Lawrence. Under the Peach Tree. 2006. pap. 8.00 (978-0-8059-7019-7(3)) Dorrance Publishing Co., Inc.

Carrier, Roch. The Longest Home Run. Fischman, Sheila, tr. from FRE. Cohen, Sheldon, illus. 2001. Orig. Title: Le Plus Long Circuit. 24p. (J). (gr. 3). pap. 7.95 (978-0-88776-312-0(X)) Tundra Bks., Inc./Livres Toundra, Inc. CAN. *Dist:* Random Hse., Inc.

Carrol, Jacqueline. Enter the Viper with Cards. 2001. (gr. k-3). lib. bdg. 13.00 (978-0-613-72449-4(6)) Tandem Library Bks.

Carroll, Yvonne. The Leprechaun Library, 5. 1999. (Illus.). 116p. (J). 16.95 (978-0-7171-3251-5(X)) Gill & MacMillan, Ltd. IRL. *Dist:* Irish Bks. & Media, Inc.

Caruso, Tina Silvio. The Magical Dream. Larsson, Rod, illus. 2000. 32p. (J). (ps-5). pap. 6.95 (978-0-9706745-0-0(3)) Caruso, Tina Silvio.

Cassedy, Sylvia. Behind the Attic Wall. 1998. (gr. 4-7). 22.50 (978-0-8446-6965-6(2)) Smith, Peter Pub., Inc.

Castilla, Julia Mercedes. El Tesoro de la Pordiosera. Diaz, Carlos Manuel, illus. 2002. (SPA.). 118p. pap. 5.30 (978-958-04-6889-9(3)) Norma S.A. COL. *Dist:* Lectorum Pubns., Inc.

Chabon, Michael. Summerland. 2004. (gr. 3-6). lib. bdg. 17.60 (978-0-613-90441-4(9)) Tandem Library Bks.

—Summerland. l.t. ed. 2003. 615p. (J). 25.95 (978-0-7862-5143-8(3)) Thorndike Pr.

—Summerland: A Novel. 2004. 512p. (J). (ps-17). reprint ed. pap. 8.95 (978-0-7868-1615-6(5)) Miramax Bks.

Chandler, Fiona. Sorcerer's Apprentice. 2007. 48p. (J). 8.99 (978-0-7945-1589-8(4) , Usborne) EDC Publishing.

Chapman, Linda. Flying High. 2006. (My Secret Unicorn Ser.). 144p. (J). pap. 4.99 (978-0-439-81384-6(0) , Scholastic Paperbacks) Scholastic, Inc.

Charbonnet, Gabrielle. Adventure in Walt Disney World. 7th ed. 1999. (Disney Girls Ser.). 128p. (J). (gr. 2-5). pap. 3.99 (978-0-7868-4390-9(X)) Disney Pr.

Chartrand, Lili. Taming Horrible Harry. Ouriou, Susan, tr. from FRE. Rogé, illus. 2006. 32p. (J). (ps-3). 16.95 (978-0-88776-772-2(9)) Tundra Bks., Inc./Livres Toundra, Inc. CAN. *Dist:* Random Hse., Inc.

Child, L. Maria. The Magician's Show Box & Other Stories. 2007. (ENG.). 124p. per. (***978-1-4065-1354-7(7))*** Dodo Pr.

Chima, Cinda Williams. The Warrior Heir. 2006. 432p. (gr. 7-17). 16.99 (978-0-7868-3916-2(3)) Hyperion Bks. for Children.

—The Warrior Heir. 2007. 448p. (gr. 7-17). pap. 8.99 (***978-0-7868-3917-9(1))*** Hyperion Pr.

Chipman, Laura. Dragonspeaker. 2005. 76p. pap. 14.95 (978-1-4241-0136-8(0)) PublishAmerica, Inc.

The Chocolate Moose. 2007. (Illus.). 48p. (J). per. 13.00 (***978-0-9767189-5-6(2))*** Better Day Publishing Co.

Chronicle Books LLC Staff. Make a Wish. 2008. (J). 15.95 (978-0-8118-5716-1(6)) Chronicle Bks. LLC.

Ciddor, Anna. Runestone. 2007. (Viking Magic Ser.). (Illus.). 192p. (Orig.). (J). (gr. 4-7). pap. 7.95 (***978-1-86508-689-7(4))*** Allen & Unwin AUS. *Dist:* Independent Pubs. Group.

—Wolfspell. 2007. (Viking Magic Ser.). (Illus.). 192p. (J). (gr. 4-7). pap. 7.95 (***978-1-74114-013-2(7))*** Allen & Unwin AUS. *Dist:* Independent Pubs. Group.

Ciencin, Scott & Burge, Constance M. Luck Be a Lady. 2004. (Charmed Ser.). (Illus.). 224p. (YA). mass mkt. 11.95 (978-0-689-85793-5(4) , Simon & Schuster Children's Publishing) Simon & Schuster Children's Publishing.

Cincotta, Wendy. Nadia's Heart. 2002. (Adventures in Evergreen Ser.: Bk. 4). 150p. (J). (gr. 3-7). pap. 9.95 (978-0-9723010-3-9(8)) Evergreen Bks.

—Return to Evergreen. Cincotta, Eva, illus. 2002. (Adventures in Evergreen Ser.: Bk. 2). 120p. (J). (gr. 3-7). pap. 9.95 (978-0-9723010-1-5(1)) Evergreen Bks.

Clamp. Master of the Clow 5. 2003. (gr. 3-6). lib. bdg. 18.80 (978-0-613-80317-5(5)) Tandem Library Bks.

Clare, Cassandra. City of Ashes. 2008. (Mortal Instruments Ser.). 480p. (YA). 17.99 (***978-1-4169-1429-7(3)*** , McElderry, Margaret K.) Simon & Schuster Children's Publishing.

Clarizio, Laura. If i Had a Magic Carpet. 2005. 48p. pap. 12.95 (978-1-4137-8557-9(3)) PublishAmerica, Inc.

Clarizio, Laura. If I Had a Magic Carpet II: Key to Kindness. 2006. (ENG.). 48p. per. 12.95 (***978-1-4241-3985-9(6))*** PublishAmerica, Inc.

Clark, Brenda, illus. Franklin & the Magic Show. 2002. (Franklin Ser.). (J). 12.40 (978-1-4046-1980-7(1)) Book Wholesalers, Inc.

Clark, Emma Chichester. The Amazing Mr Zooty! 2007. (Illus.). 32p. (J). (ps-k). 15.99 (***978-1-84270-480-6(X))*** Andersen GBR. *Dist:* Independent Pubs. Group.

Claycomb, Patty. My Magic Carpet Adventure. McMahon, Kelly, illus. 2002. (Two Can Read Ser.). 16p. (J). 2.99 (978-1-56472-657-5(6)) Edupress, Inc.

Clemens, James. Wit'ch War. 2001. (Banned & the Banished Ser.: Vol. 3). (Illus.). 560p. pap. 7.99 (978-0-345-41710-7(0) , Del Rey) Random House Publishing Group.

Clement-Davies, David. The Telling Pool. (gr. 7-17). 2007. 382p. (YA). pap. 7.95 (***978-0-8109-9257-3(4));*** 2005. (Illus.). 376p. (J). 19.95 (978-0-8109-5758-9(2) , Abrams Bks. for Young Readers) Abrams, Harry N. , Inc.

Coakley, Lena. Mrs. Goodhearth & the Gargoyle. Bailey, Wendy, illus. 2005. 32p. (J). (ps-2). 17.95 (978-1-55143-328-8(1)) Orca Bk. Pubs. USA.

Coats, Lucy. Neil's Numberless World. 2000. (J). (978-0-606-20123-0(8)) Tandem Library Bks.

Codell, Esmé Raji. Diary of a Fairy Godmother. Lillis, Rachael & Kozjan, Drazen, illus. 2006. 176p. (gr. 2-5). pap. 5.99 (978-0-7868-0966-0(3)) Hyperion Pr.

Cofer, Amadeus. Aloha Adventure: The Magic of Imagination on a Rainy Day. l.t. ed. 2004. (Illus.). 36p. (J). 14.00 (978-1-932957-01-3(4)) Legacy Pubs.

Cole, Joanna. Imperial China: Ms. Frizzle's Adventures. Degen, Bruce, illus. 2005. (Magic School Bus Ser.). 48p. (J). (ps-ps). pap. 16.95 (978-0-590-10822-5(0) , Scholastic Pr.) Scholastic, Inc.

Cole, Myke. The Wildsidhe Chronicles Bk. 6: Car Trouble. 2003. (J). pap. 7.99 (978-1-890096-18-2(0)) Padwolf Publishing, Inc.

Coleman, Alice Scovell. Engraved in Stone. Armand, Anjale Renee, illus. 2003. 152p. (J). 14.95 (978-0-9729846-0-7(7)) Tiara Bks. LLC.

Coleman, David R. Old Troop, Rainbow Fairies, & the Forget-Me-Now Potion. 2007. (J). pap. 8.99 (***978-1-60247-054-5(5))*** Tate Publishing & Enterprises, L.L.C.

Colfer, Eoin. The Arctic Incident. l.t. ed. 2003. (Artemis Fowl Ser.: Bk. 2). 296p. (J). (gr. 3-6). 16.95 (978-0-7540-7839-5(6) , Galaxy Children's Large Print) BBC Audiobooks America.

—The Arctic Incident. (Artemis Fowl Ser.: Bk. 2). 288p. (ps-17). 2003. (J). pap. 7.99 (978-0-7868-1708-5(9)); 2002. 16.95 (978-0-7868-0855-7(1)) Hyperion Bks. for Children.

—The Arctic Incident. l.t. ed. 2003. (Artemis Fowl Ser.: Bk. 2). 313p. (J). (gr. 3-6). 25.95 (978-0-7862-4825-4(4)) Thorndike Pr.

—Artemis Fowl. (Artemis Fowl Ser.: Bk. 1). (FRE.). pap. 34.95 (978-2-07-054681-7(0)) Gallimard, Editions FRA. *Dist:* Distribooks, Inc.

—Artemis Fowl. 2003. (Artemis Fowl Ser.: Bk. 1). (Illus.). 416p. (ps-17). pap. 5.99 (978-0-7868-1787-0(9)) Hyperion Bks. for Children.

—Artemis Fowl. 2002. (Artemis Fowl Ser.: Bk. 1). 304p. (J). (ps-17). pap. 7.99 (978-0-7868-1707-8(0)) Hyperion Paperbacks for Children.

—Artemis Fowl. 2001. (Artemis Fowl Ser.: Bk. 1). 288p. (gr. 8-17). 16.95 (978-0-7868-0801-4(2)) Miramax Bks.

—Artemis Fowl. abr. ed. 2001. (Artemis Fowl Ser.: Bk. 1). (Illus.). 2p. (J). (gr. 3-6). cd-rom (978-0-14-180286-2(3) , Penguin AudioBooks) Penguin Group (USA) Inc.

—Artemis Fowl. (Artemis Fowl Ser.: Bk. 1). 2003. (gr. 7-12). lib. bdg. 14.15 (978-0-613-75035-6(7)); 2002. (gr. 5-8). lib. bdg. 16.15 (978-0-613-60637-0(X)) Tandem Library Bks.

—Artemis Fowl. l.t. ed. 2001. (Artemis Fowl Ser.: Bk. 1). 312p. (J). (gr. 3-6). 28.95 (978-1-58724-092-8(0) , Wheeler Publishing, Inc.) Thomson Gale.

—Artemis Fowl: The Graphic Novel. Rigano, Giovanni & Lamanna, Paolo, illus. 2007. (Artemis Fowl Ser.). 112p. (gr. 5 up). 18.99 (***978-0-7868-4881-2(2))*** Miramax Bks.

—Artemis Fowl: The Graphic Novel. Lamanna, Paolo, illus. 2007. (Artemis Fowl Ser.). 112p. (gr. 5 up). pap. 9.99 (***978-0-7868-4882-9(0))*** Miramax Bks.

—Artemis Fowl Encuentro en el Artico: Encuentro en el Artico. 2005. (SPA., Illus.). 320p. (J). pap. 13.95 (978-0-307-34310-9(3) , Montena) Random House Mondadori ESP. *Dist:* Random Hse., Inc.

—The Artemis Fowl Files. 2004. (Artemis Fowl Ser.). (Illus.). 208p. (J). (gr. 7-17). 12.95 (978-0-7868-5639-8(4)) Hyperion Bks. for Children.

—El Cubo B. 2005. (Artemis Fowl Ser.: No. 3). (SPA., Illus.). 352p. (J). pap. 13.95 (978-0-307-34311-6(1) , Montena) Random House Mondadori ESP. *Dist:* Random Hse., Inc.

—The Eternity Code. (Artemis Fowl Ser.: Bk. 3). 2005. 446p. (YA). (gr. 5-17). mass mkt. 5.99 (978-0-7868-5628-2(9)); 2003. 320p. (ps-17). 16.95 (978-0-7868-1914-0(6)) Hyperion Bks. for Children.

Colfer, Eoin. The Opal Deception. 2005. (Artemis Fowl Ser.: Bk. 4). 352p. (gr. 5-17). 16.95 (978-0-7868-5289-5(5)) Hyperion Bks. for Children.

—The Opal Deception. (Artemis Fowl Ser.). 2007. 528p. (gr. 5 up). pap. 5.99 (***978-1-4231-0399-8(8));*** 2005. (J). pap. 7.99 (978-0-7868-3640-6(7)); 2006. 352p. (J). (gr. 5-17). reprint ed. pap. 7.99 (978-0-7868-5290-1(9)) Miramax Bks.

—The Opal Deception. l.t. ed. 2005. (Artemis Fowl Ser.: Bk. 4). 421p. (J). 23.95 (978-0-7862-7754-4(8) , Large Print Pr.) Thorndike Pr.

Collins, Max Allan. Jax Epoch & the Quicken Forbidden Vol. 1: Borrowed Magic. Beatty, Terry, illus. 2003. 156p. (gr. 8 up). pap. 14.95 (978-1-932051-11-7(2)) A i T/Planet Lar.

Constable, Kate. The Singer of All Songs. 2005. (Chanters of Tremaris Trilogy Ser.). 320p. (J). reprint ed. pap. 4.99 (978-0-439-55479-4(9) , Levine, Arthur A. Bks.) Scholastic, Inc.

—Singer of All Songs Bk. 1: In the Chanters of Tremaris Trilogy. 2004. (Chanters of Tremaris Trilogy Ser.). 304p. (J). pap. 16.95 (978-0-439-55478-7(0) , Levine, Arthur A. Bks.) Scholastic, Inc.

—The Tenth Power. (Chanters of Tremaris Trilogy Ser.: Bk. 3). (Illus.). 320p. (J). 2007. pap. 5.99 (978-0-439-55483-1(7)); 2006. (gr. 7 up). pap. 16.99 (978-0-439-55482-4(9)) Scholastic, Inc. (Levine, Arthur A. Bks.).

Coombs, Kate. The Runaway Princess. 2006. 288p. (J). 17.00 (978-0-374-35546-3(0)) Farrar, Straus & Giroux.

Cooney, Caroline B. & Shakespeare, William. Enter Three Witches: A Story of Macbeth. 2007. 281p. (***978-1-4287-3716-7(2)*** , Scholastic Pr.) Scholastic, Inc.

Cooper, Clare. Stonehead. 2000. 132p. (J). pap. 12.95 (978-1-85902-782-0(2)) Beekman Bks., Inc.

Cooper, Susan. The Dark Is Rising. (Dark Is Rising Sequence Ser.). 244p. (YA). (gr. 5 up). pap. 4.99 (978-0-8072-1533-3(3) , Listening Library) Random Hse. Audio Publishing Group.

—The Dark Is Rising. (Dark Is Rising Sequence Ser.). 2007. ???p. (YA). pap. 8.99 (***978-1-4169-4965-7(8)*** , Simon Pulse); 2005. 232p. pap. 2.99 (978-1-4169-0528-8(6) , Aladdin); 1999. 232p. (J). (gr. 7 up). pap. 5.99 (978-0-689-82983-3(3) , Aladdin); 2007. 256p. (J). (gr. 4-8). pap. 6.99 (***978-1-4169-4995-4(X)*** , Aladdin); 2007. 272p. (YA). (gr. 7). pap. 8.99 (***978-1-4169-4969-5(0)*** , Simon Pulse) Simon & Schuster Children's Publishing.

—The Dark Is Rising. 1999. (Dark Is Rising Sequence Ser.). (gr. 5-8). lib. bdg. 13.00 (978-0-613-90606-7(3)) Tandem Library Bks.

—The Dark Is Rising. l.t. ed. 2001. (Dark Is Rising Sequence Ser.). 395p. (J). (gr. 4-7). 21.95 (978-0-7862-2920-8(9)) Thorndike Pr.

—The Dark Is Rising Boxed Set: The Dark Is Rising, Greenwitch, over Sea, under Stone, Silver on the Tree, the Grey King. 2007. (Dark Is Rising Sequence Ser.). 1088p. (J). pap. 29.99 (***978-1-4169-4996-1(8)*** , Aladdin) Simon & Schuster Children's Publishing.

—Greenwitch. (Dark Is Rising Sequence Ser.). 2007. 176p. (YA). pap. 8.99 (***978-1-4169-4966-4(6)*** , Simon Pulse); 2000. 144p. (J). (gr. 4-7). pap. 5.99 (978-0-689-84034-0(9) , Aladdin) Simon & Schuster Children's Publishing.

—Greenwitch. 2000. (Dark Is Rising Sequence Ser.). (J). 11.64 (978-0-606-19710-6(9)); (gr. 3-6). lib. bdg. 13.00 (978-0-613-29971-8(X)) Tandem Library Bks.

—Greenwitch. l.t. ed. 2001. (Dark Is Rising Sequence Ser.). 131p. (J). 21.95 (978-0-7862-2923-9(3)) Thorndike Pr.

—The Grey King. 2002. (Dark Is Rising Sequence Ser.). (Illus.). (J). 13.40 (978-0-7587-0188-6(8)) Book Wholesalers, Inc.

—The Grey King. (Dark Is Rising Sequence Ser.). 2007. 192p. (YA). pap. 8.99 (***978-1-4169-4967-1(4)*** , Simon Pulse); 1999. 176p. (J). (gr. 4-7). pap. 5.99 (978-0-689-82984-0(1) , Aladdin) Simon & Schuster Children's Publishing.

—The Grey King. 1999. (Dark Is Rising Sequence Ser.). (gr. 5-8). lib. bdg. 13.00 (978-0-613-73286-4(3)) Tandem Library Bks.

—The Grey King. l.t. ed. 2002. (Dark Is Rising Sequence Ser.). 262p. (J). 21.95 (978-0-7862-2919-2(5)) Thomson Gale.

Cooper, Susan. Over Sea, under Stone. 2002. (Dark Is Rising Sequence Ser.). (Illus.). (J). 13.40 (978-0-7587-5635-0(6)) Book Wholesalers, Inc.

—Over Sea, under Stone. 2007. (Dark Is Rising Sequence Ser.). 224p. (YA). pap. 8.99 (***978-1-4169-4964-0(X)*** , Simon Pulse) Simon & Schuster Children's Publishing.

—Over Sea, under Stone. Wiesner, David, illus. 2000. (Dark Is Rising Sequence Ser.). 208p. (J). (gr. 4-7). pap. 5.99 (978-0-689-84035-7(7) , Aladdin) Simon & Schuster Children's Publishing.

—Over Sea, under Stone. 2000. (Dark Is Rising Sequence Ser.). (gr. 7-12). lib. bdg. 13.00 (978-0-613-30082-7(3)) Tandem Library Bks.

—Over Sea, under Stone. l.t. ed. 2000. (Dark Is Rising Sequence Ser.). 332p. (J). (gr. 4-7). 22.95 (978-0-7862-2918-5(7)) Thorndike Pr.

Corbett, Sue. 12 Again. 2007. 240p. (J). (gr. 5 up). pap. 5.99 (978-0-14-240729-5(1) , Puffin) Penguin Group (USA) Inc.

Corey, Irene. The Magic Garden. 2000. (J). (gr. k-3). pap. 7.00 (978-0-87602-376-1(6)) Anchorage Pr.

Corlett, William. The Bridge in the Clouds. 2001. (Magician's House Quartet Ser.: Bk. 4). 352p. (YA). mass mkt. 4.99 (978-0-7434-1004-5(1) , Simon Pulse) Simon & Schuster Children's Publishing.

—The Door in the Tree. 2000. (978-0-606-20635-8(3)) Tandem Library Bks.

Cort, Ben, illus. Will Wizard. 2005. (Fun Phones Ser.). 10p. (J). bds. 4.95 (978-0-7641-5795-0(7)) Barron's Educational Series, Inc.

Coville, Bruce. Jennifer Murdley's Toad. Lippincott, Gary A., illus. 2002. (Magic Shop Bks.). 176p. (YA). (gr. 3-7). 17.00 (978-0-15-204613-2(5)) Harcourt Children's Bks.

—Jennifer Murdley's Toad: A Magic Shop Book. Lippincott, Gary A., illus. 2007. (Magic Shop Book Ser.). 176p. (J). (gr. 3-7). pap. 5.95 (***978-0-15-206246-0(7)*** , Magic Carpet Bks.) Harcourt Children's Bks.

—Juliet Dove, Queen of Love. DiTerlizzi, Tony, illus. 2003. (Magic Shop Bks.). 208p. (J). (gr. 3-6). 17.00 (978-0-15-204561-6(9)) Harcourt Children's Bks.

—The Monster's Ring. 2002. lib. bdg. 20.00 incl. audio (978-1-932076-10-3(7) , 02009) Full Cast Audio.

—The Monster's Ring. Coville, Katherine, illus. anniv. exp. ed. 2002. (Magic Shop Bks.). 128p. (YA). (gr. 3-7). 16.00 (978-0-15-204618-7(6)) Harcourt Children's Bks.

—The Monster's Ring. Coville, Katherine, illus. 2003. (Magic Shop Bks.). 128p. mass mkt. 5.99 (978-0-689-85692-1(X) , Aladdin) Simon & Schuster Children's Publishing.

—The Skull of Truth. Lippincott, Gary A., illus. 2002. (Magic Shop Bks.). 208p. (YA). (gr. 3-7). 17.00 (978-0-15-204612-5(7)) Harcourt Children's Bks.

—The Skull of Truth. 208p. (J). (gr. 5-7). pap. 3.99 (978-0-8072-1538-8(4) , Listening Library) Random Hse. Audio Publishing Group.

—The Weeping Werewolf. Coville, Katherine, illus. 2004. (Moongobble & Me Ser.). 80p. (J). (gr. 1-4). 15.99 (978-0-689-85756-0(X)) Simon & Schuster Children's Publishing.

Craik, Dinah Maria Mulock. Little Lame Prince EasyRead Comfort Edit. 2006. pap. (***978-1-4250-2001-9(1))*** Assistedreadingbooks.com Inc.

—Little Lame Prince EasyRead Edition. 2006. pap. (***978-1-4250-1718-7(5))*** Assistedreadingbooks.com Inc.

—Little Lame Prince EasyRead Large Editio. 2006. pap. (***978-1-4250-2260-0(X))*** Assistedreadingbooks.com Inc.

—Little Lame Prince the. 2006. pap. (***978-1-4250-2683-7(4))*** Assistedreadingbooks.com Inc.

Creamer, Joan Klatil. The Magic Sceptre - the Legend of Blue Santa Claus. Creamer, Joan Klatil, illus. ed. 2006. (J). 16.95 (978-0-9778476-3-1(2)) Silver Snowflake Publishing.

Creamer, Joan Klatil. The Magic Sceptre & Reginald the Rabbit. ed. 2007. (Illus.). 32p. (J). 16.95 (***978-0-9778476-5-5(9))*** Silver Snowflake Publishing.

Cresci, Bobby. The Kingdom of Tara. 2000. 204p. pap. 12.95 (978-0-595-16180-5(4) , Writers Club Pr.) iUniverse, Inc.

Croggon, Alison. The Naming. 2006. (Pellinor Ser.: Bk. 1). 528p. (YA). (gr. 7). pap. 8.99 (978-0-7636-3162-8(0)) Candlewick Pr.

—The Riddle. (Pellinor Ser.: Bk. 2). (Illus.). (YA). (gr. 7). 2007. 528p. pap. 8.99 (***978-0-7636-3414-8(X));*** 2006. 512p. 17.99 (978-0-7636-3015-7(2)) Candlewick Pr.

Croggon, Allison. Naming: The First Book of Pellinor, No. 1. 2005. 528p. (YA). (gr. 7 up). 17.99 (978-0-7636-2639-6(2)) Candlewick Pr.

Crossley-Holland, Kevin. At the Crossing Places. 2002. (Arthur Trilogy: Bk. 2). 416p. (J). (gr. 9 up). 17.95 (978-0-439-26598-0(3) , Levine, Arthur A. Bks.) Scholastic, Inc.

—At the Crossing-Places. 2004. (Illus.). 394p. (YA). (gr. 7-12). lib. bdg. 13.64 (978-0-606-32761-9(4)) Tandem Library Bks.

—At the Crossing Places. 2004. (Arthur Trilogy: Bk. 2). 416p. (J). (gr. 4-7). reprint ed. pap. 7.99 (978-0-439-26599-7(1) , Levine, Arthur A. Bks.) Scholastic, Inc.

—King of the Middle March. 432p. (J). 2006. pap. 7.99 (978-0-439-26601-7(7)); Book 3. 2004. (gr. 7 up). 17.95 (978-0-439-26600-0(9) , Levine, Arthur A. Bks.) Scholastic, Inc.

MNO

—The Seeing Stone. 2002. (Arthur Trilogy: Vol. 1). 368p. (J). (gr. 5 up). mass mkt. 6.99 (978-0-439-43524-6(2) , Levine, Arthur A. Bks.) Scholastic, Inc.

—Seeing Stone. 2002. (gr. 7-12). lib. bdg. 15.30 (978-0-613-50642-7(1)) Tandem Library Bks.

Cuentos Magicos. l.t. ed. 2002. Tr. of Magical Stories. (SPA., Illus.). 224p. 28.00 (978-84-494-2117-4(9) , GML07104-186002) Oceano Grupo Editoria, S.A. ESP. *Dist:* Thomson Gale.

Culver, Steven. The Magic Christmas Reindeer Bell: A Ho. 2006. pap. 11.00 (***978-1-4259-7114-4(8)***) AuthorHouse.

Curley, Marianne. El Circulo de Fuego. Puig, Fernando Gari, tr. 2001. (SPA.). 256p. (978-84-7888-710-1(5) , 1952) Emece Editores.

—Old Magic. 2002. 320p. (YA). (gr. 7-9). mass mkt. 5.99 (978-0-7434-3769-1(1) , Simon Pulse) Simon & Schuster Children's Publishing.

—Old Magic. 2002. (gr. 7-12). lib. bdg. 14.15 (978-0-613-74226-9(5)) Tandem Library Bks.

Curry, Jane Louise. The Egyptian Box. 2002. (Illus.). 192p. (J). (gr. 4-7). 16.95 (978-0-689-84273-3(2) , McElderry, Margaret K.) Simon & Schuster Children's Publishing.

—The Egyptian Box. l.t. ed. 2002. 216p. (J). 21.95 (978-0-7862-4896-4(3)) Thorndike Pr.

Curry, Kenneth. The Legend of the Dancing Trees: An African American Folk Tale. 2007. 111p. (J). per. 14.95 (***978-0-9798364-0-4(9)***) Curry Brothers Publishing.

Curry, Kenneth, et al. The Legend of the Dancing Tees Teachers Resource: The Legend of the Dancing Trees. 2007. Tr. of Teachers Resource. per. 19.95 (***978-0-9798364-1-1(7)***) Curry Brothers Publishing.

Curtis, Jillian M. The Little Prince & His Magic Wand. 2005. (Illus.). 28p. (J). 24.95 (978-1-59858-015-0(9)); pap. 16.95 (978-1-59858-010-5(8)) Dog Ear Publishing, LLC.

Cussler, Clive. The Adventures of Vin Fiz. Farnsworth, William, illus. 2006. 144p. (J). (gr. 3). 15.99 (978-0-399-24474-2(3) , Philomel) Penguin Group (USA) Inc.

Cyber. The Transdimensional War Series. 2006. 67p. pap. 14.95 (978-1-4241-2778-8(5)) PublishAmerica, Inc.

D' Lacey, Chris. The Fire Within. 2005. 352p. (YA). 15.99 (978-0-439-67243-6(0)) Scholastic, Inc.

da Vinci, Leonardo. Leonardo's Fables & Jests. 2003. 48p. per. 14.95 (978-0-9719898-9-4(3)) E & E Publishing.

Dahl, Roald. Charlie & the Chocolate Factory. Blake, Quentin, illus. 40th anniv. movie tie-in ed. 2004. 160p. (J). (gr. k). 22.95 (978-0-375-83197-3(5) , Knopf Bks. for Young Readers) Random Hse. Children's Bks.

—El Dedo Magico. Marriot, Pat, illus. (SPA.). 74p. (J). (gr. 3-5). 9.95 (978-968-19-0621-4(7)) Aguilar Editorial MEX. *Dist:* Santillana USA Publishing Co., Inc.

—Le Doigt Magique. 6th ed. 1998. Tr. of Magic Finger. (FRE., Illus.). (J). (gr. 4-7). pap. 17.95 (978-2-07-051784-8(5)) Gallimard, Editions FRA. *Dist:* Distribooks, Inc.

—George's Marvelous Medicine. Blake, Quentin, illus. 2002. (J). 13.19 (978-0-7587-9421-5(5)) Book Wholesalers, Inc.

—George's Marvelous Medicine. Blake, Quentin, illus. 2007. 96p. (J). (gr. 2). 5.99 (***978-0-14-241035-6(7)*** , Puffin) Penguin Group (USA) Inc.

—George's Marvelous Medicine. Blake, Quentin, illus. 2002. 112p. (J). (gr. 3-7). 15.95 (978-0-375-82206-3(2)); lib. bdg. 17.99 (978-0-375-92206-0(7)) Random Hse. Children's Bks. (Knopf Bks. for Young Readers).

—James et la Grosse Peche.Tr. of James & the Giant Peach. (FRE.). (J). pap. 17.95 (978-2-07-051374-1(2)) Gallimard, Editions FRA. *Dist:* Distribooks, Inc.

Dale, Anna. Whispering to Witches. 304p. (J). 2004. 16.95 (978-1-58234-890-2(1) , Bloomsbury Children); 2005. reprint ed. pap. 7.95 (978-1-58234-699-1(2)) Bloomsbury Publishing.

Dalmatian Press Staff. Fairy Magic. 2004. 12p. (J). bds. 3.99 (978-1-4037-0743-7(X)) Dalmatian Pr.

Damitz, Charlie. Diving for el Corazon. Diefendorf, Cathy, illus. 2007. 100p. (J). pap. 7.95 (978-0-9744446-3-5(4)) All About Kids Publishing.

D'Andrea, Elinor. Olivia the Magical Gourd. 2007. (J). per. 11.99 (***978-1-59886-898-2(5)***) Tate Publishing & Enterprises, L.L.C.

Dashney, John. The Adventures of Walter the Weremouse ; the Adventures of Mishka the Mousewere. Somerville, Sheila, illus. 2005. 202p. (J). pap. (978-0-9633236-7-5(9)) Storm Peak Pr.

Davenport, Victoria & Davenport, Nigel. Once Upon Another Time - Another Place. 2001. 216p. pap. 14.95 (978-0-595-18338-8(7) , Writers Club Pr.) iUniverse, Inc.

David, Ryan. The Magic Raincoat. Shekerdjiska-Benatova, Sybilla, illus. 2007. 40p. (J). (ps-1). 17.95 (978-1-932425-68-0(3) , Front Street) Boyds Mills Pr.

David, Stuart. Nalda Said. 2003. (gr. 7-12). lib. bdg. 24.55 (978-0-613-61144-2(6)) Tandem Library Bks.

Davidson, Mary Janice & Alongi, Anthony. The Silver Moon Elm: A Jennifer Scales Novel. 2007. 368p. (YA). (gr. 12). pap. 9.99 (***978-0-425-21526-5(1)*** , Berkley Trade) Penguin Group (USA) Inc.

Davidson, Susanna. Dolls. Wanert, Amandine, illus. 2006. 48p. (J). 8.99 (978-0-7945-1327-6(1) , Usborne) EDC Publishing.

Davidson, Susanna. Stories of Magic Ponies. 2007. (Young Reading Series 1 Gift Bks). 48p. (J). 8.99 (***978-0-7945-1790-8(0)*** , Usborne) EDC Publishing.

Davis, Bryan. Raising Dragons. 2004. (Dragons in Our Midst Chronicles: Vol. 1). 416p. pap. 12.99 (978-0-89957-170-6(0)) AMG Pubs.

Dawn, Thomas F. The Crystal Dream. 2007. 188p. (YA). (gr. 8 up). pap. 9.95 (978-1-56315-377-8(7) , Blue Imp Bks.) SterlingHouse Pubs., Inc.

de Brunhoff, Laurent. Babar the Magician. 2005. (Illus.). 24p. (J). (ps-1). 9.95 (978-0-8109-5863-0(5)) Abrams, Harry N. , Inc.

De Matos, Isabel Freire. El Pecécito Magico. Torres, Walter, illus. 2004. (SPA.). 22p. (J). pap. 6.95 (978-1-57581-578-7(8)) Santillana USA Publishing Co., Inc.

de Paola, Tomie. Strega Nona. 2000. (J). (978-0-606-20259-6(5)) Tandem Library Bks.

de Tena, Torcuato Luca. El Fabricante de Suenos. (SPA.). 112p. (J). (978-84-348-4787-3(6)) SM Ediciones ESP. *Dist:* Lectorum Pubns., Inc.

De Valera, Sinead. The Magic Gifts: Classic Irish Fairytales. (Illus.). 224p. 16.95 (978-0-86327-822-8(1)) Wolfhound Pr. IRL. *Dist:* Irish Bks. & Media, Inc.

de Varennes, Monique. The Jewel Box Ballerinas. Juan, Ana, illus. 2007. 40p. (J). (ps-3). lib. bdg. 19.99 (***978-0-375-93605-0(X)*** , Schwartz & Wade Bks.) Random Hse. Children's Bks.

De Witt, Peter. Isabella & the Room of Lost Brooms. 2007. 210p. (J). pap. 12.95 (***978-1-933255-35-4(8)***) DNA Pr.

de Witt, Peter. Toaster Pond. 2006. 248p. (YA). pap. 14.95 (978-1-933255-21-7(8)) DNA Pr.

Dean, Pamela. Juniper, Gentian, & Rosemary. 1998. 352p. (YA). (gr. 10 up). 24.95 (978-0-312-86004-2(8) , Tor Bks.) Doherty, Tom Assocs., LLC.

Delacre, Lulu. Rafi & Rosi. 2004. (Illus.). 64p. (J). lib. bdg. 13.85 (***978-1-4242-0596-7(4)***) Fitzgerald Bks.

DeLaney, Edgar Azell. The Magical Hammock. DeLaney, Edgar Azell, illus. 2004. (Illus.). 83p. (J). 19.95 (978-0-9759013-0-4(3)) Special Edition Studios, Inc.

Dematteis, J. M. The Puppet, the Professor, & the Prophet. Ploog, Mike, illus. 3rd rev. ed. 2007. 144p. (J). (gr. 4-7). 9.99 (978-1-4231-0063-8(8)) Hyperion Pr.

DeMatteis, J.M. Stardust Kid. 2008. (Stardust Kind Ser. ; Ser.). (Illus.). 128p. pap. 14.99 (***978-1-934506-04-2(4)***) Boom! Studios.

Demers, Dominique, et al. Old Thomas & the Little Fairy. Poulin, Stephane, illus. 2001. 29p. (J). (ps-3). pap. (978-1-894363-45-7(0)) Dominique & Friends.

Demi, illus. The Magic Pillow. 2008. (J). (***978-1-4169-2470-8(1)*** , McElderry, Margaret K.) Simon & Schuster Children's Publishing.

Deriso, Christine Hurley. Do-Over. 2006. 192p. (J). (gr. 4-7). 15.95 (978-0-385-73333-5(X)); lib. bdg. 17.99 (978-0-385-90350-9(2)) Random Hse. Children's Bks. (Delacorte Bks. for Young Readers).

Deriso, Christine Hurley. Do-over. 2007. 160p. (J). (gr. 4-7). 5.99 (***978-0-440-42119-1(5)*** , Yearling) Random Hse. Children's Bks.

Desimini, Lisa. Trick-or-Treat, Smell My Feet! Desimini, Lisa, illus. 2005. (Illus.). 40p. (J). pap. 16.95 (978-0-439-23323-1(2) , Blue Sky Pr., The) Scholastic, Inc.

Desrosiers, Sylvie & Sylvestre, Daniel. Faut-Il Croire a la Magie? 2001. (FRE., Illus.). 96p. (J). pap. (978-2-89021-509-2(1)) Diffusion du livre Mirabel.

Devlin, Serena. The Red Witch. 2000. 365p. (YA). (gr. 10 up). pap. 12.95 (978-1-893221-04-8(0)) Pendleton Bks.

Dey, Frederic Van Re. The Magic Story. 2004. reprint ed. pap. 15.95 (978-0-7661-8653-8(9)) Kessinger Publishing, LLC.

Diakite, Baba Wague. Mee-an & the Magic Serpent: A Folktale from Mali. 2007. (Illus.). 32p. (J). (gr. k-4). 16.95 (978-0-88899-719-7(1)) Groundwood Bks. CAN. *Dist:* Perseus Distribution.

Diamond, Bobby. What's Waiting at Wellington Mansion. 2002. 244p. (J). per. 18.00 (978-1-58982-026-5(6) , Bedside Bks.) American Bk. Publishing Group.

Dickins, Rosie. Monkey King. Ovani, Germano, illus. 2007. (Young Reading Series 1 Gift Bks). 48p. (J). 8.99 (***978-0-7945-1593-5(2)*** , Usborne) EDC Publishing.

Dickinson, Peter. Angel Isle. 2007. 512p. (gr. 9). (J). lib. bdg. 20.99 (***978-0-385-90928-0(4)***); (YA). 17.99 (***978-0-385-74690-8(3)***) Random Hse. Children's Bks. (Lamb, Wendy).

Dickson, Louise. Vanishing Cat. 2002. (gr. 3-6). lib. bdg. 15.25 (978-0-613-53331-7(3)) Tandem Library Bks.

DiGerolamo, Tony. The Wildsidhe Chronicles Bk. 5: The Undercover Dragon. 2003. (J). pap. 7.99 (978-1-890096-17-5(2)) Padwolf Publishing, Inc.

DiMarco, Carol & Wurm, Connie. The Magical Child. 3rd rev. ed. 2007. 44p. (J). 10.99 (978-1-59092-273-6(5) , Little Blue Works) Windstorm Creative.

Disney Press Staff. Abracadabra. 2001. (gr. k-3). lib. bdg. 13.00 (978-0-613-75074-5(8)) Tandem Library Bks.

—Fight for Your Right. 2001. (gr. 3-6). lib. bdg. 13.00 (978-0-613-75081-3(0)) Tandem Library Bks.

Disney Press Staff, ed. Magical Wishes: A Deluxe Pop-up Storybook. Disney Storybook Artists Staff, illus. 2007. 12p. (ps-2). 14.99 (***978-1-4231-0537-4(0)***) Disney Pr.

Disney Storybook Artists Staff, illus. Cars: Out for a Spin. 2006. 10p. (ps-17). 12.99 (978-0-7868-3596-6(6)) Disney Pr.

Distler, Christine A. Pegasus: The Introduction. 2005. 84p. pap. 11.95 (978-1-59113-763-4(2)) Booklocker.com, Inc.

DiTerlizzi, Tony & Black, Holly. Care & Feeding of Sprites. DiTerlizzi, Tony, illus. 2006. (Spiderwick Chronicles). 48p. (J). (gr. 2 up). 15.99 (978-1-4169-2757-0(3)) Simon & Schuster Children's Publishing.

—The Wrath of Mulgarath. DiTerlizzi, Tony, illus. movie tie-in ed. 2008. (Spiderwick Chronicles: Bk. 5). 160p. (J). (gr. 2 up). 10.99 (***978-1-4169-5021-9(4)***) Simon & Schuster Children's Publishing.

—The Wrath of Mulgarath. l.t. ed. 2006. (Spiderwick Chronicles: Bk. 5). 183p. (YA). 23.95 (978-0-7862-8579-2(6)) Thorndike Pr.

Divakaruni, Chitra Banerjee. The Conch Bearer. 2005. 265p. (J). (gr. 3-7). per. 12.64 (978-0-606-33382-5(7)); per. 14.45 (978-1-4176-6930-1(6)) Tandem Library Bks.

—The Mirror of Fire & Dreaming. 2005. (Brotherhood of the Conch Ser.: Bk. 2). (Illus.). 336p. (J). (ps-17). 16.95 (978-1-59643-067-9(2)) Roaring Brook Pr.

—The Mirror of Fire & Dreaming. 2007. 336p. (J). (gr. 3-7). pap. 5.99 (978-1-4169-1768-7(3) , Aladdin) Simon & Schuster Children's Publishing.

Dixon, Andy. Sword Quest. Brooks, Felicity, ed. Boni, Simone, illus. rev. ed. 2005. 31p. (J). (ps-7). pap. 7.95 (978-0-7945-1096-1(5) , Usborne) EDC Publishing.

DK Publishing Staff. Magic Toy Shop. 2007. 12p. (J). (ps-3). 14.99 (***978-0-7566-3179-6(3)***) Dorling Kindersley Publishing, Inc.

Dokey, Cameron. Golden: A Retelling of Rapunzel. 2007. (Once upon a Time Ser.). 192p. (YA). pap. 5.99 (***978-1-4169-3926-9(1)*** , Simon Pulse) Simon & Schuster Children's Publishing.

Dolbeck, Andrew. Fever Jenny, Bk. 1. 2006. 120p. pap. 10.99 (978-1-59092-324-5(3)) Windstorm Creative.

Donaldson, Julia. Princess Mirrorbelle & the Magic Shoes. l.t. ed. 2005. pap. 16.95 (978-1-4056-6038-9(4)) BBC Audio GBR. *Dist:* BBC Audiobooks America.

Dorling Kindersley Publishing Staff. Pajama Bedtime Bear's Magic Surprise: A Lift-the-Flap Book. 2002. (Lift-the-Flap Books Ser.). (Illus.). 12p. (J). pap. 6.95 (978-0-7894-6276-3(1) , D K Ink) Dorling Kindersley Publishing, Inc.

Downer, Ann. The Dragon of Never-Was. Rayyan, Omar, illus. 2006. 320p. (J). (gr. 3-6). 16.95 (978-0-689-85571-9(0) , Atheneum) Simon & Schuster Children's Publishing.

—Hatching Magic. 256p. (J). 2006. pap. 2.99 (978-1-4169-2497-5(3) , Aladdin); 2005. pap. 2.99 (978-1-4169-0535-6(9) , Aladdin); 2003. (Illus.). (gr. 3-7). 17.95 (978-0-689-83400-4(4) , Atheneum); 2004. reprint ed. pap. 5.99 (978-0-689-87057-6(4) , Aladdin) Simon & Schuster Children's Publishing.

Doyle, Debra. The Wizard's Castle, Bk. 5. 2001. (Circle of Magic Ser.). (Illus.). (Orig.). (J). (978-0-606-20998-4(0)) Tandem Library Bks.

Drake, David. Tommy Powers & the Replicator of Rio Azul. 2005. 210p. (YA). pap. 14.99 (978-1-885631-93-0(6)) Hutchison, G.F. Pr.

Drake, Emily. Curse of Arkady. 2003. 384p. (gr. 12). mass mkt. 6.99 (978-0-7564-0103-0(8) , D A W Bks., Inc.) Penguin Group (USA) Inc.

—Curse of Arkady. 2002. (gr. 5-8). lib. bdg. 15.30 (978-0-613-67323-5(9)) Tandem Library Bks.

—Magickers. 2002. (gr. 5-8). lib. bdg. 15.30 (978-0-613-67340-2(9)) Tandem Library Bks.

—The Magickers. 2002. 384p. reprint ed. mass mkt. 6.99 (978-0-7564-0035-4(X) , D A W Bks., Inc.) Penguin Group (USA) Inc.

Drake, Gillian. The Girl in Green. 2000. 125p. pap. 12.95 (978-1-85902-872-8(1)) Beekman Bks., Inc.

The Drums of Legenderry. 2006. (J). per. (978-0-9776967-0-3(7)) Legenderry.com.

Dubosarsky, Ursula. The Magic Wand: Poof! What Happened to Becky's Brother? Vane, Mitch, illus. 2006. (Nibbles Ser.). 72p. (J). pap. 3.95 (978-0-7624-2653-9(5) , Running Pr. Kids) Running Pr. Bk. Pubs.

Dubowski, Cathy East. Dog's Life. 1998. (gr. 7-12). lib. bdg. 13.00 (978-0-613-73049-5(0)) Tandem Library Bks.

Duce, Gillian. Magic & Mayhem. 2006. 208p. per. (***978-1-894936-64-4(7)***) Saga Bks.

Duey, Kathleen. Mountains of the Moon. 2002. (gr. 3-6). lib. bdg. 11.80 (978-0-613-58375-6(2)) Tandem Library Bks.

Duey, Kathleen. Skin Hunger. Rayyan, Sheila, illus. 2007. (Resurrection of Magic Ser.). 368p. (YA). (gr. 7 up). 17.99 (***978-0-689-84093-7(4)***) Simon & Schuster Children's Publishing.

DuFalla, Anita, illus. Sumac & the Magic Lake: Levels F-M (9-28) ed. 2004. (Reader's Theater Ser.). 16p. (J). pap. 22.00 (978-1-4108-2291-8(5) , A22915) Benchmark Education Co.

Duffy, Daniel M., illus. The Magic Show Mystery, Vol. 4. 1998. (Adventures of Benny & Watch: Vol. No. 4). 32p. (J). (ps-2). pap. 3.95 (978-0-8075-4939-1(8)) Whitman, Albert & Co.

Dulaney, Kim. Maya's Magic. Beck, Sherman, illus. 1999. (Fuzzy-Feeling Bks.). (J). (ps-3). pap. 8.25 (978-1-891636-04-2(9) , 1003) Unique Expression.

Dumas, Kim Renay. The Magic Tree Whispers. 2001. (J). pap. 7.00 (978-0-8059-5072-4(9)) Dorrance Publishing Co., Inc.

Duncan, Lois. A Gift of Magic. 1999. 240p. (YA). (gr. 7-9). mass mkt. 5.99 (978-0-440-22847-9(6) , Laurel Leaf) Random Hse. Children's Bks.

—A Gift of Magic. 1999. (Illus.). (J). 11.64 (978-0-606-17033-8(2)) Tandem Library Bks.

Dunkle, Clare B. Close Kin. 2nd rev. ed. 2006. (Hollow Kingdom Trilogy Ser.). 224p. (YA). (gr. 7 up). pap. 6.95 (978-0-8050-8109-1(7) , Holt, Henry & Co. Bks. For Young Readers) Holt, Henry & Co.

—Close Kin. Simonsen, Reka, ed. 2nd rev. ed. 2004. (Hollow Kingdom Trilogy Ser.: Bk. II). (Illus.). 224p. (YA). 16.95 (978-0-8050-7497-0(X) , Holt, Henry & Co. Bks. For Young Readers) Holt, Henry & Co.

—The Hollow Kingdom. 2003. (Hollow Kingdom Trilogy Ser.). (Illus.). 240p. (YA). (gr. 7). 16.95 (978-0-8050-7390-4(6) , Holt, Henry & Co. Bks. For Young Readers) Holt, Henry & Co.

—Hollow Kingdom. 2006. (Hollow Kingdom Trilogy Ser.). 240p. (YA). reprint ed. pap. 6.95 (978-0-8050-8108-4(9) , Holt, Henry & Co. Bks. For Young Readers) Holt, Henry & Co.

—The Hollow Kingdom, Vol. 5. l.t. ed. 2004. 360p. 21.95 (978-0-7862-6769-9(0) , Large Print Pr.) Thorndike Pr.

—In the Coils of the Snake. 3rd rev. ed. (Hollow Kingdom Trilogy Ser.). 240p. (YA). (gr. 7 up). 2006. pap. 6.95 (978-0-8050-8110-7(0) , Holt, Henry & Co. Bks. For Young Readers); 2005. 16.95 (978-0-8050-7747-6(2)) Holt, Henry & Co.

Dunn, John B. Dr. John's Traveling Magic Show. 2000. 15p. (J). pap. 4.00 (978-1-58193-188-4(3)) Brown Bag Productions.

Dyer, Heather. Ibby's Magic Weekend. 2008. 160p. pap. 16.99 (***978-0-545-03209-4(1)***) Scholastic, Inc.

Eager, Edward. Half Magic. Bodecker, N. M., illus. 1999. 208p. (YA). (gr. 3-6). pap. 6.00 (978-0-15-202068-2(3) , Odyssey Classics); 50th anniv. ed. 2004. 240p. (J). 18.95 (978-0-15-205302-4(6)) Harcourt Children's Bks.

—Half Magic. 192p. (J). (gr. 2-4). pap. 6.00 (978-0-8072-1534-0(1)); 1999. (gr. 3-7). pap. 29.00 incl. audio (978-0-8072-8066-9(6) , YA992SP) Random Hse. Audio Publishing Group. (Listening Library).

—Half Magic. Bodecker, N. M., illus. l.t. ed. 2005. 216p. (J). (gr. 3-7). pap. 10.95 (978-0-7862-7952-4(4)) Thorndike Pr.

—Knight's Castle. Bodecker, N. M., illus. 1999. 208p. pap. 6.00 (978-0-15-202073-6(X) , Odyssey Classics) Harcourt Children's Bks.

—Magic by the Lake. Bodecker, N. M., illus. 1999. 208p. (YA). pap. 6.00 (978-0-15-202076-7(4) , Odyssey Classics) Harcourt Children's Bks.

—Magic by the Lake. 1999. (gr. 3-6). lib. bdg. 14.15 (978-0-613-15895-4(4)) Tandem Library Bks.

—Magic or Not? Bodecker, N. M., illus. 1999. (Odyssey Classics). 208p. (J). (gr. 3-7). pap. 7.00 (978-0-15-202080-4(2) , Odyssey Classics) Harcourt Children's Bks.

—Magic or Not? 1999. (J). (978-0-606-19001-5(5)) Tandem Library Bks.

—Seven-Day Magic. 1999. (gr. 3-6). lib. bdg. 14.15 (978-0-613-22363-8(2)) Tandem Library Bks.

—The Time Garden. Bodecker, N. M., illus. 1999. 208p. (YA). pap. 6.00 (978-0-15-202070-5(5) , Odyssey Classics) Harcourt Children's Bks.

—The Time Garden. 1999. (gr. 5-8). lib. bdg. 14.15 (978-0-613-70941-5(1)) Tandem Library Bks.

—The Well-Wishers. Bodecker, N. M., illus. 1999. 220p. (J). (ps-7). per. 14.15 (978-0-613-22594-6(5)) Tandem Library Bks.

Ediciones B & Outhwaite, Ida Rentoul. La Magia de Las Hadas. 2005. (SPA., Illus.). 64p. (J). (gr. 2-4). 12.95 (978-84-666-1610-2(1)) Ediciones B ESP. *Dist:* Independent Pubs. Group.

Edwards, Gerry. Candy Klaus Trick or Treat. 2004. 56p. per. 10.95 (978-1-59453-394-5(6) , 1074) Airleaf Publishing & Bookselling.

Egan, Kate, adapted by. World's Apart. 2005. (W. I. T. C. H. Ser.: Bk. 14). 134p. (J). lib. bdg. 16.92 (***978-1-4242-0788-6(6)***) Fitzgerald Bks.

Eggleton, Jill. The Magic Show: Emergent Level Satellite Individual Title Six-Packs. Taylor, Clive, illus. (Sails Literacy Ser.). (gr. k-1). 27.00 (978-0-7578-7921-0(7)) Rigby Education.

Egielski, Richard. Jazper. Egielski, Richard, illus. 1998. (Illus.). 32p. (J). (ps-2). 14.95 (978-0-06-027817-5(X)) HarperCollins Pubs.

—Three Magic Balls. Egielski, Richard, illus. 2000. (Illus.). 40p. (J). (ps-2). 15.89 (978-0-06-026033-0(5) , Geringer, Laura Book) HarperCollins Pubs.

Ehrlich, Amy. Bravo, Kazam! Saltzberg, Barney, illus. 2002. (Brand New Readers Ser.). (J). (ps-2). 8p. 12.99 (978-0-7636-1315-0(0)); 32p. pap. 5.99 (978-0-7636-1316-7(9)) Candlewick Pr.

—Kazam's Magic. Saltzberg, Barney, illus. 2001. (Brand New Readers Ser.). 1p. (J). (ps-2). pap. 5.99 (978-0-7636-1310-5(X)) Candlewick Pr.

Elschner, Geraldine. Max's Magic Seeds. Myngheer, Charise, tr. Corderoc'h, Jean-Pierre, illus. 2007. 32p. (J). (ps-2). 16.99 (***978-0-698-40059-7(3)*** , Minedition) Penguin Group (USA) Inc.

ElvenWolf. Binding Magic. 2006. 75p. pap. 14.95 (978-1-4241-2700-9(9)) PublishAmerica, Inc.

Emmett, Jonathan. The Conjuror's Cookbook Vol. I: Goblin Stew. (Illus.). 64p. (J). pap. 7.99 (978-0-7475-4403-6(4)) Bloomsbury Publishing Plc GBR. *Dist:* Trafalgar Square Publishing.

—The Conjuror's Cookbook Vol. II: Serpent Soup. (Illus.). 64p. (J). pap. 7.99 (978-0-7475-4408-1(5)) Bloomsbury Publishing Plc GBR. *Dist:* Trafalgar Square Publishing.

—The Conjuror's Cookbook Vol. III: Ghostly Goulash. (Illus.). 64p. (J). pap. 7.99 (978-0-7475-4413-5(1)) Bloomsbury Publishing Plc GBR. *Dist:* Trafalgar Square Publishing.

Emshwiller, Carol. Mister Boots. 2007. (Firebird Ser.). 192p. (YA). pap. 6.99 (978-0-14-240770-7(4) , Puffin) Penguin Group (USA) Inc.

Enderle, Dotti. The Magic Shades: Fortune Tellers Club. 2003. (gr. 7-12). lib. bdg. 13.00 (978-0-613-87047-4(6)) Tandem Library Bks.

Ensor, Barbara. Cinderella (As If You Didn't Already Know the Story) Ensor, Barbara, illus. 2006. (Illus.). 128p. (J). (gr. 2-5). lib. bdg. 14.99 (978-0-375-93620-3(3) , Schwartz & Wade Bks.) Random Hse. Children's Bks.

Entara Ltd. Staff, photos by. Piggley & the Magic Doll. 2006. (Jakers! Ser.). 24p. (J). pap. 3.99 (978-0-689-87611-0(4) , Simon Spotlight) Simon & Schuster Children's Publishing.

Epner, Paul. Herbert Hilligan & His Magical Lunchbox. Kuon, Vuthy & Nguyen, Duke, illus. rev. ed. (Herbert Hilligan Ser.). 15.95 (978-1-57168-549-0(9)) Eakin Pr.

—Herbert Hilligan's Lone Star Adventure, Vol. 4. Kuon, Vuthy & Nguyen, Duke, illus. 2002. (Herbert Hilligan Ser.). 15.95 (978-1-57168-678-7(9)) Eakin Pr.

—Herbert Hilligan's Lone Star Adventure. Kuon, Vuthy & Nguyen, Duke, illus. 2003. 32p. (J). 15.95 (978-0-9743335-3-3(0)) Imaginative Publishing, Ltd.

—Herbert Hilligan's Tropical Adventure. Kuon, Vuthy & Nguyen, Duke, illus. 2003. 32p. (J). 15.95 (978-0-9743335-2-6(2)) Imaginative Publishing, Ltd.

Erenberger, Timothy D. Abacar the Wizard Book One: A Tale of Magic, War, Elves, Goblins, Orcs, Monsters, Fantasy, & Adventure. 2001. 210p. pap. 14.95 (978-0-595-21261-3(1) , Writer's Showcase Pr.) iUniverse, Inc.

Escondete y Grita, Vol. II. (Fantasmas de Fear Street Coleccion: No. 1). (SPA.). (J). (gr. 4-7). pap. 7.95 (978-950-04-1999-4(8) , EM4474) Emecé Editores S.A. ARG. *Dist:* Lectorum Pubns., Inc., Planeta Publishing Corp.

Eubank, Patti Reeder, illus. The Princess & the Snarls. 2006. 32p. (J). (ps). 16.95 (978-0-8249-5536-6(6) , Ideals Children's Bks.) Ideals Pubns.

Evans, Douglas. Mouth Moths: And More Classroom Tales. Di Fiori, Lawrence, illus. 2006. 112p. (J). 15.95 (978-1-932425-23-9(3) , Lemniscaat) Boyds Mills Pr.

Evans, Pamela. Tina Queen of the Dragons. 2006. 101p. pap. 14.95 (978-1-4241-3356-7(4)) PublishAmerica, Inc.

Evans, Richard Paul. The Christmas Candle. Collins, Jacob, illus. 32p. (J). (ps-3). 2007. 9.99 ***978-1-4169-5047-9(8));*** 2006. 7.99 (978-1-4169-2682-5(8) , Aladdin); 1998. 16.95 (978-0-689-82319-0(3)) Simon & Schuster Children's Publishing.

Faber, Roger A. What Happened to Milly? Monroe, John, illus. 1998. (J). (gr. 3 up). pap. (978-1-880122-07-5(3)) White Stone Co., The.

Fairy Tale- Beauty & the Beast. 2005. (J). bds. (978-1-4194-0038-4(X)) Paradise Pr., Inc.

Fairy Tales - Beauty & the Beast. 2005. (J). bds. (978-1-4194-0099-5(1)) Paradise Pr., Inc.

Fairy Tales s/s Beauty & the Beast. 2005. (J). bds. (978-1-4194-0065-0(7)) Paradise Pr., Inc.

Farooqi, Imran A. The Spell of the Witch-Queen. 2006. (Illus.). 60p. pap. (***978-1-84401-816-1(4))*** Athena Pr.

Farr, Dan. Mr. Finnegan's Giving Chest. 2005. (Illus.). 32p. (J). (ps-3). 19.95 incl. audio compact disk (978-1-59038-555-5(1) , Shadow Mountain) Deseret Bk. Co.

Farrell, Patricia. Jessicah the Mountain Slayer. 1999. 92p. pap. (978-1-77901-095-7(8)) Zimbabwe Publishing House Ltd, Zimbabwe.

Fénelon, Marie Jirlande. The Two Best Friends & the Old Lady. 2004. (Illus.). 28p. (J). bds. 19.00 (978-1-58432-128-6(8)) Educa Vision.

Fequiere, Marie A. Devil Rain & the Bearded Child of the Desert. 2007. (J). pap. 8.00 (***978-0-8059-7366-2(4))*** Dorrance Publishing Co., Inc.

Fernandez, Giselle. Gigi & the Birthday Ring. Petersen, Sheli, illus. 2005. (J). (978-1-56492-358-5(4)) Laredo Publishing Co., Inc.

Fienberg, Anna & Fienberg, Barbara. Tashi & the Dancing Shoes. Gamble, Kim, illus. (Tashi Ser.). 64p. (Orig.). (J). (gr. k-2). 2007. pap. 5.95 (***978-1-74114-972-2(X));*** 2002. pap. 5.95 (978-1-86508-552-4(9)) Allen & Unwin AUS. *Dist:* Independent Pubs. Group.

—Tashi & the Royal Tomb. Gamble, Kim, illus. (Tashi Ser.). 64p. (Orig.). (J). (gr. k-2). 2007. pap. 5.95 (***978-1-74114-973-9(8));*** Vol. 10. 2004. pap. 5.95 (978-1-74114-090-3(0)) Allen & Unwin AUS. *Dist:* Independent Pubs. Group.

Figueroa, M. A. & Figueroa, P. A. Melissa & the Magic Pen. Barnoski, Karel, illus. 2004. 36p. pap. 17.95 (978-1-4137-3441-6(3)) PublishAmerica, Inc.

Filaretos, William. The Potion of Time: A Story of Demetrios. 2006. per. 12.95 (978-0-9724520-0-7(1)) Filaretos, William.

Findlay, Andrew. Roddy & the Magic Mattress. 2005. 54p. pap. 5.61 (978-1-4116-3612-5(0)) Lulu.com.

Finks, Jan. Rainy Day Magic. 2000. II17p. (J). (ps-5). spiral bd. 15.00 (978-0-615-11137-7(8)) Hope Chest Publishing.

Fisher, Catherine. Corbenic. 2006. 288p. (J). 16.99 (978-0-06-072470-2(6) , Greenwillow Bks.); lib. bdg. 17.89 (978-0-06-072471-9(4)) HarperCollins Pubs.

—Darkhenge. (J). 2007. 432p. pap. 7.99 (978-0-06-078584-0(5)); 2006. 352p. 15.99 (978-0-06-078582-6(9)) HarperCollins Pubs.

Fisscher, Tiny. RUBY & MAGIC TWIG. 2008. 48p. 11.95 (***978-1-60136-013-7(4))*** Mars Media Pubs.

Flaker, Tracey. Around the Corner: Gwenever's Quest. 2006. 55p. pap. 12.95 (978-1-4241-1886-1(7)) PublishAmerica, Inc.

Fletcher, Claire & Haswell. X-Ray Mabel & Her Magic Specs. 1999. (Illus.). 14p. (J). 22.00 (978-0-370-32314-5(9)) Random Hse. GBR. *Dist:* Independent Pubs. Group.

Fletcher, Ralph J. Tommy Trouble & the Magic Marble. Caldwell, Benjamin H., Jr., illus. 2002. 64p. pap. 3.99 (978-0-439-34048-9(9)) Scholastic, Inc.

Forbeck, Matt. Secret of the Spiritkeeper. 2004. (Dungeons & Dragons Ser.). (Illus.). 192p. (J). (gr. 3-7). pap. 5.99 (978-0-7869-3143-9(4)) Wizards of the Coast.

Ford, Laura. Buster Brown & Tige in Misfit Heroes. 2004. (Illus.). 320p. 19.95 (978-1-881554-28-8(7)) Skyward Publishing Co.

Forrestal, Elaine. Watching Lake. 2002. 104p. reprint ed. pap. 12.95 (978-1-86368-360-9(7)) Fremantle Pr. AUS. *Dist:* International Specialized Bk. Services.

Forrester, Sandra. Witches of Friar's Lantern. 2003. (gr. 3-6). lib. bdg. 12.95 (978-0-613-84057-6(7)) Tandem Library Bks.

—The Witches of Winged-Horse Mountain: The Adventures of Beatrice Bailey. 2004. (Adventures of Beatrice Bailey Ser.). 256p. (J). pap. 4.95 (978-0-7641-2784-7(5)) Barron's Educational Series, Inc.

Forward, Toby. Travelling Backwards. 2003. (Illus.). 128p. (J). 9.99 (978-1-84270-293-2(9)) Andersen GBR. *Dist:* Independent Pubs. Group.

Fox, Mem. The Magic Hat. Tusa, Tricia, illus. 2002. 32p. (J). (ps-3). 16.00 (978-0-15-201025-6(4)) Harcourt Children's Bks.

Frabetti, Carlo. La Magia Mas Poderosa. 11th ed. 2003. (SPA., Illus.). 120p. (J). 15.95 (978-84-204-4844-2(3)) Alfaguara, Ediciones, S.A.- Grupo Santillana ESP. *Dist:* Santillana USA Publishing Co., Inc.

—La Magia Mas Poderosa. 2000. (SPA.). (gr. 5-8). lib. bdg. 18.75 (978-0-613-82085-1(1)) Tandem Library Bks.

Francis-Harris, Annabel. The Other Side of the Forest. 2006. pap. 19.95 (***978-1-59526-458-9(2))*** Media Creations, Inc.

Franson, Scott E. Un-Brella. 2007. (Illus.). 40p. (J). (ps-3). 15.95 (978-1-59643-179-9(2)) Roaring Brook Pr.

Franz, Kevin. Into the Hidden Lands: A Castle Rose Adventure. Stigler, Marilyn, illus. 2004. 112p. (J). per. 7.99 (978-0-9747774-0-5(4)) Starbell Bks.

Frederick, Mary. Peeka, Pooka, & the Dinosaur. Williams, Allen, illus. 2000. 108p. (ps-3). pap. 9.95 (978-0-595-12812-9(2)) iUniverse, Inc.

Freeman, Faith L. Beyond the Magic Waterfall. 2006. 79p. pap. 26.38 (978-1-4116-8202-3(5)) Lulu.com.

Freeman, Richard. The Legend of Booga Bearia. 2004. 117p. pap. 16.95 (978-1-4137-2016-7(1)) PublishAmerica, Inc.

Frei, Greg & Frei, Greg. Discovery. 2006. 44p. (J). 10.99 (978-1-59092-253-8(0) , Little Blue Works) Windstorm Creative.

French, Vivian. Princess Alice & the Magical Mirror. Gibb, Sarah, illus. 2007. 67p. (J). (***978-1-4287-2734-2(5))*** HarperCollins Pubs.

—The Princess Alice & the Magical Mirror. Gibb, Sarah, illus. 2007. (Tiara Club Ser.: Vol. 4). 80p. (J). 15.99 (978-0-06-112440-2(0) , Tegen, Katherine Bks) HarperCollins Pubs.

French, Vivian. Princess Daisy & the Magical Merry-Go-Roun. Gibb, Sarah, illus. 2007. (Tiara Club Ser.: No. 9). 80p. (J). pap. 3.99 (***978-0-06-112445-7(1)*** , Harper Trophy) HarperCollins Pubs.

Fujishima, Kosuke. Oh My Goddess! Mara Strikes Back. 2000. (gr. 7-12). lib. bdg. 24.55 (978-0-613-55175-5(3)) Tandem Library Bks.

Funke, Cornelia. Igraine the Brave. Bell, Anthea, tr. from GER. 2007. 224p. (J). (gr. 4-7). pap. 16.99 (***978-0-439-90379-0(3)*** , Chicken Hse., The) Scholastic, Inc.

—Inkheart. 2008. (Inkheart Movie Ser.). 576p. (J). 9.99 (***978-0-545-04626-8(2)*** , Scholastic) Scholastic, Inc.

—Inkheart. Bell, Anthea, tr. 2005. (Illus.). 560p. (ps-7). pap. 8.99 (978-0-439-70910-1(5)) Scholastic, Inc.

—Inkheart. 2003. 544p. (J). 60.00 (978-0-439-61671-3(9) , Chicken Hse., The) Scholastic, Inc.

—Inkheart. Bell, Anthea, tr. from GER. 2003. (Illus.). 544p. (J). (gr. 3-6). pap. 19.95 (978-0-439-53164-1(0) , Chicken Hse., The) Scholastic, Inc.

—Inkheart. Bell, Anthea, tr. 2005. 550p. (J). (ps-7). lib. bdg. 15.04 (978-0-606-33803-5(9)) Tandem Library Bks.

—Inkheart. l.t. ed. 2006. 709p. (YA). pap. 10.95 (978-0-7862-8363-7(7)) Thorndike Pr.

—Inkheart. Bell, Anthea, tr. l.t. ed. 2005. (Illus.). 709p. (J). (gr. 3-7). 23.95 (978-0-7862-8041-4(7) , Large Print Pr.) Thorndike Pr.

—Inkspell. 2007. 656p. (J). (gr. 4-7). pap. 9.99 (978-0-439-55401-5(2) , Chicken Hse., The) Scholastic, Inc.

—Inkspell. l.t. ed. 2006. 779p. (YA). 23.95 (978-0-7862-8040-7(9)) Thorndike Pr.

Furlong, Monica. Colman. 2005. 288p. (J). (gr. 5). reprint ed. pap. 5.99 (978-0-375-81515-7(5) , Laurel Leaf) Random Hse. Children's Bks.

Gaiman, Neil. M Is for Magic. Kristiansen, Teddy, illus. 2007. 272p. (J). (gr. 5 up). lib. bdg. 17.89 (***978-0-06-118645-5(7));*** 16.99 (***978-0-06-118642-4(2))*** HarperCollins Pubs.

Gaiman, Neil. Stardust. movie tie-in ed. 2007. 368p. (J). (gr. 7 up). pap. 6.99 (978-0-06-124048-5(6) , Harper Entertainment) HarperCollins Pubs.

Gallagher, Diana. Dark Vengeance. 2002. 202p. (YA). (gr. 7-12). lib. bdg. 14.15 (978-0-613-73371-7(1)) Tandem Library Bks.

Gallagher, Diana G. Dark Vengeance. 2002. (Charmed Ser.). 208p. (YA). pap. 5.99 (978-0-689-85079-0(4) , Simon Pulse) Simon & Schuster Children's Publishing.

Gallagher, Diana G. & Burge, Constance M. Mystic Knoll. 2005. 217p. (J). (978-1-4155-8004-2(9) , Simon Spotlight) Simon & Schuster Children's Publishing.

Gallego García, Laura & Peden, Margaret Sayers. The Valley of the Wolves. 2006. 247p. (J). pap. (978-0-439-58554-5(6) , Levine, Arthur A. Bks.) Scholastic, Inc.

Gandolfi, Silvana & Schwartz, Lynne Sharon. Aldabra, or, the Tortoise Who Loved Shakespeare. 2004. 151p. (J). (978-0-439-49744-2(2) , Levine, Arthur A. Bks.) Scholastic, Inc.

Garcia, Gloria. Magia. (SPA.). 8p. 9.95 (978-84-272-7275-0(8)) Molino, Editorial ESP. *Dist:* Distribooks, Inc.

Garcia, Laura Gallego. The Valley of the Wolves. 2006. 336p. (J). (gr. 4-7). pap. 16.99 (978-0-439-58553-8(8) , Levine, Arthur A. Bks.) Scholastic, Inc.

Gardner, Sally. I, Coriander. 2007. 288p. (J). (gr. 5 up). pap. 6.99 (978-0-14-240763-9(1) , Puffin) Penguin Group (USA) Inc.

—Magical Kids: The Strongest Girl in the World & the Invisible Boy. 2007. (Illus.). 224p. (J). (gr. 2-5). 15.99 (978-0-8037-3158-5(2) , Dial) Penguin Group (USA) Inc.

Gardner, Sally, illus. Magical Kids: The Smallest Girl Ever: The Boy Who Could Fly. 2008. (J). (***978-0-8037-3159-2(0)*** , Dial) Penguin Group (USA) Inc.

Garland, Michael. Miss Smith Reads Again! Garland, Michael, illus. 2006. (Illus.). 32p. (J). (ps). 15.99 (978-0-525-47722-8(5) , Dutton Juvenile) Penguin Group (USA) Inc.

—Miss Smith Reads Again! 2006. (Illus.). (J). (***978-1-4156-8098-8(1)*** , Dutton Juvenile) Penguin Group (USA) Inc.

Garland, Michael. Miss Smith's Incredible Storybook. Garland, Michael, illus. 32p. (J). 2005. pap. 6.99 (978-0-14-240282-5(6) , Puffin); 2003. (Illus.). 16.99 (978-0-525-47133-2(2) , Dutton Juvenile) Penguin Group (USA) Inc.

—Miss Smith's Incredible Storybook. 2007. 27.95 incl. audio (***978-0-8045-6945-3(2));*** 29.95 incl. audio compact disk (***978-0-8045-4159-6(0))*** Spoken Arts, Inc.

Garrido, Pedro Gelabert. El Libro del Abuelo: Un Mundo de Aventuras Entre la Realidad y la Fantasma. Velert, Miriam, illus. 2003. (Ficcion Interactiva Series Ser.). (SPA.). 160p. pap. 14.95 (978-84-89984-11-0(5)) Recursos, Ediciones ESP. *Dist:* Independent Pubs. Group.

Garrison, Terie. AutumnQuest. 2006. 192p. (YA). (gr. 7-9). pap. 8.95 (978-0-7387-0926-0(3) , Flux) Llewellyn Pubns.

—SpringFire. 2007. (DragonSpawn Cycle Ser.: Bk. 3). 240p. (J). pap. 8.95 (978-0-7387-1096-9(2) , Flux) Llewellyn Pubns.

—SummerDanse. 2007. 240p. (J). (gr. 4-7). pap. 8.95 (***978-0-7387-1112-6(8)*** , Flux) Llewellyn Pubns.

Garrison, Terie. WinterMaejic. 2007. 192p. (J). (gr. 7-9). pap. 8.95 (978-0-7387-1028-0(8) , Flux) Llewellyn Pubns.

Gaskin, Sharon. The Magic Mat. 2000. (Illus.). 24p. (J). pap. 7.00 (978-0-8059-4856-1(2)) Dorrance Publishing Co., Inc.

Geeslin, Campbell. Clara & Senor Frog. Sanchez, Ryan, illus. 2007. 40p. (J). (ps-3). 16.99 (978-0-375-83613-8(6) , Schwartz & Wade Bks.) Random Hse. Children's Bks.

Geist, Ken, ed. Friends Forever: 4 Favorite Stories. 2005. (Scholastic Reader Collection Level 3 Ser.). 160p. (J). pap. 6.99 (978-0-439-76314-1(2) , Cartwheel Bks.) Scholastic, Inc.

Gerstein, Mordicai. Fox Eyes. 2001. (gr. k-3). lib. bdg. 11.80 (978-0-613-43036-4(0)) Tandem Library Bks.

Gibson, Betty & Denton, Kady MacDonald. Little Quack.Tr. of Couac, la Petite Cane. (FRE., Illus.). (J). 13.99 (978-0-590-73930-6(1)) Scholastic, Inc.

Giles, Chauncey. The Magic Spectacles: A Fairy Story. 2004. reprint ed. pap. 22.95 (978-0-7661-8731-3(4)) Kessinger Publishing, LLC.

Gill, Janie S. The Magic Disc. 1999. 23p. (J). 5.95 (978-0-89868-492-6(7)); pap. 3.95 (978-0-89868-491-9(9)); lib. bdg. 10.95 (978-0-89868-490-2(0)) ARO Publishing Co.

Gilliland, Judith Heide. Not in the House, Newton! Sayles, Elizabeth, illus. 2002. 32p. (J). (gr. k-3). 5.95 (978-0-618-24619-9(3) , Clarion Bks.) Houghton Mifflin Co. Trade & Reference Div.

—Not in the House, Newton! 2002. (gr. k-3). lib. bdg. 14.10 (978-0-613-72909-3(9)) Tandem Library Bks.

Gilman, Laura Anne. The Camelot Spell. 2006. (Grail Quest Trilogy Ser.: No. 1). 304p. (J). 10.99 (978-0-06-077279-6(4)); lib. bdg. 14.89 (978-0-06-077280-2(8)) HarperCollins Pubs.

—Morgain's Revenge. 2006. (Grail Quest Trilogy Ser.: No. 2). 288p. (J). lib. bdg. 14.89 (978-0-06-077283-3(2)) HarperCollins Pubs.

Gilman, Phoebe. The Balloon Tree. ed. 2004. (J). (gr. k-3). spiral bd. (978-0-616-01650-3(6)) Canadian National Institute for the Blind/Institut National Canadien pour les Aveugles.

—The Balloon Tree. (Tell Me a Story Ser.). (FRE., Illus.). (J). 13.99 (978-0-590-24399-5(3)) Scholastic, Inc.

Gilmour, H. B. & Reisfeld, Randi. Dead Wrong. 2002. (T*Witches Ser.: No. 4). (Illus.). 176p. (J). pap. 4.99 (978-0-439-24073-4(5)) Scholastic, Inc.

Gilson. Melusine: Hocus Pocus. Jeffrey, Erica, tr. from FRE. Clarke, illus. 2007. 48p. pap. 9.99 (***978-1-905460-20-5(1))*** CineBook GBR. *Dist:* Biblio Distribution.

Glasco, Eileen. Travels with Sir Brolly: The Magic Umbrella. 2006. 31p. pap. 12.95 (978-0-9774603-0-4(4) , 704-001) Pollyanna Publishing.

Glassman, Peter. The Magical Land of Noom. 1998. (Books of Wonder). (Illus.). 192p. (J). (gr. 3-7). reprint ed. 22.00 (978-0-688-14117-2(X)) HarperCollins Pubs.

Gliori, Debi. Pure Dead Batty. (Illus.). (J). 2007. 320p. (gr. 4-7). 6.50 (***978-0-440-42074-3(1)*** , Yearling); 2006. 304p. (gr. 5). 15.95 (978-0-375-83316-8(1) , Knopf Bks. for Young Readers); 2006. 304p. (gr. 5). lib. bdg. 17.99 (978-0-375-93316-5(6) , Knopf Bks. for Young Readers) Random Hse. Children's Bks.

—Pure Dead Brilliant. l.t. ed. 2004. (Pure Dead Ser.: Vol. 5). (Illus.). 378p. (J). 21.95 (978-0-7862-6148-2(X)) Thorndike Pr.

—Pure Dead Frozen. 2007. (J). (gr. 5). 320p. 15.99 (***978-0-375-83317-5(X));*** 304p. lib. bdg. 18.99 (***978-0-375-93317-2(4))*** Random Hse. Children's Bks. (Knopf Bks. for Young Readers).

—Pure Dead Magic. 2002. (Illus.). 208p. (gr. 5). mass mkt. 6.50 (978-0-440-41849-8(6) , Yearling) Random Hse. Children's Bks.

—Pure Dead Trouble. 2006. 304p. (J). (gr. 4-7). 6.50 (978-0-440-42070-5(9) , Yearling) Random Hse. Children's Bks.

—Pure Dead Wicked. 2003. 240p. (gr. 5 up). 6.50 (978-0-440-41936-5(0) , Yearling) Random Hse. Children's Bks.

—Pure Dead Wicked. 2003. (gr. 3-6). lib. bdg. 13.00 (978-0-613-72261-2(2)) Tandem Library Bks.

Goble, Paul. Iktomi Loses His Eyes. Goble, Paul, illus. 1999. (Illus.). 32p. (J). (ps-2). pap. 16.95 (978-0-531-30200-2(8) , Orchard Bks.) Scholastic, Inc.

Going, K. L. The Garden of Eve. 2007. (Illus.). 240p. (J). (gr. 3-7). 17.00 (***978-0-15-205986-6(5))*** Harcourt Children's Bks.

Goldberg, Dennis. Double Bubble Trouble. 2007. (J). 14.95 (***978-1-933769-19-6(X))*** Level 4 Press, Inc.

Golden Books Staff. Journey to Fairytale Land. 2007. (Book & CD Ser.). (Illus.). 24p. (J). (ps-2). 9.99 (978-0-375-84025-8(7) , Golden Bks.) Random Hse. Children's Bks.

—The Magical Paintbrush. Duarte, Pamela, illus. 2002. 32p. (J). (ps-2). pap. 3.99 (978-0-307-29963-5(5) , Golden Bks.) Random Hse. Children's Bks.

—Stick Together! 2007. (Illus.). 32p. (J). (ps-3). 2.99 (978-0-375-83485-1(0) , Golden Bks.) Random Hse. Children's Bks.

Golden Books Staff. Unicorn Magic. 2008. (Color Plus Chunky Crayons Ser.). (Illus.). 48p. (J). (ps-2). pap. 3.99 (***978-0-375-84212-2(8)*** , Golden Bks.) Random Hse., Inc.

Goldman, Leslie. Truth Hurts. 2003. (gr. 3-6). lib. bdg. 13.00 (978-0-613-66471-4(X)) Tandem Library Bks.

Goldsborough, F. The Crimson Spell. 2000. (Charmed Ser.: Vol. 3). 192p. (YA). (gr. 7 up). pap. 6.99 (978-0-671-04164-9(9) , Simon Pulse) Simon & Schuster Children's Publishing.

Gonzalez, Eladia. El Misterio de las Damas Chinas. 2000. (SPA.). 30p. (J). (gr. 2-4). (978-968-494-094-9(7) , CI30454) Centro de Informacion y Desarrollo de la Comunicacion y la Literatura MEX. *Dist:* AIMS International Bks., Inc., Continental Bk. Co., Inc., Lectorum Pubns., Inc.

Goode, Suzi. The Lost Wizard Series Bk 1. 2007. pap. 11.95 (***978-1-59374-817-3(5))*** Whiskey Creek Pr., LLC.

Goodyear-Brown, Paris. Gabby the Gecko. 2003. per. (978-1-932203-54-7(0)) Sundog, Ltd.

Gordon, Amy. Magic by Heart. Gustavson, Adam, illus. 2007. 128p. (J). (gr. 3-7). 16.95 (***978-0-8234-1995-1(9))*** Holiday Hse., Inc.

Gormley, Beatrice. More Fifth Grade Magic. McCully, Emily Arnold, illus. 2001. 116p. (YA). (gr. 4-7). pap. 9.95 (978-0-595-15203-2(1) , Backinprint.com) iUniverse, Inc.

Gormley, Greg. Grandad's Busy Day. 2007. (Fantastic Phones Ser.). (Illus.). 12p. (J). 9.99 (***978-0-7475-8377-6(3))*** Bloomsbury Publishing Plc GBR. *Dist:* Independent Pubs. Group.

Gormon: The Sentinel Awakes. 2004. per. 2.75 (978-0-9762294-0-7(4)) Corbett Features.

Goudge, Elizabeth. Linnets & Valerians. 2001. 256p. (J). pap. 6.99 (978-0-14-230026-8(8) , Puffin) Penguin Group (USA) Inc.

—The Little White Horse. 2001. 240p. (YA). (gr. 3-6). pap. 5.99 (978-0-14-230027-5(6) , Puffin) Penguin Group (USA) Inc.

—Little White Horse. 2001. (gr. 5-8). lib. bdg. 14.15 (978-0-613-44399-9(3)) Tandem Library Bks.

Graff, Lisa. Bernetta Wallflower: A Novel. 2008. 256p. (J). 16.99 (***978-0-06-087592-3(5));*** lib. bdg. 17.89 (***978-0-06-087593-0(3))*** HarperCollins Pubs. (Geringer, Laura Book).

Graham, Edgar Earl. The Magic Orange. 2001. (J). pap. 8.00 (978-0-8059-5230-8(6)) Dorrance Publishing Co., Inc.

Graham-Larkin, Debbie. Magic in the Air. 2005. (Graham Cracker Kids Adventure Ser.). (Illus.). (J). pap. 12.95 (978-0-9716475-1-0(8)) Graham Cracker Kids.

Grandma's Magical Storybook. 2003. (Illus.). 256p. (J). 12.98 (978-1-4054-0968-1(1)) Parragon, Inc.

Gray, Kes. Duperball. Mould, Chris, illus. 2006. (Read-It! Chapter Books). 48p. (J). lib. bdg. (***978-1-4048-3118-6(5)*** , 1265805) Picture Window Bks.

Gray, Luli. Falcon & the Carousel of Time. 2005. 128p. (J). (gr. 5-9). 15.00 (978-0-618-44895-1(0)) Houghton Mifflin Co. Trade & Reference Div.

—Falcon & the Charles Street Witch. 2002. 144p. (J). (gr. 5-9). 16.00 (978-0-618-16410-3(3)) Houghton Mifflin Co. Trade & Reference Div.

Gray, Margaret. The Ugly Princess & the Wise Fool. Cecil, Randy, illus. rev. ed. 2002. 176p. (J). (gr. 3-5). 16.95 (978-0-8050-6847-4(3) , Holt, Henry & Co. Bks. For Young Readers) Holt, Henry & Co.

Graziani, Maria. A Black Cat on Halloween: Un Gato Negro en Dia de Brujas. Elejalde, Eliana, illus. l.t. ed. 2004. (SPA.). 23p. (J). 7.00 (978-0-9762361-1-5(7)) Ed. Acespanish S.A.C.- Lima, Peru.

Grban, Tanguy. Sarah So Small. 2004. 32p. (978-1-59687-179-3(2) , Milk & Cookies) ibooks, Inc.

Greenburg, Dan. My Grandma, Major League Slugger. Davis, Jack E., illus. 2001. (Zack Files Ser.: No. 24). 64p. (J). (gr. 2-5). pap. 4.99 (978-0-448-42550-4(5) , Grosset & Dunlap) Penguin Group (USA) Inc.

—My Grandma, Major League Slugger. 2001. (gr. 3-6). lib. bdg. 13.00 (978-0-613-58376-3(0)) Tandem Library Bks.

Greenspan, Deborah. Kids' Day. 2004. (J). pap. 10.95 (978-1-59526-197-7(4)) Media Creations, Inc.

Griffin, Adele. Witch Twins & Melody Malady. Rogers, Jacqueline, illus. 2004. 144p. (gr. 2-6). pap. 5.99 (978-0-7868-0964-6(7)) Hyperion Pr.

Griffin, Lydia. BeBa & the Curious Creature Catchers. Lostimolo, Stephanie, illus. l.t. ed. 2006. 32p. (J). 16.95 (978-0-9770516-0-1(9)) Laffin Minor Pr.

Griggs, Terry. Cat's Eye Corner. 2003. (Cat's Eye Corner Ser.). (Illus.). 168p. (J). pap. 7.95 (978-1-55192-350-5(5)) Raincoast Bk. Distribution CAN. *Dist:* Perseus Distribution.

—Cat's Eye Corner. 2003. (gr. 3-6). lib. bdg. 16.40 (978-0-613-78641-6(6)) Tandem Library Bks.

Grindley, Sally. The Kingfisher Book of Magical Tales: Tales of Enchantment. Field, Susan Anna, illus. 2002. (Story Collections). 80p. (J). (gr. 3-5). pap. 10.95 (978-0-7534-5388-9(6) , Kingfisher) Houghton Mifflin Co. Trade & Reference Div.

Grosset & Dunlap. New Enemy with Cards. 2002. (gr. 3-6). lib. bdg. 13.00 (978-0-613-72452-4(6)) Tandem Library Bks.

Gruelle, Johnny. The Paper Dragon: A Raggedy Ann Adventure. Gruelle, Johnny, illus. 2003. (Raggedy Ann Ser.). (Illus.). 96p. (J). 17.95 (978-0-689-84969-5(9)) Simon & Schuster Children's Publishing.

—Raggedy Ann's Wishing Pebble. Gruelle, Johnny, illus. 2004. reprint ed. pap. 15.95 (978-1-4179-0709-0(6)) Kessinger Publishing, LLC.

Gruelle, Johnny & Palmer, Jan. Raggedy Ann & Andy & the Nice Police Officer. 2002. (My First Raggedy Ann Ser.). (Illus.). 40p. (J). pap. 6.99 (978-0-689-85344-9(0) , Aladdin) Simon & Schuster Children's Publishing.

Guess, Catherine Ritch. Rudy & the Magic Sleigh. 2006. (Illus.). 32p. 14.95 (*978-1-933341-18-7(1)) CRM.

Guillain, Adam. Bella Balistica & the Temple of Tikal. 2004. (Bella Balistica Ser.). (Illus.). 288p. (J). pap. 9.95 (978-1-84059-394-5(6)) Milet Publishing.

Gummelt, Donna & Melchiorre, Dondino. Michelina the Magical Musical Good Witch of the Forest. Wall, Randy Hugh, ed. Varela, Juan D., tr. Varela, Juan D., illus. 2006. (SPA.). 34p. (J). 14.95 (978-0-9764798-6-4(9)) Story Store Collection Publishing.

Gunderson, Jeff. The Magic. 2007. pap. 7.95 (*978-0-533-15572-9(X)) Vantage Pr., Inc.

Hahner, Aaron. The Magic of Midnight. 2004. per. 8.95 (978-1-932560-58-9(0)) Media Creations, Inc.

Hahnke. Through the Eyes of a Raptor. 2007. 424p. per. 19.95 (*978-0-595-42609-6(3)) iUniverse, Inc.

Haining, Peter, ed. Magician's Circle: More Spellbinding Stories of Wizards & Wizardry. 2004. (Illus.). 256p. (J). 19.95 (978-0-285-63681-1(2)) Souvenir Pr. Ltd. GBR. *Dist:* Independent Pubs. Group.

Haining, Peter & Strings Magazine Staff. The Wizard's Den: Spellbinding Stories of Magic & Magicians. 2003. (Illus.). 320p. (J). 22.95 (978-0-285-63628-6(6)) Souvenir Pr. Ltd. GBR. *Dist:* Independent Pubs. Group.

Hale, Bruce. Pirates of Underwhere. Hillman, Shane, illus. 2008. (Underwhere Ser.). 160p. (J). 15.99 (*978-0-06-085127-9(9)); lib. bdg. 16.89 (*978-0-06-085128-6(7)) HarperCollins Pubs.

—Prince of Underwhere. Hillman, Shane, illus. 2008. (Underwhere Ser.). 176p. (J). lib. bdg. 16.89 (*978-0-06-085125-5(2)); (gr. 3-7). 15.99 (*978-0-06-085124-8(4)) HarperCollins Pubs.

Hale, Nathan. The Devil You Know. Hale, Nathan, illus. 2005. (Illus.). 32p. (J). (ps-3). 16.95 (978-0-8027-8981-5(1)) Walker & Co.

Halfmann, Janet. Bewitching the Chickadees. 2007. 88p. (J). pap. 14.99 (978-1-59092-573-7(4) , Orchard Academy Pr.) Windstorm Creative.

Hall, John. The Casebook of Janet Moore, Vol. I. 2003. 265p. 18.95 (978-1-59286-403-4(1)) PublishAmerica, Inc.

Hall, Kirsten. Revamp Your Room. 2005. (Illus.). 48p. pap. (*978-0-439-80296-3(2)) Scholastic, Inc.

Ham, David A. & Sibley, Janice B. Magic Baseball Cap. Bostick, Blair, illus. 2006. 48p. (J). 16.95 (978-0-9746920-2-9(6)) CRM Pubs., LLC.

Hamilton, C. After Ever Happily. 2006. 80p. pap. 14.95 (978-1-4241-3190-7(1)) PublishAmerica, Inc.

Hamilton, Tisha, adapted by. Five Times the Trouble. 2006. (Trollz Ser.). (Illus.). 32p. (J). (*978-1-4156-8962-2(8)) Scholastic, Inc.

Hao, Kuang-ts'ai. Seven Magic Brothers. 2000. (J). (KOR & ENG.). 18.95 (978-957-32-2168-5(3)); (TAG & ENG.). 18.95 (978-957-32-2169-2(1)) Yuan-liou Publishing Co., Ltd. TWN. *Dist:* AIMS International Bks., Inc.

Haptie, Charlotte. Otto & the Bird Charmers: The Second Book of the Karmidee. 2005. (Illus.). 417p. (J). 17.95 (978-0-8234-1883-1(9)) Holiday Hse., Inc.

—Otto & the Flying Twins: The First Book of the Karmidee. 2004. (Illus.). 320p. (J). (gr. 4-6). 17.95 (978-0-8234-1826-8(X)) Holiday Hse., Inc.

Hardinge, Frances. Well Witched. 2008. 400p. (J). 16.99 (*978-0-06-088038-5(4)); lib. bdg. 17.89 (*978-0-06-088039-2(2)) HarperCollins Pubs.

Hardy, Lorien. The Snow Dance. Trover, Zachary, illus. 2006. (Read-It! Readers Ser.). (J). 19.93 (978-1-4048-2421-8(9)) Picture Window Bks.

Hargreaves, Roger. Little Miss Magic. Hargreaves, Roger, illus. rev. ed. 2000. (Mr. Men & Little Miss Ser.). (Illus.). 32p. (J). (gr. k-3). pap. 3.99 (978-0-8431-7565-3(6) , Price Stern Sloan) Penguin Group (USA) Inc.

—Little Miss Magic. 2000. (ps-2). lib. bdg. 10.65 (978-0-613-26028-2(7)) Tandem Library Bks.

Harris, Joanne. Runemarks. 2008. 544p. (J). (gr. 5). 18.99 (*978-0-375-84444-7(9) , Knopf Bks. for Young Readers) Random Hse. Children's Bks.

Harrison, J. The Adventurous Journey of Willowby Went. 2005. 350p. pap. 24.95 (978-1-4137-7249-4(8)) PublishAmerica, Inc.

Harrison, Mette. Mira, Mirror. 2006. 320p. (YA). (gr. 7). pap. 6.99 (978-0-14-240643-4(0) , Puffin) Penguin Group (USA) Inc.

Harry Potter & the Chamber of Secrets. 2002. (Harry Potter Ser.). (Illus.). (J). 15.23 (978-0-7587-4426-5(9)) Book Wholesalers, Inc.

Harry Potter & the Sorcerer's Stone. 2002. (Harry Potter Ser.). (Illus.). (J). 15.23 (978-0-7587-0016-2(4)) Book Wholesalers, Inc.

Harvey, Matthea. The Little General & the Giant Snowflake. Zechel, Elizabeth, illus. 2007. 64p. (J). 12.95 (*978-1-933368-83-2(7)) Counterpoint.

Hauman, Carrie. Zoe the Magic Love Dog. 2003. (Illus.). 32p. (J). 16.00 (978-0-9746333-8-1(0)) Alma Pr.

Hausman, Gerald. Doctor Moledinky's Castle: A Hometown Tale. rev. ed. 1999. 151p. (YA). (gr. 5 up). pap. 10.00 (978-0-9709112-1-6(1)) Irie Bks.

Haworth-Atlard, Barbara. WyndMagic. 1999. (Out of This World Ser.). 136p. (YA). (gr. 5-8). pap. 5.95 (978-1-896184-54-8(5)) Roussan Pubs., Inc./Roussan Editeur, Inc. CAN. *Dist:* Orca Bk. Pubs. USA.

Hawthorne, Nathaniel & San Souci, Robert D. Feathertop: Based on the Tale by Nathaniel Hawthorne. San Souci, Robert D. & San Souci, Daniel, illus. 2006. (J). reprint ed. pap. 10.95 (978-1-59078-382-5(4)) Boyds Mills Pr.

Hayes, Joe. Little Gold Star: A Cinderella Cuento. 2002. (gr. k-3). lib. bdg. 16.40 (978-0-613-77773-5(5)) Tandem Library Bks.

Hayes, Rosemary. The Magic Sword. 2005. (Cambridge Storybooks Ser.). 32p. pap. 7.00 (978-0-521-67475-1(1)) Cambridge Univ. Pr.

Hearne, Betsy. Wishes, Kisses, & Pigs. 2003. 144p. (J). pap. 4.99 (978-0-689-86347-9(0) , Aladdin) Simon & Schuster Children's Publishing.

—Wishes, Kisses, & Pigs. 2003. (gr. 3-6). lib. bdg. 13.00 (978-0-613-70812-8(1)) Tandem Library Bks.

Helgerson, Joseph. Horns & Wrinkles. Ceccoli, Nicoletta, illus. 2006. 368p. (J). (gr. 4-6). 16.00 (978-0-618-61679-4(9)) Houghton Mifflin Co.

Helgerson, Joseph. Horns & Wrinkles. Ceccoli, Nicoletta, illus. 2008. 240p. (J). (gr. 5-9). pap. 4.95 (*978-0-618-98178-6(0)) Houghton Mifflin Co. Trade & Reference Div.

Heller, Nicholas. Elwood & the Witch. Smith, Jos. A., illus. 2000. 32p. (J). (gr. k-3). 15.89 (978-0-688-16946-6(5)) HarperCollins Pubs.

—Elwood & the Witch. Smith, Jos. A., illus. 2000. 32p. (J). (gr. k-3). 15.95 (978-0-688-16945-9(7)) HarperCollins Pubs.

Helliwell, Sheila. Hoonraki Moon: The Murphy Stories. 2006. (J). pap. 9.00 (978-0-8059-7027-2(4)) Dorrance Publishing Co., Inc.

Henighan, Tom. Mercury Man. 2004. 200p. pap. 9.99 (978-1-55002-508-8(2)) Dundurn Group, The CAN. *Dist:* Univ. of Toronto Pr.

Henry, Heather French. Claire's Magic Sades. Henry, Heather French, illus. 2004. (Claire's Everyday Adventures Ser.). (Illus.). 32p. (J). (gr. k-4). pap. 8.95 (978-0-9706341-7-7(X) , 1231609) Cubbie Blue Publishing.

Herbert Hilligan & His Magical Adventure Curriculum Guide. 2004. ring bd. 24.95 (978-0-9743335-4-0(9)) Imaginative Publishing, Ltd.

Herbert Hilligan's Lone Star Adventure Curriculum Guide. 2004. ring bd. 24.95 (978-0-9743335-7-1(3)) Imaginative Publishing, Ltd.

Herbert Hilligan's Tropical Adventure Curriculum Guide. 2004. ring bd. 24.95 (978-0-9743335-6-4(5)) Imaginative Publishing, Ltd.

Herbert, James. The Magic Cottage. 1999. 394p. 32.50 (978-0-333-76129-8(4)) Macmillan Publishers Ltd. GBR. *Dist:* Independent Pubs. Group.

Here Is a Bird: Individual Title Six-Packs. (Sails Literacy Ser.). 16p. (gr. k up). 27.00 (978-0-7635-4412-6(4)) Rigby Education.

Herman, Gail. A Little Magic. 2007. (Mr. Magorium's Wonder Emporium Ser.). 32p. (J). pap. 3.99 (*978-0-439-91249-5(0)) Scholastic, Inc.

Herman, Gail. The Potion Plan. Mones, Marc & Mones, Isidre, illus. 2004. (Shrek 2 Ser.). 32p. (J). pap. 3.99 (978-0-439-63401-4(6)) Scholastic, Inc.

Herrera, Joaquin. Horris, Little Eli & the Lens of Truth. 2007. (DreamFever Chronicles Ser.: Bk. 1). 208p. (978-1-59258-245-7(1)) Hylas Publishing.

Hess, Brian F. Lynquest & the Search for Greatness. 2006. (ENG.). 116p. per. 16.95 (978-1-4241-4503-4(1)) PublishAmerica, Inc.

Hibbett, Myles. Zephyr: Spheres & the Sword of Wonders. 2001. 200p. pap. 14.95 (978-0-595-17452-2(3) , Writer's Showcase Pr.) iUniverse, Inc.

—Zephyr Spheres & the Lost Spell. 2004. 156p. (YA). 22.95 (978-0-595-66307-1(9)); pap. 12.95 (978-0-595-31395-2(7)) iUniverse, Inc.

Hill, Pamela Smith. The Last Grail Keeper. 2001. 240p. (J). (gr. 7 up). tchr. ed. 17.95 (978-0-8234-1574-8(0)) Holiday Hse., Inc.

Hillert, Margaret. The Magic Beans. Pekarsky, Mel, illus. rev. ed. 2006. (Beginning to Read Ser.). 30p. (J). lib. bdg. 18.60 (978-1-59953-025-3(2)) Norwood Hse. Pr.

Hobbs, Will. Kokopelli's Flute. 2005. 160p. (J). (gr. k-9). pap. 4.99 (978-1-4169-0250-8(3) , Aladdin) Simon & Schuster Children's Publishing.

Hodges, Betty June. Nasturtium & His Magic Doors. Oroyan, Thomas, illus. 2002. 23.95 (978-1-58597-161-9(8)) Leathers Publishing.

Hoffman, Mary. City of Flowers. 2005. (Illus.). 250p. (YA). (gr. 7-12). 17.95 (978-1-58234-887-2(1) , Bloomsbury Children) Bloomsbury Publishing.

—City of Stars. 2005. (Illus.). 464p. (YA). (ps-17). reprint ed. pap. 7.95 (978-1-58234-982-4(7) , Bloomsbury Children) Bloomsbury Publishing.

Holbrook, John Robert. Gingerbread Jimmi: Magical Storybook. Scott, Catherine, ed. Stensaas, Martin & Strasburg, Sunny, illus. 2004. (J). 19.95 (978-0-9762440-0-4(4)) Holbrook Studios.

Holder, Nancy. Spirited. 2004. (Once upon a Time Ser.). 272p. (YA). pap. 13.95 (978-0-689-87063-7(9) , Simon Pulse) Simon & Schuster Children's Publishing.

—Witch. 2002. lib. bdg. 14.15 (978-0-613-74180-4(3)) Tandem Library Bks.

Holder, Nancy & Viguié, Debbie. Witch. 2002. (Wicked Ser.). 368p. (YA). (gr. 7 up). pap. 5.99 (978-0-7434-2696-1(7) , Simon Pulse) Simon & Schuster Children's Publishing.

Holub, Joan. Abby Cadabra, Super Speller. Holub, Joan, illus. 2000. (All Aboard Reading Ser.). (Illus.). 48p. (J). (gr. 1-3). pap. 3.99 (978-0-448-42168-1(2) , Grosset & Dunlap) Penguin Group (USA) Inc.

—Abby Cadabra, Super Speller. 2000. (All Aboard Reading Ser.). (978-0-606-18849-4(5)); lib. bdg. 11.80 (978-0-613-24083-3(9)) Tandem Library Bks.

Honigsberg, Peter Jan. Pillow of Dreams. Morse, Tony, illus. 2004. 32p. (gr. k-4). 17.95 (978-1-57143-076-2(8)) RDR Bks.

Horn, S. Silkie. (Illus.). 89p. pap. 7.95 (978-0-340-67265-5(X) , Hodder & Stoughton) Hodder General Publishing Division GBR. *Dist:* Trafalgar Square Publishing.

Hornik, Laurie Miller. The Secrets of Ms. Snickle's Class. Tilley, Debbie, illus. 2001. 144p. (J). (gr. 4-6). tchr. ed. 15.00 (978-0-618-03435-2(8) , Clarion Bks.) Houghton Mifflin Co. Trade & Reference Div.

Horowitz, Alena Netia. The Tlytiettlym Tree. Horowitz, Alena Netia & De La Fuente, Mary, illus. l.t. ed. 2003. 64p. (J). per. 12.95 (978-0-923550-42-4(9)) Tetrahedron Publishing LLC.

Horwitz, Elinor Lander. When the Sky Is Like Lace. Cooney, Barbara, illus. 2004. 32p. (J). (ps-3). reprint ed. 16.99 (978-0-670-05909-6(9) , Viking Juvenile) Penguin Group (USA) Inc.

Howells, Andrea. Finding Peace & the True Soul. 2006. 60p. (J). per. 11.95 (978-0-9765072-4-6(2)) Tribute Bks.

Howland, Naomi. Latkes, Latkes, Good to Eat: A Chanukah Story. 2004. (Illus.). 32p. (J). (ps-3). pap. 5.95 (978-0-618-49295-4(X) , Clarion Bks.) Houghton Mifflin Co. Trade & Reference Div.

—Latkes, Latkes, Good to Eat: A Chanukah Story. Howland, Naomi, illus. 1999. (Illus.). 32p. (J). (gr. k-3). tchr. ed. 16.00 (978-0-395-89903-8(6) , Clarion Bks.) Houghton Mifflin Co. Trade & Reference Div.

Hoylie, Gerry. Byron Unleashed. 2005. 60p. pap. 14.95 (978-1-59113-670-5(9)) Booklocker.com, Inc.

Hudson, Margaret Parker. The Blue Umbrella. 2005. (Illus.). (J). 15.95 (978-0-9771301-0-8(X)) FayRe Pr.

Hughes, Monica. The Isis Trilogy. ed. 2006. 568p. (J). (gr. 4-7). (978-0-88776-792-0(3)) Tundra Bks., Inc./Livres Toundra, Inc. CAN. *Dist:* Random Hse., Inc.

Hult, Robert William. Time Dancer. 2004. (Illus.). (YA). pap. 14.00 (978-0-9754114-0-7(3)) Hegemony Pr.

Hunter, Erin. Moonrise. 2005. (Warriors Ser.: Bk. 2). (Illus.). 304p. (YA). (gr. 5 up). 15.99 (978-0-06-074452-6(9)) HarperCollins Pubs.

Hutchins, Hazel. Sarah & the Magic Science Project. Delezenne, Christine, illus. 2005. 152p. (J). (gr. 3-6). 18.95 (978-1-55037-931-0(3)); pap. 7.95 (978-1-55037-930-3(5)) Annick Pr., Ltd. CAN. *Dist:* Firefly Bks., Ltd.

Hyperion, ed. An Unexpected Return - #8: W. I. T. C. H. Graphic Novel. 8th rev. ed. 2007. 128p. (gr. 3-7). pap. 4.99 (*978-1-4231-0903-7(1)) Hyperion Pr.

Hyperion Staff. A Choice Is Made. rev. ed. 2006. (W. I. T. C. H. Ser.: Bk. 22). 144p. (gr. 3-7). pap. 4.99 (978-0-7868-4878-2(2)) Hyperion Pr.

—Forces of Change. rev. ed. 2006. (W. I. T. C. H. Graphic Novels Ser.: Bk. 6). 128p. (gr. 3-7). pap. 4.99 (978-0-7868-4877-5(4)) Hyperion Pr.

—Legends Revealed. rev. ed. 2006. (W. I. T. C. H. Graphic Novels Ser.: Bk. 6). (Illus.). 128p. (gr. 3-7). pap. 4.99 (978-0-7868-4876-8(6)) Hyperion Pr.

—Walt Disney World: Where Magic Lives 2006. 2006. 96p. (ps-17). pap. 9.95 (978-1-4231-0257-1(6) , Disney Editions) Disney Pr.

Ibbotson, Eva. The Ibbotson Reader: The Secret of Platform 13, Which Witch? Island of the Aunts. Hawkes, Kevin et al, illus. 2001. 768p. (J). (gr. 4-7). 14.98 (978-0-525-46776-2(9) , Dutton Juvenile) Penguin Group (USA) Inc.

—Island of the Aunts. 2002. (Illus.). (YA). 13.19 (978-1-4046-0936-5(9)) Book Wholesalers, Inc.

—Island of the Aunts. 2001. (J). 12.64 (978-0-606-21782-8(7)); (gr. 3-6). lib. bdg. 14.15 (978-0-613-44394-4(2)) Tandem Library Bks.

—Which Witch? 2002. (Illus.). 13.19 (978-1-4046-1490-1(7)) Book Wholesalers, Inc.

—Which Witch? Large, Annabel, illus. 2000. 256p. (YA). (gr. 3-7). pap. 5.99 (978-0-14-130427-4(8) , Puffin); 1999. 224p. (J). (gr. 4-7). 15.99 (978-0-525-46164-7(7) , Dutton Juvenile) Penguin Group (USA) Inc.

—Which Witch? 2000. (J). (978-0-606-19882-0(2)); (gr. 3-6). lib. bdg. 14.15 (978-0-613-31926-3(5)) Tandem Library Bks.

Impey, Rose. Wanda Witch & the Wobbly Fang. Mcewen, Katharine, illus. 2006. (Scholastic Reader Level 3 Ser.). 32p. (J). pap. 3.99 (978-0-439-78450-4(6) , Cartwheel Bks.) Scholastic, Inc.

—Wanda Witch & Too Many Frogs. McEwen, Katharine, illus. 2006. (Scholastic Reader Ser.). 32p. (J). pap. 3.99 (978-0-439-78451-1(4) , Cartwheel Bks.) Scholastic, Inc.

Inches, Alison. In the Mushroom Meadow. 2002. (gr. k-3). lib. bdg. 10.95 (978-0-613-86241-7(4)) Tandem Library Bks.

The Indian in the Cupboard. 1998. (J). pap. 3.95 (978-0-439-04474-5(X)) Scholastic, Inc.

Innes, Grant. The Flight of the Whirligigs. Innes, Grant, illus. 1999. (Illus.). 24p. (J). (ps-k). lib. bdg. 17.95 (978-1-55037-587-9(3)) Annick Pr., Ltd. CAN. *Dist:* Firefly Bks., Ltd.

Island, Fiona. Wishbone's Magic Garden. 2006. 120p. pap. (*978-1-84401-733-1(8)) Athena Pr.

Jablonski, Carla. Bindings. 2003. (gr. 7-12). lib. bdg. 14.15 (978-0-613-65686-3(5)) Tandem Library Bks.

—The Gypsy Enchantment. 2001. 181p. (YA). (gr. 7-12). lib. bdg. 14.15 (978-0-613-74199-6(4)) Tandem Library Bks.

Jackson, Stephen. Mundoespejo. Abreu, Carlos, tr. 2005. (SPA., Illus.). 28p. (J). (gr. 2-4). 15.95 (978-84-666-1495-5(8)) Ediciones B ESP. *Dist:* Independent Pubs. Group.

Jane, Pamela. Milo & the Greatest Trick Ever! Johnson, Meredith, ed. Johnson, Meredith, illus. 2002. 32p. (J). 13.95 (978-1-59034-187-2(2)); (gr. 1-3). pap. 13.95 (978-1-59034-184-1(8)) Mondo Publishing.

—Take a Bow, Winky Blue! Tilley, Debbie, illus. 1998. (Mondo Ser.). 56p. (J). (gr. 2-6). pap. 3.95 (978-1-57255-550-1(5)) Mondo Publishing.

Janer Manila, Gabriel. Esto Que Ves Es el Mar. 3rd ed. (SPA., Illus.). 88p. (YA). (gr. 5-8). (978-84-246-8627-7(6) , GL2774) La Galera, S.A. Editorial ESP. *Dist:* Lectorum Pubns., Inc.

Jarman, Julia. The Magic Backpack. Gon, Adriano, illus. 2004. (Flying Foxes Ser.). 48p. (J). (978-0-7787-1487-3(X)); pap. (978-0-7787-1533-7(7)) Crabtree Publishing Co.

Jarrell, Randall. Gingerbread Rabbit. 2004. (gr. k-3). lib. bdg. 15.30 (978-0-613-70970-5(5)) Tandem Library Bks.

Jeffers, Susan. The Nutcracker. Jeffers, Susan, illus. 2007. 40p. (J). (ps-3). lib. bdg. 17.89 (*978-0-06-074387-1(5)); (Illus.). 16.99 (*978-0-06-074386-4(7)) HarperCollins Pubs.

Jenkins, Gloria. Storm: The Peace Maker. 2006. (J). pap. 8.00 (*978-0-8059-7116-3(5)) Dorrance Publishing Co., Inc.

Jenkins, Susan. Franklin & the Magic Show. 2004. (Kids Can Read Ser.). (Illus.). 32p. (J). (gr. k-3). (978-1-55074-992-2(7)); (978-1-55074-990-8(0)) Kids Can Pr., Ltd.

Jessop, Sherry. The Great BooDinie Bird: Faith, 5 vols., Vol. 1. Staples, Deb, ed. Sketchit, Elly, illus. 2000. cd-rom 6.50 (978-1-931540-25-4(X)) SynergEbks.

Jocelyn, Marthe. The Invisible Day. 1999. (Illus.). (J). (978-0-606-18413-7(9)) Tandem Library Bks.

—The Invisible Day. Carter, Abby, illus. 1999. 160p. (J). (gr. 3-7). reprint ed. pap. 6.99 (978-0-88776-477-6(0)) Tundra Bks., Inc./Livres Toundra, Inc. CAN. *Dist:* Random Hse., Inc.

Johnson, Gillian. Thora: A Half-Mermaid Tale. Johnson, Gillian, illus. 2005. (Illus.). 256p. (J). 15.99 (978-0-06-074378-9(6)); lib. bdg. 15.89 (978-0-06-074379-6(4)) HarperCollins Pubs.

Johnson, Jane. The Secret Country. Stower, Adam, illus. 336p. (J). 2007. (Eidolon Chronicles Ser.). pap. 5.99 (*978-1-4169-3815-6(X) , Aladdin); 2006. (Chronicles of Eidolon Ser.: Bk. 1). (gr. 3-7). 14.95 (978-1-4169-0712-1(2)) Simon & Schuster Children's Publishing.

Johnson, Sandi. Dittle's Christmas Wish. Johnson, Britt, ed. Sturgen, Bobbi, illus. 2000. 17p. (J). (gr. k-5). spiral bd. 5.99 (978-1-929063-65-9(2) , 164) Moons & Stars Publishing For Children.

Johnston, Tony. The Spoon in the Bathroom Wall. 2006. (Illus.). 144p. (J). pap. 5.95 (978-0-15-205625-4(4) , Harcourt Paperbacks) Harcourt Children's Bks.

Johnston, Tony & Johnston, Tony. The Spoon in the Bathroom Wall. 2005. 144p. (J). (ps-7). 16.00 (978-0-15-205292-8(5)) Harcourt Trade Pubs.

Jones, Christianne C. & Kipling, Rudyard. How the Camel Got Its Hump: A Retelling of the Classic Folktale. Rooney, Ronnie, illus. 2005. (Read-It! Readers Ser.). 32p. (J). (gr. k-3). 18.60 (978-1-4048-1003-7(X)) Picture Window Bks.

Jones, Diana Wynne. The Chronicles of Chrestomanci, 2 vols. 2001. (Chronicles of Chrestomanci Ser.: Vol. I). (J). (gr. 7-12). Vol. I. 608p. pap. 7.99 (978-0-06-447268-5(X) , Harper Trophy); Vol. II. 560p. pap. 7.99 (978-0-06-447269-2(8)) HarperCollins Pubs.

—Chronicles of Chrestomanci: Lives of Christopher Chant & Charmed Life. 2001. (gr. 5-8). lib. bdg. 15.30 (978-0-613-31070-3(5)) Tandem Library Bks.

—Chronicles of Chrestomanci: Magicians of Caprona & Witch Week. 2001. (gr. 5-8). lib. bdg. 15.30 (978-0-613-31071-0(3)) Tandem Library Bks.

—Conrad's Fate. (J). 2006. 400p. pap. 6.99 (978-0-06-074745-9(5)); 2005. 384p. (gr. k-17). lib. bdg. 17.89 (978-0-06-074744-2(7)); 2005. 384p. (gr. 5 up). 16.99 (978-0-06-074743-5(9)) HarperCollins Pubs.

—Conrad's Fate: Read-Along/Homework Pack. 2005. (Chrestomanci Ser.). (YA). (gr. 5-8). 102.74 incl. audio (978-1-4193-3551-8(0) , 42039) Recorded Bks., LLC.

—Dark Lord of Derkholm. 2001. (gr. 7-12). lib. bdg. 15.30 (978-0-613-35925-2(9)) Tandem Library Bks.

—Magicians of Caprona. Stevens, Tim, illus. l.t. ed. 2005. 288p. (J). pap. (978-0-7540-6151-9(5) , CLP 345) BBC Audio.

—Magicians of Caprona. 1999. (gr. 5-8). lib. bdg. 14.15 (978-0-613-16750-5(3)) Tandem Library Bks.

—The Merlin Conspiracy. 480p. (J). (gr. 5 up). 2004. pap. 6.99 (978-0-06-052320-6(4) , Harper Trophy); 2003. 17.89 (978-0-06-052319-0(0)); 2003. 16.99 (978-0-06-052318-3(2)) HarperCollins Pubs.

—Mixed Magics: Four Tales of Chrestomanci. 2001. (Chronicles of Chrestomanci Ser.: Bk. 4). 144p. (J). (gr. 5 up). 15.89 (978-0-06-029706-0(9)) HarperCollins Pubs.

—Ogre Downstairs. 2002. (gr. 3-6). lib. bdg. 14.10 (978-0-613-68455-2(9)) Tandem Library Bks.

—The Pinhoe Egg: A Chrestomanci Book. (J). 2007. 480p. pap. 7.99 (*978-0-06-113126-4(1) , Eos); 2006. 528p. 17.99 (978-0-06-113124-0(5) , Greenwillow Bks.); 2006. 528p. lib. bdg. 18.89 (978-0-06-113125-7(3)) HarperCollins Pubs.

—Stopping for a Spell. Zug, Mark, illus. 2004. 144p. (J). (gr. 3 up). pap. 5.99 (978-0-06-056206-9(4) , Harper Trophy) HarperCollins Pubs.

—Stopping for a Spell. 2004. (gr. 3-6). lib. bdg. 14.15 (978-0-613-81137-8(2)) Tandem Library Bks.

—Witch's Business. 2002. 208p. (J). (gr. 3 up). 15.99 (978-0-06-008782-1(X)); lib. bdg. 17.89 (978-0-06-008783-8(8)) HarperCollins Pubs.

—Year of the Griffin. (J). 2001. 400p. (gr. 7 up). pap. 7.99 (978-0-06-447335-4(X) , Harper Trophy); 2000. 272p. (gr. 5 up). 15.89 (978-0-06-029158-7(3)) HarperCollins Pubs.

—Year of the Griffin. 2001. (J). (978-0-606-21708-8(8)); (gr. 5-8). lib. bdg. 15.30 (978-0-613-44275-6(X)) Tandem Library Bks.

Jones, Jasmine. Enchanted: The Junior Novelization. rev. ed. 2007. 160p. (gr. 3-7). pap. 4.99 (*978-1-4231-0471-1(4)) Disney Pr.

Jones, Katina. Cool School Story: Little Lucy & Friends. Ottinger, Jon, illus. Zaidan, Rick, photos by. 2001. (Little Lucy & Friends Ser.). 24p. (J). (ps-3). 9.99 (978-1-57151-700-5(6)) Playhouse Publishing.

Jones, Miranda. Castle Magic. 2006. (Little Genie Ser.). (Illus.). 96p. (J). (gr. 1-3). pap. 4.99 (978-0-440-41976-1(X) , Yearling) Random Hse. Children's Bks.

—Double Trouble. 2005. 128p. (J). (gr. 1-3). pap. 4.99 (978-0-440-41974-7(3) , Yearling) Random Hse. Children's Bks.

—Double Trouble. Calver, David, illus. 2004. (Little Genie Ser.). 128p. (J). (gr. 1-3). 8.95 (978-0-385-73138-6(8) , Delacorte Bks. for Young Readers) Random Hse. Children's Bks.

—Home on the Range. Calver, David, illus. 2008. (J). pap. (*978-0-440-42226-6(4)); 128p. lib. bdg. (*978-0-385-90532-9(7)) Random Hse. Children's Bks. (Yearling).

—Little Genie: A Puff of Pink. Calver, David, tr. Calver, David, illus. 2004. 128p. (gr. 1-3). lib. bdg. 10.99 (978-0-385-90188-8(7) , Delacorte Bks. for Young Readers) Random Hse. Children's Bks.

—Little Genie No. 4: Castle Magic. Calver, David, illus. 2004. 144p. (gr. 1-3). 8.95 (978-0-385-73165-2(5) , Delacorte Bks. for Young Readers) Random Hse. Children's Bks.

—Make a Wish. Calver, David, illus. 2004. (Little Genie Ser.). 128p. (gr. 1-3). 8.95 (978-0-385-73137-9(X) , Delacorte Bks. for Young Readers) Random Hse. Children's Bks.

—Meanie Genie. Calver, David, illus. 2008. 128p. (J). lib. bdg. (*978-0-385-90533-6(5)); (gr. 1-4). 4.99 (*978-0-440-42227-3(2)) Random Hse. Children's Bks. (Yearling).

Jones, Miranda. Puff of Pink. 2006. (Little Genie Ser.). (Illus.). 128p. (J). (gr. 1-3). pap. 4.99 (978-0-440-41975-4(1) , Yearling) Random Hse. Children's Bks.

Jones, Ursula. The Witch's Children. Ayto, Russell, illus. 2003. 32p. (J). (ps-2). 16.95 (978-0-8050-7205-1(5) , Holt, Henry & Co. Bks. For Young Readers) Holt, Henry & Co.

Joseph, Elaine. Dreamstealer. (Illus.). 32p. (J). 2002. (TUR & ENG.). 19.95 (978-1-85269-156-1(5)); 2000. (BEN, ENG & GUJ., 19.95 (978-1-85269-153-0(0)); 2000. (GUJ, ENG & BEN., 19.95 (978-1-85269-155-4(7)); 2000. (SOM & ENG., 18.95 (978-1-85269-159-2(X)); 2000. (URD & ENG., 19.95 (978-1-85269-157-8(3)) Mantra Publishing, Ltd. GBR. *Dist:* AIMS International Bks., Inc.

—Dreamstealer. 2000. (CHI & ENG., Illus.). 32p. (J). 15.95 (978-1-85269-154-7(9)) Yuan-liou Publishing Co., Ltd. TWN. *Dist:* AIMS International Bks., Inc.

Jullie A. Smith. The Magic Carpet Adventures: A Trip to the Park. 2007. (ENG.). 32p. per. 12.99 (*978-1-4259-7358-2(2)) AuthorHouse.

Juster, Norton. Casello Magico. pap. 19.95 (978-88-452-3854-3(7)) Fabbri - RCS Libri ITA. *Dist:* Distribooks, Inc.

Kaaberbol, Lene. Heartbreak Island. 2005. (W. I. T. C. H. Adventures Ser. : Bk. 3). (Illus.). 105p. (J). lib. bdg. 11.00 (*978-1-4242-0786-2(X)) Fitzgerald Bks.

—Heartbreak Island, Vol. 2. rev. ed. 2005. (W. I. T. C. H. Adventures Ser. : Bk. 3). (Illus.). 112p. (J). (gr. 3-7). pap. 4.99 (978-0-7868-0981-3(7) , Volo) Hyperion Bks. for Children.

Kadono, Eiko. Kiki's Delivery Service. Riggs, Lynne E., tr. from JPN. Hayashi, Akiko, illus. 2003. 176p. (J). (gr. 4 up). 18.95 (978-1-55037-789-7(2)); pap. 6.95 (978-1-55037-788-0(4)) Annick Pr., Ltd. CAN. *Dist:* Firefly Bks., Ltd.

—Kiki's Delivery Service. 2003. (gr. 3-6). lib. bdg. 15.25 (978-0-613-67558-1(4)) Tandem Library Bks.

Kanaan, Hanan S. The Jewel of Love. 2003. (Illus.). 114p. (J). per. 11.95 (978-1-59405-000-8(7) , New Age World Pr.) New Age World Publishing.

Kane, James. Ellie's Magic Kingdom. 2005. 73p. pap. 14.95 (978-1-4137-6420-8(7)) PublishAmerica, Inc.

Katschke, Judy. Jade Monkey. 2002. (gr. 3-6). lib. bdg. 13.00 (978-0-613-72495-1(X)) Tandem Library Bks.

—The Magic of the Five. Noel, Aragon & Hwan, Choi Sung, illus. 2006. (Trollz Ser.). 136p. (J). pap. 4.99 (978-0-439-78932-5(X)) Scholastic, Inc.

Katz, Bebe Weinberg. Princess Claudia & the Freckles. 2007. (ENG.). 48p. per. 12.95 (*978-1-4241-6446-2(X)) PublishAmerica, Inc.

Katz, Welwyn W. The Third Magic. 2nd ed. 2000. (Illus.). 218p. (J). (gr. 4-7). pap. 6.95 (978-0-88899-385-4(4) , Libros Tigrillo) Groundwood Bks. CAN. *Dist:* Perseus Distribution.

Kay, Elizabeth. Back to the Divide. 2007. 384p. (J). 6.99 (*978-0-439-63555-4(1)) Scholastic, Inc.

—The Jinx on the Divide. 2007. 384p. (J). pap. 6.99 (*978-0-439-72456-2(2)) Scholastic, Inc.

Keehn, Sally M. Gnat Stokes & the Foggy Bottom Swamp Queen. 2005. 160p. (YA). (gr. 5-7). 16.99 (978-0-399-24287-8(2) , Philomel) Penguin Group (USA) Inc.

Kemler, Nancy. Dragon Box: The Key to Magic. 2005. 108p. pap. 16.95 (978-1-4137-8445-9(3)) PublishAmerica, Inc.

Kemp, Kristen. How to Trick Your Biggest Enemy. 2002. (Genny in a Bottle Ser.: No. 3). 128p. pap. 4.50 (978-0-439-21180-2(8)) Scholastic, Inc.

Kendall, Cassie. Laurel. 1999. (Stardust Classics). (J). 16.95 (978-1-889514-22-2(5)) Dolls Corp.

Kendall, Jack. The Magic Apple Tree. Bostrom, Sally, illus. l.t. ed. 2006. (ENG.). 48p. (J). per. 9.95 (978-0-9787740-4-2(3)) Peppertree Pr., The.

Kennemore, Tim. Circle of Doom. 2003. 208p. (J). 16.00 (978-0-374-31284-8(2) , Farrar, Straus & Giroux (BYR)) Farrar, Straus & Giroux.

Kennemore, Tim & Archbold, Tim. Circle of Doom. 2006. (Illus.). 208p. (J). pap. 6.95 (978-0-374-41198-5(0)) Macmillan.

Kerr, Katharine. The Black Raven. 1999. (Dragon Mage Ser.: Bk. 2). (gr. 7-12). lib. bdg. 15.30 (978-0-613-63018-4(1)) Tandem Library Bks.

Kerr, P. B. The Akhenaten Adventure. 2004. (Children of the Lamp Ser.: Bk. 1). 368p. (J). (gr. 4-7). pap. 16.95 (978-0-439-67019-7(5) , Orchard Bks.) Scholastic, Inc.

—The Akhenaten Adventure No. 1: Children of the Lamp. l.t. ed. 2005. 430p. 23.95 (978-0-7862-7299-0(6) , Large Print Pr.) Thorndike Pr.

—Blue Djinn of Baby. 2006. (Children of the Lamp Ser.: No. 2). 384p. (J). pap. 6.99 (978-0-439-67022-7(5)) Scholastic, Inc.

—The Blue Djinn of Babylon. 2006. (Children of the Lamp Ser.: Bk. 2). 384p. (J). (gr. 4-7). pap. 16.99 (978-0-439-67021-0(7) , Orchard Bks.) Scholastic, Inc.

—Cobra King of Kathmandu. 2007. (Children of the Lamp Ser.: No. 3). 400p. (J). pap. 6.99 (*978-0-439-67024-1(1) , Scholastic Paperbacks) Scholastic, Inc.

—The Cobra King of Kathmandu. 2007. (Children of the Lamp Ser.: No. 3). (Illus.). 384p. (J). (gr. 4-7). pap. 16.99 (978-0-439-67023-4(3) , Orchard Bks.) Scholastic, Inc.

Kerr, P. B. The Day of the Djinn Warriors. 2008. (Scholastic First Discovery Ser.). 400p. (J). pap. 17.99 (*978-0-439-93214-1(9) , Orchard Bks.) Scholastic, Inc.

Kerven, Rosalind. Coyote Girl. 2005. (Cambridge Storybooks Ser.). 32p. pap. 7.00 (978-0-521-67483-6(2)); pap. 7.00 (978-0-521-67485-0(9)) Cambridge Univ. Pr.

Kimmel, Eric A. Anansi & the Magic Stick. Stevens, Janet, illus. (J). 2005. pap. 16.95 incl. audio (978-1-59112-481-8(6)); 2005. pap. 18.95 incl. audio compact disk (978-1-59112-506-8(5)); 2003. 25.95 incl. audio (978-1-59112-482-5(4)); 2003. 28.95 incl. audio compact disk (978-1-59112-507-5(3)); 2003. pap. 37.95 incl. audio (978-1-59112-483-2(2)); 2003. pap. 39.95 incl. audio compact disk (978-1-59112-519-8(7)) Live Oak Media.

Kimmons, Janet M. The Jewel in the Attic & the Adventures of Tiger. Farmer, Zoe, illus. 2007. 108p. (J). (gr. 1-3). pap. (978-1-58690-028-1(5)) Mould, Paul Publishing.

Kingfisher Editors, ed. Marvelous Magical Stories. 2007. (Super Shorts Ser.). 160p. (J). (gr. k-3). pap. 6.95 (978-0-7534-6072-6(6) , Kingfisher) Houghton Mifflin Co. Trade & Reference Div.

Kingsley, Kaza. Erec Rex: The Dragon's Eye. Payne, John, ed. 2007. 343p. (J). pap. 9.99 (*978-0-9786555-3-2(2)) Firelight Press, Inc.

—Erec Rex: The Dragon's Eye. Payne, John, ed. Grant, Melvyn, illus. 2006. 360p. (J). 17.99 (978-0-9786555-6-3(7)) Firelight Press, Inc.

Kitamura, Satoshi. Me & My Cat? Kitamura, Satoshi, illus. 2000. (Illus.). 40p. (J). (ps-3). 16.00 (978-0-374-34906-6(1) , Farrar, Straus & Giroux (BYR)) Farrar, Straus & Giroux.

—Me & My Cat? 2005. (Illus.). 40p. (J). reprint ed. pap. 6.95 (978-0-374-44796-0(9) , Sunburst) Farrar, Straus & Giroux.

—Yo y Mi Gato? (Los Especiales de A la Orilla Del Viento Ser.). (SPA., Illus.). 36p. (J). (gr. k-3). 13.99 (978-968-16-6234-9(2) , FC30958) Fondo de Cultura Economica USA.

Kladstrup, Kristin. The Book of Story Beginnings. 2006. 368p. (J). (gr. 5-8). 15.99 (978-0-7636-2609-9(0)) Candlewick Pr.

Klein, Abby. Talent Show Scaredy-Pants. McKinley, John, illus. 2005. (J). pap. (978-0-439-55603-3(1) , Blue Sky Pr., The); 5th ed. (Ready, Freddy! Ser.: No. 5). 96p. pap. 3.99 (978-0-439-55604-0(X)) Scholastic, Inc.

Klutz Editors. No-Practice Magic. 2005. (Illus.). 42p. (J). spiral bd. (978-1-59174-303-3(6)) Klutz.

K.M. Mohr, John Kelley and Waking Dalifi. 2005. 72p. pap. 9.95 (978-1-4116-6364-0(0)) Lulu.com.

Knight, Caitlyn. Anastasia: the Tapestry of the Silver Unicorns. 2007. 386p. pap. 19.98 (*978-0-615-15145-8(0)) Neugard, S.L.

Kochalka, James. James Kochalka's Magic Boy & Robot Elf. 2003. (Illus.). 80p. (YA). pap. 9.95 (978-1-891830-33-4(3)) Top Shelf Productions.

Koda-Callan, Elizabeth, illus. The Magic Locket. 2004. 48p. (J). 9.95 (978-0-7611-3636-1(3) , 13636) Workman Publishing Co., Inc.

Kollars, Helmut. The Lonely Wizard. Kollars, Helmut, illus. 1998. Tr. of Es War Einmal Zauberer Ganz Allein. (Illus.). 32p. (J). (ps-3). 23.69 (978-1-56711-804-9(6) , Blackbirch Pr., Inc.) Thomson Gale.

Komorn, Julie, adapted by. Out of the Dark. 2004. (W. I. T. C. H. Ser.: Bk. 8). (Illus.). 128p. (J). lib. bdg. 16.92 (*978-1-4242-0789-3(4)) Fitzgerald Bks.

Komorn, Julie & Lenhard, Elizabeth, adapted by. The Light of Meridian. 2004. (W. I. T. C. H. Ser.: Bk. 7). (Illus.). 144p. (J). lib. bdg. 16.92 (*978-1-4242-0794-7(0)) Fitzgerald Bks.

Korelitz, Jean Hanff. Interference Powder. 144p. (J). 2006. pap. 5.95 (978-0-7614-5275-1(3)); 2003. 15.95 (978-0-7614-5139-6(0)) Cavendish, Marshall Corp.

Korman, Gordon. Head over the Heels. 2001. (Jersey Ser.: No. 6). (Illus.). 128p. (J). (gr. 3-7). reprint ed. pap. 4.99 (978-0-7868-4447-0(7)) Disney Pr.

—It's Magic. 2000. (gr. 3-6). lib. bdg. 13.00 (978-0-613-31370-4(4)) Tandem Library Bks.

—Need for Speed. 2001. (Jersey Ser.: 8). (Illus.). 128p. (gr. 3-7). reprint ed. pap. 4.99 (978-0-7868-4467-8(1)) Disney Pr.

—Nick's a Chick. 2000. (gr. 3-6). lib. bdg. 13.00 (978-0-613-31525-8(1)) Tandem Library Bks.

—No Girly-Girls Allowed! 2000. (gr. 3-6). lib. bdg. 13.00 (978-0-613-31529-6(4)) Tandem Library Bks.

—This Rocks! 2000. (gr. 3-6). lib. bdg. 13.00 (978-0-613-31807-5(2)) Tandem Library Bks.

Krensky, Stephen. Too Many Leprechauns: Or How That Pot o' Gold Got to the End of the Rainbow. Andreasen, Dan, illus. 2007. 32p. (J). 12.99 (978-0-689-85112-4(X) , Simon & Schuster Children's Publishing) Simon & Schuster Children's Publishing.

Krulik, Nancy E. Any Way You Slice It, No. 9. John and Wendy Staff, illus. 2003. (Katie Kazoo, Switcheroo Ser.: No. 9). 80p. (J). (gr. 2-6). pap. 3.99 (978-0-448-43204-5(8) , Grosset & Dunlap) Penguin Group (USA) Inc.

—Anyone but Me, No. 1. John and Wendy Staff, illus. 2002. (Katie Kazoo, Switcheroo Ser.: No. 1). 80p. (gr. 2-5). pap. 3.99 (978-0-448-42653-2(6) , Grosset & Dunlap) Penguin Group (USA) Inc.

—Anyone but Me, No. 1. 2002. (Katie Kazoo, Switcheroo Ser.: No. 1). (gr. 3-6). lib. bdg. 11.80 (978-0-613-58350-3(7)) Tandem Library Bks.

—Be Nice to Mice, No. 20. John and Wendy Staff, illus. 2006. (Katie Kazoo, Switcheroo Ser.: No. 20). 80p. (J). (gr. 2-5). mass mkt. 3.99 (978-0-448-44132-0(2) , Grosset & Dunlap) Penguin Group (USA) Inc.

—Be Nice to Mice, No. 20. 2006. (Katie Kazoo, Switcheroo Ser.: No. 20). (Illus.). 78p. (J). (*978-1-4156-7185-6(0) , Grosset & Dunlap) Penguin Group (USA) Inc.

—Doggone It!, No. 8. John and Wendy Staff, illus. 2003. (Katie Kazoo, Switcheroo Ser.: No. 8). 80p. (J). (gr. 2-4). pap. 3.99 (978-0-448-43172-7(6) , Grosset & Dunlap) Penguin Group (USA) Inc.

—Doggone It!, No. 8. 2003. (Katie Kazoo, Switcheroo Ser.: No. 8). (gr. 3-6). lib. bdg. 11.80 (978-0-613-67541-3(X)) Tandem Library Bks.

—Drat! You Copycat, No. 7. 2003. (Katie Kazoo, Switcheroo Ser.: No. 7). (gr. 3-6). lib. bdg. 11.80 (978-0-613-62943-0(4)) Tandem Library Bks.

—Drat! You Copycat!, No. 7. 2003. (Katie Kazoo, Switcheroo Ser.: No. 7). (Illus.). 80p. (J). (gr. 2-4). pap. 3.99 (978-0-448-43171-0(8) , Grosset & Dunlap) Penguin Group (USA) Inc.

—Flower Power, No. 27. 2008. (Katie Kazoo, Switcheroo Ser.: No. 27). 80p. (J). (gr. 2-5). 3.99 (*978-0-448-44674-5(X) , Grosset & Dunlap) Penguin Group (USA) Inc.

—Free the Worms!, No. 28. John and Wendy Staff, illus. 2008. (Katie Kazoo, Switcheroo Ser.: No. 28). 80p. (J). (gr. 2-5). pap. 3.99 (*978-0-448-44675-2(8) , Grosset & Dunlap) Penguin Group (USA) Inc.

—Friends for Never, No. 14. John and Wendy Staff, illus. 2004. (Katie Kazoo, Switcheroo Ser.: No. 14). 80p. (J). (gr. 2-5). pap. 3.99 (978-0-448-43606-7(X) , Grosset & Dunlap) Penguin Group (USA) Inc.

—Get Lost!, No. 6. 2003. (Katie Kazoo, Switcheroo Ser.: No. 6). (Illus.). 80p. (J). (gr. 2-6). pap. 3.99 (978-0-448-43101-7(7) , Grosset & Dunlap) Penguin Group (USA) Inc.

—Get Lost!, No. 6. 2003. (Katie Kazoo, Switcheroo Ser.: No. 6). (gr. 3-6). lib. bdg. 11.80 (978-0-613-60289-1(7)) Tandem Library Bks.

—I Hate Rules! 2003. (Katie Kazoo, Switcheroo Ser.: Vol. 5). (gr. 3-6). lib. bdg. 11.80 (978-0-613-60296-9(X)) Tandem Library Bks.

—I Hate Rules, No. 5. 2003. (Katie Kazoo, Switcheroo Ser.: No. 5). (Illus.). 80p. (J). (gr. 2-6). pap. 3.99 (978-0-448-43100-0(9) , Grosset & Dunlap) Penguin Group (USA) Inc.

—I'm Game, No. 21. John and Wendy Staff, illus. 2006. (Katie Kazoo, Switcheroo Ser.: No. 21). 80p. (J). (gr. 2-5). pap. 3.99 (978-0-448-44133-7(0) , Grosset & Dunlap) Penguin Group (USA) Inc.

—It's Snow Joke, No. 22. John and Wendy Staff, illus. 2006. (Katie Kazoo, Switcheroo Ser.: No. 22). 80p. (J). (gr. 2-5). pap. 3.99 (978-0-448-44396-6(1) , Grosset & Dunlap) Penguin Group (USA) Inc.

—Karate Katie, No. 18. John and Wendy Staff, illus. 2006. (Katie Kazoo, Switcheroo Ser.: No. 18). 80p. (J). (gr. 2-5). pap. 3.99 (978-0-448-43767-5(8) , Grosset & Dunlap) Penguin Group (USA) Inc.

—No Biz Like Show Biz, No. 24. John and Wendy Staff, illus. 2007. (Katie Kazoo, Switcheroo Ser.: No. 24). 80p. (J). pap. 3.99 (978-0-448-44440-6(2) , Grosset & Dunlap) Penguin Group (USA) Inc.

—No Bones about It. 2004. (Katie Kazoo, Switcheroo Ser.: Vol. 12). (gr. 3-6). lib. bdg. 11.80 (978-0-613-72571-2(9)) Tandem Library Bks.

—No Messin' with My Lesson, No. 11. 2004. (Katie Kazoo, Switcheroo Ser.: No. 11). (gr. 3-6). lib. bdg. 11.80 (978-0-613-72569-9(7)) Tandem Library Bks.

—On Your Mark, Get Set, Laugh!, No. 13. John and Wendy Staff, illus. 2004. (Katie Kazoo, Switcheroo Ser.: No. 13). 80p. (J). mass mkt. 3.99 (978-0-448-43605-0(1) , Grosset & Dunlap) Penguin Group (USA) Inc.

—Open Wide, No. 23. John and Wendy Staff, illus. 2007. (Katie Kazoo, Switcheroo Ser.: No. 23). 80p. (J). pap. 3.99 (978-0-448-44439-0(9) , Grosset & Dunlap) Penguin Group (USA) Inc.

—Out to Lunch, No. 2. 2002. (Katie Kazoo, Switcheroo Ser.: No. 2). (Illus.). 80p. (J). (gr. 2-4). pap. 3.99 (978-0-448-42654-9(4) , Grosset & Dunlap) Penguin Group (USA) Inc.

—Out to Lunch, No. 2. 2002. (Katie Kazoo, Switcheroo Ser.: No. 2). (gr. 3-6). lib. bdg. 11.80 (978-0-613-58381-7(7)) Tandem Library Bks.

—Quiet on the Set!, No. 10. John and Wendy Staff, illus. 2003. (Katie Kazoo, Switcheroo Ser.: No. 10). 80p. (J). pap. 3.99 (978-0-448-43214-4(5) , Grosset & Dunlap) Penguin Group (USA) Inc.

—Something's Fishy, No. 26. John and Wendy Staff, illus. 2007. (Katie Kazoo, Switcheroo Ser.: No. 26). 80p. (J). (gr. 2-5). pap. 3.99 (*978-0-448-44442-0(9) , Grosset & Dunlap) Penguin Group (USA) Inc.

—Super Special on Thin Ice. John and Wendy Staff, illus. 2007. (Katie Kazoo, Switcheroo Ser.). 160p. (J). (gr. 2-5). pap. 4.99 (*978-0-448-44447-5(X) , Grosset & Dunlap) Penguin Group (USA) Inc.

Krulik, Nancy E. Witch Switch. John and Wendy Staff, illus. 2006. (Katie Kazoo, Switcheroo Ser.). 160p. (J). (gr. 2-5). mass mkt. 4.99 (978-0-448-44330-0(9) , Grosset & Dunlap) Penguin Group (USA) Inc.

Kulick Triscila, Verne. Joel & the Magic Toy Tree. 2005. 36p. (J). 11.99 (978-1-4116-6985-7(1)) Lulu.com.

Kunkel, Mike. Inheritance. 2003. (gr. k-3). lib. bdg. 30.35 (978-0-613-77882-4(0)) Tandem Library Bks.

Kurzweil, Allen. Leon & the Champion Chip. Bertholf, Bret, illus. 2005. 352p. (J). lib. bdg. 16.89 (978-0-06-053934-4(8)) HarperCollins Pubs.

—Leon & the Spitting Image. Bertholf, Bret, illus. 320p. (J). (gr. 3 up). 2005. pap. 6.99 (978-0-06-053932-0(1) , Harper Trophy); 2003. 16.99 (978-0-06-053930-6(5)); 2003. lib. bdg. 16.89 (978-0-06-053931-3(3)) HarperCollins Pubs.

Kusaka, Hidenori. Pokemon Yellow Caballero: The Gym Leader's Alliance. MATO Staff, illus. 2002. (Pokemon Adventures Ser.). 53p. (YA). (gr. 4-7). pap. 4.95 (978-1-56931-563-7(9)) Viz Media.

LaFevers, R. L. Theodosia & the Serpents of Chaos. Tanaka, Yoko, illus. 2007. 368p. (J). (gr. 5-7). 16.00 (*978-0-618-75638-4(8)) Houghton Mifflin Co. Trade & Reference Div.

Lake, A. J. The Book of the Sword: The Darkest Age II. 2007. 240p. (J). 16.95 (*978-1-59990-039-1(4) , Bloomsbury Children) Bloomsbury Publishing.

—The Coming of Dragons. 2006. (Darkest Age Ser.: Bk. 1). (Illus.). 250p. (J). 16.95 (978-1-58234-965-7(7) , Bloomsbury Children) Bloomsbury Publishing.

—The Coming of Dragons Bk. 1: Darkest Age I. 2007. (Illus.). 240p. (YA). pap. 6.95 (978-1-58234-902-2(9) , Bloomsbury Children) Bloomsbury Publishing.

Lamb, Charles & Lamb, Mary. Tales from Shakespeare: "A Midsummer Night's Dream" Strang, Kay, ed. Andrews, Gary, illus. rev. ed. 2005. 40p. pap. 4.95 (978-0-9542905-3-5(4)) Capercaillie Bks., Ltd GBR. *Dist:* Wilson & Assocs.

Lamere, Jill. The King's Crown. 2007. (Illus.). 5p. (J). 14.95 (*978-0-9772320-2-4(6)) Minikin Pr.

Lancett, Peter. Dark Words. 2007. (Dark Man Ser.). 36p. pap. 6.95 (*978-1-84167-602-9(0)) Ransom Publishing Ltd. GBR. *Dist:* International Publishers Marketing.

Landy, Derek. Skulduggery Pleasant. (Skulduggery Pleasant Ser.). (J). 2008. 416p. pap. 7.99 (*978-0-06-123117-9(7) , Harper Trophy); 2007. 400p. (gr. 3-7). 17.99 (*978-0-06-123115-5(0)); 2007. 400p. (gr. 5 up). lib. bdg. 18.89 (*978-0-06-123116-2(9)) HarperCollins Pubs.

Lane, Nickel. The Ferret Crusaders: Quest of the Wish A Pod. 2nd ed. 2004. 73p. (J). per. 8.49 (978-1-4116-0459-9(8)) Lulu.com.

Lang, Andrew. The Violet Fairy Book. 2005. 404p. pap. 16.95 (978-1-4218-0107-0(8) , 1st World Library - Literary Society) 1st World Publishing, Inc.

Langton, Jane. The Mysterious Circus. 2005. (Hall Family Chronicles). 224p. (J). lib. bdg. 16.89 (978-0-06-009487-4(7)) HarperCollins Pubs.

Larbalestier, Justine. Magic Lessons. 2007. 304p. (YA). pap. 7.99 (978-1-59514-124-8(3)); 2006. 288p. (J). (gr. 7-12). 16.99 (978-1-59514-054-8(9)) Penguin Group (USA) Inc. (Razorbill).

—Magic or Madness. (gr. 7-12). 2006. 304p. (YA). pap. 7.99 (978-1-59514-070-8(0)); 2005. 288p. (J). 16.99 (978-1-59514-022-7(0)) Penguin Group (USA) Inc. (Razorbill).

—Magic's Child. 2007. 304p. (YA). 16.99 (978-1-59514-064-7(6) , Razorbill) Penguin Group (USA) Inc.

Larsen, C. S. The Chronicles of Marvin Archibald Trekker Boy Magician Book 1 - Penguins of Choice. l.t. ed. 2006. (Illus.). 163p. (YA). per. 5.99 (978-0-9779844-1-1(9)) KnowledgeGain Inc.

Laurie, Peter. Mauby's Quest for the Magic Flower. Dodson, H. Ann, illus. rev. ed. 2002. 48p. (J). 12.95 (978-0-333-95313-6(4)) Macmillan Caribbean GBR. *Dist:* Interlink Publishing Group, Inc.

Laybourn, Emma. Missing Magic. 2007. 192p. (J). (gr. 4 up). 16.99 (978-0-8037-3219-3(8) , Dial) Penguin Group (USA) Inc.

Le Gallienne, Richard. The Book Bills of Narcissus. 2004. reprint ed. pap. 15.95 (978-1-4191-5479-9(6)); pap. 1.99 (978-1-4192-5479-6(0)) Kessinger Publishing, LLC.

Le Guin, Ursula K. The Farthest Shore. 2001. (Earthsea Ser.: Vol. 3). (YA). lib. bdg. 13.00 (978-0-613-88305-4(5)); lib. bdg. 15.30 (978-0-613-73333-5(9)) Tandem Library Bks.

LeapFrog Staff, compiled by & des. Magic Tree House - Knights at Dawn. LeapFrog Staff, des. 2002. (J). spiral bd. 14.99 (978-1-58605-829-6(0)) LeapFrog Enterprises, Inc.

Leavitt, Martine. The Dollmage. 2004. (Illus.). 160p. (YA). (gr. 7 up). pap. 8.95 (978-0-88995-233-1(7)) Red Deer Pr. CAN. *Dist:* Fitzhenry & Whiteside, Ltd.

Lee, Brian. Bouncey the Elf & Friends - Bedtime St. 2005. (ENG., Illus.). 53p. pap. (*978-0-7552-1023-7(9)) Authors OnLine, Ltd.

Lee, Quinlan B. Twink & the Sprites. Langer, Jutta, illus. 2004. (Rainbow Brite Ser.). 33p. (J). (ps-3). pap. 3.99 (978-0-439-68114-8(6)) Scholastic, Inc.

Lee, Shell. Teenie's Treehouse Adventures: The Magic Begins. 2004. 37p. pap. 17.95 (978-1-4137-2879-8(0)) PublishAmerica, Inc.

Lehman, Seth. The Color Pets. 2006. (Illus.). 52p. (J). 7.00 net. (*978-0-9787986-0-4(0)) 4All Ages LLC.

M
N
O

LeMieux, Anne Connelly. A Safe Place. 1998. (Fairy Lair Ser.: 2). 160p. (J). (gr. 3-7). mass mkt. 4.50 (978-0-689-81726-7(6) , Simon Pulse) Simon & Schuster Children's Publishing.

Lemire, Lillie. A Young Witch's Magical Adventure. 2006. (ENG.). 48p. per. 12.95 (*978-1-4241-5413-5(8)) PublishAmerica, Inc.

Lenhard, Elizabeth. A Bridge Between Worlds. 2004. (W. I. T. C. H. Ser.: Bk. 10). 158p. (J). lib. bdg. 16.92 (*978-1-4242-0796-1(7)) Fitzgerald Bks.

—Different Path. 2004. (W. I. T. C. H. Ser.: Bk. 13). 158p. (J). lib. bdg. 16.92 (*978-1-4242-0791-6(6)) Fitzgerald Bks.

—The Disappearance. 2004. (W. I. T. C. H. Ser.: Bk. 2). 158p. (J). lib. bdg. 16.92 (*978-1-4242-0799-2(1)) Fitzgerald Bks.

—Finding Meridian. 2004. (W. I. T. C. H. Ser.: Bk. 3). 158p. (J). lib. bdg. 16.92 (*978-1-4242-0801-2(7)) Fitzgerald Bks.

—Power of Five. 2004. 158p. (J). lib. bdg. 16.92 (*978-1-4242-0795-4(9)) Fitzgerald Bks.

Lenhard, Elizabeth, adapted by. The Crown of Light, Bk. 11. rev. ed. 2004. (W. I. T. C. H. Ser.: Bk. 11). (Illus.). 160p. (J). (gr. 3-7). pap. 4.99 (978-0-7868-5139-3(2) , Volo) Hyperion Bks. for Children.

Lenhard, Elizabeth, adapted by. The Return of a Queen. 2004. (W. I. T. C. H. Ser.: Bk. 12). 152p. (J). lib. bdg. 16.92 (*978-1-4242-0797-8(5)) Fitzgerald Bks.

Lerangis, Peter. Boo! Ghosts in the School. 2001. (gr. 3-6). lib. bdg. 11.80 (978-0-613-53484-0(0)) Tandem Library Bks.

—Whoa! Amusement Park Gone Wild! Talbot, Jim, illus. 2003. (Abracadabra Ser.: No. 7). 112p. (J). pap. 3.99 (978-0-439-38938-9(0) , Scholastic Paperbacks) Scholastic, Inc.

—Wow! Blast from the Past! Talbot, Jim, illus. 2003. (Abracadabra Ser.: No. 8). 112p. (J). pap. 3.99 (978-0-439-38939-6(9) , Scholastic Paperbacks) Scholastic, Inc.

Lethcoe, Jason. Wishful Thinking. 2007. (Benjamin Bartholomew Piff Ser.: No. 2). 224p. (J). (gr. 3-7). 9.99 (978-0-448-44497-0(6) , Grosset & Dunlap) Penguin Group (USA) Inc.

—Wishing Well. Damkoehler, Katrina, illus. 2007. (Benjamin Bartholomew Piff Ser.: No. 3). 224p. (J). (gr. 3-7). 9.99 (*978-0-448-44498-7(4) , Grosset & Dunlap) Penguin Group (USA) Inc.

Lethcoe, Jason. You Wish, No. 1. Lethcoe, Jason, illus. 2007. (Misadventures of Benjamin Bartholomew Piff Ser.: No. 1). (Illus.). 224p. (J). (gr. 4-7). 9.99 (978-0-448-44496-3(8) , Grosset & Dunlap) Penguin Group (USA) Inc.

Levine, Gail Carson. For Biddle's Sake. Elliott, Mark, illus. 2002. (Princess Tales Ser.). 112p. (J). (gr. 2-6). 9.99 (978-0-06-000094-3(5)) HarperCollins Pubs.

—The Two Princesses of Bamarre. (J). 2003. 256p. (gr. 5 up). pap. 6.99 (978-0-06-440966-7(X)); 2001. 256p. (gr. 5 up). 17.99 (978-0-06-029315-4(2)); 2001. 256p. (gr. 5 up). lib. bdg. 17.89 (978-0-06-029316-1(0)); 2004. (Illus.). 304p. (gr. 7 up). reprint ed. pap. 6.99 (978-0-06-057580-9(8)) HarperCollins Pubs.

—The Two Princesses of Bamarre. 2003. (Illus.). (gr. 7-12). lib. bdg. 14.15 (978-0-613-67233-7(X)) Tandem Library Bks.

Levine, Terri. Abigail & the Purple Fairy. Harr, Lynn, illus. 2007. 34p. (J). (ps-3). per. 14.99 (*978-1-60002-314-9(2) , Airleaf Publishing) Airleaf Publishing & Bookselling.

Levinson, Marilyn. Rufus & Magic Run Amok. 112p. 2005. (YA). pap. 5.95 (978-0-7614-5176-1(5)); 2001. (Illus.). (J). (gr. 2-6). 14.25 (978-0-7614-5102-0(1) , Cavendish Children's Bks.) Cavendish, Marshall Corp.

Lewis, C. S. Las Cronicas de Narnia. 2006. (SPA.). 816p. pap. 19.99 (978-0-06-119900-4(1) , Rayo) HarperCollins Pubs.

—The Magician's Nephew. Baynes, Pauline, illus. gif. ed. 2003. (Narnia Ser.). 112p. (J). (gr. 3 up). 19.99 (978-0-06-053084-6(7)) HarperCollins Pubs.

Lewis, H. B. Winnie Mae. 2001. (Illus.). 40p. (J). (gr. 3). pap. 8.95 (978-0-89812-013-4(6) , Creative Paperbacks) Creative Co., The.

Lewis, Regina N. The Smallest Schoolhouse. Moore, P. M., illus. 2007. 56p. (J). pap. 12.95 (*978-0-9776958-3-6(2)) CyPress Pubns.

Lewis, Regina N. The Smallest Toy Store, A Christmas Story. Moore, Phyllis M., illus. 2004. 44p. (J). per. 12.95 (978-0-9672585-8-4(8)) CyPress Pubns.

Lewison, Wendy Cheyette. Princess Buttercup: A Flower Princess Story. Smath, Jerry, illus. 2001. (All Aboard Reading Ser.). 32p. (J). (ps-3). pap. 3.99 (978-0-448-42472-9(X) , Grosset & Dunlap) Penguin Group (USA) Inc.

Leyva, Barbara. Henry & the Magic Window. Leyva, Barbara, illus. l.t. ed. 2003. (Illus.). 50p. (J). 3.50 (978-0-9729056-0-2(X) , 0, Balticbard Publishing) Leyva, Barbara.

Liberto, Lorenzo. Matt the Rat & His Sister Maggie (Raton Mateo y Su Hermana Maggie) When I Grow Up (Cuando Yo Crezca) Gomez, Rocio, ed. Torres, Irving, illus. 2003. (Matt the Rat Ser. / La Serie de Raton Mateo). (SPA & ENG.). 40p. (J). lib. bdg. 20.00 (978-0-9743668-1-4(1)) Harvest Sun Pr., LLC.

Lindner, Simone. Aelin the Water Fairy. Unzner, Christa, illus. 2008. 32p. (J). (ps). 9.99 (*978-0-698-40070-2(4) , Minedition) Penguin Group (USA) Inc.

—Runia the Fire Fairy. Unzner, Christa, illus. 2008. 32p. (J). (ps). 9.99 (*978-0-698-40071-9(2) , Minedition) Penguin Group (USA) Inc.

Lindsay, Elizabeth. Annie Saves the Day. Eastwood, John, illus. 2003. 92p. (J). (978-0-439-44651-8(1)) Scholastic, Inc.

Lisle, Janet Taylor. The Lost Flower Children. 2001. (J). (978-0-606-21305-9(8)) Tandem Library Bks.

Little, Berta. Nights in Nemra. 2003. 137 p. pap. 19.95 (978-1-4137-0511-9(1)) PublishAmerica, Inc.

Little, Jean. Emma's Magic Winter. Plecas, Jennifer, illus. (I Can Read Bks.). 64p. (J). (ps-3). 2000. pap. 3.99 (978-0-06-443706-6(X) , Harper Trophy); 1998. 15.95 (978-0-06-025389-9(4)); 1998. 15.89 (978-0-06-025390-5(8)) HarperCollins Pubs.

—Emma's Magic Winter. 2000. (gr. k-3). lib. bdg. 11.80 (978-0-613-27805-8(4)) Tandem Library Bks.

The Little Mermaid. 2002. (Classic Tales Mini Bks.). (Illus.). 32p. (J). (978-1-59069-038-3(9) , T1007) Studio Mouse LLC.

Littler, Keith. Merlin, King of the Castle. 2002. (Illus.). 24p. (J). (ps-3). pap. 7.99 (978-1-84222-617-9(7)) Carlton Bks., Ltd. GBR. Dist: Independent Pubs. Group.

—Merlin the Magical Puppy on Ice. 2002. (Illus.). 24p. pap. 7.99 (978-1-84222-616-2(9)) Carlton Bks., Ltd. GBR. Dist: Trafalgar Square Publishing.

Loehr, Mallory. Fire Dreams. 2001. (gr. 3-6). lib. bdg. 11.80 (978-0-613-35687-9(X)); (Illus.). (J). 10.64 (978-0-606-21185-7(3)) Tandem Library Bks.

—Unicorn Wings. Silin-Palmer, Pamela, illus. 2006. (Step into Reading Ser.). 32p. (J). (ps-2). lib. bdg. 11.99 (978-0-375-93117-8(1)); 3.99 (978-0-375-83117-1(7)) Random Hse. Children's Bks. (Random Hse. Bks. for Young Readers).

Lomas Garza, Carmen. Magic Windows: Ventanas Magicas. Lomas Garza, Carmen, illus. 2003. (ENG & SPA., Illus.). 32p. (J). pap. 7.95 (978-0-89239-183-7(9)) Children's Bk. Pr.

Lopez, David Mark. Run Like a Fugitive. 2006. (J). (gr. 4-8). (*978-0-9744097-2-6(3)) Lopez, David.

—Walk Like an Egyptian. 2006. (J). (gr. 3-7). (*978-0-9744097-0-2(7)) Lopez, David.

Love, D. Anne. The Secret Prince. 2005. 240p. (J). 16.95 (978-0-689-84426-3(3) , McElderry, Margaret K.) Simon & Schuster Children's Publishing.

Lovhaug, Lewis J. Angel Armor: The Cassandra Conflict. 2004. 188p. (YA). pap. 13.95 (978-0-595-30869-9(4)) iUniverse, Inc.

Lowe, Wesley. The Griffin's Gauntlet. 2003. (Illus.). (YA). per. 14.95 (978-0-9723011-2-1(7)) Helm Publishing.

—The Griffin's Gauntlet. 2003. (YA). per. 14.95 (978-1-59453-013-5(0) , 1171) Airleaf Publishing & Bookselling.

Lubar, David. Wizards of the Game. 2004. 176p. (J). (gr. 5). pap. 5.99 (978-0-14-240215-3(X) , Puffin) Penguin Group (USA) Inc.

Lucas, David. Nutmeg. 2006. (Illus.). 32p. (J). (ps-3). 16.95 (978-0-375-83519-3(9)); lib. bdg. 18.99 (978-0-375-93519-0(3)) Random Hse. Children's Bks. (Knopf Bks. for Young Readers).

Luckett, Dave. Girl Dragon, & the Wild Magic. 2003. (gr. 3-6). lib. bdg. 13.00 (978-0-613-72141-7(1)) Tandem Library Bks.

Lukas, Catherine. Three Wishes. Hall, Susan', illus. 2007. (Backyardigans Ser.). 24p. (J). pap. 3.99 (*978-1-4169-3437-0(5) , Simon Spotlight/Nickelodeon) Simon & Schuster Children's Publishing.

Maccarone, Grace. Magic Matt & the Dinosaur. Bridwell, Norman, illus. 2004. (Scholastic Reader Ser.). 32p. (J). 3.99 (978-0-439-37607-5(6) , Cartwheel Bks.) Scholastic, Inc.

—Magic Matt & the Jack O' Lantern. 2003. (ps-2). lib. bdg. 11.80 (978-0-613-72183-7(7)) Tandem Library Bks.

—Magic Matt & the Jack O'Lantern, Level 1. Bridwell, Norman, illus. 2003. (Reader Ser.). 32p. (J). pap. 3.99 (978-0-439-43992-3(2) , Cartwheel Bks.) Scholastic, Inc.

—Magic Matt & the Skunk in the Tub. Bridwell, Norman, illus. 2003. (Reader Ser.). 32p. (J). pap. 3.99 (978-0-439-40570-6(X) , Cartwheel Bks.) Scholastic, Inc.

—Magic Matt & the Skunk in the Tub. 2003. (gr. k-3). lib. bdg. 11.80 (978-0-613-63556-1(6)) Tandem Library Bks.

MacDonald, Betty Bard. Hello, Mrs. Piggle-Wiggle. 2000. (YA). pap. 40.20 incl. audio (978-0-7887-4171-5(3) , 41089) Recorded Bks., LLC.

MacDonald, George. Light Princess Large Print. 2006. pap. (*978-1-84702-350-6(9)) Echo Library.

MacDonald, George. The Princess & the Goblin Book & Charm. 2004. (Charming Classics). (Illus.). 272p. (J). pap. 6.99 (978-0-06-009552-9(0) , Harper Festival) HarperCollins Pubs.

Mack, Michele. Henry Fickle & the Secret Laboratory. 2005. (Illus.). 112p. (J). 18.00 (978-0-9667747-1-9(X) , 1239658) Sorcerer's Pr., The.

MacMillan, Dianne M. The Curse of Rafferty Mcgill. Porfirio, Guy, illus. 2003. 72p. (J). (gr. 2-5). 13.95 (978-0-8075-3779-4(9)) Whitman, Albert & Co.

Magic Box. (ARA., Illus.). 100p. (YA). pap. 5.95 (978-0-86685-743-7(5) , LDL946) Librairie du Liban Pubns. FRA. Dist: International Bk. Ctr., Inc.

The Magic King. 2003. (J). (978-1-4120-3345-9(4)) Black Dot Pubns.

The Magic of Tobias Twissle. 2003. (J). lib. bdg. (978-0-9744923-0-8(2)) Purple Plume Pr.

The Magical Horses Vol. 2000: A Fairy Tale for the Young & the Young at Heart. l.t. ed. 2005. (Illus.). 127p. (J). per. (978-0-9738625-0-8(5)) Blue Cat Publishing.

Magical Max Makes Friends. 2005. (Adventures of Magical Max, Scarlet Feather & Little Lilly Woo-Woo Ser.). (Illus.). 16p. (J). (gr. k-4). 14.95 (978-0-9762408-0-8(7)) Lead Life Pr., LLC.

Magness, Lee. Silver Dasher. 2003. 164p. pap. 12.95 (978-0-595-29043-7(4)) iUniverse, Inc.

Magnificent Staff. The Road to Paradise. Clouche, Armelle, ed. Heyer, Marilee, illus. 2000. 88p. (J). (gr. 4-7). 16.95 (978-0-615-11546-7(2)) Armelle Prod.

Mahy, Margaret. Alchemy. (Illus.). 224p. (YA). 2003. (gr. 7-12). 16.95 (978-0-689-85053-0(0) , McElderry, Margaret K.); 2004. reprint ed. pap. 7.99 (978-0-689-85054-7(9) , Simon Pulse) Simon & Schuster Children's Publishing.

—Alchemy. 2004. 207p. (YA). (gr. 7-12). per. 16.75 (978-1-4176-3556-6(8)) Tandem Library Bks.

—Maddigan's Fantasia. 2007. 512p. (J). (gr. 5 up). 17.99 (978-1-4169-1812-7(4) , McElderry, Margaret K.) Simon & Schuster Children's Publishing.

Major, Roberta Olsen. The Prince in the Flower Bed. 2001. 147p. (YA). pap. 13.95 (978-1-59088-977-0(0)) Wings ePress, Inc.

—Royal Pains Bk. 4: The Bottle of DJINN. 2006. (YA). pap. 9.95 (978-1-59705-824-7(6)) Wings ePress, Inc.

Maloney, Peter. The Magic Hockey Stick. ed. 2001. (J). (gr. 1). spiral bd. (978-0-616-07240-0(6)); (gr. 2). spiral bd. (978-0-616-07241-7(4)) Canadian National Institute for the Blind/Institut National Canadien pour les Aveugles.

—The Magic Hockey Stick. 2001. (978-0-606-22510-6(2)) Tandem Library Bks.

Mammola-Koravos, Beth. Olivia's Magical Christmas. 2006. (J). pap. 16.95 (*978-1-59526-631-6(3)) Media Creations, Inc.

Man-Kong, Mary. Barbie & the Magic of Pegasus. 2006. (Illus.). 22p. (J). (gr. k-ps). bds. 4.99 (978-0-375-83539-1(3) , Golden Bks.) Random Hse. Children's Bks.

Man-Kong, Mary. The Magic of the Rainbow. 2008. 24p. (J). (gr. k-k). bds. 4.99 (*978-0-375-84796-7(0) , Golden Bks.) Random Hse., Inc.

Man-Kong, Mary & Golden Books Staff. The Magic of Pegasus: A Storybook. 2005. (Random House Pictureback Book Ser.). (Illus.). 24p. (J). (ps-2). pap. 3.99 (978-0-375-83337-3(4) , Golden Bks.) Random Hse. Children's Bks.

Mantell, Paul. Fight for Your Right. 2001. (Jersey Ser.: No. 7). (Illus.). 128p. (J). (gr. 3-7). reprint ed. pap. 4.99 (978-0-7868-4466-1(3)) Disney Pr.

Marillier, Juliet. Wildwood Dancing. 2008. 416p. (J). (gr. 7). pap. 9.99 (*978-0-375-84474-4(0) , Knopf Bks. for Young Readers) Random Hse. Children's Bks.

Marriotte, Jeff. Door to Alternity. 2001. (gr. 7-12). lib. bdg. 15.30 (978-0-613-63279-9(6)) Tandem Library Bks.

Marshall, Heidi Amenda. Petra's Adventure in Nievenheim. Marshall, Heidi Amenda, illus. l.t. ed. 2003. (Illus.). 57p. (J). per. 7.99 (978-0-9747445-0-6(6)) Landfall Co., The.

Martin, Ann M. On Christmas Eve. 160p. (J). 2007. pap. 5.99 (*978-0-439-74589-5(6) , Scholastic Paperbacks); 2006. (Illus.). pap. 15.99 (978-0-439-74588-8(8) , Scholastic) Scholastic, Inc.

Martin, Sharene. Lilah Birdsong's Original Little Perrytales. 2004. 49p. pap. 12.95 (978-1-4137-1367-1(X)) PublishAmerica, Inc.

Martineck, Michael J. The Misspellers. 2002. 150p. (J). (gr. 4-8). pap. 8.00 (978-0-9720978-0-2(5)) Our Little Secret Pr.

—The Wrong Channel. 2005. 160p. (J). (gr. 4-8). 8.00 (978-0-9720978-1-9(3)) Our Little Secret Pr.

Marvin Redpost: A Magic Crystal. 2002. (Marvin Redpost Ser.). (Illus.). (J). 11.91 (978-0-7587-6198-9(8)) Book Wholesalers, Inc.

Mason, Adrienne. The Carnival Caper. Cupples, Pat, illus. 2002. (Lu & Clancy Ser.). 40p. (J). (gr. k-3). (978-1-55074-838-3(6)); (978-1-55337-027-7(9)) Kids Can Pr., Ltd.

Mason, Jane B. & Stephens, Sarah Hines. Appley Ever After. 2005. (Princess School Ser.: No. 6). (Illus.). 128p. (J). (ps-7). pap. 4.99 (978-0-439-69814-6(6) , Scholastic Paperbacks) Scholastic, Inc.

Massie. The Secret of the Silver Shoes. 1999. (Illus.). pap. 6.20 (978-0-7398-0880-1(X)) Steck-Vaughn.

Masson, Sophie. Snow, Fire, Sword. 2006. 368p. (J). 15.99 (978-0-06-079091-2(1)); lib. bdg. 16.89 (978-0-06-079092-9(X)) HarperCollins Pubs.

Mayer, Mercer. Wizard Comes to Town. 2002. (gr. k-3). lib. bdg. 14.10 (978-0-613-86842-6(0)) Tandem Library Bks.

Mayfield, Julie. The Magical First Day. Reis, Michael, illus. 1998. (J). pap. 5.95 (978-1-56763-337-5(4)); lib. bdg. 17.25 (978-1-56763-336-8(6)) Ozark Publishing.

Mazer, Anne. Mabel Makes the Grade. 2007. (Sister Magic Ser.). 96p. (J). pap. 3.99 (*978-0-439-87248-5(0) , Scholastic Paperbacks) Scholastic, Inc.

—Sister Magic. 2007. (Sister Magic Ser.: Bk. 2). 112p. (J). pap. 3.99 (*978-0-439-87247-8(2)) Scholastic, Inc.

—The Trouble with Violet. Brown, Bill, illus. 2007. (Sister Magic Ser.: Bk. 1). 112p. (J). (gr. 2-4). pap. 4.99 (*978-0-439-87246-1(4)) Scholastic, Inc.

McAllister, Margaret. The Magic Porridge Pot. Utton, Peter, illus. 2006. 32p. (J). (*978-1-4048-3122-3(3)) Picture Window Bks.

McCafferty, Catherine. Rapunzel. Spong, Clive, illus. 2002. (Brighter Child Keepsake Stories Ser.). 32p. (J). (ps-3). pap. 3.99 (978-1-57768-379-7(X) , Brighter Child) School Specialty Publishing.

McCaffrey, Anne. An Exchange of Gifts. 2002. (YA). pap. 7.99 (978-1-880448-44-1(0)) Wildside Pr.

McCaffrey, Laura Williams. Water Shaper. 2006. 224p. (J). (gr. 5-9). 16.00 (978-0-618-61489-9(3) , Clarion Bks.) Houghton Mifflin Co. Trade & Reference Div.

McCaughrean, Geraldine. Peter Pan. 2006. 232p. pap. 17.95 (*978-958-704-467-6(3)) Alfaguara, Ediciones, S.A.-Grupo Santillana ESP. Dist: Santillana USA Publishing Co., Inc.

McClear, Preston. Old Man Brown & His Magic Bike. Dollak, Nicholas, illus. 1999. 30p. (J). (gr. k-5). 16.95 (978-1-929084-06-7(4)); pap. 12.95 (978-1-929084-07-4(2)) Malibu Bks. for Children.

McClintock, Barbara. Molly & the Magic Wishbone. abr. ed. 2002. (J). (gr. k-3). 26.95 incl. audio (978-0-8045-6888-3(X)) Spoken Arts, Inc.

McCombie, Karen. Marshmallow Magic & the Wild Rose Roug. l.t. ed. 2005. pap. 16.95 (978-1-4056-6036-5(8)) BBC Audio GBR. Dist: BBC Audiobooks America.

McConnell, Robert. Norbert Nipkin & the Magic Riddle Stone. Pilcher, Steve, illus. 2nd anniv. ed. 2004. 42p. (J). 20.95 (978-0-929141-79-4(2)) Napoleon Publishing/Rendezvous Pr. CAN. Dist: AtlasBooks Distribution.

Mccullagh, Sheila. Magic Griffle & Other Stories. 2007. (Tales from Puddle Lane Ser.). (Illus.). 96p. 19.95 (*978-1-84560-041-9(X)) Mercury Bks. Ltd. GBR. Dist: International Publishers Marketing.

—Magician of Puddle Lane & Other Stories. 2007. (Tales from Puddle Lane Ser.). (Illus.). 96p. 19.95 (*978-1-84560-040-2(1)) Mercury Bks. Ltd. GBR. Dist: International Publishers Marketing.

—Wideawake Mice & Other Stories. 2007. (Illus.). 96p. 19.95 (*978-1-84560-038-9(X)) Mercury Bks. Ltd. GBR. Dist: International Publishers Marketing.

—Wideawake Mice in Danger & Other Stories. 2007. (Tales from Puddle Lane Ser.). (Illus.). 96p. 19.95 (*978-1-84560-039-6(8)) Mercury Bks. Ltd. GBR. Dist: International Publishers Marketing.

McCutchen, Heather L. LightLand. (Illus.). 240p. (J). 2002. (gr. 3-7). pap. 16.95 (978-0-439-39565-6(8)); 2004. reprint ed. pap. 4.99 (978-0-439-39566-3(6)) Scholastic, Inc. (Orchard Bks.).

McDonald, Ann-Eve. The Tale of the Black Square. 2004. (J). (978-0-9770158-2-5(3)) BeachWalk Bks. Inc.

McElroy, B. Roland. The Great Mizzariddle. Smith, Donald A., ed. 1999. (Illus.). 32p. (J). (ps-6). pap. 6.95 (978-0-9673917-0-0(9)) McElroy & Assocs.

McGaw, Wayne T. T-Boy of the Bayou. Crespo, George, illus. 2003. 32p. (J). (ps-3). 15.95 (978-0-87614-648-4(5) , Carolrhoda Bks.) Lerner Publishing Group.

McKinty, Adrian. The Lighthouse Land. 2007. 416p. (YA). (gr. 7-17). pap. 7.95 (*978-0-8109-9361-7(9)) Abrams, Harry N. , Inc.

—The Lighthouse War. 2007. 403p. (J). (gr. 7-17). 16.95 (*978-0-8109-9354-9(6)) Abrams, Harry N. , Inc.

McMullan, Kate. Danger! Wizard at Work. Basso, Bill, illus. 2004. (Dragon Slayers' Academy Ser.: No. 11). 112p. (J). (gr. 2-5). pap. 4.99 (978-0-448-43529-9(2) , Grosset & Dunlap) Penguin Group (USA) Inc.

—The New Kid at School. 2003. (Dragon Slayers' Academy Ser.: No. 1). (gr. 3-6). lib. bdg. 13.00 (978-0-613-72614-6(6)) Tandem Library Bks.

McMullan, Kate & Basso, Bill, illus. The New Kid at School. 2003. (Dragon Slayers' Academy Ser.: No. 1). 112p. (J). (gr. 1-4). mass mkt. 4.99 (978-0-448-43108-6(4) , Grosset & Dunlap) Penguin Group (USA) Inc.

McOmber, Rachel B., ed. McOmber Phonics Storybooks: The Magic "E" rev. ed. (Illus.). (J). (978-0-944991-37-4(8)) Swift Learning Resources.

—McOmber Phonics Storybooks: The Neat Trick. rev. ed. (Illus.). (J). (978-0-944991-55-8(6)) Swift Learning Resources.

—McOmber Phonics Storybooks: The Prime Time Trick. rev. ed. (Illus.). (J). (978-0-944991-56-5(4)) Swift Learning Resources.

McPhail, David. Water Boy. 2007. (Illus.). (J). (ps-3). 32p. 15.95 (978-0-8109-1784-2(X)); (*978-1-4287-3988-8(2)) Abrams, Harry N. , Inc. (Abrams Bks. for Young Readers).

Mcshane, Pol. The Magic Elevator: The Adventures of Johnny & Joey. 2005. 129p. pap. 17.95 (978-1-4241-0014-9(3)) PublishAmerica, Inc.

Mead, Richelle. Vampire Academy. 2007. 336p. (J). (gr. 7). pap. 8.99 (*978-1-59514-174-3(X) , Razorbill) Penguin Group (USA) Inc.

Meadows, Daisy. Abigail the Breeze Fairy. 2006. (Weather Fairies Ser.: No. 2). (Illus.). 80p. (J). pap. 4.99 (978-0-439-81386-0(7) , Scholastic Paperbacks) Scholastic, Inc.

—Amy the Amethyst Fairy. 2007. (Jewel Fairies Ser.). 80p. (Orig.). (J). pap. 4.99 (*978-0-439-93532-6(6) , Scholastic Paperbacks) Scholastic, Inc.

—Chloe the Topaz Fairy. 2007. (Jewel Fairies Ser.: No. 4). 80p. (Orig.). (J). 4.99 (*978-0-439-93531-9(8)) Scholastic, Inc.

—Emily the Emerald Fairy. 2007. (Jewel Fairies Ser.: No. 3). 80p. (Orig.). (J). 4.99 (*978-0-439-93530-2(X)) Scholastic, Inc.

—India the Moonstone Fairy. 2007. (Jewel Fairies Ser.: No. 1). 80p. (Orig.). (J). 4.99 (*978-0-439-93528-9(8)) Scholastic, Inc.

—Lucy the Diamond Fairy. 2008. (Scholastic First Discovery Ser.: No. 7). 80p. (Orig.). (J). pap. 4.99 (*978-0-439-93534-0(2) , Scholastic Paperbacks) Scholastic, Inc.

—Rainbow Magic: Inky the Indigo Fairy. Ripper, Georgie, illus. 2006. (Rainbow Magic Ser.: No. 6). 80p. (J). pap. 4.99 (978-0-439-74685-4(X) , Scholastic Paperbacks) Scholastic, Inc.

—Sunny the Yellow Fairy. Ripper, Georgie, illus. 2005. (Rainbow Magic Ser.: No. 3). 70p. (J). 4.99 (978-0-439-74466-9(0)) Scholastic, Inc.

Meadows, Melissa. What's the Word, Thunderbird? (Illus.). 80p. (J). 2008. (ENG.). (*978-1-934517-01-7(1)); 2007. pap. 4.99 (*978-1-934517-00-0(3)) Firelight Press, Inc.

Meddaugh, Susan. Cinderella's Rat. Meddaugh, Susan, illus. 2002. (Illus.). 32p. (J). (gr. k-3). pap. 5.95 (978-0-618-12540-1(X) , Walter Lorraine) Houghton Mifflin Co. Trade & Reference Div.

—Cinderella's Rat. 2002. (gr. k-3). lib. bdg. 14.10 (978-0-613-72920-8(X)) Tandem Library Bks.

—The Witch's Walking Stick. 2005. (Illus.). 32p. (J). (gr. k-3). 16.00 (978-0-618-52948-3(9) , Walter Lorraine) Houghton Mifflin Co. Trade & Reference Div.

Melling, David. The Tale of Jack Frost. 2003. (Illus.). 32p. (J). 14.95 (978-0-7641-5675-5(6)) Barron's Educational Series, Inc.

Melling, O. R. The Hunter's Moon. 2005. (Chronicles of Faerie Ser.: No. 1). (Illus.). 296p. (J). (gr. 5-10). 16.95 (978-0-8109-5857-9(0)) Abrams, Harry N., Inc.

—Hunter's Moon. 2006. (Chronicles of Faerie Ser.: No. 1). 304p. (J). (gr. 5-10). pap. 7.95 (978-0-8109-9214-6(0)) Abrams, Harry N., Inc.

Mello, Alondra. Alanora's Magic Tree: Alanora's Spirit Journey. 2007. 48p. per. 12.97 (*978-1-932344-77-6(2)) Thornton Publishing.

Melmed, Laura Krauss. Moishe's Miracle: A Hanukkah Story. Slonim, David, illus. 2005. 32p. (J). (ps-3). pap. 6.95 (978-0-8118-5234-0(2)) Chronicle Bks. LLC.

—Moishe's Miracle: A Hanukkah Story. Slonim, David, illus. 2000. 32p. (J). (ps up). 15.95 (978-0-688-14682-5(1)); lib. bdg. 15.89 (978-0-688-14683-2(X)) HarperCollins Pubs.

Meredith Books Staff & Forlini, Victoria, eds. A Berry Picnic Surprise: Deluxe Sound Storybook. 2004. (Strawberry Shortcake Ser.). (ENG., Illus.). 22p. (J). (gr. k-3). 15.95 (978-0-696-22243-6(4)) Meredith Bks.

Merlin, Master. Wizardology: The Book of the Secrets of Merlin. Steer, Dugald, ed. Gilbert, Anne Yvonne et al, illus. gif. ed. 2005. (Ologies Ser.). 32p. (J). (gr. 3 up). 19.99 (978-0-7636-2895-6(6)) Candlewick Pr.

Merritt, Gail. Silver Mantle. 2002. (Illus.). 160p. (YA). pap. (978-0-7344-0177-9(9) , Lothian Bks.) Hachette Livre Australia.

—Silver Mantle. 2001. (gr. 7-12). lib. bdg. 22.20 (978-0-613-90916-7(X)) Tandem Library Bks.

Meyer, Kai. The Glass Word. Crawford, Elizabeth D., tr. from GER. 2008. (Dark Reflections Trilogy Ser.). 288p. (YA). (gr. 7 up). 16.99 (*978-0-689-87791-9(9) , McElderry, Margaret K.) Simon & Schuster Children's Publishing.

—Pirate Curse. Crawford, Elizabeth D., tr. from GER. 2006. (Wave Walkers Ser.). 336p. (J). (gr. 5-9). 15.95 (978-1-4169-2421-0(3) , McElderry, Margaret K.) Simon & Schuster Children's Publishing.

—The Stone Light. Crawford, Elizabeth D., tr. (Dark Reflections Trilogy Ser.). (YA). 2007. 384p. pap. 8.99 (*978-0-689-87790-2(0) , Simon Pulse); 2006. 368p. (gr. 7 up). 16.95 (978-0-689-87789-6(7) , McElderry, Margaret K.) Simon & Schuster Children's Publishing.

Meyer, Kai. The Water Mirror. Crawford, Elizabeth D., tr. 2006. (Dark Reflections Trilogy Ser.). 272p. (YA). pap. 7.99 (978-0-689-87788-9(9) , Simon Pulse); 2005. (Dark Reflections Ser.: Bk. 1). 256p. (J). (gr. 7 up). 15.95 (978-0-689-87787-2(0) , McElderry, Margaret K.) Simon & Schuster Children's Publishing.

—The Water Mirror. l.t. ed. 2006. 260p. (YA). 22.95 (978-0-7862-8288-3(6)) Thorndike Pr.

Meyer, Kai & Crawford, Elizabeth D. The Water Mirror. 2005. (J). (978-978-068-987-2(7) , McElderry, Margaret K.) Simon & Schuster Children's Publishing.

Mhlophe, Gcina. Our Story Magic. 2006. 100p. 29.95 (*978-1-86914-111-0(3)) Univ. of Natal Pr. ZAF. *Dist:* International Specialized Bk. Services.

Miller, Jennifer. Best Friends for Life. Choi Sung Hwan, Aragon Noel, illus. 2006. (Trollz Ser.). 120p. (J). pap. 4.99 (978-0-439-80311-3(X)) Scholastic, Inc.

Miller, Olive Beaupr. The Magic Garden of My Book House. 2005. reprint ed. pap. 24.95 (978-1-4191-4169-0(4)) Kessinger Publishing, LLC.

Mills, Lauren A. The Dog Prince. Mills, Lauren A. & Nolan, Dennis, illus. 2001. 32p. (J). (gr. 1-3). 15.95 (978-0-316-57417-4(1)) Little, Brown Bks. for Young Readers.

Mitchell, Stephen. Genies, Meanies, & Magic Rings: Three Tales from the 1001 Nights. Pohrt, Tom & Campbell Pearson, Tracey, illus. 2007. 192p. (J). 16.95 (*978-0-8027-9639-4(7)) Walker & Co.

Mitton, Tony & Rider, Cynthia. The Magic Porridge Pot. Shaw-Smith, Emma, illus. 2001. (Cambridge Reading Ser.). 16p. pap., stu. ed. 8.00 (978-0-521-01429-8(8)) Cambridge Univ. Pr.

Miyazaki, Hayao. Spirited Away. Orig. Title: Sen to Chihiro no kamikakushi. (gr. 3-6). 2003. lib. bdg. 18.75 (978-0-613-79014-7(6)); 2002. lib. bdg. 18.75 (978-0-613-79012-3(X)); 2002. lib. bdg. 18.75 (978-0-613-79013-0(8)); 2002. lib. bdg. 18.75 (978-0-613-79011-6(1)) Tandem Library Bks.

—Spirited Away. Miyazaki, Hayao, illus. (Spirited Away Ser.). Orig. Title: Sen to Chihiro no kamikakushi. (Illus.). (YA). Vol. 1. 2002. 172p. pap. 9.95 (978-1-56931-791-4(7)); Vol. 2. 2002. 172p. pap. 9.95 (978-1-56931-792-1(5)); Vol. 3. 2003. 172p. pap. 9.95 (978-1-56931-793-8(3)); Vol. 4. 2003. 172p. pap. 9.95 (978-1-56931-794-5(1)); Vol. 5. 2003. 184p. pap. 9.95 (978-1-56931-795-2(X)) Viz Media.

Mlynowski, Sarah. Frogs & French Kisses. (gr. 7). 2007. 304p. (YA). pap. 8.99 (*978-0-385-73185-0(X)); 2006. (Illus.). 288p. (J). 15.95 (978-0-385-73182-9(5)); 2006. (Illus.). 288p. (YA). lib. bdg. 17.99 (978-0-385-90219-9(0)) Random Hse. Children's Bks. (Delacorte Bks. for Young Readers).

Moffit, Linda L. The Magic Mirror. 2003. (Illus.). 80p. (Orig.). (gr. k-7). 10.95 (978-0-87516-615-5(6) , Devorss Pubns.) DeVorss & Co.

Molesworth, Mary Louisa. The Cuckoo Clock. 2004. reprint ed. pap. 19.95 (978-1-4191-5839-1(2)); pap. 1.99 (978-1-4192-5839-8(7)) Kessinger Publishing, LLC.

Molloy, Michael. The House on Falling Star Hill. 2004. (Illus.). 384p. (J). pap. 16.95 (978-0-439-57740-3(3) , Chicken Hse., The) Scholastic, Inc.

Moody, Betty G. Magical Wish. 1998. (Illus.). (J). 15.95 (978-0-9663522-1-4(1)) Character Lines Publishing.

Moon, Grace. The Magic Trail. Moon, Carl, illus. 2004. reprint ed. pap. 26.95 (978-1-4179-4224-4(X)) Kessinger Publishing, LLC.

Mooney, E. S. Cartoon Crazy. 2000. (gr. k-3). lib. bdg. 11.80 (978-0-613-32373-4(4)) Tandem Library Bks.

—Teacher's Pest, No. 5. Maher, Alex, illus. 2001. (Powerpuff Girls Chapter Bks.: Vol. 5). 64p. (J). (ps-2). pap. 3.99 (978-0-439-24325-4(4)) Scholastic, Inc.

Moore, Clement C. Magie de Noel. pap. 16.95 (978-2-07-054886-6(4)) Gallimard, Editions FRA. *Dist:* Distribooks, Inc.

Moran, Maggie A. The Magic in Me. Sasaki, Chie, illus. 2002. 28p. (J). 14.95 (978-1-931642-02-6(8)) New Voices Publishing Co.

Morden, Daniel. Weird Tales from the Storyteller. Jones, Jac, tr. Jones, Jac, illus. 2003. 64p. pap. 12.95 (978-1-84323-210-0(3)) Beekman Bks., Inc.

Morgan, Melissa J. Charmed Forces No. 19: Super Special. 2008. (Camp Confidential Ser.). 256p. (J). (gr. 4-7). 5.99 (*978-0-448-44722-3(3) , Grosset & Dunlap) Penguin Group (USA) Inc.

Morgan, Nikki. Mithendrove: Escaping Callendae. 2003. 110p. (YA). pap. 9.95 (978-0-595-27138-2(3)) iUniverse, Inc.

Moriarty, Jaclyn. The Spell Book of Listen Taylor. 2007. (YA). (*978-0-439-84679-0(X)); 496p. (J). (gr. 9 up). 16.99 (*978-0-439-84678-3(1)) Scholastic, Inc. (Levine, Arthur A. Bks.).

Morpurgo, Michael. The Butterfly Lion. 2000. (Illus.). (J). pap. 4.99 (978-0-14-038550-2(9) , Puffin) Penguin Group (USA) Inc.

Morressy, John. Juggler. 1998. (978-0-606-13545-0(6)) Tandem Library Bks.

Morris, Gerald. The Princess, the Crone, & the Dung-Cart Knight. (Squire's Tales Ser.). 320p. (YA). (gr. 5-9). 2006. pap. 6.95 (978-0-618-73748-2(0)); 2004. tchr. ed. 16.00 (978-0-618-37823-4(5)) Houghton Mifflin Co. Trade & Reference Div.

—The Savage Damsel & the Dwarf. (Squire's Tales Ser.). 224p. (gr. 5-9). 2004. (YA). pap. 5.95 (978-0-618-19681-4(1)); 2000. (J). tchr. ed. 16.00 (978-0-395-97126-0(8)) Houghton Mifflin Co. Trade & Reference Div.

—The Squire & His Knight. l.t. ed. 2001. (Illus.). 257p. (J). (gr. 4-7). 21.95 (978-0-7862-3039-6(8)) Thorndike Pr.

—The Squire, His Knight, & His Lady. 1999. (Squire's Tales Ser.). 240p. (J). (gr. 5-9). tchr. ed. 16.00 (978-0-395-91211-9(3)) Houghton Mifflin Co. Trade & Reference Div.

—The Squire's Tale. 1998. (Squire's Tales Ser.). 224p. (J). (gr. 5-9). tchr. ed. 16.00 (978-0-395-86959-8(5)) Houghton Mifflin Co. Trade & Reference Div.

—Squire's Tale. 2000. (978-0-606-17839-6(2)) Tandem Library Bks.

Morrissey, Dean. The Christmas Ship. 2000. (Illus.). 40p. (J). (gr. k-4). 16.89 (978-0-06-028576-0(1)) HarperCollins Pubs.

—Christmas Ship. 2000. (gr. k-3). lib. bdg. 14.15 (978-0-613-68414-9(1)) Tandem Library Bks.

Morrissey, Dean & Krensky, Stephen. The Moon Robber. 2001. (Magic Door Ser.). (Illus.). 64p. (J). (gr. 2-5). pap. 5.95 (978-0-06-442113-3(9) , Harper Trophy) HarperCollins Pubs.

Morse, Scott. Magic Pickle vs. the Egg Poacher. 2008. 144p. (J). pap. 5.99 (*978-0-439-87997-2(3) , Graphix) Scholastic, Inc.

Mortenson, R. K. Landon Snow & the Auctors Kingdom # 5. 2007. (Landon Snow Ser.). 224p. (J). 9.97 (*978-1-59789-297-1(1)) Barbour Publishing, Inc.

Mortimer, Sheila. Finn & the Magic Harp. Catchpole, Diana, illus. 2004. (J). 10.95 (978-0-7171-3767-1(8)) Gill & MacMillan, Ltd. IRL. *Dist:* Irish Bks. & Media, Inc.

Moshonas, Spyridon. Escape from Argopoli. 2002. 108p. pap. 16.95 (978-1-59129-661-4(7)) PublishAmerica, Inc.

Mosley, Walter. 47. 240p. (gr. 7-17). 2005. (YA). 16.99 (978-0-316-11035-8(3)); 2006. (J). reprint ed. pap. 7.99 (978-0-316-01635-3(7)) Little Brown & Co.

Mudenda, Duly & Nagunga, Kansi. Syankombo. 2004. (Illus.). 20p. 16.95 (978-1-77936-005-2(3)) Africa Community Publishing & Development Trust ZWE. *Dist:* Michigan State Univ. Pr.

Mull, Brandon. The Candy Shop War. 2007. 358p. (YA). (gr. 4 up). 17.95 (*978-1-59038-783-2(X) , Shadow Mountain) Deseret Bk. Co.

—Fablehaven. 2006. (Illus.). 368p. (J). 16.95 (978-1-59038-581-4(0) , Shadow Mountain) Deseret Bk. Co.

—Fablehaven. Dorman, Brandon, illus. 2007. (Fablehaven Ser.). 368p. (J). pap. 6.99 (*978-1-4169-4720-2(5) , Aladdin) Simon & Schuster Children's Publishing.

—Fablehaven: Rise of the Evening Star. 2007. 456p. 17.95 (*978-1-59038-742-9(2) , Shadow Mountain) Deseret Bk. Co.

Muller, Rachel Dunstan. When the Curtain Rises. 2007. 144p. (J). (gr. 4-7). pap. (*978-1-55143-615-9(9)) Orca Bk. Pubs.

Muneefa. My Tales for Children. 2006. 90p. (J). pap. 13.95 (978-1-58909-339-3(9)) Bookstand Publishing.

Myers, Bill. Curse. 2002. (gr. 3-6). lib. bdg. 13.00 (978-0-613-76881-8(7)) Tandem Library Bks.

Myers, Tim. The Furry-Legged Teapot: A Unique Retelling. McGuire, Robert, illus. 2007. (J). 16.99 (978-0-7614-5295-9(8)) Cavendish, Marshall Corp.

Nahu. Dolphina's World: And Other Stories. 2006. 80p. pap. 12.95 (978-1-59800-178-5(7)) Outskirts Press, Inc.

Naidu, Vayu. Magic Vessels. 1998. (Under the Banyan Ser.). (Illus.). 22p. (YA). (gr. 2 up). 11.99 incl. audio (978-81-86838-29-7(5)) APG Sales and Fulfillment.

Naifeh, Ted. Courtney Crumrin & the Night Things, 2 vols., Vol. 1. Jones, James Lucas, ed. 2nd ed. 2003. (Courtney Crumrin Ser.: Vol. 1). (Illus.). 128p. (YA). pap. 11.95 (978-1-929998-60-9(0)) Oni Pr., Inc.

—Courtney Crumrin & the Night Things. Jones, James Lucas, ed. 2005. (Illus.). 120p. lib. bdg. 19.00 (978-0-606-33365-8(7)) Tandem Library Bks.

Nakagawa, Rieko. Guri & Gura's Magical Friend. Yamawaki, Yuriko, illus. 2003. 32p. 10.95 (978-0-8048-3356-1(7)) Tuttle Publishing.

Namy, Verna. Ali Baba & His Magical Pajamas. Martin, Mary, illus. 1998. 38p. (J). (ps-12). pap. 7.95 (978-0-944851-15-9(0)) Earth Star Pubns.

Napoli, Donna Jo. Breath. 2003. (Illus.). 272p. (YA). 17.95 (978-0-689-86174-1(5) , Atheneum) Simon & Schuster Children's Publishing.

—Breath. l.t. ed. 2005. 251p. 21.95 (978-0-7862-7420-8(4) , Large Print Pr.) Thorndike Pr.

—Crazy Jack. 2001. 12.15 (978-0-606-20617-4(5)) Tandem Library Bks.

—Gracie: The Pixie of the Puddle. Schachner, Judith B., illus. 2004. 160p. (J). (gr. 3). 16.99 (978-0-525-47264-3(9) , Dutton Juvenile) Penguin Group (USA) Inc.

Nash, Mary. Lost Treasures Bk. 2: Mrs. Coverlet's Magician. 2001. 128p. (J). 13.49 (978-0-7868-2597-4(9)) Hyperion Pr.

Nathan, Sarah. A Dream Come True. 2007. 32p. (gr. 1). pap. 3.99 (*978-1-4231-0909-9(0)) Disney Pr.

—Enchanted Storybook. rev. ed. 2007. 48p. (J). (gr. 2-7). 8.99 (*978-1-4231-0911-2(2)) Disney Pr.

Nazemi, Mary. Kaveh, Jolly & the Super Giant. 2006. (J). pap. 15.00 (978-0-8059-7001-2(0)) Dorrance Publishing Co., Inc.

Neff, Henry H. The Hound of Rowan. 2007. (Tapestry Ser.: Bk. 1). (Illus.). 414p. (J). (gr. 3-7). 17.99 (978-0-375-83894-1(5) , Random Hse. Bks. for Young Readers) Random Hse. Children's Bks.

—The Hound of Rowan. Neff, Henry H., illus. 2007. (Tapestry Ser.: Bk. 1). (Illus.). 414p. (J). (gr. 3-7). lib. bdg. 20.99 (978-0-375-93894-8(X) , Random Hse. Bks. for Young Readers) Random Hse. Children's Bks.

—The Hound of Rowan. 2007. (J). pap. (978-0-375-83895-8(3)) Random Hse., Inc.

Negrin, Fabian, illus. Wizard Tales. 2003. 96p. 19.95 (978-1-55285-558-4(9)) Whitecap Bks., Ltd. CAN. *Dist:* Graphic Arts Ctr. Publishing Co.

Nelson, Brett Alan. The Magical Forest. Ueda, Kumiko, illus. 2003. 42p. (J). (978-0-9655078-7-5(4)) Windsong Publishing Co.

Nelson, S. D. Coyote's Christmas: A Lakota Story. 2007. (Illus.). 40p. (J). (gr. k-4). 15.95 (*978-0-8109-9367-9(8) , Abrams Bks. for Young Readers) Abrams, Harry N., Inc.

Nesbit, E. The Enchanted Castle. l.t. ed. 2005. 388p. pap. (978-1-84637-202-5(X)) Echo Library.

—Five Children & IT. Zelinsky, Paul O., illus. 1999. (Books of Wonder). 256p. (gr. 4-7). 22.95 (978-0-688-13545-4(5)) HarperCollins Pubs.

—The House of Arden. 2006. (New York Review Children's Collection). 248p. (J). (gr. 3). 17.95 (978-1-59017-202-5(7) , NYR Children's Collection) New York Review of Bks., Inc., The.

—Lionel & the Book of Beasts. Hague, Michael, illus. 2006. 48p. (J). (gr. 2-4). lib. bdg. 17.89 (978-0-06-084272-7(5)); 16.99 (978-0-688-14006-9(8)) HarperCollins Pubs.

Nesbit, E. Phoenix & the Carpet. 2006. pap. (*978-1-4068-3504-5(8)) Echo Library.

Newman, Robert. Lost Treasures Bk. 5: Merlin's Mistake. 2001. 240p. (J). 13.49 (978-0-7868-2600-1(2)) Hyperion Pr.

Newton, Astora. Fabulous Friends! 2003. (Color Plus Ser.). (Illus.). 32p. (J). (ps-3). pap. 4.99 (978-0-7364-2081-5(9) , Golden/Disney) Random Hse. Children's Bks.

Nicholetti, Terry & Campbell, Annie. Noralee's Adventures on Planet Ifwee. 2002. pap. 10.95 (978-0-9716488-0-7(8)) Goldstar Magic.

Nimmo, Jenny. Charlie Bone & the Hidden King. 2006. (Children of the Red King Ser.: Bk. 5). xx, 441p. (J). (*978-1-4156-7832-9(4) , Orchard Bks.) Scholastic, Inc.

—Charlie Bone & the Invisible Boy. 2004. (Children of the Red King Ser.: Bk. 3). (Illus.) 432p. (J). 9.95 (978-0-439-54526-6(9) , Orchard Bks.) Scholastic, Inc.

—The Chestnut Soldier. 2007. (Snow Spider Trilogy: Bk. 3). 208p. (J). (gr. 4-7). 9.99 (978-0-439-84677-6(3) , Orchard Bks.) Scholastic, Inc.

—Emlyn's Moon. 2007. (Snow Spider Trilogy: Bk. 2). 176p. (J). (gr. 4-7). 9.99 (978-0-439-84676-9(5) , Orchard Bks.) Scholastic, Inc.

—Midnight for Charlie Bone. 2003. (Children of the Red King Ser.: Bk. 1). (J). (gr. 2-6). per. 4.99 (978-0-439-48839-6(7)); 416p. (gr. 4-6). 9.95 (978-0-439-47429-0(9) , Orchard Bks.) Scholastic, Inc.

—The Snow Spider. 2006. (Snow Spider Trilogy: Bk. 1). (J). 39.95 (978-0-439-89844-7(7)); 160p. (gr. 3-7). 9.99 (978-0-439-84675-2(7) , Orchard Bks.) Scholastic, Inc.

Nishimori, Hiroyuki. Cheeky Angel, Volume 17. 2007. (Cheeky Angel Ser.). 192p. (YA). pap. 9.99 (978-1-4215-0886-3(9)) Viz Media.

Nister, Ernest. Magic Windows. (Illus.). (J). (978-0-399-22355-6(X) , Philomel) Penguin Group (USA) Inc.

Nix, Garth. Across the Wall: A Tale of the Abhorsen & Other Stories. 2006. 432p. (J). pap. 7.99 (978-0-06-074715-2(3)) HarperCollins Pubs.

—The Keys to the Kingdom, 3 bks., Set. Incl. Drowned Wednesday. 400p. pap. 15.95 (978-0-439-70086-3(8)); Grim Tuesday. 336p. pap. 15.95 (978-0-439-70370-3(0) , Scholastic Pr.); (J). (gr. 4-7). 2005. 2006. 47.85 (978-0-439-78080-3(2) , Scholastic Pr.) Scholastic, Inc.

—Lirael: Daughter of the Clayr. (Old Kingdom Ser.: No. 2). (gr. 7 up). 2002. 720p. pap. 7.99 (978-0-06-000542-9(4) , Harper Trophy); 2001. (Illus.). 496p. (YA). 18.99 (978-0-06-027823-6(4)) HarperCollins Pubs.

—Lirael: Daughter of the Clayr. 2002. (Old Kingdom Ser.: No. 2). (gr. 7-12). lib. bdg. 15.30 (978-0-613-62468-8(8)) Tandem Library Bks.

—Sir Thursday. (Keys to the Kingdom Ser.: No. 4). 352p. (J). 2007. pap. 6.99 (*978-0-439-43657-1(5) , Scholastic Paperbacks); 2006. (gr. 4-7). pap. 16.99 (978-0-439-70087-0(6) , Scholastic Pr.) Scholastic, Inc.

Nix, Garth. The Violet Keystone. 2001. (Seventh Tower Ser.: Bk. 6). 233p. (gr. 3-6). lib. bdg. 13.00 (978-0-613-43905-3(8)) Tandem Library Bks.

Nixon, Joan Lowery. A Deadly Game of Magic. 2004. 240p. (YA). pap. 5.95 (978-0-15-205030-6(2) , Harcourt Paperbacks) Harcourt Children's Bks.

—A Deadly Game of Magic. 2004. (gr. 7-12). lib. bdg. 14.10 (978-0-613-71631-4(0)) Tandem Library Bks.

Nolan, Lucy A. A Fairy in a Dairy. Bryant, Laura J., illus. 2003. 32p. (J). 16.95 (978-0-7614-5130-3(7)) Cavendish, Marshall Corp.

Noland, Charles. The Adventures of Drew & Ellie: The Daring Rescue. Moyer, Tom, illus. 2nd ed. 2006. (J). per. 7.95 (*978-0-9789297-2-5(1)) TMD Enterprises.

Norac, Carl. My Mommy Is Magic. Godon, Ingrid, illus. 2007. 32p. (J). (ps-k). 16.00 (978-0-618-75766-4(X) , Clarion Bks.) Houghton Mifflin Co. Trade & Reference Div.

Norris, Christine. Talisman of Zandria, 1. Nagy, Robert, illus. 2005. 187p. (YA). pap. 14.95 (978-1-885093-44-8(6) , LBF/Hadrosaur) Hadrosaur Pr.

Norton, Andre. Fur Magic: The Magic Books #3. 2006. (Magic Bks.). 160p. (J). 5.99 (978-0-7653-5299-6(0) , Starscape) Doherty, Tom Assocs., LLC.

—Octagon Magic. 2005. (Magic Bks.: No. 2). 192p. (J). (gr. 5). 5.99 (978-0-7653-5298-9(2) , Starscape) Doherty, Tom Assocs., LLC.

—Steel Magic. 2005. (Magic Bks.: Bk. 1). 128p. (J). 5.99 (978-0-7653-5297-2(4) , Starscape) Doherty, Tom Assocs., LLC.

Norton, Mary. Bedknob & Broomstick. 2000. 12.65 (978-0-606-20322-7(2)); (J). (978-0-606-20159-9(9)); (gr. 3-6). lib. bdg. 14.15 (978-0-613-29886-5(1)) Tandem Library Bks.

Novak, Joseph. Day of Magic. 2003. pap. 7.95 (978-0-533-14349-8(7)) Vantage Pr., Inc.

Nugent, Cynthia. Francesca & the Magic Bike. 2005. (Illus.). 200p. (J). pap. 7.95 (978-1-55192-561-5(3)) Raincoast Bk. Distribution CAN. *Dist:* Perseus Distribution.

—Francesca & the Magic Bike Teacher Guide. 2005. 4p. (J). pap. (978-1-55192-825-8(6)) Raincoast Bk. Distribution CAN. *Dist:* Transition Vendor.

O'Connor, Ilett. Alexandra & the Blue Button. Kahn, Alisha, illus. Wells, Wadell, photos by. 2002. 32p. pap. 10.00 (978-0-9717003-0-7(3)) O'Connor, Ilett K.

—The Dancer 2 Cristina & the Magic Ball. unabr. ed. 2002. 45p. (J). pap. 12.00 (978-0-9717003-5-2(4)) O'Connor, Ilett K.

Ogilvy, Ian. Measle & the Dragodon. 2006. 352p. (J). pap. 6.99 (978-0-06-058690-4(7) , Harper Trophy) HarperCollins Pubs.

—Measle & the Mallockee. 2006. 384p. (J). 15.99 (978-0-06-058691-1(5)) HarperCollins Pubs.

Oldfield, Jenny. Bright Eyes 3. 2007. (Illus.). 144p. pap. 6.95 (*978-0-340-91075-7(5)) Hodder Children's Division GBR. *Dist:* Independent Pubs. Group.

—Dawn Light. 2007. (Illus.). 128p. pap. 6.95 (*978-0-340-91078-8(X)) Hodder Children's Division GBR. *Dist:* Independent Pubs. Group.

—Midnight Snow 4. 2007. (Illus.). 128p. pap. 6.95 (*978-0-340-91076-4(3)) Hodder Children's Division GBR. *Dist:* Independent Pubs. Group.

—Sea Haze. 2008. (Illus.). 144p. pap. 6.95 (*978-0-340-91842-5(X)) Hodder Children's Division GBR. *Dist:* Independent Pubs. Group.

—Shining Star. 2007. (My Magical Pony Ser.). (Illus.). 128p. (J). pap. 6.95 (*978-0-340-90323-0(6)) Hodder Children's Division GBR. *Dist:* Independent Pubs. Group.

—Silver Mist 2. 2007. (Illus.). 144p. pap. 6.95 (*978-0-340-90324-7(4)) Hodder Children's Division GBR. *Dist:* Independent Pubs. Group.

—Summer Shadows 5. 2007. (Illus.). 128p. pap. 6.95 (*978-0-340-91077-1(1)) Hodder Children's Division GBR. *Dist:* Independent Pubs. Group.

O'Leary-Coggins, Annette C. Nanny Reilly. 2007. 116p. per. 10.95 (*978-0-595-44994-1(8)) iUniverse, Inc.

Oliver, Mark Herren. Trish & the Wishing Star. 2006. (ENG.). 32p. per. 18.65 (*978-1-4134-9402-0(1)) Xlibris Corp.

Oracle of the Horses. 2005. (YA). per. (978-0-615-12836-8(X)) Miller, Don G.

Oryan, Ellie. Winx Club Magical Magix. MacKenzie, Kevin, illus. 2005. (Winx Club Ser.). 32p. (J). (ps-k). pap. 4.99 (978-0-439-74421-8(0)) Scholastic, Inc.

Osborne, Mary Pope. Blizzard of the Blue Moon. Murdocca, Sal, illus. 2007. (Magic Tree House Ser.: No. 36). 144p. (J). (gr. 2-5). pap. 4.99 (978-0-375-83038-9(3) , Random Hse. Bks. for Young Readers) Random Hse. Children's Bks.

—Blizzard of the Blue Moon. 2006. (Magic Tree House Ser.: No. 36). (Illus.). 128p. (J). (gr. k-3). lib. bdg. 13.99 (978-0-375-93037-9(X)); (gr. 2-5). 11.95 (978-0-375-83037-2(5)) Random Hse. Children's Bks. (Random Hse. Bks. for Young Readers).

—Buffalo Before Breakfast. 2004. (Magic Tree House Ser. : No. 18). 72p. (J). (gr. k-3). pap. 17.00 incl. audio (978-0-8072-0927-1(9) , Listening Library) Random Hse. Audio Publishing Group.

—Buffalo Before Breakfast. Murdocca, Sal, illus. 1999. (Magic Tree House Ser.: No. 18). (J). (gr. k-3). 20.00 (978-0-375-80041-2(7)); 96p. lib. bdg. 11.99 (978-0-679-99064-2(X)); Vol. 18. 96p. mass mkt. 3.99 (978-0-679-89064-5(5)) Random Hse. Children's Bks. (Random Hse. Bks. for Young Readers).

MNO

—Buffalo Before Breakfast. Murdocca, Salvatore, illus. 1999. (Magic Tree House Ser.: No. 18). 72p. (J). (gr. k-3). lib. bdg. 11.80 (978-0-613-16067-4(3)) Tandem Library Bks.

—Buffalo Before Breakfast. 1999. (Magic Tree House Ser. ; No. 18). (J). (gr. k-3). lib. bdg. 10.79 (978-0-606-16841-0(9)) Tandem Library Bks.

—Carnival at Candlelight. 2006. (Magic Tree House Ser.: No. 33). (Illus.). 144p. (J). (gr. 2-6). pap. 4.99 (978-0-375-83034-1(0) , Random Hse. Bks. for Young Readers) Random Hse. Children's Bks.

—Christmas in Camelot. Murdocca, Sal, illus. 2001. (Magic Tree House Ser.: No. 29). 128p. (J). (gr. k-3). 11.95 (978-0-375-81373-3(X)); lib. bdg. 13.99 (978-0-375-91373-0(4)) Random Hse. Children's Bks. (Random Hse. Bks. for Young Readers).

—Civil War on Sunday, Vol. 21. unabr. ed. 2004. (Magic Tree House Ser. : No. 21). 76p. (J). (gr. k-3). pap. 17.00 incl. audio (978-0-8072-0930-1(9) , S FTR 253 SP, Listening Library) Random Hse. Audio Publishing Group.

—Civil War on Sunday. Murdocca, Sal, illus. 2000. (Magic Tree House Ser.: No. 21). 96p. (J). (gr. k-3). lib. bdg. 11.99 (978-0-679-99067-3(4)); mass mkt. 3.99 (978-0-679-89067-6(X)) Random Hse. Children's Bks. (Random Hse. Bks. for Young Readers).

—Civil War on Sunday. 2000. (Magic Tree House Ser. : No. 21). (J). (gr. k-3). lib. bdg. 11.80 (978-0-613-24596-8(2)); (Illus.). 10.79 (978-0-606-18852-4(5)) Tandem Library Bks.

—Dark Day in the Deep Sea. Murdocca, Sal, illus. 2008. (Stepping Stone Bks.). 128p. (J). (gr. 3-7). lib. bdg. 14.99 (*978-0-375-93731-6(5)* , Random Hse. Bks. for Young Readers) Random Hse. Children's Bks.

—Day of the Dragon King, Vol. 14. unabr. ed. 2004. (Magic Tree House Ser. : No. 14). 68p. (J). (gr. k-3). pap. 17.00 incl. audio (978-0-8072-0783-3(7) , S FTR 242 SP, Listening Library) Random Hse. Audio Publishing Group.

—Day of the Dragon King. Murdocca, Sal, illus. 1998. (Magic Tree House Ser.: No. 14). 96p. (J). (gr. k-3). lib. bdg. 11.99 (978-0-679-99051-2(8)); 14th ed. pap. 3.99 (978-0-679-89051-5(3)) Random Hse. Children's Bks. (Random Hse. Bks. for Young Readers).

—Day of the Dragon King. Murdocca, Sal, illus. 1998. (Magic Tree House Ser. : No. 14). (J). (gr. k-3). 10.79 (978-0-606-13958-8(3)) Tandem Library Bks.

—Dinosaurs Before Dark. unabr. ed. 2004. (Magic Tree House Ser. : No. 1). 68p. (J). (gr. k-5). pap. 17.00 incl. audio (978-0-8072-0330-9(0) , FTR208SP, Listening Library) Random Hse. Audio Publishing Group.

—Dragon of the Red Dawn. Murdocca, Sal, illus. 2007. (Magic Tree House Ser.: No. 37). 128p. (J). (gr. k-3). 11.99 (978-0-375-83727-2(2) , Random Hse. Bks. for Young Readers) Random Hse. Children's Bks.

—Dragon of the Red Dawn. Murdocca, Sal, illus. 2007. (Magic Tree House Ser.: No. 37). 108p. (J). (gr. k-3). pap. (978-0-375-83728-9(0)) Random Hse., Inc.

—Earthquake in the Early Morning, Vol. 24. unabr. ed. 2004. (Magic Tree House Ser. : No. 24). 71p. (J). (gr. k-3). pap. 17.00 incl. audio (978-0-8072-0933-2(3) , S FTR 256 SP, Listening Library) Random Hse. Audio Publishing Group.

—Earthquake in the Early Morning. Murdocca, Sal, illus. 2001. (Magic Tree House Ser.: No. 24). 96p. (J). (gr. k-3). 11.99 (978-0-679-99070-3(4)); mass mkt. 3.99 (978-0-679-89070-6(X)) Random Hse. Children's Bks. (Random Hse. Bks. for Young Readers).

—Earthquake in the Early Morning. 2001. (Magic Tree House Ser. : No. 24). (J). (gr. k-3). lib. bdg. 11.80 (978-0-613-35684-8(5)); (Illus.). 10.79 (978-0-606-21166-6(7)) Tandem Library Bks.

—Ghost Town at Sundown. unabr. ed. 2004. (Magic Tree House Ser. : No. 10). 73p. (J). (gr. k-3). pap. 17.00 incl. audio (978-0-8072-0535-8(4) , Listening Library) Random Hse. Audio Publishing Group.

—Haunted Castle on Hallows Eve. Murdocca, Sal, illus. 2003. (Magic Tree House Ser.: No. 30). 128p. (J). (gr. k-3). 11.95 (978-0-375-82521-7(5)); lib. bdg. 13.99 (978-0-375-92521-4(X)) Random Hse. Children's Bks. (Random Hse. Bks. for Young Readers).

—High Tide in Hawaii. Murdocca, Sal, illus. 2003. (Magic Tree House Ser.: No. 28). 96p. (J). (gr. k-3). lib. bdg. 11.99 (978-0-375-90616-9(9)); (gr. 1-4). pap. 3.99 (978-0-375-80616-2(4)) Random Hse. Children's Bks. (Random Hse. Bks. for Young Readers).

—High Tide in Hawaii. 2003. (Magic Tree House Ser. : No. 28). (J). (gr. k-3). lib. bdg. 11.80 (978-0-613-62386-5(X)) Tandem Library Bks.

—Hour of the Olympics. unabr. ed. 2004. (Magic Tree House Ser. : No. 16). 70p. (J). (gr. k-3). pap. 17.00 incl. audio (978-0-8072-0785-7(3) , LFTR 244 SP, Listening Library) Random Hse. Audio Publishing Group.

—Hour of the Olympics. Murdocca, Sal, illus. 1998. (Magic Tree House Ser.: No. 16). 96p. (J). (gr. k-3). lib. bdg. 11.99 (978-0-679-99062-8(3)); mass mkt. 3.99 (978-0-679-89062-1(9)) Random Hse. Children's Bks. (Random Hse. Bks. for Young Readers).

—The Knight at Dawn. unabr. ed. 2004. (Magic Tree House Ser. : No. 2). 66p. (J). (gr. k-3). pap. 17.00 incl. audio (978-0-8072-0331-6(9) , Listening Library) Random Hse. Audio Publishing Group.

—The Knight at Dawn Book & CD. Murdocca, Sal, illus. 2008. (Stepping Stone Book(TM) Ser.). (J). (gr. k-3). 9.99 (*978-0-375-84406-5(6)* , Random Hse. Bks. for Young Readers) Random Hse. Children's Bks.

—Magic Tree House #1-4, 4 bks., Vol. 1-4. Murdocca, Sal, illus. 2001. (J). (gr. 1-3). pap. 15.96 (978-0-375-81365-8(9) , Random Hse. Bks. for Young Readers) Random Hse. Children's Bks.

—Magic Tree House #5-8, Bks. 5-8. 2002. (Illus.). (J). (ps-3). pap. 15.96 (978-0-375-82266-7(6) , Random Hse. Bks. for Young Readers) Random Hse. Children's Bks.

—Magic Treehouse Goes to America. 1999. (J). pap. (978-0-679-88608-2(7) , Random Hse. Bks. for Young Readers) Random Hse. Children's Bks.

—Magische Baumhaus der Ruf. 18.95 (978-3-7855-4185-2(6)) Loewe Verlag GmbH DEU. *Dist:* Distribooks, Inc.

—Midnight on the Moon, Vol. 8. unabr. ed. 2004. (Magic Tree House Ser. : No. 8). 70p. (J). (gr. k-3). pap. 17.00 incl. audio (978-0-8072-0341-5(6) , Listening Library) Random Hse. Audio Publishing Group.

—Una Momia en la Manana. 2004. (Coleccion la Casa Del Arbol the Magic Tree House Ser.). (SPA.). (J). pap. 4.95 (978-1-930332-51-5(3)) Lectorum Pubns., Inc.

—Una Momia en la Manana. 2003. (SPA.). (gr. 3-6). lib. bdg. 12.95 (978-0-613-64609-3(6)) Tandem Library Bks.

—Monday with a Mad Genius. Murdocca, Sal, illus. 2007. (Stepping Stone Bks.). 128p. (J). (gr. 2-6). 11.99 (*978-0-375-83729-6(9)*); lib. bdg. 14.99 (*978-0-375-93729-3(3)*) Random Hse. Children's Bks. (Random Hse. Bks. for Young Readers).

—Monday with a Mad Genius. Murdocca, Sal, illus. 2007. (J). pap. (*978-0-375-83730-2(2)*) Random Hse., Inc.

—Night of the New Magicians. Murdocca, Sal, illus. 2006. (Magic Tree House Ser.: No. 35). 128p. (J). (gr. k-3). 11.95 (978-0-375-83035-8(9)); lib. bdg. 13.99 (978-0-375-93035-5(3)) Random Hse. Children's Bks. (Random Hse. Bks. for Young Readers).

—La Noche de los Ninjas. 2004. (Coleccion la Casa Del Arbol the Magic Tree House Ser.).Tr. of Night of the Ninjas. (SPA., Illus.). (J). pap. 4.95 (978-1-930332-66-9(1)) Lectorum Pubns., Inc.

—Pirates Past Noon. unabr. ed. 2000. (Magic Tree House Ser. : No. 4). (J). (gr. k-3). pap. 17.00 incl. audio Random Hse. Audio Publishing Group.

—Revolutionary War on Wednesday, Vol. 22. unabr. ed. 2004. (Magic Tree House Ser. : No. 22). 69p. (J). (gr. k-3). pap. 17.00 incl. audio (978-0-8072-0931-8(7) , S FTR 254 SP, Listening Library) Random Hse. Audio Publishing Group.

—Revolutionary War on Wednesday. Loehr, Mallory, ed. Murdocca, Sal, illus. 2000. (Magic Tree House Ser.: No. 22). 96p. (J). (gr. k-3). lib. bdg. 11.99 (978-0-679-99068-0(2)); pap. 3.99 (978-0-679-89068-3(8)) Random Hse. Children's Bks. (Random Hse. Bks. for Young Readers).

—Revolutionary War on Wednesday. Murdocca, Salvatore, illus. 2000. (Magic Tree House Ser. : No. 22). 69p. (J). (gr. k-3). lib. bdg. 11.80 (978-0-613-28355-7(4)) Tandem Library Bks.

—Revolutionary War on Wednesday. Murdocca, Sal, illus. 2000. (Magic Tree House Ser. : No. 22). (J). (gr. k-3). (978-0-606-19907-0(1)) Tandem Library Bks.

—Season of the Sandstorms. 2006. (Magic Tree House Ser.: No. 34). 144p. (J). (gr. k-3). pap. 4.99 (978-0-375-83032-7(4) , Random Hse. Bks. for Young Readers) Random Hse. Children's Bks.

—Stage Fright on a Summer Night. Murdocca, Sal, illus. 2002. (Magic Tree House Ser.: No. 25). 96p. (J). (gr. k-3). lib. bdg. 11.99 (978-0-375-90611-4(8)); 25. pap. 3.99 (978-0-375-80611-7(3)) Random Hse. Children's Bks. (Random Hse. Bks. for Young Readers).

—Stage Fright on a Summer Night. Murdocca, Salvatore, illus. 2002. (Magic Tree House Ser.: No. 25). 70p. (J). (gr. k-3). lib. bdg. 10.79 (978-0-606-24092-5(6)) Tandem Library Bks.

—Stage Fright on a Summer Night. 2002. (Magic Tree House Ser. : No. 25). (J). (gr. k-3). lib. bdg. 11.80 (978-0-613-50506-2(9)) Tandem Library Bks.

—Summer of the Sea Serpent. Murdocca, Sal, tr. Murdocca, Sal, illus. 2004. (Magic Tree House Ser.: No. 31). 128p. (J). (gr. k-3). lib. bdg. 13.99 (978-0-375-92735-5(2)); (gr. 2-5). 11.95 (978-0-375-82735-8(8)) Random Hse. Children's Bks. (Random Hse. Bks. for Young Readers).

—Una Tarde en el Amazonas. 2004. (Coleccion la Casa Del Arbol the Magic Tree House Ser.).Tr. of Afternoon on the Amazon. (SPA., Illus.). (J). pap. 4.95 (978-1-930332-67-6(X)) Lectorum Pubns., Inc.

—Tigers at Twilight, Vol. 19. unabr. ed. 2004. (Magic Tree House Ser. : No. 19). 72p. (J). (gr. k-3). pap. 17.00 incl. audio (978-0-8072-0928-8(7) , S FTR 251 SP, Listening Library) Random Hse. Audio Publishing Group.

—Tigers at Twilight. Murdocca, Sal, illus. 1999. (Magic Tree House Ser.: No. 19). 96p. (J). (gr. k-3). lib. bdg. 11.99 (978-0-679-99065-9(8)); mass mkt. 3.99 (978-0-679-89065-2(3)) Random Hse. Children's Bks. (Random Hse. Bks. for Young Readers).

—Tigers at Twilight. 1999. (Magic Tree House Ser. : No. 19). (J). (gr. k-3). (Illus.). 71p. lib. bdg. 10.79 (978-0-606-16957-8(1)); lib. bdg. 11.80 (978-0-613-16224-1(2)) Tandem Library Bks.

—Un Tigre Dientes de Sable en el Ocaso. 2004. (Coleccion la Casa Del Arbol the Magic Tree House Ser.).Tr. of Sunset of the Sabretooth. (SPA., Illus.). (J). pap. 4.95 (978-1-930332-68-3(8)) Lectorum Pubns., Inc.

—Tonight on the Titanic. unabr. ed. 2004. (Magic Tree House Ser. : No. 17). 71p. (J). (gr. k-3). pap. 17.00 incl. audio (978-0-8072-0926-4(0) , S FTR 249 SP, Listening Library) Random Hse. Audio Publishing Group.

—Tonight on the Titanic. Murdocca, Sal, illus. 1999. (Magic Tree House Ser.: No. 17). (J). (gr. k-3). 96p. lib. bdg. 11.99 (978-0-679-99063-5(1)); 71p. pap. 3.99 (978-0-679-89063-8(7)) Random Hse. Children's Bks. (Random Hse. Bks. for Young Readers).

—Tonight on the Titanic. Murdocca, Sal, illus. 1999. (Magic Tree House Ser. : No. 17). 70p. (J). (gr. k-3). lib. bdg. 11.19 (978-0-606-16894-6(X)) Tandem Library Bks.

—Tonight on the Titanic. 1999. (Magic Tree House Ser. : No. 17). (J). (gr. k-3). lib. bdg. 11.80 (978-0-613-16226-5(9)) Tandem Library Bks.

—Twister on Tuesday, Vol. 23. 2004. (Magic Tree House Ser. : No. 23). 70p. (J). (gr. k-3). pap. 17.00 incl. audio (978-0-8072-9932-6(4) , Listening Library) Random Hse. Audio Publishing Group.

—Twister on Tuesday. Murdocca, Sal, illus. 2001. (Magic Tree House Ser.: No. 23). 96p. (J). (gr. k-3). 11.99 (978-0-679-99069-7(0)); 23. pap. 3.99 (978-0-679-89069-0(6)) Random Hse. Children's Bks. (Random Hse. Bks. for Young Readers).

—Twister on Tuesday. 2001. (Magic Tree House Ser. : No. 23). (J). (gr. k-3). lib. bdg. 11.80 (978-0-613-35706-7(X)); (Illus.). (978-0-606-21498-8(4)) Tandem Library Bks.

—Viking Ships at Sunrise, Vol. 15. unabr. ed. 2004. (Magic Tree House Ser. : No. 15). 71p. (J). (gr. k-3). pap. 17.00 incl. audio (978-0-8072-0784-0(5) , LFTR 243 SP, Listening Library) Random Hse. Audio Publishing Group.

—Viking Ships at Sunrise. Murdocca, Sal, illus. 1998. (Magic Tree House Ser.: No. 15). 96p. (J). (gr. k-3). lib. bdg. 11.99 (978-0-679-99061-1(5)); mass mkt. 3.99 (978-0-679-89061-4(0)) Random Hse. Children's Bks. (Random Hse. Bks. for Young Readers).

—Viking Ships at Sunrise. Murdocca, Salvatore, illus. 1998. (Magic Tree House Ser. : No. 15). 71p. (J). lib. bdg. 10.79 (978-0-606-15755-1(7)) Tandem Library Bks.

Osterweil, Adam. The Amulet of Komondor. Thorpe, Peter, illus. 2004. 112p. (J). (gr. 3-7). 15.95 (978-1-886910-81-2(2) , Lemniscaat) Boyds Mills Pr.

Ostow, Micol & Burge, Constance M. Changeling Places: An Original Novel. 2005. 152p. (J). (978-1-4155-8183-4(5) , Simon Spotlight) Simon & Schuster Children's Publishing.

Ottolenghi, Carol. Jack & the Beanstalk. Porfirio, Guy, illus. 2002. (Brighter Child Keepsake Stories Ser.). 32p. (J). (ps-3). pap. 3.99 (978-1-57768-377-3(3) , Brighter Child) School Specialty Publishing.

Panamkat, Matthew. Karan Quma & the Meluha Tree. 2007. 348p. per. 19.95 (*978-0-595-41816-9(3)*) iUniverse, Inc.

Paolini, Christopher. Eldest. (Inheritance Trilogy: Bk. 2). (gr. 7 up). 2007. 704p. (YA). pap. 12.99 (978-0-375-84040-1(0)); 2006. 736p. (J). 24.00 (978-0-375-84060-9(5)); 2006. 736p. (J). lib. bdg. 27.99 (978-0-375-94060-6(X)) Random Hse. Children's Bks. (Knopf Bks. for Young Readers).

Papineau, Lucie. Lulu & the Magic Box/Lucie Papineau ; Illustrated by Catherine Lepage. Lepage, Catherine, illus. 2005. (Read-It! Readers Ser.). 32p. (J). (gr. k-3). 18.60 (978-1-4048-1066-2(8)) Picture Window Bks.

Park, Linda Sue. Archer's Quest. 2006. (Illus.). 176p. (J). (gr. 5-9). 16.00 (978-0-618-59631-7(3) , Clarion Bks.) Houghton Mifflin Co. Trade & Reference Div.

Partridge, Elizabeth. Clara & the Hoodoo Man. 1998. (J). (978-0-606-13278-7(3)) Tandem Library Bks.

Pasch, J. A. Arthur P. Snittles: The Magic Barrel. 2006. 116p. (YA). per. 10.95 (978-1-59886-199-0(9)) Tate Publishing & Enterprises, L.L.C.

Pasillo, Susan. The Perfect Pumpkin. 2006. (J). lib. bdg. 20.95 (*978-1-933732-14-5(8)* , Bear Hug Bks.) MidAmerica Publishing Co.

Patrick, Ruthven. Prisoners under Glass. 2005. (YA). per. (978-0-9735422-2-6(5)) Scroll Pr.

Patterson, James. SantaKid. Garland, Michael, illus. 2004. 48p. (J). (gr. k-3). 14.99 (978-0-316-00061-1(2)) Little, Brown Bks. for Young Readers.

Pearce, Philippa. The Little Gentleman. Pohrt, Tom, illus. 2004. 208p. (J). (gr. 3 up). 15.99 (978-0-06-073160-1(5)); lib. bdg. 16.89 (978-0-06-073161-8(3)) HarperCollins Pubs.

Peel, John. Book of Magic, Vol. 3. Karre, Andrew, ed. 2004. (Diadem Worlds of Magic Ser.). 208p. pap. 4.99 (978-0-7387-0615-3(9)) Llewellyn Pubns.

—Book of Names. Karre, Andrew, ed. 2004. (Diadem Worlds of Magic Ser.). 208p. pap. 6.99 (978-0-7387-0617-7(5)) Llewellyn Pubns.

—Book of Nightmares, Vol. 6. 2005. (Diadem: World Magic Ser.: Book 6). 192p. pap. 4.99 (978-0-7387-0612-2(4)) Llewellyn Pubns.

—Book of Oceans. 2005. 216p. (ps-7). pap. 4.99 (978-0-7387-0748-8(1)) Llewellyn Pubns.

—Book of Reality. 2006. 216p. pap. 4.99 (978-0-7387-0843-0(7)) Llewellyn Pubns.

—Book of Signs, Vol. 2. Karre, Andrew, ed. 2004. (Diadem Worlds of Magic Ser.). (Illus.). 208p. pap. 5.99 (978-0-7387-0616-0(7)) Llewellyn Pubns.

—Double Disaster! 2002. (gr. 3-6). lib. bdg. 13.00 (978-0-613-70890-6(3)) Tandem Library Bks.

—Twice the Trouble. 2001. (Magical States Ser.: Vol. 2). 160p. (J). pap. 9.95 (978-0-7434-1763-1(1) , Aladdin) Simon & Schuster Children's Publishing.

Peel, John & Peel, John. Twice the Trouble! 2001. 145p. (J). (gr. 3-6). per. 13.00 (978-0-613-70906-4(3)) Tandem Library Bks.

Pelletier, Andrew T. The Toy Farmer. Nash, Scott, illus. 2007. 32p. (J). (ps). 16.99 (978-0-525-47649-8(0) , Dutton Juvenile) Penguin Group (USA) Inc.

Penick Phillips-Cermak, Mosetta. The Wishing Flower. 2007. 24p. 16.50 (*978-0-615-15573-9(1)*) PM Moon Pubs.

Pennypacker, Sara. Stuart Goes to School. Matje, Martin, illus. 64p. (J). 2003. pap. 15.95 (978-0-439-30182-4(3) , Orchard Bks.); 2005. reprint ed. pap. 4.99 (978-0-439-30183-1(1) , Scholastic Paperbacks) Scholastic, Inc.

—Stuart's Cape. Matje, Martin, illus. 2004. 64p. (J). (ps-3). reprint ed. pap. 3.99 (978-0-439-30181-7(5) , Scholastic Paperbacks) Scholastic, Inc.

Perrault, Charles. Las Hadas. Trias, Margarida, tr. Dumas, Philippe, illus. 2002. (SPA.). 52p. (978-84-8470-058-6(5)) Corimbo, Editorial S.L.

Perry, Shannon. Marietta & the Creeping Nasties. Keenan Dalrymple, Anne, illus. 2002. 160p. (J). per. 7.00 (978-0-9723902-0-0(0) , 3000) Walters, Charles E. Co., The.

Peterson, John. Littles First Readers: The Littles & the Big Blizzard. Rogers, Jacqueline, illus. 2001. (J). (978-0-606-19929-2(2)) Tandem Library Bks.

Pierce, Angelica. Wizard in Blue Jeans. 2007. 184p. pap. 10.95 (*978-1-4303-0647-4(5)*) Lulu.com.

Pierce, Tamora. Bloodhound. 2008. (Beka Cooper Ser.: No. 2). 240p. (J). (gr. 7-11). 18.99 (*978-0-375-81469-3(8)*); lib. bdg. 21.99 (*978-0-375-91469-0(2)*) Random Hse. Children's Bks. (Random Hse. Bks. for Young Readers).

—Briar's Book. (Circle of Magic Ser.: No. 4). (Illus.). 272p. (J). 2000. 5.99 (978-0-590-55411-4(5) , Scholastic Paperbacks); 1999. (gr. 6-12). pap. 15.95 (978-0-590-55359-9(3)) Scholastic, Inc.

—Briar's Book. (Circle of Magic Ser.: No. 4). 2000. (gr. 5-8). lib. bdg. 13.00 (978-0-613-24415-2(X)); 1999. (J). 11.64 (978-0-606-19550-8(5)) Tandem Library Bks.

—Cold Fire. (Circle Opens Ser.: No. 3). (J). 2003. 384p. 5.99 (978-0-590-39656-1(0) , Scholastic Paperbacks); 2002. (Illus.). 368p. (gr. 5 up). pap. 16.95 (978-0-590-39655-4(2) , Scholastic Pr.) Scholastic, Inc.

—Cold Fire. 2003. (Circle Opens Ser.: No. 3). (gr. 7-12). lib. bdg. 14.15 (978-0-613-72894-2(7)) Tandem Library Bks.

—Daja's Book. (Circle of Magic Ser.: No. 3). (Illus.). 240p. (J). 2000. 5.99 (978-0-590-55410-7(7) , Scholastic Paperbacks); 1998. (gr. 6-12). pap. 15.95 (978-0-590-55358-2(5)) Scholastic, Inc.

—Daja's Book. 2000. (Circle of Magic Ser.: No. 3). (gr. 5-8). lib. bdg. 13.00 (978-0-613-28460-8(7)) Tandem Library Bks.

—Magic Steps. (Circle Opens Ser.: No. 1). 272p. (J). 2000. (Illus.). (gr. 4-7). pap. 16.95 (978-0-590-39588-5(2) , Scholastic Pr.); 2001. (gr. 6-12). pap. 5.99 (978-0-590-39605-9(6)) Scholastic, Inc.

—Magic Steps. (Circle Opens Ser.: No. 1). 2001. (gr. 5-8). lib. bdg. 13.00 (978-0-613-35738-8(8)); 2000. (Illus.). (J). (978-0-606-21109-3(8)) Tandem Library Bks.

—Sandry's Book. var. ed. 2002. (Circle of Magic Ser.: No. 1). (YA). (gr. 6-9). lib. bdg. 29.00 incl. audio (978-0-9717540-9-6(8) , 02004L) Full Cast Audio.

—Sandry's Book. 1999. (Circle of Magic Ser.: No. 1). 272p. (YA). (gr. 6-12). mass mkt. 6.99 (978-0-590-55408-4(5)) Scholastic, Inc.

—Sandry's Book. 1999. (Circle of Magic Ser.: No. 1). (gr. 5-8). lib. bdg. 13.00 (978-0-613-17935-5(8)); (Illus.). (J). (978-0-606-20509-2(8)) Tandem Library Bks.

—Shatterglass. (Circle Opens Ser.: No. 4). 368p. (J). 2004. pap. 5.99 (978-0-590-39696-7(X) , Scholastic Paperbacks); 2003. pap. 16.95 (978-0-590-39683-7(8)) Scholastic, Inc.

—Street Magic. (Circle Opens Ser.: No. 2). (J). 2001. 304p. pap. 16.95 (978-0-590-39628-8(5)); 2002. (Illus.). 312p. pap. 6.99 (978-0-590-39643-1(9)) Scholastic, Inc.

—Street Magic. 2002. (Circle Opens Ser.: No. 2). (gr. 5-8). lib. bdg. 13.00 (978-0-613-53870-1(6)) Tandem Library Bks.

—Terrier. (Beka Cooper Ser.: No. 1). (gr. 7-11). 2007. 608p. (YA). pap. 9.99 (*978-0-375-83816-3(3)*); 2006. (Illus.). 592p. (J). lib. bdg. 20.99 (978-0-375-91468-3(4)) Random Hse. Children's Bks. (Random Hse. Bks. for Young Readers).

—Tris's Book. 1999. (Circle of Magic Ser.: No. 2 2). 272p. (YA). (gr. 6-12). mass mkt. 5.99 (978-0-590-55409-1(3)) Scholastic, Inc.

—Wild Magic. 2005. (Immortals Ser.: No. 1). 384p. (YA). pap. 6.99 (978-1-4169-0343-7(7) , Simon Pulse) Simon & Schuster Children's Publishing.

—The Will of the Empress. (Circle Reforged Ser.: Bk. 1). 560p. (J). 2006. pap. 8.99 (978-0-439-44172-8(2)); 2005. (Illus.). (gr. 9-12). pap. 17.99 (978-0-439-44171-1(4) , Scholastic Pr.) Scholastic, Inc.

Pierce, Walter. Dreams Unseen: The Dragon of Mists. 2007. 260p. (YA). per. 16.95 (*978-0-595-45171-5(3)*) iUniverse, Inc.

Plant, Timothy. Beyond the Wall. 2005. (Illus.). 192p. pap. 8.95 (978-1-56315-368-6(8)) SterlingHouse Pubs., Inc.

Plourde, Paulette. My Magic Pillow. 2005. (Illus.). 40p. (J). per. 8.99 (978-1-932338-76-8(4)) Lifevest Publishing, Inc.

Polacco, Patricia. Rechenka's Eggs. Polacco, Patricia, illus. 2002. (Illus.). (J). 14.04 (978-0-7587-3502-7(2)) Book Wholesalers, Inc.

Pollack, Pam. The Bad Luck Charm. 2001. (Malcolm in the Middle Ser.: No. 3). 144p. (J). (gr. 3-7). pap. 4.99 (978-0-439-23078-0(0)) Scholastic, Inc.

Pollack, Pamela & Belviso, Meg. Mimi's Crest of Sincerity. 2001. (Digimon Ser.: No. 7). (Illus.). 96p. (J). (gr. 1-4). pap. 4.50 (978-0-06-107203-1(6) , Harper Entertainment) HarperCollins Pubs.

Preble, Laura. Lica's Angel. 2003. 142p. (YA). 21.95 (978-0-595-74914-0(3)); pap. 11.95 (978-0-595-28253-1(9)) iUniverse, Inc.

The Princess & the Magic Locket. 2003. (Illus.). 32p. (J). 5.98 (978-1-4054-1022-9(1)) Parragon, Inc.

Prineas, Sarah. Stolen. 2008. (Magic Thief Ser.). 416p. (J). 16.99 (*978-0-06-137587-3(X)*) HarperCollins Pubs.

Provencher, Olga J. Joey & Mup. 2005. 134p. per. 9.95 (978-1-59824-048-1(X)) E-BookTime LLC.

Pullman, Philip. The Firework-Maker's Daughter. 1999. 120p. (J). 16.95 (978-0-7540-6055-0(1) , Galaxy Children's Large Print) BBC Audiobooks America.

—The Firework-Maker's Daughter. Gallagher, Susan Saelig, illus. 1999. (J). pap. (978-0-590-12943-5(0) , Levine, Arthur A. Bks.) Scholastic, Inc.

—His Dark Materials Omnibus. 2007. (His Dark Materials Ser.: Bks. 1-3). 944p. (YA). (gr. 7-12). pap. 21.99 (*978-0-375-84722-6(7)* , Knopf Bks. for Young Readers) Random Hse. Children's Bks.

M N O

—Lyra's Oxford. Lawrence, John, illus. 2007. 64p. (YA). (gr. 7-12). per. 6.99 (*978-0-375-84369-3(8) , Knopf Bks. for Young Readers) Random Hse. Children's Bks.

—Das Magische Messer. (GER.). pap. 22.95 (978-3-453-15227-4(1)) Verlag Wilhelm Heyne DEU. Dist: Distribooks, Inc.

Pullman, Philip. The Subtle Knife. deluxe anniv. ed. 2007. (His Dark Materials Ser.: Bk. 2). 368p. (YA). (gr. 7-12). 22.99 (*978-0-375-84672-4(7)); lib. bdg. 25.99 (*978-0-375-94672-1(1)) Random Hse. Children's Bks. (Knopf Bks. for Young Readers).

Purnell, Pamela. Denny & the Magic Pool. 2000. 133p. (J). pap. 11.95 (978-0-8464-4841-9(6)) Beekman Bks., Inc.

Pye, Sylvia. Dusty & the Magic Gold Dust. 2004. 108p. pap. 16.95 (978-1-4137-1124-0(3)) PublishAmerica, Inc.

Pyne, Erin A. A Fandom of Magical Proportions: S: an Unauthorized History of the Harry Potter Phenomenon. 2007. (Illus.). 84p. (J). per. 8.36 (*978-0-9788138-8-8(X)) Nimble Bks. LLC.

Quest, Stacy. Sad Sam & the Magic Cookies. 2006. (Illus.). (J). lib. bdg. 16.95 (978-1-932367-01-0(2)) BookBound Publishing.

Quinn, Zoe. Lightning Strikes! 2006. (Illus.). 128p. (J). (gr. 4-7). 4.99 (978-0-440-42081-1(4) , Yearling) Random Hse. Children's Bks.

Rabe, Tish. Harry's Magic Hat. Watson, Richard, illus. 2007. 24p. (J). (ps-1). pap. 6.99 (*978-1-58476-610-0(7) , IKIDS) Innovative Kids.

Ramsby, H. S. Neverlore. Velario, Jackie, illus. 2005. (YA). 16.95 (978-0-9785075-6-5(8) , Ferne Pr.) Nelson Publishing & Marketing.

Rand, Jonathan. The Magical Wading Pool, Freddie Fernortner Bk 7: Fearless First Grader. 2007. pap. 4.99 (*978-1-893699-91-5(9)) AudioCraft Publishing, Inc.

Rand, Kathleen G. Marianne's Magical Journey. 1998. (Illus.). 15p. (J). (ps-8). pap. 6.95 (978-1-880710-18-0(8)) Monterey Pacific Pubs.

Random House Staff & Golden Books Staff. Barbie & the Magic of Pegasus. 2005. (Illus.). 32p. (J). (ps-2). pap. 3.99 (978-0-375-83296-3(3) , Random Hse. Bks. for Young Readers) Random Hse. Children's Bks.

Ransom, Candice. Horses in the Wind: A Tale of Seabiscuit. 2007. 128p. (J). (gr. 1-5). pap. 4.99 (*978-0-7869-4355-5(6) , Mirrorstone) Wizards of the Coast.

Ransom, Candice. Signals in the Sky. 2007. 128p. (J). 4.99 (978-0-7869-4353-1(X) , Mirrorstone) Wizards of the Coast.

Rao, Chatura. Amie & the Chawl of Colour. Pathak, Ashutosh, illus. 2004. 100p. pap. (978-0-14-333592-4(8) , Puffin) Penguin Group (USA) Inc.

Rawson, Christopher. Wizards. 2002. (gr. k-3). lib. bdg. 14.10 (978-0-613-65138-7(3)) Tandem Library Bks.

Redbank, Tennant. Enchanted: A Storybook Life. 2nd rev. ed. 2007. 24p. (gr. 1). pap. 3.99 (*978-1-4231-1080-4(3)) Disney Pr.

—Enchanted: Before the Fall. 2007. 24p. (gr. 1). pap. 3.99 (*978-1-4231-1079-8(X)) Disney Pr.

Reilly, Matthew. Full Throttle. Raimondi, Pablo, illus. 2007. (Hover Car Racer Ser.). 224p. (J). 9.95 (978-1-4169-0227-0(9)) Simon & Schuster Children's Publishing.

Reiss, Kathryn. Paint by Magic. 2003. (Time Travel Mystery Ser.). 288p. (J). (gr. 5 up). pap. 6.95 (978-0-15-204925-6(8) , Harcourt Paperbacks) Harcourt Children's Bks.

—Paint by Magic. 2002. (gr. 5-8). lib. bdg. 14.10 (978-0-613-70531-8(9)) Tandem Library Bks.

Rene, Richard. The Nightmare Tree. 2007. 240p. (YA). (gr. 5-8). 8.95 (*978-1-55050-363-0(4)) Coteau Bks. CAN. Dist: Fitzhenry & Whiteside, Ltd.

Reviejo, Carlos. Dejame Que te Cuente: Cincuenta Cuentos de Animales para Ninos. 2003. (SPA., Illus.). 212p. (978-84-348-7166-3(1) , SM31147) SM Ediciones ESP. Dist: Lectorum Pubns., Inc.

Richards, L. B. The Adventures of Charley Tooth, Vol. 1. 2004. (Illus.). mass mkt. 12.95 (978-0-8439-5136-3(2)) Dorchester Publishing Co., Inc.

Rickis, Andrew. The Magic Oak: (A Baseball Story) A Novel for Young Adults. 2003. 114p. pap. 16.95 (978-1-4137-0665-9(7)) PublishAmerica, Inc.

Rinaldi, Ann. Millicent's Gift. 2002. (Illus.). 224p. (J). (ps-3). 15.95 (978-0-06-029636-0(4)) HarperCollins Pubs.

Riva, Jim. Marvin Mallard & the Magic Medallion. Steinmark, Sharyl, illus. 2004. 64p. (YA). pap. 14.95 (978-1-891262-03-6(3)) Soaring Sparrow Pr.

Roberts, Rachel. All That Glitters. 2007. (Avalon Ser.: Bk. 2). 175p. (J). (gr. 3-7). 9.99 (*978-1-933164-65-6(4)) Seven Seas Entertainment, LLC.

—All That Glitters. 2001. (Avalon Ser.: Bk. 2). (J). (978-0-606-22175-7(1)) Tandem Library Bks.

—All's Fairy in Love & War. 2003. (Avalon Ser.: Vol. 2). 200p. (J). pap. 4.99 (978-1-59315-011-2(3)) Perseus Bks. Group.

—All's Fairy in Love & War. 2003. (gr. 3-6). lib. bdg. 13.00 (978-0-613-79959-1(3)) Tandem Library Bks.

—The Avalon Collection, 3 vols., Bks. 1 - 3. 2005. (Avalon Ser.). 656p. (J). (gr. 2-6). pap. 9.95 (978-1-59315-320-5(1)) Vanguard Pr.

—Avalon Collections, 2 vols. 2004. (Avalon Ser.). 544p. (J). pap. 9.95 (978-1-59315-146-1(2)); Vol. 2. pap. 9.95 (978-1-59315-147-8(0)) Perseus Bks. Group.

—Cry of the Wolf. 2001. (Avalon Ser.: Bk. 3). (J). (gr. 3-7). (978-0-606-22236-5(7)) Tandem Library Bks.

—The Dark Mage: Avalon Quest for Magic. 2006. (Avalon Ser.: Vol. 5). 224p. (J). pap. 5.99 (978-1-59315-014-3(8)) Vanguard Pr.

—The Secret of the Unicorn. 2003. (Avalon Ser.: Bk. 4). 187p. (YA). (gr. 3-7). pap. 4.99 (978-1-59315-006-8(7)) Perseus Bks. Group.

—The Secret of the Unicorn. 2002. (Avalon Ser.: Bk. 4). (J). (gr. 3-6). lib. bdg. 13.00 (978-0-613-50572-7(7)) Tandem Library Bks.

—Spellsinger. 2003. (Avalon Ser.: Bk. 5). 176p. (gr. 3-7). pap. 4.99 (978-1-59315-007-5(5)) Perseus Bks. Group.

—Spellsinger. 2002. (Avalon Ser.: Bk. 5). (Illus.). 176p. (J). (gr. 3-7). pap. 4.99 (978-0-439-22170-2(6)) Scholastic, Inc.

—Trial by Fire. 2003. (Avalon Ser.: Bk. 6). 176p. (YA). (gr. 3-7). pap. 4.99 (978-1-59315-008-2(3)) Perseus Bks. Group.

Robertson, Barbara. Rosemary & the Island Treasure: Back to 1947. 2001. (Hourglass Adventures Ser.: Bk. 4). (Illus.). 128p. (J). (gr. 3-5). pap. 4.95 (978-1-890817-58-9(9)) Winslow Pr.

—Rosemary at Sea: Back to 1919. 2001. (Hourglass Adventures Ser.: Bk. 3). (Illus.). 128p. (J). (gr. 4-6). pap. 4.95 (978-1-890817-57-2(0)) Winslow Pr.

—Rosemary in Paris: Back to 1889. 2001. (Hourglass Adventures Ser.: Bk. 2). (Illus.). 121p. (J). (gr. 4-7). pap. 4.95 (978-1-890817-56-5(2)) Winslow Pr.

—Rosemary Meets Rosemarie Bk. 1: Berlin in 1870. 2001. (Hourglass Adventures Ser.: Bk. 1). (Illus.). 128p. (J). (gr. 4-6). pap. 5.95 (978-1-890817-55-8(4)) Winslow Pr.

Robertson, Elysia Hill. Santa the Chimney Sweep / The Candy Cane That Found A Home. Robertson, Elysia Hill, illus. 2005. (Illus.). 37p. (J). per. 6.95 (978-0-9764444-9-7(6)) E. J. Publishing.

Robey, M. Ye Olde Witch Club in the Order of the C. 2005. 226p. pap. 19.95 (978-1-4137-6627-1(7)) PublishAmerica, Inc.

Robinson, Marcus. Samurai Baby the Adventure Begins. 2007. 87p. pap. 11.98 (*978-1-4303-0350-3(6)) Lulu.com.

Rodda, Emily. The Charm Bracelet. Vitale, Raoul, illus. 2003. (Fairy Realm Ser.: No. 1). 128p. (J). (gr. 2-5). 8.99 (978-0-06-009583-3(0)); lib. bdg. 15.89 (978-0-06-009584-0(9)) HarperCollins Pubs.

—The Charm Bracelet. Vitale, Raoul, illus. 2007. (Fairy Realm Ser.). 128p. (J). (gr. 3-6). 25.65 (978-1-59961-323-9(9)) Spotlight.

—The Flower Fairies. Vitale, Raoul, illus. 2003. (Fairy Realm Ser.: No. 2). 128p. (J). 8.99 (978-0-06-009586-4(5)); lib. bdg. 15.89 (978-0-06-009587-1(3)) HarperCollins Pubs.

—The Forests of Silence. 2007. (Deltora Quest Ser.: No. 1). 144p. (J). pap. 2.99 (*978-0-545-01031-3(4)) Scholastic, Inc.

—The Forests of Silence. 2001. (gr. 5-8). lib. bdg. 13.00 (978-0-613-35718-0(3)) Tandem Library Bks.

—Isle of the Dead. 2004. 195p. (J). lib. bdg. 16.92 (*978-1-4242-0273-7(6)) Fitzgerald Bks.

—The Key to Rondo. 2008. (J). (*978-0-545-03536-1(8)); 224p. pap. 16.99 (*978-0-545-03535-4(X)) Scholastic, Inc. (Scholastic Pr.).

—The Last Fairy-Apple Tree. Vitale, Raoul, illus. 2003. (Fairy Realm Ser.: No. 4). 128p. (J). 8.99 (978-0-06-009592-5(X)); lib. bdg. 15.89 (978-0-06-009593-2(8)) HarperCollins Pubs.

—The Magic Key. Vitale, Raoul, illus. 2004. (Fairy Realm Ser.: No. 5). 128p. (J). lib. bdg. 15.89 (978-0-06-009596-3(2)); Book 5. 8.99 (978-0-06-009595-6(4)) HarperCollins Pubs.

—The Magic Key. Vitale, Raoul, illus. 2007. (Fairy Realm Ser.). 128p. (J). (gr. 3-6). 25.65 (978-1-59961-327-7(1)) Spotlight.

—Maze of the Beast. 2001. (gr. 5-8). lib. bdg. 13.00 (978-0-613-35786-9(8)) Tandem Library Bks.

—The Peskie Spell. Vitale, Raoul, illus. 2006. (Fairy Realm Ser.). 128p. (J). 8.99 (978-0-06-077764-7(8)); lib. bdg. 14.89 (978-0-06-077766-1(4)) HarperCollins Pubs.

—The Rainbow Wand. Vitale, Raoul, illus. 2006. (Fairy Realm Ser.: No. 10). 128p. (J). lib. bdg. 14.89 (978-0-06-077769-2(9)); 8.99 (978-0-06-077768-5(0)) HarperCollins Pubs.

—The Rainbow Wand. Vitale, Raoul, illus. 2007. (Fairy Realm Ser.). 128p. (J). (gr. 3-6). 25.65 (978-1-59961-332-1(8)) Spotlight.

Rowan & the Ice Creepers. 2004. (Rowan of Rin Ser.). (Illus.). 272p. (J). (gr. 3 up). pap. 5.99 (978-0-06-441023-6(4)) HarperCollins Pubs.

—Shadowgate. 2004. 195p. (J). lib. bdg. 16.92 (*978-1-4242-0274-4(4)) Fitzgerald Bks.

—The Star Cloak. Vitale, Raoul, illus. 2005. (Fairy Realm Ser.: No. 7). 128p. (J). lib. bdg. 14.89 (978-0-06-077759-3(1)); 8.99 (978-0-06-077758-6(3)) HarperCollins Pubs.

—Tales of Deltora. 2006. (Illus.). 176p. (J). pap. 14.99 (978-0-439-87785-5(7)); pap. 7.99 (978-0-439-82909-0(7) , Scholastic Paperbacks) Scholastic, Inc.

—The Third Wish. Vitale, Raoul, illus. 2003. (Fairy Realm Ser.: No. 3). 128p. (J). 8.99 (978-0-06-009589-5(X)); lib. bdg. 15.89 (978-0-06-009590-1(3)) HarperCollins Pubs.

—The Unicorn. Vitale, Raoul, illus. 2004. (Fairy Realm Ser.: No. 6). 112p. (J). 8.99 (978-0-06-009598-7(9)); lib. bdg. 14.89 (978-0-06-009599-4(7)) HarperCollins Pubs.

—The Valley of the Lost. 2001. (gr. 5-8). lib. bdg. 13.00 (978-0-613-43903-9(1)) Tandem Library Bks.

Roderman, Anna Marie. Two Tales of Courage. 2004. 116p. (YA). pap. 7.95 (978-0-87714-318-5(8)) Denlingers Pubs., Ltd.

Rodgers, Frank. Little T & Lizard the Wizard. 2007. (Read-It! Chapter Books). (J). 21.26 (978-1-4048-2725-7(0)) Picture Window Bks.

Rolly's Magic Pencil. 2005. (J). per. 6.99 (978-0-9769985-0-1(5) , 1-206-818-9769) Grace Publishing.

Roman, Javier. Adventures of Tinturu & Kumachan the M. 2007. (Illus.). 48p. pap. 12.95 (*978-1-4241-1626-3(0)) PublishAmerica, Inc.

Roop, Peter. Houdini: Prince of Air. 2003. (Illus.). 14.95 (978-1-59319-023-1(9)) LeapFrog Enterprises, Inc.

Rosario, Joann. The Trick That Turned into Poop! Rosario, Joann, illus. 2004. (Illus.). 20p. (J). (ps-13). pap. 10.00 (978-0-9758746-5-3(9) , 1246169) J.G.R. Enterprises.

Rosasco, Jose Luis. La Mariposa Negra y Otros Cuentos. 2003. (SPA.). pap. (978-956-13-1661-4(7) , AB12831) Bello, Andres CHL. Dist: Lectorum Pubns., Inc.

Rose, Maddy. The Adventures of Pinkie: Tricky Tricksters. 2008. 24p. (J). pap. 9.95 (*978-1-86230-489-5(0)) Transworld Publishers Ltd. GBR. Dist: Independent Pubs. Group.

Rose, Simon. The Alchemist's Portrait. 2006. (Illus.). 134p. (J). 6.95 (978-1-896580-29-6(7)) Tradewind Bks. CAN. Dist: Orca Bk. Pubs. USA.

Ross, Jillian. Alissa & the Castle Ghost. Backes, Nick, illus. 2nd ed. 1998. (Stardust Classics). (J). (gr. 2-6). 113p. 12.95 (978-1-889514-07-9(1)); 119p. pap. 5.95 (978-1-889514-08-6(X)) Dolls Corp.

Rowe, Melissa J. When the Tooth Fairy Comes... 2007. (J). per. 10.99 (*978-1-59879-369-7(1)) Lifevest Publishing, Inc.

Rowling, J. K. Harrius Potter et Camera Secretorum. Needham, Peter, tr. from ENG. 2006. Orig. Title: Harry Potter & the Chamber of Secrets. (LAT., Illus.). 300p. (J). 23.95 (978-1-59990-067-4(X) , Bloomsbury Children) Bloomsbury Publishing.

—Harry Potter a l'Ecole des Sorciers. l.t. ed. 2005. (Harry Potter Ser.). (Illus.). 408p. 30.99 (978-2-84011-646-2(4)) Ulverscroft Large Print Bks. GBR. Dist: Ulverscroft Large Print Bks., Ltd.

—Harry Potter & the Chamber of Secrets. braille ed. 1999. (Harry Potter Ser.: Year 2). 520p. (YA). (gr. 3 up). pap. 17.99 (978-0-939173-35-8(2)) National Braille Pr.

—Harry Potter & the Chamber of Secrets. unabr. ed. 2004. (Harry Potter Ser.: Year 2). 352p. (J). (gr. 3 up). pap. 46.00 incl. audio (978-0-8072-8207-6(3) , S YA 137 SP, Listening Library) Random Hse. Audio Publishing Group.

—Harry Potter & the Chamber of Secrets. (RUS., Illus.). 28.95 (978-5-8451-0947-7(7)) Rosmen-Izdat RUS. Dist: Distribooks, Inc.

—Harry Potter & the Chamber of Secrets. 2003. (Harry Potter Ser.: Year 2). 352p. (J). 24.95 (978-0-439-55489-3(6) , Levine, Arthur A. Bks.) Scholastic, Inc.

—Harry Potter & the Chamber of Secrets. GrandPré, Mary, illus. (Harry Potter Ser.: Year 2). (J). 2002. 448p. mass mkt. 6.99 (978-0-439-42010-5(5) , Levine, Arthur A. Bks.); 2000. 352p. (gr. 3 up). mass mkt. 8.99 (978-0-439-06487-3(2)); 2002. 352p. 75.00 (978-0-439-20353-1(8) , Levine, Arthur A. Bks.) Scholastic, Inc.

—Harry Potter & the Chamber of Secrets. l.t. ed. 2003. 464p. 13.95 (978-1-59413-001 4(9)) Thorndike Pr.

—Harry Potter & the Chamber of Secrets. GrandPré, Mary, illus. l.t. ed. 2000. (Harry Potter Ser.: Year 2). 464p. (gr. 3 up). 24.95 (978-0-7862-2273-5(5) , Large Print Pr.) Thorndike Pr.

—Harry Potter & the Deathly Hallows. braille ed. 2007. (Harry Potter Ser.: Year 7). 34.99 (*978-0-939173-57-0(3)) National Braille Pr.

—Harry Potter & the Deathly Hallows. GrandPré, Mary, illus. 2007. (Harry Potter Ser.: Year 7). 784p. (J). (gr. 4-7). 34.99 (*978-0-545-01022-1(5)); 784p. (YA). (gr. 6 up). 39.99 (*978-0-545-02936-0(8)); 816p. (J). 65.00 (*978-0-545-02937-7(6)) Scholastic, Inc. (Levine, Arthur A. Bks.).

—Harry Potter & the Deathly Hallows. l.t. ed. 2007. (Harry Potter Ser.: Year 7). (YA). 34.95 (*978-0-7862-9665-1(8)) Thorndike Pr.

—Harry Potter & the Goblet of Fire. braille ed. 2000. (Harry Potter Ser.: Year 4). 650p. (YA). (gr. 3 up). pap. 25.95 (978-0-939173-37-2(9)) National Braille Pr.

—Harry Potter & the Goblet of Fire. 2003. (Harry Potter Ser.: Year 4). 752p. (J). 30.95 (978-0-439-55490-9(X) , Levine, Arthur A. Bks.) Scholastic, Inc.

—Harry Potter & the Goblet of Fire. GrandPré, Mary, illus. (Harry Potter Ser.: Year 4). 752p. (J). (gr. 3 up). 2002. mass mkt. 9.99 (978-0-439-13960-1(0)); 2000. 29.99 (978-0-439-13959-5(7)) Scholastic, Inc. (Levine, Arthur A. Bks.).

—Harry Potter & the Goblet of Fire. 2002. (gr. 3-6). lib. bdg. 17.60 (978-0-613-49674-2(4)) Tandem Library Bks.

—Harry Potter & the Goblet of Fire. l.t. ed. 2003. 936p. 14.95 (978-1-59413-003-8(5)) Thorndike Pr.

—Harry Potter & the Goblet of Fire. GrandPré, Mary, illus. l.t. ed. 2000. (Harry Potter Ser.: Year 4). 936p. (gr. 3 up). 25.95 (978-0-7862-2927-7(6) , Large Print Pr.) Thorndike Pr.

—Harry Potter & the Half-Blood Prince, 9 vols. braille ed. 2005. (Harry Potter Ser.: 6). (YA). 29.99 (978-0-939173-39-6(5) , HALF) National Braille Pr.

—Harry Potter & the Half-Blood Prince. 2003. (Harry Potter Ser.). 496p. 24.95 (*978-7-02-005323-0(8) , HAP06) People's Literature Publishing Hse. CHN. Dist: China Bks. & Periodicals, Inc.

—Harry Potter & the Half-Blood Prince. GrandPré, Mary, illus. (J). 2005. (Harry Potter Ser.: Year 6). 672p. 34.99 (978-0-439-78677-5(0)); 2005. (Harry Potter Ser.: Year 6). 672p. 29.99 (978-0-439-78454-2(9)); 2005. (Harry Potter Ser.: Year 6). 704p. 60.00 (978-0-439-79132-8(4)); 2006. 672p. reprint ed. pap. 9.99 (978-0-439-78596-9(0)) Scholastic, Inc. (Levine, Arthur A. Bks.).

—Harry Potter & the Half-Blood Prince. 832p. 2007. pap. 14.95 (*978-1-59413-221-6(6)); 2005. (Harry Potter Ser.: Year 6). 29.95 (978-0-7862-7745-2(9)) Thorndike Pr. (Large Print Pr.).

—Harry Potter & the Order of the Phoenix, 13 vols. braille ed. 2003. (Harry Potter Ser.: Year 5). (YA). 29.99 (978-0-939173-38-9(7)) National Braille Pr.

—Harry Potter & the Order of the Phoenix. 2003. (Harry Potter Ser.). 575p. 25.95 (978-7-02-004327-9(5) , HAP05) People's Literature Publishing Hse. CHN. Dist: China Bks. & Periodicals, Inc.

—Harry Potter & the Order of the Phoenix. GrandPré, Mary, illus. (Harry Potter Ser.: Year 5). (J). 2004. 896p. (gr. 4-7). mass mkt. 9.99 (978-0-439-35807-1(8) , Scholastic Paperbacks); 2003. 870p. (gr. 3-6). 29.99 (978-0-439-35806-4(X)); 2003. 896p. (gr. 3-6). 34.99 (978-0-439-56761-9(0)) Scholastic, Inc.

—Harry Potter & the Order of the Phoenix. l.t. ed. 2003. (Harry Potter Ser.: Year 5). 1093p. 29.95 (978-0-7862-5778-2(4) , Large Print Pr.) Thorndike Pr.

—Harry Potter & the Order of the Phoenix. GrandPré, Mary, illus. l.t. ed. 2003. 1232p. (J). (gr. 4-7). pap. 14.95 (978-1-59413-112-7(0) , Large Print Pr.) Thorndike Pr.

—Harry Potter & the Prisoner of Azkaban. 2002. (Harry Potter Ser.). (Illus.). (YA). 16.26 (978-0-7587-5662-6(3)) Book Wholesalers, Inc.

—Harry Potter & the Prisoner of Azkaban. braille ed. 1999. (Harry Potter Ser.: Year 3). (YA). (gr. 3 up). pap. 19.95 (978-0-939173-36-5(0)) National Braille Pr.

—Harry Potter & the Prisoner of Azkaban. 2000. (J). tchr. ed. 9.95 (978-1-58130-656-9(3)); stu. ed. 11.95 (978-1-58130-657-6(1)) Novel Units, Inc.

—Harry Potter & the Prisoner of Azkaban. (Harry Potter Ser.: Year 3). 2004. 560p. mass mkt. 7.99 (978-0-439-65548-4(X) , Scholastic Paperbacks); 2003. 448p. (J). 24.95 (978-0-439-55492-3(6) , Levine, Arthur A. Bks.) Scholastic, Inc.

—Harry Potter & the Prisoner of Azkaban. GrandPré, Mary, illus. (Harry Potter Ser.: Year 3). 448p. (gr. 3 up). 2001. (YA). mass mkt. 8.99 (978-0-439-13636-5(9) , Levine, Arthur A. Bks.); 1999. (J). 22.99 (978-0-439-13635-8(0)) Scholastic, Inc.

—Harry Potter & the Prisoner of Azkaban. 2001. (gr. 3-6). lib. bdg. 16.45 (978-0-613-37106-3(2)); (Illus.). (J). 14.64 (978-0-606-21584-8(0)) Tandem Library Bks.

—Harry Potter & the Prisoner of Azkaban. l.t. ed. 2003. 592p. 13.95 (978-1-59413-002-1(7)) Thorndike Pr.

—Harry Potter & the Prisoner of Azkaban. GrandPré, Mary, illus. l.t. ed. 2000. (Harry Potter Ser.: Year 3). 592p. (gr. 3 up). 24.95 (978-0-7862-2274-2(3) , Large Print Pr.) Thorndike Pr.

—Harry Potter & the Sorcerer's Stone. unabr. ed. (Harry Potter Ser.: Year 1). 320p. (gr. 3 up). (YA). pap. 62.00 incl. audio (978-0-8072-1547-0(3)); 2004. (J). pap. 46.00 incl. audio (978-0-8072-8119-2(0) , S YA 108 SP) Random Hse. Audio Publishing Group. (Listening Library).

—Harry Potter & the Sorcerer's Stone. GrandPré, Mary, illus. (Harry Potter Ser.: Year 1). (gr. 3 up). 2001. 400p. (J). mass mkt. 6.99 (978-0-439-36213-9(X)); 1999. 320p. (YA). mass mkt. 8.99 (978-0-590-35342-7(X)); 1998. 320p. (J). pap. 22.99 (978-0-590-35340-3(3) , Levine, Arthur A. Bks.) Scholastic, Inc.

—Harry Potter & the Sorcerer's Stone. collector's ed. 2000. (Harry Potter Ser.: Year 1). 320p. (YA). (gr. 3 up). 75.00 (978-0-439-20352-4(X)) Scholastic, Inc.

—Harry Potter & the Sorcerer's Stone. l.t. ed. 2003. 423p. 13.95 (978-1-59413-000-7(0)) Thorndike Pr.

—Harry Potter & the Sorcerer's Stone. GrandPré, Mary, illus. l.t. ed. 1999. (Harry Potter Ser.: Year 1). 422p. (gr. 3 up). 24.95 (978-0-7862-2272-8(7) , Large Print Pr.) Thorndike Pr.

—Harry Potter Boxed Set, Bks. 1-7. 2007. (Harry Potter Ser.: Years 1-7). (J). 195.00 (*978-0-545-04425-7(1) , Levine, Arthur A. Bks.) Scholastic, Inc.

—Harry Potter Boxed Set: Harry Potter & the Sorcerer's Stone; Harry Potter & the Chamber of Secrets; Harry Potter & the Prisoner of Azkaban, 3 vols. GrandPré, Mary, illus. (Harry Potter Ser.: Years 1-3). (YA). 2002. pap. 21.97 (978-0-439-32466-3(1)); 1999. (gr. 3 up). 55.85 (978-0-439-13316-6(5)) Scholastic, Inc. (Levine, Arthur A. Bks.).

—Harry Potter Boxed Set: Harry Potter & the Sorcerer's Stone; Harry Potter & the Chamber of Secrets; Harry Potter & the Prisoner of Azkaban; Harry Potter & the Goblet of Fire, 4 vols. GrandPré, Mary, illus. 2000. (Harry Potter Ser.: Years 1-4). (YA). (gr. 3 up). 85.80 (978-0-641-06631-3(7) , Levine, Arthur A. Bks.) Scholastic, Inc.

—Harry Potter Coffret: Harry Potter a l'Ecole des Sorciers; Harry Potter et la Chambre des Secrets; Harry Potter et le Prisonnier d'Azkaban. 1999. (Harry Potter Ser.: Years 1-3). Tr. of Harry Potter Boxed Set: Harry Potter & the Chamber of Secrets; Harry Potter & the Sorcerer's Stone; Harry Potter & the Prisoner of Azkaban. (FRE.). (YA). (gr. 3 up). pap. 43.95 (978-2-07-052929-2(0)) Gallimard, Editions FRA. Dist: Distribooks, Inc.

—Harry Potter Coffret: Harry Potter a l'Ecole des Sorciers; Harry Potter et la Chambre des Secrets; Harry Potter et le Prisonnier d'Azkaban; Harry Potter et la Coupe de Feu. 1999. (Harry Potter Ser.: Years 1-3). Tr. of Harry Potter Boxed Set: Harry Potter & the Chamber of Secrets; Harry Potter & the Sorcerer's Stone; Harry Potter & the Prisoner of Azkaban; Harry Potter et la COupe de Feu. (FRE.). 1400p. (YA). (gr. 3 up). pap. 34.95 (978-0-320-03843-3(2)) French & European Pubns., Inc.

—Harry Potter e a Camara Secreta. (POR.). pap. 28.95 (978-85-325-1166-9(X)) Rocco, Editora, Ltda BRA. Dist: Distribooks, Inc.

—Harry Potter et la Chambre des Secrets. 1999. (Harry Potter Ser.: Year 2). Tr. of Harry Potter & the Chamber of Secrets. (FRE.). (YA). (gr. 3 up). pap. 13.95 (978-0-320-03778-8(9)) French & European Pubns., Inc.

—Harry Potter et la Chambre des Secrets. 1999. (Harry Potter Ser.: Year 2). Tr. of Harry Potter & the Chamber of Secrets. (FRE., Illus.). 358p. (YA). (gr. 3 up). pap. 16.95 (978-2-07-052455-6(8)) Gallimard, Editions FRA. Dist: Distribooks, Inc.

—Harry Potter et le Prisonnier d'Azkaban. 1999. (Harry Potter Ser.: Year 3). Tr. of Harry Potter & the Prisoner of Azkaban. (FRE.). 465p. (YA). (gr. 3 up). pap. 16.95 (978-2-07-052818-9(9)) Gallimard, Editions FRA. Dist: Distribooks, Inc.

—Harry Potter et l'Ecole des Sorciers. 3rd ed. 1998. (Harry Potter Ser.: Year 1). Tr. of Harry Potter & the Sorcerer's Stone. (FRE., Illus.). (YA). (gr. 3 up). pap. 14.95 (978-2-07-050142-7(6)) Distribooks, Inc.

—Harry Potter et l'Ecole des Sorciers. 1999. (Harry Potter Ser.: Year 1). Tr. of Harry Potter & the Sorcerer's Stone. (FRE.). (YA). (gr. 3 up). pap. 16.95 (978-0-320-03780-1(0)) French & European Pubns., Inc.

—Harry Potter et l'Ecole des Sorciers. 2000. Tr. of Harry Potter & the Sorcerer's Stone. (FRE.). (J). pap. 14.95 (978-2-07-051426-7(9)) Gallimard, Editions FRA. *Dist:* Distribooks, Inc.

—Harry Potter und der Gefangene von Azkaban. 1999. (Harry Potter Ser.: Year 3). Tr. of Harry Potter & the Prisoner of Azkaban. (GER.). (YA). (gr. 3 up). pap. 34.95 (978-3-551-55169-6(3)) Carlsen Verlag DEU. *Dist:* Distribooks, Inc.

—Harry Potter und der Stein der Weisen. 1999. (Harry Potter Ser.: Year 1). (GER.). 335p. (YA). (gr. 3 up). pap. 34.95 (978-3-551-55167-2(7)) Carlsen Verlag DEU. *Dist:* Distribooks, Inc.

—Harry Potter und die Kammer des Schreckens. 1999. (Harry Potter Ser.: Year 2). Tr. of Harry Potter & Chamber of Secrets. (GER.). (YA). (gr. 3 up). pap. 36.95 (978-3-551-55168-9(5)) Carlsen Verlag DEU. *Dist:* Distribooks, Inc.

—Harry Potter y el Caliz de Fuego. 2001. (SPA.). 640p. (978-84-7888-664-7(8) , 1950) Emece Editores.

—Harry Potter y el Caliz de Fuego. 2004. (Harry Potter Ser.). (SPA., Illus.). (YA). 240p. 19.95 (978-84-7888-645-6(1) , SAL30169); pap. 16.50 (978-84-7888-646-3(X) , SAL30171) Emece Editores ESP. *Dist:* Lectorum Pubns., Inc.

—Harry Potter y el Caliz de Fuego. 2000. 636p. 39.95 (978-0-320-04849-4(7)) French & European Pubns., Inc.

—Harry Potter y el Caliz de Fuego. 2001. (SPA.). (gr. 3-6). lib. bdg. 26.35 (978-0-613-35957-3(7)); (Illus.). (J). 23.15 (978-0-606-21227-4(2)) Tandem Library Bks.

—Harry Potter y el Prisionero de Azkaban. 2004. (Harry Potter Ser.: Year 3). (SPA., Illus.). 360p. (gr. 3 up). 17.95 (978-84-7888-519-0(6) , SAL1889) Emece Editores ESP. *Dist:* Lectorum Pubns., Inc.

—Harry Potter y el Prisionero de Azkaban. 2000. (Harry Potter Ser.: Year 3). (SPA.). (YA). (gr. 3 up). 16.95 (978-0-320-03783-2(5)); 360p. 29.95 (978-0-320-04846-3(2)) French & European Pubns., Inc.

—Harry Potter y el Prisionero de Azkaban. 2001. (SPA.). (gr. 3-6). lib. bdg. 21.10 (978-0-613-35958-0(5)); (Illus.). (J). 18.65 (978-0-606-20490-3(3)) Tandem Library Bks.

—Harry Potter y la Camara Secreta. 2000. (SPA.). 288p. (978-84-7888-614-2(1) , 1950) Emece Editores.

—Harry Potter y la Camara Secreta. 2004. (Harry Potter Ser.). (SPA.). (YA). 286p. pap. 9.99 (978-84-7888-656-2(7) , SAL30173); (Illus.). 288p. (gr. 3 up). 15.95 (978-84-7888-495-7(5) , SAL4595) Emece Editores ESP. *Dist:* Lectorum Pubns., Inc.

—Harry Potter y la Camara Secreta. 2000. (SPA.). 290p. (YA). (gr. 7 up). 15.95 (978-950-04-2068-6(6)) Emecé Editores S.A. ARG. *Dist:* Libros Sin Fronteras.

—Harry Potter y la Camara Secreta. 1999. (Harry Potter Ser.: Year 2). (SPA.). (YA). (gr. 3 up). 14.95 (978-0-320-03781-8(9)) French & European Pubns., Inc.

—Harry Potter y la Camara Secreta. 2001. (SPA.). (gr. 3-6). lib. bdg. 18.80 (978-0-613-35959-7(3)); (Illus.). (J). 16.64 (978-0-606-20491-0(1)) Tandem Library Bks.

—Harry Potter y la Orden del Fenix. 2004. (Harry Potter Ser.). (SPA.). 893p. (YA). 23.99 (978-84-7888-901-3(9)) Emece Editores ESP. *Dist:* Lectorum Pubns., Inc.

—Harry Potter y la Orden del Fenix. Ortega, Gemma Rovira, tr. 2004. (Harry Potter Ser.). (SPA.). 893p. (YA). pap. 17.99 (978-84-7888-884-9(5)) Emece Editores ESP. *Dist:* Lectorum Pubns., Inc.

—Harry Potter y la Piedra Filosofal. 2000. (SPA.). 256p. (978-84-7888-612-8(5) , 1950) Emece Editores.

—Harry Potter y la Piedra Filosofal. 2004. (Harry Potter Ser.). (SPA., Illus.). 256p. (YA). pap. 9.99 (978-84-7888-654-8(0) , SAL30172); (gr. 7 up). 15.95 (978-84-7888-445-2(9) , SAL2819) Emece Editores ESP. *Dist:* Lectorum Pubns., Inc.

—Harry Potter y la Piedra Filosofal. 2000. 254p. 29.95 (978-0-320-04848-7(9)); 1999. (Harry Potter Ser.: Year 1). (SPA.). (YA). (gr. 3 up). 14.95 (978-0-320-03782-5(7)) French & European Pubns., Inc.

—Harry Potter y la Piedra Filosofal. 2001. (SPA.). (gr. 3-6). lib. bdg. 18.80 (978-0-613-35960-3(7)); (Illus.). (J). 16.64 (978-0-606-20489-7(X)) Tandem Library Bks.

Rowling, J. K. & Dale, Jim. Harry Potter & the Goblet of Fire. unabr. ed. 2004. (Harry Potter Ser.). 752p. (J). pap. 65.00 incl. audio (978-0-8072-1196-0(6) , S YA 270 SP, Listening Library) Random Hse. Audio Publishing Group.

Ruditis, Paul & Burge, Constance M. As Puck Would Have It. 2006. (Charmed Ser.). 240p. (YA). pap. 6.99 (978-1-4169-1468-6(4) , Simon Spotlight Entertainment) Simon & Schuster.

Ruditis, Paul & Burge, Constance M. Leo Rising. 2007. (Charmed Ser.). 224p. (YA). pap. 6.99 (***978-1-4169-3669-5(6)** , Simon Spotlight Entertainment) Simon & Schuster.

Running Press Staff. Magic Mother Goose: Pull the Tabs! Change the Pictures! 2004. (Magic Windows Ser.). (Illus.). 12p. (J). pap. 12.95 (978-0-7624-1574-8(6) , Running Pr. Kids) Running Pr. Bk. Pubs.

Rupp, Rebecca. The Dragon of Lonely Island. ed. 2006. 192p. (J). (gr. 3-6). pap. 5.99 (978-0-7636-2805-5(0)) Candlewick Pr.

Russon, Penni. Breathe. 2007. (Illus.). 368p. (J). (gr. 9 up). 16.99 (978-0-06-079393-7(7)); lib. bdg. 17.89 (978-0-06-079394-4(5)) HarperCollins Pubs.

—Undine. 2006. (Illus.). 336p. (J). 16.99 (978-0-06-079389-0(9)); lib. bdg. 17.89 (978-0-06-079390-6(2)) HarperCollins Pubs.

Ryan. Me Two. Sauber, Rob, illus. 2001. 192p. (YA). (gr. 4-7). pap. 14.95 (978-0-595-17594-9(5)) iUniverse, Inc.

Ryan, Brittney. Holly Claus: The Christmas Princess. Long, Laurel & Bedrick, Jeffrey K., illus. 2007. 48p. (J). lib. bdg. 19.89 (***978-0-06-144023-6(X));** 18.99 (***978-0-06-144022-9(1))** HarperCollins Pubs. (Julie Andrews Collection).

—The Legend of Holly Claus. Long, Laurel, illus. 2004. 544p. (J). (gr. 4 up). 16.99 (978-0-06-058511-2(0)); lib. bdg. 17.89 (978-0-06-058514-3(5)) HarperCollins Pubs. (Julie Andrews Collection).

—Legend of Holly Claus. Long, Laurel, illus. 2006. 544p. (J). pap. 7.99 (978-0-06-058515-0(3) , Julie Andrews Collection) HarperCollins Pubs.

Ryan, Margaret. Magic Mess! Murfin, Teresa, illus. 2005. (Airy Fairy Bks.). 80p. (J). pap. 3.95 (978-0-7641-3188-2(5)) Barron's Educational Series, Inc.

—Magic Mischief! Murfin, Teresa, illus. 2005. (Airy Fairy Bks.: Vol. 1). 80p. (J). pap. 3.95 (978-0-7641-3186-8(9)) Barron's Educational Series, Inc.

—Magic Mistakes! Murfin, Teresa, illus. 2005. (Airy Fairy Bks.). 80p. (J). pap. 3.99 (978-0-7641-3426-5(4)) Barron's Educational Series, Inc.

—Magic Mix-up! Murfin, Teresa, illus. 2005. (Airy Fairy Bks.: Vol. 4). 80p. (J). pap. 3.95 (978-0-7641-3189-9(3)) Barron's Educational Series, Inc.

Rylant, Cynthia. The Van Gogh Cafe. 2006. (Illus.). 64p. (J). (gr. 3-7). pap. 5.95 (978-0-15-205750-3(1) , Harcourt Paperbacks) Harcourt Children's Bks.

Sabin, E. Rose. School for Sorcery. 2003. (gr. 5-8). lib. bdg. 14.15 (978-0-613-67854-4(0)) Tandem Library Bks.

—A School for Sorcery. rev. ed. 2002. 318p. 17.95 (978-0-7653-0289-2(6) , Forge Bks.) Doherty, Tom Assocs., LLC.

Sachar, Louis. A Magic Crystal? Loehr, Mallory, ed. Wummer, Amy, illus. 2000. (Marvin Redpost Ser.: No. 8). 96p. (J). (gr. k-3). lib. bdg. 11.99 (978-0-679-99002-4(X)); 3.99 (978-0-679-89002-7(5)) Random Hse. Children's Bks. (Random Hse. Bks. for Young Readers).

—A Magic Crystal? 2000. (Marvin Redpost Ser.: Bk. 8). (gr. 3-6). lib. bdg. 11.80 (978-0-613-28343-4(0)) Tandem Library Bks.

—A Magic Crystal? Wummer, Amy, illus. 2000. (J). (978-0-606-19902-5(0)) Tandem Library Bks.

Sadler, Marilyn. P. J. Funnybunny's Bag of Tricks. Bollen, Roger, illus. 2004. (Step into Reading Ser.). 32p. (J). (ps-2). pap. 3.99 (978-0-375-82444-9(8) , Random Hse. Bks. for Young Readers) Random Hse. Children's Bks.

—P J Funnybunny's Bag of Tricks. 2004. (ps-2). lib. bdg. 11.80 (978-0-613-83535-0(2)) Tandem Library Bks.

Sage, Angie. Flyte. Zug, Mark, illus. (Septimus Heap Ser.: Bk. 2). 544p. (J). (gr. 4 up). 2007. pap. 7.99 (978-0-06-057736-0(3) , Harper Trophy); 2006. lib. bdg. 18.89 (978-0-06-057735-3(5)); 2006. 17.99 (978-0-06-057734-6(7) , Tegen, Katherine Bks) HarperCollins Pubs.

—Magyk. Zug, Mark, illus. (Septimus Heap Ser.: Bk. 1). (J). (gr. 4 up). 2005. 576p. 17.99 (978-0-06-057731-5(2) , Tegen, Katherine Bks); 2005. 576p. lib. bdg. 18.89 (978-0-06-057732-2(0)); 2006. 608p. reprint ed. pap. 7.99 (978-0-06-057733-9(9) , Harper Trophy) HarperCollins Pubs.

—Physik. Zug, Mark, illus. (Septimus Heap Ser.: Bk. 3). 560p. (J). (gr. 4-6). 2008. pap. 7.99 (***978-0-06-057739-1(8)** , Harper Trophy); 2007. 17.99 (978-0-06-057737-7(1) , Tegen, Katherine Bks); 2007. lib. bdg. 18.89 (978-0-06-057738-4(X) , Tegen, Katherine Bks) HarperCollins Pubs.

—Septimus Heap Box Set: Books 1 And 2. Zug, Mark, illus. 2007. (Septimus Heap Ser.). (J). pap. 15.99 (***978-0-06-136195-1(X)** , Harper Trophy) HarperCollins Pubs.

Sakura's Never-Ending Day. 2001. (gr. 3-6). lib. bdg. 11.80 (978-0-613-33016-9(1)) Tandem Library Bks.

Sample, Stephanie & Sample, Scott. Audreena the Birthday Fairy. 2001. (Illus.). 32p. (J). (ps-3). 15.95 (978-0-86573-485-2(2) , Creative Publishing International) Quayside.

Sampson, Fay. Pangur Ban, the White Cat, Vol. 2. 2002. 160p. (J). (gr. 5-8). pap. 7.99 (978-0-7459-4763-1(8) , Lion) Lion Hudson plc GBR. *Dist:* Independent Pubs. Group.

—Shape-Shifter: The Naming of Pangur Ban. 2002. (Illus.). 160p. (J). (gr. 5-8). pap. 7.99 (978-0-7459-4762-4(X) , Lion) Lion Hudson plc GBR. *Dist:* Independent Pubs. Group.

Sampson, Fay. The Sorcerer's Daughter. 2007. 224p. (J). (gr. 4-7). pap. 9.95 (***978-0-7459-6072-2(3))** Lion Hudson plc GBR. *Dist:* Independent Pubs. Group.

Sampson, Jeff. The Stolen Sun. 2007. (Suncatcher Trilogy Ser.: Vol. 3). (J). (gr. 5-9). pap. 5.99 (***978-0-7869-4291-6(6)** , Mirrorstone) Wizards of the Coast.

—Wizard's Betrayal. 2006. (New Adventures Ser.). (Illus.). 241p. (J). (***978-1-4156-4798-1(4)** , Mirrorstone) Wizards of the Coast.

San Souci, Robert D. Cinderella Skeleton. Catrow, David, illus. 2004. 32p. (J). reprint ed. pap. 6.00 (978-0-15-205069-6(8) , Voyager Bks./Libros Viajeros) Harcourt Children's Bks.

—Faithful Friend. 1999. (gr. 3-6). lib. bdg. 15.30 (978-0-613-11526-1(0)) Tandem Library Bks.

Santillo, LuAnn. Look at Me. Santillo, LuAnn, ed. 2003. (Half-Pint Kids Readers Ser.). (Illus.). 7p. (J). (ps-1). pap. (978-1-59256-052-3(0)) Half-Pint Kids, Inc.

Sato, Wakiko. Grandma Baba's Magic Watermelon!, Vol. 8. Carpenter, Richard, tr. from JPN. 2004. (Grandma Baba Ser.). (Illus.). 28p. (J). 10.95 (978-0-8048-3567-1(5)) Tuttle Publishing.

Saunders, Kate. The Belfry Witches: Witch You Were Here. l.t. ed. 2005. (Illus.). 128p. (J). pap. (978-0-7540-6161-8(2) , CLP 355) BBC Audio.

Sauvant, Henriette. Rapunzel & Other Magic Fairy Tales. Bell, Anthea, tr. from MUL. 2007. (Illus.). 160p. (J). (gr. k-2). pap. 15.95 (***978-1-4052-2702-5(8))** Egmont Bks., Ltd. GBR. *Dist:* Independent Pubs. Group.

Sawler, Kimberley. Rocket & the Magical Cosmic Candies. 2007. (YA). 18.95 (***978-1-933285-51-1(6))** Brown Bks. Publishing Group.

Sawyer, Ruth. The Wee Christmas Cabin of Carn-Na-Ween. Grafe, Max, illus. 2005. 40p. (J). (gr. 3 up). 14.99 (978-0-7636-2553-5(1)) Candlewick Pr.

Scheunemann, Pam. Pelican's Pouch. Nobens, C. A., illus. 2007. (Fact & Fiction Ser.). 24p. (J). pap. (978-1-59928-463-7(4)); 21.35 (978-1-59928-462-0(6)) ABDO Publishing Co.

Schlesinger, Gretchen. Send Me the Soap #1: The Emerald Isle Adventure. Pietila, David, illus. 2006. (J). 11.95 (978-0-9778536-0-1(8)) Eco-thumb Publishing Co.

—Send Me the Soap #1: The Emerald Isle Adventure (lib. Bdg.) Pietila, David, illus. 2006. (J). lib. bdg. (978-0-9778536-1-8(6)) Eco-thumb Publishing Co.

Schoberle, Cecile. Snowflake Fairy Magic. Regan, Dana, illus. 2000. (J). 2.00 (978-0-689-84287-0(2) , Little Simon) Simon & Schuster Children's Publishing.

Scholastic, Inc. Staff. Mr Magorium's Wonder Emporium: Movie Reader. 2007. (Mr. Magorium's Wonder Emporium Ser.). 32p. (J). pap. 3.99 (***978-0-545-00516-6(7)** , Scholastic en Espanol) Scholastic, Inc.

Scholastic, Inc. Staff. World of Rainbow Brite. Swendsen, Silje, ed. 2004. (Rainbow Brite Ser.). (Illus.). 17p. (J). (ps-3). pap. 5.99 (978-0-439-65937-6(X)) Scholastic, Inc.

School Zone Publishing Company Staff & Hoenecke, Karen. The Magic Wand. 2000. (Start to Read Board Bks.). (Illus.). 10p. (J). (ps-k). bds. 4.99 (978-0-88743-809-7(1) , 06806) School Zone Publishing Co.

Schraff, Anne. Wishstone. 2001. (gr. 5-8). lib. bdg. 11.80 (978-0-613-63145-7(5)) Tandem Library Bks.

Schurch, Maylan. Beware of the Crystal Dragon. 2001. (J). mass mkt. 1.99 (978-0-8280-1610-0(0) , 21-660) Review & Herald Publishing Assn.

Schusterman, Neal. The Dark Side of Nowhere. unabr. ed. 2004. 192p. (J). (gr. 4-7). pap. 36.00 incl. audio (978-0-8072-8757-6(1) , YA258SP, Listening Library) Random Hse. Audio Publishing Group.

Schwabacher, Martin. The Magic School Bus Flies with the Dinosaurs. Bracken, Carolyn, illus. 2008. (Scholastic Reader Ser.). 32p. (J). pap. 3.99 (***978-0-439-80106-5(0))** Scholastic, Inc.

Schwartz, Howard. Day the Rabbi Disappeared: Jewish Holiday Tales of Magic. 2003. (gr. 3-6). lib. bdg. 18.75 (978-0-613-89176-9(7)) Tandem Library Bks.

Scieszka, Jon. Knights of the Kitchen Table. unabr. ed. 1998. (Time Warp Trio Ser.: No. 1). 55p. (J). (gr. 2-5). pap. 17.00 incl. audio (978-0-8072-0391-0(2) , FTR193SP, Listening Library) Random Hse. Audio Publishing Group.

—Me Oh Maya. McCauley, Adam, illus. 2005. (Time Warp Trio Ser.: No. 13). 96p. (J). pap. 4.99 (978-0-14-240300-6(8) , Puffin) Penguin Group (USA) Inc.

—South Pole or Bust (an Egg) 2007. (Time Warp Trio). 48p. (J). pap. 3.99 (978-0-06-111640-7(8) , Harper Trophy) HarperCollins Pubs.

—Summer Reading Is Killing Me! Smith, Lane, illus. 2004. (Time Warp Trio Ser.: No. 7). 80p. (J). (gr. 2-6). pap. 4.99 (978-0-14-240115-6(3) , Puffin) Penguin Group (USA) Inc.

—Summer Reading Is Killing Me! Smith, Lane & McCauley, Adam, illus. 1998. (Time Warp Trio Ser.: No. 7). 64p. (J). (gr. 3-7). 14.99 (978-0-670-88041-6(8) , Viking Juvenile) Penguin Group (USA) Inc.

Scott, Mavis. Magic Palace. Spoor, Mike, illus. 96p. pap. 8.95 (978-0-7022-2528-4(2)) Univ. of Queensland Pr. AUS. *Dist:* International Specialized Bk. Services.

Scott, Michael. The Alchemyst. 2007. (Secrets Imrtl Nicholas Flamel Ser.). (Illus.). 400p. (YA). (gr. 7 up). 16.99 (978-0-385-73357-1(7)); lib. bdg. 19.99 (978-0-385-90372-1(3)) Random Hse. Children's Bks. (Delacorte Bks. for Young Readers).

Scott, Susan Carlson. Fip's Magical World of Color, Vol. 14. Scott, Susan Carlson, illus. l.t. ed. 2002. (Illus.). 64p. (J). 15.95 (978-1-887932-94-3(1) , New Concord Pr.) Equine Graphics Publishing Group.

Scotton, Rob. Russell's Christmas Magic. Scotton, Rob, illus. 2007. 32p. (J). lib. bdg. 17.89 (***978-0-06-059855-6(7))** HarperCollins Pubs.

Sedgwick, Marcus. The Book of Dead Days. 2006. pap. 5.50 (978-0-440-41909-9(3)); 288p. (J). (gr. 5). reprint ed. pap. 7.95 (978-0-385-74704-2(7) , Lamb, Wendy) Random Hse. Children's Bks.

Sedgwick, Marcus. The Dark Flight Down. 240p. 2008. (YA). (gr. 7). pap. 7.99 (***978-0-553-48784-8(1));** 2005. (J). (gr. 5-7). 15.95 (978-0-385-74645-8(8)) Random Hse. Children's Bks. (Lamb, Wendy).

See, Linda. Cindy & Sean Centipede's: It Was Magical, Granny Wise Owl. 1998. (Illus.). 32p. (J). (gr. k-3). pap. 8.00 (978-0-8059-4458-7(3)) Dorrance Publishing Co., Inc.

Selman, Marty. Nick's a Chick. Weizman, Daniel, ed. 2000. (Jersey Ser.: 3). (Illus.). 128p. (gr. 3-7). pap. 4.99 (978-0-7868-4423-4(X)) Disney Pr.

—Nick's a Chick. 2000. (Jersey Ser.). (Illus.). (J). (978-0-606-20738-6(4)) Tandem Library Bks.

—This Rocks! Weizman, Daniel, ed. 2000. (Jersey Ser.: 4). (Illus.). 128p. (gr. 3-7). pap. 4.99 (978-0-7868-4424-1(8)) Disney Pr.

—This Rocks! 2000. (Jersey Ser.). (Illus.). (J). (978-0-606-20739-3(2)) Tandem Library Bks.

Service, Pamela F. Yesterday's Magic. 2008. (J). (gr. 3-7). 224p. 16.99 (***978-0-375-85577-1(7));** 320p. lib. bdg. 19.99 (***978-0-375-95577-8(1))** Random Hse. Children's Bks. (Random Hse. Bks. for Young Readers).

Seward, Angela. Maxx & the Wishing Bone. Easter, Avery, illus. 2001. 42p. (J). (ps-3). 15.95 (978-0-9710809-0-4(9)) Summer Sun Publishing.

Shah, Idries. The Magic Horse. Freeman, Julie, illus. 2001. 34p. (J). 6.99 (978-1-883536-26-8(X) , MAHO2, Hoopoe Bks.) ISHK.

Shalant, Phyllis. The Great Cape Rescue. 2007. (Society of Super Secret Heroes Ser.: Bk. 1). 128p. (J). (gr. 2-4). 15.99 (978-0-525-47404-3(8) , Dutton Juvenile) Penguin Group (USA) Inc.

Shan, Darren, pseud. Slawter. 2006. (Demonata Ser.: No. 3). 240p. (J). (gr. 10-17). 16.99 (978-0-316-01387-1(0)) Little Brown & Co.

—Slawter. 2007. (Demonata Ser.: No. 3). 240p. (J). (gr. 10-17). pap. 8.99 (***978-0-316-01388-8(9))** Little, Brown Bks. for Young Readers.

Shannon, David. Alicia el Hada. Shannon, David, illus. 2004. (SPA., Illus.). 40p. (J). (gr. k-ps). pap. 15.95 (978-0-439-66203-1(6) , Blue Sky Pr., The) Scholastic, Inc.

Sharp, D. L. M. A Pocket of Magic on Beechwood Street. 2004. (J). pap. (978-0-9762626-0-2(6)) Sharp, Diana Consulting.

Sharpe, Gerald. What Lies Beneath the Bed: Parade of Lights. 2007. 496p. (YA). pap. 11.00 (***978-1-933894-01-0(6))** IJN Publishing, Inc.

Sharratt, Nick. Muddlewitch on the Farm. 2007. (Illus.). 18p. (J). (ps-k). bds. 14.95 (***978-1-4052-2651-6(X))** Egmont Bks., Ltd. GBR. *Dist:* Independent Pubs. Group.

Shaskan, Trisha Speed. Marconi the Wizard. 2007. (Illus.). 24p. (J). (***978-1-4048-1234-5(2))** Picture Window Bks.

—Marconi the Wizard. Muehlenhardt, Amy Bailey, illus. 2006. 24p. (J). lib. bdg. (***978-1-4048-3167-4(3))** Picture Window Bks.

Shepard, Aaron. The Mountain of Marvels: A Celtic Tale of Magic, Retold from the Mabinogion. 2007. (Ancient Fantasy Ser.: 1). 46p. (J). pap. 6.00 (978-0-938497-36-3(7)); lib. bdg. 15.00 (978-0-938497-34-9(0)) Shepard Pubns. (Skyhook Pr.).

—The Songs of Power: A Finnish Tale of Magic, Retold from the Kalevala. 2007. (Ancient Fantasy Ser.: 2). 54p. (J). lib. bdg. 15.00 (978-0-938497-35-6(9)); lib. bdg. 6.00 (978-0-938497-37-0(5)) Shepard Pubns. (Skyhook Pr.).

Shetterly, Will. Nevernever. 2004. 226p. (YA). (gr. 9-12). lib. bdg. 13.60 (978-0-606-33013-8(5)) Tandem Library Bks.

Shire, Poppy. Brightheart the Knight's Pony. Berg, Ron, illus. 2007. (Magic Pony Carousel Ser.: No. 2). 96p. (J). pap. 3.99 (978-0-06-083782-2(9)); 14.99 (978-0-06-083780-8(2)) HarperCollins Pubs. (Harper Trophy).

—Magic Pony Carousel #4: Jewel the Midnight Pony. Berg, Ron, illus. 2008. (Magic Pony Carousel Ser.). 96p. (J). pap. 3.99 (***978-0-06-083788-4(8)** , Harper Trophy) HarperCollins Pubs.

—Sparkle the Circus Pony. Berg, Ron, illus. 2007. (Magic Pony Carousel Ser.: No. 1). 96p. (J). pap. 3.99 (978-0-06-083779-2(9)); 14.99 (978-0-06-083777-8(2)) HarperCollins Pubs. (Harper Trophy).

Shire, Poppy. Star the Western Pony. Berg, Ron, illus. 2007. (J). (***978-0-06-083783-9(7));** (Magic Pony Carousel Ser.: No.3). 96p. (gr. 2-5). pap. 3.99 (***978-0-06-083785-3(3))** HarperCollins Pubs. (Harper Trophy).

Shiro Amano. Kingdom Hearts, 4 vols., Vol. 4. 4th rev. ed. 2006. (Disney Squaresoft Ser.). (Illus.). pap. 5.99 (978-1-59816-220-2(9) , Tokyopop Kids) TOKYOPOP, Inc.

Shulman, Dee. Hetty the Yeti. Shulman, Dee, illus. 2005. (Read-It! Chapter Bks.). (Illus.). 52p. (J). (ps-k). lib. bdg. 19.95 (978-1-4048-1276-5(8)) Picture Window Bks.

Silverman. Mirror Mirror. 2004. 176p. (J). pap. 4.50 (978-0-439-44086-8(6) , Scholastic Paperbacks) Scholastic, Inc.

Silverman, A. O. Mirror, Mirror: Twisted Tales. 2002. (Illus.). 176p. (J). (gr. 5). pap. 15.95 (978-0-439-29593-2(9) , Chicken Hse., The) Scholastic, Inc.

Silvestre y la Piedrecita Magica. 1999. (SPA.). (J). 9.95 (978-1-56137-549-3(7)) Novel Units, Inc.

Simard, Remy. La Bottine Magique de Pipo. ed. 2004. (FRE., Illus.). (J). (gr. k-2). spiral bd. (978-0-616-01841-5(X)) Canadian National Institute for the Blind/Institut National Canadien pour les Aveugles.

Simmons, Marcia, et al. Annie's Shoes PC Book. 2002. cd-rom 5.00 (978-0-9721586-2-6(6)) Family Treasures Publishing Co.

Simmons, Steven J. Alice & Greta: A Tale of Two Witches. Moore, Cyd, illus. 1999. 32p. (J). (ps-3). pap. 6.95 (978-0-88106-976-1(0)) Charlesbridge Publishing, Inc.

—Alicia y Greta: Un Cuento de Dos Brujas. Mlawer, Teresa, tr. Moore, Cyd, illus. 2004. Tr. of Alice & Greta. (SPA.). 32p. (J). (gr. k-2). pap. 7.95 (978-0-88106-133-8(6) , CH5119) Charlesbridge Publishing, Inc.

Sims, Lesley. Enchanted Castle. Marks, Alan, illus. 2007. (Young Reading Series 2 Gift Bks). 64p. (J). 8.99 (***978-0-7945-1347-4(6)** , Usborne) EDC Publishing.

—Magical Book. 2007. (Young Reading Series 2 Gift Bks). 64p. (J). 8.99 (***978-0-7945-1703-8(X)** , Usborne) EDC Publishing.

Sinclair, Jay. It's Magic. 2000. (Jersey Ser.: 1). 128p. (gr. 3-7). pap. 4.99 (978-0-7868-4261-2(X)) Disney Pr.

—The Jersey. 2000. (Jersey Ser.). (Illus.). (J). 11.64 (978-0-606-20736-2(8)) Tandem Library Bks.

—No Girly-Girls Allowed! 2000. (Jersey Ser.). (Illus.). (J). (978-0-606-20737-9(6)) Tandem Library Bks.

Singh, Rina. The Magic Braid. Zaman, Farida, illus. Date not set. 134p. (J). pap. (978-0-920813-25-6(9)) Sister Vision Pr.

Singleton, Linda Joy. Sea Switch. 2005. (Illus.). 264p. (ps-7). pap. 5.99 (978-0-7387-0712-9(0)) Llewellyn Pubns.

—Shamrocked! 2005. 216p. pap. 4.99 (978-0-7387-0594-1(2)) Llewellyn Pubns.

M
N
O

Sisters of Isis3 & Ewing, Lynne. Enchantress. 3rd rev. ed. 2007. 256p. (gr. 7 up). 9.99 (***978-1-4231-0684-5(9)***) Hyperion Bks. for Children.

Skene, Pat. The Whoosh of Gadoosh. Keith, Doug, illus. 2002. 32p. 15.95 (978-0-9701907-0-3(0)) Illumination Arts Publishing Co., Inc.

Skye, Obert. Leven Thumps & the Gateway to Foo. 2005. (Leven Thumps Ser.: Bk. 1). (Illus.). 384p. (J). 17.95 (978-1-59038-369-8(9) , Shadow Mountain) Deseret Bk. Co.

—Leven Thumps & the Gateway to Foo. Sowards, Ben, illus. 2006. (Leven Thumps Ser.: Bk. 1). 400p. (J). (gr. 4 up). pap. 7.99 (978-1-4169-2806-5(5) , Aladdin) Simon & Schuster Children's Publishing.

Slack, David. Shendu Escapes! with Cards. 2002. (gr. 3-6). lib. bdg. 13.00 (978-0-613-72451-7(8)) Tandem Library Bks.

The Sleeping Beauty: Individual Title Six-Packs. 32p. (gr. 3 up). 37.00 (978-0-7635-9680-4(9)) Rigby Education.

Sleigh, Barbara. Carbonel: The King of Cats. Drummond, V. H., illus. 2004. 216p. (J). reprint ed. 16.95 (978-1-59017-126-4(8) , NYR Children's Collection) New York Review of Bks., Inc., The.

Smallcomb, Pam. Trimoni Twins & the Changing Coin. 2004. 175p. (J). 15.95 (978-1-58234-939-8(8) , Bloomsbury Children) Bloomsbury Publishing.

Smiletown's Upside Down. 2007. (J). per. 14.95 (***978-0-9785132-3-8(1)***) Smile-a-Lot, LLP.

Smith, Gordon. The Forest in the Hallway. 2006. 160p. (J). (gr. 5-9). 16.00 (978-0-618-68847-0(1) , Clarion Bks.) Houghton Mifflin Co. Trade & Reference Div.

Smith, Janice Lee. Wizard & Wart in Trouble. Meisel, Paul, illus. (I Can Read Bks.). 48p. (J). (ps-3). 2000. pap. 3.99 (978-0-06-444274-9(8)); 1998. 15.89 (978-0-06-027762-8(9)) HarperCollins Pubs.

—Wizard & Wart in Trouble. 2000. (I Can Read Bks.). (978-0-606-18731-2(6)) Tandem Library Bks.

Smith, Jullie. The Magic Carpet Adventures: Finding the Magic Carpet, Vol. 1. 2005. (ENG., Illus.). 36p. per. 19.25 (978-1-4208-6725-1(3)) AuthorHouse.

Smith, Linda. Talisa's Song. 2006. 272p. (YA). pap. 8.95 (978-1-55050-327-2(8)) Coteau Bks. CAN. *Dist:* F & W Pubns., Inc.

Smith, Linda. The Weathermage. 2007. (Tales of Three Lands Ser.). 384p. (YA). (gr. 6-8). 8.95 (***978-1-55050-352-4(9)***) Coteau Bks. CAN. *Dist:* Fitzhenry & Whiteside, Ltd.

Smith, Tara Bray. Betwixt. 2007. 488p. (YA). (gr. 10-17). 17.99 (***978-0-316-06033-2(X)***) Little, Brown Bks. for Young Readers.

Snell Jr., Mark "Jonathan". The Bee & the Magic Mirror: la Abela y el Espejo M+?gico. 2006. (ENG.). 32p. per. 13.24 (***978-1-4259-7214-1(4)***) AuthorHouse.

Snow White & the Seven Dwarfs: Individual Title Six-Packs. 32p. (gr. 2 up). 37.00 (978-0-7635-9401-5(6)) Rigby Education.

Snyder, Midori. Beldan's Fire. 2005. (Queen's Quarter Ser.: Bk. 3). 384p. (YA). (gr. 6-11). pap. 7.99 (978-0-14-240348-8(2) , Puffin) Penguin Group (USA) Inc.

Snyder, Zilpha Keatley. The Bronze Pen. 2008. 208p. (J). 16.99 (***978-1-4169-4201-6(7)***) Simon & Schuster Children's Publishing.

—The Headless Cupid. 2002. (Illus.). (J). 13.38 (978-0-7587-0269-2(8)) Book Wholesalers, Inc.

—The Unseen. 2005. 208p. 5.99 (978-0-440-41930-3(1) , Yearling) Random Hse. Children's Bks.

—The Witches of Worm. 2006. 22.00 (978-0-8446-7290-8(4)) Smith, Peter Pub., Inc.

Sobel, Gerrie. Jacob & His Magical Flying Bears: A Christmas Story. Torres, Dottie, illus. 2007. 32p. (J). 12.95 (***978-0-9798244-4-9(3)***) TRIAD Publishing Group.

Soesbee, Ree. Riddle in Stone. Fiegenshuh, Emily, illus. 2004. (Dungeons & Dragons Ser.). 192p. (YA). pap. 5.99 (978-0-7869-3211-5(2)) Wizards of the Coast.

Sokol, Edward. Meet Stinky Magee. Sokol, Edward, illus. 2000. (Illus.). 32p. (J). (ps-3). 14.95 (978-0-688-17416-3(7)) HarperCollins Pubs.

—Meet Stinky Magee. 2000. (Illus.). 32p. (J). (ps-3). 14.89 (978-0-688-17417-0(5)) HarperCollins Pubs.

Soloman, Ms Debra. Jasper & his magical Tail. 2006. 21p. (J). 10.00 (978-1-4116-3963-8(4)) Lulu.com.

Sonenklar, Carol. Bug Girl. 2000. (Illus.). (J). (978-0-606-18100-6(8)) Tandem Library Bks.

Spalding, Andrea. Dance of the Stones. 2003. (Summer of Magic Quartet Ser.). (Illus.). 192p. (J). (gr. 3-7). pap. 7.95 (978-1-55143-268-7(4)) Orca Bk. Pubs. USA.

—Heart of the Hill. 2005. (Dinah Galloway Mystery Ser.: Bk. 3Three). 192p. (J). (gr. 3-7). pap. 7.95 (978-1-55143-486-5(5)) Orca Bk. Pubs. USA.

—The Keeper & the Crows. 1999. (Young Reader Ser.). (Illus.). 128p. (J). (gr. 3-6). pap. 5.95 (978-1-55143-141-3(6)) Orca Bk. Pubs. USA.

—The Keeper & the Crows. 2000. (gr. 3-6). lib. bdg. 12.40 (978-0-613-83717-0(7)) Tandem Library Bks.

Spann, Bill. The Agents of Little Woods. 2005. 116p. pap. 16.95 (978-1-4137-6574-8(2)) PublishAmerica, Inc.

Spicer, Lin. Faerie Baby. 2006. pap. (***978-1-84426-384-4(3)***) Upfront Publishing Ltd.

Spinner, Stephanie. The Magic of Merlin. Sokolova, Valerie, illus. 2004. (Road to Reading Ser.). 48p. (J). (gr. k-3). pap. 3.99 (978-0-307-26403-9(3) , Random Hse. Bks. for Young Readers) Random Hse. Children's Bks.

—Magic of Merlin. 2000. (Road to Reading Ser.). (Illus.). (J). (978-0-606-20442-2(3)) Tandem Library Bks.

Spring, Manda. Emerald & the Magic of Raynon. 2004. 118p. pap. 16.95 (978-1-4137-3708-0(0)) PublishAmerica, Inc.

Springer, Nancy. I Am Morgan le Fay: A Tale from Camelot. 2002. (Firebird Ser.). 240p. (YA). pap. 6.99 (978-0-698-11974-1(6) , Puffin) Penguin Group (USA) Inc.

—I Am Morgan le Fay: A Tale from Camelot. 2002. (gr. 7-12). lib. bdg. 14.15 (978-0-613-55214-1(8)) Tandem Library Bks.

Stainer, M. L. Joachim's Magic. Melvin, James, illus. unabr. ed. 2001. (Heretics & Magic Ser.: Bk. 1). 180p. (YA). (gr. 6-9). pap. 6.95 (978-1-893337-07-7(3)); lib. bdg. 9.95 (978-1-893337-06-0(5)) Chicken Soup Pr., Inc.

Stainton, Sue. Christmas Magic. Melhuish, Eva, illus. 2007. 32p. (J). lib. bdg. 16.89 (***978-0-06-078572-7(1));*** 15.99 (***978-0-06-078571-0(3)***) HarperCollins Pubs. (Tegen, Katherine Bks).

Stampfl, Barbara. Lost Magic. 2001. (Illus.). 32p. (J). (ps-2). 10.00 (978-0-9713219-0-8(6)) Jumping Jack Holidays.

Stanek, Robert. In the Service of Dragons III. 2005. (Illus.). 240p. (J). (ps-7). pap. 14.00 (978-1-57545-093-3(3)) Reagent Pr.

—In the Service of Dragons IV. 2005. 240p. (YA). pap. 14.00 (978-1-57545-094-0(1)) Reagent Pr.

—The Kingdoms & the Elves of the Reaches. (Keeper Martin's Tales Ser.: Bk. 1). 2002. (YA). 22.95 (978-1-57545-073-5(9)); 2005. (Illus.). 240p. (J). pap. 14.00 (978-1-57545-059-9(3)) Reagent Pr.

—The Kingdoms & the Elves of the Reaches Bk. 1: Keeper Martin's Tales. Stanek, Robert, illus. alt. gif. ed. 2004. (Illus.). 176p. (YA). pap. 10.99 (978-1-57545-501-3(3) , Reagent Pr. Echo) Reagent Pr.

—The Kingdoms & the Elves of the Reaches II. (Keeper Martin's Tales Ser.: No. 2). 2002. (YA). 22.95 (978-1-57545-074-2(7)); 2005. (Illus.). 240p. (J). pap. 14.00 (978-1-57545-060-5(7)) Reagent Pr.

—The Kingdoms & the Elves of the Reaches II Bk. 2: Keeper Martin's Tales. Stanek, Robert, illus. alt. gif. ed. 2004. 180p. (YA). pap. 10.99 (978-1-57545-502-0(1) , Reagent Pr. Echo) Reagent Pr.

—The Kingdoms & the Elves of the Reaches III. (Keeper Martin's Tales Ser.: No. 3). 2003. (YA). 22.50 (978-1-57545-080-3(1)); 2005. (Illus.). 240p. (J). pap. 14.00 (978-1-57545-063-6(1)) Reagent Pr.

—The Kingdoms & the Elves of the Reaches III Bk. 3: Keeper Martin's Tales. Stanek, Robert, illus. alt. gif. ed. 2004. 172p. (YA). pap. 10.99 (978-1-57545-503-7(X) , Reagent Pr. Echo) Reagent Pr.

—The Kingdoms & the Elves of the Reaches IV. (Keeper Martin's Tales Ser.: No. 4). (YA). 2003. 22.50 (978-1-57545-081-0(X)); 2005. (Illus.). 240p. pap. 14.00 (978-1-57545-065-0(8)) Reagent Pr.

—The Kingdoms & the Elves of the Reaches IV Bk. 4: Keeper Martin's Tales. Stanek, Robert, illus. alt. gif. ed. 2005. 172p. (YA). pap. 10.99 (978-1-57545-504-4(8) , Reagent Pr. Echo) Reagent Pr.

Stanley, Diane. The Mysterious Matter of I. M. Fine. 208p. (J). (gr. 4 up). 2002. pap. 5.99 (978-0-380-73327-9(7)); 2001. (Illus.). 15.99 (978-0-688-17546-7(5)); 2001. (Illus.). lib. bdg. 16.89 (978-0-06-029619-3(4)) HarperCollins Pubs.

—The Mysterious Matter of I. M. Fine. 2002. (gr. 3-6). lib. bdg. 14.15 (978-0-613-60392-8(3)) Tandem Library Bks.

Staub, Wendy Corsi. Voodoo Moon. 2000. (Charmed Ser.: Vol. 5). 192p. (YA). (gr. 7 up). mass mkt. 6.99 (978-0-671-04166-3(5) , Simon Pulse) Simon & Schuster Children's Publishing.

Steele, Michael Anthony. Mr. Magorium's Wonder Emporium: Magical Movie Storybook. 2007. (Mr. Magorium's Wonder Emporium Ser.). 48p. (J). pap. 8.99 (***978-0-439-91252-5(0)***) Scholastic, Inc.

Stefano, Roberto D. La Magia de Pablo y Otros Cuentos con Poderes. Martin, Silvia, illus. 2000. (Chicos de la Valija Ser.).Tr. of Pablo's Magic Tricks & Other Magical Tales. (SPA.). 61p. (J). (gr. k-2). pap. 8.95 (978-950-739-829-2(5)) Errepar ARG. *Dist:* Baker & Taylor Bks.

Steig, William. The Amazing Bone. Steig, William, illus. 2002. (Illus.). (J). 14.43 (978-0-7587-0089-6(X)) Book Wholesalers, Inc.

—Sylvester & the Magic Pebble. Steig, William, illus. (Stories to Go! Ser.). (J). 2006. 32p. 4.99 (978-1-4169-1857-8(4) , Aladdin); 2005. (Illus.). 42p. 17.99 (978-1-4169-0206-5(6)) Simon & Schuster Children's Publishing.

Stein, Mathilde. Brave Ben. 2006. (Illus.). 32p. (J). 15.95 (978-1-932425-64-2(0) , Lemniscaat) Boyds Mills Pr.

Stephenson, Larry K. & Weinbrenner, Patti. The Butterfly King: A Legend for the New Millennium. Stephenson, Larry K., illus. 1999. (Illus.). v, 45p. (J). (gr. 4). 19.95 (978-0-9672202-0-8(3)) Jewel Box & Friends.

Stevens, Janet & Crummel, Susan Stevens. Jackalope. Stevens, Janet, illus. 2003. (Illus.). 56p. (J). (gr. k-3). 17.00 (978-0-15-216736-3(6)) Harcourt Children's Bks.

Stevermer, Caroline. A College of Magics. 2002. 468p. (gr. 7-12). per. 14.15 (978-0-613-62606-4(0)) Tandem Library Bks.

Stevermer, Caroline & Wrede, Patricia C. Sorcery & Cecelia or the Enchanted Chocolate Pot: Being the Correspondence of Two Young Ladies of Quality Regarding Various Magical Scandals in London & the Country. 2004. (Illus.). 336p. (YA). pap. 6.95 (978-0-15-205300-0(X) , Magic Carpet Bks.) Harcourt Children's Bks.

Stewart, Pat. Invisible Wizards Magic Picture Book. 2003. (Dover Little Activity Bks.). (Illus.). 16p. (J). pap. 1.50 (978-0-486-42636-5(X)) Dover Pubns., Inc.

Stine, Megan. Power of the Rat. 2002. (gr. 3-6). lib. bdg. 13.00 (978-0-613-72454-8(2)) Tandem Library Bks.

Stine, R. L. Chicken Chicken. rev. ed. 2007. (Goosebumps Ser.). 144p. (J). pap. 4.99 (978-0-439-89113-4(2)) Scholastic, Inc.

—Nightmare Hour. 2000. (Illus.). 160p. (J). (gr. 5 up). pap. 5.99 (978-0-06-440842-4(6) , Avon) HarperCollins Pubs.

—Nightmare Hour: Time for Terror. 1999. (Illus.). 160p. (J). (gr. 3 up). 16.99 (978-0-06-028688-0(1)) HarperCollins Pubs.

—Nightmare Hour: Time for Terror. 2000. (gr. 5-8). lib. bdg. 14.15 (978-0-613-71481-5(4)) Tandem Library Bks.

Stockham, Jess, et al, illus. The Frog Prince. 2007. 24p. pap. 5.99 (***978-1-84643-077-0(1)***) Child's Play International Ltd. GBR. *Dist:* Child's Play-International.

Stockton, Frank Richard. The Bee-Man of Orn: And Other Fanciful Tales. 2007. 140p. pap. 10.99 (***978-1-4264-5788-3(X));*** 154p. pap. 14.99 (***978-1-4264-5848-4(7)***) BiblioBazaar.

Stolarz, Laurie Faria. The Blue Is for Nightmares Collection. 2006. 1224p. pap., pap. 29.95 (978-0-7387-0988-8(3) , Flux) Llewellyn Pubns.

—Silver Is for Secrets. 2005. (Blue Is for Nightmares Ser.: Vol. 3). 288p. pap. 8.95 (978-0-7387-0631-3(0)) Llewellyn Pubns.

—White Is for Magic. Karre, Andrew, ed. 2004. (Blue Is for Nightmares Ser.: Vol. 2). 312p. pap. 8.95 (978-0-7387-0443-2(1)) Llewellyn Pubns.

Stone, David Lee. The Ratastrophe Catastrophe. Lea, Bob, illus. 2004. (Illmoor Chronicles Ser.: Bk. 1). 288p. (gr. 5-9). 16.99 (978-0-7868-5128-7(7)) Hyperion Bks. for Children.

Stone, Forrest. Loki & the Magic Hammer: A Norse Myth. 2006. 42.00 (***978-1-4108-6178-8(3)***) Benchmark Education Co.

Stone, Kelsey. The Predahil Chronicles. 2005. (YA). per. 6.49 (978-1-59196-995-2(6)) Instantpublisher.com.

Strasser, Todd. Here Comes Heavenly: Pastabilities. 2000. (J). (978-0-606-19054-1(6)) Tandem Library Bks.

Strauss, Linda Leopold. A Fairy Called Hilary. Truesdell, Sue, illus. 1999. 96p. (J). (gr. 4-6). tchr. ed. 15.95 (978-0-8234-1418-5(3)) Holiday Hse., Inc.

Strega Nona. 2005. (J). (978-1-59564-834-1(8)) Steps To Literacy, LLC.

Strickland, Brad. Grimoire: Curse of the Midions. 2006. 240p. (J). (gr. 4). 11.99 (978-0-8037-3060-1(8) , Dial) Penguin Group (USA) Inc.

—Grimoire: Tracked by Terror. 2007. 192p. (J). (gr. 4-3). 15.99 (***978-0-8037-3061-8(6)*** , Dial) Penguin Group (USA) Inc.

—The House Where Nobody Lived. 2006. 176p. (J). (gr. 4-7). 16.99 (978-0-8037-3148-6(5) , Dial) Penguin Group (USA) Inc.

—The Tower at the End of the World. Schindler, S. D., illus. 2001. (Lewis Barnavelt Ser.). 160p. (J). 16.99 (978-0-8037-2620-8(1) , Dial) Penguin Group (USA) Inc.

—The Whistle, the Grave & the Ghost. 2003. (Lewis Barnavelt Ser.). 160p. (J). (gr. 4). 16.99 (978-0-8037-2622-2(8) , Dial) Penguin Group (USA) Inc.

Stroud, Jonathan. The Amulet of Samarkand. 2003. (Bartimaeus Trilogy Ser.: Bk. 1). (Illus.). 464p. (gr. 5-17). 17.95 (978-0-7868-1859-4(X)) Hyperion Bks. for Children.

—The Golem's Eye. 2nd rev. ed. 2006. (Bartimaeus Trilogy Ser.: Bk. 2). 576p. (gr. 5-17). reprint ed. pap. 7.99 (978-0-7868-3654-3(7)) Miramax Bks.

—Ptolemy's Gate. 3rd rev. ed. 2006. (Bartimaeus Trilogy Ser.: Bk. 3). 512p. (gr. 5-17). 17.95 (978-0-7868-1861-7(1)) Miramax Bks.

Stuart, Guyla W. The Magic Camera. 2004. 10.95 (978-0-533-12793-1(9)) Vantage Pr., Inc.

Stutzman, D. J. The Promise Ring. 2007. (J). pap. 9.00 (***978-0-8059-7365-5(6)***) Dorrance Publishing Co., Inc.

Suarez, Sergio Lopez. Huakala! a los Miedos. Suarez, Sergio Lopez, illus. 2003. (SPA., Illus.). 32p. (J). (gr. k-3). 9.95 (978-968-19-0556-9(3)) Aguilar, Altea, Taurus, Alfaguara, S.A. de C.V MEX. *Dist:* Santillana USA Publishing Co., Inc.

—Huakala! a los Miedos. 2000. (SPA.). 32p. (J). (ps-3). 15.95 (978-84-204-4936-4(9)) Alfaguara, Ediciones, S.A.- Grupo Santillana ESP. *Dist:* Santillana USA Publishing Co., Inc.

Suhay, Lisa. Our Fantasy Island. 2006. 30p. (J). pap. 8.00 (***978-0-9766628-0-8(9)***) Fantasy Island Pr.

Sula, Sondra. Zander's Portal: The Magic Scroll. 2000. mass mkt. 4.50 (978-1-931179-55-3(7)); mass mkt. 8.95 (978-1-931179-56-0(5)) Long Hill Productions, Inc.

Sullivan, Jenny. Gwydion & the Flying Wand. 2000. 76p. pap. 11.95 (978-1-85902-836-0(5)) Beekman Bks., Inc.

—Magic Maldwyn. 2002. (WEL.). 72p. pap. 11.95 (978-1-84323-074-8(7)) Beekman Bks., Inc.

Summers, Gillian. Into the Wildewood. 2008. 312p. (J). pap. 9.95 (***978-0-7387-1332-8(5)*** , Flux) Llewellyn Pubns.

Sutherland, David, et al. Siriol Llywelyn a'r Salwch Chwyrlio Erchyll. 2005. (WEL., Illus.). 45p. (978-1-85596-679-6(4)) Dref Wen.

Sutherland, Tui. So This Is How It Ends. 2006. (Avatars Ser.: Bk. 1). 368p. (J). 16.99 (978-0-06-075024-4(3) , Eos); lib. bdg. 17.89 (978-0-06-075028-2(6)) HarperCollins Pubs.

Swanson, Stan. The Misadventures of Hobart Huckleback. 2007. (J). 16.95 (***978-0-9787925-3-4(X));*** per. 9.95 (***978-0-9787925-2-7(1)***) Stony Meadow Publishing.

Swope, Sam. Jack & the Seven Deadly Giants. Cneut, Carll, illus. 2004. 112p. (J). 16.00 (978-0-374-33670-7(9) , Frances Foster Bks.) Farrar, Straus & Giroux.

Tabori, Lena & Tabori-Fried, Natasha, eds. The Little Big Book of Chills & Thrills. (Illus.). 352p. (J). (ps-7). 24.95 (978-1-932183-85-6(X) , Welcome Bks.) Welcome Enterprises, Inc.

Takahashi, Rumiko. Inu-Yasha: Anime/Manga Box Set. Takahashi, Rumiko, illus. 2003. (Inuyasha Ser.). 200p. (YA). pap. 39.98 (978-1-59116-235-3(1) , Viz Comics) Viz Media.

Talbert, Marc. Double or Nothing. 2001. 136p. (gr. 4-7). pap. 9.95 (978-0-595-15009-0(8) , Backinprint.com) iUniverse, Inc.

The Tale of Jackie Berry. 2005. (J). per. 12.95 (978-0-9677047-5-3(8)) Marble House Editions.

Tandi's World. 2006. (J). (978-0-9772634-0-0(1)) Hall, Monique P. Productions.

Tarver, S., 1st. Imaga & the Magic Pearls, 2nd l.t. ed. 2003. (Illus.). 20p. (J). 6.99 (978-0-9743568-0-8(8)) Tarver, Monroe.

Taulbert, Clifton L. Little Rooster's Little Cliff & the Porch People. Kane, Cindy, ed. Lewis, Earl, illus. 1999. 32p. (J). (ps-3). 16.99 (978-0-8037-2174-6(9) , Dial) Penguin Group (USA) Inc.

Taylor, Cora. Murder in Mexico. 2007. (Spy Who Wasn't There Ser.). (Illus.). 360p. (J). (gr. 4-7). pap. 7.95 (***978-1-55050-353-1(7)***) Coteau Bks. CAN. *Dist:* Fitzhenry & Whiteside, Ltd.

Taylor, G. P. Shadowmancer. 2003. (Illus.). 304p. (J). pap. (978-0-571-22046-5(0)) Faber & Faber, Ltd.

—Shadowmancer. (YA). 2005. 288p. (gr. 7). pap. 7.99 (978-0-14-240341-9(5) , Puffin); 2004. 304p. (gr. 4 up). 16.99 (978-0-399-24256-4(2) , Putnam Juvenile) Penguin Group (USA) Inc.

—Shadowmancer. 2004. (Illus.). 280p. 16.99 (978-1-59185-613-9(2)) Strang Communications Co.

—The Shadowmancer Returns: The Curse of Salamander Street. 2007. 272p. (YA). (gr. 7 up). 17.99 (978-0-399-24346-2(1) , Putnam Juvenile) Penguin Group (USA) Inc.

Taylor, James Henry. Honeysuckle & Other Stories. 2001. 83p. per. 6.50 (978-0-9713497-0-4(3)) Cave Hollow Pr.

Taylor, Laini. Blackbringer. 2007. (Faeries of Dreamdark Ser.). 368p. (J). (gr. 5 up). 17.99 (978-0-399-24630-2(4) , Putnam Juvenile) Penguin Group (USA) Inc.

Taylor, S. G. Books of Merlin I. 2006. pap. 10.49 (***978-1-4259-6740-6(X)***) AuthorHouse.

Taylor, Terry. Tim the Young Magician: Tim Discovers Magic. 2005. 48p. pap. 12.95 (978-1-4137-6023-1(6)) PublishAmerica, Inc.

Temple-West, Mariga. Louise & Edna. 2001. 128p. per. 12.75 (978-1-931633-05-5(3)) New World Media, Inc.

Terry, Will, illus. Little Rooster's Diamond Button. 2007. 32p. (J). (ps-2). 16.95 (978-0-8075-4644-4(5)) Whitman, Albert & Co.

Thomas, Joyce Carol. Christmas & the Magic Pie Pan. 32p. (J). Date not set. lib. bdg. 15.89 (978-0-06-025386-8(X)); 2001. (978-0-06-025385-1(1)) HarperCollins Pubs. (Cotler, Joanna Books).

Thomas, Patrick. The Wildsidhe Chronicles Bk. 1: Welcome to the Wildsidhe. 2002. (J). pap. 7.99 (978-1-890096-12-0(1)) Padwolf Publishing, Inc.

—The Wildsidhe Chronicles Bk. 2: Double Cross. 2002. (J). pap. 7.99 (978-1-890096-14-4(8)) Padwolf Publishing, Inc.

Thompson, Colin. The Floods #1: Good Neighbors. Scrambly, Crab, illus. 2008. (Floods Ser.). 224p. (J). 15.99 (***978-0-06-113196-7(2));*** lib. bdg. 16.89 (***978-0-06-113199-8(7)***) HarperCollins Pubs.

Thompson, John M. & Schultz, George M. Just Imagine. Wodin, illus. 2006. 32p. 16.95 (***978-0-9740190-6-2(2)***) Illumination Arts Publishing Co., Inc.

Thornton, Duncan. Kalifax. Noblet, Yves, illus. 1999. 184p. (J). (gr. 5-9). 8.95 (978-1-55050-152-0(6)) Coteau Bks. CAN. *Dist:* Fitzhenry & Whiteside, Ltd.

Thumbelina. 2002. (Classic Tales Mini Bks.). (Illus.). 32p. (J). (978-1-59069-036-9(2) , T1005); incl. audio compact disk (978-1-59069-103-8(2) , T1105) Studio Mouse LLC.

Tich, Jan & Jantti, Mariana. The Sea Fairy's Hat. 2006. (Magical Stories Ser.). (Illus.). 28p. (J). 16.95 (978-9974-7896-8-5(0)) Hardenville SA URY. *Dist:* Independent Pubs. Group.

Tiernan, Cate. Dark Magick. 2001. (Sweep Ser.: Bk. 4). 192p. (YA). (gr. 7 up). pap. 5.99 (978-0-14-131112-8(6) , Puffin) Penguin Group (USA) Inc.

—Dark Magick. 2001. (gr. 7-12). lib. bdg. 13.00 (978-0-613-64035-0(7)) Tandem Library Bks.

—Spellbound. 2001. (Sweep Ser.: Bk. 6). 192p. (YA). (gr. 7 up). pap. 6.99 (978-0-14-230046-6(2) , Puffin) Penguin Group (USA) Inc.

—Spellbound. 2001. (gr. 7-12). lib. bdg. 13.00 (978-0-613-64112-8(4)) Tandem Library Bks.

Toda, Akihito & Wada, Junko. Don't Laugh Charizard. Kimura, Naoyo et al, illus. 2001. (Pokemon Tales Ser.: Vol. 19). 18p. (YA). (ps-k). 4.95 (978-1-56931-570-5(1)) Viz Media.

Tomizawa, Hitoshi. Treasure Hunter 1: Eternal Youth, 3 vols., Vol. 1. Pannone, Frank, ed. Kobayashi, Mayumi, tr. from JPN. Tomizawa, Hitoshi, illus. 2004. Orig. Title: Hizenya Jyubei 2. (Illus.). 200p. pap. 9.99 (978-1-58664-921-0(3) , CMX 65101G, CPM Manga) Central Park Media Corp.

Tomlinson, Heather. The Swan Maiden. 2007. 304p. (YA). (gr. 7 up). 17.95 (***978-0-8050-8275-3(1)***) Holt, Henry & Co.

Torba, Ed. The Magic Trip. Hansen, Kate, illus. 2002. (YA). per. 15.00 (978-0-9765748-0-4(2)) Torba Publishing.

Touring Europe on a Magic Carpet. 2004. (J). ring bd. 4.50 (978-0-9762740-9-4(4)) Smart Smiles Co., The.

Towell, Katy. The Little Girl Who Was Forgotten by Absolutely Everyone (Even the Postman) 2005. 56p. (YA). pap. 16.99 (978-1-4116-5919-3(8)) Lulu.com.

Town, Nathan. Ned Stapleton & the Wrath of the Death Gods. 2006. 174p. (YA). (***978-0-9781040-0-9(5)***) Emerald City Storytellers.

Townsend, Tom. Never Trust a One-Eyed Wizard: The Fairie Ring, Vol. 2. 2000. (Fairie Ring Ser.: Vol. 2). 171p. (YA). (gr. 8 up). 9.99 (978-0-88092-526-6(4)) Royal Fireworks Publishing Co.

Tracy, Judith. The Wildsidhe Chronicles Bk. 3: Dark Proposal. 2003. (J). pap. 7.99 (978-1-890096-15-1(6)) Padwolf Publishing, Inc.

—The Wildsidhe Chronicles Bk. 4: Legacy. 2002. (J). pap. 7.99 (978-1-890096-16-8(4)) Padwolf Publishing, Inc.

Travers, P. L. Mary Poppins. Shepard, Mary, illus. 2006. 224p. (J). 12.95 (978-0-15-205810-4(9) , Harcourt Young Classics) Harcourt Children's Bks.

MNO

—Mary Poppins Vintage Boxed Set: Three Enchanting Classics: Mary Poppins, Mary Poppins Comes Back, & Mary Poppins Opens the Door. 2007. (Illus.). (J). 38.85 (978-0-15-205858-6(3)) Harcourt Children's Bks.

Trejo, Delia. A Fairy Tale for Artemis. 2002. 238p. pap. 14.95 (978-0-595-23437-0(2) , Writer's Showcase Pr.) iUniverse, Inc.

Trimble, Marcia. Witchy's Turned-Around House. Cameron, Chad, illus. 1998. 32p. (J). (ps-5). 15.95 (978-1-891577-27-7(1)) Images Pr.

Trondheim, Lewis. McConey Vol. 2: The Hoodoodad. 1998. (Fantagraphics Ser.). (Illus.). 48p. (gr. 10 up). pap. 10.95 (978-1-56097-338-6(2)) Fantagraphics Bks.

Trondhein, Lewis. Harum Scarum: The Spiffy Adventures of McConey, Vol. 1. (Illus.). 48p. (gr. 10 up). pap. 10.95 (978-1-56097-288-4(2)) Fantagraphics Bks.

Troulis, Jennifer. Penelope & Priscilla & the City of the Banished. 2007. (J). per. 14.95 (***978-0-9768602-1-1(X)***) Twin Monkeys Pr.

Troulis, Jennifer. Penelope & Priscilla & the Enchanted House of Whispers. 2005. (Illus.). (J). pap. 13.95 (978-0-9768602-0-4(1)) Twin Monkeys Pr.

Trudeau, Scott & Holzbauer, David. A Treasure to Share: Adventures in Social Skills. Trudeau, Scott, illus. 2003. (Illus.). 68p. (J). (978-0-9743805-0-6(4)) Intellipop, LLC.

Tsukirino, Yumi. Incredible Shrinking Hazel, Pt. 4. Tsukirino, Yumi, illus. 2001. (Magical Pokemon Journey Ser.: Pt. 4, No. 3). (Illus.). 40p. (YA). pap. 4.95 (978-1-56931-676-4(7)) Viz Media.

—Magical Pokemon Journey Vol. 4: Kadabra's Magic Show. Tsukirino, Yumi, illus. 2001. (Magical Pokemon Journey, Part 3 Ser.: No. 4). (Illus.). 40p. (YA). (ps-3). pap. 4.95 (978-1-56931-557-6(4)) Viz Media.

Tucker, Kathy. Leprechaun in the Basement. 2002. (gr. k-3). lib. bdg. 15.25 (978-0-613-75744-7(0)) Tandem Library Bks.

Turner, Jessie E. Moon in the Day Sky. 2006. 19p. (YA). pap. 19.95 (***978-1-59299-238-6(2)***) Inkwater Pr.

Turner, Megan Whalen. Instead of Three Wishes: Magical Short Stories. 2006. 160p. (J). pap. 5.99 (978-0-06-084231-4(8)) HarperCollins Pubs.

Tyrrell, Melissa. The Gingerbread Man. McMullen, Nigel, illus. 2005. (Fairytale Friends Ser.: Vol. 8). 12p. (J). (ps-k). bds. 5.95 (978-1-58117-154-9(4) , Intervisual/Piggy Toes) Dalmatian Pr.

Uderzo, Albert & Goscinny, René. Asterix & the Vikings. 2007. (Illus.). 64p. 12.95 (978-0-7528-8590-2(1)) Orion Bks. Ltd. GBR. *Dist:* Sterling Publishing Co., Inc.

Umansky, Kaye. Pongwiffy & the Spell of the Year. Smedley, Chris, illus. 2002. 160p. (YA). mass mkt. 4.50 (978-0-7434-1914-7(6) , Aladdin) Simon & Schuster Children's Publishing.

Ungerer, Tomi. Tortoni Tremolo: The Cursed Musician. Ungerer, Tomi, illus. 2004. (Illus.). 28p. (J). (gr. k-4). reprint ed. 17.00 (978-0-7567-9047-9(6)) DIANE Publishing Co.

—Tortoni Tremolo the Cursed Magician. Ungerer, Tomi, illus. 1998. (Illus.). 32p. (J). (gr. 1-5). 16.95 (978-1-57098-226-2(0)) Rinehart, Roberts Pubs.

Valdés, Zoé. Los Aretes de la Luna. 2nd ed. 2000. (SPA., Illus.). 72p. (J). (gr. 3-5). 6.36 net. (978-84-241-7888-8(2)) Lectorum Pubns., Inc.

Van Allsburg, Chris. Probuditi! 2006. (Illus.). 32p. (J). (gr. 3-5). 18.95 (978-0-618-75502-8(0)) Houghton Mifflin Co. Trade & Reference Div.

Vande Velde, Vivian. Curses, Inc. & Other Stories. 2007. (Illus.). 240p. (J). pap. 6.95 (***978-0-15-206107-4(X)*** , Magic Carpet Bks.) Harcourt Children's Bks.

—Magic Can Be Murder. 2002. 197p. (J). (gr. 4-7). per. 14.15 (978-0-613-53832-9(3)) Tandem Library Bks.

—Now You See It... 2005. (Illus.). 288p. (YA). 17.00 (978-0-15-205311-6(5)) Harcourt Children's Bks.

—Wizard at Work. 2003. (Illus.). 144p. (YA). 16.00 (978-0-15-204559-3(7)) Harcourt Children's Bks.

—Wizard at Work: A Novel in Stories. 2004. (Illus.). 144p. (J). pap. 5.95 (978-0-15-205309-3(3) , Magic Carpet Bks.) Harcourt Children's Bks.

Varennes, Monique de. Bibi & the Sad Ballerinas. Juan, Ana, illus. 2006. (J). 16.95 (978-0-689-87665-3(3) , Atheneum) Simon & Schuster Children's Publishing.

Varennes, Monique de. The Jewel Box Ballerinas. Juan, Ana, illus. 2007. 40p. (J). (ps-3). 16.99 (***978-0-375-83605-3(5)*** , Schwartz & Wade Bks.) Random Hse. Children's Bks.

Vaughan, Christina. Badda-Badda's Bad Spells. 2000. (Illus.). (J). (gr. 2-6). spiral bd. 18.95 (978-0-9641697-4-6(6) , You-Draw-It Bks.) Castlebrook Pubns.

Velde, Vivan V. A Hidden Magic. 176p. (J). pap. 5.00 (978-0-8072-1519-7(8) , Listening Library) Random Hse. Audio Publishing Group.

Venable, Alan. Take Me with You When You Go. Marshall, Laurie, illus. 2008. 112p. (J). 12.95 (***978-0-9777082-7-7(6)***) One Monkey Books.

Vercz, Carol A. The Magic of Hildie. (J). 6.95 (978-0-910119-44-3(9)) S.O.C.O. Pubns.

Verne, Jules. Viaje Al Centro de la Tierra. 2004. (Illus.). 48p. (J). (ps-ps). lib. bdg. 12.75 (978-0-606-30424-5(X)) Tandem Library Bks.

Verrillo, Erica F. Elissa's Quest. 2007. (Phoenix Rising Trilogy Ser.). 352p. (J). (gr. 4-7). 16.99 (978-0-375-83946-7(1)); lib. bdg. 19.99 (978-0-375-93946-4(6)) Random Hse. Children's Bks. (Random Hse. Bks. for Young Readers).

—Elissa's Quest. 2007. (J). pap. (978-0-375-83947-4(X)) Random Hse., Inc.

Villaseñor, Victor. Walking Stars: Stories of Magic & Power. 2003. (gr. 7-12). lib. bdg. 19.90 (978-0-613-89452-4(9)); 1998. 180p. (YA). (gr. 8-12). lib. bdg. 22.20 (978-0-613-59028-0(7)) Tandem Library Bks.

Vornholt, John. The Troll King. 2003. 272p. (J). 22.95 (978-0-7862-5049-3(6)) Thorndike Pr.

—Troll King. 2002. (gr. 5-8). lib. bdg. 13.00 (978-0-613-70774-9(5)) Tandem Library Bks.

—The Troll Queen. l.t. ed. 2004. (Troll King Ser.). 241p. 20.95 (978-0-7862-6517-6(5)) Thorndike Pr.

Waite, Judy. A Trick of the Mind. 2005. (Illus.). 272p. (YA). (gr. 7). 16.95 (978-0-689-87014-9(0) , Atheneum) Simon & Schuster Children's Publishing.

—Trick of the Mind. 2006. 288p. (YA). pap. 6.99 (978-0-689-87015-6(9) , Simon Pulse) Simon & Schuster Children's Publishing.

Waldman, Thomas. 1 ! 2 ! 3 ! 4 ! Saisons. 2005. 10p. 8.53 (978-1-4116-3332-2(6)) Lulu.com.

Walker, Richard. Jack & Beanstalk. Sharkey, Niamh, illus. 2006. 0040p. 9.99 (978-1-905236-69-5(7)) Barefoot Bks., Inc.

Walker, Russell D. Michelle & the Magic Timepiece. 2006. 108p. pap. 16.95 (978-1-4241-3143-3(X)) PublishAmerica, Inc.

Walker, Victoria. The Winter of Enchantment. 2007. (J). (***978-1-930900-33-2(3)***) Purple Hse. Pr.

Walkow, Jim. The Zabbit: The Magic's in You. Carson, Shawn, illus. 2001. 40p. (J). 19.95 (978-0-9710394-0-7(2)) Cloud 9 Publishing, L L C.

Wallace, Karen. Queen Carrion's Big Bear Hug. Flook, Helen, illus. 2007. (J). lib. bdg. (***978-1-4048-3709-6(4)***) Picture Window Bks.

Wallace, Karen. Where Are My Shoes? Allwright, Deborah, illus. 2005. (Reading Corner Ser.). 24p. (J). (gr. k-3). lib. bdg. 22.80 (978-1-59771-002-2(4)) Sea-To-Sea Pubns.

Wang, An. Anywhere but Here. 2006. 100p. (YA). pap. 9.95 (978-0-88100-140-2(6)) National Writers Pr., The.

Ward, John. The Stone of Sorrow: The Revealer of Wonders. 2004. (Fate of the Stone Ser.: Pt. 2). 256p. (YA). pap. (978-1-55207-080-2(8)) Studio 9 Bks. and Music.

Warner, Mike. The Titanic Game. Ordaz, Frank, illus. 2007. 201p. (J). pap. 9.95 (978-0-9744446-2-8(6)) All About Kids Publishing.

Watase, Yuu. Alice 19th Vol. 1: Lotis Master. Watase, Yuu, illus. 2003. (Alice 19th Ser.). (Illus.). 192p. (YA). pap. 9.95 (978-1-59116-215-5(7)) Viz Media.

—Alice 19th Vol. 2: Inner Heart. JN Productions Staff, tr. 2003. (Alice 19th Ser.). (Illus.). 200p. (YA). pap. 9.95 (978-1-59116-229-2(7)) Viz Media.

Watson, Richard Jesse. The Magic Rabbit. Watson, Richard Jesse, illus. 2005. (Illus.). 40p. (J). pap. 15.95 (978-0-590-47964-6(4) , Blue Sky Pr., The) Scholastic, Inc.

Weber, Jen Funk. Hogsqueal's Activity Book. 2008. (Spiderwick Chronicles). 64p. 4.99 (***978-1-4169-4951-0(8)*** , Simon Scribbles) Simon & Schuster Children's Publishing.

Weinberg, Jennifer. Surprise for a Princess. Emslie, Peter & Marrucchi, Elisa, illus. 2003. (Disney Princess Ser.). 32p. (J). (ps-1). pap. 3.99 (978-0-7364-2132-4(7) , RH/Disney) Random Hse. Children's Bks.

—Surprise for a Princess. 2003. (Disney Princess Ser.). (ps-2). lib. bdg. 11.80 (978-0-613-73686-2(9)) Tandem Library Bks.

Weinberger, Kimberly. Sakura & the New Boy. 2001. (Cardcaptors Ser.: Bk. 1). (Illus.). 48p. (J). (ps-3). pap. 3.99 (978-0-439-25186-0(9)) Scholastic, Inc.

Weis, Margaret & Hickman, Tracy. To the Gates of Palanthas. 2003. (Dragonlance Ser.: Pt. 4). (Illus.). 256p. (YA). pap. 5.99 (978-0-7869-3096-8(9)) Wizards of the Coast.

Weller, Duncan. The Boy from the Sun. 2007. (Illus.). 36p. 16.95 (978-1-894965-33-0(7)) Simply Read Bks. CAN. *Dist:* Perseus Distribution.

Welles, Lee. Gaia Girls Enter the Earth. 2006. (Gaia Girls Ser.). (Illus.). 336p. (YA). 18.95 (978-1-933609-00-3(1)) Daisyworld Pr.

Wells, Carolyn. Patty Fairfield. 2004. reprint ed. pap. 20.95 (978-1-4191-4033-4(7)); pap. 1.99 (978-1-4192-4033-1(1)) Kessinger Publishing, LLC.

Wells, H. G. The Magic Shop. Roca, Francois, illus. 2005. 32p. (J). (gr. 1-4). lib. bdg. 16.85 (978-1-933327-06-8(5)) Purple Bear Bks., Inc.

Wells, H. G. & Roca, Francois. The Magic Shop. ed. 2005. (Illus.). 32p. (J). 15.95 (978-1-933327-02-0(2)) Purple Bear Bks., Inc.

Werner, Teresa O. A Quilt of Wishes. Tremlin, Nathan, illus. l.t. ed. 2005. 21p. (J). per. 9.99 (978-1-59879-037-5(4)) Lifevest Publishing, Inc.

West, Tracey. Abracadanger. 2003. (gr. 3-6). lib. bdg. 13.00 (978-0-613-72531-6(X)) Tandem Library Bks.

West, Tracey. Yu-Gi-Oh GX: Jaden's Secret. 2007. 32p. (J). pap. 3.99 (***978-0-439-88838-7(7)***) Scholastic, Inc.

Wheeler, Lisa. The Christmas Boot. Monroe, Michael Glenn, illus. 2007. 32p. (J). 18.95 (***978-1-58726-327-9(0)*** , Mitten Pr.) Ann Arbor Media Group, LLC.

Whelan, Olwyn. The Star Child. Maidment, Stella, illus. 2004. 40p. (J). 14.95 (978-1-84458-039-2(3)) Chrysalis Children's Bks. GBR. *Dist:* Transition Vendor.

White, Amanda. Sand Sister. Morales, Yuyi, illus. 2004. 32p. (J). 16.99 (978-1-84148-617-8(5)) Barefoot Bks., Inc.

Whittemore, JoAnne. Curse of Arastold. 2006. 312p. (J). pap. 8.95 (978-0-7387-0917-8(4)) Llewellyn Pubns.

—Escape from Arylon. 2006. 360p. pap. 8.95 (978-0-7387-0869-0(0)) Llewellyn Pubns.

Whittle, J. Robert & Sandilands, Joyce. Leprechaun Magic. Galego, Ane M., illus. 2004. 64p. (J). (978-0-9685061-2-7(7)) Whitlands Publishing, Ltd.

Whybrow, Ian. Parcel for Stanley. Hobson, Sally, illus. 1998. 32p. (J). (ps-3). 14.95 (978-1-899607-53-2(6)) Sterling Publishing Co., Inc.

—Parcel for Stanley. Hobson, Sally, illus. 1999. (J). (ps-ps). lib. bdg. 15.25 (978-0-613-22155-9(9)) Tandem Library Bks.

—A Parcel for Stanley. Hobson, Sally, illus. 1999. 32p. (J). pap. 6.95 (978-1-86233-082-5(4)) Sterling Publishing Co., Inc.

—The Unvisibles. 2005. 184p. (J). 16.95 (978-0-8234-1972-2(X)) Holiday Hse., Inc.

Wicke, Ed. Akayzia Adams & the Masterdragon's Secret. Warne, Tom, illus. 2003. 280p. (J). per. 9.99 (978-0-9677652-3-5(4) , BlacknBlue Pr. UK) Blacknblue Pr.

Wilkinson, Doris J. Alphabet. Wilkinson, Doris J., ed. Chipping, Oliver, illus. 2000. (Jacob's Magic Box Discovery Ser.). 20p. (J). (ps). pap. 4.95 (978-0-9700386-7-8(4)) Magic Box Pubns.

—Jacob in the Magic Box. Wilkinson, Doris J., ed. Chipping, Oliver, illus. 2000. (Jacob's Magic Box Discovery Ser.). 20p. (J). (ps). pap. 4.95 (978-0-9700386-6-1(6)) Magic Box Pubns.

Willard, Eliza. Dark Hand with Cards. 2001. (gr. k-3). lib. bdg. 13.00 (978-0-613-72445-6(3)) Tandem Library Bks.

—Revenge of the Dark Hand with Cards. 2002. (gr. 3-6). lib. bdg. 13.00 (978-0-613-72453-1(4)) Tandem Library Bks.

Willett, Edward. The Dark Unicorn. 18th ed. 1998. 158p. (YA). (gr. 6 up). 9.99 (978-0-88092-414-6(4) , 4144) Royal Fireworks Publishing Co.

Willever, Lisa Funari & Funari, Lorraine. Maximilian the Great. Corsi, Adam, illus. 2000. 32p. (J). (ps-2). 9.95 (978-0-9679227-3-7(9) , 329-007) Franklin Mason Pr.

Williams, Suzanne. The Gigantic, Genuine Genie. Gonzales, Chuck, illus. 2007. (Princess Power Ser.: No. 6). 128p. (J). 15.99 (***978-0-06-078309-9(5)***); (gr. 3-7). pap. 4.99 (***978-0-06-078308-2(7)*** , Harper Trophy) HarperCollins Pubs.

—The Stubbornly Secretive Servant. Gonzales, Chuck, illus. 2007. (Princess Power Ser.). 128p. (J). 15.99 (***978-0-06-078307-5(9)***); pap. 4.99 (***978-0-06-078306-8(0)*** , Harper Trophy) HarperCollins Pubs.

Williston, Teresa Pierce. The Bamboo Cutter & the Moon Maiden: A Japanese Folk Tale. Marsh, Dilleen, illus. 2006. 32p. (J). 16.95 (978-1-933317-39-7(6)) Silverleaf Pr.

Wilson, Barbara Ker. Maui & the Big Fish. Lessac, Frane, illus. 2004. 32p. (J). (978-0-7112-2066-9(2)); pap. 7.95 (978-1-84507-159-2(X)) Lincoln, Frances Ltd. GBR. *Dist:* Transition Vendor, Perseus Distribution.

Wilson, Karma. Baby Cakes. Williams, Sam, illus. 2006. 32p. (J). 7.99 (978-1-4169-0289-8(9) , Little Simon) Simon & Schuster Children's Publishing.

Wilson, N. D. 100 Cupboards. 2007. (J). pap. (***978-0-375-83882-8(1)***); 304p. lib. bdg. (***978-0-375-93881-8(8)***); 304p. (gr. 3-7). 16.99 (***978-0-375-83881-1(3)***) Random Hse., Inc.

Wingerter, Linda S., illus. My Magic Diary. 2005. 192p. 9.99 (978-0-7353-0099-6(2)) Galison.

Winker, Michael & Ashley. One Good Quest Deserves Another: A Crown of Amaranth Story. 2007. 232p. 25.95 (***978-0-595-68779-4(2)***); per. 15.95 (***978-0-595-43799-3(0)***) iUniverse, Inc.

Winkler, Henry & Oliver, Lin. Niagara Falls, or Does It? 2004. (Hank Zipzer Ser.: No. 1). 128p. (J). (gr. 2-6). pap. 29.00 incl. audio (978-1-4000-9006-8(7) , Listening Library) Random Hse. Audio Publishing Group.

—Niagara Falls, or Does It? 2006. (Hank Zipzer Ser.: No. 1). (J). (gr. 3-8). 24.21 (978-1-59961-108-2(2)) Spotlight.

—Niagara Falls, or Does It? 2003. (Hank Zipzer Ser.: No. 1). lib. bdg. 13.00 (978-0-613-63737-4(2)) Tandem Library Bks.

The Wish. 2000. (J). (978-0-06-029060-3(9)) HarperCollins Pubs.

Wittner, Shirley. Kemira & the Ancient Book of Spells. 2006. 51p. pap. 12.95 (***978-1-4241-4840-0(5)***) PublishAmerica, Inc.

Wojciechowski, Susan. Beany (Not Beanhead) & the Magic Crystal. 2001. (Illus.). (J). 12.79 (978-0-606-21052-2(0)) Tandem Library Bks.

—Christmas Miracle of Jonathan Toomey. Lynch, P. J., illus. 2004. 40p. (J). (gr. 1-7). reprint ed. 12.99 incl. audio compact disk (978-0-7636-2621-1(X)) Candlewick Pr.

Wood, Audrey. Magic Shoelaces. Wood, Audrey, illus. 2005. (Illus.). 32p. (J). pap. 7.99 (978-1-904550-51-8(7)) Child's Play-International.

Wood, Dominic. Dominic Wood's Spooky Magic. 2005. (Illus.). 48p. pap. 10.99 (978-0-09-944768-9(1) , Red Fox) Random Hse. Children's Bks. GBR. *Dist:* Trafalgar Square Publishing.

Wood, Jamie Martinez. Rogelia's House of Magic. 2008. 320p. (J). (gr. 7). 15.99 (***978-0-385-73477-6(8)*** , Delacorte Bks. for Young Readers) Random Hse. Children's Bks.

Wood, Robert E. Candle & the Magic Boat. Femrite, Gina, illus. l.t. ed. 1999. (Oozooland Adventures Ser.: Vol. 1). 52p. (J). (ps-7). 18.95 (978-1-892458-00-1(4)) Life's Footprints, Inc.

Woods, Shirley. The Magical Mystery. 2005. (Illus.). 102p. (J). per. 11.95 (978-1-59453-100-2(5) , 3679) Airleaf Publishing & Bookselling.

Worthington, Lisa & Moon, Susan. My Magic Bike. Harston, Jerry, illus. 2003. 16p. (J). (gr. k-2). pap. 4.95 (978-1-57874-039-0(8)) Kaeden Corp.

Wrede, Patricia C. Book of Enchantments. 2005. 256p. (J). (gr. 5). pap. 5.95 (978-0-15-205508-0(8) , Magic Carpet Bks.) Harcourt Children's Bks.

—Calling on Dragons. 2003. (Enchanted Forest Chronicles: Bk. 3). (Illus.). 272p. (YA). pap. 5.95 (978-0-15-204692-7(5) , Magic Carpet Bks.) Harcourt Children's Bks.

—Calling on Dragons. unabr. ed. 2004. (Enchanted Forest Ser.: Vol 3). 244p. (J). (gr. 6 up). pap. 38.00 incl. audio (978-0-8072-0792-5(6) , LYA 347 SP, Listening Library) Random Hse. Audio Publishing Group.

—Calling on Dragons. 2003. (gr. 7-12). lib. bdg. 14.10 (978-0-613-59887-3(3)) Tandem Library Bks.

—Mairelon the Magician. 2002. (Magician Ser.). 288p. (J). 5.99 (978-0-7653-4232-4(4) , Starscape) Doherty, Tom Assocs., LLC.

—Mairelon the Magician. 2002. (gr. 7-12). lib. bdg. 14.15 (978-0-613-58076-2(1)) Tandem Library Bks.

—Talking to Dragons. 2003. (Enchanted Forest Chronicles: Bk. 4). (Illus.). 272p. (YA). pap. 5.95 (978-0-15-204691-0(7) , Magic Carpet Bks.) Harcourt Children's Bks.

—Talking to Dragons. unabr. ed. 2004. (Enchanted Forest Chronicles Ser.). 255p. (J). (gr. 6 up). pap. 38.00 incl. audio (978-0-8072-0983-7(X) , S YA 385 SP, Listening Library) Random Hse. Audio Publishing Group.

—Talking to Dragons. 2003. (gr. 7-12). lib. bdg. 14.10 (978-0-613-59931-3(4)) Tandem Library Bks.

Wright, Joshua. Goom. 2005. (Illus.). 168p. (J). (ps-7). pap. 6.95 (978-1-74114-435-2(3)) Allen & Unwin AUS. *Dist:* Independent Pubs. Group.

Wright, Mary J. The Brave Knight. 2005. 108p. pap. 16.95 (978-1-4137-8185-4(3)) PublishAmerica, Inc.

Wright, Timothy. Childish Things. 2006. 163p. pap. 11.49 (978-1-4116-6987-1(8)) Lulu.com.

Yee, Paul. Bamboo. Wang, Shaoli, illus. 2006. 32p. (J). 16.95 (978-1-894965-53-8(1)) Simply Read Bks. CAN. *Dist:* Perseus Distribution.

Yeoman. Princes' Gift Magic Folk Tales. (Illus.). 128p. (YA). (gr. 1 up). 19.99 (978-1-85793-879-1(8) , Pavilion Bks., Ltd.) Anova Bks. GBR. *Dist:* Trafalgar Square Publishing.

Yep, Laurence. The Magic Paintbrush. Wang, Suling, illus. 2003. 96p. (J). (gr. 3-7). pap. 4.99 (978-0-06-440852-3(3)) HarperCollins Pubs.

—The Magic Paintbrush. 2003. (gr. 3-6). lib. bdg. 13.00 (978-0-613-65808-9(6)) Tandem Library Bks.

—Tiger Magic. 2006. (Tiger's Apprentice Ser.). 288p. (J). 16.99 (978-0-06-001019-5(3)); lib. bdg. 17.89 (978-0-06-001020-1(7)) HarperCollins Pubs.

—Tiger's Apprentice. 2005. 184p. (J). lib. bdg. 24.62 (***978-1-4242-0449-6(6)***) Fitzgerald Bks.

—Tiger's Apprentice. 2005. 184p. (J). (gr. k-9). per. 12.64 (978-0-606-33327-6(4)) Tandem Library Bks.

—The Tiger's Apprentice. 2005. (Tiger's Apprentice Ser.: Bk. 1). 208p. (J). (gr. 5 up). reprint ed. pap. 5.99 (978-0-06-001015-7(0) , Harper Trophy) HarperCollins Pubs.

—Tiger's Blood. 2005. (Tiger's Apprentice Ser.: Bk. 2). 240p. (J). (gr. 5 up). 15.99 (978-0-06-001016-4(9)); lib. bdg. 16.89 (978-0-06-001017-1(7)) HarperCollins Pubs.

—Tiger's Blood. 2006. (Tiger's Apprentice Ser.: Bk. 2). 240p. (J). pap. 5.99 (978-0-06-001018-8(5) , Harper Trophy) HarperCollins Pubs.

Yolen, Jane. The Bagpiper's Ghost. 2003. (Tartan Magic Ser.: Bk. 3). (Illus.). 144p. (J). pap. 5.95 (978-0-15-204913-4(3) , Magic Carpet Bks.) Harcourt Children's Bks.

—Pictish Child. 2002. (gr. 3-6). lib. bdg. 14.10 (978-0-613-53854-1(4)) Tandem Library Bks.

—The Wizard of Washington Square. 2005. 96p. (J). 5.99 (978-0-7653-5016-9(5) , Starscape) Doherty, Tom Assocs., LLC.

—Wizard's Hall. 1999. 144p. (YA). pap. 6.95 (978-0-15-202085-9(3) , Magic Carpet Bks.) Harcourt Children's Bks.

—Wizard's Hall. 144p. (J). (gr. 3-5). pap. 6.00 (978-0-8072-1544-9(9) , Listening Library) Random Hse. Audio Publishing Group.

—Wizard's Hall. 1999. (978-0-606-16528-0(2)); (gr. 3-6). lib. bdg. 14.15 (978-0-7857-1069-1(8)) Tandem Library Bks.

—The Wizard's Map. (Tartan Magic Ser.: Bk. 1). (YA). 2002. 156p. pap. 5.95 (978-0-15-216365-5(4) , Magic Carpet Bks.); 1999. 144p. (gr. 3-7). 16.00 (978-0-15-202067-5(5)) Harcourt Children's Bks.

—Wizard's Map. 2002. (gr. 3-6). lib. bdg. 14.10 (978-0-613-53882-4(X)) Tandem Library Bks.

Yolen, Jane & Stemple, Adam. Pay the Piper: A Rock 'n' Roll Fairy Tale. 2006. 192p. (J). 5.99 (978-0-7653-5041-1(6) , Starscape) Doherty, Tom Assocs., LLC.

Yoo, Tae-Eun. The Little Red Fish. 2007. (Illus.). (J). (***978-1-4287-3601-6(8)*** , Dial) Penguin Group (USA) Inc.

Yoshizuki, Kumichi. Someday's Dreamers. 2nd rev. ed. 2006. (Illus.). pap. 9.99 (978-1-59816-179-3(2) , Tokyopop Kids) TOKYOPOP, Inc.

Young, Cleous. The Magical Rug. 2004. 25p. pap. 14.95 (978-1-4137-3555-0(X)) PublishAmerica, Inc.

Young, Steve. 15 Minutes. 2006. 176p. (J). 15.99 (978-0-06-072508-2(7)); lib. bdg. 16.89 (978-0-06-072509-9(5)) HarperCollins Pubs.

Yu, Li, et al. The Holy Spark: Rogel & the Goddess of Liberty. 2006. (J). (978-1-931907-42-2(0)) Homa & Sekey Bks.

Zalben, Jane Breskin. The Magic Menorah: A Modern Chanukah Tale. Diamond, Donna, illus. 2001. 64p. (J). (gr. 3-5). 15.00 (978-0-689-82606-1(0)) Simon & Schuster Children's Publishing.

Zellers, Michelle. Maya's Magic Carpet. 2006. (J). per. 11.95 (978-1-889743-48-6(8)) Robbie Dean Pr.

Zinsser, Anne. More Dolphin Magic: The Adventure Continues. Sohl, Lee Ellen, illus. 2001. viii, 120p. (J). per. 6.95 (978-0-933951-20-4(5)) Locust Hill Pr.

MAGIC—HISTORY

Savage, Candace. Wizards: An Amazing Journey Through the Last Great Age of Magic. 2004. (Illus.). 80p. pap. 12.00 (978-1-55365-039-3(5)) Douglas & McIntyre, Ltd. CAN. *Dist:* Transition Vendor.

MAGIC TRICKS

Here are entered works on performance of sleight of hand or tricks involving various types of illusion for purposes of entertainment. Works on the use of charms, spells, etc., believed to have supernatural power to produce or prevent a particular result considered unobtainable by natural means are entered under Magic.

Amazing Magic. 2004. (Fun Kits Ser.). (Illus.). 48p. (J). (978-1-84229-859-6(3)) Top That! Publishing PLC.

Andrews, Ted. Faerie Charms. 2001. (Young Person's School of Magic & Mystery Ser.: Vol. 6). (Illus.). 256p. (J). (gr. 7 up). 18.95 (978-1-888767-42-1(1)) Dragonhawk Publishing.

Austin, Mike. The Unbelievable Levitating Card Tricks. Krul, Paige, ed. 2001. (Mini-Maestro Ser.). 48p. (J). (gr. 1-3). lthr. 7.95 (978-0-439-31763-4(0) , Tangerine Pr.) Scholastic, Inc.

Balloon Oriented Magic. 2004. (Illus.). 139p. (YA). spiral bd. 16.95 (978-1-931084-01-7(7)) Balloon Magic.

Blackstone, Bellamie. Everyday Magic. (978-1-59093-002-1(9) , Eager Minds Pr.) Warehousing & Fulfillment Specialists, LLC (WFS, LLC).

Book of Magic Tricks Kid Kit. 2004. 64p. (J). 15.99 (978-1-58086-454-1(6)) EDC Publishing.

Bree, Loris. Kids' Magic Secrets: Simple Magic Tricks & Why They Work. Bree, Marlin, illus. 2003. 110p. (J). pap. 9.95 (978-1-892147-08-0(4)) Marlor Pr., Inc.

Bryant, Page. Star Magic. Haugen, Diane, ed. 2001. (Young Person's School of Magic & Mystery Ser.: Vol. 4). (Illus.). 256p. (YA). (gr. 7 up). 18.95 (978-1-888767-44-5(8)) Dragonhawk Publishing.

Burgess, Ron. Make Magic! 50 Tricks to Mystify & Amaze. 2004. (Quick Starts for Kids! Ser.). (Illus.). 128p. (J). pap. 12.95 (978-1-885593-87-0(2) , Williamson Bks.) Ideals Pubns.

Buttitta, Hope. It's Not Magic, It's Science! 50 Science Tricks that Mystify, Dazzle & Astound. La Baff, Tom & Lundgren, Orrin, illus. 2007. 80p. pap. 7.95 (978-1-57990-883-6(7)) Lark Bks.

Cassidy, John. Klutz Book of Magic. 2006. (Illus.). 96p. (J). 16.95 (978-1-57054-891-8(9)) Klutz.

Charney, Steve. Hocus-Jokus: 50 Funny Magic Tricks Complete with Jokes. 2003. (Illus.). ix, 132p. (J). (978-0-88166-376-1(X)) Meadowbrook Pr.

—Hocus Jokus 50 Funny Magic Tricks Complete With Jokes. 2003. 144p. (J). pap. 7.95 (978-0-684-01866-9(7)) Meadowbrook Pr.

Denne, B. Amazing Magic Tricks. 2004. (Illus.). 32p. (J). pap., act. bk. ed. 6.95 (978-0-7945-0601-8(1)) EDC Publishing.

Denne, Ben. Amazing Magic Tricks Kid Kit. 2004. (Kid Kits Ser.). 32p. (J). 12.99 (978-1-58086-729-0(4)); 12.99 (978-1-58086-736-8(7)) EDC Publishing. (Usborne).

Diagram Visual. Super Little Giant Book of Magic. 2007. (Illus.). 288p. (J). pap. 6.95 (978-1-4027-3905-7(2)) Sterling Publishing Co., Inc.

Dickson, Louise. The Vanishing Cat. Cupples, Pat, illus. 2001. (Lu & Clancy Ser.). 40p. (J). (gr. k-3). (978-1-55074-836-9(X)); (978-1-55337-026-0(0)) Kids Can Pr., Ltd.

Eldin, Peter. How to Be a Magician. 2006. (Most Excellent Book Of- Ser.). (Illus.). 32p. (J). (978-1-59604-123-3(4)) Stargazer Bks.

—Magic for Fun. 2002. (gr. 3-6). lib. bdg. 24.55 (978-0-613-81353-2(7)) Tandem Library Bks.

Fleming, Sarah. Do the Loops Trick, 6 vols, Pack. 2000. (Cambridge Reading Ser.). 8p. pap. 28.00 (978-0-521-78769-7(6)) Cambridge Univ. Pr.

Folder, Alan. Paper Tricks. Galvani, Maureen, illus. 2001. (Paper Magic Ser.). 48p. (J). (gr. 3-7). 7.95 (978-0-439-26034-3(5)) Scholastic, Inc.

Fulves, Karl. Self-Working Table Magic: 97 Foolproof Tricks with Everyday Objects. Schmidt, Joseph K., illus. 1998. 122p. (Orig.). pap. 6.95 (978-0-486-24116-6(5)) Dover Pubns., Inc.

Gardner, Martin. Smart Science Tricks. Steimle, Bob, illus. 2005. 144p. (J). (gr. k-9). pap. 5.95 (978-1-4027-2220-2(6)) Sterling Publishing Co., Inc.

Gardner, Robert. Science Projects about the Science Behind Magic. 2000. (Science Projects Ser.). (Illus.). 128p. (YA). (gr. 6-12). lib. bdg. 26.60 (978-0-7660-1164-9(X)) Enslow Pubs., Inc.

Hill, Gordon. Magic Tricks. 2001. (Mini-Maestro Ser.). (Illus.). 48p. (J). (gr. 1-3). 7.95 (978-0-439-22012-5(2)) Scholastic, Inc.

Ho, Oliver. Card Tricks. Garbot, David, illus. 2005. (Young Magician Ser.). 48p. (J). (ps). pap. 4.95 (978-1-4027-2807-5(7)) Sterling Publishing Co., Inc.

—How to Read Minds: And Other Magic Tricks. Garbot, Dave, illus. 2002. 96p. (gr. 4-7). pap. 5.95 (978-0-8069-7645-7(4)) Sterling Publishing Co., Inc.

—Magic Tricks. Garbot, David, illus. 2005. (Young Magician Ser.). 48p. (J). (ps). pap. 4.95 (978-1-4027-2808-2(5)) Sterling Publishing Co., Inc.

—Young Magician. Garbot, Dave, illus. 2005. 96p. (J). (978-1-4027-2920-1(0) , Sterling/Main St.) Sterling Publishing Co., Inc.

Huckleberry, Bea. Magnificent Magic Tricks. 2001. (Fun Factory... Ser.). (Illus.). 64p. pap. 6.95 (978-1-84215-491-5(5) , Southwater) Anness Publishing GBR. *Dist:* National Bk. Network.

Johnson, Ginger. Paper-Folding Fun! 50 Awesome Crafts to Weave, Twist, & Curl. Day, Betsy, illus. 2002. (Williamson Kids Can!(R) Ser.). 128p. (J). (gr. 3 up). pap. 12.95 (978-1-885593-67-2(8) , Williamson Bks.) Ideals Pubns.

Klingel, Cynthia Fitterer & Noyed, Robert B. Card Tricks. 2002. (Games Around the World Ser.). (Illus.). 32p. (J). (gr. 3 up). lib. bdg. 21.26 (978-0-7565-0190-7(3)) Compass Point Bks.

—Magic Tricks. 2002. (Games Around the World Ser.). (Illus.). 32p. (J). (gr. 3 up). lib. bdg. 21.26 (978-0-7565-0192-1(X)) Compass Point Bks.

Knoles, David. Spine-Tingling Magic Tricks. 2001. (Illus.). 128p. pap. 5.95 (978-0-8069-7569-6(5)) Sterling Publishing Co., Inc.

Kole, Andre. Tricks & Twists. 2004. 168p. pap. (978-0-9727279-7-6(3)) Pine Hill Graphics.

Longe, Bob. Card Tricks Galore. 1999. (gr. 3-6). lib. bdg. 14.10 (978-0-613-75480-4(8)) Tandem Library Bks.

—Easy Hand Tricks. 2004. (Illus.). 128p. pap. 5.95 (978-1-4027-0779-7(7)) Sterling Publishing Co., Inc.

Magic Card Tricks. 2007. (J). 8.99 ***(978-0-439-85308-8(7))*** Scholastic, Inc.

Magic Card Tricks. 2004. (Whizz Kits Ser.). (Illus.). 48p. (J). (978-1-84229-943-2(3)) Top That! Publishing PLC.

Mandelberg, Robert. Mystifying Mind Reading Tricks. Sardella, Ferruccio, illus. 2002. 96p. pap. 6.95 (978-0-8069-8811-5(8)) Sterling Publishing Co., Inc.

Markle, Sandra. Magic. Smith, Jamie, tr. Smith, Jamie, illus. 2001. (Super Science Ser.). 61p. (J). pap. (978-0-439-28136-2(9)) Scholastic, Inc.

Mason, Tom & Danko, Dan. The Book of All-Stars Magic. 2002. (Illus.). 74p. (J). (978-0-439-32712-1(1)) Scholastic, Inc.

—The Book of Body & Mind Magic. 2002. (Illus.). 74p. (J). (978-0-439-32711-4(3)) Scholastic, Inc.

—The Book of Comedy Magic. 2002. (Illus.). 74p. (J). (978-0-439-32708-4(3)) Scholastic, Inc.

—The Book of Transpositions. 2002. (Illus.). 74p. (J). (978-0-439-32706-0(7)) Scholastic, Inc.

Mason, Tom, et al. The Book of Impossibility. 2002. (Illus.). 74p. (J). (978-0-439-32707-7(5)) Scholastic, Inc.

—The Book of Mealtime Magic. 2002. (Illus.). 74p. (J). (978-0-439-32710-7(5)) Scholastic, Inc.

Mayne, Andrew. Handbook of Super Powers: Magic Tricks that Make It Look Like You Possess Super-human Abilities. 2004. (Illus.). 96p. (YA). per. 11.95 (978-0-9715183-6-0(X)) Maynestream Pr.

McMaster, Shawn. The First-Timer's Guide to Magic Tricks. 1999. (Illus.). 80p. (J). (gr. 1-4). pap. 8.95 (978-0-7373-0229-5(1) , 02291W) McGraw-Hill/Contemporary.

—Kidsource: Magic Tricks. 2000. (Kidsource Ser.). (Illus.). 119p. (J). (gr. 3-7). pap. 9.95 (978-0-7373-0231-8(3) , 02313W) McGraw-Hill/Contemporary.

Mouser, David B. Harry Potter's Muggles Guide to Magic. deluxe l.t. ed. 2001. 80p. (J). lib. bdg. 15.95 (978-1-929771-04-2(5)) H P Pubns., LTD.

Presto, Fay. Magic for Kids. 1999. (J). (978-0-7534-5187-8(5) , Kingfisher) Houghton Mifflin Co. Trade & Reference Div.

—Magic for Kids. 1999. (gr. 3-6). lib. bdg. 21.05 (978-0-613-90586-2(5)) Tandem Library Bks.

Railing, John & Orleans, Danny. The Book of Master Magician's Magic. 2002. (Illus.). 74p. (J). (978-0-439-42791-3(6)) Scholastic, Inc.

Schendlinger, Mary. Prepare to be Amazed: The Geniuses of Modern Magic. 2005. (Illus.). 79p. (J). (gr. 3-6). pap. 12.95 (978-1-55037-926-6(7)) Annick Pr., Ltd. CAN. *Dist:* Firefly Bks., Ltd.

—Prepare to be Amazed: The Geniuses of Modern Magic. Clark, Warren, illus. 2005. 79p. (J). (gr. 3-6). 24.95 (978-1-55037-927-3(5)) Annick Pr., Ltd. CAN. *Dist:* Firefly Bks., Ltd.

Southwater Staff. Outrageously Magic Tricks & Puzzles. 2002. (Outrageously... Ser.). (Illus.). 96p. pap. 9.99 (978-1-84215-670-4(5) , Southwater) Anness Publishing GBR. *Dist:* National Bk. Network.

Spelling, Phoebe. Hocus Pocus: A Whole Book of Magical Fun! 2001. (Illus.). 160p. (J). pap. 4.99 (978-0-439-29652-6(8)) Scholastic, Inc.

Szwast, Ursula. Magic. 2004. (Get Going! Hobbies Ser.). (Illus.). 32p. (J). pap. (978-1-4034-6126-1(0)); (gr. 4-6). lib. bdg. 24.22 (978-1-4034-6119-3(8)) Heinemann Library.

Top That Publishing Editors, ed. Magical Mischief. Dahl, Roald, illus. 2005. 24p. (J). pap. (978-1-905359-51-6(9)) Top That! Publishing PLC.

Townsend, Charles Barry. World's Greatest Magic Tricks. 2005. (Illus.). 128p. (gr. 7-12). pap. 5.95 (978-1-4027-2545-6(0)) Sterling Publishing Co., Inc.

Whiter, Barbara. 101 Cool Magic Tricks. 2002. 208p. (YA). mass mkt. 5.95 (978-0-689-02424-5(X)) Meadowbrook Pr.

Wilson. 6 Pkt Mini/Classic Black. 2000. 4.95 (978-1-56138-810-3(6)) Running Pr. Bk. Pubs.

Wood, Dominic. Party Tricks. 2004. (Illus.). 64p. (J). pap. (978-0-09-945137-2(9) , Red Fox) Random Hse. Children's Bks.

—Playground Pranks. 2004. (Illus.). 64p. (J). pap. (978-0-09-945138-9(7) , Red Fox) Random Hse. Children's Bks.

Zenon, Paul. Magic of the Mind: Tricks for the Master Magician. 2007. (J). ***(978-1-4042-1072-1(5))*** Rosen Publishing Group, Inc., The.

—Simple Sleight-Of-Hand: Card & Coin Tricks for the Beginning Magician. 2007. (J). ***(978-1-4042-1070-7(9))*** Rosen Publishing Group, Inc., The.

MAGICIANS

see also Wizards

Eldin, Peter. How to Be a Magician. 2006. (Most Excellent Book Of- Ser.). (Illus.). 32p. (J). (978-1-59604-123-3(4)) Stargazer Bks.

Fleischman, Sid. Escape! The Story of the Great Houdini. 2006. (Illus.). 224p. (J). (gr. 4-8). 18.99 (978-0-06-085094-4(9)); lib. bdg. 19.89 (978-0-06-085095-1(7)) HarperCollins Pubs.

Haskins, James & Benson, Kathleen. Conjure Times: Black Magicians in America. 2001. (Illus.). 192p. (J). (gr. 5-10). 17.85 (978-0-8027-8763-7(0)) Walker & Co.

—Conjure Times: The History of Black Magicians in America. 2001. (Illus.). 192p. (J). (gr. 5-10). 16.95 (978-0-8027-8762-0(2)) Walker & Co.

Hill, Douglas. Brujas y Magos. Wilson, Alex, illus. 2003. (SPA.). 64p. (J). 14.95 (978-84-372-2321-6(0)) Altea, Ediciones, S.A. - Grupo Santillana ESP. *Dist:* Santillana USA Publishing Co., Inc.

Krull, Kathleen. Houdini: World's Greatest Mystery Man & Escape King. Velasquez, Eric, illus. 32p. (J). 2007. pap. 6.95 ***(978-0-8027-9646-2(X));*** 2005. 17.85 (978-0-8027-8954-9(4)); 2005. 16.95 (978-0-8027-8953-2(6)) Walker & Co.

Kulling, Monica. The Great Houdini. 1999. (J). (978-0-606-16897-7(4)) Tandem Library Bks.

—The Great Houdini: World Famous Magician & Escape Artist. Reas, Anne, illus. 2003. (Step into Reading Step 3 Bks.). 48p. (J). (gr. 2-4). pap. 3.99 (978-0-679-88573-3(0) , Random Hse. Bks. for Young Readers) Random Hse. Children's Bks.

Lakin, Patricia. Harry Houdini: Esape Artist. Geary, Rick, illus. 2002. (Ready-to-Read Ser.). 32p. (J). pap. 3.99 (978-0-689-84815-5(3) , Aladdin) Simon & Schuster Children's Publishing.

MacLeod, Elizabeth. Harry Houdini: A Magical Life. (Illus.). 32p. (978-1-55337-769-6(9)); 2005. (J). (gr. 3-7). (978-1-55337-770-2(2)) Kids Can Pr., Ltd.

Marsh, Carole. Harry Houdini. 2002. (One Thousand Readers Ser.). (Illus.). 12p. (J). (gr. k-4). 2.95 (978-0-635-01511-2(0) , 15110) Gallopade International.

Mullin, Rita Thievon. Sterling Biographies: Harry Houdini: Death-Defying Showman. 2007. (Sterling Biographies Ser.). (Illus.). 128p. (J). 12.95 ***(978-1-4027-4953-7(8))*** Sterling Publishing Co., Inc.

Shakespeare, William. The Tempest. Ermitage, Kathleen, ed. 2002. (Simply Shakespeare Ser.). (Illus.). 288p. pap. 8.99 (978-0-7641-2087-9(5)) Barron's Educational Series, Inc.

Sutherland, Tui. Who Was Harry Houdini? 2002. (gr. 3-6). lib. bdg. 13.00 (978-0-613-45331-8(X)) Tandem Library Bks.

Sutherland, Tui & O'Brien, John. Who Was Harry Houdini? Harrison, Nancy, illus. 2002. (Who Was...? Ser.). 112p. (J). pap. 4.99 (978-0-448-42686-0(2) , Grosset & Dunlap) Penguin Group (USA) Inc.

MAGICIANS—FICTION

Abbott, Tony. Sorcerer. ed. 2006. (Secrets of Droon Ser.: No. 4). 176p. (J). pap. 5.99 (978-0-439-67178-1(7) , Scholastic Paperbacks) Scholastic, Inc.

Akita, Yoshinobu. Orphen, Vol. 5. 2006. (Illus.). 168p. (YA). pap. (978-1-4139-0270-9(7)) ADV Manga.

—Orphen Volume 6. 2006. (Illus.). 168p. (YA). pap. (978-1-4139-0271-6(5)) ADV Manga.

Alexander, Lloyd. The Cat Who Wished to Be a Man. 2000. 107p. (J). (ps-7). per. 13.00 (978-0-613-12359-4(X)) Tandem Library Bks.

—The Rope Trick. 2002. 192p. (J). (gr. 3-6). 16.99 (978-0-525-47020-5(4) , Dutton Juvenile) Penguin Group (USA) Inc.

Alexander, Lloyd, contrib. by. The Rope Trick. 2004. 195p. (J). (gr. 5). lib. bdg. 13.64 (978-0-606-30794-9(X)) Tandem Library Bks.

Ashman, Linda. Maxwell's Magic Mix-up. Dunnick, Regan, illus. 2004. 30p. (J). (gr. k-3). reprint ed. 16.00 (978-0-7567-7156-0(0)) DIANE Publishing Co.

Asprin, Robert. M. Y. T. H. Inc. Link. 2006. 176p. (gr. 12). mass mkt. 6.99 (978-0-441-01449-1(6) , Ace Bks.) Penguin Group (USA) Inc.

Auer, Chris. The Littlest Magi: A Christmas Tale. Eagle, Bruce, illus. 2004. 32p. (J). 15.99 (978-0-310-70663-2(7)) Zonderkidz.

Avi. Magia de Medianoche. 2004. (SPA.). 194p. (YA). 10.99 (978-84-348-9112-8(3)) SM Ediciones ESP. *Dist:* Lectorum Pubns., Inc.

—Midnight Magic. 2001. (978-0-606-22158-0(1)); (gr. 5-8). lib. bdg. 13.00 (978-0-613-54286-9(X)) Tandem Library Bks.

Banerjee, Anjali. Looking for Bapu. 2006. 176p. (J). (gr. 3-6). lib. bdg. 17.99 (978-0-385-90894-8(6) , Lamb, Wendy) Random Hse. Children's Bks.

Barron, T. A. The Lost Years of Merlin. 1998. (J). (gr. 4-7). mass mkt. 4.99 (978-0-8125-7777-8(9) , Tor Bks.) Doherty, Tom Assocs., LLC.

—The Lost Years of Merlin, Bk. 1. 1999. (Lost Years of Merlin Ser.). (Illus.). 304p. (gr. 4-7). reprint ed. mass mkt. 6.99 (978-0-441-00668-7(X) , Ace Bks.) Penguin Group (USA) Inc.

Bates, Martine. The Taker's Key, Vol. 3. 1998. (Praise for the Marmawell Ser.). 208p. (J). pap. 8.95 (978-0-88995-184-6(5)) Red Deer Pr. CAN. *Dist:* Fitzhenry & Whiteside, Ltd.

Baynton, Martin. Jane & the Magician. Baynton, Martin, illus. 2007. (Illus.). 32p. (J). (ps-3). pap. 4.99 ***(978-0-7636-3571-8(5))*** Candlewick Pr.

Bemelmans, Ludwig. Madeline's Christmas. Bemelmans, Ludwig, illus. 2007. (Puffin Storytime Ser.). 32p. (J). (ps). 9.99 ***(978-0-14-240897-1(2)*** , Puffin) Penguin Group (USA) Inc.

Birch, Beverley. Tempest. 2007. (Illus.). 80p. 13.95 ***(978-0-7502-4961-4(7)*** , Hodder Wayland) Hodder Children's Division GBR. *Dist:* Independent Pubs. Group.

Bosch, Pseudonymous. The Name of This Book Is Secret. Ford, Gilbert, illus. rev. ed. 2007. 384p. (J). (gr. 3-7). 16.99 ***(978-0-316-11366-3(2))*** Little, Brown Bks. for Young Readers.

Burleigh, Robert. The Secret of the Great Houdini. Gore, Leonid, illus. 2002. 40p. (J). (gr. 2-5). 16.95 (978-0-689-83267-3(2) , Atheneum) Simon & Schuster Children's Publishing.

Campbell-Ernst, Lisa & Ernst, Lisa Campbell. Tangram Magician. Ernst, Lee, illus. 2005. 28p. bds. 15.95 (978-1-59354-106-4(6)) Blue Apple Bks.

Cate, Annette LeBlanc. The Magic Rabbit. Cate, Annette LeBlanc, illus. 2007. (Illus.). 32p. (J). (ps-3). 15.99 ***(978-0-7636-2672-3(4))*** Candlewick Pr.

Cerda, Alfredo Gomez. Manolo Multon y el Mago Guason. Antonio & Covi, illus. 2004. Tr. of Manolo Citation & Boring the Magician. (SPA.). (J). pap. 7.99 (978-84-236-6322-4(1)) Edebé ESP. *Dist:* Lectorum Pubns., Inc.

Chandler, Fiona. Sorcerer's Apprentice. 2007. 48p. (J). 8.99 (978-0-7945-1589-8(4) , Usborne) EDC Publishing.

Child, L. Maria. The Magician's Show Box & Other Stories. 2007. (ENG.). 124p. per. ***(978-1-4065-1354-7(7))*** Dodo Pr.

Child, Lydia Maria. The Magician's Show Box & Other Stories. 2004. reprint ed. pap. 19.95 (978-1-4191-7122-2(4)); pap. 1.99 (978-1-4192-7122-9(9)) Kessinger Publishing, LLC.

Clarke, Jane. G. E. M. 2008. (Illus.). 32p. (J). pap. 9.95 ***(978-0-09-948012-9(3))*** Transworld Publishers Ltd. GBR. *Dist:* Independent Pubs. Group.

Cooper, Susan. The Magician's Boy. Riglietti, Serena, illus. 2006. 112p. (J). (gr. 3-7). pap. 6.99 (978-1-4169-1555-3(9) , Aladdin) Simon & Schuster Children's Publishing.

Corlett, William. The Door in the Tree. 2000. 289p. (J). (gr. 5-8). per. 13.00 (978-0-613-74171-2(4)) Tandem Library Bks.

—The Tunnel Behind the Waterfall. 2001. (gr. 7-12). lib. bdg. 13.00 (978-0-613-74172-9(2)) Tandem Library Bks.

Coville, Bruce. The Dragon of Doom. Coville, Katherine, illus. (Moongobble & Me Ser.). 80p. (J). 2005. pap. 3.99 (978-0-689-85757-7(8) , Aladdin); 2003. (gr. 1-5). 14.95 (978-0-689-85754-6(3)) Simon & Schuster Children's Publishing.

—The Dragon of Doom. Coville, Katherine, illus. 2005. 69p. (J). (ps-k). lib. bdg. 10.64 (978-0-606-33373-3(8)) Tandem Library Bks.

—The Mischief Monster. Coville, Katherine, illus. 2007. (Moongobble & Me Ser.). 80p. (J). 15.99 (978-1-4169-0807-4(2) , Simon & Schuster Children's Publishing) Simon & Schuster Children's Publishing.

—The Weeping Werewolf. Coville, Katherine, illus. (Moongobble & Me Ser.). (J). (gr. 1-4). 2006. 80p. pap. 3.99 (978-0-689-85759-1(4)); 2005. 71p. pap. 3.99 (978-0-689-85758-4(6)) Simon & Schuster Children's Publishing. (Aladdin).

Cross, Frances. Butternut Blobber & the Blue Jade. 2007. (Blobber Trilogy Ser.). 98p. pap. 7.95 ***(978-1-84167-561-9(X))*** Ransom Publishing Ltd. GBR. *Dist:* International Publishers Marketing.

Dadey, Debbie & Jones, Marcia Thornton. Sorciers N'Ont Pas Besoin d'Ordinateurs. (Adventures of the Bailey School Kids Ser.). (FRE., Illus.). 88p. (J). pap. 5.99 (978-0-590-16024-7(9)) Scholastic, Inc.

Davies, Margaret, et al. Y Dewin Diog. 2005. (WEL., Illus.). 32p. pap. (978-1-85596-219-4(5)) Dref Wen.

Delgado, Luis Cabrera. Catalina la Maga. (Torre de Papel Ser.). (J). (gr. 2). 7.95 (978-958-04-4220-2(7)) Norma S.A. COL. *Dist:* Distribuidora Norma, Inc.

Dickinson, Peter. Angel Isle. 2007. 512p. (gr. 9). (J). lib. bdg. 20.99 ***(978-0-385-90928-0(4));*** (YA). 17.99 ***(978-0-385-74690-8(3))*** Random Hse. Children's Bks. (Lamb, Wendy).

Everson, Chance. Verlin's Magical Blunder: Tales of the Mandrasaurs, Volume the Seventh. Geary, Steve, illus. 2004. cd-rom 9.95 (978-0-9760303-6-2(5)) R.A.R.E. TALES.

Fagan, Cary. Daughter of the Great Zandini. Young, Cybele, illus. 2001. 64p. (J). (gr. 3-7). 16.95 (978-0-88776-534-6(3)) Tundra Bks., Inc./Livres Toundra, Inc. CAN. *Dist:* Random Hse., Inc.

Frost-Snyder, M. G. The Hallu Realm. 2001. (Illus.). 80p. (J). pap. 9.00 (978-0-8059-5418-0(X)) Dorrance Publishing Co., Inc.

Gauthier, Bertrand. Zunik dans le Grand Magicien. ed. 2004. (FRE., Illus.). (J). (ps-2). spiral bd. (978-0-616-01831-6(2)) Canadian National Institute for the Blind/Institut National Canadien pour les Aveugles.

Graham, Bob. Benny: An Adventure Story. Graham, Bob, illus. 2003. (Illus.). 32p. (J). (ps-2). pap. 6.99 (978-0-7636-1703-5(2)) Candlewick Pr.

Heitz, Bruno. Yoyo el Mago. (la Orilla Del Viento Ser.). (SPA., Illus.). 32p. (J). reprint ed. 6.99 (978-968-16-5802-1(7) , 110) Fondo de Cultura Economica USA.

—Yoyo sin Miedo. Sanchez, Diana Luz, tr. (la Orilla Del Viento Ser.).Tr. of Jojo sans peur. (SPA.). 33p. (J). reprint ed. 6.99 (978-968-16-6232-5(6) , 141) Fondo de Cultura Economica USA.

Howe, James. Rabbit-Cadabra! Daniel, Alan, illus. 1999. (Bunnicula & Friends Ser.). 48p. (J). (gr. k-3). pap. 5.95 (978-0-688-16699-1(7)) HarperCollins Pubs.

—Rabbit-Cadabra! Mack, Jeff, illus. 2006. (Bunnicula & Friends Ser.: Vol. 4). 48p. (J). 14.95 (978-0-689-85727-0(6) , Atheneum) Simon & Schuster Children's Publishing.

Howe, James. Rabbit-cadabra! Mack, Jeff, illus. 2007. (Bunnicula & Friends Ser.). 48p. (J). pap. 3.99 ***(978-0-689-85752-2(7)*** , Aladdin) Simon & Schuster Children's Publishing.

Hoye, Regena. Ala Voom, Vol. 1. Hoye, Regena, illus. 1998. (Illus.). 65p. (J). (ps-6). 12.00 (978-0-9636906-0-9(4)) Ishnuvu Publishing Co.

Jones, Diana Wynne. Archer's Goon. 2003. (Illus.). 336p. (J). (gr. 5 up). pap. 5.99 (978-0-06-447356-9(2) , Harper Trophy) HarperCollins Pubs.

—The Lives of Christopher Chant. l.t. ed. 2005. 360p. (J). pap. (978-0-7540-6163-2(9) , CLP 359) BBC Audio.

—The Magicians of Caprona. 1999. (978-0-606-22058-3(5)) Tandem Library Bks.

—Mixed Magics: Four Tales of Chrestomanci. 2003. 193p. (J). (ps-7). lib. bdg. 14.15 (978-0-613-68452-1(4)) Tandem Library Bks.

King-Smith, Dick. Clever Lollipop. Barton, Jill, illus. 2003. 144p. (J). (gr. 2-5). 15.99 (978-0-7636-2174-2(9)) Candlewick Pr.

M
N
O

Kolosov, Jacqueline. The Red Queen's Daughter. rev. ed. 2007. 399p. (YA). (gr. 7 up). 16.99 (***978-1-4231-0797-2(7)***) Hyperion Pr.

Lackey, Mercedes. The Black Swan. 1999. (gr. 7-12). lib. bdg. 15.30 (978-0-613-27746-4(5)) Tandem Library Bks.

Lalicki, Tom. Danger in the Dark. 2006. (Houdini & Nate Mysteries Ser.). (Illus.). 192p. (J). 14.95 (978-0-374-31680-8(5)) Farrar, Straus & Giroux.

Lalicki, Tom. Shots at Sea. Cerniglia, Carlyn, illus. 2007. (Houdini & Nate Mysteries Ser.). 208p. (J). (gr. 3-7). 15.95 (***978-0-374-31679-2(1)***) Farrar, Straus & Giroux.

Lee, Shell. Teenie's Treehouse Adventures: The Magic Begins. 2004. 37p. pap. 17.95 (978-1-4137-2879-8(0)) PublishAmerica, Inc.

Lieshout, Ted van. Uncle Gus's Magic Box. Sideri, Simona, tr. from DUT. Hopman, Philip, illus. 2005. 60p. (J). (gr. 2-4). 18.95 (978-1-55037-935-8(6)) Annick Pr., Ltd. CAN. *Dist:* Firefly Bks., Ltd.

El Mago de Oz. 2000. Tr. of Wizard of Oz. (SPA., Illus.). (YA). (gr. 5-8). 12.95 incl. audio (978-84-207-6731-4(X)) Grupo Anaya, S.A. ESP. *Dist:* Distribooks, Inc.

Mahy, Margaret. Alchemy. (Illus.). 224p. (YA). 2003. (gr. 7-12). 16.95 (978-0-689-85053-0(0) , McElderry, Margaret K.); 2004. reprint ed. pap. 7.99 (978-0-689-85054-7(9) , Simon Pulse) Simon & Schuster Children's Publishing.

Meddaugh, Susan. Lulu's Hat. (Illus.). 80p. (J). (gr. 3-5). 2006. pap. 5.95 (978-0-618-77127-1(1)); 2002. 15.00 (978-0-618-15277-3(6)) Houghton Mifflin Co. Trade & Reference Div. (Walter Lorraine).

Merola, Caroline. Toni Biscotti's Magic Trick. Cummins, Sarah, tr. from FRE. Merola, Caroline, illus. 2006. (First Novel Ser.). (Illus.). 64p. (J). (gr. 2-5). (***978-0-88780-719-0(4)***); 4.95 (***978-0-88780-715-2(1)***) Formac Publishing Co., Ltd. CAN. *Dist:* Casemate Pubs. & Bk. Distributors, LLC.

Modesitt, L. E., Jr. The Spellsong War. 1999. (Spellsong Cycle Ser.: Bk. 2). (gr. 7-12). lib. bdg. 15.30 (978-0-613-22421-5(3)) Tandem Library Bks.

Monreal, Violeta. Sos Se Necesita Sonrisa. 2004. (Coleccion Pictogramas Pictograms Ser.). (SPA.). 36p. (J). 8.50 (978-84-241-8101-7(8)) Everest de Ediciones y Distribucion, S.L. ESP. *Dist:* Continental Bk. Co., Inc., Lectorum Pubns., Inc.

A Mouse Named Sam. 2006. pap. 13.95 (***978-1-59526-381-0(0)***) Media Creations, Inc.

Omishi, Ray, illus. Sorcerer Hunters Authentic Relaunch, Vol. 1. 2005. 208p. pap. 9.99 (978-1-59532-494-8(1) , TOKYOPOP Adult) TOKYOPOP, Inc.

Ransom, Candice. Magician in the Trunk. 2007. (Time Spies Ser.: Bk. 4). (Illus.). 128p. (J). (gr. 1-5). 4.99 (978-0-7869-4070-7(0) , Mirrorstone) Wizards of the Coast.

Risso, Eduardo. Los misterios de la Luna Roja Vol. 1: Mysteries of the Red Moon. 2006. (SPA.). 48p. pap. 16.95 (978-1-59497-162-4(5)) Public Square Bks.

—Mysteries of the Red Moon, Vol. 3. 2006. (SPA.). 48p. pap. 16.95 (978-1-59497-163-1(3)) Public Square Bks.

Romey, Elizabeth A. Lera of Tymoria: The Dragonmage. Beletskaya, Maryana, illus. 2002. 252p. (YA). (gr. 5 up). pap. 9.99 (978-0-88092-570-9(1) , 5701) Royal Fireworks Publishing Co.

Sawada, Hijime & Akita, Yoshinobu. Orphen, Vol. 4. 2006. (Illus.). 168p. (YA). pap. (978-1-4139-0269-3(3)) ADV Manga.

Sedgwick, Marcus. The Book of Dead Days. 2006. pap. 5.50 (978-0-440-41909-9(3)); 2004. 288p. (J). (gr. 5). 15.95 (978-0-385-73055-6(1) , Lamb, Wendy); 2006. 288p. (J). (gr. 5). reprint ed. pap. 7.95 (978-0-385-74704-2(7) , Lamb, Wendy) Random Hse. Children's Bks.

Sedgwick, Marcus. The Dark Flight Down. 240p. 2008. (YA). (gr. 7). pap. 7.99 (***978-0-553-48784-8(1)***); 2005. (J). (gr. 5-7). 15.95 (978-0-385-74645-8(8)) Random Hse. Children's Bks. (Lamb, Wendy).

Seeger, Pete & Jacobs, Paul DuBois. Abiyoyo Returns. Hays, Michael, illus. 2004. (J). (ps-3). lib. bdg. 14.19 (978-0-606-32677-3(4)) Tandem Library Bks.

Selznick, Brian. The Houdini Box. Selznick, Brian, illus. 2001. (Illus.). 64p. (J). 17.00 (978-0-689-84488-1(3) , Atheneum/Anne Schwartz Bks.); pap. 5.99 (978-0-689-84451-5(4) , Aladdin) Simon & Schuster Children's Publishing.

—Houdini Box. 2001. (gr. 3-6). lib. bdg. 14.15 (978-0-613-37147-6(X)) Tandem Library Bks.

Smallcomb, Pam. Trimoni Twins & the Changing Coin. 2004. 175p. (J). 15.95 (978-1-58234-939-8(8) , Bloomsbury Children) Bloomsbury Publishing.

Stockton, Frank Richard. The Bee Man of Orn & Other Fanciful Tales. 2004. reprint ed. pap. 20.95 (978-1-4191-5383-9(8)); pap. 1.99 (978-1-4192-5383-6(2)) Kessinger Publishing, LLC.

Taylor, Terry. Tim the Young Magician: Tim & the Circus. 2005. 48p. pap. 12.95 (978-1-4137-6618-9(8)) PublishAmerica, Inc.

Taylor, Theodore. The Boy Who Could Fly Without a Motor. (Illus.). 2004. 168p. (J). pap. 5.95 (978-0-15-204767-2(0) , Harcourt Paperbacks); 2002. 144p. (YA). (gr. 3-6). 15.00 (978-0-15-216529-1(0)) Harcourt Children's Bks.

Temperley, Alan. The Magician of Samarkand. l.t. ed. 2005. 216p. (J). pap. (978-0-7540-7883-8(3) , CLP 459) BBC Audio.

—The Magician of Samarkand. 2004. (J). pap. 29.95 incl. audio (978-0-7540-6279-0(1) , Chivers Children's Audio Bks.) BBC Audiobooks America.

Thompson, Colin. The Great Montefiasco. Redlich, Ben, illus. 2004. 40p. (J). (ps-ps). 16.95 (978-1-59572-008-5(1)) Star Bright Bks., Inc.

The Three Magicians, 6 Packs. (Literatura 2000 Ser.). (gr. 2-3). 33.00 (978-0-7635-0241-6(3)) Rigby Education.

Tiffany, Grace. Ariel. 2005. 240p. (J). 16.99 (978-0-06-075327-6(7)); lib. bdg. 17.89 (978-0-06-075328-3(5)) HarperCollins Pubs.

Los tres Magos: Individual Title, 6 Packs. (Literatura 2000 Ser.). (SPA.). (gr. 2-3). 33.00 (978-0-7635-1275-0(3)) Rigby Education.

Van Lieshout, Ted. Uncle Gus's Magic Box. Sideri, Simona, tr. from DUT. Hopman, Philip, illus. 2005. 60p. (J). (gr. 2-4). pap. 5.95 (978-1-55037-934-1(8)) Annick Pr., Ltd. CAN. *Dist:* Firefly Bks., Ltd.

Villalobos, Ligiah. Save the Elephants. Zalme, Ronald, illus. 2007. (Go, Diego, Go! Ser.). 24p. (J). pap. 3.99 (***978-1-4169-3821-7(4)*** , Simon Spotlight) Simon & Schuster Children's Publishing.

Watson-Dubisch, Carolyn. Andy! & the Magician's Horn, 1. l.t. ed. 2006. (Illus.). 32p. (J). per. 9.95 (978-0-9779295-0-4(7)) Medusa Road Pr.

Wilkins, Kim. Tide Stealers: Sunken Kingdom #2. Cornish, D. M., illus. 2008. 96p. (J). (gr. 4-7). pap. 5.99 (***978-0-375-84807-0(X)***); lib. bdg. 11.99 (***978-0-375-94807-7(4)***) Random Hse. Children's Bks. (Random Hse. Bks. for Young Readers).

Willever, Lisa Funari & Funari, Lorraine. Maximilian the Great. Corsi, Adam, illus. 2000. 32p. (J). (ps-2). 9.95 (978-0-9679227-3-7(9) , 329-007) Franklin Mason Pr.

Wilson, Wendy. The First Book of Red. 2005. 99p. pap. 14.95 (978-1-4137-5570-1(4)) PublishAmerica, Inc.

Yee, Wong Herbert. Abracadabra! Magic with Mouse & Mole. 2007. 48p. (J). (gr. k-3). 15.00 (***978-0-618-75926-2(3)***) Houghton Mifflin Co.

MAGNA CARTA

Daugherty, James. The Magna Charta. Daugherty, James, illus. 1998. (Illus.). 181p. (YA). (gr. 5 up). reprint ed. pap. 10.95 (978-0-9643803-5-6(8)) Beautiful Feet Bks.

MAGNET WINDING

see Electromagnets

MAGNETIC RECORDERS AND RECORDING

Chambers, Catherine. Personal Stereo. 1998. (Look Inside Ser.). (Illus.). 24p. 19.92 (978-1-57572-623-6(8)) Heinemann Library.

Sloan, Peter. Making a Tape. 1999. (gr. k-3). lib. bdg. 11.80 (978-0-613-30586-0(8)) Tandem Library Bks.

MAGNETISM

see also Electricity; Electromagnetism; Electromagnets; Magnets

Angliss, Sarah. Electricity & Magnets. Le Jars, David, illus. 2001. (Hands-On Science Ser.). 40p. (J). (gr. 3-5). pap. 6.95 (978-0-7534-5349-0(5) , Kingfisher) Houghton Mifflin Co. Trade & Reference Div.

—Electricity & Magnets. 2001. (Hands-On Science Ser.). (Illus.). (J). 13.75 (978-0-606-21172-7(1)) Tandem Library Bks.

Benchmark Education Staff, compiled by. Electricity & Magnetism. 2006. spiral bd. 85.00 (***978-1-4108-7035-3(9)***); spiral bd. 119.00 (***978-1-4108-7136-7(3)***) Benchmark Education Co.

Bryant-Mole, Karen & Ansary, Mir Tamim. Magnets. 2002. (Science All Around Me Ser.). (Illus.). 24p. (J). (gr. 1-3). pap. 6.50 (978-1-4034-0052-9(0) , 91496) Heinemann Library.

Burton, Margie, et al. Magnets. Evento, Susan, ed. 1998. (Early Connections Ser.). 16p. (J). (gr. k-2). pap. 4.25 (978-1-892393-57-9(3)) Benchmark Education Co.

Cheshire, Gerard. Electricity & Magnetism. 2006. (Illus.). 48p. (J). (978-1-58340-994-7(7) , 1262672) Smart Apple Media.

Clemmet, Mike. Electricity & Magnetism. 1998. (Fact Finders Ser.). (Illus.). 48p. (J). (gr. 3-7). pap. (978-0-563-37308-7(3)) BBC Worldwide.

Cobb, Vicki. Sources of Forces: Science Fun with Force Fields. Haefele, Steve, illus. 2002. (Science Fun with Vicki Cobb Ser.). 48p. (gr. 3-6). lib. bdg. 24.90 (978-0-7613-1574-2(8) , Millbrook Pr.) Lerner Publishing Group.

Cooper, Christopher. Magnetism: From Pole to Pole. 2003. (Science Answers Ser.). (Illus.). 32p. (J). pap. 7.50 (978-1-4034-3551-4(0)); lib. bdg. 24.22 (978-1-4034-0954-6(4)) Heinemann Library.

Cooper, Jason. Magnets. 2003. (Science Secrets Discovery Library). (Illus.). 24p. (gr. 1-4). 14.95 (978-1-58952-412-5(8)) Rourke Publishing, LLC.

Davis, Beth. Electricity & Magnetism. 2000. (Inquiry Science Ser.). 32p. (J). (gr. 4-5). pap. 4.99 (978-1-56822-950-8(X) , IF20857) School Specialty Publishing.

DiSpezio, Michael A. Awesome Experiments in Electricity & Magnetism. 2006. (Illus.). 160p. pap. 6.95 (978-1-4027-2370-4(9)) Sterling Publishing Co., Inc.

Electricidad y magnetismo: Cuaderno de Evaluacion: Unit 5: Electricidad y magnetismo (Electricity & Magnetism) 2000. (McGraw-Hill Ciencias Ser.). (ENG & SPA.). (gr. 4 up). (978-0-02-278664-9(3)) Macmillan/McGraw-Hill Schl. Div.

Electricidad y magnetismo: Recursos para el maestro con clave de Respuestas: Unit 5: Electricidad y magnetismo (Electricity & Magnetism) 2000. (McGraw-Hill Ciencias Ser.). (ENG & SPA.). (gr. 4 up). (978-0-02-278704-2(6)) Macmillan/McGraw-Hill Schl. Div.

Fairley, Peter. Electricity & Magnetism. 2007. (J). lib. bdg. (***978-0-8225-6605-2(2)***) Twenty First Century Bks.

Farndon, John. Magnetism. 2001. (Science Experiments Ser.). (Illus.). 32p. (J). (gr. 3-5). lib. bdg. 25.64 (978-0-7614-1343-1(X) , Benchmark Bks.) Cavendish, Marshall Corp.

Frank, Marjorie Slavick, et al. Science Instant Readers Bk. 12: Jeff's Magnet. 1999. (Harcourt Science Ser.). (gr. 1 up). pap. 15.50 (978-0-15-316210-7(4)) Harcourt Schl. Pubs.

Frisch, Joy. Magnetism. 2008. (J). (***978-1-58341-577-1(7)*** , Creative Education) Creative Co., The.

Furgang, Kathy. Trabajar con la electricidad y el magnetismo & Working with Electricity & Magnetism. 2005. spiral bd. 84.00 (***978-1-4108-5719-4(0)***) Benchmark Education Co.

Gareth Stevens Publishing Staff, contrib. by. Magnetism. 2003. (Discovery Channel School Science Ser.). (Illus.). 32p. (J). (gr. 5 up). lib. bdg. 24.67 (978-0-8368-3360-7(0)) Stevens, Gareth Inc.

Gianopoulos, Andrea. The Attractive Story of Magnetism with Max Axiom, Super Scientist. Martin, Cynthia & Schulz, Barbara, illus. 2008. (J). (***978-1-4296-0141-2(8)***) Capstone Pr., Inc.

Hands on Science: Electricity & Magnetism. 1999. (Illus.). (J). 74.20 (978-0-7398-1679-0(9)) Raintree.

Hantula, Richard. Electricity & Forces. 2006. (Real World Science Ser.). (Illus.). 32p. (J). 24.67 (978-0-8368-6305-5(4)) Stevens, Gareth Inc.

Harcourt School Publishers Staff. Harcourt Science: Jeff's Magnet Reader. 1999. (Illus.). pap. 3.10 (978-0-15-314862-0(4)) Harcourt Schl. Pubs.

Haslam, Andrew. Electricity: The Hands-on Approach to Science. 2001. (gr. 3-6). lib. bdg. 15.25 (978-0-613-43318-1(1)) Tandem Library Bks.

Holt, Rinehart and Winston Staff. Holt Science & Technology Pt. N: Electricity & Magnetism. 3rd ed. 2003. (SPA.). 18.60 (978-0-03-069329-8(2)) Holt, Rinehart & Winston.

Hunter, Rebecca M. Electricity & Magnetism. 2000. (Discovering Science Ser.). (Illus.). 32p. (J). (gr. 3-5). lib. bdg. 25.69 (978-0-7398-2970-7(X)) Raintree.

—Electricity & Magnetism. 2000. (Discovering Science Ser.). (Illus.). 32p. (J). (gr. 3-5). pap. 8.95 (978-0-7398-3015-4(5)) Steck-Vaughn.

Jennings, Terry. Electricidad y Magnetismo (Electricity & Magnetism) (SPA.). 32p. (J). 6.95 (978-84-348-1741-8(1)) SM Ediciones ESP. *Dist:* AIMS International Bks., Inc.

Kids Publishing Science Staff. Amazing Force Fields: The Story of Electricity & Magnetism. 1999. pap. 6.95 (978-1-891418-18-1(1)) Science Kids.

Larousse Mexico Staff, ed. Imanes y Electricidad. 2005. (40 Fantasticos Experimentos Ser.). (SPA.). 40p. (gr. 3-5). pap. 5.95 (978-970-22-0864-8(5)) Larousse, Ediciones, S. A. de C. V. MEX. *Dist:* Houghton Mifflin Co. Trade & Reference Div.

Lauw, Darlene. Magnets. 2002. (gr. 3-6). lib. bdg. 16.40 (978-0-613-52877-1(8)) Tandem Library Bks.

Lauw, Darlene & Puay, Lim Cheng. Magnets. 2002. (Science Alive! Ser.). (Illus.). 32p. (J). (gr. 4-5). pap. (978-0-7787-0609-0(5)); lib. bdg. (978-0-7787-0563-5(3)) Crabtree Publishing Co.

Magnetism & Electricity. (Jump Ser.). (Illus.). 32p. (J). (gr. 2-7). pap. (978-1-882210-27-5(1)) Action Publishing, Inc.

Magnets. (Amazing Science Ser.). 24p. (J). 7.95 (978-1-4048-0333-6(5)) Picture Window Bks.

A Magnets Set, 6 vols. (Phonics Readers Ser.). (gr. k-2). 17.50 (978-0-7368-3195-6(9)) Red Brick Learning.

McGraw-Hill Staff. Glencoe Science: Electricy & Magnetism. 2nd ed. 2004. stu. ed. 20.64 (978-0-07-861773-7(1) , 9780078617737) Glencoe/McGraw-Hill.

Meiani, Antonella. Magnetism. 2003. (Experimenting with Science Ser.). (Illus.). 40p. (J). (gr. 4-8). lib. bdg. 23.93 (978-0-8225-0085-8(X)) Lerner Publishing Group.

Merrill, Amy French. Everyday Physical Science Experiments with Magnetism. 2002. (Science Surprises Ser.). (Illus.). 24p. (J). lib. bdg. 19.95 (978-0-8239-5800-9(0) , PowerKids Pr.) Rosen Publishing Group, Inc., The.

Mondello, Cindy, ed. Investigating Science - Energy, Magnetism, & Machines. 2000. 48p. 9.95 (978-1-56234-446-7(3) , Mailbox Bks., The) Education Ctr., Inc.

Murphy, Brian. Magnetism. 2004. (Experiment with Ser.). (SPA., Illus.). 32p. (gr. 2-5). (J). pap. 5.95 (978-1-58728-115-0(5)); 9.95 (978-1-58728-243-0(7)) T&N Children's Publishing. (Two Can Publishing).

Murray, Julie. Magnets. 2007. (Illus.). 24p. (J). 21.35 (978-1-59679-827-4(0)) ABDO Publishing Co.

Nelson, Robin. Magnets. 2005. (First Step Nonfiction Ser.). (Illus.). 24p. (J). (gr. k-2). lib. bdg. 18.60 (978-0-8225-5132-4(2)) Lerner Publishing Group.

Newson, Lesley & Wadsworth, Pamela. Trydan a Magnetedd. 2005. (WEL., Illus.). 24p. pap. (978-1-85596-225-5(X)) Dref Wen.

O'Daley, Anne. Magnetism. 2003. (Illus.). 24p. (J). 22.45 (978-1-4103-0080-5(3) , Blackbirch Pr., Inc.) Thomson Gale.

Olien, Rebecca. Magnets. 2002. (Bridgestone Science Library). (Illus.). 24p. (J). (gr. 1-2). lib. bdg. 18.60 (978-0-7368-1406-5(X) , Bridgestone Bks.) Capstone Pr., Inc.

Parker, Steve. Electricity & Magnetism. 2004. (Science View Ser.). (Illus.). 32p. (J). (gr. 4-8). 28.00 (978-0-7910-8208-9(3) , Chelsea Hse.) Facts On File, Inc.

—Electricity & Magnetism. 2000. (Science Fact Files Ser.). (Illus.). 48p. (J). (gr. 4-7). lib. bdg. 27.12 (978-0-7398-1010-1(3)) Raintree.

—Opposites Attract: Magnetism. (Illus.). 56p. (J). 2005. (gr. 6-8). pap. 8.90 (978-1-4034-6421-7(9)); 2004. lib. bdg. (978-1-4034-4815-6(9)) Heinemann Library.

—The Science of Electricity & Magnetism: Projects & Experiments with Electricity & Magnets. 2005. (Illus.). 32p. (J). (ps-6). lib. bdg. 29.29 (978-1-4034-7283-0(1)); pap. 7.95 (978-1-4034-7290-8(4)) Heinemann Library.

Pipe, Jim. Magnets: Magic Forces. 2005. (Science Starters Ser.). (Illus.). 32p. (J). (gr. 3-7). lib. bdg. 27.10 (978-1-59604-015-1(7)) Stargazer Bks.

Project Kit for Kids: Magnetism. 2004. (Illus.). 28p. pap. 14.95 (978-0-9724983-1-9(1)) Jazwares Distribution, Inc.

Raum, Elizabeth. What's the Attraction? 2006. (Illus.). 32p. (J). (978-1-4109-2586-2(2)); pap. (978-1-4109-2615-9(X)) Steck-Vaughn.

Richardson, Adele. Magnetism: A Question & Answer Book. 2006. (Fact Finders Ser.). (Illus.). 32p. (J). (978-0-7368-5447-4(9)) Capstone Pr., Inc.

Riley, Peter D. Magnetism. 1999. (Straightforward Science Ser.). (Illus.). 32p. (J). (gr. 3-5). pap. 6.95 (978-0-531-15372-7(X) , Watts, Franklin) Scholastic Library Publishing.

—Magnetism. 1999. (gr. 3-6). lib. bdg. 15.25 (978-0-613-31440-4(9)) Tandem Library Bks.

Riley, Peter D. & Snedden, Robert. Electricity & Magnetism. 1999. (Smart Science Ser.). (Illus.). 32p. (YA). (gr. 4-7). lib. bdg. 22.79 (978-1-57572-868-1(0)) Heinemann Library.

Rosinsky, Natalie M. Magnets: Pulling Together, Pushing Apart. Boyd, Sheree, illus. 2004. (Amazing Science Ser.). 24p. (C). (gr. k-4). 22.60 (978-1-4048-0014-4(X)) Picture Window Bks.

Royston, Angela. Magnetic & Non-Magnetic. 2003. (My World of Science Ser.). (Illus.). 32p. (J). (gr. k-2). lib. bdg. 22.79 (978-1-4034-0855-6(6)) Heinemann Library.

—Magnetic & Nonmagnetic. 2003. (Illus.). 32p. pap. 6.50 (978-1-4034-3168-4(X)) Heinemann Library.

—Magnets. (Illus.). 32p. (J). (gr. k-2). 2002. pap. 6.95 (978-1-4034-0042-0(3) , 91486); 2001. lib. bdg. 21.36 (978-1-58810-243-0(2)) Heinemann Library.

—Magnets. 2002. (gr. k-3). lib. bdg. 14.75 (978-0-613-88700-7(X)) Tandem Library Bks.

Sadler, Wendy. Magnets: Sticking Together! 2005. (Raintree Perspectives Ser.). (Illus.). 32p. (J). (978-1-4109-1555-9(7)); pap. (978-1-4109-1563-4(8)) Steck-Vaughn.

Saunders, N. Electricity & Magnetism. 2007. (J). lib. bdg. (***978-1-4042-3749-0(6)*** , PowerKids Pr.) Rosen Publishing Group, Inc., The.

School Specialty Publishing. Magnetism. (Science Search Lab Ser.). (J). 2005. (gr. 3-5). pap. 24.95 (978-0-7682-2835-9(2) , Ideal School Supply); 2004. 4p. (gr. 5-7). ring bd. 4.99 (978-0-7424-2922-2(9) , Instructional Fair) Schaffer, Frank Pubns.

Schuh, Mari. Magnetism. 2007. (Illus.). 24p. (J). lib. bdg. 19.95 (978-1-60014-098-3(X)) Bellwether Media.

Sources of Forces: Science Fun with Force Fields. 2007. (J). pap. 7.95 (***978-0-8225-7023-3(8)*** , First Avenue Editions) Lerner Publishing Group.

Spilsbury, Richard & Spilsbury, Louise. What Is Electricity & Magnetism? Exploring Science with Hands-On Activities. 2008. (In Touch with Basic Science Ser.). 32p. (J). (gr. 3-4). lib. bdg. 22.60 (***978-0-7660-3096-1(2)***) Enslow Pubs., Inc.

Stille, Darlene R. Magnets. 2001. (Simply Science Ser.). (Illus.). 32p. (J). (gr. 3 up). lib. bdg. 19.93 (978-0-7565-0091-7(5)) Compass Point Bks.

Tiner, John Hudson. Magnetism. 2002. (Understanding Science (Mankato, Minn.) Ser.). (Illus.). 32p. (J). lib. bdg. 24.25 (978-1-58340-158-3(X)) Smart Apple Media.

Top That Publishing Staff, ed. Magnet Science. 2004. (Top That! Labs Ser.). (Illus.). 24p. (J). (978-1-84510-154-1(5)) Top That! Publishing PLC.

Wadsworth, Pamela. Golwg Gyntaf Ar Drydan a Magnetau. 2005. (WEL., Illus.). 24p. pap. (978-1-85596-255-2(1)) Dref Wen.

Walker, Sally M. Magnetism. King, Andy, photos by. 2006. (Early Bird Energy Ser.). (Illus.). 48p. (J). (gr. 3-7). 25.26 (978-0-8225-2932-3(7) , Lerner Pubns.) Lerner Publishing Group.

Walker, Sally M. El Magnetismo (Magnetism) 2007. (Libros de Energía para madrugadores (Early Bird Energy) Ser.). (SPA.). 48p. (J). (gr. 2-5). 26.60 (***978-0-8225-7720-1(8)*** , Ediciones Lerner) Lerner Publishing Group.

Whalley, Margaret. Electricity & Magnetism. (Illus.). 48p. (J). 2004. (Interfact Ser.). (SPA.). (gr. 3-6). 14.95 incl. cd-rom (978-1-58728-451-9(0)); 2000. (Collectafact Ser.: Vol. 4). (gr. 1-5). 4.95 (978-1-58728-751-0(X)) T&N Children's Publishing. (Two Can Publishing).

Whyman, Kathryn. Electricity & Magnetism. 2004. (J). lib. bdg. (978-1-932799-19-4(2)) Stargazer Bks.

Wood, Robert W. Electricity & Magnetism Fundamentals. 1999. (Funtastic Science Activities for Kids Ser.). (Illus.). 160p. (YA). (gr. 4-7). lib. bdg. 25.25 (978-0-7910-4841-2(1) , Chelsea Hse.) Facts On File, Inc.

MAGNETS

see also Electromagnets

Bailey, Jacqui. What Does a Magnet Do? 2007. (Illus.). 30p. (J). (***978-1-58340-929-9(7)***) Smart Apple Media.

Blevins, Wiley. Magnets. 2003. (Compass Point Phonics Readers Ser.). (Illus.). 16p. (J). (gr. 1 up). 13.26 (978-0-7565-0511-0(9)) Compass Point Bks.

Bliss, Pamela. The Mystery of Magnets. 2004. (National Geographic Reading Expeditions Ser.). (Illus.). 32p. (J). pap. (978-0-7922-4581-0(4)) National Geographic Society.

Bocknek, Jonathan. The Science of Magnets. 1999. (Living Science Ser.). (Illus.). 32p. (J). (gr. 2 up). lib. bdg. 23.93 (978-0-8368-2572-5(1)) Stevens, Gareth Inc.

The Bridgestone Science Library: Our Physical World, 4 bks. Incl. Electricity. Olien, Rebecca. lib. bdg. 18.60 (978-0-7368-1404-1(3)); Light. Olien, Rebecca. lib. bdg. 18.60 (978-0-7368-1405-8(1)); Magnets. Olien, Rebecca. lib. bdg. 18.60 (978-0-7368-1406-5(X)); Sound. Olien, Becky. lib. bdg. 18.60 (978-0-7368-1407-2(8)); 24p. (J). (gr. 1-2). 2002. (Illus.). 2002. Set lib. bdg. 74.40 (978-0-7368-1408-9(6) , Bridgestone Bks.) Capstone Pr., Inc.

Bryant-Mole, Karen & Ansary, Mir Tamim. Magnets. 2002. (Science All Around Me Ser.). (Illus.). 24p. (J). (gr. 1-3). pap. 6.50 (978-1-4034-0052-9(0) , 91496) Heinemann Library.

Carmi, Rebecca. Amazing Magnetism. Speirs, John, illus. 2002. (Magic School Bus Chapter Bks.: Bk. 12). 80p. (J). (gr. 2-4). pap. 4.99 (978-0-439-31432-9(1) , Scholastic Paperbacks) Scholastic, Inc.

—Amazing Magnetism. 2001. (gr. 3-6). lib. bdg. 11.80 (978-0-613-63245-4(1)) Tandem Library Bks.

Doherty, Paul & Cassidy, John. Magia Magnetica. 2005. (SPA., Illus.). 68p. (J). spiral bd. 15.95 (978-987-1078-40-0(4)) Klutz Latino MEX. *Dist:* Independent Pubs. Group.

Electricidad e Imanes. (Coleccion Jugando Con la Ciencia). (SPA., Illus.). 39p. (J). pap. 9.95 (978-950-11-0828-6(7) , SGM309) Sigmar ARG. *Dist:* Continental Bk. Co., Inc.

Fun with Magnets: Individual Title Six-Packs. (Rigby Focus Ser.). 24p. (gr. 2 up). 28.00 (978-0-7578-5357-9(9)); 30.00 (978-0-7578-5587-0(3)) Rigby Education.

Gianopoulos, Andrea. The Attractive Story of Magnetism with Max Axiom, Super Scientist. Martin, Cynthia & Schulz, Barbara, illus. 2008. (J). ***978-1-4296-0141-2(8))** Capstone Pr., Inc.

Glover, David. Batteries, Bulbs, & Wires. 2002. (Young Discoverers Ser.). (Illus.). 32p. (J). (gr. k-3). pap. 7.95 (978-0-7534-5510-4(2) , Kingfisher) Houghton Mifflin Co. Trade & Reference Div.

Hirschmann, Kris. Magnets. 2006. 48p. (gr. 4-8). 26.20 (978-0-7377-1016-8(0) , Kidhaven) Thomson Gale.

Hixson, Bryce. Opposites Attract. Hixson, Bryce, illus. 2002. (Illus.). (J). per. 14.95 (978-0-9660965-1-4(7)) Loose In The Lab.

Inquiry Investigations: Magnets. 2004. 48p. (J). pap. 6.99 (978-0-88724-265-6(0) , CD-2362) Carson-Dellosa Publishing Co., Inc.

Lauw, Darlene. Magnets. 2002. (gr. 3-6). lib. bdg. 16.40 (978-0-613-52877-1(8)) Tandem Library Bks.

Lauw, Darlene & Puay, Lim Cheng. Magnets. 2002. (Science Alive! Ser.). (Illus.). 32p. (J). (gr. 4-5). pap. (978-0-7787-0609-0(5)); lib. bdg. (978-0-7787-0563-5(3)) Crabtree Publishing Co.

The Letter Tt: Magnets, 6 vols. (gr. k-2). 17.50 (978-0-7368-4119-1(9)) Red Brick Learning.

Levine, Shar & Johnstone, Leslie. Magnet Power! Harpster, Steve, illus. 2006. (First Science Experiments Ser.). 48p. (J). 14.95 (978-1-4027-2438-1(1)) Sterling Publishing Co., Inc.

Magnets. (Our Physical World Ser.). 24p. (J). 6.95 (978-0-7368-3428-5(1)) Capstone Pr., Inc.

Magnets. (Amazing Science Ser.). 24p. (J). 7.95 (978-1-4048-0333-6(5)) Picture Window Bks.

Magnets & Electricity. 2002. (Super Science Activities Ser.). 48p. (J). (gr. 2-5). 7.99 (978-0-7439-3664-4(7) , 3664) Teacher Created Materials, Inc.

Murray, Julie. Magnets. 2007. (Illus.). 24p. (J). 21.35 (978-1-59679-827-4(0)) ABDO Publishing Co.

Nelson, Robin. Los Imanes (Magnets) 2007. (Mi Primer Paso al Mundo Real - Fuerzas y Movimiento (First Step Nonfiction - Forces & Motion) Ser.). (SPA.). 24p. (J). (gr. k-2). lib. bdg. 18.60 (***978-0-8225-7809-3(3)** , Ediciones Lerner) Lerner Publishing Group.

Nelson, Robin. Magnets. 2005. (First Step Nonfiction Ser.). (Illus.). 24p. (J). (gr. k-2). lib. bdg. 18.60 (978-0-8225-5132-4(2)) Lerner Publishing Group.

Olien, Rebecca. Magnets. 2002. (Bridgestone Science Library). (Illus.). 24p. (J). (gr. 1-2). lib. bdg. 18.60 (978-0-7368-1406-5(X) , Bridgestone Bks.) Capstone Pr., Inc.

Parker, S. Magnets. 2002. (Fantastic Facts Ser.). (Illus.). 64p. (gr. 3-7). pap. 6.95 (978-1-84215-613-1(6) , Southwater) Anness Publishing GBR. *Dist:* National Bk. Network.

Parker, Steve. Opposites Attract: Magnetism. (Illus.). 56p. (J). 2005. (gr. 6-8). pap. 8.90 (978-1-4034-6421-7(9)); 2004. lib. bdg. (978-1-4034-4815-6(9)) Heinemann Library.

Pipe, Jim. Magnets: Magic Forces. 2005. (Science Starters Ser.). (Illus.). 32p. (J). (gr. 3-7). lib. bdg. 27.10 (978-1-59604-015-1(7)) Stargazer Bks.

Prior, Jennifer Overend. Magnets. Hale, Janet A., ed. Chaney, Howard, illus. 1999. (Thematic Units Ser.). 80p. (J). pap., tchr. ed. 9.99 (978-1-57690-377-3(X) , TCM2377) Teacher Created Materials, Inc.

Raum, Elizabeth. What's the Attraction? 2006. (Illus.). 32p. (J). (978-1-4109-2586-2(2)); pap. (978-1-4109-2615-9(X)) Steck-Vaughn.

Richardson, Adele. Magnetism: A Question & Answer Book. 2006. (Fact Finders Ser.). (Illus.). 32p. (J). (978-0-7368-5447-4(9)) Capstone Pr., Inc.

Rosinsky, Natalie M. Magnets: Pulling Together, Pushing Apart. Boyd, Sheree, illus. 2004. (Amazing Science Ser.). 24p. (C). (gr. k-4). 22.60 (978-1-4048-0014-4(X)) Picture Window Bks.

Royston, Angela. Imanes. 2006. (Ciencia en Mi Mundo Ser.). (SPA., Illus.). 32p. (J). lib. bdg. 25.36 (978-1-4034-9110-7(0)) Heinemann Library.

—Magnetic & Non-Magnetic. 2003. (My World of Science Ser.). (Illus.). 32p. (J). (gr. k-2). lib. bdg. 22.79 (978-1-4034-0855-6(6)) Heinemann Library.

—Magnets. (Illus.). 32p. (J). (gr. k-2). 2002. pap. 6.95 (978-1-4034-0042-0(3) , 91486); 2001. lib. bdg. 21.36 (978-1-58810-243-0(2)) Heinemann Library.

—Magnets. 2002. (gr. k-3). lib. bdg. 14.75 (978-0-613-88700-7(X)) Tandem Library Bks.

Sadler, Wendy. Magnets: Sticking Together! 2005. (Raintree Perspectives Ser.). (Illus.). 32p. (J). (978-1-4109-1555-9(7)); pap. (978-1-4109-1563-4(8)) Steck-Vaughn.

Schreiber, Anne. Magnets. Sinnott, Adrian C., illus. 2003. (All Aboard Science Reader Ser.). 48p. (J). (gr. 2-4). pap. 3.99 (978-0-448-43149-9(1) , Grosset & Dunlap) Penguin Group (USA) Inc.

—Magnets. 2003. (gr. k-3). lib. bdg. 11.80 (978-0-613-68361-6(7)) Tandem Library Bks.

Science with Magnets Kid Kit. 2004. (Kid Kits Ser.). (Illus.). 24p. (J). 14.95 (978-1-58086-420-6(1)) EDC Publishing.

Sian Revision Magnet Magic. 2004. (Science in A Nutshell(R) Ser.). (J). (978-1-59242-043-8(5)) Delta Education, LLC.

Smuskiewicz, Alfred J. Magnets & Electromagnetism. 2007. (J). (***978-1-4034-9927-1(6)**); pap. (***978-1-4034-9935-6(7))** Heinemann Library.

Stewart, Josie & Salem, Lynn. Magnets. Durney, Ryan, illus. 2000. 8p. (J). (gr. k-2). pap. 3.75 (978-1-58323-007-7(6) , Seedling Pubns.) Continental Pr., Inc.

Stille, Darlene R. Magnets. 2001. (Simply Science Ser.). (Illus.). 32p. (J). (gr. 3 up). lib. bdg. 19.93 (978-0-7565-0091-7(5)) Compass Point Bks.

Tiner, John Hudson. Magnetism. 2002. (Understanding Science (Mankato, Minn.) Ser.). (Illus.). 32p. (J). lib. bdg. 24.25 (978-1-58340-158-3(X)) Smart Apple Media.

Tocci, Salvatore. Experiments with Magnets. 2001. (True Science Experiments Bks.). (Illus.). 48p. (J). (gr. 3-5). 25.00 (978-0-516-22248-6(1) , Children's Pr.) Scholastic Library Publishing.

—Experiments with Magnets. 2002. 13.75 (978-0-606-22882-4(9)); 2001. (gr. 3-6). lib. bdg. 15.25 (978-0-613-54210-4(X)) Tandem Library Bks.

Vecchione, Glen. Magnet Science. 2007. (Illus.). 128p. (J). 14.95 (978-1-4027-2291-2(5)) Sterling Publishing Co., Inc.

Walker, Richard. Magnets. 1998. (Detective Files Ser.). (Illus.). 32p. (J). (gr. 3-7). 19.95 (978-1-57145-323-5(7) , Silver Dolphin Bks.) Advantage Pubs. Group.

Walker, Sally M. Magnetism. King, Andy, photos by. 2006. (Early Bird Energy Ser.). (Illus.). 48p. (J). (gr. 3-7). 25.26 (978-0-8225-2932-3(7) , Lerner Pubns.) Lerner Publishing Group.

Walker, Sally M. El Magnetismo (Magnetism) 2007. (Libros de Energía para madrugadores (Early Bird Energy) Ser.). (SPA.). 48p. (J). (gr. 2-5). 26.60 (***978-0-8225-7720-1(8)** , Ediciones Lerner) Lerner Publishing Group.

MAGPIES—FICTION

Doust, Jon & Spillman, Ken. Magpie Mischief. Sorensen, Gert, ed. 2002. (Illus.). 72p. pap. 11.95 (978-1-86368-355-5(0)) Fremantle Pr. AUS. *Dist:* International Specialized Bk. Services.

Ferguson, Sarah. Little Red's Summer Adventure. Williams, Sam, illus. 2006. 40p. (J). (ps-2). 15.95 (978-0-689-85562-7(1)) Simon & Schuster Children's Publishing.

Wild, Margaret. Fox. Brooks, Ron, illus. 2000. 40p. (J). (978-1-86448-465-6(9)); mass mkt. (978-1-86448-933-0(2)) Allen & Unwin.

MAGRUDER, BERNIE (FICTITIOUS CHARACTER)—FICTION

Naylor, Phyllis Reynolds. Bernie Magruder & the Case of the Big Stink. 2001. 11.64 (978-0-606-22812-1(8)) Tandem Library Bks.

—Bernie Magruder & the Disappearing Bodies. 2001. 11.64 (978-0-606-22813-8(6)) Tandem Library Bks.

—Bernie Magruder & the Haunted Hotel. 2001. 11.64 (978-0-606-22814-5(4)) Tandem Library Bks.

—Bernie Magruder & the Haunted Hotel. l.t. ed. 2001. 127p. (J). 20.95 (978-0-7862-3600-8(0)) Thorndike Pr.

—Bernie Magruder & the Pirate's Treasure. 2001. (978-0-606-22788-9(1)) Tandem Library Bks.

MAINE

Brown, Jonatha A. Maine. 2006. (Portraits of the States Ser.). (J). pap. (978-0-8368-4718-5(0)); lib. bdg. (978-0-8368-4701-7(6)) Stevens, Gareth Inc.

Craig, Janet. Maine: The Pine Tree State. 2003. (World Almanac Library of the States). (Illus.). 48p. (J). (gr. 5 up). pap. 14.95 (978-0-8368-5322-3(9)); lib. bdg. 30.00 (978-0-8368-5151-9(X)) Stevens, Gareth Inc. (World Almanac Library).

Dean, Carol. The Hen House: A True Story of Growing up on a Maine Farm. Dunn, Sandy, illus. 2003. 32p. 15.95 (978-0-89272-609-7(1)) Down East Bks.

Dornfeld, Margaret. Maine. 2001. (Celebrate the States Ser.). (Illus.). 144p. (J). (gr. 4-8). lib. bdg. 37.07 (978-0-7614-1071-3(6) , Benchmark Bks.) Cavendish, Marshall Corp.

Engfer, LeeAnne. Maine. (Hello U. S. A. Ser.). (gr. 3-6). 1999. 72p. pap. 5.95 (978-0-8225-9787-2(X)); 2nd exp. rev. ed. 2003. (Illus.). 84p. (J). pap. 6.95 (978-0-8225-4138-7(6)); 2nd exp. rev. ed. 2002. (Illus.). 84p. (J). lib. bdg. 25.26 (978-0-8225-4071-7(1)) Lerner Publishing Group.

Foran, Jill. A Guide to Maine. 2001. (American States Ser.). (Illus.). 32p. (J). lib. bdg. 16.95 (978-1-930954-69-4(7)) Weigl Pubs., Inc.

Furlong Reynolds, Cynthia. L Is for Lobster: A Maine Alphabet. Brett, Jeannie, illus. 2001. 40p. (J). (ps-3). 17.95 (978-1-58536-024-6(4)) Sleeping Bear Pr.

Graham, Amy. Maine: A MyReportLinks.com Book. 2002. (States Ser.). (Illus.). 48p. (J). (gr. 4-10). lib. bdg. 25.26 (978-0-7660-5017-4(3) , MyReportLinks.com Bks.) Enslow Pubs., Inc.

Heinrichs, Ann. Maine. 2003. (This Land Is Your Land Ser.). (Illus.). 48p. (J). (gr. 3 up). lib. bdg. 22.60 (978-0-7565-0347-5(7)) Compass Point Bks.

—Maine. 2007. (America the Beautiful, Third Ser.). 144p. (J). spiral bd. 38.00 (***978-0-531-18575-9(3)** , Children's Pr.) Scholastic Library Publishing.

Hicks, Terry Allan. Maine. 2005. (It's My State! Ser.). (Illus.). 80p. (J). (978-0-7614-1910-5(1) , Benchmark Bks.) Cavendish, Marshall Corp.

Knox, Barbara. Maine. 2003. (Land of Liberty Ser.). (Illus.). 64p. (J). (gr. 3-4). lib. bdg. 23.93 (978-0-7368-1587-1(2) , Bridgestone Bks.) Capstone Pr., Inc.

Kummer, Patricia K. Maine. rev. ed. 2002. (One Nation Ser.). (Illus.). 48p. (J). (gr. 3-4). lib. bdg. 22.60 (978-0-7368-1243-6(1) , Bridgestone Bks.) Capstone Pr., Inc.

Maine. 2000. (Switched on Schoolhouse Ser.). (Illus.). (YA). (gr. 7-12). pap. 24.95 incl. cd-rom (978-0-7403-0271-8(X) , SOSME) Alpha Omega Pubns., Inc.

Marsh, Carole. The Big Maine Reproducible Activity Book. 2001. (Carole Marsh Maine Bks.). (Illus.). 96p. (J). (gr. 2-6). pap., act. bk. ed. 9.95 (978-0-7933-9944-4(0)) Gallopade International.

—Maine Classic Christmas Trivia. 2002. (Carole Marsh Maine Bks.). (Illus.). 32p. pap. 6.95 (978-0-635-01405-4(X) , 1405X); lib. bdg. 21.95 (978-0-635-01406-1(8) , 14068, Marsh, Carole Bks.) Gallopade International.

—Maine Current Events Projects: 30 Cool, Activities, Crafts, Experiments & More for Kids to Do to Learn about Your State! 2003. (Maine Experience Ser.). 32p. (gr. k-8). pap. 5.95 (978-0-635-02038-3(6) , Marsh, Carole Bks.) Gallopade International.

—The Maine Experience Pocket Guide. 2001. (Carole Marsh Maine Bks.). (Illus.). 96p. (J). (gr. 3-8). pap. 6.95 (978-0-7933-9915-4(7)) Gallopade International.

—Maine Geography Projects: 30 Cool, Activities, Crafts, Experiments & More for Kids to Do to Learn about Your State! 2003. (Maine Experience Ser.). 32p. (gr. k-5). pap. 5.95 (978-0-635-01838-0(1) , Marsh, Carole Bks.) Gallopade International.

—Maine Government Projects: 30 Cool, Activities, Crafts, Experiments & More for Kids to Do to Learn about Your State! 2003. (Maine Experience Ser.). 32p. (gr. k-5). pap. 5.95 (978-0-635-01938-7(8) , Marsh, Carole Bks.) Gallopade International.

—Maine Jeopardy! Answers & Questions about Our State! 2001. (Illus.). 32p. (J). (gr. 3-8). pap. 7.95 (978-0-7933-9799-0(5)) Gallopade International.

—Maine "Jography" A Fun Run Thru Our State! 2001. (Carole Marsh Maine Bks.). (Illus.). 32p. (J). (gr. 3-8). pap. 7.95 (978-0-7933-9828-7(2)) Gallopade International.

—Maine Millionaire: Game Book. 2001. (Carole Marsh Maine Bks.). (Illus.). 32p. (J). (gr. 3-8). pap., act. bk. ed. 9.95 (978-0-635-00054-5(7)) Gallopade International.

—Maine People Projects: 30 Cool, Activities, Crafts, Experiments & More for Kids to Do to Learn about Your State! 2003. (Maine Experience Ser.). 32p. (gr. k-5). pap. 5.95 (978-0-635-01988-2(4) , Marsh, Carole Bks.) Gallopade International.

—Maine Survivor: Game Book. 2001. (Carole Marsh Maine Bks.). (Illus.). 32p. (J). (gr. 3-8). pap., act. bk. ed. 9.95 (978-0-635-00540-3(9)) Gallopade International.

—Maine Symbols & Facts Projects: 30 Cool, Activities, Crafts, Experiments & More for Kids to Do to Learn about Your State! 2003. (Maine Experience Ser.). 32p. (gr. k-5). pap. 5.95 (978-0-635-01888-5(8) , Marsh, Carole Bks.) Gallopade International.

—My First Book about Maine. 2001. (Carole Marsh Maine Bks.). (Illus.). 32p. (J). (gr. k-4). pap. 7.95 (978-0-7933-9886-7(X)) Gallopade International.

—The Survivor: A Class Challenge. 2001. (Carole Marsh Maine Bks.). lib. bdg. 29.95 (978-0-635-00665-3(0)) Gallopade International.

McAuliffe, Emily. Maine: Facts & Symbols. 1999. (States & Their Symbols Ser.). (Illus.). 24p. (J). (gr. k-3). pap. 15.00 (978-0-531-12002-6(3) , Watts, Franklin) Scholastic Library Publishing.

Morris, Ann. Grandma Susan Remembers: A British-American Family Story. Linenthal, Peter, illus. 2002. (What Was It Like, Grandma? Ser.). 32p. (gr. k-3). lib. bdg. 22.90 (978-0-7613-2319-8(8) , Millbrook Pr.) Lerner Publishing Group.

—Grandma Susan Remembers: A British-American Family Story. 2002. (gr. k-3). lib. bdg. 16.40 (978-0-613-56398-7(0)) Tandem Library Bks.

Murray, Julie. Maine. 2006. (Illus.). 32p. (J). (gr. k-4). lib. bdg. 22.78 (978-1-59197-678-3(2) , Buddy Bks.) ABDO Publishing Co.

Obregon, Jose M. Maine. Brusca, Maria Cristina, tr. 2005. (Bilingual Library of the United States of America: Set 1). (ENG & SPA., Illus.). 32p. (J). (gr. 2-5). lib. bdg. 22.50 (978-1-4042-3084-2(X) , Buenas Letra) Rosen Publishing Group, Inc., The.

Pelletier, Fran. Little Pine to King Spruce: A Franco-American Childhood. 2003. (Illus.). 192p. pap. 15.00 (978-0-88448-254-3(5)) Tilbury Hse. Pubs.

Peterson, Sheryl. Maine. 2008. (J). (***978-1-58341-644-0(7)** , Creative Education) Creative Co., The.

Reynolds, Cynthia Furlong. Fishing for Numbers: A Maine Number Book. Brett, Jeannie, illus. 2005. (Count Your Way Across the USA Ser.). 40p. (J). (gr. k-5). 16.95 (978-1-58536-035-2(X)) Sleeping Bear Pr.

Ross, D. J. Uniquely Maine. 2004. (Heinemann State Studies). (Illus.). 48p. (J). pap. 8.50 (978-1-4034-4724-1(1)); lib. bdg. 27.07 (978-1-4034-4655-8(5)) Heinemann Library.

Walker, Cynthia. Maine. (J). 2006. 32p. (gr. 1-2). pap. 5.95 (978-0-516-25157-8(0)); 2005. (Illus.). 31p. (ps-ps). 20.50 (978-0-516-25255-1(0)) Scholastic Library Publishing. (Children's Pr.).

Webster, Christine. Maine. 2003. (From Sea to Shining Sea Ser.: 2). (Illus.). 80p. (J). 30.50 (978-0-516-22323-0(2) , Children's Pr.) Scholastic Library Publishing.

Zschock, Martha Day. Journey Around Maine from A to Z. Zschock, Martha Day, illus. 2007. (J). 17.95 (***978-1-933212-31-9(4))** Commonwealth Editions.

MAINE—FICTION

Agell, Charlotte. Welcome Home or Someplace Like It. rev. ed. 2003. (Illus.). 240p. (J). 16.95 (978-0-8050-7083-5(4) , Holt, Henry & Co. Bks. For Young Readers) Holt, Henry & Co.

Aldridge, Janet. The Meadow-Brook Girls in the Hills: Or the Missing Pilot of the White Mountains. 2006. pap. (***978-1-4065-0694-5(X))** Dodo Pr.

Austin, Heather. Visiting Aunt Sylvia's: A Maine Adventure. Austin, Heather, illus. 2002. (Illus.). 32p. (gr. k-3). 15.95 (978-0-89272-523-6(0)) Down East Bks.

Banghart, Tracy E. What the Sea Wants. Blum, Julia C., illus. 2006. 64p. (YA). kivar 16.00 (978-0-9779753-0-3(4)) LizStar Bks.

Bartlett, Susan. Seal Island School. Bonnell, J., ed. Tusa, Tricia, illus. 2001. (Chapters Ser.). 80p. (J). (gr. 2-5). pap. 4.99 (978-0-14-131104-3(5) , Puffin) Penguin Group (USA) Inc.

—Seal Island School. Tusa, Tricia, illus. 1999. 80p. (J). (gr. 2-5). 15.99 (978-0-670-88349-3(2) , Viking Juvenile) Penguin Group (USA) Inc.

—Seal Island School. 2001. (gr. 3-6). lib. bdg. 13.00 (978-0-613-63991-0(X)) Tandem Library Bks.

Beckhorn, Susan Williams. Sarey by Lantern Light. 2003. (Illus.). 150p. pap. 9.95 (978-0-89272-612-7(1)) Down East Bks.

—Sarey by Lantern Light. 2003. (gr. 7-12). lib. bdg. 18.75 (978-0-613-77418-5(3)) Tandem Library Bks.

Bennett, Dean. The Late Loon. 2006. (Illus.). 32p. 15.95 (978-0-89272-730-8(6)) Down East Bks.

Blume, Judy. Fudge-a-Mania. 2007. (Fudge Ser.). 160p. (J). (gr. 2). pap. 5.99 (978-0-14-240877-3(8) , Puffin) Penguin Group (USA) Inc.

Brown, Margaret Wise. The Little Island. Weisgard, Leonard, illus. 2003. 48p. (J). (gr. k-3). 14.95 (978-0-385-74640-3(7)); lib. bdg. 16.99 (978-0-385-90872-6(5)) Random Hse. Children's Bks. (Doubleday Bks. for Young Readers).

Buzzeo, Toni. The Sea Chest. GrandPré, Mary, illus. 2002. 32p. (J). (gr. k up). 16.99 (978-0-8037-2703-8(8) , Dial) Penguin Group (USA) Inc.

Carlton, Susan. Lobsterland. 2007. 224p. (YA). (gr. 9 up). 16.95 (***978-0-8050-8096-4(1))** Holt, Henry & Co.

Chetkowski, Emily. Mabel Takes a Sail. 2000. (gr. k-3). lib. bdg. 19.35 (978-0-613-85830-4(1)) Tandem Library Bks.

—Mabel Takes a Sail. Peterson, Dawn, illus. 2000. 64p. (J). (ps-3). pap. 10.50 (978-1-880158-26-5(4)) Townsend, J.N. Publishing.

—Mabel Takes the Ferry. Peterson, Dawn, illus. 2001. 40p. (J). pap. 11.95 (978-1-880158-37-1(X)) Townsend, J.N. Publishing.

Clark, Catherine. Maine Squeeze. 2004. 368p. (J). (gr. 8 up). pap. 5.99 (978-0-06-056725-5(2)) HarperCollins Pubs.

Cooney, Barbara. Lost Treasures Bk. 1: The Kellyhorns. 2001. 256p. (J). 13.49 (978-0-7868-2596-7(0)) Hyperion Pr.

Copeland, Cynthia L. Elin's Island. 2003. (Single Titles Ser.: up). 144p. (gr. 6 up). lib. bdg. 22.90 (978-0-7613-2522-2(0) , Millbrook Pr.) Lerner Publishing Group.

Crossman, David A. The Secret of the Missing Grave. 1999. (Bean & Ab Mystery Ser.). 184p. (YA). (gr. 4-10). 16.95 (978-0-89272-456-7(0)) Down East Bks.

Dalmatian Press Staff, adapted by. Rebecca of Sunnybrook Farm. 2003. (Spot the Classics Ser.). 192p. (J). 4.99 (978-1-57759-563-2(7)) Dalmatian Pr.

Dean, Carol S. The Live Bale of Hay: A Real Maine Adventure. Dunn, Sandra, illus. 2005. 32p. (ps-ps). 15.95 (978-0-89272-674-5(1)) Down East Bks.

Deans, Sis Boulos. Rainy. 2005. 208p. (J). (ps-7). 16.95 (978-0-8050-7831-2(2)) Holt, Henry & Co.

Draper, Rochelle, illus. The Stone Wall Dragon. 2007. 32p. 15.95 (***978-0-89272-690-5(3))** Down East Bks.

Eaton, Walter Prichard. Boy Scouts in the White Mountains: the Story of a Long Hike. Merrill, Frank T., illus. 2006. (ENG.). 316p. per. 30.95 (***978-1-4286-4117-4(3))** Kessinger Publishing, LLC.

Flint, Garrison. The Butler Did It! A Raymond Masrters Mystery. 2003. (Raymond Masters Mystery: 10). 206p. per. 13.99 (978-1-885631-72-5(3)) Hutchison, G.F. Pr.

Frey, G. Hildegard. Camp Fire Girls in the Maine Woods or Th. 2006. 95.99 (***978-1-4280-4028-1(5)**); pap. 88.99 (***978-1-4280-4023-6(4))** IndyPublish.com.

Gamble, Adam. Good Night Maine. Chan, Suwin, illus. 2006. (J). bds. 9.95 (978-0-9758502-8-2(8)) On Cape Pubns.

—Good Night Maine. Chan, Suwin, illus. 2007. (Good Night Our World Ser.). 18p. (J). bds. 9.95 (***978-1-60219-010-8(0))** Our World of Books.

Garfield, Henry. Tartabull's Throw. 2001. (Illus.). 272p. (J). (gr. 7 up). 16.00 (978-0-689-83840-8(9) , Atheneum/Richard Jackson Bks.) Simon & Schuster Children's Publishing.

—Tartabull's Throw. 2003. (gr. 7-12). lib. bdg. 14.15 (978-0-613-61823-6(8)) Tandem Library Bks.

Gerritsen, Tess. Bloodstream: A Novel of Medical Suspense. 1999. (gr. 7-12). lib. bdg. 16.45 (978-0-613-24020-8(0)) Tandem Library Bks.

Goldsberry, Booty. Scaredy-Cat, I'm Not. 2007. (Illus.). 40p. pap. 9.95 (***978-0-9792875-0-3(2))** Goldsberry, Booty.

Gutman, Dan. The Get Rich Quick Club. 128p. (J). 2006. pap. 5.99 (978-0-06-053442-4(7) , Harper Trophy); 2004. 15.99 (978-0-06-053440-0(0)); 2004. lib. bdg. 16.89 (978-0-06-053441-7(9)) HarperCollins Pubs.

Harcourt School Publishers Staff. Skylark: Reader's Choice Book. 2001. (Collections Ser.). (Illus.). (J). 6.90 (978-0-15-314358-8(4)) Harcourt Schl. Pubs.

Harlow, Joan Hiatt. Shadows on the Sea. (Illus.). 256p. (J). 2005. pap. 4.99 (978-0-689-84927-5(3) , Aladdin); 2003. (gr. 3-6). 17.99 (978-0-689-84926-8(5) , McElderry, Margaret K.) Simon & Schuster Children's Publishing.

—Shadows on the Sea. l.t. ed. 2003. 214p. 20.95 (978-0-7862-6145-1(5) , Large Print Pr.) Thorndike Pr.

Hawkes, Kevin. The Wicked Big Toddlah. 2007. 40p. (J). (ps-3). 16.99 (978-0-375-82427-2(8)); lib. bdg. 19.99 (978-0-375-92427-9(2)) Random Hse. Children's Bks. (Knopf Bks. for Young Readers).

Holmes, Barbara W. Following Fake Man. 2002. (gr. 3-6). lib. bdg. 13.00 (978-0-613-61839-7(4)) Tandem Library Bks.

Hopkinson, Deborah. Birdie's Lighthouse. Root, Kimberly B., illus. 2000. 32p. (J). (ps-3). 6.99 (978-0-689-83529-2(9) , Aladdin) Simon & Schuster Children's Publishing.

—Birdie's Lighthouse. 2000. (gr. 3-6). lib. bdg. 14.15 (978-0-613-28424-0(0)); (Illus.). (J). (978-0-606-17913-3(5)) Tandem Library Bks.

Horvath, Polly. The Canning Season. 2003. (J). pap. (978-0-88899-552-0(0)) Douglas & McIntyre, Ltd.

—The Canning Season. 208p. (YA). 2003. (gr. 6-9). 16.00 (978-0-374-39956-6(5)); 2005. (gr. 7). reprint ed. pap. 6.95 (978-0-374-41042-1(9)) Farrar, Straus & Giroux. (Farrar, Straus & Giroux (BYR)).

—The Canning Season. l.t. ed. 2005. 269p. (YA). (gr. 7). pap. 10.95 (978-0-7862-8088-9(3)) Thorndike Pr.

Jahn-Clough, Lisa. Country Girl, City Girl. 2004. 192p. (YA). (gr. 5). tchr. ed. 15.00 (978-0-618-44791-6(1) , Walter Lorraine) Houghton Mifflin Co. Trade & Reference Div.

Jewett, Sarah Orne. The Country of the Pointed Firs & Other Stories. 2000. (gr. 7-12). lib. bdg. 11.80 (978-0-613-27778-5(3)) Tandem Library Bks.

Jones, Carrie. Tips on Having a Gay (ex) Boyfriend. 2008. 264p. (J). pap. 9.95 (*978-0-7387-1341-0(4)* , Flux) Llewellyn Pubns.

Jones, Kimberly K. Sand Dollar Summer. 2006. 224p. (J). 15.95 (978-1-4169-0362-8(3) , McElderry, Margaret K.) Simon & Schuster Children's Publishing.

Jones, Molly. The Choosing Tree. 2006. 126p. pap. 17.95 (*978-1-4241-5076-2(0)*) PublishAmerica, Inc.

Jordan, Evora. Annie Love: A Hannah Gray Dog Story. 2003. (Hannah Gray Mysteries). (J). per. (978-0-9725071-2-7(4)) EvoraBooks, LLC.

Keizer, Garret. God of Beer. 256p. (J). 2003. pap. 6.99 (978-0-06-447276-0(0)); 2002. (gr. 8 up). 15.95 (978-0-06-029456-4(6)) HarperCollins Pubs.

—God of Beer. 2003. (gr. 7-12). lib. bdg. 15.30 (978-0-613-71500-3(4)) Tandem Library Bks.

Levin, Betty. That'll Do, Moss. 2002. (Illus.). 128p. (J). (gr. 3 up). 15.89 (978-0-06-000532-0(7)) HarperCollins Pubs.

Lewis, Carolyn & DeVince, James. Hairy Beary Book Three: The Blue Ribbon Hero, 3 bks., Vol. 3. DeVince, James, ed. Porcheron, Tammy, illus. 2003. (Hairy Beary Ser.: 3). 46p. (J). pap. 9.95 (978-0-9712641-2-0(0)) J M D's Business Services.

Libhart, Virginia B. Carrie's Dream. 2005. (978-0-9652963-7-3(7)) Harborseal Publishing Co.

Love, Pamela. A Loon Alone. Sycks, Shannon, illus. 2002. 30p. pap. 9.95 (978-0-89272-526-7(5) , 1078); 29p. 14.95 (978-0-89272-571-7(0)) Down East Bks.

Mackinnon, Bernard. The Boy Who Turned Green. 2005. 119p. pap. 16.95 (978-1-4137-7262-3(5)) PublishAmerica, Inc.

Mariconda, Barbara. Turn the Cup Around. 1998. (978-0-606-13878-9(1)) Tandem Library Bks.

Martin, Jacqueline Briggs. Grandmother Bryant's Pocket. Mathers, Petra, illus. 2000. 48p. (J). (gr. k-3). pap. 5.95 (978-0-618-03309-6(2)) Houghton Mifflin Co. Trade & Reference Div.

—Grandmother Bryant's Pocket. 2000. (Illus.). (J). (978-0-606-18209-6(8)) Tandem Library Bks.

McCloskey, Robert. Blueberries for Sal. McCloskey, Robert, illus. 2002. (Illus.). (J). 14.04 (978-0-7587-0097-1(0)) Book Wholesalers, Inc.

—Blueberries for Sal. 2000. (J). pap. 19.97 incl. audio (978-0-7366-9193-2(6)) Books on Tape, Inc.

—Blueberries for Sal. (J). (ps-k). pap. 12.95 incl. audio Weston Woods Studios, Inc.

—Burt Dow: Deep-Water Man. 2001. (J). (gr. 1-4). 12.00 (978-0-7887-5510-1(2)) Recorded Bks., LLC.

McKenzie, Lyn. Betsy, Girl Scout of Woodward Center 1935. 2007. 244p. (YA). pap. 17.95 net. (*978-0-9722839-0-8(0)*) Just Write Bks.

Nugent, Matthew. Nightmares on Goose Rocks Beach in Kennebunkport, Maine: Book 4 of the Goose Rocks Tales. 2003. (Illus.). 204p. (J). per. 14.95 (978-0-9705812-3-5(8)) CBI Pr.

Nugent, Matthew A. The Legend of Goose Rocks Beach. Nugent, Louise, illus. 2001. 84p. (YA). (gr. 3-8). pap. 14.95 (978-0-9705812-0-4(3)) CBI Pr.

Ogilvie, Elizabeth. The Pigeon Pair. (J). reprint ed. lib. bdg. 19.95 (978-0-88411-336-2(1)) Amereon LTD.

Padian, Maria. Brett McCarthy: Work In Progress. 2008. (J). 288p. (*978-0-375-84675-5(1)); (*978-0-375-94675-2(6)*) Knopf, Alfred A. Inc.

Page, Katherine Hall. Down East. 1998. (Christie & Company Ser.). (YA). (gr. 6-8). reprint ed. pap. 3.99 (978-0-380-78033-4(X)) HarperCollins Pubs.

Perkins, T J. Wound Too Tight. 2006. (Illus.). 141p. (YA). 10.99 (978-0-9777538-5-7(9)) GumShoe Press.

Perrow, Angeli. Captain's Castaway. Harris, Emily, illus. 1998. 32p. (J). (ps-3). 15.95 (978-0-89272-419-2(6)) Down East Bks.

—Lighthouse Dog to the Rescue. Harris, Emily, illus. 2000. 30p. pap. 9.95 (978-0-89272-600-4(8)); 32p. (J). 14.95 (978-0-89272-487-1(0)) Down East Bks.

—Lighthouse Dog to the Rescue. 2000. (gr. k-3). lib. bdg. 18.75 (978-0-613-65727-3(6)) Tandem Library Bks.

Pochocki, Ethel. The Gazebo. Owens, Mary Beth, illus. 2002. 30p. (gr. 3-6). 15.95 (978-0-89272-516-8(8)) Down East Bks.

—A Penny for a Hundred. Owens, Mary Beth, illus. 2005. 32p. (J). pap. 9.95 (978-1-883937-52-2(3)) Bethlehem Bks.

Reynolds, Cynthia Furlong. Across the Reach. 2007. 144p. (J). 16.95 (*978-1-58726-518-1(4)* , Mitten Pr.) Ann Arbor Media Group, LLC.

Roselle, Gayle. Moozelville Playground. 2007. (Illus.). 74p. (J). pap. 12.95 (*978-0-9788628-8-6(0)*) Just Write Bks.

Roy, Ron. The White Wolf. Gurney, John Steven, tr. Gurney, John Steven, illus. 2004. (A to Z Mysteries Ser.: No. 23). 96p. (J). (gr. 1-4). pap. 3.99 (978-0-375-82480-7(4)); lib. bdg. 11.99 (978-0-375-92480-4(9)) Random Hse. Children's Bks. (Random Hse. Bks. for Young Readers).

Schmidt, Gary D. Lizzie Bright & the Buckminster Boy. 2004. 224p. (YA). (gr. 5 up). 15.00 (978-0-618-43929-4(3) , Clarion Bks.) Houghton Mifflin Co. Trade & Reference Div.

—Lizzie Bright & the Buckminster Boy. (gr. 5). 2008. 240p. (YA). mass mkt. 6.99 (*978-0-375-84169-9(5)* , Laurel Leaf); 2006. 224p. (J). reprint ed. pap. 6.50 (978-0-553-49495-2(3) , Yearling) Random Hse. Children's Bks.

Sedita, Francesco. Miss Popularity. 2007. (Candy Apple Ser.: No. 3). 144p. (J). pap. 4.99 (*978-0-439-88814-1(X)* , Scholastic Paperbacks) Scholastic, Inc.

Simmons, Derek. Flash of Life. 2006. 85p. pap. 14.95 (*978-1-4241-3890-6(6)*) PublishAmerica, Inc.

Smith, Constance. Pea Soup Fog. Cart, Jen, illus. 2004. 32p. 15.95 (978-0-89272-643-1(1)) Down East Bks.

Smith, George. The Journey of the Little Red Boat: A Story from the Coast of Maine. 2nd ed. 2004. (Illus.). 50p. (J). per. 7.99 (978-0-9740434-1-8(9) , 255-3716) Smith, George Publishing.

Smith, Lauren. Ashley Enright & the Mystery at Miller's Pond. 2006. (ENG.). 60p. per. 12.95 (*978-1-4241-5268-1(2)*) PublishAmerica, Inc.

Smith, Lauren E. Ashley Enright Investigations. 2006. 48p. pap. 12.95 (978-1-4241-2963-8(X)) PublishAmerica, Inc.

Sockabasin, Allen. Thanks to the Animals. Raye, Rebekah, illus. 2005. 32p. (J). (ps-2). 16.95 (978-0-88448-270-3(7)) Tilbury Hse. Pubs.

Standish, Burt L. Frank Merriwell in Maine. Rudman, Jack, ed. 2003. (Frank Merriwell Ser.). (YA). (gr. 9 up). 29.95 (978-0-8373-9328-5(0)); pap. 9.95 (978-0-8373-9028-4(1) , FM-028) Merriwell, Frank Inc.

Stengel, Joyce A. Mystery at Kittiwake Bay. 2001. 176p. (J). pap. 9.95 (978-0-689-84595-6(2) , Aladdin) Simon & Schuster Children's Publishing.

Stockwell, Jeff. Fandango: The Key to the Wind. Stockwell, Pel, illus. 2007. 58p. (YA). per. 22.50 (*978-0-9785594-0-3(1)*) Stockwell Publishing.

Testa, Maria. Some Kind of Pride. 2003. 128p. (gr. 3-7). 4.99 (978-0-440-41669-2(8) , Yearling) Random Hse. Children's Bks.

—Some Kind of Pride. 2003. (gr. 3-6). lib. bdg. 13.00 (978-0-613-62119-9(0)) Tandem Library Bks.

Voigt, Cynthia. Angus & Sadie. Leigh, Tom, illus. 2005. 208p. (J). lib. bdg. 16.89 (978-0-06-074583-7(5)); 15.99 (978-0-06-074582-0(7)) HarperCollins Pubs.

Wait, Lea. Finest Kind. 2006. 256p. (J). 16.95 (978-1-4169-0952-1(4) , McElderry, Margaret K.) Simon & Schuster Children's Publishing.

—Stopping to Home. 2001. (Illus.). 160p. (J). (gr. 3-7). 16.00 (978-0-689-83832-3(8) , McElderry, Margaret K.) Simon & Schuster Children's Publishing.

—Stopping to Home. 2003. (gr. 3-6). lib. bdg. 13.00 (978-0-613-61659-1(6)) Tandem Library Bks.

—Wintering Well. (Illus.). 192p. (J). 2006. pap. 5.99 (978-0-689-85647-1(4) , Aladdin); 2004. 16.95 (978-0-689-85646-4(6) , McElderry, Margaret K.) Simon & Schuster Children's Publishing.

Wiggin, Kate Douglas. Rebecca of Sunnybrook Farm. McClintock, Barbara, illus. anniv. ed. 2006. 290p. (J). (gr. 4-8). reprint ed. 22.00 (978-1-4223-5332-5(X)) DIANE Publishing Co.

—Rose O' the River. 2004. reprint ed. pap. 15.95 (978-1-4179-9998-9(5)); pap. 1.99 (978-1-4179-9948-4(9)) Kessinger Publishing, LLC.

Wigington, Patti. Summer's Ashes. 2007. 208p. (YA). pap. 15.00 (*978-0-9766805-9-8(9)*) Keene Publishing.

Woodruff, Elvira. The Ghost of Lizard Light. Clayton, Elaine, illus. 2001. 192p. (gr. 3-7). pap. 4.99 (978-0-440-41655-5(8) , Yearling) Random Hse. Children's Bks.

—The Ghost of Lizard Light. 2001. (gr. 3-6). lib. bdg. 13.00 (978-0-613-36814-8(2)) Tandem Library Bks.

MAINE—HISTORY

Deinard, Jenny. How to Draw Maines Sights & Symbols. 2002. (Kids Guide to Drawing America Ser.). 32p. (J). lib. bdg. 25.25 (978-0-8239-6075-0(7) , PowerKids Pr.) Rosen Publishing Group, Inc., The.

Malone, Richard & Shettleworth, Earle. Rediscovering S. P. Rolt Triscott: Monhegan Island Artist & Photographer. 2002. (Illus.). xi, 196p. pap. 30.00 (978-0-88448-240-6(5)) Tilbury Hse. Pubs.

Marsh, Carole. Maine History Projects: 30 Cool, Activities, Crafts, Experiments & More for Kids to Do to Learn about Your State! 2003. (Maine Experience Ser.). 32p. (gr. k-5). pap. 5.95 (978-0-635-01788-8(1) , Marsh, Carole Bks.) Gallopade International.

—My First Pocket Guide Maine. 2000. (Maine Experience! Ser.). (Illus.). 96p. (J). (gr. 3-8). 12.95 (978-0-635-01311-8(8) , 13118) Gallopade International.

Phillips, Margaret Coull. Maine. 2004. (Seeds of a Nation Ser.). (Illus.). 48p. (J). 26.20 (978-0-7377-2080-8(8) , Greenhaven Pr., Inc.) Thomson Gale.

Schneider, Jack. Allagash River Towboat: A Maine Logging Adventure. 2003. (Illus.). 108p. pap. 10.95 (978-0-89272-601-1(6)) Down East Bks.

Smolik, Jane. The Great State of Maine Activity Book: Over 75 Puzzles about Life in Maine. rev. ed. 2006. (J). per. 11.95 (978-0-9664095-6-7(6)) MidRun Pr.

MAINE—POETRY

Bull, Webster. A Kittery Kayaker. Decker, Jacqueline, illus. 2007. (J). 12.95 (*978-1-933212-36-4(5)*) Commonwealth Editions.

MAINE (BATTLESHIP)

McNeese, Tim. Remember the Maine! The Spanish-American War Begins. 2004. (First Battles Ser.). (Illus.). 112p. (YA). (gr. 6-12). 23.95 (978-1-883846-79-4(X) , First Biographies) Reynolds, Morgan Inc.

Sinking of the Maine. 2002. (History in the Headlines Ser.). 32p. (gr. 6-8). 6.99 (978-0-7682-0222-9(1) , GA13022) School Specialty Publishing.

MAISY (FICTITIOUS CHARACTER)—FICTION

Cousins, Lucy. Los Amigos de Maisy. 2000. (Maisy Bks.).Tr. of Maisy's Friends. (SPA., Illus.). 16p. (J). (ps). 8.95 (978-84-95040-11-4(5)) Lectorum Pubns., Inc.

—El Autobus de Maisy. 2000. (Maisy Bks.). (CAT., Illus.). 24p. (J). (ps). 10.95 (978-84-95040-70-1(0)) Serres, Ediciones, S. L. ESP. *Dist:* Lectorum Pubns., Inc.

—Bathtime, Maisy! Cousins, Lucy, illus. 2001. (Maisy Bks.). (Illus.). 6p. (J). (gr. k-ps). pap. 6.99 (978-0-7636-1600-7(1)) Candlewick Pr.

—Bedtime, Maisy! Cousins, Lucy, illus. 2001. (Maisy Bks.). (Illus.). 6p. (J). (gr. k-ps). pap. 6.99 (978-0-7636-1601-4(X)) Candlewick Pr.

—El Carnaval de Maisy. 2000. (Maisy Bks.). (Illus.). 24p. (J). (ps). (CAT.). 10.95 (978-84-95040-41-1(7)); (SPA., 10.95 (978-84-95040-40-4(9) , RR1669) Serres, Ediciones, S. L. ESP. *Dist:* Lectorum Pubns., Inc.

—Los Colores de Maisy. 2000. (Maisy Bks.). (SPA.). 24p. (J). (ps). (978-84-88061-63-8(3)) Lectorum Pubns., Inc.

—Los Colores de Maisy. 2001. (Illus.). (J). (ps). (CAT.). 16p. 10.95 (978-84-95040-60-2(3)); (SPA., 24p. 15.95 (978-84-95040-75-6(1) , RR7142) Serres, Ediciones, S. L. ESP. *Dist:* Lectorum Pubns., Inc., Lectorum Pubns., Inc., Libros Sin Fronteras.

—Las Cosas Favoritas de Maisy. 2000. (Maisy Bks.).Tr. of Maisy's Favorite Things. (SPA., Illus.). 16p. (J). (ps). 8.95 (978-84-95040-12-1(3)) Lectorum Pubns., Inc.

—Count with Maisy. Cousins, Lucy, illus. 2nd ed. 1999. (Maisy Bks.). (Illus.). 24p. (J). (gr. k-ps). bds. 5.99 (978-0-7636-0234-5(5)) Candlewick Pr.

—Cuenta con Maisy. 2000. (Maisy Bks.). (SPA.). 24p. (J). (ps). 11.95 (978-84-88061-62-1(5)) Lectorum Pubns., Inc.

—Cuenta con Maisy. 2001. (Illus.). (J). (CAT.). 16p. 10.95 (978-84-95040-74-9(3)); (SPA., 24p. 10.95 (978-84-95040-73-2(5) , RR6313) Serres, Ediciones, S. L. ESP. *Dist:* Lectorum Pubns., Inc.

—Un Dia con Maisy. 2000. (Maisy Bks.). (SPA., Illus.). 16p. (J). (ps). 10.50 (978-84-95040-09-1(3)) Lectorum Pubns., Inc.

—Los Disfraces de Maisy. 2000. (Maisy Bks.). (SPA., Illus.). 16p. (J). (ps). 13.95 (978-84-95040-19-0(0)) Lectorum Pubns., Inc.

—Doctor Maisy. Cousins, Lucy, illus. 2001. (Maisy Bks.). (Illus.). 24p. (J). (gr. k-k). pap. 3.99 (978-0-7636-1613-7(3)) Candlewick Pr.

—Doctor Maisy. 2001. (ps-2). lib. bdg. 11.00 (978-0-613-74783-7(6)) Tandem Library Bks.

—Donde Esta el Panda de Maisy? 1999. (Maisy Bks.). (Illus.). 16p. (J). (ps). (CAT.). 10.95 (978-84-95040-08-4(5)); (SPA., 11.50 (978-84-95040-07-7(7) , RR4459) Serres, Ediciones, S. L. ESP. *Dist:* Lectorum Pubns., Inc.

—Donde Se Esconde Maisy? 1999. (Maisy Bks.). (Illus.). 16p. (J). (ps). (CAT.). 10.95 (978-84-95040-06-0(9)); (SPA., 10.99 (978-84-95040-05-3(0) , RR4499) Serres, Ediciones, S. L. ESP. *Dist:* Lectorum Pubns., Inc.

—Donde Vive Maisy? 2000. (Maisy Bks.). (Illus.). 16p. (J). (ps). (CAT.). 10.95 (978-84-95040-47-3(6)); (SPA., 11.50 (978-84-95040-46-6(8)) Serres, Ediciones, S. L. ESP. *Dist:* Lectorum Pubns., Inc.

—Feliz Cumpleanos, Maisy. 1999. (Maisy Bks.). (Illus.). 16p. (J). (ps). (CAT.). 16.95 (978-84-88061-95-9(1)); (SPA., 17.99 (978-84-88061-96-6(X) , RR3371) Serres, Ediciones, S. L. ESP. *Dist:* Lectorum Pubns., Inc.

—Feliz Navidad, Maisy! 2000. (Maisy Bks.). (Illus.). (J). (ps). (CAT.). 18p. 19.95 (978-84-95040-62-6(X)); (SPA., 316p. 19.95 (978-84-95040-61-9(1) , RR1434) Serres, Ediciones, S. L. ESP. *Dist:* Lectorum Pubns., Inc.

—Fun with Maisy. 2002. (ps-2). lib. bdg. 11.80 (978-0-613-74761-5(5)) Tandem Library Bks.

—Go, Maisy, Go! Cousins, Lucy, illus. 2003. (Maisy Ser.). (Illus.). 10p. (J). (gr. k-k). bds. 8.99 (978-0-7636-2118-6(8)) Candlewick Pr.

—Happy Birthday, Maisy: Mini Edition. 2004. (Maisy Ser.). (Illus.). 14p. (J). (gr. k-k). 4.99 (978-0-7636-2454-5(3)) Candlewick Pr.

—Happy Easter, Maisy! Cousins, Lucy. 2007. 14p. (J). (gr. k-k). bds. 4.99 (978-0-7636-3230-4(9)) Candlewick Pr.

—Maisy at the Fair. 2001. (Maisy Bks.). (Illus.). 24p. (J). (gr. k-k). pap. 3.99 (978-0-7636-1502-4(1)) Candlewick Pr.

—Maisy at the Fair. 2001. (ps-2). lib. bdg. 11.00 (978-0-613-74784-4(4)) Tandem Library Bks.

—Maisy Dresses Up. Cousins, Lucy, illus. 1999. (Maisy Bks.). (Illus.). 24p. (J). (gr. k-k). pap. 3.99 (978-0-7636-0909-2(9)) Candlewick Pr.

—Maisy Dresses Up. 1999. (gr. k-3). lib. bdg. 11.00 (978-0-613-21952-5(X)) Tandem Library Bks.

—Maisy Drives the Bus. Cousins, Lucy, illus. 2000. (Maisy Bks.). (Illus.). 24p. (J). (gr. k-k). pap. 3.99 (978-0-7636-1085-2(2)) Candlewick Pr.

—Maisy en la Granja. 1999. (Maisy Bks.). (Illus.). (J). (ps). (CAT.). 16p. 16.95 (978-84-88061-94-2(3)); (SPA., 24p. 17.88 (978-84-88061-97-3(8) , RR3457) Serres, Ediciones, S. L. ESP. *Dist:* Lectorum Pubns., Inc.

—Maisy Goes Camping. Cousins, Lucy, illus. 2004. (Maisy Ser.). (Illus.). 32p. (J). (gr. k-k). 12.99 (978-0-7636-2369-2(5)) Candlewick Pr.

—Maisy Goes Shopping. Cousins, Lucy, illus. 2001. (Maisy Bks.). (Illus.). 24p. (J). (gr. k-k). pap. 3.99 (978-0-7636-1503-1(X)) Candlewick Pr.

—Maisy Goes to Bed. Cousins, Lucy, illus. ed. 2006. 14p. (J). (ps). 4.99 (978-0-7636-3123-9(X)) Candlewick Pr.

—Maisy Likes Music. Cousins, Lucy, illus. 2002. (Maisy Ser.). (Illus.). 12p. (J). (ps-k). bds. 6.99 (978-0-7636-1915-2(9)) Candlewick Pr.

—Maisy Loves You. 2004. (Illus.). 10p. (J). (gr. k-k). bds. 4.99 (978-0-7636-2687-7(2)) Candlewick Pr.

—Maisy Loves You. Cousins, Lucy, illus. 2003. (Maisy Ser.). (Illus.). 10p. (J). (gr. k-k). bds. 5.99 (978-0-7636-2065-3(3)) Candlewick Pr.

—Maisy Loves You: Book & Toy Gift Set. 2004. (Illus.). 1p. (J). 12.99 (978-0-7636-2564-1(7)) Candlewick Pr.

—Maisy Makes Lemonade. 2002. (Maisy Ser.). (Illus.). 24p. (J). (ps-k). pap. 3.99 (978-0-7636-1729-5(6)) Candlewick Pr.

—Maisy Makes Lemonade. 2002. (ps-2). lib. bdg. 11.00 (978-0-613-51316-6(9)) Tandem Library Bks.

—Maisy Plays. Cousins, Lucy, illus. 2001. (Maisy Bks.). (Illus.). 16p. (J). (gr. k-k). bds. 4.99 (978-0-7636-1462-1(9)) Candlewick Pr.

—Maisy Se Va a la Cama. 2000. (Maisy Bks.). (Illus.). 16p. (J). (ps). (CAT.). 16.95 (978-84-88061-50-8(1)); (SPA., 16.95 (978-84-88061-33-1(1) , RR7051) Serres, Ediciones, S. L. ESP. *Dist:* Lectorum Pubns., Inc.

—Maisy Se Va a Nadar. 2000. (Maisy Bks.). (SPA., Illus.). 24p. (J). (ps). 16.95 (978-84-88061-32-4(3) , RR7052) Serres, Ediciones, S. L. ESP. *Dist:* Lectorum Pubns., Inc.

—Maisy Takes a Bath. Cousins, Lucy, illus. 2000. (Maisy Bks.). (Illus.). 24p. (J). (gr. k-k). pap. 3.99 (978-0-7636-1084-5(4)) Candlewick Pr.

—Maisy Takes a Bath. 2000. (Maisy Bks.). (Illus.). (J). (ps). 9.99 (978-0-7636-0182-9(9)) Candlewick Pr.

—Maisy Takes a Bath. 2000. (ps-2). lib. bdg. 11.00 (978-0-613-27962-8(X)) Tandem Library Bks.

—Maisy y Sus Amigos. 1999. (Maisy Bks.). (Illus.). 16p. (J). (ps). (CAT & SPA.). 16.95 (978-84-95040-03-9(4)); (SPA., 17.99 (978-84-95040-02-2(6) , RR2456) Serres, Ediciones, S. L. ESP. *Dist:* Lectorum Pubns., Inc.

—Maisy's Bedtime. Cousins, Lucy, illus. 1999. (Maisy Bks.). (Illus.). 24p. (J). pap. 3.99 (978-0-7636-0908-5(0)) Candlewick Pr.

—Maisy's Big Flap Book. Cousins, Lucy, illus. 2001. (Maisy Bks.). (Illus.). 10p. (J). (gr. k-k). bds. 8.99 (978-0-7636-1189-7(1)) Candlewick Pr.

—Maisy's Colors. Cousins, Lucy, illus. 2nd ed. 1999. (Maisy Bks.). (Illus.). 24p. (J). (gr. k-ps). bds. 5.99 (978-0-7636-0237-6(X)) Candlewick Pr.

—Maisy's Favorite Animals. Cousins, Lucy, illus. 2001. (Maisy Bks.). (Illus.). 22p. (J). (gr. k-k). bds. 3.99 (978-0-7636-1572-7(2)) Candlewick Pr.

—Maisy's Favorite Things. Cousins, Lucy, illus. 2001. (Maisy Bks.). (Illus.). 22p. (J). (gr. k-k). bds. 3.99 (978-0-7636-1574-1(9)) Candlewick Pr.

—Maisy's Favorite Toys. Cousins, Lucy, illus. 2001. (Maisy Bks.). (Illus.). 22p. (J). (gr. k-k). bds. 3.99 (978-0-7636-1571-0(4)) Candlewick Pr.

—Maisy's Fire Engine. Cousins, Lucy, illus. 2002. (Maisy Bks.). (Illus.). 16p. (J). (gr. k-k). bds. 4.99 (978-0-7636-1780-6(6)) Candlewick Pr.

—Maisy's First Game Book. Cousins, Lucy, illus. 2006. (Illus.). 8p. (J). (ps). bds. 9.99 (978-0-7636-2812-3(3)) Candlewick Pr.

—Maisy's Garden: Sticker Book. 2001. (Maisy Bks.). (Illus.). 16p. (J). (ps-k). pap. 3.99 (978-0-7636-1505-5(6)) Candlewick Pr.

—Maisy's Morning on the Farm. Cousins, Lucy, illus. 2001. (Maisy Bks.). (Illus.). 24p. (J). (gr. k-k). pap. 3.99 (978-0-7636-1611-3(7)) Candlewick Pr.

—Maisy's Morning on the Farm. 2001. (ps-2). lib. bdg. 11.00 (978-0-613-74782-0(8)) Tandem Library Bks.

—Maisy's Noisy Day. Cousins, Lucy, illus. 2003. (Maisy Ser.). (Illus.). 12p. (J). (ps-k). bds. 6.99 (978-0-7636-1917-6(5)) Candlewick Pr.

—Maisy's Pool. Cousins, Lucy, illus. 1999. (Maisy Bks.). (Illus.). 24p. (J). pap. 3.99 (978-0-7636-0907-8(2)) Candlewick Pr.

—Maisy's Seasons. 2002. (Maisy Ser.). (Illus.). 12p. (J). (gr. k-k). bds. 8.99 (978-0-7636-1914-5(0)) Candlewick Pr.

—Maisy's Train. Cousins, Lucy, illus. 2002. (Maisy Noisy Board Bks.). (Illus.). 16p. (J). (gr. k-k). bds. 4.99 (978-0-7636-1781-3(4)) Candlewick Pr.

—Maisy's Wonderful Weather Book. Cousins, Lucy, illus. 2006. 14p. (J). (ps). 11.99 (978-0-7636-2987-8(1)) Candlewick Pr.

—Merry Christmas Maisy. Cousins, Lucy, illus. ed. 2003. (Maisy Ser.). (Illus.). 16p. (J). (ps). 4.99 (978-0-7636-2241-1(9)) Candlewick Pr.

—La Piscina de Maisy. 2002. (Illus.). 24p. (J). (CAT.). 10.95 (978-84-95040-77-0(8)); (SPA., 9.99 (978-84-95040-76-3(X) , RR4185) Serres, Ediciones, S. L. ESP. *Dist:* Lectorum Pubns., Inc.

—Playtime, Maisy! Cousins, Lucy, illus. 2001. (Maisy Bks.). (Illus.). 6p. (J). (gr. k-ps). pap. 6.99 (978-0-7636-1602-1(8)) Candlewick Pr.

—Que Hora Es, Maisy? 2002. (Illus.). (J). (SPA.). 12p. (978-84-8488-048-6(6)); (CAT., 14p. (978-84-8488-049-3(4)) Serres, Ediciones, S. L. ESP. *Dist:* Lectorum Pubns., Inc.

—Snacktime, Maisy! Cousins, Lucy, illus. 2001. (Maisy Bks.). (Illus.). 6p. (J). (gr. k-ps). pap. 6.99 (978-0-7636-1603-8(6)) Candlewick Pr.

—Where Are Maisy's Friends? A Lift-the-Flap Book. Cousins, Lucy, illus. 2000. (Maisy Bks.). (Illus.). 12p. (J). (gr. k-k). bds. 4.99 (978-0-7636-1119-4(0)) Candlewick Pr.

—Where Does Maisy Live? Cousins, Lucy, illus. 2000. (Maisy Bks.). (Illus.). 12p. (J). (gr. k-ps). bds. 4.99 (978-0-7636-1163-7(8)) Candlewick Pr.

—Where Is Maisy? A Lift-the-Flap Book. Cousins, Lucy, illus. 1999. (Maisy Bks.). (Illus.). 12p. (J). (gr. k-k). bds. 4.99 (978-0-7636-0752-4(5)) Candlewick Pr.

—Where Is Maisy's Panda? A Lift-the-Flap Book. Cousins, Lucy, illus. 1999. (Maisy Bks.). (Illus.). 14p. (J). (gr. k-k). bds. 4.99 (978-0-7636-0753-1(3)) Candlewick Pr.

—With Love from Maisy. 2004. (Maisy Ser.). (Illus.). 16p. (J). (gr. k-k). 13.99 (978-0-7636-2513-9(2)) Candlewick Pr.

Cousins, Lucy. With Love from Maisy: Mini Edition. Cousins, Lucy, illus. 2007. (Maisy Ser.). (Illus.). 16p. (J). (ps). 4.99 (***978-0-7636-3539-8(1)***) Candlewick Pr.

MAIZE

see Corn

MAKE-UP (COSMETICS)

see Cosmetics

MAKE-UP, THEATRICAL

Quinlan, Kathryn A. Makeup Artist. 1999. (Careers Without College Ser.). (Illus.). 48p. (J). (gr. 3-4). lib. bdg. 21.26 (978-0-7368-0175-1(8) , LifeMatters Bks.) Capstone Pr., Inc.

MALADJUSTED CHILDREN

see Problem Children

MALAGASY REPUBLIC

see Madagascar

MALARIA

Abramovitz, Melissa. Malaria. 2005. (Diseases & Disorders Ser.). (Illus.). 112p. (YA). (gr. 7-10). lib. bdg. 32.45 (978-1-59018-592-6(7) , Lucent Bks.) Thomson Gale.

Day, Nancy. Malaria, West Nile & Other Mosquito-Borne Diseases. 2001. (Diseases & People Ser.). (Illus.). 128p. (YA). (gr. 6-12). lib. bdg. 26.60 (978-0-7660-1597-5(1)) Enslow Pubs., Inc.

Isle, Mick. Malaria. 2001. (Epidemics Ser.). (Illus.). 64p. (J). (gr. 4-6). lib. bdg. 26.50 (978-0-8239-3342-6(3)) Rosen Publishing Group, Inc., The.

Lynette, Rachel. Malaria. 2005. (Understanding Diseases & Disorders Ser.). (Illus.). 48p. (J). (ps-8). lib. bdg. 26.20 (978-0-7377-2641-1(5) , Greenhaven Pr., Inc.) Thomson Gale.

Marcus, Bernard A. Malaria. 2003. (Deadly Diseases & Epidemics Ser.). (Illus.). 112p. (gr. 9-13). 31.95 (978-0-7910-7466-4(8) , Chelsea Hse.) Facts On File, Inc.

Wyborny, Sheila. The Malaria Parasite. 2005. (Parasites Ser.). (Illus.). 32p. (J). (ps-8). lib. bdg. 24.95 (978-0-7377-3051-7(X) , Greenhaven Pr., Inc.) Thomson Gale.

MALAWI

Lilly, Melinda. Zimani's Drum: A Malawian Legend. Reasoner, Charles, illus. 1998. (African Tales & Myths Ser.). (J). lib. bdg. (978-0-86625-633-9(4)) Rourke Publishing, LLC.

MALAYSIA

Di Piazza, Francesca. Malaysia in Pictures. 2006. (Visual Geography Series, Second Ser.). (Illus.). 80p. (J). 27.93 (978-0-8225-2674-2(3) , Twenty-First Century Bks.) Lerner Publishing Group.

Glendinning, Aiden & Holmes, Jimmy. Malaysia. 2004. (Changing Face Of... Ser.). (J). 28.56 (978-0-7398-6830-0(6)) Harcourt Schl. Pubs.

Goodman, Susan E. Chopsticks for My Noodlesoup: Eliza's Life in Malaysia. Doolittle, Michael, illus. 1999. (Around the World Ser.). 32p. (gr. k-3). lib. bdg. (978-0-7613-1552-0(7) , Millbrook Pr.) Lerner Publishing Group.

Heinrichs, Ann. Malaysia. (True Bks.). (J). 2005. (Illus.). 48p. (gr. 3-5). pap. 6.95 (978-0-516-26957-3(7)); 2004. 25.00 (978-0-516-22812-9(9)) Scholastic Library Publishing. (Children's Pr.).

McNair, Sylvia. Malaysia. 2002. (Enchantment of the World, Second Ser.). (Illus.). 144p. (YA). (gr. 5-9). pap. 36.00 (978-0-516-21009-4(2) , Children's Pr.) Scholastic Library Publishing.

Munan, Heidi & Foo, Y. Malaysia. 2nd ed. 2001. (Cultures of the World Ser.). (Illus.). 144p. (gr. 5 up). lib. bdg. 37.07 (978-0-7614-1351-6(0) , Benchmark Bks.) Cavendish, Marshall Corp.

Petrini, Catherine M. The Petronas Towers. 2004. (Building World Landmarks Ser.). (J). 24.95 (978-1-56711-346-4(X) , Blackbirch Pr., Inc.) Thomson Gale.

Pundyk, Grace & Radhakrishnan, Anand. Welcome to Malaysia. 2004. (Welcome to My Country Ser.). (Illus.). 48p. (J). (gr. 2 up). lib. bdg. 26.00 (978-0-8368-2560-2(8)) Stevens, Gareth Inc.

Radhakrishnan, Anand. Malaysia. 2002. (Countries of the World Ser.). (Illus.). 96p. (J). (gr. 6 up). lib. bdg. 30.00 (978-0-8368-2360-8(5)) Stevens, Gareth Inc.

Roberts, Allen. Malaysia. 2002. (Ask about Asia Ser.). (Illus.). 48p. (J). (gr. 4 up). lib. bdg. (978-1-59084-201-0(4)) Mason Crest Pubs.

Staub, Frank. Children of Malaysia. 2000. (World's Children Ser.). (Illus.). 48p. (J). (gr. 4-7). 23.93 (978-1-57505-449-0(3) , Carolrhoda Bks.) Lerner Publishing Group.

Thomas, Mark. Las Torres Gemelas Petronas. 2004. (Record-Breaking Structures Ser.). (SPA.). 24p. (J). (gr. 3-6). lib. bdg. 17.25 (978-0-8239-6862-6(6) , Buenas Letra) Rosen Publishing Group, Inc., The.

—The Petronas Twin Towers: World's Tallest Buildings. 2002. (Reading Power Ser.). (Illus.). 24p. (J). (gr. 1). lib. bdg. 17.25 (978-0-8239-5989-1(9) , PowerKids Pr.) Rosen Publishing Group, Inc., The.

MALAYSIA—FICTION

Buchmann, Stephen L. & Cohn, Diana. The Bee Tree. Mirocha, Paul, illus. 2007. 40p. (J). (gr. 2-6). 17.95 (***978-0-938317-98-2(9)***) Cinco Puntos Pr.

Geras, Adele. Other Echoes. 2005. 144p. (J). (gr. 7). 15.95 (978-0-385-75054-7(4) , Fickling, David Bks.) Random Hse. Children's Bks.

Lat. Kampung Boy. Lat, illus. rev. ed. 2006. (Illus.). 144p. (J). (gr. 6-8). pap. 16.95 (978-1-59643-121-8(0) , First Second Bks.) Roaring Brook Pr.

MALCOLM X, 1925-1965

see X, Malcolm, 1925-1965

MALE GROOMING

see Grooming for Men

MALI

Armentrout, David & Armentrout, Patricia. Ghana, Mali & Songhay. 2003. (Timelines of Ancient Civilizations Ser.). (Illus.). 32p. (J). 28.50 (978-1-58952-721-8(6)) Rourke Publishing, LLC.

Blauer, Ettagale & Lauré, Jason. Mali. 2007. (Cultures of the World Ser.). (J). lib. bdg. (***978-0-7614-2568-7(3)*** , Benchmark Bks.) Cavendish, Marshall Corp.

Brook, Larry & Brooks, Larry. Daily Life in Ancient & Modern Timbuktu. Webb, Ray, illus. 1999. (Cities Through Time Ser.). 64p. (gr. 5-12). 25.26 (978-0-8225-3215-6(8)) Lerner Publishing Group.

Conrad, David C. Empires of Medieval West Africa: Ghana, Mali, & Songhay. 2005. (Great Empires of the Past Ser.). (Illus.). (J). (gr. 6-12). 35.00 (978-0-8160-5562-3(9)) Facts On File, Inc.

DiPiazza, Francesca Davis. Mali in Pictures. 2007. (Visual Geography Ser.). (Illus.). 80p. (J). (gr. 5-12). 27.93 (978-0-8225-6591-8(9) , Twenty-First Century Bks.) Lerner Publishing Group.

Masoff, Joy. Mali: Land of Gold & Glory. 2002. (Illus.). 48p. (J). pap. 9.95 (978-0-9727156-0-7(6)) Five Ponds Pr.

Pancella, Peggy. Mansa Musa. 2003. (Historical Biographies Ser.). (Illus.). 32p. (J). pap. 7.50 (978-1-4034-3711-2(4)); lib. bdg. 22.79 (978-1-4034-3703-7(3)) Heinemann Library.

Quigley, Mary. Ancient West African Kingdoms: Ghana, Mali, & Songhai. 2002. (Understanding People in the Past Ser.). (Illus.). 64p. (J). (gr. 4-6). lib. bdg. 28.50 (978-1-58810-425-0(7)) Heinemann Library.

Supples, Kevin. Mali. 2004. (Civilizations Past to Present Ser.). (Illus.). 24p. (J). pap. (978-0-7922-4539-1(3)) National Geographic Society.

Wisniewski, David, retold by. Sundiata: Lion King of Mali. 1999. (Illus.). 32p. (J). (gr. k-3). 6.95 (978-0-395-76481-7(5) , Clarion Bks.) Houghton Mifflin Co. Trade & Reference Div.

MALI—FICTION

Burns, Khephra. Mansa Musa: The Lion of Mali. Dillon, Leo & Dillon, Diane, illus. 2001. 56p. (J). (gr. 3-5). 18.00 (978-0-15-200375-3(4) , Gulliver Bks.) Harcourt Children's Bks.

Diakite, Baba Wague. Mee-an & the Magic Serpent: A Folktale from Mali. 2007. (Illus.). 32p. (J). (gr. k-4). 16.95 (978-0-88899-719-7(1)) Groundwood Bks. CAN. *Dist:* Perseus Distribution.

Diakite, Penda. I Lost My Tooth in Africa. Diakite, Baba Wague, illus. 2006. 32p. (J). (ps-3). pap. 16.99 (978-0-439-66226-0(5) , Scholastic Pr.) Scholastic, Inc.

McDowell, Josh & Hostetler, Bob. The Truth Twisters. 2006. 170p. (YA). pap. 11.99 (978-1-932587-84-5(5)) Green Key Bks.

Tellem, Sundiata. Chaka Goes to Mali. 2005. (Illus.). 24p. (J). per. 8.99 (978-1-932338-72-0(1)) Lifevest Publishing, Inc.

MALLORY, GEORGE HERBERT LEIGH-, 1886-1924

see Leigh-Mallory, George Herbert, 1886-1924

MALTA

Stafford, James. Malta. 2006. (European Union Ser.). (Illus.). 88p. (J). (gr. 5 up). lib. bdg. (978-1-4222-0056-8(6)) Mason Crest Pubs.

MALTA—FICTION

Clizbe, Kent. Xrina at Hagar Qim: The Temple Builders of Malta. Konstantinov, Ignat, illus. 1998. (Children of Malta Ser.: Vol. 1). 40p. (J). (gr. k-5). pap. 12.95 (978-0-9656252-1-0(4) , MAL001) O.T.S.

MAMMALS

see also Primates

also names of mammals, e.g. Bats

Batten, Mary. Who Has a Belly Button? Bond, Higgins, illus. 2004. 32p. (J). (gr. 2-3). 15.95 (978-1-56145-235-4(1)) Peachtree Pubs., Ltd.

Beer, Amy-Jane & Morris, Pat. Mammals. 2006. (Facts at Your Fingertips Ser.). (Illus.). 64p. (J). (***978-1-933834-03-0(X)***) Brown Bear Books.

Bloom & Ronzani, Maggie. Mammals: Grades 2 Through 4. (Illus.). (J). pap., wbk. ed. 4.99 (978-0-88743-963-6(2)) School Zone Publishing Co.

Brewer, Duncan. 1000 Things You Should Know about Mammals. 2002. (1000 Things You Should Know about Ser.). (Illus.). 64p. (YA). (gr. 5 up). lib. bdg. (978-1-59084-467-0(X)) Mason Crest Pubs.

Bruce, Jim. Mammals: Explore & Discover Mammals. 2001. (Question Time Ser.). (Illus.). 32p. (J). (gr. k-3). tchr. ed. 11.95 (978-0-7534-5340-1(1) , Kingfisher) Houghton Mifflin Co. Trade & Reference Div.

—Mammals: Explore & Discover Mammals. Kingfisher Publications, Inc. Staff, ed. 2001. (Question Time Ser.). (Illus.). 32p. (J). (gr. k-3). pap. 6.95 (978-0-7534-5408-4(4) , Kingfisher) Houghton Mifflin Co. Trade & Reference Div.

—Question Time: Mammals. 2001. (Explore & Discover Ser.). (Illus.). (J). (978-0-606-21390-5(2)) Tandem Library Bks.

Bulletpoints Mammals. 2005. (Illus.). (J). per. 4.99 (978-1-933581-04-0(2)) Byeway Bks.

Burroughs, John. Squirrels & Other Fur-Bearers (Yesterday's Classics) 2006. (Illus.). 144p. (J). per. 8.95 (978-1-59915-070-3(0)) Yesterday's Classics.

Carper, Virginia. Animal Teachings: Mammals. 2005. ring bd., wbk. ed. 20.00 (978-0-9788858-0-9(5)) Animal Teachers Enterprises.

Cobb, Vicki. This Place Is Wild: East Africa. 2000. (Imagine Living Here Ser.). (978-0-606-18744-2(8)); (gr. 3-6). lib. bdg. 16.40 (978-0-613-27231-5(5)) Tandem Library Bks.

—This Place Is Wild: East Africa. Lavallee, Barbara, illus. 1998. (Imagine Living Here Ser.: Vol. 7). 33p. (J). (gr. k-3). lib. bdg. 16.85 (978-0-8027-8633-3(2)); 15.95 (978-0-8027-8632-6(4)) Walker & Co.

Cobb, Vicki & Lavallee, Barbara. This Place Is Wild: East Africa. 2000. (Imagine Living Here Ser.). (Illus.). 32p. (J). (gr. 2-5). pap. 7.95 (978-0-8027-7579-5(9)) Walker & Co.

Cooper, Jason. Esp Vaquitas. 2005. (SPA.). 24p. pap. 5.45 (978-1-59515-698-3(4)) Rourke Publishing, LLC.

Coupe, Robert. Mammals of the Sea. 2002. (Junior Adventure Ser.). (Illus.). 32p. (J). (gr. 3 up). lib. bdg. (978-1-59084-166-2(2)) Mason Crest Pubs.

Dalgleish, Sharon. Mighty Mammals. 2002. (Junior Adventure Ser.). (Illus.). 32p. (J). (gr. 3 up). lib. bdg. (978-1-59084-176-1(X)) Mason Crest Pubs.

—Mini Mammals. Cavaluzzo, Laura & McEwen, Rebecca, eds. 1999. (Explorers Ser.). (Illus.). 32p. (J). (978-0-7699-0491-7(2)) Shortland Pubns. (U. S. A.) Inc.

Dancing with Mana. 1998. (J). (gr. 2). pap. 3.95 (978-0-439-04438-7(3)) Scholastic, Inc.

Dietz, James M. African Animal Giants. Cremins, Robert & Morrison, Robert, illus. 2004. 12p. (J). (gr. k-4). reprint ed. 16.00 (978-0-7567-7641-1(4)) DIANE Publishing Co.

Discovery Books Staff & Myers, Philip. Mammals: An Explore Your World Handbook. 2000. (Explore Your World Ser.). (Illus.). 192p. pap. 14.95 (978-1-56331-838-2(5)) Discovery Bks.

DK Publishing. Eye Know Mammal. 2008. (Eye Know Ser.). 24p. (J). (gr. k-3). 8.99 (***978-0-7566-3870-2(4)***) Dorling Kindersley Publishing, Inc.

Dorling Kindersley Publishing Staff, ed. Mammal. 2004. (Dk Eyewitness Books Ser.). (Illus.). 72p. (J). 15.99 (978-0-7566-0703-6(5)) Dorling Kindersley Publishing, Inc.

Doudna, Kelly. Frisky Ferrets. Nobens, C. A., illus. 2007. (Perfect Pets Ser.). 24p. (J). (gr. k-3). lib. bdg. 19.93 (***978-1-59928-748-5(X)*** , SandCastle) ABDO Publishing Co.

Endangered Mammals - Africa: An Educational Coloring Book. (J). (gr. 3 up). pap. 1.99 (978-0-86545-213-8(X)) Spizzirri Pr., Inc.

Endangered Mammals - Asia & China: An Educational Coloring Book. (J). (gr. 3 up). pap. 1.99 (978-0-86545-214-5(8)) Spizzirri Pr., Inc.

Endangered Mammals - South America: An Educational Coloring Book. (J). pap. 1.99 (978-0-86545-215-2(6)) Spizzirri Pr., Inc.

Feldman, Thea. Migrating Animals of the Land. 2007. (J). pap. (***978-0-8368-8423-4(X)***); 24p. (gr. 2-4). lib. bdg. 19.93 (***978-0-8368-8418-0(3)***) Stevens, Gareth Inc. (Weekly Reader Early Learning Library).

Field, Nancy, ed. Wild Stickers - Marine Mammals. Maydak, Michael S., illus. 1998. (Wild Stickers Ser.: Vol. 3). 8p. (J). (gr. k-6). pap. 2.50 (978-0-941042-23-9(5)) Dog-Eared Pubns.

Florian, Douglas. Mammalabilia. 2000. (Illus.). 48p. (J). (ps-3). 16.98 (978-0-7398-2199-2(7)) Raintree.

—Mammalabilia. 2004. (gr. 3-6). lib. bdg. 15.30 (978-0-613-81145-3(3)) Tandem Library Bks.

Foley, Cate. Find the Wild Animal. 2000. (Welcome Bks.). (Illus.). 24p. (J). (ps-2). 17.00 (978-0-516-23098-6(0) , Children's Pr.) Scholastic Library Publishing.

—Find the Wild Animal. 2000. (gr. k-3). lib. bdg. 12.95 (978-0-613-52048-5(3)) Tandem Library Bks.

Fowler, Allan. Mammals of Long Ago. (Rookie Read-About Science Ser.). (Illus.). 32p. (J). (gr. 1-2). 2001. pap. 4.95 (978-0-516-27090-6(7)); 2000. 20.50 (978-0-516-21209-8(5)) Scholastic Library Publishing. (Children's Pr.).

—Mammals of Long Ago. 2001. (Illus.). 31p. (J). (ps-3). lib. bdg. 12.95 (978-0-613-54609-6(1)) Tandem Library Bks.

Franchino, Vicky. Mammals. 2000. (Simply Science Ser.). (Illus.). 32p. (J). (gr. 3 up). lib. bdg. 19.93 (978-0-7565-0032-0(X)) Compass Point Bks.

Gareth Stevens Publishing Staff, contrib. by. Mammals. 2002. (Discovery Channel School Science Ser.). (Illus.). 32p. (J). (gr. 5 up). lib. bdg. 24.67 (978-0-8368-3217-4(5)) Stevens, Gareth Inc.

Gentle, Victor & Perry, Janet. Jackals. 2002. (Imagination Library). (Illus.). 24p. (J). (gr. 2 up). lib. bdg. 22.00 (978-0-8368-3097-2(0)) Stevens, Gareth Inc.

Gierecke, Ernestine. Mammals. 1999. (Outside My Window Ser.). 24p. (J). (gr. 1-3). lib. bdg. 21.36 (978-1-57572-681-6(5)) Heinemann Library.

Goodall, Jane. In the Shadow of Man. 2000. (gr. 7-12). lib. bdg. 24.60 (978-0-613-45778-1(1)) Tandem Library Bks.

Grambo, Rebecca L., et al. Animal Kingdom. 2000. (Eyes on Nature Ser.). (Illus.). 109p. (J). (978-1-56156-882-6(1)) Kidsbooks, Inc.

Green. Mammals. 2003. (Weird Wildlife Ser.). (Illus.). 32p. (J). pap. 7.95 (978-1-4109-0078-4(9)) Raintree.

Green, Jen. Mammal. 2007. (Dk Online Ser.). 96p. (J). (gr. 3-8). pap. 9.99 (***978-0-7566-3137-6(8)***) Dorling Kindersley Publishing, Inc.

Green, Jen. Mammals. 2002. (Young Library - Weird Wildlife Ser.). (Illus.). 32p. (J). lib. bdg. 25.69 (978-0-7398-4856-2(9)) Raintree.

Green, Jen, et al. Mammal. 2005. (Google E Guides Ser.). (Illus.). 96p. (J). 17.99 (978-0-7566-1139-2(3)) Dorling Kindersley Publishing, Inc.

Grzimek, Bernhard & McDade, Melissa C. Grzimek's Student Animal Life Resource. 2004. (J). (978-0-7876-9184-4(4)); (978-0-7876-9187-5(9)); (978-0-7876-9188-2(7)); (978-0-7876-9234-6(4)); (Illus.). (978-0-7876-9185-1(2)) Thomson Gale. (UXL).

—Mammal, Grzimeks Student Animal, 5 vols. 2004. (Grzimek's Student Animal Life Resource Ser.). (Illus.). 1,000p. (J). 290.00 (978-0-7876-9183-7(6) , UXL) Thomson Gale.

Gustafson, Sarah. Whales, Dolphins, & More Marine Mammals. 2005. (Illus.). 48p. (J). pap. (978-0-439-71189-0(4)) Scholastic, Inc.

Hairy Little Critters: Individual Title Six-Packs. (Action Packs Ser.). 104p. (gr. 3-5). 44.00 (978-0-7635-8404-7(5)) Rigby Education.

Hare, Tony. Animal Habitats: Discovering How Animals Live in the Wild. 2001. (Animal Life Ser.). (Illus.). 188p. (J). (gr. 4-8). 40.00 (978-0-8160-4593-8(3) , Checkmark Bks.) Facts On File, Inc.

—Animal Life Cycles: Growing up in the Wild. 2001. (Animal Life Ser.). (Illus.). 160p. (J). (gr. 4-9). 40.00 (978-0-8160-4595-2(X) , Checkmark Bks.) Facts On File, Inc.

Harman, Amanda. Ferrets. 2004. (Nature's Children Ser.). (J). (978-0-7172-5963-2(3) , Grolier) Scholastic Library Publishing.

Harris, Tim. Meerkats. 2004. (Nature's Children Ser.). (J). (978-0-7172-5969-4(2) , Grolier) Scholastic Library Publishing.

Harvey, Bev. Mammals. 2002. (Animal Kingdom Ser.). (Illus.). 32p. (gr. k-2). 23.00 (978-0-7910-6981-3(8) , Chelsea Hse.) Facts On File, Inc.

Hay DeSimone, Corkey. Mammal Animal Coloring & Activity Book: What Is a mammal? You are a mammal Too! 2005. (J). 4.95 (978-0-9747921-2-5(8)) Gentle Giraffe Pr.

Herriges, Ann. Manatees. 2006. (Oceans Alive! Ser.). (Illus.). 24p. (J). lib. bdg. 16.95 (978-1-60014-048-8(3)) Bellwether Media.

Holt, Rinehart and Winston Staff. Birds & Mammals: Chapter Resources: Tennessee Edition. 3rd ed. 2003. (Holt Science & Technology Ser.). pap. 11.40 (978-0-03-069141-6(9)) Holt, Rinehart & Winston.

—Holt Science & Technology Chapter 17: Life Science: Birds & Mammals. 5th ed. 2004. (Illus.). pap. 12.86 (978-0-03-030226-8(9)) Holt, Rinehart & Winston.

Hudak, Heather C. Land Mammals. 2004. (Animal Facts Ser.). (Illus.). 24p. (J). lib. bdg. 24.45 (978-1-59036-200-6(4)) Weigl Pubs., Inc.

Jacobs, Daniel. Big Babies. 2005. (Yellow Umbrella Ser.). (Illus.). 16p. (J). (978-0-7368-5257-9(3)); (978-0-7368-5293-7(X)) Capstone Pr., Inc.

Jeffrey, Laura S. Hamsters, Gerbils, Guinea Pigs, Rabbits, Ferrets, Mice, & Rats: How to Choose & Care for a Small Mammal. 2004. (American Humane Pet Care Library). (Illus.). 48p. (J). lib. bdg. 23.93 (978-0-7660-2518-9(7)) Enslow Pubs., Inc.

John Farndon. Mammals. 2004. (Illus.). 32p. (J). 23.70 (978-1-4103-0119-2(2) , Blackbirch Pr., Inc.) Thomson Gale.

Johnson, Jinny. Mammals. 2003. (Illus.). 48p. (J). (gr. 3 up). lib. bdg. (978-1-59084-451-9(3)) Mason Crest Pubs.

Kalman, Bobbie. Animales llamados Mamíferos. 2007. (SPA.). 32p. (J). (gr. 1-2). (***978-0-7787-8836-2(9)***) Crabtree Publishing Co.

—Les Mammiferes. 2002. (FRE., Illus.). 32p. (J). pap. (978-2-920660-81-6(0)) Crabtree Publishing Co.

—What Is a Mammal? 1999. (Science of Living Things Ser.). (Illus.). 32p. (J). (gr. 2-3). (978-0-86505-878-1(4)); pap. (978-0-86505-890-3(3)) Crabtree Publishing Co.

—What Is a Marine Mammal? 2000. (Science of Living Things Ser.). (978-0-606-18071-9(0)) Tandem Library Bks.

Kalman, Bobbie & Dyer, Hadley. Endangered Manatees. 2006. (Illus.). 32p. (J). (gr. 2-8). (978-0-7787-1868-0(9)) Crabtree Publishing Co.

Kalman, Bobbie & Johnson, Robin. Koalas & Other Marsupials. 2005. (What Kind of Animal Is It? Ser.). (Illus.). 32p. (J). (gr. k-6). (978-0-7787-2162-8(0)); pap. (978-0-7787-2220-5(1)) Crabtree Publishing Co.

Kalman, Bobbie & Langille, Jacqueline. What Is a Marine Mammal? 1999. (Science of Living Things Ser.). (Illus.). 32p. (J). (gr. 2-3). (978-0-86505-936-8(5)); pap. (978-0-86505-954-2(3)) Crabtree Publishing Co.

—What Is a Marine Mammal? 1999. (Illus.). 32p. (J). (ps-7). lib. bdg. 14.10 (978-0-613-22604-2(6)) Tandem Library Bks.

Kalman, Bobbie & Lundblad, Kristina. Animales llamados Mamíferos. rev. ed. 2007. (SPA.). 32p. (J). (gr. 1-2). pap. (***978-0-7787-8872-0(5)***) Crabtree Publishing Co.

Kalman, Bobbie & Lundblad, Kristina. Animals Called Mammals. 2005. (What Kind of Animal Is It? Ser.). (Illus.). 32p. (J). (978-0-7787-2157-4(4)); pap. (978-0-7787-2215-1(5)) Crabtree Publishing Co.

Kingfisher Books Staff. Mammals. 2002. (gr. 3-6). lib. bdg. 16.40 (978-0-613-90361-5(7)) Tandem Library Bks.

Klevansky, Rhonda, et al. The Illustrated Wildlife Encyclopedia: Big Mammals. 2001. (Illus.). 256p. pap. 19.95 (978-1-84215-526-4(1) , Southwater) Anness Publishing GBR. *Dist:* National Bk. Network.

LeapFrog Staff, compiled by. Amazing Mammals. 2001. (J). (ps-2). spiral bd. 14.99 (978-1-58605-031-3(1)) LeapFrog Enterprises, Inc.

Lithgow, John & Blackaby, Susan. Splishy, Splashy Mammals: Level 2. 2007. (Lithgow Palooza Readers Ser.). (Illus.). 32p. (J). (gr. k-1). pap. 3.95 (978-0-7696-4252-9(7)) School Specialty Publishing.

Long, Olivia. Why Don't Cats Lay Eggs? Long, Olivia, illus. Date not set. (Our Precious Planet Ser.). (Illus.). 32p. (J). (ps-4). (978-1-880042-12-0(6)) Shelf-Life Bks.

Lunde, Darrin. Meet the Meerkat. Wynne, Patricia J., illus. 2007. (J). (ps-1). 15.95 (978-1-58089-110-3(1)) Charlesbridge Publishing, Inc.

Lunde, Darrin P. Discovering a New Animal with a Scientist. 2007. (I Like Science! Ser.). (Illus.). 24p. (J). (gr. 1-3). lib. bdg. 21.26 (***978-0-7660-2815-9(1)*** , Enslow Elementary) Enslow Pubs., Inc.

MacAulay, Kelley & Kalman, Bobbie. Dolphins & Other Marine Mammals. 2005. (What Kind of Animal Is It? Ser.). (Illus.). 32p. (J). (gr. k-6). (978-0-7787-2164-2(7)); pap. (978-0-7787-2222-9(8)) Crabtree Publishing Co.

Macken, JoAnn Early. Mountain Goats: Cabra Montés. 2006. (ENG & SPA., Illus.). 24p. (J). pap. (978-0-8368-6458-8(1)); lib. bdg. 19.33 (978-0-8368-6451-9(4)) Stevens, Gareth Inc.

Mamiferos Pequenos, 6 vols., Vol. 3. (Explorers. Exploradores Nonfiction Sets Ser.). (SPA.). (gr. 3-6). (978-0-7699-0651-5(6)) Shortland Pubns. (U. S. A.) Inc.

Mamlferos de Gran TamanO, 6 vols., Vol. 2. (Explorers. Exploradores Nonfiction Sets Ser.). (SPA.). 32p. (gr. 3-6). 44.95 (978-0-7699-0638-6(9)) Shortland Pubns. (U. S. A.) Inc.

Los Mamlferos Del Mar, 6 vols. (Explorers. Exploradores Nonfiction Sets Ser.). (SPA.). 32p. (gr. 3-6). 44.95 (978-0-7699-0629-4(X)) Shortland Pubns. (U. S. A.) Inc.

Mammals. 2001. 63p. (YA). 8.65 (978-0-7525-4876-0(X)) Parragon, Inc.

Mammals. 2003. (Science Card Games Ser.). (gr. 1-3). 9.99 (978-0-7682-1991-3(4) , J53019) School Specialty Publishing.

Mammals; Dinosaurs; Human Body, 3 vols., Set. 2001. 192p. (J). 25.95 (978-0-7525-5456-3(5)) Parragon, Inc.

Mammals Set 1: Mammals of North America. 2005. (J). spiral bd. 23.40 (978-0-9770248-9-6(X)) Sidedoor Publishing LLC.

Markle, Sandra. Jackals. 2005. (Animal Scavengers Ser.). (Illus.). 40p. (J). (ps-7). 25.26 (978-0-8225-3197-5(6) , Lerner Pubns.) Lerner Publishing Group.

Marsico, Katie. A Manatee Calf Grows Up. 2007. (Scholastic News Nonfiction Readers Ser.). 24p. (J). (gr. 1-2). 19.00 (978-0-531-17479-1(4) , Children's Pr.) Scholastic Library Publishing.

Martin-James, Kathleen. Gentle Manatees. 2005. (Pull Ahead Bks.). (J). 22.60 (978-0-8225-2422-9(8) , Lerner Pubns.); 32p. pap. 5.95 (978-0-8225-2441-0(4)) Lerner Publishing Group.

Martin, Patricia. Manatees. 2002. (gr. 3-6). lib. bdg. 15.25 (978-0-613-59512-4(2)) Tandem Library Bks.

Martin, Patricia A. Fink. Lemurs, Lorises, & Other Lower Primates. 2000. (True Bks.). (Illus.). 48p. (J). (gr. 3-5). 25.00 (978-0-516-21575-4(2) , Children's Pr.) Scholastic Library Publishing.

McCourt, Lisa. Hairy 'n Weird: The Strangest Mammals You Ever Saw. Nathan, Cheryl, illus. 2000. (Roxbury Park Bks.). 32p. (J). (gr. k-3). pap. 7.95 (978-0-7373-0404-6(9) , 04049W, Roxbury Park Juvenile) Lowell Hse. Juvenile.

McDonald, Mary Ann. Manatees. 2006. (New Naturebooks). (Illus.). 32p. (J). (gr. 1-5). 27.07 (978-1-59296-643-1(8)) Child's World, Inc.

McEvoy, Paul. Mammals. 2003. (Animal Facts Ser.). (Illus.). 24p. (gr. 2-4). 23.00 (978-0-7910-7282-0(7) , Chelsea Hse.) Facts On File, Inc.

McLaurin, Thad, ed. Investigating Science - Mammals. 2000. 48p. 9.95 (978-1-56234-400-9(5) , Mailbox Bks., The) Education Ctr., Inc.

McRae, Anne & Agosta, Loredana. Mammals. 2007. (J). (***978-88-6098-047-2(X)***) McRae Bks. Srl.

Meerkats. (Animals Ser.). 32p. (J). 6.95 (978-0-7368-8411-2(4)) Capstone Pr., Inc.

Michels, Dia L. If My Mom Were A Platypus: Animal Babies & Their Mothers. Barthelmes, Andrew, illus. 2005. 64p. 29.95 (978-1-930775-13-8(X)); pap. 22.95 (978-1-930775-30-5(X)) Platypus Media, L.L.C.

—If My Mom Were a Platypus: Animal Babies & Their Mothers. Barthelmes, Andrew, illus. rev. ed. 2001. 64p. 16.95 (978-1-930775-02-2(4)) Platypus Media, L.L.C.

—If My Mom Were a Platypus: Mammal Babies & Their Mothers. Barthelmes, Andrew, illus. 2005. 64p. (ps-7). pap. 9.95 (978-1-930775-19-0(9)) Platypus Media, L.L.C.

—If My Mom Were a Platypus: Mammal Babies & Their Mothers. 2nd rev. ed. 2005. (Illus.). 64p. 16.95 (978-1-930775-35-0(0)) Platypus Media, L.L.C.

—If My Mom Were A Platypus- Hebrew Language Edition. 2006. Orig. Title: #1488;#1501; #1488;#1502;#1497; #1492;#1497;#1514;#1492; #1508;#1500;#1496;#1497;#1508;#1493;#1505;. (HEB.). 64p. (J). 16.95 (978-0-9678020-8-4(3)) Science, Naturally!.

—If My Mom Were A Platypus- Hebrew Language Edition. Barthelmes, Andrew, illus. 2006. Orig. Title: #1488;#1501; #1488;#1502;#1497; #1492;#1497;#1514;#1492; #1508;#1500;#1496;#1497;#1508;#1493;#1505;. 64p. (J). 29.95 (978-0-9678020-9-1(1)) Science, Naturally!.

Mighty Mammals: Level O, 6 vols., Vol. 2. (Explorers Ser.). 32p. (gr. 3-6). 44.95 (978-0-7699-0602-7(8)) Shortland Pubns. (U. S. A.) Inc.

Miller, Ruth. Mammals. 2004. (Illus.). 64p. (J). (978-1-4109-1050-9(4)); pap. (978-1-4109-1346-3(5)) Harcourt Schl. Pubs.

Miller, Sara Swan. Mammal Misfits. 2001. (Animals Ser.). (Illus.). 64p. (J). (gr. 5-7). 25.50 (978-0-531-11795-8(2) , Watts, Franklin) Scholastic Library Publishing.

—Mammal Misfits. 2001. (gr. 3-6). lib. bdg. 17.60 (978-0-613-37446-0(0)) Tandem Library Bks.

Mini Mammals: Level P, 6 vols., Vol. 3. (Explorers Ser.). 32p. (gr. 3-6). 44.95 (978-0-7699-0615-7(X)) Shortland Pubns. (U. S. A.) Inc.

Moncrief, Nancy D. Fun with Mammals. Burns, Jasper, illus. 1999. 36p. (J). (gr. 1-3). pap. 4.95 (978-1-884549-13-7(6)) Virginia Museum of Natural History.

Morgan, Ben. Mammals. 2006. (DK Guides Ser.). 64p. (J). pap. 7.99 (978-0-7566-1792-9(8)) Dorling Kindersley Publishing, Inc.

Morgan, Ben & Dorling Kindersley Publishing Staff. Mammals. 2003. (DK Guides Ser.). (Illus.). 64p. (J). 15.99 (978-0-7894-9581-5(3)) Dorling Kindersley Publishing, Inc.

Morgan, Sally. Cats & Other Mammals. 2001. (Illus.). 32p. (J). lib. bdg. 24.25 (978-1-930643-43-7(8)) Chrysalis Education.

Morris, Pat, et al. Insectivores & Bats, 10 vols., Vol. 9. 2003. (Illus.). (J). (978-0-7172-5751-5(7) , Grolier) Scholastic Library Publishing.

—Large Carnivores, 10 vols., Vol. 2. 2003. (Illus.). (J). (978-0-7172-5744-7(4) , Grolier) Scholastic Library Publishing.

—Large Herbivores, 10 vols., Vol. 5. 2003. (Illus.). (J). (978-0-7172-5747-8(9) , Grolier) Scholastic Library Publishing.

—Mammals: World of Animals, 10 vols. Incl. Vol. 1. Small Carnivores. (978-0-7172-5743-0(6)); Vol. 2. Large Carnivores. (978-0-7172-5744-7(4)); Vol. 3. Sea Mammals. (978-0-7172-5745-4(2)); Vol. 4. Primates. (978-0-7172-5746-1(0)); Vol. 5. Large Herbivores. (978-0-7172-5747-8(9)); Vol. 6. Ruminant (Horned) Herbivores. (978-0-7172-5748-5(7)); Vol. 7. Rodents 1. (978-0-7172-5749-2(5)); Vol. 8. Rodents 2 & Lagomorphs. (978-0-7172-5750-8(9)); Vol. 9. Insectivores & Bats. (978-0-7172-5751-5(7)); Vol. 10. Marsupials. (978-0-7172-5752-2(5)); (J). (World of Animals Ser.: Vol. 1). (Illus.). 1280p. 2003. 499.00 (978-0-7172-5742-3(8) , Grolier) Scholastic Library Publishing.

—Marsupials, 10 vols., Vol. 10. 2003. (Illus.). (J). (978-0-7172-5752-2(5) , Grolier) Scholastic Library Publishing.

—Rodents 2 & Lagomorphs, 10 vols., Vol. 8. 2003. (Illus.). (J). (978-0-7172-5750-8(9) , Grolier) Scholastic Library Publishing.

—Ruminant (Horned) Herbivores, 10 vols., Vol. 6. 2003. (Illus.). (J). (978-0-7172-5748-5(7) , Grolier) Scholastic Library Publishing.

—Sea Mammals, 10 vols., Vol. 3. 2003. (Illus.). (J). (978-0-7172-5745-4(2) , Grolier) Scholastic Library Publishing.

—Small Carnivores, 10 vols., Vol. 1. 2003. (Illus.). (J). (978-0-7172-5743-0(6) , Grolier) Scholastic Library Publishing.

Murray, Peter. Mammals. 2004. (Science Around Us Ser.). 32p. (J). (gr. 2-6). 27.07 (978-1-59296-216-7(5)) Child's World, Inc.

National Audubon Society Staff & Grassy, John. Mammals. 1998. (Audubon Society First Field Guide Ser.). (Illus.). 160p. (YA). (gr. 3-7). pap. 17.95 (978-0-590-05471-3(6)); pap. 11.95 (978-0-590-05489-8(9)) Scholastic, Inc. (Scholastic Reference).

National Geographic Society Staff. Great Mammals. 2002. (Illus.). 80p. (J). (gr. 3-7). pap. 5.95 (978-0-7922-6582-5(3) , National Geographic Children's Bks.) National Geographic Society.

Nature Files. 2005. (Illus.). 32p. (gr. 4-8). pap. 168.00 (978-0-7910-8446-5(9) , Chelsea Hse.) Facts On File, Inc.

O'Connell, Kim A. The Wallaby: A MyReportLinks. com Book. 2005. (Endangered & Threatened Animals Ser.). (Illus.). 48p. (J). lib. bdg. 25.26 (978-0-7660-5064-8(5) , MyReportLinks.com Bks.) Enslow Pubs., Inc.

O'Hare, Ted. Mammals. 2006. (What Is an Animal Ser.). (Illus.). 24p. (gr. 1-4). 14.95 (978-1-59515-420-0(5)) Rourke Publishing, LLC.

Ohare, Ted. Mammals. 2005. 24p. pap. 5.45 (978-1-59515-734-8(4)) Rourke Publishing, LLC.

O'Reilly, Wenda. Go fish wildlife Mammals. 2007. n/ap. pap. 119.40 (***978-1-59960-016-1(1)***) Birdcage Pr.

—Wild Cards. 2007. n/ap. pap. 119.40 (***978-1-59960-012-3(9)***) Birdcage Pr.

Parker, Edward, photos by. Mammals. 2002. (Rain Forest Pilot Ser.). (Illus.). 48p. (J). lib. bdg. 27.12 (978-0-7398-5241-5(8)) Raintree.

Parker, Steve. Bats, Blue Whales & Other Mammals. 2005. (Animal Kingdom Classification Ser.). (Illus.). 48p. (J). (gr. 4-6). (978-0-7565-1253-8(0)) Compass Point Bks.

—Mamiferos. 2005. (Dk eyewitness Bks.). 72p. (J). 15.99 (978-0-7566-1484-3(8)); lib. bdg. 19.99 (978-0-7566-1490-4(2)) Dorling Kindersley Publishing, Inc.

—Mamiferos. 2nd ed. Date not set. (SPA., Illus.). 64p. 14.95 (978-84-372-3714-5(9)) Santillana USA Publishing Co., Inc.

—Mammal: Eyewitness Books. Burton, Jane & King, Dave, photos by. 2004. (Illus.). 63p. (gr. 4-8). reprint ed. 16.00 (978-0-7567-7286-4(9)) DIANE Publishing Co.

Parker, Steve & Dorling Kindersley Publishing Staff. Mammal. Burton, Jane, illus. Burton, Jane, photos by. 2004. (Eyewitness Books). 72p. (J). lib. bdg. 19.99 (978-0-7566-0702-9(7)) Dorling Kindersley Publishing, Inc.

Penner, Lucille Recht & Rabe, Tish. Is a Camel a Mammal? 1998. (Cat in the Hat's Learning Library). (Illus.). 48p. (J). (gr. k-3). lib. bdg. 11.99 (978-0-679-97302-7(8) , Random Hse. Bks. for Young Readers) Random Hse. Children's Bks.

Perry, Phyllis J. Freshwater Giants: Hippopotamuses, River Dolphins, & Manatees. 1999. (gr. 3-6). lib. bdg. 17.60 (978-0-613-29429-4(7)) Tandem Library Bks.

Peterson, Roger T. & Alden, Peter C. Peterson First Guide to Mammals of North America. Grossenheider, Richard Philip, illus. 2nd ed. 1998. (First Guides). 128p. pap. 5.95 (978-0-395-91181-5(8)) Houghton Mifflin Co. Trade & Reference Div.

Phillips, Dee. Mammals. 2006. (Blue Zoo Guides Ser.). (Illus.). 96p. 18.95 (978-1-58728-519-6(3) , Two Can Publishing) T&N Children's Publishing.

Pyers, Greg. Why Am I a Mammal? 2005. (Illus.). 32p. (J). (978-1-4109-2016-4(X)); (gr. 5-8). pap. 7.85 (978-1-4109-2023-2(2)) Steck-Vaughn.

Raintree Steck-Vaughn Staff. Encyclopedia of Mammals. 2nd ed. 1999. (Encyclopedias of Animals Ser.). (Illus.). 240p. (J). (gr. 4-7). pap. 68.50 (978-0-7398-0682-1(3)) Raintree.

Rake, Jody Sullivan. Manatees. 2007. (Illus.). 24p. (J). (978-0-7368-6723-8(6) , 1264889) Capstone Pr., Inc.

Richardson, Adele D. Mammals. 2004. (First Facts Ser.). 24p. (J). lib. bdg. 21.26 (978-0-7368-2624-2(6)) Capstone Pr., Inc.

Richardson, Joy. Mammals. 2005. (Illus.). 32p. (J). lib. bdg. 23.33 (978-0-8368-4506-8(4)) Stevens, Gareth Inc.

Ring, Susan. Mammals. 2003. (Illus.). 17p. (J). 15.93 (978-0-7368-2919-9(9)); pap. (978-0-7368-2878-9(8)) Yellow Umbrella Pr.

Robinson, W. Wright. How Mammals Build Their Amazing Homes. Iverson, Carlyn, illus. 1999. (Animal Architects Ser.). 64p. (J). (gr. 5-9). 27.44 (978-1-56711-381-5(8) , Blackbirch Pr., Inc.) Thomson Gale.

Romeu, Emma. El Gran Manati. Sanchez Vigil, Luis Gerardo & Vanden Broeck, Fabricio, illus. 2004. (Coleccion Animales de America). (SPA.). 24p. (J). (gr. 5-8). pap. 7.95 (978-970-29-0513-4(3)) Santillana USA Publishing Co., Inc.

Royston, Angela. Mammals. (Illus.). 32p. (YA). (gr. 2 up). lib. bdg. 27.10 (978-1-932333-37-4(1)) Chrysalis Education.

Salzmann, Mary Elizabeth. What Has Horns? 2007. (Creature Features Ser.). (ENG., Illus.). 24p. (J). (ps-3). lib. bdg. 24.21 (***978-1-59928-868-0(0)*** , Super SandCastle) ABDO Publishing Co.

Savage, Stephen. Mammals. 2000. (What's the Difference? Ser.). (Illus.). (J). (978-0-07-398135-2(4)) McGraw-Hill Cos., The.

—Mammals. 1999. (What's the Difference? Ser.). (Illus.). 32p. (J). (gr. 2-4). lib. bdg. 25.69 (978-0-7398-1354-6(4)) Raintree.

—Mammals. 1999. (What's the Difference? Ser.). (Illus.). 32p. (J). (gr. k-3). pap. 7.95 (978-0-7398-1476-5(1)) Steck-Vaughn.

Schaefer, Lola M. El Equidna. Abello, Patricia, tr. 2004. (SPA., Illus.). 12p. (J). 12.95 (978-1-4034-4299-4(1)) Heinemann Library.

—El Puerco Espin. Abello, Patricia, tr. 2004. (SPA., Illus.). 12p. (J). 12.95 (978-1-4034-4301-4(7)) Heinemann Library.

—What Is a Mammal? Saunders-Smith, Gail, ed. 2001. (Animal Kingdom Ser.). (Illus.). 24p. (J). (gr. k-1). lib. bdg. 14.60 (978-0-7368-0867-5(1) , Pebble Bks.) Capstone Pr., Inc.

School Specialty Publishing. Mammals. 2004. (On-File Ser.). 4p. (J). (gr. 3-5). ring bd. 4.99 (978-0-7424-2900-0(8) , Instructional Fair) Schaffer, Frank Pubns.

School Zone Publishing Company Staff. Mammals. (Illus.). (J). 19.99 incl. audio compact disk (978-0-88743-972-8(1)) School Zone Publishing Co.

Schulte, Mary Knudson. Monkeys & Other Mammals. 2005. (Scholastic News Nonfiction Readers Ser.). (Illus.). 24p. (J). (gr. 1-2). 19.00 (978-0-516-24933-9(9) , Children's Pr.) Scholastic Library Publishing.

Sill, Cathryn P. About Mammals: A Guide for Children. 2000. (Illus.). 48p. (J). (ps-3). pap. 7.95 (978-1-56145-174-6(6)) Peachtree Pubs., Ltd.

Snedden, Robert. Mammals. 2007. (J). (***978-1-59920-081-1(3)***) Smart Apple Media.

Solway, Andrew. Classifying Mammals. 2003. (Classifying Living Things Ser.). (Illus.). 32p. (J). (gr. 3-5). lib. bdg. 24.22 (978-1-4034-0847-1(5)); pap. (978-1-4034-3347-3(X)) Heinemann Library.

—Lions & Other Mammals. 2006. (Illus.). 48p. (J). (978-1-4034-8220-4(9)); pap. (978-1-4034-8227-3(6)) Heinemann Library.

Spilsbury, Louise & Spilsbury, Richard. Save the Florida Manatee. 2006. (Illus.). 32p. (J). 25.36 (978-1-4034-7806-1(6)); pap. (978-1-4034-7814-6(7)) Heinemann Library.

Sterling Publishing Company Staff & Ward, Adam, contrib. by. Pocket Factfiles: Mammals. 2004. (Illus.). 256p. (J). 4.98 (978-1-4027-1851-9(9)) Sterling Publishing Co., Inc.

Stewart, Melissa. Mammals. 2001. (True Bks.). (Illus.). 48p. (J). (gr. 3-5). pap. 6.95 (978-0-516-25952-9(0)); 25.00 (978-0-516-22035-2(7)) Scholastic Library Publishing. (Children's Pr.).

—Mammals. 2001. (gr. 3-6). lib. bdg. 15.25 (978-0-613-53997-5(4)) Tandem Library Bks.

Storad, Conrad J. Meerkats. 2007. (Early Bird Nature Books Ser.). (J). 25.26 (***978-0-8225-6466-9(1)*** , Lerner Pubns.) Lerner Publishing Group.

Swinburne, Stephen R. Saving Manatees. 2006. (Illus.). 40p. (J). (gr. 3-7). 16.95 (978-1-59078-319-1(0)) Boyds Mills Pr.

Taylor, Barbara. Big Mammals: Elephants, Big Cats, Bears & Pandas, Whales & Dolphins. 2001. (gr. 3-6). lib. bdg. 30.35 (978-0-613-82096-7(7)) Tandem Library Bks.

—Large Mammals: Elephants, Bears & Pandas, Big Cats, Whales & Dolphins. 2003. (Illus.). 264p. pap. 19.99 (978-0-7548-1203-6(0)) Anness Publishing GBR. *Dist:* National Bk. Network.

—Mammals. 2002. (Questions & Answers about... Ser.). (Illus.). 40p. (J). (gr. 4-8). pap. 7.95 (978-0-7534-5489-3(0) , Kingfisher) Houghton Mifflin Co. Trade & Reference Div.

Taylor, Barbara, et al. Mammals. 1998. (Pockets Ser.). (Illus.). 128p. (J). (gr. 3-7). pap. 6.99 (978-0-7894-3417-3(2)) Dorling Kindersley Publishing, Inc.

Theodorou, Rod. Mammals. 2007. (Illus.). 32p. (J). (***978-1-4034-9252-4(2)***); (***978-1-4034-9245-6(X)***) Heinemann Library.

Townsend. Incredible Mammals, 6 Packs. 2004. (Illus.). (J). pap. 51.30 (978-1-4109-0864-3(X)) Harcourt Schl. Pubs.

Townsend, John. Incredible Mammals. 2004. (J). pap. 9.50 (978-1-4109-0855-1(0)); (Illus.). 56p. lib. bdg. 31.36 (978-1-4109-0531-4(4)) Harcourt Schl. Pubs.

—Incredible Mammals. 2005. 56p. (J). (ps-1). (Illus.). lib. bdg. 32.86 (978-1-4109-1712-6(6)); (978-1-4109-1721-8(5)) Steck-Vaughn.

Unwin, Mike. The Life Cycle of Mammals. 2003. (From Egg to Adult Ser.). (J). lib. bdg. 24.22 (978-1-4034-0782-5(7)); (Illus.). 32p. pap. 7.50 (978-1-4034-3407-4(7)) Heinemann Library.

VanVoorst, Jennifer. Mamiferos. 2005. Tr. of Mammals. (SPA., Illus.). 16p. (J). (gr. 1 up). lib. bdg. 15.93 (978-0-7368-4163-4(6)) Capstone Pr., Inc.

Vastola, Pam. Huge Animals: Learning the Long U Sound. (PowerPhonics Ser.). (Illus.). (J). 2002. 24p. (gr. 1). lib. bdg. 18.50 (978-0-8239-5931-0(7)); 2001. 23p. pap. 26.40 (978-0-8239-8276-9(9)) Rosen Publishing Group, Inc., The. (PowerKids Pr.).

Walker, Sarah. Mammals. 2002. (Eye Wonder Ser.). (Illus.). 48p. (J). (gr. k-3). 9.99 (978-0-7894-8869-5(8)) Dorling Kindersley Publishing, Inc.

Walker, Sarah & Dorling Kindersley Publishing Staff. Mammals. 2002. (Eye Wonder Ser.). (Illus.). 48p. (J). (gr. k-3). lib. bdg. 17.99 (978-0-7894-8900-5(7)) Dorling Kindersley Publishing, Inc.

What Is a Mammal? 2005. (Animals, Animals, Animals Ser.). (YA). (gr. k-3). (978-0-7368-9096-0(3) , Pebble Bks.) Capstone Pr., Inc.

What Is a Mammal?, 6 vols. (gr. k-2). 28.95 (978-0-7368-9117-2(X)) Red Brick Learning.

Wilkes, Sarah. Mammals. 2006. (J). pap. (978-0-8368-6231-7(7)); (Illus.). 48p. lib. bdg. 30.00 (978-0-8368-6212-6(0)) Stevens, Gareth Inc. (World Almanac Library).

Woods, Samuel G. Sorting Out Mammals: Everything You Want to Know about Marsupials, Carnivores, Herbivores & More! 1999. (Sorting Out Ser.). (Illus.). 32p. (J). (gr. 4-8). 23.70 (978-1-56711-372-3(9) , Blackbirch Pr., Inc.) Thomson Gale.

Woodward, John. Jackals. 2004. (Nature's Children Ser.). (J). (978-0-7172-5967-0(6) , Grolier) Scholastic Library Publishing.

—Wildebeest. 2004. (Nature's Children Ser.). (J). (978-0-7172-5978-6(1) , Grolier) Scholastic Library Publishing.

World Book, Inc. Staff, contrib. by. Mammals of the United States & Canada. 2004. (World Book's Science & Nature Guides Ser.). (Illus.). 80p. (J). (978-0-7166-4215-2(8)) World Bk., Inc.

World of Mammals. 2005. (Illus.). (J). (gr. 2-3). lib. bdg. 212.60 (978-0-7368-4417-8(1)) Capstone Pr., Inc.

MAMMALS—FICTION

Anderson, Laurie Halse. Manatee Blues, No. 4. 2008. (Vet Volunteers Ser.). 144p. (J). (gr. 3). 6.99 (***978-0-14-241084-4(5)*** , Puffin) Penguin Group (USA) Inc.

Arnosky, Jim. A Manatee Morning. 2001. (J). (978-0-606-21615-9(4)) Tandem Library Bks.

Bailey, Arthur. The Tale of Fatty Coon. 2002. 128p. pap. 19.95 (978-1-932080-45-2(7)) Ross & Perry, Inc.

Balzola, Asun. Historia de un Erizo. 2001. Tr. of Hedgehog Story. (SPA.). 26p. (978-84-305-7197-0(3)) Lectorum Pubns., Inc.

Bone, Thomas H. & LeTourneau, Anthony Alex, illus. Mama, Can Armadillos Swim? 2004. (J). 17.00 (978-0-9674602-6-0(3)) Blue Marlin Pubns.

Brown, Tricia. Itchy Little Musk Ox. Dubac, Debbie, illus. 2006. 32p. (J). 15.95 (978-0-88240-613-8(2)); pap. 8.95 (978-0-88240-614-5(0)) Graphic Arts Ctr. Publishing Co. (Alaska Northwest Bks.).

Clarke, Jane & Gale, Cathy. Plodney Creeper, Supersloth. 2006. (Blue Bananas Ser.). (Illus.). 48p. (J). pap. (978-0-7787-0896-4(9)) Crabtree Publishing Co.

Davis, Maggie Steincrohn. Garden of Whales. 2000. (gr. k-3). lib. bdg. 15.25 (978-0-613-77755-1(7)) Tandem Library Bks.

The Girl Who Loved Meerkats. 2005. (J). (978-1-933248-04-2(1)) World Quest Learning.

Harms, John. Saving of Arma Armadillo. 2001. (gr. 3-6). lib. bdg. 15.25 (978-0-613-77813-8(8)) Tandem Library Bks.

Hermes, Patricia. Emma Dilemma & the New Nanny. 2006. (Illus.). 112p. (J). 15.95 (978-0-7614-5286-7(9)) Cavendish, Marshall Corp.

King, Jamie R. Marybelle the Manatee. Lemmon, David, illus. 1999. (Zoooo Stories Ser.). (J). (978-1-893993-02-0(7)) Medias & Co., Inc.

Maccarone, Grace. Mother, May I? 2006. 28p. (J). bds. 8.99 (978-0-439-77015-6(7) , Cartwheel Bks.) Scholastic, Inc.

McCluskey, Jeffrey. The Adventures of Peter the Pleasant Platypus & Friends, Second Adventure: Brown Water. 2005. 52p. pap. 19.95 (978-1-4116-4880-7(3)) Lulu.com.

Navarro, Laura. Un tesoro Inesperado: An Unexpected Treasure. Sebastian, Juan, illus. 2003. (SPA & ENG.). 49p. pap. 8.95 (978-0-9742379-0-9(6)) Bat Conservation International, Inc.

Ross, Michael Elsohn. Mama's Milk. Wolff, Ashley, illus. 2007. 32p. (J). 12.95 (***978-1-58246-181-6(3)*** , Tricycle Pr.) Ten Speed Pr.

Torres, Jotam. Weagol's Big Mess. 2007. 28p. per. 12.99 (***978-1-59886-758-9(X)***) Tate Publishing & Enterprises, L.L.C.

Woods, Shirley. Jack: The Story of a Beaver. 2004. (gr. 3-6). lib. bdg. 16.40 (978-0-613-70894-4(6)) Tandem Library Bks.

Zoehfeld, Kathleen Weidner. Manatee Winter: Smithsonains Oceanic. 2005. (Illus.). 32p. (J). (ps-2). pap. 6.95 (978-1-56899-936-4(4) , S4003) Soundprints.

MAMMALS, FOSSIL

see also names of extinct animals, e.g. Mastodon; etc.

Aliki. Wild & Woolly Mammoths. Aliki, illus. 2nd rev. ed. 1998. (Trophy Picture Bk.). (Illus.). 32p. (J). (ps-3). pap. 6.99 (978-0-06-446179-5(3) , Harper Trophy) HarperCollins Pubs.

—Wild & Woolly Mammoths. rev. ed. 1998. (Trophy Picture Bks.). (J). (978-0-606-13068-4(3)) Tandem Library Bks.

Blashfield, Jean F. & Jacobs, Richard P. When Giant Mammals Thundered: The Cenozoic Era. 2005. (Illus.). 80p. (J). (978-1-4034-7661-6(6)) Heinemann Library.

Brown, Charlotte Lewis. After the Dinosaurs: Mammoths & Fossil Mammals. Wilson, Phil, illus. (I Can Read Bks.). (J). 2007. 32p. pap. 3.99 (*978-0-06-053055-6(3)* , Harper Trophy); 2006. 48p. 15.99 (978-0-06-053053-2(7)); 2006. 48p. lib. bdg. 16.89 (978-0-06-053054-9(5)) HarperCollins Pubs.

Fowler, Allan. Mammals of Long Ago. 2000. (Rookie Read-About Science Ser.). (Illus.). 32p. (J). (gr. 1-2). 20.50 (978-0-516-21209-8(5) , Children's Pr.) Scholastic Library Publishing.

Holmes & Thom. Age of Mammals: The Oligocene & Miocene Periods. 2008. (Prehistoric Earth Ser.). 208p. (gr. 6-12). 35.00 (*978-0-8160-5964-5(0)* , Chelsea Hse.) Facts On File, Inc.

Jay, Michael. Flying Creatures. 2003. (Illus.). 32p. (J). lib. bdg. 25.70 (978-1-4109-0007-4(X)) Raintree.

—Ice Age Beasts. 2003. (Illus.). 32p. (J). lib. bdg. 25.70 (978-1-4109-0008-1(8)) Raintree.

Lindeen, Carol. Giant Ripper Lizard: Megalania Prisca. 2008. (J). (*978-1-4296-0115-3(9)*) Capstone Pr., Inc.

Riehecky, Janet. Cave Bear: Ursus Spelaeus. 2008. (*978-1-4296-0113-9(2)*) Capstone Pr., Inc.

MAMMOTH

Agenbroad, Larry. Mammoths: Ice-Age Giants. 2002. (gr. 5-8). lib. bdg. 16.40 (978-0-613-46148-1(7)) Tandem Library Bks.

Agenbroad, Larry D. & Nelson, Lisa W. Mammoths: Ice-Age Giants. 2003. (Illus.). 120p. (J). (gr. 7-12). pap. 7.95 (978-0-8225-0470-2(7)) Lerner Publishing Group.

Aliki. Wild & Woolly Mammoths. Aliki, illus. 2nd rev. ed. 1998. (Trophy Picture Bk.). (Illus.). 32p. (J). (ps-3). pap. 6.99 (978-0-06-446179-5(3) , Harper Trophy) HarperCollins Pubs.

—Wild & Woolly Mammoths. rev. ed. 1998. (Trophy Picture Bks.). (J). (978-0-606-13068-4(3)) Tandem Library Bks.

Arnold, Caroline. When Mammoths Walked the Earth. Caple, Laurie A., illus. 2002. 40p. (J). (gr. k-3). tchr. ed. 16.00 (978-0-618-09633-6(7) , Clarion Bks.) Houghton Mifflin Co. Trade & Reference Div.

Dixon, Dougal. Frozen Mammoth. 2003. (History Hunters Ser.). (Illus.). 32p. (J). (gr. 3 up). lib. bdg. 24.67 (978-0-8368-3740-7(1)) Stevens, Gareth Inc.

Frost, Helen. Woolly Mammoth. 2005. (Dinosaurs & Prehistoric Animals Ser.). (Illus.). 24p. (J). 19.93 (978-0-7368-3649-4(7)) Capstone Pr., Inc.

Goecke, Michael P. Woolly Mammoth. 2003. (Prehistoric Animals Ser.). (Illus.). 24p. (J). (gr. k-4). lib. bdg. 21.35 (978-1-57765-971-6(6)) ABDO Publishing Co.

Johnston, Marianne. Mastodons, Mammoths, & Modern-Day Elephants. 2000. (Prehistoric Animals & Their Modern-Day Relatives Ser.). 24p. (J). (gr. k-4). lib. bdg. 18.75 (978-0-8239-5202-1(9) , PowerKids Pr.) Rosen Publishing Group, Inc., The.

Levy, Elizabeth. Who Are You Calling a Woolly Mammoth? Prehistoric America. 2001. (America's Horrible Histories Ser.: No. 1). (Illus.). 128p. (J). (gr. 4-6). pap. 4.99 (978-0-590-12938-1(4)) Scholastic, Inc.

Mammoth: MainSails, 6 Packs. (Sails Literacy Ser.). (gr. 5 up). 37.00 (978-0-7578-8047-6(9)) Rigby Education.

Mammoth: Riddle of the Ice Age. 2000. (YA). 0.75 (978-1-893345-24-9(6)) Answers in Genesis Ministries.

Markle, Sandra. Outside & Inside Woolly Mammoths. 2007. (Illus.). 40p. (J). (gr. 4-8). 17.95 (*978-0-8027-9589-2(7)*); 18.85 (*978-0-8027-9590-8(0)*) Walker & Co.

Matthews, Rupert. Woolly Mammoth. 2003. (Gone Forever Ser.). (Illus.). 32p. pap. 6.50 (978-1-4034-3417-3(4)); (J). lib. bdg. 22.79 (978-1-4034-0789-4(4)) Heinemann Library.

Myers, Jack. What Happened to the Mammoths? And Other Explorations of Science in Action. Rice, John, illus. 2004. 64p. (YA). (gr. 4-6). 17.95 (978-1-56397-801-2(6)); pap. 9.95 (978-1-59078-280-4(1)) Boyds Mills Pr.

Nelson, Lisa W. & Agenbroad, Larry D. Mammoths: Ice-Age Giants. Jansen, Paula, illus. Jansen, Paula, photos by. 2005. (Discovery! Ser.). 120p. (gr. 5-12). lib. bdg. 27.93 (978-0-8225-2862-3(2)) Lerner Publishing Group.

O'Brien, Patrick. Mammoth. rev. ed. 2002. (Illus.). 40p. (J). 16.95 (978-0-8050-6596-1(2) , Holt, Henry & Co. Bks. For Young Readers) Holt, Henry & Co.

Philippo, Sophie. Meet the Woolly Mammoth. Dutertre, Charles, illus. 2005. 45p. (978-1-58728-521-9(5) , Two Can Publishing) T&N Children's Publishing.

Wadsworth, Ginger. Woolly Mammoths. Zalewski, Todd, illus. 2006. (On My Own Science Ser.). 48p. (J). (gr. 2-4). lib. bdg. 25.26 (978-1-57505-879-5(0) , Millbrook Pr.) Lerner Publishing Group.

Wheeler, Lisa. Mammoths on the Move. Cyrus, Kurt, illus. 2006. 32p. (J). 16.00 (978-0-15-204700-9(X)) Harcourt Trade Pubs.

Woolly Mammoths. 2007. (J). pap. 5.95 (*978-0-8225-6447-8(5)* , First Avenue Editions) Lerner Publishing Group.

MAN

see Human Beings

MAN—COLOR

see Human Skin Color

MAN, PREHISTORIC

see Prehistoric Peoples

MAN IN SPACE

see Manned Space Flight

MANAGEMENT

see also Industrial Management

Aikins, Anne Marie. Authority: Before It Deals with You. Murray, Steven, illus. 2005. (Deal with It Ser.). 32p. (J). (gr. 4-8). 12.95 (978-1-55028-869-8(5)) Lorimer, James & Co., Ltd., Pubs. CAN. *Dist:* Casemate Pubs. & Bk. Distributors, LLC.

Ferguson. Mastering Career Skills: Organization Skills. 2nd rev. ed. (Mastering Career Skills Ser.). 144p. pap. 12.95 (*978-0-8160-7116-6(0)* , Checkmark Bks.) Facts On File, Inc.

Giesecke, Ernestine. Be Your Own Boss: Small Businesses. 2003. (Everyday Economics Ser.). (Illus.). 48p. (J). (gr. 3-5). lib. bdg. (978-1-58810-493-9(1)) Heinemann Library.

Griffin. Hm E-study: Used With ... Griffin-Management. 8th ed. 2004. (Illus.). xxxii, 808p. cd-rom 2.76 (978-0-618-35463-4(8) , 335024) Houghton Mifflin College Div.

—Study Guide: Used with ... Griffin-Management. 8th ed. 2006. (YA). stu. ed. 45.56 (978-0-618-35461-0(1) , 335022) Houghton Mifflin College Div.

Griffin, Ricky. Management: Text with HM e-Study. 8th ed. 2004. (Illus.). 808p. (YA). 155.96 incl. cd-rom (978-0-618-49927-4(X) , 335032) Houghton Mifflin College Div.

J. G. Ferguson Publishing Company Staff. Careers in Focus: Business Managers. 2003. (Careers in Focus Ser.). 192p. (YA). (gr. 6-12). 22.95 (978-0-89434-414-5(5) , Ferguson Publishing Co.) Facts On File, Inc.

Kennerdell, Peter, et al. Business Studies for OCR GCSE. 2001. (Illus.). 288p. pap. 47.50 (*978-0-340-79052-6(0)* , Hodder Arnold) Hodder Education GBR. *Dist:* Trans-Atlantic Pubns., Inc.

Rossiter, Diane E. Leadership Skills. 2nd ed. 2004. (Career Skills Library). (Illus.). 128p. (YA). (gr. 6-12). 21.95 (978-0-8160-5519-7(X) , Ferguson Publishing Co.) Facts On File, Inc.

Thompson, Tamara. Emergency Response. 2004. (Careers for the Twenty-First Century Ser.). (Illus.). 112p. (J). (gr. 7-10). 29.95 (978-1-59018-396-0(7) , Lucent Bks.) Thomson Gale.

Vitale, Ann E. Manager. 2002. (Careers with Character Ser.). (Illus.). 96p. (J). (gr. 7 up). (978-1-59084-317-8(7)) Mason Crest Pubs.

MANAGEMENT—EMPLOYEE PARTICIPATION

Connolly, Sean. Rights at Work. 2005. (Campaigns for Change Ser.). (Illus.). 48p. (J). (gr. 6-9). lib. bdg. 29.95 (978-1-58340-518-5(6) , 1247340) Smart Apple Media.

MANAGEMENT, INDUSTRIAL

see Industrial Management

MANAGEMENT, SCIENTIFIC

see Management

MANAGEMENT OF CHILDREN

see Child Rearing

MANDELA, NELSON, 1918-

Andy Koopmans. Nelson Mandela. 2004. (Heroes & Villains Ser.). (Illus.). 112p. (J). 29.95 (978-1-59018-426-4(2)) Thomson Gale.

Beecroft, Simon. The Release of Nelson Mandela. 2004. (Days That Changed the World Ser.). (Illus.). 48p. (J). (gr. 5 up). pap. 11.95 (978-0-8368-5578-4(7)); lib. bdg. 30.00 (978-0-8368-5571-5(X)) Stevens, Gareth Inc. (World Almanac Library).

Boothroyd, Jennifer. Nelson Mandela: A Life of Persistence. 2007. (Pull Ahead Books). (Illus.). 32p. (J). 22.60 (978-0-8225-6385-3(1) , Lerner Pubns.) Lerner Publishing Group.

Connolly, Sean. Nelson Mandela: An Unauthorized Biography. 2000. (Profiles Ser.). (Illus.). 56p. (J). (gr. 4-6). lib. bdg. 24.22 (978-1-57572-225-2(9)) Heinemann Library.

Cooper, Floyd. Mandela: From the Life of the South African Statesman. Cooper, Floyd, illus. 2000. (Illus.). 40p. (J). (gr. k-5). pap. 6.99 (978-0-698-11816-4(2) , Putnam Juvenile) Penguin Group (USA) Inc.

—Mandela: From the Life of the South African Statesman. 2000. (978-0-606-18430-4(9)); lib. bdg. 15.30 (978-0-613-23016-2(7)) Tandem Library Bks.

Crompton, Samuel Willard. Nelson Mandela: Ending Apartheid in South Africa. 2006. (Modern Peacemakers Ser.). (Illus.). 128p. (J). (gr. 9 up). 30.00 (978-0-7910-8997-2(5) , Chelsea Hse.) Facts On File, Inc.

Finlayson, Reggie. Nelson Mandela. (Just the Facts Biographies Ser.). 2006. (Illus.). 112p. (J). (gr. 3-7). 27.93 (978-0-8225-2644-5(1)); 2004. (J). pap. (978-0-8225-5360-1(0)); 1998. (Illus.). 112p. (YA). (gr. 6-12). 27.93 (978-0-8225-4936-9(0)) Lerner Publishing Group. (Lerner Pubns.).

Gogerly, Liz. The Freeing of Nelson Mandela. 2004. (Days That Shook the World Ser.). (Illus.). 47p. (J). lib. bdg. 28.56 (978-0-7398-6648-1(6)) Raintree.

—Nelson Mandela. 2003. (Leading Lives Ser.). (Illus.). 64p. (J). lib. bdg. 28.50 (978-1-4034-0834-1(3)) Heinemann Library.

Grant, Karima. Nelson Mandela. (Illus.). (J). 2006. 32p. (gr. 1-2). pap. 4.95 (978-0-516-25537-8(1)); 2005. 31p. (ps-ps). 20.50 (978-0-516-25270-4(4)) Scholastic Library Publishing. (Children's Pr.).

Harcourt School Publishers Staff. A New Day for South Africa. 3rd ed. 2002. (Horizons Ser.). (Illus.). (J). pap. 7.30 (978-0-15-333630-0(7)) Harcourt Schl. Pubs.

Hort, Lenny & Brown, Laaren. Nelson Mandela. 2006. (Biography Ser.). (Illus.). 128p. (J). 14.99 (978-0-7566-2110-0(0)); pap. 4.99 (978-0-7566-2109-4(7)) Dorling Kindersley Publishing, Inc.

Keller, Bill. Tree Shaker: The Story of Nelson Mandela. 2008. (New York Times Ser.). 128p. (J). (gr. 5-9). 17.95 (*978-0-7534-5992-8(2)* , Kingfisher) Houghton Mifflin Co. Trade & Reference Div.

Kramer, Ann. Mandela: The Rebel Who Led His Nation to Freedom. 2005. (World History Biographies Ser.). (Illus.). 64p. (J). (gr. 3-7). 17.95 (978-0-7922-3658-0(0) , National Geographic Children's Bks.) National Geographic Society.

—Nelson Mandela. 2003. (20th Century History Makers Ser.). (Illus.). 112p. (J). lib. bdg. 32.85 (978-0-7398-5258-3(2)) Raintree.

—Nelson Mandela: The Rebel Who Led His Country to Freedom. 2005. (World History Biographies Ser.). (Illus.). 64p. (J). (gr. 3-7). 27.90 (978-0-7922-3659-7(9) , National Geographic Children's Bks.) National Geographic Society.

McDonough, Yona Zeldis & Zeldis, Malcah. Peaceful Protest. 2006. (Illus.). 40p. (J). pap. 8.95 (978-0-8027-8948-8(X)) Walker & Co.

O'Hern, Kerri & Holland, Gini. Nelson Mandela. 2006. (Illus.). (J). pap. 8.95 (978-0-8368-6249-2(X)); 32p. lib. bdg. 26.00 (978-0-8368-6197-6(3)) Stevens, Gareth Inc. (World Almanac Library).

O'Hern, Kerri, et al. Nelson Mandela. 2006. (ENG & SPA.). (J). pap. (*978-0-8368-7888-2(4)*); lib. bdg. (*978-0-8368-7881-3(7)*) Stevens, Gareth Inc. (World Almanac Library).

Schuldt, Lori Meek. Martin Luther King, Jr: With Profiles of Mohandas K. Gandhi & Nelson Mandela. 2006. (Biographical Connections Ser.). (Illus.). 112p. (J). (978-0-7166-1822-5(2)) World Bk., Inc.

Shone, Rob. Nelson Mandela: The Life of an African Statesman. Reed, Neil, illus. 2006. 48p. (J). (978-1-4042-0922-0(0)); pap. (978-1-4042-0923-7(9)) Rosen Publishing Group, Inc., The.

—Nelson Mandela: The Life of an African Statesman. 2006. (Graphic Biographies Ser.). (Illus.). 48p. (J). lib. bdg. 29.95 (978-1-4042-0860-5(7)) Rosen Publishing Group, Inc., The.

Stamper, G. C. Nelson Mandela. 2005. (Illus.). 32p. (J). pap. (*978-0-7367-2922-2(4)*) Zaner-Bloser, Inc.

Trailblazers of the Modern World: Neil Armstrong; Bob Dylan; Bill Gates; Nelson Mandela; Eleanor Roosevelt; Steven Spielberg, 6 bks. 2002. (Illus.). (J). (gr. 5 up). pap. 87.60 (978-0-8368-5234-9(6) , World Almanac Library) Stevens, Gareth Inc.

MANET, EDOUARD, 1832-1883

Dorling Kindersley Publishing Staff & Wright, Patricia. Manet. 1999. (Eyewitness Art Ser.). (Illus.). 64p. (J). (gr. 3-7). 15.99 (978-0-7894-4879-8(3)) Dorling Kindersley Publishing, Inc.

Manet, Edouard. Color Your Own Manet Paintings. 2008. 32p. pap. 3.95 (*978-0-486-46202-8(1)*) Dover Pubns., Inc.

Mis, Melody S. Edouard Manet. 2008. (J). lib. bdg. (*978-1-4042-3841-1(7)* , PowerKids Pr.) Rosen Publishing Group, Inc., The.

MANGROVE

Blaxland, Beth. Mangroves. 2001. (Water Worlds Ser.). (Illus.). 32p. (J). (gr. 4 up). 28.00 (978-0-7910-6565-5(0) , 010354, Chelsea Hse.) Facts On File, Inc.

Pryor, Kimberley Jane. Mangrove Swamps. 2007. (J). (*978-1-59920-138-2(0)*) Smart Apple Media.

MANNED SPACE FLIGHT

see also Astronauts; Outer Space—Exploration

also names of projects, e.g. Gemini Project; etc.

Angelo, Joseph A., Jr. Human Spaceflight. 2007. (Frontiers in Space Ser.). 384p. (J). (gr. 9). 39.50 (978-0-8160-5775-7(3)) Facts On File, Inc.

Atkinson, Stuart. Space Travel. 2002. (Young Library - Space Busters Ser.). (Illus.). 32p. (J). lib. bdg. 25.69 (978-0-7398-4852-4(6)) Raintree.

Aylmore, Angela. We Work in Space. 2006. (Where We Work Ser.). (Illus.). 24p. (J). (978-1-4109-2249-6(9)); 21.36 (978-1-4109-2244-1(8)) Steck-Vaughn.

Belfiore, Michael P. Life Aboard a Space Station. 2004. (Way People Live Ser.). (Illus.). 112p. (J). (gr. 7-10). 29.95 (978-1-59018-460-8(2) , Lucent Bks.) Thomson Gale.

Bergin, Mark. Space Shuttle. 1999. (Fast Forward Ser.). (Illus.). 32p. (J). (gr. 4-8). 29.00 (978-0-531-14573-9(5) , Watts, Franklin) Scholastic Library Publishing.

—Space Shuttle. 1999. (gr. 3-6). lib. bdg. 18.75 (978-0-613-34966-6(0)) Tandem Library Bks.

Bondar, Barbara & Bondar, Roberta. On the Shuttle: Eight Days in Space. 2003. (Illus.). 64p. (J). (gr. 4-7). 16.95 (978-1-895688-12-2(4) , Owl Bks.) Maple Tree Pr. CAN. *Dist:* Firefly Bks., Ltd.

Bredeson, Carmen. Nave Espacial. 2004. (Rookie Readers - Spanish Ser.). (J). 19.50 (978-0-516-25101-1(5) , Watts, Franklin) Scholastic Library Publishing.

Deady, Kathleen W. Space Walks. 2002. (Explore Space! Ser.: 2). (Illus.). 24p. (J). (gr. 1-2). lib. bdg. 18.60 (978-0-7368-1402-7(7) , Bridgestone Bks.) Capstone Pr., Inc.

Green, Carl R. The Gemini 4 Spacewalk Mission: A MyReportLinks. com Book. 2004. (Space Flight Adventures & Disasters Ser.). (Illus.). 48p. (J). lib. bdg. 25.26 (978-0-7660-5163-8(3) , MyReportLinks.com Bks.) Enslow Pubs., Inc.

Herrod, Robin. Space Pioneers. 2004. (History of Space Exploration Ser.). (Illus.). 48p. (J). pap. 11.95 (978-0-8368-5714-6(3)); lib. bdg. 30.00 (978-0-8368-5707-8(0)) Stevens, Gareth Inc. (World Almanac Library).

Hilliard, Richard, illus. Ham, the Astrochimp. 2007. 32p. (J). (gr. 4-7). 16.95 (*978-1-59078-459-4(6)*) Boyds Mills Pr.

Ingebretsen, Karen, et al. Human Space Exploration. 2006. (World Book's Solar System & Space Exploration Library). (Illus.). 63p. (J). (978-0-7166-9509-7(X)) World Bk., Inc.

Jefferis, David. Flight into Orbit. 2007. (Illus.). 32p. (J). (gr. 3-7). (*978-0-7787-3101-6(4)*); pap. (*978-0-7787-3115-3(4)*) Crabtree Publishing Co.

Kortenkamp, Steve. Working in Space. 2008. (*978-1-4296-1261-6(4)*) Capstone Pr., Inc.

Lieurance, Suzanne. The Space Shuttle Challenger Disaster in American History. 2001. (In American History Ser.). (Illus.). 128p. (J). (gr. 5-12). lib. bdg. 26.60 (978-0-7660-1419-0(3)) Enslow Pubs., Inc.

Raketen und Raumfahrt. (GER.). 40p. (978-3-411-08191-2(0)) Bibliographisches Institut & F. A. Brockhaus AG DEU. *Dist:* i.b.d., Ltd.

Rau, Dana Meachen & Higgins, Nadia. Space Walks. 2004. (Our Solar System Ser.). (Illus.). 32p. (J). (978-0-7565-0851-7(7)) Compass Point Bks.

Richie, Jason. Space Flight: Crossing the Last Frontier. 2001. (Innovators Ser.: Vol. 10). (Illus.). 144p. (gr. 5 up). lib. bdg. 21.95 (978-1-881508-77-9(3)) Oliver Pr., Inc.

Shearer, Deborah A. Walking on the Moon. 2002. (Explore Space! Ser.). (Illus.). 24p. (J). (gr. 1-2). lib. bdg. 18.60 (978-0-7368-1145-3(1) , Bridgestone Bks.) Capstone Pr., Inc.

Space Busters, 5 bks., Set. 2003. (Illus.). (J). pap. (978-1-4109-0150-7(5)) Raintree.

Spangenburg, Ray. Onboard the Space Shuttle. 2002. (gr. 5-8). lib. bdg. 24.55 (978-0-613-53847-3(1)) Tandem Library Bks.

Sparrow, Giles. Astronauts. 2006. (Illus.). 48p. (J). pap. (978-0-8368-7282-8(7)); lib. bdg. (978-0-8368-7275-0(4)) Stevens, Gareth Inc. (World Almanac Library).

Taylor, Robert. Life Aboard the Space Shuttle. 2002. (Way People Live Ser.). (Illus.). 112p. (J). (gr. 7-10). 29.95 (978-1-59018-154-6(9) , LML00902-181109, Lucent Bks.) Thomson Gale.

Tesar, Jenny. Space Travel. 1998. (Space Observer Ser.). (Illus.). 24p. (ps-3). pap. (978-1-57572-581-9(9)) Heinemann Library.

Vogt, Gregory L. Spacewalks: The Ultimate Adventure in Orbit. 2000. (Countdown to Space Ser.). (Illus.). 48p. (YA). (gr. 4-10). lib. bdg. 23.93 (978-0-7660-1305-6(7)) Enslow Pubs., Inc.

Whitehouse, Patricia. Living in Space. 2004. (J). 24.21 (978-1-4034-5151-4(6)); pap. 6.95 (978-1-4034-5655-7(0)) Heinemann Library.

World Book, contrib. by. Human Space Exploration. 2nd ed. 2006. (World Book's Solar System & Space Exploration Library). (Illus.). 64p. (J). (*978-0-7166-9514-1(6)*) World Bk., Inc.

Zelon, Helen. The First American Space Walk: The Gemini IV Mission. 2002. (Space Missions Ser.). (Illus.). 24p. (J). lib. bdg. 19.95 (978-0-8239-5771-2(3) , PowerKids Pr.) Rosen Publishing Group, Inc., The.

MANNERS

see Courtesy; Etiquette

MANNERS AND CUSTOMS

see also Chivalry; Clothing and Dress; Costume; Etiquette; Food Habits; Funeral Rites and Ceremonies; Holidays; Marriage Customs and Rites; Social Classes; Travel

Ajmera, Maya. Ser Nino. 2000. (J). (978-0-606-19332-0(4)); (SPA.). lib. bdg. 15.25 (978-0-613-51267-1(7)) Tandem Library Bks.

—To Be a Kid. 2000. (J). (978-0-606-19334-4(0)); 1999. lib. bdg. 15.25 (978-0-613-30161-9(7)) Tandem Library Bks.

Ajmera, Maya & Ivanko, John D. To Be a Kid. (Illus.). 32p. (J). 2004. bds. 6.95 (978-1-57091-371-6(4)); 2004. pap. 6.95 (978-0-88106-842-9(X)); 1999. 16.95 (978-0-88106-841-2(1)) Charlesbridge Publishing, Inc.

Alexander, Florence & Alexander, Stanley. Come with Me & See... Children of the World. Lt. ed. 2003. (ENG & SPA., Illus.). 32p. (J). 9.99 (978-0-9648313-9-1(2)) Ebon Research Systems Publishing, LLC.

Andrade, Mary J. The Vigil of Little Angels, Day of the Dead in Mexico. Murguia, Jose, illus. 2001. 36p. (J). (gr. 1-6). 19.95 (978-0-9665876-3-0(4)) La Oferta Publishing Co.

Before You Say Yes to a Guest. 2003. (YA). (978-0-9729586-0-8(6)) Imani-MCHS.

Berry, Joy. Bad Habits. 3rd ed. 2005. (Winning skills series, get over It! Ser.). (Illus.). 48p. (J). 3.95 (978-1-57687-280-2(7) , PowerHouse Kids) powerHouse Cultural Entertainment, Inc.

Bracken, Thomas. Customs of the World. 1999. (Looking Into the Past Ser.). (Illus.). 64p. (YA). (gr. 5 up). 14.00 (978-0-7910-4679-1(6) , 036655, Chelsea Hse.) Facts On File, Inc.

Breaud, Odile, et al. Cultures of the World. 1998. (Creative Discoveries Ser.: Vol. 8). Orig. Title: Living Around the World. (Illus.). 75p. (J). (gr. 2-8). lib. bdg. 23.95 (978-0-88682-957-5(7) , Creative Education) Creative Co., The.

Carter, Jennifer, illus. Christmas Treasures. 2005. 33p. pap. 3.99 (978-1-904726-00-5(3)) Authentic Media.

Casey & the Growing Spurt: Learning Patriotism, Citizenship, & Character. 2002. (Kamaron Concept Book). 94p. (J). per. 9.99 (978-0-9715713-2-7(5)) Kamaron Institute Pr.

Chelsea House Publishing Staff. People & Customs of the World, 4 bks. 1998. (Illus.). (gr. 5-12). 79.80 (978-0-7910-5137-5(4) , Chelsea Hse.) Facts On File, Inc.

A Child's Book of Manners. 2006. 16p. (J). pap. 1.99 (978-0-7847-1684-7(6) , 02986) Standard Publishing.

Coppendale, Jean. Life & Death. 2006. (Illus.). 32p. (YA). (gr. 1 up). lib. bdg. 27.10 (978-1-931983-99-0(2)) Chrysalis Education.

Cultures of the World - Group 16, 6 vols. Incl. Belarus. Levy, Patricia. lib. bdg. 37.07 (978-0-7614-0811-6(8)); Guatemala. Sheehan, Sean. lib. bdg. 37.07 (978-0-7614-0812-3(6)); Liberia. Levy, Patricia. lib. bdg. 37.07 (978-0-7614-0810-9(X)); New Zealand. Smelt, Roselynn. lib. bdg. 37.07 (978-0-7614-0808-6(8)); Papua New Guinea. Gascoigne, Ingrid. lib. bdg. 37.07 (978-0-7614-0813-0(4)); Tanzania. Heale, Jay. lib. bdg. 37.07 (978-0-7614-0809-3(6)); 128p. (gr. 5-12). 1998. (Illus.). 1998. 222.43 (978-0-7614-0807-9(X) , Benchmark Bks.) Cavendish, Marshall Corp.

Delasfosse, Claude & Jeunesse, Gallimard. Houses. Grant, Donald, illus. 1998. (First Discovery Book Ser.). 24p. (J). (ps-2). 12.95 (978-0-590-38152-9(0)) Scholastic, Inc.

Do, Elisa Shipon-Blum. Understanding Katie: A Day in the Life Of. Salus, Diane, illus. 2003. 28p. (J). (ps up). pap. (978-0-9714800-3-2(6)) Selective Mutism Anxiety Research & Treatment Ctr.

Doudna, Kelly. Culture Around the World. 2004. (Around the World Ser.). (Illus.). 23p. (J). (ps-3). lib. bdg. 19.93 (978-1-59197-566-3(2)) ABDO Publishing Co.

Ever Wonder What to Do Manners. 2004. pap. 1.50 (978-0-87162-918-0(6)) Warner Pr. Pubs.

Forrester, Tina & Shapiro, Sheryl. The Birthday Book. Langlois, Suzane, illus. 2003. 24p. (J). (gr. 1-4). lib. bdg. 18.95 (978-1-55037-829-0(5)) Annick Pr., Ltd. CAN. *Dist:* Firefly Bks., Ltd.

Fox, Mem. Whoever You Are. Staub, Leslie, illus. 2001. 32p. (J). (gr. k-2). pap. 7.00 (978-0-15-216406-5(5) , Voyager Bks./Libros Viajeros) Harcourt Children's Bks.

Goodman, Susan E. Chopsticks for My Noodlesoup: Eliza's Life in Malaysia. Doolittle, Michael, illus. 1999. (Around the World Ser.). 32p. (gr. k-3). lib. bdg. (978-0-7613-1552-0(7) , Millbrook Pr.) Lerner Publishing Group.

Gordon, Sharon. We Are Kind. 2005. (Bookworms Ser.). (ENG & SPA., Illus.). 24p. (J). (gr. 3-7). lib. bdg. (978-0-7614-1992-1(6) , Benchmark Bks.) Cavendish, Marshall Corp.

Gray, Carolyn. All about M. E. Manners & Etiquette for TWEENS & TEENS. 2007. 28p. (J). pap. 12.95 (***978-1-60131-010-1(2)***) Big Tent Bks.

Grolier Educational Staff, contrib. by. Canada. 2003. (Illus.). 32p. (J). (978-0-7172-5790-4(8) , Grolier) Scholastic Library Publishing.

—Colombia. 2003. (Illus.). 32p. (J). (978-0-7172-5791-1(6) , Grolier) Scholastic Library Publishing.

—Haiti. 2003. (Illus.). 32p. (J). (978-0-7172-5792-8(4) , Grolier) Scholastic Library Publishing.

—Iran. 2003. (Illus.). 32p. (J). (978-0-7172-5794-2(0) , Grolier) Scholastic Library Publishing.

—Mongolia. 2003. (Illus.). 32p. (J). (978-0-7172-5796-6(7) , Grolier) Scholastic Library Publishing.

—Nicaragua. 2003. (Illus.). 32p. (J). (978-0-7172-5797-3(5) , Grolier) Scholastic Library Publishing.

—Norway. 2003. (Illus.). 32p. (J). (978-0-7172-5798-0(3) , Grolier) Scholastic Library Publishing.

—Portugal. 2003. (Illus.). 32p. (J). (978-0-7172-5799-7(1) , Grolier) Scholastic Library Publishing.

—Scotland. 2003. (Illus.). 32p. (J). (978-0-7172-5800-0(9) , Grolier) Scholastic Library Publishing.

—Sri Lanka. 2003. (Illus.). 32p. (J). (978-0-7172-5801-7(7) , Grolier) Scholastic Library Publishing.

—Syria. 2003. (Illus.). 32p. (J). (978-0-7172-5802-4(5) , Grolier) Scholastic Library Publishing.

Groves, Marsha. Manners & Customs in the Middle Ages. 2005. (Medieval World Ser.). (Illus.). 32p. (J). (gr. 4-9). pap. (978-0-7787-1389-0(X)) Crabtree Publishing Co.

Gurkow, Malkie. Building a Better Me: Student's Workbook. 2005. 29p. pap., wbk. ed. 7.50 (978-1-878895-44-8(3)) Torah Umesorah Pubns.

Gustafson, Angela. Imagine a House: A Journey to Fascinating Houses Around the World. 2003. (What a World We Live in Ser.). (Illus.). 32p. (J). (gr. k-6). lib. bdg. 16.95 (978-0-9726849-0-3(5)) Out of the Box.

Guy, John. Victorian Life. 2004. (Illus.). 32p. (J). (gr. 4-7). pap. (978-1-86007-005-1(1)) Ticktock Media Ltd.

Hallinan, P. K. I'm Thankful Each Day! 2001. (Illus.). 24p. (J). 7.95 (978-0-8249-5396-6(7) , Ideals) Ideals Pubns.

Halstead, Rachel & Reid, Struan. Customs. 2004. (Hands-On History Ser.). (Illus.). 64p. pap. 10.99 (978-1-84215-859-3(7) , Southwater) Anness Publishing GBR. *Dist:* National Bk. Network.

Harcourt School Publishers Staff. Horizons Unit 4: Learn About People. 3rd ed. 2001. (Illus.). pap. 169.80 (978-0-15-322579-6(3)) Harcourt Schl. Pubs.

Harris, Nicholas, ed. People of the World. 2002. (Blackbirch Visual Encyclopedia Ser.). (Illus.). 64p. (J). 37.44 (978-1-56711-518-5(7) , Blackbirch Pr., Inc.) Thomson Gale.

Hollyer, Beatrice. Wake up, World! A Day in the Life of Children Around the World. rev. ed. 1999. (Illus.). 48p. (J). (gr. 1-4). 17.95 (978-0-8050-6293-9(9) , Holt, Henry & Co. Bks. For Young Readers) Holt, Henry & Co.

Holyoke, Nancy. A Smart Girl's Guide to Manners: The Secrets to Grace, Confidence, & Being Your Best. Watkins, Michelle, ed. Mingus, Cathi, illus. 2005. (American Girl Library). 120p. (J). (gr. 3). pap. 9.95 (978-1-58485-983-3(0) , American Girl) American Girl Publishing, Inc.

I'm Thankful Each Day! 2001. (Illus.). 28p. (J). pap. 5.95 (978-0-8249-5397-3(5)) Ideals Pubns.

Israel, Fred L., intro. Greetings of the World. 1999. (Looking Into the Past Ser.). (Illus.). 64p. (YA). (gr. 5 up). lib. bdg. 19.75 (978-0-7910-4680-7(X) , Chelsea Hse.) Facts On File, Inc.

Jackson, Abby. Fancy Feet. 2005. (Yellow Umbrella Ser.). (J). (978-0-7368-5313-2(8)); (Illus.). 16p. (978-0-7368-5277-7(8)) Capstone Pr., Inc.

Joosse, Barbara. Please Is a Good Word to Say. Plecas, Jennifer, illus. 2007. 40p. (J). (ps-3). 12.99 (978-0-399-24217-5(1) , Philomel) Penguin Group (USA) Inc.

Kane-Wood, Deborah. Where Everything Belongs: Table Setting & Manners for Children. 2003. (Illus.). 32p. (J). pap. 24.99 (978-1-57921-717-4(6)) WinePress Publishing.

Kids Talk, 12 bks. Incl. Do I Have To? Kids Talk about Responsibility. Loewen, Nancy. Wesley, Omarr, illus. (C). 23.93 (978-1-4048-0030-4(1)); How Could You? Kids Talk about Trust. Loewen, Nancy. Wesley, Omarr, illus. (C). 23.93 (978-1-4048-0031-1(X)); I Can Do It! Kids Talk about Courage. Loewen, Nancy. Wesley, Omarr, illus. (C). 23.93 (978-1-4048-0032-8(8)); Is That True? Kids Talk about Honesty. Nettleton, Pamela Hill. Muehlenhardt, Amy Bailey, illus. (C). 23.93 (978-1-4048-0619-1(9)); Let's Get Along! Kids Talk about Tolerance. Nettleton, Pamela Hill. Muehlenhardt, Amy Bailey, illus. (J). 23.93 (978-1-4048-0622-1(9)); May I Help You? Kids Talk about Caring. Nettleton, Pamela Hill. Muehlenhardt, Amy Bailey, illus. (C). 23.93 (978-1-4048-0620-7(2)); No Fair! Kids Talk about Fairness. Loewen, Nancy. Wesley, Omarr, illus. (C). 23.93 (978-1-4048-0033-5(6)); Pitch In! Kids Talk about Cooperation. Nettleton, Pamela Hill. Muehlenhardt, Amy Bailey, illus. (C). 23.93 (978-1-4048-0621-4(0)); Treat Me Right! Kids Talk about Respect. Loewen, Nancy. Wesley, Omarr, illus. (C). 23.93 (978-1-4048-0034-2(4)); Want to Play? Kids Talk about Friendliness. Nettleton, Pamela Hill. Muehlenhardt, Amy Bailey, illus. (C). 23.93 (978-1-4048-0623-8(7)); We Live Here Too! Kids Talk about Good Citizenship. Loewen, Nancy. Wesley, Omarr, illus. (C). pap. 23.93 (978-1-4048-0035-9(2)); You First! Kids Talk about Consideration. Nettleton, Pamela Hill. Muehlenhardt, Amy Bailey, illus. (C). 23.93 (978-1-4048-0624-5(5)); 32p. (gr. 2-5). 2004. 2002. Set lib. bdg. 287.16 (978-1-4048-0635-1(0)) Picture Window Bks.

King, Alyson L. Chores Around the House. 2007. (Illus.). 24p. pap. (***978-1-59515-963-2(0)***) Rourke Publishing, LLC.

King, Elizabeth. Quinceanera: Celebrating Fifteen. King, Elizabeth, photos by. 2006. (Illus.). 40p. (YA). (gr. 8-11). reprint ed. 17.00 (978-1-4223-5728-6(7)) DIANE Publishing Co.

Leaf, Munro. How to Speak Politely & Why. 2005. (Illus.). 56p. (J). (gr. k). 14.95 (978-0-7893-1352-2(9)) Universe Publishing.

Lee, Quinlan B. Look at Me! Langer S.L., Jutta, illus. 2004. (Barney Ser.). 80p. (J). pap. 2.99 (978-0-439-62503-6(3)) Scholastic, Inc.

Long Ago & Today. 2002. pap. 3.74 (978-0-7398-5845-5(9)) Steck-Vaughn.

Love, Mary A. Learning Through Symbolism & Celebrations. Flournoy, L. Diana, illus. 1998. x, 150p. (J). pap. 18.00 (978-1-929548-00-2(1)) Love's Creative Resources.

MacDonald, Fiona. History of Culture. 2003. (Culture Encyclopedia Ser.). (Illus.). 40p. (J). (gr. 5 up). lib. bdg. (978-1-59084-477-9(7)) Mason Crest Pubs.

Manners. (First Facts Ser.). (Illus.). (J). (gr. 1-2). lib. bdg. 127.56 (978-0-7368-2756-0(0)) Capstone Pr., Inc.

Marsh, Carole. Christmas Traditions Around the World. 2003. 12p. (J). (gr. k-4). pap. 2.95 (978-0-635-02154-0(4)) Gallopade International.

—Why Do We Hang Christmas Stockings. 2003. 12p. (J). (gr. k-4). pap. 2.95 (978-0-635-02152-6(8)) Gallopade International.

Mason, Paul. Body Piercing & Tattooing. 2003. (Just the Facts Ser.). (Illus.). 56p. (J). lib. bdg. 25.64 (978-1-4034-0817-4(3)) Heinemann Library.

Mattern, Joanne. Getting Ready for School: Me Preparo para Ir a la Escuela. 2006. (ENG & SPA., Illus.). 24p. (J). pap. (978-0-8368-7366-5(1)); lib. bdg. (978-0-8368-7359-7(9)) Stevens, Gareth Inc. (Weekly Reader Early Learning Library).

McDonald, Fiona. Hats & Headdresses Through History. 2006. (Why Do We Wear? Ser.). (Illus.). 32p. (J). lib. bdg. (978-0-8368-6854-8(4)) Stevens, Gareth Inc.

Milord, Susan. Mexico! 40 Activities to Experience Mexico Past & Present. 1999. (Kaleidoscope Kids Bks.). (Illus.). 96p. (J). (gr. 2-8). pap. 12.95 (978-1-885593-22-1(8) , Williamson Bks.) Ideals Pubns.

Minnis. Ancient Rome. 2004. (Raintree Perspectives Ser.). (Illus.). 32p. (J). 25.70 (978-1-4109-0618-2(3)) Harcourt Schl. Pubs.

Montanari, Donata. Children Around the World. Montanari, Donata, illus. (Illus.). 32p. (J). (gr. k-3). 2004. (978-1-55337-684-2(6)); 2001. (978-1-55337-064-2(3)) Kids Can Pr., Ltd.

Mundy, Michaelene. Saying Goodbye, Saying Hello: When Your Family Is Moving. Alley, Robert W., illus. 2005. (Elf-Help Books for Kids). 32p. (J). (ps-ps). per. 7.95 (978-0-87029-393-1(1)) Abbey Pr.

Newcomer, Ruth. Silly Songs for Little People. 2004. (Illus.). 42p. (J). spiral bd. 18.00 (978-1-883911-63-8(X)) Brandylane Pubs., Inc.

One City, One School, Many Foods: Six-Pack. (Greetings Ser.: Vol. 1). (gr. 3-5). 31.00 (978-0-7635-1797-7(6)) Rigby Education.

Pacileo, Cindy, creator. The Virtues Activity & Coloring Book, Ages 5-7. 2005. (J). 4.50 (978-0-9741930-0-7(3)) Changing-Times.net.

—The Virtues Activity & Coloring Book, Ages 8-10. 2005. (J). 4.50 (978-0-9741930-1-4(1)) Changing-Times.net.

Parish, Scott. Tiger at the Table. 2005. 14p. (J). 10.00 (978-1-4116-4704-6(1)) Lulu.com.

People of the World. (J). (gr. 6). (978-0-8374-1460-7(1) , 208) Weekly Reader Corp.

Pickels, Dwayne E. Ancient & Annual Customs. 1999. (Looking Into the Past Ser.). (Illus.). 64p. (YA). (gr. 5 up). 14.00 (978-0-7910-4682-1(6) , Chelsea Hse.) Facts On File, Inc.

PoliteKids 101. . . Social Skills Your Child Needs for Success in Life! 2004. (J). (978-0-9729706-7-9(3)); wbk. ed. (978-0-9729706-8-6(1)) Production 101, Inc.

Powell, Jillian. A New Baby. 2006. (Illus.). 30p. (J). (978-1-58340-949-7(1)) Smart Apple Media.

Raatma, Lucia. Generosity. 2002. (Character Education Ser.). (Illus.). 24p. (J). (gr. 1-2). lib. bdg. 18.60 (978-0-7368-1388-4(8) , Bridgestone Bks.) Capstone Pr., Inc.

Raintree Steck-Vaughn Staff. Con Buenos Modales, Por Favor! 1999. (Coleccion en Parejas). (SPA.). (J). pap., stu. ed. 21.50 (978-0-7398-0837-5(0)) Steck-Vaughn.

Ring, Susan. Places We Live. (J). (gr. k-2). 2006. (Illus.). 16p. 15.93 (978-0-7368-5850-2(4) , Yellow Umbrella Bks.); 2005. (978-0-7368-5316-3(2)); 2005. (Illus.). 16p. (978-0-7368-5280-7(8)) Capstone Pr., Inc.

Roca, Nuria. Boys & Girls of the World: From One End... to the Other. Curto, Rosa Maria, illus. 2002. (From ... to Ser.). 36p. (J). (ps-1). pap. 7.99 (978-0-7641-2141-8(3)) Barron's Educational Series, Inc.

Rosson, Denise & Tumblacer, Margaret. Tadpole Dreams Etiquette & Good Manners Program Handbook. 2005. 25p. (J). 12.95 (978-0-9769320-1-7(6) , ss0002) Smith, S. Pubns.

Sato, Shozo. Tea Ceremony. 2005. (Asian Arts & Crafts for Creative Kids Ser.). (Illus.). 64p. 12.95 (978-0-8048-3500-8(4)) Tuttle Publishing.

Schaefer, Lola M. Understanding Differences, 4 bks. Saunders-Smith, Gail, ed. Incl. Some Kids Are Blind. 2001. lib. bdg. 15.93 (978-0-7368-0664-0(4)); Some Kids Are Deaf. 2001. lib. bdg. 15.93 (978-0-7368-0665-7(2)); Some Kids Use Wheelchairs. 2000. lib. bdg. 15.93 (978-0-7368-0666-4(0)); Some Kids Wear Leg Braces. 2000. lib. bdg. 15.93 (978-0-7368-0667-1(9)); 24p. (J). (gr. k-1). (Illus.). 2001. Set lib. bdg. 63.72 (978-0-7368-0691-6(1) , Pebble Bks.) Capstone Pr., Inc.

Scott, Janine. Cool Customs. 2002. (Spyglass Books). (Illus.). 24p. (J). (gr. 1 up). lib. bdg. 18.60 (978-0-7565-0364-2(7)) Compass Point Bks.

Small, Mary. Being Respectful: A Book about Respectfulness. Previn, Stacey, illus. 2005. (Way to Be! Ser.). 24p. (J). (ps). lib. bdg. 22.60 (978-1-4048-1053-2(6)) Picture Window Bks.

Sonnier, Suzanne. Shinto, Spirits, & Shrines: Religion in Japan. 2007. (Lucent Library of Historical Eras:Twentieth-Century Japan Ser.). (Illus.). 128p. (gr. 7-10). 31.20 (***978-1-4205-0029-5(5)*** , Lucent Bks.) Thomson Gale.

Spangenburg, Ray & Moser, Kit. Teen Fads: Fun, Foolish, or Fatal? 2003. (Teen Issues Ser.). (Illus.). 64p. (J). (gr. 6-12). lib. bdg. 22.60 (978-0-7660-1665-1(X)) Enslow Pubs., Inc.

Spier, Peter. Gente. 2000. Tr. of People. (SPA., Illus.). 44p. (J). (gr. 2-4). 17.95 (978-84-264-3604-7(8) , LC0759) Editorial Lumen ESP. *Dist:* Lectorum Pubns., Inc.

Stefoff, Rebecca. The Medieval World. 2003. (Illus.). 48p. (J). 27.07 (978-0-7614-1642-5(0) , Benchmark Bks.) Cavendish, Marshall Corp.

Stephens, Chris S. A Christmas Box. 32p. 2003. pap. 20.95 (978-1-84323-306-0(1)); 2002. (Illus.). pap. 13.95 (978-1-84323-037-3(2)) Beekman Bks., Inc.

Summers, Jean. The Kids' Guide to Writing Great Thank-You Notes. 2005. (Illus.). 38p. (J). pap. 11.95 (978-1-59411-125-9(1)) Writers' Collective, The.

Tadpole Dreams Etiquette & Good Manners Curriculum. 2005. (YA). ring bd. 249.95 (978-0-9769320-0-0(8) , ss0001) Smith, S. Pubns.

Thomas, Pat. My Manners Matter: A First Look at Being Polite. Harker, Lesley, illus. 2006. (First Look At... Ser.). 32p. (J). pap. 6.99 (978-0-7641-3212-4(1)) Barron's Educational Series, Inc.

Townsend, John. Freaky Fashion & Foul Food. 2006. (Raintree Freestyle Ser.). (Illus.). 48p. (J). (978-1-4109-1869-7(6)) Steck-Vaughn.

Treat Me Right! (Kids Talk Ser.). 32p. (J). 8.95 (978-1-4048-0367-1(X)) Picture Window Bks.

Trumbauer, Lisa. About 100 Years Ago. 2000. (Yellow Umbrella Books). (Illus.). 16p. (J). (gr. 1). lib. bdg. 14.60 (978-0-7368-0736-4(5) , Pebble Bks.) Capstone Pr., Inc.

Underwood, Deborah. Where Are Your Manners? 2006. (Illus.). 32p. (J). (978-1-4109-2594-7(3)); pap. (978-1-4109-2623-4(0)) Steck-Vaughn.

Vong, Yumi. Aloha Sun. 2006. 16p. pap. 6.95 (978-1-933067-16-2(0)) Beachhouse Publishing, LLC.

Wallace, Paula S. Life Around the World, 4 bks. Incl. World of Birthdays. lib. bdg. 24.67 (978-0-8368-3659-2(6)); World of Food. lib. bdg. 24.67 (978-0-8368-3660-8(X)); World of Holidays. lib. bdg. 24.67 (978-0-8368-3661-5(8)); World of Sports. lib. bdg. 24.67 (978-0-8368-3662-2(6)); 48p. (J). (gr. 2 up). 2003. (Illus.). 2002. Set lib. bdg. 98.68 (978-0-8368-3658-5(8)) Stevens, Gareth Inc.

Way to Be! (C). 135.60 (978-1-4048-1058-7(7)) Picture Window Bks.

Weber, Rebecca. Understanding Differences. 2004. (Spyglass Books). (Illus.). 24p. (J). (gr. 1 up). lib. bdg. 19.93 (978-0-7565-0651-3(4)) Compass Point Bks.

Welcome to My Country New Releases: Denmark; Haiti; Pakistan; South Korea; Sri Lanka; Ukraine, 6 bks. 2003. (Illus.). (J). (gr. 2 up). lib. bdg. 151.60 (978-0-8368-2549-7(7)) Stevens, Gareth Inc.

What Really Matters. 2007. (J). per. 10.00 (***978-1-930052-35-2(9)***) Cherokee Bks.

Wheeler, Valerie. Yes, Please! No, Thank You! Dibley, Glin, illus. 2006. 30p. (J). bds. 5.95 (978-1-4027-3929-3(X)); 2005. 32p. 14.95 (978-1-4027-1746-8(6) , 1241714) Sterling Publishing Co., Inc.

Whyte, Daniel, 3rd. Money under the Car Seat: And Other Things to Thank God For. 2004. (Illus.). 220p. per. (978-0-9763487-0-2(5)) Torch Legacy Pubns.

Wilson, Amber. Jamaica - the People. 2003. (Lands, Peoples & Cultures Ser.). (Illus.). 32p. (J). pap. (978-0-7787-9699-2(X)) Crabtree Publishing Co.

World Book, Inc. Staff, contrib. by. Everyday Celebrations & Rituals. 2003. (World Book's Celebrations & Rituals Around the World Ser.). (Illus.). 46p. (J). (978-0-7166-5016-4(9)) World Bk., Inc.

Worthy of Honor. 2003. (Humble Heart Ser.). (J). spiral bd., wbk. ed. (978-0-9746148-2-3(3)) Common Courtesy.

MANNERS AND CUSTOMS—FICTION

Alegria, Malin. Estrellas Quinceanera. 2006. (Illus.). 272p. (YA). 15.99 (978-0-689-87809-1(5)) Simon & Schuster Children's Publishing.

Alexander, Mary Helen. Please & Thank You. 2005. 23p. pap. 14.95 (978-1-4137-6240-2(9)) PublishAmerica, Inc.

Binkow, Howard. Howard B. Wigglebottom Learns to Listen. Cornelison, Susan F., illus. 2006. 32p. (J). (ps-2). 15.00 (978-0-9715390-1-3(4)) Thunderbolt Publishing.

Bloom, Becky. Leo & Lester. Biet, Pascal, illus. 2003. (J). 32p. 15.95 (978-1-59034-582-5(7)); 33p. pap. (978-1-59034-583-2(5)) Mondo Publishing.

Buckley, Charlie. How to Wash Your Hands. 2007. (Show Jo Language Development Ser.). (Illus.). 16p. (J). (ps-1). per., bds. 14.95 (***978-1-933669-09-0(8)***) Literary Architects, LLC.

Byrum, Isabel C. How John Became a Man Life Story of a Motherless Boy. 2005. reprint ed. pap. 15.95 (978-1-4179-0742-7(8)) Kessinger Publishing, LLC.

Chambers, Robert W. The Purple Emperor. 2004. reprint ed. pap. 15.95 (978-1-4191-7947-1(0)); pap. 1.99 (978-1-4192-7947-8(5)) Kessinger Publishing, LLC.

Chi Omega - My First Board Book. 2006. (J). bds. 10.95 (978-0-9776627-1-5(3)) Captus, LLC.

Cochran, Jean M. Your Tummy's Talking. Gullens, Lee, illus. 2007. 32p. (J). 16.95 (***978-0-9792035-3-4(8)***) Pleasant St. Pr.

Cole, Babette. The Sprog Owner's Manual. 2005. (Illus.). 32p. (J). (ps-3). pap., pap. 9.99 (978-0-09-944765-8(7) , Red Fox) Random Hse. Children's Bks. GBR. *Dist:* Trafalgar Square Publishing.

Dana, B. J. Tales of the Sugar Hollow Twins: And their very most favorite stories, Book #4. 2006. 100p. (J). per. 13.95 (***978-1-59453-870-4(0)*** , 3165, Airleaf Publishing) Airleaf Publishing & Bookselling.

de Paola, Tomie. The Night of las Posadas. 2001. (gr. k-3). lib. bdg. 15.30 (978-0-613-44406-4(X)) Tandem Library Bks.

Delta Delta Delta - My First Board Book. 2006. (J). bds. 10.95 (978-0-9776627-3-9(X)) Captus, LLC.

DK Publishing. Don't Forget Spike about Manners: Plush Board Book. 2008. 10p. (J). bds. 8.99 (***978-0-7566-3445-2(8)***) Dorling Kindersley Publishing, Inc.

Entara Ltd., photos by. Mind Your Manners. 2007. (Jakers! Ser.). 24p. (J). (ps-2). pap. 3.99 (***978-1-4169-4715-8(9)*** , Simon Spotlight) Simon & Schuster Children's Publishing.

Fedewa, Lanna C. Reid Rides the Railroad. Batson, Mary, illus. 2002. 18p. (J). (gr. k-3). pap. 9.95 (978-0-9702880-5-9(0)) Sun R.A.Y.S., LLC.

Freeman, Emily. God Bless Your Way: A Christmas Journey. Burr, Dan, illus. 2007. 32p. (J). (ps-3). 19.95 incl. audio compact disk (***978-1-59038-806-8(2)***) Deseret Bk. Co.

Gilmore, Rachna. When-I-Was-A-Little-Girl. Benoit, Renné, illus. 2006. 28p. 12.95 (978-1-897187-12-8(2)) Second Story Pr. CAN. *Dist:* Orca Bk. Pubs. USA.

Goldberg, Whoopi. Big Book of Manners. Olo, illus. 2006. 40p. (ps-1). 15.99 (978-0-7868-5295-6(X) , Jump at the Sun) Hyperion Bks. for Children.

Greig, Elna. Bye-Bye! 2005. (Illus.). 16p. pap. 7.95 (978-1-932915-13-6(3)) Sandvik Publishing.

—Hello! 2005. (Illus.). 16p. pap. 7.95 (978-1-932915-12-9(5)) Sandvik Publishing.

Grekul, Lisa. Kalyna's Song. 2nd ed. 2007. 472p. (YA). (gr. 10 up). pap. 12.95 (***978-1-55050-355-5(3)***) Coteau Bks. CAN. *Dist:* Fitzhenry & Whiteside, Ltd.

Grimsdell, Jeremy. Bushbaby Night. 2006. 32p. pap. 17.95 (978-1-77009-056-9(8)) Jacana Media ZAF. *Dist:* Independent Pubs. Group.

Hallinan, P. K. Let's Be Polite. 2004. (Illus.). 26p. (J). bds. 7.95 (978-0-8249-6562-4(0)) Ideals Pubns.

Hamilton, Tisha & Stephenson, Kristine. Play Fair, Have Fun: A Book about Making Good Choices. 2007. 12p. (J). (ps-k). 10.99 (***978-0-7944-1354-5(4)***) Reader's Digest Assn., Inc., The.

Helmer, Diana Star. The Cat Who Came for Tacos. Escriva, Vivi, illus. 2003. 32p. (J). (gr. 1-3). 15.95 (978-0-8075-5106-6(6)) Whitman, Albert & Co.

Holm, Jennifer L. Boston Jane. unabr. ed. 2004. (Middle Grade Cassette Librariestm Ser.). 288p. (J). (gr. 5-9). pap. 38.00 incl. audio (978-0-8072-0787-1(X) , S YA 307 SP, Listening Library) Random Hse. Audio Publishing Group.

Johnston, Annie Fellows. Mary Ware the Little Colonel's Chum. Barry, Etheldred B., illus. 2004. reprint ed. pap. 30.95 (978-1-4179-1704-4(0)) Kessinger Publishing, LLC.

Jones, Deirdre. All over the World. Dillard, Kristine, illus. 1998. 8p. (J). (gr. k-2). pap. 3.75 (978-1-880612-74-3(7) , Seedling Pubns.) Continental Pr., Inc.

Kappa Alpha Theta - My First Board Book. 2006. (J). bds. 10.95 (978-0-9776627-4-6(8)) Captus, LLC.

Kappa Delta - My First Board Book. 2006. (J). bds. 10.95 (978-0-9776627-5-3(6)) Captus, LLC.

Magi, Aria. The Lulilites: And the Star of Seven Rays. l.t. ed. 2005. (Illus.). 40p. (J). 19.95 (978-0-9759631-0-4(4)) Lulilite Productions.

Manners I. Care. 2005. (J). pap. 5.99 (***978-0-9771143-4-4(1)***) Child LIfe Bks., LLC.

Mayer, Mercer. Just a Mess. Mayer, Mercer, illus. 2000. (Little Critter Ser.). (Illus.). 24p. (J). (gr. k-k). 3.99 (978-0-307-11948-3(3) , 11948, Random Hse. Bks. for Young Readers) Random Hse. Children's Bks.

McMullan, Kate. I'm Dirty! McMullan, Jim, illus. 2006. 40p. (J). lib. bdg. 17.89 (978-0-06-009294-8(7) , Cotler, Joanna Books) HarperCollins Pubs.

Melling, David. The Scallywags. 2006. 32p. (J). (ps-2). 14.99 (978-0-7641-5991-6(7)) Barron's Educational Series, Inc.

Moses, Brian. Yo No Fui: Aprender a Ser Honesto. Gordon, Mike, illus. 2000. (SPA.). 32p. (J). (ps-k). 7.95 (978-950-24-0804-0(7)) Lectorum Pubns., Inc.

O'Connor, Jane. Fancy Nancy. Glasser, Robin Preiss, illus. 2005. (Fancy Nancy Ser.). 32p. (J). 16.99 (978-0-06-054209-2(8)); lib. bdg. 17.89 (978-0-06-054210-8(1)) HarperCollins Pubs.

—Fancy Nancy & the Posh Puppy. Glasser, Robin Preiss, illus. 2007. (Fancy Nancy Ser.). 32p. (J). lib. bdg. 17.89 ***(978-0-06-054215-3(2));*** 16.99 ***(978-0-06-054213-9(6))*** HarperCollins Pubs.

—Fancy Nancy's Glamorous Gift. Glasser, Robin Preiss, illus. gif. ed. 2007. (Fancy Nancy Ser.). 32p. (J). (ps-2). 24.99 ***(978-0-06-137182-0(3))*** HarperCollins Pubs.

Otte, Kathleen. I Can Show Good Manners. 2006. (J). pap., tchr. ed. (978-1-57332-438-0(8)); pap. (978-1-57332-439-7(6)) HighReach Learning, Inc.

Parish, Scott. Tigre a la Mesa. 2005. 14p. (J). 10.00 (978-1-4116-6003-8(X)) Lulu.com.

Paul, Ann Whitford. Everything to Spend the Night: From A to Z. 2001. (978-0-606-22366-9(5)) Tandem Library Bks.

Phillips, Betty Lou. Emily's Manners. Watts, Sharon, illus. 2005. 12p. (J). (ps). bds. 6.95 (978-1-58685-457-7(7)) Gibbs Smith, Publisher.

The Pledge of Allegiance. 2006. (J). bds. 7.95 (978-0-9776627-2-2(1)) Captus, LLC.

Ricci, Christine. Los Buenos Modales de Dora. Hall, Susan, illus. 2005. (Dora the Explorer Ser.).Tr. of Dora's Book of Manners. (SPA.). 24p. pap. 3.99 (978-1-4169-0069-6(1) , Libros Para Ninos) Simon & Schuster Children's Publishing.

—Dora's Book of Manners. Hall, Susan', illus. ed. 2005. (Dora the Explorer Ser.: No. 7). 22p. (J). lib. bdg. 15.00 (978-1-59054-793-9(4)) Fitzgerald Bks.

—Dora's Book of Manners. Hall, Susan T., illus. 2004. (Dora the Explorer Ser.). 24p. (J). pap. 3.50 (978-0-689-86533-6(3) , Simon Spotlight/Nickelodeon) Simon & Schuster Children's Publishing.

—Dora's Book of Manners. 2004. (ps-2). lib. bdg. 11.25 (978-0-613-73450-9(5)) Tandem Library Bks.

Riddle, Sharon Kay & Sanders, Nancy/Ida. The King's Silverware. Lowe, Frank Allen, illus. 2007. 32p. (J). pap. 15.00 ***(978-0-9761583-5-6(3))*** Olive Leaf Pubns.

Santanach, Tino, illus. Happy Brush Day! 2007. (LazyTown Ser.). 24p. (J). pap. 3.99 (978-1-4169-0795-4(5) , Simon Spotlight/Nickelodeon) Simon & Schuster Children's Publishing.

Shealy, Dennis. Please & Thank You, God. Nakata, Hiroe, illus. 2007. 36p. (J). (gr. k-k). 6.99 (978-0-375-83656-5(X) , Golden Inspirational) Random Hse. Children's Bks.

Sigma Kappa - My First Board Book. 2006. (J). bds. 10.95 (978-0-9776627-6-0(4)) Captus, LLC.

Simon Minds His Manners. 2006. 16p. (J). pap. 1.99 (978-0-7847-1698-4(6) , 03000) Standard Publishing.

Tayleur, Karen. Excuses! Survive & Succeed with David Mortimore Baxter. Garvey, Brann, illus. 2007. (David Mortimore Baxter Ser.). 71p. (J). (gr. 3-6). lib. bdg. 23.93 (978-1-59889-073-0(5)) Stone Arch Bks.

Wax, Wendy. Hippo Rules: A Tale of Good Manners. Terry, Michael, illus. 2007. 12p. (J). 12.99 ***(978-0-7944-1289-0(0))*** Reader's Digest Assn., Inc., The.

Wong-Avery, Sally. Chinese Manners. 2007. (Illus.). (J). pap. ***(978-0-9798874-0-6(2))*** Tsui Wong-Avery, Sally.

Zima, Gordon. Sunbirds & Evergreens. 2006. (J). (978-0-9742894-5-8(0)) Hutton Electronic Publishing.

Zima, Gordon & Zima, Paula, illus. Sun Birds & Evergreens: The Nuk-Chuk Stories. 2005. (J). (978-0-9742894-3-4(4)) Hutton Electronic Publishing.

MANTLE, MICKEY, 1931-1995

Marlin, John. Mickey Mantle. 2005. (Sports Heroes & Legends Ser.). (Illus.). 112p. (J). (gr. 6-12). lib. bdg. 27.93 (978-0-8225-1796-2(5)) Lerner Publishing Group.

MANUFACTURES

see also Machinery; Waste Products

Adil, Janeen R. Goods & Services. 2006. (First Facts. Learning about Money Ser.). (Illus.). 24p. (J). (978-0-7368-5395-8(2)) Capstone Pr., Inc.

Gale Research Staff. CDs, Super Glue & Salsa Series 3: How Everyday Products Are Made, 2 vols. 2002. (Illus.). 400p. (J). 120.00 (978-0-7876-6476-3(6) , GML00402-182081) Thomson Gale.

Giacobello, John. Choosing a Career in the Toy Industry. 2005. (World of Work Ser.). (Illus.). 64p. (YA). (gr. 7-12). lib. bdg. 25.25 (978-0-8239-3438-6(1)) Rosen Publishing Group, Inc., The.

Lafferty, Peter. How Things Are Made. 2004. (Knowledge Masters Plus Ser.). (Illus.). 32p. (YA). pap. incl. cd-rom (978-1-903954-42-3(8)) Chrysalis Children's Bks.

Manufacturing TCG. 3rd rev. ed. 2004. 48p. pap. (978-0-86657-513-3(8)) Lab-Volt Systems, Inc.

Miller, Raymond H. Milton Bradley. 2004. (Inventors & Creators Ser.). (Illus.). 48p. (J). (gr. 4-7). 26.20 (978-0-7377-2613-8(X) , Greenhaven Pr., Inc.) Thomson Gale.

Ottenheimer-Maquet, L. How Things Are Made. 1998. Orig. Title: What Are Things Made Of?. (Illus.). 75p. (J). (gr. 2-9). lib. bdg. 23.95 (978-0-88682-955-1(0) , Creative Education) Creative Co., The.

Reeves, Diane Lindsey. Career Ideas for Teens in Manufacturing. 2005. (Career Ideas for Teens Ser.). (Illus.). 183p. (J). (gr. 6-12). per. 40.00 (978-0-8160-5294-3(8) , Ferguson Publishing Co.) Facts On File, Inc.

Rein, Mei Ling, ed. CD's, Super Glue, & Salsa: How Everyday Products Are Made: Series 3, 2 vols. 2002. (Illus.). (J). (978-0-7876-6477-0(4)); (978-0-7876-6478-7(2)) Thomson Gale. (UXL).

Royston, Angela. How Is a Pencil Made? 2005. (How Are Things Made? Ser.). (J). (978-1-4030-5045-8(7)); pap. (978-1-4034-6647-1(5)); (Illus.). 32p. (978-1-4034-6640-2(8)) Heinemann Library.

—Pencil. 2005. (How Are Things Made? Ser.). (Illus.). 32p. (J). tchr. ed. (978-0-431-05045-4(7)); pap. (978-0-431-05052-2(X)) Steck-Vaughn.

Scott, Janine. Make It! Ship It! 2002. (Spyglass Books). (Illus.). 24p. (J). (gr. 1 up). lib. bdg. 18.60 (978-0-7565-0363-5(9)) Compass Point Bks.

Slavin, Bill. Transformed: How Everyday Things Are Made. Slavin, Bill, illus. 2005. (Illus.). 160p. (J). (gr. 3-7). (978-1-55337-179-3(8)) Kids Can Pr., Ltd.

Smith, Penny & Mack, Lorrie. See How It's Made: Clothes, Toys, Shoes, Food, Drinks, Skateboards. Smith, Penny & Mack, Lorrie, eds. 2007. (Illus.). 96p. (J). (gr. 2-4). 15.99 ***(978-0-7566-3204-5(8))*** Dorling Kindersley Publishing, Inc.

Stone, Tanya Lee. Toothpaste: From Start to Finish. Brady, Jill C., illus. 2001. (Made in the U. S. A. Ser.). 32p. (J). (gr. 3-6). 23.70 (978-1-56711-481-2(4) , Blackbirch Pr., Inc.) Thomson Gale.

MAO, TSE-TUNG, 1893-1976

see Mao, Zedong, 1893-1976

MAO, ZEDONG, 1893-1976

Gay Kathlyn. Mao Zedong's China. 2007. (Dictatorships Ser.). (Illus.). 160p. (YA). (gr. 9-12). lib. bdg. 38.60 ***(978-0-8225-7285-5(0)*** , Twenty-First Century Bks.) Lerner Publishing Group.

Hatt, Christine. Mao Zedong. 2003. (Judge for Yourself Ser.). (Illus.). 64p. (J). pap. (978-0-8368-5539-5(6) , World Almanac Library) Stevens, Gareth Inc.

Macdonald, Fiona & Geyer, Flora. Mao Zedong: The Rebel Who Led a Revolution. 2007. (World History Biographies Ser.). (Illus.). 64p. (J). (gr. 3-7). 17.95 (978-1-4263-0062-2(X)); lib. bdg. 27.90 (978-1-4263-0063-9(8)) National Geographic Society. (National Geographic Children's Bks.).

MAORI (NEW ZEALAND PEOPLE)

Strudwick, Leslie. Maori. (Indigenous Peoples Ser.). 32p. 2005. pap. 7.95 (978-1-59036-256-3(X)); 2004. (Illus.). (J). lib. bdg. 24.25 (978-1-59036-221-1(7)) Weigl Pubs., Inc.

Theunissen, Steve. The Maori of New Zealand. 2005. (First Peoples Ser.). (Illus.). 48p. (gr. 4-8). lib. bdg. 23.95 (978-0-8225-0665-2(3)) Lerner Publishing Group.

MAORI (NEW ZEALAND PEOPLE)—FICTION

Cowley, Joy. Hunter. 2004. 176p. (YA). (gr. 5). 17.99 (978-0-399-24227-4(9) , Philomel) Penguin Group (USA) Inc.

Ihimaera, Witi. The Whale Rider. 2003. Orig. Title: Te Kaieke Tohora. 152p. (YA). (gr. 3-6). 17.00 (978-0-15-205017-7(5)) Harcourt Children's Bks.

—Whale Rider. 2003. (gr. 5-8). lib. bdg. 16.45 (978-0-613-70660-5(9)) Tandem Library Bks.

MAP DRAWING

see also Atlases

Beasant, Pam & Smith, Alastair. How to Draw Maps. 2001. (Illus.). 24p. (J). (978-0-439-47423-8(X)) Scholastic, Inc.

Bramwell, Martyn. Mapping the Seas & Airways. 1998. (Maps & Mapmakers Ser.). (Illus.). 48p. (J). (gr. 5-7). lib. bdg. 22.60 (978-0-8225-2921-7(1) , Lerner Pubns.) Lerner Publishing Group.

Burstein, John. Making Maps: Where's the Party? Destiny Images Staff, illus. 2003. (Math Monsters Ser.). 24p. (YA). (gr. 1 up). lib. bdg. 19.33 (978-0-8368-3811 4(4) , Weekly Reader Early Learning Library) Stevens, Gareth Inc.

—Making Maps: Where's the Party? 2003. (Weekly Reader Early Learning Library). (Illus.). 24p. (J). (gr. 1 up). pap. 7.93 (978-0-8368-3826-8(2) , Weekly Reader Early Learning Library) Stevens, Gareth Inc.

Sammis, Fran. Europe & the Middle East. 1998. (Mapping Our World Ser.). (Illus.). 64p. (J). (gr. 4-8). lib. bdg. 27.07 (978-0-7614-0370-8(1) , Benchmark Bks.) Cavendish, Marshall Corp.

—Maps & Mapmaking. 1999. (Mapping Our World Ser.). (Illus.). 64p. (J). (gr. 4-8). lib. bdg. 27.07 (978-0-7614-0367-8(1) , Benchmark Bks.) Cavendish, Marshall Corp.

—North America. 1998. (Mapping Our World Ser.). (Illus.). 64p. (J). (gr. 4-8). lib. bdg. 27.07 (978-0-7614-0368-5(X) , Benchmark Bks.) Cavendish, Marshall Corp.

MAP-MAKING

see Cartography

MAPLE

Bernard, Robin. A Tree for All Seasons. 1999. (J). (978-0-7922-9427-6(0)); pap. (978-0-7922-9435-1(1)) National Geographic Society.

—Tree for All Seasons. 2001. (Illus.). 16p. (J). (gr. 3-7). pap. 5.95 (978-0-7922-6674-7(9) , National Geographic Children's Bks.) National Geographic Society.

—Tree for All Seasons. 2001. (ps-2). lib. bdg. 14.10 (978-0-613-56662-9(9)) Tandem Library Bks.

Carney, Margaret. At Grandpa's Sugar Bush. Wilson, Janet, illus. 1998. 32p. (J). (gr. k-3). (978-1-55074-341-8(4)) Kids Can Pr., Ltd.

Fowler, Allan. Maple Trees. (Rookie Read-About Science Ser.). (Illus.). 32p. (J). (gr. 1-2). 2002. pap. 4.95 (978-0-516-25985-7(7)); 2001. 20.50 (978-0-516-21684-3(8)) Scholastic Library Publishing. (Children's Pr.).

—Maple Trees. 2002. (Illus.). 31p. (J). (ps-3). lib. bdg. 12.95 (978-0-613-54439-9(0)) Tandem Library Bks.

Freeman, Marcia S. Maple Trees. Saunders-Smith, Gail, ed. 1998. (Trees Ser.). (Illus.). 24p. (J). (gr. k-1). lib. bdg. 15.93 (978-0-7368-0092-1(1) , Pebble Bks.) Capstone Pr., Inc.

Hibbert, Clare. The Life of a Tree. 2004. (Raintree Perspectives Ser.). (Illus.). 32p. (J). pap. (978-1-4109-0818-6(6)) Harcourt Schl. Pubs.

—The Life of a Tree. 2004. (Life Cycles (Perspectives) Ser.). (Illus.). 32p. (J). (gr. 3-5). lib. bdg. 19.25 (978-1-4109-0545-1(4)) Raintree.

Keller, Kristin Thoennes. Maple Trees to Maple Syrup. 2004. (First Facts Ser.). (Illus.). 24p. (J). lib. bdg. 21.26 (978-0-7368-2634-1(3)) Capstone Pr., Inc.

Lasky, Kathryn. Sugaring Time. 1998. (J). pap. 4.95 (978-0-87628-350-9(4)) Ctr. for Applied Research in Education, The.

Maple Trees. (Trees Ser.). 24p. (J). 5.95 (978-0-7368-8093-0(3)) Capstone Pr., Inc.

Maple Trees, 6 vols. (gr. k-2). 28.95 (978-0-7368-8117-3(4)) Red Brick Learning.

Mitchell, Melanie. From Maple Tree to Syrup. pap. 4.95 (978-0-8225-2144-0(X)) Lerner Publishing Group.

Reed, Janet. Del arbol a la Mesa. 2005. Tr. of From Tree to Table. (SPA., Illus.). 16p. (J). (gr. 1 up). lib. bdg. 15.93 (978-0-7368-4142-9(3)) Capstone Pr., Inc.

Ring, Susan. From Tree to Table. 2003. (Yellow Umbrella Books). (Illus.). 16p. (J). (gr. 1). lib. bdg. 14.60 (978-0-7368-2026-4(4) , Pebble Bks.) Capstone Pr., Inc.

—From Tree to Table. 2003. (J). (978-0-7368-1723-3(9)) Yellow Umbrella Pr.

Schwartz, David M. Maple Tree. Kuhn, Dwight, photos by. (Life Cycles Ser.). (Illus.). 16p. (J). (gr. 1-3). pap. 2.99 (978-1-57471-556-9(9) , 3066) Creative Teaching Pr., Inc.

—Maple Tree. Kuhn, Dwight, photos by. 2001. (Springboards into Science Ser.). (Illus.). 24p. (J). (gr. 1 up). lib. bdg. 20.67 (978-0-8368-2978-5(6)) Stevens, Gareth Inc.

MAPS

Here are entered works about maps. Works on the mapping of small areas and the drawing of maps in elementary schools are entered under Map Drawing. Works on the general science of map-making, including map projection and the mapping of large areas are entered under Cartography.

Aberg, Rebecca. Claves de Mapas. 2006. (SPA.). 32p. (J). (gr. k-2). pap. 5.95 (978-0-516-25041-0(8) , Children's Pr.) Scholastic Library Publishing.

—Latitude & Longitude. 2003. (Rookie Read-About Geography Ser.). (Illus.). 32p. (J). (gr. 1-2). 20.50 (978-0-516-22723-8(8) , Children's Pr.) Scholastic Library Publishing.

—Map Keys. 2003. (Rookie Read-About Geography Ser.). (gr. 1-2). pap. 5.95 (978-0-516-27773-8(1)); (Illus.). 32p. (J). 20.50 (978-0-516-22722-1(X)) Scholastic Library Publishing. (Children's Pr.).

—Map Keys. 2003. (gr. k-3). lib. bdg. 14.10 (978-0-613-67911-4(3)) Tandem Library Bks.

Aberg, Rebecca & Rebecca, Aberg. Claves de Mapas: Map Keys. 2005. (Rookie Espaanol Geografia Ser.). (SPA & ENG., Illus.). 32p. (J). (ps-ps). 19.50 (978-0-516-25242-1(9) , Children's Pr.) Scholastic Library Publishing.

Alter, Judy. Exploring & Mapping the American West. 2001. (gr. 3-6). lib. bdg. 14.10 (978-0-613-52037-9(8)) Tandem Library Bks.

American Education Staff. Complete Book of Map & Geography. 1998. (ps-2). lib. bdg. 24.55 (978-0-613-82802-4(X)) Tandem Library Bks.

Andersen, Scoular. Space Pirates & the Monster of the Malswamp Cave. 2007. (Illus.). 32p. (J). (gr. k-3). 16.95 ***(978-1-84507-480-7(7))*** Lincoln, Frances Ltd. GBR. *Dist:* Perseus Distribution.

Anderson, Jackie, et al. Children Map the World: Selections from the Barbara Petchenik Children's World Map Competition. Wood, Alberta Auringer et al, eds. 2005. (Illus.). 120p. pap. 24.95 (978-1-58948-125-1(9) , ESRI Pr.) ESRI, Inc.

Anderson, Scoular. Space Pirates: A Map-Reading Adventure. Anderson, Scoular, illus. 2004. (Illus.). 32p. (J). (gr. 1-4). pap., act. bk. ed. 8.95 (978-1-55037-880-1(5)) Annick Pr., Ltd. CAN. *Dist:* Firefly Bks., Ltd.

Ashcroft, Minnie. Marvelous Map Activities for Young Learners. 2003. 64p. 11.95 (978-0-439-17887-7(8)) Scholastic, Inc.

Axelrod, Amy. The News Hounds Catch a Wave: A Geography Adventure. Bowers, Tim, illus. 2001. (J). 13.00 (978-0-689-82410-4(6) , Simon & Schuster Children's Publishing) Simon & Schuster Children's Publishing.

Baber, Maxwell. Map Basics. (Map Readers Ser.). (Illus.). 32p. (J). 2007. pap. ***(978-1-4034-6680-8(7));*** 2006. 27.07 (978-1-4034-6794-2(3)); 2006. pap. (978-1-4034-6801-7(X)) Heinemann Library.

Ball, Jackie. Mapping Earth. 2004. (Discovery Channel School Science Ser.). (Illus.). 32p. (J). (gr. 5 up). lib. bdg. 24.67 (978-0-8368-3382-9(1)) Stevens, Gareth Inc.

Baltas, Denise & Baltas, Joyce. Follow the Directions! Vol. 1: 180 Daily Exercises That Help Kids Learn to Follow Written Directions. 1999. (Illus.). 80p. pap. 10.95 (978-0-590-66131-7(0)) Scholastic, Inc.

Bellamy, David. The Roadside. Dow, Jill, illus. 1999. (Our Changing World Ser.). 32p. (J). (gr. 1-5). pap. 7.99 (978-0-7112-1383-8(6)) Lincoln, Frances Ltd. GBR. *Dist:* Antique Collectors' Club.

Berger, Melvin & Berger, Gilda. The Whole World in Your Hands: Looking at Maps. Quackenbush, Robert, illus. 1999. (Discovery Readers Ser.). 48p. (J). (gr. 4-7). lib. bdg. 17.55 (978-0-7910-5073-6(4) , Chelsea Hse.) Facts On File, Inc.

Blevins, Wiley. Maps. 2003. (Compass Point Phonics Readers Ser.). (Illus.). 16p. (J). (gr. 1 up). 13.26 (978-0-7565-0512-7(7)) Compass Point Bks.

Bowles, Rachel & Evans, Peter. Maps. 1998. (Fact Finders Ser.). (Illus.). 48p. (J). (gr. 3-7). pap. (978-0-563-37274-5(5)) BBC Worldwide.

Bramwell, Martyn. Mapping the Seas & Airways. 1998. (Maps & Mapmakers Ser.). (Illus.). 48p. (J). (gr. 5-7). lib. bdg. 22.60 (978-0-8225-2921-7(1) , Lerner Pubns.) Lerner Publishing Group.

Bredeson, Carmen. Looking at Maps & Globes. (Rookie Read-About Geography Ser.). (Illus.). 32p. (J). (gr. 1-2). 2002. pap. 5.95 (978-0-516-25982-6(2)); 2001. 20.50 (978-0-516-22351-3(8)) Scholastic Library Publishing. (Children's Pr.).

—Looking at Maps & Globes. 2001. (gr. k-3). lib. bdg. 14.10 (978-0-613-54284-5(3)) Tandem Library Bks.

—Mapas y Globos Terraqueos. (J). (gr. k-2). 2006. (SPA.). 32p. pap. 5.95 (978-0-516-25043-4(4)); 2005. (ENG & SPA., Illus.). 31p. 19.50 (978-0-516-25241-4(0)) Scholastic Library Publishing. (Children's Pr.).

Campbell, Mel. Walk on Maps. 2007. (Illus.). 24p. (J). (978-1-59515-979-3(7)) Rourke Publishing, LLC.

Chancellor, Deborah. Maps & Mapping. (Science Kids Ser.). (Illus.). 48p. (J). 2007. pap. 6.95 ***(978-0-7534-6164-8(1));*** 2004. 9.95 (978-0-7534-5759-7(8)) Houghton Mifflin Co. Trade & Reference Div. (Kingfisher).

Como Ser un Experto en Mapas. (Coleccion Ciencia y Proyectos). (SPA., Illus.). (YA). (gr. 5-8). pap. (978-950-724-562-6(6) , LMA8239) Lumen ARG. *Dist:* Lectorum Pubns., Inc.

The Continent. (Poster Projects Ser.). (gr. 3-6). 9.99 (978-0-7424-1498-3(1) , IF22457) School Specialty Publishing.

Coupe, Robert. Maps & Our World. 2002. (Junior Adventure Ser.). (Illus.). 32p. (J). (gr. 3 up). lib. bdg. (978-1-59084-175-4(1)) Mason Crest Pubs.

—Maps & Our World. 1999. (Explorers Ser.). (Illus.). 32p. (J). (978-0-7699-0486-3(6)) Shortland Pubns. (U. S. A.) Inc.

De Capua, Sarah. Como Nos Orientamos? 2006. (SPA.). 32p. (J). (gr. k-2). pap. 5.95 (978-0-516-24691-8(7) , Children's Pr.) Scholastic Library Publishing.

Dispenzio, Michael A. Map Mania: Discovering Where You Are & Getting to Where You Aren't. Garbot, Dave, illus. 2006. 80p. (J). (gr. 4-8). reprint ed. 20.00 (978-0-7567-9893-2(0)) DIANE Publishing Co.

DiSpezio, Michael Anthony. Map Mania: Discovering Where You Are & Getting to Where You Aren't. Garbot, Dave, illus. 2003. 80p. (J). pap. 6.95 (978-1-4027-0599-1(9)) Sterling Publishing Co., Inc.

—Map Mania: Discovering Where You Are & Getting to Where You Aren't. 2003. (gr. 3-6). lib. bdg. 15.25 (978-0-613-77999-9(1)) Tandem Library Bks.

Edson, Ann & Insel, Eunice. Reading Maps, Globes, Charts, Graphs. (J). (gr. 4-6). stu. ed., instr.'s gde. ed. 39.00 incl. audio (978-0-89525-175-6(2) , AKC 356) Educational Activities, Inc.

Facts on File, Inc. Staff. Maps on File. 2005. (Maps on File Ser.). (Illus.). 526p. (gr. 6-12). 250.00 (978-0-8160-6413-7(X)) Facts On File, Inc.

Finch, Spencer. World. 2004. (Instant Map Skills Ser.). 32p. pap. 9.99 (978-0-439-54048-3(8) , Teaching Resources) Scholastic, Inc.

Fleming, Sarah. I Made a Map. 2000. (Cambridge Reading Ser.). (Illus.). 10p. pap. 5.00 (978-0-521-77459-8(4)) Cambridge Univ. Pr.

—I Made a Map American English Edition, 6 bks., Set. 2000. (Cambridge Reading Ser.). (Illus.). 8p. pap. 28.00 (978-0-521-79887-7(6)) Cambridge Univ. Pr.

Geography, Rookie Read-About Geography: Maps & Globes. 2004. (Illus.). 114.00 (978-0-516-29652-4(3)) Scholastic Library Publishing.

Gillis, Jennifer Blizin. Estas Aquí. 2007. (SPA & ENG., Illus.). 24p. (J). ***(978-1-60044-294-0(3))*** Rourke Publishing, LLC.

Gillis, Jennifer Blizin. You Are Here. (Illus.). 24p. 2007. (J). (978-1-60044-205-6(6)); 2005. pap. 18.00 ***(978-1-59515-554-2(6))*** Rourke Publishing, LLC.

Gonzales, Doreen. Up North & down South: Using Map Directions. 2008. (J). ***(978-1-4296-0055-2(1)*** , First Facts) Capstone Pr., Inc.

Gravois, Michael. Comic Strip Map Skills: 30 Reproducible, Rib-Tickling Cartoons with Related Maps & Questions That Build Map Skills. 2001. 64p. pap. 10.95 (978-0-439-21557-2(9)) Scholastic, Inc.

Grolier Educational Staff, contrib. by. City Maps, 8 vols., Vol. 7. 2002. (Illus.). (J). (978-0-7172-5626-6(X) , Grolier) Scholastic Library Publishing.

—Mapping for Governments, 8 vols., Vol. 6. 2002. (Illus.). (J). (978-0-7172-5625-9(1) , Grolier) Scholastic Library Publishing.

—Mapping for Today & Tomorrow, 8 vols., Vol. 8. 2002. (Illus.). (J). (978-0-7172-5627-3(8) , Grolier) Scholastic Library Publishing.

—Mapping New Lands, 8 vols., Vol. 5. 2002. (Illus.). (J). (978-0-7172-5624-2(3) , Grolier) Scholastic Library Publishing.

—Mapping the World, 8 vols., set. Incl. Vol. 1. Ways of Mapping the World. (978-0-7172-5620-4(0)); Vol. 2. Observation & Measurement. (978-0-7172-5621-1(9)); Vol. 3. Maps for Travelers. (978-0-7172-5622-8(7)); Vol. 4. Navigation. (978-0-7172-5623-5(5)); Vol. 5. Mapping New Lands. (978-0-7172-5624-2(3)); Vol. 6. Mapping for Governments. (978-0-7172-5625-9(1)); Vol. 7. City Maps. (978-0-7172-5626-6(X)); Vol. 8.

Mapping for Today & Tomorrow. (978-0-7172-5627-3(8)); (J). 2002. (Illus.). 239.00 (978-0-7172-5619-8(7) , Grolier) Scholastic Library Publishing.

—Maps for Travelers, 8 vols., Vol. 3. 2002. (Illus.). (J). (978-0-7172-5622-8(7) , Grolier) Scholastic Library Publishing.

—Navigation, 8 vols., Vol. 4. 2002. (Illus.). (J). (978-0-7172-5623-5(5) , Grolier) Scholastic Library Publishing.

—Observation & Measurement, 8 vols., Vol. 2. 2002. (Illus.). (J). (978-0-7172-5621-1(9) , Grolier) Scholastic Library Publishing.

—Ways of Mapping the World, 8 vols., Vol. 1. 2002. (Illus.). (J). (978-0-7172-5620-4(0) , Grolier) Scholastic Library Publishing.

Hammond World Atlas Corporation Staff. World Flip View Map. 2003. 1p. 3.95 (978-0-8437-1861-4(7)); 12p. pap. 47.40 (978-0-8437-1870-6(6)) Langenscheidt Pubs Inc.

Harcourt School Publishers Staff. Geography Tools. 3rd ed. 2002. (Horizons Ser.). (Illus.). (J). pap. 5.50 (978-0-15-333286-9(7)) Harcourt Schl. Pubs.

—Getting to Grandpa's Below Level. 3rd ed. 2002. (Trophies Reading Program Ser.). (Illus.). pap. 5.10 (978-0-15-323067-7(3)) Harcourt Schl. Pubs.

—How Maps Came to Be On Level. 3rd ed. 2002. (Trophies Reading Program Ser.). (Illus.). pap. 5.10 (978-0-15-323097-4(5)) Harcourt Schl. Pubs.

—Maps Old & New. 3rd ed. 2002. (Horizons Ser.). (Illus.). (J). pap. 3.70 (978-0-15-333206-7(9)) Harcourt Schl. Pubs.

Holt, Rinehart and Winston Staff. Holt Science & Technology Chptr. 6: Maps & Models: Chapter Resources - Tennessee Edition. 3rd ed. 2003. (YA). pap. 11.40 (978-0-03-069164-5(8)) Holt, Rinehart & Winston.

Home & School. (J). (gr. k-1). (978-84-342-2416-2(X) , PR30570) Parramon Ediciones S.A. ESP. *Dist:* Lectorum Pubns., Inc.

Home & School. (J). (gr. 1). 3.80 (978-0-8374-1450-8(4) , 401) Weekly Reader Corp.

Hudak, Heather C. Mapping. 2007. (J). (***978-1-59036-762-9(6)***); lib. bdg. (***978-1-59036-761-2(8)***) Weigl Pubs., Inc.

In the World. (J). (gr. 6). 3.80 (978-0-8374-1455-3(5) , 406) Weekly Reader Corp.

Instructional Fair. Facts about our 50 States Ready Reference Cards. 1999. (Ready Reference Ser.). 12p. (J). (gr. 3-6). ring bd. 11.50 (978-0-7424-0733-6(0) , IF653R) School Specialty Publishing.

Jackson, Kay. Ways to Find Your Way: Types of Maps. 2008. (J). (***978-1-4296-0058-3(6)*** , First Facts) Capstone Pr., Inc.

Johnson, Jinny. Maps & Mapping. 2007. (Inside Access Ser.). 32p. (J). 9.95 (***978-0-7534-6062-7(9)*** , Kingfisher) Houghton Mifflin Co. Trade & Reference Div.

Julio, Susan. Great Map Games: 20 Super Fun, Easy Reproducible Games That Build Key Map & Geography Skills-And Help Kids Navigate Their World. 2000. (Illus.). 80p. pap. 11.95 (978-0-439-07753-8(2)) Scholastic, Inc.

Kachur, Matthew. Making Maps. 2004. (Navigators Ser.). (J). pap. 42.00 (978-1-4108-0416-7(X)) Benchmark Education Co.

The Language of Maps. 128p. (gr. 4-8). 14.99 (978-0-7682-0329-5(5) , GA13060) School Specialty Publishing.

The Letter Rr: Maps, 6 vols. (gr. k-2). 17.50 (978-0-7368-4117-7(2)) Red Brick Learning.

Levy, Janey. The Silk Road: Using a Map Scale to Measure Distances. 2005. (PowerMath Ser.). (Illus.). 32p. (J). 22.50 (978-1-4042-2938-9(8) , PowerKids Pr.); pap. (978-1-4042-5140-3(5)) Rosen Publishing Group, Inc., The.

Lierman, Jane. Standards-Based Map Activities: Easy & Engaging Lessons, Activities, & Practice Pages That Build Key Map & Geography Skills. 2005. (Illus.). 64p. (ps-k). pap. 12.99 (978-0-439-51774-4(5) , Teaching Resources) Scholastic, Inc.

Lomas, Sue. Maps & Symbols. 2004. (Geography First Ser.). (J). 23.70 (978-1-4103-0113-0(3) , Blackbirch Pr., Inc.) Thomson Gale.

Mahaney, Ian F. Map It: A Kid's Guide to Map Skills & Symbols. 2006. (Illus.). 24p. (J). lib. bdg. (978-1-4042-3053-8(X)) Rosen Publishing Group, Inc., The.

—Political Maps. 2007. (Illus.). 24p. (J). (978-1-4042-3055-2(6)); (978-1-4042-2211-3(1)); (978-1-4042-2401-8(7)) Rosen Publishing Group, Inc., The. (PowerKids Pr.).

—Reading Physical Maps. 2006. (J). (978-1-4042-3455-0(1)); (Illus.). 24p. pap. (978-1-4042-2210-6(3)); (Illus.). 24p. lib. bdg. (978-1-4042-3054-5(8)) Rosen Publishing Group, Inc., The. (PowerKids Pr.).

—Reading Political Maps. 2007. (NASCAR Champions Ser.). (Illus.). 24p. (J). lib. bdg. (978-1-4042-3456-7(X) , PowerKids Pr.) Rosen Publishing Group, Inc., The.

—Reading Topographic Maps. 2007. (J). lib. bdg. (978-1-4042-3454-3(3) , PowerKids Pr.) Rosen Publishing Group, Inc., The.

—Topographic Maps. 2007. (Illus.). 24p. (J). pap. (978-1-4042-2209-0(X) , PowerKids Pr.) Rosen Publishing Group, Inc., The.

Making a Map, 6 Pks. (Rigby Focus Ser.). 24p. (gr. 2 up). 30.00 (978-0-7578-5580-1(6)) Rigby Education.

Making a Map: Individual Title Six-Packs. (Rigby Focus Ser.). 24p. (gr. 2 up). 28.00 (978-0-7578-5350-0(1)) Rigby Education.

Map Mysteries, 6 vols., Pack. (gr. k-1). 23.00 (978-0-7635-9071-0(1)) Rigby Education.

Map Search. 2002. (Illus.). (J). pap. 5.43 (978-0-7398-5930-8(7)) Steck-Vaughn.

Map Skills: Grade 1. 2003. 48p. (J). 5.99 (978-0-88724-959-4(0) , CD-4700) Carson-Dellosa Publishing Co., Inc.

Map Skills: Grade 2. 2003. 48p. (J). 5.99 (978-0-88724-960-0(4) , CD-4701) Carson-Dellosa Publishing Co., Inc.

Map Skills: Grade 3. 2003. 48p. (J). 5.99 (978-0-88724-961-7(2) , CD-4702) Carson-Dellosa Publishing Co., Inc.

Map Skills: Grade 4. 2003. 48p. (J). 5.99 (978-0-88724-962-4(0) , CD-4703) Carson-Dellosa Publishing Co., Inc.

Map Skills: Grade 5. 2003. 48p. (J). 5.99 (978-0-88724-963-1(9) , CD-4704) Carson-Dellosa Publishing Co., Inc.

Map Skills Book Grade 3. 2002. (978-0-8374-0002-0(3)) Weekly Reader Corp.

Map Skills Book Grade 4. 2002. (978-0-8374-0003-7(1)) Weekly Reader Corp.

Map Skills Books Grade 5. 2002. (978-0-8374-0004-4(X)) Weekly Reader Corp.

Map Skills Books Grade 6. 2002. (978-0-8374-0005-1(8)) Weekly Reader Corp.

Map Skills for Today Gr. 1 -revised 2003- rev. ed. 2003. (YA). (978-0-8374-0000-6(7)) Weekly Reader Corp.

Mapping Specialists. US & World Map Outlines, Vol. 8305. 2004. (Power Practice Ser.). (Illus.). 128p. (J). pap. 12.99 (978-1-59198-075-9(5) , 8305) Creative Teaching Pr., Inc.

Maps, Maps, Maps. (Rosen Real Readers Big Bookstm Ser.). 8p. (J). (gr. k-1). 27.95 (978-1-4042-6211-9(3)) Rosen Publishing Group, Inc., The.

Maps Show Us the Way. (Rosen Real Readers Big Bookstm Ser.). 12p. (J). (gr. 1-2). 31.95 (978-1-4042-6218-8(0)) Rosen Publishing Group, Inc., The.

Maps Skills Books Grade 2. 2002. (978-0-8374-0001-3(5)) Weekly Reader Corp.

McKay, Sindy. We Both Read-My Town. Johnson, Meredith, illus. 2007. (We Both Read Ser.). 44p. (J). 7.99 (***978-1-60115-001-1(6)***); pap. 3.99 (***978-1-60115-002-8(4)***) Treasure Bay, Inc.

Neighborhood. (J). (gr. 2). 3.80 (978-0-8374-1451-5(2) , 402) Weekly Reader Corp.

Nelson, Robin. Maps. 2004. (First Step Nonfiction Ser.). (J). pap. (978-0-8225-5393-9(7)) Lerner Publishing Group.

Nunan, David. Go for It!, Bk. 4. 1999. (Global ESL/ELT Ser.). (Illus.). 112p. (J). pap. 23.95 (978-0-8384-6785-5(7)) Thomson Heinle.

Oleksy, Walter. Maps in History. (Watts Library). (Illus.). 64p. (J). 2003. (gr. 5-7). pap. 8.95 (978-0-531-16633-8(3)); 2002. (gr. 4-6). pap. 25.50 (978-0-531-12028-6(7)) Scholastic Library Publishing. (Watts, Franklin).

Olesky, Walter. Mapping the World. 2002. (gr. 3-6). lib. bdg. 17.60 (978-0-613-59515-5(7)) Tandem Library Bks.

—Maps in History. 2002. (gr. 3-6). lib. bdg. 17.60 (978-0-613-59516-2(5)) Tandem Library Bks.

On the Map. (Rigby Infoquest Ser.). (gr. 3 up). 30.00 (978-0-7578-3903-0(7)) Rigby Education.

On the Right Track, 6, Pack. (gr. k-1). 23.00 (978-0-7635-9070-3(3)) Rigby Education.

Our Book of Maps: Individual Title Six-Packs. (Discovery World Ser.). 24p. (gr. 1-2). 33.00 (978-0-7635-8470-2(3)) Rigby Education.

Phillips, Larissa. A Historical Atlas of Iraq. 2003. (Historical Atlases of South Asia, Central Asia & the Middle East Ser.). (Illus.). 64p. (YA). lib. bdg. 30.60 (978-0-8239-3865-0(4)) Rosen Publishing Group, Inc., The.

Raintree Steck-Vaughn Staff. Map Skills. 2002. (J). (gr. 2). pap. (978-0-7398-6130-1(1)) Steck-Vaughn.

Rand McNally Staff. Atlas Schoolhouse Beginner's Workbook. 2005. 128p. (J). pap. 7.95 (978-0-528-93469-8(4)) Rand McNally.

—Atlas Schoolhouse Illustrated World Atlaas. 2005. 112p. (J). 9.95 (978-0-528-93458-2(9)) Rand McNally.

—Atlas Schoolhouse Intermediate World Atlas. 2005. 128p. (J). pap. 6.95 (978-0-528-93460-5(0)) Rand McNally.

—Atlas Scoolhouse Beginner's World Atlas. 2005. 48p. (J). pap. 5.95 (978-0-528-93463-6(5)) Rand McNally.

Rand McNally Staff, creator. Intermediate Geography & Map Activities. 2005. (Illus.). 128p. pap. 7.95 (978-0-528-93470-4(8)) Rand McNally.

Ready to Go Super Book of Outline Maps. 2003. (J). 14.95 (978-0-439-11761-6(5)) Scholastic, Inc.

Resnick, Abraham. Maps Tell Stories Too: Geographic Connections to American History. 2002. 170p. pap. 12.95 (978-0-595-24076-0(3) , Writers Club Pr.) iUniverse, Inc.

Risby, Bonnie. Maps Bk. 1: Map Activities for Primary Students. 2005. 32p. 10.95 (978-1-59363-093-5(X)) Prufrock Pr.

—Maps Vol. 2: Map Activities for Primary Students, Vol. 2. 2005. 32p. 10.95 (978-1-59363-094-2(8)) Prufrock Pr.

Ross, Simon. Basic Mapwork Skills. 2003. (Illus.). 128p. pap. (978-0-7487-7409-8(2)) Nelson Thornes Ltd.

Royston, Angela. Maps & Symbols. 1998. (Geography Starts Here Ser.). (Illus.). 32p. (J). (gr. 1-4). lib. bdg. 25.69 (978-0-8172-5113-0(8)) Raintree.

—Maps & Symbols. 1998. (Geography Starts Here Ser.). (Illus.). 32p. (978-0-7502-1987-7(4)) Steck-Vaughn.

Rutten, Robert J. Map, Compass, GPS: An Introduction. Rutten, Robert J., illus. 5th ed. 2000. (Illus.). 110p. (YA). (gr. 7 up). pap. (978-0-9678156-0-2(6)) Outdoor Communications Co.

Salisbury, Kent. Route 1-2-3: Follow the Road Through the World of Numbers. 1998. (Illus.). 13p. (J). (ps-k). 6.99 (978-0-7681-0085-3(2) , McClanahan Bk.) Learning Horizons, Inc.

Sammis, Fran. Africa. 1998. (Mapping Our World Ser.). (Illus.). 64p. (J). (gr. 4-8). lib. bdg. 27.07 (978-0-7614-0372-2(8) , Benchmark Bks.) Cavendish, Marshall Corp.

—Asia. 1998. (Mapping Our World Ser.). (Illus.). 64p. (J). (gr. 4-8). lib. bdg. 27.07 (978-0-7614-0371-5(X) , Benchmark Bks.) Cavendish, Marshall Corp.

—South America. 1999. (Mapping Our World Ser.). (Illus.). 64p. (J). (gr. 4-8). lib. bdg. 27.07 (978-0-7614-0369-2(8) , Benchmark Bks.) Cavendish, Marshall Corp.

Scholastic, Inc. Staff, contrib. by. Map Skills. 2003. (Practice Makes Perfect Ser.). (Illus.). 48p. (J). (gr. 4). pap. 4.99 (978-0-7439-3729-0(5)) Teacher Created Materials, Inc.

School Specialty Publishing. Flip-Flash Facts: States & Capitals. 2002. (Flip-Flashtm Phonics Ser.). 160p. (J). (gr. k-5). pap. 7.99 (978-1-56451-395-3(5) , ID2450) School Specialty Publishing.

Scott, Janine. Mapping Our World. 2002. (Spyglass Books). (Illus.). 24p. (J). (gr. 1 up). lib. bdg. 18.60 (978-0-7565-0362-8(0)) Compass Point Bks.

Shireman, Myrl. Map Reading, Laitude, Longitude, & Time. 1998. (Illus.). 80p. (YA). (gr. 5). pap. 9.95 (978-1-58037-079-0(9)) Twain, Mark Media, Inc. Pubs.

Silver, Donald M. & Wynne, Patricia J. Interactive 3-D Maps: Easy-to-Assemble 3-D Maps That Students Make & Manipulate to Learn Key Facts & Concepts-in a Kinesthetic Way! 2005. 112p. pap. 15.99 (978-0-439-24114-4(6) , Teaching Resources) Scholastic, Inc.

Smith, A. G. Where Am I? The Story of Maps & Navigation. (Illus.). 89p. (YA). (gr. 4-9). pap. 15.95 (978-0-7737-6220-6(5)) Stoddart Kids CAN. *Dist:* Fitzhenry & Whiteside, Ltd.

—Where Am I? The Story of Maps & Navigation. 2001. (gr. 3-6). lib. bdg. 25.70 (978-0-613-81884-1(9)) Tandem Library Bks.

Steck-Vaughn Staff. Map Skills. 2002. (Illus.). (J). (gr. 3). pap. (978-0-7398-6131-8(X)); (gr. 4). pap. (978-0-7398-6132-5(8)); (gr. 5). pap. (978-0-7398-6133-2(6)); (gr. 6). pap. (978-0-7398-6134-9(4)) Steck-Vaughn.

Sweeney, Joan. Me on the Map. Cable, Annette, illus. 1998. 32p. (J). (gr. k-3). pap. 6.99 (978-0-517-88557-4(3) , Dragonfly Bks.) Random Hse. Children's Bks.

Taylor, Barbara. Looking at Maps. 2007. (J). (***978-1-59920-050-7(3)***) Smart Apple Media.

—Maps. 2004. (Make It Work! Geography Ser.). (Illus.). 48p. (gr. 3-6). 12.95 (978-1-58728-258-4(5) , Two Can Publishing) T&N Children's Publishing.

—Maps. Haslam, Andrew, illus. 2004. (Make It Work! Geography Ser.). 48p. (J). (gr. 3-6). pap. 6.95 (978-1-58728-250-8(X) , Two Can Publishing) T&N Children's Publishing.

—Maps: The Hands-on Approach to Geography. 2001. (gr. 3-6). lib. bdg. 15.25 (978-0-613-43352-5(1)) Tandem Library Bks.

—Maps & Mapping. 2002. (Young Discoverers Ser.). (Illus.). 32p. (J). (gr. k-3). 7.95 (978-0-7534-5506-7(4) , Kingfisher) Houghton Mifflin Co. Trade & Reference Div.

—Maps & Mapping. 2002. (gr. k-3). lib. bdg. 16.40 (978-0-613-90578-7(4)) Tandem Library Bks.

TNI Stone and Associates Staff & Peteric Design Partners Staff. Quik View Map of the United States & World. 1998. (Illus.). 2p. pap. 2.95 (978-1-58220-018-7(1) , 21213, PowerTools for Kids) Navigator Systems, Inc.

TNT Stone and Associates Staff & Petertil Design Partners Staff, illus. My United States & World Map. 1998. (Powertools for Kids Ser.: No. 18). 4p. (J). (gr. k-8). pap. 4.95 (978-1-58220-017-0(3) , 32508, PowerTools for Kids) Navigator Systems, Inc.

Trumbauer, Lisa. Lost! 2006. (Illus.). 32p. (J). pap. (978-1-4109-2625-8(7)); lib. bdg. (978-1-4109-2596-1(X)) Steck-Vaughn.

US Map. (Poster Projects Ser.). (gr. 3-6). 9.99 (978-0-7424-0697-1(0) , IF22454) School Specialty Publishing.

Vierow, Wendy. Africa. 2004. (Atlas of the Seven Continents Ser.). (Illus.). 24p. (J). lib. bdg. 21.25 (978-0-8239-6687-5(9) , PowerKids Pr.) Rosen Publishing Group, Inc., The.

—Asia. 2004. (Atlas of the Seven Continents Ser.). (Illus.). 24p. (J). lib. bdg. 21.25 (978-0-8239-6689-9(5) , PowerKids Pr.) Rosen Publishing Group, Inc., The.

—Australia. 2004. (Atlas of the Seven Continents Ser.). (Illus.). 24p. (J). lib. bdg. 21.25 (978-0-8239-6690-5(9) , PowerKids Pr.) Rosen Publishing Group, Inc., The.

Wade, Mary Dodson. Map Scales. 2003. (Rookie Read-About Geography Ser.). (Illus.). 32p. (J). (gr. 1-2). 20.50 (978-0-516-22720-7(3) , Children's Pr.) Scholastic Library Publishing.

—Tipos de Mapas. 2006. (SPA.). 32p. (J). (gr. k-2). pap. 5.95 (978-0-516-25044-1(2) , Children's Pr.) Scholastic Library Publishing.

—Tipos de Mapas. DelRisco, Eida, tr. from ENG. 2005. (Rookie Espaanol Geografia Ser.). (ENG & SPA., Illus.). 32p. (J). (ps-ps). 19.50 (978-0-516-25243-8(7) , Children's Pr.) Scholastic Library Publishing.

—Types of Maps. 2003. (Rookie Read-About Geography Ser.). (gr. 1-2). pap. 5.95 (978-0-516-27768-4(5)); (Illus.). 32p. (J). 20.50 (978-0-516-22721-4(1)) Scholastic Library Publishing. (Children's Pr.).

—Types of Maps. 2003. (gr. k-3). lib. bdg. 14.10 (978-0-613-67941-1(5)) Tandem Library Bks.

Weidenman, Lauren. What Is a Map? 2000. (Yellow Umbrella Books). (Illus.). 16p. (J). (gr. 1). lib. bdg. 14.60 (978-0-7368-0742-5(X) , Pebble Bks.) Capstone Pr., Inc.

The Whole World in Your Hands. (Discovery Readers Ser.). 48p. (J). pap. 3.95 (978-0-8249-5315-7(0) , Ideals Children's Bks.) Ideals Pubns.

Wiggers, George & Wiggers, Hannah. Uncle Josh's Outline Maps. 2002. (J). cd-rom 26.95 (978-1-931397-10-0(4)) Geography Matters, Inc.

Wiggers, George W. & Wiggers, Hannah L. Uncle Josh's Outline Map Book. 2000. (Illus.). 112p. (J). per. 19.95 (978-0-9702403-0-9(9)) Geography Matters, Inc.

Williams, Brian. Latitude & Longitude. 2002. (Illus.). 32p. (J). lib. bdg. 24.25 (978-1-58340-209-2(8)) Smart Apple Media.

World Map Wall Chart. 2004. (Wall Charts Ser.). (Illus.). (J). 4.99 (978-1-85997-235-9(7)) Byeway Bks.

X Marks the Spot, 6 Packs. (gr. k-1). 23.00 (978-0-7635-9064-2(9)) Rigby Education.

Your Community. (J). (gr. 3). 3.80 (978-0-8374-1452-2(0) , 403) Weekly Reader Corp.

Zuravicky, Orli. Map Math: Learning about Latitude & Longitude Using Coordinate Systems. 2005. (PowerMath Ser.). (J). 22.50 (978-1-4042-2935-8(3)); pap. 22.50 (978-1-4042-5133-5(2)) Rosen Publishing Group, Inc., The. (PowerKids Pr.).

MAPS, HISTORICAL

see Historical Geography—Maps

MARATHON, BATTLE OF, 490 B.C.

Califf, David J. Marathon. 2002. (Battles That Changed the World Ser.). (Illus.). 112p. (J). (gr. 7-10). 30.00 (978-0-7910-6679-9(7) , Chelsea Hse.) Facts On File, Inc.

Reynolds, Susan. The First Marathon: The Legend of Pheidippides. Minter, Daniel, illus. 2006. 32p. (J). 16.95 (978-0-8075-0867-1(5)) Whitman, Albert & Co.

Ross, Stewart. Athens Is Saved. 2007. (Flashbacks Ser.). (Illus.). 64p. (J). (gr. 4-7). pap. 8.95 (***978-0-237-53152-2(6)*** , Evans Brothers, Limited) Evans Publishing Group GBR. *Dist:* Independent Pubs. Group.

MARCH FAMILY (FICTITIOUS CHARACTERS)

Dreibrodt, Stacie Champlin. Little Women. 2000. (YA). 9.95 (978-1-58130-630-9(X)); 11.95 (978-1-58130-631-6(8)) Novel Units, Inc.

MARCH FAMILY (FICTITIOUS CHARACTERS)—FICTION

Alcott, Louisa May. Jo's Boys. 2000. 252p. (J). pap. 9.95 (978-0-594-05147-3(9)) 1873 Pr.

—Jo's Boys. 1999. (Dover Children's Thrift Classics Ser.). (Illus.). 80p. (J). pap. 1.00 (978-0-486-40789-0(6)) Dover Pubns., Inc.

—Little Women. 2002. (Great Illustrated Classics Ser.). (Illus.). 240p. (J). (gr. 3-8). 21.35 (978-1-57765-693-7(8) , ABDO & Daughters) ABDO Publishing Co.

—Little Women. Dryhurst, Dinah, illus. 2000. 288p. (J). pap. 8.99 (978-1-86205-220-8(4) , Pavilion Bks., Ltd.) Anova Bks. GBR. *Dist:* Trafalgar Square Publishing.

—Little Women. 2002. (YA). 14.04 (978-0-7587-7589-4(X)) Book Wholesalers, Inc.

—Little Women. Alton, Anne Hiebert, ed. 2001. (Broadview Literary Texts Ser.). (Illus.). 619p. (J). pap. (978-1-55111-191-9(8)) Broadview Pr.

—Little Women. unabr. ed. 2004. (Chrysalis Children's Classics Ser.). (Illus.). 190p. (YA). pap. (978-1-84365-049-2(5)) Chrysalis Children's Bks.

—Little Women. unabr. ed. 2000. (Dover Juvenile Classics Ser.). (Illus.). 608p. (J). (gr. 4-7). pap. 4.00 (978-0-486-41023-4(4)) Dover Pubns., Inc.

—Little Women. 2001. (Young Reader's Classics Ser.). 94p. (J). pap. 9.95 (978-1-55013-783-5(2) , Key Porter kids) Key Porter Bks. CAN. *Dist:* Firefly Bks., Ltd.

—Little Women. Lauter, Richard, illus. 192p. (J). 9.95 (978-1-56156-371-5(4)) Kidsbooks, Inc.

—Little Women. 1998. 559p. (J). reprint ed. lib. bdg. 25.00 (978-1-58287-046-5(2)) North Bks.

—Little Women. Lindskoog, Kathryn, ed. Chitouras, Barbara, illus. 2003. (Classics for Young Readers Ser.). 432p. (J). per. 12.99 (978-0-87552-734-5(5)) P & R Publishing.

—Little Women. 2001. (Classics Ser.). (Illus.). 528p. pap. 7.95 (978-0-375-75672-6(8) , Modern Library) Random House Publishing Group.

—Little Women. Smith, Jessie Willcox, illus. 2002. (Illustrated Library for Children). 400p. (J). 12.99 (978-0-517-22116-7(0) , Gramercy) Random Hse. Value Publishing.

—Little Women. 1998. (Children's Classics Ser.). (Illus.). 400p. (J). 6.99 (978-0-517-18954-2(2)) Random Hse. Value Publishing.

—Little Women. 2000. 576p. (J). (gr. 4-7). pap. 4.99 (978-0-439-10136-3(0)) Scholastic, Inc.

—Little Women. 2000. (Classics Ser.). 704p. (J). (gr. 4-7). pap. 5.99 (978-0-689-83531-5(0) , Aladdin) Simon & Schuster Children's Publishing.

—Little Women. 2001. (gr. k-3). lib. bdg. 14.15 (978-0-613-86261-5(9)); 2000. (gr. 3-6). lib. bdg. 10.65 (978-0-613-90409-4(5)); 2000. (gr. 3-6). lib. bdg. 14.15 (978-0-613-63211-9(7)); 2000. (gr. 5-8). lib. bdg. 13.00 (978-0-613-66717-3(4)); Bk. 1. 2003. (gr. 3-6). lib. bdg. 15.30 (978-0-613-70764-0(8)) Tandem Library Bks.

—Little Women. (Signature Classics Ser.). (Illus.). 544p. (J). 2001. 12.95 (978-1-58279-069-5(8) , 64); 2000. (978-1-58279-075-6(2)) Trident Pr. International.

—Little Women: Book & Charm. (Charming Classics). (Illus.). (J). 2003. 384p. 6.99 (978-0-06-051180-7(X)); 2000. 5.95 (978-0-694-01527-6(X)) HarperCollins Pubs. (Harper Festival).

—Little Women Bk. 2: Good Wives: Book with Charm. 2004. (Charming Classics). 416p. (J). pap. 6.99 (978-0-06-055991-5(8) , Harper Festival) HarperCollins Pubs.

—Little Women & Good Wives. 1998. (Children's Classics). (ENG.). 224p. (J). (gr. 4-7). pap. (978-1-85326-116-9(5) , 1165WW) Wordsworth Editions, Ltd.

—Mujercitas. (SPA., Illus.). 192p. (YA). 11.95 (978-84-7281-101-0(8) , AF1101) Auriga, Ediciones S.A. ESP. *Dist:* Continental Bk. Co., Inc.

—Mujercitas. 2002. (Classics for Young Readers Ser.). (SPA.). (YA). 14.95 (978-84-392-0901-0(0) , EV30608) Lectorum Pubns., Inc.

—Mujercitas. (YA). 7.95 (978-84-95311-16-0(X)) Mestas, Jorge A. Ediciones Escolares La Escuela Nueva y Alinorma, S.L. ESP. *Dist:* Continental Bk. Co., Inc.

—Mujercitas. 1998. (SPA., Illus.). 304p. (J). (978-84-01-46257-3(6)) Plaza & Janes Editories, S.A.

—Mujercitas. (Coleccion Estrella). (SPA., Illus.). 64p. (J). 14.95 (978-950-11-0010-5(3) , SGM010) Sigmar ARG. *Dist:* Continental Bk. Co., Inc.

—Mujercitas. 2000. (Coleccion "Clasicos Juveniles" Ser.). (SPA., Illus.). 292p. (gr. 4-7). pap. 12.95 (978-1-58348-784-6(0)) iUniverse, Inc.

Alcott, Louisa May & Dorling Kindersley Publishing Staff. Little Women. Gerver, Jane E., ed. Molan, Chris, illus. 1999. (Eyewitness Classics Ser.). 64p. (J). (gr. 2 up). 14.99 (978-0-7894-4767-8(3)) Dorling Kindersley Publishing, Inc.

Alcott, Louisa May & Eiselein, Gregory. Little Women. 2003. (Illus.). 352p. (YA). pap. 13.00 (978-0-393-97614-4(9)) Norton, W. W. & Co., Inc.

Alcott, Louisa May, et al. Mujercitas. Prunier, James, tr. 2002. (SPA., Illus.). 268p. (J). 29.95 (978-84-348-5324-9(8)) SM Ediciones ESP. *Dist:* AIMS International Bks., Inc.

Francis, Pauline & Alcott, Louisa May. Little Women. 2003. (Fast Track Classics Ser.). (Illus.). 48p. (YA). pap. 9.99 (978-0-237-52533-0(X) , Evans Brothers, Limited) Evans Publishing Group GBR. *Dist:* Independent Pubs. Group.

Glencoe McGraw-Hill Staff & McGraw-Hill - Jamestown Education Staff. Topics from the Restless, Bk. 1. unabr. ed. 1999. (Wordsworth Classics Ser.). (gr. 10 up). pap. 24.64 (978-0-89061-116-6(5) , 9780890611166) Jamestown.

Swicord, Robin. Little Women: The Children's Picture Book. 2004. (Illus.). 96p. (gr. 2 up). 15.95 (978-1-55704-216-3(0)) Newmarket Pr.

MARCONI, GUGLIELMO, MARCHESE, 1874-1937

Auch, Allison. Personalidades electrizantes & Electrifying Personalities. 2005. spiral bd. 84.00 (*978-1-4108-5713-2(1)) Benchmark Education Co.

Goldsmith, Mike. Guglielmo Marconi. 2002. (Scientists Who Made History Ser.). (Illus.). 48p. (J). lib. bdg. 27.12 (978-0-7398-5227-9(2)) Raintree.

O'Shei, Tim. Marconi & Tesla: Pioneers of Radio Communication. 2008. (Inventors Who Changed the World Ser.). (Illus.). 128p. (J). (gr. 6 up). lib. bdg. 33.27 (*978-1-59845-076-7(X) , MyReportLinks.com Bks.) Enslow Pubs., Inc.

Sherrow, Victoria. Guglielmo Marconi: Inventor of Radio & Wireless Communication. 2004. (Nobel Prize-Winning Scientists Ser.). (Illus.). 112p. (J). lib. bdg. 26.60 (978-0-7660-2280-5(3)) Enslow Pubs., Inc.

Sonneborn, Liz. Guglielmo Marconi: Inventor of Wireless Technology. 2005. (Great Life Stories Ser.). (Illus.). 111p. (J). 30.50 (978-0-531-16752-6(6) , Watts, Franklin) Scholastic Library Publishing.

Zannos, Susan. Guglielmo Marconi & Radio Waves. 2004. (Uncharted, Unexplored, & Unexplained Ser.). (Illus.). 48p. (J). (gr. 4-8). lib. bdg. 29.95 (978-1-58415-265-1(6)) Mitchell Lane Pubs., Inc.

MARIE ANTOINETTE, QUEEN, CONSORT OF LOUIS XVI, KING OF FRANCE, 1755-1793

Daynes, Katie. Marie Antoinette. Mistry, Nilesh, illus. 2005. 64p. (J). 8.95 (978-0-7945-1049-7(3) , Usborne) EDC Publishing.

Lotz, Nancy & Phillips, Carlene. Marie Antoinette & the Decline of French Monarchy. 2004. (World Leaders Ser.). (Illus.). 160p. (YA). (gr. 6-12). lib. bdg. 26.95 (978-1-931798-28-0(1)) Reynolds, Morgan Inc.

MacDonald, Fiona. Marie Antoinette. 2000. (World in the Time of... Ser.). (Illus.). 48p. (J). (gr. 4-7). 22.95 (978-0-7910-6034-6(9) , Chelsea Hse.) Facts On File, Inc.

Plain, Nancy. Louis XVI, Marie Antoinette & the French Revolution. 2001. (Rulers & Their Times Ser.). (Illus.). 80p. (J). (gr. 6 up). lib. bdg. 29.93 (978-0-7614-1029-4(5) , Benchmark Bks.) Cavendish, Marshall Corp.

MARIE ANTOINETTE, QUEEN, CONSORT OF LOUIS XVI, KING OF FRANCE, 1755-1793—FICTION

Cullen, Lynn. Moi & Marie Antoinette. Young, Amy, illus. 2006. 32p. (J). 16.95 (978-1-58234-958-9(4)) Bloomsbury Publishing.

Lasky, Kathryn. Marie Antoinette: Princess of Versailles, Austria-France, 1769. 2000. (Royal Diaries Ser.). (Illus.). 240p. (J). (gr. 4-8). pap. 10.95 (978-0-439-07666-1(8)) Scholastic, Inc.

MARIJUANA

Dudley, William, ed. Marijuana. 1998. (At Issue Ser.). 95p. (YA). (gr. 9-12). pap. 17.45 (978-0-7377-0006-0(8)); lib. bdg. 26.20 (978-0-7377-0007-7(6)) Thomson Gale. (Greenhaven Pr., Inc.).

Ingram, Scott & Brogan, Ronald J. Marijuana. 2008. (Junior Drug Awareness Ser.). 112p. (J). (gr. 5-8). 30.00 (*978-0-7910-9695-6(5) , Chelsea Hse.) Facts On File, Inc.

Nakaya, Andrea C. Marijuana. 2007. (Compact Research Ser.). 112p. (YA). lib. bdg. (*978-1-60152-000-5(X)) ReferencePoint Pr., Inc.

Ruschmann, Paul. Legalizing Marijuana/By Paul Ruschmann. 2003. (Point/Counterpoint Ser.). (Illus.). 112p. (gr. 9-13). 32.95 (978-0-7910-7483-1(8) , Chelsea Hse.) Facts On File, Inc.

Sanna, E. J. Marijuana: Mind-Altering Weed. 2008. (J). (978-1-4222-0158-9(9)) Mason Crest Pubs.

Somdahl, Gary L. Marijuana Drug Dangers. 1999. (Drug Dangers Ser.). (Illus.). 64p. (YA). (gr. 4-10). lib. bdg. 27.93 (978-0-7660-1214-1(X)) Enslow Pubs., Inc.

Stanley, Debbie. Marijuana & Your Lungs: The Incredibly Disgusting Story. rev. ed. 2005. (Incredibly Disgusting Drugs Ser.). (Illus.). 48p. (YA). (gr. 5-8). lib. bdg. 25.25 (978-0-8239-3252-8(4) , DDMALU) Rosen Publishing Group, Inc., The.

Tardiff, Joe. Marijuana. 2007. (Contemporary Issues Companion Ser.). (Illus.). 240p. (YA). (gr. 10-12). 36.20 (*978-0-7377-2775-3(6)); pap. 24.95 (*978-0-7377-2776-0(4)) Thomson Gale. (Greenhaven Pr., Inc.).

MARIJUANA—FICTION

It's Just a Plant: A Children's Story about Marijuana. 2nd rev. ed. 2006. (J). per. 20.00 (978-0-9760117-2-9(7)) Magic Propaganda Mill.

Lurie, April. The Latent Powers of Dylan Fontaine. 2008. 224p. (YA). (gr. 9). 15.99 (*978-0-385-73125-6(6) , Delacorte Bks. for Young Readers) Random Hse. Children's Bks.

Myracle, Lauren. TTFN (Ta-Ta for Now) 2007. (Internet Girls Ser.). 256p. (J). (gr. 2-8). pap. 6.95 (*978-0-8109-9279-5(5) , Amulet Bks.) Abrams, Harry N. , Inc.

MARINE ANIMALS

see also Corals; Fishes; Fresh-Water Animals

Advantage Publishers Group & DePrisco, Dorothea. A Swim in the Ocean. 2007. (Illus.). 14p. (J). bds. 12.95 (*978-1-59223-475-2(5) , Silver Dolphin Bks.) Advantage Pubs. Group.

Advantage Publishers Group & Pledger, Maurice. All about Ocean Animals. 2007. (All About Ser.). (Illus.). 80p. (J). 12.95 (978-1-59223-457-8(7) , Silver Dolphin Bks.) Advantage Pubs. Group.

Allen, Francesca, illus. Under the Sea. 2005. 10p. (J). 4.99 (978-0-7945-0857-9(X) , Usborne) EDC Publishing.

Anastasio, Dina. Escondidos en el mar & Hiding in the Sea. 2005. spiral bd. 66.00 (*978-1-4108-5643-2(7)) Benchmark Education Co.

Anderson, Jill, ed. Let's Dive in the Ocean! !Vamos a Bucear! Holmes, Steve, illus. 2005. (ENG & SPA.). 20p. (J). (gr. 3-7). bds. 6.95 (978-1-58728-524-0(X) , Two Can Publishing) T&N Children's Publishing.

Animales Marinos, 6 vols. (Explorers. Exploradores Nonfiction Sets Ser.).Tr. of Marine Animals. (SPA.). 32p. (gr. 3-6). 44.95 (978-0-7699-0627-0(3)) Shortland Pubns. (U. S. A.) Inc.

Animales Marinos. 2005. (Collection Abre Tus Ojos, Collection Eye Openers Ser.).Tr. of Marine Animals. (SPA.). (J). (gr. k-2). 6.95 (978-950-11-0966-5(6)) Sigmar ARG. *Dist:* Iaconi, Mariuccia Bk. Imports.

Animals of the Ocean Series, (Illus.). (J). (gr. 2-6). lib. bdg. 44.85 (978-1-56674-947-3(6)) Forest Hse. Publishing Co., Inc.

Animals of the Reef, 12 bks. 2002. (978-0-7398-5373-3(2)) Raintree.

Armour, Michael C., et al. Big Box of Ocean Animals, 4 bks., Set. Lee, Katie et al, illus. 2002. (Big Box of Board Bks.). 10p. (J). (ps-k). (978-1-59069-178-6(4)) Studio Mouse LLC.

Arnold, Caroline. Shockers of the Sea: And Other Electric Animals. Forest, Crista, illus. 1999. 32p. (J). (ps-3). pap. 6.95 (978-0-88106-874-0(8)) Charlesbridge Publishing, Inc.

Arnold, Caroline. Super Swimmers: Whales, Dolphins, & Other Mammals of the Sea. Wynne, Patricia J., illus. 2007. 32p. (J). (gr. 1-4). 16.95 (*978-1-57091-588-8(1)); pap. 6.95 (*978-1-57091-589-5(X)) Charlesbridge Publishing, Inc.

Arnosky, Jim. All about Manatees. 2008. (All About Ser.). 32p. (J). pap. 5.99 (*978-0-439-90361-5(0)) Scholastic, Inc.

—The Brook Book. 2008. 32p. (J). (gr. 2). 15.99 (*978-0-525-47716-7(0) , Dutton Juvenile) Penguin Group (USA) Inc.

Aubinais, Marie. Sea Animals. Martin, Jean-Francois, illus. 1998. (Big, Bigger, Biggest Ser.). 32p. (J). 16.95 (978-0-7892-0386-1(3) , Abbeville Kids) Abbeville Pr., Inc.

Baby Orca. 2005. (Seaworld Animal Library: Vol. 1). (Illus.). 24p. (J). (ps-k). bds. 6.95 (978-0-8249-6615-7(5)) Ideals Pubns.

Baggott, Stella. Glug, Glug, Glug Bath Book. 2007. (Bath Bks). 5p. (J). 14.99 (*978-0-7945-1784-7(6) , Usborne) EDC Publishing.

Bajo el Mar. 2004. (Ladders—Spanish Ser.). (SPA., Illus.). 32p. (J). (gr. 1-3). pap. 9.95 (978-1-58728-476-2(6) , Two Can Publishing) T&N Children's Publishing.

Baker, Lucy. Oceans. 2004. (Life In... Ser.). (SPA., Illus.). (gr. 3-6). 32p. (J). pap. 6.95 (978-1-58728-570-7(3)); 31p. 12.95 (978-1-58728-555-4(X)) T&N Children's Publishing. (Two Can Publishing).

Barnhill, Kelly Regan. Monsters of the Deep: Deep Sea Adaptation. 2008. (J). (*978-1-4296-1264-7(9) , Fact Finders) Capstone Pr., Inc.

Bateman, Helen & Denshire, Jayne. Of the Oceans. 2005. (Illus.). 32p. (J). (gr. 4-7). lib. bdg. 27.10 (978-1-58340-768-4(5)) Smart Apple Media.

Bauman, Amy, et al. The Wonder of Manatees. 2000. (Animal Wonders Ser.). (Illus.). 48p. (J). (gr. 1 up). lib. bdg. 26.00 (978-0-8368-2663-0(9)) Stevens, Gareth Inc.

Becker, John. Manatees. 2002. (Returning Wildlife Ser.). (Illus.). 48p. (J). (gr. 3-5). 23.70 (978-0-7377-1010-6(1) , Kidhaven) Thomson Gale.

Benchmark Education Staff, compiled by. Watery World & Animal Adaptations. 2005. spiral bd. 225.00 (*978-1-4108-5814-6(6)) Benchmark Education Co.

Beneath the Waves, 6 Packs. (Rigby Infoquest Ser.). 32p. (gr. 4 up). 37.00 (978-0-7578-5728-7(0)) Rigby Education.

Berger, Gilda & Berger, Melvin. Sharks & Other Wild Water Animals. 2006. (Scholastic Reader Collection Level 3 Ser.). 160p. (J). pap. 6.99 (978-0-439-84802-2(4) , Cartwheel Bks.) Scholastic, Inc.

Berger, Melvin. Dive! A Book of Deep-Sea Creatures. 2000. (Hello Reader! Science Ser.). (Illus.). 40p. (J). (ps-3). pap. 3.99 (978-0-439-08747-6(3)) Scholastic, Inc.

—Dive! A Book of Deep Sea Creatures. 2000. (Illus.). (J). 10.79 (978-0-606-18536-3(4)) Tandem Library Bks.

—Dive! a Book of Deep Sea Creatures. 2000. (gr. k-3). lib. bdg. 11.80 (978-0-613-24860-0(0)) Tandem Library Bks.

Berger, Melvin & Berger, Gilda. Manta Rays. 2003. (Illus.). (J). pap. (978-0-439-47393-4(4)) Scholastic, Inc.

Beylon, Cathy. Aquarium Show Sticker Activity Book. 2000. (Dover Little Activity Bks.). (Illus.). 4p. (J). (ps-3). pap., act. bk. ed. 1.50 (978-0-486-40985-6(6)) Dover Pubns., Inc.

BHB International Staff. Sea Animals. 1998. (Our Animal World in Pictures Ser.). (J). (978-2-215-06160-1(X)) Editions Fleurus.

Birds; Insects; Sharks, 3 vols., Set. 2001. 192p. (J). 25.95 (978-0-7525-5454-9(9)) Parragon, Inc.

Blaxland, Beth. Cephalopods: Octopuses, Squids, & Their Relatives. 2002. (Invertebrates Ser.). (Illus.). 32p. (gr. 4-8). 28.00 (978-0-7910-6992-9(3) , Chelsea Hse.) Facts On File, Inc.

—Echinoderms: Sea Stars, Sea Urchins, & Their Relatives. 2002. (Invertebrates Ser.). (Illus.). 32p. (gr. 4-8). 28.00 (978-0-7910-6996-7(6) , Chelsea Hse.) Facts On File, Inc.

Blevins, Wiley. Ocean Life. 2006. (Let's Find Out Ser.). (Illus.). 24p. (J). pap. 8.99 (978-0-439-72605-4(0) , Cartwheel Bks.) Scholastic, Inc.

Blocksma, Mary. What's on the Beach? A Great Lakes Treasure Hunt. 2003. (Illus.). 48p. (YA). pap. 10.95 (978-0-9708575-2-1(7)) Beaver Island Arts.

—What's on the Beach? A Great Lakes Treasure Hunt. Blocksma, Mary, illus. 2003. (Great Lakes Treasure Hunts Ser.: No. 1). (Illus.). 48p. (J). pap. 9.95 (978-0-9708575-1-4(9)) Beaver Island Arts.

Book Company Staff. Moon Dance. Lassen, Christian R., illus. 2005. (Sparkle Books Minis Ser.). 16p. (J). (gr. 3-9). bds. 8.95 (978-1-74047-591-4(7) , Penton Kids) Penton Overseas, Inc.

Booth, Jack. The 10 Deadliest Sea Creatures. 2008. (Ten-trade; Ser.). 48p. (J). pap. 14.99 (*978-1-55448-482-9(0) , Watts, Franklin) Scholastic Library Publishing.

Brown Bear Books (Firm) Staff, contrib. by. Ocean Life. 2007. (J). (*978-1-933834-16-0(1)) Brown Bear Books.

Brown, Carron. Animal Babies in Ponds & Rivers. 2007. (Illus.). 24p. (J). bds. 6.95 (978-0-7534-6059-7(9) , Kingfisher) Houghton Mifflin Co. Trade & Reference Div.

Bull, Peter, illus. Under the Sea. 2004. (Out & about Ser.). 12p. (J). bds. 4.99 (978-1-85997-806-1(1)) Byeway Bks.

—Under the Sea. (Puzzle Shapes Ser.). (J). 10p. bds. (978-2-89393-938-4(4)); 8p. bds. (978-2-7643-0146-3(4)) Phidal Publishing, Inc./Editions Phidal, Inc.

Burnard, Damon. I Spy in the Ocean. Cairns, Julia, illus. 2001. 24p. (J). (ps-5). bds. 6.95 (978-0-8118-2988-5(X)) Chronicle Bks. LLC.

Butterfield, Moira. Animals in Rivers & Lakes. 1999. (Looking at...Ser.). (Illus.). 32p. (J). (gr. 1-4). lib. bdg. 24.26 (978-0-7398-0108-6(2)) Raintree.

—Animals in the Oceans. 1999. (Looking at...Ser.). 32p. (J). (gr. 1-4). lib. bdg. 24.26 (978-0-7398-0107-9(4)) Raintree.

Cando, Kinder. Creatures under the Sea Take Home. (J). 7.95 (978-0-8136-0667-5(5)) Modern Curriculum Pr.

Canizares, Susan, et al. Aquarium. 2000. (Scholastic Placebook Ser.). (Illus.). (J). pap. (978-0-439-15372-0(7)) Scholastic, Inc.

Carson, Mary Kay. In the Deep. 2003. (Science Links Ser.). (Illus.). 32p. (gr. 3-5). 23.00 (978-0-7910-7420-6(X) , Chelsea Hse.) Facts On File, Inc.

Cecchini, Marie E. Under the Sea: A Cross-Curricular Unit for Grades 1-3. Mitchell, Judy & Lindeen, Mary, eds. Armbrust, Janet & Skiles, Janet, illus. 2007. 32p. (J). pap. 6.95 (*978-1-57310-529-3(5)) Teaching & Learning Co.

Cerullo, Mary M. Life under Ice. Curtsinger, Bill, illus. Curtsinger, Bill, photos by. 2005. 40p. (J). (gr. 3-7). 16.95 (978-0-88448-246-8(4)) Tilbury Hse. Pubs.

—Life Under Ice. Curtsinger, Bill, photos by. 2005. (Illus.). 40p. (J). (gr. 3-7). 7.95 (978-0-88448-247-5(2)) Tilbury Hse. Pubs.

—The Truth about Dangerous Sea Creatures. Wertz, Michael, illus. Rotman, Jeffrey L., photos by. 2003. 48p. (J). 15.95 (978-0-8118-4050-7(6)) Chronicle Bks. LLC.

—The Truth about Great White Sharks. Wertz, Michael, illus. Rotman, Jeffrey L., photos by. 2000. 48p. (J). (gr. 3-7). 15.95 (978-0-8118-2467-5(5)) Chronicle Bks. LLC.

Chanko, Pamela. Sea Creatures: Criaturas Marinas. 2002. (Science Emergent Readers Ser.). (ENG & SPA., Illus.). (J). pap. (978-0-439-41161-5(0)) Scholastic, Inc.

Clarke, Phil. Seas & Oceans Sticker Atlas. 2006. 24p. (J). pap. 8.95 (978-0-7945-1218-7(6) , Usborne) EDC Publishing.

Clemson, Wendy & Clemson, David. Ocean Giants. 2006. (Illus.). 32p. (J). pap. (*978-0-8368-8139-4(7)); lib. bdg. (*978-0-8368-7840-0(X)) Stevens, Gareth Inc.

Cole, Joanna. The Magic School Bus on the Ocean Floor. Degen, Bruce, illus. (Magic School Bus Ser.). (FRE.). (J). (gr. 1-4). pap. 6.99 (978-0-590-24318-6(7)) Scholastic, Inc.

Cole, Melissa S. Kelp Forests. 2004. (Illus.). 24p. (J). 22.45 (978-1-56711-909-1(3) , Blackbirch Pr., Inc.) Thomson Gale.

Collard, Sneed B., III. The Deep-Sea Floor. Wenzell, Gregory, illus. 2003. 32p. (J). (gr. 2-6). 16.95 (978-1-57091-402-7(8)); pap. 6.95 (978-1-57091-403-4(6)) Charlesbridge Publishing, Inc.

—One Night in the Coral Sea. Brickman, Robin, illus. 2006. 32p. (J). pap. 6.95 (978-1-57091-390-7(0)) Charlesbridge Publishing, Inc.

Cooper, Jason. Crayfish. 2003. (Life Cycles II Ser.). (Illus.). 24p. (J). 25.64 (978-1-58952-704-1(6)) Rourke Publishing, LLC.

Corrigan, Patricia, et al. Ocean Animals. 2001. (Our Wild World Ser.). (Illus.). 192p. (J). (gr. 2-5). 16.95 (978-1-55971-781-6(5) , NorthWord Bks. for Young Readers) T&N Children's Publishing.

Cosson, M. J. Sea Monsters: Myth & Truth. 2000. (Cover-to-Cover Bks.). (Illus.). 56p. (J). pap. 8.95 (978-0-7891-5047-9(6)); (gr. 4-7). lib. bdg. 17.95 (978-0-7807-9013-1(8)) Perfection Learning Corp.

Costain, Meredith. Tidal Pools. 2000. (gr. k-3). lib. bdg. 11.80 (978-0-613-30791-8(7)) Tandem Library Bks.

Coupe, Robert. Mammals of the Sea. 1999. (Explorers Ser.). (Illus.). 32p. (J). (978-0-7699-0470-2(X)) Shortland Pubns. (U. S. A.) Inc.

Court, Rob. How to Draw Underwater Animals. 2007. (Doodle Bks.). 32p. (J). 21.36 (*978-1-59296-810-7(4)) Child's World, Inc.

Creative Team at Walter Foster Publishing Staff & Farrell, Russell. Sea Creatures. 2005. (Draw & Color Ser.). (Illus.). 40p. (J). pap. 4.95 (978-1-56010-863-4(0)) Foster, Walter Publishing, Inc.

Cutchins, Judy & Johnston, Ginny. Giant Predators of the Ancient Seas. Cutchins, Judy, illus. 2001. (Southern Fossil Discoveries Ser.). (Illus.). 48p. (J). (gr. 3-7). 14.95 (978-1-56164-237-3(1)) Pineapple Pr., Inc.

Dahl, Michael. One Giant Splash: A Counting Book about the Ocean. Ouren, Todd, illus. 2004. (Know Your Numbers Ser.). 24p. (C). (gr. k-3). 22.60 (978-1-4048-0577-4(X) , 1229523) Picture Window Bks.

Dalgleish, Sharon. Hidden World. 1999. (Explorers Ser.). 32p. (J). (978-0-7699-0492-4(0)) Shortland Pubns. (U. S. A.) Inc.

—Ocean Life. Cavaluzzo, Laura & McEwen, Rebecca, eds. 1999. (Explorers Ser.). (Illus.). 32p. (J). (978-0-7699-0480-1(7)) Shortland Pubns. (U. S. A.) Inc.

—Underwater Animals. 2002. (Junior Adventure Ser.). (Illus.). 32p. (J). (gr. 3 up). lib. bdg. (978-1-59084-173-0(5)) Mason Crest Pubs.

Daynes, Katie. 1001 Things to Spot in the Sea. 2004. (1001 Things to Spot Ser.). 32p. (J). pap. 6.95 (978-0-7945-0229-4(6)) EDC Publishing.

Delafosse, Claude. Hidden World: Under the Sea. De Hugo, Pierre, illus. 1998. (Hidden World Ser.). 26p. (J). (ps-2). 12.95 (978-0-590-10992-5(8)) Scholastic, Inc.

Delano, Marfe Ferguson. Sea Monsters: A Prehistoric Adventure. 2007. (Illus.). 32p. (J). (gr. 3-7). 6.95 (*978-1-4263-0162-9(6)); lib. bdg. 22.90 (*978-1-4263-0119-3(7)) National Geographic Society. (National Geographic Children's Bks.).

Diagram Visual & Lambert, David. Super Little Giant Book of Undersea Creatures. 2007. (Illus.). 288p. (J). pap. 6.95 (978-1-4027-3904-0(4)) Sterling Publishing Co., Inc.

Discovery Kids Staff. Terror under the Sea. 2000. (Illus.). (J). (978-0-606-18466-3(X)) Tandem Library Bks.

Dixon, Dougal. In the Sea. 2001. (Dinosaurs Ser.). (Illus.). 36p. (J). (gr. 4 up). lib. bdg. 24.67 (978-0-8368-2917-4(4)) Stevens, Gareth Inc.

DK Publishing Staff. Deep Blue Sea. 2007. 14p. (J). (gr. k-2). 12.99 (978-0-7566-2995-3(0)) Dorling Kindersley Publishing, Inc.

—Splishy, Splashy, Sparkly Sea Life. 2007. (Touchables Ser.). 10p. (J). (ps-1). 8.99 (978-0-7566-2936-6(5)) Dorling Kindersley Publishing, Inc.

Donovan, Sandy. Ocean Animals. 2002. (Animals of the Biomes Ser.). (Illus.). 48p. (J). lib. bdg. 25.70 (978-0-7398-5689-5(8)) Raintree.

—Ocean Animals. 2002. (Animals of the Biomes Ser.). (Illus.). 48p. (J). pap. 7.20 (978-0-7398-6409-8(2)) Steck-Vaughn.

Dorling Kindersley Publishing Staff. Fishy Tales. 2003. (Dorling Kindersley Readers Ser.). (Illus.). 32p. (J). (gr. 5). pap. 3.99 (978-0-7894-9797-0(2)) Dorling Kindersley Publishing, Inc.

—Glow in the Dark Ocean Creatures. 2003. (Ultimate Sticker Bks.). (Illus.). 16p. (J). pap. 6.99 (978-0-7894-9277-7(6)) Dorling Kindersley Publishing, Inc.

—Sea Creatures. 2005. (Look Closer Ser.). (Illus.). 24p. (J). (ps-ps). 9.99 (978-0-7566-1431-7(7)) Dorling Kindersley Publishing, Inc.

—Sea Star. 2005. 8p. (J). 5.99 (978-0-7566-1712-7(X)) Dorling Kindersley Publishing, Inc.

Earle, Sylvia A. Sea Critters. Henry, Wolcott, photos by. 2000. (Illus.). 32p. (J). (gr. 1-4). 16.95 (978-0-7922-7181-9(5) , National Geographic Children's Bks.) National Geographic Society.

—Sea Critters. 2006. 32p. (J). (gr. 1-4). pap. 6.95 (978-0-7922-5584-0(4) , National Geographic Children's Bks.) National Geographic Society.

Encyclopaedia Britannica Publishers, Inc. Staff. Creatures of the Waters. 2004. (Illus.). 64p. 14.95 (978-1-59339-014-3(9)) Encyclopaedia Britannica, Inc.

Fabiny, Sarah. Under the Sea. Smith, Jan, illus. 2004. (Pinwheel Ser.). 12p. (J). 9.95 (978-1-4027-1213-5(8)) Sterling Publishing Co., Inc.

Faundez, Anne. Sea Ceatures. 2004. (QEB Start Reading Ser.). (Illus.). 24p. (J). lib. bdg. 15.95 (978-1-59566-008-4(9)) QEB Publishing Inc.

Fecher, Sarah. On the Move. 2000. (ps-2). lib. bdg. 15.25 (978-0-613-43486-7(2)) Tandem Library Bks.

Fredericks, Anthony D. In One Tidepool: Crabs, Snails, & Salty Tails. 2002. (gr. k-3). lib. bdg. 16.40 (978-0-613-52762-0(3)) Tandem Library Bks.

—Surprising Swimmers. 2000. (Exhortation Ser.). (Illus.). 32p. (ps-3). pap. 7.95 (978-1-55971-629-1(0) , NorthWord Bks. for Young Readers) T&N Children's Publishing.

Galko, Francine. Coral Reef Animals. 2003. (Animals in Their Habitats Ser.). (Illus.). 32p. (J). (gr. k-2). lib. bdg. 21.36 (978-1-4034-0177-9(2)) Heinemann Library.

—Pond Animals. 2003. (Animals in Their Habitats Ser.). (Illus.). 32p. (J). (gr. k-2). lib. bdg. 21.36 (978-1-4034-0181-6(0)) Heinemann Library.

—Sea Animals. 2003. (Animals in Their Habitats Ser.). 32p. (gr. k-2). (Illus.). (J). lib. bdg. 21.36 (978-1-4034-0184-7(5)); pap. 6.95 (978-1-4034-0441-1(0)) Heinemann Library.

—Sea Animals. 2003. (gr. k-3). lib. bdg. 14.75 (978-0-613-45826-9(5)) Tandem Library Bks.

M N O

Galvin, Laura Gates. Alphabet of Ocean Animals. 2007. (Illus.). 40p. 15.95 (***978-1-59249-690-7(3)***) Soundprints.

Gambrell, Linda B. & Dorling Kindersley Publishing Staff. Fishy Tales. 2003. (Readers Ser.). (Illus.). 32p. (J). 12.99 (978-0-7894-9796-3(4)) Dorling Kindersley Publishing, Inc.

Ganeri, Anita. I Wonder Why the Sea Is Salty: And Other Questions about the Oceans. 2003. (I Wonder Why Ser.). 32p. (J). (gr. k-3). pap. 6.95 (978-0-7534-5611-8(7) , Kingfisher) Houghton Mifflin Co. Trade & Reference Div.

—I Wonder Why the Sea Is Salty: And Other Questions about the Oceans. 2003. (gr. k-3). lib. bdg. 14.10 (978-0-613-63165-5(X)) Tandem Library Bks.

Garrett, Ann & Higney, Gene-Michael. Fins & Flippers, Scales & Nippers. 2003. (Illus.). 32p. (J). pap. (978-1-59034-871-0(0)); 15.95 (978-1-59034-869-7(9)) Mondo Publishing.

Gibbons, Gail. Sea Turtles. Gibbons, Gail, illus. unabr. ed. 1999. (Gail Gibbons' Creatures Great & Small Ser.). (Illus.). (J). (gr. 1-6). pap. 16.95 incl. audio (978-0-87499-583-1(3)) BBC Audiobooks America.

—Sea Turtles. Gibbons, Gail, illus. unabr. ed. 1999. (Gail Gibbons' Creatures Great & Small Ser.). (Illus.). (J). (gr. 1-6). 25.95 incl. audio (978-0-87499-584-8(1)) Live Oak Media.

Gigantes marinos de la época de los dinosaurios (Sea Giants of Dinosaur Time) 2006. (J). pap. 6.95 (978-0-8225-6638-0(9) , Ediciones Lerner) Lerner Publishing Group.

Gilpin, Daniel. Starfish, Urchins & Other Echinoderms. 2006. (Animal Kingdom Classification Ser.). (Illus.). 48p. (J). (gr. 4-6). 26.60 (978-0-7565-1611-6(0)) Compass Point Bks.

Goldish, Meish. Florida Manatees: Warm Water Miracles. 2008. (J). lib. bdg. 25.27 (***978-1-59716-507-5(7)***) Bearport Publishing Co., Inc.

Goldsack, Gaby. Ocean Animals. Bampton, Bob, illus. (J). (978-1-57755-508-7(2)) Allied Publishing.

Gordon, Sharon. Adivina Quién Atrapa. 2006. (Bookworms Ser.). (SPA & ENG.). 32p. (J). lib. bdg. 22.79 (978-0-7614-2383-6(4)) Cavendish, Marshall Corp.

—Guess Who Grabs (Adivina Quién Atrapa) 2006. (Bookworms Ser.). (ENG & SPA.). 32p. (J). lib. bdg. 22.79 (978-0-7614-2464-2(4)) Cavendish, Marshall Corp.

Gray, Samantha & Dorling Kindersley Publishing Staff. Ocean. 2001. (Eye Wonder Ser.). (Illus.). 48p. (J). (gr. k-3). lib. bdg. 17.99 (978-0-7894-8180-1(4)) Dorling Kindersley Publishing, Inc.

Gray, Samantha & Thornton, Sue. Ocean. Ling, Mary, ed. 2001. (Eye Wonder Ser.). (Illus.). 48p. (J). (gr. k-3). 9.99 (978-0-7894-7852-8(8)) Dorling Kindersley Publishing, Inc.

Green, Jen. A Coral Reef. 2002. (Small Worlds Ser.). (Illus.). 32p. (J). (gr. 3-4). (978-0-7787-0138-5(7)); pap. (978-0-7787-0152-1(2)) Crabtree Publishing Co.

Greenaway, Theresa, ed. Ocean: A Foldout Book & Wall Chart. 2005. (Illus.). 12p. (J). (gr. k-4). reprint ed. 10.00 (978-0-7567-8533-8(2)) DIANE Publishing Co.

Grimm, Phyllis W. Crayfish. Boucher, Jerry, photos by. 2000. (Early Bird Nature Bks.). (Illus.). 48p. (J). (gr. 2-4). lib. bdg. 25.26 (978-0-8225-3030-5(9) , Lerner Pubns.) Lerner Publishing Group.

Gross, Miriam J. The Moray Eel. 2005. (Illus.). 24p. (J). lib. bdg. (978-1-4042-3189-4(7)) Rosen Publishing Group, Inc., The.

—The Octopus. 2006. (Weird Sea Creatures Ser.). (Illus.). 23p. (J). lib. bdg. (978-1-4042-3188-7(9) , PowerKids Pr.) Rosen Publishing Group, Inc., The.

—The Sea Slug. 2006. (Illus.). 24p. (J). lib. bdg. (978-1-4042-3191-7(9) , PowerKids Pr.) Rosen Publishing Group, Inc., The.

—The Stingray. 2006. (Illus.). 24p. (J). lib. bdg. (978-1-4042-3190-0(0) , PowerKids Pr.) Rosen Publishing Group, Inc., The.

Group/McGraw-Hill, Wright. Under the Sea, 6 vols. (Wildcats Ser.). 32p. (gr. 2-8). (978-0-322-05862-0(7)) Wright Group, The.

Grupper, Jonathan. Destination: Deep Sea. 2000. (Illus.). 32p. (J). (gr. 1-5). 16.95 (978-0-7922-7693-7(0) , National Geographic Children's Bks.) National Geographic Society.

Guiberson, Brenda Z. Ocean Life. 2001. (Science Readers Ser.). (Illus.). (J). (978-0-439-20550-4(6)) Scholastic, Inc.

Halfmann, Janet. Life in a Tide Pool. 2000. (Lifeviews Ser.). (Illus.). 32p. (J). lib. bdg. (978-1-58341-076-9(7) , Creative Education) Creative Co., The.

Hall, David, illus. & photos by. Survival Secrets of Sea Animals. Hall, David, photos by. 2006. (Undersea Encounters Ser.). 48p. (J). (gr. 3-5). 27.00 (978-0-516-24398-6(5) , Children's Pr.) Scholastic Library Publishing.

Hall, David, photos by & text. Dolphins, Seals & Other Sea Mammals. Hall, David, text. 2006. (Undersea Encounters Ser.). (Illus.). 48p. (J). (gr. 3-5). 27.00 (978-0-516-24392-4(6) , Children's Pr.) Scholastic Library Publishing.

Hall, Howard. The Secrets of Kelp Forests: Life's Ebb & Flow in the Sea's Richest Habitat. Leon, Vicki, ed. 2nd ed. 2007. (Jean-Michel Cousteau Presents Ser.). (Illus.). 48p. (J). pap. 8.95 (***978-0-9766134-9-7(2)***) London Town Pr.

Hansen, Judith. Seashells in My Pocket: AMC Family Guide to Exploring Nature along the Atlantic Coast from Maine to Florida. Sabaka, Donna R., illus. 3rd ed. 2008. (ENG.). 160p. pap. 14.95 (978-1-929173-61-7(X)) Appalachian Mountain Club Bks.

Harcourt School Publishers Staff. Ocean Animals. 3rd ed. 2002. (Trophies English Language Learners Ser.). (gr. 3). pap. 5.10 (978-0-15-327697-2(5)) Harcourt Schl. Pubs.

—Splash in the Ocean: Little Book. 2000. (Collections Ser.). (Illus.). (J). pap. 10.20 (978-0-15-314506-3(4)) Harcourt Schl. Pubs.

Hardy, A. S. Sea Stories for Wonder Eyes. 2005. reprint ed. pap. 21.95 (978-1-4191-0670-5(8)) Kessinger Publishing, LLC.

Harris, Caroline. Whales Sing & Other Questions about Sea Creatures. 2006. (I Wonder Why Ser.). (Illus.). 32p. (J). (gr. k-3). 12.95 (978-0-7534-5965-2(5) , Kingfisher) Houghton Mifflin Co. Trade & Reference Div.

Helbrough, Emma. Ocean Life. 2006. (First Library of Knowledge). 32p. (J). (gr. 2-4). 23.70 (978-1-4103-0342-4(X) , Blackbirch Pr., Inc.) Thomson Gale.

Henley, Claire. In the Ocean. Henley, Claire, illus. 1999. (Illus.). 24p. (J). (ps-k). reprint ed. 12.00 (978-0-7881-6616-7(6)) DIANE Publishing Co.

Hewitt, Sally. Sea Creatures: A Squirmy, Scary, Prickly Pop-up. Gilvan-Cartwright, Chris, illus. 2008. 12p. (J). (ps-3). 14.95 (978-0-8109-5877-5(9)) Abrams, Harry N., Inc.

Himmelman, John. What Can You See at the Seashore? A Roundabout Nature Book. 2008. (J). (***978-1-55971-996-4(6)*** , NorthWord Bks. for Young Readers) T&N Children's Publishing.

Hirschi, Ron. Ocean Seasons. Carlson, Kirsten, illus. 2007. 32p. (J). (gr. k-4). pap. 8.95 (***978-1-934359-16-7(5)***) Sylvan Dell Pubng.

Hirschmann, Kris. Creatures That Glow. 2005. (Creatures of the Sea Ser.). (Illus.). 48p. (J). (gr. 4-8). 26.20 (978-0-7377-2340-3(8) , Greenhaven Pr., Inc.) Thomson Gale.

—Sea Urchins. 2005. (Creatures of the Sea Ser.). (Illus.). 48p. (J). (ps-8). lib. bdg. 26.20 (978-0-7377-3012-8(9) , Greenhaven Pr., Inc.) Thomson Gale.

Hodgkins, Fran. Between the Tides. Sollers, Jim, illus. 2007. 32p. pap. 15.95 (978-0-89272-727-8(6)) Down East Bks.

Horsman, Paul. Out of the Blue: A Journey Through the World's Oceans. Seapics.Com, photos by. 2005. (Illus.). 160p. (gr. 3-7). 29.95 (978-0-262-08341-6(8)) MIT Pr.

Hubbell, Patricia. Papa Fish's Lullaby. Eaddy, Susan, illus. 2007. 32p. (J). (ps-1). 16.95 (978-1-55971-965-0(6) , NorthWord Bks. for Young Readers) T&N Children's Publishing.

Hudak, Heather C. Marine Mammals. 2004. (Animal Facts Ser.). (Illus.). 24p. (J). lib. bdg. 24.45 (978-1-59036-201-3(2)) Weigl Pubs., Inc.

Hughes, Monica. Swimming Giants. 2008. (J). lib. bdg. (***978-1-59716-542-6(5)***) Bearport Publishing Co., Inc.

Humann, Paul & DeLoach, Ned. The Reef Set Florida Caribbean Bahamas. 2nd ed. 2002. (Reef Set Ser.). 120.00 (978-1-878348-33-3(7)) New World Pubns., Inc.

Innes, Brian. Water Monsters. 1999. (Unsolved Mysteries Ser.). (Illus.). 48p. (YA). (gr. 3 up). lib. bdg. 25.69 (978-0-8172-5479-7(X)) Raintree.

—Water Monsters. 1998. (Unsolved Mysteries Ser.). (Illus.). 48p. (gr. 3-7). pap. 8.05 (978-0-8172-4276-3(7)) Steck-Vaughn.

—Water Monsters. 1999. (gr. 3-6). lib. bdg. 15.25 (978-0-613-76291-5(6)) Tandem Library Bks.

Jablonsky, Alice & Webster, Steven K. Discover Ocean Life. O'Neill, Pablo Montes & Robare, Lorie, trs. O'Neill, Pablo Montes & Robare, Lorie, illus. 2005. (Discover Ser.). 48p. (J). (978-0-7853-6111-4(1) , 3013407) Publications International, Ltd.

James, Diane. Bajo el Agua. 2001. Tr. of Underwater. 12.75 (978-0-606-22731-5(8)) Tandem Library Bks.

James, Jasper, et al. Chased by Sea Monsters. 2004. (Illus.). 168p. 25.00 (978-0-7566-0375-5(7)) Dorling Kindersley Publishing, Inc.

Jango-Cohen, Judith. Real-Life Sea Monsters: Truth & Tales. Durney, Ryan, illus. 2007. (On My Own Science Ser.). 48p. (J). (gr. 2-4). lib. bdg. 25.26 (978-0-8225-6747-9(4) , Millbrook Pr.) Lerner Publishing Group.

Jay, Michael. Sea Monsters. 2003. (Illus.). 32p. (J). lib. bdg. 25.70 (978-1-4109-0010-4(X)) Raintree.

Jerome, Kate Boehm. Science at the Aquarium. 2004. (National Geographic Reading Expeditions Ser.). (Illus.). 24p. (J). pap. (978-0-7922-8625-7(1)) National Geographic Society.

Johnson, Jinny. Children's Guide to Sea Creatures. 1998. (Simon & Schuster Children's Guides Ser.). (Illus.). 80p. (J). (gr. 3-7). 22.95 (978-0-689-81534-8(4)) Simon & Schuster Children's Publishing.

Kalman, Bobbie & Dyer, Hadley. Endangered Manatees. 2006. (Illus.). 32p. (J). (gr. 2-8). pap. (978-0-7787-1914-4(6)) Crabtree Publishing Co.

Kalman, Bobbie & Langille, Jacqueline. Les Mammiferes Marins. 2003. (FRE., Illus.). 32p. pap. (978-2-920660-97-7(7)) Crabtree Publishing Co.

Kenah, Katharine. Creatures of the Deep. 2004. (Extreme Readers Ser.). (Illus.). 32p. (J). (ps-2). pap. 3.95 (978-0-7696-3177-6(0)) School Specialty Publishing.

Kingsley, Charles. Glaucus: The Wonders of the Shore. 2006. 122p. pap. 10.99 (978-1-4264-0318-7(6)); 116p. pap. 13.99 (978-1-4264-0369-9(0)) BiblioBazaar.

Knox, Barbara. ABC under the Sea: An Ocean Life Alphabet Book. 2003. (A+ Alphabet Books). (Illus.). 32p. (J). (gr. k-1). lib. bdg. 22.60 (978-0-7368-1684-7(4) , Aplus Bks.) Capstone Pr., Inc.

—Under the Sea 1, 2, 3: An Ocean Life Counting Book. 2003. (A+ Counting Books). (Illus.). 32p. (J). (gr. k-1). lib. bdg. 22.60 (978-0-7368-1677-9(1) , Aplus Bks.) Capstone Pr., Inc.

Kravetz, Jonathan. Ticks. 2006. (Illus.). 24p. (J). lib. bdg. (978-1-4042-3046-0(7) , PowerKids Pr.) Rosen Publishing Group, Inc., The.

Kronstadt, Jonathan. Ocean Extremes: Life in the Darkest Depths & under the Ice. 2005. (Illus.). 48p. (J). (***978-0-439-71190-6(8)***) Scholastic, Inc.

LaBella, Susan. Migrating Animals of the Water. 2007. (J). pap. (***978-0-8368-8424-1(8)***); 24p. (gr. 2-4). lib. bdg. 19.93 (***978-0-8368-8419-7(1)***) Stevens, Gareth Inc. (Weekly Reader Early Learning Library).

Lambilly-Bresson, Elisabeth de. Animals at the Pond. 2006. (Illus.). 14p. (J). lib. bdg. (***978-0-8368-7830-1(2)***) Stevens, Gareth Inc.

Lambilly, Elisabeth de. Sea Animals. 2006. (Illus.). 14p. (J). lib. bdg. (***978-0-8368-8160-8(5)***) Stevens, Gareth Inc.

Landau, Elaine. Sea Horses. 1999. (True Bks.). (Illus.). 48p. (J). (gr. 3-5). pap. 6.95 (978-0-516-26503-2(2) , Children's Pr.) Scholastic Library Publishing.

Larousse Mexico Staff, ed. Delfines y Ballenas. 2005. (Mi Pequena Enciclopedia Ser.). (SPA.). 38p. (ps-k). pap. 3.95 (978-970-22-0856-3(4)) Larousse, Ediciones, S. A. de C. V. MEX. *Dist:* Houghton Mifflin Co. Trade & Reference Div.

Laskey, Elizabeth. Seahorses. 2003. (Sea Creatures Ser.). (Illus.). 32p. (J). pap. 6.95 (978-1-4034-3565-1(0)); lib. bdg. 22.79 (978-1-4034-0963-8(3)) Heinemann Library.

Lassieur, Allison. Crabs, Lobsters, & Shrimps. 2003. (Animals in Order Ser.). 48p. (J). (gr. 4-6). pap. 6.95 (978-0-531-16659-8(7) , Watts, Franklin) Scholastic Library Publishing.

Leardi, Jeanette. Southern Sea Otters: Fur-tastrophe Avoided. 2008. (J). lib. bdg. 25.27 (***978-1-59716-534-1(4)***) Bearport Publishing Co., Inc.

Lensch, Chris, illus. Coral Reef: Hide & Seek. 2005. 10p. (J). bds. 7.95 (978-1-58117-362-8(8) , Intervisual/Piggy Toes) Dalmatian Pr.

Leon, Vicki. A Raft of Sea Otters: The Playful Life of a Furry Survivor. 2nd ed. 2005. (Jean-Michel Cousteau Presents Ser.). (Illus.). 48p. (J). pap. 8.95 (978-0-9666490-4-8(4)) London Town Pr.

Leon, Vicki. The Secrets of Tidepools: The Bright World of the Rocky Shoreline. 2nd ed. 2006. (Jean-Michel Cousteau Presents Ser.). (Illus.). 48p. (J). pap. 8.95 (978-0-9766134-6-6(8)) London Town Pr.

Lessem, Don. Sea Giants of Dinosaur Time. Bindon, John, illus. 2005. 32p. (J). (gr. 2-5). pap. 6.95 (978-0-8225-2623-0(9)); 23.93 (978-0-8225-1425-1(7)) Lerner Publishing Group.

L'Hommedieu, Arthur John. Ocean Tidepool. 1998. (Habitats Ser.). (Illus.). 32p. (J). (gr. 2-3). pap. 6.95 (978-0-516-20373-7(8) , Children's Pr.) Scholastic Library Publishing.

Lindeen, Carol. Life in an Ocean. 2003. (Pebble Plus: Living in a Biome Ser.). (Illus.). 24p. (J). lib. bdg. 17.26 (978-0-7368-2099-8(X) , Pebble Bks.) Capstone Pr., Inc.

Lindeen, Carol K. Life in an Ocean, Vol. 3. 2005. (Earth & Outer Space Ser.). 24p. (YA). (gr. k-3). pap. (978-0-7368-3406-3(0) , Pebble Bks.) Capstone Pr., Inc.

Listen-Read-Think Science: Sea Creatures. 2006. pap. 4.49 (978-1-4206-8150-5(8)) Teacher Created Materials, Inc.

Lithgow, John & Blackaby, Susan. Drop, Drip, an Underwater Trip: Level 3. 2007. (Lithgow Palooza Readers Ser.). (Illus.). 32p. (J). (gr. 1-2). pap. 3.95 (978-0-7696-4253-6(5)) School Specialty Publishing.

—Sea Cows Don't Moo! Level 3. 2007. (Lithgow Palooza Readers Ser.). (Illus.). 32p. (J). (gr. 1-2). pap. 3.95 (978-0-7696-4243-7(8)) School Specialty Publishing.

—Splishy, Splashy Mammals: Level 2. 2007. (Lithgow Palooza Readers Ser.). (Illus.). 32p. (J). (gr. k-1). pap. 3.95 (978-0-7696-4252-9(7)) School Specialty Publishing.

Llewellyn, Claire. Sea Animals. 2005. (Illus.). 24p. (YA). (gr. 1 up). lib. bdg. 22.80 (978-1-932889-32-1(9)) Sea-To-Sea Pubns.

Logue, Mary. Sponges. 2004. (Science Around Us Ser.). 32p. (J). (gr. 2-6). 27.07 (978-1-59296-274-7(2)) Child's World, Inc.

Longnecker, Theresa. Who Grows Up in the Ocean? A Book about Ocean Animals & Their Offspring. Carpenter, Melissa, illus. 2004. (Who Grows Up Here? Ser.). 24p. (C). (gr. k-4). 21.26 (978-1-4048-0026-7(3)) Picture Window Bks.

Iunis, Natalie. Slimy Sea Slugs. 2008. (J). lib. bdg. 21.28 (***978-1-59716-511-2(5)***) Bearport Publishing Co., Inc.

Macken, JoAnn Early. Rivers: Rios. 2005. (SPA.). (J). (978-0-8368-6038-2(1)) Stevens, Gareth Inc.

—Sea Lions: Los Leones Marinos. 2004. (ENG & SPA., Illus.). 24p. (J). pap. (978-0-8368-4389-7(4)); lib. bdg. 19.33 (978-0-8368-4384-2(3)) Stevens, Gareth Inc.

Makowski, Robin Lee. Sea Creatures. 2001. (How to Draw Ser.). (Illus.). 32p. (J). (gr. 2-5). lib. bdg. 25.27 (978-1-58952-156-8(0)) Rourke Publishing, LLC.

Makowski, Robin Lee, illus. Sea Creatures. 2004. (J). (978-1-59203-090-3(4)) Learning Challenge, Inc.

Mammals of the Sea: Level N, 6 vols. (Explorers Ser.). 32p. (gr. 3-6). 44.95 (978-0-7699-0593-8(5)) Shortland Pubns. (U. S. A.) Inc.

Manatees Oceans Alive. 2006. (Illus.). 24p. (J). (gr. k-2). 18.50 (***978-0-531-17870-6(6)***) Scholastic Library Publishing.

Mannis, Celeste Davidson. Snapshots: The Wonders of Monterey Bay. 2006. (Illus.). 32p. (J). (gr. 1). 16.99 (978-0-670-06062-7(3) , Viking Adult) Penguin Group (USA) Inc.

Markle, Sandra. Really Wild Animals: Sea Babies. 2002. (Illus.). 30p. (J). (978-0-439-33489-1(6)) Scholastic, Inc.

Marshall Cavendish Corporation Staff. Aquatic Life of the World, 11 vols., Vols. 1-10. 2000. (Illus.). (J). (978-0-7614-7181-3(2)) Cavendish, Marshall Corp.

Marshall Cavendish Corporation Staff, contrib. by. Aquatic Life of the World, 11 vols., Set. 2000. (Illus.). 700p. (gr. 4-6). 471.36 (978-0-7614-7170-7(7) , Cavendish, Marshall Reference Bks.) Cavendish, Marshall Corp.

Marshall Cavendish Corporation Staff, ed. Aquatic Life of the World, 11 vols. 2000. (Illus.). (J). (978-0-7614-7171-4(5)); 700p. 329.95 (978-0-7614-7172-1(3)); (978-0-7614-7173-8(1)); (978-0-7614-7174-5(X)); (978-0-7614-7175-2(8)); (978-0-7614-7176-9(6)); (978-0-7614-7177-6(4)); (978-0-7614-7178-3(2)); (978-0-7614-7179-0(0)); (978-0-7614-7180-6(4)) Cavendish, Marshall Corp.

Marsico, Katie. A Baby Lobster Grows Up. 2007. (Scholastic News Nonfiction Readers Ser.). (Illus.). 24p. (J). (gr. 1-2). 19.00 (978-0-531-17475-3(1) , Children's Pr.) Scholastic Library Publishing.

Marsico, Katie. A Manatee Calf Grows Up. 2007. (Scholastic News Nonfiction Readers: Life Cycles Ser.). 24p. (J). pap. 6.95 (***978-0-531-18698-5(9)*** , Children's Pr.) Scholastic Library Publishing.

Marston, Hope Irvin. Wings in the Water: The Story of a Manta Ray. Petruccio, Steven James, illus. 1998. (Smithsonian Oceanic Collection: Vol. 16). 32p. (J). (ps-2). 19.95 incl. audio (978-1-56899-579-3(2) , BC4016); Incl. toy. 29.95 (978-1-56899-581-6(4)); Incl. toy. 34.95 incl. audio (978-1-56899-583-0(0)) Soundprints.

—Wings in the Water: The Story of a Manta Ray - Micro Book, Incl. micro toy. Petruccio, Steven James, illus. 1998. (Smithsonian Oceanic Collection: Vol. 16). 32p. (J). (ps-2). 9.95 incl. audio (978-1-56899-584-7(9)) Soundprints.

—Wings in the Water: The Story of a Manta Ray - Micro Edition. Petruccio, Steven James, illus. 1998. (Smithsonian Oceanic Collection: Vol. 16). 32p. (J). (ps-2). incl. audio (978-1-56899-580-9(6)) Soundprints.

Mason, Adrienne. World of Marine Mammals. 1999. (gr. 3-6). lib. bdg. 18.75 (978-0-613-54792-5(6)) Tandem Library Bks.

Mattern, Joanne. What River Animals Eat: Qué Comen Los Animales de Los Ríos? 2006. (ENG & SPA., Illus.). 24p. (J). pap. (978-0-8368-7382-5(3)); lib. bdg. (978-0-8368-7375-7(0)) Stevens, Gareth Inc. (Weekly Reader Early Learning Library).

—What Sea Animals Eat. 2006. (Nature's Food Chains Ser.). (Illus.). 24p. (J). (gr. 1-2). pap. 5.95 (978-0-8368-6882-1(X)); lib. bdg. 19.93 (978-0-8368-6875-3(7)) Stevens, Gareth Inc.

—What Sea Animals Eat: Qué Comen Los Animales Del Mar? 2006. (ENG & SPA., Illus.). 24p. (J). pap. (978-0-8368-7383-2(1) , Weekly Reader Early Learning Library) Stevens, Gareth Inc.

McCall, Gerrie. Fierce Water Creatures. 2006. (Nature's Monsters Ser.). (Illus.). 32p. (J). lib. bdg. 23.33 (978-0-8368-6177-8(9)) Stevens, Gareth Inc.

McCourt, Lisa. Wet 'n' Weird: The Strangest Sea Creatures You Ever Seen. Nathan, Cheryl, illus. 2000. (Roxbury Park Bks.). 32p. (J). (gr. k-3). pap. 7.95 (978-0-7373-0405-3(7) , 04057W, Roxbury Park Juvenile) Lowell Hse. Juvenile.

McCurry, Kristen & Jackson, Aimee. Ocean Babies. NorthWord Books for Young Readers Staff, ed. 2004. (Illus.). 22p. (J). (ps up). bds. 5.95 (978-1-55971-898-1(6) , NorthWord Bks. for Young Readers) T&N Children's Publishing.

McKenzie, Michelle. Ocean Pop & Pull. 2001. 12p. (J). 12.95 (978-1-878244-36-9(1)) Monterey Bay Aquarium.

McKissack, Fredrick, Jr. & McKissack, Lisa Beringer. Counting in the Oceans. 2008. (J). (***978-0-7660-2994-1(8)***) Enslow Pubs., Inc.

McKnight, Diane. The Lost Seal. Emerling, Dorothy, illus. 2006. 40p. 19.95 (978-0-9723422-7-8(3)) Moonlight Publishing.

McNeil, Niki, et al. HOCPP 1077 Predators of the Deep. 2006. spiral bd. 16.50 (***978-1-60308-077-4(5)***) In the Hands of a Child.

Mead, Brian. Creatures of the Deep Coloring Book. 2003. 32p. (J). (ps-3). pap. 3.99 (978-0-9717509-3-7(9)) Mead, Brian Publishing.

Merlino, Kim. Ocean Life: Grades 2 Through 4. (Illus.). (J). pap., wbk. ed. 4.99 (978-0-88743-966-7(7)) School Zone Publishing Co.

Meucci, Antonella. Seas & Oceans. Chesi, Matteo, illus. 2000. (Nature's Record-Breakers Ser.). 32p. (J). (gr. 3 up). lib. bdg. 23.33 (978-0-8368-2475-9(X)) Stevens, Gareth Inc.

Milbourne, Anna. Under the Sea Lift-the-Flap. 2001. (1001 Things to Spot Ser.). 16p. (J). (gr. 1 up). 11.95 (978-0-7945-0509-7(0)) EDC Publishing.

Milbourne, Anna. Under the Sea (Picture Book) 2007. (Picture Bks). 24p. (J). 9.99 (***978-0-7945-1801-1(X)*** , Usborne) EDC Publishing.

Miller, Sara Swan. Seahorses, Pipefishes, & Their Kin. 2003. (Animals in Order Ser.). (Illus.). 48p. (J). (gr. 4-6). pap. 6.95 (978-0-531-16379-5(2) , Watts, Franklin) Scholastic Library Publishing.

Miller-Schroeder, Patricia. The Science of Underwater Life. 2000. (Living Science Ser.). (Illus.). 32p. (J). (gr. 2 up). lib. bdg. 24.67 (978-0-8368-2683-8(3)) Stevens, Gareth Inc.

Morrison, Gordon. Pond. Morrison, Gordon, illus. 2002. (Illus.). 32p. (J). (gr. k-3). tchr. ed. 16.00 (978-0-618-10271-6(X) , Walter Lorraine) Houghton Mifflin Co. Trade & Reference Div.

Murphy, Patricia J. Discovering Underwater Secrets with a Nature Photographer. 2007. (I Like Science! Ser.). (Illus.). 24p. (J). (gr. 1-3). lib. bdg. 21.26 (***978-0-7660-2816-6(X)*** , Enslow Elementary) Enslow Pubs., Inc.

Nature Series Books 25 & 26: Activities. 2004. (J). pap., instr.'s gde. ed. 2.95 (978-1-878405-48-7(9)) Nags Head Art, Inc.

Needham, Kate. Great Undersea Search. Jackson, Ian, illus. rev. ed. 2005. 32p. (J). pap. 7.99 (978-0-7945-1228-6(3) , Usborne) EDC Publishing.

Nelson, Robert Lyn. Ocean Friends. 2003. (Illus.). 32p. (gr. k-3). 15.95 (978-1-55971-840-0(4) , NorthWord Bks. for Young Readers) T&N Children's Publishing.

Nichols, Catherine. One Big Ocean. 2002. (We Can Read about Nature! Ser.). (Illus.). 32p. (J). 21.36 (978-0-7614-1433-9(9) , Benchmark Bks.) Cavendish, Marshall Corp.

Nicholson, Sue. Animal Babies in Seas. Kingfisher Editors, ed. 2006. (Animal Babies Ser.). (Illus.). 24p. (J). (ps-k). bds. 6.95 (978-0-7534-5945-4(0) , Kingfisher) Houghton Mifflin Co. Trade & Reference Div.

—Ocean Explorer. 2002. 48p. (J). pap. 6.95 (978-0-439-31688-0(X)) Scholastic, Inc.

NorthWord Books for Young Readers Editors. Ocean Babies. 2005. (SPA.). (J). bds. 5.95 (978-1-55971-908-7(7) , NorthWord Bks. for Young Readers) T&N Children's Publishing.

Nye, Bill & Saunders, Ian G. Bill Nye the Science Guy's Big Blue Ocean. Dykes, John S., illus. 2003. 48p. (gr. 2-5). pap. 6.99 (978-0-7868-1757-3(7)) Hyperion Bks. for Children.

Ocean Animals. 2004. (Illus.). lib. bdg. 7.95 (978-0-8225-4511-8(X)) Lerner Publishing Group.

Ocean Animals. Date not set. (Illus.). 16p. (J). 5.98 (978-0-7525-7698-5(4)); 2.98 (978-0-7525-9762-1(0)) Parragon, Inc.

Ocean Animals. (Little Tot Dot-to-Dots Ser.). 32p. (ps-2). 4.29 (978-0-7682-0227-4(2) , FS130305) Schaffer, Frank Pubns.

Oceans Alive!, 10 vols., Set. 2006. (Blastoff! Readers Ser.). (Illus.). (J). (gr. k-2). 185.00 (***978-0-531-16877-6(8)***) Scholastic Library Publishing.

Oceans Alive, Level 2, 4 bks., Set. Incl. Clown Fish. Sexton, Colleen. 18.50 (***978-0-531-17562-0(6));*** Sea Dragons. Schach, David. 18.50 (***978-0-531-17563-7(4));*** Seals. Sexton, Colleen. (Illus.). 18.50 (***978-0-531-17564-4(2));*** Stingrays. Rustad, Martha E. H. lib. bdg. 18.50 (***978-0-531-17570-5(7));*** 24p. (J). (gr. k-2). (Blastoff! Readers Ser.). 2007. 74.00 (***978-0-531-17742-6(4)*** , Children's Pr.) Scholastic Library Publishing.

Octopuses & Squids: Level N, 6 vols. (Wonder Worldtm Ser.). 48p. 34.95 (978-0-7802-2902-0(9)) Wright Group, The.

O'Donnell, Kerri. Ugly Sea Creatures. 2006. (Illus.). 24p. (J). lib. bdg. (978-1-4042-3528-1(0)) Rosen Publishing Group, Inc., The.

Oliver. Sea Creatures. 2003. (Weird Wildlife Ser.). (Illus.). 32p. pap. 7.95 (978-1-4109-0081-4(9)) Raintree.

Oliver, Clare. Sea Creatures. 2002. (Weird Wildlife Ser.). (Illus.). 32p. (J). lib. bdg. 25.69 (978-0-7398-4859-3(3)) Raintree.

One Giant Splash. (Know Your Numbers Ser.). 24p. (J). 7.95 (978-1-4048-1122-5(2)) Picture Window Bks.

O'Neil, Sarah. Under the Sea. 2001. (gr. k-3). lib. bdg. 11.80 (978-0-613-33449-5(3)) Tandem Library Bks.

O'Reilly, Wenda. Go fish wildlife sea Creatures. 2007. n/ap. pap. 119.40 (***978-1-59960-020-8(X)***) Birdcage Pr.

Orme, Helen. In the Sea. Eye View Staff, ed. 2003. (Eye View Ser.). (Illus.). 32p. (J). 14.95 (978-1-57768-566-1(0) , Waterbird Bks.) School Specialty Publishing.

Osborne, Mary Pope & Boyce, Natalie Pope. Sea Monsters. Murdocca, Sal, illus. 2008. (J). (***978-0-375-84663-2(8));*** lib. bdg. 11.99 (***978-0-375-94663-9(2)***) Random Hse., Inc.

O'Sullivan, Robyn. Spitting Cobras, Weedy Sea Dragons: And Other Wild & Amazing Animals. 2006. (National Geographic Science Chapters Ser.). (Illus.). 48p. (gr. 1-4). 17.90 (978-0-7922-5941-1(6) , National Geographic Children's Bks.) National Geographic Society.

Pallotta, Jerry. The Ocean Alphabet Board Book. Mazzola, Frank, Jr., illus. 2004. 28p. (J). bds. 6.95 (978-1-57091-524-6(5)) Charlesbridge Publishing, Inc.

Palotta, Jerry. Underwater Counting: Even Numbers. 2001. (gr. 3-6). lib. bdg. 15.25 (978-0-613-51270-1(7)) Tandem Library Bks.

—Underwater Counting Even Numbers. Biedrzycki, David, illus. 2001. 32p. (J). (gr. 1-4). 16.95 (978-0-88106-952-5(3)); pap. 6.95 (978-0-88106-800-9(4)) Charlesbridge Publishing, Inc.

Pfeffer, Wendy. Deep Oceans. 2002. (Living on the Edge Ser.). (Illus.). 39p. (J). 25.64 (978-0-7614-1439-1(8) , Benchmark Bks.) Cavendish, Marshall Corp.

Phillips, Dee. Find It at the Beach. 2005. (Can You Find It? Ser.). (Illus.). 24p. (J). lib. bdg. 22.00 (978-0-8368-6298-0(8)) Stevens, Gareth Inc.

Phillips, Dee & Howard, Allison. Ocean Life: Blue Zoo Guides. 2006. (Blue Zoo Guides Ser.). (Illus.). 96p. 18.95 (978-1-58728-560-8(6) , Two Can Publishing) T&N Children's Publishing.

Pierce, Terry & Kofsky, Kristen. Dangerous Sea Creatures A to Z Coloring Book. 2004. (Illus.). 24p. pap. 4.95 (978-1-57306-177-3(8)) Bess Pr., Inc.

Pike, Katy & Turner, Garda. Coral Reefs. 2003. (Ocean Facts Ser.). (Illus.). 24p. (gr. 2-4). 23.00 (978-0-7910-7285-1(1) , Chelsea Hse.) Facts On File, Inc.

—Sea Life. 2003. (Ocean Facts Ser.). (Illus.). 24p. (gr. 2-4). 23.00 (978-0-7910-7288-2(6) , Chelsea Hse.) Facts On File, Inc.

Pipe, Jim. Sea Animals. 2007. (J). (***978-1-59604-163-9(3)***) Stargazer Bks.

Pohl, Kathleen. Animals of the Ocean. 2007. (Animal Show & Tell Ser.). 16p. (J). (ps-2). lib. bdg. 17.27 (***978-0-8368-8208-7(3)***) Stevens, Gareth Inc.

Pountney, Beth. Ocean Buddies. 2007. (Touchy Feely Ser.). (Illus.). 12p. (ps). per., bds. 5.95 (978-1-84610-457-2(2)) Make Believe Ideas GBR. *Dist:* Ingram Pub. Services.

Pratt-Serafini, Kristin Joy. A Swim Through the Sea. Pratt-Serafini, Kristin Joy, illus. 2006. (Illus.). 26p. (J). bds. 7.95 (978-1-58469-080-1(1)) Dawn Pubns.

Press, Judy. Little Hands Sea Life Art & Activities: Creative Learning Experiences for 3- to 7-Year Olds. 2004. (Williamson's Little Hands Book Ser.). (Illus.). 128p. (J). 12.95 (978-1-885593-94-8(5) , Williamson Bks.) Ideals Pubns.

Price-Goff, Claire. The Manatee. 1999. (Endangered Animals & Habitats Ser.). (Illus.). 112p. (YA). (gr. 4-12). 27.45 (978-1-56006-445-9(5) , Lucent Bks.) Thomson Gale.

Priddy, Roger. Ocean: Amazing Photo Pop-Ups Like You've Never Seen Before! 2005. (Illus.). 18p. (J). (ps-ps). 12.95 (978-0-312-49465-0(3) , Priddy Bks.) St. Martin's Pr.

QEB Start Reading Together National Book Stores Edition: Sea Creatures. 2006. (J). per. (978-1-59566-258-3(8)) QEB Publishing Inc.

Raintree Steck-Vaughn Staff. Criaturas de la Playa. (SPA.). (J). 2000. pap. 29.12 (978-0-7398-0739-2(0)); 1999. pap., stu. ed. 31.05 (978-0-7398-0766-8(8)) Steck-Vaughn.

—The Ocean Life: Tide Pool Creatures. 1999. (Illus.). (J). pap. 35.60 (978-0-7398-0900-6(8)) Steck-Vaughn.

Rake, Jody Sullivan. Sea Urchins. 2007. 24p. (J). (978-0-7368-6724-5(4) , Pebble Bks.) Capstone Pr., Inc.

—Sponges. 2006. (Under the Sea Ser.). (Illus.). 24p. (J). (gr. k-2). lib. bdg. 19.93 (978-0-7368-6366-7(4) , Pebble Bks.) Capstone Pr., Inc.

Redmond, Shirley Raye. Tentacles! Tales of the Giant Squid. Barnard, Bryn, illus. 2003. (Step into Reading Ser.). 48p. (J). (gr. k-2). pap. 3.99 (978-0-375-81307-8(1) , Random Hse. Bks. for Young Readers) Random Hse. Children's Bks.

Reiser, Lynn W. Little Clam. Reiser, Lynn W., illus. 1998. (Illus.). 24p. (J). (ps-3). 14.89 (978-0-688-15909-2(5)) HarperCollins Pubs.

Reyes, Blanca Matilde. Sea Animals. ed. 2006. (Illus.). 16p. (J). 0.75 (978-1-933984-03-2(1)) Two Lands.

Rhodes, Mary Jo. Predators of the Sea. Hall, David, photos by. 2006. (Undersea Encounters Ser.). (Illus.). 48p. (J). (gr. 3-5). 27.00 (978-0-516-24399-3(3) , Children's Pr.) Scholastic Library Publishing.

Rhodes, Mary Jo & Hall, David. Partners in the Sea. 2006. (Undersea Encounters Ser.). (Illus.). 48p. (J). (gr. 3-5). pap. 6.95 (978-0-516-25492-0(8) , Children's Pr.) Scholastic Library Publishing.

—Partners in the Sea. Hall, David, photos by. 2005. (Undersea Encounters Ser.). (Illus.). 48p. (J). (ps-7). 27.00 (978-0-516-24397-9(7) , Children's Pr.) Scholastic Library Publishing.

—Sea Turtles. 2006. (Undersea Encounters Ser.). (Illus.). 48p. (J). (gr. 3-5). pap. 6.95 (978-0-516-25353-4(0) , Children's Pr.) Scholastic Library Publishing.

—Sea Turtles. Hall, David, photos by. 2005. (Undersea Encounters Ser.). (Illus.). 48p. (J). (ps-7). 27.00 (978-0-516-24391-7(8) , Children's Pr.) Scholastic Library Publishing.

Rigby Education Staff. Big Animals in the Sea. (Sails Literacy Ser.). (Illus.). 16p. (gr. k-1). 27.00 (978-0-7635-9868-6(2) , 698682C99) Rigby Education.

—On the Seashore. (Sails Literacy Ser.). (Illus.). 16p. (gr. k-1). 27.00 (978-0-7635-9865-5(8) , 698658C99) Rigby Education.

Rivera, Sheila. Ocean. 2005. (First Step Nonfiction Ser.). (Illus.). 23p. (J). (ps-7). 18.60 (978-0-8225-2795-4(2) , Lerner Pubns.) Lerner Publishing Group.

Rogers, Kirsteen. Under the Sea Jigsaw Bk. Scott, Peter, illus. 2007. 14p. (J). bds. 14.99 (978-0-7945-1330-6(1) , Usborne) EDC Publishing.

Rose, Deborah Lee. Ocean Babies. Nakata, Hiroe, illus. 2005. 32p. (J). (ps-3). 25.90 (978-0-7922-8312-6(0)); 16.95 (978-0-7922-6669-3(2)) National Geographic Society. (National Geographic Children's Bks.).

—One Nighttime Sea. Jenkins, Steve, illus. 2003. 40p. (J). pap. 16.95 (978-0-439-33906-3(5)) Scholastic, Inc.

Rose, Deborah Lee & Jenkins, Steve. Into the A, B, Sea. 2000. (Illus.). (J). (978-0-439-09697-3(9)) Scholastic, Inc.

Rubin, Alan. How Many Fish? 2003. (Yellow Umbrella Books). (Illus.). 16p. (J). (gr. 1). lib. bdg. 14.60 (978-0-7368-2013-4(2) , Pebble Bks.) Capstone Pr., Inc.

—How Many Fish? 2003. (Math Ser.). (J). (978-0-7368-1699-1(2)) Yellow Umbrella Pr.

Rudy, Lisa Jo. Learn All About: Ocean Life. 2003. (Learn All About Ser.). (Illus.). 64p. pap. 10.95 (978-0-439-51884-0(9)) Scholastic, Inc.

Rustad, Martha E. Manatees. 2005. (Ocean Life Ser.). 24p. (YA). (gr. k-3). pap. (978-0-7368-3414-8(1) , Pebble Bks.) Capstone Pr., Inc.

Rustad, Martha E. H. Sea Anemones. 2007. (Illus.). 24p. (J). lib. bdg. 19.95 (978-1-60014-081-5(5)) Bellwether Media.

—Sea Urchins. 2007. (Illus.). 24p. (J). lib. bdg. 19.95 (978-1-60014-109-6(9)) Bellwether Media.

—Stingrays. 2007. (Illus.). 24p. (J). lib. bdg. 16.95 (978-1-60014-080-8(7)) Bellwether Media.

—Stingrays. 2007. (Blastoff! Readers Ser.). 24p. (J). (gr. k-2). lib. bdg. 18.50 (***978-0-531-17570-5(7)*** , Children's Pr.) Scholastic Library Publishing.

Sabuda, Robert & Reinhart, Matthew. Encyclopedia Prehistorica: Sharks & Other Sea Monsters. Sabuda, Robert & Reinhart, Matthew, illus. 2006. (Illus.). 12p. (J). (gr. k). 27.99 (978-0-7636-2229-9(X)) Candlewick Pr.

Saffer, Barbara. Science Questions & Answers: The Ocean. 1999. (Science Questions & Answers Ser.). (Illus.). 63p. (J). (gr. 1-3). pap. 5.95 (978-0-7373-0210-3(0)) Lowell Hse.

Santillo, LuAnn. Under the Sea, 6 vols. Santillo, LuAnn, ed. 2003. (Half-Pint Kids Readers Ser.). (Illus.). 42p. (J). (ps-1). pap. 6.99 (978-1-59256-091-2(1)) Half-Pint Kids, Inc.

Saunders-Smith, Gail, ed. Under the Sea. 2005. (Pebble Plus Ser.). (Illus.). (J). (gr. k-1). lib. bdg. 279.02 (978-0-7368-4408-6(2)) Capstone Pr., Inc.

Sautter, Aaron. Sea Monsters. 2007. (Blazers Ser.). (Illus.). 32p. (J). 19.93 (978-0-7368-6442-8(3)) Capstone Pr., Inc.

Schach, David. Sea Dragons. 2007. (Illus.). 24p. (J). lib. bdg. 16.95 (978-1-60014-055-6(6)) Bellwether Media.

—Sea Dragons. 2007. (Blastoff! Readers Ser.). 24p. (J). (gr. k-2). 18.50 (***978-0-531-17563-7(4)*** , Children's Pr.) Scholastic Library Publishing.

Schaefer, Lola M. La Bellota de Mar. 2002. (Animales Acorazados (Musty-Crusty Animals) Ser.). (SPA.). 24p. (J). (ps-1). lib. bdg. 18.50 (978-1-58810-771-8(X)); (Illus.). pap. 5.25 (978-1-58810-815-9(5) , 91561) Heinemann Library.

—Corals. Saunders-Smith, Gail, ed. 1999. (Ocean Life Ser.). (Illus.). 24p. (J). (gr. k-1). lib. bdg. 15.93 (978-0-7368-0244-4(4) , Pebble Bks.) Capstone Pr., Inc.

—Corals. 1999. 13.25 (978-0-516-21832-8(8) , Children's Pr.) Scholastic Library Publishing.

—Crabs. Saunders-Smith, Gail, ed. 1999. (Ocean Life Ser.). (Illus.). 24p. (J). (gr. k-1). lib. bdg. 15.93 (978-0-7368-0245-1(2) , Pebble Bks.) Capstone Pr., Inc.

—Crabs. 1999. lib. bdg. 13.25 (978-0-516-21833-5(6) , Children's Pr.) Scholastic Library Publishing.

—Octopuses. Saunders-Smith, Gail, ed. 1999. (Ocean Life Ser.). (Illus.). 24p. (J). (gr. k-1). lib. bdg. 15.93 (978-0-7368-0246-8(0) , Pebble Bks.) Capstone Pr., Inc.

—Sea Anemones. Saunders-Smith, Gail, ed. 1999. (Ocean Life Ser.). (Illus.). 24p. (J). (gr. k-1). lib. bdg. 15.93 (978-0-7368-0248-2(7) , Pebble Bks.) Capstone Pr., Inc.

—Sea Anemones. 2002. (Heinemann Read & Learn Ser.). (Illus.). 24p. (J). (ps-1). pap. (978-1-58810-717-6(5) , 91372); lib. bdg. (978-1-58810-508-0(3)) Heinemann Library.

—Sea Anemones. 1999. lib. bdg. 13.25 (978-0-516-21836-6(0) , Children's Pr.) Scholastic Library Publishing.

—Sea Horses. Saunders-Smith, Gail, ed. 1999. (Ocean Life Ser.). (Illus.). 24p. (J). (gr. k-1). lib. bdg. 15.93 (978-0-7368-0249-9(5) , Pebble Bks.) Capstone Pr., Inc.

—Sea Stars. Saunders-Smith, Gail, ed. 1999. (Ocean Life Ser.). (Illus.). 24p. (J). (gr. k-1). lib. bdg. 15.93 (978-0-7368-0250-5(9) , Pebble Bks.) Capstone Pr., Inc.

—Sea Stars, Vol. 2. 2005. (Ocean Life Ser.). 24p. (YA). (gr. k-3). pap. (978-0-7368-8221-7(9) , Pebble Bks.) Capstone Pr., Inc.

—Sea Urchins. Saunders-Smith, Gail, ed. 1999. (Ocean Life Ser.). (Illus.). 24p. (J). (gr. k-1). lib. bdg. 15.93 (978-0-7368-0251-2(7) , Pebble Bks.) Capstone Pr., Inc.

—Sea Urchins. 2003. (Heinemann Read & Learn Ser.). (Illus.). 24p. (J). lib. bdg. 18.50 (978-1-4034-3245-2(7)) Heinemann Library.

—Sea Urchins, Vol. 2. 2005. (Ocean Life Ser.). 24p. (YA). (gr. k-3). pap. (978-0-7368-8222-4(7) , Pebble Bks.) Capstone Pr., Inc.

Schatz, Dennis. Totally Sea Creatures. 2004. (Totally Ser.). (Illus.). 32p. (J). 16.95 (978-1-59223-087-7(3)) Advantage Pubs. Group.

Scheafer, Lola M. Sea Anemones. 2005. (Ocean Life Ser.). 24p. (YA). (gr. k-3). pap. (978-0-7368-8219-4(7) , Pebble Bks.) Capstone Pr., Inc.

Schlepp, Tammy J. Sea Animals. 2001. (978-0-606-22444-4(0)) Tandem Library Bks.

School Specialty Publishing. Dot-to-Dots, Mazes & More: Sea Creatures. 2002. (Homework Booklets Ser.). 80p. (J). (gr. k-1). pap. 2.99 (978-0-7424-0257-7(6) , IF0413) School Specialty Publishing.

Scott, Janine. A Sea of Animals. 2002. (Spyglass Books). (Illus.). 24p. (J). (gr. 1 up). lib. bdg. 18.60 (978-0-7565-0240-9(3)) Compass Point Bks.

Sea Anemones. 2006. (Under the Sea Ser.). 24p. (J). 6.95 (978-0-7368-6134-2(3)) Capstone Pr., Inc.

Sea Anemones, 6 vols. (gr. k-2). 28.95 (978-0-7368-8259-0(6)) Red Brick Learning.

Sea Animals. 2007. (My First Sticker Encyclopedia Ser.). (Illus.). 18p. (J). pap. 5.95 (***978-1-59496-148-9(4)***) Teora USA LLC.

Sea Creatures. 2000. 32p. (YA). 9.95 (978-0-7525-4322-2(9)) Parragon, Inc.

Sea Horses. (Under the Sea Ser.). 24p. (J). 6.95 (978-0-7368-5118-3(6)) Capstone Pr., Inc.

Sea Mammals. (Illus.). (J). (ps-6). pap., act. bk. ed. 2.95 (978-0-565-00974-8(5)) Natural History Museum Pubns. GBR. *Dist:* Parkwest Pubns., Inc.

Sea Shapes. (Illus.). 12p. (J). (978-2-7643-0150-0(2)) Phidal Publishing, Inc./Editions Phidal, Inc.

Sea Splash. (My Animal Library). (Illus.). 10p. (J). (978-2-7643-0103-6(0)) Phidal Publishing, Inc./Editions Phidal, Inc.

Sea Stars, 6 vols. (gr. k-2). 28.95 (978-0-7368-8261-3(8)) Red Brick Learning.

Sea Urchins, 6 vols. (gr. k-2). 28.95 (978-0-7368-8262-0(6)) Red Brick Learning.

Seaworld Photographers, photos by. Baby Manatee. 2006. (SeaWorld Library: Vol. 5). (Illus.). 24p. (J). bds. 6.95 (978-0-8249-6644-7(9) , Candy Cane Pr.) Ideals Pubns.

Seuss, Dr. & Worth, Bonnie. Wish for a Fish: All about Sea Creatures. 1999. (Cat in the Hat's Learning Library Ser.). (Illus.). 48p. (J). (gr. k-3). 8.99 (978-0-679-89116-1(1) , Random Hse. Bks. for Young Readers) Random Hse. Children's Bks.

Sharks & Other Sea Creatures. 2001. 64p. (YA). 8.65 (978-0-7525-4882-1(4)) Parragon, Inc.

Sheather, Allan. Neptune's Nursery. 2000. (J). (978-0-606-19331-3(6)) Tandem Library Bks.

—One Less Fish. Toft, Kim Michelle, illus. 1998. 32p. (J). (ps-3). 15.95 (978-0-88106-322-6(3)); pap. 6.95 (978-0-88106-323-3(1)) Charlesbridge Publishing, Inc.

Shi, Sharon. Ocean Creatures. Jensen, Keli, illus. 2000. 24p. (J). (gr. 2-8). mass mkt. 4.99 (978-0-9702195-1-0(2) , B012, Tattootles Bks.) Tattoo Manufacturing.

Sill, Cathryn P. About Crustaceans: A Guide for Children. Sill, John, illus. 2007. 40p. (J). (ps-3). pap. 7.95 (***978-1-56145-405-1(2)***) Peachtree Pubs., Ltd.

Sill, Cathryn P. & Sill, John. About Crustaceans: A Guide for Children. Sill, Cathryn P. & Sill, John, trs. 2004. (Illus.). 40p. (J). 15.95 (978-1-56145-301-6(3)) Peachtree Pubs., Ltd.

Silver Dolphin en Español Editors. Baby Einstein: el mundo a mi alrededor, el Oceano: Baby Einstein: the World Around Me: Oceans. 2007. (Illus.). 12p. (J). bds. 15.95 (***978-970-718-457-2(4)*** , Silver Dolphin en Español) Advanced Marketing, S. de R. L. de C. V. MEX. *Dist:* Perseus Distribution.

Sladen, Louisa. Sea Creatures. Rinaldo, Luana, illus. 2005. (Magic Color Bks.). 10p. (J). 3.95 (978-1-4027-2056-7(4) , Sterling/Pinwheel) Sterling Publishing Co., Inc.

Slater, Patrick. Australian Marine Fish. 2002. (Nature Kids Ser.). (Illus.). 52p. (J). (gr. 3 up). lib. bdg. (978-1-59084-215-7(4)) Mason Crest Pubs.

—Australian Sealife. 2002. (Nature Kids Ser.). (Illus.). 52p. (J). (gr. 3 up). lib. bdg. (978-1-59084-211-9(1)) Mason Crest Pubs.

Smith. Criaturas de la Playa. 1999. pap. 5.18 (978-0-7398-0731-6(5)) Steck-Vaughn.

Smith, Alastair & Howell, Laura. On the Beach. 2004. (Lift-the-Flap Learners Ser.). (Illus.). 16p. (J). (gr. 1 up). pap. 8.95 (978-0-7945-0213-3(X) , Usborne) EDC Publishing.

Smith, Alastair & Tatchell, Judy. En el Mar. 2004. (SPA., Illus.). 20p. (J). 11.95 (978-0-7460-6398-9(9) , Usborne) EDC Publishing.

Smith, Carrie & Swain, Cameron. Life at the Beach. 2006. (Early Explorers Ser.). (J). 30.00 (***978-1-4108-6020-0(5)***) Benchmark Education Co.

Soloff-Levy, Barbara. How to Draw Sea Creatures. 2002. (gr. 3-6). lib. bdg. 11.80 (978-0-613-89988-8(1)) Tandem Library Bks.

Souza, Dorothy M. Sea Creatures with Many Arms. 1998. (Creatures All Around Us Ser.). (Illus.). 40p. (J). (gr. 2-4). lib. bdg. (978-1-57505-262-5(8) , Carolrhoda Bks.) Lerner Publishing Group.

—Sea Snakes. 1998. (Creatures All Around Us Ser.). (Illus.). 40p. (J). (gr. 2-4). lib. bdg. (978-1-57505-263-2(6) , Carolrhoda Bks.) Lerner Publishing Group.

Spizzirri, Linda, ed. Prehistoric Sea Life. Kohn, Arnie, illus. 32p. (J). (gr. 1-8). pap. 4.98 incl. audio (978-0-86545-020-2(X)) Spizzirri Pr., Inc.

Squire, Ann O. Animals of the Sea & Shore. 2001. (gr. 3-6). lib. bdg. 15.25 (978-0-613-51613-6(3)) Tandem Library Bks.

Steck-Vaughn Staff. Endangered Marine Animals. 2000. (Primary Source Science Collection). (J). pap. incl. VHS (978-0-7398-3212-7(3)) Raintree.

Stewart, David. Ocean Life! (World of Wonder Ser.). 32p. (J). 2008. pap. 9.95 (***978-0-531-20542-6(8));*** 2007. spiral bd. 29.00 (***978-0-531-20451-1(0)***) Scholastic Library Publishing. (Children's Pr.).

Stewart, Melissa. Extreme Coral Reef! Q & A. 2008. 48p. (J). 16.99 (***978-0-06-111577-6(0)***); pap. 6.99 (***978-0-06-111575-2(4)***) Smithsonian Institution Pr.

Stewart, Pat. Sea Animals. 1998. (Illus.). 32p. (J). pap. 2.95 (978-0-486-40558-2(3)) Dover Pubns., Inc.

Stierle, Cynthia & Crawley, Annie. Ocean Life from A to Z Book. 2007. (Readers Book & DVD Ser.). 32p. (J). (ps-3). bds. 17.99 incl. DVD (978-0-7944-1222-7(X)) Reader's Digest Assn., Inc., The.

Stille, Darlene. I Live in the Ocean, 6 bks. Ouren, Todd, illus. Incl. I Am a Dolphin : The Life of a Bottlenose Dolphin. (J). lib. bdg. 22.60 (978-1-4048-0596-5(6)); I Am a Fish : The Life of a Clown Fish. (J). lib. bdg. 22.60 (978-1-4048-0595-8(8)); I Am a Sea Turtle : The Life of a Green Sea Turtle. (C). 22.60 (978-1-4048-0597-2(4)); I Am a Seal : The Life of an Elephant Seal. (J). lib. bdg. 22.60 (978-1-4048-0598-9(2)); I Am a Shark : The Life of a Great Hammerhead Shark. (J). lib. bdg. 22.60 (978-1-4048-0599-6(0)); I Am a Whale : The Life of a Humpback Whale. (J). lib. bdg. 22.60 (978-1-4048-0600-9(8)); 24p. (gr. k-2). (Illus.). 2004. 135.60 (978-1-4048-0631-3(8)) Picture Window Bks.

Stone, Lynn M. Animals of the Coral Reef. 2001. (Under the Sea Ser.). (Illus.). 24p. (J). (gr. 1-4). lib. bdg. 20.64 (978-1-58952-109-4(9)) Rourke Publishing, LLC.

—Getting Around. 2001. (Under the Sea Ser.). (Illus.). 24p. (J). (gr. 1-4). lib. bdg. 20.64 (978-1-58952-110-0(2)) Rourke Publishing, LLC.

—How Do Animals Use Their Flippers? 2008. (J). (***978-1-60044-505-7(5)***) Rourke Publishing, LLC.

—Life of the Kelp Forest. 2001. (Under the Sea Ser.). (Illus.). 24p. (J). (gr. 1-4). lib. bdg. 20.64 (978-1-58952-112-4(9)) Rourke Publishing, LLC.

—Ocean Hunters. 2001. (Under the Sea Ser.). (Illus.). 24p. (J). (gr. 1-4). lib. bdg. 20.64 (978-1-58952-111-7(0)) Rourke Publishing, LLC.

—Partners. 2001. (Under the Sea Ser.). (Illus.). 24p. (J). (gr. 1-4). lib. bdg. 20.64 (978-1-58952-114-8(5)) Rourke Publishing, LLC.

—Sea Horses. 2002. (Rourke Discovery Library). (Illus.). 24p. (J). lib. bdg. 20.64 (978-1-58952-319-7(9)) Rourke Publishing, LLC.

—Sea Otter. 2003. (Animals in U.S. History Ser.). (Illus.). 24p. (J). 25.64 (978-1-58952-701-0(1)) Rourke Publishing, LLC.

Sullivan, Jody. Sea Anemones. 2005. (Illus.). 24p. (J). (ps-7). lib. bdg. 19.93 (978-0-7368-4271-6(3)) Capstone Pr., Inc.

Swanson, Diane. Safari Beneath the Sea: The Wonder World of the North Pacific Coast. Royal British Columbia Museum Staff, photos by. (Illus.). 64p. (J). (gr. 3-2). pap. 12.95 (978-1-55110-441-6(5)) Whitecap Bks., Ltd. CAN. *Dist:* Graphic Arts Ctr. Publishing Co.

Swinburne, Stephen R. Turtle Tide: The Ways of Sea Turtles. Hiscock, Bruce, illus. 2005. 32p. (J). (ps-7). 15.95 (978-1-59078-081-7(7)) Boyds Mills Pr.

Tatham, Betty. Baby Sea Otter. Paley, Joan, illus. rev. ed. 2005. 40p. (J). (ps). 17.95 (978-0-8050-7504-5(0)) Holt, Henry & Co.

Tejada, Susan. Life on a Coral Reef. 2001. (All-Star Readers: Level 3 Ser.). (Illus.). 48p. (J). 3.99 (978-1-57584-727-6(2)) Reader's Digest Children's Publishing, Inc.

Telford, Carole & Theodorou, Rod. Down a River. 2006. (Illus.). 32p. (J). (*978-1-4034-8789-6(8)) Heinemann Library.

—Down a River. 2nd ed. 2006. (Illus.). 32p. (J). pap. (*978-1-4034-8796-4(0)) Heinemann Library.

Thomas, Peggy. Bird Alert. 2000. (Science of Saving Animals Ser.: 8). (Illus.). 64p. (gr. 5-8). lib. bdg. (978-0-7613-1457-8(1) , Twenty-First Century Bks.) Lerner Publishing Group.

Thompson, Lisa. Creatures of the Deep. 2006. (Real Deal - Yellow Ser.). (Illus.). 32p. (gr. 4-8). 19.00 (978-0-7910-9058-9(2)) Facts On File, Inc.

Toft, Kim Michelle. Neptune's Nursery. 2000. (gr. k-3). lib. bdg. 15.25 (978-0-613-35189-8(4)) Tandem Library Bks.

Toft, Kim Michelle & Sheather, Allan. Neptunes Nursery. Toft, Kim Michelle, illus. 1999. (Illus.). 32p. 19.95 (978-0-7022-3079-0(0)) Univ. of Queensland Pr. AUS. *Dist:* International Specialized Bk. Services.

Top That Publishing Staff, ed. Ocean Predators. 2004. (Stickertastic Ser.). (Illus.). 24p. (J). pap. (978-1-84510-117-6(0)) Top That! Publishing PLC.

Twist, Clint. Shark & Other Sea Creatures Dictionary: An a to Z of Sea Life. 2002. (Illus.). 64p. (J). (978-0-439-46133-7(2)) Scholastic, Inc.

Underwater Animals. 2004. 23.70 (978-1-4103-0126-0(5) , Blackbirch Pr., Inc.) Thomson Gale.

Underwater Animals: Level O, 6 vols. (Explorers Ser.). 32p. (gr. 3-6). 44.95 (978-0-7699-0591-4(9)) Shortland Pubns. (U. S. A.) Inc.

Van Zandt, Steve. River Song: With the Banana Slug String Band (Includes Music CD) Zecca, Katherine, illus. 2007. 32p. (J). (gr. k-4). 17.95 (*978-1-58469-093-1(3)); pap. 9.95 (*978-1-58469-094-8(1)) Dawn Pubns.

Vida Marina. 2005. 130p. (J). spiral bd. 14.99 (978-1-59441-460-2(2) , K04011) Carson-Dellosa Publishing Co., Inc.

Vogel, Carole G. Ocean Wildlife. 2003. (Restless Sea Ser.). (Illus.). 96p. (J). (gr. 5-8). 30.50 (978-0-531-12324-9(3) , Watts, Franklin) Scholastic Library Publishing.

—Ocean Wildlife. 2003. (gr. 5-8). lib. bdg. 22.20 (978-0-613-67836-0(2)) Tandem Library Bks.

Wade, Laura. Sea & Sealife. 2003. (Knowledge Masters Ser.). (Illus.). 32p. (YA). pap. incl. cd-rom (978-1-903954-10-2(X)) Chrysalis Children's Bks.

Walker, Pam & Wood, Elaine. The Open Ocean. 2005. (Life in the Sea Ser.). (Illus.). 132p. (J). (gr. 4-9). 35.00 (978-0-8160-5705-4(2)) Facts On File, Inc.

Walker, Sally M. Manatees. 1999. (Nature Watch Ser.). (Illus.). 48p. (J). (gr. 3-6). lib. bdg. 25.26 (978-1-57505-299-1(7) , Carolrhoda Bks.) Lerner Publishing Group.

Walsh, Melanie. Ocean Animals. Walsh, Melanie, illus. 2002. (Tiny Teether Ser.). (Illus.). 14p. (J). (gr. k-ps). bds. 4.99 (978-0-7636-1807-0(1)) Candlewick Pr.

Weber, Valerie. Sea Slugs. 2005. (Weird Wonders of the Deep Ser.). (Illus.). 24p. (J). lib. bdg. 22.00 (978-0-8368-4563-1(3)) Stevens, Gareth Inc.

—Squids. 2005. (Weird Wonders of the Deep Ser.). (Illus.). 24p. (J). lib. bdg. 22.00 (978-0-8368-4564-8(1)) Stevens, Gareth Inc.

Weber, Valerie J. Wird Wonders of the Deep. 24p. (YA). 132.00 (978-0-8368-4559-4(5)) Stevens, Gareth Inc.

Weird Sea Creatures. (Illus.). (J). (gr. k-6). 112.50 (978-1-4042-3298-3(2)) Rosen Publishing Group, Inc., The.

Whitehouse, Patricia. Hiding in a Coral Reef. 2003. (Illus.). 32p. pap. 6.50 (978-1-4034-3185-1(X)); (J). lib. bdg. 22.79 (978-1-4034-0795-5(9)) Heinemann Library.

—Hiding in the Ocean. 2003. (Illus.). 32p. pap. 6.50 (978-1-4034-3189-9(2)); (J). lib. bdg. 22.79 (978-1-4034-0798-6(3)) Heinemann Library.

Who Grows up in the Ocean? (Who Grows up Here? Ser.). 24p. (J). 7.95 (978-1-4048-0208-7(8)) Picture Window Bks.

Who Lives in the Coral Reef. 2004. (J). 4.99 (978-0-931548-12-3(8)) Island Heritage Publishing.

Wicker, Jan Lee. Those Magical Manatees. 2007. pap. 8.95 (*978-1-56164-383-7(1)); 14.95 (*978-1-56164-382-0(3)) Pineapple Pr., Inc.

Wickings, Ruth. Animals in the Sea. 2006. (First Fun Pop-ups Ser.). (Illus.). 12p. bds. 8.95 (978-1-84560-023-5(1)) Mercury Bks. Ltd. GBR. *Dist:* International Publishers Marketing.

Wieland, Carl. Dragons of the Deep: Ocean Monsters Past & Present. Wiskur, Darrell, illus. 2005. 78p. (J). 15.99 (978-0-89051-424-5(0)) Master Bks.

Wilkes, Angela, contrib. by. Bajo el Mar: Under the Sea. 2004. (Ladders—Spanish Ser.). (SPA., Illus.). 32p. 12.95 (978-1-58728-475-5(8) , Two Can Publishing) T&N Children's Publishing.

Wilkes, Angela & Webster, Belinda. Under the Sea, 4 vols., Set. 1999. (Ladders Ser.). (Illus.). 32p. (J). (gr. k-3). (978-0-7166-7705-5(9)) World Bk., Inc.

Windsor, Jo. Toothwalkers: Individual Title Six-Packs. (Sails Literacy Ser.). 16p. (gr. 2-3). 27.00 (978-0-7578-0712-1(7)) Rigby Education.

Winkelman, Barbara Gaines. Puffer's Surprise. 2005. (Illus.). 32p. (J). (ps-2). 8.95 incl. audio (978-1-59249-062-2(X) , SC4024) Soundprints.

Wiskur, Darrell. Undersea Journey. 2002. (Take a Trip on the Silver Ship Ser.). (Illus.). (J). 6.99 (978-0-89051-379-8(1)) Master Bks.

Wlodarski, Loran. The Story of Manatees: Siren's Song. 2nd rev. ed. 1998. (Education Department Animal Information Publications). (Illus.). 64p. (gr. 4-12). per. 7.99 (978-1-893698-00-0(9) , B07, SeaWorld Education Dept.) SeaWorld, Inc.

Woodward, John. Eels. 2004. (Nature's Children Ser.). (Illus.). 48p. (J). 199.00 (978-0-7172-5957-1(9)); (978-0-7172-5962-5(5)) Scholastic Library Publishing. (Grolier).

World Book, Inc Staff, contrib. by. Under the Sea. 2007. (J). (*978-0-7166-7731-4(8)) World Bk., Inc.

Wymarra, Elizabeth & Wymarra, Wandihnu. Wandihnu & the Old Dugong. 2007. 28p. pap. 17.00 (*978-1-921248-18-4(1)) Magabala Bks. AUS. *Dist:* International Specialized Bk. Services.

Yelagalawadi, Jyoti. Deep Sea Creatures. Nagaraju, Harsha, illus. 2004. 32p. (J). 14.99 (978-0-9725901-2-9(9)) Lekha Pubs., LLC.

Yoon, Salina, creator. Sea Creatures: A Sparkling Little Colors Book, 4 vols. 2005. (Illus.). 12p. (J). 5.95 (978-1-58117-169-3(2) , Intervisual/Piggy Toes) Dalmatian Pr.

Young, Karen Romano. Across the Wide Ocean: The Why, How, & Where of Navigation for Humans & Animals at Sea. Young, Karen Romano, illus. 2007. 80p. (J). (gr. 5-7). lib. bdg. 19.89 (978-0-06-009087-6(1)); (Illus.). 18.99 (978-0-06-009086-9(3)) HarperCollins Pubs.

MARINE ANIMALS—FICTION

Aigner-Clark, Julie. World Around Me: Oceans. 2003. (Baby Einstein Ser.). 12p. (ps-17). 15.99 (978-0-7868-1913-3(8)) Disney Pr.

Amato, Carol A. Chessie, the Meandering Manatee, Vol. 8. Wenzel, David, illus. 1998. (Young Reader Ser.). 48p. (J). (gr. 3-6). lib. bdg. 13.45 (978-1-56674-239-9(0)) Forest Hse. Publishing Co., Inc.

Anderson, R. P., et al. Curious George at the Aquarium. Hines, Anna Grossnickle, illus. 2007. 24p. (J). (ps-k). 12.95 (*978-0-618-80067-4(0)); pap. 3.95 (*978-0-618-80068-1(9)) Houghton Mifflin Co.

Andreae, Giles. The Pop-Up Commotion in the Ocean. Wojtowycz, David, illus. 2002. 12p. (J). tchr. ed. 14.95 (978-1-58925-680-4(8) , tiger tales) ME Media LLC.

Arnosky, Jim. A Manatee Morning. 2001. (J). per. 5.99 (978-0-689-81605-5(7) , Aladdin) Simon & Schuster Children's Publishing.

Artifact Group. Atlantis SquarePantis. 2007. (SpongeBob SquarePants Ser.). 24p. (J). pap. 3.99 (*978-1-4169-3799-9(4) , Simon Spotlight/Nickelodeon) Simon & Schuster Children's Publishing.

Auerbach, Annie. Spongebob Superstar, Vol. 5. 2004. 64p. (J). (gr. 2-5). pap. 17.00 incl. audio (978-1-4000-8628-3(0) , Listening Library) Random Hse. Audio Publishing Group.

Banks, Steven. The Big Halloween Scare. Martinez, Heather, illus. 2005. (Ready-to-Read Ser. Level 2: 1). 32p. (J). lib. bdg. 15.00 (978-1-59054-987-2(2)) Fitzgerald Bks.

—The Big Halloween Scare. Martinez, Heather, illus. 2003. (SpongeBob SquarePants Ready-To-Read Ser.: Vol. 1). 32p. (J). (gr. k-2). pap. 3.99 (978-0-689-84196-5(5) , Simon Spotlight/Nickelodeon) Simon & Schuster Children's Publishing.

—The Big Halloween Scare. Martinez, Heather, illus. 2003. 32p. (J). (gr. k-2). lib. bdg. 11.80 (978-0-613-73339-7(8)) Tandem Library Bks.

—Lost in Time. The Artifact Group, illus. 2006. 22p. (J). lib. bdg. 15.00 (*978-1-4242-0977-4(3)) Fitzgerald Bks.

—Lost in Time. 2007. 24p. (J). 21.35 (*978-1-59961-367-3(0)) Spotlight.

—Show Me the Bunny! 2004. (gr. k-3). lib. bdg. 11.80 (978-0-613-73446-2(7)) Tandem Library Bks.

—Special Delivery! DePorter, Vince, illus. 2003. (SpongeBob SquarePants Ready-To-Read Ser.: Vol. 2). 32p. (J). pap. 3.99 (978-0-689-85887-1(6) , Simon Spotlight/Nickelodeon) Simon & Schuster Children's Publishing.

—Spongebob Goes to the Doctor. Saunders, Zina, illus. 2005. 22p. (J). lib. bdg. 15.00 (*978-1-4242-0976-7(5)) Fitzgerald Bks.

—Stop the Presses! DePorter, Vince, illus. 2005. 22p. (J). lib. bdg. 15.00 (*978-1-4242-0973-6(0)) Fitzgerald Bks.

Banks, Steven & Artifact Group. For the Love of Bubbles. 2006. (SpongeBob SquarePants Ser.). 64p. (J). pap. 4.99 (978-1-4169-1633-8(4) , Simon Spotlight/Nickelodeon) Simon & Schuster Children's Publishing.

Banks, Steven & Hillenburg, Stephen. Show Me the Bunny! Greenblatt, C. H. & Reiss, William, illus. 2004. (SpongeBob SquarePants Ready-To-Read Ser.: Vol. 3). 32p. (J). pap. 3.99 (978-0-689-86485-8(X) , Simon Spotlight/Nickelodeon) Simon & Schuster Children's Publishing.

Banks, Steven & Hillenburg, Stephen. SpongeBob Goes to the Doctor. Saunders, Zina, illus. 2005. (J). (*978-1-4156-3131-7(X) , Simon Spotlight/Nickelodeon) Simon & Schuster Children's Publishing.

Base, Graeme. The Sign of the Seahorse: A Tale of Greed & High Adventure in Two Acts. 1998. (Picture Puffin Ser.). (Illus.). 48p. (J). (gr. 1-4). pap. 8.99 (978-0-14-056387-0(3) , Puffin) Penguin Group (USA) Inc.

Baum, L. Frank. The Sea Fairies. l.t. ed. 2004. (Large Print Ser.). lib. bdg. 25.00 (978-1-58287-793-8(9)) North Bks.

Bedford, David. Little Otter's Big Journey. Winter, Susan, illus. 2006. 28p. (J). 16.00 (978-1-56148-548-2(9)) Good Bks.

Blackstone, Stella. Secret Seahorse. Beaton, Clare, illus. 24p. (J). 2005. pap. 6.99 (978-1-84148-937-7(9)); 2005. 15.99 (978-1-84148-704-5(X)); 2004. per. 6.99 (978-1-905236-15-2(8)) Barefoot Bks., Inc.

Boey, Stephanie. Undersea Treasure Hunt: Find the Treasure with Little Fish & Friends. Boey, Stephanie, illus. 2005. (Illus.). 20p. (J). 15.95 (978-0-8118-4622-6(9)) Chronicle Bks. LLC.

Bonnell, Kris. Down in the Sea. 2006. (J). 3.95 (*978-1-933727-38-7(1)) Reading Reading Bks., LLC.

—Mudskipper & the Water. 2006. (J). 3.95 (*978-1-933727-21-9(7)) Reading Reading Bks., LLC.

Bonnell, Kris. Who Goes in the Water. 2005. (J). 3.75 (978-1-933727-20-2(9)) Reading Reading Bks., LLC.

Book Company Staff. Ocean Friends. Lassen, Christian R., illus. 2003. (Puzzles Ser.). (J). bds. 14.95 (978-1-74047-381-1(7)) Book Co. Publishing Pty, Ltd., The AUS. *Dist:* Penton Overseas, Inc.

—Treasures of the Sea: Birthday & Address Book. Lassen, Christian R., illus. 2003. (Stationery Ser.). (J). 14.95 (978-1-86309-793-2(7)) Book Co. Publishing Pty, Ltd., The AUS. *Dist:* Penton Overseas, Inc.

Brookes, C. Avery. Sea Breezes, Salt Air. 1999. (Illus.). 53 p. (J). 6.95 (978-0-9666246-0-1(2) , Bunny Express Pr.) Brookes, C. Avery Ltd.

Brooks, David. You Can Count at the Ocean. 2005. (Illus.). 24p. (J). bds. (978-1-55971-930-8(3) , NorthWord Bks. for Young Readers) T&N Children's Publishing.

Brooks, John. Balloons, Sea Creatures, & Me. 2006. 34p. (J). 14.58 (978-0-9661789-3-7(9)) Lulu.com.

Burns, Joanne. Ollie Oyster's Ouch. 2005. 21p. 8.99 (978-1-4116-5337-5(8)) Lulu.com.

Carle, Eric. A House for a Hermit Crab. 2002. (gr. k-3). lib. bdg. 15.30 (978-0-613-90187-1(8)) Tandem Library Bks.

Carty, Jay, et al. O. Whillikers in the Hall of Champions. 2000. (Illus.). 112p. (J). pap. 13.00 (978-0-8307-2634-9(9) , Gospel Light) Gospel Light Pubns.

Chanda, J-P. Happy Birthday, SpongeBob! Martinez, Heather, illus. 2005. (Ready-To-Read Ser.). 24p. (J). pap. 3.99 (978-0-689-87674-5(2) , Simon Spotlight/Nickelodeon) Simon & Schuster Children's Publishing.

Cherry, Lynne. The Sea, the Storm, & the Mangrove Tangle. 2004. (Illus.). 40p. (J). 17.00 (978-0-374-36482-3(6) , Farrar, Straus & Giroux (BYR)) Farrar, Straus & Giroux.

Chipponeri, Kelli. SpongeBob Rocks! Martinez, Heather, illus. 2006. (SpongeBob SquarePants Ready-To-Read Ser.: Vol. 9). 32p. (J). pap. 3.99 (978-1-4169-1314-6(9) , Simon Spotlight/Nickelodeon) Simon & Schuster Children's Publishing.

Collins, Terry. Tea at the Treedome. 2004. 64p. (J). (gr. 2-5). pap. 17.00 incl. audio (978-0-8072-1986-7(X) , Listening Library) Random Hse. Audio Publishing Group.

Conrique, Samantha. The Pod-Poppers. 2007. (J). pap. 8.00 (*978-0-8059-7200-9(5)) Dorrance Publishing Co., Inc.

Cummings, Priscilla. Meet Chadwick & His Chesapeake Bay Friends. Cohen, A. R., illus. 1999. 30p. (J). (ps-3). 11.95 (978-0-87033-516-7(2) , Tidewater Pubs.) Cornell Maritime Pr., Inc.

De Armond, Garry E. Bugaroos: The Adventure Begins. Huff, Nichalos, illus. 2000. 32p. (YA). (gr. k-4). 19.95 (978-0-9676287-0-7(9)) De Armond, Garry.

DePrisco, Dorothea. Mini Whos in the Ocean. 2006. 10p. 4.95 (978-1-58117-509-7(4) , Intervisual/Piggy Toes) Dalmatian Pr.

Diesen, Deborah. The Pout-Pout Fish. Hanna, Dan, illus. 2008. 32p. (J). 16.00 (*978-0-374-36096-2(0)) Farrar, Straus & Giroux.

Donovan, Gail. !Listos... Ya! Clar, David Austin, illus. 2003. (Rainbow Fish & Friends Ser.). 24p. (J). mass mkt. 3.99 (978-1-59014-123-6(7)) Night Sky Bks.

Douglas, Vincent & School Specialty Publishing Staff. Sandy Starfish. 2006. (Bath Buddies Ser.). 7p. (J). 12.95 (978-0-7696-4597-1(6) , Brighter Child) School Specialty Publishing.

Edgemon, Darcie. Seamore, the Very Forgetful Porpoise. Seibold, J. Otto, illus. 2008. 48p. (J). 16.99 (*978-0-06-085075-3(2)); lib. bdg. 17.89 (*978-0-06-085076-0(0)) HarperCollins Pubs.

Farrelly, Peter. Abigale the Happy Whale. Rama, Jamie, illus. 2006. 32p. (J). (ps-1). 15.99 (978-0-316-01190-7(8) , Tingley, Megan Bks.) Little, Brown Bks. for Young Readers.

Ferris, Aimee. Girl Overboard. 2007. (S. A. S. S. (Students Across the Seven Seas) Ser.). 224p. (YA). (gr. 7). pap. 6.99 (978-0-14-240799-8(2) , Puffin) Penguin Group (USA) Inc.

Fogle, Llynda, et al. A Pond Full of Feelings. Bicking, Judy, illus. 2005. (SPA.). (J). (978-0-9760282-9-1(8)) RAPC - Sparkle & Shine Project.

Fontes, Justine. Who Lives at the Pond? Tagel, Peggy, illus. 2000. (Wiggly Tab Bks.). 6p. (J). (ps-k). bds. 5.99 (978-1-57584-351-3(X)) Reader's Digest Children's Publishing, Inc.

Fraknoi, Andrew & Gordon, David George. Disney Sea Creatures. Disney Press Staff, ed. Becker and Mayer, Ltd. Staff, illus. 2007. 48p. (gr. 1-4). 15.99 (*978-1-4231-0224-3(X)) Disney Pr.

Frasier, Debra. Out of the Ocean. 2002. (Illus.). 40p. (J). pap. 7.00 (978-0-15-216354-9(9) , Voyager Bks./Libros Viajeros) Harcourt Children's Bks.

—Out of the Ocean. 2002. (gr. 3-6). lib. bdg. 15.30 (978-0-613-53850-3(1)) Tandem Library Bks.

Freeman, Jeanne M. Katie's Pond. Recchia, Anne, illus. unabr. ed. 2001. 65p. (J). (ps-3). pap. 14.95 (978-0-9717284-1-7(0)) Sonrel Pr.

Gall, Steve J. Sea Serpent's Birthday Present. Hume, Pepper, illus. 2002. (J). pap. 10.00 incl. audio compact disk (978-1-931457-14-9(X)) Stargate Electronic Library, Inc.

Galloway, Ruth. Smiley Shark. Galloway, Ruth, illus. (Illus.). 32p. (J). 2005. 6.95 (978-1-58925-391-9(4)); 2003. tchr. ed. 15.95 (978-1-58925-028-4(1)) ME Media LLC. (tiger tales).

Gerstein, Sherry. My Great Aunt Phibian. Reader's Digest Editors, ed. Van Fleet, Mara, illus. 2005. 10p. (J). bds. 12.99 (978-0-7944-0506-9(1) , Reader's Digest Children's Bks.) Reader's Digest Children's Publishing, Inc.

Ginger & the Seagull. 2000. 26p. (J). 7.95 (978-1-931015-01-1(5)) Distant Waters Publishing & Designs.

Gould, Robert. Sea Creatures. Epstein, Eugene, illus. Gould, Robert, photos by. 2005. (Big Stuff Ser.: 8). 16p. (J). bds. 7.95 (978-1-929945-59-7(0)) Big Guy Bks., Inc.

Greenburg, J. C. In the Deep. Gerardi, Jan, illus. 2004. (Andrew Lost Ser.: Bk. 8). 96p. (J). (gr. 2-5). pap. 3.99 (978-0-375-82526-2(6) , Random Hse. Bks. for Young Readers) Random Hse. Children's Bks.

—In the Deep, No. 8. Reed, Mike, illus. 2004. (Andrew Lost Ser.: Bk. 8). 96p. (J). (gr. 2-5). lib. bdg. 11.99 (978-0-375-92526-9(0) , Random Hse. Bks. for Young Readers) Random Hse. Children's Bks.

—On the Reef. Reed, Mike, tr. Reed, Mike & Gerardi, Jan, illus. 2004. (Andrew Lost Ser.: Bk. 7). 96p. (J). (gr. 2-5). lib. bdg. 11.99 (978-0-375-92525-2(2)); pap. 3.99 (978-0-375-82525-5(8)) Random Hse. Children's Bks. (Random Hse. Bks. for Young Readers).

—Under Water. Reed, Mike, illus. 2003. (Andrew Lost Ser.: Bk. 5). 96p. (J). (gr. 2-5). mass mkt. 3.99 (978-0-375-82523-1(1) , Random Hse. Bks. for Young Readers) Random Hse. Children's Bks.

Grindley, Sally & Foreman, Michael. La Playa de Pedro. 2004. (SPA., Illus.). 32p. (J). 19.99 (978-84-261-3314-4(2)) Juventud, Editorial ESP. *Dist:* Lectorum Pubns., Inc.

Harcourt School Publishers Staff. At the Beach. 3rd ed. 2002. (Trophies English Language Learners Ser.). (Illus.). pap. 5.10 (978-0-15-327888-4(9)) Harcourt Schl. Pubs.

—At the Beach: Independent Reader. 3rd ed. 2002. (Trophies Reading Program Ser.). (Illus.). (J). pap. 2.90 (978-0-15-325501-4(3)) Harcourt Schl. Pubs.

—I Swam with a Seal Little Book. 3rd ed. 2002. (Trophies Reading Program Ser.). (Illus.). (J). pap. 10.20 (978-0-15-329364-1(0)) Harcourt Schl. Pubs.

—Tidal Camp On Level. 3rd ed. 2002. (Trophies Reading Program Ser.). (Illus.). pap. 5.10 (978-0-15-323449-1(0)) Harcourt Schl. Pubs.

Harms, John, II. The Saving of Okee & Dokee Sea Turtle. Belizar, Denise H., ed. Makowski, Robin Lee, illus. 2001. 32p. (gr. 7-12). (J). lib. bdg. 18.95 (978-1-931329-03-3(6)); (YA). 14.95 (978-0-9653871-4-9(3)); (YA). pap. 6.95 (978-0-9653871-5-6(1)) Frederick Pr.

Holman, Doris Anne. Mandy & Sally Manatee. 2001. (Illus.). 26p. (J). (gr. 3-7). pap. (978-0-9667192-4-6(7)) Holman, Doris Anne.

Holmes, Steve, illus. Animales Marinos: Mezcla y Diviertete. 2005. (Mezcla y Diviertete Ser.). (SPA.). 5p. (J). (ps-7). 7.95 (978-970-718-291-2(1) , Silver Dolphin en Español) Advanced Marketing, S. de R. L. de C. V. MEX. *Dist:* Perseus Distribution.

Ibbotson, Eva. Island of the Aunts. 2001. 304p. (YA). (gr. 4-7). pap. 5.99 (978-0-14-230049-7(7) , Puffin) Penguin Group (USA) Inc.

—Monster Mission. l.t. ed. 2006. pap. 16.95 (978-1-4056-6057-0(0)) BBC Audio GBR. *Dist:* BBC Audiobooks America.

Kennedy, Lisa. The Seashell. Kennedy, Darlene, illus. 2000. 9p. (J). (ps-6). pap. 4.95 (978-0-9708610-0-9(1)) Wee Wonder Bks.

Kono Juliet. Bravest Opihi. Fujitake Dennis, illus. 2005. 32p. 14.95 (978-1-933067-12-4(8)) Beachhouse Publishing, LLC.

Korman, Susan. Swordfish Returns. Stegos, Daniel, illus. 2005. 32p. (J). (ps-2). 4.95 (978-1-59249-126-1(X) , B4075); 9.95 (978-1-59249-132-2(4) , PB4075); 19.95 incl. audio (978-1-59249-128-5(6) , BC4025) Soundprints.

—Swordfish Returns. Stegos, Daniel, tr. Stegos, Daniel, illus. 2005. 32p. (J). (ps-2). 15.95 (978-1-59249-125-4(1) , B4025); pap. 6.95 (978-1-59249-127-8(8) , S4025) Soundprints.

—Swordfish Returns. Stegos, Daniel, illus. 2003. 32p. (J). (ps-2). 8.95 incl. audio (978-1-59249-129-2(4) , SC4025) Soundprints.

Lavelle, Sheila. Ursula by the Sea. (Illus.). 1p. (J). 13.95 (978-0-241-11914-3(6) , Hamilton, Hamish) Penguin Bks., Ltd. GBR. *Dist:* Trafalgar Square Publishing.

Lewman, David. Bubble Blowers, Beware! Goldberg, Barry, illus. 2004. 22p. (J). lib. bdg. 15.00 (*978-1-4242-0974-3(9)) Fitzgerald Bks.

—Jokes from the Krusty Krab. Style Guide Staff, illus. 2005. (Spongebob Squarepants Ser.). 48p. (J). pap. 3.99 (978-1-4169-0652-0(5) , Simon Spotlight) Simon & Schuster Children's Publishing.

—SpongeBob & the Princess. Bond, Clint, illus. 2004. (SpongeBob SquarePants 8 X 8 Paperback ; #5 Ser.). 24p. (J). pap. 3.99 (978-0-689-86581-7(3) , Simon Spotlight/Nickelodeon) Simon & Schuster Children's Publishing.

Lewman, David, et al. Zoo Day Disaster. Dress, Robert, illus. 2005. (SpongeBob SquarePants Chapter Book Ser.: Vol. 10). 60p. (J). (*978-1-4156-0765-7(6) , Simon Spotlight/Nickelodeon) Simon & Schuster Children's Publishing.

Lumry, Amanda & Hurwitz, Laura. Adventures of Riley: Dolphins in Danger. McIntyre, Sarah, illus. 2005. 36p. 15.95 (978-0-9748411-1-3(0)) Eaglemont Pr.

Macveety, Sue Maney. Singing Sea/el Mar Que Canta. Zantay, Valerie, tr. 2005. (SPA., Illus.). 36p. per. 15.99 (978-1-4134-7275-2(3)) Xlibris Corp.

Martenz, Arden. Ocho: A Character-Education Story. 2002. 32p. (J). 6.95 (978-1-57543-112-3(2)) MAR*CO Products, Inc.

Miglis, Jenny. And the Winner Is... 2007. 24p. (J). 21.35 (*978-1-59961-363-5(8)) Spotlight.

MNO

Miles, Victoria. Pup's Supper. Tachiera, Andrea Z., illus. 1998. (J). bds. 5.95 (978-1-878244-22-2(1)) Monterey Bay Aquarium.

Miller, Edward. Captain Barnacle's Aquarium: Filled with Fun, Fishy Facts! 2006. 32p. (J). (ps-1). 14.95 (978-0-8109-5985-9(2)) Abrams, Harry N. , Inc.

Moeller, Kathleen H. Hoketichee & the Manatee. Soper, Pat, illus. 1998. (Books for Young Learners). 16p. (J). (gr. k-2). pap. 5.00 (978-1-57274-117-1(1) , A2745) Owen, Richard C. Pubs., Inc.

—Hoketichee y el Manati. Romo, Alberto, tr. Soper, Pat, illus. 1999. (Books for Young Learners).Tr. of Hoketichee & the Manatee. (SPA.). 16p. (J). (gr. k-2). pap. 5.00 (978-1-57274-292-5(5)) Owen, Richard C. Pubs., Inc.

Momi a Hawaiian Mermaid in the Land of Delight. 2001. (J). 8.99 (978-0-89610-356-6(0)) Island Heritage Publishing.

Mora, Ebie. Kai: The Honu Didn't Know He Was Brave. Tackett, Mike, illus. 2005. 24p. (J). 10.95 (978-1-56647-755-0(7)) Mutual Publishing LLC.

Morgan, Christopher. Pirates Drive Buses. 2008. 80p. (J). 14.95 (***978-1-59643-313-7(2)***) Roaring Brook Pr.

Narvick, the Whark (or a Shwale) 2003. (J). 8.95 (978-0-9729703-1-0(2)) Kidderature Publishing.

Oberheu, John. The Manatee That Flew. 2006. pap. 12.95 (978-0-9759818-8-7(9)) High-Pitched Hum Inc.

O'Neill, Michael Patrick. Fishy Friends: A Journey Through the Coral Kingdom. O'Neill, Michael Patrick, photos by. 2003. (Illus.). 64p. (J). 19.95 (978-0-9728653-0-2(6)) Batfish Bks.

Osborne, Mary Pope. Magische Baumhaus der Ruf. 18.95 (978-3-7855-4185-2(6)) Loewe Verlag GmbH DEU. *Dist:* Distribooks, Inc.

Ostrow, Kim. Great Snail Race. 2007. 24p. (J). 21.35 (***978-1-59961-364-2(6)***) Spotlight.

Pallotta, Jerry. Dory Story. Biedrzycki, David, illus. 32p. (J). (gr. k-2). 2004. pap. 7.95 (978-0-88106-076-8(3)); 2000. 15.95 (978-0-88106-075-1(5)) Charlesbridge Publishing, Inc.

—Dory Story. Biedrzycki, David, illus. 2004. (J). (ps-ps). lib. bdg. 14.50 (978-0-606-30230-2(1)) Tandem Library Bks.

Pass, Erica & Artifact Group. Hooray for Dads! 2007. (SpongeBob SquarePants Ser.). 24p. (J). pap. 3.99 (978-1-4169-2782-2(4) , Simon Spotlight/Nickelodeon) Simon & Schuster Children's Publishing.

Peck, Jan. Way down Deep in the Deep Blue Sea. Petrone, Valeria, illus. 2004. 32p. (J). 16.99 (978-0-689-85110-0(3)) Simon & Schuster Children's Publishing.

Pierre, Stephanie. What the Sea Saw. Doyle, Beverly, illus. 2006. 48p. (J). 16.95 (978-1-56145-359-7(5)) Peachtree Pubs., Ltd.

Rathmell, Donna & Rathmell, Doreen. Octavia Octopus & Her Purple Ink Cloud. McLennan, Connie, illus. 2006. 32p. (J). 15.95 (978-0-9764943-5-5(3)) Sylvan Dell Pubng.

Riddle, Jamie. Beach Bum Babies & Sand Sisters Stormy. 2006. 48p. pap. 12.95 (978-1-4241-3600-1(8)) PublishAmerica, Inc.

Ridinger, Gayle. A Star at the Bottom of the Sea. Parpajola, Andreina, illus. 2002. 32p. (J). (ps up). lib. bdg. 24.67 (978-0-8368-3175-7(6)) Stevens, Gareth Inc.

Ring, Susan. Innovative Kids Readers: the Great Barrier Reef - an Undersea Adventure. 2007. 32p. (J). (gr. 1-3). pap. 6.99 (978-1-58476-543-1(7)) Innovative Kids.

Roberts, Lynne. SpongeBob SquarePants. Mawhinney, Art, illus. 2004. (Look & Find Ser.). 24p. (J). (978-0-7853-9837-0(6) , 7208400) Publications International, Ltd.

Rohmann, Eric. The Cinder-Eyed Cats. 2001. 40p. (J). (gr. k-3). pap. 6.99 (978-0-440-41743-9(0) , Dragonfly Bks.) Random Hse. Children's Bks.

—The Cinder-Eyed Cats. 2001. 13.79 (978-0-606-22187-0(5)) Tandem Library Bks.

Romeu, Emma. My Manatee Friend. Vigil, Luis Gerardo Sanchez & Broeck, Fabricio Vanden, illus. (SPA.). 24p. (J). (gr. 3-5). pap. 7.95 (978-1-59437-845-4(2)) Santillana USA Publishing Co., Inc.

Rovetch, Lissa. 1,2,3 Octopus & Me. Gévry, Claudine, illus. 2006. (J). (978-1-58987-011-6(5)) Kindermusik International.

Salton, Liz. Eelfish, a Rock & Roll King. Hathaway, Karen, illus. 2004. 38p. pap. 17.95 (978-1-4137-1847-8(7)) PublishAmerica, Inc.

Saunders, Zina, illus. Trouble at the Krusty Krab! 2004. (Ready-to-Read Ser.). 32p. (J). pap. 3.99 (978-0-689-86838-2(3) , Simon Spotlight/Nickelodeon) Simon & Schuster Children's Publishing.

Schwarz, Viviane. Shark & Lobster's Amazing Undersea Adventure. Stewart, Joel, illus. 2006. 34p. (J). (***978-1-4156-8140-4(6)***) Candlewick Pr.

Seahorse's Surprise. 2002. (Oceanic Mini Bks.). (Illus.). 32p. (J). (978-1-59069-009-3(5) , H1010) Studio Mouse LLC.

Shahan, Sherry. La Estrella de Mar Tiene Hambre. Romo, Alberto, tr. Torrisi, Gary, illus. 1999. (Books for Young Learners).Tr. of Hungry Sea Star. (SPA.). 12p. (J). (gr. k-2). pap. 5.00 (978-1-57274-290-1(9)) Owen, Richard C. Pubs., Inc.

Shepherd, Jodie. Ocean Friends. Ovresat, Laura, illus. 2007. 12p. (J). bds. 7.99 (978-0-7944-1122-0(3)) Reader's Digest Assn., Inc., The.

Sherry, Kevin. I'm the Biggest Thing in the Ocean. 2007. (Illus.). 32p. (J). (ps). 16.99 (978-0-8037-3192-9(2) , Dial) Penguin Group (USA) Inc.

Silver Dolphin en Español Staff. Imanes Magicos: Amigos Del Mar: Magnets on the Move: Ocean Friends, Spanish-Language Editon. 2006. (Illus.). 8p. (J). bds. 12.95 (978-970-718-368-1(3) , Silver Dolphin en Español) Advanced Marketing, S. de R. L. de C. V. MEX. *Dist:* Perseus Distribution.

Sloat, Teri. There Was an Old Lady Who Swallowed a Trout. Ruffins, Reynold, illus. 2002. (J). 26.47 (978-0-7587-3781-6(5)) Book Wholesalers, Inc.

—There Was an Old Lady Who Swallowed a Trout. Ruffins, Reynold, illus. rev. ed. 32p. (J). (gr. k-2). 2002. pap. 7.95 (978-0-8050-6900-6(3)); 1998. 17.95 (978-0-8050-4294-8(6)) Holt, Henry & Co. (Holt, Henry & Co. Bks. For Young Readers).

—There Was an Old Lady Who Swallowed a Trout. 2002. (ps-2). lib. bdg. 15.25 (978-0-613-88115-9(X)) Tandem Library Bks.

Smiley, Minerva J. Billy's Search for Florida Undersea Treasure. Smiley, Russ, illus. 2002. 44p. (J). lib. bdg. 16.95 (978-0-89317-047-9(X) , RS-047X, Windward Publishing) Finney Co., Inc.

Soundprints. Ocean Adventures: Story-Time Treasury. 2005. (Smithsonian Institution Story-Time Treasures Ser.). (Illus.). 256p. (J). (ps-2). 14.95 (978-1-59069-226-4(8) , HT1001) Studio Mouse LLC.

SpongeBob SquarePants. 2007. (J). 128.10 (***978-1-59961-361-1(1)***) Spotlight.

Stadler, John. One Seal. Stadler, John, illus. 1999. (Illus.). 32p. (J). (ps-2). pap. 15.95 (978-0-531-30195-1(8) , Orchard Bks.) Scholastic, Inc.

Stanley, Jacqueline Vickery. Wolfie the Wolf-Eel: The Adventures of an Undersea Creature. Bastedo, Suzanne, ed. Stanley, Jacqueline Vickery, illus. 2000. (Illus.). 424p. (J). (gr. k-6). 18.95 (978-0-89716-828-1(3)) Peanut Butter Publishing.

Sula, Sondra & Sula, Robert. Briny Town: Shark Showdown. Sula, Robert, illus. 2000. (Illus.). 32p. (J). (gr. 1-3). pap. (978-0-9701450-6-2(3)) Long Hill Productions, Inc.

Tate, Suzanne. Sandy Seal: A Tale of Sea Dogs. Melvin, James, illus. l.t. ed. 2004. (Suzanne Tate's Nature Ser.). 28p. (J). pap. 4.95 (978-1-878405-49-4(7)) Nags Head Art, Inc.

Tokyopop Staff. Spongebob Squarepants. 2003. (gr. 3-6). lib. bdg. 16.45 (978-0-613-79933-1(X)); lib. bdg. 16.45 (978-0-613-79935-5(6)) Tandem Library Bks.

Vanier, Jolie. Puwaii Adventures with Joliea & Friends. 2006. 16.95 (***978-0-9787949-1-0(5)***) Puwaii International, LLC.

Ward, Jennifer. Somewhere in the Ocean. 2000. (J). (978-0-606-19468-6(1)) Tandem Library Bks.

Ward, Jennifer, et al. Somewhere in the Ocean. Spengler, Kenneth J., illus. 2000. 32p. (ps-2). 15.95 (978-0-87358-748-8(0) , Rising Moon Bks. for Young Readers) Northland Publishing.

Warnes, Tim & Galloway, Ruth. Fidgety Fish. 2001. (Illus.). 32p. (J). (ps-3). tchr. ed. 14.95 (978-1-58925-012-3(5) , tiger tales) ME Media LLC.

The Water Park, 6 Pack. (Sails Literacy Ser.). 16p. (gr. k up). 27.00 (978-0-7635-4415-7(9)) Rigby Education.

Weathers, Andrea. Hermy the Hermit Crab Goes Shopping. Thames, Bob, illus. 2001. 40p. (J). 15.99 (978-0-933101-20-3(1)) Legacy Pubns.

Wlodarski, Loran. If a Dolphin Were a Fish. Klein, Laurie Allen, illus. 2007. 1p. (J). 8.95 (***978-1-934359-03-7(3)***) Sylvan Dell Pubng.

Zimmerman, Andrea. My Manatee Mom. 2005. (Silly Millies Ser.). (Illus.). 32p. (J). (ps-4). pap. 4.99 (978-0-7613-1829-3(1) , First Avenue Editions) Lerner Publishing Group.

Zimmerman, Andrea & Clemesha, David. Manatee Mom. Swisher, Michael-Che, illus. 2005. (Silly Millies Ser.). 32p. (J). (ps-ps). lib. bdg. 18.60 (978-0-7613-2404-1(6) , Millbrook Pr.) Lerner Publishing Group.

MARINE ARCHITECTURE

see Naval Architecture; Shipbuilding

MARINE BIOLOGY

see also Fresh-Water Biology; Marine Animals; Marine Ecology; Marine Plants; Marine Resources

Allman, Toney. From Fish Gills to Underwater Breathing. 2006. (Imitating Nature Ser.). 32p. (J). (gr. 3-6). 24.95 (978-0-7377-3608-3(9) , Kidhaven) Thomson Gale.

Arnold, Caroline. Shockers of the Sea: And Other Electric Animals. Forest, Crista, illus. 1999. 32p. (J). (ps-3). 15.95 (978-0-88106-873-3(X)); pap. 6.95 (978-0-88106-874-0(8)) Charlesbridge Publishing, Inc.

Baines, Francesca. Ocean Worlds. 2004. (Discovery Guides Ser.). (SPA., Illus.). 32p. (J). (gr. 2-5). pap. 6.95 (978-1-58728-215-7(1) , Two Can Publishing) T&N Children's Publishing.

—Ocean Worlds. 2001. (gr. 3-6). lib. bdg. 15.25 (978-0-613-43482-9(X)) Tandem Library Bks.

Baker, Beth. Sylvia Earle. 2006. (Just the Facts Biographies Ser.). (Illus.). 112p. (J). 27.93 (978-0-8225-3422-8(3) , Lerner Pubns.) Lerner Publishing Group.

Baker, Lucy. Life in the Oceans. 2001. (World Book Ecology Ser.). (Illus.). 32p. (J). (978-0-7166-5222-9(6)) World Bk., Inc.

Bennett, Paul. Ocean Habitats. 2006. (Exploring Habitats Ser.). (Illus.). 36p. (J). lib. bdg. (978-0-8368-7255-2(X)) Stevens, Gareth Inc.

Berger, Melvin. What Makes an Ocean Wave? Questions & Answers about Oceans. 2001. (Question & Answer Ser.). (Illus.). (J). (978-0-606-20985-4(9)) Tandem Library Bks.

Brighter Vision Publishing Staff. Ocean Life. 1999. (Learning Adventures Preschool Ser.). (Illus.). (J). (ps-k). pap. 2.25 (978-1-55254-056-5(1) , BV12005) Brighter Vision Pubns.

Burton, Margie, et al. Ocean Animals. Adams, Alison, ed. 1999. (Early Connections Ser.). 16p. (J). (gr. k-2). pap. 4.50 (978-1-58344-074-2(7)) Benchmark Education Co.

Cerullo, Mary M. Sea Soup: Zooplankton. Curtsinger, Bill, photos by. 2005. (Illus.). 40p. (J). (gr. 3-7). 16.95 (978-0-88448-219-2(7)) Tilbury Hse. Pubs.

Collard, Sneed B., III. A Whale Biologist at Work. (Wildlife Conservation Society Bks.). (Illus.). 48p. (J). (gr. 4-6). 2001. pap. 6.95 (978-0-531-16526-3(4)); 2000. 24.50 (978-0-531-11786-6(3)) Scholastic Library Publishing. (Watts, Franklin).

—A Whale Biologist at Work. 2000. (Illus.). (J). (978-0-606-20984-7(0)) Tandem Library Bks.

Conlan, Kathy. Under the Ice. Conlan, Kathy, illus. 2002. (Illus.). 56p. (J). (gr. 4-6). (978-1-55337-001-7(5)) Kids Can Pr., Ltd.

Cooper, Jason. Crayfish. 2003. (Life Cycles II Ser.). (Illus.). 24p. (J). 25.64 (978-1-58952-704-1(6)) Rourke Publishing, LLC.

Crowson, Andrew. Flip Flap Ocean. 2003. (Illus.). 12p. bds. (978-1-85602-431-0(8)) Chrysalis Children's Bks.

Dalgleish, Sharon. Hidden World. 1999. (Explorers Ser.). 32p. (J). (978-0-7699-0492-4(0)) Shortland Pubns. (U. S. A.) Inc.

—Mini Mammals. 2002. (Junior Adventure Ser.). (Illus.). 32p. (J). lib. bdg. (978-1-59084-193-8(X)) Mason Crest Pubs.

—Ocean Life. 2002. (Junior Adventure Ser.). (Illus.). 32p. (J). (gr. 3 up). lib. bdg. (978-1-59084-177-8(8)) Mason Crest Pubs.

—Ocean Life. Cavaluzzo, Laura & McEwen, Rebecca, eds. 1999. (Explorers Ser.). (Illus.). 32p. (J). (978-0-7699-0480-1(7)) Shortland Pubns. (U. S. A.) Inc.

Davis, Buddy & Davis, Kay. Special Wonders of the Sea World. 1999. (Special Wonders Ser.). (Illus.). 80p. (J). (gr. 3-7). 12.99 (978-0-89051-253-1(1) , 303-056) Master Bks.

Day, Trevor. Exploring the Oceans, 4 vols. 2003. (Illus.). (J). (978-0-19-521967-8(8)); (978-0-19-521968-5(6)); (978-0-19-521969-2(4)); (978-0-19-521970-8(8)) Oxford Univ. Pr., Inc.

DK Publishing. Ocean. 2008. 512p. pap. 24.95 (***978-0-7566-3692-0(2)***) Dorling Kindersley Publishing, Inc.

—Sharkpedia. 2008. 128p. (J). (gr. 2-8). 12.99 (***978-0-7566-3761-3(9)***) Dorling Kindersley Publishing, Inc.

Esbensen, Barbara Juster. Sponges Are Skeletons, Stage 2. 1998. (Let's-Read-and-Find-Out Science Ser.). (978-0-606-13796-6(3)) Tandem Library Bks.

Exploring Creation Marine Biology. 2006. cd-rom 58.50 (978-1-932012-66-8(4)) Apologia Educational Ministries, Inc.

Exploring Creation Marine Biology Companion CD-ROM. 2006. cd-rom 13.50 (978-1-932012-67-5(2)) Apologia Educational Ministries, Inc.

Field, Nancy H. Discovering Sharks & Rays. Maydak, Michael S., illus. 2003. (Discovering Nature Library). 40p. (J). (gr. 2-6). pap. 7.95 (978-0-941042-33-8(2)) Dog-Eared Pubns.

Ganeri, Anita. Protecting Ocean Habitats. 2005. (Protecting Habitats Ser.). (Illus.). 32p. (J). lib. bdg. 24.67 (978-0-8368-4992-9(2)) Stevens, Gareth Inc.

Gilpin, Daniel. Life-Size Sharks & Other Underwater Creatures. Knowelden, Martin, illus. 2005. (Life-Size Ser.). 28p. (J). (ps-7). 9.95 (978-1-4027-2537-1(X)) Sterling Publishing Co., Inc.

Gilvan-Cartwright, Chris, illus. Who's in the Ocean? 2005. (Lift-The-Flap 'n' Learn Ser.). 10p. (J). 9.95 (978-1-58117-213-3(3) , Intervisual/Piggy Toes) Dalmatian Pr.

Goodman, Susan E. Wading into Marine Biology. 2000. (Ultimate Field Trip Ser.: Vol. 3). (J). (978-0-606-19253-8(0)) Tandem Library Bks.

Gross, Miriam J. The Sea Dragon. 2006. (Illus.). 24p. (J). lib. bdg. (978-1-4042-3193-1(5) , PowerKids Pr.) Rosen Publishing Group, Inc., The.

Guiberson, Brenda Z. Ocean Life. 2002. (Science Readers Level 2 Ser.). (Illus.). 48p. (J). (gr. 2-3). pap. 3.99 (978-0-439-31632-3(4) , Scholastic Reference) Scholastic, Inc.

Harcourt School Publishers Staff. Asombrosas Aranas: Take-Home Book. 2001. (Vamos Ser.). (SPA., Illus.). (J). pap. 2.80 (978-0-15-319934-9(2)) Harcourt Schl. Pubs.

—A Conversation about Life in the Ocean - 5 Pack - Grade 6, On-Level. 3rd ed. 2002. (Trophies Reading Program Ser.). pap. 25.60 (978-0-15-327528-9(6)) Harcourt Schl. Pubs.

Hart, Melissa. Exploring Ocean Life. 2007. 96p. pap. 19.99 (***978-1-4206-8877-1(4)***) Teacher Created Resources, Inc.

Haydon, Julie. Marine Biologists. 2004. (J). lib. bdg. 27.10 (978-1-58340-540-6(2)) Smart Apple Media.

Hemmel, David Lee & Knutson, Janette C. Alexis' Island: Growing up in the Tropical Paradise of Key West. 2006. (J). per. 14.95 (978-0-9745637-2-5(2)) Duval Publishing.

Hirschmann, Kris. Ocean Hunters. 2001. (Planet Reader Ser.). (Illus.). (J). (978-0-606-21361-5(9)) Tandem Library Bks.

Hitchcock, Susan Tyler. Sylvia A. Earle: Deep Sea Explorer. 2004. (Women Explorers Ser.). (Illus.). 120p. 30.00 (978-0-7910-7712-2(8) , Chelsea Hse.) Facts On File, Inc.

Howard, Fran. Oceans. 2007. (Habitats Ser.). (Illus.). 32p. (J). (gr. k-4). lib. bdg. 22.78 (978-1-59679-781-9(9)) ABDO Publishing Co.

Jablonsky, Alice & Webster, Steven K. Discover Ocean Life. O'Neill, Pablo Montes & Robare, Lorie, trs. O'Neill, Pablo Montes & Robare, Lorie, illus. 2005. (Discover Ser.). 48p. (J). (978-0-7853-6111-4(1) , 3013407) Publications International, Ltd.

Johnson, Rebecca L. Sylvia Earle: Protecting the Seas. 2002. (Scientists in the Field Ser.). (Illus.). 32p. (J). (978-0-7922-8879-4(3)) National Geographic Society.

Kalman, Bobbie. Ocean Biome. 2003. (gr. 3-6). lib. bdg. 15.25 (978-0-613-59134-8(8)) Tandem Library Bks.

Klingel, Cynthia Fitterer & Noyed, Robert B. Oceans. 2001. (Wonder Books Level 2: Habitats Ser.). (Illus.). 24p. (J). (ps-3). 22.79 (978-1-56766-974-9(3)) Child's World, Inc.

Kosek, Jane Kelly. What's Inside the Ocean? 1999. (What's Inside Library). 24p. (J). (gr. k-4). lib. bdg. 18.75 (978-0-8239-5278-6(9) , PowerKids Pr.) Rosen Publishing Group, Inc., The.

Lalley. Ocean Scientists. 2001. (Scientists of the Biomes Ser.). (Illus.). (J). pap. (978-0-7398-4938-5(7)) Steck-Vaughn.

Lalley, Pat & Kittmans-Lalley, Janet. Ocean Scientists. 2001. (Scientists of the Biomes Ser.). (Illus.). 48p. (J). lib. bdg. 24.26 (978-0-7398-4750-3(3)) Raintree.

Lantz, Peggy S. & Hale, Wendy A. The Florida Water Story: From Raindrops to the Sea. Barnes, Jean, illus. 1998. 132p. (J). (gr. 5-7). 19.95 (978-1-56164-099-7(9)) Pineapple Pr., Inc.

Lassen, Christian Riese. Sea Creatures: A Read & Play Carry Puzzle Book. 2001. (Illus.). 10p. (J). (ps-3). 12.95 (978-0-7407-1800-7(2)) Andrews McMeel Publishing.

Leonhardt, Alice. Ocean Life: Tide Pool Creatures. 1999. (Pair-It Books). (Illus.). 40p. (J). pap. 5.65 (978-0-7398-0869-6(9)); (gr. 2-4). pap. 5.95 (978-0-7398-1481-9(8)) Steck-Vaughn.

Look Who's Popping Up: Under the Sea. 2003. (J). (ps-k). 4.98 (978-0-7525-8904-6(0)) Parragon, Inc.

MacAulay, Kelley & Kalman, Bobbie. Tropical Oceans. 2005. (Living Ocean Ser.). (Illus.). 32p. (J). (978-0-7787-1300-5(8)) Crabtree Publishing Co.

MacQuitty, Miranda. Ocean. 2008. (DK Eyewitness Bks.). 72p. (J). (gr. 3-8). 15.99 (***978-0-7566-3776-7(7)***) Dorling Kindersley Publishing, Inc.

Marine Science. 2001. (J). Book 1. per. 12.95 (978-1-883055-45-5(8)); Book 2. per. 12.95 (978-1-883055-46-2(6)); Book 3. per. 12.95 (978-1-883055-47-9(4)) Dandy Lion Pubns.

Marshall Cavendish Corporation Staff. Aquatic Life of the World, 11 vols., Vols. 1-10. 2000. (Illus.). (J). (978-0-7614-7181-3(2)) Cavendish, Marshall Corp.

Marshall Cavendish Corporation Staff, contrib. by. Aquatic Life of the World, 11 vols., Set. 2000. (Illus.). 700p. (gr. 4-6). 471.36 (978-0-7614-7170-7(7) , Cavendish, Marshall Reference Bks.) Cavendish, Marshall Corp.

Marshall Cavendish Corporation Staff, ed. Aquatic Life of the World, 11 vols. 2000. (Illus.). (J). (978-0-7614-7171-4(5)); 700p. 329.95 (978-0-7614-7172-1(3)); (978-0-7614-7173-8(1)); (978-0-7614-7174-5(X)); (978-0-7614-7175-2(8)); (978-0-7614-7176-9(6)); (978-0-7614-7177-6(4)); (978-0-7614-7178-3(2)); (978-0-7614-7179-0(0)); (978-0-7614-7180-6(4)) Cavendish, Marshall Corp.

Meucci, Antonella. Seas & Oceans. Chesi, Matteo, illus. 2000. (Nature's Record-Breakers Ser.). 32p. (J). (gr. 3 up). lib. bdg. 23.33 (978-0-8368-2475-9(X)) Stevens, Gareth Inc.

Moor, Jo Ellen. Life in the Ocean. Evans, Marilyn, ed. Larsen, Jo, illus. 1998. (Science Picture Cards Ser.: Vol. 3). 24p. (J). (gr. 1-3). pap., tchr. ed. 12.95 (978-1-55799-694-7(6) , EMC 865) Evan-Moor Educational Pubs.

Morgan, Sally. Oceans. (Extreme Survival Ser.). (Illus.). 32p. (J). 2004. pap. 7.95 (978-1-4109-0361-7(3)); 2003. lib. bdg. 25.70 (978-1-4109-0002-9(9)) Raintree.

—Oceans. 2003. (gr. 3-6). lib. bdg. 16.40 (978-0-613-78254-8(2)) Tandem Library Bks.

Morrison, Marianne. Science Chapters: Mysteries of the Sea: How Divers Explore the Ocean Depths. 2006. (National Geographic Science Chapters Ser.). (Illus.). 48p. (gr. 1-4). 17.90 (978-0-7922-5954-1(8) , National Geographic Children's Bks.) National Geographic Society.

Niesen, Thomas M. & Coloring Concepts Inc. Staff. The Marine Biology Coloring Book. 2nd ed. 2000. (Coloring Bks.). (Illus.). 272p. pap. 21.95 (978-0-06-273718-2(X)) HarperCollins Pubs.

Ocean Life, 14 bks. Incl. Corals. Schaefer, Lola M. Saunders-Smith, Gail, ed. 1999. lib. bdg. 15.93 (978-0-7368-0244-4(4)); Crabs. Schaefer, Lola M. Saunders-Smith, Gail, ed. 1999. lib. bdg. 15.93 (978-0-7368-0245-1(2)); Dolphins. Rustad, Martha E. H. Saunders-Smith, Gail, ed. 2001. lib. bdg. 15.93 (978-0-7368-0857-6(4)); Jellyfish. Rustad, Martha E. H. 2003. lib. bdg. 15.93 (978-0-7368-1656-4(9)); Manatees. Rustad, Martha E. H. 2003. lib. bdg. 15.93 (978-0-7368-1657-1(7)); Octopuses. Schaefer, Lola M. Saunders-Smith, Gail, ed. 1999. lib. bdg. 15.93 (978-0-7368-0246-8(0)); Parrotfish. Schaefer, Lola M. Saunders-Smith, Gail, ed. 1999. lib. bdg. 15.93 (978-0-7368-0247-5(9)); Rays. Rustad, Martha E. H. Saunders-Smith, Gail, ed. 2001. lib. bdg. 15.93 (978-0-7368-0858-3(2)); Sea Anemones. Schaefer, Lola M. Saunders-Smith, Gail, ed. 1999. lib. bdg. 15.93 (978-0-7368-0248-2(7)); Sea Horses. Schaefer, Lola M. Saunders-Smith, Gail, ed. 1999. lib. bdg. 15.93 (978-0-7368-0249-9(5)); Sea Snakes. Rustad, Martha E. H. 2003. lib. bdg. 15.93 (978-0-7368-1658-8(5)); Sea Stars. Schaefer, Lola M. Saunders-Smith, Gail, ed. 1999. lib. bdg. 15.93 (978-0-7368-0250-5(9)); Sea Turtles. Rustad, Martha E. H. Saunders-Smith, Gail, ed. 2001. lib. bdg. 15.93 (978-0-7368-0859-0(0)); Sea Urchins. Schaefer, Lola M. Saunders-Smith, Gail, ed. 1999. lib. bdg. 15.93 (978-0-7368-0251-2(7)); Seals. Rustad, Martha E. H. Saunders-Smith, Gail, ed. 2001. lib. bdg. 15.93 (978-0-7368-0860-6(4)); Sharks. Rustad, Martha E. H. Saunders-Smith, Gail, ed. 2001. lib. bdg. 15.93 (978-0-7368-0861-3(2)); Walrus. Rustad, Martha E. H. 2003. lib. bdg. 15.93 (978-0-7368-1659-5(3)); Whales. Rustad, Martha E. H. Saunders-Smith, Gail, ed. 2001. lib. bdg. 15.93 (978-0-7368-0862-0(0)); 24p. (J). (gr. k-1). (Illus.). Set lib. bdg. 286.74 (978-0-7368-1672-4(0) , Pebble Bks.) Capstone Pr., Inc.

Ocean Life. gif. ed. (Illus.). (J). (ps-k). 6.95 (978-1-55254-261-3(0) , BV50004) Brighter Vision Pubns.

Ocean Life: Level Q, 6 vols., Vol. 2. (Explorers Ser.). 32p. (gr. 3-6). 44.95 (978-0-7699-0604-1(4)) Shortland Pubns. (U. S. A.) Inc.

Ocean Life II Set. (gr. k-2). 172.95 (978-0-7368-9119-6(6)) Red Brick Learning.

A Ocean Life, Set. 2005. (Ocean Life Ser.). (YA). (gr. k-3). 267.30 (978-0-7368-4214-3(4) , Pebble Bks.) Capstone Pr., Inc.

Ocean Life Set. (gr. k-2). 230.95 (978-0-7368-9044-1(0)) Red Brick Learning.

Ocean Life, Set B. 2005. (Ocean Life Ser.). (YA). (gr. k-3). 267.30 (978-0-7368-4215-0(2) , Pebble Bks.) Capstone Pr., Inc.

Oceans & Underwater Life. 2001. (J). (978-0-307-10539-4(3) , 10539, Golden Bks.) Random Hse. Children's Bks.

Pallotta, Jerry. Underwater Counting: Even Numbers. 2001. (Illus.). (J). (978-0-606-20964-9(6)) Tandem Library Bks.

Patchett, Fiona. Under the Sea. Kushii, Tetsuo & Wray, Zoë, illus. 2006. (Usborne Beginners Ser.). 32p. (J). ***(978-0-439-02673-4(3))*** Scholastic, Inc.

Patchett, Fiona. Under the Sea (Level 1) - Internet Referenced. 2006. (Illus.). 32p. (J). 4.99 (978-0-7945-1336-8(0) , Usborne) EDC Publishing.

Pebble Books: Ocean Life. 2005. (YA). (gr. k-3). 534.60 (978-0-7368-4223-5(3) , Pebble Bks.) Capstone Pr., Inc.

Petach, Heidi. Sea Life Dot-to-Dot. 2001. (Illus.). 32p. (J). (ps-2). pap. 3.95 (978-0-486-41541-3(4)) Dover Pubns., Inc.

Piano, Maureen. My Adventure with Tidepools. 2007. 44p. (J). 8.99 (978-1-59092-473-0(8) , Orchard Academy Pr.) Windstorm Creative.

Pitkin, Linda M. Journey under the Sea. 2003. (Illus.). 48p. (YA). 22.95 (978-0-19-521971-5(6)) Oxford Univ. Pr., Inc.

Rhodes, Mary Jo & Hall, David. Life in a Kelp Forest. 2006. (Undersea Encounters Ser.). (Illus.). 48p. (J). (gr. 3-5). pap. 6.95 (978-0-516-25491-3(X) , Children's Pr.) Scholastic Library Publishing.

—Life in a Kelp Forest. Hall, David, photos by. 2005. (Undersea Encounters Ser.). (Illus.). 48p. (J). (ps-7). 27.00 (978-0-516-24396-2(9) , Children's Pr.) Scholastic Library Publishing.

Riley, Peter D. Floating & Sinking. Moller, Ray, photos by. 2002. (Everyday Science Ser.). (Illus.). 32p. (J). (gr. 1 up). lib. bdg. 23.33 (978-0-8368-3248-8(5)) Stevens, Gareth Inc.

Salas, Laura Purdie. Oceans. 2007. (Amazing Science Ser.). (Illus.). 24p. (J). ***(978-1-4048-3471-2(0)*** , 1265693) Picture Window Bks.

Salas, Laura Purdie. Oceans: Underwater Worlds. Yesh, Jeff, illus. 2006. (Amazing Science Ser.). 24p. (J). (978-1-4048-3097-4(9) , 1265693) Picture Window Bks.

Sauter Hill, Amy. Marine Biology: An Introduction to Ocean Ecosystems. 2002. (gr. 9-12). 46p. lab manual ed. 12.99 (978-0-8251-4401-1(9) , 0-44019); 2nd ed. 58p. tchr. ed. 13.99 (978-0-8251-4402-8(7) , 0-44027); 2nd ed. 144p. stu. ed. 36.99 (978-0-8251-4323-6(3)) Walch Publishing.

Schaefer, Lola M. La Anemona de Mar. 2002. (Animales Resbalosos (Ooey-Gooey Animals) Ser.). (SPA.). 24p. (J). (ps-1). lib. bdg. 18.50 (978-1-58810-872-2(4)); (Illus.). pap. 5.25 (978-1-58810-873-9(2) , 91516) Heinemann Library.

—Crayfish. 2002. (Musty-Crusty Animals Ser.). (Illus.). 24p. (J). (ps-1). pap. 5.25 (978-1-58810-722-0(1) , 91375); lib. bdg. 17.08 (978-1-58810-513-4(X)) Heinemann Library.

—Sea Horses. 2002. (Musty-Crusty Animals Ser.). (Illus.). 24p. (J). (ps-1). pap. 5.25 (978-1-58810-726-8(4) , 91381); lib. bdg. 17.08 (978-1-58810-517-2(2)) Heinemann Library.

Seligson, Sherri. Exploring Creation with Marine Biology. Wile, Jay L., ed. 2005. stu. ed., per. 20.00 ***(978-1-932012-59-0(1))***; Set. 85.00 ***(978-1-932012-60-6(5))*** Apologia Educational Ministries, Inc.

—Exploring Creation with Marine Biology: Student Text. Wile, Jay L., ed. 2005. 65.00 ***(978-1-932012-58-3(3))*** Apologia Educational Ministries, Inc.

Smith, Robert. Exploring Ocean Life. 2007. 112p. pap. 21.99 ***(978-1-4206-8878-8(2))***; pap. 21.99 ***(978-1-4206-8879-5(0))*** Teacher Created Resources, Inc.

Smithyman, Kathryn. The Ocean Biome. 2003. (Living Ocean Ser.). (Illus.). 32p. (J). (gr. 2-9). (978-0-7787-1296-1(6)) Crabtree Publishing Co.

Smithyman, Kathryn & Kalman, Bobbie. El bioma Marino. 2006. (SPA., Illus.). 32p. (gr. 3-4). pap. (978-0-7787-8414-2(2)) Crabtree Publishing Co.

Somervill, Barbara A. Our Living World: Earth's Biomes, 7 vols., Set. 2005. (Illus.). (J). (gr. 4-8). 350.00 (978-1-59187-052-4(6)) Tradition Publishing Co.

Stern, Leonard & Price, Roger. Under the Sea Mad Libs Junior. 2005. 48p. (J). (gr. k-3). mass mkt. 3.99 (978-0-8431-1350-1(2) , Price Stern Sloan) Penguin Group (USA) Inc.

Swanson, Diane. Safari Beneath the Sea: The Wonder World of the North Pacific Coast. Royal British Columbia Museum Staff, photos by. (Illus.). 64p. (J). (gr. 3-2). pap. 12.95 (978-1-55110-441-6(5)) Whitecap Bks., Ltd. CAN. *Dist:* Graphic Arts Ctr. Publishing Co.

Tagliaferro, Linda. How Many Fish in the Sea? A Book about Oceans. 2007. (First Facts Ser.). (Illus.). 24p. (J). (978-0-7368-6786-3(4) , 1264904) Capstone Pr., Inc.

Tahta, Sophie. What's under the Sea. rev. ed. 2006. 24p. (J). pap. 4.99 (978-0-7945-1409-9(X) , Usborne) EDC Publishing.

Tant, Carl. Awesome Oceans: Advances in Marine Biotechnology. Crask, Tammy, illus. 1998. (Awesome Science of Biology Ser.). (Orig.). (YA). (gr. 9-12). pap. 18.95 (978-1-880319-15-4(2)) Biotech Publishing.

Unwin, Mike. Scientists at Work: Pack A of 6 Paperback. 2007. (Illus.). 32p. (J). ***(978-0-431-14936-3(4))*** Heinemann Library.

—Scientists at Work: Secrets of the Deep: Marine Biologists Hardback. 2007. (Illus.). 32p. (J). ***(978-0-431-14928-8(3))*** Heinemann Library.

—Secrets of the Deep: Marine Biologists. 2007. (J). ***(978-1-4034-9952-3(7))***; pap. ***(978-1-4034-9959-2(4))*** Heinemann Library.

Vogel, Carole G. Ocean Wildlife. 2003. (Restless Sea Ser.). (gr. 5-8). pap. 12.95 (978-0-531-16681-9(3) , Watts, Franklin) Scholastic Library Publishing.

—Savage Waters. 2003. (Restless Sea Ser.). (Illus.). 80p. (gr. 5-8). pap. 12.95 (978-0-531-16682-6(1) , Watts, Franklin) Scholastic Library Publishing.

Walker, Pam & Wood, Elaine. The Continental Shelf. 2005. (Life in the Sea Ser.). (Illus.). 142p. (J). (gr. 4-9). 35.00 (978-0-8160-5704-7(4)) Facts On File, Inc.

Wallace, Karen. Think of an Eel. Bostock, Mike & Jenkins, Martin, illus. 2001. (Read & Wonder Ser.). 32p. (J). (ps up). pap. 6.99 (978-0-7636-1522-2(6)) Candlewick Pr.

Wilkes, Angela. Question Time: Seashore. 2001. (Explore & Discover Ser.). (Illus.). (J). (978-0-606-21391-2(0)) Tandem Library Bks.

—Seashore. 2001. (Question Time Ser.). (Illus.). 32p. (J). (gr. k-3). 6.95 (978-0-7534-5407-7(6) , Kingfisher) Houghton Mifflin Co. Trade & Reference Div.

Williams, Andy. Nature Unfolds Oceans. 2002. (gr. 5-8). lib. bdg. 18.75 (978-0-613-81879-7(2)) Tandem Library Bks.

—Nature Unfolds the Oceans. Camm, Martin, illus. 2002. (Nature Unfolds Ser.). 40p. (J). (gr. 4). pap. (978-0-7787-0322-8(3)); lib. bdg. (978-0-7787-0310-5(X)) Crabtree Publishing Co.

MARINE BIOLOGY—FICTION

Baldwin, Robert F. This Is the Sea That Feeds Us. Dyen, Don, illus. 1998. 32p. (YA). (ps-3). 16.95 (978-1-883220-69-3(6)); pap. 7.95 (978-1-883220-70-9(X)) Dawn Pubns.

Deans, Sis Boulos. Every Day & All the Time, Vol. 5. l.t. ed. 2004. 304p. 21.95 (978-0-7862-6386-8(5)) Thorndike Pr.

Farber, Erica. Octopus Island. Mayer, Mercer, illus. 2006. (Critter Kids Adventure Ser.). 32p. (J). (gr. 2-5). pap. 4.95 (978-0-7696-4766-1(9) , Gingham Dog Pr.) School Specialty Publishing.

Kranking, Kathy & Kranking, Kathleen W. The Ocean Is. . . Wu, Norbert, photos by. 2003. (Illus.). 32p. (J). (ps-2). 17.95 (978-0-8050-7097-2(4) , Holt, Henry & Co. Bks. For Young Readers) Holt, Henry & Co.

McKaige, Andrew. The Big Clean-Up: The Adventures of Sophie the Squid & Eddy the Eel. Wells, Malcolm, illus. 2001. 36p. (J). (ps-2). pap. 9.95 (978-1-880812-30-3(4)) Storytellers Ink, Inc.

Mullican, Judy. Under the Sea. Carroll, Ken, Jr., illus. 1998. (Big Bks.). 8p. (J). (ps-k). pap. 10.95 (978-1-57332-093-1(5)); pap. 10.95 (978-1-57332-092-4(7)) High-Reach Learning, Inc.

Reasoner, Charles. Who's in the Sea? Reasoner, Charles, illus. 2003. (Sliding Surprise Bks.). (Illus.). 12p. (J). (ps). bds. 7.99 (978-0-8431-0599-5(2) , Price Stern Sloan) Penguin Group (USA) Inc.

Treasures of the Barrier Reef. 2005. (J). audio, cd-rom 24.95 (978-0-9771381-7-3(8)) Williams, Geoffrey T.

MARINE ECOLOGY

Aloian, Molly. Habitats Acuaticos. 2007. (SPA.). 32p. (J). (gr. 1-2). ***(978-0-7787-8325-1(1))*** Crabtree Publishing Co.

Aloian, Molly. Water Habitats. 2006. (Illus.). 32p. (J). (gr. 2). pap. (978-0-7787-2977-8(X)) Crabtree Publishing Co.

Aloian, Molly & Kalman, Bobbie. Habitats Acuaticos. rev. ed. 2007. (SPA.). 32p. (J). (gr. 1-2). pap. ***(978-0-7787-8349-7(9))*** Crabtree Publishing Co.

Aloian, Molly & Kalman, Bobbie. Water Habitats. 2006. (Illus.). 32p. (J). (978-0-7787-2949-5(4)) Crabtree Publishing Co.

Animals of the Ocean Series, (Illus.). (J). (gr. 2-6). lib. bdg. 44.85 (978-1-56674-947-3(6)) Forest Hse. Publishing Co., Inc.

Baker, Lucy. Life in the Oceans: Animals, People, Plants. 2000. (gr. 3-6). lib. bdg. 15.25 (978-0-613-43345-7(9)) Tandem Library Bks.

—la Vida en los Oceanos: Animales, Gente, Plantes. 2000. (Illus.). (J). (978-0-606-20973-1(5)) Tandem Library Bks.

Barnham, Kay. Coasts. 2004. (Geography First Ser.). (J). 23.70 (978-1-4103-0112-3(5) , Blackbirch Pr., Inc.) Thomson Gale.

Bayrock, Fiona. The Ocean Explorer's Handbook. 2005. (Undersea University Ser.). (Illus.). 48p. (J). pap. (978-0-439-71184-5(3)) Scholastic, Inc.

Beatty, Richard. Rivers, Lakes, Streams, & Ponds. 2002. (Biomes Atlases Ser.). (Illus.). 64p. (J). lib. bdg. 31.42 (978-0-7398-5513-3(1)) Raintree.

—Rivers, Lakes, Streams, & Ponds. 2003. (gr. 5-8). lib. bdg. 18.20 (978-0-613-78187-9(2)) Tandem Library Bks.

Berger, Melvin & Berger, Gilda. What Makes an Ocean Wave? Questions & Answers about Oceans. 2001. (Scholastic Question & Answer Ser.). (J). pap. 4.99 (978-0-439-09589-1(1)) Scholastic, Inc.

—What Makes an Ocean Wave? Questions & Answers about Oceans. Rice, John, illus. 2001. (Question & Answer Ser.). 48p. (J). (gr. 2-4). pap. 14.95 (978-0-439-09588-4(3)) Scholastic, Inc.

Blocksma, Mary. What's on the Beach? A Great Lakes Treasure Hunt. 2003. (Illus.). 48p. (YA). pap. 10.95 (978-0-9708575-2-1(7)) Beaver Island Arts.

—What's on the Beach? A Great Lakes Treasure Hunt. Blocksma, Mary, illus. 2003. (Great Lakes Treasure Hunts Ser.: No. 1). (Illus.). 48p. (J). pap. 9.95 (978-0-9708575-1-4(9)) Beaver Island Arts.

Bredeson, Carmen. Tide Pools. 1999. (First Bks.). (Illus.). 64p. (J). (gr. 5-7). pap. 6.95 (978-0-531-15958-3(2) , Watts, Franklin) Scholastic Library Publishing.

—Tide Pools. 1999. (gr. 5-8). lib. bdg. 15.25 (978-0-613-54707-9(1)) Tandem Library Bks.

Breidahl, Harry. Diminutive Drifters: Microscopic Aquatic Life. 2001. (Life in Strange Places Ser.). (Illus.). 32p. (J). (gr. 4 up). 28.00 (978-0-7910-6618-8(5) , 011002, Chelsea Hse.) Facts On File, Inc.

Butterfield, Moira. Who Eats Who at the Seashore? 2007. (Food Chains in Action Ser.). (Illus.). 32p. (J). ***(978-1-58340-963-3(7)*** , 1262631) Smart Apple Media.

Cefrey, Holly. Oceans. 2003. (Reading Power Ser.). (Illus.). 24p. (J). lib. bdg. 17.25 (978-0-8239-6453-6(1) , PowerKids Pr.) Rosen Publishing Group, Inc., The.

Champion, Neil. Seas & Oceans. 2005. (Caring for the Planet Ser.). (Illus.). 48p. (J). (978-1-58340-511-6(9)) Smart Apple Media.

Cole, Melissa S. Coral Reefs. 2004. (Illus.). 24p. (J). 22.45 (978-1-56711-908-4(5) , Blackbirch Pr., Inc.) Thomson Gale.

—Kelp Forests. 2004. (Illus.). 24p. (J). 22.45 (978-1-56711-909-1(3) , Blackbirch Pr., Inc.) Thomson Gale.

—Sand Bottoms. 2004. (Illus.). 24p. (J). 22.45 (978-1-56711-910-7(7) , Blackbirch Pr., Inc.) Thomson Gale.

Collard, Sneed B., III. Lizard Island: Science & Scientists on Australia's Great Barrier Reef. (Single Title Science Pb Ser.). (Illus.). 144p. (YA). (gr. 9-12). 2001. pap. 12.95 (978-0-531-16519-5(1)); 2000. 26.00 (978-0-531-11719-4(7)) Scholastic Library Publishing. (Watts, Franklin).

Crossingham, John & Kalman, Bobbie. Cadenas Alimentarias de la Costa Marina. (Cadenas Alimentarias Ser.). (SPA., Illus.). 32p. (J). (978-0-7787-8531-6(9)) Crabtree Publishing Co.

Culen, Gerald R., et al. Coastal Marine Environmental Issues: An Extended Case Study for the Investigation & Evaluation of Marine Issues of the Gulf Coast & Florida Peninsula. 2000. (Illus.). 131p. (YA). (gr. 6-12). spiral bd. 14.80 (978-1-58874-025-0(0)) Stipes Publishing L.L.C.

Davies, Nicola. Oceans & Seas. (Science Kids Ser.). (Illus.). 48p. (J). 2007. pap. 6.95 ***(978-0-7534-6165-5(X))***; 2004. 9.95 (978-0-7534-5758-0(X)) Houghton Mifflin Co. Trade & Reference Div. (Kingfisher).

Davis, Kate & Innovative Kids Staff. High Tide. Filipowich, Bob, illus. 2001. (Textured Soft Shapes Ser.). 8p. (J). (ps-ps). 10.99 (978-1-58476-067-2(2)) Innovative Kids.

Davis, Wendy & Knight, Bertram T. Working at a Marine Institute. (Working Here Ser.). (Illus.). 32p. (J). (gr. 2-4). 1999. pap. 6.95 (978-0-516-26453-0(2)); 1998. 23.50 (978-0-516-21223-4(0)) Scholastic Library Publishing. (Children's Pr.).

Day. Oceans & Beaches. 2003. (Biomes Atlas Ser.). (Illus.). (J). pap. 48.30 (978-1-4109-0248-1(X)) Raintree.

Day, Trevor. Oceans & Beaches. 2003. (Biomes Atlases Ser.). (Illus.). 64p. (J). lib. bdg. 31.42 (978-0-7398-5512-6(3)) Raintree.

Fleisher, Paul. Ocean Food Webs. 2007. (Early Bird Food Webs Ser.). 48p. (J). (gr. 2-5). 26.60 ***(978-0-8225-6732-5(6)*** , Lerner Pubns.) Lerner Publishing Group.

Ganeri, Anita. I Wonder Why the Sea Is Salty: And Other Questions about the Oceans. 2003. (I Wonder Why Ser.). 32p. (J). (gr. k-3). pap. 6.95 (978-0-7534-5611-8(7) , Kingfisher) Houghton Mifflin Co. Trade & Reference Div.

—I Wonder Why the Sea Is Salty: And Other Questions about the Oceans. 2003. (gr. k-3). lib. bdg. 14.10 (978-0-613-63165-5(X)) Tandem Library Bks.

Gottlieb. Water Life. 2004. (Illus.). pap. 15.60 incl. cd-rom (978-0-7398-9178-0(2)) Steck-Vaughn.

Group/McGraw-Hill, Wright. La Vida en el Oceano, 6 vols., Vol. 2. (Explorers. Exploradores Nonfiction Sets Ser.). (SPA.). 32p. (gr. 3-6). 44.95 (978-0-7699-0740-6(7)) Shortland Pubns. (U. S. A.) Inc.

Haugen, Hayley Mitchell. Life in a Coral Reef. 2003. (Ecosystems Library). (Illus.). 48p. (J). 23.70 (978-0-7377-1370-1(4) , Greenhaven Pr., Inc.) Thomson Gale.

Helbrough, Emma. Ocean Life. 2006. (First Library of Knowledge). 32p. (J). (gr. 2-4). 23.70 (978-1-4103-0342-4(X) , Blackbirch Pr., Inc.) Thomson Gale.

Hidden World: Level P, 6 vols., Vol. 3. (Explorers Ser.). 32p. (gr. 3-6). 44.95 (978-0-7699-0616-4(8)) Shortland Pubns. (U. S. A.) Inc.

Hirschi, Ron. Ocean Seasons. Carlson, Kirsten, illus. 2007. 32p. (J). (gr. k-4). 15.95 ***(978-0-9777423-2-5(6))***; pap. 8.95 ***(978-1-934359-16-7(5))*** Sylvan Dell Pubng.

Hodge, Susie. Ocean Survival. 2007. (Extreme Habitats Ser.). 32p. (J). (gr. 4-6). lib. bdg. 25.27 ***(978-0-8368-8247-6(4))*** Stevens, Gareth Inc.

Hodgkins, Fran. Between the Tides. Sollers, Jim, illus. 2007. 32p. pap. 15.95 (978-0-89272-727-8(6)) Down East Bks.

Hudak, Heather C. Oceans. 2005. (Illus.). 32p. (J). (ps-6). lib. bdg. 24.45 (978-1-59036-348-5(5)); pap. 7.95 (978-1-59036-354-6(X)) Weigl Pubs., Inc.

Inskipp, Carol. Healthy Seas. 2006. (Sustainable Futures Ser.). (Illus.). 48p. (J). (978-1-58340-980-0(7) , 1262623) Smart Apple Media.

Jackson, Kay. Explore the Ocean. 2007. (Fact Finders Ser.). (Illus.). 32p. (J). 22.60 (978-0-7368-6406-0(7)) Capstone Pr., Inc.

James, Diane. Underwater. Lynn, Sara, illus. rev. ed. 2004. (My First Look at Animals Ser.). (SPA.). 24p. (ps-2). (J). pap. 5.95 (978-1-58728-861-6(3)); 9.95 (978-1-58728-854-8(0)) T&N Children's Publishing. (Two Can Publishing).

Johnson, Rebecca L. A Journey into the Ocean. Saroff, Phyllis V., illus. 2004. (J). pap. 6.95 (978-0-8225-2046-7(X) ,); 48p. (gr. 3-6). lib. bdg. 23.93 (978-1-57505-591-6(0)) Lerner Publishing Group.

King, Roger. Jacques Cousteau & the Undersea World. 2000. (Explorers of the New World Ser.). (Illus.). (J). (gr. 4-7). pap. 25.00 (978-0-7910-6166-4(3)); 64p. (gr. 8-12). 25.00 (978-0-7910-5956-2(1)) Facts On File, Inc. (Chelsea Hse.).

Kurtz, Kevin. A Day in the Salt Marsh. 2007. (Illus.). 32p. (J). (ps-3). 8.95 ***(978-1-934359-19-8(X))*** Sylvan Dell Pubng.

L'Hommedieu, Arthur John. Ocean Tidepool. 1998. (Habitats Ser.). (Illus.). 32p. (J). (gr. 2-3). pap. 6.95 (978-0-516-20373-7(8) , Children's Pr.) Scholastic Library Publishing.

Lindop, Laurie. Venturing the Deep Sea. 2006. (Science on the Edge Ser.). (Illus.). 80p. (J). 27.93 (978-0-7613-2701-1(0) , Twenty-First Century Bks.) Lerner Publishing Group.

Littlefield, Cindy A. Awesome Ocean Science: Investigating the Secrets of the Underwater World. 2004. (Kids Can Bks.). (Illus.). 120p. (J). (gr. 3-5). pap. 12.95 (978-1-885593-71-9(6) , Williamson Bks.) Ideals Pubns.

Lynch, Emma. Ocean Food Chains. 2004. (Food Webs Ser.). (Illus.). 32p. (J). pap. 7.50 (978-1-4034-5864-3(2)) Heinemann Library.

—Ocean Food Chains: Emma Lynch. 2004. (Food Webs Ser.). (Illus.). 32p. (J). 24.22 (978-1-4034-5857-5(X)) Heinemann Library.

Macken, JoAnn Early. Water Habutats. 24p. (YA). 115.98 (978-0-8368-6026-9(8)) Stevens, Gareth Inc.

Matsen, Bradford. The Incredible Submersible Alvin Discovers a Strange Deep-Sea World. 2003. (Incredible Deep-Sea Adventures Ser.). (Illus.). 48p. (J). (gr. 4-10). lib. bdg. 23.93 (978-0-7660-2189-1(0)) Enslow Pubs., Inc.

Mayer, Cassie. Ocean. 2007. (J). ***(978-1-4034-9430-6(4))***; pap. ***(978-1-4034-9436-8(3))*** Heinemann Library.

McKissack, Fredrick, Jr. & McKissack, Lisa Beringer. Counting in the Oceans. 2008. (J). ***(978-0-7660-2994-1(8))*** Enslow Pubs., Inc.

Meucci, Antonella. Seas & Oceans. Chesi, Matteo, illus. 2000. (Nature's Record-Breakers Ser.). 32p. (J). (gr. 3 up). lib. bdg. 23.33 (978-0-8368-2475-9(X)) Stevens, Gareth Inc.

Milbourne, Anna. Under the Sea (Picture Book) 2007. (Picture Bks). 24p. (J). 9.99 ***(978-0-7945-1801-1(X)*** , Usborne) EDC Publishing.

Miller-Schroeder, Patricia. The Science of Underwater Life. 2000. (Living Science Ser.). (Illus.). 32p. (J). (gr. 2 up). lib. bdg. 24.67 (978-0-8368-2683-8(3)) Stevens, Gareth Inc.

Miller-Schroeder, Patricia. Underwater Life. 2007. (J). ***(978-1-59036-713-1(8))***; ***(978-1-59036-714-8(6))*** Weigl Pubs., Inc.

Morey, Allan. Ocean Food Chains. 2003. (What Eats What? Ser.). (J). pap. (978-1-58417-219-2(3)); lib. bdg. (978-1-58417-218-5(5)) Lake Street Pubs.

Morgan, Sally. Oceans. (Extreme Survival Ser.). (Illus.). 32p. (J). 2004. pap. 7.95 (978-1-4109-0361-7(3)); 2003. lib. bdg. 25.70 (978-1-4109-0002-9(9)) Raintree.

—Oceans. 2003. (gr. 3-6). lib. bdg. 16.40 (978-0-613-78254-8(2)) Tandem Library Bks.

O'Clair, Rita M. & Hocker, Katherine M. Where Is Dinah Diatom? 2000. (Illus.). 16p. (J). (ps-4). pap. (978-0-9664245-2-2(2)) Plant Pr.

Pratt-Serafini, Kristin Joy. A Swim Through the Sea. Pratt-Serafini, Kristin Joy, illus. 2006. (Illus.). 26p. (J). bds. 7.95 (978-1-58469-080-1(1)) Dawn Pubns.

Pringle, Laurence P. Come to the Ocean's Edge: A Nature Cycle Book. Chesworth, Michael, illus. 2003. 32p. (YA). (gr. k-2). 15.95 (978-1-56397-779-4(6)) Boyds Mills Pr.

Pryor, Kimberley Jane. Icy Seas. 2007. (J). ***(978-1-59920-143-6(7))*** Smart Apple Media.

—The Open Sea. 2007. (J). ***(978-1-59920-142-9(9))*** Smart Apple Media.

—Sea-Grass Beds. 2007. (J). ***(978-1-59920-141-2(0))*** Smart Apple Media.

Pyers, Greg. Ocean Explorer. 2004. (Habitat Explorer Ser.). (Illus.). 32p. (J). (ps-ps). lib. bdg. 25.70 (978-1-4109-0510-9(1)) Raintree.

Reid, Greg. Oceans. 2004. (Ecosystems Ser.). (Illus.). 32p. (J). (gr. 3-5). 23.00 (978-0-7910-7940-9(6) , Chelsea Hse.) Facts On File, Inc.

Rigby Education Staff. Gardens of the Sea. (Sails Literacy Ser.). (Illus.). 16p. (J). (gr. 1-2). 27.00 (978-0-7635-9923-2(9) , 699239C99) Rigby Education.

Riley, Peter D. The Ocean. 2004. (Survivor's Science Ser.). 28.56 (978-1-4109-0229-0(3)) Harcourt Schl. Pubs.

Sacks, Janet. Oceans & Art Activities. 2002. (gr. 3-6). lib. bdg. 17.60 (978-0-613-52889-4(1)) Tandem Library Bks.

Sacks, Janet & Goodman, Polly, texts. Oceans & Art Activities. 2002. (Arty Facts Ser.). (Illus.). 48p. (J). (gr. 3-4). pap. (978-0-7787-1143-8(9)); lib. bdg. (978-0-7787-1115-5(3)) Crabtree Publishing Co.

Schaefer, Lola M. Barnacles. 2002. (Musty-Crusty Animals Ser.). (Illus.). 24p. (J). (ps-1). pap. 5.25 (978-1-58810-721-3(3) , 91374); lib. bdg. 17.08 (978-1-58810-512-7(1)) Heinemann Library.

Smithyman, Kathryn. The Ocean Biome. 2003. (Living Ocean Ser.). (Illus.). 32p. (J). (gr. 2-9). (978-0-7787-1296-1(6)) Crabtree Publishing Co.

Smithyman, Kathryn & Kalman, Bobbie. El bioma Marino. 2006. (SPA., Illus.). 32p. (gr. 3-4). pap. (978-0-7787-8414-2(2)) Crabtree Publishing Co.

Steck-Vaughn Staff. The Living Ocean. 2002. (J). pap. (978-0-7398-6162-2(X)) Steck-Vaughn.

Steele, Philip. A Tidal Pool. 1999. (Small Worlds Ser.). (Illus.). 32p. (J). (gr. 3-4). pap. (978-0-7787-0149-1(2)) Crabtree Publishing Co.

Stewart, Melissa. Extreme Coral Reef! Q & A. 2008. 48p. (J). 16.99 (***978-0-06-111577-6(0)***); pap. 6.99 (***978-0-06-111575-2(4)***) Smithsonian Institution Pr.

Stone, Lynn M. The Food Chain. 2001. (Under the Sea Ser.). (Illus.). 24p. (J). (gr. 1-4). lib. bdg. 20.64 (978-1-58952-113-1(7)) Rourke Publishing, LLC.

—Oceans. 2003. (Illus.). 24p. (J). 20.64 (978-1-58952-686-0(4)) Rourke Publishing, LLC.

Storey Publishing Staff. Under the Sea Poster Book. 2005. (Illus.). 64p. (J). pap. 9.95 (978-1-58017-623-1(2)) Storey Publishing, LLC.

Tocci, Salvatore. Marine Habitats: Life in Saltwater. 2005. (Watts Library). (Illus.). 64p. (J). (gr. 5-7). pap. 8.95 (978-0-531-16670-3(8), Watts, Franklin) Scholastic Library Publishing.

—Marine Habitats: Life in the Ocean. 2004. (Watts Library Ser.). (J). 25.50 (978-0-531-12306-5(5), Watts, Franklin) Scholastic Library Publishing.

Wade, Laura. Sea & Sealife. 2003. (Knowledge Masters Ser.). (Illus.). 32p. (YA). pap. incl. cd-rom (978-1-903954-10-2(X)) Chrysalis Children's Bks.

Walker, Pam & Wood, Elaine. The Open Ocean. 2005. (Life in the Sea Ser.). (Illus.). 132p. (J). (gr. 4-9). 35.00 (978-0-8160-5705-4(2)) Facts On File, Inc.

West, Krista, ed. Critical Perspectives on the Oceans. 2006. (Scientific American Critical Anthologies on Environment & Climate Ser.). (Illus.). 200p. (J). (978-1-4042-0692-2(2)) Rosen Publishing Group, Inc., The.

Whitehouse, Patricia. Living in an Ocean. 2007. (Illus.). 24p. (J). (978-1-60044-187-5(4)) Rourke Publishing, LLC.

Wilkes, Angela. Under the Sea. rev. ed. 2004. (Ladders Ser.). (Illus.). 32p. (J). (ps-3). pap. 6.95 (978-1-58728-615-5(7), Two Can Publishing) T&N Children's Publishing.

—Under the Sea. Holmes, Steve, illus. rev. ed. 2004. (Ladders Ser.). 30p. (ps-3). 12.95 (978-1-58728-607-0(6), Two Can Publishing) T&N Children's Publishing.

—Under the Sea. 2000. (ps-2). lib. bdg. 15.25 (978-0-613-43515-4(X)) Tandem Library Bks.

Woodward, John. The Sunlit Zone. 2004. (Illus.). 48p. (J). pap. 8.50 (978-1-4034-5133-0(8)); lib. bdg. (978-1-4034-5127-9(3)) Heinemann Library.

Working on Water: Individual Title Six-Packs. (gr. k-1). 23.00 (978-0-7635-8853-3(9)) Rigby Education.

Wright, Alexandra. At Home in the Tide Pool. 1999. (Illus.). (J). 14.75 (978-0-606-18022-1(2)) Tandem Library Bks.

MARINE FAUNA

see Marine Animals

MARINE FLORA

see Marine Plants

MARINE GEOLOGY

see Submarine Geology

MARINE PAINTING

Baumbusch, Brigitte. Oceans in Art. 2005. (Illus.). 32p. (J). lib. bdg. 22.00 (978-0-8368-4782-6(2)) Stevens, Gareth Inc.

Draw 50 Boats, Ships, Trucks & Trains. 2002. (Draw 50 Ser.). (Illus.). (J). 17.60 (978-0-7587-6968-8(7)) Book Wholesalers, Inc.

Howell, David Sanders, frwd. Seascapes by David Sanders Howell. 2004. (Illus.). 64p. per. 20.00 (978-1-886438-02-6(1), 305-538-1033) Grassfield Pr., Inc.

MARINE PLANTS

see also Algae; Fresh-Water Plants

Cole, Melissa S. Kelp Forests. 2004. (Illus.). 24p. (J). 22.45 (978-1-56711-909-1(3), Blackbirch Pr., Inc.) Thomson Gale.

Dell, Pamela. Ocean Plants. 2006. (Life in the World's Biomes Ser.). (Illus.). 24p. (J). (978-0-7368-4322-5(1)) Capstone Pr., Inc.

Hardy, A. S. Sea Stories for Wonder Eyes. 2005. reprint ed. pap. 21.95 (978-1-4191-0670-5(8)) Kessinger Publishing, LLC.

Hirschmann, Kris. Creatures That Glow. 2005. (Creatures of the Sea Ser.). (Illus.). 48p. (J). (gr. 4-8). 26.20 (978-0-7377-2340-3(8), Greenhaven Pr., Inc.) Thomson Gale.

Horsman, Paul. Out of the Blue: A Journey Through the World's Oceans. Seapics.Com, photos by. 2005. (Illus.). 160p. (gr. 3-7). 29.95 (978-0-262-08341-6(8)) MIT Pr.

Lindeen, Carol. Life in an Ocean. 2003. (Pebble Plus: Living in a Biome Ser.). (Illus.). 24p. (J). lib. bdg. 17.26 (978-0-7368-2099-8(X), Pebble Bks.) Capstone Pr., Inc.

Lindeen, Carol K. Life in an Ocean, Vol. 3. 2005. (Earth & Outer Space Ser.). 24p. (YA). (gr. k-3). pap. (978-0-7368-3406-3(0), Pebble Bks.) Capstone Pr., Inc.

Littlefield, Cindy A. Awesome Ocean Science: Investigating the Secrets of the Underwater World. 2004. (Kids Can Bks.). (Illus.). 120p. (J). (gr. 3-5). pap. 12.95 (978-1-885593-71-9(6), Williamson Bks.) Ideals Pubns.

May, Suellen. Invasive Aquatic & Wetland Plants. 2006. (Invasive Species Ser.). (Illus.). 112p. (J). (gr. 6-12). 30.00 (978-0-7910-9130-2(9), Chelsea Hse.) Facts On File, Inc.

Merlino, Kim. Ocean Life: Grades 2 Through 4. (Illus.). (J). pap., wbk. ed. 4.99 (978-0-88743-966-7(7)) School Zone Publishing Co.

Morrison, Gordon. Pond. Morrison, Gordon, illus. 2002. (Illus.). 32p. (J). (gr. k-3). tchr. ed. 16.00 (978-0-618-10271-6(X), Walter Lorraine) Houghton Mifflin Co. Trade & Reference Div.

Nicholson, Sue. Ocean Explorer. 2002. 48p. (J). pap. 6.95 (978-0-439-31688-0(X)) Scholastic, Inc.

O'Neil, Sarah. Under the Sea. 2001. (gr. k-3). lib. bdg. 11.80 (978-0-613-33449-5(3)) Tandem Library Bks.

Rivera, Sheila. Ocean. 2005. (First Step Nonfiction Ser.). (Illus.). 23p. (J). (ps-7). 18.60 (978-0-8225-2795-4(2), Lerner Pubns.) Lerner Publishing Group.

Stone, Lynn M. Life of the Kelp Forest. 2001. (Under the Sea Ser.). (Illus.). 24p. (J). (gr. 1-4). lib. bdg. 20.64 (978-1-58952-112-4(9)) Rourke Publishing, LLC.

—Sea Anemones. 2003. (Rourke Discovery Library). (Illus.). 24p. (gr. 2-5). 14.95 (978-1-58952-317-3(2)) Rourke Publishing, LLC.

Swanson, Diane. Safari Beneath the Sea: The Wonder World of the North Pacific Coast. Royal British Columbia Museum Staff, photos by. (Illus.). 64p. (J). (gr. 3-2). pap. 12.95 (978-1-55110-441-6(5)) Whitecap Bks., Ltd. CAN. *Dist:* Graphic Arts Ctr. Publishing Co.

MARINE RESOURCES

see also Fisheries

Davis, Wendy & Knight, Bertram T. Working at a Marine Institute. 1998. (Working Here Ser.). (Illus.). 32p. (J). (gr. 2-4). 23.50 (978-0-516-21223-4(0), Children's Pr.) Scholastic Library Publishing.

Green, Jen. Saving Oceans & Wetlands. 2004. (J). lib. bdg. 27.10 (978-1-59389-139-8(3)) Chrysalis Education.

Harper, Joel. All the Way to the Ocean. Spusta, Marq, illus. 2006. (J). (***978-0-9714254-1-5(8)***) Harper, Joel D.

Mallory, Kenneth. A Home by the Sea: Protecting Coastal Wildlife. 2003. (Illus.). 64p. (YA). (gr. 4-8). reprint ed. 20.00 (978-0-7567-6562-0(5)) DIANE Publishing Co.

MARINE ZOOLOGY

see Marine Animals

MARINERS

see Sailors

MARION, FRANCIS, 1732-1795

Cornelius, Kay. Francis Marion: Swamp Fox. 2000. (Revolutionary War Leaders Ser.). (Illus.). 80p. (J). (gr. 4-7). pap. 27.50 (978-0-7910-6134-3(5)); (gr. 8-12). 31.00 (978-0-7910-5976-0(6)) Facts On File, Inc. (Chelsea Hse.).

—Francis Marion: The Swamp Fox. 2001. (gr. 5-8). lib. bdg. 17.60 (978-0-613-32583-7(4)) Tandem Library Bks.

Kauffman, Scott. Francis Marion: Swamp Fox of South Carolina. 2006. (Forgotten Heroes of the American Revolution Ser.). (Illus.). 88p. (YA). (gr. 5-11). lib. bdg. 23.95 (978-1-59556-014-8(9)) OTTN Publishing.

Towles, Louis P. Francis Marion: The Swamp Fox of the American Revolution. 2005. (Library of American Lives & Times). (Illus.). 112p. (J). (gr. 4-8). lib. bdg. 31.95 (978-0-8239-5728-6(4)) Rosen Publishing Group, Inc., The.

MARITIME DISCOVERIES

see Discoveries in Geography

MARK, SAINT

Woodman, Ros. Bible Detectives: Mark. 64p. (YA). pap., act. bk. ed. 7.99 (978-1-85792-674-3(9), Christian Focus) Christian Focus Pubns. GBR. *Dist:* Riverside.

MARKET GARDENING

see Vegetable Gardening

MARKETING

Etzel. Marketing: Student Study Guide. 13th rev. ed. 2004. 368p. (gr. 6-12). pap. (978-0-07-283785-8(3)) Glencoe/McGraw-Hill.

Gifford, Clive. Advertising & Marketing: Developing the Marketplace. 2005. (Influence & Persuasion Ser.). (Illus.). 64p. (J). (gr. 6-8). lib. bdg. 31.43 (978-1-4034-7651-7(9)) Heinemann Library.

Landau, Elaine. All-American Companies. 2003. (Single Titles Ser.). 112p. (J). lib. bdg. 32.90 (978-0-7613-2350-1(3), Twenty-First Century Bks.) Lerner Publishing Group.

Wesley, Sonya L. Business Management Ethical Marketing: A Discussion & Activity Tool. 2000. (Sport Ser.). (Illus.). (C). spiral bd. (978-0-9706421-8-9(0)) Game Plan Pubns.

Wilson, Antoine. The Young Zillionaire's Guide to Distributing Goods & Services. 2000. (Be a Zillionaire Ser.). (Illus.). 48p. (YA). (gr. 5-8). lib. bdg. 23.95 (978-0-8239-3259-7(1), ZIDIST, Rosen Central) Rosen Publishing Group, Inc., The.

MARKETING—VOCATIONAL GUIDANCE

Ferguson, creator. Discovering Careers for Your Future: Advertising & Marketing. 2005. (Discovering Careers for Your Future Ser.). (Illus.). 92p. (YA). (gr. 4-9). 21.95 (978-0-8160-5847-1(4), Ferguson Publishing Co.) Facts On File, Inc.

J. G. Ferguson Publishing Company Staff, contrib. by. Careers in Focus. 2003. (Careers in Focus Ser.). (Illus.). 192p. (J). (gr. 6-12). 22.95 (978-0-8160-5482-4(7), Ferguson Publishing Co.) Facts On File, Inc.

MARKETING (HOME ECONOMICS)

see Shopping

MARKETING OF FARM PRODUCE

see Farm Produce—Marketing

MARKETS

see also Fairs

Anderson, Sara. A Day at the Market. 2006. (Illus.). 12p. (J). bds. 14.95 (978-1-59354-149-1(X)) Handprint Bks.

Burns, Peggy. Stores & Markets. (Stepping Through History Ser.). (Illus.). 32p. (J). (gr. 3-7). lib. bdg. 5.00 (978-1-56847-344-4(3)) Raintree.

Gorman, Jacqueline Laks. The Shopping Mall: El Centro Comercial. 2005. (ENG & SPA., Illus.). 24p. (J). pap. (978-0-8368-4606-5(0)); lib. bdg. 19.33 (978-0-8368-4599-0(4)) Stevens, Gareth Inc.

Harcourt School Publishers Staff. Trofeos Advanced Level: El Mercado Pescado. 3rd ed. 2002. (SPA., Illus.). pap. 5.50 (978-0-15-323929-8(8)) Harcourt Schl. Pubs.

Lewin, Ted. How Much? Visiting Markets Around the World. Lewin, Ted, illus. 2006. (Illus.). 40p. (J). 16.99 (978-0-688-17552-8(X)); lib. bdg. 17.89 (978-0-688-17553-5(8)) HarperCollins Pubs.

—Market! 2000. (978-0-606-18705-3(7)) Tandem Library Bks.

The Market: First Wave Satellite, 6 Packs. (Sails Literacy Ser.). 16p. (gr. k up). 27.00 (978-0-7578-6874-0(6)) Rigby Education.

Mayer, Cassie. Markets. 2007. (J). (***978-1-4034-9404-7(5)***); pap. (***978-1-4034-9413-9(4)***) Heinemann Library.

Rauen, Amy. Counting at the Market. 2008. (J). pap. (***978-0-8368-8986-4(X)***); lib. bdg. (***978-0-8368-8981-9(9)***) Stevens, Gareth Inc.

Ravishankar, Anushka. To Market! To Market! Scanziani, Emanuele, illus. 2007. 24p. (J). 16.95 (***978-81-86211-99-1(3)***) Tara Publishing IND. *Dist:* Consortium Bk. Sales & Distribution.

MARKETS—FICTION

Alakija, Polly. Catch That Goat! (Illus.). 32p. (J). 2004. pap. 6.99 (978-1-84148-161-6(0)); 2002. 16.99 (978-1-84148-908-7(5)) Barefoot Bks., Inc.

Amollo, Regina. When Mother Leaves Home. 2004. (Illus.). 35p. pap. 9.95 (978-9970-02-435-3(3)) Fountain Pubs. Ltd. UGA. *Dist:* Michigan State Univ. Pr.

Bunting, Eve. Market Day. 1999. (J). (978-0-606-14263-2(0)) Tandem Library Bks.

Chanchani, Vishakha. Spectacular Spectacle Man. 2005. (Illus.). 16p. pap. 14.95 (978-81-86211-18-2(7)) Tara Publishing IND. *Dist:* Consortium Bk. Sales & Distribution.

Charles, Bob. A Trip to the Market. ed. 2003. (Early Connections Ser.). (J). pap. 33.00 (978-1-4108-1359-6(2)) Benchmark Education Co.

Charles, Bob. A una visita al mercado & Trip to the Market. 2005. spiral bd. 66.00 (***978-1-4108-5642-5(9)***) Benchmark Education Co.

deRubertis, Barbara. Count on Pablo. Thornburgh, Rebecca McKillip, illus. 1999. (Math Matters Ser.). 32p. (gr. k-2). pap. 4.95 (978-1-57565-090-6(8)) Kane Pr., The.

—Count on Pablo. 1999. (ps-2). lib. bdg. 12.95 (978-0-613-17153-3(5)); (Illus.). (J). 11.75 (978-0-606-18217-1(9)) Tandem Library Bks.

Ehlert, Lois. Dia de Mercado: Una Historia Contado a Traves del Arte Popular. Campoy, F. Isabel & Ada, Alma Flor, trs. 2003. (SPA., Illus.). 36p. (J). pap. 7.00 (978-0-15-216814-8(1), Voyager Bks./Libros Viajeros) Harcourt Children's Bks.

—Dia de Mercado: Una Historia Contado A Traves Del Arte Popular. 2003. (SPA.). lib. bdg. 15.30 (978-0-613-59890-3(3)) Tandem Library Bks.

—Market Day: A Story Told with Folk Art. Ehlert, Lois, illus. 2002. (Illus.). (J). 23.40 (978-0-7587-4281-0(9)) Book Wholesalers, Inc.

—Market Day: A Story Told with Folk Art. (Illus.). 36p. (J). (gr. k-2). 2002. pap. 7.00 (978-0-15-216820-9(6), Voyager Bks./Libros Viajeros); 2000. 16.00 (978-0-15-202158-0(2)) Harcourt Children's Bks.

—Market Day: A Story Told with Folk Art. 2002. (gr. k-3). lib. bdg. 14.15 (978-0-613-53833-6(1)) Tandem Library Bks.

Get Together Girls - Going to the Mall. 2005. (J). bds. (978-1-4194-0087-2(8)) Paradise Pr., Inc.

Harcourt School Publishers Staff. The Fish Market, 6 Nos., Pack. 3rd ed. 2002. (Trophies Reading Program Ser.). (Illus.). (gr. 1). pap. 20.10 (978-0-15-326868-7(9)) Harcourt Schl. Pubs.

—Joey Goes to the Market: Take-Home Book. 1999. (Collections Ser.). (Illus.). (J). pap. 1.90 (978-0-15-317207-6(X)) Harcourt Schl. Pubs.

Jonathan Buys a Present: Individual Title Six-Packs. 16p. (gr. 1-2). 35.00 (978-0-7635-8931-8(4)) Rigby Education.

Leto, Frank & Scelsa, Greg. Let's Go to the Market. Faulkner, Stacey, ed. 2006. (J). pap. 2.99 (***978-1-59198-317-0(7)***) Creative Teaching Pr., Inc.

Losi, Carol A. Salt & Pepper at the Pike Place Market. Meissner, Amy, illus. 2004. 32p. (J). 15.95 (978-1-55868-800-1(5)); pap. 8.95 (978-1-55868-801-8(3)) Graphic Arts Ctr. Publishing Co. (West Winds Pr.).

Mom at the Market: Individual Title Six-Packs. (Sails Literacy Ser.). (gr. 1-2). 36.00 (978-0-7578-6721-7(9)) Rigby Education.

Nabb, Magdalen. Josie Smith at the Market. 2000. (Illus.). 125p. (J). 6.95 (978-0-00-675064-2(8)) Zondervan.

Rondon, Javier. The Absent-Minded Toad. Cabrera, Marcela, illus. 2002. 28p. (J). pap. 6.95 (978-1-929132-39-3(5)) Kane/Miller Bk. Pubs., Inc.

Shaw. At the Farmer's Market. 2002. (J). 15.95 (978-0-8050-3763-0(2), Holt, Henry & Co. Bks. For Young Readers) Holt, Henry & Co.

Stockwell, Peter. The Market. 2005. 54p. pap. 12.95 (978-1-4137-6087-3(2)) PublishAmerica, Inc.

Thong, Roseanne. Gai See: What You Can See in Chinatown. Choi, Yangsook, illus. 2007. 40p. (J). (ps-3). 16.95 (***978-0-8109-9337-2(6)***, Abrams Bks. for Young Readers) Abrams, Harry N., Inc.

Vonthron, Satanta C. Caillov Visits the Farmer's Market. Meier, Kerry L., illus. l.t. ed. 2005. (Hrl Board Book Ser.). (J). (ps-k). pap. 10.95 (978-1-57332-310-9(1)) HighReach Learning, Inc.

Wellington, Monica. Apple Farmer Annie/ Anna Cultiva Manzanas. Del Risco, Eida, tr. Wellington, Monica, illus. 2004. (ENG & SPA., Illus.). 32p. (J). (ps). 10.99 (978-0-525-47252-0(5), Dutton Juvenile) Penguin Group (USA) Inc.

MARKSMANSHIP

see Shooting

MARLEY, BOB, 1945-1981

Jeffrey, Gary. Bob Marley: The Life of a Reggae Superstar. Riley, Terry, illus. 2006. (Graphic Biographies Ser.). 48p. (J). lib. bdg. 29.95 (978-1-4042-0854-4(2)) Rosen Publishing Group, Inc., The.

Marley, Bob. Bob Marley. 1999. (They Died Too Young Ser.). (Illus.). 48p. (YA). 27.00 (978-0-7910-5228-0(1), Chelsea Hse.) Facts On File, Inc.

Marley, Cedella & Hausman, Gerald. The Boy from Nine Miles: The Early Life of Bob Marley. Fox, Mariah, illus. 2002. (Young Spirit Books). 64p. (J). (gr. 3-4). 17.95 (978-1-57174-282-7(4)) Hampton Roads Publishing Co., Inc.

Waters, Rosa. Bob Marley & the Wailers. 2008. (J). (***978-1-4222-0192-3(9)***) Mason Crest Pubs.

MARMOTS

see also Woodchuck

Richardson, Adele D. Groundhogs: Woodchucks, Marmots, & Whistle Pigs. 2002. (Wild World of Animals Ser.). (Illus.). 24p. (J). (gr. 1). lib. bdg. 18.60 (978-0-7368-1397-6(7), Bridgestone Bks.) Capstone Pr., Inc.

Royer, Anne. Little Marmots. Castile, Muriel, tr. from FRE. 2005. (Born to Be Wild Ser.). (Illus.). 24p. (J). (gr. 1-3). lib. bdg. 22.00 (978-0-8368-4439-9(4)) Stevens, Gareth Inc.

MARMOTS—FICTION

Elschner, G. & Devos, X. Friends for All Seasons. 2006. (Illus.). 32p. (J). 15.95 (978-0-7358-2003-6(1)) North-South Bks., Inc.

Knister. A Promise Is a Promise. Tharlet, Eve, illus. 2006. 32p. (J). (ps-3). 16.99 (978-0-698-40040-5(2), Minedition) Penguin Group (USA) Inc.

MARQUETTE, JACQUES, 1637-1675

Donaldson-Forbes, Jeff. Jacques Marquette & Louis Jolliet. 2002. (Famous Explorers Ser.). (Illus.). 24p. (J). (gr. 3). lib. bdg. 18.75 (978-0-8239-5835-1(3), PowerKids Pr.) Rosen Publishing Group, Inc., The.

Harkins, Susan and William. The Life & Times of Father Jacques Marquette. 2007. (Profiles in American History Ser.). (J). lib. bdg. (***978-1-58415-528-7(0)***) Mitchell Lane Pubs., Inc.

Harmon, Daniel E. Jolliet & Marquette: Explorers of the Mississippi River. 2001. (Explorers of New Worlds Ser.). (Illus.). (J). 63p. pap. 25.00 (978-0-7910-6427-6(1)); 64p. 25.00 (978-0-7910-6426-9(3)) Facts On File, Inc. (Chelsea Hse.).

—Jolliet & Marquette: Explorers of the Mississippi River. 2001. (Illus.). 63p. (J). (gr. 4-7). lib. bdg. 17.60 (978-0-613-65434-0(X)) Tandem Library Bks.

Marsh, Carole. Father Jacques Marquette. 2002. (One Thousand Readers Ser.). (Illus.). 12p. (J). (gr. k-4). 2.95 (978-0-635-01514-3(5), 15145) Gallopade International.

Petrie, Kristin. Marquette & Jolliet. 2007. (Illus.). 32p. (J). 22.78 (978-1-59679-745-1(2)) ABDO Publishing Co.

Zelenyi, Alexander. Marquette & Jolliet: Quest for the Mississippi. 2006. (In the Footsteps of Explorers Ser.). (Illus.). 32p. (J). (gr. 3-9). (978-0-7787-2431-5(X)); pap. (978-0-7787-2467-4(0)) Crabtree Publishing Co.

MARRIAGE

see also Dating (Social Customs); Domestic Relations; Family; Family Life; Family Life Education; Intermarriage; Sex; Sexual Ethics

Ayer, Eleanor H. El Matrimonio Adolescente. 2002. (Todo lo Que Necesitas Saber Ser.). (SPA & ENG., Illus.). 64p. (YA). lib. bdg. 26.50 (978-0-8239-3586-4(8), Buenas Letra) Rosen Publishing Group, Inc., The.

Butler, Brian, et al. Theology of the Body for Teens: Student Workbook. 2006. per. 14.95 (***978-1-932927-86-3(7)***) Ascension Pr.

Center for Learning Network Staff. Charming Billy/at Weddings & Wakes: Curriculum Unit. 2005. (Novel Ser.). 64p. (YA). tchr. ed. 19.95 (978-1-56077-788-5(5)) Ctr. for Learning, The.

Chronicle Books LLC Staff. Fiona the Flower Girl. 2008. 40p. (J). 15.99 (978-0-8118-5903-5(7)) Chronicle Bks. LLC.

The Fighting Marriage. 2004. (Focus on the Family Marriage Ser.).Tr. of El Conflicto en el Matrimonio. 80p. 7.99 (978-0-8307-3149-7(0), Gospel Light) Gospel Light Pubns.

The Giving Marriage. 2004. (Focus on the Family Marriage Ser.).Tr. of La Abnegacion en el Matrimonio. 80p. 7.99 (978-0-8307-3151-0(2), Gospel Light) Gospel Light Pubns.

Gold, Shannon & Gold, Erica. Flower Petals Falling Down: How to Be a Flower Girl. Masar, Corey N., illus. 2000. 43p. (J). (ps-7). pap. 14.95 (978-0-9671047-0-6(X)) Peacock Publishing.

Hossler, Margaret. Spenser Rose Is Born. 2003. 32p. 12.99 (978-0-9650491-4-6(0)) STL Distribution North America.

Lindsay, Jeanne Warren. Teenage Couples - Caring, Commitment & Change: How to Build a Relationship That Lasts. Crawford, David, photos by. 2003. (Teenage Couples Ser.). (Illus.). 208p. (J). (gr. 7 up). 15.95 (978-0-930934-92-7(X)) Morning Glory Pr., Inc.

—Teenage Couples - Caring, Commitment & Change: How to Build a Relationship That Lasts. Crawford, David, photos by. 2003. (Teenage Couples Ser.). (Illus.). 208p. (J). (gr. 7 up). pap. 9.95 (978-0-930934-93-4(8)) Morning Glory Pr., Inc.

—Teenage Couples - Coping with Reality: Dealing with Money, In-Laws, Babies & Other Details of Daily Life. Crawford, David, photos by. 2003. (Teen Pregnancy & Parenting Ser.). (Illus.). 188p. (J). (gr. 7-12). 15.95 (978-0-930934-87-3(3)); pap. 9.95 (978-0-930934-86-6(5)) Morning Glory Pr., Inc.

The Masterpiece Marriage. 2004. (Focus on the Family Marriage Ser.).Tr. of La obra Maestra del matrimonio. 72p. 7.99 (978-0-8307-3120-6(2) , Gospel Light) Gospel Light Pubns.

The Model Marriage. 2004. (Focus on the Family(R) Marriage Ser.).Tr. of El Modelo para el Matrimonio. 72p. 7.99 (978-0-8307-3150-3(4) , Gospel Light) Gospel Light Pubns.

Ruhnke, Robert A. For Better & for Ever 3.2 - Roman Catholic Edition. 1999. (Illus.). 200p. (YA). pap. 12.50 (978-0-9677223-0-6(6)) Redemptorists Marriage Preparation Resources.

Smalley, Gary. The Covenant Marriage. 2004. (Focus on the Family Marriage Ser.). 72p. 7.99 (978-0-8307-3119-0(9) , Gospel Light) Gospel Light Pubns.

—The Passionate Marriage. 2004. (Focus on the Family Marriage Ser.). 72p. 7.99 (978-0-8307-3152-7(0) , Gospel Light) Gospel Light Pubns.

Snyder, Gail. Marriage & Family Issues. 2006. (Gallup Major Trends & Events Ser.). (Illus.). 112p. (J). (gr. 7 up). lib. bdg. (978-1-59084-966-8(3) , 1260831) Mason Crest Pubs.

The Surprising Marriage. 2004. (Focus on the Family Marriage Ser.).Tr. of La Expectacion en el Matrimonio. 80p. 7.99 (978-0-8307-3153-4(9) , Gospel Light) Gospel Light Pubns.

Whelan, Shane LeGrande. More Than One: Plural Marriage - A Sacred Heritage, a Promise for Tomorrow. 2nd rev. ed. 2002. (Illus.). 262p. pap. 16.95 (978-0-9717704-2-3(5)) Zion Pubs.

Ziefert, Harriet. What Is a Wedding? Schumacher, Claire, illus. 2006. 16p. pap. 5.95 (978-1-4027-3648-3(7)) Sterling Publishing Co., Inc.

MARRIAGE—FICTION

Adee, Donna J. Miriam & Timothy Face Life, Vol. 3. Babcock, Marci, illus. 2000. 384p. (J). pap. 12.95 (978-0-9654272-3-4(4)) Harvest Pubns.

Ain, Beth Levine. The Portrait. 2008. (J). (*978-0-7636-3396-7(8)) Candlewick Pr.

Amelia Bedelia & the Surprise Shower. 2002. (Amelia Bedelia Ser.). (Illus.). (J). 12.34 (978-0-7587-5974-0(6)) Book Wholesalers, Inc.

Artigas de Sierra, Ione M. Las Bodas del Gallo Perico. (Superbks./Superlibros). (J). (gr. k-1). (SPA.). 21.95 (978-0-88272-488-1(6)); (SPA.). pap. 6.95 (978-0-88272-489-8(4)); (Illus.). 16p. pap. 6.95 (978-0-88272-491-1(6)) Santillana USA Publishing Co., Inc.

Barasch, Lynne. The Reluctant Flower Girl. Barasch, Lynne, illus. 2001. (Illus.). 40p. (J). (gr. k-3). 14.95 (978-0-06-028809-9(4)) HarperCollins Pubs.

Bennett, Cherie. The Wedding That Almost Wasn't. 1998. (J). (gr. 3-7). pap. 4.50 (978-0-590-05959-6(9) , Scholastic Paperbacks) Scholastic, Inc.

Berman, Ron. Old MacDonald Had a Wedding. Gerrity, Brian, illus. 2007. 24p. (J). pap. 5.99 (978-0-8431-2189-6(0) , Price Stern Sloan) Penguin Group (USA) Inc.

Boonstra, Jean Elizabeth. A Wedding in Avondale. 2004. 95p. (J). (978-0-8163-2018-9(7)) Pacific Pr. Publishing Assn.

Bradbury, Bianca. Flight into Spring. 2005. 184p. (YA). pap. (*978-1-932350-01-2(2)) Bethlehem Bks.

Brannen, Sarah S. Uncle Bobby's Wedding. Brennen, Sarah S., illus. 2008. 32p. (J). (ps). 15.99 (*978-0-399-24712-5(2) , Putnam Juvenile) Penguin Group (USA) Inc.

Buehner, Caralyn. Fanny's Dream. 2003. (gr. k-3). lib. bdg. 15.30 (978-0-613-67452-2(9)) Tandem Library Bks.

Buehner, Caralyn & Buehner, Mark. Fanny's Dream. Buehner, Caralyn & Buehner, Mark, illus. 2003. (Illus.). 32p. (J). (gr. k-3). pap. 6.99 (978-0-14-250060-6(7) , Puffin) Penguin Group (USA) Inc.

Bunting, Eve. My Mom's Wedding. Papp, Lisa, illus. 2006. 32p. (J). (gr. 1-5). 16.95 (978-1-58536-288-2(3)) Sleeping Bear Pr.

Burge, Constance M. Soul of the Bride. 2001. (gr. 7-12). lib. bdg. 14.15 (978-0-613-74202-3(8)) Tandem Library Bks.

Campbell, Joanna. Bridal Dreams. 2004. (Thoroughbred Ser.: No. 65). 176p. (J). pap. 4.99 (978-0-06-059524-1(8) , Harper Entertainment) HarperCollins Pubs.

Cohn, Rachel. Two Steps Forward. 2007. 240p. (J). (gr. 4-8). pap. 8.99 (*978-0-689-86615-9(1)) Kaplan Bks.

Crook, Carol. The Prophetic Wedding of the Bride. 2001. (Illus.). 61p. (YA). (gr. 10 up). pap. 5.95 (978-0-939399-44-4(X)) Books of Truth.

Cushman, Karen. El Libro de Catherine. 2003. (SPA.). 237p. (978-84-236-4600-5(9) , ED8017) Edebé ESP. *Dist:* Lectorum Pubns., Inc.

de Brunhoff, Jean, et al. Isabelle the Flower Girl. 2004. (Babar Ser.). (Illus.). 24p. (J). (ps-3). 9.95 (978-0-8109-5039-9(1)) Abrams, Harry N. , Inc.

Delton, Judy. Angel's Mother's Wedding. Weber, Jill, illus. 2001. 176p. (J). (gr. 4-6). pap. 4.95 (978-0-618-11118-3(2)) Houghton Mifflin Co. Trade & Reference Div.

—Angel's Mother's Wedding. 2001. (J). 11.60 (978-0-606-21032-4(6)); (gr. 3-6). lib. bdg. 12.95 (978-0-613-35483-7(4)) Tandem Library Bks.

Dessen, Sarah. That Summer. 1998. (J). (978-0-606-13842-0(0)) Tandem Library Bks.

Dhami, Narinder. Bhangra Babes. 2007. 192p. (J). (gr. 4-7). 5.99 (*978-0-440-42106-1(3) , Yearling) Random Hse. Children's Bks.

Dijkstra, Lida. Little Mouse. Grobler, Piet, illus. 2004. 32p. (J). 15.95 (978-1-932425-06-2(3) , Lemniscaat) Boyds Mills Pr.

Doudna, Kelly. Crab Cakes. Haberstroh, Anne, illus. (Fact & Fiction Ser.). 24p. (J). 2007. 21.35 (978-1-59928-434-7(0)); 2006. (978-1-59928-435-4(9)) ABDO Publishing Co.

Dower, Laura. From the Files of Madison Finn: Sink or Swim. 2003. (gr. 3-6). lib. bdg. 13.00 (978-0-613-88965-0(7)) Tandem Library Bks.

—Sink or Swim. rev. ed. 2003. (From the Files of Madison Finn Ser.: No. 13). 176p. (J). (gr. 3-7). pap. 4.99 (978-0-7868-1735-1(6) , Volo) Hyperion Bks. for Children.

DuJardin, Rosamond. Double Wedding: A Pam & Penny Story. 2002. 187p. (YA). pap. 12.95 (978-1-930009-52-3(6) , 800-691-7779) Image Cascade Publishing.

—Wedding in the Family. 2003. (YA). pap. 12.95 (978-1-930009-72-1(0) , 800-691-7779) Image Cascade Publishing.

Dunkle, Clare B. Close Kin. 2nd rev. ed. 2006. (Hollow Kingdom Trilogy Ser.). 224p. (YA). (gr. 7 up). pap. 6.95 (978-0-8050-8109-1(7) , Holt, Henry & Co. Bks. For Young Readers) Holt, Henry & Co.

—Close Kin. Simonsen, Reka, ed. 2nd rev. ed. 2004. (Hollow Kingdom Trilogy Ser.: Bk. II). (Illus.). 224p. (YA). 16.95 (978-0-8050-7497-0(X) , Holt, Henry & Co. Bks. For Young Readers) Holt, Henry & Co.

—In the Coils of the Snake. 3rd rev. ed. (Hollow Kingdom Trilogy Ser.). 240p. (YA). (gr. 7 up). 2006. pap. 6.95 (978-0-8050-8110-7(0) , Holt, Henry & Co. Bks. For Young Readers); 2005. 16.95 (978-0-8050-7747-6(2)) Holt, Henry & Co.

Finley, Martha. Elsie's New Life, Vol. 3. 2006. (Life of Faith': Elsie Dinsmore Ser.). 224p. (J). pap. 7.99 (978-1-928749-82-0(8)) Zonderkidz.

—Elsie's Troubled Times, Vol. 6. 2006. (Life of Faith': Elsie Dinsmore Ser.). 224p. (J). pap. 7.99 (978-1-928749-88-2(7)) Zonderkidz.

—Elsie's True Love, Vol. 5. 2006. (Life of Faith': Elsie Dinsmore Ser.). 224p. (J). pap. 7.99 (978-1-928749-84-4(4)) Zonderkidz.

—Mildred & Elsie, Vol. 3. (Mildred Classics Ser.: Vol. 3). 288p. pap. 6.95 (978-1-58182-229-8(4)) Cumberland Hse. Publishing.

Friedman, Laurie. Heart to Heart with Mallory. Pollak, Barbara, illus. 2007. (Mallory Ser.). 160p. (J). (gr. 2-7). pap. 5.95 (*978-0-8225-7133-9(1) , First Avenue Editions) Lerner Publishing Group.

Friedman, Laurie B. Heart to Heart with Mallory. Pollak, Barbara, illus. 2006. 160p. (J). (gr. 2-5). 15.95 (978-1-57505-932-7(0) , Twenty-First Century Bks.) Lerner Publishing Group.

—Mallory on Board. Pollak, Barbara, illus. 2007. 160p. (J). (gr. 2-6). 15.95 (978-0-8225-6194-1(8) , Carolrhoda Bks.) Lerner Publishing Group.

—A Style All Her Own. Watts, Sharon, illus. 2005. 32p. (J). (ps-3). lib. bdg. 15.95 (978-1-57505-599-2(6)) Lerner Publishing Group.

Furgang, Kathy. Flower Girl. Jessup, Harley, illus. 2005. 32p. (J). (gr. k-3). reprint ed. pap. pap. 5.99 (978-0-14-240238-2(9) , Puffin) Penguin Group (USA) Inc.

Godwin, Laura. Flower Girl. Wallace, John, illus. 2000. 24p. (ps-k). 12.99 (978-0-7868-0408-5(4)) Hyperion Bks. for Children.

Grindley, Sally. Spilled Water. 2004. 224p. (J). 15.95 (978-1-58234-937-4(1) , Bloomsbury Children) Bloomsbury Publishing.

H. Kraus, Joanna & Luisa, Anna. A Night of Tamales & Roses. 2007. 32p. (J). 15.95 (*978-0-9726614-4-7(1)) Shenanigan Bks.

Hamilton, Elizabeth L. Date with Responsibility. 2004. (Character-in-Action Ser.: No. 2). (Illus.). 384p. (YA). per. 19.95 (978-0-9713749-0-4(2) , Character-in-Action) Quiet Impact, Inc.

Harcourt School Publishers Staff. The Best Race of All On Level. 3rd ed. 2002. (Trophies Reading Program Ser.). (Illus.). pap. 5.10 (978-0-15-323431-6(8)) Harcourt Schl. Pubs.

—The Red & Blue Hat On Level. 3rd ed. 2002. (Trophies Reading Program Ser.). (Illus.). pap. 5.10 (978-0-15-323347-0(8)) Harcourt Schl. Pubs.

Helmso, Candy G. Saltar la Escoba. Romo, Alberto, tr. Friar, Joanne, illus. 1998. (Books for Young Learners).Tr. of Jump the Broom. (SPA.). 16p. (J). (gr. k-2). pap. 5.00 (978-1-57274-202-4(X) , A2900) Owen, Richard C. Pubs., Inc.

Henkes, Kevin. Lilly's Big Day. Henkes, Kevin, illus. 2006. (Illus.). 40p. (J). 16.99 (978-0-06-074236-2(4)); lib. bdg. 17.89 (978-0-06-074237-9(2)) HarperCollins Pubs.

Hernandez, Mary. Wedding on Mudpie Island. Wise, Noreen, ed. Wethington, Liz, illus. 2000. (Book-a-Day Collection). 32p. (YA). (ps up). pap. 5.95 (978-1-58584-440-1(3)) Huckleberry Pr.

Hicks, Betty. Out of Order. 2007. 176p. (J). pap. 6.99 (*978-0-312-37355-9(4)) Square Fish.

Hillcrest, Dayne. Letena, Forever A-Flutter. 1999. (J). (gr. k-4). pap. 6.95 (978-0-533-12757-3(2)) Vantage Pr., Inc.

Hingoro, Samira, creator. A Marriage Proposal. 2003. (YA). per. 12.95 (978-0-9743167-0-3(9)) Faith Pubns.

Holabird, Katharine. The Angelina's Diary No. 4. Craig, Helen, illus. 2006. (Angelina Ballerina Ser.). 80p. (J). (gr. 1-3). 3.99 (978-0-448-44386-7(4) , Grosset & Dunlap) Penguin Group (USA) Inc.

Hook, Jacqueline A. You're Going to Be a Flower Girl. 2005. (J). per. (978-0-9664783-3-4(9)) Jacqueline Beverly Hills.

Hooper, Mary. The Revolting Bridesmaid. 2007. (Katie Ser.). (Illus.). 80p. (J). (gr. 2-4). pap. 8.95 (*978-0-7475-8611-1(X)) Bloomsbury Publishing Plc GBR. *Dist:* Independent Pubs. Group.

—The Revolting Wedding. 2007. (Katie Ser.). (Illus.). 96p. (J). (gr. 2-4). pap. 8.95 (*978-0-7475-8612-8(8)) Bloomsbury Publishing Plc GBR. *Dist:* Independent Pubs. Group.

Howard, Annabelle. As the Mayan Calendars Turn. 2005. 40.00 (*978-1-4108-4223-7(1)) Benchmark Education Co.

Howard, Elizabeth Fitzgerald. Flower Girl Butterflies. Kromer, Christiane, illus. 2004. 32p. (J). 16.89 (978-0-688-17810-9(3)) HarperCollins Pubs.

Howe, James. Pinky & Rex Get Married. 1999. (Pinky & Rex Ser.). (J). (gr. 1-4). (978-0-606-16307-1(7)) Tandem Library Bks.

Hunt, Angela Elwell. Keeping Your Life Together When Your Parents Pull Apart: A Teen's Guide to Surviving Divorce. 2000. 136p. (YA). (gr. 7-12). pap. 10.95 (978-0-595-08999-4(2)) iUniverse, Inc.

Irvine, Abby. La increible boda de mi tia Lola. Abbott, Simon, illus. 2005. (SPA.). 16p. (J). bds. 13.95 (978-84-7864-792-7(9)) Combel Editorial, S.A. ESP. *Dist:* Independent Pubs. Group.

James, Elizabeth. The Woman Who Married a Bear. Atanas, illus. 2007. 40p. (J). (gr. k up). 16.95 (*978-1-894965-49-1(3)) Simply Read Bks. CAN. *Dist:* Perseus Distribution.

Jensen, Roberta Joan. The Marriage of Princess Winter Bk. 1: Princess Winter. 2005. 64p. pap. 12.95 (978-1-4137-7769-7(4)) PublishAmerica, Inc.

Johnson, Angela. The Wedding. Soman, David, illus. 1999. 32p. (J). (ps-2). 17.99 (978-0-531-33139-2(3)); pap. 16.95 (978-0-531-30139-5(7)) Scholastic, Inc. (Orchard Bks.).

Johnson, Annabel & Johnson, Edgar. Wilderness Bride. 2003. 232p. 12.95 (978-0-9714612-7-7(9)) Green Mansion Pr. LLC.

Kanefield, Teri. Rivka's Way. 2001. (Illus.). 144p. (J). (gr. 5-9). 15.95 (978-0-8126-2870-8(5)) Cricket Bks.

Katies Choice. 2005. (YA). per. (978-1-59872-217-8(4)) Instantpublisher.com.

Keane, Dave. The Missing Monkey-Eye Diamond. Keane, Dave, illus. 2006. (Joe Sherlock Ser.: No. 3). (Illus.). 128p. (J). 15.99 (978-0-06-076191-2(1)) HarperCollins Pubs.

Keane, David & Keane, Dave. The Missing Monkey-Eye Diamond. Keane, Dave, illus. 2006. (Joe Sherlock Ser.). (Illus.). 128p. (J). pap. 3.99 (978-0-06-076190-5(3) , Harper Trophy) HarperCollins Pubs.

Kiser, Dolores White. The Marriage of White Rabbit. 2005. (J). 10.00 net. (978-0-9766648-3-3(6)) White Kiser, Dolores.

Korba, Joanna. Rough-Face Girl: A Native AMER Cinderella Story. 2006. 42.00 (*978-1-4108-6163-4(5)) Benchmark Education Co.

LaFaye, A. The Year of the Sawdust Man. 1999. (978-0-606-17947-8(X)) Tandem Library Bks.

Lambert, Janet. Wedding Bells. 2001. (Jordon Ser.: Vol. 8). (YA). pap. 12.95 (978-1-930009-39-4(9)) Image Cascade Publishing.

Levine, Gail Carson. The Princess Test. Elliott, Mark, illus. 1999. (Princess Tales Ser.). 96p. (J). (gr. 2-7). 9.99 (978-0-06-028062-8(X)) HarperCollins Pubs.

Lewison, Wendy Cheyette. I Am a Flower Girl. Hathon, Elizabeth, illus. 1999. (Grosset & Dunlap All Aboard Books & Cassettes Ser.). 32p. (J). (ps-3). pap. 2.99 (978-0-448-41956-5(4) , Grosset & Dunlap) Penguin Group (USA) Inc.

Liberts, Jennifer & Random House Disney Staff. Wishes Come True - Wedding Bells. 2001. (Illus.). 80p. (J). (ps-3). pap. 2.99 (978-0-7364-1196-7(8) , Golden/ Disney) Random Hse. Children's Bks.

Literature Connections English: Picture Bride. 2004. (gr. 6-12). (978-0-395-77540-0(X) , 2-80109) McDougal Littell Inc.

Literature Connections English: Pride & Prejudice. 2004. (gr. 6-12). (978-0-395-77556-1(6) , 2-80125) McDougal Littell Inc.

The Littles Have a Wedding. 2002. (Littles Ser.). (Illus.). (J). 12.17 (978-0-7587-8431-5(7)) Book Wholesalers, Inc.

Lollino, Jessica. Lily & the Big Italian Wedding. Lollino, Jessica, ed. 2006. (Little Lily Mays Ser.: Vol. 2). (Illus.). 32p. (J). pap. 20.00 (978-0-9712383-2-9(4)) Culture Connection, The.

Looper, Grace W. Great-Grandpa's Hidden Treasure. 2006. (YA). pap. (*978-1-933523-18-7(2)) Bella Rosa Bks.

Marsoli, Lisa Ann. My Perfect Wedding. 2004. (Random House Pictureback Book Ser.). (Illus.). 24p. (J). (ps-2). pap. 3.99 (978-0-7364-2219-2(6) , RH/Disney) Random Hse. Children's Bks.

Mathers, Petra. Dodo Gets Married. Mathers, Petra, illus. 2001. (Illus.). 32p. (J). (ps-3). 16.00 (978-0-689-83018-1(1) , Atheneum/Anne Schwartz Bks.) Simon & Schuster Children's Publishing.

McDonald, Megan. Daisy Jane, Best-Ever Flower Girl. Gévry, Claudine, illus. 2007. (Step into Reading Ser.). 48p. (J). (gr. k-3). 3.99 (978-0-375-83110-2(X) , Random Hse. Bks. for Young Readers) Random Hse. Children's Bks.

—Daisy Jane, Best-Ever Flower Girl! Gévry, Claudine, illus. 2007. (Step into Reading Ser.). 48p. (J). (gr. k-3). lib. bdg. 11.99 (978-0-375-93110-9(4) , Random Hse. Bks. for Young Readers) Random Hse. Children's Bks.

McKay, Hilary. Caddy Ever After. 224p. (J). 2007. pap. 5.99 (*978-1-4169-0931-6(1) , Aladdin); 2006. (gr. 5-9). 15.95 (978-1-4169-0930-9(3) , McElderry, Margaret K.) Simon & Schuster Children's Publishing.

Milde, Jeanette. Once upon a Wedding. Sandin, Joan, tr. from SWE. 2004. (Illus.). 32p. (J). 15.00 (978-91-29-66048-7(3)) R & S Bks. SWE. *Dist:* Macmillan.

Miller, Mary. Where Angels Sing. 1998. (Illus.). pap. 7.50 (978-1-884377-04-4(1)) Green Pastures Pr.

Monnar, Ana. Heart of Stone. Michaud, Nancy, illus. 2007. 24p. (J). per. 11.99 (*978-0-9768035-5-3(0)) Readers Are Leaders U.S.A., Inc.

Morgan, Robert. Gap Creek: The Story of A Marriage. 2001. (gr. 5-8). lib. bdg. 16.45 (978-0-613-58965-9(3)) Tandem Library Bks.

Munsch, Robert. Ribbon Rescue. ed. 2004. (Illus.). (J). (gr. k-3). spiral bd. (978-0-616-01742-5(1)); spiral bd. (978-0-616-01743-2(X)) Canadian National Institute for the Blind/Institut National Canadien pour les Aveugles.

—Ribbon Rescue. Fernandes, Eugenie, illus. 1999. 32p. (J). (ps-1). pap. 11.95 (978-0-590-89012-0(3)) Scholastic, Inc.

Munsch, Robert & Fernandes, Eugenie. Ribbon Rescue. 2002. (Illus.). 32p. (J). pap. 3.99 (978-0-590-89597-2(4)) Scholastic, Inc.

My Sister's Wedding: A Story of Kenya. 2005. (Make Friends Around the World Ser.). (Illus.). 32p. (J). (gr. k-3). 8.95 incl. reel tape (978-1-56899-900-5(3) , SC8006) Soundprints.

Naylor, Phyllis Reynolds. Including Alice. 2004. (Alice Ser.). 288p. (YA). 15.95 incl. audio compact disk (978-0-689-82637-5(0) , Atheneum) Simon & Schuster Children's Publishing.

—Patiently Alice. (Alice Ser.). 256p. (YA). 2004. mass mkt. 5.99 (978-0-689-87073-6(6) , Simon Pulse); 2003. (Illus.). 15.95 (978-0-689-82636-8(2) , Atheneum) Simon & Schuster Children's Publishing.

Naylor, Phyllis Reynolds & Vaccaro, Nick. Including Alice. 2005. (Alice Ser.). 288p. (YA). mass mkt. 5.99 (978-0-689-87074-3(4) , Simon Pulse) Simon & Schuster Children's Publishing.

Newhall, Mary. Bridal Dreams. 2004. 163p. (J). (gr. 3-7). per. 12.04 (978-0-606-32970-5(6)) Tandem Library Bks.

Nilsen, Anna. Bella & the Royal Wedding. 2006. (Illus.). 20p. (J). 10.95 (978-0-7624-2757-4(4) , Running Pr. Kids) Running Pr. Bk. Pubs.

Paine, Penelope C. 10 Neat Things about Being a Flower Girl. 2002. (Illus.). 24p. (J). 8.95 (978-0-9707944-1-3(X)) Paper Posie.

Paratore, Coleen Murtagh. The Wedding Planner's Daughter. 2005. (Wedding Planner's Daughter Ser.). 208p. (J). 15.95 (978-0-689-87340-9(9)) Simon & Schuster Children's Publishing.

Paratore, Coleen Murtagh. Willa by Heart. 2008. (Wedding Planner's Daughter Ser.). 240p. (J). 15.99 (*978-1-4169-4076-0(6)) Simon & Schuster Children's Publishing.

Park, Barbara. Junie B. Jones Is (Almost) a Flower Girl. Brunkus, Denise, illus. 1999. (Junie B. Jones Ser.: No. 13). 80p. (J). (gr. 1-4). lib. bdg. 11.99 (978-0-375-90038-9(1)); (gr. k-3). pap. 3.99 (978-0-375-80038-2(7)) Random Hse. Children's Bks. (Random Hse. Bks. for Young Readers).

—Junie B. Jones Is (Almost) a Flower Girl. 1999. (Junie B. Jones Ser.: No. 13). (J). (gr. k-3). lib. bdg. 11.80 (978-0-613-16138-1(6)) Tandem Library Bks.

Paterson, Aileen. Maisie Goes to a Wedding. Paterson, Aileen, illus. 2000. (Illus.). 32p. (J). (gr. 1-3). pap. (978-1-871512-54-0(9)) Glowworm Bks., Ltd.

Picard, Barbara Leonie. The Midsummer Bride. 1999. (Illus.). 26p. (J). (978-0-19-272354-3(5)) Oxford Univ. Pr., Inc.

Porte, Barbara Ann. Harry Gets an Uncle. 2002. (I Can Read Bks.). (Illus.). 48p. (J). (gr. k-3). 15.95 (978-0-06-001150-5(5)) HarperCollins Pubs.

—Harry Gets an Uncle. 2002. (gr. k-3). lib. bdg. 11.80 (978-0-613-62143-4(3)) Tandem Library Bks.

Porter, Eleanor H. Miss BillyMarried. 2006. pap. (*978-1-4068-3238-9(3)) Echo Library.

—Miss Billys Decision. 2006. pap. (*978-1-4068-3240-2(5)) Echo Library.

Random House Disney Staff. Make Believe Bride. 2004. (Illus.). 24p. (J). (ps-2). pap. 3.99 (978-0-7364-2220-8(X) , RH/Disney) Random Hse. Children's Bks.

Rinaldi, Ann. Brooklyn Rose. 240p. (YA). 2005. 17.00 (978-0-15-205117-4(1)); 2006. (Illus.). reprint ed. pap. 6.95 (978-0-15-205538-7(X) , Harcourt Paperbacks) Harcourt Children's Bks.

Roy, Ron. A Spy in the White House. Bush, Timothy, tr. Bush, Timothy, illus. 2004. (Capital Mysteries Ser.: Vol. 4). 96p. (J). (gr. 1-4). pap. 3.99 (978-0-375-82557-6(6)); lib. bdg. 11.99 (978-0-375-92557-3(0)) Random Hse. Children's Bks. (Random Hse. Bks. for Young Readers).

Rylant, Cynthia. Wedding Flowers. Halperin, Wendy Anderson, illus. 2003. (Cobble Street Cousins Ser.: No. 6). 80p. (J). pap. 3.99 (978-0-689-83418-9(7) , Aladdin) Simon & Schuster Children's Publishing.

—Wedding Flowers. 2003. (Cobble Street Cousins Ser.: No. 6). (gr. 3-6). lib. bdg. 11.80 (978-0-613-66444-8(2)) Tandem Library Bks.

Rylant, Cynthia & Halperin, Wendy Anderson. Wedding Flowers. 2002. (Cobble Street Cousins Ser.: No. 6). (Illus.). 80p. (J). (gr. 2-5). 15.00 (978-0-689-83242-0(7)) Simon & Schuster Children's Publishing.

Sayres, Meghan Nuttall. Anahita's Woven Riddle. 2006. 368p. (YA). (gr. 5-9). 16.95 (978-0-8109-5481-6(8)) Abrams, Harry N. , Inc.

Shacter, Sara F. Heading to the Wedding: You're invited to join Patrick & Evie on the Great Adventure of Becoming (almost) perfect Guests. Thornton, Christine, illus. 2006. 32p. 18.95 (978-1-933176-05-5(9) , Red Pebble Bks.) Red Rock Pr., Inc.

Shanahan, Lisa. The Sweet, Terrible, Glorious Year I Truly, Completely Lost It. 2007. 304p. (YA). (gr. 7-10). 15.99 (*978-0-385-73516-2(2)); lib. bdg. 18.99 (*978-0-385-90505-3(X)) Random Hse. Children's Bks. (Delacorte Bks. for Young Readers).

Sharp, N. L. Ring Bear. Hassler, Michael T., illus. 2006. 32p. 17.95 (978-1-886225-91-6(5)) Prairieland Pr.

Slater, David Michael. The Ring Bear. Brooks, S. G., illus. 2004. 32p. (J). 15.95 (978-0-9729225-1-7(2) , 1231960) Flashlight Pr.

Small, David. Hoover's Bride. 2006. (Illus.). 40p. (J). pap. 5.99 (978-0-439-81218-4(6) , Scholastic Paperbacks) Scholastic, Inc.

Smith, Betty. Joy in the Morning. 2000. (gr. 7-12). lib. bdg. 22.25 (978-0-8085-1474-9(1)) Tandem Library Bks.

Soto, Gary. Snapshots from the Wedding. Garcia, Stephanie, illus. 1998. 32p. (J). (ps-3). pap. 5.99 (978-0-698-11752-5(2) , Putnam Juvenile) Penguin Group (USA) Inc.

Soto, Gary & Soto, Gary. Snapshots from the Wedding. Garcia, Stephanie, illus. 1998. (J). (ps-ps). lib. bdg. 14.15 (978-0-613-12117-0(1)) Tandem Library Bks.

Stacy & the Greek Village Wedding. 2001. 80p. (J). pap. 5.25 (978-0-9658730-2-4(1)) Drew Publishing Co.

Standish, Burt L. Frank Merriwell's Marriage. Rudman, Jack, ed. 2003. (Frank Merriwell Ser.). pap. 9.95 (978-0-8373-9125-0(3)) Merriwell, Frank Inc.

Stanley, Mandy. Lettice: The Flower Girl. Stanley, Mandy, illus. 2006. (Illus.). 32p. (J). (ps-3). 9.95 (978-1-4169-1157-9(X)) Simon & Schuster Children's Publishing.

Surace, Joan. The Story of Lucia. Rockford, Nancy, illus. 2006. (YA). pap. 8.00 (*978-0-8059-7062-3(2)) Dorrance Publishing Co., Inc.

Sypolt, Carl W. Adventures of David the Honeybee. 2003. 51p. pap. 9.95 (978-0-7414-1526-4(7)) Infinity Publishing.

The Three Sillies, 6, Pack. (Literatura 2000 Ser.). (gr. 2-3). 33.00 (978-0-7635-0242-3(1)) Rigby Education.

Tytler, Sarah. Girlhood & Womanhood the Story of Some. 2007. 43.99 (*978-1-4280-5160-7(0)); pap. 36.99 (*978-1-4280-5161-4(9)) IndyPublish.com.

Walters, Jennie. Caz's Confetti Crisis. 2002. (Illus.). mass mkt. 7.99 (978-0-340-85413-6(8) , Hodder & Stoughton) Hodder General Publishing Division GBR. *Dist:* Trafalgar Square Publishing.

Weber, Lenora Mattingly. Something Borrowed, Something Blue. 1999. (Beany Malone Ser.). 273p. (J). pap. 12.95 (978-1-930009-05-9(4)) Image Cascade Publishing.

—Tarry Awhile. 1999. (Beany Malone Ser.). 292p. (J). reprint ed. pap. 12.95 (978-1-930009-04-2(6)) Image Cascade Publishing.

The Wedding of the Mouse: An Asian Folktale. 2006. (J). 17.95 (*978-0-9790033-0-1(X)) Playground Pr.

Wenzel, Karen M. The Fan Tom Spider: A Flower Forest Wedding. Stadlberger, Kristy G., illus. 1999. 39p. (J). (gr. k-4). pap. (978-0-9656714-7-7(X)) WNZ Pubns.

Wharton, Edith. Ethan Frome, Level 3. 2nd abr. ed. 2000. (Bookworms Ser.). (Illus.). 80p. 6.50 (978-0-19-423002-5(3)) Oxford Univ. Pr., Inc.

Whelan, Gloria. Homeless Bird. (gr. 5 up). 2001. 192p. pap. 5.99 (978-0-06-440819-6(1)); 2000. 240p. (J). 16.99 (978-0-06-028454-1(4)) HarperCollins Pubs.

—Homeless Bird. 2001. 186p. (YA). (gr. 8-12). lib. bdg. 14.15 (978-0-613-44393-7(4)) Tandem Library Bks.

—Homeless Bird. l.t. ed. 2002. 147p. (J). 23.95 (978-0-7862-4060-9(1)) Thomson Gale.

—Pajaro Sin Hogar. 2003. (SPA., Illus.). (YA). 152p. (978-84-241-8106-2(9) , EV5099); (978-84-241-8077-5(1) , EV3047) Everest de Ediciones y Distribucion, S.L. ESP. *Dist:* Lectorum Pubns., Inc.

—Pajaro Sin Hogar. 2002. (gr. 7-12). lib. bdg. 18.75 (978-0-613-52285-4(0)) Tandem Library Bks.

Whitney, Kim Ablon. See You down the Road. 2005. 192p. (YA). (gr. 7-12). mass mkt. 5.99 (978-0-440-23809-6(9) , Laurel Leaf) Random Hse. Children's Bks.

Wierenga, Kathy & Johnson, Lissa Halls. Double Exposure, Vol. 4. 2005. (Brio Girls Ser.). 192p. (YA). pap. 7.99 (978-1-56179-954-1(8)) Focus on the Family Publishing.

Zalben, Jane Breskin. Brenda Berman, Wedding Expert. Chess, Victoria, illus. 2007. (J). (*978-0-618-31321-1(4) , Clarion Bks.) Houghton Mifflin Co. Trade & Reference Div.

10 Cool Things about Being a Ring Bearer. 2002. 24p. (J). 8.95 (978-0-9707944-2-0(8)) Paper Posie.

MARRIAGE, INTERRACIAL

see Interracial Marriage

MARRIAGE, MIXED

see Intermarriage

MARRIAGE CUSTOMS AND RITES

Allen, Amy. What Is It? 2000. (Illus.). 30p. (ps-1). 4.99 (978-1-887169-10-3(5)) Wedding Solutions Publishing, Inc.

Ariel Books Staff. The Bride. 2003. (Illus.). 80p. 5.99 (978-0-7407-3364-2(8)) Andrews McMeel Publishing.

Ganeri, Anita. Wedding Days: Celebrations of Marriage. 1999. (Life Times Ser.). (Illus.). 32p. (J). 15.95 (978-0-87226-288-1(X) , 6288XB, Bedrick, Peter Bks.) School Specialty Publishing.

Gelber, Carol. Love & Marriage Around World. 1998. (Illus.). 72p. (gr. 4-6). lib. bdg. 23.90 (978-0-7613-0102-8(X) , Millbrook Pr.) Lerner Publishing Group.

Hook, Jacqueline A. You're Going to Be a Ring Bearer. 2005. (J). per. (978-0-9664783-4-1(7)) Jacqueline Beverly Hills.

Jackson, Ellen B. Here Come the Brides. Heyer, Carol, illus. 1998. 32p. (J). (ps-3). 15.95 (978-0-8027-8468-1(2)); lib. bdg. 16.85 (978-0-8027-8469-8(0)) Walker & Co.

Mason, Paul. Weddings. 2003. (Rites of Passage Ser.). (Illus.). 32p. (J). pap. (978-1-4034-2515-7(9)); lib. bdg. 24.22 (978-1-4034-3990-1(7)) Heinemann Library.

Mattox, Brenda Sneathen. Wedding Traditions from Around the World Coloring Book. 2007. 32p. pap. 3.95 (*978-0-486-46232-5(3)) Dover Pubns., Inc.

Powell, Jillian. A Wedding. 2006. (Illus.). 30p. (978-1-58340-948-0(3)) Smart Apple Media.

Sonntag, Linda. Weddings. 2001. (Ceremonies & Celebrations Ser.). (Illus.). 32p. (J). (ps-3). lib. bdg. 25.69 (978-0-7398-3272-1(7)) Raintree.

World Book, Inc. Staff, contrib. by. Marriage Celebrations. 2003. (World Book's Celebrations & Rituals Around the World Ser.). (Illus.). 46p. (J). (978-0-7166-5012-6(6)) World Bk., Inc.

MARRIAGE CUSTOMS AND RITES—FICTION

Emecheta, Buchi & Border, Rosemary. The Bride Price. 2nd ed. 2000. (Oxford Bookworms Ser.). (Illus.). 106p. 6.50 (978-0-19-423059-9(7)) Oxford Univ. Pr., Inc.

English, Karen. Nadia's Hands. Weiner, Jonathan, illus. 2003. 32p. (J). (gr. k-2). 16.95 (978-1-56397-667-4(6)) Boyds Mills Pr.

Fagan, Cary. The Market Wedding. Ricci, Regolo, illus. 2000. 32p. (J). (gr. 2-5). 16.95 (978-0-88776-492-9(4)) Tundra Bks., Inc./Livres Toundra, Inc. CAN. *Dist:* Random Hse., Inc.

Gantos, Jack. Wedding Bells for Rotten Ralph. Rubel, Nicole, illus. 1999. (Rotten Ralph Ser.: Vol. 2). (J). (ps-3). 40p. 15.99 (978-0-06-027533-4(2)); Bk. 2. 32p. 14.89 (978-0-06-027534-1(0)) HarperCollins Pubs.

Godwin, Laura. The Ring Bearer. Wallace, John, illus. 2006. 32p. (ps-k). 12.99 (978-0-7868-5510-0(X)) Hyperion Pr.

Gunn, Robin Jones. With This Ring. 1998. (Sierra Jensen Ser.: Bk. 6). 160p. (J). (gr. 7-11). pap. (978-1-56179-540-6(2)) Focus on the Family Publishing.

Onyefulu, Ifeoma, illus. Here Comes Our Bride an African Wedding Story. 2004. 32p. (J). 15.95 (978-1-84507-047-2(X)) Lincoln, Frances Ltd. GBR. *Dist:* Perseus Distribution.

Peterson, John. The Littles Have a Wedding. Clark, Roberta C., illus. 2007. (Littles Ser.). 96p. (J). (gr. 1-5). pap. 3.99 (978-0-590-46224-2(5)) Scholastic, Inc.

Russell, Ching Yeung. Child Bride. 136p. 2003. (YA). (gr. 4-6). pap. 9.95 (978-1-59078-024-4(8)); 1999. (Illus.). (J). (gr. 3-7). 15.95 (978-1-56397-748-0(6)) Boyds Mills Pr.

Staples, Suzanne Fisher. Shabanu: Daughter of the Wind. 3rd ed. (J). pap. 3.99 (978-0-13-800053-0(0)) Prentice Hall (Schl. Div.).

—Shabanu: Daughter of the Wind. 2003. 288p. (YA). (gr. 7). pap. 6.99 (978-0-440-23856-0(0) , Laurel Leaf) Random Hse. Children's Bks.

—Shabanu: Daughter of the Wind. 2003. (gr. 7-12). lib. bdg. 14.75 (978-0-613-72260-5(4)) Tandem Library Bks.

MARS (PLANET)

Adamson, Thomas K. Mars. (J). 2008. (*978-1-4296-0737-7(8)); 2003. (Illus.). 24p. lib. bdg. 17.26 (978-0-7368-2113-1(9) , Pebble Bks.) Capstone Pr., Inc.

Adamson, Thomas K. Marte: Mars. 2006. (ENG & SPA., Illus.). 24p. (J). (978-0-7368-5880-9(6)) Capstone Pr., Inc.

Asimov, Isaac. The Solar System: Mars. 2004. (Isaac Asimov's 21st Century Library of the Universe). (Illus.). 32p. 14.00 (978-1-59102-124-7(3)) Prometheus Bks., Pubs.

Asimov, Isaac & Hantula, Richard. Mars. rev. ed. 2003. (Isaac Asimov's 21st Century Library of the Universe). (Illus.). 32p. (YA). (gr. 3 up). lib. bdg. 24.67 (978-0-8368-3236-5(1)) Stevens, Gareth Inc.

—Mars: Our Mysterious Neighbor. 2003. (Isaac Asimov's 21st Century Library of the Universe). (Illus.). 32p. (J). (gr. 3 up). pap. (978-0-8368-3940-1(4) , Weekly Reader Early Learning Library) Stevens, Gareth Inc.

Bergin, Mark. Exploration of Mars. 2001. (Fast Forward Ser.). (Illus.). 32p. (J). (gr. 4-8). 29.00 (978-0-531-14615-6(4) , Watts, Franklin) Scholastic Library Publishing.

Birch, Robin. Mars. 2004. (Solar System Ser.). (Illus.). 32p. (gr. 3-5). 23.00 (978-0-7910-7927-0(9) , Chelsea Hse.) Facts On File, Inc.

Branley, Franklyn M. Mission to Mars. 2002. (gr. k-3). lib. bdg. 13.00 (978-0-613-59380-9(4)) Tandem Library Bks.

Bridges, Andrew. The Inside Story of Mars. 2006. (J). 7.80 (978-0-9753920-8-9(5)) Sally Ride Science.

Brimner, Larry Dane. Mars. 1999. (Illus.). 47p. (J). (gr. 2-4). lib. bdg. 15.25 (978-0-613-37448-4(7)) Tandem Library Bks.

Carson, Mary Kay. Mars. 2003. (Science Links Ser.). (Illus.). 32p. (gr. 3-5). 23.00 (978-0-7910-7426-8(9) , Chelsea Hse.) Facts On File, Inc.

Chrismer, Melanie. Mars. (Scholastic News Nonfiction Readers: Space Science Ser.). 24p. (J). 2008. pap. 6.95 (*978-0-531-14762-7(2)); 2007. (Illus.). (gr. 1-2). lib. bdg. 20.00 (*978-0-531-14697-2(9)) Scholastic Library Publishing. (Children's Pr.).

Cobb, Allan B. Mars. 2004. (Library of the Nine Planets). (Illus.). 48p. (J). lib. bdg. 26.50 (978-1-4042-0169-9(6)) Rosen Publishing Group, Inc., The.

Cole, Michael D. Living on Mars: Mission to the Red Planet. 1999. (Countdown to Space Ser.). (Illus.). 48p. (J). (gr. 4-10). lib. bdg. 23.93 (978-0-7660-1121-2(6)) Enslow Pubs., Inc.

—Mars: The Fourth Planet. 2002. (Countdown to Space Ser.). (Illus.). 48p. (J). (gr. 4-10). lib. bdg. 23.93 (978-0-7660-1949-2(7)) Enslow Pubs., Inc.

Cutting, Robert. Mars Colony. Jeevan, Dhamindra, illus. 2007. 48p. (J). lib. bdg. 23.08 (*978-1-4242-1630-7(3)) Fitzgerald Bks.

Davis, Lucile. The Mars Rovers. 2004. (KidHaven Science Library). (Illus.). 48p. (J). (gr. 4-7). 26.20 (978-0-7377-3074-6(9) , Greenhaven Pr., Inc.) Thomson Gale.

Demuth, Patricia B. Mars: The Red Planet. Marchesi, Stephen, illus. 1998. (All Aboard Reading Ser.). 48p. (J). (gr. 2-4). pap. 3.99 (978-0-448-41843-8(6) , Grosset & Dunlap) Penguin Group (USA) Inc.

El descubrimiento de Marte. 2000. (McGraw-Hill Ciencias Ser.). (ENG & SPA.). (gr. 3 up). (978-0-02-279630-3(4)) Macmillan/McGraw-Hill Schl. Div.

Dorling Kindersley Publishing Staff, ed. Mars. 2004. (Eyewitness Books). (Illus.). 72p. (J). (ps-12). lib. bdg. 19.99 (978-0-7566-0766-1(3)); 15.99 (978-0-7566-0765-4(5)) Dorling Kindersley Publishing, Inc.

Doyle, Bill. The Space Explorer's Guide to Mars— in 3-D! 2004. (Space University Ser.). (Illus.). 47p. (J). (978-0-439-55748-1(8)) Scholastic, Inc.

Dunn, Mary R. A Look at Mars. 2008. (J). lib. bdg. (*978-1-4042-3828-2(X) , PowerKids Pr.) Rosen Publishing Group, Inc., The.

Eckold, David. The Ultimate Mars Rover Kit. 2004. (Illus.). 1p. (J). 29.99 (978-0-7566-0799-9(X)) Dorling Kindersley Publishing, Inc.

Feinstein, Stephen. Mars: A Myreportlinks. com Book. 2005. (Solar System Ser.). (Illus.). 48p. (J). (ps-10). lib. bdg. 25.26 (978-0-7660-5302-1(4) , MyReportLinks.com Bks.) Enslow Pubs., Inc.

Gaines, Ann Graham & Richardson, Adele D. Journey to Mars. 1999. (Above & Beyond Ser.). (Illus.). 32p. (J). (gr. 4-7). lib. bdg. 16.95 (978-1-58340-048-7(6)) Smart Apple Media.

Getz, David. Life on Mars. McCarty, Peter, illus. rev. ed. 2004. 64p. (J). 14.95 (978-0-8050-7729-2(4) , Holt, Henry & Co. Bks. For Young Readers) Holt, Henry & Co.

Golden Books Staff. Blast off to Mars! 2006. (Illus.). 64p. (J). (ps-2). pap. 3.99 (978-0-375-83663-3(2) , Golden Bks.) Random Hse. Children's Bks.

Goldstein, Margaret J. Mars. 2005. (Pull Ahead Bks.). (Illus.). 32p. (gr. 2-4). lib. bdg. 22.60 (978-0-8225-4651-1(5)) Lerner Publishing Group.

Goss, Tim. Mars. 2003. (Universe Ser.). (Illus.). 32p. (J). (gr. 3-5). lib. bdg. 22.79 (978-1-58810-912-5(7)); pap. 7.50 (978-1-4034-0613-2(8)) Heinemann Library.

Howard, Fran. Mars. 2007. (Planets Ser.). (ENG., Illus.). 32p. (J). (gr. k-4). lib. bdg. 24.21 (*978-1-59928-826-0(5) , Buddy Bks.) ABDO Publishing Co.

Jefferis, David. Exploring Planet Mars. 2007. (Illus.). 32p. (J). (gr. 3-7). (*978-0-7787-3100-9(6)); pap. (*978-0-7787-3114-6(6)) Crabtree Publishing Co.

Kerrod, Robin. Mars. 2005. (Planet Library). (Illus.). 32p. (gr. 3-8). 21.27 (978-0-8225-3906-3(3)) Lerner Publishing Group.

Kipp, Steven L. Mars. 2000. (Galaxy Ser.). (Illus.). 24p. (J). (gr. 2-3). lib. bdg. 18.60 (978-0-7368-0520-9(6) , Bridgestone Bks.) Capstone Pr., Inc.

LaFontaine, Bruce. Mars Exploration: Fact & Fantasy. 2002. (Pictorial Archive Ser.). (Illus.). 48p. (J). pap. 3.95 (978-0-486-41864-3(2)) Dover Pubns., Inc.

Landau, Elaine. Mars. (True Booktrade;: Space Ser.). (J). 2008. 48p. pap. 6.95 (*978-0-531-14790-0(8) , Children's Pr.); 2007. (Illus.). 48p. (gr. 3-5). lib. bdg. 26.00 (*978-0-531-12560-1(2) , Children's Pr.); 1999. (Illus.). 64p. (gr. 5-7). 25.50 (978-0-531-20388-0(3) , Watts, Franklin) Scholastic Library Publishing.

—Mars. 1999. (gr. 5-8). lib. bdg. 17.60 (978-0-613-37449-1(5)) Tandem Library Bks.

Leedy, Loreen & Schuerger, Andrew. Messages from Mars. Leedy, Loreen, illus. 2006. (Illus.). 40p. (J). 16.95 (978-0-8234-1954-8(1)) Holiday Hse., Inc.

Lomberg, Michelle. Mars. (Exploring Planets Ser.). (Illus.). (J). 2004. pap. (978-1-59036-226-6(8)); 2003. 24p. lib. bdg. 15.95 (978-1-59036-099-6(0)) Weigl Pubs., Inc.

Margaret, Amy, et al, contrib. by. Mars. 2001. (Library of the Planets). (Illus.). 24p. (J). lib. bdg. 21.25 (978-0-8239-5645-6(8) , PowerKids Pr.) Rosen Publishing Group, Inc., The.

Mars: Individual Title Six-Packs. (Rigby Focus Ser.). 16p. (gr. 1 up). 28.00 (978-0-7578-5329-6(3)); 30.00 (978-0-7578-5561-0(X)) Rigby Education.

McMorrow, Annalisa. Mars. Chalk, Philip, illus. 1998. 48p. (J). (gr. 1-3). pap. 7.95 (978-1-57612-058-3(9) , MM2072) Monday Morning Bks., Inc.

Miller, Ron. Mars. 2006. (Worlds Beyond Ser.). (Illus.). 96p. (J). (gr. 5-9). 27.93 (978-0-7613-2362-4(7) , Twenty-First Century Bks.) Lerner Publishing Group.

Orme, Helen & Orme, David. Let's Explore Mars. 2006. (J). pap. (*978-0-8368-8126-4(5)); lib. bdg. (*978-0-8368-7941-4(4)) Stevens, Gareth Inc.

Oxlade, Chris. Mercury, Mars & the Inner Planets. 2007. (J). lib. bdg. (*978-1-4042-3735-3(6) , Rosen Central) Rosen Publishing Group, Inc., The.

Potts, Steve. Mars. 2001. (Illus.). 24p. (J). 21.35 (978-1-58340-095-1(8)) Smart Apple Media.

Quigley, Sebastian, illus. Mars Mission Masterbuilders. 2000. (LEGO Masterbuilders Ser.). (J). (ps-3). 19.99 (978-1-903276-16-7(0)) Lego Media International, Inc.

Rau, Dana Meachen. Mars. 2002. (Our Solar System Ser.). (Illus.). 32p. (J). (gr. 3 up). lib. bdg. 21.26 (978-0-7565-0199-0(7)) Compass Point Bks.

Richardson, Adele. Mars. 2008. (J). (*978-1-4296-0723-0(8)) Capstone Pr., Inc.

Richardson, Adele D. Mars. 2005. (Illus.). 24p. (J). 21.26 (978-0-7368-3689-0(6)) Capstone Pr., Inc.

Romero, Libby. Discover Mars & Venus. 2006. pap. 39.00 (*978-1-4108-6507-6(X)) Benchmark Education Co.

—Mars & Venus. 2006. pap. 39.00 (*978-1-4108-6504-5(5)) Benchmark Education Co.

Shearer, Deborah A. Exploring Mars. 2002. (Explore Space! Ser.). (Illus.). 24p. (J). (gr. 1-2). lib. bdg. 18.60 (978-0-7368-1399-0(3) , Bridgestone Bks.) Capstone Pr., Inc.

Simon, Seymour. Destination: Mars. 32p. (J). 2004. pap. 6.99 (978-0-06-054638-0(7) , Harper Trophy); 2000. (Illus.). 15.95 (978-0-688-15770-8(X)) HarperCollins Pubs.

—Destination: Mars. 2004. (gr. k-3). lib. bdg. 15.30 (978-0-613-83565-7(4)) Tandem Library Bks.

—Planet Mars. 2006. (Illus.). 32p. (J). 14.50 (978-0-8118-5404-7(3)); pap. 3.95 (978-0-8118-5405-4(1)) Chronicle Bks. LLC.

Skurzynski, Gloria. Discover Mars. 1998. (Illus.). 48p. (J). (gr. 4-7). 17.95 (978-0-7922-7099-7(1) , National Geographic Children's Bks.) National Geographic Society.

Spangenburg, Ray. Look at Mars. 2000. (gr. 7-12). lib. bdg. 24.55 (978-0-613-34337-4(9)) Tandem Library Bks.

Sparrow, Giles. Mars. (Exploring the Solar System Ser.). (Illus.). (J). (gr. 4-6). 2002. 40p. pap. 7.95 (978-1-58810-961-3(5) , 91444); 2001. 39p. lib. bdg. 24.22 (978-1-57572-394-5(8)) Heinemann Library.

Stille, Darlene R. Mars. 2003. (Planets Ser.). (Illus.). 32p. (J). (gr. 2-6). 27.07 (978-1-59296-050-7(2)) Child's World, Inc.

Stone, Tanya Lee. Mars. 2002. (Blastoff! Ser.). (Illus.). 64p. (J). (gr. 5 up). lib. bdg. 28.50 (978-0-7614-1233-5(6) , Benchmark Bks.) Cavendish, Marshall Corp.

Sumners, Carolyn T. & Handron, Kerry. An Earthling's Guide to Mars: Travel to Mars with Pathfinder. 2003. (Illus.). 138p. (YA). (gr. 4-7). pap. 12.95 (978-0-07-069635-8(7)) McGraw-Hill Trade.

Teitelbaum, Michael. Mars & Venus Space Exploration. 2006. (Navigators Ser.). (J). pap. 44.00 (*978-1-4108-6243-3(7)) Benchmark Education Co.

Vogt, Gregory L. Mars. 2000. (Our Universe Ser.). (Illus.). 48p. (J). (gr. 4-7). lib. bdg. 22.83 (978-0-7398-3104-5(6)) Raintree.

—Mars. 2000. (Our Universe Ser.). (Illus.). (J). pap. (978-0-7398-3343-8(X)) Steck-Vaughn.

—Mars: A Visual Journey Across an Alien Landscape. 2007. (Illus.). 128p. (*978-0-387-75467-3(9)) Springer.

Vogt, Gregory L. Mercury, Venus, Earth & Mars. 2000. (Our Universe Ser.). (Illus.). 48p. (J). (gr. 4-7). lib. bdg. 22.83 (978-0-7398-3110-6(0)) Raintree.

Ward, David J. Exploring Mars. 2007. (Cool Science Ser.). (Illus.). 48p. (J). (gr. 4-8). lib. bdg. 26.60 (978-0-8225-5936-8(6) , Lerner Pubns.) Lerner Publishing Group.

Wethered, Peggy & Edgett, Ken. Touchdown Mars! An ABC Adventure. Chesworth, Michael, illus. 2000. 1p. (J). (ps-3). 15.99 (978-0-399-23214-5(1) , Putnam Juvenile) Penguin Group (USA) Inc.

Wimmer, Teresa. Mars. 2007. (J). (978-1-58341-518-4(1) , Creative Education) Creative Co., The.

World Book, contrib. by. Mars. 2nd ed. 2006. (World Book's Solar System & Space Exploration Library). (Illus.). 64p. (J). (*978-0-7166-9516-5(2)) World Bk., Inc.

Wunsch, Susi Trautmann. The Adventures of Sojourner: The Mission to Mars That Thrilled the World. 1998. (Illus.). 60p. (J). (ps-7). lib. bdg. 18.75 incl. 5.25 hd (978-0-613-23064-3(7)) Tandem Library Bks.

MARS (PLANET)—FICTION

Bennett, Jeffrey. Max Goes to Mars: A Science Adventure. Okamoto, Alan, illus. 2003. (Science Adventures with Max the Dog Ser.). 32p. (J). 16.95 (978-0-9721819-1-4(1)) Big Kid Science.

Book, Rita. My Soccer Mom from Mars. Wummer, Amy, illus. 2001. (All Aboard Reading Ser.). 48p. (J). pap. 3.99 (978-0-448-42599-3(8) , Grosset & Dunlap) Penguin Group (USA) Inc.

—My Soccer Mom from Mars. 2001. (gr. k-3). lib. bdg. 11.80 (978-0-613-64077-0(2)) Tandem Library Bks.

Brouwer, Sigmund. Alien Pursuit. 2000. (gr. 5-8). lib. bdg. 13.00 (978-0-613-76892-4(2)) Tandem Library Bks.

—Countdown. 2001. (gr. 5-8). lib. bdg. 13.00 (978-0-613-76821-4(3)) Tandem Library Bks.

—Hammerhead. 2001. (gr. 3-6). lib. bdg. 13.00 (978-0-613-76893-1(0)) Tandem Library Bks.

—Last Stand. 2002. (gr. 3-6). lib. bdg. 13.00 (978-0-613-76883-2(3)) Tandem Library Bks.

—Manchurian Sector. 2002. (gr. 3-6). lib. bdg. 13.00 (978-0-613-76880-1(9)) Tandem Library Bks.

—Mission 10: Last Stand. 2002. (Mars Diaries Ser.: Mission 10). 144p. (J). mass mkt. 4.99 (978-0-8423-5634-3(7)) Tyndale Hse. Pubs.

—Mission 2: Alien Pursuit. 2000. (Mars Diaries Ser.: Mission 2). (Illus.). 144p. (J). (gr. 5-9). mass mkt. 4.99 (978-0-8423-4305-3(9)) Tyndale Hse. Pubs.

—Mission 4: Hammerhead. 2001. (Mars Diaries Ser.: Mission 4). (Illus.). 128p. (J). (gr. 4-7). mass mkt. 4.99 (978-0-8423-4307-7(5)) Tyndale Hse. Pubs.

—Mission 5: Sole Survivor. 2001. (Mars Diaries Ser.: Mission 5). (Illus.). 128p. (J). (gr. 4-7). mass mkt. 4.99 (978-0-8423-4308-4(3)) Tyndale Hse. Pubs.

—Mission 9: Manchurian Sector. 2002. (Mars Diaries Ser.: Mission 9). 160p. (J). mass mkt. 4.99 (978-0-8423-5633-6(9)) Tyndale Hse. Pubs.

—Moon Racer. 2001. (gr. 5-8). lib. bdg. 13.00 (978-0-613-76814-6(0)) Tandem Library Bks.

—Oxygen Level Zero Level Zero. 2000. (gr. 5-8). lib. bdg. 10.65 (978-0-613-76779-8(9)) Tandem Library Bks.

—Robot War. 2001. (gr. 5-8). lib. bdg. 13.00 (978-0-613-76822-1(1)) Tandem Library Bks.

—Sole Survivor. 2001. (gr. 3-6). lib. bdg. 13.00 (978-0-613-76817-7(5)) Tandem Library Bks.

—Time Bomb. 2000. (gr. 5-8). lib. bdg. 13.00 (978-0-613-76816-0(7)) Tandem Library Bks.

Cahill, Byron. Space Pox. 2005. 40.00 (*978-1-4108-4220-6(7)) Benchmark Education Co.

Corey, Shana. First Graders from Mars. Teague, Mark, illus. 2003. (First Graders from Mars Ser.: No. 4). 32p. (J). pap. 4.99 (978-0-439-45219-9(8) , Scholastic Pr.) Scholastic, Inc.

—Horus's Horrible Day. Teague, Mark, illus. 2001. (First Graders from Mars Ser.: No. 1). 32p. (J). (gr. k-2). pap. 14.95 (978-0-439-26220-0(8)); pap. 4.99 (978-0-439-31955-3(2)) Scholastic, Inc. (Levine, Arthur A. Bks.).

Corey, Shana & Teague, Mark. Tera, Star Student. 2003. (First Graders from Mars Ser.: No. 4). (Illus.). 32p. (J). pap. 15.95 (978-0-439-26634-5(3) , Scholastic Pr.) Scholastic, Inc.

Dress, Robert, illus. Mars, Here We Come! 2006. (Backyardigans Ser.). 16p. (J). bds. 7.99 (978-1-4169-1471-6(4) , Simon Spotlight/Nickelodeon) Simon & Schuster Children's Publishing.

A Flag on Mars, Bk. 3. 1999. (Junior Academic Ser.). (Illus.). 16p. (J). (gr. k-1). pap. 2.99 (978-1-57768-530-2(X)) School Specialty Publishing.

Fontenay, Charles L. Kipton & the Delusions of Tante Else, 18 vols. 1999. (Kipton Chronicles Ser.: Bk. 17). 189p. (YA). (gr. 6-9). 9.99 (978-0-88092-456-6(X) , 456-X) Royal Fireworks Publishing Co.

Gall, Chris. There's Nothing to Do on Mars. 2008. 32p. (J). (ps-1). 16.99 (***978-0-316-16684-3(7)***) Little Brown & Co.

Hobbs, Leigh. Old Tom Goes to Mars. Hobbs, Leigh, illus. 2005. (Illus.). 112p. (gr. 1-3). pap. 3.99 (978-0-7868-5514-8(2)) Hyperion Pr.

The Imaginer: Individual Title Six-Packs. (Bookweb Ser.). 32p. (gr. 6 up). 34.00 (978-0-7578-0900-2(6)) Rigby Education.

Knife & Packer. Captain Fact: Space Adventure. 2004. (Illus.). 103p. (J). (***978-1-4156-0561-5(0)***) Hyperion Bks. for Children.

McGee, Warner, illus. Mision a Marte. 2006. (Backyardigans Ser.). (SPA.). 24p. (J). pap. 3.99 (978-1-4169-1567-6(2) , Libros Para Ninos) Simon & Schuster Children's Publishing.

—Mission to Mars. 2006. (Backyardigans Ser.). 24p. (J). pap. 3.99 (978-1-4169-1486-0(2) , Simon Spotlight/ Nickelodeon) Simon & Schuster Children's Publishing.

Niven, Larry. Rainbow Mars. 2000. (gr. 7-12). lib. bdg. 15.30 (978-0-613-28032-7(6)) Tandem Library Bks.

Orme, David. Boffin Boy & the Temples of Mars. 2007. (Boffin Boy Ser.). (Illus.). 36p. pap. 7.95 (***978-1-84167-623-4(3)***) Ransom Publishing Ltd. GBR. *Dist:* International Publishers Marketing.

Robinson, Kim Stanley. The Martians. 2000. (gr. 7-12). lib. bdg. 15.30 (978-0-613-35420-2(6)) Tandem Library Bks.

Summers, Kim. Senor Mundo & Me: A Happy Birthday Story. Mariscal, Javier, illus. 2004. 31p. (J). (gr. k-4). 20.00 (978-0-7567-7759-3(3)) DIANE Publishing Co.

Thaler, Mike. Moving to Mars. 1998. (Orig.). (gr. k-3). lib. bdg. 10.60 (978-0-613-75798-0(X)) Tandem Library Bks.

Trimble, Marcia J. Marsby & the Martian Detectives. Hayden, Jennifer H., illus. 2004. 56p. (J). per. 9.95 (978-1-891577-52-9(2) , SAN299-4844) Images Pr.

MARSH, OTHNIEL CHARLES, 1831-1899

Goldish, Meish. The Fossil Feud: Marsh & Cope's Bone Wars. 2007. (Fossil Hunters Ser.). 32p. (J). (gr. 3-7). lib. bdg. 25.27 (978-1-59716-256-2(6)) Bearport Publishing Co., Inc.

Hartzog, Brooke. The Dinosaur Bone Battle Between O. C. Marsh & Edward Drinker Cope. 1999. (Dinosaurs & Their Discoverers Ser.). 24p. (J). (gr. k-4). lib. bdg. 18.75 (978-0-8239-5327-1(0) , PowerKids Pr.) Rosen Publishing Group, Inc., The.

MARSHALL, GEORGE C. (GEORGE CATLETT), 1880-1959

George C. Marshall, Reporting for Duty. 2001. (YA). (gr. 6-10). pap. 12.00 (978-0-9661582-2-9(9)) Blue Valley Bks.

Gimpel, Lee. Fighting Wars, Planning for Peace: The Story of George C. Marshall. 2005. (World Leaders Ser.). (Illus.). 176p. (J). (gr. 8 up). lib. bdg. 26.95 (978-1-931798-66-2(4)) Reynolds, Morgan Inc.

Marsh, Carole. George C. Marshall. 2002. (One Thousand Readers Ser.). (Illus.). 12p. (J). (gr. k-4). 2.95 (978-0-635-01547-1(1) , 15471) Gallopade International.

Welch, Catherine A. George C. Marshall. 2005. (History Maker Bios Ser.). 48p. (J). pap. 6.95 (978-0-8225-5460-8(7)); (Illus.). 26.60 (978-0-8225-2435-9(X) , Lerner Pubns.) Lerner Publishing Group.

MARSHALL, JOHN, 1755-1835

Kallen, Stuart A. James Monroe. 2001. (United States Presidents Ser.). (Illus.). 64p. (J). (gr. 3-8). lib. bdg. 25.65 (978-1-57765-230-4(4) , ABDO & Daughters) ABDO Publishing Co.

Susi, Geraldine Lee. My Father, My Companion: Life at the Hollow, Chief Justice John Marshall's Boyhood Home in Virginia. 2001. (Illus.). 96p. (J). (gr. 4-9). pap. 10.95 (978-1-889324-22-7(1)) EPM Pubns., Inc.

Wetterer, Charles M. & Wetterer, Margaret K. Chief Justice. Walters, Kurt K. C., illus. 2005. 32p. (J). (978-1-59336-306-2(0)); pap. (978-1-59336-307-9(9)) Mondo Publishing.

MARSHALL, THURGOOD, 1908-1993

Boerst, William J. Galileo Galilei & the Science of Motion. 2004. (Profiles in Science Ser.). (Illus.). 144p. (YA). (gr. 6-12). lib. bdg. 26.95 (978-1-931798-00-6(1)) Reynolds, Morgan Inc.

Crowe, Chris. Up Close: Thurgood Marshall: Thurgood Marshall. 2008. 208p. (YA). (gr. 6). 16.99 (***978-0-670-06228-7(6)*** , Viking Juvenile) Penguin Group (USA) Inc.

Dunham, Montrew. Thurgood Marshall. 1998. (Childhood of Famous Americans Ser.). (Illus.). 192p. (J). (gr. 3-7). pap. 5.99 (978-0-689-82042-7(9) , Aladdin) Simon & Schuster Children's Publishing.

Feldman, Ruth Tenzer. Thurgood Marshall. 2001. (Biography Ser.). (Illus.). 112p. (J). (gr. 6-12). lib. bdg. 27.93 (978-0-8225-4989-5(1) , Lerner Pubns.) Lerner Publishing Group.

Frost, Helen. Thurgood Marshall. Saunders-Smith, Gail, ed. 2003. (Famous Americans Ser.). (Illus.). 24p. (J). (gr. k-1). lib. bdg. 15.93 (978-0-7368-1643-4(7) , Pebble Bks.) Capstone Pr., Inc.

Gibson, Karen Bush. Thurgood Marshall. 2002. (Photo-Illustrated Biographies Ser.). (Illus.). 24p. (J). (gr. 2-3). lib. bdg. 18.60 (978-0-7368-1113-2(3) , Bridgestone Bks.) Capstone Pr., Inc.

Haugen, Brenda. Thurgood Marshall: Civil Rights Lawyer & Supreme Court Justice. 2006. (Illus.). 112p. (J). lib. bdg. (***978-0-7565-1877-6(6)***) Compass Point Bks.

Horn, Geoffrey M. Thurgood Marshall. 2004. (Trailblazers of the Modern World Ser.). (Illus.). 48p. (J). (gr. 5 up). pap. 11.95 (978-0-8368-5258-5(3)); lib. bdg. 30.00 (978-0-8368-5098-7(X)) Stevens, Gareth Inc. (World Almanac Library).

Mara, Wil. Thurgood Marshall: Champion for Civil Rights. 2004. (Great Life Stories Ser.). (Illus.). 125p. (J). 30.50 (978-0-531-12058-3(9) , Watts, Franklin) Scholastic Library Publishing.

Marsh, Carole. Thurgood Marshall. 2002. (One Thousand Readers Ser.). (Illus.). 12p. (J). (gr. k-4). 2.95 (978-0-635-01491-7(2) , 14912) Gallopade International.

—The Virginia Reader: Thurgood Marshall. 2001. (Virginia Experience! Ser.). (Illus.). 12p. (J). (gr. k-5). pap. 2.95 (978-0-635-00352-2(X)) Gallopade International.

Marshall, Thurgood. Thurgood Marshall: Supreme Court Justice. (Black Americans of Achievement Ser.). (Illus.). 112p. (J). (gr. 6-12). 2005. pap. 13.25 (978-0-7910-8337-6(3)); 2004. 30.00 (978-0-7910-8163-1(X)) Facts On File, Inc. (Chelsea Hse.).

McLeese, Don & Marshall, Thurgood. Thurgood Marshall. 2003. (Rourke Discovery Library). (Illus.). 24p. (gr. 2-5). 14.95 (978-1-58952-303-6(2)) Rourke Publishing, LLC.

Rowh, Mark. Thurgood Marshall: Civil Rights Attorney & Supreme Court Justice. 2002. (African-American Biographies Ser.). (Illus.). 112p. (YA). (gr. 6-12). lib. bdg. 26.60 (978-0-7660-1547-0(5)) Enslow Pubs., Inc.

Taylor-Butler, Christine. Thurgood Marshall. 2006. 32p. (gr. 1-2). (YA). pap. 4.95 (978-0-516-27099-9(0)); (Illus.). (J). 20.50 (978-0-516-25015-1(9)) Scholastic Library Publishing. (Children's Pr.).

Wheeler, Jill C. Thurgood Marshall. 2003. (Breaking Barriers Ser.). (Illus.). 64p. (J). (gr. 3-8). lib. bdg. 25.65 (978-1-57765-907-5(4)) ABDO Publishing Co.

Whitelaw, Nancy. Mr. Civil Rights: The Story of Thurgood Marshall. 2nd rev. exp. ed. 2004. (Notable Americans Ser.). (Illus.). 144p. (YA). (gr. 6-12). 23.95 (978-1-931798-02-0(8)) Reynolds, Morgan Inc.

MARSHES

Blaxland, Beth. Mangroves. 2001. (Water Worlds Ser.). (Illus.). 32p. (J). (gr. 4 up). 28.00 (978-0-7910-6565-5(0) , 010354, Chelsea Hse.) Facts On File, Inc.

Cheshire, Gerald. Nature Unfolds the Tropical Rainforest. 2001. (Nature Unfolds Ser.). (Illus.). 40p. (J). (gr. 4). lib. bdg. (978-0-7787-0308-2(8)); pap. (978-0-7787-0320-4(7)) Crabtree Publishing Co.

Declus, Jennifer. What Might I Find in a Swamp. Kalasea, illus. 2004. (J). (978-0-9743690-3-7(9)) Britt Allcroft Productions.

Dorling Kindersley Publishing Staff. Swamp Life. 2000. (978-0-606-17814-3(7)) Tandem Library Bks.

Field, Nancy, et al. Leapfrogging Through Wetlands. Maydak, Michael S., illus. 1998. (Nature Discovery Library). 40p. (J). (gr. 4-6). pap. 7.95 (978-0-941042-18-5(9)) Dog-Eared Pubns.

Garrett, Ann. Keeper of the Swamp. Chandler, Karen, illus. 1998. (SPA.). 40p. (J). (gr. 1-4). 16.95 (978-1-890515-12-6(4)) Turtle Bks.

Himmelman, John. Frog in a Bog. Himmelman, John, illus. 2004. (Illus.). 32p. (J). 15.95 (978-1-57091-517-8(2)) Charlesbridge Publishing, Inc.

Hirshberg, Jackie. Nicky the Swamp Dog: A True Story. Guillory, D. Ray, photos by. 2000. (Illus.). 40p. (J). (gr. 3-5). 14.95 (978-0-925417-36-7(X)) Acadian Hse. Publishing.

Johansson, Philip. Marshes & Swamps: A Wetland Web of Life. 2007. (Wonderful Water Biomes Ser.). (Illus.). 48p. (J). (gr. 3-4). lib. bdg. 23.93 (***978-0-7660-2814-2(3)*** , Enslow Elementary) Enslow Pubs., Inc.

Lion, David C. A Home in the Swamp. 2006. (Scholastic News Nonfiction Readers Ser.). (Illus.). 24p. (J). 19.00 (978-0-516-25349-7(2) , Children's Pr.) Scholastic Library Publishing.

Povey, Karen D. Life in a Swamp. 2005. (Ecosystems Ser.). (Illus.). 48p. (J). (gr. 4-7). lib. bdg. 26.20 (978-0-7377-3140-8(0) , Greenhaven Pr., Inc.) Thomson Gale.

Sovak, Jan. Learning about Swamp Animals. 2003. (Learning about Ser.). (Illus.). 16p. (J). (gr. 3-5). pap. 1.50 (978-0-486-43025-6(1)) Dover Pubns., Inc.

Stille, Darlene R. Wetlands. 2000. (True Bks.). (Illus.). 48p. (J). (gr. 3-5). pap. 6.95 (978-0-516-26791-3(4) , Children's Pr.) Scholastic Library Publishing.

—Wetlands. 1999. (gr. 3-6). lib. bdg. 15.25 (978-0-613-37582-5(3)) Tandem Library Bks.

MARSHES—FICTION

Butler, Mary Nyegard. Fantasy Marsh. Butler, Mary Nyegard, illus. 2000. (Illus.). 27p. (J). (ps-2). per. 6.95 (978-0-9701497-0-1(0)) Bay Tree Enterprises.

Demas, Corinne. Yuck! Stuck in the Muck. Rader, Laura, illus. 2006. (Scholastic Reader Ser.). 32p. (J). pap. 3.99 (978-0-439-79431-2(5) , Cartwheel Bks.) Scholastic, Inc.

Garrett, Ann. Guardian Del Pantano. 1999. (SPA.). (gr. 3-6). lib. bdg. 17.60 (978-0-613-35955-9(0)) Tandem Library Bks.

George, Jean Craighead. Call from the Swamp. 2007. (J). 17.99 (978-0-7868-0694-2(X)) Disney Pr.

Kurtz, Kevin. A Day in the Salt Marsh. 2007. (Illus.). 32p. (J). (ps-3). 15.95 (978-0-9768823-5-0(3)) Sylvan Dell Pubng.

Prins, Piet. The Flying Phantom. 2006. (Illus.). 142p. (J). pap. (978-1-894666-45-9(3)) Inheritance Pubns.

Stratton Porter, Gene. Freckles. 2006. 236p. (YA). 19.95 (***978-1-934169-32-2(3)***); pap. 8.95 (***978-1-934169-33-9(1)***) Norilana Bks.

—A Girl of the Limberlost. 2006. 336p. (YA). 21.95 (***978-1-934169-30-8(7)***); pap. 10.95 (***978-1-934169-31-5(5)***) Norilana Bks.

Traylor, Waverly. Tales of the Great Dismal Swamp. Traylor, Waverly, ed. 2001. (Illus.). 40p. (YA). pap. 7.95 (978-0-9715068-0-0(9)) Traylor, Waverley Publishing.

MARSUPIALS

Fenton, Julie A. Kangaroos & Other Marsupials, Vol. 6. World Book, Inc. Staff, ed. 2002. (World Book's Animals of the World Ser.: Set 1). 64p. (J). (978-0-7166-1243-8(7)) World Bk., Inc.

Kalman, Bobbie. Les Marsupiaux. 2002. (FRE., Illus.). 32p. (J). pap. (978-2-920660-71-7(3)) Crabtree Publishing Co.

—What Is a Marsupial? 2000. (gr. 3-6). lib. bdg. 14.10 (978-0-613-28131-7(4)) Tandem Library Bks.

Kalman, Bobbie & Levigne, Heather. What Is a Marsupial? 2000. (Science of Living Things Ser.). (Illus.). 32p. (J). (gr. 2-3). (978-0-86505-978-8(0)); pap. (978-0-86505-955-9(1)) Crabtree Publishing Co.

McMorrow, Annalisa. Marsupials. Clark, Philip, illus. 1998. (J). (gr. 1-3). pap. 7.95 (978-1-57612-056-9(2) , MM2070) Monday Morning Bks., Inc.

Morgan, Sally. Marsupials. 2004. (J). lib. bdg. 27.10 (978-1-59389-175-6(X)) Chrysalis Education.

Sautel, Anne. Beijing Breakaway! Stewart, Scott, illus. 2007. (Wombat Smith Ser.: Vol. 2). 96p. (J). (gr. 1-4). pap. (978-1-897073-48-3(8)) Lobster Pr.

Sill, Cathryn P. & Sill, John, illus. About Marsupials: A Guide for Children. 2006. (J). 15.95 (978-1-56145-358-0(7) , Peachtree Junior) Peachtree Pubs., Ltd.

Steele, Christy. Tasmanian Devils. 2003. (Animals of the Rain Forest Ser.). (Illus.). 32p. (J). lib. bdg. 24.28 (978-0-7398-6840-9(3)) Raintree.

Stefoff, Rebecca. The Marsupial Order. 2007. (Family Trees Ser.). 96p. (J). lib. bdg. 32.79 (***978-0-7614-2697-4(3)*** , Benchmark Bks.) Cavendish, Marshall Corp.

Swan, Erin Pembrey, et al. Meat-Eating Marsupials. 2002. (Animals in Order Ser.). (Illus.). 48p. (J). (gr. 4-6). 26.50 (978-0-531-11628-9(X) , Watts, Franklin) Scholastic Library Publishing.

MARTHA'S VINEYARD (MASS.)

The Greatest Place on Earth: A Children's Story, A History Lesson, A Scrapbook, A Lifetime Keepsake. 2006. (J). 18.95 (978-0-9777882-0-0(2) , Light Works Publishing) I.M. Enterprises.

McMahon, Patricia. Summer Tunes: A Martha's Vineyard Vacation. Simon, Peter, illus. 2003. 48p. (J). (gr. 4-6). 16.95 (978-1-56397-572-1(6)) Boyds Mills Pr.

MARTHA'S VINEYARD (MASS.)—FICTION

Czech, Jan. Grace Happens. 2007. 160p. (YA). pap. 6.99 (978-0-14-240752-3(6) , Puffin) Penguin Group (USA) Inc.

DeFelice, Cynthia C. Death at Devil's Bridge. 2000. 192p. (J). (gr. 3-7). 16.00 (978-0-374-31723-2(2) , Farrar, Straus & Giroux (BYR)) Farrar, Straus & Giroux.

—Death at Devil's Bridge. 2002. 192p. (J). (gr. 3-7). pap. 5.99 (978-0-06-441037-3(4) , Harper Trophy) HarperCollins Pubs.

Franklin, Emily. Labor of Love: The Principles of Love. 2007. 256p. (gr. 12 up). pap. 9.99 (***978-0-451-22211-4(3)*** , N A L Trade) Penguin Group (USA) Inc.

Stewart, Jane. The Island Escapade. 2003. 102p. (YA). pap. 9.95 (978-0-595-27734-6(9)) iUniverse, Inc.

MARTIAL ARTS

see also Archery; Self-Defense

The ABCs of Tae Kwon Do. 2004. (J). 5.95 (978-0-9754345-0-5(0)) Cannady, John.

Amerland, David. Tae Kwon Do. 2004. (J). lib. bdg. 24.67 (978-0-8368-4195-4(6)) Stevens, Gareth Inc.

Atwood, Jane E. Capoeira: A Martial Art & a Cultural Tradition. 1999. (Library of African American Arts & Culture). (Illus.). 64p. (YA). (gr. 7-12). lib. bdg. 26.50 (978-0-8239-1859-1(9) , AACAPO) Rosen Publishing Group, Inc., The.

Binder, C. F. Black Belt Attitude. 2003. (Illus.). 16p. (J). (978-1-4120-0351-3(2)) Trafford Publishing.

Blackall, Bernie. Martial Arts. 1999. (Top Sport Ser.). 32p. (J). (gr. 4-6). lib. bdg. 21.36 (978-1-57572-705-9(6)) Heinemann Library.

Buckley, Thomas. Jujitsu & Judo. 2004. (Child's World of Sports). (Illus.). 32p. (J). (gr. 1-5). 25.64 (978-1-59296-030-9(8)) Child's World, Inc.

—Karate. 2004. (Child's World of Sports). (Illus.). 32p. (J). (gr. 1-5). 25.64 (978-1-56766-751-6(1)) Child's World, Inc.

—Tae Kwon Do. 2004. (Child's World of Sports). (Illus.). 32p. (J). (gr. 1-5). 25.64 (978-1-59296-031-6(6)) Child's World, Inc.

Carter, Kevin. Martial Arts for Fun! 2004. (Activities for Fun Ser.). (Illus.). 48p. (J). (gr. 3 up). lib. bdg. 21.26 (978-0-7565-0586-8(0)) Compass Point Bks.

Chaline, Eric. Martial Arts for Athletic Conditioning. 2003. (Martial & Fighting Arts Ser.). (Illus.). 96p. (J). (gr. 7 up). lib. bdg. (978-1-59084-397-0(5)) Mason Crest Pubs.

—Martial Arts for Women. 2002. (Martial & Fighting Arts Ser.). (Illus.). 96p. (J). (gr. 7 up). lib. bdg. (978-1-59084-395-6(9)) Mason Crest Pubs.

—Ninjutsu. 2002. (Martial & Fighting Arts Ser.). (Illus.). 96p. (J). (gr. 7 up). lib. bdg. (978-1-59084-398-7(3)) Mason Crest Pubs.

Chesterman, Barnaby. Taekwondo. 2002. (Martial & Fighting Arts Ser.). (Illus.). 96p. (J). (gr. 7 up). lib. bdg. 22.95 (978-1-59084-391-8(6)) Mason Crest Pubs.

Collins, Paul. Kendo. 2001. (Illus.). 32p. (J). 28.00 (978-0-7910-6869-4(2) , Chelsea Hse.) Facts On File, Inc.

—Martial Arts Series, 4 bks. Incl. Judo. 28.00 (978-0-7910-6553-2(7) , 010251); Karate. 28.00 (978-0-7910-6555-6(3) , 010252); Kung Fu. 28.00 (978-0-7910-6556-3(1) , 010253); Taek Won Do. 28.00 (978-0-7910-6554-9(5) , 010254); 32p. (J). (gr. 3 up). 2001. (Illus.). 67.80 (978-0-7910-6552-5(9) , 010250S, Chelsea Hse.) Facts On File, Inc.

Compass Point Books, contrib. by. Martial Arts for Fun! (For Fun Ser.). 48p. (YA). pap. 8.95 (978-0-7565-1159-3(3)) Compass Point Bks.

Eng, Paul. Kungfu for Kids. 2005. (Martial Arts for Kids Ser.). (Illus.). 48p. (J). 11.95 (978-0-8048-3600-5(0)) Tuttle Publishing.

Escher, Ursula. Self-Defense for Kids: Learn Practical & Effective Techniques to Help You Defend Yourself. 2004. (Illus.). 47p. (J). (ps-12). pap. 6.95 (978-0-9718609-5-7(5)) High Mountain Publishing.

Figueroa, Jose & Berwick, Stephan. Tai Chi for Kids. 2006. (Martial Arts for Kids Ser.). (Illus.). 48p. (J). 11.95 (978-0-8048-3563-3(2)) Tuttle Publishing.

FitzPatrick, Bill. The Shaolin Action Principles. 2004. Orig. Title: 100 Action Principles of the Shaolin. 128p. pap. 20.00 (978-1-884864-22-3(8)) American Success Institute, Inc.

Gaines, Ann Graham. The Composite Guide to Martial Arts. 2000. (Composite Guide Ser.). (Illus.). (J). (gr. 8-12). 18.65 (978-0-7910-5866-4(2) , Chelsea Hse.) Facts On File, Inc.

Galashan, Kathy. Kick Boxing. 2001. (Livewire Ser.). (Illus.). 32p. pap. (978-0-340-80066-9(6) , Hodder Arnold) Hodder Education.

Gale, Martin. ACAMAC. 2000. (Illus.). 50p. (YA). 99.95 (978-1-58753-129-3(1) , Martial Art-Org) Aristo Agon Brun Universal Union.

Gambordella, Ted. The Ultimate Martial Arts: 36 Complete Books & 5 hrs Video. 2nd ed. 2001. (Illus.). 3000p. (YA). cd-rom 19.95 (978-0-9759744-0-7(8)) Black Belt Training.

Group/McGraw-Hill, Wright. Formas de Moverse, 6 vols. (First Explorers. Primeros Exploradores Nonfiction Sets Ser.). (SPA.). (gr. 1-2). 29.95 (978-0-7699-1473-2(X)) Shortland Pubns. (U. S. A.) Inc.

Heinrichs, Ann. Kung Fu & Tai Chi. 2004. (Child's World of Sports). (Illus.). 32p. (J). (gr. 1-5). 25.64 (978-1-59296-029-3(4)) Child's World, Inc.

Hillson, Ted. Tae Kwon Do Classic Forms: 21 Hyung—Novice White Belt Through Advanced Black Belt. Kligge, Elizabeth, illus. 2003. 232p. (YA). spiral bd. 22.50 (978-0-9729293-0-1(4)) Double Dagger Pr.

Hunter, Ruth S. Everyday Warriors. 1999. (Illus.). 112p. (J). (gr. 1-5). pap. 9.95 (978-1-880336-30-4(8) , EW) Turtle Pr. Corp.

Iedwab, Claudio A. Peaceful Way: A Children's Guide to the Traditions of the Martial Arts. 2001. (gr. 3-6). lib. bdg. 22.20 (978-0-613-77425-3(6)) Tandem Library Bks.

Jablonsky, A. A Girl's Guide to the Martial Arts. 2004. (Ener-Chi Bks.). (Illus.). 80p. (J). pap. 8.95 (978-0-7641-2841-7(8)) Barron's Educational Series, Inc.

Johnson, Nathan. Kickboxing. 2002. (Martial & Fighting Arts Ser.). (Illus.). 96p. (J). lib. bdg. (978-1-59084-392-5(4)) Mason Crest Pubs.

—Kung Fu. 2002. (Martial & Fighting Arts Ser.). (Illus.). 96p. (J). (gr. 7 up). lib. bdg. (978-1-59084-393-2(2)) Mason Crest Pubs.

—Martial Arts for Children. 2002. (Martial & Fighting Arts Ser.). (Illus.). 96p. (J). (gr. 7 up). lib. bdg. (978-1-59084-396-3(7)) Mason Crest Pubs.

—Martial Arts for the Mind. 2002. (Martial & Fighting Arts Ser.). (Illus.). 96p. (J). (gr. 7 up). lib. bdg. (978-1-59084-394-9(0)) Mason Crest Pubs.

Kanzaki, Masaomi. Street Fighter II - the Manga Volume 1. 2007. 180p. (YA). pap. 12.95 (***978-0-9781386-1-5(9)***) URON Entertainment Corp. CAN. *Dist:* Diamond Bk. Distributors.

Kickboxing. (To the Extreme Ser.). 32p. (YA). 7.95 (978-0-7368-6176-2(9)) Capstone Pr., Inc.

Knotts, Bob. Martial Arts. 2000. (gr. 3-6). lib. bdg. 15.25 (978-0-613-54004-9(2)) Tandem Library Bks.

Koopmans, Andy. Bruce Lee. 2001. (Importance of Ser.). (Illus.). 112p. (J). (gr. 7-10). 28.70 (978-1-59018-081-5(X) , Lucent Bks.) Thomson Gale.

Lawrence, Katherine Drobot. Jean-Claude Van Damme. 2005. (Martial Arts Masters Ser.). (Illus.). 112p. (YA). (gr. 7-12). lib. bdg. 25.25 (978-0-8239-3517-8(5)) Rosen Publishing Group, Inc., The.

Levigne, Heather. Les Arts Martiaux. 2007. (FRE.). 32p. pap. 7.95 (***978-2-89579-168-3(6)***) Editions Banjo CAN. *Dist:* Crabtree Publishing Co.

Levigne, Heather. Martial Arts in Action. 2000. (978-0-606-22839-8(X)) Tandem Library Bks.

Lewis, Joe. The World's Greatest Fighter Teaches You: How to Master Bruce Lee's Fighting System. 2005. (Illus.). 208p. pap. 24.95 (978-1-932835-00-7(8)) Seconds Out, Inc.

Lloyd, Bryant. Artes Marciales: Desarrollo Personal. 2002. (Juega Como un Profesional Ser.). (SPA.). (J). 23.93 (978-1-58952-443-9(8)) Rourke Publishing, LLC.

Lloyd, Bryant & Bonney, Barbara. Artes Marciales: Tecnicas. 2002. (Juega Como un Profesinal Ser.). (SPA.). (J). 23.93 (978-1-58952-442-2(X)) Rourke Publishing, LLC.

MacAulay, Kelley & Kalman, Bobbie. Taekwondo in Action. Crabtree, Marc, photos by. 2004. (Sports in Action Ser.). (Illus.). 32p. (J). (978-0-7787-0338-9(X)); pap. (978-0-7787-0358-7(4)) Crabtree Publishing Co.

Martial Arts. 2005. 32p. pap. 224.00 (978-0-7910-6880-9(3) , Chelsea Hse.) Facts On File, Inc.

Martial Arts. 32p. (YA). 98.68 (978-0-8368-4191-6(3)) Stevens, Gareth Inc.

Martial Arts Masters. 2005. (Illus.). (gr. 7-12). lib. bdg. 151.50 (978-0-8239-9691-9(3)) Rosen Publishing Group, Inc., The.

Mattern, Joanne. Ninjas: Masters of Stealth & Secrecy. 2005. (Way of the Warrior Ser.). (Illus.). 48p. (J). 24.00 (978-0-516-25120-2(1)); (gr. 7-12). pap. 6.95 (978-0-516-25089-2(2)) Scholastic Library Publishing. (Children's Pr.).

—Ninjas: Masters of Stealth & Secrecy. 2005. (Illus.). 48p. (J). (gr. 5-8). lib. bdg. 14.15 (978-0-606-33504-1(8)) Tandem Library Bks.

McNab, Chris. Martial Arts for People with Disabilities. 2004. (Martial & Fighting Arts Ser.). (Illus.). 96p. (J). (gr. 7). lib. bdg. (978-1-59084-399-4(1)) Mason Crest Pubs.

—Martial Arts for the Special Forces. 2002. (Martial & Fighting Arts Ser.). (Illus.). 96p. (J). (gr. 7 up). lib. bdg. (978-1-59084-400-7(9)) Mason Crest Pubs.

Mochizuki, Ken. Be Water, My Friend: The Early Years of Bruce Lee. Lee, Dom, illus. 2006. 32p. (J). 16.95 (978-1-58430-265-0(8)) Lee & Low Bks., Inc.

Montanha. The Brazilian Jiu-Jitsu Mind Set: To Submit Your Opponent from Any Position ! 2004. (Illus.). 108p. per. 12.95 (978-0-9743380-0-2(1)) Montanha Pr.

Page, Jason. Combat: Fencing, Judo, Wrestling, Boxing, Taekwondo & Lots, Lots More. 2000. (Zeke's Olympic Pocket Guide Ser.). (Illus.). 32p. (J). pap. 3.95 (978-0-8225-5055-6(5) , LernerSports) Lerner Publishing Group.

Park, Y. H. Taekwondo for Kids. 2005. (Tuttle Martial Arts for Kids Ser.). (Illus.). 48p. (J). (ps-7). 11.95 (978-0-8048-3631-9(0)) Tuttle Publishing.

Poolos, J. Jackie Chan. 2005. (Martial Arts Masters Ser.). (Illus.). 112p. (YA). (gr. 7-12). lib. bdg. 25.25 (978-0-8239-3518-5(3)) Rosen Publishing Group, Inc., The.

Rielly, Robin L. Karate for Kids. 2004. (Martial Arts for Kids Ser.). (Illus.). 48p. (YA). 13.95 (978-0-8048-3534-3(9)) Tuttle Publishing.

Robertson, Lauren. The Best Book of Martial Arts. 2002. (Best Book of... Ser.). (Illus.). 32p. (J). (gr. k-3). tchr. ed. 12.95 (978-0-7534-5448-0(3) , Kingfisher) Houghton Mifflin Co. Trade & Reference Div.

Roensch, Greg. Bruce Lee. 2005. (Martial Arts Masters Ser.). (Illus.). 112p. (YA). (gr. 7-12). lib. bdg. 25.25 (978-0-8239-3515-4(9)) Rosen Publishing Group, Inc., The.

Rumpf, Wolfgang. Taekwondo Kids: From White Belt to Yellow/Green Belt. Dornemann, Volker, illus. 2007. 128p. (J). pap. 14.95 (978-1-84126-214-7(5)) Meyer & Meyer Sport, Ltd. GBR. *Dist:* Perseus Distribution.

Santoro, Laura. Aikido for Kids. 1998. (Illus.). 96p. (J). (gr. 4-7). 14.95 (978-0-8069-9405-5(3)) Sterling Publishing Co., Inc.

Santoro, Laura & Corso, Jennifer. Aikido for Kids. 1998. 96p. (YA). (gr. 6-8). reprint ed. 15.00 (978-0-7567-6028-1(3)) DIANE Publishing Co.

Scandiffio, Laura. The Martial Arts Book. Debon, Nicolas, illus. 2003. 64p. (J). (gr. 4 up). pap. 9.95 (978-1-55037-776-7(0)) Annick Pr., Ltd. CAN. *Dist:* Firefly Bks., Ltd.

—The Martial Arts Book. 2003. (gr. 5-8). lib. bdg. 18.75 (978-0-613-67913-8(X)) Tandem Library Bks.

Sievert, Terri. Kickboxing. 2004. (Edge Books, X-Sports). (Illus.). 32p. (J). lib. bdg. 22.60 (978-0-7368-2710-2(2)) Capstone Pr., Inc.

Sprague, Martina. The Martial Arts Book of Physics: How to Maximize Your Power, Speed & Endurance Using the Natural Laws of Motion. Sobel, Stuart, ed. Jones, Tim, illus. 2001. 128p. (YA). (gr. 13 up). pap. 19.95 (978-1-890378-01-1(1)) Pro-Action Publishing.

Streissguth, Thomas. Kickboxing. 2008. (Illus.). 24p. (J). lib. bdg. 19.95 (***978-1-60014-140-9(4)***) Bellwether Media.

Trimble, Aidan, contrib. by. Martial & Fighting Arts, 13 vols., Set. (Illus.). 96p. (YA). (gr. 7 up). lib. bdg. (978-1-59084-387-1(8)) Mason Crest Pubs.

Webster-Doyle, Terrence. Martial Arts Masters: Black Belt Warriors for Peace. 2001. (Illus.). 128p. pap. 16.95 (978-0-8348-0487-6(5) , Weatherhill, Inc.) Shambhala Pubns., Inc.

—My First Martial Arts Book: Putting My Shoes by the Door, Just So. 2001. (Martial Arts for Peace Ser.). (Illus.). 32p. 14.95 (978-0-8348-0481-4(6) , Weatherhill, Inc.) Shambhala Pubns., Inc.

Wilson, Wayne. Bruce Lee. 2001. (Real-Life Reader Biography Ser.). (Illus.). 32p. (J). (gr. 3-8). lib. bdg. 15.95 (978-1-58415-066-4(1)) Mitchell Lane Pubs., Inc.

Winkle, Jason M. & Ozmun, John C. Teaching Martial Arts for Fitness & Fun: A Noncontact Approach for Young People. 2001. (Illus.). 96p. pap., tchr. ed. 46.95 (978-0-7360-3245-2(2)) Human Kinetics Pubs.

MARTIAL ARTS—FICTION

Artful Doodlers. TMNT: Intense Action. 2008. (Teenage Mutant Ninja Turtles Ser.). 224p. (J). 4.99 (***978-1-4169-5102-5(4)*** , Simon Scribbles) Simon & Schuster Children's Publishing.

Asai, Carrie. The Book of the Pearl. Verhoye, Annabelle & Alarcao, Renato, illus. 2003. (Samurai Girl Ser.: Bk. 3). 240p. (YA). pap. 6.99 (978-0-689-86432-2(9) , Simon Pulse) Simon & Schuster Children's Publishing.

Asai, Carrie & Gray, Mitchel. The Book of the Wind. Verhoye, Annabelle & Alarcao, Renato, illus. 2003. (Samurai Girl Ser.). 224p. (YA). pap. 6.99 (978-0-689-86433-9(7) , Simon Pulse) Simon & Schuster Children's Publishing.

Barnes, Dawn. Beware of the Haunted Eye. 2007. (Black Belt Club Ser.: No. 3). 128p. (J). pap. 4.99 (978-0-439-85657-7(4) , Blue Sky Pr., The) Scholastic, Inc.

—Night on the Mountain of Fear. Chang, Bernard, illus. 2006. (Black Belt Club Ser.: No. 2). 176p. (J). pap. 4.99 (978-0-439-63939-2(5)); (gr. 2-5). 16.99 (978-0-439-63937-8(9)) Scholastic, Inc. (Blue Sky Pr., The).

Barnes, Dawn. Seven Wheels of Power. 2007. (Black Belt Club Ser.: No. 1). 176p. (J). pap. 2.99 (***978-0-545-01029-0(2)***) Scholastic, Inc.

—Seven Wheels of Power. Chang, Bernard, illus. 2005. (Black Belt Club Ser.: No. 1). 176p. (J). 4.99 (978-0-439-63936-1(0)); pap. 16.95 (978-0-439-63935-4(2)) Scholastic, Inc. (Blue Sky Pr., The).

Cerasini, Marc. Meet Casey Jones. 2004. (gr. k-3). lib. bdg. 11.80 (978-0-613-83490-2(9)) Tandem Library Bks.

Cha, Louis. The Legendary Couple, Vol. 4. Wong, Tony, illus. 2003. 120p. (YA). (gr. 8 up). pap. 13.95 (978-1-58899-233-8(0)) ComicsOne Corp./Dr. Masters.

Dgn Production Inc Staff & Lau, Ding Kin. Chinese Hero Tales of the Blood Sword V. 2007. (Illus.). 280p. (YA). pap. 19.95 (***978-1-59796-117-2(5)***) DrMaster Pubns. Inc.

Dixon, Franklin W. Martial Law. 2006. 152p. (J). lib. bdg. 16.92 (***978-1-4242-0389-5(9)***) Fitzgerald Bks.

—Martial Law. 2006. (Illus.). 152p. (J). (978-1-4156-6852-8(3) , Aladdin) Simon & Schuster Children's Publishing.

Dong, Seung. Where Is My Black Belt? 2005. 151p. pap. 19.95 (978-1-4137-8132-8(2)) PublishAmerica, Inc.

Gerver, Jane E. The Santa Snatcher. Spaziante, Patrick, illus. 2004. 32p. (J). lib. bdg. 15.00 (***978-1-4242-0959-0(5)***) Fitzgerald Bks.

—The Santa Snatcher. 2004. (Ready-to-Read Ser.). 32p. (J). pap. 3.99 (978-0-689-87018-7(3) , Simon Spotlight) Simon & Schuster Children's Publishing.

Harper, Benjamin. TMNT Underground Art Studio. 2007. (Teenage Mutant Ninja Turtles Ser.). (Illus.). 48p. (J). (ps-3). 9.99 (***978-1-4169-3856-9(7)*** , Simon Scribbles) Simon & Schuster Children's Publishing.

Hong, Chen Jiang. Little Sima. 2007. 36p. (ps-3). 16.95 (***978-1-59270-071-4(3)***) Enchanted Lion Bks., LLC.

Kakinouchi, Narumi. Juline, 5 vols. 168p. Vol. 1. 2001. (gr. 7-12). pap. 12.99 (978-1-892213-61-3(X)); Vol. 3. 3rd rev. ed. 2002. pap. 12.99 (978-1-931514-03-3(8)) TOKYOPOP, Inc.

Kehl, Mark. Tournament of Fear: And Other Martial Arts Stories. Artenstein, Michael, ed. 1999. (Sports Shorts Ser.). (Illus.). (J). (gr. 3-7). 96p. 12.95 (978-1-56565-889-9(2) , 08892W); 95p. pap. 5.95 (978-1-56565-949-0(X) , 09499W) Lowell Hse. (Roxbury Park).

Ma, Wing Shing. Storm Riders Vol. 1: Invading Sun. 2003. (Illus.). 128p. 9.95 (978-1-58899-359-5(0)) ComicsOne Corp./Dr. Masters.

Mah, Adeline Yen. Chinese Cinderella & the Secret Dragon Society. (Illus.). 256p. (J). 2006. pap. 5.99 (978-0-06-056736-1(8) , Harper Trophy); 2005. (gr. 5 up). 15.99 (978-0-06-056734-7(1)) HarperCollins Pubs.

Mauser McCord, Pat. A Bundle of Sticks. 2nd ed. 2004. (Illus.). 170p. (J). pap. 6.99 (978-1-880336-86-1(3) , BOS) Turtle Pr. Corp.

Murphy, Steve. Look Out! It's Turtle Titan! Spaziante, Patrick, illus. 2004. (Teenage Mutant Ninja Turtles Ser.). 24p. (J). pap. 3.99 (978-0-689-86900-6(2) , Simon Spotlight) Simon & Schuster Children's Publishing.

—Look Out! It's Turtle Titan! 2004. (gr. k-3). lib. bdg. 11.80 (978-0-613-83491-9(7)) Tandem Library Bks.

Nakahira, Masahiko. Street Fighter Alpha Volume 1. 2007. (Illus.). 200p. (YA). pap. 12.95 (***978-1-897376-50-8(2)***) URON Entertainment Corp. CAN. *Dist:* Diamond Bk. Distributors.

—Street Fighter Alpha Volume 2. 2007. (Illus.). 200p. (YA). pap. 12.95 (***978-1-897376-51-5(0)***) URON Entertainment Corp. CAN. *Dist:* Diamond Bk. Distributors.

—Street Fighter Sakura Ganbaru! Volume 1. 2007. 200p. (YA). pap. 12.95 (***978-1-897376-52-2(9)***) URON Entertainment Corp. CAN. *Dist:* Diamond Bk. Distributors.

Ng, Leandro, illus. Passage 2: HIV/AIDS — First Love. 2005. (1 World Manga Ser.: Vol. 2). 40p. pap. 3.99 (978-0-8213-6406-2(5)) World Bank Pubns.

Pierce, Terry. Tae Kwon Do! Bonita, Todd, illus. 2006. (Step into Reading Ser.). 32p. (J). (ps-1). pap. 3.99 (978-0-375-83448-6(6)); lib. bdg. 11.99 (978-0-375-93448-3(0)) Random Hse. Children's Bks. (Random Hse. Bks. for Young Readers).

Pinkney, Brian. Jojo's Flying Sidekick. Pinkney, Brian, illus. 1998. (Illus.). 32p. (J). (gr. k-3). pap. 6.99 (978-0-689-82192-9(1) , Aladdin) Simon & Schuster Children's Publishing.

Redondo, Jesus, illus. Turtle Rescue! 2004. (Ready-to-Read Ser.). 32p. (J). pap. 3.99 (978-0-689-87007-1(8) , Simon Spotlight) Simon & Schuster Children's Publishing.

Saito, Takao. Golgo 13. 2006. (Golgo 13 Ser.). 208p. (YA). Vol. 3. pap. 9.99 (978-1-4215-0462-9(6)); Vol. 4. pap. 9.99 (978-1-4215-0463-6(4)) Viz Media.

Sensei Teaches Focus. 2004. (J). 10.00 (978-0-9767483-0-4(4)) Wright's Way Inc.

Sfar, Joann. Little Vampire Does Kung Fu! Sfar, Joann, illus. 2003. (Illus.). 40p. (J). 12.95 (978-0-689-85769-0(1)) Simon & Schuster Children's Publishing.

Siu-Chong, Ken. Street Fighter Legends Volume 1: Sakura: Sakura. 2007. (Illus.). 128p. pap. 11.95 (***978-0-9781386-4-6(3)***) URON Entertainment Corp. CAN. *Dist:* Diamond Bk. Distributors.

Spaziante, Patrick, illus. Meet Casey Jones. 2004. (Teenage Mutant Ninja Turtles Ser.). 24p. (J). pap. 3.99 (978-0-689-86899-3(5) , Simon Spotlight) Simon & Schuster Children's Publishing.

Stone, Jeff. Crane. 2007. (Five Ancestors Ser.: Bk. 4). 224p. (J). (gr. 5-9). lib. bdg. 17.99 (978-0-375-93077-5(9) , Random Hse. Bks. for Young Readers) Random Hse. Children's Bks.

—Crane. 2007. (Five Ancestors Ser.: Bk. 4). 248p. (J). pap. (***978-0-375-83078-5(2)***) Random Hse., Inc.

—The Five Ancestors Book #1: Tiger. (Five Ancestors Ser.: Bk. 1). 208p. (gr. 5). 2005. (J). lib. bdg. 17.99 (978-0-375-93071-3(X) , Random Hse. Bks. for Young Readers); 2005. (Illus.). (J). 15.95 (978-0-375-83071-6(5) , Random Hse. Bks. for Young Readers); 2006. reprint ed. 5.99 (978-0-375-83072-3(3) , Yearling) Random Hse. Children's Bks.

—Monkey. (Five Ancestors Ser.: Bk. 1). 208p. (gr. 5). 2006. 5.99 (978-0-375-83074-7(X) , Yearling); 2005. (J). lib. bdg. 17.99 (978-0-375-93073-7(6) , Random Hse. Bks. for Young Readers); 2005. (J). 15.95 (978-0-375-83073-0(1) , Random Hse. Bks. for Young Readers) Random Hse. Children's Bks.

—Snake. 2007. (Five Ancestors Ser.: Bk. 3). 208p. (J). (gr. 5). 5.99 (978-0-375-83076-1(6) , Yearling) Random Hse. Children's Bks.

Teitelbaum, Michael. The Legend Begins. 2002. (Samurai Jack Ser.). (Illus.). 80p. (J). (gr. 3-7). pap. 4.50 (978-0-439-40972-8(1)) Scholastic, Inc.

Thomas, Jim. Super Slam Turtles! Spaziante, Patrick, illus. 2005. 22p. (J). lib. bdg. 15.00 (***978-1-4242-0971-2(4)***) Fitzgerald Bks.

Tokyopop Staff, ed. Jackie Chan Adventures, 3 vols., Vol. 2. 2004. (Illus.). 128p. pap. 7.99 (978-1-59182-403-9(6)) TOKYOPOP, Inc.

Trembath, Don. The Bachelors. 2002. (Illus.). 160p. (J). (gr. 3-7). pap. 6.95 (978-1-55143-209-0(9)) Orca Bk. Pubs. USA.

—One Missing Finger. 2001. (Black Belt Ser.). 160p. (J). (gr. 3-7). pap. 6.95 (978-1-55143-194-9(7)) Orca Bk. Pubs. USA.

—One Missing Finger. 2001. (gr. 3-6). lib. bdg. 15.25 (978-0-613-88906-3(1)) Tandem Library Bks.

Wax, Wendy. Meet Leatherhead. Spaziante, Patrick, illus. 2005. 22p. (J). lib. bdg. 15.00 (***978-1-4242-0972-9(2)***) Fitzgerald Bks.

West, Tracey. Journey to the Impossible Islands. 2003. (gr. 3-6). lib. bdg. 12.40 (978-0-613-72173-8(X)) Tandem Library Bks.

—The Seven Labors of Jack. Rodriguez, Angel, illus. 2003. (Samurai Jack Chapter Bks.: No. 2). 80p. (J). (gr. 3-7). pap. 4.50 (978-0-439-40974-2(8)) Scholastic, Inc.

Whitman, John. Ghostwarrior: And Other Martial Arts Stories. 2000. (Sports Shorts Ser.). 96p. (J). (gr. 3-7). pap. 5.95 (978-0-7373-0461-9(8) , 06/2000, Roxbury Park) Lowell Hse.

Willard, Eliza. Dark Hand with Cards. 2001. (gr. k-3). lib. bdg. 13.00 (978-0-613-72445-6(3)) Tandem Library Bks.

MARTINIQUE—FICTION

Cendrillon.Tr. of Cinderella. (FRE.). 48p. pap. 12.95 incl. audio compact disk (978-2-89558-065-2(0)) Coffragants CAN. *Dist:* Penton Overseas, Inc.

Perrault, Charles. Cendrillon. Baudrand, Edith, illus. 2000. (FRE.). 32p. (J). 13.95 (978-2-09-202114-9(1)) Nathan, Fernand FRA. *Dist:* Distribooks, Inc.

Stengel, Joyce A. Mystery of the Island Jewels. 2002. 208p. (J). (gr. 3-7). pap. 4.99 (978-0-689-85049-3(2) , Aladdin) Simon & Schuster Children's Publishing.

—Mystery of the Island Jewels. 2002. (gr. 3-6). lib. bdg. 13.00 (978-0-613-70940-8(3)) Tandem Library Bks.

MARX, KARL, 1818-1883

Karl Marx & Christian Ethics. 2nd l.t. ed. 2000. 401p. (C). pap. 29.00 (978-0-9712616-0-0(1)) Arts Colony Pubs.

MARXISM

see Communism; Socialism

MARY, BLESSED VIRGIN, SAINT

Aston, Al. A Message for Mary. Hutchinson, Joy, illus. 2005. 16p. 2.00 (978-1-84427-176-4(5)) Scripture Union GBR. *Dist:* STL Distribution North America.

La Casa de Maria.Tr. of Mary's House. (SPA.). (J). (978-0-7899-0875-9(1) , 496234) Editorial Unilit.

De Santis, Zerlina. Journeys with Mary: Apparitions of Our Lady. Lebel, Edward, illus. rev. ed. 2001. (Encounter the Saints Ser.: Vol. 9). 132p. (J). pap. 5.95 (978-0-8198-3972-5(8) , 332-149) Pauline Bks. & Media.

Demi. Mary. Demi, illus. 2006. (Illus.). 48p. (J). (gr. 2-5). 19.95 (978-0-689-87692-9(0) , McElderry, Margaret K.) Simon & Schuster Children's Publishing.

Glen, Jo. Thirty Activity Days, Story of Mary & Joseph: The Story of Mary & Joseph. 1998. (Illus.). 24p. 9.99 (978-1-85608-367-6(5)) Hunt, John Publishing Ltd. GBR. *Dist:* APG Sales and Fulfillment.

—30 Days with Mary & Joseph. 2004. (Illus.). 30p. (ps-3). 11.95 (978-0-8294-1475-2(4)) Loyola Pr.

Harder Tangvald, Christine. Swish, Swish, Went the Giant Fish: And Other Bible Stories about Prayer. Griego, Tony, illus. 1999. (Read Aloud, Read Alone Ser.). 32p. (J). (978-0-7814-0929-2(2)) Cook, David C. Publishing Co.

Joslin, Mary. Mary, Mother of Jesus. 2004. (Illus.). 24p. (ps up). 15.95 (978-0-8294-1380-9(4)) Loyola Pr.

Kubiak, Shannon. God Called a Girl: How Mary Changed Her World — And You Can Too. 2005. 176p. (J). reprint ed. pap. 11.99 (978-0-7642-0029-8(1)) Bethany Hse. Pubs.

Orfeo, Christine Virginia. My First Book about Mary. Darrenkamp, Julia Mary, illus. 2007. 64p. (Orig.). (J). pap. 7.95 (***978-0-8198-4861-1(1)***) Pauline Bks. & Media.

Papademetriou, Dorrie. The Story of Mary, the Mother of God. 2000. (Illus.). 32p. (J). 15.00 (978-0-88141-205-5(8)) St. Vladimir's Seminary Pr.

Pingry, Patricia. Story of Mary. 2006. (Illus.). 32p. (J). pap. 3.95 (978-0-8249-5546-5(3)) Ideals Pubns.

Pingry, Patricia A. & Venturi-Pickett, Stacy. The Story of Mary. 2000. (Illus.). 26p. (J). (ps-3). bds. 6.95 (978-0-8249-4183-3(7) , Ideals Children's Bks.) Ideals Pubns.

Roux, Marie-Genevieve & Charpy, Elisabeth. Saint Catherine Laboure: Mary's Messenger. Curreli, Augusta, illus. 2000. (Along the Paths of the Gospel Ser.). 74p. (J). (gr. 5-9). 6.95 (978-0-8198-7037-7(4) , 332-346) Pauline Bks. & Media.

Sanna, Ellyn. Mary, Mother of Jesus. 1999. (Young Reader's Christian Library). (Illus.). 224p. (J). (ps-3). pap. 1.39 (978-1-57748-653-4(6)) Barbour Publishing, Inc.

Serrano, Francisco. La Virgen de Guadalupe. Davalos, Felipe, illus. Tr. of Virgin of Guadalupe. (SPA.). (J). (gr. 2-4). 18.00 (978-968-494-070-3(X)) Centro de Informacion y Desarrollo de la Comunicacion y la Literatura MEX. *Dist:* Lectorum Pubns., Inc.

Serrano, Francisco & Guzman, Eugenia. La Virgen de Guadalupe. Davalos, Felipe, illus. 1998. Tr. of Virgin of Guadalupe. (SPA.). 12p. (J). 16.95 (978-0-88899-340-3(4)) Groundwood Bks. CAN. *Dist:* Perseus Distribution.

Wangerin, Walter, Jr. Mary's First Christmas. Ladwig, Tim, illus. 1998. 48p. (J). 19.99 (978-0-310-22216-3(8)) Zonderkidz.

—Mary's First Christmas. 1998. (J). 19.99 (978-0-310-22746-5(1)) Zondervan.

Zondervan. Mary & Little Jesus. DeVries, Catherine, ed. Pulley, Kelly, illus. 2005. (Beginner's Bible' Ser.). 22p. (J). (ps). 5.99 (978-0-310-71105-6(3)) Zonderkidz.

MARY, QUEEN OF SCOTS, 1542-1587

Carruth, J. A., text. Mary Queen of Scots. (Scotland in Words & Pictures Ser.). (Illus.). 32p. pap. 3.95 (978-0-7117-0147-2(4)) Jarrold Publishing GBR. *Dist:* 7 Hills Bk. Distributors.

Douglas, Elizabeth. Mary, Queen of Scots. Philip, Carrie, illus. 1999. (Scottie Bks.). 40p. (J). (gr. 3-7). pap. 8.95 (978-0-11-494265-6(X)) NMS Enterprises Ltd. - Publishing GBR. *Dist:* Antique Collectors' Club, Balogh International, Inc.

Macdonald, Fiona. You Wouldn't Want to Be Mary Queen of Scots! A Ruler Who Really Lost Her Head. (You Wouldn't Want to... : History of the World Ser.). 32p. (J). 2008. pap. 9.95 (***978-0-531-14853-2(X)*** , Watts, Franklin); 2007. spiral bd. 29.00 (***978-0-531-13912-7(3)*** , Children's Pr.) Scholastic Library Publishing.

Vicary, Tim. Mary Queen of Scots, Level 1. 2nd ed. 2000. (Bookworms Ser.). (Illus.). 64p. 6.50 (978-0-19-422947-0(5)) Oxford Univ. Pr., Inc.

MARY, QUEEN OF SCOTS, 1542-1587—FICTION

Hendry, Frances. Quest for a Queen: The Falcon. 2006. pap. (***978-1-905665-06-8(7)***) Pollinger In Print.

—Quest for a Queen: The Jackdaw. 2006. pap. (***978-1-905665-05-1(9)***) Pollinger In Print.

—Quest for a Queen: The Lark. 2006. pap. (***978-1-905665-04-4(0)***) Pollinger In Print.

Lasky, Kathryn. Mary, Queen of Scots: Queen Without a Country, France 1553. 2002. (Royal Diaries Ser.). (Illus.). 112p. (J). (gr. 4-8). pap. 10.95 (978-0-439-19404-4(0) , Scholastic Pr.) Scholastic, Inc.

Yolen, Jane. Queen's Own Fool: A Novel of Mary Queen of Scots. 2001. (gr. 7-12). lib. bdg. 16.45 (978-0-613-44410-1(8)) Tandem Library Bks.

MARYLAND

Alderfer, Jonathan. National Geographic Field Guide to Birds: Maryland & D. C. 2006. (Illus.). 272p. pap. 14.95 (978-1-4262-0007-6(2) , National Geographic) National Geographic Society.

Bennett, Kelly. Chesapeake Bay. 2006. (Rookie Read-About Geography Ser.). (Illus.). 32p. (J). (gr. 1-2). 20.50 (978-0-516-25032-8(9) , Children's Pr.) Scholastic Library Publishing.

Blashfield, Jean F. Maryland. 2007. (America the Beautiful, Third Ser.). 144p. (J). spiral bd. 38.00 (***978-0-531-18576-6(1)*** , Children's Pr.) Scholastic Library Publishing.

Brown, Jonatha A. Maryland. 2006. (Portraits of the States Ser.). (Illus.). 32p. (J). pap. (978-0-8368-4687-4(7)); lib. bdg. 23.33 (978-0-8368-4668-3(0)) Stevens, Gareth Inc.

Brown, Vanessa. Maryland. 2005. (Bilingual Library of the United States of America: Set 1). (ENG & SPA., Illus.). 32p. (J). (gr. 2-5). lib. bdg. 22.50 (978-1-4042-3085-9(8) , Buenas Letra) Rosen Publishing Group, Inc., The.

Bunting, Elaine & D'Amario, Patricia. Counties of Central Maryland. Ramsey, Marcy Dunn, illus. 1998. (Our Maryland Counties Ser.). 160p. (J). 19.95 (978-0-87033-503-7(0)) Cornell Maritime Pr., Inc.

—Counties of Maryland's Lower Eastern Shore. Ramsey, Marcy Dunn, illus. 2004. (Our Maryland Counties Ser.). 168p. (J). 19.95 (978-0-87033-555-6(3) , Tidewater Pubs.) Cornell Maritime Pr., Inc.

—Counties of Southern Maryland. Ramsey, Marcy Dunn, illus. 2001. 138p. (J). 19.95 (978-0-87033-535-8(9) , Tidewater Pubs.) Cornell Maritime Pr., Inc.

Burgan, Michael. Maryland. 2004. (Life in the Thirteen Colonies Ser.). (Illus.). 124p. (J). 36.00 (978-0-516-24571-3(6) , Children's Pr.) Scholastic Library Publishing.

Craats, Rennay. A Guide to Maryland. 2001. (American States Ser.). (Illus.). 32p. (J). lib. bdg. 16.95 (978-1-59036-000-2(1)) Weigl Pubs., Inc.

Curtis, Alice Turner. A Little Maid of Maryland. Little, Nat, illus. 2004. (Little Maid Ser.). 192p. (J). (gr. 4-7). reprint ed. per. 9.95 (978-1-55709-327-1(X)) Applewood Bks.

Doherty, Craig A. & Doherty, Katherine M. Maryland. 2005. (Thirteen Colonies Ser.). (Illus.). 128p. (J). (gr. 4-9). 35.00 (978-0-8160-5418-3(5)) Facts On File, Inc.

Dubois, Muriel L. Maryland Facts & Symbols. (States & Their Symbols Ser.). 24p. (J). 2000. (Illus.). (gr. 2-3). lib. bdg. 18.60 (978-0-7368-0523-0(0) , Bridgestone Bks.); 2003. lib. bdg. 19.93 (978-0-7368-2250-3(X)) Capstone Pr., Inc.

Heinrichs, Ann. Maryland. 2003. (This Land Is Your Land Ser.). (Illus.). 48p. (J). (gr. 3 up). lib. bdg. 22.60 (978-0-7565-0348-2(5)) Compass Point Bks.

Johnston, Joyce. Maryland. 2nd exp. rev. ed. 2003. (Hello U. S. A. Ser.). (Illus.). 84p. (J). (gr. 3-6). lib. bdg. 25.26 (978-0-8225-4094-6(0)) Lerner Publishing Group.

—Maryland. rev. ed. 2003. (gr. 3-6). lib. bdg. 15.25 (978-0-613-52438-4(1)) Tandem Library Bks.

Kummer, Patricia K. Maryland. rev. ed. 2002. (One Nation Ser.). (Illus.). 48p. (J). (gr. 3-4). lib. bdg. 22.60 (978-0-7368-1244-3(X) , Bridgestone Bks.) Capstone Pr., Inc.

MNO

LaBella, Susan. Maryland. 2006. 32p. (J). (gr. 1-2). pap. 5.95 (978-0-516-25493-7(6) , Children's Pr.) Scholastic Library Publishing.

Labella, Susan. Maryland. 2005. (Rookie Read-About Geography Ser.). (Illus.). 31p. (J). (ps-ps). 20.50 (978-0-516-25256-8(9) , Children's Pr.) Scholastic Library Publishing.

Leese, Jennifer. Uniquely Maryland. 2003. (State Studies). (Illus.). 48p. (J). 27.07 (978-1-4034-4493-6(5)); pap. 8.50 (978-1-4034-4508-7(7)) Heinemann Library.

Marsh, Carole. The Big Maryland Reproducible Activity Book! 2004. (Maryland Experience! Ser.). (Illus.). 128p. (J). (gr. 2-6). per., act. bk. ed. 9.95 (978-0-7933-9614-6(X)) Gallopade International.

—The Magnificant Maryland Coloring Book. 2004. (Maryland Experience! Ser.). (Illus.). 32p. (J). (gr. k-2). pap. 3.95 (978-0-7933-9615-3(8)) Gallopade International.

—Maryland Classic Christmas Trivia. 2002. (Carole Marsh Maryland Bks.). (Illus.). 32p. pap. 6.95 (978-0-635-01407-8(6) , 14076); lib. bdg. 21.95 (978-0-635-01408-5(4) , 14084) Gallopade International. (Marsh, Carole Bks.).

—Maryland Current Events Projects: 30 Cool, Activities, Crafts, Experiments & More for Kids to Do to Learn about Your State! 2003. (Maryland Experience Ser.). 32p. (gr. k-8). pap. 5.95 (978-0-635-02039-0(4) , Marsh, Carole Bks.) Gallopade International.

—Maryland Geography Projects: 30 Cool, Activities, Crafts, Experiments & More for Kids to Do to Learn about Your State! 2003. (Maryland Experience Ser.). 32p. (gr. k-5). pap. 5.95 (978-0-635-01839-7(X) , Marsh, Carole Bks.) Gallopade International.

—Maryland Government Projects: 30 Cool, Activities, Crafts, Experiments & More for Kids to Do to Learn about Your State! 2003. (Maryland Experience Ser.). 32p. (gr. k-5). pap. 5.95 (978-0-635-01939-4(6) , Marsh, Carole Bks.) Gallopade International.

—Maryland Jeopardy! Answers & Questions about Our State! 2004. (Maryland Experience! Ser.). (Illus.). 32p. (J). (gr. 3-8). pap. 7.95 (978-0-7933-9612-2(3)) Gallopade International.

—Maryland "Jography" A Fun Run Thru Our State! 2004. (Maryland Experience! Ser.). (Illus.). 32p. (J). (gr. 3-8). pap. 7.95 (978-0-7933-9613-9(1)) Gallopade International.

—Maryland People Projects: 30 Cool, Activities, Crafts, Experiments & More for Kids to Do to Learn about Your State! 2003. (Maryland Experience Ser.). 32p. (gr. k-5). pap. 5.95 (978-0-635-01989-9(2) , Marsh, Carole Bks.) Gallopade International.

—Maryland Survivor: Game Book. 2001. (Carole Marsh Maryland Bks.). (Illus.). 32p. (J). (gr. 3-8). pap., act. bk. ed. 9.95 (978-0-635-00541-0(7)) Gallopade International.

—Maryland Symbols & Facts Projects: 30 Cool, Activities, Crafts, Experiments & More for Kids to Do to Learn about Your State! 2003. (Maryland Experience Ser.). 32p. (gr. k-5). pap. 5.95 (978-0-635-01889-2(6) , Marsh, Carole Bks.) Gallopade International.

—My First Book about Maryland. 2004. (Maryland Experience! Ser.). (Illus.). 32p. (J). (gr. k-4). pap. 7.95 (978-0-7933-9611-5(5)) Gallopade International.

—My First Pocket Guide: Maryland. 2004. (Maryland Experience! Ser.). (Illus.). 96p. (J). (gr. 3-8). per. 6.95 (978-0-7933-9610-8(7)) Gallopade International.

—The Survivor: A Class Challenge. 2001. (Carole Marsh Maryland Bks.). lib. bdg. 29.95 (978-0-635-00666-0(9)) Gallopade International.

Martin, Michael A. Maryland: The Old Line State. 2002. (World Almanac Library of the States). (Illus.). 48p. (J). (gr. 5 up). lib. bdg. 30.00 (978-0-8368-5137-3(4)); pap. 14.95 (978-0-8368-5307-0(5)) Stevens, Gareth Inc. (World Almanac Library).

Maryland. 2000. (Switched on Schoolhouse Ser.). (Illus.). (YA). (gr. 7-12). pap. 24.95 incl. cd-rom (978-0-7403-0272-5(8) , SOSMD) Alpha Omega Pubns., Inc.

Menendez, Shirley. B Is for Blue Crab: A Maryland Alphabet. Stutzman, Laura, illus. 2004. (State Ser.). 40p. (J). 17.95 (978-1-58536-160-1(7)) Sleeping Bear Pr.

Murray, Julie. Maryland. 2006. (Buddy Book Ser.). (Illus.). 32p. (J). (gr. k-4). lib. bdg. 22.78 (978-1-59197-679-0(0) , Buddy Bks.) ABDO Publishing Co.

Otfinoski, Steven. Maryland. 2002. (It's My State! Ser.). (Illus.). 80p. (J). 27.07 (978-0-7614-1421-6(5) , Benchmark Bks.) Cavendish, Marshall Corp.

Pell, Ed. Maryland. 2003. (Land of Liberty Ser.). (Illus.). 64p. (J). (gr. 3-4). lib. bdg. 23.93 (978-0-7368-1588-8(0) , Bridgestone Bks.) Capstone Pr., Inc.

Rollo, Vera F. Maryland Today: A Geography. 3rd ed. 1999. (Illus.). 188p. (YA). (gr. 4 up). 22.50 (978-0-917882-49-4(0)) Maryland Historical Pr.

Savage, Jeff. Maryland: A MyReportLinks.com Book. 2003. (States Ser.). (Illus.). 48p. (J). lib. bdg. 25.26 (978-0-7660-5115-7(3) , MyReportLinks.com Bks.) Enslow Pubs., Inc.

Somervill, Barbara A. Maryland. 2003. (From Sea to Shining Sea Ser.: 2). (Illus.). 80p. (J). 30.50 (978-0-516-22384-1(4) , Children's Pr.) Scholastic Library Publishing.

Wimmer, Teresa. Maryland. 2008. (J). (****978-1-58341-645-7(5)*** , Creative Education) Creative Co., The.

MARYLAND—FICTION

Carbone, Elisa. Stealing Freedom. 2001. (Illus.). 272p. (YA). (gr. 5-8). 5.99 (978-0-440-41707-1(4) , Yearling) Random Hse. Children's Bks.

Conly, Jane Leslie. While No One Was Watching. 2000. (978-0-606-18728-2(6)) Tandem Library Bks.

Cummings, Priscilla. A Face First. 2003. 208p. (J). (gr. 3-6). pap. 6.99 (978-0-14-230247-7(3) , Puffin) Penguin Group (USA) Inc.

—A Face First. 2003. (gr. 3-6). lib. bdg. 14.15 (978-0-613-61621-8(9)) Tandem Library Bks.

Delacre, Lulu. Cuentos Con Sazon. 2001. Tr. of Stories with Season. (SPA.). (gr. 3-6). lib. bdg. 12.40 (978-0-613-82235-0(8)) Tandem Library Bks.

Elise Broach. Shakespeare's Secret. l.t. ed. 2006. 350p. (J). 22.95 (978-0-7862-8735-2(7)) Thorndike Pr.

Fuqua, Jonathon Scott. Reappearance of Sam Webber. 1999. (Illus.). 232p. (YA). pap. 23.95 (978-1-890862-03-9(7)) Bancroft Pr.

—The Reappearance of Sam Webber. 2001. (Illus.). 288p. (J). (gr. 5). reprint ed. pap. 9.99 (978-0-7636-1424-9(6)) Candlewick Pr.

Furtney, Charles S. Tryconnel: An Antebellum Adventure along the C & O Canal. 2004. (Illus.). iii, 156p. (J). pap. (978-0-9711835-3-7(8)) Local History Co., The.

Hahn, Mary Downing. Anna All Year Round. deGroat, Diane, illus. 2001. 144p. (J). (gr. 4-7). pap. 4.95 (978-0-380-73317-0(X) , Harper Trophy) HarperCollins Pubs.

—Anna on the Farm. 2001. lib. bdg. 14.15 (978-0-613-68401-9(X)) Tandem Library Bks.

Hancock, Irving H. Dave Darrin's First Year at Annapolis. 2006. 78.99 (****978-1-4219-9882-4(3));*** pap. 72.99 (****978-1-4219-9880-0(7))*** IndyPublish.com.

—Dave Darrin's Fourth Year at Annapolis (2006. 78.99 (****978-1-4219-9801-5(7));*** pap. 72.99 (****978-1-4219-9805-3(X))*** IndyPublish.com.

—Dave Darrin's Second Year at Annapolis O. 2006. 95.99 (****978-1-4280-1562-3(0));*** pap. 89.99 (****978-1-4280-1578-4(7))*** IndyPublish.com.

—Dave Darrin's Third Year at Annapolis or. 2006. 95.99 (****978-1-4219-7420-0(7));*** pap. 89.99 (****978-1-4219-7419-4(3))*** IndyPublish.com.

Hollenbeck, Kathleen M. Dancing on the Sand: A Story of an Atlantic Blue Crab. 2005. (Illus.). 32p. (J). (ps-2). 8.95 incl. audio (978-1-59249-234-3(7) , SC4017) Soundprints.

—Dancing on the Sand: A Story of an Atlantic Blue Crab. Popeo, Joanie, illus. 1999. (Smithsonian Oceanic Collection: Vol. 17). 32p. (J). (ps-2). 19.95 incl. reel tape (978-1-56899-732-2(9) , BC4017) Soundprints.

Kimball, K. M. The Star-Spangled Secret. 2001. 234p. (J). (gr. 4-7). lib. bdg. 11.64 (978-0-606-22096-5(8)) Tandem Library Bks.

Klam, Cheryl. Learning to Swim. 2007. 224p. (YA). (gr. 7). pap. 8.99 (978-0-385-73372-4(0)); lib. bdg. 13.99 (978-0-385-90387-5(1)) Random Hse. Children's Bks. (Delacorte Bks. for Young Readers).

Leatherman, Diane. Rebecca, a Maryland Farm Girl. 2002. (J). (gr. 3-7). per. 7.95 (978-0-9665861-1-4(5)) Bounty Project, The.

Maxson, H. A. & Young, Claudia H. Tea Party at Chestertown. Kosits, Andrew, illus. 2003. 55p. (J). per. 8.95 (978-0-9741713-0-2(1)) Bay Oak Pubs., Ltd.

Mills, Charles. Storm on Shadow Mountain. 2003. 127p. (J). (978-0-8163-1993-0(6)) Pacific Pr. Publishing Assn.

Mills, Claudia. The Totally Made-Up Civil War Diary of Amanda MacLeish. 2008. 208p. (J). 16.00 (****978-0-374-37696-3(4))*** Farrar, Straus & Giroux.

Naylor, Phyllis Reynolds. Alice in the Know. (Alice Ser.). (YA). 2007. 320p. pap. 5.99 (****978-0-689-87093-4(0)*** , Simon Pulse); 2006. 288p. (gr. 7 up). 15.95 (978-0-689-87092-7(2)) Simon & Schuster Children's Publishing.

—Dangerously Alice. 2007. (Alice Ser.). 304p. (YA). (gr. 9 up). 15.99 (978-0-689-87094-1(9) , Atheneum) Simon & Schuster Children's Publishing.

—Lovingly Alice. (Alice Ser.). (J). 2006. 176p. pap. 5.99 (978-0-689-84400-3(X) , Aladdin); 2006. 166p. (****978-1-4156-5199-5(X)*** , Aladdin); 2004. (Illus.). 176p. 15.95 (978-0-689-84399-0(2) , Atheneum) Simon & Schuster Children's Publishing.

Otis, James. Calvert of Maryland A Story of Lord Baltimore's Colony. 2005. reprint ed. pap. 21.95 (978-1-4179-3369-3(0)) Kessinger Publishing, LLC.

Siwak, Brenda S. Counting on the Bay. Dodge, Barbara A., illus. 2006. (J). per. 14.95 (****978-0-9790906-0-8(1))*** Pleasant Plains Pr.

The Star-Spangled Banner. 2003. (Illus.). 32p. (J). 16.95 (978-0-8249-5462-8(9)) Ideals Pubns.

Trimper, Marty. Hermione: Shipwrecked! in Ocean City, Maryland. Amy, Holloway, illus. 2004. (J). (978-1-886068-28-5(3)) Fruitbearer Publishing.

Troeger, Virginia B. Secret along the St. Mary's. Swisher, Michael-Che, tr. Swisher, Michael-Che, illus. 2003. (Mysteries in Time Ser.). 92p. (J). 14.95 (978-1-893110-35-9(4)) Silver Moon Pr.

MARYLAND—HISTORY

An Academy of Every Virtue: A History of Mount de Sales Academy, Catonsville, Maryland, 1852-2002. 2001. 328p. (C). (978-0-9715386-0-3(3)) Mount de Sales Academy.

Bachmann, Elaine Rice. While a Tree Grew: The Story of Maryland's Wye Oak. Harrell, Kim, illus. 2006. (J). (****978-0-87033-577-8(4)*** , Tidewater Pubs.) Cornell Maritime Pr., Inc.

Bartoletti, Susan Campbell. The Flag Maker. Nivola, Claire A., illus. 2004. 32p. (J). (gr. 3-5). tchr. ed. 16.00 (978-0-618-26757-6(3)) Houghton Mifflin Co. Trade & Reference Div.

Bennett, Kelly. Chesapeake Bay. 2006. 32p. (YA). (gr. 1-2). pap. 5.95 (978-0-516-29702-6(3) , Children's Pr.) Scholastic Library Publishing.

Britton, Tamara L. The Maryland Colony. 2001. (Colonies Ser.). (Illus.). 32p. (J). (gr. k-6). lib. bdg. 22.78 (978-1-57765-578-7(8) , Checkerboard Library) ABDO Publishing Co.

Bunting, Elaine & D'Amario, Patricia. Counties of Northern Maryland. Ramsey, Marcy Dunn, illus. 2000. (Our Maryland Counties Ser.). 172p. (J). (gr. 4-7). 19.95 (978-0-87033-520-4(0) , Tidewater Pubs.) Cornell Maritime Pr., Inc.

Coleman, Brooke. The Colony of Maryland. 2000. (Library of the Thirteen Colonies & the Lost Colony). (Illus.). 24p. (J). (gr. 3). lib. bdg. 19.95 (978-0-8239-5483-4(8) , PowerKids Pr.) Rosen Publishing Group, Inc., The.

Deinard, Jenny. How to Draw Marylands Sights & Symbols. 2002. (Kids Guide to Drawing America Ser.). 32p. (J). lib. bdg. 25.25 (978-0-8239-6076-7(5) , PowerKids Pr.) Rosen Publishing Group, Inc., The.

Doak, Robin. Maryland, 1634-1776. 2007. (Voices from Colonial America Ser.). (Illus.). 112p. (J). (gr. 5-9). 21.95 (****978-1-4263-0143-8(X));*** lib. bdg. 32.90 (****978-1-4263-0144-5(8))*** National Geographic Society. (National Geographic Children's Bks.).

Doherty, Craig A. & Doherty, Katherine M. Maryland. 2005. (Thirteen Colonies Ser.). (Illus.). 128p. (J). (gr. 4-9). 35.00 (978-0-8160-5418-3(5)) Facts On File, Inc.

Hama, Larry. The Battle of Antietam: "The Bloodiest Day of Battle" 2007. (Graphic Battles of the Civil War Ser.). (Illus.). 48p. (J). lib. bdg. (978-1-4042-0775-2(9)) Rosen Publishing Group, Inc., The.

Heinrichs, Ann. Maryland. 2005. (Welcome to the USA Ser.). (Illus.). 40p. (J). (gr. 1-5). 27.07 (978-1-59296-445-1(1)) Child's World, Inc.

Jensen, Ann. The World Turned Upside Down: Children of 1776. Ramsey, Marcy Dunn, illus. 2001. 80p. (J). pap. 9.95 (978-0-87033-534-1(0) , Tidewater Pubs.) Cornell Maritime Pr., Inc.

Landau, Elaine. The National Anthem. 2007. (True Bks.). (Illus.). 48p. (J). (gr. 3-5). lib. bdg. 26.00 (****978-0-531-12633-2(1)*** , Children's Pr.) Scholastic Library Publishing.

Levy, Debbie. Maryland. 2003. (Seeds of a Nation Ser.). (Illus.). 48p. (J). 26.20 (978-0-7377-1447-0(6) , Greenhaven Pr., Inc.) Thomson Gale.

Loker, Aleck. The Murder of Joseph Henry Ching: A Legend Examined. 2003. (Illus.). 28p. 6.00 (978-1-928874-04-1(5)) Solitude Pr.

Lough, Loree. Lord Baltimore. (Colonial Leaders Ser.). (Illus.). 80p. (gr. 3 up). 2000. (YA). 27.50 (978-0-7910-5349-2(0)); 1999. (J). pap. 27.50 (978-0-7910-5692-9(9)) Facts On File, Inc. (Chelsea Hse.).

—Lord Baltimore: English Politician & Colonist. 2000. (gr. 5-8). lib. bdg. 17.60 (978-0-613-43350-1(5)) Tandem Library Bks.

Marsh, Carole. Maryland History Projects: 30 Cool, Activities, Crafts, Experiments & More for Kids to Do to Learn about Your State! 2003. (Maryland Experience Ser.). 32p. (gr. k-5). pap. 5.95 (978-0-635-01789-5(X) , Marsh, Carole Bks.) Gallopade International.

—My First Pocket Guide Maryland. 2000. (Maryland Experience! Ser.). (Illus.). 96p. (J). (gr. 3-8). 12.95 (978-0-635-01310-1(X)) Gallopade International.

—Who Wants to Be a Millionaire? 2001. (Carole Marsh Maryland Bks.). lib. bdg. 29.95 (978-0-635-00057-6(1)) Gallopade International.

Mis, Melody S. The Colony of Maryland: A Primary Source History. 2007. (Primary Source Library of the Thirteen Colonies & the Lost Colony). (Illus.). 24p. (J). lib. bdg. (978-1-4042-3434-5(9) , PowerKids Pr.) Rosen Publishing Group, Inc., The.

Robinson, J. Dennis. Lord Baltimore: Founders of Maryland. 2006. (Signature Lives Ser.). (Illus.). 112p. (J). (gr. 5-7). 30.60 (978-0-7565-1592-8(0)) Compass Point Bks.

Sonneborn, Liz. The Colony of Maryland. 2005. (Primary Sources of the Thirteen Colonies & the Lost Colony Ser.). (Illus.). 64p. (J). (gr. 3-7). pap. 14.60 (978-1-4042-0672-4(8)) Rosen Publishing Group, Inc., The.

—A Primary Source History of the Colony of Maryland. 2005. (Primary Sources of the Thirteen Colonies & the Lost Colony Ser.). (Illus.). 64p. (YA). (gr. 5-8). lib. bdg. 29.25 (978-1-4042-0427-0(X)) Rosen Publishing Group, Inc., The.

Streissguth, Thomas. Maryland. 2001. (Thirteen Colonies Ser.). (Illus.). 104p. (YA). (gr. 4-12). lib. bdg. 29.95 (978-1-56006-871-6(X) , LML00902-178195, Lucent Bks.) Thomson Gale.

Weintraub, A. How to Draw District of Columbias Sights & Symbols. 2002. (Kids Guide to Drawing America Ser.). 32p. (J). lib. bdg. 25.25 (978-0-8239-6063-7(3) , PowerKids Pr.) Rosen Publishing Group, Inc., The.

Whiting, Jim. The Maryland Colony: Lord Baltimore. 2007. (Illus.). 48p. (J). lib. bdg. 29.95 (****978-1-58415-547-8(7))*** Mitchell Lane Pubs., Inc.

Wiener. The 13 Colonies Pack: Maryland, 6. 2004. (Illus.). 48.30 (978-1-4109-0367-9(2)) Harcourt Schl. Pubs.

Wiener, Roberta & Arnold, James R. Maryland. 2004. (Thirteen Colonies Ser.). (Illus.). 64p. (J). 31.36 (978-0-7398-6880-5(2)); 9.50 (978-1-4109-0304-4(4)) Harcourt Schl. Pubs.

MASAI (AFRICAN PEOPLE)

Alexander, Florence & Alexander, Stanley. Come with Me & See... African People. l.t. ed. 2003. (ENG & SPA., Illus.). 13p. (J). 3.99 (978-0-9648313-8-4(4)) Ebon Research Systems Publishing, LLC.

Barber, Nicola. Living in the African Savannah. 2007. (J). pap. (****978-1-4109-2823-8(3));*** lib. bdg. (****978-1-4109-2814-6(4))*** Steck-Vaughn.

Craats, Rennay. Maasai. (Indigenous Peoples Ser.). 32p. 2005. pap. 7.95 (978-1-59036-255-6(1)); 2004. (Illus.). (J). lib. bdg. 24.25 (978-1-59036-219-8(5)) Weigl Pubs., Inc.

Lekuton, Joseph Lemasolai. Facing the Lion: Growing up Maasai on the African Savanna. (Illus.). 144p. (J). (gr. 7 up). 2005. 23.90 (978-0-7922-8328-7(7)); 2003. 15.95 (978-0-7922-5125-5(3)) National Geographic Society. (National Geographic Children's Bks.).

McQuail, Lisa. The Masai of Africa. 2002. (First Peoples Ser.). (Illus.). 48p. (J). (gr. 4-8). 23.93 (978-0-8225-4855-3(0)) Lerner Publishing Group.

MASAI (AFRICAN PEOPLE)—FICTION

Joosse, Barbara M. & Lavallee, Barbara. Papa Do You Love Me? Lavallee, Barbara, illus. 2005. (Illus.). 36p. (J). 15.95 (978-0-8118-4265-5(7)) Chronicle Bks. LLC.

Kessler, Christina. Our Secret, Siri Aang. 2007. 224p. (YA). (gr. 5). pap. 6.99 (****978-0-14-240840-7(9)*** , Puffin) Penguin Group (USA) Inc.

Kessler, Cristina. Our Secret Siri Aang. 2004. 240p. (YA). (gr. 5). 16.99 (978-0-399-23985-4(5) , Philomel) Penguin Group (USA) Inc.

Kroll. Masai & I. 1998. pap. 4.99 (978-0-87628-558-9(2)) Ctr. for Applied Research in Education, The.

MASERS, OPTICAL

see Lasers

MASKS

Animators Of The Pokemon Tv Series & Viz Comics Staff. Pokeman Paper Masks. 2000. (Pokemon Ser.). 16p. (YA). pap. 10.95 (978-1-56931-516-3(7)) Viz Media.

Doney, Meryl. Masks. 2004. (Crafts from Many Cultures Ser.). (Illus.). 32p. (J). (gr. 3 up). lib. bdg. 23.33 (978-0-8368-4044-5(5)) Stevens, Gareth Inc.

Finley, Carol. The Art of African Masks: Exploring Cultural Traditions. 1998. (Art Around the World Ser.). (Illus.). 56-64p. (gr. 4-8). 23.93 (978-0-8225-2078-8(8)) Lerner Publishing Group.

Furgang, Kathy. Mask Making Around the World. 2003. (Early Connections Ser.). (J). pap. 33.00 (978-1-4108-1069-4(0)) Benchmark Education Co.

Hodge, Susie. Masks. 2006. (Illus.). 32p. (978-1-58340-952-7(1)) Smart Apple Media.

Hummingbird, Jesse & Hummingbird, Sandy. Cherokee Masks. 2002. 32p. (gr. k-3). 4.95 (978-1-57067-131-9(1)) Book Publishing Co., The.

Humphrey, Paul. How to Make a Mask. 2007. (J). (****978-1-59771-101-2(2))*** Sea-To-Sea Pubns.

Kondeatis, Christos, contrib. by. DC Comics Masks: Nine Masks of DC Comics Heroes & Villians to Assemble & Wear. 1999. (Illus.). 60p. (gr. 4-7). pap. 25.00 (978-0-8212-2434-2(4)) Little Brown & Co.

LaFosse, Michael. Making Origami Masks Step by Step. 2004. (Kid's Guide to Origami Ser.). (Illus.). 24p. (J). lib. bdg. 21.25 (978-0-8239-6703-2(4) , PowerKids Pr.) Rosen Publishing Group, Inc., The.

Lamerand, Violaine. Making Masks. 2002. (Step by Step Ser.). (Illus.). 32p. (J). (gr. 2-3). lib. bdg. 22.60 (978-0-7368-1476-8(0) , Bridgestone Bks.) Capstone Pr., Inc.

Magnificent Masks: Individual Title Six-Packs. (Bookweb Ser.). 32p. (gr. 5 up). 34.00 (978-0-7635-3792-0(6)) Rigby Education.

Masks, 6 vols. (gr. k-2). 28.95 (978-0-7368-8131-9(X)) Red Brick Learning.

Miles, Elizabeth & Montgomery, Lee. Horror Masks. 2001. (Big Book of... Ser.). (Illus.). 24p. (J). pap. 9.95 (978-1-901323-14-6(5)) Orpheus Bks., Ltd. GBR. *Dist:* CPG Publishing, Inc.

Miles, Elizabeth & Noon, Steve. Warrior Masks. 2001. (Big Book of... Ser.). (Illus.). 24p. (J). pap. 9.95 (978-1-901323-16-0(1)) Orpheus Bks., Ltd. GBR. *Dist:* CPG Publishing, Inc.

Miles, Elizabeth & Wright, David. Animals Masks. 2001. (Big Book of... Ser.). (Illus.). 24p. (J). pap. 9.95 (978-1-901323-15-3(3)) Orpheus Bks., Ltd. GBR. *Dist:* CPG Publishing, Inc.

Morris, Ting, et al. Masks. 2006. (978-1-59771-030-5(X)) Sea-To-Sea Pubns.

Otten, Jack. Watch Me Make a Mask. 2002. (Wel-Making Things Ser.). (Illus.). 24p. (J). (ps-2). 18.00 (978-0-516-23944-6(9) , Children's Pr.) Scholastic Library Publishing.

—Watch Me Make a Mask. 2002. (gr. k-3). lib. bdg. 12.95 (978-0-613-58812-6(6)) Tandem Library Bks.

Pinsent, Lynsy. Face Art. 2001. (Illus.). 40p. (J). pap. 13.95 (978-0-439-32287-4(1)) Scholastic, Inc.

Round, Graham. Bible Masks & Christmas Play Activity Book. 2002. (Illus.). 20p. (J). 7.99 (978-0-8254-7254-1(7)) Kregel Pubns.

Rudolph, Nancy Lyn. Paper Animal Masks from Northwest Tribal Tales. 2004. (Illus.). 80p. (J). (gr. 4-8). reprint ed. 20.00 (978-0-7567-7073-0(4)) DIANE Publishing Co.

Schaefer, Lola M. Masks. Saunders-Smith, Gail, ed. 1998. (Fall Fun Ser.). (Illus.). 24p. (J). (gr. k-1). lib. bdg. 15.93 (978-0-7368-0106-5(5) , Pebble Bks.) Capstone Pr., Inc.

—Masks. (Fall Fun Ser.). 24p. (J). pap. 5.95 (978-0-7368-8107-4(7)) Capstone Pr., Inc.

Schwarz, Renee F. Making Masks. 2004. (Kids Can Do It Ser.). (Illus.). 40p. (J). (gr. 4-6). (978-1-55074-931-1(5)) Kids Can Pr., Ltd.

—Making Masks. Schwarz, Renee F., illus. unabr. ed. 2004. (Kids Can Do It Ser.). (Illus.). 40p. (J). (gr. 4-6). (978-1-55074-929-8(3)) Kids Can Pr., Ltd.

Shaffer, Christy. Farm Animals Punch-Out Masks. 1998. (Illus.). 6p. (J). (gr. 3). pap. 4.95 (978-0-486-40582-7(6)) Dover Pubns., Inc.

Smith, A. G. Masks of the World Coloring Book. 2003. (Illus.). 32p. (J). pap. 3.95 (978-0-486-43039-3(1)) Dover Pubns., Inc.

Smith, Thomasina. Face Painting. 2002. (Fun Factory Ser.). (Illus.). 64p. (gr. 3-7). pap. 6.95 (978-1-84215-605-6(5) , Southwater) Anness Publishing GBR. *Dist:* National Bk. Network.

—Mask Magic. 2002. (Fun Factory Ser.). (Illus.). 64p. (gr. 3-7). pap. 6.95 (978-1-84215-618-6(7) , Southwater) Anness Publishing GBR. *Dist:* National Bk. Network.

Southwater Staff. Outrageously Fabulous Face Painting & Disguises. 2003. (Outrageously... Ser.). (Illus.). 96p. pap. 9.99 (978-1-84215-671-1(3) , Southwater) Anness Publishing GBR. *Dist:* National Bk. Network.

Sundance, ed. Making a Mask. 2000. (ps-2). lib. bdg. 11.65 (978-0-613-37625-9(0)) Tandem Library Bks.

Valat, Pierre-Marie. Animal Faces. 2007. 32p. (J). pap. 12.95 (***978-1-59354-196-5(1)***) Handprint Bks.

Waldron, Jan L. John Pig's Halloween Masks. 1998. (Illus.). (978-0-525-46105-0(1) , Dutton Juvenile) Penguin Group (USA) Inc.

MASS COMMUNICATION

see Communication

MASS MEDIA

Ali, Dominic. Media Madness: An Insider's Guide to Media. Cho, Michael, illus. 2005. 64p. (YA). (gr. 5-9). (978-1-55337-175-5(5)); (978-1-55337-174-8(7)) Kids Can Pr., Ltd.

Ball, Jacqueline A., et al. Communication Inventions: From Hieroglyphics to DVDs. 2006. (Which Came First? Ser.). (Illus.). 32p. (J). lib. bdg. 25.27 (978-1-59716-129-9(2)) Bearport Publishing Co., Inc.

Cefrey, Holly. Coping with Media Violence. 2005. (Coping Ser.). (Illus.). 192p. (YA). (gr. 7-12). lib. bdg. 26.50 (978-0-8239-2893-4(4)) Rosen Publishing Group, Inc., The.

Cooper, Alison. Media Power? 2005. (Illus.). 32p. (J). (gr. 5-9). lib. bdg. 27.10 (978-1-932889-61-1(2)) Sea-To-Sea Pubns.

DeGaetano, Gloria. Parenting Well in a Media Age: Keeping Our Kids Human. 2004. 272p. (J). pap. 18.95 (978-1-932181-12-8(1)) Personhood Pr.

Edgar, Kathleen J. Everything You Need to Know about Media Violence. rev. ed. 2000. (Need to Know Library). (Illus.). 64p. (YA). (gr. 4-6). lib. bdg. 25.25 (978-0-8239-3108-8(0) , NTMEVI) Rosen Publishing Group, Inc., The.

Endich, Roberta. Media Literacy: Activities for Understanding the Scripted World, Grades 4-8. 2003. (Linworth Learning Ser.). (Illus.). 150p. 29.95 (978-1-58683-094-6(5)) Linworth Publishing, Inc.

Gedatus, Gus. Violence in the Media. 2000. (Perspectives on Violence Ser.). (Illus.). 64p. (J). (gr. 4-6). lib. bdg. 23.93 (978-0-7368-0425-7(0) , LifeMatters Bks.) Capstone Pr., Inc.

Gellman, Marc. Bad Stuff in the News: A Guide to Handling the Headlines. 2002. (gr. 5-8). lib. bdg. 12.95 (978-0-613-87927-9(9)) Tandem Library Bks.

Gellman, Marc & Hartman, Tom. Bad Stuff in the News: A Guide to Handling the Headlines. 2002. 128p. (J). (gr. 4-9). reprint ed. pap. 4.95 (978-1-58717-232-8(1) , Sea-Star Bks.) Chronicle Bks. LLC.

Gifford, Clive & Dorling Kindersley Publishing Staff. Media & Communication. 2000. (Eyewitness Bks.). (Illus.). 64p. (J). (gr. 4-7). 15.99 (978-0-7894-6294-7(X)) Dorling Kindersley Publishing, Inc.

—Media & Communications. 2000. (Eyewitness Bks.). (Illus.). 64p. (J). (gr. 4-7). lib. bdg. 19.99 (978-0-7894-6629-7(5)) Dorling Kindersley Publishing, Inc.

Hernandez, Roger E. Teens & the Media. 2005. (Gallup Youth Survey, Major Issues & Trends Ser.). (Illus.). 112,128p. (YA). lib. bdg. 22.95 (978-1-59084-874-6(8)) Mason Crest Pubs.

Horn, Geoffrey M. Political Parties, Interest Groups & the Media. 2003. (World Almanac Library of American Government). (Illus.). 48p. (J). (gr. 5 up). pap. 14.95 (978-0-8368-5483-1(7)); lib. bdg. 30.00 (978-0-8368-5478-7(0)) Stevens, Gareth Inc. (World Almanac Library).

Koopmans, Andy. Crime & Criminals. 2002. (Examining Pop Culture Ser.). 176p. (J). 36.20 (978-0-7377-1431-9(X)); (Illus.). (gr. 7-10). pap. 24.95 (978-0-7377-1432-6(8)) Thomson Gale. (Greenhaven Pr., Inc.).

Lane, Yvet-Renee. Cambridge Checkpoints VCE Media 2005. 2004. (Cambridge Checkpoints Ser.). pap., stu. ed. 12.00 (978-0-521-61223-4(3)) Cambridge Univ. Pr.

The Media. 2005. (Illus.). 32p. (gr. 4-8). pap. 131.70 (978-0-7910-9093-0(0) , Chelsea Hse.) Facts On File, Inc.

Morgan, Sally, et al. Behind Media: An Insider's Look at the Media Industries, 7 bks., Set. 2001. 48p. (YA). (gr. 7-8). lib. bdg. 169.54 (978-1-58810-005-4(7)) Heinemann Library.

Parker, Steve. 20s & 30s: Entertainment for All. 2002. (Twentieth Century Media Ser.). (Illus.). 32p. (J). (gr. 5 up). lib. bdg. 26.00 (978-0-8368-3183-2(7)) Stevens, Gareth Inc.

—20th Century Media, 6 bks. Incl. 20s & 30s : Entertainment for All. lib. bdg. 26.00 (978-0-8368-3183-2(7)); 40s & 50s : Power & Persuasion. lib. bdg. 26.00 (978-0-8368-3184-9(5)); 70s & 80s : Global Technology. lib. bdg. 26.00 (978-0-8368-3186-3(1)); 1900-20 : Print to Pictures. lib. bdg. 26.00 (978-0-8368-3182-5(9)); 1960s : The Satellite Age. lib. bdg. 26.00 (978-0-8368-3185-6(3)); 1990s : Electronic Media. lib. bdg. 26.00 (978-0-8368-3187-0(X)); 32p. (J). (gr. 5 up). (Illus.). 2002. Set lib. bdg. 156.00 (978-0-8368-3181-8(0)) Stevens, Gareth Inc.

—40s & 50s: Power & Persuasion. 2002. (Twentieth Century Media Ser.). (Illus.). 32p. (J). (gr. 5 up). lib. bdg. 26.00 (978-0-8368-3184-9(5)) Stevens, Gareth Inc.

—70s & 80s: Global Technology. 2002. (Twentieth Century Media Ser.). (Illus.). 32p. (J). (gr. 5 up). lib. bdg. 26.00 (978-0-8368-3186-3(1)) Stevens, Gareth Inc.

—1900-20: Print to Pictures. 2002. (Twentieth Century Media Ser.). (Illus.). 32p. (J). (gr. 5 up). lib. bdg. 26.00 (978-0-8368-3182-5(9)) Stevens, Gareth Inc.

—1960s: The Satellite Age. 2002. (Twentieth Century Media Ser.). (Illus.). 32p. (J). (gr. 5 up). lib. bdg. 26.00 (978-0-8368-3185-6(3)) Stevens, Gareth Inc.

—1990s: Electronic Media. 2002. (Twentieth Century Media Ser.). (Illus.). 32p. (J). (gr. 5 up). lib. bdg. 26.00 (978-0-8368-3187-0(X)) Stevens, Gareth Inc.

Petley, Julian. The Media: The Impact on Our Lives. 2001. (Twenty-First Century Debates Ser.). (Illus.). 64p. (YA). (gr. 6-8). lib. bdg. 27.12 (978-0-7398-3175-5(5)) Raintree.

Reeves, Diane Lindsey. Career Ideas for Kids Who Like Talking. 2nd rev. ed. (Career Ideas for Kids Ser.). (J). (gr. 4-9). 2008. 304p. pap. 18.95 (***978-0-8160-6554-7(3)***); 2007. 192p. 32.95 (***978-0-8160-6553-0(5)***) Facts On File, Inc. (Checkmark Bks.).

Robinson, Hilary. E-Mail: Jesus@anytime. Lewis, Anthony, tr. Lewis, Anthony, illus. 2004. 32p. (J). 19.95 (978-0-340-85537-9(1) , Hodder & Stoughton) Hodder General Publishing Division GBR. *Dist:* Trafalgar Square Publishing.

Summers, Sue L. Media Alert! 200 Activities to Create Media-Savvy Kids. (J). pap. 15.00 (978-0-9676616-0-5(9)) Media Alert!.

Turow, Joseph. Media Today: An Introduction to Mass Communication. 2nd ed. 2002. 615p. (YA). pap. 88.36 (978-0-618-29016-1(8) , 356149) Houghton Mifflin College Div.

Tyndale House Publishers Staff, contrib. by. Mind over Media. 2001. (Life on the Edge Ser.). (Illus.). 176p. (YA). pap. 8.99 (978-1-56179-870-4(3)) Focus on the Family Publishing.

Wan, Guofang. Virtually True: Questioning Online Media. 2007. (Fact Finders Ser.). (Illus.). 32p. (J). (***978-0-7368-7863-0(7)*** , 1264914) Capstone Pr., Inc.

Wan, Guofang & Capstone Press Staff. Virtually True: Questioning Online Media. 2007. (Fact Finders Ser.). (Illus.). 32p. (J). (gr. 4-7). lib. bdg. 22.60 (978-0-7368-6767-2(8) , 1264914) Capstone Pr., Inc.

MASSACHUSETTS

Baker, Helen. Shopping the Cape, 1 book. 2003. 160p. per. 12.95 (978-0-9743511-0-0(5)) Baker, Helen Interiors, Inc.

Barenblat, Rachel. Massachusetts: The Bay State. 2002. (World Almanac Library of the States). (Illus.). 48p. (J). (gr. 5 up). pap. 14.95 (978-0-8368-5286-8(9)); lib. bdg. 30.00 (978-0-8368-5123-6(4)) Stevens, Gareth Inc. (World Almanac Library).

—Massachusetts: The Bay State. 2002. (gr. 5-8). lib. bdg. 24.15 (978-0-613-52439-1(X)) Tandem Library Bks.

Bjorklund, Ruth. Massachusetts. 2002. (It's My State! Ser.). (Illus.). 80p. (J). 27.07 (978-0-7614-1418-6(5) , Benchmark Bks.) Cavendish, Marshall Corp.

Bruun, Erik. Massachusetts. Peterson, Rick, illus. 2006. 48p. (J). (gr. 3-7). 9.95 (978-1-57912-230-0(2)) Black Dog & Leventhal Pubs., Inc.

Capstone Press Staff, contrib. by. Massachusetts. rev. ed. 2002. (One Nation Ser.). (Illus.). 48p. (J). (gr. 3-4). lib. bdg. 22.60 (978-0-7368-1245-0(8) , Bridgestone Bks.) Capstone Pr., Inc.

De Capua, Sarah. Massachusetts. 2003. (Rookie Read-About Geography Ser.). (Illus.). 32p. (J). (gr. 1-2). pap. 5.95 (978-0-516-27491-1(0) , Children's Pr.) Scholastic Library Publishing.

De Capua, Sarah & Bredeson, Carmen. Massachusetts. 2002. (Rookie Read-About Geography Ser.). (Illus.). 32p. (J). (gr. 1-2). 20.50 (978-0-516-22666-8(5) , Children's Pr.) Scholastic Library Publishing.

DeFord, Deborah H. Massachusetts. 2004. (Life in the Thirteen Colonies Ser.). (Illus.). 124p. (J). 36.00 (978-0-516-24572-0(4) , Children's Pr.) Scholastic Library Publishing.

Deinard, Jenny. How to Draw Massachusetts's Sights & Symbols. 2002. (Kid's Guide to Drawing America Ser.). (Illus.). 32p. (J). (gr. 3-5). lib. bdg. 25.25 (978-0-8239-6077-4(3) , PowerKids Pr.) Rosen Publishing Group, Inc., The.

Domblewski, Carol. Uniquely Massachusetts. 2004. (Heinemann State Studies). (Illus.). 48p. (J). pap. 8.50 (978-1-4034-4477-6(3)); lib. bdg. 27.07 (978-1-4034-4470-7(6)) Heinemann Library.

Ewing, Juliana Horatia. Story of A Short Life. 2006. pap. 24.95 (***978-1-4286-3593-7(9)***) Kessinger Publishing, LLC.

Fairley, Melissa & Brown, Jonatha A. Massachusetts. 2005. (Portraits of the States Ser.). (Illus.). 32p. (J). pap. (978-0-8368-4645-4(1)); lib. bdg. 23.33 (978-0-8368-4626-3(5)) Stevens, Gareth Inc.

Forten, Charlotte L., et al. A Free Black Girl Before the Civil War: The Diary of Charlotte Forten, 1854. Steele, Christy & Graves, Kerry, eds. 2000. (Blue Earth Books). (Illus.). 32p. (J). (gr. 3-4). lib. bdg. 22.60 (978-0-7368-0345-8(9) , Bridgestone Bks.) Capstone Pr., Inc.

Greene, Jacqueline Dembar. Powwow: A Good Day to Dance. Greene, Jacqueline Dembar, photos by. 1998. (First Bks.). (Illus.). 64p. (J). (gr. 5-7). 22.00 (978-0-531-20337-8(9) , Watts, Franklin) Scholastic Library Publishing.

Heinrichs, Ann. Massachusetts. 2005. (Welcome to the USA Ser.). 40p. (J). (gr. 1-5). 27.07 (978-1-59296-286-0(6)) Child's World, Inc.

Hodgkins, Fran. Massachusetts. 2003. (Land of Liberty Ser.). (Illus.). 64p. (J). (gr. 3-4). lib. bdg. 23.93 (978-0-7368-1589-5(9) , Bridgestone Bks.) Capstone Pr., Inc.

Leotta, Joan. Massachusetts. 80p. (J). 2008. (From Sea to Shining Sea, Second Ser.). pap. 7.95 (***978-0-531-18805-7(1)***); 2001. (From Sea to Shining Sea Ser.: 2). (Illus.). (gr. 3-5). 30.50 (978-0-516-22486-2(7)) Scholastic Library Publishing. (Children's Pr.).

LeVert, Suzanne. Massachusetts. 2000. (Celebrate the States Ser.). (Illus.). 144p. (gr. 4-8). lib. bdg. 37.07 (978-0-7614-0666-2(2) , Benchmark Bks.) Cavendish, Marshall Corp.

Marsh, Carole. The Big Massachusetts Reproducible Activity Book. 2001. (Carole Marsh Massachusetts Bks.). (Illus.). 96p. (J). (gr. 2-6). pap., act. bk. ed. 9.95 (978-0-7933-9945-1(9)) Gallopade International.

—Massachusetts Classic Christmas Trivia. 2002. (Carole Marsh Massachusetts Bks.). (Illus.). 32p. pap. 6.95 (978-0-635-01409-2(2) , 14092); lib. bdg. 21.95 (978-0-635-01410-8(6) , 14106) Gallopade International. (Marsh, Carole Bks.).

—Massachusetts Current Events Projects: 30 Cool, Activities, Crafts, Experiments & More for Kids to Do to Learn about Your State! 2003. (Massachusetts Experience Ser.). 32p. (gr. k-8). pap. 5.95 (978-0-635-02040-6(8) , Marsh, Carole Bks.) Gallopade International.

—The Massachusetts Experience Pocket Guide. 2001. (Carole Marsh Massachusetts Bks.). (Illus.). 96p. (J). (gr. 3-8). pap. 6.95 (978-0-7933-9916-1(5)) Gallopade International.

—Massachusetts Geography Projects: 30 Cool, Activities, Crafts, Experiments & More for Kids to Do to Learn about Your State! 2003. (Massachusetts Experience Ser.). 32p. (gr. k-5). pap. 5.95 (978-0-635-01840-3(3) , Marsh, Carole Bks.) Gallopade International.

—Massachusetts Government Projects: 30 Cool, Activities, Crafts, Experiments & More for Kids to Do to Learn about Your State! 2003. (Massachusetts Experience Ser.). 32p. (gr. k-5). pap. 5.95 (978-0-635-01940-0(X) , Marsh, Carole Bks.) Gallopade International.

—Massachusetts Jeopardy! Answers & Questions about Our State! 2001. (Carole Marsh Massachusetts Bks.). (Illus.). 32p. (J). (gr. 3-8). pap. 7.95 (978-0-7933-9800-3(2)) Gallopade International.

—Massachusetts "Jography" A Fun Run Thru Our State! 2001. (Carole Marsh Massachusetts Bks.). (Illus.). 32p. (J). (gr. 3-8). pap. 7.95 (978-0-7933-9829-4(0)) Gallopade International.

—Massachusetts People Projects: 30 Cool, Activities, Crafts, Experiments & More for Kids to Do to Learn about Your State! 2003. (Massachusetts Experience Ser.). 32p. (gr. k-5). pap. 5.95 (978-0-635-01990-5(6) , Marsh, Carole Bks.) Gallopade International.

—Massachusetts Survivor: Game Book. 2001. (Carole Marsh Massachusetts Bks.). (Illus.). 32p. (J). (gr. 3-8). pap., act. bk. ed. 9.95 (978-0-635-00542-7(5)) Gallopade International.

—Massachusetts Symbols & Facts Projects: 30 Cool, Activities, Crafts, Experiments & More for Kids to Do to Learn about Your State! 2003. (Massachusetts Experience Ser.). 32p. (gr. k-5). pap. 5.95 (978-0-635-01890-8(X) , Marsh, Carole Bks.) Gallopade International.

—My First Book about Massachusetts. 2001. (Carole Marsh Massachusetts Bks.). (Illus.). 32p. (J). (gr. k-4). pap. 7.95 (978-0-7933-9887-4(8)) Gallopade International.

—The Survivor: A Class Challenge. 2001. (Carole Marsh Massachusetts Bks.). lib. bdg. 29.95 (978-0-635-00667-7(7)) Gallopade International.

—Who Wants to Be a Millionaire? 2001. (Carole Marsh Massachusetts Bks.). lib. bdg. 29.95 (978-0-635-00059-0(8)) Gallopade International.

The Massachusetts 54th, 6 vols. (gr. 2-5). 39.95 (978-0-7368-4598-4(4)) Red Brick Learning.

Massachusetts. (Switched on Schoolhouse Ser.). 2003. cd-rom 24.95 (978-0-7403-0645-7(6)); 2000. (Illus.). (YA). (gr. 7-12). pap. 24.95 incl. cd-rom (978-0-7403-0273-2(6) , SOSMA) Alpha Omega Pubns., Inc.

McAuliffe, Emily. Massachusetts Facts & Symbols. (States & Their Symbols Ser.). 24p. (J). 1998. (Illus.). (gr. 2-3). lib. bdg. 18.60 (978-0-7368-0082-2(4) , Bridgestone Bks.); 2003. lib. bdg. 19.93 (978-0-7368-2251-0(8)) Capstone Pr., Inc.

Murray, Julie. Massachusetts. 2006. (Buddy Book Ser.). (Illus.). 32p. (J). (gr. k-4). lib. bdg. 22.78 (978-1-59197-680-6(4) , Buddy Bks.) ABDO Publishing Co.

Naden, Corinne J. & Blue, Rose. Massachusetts: A MyReportLinks.com Book. 2003. (States Ser.). (Illus.). 48p. (J). (gr. 4-10). lib. bdg. 25.26 (978-0-7660-5107-2(2) , MyReportLinks.com Bks.) Enslow Pubs., Inc.

Obregon, Jose M. Massachusetts. Brusca, Maria Cristina, tr. 2005. (Bilingual Library of the United States of America: Set 1). (ENG & SPA., Illus.). 32p. (J). (gr. 2-5). lib. bdg. 22.50 (978-1-4042-3086-6(6) , Buenas Letra) Rosen Publishing Group, Inc., The.

Pezzi, Bryan. A Guide to Massachusetts. 2000. (American States Ser.). (Illus.). 32p. (J). (gr. 3-7). lib. bdg. 16.95 (978-1-930954-35-9(2)) Weigl Pubs., Inc.

Raven, Margot Theis. M Is for Mayflower: A Massachusetts Alphabet. Brett, Jeannie, illus. 2002. 40p. (J). 17.95 (978-1-58536-072-7(4)) Sleeping Bear Pr.

Stemple, Heidi E. Y. One if by Land: A Massachusetts Number Book. Brett, Jeannie, illus. 2006. 40p. (J). 17.95 (978-1-58536-186-1(0)) Sleeping Bear Pr.

Sullivan, George. Paul Revere. 1999. (gr. 3-6). lib. bdg. 12.40 (978-0-613-26542-3(4)) Tandem Library Bks.

Trueit, Trudi Strain. Massachusetts. 2007. (America the Beautiful, Third Ser.). (Illus.). 144p. (YA). (gr. 5-8). lib. bdg. 38.00 (***978-0-531-18561-2(3)*** , Children's Pr.) Scholastic Library Publishing.

Trumbauer, Lisa. Paul Revere. Saunders-Smith, Gail, ed. 2003. (First Biographies Ser.). (Illus.). 24p. (J). (gr. k-1). lib. bdg. 15.93 (978-0-7368-2085-1(X) , Pebble Bks.) Capstone Pr., Inc.

Warner, J. F. Massachusetts. 2nd exp. rev. ed. (Hello U. S. A. Ser.). (Illus.). 84p. (gr. 3-6). 2002. (J). lib. bdg. 25.26 (978-0-8225-4050-2(9)); 2003. (YA). pap. 6.95 (978-0-8225-4158-5(0)) Lerner Publishing Group.

Wimmer, Teresa. Massachusetts. 2008. (J). (***978-1-58341-646-4(3)*** , Creative Education) Creative Co., The.

Winter, Jonah. Paul Revere & the Bell Ringers. Dodson, Bert, illus. 2003. (Ready-to-Read Ser.). 32p. (J). pap. 3.99 (978-0-689-85635-8(0) , Aladdin) Simon & Schuster Children's Publishing.

—Paul Revere & the Bell Ringers. 2003. (gr. k-3). lib. bdg. 11.80 (978-0-613-89003-8(5)) Tandem Library Bks.

MASSACHUSETTS—FICTION

Allen, Kathleen. Witch Hunter. 2005. 131p. pap. 19.95 (978-1-4137-7839-7(9)) PublishAmerica, Inc.

Anagram, Nicholas C. The Compass Has Eight Points, Bk. 1. 2002. 286p. (gr. 4-7). pap. 15.95 (978-0-595-21839-4(3) , Writer's Showcase Pr.) iUniverse, Inc.

Arciero, Susan. Nantucket 1, 2, 3. Arciero, Susan, illus. l.t. ed. 2000. (Illus.). (J). (ps). 7.95 (978-0-9677548-2-6(8)) Pigtail Publishing.

Arenstam, Peter. Nicholas: A Massachusetts Tale. Holman, Karen Busch, illus. 2007. (J). 14.95 (***978-1-58726-519-8(2)*** , Mitten Pr.) Ann Arbor Media Group, LLC.

Atkins, Jeannine. Anne Hutchinson's Way. Dooling, Michael, illus. 2007. 32p. (J). (gr. 3 up). 17.00 (978-0-374-30365-5(7)) Farrar, Straus & Giroux.

Atkinson, Beth. From Alice to Zen & Everyone in Between: A Novel. 2008. (Exceptional Reading & Language Arts Titles for Intermediate Grades Ser.). (J). 15.95 (***978-0-8225-7271-8(0)*** , Carolrhoda Bks.) Lerner Publishing Group.

Autumn, Kyla. Time Era: Back in Salem's Hunt. 2005. 78p. pap. 14.95 (978-1-4137-7605-8(1)) PublishAmerica, Inc.

Bruchac, Joseph. Squanto's Journey: The Story of the First Thanksgiving. Shed, Greg, illus. 2007. 32p. (J). pap. 6.00 (***978-0-15-206044-2(8)*** , Voyager Bks./Libros Viajeros) Harcourt Children's Bks.

Bryant, Annie. Ghost Town. 2007. (Beacon Street Girls Ser.: Bk. 11). 250p. (J). (gr. 4-8). pap. 7.10 (***978-1-933566-09-2(4)***) B*tween Productions, Inc.

—Just Kidding. 2007. (Beacon Street Girls Ser.: Bk. 10). 270p. (YA). pap. 7.99 (***978-1-933566-07-8(8)***) B*tween Productions, Inc.

Burnham, Niki. Sticky Fingers. 2005. 278p. (YA). (gr. 7 up). pap. 6.99 (978-0-689-87649-3(1) , Simon Pulse) Simon & Schuster Children's Publishing.

Chetkowski, Emily. Amasa Walker's Spendid Garment. Peterson, Dawn, illus. 2003. 48p. (gr. 5-8). reprint ed. pap. 9.95 (978-0-911469-21-9(4)) Hood, Alan C. & Co., Inc.

Cocca-Leffler, Maryann. Bus Route to Boston. Cocca-Leffler, Maryann, illus. 2003. (Illus.). 32p. (J). (gr. k-2). 15.95 (978-1-56397-723-7(0)) Boyds Mills Pr.

Cohn, Rachel. Pop Princess. 2004. (Illus.), 320p. (J). 16.95 (978-0-689-85205-3(3)) Simon & Schuster Children's Publishing.

Cormier, Robert. The Rag & Bone Shop. 2001. (Illus.). 160p. (YA). (gr. 7 up). 15.95 (978-0-385-72962-8(6) , Delacorte Bks. for Young Readers) Random Hse. Children's Bks.

—The Rag & Bone Shop. l.t. ed. 2002. 141p. (J). 24.95 (978-0-7862-3873-6(9)) Thomson Gale.

Curtis, Alice Turner. A Little Maid of Massachusetts Bay Colony. Smith, Wuanita, illus. 2004. (Little Maid Ser.). 192p. (J). (gr. 4-7). reprint ed. per. 9.95 (978-1-55709-329-5(6)) Applewood Bks.

Davis, Rachel. My Life at Mapleleaf Cabin. 2nd ed. 2004. (YA). per. 10.00 (978-0-9741176-8-3(4)) Wu Li Turtle Corp.

DeFelice, Cynthia C. Death at Devil's Bridge. 2000. 192p. (J). (gr. 3-7). 16.00 (978-0-374-31723-2(2) , Farrar, Straus & Giroux (BYR)) Farrar, Straus & Giroux.

—Death at Devil's Bridge. 2002. 192p. (J). (gr. 3-7). pap. 5.99 (978-0-06-441037-3(4) , Harper Trophy) HarperCollins Pubs.

—Death at Devil's Bridge. 2002. (gr. 3-6). lib. bdg. 14.10 (978-0-613-82528-3(4)) Tandem Library Bks.

Dell, Pamela. Giles & Metacom: A Story of Plimoth & the Wampanoag. 2002. (Scrapbooks of America Ser.). (Illus.). 48p. (J). (gr. 2-6). 28.50 (978-1-59187-012-8(7)) Child's World, Inc.

Dixon, Franklin W. Thrill Ride. 2005. 154p. (J). lib. bdg. 16.92 (***978-1-4242-0386-4(4)***) Fitzgerald Bks.

—Thrill Ride. 2005. (Illus.). 154p. (J). (978-1-4156-0585-1(8) , Aladdin) Simon & Schuster Children's Publishing.

Dorato, A. P. Arthur, Donna, & the Magic Crown of Tiabora. 2006. pap. 19.95 (978-1-4137-8898-3(X)) PublishAmerica, Inc.

Duey, Kathleen & Bale, Karen A. Hurricane, New Bedford, Massachusetts, 1784. 1999. (Survival! Ser.: No. 9). 160p. (J). (gr. 4-7). per. 4.50 (978-0-689-82544-6(7) , Simon Pulse) Simon & Schuster Children's Publishing.

Dunmore, Helen. Going to Egypt. 2003. 144p. (Orig.). (J). pap. 9.99 (978-0-09-941195-6(4) , Red Fox) Random Hse. Children's Bks. GBR. *Dist:* Trafalgar Square Publishing.

Durst, Sarah. Into the Wild. 2007. 272p. (J). (gr. 5-7). 15.99 (978-1-59514-156-9(1) , Razorbill) Penguin Group (USA) Inc.

Fleming, Candace. A Big Cheese for the White House: The True Tale of a Tremendous Cheddar. Schindler, S. D., illus. 2004. 32p. (J). reprint ed. pap. 6.95 (978-0-374-40627-1(8) , Sunburst) Farrar, Straus & Giroux.

Franklin, Emily. All You Need Is Love: The Principles of Love. 2006. 256p. (gr. 12). pap. 9.99 (978-0-451-21961-9(9) , N A L Trade) Penguin Group (USA) Inc.

—The Principles of Love. 2005. 256p. (gr. 12-12). pap. 9.99 (978-0-451-21517-8(6) , N A L Trade) Penguin Group (USA) Inc.

—Summer of Love: The Principles of Love. 2007. 256p. (YA). pap. 9.99 (978-0-451-22040-0(4) , N A L Trade) Penguin Group (USA) Inc.

Frederick, Heather Vogel. The Mother-Daughter Book Club. 2007. 256p. (J). (gr. 4-7). 15.99 (978-0-689-86412-4(4)) Simon & Schuster Children's Publishing.

Friend, Natasha. Bounce. 2007. 192p. (YA). (gr. 6-8). pap. 16.99 (***978-0-439-85350-7(8)*** , Scholastic Pr.) Scholastic, Inc.

Gallagher, Diana G. & Burge, Constance M. Mystic Knoll. 2005. 217p. (J). (978-1-4155-8004-2(9) , Simon Spotlight) Simon & Schuster Children's Publishing.

Golden, Christopher. Meets the Eye. 2000. (Body of Evidence Ser.: No. 4). 256p. (YA). (gr. 7 up). pap. 4.99 (978-0-671-03495-5(2) , Simon Pulse) Simon & Schuster Children's Publishing.

Greenspan, Paul. Crystal of Dreams. 2007. 192p. pap. 12.96 (***978-0-615-13477-2(7)***) Flying Cloud Bks.

M N O

Griffin, Adele. Amandine. 2003. 208p. (gr. 5-9). pap. 6.99 (978-0-7868-1441-1(1)) Disney Pr.
—Amandine. 2001. 224p. (gr. 5-9). 15.99 (978-0-7868-0618-8(4)) Hyperion Bks. for Children.
—Amandine. 2003. 199p. (YA). (gr. 7-9). lib. bdg. 15.30 (978-0-613-69042-3(7)) Tandem Library Bks.
Hawthorne, Nathaniel. The House of the Seven Gables. 1999. reprint ed. pap. 28.00 (978-1-4047-1350-5(6)) Classic Textbooks.
—The Scarlet Letter. adapted ed. (YA). (gr. 5-12). pap. 8.50 (978-0-8359-0262-5(5)) Globe Fearon Educational Publishing.
—The Scarlet Letter. l.t. ed. 2000. (LRS Large Print Heritage Ser.). 379p. (YA). (gr. 7-12). lib. bdg. 34.95 (978-1-58118-065-7(9), 23660) LRS.
—The Scarlet Letter. 1998. (YA). 40p. 11.95 (978-1-56137-339-0(7), NU3397SP); 32p. 9.95 (978-1-56137-338-3(9), NU3389) Novel Units, Inc.
Hoffman, Alice. The River King. 2001. (gr. 7-12). lib. bdg. 23.45 (978-0-613-35818-7(X)) Tandem Library Bks.
Hughes, Lynn Gordon. To Live a Truer Life: A Story of the Hopedale Community. Lindro, illus. 2003. 32p. (J). 20.00 (978-0-9725017-2-9(X)) Blackstone Editions.
Hurst, Carol Otis. In Plain Sight. 2002. 160p. (YA). (gr. 5-9). 15.00 (978-0-618-19699-9(4), Walter Lorraine) Houghton Mifflin Co. Trade & Reference Div.
—You Come to Yokum. Life, Kay, illus. 2005. 144p. (YA). (gr. 4-6). 15.00 (978-0-618-55122-4(0), Walter Lorraine) Houghton Mifflin Co. Trade & Reference Div.
Hurst, Carol Otis & Otis, Rebecca. A Killing in Plymouth Colony. 2003. 160p. (YA). (gr. 5-9). tchr. ed. 15.00 (978-0-618-27597-7(5), Walter Lorraine) Houghton Mifflin Co. Trade & Reference Div.
Kirkpatrick, Katherine. The Voyage of the Continental. 2002. (Illus.). 256p. (J). (gr. 7 up). tchr. ed. 16.95 (978-0-8234-1580-9(5)) Holiday Hse., Inc.
Koller, Jackie French. Someday. 2002. 224p. (J). (gr. 5 up). pap. 16.95 (978-0-439-29317-4(0), Orchard Bks.) Scholastic, Inc.
Langton, Jane. The Mysterious Circus. 2005. (Hall Family Chronicles). 224p. (J). lib. bdg. 16.89 (978-0-06-009487-4(7)) HarperCollins Pubs.
Lasky, Kathryn. A Journey to the New World: The Diary of Remember Patience Whipple, Mayflower, 1620. 2003. (Dear America Ser.). 176p. (J). 12.95 (978-0-439-55504-3(3)) Scholastic, Inc.
Lewis, Maggie. Morgy Coast to Coast. Chesworth, Michael, illus. 2005. 144p. (J). (gr. 3-5). 15.00 (978-0-618-44896-8(9)) Houghton Mifflin Co. Trade & Reference Div.
—Morgy Makes His Move. Chesworth, Michael, illus. 80p. (J). 2002. (gr. 1-4). pap. 4.95 (978-0-618-19680-7(3)); 1999. (gr. 4-6). tchr. ed. 15.00 (978-0-395-92284-2(4)) Houghton Mifflin Co. Trade & Reference Div.
—Morgy Makes His Move. 1999. (gr. 3-6). lib. bdg. 12.95 (978-0-613-60698-1(1)) Tandem Library Bks.
Literature Connections English: Ethan Frome. 2004. (gr. 6-12). (978-0-395-77548-6(5), 2-80117) McDougal Littell Inc.
Marshall, Peter, et al. Mercy Clifton: Pilgrim Girl. 2007. 208p. (J). pap. 9.99 (***978-0-8054-4395-0(9)***, B&H Bks.) B&H Publishing Grp.
Murphy, T. M. The Secrets of the Twisted Cross. 2002. (Belltown Mystery Ser.). (Illus.). 176p. (J). (978-1-880158-43-2(4)) Townsend, J.N. Publishing.
O'Neal, Deborah & Westengard, Angela. The Trouble with Henry: A Tale of Walden Pond. Schindler, S. D., illus. 2005. 40p. (J). (gr. k-3). 16.99 (978-0-7636-1828-5(4)) Candlewick Pr.
Oneil, Elizabeth. Alfred Visits Massachusetts. 2006. 24p. (J). pap. 12.00 (***978-0-9771836-7-8(X)***) Funny Bone Bks.
Otis, James. Mary of Plymouth. 1999. (Illus.). 160p. (YA). 10.00 (978-1-889128-60-3(0)) Mantle Ministries.
Owens, Tom. Flames of Freedom. Muchmore, Pat, illus. 2001. (Cover-to-Cover Bks.). 56p. (J). (gr. 1-4). lib. bdg. 16.95 (978-0-7807-9040-7(5)) Perfection Learning Corp.
Paratore, Coleen Murtagh. The Wedding Planner's Daughter. 2006. (Wedding Planner's Daughter Ser.). 208p. (J). reprint ed. pap. 5.99 (978-1-4169-1854-7(X), Aladdin) Simon & Schuster Children's Publishing.
Parker, Robert Andrew. Edenville Owls. 2008. 208p. (YA). (gr. 4-6). pap. 7.99 (***978-0-14-241161-2(2)***, Puffin) Penguin Group (USA) Inc.
Paterson, John & Paterson, Katherine. Blueberries for the Queen. Jeffers, Susan, illus. 2004. 32p. (J). (ps-3). lib. bdg. 18.89 (978-0-06-623943-9(5)) HarperCollins Pubs.
—Blueberries for the Queen. Jeffers, Susan, tr. Jeffers, Susan, illus. 2004. 32p. (J). (ps-3). 17.99 (978-0-06-623942-2(7)) HarperCollins Pubs.
Paterson, Katherine. Lyddie. 2003. (Espasa Juvenil Ser.: Vol. 18). (SPA., Illus.). (J). (gr. 9-12). pap. (978-84-239-9015-3(X), EC6561) Espasa Calpe, S.A. ESP. *Dist:* Lectorum Pubns., Inc.
—Lyddie. 192p. (J). 2005. (ps-7). pap. 3.99 (978-0-14-240438-6(1)); 2004. (gr. 5). pap. 6.99 (978-0-14-240254-2(0)) Penguin Group (USA) Inc. (Puffin).
Pfeffer, Susan Beth. Beth's Story. 2001. (Portraits of Little Women Ser.). (Illus.). (J). (978-0-606-21063-8(6)) Tandem Library Bks.
Rees, Douglas. Vampire High. 2005. 240p. (YA). (gr. 7 up). mass mkt. 5.99 (978-0-440-23834-8(X), Laurel Leaf) Random Hse. Children's Bks.
Reinhardt, Dana. A Brief Chapter in My Impossible Life. (gr. 7). 2007. 256p. (YA). pap. 8.99 (***978-0-375-84691-5(3)***); 2006. 240p. (J). 15.95 (978-0-385-74698-4(9)); 2006. 240p. (J). lib. bdg. 17.99 (978-0-385-90940-2(3)) Random Hse. Children's Bks. (Lamb, Wendy).
Rosenberg, Liz. Seventeen: A Novel in Prose Poems. 2002. 160p. (YA). (gr. 9 up). 16.95 (978-0-8126-4915-4(X)) Cricket Bks.
Rue, Nancy N. The Accused. 1998. (Christian Heritage Ser.). (Illus.). 224p. (J). (gr. 3-7). pap. 5.99 (978-1-56179-398-3(1)) Bethany Hse. Pubs.
Saunders, Joanne D. Secret at the Winthrop House. 2007. 192p. per. 12.99 (***978-1-59886-622-3(2)***) Tate Publishing & Enterprises, L.L.C.
Sleator, William. The Last Universe. (J). (gr. 7-11). 2006. 240p. pap. 6.95 (978-0-8109-9213-9(2)); 2005. 224p. 16.95 (978-0-8109-5858-6(9), Amulet Bks.) Abrams, Harry N., Inc.
Smith, Patricia Clark. Weetamoo, Heart of the Pocassets: Massachusetts, 1653. 2003. (Royal Diaries Ser.). (Illus.). 208p. (J). pap. 10.95 (978-0-439-12910-7(9)) Scholastic, Inc.
Sniegoski, Tom. Billy Hooten. Powell, Eric, illus. 2007. (Owlboy Ser.). 256p. (J). (gr. 4-7). lib. bdg. 9.99 (***978-0-385-90402-5(9)***, Yearling) Random Hse. Children's Bks.
—Billy Hooten: Owlboy. Powell, Eric, illus. 2007. (Owlboy Ser.). 256p. (J). (gr. 4-7). 5.99 (***978-0-440-42180-1(2)***, Yearling) Random Hse. Children's Bks.
Speare, Elizabeth George. The Witch of Blackbird Pond. 2002. (Illus.). (J). 14.47 (978-0-7587-0227-2(2)) Book Wholesalers, Inc.
—The Witch of Blackbird Pond. Moser, Barry, illus. 2001. (Illustrated American Classics Ser.). 224p. (YA). (gr. 7-9). tchr. ed. 22.00 (978-0-395-91367-3(5)) Houghton Mifflin Co. Trade & Reference Div.
—The Witch of Blackbird Pond. 2004. 223p. (J). (gr. 4-7). pap., tchr.'s planning gde. ed. 38.00 incl. audio (978-0-8072-0862-5(0), Listening Library) Random Hse. Audio Publishing Group.
Stanley, Diane. Thanksgiving on Plymouth Plantation. Berry, Holly, illus. 2004. (Time-Traveling Twins Ser.). 48p. (J). (gr. k-5). 15.99 (978-0-06-027069-8(1)); lib. bdg. 16.89 (978-0-06-027076-6(4)) HarperCollins Pubs. (Cotler, Joanna Books).
Terry, Wendy, illus. The Cape Cod Summer Home: A Family Adventure in the Town of Chatham. 2001. 40p. (YA). 10.00 (978-0-9676082-1-1(X)) Stage Harbor Pr.
Trimble, Marcia. Witchy's Turned-Around House. Cameron, Chad, illus. 1998. 32p. (J). (ps-5). 15.95 (978-1-891577-27-7(1)) Images Pr.
Voigt, Cynthia. The Callender Papers. Duranceau, Suzanne, illus. 2000. 272p. (J). (gr. 4-8). pap. 5.99 (978-0-689-83283-3(4), Aladdin) Simon & Schuster Children's Publishing.
—The Callender Papers. 2001. (J). (gr. 4-8). 21.75 (978-0-8446-7192-5(4)) Smith, Peter Pub., Inc.
—The Callender Papers. 2000. (gr. 5-8). lib. bdg. 14.15 (978-0-8085-5948-1(6)) Tandem Library Bks.
Wallace-Brodeur, Ruth. Blue Eyes Better. 2003. (Illus.). 112p. (J). (gr. 4-7). pap. 5.99 (978-0-14-250086-6(0), Puffin) Penguin Group (USA) Inc.
—Blue Eyes Better. 2003. (gr. 5-8). lib. bdg. 14.15 (978-0-613-67139-2(2)) Tandem Library Bks.
Werlin, Nancy. The Killer's Cousin. 2000. 240p. (YA). (gr. 9-12). mass mkt. 5.99 (978-0-440-22751-9(8), Laurel Leaf) Random Hse. Children's Bks.
—The Killer's Cousin. 2000. (978-0-606-17820-4(1)) Tandem Library Bks.
—The Killer's Cousin. l.t. ed. 1999. 277p. (YA). (gr. 9-12). 21.95 (978-0-7862-2188-2(7)) Thorndike Pr.
Wharton, Edith. Ethan Frome, Level 3. 2nd abr. ed. 2000. (Bookworms Ser.). (Illus.). 80p. 6.50 (978-0-19-423002-5(3)) Oxford Univ. Pr., Inc.
White, Ellen Emerson. The President's Daughter. 2008. (YA). pap. 8.99 (***978-0-312-37488-4(7)***) Feiwel & Friends.
Wiley, Melissa. Little House by Boston Bay. Andreasen, Dan, illus. 1999. (Little House Ser.). 208p. (J). (ps-3). 16.89 (978-0-06-028201-1(0)) HarperCollins Pubs.
—Little House by Boston Bay. 1999. (gr. 3-6). lib. bdg. 14.15 (978-0-613-15882-4(2)) Tandem Library Bks.
—On Tide Mill Lane, No. 2. Andreasen, Dan, illus. 2001. (Little House Ser.). 272p. (J). (gr. k-4). 16.95 (978-0-06-027013-1(6)); (gr. 3-7). 16.89 (978-0-06-027014-8(4)) HarperCollins Pubs.
Wittlinger, Ellen. Blind Faith. (YA). 2007. 304p. pap. 8.99 (***978-1-4169-4906-0(2)***, Simon Pulse); 2006. 288p. (gr. 7 up). 16.99 (978-1-4169-0273-7(2), Simon & Schuster Children's Publishing) Simon & Schuster Children's Publishing.
—Love & Lies: Marisol's Story. 2008. 256p. (YA). (***978-1-4169-1623-9(7)***, Simon & Schuster Children's Publishing) Simon & Schuster Children's Publishing.

MASSACHUSETTS—HISTORY

Allen, David. Early Maps of Greenfield, Massachusetts, 1717-1918. 2003. (Illus.). 64p. cd-rom 27.95 (978-0-911653-10-6(4)) Old Maps.
Apel, Melanie Ann. The Pilgrims. 2003. (Daily Life Ser.). (Illus.). 48p. (J). (gr. 3-5). (978-0-7377-0993-3(6), Kidhaven) Thomson Gale.
Arenstam, Peter, et al. Mayflower 1620: A New Look at a Pilgrim Voyage. 2007. (Illus.). 48p. (J). (gr. 3-7). 6.95 (***978-0-7922-6276-3(X)***, National Geographic Children's Bks.) National Geographic Society.
Armentrout, David & Armentrout, Patricia. The Mayflower Compact. 2005. (Documents that Shaped the Nation Ser.). (Illus.). 48p. (gr. 4-6). 20.95 (978-1-59515-229-9(6)) Rourke Publishing, LLC.
—El Pacto Del Mayflower. 2005. (SPA.). (J). (978-1-59515-648-8(8)) Rourke Publishing, LLC.
Brooks, Philip. The Mayflower Compact. 2004. (Illus.). 48p. (J). (gr. 4 up). lib. bdg. 22.60 (978-0-7565-0681-0(6)) Compass Point Bks.
Burgan, Michael. John Winthrop: First Governor of Massachusetts. 2006. (Signature Lives Ser.). (Illus.). 112p. (J). (gr. 5-7). 30.60 (978-0-7565-1591-1(2)) Compass Point Bks.
Clark, Judith Freeman & Allison, Robert J. Massachusetts from Colony to Commonwealth: An Illustrated History. 2002. (Illus.). 340p. 34.95 (978-1-892724-30-4(8)) American Historical Pr.
Clark, Mary. Biographical Sketches of the Fathers of New England. 2003. 180p. 89.00 (978-0-7950-4738-1(X)) New Library Press.Net.
Colonel Edward Howland Robinson Green & the World He Created at Round Hill. 2003. 39.95 (978-0-9743731-0-2(9), 2500) Bedell, Barbara F.
Cox, Clinton. Undying Glory: The Story of the Massachusetts 54th Regiment. 2007. 196p. (YA). (gr. 4-7). per. 15.95 (***978-0-595-45116-6(0)***, Backinprint.com) iUniverse, Inc.
Doherty, Craig A. & Doherty, Katherine M. Massachusetts, 13 vols. 2005. (Thirteen Colonies Ser.). (Illus.). 160p. (J). (gr. 4-9). 35.00 (978-0-8160-5407-7(X)) Facts On File, Inc.
Donnelly, Judy. The Pilgrims & Me. Cocca-Leffler, Maryann, illus. 2002. (Smart about History Ser.). 32p. (J). pap. 5.99 (978-0-448-42699-0(4), Grosset & Dunlap) Penguin Group (USA) Inc.
—Pilgrims & Me. 2002. (gr. k-3). lib. bdg. 14.15 (978-0-613-68374-6(9)) Tandem Library Bks.
Englar, Mary. The Pilgrims & the First Thanksgiving. McDonnell, Peter, illus. 2007. (Graphic Library). 32p. (J). (***978-0-7368-9656-6(2)***) Capstone Pr., Inc.
Erickson, Paul. Daily Life in the Pilgrim Colony 1636. 2001. (Illus.). 48p. (J). (gr. 4-6). tchr. ed. 20.00 (978-0-618-05846-4(X)); pap. 9.95 (978-0-395-98841-1(1)) Houghton Mifflin Co. Trade & Reference Div. (Clarion Bks.).
—Daily Life in the Pilgrim Colony 1636. 2001. (gr. 3-6). lib. bdg. 18.75 (978-0-613-35501-8(6)) Tandem Library Bks.
Fradin, Dennis B. The Mayflower Compact. 2006. (Turning Points in U. S. History Ser.). (Illus.). 48p. (J). lib. bdg. 29.93 (978-0-7614-2125-2(4), Benchmark Bks.) Cavendish, Marshall Corp.
Giblin, James. The Many Rides of Paul Revere. 2007. 96p. (J). pap. 17.99 (***978-0-439-57290-3(8)***, Scholastic Pr.) Scholastic, Inc.
Goodman, Susan E. Pilgrims of Plymouth. (J). 2001. (Illus.). 16p. (gr. 3-7). pap. 5.95 (978-0-7922-6675-4(7), National Geographic Children's Bks.); 1999. (978-0-7922-9424-5(6)) National Geographic Society.
The Greatest Place on Earth: A Children's Story, A History Lesson, A Scrapbook, A Lifetime Keepsake. 2006. (J). 18.95 (978-0-9777882-0-0(2), Light Works Publishing) I.M. Enterprises.
Griffis, William Elliot. Young People's History of the Pilgrims. 353p. reprint ed. 98.00 (978-0-7222-6679-3(0)) Library Reprints, Inc.
Harcourt School Publishers Staff. Concord Advanced Level. 3rd ed. 2002. (Trophies Reading Program Ser.). (Illus.). pap. 5.10 (978-0-15-323213-8(7)) Harcourt Schl. Pubs.
Harness, Cheryl. The Adventurous Life of Myles Standish & the Amazing-But-True Survival Story of the Plymouth Colony. Harness, Cheryl, illus. 2006. (Illus.). 144p. (J). (gr. 5-9). lib. bdg. 25.90 (978-0-7922-5919-0(X), National Geographic Children's Bks.) National Geographic Society.
—The Adventurous Life of Myles Standish & the Amazing-but-True Survival Story of the Plymouth Colony. Harness, Cheryl, illus. 2006. (Illus.). 144p. (J). (gr. 5-9). 16.95 (978-0-7922-5918-3(1), National Geographic Children's Bks.) National Geographic Society.
Hinman, Bonnie. The Massachusetts Bay Colony: The Puritans Arrive from England. 2006. (Building America Ser.). (Illus.). 48p. (J). (gr. 4-8). lib. bdg. 20.95 (978-1-58415-460-0(8)) Mitchell Lane Pubs., Inc.
Isaacs, Sally Senzell. Life in a New England Mill Town. 2003. (Picture the Past Ser.). (Illus.). 32p. (J). (gr. 2-4). lib. bdg. (978-1-58810-693-3(4)); pap. 6.95 (978-1-4034-0525-8(5)) Heinemann Library.
Kamma, Anne. If You Lived at the Time of Squanto. Johnson, Pamela Ford, illus. 2006. 63p. (J). pap. (***978-0-439-87628-5(1)***) Scholastic, Inc.
Kauffman, Dorothy. Two Villages: Two Hundred Years Apart. 2005. (Content Area Readers Ser.). 4.95 (978-0-19-430952-3(5)) Oxford Univ. Pr., Inc.
Knowlton, MaryLee & Riehecky, Janet. The Plymouth Colony. 2002. (Events That Shaped America Ser.). (Illus.). 32p. (J). (gr. 3 up). lib. bdg. 24.67 (978-0-8368-3224-2(8)) Stevens, Gareth Inc.
Landau, Elaine. Celebrate the First Thanksgiving with Elaine Landau. 2006. (Explore Colonial America with Elaine Landau Ser.). (Illus.). 48p. (J). lib. bdg. 23.93 (978-0-7660-2556-1(X), Enslow Elementary) Enslow Pubs., Inc.
—Sacco & Vanzetti. 2004. (Cornerstones of Freedom Ser.). (Illus.). 48p. (J). 26.00 (978-0-516-24237-8(7), Children's Pr.) Scholastic Library Publishing.
—Witness the Salem Witchcraft Trials with Elaine Landau. 2006. (Explore Colonial America with Elaine Landau Ser.). (Illus.). 48p. (J). lib. bdg. 23.93 (978-0-7660-2558-5(6), Enslow Elementary) Enslow Pubs., Inc.
Lassieur, Allison. The Voyage of the Mayflower. McDonnell, Peter, illus. 2006. (Graphic Library). 32p. (J). 25.26 (978-0-7368-4371-3(X)) Capstone Pr., Inc.
Lilly, Melinda. Pilgrims in America. 2002. (Rourke Discovery Library). (Illus.). 24p. (J). lib. bdg. 20.64 (978-1-58952-360-9(1)) Rourke Publishing, LLC.
Mackall, Dandi Daley. Off to Plymouth Rock. 2006. 26p. (J). bds. 9.99 (978-1-4003-0822-4(4)) Nelson, Thomas Inc.
Mara, Wil. Paul Revere. (Rookie Biographies Ser.). (J). 2005. (Illus.). 32p. (gr. 1-2). pap. 4.95 (978-0-516-25820-1(6)); 2004. 20.50 (978-0-516-21841-0(7)) Scholastic Library Publishing. (Children's Pr.).
Marsh, Carole. Massachusetts History Projects: 30 Cool, Activities, Crafts, Experiments & More for Kids to Do to Learn about Your State! 2003. (Massachusetts Experience Ser.). 32p. (gr. k-5). pap. 5.95 (978-0-635-01790-1(3), Marsh, Carole Bks.) Gallopade International.
—My First Pocket Guide Massachusetts. 2000. (Massachusetts Experience! Ser.). (Illus.). 96p. (J). (gr. 3-8). 12.95 (978-0-635-01309-5(6), 13096) Gallopade International.
Niz, Xavier. Paul Revere's Ride. Bascle, Brian, illus. 2005. (Graphic Library). 32p. (J). (gr. 3-7). lib. bdg. 25.26 (978-0-7368-4965-4(3)) Capstone Pr., Inc.
Oney, Yannick. First American Colonies. 2004. (World Discovery History Readers Ser.). (Illus.). 32p. (J). pap. (978-0-439-66555-1(8)) Scholastic, Inc.
Osborne, Mary Pope & Boyce, Natalie Pope. Pilgrims. Murdocca, Salvatore, illus. 2005. (Magic Tree House Research Guide Ser.: No. 13). 128p. (J). (gr. k-3). pap. 4.99 (978-0-375-83219-2(X), Random Hse. Bks. for Young Readers) Random Hse. Children's Bks.
—Pilgrims: A Nonfiction Companion to Thanksgiving on Thursday. Murdocca, Salvatore, illus. 2005. (Magic Tree House Research Guide Ser.: No. 13). 128p. (J). (gr. k-3). lib. bdg. 11.99 (978-0-375-93219-9(4), Random Hse. Bks. for Young Readers) Random Hse. Children's Bks.
Owens, L. L. Pilgrims in America. 2007. (Events in American History Ser.). 48p. (J). (gr. 4-6). lib. bdg. 29.93 (978-1-60044-122-6(X)) Rourke Publishing, LLC.
Philbrick, Nathaniel. The Mayflower & the Pilgrims' New World. 2008. 304p. (J). (gr. 4-6). 19.99 (***978-0-399-24795-8(5)***, Putnam Juvenile) Penguin Group (USA) Inc.
Quasha, Jennifer. Pilgrims & Native Americans: Hands-on Projects about Life in Early America. 2001. (Great Social Studies Projects Ser.). (Illus.). 24p. (J). (gr. 3). lib. bdg. 19.95 (978-0-8239-5700-2(4), PowerKids Pr.) Rosen Publishing Group, Inc., The.
Raatma, Lucia. The Minutemen. 2004. (We the People Ser.). (Illus.). 48p. (J). 22.60 (978-0-7565-0842-5(8)) Compass Point Bks.
Riehecky, Janet. The Plymouth Colony. 2002. (Landmark Events in American History Ser.). (Illus.). 48p. (J). (gr. 5 up). lib. bdg. 30.00 (978-0-8368-5340-7(7)); pap. 14.60 (978-0-8368-5354-4(7)) Stevens, Gareth Inc. (World Almanac Library).
Rooney, Thomas L. Tobey Boland & the Blackstone Canal. Donovan, Patte, illus. 2005. 30p. (J). (978-1-929039-30-2(1)) Ambassador Bks., Inc.
Sammarco, Anthony Mitchell & Buchanan, Paul G. Milton Architecture: Massachusetts. 2000. (Images of America Ser.). 128p. pap. 18.99 (978-0-7385-0496-4(3)) Arcadia Publishing.
Santella, Andrew. The First Thanksgiving. 2003. (Cornerstones of Freedom). (Illus.). 48p. (J). (gr. 4-6). 26.00 (978-0-516-24204-0(0), Children's Pr.) Scholastic Library Publishing.
Smolik, Jane. The Great Massachusetts Puzzle Book: Over 75 Puzzles about Life in the Bay State. rev. ed. 2006. (Illus.). 96p. (J). per. 11.95 (978-0-9664095-5-0(8)) MidRun Pr.
Steele, Christy & Graves, Kerry, eds. A Free Black Girl Before the Civil War: The Diary of Charlotte Forten, 1854. 1999. (Diaries, Letters & Memoirs Ser.). 32p. (J). (gr. 2-7). pap. 21.00 (978-0-516-21339-2(3), Children's Pr.) Scholastic Library Publishing.
Stille, Darlene R. Anne Hutchinson: Puritan Protester. 2006. (Signature Lives Ser.). (Illus.). 112p. (J). (gr. 5-7). 30.60 (978-0-7565-1577-5(7)) Compass Point Bks.
Sullivan, George E. Paul Revere. 2000. (J). 11.15 (978-0-606-19925-4(X)) Tandem Library Bks.
Thompson, Jim & Thompson, Carolyn. Cape Ann in Stereoviews. 2000. (Images of America Ser.). 128p. (gr. 5 up). pap. 18.99 (978-0-7385-0491-9(2)) Arcadia Publishing.
Tieck, Sarah. Paul Revere. 2007. (First Biographies Ser.). (Illus.). 32p. (J). (gr. k-3). lib. bdg. 22.78 (978-1-59679-787-1(8)) ABDO Publishing Co.
Tracy, Kathleen. The Plymouth Colony: The Pilgrims Settle in New England. 2006. (Building America Ser.). (Illus.). 48p. (J). (gr. 4-8). lib. bdg. 20.95 (978-1-58415-459-4(4)) Mitchell Lane Pubs., Inc.
Vierow, Wendy. The Assault on Fort Wagner: Black Union Soldiers Make a Stand in South Carolina Battle. 2004. (Headlines from History Ser.). (Illus.). 24p. (J). lib. bdg. 19.95 (978-0-8239-6223-5(7), PowerKids Pr.) Rosen Publishing Group, Inc., The.
Wade, Mary Dodson. Fun Facts & Games: Massachusetts. Roader, Virginia, illus. 2000. (Fun Facts & Games Ser.). 64p. (J). (gr. 1-5). pap. 5.95 (978-1-892920-47-8(6)) GHB Publishers, LLC.
Wagner, Heather Lehr. Paul Revere: Messenger for Freedom. 2005. (Leaders of the American Revolution Ser.). (Illus.). 116p. (J). (ps-8). lib. bdg. 30.00 (978-0-7910-8624-7(0), Chelsea Hse.) Facts On File, Inc.
Whitcraft, Melissa. The Mayflower Compact. 2003. (Cornerstones of Freedom). (Illus.). 48p. (J). (gr. 4-6). 26.00 (978-0-516-24203-3(2), Children's Pr.) Scholastic Library Publishing.
Whitehurst, Susan. The Pilgrims Before the Mayflower. 2002. (Library of the Pilgrims). (Illus.). 24p. (J). (gr. 3). lib. bdg. 19.95 (978-0-8239-5811-5(6), PowerKids Pr.) Rosen Publishing Group, Inc., The.
—A Plymouth Partnership: Pilgrims & Native Americans. 2002. (Library of the Pilgrims). (Illus.). 24p. (J). (gr. 3). lib. bdg. 19.95 (978-0-8239-5810-8(8), PowerKids Pr.) Rosen Publishing Group, Inc., The.
—William Bradford & Plymouth: A Colony Grows. 2002. (Library of the Pilgrims). (Illus.). 24p. (J), (gr. 3). lib. bdg. 19.95 (978-0-8239-5808-5(6), PowerKids Pr.) Rosen Publishing Group, Inc., The.

Wiener. The 13 Colonies Pack: Massachusetts, 6. 2004. (Illus.). 51.30 (978-1-4109-0368-6(0)) Harcourt Schl. Pubs.

Wiener, Roberta & Arnold, James R. Massachusetts. 2004. (Illus.). 64p. (J). 28.56 (978-0-7398-6881-2(0)) Harcourt Schl. Pubs.

—The 13 Colonies: Massachusetts. 2004. (Illus.). 64p. (J). 8.95 (978-1-4109-0305-1(2)) Harcourt Schl. Pubs.

Witteman, Barbara. Miles Standish: Colonial Leader. 2004. (Let Freedom Ring Ser.). (Illus.). 48p. (J). 17.95 (978-0-7368-2457-6(X) , Bridgestone Bks.) Capstone Pr., Inc.

Yero, Judith Lloyd. The Mayflower Compact. 2004. (National Geographic Reading Expeditions Ser.). (Illus.). 32p. (J). pap. (978-0-7922-4553-7(9)) National Geographic Society.

MASSACHUSETTS—HISTORY—COLONIAL PERIOD, CA. 1600-1775

Armentrout, David & Armentrout, Patricia. The Mayflower Compact. 2004. (Documents That Shaped the Nation Ser.). 48p. pap. 7.95 (978-1-59515-334-0(9)) Rourke Publishing, LLC.

Aronson, Marc. John Winthrop, Oliver Cromwell, & the Land of Promise. 2004. (Illus.). 224p. (J). (gr. 5-9). tchr. ed. 20.00 (978-0-618-18177-3(6) , Clarion Bks.) Houghton Mifflin Co. Trade & Reference Div.

Bowen, Gary. Stranded at Plimoth Plantation 1626. Bowen, Gary, illus. 2001. (Illus.). 81p. (J). (gr. 2-5). reprint ed. pap. 10.00 (978-0-7881-9835-9(1)) DIANE Publishing Co.

—Stranded at Plimoth Plantation 1626. Bowen, Gary, illus. 1998. (Trophy Chapter Bks.). (Illus.). 88p. (J). (gr. 3-7). pap. 12.95 (978-0-06-440719-9(5)) HarperCollins Pubs.

Burgan, Michael. Massachusetts: 1620-1776. 2005. (Voices from Colonial America Ser.). (Illus.). 112p. (J). (gr. 5-9). 32.90 (978-0-7922-6599-3(8) , National Geographic Children's Bks.) National Geographic Society.

—Massachusetts 1620-1776. 2005. (Voices from Colonial America Ser.). (Illus.). 112p. (J). (gr. 5-9). 21.95 (978-0-7922-6383-8(9) , National Geographic Children's Bks.) National Geographic Society.

Capstone Press, contrib. by. Anne Hutchinson. (Colonial America Biographies Ser.). 48p. (YA). pap. 7.95 (978-0-7368-4483-3(X)) Capstone Pr., Inc.

Connelly, Elizabeth Russell. John Winthrop. 2001. (gr. 5-8). lib. bdg. 17.60 (978-0-613-32729-9(2)) Tandem Library Bks.

Deady, Kathleen W. The Massachusetts Bay Colony. 2005. (Fact Finders Ser.). (Illus.). 32p. (J). (ps-7). lib. bdg. 22.60 (978-0-7368-2676-1(9)) Capstone Pr., Inc.

Decapua, Sarah. Massachusetts. 2002. (gr. k-3). lib. bdg. 14.10 (978-0-613-58715-0(4)) Tandem Library Bks.

Dell, Pamela. Plymouth Colony. 2004. (Let Freedom Ring Ser.). (Illus.). 48p. (J). 23.93 (978-0-7368-2463-7(4) , Bridgestone Bks.) Capstone Pr., Inc.

Doherty, Craig A. & Doherty, Katherine M. Massachusetts, 13 vols. 2005. (Thirteen Colonies Ser.). (Illus.). 160p. (J). (gr. 4-9). 35.00 (978-0-8160-5407-7(X)) Facts On File, Inc.

Edwards, Judith. The Plymouth Colony & the Pilgrim Adventure in American History. 2003. (In American History Ser.). (Illus.). 128p. (J). (gr. 5-12). lib. bdg. 26.60 (978-0-7660-1989-8(6)) Enslow Pubs., Inc.

Englar, Mary. The Pilgrims & the First Thanksgiving. 2007. (Graphic Library). (Illus.). 32p. (J). (978-0-7368-5492-4(4)) Capstone Pr., Inc.

Erickson, Paul. Daily Life in the Pilgrim Colony,1636. 2001. 16.75 (978-0-606-22581-6(1)) Tandem Library Bks.

Freedman, Jeri. A Primary Source History of the Colony of Massachusetts. 2005. (Primary Sources of the Thirteen Colonies & the Lost Colony Ser.). (Illus.). 64p. (J). (gr. 3-7). pap. 14.60 (978-1-4042-0671-7(X)); (YA). (gr. 5-8). lib. bdg. 29.25 (978-1-4042-0428-7(8) , Rosen Central) Rosen Publishing Group, Inc., The.

Goodman, Susan E. Pilgrims of Plymouth. 1999. (J). (978-0-7922-9429-0(7)) National Geographic Society.

Hirschfelder, Arlene B. Squanto1585-1622. 2004. (American Indian Biographies Ser.). (Illus.). 32p. (J). (gr. 3-4). lib. bdg. 23.93 (978-0-7368-2446-0(4) , Blue Earth Bks.) Capstone Pr., Inc.

Italia, Bob. The Massachusetts Colony. 2001. (Colonies Ser.). (Illus.). 32p. (J). (gr. k-6). lib. bdg. 22.78 (978-1-57765-584-8(2) , Checkerboard Library) ABDO Publishing Co.

Jackson, Garnet N. First Thanksgiving. 2000. (gr. k-3). lib. bdg. 11.80 (978-0-613-35508-7(3)) Tandem Library Bks.

Kiely Miller, Barbara. Anne Hutchinson. 2007. (J). pap. (***978-0-8368-8324-4(1)*** , Weekly Reader Early Learning Library) Stevens, Gareth Inc.

Koestler-Grack, Rachel A. The Pilgrims. 2005. (American Moments Ser.). (Illus.). 48p. (J). (gr. 4-8). lib. bdg. 25.65 (978-1-59197-937-1(4)) ABDO Publishing Co.

Lutz, Norma Jean. Cotton Mather: Author, Clergyman & Scholar. 2000. (gr. 5-8). lib. bdg. 17.60 (978-0-613-43314-3(9)) Tandem Library Bks.

Miller, Barbara Kiely. Anne Hutchinson. 2007. (Great Americans Ser.). 24p. (J). (gr. 2-4). lib. bdg. 19.93 (***978-0-8368-8317-6(9)*** , Weekly Reader Early Learning Library) Stevens, Gareth Inc.

Miller, Jake. The Colony of Massachusetts: A Primary Source History. 2006. (Primary Source Library of the Thirteen Colonies & the Lost Colony). (Illus.). 24p. (J). (gr. 3-5). lib. bdg. 21.25 (978-1-4042-3028-6(9) , PowerKids Pr.) Rosen Publishing Group, Inc., The.

Miller, Susan Martins. Miles Standish. 1999. (Colonial Leaders Ser.). (Illus.). 80p. (J). (gr. 3 up). pap. 27.50 (978-0-7910-5693-6(7) , Chelsea Hse.) Facts On File, Inc.

Moe, Barbara A. The Charter of the Massachusetts Bay Colony: A Primary Source Investigation of the 1629 Charter. 2005. (Great American Political Documents Ser.). (Illus.). 112p. (YA). (gr. 7-12). lib. bdg. 26.50 (978-0-8239-3801-8(8)) Rosen Publishing Group, Inc., The.

Pell, Ed. John Winthrop: Governor of the Massachusetts Bay Colony. 2004. (Let Freedom Ring Ser.). (Illus.). 48p. (J). 23.93 (978-0-7368-2455-2(3) , Bridgestone Bks.) Capstone Pr., Inc.

Plymouth Colony. (Colonial America Ser.). 48p. (YA). 7.95 (978-0-7368-4480-2(5)) Capstone Pr., Inc.

Price Hossell, Karen. The Boston Tea Party: Rebellion in the Colonies. 2003. (Point of Impact Ser.). (Illus.). 32p. (J). (gr. 5-7). lib. bdg. 25.64 (978-1-58810-906-4(2)); pap. (978-1-4034-0534-0(4)) Heinemann Library.

Raum, Elizabeth. Anne Hutchinson. 2004. (Illus.). 32p. (J). pap. 7.50 (978-1-4034-5966-4(5)); lib. bdg. (978-1-4034-5958-9(4)) Heinemann Library.

Walsh, Kieran. Anne Hutchinson. 2005. (Discover the Life of a Colonial American Ser.). (Illus.). 24p. (J). (gr. 2-5). 14.95 (978-1-59515-137-7(0)) Rourke Publishing, LLC.

Whitehurst, Susan. The Colony of Massachusetts. 2000. (Library of the Thirteen Colonies & the Lost Colony). (Illus.). 24p. (J). (gr. 3). lib. bdg. 19.95 (978-0-8239-5475-9(7) , PowerKids Pr.) Rosen Publishing Group, Inc., The.

MASSACHUSETTS—HISTORY—FICTION

Alger, Horatio. Do & Dare: Or, A Brave Boy's Fight for Fortune. 2006. 182p. pap. 11.99 (978-1-4264-0880-9(3)); 170p. pap. 14.99 (978-1-4264-0861-8(7)) BiblioBazaar.

—Do & Dare: Or, A Brave Boy's Fight for Fortune. 2006. pap. (***978-1-4065-0701-0(6)***) Dodo Pr.

—Do & Dare: Or, A Brave Boy's Fight for Fortune. unabr. ed. 2002. (Illus.). (J). pap. 17.95 (978-1-931927-90-1(1)) Polyglot Pr., Inc.

Anderson, M. T. The Astonishing Life of Octavian Nothing, Traitor to the Nation. 2006. (Pox Party Ser.: Vol. 1). (Illus.). 368p. (YA). (gr. 9). 17.99 (978-0-7636-2402-6(0)) Candlewick Pr.

—Astonishing Life of Octavian Nothing, Traitor to the Nation: The Pox Party. rev. l.t. ed. 2007. (Astonishing Life of Octavian Nothing Ser.). 500p. (YA). 23.95 (***978-0-7862-9552-4(X)***) Thorndike Pr.

Anderson, M. T. The Serpent Came to Gloucester. Ibatoulline, Bagram, illus. 2005. 40p. (J). (gr. 1-5). 16.99 (978-0-7636-2038-7(6)) Candlewick Pr.

Brodeur, Tom. Regina Silsby's Phantom Militia. 2005. (Illus.). 267p. (J). (ps-7). 7.49 (978-1-59166-385-0(7)) Jones, Bob Univ. Pr.

Cooney, Caroline B. The Ransom of Mercy Carter. 2002. (gr. 7-12). lib. bdg. 13.55 (978-0-613-60395-9(8)) Tandem Library Bks.

Duble, Kathleen Benner & Vojnar, Kamil. The Sacrifice. 2005. 224p. (J). (gr. 4-8). 16.99 (978-0-689-87650-9(5) , McElderry, Margaret K.) Simon & Schuster Children's Publishing.

Duey, Kathleen. American Diaries; Zellie Blake: Lowell, Massachusetts 1834. 2002. 133p. (J). (ps-7). lib. bdg. 11.64 (978-0-606-22099-6(2)) Tandem Library Bks.

Fleming, Candace. Big Cheese for the White House: The True Tale of a Tremendous Cheddar. Schindler, S. D., illus. 2004. 32p. (J). (ps-ps). lib. bdg. 14.15 (978-0-606-30286-9(7)) Tandem Library Bks.

Forbes, Esther. Johnny Tremain. McCurdy, Michael, illus. 1998. (Illustrated American Classics Ser.). 304p. (YA). (gr. 5-9). tchr. ed. 22.00 (978-0-395-90011-6(5)) Houghton Mifflin Co. Trade & Reference Div.

Gomes, Linda Nunes. Special Words: A Story about Multicultural Families & Their Pets. Levine, Lenora D., illus. 2007. (YA). per. 12.99 (***978-1-934400-02-9(5)***) Rock Village Publishing.

Grote, JoAnn A. Danger in the Harbor: Grain Riots Threaten Boston. 1999. (American Adventure Ser.: No. 6). (Illus.). 144p. (J). (gr. 3-7). lib. bdg. 15.95 (978-0-7910-5046-0(7) , Chelsea Hse.) Facts On File, Inc.

—Queen Anne's War. 1999. (American Adventure Ser.: No. 5). 144p. (J). (gr. 3-7). lib. bdg. 15.95 (978-0-7910-5045-3(9) , Chelsea Hse.) Facts On File, Inc.

Harlow, Joan Hiatt. Midnight Rider. 2006. 384p. (J). pap. 5.99 (978-0-689-87010-1(8) , Aladdin) Simon & Schuster Children's Publishing.

Harlow, Joan Hiatt & Minor, Wendell. Midnight Rider. 2005. (Illus.). 416p. (J). 15.95 (978-0-689-87009-5(4) , McElderry, Margaret K.) Simon & Schuster Children's Publishing.

Hausman, Gerald & Hausman, Loretta. A Mind with Wings: The Story of Henry David Thoreau. 2006. (Illus.). 160p. (YA). 15.95 (978-1-59030-228-6(1) , Trumpeter) Shambhala Pubns., Inc.

Hearn, Julie. The Minister's Daughter. 2006. 272p. (YA). pap. 7.99 (978-0-689-87691-2(2) , Simon Pulse) Simon & Schuster Children's Publishing.

Hearn, Julie & Frost, Michael. The Minister's Daughter. 2005. 272p. (YA). (gr. 7 up). 17.99 (978-0-689-87690-5(4) , Atheneum) Simon & Schuster Children's Publishing.

Hurst, Carol Otis. Terrible Storm. Schindler, S. D., illus. 2007. 32p. (J). (gr. k-3). 16.99 (978-0-06-009001-2(4)); lib. bdg. 17.89 (978-0-06-009002-9(2)) HarperCollins Pubs.

—Torchlight. 2006. 160p. (J). (gr. 4-6). 16.00 (978-0-618-27601-1(7)) Houghton Mifflin Co.

Jackson, Dave & Jackson, Neta. The Mayflower Secret: Governor William Bradford. Jackson, Julian & McLaughlin, Catherine R., illus. 1998. (Trailblazer Bks.: Vol. 26). 160p. (J). (gr. 3-7). pap. 6.99 (978-0-7642-2010-4(1)) Bethany Hse. Pubs.

Jacobs, Paul S. James Printer: A Novel of King Philip's War. 2000. 224p. (J). (gr. 4-7). 4.50 (978-0-590-97541-4(2)) Scholastic, Inc.

Kelley, Nancy J. The Whispering Rod: A Tale of Old Massachusetts. 2002. 160p. (J). lib. bdg. 17.95 (978-1-57249-248-6(1) , White Mane Kids) White Mane Publishing Co., Inc.

Kwasney, Michelle D. Baby Blue. rev. ed. 2004. (Illus.). 208p. (YA). 16.95 (978-0-8050-7050-7(8) , Holt, Henry & Co. Bks. For Young Readers) Holt, Henry & Co.

Lasky, Kathryn. A Journey to the New World: The Diary of Remember Patience Whipple, Mayflower, 1620. 1999. (Dear America Ser.). (J). 9.95 (978-0-439-15601-1(7)) Scholastic, Inc.

Lough, Loree. Dream Seekers: Roger William's Stand for Freedom. 1999. (American Adventure Ser.: No. 3). (Illus.). 144p. (J). (gr. 3-7). lib. bdg. 15.95 (978-0-7910-5043-9(2) , Chelsea Hse.) Facts On File, Inc.

Lutz, Norma Jean. Smallpox Strikes! Cotton Mather's Bold Experiment. 1999. (American Adventure Ser.: No. 7). (Illus.). 144p. (J). (gr. 3-7). lib. bdg. 15.95 (978-0-7910-5047-7(5) , Chelsea Hse.) Facts On File, Inc.

Meltzer, Milton. Tough Times. 2007. 176p. (J). (gr. 7 up). 16.00 (***978-0-618-87445-3(3)*** , Clarion Bks.) Houghton Mifflin Co. Trade & Reference Div.

Paterson, Katherine. Bread & Roses, Too. 2006. 288p. (J). (gr. 5-9). 16.00 (978-0-618-65479-6(8) , Clarion Bks.) Houghton Mifflin Co. Trade & Reference Div.

Peacock, Carol Antoinette. Pilgrim Cat. Ettlinger, Doris, illus. 2006. 32p. (J). (gr. 2-5). 6.95 (978-0-8075-6533-9(4)) Whitman, Albert & Co.

Rees, Celia. Witch Child. 272p. (YA). (gr. 7 up). 2002. pap. 8.99 (978-0-7636-1829-2(2)); 2001. (Illus.). 15.99 (978-0-7636-1421-8(1)) Candlewick Pr.

—Witch Child. unabr. ed. 2004. (Young Adult Cassette Librariestm Ser.). 304p. (J). (gr. 5-9). pap. 40.00 incl. audio (978-0-8072-1198-4(2) , S YA 343 SP, Listening Library) Random Hse. Audio Publishing Group.

—Witch Child. 2002. (gr. 7-12). lib. bdg. 16.45 (978-0-613-60740-7(6)) Tandem Library Bks.

—Witch Child. l.t. ed. 2002. 284p. (J). 22.95 (978-0-7862-3896-5(8)) Thomson Gale.

Rinaldi, Ann. Hang a Thousand Trees with Ribbons: The Story of Phillis Wheatley. 2005. (Great Episodes Ser.). 352p. (YA). pap. 6.95 (978-0-15-205393-2(X) , Gulliver Bks.) Harcourt Children's Bks.

—The Journal of Jasper Jonathan Pierce: A Pilgrim Boy, Plymouth, 1620. 2000. (My Name Is America Ser.). (Illus.). 160p. (J). (gr. 4-8). pap. 10.95 (978-0-590-51078-3(9)) Scholastic, Inc.

Roy, Ron. Mayflower Treasure Hunt. Gurney, John Steven, illus. 2nd ed. 2007. (A to Z Mysteries Ser.: No. 28). 128p. (J). (gr. 1-4). pap. 4.99 (978-0-375-83937-5(2)); lib. bdg. 11.99 (978-0-375-93937-2(7)) Random Hse. Children's Bks. (Random Hse. Bks. for Young Readers).

Rue, Nancy N. Samaritan. 1998. (gr. 3-6). lib. bdg. 14.15 (978-0-613-88494-5(9)) Tandem Library Bks.

Sheely, Robert. In the Hands of the Enemy. Killcoyne, Hope L., ed. Martin, John F., illus. 2003. (Adventures in America Ser.: Vol. 8). 75p. (J). 14.95 (978-1-893110-31-1(1)) Silver Moon Pr.

Smith, Mary P. Boy Captive of Old Deerfield. (Illus.). (J). (gr. 5-6). reprint ed. lib. bdg. 22.95 (978-0-89190-961-3(3) , Rivercity Pr.) Amereon LTD.

Stites, Clara. Naming the Stones. Davis, Cindy, illus. 2002. 46p. (J). (978-0-932027-72-6(5)) Spinner Pubns., Inc.

Strohmeier, Lenice. Mingo. Farnsworth, Bill, illus. 2003. 32p. (J). 16.95 (978-0-7614-5111-2(0)) Cavendish, Marshall Corp.

Thomas, Carroll. Ring Out Wild Bells: A Matty Trescott Novel. 2001. (Illus.). viii, 169p. (J). 9.95 (978-1-57525-291-9(0)) Smith and Kraus Publishers, Incorporated.

Thomas, Carroll, creator. Under the Open Sky: A Matty Trescott Novel. 2005. (Illus.). 184p. (J). per. 12.95 (978-0-9762091-2-6(8)) Antrim Hse.

Vernon, Louise A. Peter & the Pilgrims. Eitzen, Allan, illus. 2nd ed. 2002. 128p. (YA). (gr. 4-9). 7.99 (978-0-8361-9226-1(5)) Herald Pr.

Warburton, Carol. Edge of Night: A Novel. 2004. (Illus.). 278p. pap. 14.95 (978-1-59156-013-5(6)) Covenant Communications, Inc.

Waters, Kate. On the Mayflower: Voyage of the Ship's Apprentice & a Passenger Girl. 1998. (J). 5.99 (978-0-590-67408-9(0)) Scholastic, Inc.

Whelan, Gloria. Fruitlands: Louisa May Alcott Made Perfect. 2002. 128p. (J). (gr. 4-7). 15.99 (978-0-06-623815-9(3)) HarperCollins Pubs.

Who's That Stepping on Plymouth Rock? 2004. (J). 24.95 incl. audio (978-1-56008-219-4(4)) Weston Woods Studios, Inc.

Wiley, Melissa. Little House by Boston Bay. 2007. (Little House Ser.). 160p. (J). pap. 5.99 (***978-0-06-114828-6(8)*** , Harper Trophy) HarperCollins Pubs.

—Little House by Boston Bay. Andreasen, Dan, illus. 1999. (Little House Ser.). 195p. lib. bdg. 13.04 (978-0-606-16684-3(X)) Tandem Library Bks.

—On Tide Mill Lane. 2007. (Little House Ser.). 176p. (J). pap. 5.99 (***978-0-06-114829-3(6)*** , Harper Trophy) HarperCollins Pubs.

Wiley, Melissa. The Road from Roxbury. 2002. (Little House Ser.). (Illus.). 256p. (J). 16.99 (978-0-06-027019-3(5)); 18.89 (978-0-06-027020-9(9)) HarperCollins Pubs.

MASTODON

Goecke, Michael P. American Mastodon. 2004. (Prehistoric Animals Set II Ser.). (Illus.). 24p. (J). (gr. k-4). lib. bdg. 21.35 (978-1-57765-973-0(2)) ABDO Publishing Co.

Lindeen, Carol. Mastodonte Americano: American Mastodon. 2007. (ENG & SPA.). (J). (978-0-7368-7634-6(0)) Capstone Pr., Inc.

Lindeen, Carol K. American Mastodon. 2006. (Pebble Plus—Dinosaurs & Prehistoric Animals Ser.). (Illus.). 24p. (J). (978-0-7368-4255-6(1)) Capstone Pr., Inc.

Morrison, Taylor. Mastodon Mystery. 2006. (Illus.). 32p. (J). (gr. k-3). pap. 6.95 (978-0-618-77130-1(1)) Houghton Mifflin Co.

MATERIA MEDICA

see also Poisons

Monroe, Judy. Herbal Drug Dangers. (Drug Dangers Ser.). (Illus.). 64p. (YA). (gr. 4-10). 2001. pap. 13.26 (978-0-7660-1964-5(0)); 2000. lib. bdg. 27.93 (978-0-7660-1319-3(7)) Enslow Pubs., Inc.

MATERIALS

Bailey, Jacqui. How Do We Use Materials? 2006. (Investigating Science Ser.). (Illus.). 30p. (J). (978-1-58340-926-8(2)) Smart Apple Media.

Ballard, Carol. Grouping Materials. 2003. (Science Answers Ser.). (Illus.). 32p. (J). 7.50 (978-1-4034-3549-1(9)); lib. bdg. 24.22 (978-1-4034-0952-2(8)) Heinemann Library.

Bentley, Joyce. Rough. 2006. (Things Around Us Ser.). (J). (978-1-59389-276-0(4)) Chrysalis Education.

—Smooth. 2006. (Things Around Us Ser.). (J). (978-1-59389-277-7(2)) Chrysalis Education.

Brill, Marlene Targ. Cement Mixers. 2007. (Pull Ahead Books). (Illus.). 32p. (J). 22.60 (978-0-8225-6011-1(9) , Lerner Pubns.) Lerner Publishing Group.

Cosway, Ted, et al. Design & Make It! Resistant Materials Technology. 1998. (Illus.). 144p. pap. 30.00 (978-0-7487-2470-3(2)) State Mutual Bk. & Periodical Service, Ltd.

Gifford, Clive. Materials: Liquids, Solids, Gases, Properties & Their Uses. 2005. (Kingfisher Young Knowledge Ser.). (Illus.). 48p. (J). (gr. k-3). 9.95 (978-0-7534-5867-9(5) , Kingfisher) Houghton Mifflin Co. Trade & Reference Div.

Glover, David. Using Materials. 2001. (Experiments in Science Ser.). (Illus.). (J). (978-0-7894-7467-4(0)) Dorling Kindersley Publishing, Inc.

Godwin, Sam. All Kinds of Everything. 2002. (Little Bees Ser.). (Illus.). 31p. (J). lib. bdg. 24.25 (978-1-58340-251-1(9)) Smart Apple Media.

Hewitt, Sally. Sleep on a Bed of Bubbles: (Materials) 2002. (Why Can't I Ser.). (Illus.). 32p. (J). lib. bdg. 24.25 (978-1-930643-68-0(3)) Chrysalis Education.

—Sorting Materials: Tough Toys, Soft Toys. 2005. (Science Starters Ser.). (Illus.). 32p. (J). (gr. 1-4). lib. bdg. 27.10 (978-1-59604-014-4(9)) Stargazer Bks.

Huggins-Cooper, Lynn. Materials. McNicholas, Shelagh & Burroughs, Dave, trs. McNicholas, Shelagh & Burroughs, Dave, illus. 2004. (J). lib. bdg. (978-1-58340-448-5(1)) Smart Apple Media.

Investigating Earth Systems Materials & Minerals. 2002. stu. ed., per. (978-1-58591-075-5(9)); stu. ed., bds. (978-1-58591-105-9(4)) It's About Time, Herff Jones Education Diiv.

Issues, Evidence & You - Water Mega Module Complete Materials Package. 2003. (Illus.). tchr. ed., ring bd. (978-1-887725-42-2(3)); (YA). tchr. ed., stu. ed., per. (978-1-887725-60-6(1)) Lab-Aids, Inc.

Issues, Evidence & You Complete Materials Package. 2003. (Illus.). (YA). tchr. ed., ring bd. (978-1-887725-71-2(7)) Lab-Aids, Inc.

Issues, Evidence & You Complete Materials Package: Includes Teacher's Guide & Student Books. 2003. (Illus.). (YA). (978-1-887725-72-9(5)) Lab-Aids, Inc.

Kassinger, Ruth. Material World, 5 vols. 2004. (Illus.). (YA). (gr. 6-8). (978-0-7613-3729-4(6) , Twenty-First Century Bks.) Lerner Publishing Group.

Kerrod, Robin. New Materials. 2003. (21st Century Science Ser.). 48p. (J). lib. bdg. 27.10 (978-1-58340-353-2(1)) Smart Apple Media.

Knapp, Brian J. Materials Science, 9 vols. 2003. (Illus.). 648p. (J). 309.00 (978-0-7172-5697-6(9) , Grolier) Scholastic Library Publishing.

Larousse Mexico Staff, ed. Materiales y Materia. 2005. (40 Fantasticos Experimentos Ser.). (SPA.). 40p. (gr. 3-5). pap. 5.95 (978-970-22-0865-5(3)) Larousse, Ediciones, S. A. de C. V. MEX. *Dist:* Houghton Mifflin Co. Trade & Reference Div.

Lauw, Darlene. Materials. 2003. (gr. 3-6). lib. bdg. 16.40 (978-0-613-52880-1(8)) Tandem Library Bks.

Lauw, Darlene & Puay, Lim Cheng. Materials. 2002. (Science Alive! Ser.). (Illus.). 32p. (J). (gr. 4-5). pap. (978-0-7787-0610-6(9)); lib. bdg. (978-0-7787-0564-2(1)) Crabtree Publishing Co.

Llewellyn, Claire. Materials. 2005. (Illus.). 24p. (J). (gr. 1-4). lib. bdg. (978-1-84234-337-1(8) , Cherrytree Books) Evans Publishing Group.

Lunis, Natalie. Squishy Sponges. 2008. (J). lib. bdg. 21.28 (***978-1-59716-512-9(3)***) Bearport Publishing Co., Inc.

Madgwick, Wendy. Super Materials. 1999. (Science Starters Ser.). (Illus.). 32p. (J). (gr. k-4). 22.83 (978-0-8172-5555-8(9)) Raintree.

—Super Materials. 1999. (Science Starters Ser.). (Illus.). 32p. (gr. k-4). pap. 7.95 (978-0-8172-5881-8(7)) Steck-Vaughn.

Mason, Adrienne. Touch It! Materials, Matter & You. Davila, Claudia, illus. 2005. (Primary Physical Science Ser.). 32p. (J). (978-1-55337-761-0(3)) Kids Can Pr., Ltd.

—Touch It! Materials, Matter & You. Davila, Claudia, illus. 2005. (Primary Physical Science Ser.). 32p. (J). (ps-ps). (978-1-55337-760-3(5)) Kids Can Pr., Ltd.

Materials. 2004. (Illus.). lib. bdg. 7.95 (978-0-8225-4789-1(9)) Lerner Publishing Group.

Materials & Their Uses, 6 vols., Pack. (Discovery World Ser.). 24p. (gr. 1-2). 33.00 (978-0-7635-8479-5(7)) Rigby Education.

McGraw-Hill Staff. Glencoe Science: Earth's Materials & Processes. 2nd ed. 2004. stu. ed. 20.64 (978-0-07-861749-2(9) , 9780078617492) Glencoe/McGraw-Hill.

Newson, Lesley & Wadsworth, Pamela. Defnyddiau. 2005. (WEL., Illus.). 24p. pap. (978-1-85596-235-4(7)) Dref Wen.

—Rhagor Am Ddefnyddiau. 2005. (WEL., Illus.). 24p. pap. (978-1-85596-236-1(5)) Dref Wen.

Newton, David E. Chemistry of New Materials. 2007. (New Chemistry Ser.). 224p. (gr. 6-12). 35.00 (978-0-8160-5278-3(6)) Facts On File, Inc.

Ottenheimer-Maquet, L. How Things Are Made. 1998. Orig. Title: What Are Things Made Of?. (Illus.). 75p. (J). (gr. 2-9). lib. bdg. 23.95 (978-0-88682-955-1(0) , Creative Education) Creative Co., The.

Oxlade, Chris. Changing Materials. 2007. (J). 32p. pap. ***978-0-7787-3648-6(2)**); (***978-0-7787-3638-7(5)**) Crabtree Publishing Co.

—Joining Materials. 2007. 32p. pap. (***978-0-7787-3649-3(0)**) Crabtree Publishing Co.

—Materials, Materials, Materials, 15 bks. (J). (gr. k-2). Set. 2003. 32p. lib. bdg. 234.96 (978-1-4034-0702-3(9)); Set 2. 2002. lib. bdg. 128.16 (978-1-58810-469-4(9)) Heinemann Library.

—Shaping Materials. 2007. 32p. pap. (***978-0-7787-3651-6(2)**) Crabtree Publishing Co.

—Using Materials, 7 vols., Set 2. 2004. (Illus.). 179.90 (978-1-4109-0608-3(6)) Raintree.

—Using Materials Set 1, 8 vols. 2004. (Illus.). pap. 54.00 (978-1-4109-0999-2(9)) Raintree.

—Using Materials Series, 6 bks., Set 2. 2004. (Illus.). (J). pap. 40.50 (978-1-4109-0899-5(2)) Raintree.

Pipe, Jim. Changing Materials: Fire & Ice. 2005. (Science Starters Ser.). (Illus.). 32p. (J). (gr. 1-4). lib. bdg. 27.10 (978-1-59604-023-6(8)) Stargazer Bks.

Raintree Steck-Vaughn Staff. Super Materials. 2000. (Science Starters Ser.). (J). (gr. k-4). lib. bdg. 25.70 (978-0-8172-5330-1(0)) Raintree.

Rigby Education Staff. Discovery World Red Materials. (Discovery World Ser.). 12p. (gr. 1-2). 31.00 (978-0-7635-2706-8(8)) Rigby Education.

Riley, Peter D. Materials. Moller, Ray, photos by. 2002. (Everyday Science Ser.). (Illus.). 32p. (J). (gr. 1 up). lib. bdg. 23.33 (978-0-8368-3251-8(5)) Stevens, Gareth Inc.

—Materials. 1998. (Cycles in Science Ser.). (Illus.). 32p. (J). (gr. 4-7). lib. bdg. (978-1-57572-619-9(X)) Heinemann Library.

—Materials & Processes. 1999. (Straightforward Science Ser.). (Illus.). 32p. (J). (gr. 3-5). pap. 6.95 (978-0-531-15369-7(X) , Watts, Franklin) Scholastic Library Publishing.

Rivera, Sheila. How Does It Feel? 2004. (First Step Nonfiction Ser.). (J). pap. (978-0-8225-5405-9(4)); lib. bdg. (978-0-8225-2863-0(0)) Lerner Publishing Group. (Lerner Pubns.).

Royston, Angela. Materials. 2002. (My World of Science Ser.). (Illus.). 32p. (J). (gr. k-2). pap. 6.95 (978-1-4034-0043-7(1) , 91487) Heinemann Library.

—Natural & Man-Made. 2003. (Illus.). 32p. pap. 6.50 (978-1-4034-3169-1(8)); (J). lib. bdg. 22.79 (978-1-4034-0856-3(4)) Heinemann Library.

Smith, A. Materials. 2004. (Internet-Linked Library of Science). 64p. (J). pap. 9.95 (978-0-7945-0085-6(4) , Usborne) EDC Publishing.

Snedden, Robert. Material World: Adventures in Material Science, 4 bks., Set. 2002. (Illus.). (YA). (gr. 6-8). lib. bdg. 96.88 (978-1-58810-013-9(8)) Heinemann Library.

—Materials Technology. 2002. (Material World Ser.). (Illus.). 32p. (YA). (gr. 6-8). lib. bdg. 24.22 (978-1-58810-071-9(5)) Heinemann Library.

Twist, Clint. Materials. 2005. (Check It Out! Ser.). (Illus.). 24p. (J). (gr. 3-7). lib. bdg. 19.96 (978-1-59716-059-9(8)) Bearport Publishing Co., Inc.

Using Materials Series, 14 vols., Set. 2004. (Using Materials Ser.). (Illus.). pap. 94.50 (978-1-4109-1395-1(3)) Raintree.

Wadsworth, Pamela. Golwg Gyntaf Ar Ddefnyddiau. 2005. (WEL., Illus.). 24p. pap. (978-1-85596-251-4(9)) Dref Wen.

Whyman, Kathryn. Structures & Materials. 2004. lib. bdg. (978-1-932799-26-2(5)) Stargazer Bks.

Wood & Other Materials: Individual Title Six-Packs. (Discovery World Ser.). 16p. (gr. 1-2). 28.00 (978-0-7635-8460-3(6)) Rigby Education.

MATERNITY

see Mothers

MATHEMATICAL DRAWING

see Geometrical Drawing; Mechanical Drawing

MATHEMATICAL RECREATIONS

Action Packed Math Games. 2003. (Basic Skills Ser.). 48p. (J). (gr. 3-5). pap. 6.99 (978-0-7424-1786-1(7) , IFG99020) School Specialty Publishing.

Activity Guide Feast of Fracts. 2004. 40p. (J). (978-1-59242-147-3(4)) Delta Education, LLC.

Activity Guide Fraction Burger. 2004. 92p. (J). (978-1-59242-146-6(6)) Delta Education, LLC.

Addition Songs. 2001. (Illus.). pap., tchr. ed., wbk. ed. 12.95 incl. audio compact disk Audio Memory Publishing.

Allen, Robert & Gale, Harold. Mensa Number Puzzles. 2002. (Mensa Word Games for Kids Ser.). (Illus.). 224p. pap. 7.95 (978-1-85868-309-6(2)) Carlton Bks., Ltd. GBR. *Dist:* Ingram Pub. Services, Simon & Schuster, Inc.

American Education Publishing Staff. Arthur's Number Match. 2001. (Illus.). 36p. 2.49 (978-1-56189-517-5(2) , 31154, American Education Publishing) School Specialty Publishing.

Anno, Mitsumasa. Anno's Magic Seeds, 1 vol. 1999. (Illus.). 40p. (J). (gr. k-4). pap. 7.99 (978-0-698-11618-4(6) , Putnam Juvenile) Penguin Group (USA) Inc.

—Anno's Magic Seeds. 1999. (J). 14.79 (978-0-606-16798-7(6)); lib. bdg. 16.45 (978-0-613-18296-6(0)) Tandem Library Bks.

Aronson, Judy. 25 Super Fun Math Spinner Games: Easy-to-Assemble, Fun-to-Play Games to Develop Mathematical Thinking. 1998. 96p. pap. 12.95 (978-0-590-34138-7(3) , Teaching Resources) Scholastic, Inc.

Babsky, Irene & Babb, Joanna. Playing with Numbers. 2003. (Illus.). 64p. 14.99 (978-0-7548-1054-4(2) , Lorenz Bks.) Anness Publishing GBR. *Dist:* National Bk. Network.

Baicker, Karen. Origami Math: Grades 2-3. 2004. (Origami Math Ser.). 48p. pap. 10.99 (978-0-439-53991-3(9) , Teaching Resources) Scholastic, Inc.

—Origami Math: Grades 4-6. 2004. (Origami Math Ser.). 48p. pap. 10.99 (978-0-439-53992-0(7) , Teaching Resources) Scholastic, Inc.

Bauer, Karen, et al. Instant Math Centers: Hands-On, Independent Math Activities. Simon, Ruth B., ed. Dunne, Kathleen, illus. 2000. 128p. (gr. k-1). pap., tchr. ed. 13.99 (978-1-57471-689-4(1) , 2597) Creative Teaching Pr., Inc.

Big Book of English & Math. 2003. (Bumper Gold Stars Ser.). (Illus.). 240p. (J). 9.98 (978-1-4054-1719-8(6)); 9.98 (978-1-4054-1720-4(X)) Parragon, Inc.

Blakely, April. Math Brainteasers. 2nd ed. 2005. 90p. pap. (978-1-59647-036-1(4)) Good Year Bks.

Blum, Raymond. Mathamazing. Sinclair, Jeff, illus. 2002. 128p. (gr. 3-7). pap. 6.95 (978-1-4027-0026-2(1)) Sterling Publishing Co., Inc.

—Mathamusements. Date not set. (J). 5.95 (978-0-8069-3190-6(6)) Sterling Publishing Co., Inc.

—Mathemania. Sinclair, Jeff, illus. 2002. 96p. (gr. 3-7). pap. 6.95 (978-1-4027-0125-2(X)) Sterling Publishing Co., Inc.

Blum, Raymond, et al. Giant Book of Science Fun/Giant Book of Math Fun: Flip Book. Sterling Publishing Company Staff, ed. (Illus.). 512p. pap. 9.98 (978-1-4027-0469-7(0)) Sterling Publishing Co., Inc.

Bodach, Vijaya. Pictographs. 2008. (J). (***978-1-4296-0041-5(1)**) Capstone Pr., Inc.

Bortz, Trudy & Rappaport, Josh. Card Game Roundup: Rompin' Fun Math Games for Little Buckaroos. 2002. (Card Game Roundup Ser.). 96p. (gr. k-2). 12.95 (978-0-9659113-9-9(X)) Singing Turtle Pr.

Brian, Sarah J. Funtastic Math: Algebra. 1998. pap. 9.95 (978-0-590-37369-2(2)) Scholastic, Inc.

—Funtastic Math! Problem Solving & Logic. 1998. (Funtastic Math Ser.). 64p. (J). pap. 9.95 (978-0-590-37368-5(4)) Scholastic, Inc.

Brighter Vision Publishing Staff. Bible Story Math 1. 1998. (J). (ps). pap. 2.25 (978-1-55254-027-5(8)) Brighter Vision Pubns.

—Bible Story Math 2. 1998. (J). (ps). pap. 2.25 (978-1-55254-028-2(6)) Brighter Vision Pubns.

—Bible Story Math 3. 1998. (J). (ps). pap. 2.25 (978-1-55254-029-9(4)) Brighter Vision Pubns.

Bruno, Janet, et al. Instant Math Centers: Hands-On, Independent Math Activities. Simon, Ruth B., ed. Dunne, Kathleen, illus. 2000. 128p. (gr. 2-3). pap., tchr. ed. 13.99 (978-1-57471-690-0(5) , 2598) Creative Teaching Pr., Inc.

Bulloch, Ivan. Fun with Math. 2004. (Action Math Ser.). (SPA., Illus.). 128p. (ps-3). 24.95 (978-1-58728-052-8(3) , Two Can Publishing) T&N Children's Publishing.

—Juegos para Aprender Matematicas Jugando. 2000. (Matematicas en Accion Ser.).Tr. of Games to Learn Math. (Illus.). (J). 12.75 (978-0-606-20747-8(3)) Tandem Library Bks.

Bulloch, Ivan & James, Diane. Let's Make & Do. 2004. (Let's Ser.). (Illus.). 96p. (J). (ps-1). 24.95 (978-1-58728-386-4(7) , Two Can Publishing) T&N Children's Publishing.

Burstein, John. Math Monsters, 14 bks. Destiny Images Staff, illus. Incl. Calculating Area : Space Rocket! lib. bdg. 19.33 (978-0-8368-3804-6(1)); Collecting Data : Pick a Pancake. lib. bdg. 19.33 (978-0-8368-3805-3(X)); Counting : Follow That Fish! lib. bdg. 19.33 (978-0-8368-3806-0(8)); Doubling : Circus Stars. lib. bdg. 19.33 (978-0-8368-3807-7(6)); Estimating : How Many Gollywomples? lib. bdg. 19.33 (978-0-8368-3808-4(4)); Geometry : Looking Down on Monster Town. lib. bdg. 19.33 (978-0-8368-3809-1(2)); Keeping Track of Time : Go Fly a Kite! lib. bdg. 19.33 (978-0-8368-3810-7(6)); Making Maps : Where's the Party? lib. bdg. 19.33 (978-0-8368-3811-4(4)); Making Tens : Groups of Gollywomples. lib. bdg. 19.33 (978-0-8368-3812-1(2)); Measuring : The Perfect Playhouse. lib. bdg. 19.33 (978-0-8368-3813-8(0)); Number Conservation : Planting Monster Melons. lib. bdg. 19.33 (978-0-8368-3814-5(9)); Number Lines : How Far to the Car? lib. bdg. 19.33 (978-0-8368-3815-2(7)); Patterns : What's on the Wall? lib. bdg. 19.33 (978-0-8368-3816-9(5)); Using Computers : Machine with a Mouse. lib. bdg. 19.33 (978-0-8368-3817-6(3)); 24p. (YA). (gr. 1 up). (Weekly Reader Early Learning Library). (Illus.). 2003. Set lib. bdg. 270.62 (978-0-8368-3803-9(3) , Weekly Reader Early Learning Library) Stevens, Gareth Inc.

—Math Monsters, 14 bks. Incl. Calculating Area : Space Rocket! pap. 7.93 (978-0-8368-3819-0(X)); Collecting Data : Pick a Pancake. pap. 7.93 (978-0-8368-3820-6(3)); Counting : Follow That Fish! pap. 7.93 (978-0-8368-3821-3(1)); Doubling : Circus Stars. pap. 7.93 (978-0-8368-3822-0(X)); Estimating : Guess How Many Gollywomples. pap. 7.93 (978-0-8368-3823-7(8)); Geometry : Looking Down on Monster Town. pap. 7.93 (978-0-8368-3824-4(6)); Keeping Track of Time : Go Fly a Kite! pap. 7.93 (978-0-8368-3825-1(4)); Making Maps : Where's the Party? pap. 7.93 (978-0-8368-3826-8(2)); Making Tens : Groups of Gollywomples. pap. 7.93 (978-0-8368-3827-5(0)); Measuring : The Perfect Playhouse. pap. 7.93 (978-0-8368-3828-2(9)); Number Conservation : Planting Monster Melons. pap. 7.93 (978-0-8368-3829-9(7)); Number Lines : How Far to the Car? pap. 7.93 (978-0-8368-3830-5(0)); Patterns : What's on the Wall? pap. 7.93 (978-0-8368-3831-2(9)); Using Computers : Machine with a Mouse. pap. 7.93 (978-0-8368-3832-9(7)); 24p. (J). (gr. 1 up). 2003. (Illus.). 2003. pap. (978-0-8368-3818-3(1) , Weekly Reader Early Learning Library) Stevens, Gareth Inc.

Cheney, Martha C. Math Puzzles & Games. 1998. (Gifted & Talented Ser.). (Illus.). 64p. (J). (gr. 1-3). pap., wbk. ed. 4.95 (978-1-56565-835-6(3) , 08353W) Lowell Hse. Juvenile.

Child's Play Staff. Fruit Salad Game: Compare & Count, Match & Measure. 1998. (J). pap. 14.99 (978-0-85953-019-4(1)) Child's Play International Ltd. GBR. *Dist:* Child's Play-International.

Chronicle Books Staff, creator. 75 Number Puzzles. 2005. (Illus.). 75p. 13.95 (978-0-8118-5199-2(0)); (gr. 2-6). 9.95 (978-0-8118-5190-9(7)) Chronicle Bks. LLC.

Clarke, Jacqueline. Hands-On Math Around the Year. 2000. (Illus.). 11p. (J). pap. 14.95 (978-0-590-96725-9(8)) Scholastic, Inc.

Clemens, Meg, et al. The Everything Kids' Math Puzzles: Brain Teasers, Games, & Activities for Hours of Fun. 2003. (Everything Ser.). (Illus.). 144p. (J). 6.95 (978-1-58062-773-3(0)) Adams Media Corp.

Clemson, David, et al. Times Tables! Multiplication Made Fun. 1998. (Illus.). 32p. (J). (gr. 1-4). 8.99 (978-0-7894-0472-5(9)) Dorling Kindersley Publishing, Inc.

Counting Money. 2004. (Illus.). (J). pap. 3.95 (978-0-8225-1289-9(0)) Lerner Publishing Group.

Counting Money. 2003. (Illus.). 48p. (J). (gr. k-2). suppl. ed. 8.99 (978-1-56451-371-7(8) , ID7522) School Specialty Publishing.

Creed, Margaret. Brain-Boosting Math Activities: More Than 50 Great Activities That Reinforce Problem-Solving & Essential Math Skills. 2001. (Joyful Learning Ser.). 64p. pap., tchr. ed., act. bk. ed. 9.95 (978-0-439-40800-4(8) , Teaching Resources) Scholastic, Inc.

D'Agnese, Joseph, et al. Brain-Boosting Math Activities: More Than 50 Great Activities That Reinforce Problem-Solving & Essential Math Skills. 2001. (Joyful Learning Ser.). (Illus.). 64p. pap., act. bk. ed. 9.95 (978-0-439-40803-5(2) , Teaching Resources) Scholastic, Inc.

Dana, Marcia. Math Practice Games. 1999. (Basic Skills Ser.). 48p. (gr. 3 up). 5.99 (978-1-56822-751-1(5) , IF5205); (Illus.). (gr. 2 up). 5.99 (978-1-56822-750-4(7) , IF5204); (Illus.). (gr. 4 up). 5.99 (978-1-56822-752-8(3) , IF5206); (Illus.). (gr. 5 up). 5.99 (978-1-56822-753-5(1) , IF5207) School Specialty Publishing.

Diffily, Deborah. Fun Filled 5 to 10 Minute Math Activities for Young Learners: 200 Instant Kid-Pleasing Activities That Build Essential Early Math Skills for Circle Time, Transition Time-or Any Time. 2002. (Illus.). 64p. pap. 11.95 (978-0-439-31890-7(4)) Scholastic, Inc.

Dinio-Durkin, Cecilia. Brain-Boosting Math Activities: More Than 50 Great Activities That Reinforce Problem-Solving & Essential Math Skills. 2001. (Joyful Learning Ser.). 64p. pap., tchr. ed., act. bk. ed. 9.95 (978-0-439-40799-1(0) , Teaching Resources) Scholastic, Inc.

Division Songs. 2001. pap. 9.95 incl. audio. (Illus.). pap., tchr. ed., wbk. ed. 12.95 incl. audio compact disk Audio Memory Publishing.

Dominguez, Marissa & Dominguez, Margaret. Mission Possible TEKS-Based Math TAAS Computer Game with Study Guide. 2000. (Illus.). 270p. (YA). (gr. 6 up). pap. 79.00 (978-1-889684-16-1(3)) Texas Testing Products.

Dot-to-Dot 1-100+ Spanish Version. 2007. (J). per. (***978-1-58232-163-9(9)**) Bryan Hse. Pubs., Inc.

Douglas, Vincent & School Specialty Publishing Staff. Number Puzzles. 2003. (Brighter Child Homework Helpers Ser.). (Illus.). 32p. (J). (gr. k-1). pap., wbk. ed. 2.99 (978-0-7696-2923-0(7) , Brighter Child) School Specialty Publishing.

Eastaway, Rob & Wyndham. Why Do Buses Come in Threes? 2004. (Illus.). 156p. pap. (978-1-86105-247-6(2) , Robson Bks. Ltd.) Anova Bks.

Egan, Lorraine Hopping. 101 Brain-Boosting Math Problems: An Awesome Assortment of Fun-to-Solve Reproducible Puzzles That Build Essential Math Skills. 1999. (Illus.). 96p. (J). 12.95 (978-0-590-37869-7(4)) Scholastic, Inc.

English/Math 3-4. 2003. (Illus.). 48p. (J). wbk. ed. 7.98 (978-1-4054-1264-3(X)) Parragon, Inc.

English/Math 4-5. 2003. (Illus.). 48p. (J). wbk. ed. 7.98 (978-1-4054-1265-0(8)) Parragon, Inc.

English/Math 5-6. 2003. (Illus.). 48p. (J). wbk. ed. 7.98 (978-1-4054-1266-7(6)) Parragon, Inc.

English/Math 6-7. 2003. (Illus.). 48p. (YA). wbk. ed. 7.98 (978-1-4054-1267-4(4)) Parragon, Inc.

Faulkner, Keith & Holmes, Stephen. Animal ? Math. Faulkner, Keith & Holmes, Stephen, illus. 2003. (Illus.). (J). (978-0-439-62755-9(9)) Scholastic, Inc.

Ferris, Julie. Galaxy Getaway: A Math Puzzle Adventure. Tassie, Jane, illus. 2000. (Math for Martians Ser.). 32p. (J). (gr. 1-3). pap. (978-0-7534-5276-9(6)) Kingfisher Publications, plc.

—Planet Omicron: A Math Puzzle Adventure. Tassie, Jane, illus. 2000. (Math for Martians Ser.). 32p. (J). (gr. 1-3). pap. (978-0-7534-5277-6(4)) Kingfisher Publications, plc.

Freudenthal. Reflections on Numbers. 3rd ed. 2003. (Math in Context Ser.). (Illus.). 7.86 (978-0-03-071704-8(3)) Holt, Rinehart & Winston.

Gave, Marc. Number Games Around the World/Juegos de numeros alrededor del Mundo: English/Spanish Pair, ed. 2004. (Navigators Ser.). (J). pap., instr.'s gde. ed. 84.00 (978-1-4108-1765-5(2)) Benchmark Education Co.

George, Rebecca. Super Smart Math. 2006. 220p. pap. 17.95 (978-1-59363-200-7(2)) Prufrock Pr.

Gonzales, Nancy A., et al. Mathematical History: Activities, Puzzles, Stories, & Games. 2nd ed. 2001. (Illus.). 91p. (J). (gr. 6-8). pap. 21.95 (978-0-87353-493-2(X)) National Council of Teachers of Mathematics.

Greenberg, Dan. Comic-Strip Math: 40 Reproducible Cartoons with Dozens of Funny Story Problems That Build Essential Skills. 1998. (Illus.). 48p. (J). pap. 8.95 (978-0-590-18737-4(6)) Scholastic, Inc.

Harcourt School Publishers Staff. Math Advantage Games & More Package. 1999. (gr. k). 92.60 (978-0-15-313707-5(X)); (gr. 1). 92.60 (978-0-15-313708-2(8)); (gr. 2). 92.60 (978-0-15-313709-9(6)) Harcourt Schl. Pubs.

Haugen, Janie & Britt, Melissa. Grocery Store Game. 1999. 16p. (J). pap., tchr. ed. (978-1-884074-84-7(7)) PCI Educational Publishing.

Highlights for Children Editorial Staff, compiled by. Mathmania. 2003. (Illus.). 48p. (YA). Vol. 9. pap. 5.95 (978-0-87534-939-8(0)); Vol. 10. pap. 5.95 (978-0-87534-940-4(4)); Vol. 11. pap. 5.95 (978-0-87534-941-1(2)); Vol. 12. pap. 5.95 (978-0-87534-942-8(0)) Highlights for Children.

Holub, Joan. Riddle-Iculous Math. Dunnick, Regan, illus. 2003. 32p. (J). (gr. 2-5). 15.95 (978-0-8075-4996-4(7)) Whitman, Albert & Co.

Howes, Jacqueline Johnson. Instant & Interactive Math Picturepages with Activities. 2000. (J). 12.95 (978-0-439-07748-4(6)) Scholastic, Inc.

HSP. Games. 2nd ed. 2002. (First-Place Math Ser.). (gr. k up). pap. 93.60 (978-0-15-335389-5(9)); (gr. 1 up). pap. 93.60 (978-0-15-335390-1(2)); (gr. 2 up). pap. 93.60 (978-0-15-335391-8(0)); (gr. 3 up). pap. 93.60 (978-0-15-335392-5(9)); (gr. 4 up). pap. 93.60 (978-0-15-335393-2(7)); (gr. 5 up). pap. 93.60 (978-0-15-335394-9(5)); (gr. 6 up). pap. 93.60 (978-0-15-335396-3(1)) Harcourt Schl. Pubs.

Keenan, Sheila. What Time Is It? a Book of Math Riddles. 1999. (gr. k-3). lib. bdg. 11.80 (978-0-613-22609-7(7)) Tandem Library Bks.

Kidzup Productions Staff. Multiplication Songs. 2002. (Learning Beat Ser.). (J). pap., wbk. ed. 13.99 (978-1-894677-35-6(8)) Kidzup Productions.

Kiernan, Denise. Fun, 5-Minute Practice Pages: Grades 4-5. 2002. 48p. (J). (gr. 4-5). 8.95 (978-0-439-29468-3(1)) Scholastic, Inc.

—Math Games to Master Basic Skills: Fractions & Decimals: Familiar & Flexible Games with Dozens of Variations That Help Struggling Learners Practice & Really Master Basic Fraction & Decimal Skills & Concepts. 2007. 48p. pap. 10.99 (978-0-439-51772-0(9) , Teaching Resources) Scholastic, Inc.

—Math Games to Master Basic Skills: Multiplication & Division: Familiar & Flexible Games with Dozens of Variations That Help Struggling Learners Practice & Really Master Multiplication & Division Facts. 2007. 48p. pap. 10.99 (978-0-439-51773-7(7) , Teaching Resources) Scholastic, Inc.

Kirkby, David. Number Play. 1998. (Mini Math Ser.). (Illus.). (J). pap. (978-1-57572-005-0(1)) Heinemann Library.

Ledwon, Peter & Mets, Marilyn. Midnight Math: Twelve Terrific Math Games. Ledwon, Peter & Mets, Marilyn, illus. 2000. (Illus.). 32p. (J). (gr. k-3). tchr. ed. 15.95 (978-0-8234-1530-4(9)) Holiday Hse., Inc.

Lee, Martin & Miller, Marcia. Menu Math. 2001. 64p. (J). (gr. 2-3). 10.95 (978-0-439-22725-4(9)) Scholastic, Inc.

—40 Fabulous Math Mysteries Kids Can't Resist: Fun-Filled Reproducible Mystery Stories That Build Essential Math Problem-Solving Skills. 2001. 96p. pap. 12.95 (978-0-439-17540-1(2)) Scholastic, Inc.

Levy, Janey. At Sea on a Viking Ship. 2004. (PowerMath Ser.). (Illus.). 24p. (J). lib. bdg. 21.25 (978-0-8239-8977-5(1) , PowerKids Pr.) Rosen Publishing Group, Inc., The.

—At Sea on a Viking Ship: Solving Problems of Length & Weight Using the Four Math Operations. 2004. (PowerMath Ser.). (Illus.). 24p. (J). pap. (978-0-8239-8922-5(4) , PowerKids Pr.) Rosen Publishing Group, Inc., The.

Lewis, J. Patrick. Arithme-Tickle: An Even Number of Odd Riddle-Rhymes. Remkiewicz, Frank, illus. 2007. 32p. (J). (gr. 1-4). pap. 6.00 (978-0-15-205848-7(6) , Voyager Bks./Libros Viajeros) Harcourt Children's Bks.

—Arithme-Tickle: An Even Number of Odd Riddle-Rhymes. Remkiewicz, Frank, illus. 2002. 32p. (J). (gr. 1-4). 16.00 (978-0-15-216418-8(9) , Silver Whistle) Harcourt Trade Pubs.

Lewis, Sue & Ciccarelli, Joellyn. Multiplication & Division Facts to 12: Over 75 Math Puzzles, Brainteasers, & Games. Hood, Christine, ed. Yamada, Jane, illus. 2002. 96p. (Orig.). (J). (gr. 2-3). pap. 11.99 (978-1-57471-820-1(7) , CTP 2580) Creative Teaching Pr., Inc.

Linde, Barbara M. Working at the Farmers' Market: Solving Money Problems Involving the Four Math Operations. 2004. (PowerMath Ser.). (Illus.). 24p. (J). lib. bdg. (978-0-8239-8920-1(8)); lib. bdg. 21.25 (978-0-8239-8975-1(5)) Rosen Publishing Group, Inc., The. (PowerKids Pr.).

Lund, Charles. Math games & activities with Dice. 2006. 84p. spiral bd. 12.55 (***978-1-934218-03-7(0)** , EM 590) White Bear Publishing, LLC.

—Place Mat Math, 1. 2006. 10.45 (***978-1-934218-04-4(9)** , EM 595) White Bear Publishing, LLC.

Lund, Charles, et al. Math Games & Activities with Cards second Addition. 2006. 64p. tchr. ed., spiral bd. 11.50 (***978-1-934218-01-3(4)** , EM 500) White Bear Publishing, LLC.

Math Card Games. 86p. (gr. 1-8). 12.99 (978-1-56451-061-7(1) , ID7220) School Specialty Publishing.

Math Discoveries with Tangrams. 64p. (gr. k-1). 7.99 (978-1-56451-089-1(1) , ID7981); (gr. 2-3). 7.99 (978-1-56451-075-4(1) , ID7982) School Specialty Publishing.

Math Games. 2003. (Practice Makes Perfect Ser.). (Illus.). 48p. (J). (gr. 3). pap. 4.99 (978-0-7439-3723-8(6)); (gr. 4). pap. 4.99 (978-0-7439-3724-5(4)); (gr. 5). pap. 4.99 (978-0-7439-3725-2(2)) Teacher Created Materials, Inc.

Math in the Cards. 2006. 186p. ring bd. 18.95 (***978-1-934218-02-0(2)***) White Bear Publishing, LLC.

Math Mind Stretchers. 2003. 96p. (gr. 5-12). 9.99 (978-1-56822-422-0(2) , IF2528) School Specialty Publishing.

Math Puzzles. 2001. (Wipe-Off Activity Bks.). 16p. (J). (gr. 1). 3.79 (978-1-58792-018-9(2)) Trend Enterprises, Inc.

McGraw-Hill Staff & School Specialty Publishing Staff. Math Activities. 2001. (Homework Helpers Activity Bks.). (Illus.). 56p. (J). (gr. k-k). pap., act. bk. ed. 2.99 (978-0-7682-0701-9(0) , FS109030); (gr. 2-2). pap., act. bk. ed. 2.99 (978-0-7682-0710-1(X) , FS109039) Schaffer, Frank Pubns. (Schaffer, Frank).

Mckell, Teresa Kane. Algebra Puzzlers. 2001. 112p. (YA). (gr. 9-12). pap. 14.99 (978-0-7682-0101-7(2) , GA1687) School Specialty Publishing.

Mental Math. 2004. (Help with Homework Ser.). 32p. (J). (gr. 1-4). wbk. ed. 3.99 (978-1-904586-26-5(0)) Byeway Bks.

Mesopotamia: Creating & Solving Word Puzzles. (Math Big Bookstm Ser.). 32p. (YA). (gr. 6-7). 53.25 (978-1-4042-6364-2(0)) Rosen Publishing Group, Inc., The.

Mitchell, Cindi. Math Skills Made Fun: Quilt Math. 2003. 112p. pap. 15.95 (978-0-439-37662-4(9) , Teaching Resources) Scholastic, Inc.

Moore, Suzanne & Henry, Lucia Kemp. Toss & Learn Games: Math. 2003. (Toss & Learn Games Ser.). (Illus.). 48p. (ps-k). pap. 10.99 (978-0-439-47116-9(8) , Teaching Resources) Scholastic, Inc.

Morgan, Rowland. Brain Bafflers. 2003. (Illus.). 96p. (J). pap. 3.99 (978-0-330-36783-7(8) , Macmillan Children's Bks.) Pan Macmillan GBR. *Dist:* Trafalgar Square Publishing.

Moscovich, Ivan. Number Games. 2000. (Illus.). 24p. (J). (gr. 3-7). 5.95 (978-0-7611-2018-6(1) , 12018) Workman Publishing Co., Inc.

—The Pattern Games. 2001. (Illus.). 24p. (J). (gr. 3-7). 6.95 (978-0-7611-2020-9(3) , 12020) Workman Publishing Co., Inc.

—The Probability Games. 2000. (Illus.). 24p. (J). (gr. 3-7). 5.95 (978-0-7611-2017-9(3) , 12017) Workman Publishing Co., Inc.

Multiplication Songs. 2001. (Illus.). pap., tchr. ed., wbk. ed. 12.95 incl. audio compact disk Audio Memory Publishing.

Neuschwander, Cindy. Sir Cumference & the Dragon of Pi: A Math Adventure. Geehan, Wayne, illus. 2004. (Make the Math-Literature Connection Ser.). 32p. (J). (gr. k-7). pap. 6.95 (978-1-57091-164-4(9)) Charlesbridge Publishing, Inc.

—Sir Cumference & the Dragon of Pi: A Math Adventure. 1999. (gr. k-3). lib. bdg. 15.25 (978-0-613-35228-4(9)) Tandem Library Bks.

—Sir Cumference & the Great Knight of Angleland: A Math Adventure. Geehan, Wayne, illus. 2004. (Make the Math-Literature Connection Ser.). 32p. (J). (gr. 4-7). 16.95 (978-1-57091-170-5(3)) Charlesbridge Publishing, Inc.

—Sir Cumference & the Sword in the Cone: A Math Adventure. Geehan, Wayne, illus. 2004. (Make the Math-Literature Connection Ser.). 32p. (J). 16.95 (978-1-57091-600-7(4)); pap. 6.95 (978-1-57091-601-4(2)) Charlesbridge Publishing, Inc.

Newman-D'Amico, Fran. My First Book of Number Fun. 2006. 64p. (J). pap. 4.95 (978-0-486-45226-5(3)) Dover Pubns., Inc.

Newmarket Press, ed. Kidoku. 2006. (Illus.). 224p. (YA). pap. 6.95 (978-1-55704-720-5(0)) Newmarket Pr.

Nichols, Jennifer. Brain-Boosting Math Activities: More Than 50 Great Activities That Reinforce Problem-Solving & Essential Math Skills. 2001. (Joyful Learning Ser.). 64p. pap., tchr. ed. 9.95 (978-0-439-40804-2(0) , Teaching Resources) Scholastic, Inc.

Niederman, Derrick. Mind-Stretching Math Puzzles. 2005. (Illus.). (gr. k-9). 352p. pap. 6.95 (978-1-4027-2194-6(3)); 112p. (J). (978-1-4156-0492-2(4)) Sterling Publishing Co., Inc.

Niederman, Derrick, et al. Mensa Math. Sinclair, Jeff, illus. 2004. (Official Mensa Puzzle Book Ser.). 287p. (J). pap. (978-1-4027-1638-6(9) , Sterling/Main St.) Sterling Publishing Co., Inc.

Nobleman, Marc Tyler. Math Puzzles: Grades 3 & 4. (Illus.). (J). pap., wbk. ed. 4.99 (978-0-88743-846-2(6)) School Zone Publishing Co.

Number Puzzles. 2002. (Wipe It Off Ser.). 24p. (J). spiral bd. 4.98 (978-0-7525-8356-3(5)) Parragon, Inc.

Olenych, Bob. Fractions, Decimals & Percents. 2004. (42 Cross-Number Puzzles Ser.). 48p. pap. 10.99 (978-0-439-51906-9(3) , Teaching Resources) Scholastic, Inc.

—40 Cross-Number Puzzles: Multiplication & Division. 2004. (40 Cross-Number Puzzles Ser.). 48p. pap. 10.99 (978-0-439-51879-6(2) , Teaching Resources) Scholastic, Inc.

—41 Cross-Number Puzzles: Addition & Subtraction. 2004. (41 Cross-Number Puzzles Ser.). 48p. pap. 10.99 (978-0-439-51904-5(7) , Teaching Resources) Scholastic, Inc.

Olenych, Bob, et al. Fun Independent Practice Pages: Word Problems. 2003. (Rtg Reproducibles Ser.). 48p. pap., tchr. ed. 10.95 (978-0-439-32316-1(9) , Teaching Resources) Scholastic, Inc.

Paré, Roger. Les Chiffres. 2004. (Livres-jeux Ser.). (FRE.). 12p. (J). (ps). pap. (978-2-89021-654-9(3)) Diffusion du livre Mirabel.

Patilla, Peter. Fun with Numbers. McDonald, Brigitte, illus. 1998. (Fun with... Ser.). 32p. (ps-2). lib. bdg. 23.90 (978-0-7613-0957-4(8) , Millbrook Pr.) Lerner Publishing Group.

Poskitt, Kjartan & Mepham, Michael. Sodoku: 100 Fun Number Puzzles. 2005. 144p. (J). pap. 4.99 (978-0-439-84570-0(X)) Scholastic, Inc.

Pressnall, Debra. Full Color File Folder Games PK-K. 2006. 160p. (J). pap. (978-0-88724-268-7(5) , CD-104047) Carson-Dellosa Publishing Co., Inc.

Prior, Jennifer. Math Games to Master Basic Skills: Time & Money: 14 Reproducible Games That Help Struggling Learners Practice & Really Master Basic Time & Money Skills & Concepts. 2007. 48p. pap. 10.99 (978-0-439-55414-5(4) , Teaching Resources) Scholastic, Inc.

Ready, Steady, Throw! 2003. pap. 9.99 (978-0-7424-1719-9(0)) School Specialty Publishing.

Ruffin, Frances E. Creating a City Park: Dividing Three-Digit Numbers by One-Digit Numbers Without Remainders. 2004. (PowerMath Ser.). (Illus.). 24p. (J). lib. bdg. (978-0-8239-8926-3(7)); lib. bdg. 21.25 (978-0-8239-8978-2(X)) Rosen Publishing Group, Inc., The. (PowerKids Pr.).

Ryan, Steve. Sit & Solve Travel Math Puzzles. 2006. (Sit & Solve Ser.). 96p. pap. 4.95 (978-1-4027-3202-7(3)) Sterling Publishing Co., Inc.

Salvadori, Mario G. Math Games for Middle School: Challenges & Skill-Builders for Students at Ever. 1998. (gr. 5-8). lib. bdg. 26.85 (978-0-613-87956-9(2)) Tandem Library Bks.

Sanger, Marsha. Multiplication Practice Puzzles. 1998. (Illus.). 128p. (J). (gr. 3-6). pap. 12.95 (978-1-56500-040-7(4)) Golden Educational Ctr.

Sargent, Brian. Grandfather's Shape Story. 2006. (Rookie Read-About Math Ser.). (Illus.). 32p. (J). (gr. k-2). 20.50 (978-0-516-29919-8(0) , Children's Pr.) Scholastic Library Publishing.

Schlegl, William. Bible Firsts. 1999. (J). pap. 7.99 (978-0-570-05256-2(4)) Concordia Publishing Hse.

Schofield, Tracey Ann. 101 Math Activities for Calculating Kids. Mitchell, Judy, ed. Glikin, Alex, illus. 2001. 112p. (J). (gr. 3-6). pap. 10.95 (978-1-57310-269-8(5)) Teaching & Learning Co.

Scholastic, Inc. Staff. 10 Monster Multiplication Wheels. 2000. (Illus.). (J). 14.95 (978-0-439-15579-3(7)) Scholastic, Inc.

School Zone Publishing Company Staff. Math War: Multiplication. rev. ed. 1998. (Game Cards Ser.). 56p. (J). (gr. 3-7). 2.79 (978-0-88743-287-3(5) , 05032) School Zone Publishing Co.

School Zone Publishing Company Staff & Nobleman, Marc Tyler. Math Puzzles. 2000. (I Know It! Workbooks Ser.). (Illus.). 32p. (J). (gr. 3-4). pap., wbk. ed. 2.49 (978-0-88743-742-7(7) , 02102) School Zone Publishing Co.

Schwartz, Linda. Mall Math. Clark, Kim, ed. Armstrong, Beverly, illus. 2002. 72p. (J). (gr. 4-6). pap. 10.99 (978-0-88160-349-1(X) , LW-204, Learning Works, The) Creative Teaching Pr., Inc.

—Math Critical Thinking, Grades 2-4: Creative Puzzles to Challenge the Brain. VanBlaricum, Pam, ed. Armstrong, Bev & Grayson, Rick, illus. 2005. 64p. (J). pap. 11.99 (978-0-88160-383-5(X) , LW-422) Creative Teaching Pr., Inc.

Sewing Cards. 2003. pap. 16.99 (978-1-56451-626-8(1)) School Specialty Publishing.

Sheldon, Ken. Sing-Along & Learn: Marvelous Math. 2001. 32p. (ps). pap. 11.95 (978-0-439-33345-0(8)) Scholastic, Inc.

Silbert, Jack. Brain-Boosting Math Activities: More Than 50 Great Activities That Reinforce Problem-Solving & Essential Math Skills. 2001. (Joyful Learning Ser.). 64p. pap., tchr. ed., act. bk. ed. 9.95 (978-0-439-40802-8(4) , Teaching Resources) Scholastic, Inc.

Smart Squares: Multiplication. (gr. k up). 7.99 (978-0-7682-2299-9(0) , J55007) School Specialty Publishing.

Stearns, Velda. Crossnumber Puzzles Grade 3: Extended Skills. Rogers, Kathy, ed. 2001. 32p. (J). pap. 3.99 (978-1-56472-251-5(1)) Edupress, Inc.

—Crossnumber Puzzles Grade 3 Operations. Rogers, Kathy, ed. 2001. 32p. (J). pap. 3.99 (978-1-56472-250-8(3)) Edupress, Inc.

—Crossnumber Puzzles Grade 4: Extended Skills. Rogers, Kathy, ed. 2001. 32p. (J). pap. 3.99 (978-1-56472-253-9(8)) Edupress, Inc.

—Crossnumber Puzzles Grade 4 Operations. Rogers, Kathy, ed. 2001. 32p. (J). pap. 3.99 (978-1-56472-252-2(X)) Edupress, Inc.

—Crossnumber Puzzles Grade 5: Extended Skills. Rogers, Kathy, ed. 2001. 64p. (J). pap. 3.99 (978-1-56472-255-3(4)) Edupress, Inc.

—Crossnumber Puzzles Grade 5 Operations. Rogers, Kathy, ed. 2001. 32p. (J). pap. 3.99 (978-1-56472-254-6(6)) Edupress, Inc.

—Crossnumber Puzzles Grade 6: Extended Skills. Rogers, Kathy, ed. 2001. 32p. (J). pap. 3.99 (978-1-56472-257-7(0)) Edupress, Inc.

—Crossnumber Puzzles Grade 6 Operations. Rogers, Kathy, ed. 2001. 32p. (J). pap. 3.99 (978-1-56472-256-0(2)) Edupress, Inc.

—Crossnumber Puzzles Grade 7: Extended Skills. Rogers, Kathy, ed. 2001. 32p. (J). pap. 3.99 (978-1-56472-259-1(7)) Edupress, Inc.

—Crossnumber Puzzles Grade 7 Operations. Rogers, Kathy, ed. 2001. 64p. (J). pap. 3.99 (978-1-56472-258-4(9)) Edupress, Inc.

—Crossnumber Puzzles Grade 8: Extended Skills. Rogers, Kathy, ed. 2001. 32p. pap. 3.99 (978-1-56472-261-4(9)) Edupress, Inc.

—Crossnumber Puzzles Grade 8 Operations. Rogers, Kathy, ed. 2001. 32p. pap. 3.99 (978-1-56472-260-7(0)) Edupress, Inc.

Steck-Vaughn Staff. Math Level H-J: How Big Is a Cat? 2003. (Illus.). pap. (978-0-7398-7657-2(0)) Steck-Vaughn.

Subtraction Songs. 2001. (Illus.). pap., tchr. ed., wbk. ed. 12.95 incl. audio compact disk Audio Memory Publishing.

Super Sticker Math. Date not set. 64p. (J). 3.98 (978-0-7525-9774-4(4)) Parragon, Inc.

Tang, Greg. The Grapes of Math. Briggs, Harry, illus. 2004. (Scholastic Bookshelf Ser.). 40p. (J). pap. 5.99 (978-0-439-59840-8(0) , Scholastic Paperbacks) Scholastic, Inc.

—Math Appeal. Briggs, Harry, illus. 2003. (J). pap. (978-0-439-21045-4(3)); 40p. (gr. 2-5). pap. 16.95 (978-0-439-21046-1(1) , Scholastic Pr.) Scholastic, Inc.

Weiss, Ellen. Math on the Playground. 2007. (Scholastic News Nonfiction Readers Ser.). (Illus.). 24p. (J). (gr. 1-2). lib. bdg. 20.00 (***978-0-531-18533-9(8)*** , Children's Pr.) Scholastic Library Publishing.

Williams, Susan. Second Grade Math Puzzles & Games: Boosting Your Way to Success in School. 1998. (Grade Boosters Ser.). (Illus.). 64p. (J). (gr. 1-3). pap. 4.95 (978-1-56565-754-0(3) , 07543W) Lowell Hse.

Wortzman, Ricki. Math Detectives: Finding Fun in Numbers. 2003. (gr. k-3). lib. bdg. 12.95 (978-0-613-78018-6(3)) Tandem Library Bks.

Wortzman, Ricki & Harcourt, Lalie. Math Detectives: Finding Fun in Numbers. 2003. (Illus.). 48p. (J). pap. 4.95 (978-1-4027-0809-1(2)) Sterling Publishing Co., Inc.

Wyatt, Valerie. The Math Book for Girls: And Other Beings Who Count. Cupples, Pat, illus. 2000. (Books for Girls Ser.). 64p. (J). (gr. 4-6). (978-1-55074-584-9(0)) Kids Can Pr., Ltd.

—The Math Book for Girls & Other Beings Who Count. Cupples, Pat, illus. 2000. (Books for Girls Ser.). 64p. (J). (gr. 4-6). (978-1-55074-830-7(0)) Kids Can Pr., Ltd.

Yeatts, Karol L. Cereal Math. 2000. (Illus.). 64p. (J). 10.95 (978-0-590-51208-4(0)) Scholastic, Inc.

Yoder, Eric. One Minute Mysteries: 65 Short Mysteries You Solve with Math! 2009. 160p. pap. 9.95 (***978-0-9678020-0-8(8)***) Science, Naturally!.

Zaslavsky, Claudia. Math Games & Activities from Around the World. 2003. (Illus.). 160p. (J). (gr. 4 up). pap. 14.95 (978-1-55652-287-1(8)) Chicago Review Pr., Inc.

—Math Games & Activities from Around the World. 1998. (gr. 3-6). lib. bdg. 24.55 (978-0-613-87958-3(9)) Tandem Library Bks.

—More Math Games & Activities from Around the World. 2003. 160p. (J). pap. 14.95 (978-1-55652-501-8(X)) Chicago Review Pr., Inc.

—More Math Games & Activities from Around the World. 2003. (gr. 7-12). lib. bdg. 24.55 (978-0-613-70817-3(2)) Tandem Library Bks.

MATHEMATICAL SETS

see Set Theory

MATHEMATICIANS

Bradley, Michael J. Mathematics Frontiers: 1950 to Present. 2006. (Pioneers in Math Ser.). 160p. (gr. 6-12). 29.95 (978-0-8160-5427-5(4)) Facts On File, Inc.

—Mathematics Frontiers Vol. 1: 1950 to Present. 2006. (Pioneers in Math Ser.). 160p. (gr. 6-12). 29.95 (978-0-8160-5423-7(1)) Facts On File, Inc.

—Mathematics Frontiers Vol. 2: 1950 to Present. 2006. (Pioneers in Math Ser.). 176p. (gr. 6-12). 29.95 (978-0-8160-5424-4(X)) Facts On File, Inc.

—Mathematics Frontiers Vol. 3: 1950 to Present. 2006. (Pioneers in Math Ser.). 176p. (gr. 6-12). 29.95 (978-0-8160-5425-1(8)) Facts On File, Inc.

—Mathematics Frontiers Vol. 4: 1950 to Present. 2006. (Pioneers in Math Ser.). 176p. (gr. 6-12). 29.95 (978-0-8160-5426-8(6)) Facts On File, Inc.

—Pioneers in Math, 5 vols., Set. 2006. (Pioneers in Math Ser.). 128p. (gr. 6-12). 149.75 (978-0-8160-5422-0(3)) Facts On File, Inc.

Bruno, Leonard C. Math & Mathematicians: The History of Math Discoveries Around the World, 2 vols., Set. Baker, Lawrence W., ed. 1999. (Illus.). xli, 420p. (J). (gr. 6-10). lib. bdg. 120.00 (978-0-7876-3812-2(9) , GML00502-113573, UXL) Thomson Gale.

Bruno, Leonard C. & Baker, Lawrence W. Math & Mathematicians: The History of Math Discoveries Around the World. 1999. (Illus.). xli, 456p. (J). (978-0-7876-3814-6(5)) Thomson Gale.

Bruno, Leonard C. & Baker, Lawrence W., eds. Math & Mathematicians: The History of Math Discoveries Around the World. 1999. (Illus.). xli, 456p. (J). (978-0-7876-3813-9(7)) Thomson Gale.

Champion, Neil & Babbage, Charles. Charles Babbage. 2000. (Groundbreakers Ser.). (Illus.). 48p. (J). (gr. 5-7). lib. bdg. 25.64 (978-1-57572-367-9(0)) Heinemann Library.

Collier, Bruce & MacLachlan, James. Charles Babbage: And the Engines of Perfection. Gingerich, Owen, ed. 1998. (Oxford Portraits in Science Ser.). (Illus.). 128p. (YA). (gr. 7 up). 30.00 (978-0-19-508997-4(9)) Oxford Univ. Pr., Inc.

Collier, Bruce & Maclachlan, James. Charles Babbage & the Engines of Perfection. 2006. (Illus.). 123p. reprint ed. pap. 12.00 (978-1-4223-5040-9(1)) DIANE Publishing Co.

Franceschetti, Donald R., ed. Biographical Encyclopedia of Mathematicians, 2 vols., Set. 1999. (Illus.). 640p. 228.50 (978-0-7614-7069-4(7) , Cavendish, Marshall Reference Bks.) Cavendish, Marshall Corp.

Gow, Mary. Archimedes: Mathematical Genius of the Ancient World. 2005. (Great Minds of Science Ser.). (Illus.). 128p. (J). (gr. 5-8). lib. bdg. 26.60 (978-0-7660-2502-8(0)) Enslow Pubs., Inc.

Hasan, Heather. Archimedes: The Father of Mathematics. 2005. (Library of Greek Philosophers). (Illus.). 112p. (J). 33.25 (978-1-4042-0774-5(0)) Rosen Publishing Group, Inc., The.

Lassieur, Allison. Benjamin Banneker: Astronomer & Mathematician. 2006. (Fact Finders Ser.). (Illus.). 32p. (J). (978-0-7368-5432-0(0)) Capstone Pr., Inc.

Leech, Bonnie Coulter. Geometry's Great Thinkers: The History of Geometry. 2006. (Math for the Real World Ser.). (Illus.). 32p. (J). pap. (978-1-4042-6073-3(0)); lib. bdg. (978-1-4042-3360-7(1)) Rosen Publishing Group, Inc., The.

Love, D. Anne. Of Numbers & Stars: The Story of Hypatia. Papparone, Pam, illus. 2005. 32p. (J). (ps-3). 16.95 (978-0-8234-1621-9(6)) Holiday Hse., Inc.

McClure, Judy. Theoreticians & Builders: Mathematicians, Physical Scientists, Inventors. 2002. (Remarkable Women). (Illus.). 80p. (YA). (gr. 6-9). lib. bdg. 32.85 (978-0-8172-5728-6(4)) Raintree.

Schaffer, Frank. Skill Drill Math: Readiness, Grade 1. 2001. 64p. (J). (gr. 1-1). pap. 8.99 (978-0-7647-0385-0(4) , FS23231) Schaffer, Frank Pubns.

Schecter, Bruce. My Brain Is Open: The Mathematical Journeys of Paul Erdos. 2000. (gr. 7-12). lib. bdg. 22.25 (978-0-613-26307-8(3)) Tandem Library Bks.

Sherman, Josepha. Charles Babbage & the Story of the First Computer. 2005. (Uncharted, Unexplored, & Unexplained Ser.). (Illus.). 48p. (J). (gr. 4-8). lib. bdg. 29.95 (978-1-58415-372-6(5)) Mitchell Lane Pubs., Inc.

Spangenburg, Ray & Moser, Diane Kit. Alan Turing: The Troubled Genius of Bletchley Park Hall. 2008. (Makers of Modern Science Ser.). 160p. (gr. 6-12). 29.95 (***978-0-8160-6175-4(0)*** , Chelsea Hse.) Facts On File, Inc.

Sullivan, Erin. Mathematical Thinkers/Los Matematicos: English/Spanish Pair, 12 texts, 2 titles, Vol. 2. ed. 2004. (Navigators Ser.). (J). pap., instr.'s gde. ed. 84.00 (978-1-4108-1773-0(3) , 17733) Benchmark Education Co.

Zannos, Susan. The Life & Times of Archimedes. 2004. (Biography from Ancient Civilizations Ser.). (Illus.). 48p. (J). (gr. 4-8). lib. bdg. 29.95 (978-1-58415-242-2(7)) Mitchell Lane Pubs., Inc.

MATHEMATICS

see also Algebra; Arithmetic; Binary System (Mathematics); Calculus; Geometry; Mechanics; Mensuration; Number Theory; Set Theory; Trigonometry

Able and Talented Program Resource Room Students Staff, Able and Talented Program Resource Room, et al. Westerville Kids Celebrate the Written Word Vol. 1: 2000-2001. 2001. 254p. pap. 14.95 (978-0-595-20772-5(3) , Writers Club Pr.) iUniverse, Inc.

Accelerated Curriculum for Mathematics Grade 11 Exit TAKS Teacher Edition. 2005. (Region IV ESC Resources for Mathematics Ser.). spiral bd. (978-1-932797-25-1(4)) Region IV Education Service Ctr.

Accelerated Curriculum for Mathematics Grade 5 Student Edition. 2005. (Region IV ESC Resources for Mathematics Ser.). spiral bd. (978-1-932797-23-7(8)) Region IV Education Service Ctr.

Accelerated Curriculum for Mathematics Grade 5 Student Edition Spanish. 2005. (Region IV ESC Resources for Mathematics Ser.). (SPA.). (J). (gr. 5). stu. ed., spiral bd. (978-1-932797-83-1(1)) Region IV Education Service Ctr.

Accelerated Math Learning Cards - Basic Math. 2004. 199.00 (978-1-59455-122-2(7)) Renaissance Learning, Inc.

Accelerated Math West Virginia State Tagged Grade 3 Library. 2004. cd-rom 1199.00 (978-1-59455-107-9(3)) Renaissance Learning, Inc.

Accelerated Math West Virginia State Tagged Grade 5 Library. 2004. cd-rom 1199.00 (978-1-59455-109-3(X)) Renaissance Learning, Inc.

Accelerated Math West Virginia State Tagged Grade 6 Library. 2004. cd-rom 1199.00 (978-1-59455-110-9(3)) Renaissance Learning, Inc.

Accelerated Math West Virginia State Tagged Grade 7 Library. 2004. cd-rom 1199.00 (978-1-59455-111-6(1)) Renaissance Learning, Inc.

Accelerated Math West Virginia State Tagged Pre-Algebra Library. 2004. cd-rom 1199.00 (978-1-59455-112-3(X)) Renaissance Learning, Inc.

ACT Mathematics Victory Student Textbook. 2nd ed. 2005. per. (978-1-58894-031-5(4)) Cambridge Educational Services, Inc.

Active Investigations with the Geometer's Sketchpad. 2001. (YA). pap., tchr. ed., wbk. ed. (978-1-58123-255-4(1)); pap., stu. ed., wbk. ed. (978-1-58123-254-7(3)) Larson Learning, Inc.

Actividades con la Calculadora: Student & Teacher Support Resources. 1999. (Matematicas en Mi Mundo Ser.). (ENG & SPA.). (gr. 2 up). (978-0-02-110752-0(1)); (gr. 3 up). (978-0-02-110753-7(X)); (gr. 5 up). (978-0-02-110755-1(6)) Macmillan/McGraw-Hill Schl. Div.

Activities for Base Ten Blocks. rev. ed. 2004. (J). per. 9.95 (978-1-56911-547-3(8)) Learning Resources, Inc.

Activity Cards for Equivalency Cubes. 2004. (J). 12.95 (978-1-56911-925-9(2)) Learning Resources, Inc.

Adams, J. W. & Beaumont, R. P. More Practice in Mathematics. Goddard, T. R., ed. 1999. (Illus.). (J). (gr. 2-7). Bk. 1. 63p. pap. 19.00 (978-0-7217-2346-4(2)); Bk. 4. 71p. pap. 19.00 (978-0-7217-2349-5(7)) Schofield & Sims Ltd. GBR. *Dist:* State Mutual Bk. & Periodical Service, Ltd.

Adams, Jim, Sr., creator. Math Made Easy As 1+2+3= 2003. (Illus.). 24p. spiral bd. 16.99 (978-0-9729189-4-7(9)) Adams Publishing.

Add-On Package. 2003. 129.95 (978-0-673-76011-1(1)); 187.95 (978-0-673-76007-4(3)); 187.95 (978-0-673-76009-8(X)) Celebration Pr.

Add Regrouping. (Self-Checks Ser.). (gr. 1-3). 8.99 (978-0-7647-0338-6(2) , FS65004) Schaffer, Frank Pubns.

Adding. 2003. (Gold Star Workbooks Ser.). (Illus.). 32p. (J). 2.98 (978-1-4054-1190-5(2)); 2.98 (978-1-4054-1191-2(0)) Parragon, Inc.

Addition & Subtracting 4-5. 2004. (Basic Skills Ser.). 48p. (J). pap. 6.99 (978-0-88724-191-8(3) , CD-4723) Carson-Dellosa Publishing Co., Inc.

M N O

Addition & Subtraction 0-12. (Classroom Helpers Ser.). 24p. (gr. 1 up). 3.99 (978-0-7682-0812-2(2) , FS194111) Schaffer, Frank Pubns.

Addition & Subtraction 1-2. 2004. (Basic Skills Ser.). 48p. (J). pap. 6.99 (978-0-88724-188-3(3) , CD-4720) Carson-Dellosa Publishing Co., Inc.

Addition & Subtraction 2-3. 2004. (Basic Skills Ser.). 48p. (J). pap. 6.99 (978-0-88724-189-5(1) , CD-4721) Carson-Dellosa Publishing Co., Inc.

Addition & Subtraction 3-4. 2004. (Basic Skills Ser.). 48p. (J). pap. 6.99 (978-0-88724-190-1(5) , CD-4722) Carson-Dellosa Publishing Co., Inc.

Addition & Subtraction with Mr Wiggle. 32p. (gr. 2 up). 4.99 (978-1-56451-972-6(4) , ID99002) School Specialty Publishing.

Addition Drill. 24p. (gr. 1 up). 5.99 (978-0-7682-0522-0(0) , FS8643); (gr. 2 up). 5.99 (978-0-7682-0523-7(9) , FS8644) Schaffer, Frank Pubns.

Addition, Subtraction, Multiplication & Division. 2004. (Basic Skills Ser.). 48p. (J). pap. 6.99 (978-0-88724-192-5(1) , CD-4724) Carson-Dellosa Publishing Co., Inc.

Addition, Subtraction, Multiplication, Division, & Fractions. (Method Math Ser.). 80p. (gr. 5 up). 10.99 (978-0-7682-0506-0(9) , FS122318) Schaffer, Frank Pubns.

Addition, Subtraction, Multiplication, Division, & Percents. (Method Math Ser.). 80p. (gr. 6 up). 10.99 (978-0-7682-0507-7(7) , FS122319) Schaffer, Frank Pubns.

Addition, Subtraction, Multiplication, Division, Money, & Fractions. (Method Math Ser.). 80p. (gr. 4 up). 10.99 (978-0-7682-0505-3(0) , FS122317) Schaffer, Frank Pubns.

Addition, Subtraction, Multiplication, Division, Time, Money, Fractions, & Decimals. (Method Math Ser.). 80p. (gr. 3 up). 10.99 (978-0-7682-0504-6(2) , FS122316) Schaffer, Frank Pubns.

Addition, Subtraction, Multiplication, Fractions, Money, & Time. (Method Math Ser.). 80p. (gr. 2 up). 10.99 (978-0-7682-0503-9(4) , FS122315) Schaffer, Frank Pubns.

Addition, Subtraction, Patterns, Time, & Money. (Method Math Ser.). 80p. (gr. 1 up). 10.99 (978-0-7682-0502-2(6) , FS122314) Schaffer, Frank Pubns.

Adler, David A. You Can, Toucan, Math: Word Problem-Solving Fun. Miller, Edward, illus. 32p. (J). (ps-3). 16.95 (978-0-8234-1919-7(3)) Holiday Hse., Inc.

Advanced Mathematics: Precalculus with Discrete Mathematics & Data Analysis. 2003. (gr. 11-12). tchr. ed. (978-0-618-00730-1(X) , 2-77973); tchr. ed. (978-0-618-25039-4(5) , 2-06020); stu. ed. (978-0-618-00729-5(6) , 2-77972); stu. ed. (978-0-618-25037-0(9) , 2-06019) McDougal Littell Inc.

Advanced Mathematics Syllabus & Tests. 1999. 18p. (J). ring bd. 2.50 (978-1-57896-069-9(X) , 1004, Hewitt Homeschooling Resources) Hewitt Research Foundation, Inc.

AfterSchool KidzMath. 2002. spiral bd. 160.00 (978-1-57621-399-5(4)) Developmental Studies Ctr.

AfterSchool KidzMath 3-6 Games. ldr.'s ed. 2004. (978-1-57621-452-7(4)) Developmental Studies Ctr.

AfterSchool KidzMath K-2 Games. ldr.'s ed. 2004. (978-1-57621-451-0(6)) Developmental Studies Ctr.

Aihara, Masaaki & Sarris, Eno, eds. Grade 1 Addition: Kumon Math Workbooks. 2008. (J). per. 6.95 (***978-1-933241-49-4(7)***) Kumon Publishing North America, Inc.

—Grade 1 Subtraction: Kumon Math Workbooks. 2008. (J). per. 6.95 (***978-1-933241-50-0(0)***) Kumon Publishing North America, Inc.

—Grade 2 Addition: Kumon Math Workbooks. 2008. (J). per. 6.95 (***978-1-933241-51-7(9)***) Kumon Publishing North America, Inc.

—Grade 2 Subtraction: Kumon Math Workbooks. 2008. (J). per. 6.95 (***978-1-933241-52-4(7)***) Kumon Publishing North America, Inc.

—Grade 3 Addition & Subtraction: Kumon Math Workbooks. 2008. (J). per. 6.95 (***978-1-933241-53-1(5)***) Kumon Publishing North America, Inc.

—Grade 3 Division: Kumon Math Workbooks. 2008. (J). per. 6.95 (***978-1-933241-55-5(1)***) Kumon Publishing North America, Inc.

—Grade 3 Multiplication: Kumon Math Workbooks. 2008. (J). per. 6.95 (***978-1-933241-54-8(3)***) Kumon Publishing North America, Inc.

—Grade 4 Division: Kumon Math Workbooks. 2008. (J). per. 6.95 (***978-1-933241-57-9(8)***) Kumon Publishing North America, Inc.

—Grade 4 Multiplication: Kumon Math Workbooks. 2008. (J). per. 6.95 (***978-1-933241-56-2(X)***) Kumon Publishing North America, Inc.

Alexander, Ellen, et al. Mathematics Standards in the Classroom: Resources for Grades 3-5. 2002. (Illus.). 320p. per. 40.00 (978-0-9707948-6-4(X)) Dana, Charles A. Ctr., Univ. of Texas at Austin.

The All-Time Greatest Mathcounts Problems. 1999. (Illus.). 80p. (YA). (gr. 7-8). pap. 12.95 (978-0-9674453-0-4(2)) Mathcounts Foundation.

Allen, Margaret. Dr. Maggie's Play & Discover, Grades Preschool-2: Math. Corker, Joanne, ed. Sopp Rae, Terri, illus. 1998. (Dr. Maggie's Play & Discover Early-Childhood Ser.). 72p. pap., tchr. ed. 12.98 (978-1-57471-360-2(4) , 2348) Creative Teaching Pr., Inc.

Alper, Lynne, et al. Interactive Mathematics Program Year 4. 2000. 478p. (YA). (gr. 9-12). stu. ed. 44.95 (978-1-55953-344-7(7) , MN53344) Key Curriculum Pr.

Alpha Omega Publishing Staff. Horizons Math Kindergarten. 2000. (Illus.). (J). Bk. 1. pap., stu. ed. 12.50 (978-0-7403-0309-8(0) , JKS021); Bk. 2. pap., stu. ed. 12.50 (978-0-7403-0310-4(4) , JKS022) Alpha Omega Pubns., Inc.

—Mathematics, 2 bks., Set. 2004. (Illus.). pap. 59.95 (978-0-7403-0313-5(9) , JKC120, Horizons) Alpha Omega Pubns., Inc.

Amato, William. Math at the Store. 2002. (gr. k-3). lib. bdg. 12.95 (978-0-613-58787-1(1)) Tandem Library Bks.

—Math in the Backyard. 2002. (Welcome Bks.). (Illus.). 24p. (J). (ps-2). pap. 4.95 (978-0-516-23596-7(6) , Children's Pr.) Scholastic Library Publishing.

—Math in the Car. 2002. (gr. k-3). lib. bdg. 12.95 (978-0-613-58789-1(8)) Tandem Library Bks.

—Math in the Kitchen. 2002. (gr. k-3). lib. bdg. 12.95 (978-0-613-58790-7(1)) Tandem Library Bks.

—Math in the Neighborhood. 2002. (gr. k-3). lib. bdg. 12.95 (978-0-613-58791-4(X)) Tandem Library Bks.

—Math on the Playground. 2002. (Illus.). 24p. (J). (ps-2). pap. 4.95 Scholastic Library Publishing.

Amer Ed Pub, ed. More SkillBuilding Act Gr1. 2007. (Skill Building Learning Activities Ser.). 416p. (J). pap. 15.95 (***978-0-7696-8441-3(6)*** , American Education Publishing) School Specialty Publishing.

—More SkillBuilding Act GrK. 2007. (Skill Building Learning Activities Ser.). 416p. (J). pap. 15.95 (***978-0-7696-8440-6(8)*** , American Education Publishing) School Specialty Publishing.

—More SkillBuilding Act PreK. 2007. (Skill Building Learning Activities Ser.). 416p. (J). pap. 15.95 (***978-0-7696-8439-0(4)*** , American Education Publishing) School Specialty Publishing.

—SkillBuilding Activities Gr1. 2007. (Skill Building Learning Activities Ser.). 416p. (J). pap. 15.95 (***978-0-7696-8431-4(9)*** , American Education Publishing) School Specialty Publishing.

—SkillBuilding Activities GrK. 2007. (Skill Building Learning Activities Ser.). 416p. (J). pap. 15.95 (***978-0-7696-8430-7(0)*** , American Education Publishing) School Specialty Publishing.

—SkillBuilding Activities PreK. 2007. (Skill Building Learning Activities Ser.). 416p. (J). pap. 15.95 (***978-0-7696-8429-1(7)*** , American Education Publishing) School Specialty Publishing.

American Education Publishing Staff. Multiplication. 2003. (Brighter Child Learning Flash Cards Ser.). (Illus.). 36p. (J). 2.99 (978-1-56189-464-2(8) , 31047, American Education Publishing) School Specialty Publishing.

Analysis II: Differenzierbarkeit von Funktionen und Kurvendiskussion. (Duden Abiturhilfen Ser.). (GER.). 112p. (YA). (gr. 11-12). (978-3-411-70172-8(2)) Bibliographisches Institut & F. A. Brockhaus AG DEU. *Dist:* International Bk. Import Service, Inc.

Anastasio, Dina. Math Fun at the Fair. 2003. (Early Connections Ser.). (J). pap. 33.00 (978-1-4108-1076-2(3)) Benchmark Education Co.

Andres, Ken & Johnson, Diane. Math Go Figure Student Book. 2004. 160p. per. (978-1-59318-179-6(5)) Sopris West Educational Services.

Andrews, Ken & Johnson, Diane. You Can Be Algebra Ready. 2003. Pt. 1. 244p. spiral bd. (978-1-57035-848-7(6) , 185STU1); Pt. 2. 256p. spiral bd. (978-1-57035-849-4(4) , 185STU2) Sopris West Educational Services.

Answers to New York State Regents Examination for Three Year Sequence for High School Mathematics (Course I) January 2001, (Course I) June 2001. 2001. (YA). pap. 9.00 (978-0-9719933-3-4(5)) Technical Manuscript.

Antologia: Student & Teacher Support Resources. 1999. (Matematicas en Mi Mundo Ser.). (ENG & SPA.). (gr. k up). (978-0-02-110173-3(6)); (gr. 1 up). (978-0-02-110174-0(4)); (gr. 2 up). (978-0-02-110175-7(2)); (gr. 3 up). (978-0-02-110176-4(0)); (gr. 4 up). (978-0-02-110177-1(9)); (gr. 6 up). (978-0-02-110179-5(5)) Macmillan/McGraw-Hill Schl. Div.

Apgar, Cheryl. Marvelous Math: Hands-On Activities That Maximize Your Math Program. Samoiloff, Sheri, ed. Yamada, Jane, illus. 2001. 96p. pap. 11.99 (978-1-57471-791-4(X)) Creative Teaching Pr., Inc.

Apple. Rosie the Counting Rabbit. (J). (gr. k-2). 75.00 (978-0-669-13447-6(3)) Houghton Mifflin Co. (Schl. Div.).

Appleby, Sue. Umoyana the Little Wind: Kiswahili Version. Lihamba, Amandina, tr. 1999. (Cambridge Reading Routes Ser.). (Illus.). 16p. pap. 3.70 (978-0-521-66886-6(7)) Cambridge Univ. Pr.

Arco Staff. High-Stakes: Math. 2002. (High-Stakes Test Ser.). 224p. (YA). pap. 16.95 (978-0-7689-1070-4(6)) Peterson's.

Arlene, Sonday. The Sonday System - Let's Play Learn: Shapes & Numbers Book. Cindy, Breckman, ed. l.t. ed. 2004. (Illus.). 29p. (J). per. (978-1-891602-12-2(8)) Winsor Learning, Inc.

Armstrong, Linda. Fast Ideas for Busy Teachers: Math, Grade 4. 2004. (Illus.). 80p. (J). (gr. 4-4). pap. 10.99 (978-0-7682-2914-1(6) , FS99308, Schaffer, Frank) Schaffer, Frank Pubns.

—Fast Ideas for Busy Teachers: Math, Grade 5. 2004. (Illus.). 80p. (J). (gr. 5-5). pap. 10.99 (978-0-7682-2915-8(4) , FS99309, Schaffer, Frank) Schaffer, Frank Pubns.

Arnold, Denise & Arnold, Graham. Cambridge HSC Mathematics Study Guide. 2003. (Cambridge HSC Study Guides). 256p. pap. 11.95 (978-0-521-53967-8(6)) Cambridge Univ. Pr.

Arnold, Ellen. Magnificent Mind Masters Multiplication. Farber, Deborah, illus. 2000. (MI Strategies for Kids Ser.). 32p. (J). (gr. 1-5). pap. 7.00 (978-1-56976-116-8(7) , 1145, Zephyr Pr.) Chicago Review Pr., Inc.

Arshaghi, Adel. SAT Mathematics: 1000 Strategies in 1000 Master Tests. 2001. 300p. (YA). per. 24.00 (978-0-9712234-0-0(8)) Megasent Pr.

Arthur's Christmas Cookies. 2003. 22.95 (978-0-673-75906-1(7)) Celebration Pr.

Asher, Sandy. Teddy Teabury's Fabulous Facts. 2nd ed. 2001. 90p. (J). (gr. 3-7). reprint ed. pap. 3.99 (978-0-9707181-0-5(1)) Stanley Bks.

Association of Christian Schools International Staff. Math Grade One Supplemental Exercises: Life in the Sea. 1999. (ACSI Elementary Mathmatics). (Illus.). (gr. 1-2). stu. ed. 21.70 (978-1-58331-192-9(0) , 7240) Assn. of Christian Schls. International.

—Math Grade Three Supplemental: Life on the Land. 1999. (ACSI Elementary Mathmatics). (gr. 3-4). stu. ed. 21.70 (978-1-58331-194-3(7) , 7244) Assn. of Christian Schls. International.

—Math Grade Two Supplemental Exercises: Life in the Air. 1999. (ACSI Elementary Mathmatics). (Illus.). stu. ed. 21.70 (978-1-58331-193-6(9) , 7242) Assn. of Christian Schls. International.

Atkinson, Sue. Maths. 2003. (Hodder Home Learning Ser.). (Illus.). 32p. (J). pap. 6.99 (978-0-340-78475-4(X) , Hodder & Stoughton) Hodder General Publishing Division GBR. *Dist:* Trafalgar Square Publishing.

—Mental Maths: Brand New Activities for Key Stage 2. 2003. (Hodder Home Learning Ser.). (Illus.). 32p. (J). pap. 6.99 (978-0-340-78477-8(6) , Hodder & Stoughton) Hodder General Publishing Division GBR. *Dist:* Trafalgar Square Publishing.

—New Cambridge Mathematics. 2005. (WEL., Illus.). 32p. (978-1-86085-267-1(X)) ICA Video.

—Times Tables: Brand New Activities for Key Stage 2. 2003. (Hodder Home Learning Ser.). (Illus.). 32p. (J). pap. 6.99 (978-0-340-78476-1(8) , Hodder & Stoughton) Hodder General Publishing Division GBR. *Dist:* Trafalgar Square Publishing.

Atkinson, Sue, et al. First Skills in Numeracy 2 Practice Book, 10 pack, Bk. 1. 1998. (First Skills in Numeracy Ser.). (Illus.). 16p. pap. 10.00 (978-0-521-63432-8(6)) Cambridge Univ. Pr.

Audiocasete: a resolver Problemas! Student & Teacher Support Resources. 1999. (Matematicas en Mi Mundo Ser.). (ENG & SPA.). (gr. 1 up). (978-0-02-110724-7(6)); (gr. 3 up). (978-0-02-110726-1(2)); (gr. 4 up). (978-0-02-110727-8(0)); (gr. 5 up). (978-0-02-110728-5(9)) Macmillan/McGraw-Hill Schl. Div.

Aufmann. Aufmann Essentials of Precalculus Plus Dvd. 2005. (YA). 121.96 (978-0-618-72285-3(8) , 397235) Houghton Mifflin College Div.

—Aufmann Essentials of Precalculus Plus Student Solutions Manual. 2005. (YA). pap., pap. 121.96 (978-0-618-72284-6(X) , 397234) Houghton Mifflin College Div.

—Aufmann Prealgebra Fourth Edition Plus Nolting Math Study Skills Workbook Second Edition Plus Eduspace One Semester. 4th ed. 2004. (YA). pap., pap., pap. 135.56 (978-0-618-54077-8(6) , 389706) Houghton Mifflin College Div.

—Prealgebra: With Math Space & Eduspace/Blackboard Platform. 4th ed. 2004. (YA). pap., pap. 117.96 incl. cd-rom (978-0-618-52295-8(6) , 389350) Houghton Mifflin College Div.

Austin and Nelson Publishers Staff, et al. Funtastic Math Games. 1999. 96p. (J). (gr. 5-8). pap. 10.99 (978-1-56822-747-4(7) , IF2505) School Specialty Publishing.

Autoadhesivos: Superlibros de Literatura/Literature Big Books. 1999. (Matematicas en Mi Mundo Ser.). (ENG & SPA.). (gr. k up). (978-0-02-110700-1(9)); (gr. 1 up). (978-0-02-110268-6(6)) Macmillan/McGraw-Hill Schl. Div.

Avenues PreK Level: Plastic Magnetic Numbers. (ps-12). 11.04 (978-0-7362-2467-3(X)) Hampton-Brown Bks.

Avery, Sue. Essential Standard General Maths. rev. ed. 2006. (Essential Mathematics Ser.). pap. 13.95 (978-0-521-61254-8(3)) Cambridge Univ. Pr.

Ayudas Graficas: Student & Teacher Support Resources. 1999. (Matematicas en Mi Mundo Ser.). (ENG & SPA.). (gr. k up). (978-0-02-110233-4(3)); (gr. 1 up). (978-0-02-110234-1(1)); (gr. 2 up). (978-0-02-110235-8(X)); (gr. 3 up). (978-0-02-110236-5(8)); (gr. 4 up). (978-0-02-110237-2(6)); (gr. 6 up). (978-0-02-110239-6(2)) Macmillan/McGraw-Hill Schl. Div.

Ayudas graficas: Transparencias: Student & Teacher Support Resources. 1999. (Matematicas en Mi Mundo Ser.). (ENG & SPA.). (gr. 1 up). (978-0-02-110678-3(9)); (gr. 3 up). (978-0-02-110680-6(0)); (gr. 4 up). (978-0-02-110681-3(9)); (gr. 6 up). (978-0-02-110683-7(5)) Macmillan/McGraw-Hill Schl. Div.

Babsky, Irene & Babb, Joanna. Playing with Numbers. 2003. (Illus.). 64p. 14.99 (978-0-7548-1054-4(2) , Lorenz Bks.) Anness Publishing GBR. *Dist:* National Bk. Network.

Baker, David. Allwedd Mathemateg TGAU. 2005. (WEL., Illus.). 468p. pap. (978-1-85644-863-5(0)) Univ. of Wales, Aberystwyth, Centre for Educational Studies.

Baker, David & Kervegant, Ffion. Allwedd Mathemateg 71. 2005. (WEL., Illus.). 410p. (978-1-85644-427-9(9)) Univ. of Wales, Aberystwyth, Centre for Educational Studies.

—Allwedd Mathemateg 83. 2005. (WEL., Illus.). 380p. (978-1-85644-576-4(3)) Univ. of Wales, Aberystwyth, Centre for Educational Studies.

—Allwedd Mathemateg TGAU. 2005. (WEL., Illus.). iv, 508p. (978-1-85644-862-8(2)) Univ. of Wales, Aberystwyth, Centre for Educational Studies.

Baker, David, et al. Key Maths 7-1. 2nd rev. ed. 2000. (Illus.). 410p. (J). (gr. 6-9). pap. 29.50 (978-0-7487-5524-0(1)) Nelson Thornes Ltd. GBR. *Dist:* Trans-Atlantic Pubns., Inc.

—Key Maths 7-2. 2nd rev. ed. 2000. (Illus.). 426p. (J). (gr. 6-9). pap. 29.50 (978-0-7487-5525-7(X)) Nelson Thornes Ltd. GBR. *Dist:* Trans-Atlantic Pubns., Inc.

Ball, Barbara & Ball, Derek. Task Maths Interactive 1: Sequence Machines. 2005. cd-rom 190.00 (978-1-84565-124-4(3)) Cambridge Univ. Pr.

—Task Maths Interactive 3: Is it Possible? 2006. cd-rom 190.00 (978-1-84565-946-2(5)) Cambridge Univ. Pr.

—Task Maths Interactive 4: Number Pyramids. 2006. cd-rom 177.00 (978-1-84565-947-9(3)) Cambridge Univ. Pr.

Ball, Johnny. Go Figure: A Totally Cool Book about Numbers. 2005. (Illus.). 96p. (J). 15.99 (978-0-7566-1374-7(4)) Dorling Kindersley Publishing, Inc.

Ball, Susan, et al. Formula One Mathematics Gold A: Year 7. 2003. (Illus.). 216p. pap., pupil's gde. ed. 39.50 (***978-0-340-86932-1(1)*** , Hodder Murray) Hodder Education GBR. *Dist:* Trans-Atlantic Pubns., Inc.

—Formula One Mathematics Gold B: Year 8. 2004. (Illus.). 228p. pap., pupil's gde. ed. 39.50 (***978-0-340-86933-8(X)*** , Hodder Murray) Hodder Education GBR. *Dist:* Trans-Atlantic Pubns., Inc.

Ballart, Elisabet. Juguemos a Contar. Capdevila, Roser, illus. 2003. (SPA.). (J). (978-970-690-757-8(2)) Planeta Mexicana Editorial S. A. de C. V.

Balloon Books Staff. Division. 1999. (Play & Learn Ser.). (Illus.). 16p. (ps-3). pap., wbk. ed. 3.95 (978-0-8069-7825-3(2)) Sterling Publishing Co., Inc.

—Multiplication. 1999. (Play & Learn Ser.). (Illus.). 16p. (ps-3). pap. 3.95 (978-0-8069-7823-9(6)) Sterling Publishing Co., Inc.

Bangs, Lawrence Bailey. Math & Music. 2000. (Bigger World Ser.: Vol. 2). (YA). incl. cd-rom (978-1-59106-013-0(3)) Wildridge Software, Inc.

Un banquete Para 10: Superlibros de Literatura/Literature Big Books. 1999. (Matematicas en Mi Mundo Ser.). (ENG & SPA.). (gr. 1 up). (978-0-02-110162-7(0)) Macmillan/McGraw-Hill Schl. Div.

Barbie Kindergarten Learning Pads: Basic Math. 2004. (Illus.). 48p. (J). (978-0-7666-0613-5(9) , 49870) Modern Publishing.

Barbour, Karen, illus. Marvelous Math: A Book of Poems. 2001. 32p. (J). 7.99 (978-0-689-84442-3(5) , Aladdin) Simon & Schuster Children's Publishing.

Barker. Barker, Essential Math with Applications, 7th Edition Plus Aufmann, Basic College Math Student Solution Manual, 8th Edition. 7th ed. 2005. (YA). pap., pap. 83.16 (978-0-618-64216-8(1) , 396089) Houghton Mifflin College Div.

Barnes, John, et al. Science, Maths & Technology. 2003. (Illus.). 184p. pap. (978-0-7487-7121-9(2)) Nelson Thornes Ltd.

Barnett, Carne S., et al. General Math. 128p. (YA). (gr. 7-12). pap. 33.95 (978-0-201-25188-3(4)) Globe Fearon Educational Publishing.

—Pre-Algebra. 152p. (YA). (gr. 7-12). pap. 33.95 (978-0-201-25976-6(1)) Globe Fearon Educational Publishing.

Barulich, Shirley. Money Math Learning Centers, Grades K-2: 10 Easy Centers with Skill-Building Activities That Teach Counting, One-to-One Correspondence, Sorting, Addition, & Subtraction-and Meet the NCTM Standards. 2005. (Illus.). 64p. pap. 11.99 (978-0-439-51381-4(2) , Teaching Resources) Scholastic, Inc.

Baseball Math Kindergarten Workbook. 2006. (J). (***978-0-9787458-0-6(9)***) Sport Workbooks.

Basic Facts To 18 (Gr. 2-3) 2003. (J). (978-1-58232-084-7(5)) Bryan Hse. Pubs., Inc.

Basic Facts to 18 Spanish Version. 2007. (J). per. (***978-1-58232-153-0(1)***) Bryan Hse. Pubs., Inc.

Basic Math Skills. 2005. 304p. (gr. 4 up). 29.99 (978-1-55799-937-5(6) , EMC 3017); 2003. (J). (gr. 1). pap. 29.99 (978-1-55799-896-5(5) , EMC 3014); 2003. (J). (gr. 2). pap. 29.99 (978-1-55799-897-2(3) , EMC 3015); 2003. (J). (gr. 3). pap. 29.99 (978-1-55799-898-9(1) ; EMC 3016) Evan-Moor Educational Pubs.

Basic Math Skills, Chapter 2, Activities. 2005. (Illus.). 52p. (YA). pap. 5.00 (978-1-59476-036-5(5)) Paradigm Accelerated Curriculum.

Basic Math Skills, Chapter 2, Text. 2005. (Illus.). 72p. (YA). pap. 7.00 (978-1-59476-024-2(1)) Paradigm Accelerated Curriculum.

Basic Math Skills, Chapter 3, Activities. 2005. (Illus.). 42p. (YA). pap. 5.00 (978-1-59476-037-2(3)) Paradigm Accelerated Curriculum.

Basic Math Skills, Chapter 3, Text. 2005. (Illus.). 68p. (YA). pap. 7.00 (978-1-59476-025-9(X)) Paradigm Accelerated Curriculum.

Basic Math Skills, Chapter 4, Activities. 2005. (Illus.). 48p. (YA). pap. 5.00 (978-1-59476-038-9(1)) Paradigm Accelerated Curriculum.

Basic Math Skills, Chapter 4, Text. 2005. (Illus.). 70p. (YA). pap. 7.00 (978-1-59476-026-6(8)) Paradigm Accelerated Curriculum.

Basic Math Skills, Chapter 5, Activities. 2005. (Illus.). 40p. (YA). pap. 5.00 (978-1-59476-039-6(X)) Paradigm Accelerated Curriculum.

Basic Math Skills, Chapter 5, Text. 2005. (Illus.). 62p. (YA). pap. 7.00 (978-1-59476-027-3(6)) Paradigm Accelerated Curriculum.

Basic Math Skills, Chapter 6, Activities. 2005. (Illus.). 52p. (YA). pap. 5.00 (978-1-59476-040-2(3)) Paradigm Accelerated Curriculum.

Basic Math Skills, Chapter 6, Text. 2005. (Illus.). 70p. (YA). pap. 7.00 (978-1-59476-028-0(4)) Paradigm Accelerated Curriculum.

Basic Skills Math Books: Math Topics. (Basic Skills Ser.). 48p. (gr. 6 up). 5.99 (978-1-56822-094-9(4) , IF5114); (gr. 7 up). 5.99 (978-1-56822-097-0(9) , IF5117) School Specialty Publishing.

Basic Skills Math Books: Numeration. (Basic Skills Ser.). 48p. (gr. k up). 5.99 (978-1-56822-081-9(2) , IF5101) School Specialty Publishing.

Basiswissen Mathematik zur Physik. (Duden Abiturhilfen Ser.). (GER.). 96p. (YA). (gr. 11-13). (978-3-411-04841-0(7)) Bibliographisches Institut & F. A. Brockhaus AG DEU. *Dist:* International Bk. Import Service, Inc.

Bassarear. Student Solutions Manual: Used with ... Bassarear-Mathematics for Elementary School Teachers. 3rd ed. 2004. (YA). stu. ed. 29.16 (978-0-618-34888-6(3) , 304152) Houghton Mifflin College Div.

Bauer, David. Adding Arctic Animals. 2003. (Yellow Umbrella Books for Early Readers). (Illus.). 17p. (J). 15.93 (978-0-7368-2913-7(X)); pap. (978-0-7368-2872-7(9)) Yellow Umbrella Pr.

Beall, Scott. Functional Melodies: Finding Mathematical Relationships in Music. 2000. (Illus.). 170p. (YA). (gr. 8-12). pap. 24.95 (978-1-55953-378-2(1) , MN53378) Key Curriculum Pr.

Bear's Book of Numbers. 2004. 12p. (J). bds. 2.99 (978-1-85997-429-2(5)) Byeway Bks.

Beck, Esther. Please Don't Laugh, I Can Use a Graph! 2006. (Illus.). 24p. (J). (978-1-59928-615-0(7)) ABDO Publishing Co.

Beck, Ray, et al. Practicing Basic Skills in Math: Grades 2-3. 2004. (One-Minute Fluency Builders Ser.). 560p. per. (978-1-59318-001-0(2) , 237MATH2-3) Sopris West Educational Services.

—Practicing Basic Skills in Math: Grades 4-5. 2004. (One-Minute Fluency Builders Ser.). 592p. per. (978-1-59318-002-7(0) , 237MATH4-5) Sopris West Educational Services.

—Practicing Basic Skills in Math: Grades 6-8. 2004. (One-Minute Fluency Builders Ser.). 558p. per. (978-1-59318-003-4(9) , 237MATH6-8) Sopris West Educational Services.

—Practicing Basic Skills in Math: Grades K-1. 2004. (One-Minute Fluency Builders Ser.). 352p. per. (978-1-59318-000-3(4) , 237MATHK-1) Sopris West Educational Services.

—Practicing Basic Skills in Math: Secondary Remedial. 2004. (One-Minute Fluency Builders Ser.). 766p. per. (978-1-59318-004-1(7) , 237MATHREM) Sopris West Educational Services.

Beckes, Shirley V., illus. Dialing Numbers. 2002. (Dial Bks.). 10p. (J). (ps-k). bds. 10.95 (978-1-57145-520-8(5) , Silver Dolphin Bks.) Advantage Pubs. Group.

Bedora, Julie. Ready-to-Go Skill-Building Math Packs for Independent Learning: Reproducible Packs of Fun Practice Pages That Help Kids Really Learn All the Math Concepts They Need to Know Independently! 2001. 180p. pap. 16.95 (978-0-439-15390-4(5)) Scholastic, Inc.

Beers, Bonnie. Everyone Uses Math. 2002. (Yellow Umbrella Books). (Illus.). 16p. (J). (gr. 1). lib. bdg. 14.60 (978-0-7368-1281-8(4) , Pebble Bks.) Capstone Pr., Inc.

Beers, Jack. Anchors Grade 1. 2003. (Voyages Ser.). (J). (gr. 1). stu. ed., per. 11.95 (978-1-58830-345-5(4)) Metropolitan Teaching & Learning Co.

—Anchors Grade 1 SP. 2004. (Voyages Ser.). (J). (gr. 1). stu. ed., per. 16.53 (978-1-58830-990-7(8)) Metropolitan Teaching & Learning Co.

—Anchors Grade 2. 2003. (Voyages Ser.). (J). (gr. 2). stu. ed., per. 13.95 (978-1-58830-346-2(2)) Metropolitan Teaching & Learning Co.

—Anchors Grade 2 SP. 2004. (Voyages Ser.). (J). (gr. 2). stu. ed., per. 16.53 (978-1-58830-991-4(6)) Metropolitan Teaching & Learning Co.

—Anchors Grade 3. 2003. (Voyages Ser.). (J). (gr. 3). stu. ed., per. 13.95 (978-1-58830-347-9(0)) Metropolitan Teaching & Learning Co.

—Anchors Grade 3 SP. 2004. (Voyages Ser.). (J). (gr. 3). stu. ed., per. 16.53 (978-1-58830-992-1(4)) Metropolitan Teaching & Learning Co.

—Anchors Grade 4. 2003. (Voyages Ser.). (J). (gr. 4). stu. ed., per. 13.95 (978-1-58830-348-6(9)) Metropolitan Teaching & Learning Co.

—Anchors Grade 5 Student Edition. 2003. (Voyages Ser.). (J). (gr. 5). per. 13.95 (978-1-58830-470-4(1)) Metropolitan Teaching & Learning Co.

—Bridges-Blue. 2003. (Metro Math Bridges Ser.). (J). (gr. 8). stu. ed., per. 13.95 (978-1-58830-191-8(5)) Metropolitan Teaching & Learning Co.

—Bridges-Gold. 2003. (Metro Math Bridges Ser.). (gr. 7). tchr. ed., per. 19.95 (978-1-58830-613-5(5)) Metropolitan Teaching & Learning Co.

—Bridges-Red. 2003. (Metro Math Bridges Ser.). (J). (gr. 6). stu. ed., per. 13.95 (978-1-58830-190-1(7)) Metropolitan Teaching & Learning Co.

—Cuales van Juntos? Metro Math Readers Red Level. 2000. (J). (gr. k-1). 3.30 (978-1-58120-384-4(5)) Metropolitan Teaching & Learning Co.

—Cuantos? 2000. (Metro Math Readers Red Level Ser.). (J). (gr. k-1). 41.95 (978-1-58830-526-8(0)) Metropolitan Teaching & Learning Co.

—Cuantos Hay en Total: Metro Math Readers Red Level. 2000. (J). 3.30 (978-1-58120-385-1(3)) Metropolitan Teaching & Learning Co.

—Dedos de cinco en cinco: Metro Math Readers Yellow Level. 2000. (Metro Math Readers Yellow Level Ser.). (J). (gr. 1-2). 3.75 (978-1-58120-485-8(X)) Metropolitan Teaching & Learning Co.

—Fingers Go Five by Five. 2000. (Metro Math Readers Yellow Level Ser.). (J). (gr. 1-2). 3.75 (978-1-58120-422-3(1)) Metropolitan Teaching & Learning Co.

—Gira a la izquierda. gira a la deracha: Metro Math Readers Yellow Level. 2000. (Metro Math Readers Yellow Level Ser.). (SPA.). (J). (gr. 1-2). 3.75 (978-1-58120-478-0(7)) Metropolitan Teaching & Learning Co.

—How Many? How Much? 2000. (Metro Math Readers Red Level Ser.). (J). (gr. k-1). 41.95 (978-1-58120-556-5(2)) Metropolitan Teaching & Learning Co.

—How Many in All? Metro Math Readers Red Level. 2000. (J). (gr. k-1). 3.30 (978-1-58120-321-9(7)) Metropolitan Teaching & Learning Co.

—It's about Time: Metro Math Readers Yellow Level. 2000. (Metro Math Readers Yellow Level Ser.). (J). (gr. 1-2). 3.75 (978-1-58120-412-4(4)) Metropolitan Teaching & Learning Co.

—The Number Four: Metro Math Readers Red Level. 2002. (Metro Reading Ser.). (gr. 12). per. 46.59 (978-1-58120-634-0(8)) Metropolitan Teaching & Learning Co.

—The Number Six. 2000. (J). 3.30 (978-1-58120-306-6(3)) Metropolitan Teaching & Learning Co.

—Ositas, de diez en diez: Metro Math Readers Yellow Level. 2000. (Metro Math Readers Yellow Level Ser.). (J). (gr. 1-2). 3.75 (978-1-58120-470-4(1)) Metropolitan Teaching & Learning Co.

—Que dos cosas son iguales? Metro Math Readers Red Level. 2000. (J). 3.30 (978-1-58120-382-0(9)) Metropolitan Teaching & Learning Co.

—Rectangles: Metro Math Readers Red Level. 2000. (J). 3.30 (978-1-58120-315-8(2)) Metropolitan Teaching & Learning Co.

—Rectangulos: Metro Math Readers Red Level. 2000. (J). 3.30 (978-1-58120-379-0(9)) Metropolitan Teaching & Learning Co.

—La Simetria: Metro Math Readers Yellow Level. 2000. (Metro Math Readers Yellow Level Ser.). (J). (gr. 1-2). 3.75 (978-1-58120-477-3(9)) Metropolitan Teaching & Learning Co.

—Step 4 Student Edition. 1999. (Problem Solving Step by Step Ser.). (J). (gr. 4). stu. ed., per. 8.95 (978-1-58120-704-0(2)) Metropolitan Teaching & Learning Co.

—Step 4 Student Edition 6-Pack. 1999. (Problem Solving Step by Step Ser.). (J). (gr. 4). stu. ed., per. 69.95 (978-1-58120-734-7(4)) Metropolitan Teaching & Learning Co.

—Step 5 Student Edition. 1999. (Problem Solving Step by Step Ser.). (J). (gr. 5). stu. ed., per. 8.95 (978-1-58120-705-7(0)) Metropolitan Teaching & Learning Co.

—Step 5 Student Edition 10-Pack. 1999. (Problem Solving Step by Step Ser.). (J). (gr. 5). stu. ed., per. 97.95 (978-1-58830-175-8(3)) Metropolitan Teaching & Learning Co.

—Step 5 Student Edition 6-Pack. 1999. (Problem Solving Step by Step Ser.). (J). (gr. 5). stu. ed., per. 69.95 (978-1-58120-735-4(2)) Metropolitan Teaching & Learning Co.

—Step 6 Student Edition. 1999. (Problem Solving Step by Step Ser.). (J). (gr. 6). stu. ed., per. 8.95 (978-1-58120-706-4(9)) Metropolitan Teaching & Learning Co.

—Step 6 Student Edition 10-Pack. 1999. (Problem Solving Step by Step Ser.). (J). (gr. 6). stu. ed., per. 97.95 (978-1-58830-176-5(1)) Metropolitan Teaching & Learning Co.

—Step 6 Student Edition 6-Pack. 1999. (Problem Solving Step by Step Ser.). (J). (gr. 6). stu. ed., per. 69.95 (978-1-58120-736-1(0)) Metropolitan Teaching & Learning Co.

—Step 7 Student Edition. 1999. (Problem Solving Step by Step Ser.). (J). (gr. 7). stu. ed., per. 8.95 (978-1-58120-673-9(9)) Metropolitan Teaching & Learning Co.

—Step 7 Student Edition 10-Pack. 1999. (Problem Solving Step by Step Ser.). (J). (gr. 7). stu. ed., per. 108.95 (978-1-58830-177-2(X)) Metropolitan Teaching & Learning Co.

—Step 7 Student Edition 6-Pack. 1999. (Problem Solving Step by Step Ser.). (J). (gr. 7). stu. ed., per. 65.95 (978-1-58120-674-6(7)) Metropolitan Teaching & Learning Co.

—Step 8 6-Pack: Student Edition & Pretests/Posttests. 1999. (Problem Solving Step by Step Ser.). (J). (gr. 8). stu. ed., per. 71.95 (978-1-58120-688-3(7)) Metropolitan Teaching & Learning Co.

—Step 8 Student Edition. 1999. (Problem Solving Step by Step Ser.). (J). (gr. 8). stu. ed., per. 8.95 (978-1-58120-681-4(X)) Metropolitan Teaching & Learning Co.

—Step 8 Student Edition 10-Pack. 1999. (Problem Solving Step by Step Ser.). (J). (gr. 8). stu. ed., per. 108.95 (978-1-58830-178-9(8)) Metropolitan Teaching & Learning Co.

—Symmetry: Metro Math Readers Yellow Level. 2000. (Metro Math Readers Yellow Level Ser.). (J). (gr. 1-2). 3.75 (978-1-58120-414-8(0)) Metropolitan Teaching & Learning Co.

—Triangles: Metro Math Readers Red Level. 2000. (J). 3.30 (978-1-58120-314-1(4)) Metropolitan Teaching & Learning Co.

—Triangulos: Metro Math Readers Red Level. 2000. (J). 3.30 (978-1-58120-378-3(0)) Metropolitan Teaching & Learning Co.

—Turn to the Left, Turn to the Right: Metro Math Reader Yellow Level. 2000. (Metro Math Readers Yellow Level Ser.). (J). (gr. 1-2). 3.75 (978-1-58120-415-5(9)) Metropolitan Teaching & Learning Co.

—Which Belong Together? Metro Math Readers Red Level. 2000. (Illus.). (J). 3.30 (978-1-58120-320-2(9)) Metropolitan Teaching & Learning Co.

—Which Two Are the Same? Metro Math Readers Red Level. 2000. (J). 3.30 (978-1-58120-318-9(7)) Metropolitan Teaching & Learning Co.

—Ya Es Hora: Metro Math Readers Yellow Level. 2000. (Metro Math Readers Yellow Level Ser.). (J). (gr. 1-2). 3.75 (978-1-58120-475-9(2)) Metropolitan Teaching & Learning Co.

Beginning Numbers. 2004. (Basic Skills Ser.). 48p. (J). pap. 6.99 (978-0-88724-187-1(5) , CD-4725) Carson-Dellosa Publishing Co., Inc.

Beginning Problem Solving with Mr Wiggle. 2003. 32p. (gr. k up). 4.99 (978-1-56451-964-1(3) , ID99045); (gr. 2 up). 4.99 (978-1-56451-966-5(X) , ID99044) School Specialty Publishing.

Beissinger, Janet & Pless, Vera. The Cryptoclub: Using Mathematics to Make & Break Secret Codes. 2006. (Illus.). 300p. pap. 35.00 (978-1-56881-223-6(X)) AK Peters, Ltd.

Bello. Topics in Contemporary Math. 8th ed. 2004. (YA). pap., stu. ed. 125.16 (978-0-618-51432-8(5) , 389231) Houghton Mifflin College Div.

—Topics in Contemporary Math 8th Edition Plus Eduspace Two Semester. 8th ed. 2004. (YA). pap. 125.16 (978-0-618-52822-6(9) , 389426) Houghton Mifflin College Div.

Benchmark Education Staff, compiled by. Math Standards Set. 2005. spiral bd. 3950.00 ***(*978-1-4108-5456-8(6))*** Benchmark Education Co.

—Math Strands Set. 2005. spiral bd. 2580.00 ***(*978-1-4108-5458-2(2));*** spiral bd. 695.00 ***(*978-1-4108-5561-9(9))*** Benchmark Education Co.

—Math Texts Set. 2005. 110.00 ***(*978-1-4108-3828-5(5));*** 130.00 ***(*978-1-4108-3833-9(1));*** 50.00 ***(*978-1-4108-3835-3(8));*** 20.00 ***(*978-1-4108-3838-4(2));*** spiral bd. 750.00 ***(*978-1-4108-3827-8(7));*** spiral bd. 3685.00 ***(*978-1-4108-3821-6(8));*** spiral bd. 835.00 ***(*978-1-4108-3832-2(3));*** spiral bd. 335.00 ***(*978-1-4108-3834-6(X));*** spiral bd. 100.00 ***(*978-1-4108-3836-0(6));*** spiral bd. 95.00 ***(*978-1-4108-3837-7(4));*** (J). spiral bd. 575.00 ***(*978-1-4108-5332-5(2))*** Benchmark Education Co.

—Math Themes. 2006. spiral bd. 1295.00 ***(*978-1-4108-7055-1(3));*** spiral bd. 1125.00 ***(*978-1-4108-7078-0(2));*** spiral bd. 659.00 ***(*978-1-4108-7095-7(2))*** Benchmark Education Co.

—Numbers & Operations. 2006. spiral bd. 235.00 ***(*978-1-4108-7094-0(4));*** 2005. spiral bd. 420.00 ***(*978-1-4108-3882-7(X));*** 2005. spiral bd. 695.00 ***(*978-1-4108-3889-6(7));*** 2005. spiral bd. 370.00 ***(*978-1-4108-3890-2(0));*** 2005. spiral bd. 75.00 ***(*978-1-4108-3904-6(4));*** 2005. spiral bd. 75.00 ***(*978-1-4108-3905-3(2));*** 2005. spiral bd. 75.00 ***(*978-1-4108-3906-0(0));*** 2005. spiral bd. 615.00 ***(*978-1-4108-3881-0(1));*** 2005. spiral bd. 50.00 ***(*978-1-4108-3907-7(9));*** 2005. spiral bd. 75.00 ***(*978-1-4108-3912-1(5));*** 2005. spiral bd. 1020.00 ***(*978-1-4108-4509-2(5));*** 2005. spiral bd. 1095.00 ***(*978-1-4108-5447-6(7));*** 2005. spiral bd. 120.00 ***(*978-1-4108-5448-3(5));*** 2005. spiral bd. 905.00 ***(*978-1-4108-5858-0(8));*** 2005. spiral bd. 120.00 ***(*978-1-4108-5859-7(6));*** 2005. spiral bd. 95.00 ***(*978-1-4108-3911-4(7))*** Benchmark Education Co.

—Read & Achieve Math Small Group Set. 2005. spiral bd. 3500.00 ***(*978-1-4108-3815-5(3));*** spiral bd. 500.00 ***(*978-1-4108-4172-8(3));*** spiral bd. 3500.00 ***(*978-1-4108-4173-5(1))*** Benchmark Education Co.

—Read & Achieve Math Whole Group Set. 2005. spiral bd. 2275.00 ***(*978-1-4108-4170-4(7));*** spiral bd. 5275.00 ***(*978-1-4108-4171-1(5))*** Benchmark Education Co.

—Spanish Math Standard Sets. 2005. spiral bd. 2775.00 ***(*978-1-4108-5867-2(7))*** Benchmark Education Co.

—Using Maps, Graphs & Charts. 2006. spiral bd. 99.00 ***(*978-1-4108-7091-9(X))*** Benchmark Education Co.

Benhoff, Susan. Measurement. 1998. (Basic Skills Ser.). (Illus.). 32p. (gr. 3-5). pap. 4.99 (978-0-88724-465-0(3) , CD-2133) Carson-Dellosa Publishing Co., Inc.

Bennett. Math: Chapter Resource: Indiana Middle School Edition. 4th ed. 2004. (J). 60.40 (978-0-03-070979-1(2)) Harcourt Schl. Pubs.

—Math: Chapter Resources: Illinois Middle School Edition. 4th ed. 2004. (J). 58.60 (978-0-03-070978-4(4)) Harcourt Schl. Pubs.

—Math: Chapter Resources: New York Middle School Edition. 4th ed. 2004. (J). 58.60 (978-0-03-070981-4(4)) Harcourt Schl. Pubs.

—Math: Chapter Resources: Virginia Middle School Edition. 4th ed. 2004. (J). 58.60 (978-0-03-070984-5(9)) Holt, Rinehart & Winston.

—Math: Chapter Resources: Florida Middle School Edition. 4th ed. 2004. (J). 60.40 (978-0-03-070977-7(6)) Harcourt Schl. Pubs.

—Math 2: Chapter Resources: Illinois Middle School Edition. 4th ed. 2004. 60.60 (978-0-03-071006-3(5)) Holt, Rinehart & Winston.

—Math 2: Chapter Resources: New York Middle School Edition. 4th ed. 2004. (J). 60.60 (978-0-03-071008-7(1)) Holt, Rinehart & Winston.

—Math 2: Chapter Resources: Virginia Middle School Edition. 4th ed. 2004. (J). 60.60 (978-0-03-071123-7(1)) Holt, Rinehart & Winston.

—Math 3: Chapter Resources: Illinois Middle School Edition. 4th ed. 2004. 60.60 (978-0-03-071137-4(1)) Holt, Rinehart & Winston.

—Math 3: Chapter Resources: New York Middle School Edition. 4th ed. 2004. (J). 60.60 (978-0-03-071139-8(8)) Holt, Rinehart & Winston.

—Math 3: Chapter Resources: Virginia Middle School Edition. 4th ed. 2004. (J). 60.60 (978-0-03-071144-2(4)) Holt, Rinehart & Winston.

—Middle School Math Course 3. 4th ed. 2004. (SPA., Illus.). 62.46 (978-0-03-071143-5(6)) Holt, Rinehart & Winston.

Berger, Debra Wolk. Getting Ready to Take the Math 10 CAPTest. 2002. (Illus.). 192p. (YA). (gr. 10-12). pap., wbk. ed. 10.95 (978-1-56762-174-7(0) , Kingsbridge Pr.) Modern Learning Pr.

Berry, Catherine, et al. Formula One Maths, Vol. 1. Porkess, Roger, ed. 2001. (Illus.). 256p. pap., stu. ed., pupil's gde. ed. 39.50 ***(*978-0-340-77974-3(8)*** , Hodder Murray) Hodder Education GBR. *Dist:* Trans-Atlantic Pubns., Inc.

—Formula One Maths, Vol. 2. 2002. (Illus.). 256p. pap., stu. ed., pupil's gde. ed. 39.50 ***(*978-0-340-80306-6(1)*** , Hodder Murray) Hodder Education GBR. *Dist:* Trans-Atlantic Pubns., Inc.

—Formula One Maths. Porkess, Roger, ed. (Illus.). Vol. 2. 2001. 256p. pap., stu. ed., pupil's gde. ed. 39.50 ***(*978-0-340-77975-0(6));*** Vol. 3. 2002. 240p. pap., stu. ed., pupil's gde. ed. 39.50 ***(*978-0-340-77978-1(0))*** Hodder Education GBR. (Hodder Murray). *Dist:* Trans-Atlantic Pubns., Inc.

—Formula One Maths: B1, Vol. 1. Porkess, Roger, ed. 2002. (Illus.). 240p. pap., pupil's gde. ed. 39.50 ***(*978-0-340-77976-7(4)*** , Hodder Murray) Hodder Education GBR. *Dist:* Trans-Atlantic Pubns., Inc.

Big Book Tote Bag, 2, Pack. 2003. (Metro Reading Ser.). (J). (gr. 12). 26.45 (978-1-58120-613-5(5)) Metropolitan Teaching & Learning Co.

Bittinger, Gayle. Fast Ideas for Busy Teachers: Math, Grade K. 2004. (Illus.). 80p. (J). (gr. k-k). pap. 10.99 (978-0-7682-2910-3(3) , FS99360, Schaffer, Frank) Schaffer, Frank Pubns.

Blau, Lisa. Easy Math for the Overhead: 10 Transparencies, Punch-Out Numbers & Manipulatives & Fun Lessons. 2000. (Illus.). 32p. pap. 11.95 (978-0-439-08679-0(5)) Scholastic, Inc.

Blevins, Wiley, ed. Grade K. 2006. (SmartSquares Ser.). 16p. 14.99 (978-0-439-83831-3(2) , Teaching Resources) Scholastic, Inc.

—Grade PreK. 2006. (SmartSquares Ser.). 16p. spiral bd. 14.99 (978-0-439-83829-0(0) , Teaching Resources) Scholastic, Inc.

Block, Cheryl. Mind Building Reading: Developing Skills Using Critical Thinking. 2004. (J). pap. 19.99 (978-0-89455-846-7(3)) Critical Thinking Bks. & Software.

Blundell, Gillian & Graham, Noel. Problem Solving Activities with Mottik. (Illus.). 64p. (J). (gr. k-4). pap. 12.50 (978-1-871098-21-1(1)) Claire Pubns. GBR. *Dist:* Parkwest Pubns., Inc.

Bodach, Vijaya. Bar Graphs. 2008. (J). ***(*978-1-4296-0040-8(3))*** Capstone Pr., Inc.

—Pie Graphs. 2008. (J). ***(*978-1-4296-0042-2(X))*** Capstone Pr., Inc.

—Tally Charts. 2008. (J). ***(*978-1-4296-0043-9(8))*** Capstone Pr., Inc.

Bolster. Mathematics Grade 3. (Illus.). (J). pap., stu. ed. 6.59 (978-0-673-11812-7(6)) Addison-Wesley Educational Pubs., Inc.

Books are Fun Exclusive Start Math, 4, Bk. 2, Set. 2005. (J). lib. bdg. (978-1-59566-163-0(8)) QEB Publishing Inc.

Boothroyd, Jennifer. Grouping. 2007. (First Step Nonfiction Ser.). (J). pap. (978-0-8225-6826-1(8)) Lerner Publishing Group.

Bostock, L. & Chandler, S. Core Maths for Advanced Level. 3rd rev. ed. 2000. (Illus.). 534p. (C). pap. 57.50 (978-0-7487-5509-7(8)) Nelson Thornes Ltd. GBR. *Dist:* Trans-Atlantic Pubns., Inc.

Bourgeois, Paulette. Fun with Franklin: Math Activity Book. Clark, Brenda, illus. 1998. (Franklin Ser.). 72p. (J). (ps-3). (978-1-55074-452-1(6)) Kids Can Pr., Ltd.

Bove, Jennifer G. & Hatch, Thomas H. Working with Fractions, Decimals, & Percents: Up-to-Speed Math. 2001. (Illus.). 96p. per. 8.95 (978-1-56254-365-5(2) , SP 3652) Saddleback Educational Publishing.

Brain-Boosting Math. 2003. 128p. (J). per. 10.99 (978-0-88724-932-7(9) , CD-4333); per. 10.99 (978-0-88724-934-1(5) , CD-4335) Carson-Dellosa Publishing Co., Inc.

Brain Boosting Math. 2003. 128p. (J). per. 10.99 (978-0-88724-933-4(7) , CD-4334) Carson-Dellosa Publishing Co., Inc.

Brandenberger, Barry Max, ed. Mathematics, 4 vols. 2001. (Science Library for Students). (Illus.). (J). Vol. 1. 192p. 85.00 (978-0-02-865562-8(1)); Vol. 2. (978-0-02-865563-5(X)); Vol. 3. (978-0-02-865564-2(8)); Vol. 4. (978-0-02-865565-9(6)) Thomson Gale. (Macmillan Reference USA).

—Mathematics: The Macmillan Science Library, 4 vols., Set. Incl. Vol. 1. Mathematics. 192p. 85.00 (978-0-02-865562-8(1)); Vol. 2. Mathematics. (978-0-02-865563-5(X)); Vol. 3. Mathematics. (978-0-02-865564-2(8)); Vol. 4. Mathematics. (978-0-02-865565-9(6)); (J). 2001. (Macmillan Science Library). (Illus.). 800p. 2001. 460.00 (978-0-02-865561-1(3) , GML00502-171725, Macmillan Reference USA) Thomson Gale.

Brase, Charles Henry & Brase, Corinne Pellillo. Understandable Statistics: Advanced Placement Edition. 7th ed. 2002. (Illus.). xxiv, 750p. (YA). (gr. 11-12). stu. ed. 133.56 (978-0-618-26509-1(0) , 307018) Houghton Mifflin College Div.

Bresser, Rusty & Holtzman, Caren. Minilessons for Math Practice, Grades 3-5. 2006. 176p. (gr. 3-5). pap. 19.95 (978-0-941355-75-9(6)) Math Solutions Pubns.

—Minilessons for Math Practice, Grades K-2. 2006. 176p. (gr. k-2). pap. 19.95 (978-0-941355-74-2(8)) Math Solutions Pubns.

Bridger, Maggie. What Time Is It? A Content Area Readermath. 2005. (Emergent/Early (Prek-2) Math Package Ser.). 16p. (YA). (ps-2). 25.20 (978-0-8215-7824-7(3)) Sadlier, William H. Inc.

Briggs, D. Sharon. Mysteries in Knowledge Challenge Your Children: Complete Multiplication Tables. 2006. (J). per. 75.00 (978-0-615-13051-4(8)) Briggs, Sharon.

Bright & Beyond - Math. 2004. (J). (978-0-9763648-0-1(8)) Pal Toys, LLC.

Brighter Vision Publishing Staff. Math-1: And Thinking Activities. 1999. (Primary Skills Ser.). (Illus.). 32p. (J). (gr. 1). pap. 2.25 (978-1-55254-116-6(9) , BV13003) Brighter Vision Pubns.

—Math-2: And Thinking Activities. 1999. (Primary Skills Ser.). (Illus.). 32p. (J). (gr. 2). pap. 2.25 (978-1-55254-118-0(5) , BV13005) Brighter Vision Pubns.

—Math-3: And Thinking Activities. 1999. (Primary Skills Ser.). (Illus.). (J). (gr. 3). pap. 2.25 (978-1-55254-120-3(7)) Brighter Vision Pubns.

—Math-a-Magic. (Math-A-Magic Ser.). (Illus.). (J). 2000. pap. 2.25 (978-1-55254-156-2(8)); 1999. 28p. (gr. 1). pap. 2.25 (978-1-55254-110-4(X) , BV26100); 1999. 28p. (gr. 2). pap. 2.25 (978-1-55254-111-1(8) , BV26101); 1999. 28p. (gr. 3). pap. 2.25 (978-1-55254-112-8(6) , BV26102); 1999. 28p. (gr. 3-4). pap. 2.25 (978-1-55254-113-5(4) , BV26103) Brighter Vision Pubns.

—Math-a-Magic Phonics Magic. 2000. (Math-A-Magic Ser.). (Illus.). (J). (ps-3). pap. 2.25 (978-1-55254-159-3(2)) Brighter Vision Pubns.

—Math K: And Thinking Activities. 1999. (Primary Skills Ser.). (Illus.). 32p. (J). pap. 2.25 (978-1-55254-114-2(2) , BV13001) Brighter Vision Pubns.

Britt, Murray, et al. Signed Numbers & Powers. 2001. (Pre-Algebra Makes Sense Ser.: Bk. 2). 64p. pap., tchr.'s training gde. ed. 11.95 (978-0-7690-2520-9(X)) Seymour, Dale Pubns.

Brown, Michael, et al. Cambridge General Mathematics Year 11. 2000. (Cambridge Secondary Maths (australia) Ser.). (Illus.). 496p. pap. 30.65 (978-0-521-64378-8(3)) Cambridge Univ. Pr.

Brown, Robin. Practice Papers: Advanced Maths. 2nd ed. (Illus.). 32p. (YA). pap. (978-0-340-72690-7(3) , Hodder & Stoughton) Hodder General Publishing Division.

—Practice Papers: Maths. 2nd ed. (Illus.). 32p. (YA). pap. (978-0-340-72689-1(X) , Hodder & Stoughton) Hodder General Publishing Division.

Brown, Sam E. One, Two, Buckle My Shoe: Math Activities for Young Children. Libonn, Jula, illus. 2004. 112p. (Orig.). (ps). pap. 8.95 (978-0-87659-103-1(9) , 10300) Gryphon Hse., Inc.

Brownlee, Joan, et al. Geofinity. 2003. (J). spiral bd. 15.95 (978-1-931334-26-6(9)) Pieces of Learning.

Broz, Christine. Mind Building Math Grade K-1: Developing Skills Using Critical Thinking. 2005. (J). pap. 19.99 (978-0-89455-844-3(7)) Critical Thinking Bks. & Software.

Bruce. Math All Around Me, 4 vols., Set. 2003. (Illus.). 74.24 (978-1-4109-0631-1(0)); pap. 19.80 (978-1-4109-0657-1(4)) Raintree.

—Math All Around Me 6 Pack, 24 bks., Set. 2004. pap. 118.80 (978-1-4109-1263-3(9)) Raintree.

Bruchgleichungen und Bruchungleichungen. (Duden-Schuelerhilfen Ser.). (GER.). 96p. (YA). (gr. 8). (978-3-411-02614-2(6)) Bibliographisches Institut & F. A. Brockhaus AG DEU. *Dist:* International Bk. Import Service, Inc.

Brueche. (Duden-Schuelerhilfen Ser.). (GER.). 112gerp. (YA). (gr. 6-7). (978-3-411-70692-1(9)) Bibliographisches Institut & F. A. Brockhaus AG DEU. *Dist:* International Bk. Import Service, Inc.

Brumbaugh, Doug, et al. Scratch Your Brain Book A1: Clever Math Ticklers. 2002. (J). (gr. 2-3). pap. 16.99 (978-0-89455-788-0(2)) Critical Thinking Bks. & Software.

Brunetto, Carolyn. Brain-Boosting Math Activities: More Than 50 Great Activities That Reinforce Problem-Solving & Essential Math Skills. 2001. (Joyful Learning Ser.). 64p. pap., tchr. ed., act. bk. ed. 9.95 (978-0-439-40801-1(6) , Teaching Resources) Scholastic, Inc.

Bruno, Leonard C. Math & Mathematicians: The History of Math Discoveries Around the World, 2 vols., Set. Baker, Lawrence W., ed. 1999. (Illus.). xli, 420p. (J). (gr. 6-10). lib. bdg. 120.00 (978-0-7876-3812-2(9) , GML00502-113573, UXL) Thomson Gale.

Bryant-Mole, Karen. Counting. Mukhida, Zul, photos by. 1999. (Mortimer's Math Ser.). (Illus.). 24p. (J). (ps up). lib. bdg. 22.00 (978-0-8368-2617-3(5)) Stevens, Gareth Inc.

—Mortimer's Math, 6 bks. Mukhida, Zul, photos by. Incl. Counting. lib. bdg. 22.00 (978-0-8368-2617-3(5)); Patterns. lib. bdg. 22.00 (978-0-8368-2618-0(3)); Shapes. lib. bdg. 22.00 (978-0-8368-2619-7(1)); Size. lib. bdg. 22.00 (978-0-8368-2620-3(5)); Sorting. lib. bdg. 22.00 (978-0-8368-2621-0(3)); Where Is Mortimer? lib. bdg. 22.00 (978-0-8368-2622-7(1)); 24p. (J). (ps up). (Illus.). 1999. Set lib. bdg. 132.00 (978-0-8368-2616-6(7)) Stevens, Gareth Inc.

—Patterns. Mukhida, Zul, photos by. 1999. (Mortimer's Math Ser.). (Illus.). 24p. (J). (ps up). lib. bdg. 22.00 (978-0-8368-2618-0(3)) Stevens, Gareth Inc.

—Shapes. Mukhida, Zul, photos by. 1999. (Mortimer's Math Ser.). (Illus.). 24p. (J). (ps up). lib. bdg. 22.00 (978-0-8368-2619-7(1)) Stevens, Gareth Inc.

—Size. Mukhida, Zul, photos by. 1999. (Mortimer's Math Ser.). (Illus.). 24p. (J). (ps up). lib. bdg. 22.00 (978-0-8368-2620-3(5)) Stevens, Gareth Inc.

—Sorting. Mukhida, Zul, photos by. 1999. (Mortimer's Math Ser.). (Illus.). 24p. (J). (ps up). lib. bdg. 22.00 (978-0-8368-2621-0(3)) Stevens, Gareth Inc.

—Where Is Mortimer? Mukhida, Zul, photos by. 1999. (Mortimer's Math Ser.). (Illus.). 24p. (J). (ps up). lib. bdg. 22.00 (978-0-8368-2622-7(1)) Stevens, Gareth Inc.

Bulloch, Ivan. Disenos. 2004. (Matematicas en Accion Ser.). (SPA., Illus.). (ps-3). 32p. (J). pap. 5.95 (978-1-58728-968-2(7)); 30p. 9.95 (978-1-58728-982-8(2)) T&N Children's Publishing. (Two Can Publishing).

—Disenos para Aprender Matematicas Jugando. 2000. (Matematicas en Accion Ser.).Tr. of Designs to Learn Math. 12.75 (978-0-606-20631-0(0)) Tandem Library Bks.

—Figuras. 2004. (Matematicas en Accion Ser.). (SPA., Illus.). (ps-3). 32p. (J). pap. 5.95 (978-1-58728-966-8(0)); 30p. 9.95 (978-1-58728-980-4(6)) T&N Children's Publishing. (Two Can Publishing).

—Figuras Para Aprender Matematicas Jugando. 2000. (Matematicas en Accion Ser.).Tr. of Figures to Learn Math. (SPA.). 12.75 (978-0-606-20658-7(2)) Tandem Library Bks.

—Fun with Math. 2004. (Action Math Ser.). (SPA., Illus.). 128p. (ps-3). 24.95 (978-1-58728-052-8(3) , Two Can Publishing) T&N Children's Publishing.

—Games. 2004. (Action Math Ser.). (SPA., Illus.). 32p. (ps-3). 9.95 (978-1-58728-280-5(1)); (J). pap. 5.95 (978-1-58728-050-4(7)) T&N Children's Publishing. (Two Can Publishing).

—Jeux Mathematiques. 2001. (Action Math Ser.). (FRE., Illus.). 32p. (J). (ps-3). pap. 5.95 (978-1-58728-147-1(3) , Two Can Publishing) T&N Children's Publishing.

—Juegos. 2004. (Matematicas en Accion Ser.). (SPA., Illus.). (ps-3). 32p. (J). pap. 5.95 (978-1-58728-969-9(5)); 30p. 9.95 (978-1-58728-987-3(3)) T&N Children's Publishing. (Two Can Publishing).

—Medidas Para Aprender Matematicas Jugando. 2000. (Matematicas en Accion Ser.).Tr. of Measurements to Learn Math. (SPA., Illus.). (J). (978-0-606-20789-8(9)) Tandem Library Bks.

—Mesurer et Assembler. 2000. (Action Math Ser.). (FRE., Illus.). 32p. (J). (ps-3). pap. 5.95 (978-1-58728-148-8(1) , Two Can Publishing) T&N Children's Publishing.

—Modeles et Motifs. 2000. (Action Math Ser.). (FRE., Illus.). 32p. (J). (ps-3). pap. 5.95 (978-1-58728-149-5(X) , Two Can Publishing) T&N Children's Publishing.

—Patterns. 2004. (Action Math Ser.). (SPA., Illus.). 32p. (ps-3). 9.95 (978-1-58728-282-9(8)); (J). pap. 5.95 (978-1-58728-053-5(1)) T&N Children's Publishing. (Two Can Publishing).

Bumcrot, Curt & Bumcrot, Jenny. Achieving Peak Performance New Edition. Krischke, Nikki, ed. 2nd rev. ed. 2003. 19p. (gr. 2 up). pap. 5.00 (978-1-888786-39-2(6)) Basic Skills Assessment & Educational Services.

Bunch, Bryan H. & Finklestein, Iris. Math. 2000. (Step Ahead Workbooks Ser.). (Illus.). 32p. (J). (gr. 5-6). pap., wbk. ed. 2.99 (978-0-307-23580-0(7) , 03580, Golden Bks.) Random Hse. Children's Bks.

Burgess, Lynne. Shapes: Individual Title Six-Packs. (Discovery World Ser.). 12p. (gr. k-1). 28.00 (978-0-7635-8446-7(0)) Rigby Education.

Burns, Marilyn. Brown Paper School Book: Math for Smarty Pants. 2006. 128p. (J). pap. 12.99 (978-0-316-05980-0(3)) Little Brown & Co.

—The I Hate Mathematics! Book. 2006. (Brown Paper School Bks.). 128p. (J). pap. 12.99 (978-0-316-05970-1(6)) Little Brown & Co.

Burrill, Gail F., et al. Advanced Modeling & Matrices. (Data-Driven Mathematics Ser.). 136p. (YA). (gr. 7-12). pap., stu. ed. 18.95 (978-1-57232-255-4(1)) Seymour, Dale Pubns.

—Exploring Symbols. (Data-Driven Mathematics Ser.). 120p. (YA). (gr. 7-12). pap., stu. ed. 18.95 (978-1-57232-230-1(6)) Seymour, Dale Pubns.

Burstein, John. Doubling: Circus Stars. Destiny Images Staff, illus. 2003. (Math Monsters Ser.). 24p. (YA). (gr. 1 up). lib. bdg. 19.33 (978-0-8368-3807-7(6) , Weekly Reader Early Learning Library) Stevens, Gareth Inc.

—Doubling: Circus Stars. 2003. (Weekly Reader Early Learning Library). (Illus.). 24p. (J). (gr. 1 up). pap. 7.93 (978-0-8368-3822-0(X) , Weekly Reader Early Learning Library) Stevens, Gareth Inc.

—Estimating: Guess How Many Gollywomples. 2003. (Weekly Reader Early Learning Library). (Illus.). 24p. (J). (gr. 1 up). pap. 7.93 (978-0-8368-3823-7(8) , Weekly Reader Early Learning Library) Stevens, Gareth Inc.

—Estimating: How Many Gollywomples? Destiny Images Staff, illus. 2003. (Math Monsters Ser.). 24p. (YA). (gr. 1 up). lib. bdg. 19.33 (978-0-8368-3808-4(4) , Weekly Reader Early Learning Library) Stevens, Gareth Inc.

Burton, Margie, et al. Everyday Math. Evento, Susan, ed. 1998. (Early Connections Ser.). 16p. (J). (gr. k-2). pap. 4.25 (978-1-892393-35-7(2)) Benchmark Education Co.

—Parts of a Whole. Evento, Susan, ed. 1998. (Early Connections Ser.). 16p. (J). (gr. k-2). pap. 4.25 (978-1-892393-41-8(7)) Benchmark Education Co.

—Patterns All Around. Evento, Susan, ed. 1998. (Early Connections Ser.). 16p. (J). (gr. k-2). pap. 4.25 (978-1-892393-33-3(6)) Benchmark Education Co.

Buxton, Laurie. Sums for Smart Kids. Lewis, Paula, illus. 2001. 80p. pap. 21.50 (978-1-903142-22-6(9)) Nelson Thornes Ltd. GBR. *Dist:* International Specialized Bk. Services.

Cain, Michael. Mathability: Math in the Real World. 2005. 80p. 12.95 (978-1-59363-106-2(5)) Prufrock Pr.

Calculate Measurements. 2004. (Math "How To" Ser.). (Illus.). 48p. (J). 7.99 (978-1-57690-953-9(0)) Teacher Created Materials, Inc.

Calendario: Student & Teacher Support Resources. 1999. (Matematicas en Mi Mundo Ser.). (ENG & SPA.). (gr. k up). (978-0-02-110715-5(7)) Macmillan/McGraw-Hill Schl. Div.

Caliente o frio? Math, 6 vols.Tr. of Hot or Cold? Math. (SPA.). (gr. k-2). 28.95 (978-0-7368-3137-6(1) , Yellow Umbrella Bks.) Capstone Pr., Inc.

Callella, Trisha. I Have, Who Has?, Math — Grades 3-4: 38 Interactive Card Games. Hamaguchi, Carla, ed. 2006. (I Have, Who Has? Ser.). 208p. pap. 19.99 (978-1-59198-230-2(8) , 2208) Creative Teaching Pr., Inc.

—I Have, Who Has?, Math — Grades 5-6: 38 Interactive Card Games. Hamaguchi, Carla, ed. 2006. (I Have, Who Has? Ser.). 208p. pap. 19.99 (978-1-59198-231-9(6) , 2209) Creative Teaching Pr., Inc.

Can You Guess? Math, 6 vols. (gr. k-2). 28.95 (978-0-7368-3008-9(1) , Yellow Umbrella Bks.) Capstone Pr., Inc.

Captain B's Boat, 6 vols. (Sunshinetm Ser.). 16p. (gr. k up). 29.50 (978-0-7802-5441-1(4)) Wright Group, The.

Carole Marsh. Math for Boys. 2004. (Math Ser.). 32p. 29.95 (978-0-635-02446-6(2)); (gr. 2-6). pap. 7.95 (978-0-635-02444-2(6)) Gallopade International.

—Math for Girls. 2004. (Math Ser.). 32p. 29.95 (978-0-635-02447-3(0)); (gr. 2-6). pap. 7.95 (978-0-635-02445-9(4)) Gallopade International.

Caron, Lucille & St. Jacques, Philip M. Math Success, 7 bks., Set. Incl. Addition & Subtraction. 2001. lib. bdg. 22.60 (978-0-7660-1432-9(0)); Fractions & Decimals. 2000. lib. bdg. 22.60 (978-0-7660-1430-5(4)); Multiplication & Division. 2001. lib. bdg. 22.60 (978-0-7660-1431-2(2)); Percents & Ratios. 2000. lib. bdg. 22.60 (978-0-7660-1435-0(5)); Pre-Algebra & Algebra. 2000. lib. bdg. 22.60 (978-0-7660-1434-3(7)); 64p. (YA). (gr. 4-10). (Illus.). Set lib. bdg. 107.70 (978-0-7660-1601-9(3)) Enslow Pubs., Inc.

—Pre-Algebra & Algebra. 2000. (Math Success Ser.). (Illus.). 64p. (YA). (gr. 4-10). lib. bdg. 22.60 (978-0-7660-1434-3(7)) Enslow Pubs., Inc.

Carroll, Danielle. Tiling with Shapes. 2005. (Illus.). 16p. (J). (978-0-7368-5287-6(5)); (978-0-7368-5323-1(5)) Capstone Pr., Inc.

Carter, Denine, ed. Gotta Have Graphs. 2003. 144p. 16.95 (978-1-56234-573-0(7) , Mailbox Bks., The) Education Ctr., Inc.

Cartland Noble, Mrs, Patricia. Activities for the Graphing Mat. 2000. 32p. (J). (gr. k-3). pap. 5.99 (978-1-56451-325-0(4) , ID7248) School Specialty Publishing.

Cato, Sheila. Counting & Numbers. Sweeten, Sami, illus. 1999. (Question of Math Ser.). 32p. (J). (gr. k-3). lib. bdg. 25.26 (978-1-57505-322-6(5) , Carolrhoda Bks.) Lerner Publishing Group.

Cavanagh, Mary. Math to Know: A Mathematics Handbook. 2000. (Illus.). 483p. (J). (gr. 3-4). 24.00 (978-0-669-47154-0(2) , 047154); pap. 19.67 (978-0-669-47153-3(4) , 047153) Great Source Education Group, Inc.

Cavill, Steve. Coursework Techniques for GCSE Maths. 2005. (Illus.). 112p. pap. 10.00 (978-0-521-67787-5(4)) Cambridge Univ. Pr.

Centro Matematico: Student & Teacher Support Resources. 1999. (Matematicas en Mi Mundo Ser.). (ENG & SPA.). (gr. k up). (978-0-02-110215-0(5)); (gr. 1 up). (978-0-02-110216-7(3)); (gr. 2 up). (978-0-02-110217-4(1)); (gr. 3 up). (978-0-02-110218-1(X)); (gr. 4 up). (978-0-02-110219-8(8)); (gr. 5 up). (978-0-02-110220-4(1)); (gr. 6 up). (978-0-02-110221-1(X)) Macmillan/McGraw-Hill Schl. Div.

Cernak, Kim & Williams, Rozanne Lanczak. Build-a-Skill Instant Books Math Facts To 20. Faulkner, Stacey, ed. Campbell, Jenny, illus. 2007. (J). 4.99 (***978-1-59198-418-4(1)***) Creative Teaching Pr., Inc.

Cernek, Kim. Math Minutes Grade 1, 2583. Wright, Marsha, ed. Hillam, Corbin & Grayson, Rick, illus. 2002. 112p. (J). (gr. 1). pap. 12.99 (978-1-57471-812-6(6) , CTP 2583) Creative Teaching Pr., Inc.

Chaktoura, Julia. El Baul de Mis Juguetes: Un Libro Sobre Figuras y Cuerpos. Maddonni, Karina, illus. (Coleccion el Baul Ser.). (SPA.). 10p. (J). (gr. k-1). (978-950-46-1159-2(1)) Santillana USA Publishing Co., Inc.

Champagne, Ruth. Friendly Math Activity Book for Addition. Champagne, Ronald, illus. 2000. 52p. (Orig.). (J). (gr. k-2). pap. (978-1-929245-02-4(5)) Friendly Math.

—Friendly Math Activity Book for Multiplication. Champagne, Ronald, illus. 1999. 52p. (Orig.). (J). (gr. 3-5). pap. (978-1-929245-01-7(7)) Friendly Math.

—Friendly Math Shape & Pattern Puzzles. Champagne, Ronald, illus. 1999. 108p. (Orig.). (J). (gr. k up). pap. (978-1-929245-00-0(9)) Friendly Math.

Chanko, Pamela. January: Dozens of Instant & Irresistible Ideas & Activities from Creative Teachers Across the Country. 2001. (Fresh & Fun Ser.). 32p. pap. 8.95 (978-0-439-21575-6(7)) Scholastic, Inc.

Chapman, Carolyn. Math Comprehension Grade 5. 2003. (Skill Builders Ser.). 80p. (gr. 5 up). 2.95 (978-1-932210-04-0(0)) Rainbow Bridge Publishing.

Charles, R., et al. Problem-Solving Experiences in Mathematics. 2nd ed. 2003. 16.50 (978-0-201-49361-0(6)) Seymour, Dale Pubns.

—Problem-Solving Experiences in Mathematics, Grade 2, BLM. Anderson, Cathy & Apple, Mali, eds. 2nd ed. 2003. (Illus.). 17.50 (978-0-201-49363-4(2)) Seymour, Dale Pubns.

Charles, Randall I. Pre-algebra, 3 vols. 2004. 954p. (YA). (gr. 9 up). 477.00 (978-0-13-068608-4(5)) Prentice Hall Pr.

—Prentice Hall Mathematics: Course 1, 3 vols. 2004. 828p. (YA). (gr. 6-8). 414.00 (978-0-13-063136-7(1)) Prentice Hall Pr.

Charles, Randall I., et al. Problem-Solving Experiences in Mathematics: Prob Solv Exper. 2005. (Problem Solving Experiences Ser.). (J). (gr. k-8). stu. ed. 56.95 (978-0-7690-3250-4(8)); (gr. 4 up). stu. ed. 56.95 (978-0-7690-3251-1(6)) Seymour, Dale Pubns.

Charlesworth, Eric. 225 Fantastic Facts Math Word Problems: Amazing Facts & Quick Companion Word Problems That Build Skills in Multiplication, Division, Fractions, Decimals, Percentages, & More. 2001. 64p. (gr. 4). pap. 10.95 (978-0-439-25618-6(6)) Scholastic, Inc.

Checkpoint Mathematics, Vol. 3. 2005. (Illus.). 192p. pap. 36.50 (***978-0-340-81293-8(1)*** , Hodder Murray) Hodder Education GBR. *Dist:* Trans-Atlantic Pubns., Inc.

Checkpoint Maths, Vol. 1. 2004. (Illus.). 178p. pap. 36.50 (***978-0-340-81295-2(8)*** , Hodder Murray) Hodder Education GBR. *Dist:* Trans-Atlantic Pubns., Inc.

Cheney, Martha C. Math, Bk. II. Nolte, Larry, illus. 1998. (Gifted & Talented Ser.). 64p. (J). (gr. 1-3). pap. 4.95 (978-1-56565-666-6(0) , 06660W) Lowell Hse. Juvenile.

Cherry Lake Publishing, compiled by. Real World Math: Health & Wellness. 2008. lib. bdg. (***978-1-60279-103-9(1)***) Cherry Lake Publishing.

Chrismer, Melanie. Multiply This. 2006. 32p. (J). (gr. 1-2). pap. 5.95 (978-0-516-25365-7(4) , Children's Pr.) Scholastic Library Publishing.

—Odd & Even Socks. (Rookie Read-About Math Ser.). (Illus.). (J). 2006. 32p. (gr. 1-2). pap. 5.95 (978-0-516-25366-4(2)); 2005. 31p. (ps-ps). 20.50 (978-0-516-25265-0(8)) Scholastic Library Publishing. (Children's Pr.).

Christopher Lee Publications Staff. Einstein's Math Terms Made Easy Flippers. 2002. (Einstein's... Made Easy Flippers Ser.). (J). pap. 7.95 (978-1-59125-132-3(X)); (Illus.). pap. 7.95 (978-1-59125-161-3(3)) Penton Overseas, Inc.

Cinetto, Liliana. El baul de mi Mundo: Un libro sobre Tamanos. Perica, illus. (Coleccion el Baul Ser.). (SPA.). 10p. (J). (gr. k-1). (978-950-46-1177-6(X)) Santillana USA Publishing Co., Inc.

El circo de los Numeros: Superlibros de Literatura/Literature Big Books. 1999. (Matematicas en Mi Mundo Ser.). (ENG & SPA.). (gr. 1 up). (978-0-02-110163-4(9)) Macmillan/McGraw-Hill Schl. Div.

City Shapes Math, 6 vols. (gr. k-2). 28.95 (978-0-7368-2992-2(X) , Yellow Umbrella Bks.) Capstone Pr., Inc.

Clarke, Jacqueline. Graphing. 2002. (Best-Ever Activities for Grades 2-3 Ser.). (Illus.). 48p. (J). (gr. 2-3). 10.95 (978-0-439-29645-8(5)) Scholastic, Inc.

Clarkson, Wes. Mathematics for New Speakers of English. 2005. 161p. (YA). per. 19.95 (978-1-56254-646-5(5) , SP6465) Saddleback Educational Publishing.

Clements, Andrew. A Million Dots. Reed, Mike, illus. 2006. 48p. (J). (ps-3). 16.95 (978-0-689-85824-6(8)) Simon & Schuster Children's Publishing.

Clemson, Wendy. Charts & Graphs. 2002. (gr. k-3). lib. bdg. 14.10 (978-0-613-45339-4(5)) Tandem Library Bks.

—Multiplying & Dividing. 2002. (gr. k-3). lib. bdg. 14.10 (978-0-613-45345-5(X)) Tandem Library Bks.

—Shape & Pattern. 2002. (gr. k-3). lib. bdg. 14.10 (978-0-613-45347-9(6)) Tandem Library Bks.

—Using Math to Conquer Extreme Sports. 2004. (Mathworks!). (Illus.). 31p. (J). lib. bdg. 24.67 (978-0-8368-4210-4(3)) Stevens, Gareth Inc.

—Using Math to Solve a Crime. 2004. (Mathworks!). (Illus.). 31p. (J). lib. bdg. 24.67 (978-0-8368-4213-5(8)) Stevens, Gareth Inc.

Clemson, Wendy & Clemson, David. Charts & Graphs. 2004. (Math Magic Ser.). (Illus.). 32p. (gr. k-3). (J). pap. 5.95 (978-1-58728-342-0(5)); 9.95 (978-1-58728-336-9(0)) T&N Children's Publishing. (Two Can Publishing).

—Digging for Dinosaurs. 2006. (J). pap. (***978-0-8368-8137-0(0)***); lib. bdg. (***978-0-8368-7838-7(8)***) Stevens, Gareth Inc.

—Firefighters to the Rescue. 2006. (Illus.). 32p. (J). pap. (***978-0-8368-8138-7(9)***); lib. bdg. (***978-0-8368-7839-4(6)***) Stevens, Gareth Inc.

—Multiplying & Dividing. 2004. (Math Magic Ser.). (Illus.). 32p. (gr. k-3). (J). pap. 5.95 (978-1-58728-273-7(9)); 9.95 (978-1-58728-269-0(0)) T&N Children's Publishing. (Two Can Publishing).

—Ocean Giants. 2006. (Illus.). 32p. (J). pap. (***978-0-8368-8139-4(7)***); lib. bdg. (***978-0-8368-7840-0(X)***) Stevens, Gareth Inc.

—Rocket to the Moon. 2006. (Illus.). 32p. (J). pap. (***978-0-8368-8140-0(0)***); lib. bdg. (***978-0-8368-7841-7(8)***) Stevens, Gareth Inc.

—Shape & Pattern. 2004. (Math Magic Ser.). (Illus.). 32p. (gr. k-3). (J). pap. 5.95 (978-1-58728-275-1(5)); 9.95 (978-1-58728-271-3(2)) T&N Children's Publishing. (Two Can Publishing).

—Times Tables! (Illus.). 32p. (J). (gr. k-3). pap. 15.95 (978-0-7894-3151-6(3)) Dorling Kindersley Publishing, Inc.

—Times Tables! (Illus.). 32p. (J). pap. 11.99 (978-0-590-24755-9(7)) Scholastic, Inc.

Clemson, Wendy & Clemson, David. Treasure Hunt in the Jungle. 2006. (Illus.). 32p. (J). pap. (***978-0-8368-8141-7(9)***); (gr. 2-4). lib. bdg. 25.27 (***978-0-8368-7842-4(6)***) Stevens, Gareth Inc.

Clemson, Wendy, et al. Using Math to Be a Zoo Vet. 2004. (Mathworks!). (Illus.). 31p. (J). lib. bdg. 24.67 (978-0-8368-4209-8(X)) Stevens, Gareth Inc.

—Using Math to Create a Movie Stunt. 2004. (Mathworks!). (Illus.). 31p. (J). lib. bdg. 24.67 (978-0-8368-4211-1(1)) Stevens, Gareth Inc.

—Win a Grand Prix. 2004. (Mathworks!). (Illus.). 31p. (J). lib. bdg. 24.67 (978-0-8368-4214-2(6)) Stevens, Gareth Inc.

CMSP Projects Staff. Applied Math Concepts: Lines & Perimeters Area & Volume. rev. ed. (Illus.). 91p. (YA). reprint ed. pap. (978-0-942851-01-4(3)) CMSP Projects.

Cognitive Tutor (R) Integrated Math I. 2002. stu. ed., per. (978-1-930804-97-5(0)) Carnegie Learning.

Cognitive Tutor (R) Integrated Math I Software Edition. 2002. per. (978-1-930804-98-2(9)) Carnegie Learning.

Cognitive Tutor (R) Integrated Math II Software Manual. 2003. spiral bd. (978-1-930804-43-2(1)) Carnegie Learning.

Cognitive Tutor (R) Integrated Math II Student. 2003. per. (978-1-930804-54-8(7)) Carnegie Learning.

Cohen, Gilles & Editions POLE Staff. 50 Mathematical Puzzles & Problems: Green Collection. 2001. (Illus.). 96p. (YA). (gr. 6-12). pap. 11.95 (978-1-55953-498-7(2) , MN53498) Key Curriculum Pr.

—50 Mathematical Puzzles & Problems: Red Collection. 2000. (Illus.). 96p. (YA). (gr. 9 up). pap. 11.95 (978-1-55953-500-7(8) , MN53500) Key Curriculum Pr.

Coins & Money Workbook. 2002. (J). pap. 8.95 (978-1-56911-045-4(X)) Learning Resources, Inc.

Color Tile Fraction Math Activity Cards. 2000. (J). 7.95 (978-1-56911-751-4(9)) Learning Resources, Inc.

The Complete Book of Math: Grades 1-2. 2000. (Complete Book Ser.). (Illus.). 352p. (J). (gr. 1-2). pap., wbk. ed. 14.95 (978-1-56189-504-5(0) , 31148, American Education Publishing) School Specialty Publishing.

Comprehensive Kindergarten 10-Student Kit. 1999. (Metro Reading Ser.). (J). (gr. k). 1111.66 (978-1-58120-122-2(2)) Metropolitan Teaching & Learning Co.

Concentrate on! — Grades 7, 8. 2003. (J). spiral bd. 15.95 (978-1-58123-333-9(7)) Larson Learning, Inc.

Concentrate on! Grades 6/7. 2003. (J). spiral bd. 15.95 (978-1-58123-335-3(3)) Larson Learning, Inc.

Concentrate on! Prealgebra. 2003. spiral bd. 15.95 (978-1-58123-334-6(5)) Larson Learning, Inc.

Conejillos de Indias: Lejos y Cerca: Superlibros de Literatura/Literature Big Books. 1999. (Matematicas en Mi Mundo Ser.). (ENG & SPA.). (gr. k up). (978-0-02-110158-0(2)) Macmillan/McGraw-Hill Schl. Div.

Conexion: Casa-Escuela: Student & Teacher Support Resources. 1999. (Matematicas en Mi Mundo Ser.). (ENG & SPA.). (gr. 3 up). (978-0-02-110222-8(8)); (gr. 4 up). (978-0-02-110223-5(6)); (gr. 6 up). (978-0-02-110225-9(2)) Macmillan/McGraw-Hill Schl. Div.

Connecting People Pattern Cards. 2003. (J). 7.95 (978-1-56911-144-4(8)) Learning Resources, Inc.

Consumer Math Syllabus. 1999. 4p. (J). ring bd. 1.00 (978-1-57896-067-5(3) , 2336, Hewitt Homeschooling Resources) Hewitt Research Foundation, Inc.

Continuum & Anghileri, Julia. Children's Mathematical Thinking in the Primary Years: Perspectives on Children's Learning. 2005. (Journal for the Study of the Old Testament Ser.). (Illus.). 192p. (978-0-8264-7911-2(1)) Continuum International Publishing Group, Ltd.

Cooper, Terry, ed. Reading & Math Jumbo Workbook, Grade 2. 2005. 320p. pap., wbk. ed. 14.99 (978-0-439-78601-0(0) , Teaching Resources) Scholastic, Inc.

—Reading & Math Jumbo Workbook: Grade 1. 2005. 320p. pap., wbk. ed. 14.99 (978-0-439-78600-3(2) , Teaching Resources) Scholastic, Inc.

—Reading & Math Jumbo Workbook Grade 3. 2005. 320p. pap. 14.99 (978-0-439-78602-7(9) , Teaching Resources) Scholastic, Inc.

—Reading & Math Jumbo Workbook: Grade K. 2005. 320p. pap. 14.99 (978-0-439-78599-0(5) , Teaching Resources) Scholastic, Inc.

—Schol Success Reading & Math Gr4. 2005. 320p. pap. 14.99 (978-0-439-78603-4(7) , Teaching Resources) Scholastic, Inc.

—1st Grade Math Practice. 2006. 48p. pap. 5.99 (978-0-439-81915-2(6) , Teaching Resources) Scholastic, Inc.

—2nd Grade Math Practice. 2006. 48p. pap. 5.99 (978-0-439-81916-9(4) , Teaching Resources) Scholastic, Inc.

—3rd Grade Math Practice. 2006. 48p. pap. 5.99 (978-0-439-81917-6(2) , Teaching Resources) Scholastic, Inc.

—4th Grade Math Practice. 2006. 48p. pap. 5.99 (978-0-439-81918-3(0) , Teaching Resources) Scholastic, Inc.

Cooperative Mathematics. 2008. (J). per. 29.00 ***978-1-879097-36-0(2))** Kagan Publishing.

Cornell, Teresa. Math Riddles & Mini-Posters That Build Early Problem-Solving Skills. 2001. 48p. pap. 10.95 (978-0-439-16236-4(X)) Scholastic, Inc.

Costello, Bill. Cartooning with Math. Costello, Bill, illus. 1998. (Illus.). 64p. (J). (ps-8). pap. 8.95 (978-1-891905-31-5(7)) Thinkorporated.

Cotter, Joan A. RightStart Mathematics: Level B Worksheets. 2001. (J). spiral bd., wbk. ed. 10.00 (978-1-931980-06-7(3) , W-B) Activities for Learning.

—RightStart Mathematics: Level C Worksheets. 2001. (J). spiral bd., wbk. ed. 10.00 (978-1-931980-07-4(1) , W-C) Activities for Learning.

—RightStart Mathematics: Level D Worksheets. 2001. spiral bd., wbk. ed. 10.00 (978-1-931980-08-1(X) , W-D); spiral bd., wbk. ed. 10.00 (978-1-931980-09-8(8) , W-E) Activities for Learning.

The Cotton Tale. abr. ed. 2004. (Thrilling Tales in Time Ser.: Vol. 41). (J). 19.95 (978-1-58123-372-8(8)) Larson Learning, Inc.

Count down to Math Grade 5. 2005. (978-0-9766802-9-1(7)) Educational Tools, Inc.

Count with Me. 2005. (Mathematics Ser.). (YA). (gr. k-2). 23.94 (978-0-8215-8928-1(8)) Sadlier, William H. Inc.

Count Your Chickens Math, 6 vols. (gr. k-2). 28.95 (978-0-7368-2995-3(4) , Yellow Umbrella Bks.) Capstone Pr., Inc.

Counting Cards Staff. Learning Wrap Ups Palette. 2004. 7.99 (978-1-59204-013-1(6)) Learning Wrap-Ups.

Counting Sheep. 2005. (Emergent/Early (Prek-2) Math Package Ser.). 12p. (YA). (ps-2). 25.20 (978-0-8215-7842-1(1)) Sadlier, William H. Inc.

Covey, Stephen R. Before I Do Math: Discovering First Number Skills. 2000. (Step Ahead Workbooks Ser.). (Illus.). 32p. (J). (ps). pap. 2.99 (978-0-307-03597-4(2) , 03597, Golden Bks.) Random Hse. Children's Bks.

Cowder, Pansy. Tens & Ones Together: Metro Math Readers Yellow Level. 2000. (Metro Math Readers Yellow Level Ser.). (J). (gr. 1-2). 3.75 (978-1-58120-408-7(6)) Metropolitan Teaching & Learning Co.

Cozens, Gaynor & Thomas, Cheryl Ann. Mathematics Grade 2: New Zambia Basic Education Course. 2006. pap., stu. ed. 3.00 (978-0-521-68858-1(2)) Cambridge Univ. Pr.

—Numeracy Matters Grade 1 IsiXhosa. 2003. (AFR.). 48p. pap., wbk. ed. 2.05 (978-0-521-53868-8(8)) Cambridge Univ. Pr.

—Numeracy Matters Grade 1 Learner's Book isiXhosa Translation. 2003. (AFR.). 48p. pap., stu. ed. 3.65 (978-0-521-53865-7(3)) Cambridge Univ. Pr.

—Numeracy Matters Grade 1 Learner's Book Sesotho Translation. 2003. (AFR.). 48p. pap., stu. ed. 3.65 (978-0-521-53863-3(7)) Cambridge Univ. Pr.

—Numeracy Matters Grade 1 Learner's Book Xitsonga Translation. 2003. (AFR.). 48p. pap., stu. ed. 3.65 (978-0-521-53864-0(5)) Cambridge Univ. Pr.

—Numeracy Matters Grade 1 Sesotho Translation. 2003. (AFR.). 48p. pap., wbk. ed. 2.05 (978-0-521-53866-4(1)) Cambridge Univ. Pr.

—Numeracy Matters Grade 1 Xitsonga Tranlation. 2003. (AFR.). 48p. pap., wbk. ed. 2.05 (978-0-521-53867-1(X)) Cambridge Univ. Pr.

—Numeracy Matters Grade 1 Zambia Basic Education. 2005. 80p. pap., stu. ed. 3.70 (978-0-521-67111-8(6)) Cambridge Univ. Pr.

—Numeracy Matters Grade 2: isiXhosa Translation. 2003. (AFR.). 56p. pap., stu. ed. 4.05 (978-0-521-53871-8(8)) Cambridge Univ. Pr.

—Numeracy Matters Grade 2 isiXhosa Translation. 2003. (AFR.). 48p. pap., wbk. ed. 2.05 (978-0-521-53874-9(2)) Cambridge Univ. Pr.

—Numeracy Matters Grade 2 Learner's Book Sesotho Translation. 2003. (AFR.). 56p. pap. 4.05 (978-0-521-53869-5(6)) Cambridge Univ. Pr.

—Numeracy Matters Grade 2 Learner's Book Xitsonga Translation. 2003. (AFR.). 56p. pap. 4.05 (978-0-521-53870-1(X)) Cambridge Univ. Pr.

—Numeracy Matters Grade 2 Sesotho Translation. 2003. (AFR.). 48p. pap., wbk. ed. 2.05 (978-0-521-53872-5(6)) Cambridge Univ. Pr.

—Numeracy Matters Grade 2 Xitsonga Translation. 2003. (AFR.). 48p. pap., wbk. ed. 2.05 (978-0-521-53873-2(4)) Cambridge Univ. Pr.

—Numeracy Matters Grade 3 isiXhosa Translation. 2003. (AFR.). 48p. pap., wbk. ed. 2.05 (978-0-521-53880-0(7)) Cambridge Univ. Pr.

—Numeracy Matters Grade 3 Learner's Book isiXhosa Translation. 2003. (AFR.). 64p. pap. 4.45 (978-0-521-53877-0(7)) Cambridge Univ. Pr.

—Numeracy Matters Grade 3 Learner's Book Sesotho Translation. 2003. (AFR.). 64p. pap. 4.45 (978-0-521-53875-6(0)) Cambridge Univ. Pr.

—Numeracy Matters Grade 3 Learner's Book Xitsonga Translation. 2003. (AFR.). 64p. pap. 4.45 (978-0-521-53876-3(9)) Cambridge Univ. Pr.

—Numeracy Matters Grade 3 Sesotho Translation. 2003. (AFR.). 48p. pap., wbk. ed. 2.05 (978-0-521-53878-7(5)) Cambridge Univ. Pr.

—Numeracy Matters Grade 3 Xitsonga Translation. 2003. (AFR.). 48p. pap., wbk. ed. 2.05 (978-0-521-53879-4(3)) Cambridge Univ. Pr.

Crawford, Sheryl Ann & Sanders, Nancy I. 15 Easy And Irresistible Math Mini Books. 2002. 80p. (J). pap. 12.95 (978-0-439-21612-8(5)) Scholastic, Inc.

Creative Publications Staff. Mathscape: Seeing & Thinking Mathematically Modular Set. 1998. (YA). pap. 77.32 (978-0-7622-1466-2(X)) Creative Pubns.

Cribb, Peter, et al. Essential Mathematics 7: The CSF II Course. 2000. (Essential Mathematics Ser.). 496p. pap. 24.00 incl. cd-rom (978-0-521-62596-8(3)) Cambridge Univ. Pr.

—Essential Mathematics 8: The CSF II Course. 2000. (Essential Mathematics Ser.). pap. 28.35 incl. cd-rom (978-0-521-62595-1(5)) Cambridge Univ. Pr.

Critical Thinking Publishing Staff & Husted, Terri. Math Detective Beginning: Higher-Order Thinking in Reading & Writing in Mathematics. 2004. (J). pap. 18.99 (978-0-89455-802-3(1)) Critical Thinking Bks. & Software.

—Math Detective Book A1: Higher-Order Thinking in Reading & Writing in Mathematics. 2003. (J). pap. 18.99 (978-0-89455-803-0(X)) Critical Thinking Bks. & Software.

Critical Thinking Puzzles with Cuisenaire Rods. 2000. (J). pap. 9.95 (978-1-56911-021-8(2)) Learning Resources, Inc.

Cron, Mary, et al. Monster Math Super Edition for Ages 6-8. Cherbak, Yvonne, illus. 2000. (Monster Math Super Editions Ser.). 256p. (J). (gr. 1-3). pap. 14.95 (978-0-7373-0216-5(X) , 0216XW) Lowell Hse. Juvenile.

Crooks, Lisa. Connecting Math with Literature: Using Childrens Literature As a Springboard for Eaching Math Concepts. Samoiloff, Sheri, ed. Grayson, Rick, illus. 2002. 96p. (J). (gr. 3-6). pap. 11.99 (978-1-57471-934-5(3)) Creative Teaching Pr., Inc.

—Munchable Math: Appetizing Adventures in Math Investigations. Simon, Ruth B. & Dashef, Jennifer, eds. Fletcher, Rusty, illus. 2000. 128p. (J). (gr. 4-6). pap., stu. ed. 13.99 (978-1-57471-740-2(5) , 2596) Creative Teaching Pr., Inc.

Cruising Through the Math A Exam. 2001. 400p. (YA). (978-1-878621-65-8(3)) D&S Marketing Systems, Inc.

Crum, Anna-Maria. Matematicas para construir & Math to Build On. 2005. spiral bd. 84.00 ***978-1-4108-5696-8(8))** Benchmark Education Co.

Crum, Anna-Maria. Math to Build On. 2004. (Navigators Ser.). (J). pap. 42.00 (978-1-4108-0421-1(6)) Benchmark Education Co.

Crump, Irving, ed. Games Galore Math. 2002. 96p. (gr. 4-6). 14.95 (978-1-56234-492-4(7) , Mailbox Bks., The) Education Ctr., Inc.

Cuaderno para repaso rapido: Clave de Respuestas: Student & Teacher Support Resources. 1999. (Matematicas en Mi Mundo Ser.). (ENG & SPA.). (gr. 1 up). (978-0-02-110692-9(4)); (gr. 2 up). (978-0-02-110693-6(2)); (gr. 3 up). (978-0-02-110694-3(0)); (gr. 4 up). (978-0-02-110695-0(9)); (gr. 6 up). (978-0-02-110697-4(5)) Macmillan/McGraw-Hill Schl. Div.

Cuantos peces? Math, 6 vols.Tr. of How Many Fish? Math. (SPA.). (gr. k-2). 28.95 (978-0-7368-3138-3(X) , Yellow Umbrella Bks.) Capstone Pr., Inc.

Cuenta Conmigo. (Mathematics Ser.). (SPA.). (J). (978-958-04-7725-9(6)); (978-958-04-7726-6(4)); (978-958-04-7727-3(2)) Norma S.A. COL. *Dist:* Distribuidora Norma, Inc.

Cuenta tus Gallinas Math, 6 vols.Tr. of Count Your Chickens Math. (SPA.). (gr. k-2). 28.95 (978-0-7368-3031-7(6) , Yellow Umbrella Bks.) Capstone Pr., Inc.

Cuisenaire Rods Addition & Subtraction Activity Cards. 2003. (J). 19.95 (978-1-56911-140-6(5)) Learning Resources, Inc.

Cuisenaire Rods Fractions & Decimals Activity Cards. 2003. (J). 19.95 (978-1-56911-142-0(1)) Learning Resources, Inc.

Cuisenaire Rods Multiplication & Division Activity Cards. 2003. (J). 19.95 (978-1-56911-141-3(3)) Learning Resources, Inc.

Cuisenaire Rods Pocket Chart Book. 2002. (J). pap. 8.95 (978-1-56911-075-1(1)) Learning Resources, Inc.

Cummings, Renee. Extra Help: Math & Language Arts. 2003. (Homework Booklets Ser.). (Illus.). 72p. (gr. 1 up). 2.99 (978-1-56822-412-1(5) , IF0285); (gr. 2 up). 2.99 (978-1-56822-413-8(3) , IF0286); (gr. 3 up). 2.99 (978-1-56822-414-5(1) , IF0287); (gr. 4 up). 2.99 (978-1-56822-415-2(X) , IF0288); (gr. 5 up). 2.99 (978-1-56822-416-9(8) , IF0289); (gr. 6 up). 2.99 (978-1-56822-417-6(6) , IF0290) School Specialty Publishing.

Cut & Paste: Math. 2003. pap. 11.99 (978-0-7439-3708-5(2)) Teacher Created Materials, Inc.

Dahl, Michael. Footprints in the Snow: Counting by Twos. Ouren, Todd, illus. 2004. (Know Your Numbers Ser.). 24p. (C). (gr. k-3). 22.60 (978-1-4048-0946-8(5)) Picture Window Bks.

—Hands Down: Counting by 5s. Ouren, Todd, illus. 2004. (Know Your Numbers Ser.). 24p. (C). (gr. k-3). 22.60 (978-1-4048-0948-2(1)) Picture Window Bks.

—Lots of Ladybugs! Counting by Fives. Ouren, Todd, illus. 2004. (Know Your Numbers Ser.). 24p. (C). (gr. k-3). 22.60 (978-1-4048-0944-4(9)) Picture Window Bks.

—Pie for Piglets: Counting by 2s. Ouren, Todd, illus. 2004. (Know Your Numbers Ser.). 24p. (C). (gr. k-3). 22.60 (978-1-4048-0943-7(0)) Picture Window Bks.

—Starry Arms: Counting by 5s. Ouren, Todd, illus. 2004. (Know Your Numbers Ser.). 24p. (C). (gr. k-3). 22.60 (978-1-4048-0947-5(3)) Picture Window Bks.

Daily Problems & Weekly Puzzlers. 64p. (gr. 4 up). 7.99 (978-1-56451-196-6(0) , ID7421); (gr. 5 up). 7.99 (978-1-56451-197-3(9) , ID7422); (gr. 6 up). 7.99 (978-1-56451-198-0(7) , ID7423); (gr. 7 up). 7.99 (978-1-56451-199-7(5) , ID7424); (gr. 8 up). 7.99 (978-1-56451-200-0(2) , ID7425) School Specialty Publishing.

Daily Problems & Weekly Puzzlers Mind Stretching Math Problems. 64p. (gr. 1 up). 7.99 (978-1-56451-257-4(6) , ID7418); (gr. 2 up). 7.99 (978-1-56451-258-1(4) , ID7419); (gr. 3 up). 7.99 (978-1-56451-195-9(2) , ID7420) School Specialty Publishing.

Dale Seymour Staff. Mathematics: Problem Solving Activities. (J). 77p. (gr. 3). 9.95 (978-0-86651-254-1(3) , DSO1527); 69p. (gr. 5). 9.95 (978-0-86651-256-5(X) , DSO1529); 71p. (gr. 6). 9.95 (978-0-86651-257-2(8) , DSO1530) Seymour, Dale Pubns.

Dalmatian Press Staff. Addition & Subtraction: Practice Tablet. 2002. (Home Learning Tools Ser.). (Illus.). 64p. (J). (gr. 1-2). pap. 2.99 (978-1-57759-231-0(X)) Dalmatian Pr.

—Easy Wipe-Off Addition. 2002. (Easy Wipe-Off Ser.). (Illus.). 16p. (J). (gr. 1 up). pap., wbk. ed. 2.99 (978-1-57759-138-2(0)) Dalmatian Pr.

—Easy Wipe-Off Division. 2002. (Easy Wipe-Off Ser.). (Illus.). 16p. (J). (gr. 3-4). pap., wbk. ed. 2.99 (978-1-57759-294-5(8)) Dalmatian Pr.

—Easy Wipe-Off Multiplication. 1999. (Easy Wipe-Off Ser.). (Illus.). 16p. (J). (gr. 3-4). pap., wbk. ed. 2.99 (978-1-57759-137-5(2)) Dalmatian Pr.

—Easy Wipe-Off Subtraction. 2003. (Easy Wipe-Off Ser.). 16p. (J). (gr. 1-2). pap., wbk. ed. 2.99 (978-1-57759-293-8(X)) Dalmatian Pr.

—Math 1. rev. ed. 2002. (Tools Ser.). (Illus.). 32p. (J). (gr. 1 up). pap. 2.29 (978-1-57759-147-4(X)) Dalmatian Pr.

—Math 2, Vol. 2. rev. ed. 1999. (Tools Ser.). (Illus.). 32p. (J). (gr. 2 up). pap. 2.29 (978-1-57759-152-8(6)) Dalmatian Pr.

—Math Skills - Counting 1-10. 1998. (Precious Moments Workbooks Ser.). (Illus.). 32p. (J). pap., wbk. ed. 2.99 (978-1-57759-116-0(X)) Dalmatian Pr.

—Multiplication & Division. 1999. (Tools Ser.). 32p. (J). (gr. 3-4). pap. 2.29 (978-1-57759-150-4(X)) Dalmatian Pr.

—Multiplication & Division: Practice Tablets. 2002. (Home Learning Tools Ser.). (Illus.). 64p. (J). (gr. 3-4). pap. 2.99 (978-1-57759-234-1(4)) Dalmatian Pr.

—Precious Moments Addition & Subtraction. 2000. (Precious Moments Workbooks Ser.). (Illus.). 32p. (J). pap., wbk. ed. 2.99 (978-1-57759-290-7(5)) Dalmatian Pr.

—Precious Moments Transition Math. 2000. (Precious Moments Workbooks Ser.). (Illus.). 32p. (J). pap., wbk. ed. 2.99 (978-1-57759-289-1(1)) Dalmatian Pr.

—Transition Math. 2002. (Tools Ser.). (Illus.). 32p. (J). (gr. k-1). pap. 2.29 (978-1-57759-149-8(6)) Dalmatian Pr.

Dalmatian Press Staff, contrib. by. Addition & Subtraction. 2002. (Tools Ser.). (Illus.). 32p. (J). (gr. 1 up). pap. 2.29 (978-1-57759-148-1(8)) Dalmatian Pr.

Dalmatian Press Staff, creator. Division: Flash Cards & Games. 2003. (Home Learning Tools Ser.). 56p. (J). 2.99 (978-1-4037-0215-9(2)) Dalmatian Pr.

Dalmatian Press Staff & School Zone Publishing Interactive Staff. Math 1. 2000. (On-Track Software Ser.). 32p. (J). (gr. 1). pap., wbk. ed. 13.99 incl. cd-rom (978-0-88743-932-2(2) , 08808) School Zone Publishing Co.

Dalton, Julie. Patterns Everywhere. (J). 2006. 32p. (gr. 1-2). pap. 5.95 (978-0-516-25367-1(0)); 2005. (Illus.). 31p. (ps-ps). 20.50 (978-0-516-25266-7(6)) Scholastic Library Publishing. (Children's Pr.).

D'Amato-Neff, Adam L. Creative Learning: Letters, Numbers, & Colors. 2002. 122p. (J). pap. 10.95 (978-0-595-23162-1(4) , Writers Club Pr.) iUniverse, Inc.

Dankberg, Tracy. Pre-Algebra: Grades 5-8. 2003. (Skill Builders Ser.). 80p. (gr. 5-8). 2.95 (978-1-932210-09-5(1)) Rainbow Bridge Publishing.

Daraonco, Mickey & Ohanesian, Diane. Is Bob Big? 2nd rev. ed. 2003. (BuildUp Ser.). (J). pap. 22.00 (978-1-4108-0742-7(8)) Benchmark Education Co.

Daronco, Mickey. Circus in the City. 2003. (BuildUp Ser.). (J). pap. 22.00 (978-1-4108-0774-8(6)) Benchmark Education Co.

—A Day to Enjoy. 2003. (BuildUp Ser.). (J). pap. 22.00 (978-1-4108-0773-1(8)) Benchmark Education Co.

—Which Part? 2nd rev. ed. 2003. (BuildUp Ser.). Orig. Title: What Will I Need?. (J). pap. 22.00 (978-1-4108-0764-9(9)) Benchmark Education Co.

Daronco, Mickey & Ohanesian, Diane. The Big Clock. 2nd rev. ed. 2004. (BuildUp Ser.). (J). pap. 22.00 (978-1-4108-1526-2(9)) Benchmark Education Co.

—Can It Fit? 2nd rev. ed. 2003. (BuildUp Ser.). (J). pap. 22.00 (978-1-4108-0737-3(1)) Benchmark Education Co.

—Can We Pick It? 2nd rev. ed. 2004. (BuildUp Ser.). (J). pap. 22.00 (978-1-4108-1534-7(X)) Benchmark Education Co.

—Is It Big? 2nd rev. ed. 2004. (BuildUp Ser.). (J). pap. 22.00 (978-1-4108-1530-9(7)) Benchmark Education Co.

—More Corn. 2nd rev. ed. 2003. (BuildUp Ser.). (J). pap. 22.00 (978-1-4108-0766-3(5)) Benchmark Education Co.

—My Turn to Fit. 2nd rev. ed. 2003. (BuildUp Ser.). Orig. Title: Will It or Will It Not?. (J). pap. 22.00 (978-1-4108-0765-6(7)) Benchmark Education Co.

—One to Five. 2nd rev. ed. 2003. (BuildUp Ser.). Orig. Title: Look at This. (J). pap. 22.00 (978-1-4108-0754-0(1)) Benchmark Education Co.

—One to Ten. 2nd rev. ed. 2004. (BuildUp Ser.). (J). pap. 22.00 (978-1-4108-1527-9(7)) Benchmark Education Co.

—Two by Two. 2nd rev. ed. 2004. (BuildUp Ser.). (J). pap. 22.00 (978-1-4108-1535-4(8)) Benchmark Education Co.

Data Analysis. 2003. (Mathematical Mind Ser.). 48p. (gr. 5-8). 5.99 (978-0-7424-0262-1(2) , IF2907) School Specialty Publishing.

Data & Negatives Student: RUA Data & Negatives Student. 2005. 95p. per. 7.50 (978-1-932976-73-1(6)) National Ctr. on Education & The Economy.

Data & Negatives Student: RUPA Data & Negatives Student. 2005. 95p. per. 7.50 (978-1-932976-52-6(3)) National Ctr. on Education & The Economy.

Davidson, James E., et al. Math Topics. 1999. (100+ Seriestm Ser.). 128p. (J). (gr. 1-2). pap. 12.99 (978-0-88012-909-1(3) , IF8745); (gr. 3-4). pap. 12.99 (978-0-88012-910-7(7) , IF8746); (gr. 5-6). pap. 12.99 (978-0-88012-911-4(5) , IF8747) School Specialty Publishing.

Davies & Ne, Harriet. Sum Fun. (Illus.). 40p. (J). 19.95 (978-1-85479-226-6(1)) O'Mara, Michael Bks., Ltd. GBR. *Dist:* Trans-Atlantic Pubns., Inc.

Davies, Anne. Fast Ideas for Busy Teachers: Math, Grade 3. 2004. (Illus.). 80p. (J). (gr. 3-3). pap. 10.99 (978-0-7682-2913-4(8) , FS99307, Schaffer, Frank) Schaffer, Frank Pubns.

Davis, Rebecca. Learn Your Times Tables in Five Days. 2002. 12p. (J). (gr. 3-6). spiral bd. 4.00 (978-0-9720881-2-1(1)) His Hands, Inc.

Davis, Steve. Math Skills Practice & Apply: Grade 4. 2000. (Illus.). 128p. (J). (gr. 4). pap. 10.95 (978-1-58037-127-8(2)) Twain, Mark Media, Inc. Pubs.

—Math Skills Practice & Apply: Grade 5. 2000. (Illus.). 128p. (J). (gr. 5). pap. 10.95 (978-1-58037-128-5(0)) Twain, Mark Media, Inc. Pubs.

—Math Skills Practice & Apply: Grade 6. 2000. (Illus.). 128p. (J). (gr. 6). pap. 10.95 (978-1-58037-129-2(9)) Twain, Mark Media, Inc. Pubs.

—Math Skills Practice & Apply: Grade 7. 2000. (Illus.). 128p. (YA). (gr. 7). pap. 10.95 (978-1-58037-130-8(2)) Twain, Mark Media, Inc. Pubs.

Day, Eileen. I'm Good at Math. 2003. (Illus.). 24p. (J). pap. 5.25 (978-1-4034-3448-7(4)); lib. bdg. 18.50 (978-1-4034-0901-0(3)) Heinemann Library.

—I'm Good at Math. 2003. (gr. k-3). lib. bdg. 14.45 (978-0-613-70659-9(5)) Tandem Library Bks.

—Soy Buena para las Matematicas. 2003. (SPA.). 24p. pap. 5.25 (978-1-4034-3580-4(4)) Heinemann Library.

Day Two PSAE Student Textbook. 3rd ed. 2005. per. (978-1-58894-035-3(7)) Cambridge Educational Services, Inc.

De Pue, Kent A. Bellwork, Math Level 1 (2001) 2001. per. (978-0-934475-95-2(4)) BELLWORK Enterprises, Inc.

Dean, Arlan. Mathematical Thinking Idea Procedures. 2004. 48p. pap. 6.95 (978-1-4042-8528-6(8)) Rosen Publishing Group, Inc., The.

Decimals & Percents Student: RUPA Decimals & Percents Student. 2005. 100p. per. 7.50 (978-1-932976-48-9(5)) National Ctr. on Education & The Economy.

Decimals with Desi- Additon & Subtraction. 2000. pap. incl. audio (978-0-9709083-0-8(X)) Smiling Butterfly Pubns.

Decoding Math Word Problems - Grade 3. 2004. (J). pap. 14.95 (978-1-56911-156-7(1)) Learning Resources, Inc.

Decoding Math Word Problems - Grade 4. 2004. (J). pap. 14.95 (978-1-56911-157-4(X)) Learning Resources, Inc.

Decoding Math Word Problems - Grade 5. 2004. (J). pap. 14.95 (978-1-56911-158-1(8)) Learning Resources, Inc.

Dezimalbrueche. (Duden-Schuelerhilfen Ser.). (GER.). 112p. (J). (gr. 6). (978-3-411-70112-4(9)) Bibliographisches Institut & F. A. Brockhaus AG DEU. *Dist:* International Bk. Import Service, Inc.

Diffily, Deborah, et al. The Scholatic Book of Early Childhood Learning Centers: Complete How-to's, Management Tips, Photos & Activities for Delightful Learning Centers That Teach Early Reading, Writing, Math & More! 96th ed. 2001. (Illus.). 96p. (ps-k). pap. 12.95 (978-0-439-20106-3(3)) Scholastic, Inc.

Disbrow, Sheri. Math Warm Ups: Developing Fluency in Math. 2005. 80p. (gr. 2 up). 12.95 (978-1-59363-103-1(0)) Prufrock Pr.

—Math Warm-Ups, Grade 2. 2004. per. 12.95 (978-1-883055-64-6(4)) Dandy Lion Pubns.

—Math Warm-Ups, Grade 3. 2004. per. 12.95 (978-1-883055-65-3(2)) Dandy Lion Pubns.

—Math Warm-Ups Grade 3: Developing Fluency in Math. 2005. 80p. (gr. 3 up). 12.95 (978-1-59363-104-8(9)) Prufrock Pr.

—Math Warm-Ups, Grade 4. 2004. per. 12.95 (978-1-883055-66-0(0)) Dandy Lion Pubns.

—Math Warm-Ups Grade 4: Developing Fluency in Math. 2005. 80p. (gr. 4 up). 12.95 (978-1-59363-105-5(7)) Prufrock Pr.

Dive into Summer School with Larson's Intermediate Math — Grade 5. 2002. (J). spiral bd. 15.95 (978-1-58123-322-3(1)) Larson Learning, Inc.

Dive into Summer School with Larson's Intermediate Math: Grade 3. 2002. (J). spiral bd. 15.95 (978-1-58123-320-9(5)) Larson Learning, Inc.

Dive into Summer School with Larson's Intermediate Math: Grade 4. 2002. (J). spiral bd. 15.95 (978-1-58123-321-6(3)) Larson Learning, Inc.

Dive into Summer School with Larson's Intermediate Math: Grade 6. 2002. (J). spiral bd. 15.95 (978-1-58123-323-0(X)) Larson Learning, Inc.

DK Publishing. Dora the Explorer Kindergarten Workbook. 2008. (Math Made Easy Ser.). 202p. (J). (gr. k-k). pap. 14.99 (***978-0-7566-3847-4(X)***) Dorling Kindersley Publishing, Inc.

—Go, Diego, Go! First Grade Workbook. 2008. (Math Made Easy Ser.). 202p. (J). (gr. 1-1). pap. 14.99 (***978-0-7566-3848-1(8)***) Dorling Kindersley Publishing, Inc.

DK Publishing Staff. Batman Fifth Grade. 2007. (Math Workbooks Ser.). 202p. (J). (gr. 5-5). 14.99 (978-0-7566-2999-1(3)) Dorling Kindersley Publishing, Inc.

—Heroes: Fourth Grade. 2007. (Math Workbooks Ser.). 202p. (J). (gr. 4-4). wbk. ed. 14.99 (978-0-7566-2998-4(5)) Dorling Kindersley Publishing, Inc.

—Marvel Heroes: Second Grade. 2007. (Math Workbooks Ser.). 202p. (J). (gr. 2-2). wbk. ed. 14.99 (978-0-7566-2985-4(3)) Dorling Kindersley Publishing, Inc.

—Superman Third Grade. 2007. (Math Workbooks Ser.). 202p. (J). (gr. 3-3). wbk. ed. 14.99 (978-0-7566-2984-7(5)) Dorling Kindersley Publishing, Inc.

Doing Basic Math with Manipulatives. 240p. (gr. 1-3). 17.99 (978-1-56451-323-6(8) , ID3091); (gr. 4-6). 17.99 (978-1-56451-324-3(6) , ID3092) School Specialty Publishing.

Dominguez, Margaret & Dominguez, Marissa. Ninth Grade Math TAKS Worksheets. Dominguez, Margaret & Dominguez, Marissa, illus. 2002. (Illus.). 69p. (YA). (gr. 9). (978-1-889684-20-8(1)) Texas Testing Products.

—Seventh Grade Math TAKS Worksheets. Dominguez, Margaret & Dominguez, Marissa, illus. 2002. (Illus.). 51p. (YA). (gr. 7). (978-1-889684-22-2(8)) Texas Testing Products.

Dominoes. 2002. (J). pap., wbk. ed. 8.95 (978-1-56911-046-1(8)) Learning Resources, Inc.

Donde? Math, 6 vols.Tr. of Where? Math. (SPA.). (gr. k-2). 28.95 (978-0-7368-3141-3(X) , Yellow Umbrella Bks.) Capstone Pr., Inc.

Donde esta el Panda? Superlibros de Literatura/Literature Big Books. 1999. (Matematicas en Mi Mundo Ser.). (ENG & SPA.). (gr. k up). (978-0-02-110154-2(X)) Macmillan/McGraw-Hill Schl. Div.

Dooley, Virginia. School Success Reading & Math Prek. Cooper, Terry, ed. 2005. 320p. pap., wbk. ed. 14.99 (978-0-439-78598-3(7) , Teaching Resources) Scholastic, Inc.

Dora the Explorer Subtraction Decoder. 2004. (J). 3.95 (***978-1-58610-884-7(0)*** , 72007) Learning Horizons, Inc.

Dorling Kindersley Publishing Staff. Math Wizard. 2006. (DK Toys & Games Ser.). 1p. (J). pap. 9.99 (978-0-7566-1766-0(9)) Dorling Kindersley Publishing, Inc.

Dot-to-Dot 1-100+ (Gr. 2-4) 2003. (J). (978-1-58232-104-2(3)) Bryan Hse. Pubs., Inc.

Doudna, Kelly. Please Don't Laugh, I Can Use a Graph. 2007. (Illus.). 24p. (J). 19.93 (978-1-59928-614-3(9) , SandCastle) ABDO Publishing Co.

Douglas, Vincent. Addition & Subtraction. 2001. (Illus.). 32p. (C). (gr. 1). pap. 2.99 (978-1-56189-627-1(6) , American Education Publishing) School Specialty Publishing.

—The Complete Book of Math: Grades 5-6. 2001. (Complete Book Ser.). (Illus.). 352p. (J). (gr. 5-6). pap., wbk. ed. 14.95 (978-1-56189-677-6(2) , 31373, American Education Publishing) School Specialty Publishing.

—The Complete Book of Math Games. American Education Publishing Staff, ed. 2000. (Complete Book Ser.). (Illus.). 352p. (J). (gr. 1-2). pap. 14.95 (978-1-56189-549-6(0) , 31246, American Education Publishing) School Specialty Publishing.

—Comprehensive Curriculum Plus Test Practice: Grade 2. 2003. (Comprehensive Curriculum Plus Test Practice Ser.). (Illus.). 616p. (J). (ps-6). pap. 24.95 (978-0-7696-2902-5(4) , American Education Publishing) School Specialty Publishing.

—Comprehensive Curriculum Plus Test Practice: Grade K. 2003. (Comprehensive Curriculum Plus Test Practice Ser.). (Illus.). 616p. (J). (ps-6). pap. 24.95 (978-0-7696-2900-1(8) , American Education Publishing) School Specialty Publishing.

—Daily Learning Drills: Grade 4. 2003. (Daily Learning Drills Ser.). (Illus.). 416p. (J). (gr. 4-4). pap., wbk. ed. 10.95 (978-0-7696-3094-6(4) , American Education Publishing) School Specialty Publishing.

—Daily Learning Drills: Grade 5. 2003. (Daily Learning Drills Ser.). (Illus.). 416p. (J). (gr. 5-5). pap., wbk. ed. 10.95 (978-0-7696-3095-3(2) , American Education Publishing) School Specialty Publishing.

—Daily Learning Drills: Grade 6. 2003. (Daily Learning Drills Ser.). (Illus.). 416p. (J). (gr. 6-6). pap. 10.95 (978-0-7696-3096-0(0) , Brighter Child) School Specialty Publishing.

—Math: Grade 6. 2003. (Brighter Child Workbooks Ser.). (Illus.). 24p. (J). (gr. 6). pap. 2.25 (978-1-56189-076-7(6) , American Education Publishing) School Specialty Publishing.

Douglas, Vincent & School Specialty Publishing Staff. The Complete Book of Challenge Math. 2005. (Complete Book Ser.). (Illus.). 352p. (J). pap. 14.95 (978-0-7696-4333-5(7) , American Education Publishing) School Specialty Publishing.

—Comprehensive Curriculum Plus Test Practice, Grade 1. 2003. (Comprehensive Curriculum Plus Test Practice Ser.). (Illus.). 616p. (J). (ps-6). pap. 24.95 (978-0-7696-2901-8(6) , American Education Publishing) School Specialty Publishing.

—Comprehensive Curriculum Plus Test Practice, Grade 3. 2003. (Comprehensive Curriculum Plus Test Practice Ser.). (Illus.). 616p. (J). (ps-6). pap. 24.95 (978-0-7696-2903-2(2) , American Education Publishing) School Specialty Publishing.

—Comprehensive Curriculum Plus Test Practice, Grade 4. 2003. (Comprehensive Curriculum Plus Test Practice Ser.). (Illus.). 616p. (J). (ps-6). pap. 24.95 (978-0-7696-2904-9(0) , American Education Publishing) School Specialty Publishing.

—Everything for Math & Reading, Grade 3. Mcgraw-Hill Editorial Staff, ed. 2004. (Everything for Early Learning Ser.). (Illus.). 320p. (J). (gr. 3-3). pap. 7.95 (978-0-7696-3363-3(3) , American Education Publishing) School Specialty Publishing.

—Everything for Math & Reading, Grade 4. Mcgraw-Hill Editorial Staff, ed. 2004. (Everything for Early Learning Ser.). (Illus.). 320p. (J). (gr. 4-4). pap. 7.95 (978-0-7696-3364-0(1) , American Education Publishing) School Specialty Publishing.

—I Can Add & Subtract. 2003. (I Can... Ser.). (Illus.). 128p. (J). pap. 3.95 (978-0-7696-2399-3(9) , American Education Publishing) School Specialty Publishing.

—I Can Multiply & Divide. 2003. (I Can... Ser.). (Illus.). 128p. (J). pap. 3.95 (978-0-7696-2917-9(2) , American Education Publishing) School Specialty Publishing.

—Language Arts & Math Skills. 2004. (My Little Heavenly Helpers Ser.). (Illus.). 64p. (J). (ps-k). pap. 3.99 (978-0-7696-3650-4(0) , Brighter Child) School Specialty Publishing.

—Math at School. 2003. (It's Everyplace You Are! Ser.). (Illus.). 48p. (J). (gr. k up). pap. 6.99 (978-0-7682-2549-5(3) , FS99019); (gr. 1-1). pap. 6.99 (978-0-7682-2542-6(6) , FS99020) Schaffer, Frank Pubns. (Schaffer, Frank).

—Math at School- Grade 3. 2003. (It's Everyplace You Are! Ser.). (Illus.). 48p. (J). (gr. 3-3). pap. 6.99 (978-0-7682-2531-0(0) , FS99022, Schaffer, Frank) Schaffer, Frank Pubns.

—Math Fact Book. Notebk Referenc, ed. 2nd rev. ed. 2006. (Notebook Reference Ser.). 144p. (J). pap. 3.95 (978-0-7696-4340-3(X) , American Education Publishing) School Specialty Publishing.

—Math, Grades 3-4. 2003. (100+ Seriestm Ser.). (Illus.). 128p. (J). (gr. 3-4). pap. 12.99 (978-0-7424-1721-2(2) , IFG99001, Instructional Fair) Schaffer, Frank Pubns.

—Math Plus Reading. 2004. (Summer Link Ser.). (Illus.). 320p. (J). (ps-6). pap. 14.95 (978-0-7696-3331-2(5)); pap. 14.95 (978-0-7696-3332-9(3)); pap. 14.95 (978-0-7696-3333-6(1)); pap. 14.95 (978-0-7696-3334-3(X)); pap. 14.95 (978-0-7696-3335-0(8)) School Specialty Publishing. (American Education Publishing).

—Practice Writing Numbers. 2002. (Edu-Slates Ser.). (Illus.). 1p. (J). 2.99 (978-1-57768-998-0(4) , Brighter Child) School Specialty Publishing.

—Spectrum Enrichment Math & Reading, Grade 4. 2002. (Starburst Spectrum Workbook Ser.). (Illus.). 150p. (J). (gr. 4-4). pap. 8.95 (978-1-57768-504-3(0) , Spectrum) School Specialty Publishing.

—Spectrum Enrichment Math & Reading, Grade 5. 2002. (Starburst Spectrum Workbook Ser.). (Illus.). 150p. (J). (gr. 5-5). pap. 8.95 (978-1-57768-505-0(9) , Spectrum) School Specialty Publishing.

—Spectrum Enrichment Math & Reading, Grade 6. 2002. (Starburst Spectrum Workbook Ser.). (Illus.). 150p. (J). (gr. 6-6). pap. 8.95 (978-1-57768-506-7(7) , Spectrum) School Specialty Publishing.

—Spectrum Math, Grade 2. 1999. (McGraw-Hill Learning Materials Spectrum Ser.). (Illus.). 150p. (J). (gr. 2-2). pap., wbk. ed. 8.95 (978-1-57768-402-2(8) , Spectrum) School Specialty Publishing.

—Spectrum Math, Grade 3. Mayer, Mercer, illus. 1999. (McGraw-Hill Learning Materials Spectrum Ser.). 150p. (J). (gr. 3-3). pap., wbk. ed. 8.95 (978-1-57768-403-9(6) , Spectrum) School Specialty Publishing.

—Spectrum Math, Grade 6. Mayer, Mercer, illus. 1999. (Spectrum Workbooks Ser.). 150p. (J). (gr. 6-6). pap., wbk. ed. 8.95 (978-1-57768-406-0(0) , Spectrum) School Specialty Publishing.

—Summer Link Math, Grades 1-2. 2004. (Summer Link Ser.). (Illus.). 96p. (J). (ps-6). pap. 6.95 (978-0-7696-3311-4(0) , American Education Publishing) School Specialty Publishing.

—Summer Link Math, Grades 4-5. 2004. (Summer Link Ser.). (Illus.). 96p. (J). (ps-6). pap. 6.95 (978-0-7696-3314-5(5) , American Education Publishing) School Specialty Publishing.

—Summer Link Math, Grades 5-6. 2004. (Summer Link Ser.). (Illus.). 96p. (J). (ps-6). pap. 6.95 (978-0-7696-3315-2(3) , American Education Publishing) School Specialty Publishing.

—Summer Link Math, Kindergarten-Grade 1. 2004. (Summer Link Ser.). (Illus.). 96p. (J). (ps-6). pap. 6.95 (978-0-7696-3310-7(2) , American Education Publishing) School Specialty Publishing.

—Summer Link Math plus Reading, Kindergarten-Grade 1. 2004. (Summer Link Ser.). (Illus.). 320p. (J). (ps-6). pap. 14.95 (978-0-7696-3330-5(7) , American Education Publishing) School Specialty Publishing.

—Summer Link Math plus Reading, Preschool-Kindergarten. 2004. (Summer Link Ser.). (Illus.). 320p. (J). (ps-6). pap. 14.95 (978-0-7696-3329-9(3) , American Education Publishing) School Specialty Publishing.

—Total Math, Grade 1. 2004. (Total Math Ser.). (Illus.). 352p. (J). (gr. 1-1). pap. 14.95 (978-0-7696-3511-8(3) , American Education Publishing) School Specialty Publishing.

—Total Math, Grade 2. 2004. (Total Math Ser.). (Illus.). 352p. (J). (gr. 2-2). pap. 14.95 (978-0-7696-3512-5(1) , American Education Publishing) School Specialty Publishing.

—Total Math, Grade 3. 2004. (Total Math Ser.). (Illus.). 352p. (J). (gr. 3-3). pap. 14.95 (978-0-7696-3513-2(X) , American Education Publishing) School Specialty Publishing.

—Total Math, Grade 4. 2004. (Total Math Ser.). (Illus.). 352p. (J). (gr. 4-4). pap. 14.95 (978-0-7696-3514-9(8) , American Education Publishing) School Specialty Publishing.

—Total Math, Grade 5. 2004. (Total Math Ser.). (Illus.). 352p. (J). (gr. 5-5). pap. 14.95 (978-0-7696-3515-6(6) , American Education Publishing) School Specialty Publishing.

—Total Math, Grade 6. 2004. (Total Math Ser.). (Illus.). 352p. (J). (gr. 6-6). pap. 14.95 (978-0-7696-3516-3(4) , American Education Publishing) School Specialty Publishing.

—Total Math, Kindergarten. 2004. (Total Math Ser.). (Illus.). 352p. (J). (ps-6). pap. 14.95 (978-0-7696-3510-1(5) , American Education Publishing) School Specialty Publishing.

—Total Math, Preschool. 2004. (Total Math Ser.). (Illus.). 352p. (J). (ps-6). pap. 14.95 (978-0-7696-3509-5(1) , American Education Publishing) School Specialty Publishing.

Doxon, Lynn Ellen. Family School Mathematics. 2008. per. 9.95 (978-1-932926-95-8(X)) Artemesia Publishing, LLC.

Draze, Dianne. The Loose Caboose & Other Math Mysteries. 2005. 64p. 11.95 (978-1-59363-136-9(7)) Prufrock Pr.

—Math-a-Logic. 2005. 81p. 12.95 (978-1-59363-107-9(3)) Prufrock Pr.

Dreieckskonstruktionen. (Duden-Schuelerhilfen Ser.). (GER.). 112p. (YA). (gr. 7-8). (978-3-411-05671-2(1)) Bibliographisches Institut & F. A. Brockhaus AG DEU. *Dist:* International Bk. Import Service, Inc.

Dreisatz, Prozente, Zinsen. (Duden-Schuelerhilfen Ser.). (GER.). 112p. (YA). (gr. 6-8). (978-3-411-70762-1(3)) Bibliographisches Institut & F. A. Brockhaus AG DEU. *Dist:* International Bk. Import Service, Inc.

Drill, Practice, & Apply (Gr. 1-2) 2003. (J). (978-1-58232-100-4(0)) Bryan Hse. Pubs., Inc.

Drill, Practice, & Apply Gr. 1-2 Spanish Version. 2007. (J). per. (***978-1-58232-159-2(0)***) Bryan Hse. Pubs., Inc.

Drill, Practice, & Apply (Gr. 2-3) 2003. (J). (978-1-58232-101-1(9)) Bryan Hse. Pubs., Inc.

Drill, Practice, & Apply Gr. 2-3 Spanish Version. 2007. (J). per. (***978-1-58232-160-8(4)***) Bryan Hse. Pubs., Inc.

Drill, Practice, & Apply (Gr. 3-4) 2003. (J). (978-1-58232-102-8(7)) Bryan Hse. Pubs., Inc.

Drill, Practice, & Apply Gr. 3-4 Spanish Version. 2007. (J). per. (***978-1-58232-161-5(2)***) Bryan Hse. Pubs., Inc.

Drill, Practice, & Apply (Gr. 4-5) 2003. (J). (978-1-58232-103-5(5)) Bryan Hse. Pubs., Inc.

Drill, Practice, & Apply Gr. 4-5 Spanish Version. 2007. (J). per. (***978-1-58232-162-2(0)***) Bryan Hse. Pubs., Inc.

Duncan, Neil. Cambridge Checkpoints VCE Further Mathematics 2004. 2003. (Cambridge Checkpoints Ser.). 231p. pap. 13.35 (978-0-521-54096-4(8)) Cambridge Univ. Pr.

—Cambridge Checkpoints VCE Further Mathematics 2006. 2005. (Cambridge Checkpoints Ser.). pap. 13.40 (978-0-521-67716-5(5)) Cambridge Univ. Pr.

—Cambridge Checkpoints VCE Mathematical Methods 2006. 2005. (Cambridge Checkpoints Ser.). pap. 13.40 (978-0-521-67715-8(7)) Cambridge Univ. Pr.

—Cambridge Checkpoints VCE Specialist Mathematics 2006. 2005. (Cambridge Checkpoints Ser.). pap. 13.40 (978-0-521-67717-2(3)) Cambridge Univ. Pr.

Dunham, Anne M. & O'Neal, Debbie M. Monopoly Everyday Math Grades 3-4. 2002. 32p. (J). 3.99 (978-1-58792-028-8(X)) Trend Enterprises, Inc.

—Monopoly Junior Grades 1-2 Math. 2002. 32p. (J). 3.99 (978-1-58792-025-7(5)) Trend Enterprises, Inc.

—Monopoly Junior Kindergarten Math. 2002. 32p. (J). 3.99 (978-1-58792-022-6(0)) Trend Enterprises, Inc.

DynaNotes Grade 9 Math Review Guide Transparency Set. 2006. (YA). trans. (978-1-933854-34-2(0)) DynaStudy, Inc.

DynaNotes Grade 9 Math TAKS Review Guide. 2006. (YA). pap. (978-1-933854-30-4(8)) DynaStudy, Inc.

e-Educators. Full-Color Standards-Based Math: Activities & Games. 2007. 176p. pap. 21.99 (***978-1-4206-8719-4(0)***) Teacher Created Resources, Inc.

Early Learning at Home Beginni. 2004. 9.95 (978-0-7647-0479-6(6)) School Specialty Publishing.

Early Math Flip Chart. 2003. (gr. k up). spiral bd., tchr.'s training gde. ed. 14.95 (978-1-58845-184-2(4)) School Specialty Publishing.

Early Math Package. 2005. (Emergent/Early (Prek-2) Math Package Ser.). (YA). (gr. k-2). 126.00 (978-0-8215-7863-6(4)) Sadlier, William H. Inc.

Ebs Trust, prod. Concepts in Abstract Algebra: Group Theory. (Concepts in Abstract Algebra: Group Theory Ser.). (YA). cd-rom 269.95 (978-0-7365-4752-9(5)) Films Media Group.

Echols, Jean C., et al. Elephants & Their Young: Science & Math Activities for Young Children. Babcock, Carl, ed. Baker, Lisa H., illus. Hoyt, Richard & Barrett, Reginald H., photos by. 2001. (Great Explorations in Math & Science Ser.). 112p. (J). pap. 18.00 (978-0-924886-55-3(2) , GEMS) Univ. of California, Berkeley, Lawrence Hall of Science.

Edmunds, Tracy. Full-Color Math Rhymes, Songs & Stories. 2007. 176p. pap. 21.99 (***978-1-4206-8857-3(X)***) Teacher Created Resources, Inc.

Edson, Ann & Schwartz, Allan A. Read & Solve Math Problems, Vol. 2. (J). (gr. 4-6). pap., act. bk. ed., pupil's gde. ed. 79.00 incl. audio (978-0-89525-196-1(5) , AKC 319) Educational Activities, Inc.

Educational Testing Service Staff. Packets Math Performance Assessment: Bike-a-Thon. 2001. tchr. ed. (978-1-57091-328-0(5)) Charlesbridge Publishing, Inc.

—Packets Math Performance Assessment: Boxing Bookmarks! 2001. tchr. ed. (978-1-57091-325-9(0)) Charlesbridge Publishing, Inc.

—Packets Math Performance Assessment: Snack Attack! 2001. tchr. ed. (978-1-57091-327-3(7)) Charlesbridge Publishing, Inc.

—Packets Math Performance Assessment: Taking Shape. 2001. tchr. ed. (978-1-57091-329-7(3)) Charlesbridge Publishing, Inc.

—Packets Math Performance Assessment: Use Your Head! 2001. (978-1-57091-326-6(9)) Charlesbridge Publishing, Inc.

Edwards, Phyllis. Third Grade Math: Basic Mathematics Skills. Evans, Marilyn, ed. Supancich, Jo, illus. Date not set. 33p. (J). (gr. 3). pap., wbk. ed. 2.50 (978-1-58610-106-0(4)) Learning Horizons, Inc.

Edwards, Roy. School Mathematics Project 11-16, Llyfr 1. 2005. (WEL., Illus.). 64p. (978-1-86085-065-3(0)) ICA Video.

Edwards, Roy, et al. Mathemateg Cynradd Caergrawnt. 2005. (WEL., Illus.). 128p. (978-1-86085-070-7(7)) ICA Video.

Einstein, el matematico Imaginativo 15: Leveled Books. 2001. (McGraw-Hill. Lectura Ser.). (ENG & SPA.). (gr. 4 up). (978-0-02-188215-1(0)) Macmillan/McGraw-Hill Schl. Div.

Eisemann, Pat & Fuko, Karen. ESPA Math: Building Math Confidence & ESPA Sense. 1999. (Illus.). 200p. (J). (gr. 3-5). wbk. ed. 39.95 (978-1-886292-37-6(X)) CEO Software Solutions.

Ekblad, Linda. Big Book Yellow Super Pack. 2000. (Metro Math Readers Yellow Level Ser.). (J). (gr. 1-2). 479.95 (978-1-58830-143-7(5)) Metropolitan Teaching & Learning Co.

—Cuadrados: Metro Math Readers Red Level. 2000. 3.30 (978-1-58120-377-6(2)) Metropolitan Teaching & Learning Co.

—Cual es? Metro Math Readers Red Level. 2000. (J). 3.30 (978-1-58120-381-3(0)) Metropolitan Teaching & Learning Co.

—Half Is Fair: Metro Math Readers Yellow Level. 2000. (Metro Math Readers Yellow Level Ser.). (J). (gr. 1-2). 3.75 (978-1-58120-423-0(X)) Metropolitan Teaching & Learning Co.

—Money Counts: Metro Math Readers Yellow Level. 2000. (Metro Math Readers Yellow Level Ser.). (J). (gr. 1-2). 3.75 (978-1-58120-411-7(6)) Metropolitan Teaching & Learning Co.

—The Number Eight: Metro Math Readers Red Level. 2000. (J). 3.30 (978-1-58120-308-0(X)) Metropolitan Teaching & Learning Co.

—Perritos Vienen y vanV: Metro Math Readers Yellow Level. 2000. (Metro Math Readers Yellow Level Ser.). (J). (gr. 1-2). 3.75 (978-1-58120-467-4(1)) Metropolitan Teaching & Learning Co.

—Puppies In, Puppies Out: Metro Math Readers Yellow Level. 2000. (Metro Math Readers Yellow Level Ser.). (J). (gr. 1-2). 3.75 (978-1-58120-404-9(3)) Metropolitan Teaching & Learning Co.

—Quien falta? Metro Math Readers Red Level. 2000. (J). 3.30 (978-1-58120-383-7(7)) Metropolitan Teaching & Learning Co.

—Squares: Metro Math Readers Red Level. 2000. (J). 3.30 (978-1-58120-313-4(6)) Metropolitan Teaching & Learning Co.

—Take a Closer Look. 2000. (Metro Math Readers Red Level Ser.). (J). (gr. k-1). 46.95 (978-1-58120-555-8(4)) Metropolitan Teaching & Learning Co.

—Twenty, More or Less: Metro Math Readers Yellow Level. 2000. (Metro Math Readers Yellow Level Ser.). (J). (gr. 1-2). 3.75 (978-1-58120-402-5(7)) Metropolitan Teaching & Learning Co.

—Which One Is It? Metro Math Readers Red Level. 2000. (J). 3.30 (978-1-58120-317-2(9)) Metropolitan Teaching & Learning Co.

—Who Is Missing: Metro Math Readers Red Level. 2000. (J). 3.30 (978-1-58120-319-6(5)) Metropolitan Teaching & Learning Co.

Elementary & Middle School Mathematics. 4th ed. 2000. (J). tchr. ed. (978-0-321-08376-0(8)) Addison-Wesley Longman, Inc.

Elementary Mathematics for Diverse Learners - Training Kit. 2004. (Region IV ESC Resources for Special Education Ser.). cd-rom (978-1-932797-04-6(1)) Region IV Education Service Ctr.

Emergent Math Package. 2005. (Emergent/Early (Prek-2) Math Package Ser.). (YA). (ps-1). 135.00 (978-0-8215-7878-0(2)) Sadlier, William H. Inc.

Emergent/Early Math Package. 2005. (Mathematics Ser.). (YA). (ps-1). 243.00 (978-0-8215-7888-9(X)) Sadlier, William H. Inc.

En el pais de los Rinocerontes: Superlibros de Literatura/Literature Big Books. 1999. (Matematicas en Mi Mundo Ser.). (ENG & SPA.). (gr. 1 up). (978-0-02-110160-3(4)) Macmillan/McGraw-Hill Schl. Div.

En la selva Tropical: Superlibros de Literatura/Literature Big Books. 1999. (Matematicas en Mi Mundo Ser.). (ENG & SPA.). (gr. 2 up). (978-0-02-110166-5(3)) Macmillan/McGraw-Hill Schl. Div.

Encyclopaedia Britannica Publishers, Inc. Staff. Math in Context. 6th ed. 2005. Level 1. 79.73 (978-0-03-040374-3(X)); Level 2. 79.73 (978-0-03-040377-4(4)); Level 3. 79.73 (978-0-03-040378-1(2)) Harcourt Schl. Pubs.

—Math in Context: Building Formulas. 6th ed. 2005. pap. 10.60 (978-0-03-038559-9(8)) Harcourt Schl. Pubs.
—Math in Context: Dealing with Data. 6th ed. 2005. pap. 10.60 (978-0-03-038566-7(0)) Harcourt Schl. Pubs.
—Math in Context: Facts & Factors. 6th ed. 2005. pap. 10.60 (978-0-03-038564-3(4)) Harcourt Schl. Pubs.
—Math in Context: Great Predictions. 6th ed. 2005. pap. 10.60 (978-0-03-038572-8(5)) Harcourt Schl. Pubs.
—Math in Context: It's All the Same. 6th ed. 2005. (gr. 8). pap. 10.60 (978-0-03-038567-4(9)) Harcourt Schl. Pubs.
—Math in Context: Made to Measure. 6th ed. 2005. (gr. 7). pap. 10.60 (978-0-03-042404-5(6)) Harcourt Schl. Pubs.
—Math in Context: More or Less. 6th ed. 2006. pap. 10.60 (978-0-03-039618-2(2)) Harcourt Schl. Pubs.
—Math in Context: Number Tools. 6th ed. 2006. pap., wbk. ed. 12.70 (978-0-03-040384-2(7)) Harcourt Schl. Pubs.
—Math in Context: Operations. 6th ed. 2005. pap. 10.60 (978-0-03-038561-2(X)) Harcourt Schl. Pubs.
—Math in Context: Ratios & Rates. 6th ed. 2005. (gr. 7). pap. 10.60 (978-0-03-039629-8(8)) Harcourt Schl. Pubs.
—Math in Context: Reallotment. 6th ed. 2005. pap. 10.60 (978-0-03-039614-4(X)) Harcourt Schl. Pubs.
—Math in Context: Second Chance. 6th ed. 2005. (gr. 7). pap. 10.60 (978-0-03-038558-2(X)) Harcourt Schl. Pubs.
—Math in Context: Take a Chance. 6th ed. 2006. (gr. 6). pap. 10.60 (978-0-03-039613-7(1)) Harcourt Schl. Pubs.
—Math in Context: Ups & Downs. 6th ed. 2005. pap. 10.60 (978-0-03-038576-6(8)) Harcourt Schl. Pubs.
Enderle, Dotti. Storytime Discoveries: Math. Ginger Illustrations Staff, illus. 2004. 64p. (J). pap. 9.95 (978-1-57310-440-1(X)) Teaching & Learning Co.
Enlace: Casa y Escuela Level B Set. 2000. (Metro Math Readers Yellow Ser.). (J). (gr. 12). 21.15 (978-1-58120-489-6(2)); 21.15 (978-1-58120-490-2(6)) Metropolitan Teaching & Learning Co.
Enrichment Math & Reading: Grade 3. 2002. (Starburst Spectrum Workbook Ser.). (Illus.). 150p. (J). (gr. 3-3), pap. 8.95 (978-1-57768-503-6(2) , Spectrum) School Specialty Publishing.
Enzensberger, Hans Magnus. The Number Devil: A Mathematical Adventure. 2000. 262p. (gr. 3-6). lib. bdg. 28.05 (978-0-613-28591-9(3)) Tandem Library Bks.
Es tiempo Math, 6 vols.Tr. of It's Time! Math. (SPA.). (gr. k-2). 28.95 (978-0-7368-3029-4(4) , Yellow Umbrella Bks.) Capstone Pr., Inc.
Essential Words Math Activity Book (Elementary) Elementary. 2006. (J). 8.95 (978-1-933655-04-8(6)) New Leaf Educ., Inc.
Essential Words Math Activity Book (Intermediate) Intermediate/Middle School. 2005. (Illus.). 42p. (J). 8.95 (978-0-9722452-9-6(4)) New Leaf Educ., Inc.
Essential Words Math Glossary (Elementary) Elementary. 2006. (J). per. 19.95 (978-1-933655-03-1(8)) New Leaf Educ., Inc.
Essential Words Math Glossary (Intermediate) Intermediate/ Middle School. 2005. (Illus.). 76p. (J). per. 19.95 (978-0-9764217-0-2(4)) New Leaf Educ., Inc.
Evans, Karen. Math Basics: Grade 6. deluxe ed. 2000. (Deluxe Wkbks.). (Illus.). 64p. (ps-3). mass mkt., wbk. ed. 3.79 (978-0-88743-142-5(9) , 02206) School Zone Publishing Co.
Evans, Michael, et al. Essential Advanced General Mathematics. (Essential Mathematics Ser.). 2nd rev. ed. 1999. 592p. (gr. 9-11). pap. 23.00 incl. cd-rom (978-0-521-66449-3(7)); 3rd ed. 2005. pap., stu. ed. 30.00 incl. cd-rom (978-0-521-61252-4(7)) Cambridge Univ. Pr.
—Essential Mathematical Methods 3 & 4. 4th ed. 2005. (Essential Mathematics Ser.). pap., stu. ed. 28.95 incl. cd-rom (978-0-521-61547-1(X)) Cambridge Univ. Pr.
—Essential Mathematical Methods CAS 3 & 4. 2005. (Essential Mathematics Ser.). pap., stu. ed. 28.95 incl. cd-rom (978-0-521-61812-0(6)) Cambridge Univ. Pr.
—Essential Specialist Mathematics. 3rd ed. 2005. (Essential Mathematics Ser.). pap., stu. ed. 32.40 incl. cd-rom (978-0-521-60999-9(2)) Cambridge Univ. Pr.
Examenes: Student & Teacher Support Resources. 1999. (Matematicas en Mi Mundo Ser.). (ENG & SPA.). (gr. k up). (978-0-02-110180-1(9)); (gr. 1 up). (978-0-02-110181-8(7)); (gr. 2 up). (978-0-02-110182-5(5)); (gr. 3 up). (978-0-02-110183-2(3)); (gr. 4 up). (978-0-02-110184-9(1)); (gr. 6 up). (978-0-02-110186-3(8)) Macmillan/McGraw-Hill Schl. Div.
Exito en pruebas Estandarizadas: Assessment. 2002. (MacMillan/McGraw-Hill Matematicas Ser.). (ENG & SPA.). (gr. 1 up). (978-0-02-111698-0(9)); (gr. 2 up). (978-0-02-111699-7(7)); (gr. 3 up). (978-0-02-111700-0(4)); (gr. 4 up). (978-0-02-111701-7(2)); (gr. 5 up). (978-0-02-111702-4(0)); (gr. 6 up). (978-0-02-111703-1(9)) Macmillan/McGraw-Hill Schl. Div.
Exito en pruebas estandarizadas, Manual del Maestro: Assessment. 2002. (MacMillan/McGraw-Hill Matematicas Ser.). (ENG & SPA.). (gr. 1 up), (978-0-02-111704-8(7)) Macmillan/McGraw-Hill Schl. Div.
Exito en pruebas estandarizadas: Manual del Maestro: Assessment. 2002. (MacMillan/McGraw-Hill Matematicas Ser.). (ENG & SPA.). (gr. 2 up). (978-0-02-111705-5(5)); (gr. 3 up). (978-0-02-111706-2(3)); (gr. 4 up). (978-0-02-111707-9(1)); (gr. 5 up). (978-0-02-111708-6(X)); (gr. 6 up). (978-0-02-111709-3(8)) Macmillan/ McGraw-Hill Schl. Div.
Explorations with Links & Link-its. 2000. (J). pap. 11.95 (978-1-56911-053-9(0)) Learning Resources, Inc.
Exploring Geometric Solids. 2004. (J). per. 4.95 (978-1-56911-538-1(9)) Learning Resources, Inc.
Exploring Math with Polyhedra Dice. 2000. (J). pap. 10.95 (978-1-56911-032-4(8)) Learning Resources, Inc.
Exploring Math with Power Polygons. 2000. (J). pap. 10.95 (978-1-56911-025-6(5)) Learning Resources, Inc.
Exploring with Pattern Blocks. 2000. (J). pap. 10.95 (978-1-56911-093-5(X)) Learning Resources, Inc.
Expressions & Equations Student's Edition: CA Math Series II. 2004. 6.00 (978-1-932230-81-9(5)) National Ctr. on Education & The Economy.
Expressions & Equations Student's Edition: Foundations of Advanced Mathematics. 2002. (Foundations of Advance Mathematics Ser.). lib. bdg., stu. ed. 5.00 (978-1-931954-94-5(1)) National Ctr. on Education & The Economy.
Extend the Day! a Guide to Using Larson's Intermediate Math in Before-School & after-School Programs. 2003. spiral bd. 0.00 (978-1-58123-339-1(6)) Larson Learning, Inc.
Extend the Day! a Guide to Using Larson's Prealgebra & Larson's Algebra 1 in Before-School & after-School Programs. 2003. spiral bd. 0.00 (978-1-58123-340-7(X)) Larson Learning, Inc.
Fact Families Staff. Learning Wrap Ups Palette. 2004. 7.99 (978-1-59204-016-2(0)) Learning Wrap-Ups.
Fech, Ralph & Comras, Jay. SAT-1 Test Excellerator, Mathematics. 2000th ed. 2000. (YA). 164p. pap., tchr. ed. (978-1-56749-498-3(6)); 166p. pap., wbk. ed. (978-1-56749-496-9(X)) Instructivision, Inc.
Feely, Jenny. One, Two, Three... Harradine, Dona, tr. 1999. (Hello! Lote Ser.). (IND., Illus.). 23p. (J). pap. 29.99 (978-0-7339-1305-1(9)) Pearson Education Australia AUS. *Dist:* Cheng & Tsui Co.
—One, Two, Three... Batt, Deleece, tr. 1999. (Hello! Lote Ser.). (JPN., Illus.). 23p. (J). pap. 29.99 (978-0-7339-1322-8(9)) Pearson Education Australia AUS. *Dist:* Cheng & Tsui Co.
Feldman, Sarah. Symmetry in Our World. 2003. (Early Connections Ser.). (J). pap. 35.00 (978-1-4108-1545-3(5)) Benchmark Education Co.
Femiano, Robert. Dr. Funster's Quick Thinks Math B1: Fun Math Brain Teasers. 2003. (J). pap. 6.99 (978-0-89455-830-6(7)) Critical Thinking Bks. & Software.
—Dr. Funster's Quick Thinks Math Level A Book 1: Fun Math Brain Teasers. 2003. (J). pap. 6.99 (978-0-89455-829-0(3)) Critical Thinking Bks. & Software.
—Dr. Funster's Quick Thinks Math Level C Book 1: Fun Math Brian Teasers. 2003. (YA). pap. 6.99 (978-0-89455-831-3(5)) Critical Thinking Bks. & Software.
Figuras y Formas: Superlibros de Literatura/Literature Big Books. 1999. (Matematicas en Mi Mundo Ser.). (ENG & SPA.). (gr. k up). (978-0-02-110155-9(8)) Macmillan/ McGraw-Hill Schl. Div.
First Addition with Answers. 2000. (Math Windows Ser.). (J). pap. 0.99 (978-0-88724-859-7(4) , CD-3072) Carson-Dellosa Publishing Co., Inc.
First Number Skills Spanish Version. 2007. (J). per. (***978-1-58232-150-9(7)***) Bryan Hse. Pubs., Inc.
First Subtraction Pack. 2000. (Math Windows Ser.). (J). pap. 4.50 (978-0-88724-854-2(3) , CD-3067) Carson-Dellosa Publishing Co., Inc.
First Subtraction with Answers. 2000. (Math Windows Ser.). (J). pap. 0.99 (978-0-88724-860-3(8) , CD-3073) Carson-Dellosa Publishing Co., Inc.
First Subtration. 2000. (Math Windows Ser.). (J). pap. 0.99 (978-0-88724-848-1(9) , CD-3061) Carson-Dellosa Publishing Co., Inc.
Fisher, Carla & Hobbs, Julia. Super Summer Challenger Math: Summer Math Comprehension. 2002. (gr. 1 up). 2.95 (978-1-887923-31-6(4)); (gr. 2 up). 2.95 (978-1-887923-32-3(2)); (gr. 3 up). 2.95 (978-1-887923-33-0(0)) Rainbow Bridge Publishing.
Fisher, Diana. Lessons in Mathematics: With Applications Across the Sciences, 2002. (YA). tchr. ed., spiral bd., wbk. ed. 99.00 (978-0-9753169-1-7(5)) Creative Learning Exchange.
Fisher-Price Jumbo First Grade Workbook. 2004. (J). wbk. ed. (978-0-7666-0301-1(6) , 11822) Modern Publishing.
Fisher-Price Jumbo Kindergarten Workbook. 2004. (J). wbk. ed. (978-0-7666-0300-4(8) , 11820) Modern Publishing.
Fisher-Price Jumbo Preschool Workbook. 2004. (J). wbk. ed. (978-0-7666-0167-3(6) , 11815) Modern Publishing.
Fitzgerald, Holly, et al. Math. 1999. (100+ Seriestm Ser.). 106p. (J). (gr. k-1). pap. 12.99 (978-0-88012-848-3(8) , IF8703) School Specialty Publishing.
Fitzhugh, Karla. Crystal Meth & Other Amphetamines. 2005. (What's the Deal? Ser.). (Illus.). 56p. (J). (978-1-4034-7026-3(X)) Heinemann.
Fitzsimmons, Jim & Whiteford, Rhona. Maths Tests. (Illus.). 32p. (J). pap. 6.99 (978-0-340-68070-4(9) , Hodder & Stoughton) Hodder General Publishing Division GBR. *Dist:* Trafalgar Square Publishing.
Flikkema, Elizabeth. Money. Morris, Susan & Seltzer, Erin, eds. 2005. 48p. (J). per. 6.99 (978-1-59441-061-1(5) , CD-104022) Carson-Dellosa Publishing Co., Inc.
—Time & Money. Morris, Susan & Seltzer, Erin, eds. 2005. 48p. (J). per. 6.99 (978-1-59441-063-5(1) , CD-104027) Carson-Dellosa Publishing Co., Inc.
Flikkema, Elizabeth. Using the Standards—Measurement. 2004. (100+ Ser.). 128p. (C). pap. 12.99 (***978-0-7424-2891-1(5)*** , Instructional Fair) Schaffer, Frank Pubns.
Flip over Math: Addition & Subtraction. 2004. (J). spiral bd. 14.95 (978-1-56911-540-4(0)) Learning Resources, Inc.
Flip over Math: Multiplication & Division. 2004. (J). spiral bd. 14.95 (978-1-56911-541-1(9)) Learning Resources, Inc.
Flip over Math: Story Problems. 2004. (J). spiral bd. 14.95 (978-1-56911-542-8(7)) Learning Resources, Inc.
Flockhart, Dan. Fantasy Baseball & Mathematics. 2007. (Fantasy Sports & Mathematics Ser.). 160p. pap., stu. ed., wbk. ed. 9.95 (978-0-7879-9447-1(2) , Jossey-Bass) Wiley, John & Sons, Inc.
—Fantasy Basketball & Mathematics: Student Workbook. 2007. (Fantasy Sports & Mathematics Ser.). 216p. pap. 9.95 (978-0-7879-9449-5(9) , Jossey-Bass) Wiley, John & Sons, Inc.
—Fantasy Football & Mathematics. 2007. (Fantasy Sports & Mathematics Ser.). 144p. pap., stu. ed., wbk. ed. 9.95 (978-0-7879-9448-8(0) , Jossey-Bass) Wiley, John & Sons, Inc.
—Fantasy Soccer & Mathematics: Student Workbook. 2007. (Fantasy Sports & Mathematics Ser.). 168p. pap. 9.95 (978-0-7879-9450-1(2) , Jossey-Bass) Wiley, John & Sons, Inc.
Foresman, Scott & Fridely, Shelley. Math. 1999. (Homework Booklets Ser.). 72p. (J). (gr. 3 up). pap. 2.99 (978-0-88012-941-1(7) , IF0274); (gr. 4 up). pap. 2.99 (978-0-88012-942-8(5) , IF0275) School Specialty Publishing.
Fornara, Sarah. Math Minutes Grade 5, 2587. Wright, Marsha, ed. Hillam, Corbin & Grayson, Rick, illus. 2002. 112p. (J). (gr. 5). pap. 12.99 (978-1-57471-816-4(9) , CTP 2587) Creative Teaching Pr., Inc.
Forte, Imogene. Ready to Learn Beginning Math. 2003. (Illus.). 64p. per. 7.95 (978-0-86530-594-6(3)) Incentive Pubns., Inc.
Forte, Imogene & Schurr, Sandra. Standards-Based Math Graphic Organizers & Rubrics. 2004. 128p. (J). per. 13.95 (978-0-86530-629-5(X)) Incentive Pubns., Inc.
Fosnot, Catherine Twomey & Dolk, Maarten. Addition & Subtraction Minilessons. 2004. (Young Mathematicians at Work Ser.). (J). (ps-3). cd-rom 15.00 (978-0-325-00680-2(6) , E00680) Heinemann.
Fractals: The Art of Math. 2005. (Book Treks Ser.). (J). 37.95 (978-0-7652-3250-2(2)) Celebration Pr.
The Fraction ThinkBook with Gridmatics. 1999. (YA). (gr. 5-9). wbk. ed. 12.95 (978-0-9677074-5-7(5)) Pi Pr.
Fractions, Decimals & Percents. 2002. (J). pap. 10.95 (978-1-58123-328-5(0)) Larson Learning, Inc.
Franco, Betsy. Counting Poems Flip Chart: 20 Playful Poems That Teach Numbers, Counting, & More. 2004. 20p. pap. 19.99 (978-0-439-51761-4(3) , Teaching Resources) Scholastic, Inc.
—Funny Fairy Tale Math: 15 Rib-Tickling, Reproducible Stories with Companion Word Problems That Build Essential Math Skills & Meet the New NCTM Standards. 2001. 48p. pap. 9.95 (978-0-439-22726-1(7)) Scholastic, Inc.
—Instant Math Practice Pages for Homework - Or Anytime! 50 Super-Fun Reproducibles That Help Kids Build Essential Math Skills & Meet the Nctm Standards. 2002. (Illus.). 64p. pap. 11.95 (978-0-439-37077-6(9) , Teaching Resources) Scholastic, Inc.
—Time to Estimate. 2002. (Yellow Umbrella Books). (Illus.). 16p. (J). (gr. 1). lib. bdg. 14.60 (978-0-7368-1288-7(1) , Pebble Bks.) Capstone Pr., Inc.
—Write-&-Read Math Story Books. 1999. 96p. pap. 12.95 (978-0-590-98391-4(1)) Scholastic, Inc.
—5-Minute Math Problem of the Day for Young Learners: 180 Fast & Fun Reproducible Problems & Puzzles That Help You Build Early Math Skills Every Day of the School Year. 2001. (Illus.). 112p. pap. 14.95 (978-0-439-20151-3(9)) Scholastic, Inc.
Freeman, Christopher M. Nim: Serious Math with a Simple Game. 2nd ed. 2001. 64p. (J). per., wbk. ed. 11.95 net. (978-1-883055-40-0(7)) Dandy Lion Pubns.
Freese, Joan. Tables & Graphs of Healthy Things. 2007. (J). pap. (***978-0-8368-8480-7(9)***); 24p. (gr. 1-3). lib. bdg. 19.93 (***978-0-8368-8471-5(X)***) Stevens, Gareth Inc. (Weekly Reader Early Learning Library).
French. Consumer Mathematics. (J). (gr. 7-12). 32.97 (978-0-13-166729-7(7)) Prentice Hall (Schl. Div.).
Freudentha. Cereal Numbers: Math/Context. 3rd ed. 2003. stu. ed. 8.33 (978-0-03-071518-1(0)) Holt, Rinehart & Winston.
—Comparing Quanities: Spanish. 2003. (Mathematics in Context Ser.). (SPA.). stu. ed. 7.86 (978-0-03-072356-8(6)) Holt, Rinehart & Winston.
—Deal with Data: Math/Context - Spanish Student Edition. 98th ed. 2002. (J). 7.86 (978-0-85229-736-0(X)) Encyclopaedia Britannica, Inc.
—Deal with Data: Spanish. 2003. stu. ed. 7.86 (978-0-03-072346-9(9)) Holt, Rinehart & Winston.
—Dealing with Data: Math/Context - Student Edition. 3rd ed. 2003. 8.33 (978-0-03-071437-5(0)) Holt, Rinehart & Winston.
—Digging Numbers. 2003. (Mathematics in Context Ser.). (SPA.). stu. ed. 7.86 (978-0-03-072426-8(0)) Holt, Rinehart & Winston.
—Digging Numbers: Math/Context. 98th ed. 2002. 7.86 (978-0-7826-1566-1(X)) Encyclopaedia Britannica, Inc.
—Digging Numbers: Math/Context - Spanish Student Edition. 98th ed. 2002. 7.86 (978-0-85229-755-1(6)) Encyclopaedia Britannica, Inc.
—Dry/Wet Numbers: Math/Context - Spanish Student Edition. 98th ed. 2002. 7.86 (978-0-85229-722-3(X)) Encyclopaedia Britannica, Inc.
—Expression/Formulas Math/Context. 98th ed. 2002. (SPA.). stu. ed. 7.86 (978-0-85229-730-8(0)) Encyclopaedia Britannica, Inc.
—Expression/Formulas Math/Context: Student Edition. 98th ed. 2002. 7.86 (978-0-7826-1521-0(X)) Encyclopaedia Britannica, Inc.
—Figures/Angles: Math/Context - Spanish Student Edition. 98th ed. 2002. 7.86 (978-0-85229-724-7(6)) Encyclopaedia Britannica, Inc.
—Fraction Times. 2002. (Math in Context Ser.). (SPA.). stu. ed. 7.86 (978-0-85229-727-8(0)); (J). stu. ed. 7.86 (978-0-7826-1518-0(X)) Encyclopaedia Britannica, Inc.
—Fraction Times: Spanish. 2003. (Mathematics in Context Ser.). (SPA.). stu. ed. 7.86 (978-0-03-072348-3(5)) Holt, Rinehart & Winston.
—Go the Distance: Math/Context - Spanish Student Edition. 98th ed. 2002. 7.86 (978-0-85229-753-7(X)) Encyclopaedia Britannica, Inc.
—Going the Distance. 2003. (Mathematics in Context Ser.). (SPA.). (YA). stu. ed. 7.86 (978-0-03-072374-2(4)) Holt, Rinehart & Winston.
—Graph Equations. 2002. (Math in Context Ser.). (Illus.). 7.86 (978-0-7826-1559-3(7)) Encyclopaedia Britannica, Inc.
—Graph Equations: Math/Context - Spanish Student Edition. 98th ed. 2002. (J). 7.86 (978-0-85229-748-3(3)) Encyclopaedia Britannica, Inc.
—Grasping Sizes Math/Context. 98th ed. 2002. stu. ed. 7.86 (978-0-7826-1505-0(8)) Encyclopaedia Britannica, Inc.
—Great Expectations: Math/Context - Spanish Student Edition. 98th ed. 2002. 7.86 (978-0-85229-756-8(4)) Encyclopaedia Britannica, Inc.
—Great Expectations: Spanish. 2003. (Mathematics in Context Ser.). (SPA.). (YA). (gr. 8). stu. ed. 7.86 (978-0-03-072377-3(9)) Holt, Rinehart & Winston.
—Growth: Math/Context - Spanish Student Edition. 98th ed. 2002. 7.86 (978-0-85229-750-6(5)) Encyclopaedia Britannica, Inc.
—Growth 1998: Math/Context. 98th ed. 2002. stu. ed. 7.86 (978-0-7826-1560-9(0)) Encyclopaedia Britannica, Inc.
—Insights: Math/Context - Spanish Student Edition. 98th ed. 2002. (J). 7.86 (978-0-85229-754-4(8)) Encyclopaedia Britannica, Inc.
—Insights into Data. 2003. (Mathematics in Context Ser.: No. 2). (SPA.). stu. ed. 7.86 (978-0-03-072421-3(X)) Holt, Rinehart & Winston.
—Insights/Data: Math/Context. 98th ed. 2002. stu. ed. 7.86 (978-0-7826-1565-4(1)) Encyclopaedia Britannica, Inc.
—Looking at an Angle: Spanish. 2003. (Mathematics in Context Ser.). 7.86 (978-0-03-072361-2(2)) Holt, Rinehart & Winston.
—Math in Context: Re-Allotment. 3rd ed. 2002. (Illus.). stu. ed. 7.86 (978-0-85229-869-5(2)) Encyclopaedia Britannica, Inc.
—Measure/Measure Math/Context. 98th ed. 2002. stu. ed. 7.86 (978-0-7826-1501-2(5)) Encyclopaedia Britannica, Inc.
—More/Less: Math/Context Spanish Student Edition. 98th ed. 2002. 7.86 (978-0-85229-728-5(9)) Encyclopaedia Britannica, Inc.
—Operations. 2002. (Math in Context Ser.). (SPA., Illus.). 7.86 (978-0-85229-733-9(5)) Encyclopaedia Britannica, Inc.
—Packages & Polygons: Spanish. 2003. (Mathematics in Context Ser.). 7.86 (978-0-03-072362-9(0)) Holt, Rinehart & Winston.
—Packages & Polygons Math/Context. 98th ed. 2002. (J). stu. ed. 7.86 (978-0-7826-1543-2(0)) Encyclopaedia Britannica, Inc.
—Patterns & Figures. 2003. (Mathematics in Context Ser.). (SPA.). stu. ed. 7.86 (978-0-03-072422-0(8)) Holt, Rinehart & Winston.
—Pattern/Symbols Math/Context: Spanish. 98th ed. 2002. 7.86 (978-0-85229-721-6(1)) Encyclopaedia Britannica, Inc.
—Per Sense: Math/Context - Spanish Student Edition. 98th ed. 2002. 7.86 (978-0-85229-719-3(X)) Encyclopaedia Britannica, Inc.
—Per Sense 1998: Math Context - Student Edition. 98th ed. 2002. 7.86 (978-0-7826-1504-3(X)) Encyclopaedia Britannica, Inc.
—Picturing #s Math/Context. 98th ed. 2002. (SPA.). 8.33 (978-0-85229-726-1(2)) Harcourt Trade Pubs.
—Polygons: Math/Context - Spanish Student Edition. 98th ed. 2002. 7.86 (978-0-85229-742-1(4)) Encyclopaedia Britannica, Inc.
—Ratio/Rates: Math/Context - Spanish Student Edition. 98th ed. 2002. 7.86 (978-0-85229-729-2(7)) Encyclopaedia Britannica, Inc.
—Ratios & Rates: Spanish. 2003. (Mathematics in Context Ser.). (SPA.). stu. ed. 7.86 (978-0-03-072353-7(1)) Holt, Rinehart & Winston.
—Reallotment Math/Context: Spanish Student Edition. 98th ed. 2002. 7.86 (978-0-85229-734-6(3)) Encyclopaedia Britannica, Inc.
—Reflections: Math/Context - Spanish Student Edition. 98th ed. 2002. 7.86 (978-0-85229-747-6(5)) Encyclopaedia Britannica, Inc.
—Reflections on Numbers. 2003. (Mathematics in Context Ser.). (SPA.). stu. ed. 7.86 (978-0-03-072423-7(6)) Holt, Rinehart & Winston.
—Side Seeing Math/Context: Spanish Student Edition. 98th ed. 2002. 7.86 (978-0-85229-723-0(8)) Encyclopaedia Britannica, Inc.
—Some of Parts Math/Context: Student Edition. 98th ed. 2002. (J). 7.86 (978-0-7826-1500-5(7)) Encyclopaedia Britannica, Inc.
—Some Parts: Math/Context - Spanish Student Edition. 98th ed. 2002. 7.86 (978-0-85229-717-9(3)) Encyclopaedia Britannica, Inc.
—Spn Se Stats/env Math/context. 3rd ed. 2003. (Mathematics in Context Ser.). 7.86 (978-0-03-072364-3(7)) Holt, Rinehart & Winston.
—Triangle & Beyond: Spanish. 2003. (Mathematics in Context Ser.). 7.86 (978-0-03-072366-7(3)) Holt, Rinehart & Winston.
—Triangles & Beyond. 2002. (Math in Context Ser.). 7.86 (978-0-7826-1545-6(7)) Encyclopaedia Britannica, Inc.
—Triangles & Patchwork. 2003. (Mathematics in Context Ser.). (SPA.). (YA). (gr. 8). stu. ed. 7.86 (978-0-03-072369-8(8)) Holt, Rinehart & Winston.
—Ups & Downs: Math/Context - Spanish Student Edition. 98th ed. 2002. (J). 7.86 (978-0-85229-739-1(4)) Encyclopaedia Britannica, Inc.
Freudentha, H. Great Expectation Math/Context. 98th ed. 2002. (J). 7.86 (978-0-7826-1567-8(8)) Encyclopaedia Britannica, Inc.
—Math in Context: Figuring & Angles. 2002. (Illus.). 7.86 (978-0-7826-1503-6(1)) Encyclopaedia Britannica, Inc.
—Math in Context: Reflections on Numbers. 2002. (Illus.). 7.86 (978-0-7826-1558-6(9)) Encyclopaedia Britannica, Inc.

M
N
O

—Math in Context: Take a Chance. 2002. (Illus.). 7.86 (978-0-7826-1507-4(4)) Encyclopaedia Britannica, Inc.
—Picturing Numbers: Math/Context. 98th ed. 2002. (J). 7.86 (978-0-7826-1502-9(3)) Encyclopaedia Britannica, Inc.
—Powers of Ten: Math Context. 3rd ed. 2003. 8.33 (978-0-03-071529-7(6)) Holt, Rinehart & Winston.
—Re-Allotment Math/Context. 3rd ed. 2003. 8.33 (978-0-03-071511-2(3)) Holt, Rinehart & Winston.
Freudenthal. Decision Making. 3rd ed. 2003. (Math in Context Ser.). (Illus.). 8.33 (978-0-03-071522-8(9)) Holt, Rinehart & Winston.
—Expressions & Formulas. 3rd ed. 2002. (Math in Context Ser.). (Illus.). (J). stu. ed. (978-0-85229-864-0(1)) Encyclopaedia Britannica, Inc.
—Expressions & Formulas. 3rd ed. 2003. (Math in Context Ser.). (Illus.). 8.33 (978-0-03-071444-3(3)) Holt, Rinehart & Winston.
—Great Expectations. 3rd ed. 2003. (Math in Context Ser.). (Illus.). 8.33 (978-0-03-071664-5(0)) Holt, Rinehart & Winston.
—Growth. 3rd ed. 2002. (Math in Context Ser.). 8.33 (978-0-85229-903-6(6)) Encyclopaedia Britannica, Inc.
—Growth. 3rd ed. 2003. (Math in Context Ser.). (Illus.). 8.33 (978-0-03-071667-6(5)) Holt, Rinehart & Winston.
—Math in Context: Building Formulas. 3rd ed. 2002. 8.33 (978-0-85229-884-8(6)) Encyclopaedia Britannica, Inc.
—Math in Context: Comparing Quantity. 3rd ed. 2002. 8.33 (978-0-85229-866-4(8)) Encyclopaedia Britannica, Inc.
—Math in Context: Decision Making. 3rd ed. 2002. 8.33 (978-0-85229-885-5(4)) Encyclopaedia Britannica, Inc.
—Math in Context: Digging Numbers. 3rd ed. 2002. 8.33 (978-0-85229-909-8(5)) Encyclopaedia Britannica, Inc.
—Math in Context: Dry & Wet Numbers. 3rd ed. 2002. 8.33 (978-0-85229-849-7(8)) Encyclopaedia Britannica, Inc.
—Math in Context: Get the Most. 3rd ed. 2002. 8.33 (978-0-85229-905-0(2)) Encyclopaedia Britannica, Inc.
—Math in Context: Great Expectations. 3rd ed. 2002. 8.33 (978-0-85229-910-4(9)) Encyclopaedia Britannica, Inc.
—Math in Context: Insights into Data. 3rd ed. 2002. 8.33 (978-0-85229-908-1(7)) Encyclopaedia Britannica, Inc.
—Math in Context: Looking at the Angle. 3rd ed. 2002. 8.33 (978-0-85229-887-9(0)) Encyclopaedia Britannica, Inc.
—Math in Context: Made to Measure. 3rd ed. 2002. 8.33 (978-0-85229-868-8(4)) Encyclopaedia Britannica, Inc.
—Math in Context: Measure for Measure. 3rd ed. 2002. 8.33 (978-0-85229-844-2(7)) Encyclopaedia Britannica, Inc.
—Math in Context: Packages & Polygons. 3rd ed. 2002. 8.33 (978-0-85229-886-2(2)) Encyclopaedia Britannica, Inc.
—Math in Context: Patterns & Figures. 3rd ed. 2002. 8.33 (978-0-85229-904-3(4)) Encyclopaedia Britannica, Inc.
—Math in Context: Patterns & Symbols. 3rd ed. 2003. (SPA.). 8.33 (978-0-03-072337-7(X)) Holt, Rinehart & Winston.
—Math in Context: Powers of Ten. 3rd ed. 2002. 8.33 (978-0-85229-882-4(X)) Encyclopaedia Britannica, Inc.
—Math in Context: Reflections & Numbers. 3rd ed. 2002. 8.33 (978-0-85229-901-2(X)) Encyclopaedia Britannica, Inc.
—Math in Context: Triangles & Patchwork. 3rd ed. 2002. 8.33 (978-0-85229-906-7(0)) Encyclopaedia Britannica, Inc.
—Patterns & Symbols. 3rd ed. 2003. (Math in Context Ser.). (Illus.). 8.33 (978-0-03-071283-8(1)) Holt, Rinehart & Winston.
—Percentage Sense. 3rd ed. 2003. (Math in Context Ser.). (Illus.). 8.33 (978-0-03-071286-9(6)) Holt, Rinehart & Winston.
—Ratio & Rates. 3rd ed. 2002. (Math in Context Ser.). (Illus.). stu. ed. (978-0-85229-863-3(3)) Encyclopaedia Britannica, Inc.
—Take a Chance. 2002. (Math in Context Ser.). (SPA., Illus.). (J). 7.86 (978-0-85229-725-4(4)) Encyclopaedia Britannica, Inc.
—Take a Chance. 3rd ed. 2003. (Math in Context Ser.). (Illus.). 8.33 (978-0-03-071431-3(1)) Holt, Rinehart & Winston.
—Ups & Downs. 3rd ed. 2002. (Math in Context Ser.). (Illus.). (J). stu. ed. (978-0-85229-883-1(8)) Encyclopaedia Britannica, Inc.
—Ups & Downs. 3rd ed. 2003. (Math in Context Ser.). (Illus.). 8.33 (978-0-03-071554-9(7)) Holt, Rinehart & Winston.
Fridely, Shelley. Basic Skills Math Books: Math Topics. 1999. (Basic Skills Ser.). 43p. (J). (gr. 5 up). pap. 5.99 (978-1-56822-091-8(X) , IF5111) School Specialty Publishing.
Fried, Ellen. What's the Chance? 2004. (National Geographic Reading Expeditions Ser.). (Illus.). 24p. (J). pap. (978-0-7922-4590-2(3)) National Geographic Society.
Frieder, David & Smith, Stephanie. Mastering Math Skills. 2002. (Get Wise! Ser.). (Illus.). 240p. pap. 12.95 (978-0-7689-1076-6(5)) Peterson's.
Friedman, Matt. Grades 3-4: 50 Reproducible, Leveled Game Sheets That Kids Can Use Independently or in Small Groups to Practice Important Math Skills. 2005. (Tic-Tac-Math Ser.). 64p. pap. 11.99 (978-0-439-62920-1(9) , Teaching Resources) Scholastic, Inc.
Fuller, Jill. Springtime Addition. (Rookie Read-About Math Ser.). (J). 2005. (Illus.). 32p. (gr. 1-2). pap. 5.95 (978-0-516-24668-0(2)); 2004. 20.50 (978-0-516-24422-8(1)) Scholastic Library Publishing. (Children's Pr.).
—Toy Box Subtraction. (Rookie Read-About Math Ser.). (J). 2005. (Illus.). 32p. (gr. 1-2). pap. 5.95 (978-0-516-24673-4(9)); 2004. 20.50 (978-0-516-24423-5(X)) Scholastic Library Publishing. (Children's Pr.).
Fun-to-Learn: Beginning Math. (ps-1). 2.99 (978-0-7424-0177-8(4) , IF0410) School Specialty Publishing.
Functions & Proportionality: CA Math Series II. 2004. stu. ed. 6.00 (978-1-932230-77-2(7)) National Ctr. on Education & The Economy.
Functions & Proportionality Student's Edition: Foundations of Advanced Mathematics. 2002. (Foundations of Advance Mathematics Ser.). lib. bdg., stu. ed. 5.00 (978-1-931954-90-7(9)) National Ctr. on Education & The Economy.
Furgang, Kathy. Pizza Parts. ed. 2003. (Early Connections Ser.). (J). pap. 35.00 (978-1-4108-1548-4(X)) Benchmark Education Co.
Gannett, Barbara. Count Your Money: A Content Area Reader-math. 2005. (Emergent/Early (Prek-2) Math Package Ser.). 20p. (YA). (ps-2). 25.20 (978-0-8215-7821-6(9)) Sadlier, William H. Inc.
Gardella. Problemas y Mas: Workbook & Activity Kit, Level B. 1999. (SPA., Illus.). pap., wbk. ed. (978-0-7398-2082-7(6)) Steck-Vaughn.
Gardner, Colin. Pythagorean Triangle Properties & Attributes Samples (Enlarged), As Independently Discovered by Colin Gardner, Physicist: Pythagorean triples are everwhere, & have an application in nearly every math lesson(6th grade thru College. 2nd ed. 2004. Orig. Title: Pythagorean Triangle Properties & Attriibutes Samples. (Illus.). 6p. (YA). (gr. 6 up). 7.95 (978-0-9720348-5-2(4)) Gardner, Colin.
Gardner, Robert. Science Projects about Math. 1999. (Science Projects Ser.). (Illus.). 112p. (YA). (gr. 6-12). lib. bdg. 26.60 (978-0-89490-950-4(9)) Enslow Pubs., Inc.
Garner, Sue. Specialist Maths VCE, Units 3 and 4. 2002. (Cambridge Wizard Subject Guides). (Illus.). 112p. pap., stu. ed. 8.00 (978-1-876367-75-6(X)) Cambridge Univ. Pr.
Gave, Marc. Number Games Around the World/Juegos de numeros alrededor del Mundo: English/Spanish Pair, ed. 2004. (Navigators Ser.). (J). pap., instr.'s gde. ed. 84.00 (978-1-4108-1765-5(2)) Benchmark Education Co.
Gaydos, Nora. Math Madness, Independent. 2003. (Now I'm Reading!). (Illus.). 128p. (J). 14.99 (978-1-58476-248-5(9)) Innovative Kids.
—Maths Madness. 2003. (Now I'm Reading! Ser.). (Illus.). 128p. (J). (ps-2). 16.99 (978-1-58476-168-6(7)) Innovative Kids.
Geometric Measure Student's Edition: CA Math Series II. 2004. 6.00 (978-1-932230-83-3(1)) National Ctr. on Education & The Economy.
GER Math Tool Kit A. 2006. (J). 19.95 (***978-1-934046-10-4(8)*** Global Education Resources, LLC.
Gerber, Carole. Math. 1999. (Master Skills Ser.). (Illus.). 128p. (J). (gr. 6-6). pap., wbk. ed. 6.95 (978-1-56189-010-1(3) , 11010, American Education Publishing) School Specialty Publishing.
—Math: Grade 3. 2003. (Brighter Child Workbooks Ser.). (Illus.). 24p. (J). (gr. 3). pap. 2.25 (978-1-56189-073-6(1) , American Education Publishing) School Specialty Publishing.
—Math: Grade K. 2000. (Brighter Child Workbooks Ser.). (Illus.). 40p. (J). pap. 2.25 (978-1-56189-070-5(7) , 41010, American Education Publishing) School Specialty Publishing.
Gerber, Carole & School Specialty Publishing Staff. Math. (Master Skills Ser.). (Illus.). 128p. (J). (gr. k-6). 2001. pap., stu. ed., wbk. ed. 6.95 (978-1-56189-014-9(6) , 11014); 1999. pap., wbk. ed. 6.95 (978-1-56189-013-2(8) , 11013) School Specialty Publishing. (American Education Publishing).
Gerber, Carole & Wasson Warfel, Laura. Math. 1999. (Homework Booklets Ser.). 72p. (J). (gr. 2 up). pap. 2.99 (978-0-88012-940-4(9) , IF0273) School Specialty Publishing.
Ghim, John Y. Ghim's Critical Exercises of HIgh School Math. 2004. (Illus.). 340p. (YA). (gr. 9-12). pap. 35.99 (978-0-9656864-1-9(8)) Ghim, John Yun.
—Ghim's Critical Exercises of High School Math Answers & Explanations. 2004. (YA). per. 12.95 (978-0-9656864-2-6(6)) Ghim, John Yun.
Gifted and Talented Staff, ed. Reading, Writing, & Math. 2003. (Gifted & Talented Ser.). 192p. (ps-4). 14.95 (978-0-7696-3060-1(X)); 14.95 (978-0-7696-3061-8(8)); 14.95 (978-0-7696-3062-5(6)); 14.95 (978-0-7696-3063-2(4)) School Specialty Publishing.
Giganti, Paul, Jr. Numeros Importantes. Grbich, Aaron, illus. (SPA.). (J). (gr. 1-3). pap. 3.16 net. (978-0-590-48700-9(0) , Scholastic Pr.) Scholastic, Inc.
Gill, Shelley & Tobola, Deborah. The Big Buck Adventure. Lin, Grace, illus. 2000. 32p. (J). (gr. k-4). 15.95 (978-0-88106-294-6(4)) Charlesbridge Publishing, Inc.
Ginsburg, Herbert P., et al. Acorn Hunt. 2003. (Illus.). 9.95 (978-0-7690-3046-3(7)) Seymour, Dale Pubns.
—Big Math for Little Kids: Classroom Manipulative Kit. 2003. (Illus.). 382.50 (978-0-7690-3063-0(7)); 251.50 (978-0-7690-3064-7(5)) Seymour, Dale Pubns.
—Dobee Doubler. 2003. (Illus.). 9.95 (978-0-7690-3042-5(4)) Seymour, Dale Pubns.
—Jenny Saves the Day. 2003. (Illus.). 9.95 (978-0-7690-3047-0(5)) Seymour, Dale Pubns.
—Leftover Muffins. 2003. (Illus.). 9.95 (978-0-7690-3040-1(8)) Seymour, Dale Pubns.
—Rafael's Messy Room. 2003. (Illus.). 9.95 (978-0-7690-3045-6(9)) Seymour, Dale Pubns.
—So Many Fives! 2003. (Illus.). 9.95 (978-0-7690-3044-9(0)) Seymour, Dale Pubns.
—The Table of Phinneas Fable. 2003. (Illus.). 9.95 (978-0-7690-3048-7(3)) Seymour, Dale Pubns.
—Tick-Tock! 2003. (Illus.). 9.95 (978-0-7690-3041-8(6)) Seymour, Dale Pubns.
—The Trees of Mrs. Mcgee. 2003. (Illus.). 9.95 (978-0-7690-3049-4(1)) Seymour, Dale Pubns.
Glass, Julie. The Fly on the Ceiling: A Math Myth. 1998. (Step into Reading & Math Step 3 Bks.). (J). (gr. 2-3). (978-0-606-13962-5(1)) Tandem Library Bks.
Gleichungen mit zwei Unbekannten. (Duden-Schuelerhilfen Ser.). (GER.). 96p. (YA). (gr. 8-9). (978-3-411-02622-7(7)) Bibliographisches Institut & F. A. Brockhaus AG DEU. *Dist:* International Bk. Import Service, Inc.
Gleichungen und Ungleichungen 1. 2nd ed. (Duden-Schuelerhilfen Ser.). (GER.). 112p. (J). (gr. 5-6). (978-3-411-70872-7(7)) Bibliographisches Institut & F. A. Brockhaus AG DEU. *Dist:* International Bk. Import Service, Inc.
Gleichungen und Ungleichungen 2. (Duden-Schuelerhilfen Ser.). (GER.). 112p. (YA). (gr. 7-8). (978-3-411-70682-2(1)) Bibliographisches Institut & F. A. Brockhaus AG DEU. *Dist:* International Bk. Import Service, Inc.
Glencoe McGraw-Hill Staff & McGraw-Hill - Jamestown Education Staff. Intermediate 1. 2001. (Jamestown's Number Power Ser.). (gr. 3-6). pap., stu. ed. 17.32 (978-0-8092-2342-8(2) , 9780809223428) Jamestown.
—Introductory. 2001. (Jamestown's Number Power Ser.). (gr. 1-3). pap., stu. ed. 17.32 (978-0-8092-2341-1(4) , 9780809223411) Jamestown.
—Jamestown's Number Power: Advanced. 2001. (Jamestown's Number Power Ser.). (gr. 8-12). pap., stu. ed. 17.32 (978-0-8092-2343-5(0) , 9780809223435) Jamestown.
Glover, J. T. Vedic Mathematics for Schools, Vol. 2. 2001. (Mathematics, Astronomy, Astrology, Palmistry & Other Positive Sciences Ser.). (Illus.). reprint ed. pap. (978-81-208-1670-1(6)) Motilal Banarsidass Publishers (Pvt. Ltd).
Glover, James T. Vedic Mathematics for Schools. 2000. (Mathematics, Astronomy, Astrology, Palmistry & Other Positive Sciences Ser.: Vol. 16). (Illus.). xii, 100, 33p. (978-81-208-1318-2(9)) Motilal Banarsidass Publishers (Pvt. Ltd).
Goba, Busisiwe, et al. Mathematics for Zambia Basic Education Grade 7 Pupil's Book. 2007. pap., stu. ed. (***978-0-521-70345-1(X)***) Cambridge Univ. Pr.
—Mathematics Matters Grade 7 Learner's Book. 2005. 224p. pap. 14.40 (978-0-521-67020-3(9)) Cambridge Univ. Pr.
—Mathematics Matters Grade 7 Learner's Book Afrikaans Translation. 2005. (AFR.). 224p. pap. 14.40 (978-0-521-67022-7(5)) Cambridge Univ. Pr.
—Study & Master Mathematical Literacy Grade 10 Learner's Book. 2005. 272p. pap. 16.65 (978-0-521-67320-4(8)) Cambridge Univ. Pr.
—Study & Master Mathematical Literacy Grade 10 Learner's Book Afikaans Translation. 2005. 272p. pap. 16.65 (978-0-521-67322-8(4)) Cambridge Univ. Pr.
Godwin, Beth & Powell, Margaret. Spectrum Mathematics Gold Year 7: Black Line Masters. 2000. (Spectrum Mathematics Ser.). 100p. pap. 62.00 (978-0-521-77582-3(5)) Cambridge Univ. Pr.
—Spectrum Mathematics Gold Year 8: Black Line Masters. 2000. (Spectrum Mathematics Ser.). 96p. pap. 37.00 (978-0-521-77580-9(9)) Cambridge Univ. Pr.
Gold, Kari Jenson. Math Stories. Date not set. (Early Math Big Bks.). (Illus.). 16p. (J). (ps-2). pap. 16.95 (978-1-58273-280-0(9)) Sundance/Newbridge Educational Publishing.
—What Comes Next? Date not set. (Early Math Big Bks.). (Illus.). 16p. (J). (ps-2). pap. 16.95 (978-1-56784-434-4(0)) Sundance/Newbridge Educational Publishing.
Golden Books Staff. Math Skillbuilders. 2000. (Step Ahead Workbooks Ser.). (Illus.). 64p. (J). (gr. 2-3). pap., wbk. ed. 3.99 (978-0-307-03655-1(3) , 03655); (gr. 1-2). pap. 3.99 (978-0-307-03653-7(7) , 03653) Random Hse. Children's Bks. (Golden Bks.).
Goldie, Sophie, et al. Formula One Mathematics, Year 9. 2004. (Illus.). 224p. pap., pupil's gde. ed. 39.50 (***978-0-340-86934-5(8)*** , Hodder Murray) Hodder Education GBR. *Dist:* Trans-Atlantic Pubns., Inc.
Goldman, Phyllis B., ed. Monkeyshines on Math, Money & Banking. 2002. (Illus.). 183p. (J). pap. 32.95 (978-1-888325-21-8(6)) Allosaurus Pubs.
Goodman, Jenny. Spectrum Mathematics Year 7: Black Line Masters. 1999. (Spectrum Mathematics Ser.). 60p. (gr. 7). pap. 41.00 (978-0-521-77585-4(X)) Cambridge Univ. Pr.
—Spectrum Mathematics Year 8: Black Line Masters. 1999. (Spectrum Mathematics Ser.). 96p. (gr. 8). pap. 41.00 (978-0-521-77584-7(1)) Cambridge Univ. Pr.
Gordon, Arthur, et al. Progresa con las Matematicas. 1999. (SPA.). 80p. (J). (gr. 7-8). pap., wbk. ed. 12.00 (978-0-9624192-2-5(2)) Bacchus, Noel Publishing, Inc.
Gordon, Juli A., ed. Grade 2 Math Skillbook. Engblom, Mark, illus. 2000. 32p. (J). (gr. 2-3). pap., wbk. ed. 2.99 (978-1-889319-62-9(7) , KidSparks) Trend Enterprises, Inc.
—Grade 3 Math Skillbook. Engblom, Mark, illus. 2000. 32p. (J). (gr. 3-4). pap., wbk. ed. 2.99 (978-1-889319-64-3(3) , KidSparks) Trend Enterprises, Inc.
—Grade 4 Math Skillbook. Engblom, Mark, illus. 2000. 32p. (J). (gr. 4). pap., wbk. ed. 2.99 (978-1-889319-66-7(X) , KidSparks) Trend Enterprises, Inc.
—Grade 5 Math Skillbook. Engblom, Mark, illus. 2000. 32p. (J). (gr. 5-6). pap., wbk. ed. 2.99 (978-1-889319-68-1(6) , KidSparks) Trend Enterprises, Inc.
Gow, Mary. Archimedes: Mathematical Genius of the Ancient World. 2005. (Great Minds of Science Ser.). (Illus.). 128p. (J). (gr. 5-8). lib. bdg. 26.60 (978-0-7660-2502-8(0)) Enslow Pubs., Inc.
Grace, Nicki Clausen. What Comes First? How a Picture Book Is Printed? 2007. (Illus.). 24p. (J). (978-1-59515-977-9(0)) Rourke Publishing, LLC.
Grade Level Manipulative Kit: Manipulative Kits. 2002. (MacMillan/McGraw-Hill Matematicas Ser.). (ENG & SPA.). (gr. 4 up). (978-0-02-100279-5(7)); (gr. 5 up). (978-0-02-100281-8(9)); (gr. 6 up). (978-0-02-100282-5(7)) Macmillan/McGraw-Hill Schl. Div.
Graham, Noel. Exploring Mathematics with Number Squares. 2001. (Illus.). 32p. (YA). (gr. 4-10). pap. 13.00 (978-1-871098-44-0(0)) Claire Pubns. GBR. *Dist:* Parkwest Pubns., Inc.
—Maths for Christmas: Ideas to Use with Younger Children. 2nd ed. 2001. (Illus.). 32p. (J). (gr. k-6). pap. 10.00 (978-1-871098-31-0(9)) Claire Pubns. GBR. *Dist:* Parkwest Pubns., Inc.
Graham, Noel & Blundell, Graham. Graph Pack. (Illus.). 22p. (J). (gr. k-3). 10.00 (978-1-871098-29-7(7)) Claire Pubns. GBR. *Dist:* Parkwest Pubns., Inc.
Grande o chiquito? Math, 6 vols.Tr. of Big or Small? Math. (SPA.). (gr. k-2). 28.95 (978-0-7368-3119-2(3) , Yellow Umbrella Bks.) Capstone Pr., Inc.
Granowsky, Alvin, et al. Take-Home Books, Blackline Masters: Content Area Readers. 2002. (J). pap. (978-0-8215-7858-2(8) , Sadlier-Oxford) Sadlier, William H. Inc.
Great Source Education Group Staff. Math on Call. 4th ed. 2004. (J). (gr. 3-6). 24.00 (978-0-669-50818-5(7)) Great Source Education Group, Inc.
—Math on Call: A Mathematics Handbook. 2003. (gr. 5-8). lib. bdg. 30.00 (978-0-613-73010-5(0)) Tandem Library Bks.
Greenberg, Dan. Comic-Strip Math: Mini-Story Problems: 60 Reproducible Cartoons with Dozens of Story Problems. 2000. (Illus.). 48p. (J). pap. 9.95 (978-0-439-04383-0(2)) Scholastic, Inc.
—200 Super - Fun, Super - Fast Math Story Problems: Quick & Funny Math Problems That Reinforce Skills in Multiplication, Division, Fractions, Decimals, Measurement & More. 2002. 96p. pap. 13.95 (978-0-590-37894-9(5)) Scholastic, Inc.
Greenes, Carol. Hot Math Topics: Estimation & Computation with Large Numbers. 2003. (J). (gr. 5). 16.95 (978-0-7690-0838-7(0)) Seymour, Dale Pubns.
Greenes, Carol, et al. Addition & Subtraction. 2003. (Illus.). 60p. (J). (ps-3). 16.95 (978-0-7690-0015-2(0)) Seymour, Dale Pubns.
—Multiplication & Division. 2003. (Illus.). 60p. (J). (gr. 4-7). 16.95 (978-0-7690-0003-9(7)) Seymour, Dale Pubns.
Greenes, Carole E., et al. Navigating through Problem Solving & Reasoning in Grade 2. House, Peggy A. & Greenes, Carole E., eds. 2004. (Navigations Ser.). (Illus.). 50p. pap. 24.95 (978-0-87353-551-9(0) , 12584) National Council of Teachers of Mathematics.
Greens, Carol. Addition & Subtraction: Grade 2. 1999. lib. bdg. 33.00 (978-0-613-74908-4(1)) Tandem Library Bks.
—Spatial Sense: Grade 1. 1999. lib. bdg. 33.00 (978-0-613-74907-7(3)) Tandem Library Bks.
—Time & Money: Grade 2. 1999. lib. bdg. 33.00 (978-0-613-74906-0(5)) Tandem Library Bks.
Greenwood, David, et al. Essential Mathematics VELS Edition Year 10 GOLD. 2nd rev. ed. 2007. (Essential Mathematics Ser.). pap. 47.00 (***978-0-521-68178-0(2)***) Cambridge Univ. Pr.
Gregorich, Barbara. Math Basics: Grade 1. Koontz, Robin Michal, illus. 2001. (Super-Deluxe Wkbks.). 128p. (J). (gr. k-1). pap., wbk. ed. 7.99 (978-1-58947-007-1(9) , 02458) School Zone Publishing Co.
—Racing Math. 2nd ed. 2005. (Illus.). 128p. (J). (gr. 4-8). pap. (978-1-59647-060-6(7)) Good Year Bks.
Gregorich, Barbara & DeYoung, Lorie. Math Basics 1. 2001. (Teacher Edition Wkbks.). (Illus.). 32p. (J). pap., tchr. ed., wbk. ed. 3.99 (978-0-88743-856-1(3) , 02837) School Zone Publishing Co.
—Math Basics 2. 2001. (Teacher Edition Wkbks.). (Illus.). 32p. (J). pap., tchr. ed. 3.99 (978-0-88743-869-1(5) , 02847) School Zone Publishing Co.
GridWorks: The Fun Game of Logical Deduction. 2004. (YA). spiral bd. 9.99 (978-0-9755330-0-0(2)) ThinkFun, Inc.
Griffith, Dave. Math in Science. 1999. (Illus.). (YA). pap., stu. ed., wbk. ed. 12.00 (978-1-886998-15-5(9)) Pasco Scientific.
Group/McGraw-Hill, Wright. Wonder World Complete Sets: Math Set - 1 Each of 30 Titles. (Wonder Worldtm Ser.). (gr. k-6). 153.95 (978-0-322-06715-8(4)) Wright Group, The.
—Wonder World Early & Upper Emergent Sets: Math Set - 1 Each of 20 Titles. (Wonder Worldtm Ser.). (gr. k-6). 92.50 (978-0-322-06722-6(7)) Wright Group, The.
—Wonder World Early Fluency & Fluency: Math Set - 1 Each of 10 Titles. (Wonder Worldtm Ser.). (gr. k-6). 61.95 (978-0-322-06718-9(9)) Wright Group, The.
Grundon, Holly & Novelli, Joan. Smart Pads! Addition & Subtraction. 2005. 48p. pap. 7.99 (978-0-439-72076-2(1) , Teaching Resources) Scholastic, Inc.
—Smartpads Addition & Subtraction Gr 2-3: 40 Fun Games to Help Kids Master Addition & Subtraction Skills. 2005. 48p. pap. 7.99 (978-0-439-72079-3(6) , Teaching Resources) Scholastic, Inc.
—Smartpads Multiplication: 40 Fun Games to Help Kids Master Multiplication Skills. 2005. 48p. pap. 7.99 (978-0-439-72080-9(X) , Teaching Resources) Scholastic, Inc.
Guia de Evaluacion: Assessment. 2002. (MacMillan/McGraw-Hill Matematicas Ser.). (ENG & SPA.). (gr. k up). (978-0-02-111583-9(4)); (gr. 1 up). (978-0-02-111584-6(2)); (gr. 2 up). (978-0-02-111585-3(0)); (gr. 3 up). (978-0-02-111586-0(9)); (gr. 5 up). (978-0-02-111588-4(5)); (gr. 6 up). (978-0-02-111589-1(3)) Macmillan/McGraw-Hill Schl. Div.
Guia de evaluacion Z: Assessment. 2002. (MacMillan/McGraw-Hill Matematicas Ser.). (ENG & SPA.). (gr. 4 up). (978-0-02-111587-7(7)) Macmillan/McGraw-Hill Schl. Div.
Guia del Maestro. 2002. (MacMillan/McGraw-Hill Matematicas Ser.). (ENG & SPA.). (gr. 6 up). (978-0-02-111560-0(5)) Macmillan/McGraw-Hill Schl. Div.

Guia del Maestro: Includes Conexion: Casa-Escuela (Home/ School Connection) 1999. (Matematicas en Mi Mundo Ser.). (ENG & SPA.). (gr. k up). (978-0-02-110407-9(7)) Macmillan/McGraw-Hill Schl. Div.

Gunningham, Sue. Cambridge VCAL Numeracy Workbook. 2006. pap., stu. ed. 18.20 (978-0-521-67964-0(8)) Cambridge Univ. Pr.

Gunzi, Christiane, contrib. by. Los Colores. 2004. (Mi Primera Mirada. . . Ser.).Tr. of MVFLA Colores. (SPA., Illus.). 24p. (ps-k). 9.95 (978-1-58728-270-6(4) , Creative Publishing International) Quayside.

Guscott, Maggie. On the Job. 2004. 104p. (YA). per. 9.95 (978-1-56254-764-6(X) , SP764X) Saddleback Educational Publishing.

Guthrie, Donna. Real World Math: Money & Other Numbers in Your Life. Kline, Robyn, illus. 1998. 128p. (gr. 7 up). 26.90 (978-0-7613-0251-3(4) , Millbrook Pr.) Lerner Publishing Group.

Haciendo formas Math, 6 vols.Tr. of Making Shapes Math. (SPA.). (gr. k-2). 28.95 (978-0-7368-3046-1(4) , Yellow Umbrella Bks.) Capstone Pr., Inc.

Hagamos una grafica Math, 6 vols.Tr. of Let's Graph Math. (SPA.). (gr. k-2). 28.95 (978-0-7368-3045-4(6) , Yellow Umbrella Bks.) Capstone Pr., Inc.

Haighton, June & Rowland, Mark. Go Figure! 2002. (Key Skills Ser.). (Illus.). 208p. (YA). pap. 27.50 (978-0-7487-6193-7(4)) Nelson Thornes Ltd. GBR. *Dist:* Trans-Atlantic Pubns., Inc.

Hake, Stephen & Saxon, John. Saxon Math 5/4: An Incremental Development. 3rd ed. 2003. (Illus.). (gr. 4-8). 640p. stu. ed. (978-1-56577-503-9(1) , 503); 320; 488p. tchr. ed. (978-1-56577-504-6(X) , 504X) Saxon Pubs., Inc.

—Saxon Math 7/6. 4th ed. 2003. (Illus.). 756p. (gr. 4-8). stu. ed. (978-1-56577-507-7(4) , 5074) Saxon Pubs., Inc.

—Saxon Math 8/7. 3rd ed. 2003. (Illus.). 944p. stu. ed. (978-1-56577-509-1(0) , 509-0) Saxon Pubs., Inc.

Hakizimana, Laurence. Quadrature: Pi, at Last, a Rational Number Equal to 3.125. 2004. 63p. pap. 12.95 (978-1-4137-4558-0(X)) PublishAmerica, Inc.

Hale, Melissa Warner. Is That Correct? Checking Math Problems. 2004. (100+ Seriestm Ser.). 128p. (J). (gr. 3 up). pap. 12.99 (978-0-7424-2783-9(8) , IFG99214); (gr. 4 up). pap. 12.99 (978-0-7424-2784-6(6) , IFG99215); (gr. 5 up). pap. 12.99 (978-0-7424-2785-3(4) , IFG99216) School Specialty Publishing.

Hall, M. C. Safari matematico Math. (SPA.). (gr. k-2). 19.95 (978-0-7368-3109-3(6)) Red Brick Learning.

Hammelef, Danielle S. Fun with Fives. 2006. (Early Explorers Ser.). (J). 34.00 (***978-1-4108-6116-0(3)***) Benchmark Education Co.

Hands: Level B, 6 vols. 8p. 24.95 (978-0-7802-8915-4(3)) Wright Group, The.

Hands-On Science, Math, & Technology. 112p. (gr. 5-8). 14.99 (978-0-7682-0218-2(3) , GA13018) School Specialty Publishing.

Hankes, Judith, creator. Lost & Found & Found Again: A Math Adventure. 2005. (J). per. 25.00 (978-0-9758592-1-6(8)) Whale's Library, The.

Hanrahan, Val. Additional Mathematics for OCR. Porkess, R., ed. 2004. (Illus.). 192p. pap. 42.00 (***978-0-340-86960-4(7)*** , Hodder Murray) Hodder Education GBR. *Dist:* Trans-Atlantic Pubns., Inc.

Hansen, Sue. Grades K-2: 50 Reproducible, Leveled Game Sheets That Kids Can Use Independently or in Small Groups to Practice Important Math Skills. 2005. (Tic-Tac-Math Ser.). 64p. pap. 11.99 (978-0-439-62919-5(5) , Teaching Resources) Scholastic, Inc.

Harcourt School Publishers Staff. Answer Key: Intervention Solutions Assignment. 2nd ed. 2002. (gr. 1). pap. 17.00 (978-0-15-338239-0(2)); (gr. 2). pap. 17.00 (978-0-15-338240-6(6)); (gr. 3). pap. 17.00 (978-0-15-338241-3(4)); (gr. 5). pap. 17.00 (978-0-15-338243-7(0)); (gr. 6). pap. 17.00 (978-0-15-338244-4(9)) Harcourt Schl. Pubs.

—Benchmark Assesment for Math: California Edition. 2nd ed. 2002. pap. 10.30 (978-0-15-335846-3(7)); pap. 19.20 (978-0-15-335855-5(6)); pap., tchr. ed. 19.20 (978-0-15-335856-2(4)); pap., tchr. ed. 19.20 (978-0-15-335857-9(2)); pap., tchr. ed. 19.20 (978-0-15-335858-6(0)); pap. 10.30 (978-0-15-335845-6(9)); pap. 10.30 (978-0-15-335847-0(5)); pap. 10.30 (978-0-15-335849-4(1)); pap. 10.30 (978-0-15-335850-0(5)); pap. 10.30 (978-0-15-335851-7(3)); pap. 19.20 (978-0-15-335854-8(8)); pap., tchr. ed. 19.20 (978-0-15-335852-4(1)) Harcourt Schl. Pubs.

—Big Book Math 2004. 2nd ed. 2002. 439.60 (978-0-15-337522-4(1)) Harcourt Schl. Pubs.

—The Caterpillar, 5 Pack, On Level. 3rd ed. 2002. (Trophies Reading Program Ser.). (Illus.). (gr. 1). pap. 20.10 (978-0-15-326835-9(2)) Harcourt Schl. Pubs.

—The Caterpillar: On Level. 3rd ed. 2002. (Trophies Reading Program Ser.). (Illus.). (J). pap. 4.10 (978-0-15-322985-5(3)) Harcourt Schl. Pubs.

—Chapter Book Collection Math: Pupils Edition. 2nd ed. 2002. pap. 27.00 (978-0-15-337517-0(5)) Harcourt Schl. Pubs.

—Collections: Big Book Collection, 12 vols. 1999. (Illus.). pap. 708.60 (978-0-15-313506-4(9)) Harcourt Schl. Pubs.

—First Place Math. 2nd ed. 2002. (Illus.). (J). Unit C. pap. 1.70 (978-0-15-335323-9(6)); Unit D. pap. 1.70 (978-0-15-335324-6(4)); Unit A. pap. 1.70 (978-0-15-335321-5(X)); Unit B. pap. 1.70 (978-0-15-335322-2(8)); Unit E. pap. 1.70 (978-0-15-335326-0(0)); Unit F. pap. 1.70 (978-0-15-335327-7(9)) Harcourt Schl. Pubs.

—First Place Math: Practice Activity Book. 2nd ed. 2002. (Illus.). pap. 4.20 (978-0-15-335372-7(4)); (J). (gr. 1). pap. 3.40 (978-0-15-335373-4(2)); (J). (gr. 2). pap. 3.40 (978-0-15-335374-1(0)); (J). (gr. 3). pap. 3.40 (978-0-15-335375-8(9)); (J). (gr. 4). pap. 3.40 (978-0-15-335376-5(7)); (J). (gr. 5). pap. 3.40 (978-0-15-335377-2(5)); (J). (gr. 6). pap. 3.40 (978-0-15-335378-9(3)) Harcourt Schl. Pubs.

—First Place Math: Test Book. 2nd ed. 2002. (Illus.). (J). pap. 1.90 (978-0-15-335379-6(1)); (gr. 1). pap. 1.90 (978-0-15-335381-9(3)); (gr. 2). pap. 1.90 (978-0-15-335382-6(1)); (gr. 3). pap. 1.90 (978-0-15-335384-0(8)); (gr. 4). pap. 1.90 (978-0-15-335386-4(4)); (gr. 5). pap. 1.90 (978-0-15-335387-1(2)); (gr. 6). pap. 1.90 (978-0-15-335388-8(0)) Harcourt Schl. Pubs.

—First Place Math Unit C. 2nd ed. 2002. (Illus.). (J). pap. 2.20 (978-0-15-335332-1(5)); pap. 2.20 (978-0-15-335339-0(2)); pap. 2.20 (978-0-15-335353-6(8)); pap. 2.20 (978-0-15-335359-8(7)); pap. 2.20 (978-0-15-335367-3(8)); (gr. 3). pap. 2.20 (978-0-15-335347-5(3)) Harcourt Schl. Pubs.

—First Place Math Unit D. 2nd ed. 2002. (Illus.). (J). pap. 2.20 (978-0-15-335333-8(3)); pap. 2.20 (978-0-15-335340-6(6)); pap. 2.20 (978-0-15-335348-2(1)); pap. 2.20 (978-0-15-335354-3(6)); pap. 2.20 (978-0-15-335361-1(9)); pap. 2.20 (978-0-15-335368-0(6)) Harcourt Schl. Pubs.

—First Place Math Unit A. 2nd ed. 2002. (Illus.). (J). (gr. 1). pap. 2.20 (978-0-15-335328-4(7)); (gr. 2). pap. 2.20 (978-0-15-335337-6(6)); (gr. 3). pap. 2.20 (978-0-15-335343-7(0)); (gr. 4). pap. 2.20 (978-0-15-335351-2(1)); (gr. 5). pap. 2.20 (978-0-15-335357-4(0)); (gr. 6). pap. 2.20 (978-0-15-335364-2(3)) Harcourt Schl. Pubs.

—First Place Math Unit B. 2nd ed. 2002. (Illus.). (J). pap. 2.20 (978-0-15-335329-1(5)); pap. 2.20 (978-0-15-335338-3(4)); pap. 2.20 (978-0-15-335344-4(9)); pap. 2.20 (978-0-15-335352-9(X)); pap. 2.20 (978-0-15-335358-1(9)); pap. 2.20 (978-0-15-335366-6(X)) Harcourt Schl. Pubs.

—First Place Math Unit E. 2nd ed. 2002. (Illus.). (J). pap. 2.20 (978-0-15-335334-5(1)); pap. 2.20 (978-0-15-335341-3(4)); pap. 2.20 (978-0-15-335349-9(X)); pap. 2.20 (978-0-15-335355-0(4)); pap. 2.20 (978-0-15-335362-8(7)); pap. 2.20 (978-0-15-335369-7(4)) Harcourt Schl. Pubs.

—First Place Math Unit F. 2nd ed. 2002. (Illus.). (J). pap. 2.20 (978-0-15-335336-9(8)); pap. 2.20 (978-0-15-335342-0(2)); pap. 2.20 (978-0-15-335350-5(3)); pap. 2.20 (978-0-15-335356-7(2)); pap. 2.20 (978-0-15-335363-5(5)); (gr. 6). pap. 2.20 (978-0-15-335371-0(6)) Harcourt Schl. Pubs.

—First Place Math, Grade 1. 2nd ed. 2002. pap., tchr. ed. 117.00 (978-0-15-334597-5(7)) Harcourt Schl. Pubs.

—First Place Math, Grade 2. 2nd ed. 2002. pap., tchr. ed. 117.00 (978-0-15-334598-2(5)) Harcourt Schl. Pubs.

—First Place Math, Grade 3. 2nd ed. 2002. pap., tchr. ed. 117.00 (978-0-15-334599-9(3)) Harcourt Schl. Pubs.

—First Place Math, Grade 4. 2nd ed. 2002. pap., tchr. ed. 117.00 (978-0-15-334600-2(0)) Harcourt Schl. Pubs.

—First Place Math, Grade 5. 2nd ed. 2002. pap., tchr. ed. 117.00 (978-0-15-334601-9(9)) Harcourt Schl. Pubs.

—First Place Math, Grade 6. 2nd ed. 2002. pap., tchr. ed. 117.00 (978-0-15-334602-6(7)) Harcourt Schl. Pubs.

—First Place Math, Grade K. 2nd ed. 2002. pap., tchr. ed. 100.50 (978-0-15-334596-8(9)) Harcourt Schl. Pubs.

—First Place Math Sample Bag. 2nd ed. 2002. (Illus.). (J). (gr. 4). pap. 273.10 (978-0-15-327972-0(9)) Harcourt Schl. Pubs.

—Harcourt Matematicas. 2nd ed. (Harcourt Matematicas Ser.). (SPA., Illus.). 2002. (gr. k-6). pupil's gde. ed. 28.90 (978-0-15-325810-7(1)); 2002. (gr. k up). pap., pupil's gde. ed. 483.50 (978-0-15-321782-1(0)); 2002. (gr. 1 up). pupil's gde. ed. 41.20 (978-0-15-325811-4(X)); 2002. (gr. 2 up). pupil's gde. ed. 41.20 (978-0-15-325812-1(8)); 2002. (gr. 3 up). pupil's gde. ed. 74.80 (978-0-15-325813-8(6)); 2002. (gr. 4 up). pupil's gde. ed. 74.80 (978-0-15-325814-5(4)); 2002. (gr. 5 up). pupil's gde. ed. 74.80 (978-0-15-325815-2(2)); 2001. (gr. 6 up). pupil's gde. ed. 74.80 (978-0-15-325816-9(0)) Harcourt Schl. Pubs.

—Harcourt Matematicas: 10 Canguros: Math Reader. 2nd ed. 2002. (SPA., Illus.). pap. 4.30 (978-0-15-321715-9(4)) Harcourt Schl. Pubs.

—Harcourt Matematicas: 3 Hormigas: Math Reader. 2nd ed. 2002. (SPA., Illus.). pap. 4.00 (978-0-15-321711-1(1)) Harcourt Schl. Pubs.

—Harcourt Matematicas: A Dormir: Math Reader. 2nd ed. 2002. (SPA., Illus.). pap. 4.20 (978-0-15-321724-1(3)) Harcourt Schl. Pubs.

—Harcourt Matematicas: Bajo el Arbol de Picnic: Math Reader. 2nd ed. 2002. (SPA., Illus.). pap. 4.00 (978-0-15-321714-2(6)) Harcourt Schl. Pubs.

—Harcourt Matematicas: CA & National Family Involvement Activities. 2nd ed. 2003. (Harcourt Matematicas Ser.). (SPA., Illus.). (gr. k-6). 25.30 (978-0-15-321566-7(6)); (gr. 1 up). 31.10 (978-0-15-321567-4(4)); (gr. 2 up). 31.10 (978-0-15-321568-1(2)); (gr. 3 up). 35.80 (978-0-15-321569-8(0)); (gr. 4 up). 35.80 (978-0-15-321570-4(4)); (gr. 5 up). 35.80 (978-0-15-321571-1(2)); (gr. 6 up). 36.20 (978-0-15-321572-8(0)) Harcourt Schl. Pubs.

—Harcourt Matematicas: Challenge Workbook. 2nd ed. 2003. (Harcourt Matematicas Ser.). (SPA., Illus.). (gr. k-6). wbk. ed., pupil's gde. ed. 11.80 (978-0-15-321642-8(5)); (gr. 1 up). wbk. ed. 12.50 (978-0-15-321643-5(3)); (gr. 2 up). wbk. ed. 12.50 (978-0-15-321644-2(1)); (gr. 3 up). wbk. ed. 13.50 (978-0-15-321645-9(X)); (gr. 4 up). wbk. ed. 13.50 (978-0-15-321646-6(8)); (gr. 5 up). wbk. ed. 13.50 (978-0-15-321647-3(6)); (gr. 6 up). wbk. ed. 14.50 (978-0-15-321648-0(4)) Harcourt Schl. Pubs.

—Harcourt Matematicas: Chapter Book. 2nd ed. 2002. (Harcourt Matematicas Ser.). (SPA., Illus.). (gr. k-6). pap., pupil's gde. ed. 32.00 (978-0-15-321861-3(4)) Harcourt Schl. Pubs.

—Harcourt Matematicas: Checklilst for Knowledge Enrichment. 2nd ed. 2003. (Harcourt Matematicas Ser.). (SPA., Illus.). (gr. 5 up). 13.10 (978-0-15-326116-9(1)) Harcourt Schl. Pubs.

—Harcourt Matematicas: Cuantos? Math Reader. 2nd ed. 2002. (SPA., Illus.). pap. 4.00 (978-0-15-321704-3(9)) Harcourt Schl. Pubs.

—Harcourt Matematicas: Desfile de Mascotas: Math Reader. 2nd ed. 2002. (SPA., Illus.). pap. 4.00 (978-0-15-321701-2(4)) Harcourt Schl. Pubs.

—Harcourt Matematicas: Dia de Limpieza: Math Reader. 2nd ed. 2002. (SPA., Illus.). pap. 4.20 (978-0-15-321729-6(4)) Harcourt Schl. Pubs.

—Harcourt Matematicas: Diez, Nueve, Ocho Little Big Book. 2nd ed. 2001. (SPA., Illus.). 80.10 (978-0-15-323616-7(7)) Harcourt Schl. Pubs.

—Harcourt Matematicas: Donde Vivimos: Math Reader. 2nd ed. 2002. (SPA., Illus.). pap. 4.00 (978-0-15-321702-9(2)) Harcourt Schl. Pubs.

—Harcourt Matematicas: El Trineo: Math Reader. 2nd ed. 2002. (SPA., Illus.). pap. 4.00 (978-0-15-321710-4(3)) Harcourt Schl. Pubs.

—Harcourt Matematicas: Figuras: Math Reader. 2nd ed. 2002. (SPA., Illus.). pap. 4.00 (978-0-15-321705-0(7)) Harcourt Schl. Pubs.

—Harcourt Matematicas: La Banda de Insectos: Math Reader. 2nd ed. 2002. (SPA., Illus.). pap. 4.00 (978-0-15-321703-6(0)) Harcourt Schl. Pubs.

—Harcourt Matematicas: La Familia Que Cuenta: Math Reader. 2nd ed. 2002. (SPA., Illus.). pap. 4.30 (978-0-15-321716-6(2)) Harcourt Schl. Pubs.

—Harcourt Matematicas: La Oruga: Math Reader. 2nd ed. 2002. (SPA., Illus.). pap. 4.30 (978-0-15-321719-7(7)) Harcourt Schl. Pubs.

—Harcourt Matematicas: La Tienda de Miel: Math Reader. 2nd ed. 2002. (SPA., Illus.). pap. 4.30 (978-0-15-321723-4(5)) Harcourt Schl. Pubs.

—Harcourt Matematicas: Las Amigas Hormigas: Math Reader. 2nd ed. 2002. (SPA., Illus.). pap. 4.30 (978-0-15-321717-3(0)) Harcourt Schl. Pubs.

—Harcourt Matematicas: Las Flores de Ema: Math Reader. 2nd ed. 2002. (SPA., Illus.). pap. 4.20 (978-0-15-321728-9(6)) Harcourt Schl. Pubs.

—Harcourt Matematicas: Las Muchas Rayas Little Big Book. 2nd ed. 2001. (SPA., Illus.). 75.90 (978-0-15-323618-1(3)) Harcourt Schl. Pubs.

—Harcourt Matematicas: Libros Revueltos: Math Reader. 2nd ed. 2002. (SPA., Illus.). (gr. 2). pap. 4.20 (978-0-15-321725-8(1)) Harcourt Schl. Pubs.

—Harcourt Matematicas: Los Cinco Patitos Little Big Book. 2nd ed. 2001. (SPA., Illus.). 66.40 (978-0-15-323619-8(1)) Harcourt Schl. Pubs.

—Harcourt Matematicas: Los Juquetes: Math Reader. 2nd ed. 2002. (SPA., Illus.). pap. 4.00 (978-0-15-321700-5(6)) Harcourt Schl. Pubs.

—Harcourt Matematicas: Mi Jardin de Conteo: Math Reader. 2nd ed. 2002. (SPA., Illus.). pap. 4.00 (978-0-15-321706-7(5)) Harcourt Schl. Pubs.

—Harcourt Matematicas: Oscar y Norman: Math Reader. 2nd ed. 2002. (SPA., Illus.). pap. 4.30 (978-0-15-321720-3(0)) Harcourt Schl. Pubs.

—Harcourt Matematicas: Perfecto! Math Reader. 2nd ed. 2002. (SPA., Illus.). (gr. 1). pap. 4.30 (978-0-15-321721-0(9)) Harcourt Schl. Pubs.

—Harcourt Matematicas: Performance Assessment. 2nd ed. 2001. (Harcourt Matematicas Ser.). (SPA., Illus.). (gr. 1 up). pap. 36.40 (978-0-15-321694-7(8)); (gr. 2 up). pap. 36.40 (978-0-15-321695-4(6)); (gr. 3 up). pap. 37.30 (978-0-15-321696-1(4)); (gr. 4 up). pap. 37.30 (978-0-15-321697-8(2)); (gr. 5 up). pap. 37.30 (978-0-15-321698-5(0)); (gr. 6 up). pap. 37.30 (978-0-15-321699-2(9)) Harcourt Schl. Pubs.

—Harcourt Matematicas: Pio y Pia: Math Reader. 2nd ed. 2002. (SPA., Illus.). (gr. 1). pap. 4.20 (978-0-15-321727-2(8)) Harcourt Schl. Pubs.

—Harcourt Matematicas: Practice Workbook. 2nd ed. (Harcourt Matematicas Ser.). (SPA., Illus.). 2003. (gr. 3 up). wbk. ed. 11.60 (978-0-15-321631-2(X)); 2003. (gr. 4 up). wbk. ed. 11.60 (978-0-15-321632-9(8)); 2003. (gr. 5 up). wbk. ed. 11.60 (978-0-15-321633-6(6)); 2003. (gr. 6 up). wbk. ed. 12.00 (978-0-15-321634-3(4)); 2002. (gr. k-6). pap., wbk. ed., pupil's gde. ed. 10.50 (978-0-15-321628-2(X)); 2002. (gr. 1 up). pap., wbk. ed. 11.40 (978-0-15-321629-9(8)); 2002. (gr. 2 up). pap., wbk. ed. 11.40 (978-0-15-321630-5(1)) Harcourt Schl. Pubs.

—Harcourt Matematicas: Problem Solving & Reading Strategies Workbook. 2nd ed. 2003. (Harcourt Matematicas Ser.). (SPA., Illus.). (gr. 1 up). wbk. ed. 11.00 (978-0-15-321668-8(9)); (gr. 2 up). wbk. ed. 11.00 (978-0-15-321669-5(7)); (gr. 3 up). wbk. ed. 12.00 (978-0-15-321670-1(0)); (gr. 4 up). wbk. ed. 12.00 (978-0-15-321671-8(9)); (gr. 5 up). wbk. ed. 12.00 (978-0-15-321672-5(7)); (gr. 6 up). wbk. ed. 12.50 (978-0-15-321673-2(5)) Harcourt Schl. Pubs.

—Harcourt Matematicas: Puedo Ir? Math Reader. 2nd ed. 2002. (SPA., Illus.). pap. 4.00 (978-0-15-321708-1(1)) Harcourt Schl. Pubs.

—Harcourt Matematicas: Que Puedo Comprar? Math Reader. 2nd ed. 2002. (SPA., Illus.). pap. 4.00 (978-0-15-321707-4(3)) Harcourt Schl. Pubs.

—Harcourt Matematicas: Quien Vive en el Zoo? Math Reader. 2nd ed. 2002. (SPA., Illus.). pap. 4.30 (978-0-15-321722-7(7)) Harcourt Schl. Pubs.

—Harcourt Matematicas: Resource Package. 2nd ed. 2003. (Harcourt Matematicas Ser.). (SPA., Illus.). (gr. k-6). 992.20 (978-0-15-321844-6(4)) Harcourt Schl. Pubs.

—Harcourt Matematicas: Un Par y Calcetinas Little Big Book. 2nd ed. 2001. (SPA., Illus.). 75.90 (978-0-15-323617-4(5)) Harcourt Schl. Pubs.

—Harcourt Matematicas: Un Poquito de Cambio: Math Reader. 2nd ed. 2002. (SPA., Illus.). pap. 4.20 (978-0-15-321726-5(X)) Harcourt Schl. Pubs.

—Harcourt Matematicas: Una Semana Ocupada: Math Reader. 2nd ed. 2002. (SPA., Illus.). pap. 4.00 (978-0-15-321709-8(X)) Harcourt Schl. Pubs.

—Harcourt Matematicas: Unit Book. 2nd ed. 2002. (Harcourt Matematicas Ser.). (SPA., Illus.). (gr. 1 up). pap., pupil's gde. ed. 44.50 (978-0-15-321868-2(1)); (gr. 2 up). pap., pupil's gde. ed. 44.50 (978-0-15-321875-0(4)) Harcourt Schl. Pubs.

—Harcourt Matematicas: Venta de Galletas: Math Reader. 2nd ed. 2002. (SPA., Illus.). pap. 4.30 (978-0-15-321718-0(9)) Harcourt Schl. Pubs.

—Harcourt Matematicas: Zapatos los Osos Comparten: Math Reader. 2nd ed. 2002. (SPA., Illus.). pap. 4.00 (978-0-15-321713-5(8)) Harcourt Schl. Pubs.

—Harcourt Matematicas: Zapatos: Math Reader. 2nd ed. 2002. (SPA., Illus.). (gr. 1). pap. 4.00 (978-0-15-321712-8(X)) Harcourt Schl. Pubs.

—Harcourt Math. (Harcourt Math Ser.). 2nd ed. 2002. (Illus.). (gr. k-6). pap., pupil's gde. ed. 26.40 (978-0-15-320744-0(2)); 2nd ed. 2002. (Illus.). (gr. 1 up). pap., pupil's gde. ed. 38.30 (978-0-15-320745-7(0)); 2nd ed. 2002. (Illus.). (gr. 2 up). pap., pupil's gde. ed. 38.30 (978-0-15-320746-4(9)); 2nd ed. 2002. (Illus.). (gr. 3 up). pupil's gde. ed. 66.70 (978-0-15-320747-1(7)); 2nd ed. 2002. (Illus.). (gr. 4 up). pupil's gde. ed. 66.70 (978-0-15-320748-8(5)); 2nd ed. 2002. (Illus.). (gr. 5 up). pupil's gde. ed. 66.70 (978-0-15-320749-5(3)); 2nd ed. 2002. (Illus.). (gr. 6 up). pupil's gde. ed. 66.70 (978-0-15-320750-1(7)); 4th ed. 2004. (SPA.). (gr. k). pap., stu. ed. 28.00 (978-0-15-341102-1(3)); 4th ed. 2004. (SPA.). (gr. k). pap., wbk. ed. 10.20 (978-0-15-341129-8(5)); 4th ed. 2004. (SPA.). (gr. 1). pap., stu. ed. 40.00 (978-0-15-341103-8(1)); 4th ed. 2004. (SPA.). (gr. 1). pap., wbk. ed. 11.00 (978-0-15-341130-4(9)); 4th ed. 2004. (SPA.). (gr. 2). pap., stu. ed. 40.00 (978-0-15-341104-5(X)); 4th ed. 2004. (SPA.). (gr. 2). pap., wbk. ed. 11.00 (978-0-15-341131-1(7)); 4th ed. 2004. (SPA.). (gr. 3). stu. ed. 72.60 (978-0-15-341105-2(8)); 4th ed. 2004. (SPA.). (gr. 3). pap., wbk. ed. 11.00 (978-0-15-341132-8(5)); 4th ed. 2004. (SPA.). (gr. 4). stu. ed. 72.60 (978-0-15-341106-9(6)); 4th ed. 2004. (SPA.). (gr. 4). pap., wbk. ed. 11.00 (978-0-15-341133-5(3)); 4th ed. 2004. (SPA.). (gr. 5). stu. ed. 72.60 (978-0-15-341107-6(4)); 4th ed. 2004. (SPA.). (gr. 5). pap., wbk. ed. 11.00 (978-0-15-341134-2(1)); 4th ed. 2004. (SPA.). (gr. 6). stu. ed. 72.60 (978-0-15-341108-3(2)); 4th ed. 2004. (SPA.). (gr. 6). pap., wbk. ed. 11.00 (978-0-15-341135-9(X)) Harcourt Schl. Pubs.

—Harcourt Math: A Pair of Socks: Little Big Book. 2nd ed. 2002. (Illus.). pap. 65.80 (978-0-15-321263-5(2)) Harcourt Schl. Pubs.

—Harcourt Math: Activity Book. 2nd ed. 2002. (Illus.). (ps). pap. 8.70 (978-0-15-337969-7(3)) Harcourt Schl. Pubs.

—Harcourt Math: Animal Seasons: Little Big Book. 2nd ed. 2002. (Illus.). pap. 54.60 (978-0-15-321268-0(3)) Harcourt Schl. Pubs.

—Harcourt Math: Answer & Solution Key. 2nd ed. 2002. (Harcourt Math Ser.). (Illus.). (gr. 6 up). pap. 23.90 (978-0-15-320847-8(3)) Harcourt Schl. Pubs.

—Harcourt Math: Assessment Guide. 2nd ed. 2002. (Harcourt Math Ser.). (Illus.). (gr. 3 up). pap. 73.80 (978-0-15-320835-5(X)) Harcourt Schl. Pubs.

—Harcourt Math: Bear in a Square: Little Big Book. 2nd ed. 2002. (Illus.). pap. 58.00 (978-0-15-321267-3(5)) Harcourt Schl. Pubs.

—Harcourt Math: Big Book Collection: National & CA Edition. 2nd ed. 2002. (Harcourt Math Ser.). (Illus.). (gr. k up). pap., pupil's gde. ed. 443.80 (978-0-15-320893-5(7)) Harcourt Schl. Pubs.

—Harcourt Math: CA Assessment Guide. 2nd ed. 2002. (Illus.). (gr. 3). pap. 73.80 (978-0-15-320686-3(1)); (gr. 4). pap. 73.80 (978-0-15-320687-0(X)); (gr. 5). pap. 73.80 (978-0-15-320688-7(8)); (gr. 6). pap. 73.80 (978-0-15-320689-4(6)) Harcourt Schl. Pubs.

—Harcourt Math: CA Chapter Book. 2nd ed. 2002. (Illus.). pap. 26.00 (978-0-15-321827-9(4)) Harcourt Schl. Pubs.

—Harcourt Math: CA Family Involvement Activities. 2nd ed. 2001. (Illus.). (CHI.). pap. 27.70 (978-0-15-321573-5(9)); (VIE., pap. 27.70 (978-0-15-321580-3(1)); (CHI., (gr. 1). pap. 34.00 (978-0-15-321574-2(7)); (VIE., (gr. 1). pap. 34.00 (978-0-15-321581-0(X)); (CHI., (gr. 2). pap. 34.00 (978-0-15-321575-9(5)); (VIE., (gr. 2). pap. 34.00 (978-0-15-321582-7(8)); (CHI., (gr. 3). pap. 39.20 (978-0-15-321576-6(3)); (VIE., (gr. 3). pap. 39.20 (978-0-15-321583-4(6)); (CHI., (gr. 4). pap. 39.20 (978-0-15-321577-3(1)); (VIE., (gr. 4). pap. 39.20 (978-0-15-321584-1(4)); (CHI., (gr. 5). pap. 39.20 (978-0-15-321578-0(X)); (VIE., (gr. 5). pap. 39.20 (978-0-15-321585-8(2)); (CHI., (gr. 6). pap. 39.60 (978-0-15-321579-7(8)); (VIE., (gr. 6). pap. 39.60 (978-0-15-321586-5(0)) Harcourt Schl. Pubs.

—Harcourt Math: California Edition. 2nd ed. 2002. (Illus.). 25.10 (978-0-15-315509-3(4)); (gr. 1). 36.40 (978-0-15-315511-6(6)); (gr. 2). 36.40 (978-0-15-315512-3(4)); (gr. 3). 66.70 (978-0-15-315513-0(2)); (gr. 4). 66.70 (978-0-15-315514-7(0)); (gr. 5). 66.70 (978-0-15-315516-1(7)); (gr. 6). 66.70 (978-0-15-315517-8(5)) Harcourt Schl. Pubs.

—Harcourt Math: Challenge Workbook. 2nd ed. 2002. (Harcourt Math Ser.). (Illus.). (gr. 5 up). pap., wbk. ed. 12.00 (978-0-15-320821-8(X)); (gr. 6 up). pap., wbk. ed. 12.60 (978-0-15-320822-5(8)) Harcourt Schl. Pubs.

—Harcourt Math: Challenge Workbook: National & CA Edition. 2nd ed. 2002. (Harcourt Math Ser.). (Illus.). (gr. k-6). pap., wbk. ed. 10.10 (978-0-15-320427-2(3)); (gr. 1 up). pap., wbk. ed. 10.80 (978-0-15-320428-9(1)); (gr. 2 up). pap., wbk. ed. 10.80 (978-0-15-320429-6(X)) Harcourt Schl. Pubs.

M N O

—Harcourt Math: Family Involvement. 2nd ed. (Harcourt Math Ser.). (Illus.). 2002. (gr. k-6). pap. 21.30 (978-0-15-321282-6(9)); 2002. (gr. 1 up). pap. 27.60 (978-0-15-321283-3(7)); 2002. (gr. 4 up). pap. 31.90 (978-0-15-320849-2(X)); 2002. (gr. 5 up). pap. 31.90 (978-0-15-320850-8(3)); 2002. (gr. 6 up). pap. 31.90 (978-0-15-320851-5(1)); 2001. (gr. 2 up). pap. 27.60 (978-0-15-321284-0(5)); 2001. (gr. 3 up). pap. 31.90 (978-0-15-320848-5(1)) Harcourt Schl. Pubs.

—Harcourt Math: Family Involvement: California Edition. 2nd ed. 2002. (Illus.). pap. 21.30 (978-0-15-320705-1(1)); (gr. 1). pap. 27.60 (978-0-15-320706-8(X)); (gr. 2). pap. 27.60 (978-0-15-320707-5(8)); (gr. 3). pap. 31.90 (978-0-15-320708-2(6)); (gr. 4). pap. 31.90 (978-0-15-320709-9(4)); (gr. 5). pap. 31.90 (978-0-15-320710-5(8)); (J). (gr. 6). pap. 25.60 (978-0-15-320711-2(6)) Harcourt Schl. Pubs.

—Harcourt Math: Five Little Ducks: Little Big Book. 2nd ed. 2002. (Illus.). pap. 62.40 (978-0-15-321265-9(9)) Harcourt Schl. Pubs.

—Harcourt Math: Graphing Component. 2nd ed. 2002. (Illus.). (gr. k). pap. 34.00 (978-0-15-337509-5(4)); (gr. 1). pap. 34.00 (978-0-15-337511-8(6)); (gr. 2). pap. 34.00 (978-0-15-337512-5(4)); (gr. 3). pap. 34.00 (978-0-15-337513-2(2)); (gr. 4). pap. 34.00 (978-0-15-337514-9(0)); (gr. 5). pap. 34.00 (978-0-15-337515-6(9)); (gr. 6). pap. 34.00 (978-0-15-337516-3(7)) Harcourt Schl. Pubs.

—Harcourt Math: Integrated Mathematics Handbook. 99th ed. 2001. (Illus.). (gr. 1-2). pap. 5.60 (978-0-15-322491-1(6)) Harcourt Schl. Pubs.

—Harcourt Math: Intervention Solutions. 2nd ed. 2002. (J). (gr. 3). pap. 5.00 (978-0-15-338223-9(6)); (gr. 5). pap. 5.00 (978-0-15-338225-3(2)); (gr. 6). pap. 5.00 (978-0-15-338226-0(0)) Harcourt Schl. Pubs.

—Harcourt Math: Math Readers Grade Level Collection. 2nd ed. 2002. (Harcourt Math Ser.). (Illus.). (gr. k-6). pap. 35.20 (978-0-15-320479-1(6)); (gr. 1 up). pap. 37.00 (978-0-15-320480-7(X)); (gr. 2 up). pap. 37.60 (978-0-15-320481-4(8)) Harcourt Schl. Pubs.

—Harcourt Math: MEAP Resource Book. 3rd ed. 2003. (gr. 1). pap. 7.50 (978-0-15-340989-9(4)); (gr. 2). pap. 7.50 (978-0-15-340990-5(8)); (gr. 3). pap. 9.60 (978-0-15-340991-2(6)); (gr. 4). pap. 9.60 (978-0-15-340992-9(4)); (gr. 5). pap. 9.60 (978-0-15-340993-6(2)); (gr. 6). pap. 9.60 (978-0-15-340994-3(0)) Harcourt Schl. Pubs.

—Harcourt Math: National Intervention Solutions. 2nd ed. 2002. (J). (gr. 1). pap. 5.00 (978-0-15-338221-5(X)) Harcourt Schl. Pubs.

—Harcourt Math: National Intervention Solutions: California Edition. 2nd ed. 2002. (J). (gr. 2). pap. 5.00 (978-0-15-338222-2(8)) Harcourt Schl. Pubs.

—Harcourt Math: National Pupils Edition. 3rd ed. 2002. 26.00 (978-0-15-334739-9(2)); (gr. 1). 36.70 (978-0-15-334740-5(6)) Harcourt Schl. Pubs.

—Harcourt Math: Performance Assessment. 2nd ed. 2002. (Harcourt Math Ser.). (gr. 5 up). pap. 33.70 (978-0-15-320845-4(7)); (Illus.). (gr. 3 up). pap. 33.70 (978-0-15-320843-0(0)); (Illus.). (gr. 4 up). pap. 33.70 (978-0-15-320844-7(9)); (Illus.). (gr. 6 up). pap. 33.70 (978-0-15-320846-1(5)) Harcourt Schl. Pubs.

—Harcourt Math: Performance Assessment: California Edition. 2nd ed. 2002. (Illus.). (gr. 3). pap. 30.00 (978-0-15-320700-6(0)); (gr. 4). pap. 30.00 (978-0-15-320701-3(9)); (gr. 5). pap. 30.00 (978-0-15-320702-0(7)); (gr. 6). pap. 30.00 (978-0-15-320703-7(5)) Harcourt Schl. Pubs.

—Harcourt Math: Practice Workbook: National & CA Edition. 2nd ed. 2002. (Harcourt Math Ser.). (Illus.). (gr. k-6). pap., wbk. ed. 9.30 (978-0-15-320434-0(6)); (gr. 1 up). pap., wbk. ed. 10.40 (978-0-15-320435-7(4)); (gr. 2 up). pap., wbk. ed. 10.40 (978-0-15-320436-4(2)) Harcourt Schl. Pubs.

—Harcourt Math: Practice Workbook: National/California Edition. 2nd ed. 2002. (Harcourt Math Ser.). (gr. 2 up). pap., tchr. ed. 22.00 (978-0-15-320660-3(8)) Harcourt Schl. Pubs.

—Harcourt Math: Reteaching Workbook. 2nd ed. 2002. (Harcourt Math Ser.). (Illus.). (gr. 3 up) pap., wbk. ed. 11.20 (978-0-15-320799-0(X)); (gr. 4 up). pap., wbk. ed. 11.20 (978-0-15-320812-6(0)); (gr. 5 up). pap., wbk. ed. 12.00 (978-0-15-320813-3(9)); (gr. 6 up). pap., wbk. ed. 12.60 (978-0-15-320814-0(7)) Harcourt Schl. Pubs.

—Harcourt Math: Reteaching Workbook: National & CA Edition. 2nd ed. 2002. (Harcourt Math Ser.). (Illus.). (gr. 1 up). pap., wbk. ed. 10.80 (978-0-15-320441-8(9)); (gr. 2 up). pap., wbk. ed. 10.80 (978-0-15-320442-5(7)) Harcourt Schl. Pubs.

—Harcourt Math: Strategies & Activites. 2nd ed. 2002. (Harcourt Math Ser.). (gr. 1 up). pap., tchr. ed. 84.70 (978-0-15-320712-9(4)); (gr. 5 up). pap., tchr. ed. 94.30 (978-0-15-320765-5(5)) Harcourt Schl. Pubs.

—Harcourt Math: Strategies & Activities. 2nd ed. 2002. (gr. 2). pap., tchr. ed. 84.70 (978-0-15-320719-8(1)); (gr. 3 up). pap., tchr. ed. 84.70 (978-0-15-320720-4(5)); (gr. 4 up). pap., tchr. ed. 94.30 (978-0-15-320764-8(7)); (gr. 6 up). pap., tchr. ed. 94.30 (978-0-15-320766-2(3)) Harcourt Schl. Pubs.

—Harcourt Math: Student Workmat. 4th ed. 2004. (SPA.). (gr. 1-2). 4.70 (978-0-15-342028-3(6)) Harcourt Schl. Pubs.

—Harcourt Math: Ten, Nine, Eight: Little Big Book. 2nd ed. 2002. (Illus.). pap. 54.60 (978-0-15-321266-6(7)) Harcourt Schl. Pubs.

—Harcourt Math: Terranova Practice. 2nd ed. 2002. (Illus.). (gr. 1). pap. 6.90 (978-0-15-333648-5(X)); (gr. 2). pap. 6.90 (978-0-15-333649-2(8)); (gr. 3). pap. 9.60 (978-0-15-333650-8(1)); (gr. 4). pap. 9.60 (978-0-15-333651-5(X)); (gr. 5). pap. 9.60 (978-0-15-333652-2(8)); (gr. 6). pap. 10.30 (978-0-15-333653-9(6)) Harcourt Schl. Pubs.

—Harcourt Math 2: Practice Workbook. 2nd ed. 2002. (J). (gr. 1). pap. 10.00 (978-0-15-336473-0(4)) Harcourt Schl. Pubs.

—Harcourt Math Collection, Grade 1, Vols. 1-3. 3rd ed. 2003. tchr. ed. 276.00 (978-0-15-338863-7(3)) Harcourt Schl. Pubs.

—Harcourt Math Collection, Grade 2, Vols. 1-3. 3rd ed. 2003. tchr. ed. 276.00 (978-0-15-338864-4(1)) Harcourt Schl. Pubs.

—Harcourt Math Collection, Grade 3, Vols. 1-3. 3rd ed. 2003. tchr. ed. 276.00 (978-0-15-338865-1(X)) Harcourt Schl. Pubs.

—Harcourt Math Collection, Grade 4, Vols. 1-3. 3rd ed. 2003. tchr. ed. 276.00 (978-0-15-338866-8(8)) Harcourt Schl. Pubs.

—Harcourt Math Collection, Grade 5, Vols. 1-3. 3rd ed. 2003. tchr. ed. 276.00 (978-0-15-338867-5(6)) Harcourt Schl. Pubs.

—Harcourt Math Collection, Grade 6, Vols. 1-3. 3rd ed. 2003. tchr. ed. 276.00 (978-0-15-338868-2(4)) Harcourt Schl. Pubs.

—Harcourt Math, Grade 1. 4th ed. 2004. (SPA.). pap., tchr. ed., wbk. ed. 24.10 (978-0-15-341137-3(6)); Vol. 1. tchr. ed. 97.10 (978-0-15-341111-3(2)); Vol. 2. tchr. ed. 97.10 (978-0-15-341112-0(0)); Vol. 3. tchr. ed. 97.10 (978-0-15-341113-7(9)) Harcourt Schl. Pubs.

—Harcourt Math, Grade 1: CA Standard Test Preparation for Benchmark Test. 2nd ed. 2002. pap., tchr. ed. 19.20 (978-0-15-321809-5(6)) Harcourt Schl. Pubs.

—Harcourt Math, Grade 1: California Edition. 2nd ed. 2002. (Harcourt Math Ser.). (gr. 1 up). pap., tchr. ed., wbk. ed. 22.00 (978-0-15-320659-7(4)) Harcourt Schl. Pubs.

—Harcourt Math, Grade 1: Terranova Practice. 2nd ed. 2002. pap., tchr. ed. 14.60 (978-0-15-333654-6(4)) Harcourt Schl. Pubs.

—Harcourt Math, Grade 2. 4th ed. 2004. (SPA.). pap., tchr. ed., wbk. ed. 24.10 (978-0-15-341138-0(4)); Vol. 1. tchr. ed. 97.10 (978-0-15-341114-4(7)); Vol. 2. tchr. ed. 97.10 (978-0-15-341115-1(5)); Vol. 3. tchr. ed. 97.10 (978-0-15-341116-8(3)) Harcourt Schl. Pubs.

—Harcourt Math, Grade 2: CA Standard Test Preparation for Benchmark Test. 2nd ed. 2002. pap., tchr. ed. 19.20 (978-0-15-321810-1(X)) Harcourt Schl. Pubs.

—Harcourt Math, Grade 2: Terranova Practice. 2nd ed. 2002. pap., tchr. ed. 14.60 (978-0-15-333655-3(2)) Harcourt Schl. Pubs.

—Harcourt Math, Grade 3. 4th ed. 2004. (SPA.). pap., tchr. ed., wbk. ed. 24.10 (978-0-15-341139-7(2)); Vol. 1. tchr. ed. 97.10 (978-0-15-341117-5(1)); Vol. 2. tchr. ed. 97.10 (978-0-15-341118-2(X)); Vol. 3. tchr. ed. 97.10 (978-0-15-341119-9(8)) Harcourt Schl. Pubs.

—Harcourt Math, Grade 3: CA Standard Test Preparation for Benchmark Test. 2nd ed. 2002. pap., tchr. ed. 19.20 (978-0-15-321811-8(8)) Harcourt Schl. Pubs.

—Harcourt Math, Grade 3: Terranova Practice. 2nd ed. 2002. pap., tchr. ed. 17.30 (978-0-15-333656-0(0)) Harcourt Schl. Pubs.

—Harcourt Math, Grade 4. 4th ed. 2004. (SPA.). pap., tchr. ed., wbk. ed. 24.10 (978-0-15-341140-3(6)); Vol. 1. tchr. ed. 97.10 (978-0-15-341120-5(1)); Vol. 2. pap., tchr. ed. 97.10 (978-0-15-341121-2(X)); Vol. 3. pap., tchr. ed. 97.10 (978-0-15-341122-9(8)) Harcourt Schl. Pubs.

—Harcourt Math, Grade 4: CA Standard Test Preparation for Benchmark Test. 2nd ed. 2002. pap., tchr. ed. 19.20 (978-0-15-321812-5(6)) Harcourt Schl. Pubs.

—Harcourt Math, Grade 4: Terranova Practice. 2nd ed. 2002. pap., tchr. ed. 17.30 (978-0-15-333657-7(9)) Harcourt Schl. Pubs.

—Harcourt Math, Grade 5. 4th ed. 2004. (SPA.). pap., tchr. ed., wbk. ed. 24.10 (978-0-15-341141-0(4)); Vol. 1. pap., tchr. ed. 97.10 (978-0-15-341123-6(6)); Vol. 2. pap., tchr. ed. 97.10 (978-0-15-341124-3(4)); Vol. 3. pap., tchr. ed. 97.10 (978-0-15-341125-0(2)) Harcourt Schl. Pubs.

—Harcourt Math, Grade 5: CA Standard Test Preparation for Benchmark Test. 2nd ed. 2002. pap., tchr. ed. 19.20 (978-0-15-321813-2(4)) Harcourt Schl. Pubs.

—Harcourt Math, Grade 5: Terranova Practice. 2nd ed. 2002. pap., tchr. ed. 17.30 (978-0-15-333658-4(7)) Harcourt Schl. Pubs.

—Harcourt Math, Grade 6. 4th ed. 2004. (SPA.). pap., tchr. ed., wbk. ed. 24.10 (978-0-15-341142-7(2)); Vol. 1. pap., tchr. ed. 97.10 (978-0-15-341126-7(0)); Vol. 2. pap., tchr. ed. 97.10 (978-0-15-341127-4(9)); Vol. 3. pap., tchr. ed. 97.10 (978-0-15-341128-1(7)) Harcourt Schl. Pubs.

—Harcourt Math, Grade 6: CA Standard Test Preparation for Benchmark Test. 2nd ed. 2002. pap., tchr. ed. 19.20 (978-0-15-321814-9(2)) Harcourt Schl. Pubs.

—Harcourt Math, Grade 6: Terranova Practice. 2nd ed. 2002. pap., tchr. ed. 17.70 (978-0-15-333659-1(5)) Harcourt Schl. Pubs.

—Harcourt Math, Grade K. 4th ed. 2004. (SPA.). pap., tchr. ed., wbk. ed. 20.90 (978-0-15-341136-6(8)); Vol. 1. tchr. ed. 145.60 (978-0-15-341109-0(0)); Vol. 2. tchr. ed. 145.60 (978-0-15-341110-6(4)) Harcourt Schl. Pubs.

—Harcourt Math, Grade K Vol. 1. 3rd ed. 2002. tchr. ed. 138.00 (978-0-15-334746-7(5)) Harcourt Schl. Pubs.

—Harcourt Math, Grade K Vol. 2. 3rd ed. 2003. tchr. ed. 138.00 (978-0-15-338908-5(7)) Harcourt Schl. Pubs.

—Harcourt Math, Grade Pre-K. 2nd ed. 2002. pap., tchr. ed. 94.50 (978-0-15-337968-0(5)) Harcourt Schl. Pubs.

—Harcourt Math Reader Bk. 1: Getting to Sleep. 2nd ed. 2000. (Illus.). (J). (gr. 2). pap. 2.60 (978-0-15-319624-9(6)) Harcourt Schl. Pubs.

—Harcourt Math Reader Bk. 1: Shoes. 2nd ed. 2002. (Illus.). (gr. 1). pap. 3.00 (978-0-15-319612-6(2)) Harcourt Schl. Pubs.

—Harcourt Math Reader Bk. 1: The Toys. 2nd ed. 2002. (Illus.). pap. 3.00 (978-0-15-319600-3(9)) Harcourt Schl. Pubs.

—Harcourt Math Reader Bk. 2: Bears Can Share. 2nd ed. 2000. (Illus.). pap. 3.00 (978-0-15-319613-3(0)) Harcourt Schl. Pubs.

—Harcourt Math Reader Bk. 2: Pet Parade. 2nd ed. 2002. (Illus.). pap. 3.00 (978-0-15-319601-0(7)) Harcourt Schl. Pubs.

—Harcourt Math Reader Bk. 2: The Mixed-up Books. 2nd ed. 2002. (Illus.). (J). pap. 2.60 (978-0-15-319625-6(4)) Harcourt Schl. Pubs.

—Harcourt Math Reader Bk. 3: A Little Bit of Change. 2nd ed. 2002. (Illus.). (J). pap. 2.60 (978-0-15-319626-3(2)) Harcourt Schl. Pubs.

—Harcourt Math Reader Bk. 3: Under the Picnic Tree. 2nd ed. 2002. (Illus.). pap. 3.00 (978-0-15-319614-0(9)) Harcourt Schl. Pubs.

—Harcourt Math Reader Bk. 3: Where We Live. 2nd ed. 2002. (Illus.). pap. 3.00 (978-0-15-319602-7(5)) Harcourt Schl. Pubs.

—Harcourt Math Reader Bk. 4: 10 Kangaroos. 2nd ed. 2002. (Illus.). (J). pap. 2.60 (978-0-15-319615-7(7)) Harcourt Schl. Pubs.

—Harcourt Math Reader Bk. 4: A Bug Band. 2nd ed. 2002. (Illus.). pap. 3.00 (978-0-15-319603-4(3)) Harcourt Schl. Pubs.

—Harcourt Math Reader Bk. 4: Tweet & Chirp. 2nd ed. 2002. (Illus.). (J). pap. 2.60 (978-0-15-319627-0(0)) Harcourt Schl. Pubs.

—Harcourt Math Reader Bk. 5: Emma's Flowers. 2nd ed. 2002. (Illus.). (J). pap. 2.60 (978-0-15-319628-7(9)) Harcourt Schl. Pubs.

—Harcourt Math Reader Bk. 5: How Many. 2nd ed. 2002. (Illus.). pap. 3.00 (978-0-15-319604-1(1)) Harcourt Schl. Pubs.

—Harcourt Math Reader Bk. 5: The Counting Family. 2nd ed. 2002. (Illus.). (J). pap. 2.60 (978-0-15-319616-4(5)) Harcourt Schl. Pubs.

—Harcourt Math Reader Bk. 6: Ant Friends. 2nd ed. 2002. (Illus.). (J). pap. 2.60 (978-0-15-319617-1(3)) Harcourt Schl. Pubs.

—Harcourt Math Reader Bk. 6: Clean up Day. 2nd ed. 2002. (Illus.). (J). pap. 2.60 (978-0-15-319629-4(7)) Harcourt Schl. Pubs.

—Harcourt Math Reader Bk. 6: Shapes. 2nd ed. 2002. (Illus.). pap. 3.00 (978-0-15-319605-8(X)) Harcourt Schl. Pubs.

—Harcourt Math Reader Bk. 7: Bake Sale. 2nd ed. 2002. (Illus.). (J). pap. 2.60 (978-0-15-319618-8(1)) Harcourt Schl. Pubs.

—Harcourt Math Reader Bk. 7: My Counting Garden. 2nd ed. 2002. (Illus.). pap. 3.00 (978-0-15-319606-5(8)) Harcourt Schl. Pubs.

—Harcourt Math Reader Bk. 7: Solid Surprises. 2nd ed. 2002. (Illus.). (J). pap. 2.60 (978-0-15-319630-0(0)) Harcourt Schl. Pubs.

—Harcourt Math Reader Bk. 8: The Caterpillar. 2nd ed. 2000. (Illus.). (J). pap. 2.60 (978-0-15-319619-5(X)) Harcourt Schl. Pubs.

—Harcourt Math Reader Bk. 8: The Morning Rush. 2nd ed. 2002. (Illus.). (J). pap. 2.60 (978-0-15-319631-7(9)) Harcourt Schl. Pubs.

—Harcourt Math Reader Bk. 8: What Can I Buy. 2nd ed. 2002. (Illus.). pap. 3.00 (978-0-15-319607-2(6)) Harcourt Schl. Pubs.

—Harcourt Math Reader Bk. 9: Can I Go. 2nd ed. 2002. (Illus.). pap. 3.00 (978-0-15-319608-9(4)) Harcourt Schl. Pubs.

—Harcourt Math Reader Bk. 9: Oscar & Noman. 2nd ed. 2000. (Illus.). (J). pap. 2.60 (978-0-15-319620-1(3)) Harcourt Schl. Pubs.

—Harcourt Math Reader Bk. 9: Recess Races. 2nd ed. 2000. (Illus.). (J). pap. 2.60 (978-0-15-319632-4(7)) Harcourt Schl. Pubs.

—Harcourt Math Reader Bk. 10: A Busy Week. 2nd ed. 2002. (Illus.). pap. 3.00 (978-0-15-319609-6(2)) Harcourt Schl. Pubs.

—Harcourt Math Reader Bk. 10: Just Right. 2nd ed. 2002. (Illus.). (J). pap. 2.60 (978-0-15-319621-8(1)) Harcourt Schl. Pubs.

—Harcourt Math Reader Bk. 10: Trouble at the Cookout. 2nd ed. 2002. (Illus.). (J). pap. 2.60 (978-0-15-319633-1(5)) Harcourt Schl. Pubs.

—Harcourt Math Reader Bk. 11: Larry's New Mitt. 2nd ed. 2002. (Illus.). (J). pap. 2.60 (978-0-15-319634-8(3)) Harcourt Schl. Pubs.

—Harcourt Math Reader Bk. 11: The Sled. 2nd ed. 2002. (Illus.). pap. 3.00 (978-0-15-319610-2(6)) Harcourt Schl. Pubs.

—Harcourt Math Reader Bk. 11: Who's at the Zoo. 2nd ed. 2002. (Illus.). (J). pap. 2.60 (978-0-15-319622-5(X)) Harcourt Schl. Pubs.

—Harcourt Math Reader Bk. 12: 3 Ants. 2nd ed. 2002. (Illus.). pap. 3.00 (978-0-15-319611-9(4)) Harcourt Schl. Pubs.

—Harcourt Math Reader Bk. 12: Messy Dragons. 2nd ed. 2000. (Illus.). (J). pap. 2.60 (978-0-15-319635-5(1)) Harcourt Schl. Pubs.

—Harcourt Math Reader Bk. 12: The Honey Shop. 2nd ed. 2002. (Illus.). (J). pap. 2.60 (978-0-15-319623-2(8)) Harcourt Schl. Pubs.

—Harcourt Mathematics: Intervention Solution Assignment. 2nd ed. 2002. (gr. 3). pap. 7.00 (978-0-15-338235-2(X)) Harcourt Schl. Pubs.

—Harcourt Mathematics: Intervention Solutions. 2nd ed. 2002. (J). (gr. 4). pap. 5.00 (978-0-15-338224-6(4)) Harcourt Schl. Pubs.

—Harcourt Mathematics: Intervention Solutions & Assessment. 2nd ed. 2002. (gr. 4). pap. 7.00 (978-0-15-338236-9(8)) Harcourt Schl. Pubs.

—Harcourt Mathematics: Intervention Solutions & Assessment: Answer Key. 2nd ed. 2002. (gr. 4). pap. 17.00 (978-0-15-338242-0(2)) Harcourt Schl. Pubs.

—Harcourt Mathematics: Intervention Solutions Assignment. 2nd ed. 2002. (gr. 1). pap. 7.00 (978-0-15-338233-8(3)); (gr. 2). pap. 7.00 (978-0-15-338234-5(1)); (gr. 5). pap. 7.00 (978-0-15-338237-6(6)); (gr. 6). pap. 7.00 (978-0-15-338238-3(4)) Harcourt Schl. Pubs.

—Harcourt Mathematics: Intervention Solutions: California Edition. 2nd ed. 2002. (J). (gr. 4). pap., wbk. ed. 5.00 (978-0-15-338206-2(6)) Harcourt Schl. Pubs.

—Harcourt Mathematics: Intervention Solutions: Teacher Resource Guide. 2nd ed. 2002. (gr. 4). pap., tchr. ed. 22.70 (978-0-15-338230-7(9)) Harcourt Schl. Pubs.

—Harcourt Mathematics: Practice Book Intervention Solutions. 2nd ed. 2002. (gr. 1). pap., tchr. ed. 18.20 (978-0-15-338251-2(1)); (J). (gr. 2). pap. 9.70 (978-0-15-338246-8(5)); (gr. 2). pap., tchr. ed. 18.20 (978-0-15-338252-9(X)); (J). (gr. 3). pap. 9.70 (978-0-15-338247-5(3)); (gr. 3). pap., tchr. ed. 18.20 (978-0-15-338253-6(8)); (J). (gr. 4). pap. 9.70 (978-0-15-338248-2(1)); (gr. 4). pap., tchr. ed. 18.20 (978-0-15-338254-3(6)); (gr. 5). pap., tchr. ed. 18.20 (978-0-15-338255-0(4)); (J). (gr. 6). pap. 9.70 (978-0-15-338250-5(3)); (gr. 6). pap., tchr. ed. 18.20 (978-0-15-338256-7(2)) Harcourt Schl. Pubs.

—Harcourt Mathematics: Practice Book/Intervention Solutions. 2nd ed. 2002. (J). (gr. 1). pap. 9.70 (978-0-15-338245-1(7)) Harcourt Schl. Pubs.

—Horizons: Test Prep: North Carolina Edition. 2nd ed. 2002. (gr. 4). pap. 10.60 (978-0-15-335719-0(3)); (Illus.). (gr. 3). pap. 9.40 (978-0-15-335718-3(5)) Harcourt Schl. Pubs.

—Intervention Problem Solving Workbook. 2nd ed. 2002. (gr. 5). pap., tchr. ed. 17.60 (978-0-15-336889-9(6)); (gr. 6). pap., tchr. ed. 17.60 (978-0-15-336891-2(8)) Harcourt Schl. Pubs.

—Intervention Problem Solving Workbook Math. 2nd ed. 2002. (gr. 1). pap. 8.30 (978-0-15-336877-6(2)); (gr. 2). pap. 8.30 (978-0-15-336878-3(0)); (gr. 3). pap. 8.30 (978-0-15-336879-0(9)); (gr. 4). pap. 8.30 (978-0-15-336881-3(0)); (gr. 5). pap. 8.30 (978-0-15-336882-0(9)); (gr. 6). pap. 8.30 (978-0-15-336883-7(7)) Harcourt Schl. Pubs.

—Intervention Solutions Harcourt Mathematics: California Edition. 2nd ed. 2002. (J). (gr. 1). pap., wbk. ed. 5.00 (978-0-15-338203-1(1)); (gr. 2). pap., wbk. ed. 5.00 (978-0-15-338204-8(X)); (gr. 3). pap., wbk. ed. 5.00 (978-0-15-338205-5(8)); (gr. 5). pap., wbk. ed. 5.00 (978-0-15-338207-9(4)); (gr. 6). pap., wbk. ed. 5.00 (978-0-15-338208-6(2)) Harcourt Schl. Pubs.

—Intervention Solutions Harcourt Mathematics: Teacher Resource Guide. 2nd ed. 2002. (gr. 1). pap., tchr. ed. 22.70 (978-0-15-338227-7(9)); (gr. 2). pap., tchr. ed. 22.70 (978-0-15-338228-4(7)); (gr. 3). pap., tchr. ed. 22.70 (978-0-15-338229-1(5)); (gr. 5). pap., tchr. ed. 22.70 (978-0-15-338231-4(7)); (gr. 6). pap., tchr. ed. 22.70 (978-0-15-338232-1(5)) Harcourt Schl. Pubs.

—Literature Bb Collection Resource Package Math. 2nd ed. 2002. pap. 357.70 (978-0-15-321269-7(1)) Harcourt Schl. Pubs.

—Matematica: Intervention Strategies & Activities Site License. 2nd ed. 2002. (SPA.). cd-rom 154.80 (978-0-15-322719-6(2)) Harcourt Schl. Pubs.

—Matematica Super Value Package. 99th ed. 1999. (SPA.). (gr. k). pap. 1657.60 (978-0-15-314723-4(7)); (gr. 1). pap. 1991.60 (978-0-15-314724-1(5)); (gr. 2). pap. 1991.60 (978-0-15-314725-8(3)); (gr. 3). 2964.30 (978-0-15-314726-5(1)); (gr. 4). 2964.30 (978-0-15-314727-2(X)); (gr. 5). 2964.30 (978-0-15-314728-9(8)); (gr. 6). 2964.30 (978-0-15-314729-6(6)) Harcourt Schl. Pubs.

—Matematicas Mi Ventaja: Enrichment Workbook. 99th ed. 1998. (SPA., Illus.). (gr. 1). pap., wbk. ed. 13.80 (978-0-15-311230-0(1)); (gr. 2). pap., wbk. ed. 13.80 (978-0-15-311231-7(X)); (gr. 3). pap., wbk. ed. 14.70 (978-0-15-311232-4(8)); (gr. 4). pap., wbk. ed. 14.70 (978-0-15-311233-1(6)); (gr. 5). pap., wbk. ed. 14.70 (978-0-15-311234-8(4)); (gr. 6). pap., wbk. ed. 15.50 (978-0-15-311235-5(2)) Harcourt Schl. Pubs.

—Matematicas Mi Ventaja: Kindergarten Big Book. 99th ed. 1998. (SPA., Illus.). pap. 415.30 (978-0-15-313587-3(5)) Harcourt Schl. Pubs.

—Matematicas Mi Ventaja: Practice Workbook. 99th ed. 1998. (SPA., Illus.). pap. 11.50 (978-0-15-310768-9(5)); (gr. 3). pap. 13.60 (978-0-15-310771-9(5)); (gr. 4). pap. 13.60 (978-0-15-310772-6(3)); (gr. 5). pap. 13.60 (978-0-15-310773-3(1)); (gr. 6). pap. 13.60 (978-0-15-310774-0(X)) Harcourt Schl. Pubs.

—Matematicas Mi Ventaja: Problem Solving Workbook. 99th ed. 1998. (SPA., Illus.). (gr. 1). pap., wbk. ed. 12.30 (978-0-15-311254-6(9)); (gr. 2). pap., wbk. ed. 12.30 (978-0-15-311255-3(7)); (gr. 4). pap., wbk. ed. 13.80 (978-0-15-311257-7(3)); (gr. 5). pap., wbk. ed. 13.80 (978-0-15-311258-4(1)); (gr. 6). pap., wbk. ed. 13.80 (978-0-15-311259-1(X)) Harcourt Schl. Pubs.

—Matematicas Mi Ventaja: Problem Solving workbook. 99th ed. 1998. (SPA., Illus.). (gr. 3). pap., wbk. ed. 13.80 (978-0-15-311256-0(5)) Harcourt Schl. Pubs.

—Matematicas Mi Ventaja: Reteaching Workbook. 99th ed. 1998. (SPA., Illus.). (gr. 1). pap., wbk. ed. 13.80 (978-0-15-311242-3(5)); (gr. 2). pap., wbk. ed. 13.80 (978-0-15-311243-0(3)); (gr. 3). pap., wbk. ed. 14.70 (978-0-15-311244-7(1)); (gr. 4). pap., wbk. ed. 14.70 (978-0-15-311245-4(X)); (gr. 5). pap., wbk. ed. 14.70 (978-0-15-311246-1(8)); (gr. 6). pap., wbk. ed. 15.50 (978-0-15-311247-8(6)) Harcourt Schl. Pubs.

—Matematicas Mi Ventaja: School-Home Connections. 99th ed. 1999. (SPA., Illus.). pap. 12.00 (978-0-15-311273-7(5)); (gr. 1). pap. 12.00 (978-0-15-311274-4(3)); (gr. 2). pap. 12.00 (978-0-15-311275-1(1)); (gr. 3). pap. 12.00 (978-0-15-311276-8(X)); (gr. 4). pap. 12.00 (978-0-15-311277-5(8)); (gr. 5). pap. 12.00 (978-0-15-311278-2(6)); (gr. 6). pap. 12.00 (978-0-15-311279-9(4)) Harcourt Schl. Pubs.

—Matematicas Mi Ventaja: Standardized Test Preparation. 99th ed. 2001. (SPA., Illus.). (gr. 1). pap. 9.20 (978-0-15-320617-7(9)); (gr. 2). pap. 9.20 (978-0-15-320618-4(7)); (gr. 3). pap. 10.90 (978-0-15-320619-1(5)); (gr. 4). pap. 10.90 (978-0-15-320620-7(9)); (gr. 5). pap. 10.90 (978-0-15-320621-4(7)) Harcourt Schl. Pubs.

—Matematicas Mi Ventaja: TAAS Practice Test. 99th ed. 1999. (SPA., Illus.). (gr. 1). pap. 8.60 (978-0-15-311290-4(5)); (gr. 2). pap. 8.60 (978-0-15-311291-1(3)); (gr. 3). pap. 8.60 (978-0-15-311292-8(1)); (gr. 4). pap. 8.60 (978-0-15-311293-5(X)); (gr. 5). pap. 8.60 (978-0-15-311294-2(8)); (gr. 6). pap. 8.60 (978-0-15-311295-9(6)) Harcourt Schl. Pubs.

—Matematicas Mi Ventaja: Texas Edition. 99th ed. 1998. (SPA., Illus.). (gr. 1). pap. 44.80 (978-0-15-309967-0(4)); (gr. 2). pap. 44.80 (978-0-15-309968-7(2)); (gr. 3). 84.70 (978-0-15-309969-4(0)); (gr. 4). 84.70 (978-0-15-309970-0(4)); (gr. 5). 84.70 (978-0-15-309971-7(2)); (gr. 6). 84.70 (978-0-15-309972-4(0)) Harcourt Schl. Pubs.

—Matematicas Mi Ventaja, Grade 3 Vol. 2: Texas Edition. 99th ed. 1998. (SPA.). tchr. ed. 199.30 (978-0-15-310631-6(X)) Harcourt Schl. Pubs.

—Matematicas Mi Ventaja, Grade 4 Vol. 2: Texas Edition. 99th ed. 1998. (SPA.). tchr. ed. 216.00 (978-0-15-310632-3(8)) Harcourt Schl. Pubs.

—Matematicas Mi Ventaja, Grade 5 Vol. 2: Texas Edition. 99th ed. 1998. (SPA.). tchr. ed. 216.00 (978-0-15-310633-0(6)) Harcourt Schl. Pubs.

—Math: National Pupils Edition. 3rd ed. 2002. (gr. 2). 36.70 (978-0-15-334741-2(4)); (gr. 3). 66.70 (978-0-15-334742-9(2)) Harcourt Schl. Pubs.

—Math: Problem Solving/Reading Strategies. 2nd ed. 2002. (Harcourt Math Ser.). (gr. 3 up). pap., tchr. ed., wbk. ed. 23.00 (978-0-15-320831-7(7)); (gr. 3 up). pap., wbk. ed. 10.50 (978-0-15-320827-0(9)); (gr. 4 up). pap., tchr. ed., wbk. ed. 23.00 (978-0-15-320832-4(5)); (gr. 4 up). pap., wbk. ed. 10.50 (978-0-15-320828-7(7)); (gr. 5 up). pap., tchr. ed., wbk. ed. 24.00 (978-0-15-320833-1(3)); (gr. 6 up). pap., tchr. ed., wbk. ed. 25.80 (978-0-15-320834-8(1)); (gr. 6 up). pap., wbk. ed. 11.50 (978-0-15-320830-0(9)) Harcourt Schl. Pubs.

—Math: Problem Solving/Reading Strategies. 2nd ed. 2002. (J). (gr. 5). wbk. ed. 9.30 (978-0-15-320829-4(5)) Harcourt Trade Pubs.

—Math 2002: Chapter Books Grade K. 2nd ed. 2001. (Harcourt Math Ser.). (gr. k-6). pap., stu. ed., pupil's gde. ed. 28.10 (978-0-15-322049-4(X)) Harcourt Schl. Pubs.

—Math 2002: Unit Books Grade 1. 2nd ed. 2001. (Harcourt Math Ser.). (gr. 1 up). pap., stu. ed., pupil's gde. ed. 39.40 (978-0-15-322050-0(3)) Harcourt Schl. Pubs.

—Math 2002: Unit Books Grade 2. 2nd ed. 2001. (Harcourt Math Ser.). (gr. 2 up). pap., stu. ed., pupil's gde. ed. 39.40 (978-0-15-322051-7(1)) Harcourt Schl. Pubs.

—Math 2004: National Pupils Edition. 3rd ed. 2002. (gr. 4). 66.70 (978-0-15-334743-6(0)); (gr. 5). 66.70 (978-0-15-334744-3(9)); (gr. 6). 66.70 (978-0-15-334745-0(7)) Harcourt Schl. Pubs.

—Math Advantage: Answer & Solution Key. 99th ed. 1999. (Illus.). (gr. 6). pap. 22.70 (978-0-15-311148-8(8)); (gr. 7). pap. 22.70 (978-0-15-311149-5(6)); (gr. 8). pap. 22.70 (978-0-15-311152-5(6)) Harcourt Schl. Pubs.

—Math Advantage: Enrichment Workbook. 99th ed. 1999. (Illus.). (gr. 1). pap., wbk. ed. 11.50 (978-0-15-311079-5(1)); (gr. 2). pap., wbk. ed. 11.50 (978-0-15-311080-1(5)); (gr. 3). pap., wbk. ed. 12.30 (978-0-15-311081-8(3)); (gr. 4). pap., wbk. ed. 12.30 (978-0-15-311082-5(1)); (gr. 5). pap., wbk. ed. 13.10 (978-0-15-311083-2(X)); (gr. 6). pap., wbk. ed. 13.90 (978-0-15-311084-9(8)); (gr. 7). pap., wbk. ed. 13.90 (978-0-15-311085-6(6)); (gr. 8). pap., wbk. ed. 13.90 (978-0-15-311086-3(4)) Harcourt Schl. Pubs.

—Math Advantage: FCAT Daily Practice. 98th ed. 1998. (Illus.). (gr. 3). pap. 10.00 (978-0-15-310676-7(X)); (gr. 4). pap. 10.00 (978-0-15-310677-4(8)) Harcourt Schl. Pubs.

—Math Advantage: GA Chapter Books with Manipulatives Pouch. 99th ed. 2000. (Illus.). pap. 33.20 (978-0-15-321541-4(0)) Harcourt Schl. Pubs.

—Math Advantage: Georgia Test Preparation. 99th ed. 2001. (Illus.). (gr. 1). pap. 9.30 (978-0-15-321593-3(3)); (gr. 2). pap. 9.30 (978-0-15-321594-0(1)); (gr. 3). pap. 9.30 (978-0-15-321595-7(X)); (gr. 4). pap. 9.30 (978-0-15-321596-4(8)); (gr. 5). pap. 9.30 (978-0-15-321597-1(6)) Harcourt Schl. Pubs.

—Math Advantage: Ohio Proficiency Test Practice. 1999. (Illus.). (YA). (gr. 7). pap. 6.90 (978-0-15-317486-5(2)); (YA). (gr. 8). pap. 6.90 (978-0-15-317487-2(0)); 99th ed. (gr. 1). pap. 8.10 (978-0-15-317478-0(1)); 99th ed. (gr. 2). pap. 8.10 (978-0-15-317479-7(X)); 99th ed. (gr. 3). pap. 8.60 (978-0-15-317481-0(1)); 99th ed. (gr. 4). pap. 8.60 (978-0-15-317482-7(X)); 99th ed. (gr. 5). pap. 8.60 (978-0-15-317483-4(8)); 99th ed. (gr. 6). pap. 8.60 (978-0-15-317484-1(6)) Harcourt Schl. Pubs.

—Math Advantage: Practice for Standardized Tests: Alabama Edition. 98th ed. 1999. (Illus.). (gr. 1). pap. 20.50 (978-0-15-311307-9(3)); (gr. 2). pap. 20.50 (978-0-15-311308-6(1)); (gr. 3). pap. 18.90 (978-0-15-311309-3(X)); (gr. 4). pap. 20.50 (978-0-15-311310-9(3)); (gr. 6). pap. 20.50 (978-0-15-311312-3(X)); (gr. 7). pap. 20.50 (978-0-15-311313-0(8)); (gr. 8). pap. 20.50 (978-0-15-311314-7(6)) Harcourt Schl. Pubs.

—Math Advantage: Practice for Standardized Tests: Alabama Practice. 98th ed. 1999. (Illus.). (gr. 5). pap. 18.90 (978-0-15-311311-6(1)) Harcourt Schl. Pubs.

—Math Advantage: Practice for Stanford 9: Virginia Edition. 99th ed. 1998. (Illus.). (gr. 1). pap. 9.30 (978-0-15-313748-8(7)); (gr. 2). pap. 9.30 (978-0-15-313749-5(5)); (gr. 3). pap. 9.30 (978-0-15-313750-1(9)); (gr. 4). pap. 9.30 (978-0-15-313751-8(7)); (gr. 5). pap. 9.30 (978-0-15-313752-5(5)); (gr. 6). pap. 9.30 (978-0-15-313753-2(3)); (gr. 7). pap. 9.30 (978-0-15-313754-9(1)); (gr. 8). pap. 9.30 (978-0-15-313755-6(X)) Harcourt Schl. Pubs.

—Math Advantage: Practice New York State Math Test. 99th ed. 1999. (Illus.). (gr. 4). pap. 9.10 (978-0-15-315659-5(7)) Harcourt Schl. Pubs.

—Math Advantage: Practice New York State Math Test Package. 1999. (Illus.). (J). pap. 23.00 (978-0-15-315660-1(0)) Harcourt Schl. Pubs.

—Math Advantage: Practice Standardized Test. 99th ed. (Illus.). 1999. (gr. 6). pap. 10.00 (978-0-15-314490-5(4)); 1999. (gr. 8). pap. 10.00 (978-0-15-314492-9(0)); 1998. (gr. 1). pap. 8.20 (978-0-15-314485-1(8)); 1998. (gr. 2). pap. 8.20 (978-0-15-314486-8(6)); 1998. (gr. 3). pap. 10.00 (978-0-15-314487-5(4)); 1998. (gr. 4). pap. 10.00 (978-0-15-314488-2(2)); 1998. (gr. 5). pap. 10.00 (978-0-15-314489-9(0)); 1998. (gr. 7). pap. 10.00 (978-0-15-314491-2(2)) Harcourt Schl. Pubs.

—Math Advantage: Practice Workbook. (Illus.). 98th ed. 1999. (gr. 3). pap., wbk. ed. 11.30 (978-0-15-307930-6(4)); 98th ed. 1999. (gr. 4). pap., wbk. ed. 11.30 (978-0-15-307931-3(2)); 98th ed. 1998. (gr. 5). pap., wbk. ed. 11.40 (978-0-15-307932-0(0)); 98th ed. 1998. (gr. 2). pap., wbk. ed. 10.30 (978-0-15-307929-0(0)); 98th ed. 1998. (gr. 7). pap., wbk. ed. 11.60 (978-0-15-307934-4(7)); 99th ed. 2002. (gr. 1). pap. 9.90 (978-0-15-311039-9(2)); 99th ed. 2001. (gr. 5). pap. 11.30 (978-0-15-311045-0(7)); 99th ed. 1999. pap. 8.40 (978-0-15-311038-2(4)); 99th ed. 1999. (gr. 2). pap. 9.90 (978-0-15-311042-9(2)); 99th ed. 1999. (gr. 3). pap. 10.60 (978-0-15-311043-6(0)); 99th ed. 1999. (gr. 4). pap. 10.60 (978-0-15-311044-3(9)); 99th ed. 1999. (gr. 6). pap. 11.50 (978-0-15-311047-4(3)); 99th ed. 1999. (gr. 7). pap. 11.50 (978-0-15-311048-1(1)); 99th ed. 1999. (gr. 8). pap. 11.50 (978-0-15-311049-8(X)) Harcourt Schl. Pubs.

—Math Advantage: Problem Solving Workbook. 99th ed. 1999. (Illus.). (gr. 1). pap., wbk. ed. 9.80 (978-0-15-311095-5(3)); (gr. 2). pap., wbk. ed. 9.80 (978-0-15-311096-2(1)); (gr. 3). pap., wbk. ed. 10.80 (978-0-15-311097-9(X)); (gr. 4). pap., wbk. ed. 10.80 (978-0-15-311098-6(8)); (gr. 5). pap., wbk. ed. 11.40 (978-0-15-311099-3(6)); (J). (gr. 6). pap., wbk. ed. 9.60 (978-0-15-311100-6(3)); (YA). (gr. 7). pap., wbk. ed. 9.60 (978-0-15-311101-3(1)); (YA). (gr. 8). pap., wbk. ed. 9.60 (978-0-15-311102-0(X)) Harcourt Schl. Pubs.

—Math Advantage: Proficiency Practice Test: Ohio Edition. 99th ed. (Illus.). 1999. (gr. 4). pap. 12.10 (978-0-15-313332-9(5)); 1999. (gr. 8). pap. 12.10 (978-0-15-313336-7(8)); 1998. (gr. 1). pap. 12.10 (978-0-15-313329-9(5)); 1998. (gr. 2). pap. 12.10 (978-0-15-313330-5(9)); 1998. (gr. 3). pap. 12.10 (978-0-15-313331-2(7)); 1998. (gr. 5). pap. 12.10 (978-0-15-313333-6(3)); 1998. (gr. 6). pap. 12.10 (978-0-15-313334-3(1)); 1998. (gr. 7). pap. 12.10 (978-0-15-313335-0(X)) Harcourt Schl. Pubs.

—Math Advantage: Reproducible Chapters Without Manipulatives. 98th ed. 1998. (Illus.). pap. 27.50 (978-0-15-309933-5(X)) Harcourt Schl. Pubs.

—Math Advantage: Reteaching Workbook. 99th ed. 1999. (Illus.). (gr. 1). pap., wbk. ed. 11.50 (978-0-15-311059-7(7)); (gr. 2). pap., wbk. ed. 11.50 (978-0-15-311064-1(3)); (gr. 3). pap., wbk. ed. 12.30 (978-0-15-311065-8(1)); (gr. 4). pap., wbk. ed. 12.30 (978-0-15-311066-5(X)); (gr. 5). pap., wbk. ed. 13.10 (978-0-15-311067-2(8)); (gr. 6). pap., wbk. ed. 13.90 (978-0-15-311068-9(6)); (gr. 7). pap., wbk. ed. 13.90 (978-0-15-311069-6(4)); (gr. 8). pap., wbk. ed. 13.90 (978-0-15-311070-2(8)) Harcourt Schl. Pubs.

—Math Advantage: School-Home Connection. 99th ed. 1999. (Illus.). pap. 10.20 (978-0-15-311139-6(9)); (gr. 1). pap. 10.20 (978-0-15-311140-2(2)); (gr. 2). pap. 10.20 (978-0-15-311141-9(0)); (gr. 3). pap. 10.20 (978-0-15-311142-6(9)); (gr. 4). pap. 10.20 (978-0-15-311143-3(7)); (gr. 5). pap. 10.20 (978-0-15-311144-0(5)); (gr. 6). pap. 10.20 (978-0-15-311145-7(3)); (gr. 7). pap. 10.20 (978-0-15-311146-4(1)); (gr. 8). pap. 10.20 (978-0-15-311147-1(X)) Harcourt Schl. Pubs.

—Math Advantage: Texas Edition. 99th ed. 1999. (Illus.). (gr. 4). pap. 75.80 (978-0-15-310695-8(6)); pap. 26.70 (978-0-15-310691-0(3)); (gr. 1). pap. 39.10 (978-0-15-310692-7(1)); (gr. 2). pap. 39.10 (978-0-15-310693-4(X)); (gr. 3). pap. 74.20 (978-0-15-310694-1(8)); (gr. 5). pap. 75.80 (978-0-15-310696-5(4)); (gr. 6). pap. 75.80 (978-0-15-310697-2(2)); (gr. 7). pap. 80.60 (978-0-15-310698-9(0)); (gr. 8). pap. 80.60 (978-0-15-310699-6(9)) Harcourt Schl. Pubs.

—Math Advantage: Topeka Library Edition. 98th ed. 1999. (Illus.). (gr. 1). 101.60 (978-0-15-311939-2(X)); (gr. 2). 97.10 (978-0-15-311943-9(8)) Harcourt Schl. Pubs.

—Math Advantage: With Manipulatives Pouch: GA Edition. 99th ed. 2000. (Illus.). pap. 33.20 (978-0-15-321542-1(9)); (gr. 1). pap. 41.40 (978-0-15-321543-8(7)); (gr. 2). pap. 41.40 (978-0-15-321544-5(5)) Harcourt Schl. Pubs.

—Math Advantage Bks. 7-12: Special FL Unit Package Chapter Books. 99th ed. 1999. (Illus.). pap. 16.50 (978-0-15-317767-5(5)) Harcourt Schl. Pubs.

—Math Advantage Companion: Mississippi Edition. 99th ed. 2001. (Illus.). pap. 26.90 (978-0-15-322810-0(5)); (gr. 1). pap. 41.60 (978-0-15-322811-7(3)); (gr. 2). pap. 41.60 (978-0-15-322812-4(1)); (gr. 3). pap. 55.50 (978-0-15-322813-1(X)); (gr. 4). pap. 51.70 (978-0-15-322814-8(8)); (gr. 5). pap. 51.70 (978-0-15-322815-5(6)); (gr. 6). pap. 51.70 (978-0-15-322816-2(4)) Harcourt Schl. Pubs.

—Math Advantage, Grade 1. 99th ed. 1998. Vol. 1. pap., tchr. ed. 138.90 (978-0-15-311446-5(0)); Vol. 2. pap., tchr. ed. 138.90 (978-0-15-311447-2(9)) Harcourt Schl. Pubs.

—Math Advantage, Grade 1: Enrichment Workbook. 99th ed. 1999. pap., tchr. ed., wbk. ed. 24.70 (978-0-15-311087-0(2)) Harcourt Schl. Pubs.

—Math Advantage, Grade 1: GA Edition, Vol. 1. 99th ed. 1999. tchr. ed. 153.00 (978-0-15-321271-0(3)) Harcourt Schl. Pubs.

—Math Advantage, Grade 1: Georgia Test Preparation. 99th ed. 2001. pap., tchr. ed. 21.00 (978-0-15-321598-8(4)) Harcourt Schl. Pubs.

—Math Advantage, Grade 2: Enrichment Workbook. 99th ed. 1999. pap., tchr. ed., wbk. ed. 24.70 (978-0-15-311088-7(0)) Harcourt Schl. Pubs.

—Math Advantage, Grade 2: Georgia Edition. 99th ed. Vol. 1. 2000. tchr. ed. 153.00 (978-0-15-321273-4(X)); Vol. 2. 2000. tchr. ed. 153.00 (978-0-15-321274-1(8)); Vol. 2. 1999. tchr. ed. 153.00 (978-0-15-321272-7(1)) Harcourt Schl. Pubs.

—Math Advantage, Grade 3. 99th ed. 1998. Vol. 1. tchr. ed. 138.90 (978-0-15-311450-2(9)); Vol. 2. pap., tchr. ed. 138.90 (978-0-15-311451-9(7)) Harcourt Schl. Pubs.

—Math Advantage, Grade 3: Enrichment Workbook. 99th ed. 1999. pap., tchr. ed., wbk. ed. 25.70 (978-0-15-311089-4(9)) Harcourt Schl. Pubs.

—Math Advantage, Grade 3: Georgia Edition. 99th ed. 2000. Vol. 1. tchr. ed. 153.00 (978-0-15-321275-8(6)); Vol. 2. tchr. ed. 153.00 (978-0-15-321276-5(4)) Harcourt Schl. Pubs.

—Math Advantage, Grade 3: Georgia Test Preparation. 99th ed. 2001. pap., tchr. ed. 21.00 (978-0-15-321600-8(X)) Harcourt Schl. Pubs.

—Math Advantage, Grade 4. 99th ed. 1999. Vol. 1. pap., tchr. ed. 138.90 (978-0-15-311452-6(5)); Vol. 2. pap., tchr. ed. 138.90 (978-0-15-311453-3(3)) Harcourt Schl. Pubs.

—Math Advantage, Grade 4: Enrichment Workbook. 99th ed. 1999. pap., tchr. ed., wbk. ed. 25.70 (978-0-15-311090-0(2)) Harcourt Schl. Pubs.

—Math Advantage, Grade 4: Georgia Edition. 99th ed. Vol. 1. 1999. tchr. ed. 153.00 (978-0-15-321277-2(2)); Vol. 2. 2000. tchr. ed. 153.00 (978-0-15-321278-9(0)) Harcourt Schl. Pubs.

—Math Advantage, Grade 4: Georgia Test Preparation. 99th ed. 2001. pap., tchr. ed. 21.00 (978-0-15-321601-5(8)) Harcourt Schl. Pubs.

—Math Advantage, Grade 5. 99th ed. 1999. Vol. 1. pap., tchr. ed. 138.90 (978-0-15-311454-0(1)); Vol. 2. pap., tchr. ed. 138.90 (978-0-15-311455-7(X)) Harcourt Schl. Pubs.

—Math Advantage, Grade 5: Chapter Planner Guide: New Mexico Edition. 99th ed. 1999. pap., tchr. ed. 18.80 (978-0-15-317463-6(3)) Harcourt Schl. Pubs.

—Math Advantage, Grade 5: Enrichment Workbook. 99th ed. 1999. pap., tchr. ed., wbk. ed. 25.70 (978-0-15-311091-7(0)) Harcourt Schl. Pubs.

—Math Advantage, Grade 5: Georgia Edition. 99th ed. 1999. Vol. 1. pap., tchr. ed. 153.00 (978-0-15-321279-6(9)); Vol. 2. tchr. ed. 153.00 (978-0-15-321280-2(2)) Harcourt Schl. Pubs.

—Math Advantage, Grade 5: Georgia Lesson Planner. 99th ed. 2001. pap. 20.20 (978-0-15-321592-6(5)) Harcourt Schl. Pubs.

—Math Advantage, Grade 5: Georgia Test Preparation. 99th ed. 2001. pap., tchr. ed. 21.00 (978-0-15-321602-2(6)) Harcourt Schl. Pubs.

—Math Advantage, Grade 6: Chapter Planner Guide: New Mexico Edition. 99th ed. 1999. pap., tchr. ed. 18.80 (978-0-15-317464-3(1)) Harcourt Schl. Pubs.

—Math Advantage, Grade 6: Enrichment Workbook. 99th ed. 1999. pap., tchr. ed., wbk. ed. 28.30 (978-0-15-311092-4(9)) Harcourt Schl. Pubs.

—Math Advantage, Grade 7: Enrichment Workbook. 99th ed. 1999. pap., tchr. ed., wbk. ed. 28.30 (978-0-15-311093-1(7)) Harcourt Schl. Pubs.

—Math Advantage, Grade 8: Enrichment Workbook. 99th ed. 1999. pap., tchr. ed., wbk. ed. 28.30 (978-0-15-311094-8(5)) Harcourt Schl. Pubs.

—Math Advantage, Grade 8: Problem Solving Workbook. 99th ed. 1999. pap., tchr. ed., wbk. ed. 24.70 (978-0-15-311114-3(3)) Harcourt Schl. Pubs.

—Math Advantage, Grade K: GA Edition. 99th ed. 1999. tchr. ed. 215.40 (978-0-15-321270-3(5)) Harcourt Schl. Pubs.

—Math Advantage Super Value Package. 99th ed. 1999. (gr. k). pap. 2333.90 (978-0-15-314697-8(4)); (gr. 1). pap. 1790.60 (978-0-15-314698-5(2)); (gr. 2). pap. 1790.60 (978-0-15-314699-2(0)); (gr. 3). 2472.50 (978-0-15-314700-5(8)); (gr. 4). 2472.50 (978-0-15-314701-2(6)); (gr. 5). 2472.50 (978-0-15-314702-9(4)); (gr. 6). 2472.50 (978-0-15-314703-6(2)); (gr. 7). 2695.10 (978-0-15-314704-3(0)); (gr. 8). 2695.10 (978-0-15-314705-0(9)) Harcourt Schl. Pubs.

—Math Unit Book Collection, Bks. 1-6. 2nd ed. 2002. (Illus.). (gr. 1). pap. 38.20 (978-0-15-337518-7(3)); (gr. 2). pap. 38.20 (978-0-15-337519-4(1)) Harcourt Schl. Pubs.

—Michigan. 2nd ed. 2002. (Horizons Ser.). (gr. 4). pap., act. bk. ed. 10.40 (978-0-15-335735-0(5)) Harcourt Schl. Pubs.

—Michigan Activity Book: Answer Book. 2nd ed. 2002. (gr. 4). pap. 14.10 (978-0-15-335736-7(3)) Harcourt Schl. Pubs.

—Patterns in Nature: Little Big Book. 2nd ed. 2002. (Harcourt Math Ser.). (Illus.). (gr. k). pap. 62.40 (978-0-15-321264-2(0)) Harcourt Schl. Pubs.

—Practice Book/Intervention Solution. 2nd ed. 2002. (J). (gr. 5). pap. 9.70 (978-0-15-338249-9(X)) Harcourt Trade Pubs.

—Practice Workbook Math 2002: Grade 3. 2nd ed. 2002. (Harcourt Math Ser.). (gr. 3 up). pap., tchr. ed., wbk. ed. 22.00 (978-0-15-320795-2(7)) Harcourt Schl. Pubs.

—Problem Solving. 4th ed. 2004. pap., tchr.'s training gde. ed. 54.90 (978-0-15-341942-3(3)); pap., pupil's gde. ed. 13.70 (978-0-15-341943-0(1)) Harcourt Schl. Pubs.

—Problem Solving for Reading Strategies Workbook Harcourt. 2nd ed. 2002. pap., wbk. ed. 10.00 (978-0-15-336522-5(6)) Harcourt Schl. Pubs.

—Standard Based Proficiency Math: 10 Package. 2002. (J). (gr. 1). pap. (978-0-7398-7126-3(9)) Steck-Vaughn.

—Standard Based Proficiency Math, Grade 1. 2002. pap., tchr. ed. (978-0-7398-7125-6(0)) Steck-Vaughn.

—Standard Based Proficiency Math, Grade 2. 2002. pap., tchr. ed. (978-0-7398-7128-7(5)) Steck-Vaughn.

—Standard Based Proficiency Math, Grade 3. 2002. pap., tchr. ed. (978-0-7398-7131-7(5)) Steck-Vaughn.

—Standard Based Proficiency Math, Grade 4. 2002. pap., tchr. ed. (978-0-7398-7134-8(X)) Steck-Vaughn.

—Standard Based Proficiency Math, Grade 5. 2002. pap., tchr. ed. (978-0-7398-7137-9(4)) Steck-Vaughn.

—Success for Ell: Harcourt Math. 2nd ed. 2002. (gr. 3). pap. 30.80 (978-0-15-336545-4(5)) Harcourt Schl. Pubs.

—Test Best CATS Math: Grade 1. 2002. pap. (978-0-7398-72?5-2(4)); pap., tchr. ed. (978-0-7398-7237-6(0)) Steck-Vaughn.

—Test Best CATS Math: Grade 2. 2002. pap. (978-0-7398-7238-3(9)); pap., tchr. ed. (978-0-7398-7240-6(0)) Steck-Vaughn.

—Test Best CATS Math: Grade 3. 2002. pap. (978-0-7398-7241-3(9)); pap., tchr. ed. (978-0-7398-7243-7(5)) Steck-Vaughn.

—Test Best CATS Math: Grade 4. 2002. pap. (978-0-7398-7245-1(1)); pap., tchr. ed. (978-0-7398-7247-5(8)) Steck-Vaughn.

—Test Best CATS Math: Grade 5. 2002. pap. (978-0-7398-7248-2(6)); pap., tchr. ed. (978-0-7398-7250-5(8)) Steck-Vaughn.

—Test Best CATS Math: Grade 6. 2002. pap. (978-0-7398-7251-2(6)); pap., tchr. ed. (978-0-7398-7253-6(2)) Steck-Vaughn.

—Test Best Sol Math Gade 7. 2002. pap., tchr. ed. (978-0-7398-7469-1(1)) Steck-Vaughn.

—Test Best Sol Math Grade 1. 2002. pap., tchr. ed. (978-0-7398-7451-6(9)) Steck-Vaughn.

—Test Best Sol Math Grade 6. 2002. pap., tchr. ed. (978-0-7398-7466-0(7)) Steck-Vaughn.

Harnadek, Anita. Math Word Problems Level A- Whole Numbers & Fractions. 2003. (J). pap. 13.99 (978-0-89455-820-7(X)) Critical Thinking Bks. & Software.

—Math Word Problems Level B- Decimals/Percents. 2004. (J). pap. 13.99 (978-0-89455-821-4(8)) Critical Thinking Bks. & Software.

—Math Word Problems Level C- Mixed Concepts: Whole Numbers-Percents. 2004. (YA). pap. 13.99 (978-0-89455-822-1(6)) Critical Thinking Bks. & Software.

Harrison, Paul & Montague-Smith, Ann. Extension for all through Problem Solving. 2003. (Apex Maths Ser.: Vol. 4). (Illus.). 48p. pap., stu. ed. 10.00 (978-0-521-75492-7(5)); pap., stu. ed. 10.00 (978-0-521-75494-1(1)) Cambridge Univ. Pr.

—Extension for All through Problem Solving. 2003. (Apex Maths Ser.: Vol. 6). (Illus.). 48p. pap., stu. ed. 10.00 (978-0-521-75496-5(8)) Cambridge Univ. Pr.

Harrison, Paul & Mumford, Jeanette. Math Extension Activities for Year 6 Plus. 2004. (Illus.). 144p. pap., stu. ed. 14.00 (978-0-521-54290-6(1)) Cambridge Univ. Pr.

Harrison, Sharon, et al. Mathemateg Newydd Caergrawnt. 2005. (WEL., Illus.). 32p. (978-1-86085-272-5(6)) ICA Video.

Hartley, Susan. I Have It! 2nd rev. ed. 2003. (StartUp Ser.). (J). pap. 22.00 (978-1-4108-0720-5(7)) Benchmark Education Co.

Hartley, William. Practice Math Vol. 1: Skill Building for School & Home, 4 vols. 2000. 48p. (J). (gr. 4). pap. 6.95 (978-1-58324-054-0(3) , World Teachers Pr.) Didax Educational Resources, Inc.

—Practice Math Vol. 2: Skill Building for School & Home, 4 vols. 2000. 48p. (J). (gr. 5). pap. 6.95 (978-1-58324-055-7(1) , World Teachers Pr.) Didax Educational Resources, Inc.

—Practice Math Vol. 3: Skill Building for School & Home, 4 vols. 2000. 48p. (J). (gr. 6). pap. 6.95 (978-1-58324-056-4(X) , World Teachers Pr.) Didax Educational Resources, Inc.

—Practice Math Vol. 4: Skill Building for School & Home, 4 vols. 2000. 48p. (YA). (gr. 7). pap. 6.95 (978-1-58324-057-1(8) , World Teachers Pr.) Didax Educational Resources, Inc.

Hartley, William D. & Linderman, Bill. Math Practice. 1999. (100+ Ser.). 128p. (J). (gr. 5-6). pap. 12.99 (978-0-88012-817-9(8) , IF8741) School Specialty Publishing.

Hartman, Bob & Patmore, Mark. Maths Workout: For Homework & Practice. 1999. (Illus.). 64p. (gr. 6-9). pap., tchr. ed., stu. ed. 9.00 (978-0-521-63489-2(X)) Cambridge Univ. Pr.

—Maths Workout Bk. 4: For Homework & Practice. 2000. (Illus.). 63p. pap., tchr. ed., stu. ed. 9.00 (978-0-521-63486-1(5)) Cambridge Univ. Pr.

—Maths Workout Bk. 5: For Homework & Practice. 2000. (Illus.). 64p. pap., tchr. ed., stu. ed. 9.00 (978-0-521-63485-4(7)) Cambridge Univ. Pr.

—Maths Workout Bk. 6: For Homework & Practice. 2000. (Illus.). 70p. pap., tchr. ed., stu. ed. 9.00 (978-0-521-63484-7(9)) Cambridge Univ. Pr.

Haugen, Janie. Menu Math Complete Set, 3 vols., Set. Britt, Melissa, ed. 1999. (Illus.). 300p. (J). rnfg bd. 169.95 (978-1-884074-74-5(X) , PCI 906) PCI Educational Publishing.

Hausmann, Gisela. Hands on Mathemagical Dice. 2005. (Illus.). 30p. (J). cd-rom 13.00 (978-0-9664217-4-3(4)) Educ-Easy Bks.

Hay muchos circulos Math. 6 vols.Tr. of So Many Circles Math. (SPA.). (gr. k-2). 28.95 (978-0-7368-3123-9(1) , Yellow Umbrella Bks.) Capstone Pr., Inc.

HB. Math Plus. 1998. (gr. 7). pap., wbk. ed. 19.00 (978-0-15-305107-4(8)); 92nd ed. (gr. 2). pap., stu. ed. 41.10 (978-0-15-300139-0(9)) Harcourt Schl. Pubs.

Head, Debby & Pollett, Libby. BBY Practice Pages: Addition Facts 0-10. 2004. (Illus.). 93p. spiral bd. 29.00 (978-1-885775-20-7(2)) BBY Pubns.

—BBY Practice Pages: Addition Facts 11-20. 2004. (Illus.). 93p. spiral bd. 29.00 (978-1-885775-26-9(1)) BBY Pubns.

—BBY Practice Pages: Beginning Addition 0-10. 2004. 93p. spiral bd. 29.00 (978-1-885775-24-5(5)) BBY Pubns.

—BBY Practice Pages: Making Change Through $1. 00. 2004. (Illus.). 95p. spiral bd. 29.00 (978-1-885775-28-3(8)) BBY Pubns.

—BBY Practice Pages: Subtraction Facts 0-10. 2004. (Illus.). 93p. spiral bd. 29.00 (978-1-885775-21-4(0)) BBY Pubns.

—BBY Practice Pages: Subtraction Facts 11-20. 2004. (Illus.). 94p. spiral bd. 29.00 (978-1-885775-27-6(X)) BBY Pubns.

Hein, Marilyn B. Math Phonics - Addition & Subtraction Bonus Book. Mitchell, Judy, ed. Wheeler, Ron, illus. 2002. 96p. (J). (gr. 1-3). pap. 9.95 (978-1-57310-345-9(4)) Teaching & Learning Co.

—Math Phonics - Fractions & Decimals Bonus Book. Mitchell, Judy, ed. Wheeler, Ron, illus. 2002. 96p. (J). pap. 9.95 (978-1-57310-347-3(0)) Teaching & Learning Co.

—Math Phonics Pre-Algebra. Wheeler, Ron, illus. 2004. 96p. (J). pap. 10.65 (978-1-57310-438-8(8)) Teaching & Learning Co.

Hepker, Sue. Baby Monkey's Bananas: Kiswahili Version. Mhando, Harold, tr. 1999. (Cambridge Reading Routes Ser.). (Illus.). 16p. pap. 3.70 (978-0-521-66889-7(1)) Cambridge Univ. Pr.

—A Long Way to Baba: Kiswahili Version. Mulokozi, M. M., tr. 1999. (Cambridge Reading Routes Ser.). (Illus.). 16p. pap. 3.70 (978-0-521-66888-0(3)) Cambridge Univ. Pr.

—A Long Way to Baba Oromo Version. Buse, Abdurahim Adem, tr. 1999. (Cambridge Reading Routes Ser.). (Illus.). 16p. pap. 3.70 (978-0-521-66842-2(5)) Cambridge Univ. Pr.

—Mama Mabena's Magic: Oromo Version. Buse, Abdurahim Adem, tr. 1999. (Cambridge Reading Routes Ser.). (Illus.). 16p. pap. 3.70 (978-0-521-66844-6(1)) Cambridge Univ. Pr.

Heranz, Carlos Andradas. Pongame un Kilo de Matem Gicas. 2001. (Barco de Vapor). (SPA., Illus.). 126p. (YA). (978-84-348-7155-7(6)) SM Ediciones ESP. *Dist:* AIMS International Bks., Inc.

Higgs, Angela. Math Minutes Grade 2, 2584. Wright, Marsha, ed. Hillam, Corbin & Grayson, Rick, illus. 2002. 112p. (J). (gr. 2). pap. 12.99 (978-1-57471-813-3(4) , CTP 2584) Creative Teaching Pr., Inc.

Highlights for Children Editorial Staff. Mathmania. (Illus.). 48p. (YA). Vol. 3. 2003. pap. 5.95 (978-0-87534-933-6(1)); Vol. 4. 2003. pap. 5.95 (978-0-87534-934-3(X)); Vol. 13. 2004. (gr. 4-7). pap., act. bk. ed. 5.95 (978-0-87534-945-9(5)); Vol. 14. 2004. (gr. 4-7). pap., act. bk. ed. 5.95 (978-0-87534-946-6(3)); Vol. 15. 2004. (gr. 4-7). pap., act. bk. ed. 5.95 (978-0-87534-969-5(2)); Vol. 16. 2004. (gr. 4-7). pap., act. bk. ed. 5.95 (978-0-87534-970-1(6)) Highlights for Children.

Highlights for Children Editorial Staff, compiled by. Mathmania. 2003. (Illus.). 48p. (YA). Vol. 5. pap. 5.95 (978-0-87534-935-0(8)); Vol. 6. pap. 5.95 (978-0-87534-936-7(6)); Vol. 7. pap. 5.95 (978-0-87534-937-4(4)); Vol. 8. pap. 5.95 (978-0-87534-938-1(2)) Highlights for Children.

Hironaka, Heisuke & Sugiyama, Yoshishige, eds. Tokyo Shoseki's Mathematics 4 for Elementary School (Grade 4A & 4B, 2 vol. Set) 2006. Orig. Title: Atarashii Sansuu 4 (Jo/Ge). pap. 24.99 (978-1-934046-04-3(3)) Global Education Resources, LLC.

—Tokyo Shoseki's Mathematics 5 for Elementary School (Grades 5A & 5B, 2 vol. Set) 2006. Orig. Title: Atarashii Sansuu 5 (Jo/Ge). pap. 24.99 (978-1-934046-05-0(1)) Global Education Resources, LLC.

—Tokyo Shoseki's Mathematics 6 for Elementary School (Grade 6A & 6B, 2 vol. Set) 2006. Orig. Title: Atarashii Sansuu 6 (Jo/Ge). pap. 24.99 (978-1-934046-06-7(X)) Global Education Resources, LLC.

Hirschmann, Kris. Mathemagic. 2002. (Necco Sweethearts Ser.). (Illus.). 32p. (J). (gr. 2-4). pap. 5.99 (978-0-439-36538-3(4) , Cartwheel Bks.) Scholastic, Inc.

Hlodan, Oksana. Monster Math Multiplication Workbook. Cherbak, Yvonne, illus. 1998. (Monster Math Ser.). 64p. (J). (ps-3). pap., wbk. ed. 4.95 (978-1-56565-678-9(4) , 06784W) Lowell Hse. Juvenile.

—Monster Math Super Edition for Ages 4-6. Cherbak, Yvonne, illus. 2000. (Monster Math Super Editions Ser.). 256p. (J). (ps-1). pap. 14.95 (978-0-7373-0214-1(3) , 02143W) Lowell Hse. Juvenile.

—Puzzles & Games. Cherbak, Yvonne, illus. 1998. (Monster Math Ser.). 64p. (J). (ps-3). pap., wbk. ed. 4.95 (978-1-56565-845-5(0) , 08450W) Lowell Hse. Juvenile.

—Puzzles & Games, Bk. 2. 1999. (Monster Math Workbook Ser.: Vol. 2). (Illus.). 64p. (J). (ps-1). pap., wbk. ed. 4.95 (978-0-7373-0212-7(7) , 02127W) McGraw-Hill/Contemporary.

HM Group Staff. HMS Math. 2000. 68p. pap., tchr. ed. 9.95 (978-0-8108-3807-9(9)) Scarecrow Pr., Inc.

Ho, Oliver. Amazing Math Magic. Sinclair, Jeff, illus. 2002. 96p. (gr. 3-7). pap. 5.95 (978-0-8069-7413-2(3)) Sterling Publishing Co., Inc.

Hobbs, Chris & Perryman, Richard. The Largest Number Smaller Than Five. 2007. (ENG.). 128p. per. 19.99 ***(978-1-4303-0630-6(0))*** Lulu.com.

Hofmeyr, Dianne. Mama Mabena's Magic: Amharic Version. Wako, Tegegn Nuresu, tr. 1999. (Cambridge Reading Routes Ser.). (AMH., Illus.). 16p. pap. 3.70 (978-0-521-66827-9(1)) Cambridge Univ. Pr.

—Mama Mabena's Magic: Kiswahili Version. Lihamba, Amandina, tr. 1999. (Cambridge Reading Routes Ser.). (Illus.). 16p. pap. 3.70 (978-0-521-66895-8(6)) Cambridge Univ. Pr.

—Mama Mabena's Magic: Sepedi Version. 2002. (Illus.). 16p. pap. 1.75 (978-0-521-52841-2(0)) Cambridge Univ. Pr.

—Mama Mabena's Magic: Sesotho Version. 2002. (Illus.). 16p. pap. 1.75 (978-0-521-52838-2(0)) Cambridge Univ. Pr.

—Mama Mabena's Magic: Setswana Version. 2002. (Illus.). 16p. pap. 1.75 (978-0-521-52839-9(9)) Cambridge Univ. Pr.

—Mama Mabena's Magic: Tigre Version. Kebebew, Amare Hagos, tr. 1999. (Cambridge Reading Routes Ser.). (TIG., Illus.). 16p. pap. 3.70 (978-0-521-66817-0(4)) Cambridge Univ. Pr.

—Mama Mabena's Magic: Xitsonga Version. 2002. (Illus.). 16p. pap. 1.75 (978-0-521-52840-5(2)) Cambridge Univ. Pr.

Hogan, Paul, et al. Key Maths: Summary & Practice with Answers. 2nd ed. 2002. (Illus.). 176p. (YA). pap. 13.50 (978-0-7487-6739-7(8)) Nelson Thornes Ltd. GBR. *Dist:* Trans-Atlantic Pubns., Inc.

Holt, Rinehart and Winston Staff. Balanced Unit Assessment. 2003. (Mathematics in Context Ser.). (Illus.). (J). (gr. 5). stu. ed., ring bd. 71.86 (978-0-03-072434-3(1)) Holt, Rinehart & Winston.

—Balanced Unit Assessment: Supplemental Materials. 2003. (Mathematics in Context Ser.: No. 20). (Illus.). (YA). (gr. 8). stu. ed. 71.86 (978-0-03-072481-7(3)) Holt, Rinehart & Winston.

—Balanced Unit Assessment Binder: Supplemental Materials. 20th ed. 2003. (Mathematics in Context Ser.). (Illus.). (J). stu. ed. 71.86 (978-0-03-072446-6(5)) Holt, Rinehart & Winston.

—Decision Making: Math Context. 3rd ed. 2003. tchr. ed. 33.53 (978-0-03-071523-5(7)) Holt, Rinehart & Winston.

—Dry & Wet Numbers: Spanish. 2003. (Mathematics in Context Ser.). (SPA.). stu. ed. 7.86 (978-0-03-072343-8(4)) Holt, Rinehart & Winston.

—Esperanza Rising. 2nd ed. 2002. pap., stu. ed. 13.20 (978-0-03-066352-9(0)) Holt, Rinehart & Winston.

—Fraction Times. 2002. (Math in Context Ser.). stu. ed. 31.60 (978-0-7826-1508-1(2)) Encyclopaedia Britannica, Inc.

—Get the Most: Math/Context - Spanish Student Edition. 98th ed. 2002. 7.86 (978-0-85229-751-3(3)) Encyclopaedia Britannica, Inc.

—Going the Distance. 2002. (Math in Context Ser.). 7.86 (978-0-7826-1564-7(3)) Encyclopaedia Britannica, Inc.

—Graph Equations. 2002. (Math in Context Ser.). tchr. ed. 31.60 (978-0-7826-1549-4(X)) Encyclopaedia Britannica, Inc.

—Great Expectations. 2002. (Math in Context Ser.). tchr. ed. 31.60 (978-0-7826-1557-9(0)) Encyclopaedia Britannica, Inc.

—Growth. 3rd ed. 2003. (Math in Context Ser.). tchr. ed. 33.53 (978-0-03-071686-7(1)) Holt, Rinehart & Winston.

—Holt Ciencias y Technologia: Math & Reading: TAAS Test Practice Guide - Texas Edition. 2nd ed. 2001. pap. 21.66 (978-0-03-064891-5(2)) Holt, Rinehart & Winston.

—Holt Science & Technology: Math & Reading: TAAS Test Practice Guide - Texas Edition - Grade 6. 2nd ed. 2001. (YA). pap. 21.66 (978-0-03-064839-7(4)) Holt, Rinehart & Winston.

—Holt Science & Technology: Math & Reading: TAAS Test Practice Guide - Texas Edition - Grade 7. 2nd ed. 2001. pap. 21.66 (978-0-03-064841-0(6)) Holt, Rinehart & Winston.

—Holt Science & Technology: Math & Reading: TAAS Test Practice Guide - Texas Edition - Grade 8. 2nd ed. 2001. pap. 21.66 (978-0-03-064842-7(4)) Holt, Rinehart & Winston.

—Holt Science & Technology: Math Skills for Science. 2001. pap. 10.80 (978-0-03-054432-3(7)) Holt, Rinehart & Winston.

—Math: CIM Test Preparation Book: Oregon High School Edition: 3rd ed. 2003. (YA). pap. 12.16 (978-0-03-070452-9(9)) Holt, Rinehart & Winston of Canada, Ltd. CAN. *Dist:* Harcourt Canada, Ltd.

—Math: Middle School: Interactive Posters & Worksheets. 4th ed. 2004. (Illus.). pap. 55.66 (978-0-03-068634-4(2)) Holt, Rinehart & Winston.

—Math Course 1: Middle School: Chapter Resources. 4th ed. Date not set. pap. 367.00 (978-0-03-070832-9(X)) Holt, Rinehart & Winston.

—Math Course 1: Middle School: Interactive Posters & Worksheets. 4th ed. 2004. (Illus.). pap. 55.66 (978-0-03-068623-8(7)) Holt, Rinehart & Winston.

—Math Course 2: Middle School: Chapter Resources. 4th ed. Date not set. pap. 367.00 (978-0-03-070833-6(8)) Holt, Rinehart & Winston.

—Math Course 2: Middle School: Interactive Study Guide. 4th ed. 2002. pap., stu. ed. 9.60 (978-0-03-068633-7(4)) Holt, Rinehart & Winston.

—Math Course 2: Middle School: Standard Test Practice. 4th ed. Date not set. (YA). pap., wbk. ed. 8.40 (978-0-03-070821-3(4)) Holt, Rinehart & Winston.

—Math Course 2: Middle School: Standard Test Practice with Answer Key. 4th ed. Date not set. pap., wbk. ed. 12.60 (978-0-03-070822-0(2)) Holt, Rinehart & Winston.

—Math Course 3: Middle School: Chapter Resources. 4th ed. Date not set. pap. 367.00 (978-0-03-070834-3(6)) Holt, Rinehart & Winston.

—Math Course 3: Middle School: Interactive Posters & Worksheets. 4th ed. 2004. (Illus.). pap. 55.66 (978-0-03-068646-7(6)) Holt, Rinehart & Winston.

—Math Course 3: Middle School: Standard Test Practice. 4th ed. Date not set. pap., wbk. ed. 8.40 (978-0-03-070823-7(0)) Holt, Rinehart & Winston.

—Math Course 3: Middle School: Standard Test Practice with Answer Key. 4th ed. Date not set. pap., wbk. ed. 12.60 (978-0-03-070824-4(9)) Holt, Rinehart & Winston.

—Math Chapter Resources: Arizona Edition. 4th ed. 2004. (YA). tchr. ed. 110.60 (978-0-03-073509-7(2)); tchr. ed. 110.60 (978-0-03-073511-0(4)); tchr. ed. 110.60 (978-0-03-073512-7(2)) Holt, Rinehart & Winston.

—Math Chapter Resources: Maine Edition. 4th ed. 2004. (YA). tchr. ed. 110.60 (978-0-03-073291-1(3)); tchr. ed. 110.60 (978-0-03-073292-8(1)); tchr. ed. 110.60 (978-0-03-073293-5(X)) Holt, Rinehart & Winston.

—Math Chapter Resources: New Jersey Edition. 4th ed. 2004. (YA). 110.60 (978-0-03-073289-8(1)); tchr. ed. 110.60 (978-0-03-073288-1(3)); (gr. 6-8). tchr. ed. 110.60 (978-0-03-073287-4(5)) Holt, Rinehart & Winston.

—Math Chapter Resources: Pennsylvania Edition. 4th ed. 2004. (YA). tchr. ed. 110.60 (978-0-03-073491-5(6)); tchr. ed. 110.60 (978-0-03-073492-2(4)); tchr. ed. 110.60 (978-0-03-073493-9(2)) Holt, Rinehart & Winston.

—Math in Context: Building Formulas. 3rd ed. 2002. tchr. ed. 31.60 (978-0-85229-894-7(3)) Encyclopaedia Britannica, Inc.

—Math in Context: Cereal Numbers. 3rd ed. 2002. tchr. ed. 33.53 (978-0-85229-891-6(9)) Encyclopaedia Britannica, Inc.

—Math in Context: Comparing Quantity. 3rd ed. 2002. tchr. ed. 33.53 (978-0-85229-876-3(5)) Encyclopaedia Britannica, Inc.

—Math in Context: Dealing with Data. 3rd ed. 2002. tchr. ed. 33.53 (978-0-85229-880-0(3)) Encyclopaedia Britannica, Inc.

—Math in Context: Decision Making. 3rd ed. 2002. tchr. ed. 33.53 (978-0-85229-895-4(1)) Encyclopaedia Britannica, Inc.

—Math in Context: Digging Numbers. 3rd ed. 2002. tchr. ed. 33.53 (978-0-85229-919-7(2)) Encyclopaedia Britannica, Inc.

—Math in Context: Dry & Wet Numbers. 3rd ed. 2002. tchr. ed. 33.53 (978-0-85229-859-6(5)) Encyclopaedia Britannica, Inc.

—Math in Context: Figuring the Angles. 3rd ed. 2002. tchr. ed. 33.53 (978-0-85229-856-5(0)) Encyclopaedia Britannica, Inc.

—Math in Context: Fraction Times. 3rd ed. 2002. tchr. ed. 33.53 (978-0-85229-871-8(4)) Encyclopaedia Britannica, Inc.

—Math in Context: Get the Most. 3rd ed. 2002. tchr. ed. 33.53 (978-0-85229-915-9(X)) Encyclopaedia Britannica, Inc.

—Math in Context: Going the Distance. 3rd ed. 2002. tchr. ed. 33.53 (978-0-85229-917-3(6)); (Illus.). stu. ed. 7.86 (978-0-85229-907-4(9)) Encyclopaedia Britannica, Inc.

—Math in Context: Graph Equations. 3rd ed. 2002. tchr. ed. 33.53 (978-0-85229-912-8(5)) Encyclopaedia Britannica, Inc.

—Math in Context: Great Expectations. 3rd ed. 2002. tchr. ed. 33.53 (978-0-85229-920-3(6)) Encyclopaedia Britannica, Inc.

—Math in Context: Growth. 3rd ed. 2002. tchr. ed. 33.53 (978-0-85229-913-5(3)) Encyclopaedia Britannica, Inc.

—Math in Context: Insights into Data. 3rd ed. 2002. tchr. ed. 33.53 (978-0-85229-918-0(4)) Encyclopaedia Britannica, Inc.

—Math in Context: Looking at Angles. 3rd ed. 2002. tchr. ed. 33.53 (978-0-85229-897-8(8)) Encyclopaedia Britannica, Inc.

—Math in Context: Made to Measure. 3rd ed. 2002. tchr. ed. 33.53 (978-0-85229-878-7(1)) Encyclopaedia Britannica, Inc.

—Math in Context: Measure for Measure. 3rd ed. 2002. tchr. ed. 33.53 (978-0-85229-854-1(4)) Encyclopaedia Britannica, Inc.

—Math in Context: Operations. 3rd ed. 2002. tchr. ed. 33.53 (978-0-85229-877-0(3)) Encyclopaedia Britannica, Inc.

—Math in Context: Packages & Polygons. 3rd ed. 2002. tchr. ed. 33.53 (978-0-85229-896-1(X)) Encyclopaedia Britannica, Inc.

—Math in Context: Patterns & Figures. 3rd ed. 2002. tchr. ed. 33.53 (978-0-85229-914-2(1)) Encyclopaedia Britannica, Inc.

—Math in Context: Per Sense. 3rd ed. 2002. tchr. ed. 33.53 (978-0-85229-857-2(9)) Encyclopaedia Britannica, Inc.

—Math in Context: Powers of Ten. 3rd ed. 2002. tchr. ed. 33.53 (978-0-85229-892-3(7)) Encyclopaedia Britannica, Inc.

—Math in Context: Ratio & Rates. 3rd ed. 2002. tchr. ed. 33.53 (978-0-85229-873-2(0)) Encyclopaedia Britannica, Inc.

—Math in Context: Reflections on Numbers. 3rd ed. 2002. tchr. ed. 33.53 (978-0-85229-911-1(7)) Encyclopaedia Britannica, Inc.

—Math in Context: Side Seeing. 2002. tchr. ed. (978-0-7826-1488-6(4)); 3rd ed. 8.33 (978-0-85229-841-1(2)) Encyclopaedia Britannica, Inc.

—Math in Context: Ups & Downs. 3rd ed. 2002. tchr. ed. 33.53 (978-0-85229-893-0(5)) Encyclopaedia Britannica, Inc.

—Math in Context: Ways to Go. 3rd ed. 2002. tchr. ed. 33.53 (978-0-85229-899-2(4)) Encyclopaedia Britannica, Inc.

—Math in Context Vol. 1: Number Tools. 2002. pap. (978-0-7826-1763-4(8)) Encyclopaedia Britannica, Inc.

—Math in Context Vol. 2: Number Tools. 2002. pap. (978-0-7826-1764-1(6)) Encyclopaedia Britannica, Inc.

—Math in Context Summer Program. 3rd ed. 2004. (SPA.). pap. 26.20 (978-0-03-072447-3(3)) Holt, Rinehart & Winston.

—Math in Context Summer School Program. 2002. pap., tchr. ed. 37.33 (978-0-85229-766-7(1)); pap., tchr. ed. 37.33 (978-0-85229-768-1(8)) Encyclopaedia Britannica, Inc.

—Math in Practice: Precalculus with Answer Key. 2nd ed. 2001. pap. 42.86 incl. cd-rom (978-0-03-065997-3(3)) Holt, Rinehart & Winston.

—Math Know-It Notebook: Middle School. 4th ed. 2004. (Illus.). pap. 13.93 (978-0-03-038016-7(2)); pap. 13.89 (978-0-03-038017-4(0)); pap. 13.93 (978-0-03-038018-1(9)) Holt, Rinehart & Winston.

—Middle School Math: New York Review & Test Preparation Workbook. 4th ed. 2004. pap. 8.40 (978-0-03-070812-1(5)); 2003. pap. 8.40 (978-0-03-070811-4(7)); 2003. pap. 8.40 (978-0-03-070809-1(5)) Holt, Rinehart & Winston.

—Middle School Math Chapter 2: Resource Book. 4th ed. 2002. pap. 38.33 (978-0-03-067959-9(1)) Holt, Rinehart & Winston.

—Middle School Math Chapter 3: Resource Book. 4th ed. 2004. pap. 38.33 (978-0-03-067961-2(3)) Holt, Rinehart & Winston.

—Middle School Math Chapter 4: Resource Book. 4th ed. 2004. pap. 38.33 (978-0-03-067962-9(1)) Holt, Rinehart & Winston.

—Middle School Math Chapter 5: Resource Book. 4th ed. 2004. pap. 38.33 (978-0-03-067963-6(X)) Holt, Rinehart & Winston.

—Middle School Math Chapter 6: Resource Book. 4th ed. 2004. pap. 38.33 (978-0-03-067964-3(8)) Holt, Rinehart & Winston.

—Middle School Math Chapter 7: Resource Book. 4th ed. 2004. pap. 38.33 (978-0-03-067966-7(4)) Holt, Rinehart & Winston.

—Middle School Math Chapter 8: Resource Book. 4th ed. 2004. pap. 38.33 (978-0-03-067967-4(2)) Holt, Rinehart & Winston.

—Middle School Math Chapter 9: Resource Book. 4th ed. 2004. pap. 38.33 (978-0-03-067968-1(0)) Holt, Rinehart & Winston.

—Middle School Math Chapter 10: Resource Book. 4th ed. 2004. pap. 38.33 (978-0-03-067969-8(9)) Holt, Rinehart & Winston.

—Middle School Math Chapter 11: Resource Book. 4th ed. 2004. pap. 38.33 (978-0-03-067971-1(0)) Holt, Rinehart & Winston.

—Middle School Math Chapter 12: Resource Book. 4th ed. 2004. pap. 38.33 (978-0-03-067972-8(9)) Holt, Rinehart & Winston.

—Middle School Math Course 1: Chapter Resources: Oregon Edition. 4th ed. 2004. (YA). tchr. ed. 110.60 (978-0-03-073513-4(0)) Holt, Rinehart & Winston.

—Middle School Math Course 1: Maryland Edition. 4th ed. 2004. (J). tchr. ed. 110.60 (978-0-03-072748-1(0)) Holt, Rinehart & Winston.

—Middle School Math Course 2: Chapter Resources: Oregon Edition. 4th ed. 2004. (YA). tchr. ed. 110.60 (978-0-03-073514-1(9)) Holt, Rinehart & Winston.

—Middle School Math Course 2: Maryland Edition. 4th ed. 2004. (J). tchr. ed. 110.60 (978-0-03-072832-7(0)) Holt, Rinehart & Winston.

—Middle School Math Course 3: Chapter Resources: Oregon Edition. 4th ed. 2004. (YA). tchr. ed. 110.60 (978-0-03-073516-5(5)) Holt, Rinehart & Winston.

—Middle School Math Course 3: Consumer/Career Mathematics. 4th ed. 2004. (Illus.). pap. 22.26 (978-0-03-066231-7(1)) Holt, Rinehart & Winston.

—Middle School Math Course 3: Homework/Practice Workbook with Answer Key - Spanish Edition. 4th ed. Date not set. pap. 11.00 (978-0-03-068296-4(7)) Holt, Rinehart & Winston.

—Middle School Math Course 3: Interdisciplinary Problem Solving. 4th ed. Date not set. pap. 30.13 (978-0-03-066318-5(0)) Holt, Rinehart & Winston.

—Middle School Math Course 3: Maryland Edition. 4th annot. ed. 2004. (J). tchr. ed. 110.60 (978-0-03-072833-4(9)) Holt, Rinehart & Winston.

—Middle School Math Course 3: Success for English Language Students. 4th ed. Date not set. pap. 79.53 (978-0-03-066257-7(5)) Holt, Rinehart & Winston.

—Middle School Math 2: Spanish Homework & Practice Workbook. 4th ed. Date not set. pap. 8.40 (978-0-03-067973-5(7)) Holt, Rinehart & Winston.

—New in Numbers. 3rd ed. 2003. (Math in Context Ser.). (Illus.). pap. 15.05 (978-0-03-072432-9(5)) Holt, Rinehart & Winston.

—Patterns & Figures. 2002. (Math in Context Ser.). 7.86 (978-0-7826-1561-6(9)) Encyclopaedia Britannica, Inc.

—Per Sense. 3rd ed. 2003. (Math in Context Ser.). tchr. ed. 33.53 (978-0-03-071287-6(4)) Holt, Rinehart & Winston.

—Picturing Numbers: Math/Context. 98th ed. 2002. (J). tchr. ed. 31.60 (978-0-7826-1492-3(2)) Encyclopaedia Britannica, Inc.

—Pre-Algebra: Hands-on Lab Activities with Answer Key. 4th ed. 2004. pap. 21.53 (978-0-03-069698-5(4)) Holt, Rinehart & Winston.

—Pre-Algebra: Tech Lab Activities with Answer Key. 4th ed. 2003. pap. 21.53 (978-0-03-069861-3(8)) Holt, Rinehart & Winston.

—Pre-Algebra: Test Preparation Tool Kit. 4th ed. 2004. pap. 264.66 (978-0-03-069616-9(X)) Holt, Rinehart & Winston.

—Pre-Algebra Chptr. 4: Resource Book with Answer Key. 4th ed. 2004. pap. 38.86 (978-0-03-069683-1(6)) Holt, Rinehart & Winston.

—Pre-Algebra Chptr. 5: Resource Book with Answer Key. 4th ed. 2004. pap. 38.86 (978-0-03-069684-8(4)) Holt, Rinehart & Winston.

—Science Spectrum: Physics Math Skills. 4th ed. 2004. pap., wbk. ed. 11.13 (978-0-03-067084-8(5)) Holt, Rinehart & Winston.

—Side Seeing Math/Context. 3rd ed. 2002. tchr. ed. 31.60 (978-0-85229-851-0(X)) Encyclopaedia Britannica, Inc.

—Some of Parts: Math/Context. 98th ed. 2002. (J). tchr. ed. 31.60 (978-0-7826-1490-9(6)) Encyclopaedia Britannica, Inc.

—Triangle/Patchwork: Math/Context. 98th ed. 2002. stu. ed. 7.86 (978-0-7826-1563-0(5)) Encyclopaedia Britannica, Inc.

Hoogeboom, Shirley. Math Discoveries with Pattern Blocks. 1999. 64p. (J). (gr. k-1). 8.99 (978-1-56451-088-4(3), ID79518); (gr. 2-3). 8.99 (978-1-56451-074-7(3), ID79519) School Specialty Publishing.

Hooked on Math: Master the Facts. 1999. (Illus.). 400p. (J). (gr. 1-6). pap. 229.95 incl. audio (978-1-887942-77-5(7)) HOP, LLC.

HOP LLC Staff. Hooked on Math - Addition & Subtraction. 2005. (J). (gr. 6-7). 64.99 (978-1-931020-50-3(7)) HOP, LLC.

Hopkins, Liz. Maths Booster. 2001. (Illus.). 144p. (J). pap. 49.50 (978-0-7487-6043-5(1)); pap. 49.50 (978-0-7487-6044-2(X)) Nelson Thornes Ltd. GBR. *Dist:* Trans-Atlantic Pubns., Inc.

Horizons Mathematics 3, Bk. 1. 1998. (J). (gr. 3). pap., stu. ed. 12.50 (978-1-58095-963-6(6), JMS031) Alpha Omega Pubns., Inc.

Horizons Mathematics 5. 1999. (Illus.). (J). (gr. 5). Bk. 1. pap., stu. ed. 13.50 (978-1-58095-997-1(0), JMS051); Bk. 2. pap., stu. ed. 13.50 (978-1-58095-998-8(9), JMS052) Alpha Omega Pubns., Inc.

Hot or Cold? Math, 6 vols. (gr. k-2). 28.95 (978-0-7368-1734-9(4), Yellow Umbrella Bks.) Capstone Pr., Inc.

Housel, Debra J. Main Idea: Grade 5 (Practice Make Perfect) 2004. 48p. pap. 4.99 (978-0-7439-8645-8(8)) Teacher Created Materials, Inc.

How Many Fish? Math, 6 vols. (gr. k-2). 28.95 (978-0-7368-1735-6(2), Yellow Umbrella Bks.) Capstone Pr., Inc.

How to Solve Math Word Problems. (J). (gr. 1). (978-0-8374-2235-0(3), 381); (gr. 2). (978-0-8374-2222-0(1), 382); (gr. 3). (978-0-8374-2203-9(5), 383); (gr. 4). (978-0-8374-2204-6(3), 384); (gr. 5). (978-0-8374-2205-3(1), 385); (gr. 6). (978-0-8374-2206-0(X), 386) Weekly Reader Corp.

Howe, Elizabeth. Hands on Numeracy Year 8. 2006. pap. 13.95 (978-0-521-68236-7(3)) Cambridge Univ. Pr.

Howes, Jacqueline Johnson. Math Bulletin Boards That Teach. 1999. (Illus.). 80p. (J). 10.95 (978-0-590-02905-6(3)) Scholastic, Inc.

Howes, Jacquelyn Johnson. Super Easy Shape Art: Fun Activities with Instant Reproducible Patterns That Teach Early Math Concepts. 2002. 48p. pap. 10.95 (978-0-439-17886-0(X), Teaching Resources) Scholastic, Inc.

Howett, Jerry & Eichhorn, Connie. Basic Skills with Math. rev. ed. 1998. (gr. 6-12). pap., tchr.'s training gde. ed. 7.95 (978-0-8359-5728-1(4)) Globe Fearon Educational Publishing.

HSP. Beginning Math, Bk. A. 2nd ed. 2002. (First-Place Math Ser.). (gr. k up). pap. 9.60 (978-0-15-334603-3(5)) Harcourt Schl. Pubs.

—Book C: Adding & Subtracting Fractions. 2nd ed. 2002. (First-Place Math Ser.). (gr. 5 up). pap. 12.60 (978-0-15-334635-4(3)); (gr. 6 up). pap. 12.60 (978-0-15-334641-5(8)) Harcourt Schl. Pubs.

—Division, Bk. C. 2nd ed. 2002. (First-Place Math Ser.). (gr. 3 up). pap. 12.60 (978-0-15-334623-1(X)) Harcourt Schl. Pubs.

—Graphing, Bk. E. 2nd ed. 2002. (First-Place Math Ser.). (gr. k up). pap. 9.60 (978-0-15-334607-1(8)) Harcourt Schl. Pubs.

—Multiplication, Bk. B. 2nd ed. 2002. (First-Place Math Ser.). (gr. 3 up). pap. 12.60 (978-0-15-334622-4(1)) Harcourt Schl. Pubs.

—Multiplication & Division, Bk. B. 2nd ed. 2002. (First-Place Math Ser.). (gr. 4 up). pap. 12.60 (978-0-15-334628-6(0)) Harcourt Schl. Pubs.

—Multiplying & Dividing Fractions, Bk. D. 2nd ed. 2002. (First-Place Math Ser.). (gr. 5 up). pap. 12.60 (978-0-15-334636-1(1)); (gr. 6 up). pap. 12.60 (978-0-15-334642-2(6)) Harcourt Schl. Pubs.

—Numbers 0 To 5, Bk. B. 2nd ed. 2002. (First-Place Math Ser.). (gr. k up). pap. 9.60 (978-0-15-334604-0(3)) Harcourt Schl. Pubs.

—Numbers 6 to 10, Bk. C. 2nd ed. 2002. (First-Place Math Ser.). (gr. k up). pap. 9.60 (978-0-15-334605-7(1)) Harcourt Schl. Pubs.

—Ratio, Percent, & Probability, Bk. F. 2nd ed. 2002. (First-Place Math Ser.). (gr. 5 up). pap. 12.60 (978-0-15-334638-5(8)); (gr. 6 up). pap. 12.60 (978-0-15-334644-6(2)) Harcourt Schl. Pubs.

—Shapes, Bk. D. 2nd ed. 2002. (First-Place Math Ser.). (gr. k up). pap. 9.60 (978-0-15-334606-4(X)) Harcourt Schl. Pubs.

Hudson, Dave. Addition I: Facts 0-20. Rogers, Kathy, ed. 1999. (Best Value Drillbooks Ser.). 32p. (J). pap., wbk. ed. 3.99 (978-1-56472-109-9(4), EP109) Edupress, Inc.

—Addition II: Review & Regrouping. Rogers, Kathy, ed. 1999. (Best Value Drillbooks Ser.). 32p. (J). pap., wbk. ed. 3.99 (978-1-56472-128-0(0), eP128) Edupress, Inc.

—Division I: Facts 1-81. Rogers, Kathy, ed. 1999. (Best Value Drillbooks Ser.). (Illus.). 32p. (J). pap., wbk. ed. 3.99 (978-1-56472-139-6(6), EP139) Edupress, Inc.

—Division II: Multi-Digit. Rogers, Kathy, ed. 1999. (Best Value Drillbooks Ser.). 32p. (J). pap., wbk. ed. 3.99 (978-1-56472-147-1(7), EP147) Edupress, Inc.

—Subtraction I: Facts 0-20. Rogers, Kathy, ed. 1999. (Best Value Drillbooks Ser.). (Illus.). 32p. (J). pap., wbk. ed. 3.99 (978-1-56472-129-7(9), EP129) Edupress, Inc.

—Subtraction II: Review & Regrouping. Rogers, Kathy, ed. 1999. (Best Value Drillbooks Ser.). (Illus.). 32p. (J). pap., wbk. ed. 3.99 (978-1-56472-136-5(1), EP136) Edupress, Inc.

Hugel, Robert. Mighty-Fun Multiplication Practice Puzzles. 2001. 48p. (gr. 2). pap. 8.95 (978-0-439-07754-5(0)) Scholastic, Inc.

Hulme, Joy N. Wild Fibonacci: Nature's Secret Code Revealed. Schwartz, Carol, illus. 2005. 32p. (J). (gr. 2-4). 14.95 (978-1-58246-154-0(6), Tricycle Pr.) Ten Speed Pr.

Hults, Alaska. Math Minutes Grade 3. Wright, Marsha, ed. Hillam, Corbin & Grayson, Rick, illus. 2002. 112p. (J). (gr. 3). pap. 12.99 (978-1-57471-814-0(2), CTP 2585) Creative Teaching Pr., Inc.

—Math Minutes Grade 4. Wright, Marsha, ed. Hillam, Corbin & Grayson, Rick, illus. 2002. 112p. (J). (gr. 4). pap. 12.99 (978-1-57471-815-7(0), CTP 2586) Creative Teaching Pr., Inc.

Hungerford. Precalculus: A Graphing Approach. 2nd ed. 2001. 85.13 (978-0-03-056511-3(1)) Holt, Rinehart & Winston.

Hunt, Barrie. Graded Exercises in Pure Mathematics. 2001. (Graded Exercises in Advanced Level Mathematics Ser.). (Illus.). 464p. pap. 19.00 (978-0-521-63753-4(8)) Cambridge Univ. Pr.

Hunt, Darleen L. Dad's Pancakes: Number Reduction. Komarck, Michael, illus. 2003. (Sherman's Math Corner Ser.). (J). (ps-3). (978-1-929591-04-6(7)) Reading Rock, Inc.

—Dog & Cat Compare: Comparing Amounts. Komarck, Michael, illus. 2003. (Sherman's Math Corner Ser.). (J). (ps-3). (978-1-929591-09-1(8)) Reading Rock, Inc.

—Dog's Dollars: Patterns. Komarck, Michael, illus. 2003. (Sherman's Math Corner Ser.). (J). (ps-3). (978-1-929591-08-4(X)) Reading Rock, Inc.

—Harvey T. Crow Puts It All Together: Addition. Komarck, Michael, illus. 2003. (Sherman's Math Corner Ser.). (J). (ps-3). (978-1-929591-02-2(0)) Reading Rock, Inc.

—Samanta Uses Patterns: Patterns. Komarck, Michael, illus. 2003. (Sherman's Math Corner Ser.). (J). (ps-3). (978-1-929591-10-7(1)) Reading Rock, Inc.

—Spider Inventories: Count & Record. Komarck, Michael, illus. 2003. (Sherman's Math Corner Ser.). (J). (ps-3). (978-1-929591-05-3(5)) Reading Rock, Inc.

Hunt, Roger & Hunt, Mary. Fun with Addition. (Basic Math Ser.: No. 678-1). (Illus.). 52p. (J). (gr. 1-3). 3.50 (978-0-7214-0704-3(8), Dutton Juvenile) Penguin Group (USA) Inc.

—Fun with Division. (Basic Math Ser.: No. 678-4). (Illus.). 52p. (J). (gr. 1-3). 3.50 (978-0-7214-0707-4(2), Dutton Juvenile) Penguin Group (USA) Inc.

Husted, Terri. Math Detective Book B1: Higher-Order Thinking in Reading & Writing in Mathematics. 2003. (YA). pap. 18.99 (978-0-89455-864-1(1)) Critical Thinking Bks. & Software.

Hutton, Kallie, et al. Mathematics for Zambia Basic Education Grade 5 Pupil's Book. 2008. pap. 3.99 (***978-0-521-69868-9(5)***) Cambridge Univ. Pr.

—Stepping into Mathematics Grade 5 Learner's Book. 2nd rev. ed. 2004. 176p. pap. 9.25 (978-0-521-54632-4(X)) Cambridge Univ. Pr.

—Stepping into Mathematics Grade 5 Learner's Book Afrikaans Translation. 2nd rev. ed. 2004. (AFR.). 176p. pap. 9.25 (978-0-521-54636-2(2)) Cambridge Univ. Pr.

—Stepping into Mathematics Grade 6 Learner's Book. 2nd rev. ed. 2004. 192p. pap. 9.55 (978-0-521-54634-8(6)) Cambridge Univ. Pr.

—Stepping into Mathematics Grade 6 Learner's Book Afrikaans Translation. 2nd rev. ed. 2004. (AFR.). 192p. pap. 9.55 (978-0-521-54638-6(9)) Cambridge Univ. Pr.

—Stepping into Mathematics Matters Grade 4 Learner's Book. 2004. 160p. pap., stu. ed. 8.85 (978-0-521-54442-9(4)) Cambridge Univ. Pr.

—Stepping into Mathematics Matters Grade 4 Learner's Book Afrikaans Translation. 2004. (AFR.). 160p. pap., stu. ed. 8.85 (978-0-521-54444-3(0)) Cambridge Univ. Pr.

I Love a Parade Math, 6 vols. (gr. k-2). 28.95 (978-0-7368-1729-5(8), Yellow Umbrella Bks.) Capstone Pr., Inc.

I Love Math Series, 12 bks. Incl. Alice in Numberland : Fantasy Math. Time-Life Books Editors. Mark, Sara et al, eds. 1993. 16.95 (978-0-8094-9978-6(9)); Case of the Missing Zebra Stripes : Zoo Math. Time-Life Books Editors. Daniels, Patricia et al, eds. 1992. 16.95 (978-0-8094-9954-0(1)); From Head to Toe : Body Math. Time-Life Books Editors. Daniels, Patricia & Crawford, Jean B., eds. 1992. 16.95 (978-0-8094-9966-3(5)); How Do Octopi Eat Pizza Pie? Pizza Math. Time-Life Books Editors. Daniels, Patricia et al, eds. 1992. 16.95 (978-0-8094-9950-2(9)); Mystery Mansion : House Math. Mark, Sara, ed. 1993. 16.95 (978-0-8094-9986-1(X)); Pterodactyl Tunnel : Amusement Park Math. Crawford, Jean B., ed. 1993. 16.95 (978-0-8094-9990-8(8)); Search for the Mystery Planet : Space Math. Time-Life Books Editors. Crawford, Jean B., ed. 1993. 16.95 (978-0-8094-9982-3(7)); (Illus.). 64p. (J). (gr. 1-4). 172.89 (978-0-8094-9991-5(6)) Time-Life, Inc.

I See Patterns Math, 6 vols. (gr. k-2). 28.95 (978-0-7368-1730-1(1), Yellow Umbrella Bks.) Capstone Pr., Inc.

I See Shapes. 2005. (Emergent/Early (Prek-2) Math Package Ser.). 12p. (YA). (ps-2). 25.20 (978-0-8215-7843-8(X)) Sadlier, William H. Inc.

I Use Math, 6 Vols. 115.98 (978-0-8368-4853-3(5)) Stevens, Gareth Inc.

Idea Book for Cuisenaire Rods at the Primary Level. 2002. pap. 12.95 (978-1-56911-748-4(9)) Learning Resources, Inc.

Ikids. Fast Facts - Addition. 2005. (Math Gear Ser.). 14p. (J). (gr. 2-17). 7.99 (978-1-58476-326-0(4)) Innovative Kids.

—Fast Facts - Division. 2005. 14p. (J). (gr. 2-17). 7.99 (978-1-58476-315-4(9)) Innovative Kids.

—Fast Facts - Multiplication. 2005. (Math Gear Ser.). 14p. (J). (gr. 2-17). 7.99 (978-1-58476-314-7(0)) Innovative Kids.

—Fast Facts - Subtraction. 2005. (Math Gear Ser.). 14p. (J). (gr. 2-17). 7.99 (978-1-58476-327-7(2)) Innovative Kids.

In Step with the Standards - Computation & Estimation. 2005. (J). spiral bd. 15.95 (978-1-58123-376-6(0)) Larson Learning, Inc.

In Step with the Standards - Data, Statistics, & Probability. 2005. (J). spiral bd. 15.95 (978-1-58123-378-0(7)) Larson Learning, Inc.

Inchworms Activity Cards. 2003. (J). 17.95 (978-1-56911-143-7(X)) Learning Resources, Inc.

Insera, Rose. Numbers. Insera, Rose, illus. 2005. (Illus.). 15p. (J). (gr. 3-6). 8.95 (978-1-74157-269-8(X)) Hinkler Bks. Pty, Ltd. AUS. *Dist:* Penton Overseas, Inc.

Instructional Fair Staff, ed. Extra Help Math & Language Arts. 1998. (100+ Seriestm Ser.). (Illus.). 128p. (gr. 2 up). 12.99 (978-1-56822-491-6(5), IF8775) School Specialty Publishing.

Integrated Mathematics. 2002. (gr. 8-12). stu. ed. (978-0-618-07394-8(9), 2-61162); cd-rom (978-0-618-09306-9(0), 2-61301); Vol. 2. tchr. ed. (978-0-618-07398-6(1), 2-61166); Vol. 2. cd-rom (978-0-618-09307-6(9), 2-61302); Vol. 3. stu. ed. (978-0-618-07400-6(7), 2-61168); Vol. 3. cd-rom (978-0-618-09308-3(7), 2-61303) McDougal Littell Inc.

Integrated Mathematics: Functions Sourcebook. 2003. (gr. 11-12). (978-0-618-39078-6(2), K-51301) McDougal Littell Inc.

Integrated Mathematics: Overhead Visuals. 2002. (gr. 8-12). (978-0-395-64433-1(X), 2-13087); Vol. 2. (978-0-395-64446-1(1), 2-13117); Vol. 3. (978-0-395-64455-3(0), 2-13137) McDougal Littell Inc.

Integrating Grade 11 TAKS Geometry into Algebra II Student Edition. 2004. (Region IV ESC Resources for Mathematics Ser.). pap. (978-1-932797-71-8(8)) Region IV Education Service Ctr.

Integrating Grade 11 TAKS Geometry Objectives into Algebra II Teacher Edition. 2004. (Region IV ESC Resources for Mathematics Ser.). pap. (978-1-932797-70-1(X)) Region IV Education Service Ctr.

Interactive Mathematics - Prealgebra: Personal Academic Notebook. 1999. (Illus.). 741p. (YA). (gr. 6 up). pap. 68.50 (978-1-928962-00-7(9), MP-501-010) Academic Systems Corp.

Interactive Mathematics - Topic 1: Personal Academic Notebook. 1999. (Illus.). 50p. (gr. 6 up). pap. 3.50 (978-1-928962-10-6(6), MP-511-010) Academic Systems Corp.

Interactive Mathematics - Topic 10: Personal Academic Notebook. 1999. (Illus.). 56p. (YA). (gr. 6 up). pap. 3.50 (978-1-928962-19-9(X), MP-520-010) Academic Systems Corp.

Interactive Mathematics - Topic 11: Personal Academic Notebook. 1999. (Illus.). 80p. (YA). (gr. 6 up). pap. 3.50 (978-1-928962-20-5(3), MP-521-010) Academic Systems Corp.

Interactive Mathematics - Topic 12: Personal Academic Notebook. 1999. (Illus.). 70p. (YA). (gr. 6 up). pap. 3.50 (978-1-928962-21-2(1), MP-522-010) Academic Systems Corp.

Interactive Mathematics - Topic 13: Personal Academic Notebook. 1999. (Illus.). 74p. (YA). (gr. 6 up) pap. 3.50 (978-1-928962-22-9(X), MP-523-010) Academic Systems Corp.

Interactive Mathematics - Topic 14: Personal Academic Notebook. 1999. (Illus.). 92p. (YA). (gr. 6 up). pap. 3.50 (978-1-928962-23-6(8), MP-524-010) Academic Systems Corp.

Interactive Mathematics - Topic 15: Personal Academic Notebook. 1999. (Illus.). 70p. (YA). (gr. 6 up). pap. 3.50 (978-1-928962-24-3(6), MP-525-010) Academic Systems Corp.

Interactive Mathematics - Topic 16: Personal Academic Notebook. 1999. (Illus.). 104p. (YA). (gr. 6 up). pap. 3.50 (978-1-928962-25-0(4), MP-526-010) Academic Systems Corp.

Interactive Mathematics - Topic 17: Personal Academic Notebook. 1999. (Illus.). 90p. (gr. 6 up). pap. 3.50 (978-1-928962-26-7(2), MP-527-010) Academic Systems Corp.

Interactive Mathematics - Topic 2: Personal Academic Notebook. 1999. (Illus.). 62p. (YA). (gr. 6 up). pap. 3.50 (978-1-928962-11-3(4), MP-512-010) Academic Systems Corp.

Interactive Mathematics - Topic 3: Personal Academic Notebook. 1999. (Illus.). 36p. (YA). (gr. 6 up). pap. 3.50 (978-1-928962-12-0(2), MP-513-010) Academic Systems Corp.

Interactive Mathematics - Topic 4: Personal Academic Notebook. 1999. (Illus.). 58p. (YA). (gr. 6 up). pap. 3.50 (978-1-928962-13-7(0), MP-514-010) Academic Systems Corp.

Interactive Mathematics - Topic 5: Personal Academic Notebook. 1999. (Illus.). 60p. (YA). (gr. 6 up). pap. 3.50 (978-1-928962-14-4(9), MP-515-010) Academic Systems Corp.

Interactive Mathematics - Topic 6: Personal Academic Notebook. 1999. (Illus.). 52p. (YA). (gr. 6 up). pap. 3.50 (978-1-928962-15-1(7), MP-516-010) Academic Systems Corp.

Interactive Mathematics - Topic 7: Personal Academic Notebook. 1999. (Illus.). 54p. (gr. 6 up). pap. 3.50 (978-1-928962-16-8(5), MP-517-010) Academic Systems Corp.

Interactive Mathematics - Topic 8: Personal Academic Notebook. 1999. (Illus.). 74p. (YA). (gr. 6 up). pap. 3.50 (978-1-928962-17-5(3), MP-518-010) Academic Systems Corp.

Interactive Mathematics - Topic 9: Personal Academic Notebook. 1999. (Illus.). 32p. (YA). (gr. 6 up). pap. 3.50 (978-1-928962-18-2(1), MP-519-010) Academic Systems Corp.

Interactive Mathematics - Topic E1: Personal Academic Notebook. 1999. (Illus.). 52p. (YA). (gr. 6 up). pap. 5.50 (978-1-928962-27-4(0), MP-528-010) Academic Systems Corp.

Interactive Mathematics - Topic E2: Personal Academic Notebook. 1999. (Illus.). 126p. (YA). (gr. 6 up). pap. 5.50 (978-1-928962-28-1(9), MP-529-010) Academic Systems Corp.

Interactive Mathematics - Topic E3: Personal Academic Notebook. 1999. (Illus.). 178p. (YA). (gr. 6 up). pap. 5.50 (978-1-928962-29-8(7), MP-530-010) Academic Systems Corp.

Interactive Mathematics - Topic F1: Personal Academic Notebook. 1999. (Illus.). 102p. (YA). (gr. 6 up). pap. 5.50 (978-1-928962-04-5(1), MP-505-010) Academic Systems Corp.

Interactive Mathematics - Topic F2: Personal Academic Notebook. 1999. (Illus.). 160p. (YA). (gr. 6 up). pap. 5.50 (978-1-928962-05-2(X), MP-506-010) Academic Systems Corp.

Interactive Mathematics - Topic F3: Personal Academic Notebook. 1999. (Illus.). 78p. (YA). (gr. 6 up). pap. 5.50 (978-1-928962-06-9(8), MP-507-010) Academic Systems Corp.

Interactive Mathematics - Topic F4: Personal Academic Notebook. 1999. (Illus.). 84p. (YA). (gr. 6 up). pap. 5.50 (978-1-928962-07-6(6), MP-508-010) Academic Systems Corp.

Interactive Mathematics - Topic F5: Personal Academic Notebook. 1999. (Illus.). 172p. (YA). (gr. 6 up). pap. 5.50 (978-1-928962-08-3(4), MP-509-010) Academic Systems Corp.

Interactive Mathematics - Topic F6: Personal Academic Notebook. 1999. (Illus.). 92p. (YA). (gr. 6 up). pap. 5.50 (978-1-928962-09-0(2), MP-510-010) Academic Systems Corp.

Intermediate Idea Book for Cuisenaire Rods. 2002. pap. 12.95 (978-1-56911-100-0(6)) Learning Resources, Inc.

Intermediate Math Skills, Chapter 1, Activities. 2005. (Illus.). 50p. (YA). per. 7.00 (978-1-59476-041-9(1)) Paradigm Accelerated Curriculum.

Intermediate Math Skills, Chapter 1, Text. 2005. (Illus.). 50p. (YA). pap. 7.00 (978-1-59476-029-7(2)) Paradigm Accelerated Curriculum.

Intermediate Math Skills, Chapter 2, Activities. 2005. (Illus.). 58p. (YA). pap. 5.00 (978-1-59476-042-6(X)) Paradigm Accelerated Curriculum.

Intermediate Math Skills, Chapter 2, Text. 2005. (Illus.). 64p. (YA). pap. 7.00 (978-1-59476-030-3(6)) Paradigm Accelerated Curriculum.

Intermediate Math Skills, Chapter 3, Activities. 2005. (Illus.). 52p. (YA). pap. 5.00 (978-1-59476-043-3(8)) Paradigm Accelerated Curriculum.

Intermediate Math Skills, Chapter 3, Text. 2005. (Illus.). 62p. (YA). pap. 7.00 (978-1-59476-031-0(4)) Paradigm Accelerated Curriculum.

Intermediate Math Skills, Chapter 4, Activities. 2005. (Illus.). 60p. (YA). pap. 5.00 (978-1-59476-044-0(6)) Paradigm Accelerated Curriculum.

Intermediate Math Skills, Chapter 4, Text. 2005. (Illus.). 70p. (YA) pap. 7.00 (978-1-59476-032-7(2)) Paradigm Accelerated Curriculum.

Intermediate Math Skills, Chapter 5, Activities. 2005. (Illus.). 68p. (YA). pap. 5.00 (978-1-59476-045-7(4)) Paradigm Accelerated Curriculum.

Intermediate Math Skills, Chapter 5, Text. 2005. (Illus.). 56p. (YA). pap. 7.00 (978-1-59476-033-4(0)) Paradigm Accelerated Curriculum.

Intermediate Math Skills, Chapter 6, Activities. 2005. 68p. (YA). pap. 5.00 (978-1-59476-046-4(2)) Paradigm Accelerated Curriculum.

Intermediate Math Skills, Chapter 6, Text. 2005. (Illus.). 68p. (YA). pap. 7.00 (978-1-59476-034-1(9)) Paradigm Accelerated Curriculum.

Intermediate Math Skills Full Course Kit with TRK & CD-ROM. 2005. (Illus.). 1042p. (YA). 87.00 (978-1-59476-203-1(1)) Paradigm Accelerated Curriculum.

Investigating with Pattern Blocks. 2000. (J). pap. 10.95 (978-1-56911-051-5(4)) Learning Resources, Inc.

Investigations in Number, Data, & Space. 2004. (gr. k-5). (978-0-328-01881-9(3), Scott Foresman) Addison-Wesley Educational Pubs., Inc.

Investigations in Number, Data, & Space: Complete Program. 2004. (gr. k up). (978-0-201-37792-7(6)); (gr. 1 up). (978-0-201-37793-4(4)); (gr. 2 up). (978-0-201-37794-1(2)); (gr. 3 up). (978-0-201-37795-8(0)); (gr. 4 up). (978-0-201-37796-5(9)); (gr. 5 up). (978-0-201-37797-2(7)) Addison-Wesley Educational Pubs., Inc. (Scott Foresman).

Investigations in Number, Data, & Space: Individual Components (Additional Resources) 2004. (gr. k-2). (978-0-201-43436-1(9)); (gr. k up). (978-0-328-01882-6(1)); (gr. k up). (978-0-328-01883-3(X)); (gr. 2 up). (978-0-201-37586-2(9)); (gr. 3-5). (978-0-201-43438-5(5)) Addison-Wesley Educational Pubs., Inc. (Scott Foresman).

Irvin, Barbara. Data Analysis & Reasoning: Up-to-Speed Math. 2001. (Illus.). 96p. per. 8.95 (978-1-56254-371-6(7) , SP 3717) Saddleback Educational Publishing.

Irvin, Barbara Bando. Multiplication Made Easy 3-4. Boyer, Robin, illus. 2004. (Activity Zone Workbook Ser.). 64p. (J). (gr. 3-4). pap. 3.79 (978-1-58947-328-7(0) , 02214) School Zone Publishing Co.

It's Game Time. 2005. 80p. (J). per. 10.99 (978-1-59441-101-4(8) , CD-104045) Carson-Dellosa Publishing Co., Inc.

It's Time! Math, 6 vols. (gr. k-2). 28.95 (978-0-7368-2993-9(8) , Yellow Umbrella Bks.) Capstone Pr., Inc.

Jacobi, Dawn Talluto. Math Fun Grade 1. 2000. (Kelley Wingate Ser.). (Illus.). 80p. (J). (gr. k-1). pap. 9.99 (978-0-88724-595-4(1)) Carson-Dellosa Publishing Co., Inc.

—Math Fun Grade 3. 2000. (Kelley Wingate Ser.). (Illus.). 80p. (J). (gr. 2-4). pap. 9.99 (978-0-88724-597-8(8)) Carson-Dellosa Publishing Co., Inc.

—Math Fun Grade 4. 2000. (Kelley Wingate Ser.). (Illus.). 80p. (J). (gr. 3-5). pap. 9.99 (978-0-88724-598-5(6)) Carson-Dellosa Publishing Co., Inc.

Jacobs, Russell F. Grade 2 Math by Design. Naughton, Abbey L. & Bobbett, Victor M., eds. 1999. (Illus.). 64p. (J). (gr. 2-3). pap., wbk. ed. 10.95 (978-0-918272-30-0(0) , 169) Jacobs Publishing Co.

—Grade 3 Math by Design. 2000. 80p. (J). (gr. 3-4). pap., wbk. ed. 12.95 (978-0-918272-31-7(9) , 1691) Jacobs Publishing Co.

—Pre-Algebra by Design. Naughton, Abbey L., ed. 1998. 53p. (J). (gr. 7-9). pap., wbk. ed. 17.95 (978-0-918272-29-4(7) , 167) Jacobs Publishing Co.

James, Russell. Essential Challenge & Review 2 with Answers: Mathematics Homework Assignments. 2nd rev. ed. 1999. 72p. pap. 10.00 (978-0-521-77565-6(5)) Cambridge Univ. Pr.

James, Russell David. Essential Challenge & Review 1 with Answers: Mathematics Homework Assignments. 2nd rev. ed. 1999. 72p. (gr. 6-9). pap. 10.00 (978-0-521-77566-3(3)) Cambridge Univ. Pr.

Jarrett, Michael, photos by. I Can Do Math, 6 bks. Incl. Adding. Williams, Rozanne Lanczak. Jarrett, Michael, illus. lib. bdg. 20.67 (978-0-8368-4108-4(5)); Crayola Counting. Williams, Rozanne Lanczak. Jarrett, Michael, illus. 20.67 (978-0-8368-4109-1(3)); Learning about Coins. Williams, Rozanne Lanczak. lib. bdg. 20.67 (978-0-8368-4110-7(7)); Making Graphs. Nechaev, Michelle Wagner. Jarrett, Michael, illus. lib. bdg. 20.67 (978-0-8368-4111-4(5)); Measuring. Gresko, Marcia S. Jarrett, Michael, illus. lib. bdg. 20.67 (978-0-8368-4112-1(3)); Subtracting. Williams, Rozanne Lanczak. lib. bdg. 20.67 (978-0-8368-4113-8(1)); 24p. (J). (gr. 1 up). (Illus.). 2004. Set lib. bdg. 124.02 (978-0-8368-4107-7(7)) Stevens, Gareth Inc.

Jason Math Adventure: Proportional Reasoning & the Disappearing Wetlands. 2004. (J). (978-0-9763809-3-1(5)) JASON Project, The.

Jennison, Christopher. Baseball Math: Grandslam Activities & Projects. 3rd ed. 2005. (Illus.). 112p. (J). pap. (978-1-59647-007-1(0)) Good Year Bks.

—Baseball Math: Grandslam Activities & Projects. 2001. (gr. 3-6). lib. bdg. 22.85 (978-0-613-39463-5(1)) Tandem Library Bks.

Jeopardy Math Grade 3. 2006. (J). 28.00 (978-1-933178-56-1(6)) Pflaum Publishing Group.

Jeopardy Math Grade 4. 2006. (J). 28.00 (978-1-933178-57-8(4)) Pflaum Publishing Group.

Jeopardy Math Grade 5. 2006. (J). 28.00 (978-1-933178-58-5(2)) Pflaum Publishing Group.

Jerome, Kate Boehm. How Many Ants in an Anthill? 2004. (Math Behind the Science Ser.). (Illus.). 24p. (J). pap. (978-0-7922-4587-2(3)) National Geographic Society.

—Number Know-How. 2004. (Math Behind the Science Ser.). (Illus.). 24p. (J). pap. (978-0-7922-4591-9(1)) National Geographic Society.

Johnson, Kay. The Mathematics of Stocks Complete Solutions Guide. 2001. (Mathematics for Everyday Living Ser.). (YA). 3.50 (978-1-58123-251-6(9)) Larson Learning, Inc.

Johnson, Rebecca L. Crunching Numbers. 2004. (Math Behind the Science Ser.). (Illus.). 24p. (J). pap. (978-0-7922-4592-6(X)) National Geographic Society.

—Decoding Data. 2004. (Math Behind the Science Ser.). (Illus.). 24p. (J). pap. (978-0-7922-4588-9(1)) National Geographic Society.

—Puzzling Out Patterns. 2004. (Math Behind the Science Ser.). (Illus.). 24p. (J). pap. (978-0-7922-4594-0(6)) National Geographic Society.

Johnson, Virginia. Hands-on Math: Manipulative Activities for the Classroom. Hamaguchi, Carla, ed. Weller, Linda & Grayson, Rick, illus. 2006. 144p. pap. 19.99 (978-1-59198-232-6(4) , 2568) Creative Teaching Pr., Inc.

Jones, Colleen. Contamos con Nuestros Amigos: Metro Math Readers Yellow Level. 2000. (Metro Math Readers Yellow Level Ser.). (Illus.). (J). (gr. 1-2). 3.75 (978-1-58120-466-7(3)) Metropolitan Teaching & Learning Co.

—Hagamos doce bolsitas de fiesta: Metro Math Readers Yellow Level. 2000. (Metro Math Readers Yellow Level Ser.). (J). (gr. 1-2). 3.75 (978-1-58120-468-1(X)) Metropolitan Teaching & Learning Co.

—Let's Share: Metro Math Readers Yellow Level. 2000. (Metro Math Readers Yellow Level Ser.). (J). (gr. 1-2). 3.75 (978-1-58120-416-2(7)) Metropolitan Teaching & Learning Co.

—Making Twelve Party Bags. 2000. (Metro Math Readers Yellow Level Ser.). (J). (gr. 1-2). 3.75 (978-1-58120-405-6(1)) Metropolitan Teaching & Learning Co.

—Making Twelve Party Bags: Metro Math Readers Yellow Level. 2000. (Metro Math Readers Yellow Level Ser.). (J). (gr. 1-2). 3.75 (978-1-58120-406-3(X)) Metropolitan Teaching & Learning Co.

—The Number Nine: Metro Math Readers Red Level. 2000. (J). 3.30 (978-1-58120-310-3(1)) Metropolitan Teaching & Learning Co.

Jones, Jill. Come TOP Math: Ages 6-7. 2004. (Illus.). 32p. pap. 5.99 (978-0-7548-1144-2(1)) Anness Publishing GBR. *Dist:* National Bk. Network.

—Coming TOP Math: Ages 3-4. 2004. (Illus.). 32p. pap. 5.99 (978-0-7548-0997-5(8)) Anness Publishing GBR. *Dist:* National Bk. Network.

—Coming TOP Math: Ages 4-5. 2004. (Illus.). 32p. pap. 5.99 (978-0-7548-1142-8(5)) Anness Publishing GBR. *Dist:* National Bk. Network.

—Coming TOP Math: Ages 5-6. 2004. (Illus.). 32p. pap. 5.99 (978-0-7548-1143-5(3)) Anness Publishing GBR. *Dist:* National Bk. Network.

Jones, Otis. Geonopolis, the Shapely City of Geometry. 2003. (Illus.). 21p. (J). (978-0-9744123-0-6(9)) Colorful Crayons For Kids Publishing, LLC.

Jones, Peter, et al. Essential Further Mathematics. 3rd rev. ed. 2005. (Essential Mathematics Ser.). pap. 30.00 incl. cd-rom (978-0-521-61328-6(0)) Cambridge Univ. Pr.

—Essential Standard General Maths. 2005. (Essential Mathematics Ser.). pap., stu. ed. 30.10 incl. cd-rom (978-0-521-67260-3(0)) Cambridge Univ. Pr.

Jooste, Zonia, et al. Mathematics Matters Grade 4. 2nd ed. 2004. 144p. pap., tchr. ed. 16.20 (978-0-521-54435-1(1)) Cambridge Univ. Pr.

—Mathematics Matters Grade 4 Afrikaans Translation. 2004. (AFR.). 136p. pap., tchr. ed. 16.20 (978-0-521-54437-5(8)) Cambridge Univ. Pr.

—Mathematics Matters Grade 4 Learner's Book. 2nd ed. 2004. 128p. pap., stu. ed. 8.85 (978-0-521-54434-4(3)) Cambridge Univ. Pr.

—Mathematics Matters Grade 4 Learner's Book Afrikaans Translation. 2004. (AFR.). 128p. pap. 8.85 (978-0-521-54436-8(X)) Cambridge Univ. Pr.

—Mathematics Matters Grade 5 Learner's Book. 2nd rev. ed. 2004. 144p. pap. 9.85 (978-0-521-54624-9(9)) Cambridge Univ. Pr.

—Mathematics Matters Grade 5 Learner's Book Arikaans Translation. 2nd rev. ed. 2004. (AFR.). 144p. pap. 9.85 (978-0-521-54628-7(1)) Cambridge Univ. Pr.

—Mathematics Matters Grade 6 Learner's Book. 2nd rev. ed. 2004. 160p. pap. 10.55 (978-0-521-54626-3(5)) Cambridge Univ. Pr.

—Mathematics Matters Grade 6 Learner's Book Afrikaans Translation. 2nd rev. ed. 2004. (AFR.). 160p. pap. 10.70 (978-0-521-54630-0(3)) Cambridge Univ. Pr.

Julio, Susan. Consumer Math: Activities to Teach Counting, Saving, Shopping, & Banking. Soles, Tracy & Vaughn, Louise, eds. Crowell, Knox, illus. 1998. 96p. (J). (gr. k-3). pap. 11.99 (978-0-88724-460-5(2) , CD-7424) Carson-Dellosa Publishing Co., Inc.

The Jumbo Book of Math Discoveries. 176p. (gr. k-2). 14.99 (978-1-56451-354-0(8) , ID7475); (gr. 3-5). 14.99 (978-1-56451-355-7(6) , ID7476); (gr. 6-8). 14.99 (978-1-56451-356-4(4) , ID7477) School Specialty Publishing.

Jung, Tori. Have Fun with Math. Chung, Haley, illus. 2005. 192p. (J). Vol. 1. pap. 12.95 (978-981-05-2238-4(X)); Vol. 2. pap. 12.95 (978-981-05-2239-1(8)) Youngjin.com Publishing Co., Ltd. KOR. *Dist:* Transition Vendor.

—Math Game, Vol. 3. Chung, Haley, illus. 2005. 160p. (J). pap. (978-981-05-2768-6(3)) Monsoon Bks. Pte. Ltd.

Kaplan, Andrew & DeBold, Carol. Math on Call: A Mathematics Handbook. 2004. (Illus.). ix, 608p. (YA). 19.67 (978-0-669-50819-2(5)) Great Source Education Group, Inc.

Kaplan Staff. SCORE! Mountain Challenge Math Workbook, Grade K/1 (Ages 5-7) 2007. (Score Mountain Challenge Ser.). 160p. 10.95 (978-1-4195-9466-3(4)) Kaplan Publishing.

—SCORE! Mountian Challenge Math Workbook, Grade 2 (Ages 7-8) 2007. (Score Mountain Challenge Ser.). 160p. pap. 10.95 (978-1-4195-9454-0(0)) Kaplan Publishing.

—Score! Mountian Challenge Math Workbook, Grade 3 (Ages 8-9) 2007. (Score Mountain Challenge Ser.). 192p. pap. 10.95 (978-1-4195-9455-7(9)) Kaplan Publishing.

—Score! Mountian Challenge Math Workbook, Grade 4 (Ages 9-10) 2007. (Score Mountain Challenge Ser.). 192p. pap. 10.95 (978-1-4195-9456-4(7)) Kaplan Publishing.

—Score! Mountian Challenge Math Workbook, Grade 5 (Ages 10-11) 2007. (Score Mountain Challenge Ser.). 192p. pap. 10.95 (978-1-4195-9457-1(5)) Kaplan Publishing.

—Score! Mountian Challenge Math Workbook, Grade 6 (Ages 11-12) 2007. (Score Mountain Challenge Ser.). 192p. pap. 10.95 (978-1-4195-9458-8(3)) Kaplan Publishing.

Karapetian, Marjam. Bilingual Content Dictionary: English to Spanish. 2004. (SPA & ENG., Illus.). 4.95 (978-0-9764829-0-1(8)) WizdomInc.

Kassirir, Sue. Math Fair Blues. 2001. (Math Matters Ser.). (Illus.). (J). (978-0-606-20786-7(4)) Tandem Library Bks.

Kauffman, Dorothy. Math Every Day. 2005. (Content Area Readers Ser.). 24p. 4.95 (978-0-19-430958-5(4)) Oxford Univ. Pr., Inc.

Keep Books Organization Staff. Mini-Sets 5 & Math Concepts. (Illus.). 8p. (ps-5). pap. (978-1-893986-15-2(2)) Keep Bks.

—Mini-Sets Caption Books & Math Caption Books. (Illus.). 8p. (ps-5). pap. (978-1-893986-05-3(5)) Keep Bks.

Kelly, Lynne. Maths Wizard. (Illus.). (J). (gr. 2-6). pap. (978-1-876367-35-0(0)) Wizard Bks.

Kessler, Colleen. Math Problem Solvers: Using Word Problems to Enhance Mathematical Problem Solving. 2005. 44p. 11.95 (978-1-59363-026-3(3)) Prufrock Pr.

Keys, J. Emergent Literacy Skills: The Foundations of Reading. 2002. 72p. pap. 8.95 (978-1-58324-138-7(8) , 2-5199, World Teachers Pr.) Didax Educational Resources, Inc.

Kids Can Press Staff, Press Can. Math Stories: Subtraction. 2004. (Kids Can Learn with Franklin Ser.). (Illus.). 32p. (J). (gr. k-3). (978-1-55337-597-5(1)) Kids Can Pr., Ltd.

—Measurement. 2004. (Kids Can Learn with Franklin Ser.). (Illus.). 32p. (J). (gr. k-3). (978-1-55337-595-1(5)) Kids Can Pr., Ltd.

Kidzup Productions Staff. Addition & Subtraction. 2003. (Interactive Learning Kits Ser.). (Illus.). 24p. (J). (gr. k-2). audio, audio compact disk 13.99 (978-1-894281-01-0(2)) Kidzup Productions.

Kiernan, Denise. Great Graphs, Charts & Tables That Build Real-Life Math Skills: High-Interest Reproducible Activities That Give Kids Practice Interpreting & Creating Bar Graphs, Line Graphs, Piecharts & More. 2001. 64p. (gr. 4). pap. 10.95 (978-0-439-11107-2(2)) Scholastic, Inc.

Kim, Hy. The Complete Book of Multiplication & Division: Basic Facts & Advanced Number Theories. Applebaum, Teri L. & Rous, Sheri, eds. 2004. (Illus.). 144p. (J). pap. 16.99 (978-1-59198-035-3(6) , CTP 2572) Creative Teaching Pr., Inc.

—The Complete Book of Multiplication & Division: Mastering the Basic Facts. Applebaum, Teri L. & Rous, Sheri, eds. 2004. (Illus.). 144p. (J). pap. 16.99 (978-1-59198-034-6(8) , CTP 2571) Creative Teaching Pr., Inc.

Kindergarten Jumbo Workbook. 1998. (Step Ahead Ser.). (J). pap., wbk. ed. 4.99 (978-0-307-11251-4(9) , Golden Bks.) Random Hse. Children's Bks.

King, Keri & Sickman, Kari. Make-It-Your-Way Math: Standards-Based Games & Activities You Can Customize. Fisch, Teri L., ed. Yamada, Jane, illus. 2002. 96p. pap. 11.99 (978-1-57471-899-7(1)) Creative Teaching Pr., Inc.

Klecker, Brion T. Alpha: A View of the Universe. 2006. 124p. (J). 18.95 (978-1-58385-048-0(1)) Cold Tree Pr., LLC.

Klein, Adria. Big Book Red Super Pack. 2000. (Metro Math Readers Red Level Ser.). (J). (gr. k-1). 259.95 (978-1-58830-142-0(7)) Metropolitan Teaching & Learning Co.

—Big Book Red Super Pack Spanish. 2000. (Metro Math Readers Red Level Ser.). (J). (gr. k-1). 259.95 (978-1-58830-467-4(1)) Metropolitan Teaching & Learning Co.

—Circles: Metro Math Readers Red Level. 2000. (J). (gr. k-1). 3.30 (978-1-58120-316-5(0)) Metropolitan Teaching & Learning Co.

—Circulos: Metro Math Readers Red Level. 2000. (J). 3.30 (978-1-58120-380-6(2)) Metropolitan Teaching & Learning Co.

—Cual es la Siguiente? Metro Math Readers Red Level. 2000. (J). 3.30 (978-1-58120-388-2(8)) Metropolitan Teaching & Learning Co.

—Cual es mas? Metro Math Readers Yellow Level. 2000. (Metro Math Readers Yellow Level Ser.). (J). (gr. 1-2). 3.75 (978-1-58120-483-4(3)) Metropolitan Teaching & Learning Co.

—Feet Go Two by Two: Metro Math Readers Yellow Level. 2000. (Metro Math Readers Yellow Level Ser.). (J). (gr. 1-2). 3.75 (978-1-58120-421-6(3)) Metropolitan Teaching & Learning Co.

—Gasto monedas de diez una a una: Metro Math Readers Yellow Level. 2000. (Metro Math Readers Yellow Level Ser.). (J). (gr. 1-2). 3.75 (978-1-58120-464-3(7)) Metropolitan Teaching & Learning Co.

—How Many Are Missing? Metro Math Readers Red Level. 2000. (J). (gr. k-1). 3.30 (978-1-58120-322-6(5)) Metropolitan Teaching & Learning Co.

—In & Out of the Toy Box: Metro Math Readers Yellow Level. 2000. (Metro Math Readers Yellow Level Ser.). (J). (gr. 1-2). 3.75 (978-1-58120-417-9(5)) Metropolitan Teaching & Learning Co.

—The Measurement Mysteries: Metro Math Readers Yellow Level. 2000. (Metro Math Readers Yellow Level Ser.). (J). (gr. 1-2). 3.75 (978-1-58120-419-3(1)) Metropolitan Teaching & Learning Co.

—El Misterio de las Medidas: Metro Math Readers Yellow Level. 2000. (Metro Math Readers Yellow Level Ser.). (SPA & ENG.). (J). (gr. 1-2). 3.75 (978-1-58120-482-7(5)) Metropolitan Teaching & Learning Co.

—The Number Five: Metro Math Readers Red Level. 2000. (J). 3.30 (978-1-58120-305-9(5)) Metropolitan Teaching & Learning Co.

—The Number One: Metro Math Readers Red Level. (Metro Reading Ser.). (J). 2002. (gr. 12-1). spiral bd. 116.55 (978-1-58120-632-6(1)); 2000. (gr. k-1). 3.30 (978-1-58120-301-1(2)) Metropolitan Teaching & Learning Co.

—The Number Seven: Metro Math Readers Red Level. 2000. (J). 3.30 (978-1-58120-307-3(1)) Metropolitan Teaching & Learning Co.

—Odd Number Thirteen: Metro Math Readers Yellow Level. 2000. (Metro Math Readers Yellow Level Ser.). (J). (gr. 1-2). 3.75 (978-1-58120-418-6(3)) Metropolitan Teaching & Learning Co.

—Pies de dos en dos: Metro Math Readers Yellow Level. 2000. (Metro Math Readers Yellow Level Ser.). (J). (gr. 1-2). 3.75 (978-1-58120-484-1(1)) Metropolitan Teaching & Learning Co.

—Que es una mitad? Metro Math Readers Red Level. 2000. (J). 3.30 (978-1-58120-387-5(X)) Metropolitan Teaching & Learning Co.

—Spending Dimes One at a Time: Metro Math Readers Red Level. 2000. (Metro Math Readers Yellow Level Ser.). (J). (gr. 1-2). 3.75 (978-1-58120-401-8(9)) Metropolitan Teaching & Learning Co.

—What Is A Half? Metro Math Readers Red Level. 2000. (J). (gr. k-1). 3.30 (978-1-58120-323-3(3)) Metropolitan Teaching & Learning Co.

—Which One Is Next? Metro Math Readers Red Level. 2000. (J). (gr. k-1). 3.30 (978-1-58120-324-0(1)) Metropolitan Teaching & Learning Co.

Kofman, Victoria. Guni-Pi Academy, Math & Logic: Hands-On Textbook for 4 - 7 Year Olds. 2006. spiral bd. (978-0-9777171-0-1(0)) VK Publishing, Inc.

—Guni-Pi Academy, Math & Logic: Hands-on Textbook for 4 - 7 Year Olds - Non-Laminated. 2006. spiral bd. (978-0-9777171-2-5(7)) VK Publishing, Inc.

Koizim, Jessica. Mathematical Thinking Expressing Ideas Strategies. 2004. 48p. pap. 6.95 (978-1-4042-8523-1(7)) Rosen Publishing Group, Inc., The.

—Mathematical Thinking Linking Math. 2004. 48p. pap. 6.95 (978-1-4042-8524-8(5)) Rosen Publishing Group, Inc., The.

Koll, Hilary, et al. Using Math in the ER. 2006. (Mathworks!). (Illus.). 31p. (J). pap. (978-0-8368-6769-5(6)); lib. bdg. (978-0-8368-6762-6(9)) Stevens, Gareth Inc.

—Using Math to Build a Skyscraper. 2006. (Mathworks!). (Illus.). 32p. (J). pap. (978-0-8368-6771-8(8)); lib. bdg. (978-0-8368-6764-0(5)) Stevens, Gareth Inc.

—Using Math to Design a Roller Coaster. 2006. (Mathworks!). (Illus.). 32p. (J). pap. (978-0-8368-6773-2(4)); lib. bdg. (978-0-8368-6766-4(1)) Stevens, Gareth Inc.

—Using Math to Survive in the Wild. 2006. (Mathworks!). (J). pap. (978-0-8368-6774-9(2)); lib. bdg. (978-0-8368-6767-1(X)) Stevens, Gareth Inc.

Kompelien, Tracy. I Know about Money, It Is So Funny! 2006. (Math Made Fun Ser.). (Illus.). 24p. (J). (978-1-59928-528-3(2)) ABDO Publishing Co.

—Let's Sort, It's a Real Sport! (Math Made Fun Ser.). (Illus.). 24p. (J). 2007. 19.93 (978-1-59928-539-9(8)); 2006. (978-1-59928-540-5(1)) ABDO Publishing Co.

—You Can Estimate, That's Really Great! 2006. (Math Made Fun Ser.). (Illus.). 24p. (J). pap. (978-1-59928-552-8(5)) ABDO Publishing Co.

Koomen, Michele. Exploring Math, 6 bks. Incl. Fractions : Making Fair Shares. lib. bdg. 18.60 (978-0-7368-0817-0(5)); Numbers : Counting It Up. lib. bdg. 18.60 (978-0-7368-0818-7(3)); Patterns : What Comes Next? lib. bdg. 18.60 (978-0-7368-0819-4(1)); Sets : Sorting into Groups. lib. bdg. 18.60 (978-0-7368-0822-4(1)); Shapes : Discovering Flats & Solids. lib. bdg. 18.60 (978-0-7368-0820-0(5)); Size : Many Ways to Measure. lib. bdg. 18.60 (978-0-7368-0821-7(3)); 24p. (J). (gr. 1-2). 2001. (Illus.). Set lib. bdg. 111.60 (978-0-7368-0881-1(7) , Bridgestone Bks.) Capstone Pr., Inc.

—Patterns: What Comes Next? 2001. (Exploring Math Ser.). (Illus.). 24p. (J). (gr. 1-2). lib. bdg. 18.60 (978-0-7368-0819-4(1) , Bridgestone Bks.) Capstone Pr., Inc.

Kopp, Jaine, et al. Treasure Boxes. Klofkorn, Lisa, illus. Hoyt, Richard, photos by. 2002. (Great Explorations in Math & Science Ser.). 102p. reprint ed. pap., tchr. ed. 16.00 (978-0-924886-64-5(1) , GEMS) Univ. of California, Berkeley, Lawrence Hall of Science.

Krajcar, Eddy. Daily Mental Math, Grade 2: Building Confidence in Math Skills. 2002. 48p. 6.95 (978-1-58324-084-7(5) , 2-5157, World Teachers Pr.) Didax Educational Resources, Inc.

—Daily Mental Math, Grade 5: Building Confidence in Math Skills. 2002. 72p. 8.95 (978-1-58324-087-8(X) , 2-5160, World Teachers Pr.) Didax Educational Resources, Inc.

—Daily Mental Math, Grade 6: Building Confidence in Math Skills. 2002. 72p. 8.95 (978-1-58324-088-5(8) , 2-5161, World Teachers Pr.) Didax Educational Resources, Inc.

—Daily Mental Math, Grade 7: Building Confidence in Math Skills. 2002. 72p. 8.95 (978-1-58324-089-2(6) , 2-5162, World Teachers Pr.) Didax Educational Resources, Inc.

Krajcar, Eddy & Tiivel, Lisa. Daily Mental Math, Grade 4: Building Confidence in Math Skills. 2002. 72p. 8.95 (978-1-58324-086-1(1) , 2-5159, World Teachers Pr.) Didax Educational Resources, Inc.

Kramer, Alan. In Search of Numbers. ed. 2004. (Reader's Theater Ser.). (J). pap. 22.00 (978-1-4108-1137-0(9)) Benchmark Education Co.

—No Math Day at School. 2004. (Reader's Theater Ser.). (J). pap. 22.00 (978-1-4108-0792-2(4)) Benchmark Education Co.

Krech, Bob. Math Word Problems Made Easy: Grade 2. 2005. (Math Word Problems Made Easy Ser.). 80p. pap. 12.99 (978-0-439-52970-9(0) , Teaching Resources) Scholastic, Inc.

—Math Word Problems Made Easy: Grade 3. 2005. (Math Word Problems Made Easy Ser.). 80p. pap. 12.99 (978-0-439-52971-6(9) , Teaching Resources) Scholastic, Inc.

—Math Word Problems Made Easy: Grade 4. 2005. (Math Word Problems Made Easy Ser.). 80p. pap. 12.99 (978-0-439-52972-3(7) , Teaching Resources) Scholastic, Inc.

—Measurement: Dozens of Activities with Engaging Reproducibles That Kids Will Love ... from Creative Teachers Across the Country. 2002. (Best-Ever Activities for Grades 2-3 Ser.). (Illus.). 48p. (gr. 2-3). pap. 10.95 (978-0-439-29644-1(7)) Scholastic, Inc.

—Multiplication. 2002. (Best-Ever Activities for Grades 2-3 Ser.). (Illus.). 48p. (J). (gr. 2). 10.95 (978-0-439-29647-2(1)) Scholastic, Inc.

Krpan, Cathy Marks. The Write Math: Writing about Math in the Classroom. 2001. 94p. (J). (gr. k-8). pap. 16.50 (978-0-7690-2505-6(6)) Seymour, Dale Pubns.

Kuczma, Marcin E., compiled by. Proble: One Hundred Forty-Four Problems of the Austrian-Polish Mathematics Competition, 1978-1993. 140p. (YA). (gr. 7-12). pap. 20.00 (978-0-9640959-0-8(4)) Academic Distribution Ctr.

Kwas, Susan Estelle. Learning Block Books: Shapes, Animals, Colors, Numbers, 26 vols. 2001. (Illus.). -1p. (J). bds. 24.95 (978-0-8118-3278-6(3)) Chronicle Bks. LLC.

LaCaria, Rena. Numbers. 2004. (Illus.). 24p. (J). spiral bd. 15.95 (978-1-932373-53-0(5) , Cedar Hill Pr.) Cedar Hill Publishing.

Lakeshore Learning Materials Staff, contrib. by. Domino Math Kit. 2000. (J). pap. 29.95 (978-1-929255-60-3(8)) Lakeshore Learning Materials.

—The Doorbell Rang Packet. 2000. (J). pap. 19.95 (978-1-929255-65-8(9)) Lakeshore Learning Materials.

—The Grouchy Ladybug Packet. 2000. (J). pap. 19.95 (978-1-929255-66-5(7)) Lakeshore Learning Materials.

—How Much Is a Million? Packet. 2000. (J). pap. 19.95 (978-1-929255-64-1(0)) Lakeshore Learning Materials.

—Literature-Based Math Packets - Complete Set, 8 vols., Set. 2000. (J). pap. 149.00 (978-1-929255-62-7(4)) Lakeshore Learning Materials.

—Measurement Kit. 2000. (J). pap. 29.95 (978-1-929255-59-7(4)) Lakeshore Learning Materials.

—Skills for Living No. 2: Coping as a Consumer. 2000. (J). pap. 29.95 (978-1-929255-95-5(0)) Lakeshore Learning Materials.

Lamoreaux, Matthew, ed. Minute Math Drills. 1998. (Illus.). 64p. (J). (gr. 1-3). pap. 9.99 (978-0-88724-453-7(X) , CD-0901); (gr. 3-6). pap. 9.99 (978-0-88724-454-4(8) , CD-0902) Carson-Dellosa Publishing Co., Inc.

Lane County Mathematics Project Staff. Problem Solving in Mathematics. 432p. (J). (gr. 4). pap. 27.95 (978-0-86651-181-0(4) , DSO1407); (YA). (gr. 8). pap. 27.95 (978-0-86651-185-8(7) , DSO1411) Globe Fearon Educational Publishing.

Lappan, Glenda. Connected Mathematics, 3 vols. 2004. (YA). 760p. (gr. 6 up). 380.00 (978-0-13-180833-1(8)); 676p. (gr. 8 up). 338.00 (978-0-13-180835-5(4)) Prentice Hall Pr.

Large, Tori. Illustrated Dictionary of Math: Internet-Linked. 2004. (Illustrated Dictionaries Ser.). 128p. (J). lib. bdg. 20.99 (978-1-58086-645-3(X) , Usborne) EDC Publishing.

—Illustrated Dictionary of Math - Internet Linked. 2004. (Illustrated Dictionaries Ser.). (Illus.). 128p. (J). pap. 12.99 (978-0-7945-0662-9(3) , Usborne) EDC Publishing.

Larson. A Graphing Approach Esolutions Webcard. 4th ed. 2004. (YA). 40.36 (978-0-618-50892-1(9) , 333028) Houghton Mifflin College Div.

—Larson, Precalculus with Limits: A Graphing Approach, with Mathspace Cd, 4th Edition Plus Eduspace. 4th ed. 2005. (YA). pap. 144.36 incl. cd-rom (978-0-618-64459-9(8) , 396109) Houghton Mifflin College Div.

—Passport to Mathematics. 1999. 67.28 (978-0-618-04137-4(0)) McDougal Littell Inc.

—Precalculus Advanced Placement. 6th ed. 2003. (YA). (gr. 11-12). 137.56 (978-0-618-31435-5(0) , 332741) Houghton Mifflin College Div.

—Precalculus AP Version. 6th ed. 2003. (YA). (gr. 11-12). 137.56 incl. cd-rom (978-0-618-38602-4(5) , 384981) Houghton Mifflin College Div.

Larson, Nancy. Lesson Planner Instruction. Saxon Publishers Staff, tr. 2nd rev. ed. 2003. (gr. k-4). incl. cd-rom (978-1-59141-299-1(4) , 2994) Saxon Pubs., Inc.

—Teacher Resource Instruction. Saxon Publishers Staff, tr. 2nd rev. ed. 2003. (gr. k-4). tchr. ed. incl. audio compact disk (978-1-59141-298-4(6) , 2986) Saxon Pubs., Inc.

Larson, Ron. Middle School Math, Course 2. l.t. ed. 2004. (YA). (gr. 6-9). stu. ed. 63.96 (978-0-618-24974-9(5) , 2-06002) McDougal Littell Inc.

—Middle School Math, Course 3. l.t. ed. 2004. (YA). (gr. 6-9). stu. ed. 66.12 (978-0-618-25000-4(X) , 2-06003) McDougal Littell Inc.

Larson, Ron & Hostetler, Robert P. The Mathematics of Taxes. 2nd ed. 2000. (Mathematics for Everyday Living Ser.). 178p. (YA). per. 9.95 (978-1-58123-204-2(7)) Larson Learning, Inc.

LarsonMath. Com: Prealgebra. 2002. (J). cd-rom (978-1-58123-306-3(X)) Larson Learning, Inc.

Larson's Algebra 1 (Network Version) 2002. (YA). cd-rom (978-1-58123-308-7(6)) Larson Learning, Inc.

Larson's Algebra 1 with Review 2001. (978 1 58123-256-1(X)) Larson Learning, Inc.

Larson's Algebra 1 with Review: Binder. 2001. (978-1-58123-263-9(2)) Larson Learning, Inc.

Larson's Algebra 1 with Review: Extra Practice. 2001. (978-1-58123-260-8(8)) Larson Learning, Inc.

Larson's Algebra 1 with Review: Extra Practice Open-Ended Journal Prompts. 2001. (978-1-58123-261-5(6)) Larson Learning, Inc.

Larson's Algebra 1 with Review: Installation Instructions. 2001. (978-1-58123-258-5(6)) Larson Learning, Inc.

Larson's Elementary Math Activities, Vol. 123. 2002. (J). cd-rom 55.95 (978-1-58123-329-2(9)); cd-rom 55.95 (978-1-58123-330-8(2)); cd-rom 55.95 (978-1-58123-331-5(0)); cd-rom 160.95 (978-1-58123-332-2(9)) Larson Learning, Inc.

Larson's Elementary Math Activities: Grade 1. 2002. Vol. 1. (J). cd-rom 19.95 (978-1-58123-312-4(4)); Vol. 2. (J). cd-rom 19.95 (978-1-58123-313-1(2)); Vol. 3. cd-rom 19.95 (978-1-58123-314-8(0)) Larson Learning, Inc.

Larson's Elementary Math Activities: Grade 2. 2002. (J). Vol. 1. cd-rom 19.95 (978-1-58123-315-5(9)); Vol. 2. cd-rom 19.95 (978-1-58123-316-2(7)); Vol. 3. cd-rom 19.95 (978-1-58123-317-9(5)) Larson Learning, Inc.

Larson's Elementary Math Activities: Kindergarten. 2002. (J). Vol. 2. cd-rom 19.95 (978-1-58123-310-0(8)); Vol. 3. cd-rom 19.95 (978-1-58123-311-7(6)) Larson Learning, Inc.

Larson's Elementary Math Activities Vol. 1: Kindergarten. 2002. (J). cd-rom 19.95 (978-1-58123-309-4(4)) Larson Learning, Inc.

Larson's Elementary Math Grade-1 (Classroom Lab Pack) 2000. (J). (978-1-58123-243-1(8)) Larson Learning, Inc.

Larson's Elementary Math Grade-1 (Computer Lab Pack) 2000. (J). otabind (978-1-58123-246-2(2)) Larson Learning, Inc.

Larson's Elementary Math Grade 1 (Extra Practice) 2001. (J). pap. (978-1-58123-198-4(9)) Larson Learning, Inc.

Larson's Elementary Math Grade 1 (Family Activity Letters) 2001. (J). pap. (978-1-58123-188-5(1)) Larson Learning, Inc.

Larson's Elementary Math Grade-1 (Network Site License) 2000. (J). otabind (978-1-58123-249-3(7)) Larson Learning, Inc.

Larson's Elementary Math Grade-1 (Single User Package) 2000. (J). (978-1-58123-240-0(3)) Larson Learning, Inc.

Larson's Elementary Math Grade 1 (Teacher's Resource Guide) 2001. (J). pap. (978-1-58123-191-5(1)) Larson Learning, Inc.

Larson's Elementary Math Grade-2 (Classroom Lab Pack) 2000. (J). (978-1-58123-244-8(6)) Larson Learning, Inc.

Larson's Elementary Math Grade-2 (Computer Lab Pack) 2000. (J). (978-1-58123-247-9(0)) Larson Learning, Inc.

Larson's Elementary Math Grade 2 (Extra Practice) 2001. (J). pap. (978-1-58123-199-1(7)) Larson Learning, Inc.

Larson's Elementary Math Grade 2 (Family Activity Letters) 2001. (J). pap. (978-1-58123-189-2(X)) Larson Learning, Inc.

Larson's Elementary Math Grade-2 (Network Site License) 2000. (J). (978-1-58123-250-9(0)) Larson Learning, Inc.

Larson's Elementary Math Grade-2 (Single User Package) 2000. (J). (978-1-58123-241-7(1)) Larson Learning, Inc.

Larson's Elementary Math Grade 2 (Teacher's Resource Guide) 2001. (J). pap. (978-1-58123-192-2(X)) Larson Learning, Inc.

Larson's Elementary Math Grade-K (Classroom Lab Pack) 2000. (J). (978-1-58123-242-4(X)) Larson Learning, Inc.

Larson's Elementary Math Grade-K (Network Site License) 2000. (J). (978-1-58123-248-6(9)) Larson Learning, Inc.

Larson's Elementary Math Grade-K (Single User Package) 2000. (J). (978-1-58123-239-4(X)) Larson Learning, Inc.

Larson's Elementary Math Kindergarten (Extra Practice) 2001. (J). pap. (978-1-58123-197-7(0)) Larson Learning, Inc.

Larson's Elementary Math Kindergarten (Family Activity Letters) 2001. (J). pap. (978-1-58123-187-8(3)) Larson Learning, Inc.

Larson's Elementary Math V 2.0 (Binder) 2001. (978-1-58123-171-7(7)) Larson Learning, Inc.

Larson's Interactive Math Series Binder (6+) 2002. (YA). (978-1-58123-295-0(0)) Larson Learning, Inc.

Larson's Interactive Math Series Binder (k-6) 2002. (J). (978-1-58123-296-7(9)) Larson Learning, Inc.

Larson's Interactive Math Series Installation Instructions. 2002. (YA). pap. (978-1-58123-301-8(9)) Larson Learning, Inc.

Larson's Intermediate Math, Binder. 2000. (J). (978-1-58123-203-5(9)) Larson Learning, Inc.

Larson's Intermediate Math V. 2.0 Extra Practice - Combined. 2000. (J). pap. (978-1-58123-183-0(0)) Larson Learning, Inc.

Larson's Intermediate Math V 2.0 Grade 3 (Extra Practice) 2000. (J). pap. (978-1-58123-174-8(1)) Larson Learning, Inc.

Larsons Intermediate Math V. 2.0 Grade 4 (Extra Practice) 2000. (J). pap. (978-1-58123-177-9(6)) Larson Learning, Inc.

Larson's Intermediate Math V. 2.0 Grade 4 (Family Activity Letters) 2000. (J). pap. (978-1-58123-176-2(8)) Larson Learning, Inc.

Larson's Intermediate Math V. 2.0 Grade 5 (Extra Practice) 2000. (J). pap. (978-1-58123-180-9(6)) Larson Learning, Inc.

Larson's Intermediate Math V. 2.0 Grade 5 (Family Activity Letters) 2000. (J). pap. (978-1-58123-179-3(2)) Larson Learning, Inc.

Larson's Intermediate Math V. 2.0 Grade 6 (Extra Practice) 2000. (J). pap. (978-1-58123-186-1(5)) Larson Learning, Inc.

Larson's Intermediate Math V. 2.0 Grade 6 (Family Activity Letters) 2000. (J). pap. (978-1-58123-185-4(7)) Larson Learning, Inc.

Larson's Matematicas Saltarinas Binder. 2001. (J). (978-1-58123-282-0(9)) Larson Learning, Inc.

Larson's Matematicas Saltarinas Extra Practice-Grade 1. 2001. (J). pap. (978-1-58123-288-2(8)) Larson Learning, Inc.

Larson's Matematicas Saltarinas Extra Practice-Grade 2. 2001. (J). pap. (978-1-58123-289-9(6)) Larson Learning, Inc.

Larson's Matematicas Saltarinas Extra Practice-Kindergarten. 2001. (J). pap. (978-1-58123-287-5(X)) Larson Learning, Inc.

Larson's Matematicas Saltarinas Family Activity Letters-Grade 1. 2001. (J). pap. (978-1-58123-291-2(8)) Larson Learning, Inc.

Larson's Matematicas Saltarinas Family Activity Letters-Grade 2. 2001. (J). pap. (978-1-58123-292-9(6)) Larson Learning, Inc.

Larson's Matematicas Saltarinas Family Activity Letters-Kindergarten. 2001. (J). pap. (978-1-58123-290-5(X)) Larson Learning, Inc.

Larson's Matematicas Saltarinas Installation Instructions. 2001. (J). pap. (978-1-58123-286-8(1)) Larson Learning, Inc.

Larson's PreAlgebra Extra Practice & Open-Ended Journal Prompts. 2002. (YA). pap. (978-1-58123-300-1(0)) Larson Learning, Inc.

Larson's PreAlgebra Family Activity Letters. 2002. (YA). pap. (978-1-58123-303-2(5)) Larson Learning, Inc.

Larson's Prealgebra (Network Version) 2002. (J). cd-rom (978-1-58123-307-0(8)) Larson Learning, Inc.

Larson's Sliding Geobeads (Activity Guide) 2000. (J). pap. (978-1-58123-170-0(9)) Larson Learning, Inc.

Larson's Sliding Geobead's (Board) 2000. (J). (978-1-58123-168-7(7)) Larson Learning, Inc.

Las formas de la ciudad Math, 6 vols.Tr. of City Shapes Math. (SPA.). (gr. k-2). 28.95 (978-0-7368-3028-7(6) , Yellow Umbrella Bks.) Capstone Pr., Inc.

Lawrence, Paul. Communicator Mathematics#8482; Content Series — Fraction Addition & Subtraction Teacher Guide: W/DVD Book G. 2005. 368p. spiral bd. 45.95 (***978-1-59699-177-4(1)***) Lawrence Educational Services, Inc.

—Communicator Mathematics#8482; Content Series - Concepts of Fractions & Decimals Teacher Guide: W/DVD Book F. 2005. 268p. spiral bd. 45.95 (***978-1-59699-170-5(4)***) Lawrence Educational Services, Inc.

—Communicator Mathematics#8482; Content Series - Whole Number Addition & Subtraction Teacher Guide: W/DVD Book C. 2005. 436p. spiral bd. 51.95 (***978-1-59699-167-5(4)***) Lawrence Educational Services, Inc.

—Communicator Mathematics#8482; Content Series - Whole Numbers: Multiplication & Division Beyond Facts Teacher Guide: W/DVD Book E. 2005. 408p. spiral bd. 51.95 (***978-1-59699-169-9(0)***) Lawrence Educational Services, Inc.

—Communicator Mathematics#8482; Content Series - Whole Numbers: Understanding & Mastering Multiplication & Division Facts Teacher Guide: W/DVD Book D. 2005. 464p. spiral bd. 49.95 (***978-1-59699-168-2(2)***) Lawrence Educational Services, Inc.

—Communicator Mathematics#8482; Content Series- Decimal Addition & Subtraction Teacher Guide I: W/DVD Book I. 2005. 210p. spiral bd. 42.95 (***978-1-59699-171-2(2)***) Lawrence Educational Services, Inc.

—Communicator Mathematics#8482; Content Series Fractions & Decimals - Decimals Multiplication & Division Teacher Guide: W/DVD Book J. 2005. 148p. spiral bd. 40.95 (***978-1-59699-176-7(3)***) Lawrence Educational Services, Inc.

—Communicator Mathematics#8482; Fractions Multiplacation & Division Teacher Guide: W/DVD Book H. 2005. 262p. spiral bd. 45.95 (***978-1-59699-178-1(X)***) Lawrence Educational Services, Inc.

—Communicator#8482; Mathematics Content Series- — Decimal Multiplication & Division: Book J Student Pak. 2005. 88p. ring bd. 3.95 (***978-1-59699-352-5(9)***) Lawrence Educational Services, Inc.

—Communicator#8482; Mathematics Content Series- Concepts of Fractions & Decimals: Book F Student Pak. 2005. 144p. spiral bd. 4.95 (***978-1-59699-353-2(7)***) Lawrence Educational Services, Inc.

—Communicator#8482; Mathematics Content Series- Fraction Multiplication & Division: Book H Student Pak. 2005. 120p. spiral bd. 3.95 (***978-1-59699-355-6(3)***) Lawrence Educational Services, Inc.

—Communicator#8482; Mathematics Content Series- Perspective on Numbers Assessment: Book B Student Pak. 2005. 232p. spiral bd. 6.95 (***978-1-59699-347-1(2)***) Lawrence Educational Services, Inc.

—Communicator#8482; Mathematics Content Series- Whole Number Addition & Subtraction: Book C Student Pak. 2005. 208p. spiral bd. 7.95 (***978-1-59699-348-8(0)***) Lawrence Educational Services, Inc.

—Communicator#8482; Mathematics Content Series- Whole Numbers: Multiplication & Division Beyond Facts: Book E Student Pak. 2005. 232p. spiral bd. 7.95 (***978-1-59699-350-1(2)***) Lawrence Educational Services, Inc.

—Communicator#8482; Mathematics Content Series- Whole Numbers: Understanding & Mastering Multiplication & Division Facts: Book D Student Pak. 2005. 312p. spiral bd. 7.95 (***978-1-59699-349-5(9)***) Lawrence Educational Services, Inc.

—Communicator#8482; Mathematics Content Series- Decimal Addition & Subtraction: Book I Student Pak. 2005. 152p. spiral bd. 4.95 (***978-1-59699-351-8(0)***) Lawrence Educational Services, Inc.

Lawrence, Paul R. Question Quest GEPA Math - Level A. 2002. (Illus.). (J). pap., stu. ed. 10.95 (978-0-9676545-9-1(9)) L L Teach.

—Question Quest GEPA Math - Level B. 2002. (Illus.). (J). pap. 10.95 (978-1-931104-01-2(8)) L L Teach.

—Question Quest GEPA Math - Level C. 2002. (Illus.). (J). pap. 10.95 (978-1-931104-03-6(4)) L L Teach.

—Question Quest GEPA Math - Level D. 2002. (Illus.). (J). pap. 10.95 (978-1-931104-05-0(0)) L L Teach.

—Question Quest HSPA Math - Level A, 1 volume. 2003. (Illus.). (YA). pap. 10.95 (978-1-931104-20-3(4)) L L Teach.

—Question Quest HSPA Math - Level B, 1 volume. 2003. (Illus.). (YA). pap. 10.95 (978-1-931104-22-7(0)) L L Teach.

—Question Quest HSPA Math Algebra Companion, 1 volume. 2003. (Illus.). (YA). pap. 8.95 (978-1-931104-18-0(2)) L L Teach.

—Question Quest HSPA Math Geometry Companion. 2003. (Illus.). (YA). pap. 8.95 (978-1-931104-16-6(6)) L L Teach.

—Right Response - Level A, Vol. 1. 2002. (Illus.). (YA). pap., stu. ed. 10.95 (978-1-931104-10-4(7)) L L Teach.

—Right Response - Level B, Vol. 1. 2002. (Illus.). (YA). pap., stu. ed. 10.95 (978-1-931104-12-8(3)) L L Teach.

—Right Response - Level C, Vol. 1. 2002. (Illus.). (YA). pap., stu. ed. 10.95 (978-1-931104-14-2(X)) L L Teach.

Leacock, Elspeth. Como Usamos el Dinero: Metro Math Readers Yellow Level Ser.). (J). (gr. 1-2). 3.75 (978-1-58120-487-2(6)) Metropolitan Teaching & Learning Co.

—How Do We Use Money. 2000. (Metro Math Readers Yellow Level Ser.). (J). (gr. 1-2). 3.75 (978-1-58120-424-7(8)) Metropolitan Teaching & Learning Co.

—How Do We Use Money? Metro Math Readers Yellow Level. 1999. (Problem Solving Step by Step Ser.). (J). (gr. 7-2). per. 78.95 (978-1-58120-678-4(X)) Metropolitan Teaching & Learning Co.

Leap Frog Cool Coins Wipe off Mat. 2006. (J). 3.95 (***978-1-59545-090-6(4)***) Learning Horizons, Inc.

Leap Frog First Grade Math Workbook. 2006. (J). spiral bd. 3.95 (***978-1-59545-082-1(3)***) Learning Horizons, Inc.

Leap Frog Kindergarten Math Workbook. 2006. (J). spiral bd. 3.95 (***978-1-59545-081-4(5)***) Learning Horizons, Inc.

Leap Frog Pre-K Math Workbook. 2006. (J). spiral bd. 3.95 (***978-1-59545-080-7(7)***) Learning Horizons, Inc.

LeapFrog It's a Blast Bindup. 2007. (J). spiral bd. 8.95 (***978-1-59545-168-2(4)***) Learning Horizons, Inc.

LeapFrog Staff, compiled by. The Great Dune Buggy Race. 2001. (J). (ps-2). spiral bd. 14.99 (978-1-58605-030-6(3)) LeapFrog Enterprises, Inc.

—Lily's Birthday Party Takes Shape. 2001. (YA). (ps up). spiral bd. 9.99 (978-1-58605-094-8(X)) LeapFrog Enterprises, Inc.

—Monster Money. 2001. (J). (ps-2). spiral bd. 14.99 (978-1-58605-127-3(X)) LeapFrog Enterprises, Inc.

—3rd Grade Math: Quantum Pad Book. 2002. (Fundamentals Ser.). (YA). (gr. 4 up). spiral bd. 14.99 (978-1-58605-830-2(4)) LeapFrog Enterprises, Inc.

Learning Company Books Staff, ed. Mighty Math: Money & Decimals. 2003. (Illus.). (J). 32p. pap., wbk. ed. 3.99 (978-0-7630-7632-0(5)); 32p. pap., wbk. ed. 3.99 (978-0-7630-7631-3(7)); 320p. (gr. 2-3). pap., wbk. ed. 14.99 (978-0-7630-7636-8(8)) Learning Co. Bks.

—Reader Rabbit Math: Addition & Subtraction. 2003. (Illus.). (J). 32p. pap., wbk. ed. 3.99 (978-0-7630-7638-2(4)); 32p. pap., wbk. ed. 3.99 (978-0-7630-7639-9(2)); 320p. pap., wbk. ed. 14.99 (978-0-7630-7637-5(6)) Learning Co. Bks.

Learning Horizons, creator. Underwater Math Adventure. 2005. (Illus.). 10p. (J). (ps-3). bds. 5.99 (978-1-59545-015-9(7)) Learning Horizons, Inc.

Learning to Add & Subtract. 2003. (Kermit the Frog & Friends Ser.). (Illus.). 16p. (J). (ps-k). pap., act. bk. ed. 4.99 (978-1-57768-707-8(8)) School Specialty Publishing.

Learning Wrap-Ups Math in Tro. 2004. 34.99 (978-0-943343-80-8(1)) Learning Wrap-Ups.

Learning Wrap Ups Palette. 2004. 7.99 (978-1-59204-005-6(5)); 7.99 (978-1-59204-009-4(8)); 7.99 (978-1-59204-011-7(X)); 7.99 (978-1-59204-017-9(9)); 7.99 (978-1-59204-018-6(7)); 7.99 (978-1-59204-019-3(5)) Learning Wrap-Ups.

Learning Wrap Ups Palette Base. 2004. 11.99 (978-1-59204-000-1(4)) Learning Wrap-Ups.

Learning Wrap-Ups Pre Algebra. 2004. 34.99 (978-0-943343-52-5(6)) Learning Wrap-Ups.

LearningExpress Editors. Seeing Numbers: A Pictoral Way of Learning Math. 2007. 272p. pap. 15.95 (***978-1-57685-645-1(3)***) LearningExpress, LLC.

Lee, Cora & O'Reilly, Gillian. The Great Number Rumble: A Story of Math in Surprising Places. Gray, Virginia, illus. 2007. 104p. (J). (gr. 4-6). 24.95 (***978-1-55451-032-0(5)***); pap. 14.95 (***978-1-55451-031-3(7)***) Annick Pr., Ltd. CAN. *Dist:* Firefly Bks., Ltd.

Lee, Martin & Miller, Marcia. Menu Math. 2001. 64p. (J). (gr. 4-5). pap. 10.95 (978-0-439-22724-7(0)) Scholastic, Inc.

Leech, Bonnie Coulter. Mesopotamia: Creating & Solving Word Problems. 2006. (Math for the Real World Ser.). (Illus.). 32p. (J). pap. (978-1-4042-6067-2(6)); (gr. 4-8). lib. bdg. 23.95 (978-1-4042-3357-7(1)) Rosen Publishing Group, Inc., The.

Leff, Lawrence F. Regents Math B Power Pack. 2002. (Regents Power Packs Ser.). 864p. pap. 17.99 (978-0-7641-7532-9(7)) Barron's Educational Series, Inc.

Lehoczky, Sandor & Rusczyk, Richard. The Art of Problem Solving Vol. 1: The Basics. Date not set. 361p. (YA). (gr 7-12). pap. 29.00 (978-1-885875-01-3(0)) Mu Alpha Theta, National High Schl. Mathematics Club.

Leimbach, Judy. Math Extension Units. 2005. 64p. Bk. 1. 11.95 (978-1-59363-099-7(9)); Vol. 2. 11.95 (978-1-59363-100-0(6)) Prufrock Pr.

Lerner, Marcia & McMullen, Doug. Math Smart Junior. 2nd ed. 2002. (Smart Junior Guides). (Illus.). 368p. (J). pap. 12.00 (978-0-375-76260-4(4) , Princeton Review) Random Hse. Information Group.

Leslie, Tonya. Divide It Up! 2005. (Rookie Read-About Math Ser.). (Illus.). 31p. (J). (ps-ps). 20.50 (978-0-516-25261-2(5) , Children's Pr.) Scholastic Library Publishing.

—Divide It Up. 2006. 32p. (J). (gr. 1-2). pap. 5.95 (978-0-516-25362-6(X) , Children's Pr.) Scholastic Library Publishing.

Let's Graph Math, 6 vols. (gr. k-2). 28.95 (978-0-7368-3009-6(X) , Yellow Umbrella Bks.) Capstone Pr., Inc.

Let's Learn Number Skills. 1998. (Richard Scarry Bks.). (Illus.). 32p. (J). (gr. 1-3). pap. 4.95 (978-0-88724-490-2(4) , CD-5854) Carson-Dellosa Publishing Co., Inc.

Let's Learn Our Numbers! 1998. (Richard Scarry Bks.). (Illus.). 32p. (J). (ps-1). pap. 4.95 (978-0-88724-488-9(2) , CD-5852) Carson-Dellosa Publishing Co., Inc.

Let's Multiply. 2000. (J). (gr. 1-2). pap., act. bk. ed. 12.99 incl. audio (978-1-894281-82-9(9) , ABCD090043) Kidzup Entertainment CAN. *Dist:* Penton Overseas, Inc.

Let's Sort Math, 6 vols. (gr. k-2). 28.95 (978-0-7368-1737-0(9) , Yellow Umbrella Bks.) Capstone Pr., Inc.

Level B. 1999. (J). (gr. 1-3). pap. (978-0-8136-0320-9(X)) Modern Curriculum Pr.

Levine, Barbara H., et al. 101 Things Everyone Should Know about Math- Test Booklet. 2009. (101 Things Everyone Should Know Ser.). 16p. (J). pap. 2.95 (978-0-9678020-2-2(4)) Science, Naturally!.

M N O

Levy, Janey. A Journey along the Erie Canal: Dividing Multidigit Numbers by a One-Digit Number Without Remainders. 2004. (PowerMath Ser.). (Illus.). 32p. (J). pap. (978-0-8239-8904-1(6)); lib. bdg. 22.50 (978-0-8239-8991-1(7)) Rosen Publishing Group, Inc., The.

Levy, Joan & Levy, Norman. Math Big 8 Review: Math Grade 8 Test Preparation. Stich, Paul, ed. 2002. (ENG., Illus.). 352p. (YA). per. 17.95 (978-0-935487-77-0(8) , Big 8 Reviews) N&N Publishing Co., Inc.

Lewis, Sue. Addition & Subtraction Facts to 20: Over 80 Math Puzzles, Brainteasers, & Games. Hood, Christine, ed. Briles, Patty, illus. 2002. 96p. (Orig.). (J). (gr. 1-2). pap. 11.99 (978-1-57471-819-5(3) , CTP 2579) Creative Teaching Pr., Inc.

Libro del Estudiante. 2002. (MacMillan/McGraw-Hill Matematicas Ser.). (ENG & SPA.). (gr. 1 up). (978-0-02-111537-2(0)); (gr. 2 up). (978-0-02-111538-9(9)); (gr. 3 up). (978-0-02-111539-6(7)) Macmillan/McGraw-Hill Schl. Div.

Lin, Jonathon. Exploring Critical Thinking. Abouzahr, H. et al, illus. 2002. 32p. cd-rom 19.95 (978-1-59022-006-1(4)) Glory Educational Resource, Inc.

—Exploring Data & Graphs. Gehrke, Carolyn, ed. Abouzahr, Mohammed, illus. 2002. 32p. cd-rom 19.95 (978-1-59022-003-0(X)) Glory Educational Resource, Inc.

Linde, Barbara M. Math in Our Solar System: Applying Problem-Solving Strategies. 2005. (PowerMath Ser.). (J). 22.50 (978-1-4042-2936-5(1) , PowerKids Pr.); pap. (978-1-4042-5135-9(9)) Rosen Publishing Group, Inc., The.

Linderman, Bill. Math Practice. 1999. (100+ Ser.). 128p. (J). (gr. 3-4). pap. 12.99 (978-0-88012-816-2(X) , IF8740) School Specialty Publishing.

—Time & Money: Building Math Skills for Daily Life. 2000. (100+ Seriestm Ser.). 128p. (J). (gr. 1-2). pap. 12.99 (978-1-56822-904-1(6) , IF87110); (gr. 2-3). pap. 12.99 (978-1-56822-905-8(4) , IF87111) School Specialty Publishing.

Lindsay, Kristine. Basic Math Practice 5 - Rounding, Reasonableness & Estimating. 2005. (YA). ring bd. 49.95 (978-1-58804-405-1(X)) PCI Educational Publishing.

—Coupon Math. 2004. (YA). ring bd. 59.95 (978-1-58804-355-9(X)) PCI Educational Publishing.

Lindstrom, Florence. Liberty Mathematics Level K. 2001. (Illus.). 192p. (J). (ps-1). pap., wbk. ed. 7.95 (978-1-930367-60-9(0) , CLP59500) Christian Liberty Pr.

Line Designs. 80p. (gr. 5-12). 8.99 (978-1-56451-081-5(6) , ID10031) School Specialty Publishing.

Litchfield, Jo. First Picture Math. 2007. (First Picture Board Bks). 16p. (J). bds. 11.99 (***978-0-7945-1642-0(4)*** , Usborne) EDC Publishing.

Literacy & Math Centers. 2005. (J). pap. (***978-1-60015-019-7(5)***) Steps To Literacy, LLC.

Lith, Daan van der. Study & Master Mathematics Grade 11 Learner's Book. 2006. 312p. pap., stu. ed. 18.70 (978-0-521-68921-2(X)) Cambridge Univ. Pr.

—Study & Master Mathematics Grade 11 Learner's Book Afrikaans Translation. 2006. 312p. pap., stu. ed. 18.70 (978-0-521-68922-9(8)) Cambridge Univ. Pr.

Littlewort, Elizabeth. Thuli's Mattress: Chilomwe Version. Nkhoma, Wilson, tr. 1999. (Cambridge Reading Routes Ser.). (Illus.). 16p. (Orig.). pap. 3.70 (978-0-521-66851-4(4)) Cambridge Univ. Pr.

—Thuli's Mattress: Chitumbuka Version. Chirambo, Reuben, tr. 1999. (Cambridge Reading Routes Ser.). (Illus.). 16p. pap. 3.70 (978-0-521-66875-0(1)) Cambridge Univ. Pr.

—Thuli's Mattress: Chiyao Version. Kaliati, Mailos, tr. 1999. (Cambridge Reading Routes Ser.). (Illus.). 16p. pap. 3.70 (978-0-521-66859-0(X)) Cambridge Univ. Pr.

—Thuli's Mattress: Kiswahili Version. Kitunga, Demere, tr. 1999. (Cambridge Reading Routes Ser.). (Illus.). 16p. pap. 3.70 (978-0-521-66893-4(X)) Cambridge Univ. Pr.

Loader, Mair. Yr Haen Fathemateg. 2005. (WEL., Illus.). 123p. (978-0-86174-782-5(8)); 112p. (978-0-86174-781-8(X)) Drake Educational Assocs. Ltd.

Lockwood, Joanne, et al. Prealgebra. 4th ed. 2004. 652p. (YA). 117.96 (978-0-618-37262-1(8) , 301320) Houghton Mifflin College Div.

Loesen von Sachaufgaben. (Duden-Schuelerhilfen Ser.). (GER.). 112p. (J). (gr. 5-6). (978-3-411-04872-4(7)) Bibliographisches Institut & F. A. Brockhaus AG DEU. *Dist:* International Bk. Import Service, Inc.

Logarithmen und Exponentialgleichungen. (Duden-Schuelerhilfen Ser.). (GER.). 112p. (YA). (gr. 10). (978-3-411-05661-3(4)) Bibliographisches Institut & F. A. Brockhaus AG DEU. *Dist:* International Bk. Import Service, Inc.

Long Division Grades 3-6. 2000. 64p. (J). pap. 8.94 (978-1-889369-40-2(3)) Teaching Ink, Inc.

Long, Lynette. Dealing with Addition. 1998. (Illus.). 32p. (J). (ps-3). 15.95 (978-0-88106-269-4(3)); pap. 6.95 (978-0-88106-270-0(7)) Charlesbridge Publishing, Inc.

—Marvelous Multiplication: Games & Activities That Make Math Easy & Fun. 2000. (gr. 3-6). lib. bdg. 22.20 (978-0-613-87290-4(8)) Tandem Library Bks.

—Marvelous Multiplication: Games & Activities That Make Math Easy & Fun. 2000. (Magical Math Ser.: Vol. 2). (Illus.). 128p. (gr. 3-7). pap. 12.95 (978-0-471-36982-0(9) , Wiley-Interscience) Wiley, John & Sons, Inc.

Look at a Calendar. 2005. (Emergent/Early (Prek-2) Math Package Ser.). 12p. (YA). (ps-2). 25.20 (978-0-8215-7845-2(6)) Sadlier, William H. Inc.

Look at Both Sides Math, 6 vols. (gr. k-2). 28.95 (978-0-7368-3013-3(8) , Yellow Umbrella Bks.) Capstone Pr., Inc.

Lowell, Laura & Willard, Carolyn. Sifting Through Science. Bergman, Lincoln et al, eds. Klofkorn, Lisa et al, illus. Hoyt, Richard & Bradley, Laurence, photos by. 1999. (Great Explorations in Math & Science Ser.). 104p. (J). (gr. k-2). pap., tchr. ed. 13.50 (978-0-924886-46-1(3) , GEMS) Univ. of California, Berkeley, Lawrence Hall of Science.

Lucado, Max. Shapes. 2004. (Beginnings Ser.: No. 3). (Illus.). 24p. (J). 9.99 (978-1-4003-0421-9(0)) Nelson, Thomas Inc.

Lucas, Vivien. A Puzzle a Day: A Collection of Mathematical Problems for Every Day of the Year. 2004. (Illus.). 96p. 14.00 (978-1-899618-52-1(X)) Tarquin Pubns. GBR. *Dist:* Parkwest Pubns., Inc.

Lund, Charles. Math Doodles. 2006. 80p. 10.45 (***978-1-934218-05-1(7)*** , Em 510) White Bear Publishing, LLC.

Lynch, Olmstead. Answer Key, Math Matters, Vol. 3. 2nd ed. 2000. (J). 25.95 net. (978-0-538-69476-6(9)) CENGAGE Learning.

—Transparencies-Lesson Warm-Ups & Color, Math Matters, Vol.3. 2nd ed. 2000. (J). 295.95 net. (978-0-538-69475-9(0)) CENGAGE Learning.

Mac: Technology: Test Generator. 1999. (Matematicas en Mi Mundo Ser.). (ENG & SPA.). (gr. 6 up). (978-0-02-111228-9(2)) Macmillan/McGraw-Hill Schl. Div.

Mac: Test Generator. 1999. (Matematicas en Mi Mundo Ser.). (ENG & SPA.). (gr. 5 up). (978-0-02-111226-5(6)) Macmillan/McGraw-Hill Schl. Div.

Maccarone, Grace. Monster Money. 1998. (Hello Reader! Math Ser.). (J). (ps-1). (978-0-606-13618-1(5)) Tandem Library Bks.

Making Connection with Measurement, Grade 11 TAKS - Student. 2004. (Region IV ESC Resources for Mathematics Ser.). pap., wbk. ed. (978-1-932797-53-4(X)) Region IV Education Service Ctr.

Making Connection with Measurement, TAKS Preparation Grade 6 - Student Workbook - Spanish. 2004. (Region IV ESC Resources for Mathematics Ser.). pap. (978-1-932797-67-1(X)) Region IV Education Service Ctr.

Making Connections with Measurement, Grade 1 - Student Workbook - Spanish. 2004. (Region IV ESC Resources for Mathematics Ser.). pap. (978-1-932797-62-6(9)) Region IV Education Service Ctr.

Making Connections with Measurement, Grade 1 TEKS - Student Workbook. 2004. (Region IV ESC Resources for Mathematics Ser.). pap. (978-1-932797-43-5(2)) Region IV Education Service Ctr.

Making Connections with Measurement, Grade 10 TAKS - Student Workbook. 2004. (Region IV ESC Resources for Mathematics Ser.). pap. (978-1-932797-52-7(1)) Region IV Education Service Ctr.

Making Connections with Measurement, Grade 2 TEKS - Student Workbook. 2004. (Region IV ESC Resources for Mathematics Ser.). pap. (978-1-932797-44-2(0)) Region IV Education Service Ctr.

Making Connections with Measurement, Grade 3 TAKS - Student Workbook. 2004. (Region IV ESC Resources for Mathematics Ser.). pap. (978-1-932797-45-9(9)) Region IV Education Service Ctr.

Making Connections with Measurement, Grade 4 TEKS - Student Workbook. 2004. (Region IV ESC Resources for Mathematics Ser.). pap. (978-1-932797-46-6(7)) Region IV Education Service Ctr.

Making Connections with Measurement, Grade 5 TAKS - Student Workbook. 2004. (Region IV ESC Resources for Mathematics Ser.). pap. (978-1-932797-47-3(5)) Region IV Education Service Ctr.

Making Connections with Measurement, Grade 5 TAKS - Teacher Edition. 2004. (Region IV ESC Resources for Mathematics Ser.). spiral bd. (978-1-932797-35-0(1)) Region IV Education Service Ctr.

Making Connections with Measurement, Grade 6 TAKS - Student Workbook. 2004. (Region IV ESC Resources for Mathematics Ser.). pap. (978-1-932797-48-0(3)) Region IV Education Service Ctr.

Making Connections with Measurement, Grade 7 TAKS - Student Workbook. 2004. (Region IV ESC Resources for Mathematics Ser.). pap. (978-1-932797-49-7(1)) Region IV Education Service Ctr.

Making Connections with Measurement, Grade 8 TAKS - Student Workbook. 2004. (Region IV ESC Resources for Mathematics Ser.). pap. (978-1-932797-50-3(5)) Region IV Education Service Ctr.

Making Connections with Measurement, Grade 9 TAKS - Student Workbook. 2004. (Region IV ESC Resources for Mathematics Ser.). pap. (978-1-932797-51-0(3)) Region IV Education Service Ctr.

Making Connections with Measurement, Grade K TEKS - Student Workbook. 2004. (Region IV ESC Resources for Mathematics Ser.). pap. (978-1-932797-42-8(4)) Region IV Education Service Ctr.

Making Connections with Measurement, Grade K TEKS - Student Workbook Spanish. 2004. (Region IV ESC Resources for Mathematics Ser.). pap. (978-1-932797-61-9(0)) Region IV Education Service Ctr.

Making Connections with Measurement, TAKS Preparation Grade 2 - Student Workbook. 2004. (Region IV ESC Resources for Mathematics Ser.). pap. (978-1-932797-63-3(7)) Region IV Education Service Ctr.

Making Connections with Measurement, TAKS Preparation Grade 3 TAKS - Student Workbook - Spanish. 2004. (Region IV ESC Resources for Mathematics Ser.). pap. (978-1-932797-64-0(5)) Region IV Education Service Ctr.

Making Connections with Measurement, TAKS Preparation Grade 4 TAKS - Student Workbook - Spanish. 2004. (Region IV ESC Resources for Mathematics Ser.). pap. (978-1-932797-65-7(3)) Region IV Education Service Ctr.

Making Connections with Measurement, TAKS Preparation Grade 5 - Student Workbook - Spanish. 2004. (Region IV ESC Resources for Mathematics Ser.). pap. (978-1-932797-66-4(1)) Region IV Education Service Ctr.

Making Fractions with Pattern Blocks. 32p. (gr. 1-3). 3.99 (978-1-56451-326-7(2) , ID79516) School Specialty Publishing.

Making Patterns with Mr Wiggle. 32p. (gr. k up). 4.99 (978-1-56451-973-3(2) , ID99009); (gr. 2 up). 4.99 (978-1-56451-975-7(9) , ID99011) School Specialty Publishing.

Making Shapes Math, 6 vols. (gr. k-2). 28.95 (978-0-7368-3010-2(3) , Yellow Umbrella Bks.) Capstone Pr., Inc.

Malchik, E., Antonia. The Los numeros de la Gran Depresion & Great Depression by the Numbers. 2005. spiral bd. 88.00 (***978-1-4108-5730-9(1)***) Benchmark Education Co.

Mandery, Mathew M. & Schneider, Marvin. Achieving Proficiency in Mathematics. rev. ed. 2000. (978-1-56765-537-7(8) , R023H) AMSCO Schl. Pubns., Inc.

—Workbook Achieving Proficiency in Mathematics. 2000. pap., wbk. ed. (978-1-56765-538-4(6) , R578W) AMSCO Schl. Pubns., Inc.

Mansk, Anne. You Can Measure: A Content Area Reader-math. 2005. (Emergent/Early (Prek-2) Math Package Ser.). 16p. (YA). (ps-2). 25.20 (978-0-8215-7825-4(1)) Sadlier, William H. Inc.

Martin, Andy, et al. Pure Mathematics: Complete Advanced Level Mathematics. 1999. (Illus.). 736p. (YA). (gr. 11 up). pap. 43.50 (978-0-7487-3558-7(5)) Nelson Thornes Ltd. GBR. *Dist:* Trans-Atlantic Pubns., Inc.

Martin, Hope & Martin, Jill. Good Morning Math. 1999. (Illus.). 122p. (J). (gr. k-4). pap. 17.95 (978-0-9659993-1-1(9)) Hope's Bks.

Martin, Jannelle. ABC Math Riddles. Levin, Freddie, illus. 2003. (ABC Riddles Ser.). 32p. (J). 13.95 (978-0-939217-57-1(0)) Peel Productions, Inc.

Martin, Sandra. Mathopedia Level 1. 2003. (Illus.). 118p. spiral bd. 49.99 (978-0-9718488-1-8(5)) Specialty Educational Pubs.

Martinelli, Marjorie. Brain Quest Grade 1 Math. rev. ed. 2006. 150p. (J). 10.95 (978-0-7611-4135-8(9)) Workman Publishing Co., Inc.

—Brain Quest Grade 2 Math. rev. ed. 2006. 150p. (J). 10.95 (978-0-7611-4136-5(7)) Workman Publishing Co., Inc.

Mastering Multiplication. 88p. (gr. 3-4). 2.99 (978-0-7424-0115-0(4) , IF0374); Vol. 2. 2.99 (978-0-7424-0116-7(2) , IF0375) School Specialty Publishing.

Matching & Sorting with Mr Wiggle. 32p. (gr. k up). 4.99 (978-1-56451-983-2(X) , ID99016); (gr. 1 up). 4.99 (978-1-56451-984-9(8) , ID99017) School Specialty Publishing.

Matematica y dinero Math, 6 vols.Tr. of Money Math Math. (SPA.). (gr. k-2). 28.95 (978-0-7368-3047-8(2) , Yellow Umbrella Bks.) Capstone Pr., Inc.

Matematicas 2000. (SPA.). (YA). (gr. 10). pap. 19.95 (978-958-02-0533-3(7) , 0333); (SPA.). (YA). (gr. 11). pap. 19.95 (978-958-02-0534-0(5) , 0334); (J). (gr. 6). pap. 19.95 (978-958-02-0529-6(9) , 0329); (SPA.). (J). (gr. 7). pap. 19.95 (978-958-02-0530-2(2) , 0330); (SPA.). (YA). (gr. 8). pap. 19.95 (978-958-02-0531-9(0) , 0331); (SPA.). (YA). (gr. 9). pap. 19.95 (978-958-02-0532-6(9) , 0332) Norma S.A. COL. *Dist:* Continental Bk. Co., Inc.

Matematicas cada dia Math. (SPA.). (gr. k-2). 19.95 (978-0-7368-2980-9(6)) Red Brick Learning.

Matematicas y canciones Audiocasete: Student & Teacher Support Resources. 1999. (Matematicas en Mi Mundo Ser.). (ENG & SPA.). (gr. 2 up). (978-0-02-110248-8(1)) Macmillan/McGraw-Hill Schl. Div.

El Matematico de Primaria 1. (Matematicos Ser.). (SPA.). (J). 15.50 (978-968-416-840-4(3) , 5101) Fernandez USA Publishing.

El Matematico de Primaria 2. (Matematicos Ser.). (SPA.). (J). 15.50 (978-968-416-841-1(1) , FN8411) Fernandez USA Publishing.

El Matematico de Primaria 3. (Matematicos Ser.). (SPA.). (J). 15.50 (978-968-416-842-8(X) , 5103) Fernandez USA Publishing.

El Matematico de Primaria 4, Level 4. (Matematicos Ser.). (SPA.). (J). 15.50 (978-968-416-843-5(8) , 5104) Fernandez USA Publishing.

El Matematico de Primaria 5, Level 5. (SPA.). (J). 15.50 (978-968-416-844-2(6) , 5105) Fernandez USA Publishing.

El Matematico Preescolar Avanzado. (Matematicos Ser.). (SPA.). (J). 11.95 (978-970-03-1141-8(4) , FN4736) Fernandez USA Publishing.

El Matematico Preescolar Basic. (Matematicos Ser.). (SPA.). (J). 11.95 (978-970-03-1140-1(6) , FN4728) Fernandez USA Publishing.

El Matematico Preescolar Inicial. (Matematicos Ser.). (SPA.). (J). 11.95 (978-970-03-1139-5(2) , FN471X) Fernandez USA Publishing.

Math. 2005. (SPA., Illus.). (J). (gr. k-1). lib. bdg. 286.74 (978-0-7368-4987-6(4)) Capstone Pr., Inc.

Math. 2001. (Early Math Ser.). (J). (gr. k-12). vinyl bd. 4.99 (978-1-58845-062-3(7)) School Specialty Publishing.

Math. 2004. (Skill Builders for Young Learners Ser.). (Illus.). 96p. 11.99 (978-0-7439-3686-6(8)) Teacher Created Materials, Inc.

Math: Grades 5 & 6. (Illus.). (J). pap., wbk. ed. 4.99 (978-0-88743-847-9(4)) School Zone Publishing Co.

Math: Student Testing Kit. 2004. (gr. 1-8). pap., stu. ed. 5.00 (978-1-58095-815-8(X) , MD001); (gr. 7-12). pap., stu. ed. 5.00 (978-1-58095-817-2(6) , MD002) Alpha Omega Pubns., Inc. (Lifepac).

Math: TestWorks. 1999. (SPA.). (gr. 1 up). cd-rom 99.00 (978-0-201-31833-3(4)); (gr. 2 up). cd-rom 99.00 (978-0-201-31834-0(2)); (gr. 3 up). cd-rom 99.00 (978-0-201-31835-7(0)); (gr. 4 up). cd-rom 99.00 (978-0-201-31836-4(9)); (gr. 5 up). cd-rom 99.00 (978-0-201-31837-1(7)); (gr. 6 up). cd-rom 99.00 (978-0-201-37011-9(5)) Addison-Wesley Educational Pubs., Inc.

Math 1 Reviews. 3rd ed. 2006. pap., act. bk. ed. 14.00 (***978-1-59166-322-5(9)***) Jones, Bob Univ. Pr.

Math 1 Student Manipulatives. 3rd ed. 2006. (J). 12.00 (***978-1-59166-325-6(3)***) Jones, Bob Univ. Pr.

Math 1 Testpack. 3rd ed. 2006. 10.00 (***978-1-59166-326-3(1)***) Jones, Bob Univ. Pr.

Math 4: Version 3. 1, 2 vols. 2003. (gr. 6-12). stu. ed. 40.00 (978-1-885145-48-2(9) , M4-489) CPM Educational Program.

Math 5: Version 3. 0, 2 vols. 2003. (gr. 6-12). stu. ed. 50.00 (978-1-931287-28-9(7) , M5-287) CPM Educational Program.

Math 65 Syllabus & Tests. 1999. 10p. (YA). ring bd. 1.00 (978-1-57896-073-6(8) , 1959, Hewitt Homeschooling Resources) Hewitt Research Foundation, Inc.

Math 76 Syllabus & Tests. 1999. 10p. (YA). ring bd. 1.00 (978-1-57896-074-3(6) , 1960, Hewitt Homeschooling Resources) Hewitt Research Foundation, Inc.

Math 87 Syllabus & Tests. 1999. 10p. (J). ring bd. 1.50 (978-1-57896-064-4(9) , 1964, Hewitt Homeschooling Resources) Hewitt Research Foundation, Inc.

Math Achievement Grade 1. 2001. (Math Achievement Ser.). 96p. (J). pap., suppl. ed. 10.99 (978-0-88724-637-1(0) , CD-2208) Carson-Dellosa Publishing Co., Inc.

Math Achievement Grade 2. 2001. (Math Achievement Ser.). 96p. (J). pap., suppl. ed. 10.99 (978-0-88724-638-8(9) , CD-2209) Carson-Dellosa Publishing Co., Inc.

Math Achievement Grade 3. 2001. (Math Achievement Ser.). 96p. (J). pap., suppl. ed. 10.99 (978-0-88724-639-5(7) , CD-2210) Carson-Dellosa Publishing Co., Inc.

Math Achievement Grade 4. 2001. (Math Achievement Ser.). 96p. (J). pap., suppl. ed. 10.99 (978-0-88724-640-1(0) , CD-2211) Carson-Dellosa Publishing Co., Inc.

Math Achievement Grade 5. 2001. (Math Achievement Ser.). 96p. (J). pap., suppl. ed. 10.99 (978-0-88724-641-8(9) , CD-2212) Carson-Dellosa Publishing Co., Inc.

Math Achievement Grade 6. 2001. (Math Achievement Ser.). 96p. (J). pap., suppl. ed. 10.99 (978-0-88724-642-5(7) , CD-2213) Carson-Dellosa Publishing Co., Inc.

Math Achievement Grade 7. 2001. (Math Achievement Ser.). 96p. (J). pap., suppl. ed. 10.99 (978-0-88724-643-2(5) , CD-2214) Carson-Dellosa Publishing Co., Inc.

Math Achievement Grade 8. 2001. (Math Achievement Ser.). 96p. (J). pap., suppl. ed. 10.99 (978-0-88724-644-9(3) , CD-2215) Carson-Dellosa Publishing Co., Inc.

Math Activities (Gr. 1) 2003. (J). (978-1-58232-046-5(2)) Bryan Hse. Pubs., Inc.

Math Activities (K) 2003. (J). (978-1-58232-044-1(6)) Bryan Hse. Pubs., Inc.

Math Activities with Dominoes: Grades 3-8. 2000. (J). pap. 10.95 (978-1-56911-083-6(2)) Learning Resources, Inc.

Math Activities with Dominoes: Grades K-3. 2000. (J). pap. 10.95 (978-1-56911-082-9(4)) Learning Resources, Inc.

Math Ad Libs: Addition & Subtraction. 2004. (J). per. 9.95 (978-1-56911-543-5(5)) Learning Resources, Inc.

Math Ad Libs: Fractions & Decimals. 2004. (J). per. 9.95 (978-1-56911-545-9(1)) Learning Resources, Inc.

Math Ad Libs: Multiplication & Division. 2004. (J). per. 9.95 (978-1-56911-544-2(3)) Learning Resources, Inc.

Math Add-on Set, Early Level. (gr. k-2). 57.95 (978-0-7368-3065-2(0) , Yellow Umbrella Bks.) Capstone Pr., Inc.

Math Add-on Set, Emergent Level. (gr. k-2). 57.95 (978-0-7368-1791-2(3) , Yellow Umbrella Bks.) Capstone Pr., Inc.

The Math Adventurers Meet the Evil Wizard. 2002. spiral bd. 20.00 (978-0-9702641-0-7(0)) MATHSTORY.COM.

Math & Reading Excelerator (Ages 8-12) 2003. cd-rom, audio compact disk 29.99 (978-1-59150-264-7(0)) TOPICS Entertainment.

Math & Science Excelerator (Ages 8-12), 4 Cds. 2003. cd-rom 29.99 (978-1-59150-266-1(7)) TOPICS Entertainment.

Math Art (Gr. 1-2) 2003. (J). (978-1-58232-105-9(1)) Bryan Hse. Pubs., Inc.

Math Art (Gr. 2-3) 2003. (J). (978-1-58232-106-6(X)) Bryan Hse. Pubs., Inc.

Math at Work, High School, 6 vols., Vol. 5. 2001. (At Work High School Ser.: Vol. 5). (YA). cd-rom 69.95 (978-1-929879-21-2(0)) Career Kids.

Math Big Books, English. (gr. k-2). 55.95 (978-0-7368-3250-2(5)) Red Brick Learning.

Math Big Books, Spanish. (SPA.). (gr. k-2). 37.95 (978-0-7368-3251-9(3)) Red Brick Learning.

Math Brain Teasers. 2003. (Practice Makes Perfect Ser.). (Illus.). 48p. (J). (gr. 3). pap. 4.99 (978-0-7439-3753-5(8)); (gr. 4). pap. 4.99 (978-0-7439-3754-2(6)); (gr. 5). pap. 4.99 (978-0-7439-3755-9(4)); (gr. 6). pap. 4.99 (978-0-7439-3756-6(2)) Teacher Created Materials, Inc.

Math Centers. 2002. (Take It to Your Seat Learning Centers). (Illus.). (J). (gr. 1-3). suppl. ed. 19.99 (978-1-55799-853-8(1) , EMC 3013) Evan-Moor Educational Pubs.

Math Centers. 2003. (Early Childhood Centers Ser.). 240p. (J). (ps-1). 18.99 (978-0-7439-3718-4(X)) Teacher Created Materials, Inc.

Math Centers, 2-3. 2004. (J). (gr. 2-3). per. 19.99 (978-1-55799-978-8(3) , EMC 3021) Evan-Moor Educational Pubs.

Math Centers, 3-4. 2004. (J). (gr. 3-4). per. 19.99 (978-1-55799-979-5(1) , EMC 3022) Evan-Moor Educational Pubs.

Math Centers, 4-6. 2002. (Take It to Your Seat Learning Centers). (Illus.). 192p. (J). (gr. 4-6). suppl. ed. 19.99 (978-1-55799-852-1(3) , EMC 3012) Evan-Moor Educational Pubs.

Math Connections Year 1. 2002. per. incl. cd-rom (978-1-58591-006-9(6)) It's About Time, Herff Jones Education Diiv.

Math Connections Year 1 Complete Set, No. 3. 2000. ring bd. (978-1-58591-048-9(1)) It's About Time, Herff Jones Education Diiv.

Math Connections Year 1A. 2001. wbk. ed. (978-1-58591-033-5(3)); 2000. tchr. ed., bds. (978-1-891629-18-1(2)); 2000. stu. ed., bds. (978-1-891629-13-6(1)); Set. 2000. stu. ed., bds. (978-1-891629-75-4(1)) It's About Time, Herff Jones Education Diiv.

MNO

Math Connections Year 1B. 2000. tchr. ed., per. (978-1-891629-83-9(2)); stu. ed., bds. (978-1-891629-12-9(3)); per., wbk. ed. (978-1-58591-034-2(1)) It's About Time, Herff Jones Education Diiv.

Math Connections Year 2, Set. 2001. stu. ed., wbk. ed. (978-1-58591-028-1(7)); 2000. stu. ed., bds. (978-1-891629-76-1(X)) It's About Time, Herff Jones Education Diiv.

Math Connections Year 2 Complete Set, No. 3. 2000. ring bd. (978-1-58591-051-9(1)) It's About Time, Herff Jones Education Diiv.

Math Connections Year 2A. 2001. wbk. ed. (978-1-58591-035-9(X)); 2000. tchr. ed., per. (978-1-891629-84-6(0)); 2000. tchr. ed., per. (978-1-891629-14-3(X)) It's About Time, Herff Jones Education Diiv.

Math Connections Year 2B. 2002. per., wbk. ed. (978-1-58591-036-6(8)); 2000. tchr. ed., per. (978-1-891629-21-1(2)); 2000. stu. ed., bds. (978-1-891629-15-0(8)) It's About Time, Herff Jones Education Diiv.

Math Core Assignment: Multiplication. 1999. 67p. (J). pap., stu. ed. 5.00 (978-1-889630-03-8(9)) National Ctr. on Education & The Economy.

Math Core Assignment: Proportionality. 1999. 69p. (YA). pap., stu. ed. 6.00 (978-1-889630-11-3(X)) National Ctr. on Education & The Economy.

Math Core Assignments: Division. 1999. 97p. (J). pap., stu. ed. 5.00 (978-1-889630-05-2(5)) National Ctr. on Education & The Economy.

Math Core Assignments: Exponential Growth. 1999. 96p. (YA). pap., stu. ed. 6.00 (978-1-889630-15-1(2)) National Ctr. on Education & The Economy.

Math Core Assignments: Numbers from 0-1. 1999. 97p. (J). pap., stu. ed. 6.00 (978-1-889630-07-6(1)) National Ctr. on Education & The Economy.

Math Core Assignments: Slope High School Student's Edition. 1999. 84p. (YA). pap., stu. ed. 6.00 (978-1-889630-13-7(6)) National Ctr. on Education & The Economy.

Math Core Assignments: Volume High School Students Edition. 1999. (Core Assignment Math Ser.). 115p. (YA). pap., stu. ed. 6.00 (978-1-889630-17-5(9)) National Ctr. on Education & The Economy.

Math Discoveries with Attribute Blocks. 64p. (gr. 1-3). 7.99 (978-1-56451-076-1(X) , ID3189) School Specialty Publishing.

Math Discoveries with Geoboards. 64p. (gr. k-1). 7.99 (978-1-56451-086-0(7) , ID75423); (gr. 2-3). 7.99 (978-1-56451-077-8(8) , ID75424) School Specialty Publishing.

Math Every Day Math. (gr. k-2). 19.95 (978-0-7368-2903-8(2)) Red Brick Learning.

The Math Explorer Calculator. 2004. (gr. 4-6). suppl. ed. 625.50 (978-0-201-24074-0(2)) Addison-Wesley Educational Pubs., Inc.

Math Fact Families: Reproducible Activities Presenting a Logical & Innovative Approach to Teaching Math Facts. 48p. (gr. 1 up). 5.99 (978-0-7424-0094-8(8) , IF5225); (gr. 2 up). 5.99 (978-0-7424-0095-5(6) , IF5226); (gr. 3 up). 5.99 (978-0-7424-0096-2(4) , IF5227); (gr. 4 up). 5.99 (978-0-7424-0097-9(2) , IF5228); (gr. 5 up). 5.99 (978-0-7424-0098-6(0) , IF5229) School Specialty Publishing.

Math Fun for Little Ones. 2006. (J). pap. ***978-1-57332-387-1(X))** HighReach Learning, Inc.

Math Fun Grade 2. 2000. (Kelley Wingate Ser.). (Illus.). 80p. (J). (gr. 1-3). pap. 9.99 (978-0-88724-596-1(X) , CD-3606) Carson-Dellosa Publishing Co., Inc.

Math Grade Eight. 2004. (ACSI Elementary Mathmatics). tchr. ed., ring bd. (978-1-58331-198-1(X) , 7225) Assn. of Christian Schls. International.

Math Home/School Conn Blms, Level B, Set. 2000. (Metro Math Readers Yellow Ser.). (J). (gr. 12). 21.15 (978-1-58120-462-9(0)) Metropolitan Teaching & Learning Co.

Math in My World - Math for You & Me! Test Generator. 1999. (Matematicas en Mi Mundo Ser.). (SPA & ENG.). (gr. 3 up). (978-0-02-111221-0(5)); (gr. 3 up). (978-0-02-111222-7(3)); (gr. 4 up). (978-0-02-111224-1(X)) Macmillan/McGraw-Hill Schl. Div.

Math Is Everywhere, 6 vols. (Sunshinetm Ser.). 16p. (gr. k up). 29.50 (978-0-7802 5442-8(2)) Wright Group, The.

Math Is Fun. 2004. (Play & Learn Pads Ser.). 48p. (J). 3.99 (978-1-85997-720-0(0)) Byeway Bks.

Math Journal. 2004. (J). pap. 19.95 (978-1-56911-182-6(0)) Learning Resources, Inc.

Math Made Fun. 2007. 478.32 (978-1-59928-503-0(7) , SandCastle) ABDO Publishing Co.

Math on Target for Grade 3. 2005. (J). stu. ed., per. 10.95 (978-1-59230-064-8(2)) Englefield & Assocs., Inc.

Math on Target for Grade 4: Student Workbook. 2006. (J). per. 10.95 (978-1-59230-161-4(4)) Englefield & Assocs., Inc.

Math on Target for Grade 5: Student Workbook. 2005. (J). stu. ed., per. 10.95 (978-1-59230-111-9(8)) Englefield & Assocs., Inc.

Math Plus Literature, Set. (J). (gr. 2). pap. (978-0-8136-8824-4(8)) Modern Curriculum Pr.

Math Practice. (J). 2003. 128p. (gr. 1-2). per. 10.99 (978-0-88724-936-5(1) , CD-4325); 2003. 128p. (gr. 3-4). per. 10.99 (978-0-88724-937-2(X) , CD-4326); 2003. 128p. (gr. 5-6). per. 10.99 (978-0-88724-938-9(8)); 2000. (Illus.). 80p. (gr. 1-2). pap. 9.99 (978-0-88724-599-2(4)); 2000. (Illus.). 80p. (gr. 2-3). pap. 9.99 (978-0-88724-600-5(1)); 2000. (Illus.). 80p. (gr. 3). pap. 9.99 (978-0-88724-601-2(X)) Carson-Dellosa Publishing Co., Inc.

Math Program, Early Level. (gr. k-2). 348.95 (978-0-7368-3064-5(2) , Yellow Umbrella Bks.) Capstone Pr., Inc.

Math Program, Emergent Level. (gr. k-2). 348.95 (978-0-7368-1792-9(1) , Yellow Umbrella Bks.) Capstone Pr., Inc.

Math Puzzles & Games. 2002. (Home Workbooks Ser.). 64p. pap. 2.49 (978-0-88724-735-4(0) , CD-4537); pap. 2.49 (978-0-88724-728-6(8) , CD-4530); pap. 2.49 (978-0-88724-741-5(5) , CD-4543) Carson-Dellosa Publishing Co., Inc.

Math Readers Red Level 6-Pk Ea of 24 Titles. 1999. (Metro Reading Ser.). (J). (gr. 12). 519.35 (978-1-58120-325-7(X)) Metropolitan Teaching & Learning Co.

Math Readers Yellow Level 6-Pk Ea of 24 Titles. 2000. (Metro Math Readers Yellow Ser.). (J). (gr. 12). 540.55 (978-1-58120-330-1(6)) Metropolitan Teaching & Learning Co.

Math Readers Yellow Level 6-Pk Ea of 24 Titles Sp. 2000. (Metro Math Readers Yellow Ser.). (J). (gr. 12). 540.55 (978-1-58120-360-8(8)) Metropolitan Teaching & Learning Co.

Math Readers Yellow Level 6-Stud Kit Sp. 2000. (Metro Math Readers Yellow Ser.). (J). (gr. 12). 582.95 (978-1-58120-463-6(9)) Metropolitan Teaching & Learning Co.

Math Readers Yellow Level 6-Student Kit. 2000. (Metro Math Readers Yellow Ser.). (J). (gr. 12). 604.15 (978-1-58120-400-1(0)) Metropolitan Teaching & Learning Co.

Math Readersyellow Level 1 Ea of 24 Titles Sp. 2000. (Metro Math Readers Yellow Ser.). (J). (gr. 12). 101.95 (978-1-58120-358-5(6)) Metropolitan Teaching & Learning Co.

Math Readiness. deluxe ed. 2004. (Activity Zone Workbook Ser.). 64p. (J). pap. 3.79 (978-1-58947-322-5(1) , 02208) School Zone Publishing Co.

Math Renaissance RP Complete Subscription Package. 2004. cd-rom (978-1-59455-185-7(5)) Renaissance Learning, Inc.

Math Renaissance RP Set Up. 2004. cd-rom 299.00 (978-1-59455-186-4(3)) Renaissance Learning, Inc.

Math Renaissance RP Starter Package. 2004. cd-rom 6995.00 (978-1-59455-184-0(7)) Renaissance Learning, Inc.

Math Renaissance RP Student Subscription. 2004. cd-rom (978-1-59455-187-1(1)) Renaissance Learning, Inc.

Math Renaissance RP Student Subscription Renewal. 2004. cd-rom (978-1-59455-188-8(X)) Renaissance Learning, Inc.

Math Resource Manager. 2002. (McGraw-Hill Mathematics Ser.). (ENG & SPA.). (gr. 4 up). (978-0-02-111490-0(0)); (gr. 5 up). (978-0-02-111491-7(9)); (gr. 6 up). (978-0-02-111492-4(7)) Macmillan/McGraw-Hill Schl. Div.

Math Review. 2003. (Practice Makes Perfect Ser.). 48p. (J). (gr. 3). pap. 4.99 (978-0-7439-3743-6(0)); (gr. 4). pap. 4.99 (978-0-7439-3744-3(9)); (gr. 5). pap. 4.99 (978-0-7439-3745-0(7)); (gr. 6). pap. 4.99 (978-0-7439-3746-7(5)) Teacher Created Materials, Inc.

Math Rod Activity Cards - Addition & Subtraction. 2004. (J). 9.95 (978-1-56911-164-2(2)) Learning Resources, Inc.

Math Rod Activity Cards - Kindergarten. 2004. (J). 9.95 (978-1-56911-163-5(4)) Learning Resources, Inc.

Math Rod Activity Cards - Multiplication & Division. 2004. (J). 9.95 (978-1-56911-165-9(0)) Learning Resources, Inc.

Math Safari Math. (gr. k-2). 19.95 (978-0-7368-1798-1(0)) Red Brick Learning.

Math Shark. 2005. (J). ***978-1-60015-034-0(9))** Steps To Literacy, LLC.

Math Skill Sharpeners: First Grade. 2002. (J). pap. 17.95 (978-1-56911-037-9(9)) Learning Resources, Inc.

Math Skill Sharpeners: Second Grade. 2002. (J). pap. 17.95 (978-1-56911-038-6(7)) Learning Resources, Inc.

Math Skill Sharpeners: Third Grade. 2002. (J). pap. 17.95 (978-1-56911-039-3(5)) Learning Resources, Inc.

Math Spanish Content Area Standard Set. 2005. spiral bd. 2095.00 ***978-1-4108-4532-0(X))** Benchmark Education Co.

Math Special Deliveries Books. 2001. (J). pap. 13.95 (978-1-56911-069-0(7)) Learning Resources, Inc.

Math Special Deliveries Books: Grades K-3. 2001. (J). pap. 13.95 (978-1-56911-084-3(0)) Learning Resources, Inc.

Math Standards Review Binder 1. 2001. (Illus.). 100p. (YA). ring bd. 29.95 (978-1-56254-518-5(3) , SP5183) Saddleback Educational Publishing.

Math Standards Review Binder 2. 2001. (Illus.). 100p (YA). ring bd. 29 95 (978 1-56254-519-2(1) , SP5191) Saddleback Educational Publishing.

Math Student Text: Grade 7. 2004. 32.00 (978-0-89084-842-5(4)) Jones, Bob Univ. Pr.

Math Teach & Test Grade 1. 2002. (Teach & Test Ser.). (Illus.). 48p. (J). per. 10.99 (978-0-88724-763-7(6) , CD-4305) Carson-Dellosa Publishing Co., Inc.

Math Traveler. 2002. (McGraw-Hill Mathematics Ser.). (ENG & SPA.). (gr. 6 up). (978-0-02-111485-6(4)); (gr. 4 up). (978-0-02-111483-2(8)); (gr. 4 up). (978-0-02-111476-4(5)); (gr. 5 up). (978-0-02-111477-1(3)); (gr. 5 up). (978-0-02-111484-9(6)); (gr. 6 up). (978-0-02-111478-8(1)) Macmillan/McGraw-Hill Schl. Div.

Math War! 1998. (High Q Books Ser.). (Illus.). 60p. (J). (ps-6). pap. 2.99 (978-0-7681-0071-6(2) , McClanahan Bk.) Learning Horizons, Inc.

Math with Connecting People. 2000. (J). pap. 9.95 (978-1-56911-023-2(9)) Learning Resources, Inc.

Math Workbook. 1999. (Step Ahead Ser.). 320p. (J). pap., wbk. ed. 4.99 (978-0-307-11252-1(7) , Golden Bks.) Random Hse. Children's Bks.

Mathematical Connections: A Bridge to Algebra & Geometry. 2001. (gr. 7-10). (978-0-618-07387-0(6) , 2-60436); tchr. ed. (978-0-618-07386-3(8) , 2-60435); stu. ed. 51.09 (978-0-618-07385-6(X) , 2-60434) McDougal Littell Inc.

Mathematics. (Illus.). 2004. (gr. 5). tchr. ed., stu. ed. 47.95 (978-1-58095-725-0(0) , MAT0515, Lifepac); 2000. (J). (gr. 3-7). pap. 66.95 incl. cd-rom (978-0-7403-0225-1(6) , SOS300M); 2005. 2004. (gr. 2). tchr. ed., stu. ed. 47.95 (978-1-58095-716-8(1) , MAT0215, Lifepac) Alpha Omega Pubns., Inc.

Mathematics. 2000. (Quick Start Masters Technology Ser.). (J). (gr. 1-2). (978-0-7725-2360-0(6)); (gr. 3-4). (978-0-7725-2364-8(9)) Thomson Nelson.

Mathematics: Algebra II, 11 vols., Set. 2004. (Illus.). (gr. 11-12). tchr. ed., stu. ed. 52.95 (978-1-58095-743-4(9) , MAT1115, Lifepac) Alpha Omega Pubns., Inc.

Mathematics: Trigonometry, 11 vols., Set. 2004. (Illus.). (gr. 12). tchr. ed., stu. ed. 52.95 (978-1-58095-746-5(3) , MAT1215, Lifepac) Alpha Omega Pubns., Inc.

Mathematics for New English Speakers of English TRG. 2005. 171p. (YA). per. 49.95 (978-1-56254-647-2(3) , SP6473) Saddleback Educational Publishing.

Mathematics in a World of Data. 2000. (YA). (gr. 7-12). 18.95 (978-1-57232-402-2(3)) Seymour, Dale Pubns.

The Mathematics of Bonds. 2002. (Mathematics for Everyday Living Ser.). (YA). per. 10.95 (978-1-58123-318-6(3)) Larson Learning, Inc.

The Mathematics of Bonds Complete Solutions Guide. 2002. (Mathematics for Everyday Living Ser.). (YA). pap. 5.00 (978-1-58123-298-1(5)) Larson Learning, Inc.

The Mathematics of Mutual Funds. 2002. (Mathematics for Everyday Living Ser.). (YA). per. 10.95 (978-1-58123-319-3(1)) Larson Learning, Inc.

The Mathematics of Mutual Funds Complete Solutions Guide. 2002. (Mathematics for Everyday Living Ser.). (YA). pap. 5.00 (978-1-58123-324-7(8)) Larson Learning, Inc.

The Mathematics of Stocks. 2001. (Mathematics for Everyday Living Ser.). (YA). per. 9.95 (978-1-58123-211-0(X)) Larson Learning, Inc.

The Mathematics of Taxes Complete Solutions Guide. 2000. (Mathematics for Everyday Living Ser.). (YA). per. 3.50 (978-1-58123-205-9(5)) Larson Learning, Inc.

The Mathematics of Taxes Complete Solutions Guide: The Mathematics of Everyday Living. 2nd ed. 2000. (Mathematics for Everyday Living Ser.). (YA). 5.00 (978-1-58123-277-6(2)) Larson Learning, Inc.

Mathematics: Structure & Method, Course 1: Pupil's Edition. 2000. (gr. 6-12). (978-0-395-48098-4(1) , 2-12745) McDougal Littell Inc.

Mathematics Today, Grades 2-3 Vol. 1: Featuring Students Working Mathematically, 3 vols. 2000. 80p. (J). (gr. 2-3). pap. 8.95 (978-1-58324-090-8(X) , World Teachers Pr.) Didax Educational Resources, Inc.

Mathematics Today, Grades 4-5 Vol. 2: Featuring Students Working Mathematically, 3 vols. 2000. 80p. (J). (gr. 4-5). pap. 8.95 (978-1-58324-091-5(8) , World Teachers Pr.) Didax Educational Resources, Inc.

Mathematics Today, Grades 6-7 Vol. 3: Featuring Students Working Mathematically, 3 vols. 2000. 80p. (YA). (gr. 6-7). pap. 8.95 (978-1-58324-092-2(6) , World Teachers Pr.) Didax Educational Resources, Inc.

Mathematik I. (Duden-Schuelerduden Ser.). (GER., Illus.). 544p. (YA). (978-3-411-04206-7(0)) Bibliographisches Institut & F. A. Brockhaus AG DEU. *Dist:* International Bk. Import Service, Inc.

Mathematik II. 4th ed. (Duden-Schuelerduden Ser.). (GER.). 480p. (YA). (978-3-411-04274-6(5)) Bibliographisches Institut & F. A. Brockhaus AG DEU. *Dist:* International Bk. Import Service, Inc.

MathFacts in a Flash Installation Guide. 2004. cd-rom 4.95 (978-1-59455-119-2(7)) Renaissance Learning, Inc.

MathFacts in a Flash Made EZ Flipchart. 2004. cd-rom 21.95 (978-1-59455-120-8(0)) Renaissance Learning, Inc.

MathFacts in a Flash Software Manual. 2004. cd-rom 12.95 (978-1-59455-118-5(9)) Renaissance Learning, Inc.

MathQueue. Place Value, Grade 1. 2005. (Illus.). 96p. (J). (gr. 1-1). pap. 12.99 (978-0-7682-3111-3(6) , Schaffer, Frank) Schaffer, Frank Pubns.

—Place Value, Grade 2. 2005. (Illus.). 96p. (J). (gr. 2-2). pap. 12.99 (978-0-7682-3112-0(4) , Schaffer, Frank) Schaffer, Frank Pubns.

—Place Value, Grade 3. 2005. (Illus.). 96p. (J). (gr. 3-3). pap. 12.99 (978-0-7682-3113-7(2) , Schaffer, Frank) Schaffer, Frank Pubns.

—Place Value, Grade 4. 2005. (Illus.). 96p (J). (gr. 4-4). pap. 12.99 (978-0-7682-3114-4(0) , Schaffer, Frank) Schaffer, Frank Pubns.

—Place Value, Grade 5. 2005. (Illus.). 96p. (J). (gr. 5-5). pap. 12.99 (978-0-7682-3115-1(9) , Schaffer, Frank) Schaffer, Frank Pubns.

Maths 3-4. Date not set. (Illus.). 32p. (J). 2.98 (978-0-7525-9560-3(1)) Parragon, Inc.

Maths 4-5. Date not set. (Gold Stars Workbook Ser.). (Illus.). 32p. (J). 2.98 (978-0-7525-9561-0(X)) Parragon, Inc.

Maths 5-6. Date not set. (Gold Stars Workbook Ser.). (Illus.). 32p. (J). 2.98 (978-0-7525-9562-7(8)) Parragon, Inc.

Maths 6-7. Date not set. (Gold Stars Workbook Ser.). (Illus.). 32p. (J). 2.98 (978-0-7525-9563-4(6)) Parragon, Inc.

Matrix Math: Innovative Educational Software for Grades 1 Thru 8+ 2004. (J). cd-rom (978-0-9763833-0-7(6)) Stellar Learning.

Matross, Vuyokasi. Vusirala the Giant: Chilomwe Version. Nkhoma, Wilson, tr. 1999. (Cambridge Reading Routes Ser.). (Illus.). 16p. pap. 3.70 (978-0-521-66855-2(7)) Cambridge Univ. Pr.

—Vusirala the Giant: Chitumbuka Version. Chirambo, Reuben, tr. 1999. (Cambridge Reading Routes Ser.). (Illus.). 16p. pap. 3.70 (978-0-521-66873-6(5)) Cambridge Univ. Pr.

—Vusirala the Giant: Chiyao Version. Kaliati, Mailos, tr. 1999. (Cambridge Reading Routes Ser.). (Illus.). 16p. pap. 3.70 (978-0-521-66860-6(3)) Cambridge Univ. Pr.

Matross, Vuyokazi. Vusirala the Giant. Tadjo, Veronique, tr. from ENG. 1998. (Cambridge African Language Library). (FRE., Illus.). 16p. pap. 3.75 (978-0-521-64790-8(8)) Cambridge Univ. Pr.

Mattern, Joanne. I Use Math. 24p. (YA). (978-0-8368-5998-0(7)) Stevens, Gareth Inc.

Matthews, Jean, et al. Formula One Maths. 2003. (Illus.). Vol. 1. 80p. pap. 18.50 ***978-0-340-85928-5(8));** Vol. 1. 80p. pap. 18.50 ***978-0-340-85926-1(1));** Vol. 2. 80p. pap. 18.50 ***978-0-340-85929-2(6));** Vol. 2. 80p. pap. 18.50 ***978-0-340-85927-8(X));** Vol. 2. 96p. pap. 18.50 ***978-0-340-85925-4(3));** Vol. 3. 80p. pap. 18.50 ***978-0-340-85930-8(X))** Hodder Education GBR. (Hodder Murray). *Dist:* Trans-Atlantic Pubns., Inc.

Mayer, Mercer. Beginning Math: Preschool. 2003. (Little Critter Preschool Workbook Ser.). (Illus.). 128p. (J). (ps-2). pap., wbk. ed. 8.95 (978-1-57768-579-1(2) , Spectrum) School Specialty Publishing.

—Mercer Mayer Math, PreK. 2003. (Little Critter(R) Workbooks Ser.). (Illus.). 32p. (J). (ps-2). pap. 2.99 (978-0-7696-3009-0(X) , Learning Materials) School Specialty Publishing.

Mayer, Mercer, illus. Spectrum Math, Grade 2. 2000. (Spectrum Workbooks Ser.). 128p. (J). (gr. 2-2). pap., wbk. ed. 8.95 (978-1-57768-802-0(3) , Spectrum) School Specialty Publishing.

Mayfield-Ingram, Karen. The Journey Through Middle School Math. Humphrey Williams, Ann, illus. Crews, Elizabeth, photos by. 2005. (Equals Ser.). 140p. pap. 18.95 (978-0-912511-31-3(1) , EQUALS) Univ. of California, Berkeley, Lawrence Hall of Science.

McCallum, Ann. The Secret Life of Math. 2005. (Kids Can Ser.). (Illus.). 128p. (J). (gr. 4-7). pap. 12.95 (978-0-8249-6755-0(0) , Williamson Bks.) Ideals Pubns.

—The Secret Life of Math: Discover How (and Why) Numbers Have Survived from the Cave Dwellers to Us! Norton, Carolyn McIntyre, illus. 2005. (Kids Can! Ser.). 128p. (YA). (gr. 9-7). 14.95 (978-0-8249-6779-6(8) , Williamson Bks.) Ideals Pubns.

McDonnell, Rose Anita, et al. Progress in Mathematics, Grade 1, Skills Update Practice Book. 1999. (Progress in Mathematics Ser.). (Illus.). 32p. (J). pap. (978-0-8215-2641-5(3) , Sadlier-Oxford) Sadlier, William H. Inc.

McDougal Littell Mathpack: Macintosh(r) 2004. (gr. 6-12). cd-rom (978-0-395-82241-8(6) , 2-91001) McDougal Littell Inc.

McDougal Littell Mathpack: Macintosh(r) (CD-ROM, 3. 5) 2004. (gr. 6-12). cd-rom (978-0-395-81001-9(9) , 2-91000); cd-rom (978-0-395-82246-3(7) , 2-91006); cd-rom (978-0-395-82244-9(0) , 2-91004); cd-rom (978-0-395-82248-7(3) , 2-91008); cd-rom (978-0-395-82250-0(5) , 2-91010) McDougal Littell Inc.

McDougal Littell Mathpack: Macintosh(r) Site License. 2004. (gr. 6-12). (978-0-395-84459-5(2) , 2-91065); (978-0-395-84460-1(6) , 2-91066); (978-0-395-84464-9(9) , 2-91070); (978-0-395-84463-2(0) , 2-91069); (978-0-395-84461-8(4) , 2-91067); (978-0-395-84462-5(2) , 2-91068) McDougal Littell Inc.

McDougal Littell Mathpack: Windows Site License. 2004. (gr. 6-12). (978-0-395-85513-3(6) , 2-91163) McDougal Littell Inc.

McDougal Littell Mathpack: Windows(r) 2004. (gr. 6-12). cd-rom (978-0-395-82243-2(2) , 2-91003) McDougal Littell Inc.

McDougal Littell Mathpack: Windows(r) (CD-ROM, 3. 5) 2004. (gr. 6-12). cd-rom (978-0-395-82242-5(4) , 2-91002); cd-rom (978-0-395-82247-0(5) , 2-91007); cd-rom (978-0-395-82245-6(9) , 2-91005); cd-rom (978-0-395-82249-4(1) , 2-91009); cd-rom (978-0-395-82251-7(3) , 2-91011) McDougal Littell Inc.

McDougal Littell Mathpack: Windows(r) Site License. 2004. (gr. 6-12). (978-0-395-85514-0(4) , 2-91164); (978-0-395-85518-8(7) , 2-91168); (978-0-395-85515-7(2) , 2-91165); (978-0-395-85517-1(9) , 2-91167); (978-0-395-85516-4(0) , 2-91166) McDougal Littell Inc.

McGraw-Hill - Jamestown Education Staff. Timed Readings Plus in Mathematics. 2005. Bk. 1. pap. 16.64 (978-0-07-872659-0(X) , 9780078726590); Bk. 2. pap. 16.64 (978-0-07-872660-6(3) , 9780078726606); Bk. 3. pap. 16.64 (978-0-07-872661-3(1) , 9780078726613); Bk. 4. pap. 16.64 (978-0-07-872662-0(X) , 9780078726620); Bk. 5. pap. 16.64 (978-0-07-872663-7(8) , 9780078726637) Glencoe/McGraw-Hill.

McGraw-Hill Staff. Contemporary Mathematics in Context: A Unified Approach. 2nd ed. 2003. 39.96 (978-0-07-827549-4(0) , 9780078275494); 2003. 39.96 (978-0-07-827550-0(4) , 9780078275500); 2002. (C). stu. ed. 38.00 (978-0-07-827546-3(6) , 9780078275463); 2002. stu. ed. 38.00 (978-0-07-827541-8(5) , 9780078275418); 2002. stu. ed. 38.00 (978-0-07-827537-1(7) , 9780078275371) Glencoe/McGraw-Hill.

—Contemporary Mathematics in Context: A Unified Approach, Course 1, Part A, Spanish Student Edition. 2004. (SPA.). (C). 38.00 (978-0-07-861819-2(3) , 9780078618192) Glencoe/McGraw-Hill.

—Contemporary Mathematics in Context: A Unified Approach, Course 2, Part A, Spanish Student Edition. 2005. 38.00 (978-0-07-869299-4(7) , 9780078692994) Glencoe/McGraw-Hill.

—Contemporary Mathematics in Context: A Unified Approach, Course 2, Part B, Spanish Student Edition. 2005. 38.00 (978-0-07-869300-7(4) , 9780078693007) Glencoe/McGraw-Hill.

—Contemporary Mathematics in Context Course 2, Pt. B: A Unified Approach. 2nd ed. 2002. stu. ed. 38.00 (978-0-07-827542-5(3) , 9780078275425); stu. ed. 38.00 (978-0-07-827538-8(5) , 9780078275388) Glencoe/McGraw-Hill.

—Contemporary Mathematics in Context Course 3, Pt. A: A Unified Approach. 2nd ed. 2002. (C). stu. ed. 38.00 (978-0-07-827545-6(8) , 9780078275456) Glencoe/McGraw-Hill.

—Glencoe Pre-Algebra. 2005. stu. ed. 79.00 (978-0-07-865108-3(5) , 9780078651083) Glencoe/McGraw-Hill.

—IMPACT Mathematics: Algebra & More, Course 3. 2004. (SPA.). (C). stu. ed. 77.32 (978-0-07-860732-5(9) , 9780078607325) Glencoe/McGraw-Hill.

MNO

—IMPACT Mathematics: Algebra & More, Course 1. 2003. stu. ed. 89.32 incl. cd-rom (978-0-07-861315-9(9) , 9780078613159); 3rd ed. stu. ed. 77.32 (978-0-07-860909-1(7) , 9780078609091) Glencoe/McGraw-Hill.

—IMPACT Mathematics: Algebra & More, Course 1, Spanish Student Edition. 2003. (SPA.). 77.32 (978-0-07-860720-2(5) , 9780078607202) Glencoe/McGraw-Hill.

—IMPACT Mathematics: Algebra & More, Course 2. 2nd ed. 2004. stu. ed. 77.32 (978-0-07-860920-6(8) , 9780078609206) Glencoe/McGraw-Hill.

—IMPACT Mathematics: Algebra & More, Course 3. 2nd ed. 2004. (C). stu. ed. 77.32 (978-0-07-860929-9(1) , 9780078609299) Glencoe/McGraw-Hill.

—IMPACT Mathematics: Algebra & More for the Middle, Grades Course 3. 2001. (C). stu. ed. 73.32 (978-0-07-827290-5(4) , 9780078272905) Glencoe/McGraw-Hill.

—Math Skills Maintenance, Course 1. 2003. (gr. 6-12). pap., wbk. ed. 10.64 (978-0-07-860721-9(3) , 9780078607219) Glencoe/McGraw-Hill.

—Math Skills Maintenance, Course 2. 2003. (C). (gr. 6-12). pap., wbk. ed. 10.64 (978-0-07-860727-1(2) , 9780078607271) Glencoe/McGraw-Hill.

—Math Skills Maintenance, Course 3. 2005. (gr. 6-12). pap., wbk. ed. 10.64 (978-0-07-860733-2(7) , 9780078607332) Glencoe/McGraw-Hill.

—Mathematics: Applications & Concepts, Course 3. 2003. stu. ed. 83.96 incl. cd-rom (978-0-07-860272-6(6) , 9780078602726) Glencoe/McGraw-Hill.

—Mathematics: Applications & Concepts, Course 1. 2003. (gr. 6-12). stu. ed. 79.96 incl. cd-rom (978-0-07-860291-7(2) , 9780078602917) Glencoe/McGraw-Hill.

—Mathematics: Applications & Concepts, Course 1, Noteables: Interactive Study Notebook with Foldables. 2004. pap. 26.64 (978-0-07-868214-8(2) , 9780078682148) Glencoe/McGraw-Hill.

—Mathematics: Applications & Concepts, Course 1, Practice Skills Workbook. 2003. (C). (gr. 6-12). pap. 10.64 (978-0-07-860086-9(3) , 9780078600869) Glencoe/McGraw-Hill.

—Mathematics: Applications & Concepts, Course 1, Practice: Word Problems Workbook. 2003. (gr. 6-12). pap. 10.64 (978-0-07-860087-6(1) , 9780078600876) Glencoe/McGraw-Hill.

—Mathematics: Applications & Concepts, Course 1, Reading to Learn Mathematics Workbook. 2003. (gr. 6-12). pap. 10.64 (978-0-07-861057-8(5) , 9780078610578) Glencoe/McGraw-Hill.

—Mathematics: Applications & Concepts, Course 1, Spanish Practice Skills Workbook. 2003. (SPA.). (C). (gr. 6-12). pap. 10.64 (978-0-07-860092-0(8) , 9780078600920) Glencoe/McGraw-Hill.

—Mathematics: Applications & Concepts, Course 1, Spanish Practice: Word Problems Workbook. 2003. (SPA.). (gr. 6-12). pap. 10.64 (978-0-07-860093-7(6) , 9780078600937) Glencoe/McGraw-Hill.

—Mathematics: Applications & Concepts, Course 1, Spanish Study Guide & Intervention Workbook. 2003. (SPA.). (C). (gr. 6-12). pap. 10.64 (978-0-07-860091-3(X) , 9780078600913) Glencoe/McGraw-Hill.

—Mathematics: Applications & Concepts, Course 1, Student Edition. 2003. (gr. 6-12). stu. ed. 71.96 (978-0-07-829631-4(5) , 9780078296314) Glencoe/McGraw-Hill.

—Mathematics: Applications & Concepts, Course 1, StudentWorks CD-ROM. 2005. (C). cd-rom 83.96 (978-0-07-869874-3(X) , 9780078698743) Glencoe/McGraw-Hill.

—Mathematics: Applications & Concepts, Course 1, Study Guide & Intervention Workbook. 2003. (gr. 6-12). pap. 10.64 (978-0-07-860085-2(5) , 9780078600852) Glencoe/McGraw-Hill.

—Mathematics: Applications & Concepts, Course 2, Noteables: Interactive Study Notebook with Foldables. 2004. pap. 26.64 (978-0-07-868215-5(0) , 9780078682155) Glencoe/McGraw-Hill.

—Mathematics: Applications & Concepts, Course 2, Practice Skills Workbook. 2nd ed. 2003. (C). (gr. 6-12). pap. 10.64 (978-0-07-860129-3(0) , 9780078601293) Glencoe/McGraw-Hill.

—Mathematics: Applications & Concepts, Course 2, Practice: Word Problems Workbook. 2003. (C). (gr. 6-12). pap. 10.64 (978-0-07-860130-9(4) , 9780078601309) Glencoe/McGraw-Hill.

—Mathematics: Applications & Concepts, Course 2, Reading to Learn Mathematics Workbook. 2003. (gr. 6-12). pap. 11.20 (978-0-07-861058-5(3) , 9780078610585) Glencoe/McGraw-Hill.

—Mathematics: Applications & Concepts, Course 2, Spanish Practice Skills Workbook. 2nd ed. 2003. (SPA.). (gr. 6-12). pap. 10.64 (978-0-07-860135-4(5) , 9780078601354) Glencoe/McGraw-Hill.

—Mathematics: Applications & Concepts, Course 2, Spanish Practice: Word Problems Workbook. 2nd ed. 2003. (SPA.). (C). (gr. 6-12). pap. 10.64 (978-0-07-860136-1(3) , 9780078601361) Glencoe/McGraw-Hill.

—Mathematics: Applications & Concepts, Course 2, Student Edition. 2003. 714p. (gr. 6-8). stu. ed. 70.00 (978-0-07-829633-8(1) , 9780078296338) Glencoe/McGraw-Hill.

—Mathematics: Applications & Concepts, Course 2, StudentWorks. 2003. (C). cd-rom 83.96 (978-0-07-860279-5(3) , 9780078602795) Glencoe/McGraw-Hill.

—Mathematics: Applications & Concepts, Course 2, StudentWorks CD-ROM. 2005. cd-rom 85.32 (978-0-07-869880-4(4) , 9780078698804) Glencoe/McGraw-Hill.

—Mathematics: Applications & Concepts, Course 3. 2003. 796p. (C). (gr. 6-8). stu. ed. 73.32 (978-0-07-829635-2(8) , 9780078296352) Glencoe/McGraw-Hill.

—Mathematics: Applications & Concepts, Course 3, Noteables: Interactive Study Notebook with Foldables. 2004. (C). pap. 26.64 (978-0-07-868216-2(9) , 9780078682162) Glencoe/McGraw-Hill.

—Mathematics: Applications & Concepts, Course 3, Practice Skills Workbook. 2003. (gr. 6-12). pap. 10.64 (978-0-07-860163-7(0) , 9780078601637) Glencoe/McGraw-Hill.

—Mathematics: Applications & Concepts, Course 3, Practice: Word Problems Workbook. 2003. (C). (gr. 6-12). pap. 10.64 (978-0-07-860164-4(9) , 9780078601644) Glencoe/McGraw-Hill.

—Mathematics: Applications & Concepts, Course 3, Reading to Learn Mathematics Workbook. 2003. (gr. 6-12). pap. 10.64 (978-0-07-861062-2(1) , 9780078610622) Glencoe/McGraw-Hill.

—Mathematics: Applications & Concepts, Course 3, Student Edition. 2004. 73.32 (978-0-07-865265-3(0) , 9780078652653) Glencoe/McGraw-Hill.

—Mathematics: Applications & Concepts, Course 3, StudentWorks CD-ROM. 2005. cd-rom 85.32 (978-0-07-869886-6(3) , 9780078698866) Glencoe/McGraw-Hill.

—Mathematics: Applications & Connections, Course 1, MathPASS Tutorial, CD-ROM. 1999. cd-rom 74.64 (978-0-02-834312-9(3) , 9780028343129) Glencoe/McGraw-Hill.

—Mathematics: Applications & Connections, Course 2, Mathpass Tutorial. 1999. cd-rom 74.64 (978-0-02-834313-6(1) , 9780028343136) Glencoe/McGraw-Hill.

—Mathematics: Applications & Connections, Course 3, Mathpass Tutorial. 1999. (C). cd-rom 74.64 (978-0-02-834314-3(X) , 9780028343143) Glencoe/McGraw-Hill.

—Mathematics Course 1: Applications & Concepts. 2004. stu. ed. 71.96 (978-0-07-865253-0(7) , 9780078652530) Glencoe/McGraw-Hill.

—Mathematics Course 2: Applications & Concepts. 2006. stu. ed. 73.32 (978-0-07-865263-9(4) , 9780078652639) Glencoe/McGraw-Hill.

—MathScape: Seeing & Thinking Mathematically, Course 1, Beside the Point. 2004. (C). pap. 11.96 (978-0-07-866800-5(X) , 9780078668005) Glencoe/McGraw-Hill.

—MathScape: Seeing & Thinking Mathematically, Course 1, Designing Spaces. 2004. pap. 11.96 (978-0-07-866798-5(4) , 9780078667985) Glencoe/McGraw-Hill.

—MathScape: Seeing & Thinking Mathematically, Course 1, from Whole to Parts. 2004. pap. 11.96 (978-0-07-866796-1(8) , 9780078667961) Glencoe/McGraw-Hill.

—MathScape: Seeing & Thinking Mathematically, Course 1, Gulliver's Worlds. 2004. pap. 11.96 (978-0-07-866802-9(6) , 9780078668029) Glencoe/McGraw-Hill.

—MathScape: Seeing & Thinking Mathematically, Course 1, Patterns in Numbers & Shapes, Student Guide. 2004. pap. 11.96 (978-0-07-866804-3(2) , 9780078668043) Glencoe/McGraw-Hill.

—MathScape: Seeing & Thinking Mathematically, Course 1, StudentWorks. 2004. cd-rom 71.96 (978-0-07-868182-0(0) , 9780078681820) Glencoe/McGraw-Hill.

—MathScape: Seeing & Thinking Mathematically, Course 1, the Language of Numbers. 2004. pap. 11.96 (978-0-07-866794-7(1) , 9780078667947) Glencoe/McGraw-Hill.

—MathScape: Seeing & Thinking Mathematically, Course 1, What Does the Data Say? 2004. pap., stu. ed. 11.96 (978-0-07-866792-3(5) , 9780078667923) Glencoe/McGraw-Hill.

—MathScape: Seeing & Thinking Mathematically, Course 2, Buyer Beware, Student Guide. 2004. pap. 11.96 (978-0-07-866806-7(9) , 9780078668067) Glencoe/McGraw-Hill.

—MathScape: Seeing & Thinking Mathematically, Course 2, Chance Encounters. 2004. pap. 11.96 (978-0-07-866808-1(5) , 9780078668081) Glencoe/McGraw-Hill.

—MathScape: Seeing & Thinking Mathematically, Course 2, from the Ground up, Student Guide. 2004. pap. 11.96 (978-0-07-866812-8(3) , 9780078668128) Glencoe/McGraw-Hill.

—MathScape: Seeing & Thinking Mathematically, Course 2, Getting down to Business. 2004. (C). pap. 11.96 (978-0-07-866816-6(6) , 9780078668166) Glencoe/McGraw-Hill.

—MathScape: Seeing & Thinking Mathematically, Course 2, Making Mathematical Arguments, Student Guide. 2004. (C). pap. 11.96 (978-0-07-866810-4(7) , 9780078668104) Glencoe/McGraw-Hill.

—MathScape: Seeing & Thinking Mathematically, Course 2, Student Modular Pack. 2004. (C). pap., pap., pap. 81.32 (978-0-07-868287-2(8) , 9780078682872) Glencoe/McGraw-Hill.

—MathScape: Seeing & Thinking Mathematically, Course 2, StudentWorks. 2004. (C). cd-rom 71.96 (978-0-07-868184-4(7) , 9780078681844) Glencoe/McGraw-Hill.

—MathScape: Seeing & Thinking Mathematically, Course 2, the Language of Algebra. 2004. (C). pap. 11.96 (978-0-07-866814-2(X) , 9780078668142) Glencoe/McGraw-Hill.

—MathScape: Seeing & Thinking Mathematically, Course 3, Consolidated Student Guide. 2nd ed. 2004. 77.32 (978-0-07-860468-3(0) , 9780078604683) Glencoe/McGraw-Hill.

—MathScape: Seeing & Thinking Mathematically, Course 3, Exploring the Unknown. 2004. (C). pap. 11.96 (978-0-07-866828-9(X) , 9780078668289) Glencoe/McGraw-Hill.

—MathScape: Seeing & Thinking Mathematically, Course 3, Family Portraits. 2004. pap. 11.96 (978-0-07-866832-6(8) , 9780078668326) Glencoe/McGraw-Hill.

—MathScape: Seeing & Thinking Mathematically, Course 3, Looking Behind the Numbers. 2004. pap. 11.96 (978-0-07-866820-3(4) , 9780078668203) Glencoe/McGraw-Hill.

—MathScape: Seeing & Thinking Mathematically, Course 3, Mathematics in Motion. 2004. (C). pap. 11.96 (978-0-07-866822-7(0) , 9780078668227) Glencoe/McGraw-Hill.

—MathScape: Seeing & Thinking Mathematically, Course 3, Roads & Ramps. 2004. pap. 11.96 (978-0-07-866830-2(1) , 9780078668302) Glencoe/McGraw-Hill.

—MathScape: Seeing & Thinking Mathematically, Course 3, Shapes & Space. 2004. pap. 11.96 (978-0-07-866824-1(7) , 9780078668241) Glencoe/McGraw-Hill.

—MathScape: Seeing & Thinking Mathematically, Course 3, Student Modular Package. 2004. pap. 77.32 (978-0-07-868285-8(1) , 9780078682858) Glencoe/McGraw-Hill.

—MathScape: Seeing & Thinking Mathematically, Course 3, StudentWorks. 2004. cd-rom 71.96 (978-0-07-868186-8(3) , 9780078681868) Glencoe/McGraw-Hill.

—MathScape: Seeing & Thinking Mathematically, Course 3, What Comes Next? 2004. pap. 11.96 (978-0-07-866826-5(3) , 9780078668265) Glencoe/McGraw-Hill.

—Quick Review Math Handbook Bk. 3, Vol. 3: Hot Words, Hot Topics. 2003. (gr. 6-12). stu. ed. 30.64 (978-0-07-860160-6(6) , 9780078601606) Glencoe/McGraw-Hill.

—Skills Intervention for Middle School Mathematics: Diagnosis & Remediation, Spanish Student Workbook. 2003. (SPA.). (C). pap. 10.64 (978-0-07-861306-7(X) , 9780078613067) Glencoe/McGraw-Hill.

—Skills Intervention for Pre-Algebra: Diagnosis & Remediation, Spanish Student Workbook. 2004. (SPA.). pap. 10.64 (978-0-07-867809-7(9) , 9780078678097) Glencoe/McGraw-Hill.

—Skills Intervention for Pre-Algebra: Diagnosis & Remediation, Student Workbook. 2004. (C). pap. 10.64 (978-0-07-867808-0(0) , 9780078678080) Glencoe/McGraw-Hill.

McGraw-Hill Staff & Schaffer, Frank. Multiplication Facts. 2001. (Homework Helpers Activity Bks.). 56p. (J). (gr. 3-3). pap., act. bk. ed. 2.99 (978-0-7682-0717-0(7) , FS109046, Schaffer, Frank) Schaffer, Frank Pubns.

McGraw, Nancy L. Simple Solutions Level 3. 2003. 280p. stu. ed., per. (978-0-9728730-0-0(7)) Bright Ideas Pr., LLC.

—Simple Solutions Level 4. 2003. stu. ed., per. (978-0-9728730-1-7(5)) Bright Ideas Pr., LLC.

—Simple Solutions Level 4 TE. 2003. tchr. ed., per. (978-0-9728730-7-9(4)) Bright Ideas Pr., LLC.

—Simple Solutions Level 5. 2003. stu. ed., per. (978-0-9728730-2-4(3)) Bright Ideas Pr., LLC.

—Simple Solutions Level 5 TE. 2003. tchr. ed., per. (978-0-9728730-8-6(2)) Bright Ideas Pr., LLC.

—Simple Solutions Level 6. 2003. stu. ed., per. (978-0-9728730-3-1(1)) Bright Ideas Pr., LLC.

—Simple Solutions Level 7. 2003. stu. ed., per. (978-0-9728730-4-8(X)) Bright Ideas Pr., LLC.

—Simple Solutions Level 7 TE. 2003. tchr. ed., per. (978-0-9740408-0-6(0)) Bright Ideas Pr., LLC.

—Simple Solutions Level 8. 2003. stu. ed., per. (978-0-9728730-5-5(8)) Bright Ideas Pr., LLC.

—Simple Solutions Level 8 TE. 2003. tchr. ed., per. (978-0-9740408-1-3(9)) Bright Ideas Pr., LLC.

—Summer Solutions Level 6. 2005. (J). per. 13.00 net. (978-0-9760153-5-2(8)) Bright Ideas Pr., LLC.

—Summer Solutions Level 7. 2005. (J). per. 13.00 net. (978-0-9760153-6-9(6)) Bright Ideas Pr., LLC.

—Summer Solutions Level 8. 2005. (YA). per. 13.00 net. (978-0-9760153-7-6(4)) Bright Ideas Pr., LLC.

McGuire, Mary. Math Success Reproducible Worksheets. 2002. 171p. (J). (gr. 4-10). ring bd. 22.60 (978-0-7660-2029-0(0)) Enslow Pubs., Inc.

McKay, Lucia & Guscott, Maggie. Budgeting & Banking. 2004. 104p. (YA). per. 9.95 (978-1-56254-758-5(5) , SP7585) Saddleback Educational Publishing.

—Everyday Life. 2004. 104p. (YA). per. 9.95 (978-1-56254-760-8(7) , SP7607) Saddleback Educational Publishing.

—Home & School. 2004. 104p. (YA). per. 9.95 (978-1-56254-762-2(3) , SP7623) Saddleback Educational Publishing.

—Smart Shopping. 2004. 104p. (YA). per. 9.95 (978-1-56254-756-1(9) , SP7569) Saddleback Educational Publishing.

McLaurin, Thad, ed. Learning Library-Math. 2003. 128p. 19.95 (978-1-56234-529-7(X) , Mailbox Bks., The) Education Ctr., Inc.

McMorrow, Annalisa. Marvelous Money. 1999. (Illus.). 80p. (J). pap. 9.95 (978-1-57612-113-9(5)) Monday Morning Bks., Inc.

McMorrow, Scott. Math Start-Ups. 1999. (Illus.). 96p. (J). pap. 11.95 (978-1-57612-114-6(3)) Monday Morning Bks., Inc.

McNeil, Niki, et al. HOCPP 1115 Multiplication Party. 2006. spiral bd. 21.00 ***978-1-60308-115-3(1))** In the Hands of a Child.

MCP Mathematics: Level A. 2005. (J). (gr. k-6). stu. ed. 28.50 (978-0-7652-6056-7(5)) Seymour, Dale Pubns.

MCP Mathematics: Level B. 2005. (J). (gr. k-6). stu. ed. 28.50 (978-0-7652-6058-1(1)) Seymour, Dale Pubns.

MCP Mathematics: Level C. 2005. (J). (gr. k-6). stu. ed. 28.50 (978-0-7652-6060-4(3)) Seymour, Dale Pubns.

MCP Mathematics: Level F. 2005. (J). (gr. k-6). stu. ed. 28.50 (978-0-7652-6066-6(2)) Seymour, Dale Pubns.

MCP Mathematics: Level K. 2005. (J). (gr. k-6). stu. ed. 28.50 (978-0-7652-6054-3(9)) Seymour, Dale Pubns.

Me gustan los desfiles Math, 6 vols.Tr. of I Love a Parade Math. (SPA.). (gr. k-2). 28.95 (978-0-7368-3120-8(7) , Yellow Umbrella Bks.) Capstone Pr., Inc.

The MEAP Solution: Middle School Edition. 2003. 70p. (YA). (gr. 5-9). 19.95 (978-0-9718019-1-2(6)) Mathematical Solutions Publishing Co.

Measurement. 2001. (Inquiry Science Ser.). 32p. (gr. 2-3). 4.99 (978-1-56822-946-1(1) , IF20853) School Specialty Publishing.

Measuring with Mr Wiggle. 32p. (gr. 1 up). 4.99 (978-1-56451-994-8(5) , ID99020); (gr. 2 up). 4.99 (978-1-56451-995-5(3) , ID99021) School Specialty Publishing.

Measuring Worms Activity Cards. 2004. (J). 7.95 (978-1-56911-529-9(X)) Learning Resources, Inc.

Meeting Math Standards: High-Interest Activities that Motivate Learning. 80p. (gr. 2-3). 9.99 (978-0-7424-0249-2(5) , IF19217); (gr. 4-5). 9.99 (978-0-7424-0250-8(9) , IF19218) School Specialty Publishing.

Mega-Fun Math Fairs 4-6. 2003. 64p. (J). 7.99 (978-0-88724-974-7(4) , CD-7434) Carson-Dellosa Publishing Co., Inc.

Meiselmann, Laura. Grades 5 & Up: 50 Reproducible, Leveled Game Sheets That Kids Can Use Independently or in Small Groups to Practice Important Math Skills. 2005. (Tic-Tac-Math Ser.). 64p. pap. 11.99 (978-0-439-62921-8(7) , Teaching Resources) Scholastic, Inc.

Mental Math. 2004. (Help with Homework Ser.). 32p. (J). (gr. 1-4). wbk. ed. 3.99 (978-1-904586-26-5(0)) Byeway Bks.

Meredith-Markowitz, Susan. The Aquarium Adds Up. 2003. (Early Connections Ser.). (J). pap. 33.00 (978-1-4108-1070-0(4)) Benchmark Education Co.

—The Class Election. 2003. (Early Connections Ser.). (J). pap. 33.00 (978-1-4108-1085-4(2)) Benchmark Education Co.

Metcalf, Paul. On Course for GCSE Maths Foundation & Intermediate Tiers. 2000. (Illus.). 208p. (YA). (gr. 9-11). spiral bd. 19.95 (978-0-7487-4511-1(4)) Nelson Thornes Ltd. GBR. *Dist:* Trans-Atlantic Pubns., Inc.

Metcalf, Paul, et al. On Course for GCSE Maths Foundation & Intermediate Tiers with Answers. 2000. (Illus.). 208p. (YA). (gr. 9-11). spiral bd. 19.95 (978-0-7487-4512-8(2)) Nelson Thornes Ltd. GBR. *Dist:* Trans-Atlantic Pubns., Inc.

—On Course for GCSE Maths Intermediate & Higher Tiers. 2000. (Illus.). 208p. (YA). (gr. 9-11). spiral bd. 19.95 (978-0-7487-4454-1(1)) Nelson Thornes Ltd. GBR. *Dist:* Trans-Atlantic Pubns., Inc.

—On Course for GCSE Maths Intermediate & Higher Tiers with Answers. 2000. (Illus.). 208p. (YA). (gr. 9-11). spiral bd. 19.95 (978-0-7487-4455-8(X)) Nelson Thornes Ltd. GBR. *Dist:* Trans-Atlantic Pubns., Inc.

Meyer, Janet A. Brain Quest Grade 3 Math. rev. ed. 2006. 150p. (J). 10.95 (978-0-7611-4137-2(5)) Workman Publishing Co., Inc.

Meyers Kleine Enzyklopaedie Mathematik. (978-3-411-07771-7(9)) Bibliographisches Institut & F. A. Brockhaus AG DEU. *Dist:* i.b.d., Ltd.

MGH. McGraw Hill Matematicas. 2002. (MacMillan/McGraw-Hill Matematicas Ser.). (ENG & SPA.). (gr. k up). (978-0-02-111536-5(2)) Macmillan/McGraw-Hill Schl. Div.

Middle & High School Math (Ages 13-18), 6 Cds. 2003. cd-rom 29.99 (978-1-59150-268-5(3)) TOPICS Entertainment.

Middle Grades Mathematics. 2002. (gr. 6-9). cd-rom (978-0-618-07908-7(4) , 2-80588); (gr. 7-10). stu. ed. incl. cd-rom (978-0-618-09515-5(2) , 2-61309); (gr. 7-10). cd-rom (978-0-618-12979-9(0) , 2-99710) McDougal Littell Inc.

Middle Grades MathThematics. 2002. (gr. 6-9). tchr. ed. (978-0-618-09798-2(8) , 2-12119); 2002. (gr. 6-9). tchr. ed. (978-0-618-09799-9(6) , 2-12120); 2002. (gr. 6-9). stu. ed. (978-0-618-09801-9(1) , 2-12118); 2002. (gr. 7-10). stu. ed. incl. cd-rom (978-0-618-07811-0(8) , 2-61205); 1999. (gr. 6-9). stu. ed. (978-0-395-77499-1(3) , 2-12060); Bk. 1. 2002. (gr. 6-9). wbk. ed. (978-0-618-21248-4(5) , 2-50407); Vol. 2. 2002. (gr. 6-9). tchr. ed. (978-0-618-09804-0(6) , 2-12123); Vol. 2. 2002. (gr. 6-9). tchr. ed. (978-0-618-09803-3(8) , 2-12122); Vol. 2. 2002. (gr. 6-9). stu. ed. (978-0-618-09802-6(X) , 2-12121); Vol. 2. 2002. (gr. 6-9). wbk. ed. (978-0-618-21249-1(3) , 2-50408); Vol. 2. 2002. (gr. 6-9). cd-rom (978-0-618-07909-4(2) , 2-80589); Vol. 2. 1999. (gr. 6-12). stu. ed. (978-0-395-77500-4(0) , 2-12061); Vol. 3. 2002. (gr. 6-9). tchr. ed. (978-0-618-09806-4(2) , 2-12125); Vol. 3. 2002. (gr. 6-9). tchr. ed. (978-0-618-09807-1(0) , 2-12126); Vol. 3. 2002. (gr. 6-9). stu. ed. (978-0-618-09805-7(4) , 2-12124); Vol. 3. 2002. (gr. 6-9). wbk. ed. (978-0-618-21250-7(7) , 2-50409); Vol. 3. 2002. (gr. 6-9). cd-rom (978-0-618-07910-0(6) , 2-80590); Vol. 3. 1999. (gr. 6-12). stu. ed. (978-0-395-77501-1(9) , 2-12062) McDougal Littell Inc.

Middle School Math, Course 1: EEdition. 2004. (gr. 6-9). cd-rom (978-0-618-36400-8(5) , 2-06524) McDougal Littell Inc.

Middle School Math, Course 1: EEdition Plus Online - Parent Purchase. 2004. (gr. 6-9). (978-0-618-39816-4(3) , 2-05646) McDougal Littell Inc.

Middle School Math, Course 1: EEdition Plus Online with print purchase - 1 Year. 2004. (gr. 6-9). (978-0-618-39416-6(8) , 2-05569) McDougal Littell Inc.

Middle School Math, Course 1: EEdition Plus Online with print purchase - 2 Years. 2004. (gr. 6-9). (978-0-618-39417-3(6) , 2-05570) McDougal Littell Inc.

Middle School Math, Course 1: EEdition Plus Online with print purchase - 3 Years. 2004. (gr. 6-9). (978-0-618-39418-0(4) , 2-05571) McDougal Littell Inc.

Middle School Math, Course 1: EEdition Plus Online with print purchase - 4 Years. 2004. (gr. 6-9). (978-0-618-39419-7(2) , 2-05572) McDougal Littell Inc.

Middle School Math, Course 1: EEdition Plus Online with print purchase - 5 Years. 2004. (gr. 6-9). (978-0-618-39420-3(6) , 2-05573) McDougal Littell Inc.

Middle School Math, Course 1: EEdition Plus Online with print purchase - 6 Years. 2004. (gr. 6-9). (978-0-618-39421-0(4) , 2-05574) McDougal Littell Inc.

Middle School Math, Course 1: EEdition Plus Online without print purchase - 6 Years. 2004. (gr. 6-9). (978-0-618-36956-0(2) , 2-06527) McDougal Littell Inc.

Middle School Math, Course 1: ETutorial. 2004. (gr. 6-9). cd-rom (978-0-618-36393-3(9) , 2-06517); cd-rom (978-0-618-39810-2(4) , 2-05640); cd-rom (978-0-618-39811-9(2) , 2-05641) McDougal Littell Inc.

Middle School Math, Course 1: ETutorial Plus Online. 2004. (gr. 6-9). (978-0-618-39410-4(9) , 2-05563) McDougal Littell Inc.

Middle School Math, Course 1: EWorkbook Plus Online. 2004. (gr. 6-9). (978-0-618-39413-5(3) , 2-05566) McDougal Littell Inc.

Middle School Math, Course 1: Exercises in Spanish. 2004. (gr. 6-9). (978-0-618-37054-2(4) , 2-06338) McDougal Littell Inc.

Middle School Math, Course 1: Notetaking Guide, PE. 2004. (gr. 6-9). (978-0-618-25035-6(2) , 2-06018) McDougal Littell Inc.

Middle School Math, Course 1: Notetaking Guide, TE. 2004. (gr. 6-9). (978-0-618-33453-7(X) , 2-06212) McDougal Littell Inc.

Middle School Math, Course 1: Practice Workbook, PE. 2004. (gr. 6-9). (978-0-618-25754-6(3) , 2-06025) McDougal Littell Inc.

Middle School Math, Course 1: Practice Workbook, TE. 2004. (gr. 6-9). (978-0-618-34360-7(1) , 2-06229) McDougal Littell Inc.

Middle School Math, Course 1: Pupil's Edition. 2004. (gr. 6-12). (978-0-618-06730-5(2) , 2-78042); (978-0-618-08759-4(1) , 2-06000) McDougal Littell Inc.

Middle School Math, Course 1: Spanish Study Guide. 2004. (gr. 6-9). (978-0-618-26962-4(2) , 2-05798) McDougal Littell Inc.

Middle School Math, Course 1: Test & Practice Generator. 2004. (gr. 6-9). cd-rom (978-0-618-15838-6(3) , 2-99755) McDougal Littell Inc.

Middle School Math, Course 1: Worked-Out Solution Key. 2004. (gr. 6-9). (978-0-618-28026-1(X) , 2-06102) McDougal Littell Inc.

Middle School Math, Course 2, Vol. 2. 2001. (gr. 6-12). stu. ed. (978-0-618-06731-2(0) , 2-78043) McDougal Littell Inc.

Middle School Math, Course 2: EEdition. 2004. (gr. 6-12). cd-rom (978-0-618-36401-5(3) , 2-06525) McDougal Littell Inc.

Middle School Math, Course 2: EEdition Plus Online - Parent Purchase. 2004. (gr. 6-12). (978-0-618-39817-1(1) , 2-05647) McDougal Littell Inc.

Middle School Math, Course 2: EEdition Plus Online with print purchase - 1 Year. 2004. (gr. 6-12). (978-0-618-39422-7(2) , 2-05575) McDougal Littell Inc.

Middle School Math, Course 2: EEdition Plus Online with print purchase - 2 Years. 2004. (gr. 6-12). (978-0-618-39423-4(0) , 2-05576) McDougal Littell Inc.

Middle School Math, Course 2: EEdition Plus Online with print purchase - 3 Years. 2004. (gr. 6-12). (978-0-618-39424-1(9) , 2-05577) McDougal Littell Inc.

Middle School Math, Course 2: EEdition Plus Online with print purchase - 4 Years. 2004. (gr. 6-12). (978-0-618-39425-8(7) , 2-05578) McDougal Littell Inc.

Middle School Math, Course 2: EEdition Plus Online with print purchase - 5 Years. 2004. (gr. 6-12). (978-0-618-39426-5(5) , 2-05579) McDougal Littell Inc.

Middle School Math, Course 2: EEdition Plus Online with print purchase - 6 Years. 2004. (gr. 6-12). (978-0-618-39427-2(3) , 2-05580) McDougal Littell Inc.

Middle School Math, Course 2: EEdition Plus Online without print purchase - 6 Years. 2004. (gr. 6-12). (978-0-618-36957-7(0) , 2-06528) McDougal Littell Inc.

Middle School Math, Course 2: ETutorial. 2004. (gr. 6-12). cd-rom (978-0-618-36396-4(3) , 2-06520); cd-rom (978-0-618-39812-6(0) , 2-05642); cd-rom (978-0-618-39813-3(9) , 2-05643) McDougal Littell Inc.

Middle School Math, Course 2: ETutorial Plus Online. 2004. (gr. 6-12). (978-0-618-39411-1(7) , 2-05564) McDougal Littell Inc.

Middle School Math, Course 2: EWorkbook Plus Online. 2004. (gr. 6-12). (978-0-618-39414-2(1) , 2-05567) McDougal Littell Inc.

Middle School Math, Course 2: Exercises in Spanish. 2004. (gr. 6-12). (978-0-618-37055-9(2) , 2-06339) McDougal Littell Inc.

Middle School Math, Course 2: Notetaking Guide, PE. 2004. (gr. 6-12). (978-0-618-25618-1(0) , 2-06021) McDougal Littell Inc.

Middle School Math, Course 2: Practice Workbook, PE. 2004. (gr. 6-12). (978-0-618-25755-3(1) , 2-06026) McDougal Littell Inc.

Middle School Math, Course 2: Spanish Study Guide. 2004. (gr. 6-12). (978-0-618-26882-5(0) , 2-06083) McDougal Littell Inc.

Middle School Math, Course 2: Worked-Out Solution Key. 2004. (gr. 6-12). (978-0-618-28036-0(7) , 2-06106) McDougal Littell Inc.

Middle School Math, Course 3, Vol. 3. 2002. (gr. 8 up). stu. ed. (978-0-618-06732-9(9) , 2-78044) McDougal Littell Inc.

Middle School Math, Course 3: EEdition. 2004. (gr. 6-12). cd-rom (978-0-618-36402-2(1) , 2-06526) McDougal Littell Inc.

Middle School Math, Course 3: EEdition Plus Online with print purchase - 1 Year. 2004. (gr. 6-12). (978-0-618-39428-9(1) , 2-05581) McDougal Littell Inc.

Middle School Math, Course 3: EEdition Plus Online with print purchase - 2 Years. 2004. (gr. 6-12). (978-0-618-39429-6(X) , 2-05582) McDougal Littell Inc.

Middle School Math, Course 3: EEdition Plus Online with print purchase - 3 Years. 2004. (gr. 6-12). (978-0-618-39430-2(3) , 2-05583) McDougal Littell Inc.

Middle School Math, Course 3: EEdition Plus Online with print purchase - 4 Years. 2004. (gr. 6-12). (978-0-618-39431-9(1) , 2-05584) McDougal Littell Inc.

Middle School Math, Course 3: EEdition Plus Online with print purchase - 5 Years. 2004. (gr. 6-12). (978-0-618-39432-6(X) , 2-05585) McDougal Littell Inc.

Middle School Math, Course 3: EEdition Plus Online with print purchase - 6 Years. 2004. (gr. 6-12). (978-0-618-39433-3(8) , 2-05586) McDougal Littell Inc.

Middle School Math, Course 3: EEdition Plus Online without print purchase - 6 Years. 2004. (gr. 6-12). (978-0-618-36958-4(9) , 2-06529) McDougal Littell Inc.

Middle School Math, Course 3: ETutorial. 2004. (gr. 6-12). cd-rom (978-0-618-36383-4(1) , 2-06507); cd-rom (978-0-618-39814-0(7) , 2-05644); cd-rom (978-0-618-39815-7(5) , 2-05645) McDougal Littell Inc.

Middle School Math, Course 3: ETutorial Plus Online. 2004. (gr. 6-12). (978-0-618-39412-8(5) , 2-05565) McDougal Littell Inc.

Middle School Math, Course 3: EWorkbook Plus Online. 2004. (gr. 6-12). (978-0-618-39415-9(X) , 2-05568) McDougal Littell Inc.

Middle School Math, Course 3: Notetaking Guide, PE. 2004. (gr. 6-12). (978-0-618-25656-3(3) , 2-06022) McDougal Littell Inc.

Middle School Math, Course 3: Practice Workbook, PE. 2004. (gr. 6-12). (978-0-618-25757-7(8) , 2-06027) McDougal Littell Inc.

Middle School Math, Course 3: Worked-Out Solution Key. 2004. (gr. 6-12). (978-0-618-28040-7(5) , 2-06110) McDougal Littell Inc.

Middle School Math Excelerator, 2 CDs. 2002. cd-rom 9.99 (978-1-59150-016-2(8)) TOPICS Entertainment.

Migachyov, Dina. Mathematics for Little Ones: How to Make Your Child Successful in Math. Migachyov, Larisa, illus. 1999. viii, 183p. (J). (gr. k-3). pap. 19.95 (978-0-9672535-0-3(0)) Quatemion Pr.

Mighton, John. JUMP at Home— Grade 3: Math Worksheets for the Elementary Curriculum. 2007. (Illus.). pap. (***978-0-88784-719-6(6)***) House of Anansi Pr.

—JUMP at Home— Grade 4: Math Worksheets for the Elementary Curriculum. 2007. (Illus.). pap. (***978-0-88784-720-2(X)***) House of Anansi Pr.

—JUMP at Home— Grade 5: Math Worksheets for the Elementary Curriculum. 2007. (Illus.). pap. (***978-0-88784-721-9(8)***) House of Anansi Pr.

—JUMP at Home— Grade 6: Math Worksheets for the Elementary Curriculum. 2007. (Illus.). pap. (***978-0-88784-722-6(6)***) House of Anansi Pr.

Miles Moran, Andrea. Math Topics. 1999. (100+ Seriestm Ser.). 128p. (YA). (gr. 7-8). pap. 12.99 (978-1-56822-139-7(8) , IF8748) School Specialty Publishing.

Miles Moran, Andrea & Linderman, Bill. Word Problems. 1999. (Homework Booklets Ser.). 72p. (J). (gr. 4-4). pap. 2.99 (978-0-88012-862-9(3) , IF0193, Instructional Fair) Schaffer, Frank Pubns.

Miller, Amanda. Let's Add to Ten, Again & Again! Michael, Joan J., illus. Levin, James, photos by. 2007. (Let's Find Out Early Learning Bks.). 32p. (J). (ps-k). lib. bdg. 18.00 (978-0-531-14869-3(6) , Children's Pr.) Scholastic Library Publishing.

Miller, Elizabeth D. Read It! Draw It! Solve It! 2003. (Illus.). 192p. (YA). (gr. 3 up). 20.50 (978-1-57232-436-7(8) , 33802) Seymour, Dale Pubns.

—Read It! Draw It! Solve It! Animal Book. 2003. (Illus.). 192p. (J). 34.95 (978-1-57232-437-4(6)) Seymour, Dale Pubns.

Millington, Jon. Mathematical Snacks: A Collection of Interesting Ideas to Fill Those Spare Moments. 2004. (Illus.). 96p. 14.00 (978-1-899618-51-4(1)) Tarquin Pubns. GBR. *Dist:* Parkwest Pubns., Inc.

—Tables Cubes: Make These Two Sets of Special Cubes & Use Them for Tables Practice. 2004. (Illus.). 24p. (J). 10.00 (978-1-899618-17-0(1)) Tarquin Pubns. GBR. *Dist:* Parkwest Pubns., Inc.

Mills, Steve & Koll, Hilary. Quick Revision KS3 Maths. 2007. 46p. pap. 9.95 (***978-0-340-94306-9(8)*** , Hodder Murray) Hodder Education GBR. *Dist:* Trans-Atlantic Pubns., Inc.

Milone, Michael. LeapTrack FCAT: Math 5th Grade. 2001. (J). (gr. k-5). spiral bd. 1.50 (978-1-58605-625-4(5)) LeapFrog Enterprises, Inc.

—LeapTrack Math: 1st Grade Beginning-of-Year. 2001. (J). (gr. k-5). spiral bd. 1.50 (978-1-58605-545-5(3)) LeapFrog Enterprises, Inc.

—LeapTrack Math: 1st Grade End-of-Year. 2001. (J). (gr. k-5). spiral bd. 1.50 (978-1-58605-547-9(X)) LeapFrog Enterprises, Inc.

—LeapTrack Math: 1st Grade Middle-of-Year. 2001. (J). (gr. k-5). spiral bd. 1.50 (978-1-58605-546-2(1)) LeapFrog Enterprises, Inc.

—LeapTrack Math: 2nd Grade Beginning-of-Year. 2001. (J). (gr. k-5). spiral bd. 1.50 (978-1-58605-555-4(0)) LeapFrog Enterprises, Inc.

—LeapTrack Math: 2nd Grade End-of-Year. 2001. (J). (gr. k-5). spiral bd. 1.50 (978-1-58605-557-8(7)) LeapFrog Enterprises, Inc.

—LeapTrack Math: 2nd Grade Middle-of-Year. 2001. (J). (gr. k-5). spiral bd. 1.50 (978-1-58605-556-1(9)) LeapFrog Enterprises, Inc.

—LeapTrack Math: 3rd Grade Beginning-of-Year. 2001. (J). (gr. k-5). spiral bd. 1.50 (978-1-58605-571-4(2)) LeapFrog Enterprises, Inc.

—LeapTrack Math: 3rd Grade End-of-Year. 2001. (J). (gr. k-5). spiral bd. 1.50 (978-1-58605-573-8(9)) LeapFrog Enterprises, Inc.

—LeapTrack Math: 3rd Grade Middle-of-Year. 2001. (J). (gr. k-5). spiral bd. 1.50 (978-1-58605-572-1(0)) LeapFrog Enterprises, Inc.

—LeapTrack Math: 4th Grade Beginning-of-Year. 2001. (J). (gr. k-5). spiral bd. 1.50 (978-1-58605-591-2(7)) LeapFrog Enterprises, Inc.

—LeapTrack Math: 4th Grade End-of-Year. 2001. (J). (gr. k-5). spiral bd. 1.50 (978-1-58605-593-6(3)) LeapFrog Enterprises, Inc.

—LeapTrack Math: 4th Grade Middle-of-Year. 2001. (J). (gr. k-5). spiral bd. 1.50 (978-1-58605-592-9(5)) LeapFrog Enterprises, Inc.

—LeapTrack Math: 5th Grade Beginning-of-Year. 2001. (J). (gr. k-5). spiral bd. 1.50 (978-1-58605-611-7(5)) LeapFrog Enterprises, Inc.

—LeapTrack Math: 5th Grade Middle-of-Year. 2001. (J). (gr. k-5). spiral bd. 1.50 (978-1-58605-612-4(3)) LeapFrog Enterprises, Inc.

—LeapTrack Math: Kindergarten Beginning-of-Year. 2001. (J). (gr. k-5). spiral bd. 1.50 (978-1-58605-539-4(9)) LeapFrog Enterprises, Inc.

—LeapTrack Math: Kindergarten End-of-Year. 2001. (J). (gr. k-5). spiral bd. 1.50 (978-1-58605-541-7(0)) LeapFrog Enterprises, Inc.

—LeapTrack Math: Kindergarten Middle-of-Year. 2001. (J). (gr. k-5). spiral bd. 1.50 (978-1-58605-540-0(2)) LeapFrog Enterprises, Inc.

Minden, Cecilia. Exercise by the Numbers. 2008. (J). lib. bdg. 25.26 (***978-1-60279-010-0(8)***) Cherry Lake Publishing.

Mira los dos lados Math, 6 vols.Tr. of Look at Both Sides Math. (SPA.). (gr. k-2). 28.95 (978-0-7368-3049-2(9) , Yellow Umbrella Bks.) Capstone Pr., Inc.

Mitchell, Cindi. Dazzling Math Line Designs: Dozens of Reproducible Activities That Help Build Addition, Subtraction. 2003. (Illus.). 64p. 9.95 (978-0-590-00086-4(1)) Scholastic, Inc.

—Great Graph Art to Build Early Math Skills: 50 Reproducible Activities That Help Kids Practice Addition, Subtraction, & Basic Graphing Skills As They Plot Their Way to Picture Surprises. 2001. 64p. (gr. 1). pap. 10.95 (978-0-439-14611-1(9)) Scholastic, Inc.

—Great States Quilt Math: 50 Reproducible Activities That Motivate Kids to Practice Multi-Digit Addition & Subtraction, Multiplication & Division, Fractions & Decimals-and Learn Facts about the 50 States. 2006. (Teaching Resources Ser.). (Illus.). 64p. pap. 11.99 (978-0-439-42067-9(9) , Teaching Resources) Scholastic, Inc.

—Math Line Designs from Around the World: Grades 2 & 3. 2008. 64p. pap. 11.99 (***978-0-439-37660-0(2)*** , Teaching Resources) Scholastic, Inc.

—Math Line Designs from Around the World: Grades 4 & 6. 2008. 64p. pap. 11.99 (***978-0-439-37661-7(0)*** , Teaching Resources) Scholastic, Inc.

—Math Skills Made Fun: Great Graph Art Multiplication & Division. 2000. (Illus.). 64p. (gr. 3-11). pap. 10.95 (978-0-590-64374-0(6)) Scholastic, Inc.

—Quilt Math: 100 Reproducible Activities That Motivate Kids to Practice Multi-Digit Addition & Subtraction, Multiplication & Division, Fractions, Decimals, & More. 2005. (Illus.). 112p. (gr. 4-6). pap. 15.99 (978-0-439-38533-6(4) , Teaching Resources) Scholastic, Inc.

Mitchell, Cindi & Mitchell, Jim. Math Skills Made Fun: Kaleidoscope Math. 2001. 64p. pap. 10.95 (978-0-439-08676-9(0)) Scholastic, Inc.

Mitchell, Cindi, et al. Math Skills Made Fun: Kaleidoscope Math. 2003. (Illus.). 64p. (gr. 4-6). pap. 10.95 (978-0-439-08675-2(2)) Scholastic, Inc.

Mitchell, Cynthia. Funtastic Math: Decimals & Fractions-:Great Skill-Building Activities, Games & Reproducibles. 1998. (Funtastic Math Ser.). (Illus.). 64p. pap. 9.95 (978-0-590-37365-4(X)) Scholastic, Inc.

Mock, Valarie. Skill Drill Math: Addition, Subtraction, Measuring, Grade 2. 2001. 64p. (J). (gr. 2-2). pap. 8.99 (978-0-7647-0386-7(2) , FS23232) Schaffer, Frank Pubns.

—Skill Drill Math: Fractions, Grade 5. 2001. 64p. (J). (gr. 5-5). pap. 8.99 (978-0-7647-0389-8(7) , FS23235) Schaffer, Frank Pubns.

—Skill Drill Math: Multiplication, Division, Grade 3. 2001. 64p. (J). (gr. 3-3). pap. 8.99 (978-0-7647-0387-4(0) , FS23233) Schaffer, Frank Pubns.

—Skill Drill Math: Multiplication, Division, Measuring, Grade 4. 2001. 64p. (J). (gr. 4-4). pap. 8.99 (978-0-7647-0388-1(9) , FS23234) Schaffer, Frank Pubns.

Modern Curriculum Press Mathematics. 2003. Level C. (J). 28.50 (978-0-8136-3111-0(4)); Level D. (J). 28.50 (978-0-8136-3112-7(2)); Level D. tchr. ed. 29.50 (978-0-8136-3119-6(X)); Level A. (J). 28.50 (978-0-8136-3109-7(2)); Level B. (J). 28.50 (978-0-8136-3110-3(6)); Level K. (J). 28.50 (978-0-8136-3108-0(4)) Modern Curriculum Pr.

Moerbeek, Kees. Numbers. 2000. (Illus.). 24p. (J). (ps-1). 10.99 (978-0-85953-648-6(3)) Child's Play-International.

Molding Mental Mathemagicians Student Worksheets. 2005. (J). pap., wbk. ed. (978-0-9766926-1-4(9)) JCTT, LLC.

Money Math Math, 6 vols. (gr. k-2). 28.95 (978-0-7368-3011-9(1) , Yellow Umbrella Bks.) Capstone Pr., Inc.

Money Matters Series. 2005. (J). pap. (***978-1-60015-017-3(9)***) Steps To Literacy, LLC.

Montague-Smith, Ann. Dividing, 8 vols. 2005. (QEB Math Club Ser.). (Illus.). 24p. (J). (gr. k-1). lib. bdg. 15.95 (978-1-59566-115-9(8)) QEB Publishing Inc.

—Numbers. 2004. (QEB Start Math Ser.). (Illus.). 24p. (J). Vol. 1. lib. bdg. 15.95 (978-1-59566-025-1(9)); Vol. 2. lib. bdg. 15.95 (978-1-59566-029-9(1)) QEB Publishing Inc.

—Subtracting, 8 vols. 2005. (QEB Readers). (Illus.). 24p. (J). (gr. k-1). lib. bdg. 15.95 (978-1-59566-097-8(6)) QEB Publishing Inc.

—Using Numbers Book 2. 2005. (QEB Math Club Ser.). (Illus.). 24p. (J). (gr. k-1). lib. bdg. 15.95 (978-1-59566-113-5(1)) QEB Publishing Inc.

—Using Numbers Book One, 8 vols. 2005. (QEB Math Club Ser.). (Illus.). 24p. (J). (gr. k-1). lib. bdg. 15.95 (978-1-59566-095-4(X)) QEB Publishing Inc.

Montague-Smith, Ann & Harrison, Paul. Extension for All Through Problem Solving. 2003. (Apex Maths Ser.: Vol. 3). (Illus.). 48p. pap., stu. ed. 10.00 (978-0-521-75490-3(9)) ; pap., stu. ed. 10.00 (978-0-521-75488-0(7)) Cambridge Univ. Pr.

Moreau, Nancy & Moreau, Wayne. Math A STAReview: Math Grade 9-10 Test Preparation. Stich, Paul, ed. 2003. (ENG., Illus.). 352p. (YA). per. 12.67 (978-0-935487-78-7(6) , STAReviews) N&N Publishing Co., Inc.

Morgan, Sarah, K. Kid-Friendly Computation Level 1: Numbers to Ten. 2002. (More Math, Please! Ser.). (Illus.). 182p. (J). (ps-4). pap. 34.95 (978-1-56976-139-7(6) , Zephyr Pr.) Chicago Review Pr., Inc.

—Kid-Friendly Computation Level 2: Numbers over 10. 2002. (More Math, Please! Ser.). (Illus.). 216p. (J). (ps-4). pap. 34.95 (978-1-56976-140-3(X) , Zephyr Pr.) Chicago Review Pr., Inc.

Morris, Susan, ed. Real-World Math. 2005. 64p. (J). pap. (978-1-59441-053-6(4) , CD-104024) Carson-Dellosa Publishing Co., Inc.

Morrison, Karen & Press, Karen. Study & Master Mathematical Literacy Grade 11 Learner's Book. 2006. 312p. pap., stu. ed. 18.70 (978-0-521-68925-0(2)) Cambridge Univ. Pr.

—Study & Master Mathematical Literacy Grade 11 Learner's Book Afrikaans Translation. 2006. 312p. pap., stu. ed. 18.70 (978-0-521-68926-7(0)) Cambridge Univ. Pr.

Mother Goose Cares about Math & Science: Professional Development Manual. 2004. (978-0-9753985-2-4(0)) Mother Goose Programs.

Mottershead, Lorraine. Metamorphosis. 196p. (J). (gr. 7-10). 15.95 (978-0-86651-466-8(X) , DS01716) Seymour, Dale Pubns.

Mountain, Lee. Math Connections 1. 2001. 58p. (gr. 1). (J). pap., stu. ed. (978-1-58079-214-1(6)) ; pap., tchr. ed. (978-1-58079-217-2(0)) Barrett Kendall Publishing, Ltd.

—Math Connections 2. 2001. 58p. (gr. 2). (J). pap., stu. ed. (978-1-58079-216-5(2)) ; pap., tchr. ed. (978-1-58079-218-9(9)) Barrett Kendall Publishing, Ltd.

—Math Connections 3. 2001. 58p. (gr. 3). (J). pap., stu. ed. (978-1-58079-215-8(4)) ; pap., tchr. ed. (978-1-58079-219-6(7)) Barrett Kendall Publishing, Ltd.

Multiples & Factors Student: RUPA Multiples & Factors Student. 2005. 95p. per. 7.50 (978-1-932976-50-2(7)) National Ctr. on Education & The Economy.

Multiplication & Division. 2004. (Help with Homework Ser.). 32p. (J). (gr. 1-4). wbk. ed. 3.99 (978-1-904586-21-0(X)) Byeway Bks.

Multiplication & Division. 2003. Level C. tchr. ed. 19.50 (978-0-7652-1316-7(8)); Level C. stu. ed. 14.50 (978-0-7652-1304-4(4)); Level D. tchr. ed. 19.50 (978-0-7652-1320-4(6)); Level D. stu. ed. 14.50 (978-0-7652-1308-2(7)); Level E. tchr. ed. 19.50 (978-0-7652-1324-2(9)); Level E. stu. ed. 14.50 (978-0-7652-1312-9(5)) Modern Curriculum Pr.

Multiplication & Division. (Active Minds(R) Ser.). 16p. (J). spiral bd., bds. (978-1-4127-3503-2(3) , 7248500) Publications International, Ltd.

Multiplication & Division Game Board Book. 2004. (J). bds. 16.95 (978-1-56911-161-1(8)) Learning Resources, Inc.

Mumford, Jeanette. Cambridge Mathematics Direct 2. 2002. (Cambridge Mathematics Direct Ser.). (Illus.). 72p. pap., stu. ed. 9.15 (978-0-521-01165-5(5)) Cambridge Univ. Pr.

Murphy. Beep Beep, Vroom Vroom. 2002. (Illus.). pap. (978-0-7398-6783-9(0)) Steck-Vaughn.

—Dinosaur Deals. 2002. (Illus.). pap. (978-0-7398-6793-8(8)) Steck-Vaughn.

—Just Enough Carrots: Comparing Amounts Big Book. 2002. (Illus.). pap. (978-0-7398-6778-5(4)) Steck-Vaughn.

—Math Start Big Book Classroom Library. 2002. (Illus.). pap. (978-0-7398-6788-4(1)) Steck-Vaughn.

—Mathstart: Complete Classroom Collection. 2000. (Illus.). (J). pap. (978-0-7398-4408-3(3)) Steck-Vaughn.

—Mathstart Level 1, Supplement: Classroom/Library Edition. 2001. (Illus.). (J). pap. (978-0-7398-5059-6(8)) Steck-Vaughn.

—Mathstart Level 1, Yellow Classroom Set. 2001. (Illus.). (J). pap. (978-0-7398-4405-2(9)) Steck-Vaughn.

—Mathstart Level 1, Yellow Set. 2001. (Illus.). (J). pap. (978-0-7398-4402-1(4)) Steck-Vaughn.

—Mathstart Level 2, Blue Classroom Set. 2001. (Illus.). (J). pap. (978-0-7398-4406-9(7)) Steck-Vaughn.

—Mathstart Level 2, Blue Set. 2001. (Illus.). (J). pap. (978-0-7398-4403-8(2)) Steck-Vaughn.

—Mathstart Level 2, Supplement: Classroom/Library Edition. 2001. (Illus.). (J). pap. (978-0-7398-5060-2(1)) Steck-Vaughn.

—Mathstart Level 3, Purple Classroom Set. 2001. (Illus.). (J). pap. (978-0-7398-4407-6(5)) Steck-Vaughn.

—Mathstart Level 3, Purple Set. 2001. (Illus.). (J). pap. (978-0-7398-4404-5(0)) Steck-Vaughn.

—Mathstart Level 3, Supplement: Classroom/Library Edition. 2001. (Illus.). (J). pap. (978-0-7398-5061-9(X)) Steck-Vaughn.

—Mathstart Collection Level 1, Supplement. 2001. (Illus.). (J). pap. (978-0-7398-5062-6(8)) Steck-Vaughn.

—Mathstart Collection Level 2, Supplement. 2001. (Illus.). (J). pap. (978-0-7398-5063-3(6)) Steck-Vaughn.

—Mathstart Collection Level 3, Supplement. 2001. (Illus.). (J). pap. (978-0-7398-5064-0(4)) Steck-Vaughn.

—Monster Musical Chairs Big Book. 2002. (Illus.). pap. (978-0-7398-6785-3(7)) Steck-Vaughn.

—Rabbits Pajama Party: Sequencing Big Book. 2002. (Illus.). pap. (978-0-7398-6782-2(2)) Steck-Vaughn.

Murphy, Debbie & Murphy, Frank. Time & Money. 2002. (Best-Ever Activities for Grades 2-3 Ser.). (Illus.). 48p. (J). (gr. 2-3). 10.95 (978-0-439-29648-9(X)) Scholastic, Inc.

Murphy, Frank & Murphy, Debbie. October. 2001. (Fresh & Fun Ser.). 32p. (J). pap. 8.95 (978-0-439-21572-5(2)) Scholastic, Inc.

Murphy, Stuart J. Bigger, Better, Best! 2002. (gr. k-3). lib. bdg. 13.00 (978-0-613-59226-0(3)) Tandem Library Bks.

—Double the Ducks. Petrone, Valeria, illus. 2003. (MathStart Ser.). 40p. (J). 15.99 (978-0-06-028922-5(8)); Vol. 1. pap. 5.99 (978-0-06-446249-5(8)) HarperCollins Pubs.

—Double the Ducks. 2003. (ps-2). lib. bdg. 13.00 (978-0-613-59239-0(5)) Tandem Library Bks.

—Earth Day—Hooray! Andriani, Renee, illus. 2004. (MathStart 3 Ser.). 40p. (J). (gr. 2 up). 16.99 (978-0-06-000127-8(5)); Vol. 50. pap. 5.99 (978-0-06-000129-2(1)) HarperCollins Pubs.

—The Greatest Gymnast of All. Jabar, Cynthia, illus. 1998. (MathStart Ser.). 40p. (J). (ps up). pap. 5.99 (978-0-06-446718-6(X)) HarperCollins Pubs.

—The Grizzly Gazette. Bjorkman, Steve, illus. 2003. (MathStart Ser.). 40p. (J). (gr. 2 up). pap. 5.99 (978-0-06-000026-4(0) , Harper Trophy) HarperCollins Pubs.

—Henry the Fourth. 1999. (Math Start Ordinals Ser.). (J). 11.79 (978-0-606-16679-9(3)) Tandem Library Bks.

—Jump, Kangaroo, Jump! O'Malley, Kevin, illus. 1999. (MathStart Ser.). 40p. (gr. 2 up). pap. 5.99 (978-0-06-446721-6(X) , Harper Trophy); (YA). 15.89 (978-0-06-027615-7(0)); (YA). 15.95 (978-0-06-027614-0(2)) HarperCollins Pubs.

—Jump, Kangaroo, Jump! 1999. (Math Start Ser.). (J). 11.79 (978-0-606-16681-2(5)); lib. bdg. 13.00 (978-0-613-11724-1(7)) Tandem Library Bks.

—Let's Fly a Kite. Floca, Brian, illus. 2000. (MathStart Ser.). 40p. (J). (gr. 1 up). pap. 5.99 (978-0-06-446737-7(6)); 15.89 (978-0-06-028035-2(2)) HarperCollins Pubs.

—Let's Fly a Kite. 2000. (gr. k-3). lib. bdg. 13.00 (978-0-613-31411-4(5)) Tandem Library Bks.

—Mall Mania. Andriani, Renee, illus. 2006. (MathStart Ser.). 40p. (J). 15.99 (978-0-06-055776-8(1)); pap. 5.99 (978-0-06-055777-5(X)) HarperCollins Pubs.

—Monster Musical Chairs. Nash, Scott, illus. 28th ed. 2000. (MathStart Ser.). 40p. (J). (ps-3). 15.95 (978-0-06-028020-8(4)) HarperCollins Pubs.

—Monster Musical Chairs. 2000. (ps-2). lib. bdg. 12.95 (978-0-613-31494-7(8)) Tandem Library Bks.

—One... Two... Three... Sassafras! Wallace, John, illus. 2002. (MathStart Ser.). 40p. (J). pap. 5.99 (978-0-06-446246-4(3)) HarperCollins Pubs.

—One Two Three Sassafras! 2002. (gr. k-3). lib. bdg. 13.00 (978-0-613-59246-8(8)) Tandem Library Bks.

—Probably Pistachio Level 2. 2001. (Math Start Ser.). (Illus.). (J). (978-0-606-20867-3(4)) Tandem Library Bks.

—Same Old Horse. Bjorkman, Steve, illus. 2005. (MathStart Ser.). 40p. (J). 15.99 (978-0-06-055770-6(2)); pap. 5.99 (978-0-06-055771-3(0)) HarperCollins Pubs.

—The Shark Swimathon Level 3: Subtracting Two Digit Numbers. 2001. (Math Start Ser.). (Illus.). (J). (978-0-606-20910-6(7)) Tandem Library Bks.

—The Sundae Scoop. Jabar, Cynthia, illus. 2003. (MathStart 2 Ser.). 40p. (J). (gr. 1 up). pap. 5.99 (978-0-06-446250-1(1) , Harper Trophy) HarperCollins Pubs.

—The Sundae Scoop. 2003. (gr. k-3). lib. bdg. 13.00 (978-0-613-59252-9(2)) Tandem Library Bks.

My Book of Number Games 1-70. 2004. (Illus.). 80p. (J). per. 6.95 (978-4-7743-0759-6(9)) Kumon Publishing North America, Inc.

My Book of Simple Multiplication. 2007. (J). per. 6.95 (***978-1-933241-41-8(1)***) Kumon Publishing North America, Inc.

My First Library. 2000. 112p. (J). bds. 15.95 (978-0-7525-3741-2(5)) Parragon, Inc.

Nagda, Ann Whitehead. Panda Math: Learning about Subtraction from Hua Mei & Mei Sheng. rev. ed. 2005. (Illus.). 32p. (J). (ps-ps). 17.95 (978-0-8050-7644-8(1)) Holt, Henry & Co.

Nagda, Ann Whitehead & Bickel, Cindy. Polar Bear Math: Learning about Fractions from Klondike & Snow. rev. ed. 2004. (Illus.). 32p. (J). 16.95 (978-0-8050-7301-0(9) , Holt, Henry & Co. Bks. For Young Readers) Holt, Henry & Co.

NCPTA Staff. Better Maths. (Illus.). 32p. pap. 6.99 (978-0-340-64668-7(3) , Coronet) Hodder General Publishing Division GBR. *Dist:* Trafalgar Square Publishing.

—Home Learning 5-7 Mathematics. (Illus.). 24p. pap. 6.99 (978-0-340-71680-9(0) , Coronet) Hodder General Publishing Division GBR. *Dist:* Trafalgar Square Publishing.

Nelson, Lynn. Book of the Abacus. 1998. (Illus.). 16p. (J). (gr. 2-12). pap. 4.95 (978-1-884727-11-5(5)) Digits International-Reflexology Institute.

Neuschwander, Cindy. Patterns in Peru: An Adventure in Patterning. Langdo, Bryan, illus. 2007. 32p. (J). (gr. 1-4). 16.95 (978-0-8050-7954-8(8)) Holt, Henry & Co.

—Sir Cumference & the First Round Table: A Math Adventure. Geehan, Wayne, illus. 1999. (Make the Math-Literature Connection Ser.). 32p. (J). (gr. k-7). 16.95 (978-1-57091-160-6(6)) Charlesbridge Publishing, Inc.

New BaseTen Fries. 2004. (J). (978-1-59242-143-5(1)) Delta Education, LLC.

New Progress in Mathematics. 2003. (YA). (gr. 7 up). stu. ed. 40.50 (978-0-8215-1677-5(9)) Sadlier, William H. Inc.

New Progress in Mathematics: Student Edition. 2003. (YA). (gr. 8 up). stu. ed. 40.50 (978-0-8215-1678-2(7)) Sadlier, William H. Inc.

New York Middle School Mathematics. 2005. (J). (gr. 7-8). pap., stu. ed. 13.95 (978-0-13-024192-4(X)) Globe Fearon Educational Publishing.

New York Middle School Mathematics: Answer Key. 2005. (J). (gr. 7-8). pap. 1.50 (978-0-13-023913-6(5)) Globe Fearon Educational Publishing.

Newman, Graham. Number Works! 2000. (Illus.). 256p. (J). (gr. 6-9). pap., stu. ed. 23.50 (978-0-7487-5448-9(2)) Nelson Thornes Ltd. GBR. *Dist:* Trans-Atlantic Pubns., Inc.

—Number Works: Homework Book. 2000. (Illus.). 168p. (J). (gr. 6-9). pap. 12.95 (978-0-7487-5449-6(0)) Nelson Thornes Ltd. GBR. *Dist:* Trans-Atlantic Pubns., Inc.

Newman, Graham & Miller, Jim. Mathematics for the Future. 2nd ed. 2000. (Illus.). viii, 390p. (YA). (gr. 9-11). ring bd. 36.50 (978-0-17-431530-8(9)) Nelson Thornes Ltd. GBR. *Dist:* Trans-Atlantic Pubns., Inc.

Newman, James R., ed. The World of Mathematics. 2000. (Dover Phoenix Editions Ser.). (Illus.). Vol. 1. 768p. pap. 17.95 (978-0-486-41153-8(2)); Vol. 2. 720p. pap. 17.95 (978-0-486-41150-7(8)); Vol. 3. 624p. pap. 17.95 (978-0-486-41151-4(6)); Vol. 4. 464p. pap. 17.95 (978-0-486-41152-1(4)) Dover Pubns., Inc.

Newton, David E. Math in Everyday Life. 2001. 214p. (YA). (gr. 7-12). act. bk. ed. 20.99 (978-0-8251-4258-1(X) , 0-4258X) Walch Publishing.

Nickson, Marilyn. Teaching & Learning Mathematics. (J). pap. (978-0-8264-7026-3(2)) Continuum International Publishing Group, Ltd.

Niederman, Derrick. Mind-Stretching Math Puzzles. 2005. (Illus.). 112p. (J). (978-1-4156-0492-2(4)) Sterling Publishing Co., Inc.

Nigro, Anthony & Bernauer, Edwin. Regents High School Mathematics B Exam Review Workbook, Pts. II-IV. 2002. (YA). (gr. 8-12). per., wbk. ed. (978-0-937820-79-7(2)) WestSea Publishing Co., Inc.

Noah, Ian & Logan, Stephanie. Mike's Math Club Presents the Monstrously Fun Fraction Book. Noah, Ian et al, eds. Milken-Noah, Joni et al, eds. 2003. (Illus.). 382p. pap. 24.95 (978-0-9646425-1-5(4)) Milken Family Foundation.

Nolan, Helen. How Much, How Many, How Far, How Heavy, How Long, How Tall Is 1,000? 2001. (Illus.). (J). 12.75 (978-0-606-21238-0(8)) Tandem Library Bks.

Nolting, Paul D. Math Study Skills. 2nd ed. 2004. (Illus.). 144p. (YA). wbk. ed. 35.16 (978-0-618-47303-8(3) , 339795) Houghton Mifflin College Div.

Number Lines. 2001. (Early Math Ser.). (J). (gr. k-12). vinyl bd. 4.95 (978-1-58845-068-5(6)) School Specialty Publishing.

Numbers All Around Math, 6 vols. (gr. k-2). 28.95 (978-0-7368-1731-8(X) , Yellow Umbrella Bks.) Capstone Pr., Inc.

Numbers Everywhere: A Content Area Reader-math. 2005. (Sadlier Phonics Reading Program). 12p. (YA). (ps-2). 25.20 (978-0-8215-7823-0(5)) Sadlier, William H. Inc.

Numbers for 3-5 Years. Date not set. (Play & Learn Ser.). (Illus.). 192p. (J). 3.98 (978-0-7525-6912-3(0)) Parragon, Inc.

Numbers for 5-7 Years. Date not set. (Play & Learn Ser.). 192p. (J). 3.98 (978-0-7525-6913-0(9)) Parragon, Inc.

Numbers on the Farm. Date not set. (Illus.). (J). bds. 9.98 (978-0-7525-9889-5(9)) Parragon, Inc.

Numeros en todas partes Math, 6 vols.Tr. of Numbers All Around Math. (SPA.). (gr. k-2). 28.95 (978-0-7368-3122-2(3) , Yellow Umbrella Bks.) Capstone Pr., Inc.

Objects in the Sky, 6 bks., Set. Incl. Exploring Comets. Way, Jennifer. lib. bdg. 21.25 (978-1-4042-3469-7(1) , PowerKids Pr.); Exploring Earth. Olien, Rebecca. lib. bdg. 21.25 (978-1-4042-3465-9(9)); Exploring Meteors. Olien, Rebecca. lib. bdg. 21.25 (978-1-4042-3468-0(3) , PowerKids Pr.); Exploring the Moon. Olien, Rebecca. lib. bdg. 21.25 (978-1-4042-3466-6(7) , PowerKids Pr.); Exploring the Planets in Our Solar System. Olien, Rebecca. lib. bdg. 21.25 (978-1-4042-3467-3(5) , PowerKids Pr.); Exploring the Sun. Olien, Rebecca. lib. bdg. 21.25 (978-1-4042-3464-2(0) , PowerKids Pr.); (Illus.). 24p. (J). (gr. 4-6). 2007. 2007. Set lib. bdg. 127.50 (978-1-4042-3502-1(7) , PowerKids Pr.) Rosen Publishing Group, Inc., The.

O'Brien, Thomas C. Off the Path Math with Tobbs, Vol. 1. Reynolds, Peter H., illus. 2003. 59p. (J). 14.50 (978-1-891405-09-8(8)) FableVision Pr.

O'Connell, Susan R. Math the Write Way, Grades 2 to 3. 2001. (Illus.). 80p. (J). (gr. 2-3). pap. 12.99 (978-0-7682-0620-3(0) , GA13070, Schaffer, Frank) Schaffer, Frank Pubns.

—Math the Write Way, Grades 4 to 5. 2001. 80p. (J). (gr. 4-5). pap. 12.99 (978-0-7682-0621-0(9) , GA13071, Schaffer, Frank) Schaffer, Frank Pubns.

—Math, the Write Way, Grades 6 to 7. 2001. (Illus.). 80p. (J). (gr. 6-7). pap. 12.99 (978-0-7682-0622-7(7) , GA13072, Schaffer, Frank) Schaffer, Frank Pubns.

O'Donnell, Kerri. The Ancient Civilizations of Greece & Rome: Solving Algebraic Equations. 2005. (PowerMath Ser.). (J). 22.50 (978-1-4042-2930-3(2)); pap. (978-1-4042-5123-6(5)) Rosen Publishing Group, Inc., The. (PowerKids Pr.).

Ohanesian, Diane C. Macaroni Math. 2000. (Illus.). 27p. (J). (ps-3). pap. 7.95 (978-0-07-134826-3(3)) McGraw-Hill Cos., The.

Ohanian, Susan. Day-by-Day Math: Activities for Grades 3-6. 2000. 184p. (J). (gr. 3-6). pap. 19.95 (978-0-941355-28-5(4)) Math Solutions Pubns.

Olenych, Bob. Ready-to-Go Reproducibles: Math Practice Puzzles. 2002. 48p. (J). 9.95 (978-0-439-28850-7(9)); 9.95 (978-0-439-30942-4(5)) Scholastic, Inc.

—Ready-to-Go Reproducibles: Math Practice Puzzles, Multiplication & Division. 2001. 48p. pap. 9.95 (978-0-439-27167-7(3)) Scholastic, Inc.

Olenych, Bob, et al. Fun Independent Practice Pages: Pre-Algebra. 2003. (Rtg Reproducibles Ser.). 48p. pap., tchr. ed. 10.95 (978-0-439-43110-1(7) , Teaching Resources) Scholastic, Inc.

O'Malley, Kevin. Dinosaur Deals: Equivalent Values. 2001. 11.79 (978-0-606-22289-1(8)) Tandem Library Bks.

One Green Frog Math, 6 vols. (gr. k-2). 28.95 (978-0-7368-2994-6(6) , Yellow Umbrella Bks.) Capstone Pr., Inc.

One to a Million: Math Concepts. 2004. 24.95 incl. audio (978-0-7882-0558-3(7)) Weston Woods Studios, Inc.

Open Court Staff. Real Math: Level 8. (J). stu. ed. (978-0-8126-0638-6(8) , 60638) Open Court Publishing Co.

Open University Worldwide, prod. Introduction to Math & Pc Skills: Water for Life. (YA). cd-rom 99.95 (978-0-7365-1439-2(2)) Films Media Group.

Operations & Fractions Student: RUPA Operations & Fractions Student. 2005. 95p. per. 7.50 (978-1-932976-51-9(5)) National Ctr. on Education & The Economy.

Opie, Brenda & McAvinn, Douglas. Masterminds Riddlemath for Elementary: Measurement, Fractions, Probability, & Logical Thinking. 2004. (Illus.). 96p. (J). per. 11.95 (978-0-86530-611-0(7)) Incentive Pubns., Inc.

—Masterminds Riddlemath for Elementary: Whole Numbers, Addition, Subtraction, Multiplication, & Division. 2004. (Illus.). 96p. (J). per. 11.95 (978-0-86530-604-2(4)) Incentive Pubns., Inc.

Oppenlander, Meredith & Coulton, Mia. Math Set "B" Includes "In the Hen House," "The Bird Feeder," "How to Make Snack Mix," "How Much Does This Hold?", 4 vols. Gedeon, Gloria et al, illus. Date not set. (J). (gr. k-2). pap. 19.25 (978-1-57874-071-0(1)) Kaeden Corp.

Osborne, Carol. Spectrum Mathematics Year 10 Standard. 2000. (Spectrum Mathematics Ser.). 432p. pap. 22.00 (978-0-521-78665-2(7)) Cambridge Univ. Pr.

Osborne, Carol, et al. Cambridge Spectrum Mathematics 5. 2 Year 9 Student Pack. 2004. (Spectrum Mathematics Ser.). pap., stu. ed. 42.00 incl. cd-rom (978-0-521-53236-5(1)) Cambridge Univ. Pr.

—Cambridge Spectrum Mathematics 5. 3 Year 9 Student Pack. 2004. (Spectrum Mathematics Ser.). pap., stu. ed. 42.00 incl. cd-rom (978-0-521-53237-2(X)) Cambridge Univ. Pr.

Osborne, J. E. Everything in Order! Date not set. (Early Math Big Bks.). (Illus.). 16p. (J). (ps-2). pap. 16.95 (978-1-58273-490-3(9)) Sundance/Newbridge Educational Publishing.

—Fact Families. Date not set. (Early Math Big Bks.). (Illus.). 16p. (J). (ps-2). pap. 16.95 (978-1-58273-142-1(X)) Sundance/Newbridge Educational Publishing.

—Give It a Guess! Date not set. (Early Math Big Bks.). (Illus.). 16p. (J). (ps-2). pap. 16.95 (978-1-58273-440-8(2)) Sundance/Newbridge Educational Publishing.

—Solve It! Date not set. (Early Math Big Bks.). (Illus.). 16p. (J). (ps-2). pap. 16.95 (978-1-56784-432-0(4)) Sundance/Newbridge Educational Publishing.

—What Is Place Value? Date not set. (Early Math Big Bks.). (Illus.). 16p. (J). (ps-2). pap. 16.95 (978-1-58273-145-2(4)) Sundance/Newbridge Educational Publishing.

Osborne, Mary Pope & Osborne, Will. Dinosaurs: A Nonfiction Companion to Dinosaurs Before Dark. Murdocca, Sal, illus. 2000. (Magic Tree House Research Guide Ser.: No. 1). 128p. (J). (gr. k-3). lib. bdg. 11.99 (978-0-375-90296-3(1) , Random Hse. Bks. for Young Readers) Random Hse. Children's Bks.

Osofsky, Jill. Addition & Subtraction. 2000. (Funtastic Frogs Ser.). 32p. (J). (gr. k-2). pap., act. bk. ed. 4.99 (978-1-56451-319-9(X) , ID43015) School Specialty Publishing.

Ostebee. Single Variable: Calculus from Graphical, Numerical, & Symbolic Points of View. 2nd ed. 2001. (Illus.). 607p. (YA). (gr. 6-12). 140.76 (978-0-618-24788-2(2) , 390083) Houghton Mifflin College Div.

Over, under, Left, Right. 2005. (Emergent/Early (Prek-2) Math Package Ser.). 12p. (YA). (ps-2). 25.20 (978-0-8215-7844-5(8)) Sadlier, William H. Inc.

Overhead Manipulative Kit: Manipulative Kits. 2002. (MacMillan/McGraw-Hill Matematicas Ser.). (ENG & SPA.). (gr. 4-6). (978-0-02-100336-5(X)) Macmillan/McGraw-Hill Schl. Div.

Owen, M. J. Using the Standards—Measurement. 2004. (100+ Ser.). 128p. (C). pap. 12.99 (***978-0-7424-2893-5(1)***); pap. 12.99 (***978-0-7424-2894-2(X)***) Schaffer, Frank Pubns. (Instructional Fair).

Pallotta, Jerry. Hershey's Milk Chocolate Bar Fractions Book. 1999. (Illus.). (J). 12.79 (978-0-606-18559-2(3)) Tandem Library Bks.

—Twizzlers Percentages Book. Bolster, Rob, illus. 2001. 32p. (J). (gr. 1-3). pap. 5.99 (978-0-439-15430-7(8) , Cartwheel Bks.) Scholastic, Inc.

—Twizzlers Percentages Book. 2001. (978-0-606-22229-7(4)); lib. bdg. 14.10 (978-0-613-54716-1(0)) Tandem Library Bks.

Pape, et al. Multiplication & Division. 2000. (Flash-Action Software Ser.). (Illus.). (J). cd-rom 12.99 (978-0-88743-738-0(9) , 08454) School Zone Publishing Co.

Pappas, Theoni. Further Adventures of Penrose the Mathematical Cat. 2004. (Illus.). 128p. (J). pap. 10.95 (978-1-884550-32-4(0)) Wide World Publishing/Tetra.

Pardoe, Mary. Formula One Interactive Oral & Mental Starters. 2005. (Illus.). cd-rom (***978-0-340-91333-8(9)***) Hodder General Publishing Division.

Parham, Donna. Splash of Math K-3: K-3. 2003. (Illus.). 28p. (J). (gr. k-3). tchr. ed. 5.99 (978-1-893698-35-2(1) , T13, SeaWorld Education Dept.) SeaWorld, Inc.

Parker, Andrew & Stamford, Jane. Key Maths. 1999. (Illus.). 31p. (J). (gr. k-2). Bk. 1. pap., wbk. ed. 15.00 (978-0-7217-2454-6(X)); Bk. 2. pap., wbk. ed. 15.00 (978-0-7217-2455-3(8)); Bk. 3. pap., wbk. ed. 15.00 (978-0-7217-2456-0(6)); Bk. 4. pap., wbk. ed. 15.00 (978-0-7217-2457-7(4)); Bk. 5. pap., wbk. ed. 15.00 (978-0-7217-2458-4(2)) Schofield & Sims Ltd. GBR. *Dist:* State Mutual Bk. & Periodical Service, Ltd.

Parks, Harold B. Mathematics in Life, Society, & the World. 2nd ed. 2000. pap., stu. ed. 58.50 (978-0-13-014927-5(6)) Prentice Hall (Schl. Div.).

Partes de un entero Math, 6 vols.Tr. of Parts of a Whole Math. (SPA.). (gr. k-2). 28.95 (978-0-7368-3048-5(0) , Yellow Umbrella Bks.) Capstone Pr., Inc.

Parts of a Whole Math, 6 vols. (gr. k-2). 28.95 (978-0-7368-3012-6(X) , Yellow Umbrella Bks.) Capstone Pr., Inc.

Un paso Mas: Student & Teacher Support Resources. 1999. (Matematicas en Mi Mundo Ser.). (ENG & SPA.). (gr. k up). (978-0-02-110201-3(5)); (gr. 1 up). (978-0-02-110202-0(3)); (gr. 2 up). (978-0-02-110203-7(1)); (gr. 3 up). (978-0-02-110204-4(X)); (gr. 4 up). (978-0-02-110205-1(8)); (gr. 5 up). (978-0-02-110206-8(6)); (gr. 6 up). (978-0-02-110207-5(4)) Macmillan/McGraw-Hill Schl. Div.

Passaporte a las Matematicas, Libro 2. 2002. Tr. of Passport to Mathematics. (SPA.). (gr. 6-12). (978-0-395-91853-1(7) , 2-80509) McDougal Littell Inc.

Passport. (gr. 6-12). Bk. 1. 2002. tchr. ed. (978-0-395-96396-8(6) , 2-99726); Bk. 1. 2002. (SPA.). (978-0-618-11092-6(5) , 2-12127); Vol. 2. 2002. (SPA.). (978-0-618-11093-3(3) , 2-12128); Vol. 3. 2004. (978-0-395-98023-1(2) , 2-77964); Vol. 3. 2002. (SPA.). (978-0-618-11094-0(1) , 2-12129) McDougal Littell Inc.

Passport to Mathematics. 2002. (gr. 6-12). stu. ed. (978-0-395-87982-5(5) , 2-77604); tchr. ed. incl. cd-rom (978-0-395-93157-8(6) , 2-99434); cd-rom (978-0-395-98643-1(5) , 2-77965); stu. ed. (978-0-618-18598-6(4) , 2-05510); Vol. 2. tchr. ed. (978-0-618-18601-3(8) , 2-05513); Vol. 2. stu. ed. (978-0-618-18599-3(2) , 2-05511); Vol. 2. stu. ed. (978-0-395-87985-6(X) , 2-77607); Vol. 2. cd-rom (978-0-395-98644-8(3) , 2-77966) McDougal Littell Inc.

Passport to Mathematics: Answer Masters. 2002. (gr. 6-12). (978-0-395-89635-8(5) , 2-77690) McDougal Littell Inc.

Passport to Mathematics: Complete Solutions Manual. 2002. (gr. 6-12). (978-0-395-89637-2(1) , 2-77692); Vol. 2. (978-0-395-89659-4(2) ; 2-77731) McDougal Littell Inc.

Passport to Mathematics: Daily Cumulative Review. 2002. (gr. 6-12). (978-0-395-89630-3(4) , 2-77685); Vol. 2. (978-0-395-89652-5(5) , 2-77724) McDougal Littell Inc.

Passport to Mathematics: Enrichment Copymasters. 2002. (gr. 6-12). (978-0-395-89634-1(7) , 2-77689); Vol. 2. (978-0-395-89656-3(8) , 2-77728) McDougal Littell Inc.

Passport to Mathematics: Math Log, Vol. 2. 2002. (gr. 6-12). (978-0-395-89654-9(1) , 2-77726) McDougal Littell Inc.

Passport to Mathematics: Middle School Tutorial. 2004. (gr. 6-12). cd-rom (978-0-395-95665-6(X) , 2-99706) McDougal Littell Inc.

Passport to Mathematics: Practice Workbook. 2002. (gr. 6-12). stu. ed., wbk. ed. (978-0-395-89626-6(6) , 2-77680); Vol. 2. (SPA.). (978-0-395-90158-8(8) , 2-77863); Vol. 2. stu. ed. (978-0-395-89648-8(7) , 2-77720) McDougal Littell Inc.

Passport to Mathematics: Problem of the Day. 2002. (gr. 6-12). (978-0-395-89633-4(9) , 2-77688); Vol. 2. (978-0-395-89655-6(X) , 2-77727) McDougal Littell Inc.

Passport to Mathematics: Warm-up Exercises. 2002. (gr. 6-12). (978-0-395-89636-5(3) , 2-77691); Vol. 2. (978-0-395-89658-7(4) , 2-77730) McDougal Littell Inc.

Payne, Ruby K. Mental Models for Math: Grades 6-12. 2006. (YA). per. 10.00 (978-1-929229-53-6(4)) aha! Process, Inc.

Pearson, Donna. Math 4 Today Grade 2-4. 2001. 144p. (J). (gr. 2-4). pap. 15.99 (978-1-56417-894-7(3) , GA1594) Schaffer, Frank Pubns.

—Math 4 Today Grade 4-5. 2001. 144p. (J). (gr. 4-5). pap. 15.99 (978-1-56417-980-7(X) , GA1659) Schaffer, Frank Pubns.

Pegoraro, Laura. We'll Practice More Math. Petertil Design Partners Staff, illus. 1998. (Powertools for Kids Ser.: No. 8). 4p. (J). (gr. 2-5). pap., wbk. ed. 4.95 (978-1-58220-007-1(6) , 32108, PowerTools for Kids) Navigator Systems, Inc.

People Together: E-Journals. (Technology: Social Studies). (SPA.). (gr. 2 up). (978-0-02-147229-1(7)) Macmillan/McGraw-Hill Schl. Div.

Petersen, Jamee. Math & Nonfiction, Grades K-2. 2004. (Illus.). 144p. (gr. k-2). pap. 19.50 (978-0-941355-61-2(6)) Math Solutions Pubns.

Pettit, Krista & Geiser, Traci Ferguson. 20 Instant Math Learning Centers Kids Will Love! Reproducible Activities & Patters That Help Young Learners Practice Math Skills Independently. 2002. 112p. pap., act. bk. ed. 14.95 (978-0-439-22729-2(1) , Teaching Resources) Scholastic, Inc.

Phillips, Vivian A. Intrique Math. Date not set. (Illus.). 16p. (Orig.). (YA). pap. (978-1-888413-04-5(2)) Seasoning Quilting (Arts & Crafts).

Pisos, Cecilia. El Baul de los Transportes: Un Libro Sobre los Numeros. Ink, Lancman, illus. (Coleccion el Baul Ser.). (SPA.). 10p. (J). (gr. k-1). (978-950-46-1161-5(3)) Santillana USA Publishing Co., Inc.

Place Value. (Classroom Helpers Ser.). 24p. (gr. 1 up). 3.99 (978-0-7682-0815-3(7) , FS194114); (gr. 3 up). 3.99 (978-0-7682-0832-0(7) , FS194131) Schaffer, Frank Pubns.

Place Value. 2001. (Early Math Ser.). (J). (gr. k-12). vinyl bd. 4.95 (978-1-58845-107-1(0)) School Specialty Publishing.

Place Value Grade 2. 2004. pap. 4.99 (978-0-7439-8602-1(4)) Teacher Created Materials, Inc.

Place Value Skills (Gr. 1-2) 2003. (J). (978-1-58232-088-5(8)) Bryan Hse. Pubs., Inc.

Place Value Skills Spanish Version. 2007. (J). per. (***978-1-58232-157-8(4)***) Bryan Hse. Pubs., Inc.

Planificadores de las Lecciones: Student & Teacher Support Resources. 1999. (Matematicas en Mi Mundo Ser.). (ENG & SPA.). (gr. k up). (978-0-02-110664-6(9)); (gr. 2 up). (978-0-02-110666-0(5)); (gr. 3 up). (978-0-02-110667-7(3)); (gr. 4 up). (978-0-02-110668-4(1)); (gr. 5 up). (978-0-02-110669-1(X)); (gr. 6 up). (978-0-02-110670-7(3)) Macmillan/McGraw-Hill Schl. Div.

Pluckrose, Henry. Let's Explore, 12 bks. Incl. Air. lib. bdg. 23.33 (978-0-8368-2957-0(3)); Day & Night. lib. bdg. 23.33 (978-0-8368-2958-7(1)); Discovering Shapes. lib. bdg. 23.33 (978-0-8368-2959-4(X)); Earth. lib. bdg. 23.33 (978-0-8368-2960-0(3)); Fire. lib. bdg. 23.33 (978-0-8368-2961-7(1)); Measuring Size. lib. bdg. 23.33 (978-0-8368-2962-4(X)); My Day. lib. bdg. 23.33 (978-0-8368-2963-1(8)); Numbers & Counting. lib. bdg. 23.33 (978-0-8368-2964-8(6)); Seasons. lib. bdg. 23.33 (978-0-8368-2965-5(4)); Sorting & Sets. lib. bdg. 23.33 (978-0-8368-2966-2(2)); Time. lib. bdg. 23.33 (978-0-8368-2967-9(0)); Water. lib. bdg. 23.33 (978-0-8368-2968-6(9)); 32p. (J). (gr. 1 up). 2001. (Illus.). Set lib. bdg. 279.96 (978-0-8368-2956-3(5)) Stevens, Gareth Inc.

Pluckrose, Henry Arthur. Sorting & Sets. 2006. (Illus.). 32p. (J). (978-1-59771-038-1(5)) Sea-To-Sea Pubns.

Pocket Chart Math: Addition. 2002. (J). pap. 9.95 (978-1-56911-080-5(8)) Learning Resources, Inc.

Pocket Chart Math: Basic Money Skills. 2001. (J). pap. 9.95 (978-1-56911-721-7(7)) Learning Resources, Inc.

Pocket Chart Math: Basic Time Telling. 2001. (J). pap. 9.95 (978-1-56911-720-0(9)) Learning Resources, Inc.

Pocket Chart Math: Beginning Fractions. 2001. (J). pap. 9.95 (978-1-56911-719-4(5)) Learning Resources, Inc.

Pocket Chart Math: Place Value. 2001. (J). pap. 9.95 (978-1-56911-722-4(5)) Learning Resources, Inc.

Pocket Chart Math: Subtraction. 2002. (J). pap. 9.95 (978-1-56911-081-2(6)) Learning Resources, Inc.

Polette, Nancy & Ebbesmeyer, Joan. Math in Fables & Myths: Solving Word Problems with Readers' Theatre. 2004. (J). pap. 14.95 (978-1-931334-58-7(7)) Pieces of Learning.

Popular Book Company. Complete Math Workout Vol 1. Popular Book Company, illus. 2007. (Illus.). 272p. pap. 14.95 ***(978-1-897164-43-3(2))*** Popular Bk. Co. (Canada) Ltd. CAN. *Dist:* AtlasBooks Distribution.

—Complete Math Workout Vol 2. Popular Book Company, illus. 2007. (Illus.). 272p. pap. 14.95 ***(978-1-897164-44-0(0))*** Popular Bk. Co. (Canada) Ltd. CAN. *Dist:* AtlasBooks Distribution.

—Complete Math Workout Vol 3. Popular Book Company, illus. 2007. (Illus.). 272p. pap. 14.95 ***(978-1-897164-45-7(9))*** Popular Bk. Co. (Canada) Ltd. CAN. *Dist:* AtlasBooks Distribution.

—Complete Math Workout Vol 4. Popular Book Company, illus. 2007. (Illus.). 272p. pap. 14.95 ***(978-1-897164-46-4(7))*** Popular Bk. Co. (Canada) Ltd. CAN. *Dist:* AtlasBooks Distribution.

—Complete Math Workout Vol 5. Popular Book Company, illus. 2007. (Illus.). 272p. pap. 14.95 ***(978-1-897164-47-1(5))*** Popular Bk. Co. (Canada) Ltd. CAN. *Dist:* AtlasBooks Distribution.

—Complete Math Workout Vol 6. Popular Book Company, illus. 2007. (Illus.). 272p. pap. 14.95 ***(978-1-897164-48-8(3))*** Popular Bk. Co. (Canada) Ltd. CAN. *Dist:* AtlasBooks Distribution.

Por que medimos? Math, 6 vols.Tr. of Why We Measure Math. (SPA.). (gr. k-2). 28.95 (978-0-7368-3142-0(8) , Yellow Umbrella Bks.) Capstone Pr., Inc.

Porzio, Joseph A. Math Test Prep That Matters! Grades 3-4: 100 Standards-Based Math Prompts That Develop Students' Critical Thinking & Deepen Their Understanding of Key Math Concepts. 2006. 64p. pap. 11.99 (978-0-439-59722-7(6) , Best Practices in Action) Scholastic, Inc.

—Math Test Prep That Matters! Grades 5 & Up: 100 Standards-Based Math Prompts That Develop Students' Critical Thinking & Deepen Their Understanding of Key Math Concepts. 2006. 64p. pap. 11.99 (978-0-439-59723-4(4) , Best Practices in Action) Scholastic, Inc.

—Math Test Prep That Matters! Grades K-2: 50 Standards-Based Math Prompts That Develop Students' Critical Thinking & Deepen Their Understanding of Key Math Concepts. 2006. 64p. pap. 11.99 (978-0-439-59721-0(8) , Best Practices in Action) Scholastic, Inc.

Poskitt, Kjartan. Esas Mortiferas Mates. (SPA.). 144p. (YA). (gr. 5-8). (978-84-272-2056-0(1)) Molino, Editorial ESP. *Dist:* Lectorum Pubns., Inc.

Power Math: Sets 7,8, And 9. (Illus.). (J). (gr. 3-6). 405.00 (978-1-4042-2967-9(1)) Rosen Publishing Group, Inc., The.

Power Math Set 10. (J). (gr. k-5). 79.50 (978-1-4042-3383-6(0)) Rosen Publishing Group, Inc., The.

Power Math Set 7. (Illus.). (J). (gr. 3-6). 135.00 (978-1-4042-2974-7(4)) Rosen Publishing Group, Inc., The.

Power Math Set 8. (Illus.). (J). (gr. 3-6). 135.00 (978-1-4042-2975-4(2)) Rosen Publishing Group, Inc., The.

Power Math Set 9. (Illus.). (J). (gr. 3-6). 135.00 (978-1-4042-2976-1(0)) Rosen Publishing Group, Inc., The.

Practica: Student & Teacher Support Resources. 1999. (Matematicas en Mi Mundo Ser.). (ENG & SPA.). (gr. k up). (978-0-02-110194-8(9)); (gr. 1 up). (978-0-02-110195-5(7)); (gr. 2 up). (978-0-02-110196-2(5)); (gr. 3 up). (978-0-02-110197-9(3)); (gr. 4 up). (978-0-02-110198-6(1)); (gr. 5 up). (978-0-02-110199-3(X)); (gr. 6 up). (978-0-02-110200-6(7)) Macmillan/McGraw-Hill Schl. Div.

Practica, Revision de ensenanza y un paso mas: Clave de Respuestas: Student & Teacher Support Resources. 1999. (Matematicas en Mi Mundo Ser.). (ENG & SPA.). (gr. 1 up). (978-0-02-110860-2(9)); (gr. 2 up). (978-0-02-110861-9(7)); (gr. 3 up). (978-0-02-110862-6(5)); (gr. 5 up). (978-0-02-110864-0(1)); (gr. 6 up). (978-0-02-110865-7(X)) Macmillan/McGraw-Hill Schl. Div.

Practica, Revision de ensenanza y un paso mas: Clave de respuestas del Maestro: Student & Teacher Support Resources. 1999. (Matematicas en Mi Mundo Ser.). (ENG & SPA.). (gr. 4 up). (978-0-02-110863-3(3)) Macmillan/McGraw-Hill Schl. Div.

Practica, y un paso mas: Clave Respuestas: Student & Teacher Support Resources. 1999. (Matematicas en Mi Mundo Ser.). (ENG & SPA.). (gr. k up). (978-0-02-110859-6(5)) Macmillan/McGraw-Hill Schl. Div.

Practice Power Flip & Learn Addition. 2000. (Illus.). 16p. (J). (gr. k-2). spiral bd. (978-1-930355-20-0(3)) Greenbrier/Scentex.

Practice Power Practice Book Addition. (Illus.). (J). (gr. k-2). 2001. 18p. spiral bd., wbk. ed. (978-1-930355-34-7(3)); 2000. 16p. spiral bd., wbk. ed. (978-1-930355-03-3(3)) Greenbrier/Scentex.

Practice Power Practice Book Division. 2000. (Illus.). 16p. (J). (gr. 2-5). spiral bd., wbk. ed. (978-1-930355-02-6(5)) Greenbrier/Scentex.

Practice Power Practice Book Multiplication. 2000. (Illus.). 16p. (J). (gr. 2-5). spiral bd., wbk. ed. (978-1-930355-01-9(7)) Greenbrier/Scentex.

Practice Power Practice Book Subtraction. (Illus.). (J). (gr. k-2). 2001. 18p. spiral bd., wbk. ed. (978-1-930355-30-9(0)); 2000. 16p. spiral bd., wbk. ed. (978-1-930355-04-0(1)) Greenbrier/Scentex.

Practice Power School Bus Book: First Grade Mathematics. 2003. (Illus.). 24p. (J). (gr. k-1). spiral bd. (978-1-930355-44-6(0)) Greenbrier/Scentex.

Practice Power Workbook Addition. 1999. (Illus.). 16p. (J). (gr. k-2). wbk. ed. (978-1-930355-13-2(0)) Greenbrier/Scentex.

Practice Power Workbook Division. 1999. (Illus.). 16p. (J). (gr. 2-5). wbk. ed. (978-1-930355-17-0(3)) Greenbrier/Scentex.

Practice Power Workbook Multiplication. 1999. (Illus.). 16p. (J). (gr. 2-5). wbk. ed. (978-1-930355-16-3(5)) Greenbrier/Scentex.

Practice Power Workbook Subtraction. 1999. (Illus.). 16p. (J). (gr. k-2). wbk. ed. (978-1-930355-12-5(2)) Greenbrier/Scentex.

Pre-Algebra: EEdition. 2005. (gr. 6-12). cd-rom (978-0-618-43339-1(2) , 2-05812) McDougal Littell Inc.

Pre-Algebra: ETutorial. 2005. (gr. 6-12). cd-rom (978-0-618-43351-3(1) , 2-05824); cd-rom (978-0-618-43355-1(4) , 2-05828); cd-rom (978-0-618-43356-8(2) , 2-05829) McDougal Littell Inc.

Pre-Algebra: ETutorial Plus Online. 2005. (gr. 6-12). (978-0-618-43357-5(0) , 2-05830) McDougal Littell Inc.

Pre-Algebra: EWorkbook Plus Online. 2005. (gr. 6-12). (978-0-618-43358-2(9) , 2-05831) McDougal Littell Inc.

Pre-Algebra: Exercises in Spanish. 2005. (gr. 6-12). (978-0-618-43362-9(7) , 2-05834) McDougal Littell Inc.

Pre-Algebra: Notetaking Guide, PE. 2005. (gr. 6-12). (978-0-618-25657-0(1) , 2-06023) McDougal Littell Inc.

Pre-Algebra: Practice Workbook, PE. 2005. (gr. 6-12). (978-0-618-25752-2(7) , 2-06024) McDougal Littell Inc.

Pre-Algebra: Pupil's Edition. 2005. (gr. 6-12). (978-0-618-25003-5(4) , 2-06006) McDougal Littell Inc.

Pre-Algebra: Worked-Out Solution Key. 2005. (gr. 6-12). (978-0-618-28044-5(8) , 2-06114) McDougal Littell Inc.

Pre-Algebra Middle School. 2003. 128p. (J). per. 10.99 (978-0-88724-952-5(3) , CD-4323) Carson-Dellosa Publishing Co., Inc.

Premium Education Bindup Grade 1. 2006. (J). per. 14.95 ***(978-1-59545-026-5(2))*** Learning Horizons, Inc.

Premium Education Bindup Grade 2. 2006. (J). per. 14.95 ***(978-1-59545-027-2(0))*** Learning Horizons, Inc.

Premium Education Bindup Grade 3. 2006. (J). per. 14.95 ***(978-1-59545-028-9(9))*** Learning Horizons, Inc.

Premium Education Bindup Grade K. 2006. (J). per. 14.95 ***(978-1-59545-025-8(4))*** Learning Horizons, Inc.

Premium Education Bindup Pre-K. 2006. (J). per. 14.95 ***(978-1-59545-024-1(6))*** Learning Horizons, Inc.

Preschool Jumbo Workbook. 1998. (Step Ahead Ser.). (J). (ps). pap., wbk. ed. 4.99 (978-0-307-11250-7(0) , Golden Bks.) Random Hse. Children's Bks.

Priddy Books Staff & Priddy, Roger. Play & Learn Numbers: Easy Learning Fun, for the Very Young. rev. ed. 2004. (Play & Learn Ser.). (Illus.). 12p. (J). bds. 8.95 (978-0-312-49394-3(0) , Priddy Bks.) St. Martin's Pr.

Priddy, Roger. Simple Math. rev. ed. 2005. (Wipe Clean Ser.). 20p. (J). spiral bd. 9.95 (978-0-312-49456-8(4) , Priddy Bks.) St. Martin's Pr.

Primary Mathematics Intensive Practice U. S. Edition 1A. 2004. per. 8.50 (978-1-932906-00-4(2)) SingaporeMath-.com, Inc.

Primary Mathematics Intensive Practice U. S. Edition 1B. 2004. per. 8.50 (978-1-932906-01-1(0)) SingaporeMath-.com, Inc.

Primary Mathematics Intensive Practice U. S. Edition 2A. 2004. per. 8.50 (978-1-932906-02-8(9)) SingaporeMath-.com, Inc.

Primary Mathematics Intensive Practice U. S. Edition 2B. 2004. per. 8.50 (978-1-932906-03-5(7)) SingaporeMath-.com, Inc.

Primary Mathematics Intensive Practice U. S. Edition 3A. 2004. per. 8.50 (978-1-932906-04-2(5)) SingaporeMath-.com, Inc.

Primary Mathematics Intensive Practice U. S. Edition 3B. 2004. per. 8.50 (978-1-932906-05-9(3)) SingaporeMath-.com, Inc.

Primary Mathematics Intensive Practice U. S. Edition 4A. 2004. per. 8.50 (978-1-932906-06-6(1)) SingaporeMath-.com, Inc.

Primary Mathematics Intensive Practice U. S. Edition 4B. 2004. per. 8.50 (978-1-932906-07-3(X)) SingaporeMath-.com, Inc.

Primary Mathematics Intensive Practice U. S. Edition 5A. 2004. per. 8.50 (978-1-932906-08-0(8)) SingaporeMath-.com, Inc.

Primary Mathematics Intensive Practice U. S. Edition 5B. 2004. per. 8.50 (978-1-932906-09-7(6)) SingaporeMath-.com, Inc.

Primary Mathematics Intensive Practice U. S. Edition 6A. 2004. per. 8.50 (978-1-932906-10-3(X)) SingaporeMath-.com, Inc.

Primary Mathematics Intensive Practice U. S. Edition 6B. 2004. per. 8.50 (978-1-932906-11-0(8)) SingaporeMath-.com, Inc.

Primary Mathematics Teacher's Guide 3B. 2004. spiral bd. 21.00 (978-0-9741573-5-1(X)) SingaporeMath.com, Inc.

Primmer, Rachel. Pentomino Piazza, Vol. 1. 2006. (J). 24.99 (978-0-9787021-0-6(7) , P001) Knowtivate, LLC.

Princeton Review Staff. Roadmap to the AIMS: High School Mathematics. 2005. (State Test Prep Guides Ser.). 304p. pap. 16.00 (978-0-375-76504-9(2) , Princeton Review) Random Hse. Information Group.

Problem Solving. 2003. Level C. tchr. ed. 19.50 (978-0-7652-1314-3(1)); Level C. stu. ed. 14.50 (978-0-7652-1112-5(2)); Level D. tchr. ed. 19.50 (978-0-7652-1318-1(4)); Level D. stu. ed. 14.50 (978-0-7652-1306-8(0)); Level E. tchr. ed. 19.50 (978-0-7652-1322-8(2)); Level E. stu. ed. 14.50 (978-0-7652-1310-5(9)) Modern Curriculum Pr.

Problem Solving. (Classroom Helpers Ser.). 24p. (gr. 3 up). 3.99 (978-0-7682-0831-3(9) , FS194130) Schaffer, Frank Pubns.

Problem Solving 2-3. 2004. (Basic Skills Ser.). 48p. (J). pap. 6.99 (978-0-88724-178-9(6) , CD-4731) Carson-Dellosa Publishing Co., Inc.

Problem Solving 3-4. 2004. (Basic Skills Ser.). 48p. (J). pap. 6.99 (978-0-88724-179-6(4) , CD-4732) Carson-Dellosa Publishing Co., Inc.

Problem Solving 4-5. 2004. (Basic Skills Ser.). 48p. (J). pap. 6.99 (978-0-88724-180-2(8) , CD-4733) Carson-Dellosa Publishing Co., Inc.

Problem Solving 5-6. 2004. (Basic Skills Ser.). 48p. (J). pap. 6.99 (978-0-88724-181-9(6) , CD-4734) Carson-Dellosa Publishing Co., Inc.

Problem-Solving Math Journals for Primary Students. 2004. (Illus.). 256p. 24.99 (978-1-57690-963-8(8)) Teacher Created Materials, Inc.

Problema del Dia: Student & Teacher Support Resources. 1999. (Matematicas en Mi Mundo Ser.). (ENG & SPA.). (gr. k up). (978-0-02-110226-6(0)); (gr. 1 up). (978-0-02-110227-3(9)); (gr. 2 up). (978-0-02-110228-0(7)); (gr. 3 up). (978-0-02-110229-7(5)); (gr. 4 up). (978-0-02-110230-3(9)); (gr. 5 up). (978-0-02-110231-0(7)); (gr. 6 up). (978-0-02-110232-7(5)) Macmillan/McGraw-Hill Schl. Div.

Problemas y Mas: Workbook & Activity Kit. 1999. (SPA., Illus.). Level C. pap., wbk. ed. (978-0-7398-2083-4(4)); Level D. pap., wbk. ed. (978-0-7398-2084-1(2)) Steck-Vaughn.

Professional Handbook: Student & Teacher Support Resources. 1999. (Matematicas en Mi Mundo Ser.). (ENG & SPA.). (gr. 6 up). (978-0-02-110240-2(6)) Macmillan/McGraw-Hill Schl. Div.

Progress in Mathematics. 2006. (YA). (gr. k-2). stu. ed. 18.99 (978-0-8215-8200-8(3)); stu. ed. 26.70 (978-0-8215-8201-5(1)); stu. ed. 26.70 (978-0-8215-8202-2(X)) Sadlier, William H. Inc.

Progress in Mathematics: Student Workbook. 2006. (YA). (gr. k-2). stu. ed. 7.65 (978-0-8215-8220-6(8)); stu. ed. 7.65 (978-0-8215-8221-3(6)); stu. ed. 7.65 (978-0-8215-8222-0(4)) Sadlier, William H. Inc.

Progress in Mathematics, Intervention Workshop, Gr. 4. 2000. (Progress in Mathematics Ser.). 32p. (J). (978-0-8215-2784-9(3) , Sadlier-Oxford) Sadlier, William H. Inc.

Progress in Mathematics, Intervention Workshop, Gr. 5. 2000. (Progress in Mathematics Ser.). 32p. (J). 3.00 (978-0-8215-2785-6(1) , Sadlier-Oxford) Sadlier, William H. Inc.

Progress in Mathematics, Intervention Workshop, Gr. 6. 2000. (Progress in Mathematics Ser.). 32p. (J). 3.00 (978-0-8215-2786-3(X) , Sadlier-Oxford) Sadlier, William H. Inc.

Progress in Mathematics, Spiral Review Practice Book, Gr. 1. 2001. (Progress in Mathematics Ser.). 96p. (J). (978-0-8215-2571-5(9) , Sadlier-Oxford) Sadlier, William H. Inc.

Progress in Mathematics, Spiral Review Practice Book, Gr. 2. 2001. (Progress in Mathematics Ser.). 96p. (J). (978-0-8215-2572-2(7) , Sadlier-Oxford) Sadlier, William H. Inc.

Progress in Mathematics, Spiral Review Practice Book, Gr. 3. 2001. (Progress in Mathematics Ser.). 96p. (J). (978-0-8215-2573-9(5) , Sadlier-Oxford) Sadlier, William H. Inc.

Progress in Mathematics, Spiral Review Practice Book, Gr. 4. 2001. (Progress in Mathematics Ser.). 96p. (J). (978-0-8215-2574-6(3) , Sadlier-Oxford) Sadlier, William H. Inc.

Progress in Mathematics, Spiral Review Practice Book, Gr. 5. 2001. (Progress in Mathematics Ser.). 96p. (J). (978-0-8215-2575-3(1) , Sadlier-Oxford) Sadlier, William H. Inc.

Progress in Mathematics, Spiral Review Practice Book, Gr. 6. 2001. (Progress in Mathematics Ser.). 96p. (J). (978-0-8215-2576-0(X) , Sadlier-Oxford) Sadlier, William H. Inc.

Pruebas de Diagnostico: Student & Teacher Support Resources. 1999. (Matematicas en Mi Mundo Ser.). (ENG & SPA.). (gr. 1 up). (978-0-02-110757-5(2)); (gr. 2 up). (978-0-02-110758-2(0)); (gr. 3 up). (978-0-02-110759-9(9)); (gr. 4 up). (978-0-02-110760-5(2)); (gr. 5 up). (978-0-02-110761-2(0)); (gr. 6 up). (978-0-02-110762-9(9)) Macmillan/McGraw-Hill Schl. Div.

Puedes adivinar? Math, 6 vols.Tr. of Can You Guess? Math. (SPA.). (gr. k-2). 28.95 (978-0-7368-3044-7(8) , Yellow Umbrella Bks.) Capstone Pr., Inc.

Pugliano-Martin, Carol. Patterns in Nature. 2003. (Early Connections Ser.). (J). pap. 33.00 (978-1-4108-1079-3(8)) Benchmark Education Co.

Pythagoras's Bow Tie: Pre-Algebra Investigations Using the 121 Geoboard. 2000. (J). pap. 14.95 (978-1-56911-058-4(1)) Learning Resources, Inc.

QEB Maths Club National Book Stores Edition: Using Numbers Book 1. 2006. (J). per. (978-1-59566-286-6(3)) QEB Publishing Inc.

QEB Maths Club National Book Stores Edition: Using Numbers Book 2. 2006. (J). per. (978-1-59566-290-3(1)) QEB Publishing Inc.

Quadling, Douglas & Neill, Hugh. Core 1 & 2 for OCR. 2004. (Cambridge Advanced Level Mathematics Ser.). (Illus.). 456p. pap. 23.00 (978-0-521-54896-0(9)) Cambridge Univ. Pr.

Quadratische Gleichungen und Ungleichungen. (Duden-Schuelerhilfen Ser.). (GER.). 112p. (YA). (gr. 9). (978-3-411-70102-5(1)) Bibliographisches Institut & F. A. Brockhaus AG DEU. *Dist:* International Bk. Import Service, Inc.

Que hace diez? Math, 6 vols.Tr. of What Makes Ten? Math. (SPA.). (gr. k-2). 28.95 (978-0-7368-3124-6(X) , Yellow Umbrella Bks.) Capstone Pr., Inc.

A Question of Math. 2004. (Illus.). lib. bdg. 5.95 (978-0-8225-4440-1(7)) Lerner Publishing Group.

Quinn, Barney. Mathnotes: Every Student's Handy Homework Notebook. 1999. (Panterra Notes Ser.). 220p. (YA). pap. 18.95 (978-1-892680-00-6(9)) Panterra Publishing, Inc.

Rainbow Bridge Publishing Staff. Math 2nd Grade: Skill Builders. 2002. (Skill Builders Ser.). (Illus.). 64p. (gr. 2 up). pap. 2.95 (978-1-887923-47-7(0)) Rainbow Bridge Publishing.

—Math 3rd Grade: Skill Builders. 2002. (Skill Builders Ser.). (Illus.). 64p. (gr. 3 up). pap. 2.95 (978-1-887923-48-4(9)) Rainbow Bridge Publishing.

—Math Comprehension 1st Grade: Mastering Basic Skills. 2nd ed. 2003. (Skill Builders Ser.). (Illus.). 80p. (gr. 1 up). 2.95 (978-1-887923-46-0(2)) Rainbow Bridge Publishing.

—Math Connection Grade 1. 2002. (Math Connection Ser.). (Illus.). 96p. (gr. 1 up). 10.95 (978-1-887923-77-4(2)) Rainbow Bridge Publishing.

—Math Connection Grade 2. 2002. (Math Connection Ser.). (Illus.). 96p. (gr. 2 up). 10.95 (978-1-887923-78-1(0)) Rainbow Bridge Publishing.

—Math Connection Grade 3. 2002. (Math Connection Ser.). (Illus.). 96p. (gr. 3 up). 10.95 (978-1-887923-79-8(9)) Rainbow Bridge Publishing.

—Math Test Prep First Grade: Mastering Basic Skills. 2002. (Math Test Prep Ser.). (Illus.). 118p. (gr. 1 up). 10.95 (978-1-887923-72-9(1)) Rainbow Bridge Publishing.

—Math Test Prep Second Grade: Mastering Basic Skills. 2002. (Math Test Prep Ser.). (Illus.). 118p. (gr. 2 up). 10.95 (978-1-887923-73-6(X)) Rainbow Bridge Publishing.

—Math Test Prep Third Grade: Mastering Basic Skills. 2002. (Math Test Prep Ser.). (Illus.). 118p. (gr. 3 up). 10.95 (978-1-887923-74-3(8)) Rainbow Bridge Publishing.

—Math Word Problems 2nd Grade: Word Problems (Real Life) 2002. (Mastering Basic Skills Ser.). (Illus.). 32p. (gr. 2 up). 4.95 (978-1-887923-63-7(2)) Rainbow Bridge Publishing.

—Math Word Problems 3rd Grade: Word Problems (Real Life) 2002. (Mastering Basic Skills Ser.). (Illus.). 32p. (gr. 3 up). 4.95 (978-1-887923-64-4(0)) Rainbow Bridge Publishing.

—Math Word Problems 4th Grade: Word Problems (Real Life) 2002. (Mastering Basic Skills Ser.). (Illus.). 32p. (gr. 4 up). 4.95 (978-1-887923-65-1(9)) Rainbow Bridge Publishing.

—Math Word Problems First Grade: Word Problems (Real Life) 2002. (Mastering Basic Skills Ser.). (Illus.). 32p. (gr. 1 up). 4.95 (978-1-887923-62-0(4)) Rainbow Bridge Publishing.

—Multiplication Third Grade: Skill Builders. 2002. (Skill Builders Ser.). (Illus.). 64p. (gr. 3 up). 2.95 (978-1-887923-76-7(4)) Rainbow Bridge Publishing.

—Subtraction First Grade: Skill Builders. 2002. (Skill Builders Ser.). (Illus.). 64p. (gr. 1 up). 2.49 (978-1-887923-49-1(7)) Rainbow Bridge Publishing.

—Subtraction Second Grade: Skill Builders. 2002. (Skill Builders Ser.). (Illus.). 64p. (gr. 2 up). 2.49 (978-1-887923-75-0(6)) Rainbow Bridge Publishing.

Rainbow Fraction Circle Activity Cards. 2000. (J). 7.95 (978-1-56911-752-1(7)) Learning Resources, Inc.

Rainbow Fraction Square Activity Cards. 2000. (J). 7.95 (978-1-56911-753-8(5)) Learning Resources, Inc.

Raintree Steck-Vaughn Staff. Critical Math B. 2002. pap. (978-0-7398-5571-3(9)) Steck-Vaughn.

—Critical Math C. 2002. pap. (978-0-7398-5573-7(5)) Steck-Vaughn.

—Critical Math E. 2002. pap. (978-0-7398-5577-5(8)) Steck-Vaughn.

—Math Problem Solving: Level C. 1998. (Illus.). (J). pap. 11.31 (978-0-8172-7592-1(4)) Steck-Vaughn.

—Math Problem Solving: Level F. 1998. (Illus.). (J). pap. 11.31 (978-0-8172-7598-3(3)) Steck-Vaughn.

Raintree Steck-Vaughn Staff, contrib. by. Computer Scoring Service: 1-300+ with Other. 2000. (J). pap. 3.58 (978-0-7398-0709-5(9)) Steck-Vaughn.

Una rana verde Math, 6 vols.Tr. of One Green Frog Math. (SPA.). (gr. k-2). 28.95 (978-0-7368-3030-0(8) , Yellow Umbrella Bks.) Capstone Pr., Inc.

Ratio & Graphs Student: RUPA Ration & Graphs Student. 2005. 95p. per. 7.50 (978-1-932976-53-3(1)) National Ctr. on Education & The Economy.

Ratio & Proportionality Student: RUA Ratio & Proportionality Student. 2005. 95p. per. 7.50 (978-1-932976-74-8(4)) National Ctr. on Education & The Economy.

Ratio, Proporton, & Percent. 2003. (Mathematical Mind Ser.). 48p. (gr. 6-8). 5.99 (978-1-56822-985-0(2) , IF2902) School Specialty Publishing.

Ratio Student's Edition: CA Math Series II. 2004. 6.00 (978-1-932230-79-6(3)) National Ctr. on Education & The Economy.

Rawlins, Jeanne. Math Comprehension Grade 6. 2003. (Skill Builders Ser.). 80p. (gr. 6 up). 2.95 (978-1-932210-05-7(9)) Rainbow Bridge Publishing.

REA Staff. New Jersey GEPA (REA) - The Best Test Preparation for 8th Grade Math. Hearne, Stephen, ed. 2005. (Test Preps Ser.). 368p. pap. 14.95 (978-0-7386-0025-3(3)) Research & Education Assn.

Real World Math. 80p. (gr. 1-3). 12.99 (978-0-7682-0099-7(7) , GA1685) School Specialty Publishing.

Realtime Associates and Mazer Corporation Staff, compiled by. Subtract up to Three-Digit Numbers. 2002. (J). (gr. 2). 66.75 (978-1-58605-342-0(6) , LeapFrog Schl. Hse.) LeapFrog Enterprises, Inc.

Realtime Associates and Mazer Corporation Staff & LeapFrog Staff, compiled by. Compare & Order Whole Numbers. 2002. (J). (gr. 2). 66.75 (978-1-58605-331-4(0) , LeapFrog Schl. Hse.); (gr. 3). 66.75 (978-1-58605-390-1(6)) LeapFrog Enterprises, Inc.

—Compare Numbers Using Place Value. 2002. (J). (gr. 4). 66.75 (978-1-58605-450-2(3) , LeapFrog Schl. Hse.) LeapFrog Enterprises, Inc.

—Divide Math Facts to 9. 2002. (J). (gr. 3). 66.75 (978-1-58605-397-0(3) , LeapFrog Schl. Hse.) LeapFrog Enterprises, Inc.

—Estimate a Product or Quotient. 2002. (J). (gr. 4). 66.75 (978-1-58605-468-7(6)) LeapFrog Enterprises, Inc.

—Estimate Sums & Differences Beyond Basic Facts. 2002. (J). (gr. 3). 66.75 (978-1-58605-407-6(4) , LeapFrog Schl. Hse.) LeapFrog Enterprises, Inc.

—Estimate to Solve Problems. 2002. (J). (gr. 5). 66.75 (978-1-58605-527-1(5) , LeapFrog Schl. Hse.) LeapFrog Enterprises, Inc.

—Extend Simple Patterns. 2002. (J). (gr. 2). 66.75 (978-1-58605-346-8(9) , LeapFrog Schl. Hse.) LeapFrog Enterprises, Inc.

—Find Distance Between Two Points on a Coordinate Grid. 2002. (J). (gr. 5). 66.75 (978-1-58605-520-2(8) , LeapFrog Schl. Hse.) LeapFrog Enterprises, Inc.

—Find the Value of a Group of Coins to $1.00. 2002. (J). (gr. 2). 66.75 (978-1-58605-340-6(X) , LeapFrog Schl. Hse.) LeapFrog Enterprises, Inc.

—Identify Missing Numbers in a Sequence. 2002. (J). (gr. 2). 66.75 (978-1-58605-348-2(5)) LeapFrog Enterprises, Inc.

—Interpret & Use Graphs. 2002. (J). (gr. 4). 66.75 (978-1-58605-461-8(9) , LeapFrog Schl. Hse.) LeapFrog Enterprises, Inc.

—LeapTrack Cards - Math 2. 2002. (J). (978-1-58605-125-9(3)) LeapFrog Enterprises, Inc.

—LeapTrack Cards - Math 3. 2002. (J). (978-1-58605-173-0(3)) LeapFrog Enterprises, Inc.

—LeapTrack Cards - Math 4. 2002. (J). (978-1-58605-183-9(0)) LeapFrog Enterprises, Inc.

—LeapTrack Cards - Math 5. 2002. (J). (978-1-58605-186-0(5)) LeapFrog Enterprises, Inc.

—Model Problems with a Number Sentence. 2002. (J). (gr. 4). 66.75 (978-1-58605-452-6(X)); (gr. 5). 66.75 (978-1-58605-511-0(9)) LeapFrog Enterprises, Inc. (LeapFrog Schl. Hse.).

—Model Problems with Number Sentences. 2002. (J). (gr. 4). 66.75 (978-1-58605-459-5(7) , LeapFrog Schl. Hse.) LeapFrog Enterprises, Inc.

—Multiply Decimals. 2002. (J). (gr. 5). 66.75 (978-1-58605-515-8(1) , LeapFrog Schl. Hse.) LeapFrog Enterprises, Inc.

—Multiply Fractions. 2002. (J). (gr. 5). 66.75 (978-1-58605-514-1(3) , LeapFrog Schl. Hse.) LeapFrog Enterprises, Inc.

—Multiply Math Facts to 9. 2002. (J). (gr. 3). 66.75 (978-1-58605-396-3(5) , LeapFrog Schl. Hse.) LeapFrog Enterprises, Inc.

—Multiply One- & Three-Digit Numbers. 2002. (J). (gr. 4). 66.75 (978-1-58605-456-4(2) , LeapFrog Schl. Hse.) LeapFrog Enterprises, Inc.

—Recognize Equivalent Fractions. 2002. (J). (gr. 4). 66.75 (978-1-58605-454-0(6) , LeapFrog Schl. Hse.) LeapFrog Enterprises, Inc.

—Recognize Fractional Parts. 2002. (J). (gr. 2). 66.75 (978-1-58605-332-1(9) , LeapFrog Schl. Hse.) LeapFrog Enterprises, Inc.

—Recognize Fractional Parts or Parts of a Set. 2002. (J). (gr. 3). 66.75 (978-1-58605-393-2(0) , LeapFrog Schl. Hse.) LeapFrog Enterprises, Inc.

—Recognize Parallel & Perpendicular Lines. 2002. (J). (gr. 5). 66.75 (978-1-58605-528-8(3)); 66.75 (978-1-58605-529-5(1)) LeapFrog Enterprises, Inc. (LeapFrog Schl. Hse.).

—Represent an Unknown with a Variable. 2002. (J). (gr. 5). 66.75 (978-1-58605-522-6(4) , LeapFrog Schl. Hse.) LeapFrog Enterprises, Inc.

—Represent Life Problems with Diagrams & Numbers. 2002. (J). (gr. 5). 66.75 (978-1-58605-525-7(9) , LeapFrog Schl. Hse.) LeapFrog Enterprises, Inc.

—Solve Multi-Step Problems. 2002. (J). (gr. 3). 66.75 (978-1-58605-400-7(7)); (Illus.). (gr. 4). 66.75 (978-1-58605-460-1(0)) LeapFrog Enterprises, Inc. (LeapFrog Schl. Hse.).

—Solve Problems Involving Ratio, Proportion, & Rate. 2002. (J). (gr. 5). 66.75 (978-1-58605-518-9(6) , LeapFrog Schl. Hse.) LeapFrog Enterprises, Inc.

—Solve Problems of the Form _+ 4 = 8. 2002. (J). (gr. 2). 66.75 (978-1-58605-337-6(X) , LeapFrog Schl. Hse.) LeapFrog Enterprises, Inc.

—Solve Problems with Lists, Tables, Charts, Diagrams. 2002. (J). (gr. 5). 66.75 (978-1-58605-524-0(0) , LeapFrog Schl. Hse.) LeapFrog Enterprises, Inc.

—Subtract Decimals up to Hundredths. 2002. (J). (gr. 3). 66.75 (978-1-58605-395-6(7) , LeapFrog Schl. Hse.) LeapFrog Enterprises, Inc.

—Subtract Fractions with Unlike Denominators. 2002. (J). (gr. 5). 66.75 (978-1-58605-513-4(5)) LeapFrog Enterprises, Inc.

—Subtract One-Digit from Two-Digit Numbers. 2002. (J). (gr. 2). 66.75 (978-1-58605-335-2(3) , LeapFrog Schl. Hse.) LeapFrog Enterprises, Inc.

—Understand a Coordinate Grid. 2002. (J). (gr. 4). 66.75 (978-1-58605-464-9(3) , LeapFrog Schl. Hse.) LeapFrog Enterprises, Inc.

—Understand Operational & Relational Symbols. 2002. (J). (gr. 4). 66.75 (978-1-58605-465-6(1) , LeapFrog Schl. Hse.) LeapFrog Enterprises, Inc.

—Understand Sequence. 2002. 66.75 (978-1-58605-411-3(2)); (J). (gr. 3). 66.75 (978-1-58605-355-0(8)); (J). (gr. 5). 66.75 (978-1-58605-471-7(6)) LeapFrog Enterprises, Inc. (LeapFrog Schl. Hse.).

—Use Mathematics Terms. 2002. (J). (gr. 3). 66.75 (978-1-58605-409-0(0) , LeapFrog Schl. Hse.) LeapFrog Enterprises, Inc.

Recreational Mathematics, 3 vols. 2004. (Illus.). 497p. spiral bd. 45.75 (978-1-931084-23-9(8)) Balloon Magic.

Recreational Mathematics Vol. 3: Mathematical Magic. 2004. (Illus.). 151p. per. 16.95 (978-1-931084-05-5(X)) Balloon Magic.

Recursos de evaluación para el Maestro: Student & Teacher Support Resources. 1999. (Matematicas en Mi Mundo Ser.). (ENG & SPA.). (gr. k up). (978-0-02-110187-0(6)); (gr. 1 up). (978-0-02-110188-7(4)); (gr. 2 up). (978-0-02-110189-4(2)); (gr. 3 up). (978-0-02-110190-0(6)); (gr. 4 up). (978-0-02-110191-7(4)); (gr. 5 up). (978-0-02-110192-4(2)); (gr. 6 up). (978-0-02-110193-1(0)) Macmillan/McGraw-Hill Schl. Div.

Reeves, Diane Lindsey. Career Ideas for Kids Who Like Math & Money. 2nd rev. ed. (Career Ideas for Kids Ser.). 208p. (J). (gr. 4-9). pap. 16.95 ***978-0-8160-6546-2(2)** , Checkmark Bks.); 2007. 32.95 (***978-0-8160-6545-5(4)** , Ferguson Publishing Co.) Facts On File, Inc.

Reeves, Diane Lindsey & Heubeck, Nancy. Career Ideas for Kids Who Like Math. Bond, Nancy, illus. 2000. (Career Ideas for Kids Ser.). (J). (gr. 4-7). 186p. pap. 12.95 (978-0-8160-4096-4(6)); 192p. 23.00 (978-0-8160-4095-7(8)) Facts On File, Inc.

Regrouping Skills (Gr. 2-3) 2003. (J). (978-1-58232-085-4(3)) Bryan Hse. Pubs., Inc.

Regrouping Skills Spanish Version. 2007. (J). per. (***978-1-58232-154-7(X)**) Bryan Hse. Pubs., Inc.

Remkiewicz, Frank. Seaweed Soup: Matching Sets. 2001. (978-0-606-22287-7(1)) Tandem Library Bks.

Renaissance Learning, Inc. Staff. Accelerated Math Learning Cards - California Version: Grade 6. 2002. 1,203p. (J). (gr. 6). 495.00 (978-1-893751-32-3(5)) Renaissance Learning, Inc.

—Accelerated Math Learning Cards - California Version: Grade 7. 2002. 1,202p. (YA). (gr. 7). 495.00 (978-1-893751-33-0(3)) Renaissance Learning, Inc.

—Getting Started with Accelerated Math & Math Renaissance (Foundation & RP) Guide may be used by Foundaton or RP Customers. 2004. 48p. per. 12.95 (978-1-931819-55-8(6)) Renaissance Learning, Inc.

—Math Power Lessons for Grade 4: Instruction for Accelerated Math Objectives. 2004. 164p. spiral bd. 39.95 (978-1-931819-53-4(X)) Renaissance Learning, Inc.

—Math Power Lessons for Grade 5: Instruction for Accelerated Math Objectives. 2004. 207p. spiral bd. 39.95 (978-1-931819-54-1(8)) Renaissance Learning, Inc.

—STAR Math Made EZ (v 3. 1) RP: Quick Guide to the Software. 2004. 27p. spiral bd. 21.95 (978-1-931819-40-4(8)) Renaissance Learning, Inc.

Repaso diario: Transparencias: Student & Teacher Support Resources. 1999. (Matematicas en Mi Mundo Ser.). (ENG & SPA.). (gr. 1 up). (978-0-02-110701-8(7)); (gr. 2 up). (978-0-02-110702-5(5)); (gr. 3 up). (978-0-02-110703-2(3)); (gr. 4 up). (978-0-02-110704-9(1)); (gr. 5 up). (978-0-02-110705-6(X)); (gr. 6 up). (978-0-02-110706-3(8)) Macmillan/McGraw-Hill Schl. Div.

Repaso Rapido: Student & Teacher Support Resources. 1999. (Matematicas en Mi Mundo Ser.). (ENG & SPA.). (gr. k up). (978-0-02-110241-9(4)); (gr. 1 up). (978-0-02-110242-6(2)); (gr. 2 up). (978-0-02-110243-3(0)); (gr. 3 up). (978-0-02-110244-0(9)); (gr. 4 up). (978-0-02-110245-7(7)); (gr. 5 up). (978-0-02-110246-4(5)); (gr. 6 up). (978-0-02-110247-1(3)) Macmillan/McGraw-Hill Schl. Div.

Resource Manager: Technology. 2002. (MacMillan/McGraw-Hill Matematicas Ser.). (ENG & SPA.). (gr. k up). (978-0-02-111512-9(5)); (gr. 1 up). (978-0-02-111513-6(3)); (gr. 2 up). (978-0-02-111514-3(1)); (gr. 3 up). (978-0-02-111515-0(X)); (gr. 4 up). (978-0-02-111516-7(8)); (gr. 5 up). (978-0-02-111517-4(6)); (gr. 6 up). (978-0-02-111518-1(4)) Macmillan/McGraw-Hill Schl. Div.

Restar Math, 6 vols.Tr. of Take Away Math. (SPA.). (gr. k-2). 28.95 (978-0-7368-3140-6(1) , Yellow Umbrella Bks.) Capstone Pr., Inc.

Revision de Ensenanza: Student & Teacher Support Resources. 1999. (Matematicas en Mi Mundo Ser.). (ENG & SPA.). (gr. 1 up). (978-0-02-110209-9(0)); (gr. 2 up). (978-0-02-110210-5(4)); (gr. 3 up). (978-0-02-110211-2(2)); (gr. 4 up). (978-0-02-110212-9(0)); (gr. 5 up). (978-0-02-110213-6(9)); (gr. 6 up). (978-0-02-110214-3(7)) Macmillan/McGraw-Hill Schl. Div.

Richards, Thomas J. Math: Grade 4. 1999. (Spectrum Workbooks Ser.). (Illus.). 150p. (J). (gr. 4-4). pap., wbk. ed. 8.95 (978-1-57768-404-6(4) , Spectrum) School Specialty Publishing.

Ring, Susan. Una rana Verde. 2005. Tr. of One Green Prog. (SPA., Illus.). 16p. (J). (gr. k-1). lib. bdg. 15.93 (978-0-7368-4157-3(1)) Capstone Pr., Inc.

Robertson, David, et al. Essential Mathematics VELS Edition Year 7 with CD-ROM. 2nd rev. ed. 2009. (Essential Mathematics Ser.). pap. incl. cd-rom (***978-0-521-69552-7(X)**) Cambridge Univ. Pr.

Robinson, C. L. MATH1on1 Units of Measure. 2006. (YA). per. 9.99 (978-0-9786767-4-2(2)) Robinson, Consuelo.

Robles, D. & Minquini, Lourdes. Los 100 Mejores Acertijos Matematicos (The One Hundred Best Word Problems) (SPA., Illus.). 151p. (J). (gr. k-6). pap. 7.95 (978-968-416-820-6(9) , FN8209) Fernandez USA Publishing.

Rock, Nathaniel. Math for Everyone 7th Grade Math. 2007. pap. 99.99 (***978-1-59980-001-1(2)**) Nathaniel Max Rock.

Rocklin, Joanne. Not Enough Room! 1998. (Hello Reader! Math Ser.). (J). (978-0-606-13669-3(X)) Tandem Library Bks.

Rodgers, Linda. King Joe's Garden: Unit 2: Data Analysis, Statistics & Probability, 6 vols. l.t. ed. 2003. (Illus.). 88p. per. (978-0-9728596-1-5(6) , K22) King Joe Educational Enterprises, Inc.

Rookie Read-About Math, 8 bks., Set. Incl. Busy Day. Sargent, Brian. 20.50 (978-0-516-24964-3(9)); Grouping at the Dog Show. Ribke, Simone T. 20.50 (978-0-516-24959-9(2)); Guess the Order. Sargent, Brian. 20.50 (978-0-516-24963-6(0)); How Much Does It Hold? Sargent, Brian. 20.50 (978-0-516-24957-5(6)); Look & Count. Dalton, Julie. 20.50 (978-0-516-24958-2(4)); Making Change at the Fair. Dalton, Julie. 20.50 (978-0-516-24960-5(6)); Math Tools. Chrismer, Melanie. 20.50 (978-0-516-24961-2(4)); Slumber Party Problem Solving. Sargent, Brian. 20.50 (978-0-516-24962-9(2)); (Illus.). 32p. (J). (gr. 1-2). 2006. 2006. 156.00 (978-0-516-25416-6(2) , Children's Pr.) Scholastic Library Publishing.

Rookie Read-About Math: Math Concepts for Beginning Readers, 8 Bks, Set. 2004. (J). (gr. 1-2). 156.00 (978-0-516-23396-3(3) , Children's Pr.) Scholastic Library Publishing.

Rose, Mary. Week-by-Week Homework for Building Math Skills. 2006. 96p. pap. 13.99 (978-0-439-53134-4(9) , Teaching Resources) Scholastic, Inc.

Rosenberg, Mandie. Mastering Math Skills. 2002. lib. bdg. 22.20 (978-0-613-52140-6(4)) Tandem Library Bks.

Rosenberg, Mary. Math Mats & Games Measurement: Dozens of Instant & Engaging Reproducible Activity Pages That Help Children Learn Essential Math Skills & Concepts-and Meet the NCTM Standards. 2004. 64p. pap. 11.99 (978-0-439-51880-2(6) , Teaching Resources) Scholastic, Inc.

—Math Mats & Games Money: Dozens of Instant & Engaging Reproducible Activity Pages That Help Children Learn Essential Math Skills & Concepts-and Meet the NCTM Standards. 2004. 64p. pap. 11.99 (978-0-439-43827-8(6) , Teaching Resources) Scholastic, Inc.

—Math Mats & Games Time: Dozens of Instant & Engaging Reproducible Activity Pages That Help Children Learn Essential Math Skills & Concepts-and Meet the NCTM Standards. 2004. 64p. pap. 11.99 (978-0-439-51881-9(4) , Teaching Resources) Scholastic, Inc.

—Month-by-Month Math Practice Pages. 2004. 96p. pap. 13.99 (978-0-439-45874-0(9) , Teaching Resources) Scholastic, Inc.

Rosner, Jerome. First Step to Building Thinking Skills Kit: Reading, Writing, & Math Readiness. 2005. (J). pap. 59.99 (978-0-89455-853-5(6)) Critical Thinking Bks. & Software.

Rovin-Murphy, Deborah. Addition. 2002. (Best-Ever Activities for Grades 2-3 Ser.). (Illus.). 48p. (J). tchr. ed. 10.95 (978-0-439-29646-5(3)) Scholastic, Inc.

Roy, Jennifer Rozines & Roy, Gregory. Holiday Fractions. 2005. (Math All Around Ser.). (Illus.). 31p. (J). (978-0-7614-2001-9(0) , Benchmark Bks.) Cavendish, Marshall Corp.

—Math All Around, 6 bks., Set. Incl. Addition in the Forest. (Illus.). 31p. (978-0-7614-2000-2(2)); Holiday Fractions. (Illus.). 31p. (978-0-7614-2001-9(0)); Numbers on the Street. (Illus.). 31p. (978-0-7614-2002-6(9)); Patterns in Nature. (Illus.). 31p. 25.64 (978-0-7614-1999-0(3)); Sorting at the Ocean. 25.64 (978-0-7614-1998-3(5)); Subtraction at School. (Illus.). 31p. 25.64 (978-0-7614-2003-3(7)); (J). 2005. 2005. (978-0-7614-1997-6(7) , Benchmark Bks.) Cavendish, Marshall Corp.

—Math All Around Group 2, 6 bks., Set. Incl. Division with Toys. lib. bdg. 28.50 (978-0-7614-2269-3(2)); Graphing in the Desert. lib. bdg. 28.50 (978-0-7614-2262-4(5)); Measuring at Home. lib. bdg. 28.50 (978-0-7614-2263-1(3)); Money at the Store. lib. bdg. 28.50 (978-0-7614-2264-8(1)); Multiplication on the Farm. lib. bdg. 28.50 (978-0-7614-2268-6(4)); Shapes in Transportation. lib. bdg. 28.50 (978-0-7614-2265-5(X)); (Illus.). 32p. (J). 2006. 2007. Set lib. bdg. 171.00 (***978-0-7614-2261-7(7)** , Benchmark Bks.) Cavendish, Marshall Corp.

Roy, Jennifer Rozines & Roy, Gregory. Patterns in Nature. 2005. (Math All Around Ser.). (Illus.). 31p. (J). 25.64 (978-0-7614-1999-0(3) , Benchmark Bks.) Cavendish, Marshall Corp.

Roza, Greg. The Art of M. C. Escher - An Optical Artist: Exploring Patterns & Symmetry. 2005. (PowerMath Ser.). (Illus.). 32p. (J). 22.50 (978-1-4042-2927-3(2) , PowerKids Pr.) Rosen Publishing Group, Inc., The.

—An Optical Artist. 2005. (PowerMath Ser.). (Illus.). 32p. (J). pap. (978-1-4042-5117-5(0)) Rosen Publishing Group, Inc., The.

—An Optical Artist: Exploring Patterns & Symmetry. 2005. (PowerMath Ser.). (Illus.). 32p. (J). (978-1-4042-5118-2(9) , PowerKids Pr.) Rosen Publishing Group, Inc., The.

—Space Math. 2003. (Reading Room Collection). (Illus.). 24p. (J). lib. bdg. 18.75 (978-0-8239-3705-9(4)) Rosen Publishing Group, Inc., The.

Ruffin, Frances E. Let's Have a Bake Sale: Calculating Profit & Unit Cost. 2004. (PowerMath Ser.). (Illus.). 24p. (J). lib. bdg. (978-0-8239-8893-8(7)); lib. bdg. 21.25 (978-0-8239-8970-6(4)) Rosen Publishing Group, Inc., The. (PowerKids Pr.).

Safro, Jill. Math Word Problems Made Easy: Grade 5. 2005. (Math Word Problems Made Easy Ser.). 80p. pap. 12.99 (978-0-439-52973-0(5) , Teaching Resources) Scholastic, Inc.

—Math Word Problems Made Easy: Grade 6. 2005. (Math Word Problems Made Easy Ser.). 80p. pap. 12.99 (978-0-439-52974-7(3) , Teaching Resources) Scholastic, Inc.

Sain, Judy L. Daily Math SKills Review Grade 4: Practice for Mastery of Math Standards. 2004. (J). spiral bd. 22.00 (978-1-929229-23-9(2)) aha! Process, Inc.

Salvadori, Mario & Wright, Joseph P. Math Games for Middle School: Challenges & Skill-Builders for Students at Every Level. 2003. (Illus.). 184p. (J). (gr. 6-9). pap. 16.95 (978-1-55652-288-8(6)) Chicago Review Pr., Inc.

Sanders, Nancy. Munch & Learn Math Story Mats: 15 Reproducible Learning Mats with Instant Activities That Use Munchable Manipulatives to Teach Important Math Skills. 2002. 96p. pap. 13.95 (978-0-439-22270-9(2)) Scholastic, Inc.

Sanschagrin, Joceline. La Hora del Bano. 2004. (Caillou Osa Menor Ser.).Tr. of Bath Time. (SPA., Illus.). 24p. (J). (ps up). bds. 5.95 (978-1-58728-274-4(7) , Creative Publishing International) Quayside.

El sapo Distraido: Superlibros de Literatura/Literature Big Books. 1999. (Matematicas en Mi Mundo Ser.). (ENG & SPA.). (gr. k up). (978-0-02-110159-7(0)) Macmillan/McGraw-Hill Schl. Div.

Sargent, Brian. Can You Guess? (Rookie Read-About Math Ser.). (J). 2005. (Illus.). 32p. (gr. 1-2). pap. 5.95 (978-0-516-24669-7(0)); 2004. 20.50 (978-0-516-24421-1(3)) Scholastic Library Publishing. (Children's Pr.).

—Everyone Uses Math. (J). 2006. 32p. (gr. 1-2). pap. 5.95 (978-0-516-25364-0(6)); 2005. (Illus.). 31p. (ps-ps). 20.50 (978-0-516-25263-6(1)) Scholastic Library Publishing. (Children's Pr.).

—Places along the Way. 2006. (Rookie Read-About Math Ser.). (Illus.). 31p. (J). (978-0-516-29917-4(4)) Children's Pr., Ltd.

Sasman, Irene D. H. Math To-Go Books & Hands-On Library, Set. 1999. (Illus.). (J). (gr. 1-2). pap. 99.95 (978-1-56831-517-1(1)); (gr. 3-5). pap. 99.95 (978-1-56831-519-5(8)); (ps-1). pap. 99.95 (978-1-56831-515-7(5)) Learning Connection, The.

Saunders, Dave & Michelson, Richard. Ten Times Better. Baskin, Leonard, illus. 2000. 40p. (J). (ps-3). 17.95 (978-0-7614-5070-2(X) , Cavendish Children's Bks.) Cavendish, Marshall Corp.

Saunders, Hal. When Are We Ever Gonna Have to Use This? (Illus.). 14p. (J). (gr. k-6). 14.95 (978-1-57232-364-3(7)) Seymour, Dale Pubns.

Saxon Manipulatives Kit. 2004. (gr. k-3). 64.50 (978-0-01-210520-7(1)) Saxon Pubs., Inc.

Saxon Math 54 Answer Key & Test. 2004. 18.00 (978-0-01-205170-2(5)) Saxon Pubs., Inc.

Saxon Math 54 Home Study Kit. 2004. 68.50 (978-1-59141-331-8(1)) Saxon Pubs., Inc.

Saxon Math 65 Answer Key & Test. 2004. 18.00 (978-0-01-205173-3(X)) Saxon Pubs., Inc.

Saxon Math 76 Answer Key & Test. 2004. 18.00 (978-0-01-205176-4(4)) Saxon Pubs., Inc.

Saxon Math 87 Answer Key & Test. 2004. pap. 18.00 (978-0-01-210332-6(2)) Saxon Pubs., Inc.

Saxon Math 87 Home Study Kit. 2004. 57.75 (978-0-01-204723-1(6)) Saxon Pubs., Inc.

Saxon Publishers, creator. Saxon Math 5/4 Homeschool Kit, 3 vols. 3rd rev. ed. 2005. pap. 64.50 (978-1-59141-347-9(8) , 3478) Saxon Pubs., Inc.

Saxon Publishers Staff & Hake, Stephen. Saxon Math 6/5 Homeschool Kit, 3 vols. rev. ed. 2004. 69.50 (978-1-59141-348-6(6) , 3486) Saxon Pubs., Inc.

Schaefer, Lola M. Animales Espinosos 1 2 3. Abello, Patricia, tr. 2004. (SPA., Illus.). 12p. (J). 12.95 (978-1-4034-4303-8(3)) Heinemann Library.

Schaffer, Frank. Skill Drill Math: Fractions, Decimals, Measuring, Grade 6. 2001. 64p. (J). (gr. 6-6). pap. 8.99 (978-0-7647-0390-4(0) , FS23236) Schaffer, Frank Pubns.

Schieber, Jennifer. A contar en las Olimpiadas: Fiction-to-Fact Big Book. enl. ed. 2004. (SPA.). (J). pap. 26.00 (978-1-4108-2360-1(1) , 23601) Benchmark Education Co.

—Insects Measure up! ed. 2004. (Shared Connections Ser.). (J). pap., instr.'s gde. ed. 27.00 (978-1-4108-1610-8(9)) Benchmark Education Co.

Schifferdanoff, Valerie. Pocket Charts for Math: Easy How-to's & Reproducible Templates for Making 15 Interactive Pocket Charts That Teach Primary Math Skills. 1999. (Illus.). 80p. pap. 11.95 (978-0-590-98336-5(9)) Scholastic, Inc.

Schofield and Sims Staff. Times Tables. 1999. (Illus.). 27p. (J). (gr. 1-6). Bk. 1. pap. 19.00 (978-0-7217-2495-9(7)); Bk. 2. pap. 19.00 (978-0-7217-2496-6(5)) Schofield & Sims Ltd. GBR. *Dist:* State Mutual Bk. & Periodical Service, Ltd.

Scholastic, Inc. Staff. Math Grade 6. 2002. (gr. 7-12). lib. bdg. 12.95 (978-0-613-86023-9(3)) Tandem Library Bks.

—Math Homework. 1998. (gr. k-3). lib. bdg. 15.25 (978-0-613-90629-6(2)) Tandem Library Bks.

—Scholastic Success with Numbers & Concepts. 2004. (Scholastic Success With Ser.). 48p. pap. 4.99 (978-0-439-55369-8(5)) Scholastic, Inc.

—Standardized Test Skill Builders: Terranova: Reading/ Math: Grade 3. 2000. (Ready-to-Go Reproducibles Ser.). (Illus.). 48p. (J). 8.95 (978-0-439-21117-8(4)) Scholastic, Inc.

—Standardized Test Skill Builders: Terranova: Reading/ Math: Grade 4. 2000. (Ready-to-Go Reproducibles Ser.). (Illus.). 48p. (J). 8.95 (978-0-439-21118-5(2)) Scholastic, Inc.

—Standardized Test Skill Builders: Terranova: Reading/ Math: Grade 5. 2000. (Ready-to-Go Reproducibles Ser.). (Illus.). 48p. (J). 8.95 (978-0-439-21119-2(0)) Scholastic, Inc.

—Standardized Test Skill Builders: Terranova: Reading/ Math: Grade 6. 2000. (Ready-to-Go Reproducibles Ser.). (Illus.). 48p. (J). 8.95 (978-0-439-21120-8(4)) Scholastic, Inc.

Scholastic, Inc. Staff, contrib. by. Addition & Subtraction. 2000. (Interactive Learning Kits Ser.). (Illus.). 24p. (J). (gr. k-2). pap. 8.99 incl. audio (978-1-894281-46-1(2)) Kidzup Entertainment CAN. *Dist:* Penton Overseas, Inc.

—Hop to 100 Game. 2000. (J). 128.00 (978-0-439-16151-0(7)) Scholastic, Inc.

—Multiplication & Division. 2002. (Illus.). 32p. (J). (gr. 3-4). pap. 2.29 (978-1-57759-131-3(3)) Dalmatian Pr.

Scholastic, Inc. Staff, ed. Scholastic Explains Math Homework: Everything Children (& Parents) Need to Survive 2nd & 3rd Grades. 1998. (Scholastic Explains Ser.). (Illus.). 64p. (J). (gr. 2-4). pap. 14.95 (978-0-590-39754-4(0)) Scholastic, Inc.

—Standardized Test Skill-Builders for Math. 2000. (Ready-to-Go Reproducibles Ser.). (Illus.). 48p. (J). (gr. 3-4). pap. 8.95 (978-0-439-16232-6(7)) Scholastic, Inc.

School Mathematics Project Staff. Mechanics 1. rev. ed. 2001. (SMP Ser.). (Illus.). 168p. pap. 19.80 (978-0-521-78800-7(5)) Cambridge Univ. Pr.

—SMP 16-19 Statistics 2: Distributions & Hypothesis Testing. rev. ed. 2002. (School Mathematics Project 16-19 Ser.). (Illus.). 112p. pap. 19.00 (978-0-521-78803-8(X)) Cambridge Univ. Pr.

—SMP Interact Book C2. 2002. (SMP Interact Key Stage 3 Ser.). (Illus.). 192p. pap. 18.00 (978-0-521-78544-0(8)) Cambridge Univ. Pr.

—SMP Interact Practice for Book 7C: For the Mathematics Framework. 2003. (SMP Interact for the Framework Ser.). (Illus.). 120p. pap. 7.00 (978-0-521-53792-6(4)) Cambridge Univ. Pr.

—SMP Interact Practice for Book 7S: For the Mathematics Framework. 2003. (SMP Interact for the Framework Ser.). (Illus.). 128p. pap. 7.00 (978-0-521-53795-7(9)) Cambridge Univ. Pr.

—SMP Interact Practice for Book 7T: For the Mathematics Framework. 2003. (SMP Interact for the Framework Ser.). (Illus.). 104p. pap. 7.00 (978-0-521-53799-5(1)) Cambridge Univ. Pr.

—SMP Interact Practice for Book 9C: For the Mathematics Framework. 2003. (SMP Interact for the Framework Ser.). (Illus.). 64p. pap. 6.00 (978-0-521-53814-5(9)) Cambridge Univ. Pr.

—SMP Interact Practice for Book C2. 2002. (SMP Interact Key Stage 3 Ser.). (Illus.). 80p. (J). pap. 6.00 (978-0-521-79869-3(8)) Cambridge Univ. Pr.

—SMP Interact Practice for Book S1. 2001. (SMP Interact Key Stage 3 Ser.). (Illus.). 96p. (J). pap. 7.00 (978-0-521-79865-5(5)) Cambridge Univ. Pr.

—SMP Interact Practice for Book S2. 2002. (SMP Interact Key Stage 3 Ser.). (Illus.). 104p. pap. 6.00 (978-0-521-79868-6(X)) Cambridge Univ. Pr.

—SMP Interact Practice for Book S3. 2002. (SMP Interact Key Stage 3 Ser.). (Illus.). 72p. (J). pap. 7.00 (978-0-521-79871-6(X)) Cambridge Univ. Pr.

—SMP Interact Practice for Book T2. 2002. (SMP Interact Key Stage 3 Ser.). (Illus.). 64p. (J). pap. 5.00 (978-0-521-79867-9(1)) Cambridge Univ. Pr.

—SMP Interact Practice for Book T3. 2002. (SMP Interact Key Stage 3 Ser.). (Illus.). 64p. (J). pap. 5.00 (978-0-521-79870-9(1)) Cambridge Univ. Pr.

School Mathematics Project Staff, contrib. by. Smp Interact: For the Mathematics Framework. 2003. (SMP Interact for the Framework Ser.). (Illus.). 152p. pap. 18.00 (978-0-521-53812-1(2)) Cambridge Univ. Pr.

—SMP Interact: For the Mathematics Framework. 2003. (SMP Interact for the Framework Ser.). (Illus.). 192p. pap. 20.00 (978-0-521-53801-5(7)) Cambridge Univ. Pr.

—SMP Interact Bk. 7S: For the Mathematics Framework. 2003. (SMP Interact for the Framework Ser.). (Illus.). 344p. pap. 22.00 (978-0-521-53790-2(8)) ; 392p. pap. 22.00 (978-0-521-53793-3(2)) Cambridge Univ. Pr.

—SMP Interact Bk. 8S: For the Mathematics Framework. 2003. (SMP Interact for the Framework Ser.). (Illus.). 232p. pap. 20.00 (978-0-521-53804-6(1)) Cambridge Univ. Pr.

—SMP Interact Bk. 9S: For the Mathematics Framework. 2003. (SMP Interact for the Framework Ser.). (Illus.). 184p. pap. 18.00 (978-0-521-53815-2(7)) Cambridge Univ. Pr.

—Smp Interact Bk. 9T: For the Mathematics Framework. 2003. (SMP Interact for the Framework Ser.). (Illus.). 144p. pap. 18.00 (978-0-521-53819-0(X)) Cambridge Univ. Pr.

—SMP Interact Book 7T: For the Mathematics Framework. 2003. (SMP Interact for the Framework Ser.). (Illus.). 248p. pap. 22.00 (978-0-521-53797-1(5)) Cambridge Univ. Pr.

—SMP Interact Book 8T: For the Mathematics Framework. 2003. (SMP Interact for the Framework Ser.). (Illus.). 224p. pap. 20.00 (978-0-521-53808-4(4)) Cambridge Univ. Pr.

—SMP Interact Book C1. 2001. (SMP Interact Key Stage 3 Ser.). (Illus.). 208p. pap. 18.00 (978-0-521-79860-0(4)) Cambridge Univ. Pr.

—SMP Interact Book S1. 2001. (SMP Interact Key Stage 3 Ser.). (Illus.). 208p. (J). pap. 18.00 (978-0-521-79859-4(0)) Cambridge Univ. Pr.

—SMP Interact Practice for Book 8C: For the Mathematics Framework. 2003. (SMP Interact for the Framework Ser.). (Illus.). 80p. pap. 6.00 (978-0-521-53803-9(3)) Cambridge Univ. Pr.

—SMP Interact Practice for Book 8S: For the Mathematics Framework. 2003. (SMP Interact for the Framework Ser.). (Illus.). 104p. pap. 6.00 (978-0-521-53806-0(8)) Cambridge Univ. Pr.

—SMP Interact Practice for Book 9S: For the Mathematics Framework. 2003. (SMP Interact for the Framework Ser.). (Illus.). 72p. pap. 6.00 (978-0-521-53817-6(3)) Cambridge Univ. Pr.

—SMP Interact Practice for Book 9T: For the Mathematics Framework. 2003. (SMP Interact for the Framework Ser.). (Illus.). 64p. pap. 6.00 (978-0-521-53821-3(1)) Cambridge Univ. Pr.

—SMP Interact Practice for Book C1. 2001. (SMP Interact Key Stage 3 Ser.). (Illus.). 80p. pap. 7.00 (978-0-521-79866-2(3)) Cambridge Univ. Pr.

—SMP Interact Practice for Book T1. 2001. (SMP Interact Key Stage 3 Ser.). (Illus.). 64p. (J). pap. 6.00 (978-0-521-79864-8(7)) Cambridge Univ. Pr.

School Mathematics Project Staff, creator. SMP Interact Book C3. 2002. (SMP Interact Key Stage 3 Ser.). (Illus.). 152p. pap. 18.00 (978-0-521-78536-5(7)) Cambridge Univ. Pr.

—SMP Interact Book T3. 2002. (SMP Interact Key Stage 3 Ser.). (Illus.). 144p. pap. 15.00 (978-0-521-78538-9(3)) Cambridge Univ. Pr.

School Renaissance Institute Staff, creator. Math Builders: Grades 3-5. 2000. (J). (gr. 3-5). 79.95 (978-1-893751-97-2(X)) Renaissance Learning, Inc.

—Math Builders: Grades 6-8. 2000. (YA). (gr. 6-8). 79.95 (978-1-893751-98-9(8)) Renaissance Learning, Inc.

School Specialty Pub. Skills for scholars-math Gr 5. 2007. (Skills for Scholars Ser.). 80p. (J). (gr. k-6). pap. 4.99 (***978-0-7696-5125-5(9)***, Schaffer, Frank) Schaffer, Frank Pubns.

—Using the Standards—Measurement. 2004. (100+ Ser.). 128p. (C). pap. 12.99 (***978-0-7424-2890-4(7)***, Instructional Fair) Schaffer, Frank Pubns.

School Specialty Publishing. Addition & Subtraction with Regrouping. 2002. (Classroom Helpers Ser.). 24p. (J). (gr. 2 up). pap. 3.99 (978-0-7682-0820-7(3), FS194119) Schaffer, Frank Pubns.

—Advanced Concepts, Grade 4. 2006. (Skills for Scholars Ser.). 80p. (C). pap. 4.99 (***978-0-7696-4974-0(2)***, Schaffer, Frank) Schaffer, Frank Pubns.

—Beginning Problem Solving with Mr Wiggle. 2003. 32p. (J). (gr. 1 up). pap. 5.99 (978-1-56451-965-8(1), ID99043) School Specialty Publishing.

—Creative Problem Solving: Multiple Solutions for the Same Answer. 2004. 64p. (J). (gr. 3 up). pap. 8.99 (978-0-7424-2853-9(2), IFG99225); (J). (gr. 4 up). pap. 8.99 (978-0-7424-2854-6(0), IFG99226); (J). (gr. 5 up). pap. 8.99 (978-0-7424-2855-3(9), IFG99227); (J). (gr. 6 up). pap. 8.99 (978-0-7696-3406-7(0), MH1023); (YA). (gr. 7 up). pap. 8.99 (978-0-7696-3407-4(9), MH1024); (YA). (gr. 8 up). pap. 8.99 (978-0-7696-3408-1(7), MH1025) School Specialty Publishing.

—Daily Estimation Adventure. 2004. 80p. (J). (gr. 1 up). pap. 10.99 (978-0-7424-2871-3(0), IFG99228); (J). (gr. 2 up). pap. 10.99 (978-0-7424-2872-0(9), IFG99229); (J). (gr. 3 up). pap. 10.99 (978-0-7424-2873-7(7), IFG99230); (J). (gr. 4 up). pap. 10.99 (978-0-7424-2874-4(5), IFG99231); (J). (gr. 5 up). pap. 10.99 (978-0-7424-2875-1(3), IFG99232); (J). (gr. 6 up). pap. 10.99 (978-0-7696-3416-6(8), MH1027); (YA). (gr. 7 up). pap. 10.99 (978-0-7696-3417-3(6), MH1028); (YA). (gr. 8 up). pap. 10.99 (978-0-7696-3418-0(4), MH1026) School Specialty Publishing.

—Daily Warmups - Math Problems & Puzzles. 2003. (100+ Seriestm Ser.). 128p. (J). (gr. 1-1). pap. 12.99 (978-0-7424-1791-5(3), IFG99039); (J). (gr. 2-2). pap. 12.99 (978-0-7424-1792-2(1), IFG99040); (J). (gr. 5-5). pap. 12.99 (978-0-7424-1795-3(6), IFG99043); (J). (gr. 3-3). pap. 12.99 (978-0-7424-1793-9(X), IFG99041); (J). (gr. 4-4). pap. 12.99 (978-0-7424-1794-6(8), IFG99042); (J). (gr. 6-6). pap. 12.99 (978-0-7424-1796-0(4), IFG99044); (YA). (gr. 7-7). pap. 12.99 (978-0-7424-1797-7(2), IFG99045); (YA). (gr. 8-8). pap. 12.99 (978-0-7424-1798-4(0), IFG99046) School Specialty Publishing.

—Fraction Flash Cards: Advanced. 1999. (J). (gr. 3 up). 6.25 (978-1-56451-560-5(5), ID7260) School Specialty Publishing.

—Funtastic Frogs Math Vol. 1: Matching & Sorting; Counting & Numbers; Balancing Numbers; Measuring; Making Patterns. 2004. 160p. (J). (gr. k-2). pap. 16.99 (978-0-7424-2770-9(6), ID99076) School Specialty Publishing.

—Funtastic Frogs Math Vol. 3: Numbers & Beginning Place Value; Operations & Beginning Place Value; Word Problems; Beginning Algebraic Thinking; Number Games. 2004. 160p. (J). (gr. k-2). pap. 16.99 (978-0-7424-2772-3(2), ID99078) School Specialty Publishing.

—Hundred Number Board Activities. 2004. 64p. (J). (gr. k-1). pap. 8.99 (978-0-7424-2778-5(1), ID99083); (gr. 2-3). pap. 8.99 (978-0-7424-2779-2(X), ID99081); (gr. 4-5). pap. 8.99 (978-0-7424-2780-8(3), ID99082) School Specialty Publishing.

—Making Graphs with Mr Wiggle. 2003. 32p. (J). (gr. k up). pap. 5.99 (978-1-56451-967-2(8), ID99048); (gr. 1 up). pap. 5.99 (978-1-56451-968-9(6), ID99046); (gr. 2 up). pap. 5.99 (978-1-56451-969-6(4), ID99047) School Specialty Publishing.

—Making Patterns with Mr Wiggle. 2003. 32p. (J). (gr. 1 up). pap. 5.99 (978-1-56451-974-0(0), ID99010) School Specialty Publishing.

—Matching & Sorting with Mr Wiggle. 2003. 32p. (J). (gr. 2 up). pap. 5.99 (978-1-56451-985-6(6), ID99018) School Specialty Publishing.

—Matematicas. 2006. (Aprendamos Ser.). 64p. (J). pap. 3.99 (978-0-7696-4326-7(4), Brighter Child) School Specialty Publishing.

—Matematicas y Lectura. 2006. (Aprendamos Ser.). 64p. (J). pap. 3.99 (978-0-7696-4327-4(2), Brighter Child) School Specialty Publishing.

—Math. 1999. (Homework Booklets Ser.). 72p. (J). (gr. 5 up). pap. 2.99 (978-0-88012-943-5(3), IF0276) School Specialty Publishing.

—Math 4 Today: Grade 2. 2005. 112p. (C). pap. 13.99 (978-0-7682-3202-8(3), Schaffer, Frank) Schaffer, Frank Pubns.

—Math 4 Today: Grade 3. 2005. 112p. (C). pap. 13.99 (978-0-7682-3203-5(1), Schaffer, Frank) Schaffer, Frank Pubns.

—Math 4 Today: Grade 4. 2005. 112p. (C). pap. 13.99 (978-0-7682-3204-2(X), Schaffer, Frank) Schaffer, Frank Pubns.

—Math 4 Today: Grade 5. 2005. 112p. (C). pap. 13.99 (978-0-7682-3205-9(8), Schaffer, Frank) Schaffer, Frank Pubns.

—Math Activities for the 100th Day. 2003. (100+ Seriestm Ser.). 128p. (J). (ps-k). pap. 12.99 (978-0-7424-1770-0(0), IFG99072) School Specialty Publishing.

—Math at Home: It's Everyplace You Are! 2004. (It's Everyplace You Are! Ser.). 48p. (J). (gr. 4 up). pap. 6.99 (978-0-7682-2904-2(9), FS99299); (gr. k up). pap. 6.99 (978-0-7682-2900-4(6), FS99301); (gr. 1 up). pap. 6.99 (978-0-7682-2901-1(4), FS99296); (gr. 2 up). pap. 6.99 (978-0-7682-2902-8(2), FS99297); (gr. 3 up). pap. 6.99 (978-0-7682-2903-5(0), FS99298); (gr. 5 up). pap. 6.99 (978-0-7682-2905-9(7), FS99300) Schaffer, Frank Pubns.

—Math, Grade 1. 2006. (Skills for Scholars Ser.). 80p. (C). pap. 4.99 (***978-0-7696-8221-1(9)***, Schaffer, Frank) Schaffer, Frank Pubns.

—Math, Grade 2. 2006. (Skills for Scholars Ser.). 80p. (C). pap. 4.99 (***978-0-7696-8222-8(7)***, Schaffer, Frank) Schaffer, Frank Pubns.

—Math, Grade 3. 2006. (Skills for Scholars Ser.). 80p. (C). pap. 4.99 (***978-0-7696-8223-5(5)***, Schaffer, Frank) Schaffer, Frank Pubns.

—Math, Grade 4. 2006. (Skills for Scholars Ser.). 80p. (C). pap. 4.99 (***978-0-7696-8224-2(3)***, Schaffer, Frank) Schaffer, Frank Pubns.

—Math in the Community: It's Everyplace You Are! 2004. 48p. (J). (gr. k up). pap. 6.99 (978-0-7682-2950-9(2), FS99340); (gr. 1 up). pap. 6.99 (978-0-7682-2951-6(0), FS99335); (gr. 2 up). pap. 6.99 (978-0-7682-2952-3(9), FS99336); (gr. 3 up). pap. 6.99 (978-0-7682-2953-0(7), FS99337); (gr. 4 up). pap. 6.99 (978-0-7682-2954-7(5), FS99338); (gr. 5 up). pap. 6.99 (978-0-7682-2955-4(3), FS99339) Schaffer, Frank Pubns.

—Math, Kindergarten. 2006. (Skills for Scholars Ser.). 80p. (C). pap. 4.99 (***978-0-7696-8220-4(0)***, Schaffer, Frank) Schaffer, Frank Pubns.

—Math Mysteries. 2004. 48p. (J). (gr. 3-3). pap. 6.99 (978-0-7682-2743-7(7), FS99249); (gr. 4-4). pap. 6.99 (978-0-7682-2744-4(5), FS99250); (gr. 5-5). pap. 6.99 (978-0-7682-2745-1(3), FS99251); (gr. 6-6). pap. 6.99 (978-0-7682-2746-8(1), FS99252) Schaffer, Frank Pubns.

—Math Practice. 1999. (100+ Ser.). 128p. (YA). (gr. 7-8). pap. 12.99 (978-1-56822-140-3(1), IF8771) School Specialty Publishing.

—Mathematics: A Step-by-Step Approach. 1999. (Practice Drills Ser.). 86p. (YA). (gr. 8-8). pap. 2.99 (978-0-88012-487-4(3), IF0180, Instructional Fair) Schaffer, Frank Pubns.

—Money. 1999. (Flip-Flashtm Math Ser.). 160p. (J). (gr. 1 up). pap. 7.99 (978-1-56451-349-6(1), ID7873, Ideal School Supply) Schaffer, Frank Pubns.

—Operations with Fractions Gr 5. 2005. (Math 2 Master Ser.). 32p. (J). pap. 3.99 (978-0-7696-3915-4(1), Brighter Child) School Specialty Publishing.

—Place Value. 2001. 24p. (J). (gr. 1-2). pap. 5.99 (978-0-7682-0540-4(9), FS8619) Schaffer, Frank Pubns.

—Problem Solving. 2002. (Classroom Helpers Ser.). 24p. (J). (gr. 2 up). pap. 3.99 (978-0-7682-0824-5(6), FS194123) Schaffer, Frank Pubns.

—Solving Problems, Grade 3. 2006. (Skills for Scholars Ser.). 80p. (C). pap. 4.99 (***978-0-7696-4973-3(4)***, Schaffer, Frank) Schaffer, Frank Pubns.

—Standard & Metric Conversions. 2005. (Math 2 Master Ser.). 32p. (J). pap. 3.99 (978-0-7696-3935-2(6), Brighter Child) School Specialty Publishing.

—Statistics & Number Patterns. 2005. (Math 2 Master Ser.). 32p. (J). pap. 3.99 (978-0-7696-3934-5(8), Brighter Child) School Specialty Publishing.

—Time. 1999. (Flip Flashtmmath Ser.). 160p. (J). (gr. 1 up). pap. 7.99 (978-1-56451-348-9(3), ID7872, Ideal School Supply) Schaffer, Frank Pubns.

—Total English Spanish Learning Kit. 2007. (Total Learning Kits Ser.). 563p. (J). pap. 49.95 (***978-0-7696-5489-8(4)***) School Specialty Publishing.

—Word Problems. 1999. (Homework Booklets Ser.). 72p. (J). (gr. 5-5). pap. 2.99 (978-0-88012-863-6(1), IF0194, Instructional Fair) Schaffer, Frank Pubns.

—Write about Math: The Test Connection. (Test Connection Ser.). 64p. 2004. (J). (gr. 5 up). pap. 9.99 (978-0-7424-1965-0(7), FS99265); 2003. (J). (gr. 2 up). pap. 9.99 (978-0-7424-1962-9(2), FS99262); 2003. (J). (gr. 3 up). pap. 9.99 (978-0-7424-1963-6(0), FS99263); 2003. (J). (gr. 4 up). pap. 9.99 (978-0-7424-1964-3(9), FS99264); 2003. (J). (gr. 6 up). pap. 9.99 (978-0-7424-1966-7(5), FS99266); 2003. (YA). (gr. 7 up). pap. 9.99 (978-0-7424-1967-4(3), FS99267); 2003. (YA). (gr. 8 up). pap. 9.99 (978-0-7424-1968-1(1), FS99268) Schaffer, Frank Pubns. (Schaffer, Frank).

School Zone, ed. Transition Math K-1. deluxe ed. 2004. (Activity Zone Workbook Ser.). 64p. (J). pap. 3.79 (978-1-58947-321-8(3), 02207) School Zone Publishing Co.

School Zone Interactive Staff. Math Basics. rev. ed. 2003. (On-Track Software Ser.). 64p. (J). (gr. k-2). pap. 15.99 incl. cd-rom (978-1-58947-802-2(9)) ; pap. 15.99 incl. cd-rom (978-1-58947-803-9(7)) School Zone Publishing Co.

School Zone Publishing. Math 1. 2003. cd-rom 19.99 (978-1-58947-908-1(4)) School Zone Publishing Co.

—Math 2. 2003. cd-rom 19.99 (978-1-58947-909-8(2)) School Zone Publishing Co.

—Math 3. 2003. cd-rom 19.99 (978-1-58947-910-4(6)) School Zone Publishing Co.

—Multiplication & Division. 2003. (J). (gr. 3-4). cd-rom 19.99 (978-1-58947-927-2(0)) School Zone Publishing Co.

School Zone Publishing Company Staff. Division 0-12. rev. ed. 1999. (Flash Cards Ser.). 56p. (J). 2.79 (978-0-88743-241-5(7), 04017) School Zone Publishing Co.

—Math: Grades 5 & 6. (Illus.). (J). 19.99 incl. audio compact disk (978-0-88743-953-7(5)) School Zone Publishing Co.

—Math 1-2 Software. 2004. 64p. (J). wbk. ed. 15.99 incl. cd-rom (978-1-58947-369-0(8)) School Zone Publishing Co.

—Math 4. (Illus.). (J). 19.99 incl. audio compact disk (978-0-88743-952-0(7)) School Zone Publishing Co.

—Math Basics 1 Bilingual: I Know It! 2004. 64p. (J). pap. 3.79 (978-1-58947-966-1(1)) School Zone Publishing Co.

—Math Basics 2 Bilingual: I Know It! 2004. 64p. (J). pap. 3.79 (978-1-58947-967-8(X)) School Zone Publishing Co.

—Math Basics 3 Bilingual: I Know It! 2004. 64p. (J). (gr. k-3). pap. 3.79 (978-1-58947-968-5(8)) School Zone Publishing Co.

—Math Fun. 2000. (Flash Cards 4-Pack Ser.). (J). 12.99 (978-0-88743-815-8(6), 04032) School Zone Publishing Co.

—Math Readiness A Wipe-off Book: Hours of Reusable Fun! rev. ed. 2005. 26p. (J). (gr. k-1). pap. 3.79 (978-1-58947-786-5(3)) School Zone Publishing Co.

—Math Readiness K-1 Bilingual: I Know It! 2004. 64p. (J). pap. 3.79 (978-1-58947-964-7(5)) School Zone Publishing Co.

—Math War: Addition & Subtraction. rev. ed. 1999. (Game Cards Ser.). 52p. (J). 2.79 (978-0-88743-273-6(5), 05016) School Zone Publishing Co.

—Multiplication 0-12. rev. ed. 1999. (Flash Cards Ser.). 56p. (J). 2.79 (978-0-938256-93-9(9), 04008) School Zone Publishing Co.

—Multiplication Race. 2000. (Mats Ser.). (J). 3.29 (978-0-88743-725-0(7), 03113) School Zone Publishing Co.

School Zone Publishing Company Staff & Evans, Karen. Math Basics: Grade 5. deluxe ed. 2000. (Deluxe Wkbks.). (Illus.). 64p. (J). (gr. 5). pap., wbk. ed. 3.79 (978-0-88743-141-8(0), 02205) School Zone Publishing Co.

School Zone Publishing Company Staff & Giglio, Judith. Summer Scholar Grade 1. deluxe ed. 2000. (Deluxe Wkbks.). (Illus.). 64p. (J). (gr. 1). pap., wbk. ed. 3.79 (978-0-88743-832-5(6), 02232) School Zone Publishing Co.

School Zone Publishing Company Staff & Hall, M. C. Summer Scholar Grade 3. deluxe ed. 2000. (Deluxe Wkbks.). (Illus.). 64p. (J). (gr. 3). pap., wbk. ed. 3.79 (978-0-88743-834-9(2), 02234) School Zone Publishing Co.

School Zone Publishing Company Staff & Kupecky, Jere M. Summer Scholar Grade 2. Carmona, Lisa, ed. Sandford, John, illus. deluxe ed. 2000. (Deluxe Wkbks.). 64p. (J). (gr. 2). pap., wbk. ed. 3.79 (978-0-88743-833-2(4), 02233) School Zone Publishing Co.

School Zone Publishing Interactive Staff. Multiplication & Division. (On-Track Software Ser.). (J). (gr. 3-4). 2001. (Illus.). 32p. pap. 13.99 incl. cd-rom (978-0-88743-951-3(9), 08827); 1999. cd-rom 12.99 (978-0-88743-633-8(1), 08404) School Zone Publishing Co.

Schorr, Andrew M. & Hatch, Thomas H. Operations: Up-to-Speed Math. 2001. (Illus.). 96p. per., wbk. ed. 8.95 (978-1-56254-363-1(6), SP 3636) Saddleback Educational Publishing.

—Patterns, Functions, & Algebra: Up-to-Speed Math. 2001. (Illus.). 96p. per. 8.95 (978-1-56254-369-3(5), SP 3695) Saddleback Educational Publishing.

Schultz, Danielle. Story Problems. 1998. (Basic Skills Ser.). (Illus.). 32p. (J). (gr. 3-5). pap. 4.99 (978-0-88724-467-4(X), CD-2135) Carson-Dellosa Publishing Co., Inc.

Schultz-Ferrell, Karren, et al. Introduction to Reasoning & Proof: Grades 3-5. 2007. (Math Process Standards Ser.). (Illus.). 160p. (C). pap. 25.00 (***978-0-325-01033-5(1)***, E01033) Heinemann.

Schwartz, David M. G Is for Googol: A Math Alphabet Book. Moss, Marissa, illus. 2004. 57p. (J). (gr. 4-7). tchr. ed. 15.95 (978-1-883672-58-4(9), Tricycle Pr.) Ten Speed Pr.

—How Much Is a Million? Kellogg, Steven, illus. 2000. (J). (gr. 1-4). pap. 12.95 incl. audio Weston Woods Studios, Inc.

—If You Hopped Like a Frog. Warhola, James, illus. 1999. (If You Ser.). 32p. (J). (gr. k-4). pap. 16.95 (978-0-590-09857-1(8)) Scholastic, Inc.

—On Beyond a Million: An Amazing Math Journey. 2001. (gr. 3-6). lib. bdg. 15.30 (978-0-613-36853-7(3)) Tandem Library Bks.

Schwartz, Linda. Math Quiz Whiz 3-5, Vol. 431. VanBlaricum, Pam, ed. Armstrong, Beverly, illus. 2004. 128p. (J). (gr. 3-5). pap. 10.99 (978-0-88160-374-3(0), LW-431) Creative Teaching Pr., Inc.

M N O

—Primary Math Quiz Whiz, Vol. 428. VanBlaricum, Pam, ed. Mason, Mark, illus. 2004. 128p. (J). (gr. 1-3). pap. 14.99 (978-0-88160-371-2(6) , LW-428) Creative Teaching Pr., Inc.

Scott Foresman - Addison Wesley Mathematics: Additional Resources. 2004. (gr. k-2). (978-0-328-08111-0(6)); (gr. 1 up). (978-0-328-07382-5(2)); (gr. 2 up). (978-0-328-07383-2(0)); (gr. 3-4). (978-0-328-08112-7(4)); (gr. 3 up). (978-0-328-07384-9(9)); (gr. 4 up). (978-0-328-07385-6(7)); (gr. 5-6). (978-0-328-08113-4(2)); (gr. 5 up). (978-0-328-07386-3(5)); (gr. 6 up). (978-0-328-07387-0(3)) Addison-Wesley Educational Pubs., Inc. (Scott Foresman).

Scott Foresman-Addison Wesley Mathematics. 2004. (gr. k up). stu. ed. (978-0-328-03015-6(5)); (gr. k up). stu. ed. (978-0-328-07586-7(8)); (gr. k up). wbk. ed. (978-0-328-04952-3(2)); (gr. k up). wbk. ed. (978-0-328-04931-8(X)); (gr. 1 up). stu. ed. (978-0-328-03016-3(3)) Addison-Wesley Educational Pubs., Inc. (Scott Foresman).

Scott Foresman-Addison Wesley Mathematics: Additional Resources. 2004. (gr. k-5). (978-0-328-08797-6(1)); (gr. k-6). (978-0-328-06313-0(4)); (gr. k-6). (978-0-328-07636-9(8)); (gr. k up). (978-0-328-07549-2(3)); (gr. k up). (978-0-328-04989-9(1)); (gr. k up). (978-0-328-03816-9(4)); (gr. k up). (978-0-328-04945-5(X)); (gr. k up). (978-0-328-07901-8(4)); (gr. k up). (978-0-328-08559-0(6)); (gr. k up). (978-0-328-07617-8(1)); (gr. k up). (978-0-328-09083-9(2)); (gr. k up). (978-0-328-06314-7(2)); (gr. 1-2). (978-0-328-07618-5(X)); (gr. 1-2). (978-0-328-07902-5(2)); (gr. 1-2). (978-0-328-06315-4(0)); (gr. 1 up). (978-0-328-04946-2(8)); (gr. 1 up). (978-0-328-07550-8(7)); (gr. 1 up). (978-0-328-04990-5(5)); (gr. 1 up). (978-0-328-08560-6(X)); (gr. 1 up). (978-0-328-09084-6(0)); (gr. 1 up). (978-0-328-03817-6(2)); (gr. 2 up). (978-0-328-09085-3(9)); (gr. 2 up). (978-0-328-07551-5(5)); (gr. 2 up). (978-0-328-04947-9(6)); (gr. 2 up). (978-0-328-03818-3(0)); (gr. 2 up). (978-0-328-04991-2(3)); (gr. 2 up). (978-0-328-08561-3(8)); (gr. 3-4). (978-0-328-07903-2(0)); (gr. 3-4). (978-0-328-07619-2(8)); (gr. 3 up). (978-0-328-04948-6(4)); (gr. 3 up). (978-0-328-08562-0(6)); (gr. 3 up). (978-0-328-07552-2(3)); (gr. 3 up). (978-0-328-04992-9(1)); (gr. 3 up). (978-0-328-03819-0(9)); (gr. 3 up). (978-0-328-09245-1(2)); (gr. 3 up). (978-0-328-09086-0(7)); (gr. 4 up). (978-0-328-04949-3(2)); (gr. 4 up). (978-0-328-03820-6(2)); (gr. 4 up). (978-0-328-05007-9(5)); (gr. 4 up). (978-0-328-09087-7(5)); (gr. 4 up). (978-0-328-09246-8(0)); (gr. 4 up). (978-0-328-08563-7(4)); (gr. 4 up). (978-0-328-07553-9(1)); (gr. 5-6). (978-0-328-07620-8(1)); (gr. 5-6). (978-0-328-07904-9(9)); (gr. 5 up). (978-0-328-08564-4(2)); (gr. 5 up). (978-0-328-09088-4(3)); (gr. 5 up). (978-0-328-03821-3(0)); (gr. 5 up). (978-0-328-09247-5(9)); (gr. 5 up). (978-0-328-04950-9(6)); (gr. 5 up). (978-0-328-07554-6(X)); (gr. 5 up). (978-0-328-04993-6(X)); (gr. 6 up). (978-0-328-04994-3(8)); (gr. 6 up). (978-0-328-09089-1(1)); (gr. 6 up). (978-0-328-03822-0(9)); (gr. 6 up). (978-0-328-08565-1(0)); (gr. 6 up). (978-0-328-09248-2(7)); (gr. 6 up). (978-0-328-04951-6(4)); (gr. 6 up). (978-0-328-07555-3(8)) Addison-Wesley Educational Pubs., Inc. (Scott Foresman).

Scott Foresman-Addison Wesley Mathematics: Assessment, Diagnosis, & Intervention. 2004. (gr. k up). (978-0-328-05519-7(0)); (gr. 1 up). (978-0-328-05520-3(4)); (gr. 1 up). (978-0-328-06131-0(X)); (gr. 1 up). (978-0-328-09313-7(0)); (gr. 1 up). (978-0-328-06125-9(5)); (gr. 2 up). (978-0-328-05521-0(2)); (gr. 2 up). (978-0-328-09314-4(9)); (gr. 2 up). (978-0-328-06126-6(3)); (gr. 2 up). (978-0-328-06132-7(8)); (gr. 3 up). (978-0-328-06127-3(1)); (gr. 3 up). (978-0-328-06133-4(6)); (gr. 3 up). (978-0-328-06137-2(9)); (gr. 3 up). (978-0-328-05522-7(0)); (gr. 3 up). (978-0-328-09315-1(7)); (gr. 4 up). (978-0-328-06138-9(7)); (gr. 4 up). (978-0-328-06128-0(X)); (gr. 4 up). (978-0-328-09316-8(5)); (gr. 4 up). (978-0-328-06134-1(4)); (gr. 4 up). (978-0-328-05523-4(9)); (gr. 5 up). (978-0-328-06139-6(5)); (gr. 5 up). (978-0-328-05524-1(7)); (gr. 5 up). (978-0-328-06129-7(8)); (gr. 5 up). (978-0-328-09317-5(3)); (gr. 5 up). (978-0-328-06135-8(2)); (gr. 6 up). (978-0-328-06136-5(0)); (gr. 6 up). (978-0-328-06130-3(1)); (gr. 6 up). (978-0-328-05525-8(5)); (gr. 6 up). (978-0-328-09318-2(1)); (gr. 6 up). (978-0-328-06140-2(9)) Addison-Wesley Educational Pubs., Inc. (Scott Foresman).

Scott Foresman-Addison Wesley Mathematics: Pre-K Mathematics. 2004. (ps-6). cd-rom (978-0-328-08590-3(1)); (978-0-328-09229-1(0)); (978-0-328-09365-6(3)); (978-0-328-09244-4(4)); (978-0-328-09228-4(2)); (978-0-328-09243-7(6)); (978-0-328-08088-5(8)); (978-0-328-09227-7(4)); (978-0-328-08086-1(1)); (978-0-328-09366-3(1)); (978-0-328-09168-3(5)); tchr. ed. (978-0-328-08087-8(X)) Addison-Wesley Educational Pubs., Inc. (Scott Foresman).

Scott Foresman-Addison Wesley Mathematics: Pupil Edition, 4 vols. 2004. (gr. k up). (978-0-328-07587-4(6)); (gr. 2 up). (978-0-328-03017-0(1)) Addison-Wesley Educational Pubs., Inc. (Scott Foresman).

Scott Foresman-Addison Wesley Mathematics: Technology. 2004. (gr. k up). (978-0-328-08602-3(9)); (gr. k up). E-Book incl. cd-rom (978-0-328-08566-8(9)); (gr. 1 up). (978-0-328-08603-0(7)); (gr. 1 up). (978-0-328-09350-2(5)); (gr. 1 up). E-Book incl. cd-rom (978-0-328-08567-5(7)); (gr. 1 up). cd-rom (978-0-328-08579-8(0)); (gr. 1 up). cd-rom (978-0-328-07764-9(X)); (gr. 1 up). cd-rom (978-0-328-08591-0(X)); (gr. 2 up). (978-0-328-08604-7(5)); (gr. 2 up). (978-0-328-09351-9(3)); (gr. 2 up). E-Book incl. cd-rom (978-0-328-08568-2(5)); (gr. 2 up). cd-rom (978-0-328-08592-7(8)); (gr. 2 up). cd-rom (978-0-328-08580-4(4)); (gr. 2 up). cd-rom (978-0-328-07765-6(8)); (gr. 3 up). (978-0-328-09352-6(1)); (gr. 3 up). (978-0-328-08605-4(3)); (gr. 3 up). E-Book incl. cd-rom (978-0-328-08569-9(3)); (gr. 3 up). cd-rom (978-0-328-08581-1(2)); (gr. 3 up). cd-rom (978-0-328-07766-3(6)); (gr. 3 up). cd-rom (978-0-328-08593-4(6)); (gr. 4-6). (978-0-328-09311-3(4)); (gr. 4-6). (978-0-328-09312-0(2)); (gr. 4 up). (978-0-328-09353-3(X)); (gr. 4 up). (978-0-328-08606-1(1)); (gr. 4 up). E-Book incl. cd-rom (978-0-328-08570-5(7)); (gr. 4 up). cd-rom (978-0-328-08594-1(4)); (gr. 4 up). cd-rom (978-0-328-08582-8(0)); (gr. 4 up). cd-rom (978-0-328-07767-0(4)); (gr. 5 up). (978-0-328-08607-8(X)); (gr. 5 up). (978-0-328-09354-0(8)); (gr. 5 up). E-Book incl. cd-rom (978-0-328-08571-2(5)); (gr. 5 up). cd-rom (978-0-328-08595-8(2)); (gr. 5 up). cd-rom (978-0-328-08583-5(9)); (gr. 5 up). cd-rom (978-0-328-07768-7(2)); (gr. 6 up). (978-0-328-09355-7(6)); (gr. 6 up). (978-0-328-08608-5(8)); (gr. 6 up). E-Book incl. cd-rom (978-0-328-08572-9(3)); (gr. 6 up). cd-rom (978-0-328-07769-4(0)); (gr. 6 up). cd-rom (978-0-328-08596-5(0)); (gr. 6 up). cd-rom (978-0-328-08584-2(7)) Addison-Wesley Educational Pubs., Inc. (Scott Foresman).

Scott Foresman-Addison Wesley Mathematics: Workbooks. 2004. (gr. 1 up). wbk. ed. (978-0-328-04953-0(0)); (gr. 1 up). wbk. ed. (978-0-328-04959-2(X)); (gr. 1 up). wbk. ed. (978-0-328-04977-6(8)); (gr. 1 up). wbk. ed. (978-0-328-04965-3(4)); (gr. 1 up). wbk. ed. (978-0-328-07556-0(6)); (gr. 1 up). wbk. ed. (978-0-328-04932-5(8)); (gr. 2 up). wbk. ed. (978-0-328-04960-8(3)); (gr. 2 up). wbk. ed. (978-0-328-04978-3(6)); (gr. 2 up). wbk. ed. (978-0-328-07557-7(4)); (gr. 2 up). wbk. ed. (978-0-328-04966-0(2)); (gr. 2 up). wbk. ed. (978-0-328-04954-7(9)); (gr. 2 up). wbk. ed. (978-0-328-04933-2(6)); (gr. 3 up). wbk. ed. (978-0-328-04967-7(0)); (gr. 3 up). wbk. ed. (978-0-328-04955-4(7)); (gr. 3 up). wbk. ed. (978-0-328-04934-9(4)); (gr. 3 up). wbk. ed. (978-0-328-04979-0(4)); (gr. 3 up). wbk. ed. (978-0-328-07558-4(2)); (gr. 3 up). wbk. ed. (978-0-328-04961-5(1)); (gr. 4 up). wbk. ed. (978-0-328-04935-6(2)); (gr. 4 up). wbk. ed. (978-0-328-04968-4(9)); (gr. 4 up). wbk. ed. (978-0-328-07559-1(0)); (gr. 4 up). wbk. ed. (978-0-328-04962-2(X)); (gr. 4 up). wbk. ed. (978-0-328-04956-1(5)); (gr. 4 up). wbk. ed. (978-0-328-04980-6(8)); (gr. 5 up). wbk. ed. (978-0-328-04963-9(8)); (gr. 5 up). wbk. ed. (978-0-328-04981-3(6)); (gr. 5 up). wbk. ed. (978-0-328-04969-1(7)); (gr. 5 up). wbk. ed. (978-0-328-07560-7(4)); (gr. 5 up). wbk. ed. (978-0-328-04957-8(3)); (gr. 5 up). wbk. ed. (978-0-328-04936-3(0)); (gr. 6 up). wbk. ed. (978-0-328-04964-6(6)); (gr. 6 up). wbk. ed. (978-0-328-04970-7(0)); (gr. 6 up). wbk. ed. (978-0-328-04937-0(9)); (gr. 6 up). wbk. ed. (978-0-328-07561-4(2)); (gr. 6 up). wbk. ed. (978-0-328-04958-5(1)); (gr. 6 up). wbk. ed. (978-0-328-04982-0(4)) Addison-Wesley Educational Pubs., Inc. (Scott Foresman).

Scott Foresman-Addison Wesley Mathematics 1: Additional Resources. 2004. (gr. k up). (978-0-328-07666-6(X)); (gr. 1 up). (978-0-328-07668-0(6)); (gr. 2 up). (978-0-328-07670-3(8)) Addison-Wesley Educational Pubs., Inc. (Scott Foresman).

Scott Foresman-Addison Wesley Mathematics 2. 2004. (gr. k up). stu. ed. (978-0-328-06321-5(5) , Scott Foresman) Addison-Wesley Educational Pubs., Inc.

Scott Foresman-Addison Wesley Mathematics 3. 2004. (gr. k up). stu. ed. (978-0-328-06322-2(3) , Scott Foresman) Addison-Wesley Educational Pubs., Inc.

Scott Foresman-Addison Wesley Mathematics 4. 2004. (gr. k up). stu. ed. (978-0-328-06323-9(1) , Scott Foresman) Addison-Wesley Educational Pubs., Inc.

Scott Foresman-Addison Wesley Mathematics 1. 2004. (gr. k up). stu. ed. (978-0-328-06320-8(7) , Scott Foresman) Addison-Wesley Educational Pubs., Inc.

Scott Foresman Math Around the Clock. 2003. (gr. 1-2). (978-0-328-01697-6(7)); (gr. 1 up). (978-0-328-07264-4(8)); (gr. 1 up). tchr. ed. (978-0-328-06304-8(5)); (gr. 1 up). wbk. ed. (978-0-328-06432-8(7)); (gr. 1 up). wbk. ed. (978-0-328-06426-7(2)); (gr. 1 up). wbk. ed. (978-0-328-06433-5(5)); (gr. 1 up). wbk. ed. (978-0-328-06431-1(9)); (gr. 1 up). wbk. ed. (978-0-328-06427-4(0)); (gr. 1 up). wbk. ed. (978-0-328-06430-4(0)); (gr. 1 up). wbk. ed. (978-0-328-06429-8(7)); (gr. 1 up). wbk. ed. (978-0-328-06428-1(9)); (gr. 2 up). (978-0-328-07265-1(6)); (gr. 2 up). tchr. ed. (978-0-328-06305-5(3)); (gr. 2 up). wbk. ed. (978-0-328-06439-7(4)); (gr. 2 up). wbk. ed. (978-0-328-06440-3(8)); (gr. 2 up). wbk. ed. (978-0-328-06434-2(3)); (gr. 2 up). wbk. ed. (978-0-328-06435-9(1)); (gr. 2 up). wbk. ed. (978-0-328-06438-0(6)); (gr. 2 up). wbk. ed. (978-0-328-06436-6(X)); (gr. 2 up). wbk. ed. (978-0-328-06437-3(8)); (gr. 3-4). (978-0-328-01698-3(5)); (gr. 3 up). (978-0-328-07266-8(4)); (gr. 3 up). tchr. ed. (978-0-328-06306-2(1)); (gr. 3 up). wbk. ed. (978-0-328-06447-2(5)); (gr. 3 up). wbk. ed. (978-0-328-06446-5(7)); (gr. 3 up). wbk. ed. (978-0-328-06445-8(9)); (gr. 3 up). wbk. ed. (978-0-328-06444-1(0)); (gr. 3 up). wbk. ed. (978-0-328-06443-4(2)); (gr. 3 up). wbk. ed. (978-0-328-06448-9(3)); (gr. 3 up). wbk. ed. (978-0-328-06442-7(4)); (gr. 3 up). wbk. ed. (978-0-328-06441-0(6)); (gr. 4 up). (978-0-328-07267-5(2)); (gr. 4 up). tchr. ed. (978-0-328-06307-9(X)); (gr. 4 up). wbk. ed. (978-0-328-06455-7(6)); (gr. 4 up). wbk. ed. (978-0-328-06453-3(X)); (gr. 4 up). wbk. ed. (978-0-328-06452-6(1)); (gr. 4 up). wbk. ed. (978-0-328-06451-9(3)); (gr. 4 up). wbk. ed. (978-0-328-06450-2(5)); (gr. 4 up). wbk. ed. (978-0-328-06449-6(1)); (gr. 4 up). wbk. ed. (978-0-328-06454-0(8)); (gr. 5-6). (978-0-328-01880-2(5)); (gr. 5 up). (978-0-328-07268-2(0)); (gr. 5 up). tchr. ed. (978-0-328-06308-6(8)); (gr. 5 up). wbk. ed. (978-0-328-06456-4(4)); (gr. 5 up). wbk. ed. (978-0-328-06457-1(2)); (gr. 5 up). wbk. ed. (978-0-328-06458-8(0)); (gr. 5 up). wbk. ed. (978-0-328-06459-5(9)); (gr. 5 up). wbk. ed. (978-0-328-06460-1(2)); (gr. 5 up). wbk. ed. (978-0-328-06463-2(7)); (gr. 5 up). wbk. ed. (978-0-328-06461-8(0)); (gr. 5 up). wbk. ed. (978-0-328-06462-5(9)); (gr. 6 up). (978-0-328-07269-9(9)); (gr. 6 up). tchr. ed. (978-0-328-06309-3(6)); (gr. 6 up). wbk. ed. (978-0-328-06464-9(5)); (gr. 6 up). wbk. ed. (978-0-328-06465-6(3)); (gr. 6 up). wbk. ed. (978-0-328-06466-3(1)); (gr. 6 up). wbk. ed. (978-0-328-06470-0(X)); (gr. 6 up). wbk. ed. (978-0-328-06469-4(6)); (gr. 6 up). wbk. ed. (978-0-328-06468-7(8)); (gr. 6 up). wbk. ed. (978-0-328-06467-0(X)) Addison-Wesley Educational Pubs., Inc. (Scott Foresman).

Scott, Janine. Take a Guess: A Look at Estimation. 2003. (Spyglass Books). (Illus.). 24p. (J). (gr. 1 up). lib. bdg. 18.60 (978-0-7565-0446-5(5)) Compass Point Bks.

Scott, Janine & Adams, Alison. Instrumentos para Medir. 2003. (Primeras Conexiones Ser.). (SPA.). (J). pap. 35.00 (978-1-4108-0330-6(9)) Benchmark Education Co.

Seltzer, Carl. Mulitlevel Math Fun Grades 3-5: Instant Games & Activities for the Multilevel Classroom. Fisch, Teri L., ed. Tom, Darcy, illus. 2002. 96p. pap. 11.99 (978-1-57471-901-7(7)) Creative Teaching Pr., Inc.

—Multilevel Math Fun Grades 1-2: Instant Games & Activities for the Multilevel Classroom. Fisch, Teri, ed. Tom, Darcy, illus. 2002. 96p. pap. 11.99 (978-1-57471-900-0(9)) Creative Teaching Pr., Inc.

Sesame Street Early Math Skills. 2006. (J). spiral bd. 5.99 ***978-1-58610-984-4(7)*** Learning Horizons, Inc.

Sesame Street Learn about Math with Bert & Ernie. 2007. (J). pap. 3.95 ***(978-1-59545-147-7(1))*** Learning Horizons, Inc.

Seymour, Dale. Balanced Assessment for the Mathematics Curriculum. 2003. (Illus.). 184p. (J). (gr. 3-5). 42.95 (978-0-7690-0063-3(0)); Package 2. 42.95 (978-0-7690-0064-0(9)) Seymour, Dale Pubns.

—Developing Skills in Estimation, Bk. A. 55p. (J). (gr. 7-8). 14.95 net. (978-0-86651-010-3(9) , DSO1161) Seymour, Dale Pubns.

Sganga, Francis. Introducing Gifted Students to the Wonders of Mathematics: Preparation for High School & Higher Mathematics, Grades 4 ¿ 8. 2004. (Illus.). 75p. (978-0-910609-47-0(0)) Gifted Education Pr.

Shaffer, Katherine A. Larson's TI-73 Math Activities: Applications for the Real World. 1999. (Illus.). 130p. wbk. ed. 29.95 (978-1-58123-072-7(9) , MC-MTI-101) Larson Learning, Inc.

Shake & Learn Mathematics. 2001. (YA). spiral bd. 119.95 incl. audio compact disk (978-0-9746001-1-6(3)) Salt Productions, Inc.

Shapes: First Grade Guided Reading Level B. (On Our Way to English Ser.). (gr. 1 up). 27.75 (978-0-7578-7031-6(7)) Rigby Education.

Shapes Around the World: Third Grade Guided Reading Level M. (On Our Way to English Ser.). (gr. 3 up). 34.50 (978-0-7578-7132-0(1)) Rigby Education.

Shea, Therese. Biosphere 2: Solving Word Problems. 2005. (PowerMath Ser.). (Illus.). 32p. (J). 22.50 (978-1-4042-2943-3(4)); (978-1-4042-5151-9(0)); pap. (978-1-4042-5150-2(2)) Rosen Publishing Group, Inc., The. (PowerKids Pr.).

—Climbing Mount Everest: Understanding Commutative, Associative, & Distributive Properties. 2005. (PowerMath Ser.). (Illus.). 32p. (J). 22.50 (978-1-4042-2939-6(6)); (978-1-4042-5143-4(X)); pap. (978-1-4042-5142-7(1)) Rosen Publishing Group, Inc., The. (PowerKids Pr.).

Sheffield, Stephanie & Gallagher, Kathleen. Math & Nonfiction, Grades 3-5. 2004. (Illus.). 232p. (gr. 3-5). pap. 22.95 (978-0-941355-62-9(4)) Math Solutions Pubns.

Sheldon, Ken. Sing along & Learn: Early Math Kit. 2006. 32p. (J). 9.99 (978-0-439-80214-7(8) , Teaching Resources) Scholastic, Inc.

Sherard, Wade H., III. Logic Number Problems. 1998. (Illus.). 64p. (J). (gr. 4-8). pap. 12.05 (978-0-7690-0000-8(2)) Seymour, Dale Pubns.

Sherran, Peter. Graphical Calculator Support Pack. 2000. (Complete Advanced Level Mathematics Ser.). (Illus.). 104p. (YA). (gr. 11). ring bd. 55.00 (978-0-7487-4524-1(6)) Nelson Thornes Ltd. GBR. *Dist:* Trans-Atlantic Pubns., Inc.

Shieber, Jennifer. Insects Measure Up! ed. 2004. (Shared Connections Ser.). (J). pap. 27.00 (978-1-4108-1634-4(6)) Benchmark Education Co.

Shields, Charles J. Standardized Test Practice for 6th Grade. 1999. 96p. (J). (gr. 6). pap., tchr. ed. 11.99 (978-1-57690-681-1(7) , TCA2681) Teacher Created Materials, Inc.

Shiotsu, Vicky. Fast Ideas for Busy Teachers: Math, Grade 1. 2004. (Illus.). 80p. (J). (gr. 1-1). pap. 10.99 (978-0-7682-2911-0(1) , FS99305, Schaffer, Frank) Schaffer, Frank Pubns.

—Fast Ideas for Busy Teachers: Math, Grade 2. 2004. (Illus.). 80p. (J). (gr. 2-2). pap. 10.99 (978-0-7682-2912-7(X) , FS99306, Schaffer, Frank) Schaffer, Frank Pubns.

—Preschool Math: Learning Basic Concepts through Experimenting & Play. Hamaguchi, Carla & Butler, Heather, eds. Campbell, Jenny & Christensen, David, illus. 2005. 128p. pap. 13.99 (978-1-59198-224-1(3) , 2567) Creative Teaching Pr., Inc.

Shireman, Myrl. Fractions, Decimals & Percentages. 1999. (Illus.). 96p. (YA). (gr. 5-8). pap. 10.95 (978-1-58037-106-3(X)) Twain, Mark Media, Inc. Pubs.

—Math Skills Made Easy. 1999. (Illus.). 96p. (YA). (gr. 5). pap. 10.95 (978-1-58037-094-3(2)) Twain, Mark Media, Inc. Pubs.

Shoemaker, James L. Solving Math Word Problems Bk. 3: Multiplication & Division. Womack, Randy L., ed. Lew, Christina, illus. 2000. 48p. (J). (gr. 4-6). pap. 7.95 (978-1-56500-045-2(5)) Golden Educational Ctr.

—Solving Math Word Problems Bk. 4: Measurements, Money & Time. Womack, Randy L., ed. Lew, Christina, illus. 2001. 48p. (J). (gr. 4-6). pap. 7.95 (978-1-56500-046-9(3)) Golden Educational Ctr.

The Short & Sweet Math Book: Arithmetic for Adults. 2001. 114p. (J). 13.50 (978-0-9708636-0-7(8)) Mansfield, Scott.

Show What You Know on the FCAT 6, New Math Student Workbook. 2006. (J). per. 16.95 ***(*978-1-59230-190-4(8))*** Englefield & Assocs., Inc.

Show What You Know on the FCAT, Grade 8 Math Student Self Study Workbook. 2006. (YA). per. 16.95 (978-1-59230-177-5(0)) Englefield & Assocs., Inc.

Show What You Know on the OAT for Grade 6 Math Student Workbook. 2007. (J). per. 16.95 ***(*978-1-59230-281-9(5))*** Englefield & Assocs., Inc.

Show What You Know on the OAT for Grade 7, Math Student Workbook. 2006. (J). per. 16.95 (978-1-59230-174-4(6)) Englefield & Assocs., Inc.

Show What You Know Publishing, ed. Show What You Know on the CSAP for Grade 6, Mathematics Student Workbook. 2007. (J). per. 14.95 ***(*978-1-59230-238-3(6))*** Englefield & Assocs., Inc.

—Show What You Know on the OAT for Grade 8 Mathematics Student Self-Study Workbook. 2007. (YA). per. 16.95 ***(*978-1-59230-283-3(1))*** Englefield & Assocs., Inc.

Showing Relationships with Graphs Student: RUA Showing Relationships with Graphs Student. 2005. 95p. per. 7.50 (978-1-932976-75-5(2)) National Ctr. on Education & The Economy.

Sico, John J., Jr. Pre-ESPA Success Work-a-Text in Mathematics. 2002. 25p. (J). pap. (978-1-56749-532-4(X)) Instructivision, Inc.

—Pre-HSPA Success Work-a-Text in Mathematics. 2001. 224p. (YA). pap. (978-1-56749-525-6(7)) Instructivision, Inc.

Siede Preis Photography (Firm) Staff & Brian Warling Photography (Firm) Staff, contrib. by. I Can Add. 2003. (Lift-A-Flap Ser.). (Illus.). 12p. (J). bds. (978-0-7853-8239-3(9) , 7190000) Publications International, Ltd.

Silbey, Robyn. Clearly Math Gr 1. 2001. 64p. (gr. 1 up). 15.99 (978-0-7682-0485-8(2) , J331001) School Specialty Publishing.

—Clearly Math Gr 2. 2001. 64p. (gr. 2 up). 15.99 (978-0-7682-0486-5(0) , J331002) School Specialty Publishing.

—Clearly Math Gr 3. 2001. 64p. (gr. 3 up). 15.99 (978-0-7682-0487-2(9) , J331003) School Specialty Publishing.

—Clearly Math Gr 4. 2001. 64p. (gr. 4 up). 15.99 (978-0-7682-0488-9(7) , J331004) School Specialty Publishing.

—Clearly Math Gr 5. 2001. 64p. (gr. 5 up). 15.99 (978-0-7682-0489-6(5) , J331005) School Specialty Publishing.

—Clearly Math Gr 6. 2001. 64p. (gr. 6 up). 15.99 (978-0-7682-0490-2(9) , J331006) School Specialty Publishing.

—Math Hooks 1. 2004. (Illus.). 80p. (gr. 1). pap. (978-0-673-58916-3(1)) Good Year Bks.

—Math Hooks 2. 2004. (Illus.). 80p. (gr. 2). pap. (978-0-673-58917-0(X)) Good Year Bks.

Simpson, Jeff. Sharing Big Numbers, 2nd Edition, Student Edition: Count, Notice & Remember Math Intervention Volume I, MD-2. Simpson, Marilyn, ed. 2nd ed. 2007. (Count, Notice & Remember Ser. : Volume I, MD-2). ring bd. 50.00 ***(*978-1-888976-44-1(6))*** Mastery Learning Systems.

Simpson, Marilyn Bohlen, ed. Percents, Ratios, & Rates, Student Edition: Count, Notice & Remember Math Intervention, Volume 3. 2007. ring bd. 59.95 ***(*978-1-888976-50-2(0))*** Mastery Learning Systems.

Skill Sharpeners, Math, Grade 1. 2005. (J). pap. 9.99 (978-1-59673-053-3(6) , emc 4545) Evan-Moor Educational Pubs.

Skill Sharpeners, Math, Grade 2. 2005. (J). pap. 9.99 (978-1-59673-054-0(4) , emc 4546) Evan-Moor Educational Pubs.

Skill Sharpeners, Math, Grade 3. 2005. (J). pap. 9.99 (978-1-59673-055-7(2) , emc 4547) Evan-Moor Educational Pubs.

Skill Sharpeners, Math, Grade 4. 2005. (J). pap. 9.99 (978-1-59673-056-4(0) , emc 4548) Evan-Moor Educational Pubs.

Skill Sharpeners, Math, Grade 5. 2005. (J). pap. 9.99 (978-1-59673-057-1(9) , emc 4549) Evan-Moor Educational Pubs.

Skill Sharpeners, Math, Grade 6. 2005. (J). pap. 9.99 (978-1-59673-058-8(7) , emc 4550) Evan-Moor Educational Pubs.

Skill Sharpeners, Math, Grade K. 2005. (J). pap. 9.99 (978-1-59673-052-6(8) , emc 4544) Evan-Moor Educational Pubs.

Skill Sharpeners, Math, Grade PreK. 2005. (J). pap. 9.99 (978-1-59673-051-9(X) , emc 4543) Evan-Moor Educational Pubs.

Skow, Donald P. No Sense in Mathematics. 4th rev. ed. 2000. 128p. (YA). (gr. 6 up). pap. 12.00 (978-0-911171-04-4(5)) D&R Enterprises.

Smith, Judi. Test-Taking Practice for Reading & Math Grades 1-2. 2002. 80p. (J). per. 10.99 (978-0-88724-697-5(4) , CD-0050) Carson-Dellosa Publishing Co., Inc.

Smith, Robert. How to Divide: Grades 3-4. 1999. (Illus.). 48p. pap., tchr. ed. 7.99 (978-1-57690-485-5(7) , TCA2485) Teacher Created Materials, Inc.

Smith, Robert W. Problem-Solving Math for Middle Grades, Grades 6-8. Ferraro, Mary P., ed. Greger, Shana, illus. 1998. 96p. pap., tchr. ed. 10.99 (978-1-57471-364-0(7) , 2604) Creative Teaching Pr., Inc.

Snap Cube Challenges. 2000. (J). Book 1. pap. 10.95 (978-1-56911-059-1(X)); Book 2. pap. 10.95 (978-1-56911-060-7(3)) Learning Resources, Inc.

Snap! Division, 1 CD. 2004. cd-rom 4.99 (978-1-59150-408-5(2)) TOPICS Entertainment.

Snap! Subtraction. 2002. cd-rom 4.99 (978-1-59150-156-5(3)) TOPICS Entertainment.

So Many Circles Math, 6 vols. (gr. k-2). 28.95 (978-0-7368-1732-5(8) , Yellow Umbrella Bks.) Capstone Pr., Inc.

Un Sol Sale: Superlibros de Literatura/Literature. 1999. (Matematicas en Mi Mundo Ser.). (ENG & SPA.). (gr. k up). (978-0-02-110157-3(4)) Macmillan/McGraw-Hill Schl. Div.

Solve Word Problems. 2004. (Math "How To" Ser.). (Illus.). 48p. (J). (gr. 4-5). 7.99 (978-1-57690-949-2(2)); (gr. 5-6). 7.99 (978-1-57690-950-8(6)) Teacher Created Materials, Inc.

Soper, Sandra. Number Workbook 1. rev. ed. 2003. (Illus.). 32p. pap., wbk. ed. 5.99 (978-0-330-32070-2(X) , Pan) Pan Macmillan GBR. *Dist:* Trafalgar Square Publishing.

—Number Workbook 2. rev. ed. 2003. (Illus.). 32p. pap., wbk. ed. 5.99 (978-0-330-32071-9(8) , Pan) Pan Macmillan GBR. *Dist:* Trafalgar Square Publishing.

Soriano, Al. Excursions Gr 1 Sp. 2004. (Voyages Ser.). (J). (gr. 1). stu. ed., per. 10.55 (978-1-58830-875-7(8)) Metropolitan Teaching & Learning Co.

—Excursions Gr 2 Sp. 2004. (Voyages Ser.). (J). (gr. 2). stu. ed., per. 10.55 (978-1-58830-876-4(6)) Metropolitan Teaching & Learning Co.

—Excursions Gr 3 Sp. 2004. (Voyages Ser.). (J). (gr. 3). stu. ed., per. 10.55 (978-1-58830-877-1(4)) Metropolitan Teaching & Learning Co.

—Excursions Grade 1. 2003. (Voyages Ser.). (J). (gr. 1). stu. ed., per. 8.95 (978-1-58830-612-8(7)) Metropolitan Teaching & Learning Co.

—Excursions Grade 2. 2003. (Voyages Ser.). (J). (gr. 2). stu. ed., per. 8.95 (978-1-58830-627-2(5)) Metropolitan Teaching & Learning Co.

—Excursions Grade 3. 2003. (Voyages Ser.). (J). (gr. 3). stu. ed., per. 8.95 (978-1-58830-628-9(3)) Metropolitan Teaching & Learning Co.

—Excursions Grade 4. 2003. (Voyages Ser.). (J). (gr. 4). stu. ed., per. 8.95 (978-1-58830-629-6(1)) Metropolitan Teaching & Learning Co.

—Excursions Grade 5. 2003. (Voyages Ser.). (J). (gr. 5). stu. ed., per. 8.95 (978-1-58830-630-2(5)) Metropolitan Teaching & Learning Co.

—Metro Math Voyages Kindergarten Kit Sp. 2004. (Voyages Ser.). (J). (gr. k). 474.75 (978-1-58830-977-8(0)) Metropolitan Teaching & Learning Co.

—Voyages Gr 1 Student Kit Sp. 2004. (Voyages Ser.). (J). (gr. 1). 31.37 (978-1-58830-980-8(0)) Metropolitan Teaching & Learning Co.

—Voyages Gr 2 Student Kit Sp. 2004. (Voyages Ser.). (J). (gr. 2). 31.37 (978-1-58830-981-5(9)) Metropolitan Teaching & Learning Co.

—Voyages Gr 3 Student Kit Sp. 2004. (Voyages Ser.). (J). (gr. 3). 31.37 (978-1-58830-982-2(7)) Metropolitan Teaching & Learning Co.

—Voyages Grade 2 Complete Program Sp. 2005. (Voyages Ser.). (J). (gr. 2). 758.67 (978-1-58830-868-9(5)) Metropolitan Teaching & Learning Co.

—Voyages Grade 3 Complete Program Sp. 2005. (Voyages Ser.). (J). (gr. 3). 758.67 (978-1-58830-869-6(3)) Metropolitan Teaching & Learning Co.

—Voyages Kinder Sp Activity Cards Deck a Sp. 2004. (Voyages Ser.). (J). (gr. k). 62.85 (978-1-58830-974-7(6)) Metropolitan Teaching & Learning Co.

—Voyages Kinder Sp Activity Cards Deck B Sp. 2004. (Voyages Ser.). (J). (gr. k). 26.45 (978-1-58830-973-0(8)) Metropolitan Teaching & Learning Co.

—Voyages Kinder Sp Student. 2004. (Voyages Ser.). (J). (gr. k). per., act. bk. ed. 13.73 (978-1-58830-975-4(4)) Metropolitan Teaching & Learning Co.

Sornson, Bob. Math Moms & Dads Home Program: Developing Symbolic Math Skills for Ages 5 to 8. 2004. 10.00 (978-0-9755415-1-7(X)) Early Learning Foundation, LLC.

Sornson, Robert. The Math Moms & Dads Home Program: Preschool & Kindergarten Level, for ages 3 to 6. 2004. (978-0-9755415-0-0(1)) Early Learning Foundation, LLC.

Sorte, Elize A. Math Snacks: Problem-Solving Fun with Food Manipulatives. Frazier, Victoria Ponikvar, illus. 1999. 144p. (J). pap., tchr. ed. 14.99 (978-1-57690-323-0(0) , TCA2323) Teacher Created Materials, Inc.

Souviney, Randal & Coffland, Jack. Solving Math Problems Kids Care About. 2nd ed. 2005. (Illus.). 144p. pap. (978-1-59647-061-3(5)) Good Year Bks.

Souviney, Randall J., et al. Mathematical Investigations, Bk. 3. 208p. (J). 21.95 (978-0-86651-585-6(2) , DS21145) Seymour, Dale Pubns.

Spanish Math Add-on Set, Early Level. (SPA.). (gr. k-2). 57.95 (978-0-7368-3067-6(7) , Yellow Umbrella Bks.) Capstone Pr., Inc.

Spanish Math Add-on Set, Emergent Level. (SPA.). (gr. k-2). 57.95 (978-0-7368-3154-3(1) , Yellow Umbrella Bks.) Capstone Pr., Inc.

Spanish Math Program, Early Level. (SPA.). (gr. k-2). 348.95 (978-0-7368-3066-9(9) , Yellow Umbrella Bks.) Capstone Pr., Inc.

Spanish Math Program, Emergent Level. (SPA.). (gr. k-2). 348.95 (978-0-7368-3153-6(3) , Yellow Umbrella Bks.) Capstone Pr., Inc.

Spanish TAKS MASTER Math, Gr. 5. 2004. (J). (978-1-57022-473-7(0)) ECS Learning Systems, Inc.

Spanish TAKS MASTER Math, Gr. 6. 2004. (J). (978-1-57022-501-7(X)) ECS Learning Systems, Inc.

Spanish TAKS MASTER Math Grade 3. 2004. (978-1-57022-466-9(8)) ECS Learning Systems, Inc.

Spanish TAKS MASTER Math Grade 4. 2004. (978-1-57022-467-6(6)) ECS Learning Systems, Inc.

Spatial Problem Solving with Cuisenaire Rods. 2000. (J). pap. 9.95 (978-1-56911-052-2(2)) Learning Resources, Inc.

Splash! Superlibros de Literatura/Literature Big Books. 1999. (Matematicas en Mi Mundo Ser.). (ENG & SPA.). (gr. 1 up). (978-0-02-110165-8(5)) Macmillan/McGraw-Hill Schl. Div.

Spyglass Books-Math Complete Set. (Spyglass Books-Math Ser.). (gr. 1-2). 159.44 (978-0-7565-0801-2(0)) Compass Point Bks.

Stamell, Jim. Cambridge HSC General Mathematics Study Guide. 2005. (Cambridge HSC Study Guides). 272p. pap., stu. ed. 12.95 (978-0-521-60898-5(8)) Cambridge Univ. Pr.

Stamper, Judith Bauer. Space Math. Andriani, Vincent, illus. 2000. (Scholastic At-Home Phonics Reading Program Ser.: Vol. 49). 24p. (J). (978-0-590-68836-9(7)) Scholastic, Inc.

—Tic-Tac-Toe: Three in a Row. 1998. (Hello Reader! Math Ser.). (J). (978-0-606-13849-9(8)) Tandem Library Bks.

Stanley, Anne, illus. Listen in Addition. 2007. 16p. (J). 16.99 ***(978-0-9796150-0-9(3))*** Jandie Jams Music LLC.

STAR Math RP Complete Subscription Package. 2004. cd-rom (978-1-59455-179-6(0)) Renaissance Learning, Inc.

STAR Math RP Norms Upgrade. 2004. cd-rom 599.00 (978-1-59455-183-3(9)) Renaissance Learning, Inc.

STAR Math RP Set Up. 2004. cd-rom 299.00 (978-1-59455-182-6(0)) Renaissance Learning, Inc.

STAR Math RP Student Subscription. 2004. cd-rom (978-1-59455-180-2(4)) Renaissance Learning, Inc.

STAR Math RP Student Subscription Renewal. 2004. cd-rom (978-1-59455-181-9(2)) Renaissance Learning, Inc.

STAR Math RP Subscription Package. 2004. cd-rom 1499.00 (978-1-59455-178-9(2)) Renaissance Learning, Inc.

Stckvagn. AC Ems Decimals & Percents. 2004. pap. (978-0-7398-9858-1(2)) Harcourt Schl. Pubs.

—AC Ems Whole Numbers. 2004. pap. (978-0-7398-9857-4(4)) Harcourt Schl. Pubs.

Steck-Vaughn Staff. Adventures in Problem Solving Lab Pack. 1999. (J). pap. (978-0-7398-0071-3(X)) Steck-Vaughn.

—Answer Key Soaring Score CRCT Math Level D. 2002. (J). pap. (978-0-7398-5576-8(X)) Steck-Vaughn.

—Answer Key Soaring Score CRCT Math Level F. 2002. (J). pap. (978-0-7398-5580-5(8)) Steck-Vaughn.

—Answer Key Soaring Score Map Math Level D. 2002. (J). pap. (978-0-7398-5600-0(6)) Steck-Vaughn.

—Answer Key Soaring Score Map Math Level H. 2002. (J). pap. (978-0-7398-5608-6(1)) Steck-Vaughn.

—Answer Key Soaring Score Map Math Level J: High Scool Edition. 2002. (YA). pap. (978-0-7398-5618-5(9)) Steck-Vaughn.

—Answer Key Soaring Scores & CAHSEE Math: High School Edition. 2002. (YA). pap. (978-0-7398-5540-9(9)) Steck-Vaughn.

—Answer Key Soaring Scores CRCT Math Level E. 2002. (J). pap. (978-0-7398-5578-2(6)) Steck-Vaughn.

—Answer Key Sorаring Score CRCT Math Level H. 2002. (J). pap. (978-0-7398-5584-3(0)) Steck-Vaughn.

—Answer Key Steck-Vaughn Berrent Gepa Success. 2001. (J). pap. (978-0-7398-3988-1(8)) Steck-Vaughn.

—Applied Math Intermediate. 2004. pap. 8.50 (978-0-7398-9849-9(3)); pap. 68.00 (978-0-7398-9930-4(9)) Harcourt Schl. Pubs.

—Applied Math Introductory. 2004. pap. 8.50 (978-0-7398-9853-6(1)) Harcourt Schl. Pubs.

—Applied Math Introductory 8-Pack. 2004. pap. 68.00 (978-0-7398-9934-2(1)) Harcourt Schl. Pubs.

—At-Home Workbooks: Addition. 2004. (Illus.). pap., wbk. ed. (978-0-7398-8533-8(2)) Steck-Vaughn.

—At-Home Workbooks: Division. 2004. (Illus.). pap., wbk. ed. (978-0-7398-8532-1(4)) Steck-Vaughn.

—At-Home Workbooks: Math. 2004. (Illus.). (gr. 1). pap., wbk. ed. (978-0-7398-8519-2(7)); (gr. 2). pap., wbk. ed. (978-0-7398-8520-8(0)); (gr. 3). pap., wbk. ed. 4.99 (978-0-7398-8521-5(9)); (gr. 4). pap., wbk. ed. 4.99 (978-0-7398-8522-2(7)) Steck-Vaughn.

—At-Home Workbooks: Multiplication. 2004. (Illus.). (J). pap., wbk. ed. 5.99 (978-0-7398-8531-4(6)) Steck-Vaughn.

—At-Home Workbooks: Subtraction. 2004. (Illus.). pap., wbk. ed. (978-0-7398-8534-5(0)) Steck-Vaughn.

—Computational & Applied Mathematics. 2004. pap. 8.50 (978-0-7398-9846-8(9)); 8 Pack. pap. 68.00 (978-0-7398-9927-4(9)) Harcourt Schl. Pubs.

—Core Skills Math. 2002. (Illus.). (J). (gr. 1) pap. 9.99 (978-0-7398-5723-6(1)); (gr. 2). pap. (978-0-7398-5724-3(X)); (gr. 3). pap. (978-0-7398-5725-0(8)); (gr. 4). pap. (978-0-7398-5726-7(6)); (gr. 5). pap. 9.99 (978-0-7398-5727-4(4)); (gr. 6). pap. 9.99 (978-0-7398-5728-1(2)) Steck-Vaughn.

—Core Skills Math - Review. 2004. (Illus.). pap. (978-0-7398-8540-6(5)) Steck-Vaughn.

—CRCT Math A: Answer Key: Soaring Scores. 2002. pap. (978-0-7398-5570-6(0)) Steck-Vaughn.

—CRCT Math A: Soaring Scores. 2002. pap. (978-0-7398-5569-0(7)) Steck-Vaughn.

—CRCT Math B: Answer Key: Soaring Scores. 2002. pap. (978-0-7398-5572-0(7)) Steck-Vaughn.

—CRCT Math C: Answer Key: Soaring Scores. 2002. pap. (978-0-7398-5574-4(3)) Steck-Vaughn.

—CRCT Math C: Key: Soaring Scores, 10 pack. 2002. pap. (978-0-7398-5587-4(5)) Steck-Vaughn.

—CRCT Math G: Answer Key: Soaring Scores. 2002. pap. (978-0-7398-5582-9(4)) Steck-Vaughn.

—CRCT Math G: Key: Soaring Scores, 10 pack. 2002. pap. (978-0-7398-5591-1(3)) Steck-Vaughn.

—CRCT Math G: Soaring Scores. 2002. pap. (978-0-7398-5581-2(6)) Steck-Vaughn.

—Early Math: 2 Digit Addition & Subtraction. 2005. pap. 2.99 (978-1-4190-0332-5(1)) Steck-Vaughn.

—Early Math: 2 Digit Addition with Regrouping. 2005. pap. 2.99 (978-1-4190-0333-2(X)) Steck-Vaughn.

—Early Math: Mixed Operations. 2005. pap. 2.99 (978-1-4190-0326-4(7)) Steck-Vaughn.

—Early Math: Money I. 2005. pap. 2.99 (978-1-4190-0328-8(3)); pap. 29.95 (978-1-4190-0352-3(6)) Steck-Vaughn.

—Early Math: Money II. 2005. pap. 2.99 (978-1-4190-0338-7(0)); pap. 29.95 (978-1-4190-0362-2(3)) Steck-Vaughn.

—Early Math: Problem Solving I. 2005. pap. 2.99 (978-1-4190-0331-8(3)); pap. 29.95 (978-1-4190-0355-4(0)) Steck-Vaughn.

—Early Math: Problem Solving II. 2005. pap. 2.99 (978-1-4190-0341-7(0)); pap. 29.95 (978-1-4190-0365-3(8)) Steck-Vaughn.

—Early Math: Readiness. 2005. pap. 2.99 (978-1-4190-0318-9(6)); pap. 29.95 (978-1-4190-0342-4(9)) Steck-Vaughn.

—Early Math: Readiness for Problem Solving. 2005. pap. 2.99 (978-1-4190-0321-9(6)); pap. 29.95 (978-1-4190-0345-5(3)) Steck-Vaughn.

—Early Math: Time I, 10 Pack. 2005. pap. 29.95 (978-1-4190-0351-6(8)) Steck-Vaughn.

—Early Math: Time II, 10 Pack. 2005. pap. 29.95 (978-1-4190-0361-5(5)) Steck-Vaughn.

—ESPA Math Practice Test D. 2000. (J). pap. (978-0-7398-2935-6(1)) Steck-Vaughn.

—FCAT Math Level B 10 Pack: Key: Soaring Scores. 2002. pap. (978-0-7398-6566-8(8)) Steck-Vaughn.

—FCAT Math Level C 10 Pack: Key: Soaring Scores. 2002. pap. (978-0-7398-6567-5(6)) Steck-Vaughn.

—FCAT Math Level D 10 Pack: Key: Soaring Scores. 2002. pap. (978-0-7398-6568-2(4)) Steck-Vaughn.

—FCAT Math Level E 10 Pack: Key: Soaring Scores. 2002. pap. (978-0-7398-6569-9(2)) Steck-Vaughn.

—FCAT Math Level G 10 Pack: Key: Soaring Scores. 2002. pap. (978-0-7398-6571-2(4)) Steck-Vaughn.

—FCAT Math Level H 10 Pack: Key: Soaring Scores. 2002. pap. (978-0-7398-6572-9(2)) Steck-Vaughn.

—Focus on Math Level C: Decimals. 2005. pap. 2.99 (978-1-4190-0268-7(6)) Harcourt Schl. Pubs.

—Focus on Math Level C: Problem Solving. 2005. pap. 2.99 (978-1-4190-0271-7(6)) Harcourt Schl. Pubs.

—Focus on Math Level C 10-pack: Decimals. 2005. pap. 29.95 (978-1-4190-0292-2(9)) Harcourt Schl. Pubs.

—Focus on Math Level C 10-pack: Problem Solving. 2005. pap. 29.95 (978-1-4190-0295-3(3)) Harcourt Schl. Pubs.

—Focus on Math Level D: Decimals. 2005. pap. 2.99 (978-1-4190-0274-8(0)) Harcourt Schl. Pubs.

—Focus on Math Level D: Measurement. 2005. pap. 2.99 (978-1-4190-0275-5(9)) Harcourt Schl. Pubs.

—Focus on Math Level D: Mixed Operations. 2005. pap. 2.99 (978-1-4190-0272-4(4)) Harcourt Schl. Pubs.

—Focus on Math Level D: Problem Solving. 2005. pap. 2.99 (978-1-4190-0277-9(5)) Harcourt Schl. Pubs.

—Focus on Math Level D 10-pack: Decimals. 2005. pap. 29.95 (978-1-4190-0298-4(8)) Harcourt Schl. Pubs.

—Focus on Math Level D 10-pack: Measurement. 2005. pap. 29.95 (978-1-4190-0299-1(6)) Harcourt Schl. Pubs.

—Focus on Math Level D 10-pack: Problem Solving. 2005. pap. 29.95 (978-1-4190-0301-1(1)) Harcourt Schl. Pubs.

—Focus on Math Level E: Decimals. 2005. pap. 2.99 (978-1-4190-0279-3(1)) Harcourt Schl. Pubs.

—Focus on Math Level E: Mixed Operations. 2005. pap. 2.99 (978-1-4190-0278-6(3)) Harcourt Schl. Pubs.

—Focus on Math Level E: Problem Solving. 2005. pap. 2.99 (978-1-4190-0283-0(X)) Harcourt Schl. Pubs.

—Focus on Math Level E: Ratio Percent. 2005. pap. 2.99 (978-1-4190-0282-3(1)) Harcourt Schl. Pubs.

—Focus on Math Level E 10-pack: Decimals. 2005. pap. 29.95 (978-1-4190-0303-5(8)) Harcourt Schl. Pubs.

—Focus on Math Level E 10-pack: Problem Solving. 2005. pap. 29.95 (978-1-4190-0307-3(0)) Harcourt Schl. Pubs.

—Focus on Math Level F: Problem Solving. 2005. pap. 2.99 (978-1-4190-0288-5(0)) Harcourt Schl. Pubs.

—Focus on Math Level F 10-pack: Problem Solving. 2005. pap. 29.95 (978-1-4190-0312-7(7)) Harcourt Schl. Pubs.

—GED Exercises: Math. 2000. pap. 11.67 (978-0-7398-3603-3(X)) Steck-Vaughn.

—Grade Level Math. 2005. (gr. k). pap. 14.99 (978-0-7398-9936-6(8)); (gr. 1). pap. 14.99 (978-0-7398-9937-3(6)); (gr. 2). pap. 14.99 (978-0-7398-9938-0(4)); (gr. 3). pap. 14.99 (978-0-7398-9939-7(2)); (gr. 4). pap. 14.99 (978-0-7398-9940-3(6)); (gr. 5). pap. 14.99 (978-0-7398-9941-0(4)); (gr. 6). pap. 14.99 (978-0-7398-9942-7(2)) Steck-Vaughn.

—Head for Home: Master Kit. 2004. (Illus.). pap. 1293.84 (978-0-7398-9295-4(9)) Steck-Vaughn.

—Hey Theres Math in My Literature. 2004. (Illus.). (J). pap. 12.99 (978-0-7398-8474-4(3)) Steck-Vaughn.

—Higher Scores on Math Standardized Tests. 2000. (Illus.). (J). (gr. 2). pap. (978-0-7398-2061-2(3)); (gr. 3). pap. (978-0-7398-2062-9(1)); (gr. 4). pap. (978-0-7398-2063-6(X)); (gr. 5). pap. (978-0-7398-2064-3(8)); (gr. 6). pap. (978-0-7398-2065-0(6)) Steck-Vaughn.

—Just-a-Minute Math: Grade 1-8. 2003. (J). (gr. 1-8). pap. (978-0-7398-7940-5(5)) Steck-Vaughn.

—Looking for Patterns. 2003. pap. 4.10 (978-0-7398-7659-6(7)) Steck-Vaughn.

—Making a Difference. 2003. pap. 4.10 (978-0-7398-7647-3(3)) Steck-Vaughn.

—Map Math A: Answer Key: Soaring Scores. 2002. pap. (978-0-7398-5594-2(8)) Steck-Vaughn.

—Map Math A: Soaring Scores. 2002. pap. (978-0-7398-5593-5(X)) Steck-Vaughn.

—Map Math A 10 Pack: Key: Soaring Scores. 2002. pap. (978-0-7398-5609-3(X)) Steck-Vaughn.

—Map Math B: Answer Key: Soaring Scores. 2002. pap. (978-0-7398-5596-6(4)) Steck-Vaughn.

—Map Math B: Soaring Scores. 2002. pap. (978-0-7398-5595-9(6)) Steck-Vaughn.

—Map Math B 10 Pack: Key: Soaring Scores. 2002. pap. (978-0-7398-5610-9(3)) Steck-Vaughn.

—Map Math C: Answer Key: Soaring Scores. 2002. pap. (978-0-7398-5598-0(0)) Steck-Vaughn.

—Map Math C: Soaring Scores. 2002. pap. (978-0-7398-5597-3(2)) Steck-Vaughn.

—Map Math C 10 Pack: Key: Soaring Scores. 2002. pap. (978-0-7398-5611-6(1)) Steck-Vaughn.

—Map Math E: Answer Key: Soaring Scores. 2002. pap. (978-0-7398-5602-4(2)) Steck-Vaughn.

—Map Math E: Soaring Scores. 2002. pap. (978-0-7398-5601-7(4)) Steck-Vaughn.

—Map Math E 10 Pack: Key: Soaring Scores. 2002. pap. (978-0-7398-5613-0(8)) Steck-Vaughn.

—Map Math F: Answer Key: Soaring Scores. 2002. pap. (978-0-7398-5604-8(9)) Steck-Vaughn.

—Map Math F: Soaring Scores. 2002. pap. (978-0-7398-5603-1(0)) Steck-Vaughn.

—Map Math F 10 Pack: Key: Soaring Scores. 2002. pap. (978-0-7398-5614-7(6)) Steck-Vaughn.

—Map Math G: Answer Key: Soaring Scores. 2002. pap. (978-0-7398-5606-2(5)) Steck-Vaughn.

—Map Math G: Soaring Scores. 2002. pap. (978-0-7398-5605-5(7)) Steck-Vaughn.

—Map Math G 10 Pack: Key: Soaring Scores. 2002. pap. (978-0-7398-5615-4(4)) Steck-Vaughn.

—Mastering Math. 2004. Level C. pap. 16.60 incl. cd-rom (978-0-7398-9202-2(9)); Level D. pap. 16.60 incl. cd-rom (978-0-7398-9203-9(7)); Level A. pap. 16.60 incl. cd-rom (978-0-7398-9200-8(2)); Level B. pap. 16.60 incl. cd-rom (978-0-7398-9201-5(0)); Level E. pap. 16.60 incl. cd-rom (978-0-7398-9204-6(5)); Level F. pap. 16.60 incl. cd-rom (978-0-7398-9205-3(3)) Steck-Vaughn.

—Mastering Math: Practice Book Level A. 2004. (Illus.). pap. 7.60 (978-0-7398-9206-0(1)) Steck-Vaughn.

—Mastering Math: Practice Book Level B. 2004. (Illus.). pap. 7.60 (978-0-7398-9207-7(X)) Steck-Vaughn.

—Mastering Math: Practice Book Level C. 2004. (Illus.). pap. 7.60 (978-0-7398-9208-4(8)) Steck-Vaughn.

—Mastering Math: Practice Book Level D. 2004. (Illus.). pap. 7.60 (978-0-7398-9209-1(6)) Steck-Vaughn.

—Mastering Math: Practice Book Level E. 2004. (Illus.). pap. 7.60 (978-0-7398-9210-7(X)) Steck-Vaughn.

—Mastering Math: Practice Book Level F. 2004. (Illus.). pap. 7.60 (978-0-7398-9211-4(8)) Steck-Vaughn.

—Math. 2002. (Reading & Math Progress Ser.). (J). (gr. 1). pap., tchr. ed. (978-0-7398-5300-9(7)); (gr. 2). pap., tchr. ed. (978-0-7398-5302-3(3)); (gr. 3). pap., tchr. ed. (978-0-7398-5304-7(X)); (gr. 4). pap., tchr. ed. (978-0-7398-5306-1(6)); (gr. 5). pap., tchr. ed. (978-0-7398-5308-5(2)) Steck-Vaughn.

—Math: Answer Key - Soaring Scores. 1999. (J). pap., tchr. ed. (978-0-7398-1124-5(X)) Steck-Vaughn.

—Math: Data Analysis & Statistics. 2004. pap. 5.00 (978-0-7398-9844-4(2)) Harcourt Schl. Pubs.

—Math 10-Pack: Data, Analysis & Statistics. 2004. pap. 44.95 (978-0-7398-9925-0(2)) Harcourt Schl. Pubs.

—Math B: Answer Key:Soaring Scores. 2002. pap. (978-0-7398-4009-2(6)) Steck-Vaughn.

—Math B: Soaring Scores, 10 pack. 2002. pap. (978-0-7398-4016-0(9)) Steck-Vaughn.

—Math C: Answer Keys: Soaring Scores. 2002. pap. (978-0-7398-4010-8(X)) Steck-Vaughn.

—Math C: Soaring Scores: 10 Pack. 2002. pap. (978-0-7398-4017-7(7)) Steck-Vaughn.

—Math Computation Intermediate. 2004. pap. 8.50 (978-0-7398-9850-5(7)) Harcourt Schl. Pubs.

—Math Computation Intermediate 8-Pack. 2004. pap. 68.00 (978-0-7398-9931-1(7)); pap. 68.00 (978-0-7398-9935-9(X)) Harcourt Schl. Pubs.

—Math Computation Introductory. 2004. pap. 8.50 (978-0-7398-9854-3(X)) Harcourt Schl. Pubs.

—Math D: Answer Key: Soaring Scores. 2002. pap. (978-0-7398-4011-5(8)) Steck-Vaughn.

—Math D 10 Packs: Soaring Scores. 2002. pap. (978-0-7398-4018-4(5)) Steck-Vaughn.

—Math E: Answer Key: Soaring Scores. 2002. pap. (978-0-7398-4012-2(6)) Steck-Vaughn.

—Math E: Soaring Scores: 10 Pack. 2002. pap. (978-0-7398-4019-1(3)) Steck-Vaughn.

—Math Enrichment. 1998. (Illus.). (gr. 1). pap. (978-0-8172-8374-2(9)) Steck-Vaughn.

—Math F 10 Pks: Soaring Scores. 2002. pap. (978-0-7398-4020-7(7)) Steck-Vaughn.

—Math H: Answer Key: Soaring Scores. 2002. pap. (978-0-7398-4015-3(0)) Steck-Vaughn.

—Math H: Soaring Scores, 10 pack. 2002. pap. 50.55 (978-0-7398-4022-1(3)) Steck-Vaughn.

—Math Hs: Soaring Scores, 10 pack. 2002. pap. (978-0-7398-4023-8(1)) Steck-Vaughn.

—Math Level D: Answer Key. 1999. (Strategies for Success Ser.). (J). pap., tchr. ed. (978-0-7398-1052-1(9)) Steck-Vaughn.

—Math Level F: Answer Key. 1999. (Strategies for Success Ser.). (J). pap., tchr. ed. (978-0-7398-1054-5(5)) Steck-Vaughn.

—Math Problem Solving, Level F. 2000. (gr. 3-6). lib. bdg. 20.30 (978-0-613-76482-7(X)) Tandem Library Bks.

—Math Problem Solving Level G. 1999. (J). pap. (978-0-7398-2351-4(5)) Steck-Vaughn.

—Math Problem Solving Level G: Answer Key. 1999. (J). pap. (978-0-7398-2352-1(3)) Steck-Vaughn.

—Math Problem Solving Level H. 1999. (J). pap. (978-0-7398-2353-8(1)) Steck-Vaughn.

—Math Problem Solving Level H: Answer Key. 1999. (J). pap. (978-0-7398-2354-5(X)) Steck-Vaughn.

—Middle School Decimals & Percent. 1999. (Illus.). (J). pap. (978-0-7398-1301-0(3)) Steck-Vaughn.

—Multistep Math: With Written Expressions. 2002. (Illus.). (J). (gr. 3). pap. 8.99 (978-0-7398-6126-4(3)); (gr. 4). pap. (978-0-7398-6127-1(1)); (gr. 5). pap. (978-0-7398-6128-8(X)); (gr. 6). pap. (978-0-7398-6129-5(8)) Steck-Vaughn.

—Problem Solving Strategies-Start Smart. 2002. (J). pap. (978-0-7398-6016-8(X)) Steck-Vaughn.

—Problems Plus: Workbook & Activity Kit. 1999. (Illus.). Level C. wbk. ed. (978-0-7398-2076-6(1)); Level D. wbk. ed. (978-0-7398-2077-3(X)); Level B. (J). wbk. ed. (978-0-7398-2075-9(3)); Level E. wbk. ed. (978-0-7398-2078-0(8)); Level F. (J). wbk. ed. (978-0-7398-2079-7(6)); Level G. wbk. ed. (978-0-7398-2080-3(X)); Level H. (J). wbk. ed. (978-0-7398-2081-0(8)) Steck-Vaughn.

—Shutterbug Math Starter Set Level A-I. 2002. (Illus.). pap. 240.00 (978-0-7398-7814-9(X)) Steck-Vaughn.

—Soaring Score CRCT Math. 2002. (J). Level D. pap. (978-0-7398-5575-1(1)); Level F. pap. (978-0-7398-5579-9(4)); Level H. pap. (978-0-7398-5583-6(2)) Steck-Vaughn.

—Soaring Score HCPS Math: Answer Key. 2002. (J). Level C. pap. (978-0-7398-5698-7(7)); Level E. pap. (978-0-7398-5702-1(9)); Level H. pap. (978-0-7398-5708-3(8)) Steck-Vaughn.

—Soaring Score Terranova Math: Computer Test Bank. 1999. (J). Level A. pap., tchr. ed. (978-0-7398-2255-5(1)); Level B. pap., tchr. ed. (978-0-7398-2257-9(8)) Steck-Vaughn.

—Soaring Scores AIMS Mathematics - High School: Alaska Edition. 2001. (Illus.). (YA). pap. (978-0-7398-3462-6(2)) Steck-Vaughn.

—Soaring Scores Illinois SAT Math: Answer Key. 1999. (J). Level C. pap. (978-0-7398-1934-0(8)); Level D. pap. (978-0-7398-1936-4(4)); Level B. pap. (978-0-7398-1932-6(1)); Level E. pap. (978-0-7398-1938-8(0)); Level F. pap. (978-0-7398-1940-1(2)); Level G. pap. (978-0-7398-1942-5(9)); Level H. pap. (978-0-7398-1944-9(5)) Steck-Vaughn.

—Soaring Scores in Math: Answer Key. 1999. (J). pap. (978-0-7398-1132-0(0)); pap., tchr. ed. (978-0-7398-1128-3(2)); pap., tchr. ed. (978-0-7398-1130-6(4)); pap., tchr. ed. (978-0-7398-1126-9(6)); pap., tchr. ed. (978-0-7398-1134-4(7)); pap., tchr. ed. (978-0-7398-1136-8(3)) Steck-Vaughn.

—Summer School Math. 2002. (J). (gr. 1). pap., tchr. ed. (978-0-7398-5296-5(5)); (gr. 2). pap., tchr. ed. (978-0-7398-5298-9(1)) Steck-Vaughn.

—Summer School Math: Grade 3. 2001. pap., tchr. ed. 34.13 (978-0-7398-4530-1(6)) Steck-Vaughn.

—Summer School Math: Grade 4. 2001. pap. 34.13 (978-0-7398-4532-5(2)) Steck-Vaughn.

—Summer School Math: Grade 5. 2001. pap. 34.13 (978-0-7398-4534-9(9)) Steck-Vaughn.

—Summer School Math: Grade 6. 2001. pap., tchr. ed. 34.13 (978-0-7398-4536-3(5)) Steck-Vaughn.

—Taks II Math B: Soaring Scores. 2002. pap. (978-0-7398-4002-3(9)) Steck-Vaughn.

—Taks II Math D: Soaring Scores. 2002. pap. (978-0-7398-4004-7(5)) Steck-Vaughn.

—Taks II Math F: Soaring Scores. 2002. pap. (978-0-7398-4006-1(1)) Steck-Vaughn.

—Test Best Sol Math Grade 2. 2002. pap., tchr. ed. (978-0-7398-7454-7(3)) Steck-Vaughn.

—Test Best Success Pack: High School, 10. rev. ed. 2002. (YA). (gr. 9-12). pap. (978-0-7398-6716-7(4)) Steck-Vaughn.

—That Makes Ten! 2003. pap. 4.10 (978-0-7398-7656-5(2)) Steck-Vaughn.

—Together & Apart. 2002. (Illus.). (J). pap. 3.74 (978-0-7398-5894-3(7)) Steck-Vaughn.

—Top Line Math: Probability. 2005. pap. 5.49 (978-1-4190-0374-5(7)) Steck-Vaughn.

—Top Line Math: Proportions. 2005. pap. 5.49 (978-1-4190-0369-1(0)) Harcourt Schl. Pubs.

—Top Line Math: Special Topics in Math. 2005. pap., tchr. ed. 5.95 (978-1-4190-0385-1(2)) Harcourt Schl. Pubs.

—Top Line Math: Special Topics in Math. 2005. pap. 5.49 (978-1-4190-0375-2(5)) Steck-Vaughn.

—Top Line Math: Tables & Maps. 2005. pap., tchr. ed. 5.95 (978-1-4190-0381-3(X)) Harcourt Schl. Pubs.

—Top Line Math: Tables & Maps. 2005. pap. 5.49 (978-1-4190-0371-4(2)) Steck-Vaughn.

—Top Line Math 10-Pack: Probability. 2005. pap. 54.95 (978-1-4190-0395-0(X)) Harcourt Schl. Pubs.

—Top Line Math 10-Pack: Proportions. 2005. pap. 54.95 (978-1-4190-0390-5(9)) Harcourt Schl. Pubs.

—Top Line Math 10-Pack: Special Topics in Math. 2005. pap. 54.95 (978-1-4190-0396-7(8)) Harcourt Schl. Pubs.

—Top Line Math 10-Pack: Tables & Maps. 2005. pap. 54.95 (978-1-4190-0392-9(5)) Harcourt Schl. Pubs.

—Weekly Math Practice. (Illus.). (J). 2002. (gr. 1). pap. (978-0-7398-5354-2(6)); 2002. (gr. 2). pap. 12.99 (978-0-7398-5355-9(4)); 2002. (gr. 6). pap. (978-0-7398-5356-6(2)); 2000. (gr. 3). pap. (978-0-7398-3438-1(X)); 2000. (gr. 4). pap. 12.99 (978-0-7398-3439-8(8)); 2000. (gr. 5). pap. 12.99 (978-0-7398-3440-4(1)) Steck-Vaughn.

Stengard-Olliges, Robert. ¿Que Viene Primero? 2007. (J). ***978-1-60044-288-9(9)*** Rourke Publishing, LLC.

Stenmark, Jean K. & Coates, Grace D. Family Math for Young Children: Comparing. Gothberg, Brian, ed. Craig, Rose & Williams, Ann, illus. 1999. (Equals Ser.). 200p. (J). (gr. k-3). pap. 19.95 (978-0-912511-27-6(3) , EQUALS) Univ. of California, Berkeley, Lawrence Hall of Science.

Stephens, Pamela Geiger. Tessellations: The History & Making of Symmetrical Designs. McNeill, Jim, illus. 2001. 40p. (J). pap. 14.95 net. (978-1-56290-243-8(1)) Crystal Productions.

Sterling/Balloon. Add & Subtract with Benjamin the Bear. 2000. (Balloon Ser.). (Illus.). 16p. (J). (gr. k-2). pap. 5.95 (978-0-8069-2665-0(1)) Sterling Publishing Co., Inc.

Stewart, Melissa. The Giraffe Graph. 2006. (Rookie Read-About Math Ser.). (Illus.). 32p. (J). (gr. k-2). 20.50 (978-0-516-23798-5(5) , Children's Pr.) Scholastic Library Publishing.

Stoffel, Doug. Middle-Grade Math Minutes. Hults, Alaska B., ed. Hillam, Corbin, illus. 2000. 112p. (YA). (gr. 6-8). pap. 12.99 (978-1-57471-723-5(5) , CTP 2595) Creative Teaching Pr., Inc.

Straker, Anita. Home Maths. 1998. (Illus.). 34p. Bk. 1. pap., stu. ed. 7.00 (978-0-521-64926-1(9)); Bk. 2. pap., stu. ed. 7.00 (978-0-521-64925-4(0)) Cambridge Univ. Pr.

—Mental Maths. 2nd rev. ed. 1998. (Illus.). 32p. pap. 7.00 (978-0-521-65561-3(7)); pap. 6.00 (978-0-521-65562-0(5)) Cambridge Univ. Pr.

Strang, Craig, et al. On Sandy Shores. Bergman, Lincoln et al, eds. Baker, Lisa H. et al, illus. Hoyt, Richard & Bradley, Laurence, photos by. 1999. (Great Explorations in Math & Science Ser.). 212p. (J). (gr. 2-4). pap., tchr. ed. 18.00 (978-0-924886-33-1(1) , GEMS) Univ. of California, Berkeley, Lawrence Hall of Science.

Strawberry Shortcake Addition. 2005. (J). 2.95 ***(978-1-59545-002-9(5))*** Learning Horizons, Inc.

Strawberry Shortcake Groups & Patterns. 2004. (J). 4.99 ***(978-1-58610-902-8(2))*** Learning Horizons, Inc.

Strazzabosco, John. Mathematical Thinking Reasoning Proof. 2004. 48p. pap. 6.95 (978-1-4042-8522-4(9)) Rosen Publishing Group, Inc., The.

Student Testing Kit: Math 1 Through 8. 2000. (Illus.). (J). pap., stu. ed. 5.00 (978-0-7403-0056-1(3)) Alpha Omega Pubns., Inc.

StudyLab Mini No. 1: Why Do I Have to Learn Math?! 2001. 16p. (J). (gr. 5 up). per. (978-1-930281-12-7(9)) FINK, Inc.

Succeed in Pre-Algebra. 2004. (Math "How To" Ser.). (Illus.). 48p. (YA). 7.99 (978-1-57690-959-1(X)) Teacher Created Materials, Inc.

Sugiyama, Yoshishige, ed. Tokyo Shoseki's Mathematics for Elementary School (Grades 1 - 6 set, 11 vol. Set), 11 vols. 2006. Orig. Title: Atarashii Sansuu 1. (Illus.). pap. 129.55 (978-1-934046-00-5(0)) Global Education Resources, LLC.

Sullivan. Computerized Test Bank to Accompany Finite Mathema Tics: An Applied Approach. 9th ed. 2004. (YA). (978-0-471-44818-1(4)) Wiley, John & Sons, Inc.

—Test Bank to Accompany Finite Mathematics: An Appl Ied Approach, Ninth Edition. 9th ed. 2004. (YA). (978-0-471-44821-1(4)) Wiley, John & Sons, Inc.

Sullivan, Erin. Mathematical Thinkers/Los Matematicos: English/Spanish Pair, 12 texts, 2 titles, Vol. 2. ed. 2004. (Navigators Ser.). (J). pap., instr.'s gde. ed. 84.00 (978-1-4108-1773-0(3) , 17733) Benchmark Education Co.

—Sports Math/Matematicas en los Deportes: English/Spanish Pair, 12 tests, 2 titles, Vol. 2. ed. 2004. (Navigators Ser.). (J). pap., instr.'s gde. ed. 84.00 (978-1-4108-1774-7(1) , 17741) Benchmark Education Co.

Sullivan, Erin Ash. Human Body Math. 2004. (Navigators Ser.). (J). pap. 38.00 (978-1-4108-0408-2(9)) Benchmark Education Co.

—Matematicas alrededor del mundo & Math Around the Globe. 2005. spiral bd. 84.00 ***(978-1-4108-5689-0(5))*** Benchmark Education Co.

—Matematicas del cuerpo humano & Human Body Math. 2005. spiral bd. 77.00 ***(978-1-4108-5682-1(8))*** Benchmark Education Co.

—Matematicas en las olimpiadas & Math at the Olympics. 2005. spiral bd. 84.00 ***(978-1-4108-5707-1(7))*** Benchmark Education Co.

—Matematicas en una democracia & Math in a Democracy. 2005. spiral bd. 84.00 ***(978-1-4108-5715-6(8))*** Benchmark Education Co.

—Matematicas métricas & Metric Math. 2005. spiral bd. 77.00 ***(978-1-4108-5681-4(X))*** Benchmark Education Co.

—Math Around the Globe. 2004. (Navigators Ser.). (J). pap. 42.00 (978-1-4108-0417-4(8)) Benchmark Education Co.

—Math at the Olympics. 2004. (Navigators Ser.). (J). pap. 42.00 (978-1-4108-0433-4(X)) Benchmark Education Co.

—Math in a Democracy. 2004. (Navigators Ser.). (J). pap. 42.00 (978-1-4108-0437-2(2)) Benchmark Education Co.

—Metric Math. 2004. (Navigators Ser.). (J). pap. 38.00 (978-1-4108-0414-3(3)) Benchmark Education Co.

—Music Counts. 2004. (Navigators Ser.). (J). pap. 38.00 (978-1-4108-0405-1(4)) Benchmark Education Co.

Sullivan, Michael & Mizrahi, Abshalom. Technology Resource Manual to Accompany Finite Mathematics: An Applied Approach. 9th rev. ed. 2004. 140p. pap. 48.95 (978-0-471-44820-4(6)) Wiley, John & Sons, Inc.

Summers, Ginger. Celebremos el 100: Metro Math Readers Yellow Level. 2000. (Metro Math Readers Yellow Level Ser.). (J). (gr. 1-2). 3.75 (978-1-58120-473-5(6)) Metropolitan Teaching & Learning Co.

—How Many is Fifty? 2000. (Metro Math Readers Yellow Level Ser.). (J). (gr. 1-2). 3.75 (978-1-58120-409-4(4)) Metropolitan Teaching & Learning Co.

Super 7: Daily Exercises in Mathematical Problem Solving. 2002. (J). per. 19.95 (978-1-883055-51-6(2)) Dandy Lion Pubns.

Superlibro 1: Big Books. 2002. (MacMillan/McGraw-Hill Matematicas Ser.). (ENG & SPA.). (gr. k up). (978-0-02-111669-0(5)) Macmillan/McGraw-Hill Schl. Div.

Superlibro 2: Big Books. 2002. (MacMillan/McGraw-Hill Matematicas Ser.). (ENG & SPA.). (gr. k up). (978-0-02-111670-6(9)) Macmillan/McGraw-Hill Schl. Div.

Superlibro 1. 2002. (MacMillan/McGraw-Hill Matematicas Ser.). (ENG & SPA.). (gr. 1 up). (978-0-02-111672-0(5)); (gr. 2 up). (978-0-02-111675-1(X)) Macmillan/McGraw-Hill Schl. Div.

Superlibro 2. 2002. (MacMillan/McGraw-Hill Matematicas Ser.). (ENG & SPA.). (gr. 1 up). (978-0-02-111673-7(3)); (gr. 2 up). (978-0-02-111676-8(8)) Macmillan/McGraw-Hill Schl. Div.

Superlibro Package. 2002. (MacMillan/McGraw-Hill Matematicas Ser.). (ENG & SPA.). (gr. k up). (978-0-02-111671-3(7)); (gr. 1 up). (978-0-02-111674-4(1)); (gr. 2 up). (978-0-02-111677-5(6)) Macmillan/McGraw-Hill Schl. Div.

Superlibros: Superlibros de Literatura/Literature. 1999. (Matematicas en Mi Mundo Ser.). (ENG & SPA.). (gr. k up). (978-0-02-110699-8(1)); (gr. 1 up). (978-0-02-110264-8(3)); (gr. 2 up). (978-0-02-110265-5(1)) Macmillan/McGraw-Hill Schl. Div.

Superlibros de literatura. 1999. (Matematicas en Mi Mundo Ser.). (ENG & SPA.). (gr. 2 up). (978-0-02-108481-4(5)) Macmillan/McGraw-Hill Schl. Div.

Superlibros de Literatura: Superlibros de Literatura/Literature. 1999. (Matematicas en Mi Mundo Ser.). (ENG & SPA.). (gr. k up). (978-0-02-108478-4(5)); (gr. 1 up). (978-0-02-108479-1(3)) Macmillan/McGraw-Hill Schl. Div.

Superlibros y Autoadhesivos: Superlibros de Literatura/Literature. 1999. (Matematicas en Mi Mundo Ser.). (ENG & SPA.). (gr. k up). (978-0-02-110698-1(3)); (gr. 1 up). (978-0-02-111021-6(2)); (gr. 2 up). (978-0-02-111022-3(0)) Macmillan/McGraw-Hill Schl. Div.

Swain, Cynthia. Sorting at the Park. 2006. (Early Explorers Ser.). (J). 30.00 ***(978-1-4108-6036-1(1))*** Benchmark Education Co.

Swann, Kristina. Meaningful Math. 2005. (YA). ring bd. 49.95 (978-1-58804-402-0(5)) PCI Educational Publishing.

Tabletop Pocket Chart Addition & Subtraction Card Set. 2004. (J). 8.95 (978-1-56911-170-3(7)) Learning Resources, Inc.

Take Away Math, 6 vols. (gr. k-2). 28.95 (978-0-7368-1738-7(7) , Yellow Umbrella Bks.) Capstone Pr., Inc.

TAKS MASTER Power Practice, Math Gr. 3. 2004. (J). (978-1-57022-535-2(4)) ECS Learning Systems, Inc.

TAKS MASTER Power Practice, Math Gr. 4. 2004. (J). (978-1-57022-536-9(2)) ECS Learning Systems, Inc.

TAKS MASTER Power Practice, Math Gr. 5. 2004. (J). (978-1-57022-537-6(0)) ECS Learning Systems, Inc.

TAKS MASTER Power Practice, Math Gr. 6. 2004. (J). (978-1-57022-538-3(9)) ECS Learning Systems, Inc.

TAKS MASTER Power Practice, Math Gr. 7. 2004. (J). (978-1-57022-539-0(7)) ECS Learning Systems, Inc.

TAKS MASTER Power Practice, Math Gr. 8. 2004. (YA). (978-1-57022-540-6(0)) ECS Learning Systems, Inc.

TAKS MASTER Practice Test Math, Gr. 3. 2004. (J). (978-1-57022-474-4(9)) ECS Learning Systems, Inc.

TAKS MASTER Practice Test Math, Gr. 4. 2004. (J). (978-1-57022-516-1(8)) ECS Learning Systems, Inc.

TAKS MASTER Practice Test Math, Gr. 5. 2004. (J). (978-1-57022-517-8(6)) ECS Learning Systems, Inc.

TAKS MASTER Practice Test Math, Gr. 6. 2004. (J). (978-1-57022-518-5(4)) ECS Learning Systems, Inc.

TAKS MASTER Practice Test Math, Gr. 7. 2004. (J). (978-1-57022-519-2(2)) ECS Learning Systems, Inc.

TAKS MASTER Practice Test Math, Gr. 8. 2004. (YA). (978-1-57022-520-8(6)) ECS Learning Systems, Inc.

TAKS Mathematics Preparation Grade 1. 2004. (Region IV ESC Resources for Mathematics Ser.). (J). (gr. 1). stu. ed., per., wbk. ed. (978-1-932524-51-2(7)) Region IV Education Service Ctr.

TAKS Mathematics Preparation Grade 1- Spanish. 2004. (SPA.). stu. ed., per., wbk. ed. (978-1-932524-81-9(9)) Region IV Education Service Ctr.

TAKS Mathematics Preparation Grade 10. 2004. (Region IV ESC Resources for Mathematics Ser.). stu. ed., per., wbk. ed. (978-1-932524-60-4(6)) Region IV Education Service Ctr.

TAKS Mathematics Preparation Grade 11 Exit. 2003. (Region IV ESC Resources for Mathematics Ser.). stu. ed., per., wbk. ed. (978-1-932524-61-1(4)) Region IV Education Service Ctr.

TAKS Mathematics Preparation Grade 2. 2004. (Region IV ESC Resources for Mathematics Ser.). (gr. 2). stu. ed., per., wbk. ed. (978-1-932524-52-9(5)) Region IV Education Service Ctr.

TAKS Mathematics Preparation Grade 2 - Spanish. 2004. (SPA.). stu. ed., per. (978-1-932524-82-6(7)) Region IV Education Service Ctr.

TAKS Mathematics Preparation Grade 3. 2004. (Region IV ESC Resources for Mathematics Ser.). (J). (gr. 3). stu. ed., per., wbk. ed. (978-1-932524-53-6(3)) Region IV Education Service Ctr.

TAKS Mathematics Preparation Grade 3 - Spanish. 2004. (SPA.). stu. ed., per., wbk. ed. (978-1-932524-83-3(5)) Region IV Education Service Ctr.

TAKS Mathematics Preparation Grade 4. 2004. (Region IV ESC Resources for Mathematics Ser.). (J). (gr. 4). stu. ed., per., wbk. ed. (978-1-932524-54-3(1)) Region IV Education Service Ctr.

TAKS Mathematics Preparation Grade 4 - Spanish. 2004. (SPA.). stu. ed., per., wbk. ed. (978-1-932524-84-0(3)) Region IV Education Service Ctr.

TAKS Mathematics Preparation Grade 5. 2003. (Region IV ESC Resources for Mathematics Ser.). (J). (gr. 5). stu. ed., per., wbk. ed. (978-1-932524-55-0(X)) Region IV Education Service Ctr.

TAKS Mathematics Preparation Grade 5 - Spanish. 2004. (SPA.). per., wbk. ed. (978-1-932524-85-7(1)) Region IV Education Service Ctr.

TAKS Mathematics Preparation Grade 6. 2004. (Region IV ESC Resources for Mathematics Ser.). (J). (gr. 6). stu. ed., per., wbk. ed. (978-1-932524-56-7(8)) Region IV Education Service Ctr.

TAKS Mathematics Preparation Grade 6 - Spanish. 2004. stu. ed., per., wbk. ed. (978-1-932524-86-4(X)) Region IV Education Service Ctr.

TAKS Mathematics Preparation Grade 7. 2004. (Region IV ESC Resources for Mathematics Ser.). (YA). (gr. 7). stu. ed., per., wbk. ed. (978-1-932524-57-4(6)) Region IV Education Service Ctr.

TAKS Mathematics Preparation Grade 8. 2003. (Region IV ESC Resources for Mathematics Ser.). stu. ed., per., wbk. ed. (978-1-932524-58-1(4)) Region IV Education Service Ctr.

TAKS Mathematics Preparation Grade 9. 2004. (Region IV ESC Resources for Mathematics Ser.). stu. ed., per., wbk. ed. (978-1-932524-59-8(2)) Region IV Education Service Ctr.

TAKS Mathematics Preparation Grade K. 2004. (Region IV ESC Resources for Mathematics Ser.). stu. ed., per., wbk. ed. (978-1-932524-50-5(9)) Region IV Education Service Ctr.

TAKS Mathematics Preparation Grade K - Spanish. 2004. (SPA.). stu. ed., per., wbk. ed. (978-1-932524-80-2(0)) Region IV Education Service Ctr.

Tamambang, Andrew Tangang, et al. Mastering Mathematics Form 3 Student's Book: Volume 0, Part 0. 2007. pap. 6.00 ***(978-0-521-70145-7(7))*** Cambridge Univ. Pr.

Tambien los insectos son Perfectos: Superlibros de Literatura/Literature Big Books. 1999. (Matematicas en Mi Mundo Ser.). (ENG & SPA.). (gr. 2 up). (978-0-02-110167-2(1)) Macmillan/McGraw-Hill Schl. Div.

Tang, Greg. The Best of Times: Math Strategies That Multiply. Briggs, Harry, illus. 2002. 32p. (J). (gr. 1-5). pap. 16.95 (978-0-439-21044-7(5) , Scholastic Pr.) Scholastic, Inc.

—The Grapes of Math. Briggs, Harry, illus. 2001. (J). pap. (978-0-439-21040-9(2)); 40p. (gr. 2-5). pap. 16.95 (978-0-439-21033-1(X) , Scholastic Pr.) Scholastic, Inc.

—Math Appeal. Briggs, Harry, illus. 2003. (J). pap. (978-0-439-21045-4(3)); 40p. (gr. 2-5). pap. 16.95 (978-0-439-21046-1(1) , Scholastic Pr.) Scholastic, Inc.

—Math for All Seasons. Briggs, Harry, illus. 2005. 40p. (J). (ps-ps). 5.99 (978-0-439-75537-5(9) , Scholastic Paperbacks) Scholastic, Inc.

—Un, Dos, Tres, el Ano Se Fue. Briggs, Harry, illus. 2004. Tr. of Math for All Seasons. (SPA.). (J). 14.99 (978-84-241-8074-4(7)) Everest de Ediciones y Distribucion, S.L. ESP. *Dist:* Lectorum Pubns., Inc.

Tangang Tamambang, Andrew, et al. Mastering Mathematics Form 1 Student's Book. 2008. pap., stu. ed. 4.00 (978-0-521-69301-1(2)) Cambridge Univ. Pr.

—Mastering Mathematics Form 2 Student's Book. 2008. pap., stu. ed. 6.00 (978-0-521-69300-4(4)) Cambridge Univ. Pr.

Tangram Blocks Activities. 2000. (J). pap. 13.95 (978-1-56911-055-3(7)) Learning Resources, Inc.

Tangram Blocks Exploration Book. 2000. (J). pap. 13.95 (978-1-56911-056-0(5)) Learning Resources, Inc.

Taragan, Barbara. The Number Eleven: Metro Math Readers Red Level. 2000. (J). 3.30 (978-1-58120-311-0(X)) Metropolitan Teaching & Learning Co.

—The Number Three: Metro Math Readers Red Level. (Metro Reading Ser.). 2002. (gr. 12). 41.25 (978-1-58120-633-3(X)); 2000. (J). 3.30 (978-1-58120-303-5(9)) Metropolitan Teaching & Learning Co.

—The Number Twelve: Metro Math Readers Red Level. 2000. (J). 3.30 (978-1-58120-312-7(8)) Metropolitan Teaching & Learning Co.

—El Numero Diez: Math Math Readers Red Level. 2000. (J). 3.30 (978-1-58120-374-5(8)) Metropolitan Teaching & Learning Co.

—El Numero Doce: Metro Math Readers Red Level. 2000. (J). 3.30 (978-1-58120-376-9(4)) Metropolitan Teaching & Learning Co.

—El Numero Once: Metro Math Readers Red Level. 2000. (J). 3.30 (978-1-58120-375-2(6)); 18.95 (978-1-58120-510-7(4)) Metropolitan Teaching & Learning Co.

Tarea diaria: Practica: Teacher Resources. 2002. (MacMillan/McGraw-Hill Matematicas Ser.). (ENG & SPA.). (gr. 1 up). (978-0-02-111615-7(6)); (gr. 2 up). (978-0-02-111616-4(4)); (gr. 3 up). (978-0-02-111617-1(2)); (gr. 4 up). (978-0-02-111618-8(0)); (gr. 5 up). (978-0-02-111619-5(9)); (gr. 6 up). (978-0-02-111620-1(2)) Macmillan/McGraw-Hill Schl. Div.

Tastes Like Math. 2003. (J). pap., stu. ed. 10.95 (978-1-58123-341-4(8)) Larson Learning, Inc.

Taylor, Hope, ed. Games Galore Math. 2002. 96p. 14.95 (978-1-56234-491-7(9) , Mailbox Bks., The) Education Ctr., Inc.

Taylor, Loretta & Taylor, Harold. Quizzes & Tests Bk. 10: Test Book. 2000. (Basic Computation Ser.). 224p. (YA). (gr. 6-12). pap. 18.95 (978-0-7690-0123-4(8)) Seymour, Dale Pubns.

—Working with Decimals. 2000. (Basic Computation Ser.: Bk. 4). 124p. (YA). (gr. 6-12). pap. 18.95 (978-0-7690-0117-3(3)) Seymour, Dale Pubns.

—Working with Percents. 2000. (Basic Computation Ser.: Bk. 5). 98p. (YA). (gr. 6-12). pap. 18.95 (978-0-7690-0118-0(1)) Seymour, Dale Pubns.

—Working with Perimeter & Area. 2000. (Basic Computation Ser.: Bk. 7). 94p. (YA). (gr. 6-12). pap. 18.95 (978-0-7690-0120-3(3)) Seymour, Dale Pubns.

—Working with Surface Area & Volume. 2000. (Basic Computation Ser.: Bk. 8). 94p. (YA). (gr. 6-12). pap. 18.95 (978-0-7690-0121-0(1)) Seymour, Dale Pubns.

Teacher Created Materials Staff. Pre-Algebra Brain Teasers. 1998. (Brain Teasers Ser.). (Illus.). 112p. (YA). (gr. 5-8). pap., tchr. ed. 11.99 (978-1-57690-039-0(8) , TCA2039) Teacher Created Materials, Inc.

Teamwork Test Practice: Math. 2005. 48p. (J). per. 5.99 (978-1-59441-138-0(7) , CD-104057); per. 5.99 (978-1-59441-139-7(5) , CD-104058); per. 5.99 (978-1-59441-140-3(9) , CD-104059); per. 5.99 (978-1-59441-141-0(7) , CD-104060); per. 5.99 (978-1-59441-142-7(5) , CD-104061); per. 5.99 (978-1-59441-143-4(3) , CD-104062); per. 5.99 (978-1-59441-144-1(1) , CD-104063) Carson-Dellosa Publishing Co., Inc.

Test Best For Success, 10 Packs. 2002. pap. (978-0-7398-6746-4(6)) Steck-Vaughn.

Test Best for Success Level A, 10 Packs. 2002. pap. (978-0-7398-6740-2(7)) Steck-Vaughn.

Test Best for Success Level B, 10 Packs. 2002. pap. (978-0-7398-6741-9(5)) Steck-Vaughn.

TestSMART Plus Math Processes, Level B-1. 2004. (J). (978-1-57022-507-9(9)) ECS Learning Systems, Inc.

TestSMART Plus Math Processes, Level B-2. 2004. (J). (978-1-57022-508-6(7)) ECS Learning Systems, Inc.

TestSMART Plus Math Processes, Level C. 2004. (J). (978-1-57022-509-3(5)) ECS Learning Systems, Inc.

TestSMART Plus Math Processes, Level D. 2004. (J). (978-1-57022-510-9(9)) ECS Learning Systems, Inc.

TestSMART Plus Math Processes, Level E. 2004. (J). (978-1-57022-511-6(7)) ECS Learning Systems, Inc.

TestSMART Plus Math Processes, Level F. 2004. (J). (978-1-57022-512-3(5)) ECS Learning Systems, Inc.

TestSMART Plus Math Processes, Level G. 2004. (J). (978-1-57022-513-0(3)) ECS Learning Systems, Inc.

TestSMART Plus Math Processes, Level H. 2004. (J). (978-1-57022-514-7(1)) ECS Learning Systems, Inc.

TestSMART Plus Math Processes, Level I. 2004. (YA). (978-1-57022-515-4(X)) ECS Learning Systems, Inc.

TestSMART Plus Numeration, Level A-1. 2004. (J). (978-1-57022-522-2(2)) ECS Learning Systems, Inc.

TestSMART Plus Numeration, Level A-2. 2004. (J). (978-1-57022-523-9(0)) ECS Learning Systems, Inc.

TestSMART Plus Numeration, Level B. 2004. (J). (978-1-57022-524-6(9)) ECS Learning Systems, Inc.

TestSmart Plus Numeration Level C/D. 2004. (J). (978-1-57022-525-3(7)) ECS Learning Systems, Inc.

TestSmart Plus Numeration Level E/F. 2004. (J). (978-1-57022-526-0(5)) ECS Learning Systems, Inc.

TestSmart Plus Numeration Level G/H. 2004. (J). (978-1-57022-527-7(3)) ECS Learning Systems, Inc.

TestSMART Plus Whole Numbers, Level A. 2004. (J). (978-1-57022-488-1(9)) ECS Learning Systems, Inc.

That Is Math! First Grade Guided Reading Level D. (On Our Way to English Ser.). (gr. 1 up). 27.75 (978-0-7578-7041-5(4)) Rigby Education.

Thinking Mathematically: Discovering Quantitative Relationships. 2000. (J). (gr. 4-8). (978-0-13-026440-4(7)) Prentice Hall PTR.

Thompson, Karen. Math. 1999. (Homework Booklets Ser.). 72p. (J). (gr. 1 up). pap. 2.99 (978-0-88012-939-8(5) , IF0272) School Specialty Publishing.

Thompson, Kim Mitzo & Hilderbrand, Karen Mitzo. Subtraction. 2000. pap. 13.99 incl. audio compact disk (978-1-57583-333-0(6) , TWIN 444CD) Twin Sisters Productions, LLC.

Thompson, Michelle. Math Activities for the 100th Day. 2003. (100+ Seriestm Ser.). 128p. (J). (gr. 1-2). pap. 12.99 (978-0-7424-1780-9(8) , IFG99073) School Specialty Publishing.

Thornford, Charles. The World Today Exercises. 1999. (Illus.). (J). (gr. 3-7). pap. 29.00 (978-0-7217-1075-4(1)) Schofield & Sims Ltd. GBR. *Dist:* State Mutual Bk. & Periodical Service, Ltd.

Three Bear Family: Addition & Subtraction Activity Book. 2003. (J). pap. 4.95 (978-1-56911-103-1(0)) Learning Resources, Inc.

Three Bear Family: Matching & Sorting Activity Book. 2003. (J). pap. 4.95 (978-1-56911-101-7(4)) Learning Resources, Inc.

The TI-108 Calculator. 2004. (gr. k-6). suppl. ed. 74.25 (978-0-201-23150-2(6)); suppl. ed. 202.50 (978-0-201-23151-9(4)) Addison-Wesley Educational Pubs., Inc. (Scott Foresman).

Time & Money Skills (Gr. 1-2) 2003. (J). (978-1-58232-082-3(9)) Bryan Hse. Pubs., Inc.

Tiner, John. Exploring the World of Mathematics: From the Checker Board to the Super Computer. 2004. (Sense of Wonder Ser.). 160p. (YA). pap. 13.99 (978-0-89051-412-2(7) , 303-050) Master Bks.

Tipler, M. J. & Vickers, K. M. New National Curriculum Mathematics: Target Book 4. 2000. (Illus.). 342p. (YA). (gr. 6-11). pap. 27.50 (978-0-7487-3549-5(6)) Nelson Thornes Ltd. GBR. *Dist:* Trans-Atlantic Pubns., Inc.

—New National Curriculum Mathematics: Target Book 5. 2000. (Illus.). 368p. (YA). (gr. 6-10). pap. 27.50 (978-0-7487-3550-1(X)) Nelson Thornes Ltd. GBR. *Dist:* Trans-Atlantic Pubns., Inc.

To Market, to Market. 2004. cd-rom 119.00 (978-1-889775-52-4(5)) Learning in Motion.

Tobin, Catherine D. Hm Study Skills Math. Marshak, David et al, eds. 2000. 112p. pap., stu. ed. 12.95 (978-0-8108-3806-2(0)) Scarecrow Pr., Inc.

Torres Moliner, Isabel & Soriano Puche, Lola. Domino Domino. 2005. (In-genio Ser.). 48p. (J). pap. 14.95 (978-84-95895-01-1(3)) Editorial Brief ESP. *Dist:* Independent Pubs. Group.

—Espacio Espacial. 2005. (In-genio Ser.). 48p. (J). pap. 14.95 (978-84-95895-09-7(9)) Editorial Brief ESP. *Dist:* Independent Pubs. Group.

Transicion hacia el computo de 2 Digitos: Student & Teacher Support Resources. 1999. (Matematicas en Mi Mundo Ser.). (ENG & SPA.). (gr. 1 up). (978-0-02-110866-4(8)) Macmillan/McGraw-Hill Schl. Div.

Trautman, Jan, ed. Gotta Have Graphs. 2002. 64p. 11.95 (978-1-56234-510-5(9) , Mailbox Bks., The) Education Ctr., Inc.

Triola, Chris. Geometreats: Math with Munchies. 2nd ed. 2001. 88p. (YA). stu. ed., per., wbk. ed. (978-1-58123-252-3(7)) Larson Learning, Inc.

—Math Trips. 2000. 82p. (J). per. 12.95 (978-1-58123-202-8(0)) Larson Learning, Inc.

Trumbauer, Lisa. Math: Grade 2. del Sur, Duendes, illus. 2000. (Jumpstart Ser.). 32p. (J). (gr. 2). pap. 3.99 (978-0-439-17643-9(3)) Scholastic, Inc.

Try It! Hundred Number Boards. 2000. (J). pap. 10.95 (978-1-56911-094-2(8)) Learning Resources, Inc.

Try It! Pentominoes. 2000. (J). pap. 10.95 (978-1-56911-057-7(3)) Learning Resources, Inc.

Tucker, Bethanie H. Mr. Base Ten Invents Mathematics. l.t. ed. 2002. (Illus.). 205p. (J). pap. 22.00 (978-1-929229-24-6(0)) aha! Process, Inc.

Two Piece Math Flip Over Books - Adding. 2000. (Illus.). (J). (978-1-58805-114-1(5)) DS-Max USA, Inc.

Two Piece Math Flip Over Books - Times Tables. 2000. (Illus.). (J). (978-1-58805-115-8(3)) DS-Max USA, Inc.

Tyler, Jenny. First Learning Time. 2000. (gr. k-3). lib. bdg. 12.95 (978-0-613-90025-6(1)) Tandem Library Bks.

Underwood, Deborah. Safari Adventure. 2007. (J). ***(978-1-4109-2843-6(8)); (978-1-4109-2860-3(8))*** Steck-Vaughn.

University of Cambridge Local Examinations Syndication Staff. HIGCSE Mathematics Module 3, 1998. (Cambridge Open Learning Project in South Africa Ser.). 196p. pap. 9.15 (978-0-521-59515-5(0)) Cambridge Univ. Pr.

—HIGCSE Mathematics Module 4. 1998. (Cambridge Open Learning Project in South Africa Ser.). 208p. pap. 9.15 (978-0-521-59514-8(2)) Cambridge Univ. Pr.

Up-to-Speed Math Story Problems 1. 2002. (Illus.). 96p. (YA). per. 8.95 (978-1-56254-521-5(3) , SP5213) Saddleback Educational Publishing.

Up-to-Speed Math Story Problems 2. 2002. (Illus.). 20p. (YA). per. 8.95 (978-1-56254-522-2(1) , SP5221) Saddleback Educational Publishing.

Up-to-Speed Math Story Problems 3. 2002. (Illus.). 96p. (YA). per. 8.95 (978-1-56254-523-9(X) , SP523X) Saddleback Educational Publishing.

Vamos a clasificar Math, 6 vols.Tr. of Let's Sort Math. (SPA.). (gr. k-2). 28.95 (978-0-7368-3139-0(8) , Yellow Umbrella Bks.) Capstone Pr., Inc.

Van der Meer, Ron. Mathsmaster 5. 2000. (J). 19.95 (978-3-8290-2504-1(1)) Konemann.

VanLeeuwen. Math Connection Grade 4. 2003. (Math Connection Ser.). 160p. (gr. 4 up). 8.95 (978-1-932210-16-3(4)) Rainbow Bridge Publishing.

—Math Connection Grade 5. 2003. (Math Connection Ser.). 160p. (gr. 5 up). 8.95 (978-1-932210-17-0(2)) Rainbow Bridge Publishing.

—Math Connection Grade 6. 2003. (Math Connection Ser.). 160p. (gr. 6 up). 8.95 (978-1-932210-18-7(0)) Rainbow Bridge Publishing.

Various Authors. Cambridge Mathematics Direct Reception Handwriting, 10 vols., Pack. 2002. (Cambridge Mathematics Direct Ser.). (Illus.). 16p. pap., wbk. ed. 12.00 (978-0-521-01123-5(X)) Cambridge Univ. Pr.

Vedic Mathematics. 2003. per. (978-0-9727877-0-3(4)) Consciousness-Based Education Association.

Vegetales: Superlibros de Literatura/Literature Big Books. 1999. (Matematicas en Mi Mundo Ser.). (ENG & SPA.). (gr. 2 up). (978-0-02-110171-9(X)) Macmillan/McGraw-Hill Schl. Div.

Una vela Blanca: Superlibros de Literatura/Literature Big Books. 1999. (Matematicas en Mi Mundo Ser.). (ENG & SPA.). (gr. k up). (978-0-02-110156-6(6)) Macmillan/McGraw-Hill Schl. Div.

Veo patrones Math, 6 vols.Tr. of I See Patterns Math. (SPA.). (gr. k-2). 28.95 (978-0-7368-3121-5(5) , Yellow Umbrella Bks.) Capstone Pr., Inc.

Vervoort, Gerardus & Mason, Dale J. Calculator Math, Level B. 2001. 96p. (J). (gr. 3-5). 12.99 (978-0-86653-877-0(1) , FE0877, Fearon Teacher Aids) Schaffer, Frank Pubns.

Viajando a traves de los Numeros - America Aponte. 2005. 32.95 (978-1-881744-70-2(1)) Editorial Panamericana.

Vilsaint, Henock. Math Pack Bilingual English, Haitian Creole: PakMat. Date not set. (Illus.). 64p. (J). (gr. 1-3). wbk. ed. 5.50 (978-1-881839-64-4(8)) Educa Vision.

Vincent, Douglas. Math: Grade 5. 2003. (Brighter Child Workbooks Ser.). (Illus.). 24p. (J). (gr. 5). pap. 2.25 (978-1-56189-075-0(8) , American Education Publishing) School Specialty Publishing.

Virtual Math Tutor V2. 0: CD Installable. 2005. (YA). cd-rom 60.00 (978-1-59807-032-3(0)) American Bk. Co.

Virtual Math Tutor V2. 0: CD Playable. 2005. (YA). cd-rom 60.00 (978-1-59807-031-6(2)) American Bk. Co.

Vohrer, Susan. Real-World Math. Morris, Susan & Traylor, Susan, eds. 2005. 64p. (J). pap. (978-1-59441-052-9(6) , CD-104023) Carson-Dellosa Publishing Co., Inc.

—Real-World Math. Morris, Susan, ed. 2005. 64p. (J). pap. (978-1-59441-054-3(2) , CD-104025) Carson-Dellosa Publishing Co., Inc.

Vorderman, Carol. How Math Works: 100 Ways Parents & Kids Can Share the Wonders of Mathematics. 1999. (How It Works Ser.). (Illus.). 192p. (gr. 12-9). pap. 16.95 (978-0-7621-0233-4(0)) Reader's Digest Assn., Inc., The.

—Math Made Easy. 1998. 48p. (J). (gr. 2-6). 15.95 (978-0-7894-2799-1(0)) Dorling Kindersley Publishing, Inc.

Walch. Assessment Strategies for Math. 2003. 86p. 24.99 (978-0-8251-4492-9(2)) Walch Publishing.

Walsh, Kieran. Kitchen Math. 2003. (Math & My World Ser.). (Illus.). 48p. (J). 29.93 (978-1-58952-382-1(2)) Rourke Publishing, LLC.

—Map Math. 2003. (Illus.). 48p. (J). 29.93 (978-1-58952-379-1(2)) Rourke Publishing, LLC.

—Medical Math. 2003. (Illus.). 48p. (J). 29.93 (978-1-58952-380-7(6)) Rourke Publishing, LLC.

—Travel Math. 2003. (Illus.). 48p. (J). 29.93 (978-1-58952-383-8(0)) Rourke Publishing, LLC.

—Weather Math. 2003. (Math & My World Ser.). (Illus.). 48p. (J). 29.93 (978-1-58952-384-5(9)) Rourke Publishing, LLC.

Walton, Jocelyn C. & Klein, Sheryl. Achieving GEPA Mathematical Standards: A Problem Solving Approach. 2001. 385p. (YA). (gr. 6-11). 59.95 (978-1-886292-31-4(0)) CEO Software Solutions.

—Achieving GEPA Mathematical Standards Answer Key. 2001. 50p. (YA). (gr. 6-11). pap. 19.95 (978-1-886292-32-1(9)) CEO Software Solutions.

—GEPA Math: A Collection of Activities. 1998. (Illus.). 118p. (J). (gr. 7-9). stu. ed., wbk. ed. 229.95 (978-1-886292-27-7(2)) CEO Software Solutions.

Wang, Cheng Dong. Explore the Secrets of Math Level 2. 2002. (Illus.). (J). Bk. 1. 194p. pap. 12.00 (978-0-9719967-4-8(1)); Bk. 2. 12.99 (978-0-9719967-5-5(X)) Wang, Cheng Dong.

—Explore the Secrets of Math Level 3, Bk. 1. 2002. (Illus.). (J). 12.99 (978-0-9719967-6-2(8)) Wang, Cheng Dong.

Warnick, Theresa. 1-Minute Math Addition 0-10. 2001. (One-Minute Math Drills Ser.). 64p. (J). (gr. 1-2). pap. 9.99 (978-0-7647-0391-1(9) , FS23241) Schaffer, Frank Pubns.

—1-Minute Math Addition 11-18. 2001. (One-Minute Math Drills Ser.). 64p. (J). (gr. 1-2). pap. 9.99 (978-0-7647-0392-8(7) , FS23242) Schaffer, Frank Pubns.

—1-Minute Math Mult Factors 0-5. 2001. (One-Minute Math Drills Ser.). 64p. (J). (gr. 2-3). pap. 9.99 (978-0-7647-0395-9(1) , FS23245) Schaffer, Frank Pubns.

—1-Minute Math Mult Factors 6-9. 2001. (One-Minute Math Drills Ser.). 64p. (J). (gr. 2-3). pap. 9.99 (978-0-7647-0396-6(X) , FS23246) Schaffer, Frank Pubns.

—1-Minute Math Subtraction 0-10. 2001. (One-Minute Math Drills Ser.). 64p. (J). (gr. 1-2). pap. 9.99 (978-0-7647-0393-5(5) , FS23243) Schaffer, Frank Pubns.

—1-Minute Math Subtraction 11-18. 2001. (One-Minute Math Drills Ser.). 64p. (J). (gr. 1-2). pap. 9.99 (978-0-7647-0394-2(3) , FS23244) Schaffer, Frank Pubns.

Watt, Fiona & Wells, Rachel. Numbers. 2004. (Usborne Sticker Math Ser.). (Illus.). 28p. (J). (gr. k-1). pap., act. bk. ed. 6.95 (978-0-7460-3731-7(7)) EDC Publishing.

—Sticker Maths: Adding. 2004. (Usborne Sticker Math Ser.). (Illus.). 28p. (J). (gr. k-1). pap., act. bk. ed. 6.95 (978-0-7460-3728-7(7)) EDC Publishing.

—Sticker Maths: Taking Away. 2004. (Usborne Sticker Math Ser.). (Illus.). 28p. (J). (gr. k-1). pap., act. bk. ed. 6.95 (978-0-7460-3734-8(1)) EDC Publishing.

—Sticker Maths: Times Tables. 2004. (Sticker Math Ser.). (Illus.). 28p. (J). (gr. 1-2). pap., act. bk. ed. 6.95 (978-0-7945-0010-8(2) , Usborne) EDC Publishing.

Weiss, Ellen. Math at the Store. 2007. (Scholastic News Nonfiction Readers: Everyday Math—NEW SUBSET Ser.). 24p. (J). pap. 6.95 ***(978-0-531-18781-4(0));*** (Illus.). (gr. 1-2). lib. bdg. 20.00 ***(978-0-531-18528-5(1))*** Scholastic Library Publishing. (Children's Pr.).

—Math in the Backyard. 2007. (Scholastic News Nonfiction Readers: Everyday Math—NEW SUBSET Ser.). 24p. (J). pap. 6.95 ***(978-0-531-18782-1(9));*** (Illus.). (gr. 1-2). lib. bdg. 20.00 ***(978-0-531-18529-2(X))*** Scholastic Library Publishing. (Children's Pr.).

—Math in the Car. 2007. (Scholastic News Nonfiction Readers: Everyday Math—NEW SUBSET Ser.). 24p. (J). pap. 6.95 ***(978-0-531-18783-8(7));*** (Illus.). (gr. 1-2). lib. bdg. 20.00 ***(978-0-531-18530-8(3))*** Scholastic Library Publishing. (Children's Pr.).

—Math in the Kitchen. 2007. (Scholastic News Nonfiction Readers: Everyday Math—NEW SUBSET Ser.). 24p. (J). pap. 6.95 ***(978-0-531-18784-5(5));*** (Illus.). (gr. 1-2). lib. bdg. 20.00 ***(978-0-531-18531-5(1))*** Scholastic Library Publishing. (Children's Pr.).

—Math in the Neighborhood. 2007. (Scholastic News Nonfiction Readers: Everyday Math—NEW SUBSET Ser.). 24p. (J). pap. 6.95 ***(978-0-531-18785-2(3));*** (Illus.). (gr. 1-2). lib. bdg. 20.00 ***(978-0-531-18532-2(X))*** Scholastic Library Publishing. (Children's Pr.).

—Math on the Playground. 2007. (Scholastic News Nonfiction Readers: Everyday Math—NEW SUBSET Ser.). 24p. (J). pap. 6.95 ***(978-0-531-18786-9(1)*** , Children's Pr.) Scholastic Library Publishing.

Welch, Clare & Bartholomew, Barb. Math Practice. 1999. (100+ Ser.). 128p. (J). (gr. 1-2). pap. 12.99 (978-0-88012-815-5(1) , IF8739) School Specialty Publishing.

Wells, Rosemary. Adding It Up: Based on Timothy Goes to School & Other Stories. Wells, Rosemary & Koelsch, Michael, illus. 2001. (Get Set for Kindergarten Ser.). 24p. (J). pap. 5.99 (978-0-14-230040-4(3) , Puffin) Penguin Group (USA) Inc.

—Adding It Up: Based on Timothy Goes to School & Other Stories. Koelsch, Michael, illus. 2001. (Get Set for Kindergarten Ser.: No. 6). 24p. (J). 13.99 (978-0-670-03519-9(X) , Viking Juvenile) Penguin Group (USA) Inc.

—Adding It Up: Based on Timothy Goes to School & Other Stories. 2001. 12.79 (978-0-606-22482-6(3)) Tandem Library Bks.

—How Many? How Much? 2001. (ps-2). lib. bdg. 14.15 (978-0-613-31328-5(3)) Tandem Library Bks.

What Makes Ten? Math, 6 vols. (gr. k-2). 28.95 (978-0-7368-1733-2(6) , Yellow Umbrella Bks.) Capstone Pr., Inc.

Wheeler. Wheeler Discrete Math for Educators Preliminary Plus Study & Solution Manual Preliminary. 2004. (YA). pap. 92.76 (978-0-618-53798-3(8) , 389624) Houghton Mifflin College Div.

Where? Math, 6 vols. (gr. k-2). 28.95 (978-0-7368-1736-3(0) , Yellow Umbrella Bks.) Capstone Pr., Inc.

White, Nancy. Make a Pattern: A Content Area Reader-math. 2005. (Emergent/Early (Prek-2) Math Package Ser.). 12p. (YA). (ps-2). 25.20 (978-0-8215-7822-3(7)) Sadlier, William H. Inc.

Whiteford, Rhona & Fitzsimmons, Jim. Complete Math, 4 bks. in 1. (Illus.). 96p. (YA). pap. 15.99 (978-0-340-71581-9(2) , Hodder & Stoughton) Hodder General Publishing Division GBR. *Dist:* Trafalgar Square Publishing.

Whitehouse, Patricia. Matematicas del Zoologico, 7 bks., Set. 2002. (SPA.). (J). (ps-1). lib. bdg. 111.00 (978-1-58810-807-4(4)) Heinemann Library.

—The Math Zoo. 2002. 24p. (J). (ps-1). pap. (978-1-58810-756-5(6) , 91409); (Illus.). lib. bdg. 17.08 (978-1-58810-548-6(2)) Heinemann Library.

—Pares en el Zoologico. 2002. (Matematicas del Zoologico (Zoo Math) Ser.).Tr. of Zoo Pairs. (SPA.). 24p. (J). (ps-1). pap. 5.25 (978-1-58810-862-3(7) , 91627); lib. bdg. 18.50 (978-1-58810-803-6(1)) Heinemann Library.

—Partes Iguales en el Zoologico. 2002. (Matematicas del Zoologico (Zoo Math) Ser.). (SPA.). 24p. (J). (ps-1). 18.50 (978-1-58810-801-2(5)); pap. 5.25 (978-1-58810-860-9(0) , 91628) Heinemann Library.

—El Zoologico Matematico. 2002. (Matematicas del Zoologico (Zoo Math) Ser.). 24p. (J). (ps-1). (SPA.). 18.50 (978-1-58810-802-9(3)); pap. 5.25 (978-1-58810-861-6(9) , 91625) Heinemann Library.

Why We Measure Math, 6 vols. (gr. k-2). 28.95 (978-0-7368-1739-4(5) , Yellow Umbrella Bks.) Capstone Pr., Inc.

Williams, Rozanne Lanczak. Adding. Jarrett, Michael, illus. Jarrett, Michael, photos by. 2004. (I Can Do Math Ser.). 24p. (J). (gr. 1 up). lib. bdg. 20.67 (978-0-8368-4108-4(5)) Stevens, Gareth Inc.

—Subtracting. Jarrett, Michael, photos by. 2004. (I Can Do Math Ser.). (Illus.). 24p. (J). (gr. 1 up). lib. bdg. 20.67 (978-0-8368-4113-8(1)) Stevens, Gareth Inc.

Willoughby, Alana. Real Math Fourth Grade. (J). (gr. 4). stu. ed. (978-0-8126-0504-4(7) , 60504) SRA/McGraw-Hill.

Wilson, Robert B. Learn it Fast! NJ ASK4 Math. 2005. per. 34.95 (978-0-9772020-0-3(3)) Global Institute for Maximizing Potential, Incorporated.

Windows: Technology: Test Generator. 1999. (Matematicas en Mi Mundo Ser.). (ENG & SPA.). (gr. 4 up). (978-0-02-111225-8(8)); (gr. 6 up). (978-0-02-111229-6(0)) Macmillan/McGraw-Hill Schl. Div.

Windows: Test Generator. 1999. (Matematicas en Mi Mundo Ser.). (ENG & SPA.). (gr. 5 up). (978-0-02-111227-2(4)) Macmillan/McGraw-Hill Schl. Div.

Wingard-Nelson, Rebecca. Division & Multiplication. 2008. (Math Busters Ser.). (Illus.). 64p. (J). (gr. 5 up). lib. bdg. 27.93 ***(978-0-7660-2876-0(3))*** Enslow Pubs., Inc.

—Fractions & Decimals Made Easy. 2005. (Making Math Easy Ser.). (Illus.). 48p. (J). (gr. 2-4). lib. bdg. 23.93 (978-0-7660-2513-4(6) , Enslow Elementary) Enslow Pubs., Inc.

—Ratios & Percents. 2008. (Math Busters Ser.). (Illus.). 64p. (J). (gr. 5 up). lib. bdg. 27.93 ***(978-0-7660-2878-4(X))*** Enslow Pubs., Inc.

Wingard-Nelson, Rebecca. Word Problems Made Easy. LaBaff, Tom, illus. 2005. (Making Math Easy Ser.). 48p. (J). (gr. 2-4). lib. bdg. 23.93 (978-0-7660-2512-7(8) , Enslow Elementary) Enslow Pubs., Inc.

Wipe-Away Books: Multiplication. 2003. (Illus.). 16p. (J). (gr. 3 up). pap. 3.99 (978-0-7682-0074-4(1)) School Specialty Publishing.

Wise & Paco Dog's Multiplication Books. 2003. 3.99 (978-0-915960-35-4(4)) Ebon Research Systems Publishing, LLC.

Witt, Joe & Gallaway, Kate. Managing Your Mathematics Classroom. 2005. 88p. per. (978-1-59318-484-1(0)) Sopris West Educational Services.

Wolf, Kathy, ed. Learning Library-Math. 2003. 128p. 19.95 (978-1-56234-526-6(5) , Mailbox Bks., The) Education Ctr., Inc.

—Learning Library Math. 2002. 128p. 19.95 (978-1-56234-476-4(5)); 19.95 (978-1-56234-477-1(3)); 19.95 (978-1-56234-478-8(1)); 19.95 (978-1-56234-479-5(X)) Education Ctr., Inc. (Mailbox Bks., The).

Wolff, Jean. Word Problems. 1999. (Homework Booklets Ser.). 72p. (J). (gr. 2-2). pap. 2.99 (978-1-56822-130-4(4) , IF0181, Instructional Fair) Schaffer, Frank Pubns.

Woodward, Earnest & Woodward, Marilyn, contrib. by. Larson's Sliding Geobeads & Activity Guide (Combination Pack) 2000. (J). per. (978-1-58123-210-3(1)) Larson Learning, Inc.

Working It Out Math. (gr. k-2). 19.95 (978-0-7368-7104-4(7)) Red Brick Learning.

World Book, Inc. Staff. Power Series, 6 vols., Set. 2001. (YA). (gr. 5-12). 74.00 (978-0-7166-3590-1(9) , 60044) World Bk., Inc.

Wortzman, Ricki. Math Detectives: Finding Fun in Numbers. 2003. (gr. k-3). lib. bdg. 12.95 (978-0-613-78018-6(3)) Tandem Library Bks.

Wortzman, Ricki & Harcourt, Lalie. Math Detectives: Finding Fun in Numbers. 2003. (Illus.). 48p. (J). pap. 4.95 (978-1-4027-0809-1(2)) Sterling Publishing Co., Inc.

Wren, Coretta. Counting on God. 2006. 82p. (YA). per., act. bk. ed. ***(978-0-9790934-0-1(6))*** Know Me Pubn. LLC.

Wright, Marsha Elyn. Addition & Subtraction with Mr. Wiggle, Grade 1. 2003. 32p. (J). (gr. 1-1). pap. 5.99 (978-1-56451-971-9(6) , ID99001, Ideal School Supply) Schaffer, Frank Pubns.

WRITE IT! Problem Solving with Numbers & Words, Grades 1-2. 2004. (J). per. 10.95 (978-1-58123-363-6(9)) Larson Learning, Inc.

WRITE IT! Problem Solving with Numbers & Words Grades 3-4 SE. 2004. (J). per. 10.95 (978-1-58123-361-2(2)) Larson Learning, Inc.

WRITE IT! Problem Solving with Numbers & Words, Grades 5-6. 2004. (J). per. 10.95 (978-1-58123-365-0(5)) Larson Learning, Inc.

WRITE IT! Problem Solving with Numbers & Words, Grades 7-8. 2004. (J). per. 10.95 (978-1-58123-367-4(1)) Larson Learning, Inc.

Wyatt, Valerie. Math Book for Girls & Other Beings Who Count. 2000. (gr. 3-6). lib. bdg. 18.75 (978-0-613-30599-0(X)) Tandem Library Bks.

Yeatts, Karol, et al. Navigating through problem Solving & Reasoning in Grade 3. House, Peggy A. & Litwiller, Bonnie H., eds. 2004. (Principles & Standards for School Mathematics Navigations Ser.). (Illus.). 65p. pap. 28.95 (978-0-87353-557-1(X) , 12719) National Council of Teachers of Mathematics.

Yellow Umbrella Add-on Set. (gr. k-2). 346.95 (978-0-7368-1780-6(8) , Yellow Umbrella Bks.) Capstone Pr., Inc.

Yellow Umbrella Books - Math: Adding It Up at the Zoo; Can You Eat a Fraction?; Counting Many Ways; Everone Uses Math; Graph It!; It's about Time; Looking at Shapes; Many Ways to 100; Odd & Even Numbers; Subtraction Fun; Time to Estimate; What's Zero?, 12 bks. 2002. (Illus.). (J). (gr. 1). lib. bdg. 175.20 (978-0-7368-1290-0(3) , Pebble Bks.) Capstone Pr., Inc.

Yellow Umbrella Books: Math, 12 bks. Incl. Adding It up at the Zoo. Nayer, Judy. 2002. lib. bdg. 14.60 (978-0-7368-1278-8(4)); Can You Eat a Fraction? Jaffe, Elizabeth Dana. 2002. lib. bdg. 14.60 (978-0-7368-1279-5(2)); Counting Many Ways. Giganti, Paul, Jr. 2002. lib. bdg. 14.60 (978-0-7368-1280-1(6)); Everyone Uses Math. Beers, Bonnie. 2002. lib. bdg. 14.60 (978-0-7368-1281-8(4)); Graph It! Trumbauer, Lisa. 2002. lib. bdg. 14.60 (978-0-7368-1282-5(2)); Hot or Cold? Martin, Elena. 2003. lib. bdg. 14.60 (978-0-7368-2012-7(4)); How Many Fish? Rubin, Alan. 2003. lib. bdg. 14.60 (978-0-7368-2013-4(2)); It's about Time. Nayer, Judy. 2002. lib. bdg. 14.60 (978-0-7368-1283-2(0)); Let's Sort. Bauer, David. 2003. lib. bdg. 14.60 (978-0-7368-2014-1(0)); Looking at Shapes. Tucker, Shirley & Rambo, Jane. 2002. lib. bdg. 14.60 (978-0-7368-1284-9(9)); Many Ways to 100. Franco, Betsy. 2002. lib. bdg. 14.60 (978-0-7368-1285-6(7)); Odd & Even Numbers. Tucker, Shirley & Rambo, Jane. 2002. lib. bdg. 14.60 (978-0-7368-1286-3(5)); Subtraction Fun. Franco, Betsy. 2002. lib. bdg. 14.60 (978-0-7368-1287-0(3)); Take Away. Trumbauer, Lisa. 2003. lib. bdg. 14.60 (978-0-7368-2015-8(9)); Time to Estimate. Franco, Betsy. 2002. lib. bdg. 14.60 (978-0-7368-1288-7(1)); What's Zero? Franco, Betsy. 2002. lib. bdg. 14.60 (978-0-7368-1289-4(X)); Where? Ring, Susan. 2003. lib. bdg. 14.60 (978-0-7368-2016-5(7)); Why We Measure. Trumbauer, Lisa. 2003. lib. bdg. 14.60 (978-0-7368-2017-2(5)); 16p. (J). (gr. 1). (Illus.). 2001. Set lib. bdg. 262.80 (978-0-7368-2024-0(8) , Pebble Bks.) Capstone Pr., Inc.

Yelvington, Susan. Multiplication. 1998. (Basic Skills Ser.). (Illus.). 32p. (J). (gr. 1-5). pap. 4.99 (978-0-88724-463-6(7) , CD-2131) Carson-Dellosa Publishing Co., Inc.

—Multiplication Basic Facts. 1998. (Basic Skills Ser.). (Illus.). 32p. (gr. 1-5). pap. 4.99 (978-0-88724-462-9(9) , CD-2130) Carson-Dellosa Publishing Co., Inc.

Yes, You Can. 2005. (Mathematics Ser.). (YA). (gr. k-2). 23.94 (978-0-8215-8918-2(0)) Sadlier, William H. Inc.

York, Jamie. Making Math Meaningful: A 6th Grade. 2003. stu. ed. 8.95 (978-1-892857-05-7(7)) Whole Spirit Pr.

—Making Math Meaningful: A 7th Grade. 2004. (YA). tchr. ed., spiral bd. 18.95 (978-1-892857-11-8(1)) Whole Spirit Pr.

—Making Math Meaningful: A 7th Grade Student's Workbook. 2004. (YA). wbk. ed. 15.95 (978-1-892857-12-5(X)) Whole Spirit Pr.

—Making Math Meaningful: A Middle School Math Curriculum for Teachers & Parents. 2nd ed. 2003. (J). spiral bd. 17.95 (978-1-892857-04-0(9)); 3rd ed. 2004. per. 22.95 (978-1-892857-08-8(1)) Whole Spirit Pr.

—Making Math Meaningful: An 8th Grade. 2004. (YA). tchr. ed., spiral bd. 18.95 (978-1-892857-09-5(X)) Whole Spirit Pr.

—Making Math Meaningful: An 8th Grade Student's Workbook. 2004. (YA). wbk. ed. 15.95 (978-1-892857-10-1(3)) Whole Spirit Pr.

You Can Sort. 2005. (Emergent/Early (Prek-2) Math Package Ser.). 12p. (YA). (ps-2). 25.20 (978-0-8215-7841-4(3)) Sadlier, William H. Inc.

Youngs, Dave & Pauls, Michelle. Puzzle Play. Pauls, Michelle & Cordel, Betty, eds. Schlotterback, Dave, illus. 2001. 211p. (J). pap. 18.95 (978-1-881431-95-4(9) , 1722) AIMS Education Foundation.

Youngs, Dave & Youngs, Michelle. Just for the Fun of It! A Collection of AIMS Mathematical Investigations. Cordel, Betty, ed. Richmond, Brenda, illus. 1999. vii, 125p. (J). tchr. ed. 18.95 (978-1-881431-79-4(7) , 1718) AIMS Education Foundation.

Zable, Stacy. City by the Lake. ed. 2003. (Early Connections Ser.). (J). pap. 35.00 (978-1-4108-1542-2(0)) Benchmark Education Co.

—Four Faces in Rock. ed. 2003. (Early Connections Ser.). (J). pap. 35.00 (978-1-4108-1539-2(0)) Benchmark Education Co.

Zolty, Howard. What Is Math? Answer: Math Is Everything. 2005. 28p. 14.21 (978-1-4116-6717-4(4)) Lulu.com.

Zoo Math, 6 bks., Set. 2002. (J). (ps-1). lib. bdg. 102.48 (978-1-58810-473-1(7)) Heinemann Library.

1st Math Booster. 2005. 64p. (J). per. 1.49 (978-1-59441-337-7(1) , C04013) Carson-Dellosa Publishing Co., Inc.

2nd Math Booster. 2005. 64p. (J). per. 1.49 (978-1-59441-341-4(X) , C04017) Carson-Dellosa Publishing Co., Inc.

3rd & 4th Grade Excelerator, 2 CDs. 2002. cd-rom 9.99 (978-1-59150-014-8(1)) TOPICS Entertainment.

3rd Math Booster. 2005. 64p. (J). per. 1.49 (978-1-59441-345-2(2) , C04021) Carson-Dellosa Publishing Co., Inc.

4-Step Math Wall Book: Addition & Subtraction. 2000. (Math Workbooks Ser.). 112p. (J). (ps). pap., wbk. ed. 10.95 (978-1-57882-047-4(2)) Teacher's Friend Pubns., Inc.

4-Step Math Wall (Multiplication & Division) 2000. (Math Workbooks). 112p. (J). pap. 10.95 (978-1-57882-048-1(0)) Teacher's Friend Pubns., Inc.

4th Math Booster. 2005. 64p. (J). per. 1.49 (978-1-59441-349-0(5) , C04025) Carson-Dellosa Publishing Co., Inc.

100 Day Count up Calendar W/100 Open & Peek Door. 2003. (J). 12.95 (978-0-439-08248-8(X)) Scholastic, Inc.

MATHEMATICS—DATA PROCESSING

Allen-Conn, B. J. & Rose, Kim. Powerful Ideas in the Classroom Using Squeak to Enhance Math & Science Learning. 2003. (Illus.). 86p. per. (978-0-9743131-0-8(6)) Viewpoints Research Institute, Inc.

Math Computation Skills & Stratagies Level 4. 2006. (YA). per. (978-1-56254-967-1(7)) Saddleback Educational Publishing.

Math Computation Skills & Strategies Level 3. 2006. (YA). per. (978-1-56254-966-4(9)) Saddleback Educational Publishing.

Math Computation Skills & Strategies Level 5. 2006. (YA). per. (978-1-56254-968-8(5)) Saddleback Educational Publishing.

Math Computation Skills & Strategies Level 6. 2006. (J). per. (978-1-56254-969-5(3)) Saddleback Educational Publishing.

Math Computation Skills & Strategies Level 7. 2006. (J). per. (978-1-56254-970-1(7)) Saddleback Educational Publishing.

Math Computation Skills & Strategies Level 8. 2006. (J). per. (978-1-56254-971-8(5)) Saddleback Educational Publishing.

MATHEMATICS—DICTIONARIES

De Klerk, Judith. Illustrated Maths Dictionary for Australian Schools. 2nd ed. Date not set. (Illus.). 123p. pap. 59.50 (978-0-582-87045-1(3)) Addison-Wesley Longman, Ltd. GBR. *Dist:* Trans-Atlantic Pubns., Inc.

Eather, Jenny. Maths Dictionary for Kids. 2004. (J). cd-rom 152.00 (978-1-84565-033-9(6)) Cambridge Univ. Pr.

Fitzgerald, Theresa. The Absolutely Essential Math Dictionary: Every Kid's Guide to Mathematical Terms, Strategies & Tables. 2002. (Illus.). 80p. (J). per. 13.95 (978-1-883055-50-9(4)) Dandy Lion Pubns.

—Math Dictionary: The Essential Guide to Math Terms, Strategies, & Tables. 2005. (Illus.). 110p. (J). pap. 12.95 (978-1-59363-160-4(X)) Prufrock Pr.

Kaplan Staff. Math Field Trip: A Grade-Raising Math Dictionary for Students Ages 9-12. 2006. (G - Reference,Information & Interdisciplinary Subjects Ser.). 208p. mass mkt. 4.99 (978-1-4195-9149-5(5)) Kaplan Publishing.

Middle School Math, Course 1: Multi-Language Visual Glossary. 2004. (gr. 6-9). (978-0-618-26963-1(0) , 2-05799) McDougal Littell Inc.

Nichols, Eugene D. & Schwartz, Sharon. Mathematics Dictionary & Handbook. 3rd ed. 1999. 464p. (J). (gr. 5-10). 29.95 (978-1-882269-09-9(8)) Nichols Schwartz Publishing.

PRAESA & Press, Karen. The Cambridge Mathematics Dictionary for Schools Afrikaans Translation. 2008. pap. ***978-0-521-70883-8(4)*** Cambridge Univ. Pr.

Rogers, Kirsteen. Illustrated Dict of Math - Internet Referenced. 2007. 128p. (J). pap. 12.99 (978-0-7945-1629-1(7) , Usborne) EDC Publishing.

Tapson, Frank & Atkins, Robert A. Barron's Math Study Dictionary. 1998. (Illus.). 128p. pap. 14.99 (978-0-7641-0303-2(2)) Barron's Educational Series, Inc.

University of Cape Town Staff & Press, Karen. The Cambridge Mathematics Dictionary for Schools. 2008. pap. ***978-0-521-70882-1(6)*** Cambridge Univ. Pr.

MATHEMATICS—HISTORY

Bruno, Leonard C. & Baker, Lawrence W. Math & Mathematicians: The History of Math Discoveries Around the World. 1999. (Illus.). xli, 456p. (J). (978-0-7876-3814-6(5)) Thomson Gale.

Bruno, Leonard C. & Baker, Lawrence W., eds. Math & Mathematicians: The History of Math Discoveries Around the World. 1999. (Illus.). xli, 456p. (J). (978-0-7876-3813-9(7)) Thomson Gale.

Downey, Tika. How the Arabs Invented Algebra: The History of the Concept of Variables. 2004. (Powermath Ser.). (Illus.). 32p. (J). lib. bdg. (978-0-8239-8879-2(1)); lib. bdg. 22.50 (978-0-8239-8986-7(0)) Rosen Publishing Group, Inc., The. (PowerKids Pr.).

Tabak, John. The History of Mathematics Set. 2004. (History of Mathematics Ser.). (gr. 6-12). pap. 200.00 (978-0-8160-4952-3(1)) Facts On File, Inc.

Woods, Mary B. & Woods, Michael. Ancient Computing: From Counting to Calendars. 2005. (Ancient Technology Ser.). (Illus.). 96p. (gr. 6-12). 25.26 (978-0-8225-2997-2(1)) Lerner Publishing Group.

MATHEMATICS—POETRY

Fehl, Mitzi & Williams, Bobbie. 15 Fun-to-Sing Collaborative Math Learning Songs & Activities: Delightful Math Songs Set to Your Favorite Tunes with Lessons & Easy-to-Make Books That Teach Early Math Skills - And Help Meet the NCTM Standards, Grades K-2. 2002. (Illus.). 80p. pap., tchr. ed. 11.95 (978-0-439-18724-4(9)) Scholastic, Inc.

Franco, Betsy. Counting Caterpillars..., 1 vol. 1998. 64p. pap. 9.95 (978-0-590-64210-1(3)) Scholastic, Inc.

Franco, Betsy & Salerno, Steven. Mathematickles! 2003. (Illus.). 40p. (J). (gr. k-5). 17.95 (978-0-689-84357-0(7) , McElderry, Margaret K.) Simon & Schuster Children's Publishing.

Maioli, Elizabeth, illus. Arrest That Asparagus! Manna, Elizabeth, photos by. 2000. 30p. (J). (gr. 1-5). pap. 9.95 (978-0-9729807-1-5(7)) Murray, David M.

Robinson, Elizabeth Keeler. Making Cents. McMahon, Bob, illus. 2007. (J). ***978-1-58246-214-1(3)*** , Tricycle Pr.) Ten Speed Pr.

Yolen, Jane. Shape Me a Rhyme: Nature's Forms in Poetry. Stemple, Jason, illus. Stemple, Jason, photos by. 2007. 32p. (J). (gr. 5-7). 17.95 ***978-1-59078-450-1(2)*** , Wordsong) Boyds Mills Pr.

MATHEMATICS—STUDY AND TEACHING

Aigner-Clark, Julie. Baby Einstein - Shape Sorted Set. Zaidi, Nadeem, illus. 2006. (Baby Einstein Ser.). 54p. (J). (ps-17). 18.99 (978-1-4231-0000-3(X)) Baby Einstein Co., LLC, The.

APTE, Inc. Staff. Internet Coach: Discover Math & Science. 2001. (Illus.). 16p. (J). (gr. 4-8). pap. 9.95 (978-1-889651-77-4(X)) APTE, Inc.

Association of Christian Schools International Staff. Math Grade Four: The Earth Below. 2000. (ACSI Elementary Mathmatics). (Illus.). (gr. 3-4). pap., stu. ed. 15.95 (978-1-58331-186-8(6) , 7216) Assn. of Christian Schls. International.

Atkinson, Sue. Supermaths: Age 4-5. 2003. (Illus.). 32p. pap. (978-0-340-80559-6(5) , Hodder Children's Books) Hodder Children's Division.

—Supermaths 3: Age 3-6. 2003. (Illus.). 32p. pap. (978-0-340-80561-9(7) , Hodder Children's Books) Hodder Children's Division.

Beers, Jack. Bridges - Red. 2002. (Math Bridges Ser.). (J). tchr. ed., per. 19.95 (978-1-58830-320-2(9)); (gr. 6). stu. ed., per. 13.95 (978-1-58830-300-4(4)) Metropolitan Teaching & Learning Co.

Bennett. Middle School Math Course 1. 4th ed. 2004. (SPA., Illus.). 60.40 (978-0-03-070976-0(8)) Holt, Rinehart & Winston.

—Middle School Math Course 2. 4th ed. 2004. (SPA., Illus.). 62.46 (978-0-03-071098-8(7)) Holt, Rinehart & Winston.

Bolster. Exploring Mathematics. (J). pap., wbk. ed. 9.10 (978-0-673-33130-4(X)); (gr. 1). pap., wbk. ed. 9.95 (978-0-673-33131-1(8)); (gr. 5). pap., wbk. ed. 11.85 (978-0-673-33135-9(0)) Addison-Wesley Educational Pubs., Inc.

Buck, Caroline & Voice, Elaine. Cambridge Mathematics Direct Reception Assess & Review Lesson Plans. 2002. (Cambridge Mathematics Direct Ser.). (Illus.). 24p. pap. 14.20 (978-0-521-89241-4(4)) Cambridge Univ. Pr.

Burger. Thinkwell Precalculus: Multimedia Package. 4th ed. 2004. 86.66 (978-0-03-036938-4(X)) Holt, Rinehart & Winston.

Clark, Jacqueline. Shoe Box Math Learning Centers: Forty Easy-to-Make, Fun-to-Use Centers with Instant Reproducibles & Activities That Help Kids Practice Important Math Skills-Independently. 2002. 80p. pap. 12.95 (978-0-439-20574-0(3)) Scholastic, Inc.

Collins, S. Harold. Percent. 2000. (Straight Forward Math Ser.). 40p. (J). (gr. 4-8). pap., wbk. ed. 3.95 (978-0-931993-25-1(3) , GP-025) Garlic Pr.

Cousins, Coleen, et al. Ntsiki's Surprise: Siswati Version. 2002. (Illus.). 16p. pap. 1.75 (978-0-521-52821-4(6)) Cambridge Univ. Pr.

Crowden, et al. Cambridge Mathematics Direct 5 Measures, Shape, Space & Handling Data Solutions. 2001. (Cambridge Mathematics Direct Ser.). (Illus.). 32p. (J). (gr. 2-6). pap. 7.95 (978-0-521-79831-0(0)) Cambridge Univ. Pr.

—Cambridge Mathematics Direct 6: Calculations Solutions. 2001. (Cambridge Mathematics Direct Ser.). 32p. (J). (gr. 2-6). pap. 9.95 (978-0-521-79834-1(5)) Cambridge Univ. Pr.

—Cambridge Mathematics Direct 6 Measures, Shape, Space & Handling Data Solutions. 2001. (Cambridge Mathematics Direct Ser.). (Illus.). 38p. (J). (gr. 2-6). pap. 7.95 (978-0-521-79835-8(3)) Cambridge Univ. Pr.

—Cambridge Mathematics Direct 6 Numbers & the Number System Solutions. 2001. (Cambridge Mathematics Direct Ser.). 24p. (J). pap. 6.95 (978-0-521-79833-4(7)) Cambridge Univ. Pr.

Crowden, Jane, et al, eds. Measures, Shape, Space & Handling Data, 4 vols., No. 3. 2001. (Cambridge Mathematics Direct Ser.). (Illus.). 72p. pap. 10.00 (978-0-521-78463-4(8)) Cambridge Univ. Pr.

Crowden, Jane, et al. Cambridge Mathematics Direct 5 Calculations Solutions. 2001. (Cambridge Mathematics Direct Ser.). (Illus.). 40p. (gr. 2-6). pap. 9.00 (978-0-521-79830-3(2)) Cambridge Univ. Pr.

Dorling Kindersley Publishing Staff. Kindergarten. 2001. (Math Made Easy Ser.). (Illus.). 160p. (J). pap., wbk. ed. 14.99 (978-0-7894-5720-2(2)) Dorling Kindersley Publishing, Inc.

—Third Grade. 2001. (Math Workbooks Ser.). (Illus.). 200p. (J). (gr. 3). pap., wbk. ed. 14.99 (978-0-7894-5729-5(6)) Dorling Kindersley Publishing, Inc.

Egan, Lorraine Hopping. 25 Super Cool Math Board Games: Easy-to-Play Reproducible Games That Teach Essential Math Skills. 1999. (Illus.). 64p. pap. 12.95 (978-0-590-37872-7(4)) Scholastic, Inc.

Erickson, Tim. Learning Mathematics with Graphing Calculator 1.3. 2001. 99p. act. bk. ed. 19.95 incl. cd-rom (978-0-9648496-1-7(5) , eeps media) Epistemological Engineering.

Exploring Mathematics. (J). (gr. 2). pap., wbk. ed. 9.95 (978-0-673-33132-8(6)); (gr. 3). pap., wbk. ed. 11.85 (978-0-673-33133-5(4)) Addison-Wesley Educational Pubs., Inc.

Facts in a Flash, Startegies for Fast Fact Recall: Multiplication & Division. 2003. 64p. (gr. 3-6). 6.99 (978-1-56451-329-8(7) , ID7141) School Specialty Publishing.

Facts in a Flash, Strategies for Fast Fact Recall: Addition & Subtraction. 2003. 64p. (gr. 1-3). 6.99 (978-1-56451-328-1(9) , ID7140) School Specialty Publishing.

Fehl, Mitzi & Williams, Bobbie. 15 Fun-to-Sing Collaborative Math Learning Songs & Activities: Delightful Math Songs Set to Your Favorite Tunes with Lessons & Easy-to-Make Books That Teach Early Math Skills - And Help Meet the NCTM Standards, Grades K-2. 2002. (Illus.). 80p. pap., tchr. ed. 11.95 (978-0-439-18724-4(9)) Scholastic, Inc.

French, Kathy J. Math & More Directed Activities: Kindergarten. Hollister, Michele, ed. l.t. ed. 2001. 200p. (J). pap. (978-1-893632-05-9(9) , 300-108) Math Concepts, Inc.

—Mental Math: 1st Grade. Hollister, Michele, ed. l.t. ed. 1998. 150p. (J). (gr. 1). pap. 19.95 (978-1-893632-00-4(8) , 300-103) Math Concepts, Inc.

—Mental Math: 2nd Grade. Hollister, Michele, ed. l.t. ed. 1998. 140p. (J). (gr. 2). pap. 19.95 (978-1-893632-01-1(6) , 300-104) Math Concepts, Inc.

—Mental Math: 3rd Grade. Hollister, Michele, ed. l.t. ed. 1998. 150p. (J). (gr. 3). pap. 19.95 (978-1-893632-02-8(4) , 300-105) Math Concepts, Inc.

—Mental Math: 4th Grade. Hollister, Michele, ed. l.t. ed. 1998. 150p. (J). (gr. 4). pap. 19.95 (978-1-893632-03-5(2) , 300-106) Math Concepts, Inc.

—Mental Math: 5th Grade. Hollister, Michele, ed. l.t. ed. 1998. 150p. (J). (gr. 5). pap. 19.95 (978-1-893632-04-2(0) , 300-107) Math Concepts, Inc.

Freudentha. Building Formulas. 2002. (Math in Context Ser.). (Illus.). (J). 7.86 (978-0-7826-1541-8(4)); (SPA.). 7.86 (978-0-85229-740-7(8)) Encyclopaedia Britannica, Inc.

—Building Formulas: Spanish. 2003. (Mathematics in Context Ser.). (SPA.). stu. ed. 7.86 (978-0-03-072368-1(X)) Holt, Rinehart & Winston.

—Cereal Numbers: Math/Context - Spanish Student Edition. 98th ed. 2002. (J). 7.86 (978-0-85229-737-7(8)) Encyclopaedia Britannica, Inc.

—Cereal Numbers: Spanish. 2003. (SPA.). stu. ed. 7.86 (978-0-03-072358-2(2)) Holt, Rinehart & Winston.

—Decision Making: Math Context - Spanish Student Edition. 98th ed. 2002. (J). 7.86 (978-0-85229-741-4(6)) Encyclopaedia Britannica, Inc.

—Decision Making: Math/Context. 98th ed. 2002. stu. ed. 7.86 (978-0-7826-1542-5(2)) Encyclopaedia Britannica, Inc.

—Decision Making: Spanish. 2003. (Mathematics in Context Ser.). (SPA.). 7.86 (978-0-03-072359-9(0)) Holt, Rinehart & Winston.

—Dry & Wet Numbers Math/Context. 98th ed. 2002. stu. ed. 7.86 (978-0-7826-1506-7(6)) Encyclopaedia Britannica, Inc.

—Expressions & Formulas: Spanish. 2003. (Mathematics in Context Ser.). (SPA.). stu. ed. 7.86 (978-0-03-072347-6(7)) Holt, Rinehart & Winston.

—Looking at Angles. 2002. (Math in Context Ser.). 7.86 (978-0-7826-1544-9(9)) Encyclopaedia Britannica, Inc.

—Made to Measure: Math/Context. 98th ed. 2002. 7.86 (978-0-7826-1525-8(2)) Encyclopaedia Britannica, Inc.

—Math in Context: Cereal Numbers. 3rd ed. 2002. (Illus.). stu. ed. 7.86 (978-0-85229-881-7(1)) Encyclopaedia Britannica, Inc.

—More or Less: Spanish. 2003. (Mathematics in Context Ser.). (SPA.). stu. ed. 7.86 (978-0-03-072351-3(5)) Holt, Rinehart & Winston.

—Operations Math/Context. 98th ed. 2002. stu. ed. 7.86 (978-0-7826-1524-1(4)) Encyclopaedia Britannica, Inc.

—Powers of Ten: Spanish. 2003. (Mathematics in Context Ser.). 7.86 (978-0-03-072363-6(9)) Holt, Rinehart & Winston.

—Ratios & Rates. 2002. (Math in Context Ser.). 7.86 (978-0-7826-1520-3(1)) Encyclopaedia Britannica, Inc.

—Tracking Graphs. 2002. (Math in Context Ser.). 7.86 (978-0-7826-1522-7(8)) Encyclopaedia Britannica, Inc.

—Tracking Graphs. 2003. (Mathematics in Context Ser.). (SPA.). stu. ed. 7.86 (978-0-03-072344-5(2)) Holt, Rinehart & Winston.

—Ups & Downs. 2002. (Math in Context Ser.). 7.86 (978-0-7826-1540-1(6)) Encyclopaedia Britannica, Inc.

—Ups & Downs: Spanish. 2003. (Mathematics in Context Ser.). pap. 7.86 (978-0-03-072367-4(1)) Holt, Rinehart & Winston.

—Ways to Go. 2002. (Math in Context Ser.). (Illus.). (J). (SPA.). 7.86 (978-0-85229-745-2(9)); stu. ed. 7.86 (978-0-7826-1546-3(5)) Encyclopaedia Britannica, Inc.

—Ways to Go: Spanish. 2003. (Mathematics in Context Ser.). (SPA.). stu. ed. 7.86 (978-0-03-072357-5(4)) Holt, Rinehart & Winston.

Freudentha, H. Dealing with Data Math/Context. 3rd ed. 2002. (J). 7.86 (978-0-85229-870-1(6)) Encyclopaedia Britannica, Inc.

—Digging Numbers: Math/Context. 3rd ed. 2003. (J). 7.86 (978-0-03-071716-1(7)) Holt, Rinehart & Winston of Canada, Ltd. CAN. *Dist:* Harcourt Canada, Ltd.

—Math in Context: Dealing with Data. 2002. (Illus.). 7.86 (978-0-7826-1527-2(9)) Encyclopaedia Britannica, Inc.

—Math in Context: More or Less. 2002. (Illus.). 7.86 (978-0-7826-1519-7(8)) Encyclopaedia Britannica, Inc.

—Math in Context: Operations. 3rd ed. 2003. (Math in Context Ser.). (SPA., Illus.). 7.86 (978-0-03-072352-0(3)) Holt, Rinehart & Winston.

—Math in Context: Re-Allotment. 2002. (Illus.). 7.86 (978-0-7826-1526-5(0)) Encyclopaedia Britannica, Inc.

—Pattern & Figures: Math/Context. 3rd ed. 2003. (J). 7.86 (978-0-03-071702-4(7)) Holt, Rinehart & Winston of Canada, Ltd. CAN. *Dist:* Harcourt Canada, Ltd.

—Powers of Ten Math/Context. 98th ed. 2002. (J). 7.86 (978-0-7826-1539-5(2)) Encyclopaedia Britannica, Inc.

—Re-Allotment: Math/Context. 3rd ed. 2003. (SPA.). (J). 7.86 (978-0-03-072354-4(X)) Holt, Rinehart & Winston of Canada, Ltd. CAN. *Dist:* Harcourt Canada, Ltd.

Freudenthal. Comparing Quantity. 2002. (Math in Context Ser.). stu. ed. 7.86 (978-0-7826-1523-4(6)) Encyclopaedia Britannica, Inc.

Gerber, Carole & School Specialty Publishing Staff. Math. 2001. (Master Skills Ser.). (Illus.). 128p. (J). (gr. k-6). pap., stu. ed., wbk. ed. 6.95 (978-1-56189-014-9(6) , 11014, American Education Publishing) School Specialty Publishing.

Giglio, Julie. Third Grade Enrichment. 2001. (Enrichment Wkbks.). (Illus.). 32p. (J). (gr. 3). pap. 2.49 (978-0-88743-458-7(4) , 02153) School Zone Publishing Co.

Greenberg, Dan. Mega-Funny Math Poems & Problems. 1999. 56p. pap. 9.95 (978-0-590-18735-0(X)) Scholastic, Inc.

Hall, M. C. First Grade Enrichment. 2001. (Enrichment Wkbks.). 32p. (J). (gr. 1). pap., wbk. ed. 2.49 (978-0-88743-456-3(8) , 02151) School Zone Publishing Co.

—Second Grade Enrichment. 2001. (Enrichment Wkbks.). (Illus.). 32p. (J). (gr. 2). pap., wbk. ed. 2.49 (978-0-88743-457-0(6) , 02152) School Zone Publishing Co.

Harcourt School Publishers Staff. Calculating Crew: Guide to CD-ROM. 98th ed. 1998. (Mighty Mathtm Ser.). (Illus.). (gr. 3-6). pap. 11.00 (978-0-15-307976-4(2)) Harcourt Schl. Pubs.

—Carnival Countdown. 98th ed. 1998. (Harcourt Math Ser.). (gr. k-3). pap., tchr. ed. 11.00 (978-0-15-307967-2(3)) Harcourt Schl. Pubs.

—Cosmic Geometry: User's Guide. 98th ed. 1998. (Mighty Mathtm Ser.). (Illus.). (gr. 6-8). pap., pupil's gde. ed. 11.00 (978-0-15-307982-5(7)) Harcourt Schl. Pubs.

—Harcourt Matematicas: 3 Dragones Desordenados: Math Reader. 2nd ed. 2002. (SPA., Illus.). pap. 4.20 (978-0-15-321735-7(9)) Harcourt Schl. Pubs.

—Harcourt Matematicas: CA Edition. 2nd ed. 2002. (SPA., Illus.). (J). pap. 25.70 (978-0-15-321608-4(5)); (gr. 1). pap. 34.30 (978-0-15-321609-1(3)); (gr. 2). pap. 34.30 (978-0-15-321610-7(7)); (gr. 3). pap. 64.20 (978-0-15-321611-4(5)); (gr. 4). pap. 65.60 (978-0-15-321612-1(3)); (gr. 5). pap. 65.60 (978-0-15-321613-8(1)); (gr. 6). pap. 65.60 (978-0-15-321614-5(X)) Harcourt Schl. Pubs.

—Harcourt Matematicas: Carreras del Recreo: Math Reader. 2nd ed. 2002. (SPA., Illus.). pap. 4.20 (978-0-15-321732-6(4)) Harcourt Schl. Pubs.

—Harcourt Matematicas: Diez, Nueve, Ocho Little Library Book. 2nd ed. 2001. (SPA., Illus.). pap. 17.20 (978-0-15-323623-5(X)) Harcourt Schl. Pubs.

—Harcourt Matematicas: El Guante Nuevo de Larry: Math Reader. 2nd ed. 2002. (SPA., Illus.). pap. 4.20 (978-0-15-321734-0(0)) Harcourt Schl. Pubs.

—Harcourt Matematicas: El Oso es Cuadrado Little Big Book. 2nd ed. 2001. (SPA., Illus.). 70.60 (978-0-15-323620-4(5)) Harcourt Schl. Pubs.

—Harcourt Matematicas: El Oso y Cuadrado Little Library Book. 2nd ed. 2001. (SPA., Illus.). pap. 15.20 (978-0-15-323627-3(2)) Harcourt Schl. Pubs.

—Harcourt Matematicas: Las Estaciones Liltle Library Book. 2nd ed. 2001. (SPA., Illus.). pap. 14.80 (978-0-15-323628-0(0)) Harcourt Schl. Pubs.

—Harcourt Matematicas: Las Estaciones Little Big Book. 2nd ed. 2001. (SPA., Illus.). 66.40 (978-0-15-323621-1(3)) Harcourt Schl. Pubs.

—Harcourt Matematicas: Las Muchas Rayas Little Library Book. 2nd ed. 2001. (SPA., Illus.). pap. 16.70 (978-0-15-323625-9(6)) Harcourt Schl. Pubs.

—Harcourt Matematicas: Los Cinco Patitos Little Library Book. 2nd ed. 2001. (SPA., Illus.). pap. 14.80 (978-0-15-323626-6(4)) Harcourt Schl. Pubs.

—Harcourt Matematicas: Por la Manana: Math Reader. 2nd ed. 2002. (SPA., Illus.). pap. 4.20 (978-0-15-321731-9(6)) Harcourt Schl. Pubs.

—Harcourt Matematicas: Sorpresas Solidas: Math Reader. 2nd ed. 2002. (SPA., Illus.). (gr. 2). pap. 4.20 (978-0-15-321730-2(8)) Harcourt Schl. Pubs.

—Harcourt Matematicas: Un Lio en la Parrillada: Math Reader. 2nd ed. 2002. (SPA., Illus.). pap. 4.20 (978-0-15-321733-3(2)) Harcourt Schl. Pubs.

—Harcourt Matematicas: Un Par y Calcetinas Little Library Book. 2nd ed. 2001. (SPA., Illus.). pap. 16.70 (978-0-15-323624-2(8)) Harcourt Schl. Pubs.

—Harcourt Matematicas, Grade 1. 2nd ed. 2003. (Harcourt Matematicas Ser.). (SPA.). (gr. 1 up). Vol. 1. tchr. ed. 140.60 (978-0-15-321616-9(6)); Vol. 2. tchr. ed. 140.60 (978-0-15-321617-6(4)) Harcourt Schl. Pubs.

—Harcourt Matematicas, Grade 2. 2nd ed. 2003. (Harcourt Matematicas Ser.). (SPA.). (gr. 2 up). Vol. 1. tchr. ed. 140.60 (978-0-15-321618-3(2)); Vol. 2. tchr. ed. 140.60 (978-0-15-321619-0(0)) Harcourt Schl. Pubs.

—Harcourt Matematicas, Grade 3. 2nd ed. 2003. (Harcourt Matematicas Ser.). (SPA.). (gr. 3 up). Vol. 1. tchr. ed. 157.50 (978-0-15-321620-6(4)); Vol. 2. tchr. ed. 157.50 (978-0-15-321621-3(2)) Harcourt Schl. Pubs.

—Harcourt Matematicas, Grade 4. 2nd ed. 2003. (Harcourt Matematicas Ser.). (SPA.). (gr. 4 up). Vol. 1. tchr. ed. 158.90 (978-0-15-321622-0(0)); Vol. 2. tchr. ed. 158.90 (978-0-15-321623-7(9)) Harcourt Schl. Pubs.

—Harcourt Matematicas, Grade 4: Practice Workbook. 2nd ed. 2003. (Harcourt Matematicas Ser.). (SPA.). (gr. 4 up). tchr. ed., wbk. ed. 23.30 (978-0-15-321639-8(5)) Harcourt Schl. Pubs.

—Harcourt Matematicas, Grade 5. 2nd ed. 2003. (Harcourt Matematicas Ser.). (SPA.). (gr. 5 up). Vol. 1. tchr. ed. 158.90 (978-0-15-321624-4(7)); Vol. 2. tchr. ed. 158.90 (978-0-15-321625-1(5)) Harcourt Schl. Pubs.

—Harcourt Matematicas, Grade 6. 2nd ed. 2003. (Harcourt Matematicas Ser.). (SPA.). (gr. 6 up). Vol. 1. tchr. ed. 158.90 (978-0-15-321626-8(3)); Vol. 2. tchr. ed. 158.90 (978-0-15-321627-5(1)) Harcourt Schl. Pubs.

—Harcourt Matematicas, Grade K. 2nd ed. 2002. (Harcourt Matematicas Ser.). (SPA.). (gr. k-6). tchr. ed. 299.10 (978-0-15-321615-2(8)) Harcourt Schl. Pubs.

—Harcourt Matematicas, Grade K: Teacher's Resource Book. 2nd ed. 2003. (Harcourt Matematicas Ser.). (SPA.). (gr. k-6). tchr. ed. 63.90 (978-0-15-321680-0(8)) Harcourt Schl. Pubs.

—Harcourt Math: A Pair of Socks Little Book. 2nd ed. 2000. (Illus.). pap. 13.30 (978-0-15-321883-5(5)) Harcourt Schl. Pubs.

—Harcourt Math: Animal Seasons Little Book. 2nd ed. 2000. (Illus.). pap. 11.30 (978-0-15-321888-0(6)) Harcourt Schl. Pubs.

—Harcourt Math: Answer Key/Enrichment Book. 2nd ed. 2002. (Harcourt Math Ser.). (Illus.). (gr. 3 up). pap. 10.60 (978-0-15-324460-5(7)); (gr. 4 up). pap. 10.60 (978-0-15-324461-2(5)); (gr. 5 up). pap. 10.60 (978-0-15-324462-9(3)); (gr. 6 up). pap. 10.60 (978-0-15-324463-6(1)) Harcourt Schl. Pubs.

—Harcourt Math: Bear in a Square Little Book. 2nd ed. 2000. (Illus.). (J). pap. 9.70 (978-0-15-321887-3(8)) Harcourt Schl. Pubs.

—Harcourt Math: CA Challenge Workbook. 2nd ed. 2002. (Illus.). (gr. 3). pap., wbk. ed. 12.00 (978-0-15-320430-2(3)); (gr. 4). pap., wbk. ed. 12.00 (978-0-15-320431-9(1)); (gr. 5). pap., wbk. ed. 12.00 (978-0-15-320432-6(X)); (J). (gr. 6). pap., wbk. ed. 10.60 (978-0-15-320433-3(8)) Harcourt Schl. Pubs.

—Harcourt Math: CA Practice Workbook. 2nd ed. 2002. (Illus.). (gr. 3). pap., wbk. ed. 10.40 (978-0-15-320437-1(0)); (gr. 4). pap., wbk. ed. 10.40 (978-0-15-320438-8(9)); (gr. 5). pap., wbk. ed. 10.40 (978-0-15-320439-5(7)); (gr. 6). pap., wbk. ed. 10.40 (978-0-15-320440-1(0)) Harcourt Schl. Pubs.

—Harcourt Math: CA Problem Solving & Reading Strategy Workbook. 2nd ed. 2002. (Illus.). (gr. 12). pap., wbk. ed. 10.50 (978-0-15-320447-0(8)); (gr. 2). pap., wbk. ed. 10.50 (978-0-15-320448-7(6)); (gr. 4). pap., wbk. ed. 10.50 (978-0-15-320450-0(8)); (gr. 5). pap., wbk. ed. 10.50 (978-0-15-320451-7(6)); (gr. 6). pap., wbk. ed. 11.50 (978-0-15-320452-4(4)) Harcourt Schl. Pubs.

—Harcourt Math: CA Resource Package. 2nd ed. 2002. (Illus.). (J). pap. 842.40 (978-0-15-321842-2(8)) Harcourt Schl. Pubs.

—Harcourt Math: CA Reteaching Workbook. 2nd ed. 2002. (Illus.). (gr. 3). pap., wbk. ed. 11.20 (978-0-15-320443-2(5)); (gr. 4). pap., wbk. ed. 11.20 (978-0-15-320444-9(3)); (gr. 5). pap., wbk. ed. 12.00 (978-0-15-320445-6(1)); (gr. 6). pap., wbk. ed. 12.60 (978-0-15-320446-3(X)) Harcourt Schl. Pubs.

—Harcourt Math: CA Success for English Language Learners. 2nd ed. 2002. (Illus.). (gr. 3). pap. 31.70 (978-0-15-320734-1(5)); (gr. 4). pap. 31.70 (978-0-15-320735-8(3)); (gr. 5). pap. 31.70 (978-0-15-320736-5(1)); (gr. 6). pap. 31.70 (978-0-15-320737-2(X)) Harcourt Schl. Pubs.

—Harcourt Math: CA Unit Book. 2nd ed. 2002. (Illus.). (gr. 1). pap. 37.50 (978-0-15-321834-7(7)); (gr. 2). pap. 37.50 (978-0-15-321841-5(X)) Harcourt Schl. Pubs.

—Harcourt Math: Calculator Handbook. 2nd ed. 2002. (Harcourt Math Ser.). (Illus.). (gr. 3 up). pap. 20.50 (978-0-15-324408-7(9)); (gr. 4 up). pap. 20.50 (978-0-15-324409-4(7)); (gr. 5 up). pap. 20.50 (978-0-15-324410-0(0)); (gr. 6 up). pap. 20.50 (978-0-15-324411-7(9)) Harcourt Schl. Pubs.

—Harcourt Math: Enrichment Book. 2nd ed. 2002. (Harcourt Math Ser.). (Illus.). (gr. 3 up). pap. 12.00 (978-0-15-324454-4(2)); (gr. 4 up). pap. 12.00 (978-0-15-324455-1(0)); (gr. 5 up). pap. 12.80 (978-0-15-324456-8(9)); (gr. 6 up). pap. 13.30 (978-0-15-324457-5(7)) Harcourt Schl. Pubs.

—Harcourt Math: Practice Workbook. 2nd ed. (Harcourt Math Ser.). 2003. (Illus.). (gr. 3 up). wbk. ed. 9.80 (978-0-15-320768-6(X)); 2003. (Illus.). (gr. 4 up). wbk. ed. 9.80 (978-0-15-320769-3(8)); 2003. (Illus.). (gr. 5 up). wbk. ed. 9.80 (978-0-15-320785-3(X)); 2003. (Illus.). (gr. 6 up). wbk. ed. 9.80 (978-0-15-320786-0(8)); 2002. pap. 9.30 (978-0-15-336472-3(6)); 2002. pap., tchr. ed., wbk. ed. 19.00 (978-0-15-336479-2(3)); 2002. (gr. 1). pap., tchr. ed., wbk. ed. 22.00 (978-0-15-336480-8(7)); 2002. (J). (gr. 2). pap. 10.00 (978-0-15-336474-7(2)); 2002. (gr. 2). pap., tchr. ed., wbk. ed. 22.00 (978-0-15-336481-5(5)); 2002. (J). (gr. 3). pap. 10.00 (978-0-15-336475-4(0)); 2002. (gr. 3). pap., tchr. ed., wbk. ed. 22.00 (978-0-15-336482-2(3)); 2002. (J). (gr. 4). pap., wbk. ed. 10.00 (978-0-15-336476-1(9)); 2002. (gr. 4). pap., tchr. ed. 22.00 (978-0-15-336483-9(1)); 2002. (J). (gr. 5). pap., wbk. ed. 10.00 (978-0-15-336477-8(7)); 2002. (J). (gr. 6). pap., wbk. ed. 10.00 (978-0-15-336478-5(5)) Harcourt Schl. Pubs.

—Harcourt Math: Problem Solving & Reading Strategies Workbook. 2nd ed. 2002. (Harcourt Math Ser.). (Illus.). (gr. 1 up). pap., wbk. ed. 10.50 (978-0-15-324472-8(0)); (gr. 2 up). pap., wbk. ed. 10.50 (978-0-15-324473-5(9)) Harcourt Schl. Pubs.

—Harcourt Math: Ten, Nine, Eight Little Book. 2nd ed. 2000. (Illus.). pap. 11.30 (978-0-15-321886-6(X)) Harcourt Schl. Pubs.

—Harcourt Math: Zebra Stripes Little Book. 2nd ed. 2000. (Illus.). (J). pap. 10.60 (978-0-15-321884-2(3)) Harcourt Schl. Pubs.

—Harcourt Math, Grade 1: Problem Solving & Reading Strategies Workbook. 2nd ed. 2002. (Harcourt Math Ser.). (gr. 1 up). pap., tchr. ed., wbk. ed. 21.20 (978-0-15-324474-2(7)) Harcourt Schl. Pubs.

—Harcourt Math, Grade 2: Problem Solving & Reading Strategies Workbook. 2nd ed. 2002. (Harcourt Math Ser.). (gr. 2 up). pap., tchr. ed., wbk. ed. 21.20 (978-0-15-324475-9(5)) Harcourt Schl. Pubs.

—Harcourt School: CA Problem Solving & Reading Strategy Workbook. 2nd ed. 2002. (Illus.). (gr. 3). pap., wbk. ed. 10.50 (978-0-15-320449-4(4)) Harcourt Schl. Pubs.

—Matematicas Mi Ventaja. 99th ed. 1998. (SPA., Illus.). pap. 39.90 (978-0-15-309966-3(6)); (gr. 1). pap. 44.80 (978-0-15-312659-8(0)); (gr. 2). pap. 44.80 (978-0-15-312661-1(2)); (gr. 3). 84.70 (978-0-15-312662-8(0)); (gr. 4). 84.70 (978-0-15-312663-5(9)); (gr. 5). 84.70 (978-0-15-312664-2(7)); (gr. 6). 84.70 (978-0-15-312666-6(3)) Harcourt Schl. Pubs.

—Matematicas Mi Ventaja: Chapter Books. 99th ed. 1998. (SPA., Illus.). pap. 39.90 (978-0-15-311331-4(6)) Harcourt Schl. Pubs.

—Math Advantage: Chapter Book. 99th ed. 1999. (Illus.). pap. 28.40 (978-0-15-311330-7(8)) Harcourt Schl. Pubs.

—Math Advantage: Practice for Stanford 9: West Virginia Edition. 99th ed. 1998. (Illus.). (gr. 4). pap. 9.30 (978-0-15-313612-2(X)); (gr. 5). pap. 9.30 (978-0-15-313613-9(8)); (gr. 6). pap. 9.30 (978-0-15-313614-6(6)); (gr. 7). pap. 9.30 (978-0-15-313616-0(2)); (gr. 8). pap. 9.30 (978-0-15-313617-7(0)) Harcourt Schl. Pubs.

—Math Advantage: Terra Nova: Daily Pracitce. 99th ed. 1998. (Illus.). (gr. 3). pap. 9.60 (978-0-15-313098-4(9)) Harcourt Schl. Pubs.

—Math Advantage: Terra Nova: Daily Practice. 99th ed. 1998. (Illus.). (gr. 1). pap. 6.90 (978-0-15-313094-6(6)); (gr. 2). pap. 6.90 (978-0-15-313096-0(2)); (gr. 4). pap. 9.60 (978-0-15-313099-1(7)); (gr. 5). pap. 9.60 (978-0-15-313101-1(2)); (gr. 6). pap. 10.20 (978-0-15-313102-8(0)); (gr. 7). pap. 10.20 (978-0-15-313103-5(9)); (gr. 8). pap. 10.20 (978-0-15-313104-2(7)) Harcourt Schl. Pubs.

—Stanley's Sticker Stories Guide, Grades K-2. 98th ed. 1998. (Harcourt Ser.). (gr. k-6). pap. 11.00 (978-0-15-307964-1(9)) Harcourt Schl. Pubs.

—Success for Ell: Harcourt Math. 2nd ed. 2002. (gr. 2). pap. 26.60 (978-0-15-336544-7(7)); (gr. 5). pap. 30.80 (978-0-15-336547-8(1)); (gr. 6). pap. 30.80 (978-0-15-336548-5(X)) Harcourt Schl. Pubs.

—Zoo Zillions: User's Guide. 98th ed. 2003. (Mighty Mathtm Ser.). (Illus.). (gr. k-3). pap., pupil's gde. ed. 11.00 (978-0-15-307970-2(3)) Harcourt Schl. Pubs.

Hereford, Jane. Challenge the PACT: South Carolina 5th Grade Mathematics. 1999. (Illus.). 300p. (J). pap. 12.00 (978-0-89892-209-7(7)) Contemporary Publishing Co. of Raleigh, Inc.

—Challenge the PACT: South Carolina 6th Grade Mathematics. 1999. (Illus.). 304p. (J). pap. 12.00 (978-0-89892-196-0(1)) Contemporary Publishing Co. of Raleigh, Inc.

—Challenge the PACT: South Carolina 8th Grade Mathematics. 1999. (Illus.). 300p. (J). pap. 12.00 (978-0-89892-194-6(5)) Contemporary Publishing Co. of Raleigh, Inc.

—The Competitive Edge: Passing the EOG in 3rd Grade Math. 1999. (Illus.). 224p. (J). pap. 12.00 (978-0-89892-186-1(4)) Contemporary Publishing Co. of Raleigh, Inc.

—The Competitive Edge: Passing the EOG in 4th Grade Mathematics. 1999. (Illus.). 228p. (J). pap. 12.00 (978-0-89892-183-0(X)) Contemporary Publishing Co. of Raleigh, Inc.

—The Competitive Edge: Passing the EOG in 5th Grade Mathematics. 1999. (Illus.). 284p. (J). pap. 12.00 (978-0-89892-180-9(5)) Contemporary Publishing Co. of Raleigh, Inc.

—Passing the Georgia High School Graduation Test in Mathematics. 1999. (Illus.). 320p. (J). pap. 12.00 (978-0-89892-188-5(0)) Contemporary Publishing Co. of Raleigh, Inc.

Hoffman, Joan. Math Readiness. rev. ed. 2001. (I Know It! Workbooks Ser.). (Illus.). 32p. (J). (gr. k-1). pap., wbk. ed. 2.49 (978-0-88743-729-8(X) , 02049) School Zone Publishing Co.

Holt, Rinehart and Winston Staff. Building Formulas. 3rd ed. 2003. (Math in Context Ser.). tchr. ed. 31.60 (978-0-03-071721-5(3)) Holt, Rinehart & Winston.

—Digging Numbers: Math/Context. 3rd ed. 2003. (J). tchr. ed. 31.60 (978-0-03-071717-8(5)) Holt, Rinehart & Winston of Canada, Ltd. CAN. *Dist:* Harcourt Canada, Ltd.

—Holt Science & Technology: Math Skills Worksheets. 5th ed. 2004. (Illus.). pap., wbk. ed. 11.60 (978-0-03-035198-3(7)) Holt, Rinehart & Winston.

—Insights & Data: Math/Context. 3rd ed. 2003. (J). tchr. ed. 31.60 (978-0-03-071701-7(9)) Holt, Rinehart & Winston of Canada, Ltd. CAN. *Dist:* Harcourt Canada, Ltd.

—Math Course 1: Middle School: Standard Test Practice. 4th ed. 2002. pap., wbk. ed. 8.40 (978-0-03-070797-1(8)) Holt, Rinehart & Winston.

—Math Course 1: Middle School: Standard Test Practice with Answer Key. 4th ed. 2002. pap., wbk. ed. 12.60 (978-0-03-070798-8(6)) Holt, Rinehart & Winston.

—Number Tools: Math Context. 3rd ed. 2003. (SPA.). (J). pap. 42.66 (978-0-03-072433-6(3)) Holt, Rinehart & Winston of Canada, Ltd. CAN. *Dist:* Harcourt Canada, Ltd.

—Number Tools Vol. 2: Math/Context. 3rd ed. 2003. (SPA.). (J). 42.66 (978-0-03-072428-2(7)) Holt, Rinehart & Winston of Canada, Ltd. CAN. *Dist:* Harcourt Canada, Ltd.

—Number Tools Workbook Math/Contt. 3rd ed. 2003. (J). pap., wbk. ed. 24.66 (978-0-03-072582-1(8)) Holt, Rinehart & Winston of Canada, Ltd. CAN. *Dist:* Harcourt Canada, Ltd.

—Preparing for the Regents Exam in Math: New York Edition. 3rd ed. 2003. (J). pap. 12.20 (978-0-03-068552-1(4)) Holt, Rinehart & Winston.

—Reflections & Numbers: Math/Context. 3rd ed. 2003. (J). tchr. ed. 31.60 (978-0-03-071709-3(4)) Holt, Rinehart & Winston of Canada, Ltd. CAN. *Dist:* Harcourt Canada, Ltd.

—Teaching Math to All Students Package. 4th ed. 2004. 1200.00 (978-0-03-037951-2(2)); 2266.67 (978-0-03-037952-9(0)); 5333.36 (978-0-03-037953-6(9)) Holt, Rinehart & Winston.

—Triangles & Beyond. 3rd ed. 2002. (Math in Context Ser.). tchr. ed. (978-0-85229-898-5(6)) Encyclopaedia Britannica, Inc.

HSP. Practice Activities. 2nd ed. 2002. (First-Place Math Ser.). (gr. k up). pap. 20.80 (978-0-15-335148-8(9)); (gr. 1 up). pap. 19.00 (978-0-15-335149-5(7)); (gr. 2 up). pap. 19.00 (978-0-15-335150-1(0)); (gr. 3 up). pap. 19.00 (978-0-15-335151-8(9)); (gr. 4 up). pap. 19.00 (978-0-15-335152-5(7)); (gr. 5 up). pap. 19.00 (978-0-15-335153-2(5)); (gr. 6 up). pap. 19.00 (978-0-15-335154-9(3)) Harcourt Schl. Pubs.

J. G. Ferguson Publishing Company Staff. Careers in Focus: Mathmatics. 2003. (Careers in Focus Ser.). (Illus.). 192p. (YA). (gr. 6-12). 22.95 (978-0-89434-413-8(7) , Ferguson Publishing Co.) Facts On File, Inc.

Jacobi, Dawn Talluto. Math & Test Taking Grade 5. 2000. (Kelley Wingate Math & Test Taking Ser.). 128p. (gr. 5). pap. 11.99 (978-0-88724-536-7(6) , CD-3755) Carson-Dellosa Publishing Co., Inc.

—Math & Test Taking Grade 6. 2000. (Kelley Wingate Math & Test Taking Ser.). 128p. (gr. 6). pap. 11.99 (978-0-88724-537-4(4) , CD-3756) Carson-Dellosa Publishing Co., Inc.

—Math & Test Taking Grade 7. 2000. (Kelley Wingate Math & Test Taking Ser.). 128p. (gr. 7). pap. 11.99 (978-0-88724-538-1(2) , CD-3757) Carson-Dellosa Publishing Co., Inc.

—Math & Test Taking Grade 8. 2000. (Kelley Wingate Math & Test Taking Ser.). 128p. (gr. 8). pap. 11.99 (978-0-88724-539-8(0) , CD-3758) Carson-Dellosa Publishing Co., Inc.

Jooste, Zonia. Mathematics Matters: Grade 4. 2000. 136p. (gr. 4). pap., tchr. ed. 9.20 (978-0-521-78868-7(4)) Cambridge Univ. Pr.

—Mathematics Matters Grade 4 Learner's Book. 2000. 160p. (gr. 4). pap. 7.35 (978-0-521-78867-0(6)) Cambridge Univ. Pr.

Jooste, Zonia & Macgregor, Fiona. Mathematics Matters Grade 5 Learner's Book. 2001. 144p. pap. 6.90 (978-0-521-75000-4(8)) Cambridge Univ. Pr.

Kiernan, Denise. Sports Math: Slam-Dunk Math Learning with Super-Fun Reproducible Activities That Build Essential, Vol. 1. 1999. (Illus.). 64p. pap. 10.95 (978-0-590-21966-2(9)) Scholastic, Inc.

Konemann Staff. MathMaster 5+ 1999. (Illus.). (gr. 4-7). 19.95 (978-3-8290-3044-1(4)) Konemann.

Lacret-Subirat, Fabian. Lacret HS-Math Self-Tutoring (Solving Word-Problems) 2000. (Illus.). 220p. (YA). (gr. 9-12). pap. 32.00 (978-0-943144-45-0(0)) Lacret Publishing Co.

Lakeshore Learning Materials Staff, contrib. by. Blue Sea Packet. 2000. (J). pap. 19.95 (978-1-929255-67-2(5)) Lakeshore Learning Materials.

Lawrence, H. S. Word Problems, Bk 2. 1999. (Straight Forward Math Ser.). 40p. (J). (gr. 3-6). pap. 3.95 (978-0-931993-42-8(3) , GP-042) Garlic Pr.

Levy, Aaron Uri, ed. Math Practice. 1999. (Kelley Wingate Math Practice Ser.). (Illus.). 128p. (J). (gr. k-1). pap. 11.90 (978-0-88724-529-9(3) , CD-3748); iii, 128p. (J). (gr. k-1). pap. 10.95 (978-0-88724-527-5(7) , CD-3746); 128p. (gr. 4-5). pap. 11.99 (978-0-88724-528-2(5) , CD-3747); 128p. (gr. 6-7). pap. 11.99 (978-0-88724-530-5(7) , CD-3749); 128p. (gr. 7-8). pap. 11.99 (978-0-88724-531-2(5) , CD-3750) Carson-Dellosa Publishing Co., Inc.

Maletsky, Evan A., et al. Carpeta de Recursos Del Capitulo: Chapter Resource Binder. 2nd ed. 2002. (Harcourt Matematicas Ser.). (SPA.). (gr. k-6). pap. 189.60 (978-0-15-325307-2(X)) Harcourt Schl. Pubs.

—Carpeta de Recursos Del Capitulo: Chapter Resource Binders. 2nd ed. 2002. (Harcourt Matematicas Ser.). (SPA.). (gr. 1 up). pap. 358.30 (978-0-15-325308-9(8)); (gr. 2 up). pap. 358.30 (978-0-15-325309-6(6)); (gr. 3 up). pap. 357.10 (978-0-15-325310-2(X)); (gr. 4 up). pap. 365.90 (978-0-15-325311-9(8)); (gr. 5 up). pap. 388.70 (978-0-15-325312-6(6)); (gr. 6 up). pap. 335.70 (978-0-15-325313-3(4)) Harcourt Schl. Pubs.

—Check What You Know: Enrichment Books. 2nd ed. 2002. (Harcourt Math Ser.). (gr. 1 up). pap. 11.20 (978-0-15-324452-0(6)); (gr. 1 up). pap. 10.60 (978-0-15-324458-2(5)); (gr. 2 up). pap. 11.20 (978-0-15-324453-7(4)); (gr. 2 up). pap. 10.60 (978-0-15-324459-9(3)) Harcourt Schl. Pubs.

—Check What You Know: Intervention Practice Books. (Harcourt Math Ser.). 2003. (gr. 3 up). 10.70 (978-0-15-324442-1(9)); 2003. (gr. 4 up). 10.70 (978-0-15-324443-8(7)); 2003. (gr. 5 up). 11.50 (978-0-15-324444-5(5)); 2003. (gr. 6 up). 12.10 (978-0-15-324445-2(3)); 2nd ed. 2002. (gr. 1 up). pap. 11.10 (978-0-15-324440-7(2)); 2nd ed. 2002. (gr. 1 up). pap. 26.10 (978-0-15-324446-9(1)); 2nd ed. 2002. (gr. 2 up). pap. 11.10 (978-0-15-324441-4(0)); 2nd ed. 2002. (gr. 2 up). pap. 26.10 (978-0-15-324447-6(X)); 2nd ed. 2002. (gr. 3 up). pap. 30.90 (978-0-15-324448-3(8)); 2nd ed. 2002. (gr. 4 up). pap. 30.90 (978-0-15-324449-0(6)); 2nd ed. 2002. (gr. 5 up). pap. 30.90 (978-0-15-324450-6(X)); 2nd ed. 2002. (gr. 6 up). pap. 30.90 (978-0-15-324451-3(8)) Harcourt Schl. Pubs.

—Estrategias y Actividades de Intervencion Guia Del Maestro Con Hojas Reproducibles: Teacher's Guide with Copying Masters. 2nd ed. 2002. (Harcourt Matematicas Ser.). (SPA.). (gr. 1 up). pap., tchr. ed. 103.80 (978-0-15-321766-1(9)); (gr. 2 up). pap., tchr. ed. 103.80 (978-0-15-321767-8(7)); (gr. 3 up). pap., tchr. ed. 103.80 (978-0-15-321768-5(5)); (gr. 4 up). pap., tchr. ed. 115.50 (978-0-15-321769-2(3)); (gr. 5 up). pap., tchr. ed. 115.50 (978-0-15-321770-8(7)); (gr. 6 up). pap., tchr. ed. 115.50 (978-0-15-321771-5(5)) Harcourt Schl. Pubs.

—Harcourt Electronic Test System: Math Practice & Assessment. 2nd ed. 2001. (Harcourt Ser.). (gr. 1 up). pap. 10.70 (978-0-15-322160-6(7)); (gr. 2 up). pap. 10.70 (978-0-15-322161-3(5)); (gr. 3 up). pap. 10.70 (978-0-15-322162-0(3)); (gr. 4 up). pap. 10.70 (978-0-15-322163-7(1)); (gr. 5 up). pap. 10.70 (978-0-15-322164-4(X)); (gr. 6 up). pap. 10.70 (978-0-15-322165-1(8)) Harcourt Schl. Pubs.

M
N
O

—Harcourt Math Kindergarten: How Many? 2nd ed. 2000. (Harcourt Math Ser.). (gr. k-6). pap. 14.60 (978-0-15-320486-9(9)) Harcourt Schl. Pubs.

McCallum, Ann. A Kid's Multicultural Math Adventure: Amazing Activities to Explore Math's Global Roots! Norton, Carolyn, illus. 2004. (Williamson Multicultural Kids Can! Book Ser.). 128p. (J). pap. 14.95 (978-1-885593-92-4(9), Williamson Bks.) Ideals Pubns.

McGraw-Hill Staff. Advanced Mathematical Concepts: Pre-calculus with Applications, Student Edition. 6th ed. 2003. (gr. 6-12). stu. ed. 94.00 (978-0-07-860861-2(9), 9780078608612) Glencoe/McGraw-Hill.

—Defeat Dirty D: Grade 3 Math. 1999. (J). (gr. 2-3). pap. 19.95 (978-1-57768-313-1(7)) School Specialty Publishing.

—Freezing Frenzy: Math. 1999. (J). (gr. k-1). 19.95 (978-1-57768-333-9(1)) School Specialty Publishing.

—Mathematics: Applications & Concepts, Course 1, Spanish Student Edition. 2003. (SPA.). (gr. 6-12). stu. ed. 71.96 (978-0-07-860787-5(6), 9780078607875) Glencoe/McGraw-Hill.

—Mathematics: Applications & Concepts, Course 2, Spanish Student Edition. 2003. (SPA.). (gr. 6-12). stu. ed. 73.32 (978-0-07-860788-2(4), 9780078607882) Glencoe/McGraw-Hill.

—Mathematics: Applications & Concepts, Course 3, Spanish Student Edition. 2003. (SPA.). (C). (gr. 6-12). stu. ed. 73.32 (978-0-07-860789-9(2), 9780078607899) Glencoe/McGraw-Hill.

—Meet Mudflat Joe: Math. 1999. (J). (gr. 5). 19.95 (978-1-57768-315-5(3)) School Specialty Publishing.

—Quick Review Math Handbook Bk. 1: Hot Words, Hot Topics, Spanish. 2003. (SPA.). (C). (gr. 6-12). stu. ed. 37.32 (978-0-07-860751-6(5), 9780078607516) Glencoe/McGraw-Hill.

MCP Mathematics, Level E. 2003. (J). 28.50 (978-0-8136-3113-4(0)) Modern Curriculum Pr.

MCP Mathematics. 2005. (J). (gr. k-6). tchr. ed. 29.95 (978-0-7652-6063-5(8)); tchr. ed. 29.95 (978-0-7652-6065-9(4)); stu. ed. 28.50 (978-0-7652-6064-2(6)); stu. ed. 28.50 (978-0-7652-6062-8(X)) Seymour, Dale Pubns.

Miles Kelly Staff. Science & Maths. 2003. (Flip Quiz Ser.). (Illus.). 38p. (J). (gr. 10-11). spiral bd. 5.95 (978-1-84236-032-3(9)); (gr. 11-12). spiral bd. 5.95 (978-1-84236-033-0(7)); (gr. 7-9). spiral bd. 5.95 (978-1-84236-030-9(2)); (gr. 9-10). spiral bd. 5.95 (978-1-84236-031-6(0)) Miles Kelly Publishing, Ltd. GBR. *Dist:* Independent Pubs. Group.

Moredock, Janet, et al. Handy Homework Helper. 2005. (Illus.). 128p. (J). ***978-1-4127-1179-1(7))** Publications International, Ltd.

Mumford, Jeanette. Mathematics Direct 2: Planning Pack. 2002. (Cambridge Mathematics Direct Ser.). (Illus.). 42p. pap. (978-0-521-01170-9(1)) Cambridge Univ. Pr.

Muschla, Gary Robert & Muschla, Judith A. Math Games: 180 Reproducible Activities to Motivate, Excite, & Challenge Students, Grades 6-12. 2004. (Educational Trade Ser.). 240p. pap. 29.95 (978-0-7879-7081-9(6), Jossey-Bass) Wiley, John & Sons, Inc.

Novelli, Joan. Irresistible 1- 2- 3's: 50 Easy, Fun, Multi-Sensory Activities to Help All Kids Explore & Learn Numbers. 2000. (Little Learners Ser.). (Illus.). 48p. pap. 8.95 (978-0-439-04095-2(7)) Scholastic, Inc.

Nurk, Enn & Telgmaa, Aksel. Mathematics 6. Harte, Will, tr. from RUS. 2003. Orig. Title: Matematika 6. Uchebnik Dlya Obscheobrazovatel'Nykh Uchebnikh Zavedenij. (Illus.). ix, 310p. per. 38.50 (978-0-9740234-0-3(X)) Perpendicular Pr.

Opie, Brenda & McAvinn, Douglas. Masterminds Skills Boosters for the Reluctant Math Student: Reproducible Skill Builders & Higher Order Thinking Activities Based on NCTM Standards. McAvinn, Douglas, illus. 2000. (Riddle Math Ser.). (Illus.). 96p. (J). (gr. 4-8). pap. 10.95 (978-0-86530-448-2(3), IP 200-7) Incentive Pubns., Inc.

Palmer, Martha. Transition Math. 2001. (Teacher Edition Wkbks.). (Illus.). 32p. (J). (gr. k-1). pap. 3.99 (978-0-88743-398-6(7), 02867) School Zone Publishing Co.

Pedigo, Patricia & DeSanti, Roger. Math & Test Taking Grade 1. 2000. (Kelley Wingate Math & Test Taking Ser.). 128p. (gr. 1). pap. 11.99 (978-0-88724-532-9(3), CD-3751) Carson-Dellosa Publishing Co., Inc.

—Math & Test Taking Grade 2. 2000. (Kelley Wingate Math & Test Taking Ser.). 128p. (gr. 2). pap. 11.99 (978-0-88724-533-6(1), CD-3752) Carson-Dellosa Publishing Co., Inc.

—Math & Test Taking Grade 3. 2000. (Kelley Wingate Math & Test Taking Ser.). 128p. (gr. 3). pap. 11.99 (978-0-88724-534-3(X), CD-3753) Carson-Dellosa Publishing Co., Inc.

—Math & Test Taking Grade 4. 2000. (Kelley Wingate Math & Test Taking Ser.). 128p. (gr. 4). pap. 11.99 (978-0-88724-535-0(8), CD-3754) Carson-Dellosa Publishing Co., Inc.

Pegoraro, Laura. We'll Practice Addition 1. Petertil Design Partners Staff, illus. 1998. (Powertools for Kids Ser.). 4p. (J). (ps-2). pap., wbk. ed. 4.95 (978-1-58220-000-2(9), 32101, PowerTools for Kids) Navigator Systems, Inc.

—We'll Practice Addition 2. Petertil Design Partners Staff, illus. 1998. (Powertools for Kids Ser.: No. 5). 4p. (J). (gr. 1-4). pap., wbk. ed. 4.95 (978-1-58220-004-0(1), 32105, PowerTools for Kids) Navigator Systems, Inc.

—We'll Practice Division. Petertil Design Partners Staff, illus. 1998. (Powertools for Kids Ser.: No. 4). 4p. (J). (gr. k-4). pap., wbk. ed. 4.95 (978-1-58220-003-3(3), 32104, PowerTools for Kids) Navigator Systems, Inc.

—We'll Practice More Math. Petertil Design Partners Staff, illus. 1998. (Powertools for Kids Ser.: No. 8). 4p. (J). (gr. 2-5). pap., wbk. ed. 4.95 (978-1-58220-007-1(6), 32108, PowerTools for Kids) Navigator Systems, Inc.

—We'll Practice Multiplication 2. Petertil Design Partners Staff, illus. 1998. (Powertools for Kids Ser.: No. 7). 4p. (J). (gr. 1-4). pap., wbk. ed. 4.95 (978-1-58220-006-4(8), 32107, PowerTools for Kids) Navigator Systems, Inc.

—We'll Practice Subtraction 1. Petertil Design Partners Staff, illus. 1998. (Powertools for Kids Ser.: No. 2). 4p. (J). (ps-3). pap., wbk. ed. 4.95 (978-1-58220-001-9(7), 32102, PowerTools for Kids) Navigator Systems, Inc.

—We'll Practice Subtraction 2. Petertil Design Partners Staff, illus. 1998. (Powertools for Kids Ser.: No. 6). 4p. (J). (gr. 1-4). pap., wbk. ed. 4.95 (978-1-58220-005-7(X), 32106, PowerTools for Kids) Navigator Systems, Inc.

Pegoraro, Laura, ed. We'll Practice Multiplication 1. Petertil Design Partners Staff, illus. 1998. (Powertools for Kids Ser.: No. 3). 4p. (J). (gr. 1-3). pap., wbk. ed. 4.95 (978-1-58220-002-6(5), 32103, PowerTools for Kids) Navigator Systems, Inc.

Primary Grade Challenge Math. 2003. 311p. (J). per. 24.95 (978-0-9679915-3-5(6)) Hickory Grove Pr.

Read & Learn Math Collection, 17 bks., Set. 2003. (Illus.). (J). (ps-1). lib. bdg. 314.50 (978-1-4034-4606-0(7)) Heinemann Library.

Rocklin, Joanne & Burns, Marilyn. The Incredibly Awesome Box. Pillo, Cary, illus. 2000. (Hello Reader! Math Ser.). (J). pap. 3.99 (978-0-439-09955-4(2)) Scholastic, Inc.

School Zone Publishing. Transition Math. 2003. (J). (gr. k-1). cd-rom 19.99 (978-1-58947-911-1(4)) School Zone Publishing Co.

School Zone Publishing Company Staff. Grades 3-4 Big Get Ready! 2002. (Big Get Ready Ser.). (Illus.). 320p. (J). (gr. 3-4). pap. 9.99 (978-1-58947-017-0(6), 06320) School Zone Publishing Co.

School Zone Staff, ed. Third Grade Scholar. 2005. (Illus.). 128p. (J). (gr. k-3). pap. 7.99 (978-1-58947-015-6(X), 02466) School Zone Publishing Co.

Schymkiw, Gunter. Math Speed Tests Vol. 1: Reinforcing Essential Table Facts, 2 vols. 2000. 96p. (J). (gr. 1-3). pap. 8.95 (978-1-58324-058-8(6), World Teachers Pr.) Didax Educational Resources, Inc.

—Math Speed Tests Vol. 2: Reinforcing Essential Table Facts, 2 vols. 2000. 96p. (J). (gr. 3-6). pap. 8.95 (978-1-58324-059-5(4), World Teachers Pr.) Didax Educational Resources, Inc.

Silbey, Robyn. Get Ready to Teach Math Gr2. 2004. 144p. (J). (gr. 2 up). pap. 15.99 (978-0-7682-2932-5(4), FS99311) Schaffer, Frank Pubns.

Slamang, Moeneba, et al. Mathematics Matters Grade 6 Learner's Book. 2002. (Illus.). 144p. pap., stu. ed. 5.05 (978-0-521-75317-3(1)) Cambridge Univ. Pr.

Slavin, Robert E. Introduction to Division. 1998. (TAI Mathematics Ser.). (J). pap. 7.50 (978-0-88106-156-7(5), M004) Charlesbridge Publishing, Inc.

—Introduction to Multiplication. 1998. (TAI Mathematics Ser.). (J). pap. 7.50 (978-0-88106-155-0(7), M003) Charlesbridge Publishing, Inc.

Stamper, Judith Bauer. Space Math. Andriani, Vincent, illus. 2000. (Scholastic At-Home Phonics Reading Program Ser.: Vol. 49). 24p. (J). (978-0-590-68836-9(7)) Scholastic, Inc.

Steck-Vaughn Staff. Just Add One Big Book. 2002. (Illus.). pap. (978-0-7398-5982-7(X)) Steck-Vaughn.

Straker, Anita. Home Maths. 2nd rev. ed. 1998. (Illus.). 32p. pap. 6.00 (978-0-521-65550-7(1)); 48p. pap. 6.00 (978-0-521-65552-1(8)); 32p. pap. 6.00 (978-0-521-65553-8(6)) Cambridge Univ. Pr.

—Home Maths: Ages 6-7. 2nd rev. ed. 1998. (Illus.). 32p. pap. 6.00 (978-0-521-65556-9(0)) Cambridge Univ. Pr.

—Mental Maths. 2nd rev. ed. 1998. (Illus.). 32p. pap. 7.00 (978-0-521-65561-3(7)); pap. 6.00 (978-0-521-65562-0(5)) Cambridge Univ. Pr.

Test-Taking Practice for Reading & Math: With Open-Ended Questions & Scoring Rubrics. 2000. (Illus.). 80p. (gr. 3-5). pap. 10.99 (978-0-88724-564-0(1), CD-0052) Carson-Dellosa Publishing Co., Inc.

Walsh, Kieran. Money Math. 2003. (Illus.). 48p. (J). 29.93 (978-1-58952-381-4(4)) Rourke Publishing, LLC.

Willis, Shirley. Dime Cuanto Pesa. 2000. (gr. k-3). (SPA.). lib. bdg. 14.10 (978-0-613-72666-5(9)); (J). 12.75 (978-0-606-20148-3(3)) Tandem Library Bks.

—Dime Que Tan Lejos Esta de Aqui. 2000. (gr. k-3). (SPA.). lib. bdg. 14.10 (978-0-613-72672-6(3)); (J). 12.75 (978-0-606-20153-7(X)) Tandem Library Bks.

Zaslavsky, Claudia. Number Sense & Nonsense: Building Math Creativity & Confidence Through Number Play. 2001. (Illus.). 160p. (J). (gr. 3-7). pap. 14.95 (978-1-55652-378-6(5)) Chicago Review Pr., Inc.

MATINICUS ROCK LIGHTHOUSE (ME.)

Keep the Lights Burning. 9.95 (978-1-59112-293-7(7)) Live Oak Media.

Roop, Peter & Roop, Connie. Manten las Luces Encendidas, Abbie. Hanson, Peter E., illus. 2005. (Yo Solo - Historia (on My Own - History) Ser.).Tr. of Keep the Lights Burning, Abbie. (SPA.). 40p. (J). (gr. 2-5). lib. bdg. 25.26 (978-0-8225-3098-5(8), Ediciones Lerner) Lerner Publishing Group.

MATISSE, HENRI, 1869-1954

Flux, Paul. Henri Matisse. 2002. (Life & Work of... Ser.). (Illus.). 32p. (J). (gr. k-2). lib. bdg. 22.79 (978-1-58810-604-9(7)) Heinemann Library.

—The Life & Work of Henri Matisse, Set 2. 2002. (Illus.). 32p. (J). (gr. k-2). pap. 6.50 (978-1-4034-0002-4(4), 91620) Heinemann Library.

Hartland, Jessie, illus. Henri Matisse: Drawing with Scissors. 2002. (J). (ps-ps). lib. bdg. 14.15 (978-0-613-45270-0(4)) Tandem Library Bks.

Hollein, Max & Hollein, Nina. Matisse: Cut-Out Fun with Matisse. 2003. (Adventures in Art Ser.). (Illus.). 38p. (gr. 5 up). 14.95 (978-3-7913-2858-4(1)) Prestel Publishing.

Hopps, Walter, ed. & contrib. by. Henri Matisse. Hopps, Walter, contrib. by. 2002. (Art Ed Books & Kits Ser.). (Illus.). 24p. (J). 19.95 (978-0-8109-6794-6(4)) Abrams, Harry N., Inc.

Hyde, Margaret E., ed. Matisse for Kids. 2004. (Great Art for Kids Ser.). (Illus.). 10p. (J). pap. 8.95 (978-1-58980-204-9(7)) Pelican Publishing Co., Inc.

Le Tord, Bijou. A Bird or Two: A Story about Henri Matisse. Le Tord, Bijou, illus. 2004. (Illus.). 32p. (gr. 2-7). 17.00 (978-0-8028-5184-0(3)) Eerdmans, William B. Publishing Co.

Niepold, Mil & Verdu, Jeanyves. Ooh! Matisse. 2007. (Illus.). 48p. (J). (ps-k). 14.95 ***978-1-58246-227-1(5)**, Tricycle Pr.) Ten Speed Pr.

O'Connor, Jane. Henri Matisse: Drawing with Scissors. Hartland, Jessie, illus. 2002. (Smart about Art Ser.). 32p. (J). (gr. k-4). pap. 5.99 (978-0-448-42519-1(X), Grosset & Dunlap) Penguin Group (USA) Inc.

Stephens, Pamela Geiger. Dropping in on Matisse. McNeill, Jim, illus. 2004. 32p. (J). (978-1-56290-322-0(5)) Crystal Productions.

Sturm, Ellen. Matisse. 2003. (Masterpieces, Artists & Their Works). (Illus.). 24p. (J). lib. bdg. 19.93 (978-0-7368-2227-5(5), Bridgestone Bks.) Capstone Pr., Inc.

Welton, Jude. Henri Matisse. 2002. (Artists in Their Time Ser.). (Illus.). (J). (gr. 5-7). 46p. pap. 6.95 (978-0-531-16621-5(X)); 48p. pap. 23.50 (978-0-531-12228-0(X)) Scholastic Library Publishing. (Watts, Franklin).

—Henri Matisse. 2002. (gr. 5-8). lib. bdg. 15.25 (978-0-613-54241-8(X)) Tandem Library Bks.

MATRIMONY

see Marriage

MATTER

Anderson, Lynne. States of Matter. 2003. (Early Connections Ser.). (J). pap. 33.00 (978-1-4108-1083-0(6)) Benchmark Education Co.

Ansary, Mir Tamim & Bryant-Mole, Karen. Matter: Solids, Liquids & Gasses. 2002. (Science All Around Me Ser.). (Illus.). 24p. (J). (gr. 1-3). pap. 6.50 (978-1-4034-0053-6(9), 91497) Heinemann Library.

Bailey, Jacqui. How Can Solids Be Changed? 2007. (Illus.). 30p. (J). ***978-1-58340-930-5(0))** Smart Apple Media.

Baldwin. States of Matter 6-Pack. 2004. (Illus.). pap. 45.90 (978-1-4109-0947-3(6)) Raintree.

Barkan, Joanne. What Is Density? 2006. 32p. (YA). (gr. 1-2). pap. 4.95 (978-0-516-24660-4(7), Children's Pr.) Scholastic Library Publishing.

Benchmark Education Staff. Matter Is Everywhere: Solids, Liquids, & Gases. 2005. 2.00 ***978-1-4108-4658-7(X))** Benchmark Education Co.

—Measuring Matter: Solids, Liquids, & Gases. 2005. 2.00 ***978-1-4108-4651-8(2))** Benchmark Education Co.

—This Is Matter: Solids, Liquids, & Gases. 2005. 2.00 ***978-1-4108-4644-0(X))** Benchmark Education Co.

Benchmark Education Staff, compiled by. Matter. 2006. spiral bd. 330.00 ***978-1-4108-7013-1(8));** 2006. spiral bd. 139.00 ***978-1-4108-7032-2(4));** 2006. spiral bd. 95.00 ***978-1-4108-7060-5(X));** 2005. (J). spiral bd. 265.00 ***978-1-4108-5757-6(3))** Benchmark Education Co.

—Science Theme: Matter. 2005. spiral bd. 115.00 ***978-1-4108-5311-0(X))** Benchmark Education Co.

Curry, Don L. What Is Matter? (Rookie Read-About Science Ser.). (J). 2005. (Illus.). 32p. (gr. 1-2). pap. 4.95 (978-0-516-24667-3(4)); 2004. 20.50 (978-0-516-23620-9(2)) Scholastic Library Publishing. (Children's Pr.).

Dalton, Cindy Devine. Atoms. 2001. (How Can I Experiment With? Ser.). (Illus.). 32p. (J). (gr. 1-4). lib. bdg. 28.50 (978-1-58952-010-3(6)) Rourke Publishing, LLC.

Dorling Kindersley Publishing Staff & Cooper, Christopher. Matter. 1999. (Eyewitness Bks.). (Illus.). 64p. (J). (gr. 3-7). 15.99 (978-0-7894-4886-6(6)) Dorling Kindersley Publishing, Inc.

Fleisher, Paul & Seeley, Tim. Matter & Energy: Principles of Matter & Thermodynamics. 2005. (Secrets of the Universe Ser.). (Illus.). 80p. (gr. 6-12). 25.26 (978-0-8225-2986-6(6)) Lerner Publishing Group.

Freeman, Marcia S. Everything under the Sun. 2005. (Everything Science Ser.). (Illus.). 24p. (gr. 1-4). 14.95 (978-1-59515-122-3(2)) Rourke Publishing, LLC.

Fullick, Ann. Matter. 2003. (Science Topics Ser.). (Illus.). 32p. (YA). (gr. 6-8). lib. bdg. 24.22 (978-1-57572-767-7(6)) Heinemann Library.

Gifford, Clive. Materials: Liquids, Solids, Gases, Properties & Their Uses. 2005. (Kingfisher Young Knowledge Ser.). (Illus.). 48p. (J). (gr. k-3). 9.95 (978-0-7534-5867-9(5), Kingfisher) Houghton Mifflin Co. Trade & Reference Div.

Glover, David. Solids & Liquids: Science Facts & Experiments. 2002. (gr. k-3). lib. bdg. 16.40 (978-0-613-90580-0(6)) Tandem Library Bks.

Holt, Rinehart and Winston Staff. Holt Science & Technology Chptr. 18: Properties of Matter: Chapter Resources - Tennessee Edition. 3rd ed. 2003. (YA). pap. 11.40 (978-0-03-069151-5(6)) Holt, Rinehart & Winston.

—Holt Science & Technology Chptr. 19: States of Matter: Chapter Resources - Tennessee Edition. 3rd ed. 2003. (YA). pap. 11.40 (978-0-03-069152-2(4)) Holt, Rinehart & Winston.

—Holt Science & Technology No. 1: Matter & Forces Resources: Texas Edition - Grade 7. 2nd ed. 2001. pap. 26.00 (978-0-03-064858-8(0)) Holt, Rinehart & Winston.

—Holt Science & Technology No. 1: Matter & Interactions Resources: Texas Edition - Grade 8. 2nd ed. 2001. pap. 26.00 (978-0-03-064868-7(8)) Holt, Rinehart & Winston.

—Holt Science & Technology 2002 Pt. L: Matter - Intermediate. 2nd ed. 2002. 18.60 (978-0-03-064799-4(1)) Holt, Rinehart & Winston.

—Holt Science Spectrum Chptr. 3: States of Matter. 4th ed. Date not set. pap. 11.20 (978-0-03-068586-6(9)) Holt, Rinehart & Winston.

Hunter, Rebecca M. Matter. 2000. (Discovering Science Ser.). (Illus.). 32p. (J). (gr. 3-5). lib. bdg. 25.69 (978-0-7398-2969-1(6)) Raintree.

Kjelle, Marylou Morano. The Properties of Metals. 2007. (Library of Physical Sciences). (Illus.). 24p. (J). pap. (978-1-4042-2164-2(6), PowerKids Pr.) Rosen Publishing Group, Inc., The.

—The Properties of Salts. 2007. (Library of Physical Science). (Illus.). 24p. (J). lib. bdg. (978-1-4042-3425-3(X), PowerKids Pr.) Rosen Publishing Group, Inc., The.

—The Properties of Solids. 2007. (Library of Physical Sciences). (Illus.). 24p. (J). lib. bdg. (978-1-4042-3421-5(7), PowerKids Pr.) Rosen Publishing Group, Inc., The.

Larson, Daniel T. The Nature of Matter. 2007. (Physics in Action Ser.). 112p. (gr. 9). 30.00 ***978-0-7910-8929-3(0)**, Chelsea Hse.) Facts On File, Inc.

Lilly, Melinda. Solid, Liquid, & Gas. Thompson, Scott M., illus. 2003. 24p. (J). 20.64 (978-1-58952-648-8(1)) Rourke Publishing, LLC.

Manolis, Kay. Matter. 2007. (Illus.). 24p. (J). lib. bdg. 19.95 ***978-1-60014-130-0(7))** Bellwether Media.

Matos, Rebecca. Matter Is Everywhere: Solids, Liquids, & Gases. 2005. 42.00 ***978-1-4108-4610-5(5))** Benchmark Education Co.

—Measuring Matter: Solids, Liquids, & Gases. 2005. 39.00 ***978-1-4108-4603-7(2))** Benchmark Education Co.

—This Is Matter: Solids, Liquids, & Gases. 2005. 39.00 ***978-1-4108-4596-2(6))** Benchmark Education Co.

Matter. (Our Physical World Ser.). 24p. (J). 6.95 (978-0-7368-5157-2(7)) Capstone Pr., Inc.

Matter. (Amazing Science Ser.). 24p. (J). 7.95 (978-1-4048-0344-2(0)) Picture Window Bks.

Matter. 2001. (Physical Science Ser.). (J). (gr. k-12). vinyl bd. 4.95 (978-1-58845-115-6(1)); 32p. (gr. 2-3). 4.99 (978-1-56822-677-4(2), IF20848) School Specialty Publishing.

Matter. 2002. (Super Science Activities Ser.). 48p. (J). (gr. 2-5). 7.99 (978-0-7439-3660-6(4), 3660) Teacher Created Materials, Inc.

McLuskey, Krista. The Science of Liquids & Solids. 2001. (Living Science Ser.). (Illus.). 32p. (J). (gr. 2 up). lib. bdg. 24.67 (978-0-8368-2789-7(9)) Stevens, Gareth Inc.

Morgan, Sally. Energy. 2007. ***978-1-4034-9924-0(1)**; pap. ***978-1-4034-9932-5(2))** Heinemann Library.

—From Greek Atoms to Quarks: Discovering Atoms. 2007. (Chain Reactions Ser.). (Illus.). 64p. (YA). (gr. 6-9). lib. bdg. 34.29 ***978-1-4034-9551-8(3))** Heinemann Library.

Murray, Julie. Matter. 2007. (Illus.). 24p. (J). 21.35 (978-1-59679-828-1(9)) ABDO Publishing Co.

Oxlade, Chris. Atoms. (Chemicals in Action Ser.). 48p. (J). (gr. 6-8). 2002. (Illus.). lib. bdg. 25.64 (978-1-58810-195-2(9)); 2nd ed. 2007. lib. bdg. 22.00 ***978-1-4329-0051-9(X))** Heinemann Library.

Oxlade, Chris. States of Matter. rev. ed. 2007. (Chemicals in Action Ser.). 48p. (YA). (gr. 6-8). 22.00 ***978-1-4329-0055-7(2))** Heinemann Library.

Parker, Janice. The Science of Liquids & Solids. 2003. (Living Science Ser.). (Illus.). 32p. (J). (gr. 1-3). pap. 7.95 (978-1-930954-11-3(5)) Weigl Pubs., Inc.

Riley, Peter D. Materials & Matter. 2005. (Illus.). 32p. (J). (gr. 4-7). lib. bdg. 27.10 (978-1-58340-716-5(2)) Smart Apple Media.

Rivera, Sheila. Cutting. 2007. (First Step Nonfiction Ser.). (J). pap. (978-0-8225-6413-3(0)) Lerner Publishing Group.

—Dissolving. 2007. (First Step Nonfiction Ser.). (J). pap. (978-0-8225-6414-0(9)) Lerner Publishing Group.

—Heating. 2007. (First Step Nonfiction Ser.). (Illus.). 8p. (J). pap. (978-0-8225-6415-7(7)) Lerner Publishing Group.

Roca, Nuria. What Are Things Made Of? Curto, Rosa M., illus. 2007. (What Do You Know about? Bks.). 36p. (J). (gr. k-1). pap. 6.99 (978-0-7641-3651-1(8)) Barron's Educational Series, Inc.

Royston, Angela. Solids, Liquids, & Gases. 2002. (gr. k-3). lib. bdg. 15.25 (978-0-613-86993-5(1)) Tandem Library Bks.

Science, Rookie Read-About Science: Physical Science. 2004. (Illus.). 304.00 (978-0-516-29323-3(0)) Scholastic Library Publishing.

Silverman, Buffy. State of Confusion. 2007. (J). ***978-1-4109-2851-1(9)**; pap. ***978-1-4109-2868-9(3))** Steck-Vaughn.

Slade, Suzanne. The Structure of Atoms. 2007. (Illus.). 24p. (J). pap. ***978-1-4042-2161-1(1)**, PowerKids Pr.) Rosen Publishing Group, Inc., The.

Stille, Darlene R. Matter & Material. 2004. (Science Around Us Ser.). (Illus.). 32p. (J). (gr. 2-6). 27.07 (978-1-59296-223-5(8)) Child's World, Inc.

Sullivan, Erin Ash. Measuring Matter. 2005. (Navigators Ser.). (J). pap. 38.00 ***978-1-4108-5070-6(6))** Benchmark Education Co.

Trumbauer, Lisa. What Are Atoms? 2005. (Rookie Read-About Science Ser.). (Illus.). 32p. (J). (gr. 1-2). pap. 4.95 (978-0-516-24665-9(8), Children's Pr.) Scholastic Library Publishing.

Walker, Denise. Materials. 2007. ***978-1-58340-817-9(7))** Smart Apple Media.

Walker, Sally M. La Materia (Matter) 2007. (Libros de Energía para madrugadores (Early Bird Energy) Ser.). (SPA.). 48p. (J). (gr. 2-5). lib. bdg. 26.60 ***978-0-8225-7721-8(6)**, Ediciones Lerner) Lerner Publishing Group.

Webster, Christine. Matter. 2004. (First Facts Ser.). 24p. (J). lib. bdg. 21.26 (978-0-7368-2617-4(3)) Capstone Pr., Inc.

Whitehouse, Patricia. Matter & Energy. 2007. (J). ***978-1-4034-7917-4(8))** Heinemann Library.

Young, June. Energy Is Everywhere. 2006. 32p. (gr. 1-2). (YA). pap. 4.95 (978-0-516-28003-5(1)); (Illus.). (J). 20.50 (978-0-516-25902-4(4)) Scholastic Library Publishing. (Children's Pr.).

Zoehfeld, Kathleen Weidner. What Is the World Made Of? All about Solids, Liquids, & Gases. Meisel, Paul, illus. 1998. (Let's-Read-and-Find-Out Science Ser.). 32p. (J). (gr. k-4). pap. 5.99 (978-0-06-445163-5(1)) HarperCollins Pubs.

—What Is the World Made Of? All about Solids, Liquids, & Gases. Meisel, Paul, illus. 1998. 32p. (J). (ps-ps). lib. bdg. 13.00 (978-0-613-12263-4(1)) Tandem Library Bks.

MATTER—PROPERTIES

Baldwin. States of Matter. 2004. (Matter & Materials Ser.). (Illus.). pap. 8.50 (978-1-4109-0940-4(9)) Raintree.

Baldwin, Carol. States of Matter. 2004. (Matter & Materials Ser.). (Illus.). 48p. 28.56 (978-1-4109-0553-6(5)) Raintree.

—States of Matter. 2005. (J). (978-1-4109-1675-4(8)); pap. (978-1-4109-1682-2(0)) Steck-Vaughn.

Ballard, Carol. Solids, Liquids, & Gases: From Air to Stone. 2003. (Science Answers Ser.). (Illus.). 32p. (J). pap. 7.50 (978-1-4034-3552-1(9)); lib. bdg. 22.79 (978-1-4034-0955-3(2)) Heinemann Library.

Barkan, Joanne. What Is Density? 2006. (Rookie Read-About Science Ser.). (Illus.). 32p. (J). (gr. 1-2). 20.50 (978-0-516-23618-6(0) , Children's Pr.) Scholastic Library Publishing.

Bauer, David. Everything is Matter! 2003. (Yellow Umbrella Books for Early Readers). (Illus.). 17p. (J). 15.93 (978-0-7368-2942-7(3)); pap. (978-0-7368-2901-4(6)) Yellow Umbrella Pr.

—Todo Es Materia. 2005. (Yellow Umbrella Books). (SPA., Illus.). 17p. 15.93 (978-0-7368-4160-3(1)) Yellow Umbrella Pr.

Bayrock, Fiona. States of Matter: A Question & Answer Book. 2006. (Fact Finders Ser.). (Illus.). 32p. (J). (978-0-7368-5448-1(7)) Capstone Pr., Inc.

Blevins, Wiley. Is It Hot? Is It Hot? 2003. (Compass Point Phonics Readers Ser.). (Illus.). 16p. (J). (gr. 1 up). 13.26 (978-0-7565-0510-3(0)) Compass Point Bks.

Brannon, Barbara. Discover Solids. 2005. 39.00 (***978-1-4108-5117-8(6)***) Benchmark Education Co.

Clark, John Owen Edward & Hantula, Richard. Matter & Materials. 2006. (Real World Science Ser.). (Illus.). 32p. (J). 24.67 (978-0-8368-6307-9(0)) Stevens, Gareth Inc.

Claybourne, Anna. Microworlds; Unlocking the Secrets of Atoms & Molecules. 2008. (J). (***978-1-60044-606-1(X)***) Rourke Publishing, LLC.

Curry, Don L. What Is Mass? 2005. (Rookie Read-About Science Ser.). (Illus.). 32p. (J). (gr. 1-2). pap. 4.95 (978-0-516-24666-6(6) , Children's Pr.) Scholastic Library Publishing.

Farndon, John. Solids, Liquids & Gases. 2001. (Science Experiments Ser.). (Illus.). 32p. (J). (gr. 3-5). lib. bdg. 25.64 (978-0-7614-1338-7(3) , Benchmark Bks.) Cavendish, Marshall Corp.

Flynn, James J. Air. 2003. (Matter & Materials Ser.). (J). pap. (978-1-58417-169-0(3)); lib. bdg. (978-1-58417-163-8(4)) Lake Street Pubs.

Gaff, Jackie. Looking at Solids, Liquids, & Gases: How Does Matter Change? 2008. (Looking at Science: How Things Change Ser.). 32p. (J). (gr. 1-3). lib. bdg. 22.60 (***978-0-7660-3092-3(X)***) Enslow Pubs., Inc.

Gardner, Robert. Melting, Freezing, & Boiling Science Projects with Matter. 2006. (Fantastic Physical Science Experiments Ser.). (Illus.). 48p. (J). lib. bdg. 23.93 (978-0-7660-2589-9(6) , Enslow Elementary) Enslow Pubs., Inc.

—Science Fair Projects about the Properties of Matter Using Marbles, Water, Balloons, & More. 2004. (Physics! Best Science Projects Ser.). (Illus.). 128p. (J). lib. bdg. 26.60 (978-0-7660-2128-0(9)) Enslow Pubs., Inc.

—Science Projects about Solids, Liquids & Gases. 2000. (Science Projects Ser.). (Illus.). 128p. (YA). (gr. 6-12). lib. bdg. 26.60 (978-0-7660-1168-7(2)) Enslow Pubs., Inc.

Gareth Stevens Publishing Staff, contrib. by. Matter. 2003. (Discovery Channel School Science Ser.). (Illus.). 32p. (J). (gr. 5 up). lib. bdg. 24.67 (978-0-8368-3361-4(9)) Stevens, Gareth Inc.

Garrett, Ginger. Solids, Liquids, & Gases. (Rookie Read-About Science Ser.). (J). 2005. (Illus.). 32p. (gr. 1-2). pap. 4.95 (978-0-516-24663-5(1)); 2004. 20.50 (978-0-516-23615-5(6)) Scholastic Library Publishing. (Children's Pr.).

Glover, David. Testing Materials. 2001. (Experiments in Science Ser.). (Illus.). (J). (978-0-7894-7465-0(4)) Dorling Kindersley Publishing, Inc.

Gordon, Sharon. Duro Blando. 2006. (Bookworms Ser.). (SPA & ENG., Illus.). 24p. (J). lib. bdg. 22.79 (978-0-7614-2368-3(0)) Cavendish, Marshall Corp.

—Hard Soft (Duro Blando) 2006. (Bookworms Ser.). (ENG & SPA., Illus.). 24p. (J). lib. bdg. 22.79 (978-0-7614-2448-2(2)) Cavendish, Marshall Corp.

Harcourt School Publishers Staff. Solids, Liquids & Gases: Science Reader. 2000. (SPA., Illus.). (J). pap. 3.70 (978-0-15-316124-7(8)) Harcourt Schl. Pubs.

Heating. 2004. (Illus.). 24p. (J). (ps-ps). pap. 5.75 (978-1-4034-5103-3(6)) Heinemann Library.

Hewitt, Sally. Amazing Materials. 2007. 32p. pap. (***978-0-7787-3627-1(X)***) Crabtree Publishing Co.

Holland, Gini. Soft & Hard: Blando y Duro. 2007. (SPA & ENG.). (J). pap. (***978-0-8368-8311-4(X)*** , Weekly Reader Early Learning Library) Stevens, Gareth Inc.

—Soft & Hard/Blando y Duro. 2007. (I Know Opposites/ Conceptos Contrarios Ser.). (SPA & ENG.). 24p. (J). (gr. k-2). lib. bdg. 17.27 (***978-0-8368-8306-0(3)*** , Weekly Reader Early Learning Library) Stevens, Gareth Inc.

Holt, Rinehart and Winston Staff. Holt Science & Technology Chapter 2: Physical Science: Properties of Matter. 5th ed. 2004. (Illus.). pap. 12.86 (978-0-03-030361-6(3)) Holt, Rinehart & Winston.

—Holt Science & Technology Chptr. 15: Properties of Matter: Chapter Resources - Tennessee Edition. 3rd ed. 2003. (YA). pap. 11.40 (978-0-03-069176-8(1)) Holt, Rinehart & Winston.

Huggins-Cooper, Lynn. Materials. McNicholas, Shelagh & Burroughs, Dave, trs. McNicholas, Shelagh & Burroughs, Dave, illus. 2004. (J). lib. bdg. (978-1-58340-448-5(1)) Smart Apple Media.

Hunter, Rebecca. The Facts about Solids, Liquids, & Gases. 2004. (Science the Facts Ser.). (Illus.). 32p. (J). lib. bdg. (978-1-58340-450-8(3)) Smart Apple Media.

Hunter, Rebecca M. Matter. 2000. (Discovering Science Ser.). (Illus.). 32p. (J). (gr. 3-5). lib. bdg. 25.69 (978-0-7398-2969-1(6)) Raintree.

Johnson, Penny. Ice to Steam: Changing States of Matter. 2008. (J). (***978-1-60044-605-4(1)***) Rourke Publishing, LLC.

Kjelle, Marylou Morano. The Properties of Liquids. 2007. (Library of Physical Science). (Illus.). 24p. (J). (978-1-4042-2359-2(2)); pap. (978-1-4042-2169-7(7)) Rosen Publishing Group, Inc., The. (PowerKids Pr.).

—The Properties of Metals. 2007. (Library of Physical Sciences). (Illus.). 24p. (J). (978-1-4042-2354-7(1) , PowerKids Pr.) Rosen Publishing Group, Inc., The.

—The Properties of Salts. 2007. (Library of Physical Science). (Illus.). 24p. (J). pap. (978-1-4042-2172-7(7) , PowerKids Pr.) Rosen Publishing Group, Inc., The.

—The Properties of Solids. 2007. (Library of Physical Science). (Illus.). 24p. (J). (978-1-4042-2358-5(4)); pap. (978-1-4042-2168-0(9)) Rosen Publishing Group, Inc., The. (PowerKids Pr.).

Mason, Adrienne. Change It! Solids, Liquids, Gases & You. Davila, Claudia, illus. 2006. 32p. (978-1-55337-838-9(5)); (978-1-55337-837-2(7)) Kids Can Pr., Ltd.

—Touch It! Materials, Matter & You. Davila, Claudia, illus. 2005. (Primary Physical Science Ser.). 32p. (J). (978-1-55337-761-0(3)) Kids Can Pr., Ltd.

—Touch It! Materials, Matter & You. Davila, Claudia, illus. 2005. (Primary Physical Science Ser.). 32p. (J). (ps-ps). (978-1-55337-760-3(5)) Kids Can Pr., Ltd.

McGraw-Hill Staff. Glencoe Chemistry: Matter & Change. 2001. stu. ed. 91.32 (978-0-02-828378-4(3) , 9780028283784); 2nd ed. 2004. stu. ed. 91.96 (978-0-07-866418-2(7) , 9780078664182) Glencoe/McGraw-Hill.

Mellett, Peter & Angliss, Sarah. Matter & Materials. 2001. (Hands-On Science Ser.). (Illus.). 40p. (J). (gr. 3-5). pap. 6.95 (978-0-7534-5350-6(9) , Kingfisher) Houghton Mifflin Co. Trade & Reference Div.

Mezzanotte, Jim. Gases. 2006. (States of Matter Ser.). (Illus.). 24p. (J). pap. (978-0-8368-6802-9(1)); lib. bdg. (978-0-8368-6797-8(1)) Stevens, Gareth Inc.

—Solidos. 2006. (ENG & SPA.). (J). pap. (978-0-8368-7410-5(2)); lib. bdg. (978-0-8368-7405-1(6)) Stevens, Gareth Inc. (Weekly Reader Early Learning Library).

Murray, Julie. Solids, Liquids, & Gasses. 2007. (Illus.). 24p. (J). 21.35 (978-1-59679-830-4(0) , Buddy Bks.) ABDO Publishing Co.

Oxlade, Chris. Mixing & Separating. 2007. 32p. pap. (***978-0-7787-3650-9(4)***) Crabtree Publishing Co.

Parker. Is It Slippery or Sticky? 2004. (Illus.). 24p. (J). pap. 5.50 (978-1-4109-0772-1(4)) Raintree.

Parker, Vic. Slippery or Sticky. 2004. (Illus.). 24p. (J). (ps-6). lib. bdg. 18.56 (978-1-4109-0767-7(8)) Raintree.

Parker, Victoria. Hard or Soft. 2004. (Raintree Sprouts Ser.). (Illus.). 24p. (J). lib. bdg. 20.64 (978-1-4109-0765-3(1)) Raintree.

—Is It Hard or Soft? 2004. (J). pap. (978-1-4109-0770-7(8)) Raintree.

Pipe, Jim. Changing Materials: Fire & Ice. 2005. (Science Starters Ser.). (Illus.). 32p. (J). (gr. 1-4). lib. bdg. 27.10 (978-1-59604-023-6(8)) Stargazer Bks.

Pressnall, Deb, ed. Inquiry Investigations: Matter: Properties & Physical Changes. 2005. 48p. (J). per. 6.99 (978-1-59441-057-4(7) , CD-104030) Carson-Dellosa Publishing Co., Inc.

Rivera, Sheila. Mixing. 2007. (First Step Nonfiction Ser.). (Illus.). 8p. (J). pap. (978-0-8225-6411-9(4)) Lerner Publishing Group.

Robinson, Claire. Elephants: Solids, Liquids & Gases. 1998. (Science All Around Me Ser.). (Illus.). 24p. (gr. k-2). lib. bdg. 21.36 (978-1-57572-135-4(X)) Heinemann Library.

Royston, Angela. Smooth & Rough. 2003. (My World of Science Ser.). (Illus.). 32p. (gr. k-2). (J). lib. bdg. 22.79 (978-1-4034-0859-4(9)); pap. 6.50 (978-1-4034-3172-1(8)) Heinemann Library.

—Solids, Liquids & Gasses. (My World of Science Ser.). (Illus.). 32p. (J). (gr. k-2). 2002. pap. 6.95 (978-1-4034-0044-4(X) , 91488); 2001. lib. bdg. 21.36 (978-1-58810-245-4(9)) Heinemann Library.

Ryback, Carol. Solids. 2006. (States of Matter Ser.). (Illus.). 24p. (J). pap. (978-0-8368-6805-0(6)); lib. bdg. (978-0-8368-6800-5(5)) Stevens, Gareth Inc.

Slade, Suzanne. Atoms & Chemical Reactions. 2007. (Library of Physical Sciences). (Illus.). 24p. (J). (978-1-4042-2352-3(5)); pap. (978-1-4042-2162-8(X)); (gr. 3-6). lib. bdg. 21.25 (978-1-4042-3415-4(2)) Rosen Publishing Group, Inc., The. (PowerKids Pr.).

—States of Matter. 2007. (Library of Physical Sciences). (J). (978-1-4042-2353-0(3)); (Illus.). 24p. pap. (978-1-4042-2163-5(8)) Rosen Publishing Group, Inc., The. (PowerKids Pr.).

Smith, Erica. Solid, Liquid, Gas: What Is Matter? 2002. (Reading Room Collection). (Illus.). 24p. (J). lib. bdg. 18.75 (978-0-8239-3738-7(0)) Rosen Publishing Group, Inc., The.

Snedden, Robert. States of Matter. 2002. (Material World Ser.). (Illus.). 32p. (YA). (gr. 6-8). lib. bdg. 24.22 (978-1-58810-072-6(3)) Heinemann Library.

Spilsbury, Louise & Spilsbury, Richard. Atoms & Molecules. 2007. (Illus.). 32p. (J). (978-1-4034-9341-5(3)); lib. bdg. (978-1-4034-9336-1(7)) Heinemann Library.

—Mixtures & Solutions. 2007. (Illus.). 32p. (J). (978-1-4034-9344-6(8)); lib. bdg. (978-1-4034-9339-2(1)) Heinemann Library.

Spilsbury, Richard & Spilsbury, Louise. What Is Solids, Liquids, & Gases? Exploring Science with Hands-On Activities. 2008. (In Touch with Basic Science Ser.). 32p. (J). (gr. 3-4). lib. bdg. 22.60 (***978-0-7660-3094-7(6)***) Enslow Pubs., Inc.

Stille, Darlene R. Matter: See It, Touch It, Taste It, Smell It. Boyd, Sheree, illus. 2004. (Amazing Science Ser.). 24p. (C). (gr. k-4). 22.60 (978-1-4048-0246-9(0) , 1229495) Picture Window Bks.

Tocci, Salvatore. Experiments with Solids, Liquids, & Gases. 2002. 13.75 (978-0-606-22879-4(9)) Tandem Library Bks.

Trumbauer, Lisa. Fighter Jet. 2007. (J). pap. (***978-1-4109-2869-6(1)***); lib. bdg. (***978-1-4109-2852-8(7)***) Steck-Vaughn.

Walker, Sally M. Matter. King, Andy, illus. 2006. (Early Bird Energy Ser.). 48p. (J). (ps-7). 25.26 (978-0-8225-5131-7(4) , Lerner Pubns.) Lerner Publishing Group.

Warbrick, Sarah. What Is Bendy? 1998. (What Is—? Ser.). (J). 14.60 (978-1-57572-049-4(3)) Heinemann Library.

—What Is Bouncy & Stretchy? 1998. (What Is—? Ser.). (J). 14.60 (978-1-57572-050-0(7)) Heinemann Library.

—What Is See Through? 1998. (What Is—? Ser.). (J). 14.60 (978-1-57572-051-7(5)) Heinemann Library.

—What Is Shiny? 1998. (What Is—? Ser.). (J). 14.60 (978-1-57572-053-1(1)) Heinemann Library.

—What Is Squishy? 1998. (What Is—? Ser.). (J). 14.60 (978-1-57572-048-7(5)) Heinemann Library.

—What Is Sticky? 1998. (What Is—? Ser.). (J). 14.60 (978-1-57572-052-4(3)) Heinemann Library.

Weil, Anne. A Matter of Survival: Properties of Matter. 2005. (Illus.). 32p. (J). (978-1-4109-1945-8(5)); lib. bdg. (978-1-4109-1914-4(5)) Steck-Vaughn.

West, Krista. States of Matter: Gases, Liquids, & Solids. 2007. (Essential Chemistry Ser.). 128p. (gr. 6-12). 35.00 (***978-0-7910-9521-8(5)*** , Chelsea Hse.) Facts On File, Inc.

Whitehouse, Patricia, tr. Cooling. 2004. (J). pap. (978-1-4034-5102-6(8)); lib. bdg. (978-1-4034-5097-5(8)) Heinemann Library.

—Heating. 2004. (J). lib. bdg. (978-1-4034-5098-2(6)) Heinemann Library.

Williams, Zella. Experiments with Solids, Liquids, & Gases. 2007. (Do-It-Yourself Science Ser.). (Illus.). 24p. (J). (gr. 2-5). lib. bdg. 23.95 (978-1-4042-3658-5(9) , PowerKids Pr.) Rosen Publishing Group, Inc., The.

Young, June. Look How It Changes! 2006. 32p. (gr. 1-2). (YA). pap. 4.95 (978-0-516-28178-0(X)); (Illus.). (J). 20.50 (978-0-516-25901-7(6)) Scholastic Library Publishing. (Children's Pr.).

MATTHEW, SAINT, APOSTLE

Lee, Witness. The Holy Word for Morning Revival: Matthew 1:1-7:29, Vol. 1. 2000. 71p. (J). (gr. 6). 6.00 (978-0-7363-1108-3(4) , 13-133-001) Living Stream Ministry.

Mackenzie, Carine & Gair, Cyhoeddiadau'r. 4 Mathew - Actau. 2005. (978-1-85994-271-0(7)) Cyhoeddiadau'r Gair.

Woodman, Ros. Bible Detectives: Matthew. 64p. (YA). pap., act. bk. ed. 7.99 (978-1-85792-673-6(0) , Christian Focus) Christian Focus Pubns. GBR. *Dist:* Riverside.

MAURITANIA

Foreign Policy Research Institute Staff, ed. Mauritania. 2003. (Modern Middle East Nations & Their Strategic Place in the World Ser.). (Illus.). 112,128p. (J). (gr. 7 up). lib. bdg. (978-1-59084-526-4(9)) Mason Crest Pubs.

MAXIMILLIAN, EMPEROR OF MEXICO, 1832-1867

Torres, Elizar. Maximiliam & Carlota, Emperor & Empress of Mexico 1864-1867. Torres, Anna Marie, ed. Vargas, Adriana, tr. Martinez, Adela, illus. 2000. (ENG & SPA.). 65p. (YA). (gr. 3-7). pap. 7.49 (978-0-9678599-1-0(3)) EP PUBS.

MAXIMS

see Proverbs

MAY DAY

Ditchfield, Christin. Memorial Day, Last Monday in May. 2003. (gr. 3-6). lib. bdg. 15.25 (978-0-613-89011-3(6)) Tandem Library Bks.

MAY DAY—FICTION

Mora, Pat. The Rainbow Tulip. Sayles, Elizabeth, illus. 32p. (J). (gr. k-3). 2003. pap. 6.99 (978-0-14-250009-5(7) , Puffin); 1999. 16.99 (978-0-670-87291-6(1) , Viking Juvenile) Penguin Group (USA) Inc.

MAYAS

see Indians of Mexico—Mayas

MAYFLOWER (SHIP)

Arenstam, Peter, et al. Mayflower 1620: A New Look at a Pilgrim Voyage. 2007. (Illus.). 48p. (J). (gr. 3-7). 6.95 (***978-0-7922-6276-3(X)*** , National Geographic Children's Bks.) National Geographic Society.

—Mayflower 1620: A New Look at a Pilgrim Voyage. Brimberg, Sisse & Coulson, Cotton, illus. Brimberg, Sisse & Coulson, Cotton, photos by. 2003. 48p. (J). (gr. 3-7). 17.95 (978-0-7922-6142-1(9) , National Geographic Children's Bks.) National Geographic Society.

—MayFlower 1620: A New Look at a Pilgrim Voyage. 2004. (Illus.). 47p. (J). (gr. k-4). 18.00 (978-0-7567-7967-2(7)) DIANE Publishing Co.

Armentrout, David & Armentrout, Patricia. The Mayflower Compact. (Documents that Shaped the Nation Ser.). 48p. 2005. (Illus.). (gr. 4-6). 20.95 (978-1-59515-229-9(6)); 2004. pap. 7.95 (978-1-59515-334-0(9)) Rourke Publishing, LLC.

—El Pacto Del Mayflower. 2005. (SPA.). (J). (978-1-59515-648-8(8)) Rourke Publishing, LLC.

Brooks, Philip. The Mayflower Compact. 2004. (Illus.). 48p. (J). (gr. 4 up). lib. bdg. 22.60 (978-0-7565-0681-0(6)) Compass Point Bks.

Carter, E. J. The Mayflower Compact. 2003. (Heinemann Know It Ser.). (Illus.). 48p. (J). pap. 8.50 (978-1-4034-3432-6(8)); lib. bdg. 27.07 (978-1-4034-0803-7(3)) Heinemann Library.

Cook, Peter. You Wouldn't Want to Sail on the Mayflower! A Trip That Took Entirely Too Long. Whelan, Kevin, illus. 2005. (You Wouldn't Want to... Ser.). 32p. (J). (gr. 2-5). 28.50 (978-0-531-12411-6(8)); pap. 9.95 (978-0-531-12391-1(X)) Scholastic Library Publishing. (Watts, Franklin).

Fradin, Dennis B. The Mayflower Compact. 2006. (Turning Points in U. S. History Ser.). (Illus.). 48p. (J). lib. bdg. 29.93 (978-0-7614-2125-2(4) , Benchmark Bks.) Cavendish, Marshall Corp.

Lassieur, Allison. The Voyage of the Mayflower. McDonnell, Peter, illus. 2006. (Graphic Library). 32p. (J). 25.26 (978-0-7368-4371-3(X)) Capstone Pr., Inc.

Waters, Kate. On the Mayflower: Voyage of the Ship's Apprentice & a Passenger Girl. 1999. (978-0-606-17443-5(5)) Tandem Library Bks.

Whitcraft, Melissa. The Mayflower Compact. 2003. (Cornerstones of Freedom). (Illus.). 48p. (J). (gr. 4-6). 26.00 (978-0-516-24203-3(2) , Children's Pr.) Scholastic Library Publishing.

Whitehurst, Susan. The Mayflower. 2002. (Library of the Pilgrims). (Illus.). 24p. (J). (gr. 3). lib. bdg. 19.95 (978-0-8239-5806-1(X) , PowerKids Pr.) Rosen Publishing Group, Inc., The.

—Plymouth: Surviving the First Winter. 2002. (Library of the Pilgrims). (Illus.). 24p. (J). (gr. 3). lib. bdg. 19.95 (978-0-8239-5809-2(4) , PowerKids Pr.) Rosen Publishing Group, Inc., The.

Yero, Judith Lloyd. The Mayflower Compact. 2004. (National Geographic Reading Expeditions Ser.). (Illus.). 32p. (J). pap. (978-0-7922-4553-7(9)) National Geographic Society.

MAYFLOWER (SHIP)—FICTION

Lasky, Kathryn. A Journey to the New World: The Diary of Remember Patience Whipple, Mayflower, 1620. 1999. (Dear America Ser.). (J). 9.95 (978-0-439-15601-1(7)) Scholastic, Inc.

Lawton, Wendy. Almost Home: A Story Based on the Life of the Mayflower's Mary Chilton. 2003. (Daughters of the Faith Ser.). 160p. (YA). pap. 6.99 (978-0-8024-3637-5(4)) Moody Pubs.

Peacock, Carol Anto. Pilgrim Cat. Ettlinger, Doris, illus. 2004. 32p. (J). (gr. 2-5). 16.95 (978-0-8075-6532-2(6)) Whitman, Albert & Co.

Peacock, Carol Antoinette. Pilgrim Cat. Ettlinger, Doris, illus. 2006. 32p. (J). (gr. 2-5). 6.95 (978-0-8075-6533-9(4)) Whitman, Albert & Co.

Reece, Colleen L. The Mayflower Adventure. 1999. (American Adventure Ser.: No. 1). 144p. (J). (gr. 3-7). lib. bdg. 15.95 (978-0-7910-5041-5(6) , Chelsea Hse.) Facts On File, Inc.

Rinaldi, Ann. The Journal of Jasper Jonathan Pierce: A Pilgrim Boy, Plymouth, 1620. 2000. (My Name Is America Ser.). (Illus.). 160p. (J). (gr. 4-8). pap. 10.95 (978-0-590-51078-3(9)) Scholastic, Inc.

Roy, Ron. Mayflower Treasure Hunt. Gurney, John Steven, illus. 2nd ed. 2007. (A to Z Mysteries Ser.: No. 28). 128p. (J). (gr. 1-4). pap. 4.99 (978-0-375-83937-5(2)); lib. bdg. 11.99 (978-0-375-93937-2(7)) Random Hse. Children's Bks. (Random Hse. Bks. for Young Readers).

Waters, Kate. On the Mayflower: Voyage of the Ship's Apprentice & a Passenger Girl. 1998. (J). 5.99 (978-0-590-67408-9(0)) Scholastic, Inc.

MAYO FAMILY

Davis, Lucile. The Mayo Brothers: Doctors to the World. 1999. (Community Builders Ser.). (Illus.). 48p. (J). (gr. 3-5). pap. 6.95 (978-0-516-26347-2(1) , Children's Pr.) Scholastic Library Publishing.

MAYORS

Burby, Liza N. A Day in the Life of a Mayor: Featuring New York City Mayor Rudy Giuliani. 1999. (Kids' Career Library). (Illus.). 24p. (J). (gr. 3). lib. bdg. 18.75 (978-0-8239-5303-5(3) , PowerKids Pr.) Rosen Publishing Group, Inc., The.

Compass Point Books, contrib. by. Mayors. (Community Workers Ser.). 24p. (J). pap. 7.95 (978-0-7565-1193-7(3)) Compass Point Bks.

Flanagan, Alice K. Mayors. 2001. (Community Workers Ser.). (Illus.). 32p. (J). (gr. 1 up). lib. bdg. 21.26 (978-0-7565-0064-1(8)) Compass Point Bks.

Fremont, Eleanor. Rudolph W. Giuliani: America's Mayor. 2002. (Illus.). 96p. (J). (gr. 5-9). pap. 4.99 (978-0-689-85423-1(4) , Aladdin) Simon & Schuster Children's Publishing.

Gorman, Jacqueline Laks. Mayor. 2005. (Illus.). 24p. (J). pap. (978-0-8368-4576-1(5)); lib. bdg. 19.33 (978-0-8368-4569-3(2)) Stevens, Gareth Inc.

Harris, Nancy. What's a Mayor? 2007. (J). (***978-1-4034-9507-5(6)***); pap. (***978-1-4034-9513-6(0)***) Heinemann Library.

Knudsen, Shannon. Mayors. 2006. (Pull Ahead Books). (Illus.). 32p. (J). (gr. 3-7). 22.60 (978-0-8225-2829-6(0) , Lerner Pubns.) Lerner Publishing Group.

M N O

Mara, Wil. Rudolph Giuliani. 2003. (Rookie Biographies Ser.). (Illus.). 32p. (J). (gr. 1-2). 20.50 (978-0-516-22860-0(9) , Children's Pr.) Scholastic Library Publishing.

Marsh, Carole. Harold Washington. 2002. (One Thousand Readers Ser.). (Illus.). 12p. (J). (gr. k-4). 2.95 (978-0-635-01504-4(8) , 15048) Gallopade International.

—Richard Daley. 2002. (One Thousand Readers Ser.). (Illus.). 12p. (J). (gr. k-4). 2.95 (978-0-635-01509-9(9) , 15099) Gallopade International.

Pellegrino, Marjorie White. My Grandma's the Mayor. Lund, John, illus. 1999. 32p. (J). (gr. 1-7). (978-1-55798-608-5(8) , 441-6088, Magination Pr.) American Psychological Assn.

Richter, Robert. Cuauhtemoc Cardenas & the Roots of Mexico's New Democracy. 2000. (Contemporary Profiles & Policy Series for the Younger Reader). (Illus.). 75p. (YA). (gr. 8 up). 24.00 (978-0-934272-66-7(2)); pap. 15.00 (978-0-934272-65-0(4)) Burke, John Gordon Pub., Inc.

Silate, Jennifer. Your Mayor: Local Government in Action. 2003. (Primary Source Library of American Citizenship). (Illus.). 32p. (J). pap. (978-1-4042-5095-6(6)) Rosen Publishing Group, Inc., The.

MAYS, WILLIE, 1931-

Mandel, Peter. Say Hey! A Song of Willie Mays. Tate, Don, illus. 2004. 30p. (J). (gr. k-2). reprint ed. 16.00 (978-0-7567-8162-0(0)) DIANE Publishing Co.

Smith, Linda J. Willie Mays: The Say Hey Kid. 2005. (Illus.). 112p. (J). (978-1-59421-015-0(2)) Seacoast Publishing, Inc.

MAZE PUZZLES

Adam, Winky. Native American Mazes. 2003. (Illus.). 64p. (J). (ps-3). pap. 1.50 (978-0-486-42616-7(5)) Dover Pubns., Inc.

Ahlberg, Janet & Ahlberg, Allan. Each Peach Pear Plum. Ahlberg, Janet, illus. 2002. (Illus.). (J). 12.34 (978-0-7587-2427-4(6)) Book Wholesalers, Inc.

—Each Peach Pear Plum. (Illus.). 32p. (J). pap. 9.95 (978-0-14-050919-9(4)) Penguin Bks., Ltd. GBR. *Dist:* Trafalgar Square Publishing.

—Each Peach Pear Plum. Ahlberg, Janet & Ahlberg, Allan, illus. 1999. (Illus.). 34p. (J). (ps up). 6.99 (978-0-670-88278-6(X) , Viking Juvenile) Penguin Group (USA) Inc.

The Amazing Escape: A Bible Story Maze Book. 2002. 14p. (J). (gr. k-3). 12.99 (978-0-8254-7255-8(5)) Kregel Pubns.

Amazing Mazes. 2004. (Illus.). 80p. (J). per. 6.95 (978-4-7743-0710-7(6)) Kumon Publishing North America, Inc.

Axford, Elizabeth C., compiled by. The Music Box & Other Delights. 2003. (Illus.). 72p. (J). spiral bd. 14.95 (978-1-931844-03-1(8) , PP1015) Piano Pr.

Baldus, Patrick. Amazing Alphabet Maze Book. Baldus, Patrick, illus. 2002. (Illus.). 64p. (J). pap. 5.99 (978-0-8431-4915-9(9) , Price Stern Sloan) Penguin Group (USA) Inc.

Balloon Books Staff, ed. (Almost) Impossible Mazes. 2001. (Illus.). 72p. (J). (gr. 2-4). pap. 3.95 (978-0-8069-8059-1(1) , Balloon Bks.) Sterling Publishing Co., Inc.

—Maze Craze. 2001. (Balloon Ser.). (Illus.). 72p. (J). (gr. 3-7). pap. 3.95 (978-0-8069-2272-0(9) , Balloon Bks.) Sterling Publishing Co., Inc.

—Mini Mazes. 2003. (Fun House Paperbacks Ser.). (Illus.). 72p. (J). pap. 2.95 (978-0-8069-2280-5(X) , Balloon Bks.) Sterling Publishing Co., Inc.

Bereit, Rebekah, ed. A-Maze-Ing Arizona. 2002. (Illus.). 56p. (J). act. bk. ed. 7.95 (978-0-87358-809-6(6) , Rising Moon Bks. for Young Readers) Northland Publishing.

Big Book of Mazes. 12.99 (978-1-58062-904-1(0)) Adams Media Corp.

Blair, Beth. The Everything Kids' Gross Mazes Book. 2006. (Illus.). 144p. (J). pap. 7.95 (978-1-59337-616-1(2)) Adams Media Corp.

Blair, Beth & Ericsson, Jennifer. Everything Kids' Animal Puzzles. 2005. (Illus.). 144p. (J). pap., act. bk. ed. 6.95 (978-1-59337-305-4(8)) Adams Media Corp.

Blundell, Kim & Tyler, Jenny. Treasure Mazes. rev. ed. 2004. 24p. (J). pap. 5.99 (978-0-7945-0537-0(6) , Usborne) EDC Publishing.

Carpenter, Elizabeth. Dinomaze: Colossal Fossil Maze Book. 2001. (Illus.). 50p. (J). (gr. 10 up). pap. 14.95 (978-0-7611-1275-4(8) , 11275) Workman Publishing Co., Inc.

Carpenter, Elizabeth. MummyMaze: The Tomb Treasures Maze Book. 2nd rev. ed. 2007. (J). pap. 19.99 (***978-0-9793043-0-9(X))** Mazeology.

Chronicle Books Staff, creator. 75 Mind Mazes. 2005. (Illus.). 75p. (gr. 2-6). 9.95 (978-0-8118-5188-6(5)) Chronicle Bks. LLC.

Conceptis Puzzles. Mysterious Picture Mazes. 2008. 96p. pap. 5.95 (***978-1-4027-5049-6(8))** Sterling Publishing Co., Inc.

—Perplexing Picture Mazes. 2008. 96p. (J). pap. 5.95 (***978-1-4027-5046-5(3))** Sterling Publishing Co., Inc.

Conceptis Puzzles. Sneaky Picture Mazes. 2007. 96p. (J). pap. 5.95 (978-1-4027-3867-8(6)) Sterling Publishing Co., Inc.

Conceptis Puzzles Staff. Hidden Picture Mazes. 2005. (Illus.). 96p. (J). (gr. 3-7). pap. 5.95 (978-1-4027-2491-6(8)) Sterling Publishing Co., Inc.

Conner, Carol & Fabian, Melinda, illus. Follow & Find: Follow the Numbered Dots to Complete the Picture, Then Color the Picture! l.t. ed. 2000. (Nature Friend Fun Ser.: Vol. 3). 24p. (J). (gr. k-5). pap. 4.00 (978-1-890050-45-0(8)) Carlisle Pr.- Walnut Creek.

Dalmatian Press Staff. Saban's Power Rangers Lost Galaxy Mega Maze & Puzzle Book. 1999. (Illus.). (J). (ps-3). pap. 2.99 (978-1-57759-252-5(2)) Dalmatian Pr.

de Caussin, Matthew. SpectraMaze. 2000. (Illus.). 32p. (J). pap. 14.95 (978-0-9704213-0-2(3)) Gambit Gameworks, Inc.

Diagram Visual. Super Little Giant Book of Mystery Mazes. 2007. (Illus.). 288p. (J). pap. 6.95 (***978-1-4027-4863-9(9))** Sterling Publishing Co., Inc.

Dot-to-Dots, Mazes & More: Baby Animals. (gr. k-1). 2.99 (978-0-7424-0172-3(3) , IF0405) School Specialty Publishing.

Dot-to-Dots, Mazes & More: Dinosaurs. (gr. k-1). 2.99 (978-0-7424-0171-6(5) , IF0404) School Specialty Publishing.

Douglas, Vincent & School Specialty Publishing Staff. Challenge Mazes. 2003. (Homework Helpers Ser.). (Illus.). 32p. (J). (gr. k-1). pap. 2.99 (978-0-7696-2936-0(9)); (gr. 2-2). pap. 2.99 (978-0-7696-2935-3(0)) School Specialty Publishing. (American Education Publishing).

—Challenge Puzzles & Mazes. 2003. (Homework Helpers Ser.). (Illus.). 32p. (J). (gr. 3-3). pap. 2.99 (978-0-7696-2937-7(7) , American Education Publishing) School Specialty Publishing.

—Mazes. 2003. (Homework Helpers Ser.). (Illus.). 32p. (J). (gr. k-1). pap. 2.99 (978-0-7696-2916-2(4) , American Education Publishing) School Specialty Publishing.

Guastella, Sal & Strong, Judith. Greasy, Grimy, Goofy Mazes. Guastella, Sal, illus. 1998. (Illus.). 48p. (J). (gr. 1-6). reprint ed. pap. 5.95 (978-0-9607230-1-0(3)) Tiny Paws Publishing.

Hall, Jody. Super Silly Mazes. 2002. (Illus.). 64p. (J). (gr. 4-7). pap. 5.95 (978-0-8069-7903-8(8)) Sterling Publishing Co., Inc.

Heimann, Rolf. Mega Mazes. 2006. (Illus.). 80p. (J). pap. 7.95 (978-1-4027-2461-9(6)) Sterling Publishing Co., Inc.

Hop, L. L. C. Hooked on First Grade: Puzzles & Mazes. 2006. 64p. 3.79 (978-1-931020-71-8(X)) HOP, LLC.

HOP, LLC. Hooked on Learning Puzzles & Mazes. 2006. 64p. 3.79 (978-1-933863-90-0(0)) HOP, LLC.

Howell, Theresa, ed. A-Maze-Ing Western National Parks & Monuments. 2002. (Illus.). 56p. (J). act. bk. ed. 7.95 (978-0-87358-810-2(X) , Rising Moon Bks. for Young Readers) Northland Publishing.

Kampf, Christian. Mysterious Mazes. 2003. (Illus.). 96p. (J). pap. 5.95 (978-1-4027-0297-6(3)) Sterling Publishing Co., Inc.

Kay, Keith. The Who, What & Where Book of Brain Bafflers. 2002. (Illus.). 96p. (J). (978-1-4027-0682-0(0)) Sterling Publishing Co., Inc.

Martin, Lyn. Child's Play Mazes: Animal Adventure Mazes. 2005. (Illus.). 40p. (J). pap. 4.95 (978-1-4027-1510-5(2)) Sterling Publishing Co., Inc.

Matthies, Don-Oliver. Detective Mazes. 2004. (Maze Craze Book Ser.). (Illus.). 40p. pap. 3.95 (978-1-4027-1293-7(6)) Sterling Publishing Co., Inc.

—Dinosaur Mazes. 2004. (Maze Craze Book Ser.). (Illus.). 40p. pap. 3.95 (978-1-4027-1292-0(8)) Sterling Publishing Co., Inc.

—Magician's Castle. 2005. (Maze Craze Book Ser.). (Illus.). 40p. (J). (gr. 2-4). pap. 3.95 (978-1-4027-2652-1(X)) Sterling Publishing Co., Inc.

Matthies, Don-Oliver & Arena Verlag Staff. Castle Mazes. 2003. (Maze Craze Book Ser.). (Illus.). 40p. (J). pap. 3.95 (978-1-4027-0605-9(7)) Sterling Publishing Co., Inc.

—Mummy Mazes. 2003. (Maze Craze Book Ser.). (Illus.). 40p. (J). pap. 3.95 (978-1-4027-0548-9(4)) Sterling Publishing Co., Inc.

—Pirate Mazes. 2003. (Maze Craze Book Ser.). (Illus.). 40p. (J). pap. 3.95 (978-1-4027-0603-5(0)) Sterling Publishing Co., Inc.

—Spooky Mazes. 2003. (Illus.). 40p. (J). pap. 3.95 (978-1-4027-0604-2(9)) Sterling Publishing Co., Inc.

Maze Puzzles. 2002. (Wipe It Off Ser.). 24p. (J). spiral bd. 4.98 (978-0-7525-8355-6(7)) Parragon, Inc.

Mazes. 2002. (Home Workbooks Ser.). 64p. pap. 2.49 (978-0-88724-703-3(2) , CD-4505) Carson-Dellosa Publishing Co., Inc.

Mazes & Hidden Pictures Booster. 2005. (J). per. 0.00 (978-1-59441-503-6(X) , C04035) Carson-Dellosa Publishing Co., Inc.

Mazes for 1st Grade. 2003. (J). (978-1-58232-059-5(4)) Bryan Hse. Pubs., Inc.

Mazes for 2nd Grade. 2003. (J). (978-1-58232-060-1(8)) Bryan Hse. Pubs., Inc.

McGraw-Hill Staff & Schaffer, Frank. Mazes. 2001. (Homework Helpers Activity Bks.). (Illus.). 56p. (J). (gr. k-1). pap., act. bk. ed. 2.99 (978-0-7682-0686-9(3) , FS109015, Schaffer, Frank) Schaffer, Frank Pubns.

—Mazes, Puzzles, & Games. 2001. (Homework Helpers Activity Bks.). (Illus.). 56p. (J). (gr. 2-2). pap., act. bk. ed. 2.99 (978-0-7682-0711-8(8) , FS109040, Schaffer, Frank) Schaffer, Frank Pubns.

McGraw-Hill Staff & School Specialty Publishing Staff. Challenge: Mazes. 2001. (Homework Helpers Activity Bks.). (Illus.). 56p. (J). (gr. k-1). pap., act. bk. ed. 2.99 (978-0-7682-0694-4(4) , FS109023, Schaffer, Frank) Schaffer, Frank Pubns.

—Challenge Mazes. 2001. (Homework Helpers Activity Bks.). (Illus.). 56p. (J). (gr. 2-2). pap., act. bk. ed. 2.99 (978-0-7682-0713-2(4) , FS109042, Schaffer, Frank) Schaffer, Frank Pubns.

—Challenge Puzzles & Mazes. 2001. (Homework Helpers Activity Bks.). (Illus.). 56p. (J). (gr. 3-3). pap., act. bk. ed. 2.99 (978-0-7682-0718-7(5) , FS109047, Schaffer, Frank) Schaffer, Frank Pubns.

Merrell, Patrick. Brain-Tingling Mazes. 2005. (Maze Madness Ser.). (Illus.). 64p. pap. 5.95 (978-1-4027-1877-9(2)) Sterling Publishing Co., Inc.

—Charlie & Wilbur's Dinosaur Mazes. 2007. (Illus.). 48p. (J). pap. 4.95 (978-1-4027-3800-5(5)) Sterling Publishing Co., Inc.

Moreau, Roger. Around the World Mystery Mazes: An A-Maze-Ing Colorful Discovery. 2003. (Illus.). 80p. (J). (gr. 2-7). pap. 7.95 (978-0-8069-9288-4(3)) Sterling Publishing Co., Inc.

—Backyard Bug Mazes: An A-Maze-Ing Colorful Discovery! 2006. (Illus.). 80p. (J). pap. 7.95 (978-1-4027-2846-4(8)) Sterling Publishing Co., Inc.

—Dinosaur Escape Mazes: An A-maze-ing Colorful Adventure! 2002. (Illus.). 80p. (J). (gr. 4-7). pap. 7.95 (978-0-8069-5519-3(8)) Sterling Publishing Co., Inc.

—Giant Flip Book: Mazes/Word Search Puzzles. 2001. (Illus.). 512p. pap. 9.98 (978-1-4027-0044-6(X) , Sterling/Main St.) Sterling Publishing Co., Inc.

—Natural Disaster Mazes. 1998. (Illus.). 64p. (J). (gr. 4-7). pap. 5.95 (978-0-8069-5727-2(1)) Sterling Publishing Co., Inc.

—Undersea Adventure Mazes: An A-Maze-Ing Colorful Journey! 2004. (Illus.). 64p. pap. 7.95 (978-1-4027-0908-1(0)) Sterling Publishing Co., Inc.

—Wildlife Mazes: An A-Maze-Ing Colorful Journey into the Wild! 2005. (Illus.). 80p. (J). (gr. 2-6). pap. 7.95 (978-1-4027-1552-5(8)) Sterling Publishing Co., Inc.

—Wizard Magic Mazes: An A-maze-ing Colorful Quest! 2003. (Illus.). 80p. (J). pap. 7.95 (978-1-4027-0198-6(5)) Sterling Publishing Co., Inc.

Munro, Roxie. Mazescapes. 2005. (Illus.). 36p. (J). reprint ed. pap. 6.95 (978-0-8118-4753-7(5)) Chronicle Bks. LLC.

My First Mazes (Gr. K-1) 2003. (J). (978-1-58232-058-8(6)) Bryan Hse. Pubs., Inc.

Newman-D'Amico, Fran. Alphabet Mazes. 2006. 32p. (J). pap. 2.95 (978-0-486-44894-7(0)) Dover Pubns., Inc.

—Forest Animals Mazes. 2001. (Illus.). 32p. (J). pap. 2.95 (978-0-486-41540-6(6)) Dover Pubns., Inc.

—Zoo Animal Mazes. 2004. (Illus.). 32p. (J). pap. 2.95 (978-0-486-43769-9(8)) Dover Pubns., Inc.

O'Hare, Jeff. The Giant Book of Mazes. 2003. (Illus.). 72p. (YA). (gr. 5-7). pap., stu. ed. 7.95 (978-1-56397-675-9(7)) Boyds Mills Pr.

Patilla, Peter. Fun with Numbers. McDonald, Brigitte, illus. 1998. (Fun with... Ser.). 32p. (ps-2). lib. bdg. 23.90 (978-0-7613-0957-4(8) , Millbrook Pr.) Lerner Publishing Group.

Phillips, Dave. Big Book of Adventure Mazes. 2003. (Dover Super Value Editions Ser.). 128p. (J). (gr. 2-8). pap. 7.95 (978-0-486-42900-7(8)) Dover Pubns., Inc.

—Wizards & Dragons Mazes. 2002. (Illus.). 32p. (gr. 2-8). pap. 3.95 (978-0-486-42227-5(5)) Dover Pubns., Inc.

Preston, Roy, et al. Amazing Magic Mazes: Egyptian Mazes - A Tomb-Raiding Adventure. Carter, Robin, illus. 2005. (Magic Color Bks.). 12p. (J). (gr. 1-3). 9.95 (978-1-4027-2761-0(5) , Sterling/Pinwheel) Sterling Publishing Co., Inc.

Radtke, Becky. On the Go Mazes. 2005. (Illus.). 64p. (J). (ps-ps). pap. 1.50 (978-0-486-44103-0(2)) Dover Pubns., Inc.

Rossell, Judith. The Mystery of the Golden Crocodile: An Egyptian Maze Adventure. 2007. (Illus.). 32p. (J). pap. 4.95 (***978-1-60059-118-1(3))** Lark Bks.

Rudisill, J. J., et al, illus. Wimzie's Mazes. 1999. (Wimzie's House Bks.). 32p. (J). pap. 2.99 (978-0-88724-482-7(3) , CD-4850) Carson-Dellosa Publishing Co., Inc.

Sacks, Janet. Dinosaur Mazes. Hartas, Leo, illus. 2006. (Magic Color Bks.). 12p. (J). bds. 6.95 (978-1-4027-4003-9(4) , Sterling/Pinwheel) Sterling Publishing Co., Inc.

—Mini Magic Mazes: Space Mazes. Hartas, Leo, illus. 2006. (Magic Color Bks.). 12p. (J). bds. 6.95 (978-1-4027-4004-6(2) , Sterling/Pinwheel) Sterling Publishing Co., Inc.

—Safari Mazes. Preston, Roy & Hartas, Leo, illus. ed. 2006. (Magic Color Bks.). 12p. (J). bds. 6.95 (978-1-4027-3301-7(1) , Sterling/Pinwheel) Sterling Publishing Co., Inc.

—Underwater Mazes. Preston, Roy & Hartas, Leo, illus. 2006. (Magic Color Bks.). 12p. (J). bds. 6.95 (978-1-4027-3302-4(X) , Sterling/Pinwheel) Sterling Publishing Co., Inc.

School Specialty Publishing. Dot-to-Dots, Mazes & More: The Farm. 2001. (Homework Booklets Ser.). 80p. (J). (gr. k-1). pap. 2.99 (978-0-7424-0174-7(X) , IF0407) School Specialty Publishing.

—Dot-to-Dots, Mazes & More: Things That Go. 2001. (Homework Booklets Ser.). 80p. (J). (gr. k-1). pap. 2.99 (978-0-7424-0173-0(1) , IF0406) School Specialty Publishing.

School Zone Interactive Staff. Mazes. Simard, Remy, illus. rev. ed. 2006. 64p. (J). (gr. 1-2). pap., wbk. ed. 7.99 (***978-1-58947-300-3(0))** School Zone Publishing Co.

School Zone Publishing. Mazes Activity Zone. 2004. (Activity Zone Workbook Ser.). 32p. (J). pap. 2.49 (978-1-58947-386-7(8) , 02191) School Zone Publishing Co.

School Zone Staff, ed. AZ Mazes/Preschool. 2004. (Activity Zone Workbook Ser.). 32p. (J). pap. 2.49 (978-1-58947-394-2(9) , 02196) School Zone Publishing Co.

Sloane, Paul, et al. The Who, What & Where Book of Brain Bafflers: 50 Whodunits & Puzzles for the Junior Detective. 2003. (Illus.). 96p. (J). 4.95 (978-1-4027-0681-3(2) , Sterling/Main St.) Sterling Publishing Co., Inc.

Smith, Dick. Super Mazes. 1998. (Illus.). 96p. reprint ed. pap. 0.99 (978-0-87406-905-1(X) , Willowisp Pr.) Darby Creek Publishing.

Tallarico, Tony. A-Maze-Ing Airplanes. 2002. (Illus.). 96p. (J). (978-1-58865-081-8(2)) Kidsbooks, Inc.

—A-Maze-Ing Cool Cars. 2002. (Illus.). 96p. (J). (978-1-58865-037-5(5)) Kidsbooks, Inc.

—A-Maze-Ing Dinosaurs. 2001. (Illus.). 96p. (J). (978-1-58865-025-2(1)) Kidsbooks, Inc.

—Nature Trivia Mazes. 2007. 48p. (J). pap. 4.95 (978-0-486-45364-4(2)) Dover Pubns., Inc.

The Ultimate Maze Craze. 2003. (Illus.). 40p. (J). 3.95 (978-0-9729026-0-1(0)) Midwest Cylinder Management, Inc.

University Games Staff, compiled by. i-Ballers: University Games. 2004. 48p. pap. (978-1-57528-952-6(0)) University Games.

White, Graham. Secrets of the Pyramids: National Geographic Maze Adventures. 2002. (Illus.). 32p. (J). (gr. 3-7). pap. 8.95 (978-0-7922-6938-0(1) , National Geographic Children's Bks.) National Geographic Society.

—Secrets of the Pyramids: National Geographic Maze Adventures. 2002. (gr. 3-6). lib. bdg. 17.60 (978-0-613-84045-3(3)) Tandem Library Bks.

—Storming a Castle. 2002. (gr. 3-6). lib. bdg. 17.60 (978-0-613-81333-4(2)) Tandem Library Bks.

—Storming A Castle: National Geographic Maze Adventures. 2002. (Illus.). 32p. (J). (gr. 3-7). pap. 8.95 (978-0-7922-6940-3(3) , National Geographic Children's Bks.) National Geographic Society.

Woodworth, Viki. A-B-C Mazes. 2006. 64p. (J). pap. 1.50 (978-0-486-44726-1(X)) Dover Pubns., Inc.

—Little Monster Mazes. 2006. 64p. (J). pap. 1.50 (978-0-486-45189-3(5)) Dover Pubns., Inc.

—Maze Mania. 2005. (Illus.). 32p. (J). (gr. 3-7). pap. 4.95 (978-0-486-44604-2(2)) Dover Pubns., Inc.

Woodworth, Viki. World of Mazes. 2007. 48p. (J). pap. 4.95 (***978-0-486-45640-9(4))** Dover Pubns., Inc.

MEAD, MARGARET, 1901-1978

Bankston, John. Margaret Mead: Pioneer of Social Anthropology. 2006. (Great Minds of Science Ser.). (Illus.). 128p. (J). lib. bdg. 31.93 (978-0-7660-2507-3(1)) Enslow Pubs., Inc.

Horn, Geoffrey M. Margaret Mead. 2004. (Trailblazers of the Modern World Ser.). (Illus.). 48p. (J). (gr. 5 up). pap. 11.95 (978-0-8368-5259-2(1)); lib. bdg. 30.00 (978-0-8368-5099-4(8)) Stevens, Gareth Inc. (World Almanac Library).

Mark, Joan. Margaret Mead: Coming of Age in America. Gingerich, Owen, ed. 1999. (Oxford Portraits in Science Ser.). (Illus.). 112p. (YA). (gr. 6-12). 30.00 (978-0-19-511679-3(8)) Oxford Univ. Pr., Inc.

MEAL PLANNING

see Menus; Nutrition

MEASLES

Hawkins, Trisha. Everything You Need to Know about Measles & Rubella. 2005. (Need to Know Library). (Illus.). 64p. (YA). (gr. 7-12). 25.25 (978-0-8239-3322-8(9)) Rosen Publishing Group, Inc., The.

Rosaler, Maxine. Measles. 2004. (Epidemics Ser.). (Illus.). 64p. (J). lib. bdg. 26.50 (978-1-4042-0256-6(0)) Rosen Publishing Group, Inc., The.

Saffer, Barbara. Measles & Rubella. 2005. (Diseases & Disorders Ser.). (Illus.). 112p. (J). (gr. 4-7). lib. bdg. 32.45 (978-1-59018-410-3(6) , Lucent Bks.) Thomson Gale.

MEASURES

see Weights and Measures

MEASURING

see Mensuration

MEASURING INSTRUMENTS

Aboff, Marcie. The Tallest Snowman. Gray, Sara, illus. 2007. (J). lib. bdg. (***978-1-4048-3666-2(7))** Picture Window Bks.

Benchmark Education Staff. Measuring Matter: Solids, Liquids, & Gases. 2005. 2.00 (***978-1-4108-4651-8(2))** Benchmark Education Co.

Chrismer, Melanie. Math Tools. 2006. 32p. (YA). (gr. 1-2). pap. 5.95 (978-0-516-25550-7(9) , Children's Pr.) Scholastic Library Publishing.

Clark, John Owens Edward. Electrical Measurement, 9 vols., Vol. 4. 2002. (Illus.). (J). (978-0-7172-5632-7(4) , Grolier) Scholastic Library Publishing.

—Force & Pressure, 9 vols., Vol. 3. 2002. (Illus.). (J). (978-0-7172-5631-0(6) , Grolier) Scholastic Library Publishing.

—Length & Distance, 9 vols., Vol. 1. 2002. (Illus.). (J). (978-0-7172-5629-7(4) , Grolier) Scholastic Library Publishing.

—Measuring Time, 9 vols., Vol. 2. 2002. (Illus.). (J). (978-0-7172-5630-3(8) , Grolier) Scholastic Library Publishing.

—Scientific Analysis, 9 vols., Vol. 8. 2002. (Illus.). (J). (978-0-7172-5636-5(7) , Grolier) Scholastic Library Publishing.

—Scientific Classification, 9 vols., Vol. 9. 2002. (Illus.). (J). (978-0-7172-5637-2(5) , Grolier) Scholastic Library Publishing.

—Under the Microscope: Science Tools, 9 vols., Set. Incl. Vol. 1. Length & Distance. (978-0-7172-5629-7(4)); Vol. 2. Measuring Time. (978-0-7172-5630-3(8)); Vol. 3. Force & Pressure. (978-0-7172-5631-0(6)); Vol. 4. Electrical Measurement. (978-0-7172-5632-7(4)); Vol. 5. Using Visible Light. (978-0-7172-5633-4(2)); Vol. 6. Using Invisible Light. (978-0-7172-5634-1(0)); Vol. 7. Using Sound. (978-0-7172-5635-8(9)); Vol. 8. Scientific Analysis. (978-0-7172-5636-5(7)); Vol. 9. Scientific Classification. (978-0-7172-5637-2(5)); (J). (Illus.). 432p. 2002. 239.00 (978-0-7172-5628-0(6) , Grolier) Scholastic Library Publishing.

—Using Invisible Light, 9 vols., Vol. 6. 2002. (Illus.). (J). (978-0-7172-5634-1(0) , Grolier) Scholastic Library Publishing.

—Using Sound, 9 vols., Vol. 7. 2002. (Illus.). (J). (978-0-7172-5635-8(9) , Grolier) Scholastic Library Publishing.

—Using Visible Light, 9 vols., Vol. 5. 2002. (Illus.). (J). (978-0-7172-5633-4(2) , Grolier) Scholastic Library Publishing.

Doudna, Kelly. She'll use a Ruler So You Won't Fool Her. 2007. (Illus.). 24p. (J). 19.93 (978-1-59928-618-1(1) , SandCastle) ABDO Publishing Co.

M
N
O

—She'll Use a Ruler So You Won't Fool Her! 2006. (Illus.). 24p. (J). pap. (978-1-59928-619-8(X)) ABDO Publishing Co.

Eboch, Chris. Science Measurements: How Heavy?, How Long?, How Hot? Davis, Jon, illus. 2007. (Amazing Science Ser.). (J). 23.93 (978-1-4048-2197-2(X)) Picture Window Bks.

Furgang, Kathy. Instrumentos para medir en ciencias & Science Measuring Tools. 2005. spiral bd. 88.00 (*978-1-4108-5727-9(1)) Benchmark Education Co.

Harcourt School Publishers Staff. How Many Carmens? Advanced Level. 3rd ed. 2002. (Trophies Reading Program Ser.). (Illus.). pap. 5.10 (978-0-15-323102-5(5)) Harcourt Schl. Pubs.

Hutchins, Hazel. A Second Is a Hiccup: A Child's Book of Time. Denton, Kady MacDonald, illus. (J). 2008. 16.99 (978-0-439-83110-9(5)); 2007. 40p. 16.99 (978-0-439-83106-2(7)) Scholastic, Inc. (Levine, Arthur A. Bks.).

Matos, Rebecca. Measuring Matter: Solids, Liquids, & Gases. 2005. 39.00 (*978-1-4108-4603-7(2)) Benchmark Education Co.

Pistoia, Sara. Time. 2006. (MathBooks Ser.). (Illus.). 24p. (J). 24.21 (978-1-59296-692-9(6)) Child's World, Inc.

Rivera, Sheila. Measuring Cup. 2006. (First Step Nonfiction Ser.). (Illus.). 8p. (J). pap. (978-0-8225-5714-2(2) , Lerner Pubns.) Lerner Publishing Group.

—Ruler. 2006. (First Step Nonfiction Ser.). (Illus.). 8p. (J). pap. (978-0-8225-5715-9(0) , Lerner Pubns.) Lerner Publishing Group.

Roy, Jennifer Rozines & Roy, Gregory. Measuring at Home. 2006. (Math All Around Ser.). (Illus.). 32p. (J). lib. bdg. 28.50 (978-0-7614-2263-1(3) , Benchmark Bks.) Cavendish, Marshall Corp.

Sullivan, Erin Ash. Measuring Matter. 2005. (Navigators Ser.). (J). pap. 38.00 (*978-1-4108-5070-6(6)) Benchmark Education Co.

Whitehouse, Patricia. Measure It. (Illus.). 24p. 2007. (J). (978-1-60044-209-4(9)); 2005. pap. 27.00 (*978-1-59515-563-4(5)) Rourke Publishing, LLC.

Willis, Shirley. Dime Cuanto Pesa. 2000. (gr. k-3). (SPA.). lib. bdg. 14.10 (978-0-613-72666-5(9)); (J). 12.75 (978-0-606-20148-3(3)) Tandem Library Bks.

—Dime Que Tan Lejos Esta de Aqui. 2000. (gr. k-3). (SPA.). lib. bdg. 14.10 (978-0-613-72672-6(3)); (J). 12.75 (978-0-606-20153-7(X)) Tandem Library Bks.

—Dime Que Tan Rapidamente Va. 2000. (Los Estupendos Whiz Kids, Spanish Edition Ser.). (SPA., Illus.). 32p. (J). (gr. 1-3). pap. 5.95 (978-0-531-15993-4(0) , OD30044, Watts, Franklin) Scholastic Library Publishing.

—Dime Que Tan Rapidamente Va. 2000. (gr. k-3). (SPA.). lib. bdg. 14.10 (978-0-613-72673-3(1)); (J). 12.75 (978-0-606-20154-4(8)) Tandem Library Bks.

MEAT INDUSTRY AND TRADE

Klingel, Cynthia Fitterer & Noyed, Robert B. Meat. Andersen, Gregg, photos by. 2002. (Weekly Reader Early Learning Library). (Illus.). 24p. (J). (ps up). pap. 5.95 (978-0-8368-3147-4(0)); lib. bdg. 19.33 (978-0-8368-3058-3(X)) Stevens, Gareth Inc. (Weekly Reader Early Learning Library).

Nelson, Robin. Meats & Proteins. 2003. (First Step Nonfiction Ser.). (Illus.). 24p. (J). (gr. k-2). 18.60 (978-0-8225-4630-6(2)) Lerner Publishing Group.

MECHANICAL BRAINS

see Computers; Cybernetics

MECHANICAL DRAWING

see also Geometrical Drawing; Graphic Methods; Lettering

Biesty, Stephen & Platt, Richard. The Coolest Cross-Sections Ever. 2001. (Illus.). 128p. (J). 24.99 (978-0-7894-7964-8(8)) Dorling Kindersley Publishing, Inc.

Fundamentals of Drafting Using Autocad. 2nd ed. 1998. (TP - Technology Education Ser.). 656p. (C). (gr. k-12). pap., wbk. ed. 37.95 (978-0-538-65983-3(1)) Thomson South-Western.

Hepler, Donald E., et al. Architecture: Drafting & Design. 7th rev. ed. 1999. (Illus.). 256p. (YA). (gr. 6-12). stu. ed., wbk. ed. 14.99 (978-0-02-637069-1(7)) Glencoe/McGraw-Hill.

Peach, S. Technical Drawing. 1999. (Practical Guides Ser.). (Illus.). 48p. (YA). (gr. 6 up). lib. bdg. 14.96 (978-0-88110-247-5(4)) EDC Publishing.

Spencer, Henry C., et al. Basic Technical Drawing Problems. 6th ed. 1999. (Illus.). (YA). (gr. 6-12). 18.80 (978-0-02-685661-4(1)) Glencoe/McGraw-Hill.

MECHANICAL ENGINEERING

see also Electric Engineering; Engines; Machinery; Power (Mechanics)

Armentrout, David & Armentrout, Patricia. An Inclined Plane. 2003. (How Can I Experiment with Simple Machines? Ser.). (Illus.). 32p. (gr. 1-4). 19.95 (978-1-58952-333-3(4)) Rourke Publishing, LLC.

Dahl, Michael & Shea, Denise. Desliza y Empuja: Un Libro Sobre Rampas. Shea, Denise, illus. 2007. (ENG & SPA.). lib. bdg. (*978-1-4048-3226-8(2)) Picture Window Bks.

Domaine, Helena. Robotics. 2006. (Cool Science Ser.). (Illus.). 48p. (J). (gr. 4-8). lib. bdg. 26.60 (978-0-8225-2112-9(1) , Lerner Pubns.) Lerner Publishing Group.

Douglas, Lloyd G. What Is a Pulley? 2002. (Welcome Bks.). (Illus.). 24p. (J). (ps-2). pap. 4.95 (978-0-516-24024-4(2) , Children's Pr.) Scholastic Library Publishing.

Erickson, Sheldon, et al. Constructores II: Ingenieria Creativa con Construcciones Lego. Erickson, Sheldon et al, eds. Mason, Renee, illus. 2001. (SPA.). 161p. (J). pap. 18.95 (978-1-881431-92-3(4) , 1547) AIMS Education Foundation.

Frost, Helen. What Are Wedges? Saunders-Smith, Gail, ed. 2001. (Looking at Simple Machines Ser.). (Illus.). 24p. (J). (gr. k-1). lib. bdg. 15.93 (978-0-7368-0849-1(3) , Pebble Bks.) Capstone Pr., Inc.

Holland, Gini. Soft & Hard. 2007. (J). pap. (*978-0-8368-8301-5(2)); 24p. lib. bdg. 17.27 (*978-0-8368-8296-4(2)) Stevens, Gareth Inc. (Weekly Reader Early Learning Library).

Randolph, Joanne. Gears in My World. 2006. (My World of Science Ser.). (Illus.). 24p. (J). 16.00 (978-1-4042-3311-9(3) , PowerKids Pr.) Rosen Publishing Group, Inc., The.

—Gears in My World: Engranajes en Mi Mundo. 2006. (My World of Science/ Mi mundo y la Ciencia Ser.). (ENG & SPA.). 16.00 (978-1-4042-3323-2(7) , PowerKids Pr.) Rosen Publishing Group, Inc., The.

—Inclined Planes in My World. 2006. (My World of Science Ser.). (Illus.). 24p. (J). 16.00 (978-1-4042-3312-6(1) , PowerKids Pr.) Rosen Publishing Group, Inc., The.

—Inclined Planes in My World: Planos Inclinados en Mi Mundo. 2006. (My World of Science/ Mi mundo y la Ciencia Ser.). (ENG & SPA.). 16.00 (978-1-4042-3324-9(5) , PowerKids Pr.) Rosen Publishing Group, Inc., The.

—Levers in My World. 2006. (My World of Science Ser.). (Illus.). 24p. (J). 16.00 (978-1-4042-3309-6(1) , PowerKids Pr.) Rosen Publishing Group, Inc., The.

—Levers in My World: Palancas en Mi Mundo. 2006. (My World of Science/ Mi mundo y la Ciencia Ser.). (ENG & SPA.). 16.00 (978-1-4042-3321-8(0) , Buenas Letra) Rosen Publishing Group, Inc., The.

—Pulleys in My World. 2006. (My World of Science Ser.). (Illus.). 24p. (J). 16.00 (978-1-4042-3308-9(3) , PowerKids Pr.) Rosen Publishing Group, Inc., The.

—Pulleys in My World: Poleas en Mi Mundo. 2006. (My World of Science/ Mi mundo y la Ciencia Ser.). (ENG & SPA., Illus.). 24p. (J). 16.00 (978-1-4042-3320-1(2) , PowerKids Pr.) Rosen Publishing Group, Inc., The.

—Wedges in My World. 2006. (My World of Science Ser.). (Illus.). 24p. (J). 16.00 (978-1-4042-3310-2(5) , PowerKids Pr.) Rosen Publishing Group, Inc., The.

—Wedges in My World: Cuuas en Mi Mundo. 2006. (My World of Science/ Mi mundo y la Ciencia Ser.). (ENG & SPA.). (J). 16.00 (978-1-4042-3322-5(9) , PowerKids Pr.) Rosen Publishing Group, Inc., The.

Rivera, Sheila. Bending. 2007. (First Step Nonfiction Ser.). (J). pap. (978-0-8225-6416-4(5)) Lerner Publishing Group.

Royston, Angela. Pulleys & Gears. (Machines in Action Ser.). (Illus.). 32p. (J). (gr. 3-5). 2001. pap. 7.50 (978-1-4034-4085-3(9)); 2000. lib. bdg. 22.79 (978-1-57572-320-4(4)) Heinemann Library.

VanVoorst, Jennifer. Make It Move! 2003. (J). 15.93 (978-0-7368-2939-7(3)); pap. (978-0-7368-2898-7(2)) Yellow Umbrella Pr.

MECHANICS

see also Dynamics; Force and Energy; Hydrostatics; Liquids; Machinery; Motion; Power (Mechanics); Steam-Engines; Vibration

Adams, Martin, et al. Mechanics: Complete Advanced Level Mathematics. 1999. (Illus.). 616p. (YA). (gr. 11 up). pap. 43.50 (978-0-7487-3559-4(3)) Nelson Thornes Ltd. GBR. *Dist:* Trans-Atlantic Pubns., Inc.

Auto Mechanics, 6 vols. (gr. 2-5). 36.95 (978-0-7368-8466-2(1)) Red Brick Learning.

Changing Shape. 2004. (Illus.). 24p. (J). (ps-ps). pap. 5.75 (978-1-4034-5105-7(2)) Heinemann Library.

Cipriano, Jeri. Empujar y Halar. 2005. Tr. of Push & Pull. (SPA., Illus.). 16p. (J). (gr. 1 up). lib. bdg. 15.93 (978-0-7368-4164-1(4)) Capstone Pr., Inc.

Endres, Hollie J. Push & Pull. 2003. (Yellow Umbrella Books for Early Readers). (Illus.). 17p. (J). 15.93 (978-0-7368-2921-2(0)); pap. (978-0-7368-2880-2(X)) Yellow Umbrella Pr.

Fleisher, Paul. Liquids & Gases: Principles of Fluid Mechanics. 2005. (Secrets of the Universe Ser.). (Illus.). 80p. (gr. 6-12). 25.26 (978-0-8225-2988-0(2)) Lerner Publishing Group.

—Objects in Motion: Principles of Classical Mechanics. 2005. (Secrets of the Universe Ser.). (Illus.). 80p. (gr. 6-12). 25.26 (978-0-8225-2985-9(8)) Lerner Publishing Group.

Glover, David. Levers. 2002. (Simple Machines Ser.). (Illus.). 24p. (J). (gr. 2-4). pap. 6.50 (978-1-4034-0056-7(3) , 91500) Heinemann Library.

—Screws. 2002. (Simple Machines Ser.). (Illus.). 24p. (J). (gr. 2-4). pap. 6.50 (978-1-4034-0059-8(8) , 91503) Heinemann Library.

Hoyt, Linda & Therriault, Tere. Mastering the Mechanics 2 3. 2008. 160p. pap. 19.99 (*978-0-545-04878-1(8) , Teaching Resources) Scholastic, Inc.

—Mastering the Mechanics 4 5. 2008. 160p. pap. 19.99 (*978-0-545-04879-8(6) , Teaching Resources) Scholastic, Inc.

—Mastering the Mechanics K 1. 2008. 160p. pap. 19.99 (*978-0-545-04877-4(X) , Teaching Resources) Scholastic, Inc.

Inquiry Investigations: Simple Mechanics. 2004. 48p. (J). pap. 6.99 (978-0-88724-266-3(9) , CD-2363) Carson-Dellosa Publishing Co., Inc.

Mechanik I: Bewegungslehre. (Duden Abiturhilfen Ser.). (GER.). 96p. (YA). (gr. 11). (978-3-411-04451-1(9)) Bibliographisches Institut & F. A. Brockhaus AG DEU. *Dist:* International Bk. Import Service, Inc.

Mechanik II: Erhaltungssaetze. (Duden Abiturhilfen Ser.). (GER.). 96p. (YA). (gr. 11). (978-3-411-05181-6(7)) Bibliographisches Institut & F. A. Brockhaus AG DEU. *Dist:* International Bk. Import Service, Inc.

O'Neil, Sarah. Springs. 1999. (ps-2). lib. bdg. 11.80 (978-0-613-30752-9(6)) Tandem Library Bks.

Pentland, Peter & Stoyles, Pennie. Toy & Game Science. 2003. (Science & Scientists Ser.). (Illus.). 32p. (gr. 4-8). lib. bdg. 27.00 (978-0-7910-7013-0(1) , Chelsea Hse.) Facts On File, Inc.

Pipe, Jim. Movement: Things That Go. 2005. (Science Starters Ser.). 32p. (J). (gr. 1-4). lib. bdg. 27.10 (978-1-59604-018-2(1)) Stargazer Bks.

School Mathematics Project Staff. Mechanics 1. rev. ed. 2001. (SMP Ser.). (Illus.). 168p. pap. 19.80 (978-0-521-78800-7(5)) Cambridge Univ. Pr.

Schuh, Mari C. Full Speed Ahead: The Science of Going Fast. 2008. (Shockwave: Earth & Physical Science Ser.). 32p. (J). pap. 6.95 (*978-0-531-18835-4(3) , Children's Pr.) Scholastic Library Publishing.

Spilsbury, Richard. Speed & Acceleration. 2006. (Fantastic Forces Ser.). (Illus.). 32p. (J). pap. (978-1-4034-8178-8(4)); lib. bdg. (978-1-4034-8173-3(3)) Heinemann Library.

Walker, Sally M. & Feldmann, Roseann. Tornillos. 2005. (Libros de Fisica para Madrugadores (Early Bird Physics) Ser.). (SPA & ENG., Illus.). 48p. (J). (gr. 3-7). lib. bdg. 25.26 (978-0-8225-2974-3(2) , Ediciones Lerner) Lerner Publishing Group.

—Work. King, Andy, photos by. 2002. (Illus.). 48p. (978-0-8225-2211-9(X) , Lerner Pubns.) Lerner Publishing Group.

Walker, Sally M., et al. Work. 2005. (Early Bird Physics Ser.). (Illus.). 48p. (gr. 3-6). lib. bdg. 25.26 (978-0-8225-2217-1(9)) Lerner Publishing Group.

Welsbacher, Anne. Levers. 2000. (Bridgestone Science Library). (Illus.). 24p. (J). (gr. 1-2). lib. bdg. 18.60 (978-0-7368-0611-4(3) , Bridgestone Bks.) Capstone Pr., Inc.

—Pulleys. 2000. (Bridgestone Science Library). (Illus.). 24p. (J). (gr. 1-2). lib. bdg. 18.60 (978-0-7368-0612-1(1) , Bridgestone Bks.) Capstone Pr., Inc.

Whitehouse, Patricia, tr. Changing Shape. 2004. (J). lib. bdg. (978-1-4034-5100-2(1)) Heinemann Library.

Wood, Robert W. Mechanics Fundamentals. 1999. (Funtastic Science Activities for Kids Ser.). (Illus.). xii, 148p. (J). (gr. 4-7). 16.95 (978-0-7910-4844-3(6) , Chelsea Hse.) Facts On File, Inc.

MECHANICS (PERSONS)

Frost, Helen. We Need Auto Mechanics. 2004. (Helpers in Our Community Ser.). (Illus.). 24p. (J). lib. bdg. 15.93 (978-0-7368-2574-0(6) , Pebble Bks.) Capstone Pr., Inc.

Liebman, Dan. Quiero Ser Mecanico. 2003. Tr. of I Want to Be a Mechanic. (SPA.). (gr. 5-8). lib. bdg. 14.15 (978-0-613-78622-5(X)) Tandem Library Bks.

Liebman, Daniel. I Want to Be a Mechanic. 2003. (I Want to Be Ser.). (Illus.). 24p. (J). (ps-2). pap. 3.99 (978-1-55297-693-7(9)); lib. bdg. 14.95 (978-1-55297-695-1(5)) Firefly Bks., Ltd.

—Quiero Ser Mecanico. 2003. (Quiero Ser.). (SPA., Illus.). 24p. (J). (ps-2). pap. 5.99 (978-1-55297-728-6(5)) Firefly Bks., Ltd.

Macnair, Patricia Ann. Movers & Shapers. 2004. (Bodyscope Ser.). (Illus.). 40p. (J). (gr. 3-5). 9.95 (978-0-7534-5791-7(1) , Kingfisher) Houghton Mifflin Co. Trade & Reference Div.

Weintraub, Aileen. Auto Mechanic. 2004. (Great Jobs Ser.). (Illus.). 48p. (J). 24.00 (978-0-516-24090-9(0) , Children's Pr.) Scholastic Library Publishing.

Whitehouse, Patricia. What Can Jump? 2003. (Illus.). 24p. (J). lib. bdg. 18.50 (978-1-4034-4366-3(1)) Heinemann Library.

—What Can Jump? 2003. (ps-2). lib. bdg. 28.65 (978-0-613-84306-5(1)) Tandem Library Bks.

Winne, Joanne. A Day with a Mechanic. 2001. (Welcome Bks.). (Illus.). 24p. (J). (ps-2). pap. 4.95 (978-0-516-23062-7(X) , Children's Pr.) Scholastic Library Publishing.

—Day with a Mechanic. 2001. (gr. k-3). lib. bdg. 12.95 (978-0-613-58762-4(6)) Tandem Library Bks.

MEDAL OF HONOR

Alter, Judy. Audie Murphy: War Hero & Movie Star. 2007. 72p. (YA). 14.95 (*978-1-933337-19-7(2)) State Hse. Pr.

Stevens, Paul D., ed. The Congressional Medal of Honor: The Names, the Deeds. 2003. (Illus.). 1105p. 27.50 (978-0-918495-01-3(6)) Sharp & Dunnigan.

Wachtel, Roger. The Medal of Honor. 2002. (Cornerstones of Freedom). (Illus.). 48p. (J). (gr. 4-6). 26.00 (978-0-516-22265-3(1) , Children's Pr.) Scholastic Library Publishing.

MEDICAL BOTANY

see Botany, Medical

MEDICAL CENTERS

see also Hospitals

Ethan, Eric. Ambulances. Ethan, Eric, photos by. 2002. (Emergency Vehicles Ser.). (Illus.). 24p. (YA). (gr. 1 up). lib. bdg. 20.67 (978-0-8368-3044-6(X)) Stevens, Gareth Inc.

Smith, Ian. First Experiences: Going to the Doctor. 2004. (QEB Start Talking Ser.). (Illus.). 24p. (J). lib. bdg. 15.95 (978-1-59566-003-9(8)) QEB Publishing Inc.

MEDICAL PROFESSION

see Medicine; Physicians

MEDICAL RESEARCH

see Medicine—Research

MEDICAL TECHNOLOGY

Gibson, Karen Bush. Emergency Medical Technicians. 2000. (Community Helpers Ser.). (Illus.). 92p. (J). (gr. 1-2). 18.60 (978-0-7368-0623-7(7) , Bridgestone Bks.) Capstone Pr., Inc.

Heath, David. Crime Lab Technician. (Careers Without College Ser.). pap. 6.95 (978-0-7368-8533-1(1) , LifeMatters Bks.) Capstone Pr., Inc.

Moe, Barbara. The Revolution in Medical Imaging. 2005. (Library of Medicine of the Future). (Illus.). 64p. (YA). (gr. 7-12). lib. bdg. 26.50 (978-0-8239-3672-4(4)) Rosen Publishing Group, Inc., The.

Nichols, Catherine. Medical Marvels: A Chapter Book. (True Tales Ser.). (J). 2005. (Illus.). 48p. (gr. 2-4). pap. 4.95 (978-0-516-24686-4(0)); 2004. 22.50 (978-0-516-23726-8(8)) Scholastic Library Publishing. (Children's Pr.).

Rooney, Anne. Machines in Medicine. 2006. (Illus.). 64p. (J). lib. bdg. (*978-0-8368-7867-7(1) , World Almanac Library) Stevens, Gareth Inc.

Routh, Kristina. Medicine. 2005. (Technology All Around Us Ser.). (Illus.). 32p. (J). (gr. 4-7). lib. bdg. 27.10 (978-1-58340-751-6(0)) Smart Apple Media.

Solway, Andrew. Seeing Inside the Body. 2006. (Illus.). 64p. (J). lib. bdg. (*978-0-8368-7869-1(8) , World Almanac Library) Stevens, Gareth Inc.

Williams, Kara. Fertility Technology: The Baby Debate. 2003. (Focus on Science & Society Ser.). (Illus.). 64p. (YA). (gr. 4-6). lib. bdg. 26.50 (978-0-8239-3210-8(9) , FSFETE) Rosen Publishing Group, Inc., The.

Yount, Lisa. Medical Technology. annot. ed. 1998. (Milestones in Discovery & Invention Ser.). (Illus.). 160p. (J). (gr. 6-12). 25.00 (978-0-8160-3568-7(7)) Facts On File, Inc.

MEDICAL TECHNOLOGY—VOCATIONAL GUIDANCE

Bryan, Nichol. Paramedics. 2003. (Everyday Heroes (cb) Ser.). (Illus.). 32p. (J). (gr. k-6). lib. bdg. 22.78 (978-1-57765-856-6(6)) ABDO Publishing Co.

J. G. Ferguson Publishing Company Staff, ed. Careers in Focus: Medical Technicians. 3rd ed. 2001. (Careers in Focus Ser.). (Illus.). 176-192p. (YA). (gr. 7 up). lib. bdg. 22.95 (978-0-89434-408-4(0) , F616, Ferguson Publishing Co.) Facts On File, Inc.

Mattern, Joanne. Emergency Medical Technicians. 2002. (Reading Power Ser.). (Illus.). 24p. (J). lib. bdg. 17.25 (978-0-8239-5980-8(5) , PowerKids Pr.) Rosen Publishing Group, Inc., The.

Primm, E. Russell. Emergency Medical Technician. (Careers Without College Ser.). pap. 6.95 (978-0-7368-8019-0(4) , LifeMatters Bks.) Capstone Pr., Inc.

—Emergency Medical Technician. 1998. (Careers Without College Ser.). (Illus.). 48p. (J). (gr. 3-7). pap. 19.00 (978-0-516-21281-4(8) , Children's Pr.) Scholastic Library Publishing.

—Medical Assistant. 1998. (Careers Without College Ser.). (Illus.). 48p. (J). (gr. 3-7). pap. 19.00 (978-0-516-21284-5(2) , Children's Pr.) Scholastic Library Publishing.

—Surgical Technician. 1998. (Careers Without College Ser.). (Illus.). 48p. (J). (gr. 3-7). pap. 19.00 (978-0-516-21288-3(5) , Children's Pr.) Scholastic Library Publishing.

MEDICI, LORENZO DE', 1449-1492

Greenblatt, Miriam. Lorenzo de Medici & Renaissance Italy. 2002. (Rulers & Their Times Ser.). (Illus.). 80p. (J). (gr. 8-12). lib. bdg. 29.93 (978-0-7614-1490-2(8) , Benchmark Bks.) Cavendish, Marshall Corp.

Hancock, Lee. Lorenzo de' Medici: Florence's Great Leader & Patron of the Arts. 2004. (Rulers, Scholars, & Artists of Renaissance Europe Ser.). (Illus.). 112p. (J). lib. bdg. 31.95 (978-1-4042-0315-0(X)) Rosen Publishing Group, Inc., The.

MEDICINAL PLANTS

see Botany, Medical

MEDICINE

see also Anatomy; Bacteriology; Botany, Medical; Health; Hospitals; Materia Medica; Mind and Body; Pathology; Pharmacy; Physiology

also headings beginning with the word Medical

Allergies, Asthma & Exercise: The Science of Health. 1999. (Science @ Work Ser.). (Illus.). 48p. (J). (gr. 4-6). pap. 27.12 (978-0-7398-0140-6(6)) Raintree.

Ambulances. (Mighty MacHines Ser.). 24p. (J). 6.95 (978-0-7368-5137-4(2)) Capstone Pr., Inc.

Anderson, Catherine Corley. John F. Kennedy. 2006. (First Step Nonfiction Ser.). (Illus.). 112p. (J). (gr. 3-7). 27.93 (978-0-8225-2643-8(3) , Lerner Pubns.) Lerner Publishing Group.

Anderson, Sheila. Clinic. 2008. (J). pap. (*978-0-8225-8840-5(4)) Lerner Publishing Group.

Arnold, Nick. Medicine. 1999. (Tomorrow's Technology Ser.). (Illus.). 32p. (J). lib. bdg. 16.95 (978-1-929298-39-6(0)) Chrysalis Education.

Bailey, Gerry. Healing & Medicine. Boulter, Steve & Smith, Jan, illus. 2005. (Crafty Inventions Ser.). 48p. (C). (gr. 4-6). 26.60 (978-1-4048-1040-2(4)) Picture Window Bks.

Benchmark Education Staff. Fighting Disease. 2005. 2.00 (*978-1-4108-4657-0(1)) Benchmark Education Co.

Billitteri, Thomas J. Alternative Medicine. 2001. (Medical Library: up). (Illus.). 128p. (gr. 7 up). lib. bdg. 26.90 (978-0-7613-0965-9(9) , Twenty-First Century Bks.) Lerner Publishing Group.

Binder, Rudi. The Meaning: An Odyssey in Medicine. 1998. 291p. (YA). per. 11.95 (978-1-893309-01-2(0) , 2) Red Maple Publishing.

Brill, Marlene Targ. Doctors. (Pull Ahead Bks.). (Illus.). 32p. (J). 2005. lib. bdg. 22.60 (978-0-8225-1689-7(6)); 2004. pap. 5.95 (978-0-8225-2531-8(3) , Lerner Pubns.) Lerner Publishing Group.

Carlson, Dale. ¿Adonde Vamos? Dentro y Fuera de Tumente. Guix, Joan Carles, tr. Nicklaus, Carol, illus. 2004. (SPA.). 64p. (978-84-9754-117-6(0) , 88303) Ediciones Oniro S.A.

Chandler, Alton. A Salute to African American in Medicine: Learning. Chapman, L., ed. Still, Wayne A., illus. 24p. (Orig.). (J). (gr. 3-8). pap. 1.75 (978-1-877804-17-5(7)) Chandler/White Publishing Co.

Clued in! on Medicines. 2005. (J). 4.95 (978-1-55548-149-0(3)) Human Relations Media.

Cobb, Allan B. First Responders. 2006. (Extreme Careers Ser.). (Illus.). 64p. (J). (gr. 5-8). lib. bdg. 26.50 (978-1-4042-0944-2(1)) Rosen Publishing Group, Inc., The.

Cox, Judith. The Wellness Tree. Rogers, Denny, illus. 2003. 32p. (J). (gr. k-4). 19.95 (978-1-878044-29-7(X)) Mayhaven Publishing.

Dawson, Ian. Prehistoric & Egyptian Medicine. 2005. (Illus.). 64p. (J). 19.95 (978-1-59270-035-6(7)) Enchanted Lion Bks., LLC.

Doctors. (Community Helpers Ser.). 24p. (J). 6.95 (978-0-7368-8453-2(X)) Capstone Pr., Inc.

Edelson, Edward. Sports Medicine. 1999. (Twenty-First Century Health & Wellness Ser.). (Illus.). 128p. (YA). (gr. 7 up). 36.00 (978-0-7910-5521-2(3) , Chelsea Hse.) Facts On File, Inc.

Egendorf, Laura K., ed. Medicine. 2002. (Opposing Viewpoints Ser.). (Illus.). 186p. lib. bdg. 36.20 (978-0-7377-1234-6(1)); 200p. (YA). (gr. 10-12). pap. 24.95 (978-0-7377-1233-9(3)) Thomson Gale. (Greenhaven Pr., Inc.).

Elliott, Lynne. Medieval Medicine & the Plague. 2005. (Medieval World Ser.). (Illus.). 32p. (J). (gr. 4-9). (978-0-7787-1358-6(X)) Crabtree Publishing Co.

Ellis, Catherine. Cars & Trucks. 2007. (Mega Military Machines Ser.). (Illus.). 24p. (J). (gr. k-5). lib. bdg. 21.25 (978-1-4042-3669-1(4)) Rosen Publishing Group, Inc., The.

Faison, Ashley Starr & Ackerman, Bettie Bennett. The Garden of Hope: A Story about the Hospice Experience. 2005. (Illus.). (J). (***978-0-9774691-0-9(7)***) Hospice & Community Care Pubns.

Gail Stewart. Medicine. 2004. (Yesterday & Today Ser.). (Illus.). 32p. (J). 23.70 (978-1-56711-833-9(X) , Blackbirch Pr., Inc.) Thomson Gale.

Gilpin, Daniel. Medicine. 2004. (History of Invention Ser.). (Illus.). 96p. (YA). (gr. 6-12). 35.00 (978-0-8160-5442-8(8)) Facts On File, Inc.

Gordon, James S. Holistic Medicine. 2000. (Twenty-First Century Health & Wellness Ser.). (Illus.). 116p. (J). (gr. 7-12). 36.00 (978-0-7910-5984-5(7) , Chelsea Hse.) Facts On File, Inc.

Gosselin, Kim. The ABC's of Asthma: An Asthma Alphabet Book for Kids of All Ages. Ravanelli, Terry, illus. 1998. 34p. (J). (ps-3). pap. 11.95 (978-1-891383-04-5(3)) JayJo Bks., LLC.

Goulding, Sylvia. Illness & Injury. 2005. (Healthy Kids Ser.). (Illus.). 32p. (gr. 3-6). 19.95 (978-1-59515-206-0(7)) Rourke Publishing, LLC.

Grover, Jan. Healthcare. 2007. (Current Controversies Ser.). 240p. (J). (gr. 10-12). 36.20 (***978-0-7377-3427-0(2)*** , Greenhaven Pr., Inc.) Thomson Gale.

Hapka, Cathy. My Little Doctor Bag Book. Sharp, Paul, illus. 2005. (J). (***978-1-57151-754-8(5)***) Playhouse Publishing.

Health Issues New Titles: Incl. Asthma/Cancer/Diabetes/Dyslexia, 4 bks. 2002. (Illus.). (YA). (gr. 6-8). lib. bdg. 114.16 (978-0-7398-5270-5(1)) Raintree.

Health Issues Series, 12 bks., Set. Incl. AIDS. Whelan. (YA). 2001. lib. bdg. 28.54 (978-0-7398-4771-8(6)); Alcohol. Lamb, Kirsten. (YA). 2002. lib. bdg. 28.54 (978-0-7398-4772-5(4)); Asthma. Lennard-Brown, Sarah. (J). 2002. lib. bdg. 28.54 (978-0-7398-5218-7(3)); Cancer. Lamb, Kirsten. (J). 2002. lib. bdg. 28.54 (978-0-7398-5219-4(1)); Diabetes. Whelan, Jo. (J). 2002. lib. bdg. 28.54 (978-0-7398-5220-0(5)); Drugs. Lennard-Brown, Sarah. (YA). 2002. lib. bdg. 28.54 (978-0-7398-4773-2(2)); Dyslexia. Wiltshire, Paula. (J). 2002. lib. bdg. 28.54 (978-0-7398-5221-7(3)); Eating Disorders. Whelan, Jo. (YA). 2001. lib. bdg. 28.54 (978-0-7398-4421-2(0)); Pregnancy. Lamb, Kirsten. (YA). 2001. lib. bdg. 28.54 (978-0-7398-4418-2(0)); Sexually Transmitted Diseases. Whelan, Jo. (YA). 2001. lib. bdg. 28.54 (978-0-7398-4420-5(2)); Smoking. Morgan, Sally. (YA). 2002. lib. bdg. 28.54 (978-0-7398-4774-9(0)); Stress & Depression. Lennard-Brown, Sarah. (YA). 2001. lib. bdg. 28.54 (978-0-7398-4419-9(9)); 64p. (gr. 6-8). (Illus.). 2002. Set lib. bdg. 342.72 (978-0-7398-5271-2(X)) Raintree.

Hersh, Iffy. Mommy Is an Histologist. (What Does Mommy Do? Ser.). (Illus.). (Orig.). (J). (gr. k-2). pap. 10.00 (978-0-936735-04-7(X)) Grove Educational Technologies.

Hyde, Margaret O. & Setaro, John F. Medicine's Brave New World: Bioengineering & the New Genetics. 2001. (Single Titles Ser.). (Illus.). 144p. (gr. 7 up). lib. bdg. 29.90 (978-0-7613-1706-7(6) , Twenty-First Century Bks.) Lerner Publishing Group.

Iserson, Kenneth V. Get into Medical School! A Guide for the Perplexed. 2nd ed. 2004. (Illus.). 512p. (Orig.). pap. 36.95 (978-1-883620-31-8(7)) Galen Pr., Ltd.

J. G. Ferguson Publishing Company Staff, contrib. by. Careers in Focus: Alternative Health Care. 2nd ed. 2003. (Careers in Focus Ser.). (Illus.). 224p. (YA). (gr. 6-12). 22.95 (978-0-8160-5483-1(5) , Ferguson Publishing Co.) Facts On File, Inc.

Jerome, Kate Boehm. Fighting Disease. 2003. (Human Body Ser.). (Illus.). 32p. (J). pap. (978-0-7922-8865-7(3)) National Geographic Society.

Judson, Karen. Medical Ethics: Life & Death Issues. 2001. (Issues in Focus Ser.). (Illus.). 128p. (YA). (gr. 6-12). lib. bdg. 26.60 (978-0-7660-1585-2(8)) Enslow Pubs., Inc.

Keen, Jared, ed. The Conquest of Disease: Understanding Global Issues. 2002. (Understanding Global Issues). (Illus.). 56p. (YA). (gr. 10-12). lib. bdg. 19.95 (978-1-58340-166-8(0)) Weigl Pubs., Inc.

Kerrod, Robin. Medicine. 2004. (J). lib. bdg. (978-1-58340-504-8(6)) Smart Apple Media.

Kidd, J. S. & Kidd, Renee A. Potent Natural Medicines: Mother Nature's Pharmacy. 2005. (Science & Society Ser.). 224p. (J). (gr. 6-12). 35.00 (978-0-8160-5607-1(2)) Facts On File, Inc.

Koellhoffer, Tara. Health & Medicine. 2006. (Illus.). 64p. (J). 30.00 (978-0-7910-9122-7(8) , Chelsea Clubhouse) Facts On File, Inc.

Kottke, Jan. Day with a Doctor. 2000. (gr. k-3). lib. bdg. 12.95 (978-0-613-58759-4(6)) Tandem Library Bks.

Kowalski, Kathiann M. Alternative Medicine: Is It for You? 1998. (Issues in Focus Ser.). (Illus.). 128p. (YA). (gr. 6-12). lib. bdg. 26.60 (978-0-89490-955-9(X)) Enslow Pubs., Inc.

Laney, Dawn. Biomedical Ethics. 2006. (History of Issues Ser.). (Illus.). 240p. (gr. 10-12). 36.20 (978-0-7377-2859-0(0) , Greenhaven Pr., Inc.) Thomson Gale.

Levchuck, Caroline M. & Drohan, Michele Ingber. Healthy Living, 3 vols. 2000. (J). (978-0-7876-3921-1(4)) Thomson Gale.

Levchuck, Caroline M. & Drohan, Michele Ingber, contrib. by. Healthy Living, 3 vols. 2000. (J). (978-0-7876-3919-8(2) , UXL); (978-0-7876-3920-4(6)) Thomson Gale.

The Library of Future Medicine. 2005. (Illus.). (gr. 7-12). lib. bdg. 159.00 (978-0-8239-3902-2(2)) Rosen Publishing Group, Inc., The.

Living With..., 8 bks., Set. Incl. Living with Asthma. Bee, Peta. lib. bdg. 25.69 (978-0-8172-5576-3(1)); Living with Blindness. Westcott, Patsy. lib. bdg. 25.69 (978-0-8172-5741-5(1)); 32p. (J). (gr. 1-5). 1999. (Illus.). 1999. Set lib. bdg. 205.52 o.p. (978-0-7398-1379-9(X)) Raintree.

Locke, Ian. Mad Medicine. Rowe, Alan, illus. 2003. 64p. (J). pap. 3.99 (978-0-330-37082-0(0) , Pan) Pan Macmillan GBR. *Dist:* Trafalgar Square Publishing.

MacDonald, Fiona. The Plague & Medicine in the Middle Ages. 2005. (World Almanac Library of the Middle Ages). (Illus.). 48p. (J). pap. (978-0-8368-5907-2(3) , World Almanac Library) Stevens, Gareth Inc.

—The Plague & Medicine In the Middle Ages. 2005. (World Almanac' Library of the Middle Ages). (Illus.). 48p. (J). (gr. 10-17). lib. bdg. 30.00 (978-0-8368-5898-3(0) , World Almanac Library) Stevens, Gareth Inc.

Masoff, Joy. All Better Now. Dickason, Jack, illus. 2008. 20p. (J). 9.95 (***978-1-60059-128-0(0)***) Lark Bks.

Mayo Clinic Staff, contrib. by. Alternative Medicine & Your Health. 2002. (Mayo Clinic on Health Ser.). (Illus.). 36,52p. (YA). (gr. 8 up). lib. bdg. (978-1-59084-248-5(0)) Mason Crest Pubs.

Medical Care. (YA). (gr. 6-12). pap. 10.95 (978-0-8224-4365-0(1)) Globe Fearon Educational Publishing.

Medical Language. 2001. (YA). (gr. 6-12). pap. 16.95 (978-0-8359-1512-0(3)) Globe Fearon Educational Publishing.

Medicine. 1999. (How Things Work Ser.). (Illus.). 144p. (J). (gr. 3). 19.95 (978-0-8094-7870-5(6)) Time-Life, Inc.

Miller, Heather. Doctor. 2003. (This Is What I Want to Be Ser.). (Illus.). 24p. (J). (ps-1). lib. bdg. 18.50 (978-1-4034-0367-4(8)); pap. 5.25 (978-1-4034-0589-0(1)) Heinemann Library.

Nardo, Don & Dudley, William. Biomedical Ethics. 2007. (Compact Research Ser.). 112p. (YA). lib. bdg. (***978-1-60152-013-5(1)***) ReferencePoint Pr., Inc.

Nelson, Kristin L. EMTs. (Pull Ahead Bks.). (J). 2005. (Illus.). 22.60 (978-0-8225-1690-3(X)); 2004. pap. (978-0-8225-5475-2(5) , Lerner Pubns.) Lerner Publishing Group.

Nichols, Catherine. Medical Marvels: A Chapter Book. (True Tales Ser.). (J). 2005. (Illus.). 48p. (gr. 2-4). pap. 4.95 (978-0-516-24686-4(0)); 2004. 22.50 (978-0-516-23726-8(8)) Scholastic Library Publishing. (Children's Pr.).

O'Shei, Tim. The World's Deadliest Diseases. 2006. (Edge Books, the World's Top Ten). (Illus.). 32p. (J). (978-0-7368-5452-8(5)) Capstone Pr., Inc.

Parker, Steve. Medicine. 2000. (Eyewitness Bks.). (Illus.). 64p. (J). (gr. 4-7). 15.99 (978-0-7894-5580-2(3)) Dorling Kindersley Publishing, Inc.

Parker, Steve & Dorling Kindersley Publishing Staff. Medicine. 2000. (Eyewitness Bks.). (Illus.). 64p. (J). (gr. 4-7). lib. bdg. 19.99 (978-0-7894-6722-5(4)) Dorling Kindersley Publishing, Inc.

Parry, Ann. Doctors Without Borders: Medecins Sans Frontieres. 2005. (Humanitarian Organizations Ser.). (Illus.). 32p. (J). (ps-8). lib. bdg. 22.95 (978-0-7910-8817-3(0) , Chelsea Hse.) Facts On File, Inc.

Parsons, Michelle Hyde. Fighting Disease. 2005. 42.00 (***978-1-4108-4609-9(1)***) Benchmark Education Co.

Ramutkowski, Barbara, et al. Glencoe Administrative Procedures for Medical Assisting: A Patient-Centered Approach. 1998. (Illus.). 368p. (C). (gr. 6-12). pap., stu. ed., wbk. ed. 34.00 (978-0-02-804864-2(4) , 9780028048642, McGraw-Hill Science, Engineering & Mathematics) McGraw-Hill Higher Education.

Randolph, Joanne. Ambulances. 2008. (J). lib. bdg. (***978-1-4042-4150-3(7)*** , PowerKids Pr.) Rosen Publishing Group, Inc., The.

Rattenbury, Jeanne. Understanding Alternative Medicine. 1999. (Venture Bks.). (Illus.). 128p. (YA). (gr. 8-12). 21.00 (978-0-531-11413-1(9) , Watts, Franklin) Scholastic Library Publishing.

Rau, Dana Meachen. Emergency Medical Technicians (EMT) 2007. (Tools We Use Ser.). 32p. (J). lib. bdg. 22.79 (***978-0-7614-2660-8(4)*** , Benchmark Bks.) Cavendish, Marshall Corp.

—EMTs/Los Paramédicos. 2007. (Tools We Use/ Instrumentos de Trabajo Ser.). (SPA & ENG.). 32p. (J). lib. bdg. 22.79 (***978-0-7614-2825-1(9)*** , Benchmark Bks.) Cavendish, Marshall Corp.

—Los Paramédicos. 2007. (Instrumentos de Trabajo Ser.). (SPA.). 32p. (J). lib. bdg. 22.79 (***978-0-7614-2801-5(1)*** , Benchmark Bks.) Cavendish, Marshall Corp.

Rivera, Sheila. Doctor. 2004. (First Step Nonfiction Ser.). (J). pap. (978-0-8225-5357-1(0) , Lerner Pubns.) Lerner Publishing Group.

Rohr, Ian. Emergency. 2006. (Real Deal - Yellow Ser.). (Illus.). 32p. (gr. 4-8). 19.00 (978-0-7910-9060-2(4)) Facts On File, Inc.

Rollins, Barbara B. & Dahl, Michael. Cause of Death. 2004. (Forensic Crime Solvers Ser.). (Illus.). 32p. (J). 22.60 (978-0-7368-2420-0(0)) Capstone Pr., Inc.

Romaine, Deborah S. Health Care. 2000. (Overview Ser.). (Illus.). 96p. (YA). (gr. 6-9). lib. bdg. 29.95 (978-1-56006-488-6(9) , LML00902-177851, Lucent Bks.) Thomson Gale.

Romero, Libby. Discover Medical Chemistry. 2006. pap. 39.00 (***978-1-4108-6502-1(9)***) Benchmark Education Co.

Routh, Kristina. Medicine. 2005. (Technology All Around Us Ser.). (Illus.). 32p. (J). (gr. 4-7). lib. bdg. 27.10 (978-1-58340-751-6(0)) Smart Apple Media.

Ruffin, David C. The Duties & Responsibilities of the Secretary of Health & Human Services. 2005. (Your Government in Action Ser.). (J). 21.95 (978-1-4042-2691-3(5) , PowerKids Pr.) Rosen Publishing Group, Inc., The.

Sally Ride Science Editors, Sally Ride Science. What Do You Want to Be? Explore Health Sciences. 2004. (J). 6.00 (978-0-9753920-3-4(4)) Sally Ride Science.

Schnapp, William David, et al. Medically Clueless: A Health Guide for Young People. 2002. (YA). (gr. 9-12). per. 8.95 (978-0-9719337-1-2(5)) Elma Colletes & Sons.

Sherrow, Victoria. Medical Imaging. 2006. (Great Inventions Ser.). (Illus.). 127p. (J). lib. bdg. 39.93 (978-0-7614-2231-0(5) , Benchmark Bks.) Cavendish, Marshall Corp.

Sieling, Peter. Folk Medicine. 2002. (North American Folklore Ser.). (Illus.). 112p. (YA). (gr. 7 up). lib. bdg. (978-1-59084-341-3(X)) Mason Crest Pubs.

Snedden, Robert. Medical Ethics: Changing Attitudes, 1900-2000. 1999. (Twentieth Century Issues Ser.). (Illus.). 64p. (J). (gr. 4-6). lib. bdg. 28.54 (978-0-8172-5893-1(0)) Raintree.

Snyder, Inez. Doctor Tools. 2002. (Welcome Bks.). 24p. (J). (ps-2). pap. 4.95 (978-0-516-24036-7(6) , Children's Pr.) Scholastic Library Publishing.

Soloway, Cindy. Mommy, What's an MRI? Steve, Sumner, ed. Susan, Lisbin, illus. 2006. (J). mass mkt. (978-0-9765060-2-7(5)) TouchSmart Publishing, LLC.

Solway, Andrew. Genetics in Medicine. 2006. (Illus.). 64p. (J). lib. bdg. (***978-0-8368-7865-3(5)*** , World Almanac Library) Stevens, Gareth Inc.

Stille, Darlene R. The Respiratory System. 1998. (True Bks.). (Illus.). 48p. (J). (gr. 3-5). pap. 6.95 (978-0-516-26276-5(9) , Children's Pr.) Scholastic Library Publishing.

Swanson, Diane. The Doctor & You. 2001. (Illus.). 32p. (J). (ps-2). pap. 7.95 (978-1-55037-672-2(1)) Annick Pr., Ltd. CAN. *Dist:* Firefly Bks., Ltd.

Tartakoff, Katy. Burned & Beautiful. Shields, Laurie, illus. 54p. (Orig.). (J). stu. ed. 14.95 (978-0-9629365-1-7(0)) Children's Legacy.

—Let Me Show You My World. Shields, Laurie, illus. 54p. (Orig.). (J). stu. ed. 14.95 (978-0-9629365-2-4(9)) Children's Legacy.

Toriello, James. The Human Genome Project. 2005. (Library of Future Medicine). (Illus.). 64p. (YA). (gr. 7-12). lib. bdg. 26.50 (978-0-8239-3671-7(6)) Rosen Publishing Group, Inc., The.

Torr, James D. Medical Ethics. 2000. (Current Controversies Ser.). (Illus.). 176p. (YA). (gr. 7-12). pap. 21.20 (978-0-7377-0144-9(7) , Greenhaven Pr., Inc.) Thomson Gale.

Torr, James D., ed. Health Care. 2000. (Opposing Viewpoints Ser.). (Illus.). 221p. (YA). (gr. 10-12). pap. (978-0-7377-0128-9(5)); (gr. 9 up). 32.45 (978-0-7377-0129-6(3)) Thomson Gale. (Greenhaven Pr., Inc.).

Valente, Thomas W. Evaluating Health Promotion Programs. 2002. (Illus.). 328p. 49.95 (978-0-19-514176-4(8)) Oxford Univ. Pr., Inc.

Viegas, Jennifer. Stem Cell Research. 2005. (Library of Future Medicine). (Illus.). 64p. (YA). (gr. 7-12). lib. bdg. 26.50 (978-0-8239-3669-4(4)) Rosen Publishing Group, Inc., The.

Wallerstein, Claire. Alternative Medicine. 2003. (Just the Facts Ser.). (Illus.). 56p. (YA). lib. bdg. 25.64 (978-1-4034-0816-7(5)) Heinemann Library.

Walsh, Kieran. Medical Math. 2003. (Illus.). 48p. (J). 29.93 (978-1-58952-380-7(6)) Rourke Publishing, LLC.

Weber, Rebecca. Science & Your Health. 2004. (Spyglass Books). 24p. (J). (gr. 1 up). lib. bdg. 19.93 (978-0-7565-0653-7(0)) Compass Point Bks.

Whiting, Jim. Hippocrates. 2006. (Biography from Ancient Civilizations Ser.). (Illus.). 48p. (J). lib. bdg. 20.95 (978-1-58415-512-6(4) , 1259600) Mitchell Lane Pubs., Inc.

Willett, Edward. Arthritis. 2000. (Diseases & People Ser.). (Illus.). 128p. (YA). (gr. 6-12). lib. bdg. 26.60 (978-0-7660-1314-8(6)) Enslow Pubs., Inc.

Woods, Michael & Woods, Mary B. Ancient Medicine: From Sorcery to Surgery. 1999. (Ancient Technology Ser.). (Illus.). 96p. (gr. 6-12). 25.26 (978-0-8225-2992-7(0)) Lerner Publishing Group.

MEDICINE—BIOGRAPHY

see also Nurses and Nursing; Physicians; Surgeons

Hitchcock, Susan Tyler. Karen Horney: Pioneer of Feminine Psychology. 2004. (Women in Medicine Ser.). (Illus.). 112p. (gr. 6-12). 30.00 (978-0-7910-8025-2(0) , Chelsea Hse.) Facts On File, Inc.

Kent, Jacqueline C. Women in Medicine. 1998. (Profiles Ser.). (Illus.). 160p. (YA). (gr. 5-12). lib. bdg. 19.95 (978-1-881508-46-5(3)) Oliver Pr., Inc.

Morrison, John. Mathilde Krim. 2004. (Women in Medicine Ser.). (Illus.). 112p. (gr. 6-12). 30.00 (978-0-7910-8026-9(9) , Chelsea Hse.) Facts On File, Inc.

Roberts, Russell. American Women of Medicine. 2002. (Collective Biographies Ser.). (Illus.). 104p. (YA). (gr. 6-12). lib. bdg. 26.60 (978-0-7660-1835-8(0)) Enslow Pubs., Inc.

MEDICINE, DENTAL

see Dentistry; Teeth

MEDICINE—DICTIONARIES

Burles, Kenneth T. & Hundley, David H. Fever. 1998. (Learning about Your Health Ser.). (Illus.). 32p. (J). (gr. 2-5). lib. bdg. 26.60 (978-1-57103-256-0(8)) Rourke Publishing, LLC.

The New Book of Popular Science 2008, 6 vols., Set. 2008. (YA). (gr. 7-12). lib. bdg. 299.00 (***978-0-7172-1226-2(2)***) Scholastic Library Publishing.

Scholastic Library Publishing Staff, contrib. by. The New Book of Popular Science, 6 vols., Set. 2006. (Illus.). (J). (gr. 7-12). 279.00 (978-0-7172-1225-5(4) , Grolier) Scholastic Library Publishing.

World Book, Inc. Staff. The World Book Medical Encyclopedia. 2001. (YA). (gr. 6 up). cd-rom 25.00 (978-0-7166-4205-3(0)) World Bk., Inc.

MEDICINE—FICTION

Accardo, Reba, told to. Surgery for Me? 2005. (J). pap. 8.00 (978-0-8059-6697-8(8)) Dorrance Publishing Co., Inc.

Baggette, Susan K. Jonathan Goes to the Doctor. Moriarty, William J., photos by. 1998. (Jonathan Adventures Ser.). (Illus.). 16p. (J). (ps-k). bds. 5.95 (978-0-9660172-1-2(8)) Brookfield Reader, Inc., The.

Blackman, Malorie. Pig-Heart Boy. (Illus.). 2001. 208p. pap. 9.99 (978-0-552-54684-3(4)); 2000. 207p. (J). pap. 6.95 (978-0-552-52841-2(2)) Transworld Publishers Ltd. GBR. *Dist:* Trafalgar Square Publishing.

Boldt, Mark. Awareness Is Doing Something. l.t. ed. 1998. (U-Do Book Ser.). (Illus.). 32p. (J). (gr. k-8). pap. (978-0-9662556-2-1(3) , U-DO 03) Boldt.Entertainment.

Cannon, Janell. Little Yau: A Fuzzhead Tale. 2002. (Illus.). 56p. (J). (gr. k-3). 16.00 (978-0-15-201791-0(7)) Harcourt Children's Bks.

Cushman, Karen. Matilda Bone. 2002. 13.94 (978-1-4046-1906-7(2)) Book Wholesalers, Inc.

—Matilda Bone. 2000. (Illus.). 176p. (J). (gr. 5-9). tchr. ed. 15.00 (978-0-395-88156-9(0) , Clarion Bks.) Houghton Mifflin Co. Trade & Reference Div.

—Matilda Bone. unabr. ed. 2004. (Middle Grade Cassette Librariestm Ser.). 176p. (J). (gr. 5-9). pap. 36.00 incl. audio (978-0-8072-1725-2(5) , S YA 252 SP, Listening Library) Random Hse. Audio Publishing Group.

—Matilda Bone. 2002. 176p. (J). (gr. 5-7). reprint ed. 5.99 (978-0-440-41822-1(4) , Yearling) Random Hse. Children's Bks.

—Matilda Bone. 2002. 167p. (J). (gr. 4-7). lib. bdg. 13.55 (978-0-613-45343-1(3)) Tandem Library Bks.

Dahl, Roald. La Maravillosa Medicina de Jorge. Blake, Quentin, illus. 2005. (SPA.). 118p. (J). (gr. 3-5). pap. 11.95 (978-968-19-0547-7(4)) Santillana USA Publishing Co., Inc.

Danziger, Paula. The Pistachio Prescription. (J). (gr. 4-6). 154p. pap. 3.99 (978-0-8072-1525-8(2)); 160p. pap. 3.99 (978-0-8072-1374-2(8)) Random Hse. Audio Publishing Group. (Listening Library).

—The Pistachio Prescription. 1999. (978-0-606-16845-8(1)) Tandem Library Bks.

Deem, Saitofi Anne. Myrtle Learns about Medicine. 1998. (Teachable Moments Ser.). (Illus.). 8p. (J). (ps-3). pap. 7.95 (978-1-930694-12-5(1)) Myrtle Learns.

DeFelice, Cynthia. The Apprenticeship of Lucas Whitaker. 2007. 160p. (J). pap. 6.95 (978-0-374-40014-9(8) , Farrar, Straus & Giroux (BYR)) Farrar, Straus & Giroux.

Handis, Mikey. Watch Out, He's Got AIDS. Handis, Mikey, illus. 1998. (Illus.). 48p. (J). (gr. 4-7). 12.95 (978-0-934953-58-0(9)) Water Row Pr.

Harcourt School Publishers Staff. The Pony Express to the Rescue Below Level. 3rd ed. 2002. (Trophies Reading Program Ser.). (Illus.). pap. 5.10 (978-0-15-323152-0(1)) Harcourt Schl. Pubs.

Hare, Eric B. Dr. Rabbit. Bohlmann, Siegfried, illus. fac. ed. 2004. 127p. (J). per. 11.95 (978-1-57258-278-1(2) , 945-6131) TEACH Services, Inc.

Harrison, Troon. Aaron's Awful Allergies. Fernandes, Eugenie, illus. unabr. ed. 1998. 32p. (J). (gr. k-3). (978-1-55074-299-2(X)) Kids Can Pr., Ltd.

Klein, Adria F. Max Goes to the Doctor. Gallagher-Cole, Mernie, illus. 2007. (J). lib. bdg. (***978-1-4048-3680-8(2)***) Picture Window Bks.

Ladd, Debbie. Nurse Robin's Hats. Nakasone, Shaun, illus. 2006. 52p. (J). 16.95 (978-0-9727615-3-6(5)) Deb on Air Bks.

A Life in Their Hands. 2002. (Illus.). (J). pap. (978-0-7398-5100-5(4)) Steck-Vaughn.

Marx, David F. Hello, Doctor. Hicks, Mark A., illus. (Rookie Reader Espanol Ser.). 24p. (J). (gr. k-2). 2001. pap. 4.95 (978-0-516-27076-0(1)); 2000. 19.50 (978-0-516-22033-8(0)) Scholastic Library Publishing. (Children's Pr.).

Marzollo, Jean. Doctor Show, No. 2. Evans, Shane W., illus. 2001. 24p. (J). lib. bdg. 13.49 (978-0-7868-2548-6(0) , Jump at the Sun) Hyperion Bks. for Children.

—Shanna's Princess Show. 2003. (ps-2). lib. bdg. 11.25 (978-0-613-91009-5(5)) Tandem Library Bks.

Midwife's Apprentice. 1999. (J). 9.95 (978-1-56137-801-2(1)) Novel Units, Inc.

Morgan, Nicola. Fleshmarket. 2004. 224p. (YA). (gr. 9). lib. bdg. 17.99 (978-0-385-90192-5(5) , Delacorte Bks. for Young Readers) Random Hse. Children's Bks.

Neumeyer, Peter F. & Gorey, Edward. Donald Has a Difficulty. 2004. (Illus.). 40p. (J). (ps-3). reprint ed. 12.95 (978-0-8109-4835-8(4)) Abrams, Harry N., Inc.

MNO

Parish, Herman. Calling Doctor Amelia Bedelia. Sweat, Lynn, illus. (I Can Read Bks.). 64p. (J). 2004. (gr. k-3). pap. 3.99 (978-0-06-008780-7(3) , Harper Trophy); 2002. (gr. 1-2). 15.99 (978-0-06-001421-6(0)) HarperCollins Pubs.

Pelow, Lawrence. Little Larry of Lewiston Meets Bobby the Backyard Bully. 2006. 2p. 6.71 (978-1-4116-9172-8(5)) Lulu.com.

Penson, Mary. Martha Mary Overstreet, M. D. 2007. (Chaparral Book for Young Readers Ser.). 142p. (J). pap. 11.95 (***978-0-87565-345-7(6)***) Texas Christian Univ. Pr.

Pure. 2005. 245p. (YA). pap. 7.95 (978-1-896764-96-2(7)) Second Story Pr. CAN. *Dist:* Orca Bk. Pubs. USA.

Shavatt, Donna & Shavatt, Eve. Sammy Squirrel & Friends' Medical Adventures. Mays, Luke, illus. 2000. 40p. (J). pap. 11.95 (978-0-9678630-1-6(5)) Shavatt Enterprises.

Stewart, Jennifer J. Close Encounters of a Third World Kind. 2004. 128p. (J). (gr. 4-6). tchr. ed. 16.95 (978-0-8234-1850-3(2)) Holiday Hse., Inc.

Thomas, Joyce Carol. Marked by Fire. rev. ed. 2007. 192p. (YA). (gr. 8-17). 15.99 (***978-1-4231-0143-7(X)***); pap. 7.99 (***978-1-4231-0144-4(8)***) Hyperion Bks. for Children. (Jump at the Sun).

Townson, Hazel. The Speckled Panic. 1998. (Illus.). 80p. (J). pap. 8.99 (978-0-86264-828-2(9)) Andersen GBR. *Dist:* Independent Pubs. Group.

Walsh, Ann. The Doctor's Apprentice. 2005. 160p. (YA). (gr. 3-8). pap., tchr. ed. 8.95 (978-0-88878-389-9(2)) Beach Holme Pubs., Ltd. CAN. *Dist:* Literary Pr. Group of Canada.

Walsh, Ann. The Doctors Apprentice. 2007. 160p. (J). pap. 9.99 (***978-1-55002-633-7(X)*** , Sandcastle Bks.) Dundurn Group, The. CAN. *Dist:* Univ. of Toronto Pr.

Walters, Eric. Elixir. 2005. 176p. (***978-0-670-04465-8(2)*** , Viking Canada) Penguin Group (Canada).

Ziefert, Harriet. Ouch! Rossi, Richard, illus. 2006. (I'm Going to Read Ser.). 32p. (J). pap. 3.95 (978-1-4027-3424-3(7)) Sterling Publishing Co., Inc.

MEDICINE—HISTORY

Atkinson, Mary. Pills & Potions: A History of Remedies. (Shockwave: Life Science & Medicine Ser.). (J). 2008. 32p. pap. 6.95 (***978-0-531-18839-2(6)***); 2007. (Illus.). 36p. (gr. 4-6). lib. bdg. 25.00 (***978-0-531-17767-9(X)***) Scholastic Library Publishing. (Children's Pr.).

Bankston, John. Joseph Lister & the Story of Antiseptics. 2004. (Uncharted, Unexplored, & Unexplained Ser.). (Illus.). 48p. (J). (gr. 4-8). lib. bdg. 29.95 (978-1-58415-262-0(1)) Mitchell Lane Pubs., Inc.

Cannarella, Deborah & Fournier, Jane, contrib. by. Medicine. 1999. (Into the Next Millennium Ser.). (Illus.). 31p. (J). (gr. 4-8). lib. bdg. 27.93 (978-1-57103-274-4(6)) Rourke Publishing, LLC.

Casanellas, Antonio. Great Discoveries & Inventions That Improved Human Health. Garousi, Ali, illus. 2000. (Great Discoveries & Inventions Ser.). 32p. (J). (gr. 4 up). lib. bdg. 24.67 (978-0-8368-2585-5(3)) Stevens, Gareth Inc.

Clare, John. Medicine in the Industrial Age. 2006. (History of Medicine Ser.). 64p. (J). 19.95 (978-1-59270-039-4(X)) Enchanted Lion Bks., LLC.

Davis, Lucile. Medicine in the American West. 2001. (gr. 3-6). lib. bdg. 14.10 (978-0-613-51662-4(1)) Tandem Library Bks.

Dawson, Ian. Greek & Roman Medicine. 2005. (History of Medicine Ser.). (Illus.). 64p. (J). 19.95 (978-1-59270-036-3(5)) Enchanted Lion Bks., LLC.

—Renaissance Medicine. 2005. (Illus.). 64p. (J). 19.95 (978-1-59270-038-7(1)) Enchanted Lion Bks., LLC.

Dawson, Ian, et al. Medicine for Edexcel: An SHP Study in Development. 2001. (Illus.). 216p. pap. 38.50 (***978-0-7195-7727-7(6)*** , Hodder Murray) Hodder Education GBR. *Dist:* Trans-Atlantic Pubns., Inc.

Dowswell, Paul. Medicine. 2001. (Great Inventions Ser.). (Illus.). 48p. (YA). (gr. 5-8). lib. bdg. 25.64 (978-1-58810-213-3(0)) Heinemann Library.

Elgin, Kathy. Health & Disease. 2004. (Changing Times Ser.). (Illus.). 32p. (J). 26.60 (978-0-7565-0887-6(8)) Compass Point Bks.

Farndon, John. Religion, Science, Medicine & Warfare. 2001. (Illustrated Encyclopedia Ser.). (Illus.). 256p. (gr. 3-7). pap. 19.95 (978-1-84215-518-9(0) , Southwater) Anness Publishing GBR. *Dist:* National Bk. Network.

Gates, Phil. Medicine. 2001. (History News Ser.). (Illus.). 32p. (J). (gr. 3 up). lib. bdg. 24.67 (978-0-8368-2877-1(1)) Stevens, Gareth Inc.

Gates, Philip. Medicine News. 2000. (News Ser.). (J). (978-0-606-19319-1(7)) Tandem Library Bks.

Gilpin, Daniel. Medicine. 2004. (History of Invention Ser.). (Illus.). 96p. (YA). (gr. 6-12). 35.00 (978-0-8160-5442-8(8)) Facts On File, Inc.

Goldsmith, Connie. Cutting-Edge Medicine. 2007. (Cool Science Ser.). 48p. (J). (gr. 4-8). lib. bdg. 26.60 (***978-0-8225-6770-7(9)*** , Lerner Pubns.) Lerner Publishing Group.

Green, Jen. Medicine. 2004. (Routes of Science Ser.). (Illus.). 40p. (J). pap. 11.20 (978-1-4103-0305-9(5)); (gr. 4-7). 23.70 (978-1-4103-0168-0(0)) Thomson Gale. (Blackbirch Pr., Inc.).

Jeffrey, Gary. Medical Breakthroughs. Riley, Terry, illus. 2007. (Graphic Discoveries Ser.). 48p. (J). (gr. 3-7). lib. bdg. (***978-1-4042-1086-8(5)***) Rosen Publishing Group, Inc., The.

—Medical Breakthroughs. 2007. (J). (***978-1-4042-9588-9(7)***); pap. (***978-1-4042-9587-2(9)***) Rosen Publishing Group, Inc., The.

Jennings, Gael. Bloody Moments: Highlights from the Astounding History of Medicine. Harvey, Roland, illus. 2000. 80p. (J). (gr. 3-7). 16.95 (978-1-55037-643-2(8)) Annick Pr., Ltd. CAN. *Dist:* Firefly Bks., Ltd.

Platt, Richard. Doctors Did What ?! The Weird History of Medicine. 2006. (Illus.). 48p. (J). 9.95 (978-1-58728-581-3(9)); 16.95 (978-1-58728-580-6(0)) T&N Children's Publishing. (Two Can Publishing).

Savage, Douglas J. Civil War Medicine. 2000. (Untold History of the Civil War Ser.). (Illus.). 64p. (J). (gr. 3 up). 25.00 (978-0-7910-5709-4(7) , Chelsea Hse.) Facts On File, Inc.

Senior, Kathryn & Salariya, David. You Wouldn't Want to Be Sick in the 16th Century! Diseases You'd Rather Not Catch. Antram, David, illus. 2002. (You Wouldn't Want to Ser.). 32p. (J). (gr. 2-5). 28.50 (978-0-531-14605-7(7) , Watts, Franklin) Scholastic Library Publishing.

Storring, Rod. A Doctor's Life: A Visual History of Doctors & Nurses Through the Ages. 2004. (Illus.). 48p. (J). (gr. 2-6). reprint ed. 18.00 (978-0-7567-7870-5(0)) DIANE Publishing Co.

Strom, Laura Layton. Dr. Medieval: Medicine in the Middle Ages. 2007. (Shockwave: Life Science & Medicine Ser.). 36p. (J). pap. 6.95 (***978-0-531-18797-5(7)***); (Illus.). (gr. 4-6). lib. bdg. 25.00 (***978-0-531-17765-5(3)***) Scholastic Library Publishing. (Children's Pr.).

Townsend, John. Disease: Pox, Pus & Plague. 2005. (Raintree Freestyle Ser.). (Illus.). 56p. (J). pap. (978-1-4109-1338-8(4)) Steck-Vaughn.

—Pox, Pus & Plague: A History of Disease & Infection. (J). 2006. (978-1-4109-2541-1(2)); 2006. 48p. pap. (978-1-4109-2546-6(3)); 2005. (Illus.). 56p. lib. bdg. 32.86 (978-1-4109-1333-3(3)) Steck-Vaughn.

Uschan, Michael V. Forty Years of Medical Racism: The Tuskegee Experiments. 2005. (American Secrets & Scandals Ser.). (Illus.). 112p. (J). (gr. 7-10). lib. bdg. 32.45 (978-1-59018-486-8(6) , Lucent Bks.) Thomson Gale.

Walker, Richard. The Story of Medicine: Medicine Around the World & Across the Ages, 4 vols. 2000. (Exploring History Ser.). (Illus.). 64p. (gr. 4-7). 15.00 (978-0-7548-0531-1(X) , Lorenz Bks.) Anness Publishing GBR. *Dist:* National Bk. Network.

Ward, Brian. The Story of Medicine. 2003. (History Detectives Ser.). (Illus.). 64p. pap. 7.99 (978-1-84215-710-7(8) , Southwater) Anness Publishing GBR. *Dist:* National Bk. Network.

Wilbur, C. Keith. Civil War Medicine. 1999. (Illustrated Living History Ser.). (Illus.). 119p. (J). (gr. 5-9). 14.95 (978-0-7910-5207-5(9) , Chelsea Hse.) Facts On File, Inc.

—Civil War Medicine. 1998. (Illustrated Living History Ser.). (Illus.). 128p. pap. 14.95 (978-0-7627-0341-8(5)) Globe Pequot Pr., The.

Yount, Lisa. The History of Medicine. 2001. (World History Ser.). (Illus.). 128p. (J). (gr. 8-11). 32.45 (978-1-56006-805-1(1) , LML00902-178137, Lucent Bks.) Thomson Gale.

Zach, Kim K. Prosthetics. 2005. (Great Medical Discoveries Ser.). (J). (978-1-59018-552-0(8) , Lucent Bks.) Thomson Gale.

MEDICINE, POPULAR

Here are entered medical books for the layman.

Scholastic Library Publishing Staff, contrib. by. The New Book of Popular Science, 6 vols., Set. 2006. (Illus.). (J). (gr. 7-12). 279.00 (978-0-7172-1225-5(4) , Grolier) Scholastic Library Publishing.

MEDICINE, PEDIATRIC

see Children—Diseases

MEDICINE, PREVENTIVE

see Bacteriology; Health; Immunity; Public Health

MEDICINE—RESEARCH

Brocker, Susan & Furgang, Kathy. Médicos pioneros & Pioneers in Medicine. 2005. spiral bd. 84.00 (***978-1-4108-5701-9(8)***) Benchmark Education Co.

Murphy, Wendy B. Orphan Diseases: New Hope for Rare Medical Conditions. 2002. (Twenty-First Century Medical Library). (Illus.). 144p. (gr. 7 up). lib. bdg. 26.90 (978-0-7613-1919-1(0) , Twenty-First Century Bks.) Lerner Publishing Group.

MEDICINE, TROPICAL

see Tropics—Diseases and Hygiene

MEDICINE—UNITED STATES

Hantula, Richard. Jonas Salk. 2004. (Trailblazers of the Modern World Ser.). (Illus.). 48p. (J). (gr. 5 up). pap. 11.95 (978-0-8368-5260-8(5)); lib. bdg. 30.00 (978-0-8368-5100-7(5)) Stevens, Gareth Inc. (World Almanac Library).

Schroeder-Lein, Glenna R. The Encyclopedia of Civil War Medicine. 2007. 368p. 95.00 (***978-0-7656-1171-0(6)***) Sharpe, M.E. Inc.

MEDICINE, VETERINARY

see Veterinary Medicine

MEDICINE—VOCATIONAL GUIDANCE

Adamson, Heather. A Day in the Life of a Doctor. 2003. (First Facts Ser.). (Illus.). 24p. (J). 15.95 (978-0-7368-2506-1(1)) Capstone Pr., Inc.

Asher, Dana. Epidemiologists: Life Tracking Deadly Diseases. 2005. (Extreme Careers Ser.). (Illus.). 64p. (YA). (gr. 5-8). 26.50 (978-0-8239-3633-5(3)) Rosen Publishing Group, Inc., The.

Boyd, Nicole. A Doctor's Busy Day. 2002. (Reading Room Collection). (Illus.). 24p. (J). lib. bdg. 18.75 (978-0-8239-3734-9(8)) Rosen Publishing Group, Inc., The.

Christy, Lee Louis. I Go to Work as a Doctor. 2003. (I Go to Work As Ser.). (Illus.). (J). (978-1-58417-042-6(5)); pap. (978-1-58417-107-2(3)) Lake Street Pubs.

Devantier, Alecia T. & Turkington, Carol. Extraordinary Jobs in Health & Science. 2006. (Extraordinary Jobs Ser.). 176p. (J). (gr. 6-12). 35.00 (978-0-8160-5858-7(X) , Ferguson Publishing Co.) Facts On File, Inc.

Ferguson, creator. Discovering Careers for Your Future: Food. 2005. (Discovering Careers for Your Future Ser.). (Illus.). 92p. (YA). (gr. 4-9). 21.95 (978-0-8160-5848-8(2) , Ferguson Publishing Co.) Facts On File, Inc.

—Discovering Careers for Your Future: Performing Arts. 2nd rev. ed. 2005. (Discovering Careers for Your Future Ser.). (Illus.). 92p. (YA). (gr. 4-9). 21.95 (978-0-8160-5873-0(3) , Ferguson Publishing Co.) Facts On File, Inc.

Giddens, Sandra & Giddens, Owen. Choosing a Career as a Paramedic. 2005. (World of Work Ser.). (Illus.). 64p. (YA). (gr. 7-12). lib. bdg. 25.25 (978-0-8239-3244-3(3) , WWPAME) Rosen Publishing Group, Inc., The.

Hayward, Linda & Dorling Kindersley Publishing Staff. Jobs People Do: A Day in the Life of a Doctor. 2001. (Readers Ser.). (Illus.). 32p. (J). 12.99 (978-0-7894-7950-1(8)); pap. 3.99 (978-0-7894-7951-8(6)) Dorling Kindersley Publishing, Inc.

J. G. Ferguson Publishing Company Staff. Careers in Focus: Alternative Healthcare. 1999. (Careers in Focus Ser.). (Illus.). 488p. (YA). (gr. 8-12). pap. 22.95 (978-0-89434-283-7(5) , F701, Ferguson Publishing Co.) Facts On File, Inc.

—Exploring Health Care Careers. 3rd rev. ed. 2006. 960p. (YA). (gr. 9 up). 125.00 (978-0-8160-6448-9(2) , Ferguson Publishing Co.) Facts On File, Inc.

J. G. Ferguson Publishing Company Staff, contrib. by. Careers in Focus: Alternative Health Care. 2nd ed. 2003. (Careers in Focus Ser.). (Illus.). 224p. (YA). (gr. 6-12). 22.95 (978-0-8160-5483-1(5) , Ferguson Publishing Co.) Facts On File, Inc.

—Discovering Careers for Your Future. (Discovering Careers for Your Future Ser.). 96p. (gr. 4-9). 2004. 21.95 (978-0-8160-5569-2(6)); 2nd ed. 2005. (Illus.). (J). 21.95 (978-0-8160-5871-6(7)); 2nd ed. 2004. (Illus.). 21.95 (978-0-8160-5570-8(X)) Facts On File, Inc. (Ferguson Publishing Co.).

—Discovering Careers for Your Future: English. 2nd rev. ed. 2005. (Discovering Careers for Your Future Ser.). (Illus.). 96p. (gr. 4-9). 21.95 (978-0-8160-5872-3(5) , Ferguson Publishing Co.) Facts On File, Inc.

J. G. Ferguson Publishing Company Staff, ed. Exploring Health Care Careers, 2 vols., Set. 2nd ed. 2002. (Illus.). 984p. (gr. 9). 89.95 (978-0-89434-311-7(4) , Ferguson Publishing Co.) Facts On File, Inc.

J. G. Ferguson Publishing Company Staff & Facts on File, Inc. Staff, contrib. by. Discovering Careers for Your Future. 2004. (Discovering Careers for Your Future Ser.). (Illus.). 96p. (gr. 4-9). 21.95 (978-0-8160-5568-5(8) , Ferguson Publishing Co.) Facts On File, Inc.

Kottke, Jan. A Day with Paramedics. 2000. (Welcome Bks.). (Illus.). 24p. (J). (ps-2). pap. 4.95 (978-0-516-23016-0(6) , Children's Pr.) Scholastic Library Publishing.

Mattern, Joanne. Tecnicos en Emergencias Medicas. 2004. (Trabajo en Grupo Ser.). (SPA & ENG., Illus.). 24p. (J). (gr. 3-6). lib. bdg. 17.25 (978-0-8239-6839-8(1) , Buenas Letra) Rosen Publishing Group, Inc., The.

McAlpine, Margaret. Working in Health Care. 2004. (My Future Career Ser.). (Illus.). 64p. (J). lib. bdg. 26.00 (978-0-8368-4238-8(3)) Stevens, Gareth Inc.

Moe, Barbara. Careers in Sports Medicine. 2005. (Career Resource Library). (Illus.). 192p. (YA). (gr. 7-12). lib. bdg. 26.50 (978-0-8239-3538-3(8)) Rosen Publishing Group, Inc., The.

Pasternak, Ceel & Thornburg, Linda. Cool Careers for Girls in Health. 1999. (Illus.). 148p. (YA). 19.95 (978-1-57023-125-4(7)) Impact Pubns.

—Health. 1999. (Cool Careers for Girls Ser.). (Illus.). 125p. (gr. 4-7). pap. 12.95 (978-1-57023-118-6(4)) Impact Pubns.

Reeves, Diane Lindsey, et al. Career Ideas for Teens in Health Science. (Career Ideas for Teens Ser.). 192p. (gr. 6-12). pap. 16.95 (978-0-8160-6920-0(4) , Checkmark Bks.); 2005. (Illus.). (YA). 40.00 (978-0-8160-5290-5(5) , Ferguson Publishing Co.) Facts On File, Inc.

Schamp, Virginia. If You Were a Doctor. 2000. (If You Were A... Ser.). (Illus.). 32p. (J). (gr. 2-4). lib. bdg. 22.79 (978-0 7614-1000-3(7) , Benchmark Bks.) Cavendish, Marshall Corp.

Silverstone, Michael. Paramedics to the Rescue: When Every Second Counts. 2005. (Illus.). 64p. (J). (ps-7). lib. bdg. 23.93 (978-0-7368-3877-1(5)) Capstone Pr., Inc.

—Paramedics to the Rescue When Every Second Counts. 2004. (J). (978-0-7368-3849-8(X)) Capstone Pr., Inc.

Simmers, Louise. Wkbk-Hlth Sci Career Explorati. 2004. (C). pap. 20.95 (978-1-4018-5812-4(0)) Thomson Delmar Learning.

Simmers, Louise M. Health Science Career Exploration. 2004. (Illus.). 340p. (C). pap. 62.95 (978-1-4018-5809-4(0)) Thomson Delmar Learning.

Steinfeld, Alan. Careers in Alternative Medicine. rev. ed. 2000. (Careers). (Illus.). 192p. (YA). (gr. 7-12). lib. bdg. 18.95 (978-0-8239-2963-4(9) , CAALME) Rosen Publishing Group, Inc., The.

Wallner, Rosemary. Licensed Practical Nurse. 1999. (Career Exploration Ser.). (Illus.). 48p. lib. bdg. 21.26 (978-0-7368-0329-8(7) , LifeMatters Bks.) Capstone Pr., Inc.

—Licensed Practical Nurse. 1999. (Illus.). (YA). (gr. 5-12). pap. 19.93 (978-0-516-21888-5(3) , Children's Pr.) Scholastic Library Publishing.

—Pediatrician. 1999. (Career Exploration Ser.). (Illus.). 48p. (J). (gr. 3-4). lib. bdg. 21.26 (978-0-7368-0333-5(5) , LifeMatters Bks.) Capstone Pr., Inc.

—Pediatrician. 1999. (Illus.). (YA). (gr. 5-12). pap. 19.93 (978-0-516-21892-2(1) , Children's Pr.) Scholastic Library Publishing.

Waugh, Ingela. Home Health Aide. 2004. (Great Jobs Ser.). (Illus.). 48p. (J). 24.00 (978-0-516-24087-9(0)); (gr. 7-12). pap. 6.95 (978-0-516-25934-5(2)) Scholastic Library Publishing. (Children's Pr.).

Wilkinson, Beth. Careers Inside the World of Health Care. rev. ed. 1999. (Careers & Opportunities Ser.). (Illus.). 64p. (YA). (gr. 7-12). lib. bdg. 26.50 (978-0-8239-2886-6(1) , CIHECA) Rosen Publishing Group, Inc., The.

Zannos, Susan. Careers in Science & Medicine. 2001. (Latinos at Work Ser.). (Illus.). 96p. (YA). (gr. 5-12). lib. bdg. 22.95 (978-1-58415-084-8(X)) Mitchell Lane Pubs., Inc.

MEDIEVAL ART

see Art, Medieval

MEDIEVAL CIVILIZATION

see Civilization, Medieval

MEDIEVAL LITERATURE

see Literature, Medieval

MEDITATIONS

Andrews, Linda Wasmer. Meditation. 2004. (Life Balance Ser.). 80p. (J). 20.50 (978-0-531-12219-8(0) , Watts, Franklin) Scholastic Library Publishing.

Ayer, Jane E. Guided Meditations for Junior High: Good Judgment, Gifts, Obedience, Inner Blindness. 2003. (Quiet Place Apart Ser.). 48p. pap., tchr. ed. 9.95 (978-0-88489-500-8(9)) St. Mary's Pr.

Berg, Yehuda. The 72 Names of God for Kids: A Treasury of Timeless Wisdom. 2006. (Illus.). 192p. 14.95 (978-1-57189-543-1(4)) Research Centre of Kabbalah.

Brost, Corey. Gospel Connections for Teens: Reflections for Sunday Mass, Cycle C. 2006. (YA). per. 4.95 (978-0-88489-641-8(2)) St. Mary's Pr.

Carlson, Dale. Stop the Pain: Teen Meditations. Nicklaus, Carol, illus. 2000. (Psychology for Teenagers Ser.: No. 3). 189p. (gr. 5-9). pap. 14.95 (978-1-884158-23-0(4)) Bick Publishing Hse.

Cooper, Dale J. & Vande Streek, Kevin C. Lasting Victory: Meditations for Students, Athletes, Coaches & Those Who Cheer Them On. 2002. 112p. (YA). per. 10.00 (978-0-9703693-6-9(0)) Calvin College Alumni Assn.

Dall, Jeanette, et al. My Time with God Vol. 1: 150 Ways to Start Your Own Quiet Time. 2000. (Heritage Builders Ser.). 208p. (YA). (gr. 3-7). pap. 8.99 (978-1-56179-802-5(9)) Focus on the Family Publishing.

Davis, Tom, ed. & contrib. by. Quiet Time One Year Daily Devotional with Commentary (Quiet Time Devotionals), 1. Davis, Tom, contrib. by. 2006. 432p. per. 17.99 (978-1-931235-52-5(X) , TQTWC) Word of Life Fellowship, Inc.

Dunlap, Judith & Suttman, Carleen. Praying All Ways. Kielbasa, Marilyn, ed. Thiewes, Sam, illus. 2003. (Horizons Program : Level 1, Minicourse 6). 56p. (Orig.). (YA). (gr. 9). pap., stu. ed. 9.95 (978-0-88489-364-6(2)) St. Mary's Pr.

Eastwood, Vena. Benedict Rules: Daily Readings for Young People. 2001. 140p. (J). pap. 10.95 (978-0-940147-53-9(X)) Source Bks.

Edge Ministries Staff, compiled by. One 2 One: Personal Devotions for Youth Camps, Retreats & Trips. 2000. (Essentials for Christian Youth Ser.). (Illus.). 112p. (YA). (gr. 7 up). 15.00 (978-0-687-09561-2(1)) Abingdon Pr.

Essmann, Harold A., adapted by. Praise the Lord: A Book of Bible Messages with Prayers, 1. 2002. Orig. Title: Meditations. 146p. (C). pap. 2.00 (978-1-931891-06-6(0) , 38-7392) Multi-Language Pubns.

Freeman, Laurence. A Simple Way: The Path of Christian Meditation. 2004. 43p. (YA). pap. 9.95 (978-0-9725627-6-8(1)) Medio Media Publishing.

Garth, M. Luz de la Tierra. (SPA.). 120p. 7.40 (978-84-89920-92-7(3) , 87112) Ediciones Oniro S.A. ESP. *Dist:* Lectorum Pubns., Inc.

—Rayo del Sol. (SPA.). 118p. 7.70 (978-84-89920-76-7(1) , 87107) Ediciones Oniro S.A. ESP. *Dist:* Lectorum Pubns., Inc.

Gregg-Schroeder, Susan. For Your Hospital Visit: Prayers & Meditations for Children. 1999. (Illus.). 20p. (J). (gr. 1-6). pap. 2.50 (978-1-57438-033-0(8)) Educational Ministries, Inc.

Hamilton, Amy. Indigo Dreaming. 2006. 144p. pap. (***978-0-9757953-7-8(6)***) Joshua Bks.

Harmony for the Heart: Devotionals for Young Women. 2002. (Illus.). 208p. (YA). pap. 7.50 (978-1-884377-08-2(4)) Green Pastures Pr.

Hartman, Jack & Hartman, Judy. Exchange Your Worries for God's Perfect Peace. 2003. 436p. per. 12.00 (978-0-915445-09-7(3) , Lamplight Ministries, Inc.) Lamplight Pubns.

Heagy, Wanda Powell. Inspirations from My Heart. 2001. 45p. (YA). (gr. 1 up). pap. 8.00 (978-0-9712153-0-6(8)) Heagy, Wanda Powell.

Langford, Anne. Meditation for Little People. Bethards, David, illus. 2003. 40p. (gr. k-4). reprint ed. 8.95 (978-0-87516-211-9(8) , Devorss Pubns.) DeVorss & Co.

McIntosh, Kenneth & McIntosh, Marsha. The Popularity of Meditation & Spiritual Practices: Seeking Inner Peace. 2005. (Religion & Modern Culture Ser.). (Illus.). 112p. (YA). (gr. 7 up). (978-1-59084-980-4(9)) Mason Crest Pubs.

McKeever, George. Learn to Meditate: Journey Toward Self-Discovery. 1998. 161p. (YA). (gr. 8 up). pap. 9.95 (978-1-885479-03-7(4)) Aum Pubns.

Nghiem, Thuc, et al. Each Breath a Smile. Dong, Nguyen & Hop, Nguyen Thi, illus. 2002. 32p. (J). pap. 10.95 (978-1-888375-22-0(1)) Parallax Pr.

Paynter, Roxanne. Small Souls: Meditations for Children. 2004. 86p. (Orig.). (J). pap. (978-0-9581891-0-1(2) , 305-004) Joshua Bks.

Polich, Laurie. Dive into Living Water. 2004. (Illus.). 112p. 8.00 (978-0-687-05223-3(8)) Abingdon Pr.

Reichard, Don, ed. Word of Life Challenger Quiet Time. 2001. (J). (gr. 1-2). pap. 6.95 (978-1-931235-09-9(0)) Word of Life Fellowship, Inc.

—Word of Life Champion Quiet Time. 2001. (J). (gr. 5-6). pap. 6.95 (978-1-931235-11-2(2)) Word of Life Fellowship, Inc.

—Word of Life Conqueror Quiet Time. 2001. (J). (gr. 3-4). pap. 6.95 (978-1-931235-10-5(4)) Word of Life Fellowship, Inc.

—Word of Life Preschool Quiet Time, 5 vols. 2001. (J). (ps). pap. 11.95 (978-1-931235-12-9(0)) Word of Life Fellowship, Inc.

—Word of Life Quiet Time Supplement. 2001. (YA). (gr. 7 up). pap. 6.95 (978-1-931235-08-2(2)) Word of Life Fellowship, Inc.

Rozman, Deborah. Meditating with Children: The Art of Concentration & Centering: A Workbook on New Educational Methods Using Meditation. rev. ed. 2002. (Illus.). 168p. pap. 15.95 (978-0-932040-52-7(7)) Integral Yoga Pubns.

Schneider, M. Valerie. Gospel Scenes for Teens: 23 Guided Prayer Meditations. 2000. 96p. (YA). pap. 12.95 (978-1-58595-111-6(0)) Twenty-Third Pubns./Bayard.

Swanson, Gary B. Click Here: Interactive Devotionals for Teens. 2003. 144p. (YA). pap. 10.99 (978-0-8280-1726-8(3)) Review & Herald Publishing Assn.

Tasting the Fruit of the Spirit: 30 Devotional Experiences. 2003. 64p. 9.99 (978-0-7644-2515-8(3) , Flagship Church Resources) Group Publishing, Inc.

Todt, Teresa. No More Monsters: A Parent & Child Guide to Freedom from Fear. Smith, Jeremy, illus. 2003. 15p. (J). (978-1-55306-647-7(2) , Guardian Bks.) Essence Publishing.

Viegas, Marneta. Relax Kids: And Other Fairy Tale Meditations for Princesses & Superheroes. 2004. (Illus.). 128p. 14.95 (978-1-903816-66-0(1)) O Bks. GBR. *Dist:* National Bk. Network.

Wan, Jian Q. Meditating into Wellness with San He Qigong. 2003. per. 13.00 (978-1-892686-10-7(4)) Manning, Laurie.

Wasmer, Andrews Linda. Meditation. 2004. (Life Balance Ser.). 80p. (YA). (gr. 5-8). pap. 6.95 (978-0-531-16609-3(0) , Watts, Franklin) Scholastic Library Publishing.

Word of Life Fellowship Staff. Quiet Time One Year Daily Devotional for Children in Grades 1-2 (Quiet Time Devotionals), 1. Reichard, Lisa, ed. 2006. (Illus.). 122p. (J). per. 15.99 (978-1-931235-32-7(5) , OQT1) Word of Life Fellowship, Inc.

—Quiet Time One Year Daily Devotional for Children in Grades 3-4 (Quiet Time Devotionals), 1. Armbrecht, Sue, ed. 2006. (Illus.). 120p. (J). per. 15.99 (978-1-931235-34-1(1) , OQT2) Word of Life Fellowship, Inc.

—Quiet Time One-Year Daily Devotional for Early Learners Ages 4-6 (Quiet Time Devotionals), 1. Reichard, Lisa, ed. 2006. (Illus.). 378p. (J). spiral bd. 15.99 (978-1-931235-29-7(5) , ELQT) Word of Life Fellowship, Inc.

Yaconelli, Mike. Devotion: A Raw Truth Journal for Following Jesus. 2004. (Invert Ser.). (Illus.). 80p. (YA). pap. 10.99 (978-0-310-25559-8(7)) Zondervan.

Zanzig, Thomas. Christian Meditation for Beginners. Kielbasa, Marilyn, ed. Thiewes, Sam, illus. 2003. (Horizons Program : Level II, Minicourse 3). 84p. (Orig.). (YA). (gr. 10). pap., stu. ed. 9.95 (978-0-88489-361-5(8)) St. Mary's Pr.

MEDITERRANEAN REGION

Behnke, Alison, et al. Cooking the Mediterranean Way. 2nd rev. ed. 2005. (Easy Menu Ethnic Cookbooks). (Illus.). 72p. (J). 25.26 (978-0-8225-1237-0(8) , Lerner Pubns.) Lerner Publishing Group.

Forester, C. S. Sterling Point Books: the Barbary Pirates. 2007. (Sterling Point Bks.). (Illus.). 176p. (J). 12.95 (978-1-4027-4522-5(2)); pap. 6.95 (978-1-4027-4142-5(1)) Sterling Publishing Co., Inc.

Green, Jen. Mediterranean Sea. 2006. (Illus.). 48p. (J). pap. (978-0-8368-6282-9(1)); lib. bdg. 30.00 (978-0-8368-6274-4(0)) Stevens, Gareth Inc. (World Almanac Library).

Prevost, John F. Mediterranean Sea. 2003. (Oceans & Seas Ser.). (Illus.). 24p. (J). (gr. k-6). lib. bdg. 21.35 (978-1-57765-097-3(2)) ABDO Publishing Co.

Stefoff, Rebecca. The Ancient Mediterranean World. 2004. (World Historical Atlases Ser.). (Illus.). 48p. (J). 27.07 (978-0-7614-1641-8(2) , Benchmark Bks.) Cavendish, Marshall Corp.

MEDITERRANEAN REGION—FICTION

Friesner, Esther M. Nobody's Princess. (gr. 7-11). 2008. 336p. (J). pap. 7.99 (978-0-375-87529-8(8)); 2007. 320p. (J). lib. bdg. 19.99 (978-0-375-97528-8(4)); 2007. 320p. (YA). 16.99 (978-0-375-87528-1(X)) Random Hse. Children's Bks. (Random Hse. Bks. for Young Readers).

Friesner, Esther M. Nobody's Prize. 2008. (J). (***978-0-375-87531-1(X)); (*978-0-375-87533-5(6));** pap. (***978-0-375-87532-8(8));** lib. bdg. (***978-0-375-97531-8(4))***) Random Hse., Inc.

Minter, J. Take It Off: An Insiders Novel. 2005. (Insiders Ser.). 300p. (YA). pap. 8.95 (978-1-58234-994-7(0) , Bloomsbury Children) Bloomsbury Publishing.

Napoli, Donna Jo. Sirena. 1998. 256p. (YA). (gr. 7-12). pap. 15.95 (978-0-590-38388-2(4)) Scholastic, Inc.

—Sirena. 2000. (Illus.). 210p. (YA). (gr. 7-12). lib. bdg. 13.04 (978-0-606-19626-0(9)) Tandem Library Bks.

MEDUSAE

Niz, Xavier & Bowman, Laurel. Medusa. 2004. (World Mythology Ser.). (Illus.). 24p. (J). lib. bdg. 21.26 (978-0-7368-2662-4(9) , Bridgestone Bks.) Capstone Pr., Inc.

Spinner, Stephanie. Snake Hair: The Story of Medusa. 1999. (gr. k-3). lib. bdg. 11.80 (978-0-613-15165-8(8)) Tandem Library Bks.

MEIR, GOLDA, 1898-1978

Claybourne, Anna. Golda Meir. 2003. (Leading Lives Ser.). (Illus.). 64p. (J). lib. bdg. 28.50 (978-1-4034-0835-8(1)) Heinemann Library.

Marsh, Carole. Golda Meir. 2002. (One Thousand Readers Ser.). (Illus.). 12p. (J). (gr. k-4). 2.95 (978-0-635-01513-6(7) , 15137) Gallopade International.

Wheeler, Jill C. Golda Meir. 2004. (Women of the World Ser.). (J). (978-1-59197-615-8(4)) ABDO Publishing Co.

World Book, Inc Staff, contrib. by. Golda Meir: With Profiles of David Ben-Gurion & Yitzhak Rabin. 2006. (Biographical Connections Ser.). (Illus.). 112p. (J). (978-0-7166-1829-4(X)) World Bk., Inc.

MEITNER, LISE, 1878-1968

Barron, Rachel Stiffler. Lise Meitner: Discoverer of Nuclear Fission. 2004. (Profiles in Science Ser.). (Illus.). 112p. (YA). (gr. 6-12). lib. bdg. 23.95 (978-1-883846-52-7(8) , First Biographies) Reynolds, Morgan Inc.

MEKONG RIVER DELTA (VIETNAM AND CAMBODIA)

Dramer, Kim. The Mekong River. 2001. (World of Water Ser.). (Illus.). 64p. (J). (gr. 5-7). 25.50 (978-0-531-11854-2(1) , Watts, Franklin) Scholastic Library Publishing.

—Mekong River. 2001. (gr. 3-6). lib. bdg. 17.60 (978-0-613-37451-4(7)) Tandem Library Bks.

MELVILLE, HERMAN, 1819-1891

Bloom, Harold, ed. Moby-Dick - Herman Melville. 2nd rev. ed. 2007. (Bloom's Modern Critical Interpretations Ser.). 256p. (YA). (gr. 9 up). 45.00 (978-0-7910-9363-4(8) , Chelsea Hse.) Facts On File, Inc.

Gibson, Karen Bush. Herman Melville. 2006. (J). lib. bdg. (978-1-58415-453-2(5)) Mitchell Lane Pubs., Inc.

Hegarty, Carol, ed. Moby Dick. 1998. (Classics Ser.: Set II). 48p. (YA). (gr. 5-12). pap., stu. ed. 17.95 (978-1-56254-259-7(1) , SP2591) Saddleback Educational Publishing.

Meltzer, Milton. Herman Melville: A Biography. 2006. (American Literary Greats Ser.). (Illus.). 128p. (J). (gr. 7 up). 31.93 (978-0-7613-2749-3(5) , Twenty-First Century Bks.) Lerner Publishing Group.

Snodgrass, Mary Ellen. CliffsNotes on Melville's Billy Budd & Typee. rev. ed. 2003. 80p. pap. 5.99 (978-0-7645-3950-3(7) , Cliff Notes) Wiley, John & Sons, Inc.

MEMOIRS

see Autobiographies; Biography

MEMORY

Activities for Developing Memory. 2004. 64p. (J). (gr. k-1). 7.99 (978-0-7424-2707-5(2) , IFG99151) School Specialty Publishing.

Berry, Joy Wilt. A Book about Being Forgetful. 2005. (Illus.). (J). (978-0-7172-8589-1(8)) Scholastic, Inc.

Cusimano, Addie. Achieve Levels V & VI: A Visual Memory Program, 2 vols., Set. 2003. 242p. tchr. ed., ring bd. 43.95 (978-0-9727762-1-9(4)) Achieve Pubns.

Cusimano, Adeline M. Achieve Levels I-IV: A Visual Memory Program, 4 vols., Vol. 4. 2003. 412p. tchr. ed., ring bd. 79.95 (978-0-9727762-0-2(6) , 206) Achieve Pubns.

Hill, Lee Sullivan. Monuments Help Us Remember. 2000. (Building Block Bks.). (Illus.). 32p. (J). (gr. k-3). lib. bdg. (978-1-57505-475-9(2) , Carolrhoda Bks.) Lerner Publishing Group.

Levine, Melvin D. Memory Factory: Guidelines for Use with Students. Arnold, Tim, ed. 1999. (Illus.). (YA). (gr. 7-10). pap., wbk. ed. 9.00 (978-0-8388-1982-1(6)) Educators Publishing Service, Inc.

Oke, Janette. Making Memories. Bladholm, Cheri, illus. 1999. 32p. (J). (ps-3). 14.99 (978-0-7642-2190-3(6)) Bethany Hse. Pubs.

Photographic Memory: Individual Chapter Book Title Six-Packs. Vol. 27. 32p. (gr. 4 up). 44.00 (978-0-7635-4492-8(2)) Rigby Education.

School Specialty Publishing. Activities for Developing Memory. 2004. 64p. (J). (gr. 2-3). pap. 8.99 (978-0-7424-2708-2(0) , IFG99142); (gr. 4-5). pap. 8.99 (978-0-7424-2709-9(9) , IFG99150) School Specialty Publishing.

—Memory. 2006. (Brighter Child Flash Cards Ser.). 54p. (J). 2.99 (978-0-7696-4729-6(4) , Brighter Child) School Specialty Publishing.

Strang Communications Company Staff, ed. Grades 1-2 Activities: Spring 2002. 2002. (J). (gr. 1-2). pap., act. bk. ed. 3.29 (978-1-57405-934-2(3)) CharismaLife Pubs.

—Grades 1-2 Activities: Summer 2002. 2002. (J). (gr. 1-2). pap., act. bk. ed. 3.29 (978-1-57405-972-4(6)) CharismaLife Pubs.

Swanson, Diane. Hmm? The Most Interesting Book You'll Ever Read about Memory. Cowles, Rose, illus. unabr. ed. 2004. (Mysterious You Ser.). 40p. (J). (gr. 4-6). (978-1-55074-597-9(2)); (978-1-55074-595-5(6)) Kids Can Pr., Ltd.

—Hmm? The Most Interesting Book You'll Ever Read about Memory. 2001. (gr. 5-8). lib. bdg. 15.25 (978-0-613-50321-1(X)) Tandem Library Bks.

MEN

see also Human Beings

Chin-Lee, Cynthia. Akira to Zoltan: Twenty-Six Men Who Changed the World. Halsey, Megan & Addy, Sean, illus. 2006. 32p. (J). 15.95 (978-1-57091-579-6(2)) Charlesbridge Publishing, Inc.

Guys' Guides. 2005. (Illus.). 48p. (gr. 5-8). lib. bdg. 95.80 (978-0-8239-4094-3(2)) Rosen Publishing Group, Inc., The.

Guys' Guides, 6 bks. Incl. Chillin' A Guy's Guide to Friendship. Sommers, Michael A. (YA). 2005. lib. bdg. 23.95 (978-0-8239-3160-6(9) , GUCHIL); Dating & Relating : A Guy's Guide to Girls. McCarthy, Tara. (YA). 1999. lib. bdg. 17.95 (978-0-8239-3110-1(2) , GUDARE, Rosen Central); Real Deal : A Guy's Guide to Being a Guy. Roberts, Jeremy. (YA). 2005. lib. bdg. 23.95 (978-0-8239-3104-0(8) , GUREDE); Stay Cool : A Guy's Guide to Handling Conflict. Hayhurst, Chris. (YA). 2005. lib. bdg. 23.95 (978-0-8239-3159-0(5) , GUSTCO); Top of Your Game : A Guy's Guide to Looking & Feeling Good. Eshom, Dan. (YA). 2000. lib. bdg. 17.95 (978-0-8239-3083-8(1) , GUTOGA, Rosen Central); You Ought to Know : A Guy's Guide to Sex. Kelly, Bill. (J). 2005. lib. bdg. 23.95 (978-0-8239-3084-5(X) , GUYOSH); 48p. (gr. 5-8). (Illus.). Set lib. bdg. 107.70 o.p. (978-0-8239-9088-7(5) , GUGUID, Rosen Central) Rosen Publishing Group, Inc., The.

Kyi, Tanya Lloyd. Canadian Boys Who Rocked the World. Bagley, Tom, illus. 2007. 126p. (J). (gr. 3-2). pap. 9.95 (978-1-55285-799-1(9) , Walrus Bks.) Whitecap Bks., Ltd. CAN. *Dist:* Firefly Bks., Ltd.

MENDEL, GREGOR, 1822-1884

Bankston, John. Gregor Mendel & the Discovery of the Gene. 2004. (Uncharted, Unexplored, & Unexplained Ser.). (Illus.). 48p. (J). (gr. 4-8). lib. bdg. 29.95 (978-1-58415-266-8(4)) Mitchell Lane Pubs., Inc.

Bardoe, Cheryl. Gregor Mendel: The Friar Who Grew Peas. Smith, Jos. A., illus. 2006. 40p. (J). (gr. k-4). 18.95 (978-0-8109-5475-5(3) , Abrams Bks. for Young Readers) Abrams, Harry N. , Inc.

Klare, Roger. Gregor Mendel: Father of Genetics. 2001. (Great Minds of Science Ser.). (Illus.). 128p. (YA). (gr. 4-10). pap. 10.95 (978-0-7660-1871-6(7)) Enslow Pubs., Inc.

Leech, Bonnie Coulter. Gregor Mendel's Genetic Theory: Understanding & Applying Concepts of Probability. 2006. (Math for the Real World Ser.). (Illus.). 32p. (J). pap. (978-1-4042-6063-4(3)); lib. bdg. (978-1-4042-3355-3(5)) Rosen Publishing Group, Inc., The.

Yannuzzi, Della. Gregor Mendel: Genetics Pioneer. 2004. (Great Life Stories Ser.). (Illus.). 111p. (J). 30.50 (978-0-531-12263-1(8) , Watts, Franklin) Scholastic Library Publishing.

MENDELEYEV, DMITRY IVANOVICH, 1834-1907

Zannos, Susan. Dmitri Mendeleyev & the Periodic Table. 2004. (Uncharted, Unexplored, & Unexplained Ser.). (Illus.). 48p. (J). (gr. 4-8). lib. bdg. 29.95 (978-1-58415-267-5(2)) Mitchell Lane Pubs., Inc.

MENDELSSOHN-BARTHOLDY, FELIX, 1809-1847

Hiller, Ferdinand. Mendelssohn Letters & Recollections. 2001. 228p. (YA). reprint ed. 98.00 (978-0-7222-5470-7(9)) Library Reprints, Inc.

Lampadius, Wilhelm A. The Life of Felix Mendelssohn-Bartholdy. 2001. 333p. (YA). reprint ed. 98.00 (978-0-7222-5471-4(7)) Library Reprints, Inc.

Mendelssohn-Bartholdy, Felix. Letters from Italy & Switzerland. 2001. 356p. (YA). reprint ed. 98.00 (978-0-7222-5463-9(6)) Library Reprints, Inc.

—Letters of Felix Mendelssohn to Ignaz & Charlotte Moscheles. 2001. 306p. (YA). reprint ed. 98.00 (978-0-7222-5465-3(2)) Library Reprints, Inc.

Polko, Elise V. Reminiscences of Felix Mendelssohn-Bartholdy: A Social & Artistic Biography. 2001. 334p. (YA). reprint ed. 98.00 (978-0-7222-5472-1(5)) Library Reprints, Inc.

Stratton, Stephen S. Mendelssohn. 2001. 306p. (YA). reprint ed. 98.00 (978-0-7222-5473-8(3)) Library Reprints, Inc.

MENENDEZ DE AVILES, PEDRO, 1519-1574

Roberts, Russell. Pedro Menendez de Aviles. 2002. (Latinos in American History). (Illus.). 56p. (gr. 4-8). lib. bdg. 29.95 (978-1-58415-150-0(1)) Mitchell Lane Pubs., Inc.

MENNONITES

see also Amish

Null, David. Introduction to Mennonite Doctrine & Practice. 2004. 90p. 3.35 (978-0-7399-2316-0(1) , 2356) Rod & Staff Pubs., Inc.

Therrien, Patricia. Amish & Mennonite Cooking. 2005. (American Regional Cooking Library). (Illus.). 72p. (J). lib. bdg. (978-1-59084-612-4(5)); lib. bdg. 299.25 (978-1-59084-609-4(5)) Mason Crest Pubs.

MENNONITES—FICTION

Barry, Rick. Gunner's Run. 2007. (YA). (***978-1-59166-761-2(5))*** Jones, Bob Univ. Pr.

Dueck, Adele. Nettie's Journey. 2006. (Illus.). 224p. (J). pap. 7.95 (978-1-55050-322-7(7)) Coteau Bks. CAN. *Dist:* F & W Pubns., Inc.

Gugler, Laurel Dee. Catching Forever. 2007. (Streetlights Ser.). 104p. (J). (gr. 2-5). 7.95 (***978-1-55028-954-1(3)***) Lorimer, James & Co., Ltd., Pubs. CAN. *Dist:* Casemate Pubs. & Bk. Distributors, LLC.

Horrocks, Anita. Almost Eden. 2006. 288p. (J). (gr. 5-9). pap. 9.95 (978-0-88776-742-5(7)) Tundra Bks., Inc./Livres Toundra, Inc. CAN. *Dist:* Random Hse., Inc.

Klassen, Kirsten L. Katelyn's Affection. 2004. 280p. pap. 11.99 (978-0-8361-9281-0(8)) Herald Pr.

Martin, Rebella. Joanna's Journey. Yoder, Laura, illus. 2006. 168p. (YA). pap. 10.99 (978-1-933753-01-0(3)) Carlisle Pr.- Walnut Creek.

Smith, Eunice Geil. Treasure Hunt: A Shenandoah Valley Mystery. 2006. 119p. (J). pap. 9.99 (978-0-8361-9332-9(6)) Herald Pr.

Smucker, Barbara. Selina & the Shoo-Fly Pie. Wilson, Janet & Holliday, Lucy Anne, illus. 1999. 28p. (J). (ps-3). 15.95 (978-0-7737-3018-2(4)) Stoddart Kids CAN. *Dist:* Fitzhenry & Whiteside, Ltd.

Snider, Cindy Gay. Finding Anna Bee. Chambers, Mary, illus. 2007. (J). pap. (***978-0-8361-9392-3(X)***) Herald Pr.

MENSTRUATION

Dickerson, Karle. On the Spot: Real Girls on Periods, Growing Up, & Finding Your Groove. 2005. 160p. (J). (gr. 3-7). pap. 8.95 (978-1-59337-215-6(9)) Adams Media Corp.

Feinmann, Jane. Everything a Girl Needs to Know about Her Period. 2003. (Illus.). 144p. (J). pap. 14.95 (978-1-56906-555-6(1) , BTM-555) Sellers Publishing, Inc.

Gravelle, Karen & Gravelle, Jennifer. El Libro del Periodo. Palen, Debbie, illus. 2003. (SPA.). 117p. (gr. 3 up). pap. 8.95 (978-0-8027-7650-1(7)) Walker & Co.

Gregson, Susan R. Premenstrual Syndrome. 2000. (Perspectives on Physical Health Ser.). (Illus.). 64p. (J). (gr. 4-6). lib. bdg. 23.93 (978-0-7368-0421-9(8) , LifeMatters Bks.) Capstone Pr., Inc.

Jones, Rosemary, et al. The Period Pocketbook: Honest Answers with Advice from Real Girls. 2006. (Illus.). 128p. pap. 7.95 (978-1-56975-557-0(4)) Ulysses Pr.

Jukes, Mavis. Growing Up: Straight Talk about First Bras, First Periods, & Your Changing Body. Tilley, Debbie, illus. 1998. 80p. (J). (gr. 5-8). pap. 10.00 (978-0-679-89027-0(0) , Knopf Bks. for Young Readers) Random Hse. Children's Bks.

LaFlamme, Linda M. Rites of Passage: A Celebration of Menarche. 2001. (Moontime Ser.). (Illus.). 80p. (J). (gr. 3-9). 19.95 (978-0-9673449-0-4(5)) Synchronicity Pr.

Loulan, Joann & Worthen, Bonnie. Period: A Girl's Guide to Menstruation. 4th rev. ed. 2000. (Lansky, Vicki Ser.). (Illus.). 78p. (J). pap. 9.99 (978-0-916773-96-0(5)) Book Peddlers.

Morais, Joan. A Time to Celebrate: A Celebration of a Girl's First Menstrual Period. 2004. (Illus.). 112p. (YA). per. 16.95 (978-0-9746304-5-8(4) , 1196060) Lua Publishing.

Movsessian, Shushann. Puberty Girl. 2005. (Illus.). 128p. (J). (ps-7). mass mkt. 15.95 (978-1-74114-104-7(4)) Allen & Unwin AUS. *Dist:* Independent Pubs. Group.

Owen, Charlotte. Periods. 2nd ed. 2005. (Illus.). (YA). pap. 12.00 (978-0-340-88389-1(8) , Hodder & Stoughton) Hodder General Publishing Division GBR. *Dist:* Trafalgar Square Publishing.

Waters, Sophie. Dealing with PMS. 2007. (J). (***978-1-4042-1949-6(8)***) Rosen Publishing Group, Inc., The.

MENSTRUATION—FICTION

Gordon, Lorell Cynthia. Tilly's Birthday: A Young Girl's Introduction to Menstruation. 2005. (Illus.). 64p. (J). per. 6.99 (978-0-9763961-0-9(6)) Learning All About Me, LLC.

Naylor, Phyllis Reynolds. Lovingly Alice. (J). 2006. 166p. (***978-1-4156-5199-5(X)*** , Aladdin); 2004. (Illus.). 176p. 15.95 (978-0-689-84399-0(2) , Atheneum) Simon & Schuster Children's Publishing.

MENSURATION

see also Measuring Instruments; Surveying; Weights and Measures

Beck, Esther. I'm on the Trail to Learn about Scale! 2006. (Illus.). 24p. (J). (978-1-59928-593-1(2)) ABDO Publishing Co.

Beers, Jack. Time & Measurement. 2000. (Metro Math Readers Yellow Level Ser.). (J). (gr. 12-2). 52.95 (978-1-58120-558-9(9)) Metropolitan Teaching & Learning Co.

Benchmark Education Staff, compiled by. Measurement. 2005. spiral bd. 305.00 (***978-1-4108-3887-2(0));*** spiral bd. 165.00 (***978-1-4108-3888-9(9));*** spiral bd. 270.00 (***978-1-4108-3895-7(1));*** spiral bd. 120.00 (***978-1-4108-3896-4(X));*** spiral bd. 295.00 (***978-1-4108-3902-2(8));*** spiral bd. 110.00 (***978-1-4108-3903-9(6));*** spiral bd. 50.00 (***978-1-4108-3910-7(9));*** spiral bd. 35.00 (***978-1-4108-3914-5(1));*** spiral bd. 420.00 (***978-1-4108-4513-9(3));*** spiral bd. 635.00 (***978-1-4108-5454-4(X));*** spiral bd. 315.00 (***978-1-4108-5455-1(8));*** spiral bd. 330.00 (***978-1-4108-5865-8(0));*** spiral bd. 295.00 (***978-1-4108-5866-5(9)***) Benchmark Education Co.

Benjamin, Lindsay. Measurement Action! 2006. 16p. (J). (gr. k-2). 15.93 (978-0-7368-5856-4(3) , Yellow Umbrella Bks.) Capstone Pr., Inc.

Big Bigger Biggest. 2002. (Illus.). (J). pap. 3.74 (978-0-7398-5854-7(8)) Steck-Vaughn.

Billington, Jeannie. Six Feet, Three. 2000. (Math Together Ser.). (Illus.). (J). 19.99 (978-0-7636-0957-3(9)) Candlewick Pr.

Borden, Louise & Blegvad, Erik. Sea Clocks. 2004. (Illus.). 48p. (J). 18.95 (978-0-689-84216-0(3) , McElderry, Margaret K.) Simon & Schuster Children's Publishing.

Brian, Sarah J. Measurement & Geometry. 1998. (Funtastic Math Ser.). (Illus.). 64p. pap. 9.95 (978-0-590-37370-8(6)) Scholastic, Inc.

Bryant-Mole, Karen. Starting to Measure. 2004. (First Learning Ser.). (Illus.). 24p. (J). (ps up). pap., act. bk. ed. 4.95 (978-0-7460-3801-7(1)) EDC Publishing.

Bulloch, Ivan. Measure. 2004. (Action Math Ser.). (SPA., Illus.). 32p. (ps-3). 9.95 (978-1-58728-281-2(X)); (J). pap. 5.95 (978-1-58728-051-1(5)) T&N Children's Publishing. (Two Can Publishing).

—Medidas. 2004. (Matematicas en Accion Ser.). (SPA., Illus.). (ps-3). 32p. (J). pap. 5.95 (978-1-58728-967-5(9)); 30p. 9.95 (978-1-58728-981-1(4)) T&N Children's Publishing. (Two Can Publishing).

Burstein, John. Measuring: The Perfect Playhouse. 2003. (Weekly Reader Early Learning Library). (Illus.). 24p. (J). (gr. 1 up). pap. 7.93 (978-0-8368-3828-2(9) , Weekly Reader Early Learning Library) Stevens, Gareth Inc.

Burton, Margie & French, Tammy, Cathy - Jones. ¿Qué puedes medir con una paleta? & What Can You Measure with a Lollipop? 2005. spiral bd. 66.00 (***978-1-4108-5627-2(5)***) Benchmark Education Co.

Burton, Margie, et al. Measure Up! Adams, Alison, ed. 1999. (Early Connections Ser.). 16p. (J). (gr. k-2). pap. 4.50 (978-1-58344-073-5(9)) Benchmark Education Co.

Catala, Ellen. Por que Medimos? 2005. Tr. of Why We Measure. (SPA., Illus.). 16p. (J). (gr. k-1). lib. bdg. 15.93 (978-0-7368-4134-4(2)) Capstone Pr., Inc.

Cato, Sheila. Measuring. Sweeten, Sami, illus. 1999. (Question of Math Ser.). 32p. (J). (gr. k-3). lib. bdg. 25.26 (978-1-57505-323-3(3) , Carolrhoda Bks.) Lerner Publishing Group.

M N O

Davies. Fun Size. (Illus.). 40p. (J). 19.95 (978-1-85479-230-3(X)) O'Mara, Michael Bks., Ltd. GBR. *Dist:* Trans-Atlantic Pubns., Inc.

Doudna, Kelly. I'm on the Trail to Learn about Scale. 2007. (Illus.). 24p. (J). 19.93 (978-1-59928-592-4(4) , Sand-Castle) ABDO Publishing Co.

Douglas, Kathy M. Simple Centers. 1999. 240p. (J). (gr. k up). pap. 16.99 (978-1-56822-305-6(6) , IF8666) School Specialty Publishing.

Equal Parts. 2002. (Illus.). (J). pap. (978-0-7398-5944-5(7)) Steck-Vaughn.

From Here to There with Cuisenaire Rods: Area, Perimeter & Volume. 2000. (J). pap. (978-1-56911-024-9(7)) Learning Resources, Inc.

Garcia, Joy. My Paper Ruler. 2004. (Illus.). 44p. (J). pap. 4.99 (978-1-59092-144-9(5) , Orchard Academy Pr.) Windstorm Creative.

Gardner, Robert. Far-Out Science Projects with Height & Depth: How High Is up? How Low Is Down? 2003. (Sensational Science Experiments Ser.). (Illus.). 48p. (J). (gr. 1-4). lib. bdg. 23.93 (978-0-7660-2016-0(9)) Enslow Pubs., Inc.

—Science Projects about Methods of Measuring. 2000. (Science Projects Ser.). (Illus.). 128p. (YA). (gr. 6-12). lib. bdg. 26.60 (978-0-7660-1169-4(0)) Enslow Pubs., Inc.

Gresko, Marcia S. Measuring. Jarrett, Michael, illus. Jarrett, Michael, photos by. 2004. (I Can Do Math Ser.). 24p. (J). (gr. 1 up). lib. bdg. 20.67 (978-0-8368-4112-1(3)) Stevens, Gareth Inc.

Gunzi, Christiane. My Very First Look at Sizes. 2006. (Illus.). 22p. (J). bds. 6.95 (978-1-58728-564-6(9) , Two Can Publishing) T&N Children's Publishing.

Harper, Charise Mericle. The Little Book of Not So. 2005. (Illus.). 32p. (J). (ps-k). 9.95 (978-0-618-47319-9(X)) Houghton Mifflin Co. Trade & Reference Div.

Harris, Nicholas. How Tall? 2003. (How? Ser.). (Illus.). 30p. (J). 23.70 (978-1-4103-0065-2(X) , Blackbirch Pr., Inc.) Thomson Gale.

Hewitt, Sally. Measuring. 2007. (J). (***978-1-59604-135-6(8)***) Stargazer Bks.

HSP. Geometry & Measurement, Bk. E. 2nd ed. 2002. (First-Place Math Ser.). (gr. 5 up). pap. 12.60 (978-0-15-334637-8(X)); (gr. 6 up). pap. 12.60 (978-0-15-334643-9(4)) Harcourt Schl. Pubs.

—Measurement, Bk. F. 2nd ed. 2002. (First-Place Math Ser.). (gr. 3 up). pap. 12.60 (978-0-15-334626-2(4)); (gr. 4 up). pap. 12.60 (978-0-15-334632-3(9)) Harcourt Schl. Pubs.

—Measurement, Geometry, & Fractions, Bk. F. 2nd ed. 2002. (First-Place Math Ser.). (gr. 1 up). pap. 12.60 (978-0-15-334614-9(0)); (gr. 2 up). pap. 12.60 (978-0-15-334620-0(5)) Harcourt Schl. Pubs.

Hunt, Darleen L. Mr. Reed's Class Estimates: Estimating. Komarck, Michael, illus. 2003. (Sherman's Math Corner Ser.). (J). (ps-3). (978-1-929591-06-0(3)) Reading Rock, Inc.

In Step with the Standards - Measurement. 2005. (J). spiral bd. 15.95 (978-1-58123-377-3(9)) Larson Learning, Inc.

Jerome, Kate Boehm. How Many Ants in an Anthill? 2004. (Math Behind the Science Ser.). (Illus.). 24p. (J). pap. (978-0-7922-4587-2(3)) National Geographic Society.

Kirkby, David. Measuring. 1998. (Mini Math Ser.). (Illus.). (J). (978-1-57572-004-3(3)) Heinemann Library.

Kompelien, Tracy. I Can Measure Length, It Has No Strength! (Math Made Fun Ser.). (Illus.). 24p. (J). 2007. 19.93 (978-1-59928-517-7(7) , SandCastle); 2006. pap. (978-1-59928-518-4(5)) ABDO Publishing Co.

—I Can Measure Weight at Any Rate. (Math Made Fun Ser.). (Illus.). 24p. (J). 2007. 19.93 (978-1-59928-519-1(3) , SandCastle); 2006. pap. (978-1-59928-520-7(7)) ABDO Publishing Co.

—Let's All Assume, We Can Measure Volume. 2007. (Illus.). 24p. (J). 19.93 (978-1-59928-535-1(5) , SandCastle) ABDO Publishing Co.

—Let's All Assume, We Can Measure Volume! 2006. (Illus.). 24p. (J). (978-1-59928-536-8(3)) ABDO Publishing Co.

Koomen, Michele. Size: Many Ways to Measure. 2001. (Exploring Math Ser.). (Illus.). 24p. (J). (gr. 1-2). lib. bdg. 18.60 (978-0-7368-0821-7(3) , Bridgestone Bks.) Capstone Pr., Inc.

Krishnaswami, Uma. Learn to Estimate. 2006. (Early Explorers Ser.). (J). 36.00 (***978-1-4108-6132-0(5)***) Benchmark Education Co.

Learn about Measuring with Big Bird. 2005. (Illus.). 48p. (J). (ps-ps). pap. 3.95 (978-1-58610-910-3(3)) Learning Horizons, Inc.

Lee, Frances. Who Is the Tallest? 1999. (ps-2). lib. bdg. 11.80 (978-0-613-19492-1(6)) Tandem Library Bks.

Lee, Martin & Miller, Marcia. 50 Fabulous Measurement Activities: Hands-on Activities for Exploring Length, Perimeter, Weight, Volume & Time That Will Send Kids' Measurement Skills Sky HIgh! 2000. 64p. pap. 10.95 (978-0-590-64406-8(8)) Scholastic, Inc.

Leedy, Loreen. Measuring Penny. Leedy, Loreen, illus. rev. ed. 1998. (Illus.). 32p. (J). (gr. 2-4). 17.95 (978-0-8050-5360-9(5) , Holt, Henry & Co. Bks. For Young Readers) Holt, Henry & Co.

Lets Measure It. 2002. (Illus.). (J). pap. (978-0-7398-5940-7(4)) Steck-Vaughn.

Levy, Janey. The Great Pyramid of Giza: Measuring Length, Area, Volume, & Angles. 2006. (Math for the Real World Ser.). (Illus.). 32p. (J). pap. (978-1-4042-6059-7(5)); lib. bdg. (978-1-4042-3353-9(9)) Rosen Publishing Group, Inc., The.

Long, Lynette. Measurement Mania: Games & Activities That Make Math Easy & Fun. 2001. (gr. 3-6). lib. bdg. 22.20 (978-0-613-81935-0(7)) Tandem Library Bks.

—Measurement Mania: Games & Activities That Make Math Easy & Fun. 2001. (Magical Math Ser.: Vol. 4). (Illus.). 128p. (gr. 3-7). pap. 12.95 (978-0-471-36980-6(2) , Wiley-Interscience) Wiley, John & Sons, Inc.

Loughran, Donna. How Long Is It? (Rookie Read-About Math Ser.). (J). 2005. (Illus.). 32p. (gr. 1-2). pap. 5.95 (978-0-516-24671-0(2)); 2004. 20.50 (978-0-516-24424-2(8)) Scholastic Library Publishing. (Children's Pr.).

Maxwell, Yolonda. Famous Bridges of the World: Measuring Length, Weight, & Volume. 2005. (PowerMath Ser.). (Illus.). 32p. (J). 22.50 (978-1-4042-2937-2(X)); pap. (978-1-4042-5137-3(5)) Rosen Publishing Group, Inc., The. (PowerKids Pr.).

McNabb, Jeffrey G. Rule of Thumb Measuring System: Both English & Metric. Zimmerman, Pam & Kelley, Jim, illus. l.t. ed. 1999. (J). (gr. 4-8). pap. 5.00 (978-0-9669794-0-4(0)) Rule of Thumb Publishing.

Measurement & Geometry. 2003. Level C. tchr. ed. 19.50 (978-0-7652-1317-4(6)); Level C. stu. ed. 14.50 (978-0-7652-1305-1(2)); Level D. tchr. ed. 19.50 (978-0-7652-1321-1(4)); Level D. stu. ed. 14.50 (978-0-7652-1309-9(5)); Level E. tchr. ed. 19.50 (978-0-7652-1325-9(7)); Level E. stu. ed. 14.50 (978-0-7652-1313-6(3)) Modern Curriculum Pr.

Measurement & Geometry. 2003. 16.95 (978-0-7690-0836-3(4)) Seymour, Dale Pubns.

Measuring. 2005. (J). Bk. 1. per. 8.95 (978-1-59566-156-2(5)); Bk. 2. per. 8.95 (978-1-59566-160-9(3)) QEB Publishing Inc.

Measuring. 2001. (Early Math Ser.). (J). (gr. k-12). vinyl bd. 4.95 (978-1-58845-069-2(4)) School Specialty Publishing.

Measuring with Mr Wiggle. 32p. (gr. 1 up). 4.99 (978-1-56451-994-8(5) , ID99020); (gr. 2 up). 4.99 (978-1-56451-995-5(3) , ID99021) School Specialty Publishing.

Metric & Measurement: Primary. 2003. (Basic Skills Ser.). 48p. (gr. 1-5). 5.99 (978-1-56822-256-1(4) , IF5122) School Specialty Publishing.

Mian measurement Gr4-5. 2004. (Math in A Nutshell(R) Ser.). (gr. 4-5). (978-1-59242-185-5(7)) Delta Education, LLC.

Miller Molengraft, Lisa. Simple Centers. 1999. 240p. (J). (gr. 1 up). pap. 16.99 (978-1-56822-306-3(4) , IF8667); (gr. 2 up). pap. 16.99 (978-1-56822-307-0(2) , IF8668) School Specialty Publishing.

Montague-Smith, Ann. Measuring. 2004. (QEB Start Math Ser.). (Illus.). 24p. (J). Vol. 1. lib. bdg. 15.95 (978-1-59566-027-5(5)); Vol. 2. lib. bdg. 15.95 (978-1-59566-031-2(3)) QEB Publishing Inc.

Multiplication Dot-to-Dot Spanish Version. 2007. (J). (***978-1-58232-166-0(3)***) Bryan Hse. Pubs., Inc.

Multiplication Facts Spanish Version. 2007. (J). per. (***978-1-58232-155-4(8)***) Bryan Hse. Pubs., Inc.

Multiplication Skills Spanish Version. 2007. (J). per. (***978-1-58232-156-1(6)***) Bryan Hse. Pubs., Inc.

Murphy. Racing Around. 2002. (Illus.). pap. (978-0-7398-6792-1(X)) Steck-Vaughn.

Murphy, Patricia J. Measuring Puppies & Kittens. 2007. (Puppy & Kitten Math Ser.). (Illus.). 32p. (J). lib. bdg. 22.60 (978-0-7660-2727-5(9) , Enslow Elementary) Enslow Pubs., Inc.

Murphy, Stuart J. Bigger, Better, Best! Winborn, Marsha, illus. 2002. (MathStart Ser.). 40p. (J). (gr. 1 up). pap. 5.99 (978-0-06-446247-1(1)) HarperCollins Pubs.

—Polly's Pen Pal. Simard, Remy, illus. 2005. (MathStart Ser.). 40p. (J). (gr. 2 up). 15.99 (978-0-06-053168-3(1)); pap. 5.99 (978-0-06-053170-6(3)) HarperCollins Pubs.

—Racing Around. 2001. (MathStart Ser.). (Illus.). 40p. (J). (gr. 1 up). 15.95 (978-0-06-028912-6(0)) HarperCollins Pubs.

—Racing Around. Reed, Mike, illus. 2001. (MathStart Ser.). 40p. (J). (gr. 1 up). 15.89 (978-0-06-028913-3(9)); pap. 5.99 (978-0-06-446244-0(7) , Harper Trophy) HarperCollins Pubs.

—Super Sand Castle Saturday. Gorton, Julia, illus. 1999. (MathStart Ser.). 40p. (gr. 1 up). (J). pap. 5.99 (978-0-06-446720-9(1) , Harper Trophy); (YA). 15.89 (978-0-06-027613-4(3)) HarperCollins Pubs.

—Super Sand Castle Saturday. 1999. (Math Start Ser.). (978-0-606-16680-5(7)); lib. bdg. 13.00 (978-0-613-12163-7(5)) Tandem Library Bks.

—Super Sand Castle Saturday: Level 2: Measuring. Gorton, Julia, illus. 1999. (MathStart Ser.). 40p. (YA). (gr. 1 up). 15.95 (978-0-06-027612-6(6)) HarperCollins Pubs.

Murphy, Stuart J & Murphy, Stuart J. Racing Around. Reed, Mike, illus. 2001. 33p. (J). (ps-3). lib. bdg. 12.95 (978-0-613-59248-2(4)) Tandem Library Bks.

Nagda, Ann Whitehead & Bickel, Cindy. Chimp Math: Learning about Time from a Baby Chimpanzee. rev. ed. 2002. (Illus.). 32p. (J). (gr. 2-5). 17.95 (978-0-8050-6674-6(8) , Holt, Henry & Co. Bks. For Young Readers) Holt, Henry & Co.

Osofsky, Jill. Measuring. 2000. (Funtastic Frogs Ser.). 32p. (J). (gr. k-2). pap., act. bk. ed. 4.99 (978-1-56451-317-5(3) , ID43013) School Specialty Publishing.

Owen, M. J. Using the Standards: Measurement: Measurement. 2004. (100+ Ser.). 128p. (C). pap. 12.99 (***978-0-7424-2892-8(3)*** , Instructional Fair) Schaffer, Frank Pubns.

Patilla, Peter. Length. 2001. (Illus.). 32p. (J). lib. bdg. 24.25 (978-1-930643-15-4(2)) Chrysalis Education.

—Size. 2001. (Illus.). 32p. (J). lib. bdg. 24.25 (978-1-930643-16-1(0)) Chrysalis Education.

Pisano, Sal. Measurement. 2004. 48p. pap. 6.95 (978-1-4042-8543-9(1)) Rosen Publishing Group, Inc., The.

Pistoia, Sara. Measurement. 2006. (MathBooks Ser.). (Illus.). 24p. (J). 24.21 (978-1-59296-688-2(8)) Child's World, Inc.

Pluckrose, Henry. Measuring Size. 2001. (Let's Explore Ser.). (Illus.). 32p. (J). (gr. 1 up). lib. bdg. 23.33 (978-0-8368-2962-4(X)) Stevens, Gareth Inc.

Pluckrose, Henry Arthur. What Size Is It? 2006. (Illus.). 32p. (J). (978-1-59771-040-4(7)) Sea-To-Sea Pubns.

Practice Power Practice Book Fractions & Measures. 2001. (Illus.). 18p. (J). (gr. 3-5). spiral bd., wbk. ed. (978-1-930355-33-0(5)) Greenbrier/Scentex.

Prince Wallaker, Jillayne. Using the Standards—Measurement. 2004. (100+ Ser.). 128p. (C). pap. 12.99 (***978-0-7424-2895-9(8)*** , Instructional Fair) Schaffer, Frank Pubns.

QEB Start Math Book Stores Edition: Measuring - Book 1. 2006. (J). per. (978-1-59566-274-3(X)) QEB Publishing Inc.

QEB Start Math Book Stores Edition: Measuring Book 2. 2006. (J). per. (978-1-59566-278-1(2)) QEB Publishing Inc.

Rauen, Amy. Finding Shortest & Longest Where I Live. 2008. (J). pap. (***978-0-8368-8987-1(8)***); lib. bdg. (***978-0-8368-8982-6(7)***) Stevens, Gareth Inc. (Weekly Reader Early Learning Library).

—Measuring at the Dog Show. 2007. (J). pap. (***978-0-8368-8483-8(3)***); 24p. (gr. 1-3). lib. bdg. 19.93 (***978-0-8368-8474-6(4)***) Stevens, Gareth Inc. (Weekly Reader Early Learning Library).

Read-Think-Do Math: Measuring Book 1. 2006. pap. 4.49 (978-1-4206-8167-3(2)) Teacher Created Materials, Inc.

Read-Think-Do Math: Measuring Book 2. 2006. pap. 4.49 (978-1-4206-8171-0(0)) Teacher Created Materials, Inc.

Realtime Associates and Mazer Corporation Staff & Leap-Frog Staff, compiled by. Measurement: Find Perimeter. 2002. (J). (gr. 3). 66.75 (978-1-58605-402-1(3) , Leap-Frog Schl. Hse.) LeapFrog Enterprises, Inc.

—Understand Perimeter, Time, Temperature, Area. 2002. (J). (gr. 5). 66.75 (978-1-58605-519-6(4) , LeapFrog Schl. Hse.) LeapFrog Enterprises, Inc.

—Use Measurement Tools. 2002. (J). (gr. 3). 66.75 (978-1-58605-401-4(5) , LeapFrog Schl. Hse.) LeapFrog Enterprises, Inc.

Rosenberg, Mary. Math Mats & Games Measurement: Dozens of Instant & Engaging Reproducible Activity Pages That Help Children Learn Essential Math Skills & Concepts-and Meet the NCTM Standards. 2004. 64p. pap. 11.99 (978-0-439-51880-2(6) , Teaching Resources) Scholastic, Inc.

Roy, Jennifer Rozines & Roy, Gregory. Measuring at Home. 2006. (Math All Around Ser.). (Illus.). 32p. (J). lib. bdg. 28.50 (978-0-7614-2263-1(3) , Benchmark Bks.) Cavendish, Marshall Corp.

Roza, Greg. Measurement. 2004. 48p. pap. 6.95 (978-1-4042-8537-8(7)) Rosen Publishing Group, Inc., The.

—Where We Play Sports: Measuring the Perimeters of Polygons. 2004. (PowerMath Ser.). (Illus.). 24p. (J). lib. bdg. (978-0-8239-8895-2(3)); lib. bdg. 21.25 (978-0-8239-8972-0(0)) Rosen Publishing Group, Inc., The. (PowerKids Pr.).

Sargent, Brian. How Much Does It Hold? 2006. 32p. (gr. 1-2). (YA). pap. 5.95 (978-0-516-29812-2(7)); (Illus.). (J). 20.50 (978-0-516-24957-5(6)) Scholastic Library Publishing. (Children's Pr.).

School Specialty Publishing. Measuring. 2004. (On-File Ser.). 4p. (J). (gr. 1-3). ring bd. 4.99 (978-0-7424-2913-0(X) , Instructional Fair) Schaffer, Frank Pubns.

Schwartz, David M. Millions to Measure. Kellogg, Steven, illus. 40p. (J). 2003. lib. bdg. 17.89 (978-0-06-623784-8(X)); 2003. 16.99 (978-0-688-12916-3(1)); 2006. reprint ed. pap. 6.99 (978-0-06-084806-4(5) , Harper Trophy) HarperCollins Pubs.

Science Stories Foss Spanish Measurement EA CR05. 2005. (J). (978-1-59242-586-0(0)) Delta Education, LLC.

Scott, Janine. Why We Measure. 2002. (Spyglass Books). (Illus.). 24p. (J). (gr. 1 up). lib. bdg. 18.60 (978-0-7565-0449-6(X)) Compass Point Bks.

Simpson, Jeffrey L. Measurement & Geometry, Student Edition: Count, Notice & Remember Math Intervention, Volume 6. Simpson, Marilyn Bohlen, ed. 2007. ring bd. 59.95 (***978-1-888976-59-5(4)***) Mastery Learning Systems.

Steck-Vaughn Staff. Early Math: Measurement I. 2005. pap. 2.99 (978-1-4190-0329-5(1)) Steck-Vaughn.

—Early Math: Measurement II. 2005. pap. 2.99 (978-1-4190-0339-4(9)); pap. 29.95 (978-1-4190-0363-9(1)) Steck-Vaughn.

—Early Measurement 10-pack: Measurement I. 2005. pap. 29.95 (978-1-4190-0353-0(4)) Steck-Vaughn.

—Focus on Math Level C: Measurement. 2005. pap. 2.99 (978-1-4190-0269-4(4)) Harcourt Schl. Pubs.

—Focus on Math Level C 10-pack: Measurement. 2005. pap. 29.95 (978-1-4190-0293-9(7)) Harcourt Schl. Pubs.

—Measure That Tongue! 2003. pap. 4.10 (978-0-7398-7653-4(8)) Steck-Vaughn.

—Measurement & Geometry. 2004. pap. 14.95 (978-0-7398-9855-0(8)) Harcourt Schl. Pubs.

—Top Line Math: Measurement. 2005. pap. 5.49 (978-1-4190-0370-7(4)) Harcourt Schl. Pubs.

—Top Line Math 10-Pack: Measurement. 2005. pap. 54.95 (978-1-4190-0391-2(7)) Harcourt Schl. Pubs.

Strazzabosco, John. Measurement. 2004. 48p. pap. 6.95 (978-1-4042-8530-9(X)) Rosen Publishing Group, Inc., The.

Sullivan, Navin. Area, Distance, & Volume. 2006. (Measure Up! Ser.). (Illus.). 48p. (J). (gr. 4-7). lib. bdg. 29.93 (978-0-7614-2323-2(0) , Benchmark Bks.) Cavendish, Marshall Corp.

—Measure Up!, 5 bks., Set. Incl. Area, Distance, & Volume. lib. bdg. 29.93 (978-0-7614-2323-2(0)); Speed. lib. bdg. 29.93 (978-0-7614-2325-6(7)); Temperature. lib. bdg. 29.93 (978-0-7614-2322-5(2)); Time. lib. bdg. 29.93 (978-0-7614-2321-8(4)); Weight. lib. bdg. 29.93 (978-0-7614-2324-9(9)); (Illus.). 48p. (J). (gr. 4-7). 2006. 2007. Set lib. bdg. 149.64 (***978-0-7614-2320-1(6)*** , Benchmark Bks.) Cavendish, Marshall Corp.

Sullivan, Navin. Speed. 2006. (Measure Up! Ser.). (Illus.). 48p. (J). (gr. 4-7). lib. bdg. 29.93 (978-0-7614-2325-6(7) , Benchmark Bks.) Cavendish, Marshall Corp.

Trumbauer, Lisa. Why We Measure. 2003. (Yellow Umbrella Books). (Illus.). 16p. (J). (gr. 1). lib. bdg. 14.60 (978-0-7368-2017-2(5) , Pebble Bks.) Capstone Pr., Inc.

—Why We Measure. 2003. (Math Ser.). (J). (978-0-7368-1703-5(4)) Yellow Umbrella Pr.

Tuxworth, Nicola. Sizes. 2005. (Illus.). 12p. (gr. 2-13). bds. 6.99 (978-0-7548-1412-2(2) , Lorenz Bks.) Anness Publishing GBR. *Dist:* National Bk. Network.

Waters, Jennifer. Measure It! McEwen, Rebecca & Auch, Alison, eds. 2002. (Spyglass Books). (Illus.). 24p. (J). (gr. 1 up). lib. bdg. 18.60 (978-0-7565-0237-9(3)) Compass Point Bks.

What Comes in Groups. 2002. (Illus.). (J). pap. (978-0-7398-5937-7(4)) Steck-Vaughn.

Who Has More. 2002. (J). pap. 3.74 (978-0-7398-5859-2(9)) Steck-Vaughn.

Woodford, Chris. Area. 2005. (J). 11.20 (978-1-4103-0522-0(8)); 32p. (gr. 2-5). 23.70 (978-1-4103-0366-0(7)) Thomson Gale. (Blackbirch Pr., Inc.).

—Height. 2005. (J). 11.20 (978-1-4103-0524-4(4)); 32p. (gr. 2-5). 23.70 (978-1-4103-0368-4(3)) Thomson Gale. (Blackbirch Pr., Inc.).

MENSURATION—FICTION

deRubertis, Barbara. Lulu's Lemonade. Billin-Frye, Paige, illus. 2000. (Math Matters Ser.). 32p. (J). (ps-3). pap. 4.95 (978-1-57565-093-7(2)) Kane Pr., The.

—Lulu's Lemonade. 2000. (Illus.). (J). (978-0-606-18222-5(5)) Tandem Library Bks.

Naylor, Phyllis Reynolds. Lovingly Alice. 2006. (Alice Ser.). 176p. (J). pap. 5.99 (978-0-689-84400-3(X) , Aladdin) Simon & Schuster Children's Publishing.

MENTAL DEFICIENCY

see People with Mental Disabilities

MENTAL DEPRESSION

see Depression, Mental

MENTAL DISEASES

see Mental Illness; Psychology, Pathological

MENTAL HEALTH

see also Mental Illness; Mind and Body; Psychology, Pathological

Ayer, Eleanor H. Everything You Need to Know about Depression. rev. ed. 2001. (Need to Know Library). (Illus.). 64p. (YA). (gr. 4-6). lib. bdg. 25.25 (978-0-8239-3439-3(X)) Rosen Publishing Group, Inc., The.

Bellenir, Karen, ed. Mental Health Information for Teens: Health Tips about Mental Health & Mental Illness. 2001. (Teen Health Ser.). (Illus.). 406p. (gr. 7 up). (978-0-7808-0442-5(2)) Omnigraphics, Inc.

Bonnice, Sherry. Drug Therapy for Adjustment Disorders. 2003. (Encyclopedia of Psychiatric Drugs & Their Disorders Ser.). (Illus.). 128p. (J). lib. bdg. (978-1-59084-560-8(9)) Mason Crest Pubs.

Brinkerhoff, Shirley. Drug Therapy & Anxiety Disorders. 2003. (Encyclopedia of Psychiatric Drugs & Their Disorders Ser.). (Illus.). 128p. (J). lib. bdg. (978-1-59084-561-5(7)) Mason Crest Pubs.

Culbert, Timothy & Kajander, Rebecca. Be the Boss of Your Stress: Self-Care for Kids. 2007. (Be the Boss of Your Body Ser.). (Illus.). 64p. (J). (gr. 4-7). 6.95 (***978-1-57542-256-5(5)***) Free Spirit Publishing, Inc.

Fisher, Beverly. Mental Toughness for Personal Fitness: Workbook for Life. 2004. (Illus.). 64p. pap. 10.99 (978-0-9745066-0-9(5)) Sports In Mind.

—Mental Toughness for Weight Management: Workbook for Life. 2004. (Illus.). 60p. pap. 10.99 (978-0-9745066-1-6(3)) Sports In Mind.

Gray, Shirley W. Good Mental Health. 2003. (Living Well). (Illus.). 32p. (J). (gr. 2-6). 27.07 (978-1-59296-082-8(0)) Child's World, Inc.

Lambillion, Paul. Staying Cool. 2004. (Illus.). 196p. pap. 13.95 (978-0-7171-3598-1(5)) Gill & MacMillan, Ltd. IRL. *Dist:* Hushion Hse. Publishing, Ltd.

Lecoy, Denise. Looking after Me. Hamelin, Marie-Micheline, illus. 2006. 20p. (J). pap. 10.95 (978-1-894778-29-9(4)) Theytus Bks., Ltd. CAN. *Dist:* Orca Bk. Pubs. USA.

Levchuck, Caroline M. & Drohan, Michele Ingber. Healthy Living, 3 vols. 2000. (J). (978-0-7876-3921-1(4)) Thomson Gale.

Levchuck, Caroline M. & Drohan, Michele Ingber, contrib. by. Healthy Living, 3 vols. 2000. (J). (978-0-7876-3919-8(2) , UXL); (978-0-7876-3920-4(6)) Thomson Gale.

Morse, Philip C. Kick Out Stress - Teen Stress Reduction Program: Improving Self-Esteem, Optimizing Performance in School & Sports & Improving Physical & Emotional Health. 2004. (YA). (gr. 8-12). pap. (978-0-9748548-0-9(8)) Mind/Body Workshops.

Normandi, Carol Emery. Over It: A Teen's Guide to Getting Beyond Obsessions with Food & Weight. 2001. (gr. 7-12). lib. bdg. 23.40 (978-0-613-79250-9(5)) Tandem Library Bks.

Normandi, Carol Emery & Roark, Laurelee. Over It: A Teen's Guide to Getting Beyond Obsessions with Food & Weight. 2001. (Illus.). 224p. (gr. 8-12). pap. 13.95 (978-1-57731-148-5(5)) New World Library.

Quigley, Ann. Mental Health. 2007. (Current Controversies Ser.). 240p. (gr. 10-12). pap. 23.70 (***978-0-7377-2485-1(4)*** , Greenhaven Pr., Inc.) Thomson Gale.

—Mental Health 2007. 2007. (Current Controversies Ser.). 240p. (gr. 10-12). 34.95 (***978-0-7377-2484-4(6)*** , Greenhaven Pr., Inc.) Thomson Gale.

MNO

Simpson, Carolyn & Simpson, Dwain. Coping with Post-Traumatic Stress Disorder (PTSD) Dealing with Tragedy. 2005. (Coping Ser.). (Illus.). 192p. (YA). (gr. 7-12). lib. bdg. 26.50 (978-0-8239-3456-0(X)) Rosen Publishing Group, Inc., The.

Spilsbury, Louise. Why Should I Go to Bed Now? And Other Questions about a Healthy Mind. 2003. (Body Matters Ser.). (Illus.). 32p. (J). lib. bdg. (978-1-4034-4682-4(2)) Heinemann Library.

Tousey, Ben. Acting Your Dreams: Using Acting Techniques to Interpret Your Dreams, 1. 2003. (C). per. 14.95 (978-0-9724292-0-7(4)) Yhabbut Publishing.

Ward, James. Asylum Light: Stories from the George A. Zeller Era & Beyond, Peoria State Hospital, Galesburg Mental Health Center, & George A. Zeller Mental Health Center. 2005. (Illus.). 298p. pap. 19.95 (978-0-9748742-0-3(5) , 1210408) Mental Health Historic Preservation Society Of Central Illinois.

Winkler, Kathleen. Teens, Depression & the Blues. 2000. (Hot Issues Ser.). (Illus.). 64p. (YA). (gr. 6-12). lib. bdg. 27.93 (978-0-7660-1369-8(3)) Enslow Pubs., Inc.

Wolff, Lisa. Teen Depression. 1998. (Teen Issues Ser.). (Illus.). 112p. (YA). (gr. 4-12). lib. bdg. 27.45 (978-1-56006-519-7(2) , LML00902-177877, Lucent Bks.) Thomson Gale.

MENTAL HYGIENE

see Mental Health

MENTAL ILLNESS

see also Mental Health

Abramovitz, Melissa. Bipolar Disorder. 2004. (Illus.). 112p. (J). 32.45 (978-1-59018-589-6(7) , Lucent Bks.) Thomson Gale.

Abramowitz, Melissa. Mental Retardation. 2007. (Diseases & Disorders Ser.). 128p. (J). (gr. 7-10). 32.45 (***978-1-59018-412-7(2)*** , Lucent Bks.) Thomson Gale.

Abramowitz, Mimi. Schizophrenia. 2002. (Diseases & Disorders Ser.). (Illus.). 120p. (YA). (gr. 6-9). 32.45 (978-1-56006-908-9(2) , GML12001-178216, Lucent Bks.) Thomson Gale.

Airey, David, et al. Schizophrenia. 2007. (Psychological Disorders Ser.). (Illus.). 128p. (J). (gr. 9-12). 37.50 (978-0-7910-8544-8(9) , Chelsea Hse.) Facts On File, Inc.

Bonnice, Sherry & Hoard, Carolyn. Drug Therapy & Cognitive Disorders. 2003. (Encyclopedia of Psychiatric Drugs & Their Disorders Ser.). (Illus.). 128p. (J). lib. bdg. (978-1-59084-562-2(5)) Mason Crest Pubs.

Brinkerhoff, Shirley. Drug Therapy & Personality Disorders. 2003. (Encyclopedia of Psychiatric Drugs & Their Disorders Ser.). (Illus.). 128p. (J). lib. bdg. (978-1-59084-571-4(4)) Mason Crest Pubs.

Cefrey, Holly. Antidepressants. 2005. (Drug Abuse Prevention Library). (Illus.). 64p. (J). (gr. 7-12). lib. bdg. 25.25 (978-0-8239-3283-2(4) , DRANDE) Rosen Publishing Group, Inc., The.

Chou, Joey. Crazy by the Letters. Chou, Joey, illus. 2006. 15.99 (***978-0-9788670-0-3(9)***) Choo Choo Clan.

Clarke, Lisa Anne. Wishing Wellness: A Workbook for Children of Parents with Mental Illness. Matthews, Bonnie, illus. 2006. 80p. (J). (gr. 1-7). pap. 14.95 (978-1-59147-313-8(6)) American Psychological Assn.

Dinner, Sherry H. Nothing to Be Ashamed Of: Growing up with Mental Illness in Your Family. 2000. 212p. (YA). (gr. 7-9). reprint ed. 22.00 (978-0-7881-9093-3(8)) DIANE Publishing Co.

Encyc of Psychol Disorders. 2005. pap. 665.00 (978-0-7910-9164-7(3) , Chelsea Hse.) Facts On File, Inc.

Eshom, Dan. Lithium: What You Should Know. 1999. (Drug Abuse Prevention Library). (Illus.). 64p. (YA). (gr. 7-12). lib. bdg. 25.25 (978-0-8239-2828-6(4) , DRLITH) Rosen Publishing Group, Inc., The.

Fundukian, Laurie J. & Wilson, Jeffrey. Gale Encyclopedia of Mental Disorders, 2 Vol. 2nd rev. ed. 2007. 360.00 (***978-1-4144-2987-8(8)***) Thomson Gale.

Gold, Susan Dudley. Bipolar Disorder & Depression. 2000. (Health Watch Ser.). (Illus.). 48p. (YA). (gr. 4-10). lib. bdg. 23.93 (978-0-7660-1654-5(4)) Enslow Pubs., Inc.

Hunter, David & Livingston, Phyllis. Youth with Bipolar Disorder: Achieving Stability. 2008. (J). (978-1-4222-0138-1(4)) Mason Crest Pubs.

Jovinelly, Joann. Coping with Bipolar Disorder & Manic-Depressive Illness. 2005. (Coping Ser.). (Illus.). 192p. (YA). (gr. 7-12). lib. bdg. 26.50 (978-0-8239-3193-4(5)) Rosen Publishing Group, Inc., The.

Kelly, Pat. Coping with Schizophrenia. 2005. (Coping Ser.). (Illus.). 192p. (YA). (gr. 7-12). lib. bdg. 26.50 (978-0-8239-2853-8(5)) Rosen Publishing Group, Inc., The.

Kent, Deborah. Snake Pits, Talking Cures, & Magic Bullets: A History of Mental Illness. 2003. (Single Titles Ser.). (Illus.). 160p. (gr. 7 up). lib. bdg. 26.90 (978-0-7613-2704-2(5) , Twenty-First Century Bks.) Lerner Publishing Group.

Larson, Elaine Larson. The Kaleidoscope Kid: Focusing on the Strengths of Children with Asperger Syndrome & High-Functioning Autism. 2007. (J). 17.95 (***978-1-931282-41-3(2)***) Autism Asperger Publishing Co.

Leigh, Vanora. Mental Illness. 1999. (Talking Points Ser.). (Illus.). 64p. (YA). (gr. 4-7). lib. bdg. 27.12 (978-0-8172-5311-0(4)) Raintree.

Libal, Autumn. Drug Therapy & Psychosomatic Disorders. 2003. (Encyclopedia of Psychiatric Drugs & Their Disorders Ser.). (Illus.). 128p. (J). lib. bdg. (978-1-59084-573-8(0)) Mason Crest Pubs.

—The FDA & Psychiatric Drugs: Drugs & Psychology for the Mind & Body, 19 vols., Set. 2004. (Psychiatric Disorders Ser.). (Illus.). 128p. (J). lib. bdg. (978-1-59084-559-2(5)) Mason Crest Pubs.

Marvis, B. & Worth, Richard. The Insanity Defense. 2001. (Crime, Justice & Punishment Ser.). (Illus.). 80p. (J). (gr. 9 up). 30.00 (978-0-7910-4294-6(4) , Chelsea Hse.) Facts On File, Inc.

McIntosh, Kenneth & Livingston, Phyllis. Youth with Juvenile Schizophrenia: The Search for Reality. 2008. (J). (978-1-4222-0148-0(1)) Mason Crest Pubs.

Moe, Barbara. Coping with Mental Illness. 2005. (Coping Ser.). (Illus.). 192p. (YA). (gr. 7-12). lib. bdg. 26.50 (978-0-8239-3205-4(2)) Rosen Publishing Group, Inc., The.

Partner, Daniel. Disorders First Diagnosed in Childhood. 2000. (Encyclopedia of Psychological Disorders Ser.). (Illus.). 88p. (J). (gr. 7 up). 35.00 (978-0-7910-5312-6(1) , Chelsea Hse.) Facts On File, Inc.

Phillips, Jane E. & Ketelsen, David P. Schizophrenia. 2003. (Diseases & People Ser.). (Illus.). 112p. (J). (gr. 6-12). lib. bdg. 26.60 (978-0-7660-1896-9(2)) Enslow Pubs., Inc.

Psychological Disorders. 2006. (Illus.). (gr. 6-12). 139.75 (978-0-7910-9095-4(7)) Facts On File, Inc.

Ross, Allison J. Coping When a Parent Is Mentally Ill. 2005. (Coping Ser.). (Illus.). 192p. (YA). (gr. 7-12). lib. bdg. 26.50 (978-0-8239-3359-4(8)) Rosen Publishing Group, Inc., The.

Schizophrenia 2007. 2007. 192p. (gr. 10-12). pap. 23.70 (***978-0-7377-3262-7(8)*** , Greenhaven Pr., Inc.) Thomson Gale.

Shields, Charles J. Mental Illness & Its Effect on School & Work Environments. 2000. (Encyclopedia of Psychological Disorders Ser.). 88p. (YA). (gr. 7 up). 35.00 (978-0-7910-5318-8(0) , Chelsea Hse.) Facts On File, Inc.

Smith, Christopher L. Honest Talk about Serious Mental Illness. 1998. (Illus.). 25p. (YA). (gr. 6-12). pap. 7.95 (978-1-57895-074-4(0) , Bridge Resources) Curriculum Publishing, Presbyterian Church (U. S. A.).

Sommers, Michael A. Everything You Need to Know about Bipolar Disorder & Manic Depressive Illness. (Need to Know Library). (Illus.). 64p. (gr. 4-6). 2000. (J). lib. bdg. 25.25 (978-0-8239-3106-4(4) , NTBIDI); 2005. (YA). lib. bdg. 25.25 (978-0-8239-3768-4(2)) Rosen Publishing Group, Inc., The.

Stewart, Gail B. People with Mental Illness. 2002. (Illus.). 96p. (J). 29.95 (978-1-59018-237-6(5) , Lucent Bks.) Thomson Gale.

Williams, Mary E. Mental Illness. 2006. 244p. (YA). (gr. 9 up). pap. 24.95 (978-0-7377-2948-1(1)); lib. bdg. 36.20 (978-0-7377-2947-4(3)) Thomson Gale. (Greenhaven Pr., Inc.).

MENTAL ILLNESS—FICTION

Adler, David A. Don't Talk to Me about the War. 2008. (YA). (gr. 5). 15.99 (***978-0-670-06307-9(X)*** , Viking Adult) Penguin Group (USA) Inc.

Bryant, Sharon. The Earth Kitchen. 2002. 160p. (J). (gr. 5 up). 15.89 (978-0-06-029606-3(2)) HarperCollins Pubs.

Caletti, Deb. Wild Roses. (YA). (gr. 7 up). 2006. 320p. pap. 6.99 (978-0-689-86475-9(2) , Simon Pulse); 2005. 304p. 15.95 (978-0-689-86766-8(2)) Simon & Schuster Children's Publishing.

Campbell, Bebe Moore. Sometimes My Mommy Gets Angry. Lewis, E. B., illus. 2005. 32p. (J). pap. 5.99 (978-0-14-240359-4(8) , Puffin) Penguin Group (USA) Inc.

—Sometimes My Mommy Gets Angry. Lewis, Earl, illus. 2003. 32p. (J). (ps-3). 16.99 (978-0-399-23972-4(3) , Putnam Juvenile) Penguin Group (USA) Inc.

Clark, Clara Gillow. Hattie on Her Way. Thompson, John, illus. 2005. 208p. (J). (gr. 5 up). 15.99 (978-0-7636-2286-2(9)) Candlewick Pr.

Clarke, Judith. Starry Nights. 2004. 148p. (YA). 15.95 (978-1-886910-82-9(0) , Lemniscaat) Boyds Mills Pr.

Cleaver, Vera & Cleaver, Bill. Donde Florecen los Lirios. (SPA.). 168p. (YA). (gr. 5-8). (978-84-204-3648-7(8) , AF0285) Alfaguara, Ediciones, S.A.- Grupo Santillana ESP. *Dist:* Lectorum Pubns., Inc.

Day, Marie. Edward the Crazy Man. Day, Marie, illus. 2002. (Illus.). 32p. (J). (gr. 1-2). pap. 7.95 (978-1-55037-720-0(5)); lib. bdg. 18.95 (978-1-55037-721-7(3)) Annick Pr., Ltd. CAN. *Dist:* Firefly Bks., Ltd.

Doyle, Malachy. Georgie. 2002. 150p. (YA). 13.95 (978-1-58234-753-0(0) , Bloomsbury Children) Bloomsbury Publishing.

Durmush, F. Ayshe, an Anatolian Tale. 2007. (ENG.). 84p. per. (***978-1-84747-171-0(4)***) Chipmunkapublishing.

Eden, Alexandra. Holy Smoke: A Bones & the Duchess Mystery. 2004. (Illus.). 117p. (J). 16.00 (978-1-888310-46-7(4)) Knoll, Allen A. Pubs.

Fletcher, Christine. Tallulah Falls. (YA). 2007. 400p. pap. 7.95 (***978-1-59990-095-7(5)); *** 2006. 304p. 16.95 (978-1-58234-662-5(3)) Bloomsbury Publishing. (Bloomsbury Children).

Franklin, Kristine L. Dove Song. 2006. 192p. (J). (gr. 5-9). pap. 5.99 (978-0-7636-3219-9(8)) Candlewick Pr.

Fuqua, Jonathon Scott. King of the Pygmies. 2007. (Illus.). 256p. (YA). (gr. 9). pap. 7.99 (***978-0-7636-3412-4(3)***) Candlewick Pr.

Greenberg, Joanne. I Never Promised You a Rose Garden. 2004. 288p. (gr. 12). pap. 13.95 (978-0-451-21120-0(0) , N A L Trade) Penguin Group (USA) Inc.

—I Never Promised You a Rose Garden. 256p. (YA). (gr. 7 up). pap. 5.99 (978-0-8072-1362-9(4) , Listening Library) Random Hse. Audio Publishing Group.

Griffin, Adele. Where I Want to Be. 160p. (gr. 7). 2007. (YA). 6.99 (***978-0-14-240948-0(0)*** , Puffin); 2005. (J). 15.99 (978-0-399-23783-6(6) , Putnam Juvenile) Penguin Group (USA) Inc.

Guest, Jacqueline. Racing Fear. 2004. (SideStreets Ser.). 160p. (gr. 7-12). 7.95 (978-1-55028-838-4(5)); (***978-1-55028-839-1(3)***) Lorimer, James & Co., Ltd., Pubs. CAN. *Dist:* Casemate Pubs. & Bk. Distributors, LLC.

Halliday, John. Shooting Monarchs. 2003. (Illus.). 144p. (YA). 15.95 (978-0-689-84338-9(0) , McElderry, Margaret K.) Simon & Schuster Children's Publishing.

—Shooting Monarchs. l.t. ed. 2005. 157p. 20.95 (978-0-7862-7462-8(X)) Thorndike Pr.

Halpern, Julie. Get Well Soon. 2007. 208p. (YA). (gr. 7 up). 16.95 (***978-0-312-36795-4(3)***) Feiwel & Friends.

Hautman, Pete. Invisible. Hautman, Pete, illus. 160p. (YA). 2005. (gr. 7 up). 16.99 (978-0-689-86800-9(6) , Simon & Schuster Children's Publishing); 2006. reprint ed. pap. 7.99 (978-0-689-86903-7(7) , Simon Pulse) Simon & Schuster Children's Publishing.

—Invisible. l.t. ed. 2005. 192p. (YA). 20.95 (978-0-7862-7909-8(5) , Large Print Pr.) Thorndike Pr.

Hermes, Patricia. Summer Secrets. 2004. (Illus.). 144p. (YA). 15.95 (978-0-7614-5074-0(2)) Cavendish, Marshall Corp.

Hesser, Terry Spencer. Kissing Doorknobs. 1999. (J). (978-0-606-17347-6(1)) Tandem Library Bks.

Hopkins, Ellen. Impulse. 2007. 672p. (YA). (gr. 9 up). 16.99 (978-1-4169-0356-7(9) , McElderry, Margaret K.) Simon & Schuster Children's Publishing.

Huston, Donna. Inch by Inch. 2006. (J). spiral bd. 19.95 (978-0-9771192-3-3(8)) Shayne Publishing.

Johnson, Kathleen Jeffrie. A Fast & Brutal Wing. 2007. 208p. (YA). pap. 6.99 (***978-0-312-37148-7(9)***) Square Fish.

Kempton, Linda. Who'll Catch the Nightmares? 2000. (Illus.). 188p. (J). pap. 8.99 (978-0-7497-4491-5(X)) Egmont Bks., Ltd. GBR. *Dist:* Independent Pubs. Group.

Larbalestier, Justine. Magic or Madness. (gr. 7-12). 2006. 304p. (YA). pap. 7.99 (978-1-59514-070-8(0)); 2005. 288p. (J). 16.99 (978-1-59514-022-7(0)) Penguin Group (USA) Inc. (Razorbill).

Lowenstein, Sallie Claire. Waiting for Eugene. 2006. (Illus.). 201p. (J). (***978-1-4156-6166-6(9)***) Book Wholesalers, Inc.

MacCready, Robin. Buried. 2006. 208p. (YA). (gr. 9). 16.99 (978-0-525-47724-2(1) , Dutton Juvenile) Penguin Group (USA) Inc.

McNish, Cliff. Angel. 2008. (Exceptional Reading & Language Arts Titles for Upper Grades Ser.). (J). 16.95 (***978-0-8225-8900-6(1)*** , Carolrhoda Bks.) Lerner Publishing Group.

Moore, Peter G. Caught in the Act. 2005. 274p. (J). (gr. 7). 16.99 (978-0-670-05990-4(0) , Viking Juvenile) Penguin Group (USA) Inc.

Neale, Jonathan. Lost at Sea. 112p. (J). (gr. 5-9). 2002. (Illus.). 15.00 (978-0-618-13920-0(6)); 2004. reprint ed. pap. 5.95 (978-0-618-43236-3(1)) Houghton Mifflin Co. Trade & Reference Div.

Nelson, R. A. Breathe My Name. 2007. 288p. (J). (gr. 7). 16.99 (***978-1-59514-094-4(8)*** , Razorbill) Penguin Group (USA) Inc.

Neufeld, John. Lisa, Bright & Dark. 1999. (J). (978-0-606-16776-5(5)) Tandem Library Bks.

Neufeld, John. Lisa, Bright & Dark: A Novel. 2007. 152p. per. 12.95 (***978-0-595-45048-0(2)*** , Backinprint.com) iUniverse, Inc.

Parker, Roberta N. Slam Dunk: A Young Boy's Struggle with Attention Deficit Disorder. DiMatteo, Richard A., illus. 2003. 55p. (J). (gr. 3-7). pap. 11.00 (978-0-9621629-4-7(9)) Specialty Pr., Inc.

Patneaude, David. Framed in Fire. 1999. (Illus.). 224p. (J). (gr. 6-9). 15.95 (978-0-8075-9098-0(3)) Whitman, Albert & Co.

Rosenberg, Liz. Seventeen: A Novel in Prose Poems. 2002. 160p. (YA). (gr. 9 up). 16.95 (978-0-8126-4915-4(X)) Cricket Bks.

Shaw, Susan. Black-Eyed Suzie. 2007. 176p. (YA). pap. 9.95 (***978-1-59078-533-1(9)*** , Front Street) Boyds Mills Pr.

Tashjain, Janet. Multiple Choice. rev. ed. 1999. (Illus.). 192p. (YA). (gr. 5-10). 16.95 (978-0-8050-6086-7(3) , Holt, Henry & Co. Bks. For Young Readers) Holt, Henry & Co.

Trueman, Terry. Inside Out. 128p. (J). 2003. 15.99 (978-0-06-623962-0(1)); 2003. lib. bdg. 16.89 (978-0-06-623963-7(X)); 2004. reprint ed. pap. 6.99 (978-0-06-447376-7(7) , HarperTeen) HarperCollins Pubs.

Truly Blessed Ink. I Know You Won't Forget. Jordan, Carol, illus. 2007. (ENG.). 40p. (J). 16.95 (***978-0-9789066-1-0(6)***) Square Circle Pr. LLC.

Vidal, Clara. Like a Thorn. Maudet, Y., tr. 2008. 128p. (J). (gr. 9). 14.99 (***978-0-385-73564-3(2)*** , Delacorte Bks. for Young Readers) Random Hse. Children's Bks.

Vizzini, Ned. It's Kind of a Funny Story: A Novel. 448p. (gr. 8 up). 2007. pap. 8.99 (***978-0-7868-5197-3(X));*** 2006. 16.95 (978-0-7868-5196-6(1)) Miramax Bks.

Weeks, Sarah. So B. It. (J). 2005. 272p. pap. 6.99 (978-0-06-441047-2(1) , Harper Trophy); 2004. 256p. (gr. 5 up). 16.99 (978-0-06-623622-3(3) , Geringer, Laura Book); 2004. 256p. (gr. 5 up). lib. bdg. 16.89 (978-0-06-623623-0(1) , Geringer, Laura Book) HarperCollins Pubs.

Wilson, Dawn. Saint Jude. 2000. (Illus.). 171p. (YA). (gr. 6-12). pap. 15.95 (978-0-936389-68-4(0)) Tudor Pubs., Inc.

Wilson, Jacqueline. The Illustrated Mum. 2005. 288p. (J). (gr. 5). lib. bdg. 17.99 (978-0-385-90263-2(8) , Delacorte Bks. for Young Readers) Random Hse. Children's Bks.

MENTAL PHILOSOPHY

see Philosophy; Psychology

MENTAL TELEPATHY

see Thought Transference

MENTALLY DISABLED PERSONS

see People with Mental Disabilities

MENTALLY HANDICAPPED

see People with Mental Disabilities

MENTALLY ILL

see also People with Mental Disabilities

Champion, Gina. Anna & Her Mommy. Mitchell, Nanci, illus. 2005. 36p. (J). (gr. k-6). pap. 10.00 (978-1-884363-20-7(2)) Odenwald Pr.

Clarke, Lisa Anne. Wishing Wellness: A Workbook for Children of Parents with Mental Illness. Matthews, Bonnie, illus. 2006. 80p. (J). (gr. 1-7). pap. 14.95 (978-1-59147-313-8(6)) American Psychological Assn.

Knight, S. Black Magic. 2007. (ENG.). 156p. per. (***978-1-84747-007-2(6)***) Chipmunkapublishing.

Landau, Elaine. Schizophrenia. (Life Balance Ser.). 80p. (J). 2005. (Illus.). (gr. 5-8). pap. 6.95 (978-0-531-16614-7(7)); 2004. 20.50 (978-0-531-12215-0(8)) Scholastic Library Publishing. (Watts, Franklin).

Marzilli, Alan. Mental Health Reform. 2003. (Point/Counterpoint Ser.). (Illus.). 112p. (gr. 9-13). 32.95 (978-0-7910-7372-8(6) , Chelsea Hse.) Facts On File, Inc.

Miller, Maia. Drugs & Mental Illness. 2005. (Drug Abuse Prevention Library). (Illus.). 64p. (YA). (gr. 7-12). lib. bdg. 25.25 (978-0-8239-3155-2(2) , DRMEIL) Rosen Publishing Group, Inc., The.

Muckenhoupt, Margaret. Dorothea Dix: Advocate for Mental Health Care. 2004. (Oxford Portraits Ser.). (Illus.). 128p. (YA). 28.00 (978-0-19-512921-2(0)) Oxford Univ. Pr., Inc.

Ross, Allison J. Coping When a Parent Is Mentally Ill. 2005. (Coping Ser.). (Illus.). 192p. (YA). (gr. 7-12). lib. bdg. 26.50 (978-0-8239-3359-4(8)) Rosen Publishing Group, Inc., The.

MENTALLY ILL—FICTION

Bateson, Catherine. Being Bee. 2007. 136p. (J). (gr. 3-7). 16.95 (***978-0-8234-2104-6(X)***) Holiday Hse., Inc.

Detweiler, Laurie & Bustard, Ned. Pan & the Mad Man. Bustard, Ned, illus. 2000. per. 3.00 (978-1-930710-20-7(8)) Veritas Pr., Inc.

Ford, J. One in Four. 2007. pap. (***978-1-84747-173-4(0)***) Chipmunkapublishing.

Greenberg, Joanne. I Never Promised You a Rose Garden. 2004. 288p. (gr. 12). pap. 13.95 (978-0-451-21120-0(0) , N A L Trade) Penguin Group (USA) Inc.

—I Never Promised You a Rose Garden. 256p. (YA). (gr. 7 up). pap. 5.99 (978-0-8072-1362-9(4) , Listening Library) Random Hse. Audio Publishing Group.

Heiman, Herb. Running on Dreams. 2007. (J). pap. 22.95 (***978-1-931282-28-4(5)***) Autism Asperger Publishing Co.

Kehret, Peg. I'm Not Who You Think I Am. 2001. 160p. (J). (gr. 5-9). pap. 5.99 (978-0-14-131237-8(8) , Puffin) Penguin Group (USA) Inc.

—I'm Not Who You Think I Am. 2001. (J). (978-0-606-20717-1(1)); (gr. 5-8). lib. bdg. 13.00 (978-0-613-35962-7(3)) Tandem Library Bks.

Leblanc, Louise. Les Folies de Sophie. 2000. (Premier Roman Ser.). (FRE.). 192p. (J). (gr. 2-5). pap. (978-2-89021-385-2(4)) Diffusion du livre Mirabel.

Myers, Anna. Ethan Between Us. 2000. (Illus.). (J). (978-0-606-18742-8(1)) Tandem Library Bks.

Patneaude, David. Framed in Fire. 2001. (gr. 5-8). lib. bdg. 14.10 (978-0-613-35946-7(1)) Tandem Library Bks.

—Framed in Fire. 2004. 224p. (J). (gr. 6-9). pap. 5.95 (978-0-8075-9096-6(7)) Whitman, Albert & Co.

Roorda, Julie. Wings of a Bee: A Young Adult Novel. 2007. (Illus.). 232p. pap. 9.95 (***978-1-894549-68-4(6)***) Sumach Pr. CAN. *Dist:* Univ. of Toronto Pr.

Shaw, Susan. Black-Eyed Suzie. (YA). (gr. 6-9). 2003. 176p. 15.95 (978-1-56397-729-9(X)); 2002. 167p. pap. 4.95 (978-1-56397-701-5(X)) Boyds Mills Pr.

Stauffacher, Sue. Donuthead. 2005. 176p. (J). (gr. 3-7). reprint ed. pap. 5.50 (978-0-440-41934-1(4) , Yearling) Random Hse. Children's Bks.

White, Ruth. Memories of Summer. 2000. 144p. (J). (gr. 7-10). 17.00 (978-0-374-34945-5(2) , Farrar, Straus & Giroux (BYR)) Farrar, Straus & Giroux.

MENTALLY RETARDED PERSONS

see People with Mental Disabilities

MENUS

Silate, Jennifer. Planning & Preparing Healthy Meals & Snacks: A Day-to-Day Guide to a Healthier Diet. 2004. (Library of Nutrition). (Illus.). 48p. (J). lib. bdg. 25.25 (978-1-4042-0302-0(8)) Rosen Publishing Group, Inc., The.

Windsor, Jo. Marvelous Menus: Individual Title Six-Packs. Holt, Richard, illus. (Sails Literacy Ser.). 16p. (gr. 2-3). 27.00 (978-0-7578-0709-1(7)) Rigby Education.

MERCHANDISE

see Commercial Products

MERCHANDISING

see Marketing; Retail Trade

MERCHANT MARINE—UNITED STATES

Alagna, Magdalena. Life Inside the Merchant Marine Academy. 2002. (Insider's Look Ser.). (Illus.). 48p. (J). (gr. 7-12). pap. 23.00 (978-0-516-23923-1(6) , Children's Pr.) Scholastic Library Publishing.

—Life Inside the Merchant Marine Academy. 2002. (gr. 7-12). lib. bdg. 15.25 (978-0-613-58711-2(1)) Tandem Library Bks.

Evans, Fred. Maritime & Port Security. 2003. (Securing the Nation Ser.). (Illus.). 112p. (J). (gr. 9-13). 30.00 (978-0-7910-7614-9(8) , Chelsea Hse.) Facts On File, Inc.

MERCHANTS

Behnke, Alison. Grocers. 2006. (Pull Ahead Books). (Illus.). 32p. (J). (ps-7). 22.60 (978-0-8225-2801-2(0) , Lerner Pubns.) Lerner Publishing Group.

Kallen, Stuart A. A Medieval Merchant. 2005. (Working Life Ser.). (Illus.). 112p. (YA). (gr. 7-10). lib. bdg. 29.95 (978-1-59018-581-0(1) , Lucent Bks.) Thomson Gale.

MERCURY (PLANET)

Adamson, Thomas K. Mercurio: Mercury. 2006. (ENG & SPA., Illus.). 24p. (J). (978-0-7368-5881-6(4)) Capstone Pr., Inc.

—Mercury. (J). 2008. (***978-1-4296-0735-3(1)***); 2003. (Illus.). 24p. lib. bdg. 17.26 (978-0-7368-2114-8(7) , Pebble Bks.) Capstone Pr., Inc.

Asimov, Isaac & Hantula, Richard. Mercurio: El Planeta Veloz. Porras, Carlos & D'Andrea, Patricia, trs. 2003. (Isaac Asimov's Biblioteca del Universo del Siglo XXI). (SPA., Illus.). 32p. (J). (gr. 3 up). lib. bdg. 24.67 (978-0-8368-3857-2(2)); pap. 8.95 (978-0-8368-3870-1(X) , Weekly Reader Early Learning Library) Stevens, Gareth Inc.

—Mercury. rev. ed. 2003. (Isaac Asimov's 21st Century Library of the Universe). (Illus.). 32p. (YA). (gr. 3 up). lib. bdg. 24.67 (978-0-8368-3237-2(X)) Stevens, Gareth Inc.

—Mercury: The Quick Planet. 2003. (Isaac Asimov's 21st Century Library of the Universe). (Illus.). 32p. (J). (gr. 3 up). pap. (978-0-8368-3941-8(2) , Weekly Reader Early Learning Library) Stevens, Gareth Inc.

Birch, Robin. Mercury. 2004. (Solar System Ser.). (Illus.). 32p. (gr. 3-5). 23.00 (978-0-7910-7928-7(7) , Chelsea Hse.) Facts On File, Inc.

Brimner, Larry Dane. Mercury. 1999. (True Bks.). (Illus.). 48p. (J). (gr. 3-5). pap. 6.95 (978-0-516-26436-3(2) , Children's Pr.) Scholastic Library Publishing.

Cole, Michael D. Mercury: The First Planet. 2001. (Countdown to Space Ser.). (Illus.). 48p. (YA). (gr. 4-10). lib. bdg. 23.93 (978-0-7660-1512-8(2)) Enslow Pubs., Inc.

Croce, Carlo P. Mercury. 2004. (Library of the Nine Planets). (Illus.). 48p. (J). lib. bdg. 26.50 (978-1-4042-0170-5(X)) Rosen Publishing Group, Inc., The.

Dunn, Mary R. A Look at Mercury. 2008. (J). lib. bdg. (***978-1-4042-3825-1(5)***) Rosen Publishing Group, Inc., The.

Goldstein, Margaret J. Mercury. 2005. (Pull Ahead Bks.). (Illus.). 32p. (gr. 2-4). lib. bdg. 22.60 (978-0-8225-4648-1(5)) Lerner Publishing Group.

Goss, Tim. Mercury. 2003. (Universe Ser.). (Illus.). 32p. (J). (gr. 3-5). lib. bdg. 22.79 (978-1-58810-913-2(5)); pap. 6.95 (978-1-4034-0614-9(6)) Heinemann Library.

Howard, Fran. Mercury. 2007. (Planets Ser.). (ENG., Illus.). 32p. (J). (gr. k-4). lib. bdg. 24.21 (***978-1-59928-823-9(0)*** , Buddy Bks.) ABDO Publishing Co.

Kipp, Steven L. Mercury. 2000. (Galaxy Ser.). (Illus.). 24p. (J). (gr. 2-3). lib. bdg. 18.60 (978-0-7368-0518-6(4) , Bridgestone Bks.) Capstone Pr., Inc.

Landau, Elaine. Mercury. (True Booktrade;: Space Ser.). 48p. (J). 2008. pap. 6.95 (***978-0-531-14791-7(6)***); 2007. (Illus.). (gr. 3-5). lib. bdg. 26.00 (***978-0-531-12561-8(0)***) Scholastic Library Publishing. (Children's Pr.).

Margaret, Amy. Mercury. 2001. (Library of the Planets). (Illus.). 24p. (J). lib. bdg. 21.25 (978-0-8239-5642-5(3) , PowerKids Pr.) Rosen Publishing Group, Inc., The.

Miller, Ron. Mercury & Pluto. 2003. (Worlds Beyond Ser.). (Illus.). 80p. (gr. 7 up). lib. bdg. (978-0-7613-2361-7(9) , Twenty-First Century Bks.) Lerner Publishing Group.

O'Connell, Kim A. Mercury. 2005. (Solar System Ser.). (Illus.). 48p. (J). (gr. 4-7). lib. bdg. 25.26 (978-0-7660-5209-3(5) , MyReportLinks.com Bks.) Enslow Pubs., Inc.

Orme, Helen & Orme, David. Let's Explore Mercury. 2006. pap. (***978-0-8368-8127-1(3)***); lib. bdg. (***978-0-8368-7942-1(2)***) Stevens, Gareth Inc.

Oxlade, Chris. Mercury, Mars & the Inner Planets. 2007. (J). lib. bdg. (***978-1-4042-3735-3(6)*** , Rosen Central) Rosen Publishing Group, Inc., The.

Potts, Steve. Mercury. 2001. (Illus.). 23p. (J). 21.35 (978-1-58340-093-7(1)) Smart Apple Media.

Rau, Dana Meachen. Mercury. 2002. (Our Solar System Ser.). (Illus.). 32p. (J). (gr. 3 up). lib. bdg. 21.26 (978-0-7565-0200-3(4)) Compass Point Bks.

Richardson, Adele. Mercury. 2008. (J). (***978-1-4296-0724-7(6)***) Capstone Pr., Inc.

Richardson, Adele D. Mercury. 2005. (First Facts Ser.). (Illus.). 24p. (J). 21.26 (978-0-7368-3690-6(X)) Capstone Pr., Inc.

Ring, Susan. Mercury. (Exploring Planets Ser.). (Illus.). (J). 2004. pap. (978-1-59036-225-9(X)); 2003. 24p. lib. bdg. 15.95 (978-1-59036-098-9(2)) Weigl Pubs., Inc.

Spangenburg, Ray. Look at Mercury. 2003. (gr. 7-12). lib. bdg. 24.55 (978-0-613-72730-3(4)) Tandem Library Bks.

—Mercury. 2001. (gr. 5-8). lib. bdg. 17.60 (978-0-613-37452-1(5)) Tandem Library Bks.

Spangenburg, Ray & Moser, Kit. Mercury. 2001. (Space Ser.). (Illus.). 64p. (J). (gr. 5-7). 25.50 (978-0-531-11766-8(9) , Watts, Franklin) Scholastic Library Publishing.

Sparrow, Giles. Mercury. (Exploring the Solar System Ser.). (Illus.). (J). (gr. 4-6). 2002. 40p. pap. 7.95 (978-1-58810-962-0(3) , 91445); 2001. 39p. lib. bdg. 24.22 (978-1-57572-392-1(1)) Heinemann Library.

Stille, Darlene R. Mercury. 2003. (Planets Ser.). (Illus.). 32p. (J). (gr. 2-6). 27.07 (978-1-59296-051-4(0)) Child's World, Inc.

Stone, Tanya Lee. Mercury. 2002. (Blastoff! Ser.). (Illus.). 64p. (J). 28.50 (978-0-7614-1403-2(7) , Benchmark Bks.) Cavendish, Marshall Corp.

Taylor-Butler, Christine. Mercury. (Scholastic News Nonfiction Readers: Space Science Ser.). 24p. (J). 2008. pap. 6.95 (***978-0-531-14763-4(0)***); 2007. (Illus.). (gr. 1-2). lib. bdg. 20.00 (***978-0-531-14698-9(7)***) Scholastic Library Publishing. (Children's Pr.).

Tocci, Salvatore. Mercury. 2005. (True Book Ser.). (Illus.). 47p. (J). (ps-7). 25.00 (978-0-516-23700-8(4) , Children's Pr.) Scholastic Library Publishing.

Vogt, Gregory L. Mercury, Venus, Earth & Mars. 2000. (Our Universe Ser.). (Illus.). 48p. (J). (gr. 4-7). lib. bdg. 22.83 (978-0-7398-3110-6(0)) Raintree.

Wimmer, Teresa. Mercury. 2007. (J). (978-1-58341-519-1(X) , Creative Education) Creative Co., The.

World Book, contrib. by. Mercury & Venus. 2nd ed. 2006. (World Book's Solar System & Space Exploration Library). (Illus.). 64p. (J). (***978-0-7166-9517-2(0)***) World Bk., Inc.

World Book, Inc. Staff, contrib. by. Mercury & Venus. 2006. (World Book's Solar System & Space Exploration Library). (Illus.). 63p. (J). (978-0-7166-9502-8(2)) World Bk., Inc.

MERCURY PROJECT

see Project Mercury

MERCY DEATH

see Euthanasia

MERCY KILLING

see Euthanasia

MERLIN (LEGENDARY CHARACTER)—FICTION

Barron, T. A. The Fires of Merlin. (J). (gr. 5-7). 2007. (Lost Years of Merlin (Hardcover) Ser.). 261p. 10.99 (***978-0-399-25022-4(0)***); 1998. (Lost Years of Merlin Ser.: Vol. 3). (Illus.). 272p. 20.99 (978-0-399-23020-2(3)) Penguin Group (USA) Inc. (Philomel).

—The Fires of Merlin. 2000. (J). 13.64 (978-0-606-19239-2(5)) Tandem Library Bks.

—Fires of Merlin. (gr. 3-6). 2002. lib. bdg. 14.15 (978-0-613-89067-0(1)); 2000. lib. bdg. 15.30 (978-0-613-81176-7(3)) Tandem Library Bks.

—The Fires of Merlin Bk. 3. 2000. (Lost Years of Merlin Ser.: Vol. 3). (Illus.). 304p. (gr. 4-7). reprint ed. mass mkt. 6.99 (978-0-441-00713-4(9) , Ace Bks.) Penguin Group (USA) Inc.

—The Lost Years of Merlin. 1998. (J). (gr. 4-7). mass mkt. 4.99 (978-0-8125-7777-8(9) , Tor Bks.) Doherty, Tom Assocs., LLC.

—Lost Years of Merlin. (gr. 3-6). 2002. lib. bdg. 14.15 (978-0-613-83896-2(3)); 1999. lib. bdg. 15.30 (978-0-613-23013-1(2)) Tandem Library Bks.

—The Lost Years of Merlin, Bk. 1. 1999. (Lost Years of Merlin Ser.). (Illus.). 304p. (gr. 4-7). reprint ed. mass mkt. 6.99 (978-0-441-00668-7(X) , Ace Bks.) Penguin Group (USA) Inc.

—The Merlin Effect. 2004. 288p. (gr. 12). mass mkt. 6.99 (978-0-441-01222-0(1) , Ace Bks.) Penguin Group (USA) Inc.

—Seven Songs of Merlin. 2002. (gr. 7-12). lib. bdg. 14.15 (978-0-613-81177-4(1)); 2000. (978-0-606-17833-4(3)); 2000. (gr. 5-8). lib. bdg. 15.30 (978-0-613-28637-4(5)) Tandem Library Bks.

—The Seven Songs of Merlin. 2000. (Lost Years of Merlin Ser.: Vol. 2). (Illus.). 1p. (gr. 5-9). reprint ed. mass mkt. 6.99 (978-0-441-00701-1(5) , Ace Bks.) Penguin Group (USA) Inc.

—Wings of Merlin. 2000. (Lost Years of Merlin Ser.: Vol. 5). (Illus.). 272p. (J). (gr. 6-9). 19.99 (978-0-399-23456-9(X) , Philomel) Penguin Group (USA) Inc.

—Wings of Merlin. (gr. 3-6). 2003. lib. bdg. 14.15 (978-0-613-81180-4(1)); 2002. lib. bdg. 15.30 (978-0-613-81178-1(X)) Tandem Library Bks.

Coté, Denis. La Forêt aux Mille et un Périls, Tome 2. Poulin, Stephane, illus. 2004. (Roman Jeunesse Ser.). (FRE.). 96p. (J). (gr. 4-7). pap. (978-2-89021-696-9(9)) Diffusion du livre Mirabel.

Goldwell, Bruce. Dragon Keepers. 2006. (YA). pap. (978-1-894936-47-7(7)) Saga Bks.

Goldwell, Bruce. Dragon Keepers II. 2006. per. (***978-1-894936-59-0(0)***) Saga Bks.

Hodges, Margaret & Malory, Thomas. Merlin & the Making of the King. Hyman, Trina Schart, tr. Hyman, Trina Schart, illus. 2004. 40p. (J). (gr. 4-6). tchr. ed. 16.95 (978-0-8234-1647-9(X)) Holiday Hse., Inc.

Littler, Keith. Merlin & the Big Top. 2002. (Illus.). 24p. (J). (ps-3). pap. 7.99 (978-1-84222-618-6(5)) Carlton Bks., Ltd. GBR. *Dist:* Independent Pubs. Group.

—Merlin, King of the Castle. 2002. (Illus.). 24p. (J). (ps-3). pap. 7.99 (978-1-84222-617-9(7)) Carlton Bks., Ltd. GBR. *Dist:* Independent Pubs. Group.

—Merlin the Magical Puppy on Ice. 2002. (Illus.). 24p. pap. 7.99 (978-1-84222-616-2(9)) Carlton Bks., Ltd. GBR. *Dist:* Trafalgar Square Publishing.

Mallory, James. Merlin 1: Old Magic. 1999. (978-0-606-18745-9(6)) Tandem Library Bks.

Newman, Robert. Lost Treasures Bk. 5: Merlin's Mistake. 2001. 240p. (J). 13.49 (978-0-7868-2600-1(2)) Hyperion Pr.

Service, Pamela F. Tomorrow's Magic. 2007. 448p. (J). (gr. 3-7). 15.99 (978-0-375-84087-6(7)); (gr. 4-9). lib. bdg. 18.99 (978-0-375-94087-3(1)) Random Hse. Children's Bks. (Random Hse. Bks. for Young Readers).

—Tomorrow's Magic. 2007. (J). pap. (978-0-375-84088-3(5)) Random Hse., Inc.

Service, Pamela F. Yesterday's Magic. 2008. (J). (gr. 3-7). 224p. 16.99 (***978-0-375-85577-1(7)***); 320p. lib. bdg. 19.99 (***978-0-375-95577-8(1)***) Random Hse. Children's Bks. (Random Hse. Bks. for Young Readers).

Stewart, Mary. The Last Enchantment. 2003. (gr. 7-12). lib. bdg. 24.55 (978-0-613-66978-8(9)) Tandem Library Bks.

Triola, Mary. Merlin's Door. 2004. 242p. (YA). pap. 11.95 (978-0-9744084-3-9(3)) Quiet Storm Publishing Group.

Yolen, Jane. The Young Merlin Trilogy: Passager, Hobby, & Merlin. 2004. (Illus.). 276p. (J). pap. 6.95 (978-0-15-205211-9(9) , Magic Carpet Bks.) Harcourt Children's Bks.

MERMAIDS

Apperley, Dawn. The Mermaid's Manual. 2004. (Illus.). 20p. (J). 16.95 (978-1-58234-888-9(X) , Bloomsbury Children) Bloomsbury Publishing.

Bartlett, Wendy B., des. Sparkly Mermaid. 2005. (Illus.). 12p. (J). bds. 5.99 (978-0-7566-1026-5(5)) Dorling Kindersley Publishing, Inc.

Climo, Shirley. Serenade of Mermaids: Mermaid Tales from Around the World. 1999. (978-0-606-16697-3(1)) Tandem Library Bks.

Osborne, Mary Pope. Mermaid Tales from Around the World. Howell, Troy, illus. 1999. 96p. (J). (gr. 2-6). pap. 7.99 (978-0-439-04781-4(1)) Scholastic, Inc.

—Mermaid Tales from Around the World. 1999. (J). (978-0-606-16602-7(5)) Tandem Library Bks.

Penner, Lucille Recht. Mermaids. Grant, Melvyn, illus. 2008. (J). pap. (***978-0-375-83936-8(4)***); 48p. (gr. 1-4). lib. bdg. 11.99 (***978-0-375-93936-5(9)***) Random Hse., Inc.

Pratt, Leonie. Mermaid things to make & Do. 2005. 32p. (J). pap. 6.95 (978-0-7945-1062-6(0) , Usborne) EDC Publishing.

Redmond, Shirley-Raye. Mermaids. 2007. (Monsters Ser.). (Illus.). 48p. (J). (gr. 4-8). 23.70 (***978-0-7377-3634-2(8)*** , Kidhaven) Thomson Gale.

The Summer Mermaid: R-Controlled e, i, u: Level B, 6 vols. (Wright Skills Ser.). 16p. (gr. k-3). 26.50 (978-0-322-01488-6(3)) Wright Group, The.

Watt, Fiona. Mermaids. Cartwright, Stephen, illus. 2004. 10p. (J). 15.95 (978-0-7945-0727-5(1) , Usborne) EDC Publishing.

MERMAIDS—FICTION

Aaron, Chester. Home to the Sea. 2005. (Illus.). 144p. (J). pap. 10.95 (978-0-9746481-2-5(4)) Brown Barn Bks.

Andersen, Hans Christian. Ariel & the Secret Grotto. (Read-Along Ser.). (J). 7.99 incl. audio (978-0-7634-0287-7(7)) Walt Disney Records.

—The Little Mermaid. Bell, Anthea, tr. from DAN. Zwerger, Lisbeth, illus. 2004. 48p. (J). (ps). 16.99 (978-0-698-40001-6(1) , Minedition) Penguin Group (USA) Inc.

—The Little Mermaid. 2000. (Illus.). (J). (978-0-606-18420-5(1)) Tandem Library Bks.

—The Little Mermaid. Michel, Petra, tr. Wulfing, Sulamith, illus. 2004. 32p. (ps-3). 18.95 (978-1-885394-17-0(9)) Amber Lotus Publishing.

—The Little Mermaid: My Coloring Book. 1999. Tr. of Lille Havfrue. (J). pap. 1.09 (978-0-307-08630-3(5) , 08630, Golden Bks.) Random Hse. Children's Bks.

—The Little Mermaid & Other Tales. 1998. (Library of Folklore). (Illus.). 384p. (gr. 4-7). 19.95 (978-0-7818-0720-3(4)) Hippocrene Bks., Inc.

Andersen, Hans Christian & Capdevila. The Little Mermaid. Max, illus. 2003. Tr. of La Sirenita. (ENG & SPA.). 32p. (J). pap. 6.95 (978-0-8118-3911-2(7)) Chronicle Bks. LLC.

Anjelae, Samara. My Magical Mermaid. Ferguson, Martha-Elizabeth, illus. 2002. (Wonder Window Ser.). 32p. (J). 16.95 (978-0-9634910-9-1(1) , BelleTress Bks.) Red Wheel/Weiser.

Artful Doodlers. Dora Salva a las Sirenas (Dora Saves Mermaid Kingdom!) 2007. (Dora la Exploradora Ser.). (SPA., Illus.). 24p. (J). (ps-2). pap. 3.99 (***978-1-4169-4725-7(6)*** , Libros Para Ninos) Simon & Schuster Children's Publishing.

—Dora Saves Mermaid Kingdom! 2007. (Dora the Explorer Ser.). 24p. (J). pap. 3.99 (***978-1-4169-3841-5(9)*** , Simon Spotlight/Nickelodeon) Simon & Schuster Children's Publishing.

Barry, Dave & Pearson, Ridley. Escape from the Carnivale: A Never Land Book. Call, Greg, illus. 2006. 144p. (gr. 3-17). 9.99 (978-0-7868-3789-2(6)) Hyperion Bks. for Children.

Baum, L. Frank. The Sea Fairies. 2006. pap. 45.99 (***978-1-4219-8091-1(6)***) IndyPublish.com.

Bergen, Lara. Disney's the Little Mermaid. 2006. 96p. (ps-2). 12.99 (978-0-7868-4942-0(8)) Disney Pr.

—Under the Sea. 2006. (Disney's the Little Mermaid Ser.). 24p. (ps-2). 18.99 (978-1-4231-0057-7(3)) Disney Pr.

Blackaby, Susan. The Little Mermaid: A Retelling of the Hans Christian Andersen Fairy Tale. DeLage, Charlene, illus. 2004. (Read-It! Readers Ser.). 32p. (C). (gr. k-3). 18.60 (978-1-4048-0221-6(5)) Picture Window Bks.

—La Sirenita: Version del Cuento de los Hermanos Grimm. Delage, Charlene, illus. 2006. (Read-It! Readers en Espanol Ser.).Tr. of Little Mermaid: A Retelling of the Grimm's Fairy Tale. (SPA.). 32p. (J). (ps-3). 19.95 (978-1-4048-1633-6(X)) Picture Window Bks.

Blanco, Alberto. The Desert Mermaid (La Sirena del Desierto) Revah, Patricia, illus. 2002. (ENG & SPA.). 32p. (J). (gr. 1 up). pap. 7.95 (978-0-89239-173-8(1)) Bellerophon Bks.

Borgia, Mary. Tales of the Texas Mermaid: The Charro. 2007. (J). 17.95 (***978-0-9778451-1-8(7)***) Goretti Publishing.

Bryant, Megan E. The Little Mermaid. Huxtable, John, illus. 2006. (Berry Fairy Tales Ser.). 32p. (J). pap. 3.99 (978-0-448-44346-1(5) , Grosset & Dunlap) Penguin Group (USA) Inc.

—The Little Mermaid: Berry Fairy Tales. Huxtable, John & Huxtable, Tonja, illus. 2006. (Strawberry Shortcake Ser.). 32p. (J). 6.99 (978-0-448-44523-6(9) , Grosset & Dunlap) Penguin Group (USA) Inc.

Burr, Daniela. Barbie Fairytopia: Mermaidia. Schutz, Samatha, ed. 2006. (Illus.). 80p. (J). pap. 3.99 (978-0-439-85636-2(1)) Scholastic, Inc.

Caffrey-Kira, Albina. The Bear Who Loves Apples. 2006. 25.00 (978-0-8059-9128-4(X)) Dorrance Publishing Co., Inc.

Chapman, Tessie L. Guardians of the Enchanted Island. 2006. 89p. pap. 14.95 (978-1-4137-7104-6(1)) PublishAmerica, Inc.

Clibbon, Meg. Imagine You're a Mermaid! Clibbon, Lucy, illus. 2003. (Imagine This! Ser.). 32p. (J). (gr. 1-4). 19.95 (978-1-55037-791-0(4)); pap. 7.95 (978-1-55037-790-3(6)) Annick Pr., Ltd. CAN. *Dist:* Firefly Bks., Ltd.

Climo, Shirley. A Serenade of Mermaids: Mermaid Tales from Around the World. Falkenstern, Lisa, illus. 1999. (Trophy Chapter Bks.). 112p. (J). (gr. 2-5). pap. 4.25 (978-0-06-442103-4(1) , Harper Trophy) HarperCollins Pubs.

Daynes, Katie. Little Mermaid. 2006. 24p. (J). 9.99 (978-0-7945-1349-8(2) , Usborne) EDC Publishing.

de Brunhoff, Jean. Babar & Zephir. de Brunhoff, Jean, illus. 2005. (Illus.). 38p. (J). (gr. k-4). reprint ed. 16.00 (978-0-7567-8935-0(4)) DIANE Publishing Co.

Dexter, Anthony. The Adventures of Manny the Manatee. 2004. 45p. pap. 19.95 (978-1-4137-2751-7(4)) PublishAmerica, Inc.

DiCicco, Sue, illus. The Little Mermaid. 2003. (Little Golden Bks.). 24p. (J). (gr. k-k). 2.99 (978-0-7364-2177-5(7) , Golden/Disney) Random Hse. Children's Bks.

Disney-Pixar The Little Mermaid. 2002. (J). spiral bd. (978-0-9720651-9-1(9)) Story Reader, Inc.

Dotrice, Roy, narrated by. The Little Mermaid: Read Along. 2001. (Illus.). 32p. (J). pap. 9.98 incl. audio compact disk (978-0-7634-0799-5(2)) Walt Disney Records.

Douglas, Vincent. The Little Mermaid. 2001. (Disney Parent & Child Read Together Ser.). (Illus.). 40p. (ps-k). 4.99 (978-1-57768-734-4(5)) School Specialty Publishing.

Douglas, Vincent & School Specialty Publishing Staff. The Little Mermaid. 2004. (Handle Book with CD Ser.). (Illus.). 24p. (J). 3.99 (978-1-58845-721-9(4)) School Specialty Publishing.

Dunmore, Helen. Ingo. 2008. 336p. (J). pap. 6.99 (***978-0-06-081854-8(9)*** , Harper Trophy) HarperCollins Pubs.

—The Tide Knot. 2008. (J). (***978-0-06-081857-9(3)***); 336p. 16.99 (***978-0-06-081855-5(7)***); 336p. lib. bdg. 17.89 (***978-0-06-081856-2(5)***) HarperCollins Pubs.

Durant, Alan. Dear Mermaid. Cabban, Vanessa, illus. 2007. 32p. (J). (gr. 1). 12.99 (***978-0-7636-3442-1(5)***) Candlewick Pr.

Edgar, Amy. The Little Mermaid. 1999. (Read-Aloud Storybook Ser.). (Illus.). 72p. (J). (ps-2). 8.99 (978-0-7364-0161-6(X) , RH/Disney) Random Hse. Children's Bks.

Foster, Evelyn. The Mermaid of Cafur. Whelan, Olwyn, illus. 1999. 32p. (J). (gr. k-3). 15.95 (978-1-902283-40-1(6)) Barefoot Bks., Inc.

Gallemore, M. H. Annie & the Mermaid. 2005. 9.00 (978-0-8059-9787-3(3)) Dorrance Publishing Co., Inc.

Garnham, Laura. The Tiniest Mermaid. MacCarthy, Patricia, illus. 2006. 28p. (J). 16.00 (978-1-56148-512-3(8)) Good Bks.

Golden Books Staff. Barbie Fairytopia: Mermaidia Board Book. 2007. 24p. (J). (gr. k-k). bds. 4.99 (978-0-375-83851-4(1) , Golden Bks.) Random Hse. Children's Bks.

—Journey to Mermaidia. Harchy, Atelier Philippe, illus. 2006. 32p. (J). (ps-2). pap. 3.99 (978-0-375-83692-3(6) , Golden Bks.) Random Hse. Children's Bks.

—The Little Mermaid II: A Princess in Two Worlds. 2000. (Illus.). 70p. (J). (ps-3). pap. 2.99 (978-0-307-25734-5(7) , 25734, Golden Bks.) Random Hse. Children's Bks.

—The Magical Mermaid Crown. 2007. (Hologramatic Sticker Book Ser.). (Illus.). 48p. (J). (ps-2). pap. 3.99 (***978-0-375-84213-9(6)*** , Golden Bks.) Random Hse. Children's Bks.

Golden Books Staff. Undersea ABC. 1999. (Disney Ser.). (Illus.). (J). pap. 2.99 (978-0-307-05664-1(3) , 05664, Golden Bks.) Random Hse. Children's Bks.

Gray, Nigel. Jake & the Mermaid. Dickson, Peter, illus. 1998. 32p. (J). pap. 9.95 (978-1-86368-221-3(X)) Fremantle Pr. AUS. *Dist:* International Specialized Bk. Services.

Grossman, Patricia. Ariel's Treasure Hunt, Level 1. 1998. (Disney's First Readers Ser.: No. 7). (Illus.). 24p. (J). (gr. k-1). pap. 2.95 (978-0-7868-4167-7(2)) Disney Pr.

Hilb, N. Azul. 2004. (SPA.). 32p. 6.95 (978-1-4000-9289-5(2)) Editorial Sudamericana S.A. ARG. *Dist:* Random Hse., Inc.

Hinojosa, Francisco. Mi Hermana Quiere Ser Una Sirena. El Fisgon, illus. 2003. (SPA.). 43p. (J). (gr. k-3). 14.95 (978-968-19-0546-0(6)) Santillana USA Publishing Co., Inc.

Izquierdo, Oriol, et al. Little Mermaid. Max, illus. 2003. Tr. of Sirenita. (ENG & SPA.). 32p. (J). 13.95 (978-0-8118-3910-5(9)) Chronicle Bks. LLC.

Jackson, Susan. The Secret of Mermaid Island. 2004. (J). per. 9.95 (978-0-9748087-1-0(7)) Journey Pubns., LLC.

James, Robin. Maynard's Mermaid. 2001. (gr. k-3). lib. bdg. 13.00 (978-0-613-64544-7(8)) Tandem Library Bks.

James, Robin & Cosgrove, Stephen. Maynard's Mermaid. James, Robin, illus. rev. ed. 2001. (Serendipity Bks.). (Illus.). 32p. (J). mass mkt. 4.99 (978-0-8431-7665-0(2) , Price Stern Sloan) Penguin Group (USA) Inc.

Johnson, Gillian. Thora: A Half-Mermaid Tale. Johnson, Gillian, illus. 2005. (Illus.). 256p. (J). 15.99 (978-0-06-074378-9(6)); lib. bdg. 15.89 (978-0-06-074379-6(4)) HarperCollins Pubs.

Johnson, Gillian. Thora & the Green Sea-Unicorn: Another Half-Mermaid Tale. Johnson, Gillian, illus. 2007. 288p. (J). (gr. 4-6). 15.99 (***978-0-06-074381-9(6)***); lib. bdg. 16.89 (***978-0-06-074382-6(4)***) HarperCollins Pubs. (Tegen, Katherine Bks).

Karr, Kathleen. The Lighthouse Mermaid. 1998. (Hyperion Chapters Ser.). (978-0-606-13570-2(7)) Tandem Library Bks.

Kessler, Liz. Emily Windsnap & the Castle in the Mist. Ledwidge, Natacha, illus. 2007. (Emily Windsnap Ser.). 208p. (J). (gr. 3-7). 15.99 (***978-0-7636-3330-1(5)***) Candlewick Pr.

—Emily Windsnap & the Monster from the Deep. Gibb, Sarah, illus. (Emily Windsnap Ser.). (J). (gr. 3-7). 2007. 240p. 5.99 (***978-0-7636-3301-1(1)***); 2006. 224p. 15.99 (978-0-7636-2504-7(3)) Candlewick Pr.

Kessler, Liz. The Tail of Emily Windsnap. Gibb, Sarah, illus. 2006. (Emily Windsnap Ser.). 224p. (J). (gr. 3-7). reprint ed. 5.99 (978-0-7636-2811-6(5)) Candlewick Pr.

King-Smith, Dick. The Merman. unabr. ed. 2004. 102p. (J). (gr. 3-7). pap. 29.00 incl. audio (978-0-8072-8132-1(8) , Listening Library) Random Hse. Audio Publishing Group.

—The Merman. 2001. (J). (978-0-606-21328-8(7)) Tandem Library Bks.

Knoos, Sara Marie. A Fairy's Tail. Van Eps, Ann, illus. 2002. 29p. (J). (ps-6). pap. 14.99 (978-0-9721276-0-8(7)) Mermaid Utopia, Inc.

Lagonegro, Melissa. Sealed with a Kiss. Marrucchi, Elisa, illus. 2005. 32p. (J). (ps-2). pap. 3.99 (978-0-7364-2363-2(X) , RH/Disney) Random Hse. Children's Bks.

Lanza, Barbara. Little Mermaid. 2003. (gr. k-3). lib. bdg. 11.80 (978-0-613-71999-5(9)) Tandem Library Bks.

Larkin, Rochelle, ed. The Little Mermaid & Other Stories. (Illus.). 239p. (J). 9.95 (978-0-86611-676-3(1)) Waldman Publishing Corp.

Levine, Gail Carson. Fairy Haven & the Quest for the Wand. Christiana, David, illus. rev. ed. 2007. 208p. (gr. 1-5). 17.99 ***(978-1-4231-0100-0(6))*** Disney Pr.

Little Golden Books Staff. The Little Mermaid: The Whole Story. 2000. (Illus.). 24p. (J). (ps-2). bds. 2.99 (978-0-307-00106-1(7) , Golden Bks.) Random Hse. Children's Bks.

The Little Mermaid. 2007. (Illus.). 32p. (J). 12.95 ***(978-1-934056-72-1(3))*** UMI (Urban Ministries, Inc.).

The Little Mermaid. 2002. (Classic Tales Mini Bks.). (Illus.). 32p. (J). (978-1-59069-038-3(9) , T1007); incl. audio compact disk (978-1-59069-105-2(9) , T1107) Studio Mouse LLC.

Little Reader Digital Storybook: The Little Mermaid. 2005. (J). cd-rom 11.99 (978-0-9767657-0-7(5)) Mullings Media.

Lyon, Tammie, illus. Mermaid World. 2001. (Glow Sticker Stories Ser.). 16p. (J). (ps-3). mass mkt. 4.99 (978-0-448-42172-8(0) , Grosset & Dunlap) Penguin Group (USA) Inc.

Marks, Alan, illus. The Little Mermaid. 2005. 48p. (J). (ps-7). 8.95 (978-0-7945-1122-7(8) , Usborne) EDC Publishing.

Mermaid Marina. 2002. (Dolly Board Book Ser.). (J). bds. 4.98 (978-0-7525-8280-1(1)) Parragon, Inc.

Morpurgo, Michael & Richards, Lucy. Mairi's Mermaid. 2006. (Blue Bananas Ser.). (Illus.). (J). 48p. pap. (978-0-7787-0897-1(7)); 43p. (978-0-7787-0851-3(9)) Crabtree Publishing Co.

Mouse Works Staff. Sleeping Beauty/The Little Mermaid, 2 vols. 75th anniv. ed. 1998. (Illus.). (ps-3). 9.99 (978-0-7364-0091-6(5)) Mouse Works.

Napoli, Donna Jo. Sirena. 1998. 256p. (YA). (gr. 7-12). pap. 15.95 (978-0-590-38388-2(4)) Scholastic, Inc.

—Sirena. 2000. (Illus.). 210p. (YA). (gr. 7-12). lib. bdg. 13.04 (978-0-606-19626-0(9)) Tandem Library Bks.

Nesbit, E. Wet Magic. 2006. 208p. pap. 12.95 (978-1-4116-6777-8(8)) Lulu.com.

Ortiz, Kerri L. No-it-at-er... What? & the Tale of the Misplaced Mermaids. 2005. 48p. pap. 12.95 (978-1-4137-4938-0(0)) PublishAmerica, Inc.

Page, Nick & Page, Claire. The Little Mermaid. 2007. (Ready to Read: Level 1 (Make Believe Ideas) Ser.). (Illus.). 31p. (J). (gr. k-2). 3.99 ***(978-1-84610-442-8(4))*** Make Believe Ideas GBR. *Dist:* Ingram Pub. Services.

Papademetriou, Lisa. Rani in the Mermaid Lagoon. Clarke, Judith, illus. 2006. (Stepping Stone Bks.). 128p. (J). (gr. 2-4). 5.99 (978-0-7364-2375-5(3) , RH/Disney) Random Hse. Children's Bks.

Parragon Staff. Disney's the Little Mermaid. Disney Staff, ed. 2007. 48p. (ps-2). 12.99 ***(978-1-4231-0433-9(1))*** Disney Pr.

PC Treasures, prod. The Little Mermaid. 2007. (J). ***(978-1-60072-020-8(X))*** PC Treasures, Inc.

Peck, Dale. Drift House: The First Voyage. 2006. 448p. (J). pap. 7.95 (978-1-59990-005-6(X) , Bloomsbury Children) Bloomsbury Publishing.

Peetoom, Laura. Mermaid in Bathtub. Fernandes, E., illus. 2006. 104p. (J). pap. 4.95 (978-1-55041-362-5(7)) Fitzhenry & Whiteside, Ltd. CAN. *Dist:* F & W Pubns., Inc.

La Petite Sirene.Tr. of Little Mermaid. (FRE.). 48p. (J). pap. 12.95 incl. audio compact disk (978-2-89558-071-3(5)) Coffragants CAN. *Dist:* Penton Overseas, Inc.

Random House Disney Staff. The Little Mermaid. 2006. (Illus.). 12p. (J). (ps-1). pap. 6.99 (978-0-7364-2414-1(8) , RH/Disney) Random Hse. Children's Bks.

—The Little Mermaid. Berry, Bob, illus. 2005. 48p. (J). (ps-2). pap. 2.99 (978-0-375-83058-7(8) , Golden/Disney) Random Hse. Children's Bks.

—The Little Mermaid. Mateu, Francesca, illus. 2003. (Random House Pictureback Book Ser.). 24p. (J). (gr. k-3). pap. 3.99 (978-0-7364-2128-7(9) , RH/Disney) Random Hse. Children's Bks.

Random House Disney Staff & Shealy, Dennis. The Little Mermaid. 2003. (Illus.). 24p. (J). (gr. k-k). bds. 4.99 (978-0-7364-2205-5(6) , RH/Disney) Random Hse. Children's Bks.

Robleda, Margarita. Suenos. Suarez, Maribel, illus. (Rana, Rema, Rimas Ser.). (SPA.). 16p. (J). (gr. k-3). 7.95 (978-1-59437-821-8(5)) Santillana USA Publishing Co., Inc.

Rodda, Emily. The Third Wish. Vitale, Raoul, illus. 2003. (Fairy Realm Ser.: No. 3). 128p. (J). 8.99 (978-0-06-009589-5(X)); lib. bdg. 15.89 (978-0-06-009590-1(3)) HarperCollins Pubs.

Rylant, Cynthia. The Islander. 1999. (Illus.). 112p. (J). (gr. 5-17). reprint ed. pap. 5.50 (978-0-440-41542-8(X) , Yearling) Random Hse. Children's Bks.

—The Islander. 1999. (gr. 5-8). lib. bdg. 13.00 (978-0-613-23002-5(7)) Tandem Library Bks.

Sampson, Fay. Pangur Ban, the White Cat, Vol. 2. 2002. 160p. (J). (gr. 5-8). pap. 7.99 (978-0-7459-4763-1(8) , Lion) Lion Hudson plc GBR. *Dist:* Independent Pubs. Group.

San Souci, Robert D. Sukey & the Mermaid. 1998. (J). pap. 5.99 (978-0-87628-334-9(2)) Ctr. for Applied Research in Education, The.

Saxton, Patricia Cayo. Book of Mermaids. 2006. (Illus.). 32p. 14.95 (978-0-9726614-6-1(8)) Shenanigan Bks.

Scholastic, Inc. Staff. The Little Mermaid/La Sirenita. Bordoy, Irene, illus. 2007. (Bilingual Tales Ser.). (ENG & SPA.). 24p. (J). pap. 3.99 ***(978-0-439-87198-3(0))*** Scholastic, Inc.

Scholastic, Inc. Staff, et al. The Little Mermaid. Lanza, Barbara, illus. 2003. (Scholastic Reader Ser.). 32p. (J). pap. 3.99 (978-0-439-47154-1(0) , Cartwheel Bks.) Scholastic, Inc.

Schreiber, Ellen. Teenage Mermaid. 2003. 160p. (J). (gr. 4 up). lib. bdg. 16.89 (978-0-06-008205-5(4)) HarperCollins Pubs.

Selfors, Suzanne. To Catch a Mermaid. Chien, Catia, illus. rev. ed. 2007. 254p. (J). (gr. 3-7). 14.99 ***(978-0-316-01816-6(3))*** Little, Brown Bks. for Young Readers.

The Seven Stones of Sligo: Individual Chapter Book Title Six-Packs. Vol. 27. 32p. (gr. 4 up). 44.00 (978-0-7635-4493-5(0)) Rigby Education.

Singleton, Linda Joy. Sea Switch. 2005. (Illus.). 264p. (ps-7). pap. 5.99 (978-0-7387-0712-9(0)) Llewellyn Pubns.

Skinner, Daphne. My Side of the Story Bk. 3: The Little Mermaid & Ursula. Daly, Catherine, ed. 3rd rev. ed. 2004. (Disney Princess Ser.). (Illus.). 72p. (ps-17). 12.99 (978-0-7868-3503-4(6)) Disney Pr.

Sklansky, Amy E. Little Mermaid 2 (Super Chapter Book) 2000. (Illus.). 53p. (J). (gr. 4-7). pap. 4.99 (978-0-7868-4431-9(0)) Disney Pr.

Sperring, Mark. Mermaid Dreams. 2006. (Illus.). 32p. (J). pap. 16.99 (978-0-439-79610-1(5) , Chicken Hse., The) Scholastic, Inc.

Sterling Publishing Co., Inc. & Fernleigh Books Staff. Mermaids: A Magic 3-Dimensional World of Mermaids. 2007. (Step Inside Ser.). (Illus.). 12p. (J). (ps-1). 9.95 ***(978-1-4027-4899-8(X))*** Sterling Publishing Co., Inc.

Stine, R. L. Deep Trouble. 2003. (Goosebumps Ser.). 144p. pap. 4.99 (978-0-439-56828-9(5) , 53655422, Scholastic Paperbacks) Scholastic, Inc.

—Deep Trouble. 2003. (gr. 5-8). lib. bdg. 13.00 (978-0-613-70776-3(1)) Tandem Library Bks.

Thompson, D. R. The Big Ocean: An Underwater Naptime Adventure. Thompson, D. R. & Thompson, Dave, illus. 2004. (Naptime Adventure Ser.: Vol. 2). 32p. (J). (ps-3). 14.95 (978-0-9723252-2-6(0)) This New World Publishing, LLC.

ToyBox Innovations, creator. Disney's Little Mermaid. 2006. (Disney's Read Along Ser.). (Illus.). 24p. (J). audio compact disk 7.99 (978-0-7634-2174-8(X)) Walt Disney Records.

—Disney's Princess Little Mermaid. abr. ed. 2006. (Disney's Read along Collection). (J). (ps-3). pap. 14.99 incl. audio compact disk (978-0-7634-2184-7(7)) Walt Disney Records.

Wade, Judith. Mermaid Dreams. 2005. (J). per. 5.99 (978-0-9728958-3-5(3)) Riley Pr.

—The Mermaid's Gift. 2004. 140p. (J). per. 5.99 (978-0-9728958-1-1(7) , 750) Riley Pr.

—The Secret of Mermaid Island. 2003. 136p. (J). mass mkt. 5.99 (978-0-9728958-0-4(9)) Riley Pr.

Wall, Lynn J. I Wish I Was a Mermaid. Campbell, Velva L., illus. 1998. (I Wish Ser.: Vol. 1). 24p. (J). (gr. k-6). pap. 9.95 (978-0-9660136-1-0(1)) Fowema Publishing Co.

Wax, Wendy & Disney Storybook Artists Staff. The Little Mermaid Storybook & Music Box. 2006. (Disney Princess Ser.). (Illus.). 40p. (J). bds. 24.99 (978-0-7944-1133-6(9)) Reader's Digest Assn., Inc., The.

Wickstrom, Lois June & Lorrah, Jean. Nessie & the Living Stone. Strand, Sara Silvestri, illus. 2001. (J). pap. 13.80 (978-1-58338-616-3(5) , CrossroadsPub.Org) CrossroadsPub.com.

Willis, Jeanne. Do Little Mermaids Wet Their Beds? Jossen, Penelope, illus. 2001. (Concept Book Ser.). 32p. (J). (ps-1). 15.95 (978-0-8075-1668-3(6)) Whitman, Albert & Co.

Witcher, Lillie. Ican & the Little Mermaid. 2006. (Illus.). (J). 8.95 (978-1-56167-945-4(3) , Shooting Star Edition) American Literary Pr.

MERRIMACK (FRIGATE)

Abnett, Dan. The Monitor vs. the Merrimac: Ironclads at War! 2007. (Graphic Battles of the Civil War Ser.). (Illus.). 48p. (J). lib. bdg. (978-1-4042-0778-3(3)) Rosen Publishing Group, Inc., The.

Brager, Bruce L. The Monitor vs. the Merrimack. (Great Battles Through the Ages Ser.). (Illus.). 112p. (gr. 6-12). 2004. pap. 13.25 (978-0-7910-7792-4(6)); 2003. 30.00 (978-0-7910-7439-8(0)) Facts On File, Inc. (Chelsea Hse.).

Burgan, Michael. The Battle of the Ironclads. 2006. (Illus.). 48p. (J). (gr. 4-6). 23.93 (978-0-7565-1628-4(5)) Compass Point Bks.

O'Brien, Patrick. Duel of the Ironclads: The Monitor vs. the Virginia. 2003. (Illus.). 40p. (J). (gr. 1-5). 17.95 (978-0-8027-8842-9(4)); 18.85 (978-0-8027-8843-6(2)) Walker & Co.

MERRIMACK (FRIGATE)—FICTION

Sappey, Maureen S. Dreams of Ships, Dreams of Julia: At Sea with the Monitor & the Merrimack-Virginia, 1862. 1998. (Young American Ser.: Vol. 2). (Illus.). 140p. (YA). (gr. 4-7). 5.99 (978-1-57249-134-2(5)) White Mane Publishing Co., Inc.

MERRY-GO-ROUND

Carousel Writers' Group Staff, contrib. by. Every Pony Has a Tale. 2003. (Illus.). 88p. (J). pap. (978-0-89802-787-7(X)) Beautiful America Publishing Co.

The Greatest Place on Earth: A Children's Story, A History Lesson, A Scrapbook, A Lifetime Keepsake. 2006. (J). 18.95 (978-0-9777882-0-0(2) , Light Works Publishing) I.M. Enterprises.

MERRY-GO-ROUND—FICTION

Bowdish, Lynea. The Carousel Ride. Bowdish, Lynea & Girouard, Patrick, illus. 1998. (Rookie Readers Ser.). 32p. (J). (gr. 1-2). 19.50 (978-0-516-20967-8(1) , Children's Pr.) Scholastic Library Publishing.

Branson, Terri. Mirror of the Carousel. l.t. ed. 2007. (Illus.). 24p. (J). 9.99 ***(978-0-9787421-8-8(4))*** Dragonfly Publishing, Inc.

Branson, Terri & Wilks, Jackie. Mirror of the Carousel. 2006. (Illus.). 24p. (J). lib. bdg. 24.95 (978-0-9765786-9-7(7)); per. 14.99 (978-0-9765786-8-0(9)) Dragonfly Publishing, Inc.

Cabat, Erni & Keremes, Constance A. Erni Cabat's Magical World of the Carousel. Date not set. (Illus.). 32p. (J). 23.00 (978-0-943173-60-3(4)) Cabat Studio Pubns.

Cecil, Randy. Gator. Cecil, Randy, illus. 2007. (Illus.). 40p. (J). (ps-k). 15.99 (978-0-7636-2952-6(9)) Candlewick Pr.

Demeritt, Mary Anne. The Twilight Ride of the Pink Fairy. Daniel, Ellen, illus. 2006. (J). 17.95 ***(978-1-58597-410-8(2))*** Leathers Publishing.

Fiddick, Calay. The Fortieth Horse. Levy, Shaun & Jamieson, Eden, illus. 2006. 32p. (J). (978-1-55306-876-1(9) , Epic Pr.) Essence Publishing.

French, Vivian. Princess Daisy & the Magical Merry-Go-Roun. Gibb, Sarah, illus. 2007. (Tiara Club Ser.: No. 9). 80p. (J). pap. 3.99 ***(978-0-06-112445-7(1)*** , Harper Trophy) HarperCollins Pubs.

Hiebert, Elfrieda H. & Juel, Connie. The Merry Go Round. (Little Book Practice Reader Ser.). (J). (978-0-8136-1448-9(1)) Modern Curriculum Pr.

Patterson, Christina. Jazz, a Horse of a Different Color. Nguyaen, Huy, illus. 2001. 31p. (J). (978-0-89802-759-4(4)) Beautiful America Publishing Co.

Ray, Mary Lyn. My Carousel Horse. Takaki, Gary, illus. 2000. (J). 13.95 (978-0-15-200023-3(2)) Harcourt Trade Pubs.

Rosenberg, Liz. The Carousel. LaMarche, Jim, illus. 1998. 32p. (J). (gr. k-3). pap. 7.00 (978-0-15-201887-0(5) , Harcourt Paperbacks) Harcourt Children's Bks.

Sanchez, Elaine K. The General's Secret. Hughes, Janee, illus. 2001. 40p. (J). 14.95 (978-0-89802-758-7(6)) Beautiful America Publishing Co.

Selick, Henry. Moongirl: With DVD. Chan, Peter & Booker, Courtney, illus. gif. ed. 2006. 48p. (J). (ps-2). 22.99 incl. DVD (978-0-7636-3068-3(3)) Candlewick Pr.

Shire, Poppy. Magic Pony Carousel #4: Jewel the Midnight Pony. Berg, Ron, illus. 2008. (Magic Pony Carousel Ser.). 96p. (J). pap. 3.99 ***(978-0-06-083788-4(8)*** , Harper Trophy) HarperCollins Pubs.

Walsh, Sheila. Einstein's Enormous Error: A Story about Forgiving Others. Sullivan, Don, illus. 2002. (Gnoo Zoo Ser.: Bk. 3). 40p. (J). 9.95 (978-1-57856-335-7(6) , WaterBrook Pr.) WaterBrook Pr.

MERTON, THOMAS, 1915-1968

Crompton, Samuel Willard. Thomas Merton. 2004. (Spiritual Leaders & Thinkers Ser.). (Illus.). 120p. (gr. 9-13). 30.00 (978-0-7910-7862-4(0) , Chelsea Hse.) Facts On File, Inc.

MESA VERDE NATIONAL PARK (COLO.)

Arnold, Caroline. The Ancient Cliff Dwellers of Mesa Verde. Hewett, Richard, illus. 2000. 64p. (YA). (gr. 7-7). pap. 7.95 (978-0-618-05149-6(X) , Clarion Bks.) Houghton Mifflin Co. Trade & Reference Div.

—Ancient Cliff Dwellers of Mesa Verde. 2000. (gr. 3-6). lib. bdg. 15.25 (978-0-613-29870-4(5)) Tandem Library Bks.

Brannon, Barbara. Discover Mesa Verde. 2005. 39.00 ***(978-1-4108-5143-7(5))*** Benchmark Education Co.

Crewe, Sabrina & Anderson, Dale. The Anasazi Culture at Mesa Verde. 2003. (Events That Shaped America Ser.). (Illus.). 32p. (J). (gr. 3 up). lib. bdg. 24.67 (978-0-8368-3390-4(2)) Stevens, Gareth Inc.

Dickmann, Nancy. Mesa Verde National Park. 2006. (Symbols of Freedom Ser.). (Illus.). 32p. (J). (978-1-4034-7797-2(3)) Heinemann Library.

Goodman, Susan E. Digging into Southwest Archaeology. 2000. (Ultimate Field Trip Ser.: Vol. 2). (YA). 13.79 (978-0-606-19252-1(2)) Tandem Library Bks.

Shuter, Jane. Mesa Verde. (Visiting the Past Ser.). (Illus.). 32p. (J). (gr. 5-7). 2002. pap. 6.95 (978-1-58810-407-6(9) , 91182); 1999. lib. bdg. 24.22 (978-1-57572-858-2(3)) Heinemann Library.

Young, Robert. A Personal Tour of Mesa Verde. 1999. (How It Was Ser.). (Illus.). 64p. (J). (gr. 4-6). lib. bdg. (978-0-8225-3577-5(7) , Lerner Pubns.) Lerner Publishing Group.

MESOPOTAMIA

see Iraq—History—To 634

METABOLISM

see also Nutrition

Metabolic Processes & Energy Transfers: An Anthology of Current Thought. 2005. (Contemporary Discourse in the Field of Biology Ser.). (Illus.). 192p. (J). (ps-7). lib. bdg. 30.60 (978-1-4042-0399-0(0)) Rosen Publishing Group, Inc., The.

Shryer, Donna. Body Fuel: A Guide to Good Nutrition. 2007. (Food & Fitness Ser.). 144p. (J). lib. bdg. 37.07 ***(978-0-7614-2552-6(7)*** , Benchmark Bks.) Cavendish, Marshall Corp.

Stoffwechsel und Energieumsatz: Fachliche Inhalte und Uebungsaufgaben. 2nd ed. (Duden Abiturhilfen Ser.). (GER.). 112p. (YA). (gr. 12-13). (978-3-411-04282-1(6)) Bibliographisches Institut & F. A. Brockhaus AG DEU. *Dist:* International Bk. Import Service, Inc.

METAL WORK

see Metalwork

METALLURGY

see also Alloys; Mineralogy

also names of metals, e.g. Gold; etc.

Whyman, Kathryn. Metals & the Environment. Nevett, Louise & Bishop, Simon, illus. 2004. (J). lib. bdg. (978-1-932799-33-0(8)) Stargazer Bks.

METALS

Acaster, David. Transition Elements. 2001. (Cambridge Advanced Sciences Ser.). (Illus.). 64p. pap. 14.00 (978-0-521-79752-8(7)) Cambridge Univ. Pr.

Baldwin. Metals. 2004. (Matter & Materials Ser.). (Illus.). pap. 8.50 (978-1-4109-0938-1(7)) Raintree.

—Metals 6-Pack. 2004. (Matter & Materials Ser.). (Illus.). pap. 45.90 (978-1-4109-0945-9(X)) Raintree.

Baldwin, Carol. Metals. 2004. (Material Matters (Freestyle Express) Ser.). (Illus.). 48p. (YA). (gr. 6-9). 22.00 (978-1-4109-0551-2(9)) Raintree.

—Metals. 2005. (Illus.). 48p. (978-1-4109-1672-3(3)); pap. (978-1-4109-1679-2(0)) Steck-Vaughn.

Beatty, Richard. The Lanthanides. 2007. (Elements Ser.). 32p. (J). lib. bdg. 28.50 ***(978-0-7614-2687-5(6)*** , Benchmark Bks.) Cavendish, Marshall Corp.

Beatty, Richard. Manganese. 2004. (J). 25.64 (978-0-7614-1813-9(X) , Benchmark Bks.) Cavendish, Marshall Corp.

Bryan, Nichol. Danube: Cyanide Spill. 2003. (Environmental Disasters Ser.). (Illus.). 48p. (J). (gr. 5 up). pap. 11.95 (978-0-8368-5512-8(4) , World Almanac Library) Stevens, Gareth Inc.

Fix, Alexandra. Metal. 2007. (J). ***(978-1-4034-9717-8(6));*** pap. ***(978-1-4034-9725-3(7))*** Heinemann Library.

Harcourt School Publishers Staff. Treasure Hunt On Level. 3rd ed. 2002. (Trophies Reading Program Ser.). (Illus.). pap. 5.10 (978-0-15-323276-3(5)) Harcourt Schl. Pubs.

Haydon, Julie. Is It Metal? Individual Title Six-Packs. (Rigby Focus Ser.). 16p. (gr. k up). 26.00 (978-0-7578-5281-7(5)); 28.00 (978-0-7578-5515-3(6)) Rigby Education.

Jennings, Terry. Metal. 2006. (Illus.). 32p. (YA). (gr. 1 up). lib. bdg. 27.10 (978-1-932333-01-5(0)) Chrysalis Education.

Kjelle, Marylou Morano. The Properties of Metals. 2007. (Library of Physical Sciences). (Illus.). 24p. (J). (978-1-4042-2354-7(1)); pap. (978-1-4042-2164-2(6)) Rosen Publishing Group, Inc., The. (PowerKids Pr.).

Kras, Sara Louise. Metal. 2004. (First Facts Ser.). (Illus.). 24p. (J). 15.95 (978-0-7368-2512-2(6)) Capstone Pr., Inc.

Krovatin, Christopher. Heavy Metal & You. 2006. 192p. (J). pap. 7.99 (978-0-439-74399-0(0) , PUSH) Scholastic, Inc.

Levete, Sarah. Metals. 2005. (Illus.). 32p. (J). (gr. 3-7). lib. bdg. 27.10 (978-1-59604-043-4(2)) Stargazer Bks.

Llewellyn, Claire. Metal. 2002. (Material World Ser.). (Illus.). 30p. (J). (gr. 2-4). pap. 6.95 (978-0-531-14834-1(3) , Watts, Franklin) Scholastic Library Publishing.

—Metal. 2005. (Illus.). 24p. (J). (gr. 1-4). lib. bdg. 22.80 (978-1-932889-52-9(3)) Sea-To-Sea Pubns.

—Metal. 2002. (gr. 3-6). lib. bdg. 15.25 (978-0-613-53623-3(1)) Tandem Library Bks.

McDowell, Julie. Metals. 2007. (Essential Chemistry Ser.). 128p. (gr. 6-12). 35.00 ***(978-0-7910-9535-5(5)*** , Chelsea Hse.) Facts On File, Inc.

Mitchell, Melanie S. Metal. 2003. (First Step Nonfiction Ser.). (Illus.). 24p. (J). (gr. k-2). lib. bdg. 18.60 (978-0-8225-4622-1(1)) Lerner Publishing Group.

Oxlade, Chris. How We Use Metal. 2004. (Using Materials Ser.). (Illus.). (J). 25.70 (978-1-4109-0602-1(7)); Pack. pap. 40.50 (978-1-4109-0900-8(X)) Harcourt Schl. Pubs.

—Metal. 2004. (Using Materials Ser.). (J). pap. 7.50 (978-1-4109-0893-3(3)) Harcourt Schl. Pubs.

—Metal. (Materials, Materials, Materials Ser.). 32p. pap. 6.95 (978-1-4034-4098-3(0)) Heinemann Library.

—Metals. (Chemicals in Action Ser.). 2003. 48p. (YA). lib. bdg. 25.64 (978-1-4034-2500-3(0)); 2001. (Illus.). 32p. (J). lib. bdg. 21.36 (978-1-58810-155-6(X)) Heinemann Library.

Parker, Steve. Metals. 2002. (Science Files Ser.). (Illus.). 32p. (J). (gr. 3 up). lib. bdg. 24.67 (978-0-8368-3083-5(0)) Stevens, Gareth Inc.

Parramon's Editorial Team Staff. Metal. Parramon's Editorial Team Staff, photos by. 2004. (Let's Create! Ser.). (Illus.). 32p. (J). (gr. 2 up). lib. bdg. 23.33 (978-0-8368-4016-2(X)) Stevens, Gareth Inc.

Royston, Angela. Metal: Let's Look at a Knife & Fork. 2006. (Heinemann Read & Learn Ser.). (Illus.). 24p. (J). (978-1-4034-7675-3(6)); pap. (978-1-4034-7684-5(5)) Heinemann Library.

—Metal: Let's Look at a Knife & Fork. 2005. (J). (978-1-4109-1822-2(X)); pap. (978-1-4109-1831-4(9)) Steck-Vaughn.

—Metal: Miremos un Cuchillo y un Tenedor. 2005. (Heinemann Lee y Aprende Ser.). (ENG & SPA., Illus.). 24p. (978-1-4034-7543-5(1)); pap. (978-1-4034-7552-7(0)) Heinemann Library.

Saunders, N. Calcium & the Alkaline Earth Metals. 2003. (Periodic Table Ser.). (Illus.). 64p. (J). pap. 8.95 (978-1-4034-3515-6(4)); lib. bdg. 28.50 (978-1-4034-0872-3(6)) Heinemann Library.

—Gold & the Elements of Groups. 2003. (Periodic Table Ser.). (Illus.). 64p. (J). lib. bdg. 28.50 (978-1-4034-0871-6(8)) Heinemann Library.

—Gold & the Elements of Groups 8 to 12. 2003. (Periodic Table Ser.). (Illus.). 64p. (J). pap. 8.95 (978-1-4034-3517-0(0)) Heinemann Library.

—Tungsten & the Elements of Groups 3 to 7. 2003. (Periodic Table Ser.). (Illus.). 64p. (J). pap. 8.95 (978-1-4034-3518-7(9)); lib. bdg. 28.50 (978-1-4034-0876-1(9)) Heinemann Library.

—Uranium & the Rare Earth Metals. 2003. (Periodic Table Ser.). (Illus.). 64p. (J). lib. bdg. (978-1-4034-1666-7(4)) Heinemann Library.

Saunders, Nigel. Sodium & the Alkali Metals. 2003. (Periodic Table Ser.). (Illus.). 64p. (J). lib. bdg. (978-1-4034-1665-0(6)) Heinemann Library.

Sparrow, Giles. Nickel. 2004. (J). 25.64 (978-0-7614-1811-5(3) , Benchmark Bks.) Cavendish, Marshall Corp.

Storey, Rita. Metal. 2007. (J). (***978-1-59920-003-3(1)***) Smart Apple Media.

Thomas, Jens. Silicon. 2001. (Elements Ser.). (Illus.). 32p. (J). (gr. 3-5). lib. bdg. 25.64 (978-0-7614-1274-8(3) , Benchmark Bks.) Cavendish, Marshall Corp.

Thomson, Ruth. Metal. 2006. (Illus.). 29p. (978-1-58340-937-4(8) , 1262422) Smart Apple Media.

Tocci, Salvatore. Calcium. (True Bks.). (Illus.). 48p. (J). 2005. (gr. 3-5). pap. 6.95 (978-0-516-27847-6(9)); 2004. 25.00 (978-0-516-24405-1(1)) Scholastic Library Publishing. (Children's Pr.).

—Lead. (J). 2006. 48p. (gr. 3-5). pap. 6.95 (978-0-516-25575-0(4)); 2005. (Illus.). 47p. (ps-7). 25.00 (978-0-516-23699-5(7)) Scholastic Library Publishing. (Children's Pr.).

—Tin. 2005. (True Bks.). (Illus.). (J). (gr. 3-5). 47p. pap. 6.95 (978-0-516-25573-6(8)); 48p. 25.00 (978-0-516-23697-1(0)) Scholastic Library Publishing. (Children's Pr.).

—Zinc. 2005. (True Book Ser.). (Illus.). 47p. (J). (ps-7). 25.00 (978-0-516-23703-9(9) , Children's Pr.) Scholastic Library Publishing.

Whyman, Kathryn. Metals & the Environment. Nevett, Louise & Bishop, Simon, illus. 2004. (J). lib. bdg. (978-1-932799-33-0(8)) Stargazer Bks.

Woodford, Chris. Titanium. 2002. (Elements Ser.). (Illus.). 32p. (J). lib. bdg. 25.64 (978-0-7614-1461-2(4) , Benchmark Bks.) Cavendish, Marshall Corp.

Zronik, John Paul. Metals. 2004. (Rocks, Minerals, & Resources Ser.). (Illus.). 32p. (J). (978-0-7787-1418-7(7)); pap. (978-0-7787-1450-7(0)) Crabtree Publishing Co.

METALWORK

see also Bronzes; Jewelry; Steel; Welding

Harcourt School Publishers Staff. Forging Ahead: Take-Home Book. 2001. (Collections Ser.). (Illus.). (J). pap. 1.90 (978-0-15-319562-4(2)) Harcourt Schl. Pubs.

—Forging Ahead Below Level. 3rd ed. 2002. (Trophies Reading Program Ser.). (Illus.). pap. 5.10 (978-0-15-323420-0(2)) Harcourt Schl. Pubs.

Jakab, Cheryl. Metals. 2006. (Illus.). 32p. (J). (978-1-58340-778-3(2)) Smart Apple Media.

Repp, Victor E. Metalwork: Technology & Practice. 9th ed. 1999. (Illus.). 192p. (YA). (gr. 6-12). pap., stu. ed., wbk. ed. 7.60 (978-0-02-676486-5(5)) Glencoe/ McGraw-Hill.

Willacy, David M. Craft & Design in Wood. 1998. (Illus.). 224p. pap. 36.00 (978-0-7487-1066-9(3)) State Mutual Bk. & Periodical Service, Ltd.

Working with Metal: Individual Title Six-Packs. (Rigby Focus Ser.). 24p. (gr. 2 up). 28.00 (978-0-7578-5354-8(4)); 30.00 (978-0-7578-5584-9(9)) Rigby Education.

METAMORPHIC ROCKS

see Rocks

METEORITES

Alter, Judy, text. Souvenirs from Space: The Oscar E. Monnig Meteorite Gallery at TCU. 2007. (Illus.). 24p. (J). pap. 4.95 (978-0-87565-346-4(4)) Texas Christian Univ. Pr.

Nicolson, Cynthia. Discover Space Rocks. Slavin, Bill, illus. 2006. 32p. (J). lib. bdg. 15.38 (***978-1-4242-1195-1(6)***) Fitzgerald Bks.

Nicolson, Cynthia Pratt. Comets, Asteroids & Meteorites. Slavin, Bill, illus. 1999. (Starting with Space Ser.). 40p. (J). (gr. 4-6). (978-1-55074-580-1(8)) Kids Can Pr., Ltd.

—Comets, Asteroids & Meteorites. 1999. (gr. 3-6). lib. bdg. 15.25 (978-0-613-21370-7(X)) Tandem Library Bks.

—Discover Space Rocks. Slavin, Bill, illus. 2006. 32p. 3.95 (978-1-55337-901-0(2)) Kids Can Pr., Ltd. CAN. *Dist:* Wybel Marketing Group.

Norris. Meteorite. 1999. (Illus.). (J). pap. (978-0-7398-0017-1(5)) Steck-Vaughn.

Norris, Richard. Meteorite! The Last Days of the Dinosaurs. 1999. (Turnstone Ocean Explorer Ser.). (Illus.). 64p. (YA). (gr. 5-9). pap. 8.95 (978-0-7398-1241-9(6)) Steck-Vaughn.

Parker, Steve. Comets, Asteroids, & Meteors. 2007. (J). lib. bdg. (***978-1-4042-3738-4(0)***) Rosen Publishing Group, Inc., The.

Vogt, Gregory L. Meteors & Meteorites. 2002. (Galaxy Ser.). (Illus.). 24p. (J). (gr. 2-3). lib. bdg. 18.60 (978-0-7368-1120-0(6) , Bridgestone Bks.) Capstone Pr., Inc.

METEOROLOGICAL INSTRUMENTS

see also Thermometers and Thermometry

Wills, Susan & Wills, Steven R. Meteorology: Predicting the Weather. 2003. (Innovators Ser.: Vol. 12). (Illus.). 144p. (gr. 5 up). lib. bdg. 21.95 (978-1-881508-61-8(7)) Oliver Pr., Inc.

METEOROLOGICAL SATELLITES

Cobb, Allan B. Weather Observation Satellites. 2003. (Library of Satellites). (Illus.). 64p. (YA). (gr. 5-8). lib. bdg. 26.50 (978-0-8239-3856-8(5) , Rosen Central) Rosen Publishing Group, Inc., The.

METEOROLOGISTS

Cullen, Katherine E. Weather & Climate: The People Behind the Science. 2005. (Pioneers in Science Ser.). (Illus.). 176p. (J). (gr. 6-12). 29.95 (978-0-8160-5466-4(5)) Facts On File, Inc.

Demarest, Chris L. Hurricane Hunters! Riders on the Storm. Demarest, Chris L., illus. 2006. 40p. (J). (ps-5). 17.95 (978-0-689-86168-0(0) , McElderry, Margaret K.) Simon & Schuster Children's Publishing.

Hammonds, Heather. Meteorologists. 2004. (J). lib. bdg. 27.10 (978-1-58340-542-0(9)) Smart Apple Media.

Hannah, Julie & Holub, Joan. The Man Who Named the Clouds. Billin-Frye, Paige, illus. 2006. 40p. (J). 15.95 (978-0-8075-4974-2(6)) Whitman, Albert & Co.

Lindop, Laurie. Chasing Tornadoes. 2003. (Science on the Edge Ser.). (Illus.). 80p. (gr. 5 up). lib. bdg. 26.90 (978-0-7613-2703-5(7) , Twenty-First Century Bks.) Lerner Publishing Group.

Martin, Jacqueline Briggs. Snowflake Bentley. ed. 2004. (Illus.). (J). (ps-3). spiral bd. (978-0-616-01714-2(6)) Canadian National Institute for the Blind/Institut National Canadien pour les Aveugles.

—Snowflake Bentley. Azarian, Mary, illus. 1998. 32p. (J). (gr. k-3). lib. bdg., tchr. ed. 16.00 (978-0-395-86162-2(4)) Houghton Mifflin Co. Trade & Reference Div.

Spangenburg, Ray & Moser, Diane Kit. Alfred Wegener: Puzzle of the Continents. 2008. (Makers of Modern Science Ser.). 160p. (gr. 6-12). 29.95 (***978-0-8160-6174-7(2)*** , Chelsea Hse.) Facts On File, Inc.

White, Matt. Storm Chasers: On the Trail of Deadly Tornadoes. 2002. (High Five Reading Ser.). (Illus.). 48p. (J). (gr. 2-3). lib. bdg. 22.60 (978-0-7368-9552-1(3) , Capstone High-Interest Bks.); pap. (978-0-7368-9530-9(2)) Capstone Pr., Inc.

Wills, Susan & Wills, Steven R. Meteorology: Predicting the Weather. 2003. (Innovators Ser.: Vol. 12). (Illus.). 144p. (gr. 5 up). lib. bdg. 21.95 (978-1-881508-61-8(7)) Oliver Pr., Inc.

METEOROLOGY

see also Air; Atmosphere; Climate; Clouds; Floods; Fog; Hurricanes; Lightning; Rain and Rainfall; Seasons; Snow; Solar Radiation; Storms; Thunderstorms; Tornadoes; Weather; Weather Forecasting; Winds

Adams, Simon. The Best Book of Weather. Saunders, Mike & Stewart, Roger, illus. 2001. (Best Book of... Ser.). 32p. (J). (gr. k-3). tchr. ed. 12.95 (978-0-7534-5368-1(1) , Kingfisher) Houghton Mifflin Co. Trade & Reference Div.

Allaby, Michael. The World's Weather. 2002. (Inside Look Ser.). (Illus.). 48p. (J). (gr. 4 up). lib. bdg. 26.00 (978-0-8368-3178-8(0)) Stevens, Gareth Inc.

Anaxos, Inc Staff, contrib. by. UXL Encyclopedia of Weather & Natural Disasters. 2007. (J). (***978-1-4144-1880-3(9)); (*978-1-4144-1881-0(7)); (*978-1-4144-1882-7(5)); (*978-1-4144-1883-4(3)); (*978-1-4144-1884-1(1))*** Thomson Gale.

Armentrout, David & Armentrout, Patricia. Weather. 2003. (50 Words about Ser.). (Illus.). 32p. (gr. 2-4). 19.95 (978-1-58952-346-3(6)) Rourke Publishing, LLC.

Berger, Melvin & Berger, Gilda. How's the Weather? A Look at Weather & How It Changes. Cymerman, John E., illus. 1999. (Discovery Readers Ser.). 48p. (J). (gr. 1 up). lib. bdg. 15.95 (978-0-7910-5067-5(X) , Chelsea Hse.) Facts On File, Inc.

—Hurricanes Have Eyes but Can't See: And Other Amazing Facts about Wild Weather. 2003. (Illus.). 48p. (J). (978-0-439-54980-6(9)) Scholastic, Inc.

Bortz, Fred. Dr Fred's Weather Watch: Create & Run Your Own Weather Station. 2000. (gr. 7-12). lib. bdg. 21.05 (978-0-613-71532-4(2)) Tandem Library Bks.

Breen, Mark. Kids Book of Weather Forecasting. 2000. (gr. 3-6). lib. bdg. 22.20 (978-0-613-27924-6(7)) Tandem Library Bks.

Breen, Mark & Friestad, Kathleen. The Kids' Book of Weather Forecasting: Build a Weather Station, "Read" the Sky & Make Predictions! Kline, Michael P., illus. 2000. (Kids Can Bks.). 144p. (J). (gr. 2-8). pap. 12.95 (978-1-885593-39-9(2) , Williamson Bks.) Ideals Pubns.

Challen, Paul C. Drought & Heat Wave Alert! 2004. (Disaster Alert! Ser.). (Illus.). 32p. (J). (978-0-7787-1578-8(7)); pap. (978-0-7787-1610-5(4)) Crabtree Publishing Co.

Chambers, Catherine. Big Freeze. (Illus.). 32p. (J). 2007. (***978-1-4034-9574-7(2));*** 2002. lib. bdg. 21.36 (978-1-58810-658-2(6)) Heinemann Library.

—Big Freeze. 2002. lib. bdg. 14.75 (978-0-613-45714-9(5)) Tandem Library Bks.

—Heat Wave. 2002. (Wild Weather Ser.). (Illus.). 32p. (J). (gr. k-2). lib. bdg. 21.36 (978-1-58810-657-5(8)) Heinemann Library.

Christian, Sandra J. Meteorologists. 2002. (Community Helpers Ser.). (Illus.). 24p. (J). (gr. 1-2). lib. bdg. 18.60 (978-0-7368-1130-9(3) , Bridgestone Bks.) Capstone Pr., Inc.

Cobb, Allan B. Weather Observation Satellites. 2003. (Library of Satellites). (Illus.). 64p. (YA). (gr. 5-8). lib. bdg. 26.50 (978-0-8239-3856-8(5) , Rosen Central) Rosen Publishing Group, Inc., The.

Como Ser un Experto en Clima. (Coleccion Ciencia y Proyectos). (SPA., Illus.). (YA). (gr. 5-8). pap. (978-950-724-283-0(X) , LMA8238) Lumen ARG. *Dist:* Lectorum Pubns., Inc.

Conrad, David. The Weather Watcher. McEwen, Rebecca et al, eds. 2002. (Spyglass Books). (Illus.). 24p. (J). (gr. 1 up). lib. bdg. 18.60 (978-0-7565-0247-8(0)) Compass Point Bks.

El Cuerpo Humano, 6 vols. (Explorers. Exploradores Nonfiction Sets Ser.). (SPA.). 32p. (gr. 3-6). 44.95 (978-0-7699-0635-5(4)) Shortland Pubns. (U. S. A.) Inc.

El Cuerpo Humano. (Coleccion Estrella del Saber). (SPA., Illus.). (J). 14.95 (978-950-11-0035-8(9) ; SGM035) Sigmar ARG. *Dist:* Continental Bk. Co., Inc.

D'Aubuisson, Elisabeth. Rainy Days. 2007. (What's the Weather? Ser.). (Illus.). 24p. (J). (gr. k-3). lib. bdg. 21.25 (978-1-4042-3682-0(1) , PowerKids Pr.) Rosen Publishing Group, Inc., The.

DiSpezio, Michael Anthony. Weather Mania: Discovering What's up & What's Coming Down. Garbot, Dave, illus. 2003. 80p. (J). pap. 6.95 (978-1-4027-0860-2(2)) Sterling Publishing Co., Inc.

Dolphin, Colleen. Advisories to Zero Degrees: Weather from A to Z. 2007. (Let's See A to Z Ser.). (ENG., Illus.). 32p. (J). (ps-3). lib. bdg. 25.65 (***978-1-59928-879-6(6)*** , Super SandCastle) ABDO Publishing Co.

Dussling, Jennifer. Pink Snow & Other Weird Weather. Petach, Heidi, illus. 1998. (All Aboard Reading Ser.). 48p. (J). (gr. 1-3). pap. 3.99 (978-0-448-41858-2(4) , Grosset & Dunlap) Penguin Group (USA) Inc.

Farndon, John. Amazing Planet Earth: The Story of Our World & the Forces That Shaped It With. 2001. (gr. 3-6). lib. bdg. 30.35 (978-0-613-84237-2(5)) Tandem Library Bks.

Gakken Co. Ltd. Editors. Wind & Weather. Time-Life Books Editors, tr. 1999. (Illus.). 88p. (J). (gr. 1-4). 14.95 (978-0-8094-4829-6(7)) Time-Life, Inc.

Gallant, Roy A. Atmosphere: Sea of Air. 2002. (Earthworks Ser.). (Illus.). 80p. (J). 29.93 (978-0-7614-1366-0(9) , Benchmark Bks.) Cavendish, Marshall Corp.

Ganeri, Anita. El Sol. 2004. 24p. 19.33 (978-0-8368-4365-1(7)); pap. 5.95 (978-0-8368-4370-5(3)) Stevens, Gareth Inc. (Weekly Reader Early Learning Library).

Gardner, Robert. Meteorology Projects with a Weather Station You Can Build. 2008. (Build-a-Lab! Science Experiments Ser.). (Illus.). 128p. (J). (gr. 5 up). lib. bdg. 31.93 (***978-0-7660-2807-4(0)***) Enslow Pubs., Inc.

Gilbert, Miguel Angel. Weather. 2002. (Living Planet Ser.). (Illus.). 32p. (J). 23.70 (978-1-56711-683-0(3) , Blackbirch Pr., Inc.) Thomson Gale.

Greeley, August. Burning Up: Losing Our Ozone Layer. 2003. (Reading Power Ser.). (Illus.). 24p. (J). lib. bdg. 17.25 (978-0-8239-6482-6(5) , PowerKids Pr.) Rosen Publishing Group, Inc., The.

Harcourt School Publishers Staff. Meet the Weather Forecaster. 3rd ed. 2002. (Horizons Ser.). (Illus.). (J). pap. 7.30 (978-0-15-333548-8(3)) Harcourt Schl. Pubs.

Harman, Rebecca. The Earth's Weather. 2005. (Heinemann Infosearch Ser.). (Illus.). 32p. (J). pap. (978-1-4034-7065-2(0)); lib. bdg. (978-1-4034-7058-4(8)) Heinemann Library.

Huggins-Cooper, Lynn. Weather. McNicholas, Shelagh & Burroughs, David, illus. 2004. 30p. (J). lib. bdg. (978-1-58340-445-4(7)) Smart Apple Media.

Jacobs, Marian B. Why Does It Rain? 1999. (Library of Why). (Illus.). 24p. (J). (gr. k-4). lib. bdg. 18.75 (978-0-8239-5273-1(8) , PowerKids Pr.) Rosen Publishing Group, Inc., The.

Kenah, Katharine. Wild Weather. 2004. (Extreme Readers Ser.). (Illus.). 32p. (J). (ps-2). pap. 3.95 (978-0-7696-3178-3(9)) School Specialty Publishing.

Lauw, Darlene. Weather. 2003. (gr. 3-6). lib. bdg. 16.40 (978-0-613-52927-3(8)) Tandem Library Bks.

Lauw, Darlene & Puay, Lim Cheng. Weather. 2002. (Science Alive! Ser.). (Illus.). 32p. (J). (gr. 4-5). pap. (978-0-7787-0611-3(7)); lib. bdg. (978-0-7787-0565-9(X)) Crabtree Publishing Co.

Levine, Shar & Johnstone, Leslie. First Science Experiments with Nature, Senses, Weather & Machines. Harpster, Steve, illus. 2005. 192p. (978-1-4027-2922-5(7)) Sterling Publishing Co., Inc.

Llewellyn, Claire. Weather. 2006. (Illus.). 24p. (J). (978-1-59771-020-6(2)) Sea-To-Sea Pubns.

Marsico, Katie. Wild Weather Days. 2006. (Scholastic News Nonfiction Readers Ser.). (Illus.). 24p. (J). (gr. k-2). 19.00 (978-0-531-16771-7(2) , Children's Pr.) Scholastic Library Publishing.

Merk, A. Studying Weather. 2003. (Weather Report Discovery Library). (Illus.). 24p. (gr. 1-4). 19.95 (978-1-58952-573-3(6)) Rourke Publishing, LLC.

El Mundo de la Meteorologia, 6 vols., Vol. 3. (Explorers. Exploradores Nonfiction Sets Ser.). (SPA.). (gr. 3-6). (978-0-7699-0654-6(0)) Shortland Pubns. (U. S. A.) Inc.

Nankin, Frances. Weather. 2000. (Eyes on Nature Ser.). (Illus.). 109p. (J). (978-1-56156-914-4(3)) Kidsbooks, Inc.

National Audubon Society Staff, et al. Weather. 1998. (Audubon Society First Field Guide Ser.). (Illus.). 160p. (J). (gr. 3-7). pap. 8.95 (978-0-590-05488-1(0) , Scholastic Reference) Scholastic, Inc.

Parker, Janice. The Science of Weather. 2000. (Living Science Ser.). (Illus.). 32p. (J). (gr. 2 up). lib. bdg. 24.67 (978-0-8368-2684-5(1)) Stevens, Gareth Inc.

—Sunburns, Twisters & Thunderclaps: The Science of Weather. 1999. (Science @ Work Ser.). (Illus.). 48p. (J). (gr. 4-6). lib. bdg. 27.12 (978-0-7398-0131-4(7)) Raintree.

Pettigrew, Mark. Weather. 2004. (J). lib. bdg. (978-1-932799-30-9(3)) Stargazer Bks.

Phenominal Weather Grades 4-7. 2000. 64p. (J). (gr. 4-7). pap. 8.94 (978-1-889369-47-1(0)) Teaching Ink, Inc.

Purslow, Frances. Precipitation. 2005. (Science Matters Ser.). (Illus.). 24p. (J). (ps-7). pap. 6.95 (978-1-59036-311-9(6)); lib. bdg. 24.45 (978-1-59036-305-8(1)) Weigl Pubs., Inc.

Rodgers, Alan & Streluk, Angella. Precipitation. 2002. (Measuring the Weather Ser.). (Illus.). 32p. (J). (gr. 3-5). lib. bdg. 22.79 (978-1-58810-688-9(8)) Heinemann Library.

Rogers, Allen & Streluk, Angela. Precipitation. 2002. (Illus.). 32p. (J). (gr. 3-5). pap. (978-1-4034-0128-1(4) , 91633) Heinemann Library.

Rosenberg, Pam. Fun Weather Days. 2006. (Scholastic News Nonfiction Readers Ser.). (Illus.). 24p. (J). 19.00 (978-0-531-16772-4(0) , Children's Pr.) Scholastic Library Publishing.

Rubin, Joel. Weather. 2007. (J). (***978-1-4034-7912-9(7)***) Heinemann Library.

Sacks, Janet. Weather & Art Activities. 2002. (Arty Facts Ser.). (Illus.). 48p. (J). (gr. 3-4). pap. (978-0-7787-1146-9(3)); lib. bdg. (978-0-7787-1118-6(8)) Crabtree Publishing Co.

—Weather & Art Activities. 2002. (gr. 3-6). lib. bdg. 17.60 (978-0-613-52928-0(6)) Tandem Library Bks.

Schaefer, Lola M. A Hot Day. Saunders-Smith, Gail, ed. 2000. (What Kind of Day Is It? Ser.). (Illus.). 24p. (J). (gr. k-1). lib. bdg. 15.93 (978-0-7368-0403-5(X) , Pebble Bks.) Capstone Pr., Inc.

—A Hot Day. 1999. pap. 13.25 (978-0-516-21928-8(6) , Children's Pr.) Scholastic Library Publishing.

—A Sunny Day. Saunders-Smith, Gail, ed. 1999. (What Kind of Day is It? Ser.). (Illus.). 24p. (J). (gr. k-1). lib. bdg. 15.93 (978-0-7368-0406-6(4) , Pebble Bks.) Capstone Pr., Inc.

—A Sunny Day. 1999. pap. 13.25 (978-0-516-21931-8(6) , Children's Pr.) Scholastic Library Publishing.

—A Windy Day. Saunders-Smith, Gail, ed. 1999. (What Kind of Day is It? Ser.). (Illus.). 24p. (J). (gr. k-1). lib. bdg. 15.93 (978-0-7368-0407-3(2) , Pebble Bks.) Capstone Pr., Inc.

—A Windy Day. 1999. pap. 13.25 (978-0-516-21932-5(4) , Children's Pr.) Scholastic Library Publishing.

Sherman, Joseph. Amazing Science - Weather, 6 bks. Incl. Flakes & Flurries : A Book about Snow. Wesley, Omarr, illus. (J). 22.60 (978-1-4048-0098-4(0)); Gusts & Gales : A Book about Wind. (C). 22.60 (978-1-4048-0094-6(8)); Nature's Fireworks : A Book about Lightning. Wesley, Omarr, illus. (C). 22.60 (978-1-4048-0093-9(X)); Shapes in the Sky : A Book about Clouds. Wesley, Omarr, illus. (C). 22.60 (978-1-4048-0097-7(2)); Splish! Splash! A Book about Rain. Wesley, Omarr, illus. (C). 22.60 (978-1-4048-0095-3(6)); Sunshine : A Book about Sunlight. Wesley, Omarr, illus. (C). 22.60 (978-1-4048-0096-0(4)); 24p. (gr. k-3). 2004. 2003. Set lib. bdg. 127.56 (978-1-4048-0092-2(1)) Picture Window Bks.

Sievert, Terri. Precipitation. 2005. (Weather Update Ser.). (Illus.). 24p. (J). 21.26 (978-0-7368-3737-8(X)) Capstone Pr., Inc.

Silverstein, Alvin, et al. Weather & Climate. (Illus.). 2007. (Science Concepts, Second Ser.). 96p. (YA). (gr. 6-8). lib. bdg. 31.93 (***978-0-8225-6796-7(2));*** 1998. (Science Concepts Ser.: 8). 64p. (gr. 5-8). lib. bdg. 26.90 (978-0-7613-3223-7(5)) Lerner Publishing Group. (Twenty-First Century Bks.).

Thomas, Rick. Sizzle! A Book about Heat Waves. Shea, Denise, illus. 2005. (Amazing Science Ser.). 24p. (C). (gr. k-3). 22.60 (978-1-4048-0927-7(9)) Picture Window Bks.

Thompson, Jean M. Water Wonders Every Child Should Know: L. 2005. reprint ed. pap. 26.95 (978-1-4179-3339-6(9)) Kessinger Publishing, LLC.

Trueit, Trudi Strain. Rain, Hail, & Snow. 2002. (Watts Library). (Illus.). 64p. (J). (gr. 5-7). 25.50 (978-0-531-11970-9(X) , Watts, Franklin) Scholastic Library Publishing.

—Rain, Hail, & Snow. 2002. (gr. 5-8). lib. bdg. 17.60 (978-0-613-53856-5(0)) Tandem Library Bks.

Varilla, Mary, ed. Scholastic Atlas of Weather. 2004. (Illus.). 80p. (J). pap. 17.95 (978-0-439-41902-4(6) , Scholastic Reference) Scholastic, Inc.

Williams, Judith. Searching for Stormy Weather with a Scientist. 2004. (I Like Science! Ser.). (Illus.). 24p. (J). lib. bdg. 21.26 (978-0-7660-2271-3(4)) Enslow Pubs., Inc.

Woodward, John. Weather Watcher. 2006. (Nature Activities Ser.). (Illus.). 72p. (J). pap. 9.99 (978-0-7566-2068-4(6)) Dorling Kindersley Publishing, Inc.

World Almanac Library Staff, contrib. by. Understanding the Weather. 2002. (Twenty-First Century Science Ser.). (Illus.). 64p. (J). (gr. 5 up). lib. bdg. 32.67 (978-0-8368-5009-3(2) , World Almanac Library) Stevens, Gareth Inc.

World Book, Inc Staff, contrib. by. Heat Waves. 2007. (J). (***978-0-7166-9807-4(2)***) World Bk., Inc.

METEOROLOGY—VOCATIONAL GUIDANCE

Cortinas, John. On the Job with a Meteorologist. 2003. (Adventures in Science Professions Ser.). (J). (978-1-58417-061-7(1)); pap. (978-1-58417-124-9(3)) Lake Street Pubs.

Hammonds, Heather. Meteorologists. 2004. (J). lib. bdg. 27.10 (978-1-58340-542-0(9)) Smart Apple Media.

Perez, Kim & Cohen, Judith Love. You Can Be a Woman Meteorologist. Katz, David Arthur, illus. 2002. (You Can Be a Woman... Ser.). 40p. (J). (gr. 4-6). lib. bdg. 13.95 (978-1-880599-58-7(9)); per. 7.00 (978-1-880599-57-0(0)) Cascade Pass, Inc.

METEORS

see also Meteorites

Asimov, Isaac & Hantula, Richard. Comets & Meteors. 2005. (Isaac Asimov's 21st Century Library of the Universe). (Illus.). 32p. (J). lib. bdg. 24.67 (978-0-8368-3966-1(8)) Stevens, Gareth Inc.

Birch, Robin. Comets, Asteroids, & Meteors. 2002. (Space Ser.). (Illus.). 32p. (gr. k-2). 23.00 (978-0-7910-6973-8(7) , 104051, Chelsea Hse.) Facts On File, Inc.

Cutting, Robert. Falling Star. Ng, Drew, illus. 2007. 48p. (J). lib. bdg. 23.08 (***978-1-4242-1625-3(7)***) Fitzgerald Bks.

Miller, Ron. Asteroids, Comets, & Meteors. 2006. (Worlds Beyond Ser.). (Illus.). 80p. (J). (gr. 5-9). 27.93 (978-0-7613-2363-1(5) , Twenty-First Century Bks.) Lerner Publishing Group.

Mist, Rosalind. Could an Asteroid Hit the Earth? Asteroids, Comets, Meteors, & More. 2006. (Stargazers Guides Ser.). (Illus.). 48p. (J). pap. (978-1-4034-7716-3(7)); lib. bdg. 31.43 (978-1-4034-7709-5(4)) Heinemann Library.

MNO

Olien, Rebecca. Exploring Meteors. 2007. (Objects in the Sky Ser.). (Illus.). 24p. (J). (978-1-4042-2367-7(3)); pap. (978-1-4042-2176-5(X)); (gr. 4-6). lib. bdg. 21.25 (978-1-4042-3468-0(3)) Rosen Publishing Group, Inc., The. (PowerKids Pr.).

Prinja, Raman. Comets, Asteroids, & Meteors. (Universe Ser.). (J). 2003. (Illus.). 32p. (gr. 3-5). lib. bdg. 22.79 (978-1-58810-909-5(7)); 2002. pap. (978-1-4034-0610-1(3)) Heinemann Library.

Rau, Dana Meachen. Comets, Asteroids, & Meteoroids. 2003. (Our Solar System Ser.). (Illus.). 32p. (J). (gr. 3 up). lib. bdg. 21.26 (978-0-7565-0437-3(6)) Compass Point Bks.

Simon, Seymour. Comets, Meteors & Asteroids. 1998. (J). 13.79 (978-0-606-13288-6(0)) Tandem Library Bks.

—Comets, Meteors, & Asteroids. 1998. (Illus.). 32p. (J). (ps-3). pap. 6.99 (978-0-688-15843-9(9) , Harper Trophy) HarperCollins Pubs.

Sparrow, Giles. Asteroids, Comets & Meteors. 2001. (Exploring the Solar System Ser.). (Illus.). 39p. (J). (gr. 4-6). lib. bdg. 24.22 (978-1-58810-037-5(5)) Heinemann Library.

—Asteroids, Comets, & Meteors. 2002. (Exploring the Solar System Ser.). (Illus.). 40p. (J). (gr. 4-6). pap. 7.95 (978-1-58810-959-0(3) , 91442) Heinemann Library.

Vogt, Gregory L. Asteroids, Comets, & Meteors. 2000. (Our Universe Ser.). (Illus.). 48p. (YA). (gr. 5-12). lib. bdg. 22.83 (978-0-7398-3112-0(7)) Raintree.

—Asteroids, Comets, & Meteors. 2000. (Our Universe Ser.). (Illus.). (J). pap. (978-0-7398-3351-3(0)) Steck-Vaughn.

—Meteors & Meteorites. 2002. (Galaxy Ser.). (Illus.). 24p. (J). (gr. 2-3). lib. bdg. 18.60 (978-0-7368-1120-0(6) , Bridgestone Bks.) Capstone Pr., Inc.

METER

see Versification

METHOD OF STUDY

see Study Skills

METHODIST CHURCH

Benge, Janet & Benge, Geoff. John Wesley: The World, His Parish. 2007. (J). (*978-1-57658-382-1(1)) YWAM Publishing.

Jimmy, Creech. Rise above the Law: The Appeal to the Jury: the United Methodist's Trial of Jimmy Creech. 2001. 60p. 60.00 (978-0-9704958-0-8(3)) Swing Bridge Pr., The.

Maxwell, H. M. Be Courteous or Religion the True Refine. 2006. 24.99 (*978-1-4280-3284-2(3)); pap. 18.99 (*978-1-4280-3268-2(1)) IndyPublish.com.

Nason, Ruth. Visiting a Church. 2005. (Start up Religion Ser.). (Illus.). 24p. (J). (gr. 1-4). lib. bdg. (978-1-84234-342-5(4) , Cherrytree Books) Evans Publishing Group.

Wellman, Sam. John Wesley: Founder of the Methodist Church. 1999. (Heroes of the Faith Ser.). 208p. (YA). (gr. 4-7). lib. bdg. 17.95 (978-0-7910-5036-1(X) , Chelsea Hse.) Facts On File, Inc.

METRIC SYSTEM

Benjamin, Lindsay. Measurement Action! 2005. (Yellow Umbrella Books for Early Readers). (Illus.). 17p. (J). (978-0-7368-5286-9(7)); (978-0-7368-5322-4(7)) Capstone Pr., Inc.

Fandel, Jennifer. The Metric System. 2006. (What in the World? Ser.). (Illus.). 48p. 21.95 (*978-1-58341-430-9(4) , Creative Education) Creative Co., The.

Mattern, Joanne. Let's Visit Canada: The Metric System. 2004. (PowerMath Ser.). (Illus.). 24p. (J). pap. (978-0-8239-8872-3(4)); lib. bdg. 21.25 (978-0-8239-8967-6(4)) Rosen Publishing Group, Inc., The. (PowerKids Pr.).

Miura, Taro. Ton. 2006. (Illus.). 40p. (J). 15.95 (978-0-8118-5246-3(6)) Chronicle Bks. LLC.

Murphy, Stuart J. Polly's Pen Pal. Simard, Remy, illus. 2005. (MathStart Ser.). 40p. (J). (gr. 2 up). 15.99 (978-0-06-053168-3(1)); pap. 5.99 (978-0-06-053170-6(3)) HarperCollins Pubs.

O'Donnell, Kerri. Natural Wonders of the World: Converting Distance Measurements to Metric Units. 2005. (Illus.). 32p. (J). (978-1-4042-5120-5(0)) Rosen Publishing Group, Inc., The.

—Natural Wonders of the World: Converting Measurements to Metric Units. 2005. (PowerMath Ser.). (Illus.). 32p. (J). 22.50 (978-1-4042-2928-0(0) , PowerKids Pr.); pap. (978-1-4042-5119-9(7)) Rosen Publishing Group, Inc., The.

Schwartz, David M. Millions to Measure. Kellogg, Steven, illus. 40p. (J). 2003. lib. bdg. 17.89 (978-0-06-623784-8(X)); 2003. 16.99 (978-0-688-12916-3(1)); 2006. reprint ed. pap. 6.99 (978-0-06-084806-4(5) , Harper Trophy) HarperCollins Pubs.

Sullivan, Erin Ash. Matematicas métricas & Metric Math. 2005. spiral bd. 77.00 (*978-1-4108-5681-4(X)) Benchmark Education Co.

Sullivan, Navin. Area, Distance, & Volume. 2006. (Measure Up! Ser.). (Illus.). 48p. (J). (gr. 4-7). lib. bdg. 29.93 (978-0-7614-2323-2(0) , Benchmark Bks.) Cavendish, Marshall Corp.

METROLOGY

see Mensuration; Weights and Measures

METROPOLITAN AREAS

see also Cities and Towns

Dalgleish, Sharon. Managing the Land. 2003. (Our World - Our Future Ser.). (Illus.). 32p. (gr. 4-8). 27.00 (978-0-7910-7020-8(4) , Chelsea Hse.) Facts On File, Inc.

Davis, Wendy. City Park. 1998. (Habitats Ser.). (Illus.). 32p. (J). (gr. 2-3). pap. 6.95 (978-0-516-20370-6(3) , Children's Pr.) Scholastic Library Publishing.

Roop, Peter & Roop, Connie. A Suburb. 1999. (Walk Around Ser.). (Illus.). 32p. (J). (gr. 1-3). lib. bdg. 21.36 (978-1-57572-130-9(9)) Heinemann Library.

METROPOLITAN MUSEUM OF ART (NEW YORK, N.Y.)

Metropolitan Museum of Art Staff, contrib. by. Museum Colors: The Metropolitan Museum of Art. 2006. (J). (978-1-58839-183-4(3)) Metropolitan Museum of Art, The.

METROPOLITAN MUSEUM OF ART (NEW YORK, N.Y.)—FICTION

Konigsburg, E. L. From the Mixed-Up Files of Mrs. Basil E. Frankweiler. 35th anniv. ed. 2002. 208p. (YA). mass mkt. 5.99 (978-0-689-85354-8(8) , Simon Pulse) Simon & Schuster Children's Publishing.

—From the Mixed-Up Files of Mrs. Basil E. Frankweiler. 35th anniv. ed. 2002. (gr. 5-8). lib. bdg. 14.15 (978-0-613-73358-8(4)) Tandem Library Bks.

—From the Mixed-Up Files of Mrs. Basil E. Frankweiler. l.t. ed. 2005. (Illus.). 205p. (J). 22.95 (978-0-7862-7297-6(X) , Large Print Pr.) Thorndike Pr.

Konigsburg, E. L. & Marcus, Barry David. From the Mixed-Up Files of Mrs. Basil E. Frankweiler. Konigsburg, E. L., illus. 35th anniv. ed. 2002. (Illus.). 176p. (J). (gr. 3-7). 17.99 (978-0-689-85322-7(X) , Atheneum) Simon & Schuster Children's Publishing.

Weitzman, Jacqueline Preiss. You Can't Take a Balloon into the Metropolitan Museum. Bonnell, J., ed. Glasser, Robin Preiss, illus. 2001. 40p. (J). (ps-3). pap. 6.99 (978-0-14-056816-5(6) , Puffin) Penguin Group (USA) Inc.

MEXICAN AMERICANS

see also Mexicans—United States

Abrams, Dennis. Gary Soto. 2008. (Who Wrote That? Ser.). 128p. (gr. 6-12). 30.00 (*978-0-7910-9529-4(0) , Chelsea Hse.) Facts On File, Inc.

Alter, Judy. Martin de Leon: Tejano Empresario. Messersmith, Patrick, illus. 2007. 64p. (J). 17.95 (*978-1-933337-08-1(7)) State Hse. Pr.

Ancona, George. Barrio: Jose's Neighborhood. Ancona, George, photos by. 1998. (Illus.). 48p. (J). (gr. 2-7). pap. 10.00 (978-0-15-201048-5(3) , Harcourt Paperbacks) Harcourt Children's Bks.

—Mi Casa: My House. (Somos Latinos (We Are Latinos) Ser.). (Illus.). 32p. (J). 2005. (SPA & ENG.). (gr. 1-3). pap. 8.95 (978-0-516-25065-6(5)); 2004. (ENG & SPA., 20.00 (978-0-516-23688-9(1)) Scholastic Library Publishing. (Children's Pr.).

—Mis Juegos. 32p. (J). 2006. (SPA.). (gr. 1-3). pap. 8.95 (978-0-516-25498-2(7)); 2005. (ENG & SPA.). 21.00 (978-0-516-25293-3(3)) Scholastic Library Publishing. (Children's Pr.).

Anza, Ana Luisa. Amigos del Otro Lado. Gomez, Eddie Martinez, illus. rev. ed. 2004. (Castillo de la Lectura Naranja Ser.). (SPA.). 136p. (J). pap. 7.95 (978-970-20-0130-0(7)) Castillo, Ediciones, S. A. de C. V. MEX. *Dist:* Lectorum Pubns., Inc., Macmillan.

Apte, Sunita. Cesar Chavez: We Can Do It! 2005. (Defining Moments Ser.). (Illus.). 32p. (J). (gr. 3-7). lib. bdg. 25.27 (978-1-59716-073-5(3)) Bearport Publishing Co., Inc.

Atkin, S. Beth. Voices from the Fields: Children of Migrant Farmworkers Tell Their Stories. 2000. (Illus.). 96p. (J). (gr. 5-17). pap. 14.99 (978-0-316-05620-5(0)) Little Brown & Co.

—Voices from the Fields: Children of Migrant Farmworkers Tell Their Stories. 2000. (978-0-606-17851-8(1)) Tandem Library Bks.

Behnke, Alison. Mexicans in America. 2005. (In America Ser.). (Illus.). 80p. (J). (gr. 5-8). lib. bdg. 27.93 (978-0-8225-3955-1(1)) Lerner Publishing Group.

Bloom, Barbara Lee. The Mexican Americans. 2003. (Immigrants in America Ser.). (Illus.). 112p. (J). 29.95 (978-1-56006-753-5(5) , Lucent Bks.) Thomson Gale.

Boyer Binns, Tristan. Mexican Americans. (We Are America Ser.). (Illus.). 32p. (J). 2003. (gr. 2-4). lib. bdg. 24.22 (978-1-4034-0163-2(2)); 2002. pap. 6.95 (978-1-4034-0418-3(6)) Heinemann Library.

Braun, Eric. Cesar Chavez: Fighting for Farmworkers. Roland, Harry et al, illus. 2005. (Graphic Library). 32p. (J). (gr. 3-7). lib. bdg. 25.26 (978-0-7368-4631-8(X)) Capstone Pr., Inc.

Brown, Jonatha A. Cesar Chavez. (People We Should Know Ser.). (J). 2006. 24p. pap. 5.95 (978-0-8368-4766-6(0)); 2006. 24p. lib. bdg. 19.33 (978-0-8368-4759-8(8)); 2005. (Illus.). 24p. pap. (978-0-8368-4752-9(0)); 2005. (Illus.). 24p. lib. bdg. 19.33 (978-0-8368-4745-1(8)); 2004. (Illus.). 48p. (gr. 5 up). pap. 11.95 (978-0-8368-5257-8(5) , World Almanac Library); 2004. (Illus.). 48p. (gr. 5 up). lib. bdg. 30.00 (978-0-8368-5097-0(1) , World Almanac Library) Stevens, Gareth Inc.

Bryan, Nichol. Mexican Americans. 2004. (One Nation Ser.). (Illus.). 32p. (J). (gr. k-6). lib. bdg. 22.78 (978-1-57765-987-7(2)) ABDO Publishing Co.

Cesar Chavez, Vol. 3. 2005. (First Biographies Ser.). (YA). (gr. k-3). (978-0-7368-8110-4(7) , Pebble Bks.) Capstone Pr., Inc.

Cesar Chavez: Fighter in the Fields, 6 vols. (gr. 4 up). 49.95 (978-0-7368-9539-2(6) , High Five) Red Brick Learning.

Cesar Chavez 2: Leveled Books. 2001. (McGraw-Hill. Lectura Ser.). (ENG & SPA.). (gr. 4 up). (978-0-02-188202-1(9)) Macmillan/McGraw-Hill Schl. Div.

Charlesworth, Eric. Easy Reader Biographies: Cesar Chavez: A Leader for Change. 2007. 16p. pap. 2.99 (*978-0-439-77416-1(0) , Teaching Resources) Scholastic, Inc.

Colley, Betty Bailey & Monday, Jane Clements. Tales of the Wild Horse Desert. 2001. (Jack & Doris Smothers Series in Texas History, Life, & Culture: Vol.4). (Illus.). 138p. (J). pap. 19.95 (978-0-292-71241-6(3)) Univ. of Texas Pr.

Collins, David R. Cesar Chavez. 2005. (Just the Facts Biographies Ser.). (Illus.). 112p. (J). (gr. 6-12). 27.93 (978-0-8225-2248-5(9)) Lerner Publishing Group.

Copley, Robert E. The Tall Mexican: The Life of Hank Aguirre All-Star Pitcher, Businessman, Humanitarian. 2000. (J). (978-0-606-19189-0(5)); (gr. 7-12). lib. bdg. 18.75 (978-0-613-28666-4(9)) Tandem Library Bks.

Cruz, Barbara C. Cesar Chavez: A Voice for Farmworkers. 2005. (Latino Biography Library). (Illus.). 128p. (J). (gr. 6-13). lib. bdg. 31.93 (978-0-7660-2489-2(X)) Enslow Pubs., Inc.

Davis, Barbara J. The National Grape Boycott: A Victory for Farmworkers. 2007. (J). lib. bdg. (*978-0-7565-2454-8(7)) Compass Point Bks.

Davis, Lucile. Cesar Chavez. Schon, Isabel, ed. Ferrer, Martín Luis Guzman, tr. from ENG. 1998. (Biografías Ilustradas con Fotografías Ser.). (SPA., Illus.). 24p. (J). (gr. 2-3). lib. bdg. 18.60 (978-1-56065-808-5(8) , CAP2791, Bridgestone Bks.) Capstone Pr., Inc.

Deiters, Erika & Deiters, Jim. The Mexican Community in America. 2003. (J). (978-1-58417-030-3(1)); pap. (978-1-58417-092-1(1)) Lake Street Pubs.

del Castillo, Richard Griswold. César Chavez: La lucha por la Justicia. Colin, Jose Juan, tr. from ENG. Accardo, Anthony, illus. 2001. (Hispanic Civil Rights Ser.). (ENG & SPA.). 32p. (J). (ps-3). 15.95 (978-1-55885-324-9(3) , Piñata Books) Arte Publico Pr.

Ebon Research Systems Staff. Dare to Be... A Hero Vol. 3: Cesar Chavez. l.t. ed. 2003. Tr. of Atrevete Ser... Un Heroe Cesar Chavez. (ENG & SPA., Illus.). 16p. (J). 3.99 (978-0-9648313-6-0(8)) Ebon Research Systems Publishing, LLC.

Eddy, Susan. Cesar Chavez. 2004. (Rookie Biographies Ser.). (Illus.). 31p. (J). (gr. 1-2). pap. 4.95 (978-0-516-27923-7(8) , Children's Pr.) Scholastic Library Publishing.

Feinstein, Stephen. Lee sobre César Chavez/Read about Cesar Chavez. 2006. (I Like Biographies! Bilingual Ser.). (ENG & SPA., Illus.). 24p. (J). (gr. 1-3). lib. bdg. 21.26 (978-0-7660-2744-2(9) , Enslow Elementary) Enslow Pubs., Inc.

—Read about Cesar Chavez. 2004. (I Like Biographies Ser.!). (Illus.). 24p. (J). lib. bdg. 21.26 (978-0-7660-2296-6(X)) Enslow Pubs., Inc.

Fisher, Mary McMillan. Rosita's Bridge. Whitehead, Barbara Mathews, illus. 2001. 32p. (J). (gr. 2-4). 16.95 (978-1-893271-18-0(8)) Maverick Publishing Co.

Flynn, Jean. Henry B. Gonzalez: Rebel with a Cause. 2003. (Illus.). v, 140p. (J). 16.95 (978-1-57168-780-7(7) , Eakin Pr.) Eakin Pr.

Freedman, Russell. In the Days of the Vaqueros: America's First True Cowboys. 2001. (Illus.). 80p. (J). (gr. 7-7). tchr. ed. 18.00 (978-0-395-96788-1(0) , Clarion Bks.) Houghton Mifflin Co. Trade & Reference Div.

Gaines, Ann Graham. Cesar E. Chavez: The Fight for Farm Workers' Rights. 2003. (Proud Heritage-The Hispanic Library). (Illus.). 40p. (J). (gr. 3-7). 28.50 (978-1-56766-209-2(9)) Child's World, Inc.

Gallegos, Yuliana. Mi Sueño de América/My American Dream. 2007. (SPA & ENG.). 64p. (J). (gr. 3-7). pap. 9.95 (*978-1-55885-485-7(1) , Piñata Books) Arte Publico Pr.

Gelletly, LeeAnne. Mexican Immigration. 2003. (Changing Face of North America Ser.). (Illus.). 112p. (YA). lib. bdg. (978-1-59084-680-3(X)) Mason Crest Pubs.

Gibson, Karen. Jovita Idar. 2002. (Latinos in American History). (Illus.). 56p. (gr. 4-8). lib. bdg. 29.95 (978-1-58415-151-7(X)) Mitchell Lane Pubs., Inc.

Gillis, Jennifer Blizin. Dolores Huerta. 2005. (Illus.). 32p. (J). (978-1-4034-6980-9(6)); pap. (978-1-4034-6987-8(3)) Heinemann Library.

Gotsch, Patrice. Cesar Chavez: Changing Lives. Arreola, Gil, illus. 2005. 19p. (J). pap. (*978-1-55501-780-4(0)) Ballard & Tighe Pubs.

Guzman, Lila & Guzman, Rick. César Chavez: Fighting for Fairness. 2006. (Famous Latinos Ser.). (Illus.). 32p. (J). lib. bdg. 22.60 (978-0-7660-2370-3(2) , Enslow Elementary) Enslow Pubs., Inc.

Harcourt School Publishers Staff. North of the Rio Grande: Take-Home Book. 2001. (Collections Ser.). (Illus.). (J). pap. 1.90 (978-0-15-319507-5(X)) Harcourt Schl. Pubs.

Hart, Elva Trevino. Barefoot Heart: Stories of A Migrant Child. 1999. (gr. 7-12). lib. bdg. 26.90 (978-0-613-24295-0(5)) Tandem Library Bks.

Haugen, Brenda. Cesar Chavez: Crusader for Social Change. 2007. (J). lib. bdg. (*978-0-7565-3321-2(X)) Compass Point Bks.

Herrera, Juan Felipe. Calling the Doves. 2001. Tr. of El Canto De Las Palomos. (SPA.). (gr. 3-6). lib. bdg. 16.40 (978-0-613-34098-4(1)) Tandem Library Bks.

—El Canto de las Palomas/Calling the Doves. ed. 2004. (ENG & SPA., Illus.). (J). (gr. 3-6). spiral bd. (978-0-616-14607-1(8)) Canadian National Institute for the Blind/Institut National Canadien pour les Aveugles.

—The Upside down Boy. Gomez, Elizabeth, illus. Tr. of Nino de Cabeza. 32p. (J). 2006. pap. 7.95 (978-0-89239-217-9(7)); 2000. (ENG & SPA.). (gr. 1-4). 16.95 (978-0-89239-162-2(6)) Children's Bk. Pr.

Hoyt-Goldsmith, Diane. Celebrating a Quinceanera: A Latina's Fifteenth Birthday Celebration. Migdale, Lawrence, illus. Migdale, Lawrence, photos by. 2002. 32p. (J). (gr. 4-6). tchr. ed. 16.95 (978-0-8234-1693-6(3)) Holiday Hse., Inc.

—Las Posadas: A Mexican-American Christmas Celebration. Migdale, Lawrence, illus. 1999. 32p. (YA). (gr. 4-6). tchr. ed. 17.95 (978-0-8234-1449-9(3)) Holiday Hse., Inc.

Ingram, Scott. Mexican Americans. 2006. (World Almanac Library of American Immigration). (Illus.). 48p. (J). lib. bdg. (978-0-8368-7316-0(5) , World Almanac Library) Stevens, Gareth Inc.

Jones, Veda Boyd. Selena. (Latinos in the Limelight Ser.). (Illus.). 2002. 64p. (J). pap. 17.95 (978-0-7910-6113-8(2)); 2001. 64p. (J). (gr. 3 up). 31.00 (978-0-7910-6112-1(4)); 2000. 48p. (YA). 21.95 (978-0-7910-5230-3(3)) Facts On File, Inc. (Chelsea Hse.).

Kent, Deborah. Mario Molina: Chemist & Nobel Prize Winner. 2004. (Proud Heritage: the Hispanic Library Ser.). (Illus.). 40p. (J). (gr. 3-7). 28.50 (978-1-59296-170-2(3)) Child's World, Inc.

Kirkpatrick, Rob. Oscar de la Hoya: Gold-Medal Boxer. 2000. (Reading Power Ser.). (Illus.). 24p. (J). (gr. 1). lib. bdg. 17.25 (978-0-8239-5543-5(5) , PowerKids Pr.) Rosen Publishing Group, Inc., The.

—Oscar de la Hoya, Boxeador de Medalla de Oro. 2002. (Coleccion Power Kids). (SPA & ENG., Illus.). 24p. (J). (gr. k-2). lib. bdg. 17.25 (978-0-8239-6149-8(4) , RN31302, Buenas Letra) Rosen Publishing Group, Inc., The.

Krull, Kathleen. Cosechando Esperanza: La Historia de Cesar Chavez. Campoy, F. Isabel & Ada, Alma Flor, trs. Morales, Yuyi, illus. 2004. (SPA.). 48p. (J). pap. 7.00 (978-0-15-205169-3(4) , Voyager Bks./Libros Viajeros) Harcourt Children's Bks.

—Harvesting Hope: The Story of Cesar Chavez. Morales, Yuyi, illus. 2003. 48p. (J). (gr. 3-6). 17.00 (978-0-15-201437-7(3)) Harcourt Children's Bks.

Krull, Kathleen & Morales, Yuyi. Cosechando Esperanza: La Historia de Cesar Chavez. Ada, Alma Flor & Campoy, F. Isabel, trs. from ENG. Morales, Yuyi, illus. 2003. (SPA., Illus.). 48p. (J). 17.00 (978-0-15-204755-9(7) , Voyager Bks./Libros Viajeros) Harcourt Children's Bks.

La Pierre, Yvette. Welcome to Josefina's World, 1824: Growing up on America's Southwest Frontier. 1999. (American Girls Collection). (Illus.). 64p. (J). (gr. 2 up). 16.95 (978-1-56247-769-1(2)) American Girl Publishing, Inc.

Lieurance, Suzanne. Mexico: A MyReportLinks. com Book. 2004. (Top Ten Countries of Recent Immigrants Ser.). (Illus.). 48p. (J). lib. bdg. 25.26 (978-0-7660-5177-5(3) , MyReportLinks.com Bks.) Enslow Pubs., Inc.

Lomas Garza, Carmen. Magic Windows (Ventanas Magicas) Lomas Garza, Carmen, illus. 1999. (ENG & SPA., Illus.). 32p. (J). (gr. 1-4). 15.95 (978-0-89239-157-8(X)) Children's Bk. Pr.

Magner, E. C. The Mexican American Story. 2000. Orig. Title: I Am Tejano. pap. 15.00 (978-1-929416-31-8(8)) Magner Publishing & American Binding & Publishing.

Marcovitz, Hal. Cesar Chavez. 2003. (Great Hispanic Heritage Ser.). (Illus.). 112p. (gr. 6-12). 30.00 (978-0-7910-7253-0(3)); pap. 30.00 (978-0-7910-7515-9(X)) Facts On File, Inc. (Chelsea Hse.).

Marcovitz, Hal. Pat Mora. 2007. (Who Wrote That? Ser.). 136p. (J). (gr. 6-12). 30.00 (*978-0-7910-9528-7(2) , Chelsea Hse.) Facts On File, Inc.

Marsh, Carole. Cesar Chavez. 2002. (One Thousand Readers Ser.). (Illus.). 12p. (J). (gr. k-4). 2.95 (978-0-635-01566-2(8) , 15668) Gallopade International.

Martinez, Diana Davila. A School Named for Someone Like Me (Una Escuela Con un Nombre Como el Mio) (Illus.). 48p. (YA). (gr. 3-8). pap. 7.95 (978-1-55885-334-8(0) , Piñata Books) Arte Publico Pr.

Mattern, Joanne. Celebrate Cinco de Mayo. 2006. (Celebrate Holidays Ser.). (Illus.). 104p. (J). lib. bdg. 31.93 (978-0-7660-2579-0(9)) Enslow Pubs., Inc.

Matthews, J. L. & Rasinski, Timothy V. Cesar Chavez: Fighter in the Fields. 2002. (High Five Reading Ser.). (Illus.). 48p. (J). (gr. 2-3). lib. bdg. 22.60 (978-0-7368-9550-7(7) , Capstone High-Interest Bks.); pap. 16.95 (978-0-7368-9528-6(0)) Capstone Pr., Inc.

McLeese, Don. Cesar E. Chavez. 2003. (Rourke Discovery Library). (Illus.). 24p. (gr. 2-5). 14.95 (978-1-58952-285-5(0)) Rourke Publishing, LLC.

Medina, Jane. Tomas Rivera. Martinez, Edward, illus. 2004. (Green Light Reader Ser., Level 2). 24p. (J). 12.95 (978-0-15-205146-4(5)); pap. 3.95 (978-0-15-205145-7(7)) Harcourt Children's Bks. (Green Light Readers).

Mirriam-Goldberg, Caryn. Sandra Cisneros: Latina Writer & Activist. 1998. (Hispanic Biographies Ser.). (Illus.). 112p. (YA). (gr. 6-12). lib. bdg. 26.60 (978-0-7660-1045-1(7)) Enslow Pubs., Inc.

Nava, Julian. Julian Nava: My Mexican-American Journey. 2002. (Hispanic Civil Rights Ser.). 248p. (YA). 16.95 (978-1-55885-364-5(2) , Piñata Books) Arte Publico Pr.

—Julian Nava: My Mexican-American Journey. 2002. (gr. 7-12). lib. bdg. 18.75 (978-0-613-82668-6(X)) Tandem Library Bks.

Nobleman, Marc Tyler. Cinco de Mayo. 2004. (Let's See Ser.). 24p. (J). (gr. 1 up). lib. bdg. 19.93 (978-0-7565-0768-8(5)) Compass Point Bks.

Olmstead. Cesar Chavez. (Hispanic-American Biographies Ser.). 2005. pap. 9.50 (978-1-4109-1595-5(6)); 2005. pap. 34.20 (978-1-4109-1600-6(6)); Pack. 2004. (Illus.). pap. 51.30 (978-1-4109-1192-6(6)) Harcourt Schl. Pubs.

Olmstead, Mary. Cesar Chavez. 2004. (Hispanic-American Biographies Ser.). (Illus.). 64p. (J). pap. 9.50 (978-1-4109-0916-9(6)) Harcourt Schl. Pubs.

—Cesar Chavez. 2004. (Hispanic-American Biographies Ser.). (Illus.). 64p. (J). (gr. 4-6). 32.86 (978-1-4109-0710-3(4)) Raintree.

—Judy Baca. 2004. (Hispanic-American Biographies Ser.). (Illus.). 64p. (J). pap. 9.50 (978-1-4109-0915-2(8)) Harcourt Schl. Pubs.

—Judy Baca. 2004. (Hispanic-American Biographies Ser.). (Illus.). 64p. (J). (gr. 4-6). 32.86 (978-1-4109-0709-7(0)) Raintree.

Parker, Lewis K. Why Mexican Immigrants Came to America. 2003. (Reading Power Ser.). (Illus.). 24p. (J). lib. bdg. 17.25 (978-0-8239-6459-8(0) , PowerKids Pr.) Rosen Publishing Group, Inc., The.

Parr, Ann. Low Riders. 2000. (Race Car Legends Ser.). (Illus.). 64p. (J). (gr. 4-7). 28.00 (978-0-7910-5849-7(2)); pap. 5.95 (978-0-7910-5850-3(6)) Facts On File, Inc. (Chelsea Hse.).

Perl, Lila, et al. North Across the Border: The Story of the Mexican Americans. 2002. (Great Journeys Ser.). (Illus.). 112p. (J). (gr. 5 up). lib. bdg. 32.79 (978-0-7614-1226-7(3) , Benchmark Bks.) Cavendish, Marshall Corp.

Quinn, Rob. Oscar de la Hoya. (Latinos in the Limelight Ser.). (Illus.). 64p. (J). 2001. (gr. 3 up). 27.50 (978-0-7910-6098-8(5)); 2000. pap. (978-0-7910-6099-5(3)) Facts On File, Inc. (Chelsea Hse.).

Remstein, Henna. Carlos Santana. 2001. (Latinos in the Limelight Ser.). (Illus.). 64p. (J). (gr. 4-7). 27.50 (978-0-7910-6473-3(5) , Chelsea Hse.) Facts On File, Inc.

Rinaldo, Denise. Cesar Chavez: With a Discussion of Compassion. 2003. (Values in Action Ser.). (J). (978-1-59203-064-4(5)) Learning Challenge, Inc.

Roman, Michelle. Becoming Cesar Chavez. Ballis, George, photos by. 2002. (ENG & SPA., Illus.). 48p. (J). (gr. 1-6). pap. 8.95 (978-0-938911-21-0(X)) Individualized Education Systems/Poppy Lane Publishing.

Rosinsky, Natalie M. California Ranchos. 2006. (We the People Ser.). (Illus.). 48p. (J). (gr. 4-6). 23.93 (978-0-7565-1633-8(1)) Compass Point Bks.

Sanna, Ellyn. Mexican Americans' Role in the United States: A History of Pride, a Future of Hope. 2005. (Illus.). 112p. (J). (ps-7). lib. bdg. (978-1-59084-926-2(4)) Mason Crest Pubs.

Schaefer, Lola M. Cesar Chavez. Saunders-Smith, Gail, ed. 1998. (Famous Americans Ser.). (Illus.). 24p. (J). (gr. k-1). lib. bdg. 15.93 (978-0-7368-0109-6(X) , Pebble Bks.) Capstone Pr., Inc.

Schumacher, Tyler. Cesar Chavez: Champion of Workers. 2006. (Fact Finders Ser.). (Illus.). 32p. (J). (978-0-7368-5436-8(3) , Fact Finders) Capstone Pr., Inc.

Seidman, David. Cesar Chavez: Labor Leader. 2004. (Great Life Stories Ser.). (Illus.). 127p. (J). 30.50 (978-0-531-12319-5(7) , Watts, Franklin) Scholastic Library Publishing.

Shea, Kitty. Cesar Chavez: Leader of Migrant Farm Workers. 2004. (Compass Point Early Biographies Ser.). (Illus.). 32p. (J). (gr. 1-3). lib. bdg. 21.26 (978-0-7565-0793-0(6)) Compass Point Bks.

Slade, Suzanne. Cesar Chavez: Champion & Voice of Farmworkers. Thompson, Jeffrey, illus. 2007. (J). lib. bdg. (***978-1-4048-3724-9(8)***) Picture Window Bks.

Soto, Gary. Cesar Chavez: A Hero for Everyone. Lohstoeter, Lori, illus. 2003. (Milestone Ser.). 80p. (J). pap. 3.99 (978-0-689-85922-9(8) , Aladdin) Simon & Schuster Children's Publishing.

—Cesar Chavez: A Hero for Everyone. 2003. (gr. 3-6). lib. bdg. 11.80 (978-0-613-90718-7(3)) Tandem Library Bks.

Stanford, Candice & Wroth, William. The Man Who Set the Town Dancing. Dougherty, Flo Hosa, illus. 2002. (ENG & SPA.). 40p. (J). (gr. 2-4). 16.95 (978-1-57416-050-5(8)) Clear Light Pubs.

Tait, Leia. Cinco de Mayo. 2006. (J). (978-1-59036-460-4(0)); (978-1-59036-463-5(5)) Weigl Pubs., Inc.

Tello, Jerry. Let's Read About— César Chavez. Marchesi, Stephen, illus. 2004. (Scholastic First Biographies Ser.). (J). pap. (978-0-439-68051-6(4)) Scholastic, Inc.

Thatcher, Rebecca. Dolores Huerta. 2002. (Latinos in American History). (Illus.). 56p. (gr. 4-8). lib. bdg. 29.95 (978-1-58415-155-5(2)) Mitchell Lane Pubs., Inc.

Thompson, E. L. Cesar Chavez, with Profiles of Terence V. Powderly & Dolores Huerta. 2006. (Biographical Connections Ser.). (Illus.). 112p. (J). (978-0-7166-1827-0(3)) World Bk., Inc.

Torres, John Albert. Sports Great Oscar de la Hoya. 1999. (Sports Great Bks.). (Illus.). 64p. (YA). (gr. 4-10). lib. bdg. 22.60 (978-0-7660-1066-6(X)) Enslow Pubs., Inc.

Ueda, Reed & Stotsky, Sandra, eds. Mexican-American Answer Book. 1999. (Ethnic Answer Book Ser.). (Illus.). 136p. (YA). (gr. 5 up). pap. 9.95 (978-0-7910-4887-0(X)); lib. bdg. 17.95 (978-0-7910-4886-3(1)) Facts On File, Inc. (Chelsea Hse.).

Wade, Linda R. The Mexican Americans. 2002. (Welcome to America Ser.). (Illus.). 64p. (J). (gr. 4-7). lib. bdg. (978-1-59084-111-2(5)) Mason Crest Pubs.

Wadsworth, Ginger. Cesar Chavez. Schroeder, Mark, illus. 2005. (Yo Solo - Biografías (on My Own - Biographies) Ser.). (SPA.). 48p. (J). (ps-ps). pap. 5.95 (978-0-8225-3125-8(9)) Lerner Publishing Group.

—Cesar Chavez. Schroder, Mark, illus. 2005. (Yo Solo (On My Own) Ser.). (SPA.). 48p. (J). (ps-7). lib. bdg. 23.93 (978-0-8225-3124-1(0) , Ediciones Lerner) Lerner Publishing Group.

—Cesar Chavez. 2005. (On My Own Biography Ser.). (Illus.). 48p. (J). 25.26 (978-1-57505-652-4(6) , Carolrhoda Bks.) Lerner Publishing Group.

—Cesar Chavez. Schroder, Mark, illus. 2005. 48p. (J). (gr. 1-3). pap. 5.95 (978-1-57505-826-9(X)) Lerner Publishing Group.

Wheeler, Jill C. Cesar Chavez. 2003. (Breaking Barriers Ser.). (Illus.). 64p. (J). (gr. 3-8). lib. bdg. 25.65 (978-1-57765-905-1(8)) ABDO Publishing Co.

Worth, Richard. Mexican Immigrants. 2004. (Immigration to the United States Ser.). (Illus.). 96p. (J). (gr. 4-9). 35.00 (978-0-8160-5690-3(0)) Facts On File, Inc.

Young, Jeff C. Cesar Chavez. 2007. (American Workers Ser.). 160p. (YA). (gr. 5-8). lib. bdg. 27.95 (978-1-59935-036-3(X)) Reynolds, Morgan Inc.

Zannos, Susan. Cesar Chavez. 1998. (Real-Life Reader Biographies Ser.). (Illus.). 32p. (J). (gr. 4-7). lib. bdg. 15.95 (978-1-883845-71-1(8)) Mitchell Lane Pubs., Inc.

MEXICAN AMERICANS—FICTION

Abraham, Susan Gonzales & Abraham, Denise Gonzales. Surprising Cecilia. 2005. (Latino Fiction for Young Adults Ser.). 216p. (YA). 16.95 (978-0-938317-96-8(2)) Cinco Puntos Pr.

Ada, Alma Flor. I Love Saturdays y Domingos. 1999. (SPA.). pap. 4.95 (978-0-689-80591-2(8) , Aladdin) Simon & Schuster Children's Publishing.

—I Love Saturdays y Domingos. Savadier, Elivia, illus. 2004. 32p. (J). reprint ed. pap. 6.99 (978-0-689-87409-3(X) , Aladdin) Simon & Schuster Children's Publishing.

—I Love Saturdays y Domingos. Savadier, Elivia, illus. 2004. 32p. (J). (ps-ps). lib. bdg. 14.19 (978-0-606-32672-8(3)) Tandem Library Bks.

—El Vuelo de los Colibríes. Jacobson, Judith, illus. 32p. (J). (gr. 3-6). pap. 9.95 (978-1-56492-211-3(1)) Laredo Publishing Co., Inc.

Ada, Alma Flor & Savadier, Elivia. I Love Saturdays y Domingos. 2002. (Illus.). 32p. (J). (gr. k-3). 17.99 (978-0-689-31819-1(7) , Atheneum) Simon & Schuster Children's Publishing.

Alegria, Malin. Estrella's Quinceañera. 2007. 288p. (YA). (gr. 7 up). pap. 8.99 (978-0-689-87810-7(9) , Simon Pulse) Simon & Schuster Children's Publishing.

—Estrellas Quinceanera. 2006. (Illus.). 272p. (YA). 15.99 (978-0-689-87809-1(5)) Simon & Schuster Children's Publishing.

Alexander Greene, Alesia. A Mural for Mamita. Lara, Susana, tr. Teis, Kyra, illus. 2001. Tr. of Mural Para Mamita. (ENG & SPA.). (J). 8.95 (978-1-56123-154-6(1) , MFMC) Centering Corp.

Anaya, Rudolfo A. The Santero's Miracle: A Bilingual Story. Lamadrid, Enrique E., tr. Cordova, Amy, illus. 2004. (ENG & SPA.). 32p. (J). 16.95 (978-0-8263-2847-2(4)) Univ. of New Mexico Pr.

Anzaldua, Gloria. Prietita & the Ghost Woman. 2001. Tr. of Prietita Y La Llorona. (SPA.). (gr. 3-6). lib. bdg. 16.40 (978-0-613-34419-7(7)) Tandem Library Bks.

Armas, Teresa. Remembering Grandma / Recordando a Abuela. Baeza Ventura, Gabriela, tr. from ENG. Rodriguez Howard, Pauline, illus. 2003. (ENG & SPA.). 32p. (J). 14.95 (978-1-55885-344-7(8) , Piñata Books) Arte Publico Pr.

Baca, Ana. Benito's Bizcochitos. Castilla, Julia Mercedes, tr. Accardo, Anthony, illus. 1999. Tr. of Bizcochitos de Benito. (ENG & SPA.). 32p. (J). (ps-3). 14.95 (978-1-55885-264-8(6) , Piñata Books) Arte Publico Pr.

—Benito's Sopaipillas: Las Sopaipillas de Benito. Villarroel, Carolina, tr. Accardo, Anthony, illus. (ENG & SPA.). 32p. (J). (gr. 2-4). 15.95 (978-1-55885-370-6(7) , Piñata Books) Arte Publico Pr.

—Chiles for Benito (Chiles para Benito) Colin, Jose Juan, tr. Accardo, Anthony, illus. (ENG & SPA.). 32p. (J). 15.95 (978-1-55885-389-8(8) , Piñata Books) Arte Publico Pr.

Balmes, Kathy. Thunder on the Sierra. Catapano, Vicki, illus. 2001. (Adventures in America Ser.). 96p. (J). (gr. 3-7). lib. bdg. 14.95 (978-1-893110-10-6(9)) Silver Moon Pr.

Barron, Marietta. Two Worlds. 1999. 94p. (J). (gr. 3-6). 9.99 (978-0-88092-120-6(X) , 120-X) Royal Fireworks Publishing Co.

Bertrand, Diane Gonzales. The Empanadas That Abuela Made/Las Empandas Que Hacia la Abuela. Ventura, Gabriela Baeza, tr. DeLange, Alex Pardo, illus. (ENG & SPA.). 32p. (J). 15.95 (978-1-55885-388-1(X) , Piñata Books) Arte Publico Pr.

—The Last Doll/la ultima Muñeca. Balestra, Alejandra, tr. Accardo, Anthony, illus. 2001. Tr. of Ultima Muneca. (ENG & SPA.). 32p. (J). (ps-2). 14.95 (978-1-55885-290-7(5) , Piñata Books) Arte Publico Pr.

—Trino's Choice. (Illus.). 128p. (YA). (gr. 5-11). pap., stu. ed. 9.95 (978-1-55885-268-6(9)); 1999. 124p. (J). (gr. 4-7). 16.95 (978-1-55885-279-2(4)) Arte Publico Pr. (Piñata Books).

—Trino's Choice. 1999. (978-0-606-17956-0(9)); (gr. 5-8). lib. bdg. 18.75 (978-0-613-33660-4(7)) Tandem Library Bks.

—Trino's Time. 2001. (Illus.). 176p. (J). (gr. 7 up). pap. 14.95 (978-1-55885-317-1(0)); (gr. 6 up). 14.95 (978-1-55885-316-4(2)) Arte Publico Pr. (Piñata Books).

—Trino's Time. 2001. (gr. 5-8). lib. bdg. 18.75 (978-0-613-59027-3(9)) Tandem Library Bks.

—Uncle Chente's Picnic/el picnic de Tío Chente. Castilla, Julia Mercedes, tr. Howard, Pauline Rodriguez, illus. Tr. of Picnic de Tio Chente. (ENG & SPA.). 32p. (J). (ps-3). 15.95 (978-1-55885-337-9(5) , Piñata Books) Arte Publico Pr.

Bledsoe, Lucy Jane. Cougar Canyon. 2001. 136p. (J). (gr. 4-6). tchr. ed. 16.95 (978-0-8234-1599-1(6)) Holiday Hse., Inc.

Brammer, Ethriam Cash. My Tata's Guitar / la guitarra de mi Tata. Lechon, Daniel, illus. (ENG & SPA.). 32p. (J). 15.95 (978-1-55885-369-0(3) , Piñata Books) Arte Publico Pr.

—The Rowdy, Rowdy Ranch / Alla en el Rancho Grande. Cruz, D. Nina, illus. (ENG & SPA.). 32p. 15.95 (978-1-55885-409-3(6) , Piñata Books) Arte Publico Pr.

Brightwood, Laura, illus. Growing up in East L. A. Brightwood, Laura, . 2006. (J). (978-0-9779290-8-5(6)) 3-C Institute for Social Development.

Brown, Monica & Ventura, Gabriela Baeza. Butterflies on Carmen Street/Mariposas en la Calle Carmen. Ward, April, illus. 2007. (SPA & ENG.). 32p. (J). (ps-4). 15.95 (***978-1-55885-484-0(3)*** , Piñata Books) Arte Publico Pr.

Bulla, Clyde Robert. The Paint Brush Kid. (Stepping Stone Bks.). (Illus.). 80p. (J). 1999. (gr. 1-4). lib. bdg. 11.99 (978-0-679-99282-0(0)); 1998. (gr. k-3). pap. 3.99 (978-0-679-89282-3(6)) Random Hse. Children's Bks. (Random Hse. Bks. for Young Readers).

Bunting, Eve. A Day's Work. 2002. (Illus.). (J). 13.79 (978-0-7587-2361-1(X)) Book Wholesalers, Inc.

—Going Home. Diaz, David, illus. 1998. (Trophy Picture Bk.). 32p. (J). (ps-3). pap. 6.99 (978-0-06-443509-3(1) , Harper Trophy) HarperCollins Pubs.

Campos, Tito. Muffler Man/el hombre Mofle. Vigil-Pion, Evangelina, tr. Alvarez, Lamberto & Alvarez, Beto, illus. 2001. Tr. of Hombre Mofle. (ENG & SPA.). 32p. (J). (ps-3). 14.95 (978-1-55885-318-8(9) , Piñata Books) Arte Publico Pr.

Canales, Viola. Orange Candy Slices & Other Secret Tales. 2001. 128p. (YA). pap. 9.95 (978-1-55885-332-4(4) , Piñata Books) Arte Publico Pr.

—The Tequila Worm. 208p. (YA). (gr. 7-11). 2007. pap. 7.99 (978-0-375-84089-0(3)); 2005. 15.95 (978-0-385-74674-8(1)); 2005. 17.99 (978-0-385-90905-1(5)) Random Hse. Children's Bks. (Lamb, Wendy).

Cano, Robin B. Lucita Regresa a Oaxaca (Lucita Comes Home to Oaxaca) Ricardez, Rafael E., tr. Smith, Kerry, illus. 1998. (ENG & SPA.). 32p. (J). (gr. 3-6). 16.95 (978-1-56492-111-6(5)) Laredo Publishing Co., Inc.

Cano, Robin B., et al. Ramona Viaja Al Norte (North with Ramona) 1998. (Tales in Two Languages, LS Ser.). (ENG & SPA.). (J). (gr. 3-6). 16.95 (978-1-56492-254-0(5)) Laredo Publishing Co., Inc.

Caraballo, Samuel. Estrellita se despide de su isla/Estrellita Says Good-bye to Her Island. Caraballo, Samuel, tr. Torrecilla, Pablo, illus. Tr. of Estrellita Says Good-Bye to Her Island. (ENG & SPA.). 32p. (J). stu. ed. 15.95 (978-1-55885-338-6(3) , Piñata Books) Arte Publico Pr.

Center for Learning Network Staff. The House on Mango Street: Curriculum Unit. 2005. (Novel Ser.). (YA). tchr. ed., spiral bd. 19.95 (978-1-56077-783-0(4)) Ctr. for Learning, The.

Charlton-Trujillo, E. E. Prizefighter en Mi Casa. (J). (gr. 5-7). 2007. 192p. 5.99 (***978-0-440-42117-7(9)*** , Yearling); 2006. 224p. 15.95 (978-0-385-73325-0(9) , Delacorte Bks. for Young Readers); 2006. 224p. lib. bdg. 17.99 (978-0-385-90344-8(8) , Delacorte Bks. for Young Readers) Random Hse. Children's Bks.

Chato & the Party Animals. 2004. 29.95 incl. audio compact disk (978-1-55592-703-5(3)); 24.95 incl. audio (978-1-55592-693-9(2)); pap. 14.95 incl. audio (978-1-55592-687-8(8)) Weston Woods Studios, Inc.

Chato's Kitchen. 2004. (J). 24.95 incl. audio (978-0-7882-0696-2(6)); pap. 18.95 incl. audio compact disk (978-1-55592-386-0(0)); pap. 18.95 incl. audio compact disk (978-1-55592-389-1(5)); pap. 38.75 incl. audio compact disk (978-1-55592-388-4(7)); pap. 38.75 incl. audio compact disk (978-1-55592-390-7(9)); pap. 32.75 incl. audio (978-1-55592-202-3(3)); pap. 32.75 incl. audio (978-1-55592-203-0(1)); (SPA.). pap. 14.95 incl. audio (978-0-7882-0134-9(4)); pap. 14.95 incl. audio (978-0-7882-0697-9(4)) Weston Woods Studios, Inc.

Cisneros. The House on Mango Street. 2000. (J). 12.81 (978-0-07-243517-7(8) , McGraw-Hill Humanities, Social Sciences & World Languages) McGraw-Hill Higher Education.

Cook, Jean Thor. Los Amiguitos' Fiesta. Wilson, Lincoln, ed. Shade, Judith Donoho, illus. l.t. ed. 2001. Tr. of Little Friends' Fiesta. (SPA.). 28p. (J). (ps-3). 17.00 (978-0-9708940-0-7(7)) Gently Worded Bks., LLC.

Cruise, Robin. Little Mama Forgets. Dressen-McQueen, Stacey, illus. 2006. 40p. (J). 16.00 (978-0-374-34613-3(5) , Farrar, Straus & Giroux (BYR)) Farrar, Straus & Giroux.

Cruz, Maria Colleen. Border Crossing. 128p. (YA). pap. 9.95 (978-1-55885-405-5(3) , Piñata Books) Arte Publico Pr.

—Border Crossing. 2003. (gr. 7-12). lib. bdg. 18.75 (978-0-613-90255-7(6)) Tandem Library Bks.

Cuyler, Margery. From Here to There. Pak, Yu Cha, illus. rev. ed. 1999. 32p. (J). (ps-2). 17.95 (978-0-8050-3191-1(X) , Holt, Henry & Co. Bks. For Young Readers) Holt, Henry & Co.

De Anda, Diane. Kikiriki / Quiquiriquí. Hernandez, Karina, tr. from ENG. Lechon, Daniel, illus. 2004. (ENG & SPA.). 32p. 14.95 (978-1-55885-382-9(0) , Piñata Books) Arte Publico Pr.

de la Vega, Eida, tr. from ENG. Estela en el Mercado de Pulgas. Sanchez, Enrique O., illus. 2005. (SPA.). 32p. (J). (ps-k). 16.95 (978-1-58430-245-2(3)) Lee & Low Bks., Inc.

Dorros, Arthur. Isla. Kleven, Elisa, illus. 1999. Orig. Title: The Island. 40p. (J). (ps-1). pap. 6.99 (978-0-14-056505-8(1) , Puffin) Penguin Group (USA) Inc.

—Isla. 1999. Orig. Title: The Island. (J). 12.79 (978-0-606-16810-6(9)); (J). 13.79 (978-0-606-16811-3(7)); lib. bdg. 14.15 (978-0-613-14865-8(7)); (SPA.). lib. bdg. 15.30 (978-0-613-18258-4(8)) Tandem Library Bks.

—La Isla. Kleven, Elisa, illus. 1999. (Picture Puffin Ser.). (SPA.). 40p. (J). (gr. k-3). pap. 6.99 (978-0-14-056541-6(8) , DT8806, Puffin) Penguin Group (USA) Inc.

—When the Pigs Took Over. Greenseid, Diane, illus. 2002. (SPA.). 32p. (J). (ps-2). 15.99 (978-0-525-42030-9(4) , Dutton Juvenile) Penguin Group (USA) Inc.

Dumas Lachtman, Ofelia. Looking for la Unica. 2004. (ENG & SPA., Illus.). 190p. (J). pap. 9.95 (978-1-55885-412-3(6) , Piñata Books) Arte Publico Pr.

Elya, Susan Middleton. Home at Last. Davalos, Felipe, illus. 2001. (J). 16.95 (978-1-58430-020-5(5)) Lee & Low Bks., Inc.

Estevis, Anne. Down Garrapata Road. 128p. pap. 12.95 (978-1-55885-397-3(9)) Arte Publico Pr.

Fitzgerald, Joanne. Yum! Yum! Delicious Nursery Rhymes. 2007. (Illus.). 32p. (J). (ps-1). (***978-1-55041-888-0(2)***) Fitzhenry & Whiteside, Ltd.

Flores, Carlos Nicolas. Our House on Hueco. 2006. 248p. (YA). pap. 17.95 (978-0-89672-573-7(1)) Texas Tech Univ. Pr.

Freschet, Gina. Beto & the Bone Dance. Freschet, Gina, illus. 2005. (Illus.). 30p. (J). (gr. 4-8). reprint ed. 16.00 (978-0-7567-8933-6(8)) DIANE Publishing Co.

—Beto & the Bone Dance. Freschet, Gina, illus. 2001. (Illus.). 32p. (J). (gr. k-3). 16.00 (978-0-374-31720-1(8) , Farrar, Straus & Giroux (BYR)) Farrar, Straus & Giroux.

Galindo, Mary Sue & Howard, Pauline Rodriguez. Icy Watermelon. 2000. Tr. of Sandia Fria. (SPA & ENG., Illus.). 32p. (J). (ps-2). 14.95 (978-1-55885-306-5(5) , Piñata Books) Arte Publico Pr.

Gonzales Bertrand, Diane. Family, Familia. Castilla, Julia Mercedes, tr. Howard, Pauline Rodriguez, illus. 1999. (SPA & ENG.). 32p. (J). (ps-3). 14.95 (978-1-55885-269-3(7) , Piñata Books) Arte Publico Pr.

Gonzales Bertrand, Diane, et al. Close to the Heart. 2002. (Illus.). 176p. (J). pap. 9.95 (978-1-55885-319-5(7) , Piñata Books) Arte Publico Pr.

Gonzalez, Catherine T. Chacho & Ellie Sanchez, Citizens. 1998. (Illus.). 136p. (gr. 4). 13.95 (978-1-57168-114-0(0)) Eakin Pr.

Halvorsen Schreck, Karen. Lucy's Family Tree. Gassler, Stephen, illus. 2006. 40p. (J). 7.95 (***978-0-88448-292-5(8)***) Tilbury Hse. Pubs.

Harcourt School Publishers Staff. Estrella Shining Brghtly Below Level. 3rd ed. 2002. (Trophies Reading Program Ser.). (Illus.). pap. 5.10 (978-0-15-323315-9(X)) Harcourt Schl. Pubs.

Harper, Jo. Delfino's Journey. 2000. viii, 184p. (J). (gr. 8-12). 15.95 (978-0-89672-437-2(9)) Texas Tech Univ. Pr.

—Delfino's Journey, Grades 8-12. 2000. (Illus.). viii, 184p. (J). tchr. ed. 5.95 (978-0-89672-442-6(5)) Texas Tech Univ. Pr.

Haslam, Gerald W. & Haslam, Janice E. Manuel & the Madman. 2000. viii, 206p. (J). pap. 9.95 (978-0-915685-11-0(6)) Devil Mountain Bks.

Hayes, Joe. Ghost Fever.Tr. of Mal de Fantasma. (J). 2006. (SPA.). 90p. pap. 8.95 (978-1-933693-03-3(7)); 2004. (ENG & SPA., Illus.). 80p. (gr. 3-6). 14.95 (978-0-938317-83-8(0)) Cinco Puntos Pr.

Head, Judith. Mud Soup. 2003. (gr. k-3). lib. bdg. 11.80 (978-0-613-87310-9(6)) Tandem Library Bks.

Herrera, Juan Felipe. Crashboomlove: A Novel in Verse. 2000. (J). 20.60 (978-0-606-19432-7(0)) Tandem Library Bks.

—CrashBoomLove: A Novel in Verse. 2004. 165p. (gr. 8-12). pap. 14.95 (978-0-8263-2114-5(3)); 1999. 176p. 18.95 (978-0-8263-2113-8(5)) Univ. of New Mexico Pr.

—Downtown Boy. 2005. 304p. (J). pap. 16.99 (978-0-439-64489-1(5) , Scholastic Pr.) Scholastic, Inc.

—Grandma & Me at the Flea / Los Meros Meros Remateros. Rohmer, Harriet & Cumpiano, Ina, eds. Lucio-Brock, Anita de, illus. 2002. Tr. of Los Meros Meros Remateros. (ENG & SPA.). 32p. (J). (gr. 1 up). 16.95 (978-0-89239-171-4(5)) Children's Bk. Pr.

—Super Cilantro Girl / La Supernina del Cilantro. Robledo Tapia, Honorio, illus. 2003. (ENG & SPA.). 32p. (J). 16.95 (978-0-89239-187-5(1)) Children's Bk. Pr.

Hip Hip Hooray, It's Monsoon Day! 2007. (ENG & SPA.). (YA). pap. 15.95 (***978-1-886679-36-8(3)***) Arizona Sonora Desert Museum Pr.

Hobbs, Will. Crossing the Wire. 2007. 224p. (J). pap. 5.99 (978-0-06-074140-2(6) , Harper Trophy) HarperCollins Pubs.

Iyengar, Malathi. Romina's Rangoli/By Malathi Michelle Iyengar ; Illustrated by Jennifer Wanardi. Wanardi, Jennifer, illus. 2007. (J). (***978-1-885008-32-9(5)***) Shen's Bks.

Jimenez, Francisco. Breaking Through. 2001. (gr. 7-12). lib. bdg. 15.25 (978-0-613-60762-9(7)) Tandem Library Bks.

Jiménez, Francisco. Breaking Through: A Migrant Child's Journey from the Fields. 2001. (Illus.). 208p. (YA). (gr. 7 up). tchr. ed. 16.00 (978-0-618-01173-5(0)) Houghton Mifflin Co. Trade & Reference Div.

Jimenez, Francisco. Cajas de Carton: The Circuit Spanish Edition. 2002. (SPA., Illus.). 144p. (J). (gr. 5 up). pap. 6.95 (978-0-618-22616-0(8)) Houghton Mifflin Co. Trade & Reference Div.

Jiménez, Francisco. Cajas de Carton: The Circuit Spanish Edition. 2002. (SPA., Illus.). 144p. (J). (gr. 5). tchr. ed. 16.00 (978-0-618-22615-3(X)) Houghton Mifflin Co. Trade & Reference Div.

—The Christmas Gift. Cotts, Claire B., illus. 2000. Tr. of Regalo de Navidad. (SPA & ENG.). 32p. (J). (gr. k-3). tchr. ed. 16.00 (978-0-395-92869-1(9)) Houghton Mifflin Co. Trade & Reference Div.

—La Mariposa. Silva, Simon, illus. (SPA.). 40p. (J). (gr. k-3). 2000. pap. 6.95 (978-0-618-07036-7(2) , HM3550); 2000. pap. 6.95 (978-0-618-07317-7(5)); 1998. tchr. ed. 16.00 (978-0-395-81663-9(7)) Houghton Mifflin Co. Trade & Reference Div.

—La Mariposa. Silva, Simon, illus. 2000. (SPA.). (J). (978-0-606-19813-4(X)) Tandem Library Bks.

Jimenez, Francisco. La Mariposa. Silva, Simon, illus. 2004. 38p. (J). (gr. k-4). reprint ed. pap. 14.00 (978-0-7567-8433-1(6)) DIANE Publishing Co.

—Senderos Fronterizos. 2002. (SPA.). (gr. 7-12). lib. bdg. 15.25 (978-0-613-60784-1(8)) Tandem Library Bks.

—Senderos Fronterizos: Breaking Through Spanish Edition. 2002. (SPA., Illus.). 240p. (J). tchr. ed. 16.00 (978-0-618-22617-7(6)) Houghton Mifflin Co. Trade & Reference Div.

Jiménez, Francisco. Senderos Fronterizos: Breaking Through Spanish Edition. 2002. (SPA., Illus.). 240p. (J). (gr. 5 up). pap. 6.95 (978-0-618-22618-4(4)) Houghton Mifflin Co. Trade & Reference Div.

Johnston, Tony. Angel City. Byard, Carole M., illus. 2006. 40p. (J). (ps). 15.99 (978-0-399-23405-7(5) , Philomel) Penguin Group (USA) Inc.

—Any Small Goodness: A Novel of the Barrio. Colon, Raul, illus. 128p. (J). (gr. 4 up). 2003. pap. 4.99 (978-0-439-23384-2(4) , Scholastic Paperbacks); 2001. 16.95 (978-0-439-18936-1(5) , Blue Sky Pr., The) Scholastic, Inc.

—Any Small Goodness: A Novel of the Barrio. 2002. (gr. 3-6). lib. bdg. 13.00 (978-0-613-67479-9(0)) Tandem Library Bks.

MNO

—Uncle Rain Cloud. Vanden Broeck, Fabricio, illus. 2001. 32p. (J). (gr. k-4). 15.95 (978-0-88106-371-4(1)) Charlesbridge Publishing, Inc.

Johnston, Tony & Johnston, Tony. Uncle Rain Cloud. VandenBroeck, Fabricio, illus. 2003. (J). (ps-3). lib. bdg. 15.25 (978-0-613-90105-5(3)) Tandem Library Bks.

Johnston, Tony & Vanden Broeck, Fabrizio. Uncle Rain Cloud. 2003. pap. 6.95 (978-0-88106-372-1(X)) Charlesbridge Publishing, Inc.

Juan, Felipe Herrera. Coralito's Bay: Bahia de Coralito. 2004. (SPA & ENG.). 41p. 14.95 (978-0-9742810-0-1(X)) Monterey Bay Sancturary Foundation.

Lachtman, Ofelia Dumas. The Summer of El Pintor. 2001. (Illus.). 240p. (J). (gr. 11 up). pap. 9.95 (978-1-55885-327-0(8) , Piñata Books) Arte Publico Pr.

—Summer of el Pintor. 2001. (gr. 5-8). lib. bdg. 18.75 (978-0-613-59023-5(6)) Tandem Library Bks.

Lee, Marie G. Night of the Chupacabras. 1999. 128p. (gr. 3-7). pap. 3.99 (978-0-380-79773-8(9)) HarperCollins Pubs.

—Night of the Chupacabras. 1999. (978-0-606-17336-0(6)) Tandem Library Bks.

Levy, Janice. Abuelito Eats with His Fingers. Johnson, Layne, illus. 1998. 32p. 14.95 (978-1-57168-177-5(9)) Eakin Pr.

Lopez, Jack. In the Break. 2006. (Illus.). 208p. (J). (gr. 7-17). 16.99 (978-0-316-00874-7(5)) Little Brown & Co.

Lopez, Loretta. The Birthday Swap. Lopez, Loretta, illus. 1999. (Illus.). 32p. (J). (gr. k-3). pap. 6.95 (978-1-880000-89-2(X)) Lee & Low Bks., Inc.

Luenn, Nancy. A Gift for Abuelita: Celebrating the Day of the Dead. Chapman, Robert, illus. 1998. Tr. of Un Regalo para Abuelita: En Celebration del Dia de los Muertos. (ENG & SPA.). 32p. (gr. k-3). 15.95 (978-0-87358-688-7(3) , Rising Moon Bks. for Young Readers) Northland Publishing.

Lupita Manana. 3rd ed. (J). pap., stu. ed. (978-0-13-772500-7(0)) Prentice Hall (Schl. Div.).

The Magic Paper (Mexicans) 76p. (YA). (gr. 6-12). pap. 9.95 (978-0-8224-3686-7(8)) Globe Fearon Educational Publishing.

Marquez, Pablo. Benito's Treasure Hunt. 2000. (J). pap. 7.00 (978-0-533-13567-7(2)) Vantage Pr., Inc.

Marsden, Carolyn. Mama Had to Work on Christmas. Casilla, Robert, illus. 2003. 80p. (J). (gr. 2-5). 14.99 (978-0-670-03635-6(8) , Viking Juvenile) Penguin Group (USA) Inc.

Martínez, Arturo O. Pedrito's World. 2007. (Illus.). 160p. (J). 16.95 (***978-0-89672-600-0(2)***) Texas Tech Univ. Pr.

Martinez, Victor. El Loro en el Horno. 2001. (SPA.). (gr. 7-12). lib. bdg. 19.90 (978-0-613-80733-3(2)) Tandem Library Bks.

—El Loro en el Horno: Mi Vida. 2003. (SPA., Illus.). 189p. (YA). (gr. 5-8). (978-84-279-3238-8(3) , NG9012) Noguer y Caralt Editores, S. A. ESP. *Dist:* Lectorum Pubns., Inc.

—Parrot in the Oven: Mi Vida. Scott, Steve, illus. rev. ed. 1998. 240p. (J). (gr. 7 up). pap. 5.99 (978-0-06-447186-2(1) , Harper Trophy) HarperCollins Pubs.

—Parrot in the Oven: Mi Vida. 1998. (978-0-606-13695-2(9)) Tandem Library Bks.

McGinley, Jerry. Joaquin Strikes Back. 1998. 158p. (YA). (gr. 5-10). 18.95 (978-0-936389-58-5(3)) Tudor Pubs., Inc.

Medina, Jane. My Name Is Jorge: On Both Sides of the River. Vanden Broeck, Fabricio, illus. 2003. (SPA & ENG.). 48p. (YA). (gr. 2-4). 15.95 (978-1-56397-811-1(3)) Boyds Mills Pr.

Mikaelsen, Ben. Sparrow Hawk Red. 1999. 192p. pap. 5.99 (978-0-7868-1002-4(5)) Hyperion Pr.

Mora, Pat. The Bakery Lady/la señora de la Panadería. Mora, Pat & Ventura, Gabriela Baeza, trs. Torrecilla, Pablo, illus. Tr. of Señora de la Panaderia. (ENG & SPA.). 32p. (J). (ps-3). 15.95 (978-1-55885-343-0(X) , Piñata Books) Arte Publico Pr.

—A Birthday Basket for Tia. 1998. (J). pap. 4.99 (978-0-87628-395-0(4)) Ctr. for Applied Research in Education, The.

—Una Cesta de Cumpleanos para Tia Abuela. Lang, Cecily, illus. (SPA.). (J). (gr. k-2). pap. 3.16 net. (978-0-395-78817-2(X) , HMS088) Houghton Mifflin Co.

—Maria Paints the Hills. Hesch, Maria, illus. 2002. 32p. 19.95 (978-0-89013-401-6(4)); 1p. pap. 9.95 (978-0-89013-410-8(3)) Museum of New Mexico Pr.

—The Rainbow Tulip. Sayles, Elizabeth, illus. 32p. (J). (gr. k-3). 2003. pap. 6.99 (978-0-14-250009-5(7) , Puffin); 1999. 16.99 (978-0-670-87291-6(1) , Viking Juvenile) Penguin Group (USA) Inc.

—Tomas & the Library Lady. Colon, Raul, illus. 2000. 40p. (J). (gr. k-3). pap. 6.99 (978-0-375-80349-9(1) , Dragonfly Bks.) Random Hse. Children's Bks.

—Tomas & the Library Lady. 2000. (978-0-606-18093-1(1)); lib. bdg. 15.30 (978-0-613-28362-5(7)) Tandem Library Bks.

—Tomas y la Senora de la Biblioteca. ed. 2004. (SPA., Illus.). (J). (gr. k-3). spiral bd. (978-0-616-03092-9(4)) Canadian National Institute for the Blind/Institut National Canadien pour les Aveugles.

Myers, Anna. Stolen by the Sea. 2006. 144p. (J). pap. 6.95 (978-0-8027-8976-1(5)) Walker & Co.

O'Neill, Alexis. Estela en el Mercado de Pulgas. de la Vega, Eida, tr. from ENG. Sanchez, Enrique O., illus. 2005. (SPA.). 32p. (J). (ps-k). pap. 7.95 (978-1-58430-246-9(1)) Lee & Low Bks., Inc.

Ortega, Cristina. The Eyes of the Weaver: Los Ojos Del Tejedor. Garcia, Patricio, illus. 2006. 64p. (J). 17.95 (978-0-8263-3990-4(5)) Univ. of New Mexico Pr.

Parra, Kelly. Graffiti Girl. 2007. 256p. pap. 9.95 (978-1-4165-3461-7(X) , MTV) Simon & Schuster.

Perez, Amada Irma. Mi Propio Cuartito. ed. 2004. (SPA & ENG., Illus.). (J). (gr. k-3). spiral bd. (978-0-616-14609-5(4)) Canadian National Institute for the Blind/Institut National Canadien pour les Aveugles.

—My Diary from Here to There / Mi Diario de Aqui Hasta Alla. Gonzalez, Maya Christina, illus. 2002. Tr. of Mi Diario de Aqui Hasta Alla. (ENG & SPA.). 32p. (J). (gr. 2-5). 16.95 (978-0-89239-175-2(8)) Children's Bk. Pr.

—My Very Own Room (Mi Propio Cuartito) Gonzalez, Maya Christina, illus. 2000. (ENG & SPA.). 32p. (J). (gr. 1 up). 16.95 (978-0-89239-164-6(2)) Children's Bk. Pr.

—Nana's Big Surprise/¡Nana, Que Sorpresa! Gonzalez, Maya Christina, tr. Gonzalez, Maya Christina, illus. 2007. (ENG & SPA.). 32p. (J). (gr. 1-2). 16.95 (978-0-89239-190-5(1)) Children's Bk. Pr.

Perez, L. King. First Day in Grapes. Casilla, Robert, illus. 2002. 32p. (J). (gr. 1-3). 16.95 (978-1-58430-045-8(0)) Lee & Low Bks., Inc.

Podoshen, Lois. Paco's Garden. Buket, illus. 1999. (Books for Young Learners). 12p. (J). (gr. k-2). pap. 5.00 (978-1-57274-235-2(6)) Owen, Richard C. Pubs., Inc.

Rice, David Talbot. Crazy Loco: Stories about Growing up Chicano in Southern Texas. 2003. (gr. 7-12). lib. bdg. 14.15 (978-0-613-67142-2(2)) Tandem Library Bks.

Rodriguez, Luis J. America Is Her Name. Vazquez, Carlos, illus. 2004. 32p. (gr. 4-7). reprint ed. 16.95 (978-1-880684-40-5(3)) Curbstone Pr.

—La Llaman America. Villanueva, Tino, tr. Vazquez, Carlos, illus. 2004. (SPA.). 32p. (gr. 4-7). reprint ed. 16.95 (978-1-880684-41-2(1)) Curbstone Pr.

Romeyn, Debra. Passage to Monterey. May, Dan, tr. May, Dan, illus. 2003. (Adventures of Juan & Mariano Ser.: No. 1). 39p. (J). pap. 9.95 (978-0-9729016-0-4(4)) Gossamer Bks.

Ruiz, Joseph J. Angel on Daniel's Shoulder. 2004. (SPA & ENG., Illus.). 108p. (J). pap. 12.95 (978-0-86534-402-0(7)) Sunstone Pr.

—Manuel & the Magic Ring. 2003. (SPA & ENG., Illus.). 108p. (J). pap. 12.95 (978-0-86534-399-3(3)) Sunstone Pr.

Ryan, Pam Muñoz. Becoming Naomi Leon. 2005. 272p. (J). (gr. 4-7). reprint ed. pap. 5.99 (978-0-439-26997-1(0) , Scholastic Paperbacks) Scholastic, Inc.

—Esperanza Renace. Selznick, Bryan, illus. 2002. (SPA.). 272p. (J). (gr. 4-9). pap. 4.99 (978-0-439-39885-5(1) , Scholastic en Espanol) Scholastic, Inc.

—Esperanza Rising. (Illus.). (J). (gr. 4-9). 2007. 307p. 5.99 (978-0-439-12042-5(X)); 2000. 272p. pap. 15.95 (978-0-439-12041-8(1) , Scholastic Pr.) Scholastic, Inc.

Saenz, Benjamin Alire. Gift from Papa Diego.Tr. of Regalo De Papa Diego. (gr. k-3). lib. bdg. 19.90 (978-0-613-06587-0(5)) Tandem Library Bks.

—A Gift from Papa Diego (Un Regalo de Papa Diego) Garcia, Geronimo, illus. 2004. (ENG & SPA.). 40p. (gr. k-7). pap. 10.95 (978-0-938317-33-3(4)) Cinco Puntos Pr.

—He Forgot to Say Good-Bye. 2008. 272p. (YA). (***978-1-4169-4963-3(1)*** , Simon & Schuster Children's Publishing) Simon & Schuster Children's Publishing.

Saenz, Benjamin Alire. Sammy & Juliana in Hollywood. 2006. 368p. (J). pap. 7.99 (978-0-06-084374-8(8)) HarperCollins Pubs.

Sagel, Jim. Always the Heart. 1998. (Red Crane Literature Ser.).Tr. of Siempre el Corazon. (ENG & SPA., Illus.). 168p. (gr. 8-12). pap. 12.95 (978-1-878610-68-3(6)) Red Crane Bks., Inc.

—Always the Heart. 1998. Tr. of Siempre el Corazon. (gr. 7-12). lib. bdg. 22.20 (978-0-613-80111-9(3)) Tandem Library Bks.

Saldana, Rene, Jr. Finding Our Way: Stories. 2004. 117p. (YA). (gr. 7-12). per. 13.04 (978-0-606-32790-9(8)) Tandem Library Bks.

—The Jumping Tree. 2002. (Illus.). 192p. (YA). (gr. 5). pap. 5.99 (978-0-440-22881-3(6) , Laurel Leaf) Random Hse. Children's Bks.

—Jumping Tree. 2002. (gr. 5-8). lib. bdg. 13.55 (978-0-613-72279-7(5)) Tandem Library Bks.

Sanchez, Alex. Getting It. 2006. 224p. (YA). 16.95 (978-1-4169-0896-8(X)) Simon & Schuster Children's Publishing.

—So Hard to Say. 240p. 2004. (J). 15.95 (978-0-689-86564-0(3)); 2006. (Illus.). (YA). reprint ed. pap. 7.99 (978-1-4169-1189-0(8) , Aladdin) Simon & Schuster Children's Publishing.

Sanchez, Alex & Frost, Michael. Getting It. 2007. 240p. (YA). pap. 8.99 (***978-1-4169-0898-2(6)*** , Simon Pulse) Simon & Schuster Children's Publishing.

Sandin, Joan. Coyote School News. Sandin, Joan, illus. rev. ed. 2003. (Illus.). 48p. (J). 17.95 (978-0-8050-6558-9(X) , Holt, Henry & Co. Bks. For Young Readers) Holt, Henry & Co.

Sandoval, Victor. Roll over, Big Toben. 128p. (YA). pap. 9.95 (978-1-55885-401-7(0) , Piñata Books) Arte Publico Pr.

Santana, Patricia. Motorcycle Ride on the Sea of Tranquility. 2002. 270p. (YA). 19.95 (978-0-8263-2435-1(5)) Univ. of New Mexico Pr.

Serros, Michele. Scandalosa. 2007. 320p. (YA). (gr. 9 up). 15.99 (978-1-4169-1593-5(1) , Simon Pulse) Simon & Schuster Children's Publishing.

Soto, Gary. The Afterlife: A Novel. 2003. 176p. (J). (gr. 6 up). 17.00 (978-0-15-204774-0(3) , 53597422) Harcourt Children's Bks.

—Baseball in April & Other Stories. 10th anniv. ed. 2000. 128p. (YA). (gr. 3-7). (SPA.). 17.00 (978-0-15-202573-1(1)); pap. 6.00 (978-0-15-202567-0(7) , Harcourt Paperbacks) Harcourt Children's Bks.

—Buried Onions. 2006. (Illus.). 168p. (J). pap. 6.95 (978-0-15-206265-1(3) , Harcourt Paperbacks) Harcourt Children's Bks.

—Buried Onions. 10th ed. 1999. (Ageless Bks.). 160p. (J). (gr. 7-10). pap. 11.00 (978-0-06-440771-7(3) , Harper Trophy) HarperCollins Pubs.

—Chato & the Party Animals. Guevara, Susan, illus. 25.95 incl. audio (978-1-59112-460-3(3)); 28.95 incl. audio compact disk (978-1-59112-920-2(6)); pap. 37.95 incl. audio (978-1-59112-461-0(1)); pap. 39.95 incl. audio compact disk (978-1-59112-921-9(4)) Live Oak Media.

—Chato & the Party Animals. Guevara, Susan, illus. 2000. (SPA.). 32p. (J). (ps-3). 16.99 (978-0-399-23159-9(5) , Putnam Juvenile) Penguin Group (USA) Inc.

—Chato & the Party Animals. 2004. (gr. k-3). lib. bdg. 15.30 (978-0-613-89799-0(4)) Tandem Library Bks.

—Chato & the Party Animals. Guevara, Susan, illus. 2004. (J). (ps-ps). lib. bdg. 13.79 (978-0-606-29661-8(1)) Tandem Library Bks.

—Chato & the Party Animals. Guevara, Susan, illus. 2004. 32p. (J). (gr. k-3). reprint ed. pap. 6.99 (978-0-14-240032-6(7) , Puffin) Penguin Group (USA) Inc.

—Chato Goes Cruisin' Guevara, Susan, tr. Guevara, Susan, illus. 2005. 32p. (J). (ps-3). 16.99 (978-0-399-23974-8(X) , Putnam Juvenile) Penguin Group (USA) Inc.

—Chato Goes Cruisin' Guevara, Susan, illus. 2007. 32p. (J). (ps). pap. 6.99 (978-0-14-240810-0(7) , Puffin) Penguin Group (USA) Inc.

—Chato's Kitchen. 2002. (Live Oak Readalong Ser.). (Illus.). (J). pap. 16.95 incl. audio (978-1-59112-205-0(8)); pap. 18.95 incl. audio compact disk (978-1-59112-336-1(4)) Live Oak Media.

—Chato's Kitchen. Guevara, Susan, illus. 2002. 25.95 incl. audio (978-1-59112-206-7(6)); 28.95 incl. audio compact disk (978-1-59112-528-0(6)); pap. 37.95 incl. audio (978-1-59112-207-4(4)); pap. 39.95 incl. audio compact disk (978-1-59112-527-3(8)) Live Oak Media.

—Chato's Kitchen; Chato Y Su Cena. Guevara, Susan, illus. 2002. pap. 33.95 incl. audio (978-1-59112-208-1(2)) Live Oak Media.

—Help Wanted: Stories. 2005. 224p. (YA). 17.00 (978-0-15-205201-0(1)) Harcourt Children's Bks.

—Help Wanted: Stories. 2007. (Illus.). 228p. (YA). pap. 6.95 (978-0-15-205663-6(7) , Harcourt Paperbacks) Harcourt Children's Bks.

—Jesse. 2006. (Illus.). 180p. (YA). pap. 6.95 (978-0-15-205425-0(1) , Harcourt Paperbacks) Harcourt Children's Bks.

—Jesse, unabr. ed. 2000. (YA). pap. 42.24 incl. audio (978-0-7887-3188-4(2) , 40923X4) Recorded Bks., LLC.

—My Little Car. Sawaya, Linda Dalal & Paparone, Pamela, illus. 2006. Tr. of Mi Carrito. (ENG & SPA.). 32p. (J). (ps-3). 15.99 (978-0-399-23220-6(6) , Putnam Juvenile) Penguin Group (USA) Inc.

—Petty Crimes. 2006. (Illus.). 168p. (J). pap. 5.95 (978-0-15-205437-3(5) , Harcourt Paperbacks) Harcourt Children's Bks.

—The Skirt. 2008. 80p. (J). (gr. 4-7). lib. bdg. 17.99 (***978-0-385-90534-3(3)*** , Delacorte Bks. for Young Readers) Random Hse. Children's Bks.

Soto, Gary. Snapshots from the Wedding. Garcia, Stephanie, illus. 1998. 32p. (J). (ps-3). pap. 5.99 (978-0-698-11752-5(2) , Putnam Juvenile) Penguin Group (USA) Inc.

Soto, Gary & Soto, Gary. Snapshots from the Wedding. Garcia, Stephanie, illus. 1998. (J). (ps-ps). lib. bdg. 14.15 (978-0-613-12117-0(1)) Tandem Library Bks.

Soto, Gary & Widener, Terry. If the Shoe Fits. 2002. (Illus.). 32p. (J). (gr. 4-8). 15.99 (978-0-399-23420-0(9) , Putnam Juvenile) Penguin Group (USA) Inc.

Stites, Clara. Rosalba of Santa Juanita: A California Story. 2002. (Illus.). 80p. (J). pap. 8.95 (978-1-56474-394-7(2)) Fithian Pr.

Stork, Francisco X. Behind the Eyes. 2006. 256p. (YA). (gr. 9). 16.99 (978-0-525-47735-8(7) , Dutton Adult) Penguin Group (USA) Inc.

Tafolla, Carmen. What Can You Do with a Rebozo? 2007. (J). (***978-1-58246-220-2(8)*** , Tricycle Pr.) Ten Speed Pr.

Too Many Tamales. (Lexile Levels Ser.). 9.09 (978-1-56334-704-7(0)) Hampton-Brown Bks.

Tripp, Valerie. Changes for Josefina Bk. 6: A Winter Story. Tibbles, Jean-Paul & McAliley, Susan, illus. 1998. (American Girls Collection: Bk. 6). 80p. (J). (gr. 2 up). 12.95 (978-1-56247-592-5(4)); pap. 6.95 (978-1-56247-591-8(6)) American Girl Publishing, Inc.

—Changes for Josefina Bk. 6: A Winter Story. Tibbles, Jean-Paul, illus. 1998. (American Girls Collection: Bk. 6). (YA). (gr. 2 up). 12.75 (978-0-606-13264-0(3)) Tandem Library Bks.

—Happy Birthday, Josefina! A Springtime Story. Tibbles, Jean-Paul & McAliley, Susan, illus. 1998. (American Girls Collection: Bk. 4). 80p. (J). (gr. 2 up). 6.95 (978-1-56247-587-1(8)); Bk. 4. 12.95 (978-1-56247-588-8(6)) American Girl Publishing, Inc.

—Happy Birthday, Josefina! A Springtime Story. Tibbles, Jean-Paul, illus. 1998. (American Girls Collection: Bk. 4). (YA). (gr. 2 up). 12.75 (978-0-606-13381-4(X)); 12.75 (978-0-606-13456-9(5)) Tandem Library Bks.

—Josefina Entra en Accion: Un Cuento de Verano. Tibbles, Jean-Paul, illus. 1998. (American Girls Collection: Bk. 5). Tr. of Josefina Saves the Day. (SPA.). (YA). (gr. 2 up). 12.75 (978-0-606-13540-5(5)) Tandem Library Bks.

—Josefina Saves the Day Bk. 5: A Summer Story. Tibbles, Jean-Paul, illus. 1998. (American Girls Collection: Bk. 5). 80p. (J). (gr. 2 up). pap. 6.95 (978-1-56247-589-5(4)) American Girl Publishing, Inc.

—Josefina Saves the Day Bk. 5: A Summer Story, Bk. 5. Tibbles, Jean-Paul & McAliley, Susan, illus. 1998. (American Girls Collection: Bk. 5). 80p. (J). (gr. 2 up). 12.95 (978-1-56247-590-1(8)) American Girl Publishing, Inc.

—Josefina Saves the Day Bk. 5: A Summer Story. Tibbles, Jean-Paul, illus. 1998. (American Girls Collection: Bk. 5). (YA). (gr. 2 up). 12.75 (978-0-606-13541-2(3)) Tandem Library Bks.

Tripp, Valerie. Josefina's Short Story Collection. Tibbes, Jean-Paul & Graef, Renee, illus. 2006. 236p. (J). 12.95 (***978-1-59369-124-0(6)***) American Girl Publishing, Inc.

Velasquez, Gloria. Teen Angel. (Roosevelt High School Ser.). 160p. (YA). pap. 9.95 (978-1-55885-391-1(X) , Piñata Books) Arte Publico Pr.

Whitney, Kim Ablon. The Perfect Distance. 2007. 256p. (YA). (gr. 7). pap. 5.99 (978-0-553-49467-9(8) , Laurel Leaf) Random Hse. Children's Bks.

Whitney, Phyllis A. A Long Time Coming. l.t. ed. 2002. (YA). lib. bdg. 27.95 (978-1-58547-184-3(4) , Premier) Center Point Large Print.

MEXICAN WAR, 1846-1848

Bardhan-Quallen, Sudipta. The Mexican-American War. 2005. (People at the Center of Ser.). (Illus.). 48p. (J). (ps-7). lib. bdg. 24.95 (978-1-56711-927-5(1) , Blackbirch Pr., Inc.) Thomson Gale.

Cantor, Carrie. The Mexican War: How the United States Gained Its Western Lands. 2003. (Proud Heritage-The Hispanic Library). (Illus.). 40p. (J). (gr. 3-7). 28.50 (978-1-56766-176-7(9)) Child's World, Inc.

Carey, Charles W., Jr. The Mexican War: Mr. Polk's War. 2002. (American War Ser.). (Illus.). 128p. (YA). (gr. 5-12). lib. bdg. 26.60 (978-0-7660-1853-2(9)) Enslow Pubs., Inc.

Deem, James M. Primary Source Accounts of the Mexican-American War. 2006. (America's Wars Through Primary Sources Ser.). (Illus.). 128p. (J). lib. bdg. 33.27 (978-1-59845-005-7(0) , MyReportLinks.com Bks.) Enslow Pubs., Inc.

Feldman, Ruth Tenzer. The Mexican-American War. 2004. (Chronicle of America's Wars Ser.). (Illus.). 96p. (J). (gr. 5-12). 27.93 (978-0-8225-0831-1(1)) Lerner Publishing Group.

Gale Research Staff. Mexican-American War. 2002. (Illus.). 225p. (J). lib. bdg. 67.00 (978-0-7876-6537-1(1) , GML00502-182439, UXL) Thomson Gale.

Haberle, Susan E. The Mexican War, 1846-1848. 2003. (Let Freedom Ring Ser.). (Illus.). 48p. (J). (gr. 3-4). lib. bdg. 22.60 (978-0-7368-1558-1(9) , Bridgestone Bks.) Capstone Pr., Inc.

Kachur, Matthew & Sterngass, Jon. The Mexican-American War. 2006. (Wars That Changed American History Ser.). (Illus.). 48p. (J). pap. (978-0-8368-7299-6(1)); lib. bdg. (978-0-8368-7290-3(8)) Stevens, Gareth Inc. (World Almanac Library).

The Mexican-American War: Individual Title Six-Packs. (On Deck Ser.: Vol. 2). 24p. (gr. 4-5). 35.00 (978-0-7578-5808-6(2)) Rigby Education.

Mills, Bronwyn. U. S. - Mexican War. 2nd ed. 2003. (America at War Ser.). (Illus.). 160p. (J). (gr. 6-12). 35.00 (978-0-8160-4932-5(7)) Facts On File, Inc.

Nardo, Don. The Mexican-American War. 1999. (World History Ser.). (Illus.). 128p. (YA). (gr. 8-11). 31.20 (978-1-56006-495-4(1) , LML00902-177858, Lucent Bks.) Thomson Gale.

Nobleman, Marc Tyler. The Mexican War. 2004. (We the People Ser.). (Illus.). 48p. (J). 22.60 (978-0-7565-0841-8(X)) Compass Point Bks.

O'Connell, Kim A. The Mexican-American War: A MyReportLinks.com Book. 2003. (U.S. Wars Ser.). (Illus.). 48p. (J). lib. bdg. 25.26 (978-0-7660-5131-7(5) , MyReportLinks.com Bks.) Enslow Pubs., Inc.

Porterfield, Jason. The Treaty of Guadalupe-Hidalgo, 1848: A Primary Source Examination of the Treaty That Ended the Mexican-American War. 2005. (Primary Sources of American Treaties Ser.). (J). lib. bdg. (978-1-4042-0440-9(7)) Rosen Publishing Group, Inc., The.

Poulakidas, Georgene. The Mexican-American War. 2005. (Primary Sources of American Wars Ser.). (Illus.). 24p. (J). lib. bdg. (978-1-4042-2683-8(4)) Rosen Publishing Group, Inc., The.

Raabe, Emily. The Mexican-American War. 2003. (Reading Power Ser.). (Illus.). 24p. (J). lib. bdg. 17.25 (978-0-8239-6497-0(3) , PowerKids Pr.) Rosen Publishing Group, Inc., The.

Sonneborn, Liz. The Mexican-American War. 2005. (Illus.). 64p. (J). (gr. 5-8). lib. bdg. 29.25 (978-1-4042-0180-4(7)) Rosen Publishing Group, Inc., The.

MEXICAN WAR, 1846-1848—FICTION

Dell, Pamela. Blood in the Water: A Story of Friendship During the Mexican War. 2003. (Scrapbooks of America Ser.). (Illus.). 48p. (J). (gr. 2-6). 28.50 (978-1-59187-042-5(9)) Child's World, Inc.

Fleischman, Sid. The Giant Rat of Sumatra: Or Pirates Galore. Hendrix, John, illus. 208p. (J). 2005. (gr. 5 up). 15.99 (978-0-06-074238-6(0)); 2005. (gr. 5 up). lib. bdg. 16.89 (978-0-06-074239-3(9)); 2006. reprint ed. pap. 5.99 (978-0-06-074240-9(2) , Harper Trophy) HarperCollins Pubs.

MEXICANS—UNITED STATES

Taylor, Theodore. Maldonado Miracle. 2003. (gr. 5-8). lib. bdg. 6.95 (978-0-613-70532-5(7)) Tandem Library Bks.

—The Maldonado Miracle. 2003. 176p. (YA). (gr. 3-6). pap. 6.95 (978-0-15-205036-8(1) , Harcourt Paperbacks) Harcourt Children's Bks.

MEXICO

Alcraft, Rob. Mexico. (Visit to Ser.). 32p. pap. 6.50 (978-1-4034-4151-5(0)) Heinemann Library.

Alcraft, Rob & Sprague, Sean. Mexico. 1998. (Worldfocus Ser.). (Illus.). 32p. (J). pap. (978-1-57572-078-4(7)) Heinemann Library.

Armentrout, David & Armentrout, Patricia. Treasures from Mexico. 2000. (Treasures from the Past Ser.). (Illus.). 48p. (J). (gr. 4-8). lib. bdg. 29.93 (978-1-55916-290-6(2)) Rourke Publishing, LLC.

Asher, Sandy. Mexico. 2002. (Discovering Cultures Ser.). (Illus.). 48p. (J). 25.64 (978-0-7614-1175-8(5) , Benchmark Bks.) Cavendish, Marshall Corp.

Auch, Alison. Welcome to Mexico. 2002. (Spyglass Books). (Illus.). 24p. (J). (gr. 1 up). lib. bdg. 18.60 (978-0-7565-0373-4(6)) Compass Point Bks.

Aykroyd, Clarissa. The Government of Mexico. 2002. (Encyclopedia of Mexico Ser.). (Illus.). 64,80p. (J). (gr. 5 up). lib. bdg. (978-1-59084-090-0(9)) Mason Crest Pubs.

Bentley, Joyce. Mexico. 2005. (Our Lives, Our World Ser.). (Illus.). 32p. (J). (gr. 3 up). lib. bdg. 27.10 (978-1-59389-226-5(8)) Chrysalis Education.

Boraas, Tracey. Japan. 2001. (Countries & Cultures Ser.). (Illus.). 64p. (J). (gr. 3-4). lib. bdg. 23.93 (978-0-7368-0770-8(5) , Bridgestone Bks.) Capstone Pr., Inc.

Burt, Janet. The Pacific North States of Mexico. 2002. (Encyclopedia of Mexico Ser.). (Illus.). 64,80p. (J). (gr. 5 up). lib. bdg. (978-1-59084-089-4(5)) Mason Crest Pubs.

—The States of Northern Mexico. 2002. (Encyclopedia of Mexico Ser.). (Illus.). 64,80p. (YA). (gr. 5 up). lib. bdg. (978-1-59084-086-3(0)) Mason Crest Pubs.

Canizares, Susan & Chanko, Pamela. Mexico. 1999. (Social Studies Emergent Readers). (J). 2.50 (978-0-439-04570-4(3)) Scholastic, Inc.

—Mexico. 1999. (ps-2). lib. bdg. 10.10 (978-0-613-21987-7(2)) Tandem Library Bks.

Chakin, Judy & Wool, Ida. Los Cabos Guide to Good Eating. 2001. 32p. (YA). pap. 5.00 (978-0-9708674-0-7(9)) One Step Productions.

Chronicle Books LLC Staff. My First Book of Travel: Mexico. 2007. (J). 12.95 (978-0-8118-5608-9(9)) Chronicle Bks. LLC.

Cory, Steven. Daily Life in Ancient & Modern Mexico City. Webb, Ray, illus. 1999. (Cities Through Time Ser.). 64p. (gr. 5-12). 25.26 (978-0-8225-3212-5(3)) Lerner Publishing Group.

Dahl, Michael. Mexico, 6 vols. (gr. 2-5). 36.95 (978-0-7368-8169-2(7)) Red Brick Learning.

Day-McLeod, Deirdre. The States of Central Mexico. 2002. (Mexico Ser.). (Illus.). 64,80p. (YA). (gr. 5 up). lib. bdg. (978-1-59084-087-0(9)) Mason Crest Pubs.

DeAngelis, Gina. Mexico. 2003. (Many Cultures, One World Ser.). (Illus.). 32p. (J). (gr. 2-3). lib. bdg. 23.93 (978-0-7368-1534-5(1) , Bridgestone Bks.) Capstone Pr., Inc.

Dolan, Sean. Mexico. 2002. (Steadwell Books World Tour). (Illus.). 48p. (J). lib. bdg. (978-0-7398-4714-5(7)) Raintree.

Field, Randi. The Gulf States of Mexico. 2002. (Encyclopedia of Mexico Ser.). (Illus.). 64,80p. (YA). (gr. 5 up). lib. bdg. (978-1-59084-080-1(1)) Mason Crest Pubs.

Fontes, Justine & Fontes, Ron. Mexico. 2004. (to Z Ser.). (Illus.). 40p. (J). (gr. 2-4). pap. 6.95 (978-0-516-26815-6(5) , Children's Pr.) Scholastic Library Publishing.

Franklin, Sharon, et al. Mexico & Central America: Understanding Geography & History Through Art. 1999. (Artisans Around the World Ser.). (Illus.). 48p. (J). (gr. 4-8). lib. bdg. 27.12 (978-0-7398-0121-5(X)) Raintree.

Frost, Helen. A Look at Mexico. Saunders-Smith, Gail, ed. 2001. (Our World Ser.). (Illus.). 24p. (J). (gr. k-1). lib. bdg. 15.93 (978-0-7368-0985-6(6) , Pebble Bks.) Capstone Pr., Inc.

—A Look at Mexico. 2005. (One World, Many Cultures Ser.). 24p. (YA). (gr. k-3). pap. (978-0-7368-9422-7(5) , Pebble Bks.) Capstone Pr., Inc.

Furlong, Kate A. Mexico. 2000. (Countries Ser.). (Illus.). 40p. (J). (gr. k-6). lib. bdg. 22.78 (978-1-57765-390-5(4) , Checkerboard Library) ABDO Publishing Co.

Gall, Timothy L. & Gall, Susan B. Junior Worldmark Encyclopedia of Mexican States. 2nd rev. ed. 2007. 67.00 (978-1-4144-1112-5(X) , UXL) Thomson Gale.

Ganeri, Anita & Wright, Rachel. Mexico. 2005. (Illus.). 32p. (J). (gr. 4-7). lib. bdg. 27.10 (978-1-932889-94-9(9)) Sea-To-Sea Pubns.

George, Lynn. Teotihuacan: Designing an Ancient Mexican City: Calculating Perimeters & Areas of Squares & Rectangles. 2004. (PowerMath Ser.). (Illus.). 32p. (J). lib. bdg. (978-0-8239-8876-1(7)); lib. bdg. 22.50 (978-0-8239-8983-6(6)) Rosen Publishing Group, Inc., The. (PowerKids Pr.).

Golden, Nancy. Exploring Mexico with the Five Themes of Geography. 2005. (Library of the Western Hemisphere). (Illus.). 24p. (J). 19.95 (978-1-4042-2668-5(0) , PowerKids Pr.); pap. (978-0-8239-4628-0(2)) Rosen Publishing Group, Inc., The.

Goodwin, William. Mexico. 1998. (Modern Nations of the World Ser.). (Illus.). 128p. (YA). (gr. 7-10). 27.45 (978-1-56006-351-3(3) , Lucent Bks.) Thomson Gale.

Gray, Shirley W. Mexico. 2000. (First Reports). (Illus.). 48p. (J). (gr. 3 up). lib. bdg. 22.60 (978-0-7565-0031-3(1)) Compass Point Bks.

Green, Jen. Caribbean Sea & Gulf of Mexico. 2006. (Illus.). 48p. (J). lib. bdg. 30.00 (978-0-8368-6272-0(4) , World Almanac Library) Stevens, Gareth Inc.

Green, Jen. Mexico. 2000. (Nations of the World Ser.). (Illus.). 128p. (YA). (gr. 6-8). lib. bdg. 34.26 (978-0-8172-5779-8(9)) Raintree.

—Mexico. 2006. (Illus.). 48p. (J). lib. bdg. ***(*978-1-4109-2463-6(7))*** Steck-Vaughn.

Green, Marianna Y. & Keil, Sande. Everything for Cinco de Mayo. 2000. 48p. (J). (gr. 2-5). pap. 5.99 (978-1-56822-940-9(2) , IF8872) School Specialty Publishing.

Gritzner, Charles F. Mexico. (Modern World Nations Ser.). 2005. 150p. (J). 30.00 (978-0-7910-8653-7(4)); 2003. (Illus.). 200p. (gr. 6-12). 35.00 (978-0-7910-6929-5(X)); 2003. (Illus.). 200p. (gr. 6-12). pap. 30.00 (978-0-7910-7179-3(0)) Facts On File, Inc. (Chelsea Hse.).

Group/McGraw-Hill, Wright. Mexico: Land of Old & New, 6 vols. (Book2WebTM Ser.). (gr. 4-8). 36.50 (978-0-322-04445-6(6)) Wright Group, The.

Hamilton, Janice. Mexico in Pictures. 2nd rev. ed. 2003. (Visual Geography Ser.). (Illus.). 80p. (J). (gr. 5-12). 27.93 (978-0-8225-1960-7(7)) Lerner Publishing Group.

Harcourt School Publishers Staff. Buenos Dias, Mexico. 3rd ed. 2002. (Horizons Ser.). (Illus.). (J). pap. 7.30 (978-0-15-333614-0(5)) Harcourt Schl. Pubs.

Hardwick, Susan, ed. Mexico. 2004. (World-Wise Kids Project Guides). (Illus.). 96p. (978-1-59258-079-8(3)) Hylas Publishing.

Harvey, Miles. Look What Came from Mexico. 1999. (Look What Came from Ser.). (Illus.). 32p. (gr. 2-4). pap. 6.95 (978-0-531-15939-2(6) , Watts, Franklin) Scholastic Library Publishing.

Hernandez, Roger, ed. & intro. Mexico: Our Southern Neighbor, 16 vols., Set. Hernandez, Roger, intro. 2002. (Illus.). 64,80p. (YA). (gr. 5 up). lib. bdg. (978-1-59084-074-0(7)) Mason Crest Pubs.

Hodgkins, Fran. Mexico: A Question & Answer Book. 2004. (Fact Finders Ser.). (Illus.). 32p. (J). lib. bdg. 22.60 (978-0-7368-2479-8(0)) Capstone Pr., Inc.

Jen Green. Mexico. 2006. (Illus.). 48p. (J). pap. ***(*978-1-4109-2470-4(X))*** Steck-Vaughn.

Jermyn, Leslie & Conboy, Fiona. Welcome to Mexico. 1999. (Welcome to My Country Ser.). (Illus.). 48p. (J). (gr. 2 up). lib. bdg. 26.00 (978-0-8368-2398-1(2)) Stevens, Gareth Inc.

Juniyn, Leslie. Mexico. 1998. (Countries of the World Ser.). (Illus.). 96p. (J). (gr. 6 up). lib. bdg. 30.00 (978-0-8368-2127-7(0)) Stevens, Gareth Inc.

Kalman, Bobbie. Mexico: The Land. 2002. (gr. 3-6). lib. bdg. 16.40 (978-0-613-52982-2(0)) Tandem Library Bks.

—Mexico: The People. 2002. (gr. 3-6). lib. bdg. 16.40 (978-0-613-52983-9(9)) Tandem Library Bks.

—Mexico - The Culture. 2nd rev. ed. 2001. (Lands, Peoples & Cultures Ser.). (Illus.). 32p. (J). (gr. 4-5). (978-0-7787-9363-2(X)); pap. (978-0-7787-9731-9(7)) Crabtree Publishing Co.

—Mexico - The Land. 2nd rev. ed. 2001. (Lands, Peoples & Cultures Ser.). (Illus.). 32p. (J). (gr. 4-5). (978-0-7787-9361-8(3)); pap. (978-0-7787-9729-6(5)) Crabtree Publishing Co.

—Mexico from A to Z. 1999. (Illus.). (J). (gr. k-3). lib. bdg. 16.40 (978-0-613-11864-4(2)) Tandem Library Bks.

Kalman, Bobbie & Lewis, Jane. Mexico from A to Z. 1999. (AlphaBasiCs Ser.). (Illus.). 32p. (J). (gr. 2-3). pap. (978-0-86505-412-7(6)); lib. bdg. (978-0-86505-382-3(0)) Crabtree Publishing Co.

Kramme, Michael. Mexico. 1999. (Illus.). 96p. (YA). (gr. 5-8). pap. 10.95 (978-1-58037-088-2(8)) Twain, Mark Media, Inc. Pubs.

Landau, Elaine. Mexico. 2007. (True Booktrade;: Geography: Countries Ser.). 48p. (J). spiral bd. 26.00 ***(*978-0-531-16853-0(0)*** , Children's Pr.) Scholastic Library Publishing.

Lieurance, Suzanne. Mexico: A MyReportLinks. com Book. 2004. (Top Ten Countries of Recent Immigrants Ser.). (Illus.). 48p. (J). lib. bdg. 25.26 (978-0-7660-5177-5(3) , MyReportLinks.com Bks.) Enslow Pubs., Inc.

A Look at Mexico, 6 vols. (gr. k-2). 28.95 (978-0-7368-9423-4(3)) Red Brick Learning.

El maravilloso maiz de Mexico: 6 Small Books. (Saludos Ser.: Vol. 2). (SPA.). (gr. 3-5). 31.00 (978-0-7635-1815-8(8)) Rigby Education.

Marquez, Heron. Destination Veracruz. 1998. (Port Cities of North America Ser.). (Illus.). 72p. (J). (gr. 6-8). lib. bdg. 23.93 (978-0-8225-2791-6(X)) Lerner Publishing Group.

Marsh, Carole. America's Important Neighbors: Canada, Mexico & Cuba. 2001. (Here & Now Series!). (Illus.). 48p. (J). (gr. 3-8). pap. 7.95 (978-0-635-00262-4(0)) Gallopade International.

Marx, David F. Mexico. 2001. (Rookie Read-About Geography Ser.). (Illus.). 32p. (J). (gr. 1-2). pap. 5.95 (978-0-516-27086-9(9) , Children's Pr.) Scholastic Library Publishing.

—Mexico. 2000. (gr. k-3). lib. bdg. 14.10 (978-0-613-54019-3(0)) Tandem Library Bks.

McNamara, Margaret. Mexico. 2006. pap. 39.00 ***(*978-1-4108-6456-7(1))*** Benchmark Education Co.

Meister, Cari. Mexico. 2000. (Going Places Ser.). (Illus.). 24p. (J). (gr. k-6). lib. bdg. 21.35 (978-1-57765-029-4(8) , Checkerboard Library) ABDO Publishing Co.

Milord, Susan. Mexico! 40 Activities to Experience Mexico Past & Present. 1999. (Kaleidoscope Kids Bks.). (Illus.). 96p. (J). (gr. 2-8). pap. 12.95 (978-1-885593-22-1(8) , Williamson Bks.) Ideals Pubns.

—Mexico: 40 Activities to Experience Mexico Past & Present. 1999. (J). (978-0-606-16815-1(X)) Tandem Library Bks.

Nantus, Sheryl. The Pacific South States of Mexico. 2002. (Encyclopedia of Mexico Ser.). (Illus.). 64,80p. (J). (gr. 5 up). lib. bdg. (978-1-59084-084-9(4)) Mason Crest Pubs.

O'Donnell, Kerri. A Primary Source Guide to Mexico. 2004. (Countries of the World : A Primary Source Journey Ser.). (Illus.). 24p. (J). lib. bdg. (978-0-8239-8076-5(6)); lib. bdg. 19.95 (978-0-8239-6592-2(9)) Rosen Publishing Group, Inc., The. (PowerKids Pr.).

Olawsky, Lynn Ainsworth. Colors of Mexico. 2000. (Colors of the World Ser.). (Illus.). (J). 13.75 (978-0-606-21929-7(3)) Tandem Library Bks.

Park, Ted. Mexico. 1999. (Taking Your Camera to Ser.). (Illus.). 32p. (J). (gr. 4-7). lib. bdg. 22.83 (978-0-7398-1804-6(X)) Raintree.

—Taking Your Camera to Mexico. 1999. (Illus.). pap. (978-0-7398-2156-5(3)) Steck-Vaughn.

Parker, Edward. Mexico. 2004. (Countries of the World Ser.). (Illus.). 64p. (J). (gr. 6-12). 30.00 (978-0-8160-5503-6(3)) Facts On File, Inc.

—Mexico. 2002. (Changing Face Of... Ser.). (Illus.). 48p. (J). lib. bdg. 27.12 (978-0-7398-4967-5(0)) Raintree.

Parker, Lewis K. Why Mexican Immigrants Came to America. 2003. (Reading Power Ser.). (Illus.). 24p. (J). lib. bdg. 17.25 (978-0-8239-6459-8(0) , PowerKids Pr.) Rosen Publishing Group, Inc., The.

Pohl, Kathleen. Looking at Mexico. 2007. (J). pap. ***(*978-0-8368-8179-0(6));*** 32p. (gr. 2-4). lib. bdg. 25.27 ***(*978-0-8368-8172-1(9))*** Stevens, Gareth Inc.

Reilly, M. J. & Jermyn, L. Mexico. 2nd ed. 2001. (Cultures of the World Ser.). (Illus.). 144p. (gr. 5 up). lib. bdg. 37.07 (978-0-7614-1363-9(4) , Benchmark Bks.) Cavendish, Marshall Corp.

Richardson, Adele. Mexico. 2006. (My First Look at Countries Ser.). (Illus.). 24p. (J). (gr. 1-2). lib. bdg. 15.95 (978-1-58341-448-4(7) , Creative Education) Creative Co., The.

Richardson, Adele D. Mexico. 2000. (Let's Investigate Ser.). (Illus.). 32p. (J). pap. 10.60 (978-0-89812-006-6(3) , Creative Paperbacks) Creative Co., The.

—Mexico. 1998. (Let's Investigate Ser.: Vol. 12). (Illus.). 32p. (J). (ps-3). lib. bdg. (978-0-88682-984-1(4) , Creative Education) Creative Co., The.

Richter, Robert. Cuauhtemoc Cardenas & the Roots of Mexico's New Democracy. 2000. (Contemporary Profiles & Policy Series for the Younger Reader). (Illus.). 75p. (YA). (gr. 8 up). 24.00 (978-0-934272-66-7(2)) Burke, John Gordon Pub., Inc.

Ring, Susan. Come to Mexico. (Yellow Umbrella Books for Early Readers). (J). 2006. (Illus.). 16p. 15.93 (978-0-7368-5844-1(X)); 2005. (978-0-7368-5310-1(3)); 2005. (Illus.). 17p. (978-0-7368-5274-6(3)) Capstone Pr., Inc.

Ruth, Angie. My Adventure in Mexico. 2007. 44p. (J). 8.99 (978-1-59092-432-7(0) , Orchard Academy Pr.) Windstorm Creative.

Sabeca International Investment Staff. Enciclopedia de Mexico. 2004. (SPA., Illus.). (YA). cd-rom (978-1-56409-069-0(8)) EBP Latin America Group, Inc.

Sanna, Ellyn. Mexico: Facts & Figures. 2002. (Encyclopedia of Mexico Ser.). (Illus.). 64,80p. (J). (gr. 5 up). lib. bdg. (978-1-59084-088-7(7)) Mason Crest Pubs.

Simpson, Kathleen. Geography of Mexico. 2006. (Navigators Ser.). (J). pap. 44.00 ***(*978-1-4108-6263-1(1))*** Benchmark Education Co.

Stein, R. Conrad. Mexico. rev. ed. 2006. (Enchantment of the World, Second Ser.). (Illus.). 144p. (J). 36.00 (978-0-516-24868-4(5) , Children's Pr.) Scholastic Library Publishing.

Stgrei, Lynita. Mexico. 2000. (Countries & Cultures for Young Explorers Ser.). 48p. (J). (gr. k-3). pap. 6.99 (978-0-7424-0035-1(2) , IF2634) School Specialty Publishing.

Stokes, Erica M. The Economy of Mexico. 2002. (Encyclopedia of Mexico Ser.). (Illus.). 64,80p. (YA). (gr. 5 up). lib. bdg. (978-1-59084-083-2(6)) Mason Crest Pubs.

Streissguth, Thomas. Mexico. 2007. (Country Explorers Ser.). 48p. (J). (gr. 4-8). lib. bdg. 27.93 ***(*978-0-8225-7130-8(7)*** , Lerner Pubns.) Lerner Publishing Group.

Tidmarsh, Celia. Focus on Mexico. 2006. (Illus.). 64p. (J). pap. (978-0-8368-6238-6(4)); lib. bdg. 32.67 (978-0-8368-6219-5(8)) Stevens, Gareth Inc. (World Almanac Library).

Urrutia, Maria C., et al. Cinco de Mayo: Yesterday & Today. 2002. (SPA., Illus.). 32p. (J). (gr. 5 up). pap. 6.95 (978-0-88899-484-4(2)) Groundwood Bks. CAN. *Dist:* Perseus Distribution.

Walsh, Kieran. Mexico. 2005. (Countries in the News Ser.). (Illus.). 24p. (J). (gr. 1-4). 17.95 (978-1-59515-176-6(1)) Rourke Publishing, LLC.

Williams, Brian. Guide to Mexico. 1998. (World Guides Ser.). (Illus.). 32p. (J). (gr. 2-6). lib. bdg. 21.27 (978-1-884756-51-1(4)) Davidson Titles, Inc.

Williams, Colleen Madonna Flood. The Geography of Mexico. 2002. (Mexico Ser.). (Illus.). 64,80p. (YA). (gr. 5 up). lib. bdg. (978-1-59084-075-7(5)) Mason Crest Pubs.

Zocchi, Judy. In Mexico. Brodie, Neale, illus. 2005. (Global Adventures II Ser.). 32p. (J). per. 9.95 (978-1-59646-136-9(5)) Dingles & Co.

—In Mexico/en México. Brodie, Neale, illus. 2005. (Global Adventures II Ser.).Tr. of En México. (ENG & SPA.). 32p. (J). per. 9.95 (978-1-59646-138-3(1)) Dingles & Co.

MEXICO—ANTIQUITIES

Kirkpatrick, Naida. The Maya. 2003. (Understanding People in the Past Ser.: Set. 3). (J). pap. 8.95 (978-1-4034-0606-4(5)); (Illus.). 64p. pap. 28.50 (978-1-4034-0386-5(4)) Heinemann Library.

Owens, L. L. The Great Aztecs. 2002. (Cover-To-Cover Chapter Books). (Illus.). 56p. (J). pap. (978-0-7891-5742-3(X)); (gr. 1-4). lib. bdg. 16.95 (978-0-7569-0910-9(4)) Perfection Learning Corp.

Peppas, Lynn. Life in Ancient Mesoamerica. 2004. (Peoples of the Ancient World Ser.). (Illus.). 32p. (J). (978-0-7787-2039-3(X)) Crabtree Publishing Co.

MEXICO—BIOGRAPHY

Amberson, Mary Margaret McAllen. A Brave Boy & a Good Soldier: John C. C. Hill & the Texas Expedition to Mier. 2006. (Illus.). 100p. (J). pap. 12.95 (978-0-87611-230-4(0)) Texas State Historical Assn.

Carew-Miller, Anna. Famous People of Mexico. 2002. (Encyclopedia of Mexico Ser.). (Illus.). 64,80p. (J). (gr. 5 up). lib. bdg. (978-1-59084-076-4(3)) Mason Crest Pubs.

Delano, Poli. El Tejon Traicionero. 2002. (SPA., Illus.). 24p. (J). (978-968-494-123-6(4)) Centro de Informacion y Desarrollo de la Comunicacion y la Literatura.

Gaines, Ann Graham. Vicente Fox: The Road to the Mexican Presidency. 2003. (Proud Heritage-The Hispanic Library). (Illus.). 40p. (J). (gr. 3-7). 28.50 (978-1-56766-177-4(7)) Child's World, Inc.

Guidici, Cynthia. Mario Molina. 2006. (Biografías Hispanoamericanas Ser.). (Illus.). 64p. (978-1-4109-2131-4(X)); pap. (978-1-4109-2138-3(7)) Steck-Vaughn.

Guzman, Lila & Guzman, Rick. Diego Rivera: Artist of Mexico. 2006. (Famous Latinos Ser.). (Illus.). 32p. (J). lib. bdg. 22.60 (978-0-7660-2641-4(8) , Enslow Elementary) Enslow Pubs., Inc.

Hillstrom, Laurie. Diego Rivera. 2007. (Twentieth Century Most Influential Hispanics Ser.). (Illus.). 128p. (gr. 7-10). 31.20 ***(*978-1-4205-0018-9(X)*** , Lucent Bks.) Thomson Gale.

January, Brendan. Hernan Cortes. 2003. (Groundbreakers Ser.). (Illus.). 48p. (J). (gr. 5-7). lib. bdg. 27.07 (978-1-4034-0243-1(4)) Heinemann Library.

Mora, Pat. A Library for Juana: The World of Sor Juana Ines. Vidal, Beatriz, illus. 2002. 40p. (J). (gr. k-3). 15.95 (978-0-375-80643-8(1) , Knopf Bks. for Young Readers) Random Hse. Children's Bks.

Richter, Robert. Cuauhtemoc Cardenas & the Roots of Mexico's New Democracy. 2000. (Contemporary Profiles & Policy Series for the Younger Reader). (Illus.). 75p. (YA). (gr. 8 up). pap. 15.00 (978-0-934272-65-0(4)) Burke, John Gordon Pub., Inc.

Schumacher, Tyler. Junípero Serra: Explorer & Missionary. 2006. (Fact Finders Ser.). (Illus.). 32p. (J). (978-0-7368-5440-5(1)) Capstone Pr., Inc.

Soler Blanch, Carmen. Hernan Cortes. (SPA., Illus.). 160p. (YA). 11.95 (978-84-7281-174-4(3) , AF1174) Auriga, Ediciones S.A. ESP. *Dist:* Continental Bk. Co., Inc.

Stein, R. Conrad. Emiliano Zapata: Revolutionary & Champion of Poor Farmers. 2004. (Proud Heritage: the Hispanic Library Ser.). 40p. (J). (gr. 3-7). 28.50 (978-1-59296-166-5(5)) Child's World, Inc.

—Hernando Cortés: Conquistador & Empire Builder. 2004. (Proud Heritage: the Hispanic Library Ser.). 40p. (J). (gr. 3-7). 28.50 (978-1-59296-169-6(X)) Child's World, Inc.

—Pancho Villa: Mexican Revolutionary Hero. 2004. (Proud Heritage: the Hispanic Library Ser.). 40p. (J). (gr. 3-7). 28.50 (978-1-59296-171-9(1)) Child's World, Inc.

Tieck, Sarah & Rivera, Diego. Diego Rivera. 2007. (Illus.). 32p. (J). 22.78 (978-1-59679-785-7(1)) ABDO Publishing Co.

Walker, Paul Robert. Remember the Alamo: Texians, Tejanos, & Mexicans Tell Their Stories. 2007. (Illus.). 64p. (J). (gr. 4-8). lib. bdg. 27.90 (978-1-4263-0011-0(5) , National Geographic Children's Bks.) National Geographic Society.

Winter, Jonah. Frida. Juan, Ana, illus. 2002. 32p. (J). (ps-4). (SPA.). 16.95 (978-0-439-37308-1(5)); pap. 16.95 (978-0-590-20320-3(7)); (SPA.). pap. 5.99 (978-0-439-33118-0(8)) Scholastic, Inc. (Levine, Arthur A. Bks.).

—Frida. 2002. (SPA.). (ps-2). lib. bdg. 14.15 (978-0-613-49429-8(6)) Tandem Library Bks.

Winter, Jonah, et al. Frida. 2002. (Illus.). (J). (978-0-590-20321-0(5)) Scholastic, Inc.

Zronik, John Paul. Hernando Cortés: Spanish Invader of Mexico. 2006. (In the Footsteps of Explorers Ser.). (Illus.). 32p. (J). (gr. 3-9). (978-0-7787-2434-6(4)) Crabtree Publishing Co.

MEXICO CITY (MEXICO)

Bingham, Jane. The Aztec Empire. 2007. (Time Travel Guides Ser.). (Illus.). 64p. (YA). (gr. 5-8). lib. bdg. 34.29 ***(*978-1-4109-2730-9(X))*** Raintree.

—The Aztec Empire. 2007. (Time Travel Guides Ser.). (Illus.). 64p. (J). ***(*978-1-4109-2737-8(7))*** Steck-Vaughn.

Mattern, Joanne. Mexico City. 2006. (Cities Ser.). (J). (978-1-59679-716-1(9)) ABDO Publishing Co.

Morrison, Marion. Mexico City. 2003. (Great Cities of the World Ser.). (Illus.). 48p. (J). (gr. 5 up). pap. 11.95 (978-0-8368-5183-0(8)); lib. bdg. 30.00 (978-0-8368-5023-9(8)) Stevens, Gareth Inc. (World Almanac Library).

Parker, Edward. Mexico City. 2006. (Global Cities Ser.). (Illus.). 64p. (YA). (gr. 5-8). 30.00 (978-0-7910-8854-8(5) , Chelsea Hse.) Facts On File, Inc.

Pugliano-Martin, Carol. Discover Mexico City. 2006. pap. 39.00 ***(*978-1-4108-6423-9(5))*** Benchmark Education Co.

—Mexico City, Mexico. 2006. pap. 39.00 ***(*978-1-4108-6420-8(0))*** Benchmark Education Co.

MEXICO—FICTION

Abraham, Susan Gonzales. Cecilia's Year. 2004. (Latino Fiction for Young Adults Ser.). (Illus.). 160p. (J). (gr. 5 up). 16.95 (978-0-938317-87-6(3)) Cinco Puntos Pr.

Agustin, Jose. La Panza del Tepozteco. Tino, illus. 2003. (SPA.). 118p. (J). (gr. 8-12). pap. 12.95 (978-968-19-0187-5(8)) Santillana USA Publishing Co., Inc.

—La Panza del Tepozteco. Tino, illus. 1998. (SPA.). 118p. (YA). (gr. 9-12). pap. 16.95 (978-968-29-4573-1(9)) Secretaria de Educacion Publica MEX. *Dist:* Santillana USA Publishing Co., Inc.

Ahern, Carolyn L. Tino Turtle Travels to Mexico City, Mexico. 2007. (ENG & SPA., Illus.). 36p. (J). 17.95 incl. audio compact disk ***(*978-0-9793158-2-4(4))*** Tino Turtle Travels, LLC.

Amado, Elisa. Barrilete: A Kite for the Day of the Dead. 1999. (SPA., Illus.). (J). (ps-3). pap. 6.95 (978-0-88899-381-6(1) , Libros Tigrillo) Groundwood Bks. CAN. *Dist:* Transition Vendor.

Anaya, Rudolfo. Curse of the ChupaCabra. 2006. 174p. (YA). 24.95 (978-0-8263-4114-3(4)) Univ. of New Mexico Pr.

Anaya, Rudolfo. The First Tortilla: A Bilingual Story. Lamadrid, Enrique R., tr. Cordova, Amy, illus. 2007. (SPA & ENG.). 32p. (J). (gr. 2-4). 16.95 ***(*978-0-8263-4214-0(0))*** Univ. of New Mexico Pr.

And Then it was Sugar, 6 vols. (Multicultural Programs Ser.). 16p. (gr. 1-6). 31.95 (978-0-7802-8324-4(4)) Wright Group, The.

Anza, Ana Luisa. El Misterio de la Casa Chueca (y el Bulto Color Mugre) Escobar, Antonio Rocha, illus. rev. ed. 2006. (Castillo de la Lectura Naranja Ser.). (SPA.). 120p. (J). pap. 7.95 (978-970-20-0200-0(1)) Castillo, Ediciones, S. A. de C. V. MEX. *Dist:* Macmillan.

Appleton, Victor. Tom Swift in the City of Gold or Marvelo. 2006. pap. (****978-1-4065-0916-8(7)***) Dodo Pr.

Bang, Molly Garrett. Tiger's Fall. Bang, Molly Garrett, illus. rev. ed. 2001. (Illus.). 112p. (J). (gr. 4-7). 15.95 (978-0-8050-6689-0(6) , Holt, Henry & Co. Bks. For Young Readers) Holt, Henry & Co.

Bernard, Virginia. Eliza & the Sacred Mountain. 2000. (Going to Ser.). (Illus.). 121p. (J). (gr. 4-8). pap. 6.95 (978-1-893577-05-3(8)) Four Corners Publishing Co., Inc.

Best, Cari. Montezuma's Revenge. Palmisciano, Diane, illus. 1999. 32p. (J). (ps-2). 16.99 (978-0-531-33198-9(9) , Orchard Bks.) Scholastic, Inc.

Blair, Kathryn S. Diario de Lucia (1939) 2003. (Mexican Diaries). (SPA., Illus.). 132p. (J). pap. (978-970-690-039-5(X) , SOM7943) Planeta Mexicana Editorial S. A. de C. V. MEX. *Dist:* Lectorum Pubns., Inc.

Brammer, Ethriam Cash. The Rowdy, Rowdy Ranch / Alla en el Rancho Grande. Cruz, D. Nina, illus. (ENG & SPA.). 32p. 15.95 (978-1-55885-409-3(6) , Piñata Books) Arte Publico Pr.

Brown, Sally. Alexandra's Travel Adventure: Making Friends in Mexico. Lyons, Deborah, illus. 2005. 32p. (J). pap. 9.95 (978-1-57860-232-2(7)) Emmis Bks.

Buel, Hubert & Erskine, Dorothy Ward. North with de Anza. 2004. (Illus.). 234p. (J). (gr. 6-10). pap. 9.95 (978-0-8263-3631-6(0)) Univ. of New Mexico Pr.

Bundschuh, Rick & Hamilton, Bethany. Soul Surfer Crunch. 2007. (Soul Surfer#8482; Ser.). 144p. (J). pap. 6.99 (978-0-310-71225-1(4)) Zonderkidz.

Bunting, Eve. Going Home. Diaz, David, illus. 1998. (Trophy Picture Bk.). 32p. (J). (ps-3). pap. 6.99 (978-0-06-443509-3(1) , Harper Trophy) HarperCollins Pubs.

Cahill, Doris. Nina. Blackwell, Anne, illus. John, Chirs, photos by. 2001. 80p. (J). 15.95 (978-0-9713224-0-0(6)) Johnson, J LLC.

Capucilli, Alyssa Satin. Pedro's Burro. Estrada, Pau, illus. 2007. (My First I Can Read Bks.). 32p. (J). lib. bdg. 16.89 (****978-0-06-056032-4(0)***) HarperCollins Pubs.

Carr, Pat. Border Ransom. 2006. (Illus.). 146p. (J). pap. 11.95 (978-0-87565-332-7(4)) Texas Christian Univ. Pr.

Carter, Aubrey Smith. The Enchanted Lizard: La Lagartijita Magica. Nelson, Esther Whitt, ed. Branton, Molly, illus. 2006. (ENG & SPA.). 96p. (J). 18.95 (978-1-893271-38-8(2)) Maverick Publishing Co.

Cerasini, Marc. Nacho Libre Movie Novelization. 2006. 128p. (J). pap. 4.99 (978-1-4169-2762-4(X) , Simon Spotlight) Simon & Schuster Children's Publishing.

Charles, Norma M. All the Way to Mexico. 2003. (gr. 5-8). lib. bdg. 15.25 (978-0-613-78580-8(0)) Tandem Library Bks.

Cohn, Diana. Dream Carver. Cordova, Amy, illus. 2002. 40p. (J). (ps-3). 16.95 (978-0-8118-1244-3(8)) Chronicle Bks. LLC.

Colato Lainez, Rene. Playing Loteria Mexicana: El Juego de la Loteria Mexicana. Arena, Jillayne, illus. 2005. (ENG & SPA.). 32p. (gr. 1-3). 15.95 (978-0-87358-881-2(9) , Rising Moon Bks. for Young Readers) Northland Publishing.

Corpi, Lucha. Where Fireflies Dance (Ahi, Donde Bailan las Luciernagas) Reisberg, Mira, illus. 2002. 32p. (J). (gr. 1 up). pap. 7.95 (978-0-89239-177-6(4)) Children's Bk. Pr.

Cruz, Maria Colleen. Border Crossing. 128p. (YA). pap. 9.95 (978-1-55885-405-5(3) , Piñata Books) Arte Publico Pr.

—Border Crossing. 2003. (gr. 7-12). lib. bdg. 18.75 (978-0-613-90255-7(6)) Tandem Library Bks.

Cuesy, Silvia. Diario de Mercedes (1844-48) 2003. (Mexican Diaries). (SPA., Illus.). 161p. (J). pap. (978-970-690-037-1(3) , SOM7983) Planeta Mexicana Editorial S. A. de C. V. MEX. *Dist:* Lectorum Pubns., Inc.

DaColl, Ivar. El Dia de Muertos. 2004. Tr. of Day of the Dead. (SPA., Illus.). (J). 14.95 (978-1-930332-44-7(0)) Lectorum Pubns., Inc.

Damitz, Charlie. Diving for el Corazon. Diefendorf, Cathy, illus. 2007. 100p. (J). pap. 7.95 (978-0-9744446-3-5(4)) All About Kids Publishing.

Dear Abuelita. 6, Pack. (Greetings Ser.: Vol. 2). (gr. 3-5). 31.00 (978-0-7635-1765-6(8)) Rigby Education.

Death at the Border. 64p. (YA). (gr. 6-12). pap. (978-0-8224-2361-4(8)) Globe Fearon Educational Publishing.

Dorros, Arthur. Julio's Magic. Grifalconi, Ann, illus. 2005. 32p. (J). (ps-4). lib. bdg. 17.89 (978-0-06-029005-4(6)) HarperCollins Pubs.

Erdman & Perez. Mitos y Leyendas Indigenas. 2005. (SPA.). 72p. 13.99 (978-84-241-8013-3(5)) Everest de Ediciones y Distribucion, S.L. ESP. *Dist:* Lectorum Pubns., Inc.

Estrada Michel, Rafael, tr. Diario de Lupita. 2003. (Mexican Diaries). (SPA., Illus.). 179p. (J). pap. (978-970-690-114-9(0)) Planeta Mexicana Editorial S. A. de C. V.

Estrada, Pau, illus. Pedro's Burro. 2007. (My First I Can Read Bks.). 32p. (J). 15.99 (****978-0-06-056031-7(2)***) HarperCollins Pubs.

Farnes, Catherine. Out of Hiding. 2000. 174p. (YA). (gr. 9 up). pap. 6.49 (978-1-57924-329-6(0) , 122085) Jones, Bob Univ. Pr.

—Out of Hiding. 2000. (gr. 7-12). lib. bdg. 14.70 (978-0-613-83927-3(7)) Tandem Library Bks.

Fine, Edith Hope. Bajo la Luna de Limon. ed. 2004. (SPA., Illus.). (J). (gr. k-3). spiral bd. (978-0-616-03089-9(4)) Canadian National Institute for the Blind/Institut National Canadien pour les Aveugles.

—Bajo la Luna de Limon. de la Vega, Eida, tr. Moreno, Rene King, illus. 1999. (SPA.). 32p. (J). (gr. 1-3). pap. 6.95 (978-1-880000-91-5(1) , LW2628); lib. bdg. 15.95 (978-1-880000-90-8(3) , LW5634) Lee & Low Bks., Inc.

—Bajo la Luna de Limon. 1999. (SPA., Illus.). (J). 13.75 (978-0-606-17377-3(3)) Tandem Library Bks.

—Under the Lemon Moon. 2002. Tr. of Bajo la Luna de Limon. (Illus.). 32p. (J). pap. 6.95 (978-1-58430-051-9(5)) Lee & Low Bks., Inc.

—Under the Lemon Moon. Moreno, Rene King, illus. 1999. Tr. of Bajo la Luna de Limon. 32p. (J). (ps-3). 16.95 (978-1-880000-69-4(5)) Lee & Low Bks., Inc.

—Under the Lemon Moon. 2002. Tr. of Bajo la Luna de Limon. (gr. k-3). lib. bdg. 15.25 (978-0-613-82632-7(9)) Tandem Library Bks.

Fine, Edith Hope & Josephson, Judith Pinkerton. Armando & the Blue Tarp School. Sosa, Hernan, illus. 2007. 32p. (J). (gr. k-4). 16.95 (****978-1-58430-278-0(X)***) Lee & Low Bks., Inc.

Galvan, Nelinda. Cuentos de la Tradicion Mexicana. 1999. (Stories for Children Ser.).Tr. of Traditional Mexican Stories. (SPA.). 125p. (J). 7.95 (978-970-643-187-5(X)) Selector, S.A. de C.V. MEX. *Dist:* Libros Sin Fronteras.

Garza, Xavier. Lucha Libre: The Man in the Silver Mask. Garza, Xavier, illus. 2007. (SPA.). 40p. (J). pap. 8.95 (****978-1-933693-10-1(X)***) Cinco Puntos Pr.

—Lucha Libre: The Man in the Silver Mask. Crosthwaite, Luis Humberto, tr. 2005. (ENG & SPA., Illus.). 40p. (gr. 2-5). 17.95 (978-0-938317-92-0(X)) Cinco Puntos Pr.

Geeslin, Campbell. Clara & Senor Frog. Sanchez, Ryan, illus. 2007. 40p. (J). (ps-3). 16.99 (978-0-375-83613-8(6)); lib. bdg. 19.99 (978-0-375-93613-5(0)) Random Hse. Children's Bks. (Schwartz & Wade Bks.).

—Elena's Serenade. Juan, Ana, illus. 2004. 40p. (J). 17.95 (978-0-689-84908-4(7) , Atheneum) Simon & Schuster Children's Publishing.

Gonzalez, Eladia. El Misterio de las Damas Chinas. 2000. (SPA.). 30p. (J). (gr. 2-4). (978-968-494-094-9(7) , CI30454) Centro de Informacion y Desarrollo de la Comunicacion y la Literatura MEX. *Dist:* AIMS International Bks., Inc., Continental Bk. Co., Inc., Lectorum Pubns., Inc.

Grey, Zane. Ken Ward in the Jungle. l.t. ed. 1999. 272p. (J). pap. (978-0-7540-3608-1(1)) BBC Audiobooks America.

Hancock, H. Irving. Dave Darrin at Vera Cruz. rev. ed. 2006. 216p. 27.95 (978-1-4218-1745-3(4)); pap. 12.95 (978-1-4218-1845-0(0)) 1st World Publishing, Inc. (1st World Library - Literary Society).

—The Young Engineers in Mexico. rev. ed. 2006. 208p. 27.95 (978-1-4218-1738-5(1)); pap. 12.95 (978-1-4218-1838-2(8)) 1st World Publishing, Inc. (1st World Library - Literary Society).

Hancock, Irving H. Dave Darrin at Vera Cruz. 2006. 78.99 (****978-1-4219-9910-4(2)***); pap. 72.99 (****978-1-4219-9913-5(7)***) IndyPublish.com.

—The Young Engineers in Mexico or Fightin. 2006. pap. 71.99 (****978-1-4219-9885-5(8)***) IndyPublish.com.

—Young Engineers in Mexico or Fighting Th. 2006. 78.99 (****978-1-4219-9889-3(0)***) IndyPublish.com.

Harcourt School Publishers Staff. The Emperor & the Peasant Boy Below Level. 3rd ed. 2002. (Trophies Reading Program Ser.). (Illus.). pap. 5.10 (978-0-15-323238-1(2)) Harcourt Schl. Pubs.

—My School Year. 3rd ed. 2002. (Trophies English Language Learners Ser.). (Illus.). pap. 5.10 (978-0-15-327715-3(7)) Harcourt Schl. Pubs.

Herbst, Judith. Ivy's Journal. O'Gorman, Molly, illus. 2000. 32p. (J). (gr. 3-7). 15.95 (978-1-57255-839-7(3)) Mondo Publishing.

Hill, Laban Carrick. Casa Azul: An Encounter with Frida Kahlo. 2005. (Art Encounters Ser.). (Illus.). 160p. (YA). 15.95 (978-0-8230-0411-9(2)) Watson-Guptill Pubns., Inc.

Hinojosa, Francisco. A Golpe de Calcetin. Barajas, Rafael, illus. 2000. (la Orilla Del Viento Ser.). (SPA.). 46p. (J). (ps-ps). reprint ed. pap. 6.99 (978-968-16-6132-8(X) , 130) Fondo de Cultura Economica USA.

Jaramillo, Ann. La Linea. 2006. (SPA.). 144p. (J). 16.95 (978-1-59643-154-6(7)) Roaring Brook Pr.

—La Linea. 2008. 160p. (YA). pap. 7.99 (****978-0-312-37354-2(6)***) Square Fish.

Johnston, Tony. Day of the Dead. 2000. 12.80 (978-0-606-20323-4(0)) Tandem Library Bks.

—Isabel's House of Butterflies. Guevara, Susan, illus. 2003. 32p. (J). (ps-3). 15.95 (978-0-87156-409-2(2)) Sierra Club Bks. for Children.

—Isabel's House of Butterflies. Guevara, Susan, illus. 2005. 32p. pap. 6.95 (978-1-58685-844-5(0)) Gibbs Smith, Publisher.

—My Mexico/Mexico Mio. Sierra, F. John, illus. 1999. (SPA.). 32p. (J). (gr. k-3). pap. 6.99 (978-0-698-11757-0(3) , Putnam Juvenile) Penguin Group (USA) Inc.

Johnston, Tony & Johnston, Tony. Day of the Dead. Winter, Jeannette, illus. 2000. (J). (ps-17). lib. bdg. 14.15 (978-0-613-29921-3(3)) Tandem Library Bks.

Kasischke, Laura. Feathered. 2008. 272p. (J). 16.99 (****978-0-06-081317-8(2)***); lib. bdg. 17.89 (****978-0-06-081318-5(0)***) HarperCollins Pubs. (HarperTeen).

Keep, Linda Lowery. Truth & Salsa. 2006. 176p. (J). 14.95 (978-1-56145-366-5(8) , Peachtree Junior) Peachtree Pubs., Ltd.

Keep, Richard Cleminson, illus. Clatter Bash! A Day of the Dead Celebration. 2004. 32p. (J). (ps-3). 15.95 (978-1-56145-322-1(6)) Peachtree Pubs., Ltd.

Kimmel, Eric. Sopa de Cactus. Huling, Phil, illus. 2007. 32p. (J). 16.99 (****978-0-7614-5344-4(X)***) Cavendish, Marshall Corp.

Kirwan, Anna. Lady of Palenque: Flower of Bacal, Mesoamerica, A. D. 749. 2004. (Royal Diaries). (Illus.). 208p. (J). pap. 10.95 (978-0-439-40971-1(3)) Scholastic, Inc.

Langlais, Heather M. Mummy's Home Town: The Curse of the Amulet. Gillespie, P. J., illus. 1999. 144p. (J). (gr. 4-8). pap. 7.95 (978-1-930506-00-8(7)) March Forth Pubns.

Lee, Marie G. Night of the Chupacabras. 1999. 128p. (gr. 3-7). pap. 3.99 (978-0-380-79773-8(9)) HarperCollins Pubs.

—Night of the Chupacabras. 1999. (978-0-606-17336-0(6)) Tandem Library Bks.

Literature Connections English: A Place Where the Sea Remembers. 2004. (gr. 6-12). (978-0-395-83361-2(2) , 2-70784) McDougal Littell Inc.

Madrigal, Antonio Hernandez. Erandi's Braids. Peskin, Joy, ed. de Paola, Tomie, illus. 2001. 1p. (J). (ps-3). pap. 6.99 (978-0-698-11885-0(5) , Putnam Juvenile) Penguin Group (USA) Inc.

—Erandi's Braids. de Paola, Tomie, illus. 1999. 32p. (J). (ps-3). 15.99 (978-0-399-23212-1(5) , Putnam Juvenile) Penguin Group (USA) Inc.

—Erandi's Braids. 2001. (gr. k-3). lib. bdg. 15.30 (978-0-613-35941-2(0)) Tandem Library Bks.

Manning, Brennan. The Boy Who Cried Abba: A Parable of Trust & Acceptance. 2001. 85p. (J). pap. 13.95 (978-1-879290-19-8(7) , PageMill Pr.) Council Oak Bks.

Martin, Hugo. Pablo's Christmas. Chapman, Lee, illus. 2006. 24p. (J). 14.95 (978-1-4027-2560-9(4)) Sterling Publishing Co., Inc.

Marzollo, Jean. Companeros en el Futbol. 1999. (J). lib. bdg. 10.79 (978-0-606-17055-0(3)) Tandem Library Bks.

Matthews. Death in the Desert. (Thumbprint Mysteries Ser.). 32.86 (978-0-8092-0416-8(9)) McGraw-Hill/ Contemporary.

McAlister, Caroline. Holy Molé! A Folktale from Mexico. Czernecki, Stefan, illus. 2007. 32p. (gr. k-3). 16.95 (978-0-87483-775-9(8)) August Hse. Pubs., Inc.

Meunier, Brian & Edgerton, Perky. Bravo, Tavo! 2007. (Illus.). 32p. (J). (gr. k-3). 16.99 (978-0-525-47478-4(1) , Dutton Juvenile) Penguin Group (USA) Inc.

Mikaelsen, Ben. Sparrow Hawk Red. 1999. 192p. pap. 5.99 (978-0-7868-1002-4(5)) Hyperion Pr.

Morrow, Elizabeth. The Painted Pig: A Mexican Picture Book. D'Harnoncourt, Rene, illus. 2001. 1p. 13.95 (978-0-8263-2769-7(9)) Univ. of New Mexico Pr.

Nelson, Suzanne Johnson. Heart & Salsa. 2006. (S. A. S. S. (Students Across the Seven Seas) Ser.). 224p. (YA). (gr. 7). pap. 6.99 (978-0-14-240647-2(3) , Puffin) Penguin Group (USA) Inc.

O'Dell, Scott. The King's Fifth. 2006. 272p. (YA). (gr. 7). pap. 6.95 (978-0-618-74783-2(4)) Houghton Mifflin Co. Trade & Reference Div.

Olds, Sara V. Anna - a Farewell to Juarez. Roy, T. M., illus. 2003. Orig. Title: Hanne's Farewell to Juarez. (J). pap. 10.50 (978-0-9715433-7-9(2) , AFJ-TP) Zapstone Productions.

Oppenheim, Joanne. El Milagro de la Primera Flora de Nochebuena: Un Cuento Mexicano Sobre la Navidad. Negrin, Fabian, illus. 2003. (SPA.). 32p. (J). 16.99 (978-1-84148-308-5(7)) Barefoot Bks., Inc.

—The Miracle of the First Poinsettia: A Mexican Christmas Story. Negrin, Fabian, illus. 2003. 32p. (J). 16.99 (978-1-84148-245-3(5)) Barefoot Bks., Inc.

Orozco, Rebeca & Muro, Claudia Burr. Dona Josefa y sus Conspiraciones. 2005. (Ya Veras Ser.). (SPA., Illus.). (J). (gr. 3-5). pap. 9.95 (978-968-7381-29-9(9)) Tecolote, Ediciones, S.A. de C.V. MEX. *Dist:* Iaconi, Mariuccia Bk. Imports.

Paulsen, Gary. The Crossing. 2006. 128p. (J). pap. 6.99 (978-0-439-78661-4(4) , Scholastic Paperbacks) Scholastic, Inc.

Pequeña the Burro: Evaluation Guide. 2006. (J). (978-1-55942-420-2(6)) Marsh Media.

Pugliano-Martin, Carol. Quetzacoati Brings Corn to His People: A Legend from Mexico. 2006. spiral bd. 42.00 (****978-1-4108-7168-8(1)***) Benchmark Education Co.

Resau, Laura. Red Glass. 2007. 288p. (gr. 5). (J). lib. bdg. 18.99 (****978-0-385-90464-3(9)***); (YA). 15.99 (****978-0-385-73466-0(2)***) Random Hse. Children's Bks. (Delacorte Bks. for Young Readers).

Resau, Laura. What the Moon Saw. 2006. 272p. (gr. 5). (J). 15.95 (978-0-385-73343-4(7)); (YA). lib. bdg. 17.99 (978-0-385-90360-8(X)) Random Hse. Children's Bks. (Delacorte Bks. for Young Readers).

—What the Moon Saw. l.t. rev. ed. 2007. 300p. (YA). 22.95 (****978-0-7862-9278-3(4)***) Thorndike Pr.

Richardson, Kara, illus. Simon & Barklee in Mexico. 2002. (Simon & Barklee in Mexico). 64p. (J). per. 15.00 (978-0-9714502-0-2(X) , Explorer Media) Simon & Barklee, Inc./ExplorerMedia.

Romeu, Emma. Gregorio Vuelve a Mexico. 2003. (SPA., Illus.). 148p. (J). (gr. 5-8). pap. 12.95 (978-968-19-0367-1(6)) Santillana USA Publishing Co., Inc.

—Gregorio Vuelve a Mexico. 2000. (SPA.). (gr. 5-8). lib. bdg. 18.75 (978-0-613-82709-6(0)) Tandem Library Bks.

Rosas, Alejandro. Diario de Aurora. 2003. (Mexican Diaries). (SPA.). 164p. (J). pap. (978-968-406-990-9(1) , SOM7961) Planeta Mexicana Editorial S. A. de C. V. MEX. *Dist:* Lectorum Pubns., Inc.

Roth, Judith L. & Rothshank, Brooke, illus. Cups Held Out. 2006. 40p. (J). (978-0-8361-9316-9(4)) Herald Pr.

Ryan, Pam Muñoz. Becoming Naomi Leon. (J). (gr. 4-7). 2004. 240p. pap. 16.95 (978-0-439-26969-8(5) , Scholastic Pr.); 2005. 272p. reprint ed. pap. 5.99 (978-0-439-26997-1(0) , Scholastic Paperbacks) Scholastic, Inc.

—Esperanza Renace. 2002. (SPA.). (gr. 3-6). lib. bdg. 13.00 (978-0-613-82250-3(1)) Tandem Library Bks.

—Esperanza Rising. 2001. (gr. 5-8). lib. bdg. 13.00 (978-0-613-53807-7(2)) Tandem Library Bks.

—Mice & Beans. Cepeda, Joe, illus. 2001. 32p. (J). (ps-2). pap. 16.95 (978-0-439-18303-1(0) , Levine, Arthur A. Bks.) Scholastic, Inc.

Saldana, Rene, Jr. Jumping Tree. 2002. (gr. 5-8). lib. bdg. 13.55 (978-0-613-72279-7(5)) Tandem Library Bks.

Sanroman, Susana. Senora Reganona: A Mexican Bedtime Story. 2000. (Illus.). 32p. (J). (ps-k). pap. 5.95 (978-0-88899-389-2(7) , Libros Tigrillo) Groundwood Bks. CAN. *Dist:* Perseus Distribution.

—Senora Reganona: A Mexican Bedtime Story. Domi, illus. 1998. (SPA.). 24p. (J). (ps-k). 14.95 (978-0-88899-320-5(X)) Groundwood Bks. CAN. *Dist:* Perseus Distribution.

—Senora Reganona: A Mexican Bedtime Story. 2000. (978-0-606-18344-4(2)); lib. bdg. 14.10 (978-0-613-28059-4(8)) Tandem Library Bks.

Sawyer, Timothy L., Jr. Stories of Mexico's Independence Days & Other Bilingual Children's Fables. Torres, Eliseo, ed. Ramirez, Herman, illus. 2005. (ENG & SPA.). 70p. (J). (gr. 3-7). pap. 13.95 (978-0-8263-3886-0(0)) Univ. of New Mexico Pr.

Scieszka, Jon. Me Oh Maya. McCauley, Adam, illus. 2005. (Time Warp Trio Ser.: No. 13). 96p. (J). pap. 4.99 (978-0-14-240300-6(8) , Puffin) Penguin Group (USA) Inc.

Silva, Carlos. Diario de Fernando. 2003. (Mexican Diaries). (SPA., Illus.). 172p. (J). pap. (978-970-690-244-3(9)) Planeta Mexicana Editorial S. A. de C. V.

Simon & Barklee in Mexico. 2002. 70p. tchr. ed. 20.00 (978-0-9714502-2-6(6) , Explorer Media) Simon & Barklee, Inc./ExplorerMedia.

Soros, Barbara. Grandmother's Song. Morris, Jackie, illus. 1998. 32p. (J). (gr. 3-7). 15.95 (978-1-902283-02-9(3)) Barefoot Bks., Inc.

Stanton, Karen. Papi's Gift. Moreno, Rene King, illus. 2007. 32p. (J). (gr. k-3). 16.95 (978-1-59078-422-8(7)) Boyds Mills Pr.

Steinbeck, John. Perla. 2000. (SPA.). (gr. 7-12). lib. bdg. 15.25 (978-0-613-62435-0(1)) Tandem Library Bks.

Taylor, Cora. Murder in Mexico. 2007. (Spy Who Wasn't There Ser.). (Illus.). 360p. (J). (gr. 4-7). pap. 7.95 (****978-1-55050-353-1(7)***) Coteau Bks. CAN. *Dist:* Fitzhenry & Whiteside, Ltd.

Turner, Anna & Kitching, Beth. El Pato Paco, 2 vols., Set. 2000. (SPA., Illus.). (J). (ps-5). pap. 10.98 incl. audio (978-0-89084-900-2(5) , 078865) Jones, Bob Univ. Pr.

Villalpando, Jose Manuel. Diario de Clara Eugenia (1864-67) 2003. (Diarios Mexicanos Coleccion). (SPA., Illus.). 174p. (J). (gr. 5-8). pap. (978-968-406-900-8(6) , SOM7940) Planeta Mexicana Editorial S. A. de C. V. MEX. *Dist:* Lectorum Pubns., Inc.

Walker, Alice. By the Light of My Father's Smile. 1999. (gr. 7-12). lib. bdg. 23.40 (978-0-613-21276-2(2)) Tandem Library Bks.

West-Rodiguez, Helen & Rodriguez, Carmen J. Hands Across the Border (Manos a Traves de la Frontera) Raymer, M. Loys, illus. 1999. (SPA & ENG.). 22p. 14.95 (978-0-9668452-5-9(0)) Brown Bks.

Williams, Jeanne. Mission in Mexico. 2000. 196p. (YA). pap. 12.95 (978-0-595-14642-0(2) , Backinprint.com) iUniverse, Inc.

Yacowitz, Caryn. Pumpkin Fiesta. Cepeda, Joe, illus. 1998. 32p. (J). (ps-1). 16.99 (978-0-06-027658-4(4)) HarperCollins Pubs.

Zepeda, Monique. Las Pinatas. Graullera, Fabiola, illus. Tr. of Pinatas. (SPA.). 26p. (J). (gr. 3-5). pap. 6.95 (978-968-19-0612-2(8)) Santillana USA Publishing Co., Inc.

MEXICO—HISTORY

Ancona, George. The Past: Viva Mexico. 2001. (Viva Mexico! Ser.). (Illus.). 48p. (J). (gr. 3 up). lib. bdg. 27.07 (978-0-7614-1330-1(8) , Benchmark Bks.) Cavendish, Marshall Corp.

Blue, Rose & Naden, Corinne J. Exploring Central America, Mexico, & the Caribbean. 2003. (Illus.). 64p. pap. 9.50 (978-1-4109-0334-1(6)); lib. bdg. 28.56 (978-0-7398-4952-1(2)) Raintree.

Botello Mier, Oscar. Audacia/Hermenegildo Galeana. 2002. Tr. of Daring Hermenegildo Galeana. (SPA.). (J). 7.50 (978-968-24-3117-3(4)) Trillas Editorial, S. A. MEX. *Dist:* AIMS International Bks., Inc.

Burr, Claudia, et al. When the Viceroy Came. 1999. (Illus.). 32p. (J). (gr. 5-9). 15.95 (978-0-88899-354-0(4)) Groundwood Bks. CAN. *Dist:* Perseus Distribution.

Crisfield, Deborah. The Travels of Hernan Cortes. 2000. (Explorers & Exploration Ser.). (Illus.). 48p. (J). (gr. 4-7). lib. bdg. 22.83 (978-0-7398-1488-8(5)) Raintree.

Dawson, Imogen. Food & Feasts with the Aztecs. 2004. (Illus.). 32p. (J). (gr. 4-8). reprint ed. 14.00 (978-0-7567-7143-0(9)) DIANE Publishing Co.

Englar, Mary. Pancho Villa, Rebel of the Mexican Revolution. 2006. (Fact Finders Ser.). (Illus.). 32p. (J). (978-0-7368-5441-2(X)) Capstone Pr., Inc.

Frias. Padiema Churubusco y Chapultec. (Fondo 2000 Ser.). (SPA.). (J). 2.99 (978-968-16-5284-5(3)) Fondo de Cultura Economica USA.

García Davila, Sandra. Antepasados para Ninos. 2006. (SPA.). 142p. (YA). pap. (978-970-643-359-6(7)) Selector, S.A. de C.V.

Garner, Paul. Porfirio Diaz. 2001. (Profiles in Power Ser.). (Illus.). 280p. (C). pap. 20.60 (978-0-582-29267-3(0)) Longman Publishing.

Goddard, Phyllis M. Spratling Silver: Recognizing a Spratling Silver Treasure: a Field Guide. 2003. (Illus.). 152p. per. 39.95 (978-0-9740907-3-3(5)) Keenan Tyler Paine.

Harcourt School Publishers Staff. Canada/Mexico/Central America: Assignment Program. 2nd ed. 2002. (Horizons Ser.). (gr. k-7). pap. 128.10 (978-0-15-335844-9(0)) Harcourt Schl. Pubs.

Higgins, Nadia. Spanish Missions of the Old West. 2007. (Events in American History Ser.). (Illus.). 48p. (J). (gr. 4-6). lib. bdg. 29.93 (978-1-60044-128-8(9)) Rourke Publishing, LLC.

Hoyt-Goldsmith, Diane. Cinco de Mayo: Celebrating Mexican-American Traditions. Migdale, Lawrence, illus. Migdale, Lawrence, photos by. 2008. (J). ***(978-0-8234-2107-7(4))*** Holiday Hse., Inc.

Hunter, Amy Nicole. The History of Mexico. 2002. (Mexico Ser.). (Illus.). 64,80p. (YA). (gr. 5 up). lib. bdg. (978-1-59084-079-5(8)) Mason Crest Pubs.

Ingram, Scott. Mexican Americans. 2006. (World Almanac Library of American Immigration). (Illus.). 48p. (J). pap. (978-0-8368-7329-0(7)); lib. bdg. (978-0-8368-7316-0(5)) Stevens, Gareth Inc. (World Almanac Library).

Jovinelly, Joann & Netelkos, Jason. The Crafts & Culture of the Aztecs. 2002. (Crafts of the Ancient World Ser.). (Illus.). 48p. (YA). (gr. 5-8). lib. bdg. 29.25 (978-0-8239-3512-3(4) , Rosen Central) Rosen Publishing Group, Inc., The.

Kalman, Bobbie & Walker, Niki. Spotlight on Mexico. 2007. (Spotlight on My Country Ser.). (Illus.). 32p. (J). (gr. 2-5). pap. ***(978-0-7787-3477-2(3))*** Crabtree Publishing Co.

Kauffman, Dorothy. Letters from Canada & Mexico. 2005. (Content Area Readers Ser.). (Illus.). 4.95 (978-0-19-430951-6(7)) Oxford Univ. Pr., Inc.

King, David C. Projects about the Ancient Aztecs. 2006. (Hands-On History Ser.). (Illus.). 48p. (J). lib. bdg. 29.93 (978-0-7614-2256-3(0) , Benchmark Bks.) Cavendish, Marshall Corp.

Levy, Janey. Mexico. 2006. (Tony Stead Independent Reading Collection). (J). pap. (978-1-4042-5669-9(5)) Rosen Publishing Group, Inc., The.

Lourie, Peter. The Mystery of the Maya: Uncovering the Lost City of Palenque. Lourie, Peter, photos by. 2003. (Illus.). 48p. (J). (gr. 4-6). 19.95 (978-1-56397-839-5(3)) Boyds Mills Pr.

Marcovitz, Hal. Pancho Villa. 2003. (Great Hispanic Heritage Ser.). (Illus.). 112p. (gr. 6-12). 30.00 (978-0-7910-7257-8(6) , Chelsea Hse.) Facts On File, Inc.

Mathews, Sally Schofer. The Sad Night: The Story of an Aztec Victory & a Spanish Loss. 2001. (Illus.). 40p. (J). (gr. k-3). pap. 6.95 (978-0-618-11745-1(8) , Clarion Bks.) Houghton Mifflin Co. Trade & Reference Div.

McNamara, Margaret. Discover Mexico. 2006. pap. 39.00 ***(978-1-4108-6459-8(6))*** Benchmark Education Co.

Mexican Revolution, 2003. (Illus.). (YA). spiral bd. (978-0-9759194-6-0(6)) Publicaciones Papelandia.

Mexico's Desert Country, 2003. (Illus.). (YA). spiral bd. (978-0-9759194-7-7(4)) Publicaciones Papelandia.

Mihelakis, Laura & Lang, Karen. Something Special: A Lessom to Remember about Mexican Jumping Beans. 2002. (Illus.). (978-0-9725414-0-4(3)) Mihelakis, Laura.

Morris, Ting & Young, E. Aztecs & Maya. 2006. (Illus.). 32p. (J). (978-1-58340-915-2(7) , 1262694) Smart Apple Media.

Noticias de Fin de Siglo. 2005. (SPA.). (J). pap. 9.95 (978-968-7381-10-7(8)) Tecolote, Ediciones, S.A. de C.V. MEX. *Dist:* Iaconi, Mariuccia Bk. Imports.

Palos, Lilia. Acercate a la Historia 3 de las Raices Indigenas al Mexico Contemprineo Actores Sociales, Vida Cotidiana, Mentalidades y Cultura. 2003. (SPA.). 350p. (YA). (978-968-7903-42-2(2)) Edere, S. A. de C. V.

Pliego, Jane. La Reforma para Ninos. (SPA.). (J). 8.98 (978-970-643-394-7(5)) Selector, S.A. de C.V. MEX. *Dist:* AIMS International Bks., Inc.

Revolucion a Todo Vapor (Rev. Full Stream Ahead) 2005. (SPA.). (J). pap. 9.95 (978-968-7381-08-4(6)) Tecolote, Ediciones, S.A. de C.V. MEX. *Dist:* Iaconi, Mariuccia Bk. Imports.

Sandoval & Aboites. La Fortuna de Manuel / el Aprendizde Actor, Vol. 7. 2004. (Historias de Mexico Ser.). (SPA.). 76p. (978-968-16-5632-4(6)) Fondo de Cultura Economica USA.

Sanna, Ellyn. Mexican Americans' Role in the United States: A History of Pride, a Future of Hope. 2005. (Illus.). 112p. (J). (ps-7). lib. bdg. (978-1-59084-926-2(4)) Mason Crest Pubs.

Schumacher, Tyler. Junípero Serra: Explorer & Missionary. 2006. (Fact Finders Ser.). (Illus.). 32p. (J). (978-0-7368-5440-5(1)) Capstone Pr., Inc.

Serrano, Francisco. The Poet King of Tezcoco: A Great Leader of Ancient Mexico. Serrano, Pablo, illus. 2007. 48p. (J). 18.95 (978-0-88899-787-6(6)) Groundwood Bks. CAN. *Dist:* Perseus Distribution.

Stein, R. Conrad. Emliano Zapata: Revolutionary & Champion of Poor Farmers. 2004. (Proud Heritage: the Hispanic Library Ser.). 40p. (J). (gr. 3-7). 28.50 (978-1-59296-166-5(5)) Child's World, Inc.

—Hernando Cortés: Conquistador & Empire Builder. 2004. (Proud Heritage: the Hispanic Library Ser.). 40p. (J). (gr. 3-7). 28.50 (978-1-59296-169-6(X)) Child's World, Inc.

Stokes, Erica M. Sports of Mexico. 2002. (Encyclopedia of Mexico Ser.). (Illus.). 64,80p. (YA). (gr. 5 up). lib. bdg. (978-1-59084-082-5(8)) Mason Crest Pubs.

Trueba, Jose Luis. Descubre... Las Raices de Mexico. Cortes, Osvaldo, illus. 2004. (Ser. Descubre). (SPA.). 96p. (J). (gr. 3-5). pap. 18.95 (978-970-29-0508-0(7)) Santillana USA Publishing Co., Inc.

Truillo, Francisco. Conquista para Ninos. (SPA.). (J). 7.98 (978-970-643-360-2(0)) Selector, S.A. de C.V. MEX. *Dist:* AIMS International Bks., Inc.

Worth, Richard. Independence for Latino America. 2006. (Latino-American History Ser.). 112p. (J). (gr. 5-8). 35.00 (978-0-8160-6441-0(5) , Chelsea Hse.) Facts On File, Inc.

Zocchi, Judy. In Mexico. Brodie, Neale, illus. 2005. (Global Adventures I Ser.). 32p. (J). pap. 9.95 (978-1-59646-135-2(7)); lib. bdg. 20.65 (978-1-59646-002-7(4)) Dingles & Co.

—In Mexico/en México. Brodie, Neale, illus. 2005. (Global Adventures I Ser.).Tr. of En México. (ENG & SPA.). 32p. (J). pap. 9.95 (978-1-59646-137-6(3)); lib. bdg. 20.65 (978-1-59646-003-4(2)) Dingles & Co.

MEXICO—HISTORY—CONQUEST, 1519-1540

Abnett, Dan. Hernan Cortes & the Fall of the Aztec Empire. 2007. (Jr. Graphic Biographies Ser.). (J). (978-1-4042-2334-9(7)); (Illus.). 24p. pap. (978-1-4042-2144-4(1)); (Illus.). 24p. (gr. 2-6). lib. bdg. 21.25 (978-1-4042-3391-1(1)) Rosen Publishing Group, Inc., The. (PowerKids Pr.).

Blue, Rose & Naden, Corinne J. Exploring Central America, Mexico, & the Caribbean. 2003. (Illus.). 64p. lib. bdg. 28.56 (978-0-7398-4952-1(2)) Raintree.

Calvert, Patricia. Hernando Cortes: Fortune Favored the Bold. 2002. (Great Explorations Ser.). (Illus.). 80p. (J). 29.93 (978-0-7614-1482-7(7) , Benchmark Bks.) Cavendish, Marshall Corp.

De Angelis, Gina. Hernan Cortes & the Conquest of Mexico. 1999. (Explorers of the New World Ser.). (Illus.). 64p. (YA). (gr. 4 up). 31.00 (978-0-7910-5516-8(7) , Chelsea Hse.) Facts On File, Inc.

Flowers, Charles. Cortes & the Conquest of the Aztec Empire in World History. 2001. (In World History Ser.). (Illus.). 128p. (J). (gr. 5-12). lib. bdg. 26.60 (978-0-7660-1395-7(2)) Enslow Pubs., Inc.

Gaff, Jackie. Hernan Cortes: The Life of a Spanish Conquistador. 2005. (Graphic Nonfiction Ser.). (Illus.). 48p. (J). (gr. 4-6). lib. bdg. 26.50 (978-1-4042-0244-3(7)) Rosen Publishing Group, Inc., The.

Henty, G. A. By Right of Conquest: Or with Cortez in Mexico. 2000. 348p. (YA). (gr. 3 up). mass mkt. 7.99 (978-1-887159-67-8(3)) Preston-Speed Pubns.

January, Brendan. Hernan Cortes. (Groundbreakers Ser.). (Illus.). 48p. 2003. (J). (gr. 5-7). lib. bdg. 27.07 (978-1-4034-0243-1(4)); 2002. pap. (978-1-4034-0479-4(8)) Heinemann Library.

Kimmel, Eric A. Montezuma & the Fall of the Aztecs. San Souci, Daniel, illus. 2000. 32p. (J). (gr. 4-6). tchr. ed. 16.95 (978-0-8234-1452-9(3)) Holiday Hse., Inc.

Kline, Trish. Hernan Cortes. (Rourke Discovery Library). 2003. (Illus.). 24p. (gr. 2-5). 14.95 (978-1-58952-293-0(1)); 2002. 19.27 (978-1-58952-427-9(6)) Rourke Publishing, LLC.

Koestler-Grack, Rachel A. Hernando Cortes: And the Fall of the Aztecs. Goetzmann, William H., ed. 2005. (Explorers of New Lands Ser.). (Illus.). 158p. (J). (ps-8). lib. bdg. 30.00 (978-0-7910-8609-4(7) , Chelsea Hse.) Facts On File, Inc.

Orozco, Fernando. Conquista de Mexico. 2000. Tr. of Conquest of Mexico. (SPA.). 255p. (J). pap. 12.98 (978-968-38-0289-7(3)) Panorama Editorial MEX. *Dist:* Giron Bks., Libros Sin Fronteras.

Petrie, Kristin. Hernan Cortes. 2004. (Explorers Set I Ser.). (Illus.). 32p. (J). (gr. k-6). lib. bdg. 22.78 (978-1-59197-598-4(0)) ABDO Publishing Co.

Reid, Struan. Montezuma. 2002. (Historical Biographies Ser.). (Illus.). 32p. (J). (gr. 2-4). lib. bdg. 22.79 (978-1-58810-566-0(0)) Heinemann Library.

Stein, R. Conrad. The Story of Mexico. 2007. (J). ***(978-1-59935-053-0(X))*** Reynolds, Morgan Inc.

Whiting, Jim. The Life & Times of Hernando Cortes. 2006. (Profiles in American History Ser.). (Illus.). 48p. (J). (gr. 4-8). lib. bdg. 29.95 (978-1-58415-449-5(7)) Mitchell Lane Pubs., Inc.

Wilson, Mike. The Conquest of Mexico. 2002. (Exploration & Discovery Ser.). (Illus.). 64p. (YA). (gr. 5 up). lib. bdg. (978-1-59084-050-4(X)) Mason Crest Pubs.

Zronik, John Paul. Hernando Cortés: Spanish Invader of Mexico. 2006. (In the Footsteps of Explorers Ser.). (Illus.). 32p. (J). (gr. 3-9). (978-0-7787-2434-6(4)) Crabtree Publishing Co.

MEXICO—HISTORY—CONQUEST, 1519-1540—FICTION

Henty, A. G. By Right of Conquest or with Cortez in Mexico. 2007. (ENG.). 356p. 45.99 ***(978-1-4280-7223-7(3));*** per. 39.99 ***(978-1-4280-7201-5(2))*** IndyPublish.com.

MEXICO—HISTORY—SPANISH COLONY, 1540-1810

Burr, Claudia, et al. When the Viceroy Came. 2006. (Illus.). 29p. (J). (gr. 4-8). reprint ed. 16.00 (978-1-4223-5465-0(2)) DIANE Publishing Co.

MEXICO—HISTORY—SPANISH COLONY, 1540-1810—FICTION

Barrera, Norma. Diario de Tlauhquechol (1518) 2003. (Mexican Diaries). (SPA., Illus.). 146p. (J). pap. (978-970-690-042-5(X) , SOM7948) Planeta Mexicana Editorial S. A. de C. V. MEX. *Dist:* Lectorum Pubns., Inc.

Zarco, Carmen Saucedo. Diario de Mariana (1695-95) 2003. (Mexican Diaries). (SPA., Illus.). 164p. (J). pap. (978-970-690-113-2(2) , SOM7943) Planeta Mexicana Editorial S. A. de C. V. MEX. *Dist:* Lectorum Pubns., Inc.

MEXICO—PRESIDENTS

Mendieta, Ruben. El Porfiriato para Ninos. Garcia, Modesto, illus. 2002. (Historia para Ninos Ser.). (SPA.). 115p. (J). pap. 8.95 (978-970-643-509-5(3)) Selector, S.A. de C.V. MEX. *Dist:* Lectorum Pubns., Inc.

Paprocki, Sherry Beck. Vicente Fox. 2003. (Major World Leaders Ser.). (Illus.). 144p. (gr. 6-12). pap. 30.00 (978-0-7910-7524-1(9) , Chelsea Hse.) Facts On File, Inc.

MEXICO—SOCIAL LIFE AND CUSTOMS

Ancona, George. Charro: The Mexican Cowboy. 1999. (SPA.). (J). 16.80 (978-0-606-16529-7(0)) Tandem Library Bks.

—The Fiestas: Viva Mexico! 2001. (Viva Mexico! Ser.). (Illus.). 48p. (J). (gr. 3-6). lib. bdg. 27.07 (978-0-7614-1327-1(8) , Benchmark Bks.) Cavendish, Marshall Corp.

—The People: Viva Mexico! 2001. (Viva Mexico! Ser.). (Illus.). 48p. (J). (gr. 3 up). lib. bdg. 27.07 (978-0-7614-1329-5(4) , Benchmark Bks.) Cavendish, Marshall Corp.

Andrade, Mary J., photos by. Day of the Dead A Passion for Life: Día de los Muertos Pasion por la Vida. Andrade, Mary J., . 2nd ed. 2007. (SPA.). lib. bdg., stu. ed., tchr.'s training gde. ed. 29.95 ***(978-0-9791624-0-4(8))*** La Oferta Publishing Co.

Auch, Alison. Welcome to Mexico. 2002. (Spyglass Books). (Illus.). 24p. (J). (gr. 1 up). lib. bdg. 18.60 (978-0-7565-0373-4(6)) Compass Point Bks.

Baumgart, Brian. Teens in Mexico. 2006. (Global Connections Ser.). (Illus.). 96p. (J). (gr. 5-7). 31.93 (978-0-7565-2064-9(9)) Compass Point Bks.

Carew-Miller, Anna. Mexican Art & Architecture. 2002. (Encyclopedia of Mexico Ser.). (Illus.). 64,80p. (YA). (gr. 5 up). lib. bdg. (978-1-59084-081-8(X)) Mason Crest Pubs.

Cordero, Flor de Maria. M Is for Mexico. 2008. (World Alphabets Ser.). (Illus.). 32p. (J). 16.95 ***(978-1-84507-593-4(5))*** Lincoln, Frances Ltd. GBR. *Dist:* Perseus Distribution.

Coronado, Rosa. Cooking the Mexican Way. 2nd rev. exp. ed. (Easy Menu Ethnic Cookbooks). (Illus.). 72p. (J). (gr. 5-12). 2003. pap. 7.95 (978-0-8225-4162-2(9)); 2002. 25.26 (978-0-8225-4117-2(3) , Lerner Pubns.) Lerner Publishing Group.

—Cooking the Mexican Way. 2002. (gr. 5-8). lib. bdg. 16.40 (978-0-613-59146-1(1)) Tandem Library Bks.

Costain, Meredith & Collins, Paul, eds. Welcome to Mexico. 2002. (Countries of the World Ser.). (Illus.). 32p. (J). 28.00 (978-0-7910-6877-9(3) , Chelsea Hse.) Facts On File, Inc.

Cunningham, Patrick. Mexico. Cunningham, Susan M., photos by. 2004. (Letters from Around the World Ser.). (Illus.). (J). lib. bdg. (978-1-84234-244-2(4) , Cherrytree Books) Evans Publishing Group.

Doering, Amanda. Cinco de Mayo. 2006. (First Facts Ser.). (Illus.). 24p. (J). 15.93 (978-0-7368-5387-3(1)) Capstone Pr., Inc.

—Day of the Dead. 2006. (First Facts Ser.). (Illus.). 24p. (J). 15.93 (978-0-7368-5388-0(X)) Capstone Pr., Inc.

Flanagan, Alice K. Cinco de Mayo. Girouard, Patrick, illus. 2003. (Holidays & Festivals Ser.). 32p. (J). (gr. 3 up). lib. bdg. 22.60 (978-0-7565-0480-9(5)) Compass Point Bks.

Ganeri, Anita. The Ancient Maya. 2005. (Ancient Civilizations Ser.). (Illus.). 32p. (J). (gr. 4-6). 26.60 (978-0-7565-1677-2(3)) Compass Point Bks.

Garcia, James. Cinco de Mayo. 2003. (Proud Heritage-The Hispanic Library). (Illus.). 40p. (J). (gr. 3-7). 28.50 (978-1-56766-174-3(2)) Child's World, Inc.

Gillis, Jennifer Blizin. Las Posadas. 2002. (Candle Time Ser.). (Illus.). 24p. (J). (ps-1). lib. bdg. 18.50 (978-1-58810-531-8(8)) Heinemann Library.

Gillis, Jennifer Blizin & Jordan, Denise M. Las Posadas. 2002. (Fiestas Con Velas (Candle Time) Ser.). 24p. (J). (ps-1). (SPA.). lib. bdg. 18.50 (978-1-58810-786-2(8)); (SPA., Illus.). pap. 5.25 (978-1-58810-833-3(3) , 91592); (Illus.). pap. 5.25 (978-1-58810-740-4(X) , 91389) Heinemann Library.

Girod, Christina M. Mexico. 2003. (Teens Around the World Ser.). (J). (978-1-59018-032-7(1) , Lucent Bks.) Thomson Gale.

Gnojewski, Carol. Cinco de Mayo: Celebrating Hispanic Pride. 2002. (Finding Out about Holidays Ser.). (Illus.). 48p. (J). (gr. 1-4). lib. bdg. 23.93 (978-0-7660-1575-3(0)) Enslow Pubs., Inc.

—Day of the Dead: A Latino Celebration of Family & Life. 2005. (Finding Out about Holidays Ser.). (Illus.). 48p. (J). lib. bdg. 23.93 (978-0-7660-1780-1(X) , Enslow Elementary) Enslow Pubs., Inc.

Harcourt School Publishers Staff. Buenos Dias: Take-Home Book. 1999. (Vamos Ser.). (SPA., Illus.). (J). (gr. 1). pap. 2.50 (978-0-15-318808-4(1)) Harcourt Schl. Pubs.

Harris, Zoe & Williams, Suzanne. Pinatas & Smiling Skeletons: Celebrating Mexican Festivals. Woo, Yolanda G., illus. 1998. 48p. (YA). (gr. 2-8). lib. bdg. 19.95 (978-1-881896-19-7(6) , Dragon Bks.) Pacific View Pr.

Heinrichs, Ann. Cinco de Mayo. Petelinsek, Kathleen, illus. 2006. (Holidays, Festivals, & Celebrations Ser.). 32p. (J). (gr. k-4). 22.79 (978-1-59296-573-1(3)) Child's World, Inc.

—Día de Los Muertos. Gallagher-Cole, Mernie, illus. 2006. (Holidays, Festivals, & Celebrations Ser.). 32p. (J). (gr. k-4). 22.79 (978-1-59296-574-8(1)) Child's World, Inc.

Hiemen, Sara. Mexico ABCs: A Book about the People & Places of Mexico. Ouren, Todd, illus. 2004. (Country ABCs Ser.). 32p. (gr. k-5). 23.93 (978-1-4048-0023-6(9)) Picture Window Bks.

Hill, Sandi. Celebrating Cinco de Mayo: Fiesta Time! 1999. (ps-2). lib. bdg. 10.65 (978-0-613-34118-9(X)) Tandem Library Bks.

Hoyt-Goldsmith, Diane. Cinco de Mayo: Celebrating Mexican-American Traditions. Migdale, Lawrence, illus. Migdale, Lawrence, photos by. 2008. (J). ***(978-0-8234-2107-7(4))*** Holiday Hse., Inc.

Illsley, Linda. Mexico. 1999. (Food & Festivals Ser.). (Illus.). 32p. (J). (gr. 1-4). lib. bdg. 25.69 (978-0-8172-5553-4(2)) Raintree.

Kalman, Bobbie. Mexico: The Culture. 2002. (gr. 3-6). lib. bdg. 16.40 (978-0-613-52981-5(2)) Tandem Library Bks.

—Mexico - The People. 2nd rev. ed. 2001. (Lands, Peoples & Cultures Ser.). (Illus.). 32p. (J). (gr. 4-5). (978-0-7787-9362-5(1)); pap. (978-0-7787-9730-2(9)) Crabtree Publishing Co.

Kaplan, Leslie. Cinco de Mayo. 2004. (Library of Holidays). (Illus.). 24p. (J). lib. bdg. 18.75 (978-0-8239-6662-2(3) , PowerKids Pr.) Rosen Publishing Group, Inc., The.

Krebs, Laurie. Off We Go to Mexico. Corr, Christopher, illus. 2006. 0032p. (J). 16.99 (978-1-905236-40-4(9)) Barefoot Bks., Inc.

Laufer, Peter & Roth, Susan L. Made in Mexico. Roth, Susan L., illus. 2000. (Illus.). 32p. (J). (gr. 3-7). 16.95 (978-0-7922-7118-5(1) , National Geographic Children's Bks.) National Geographic Society.

Levy, Janice. Celebrate! It's Cinco de Mayo!/¡Celebremos! ¡Es el Cinco de Mayo! Arisa, Miguel, tr. Lopez, Loretta, illus. 2007. (ENG & SPA.). 32p. (J). (ps-2). 16.95 ***(978-0-8075-1176-3(5));*** pap. 6.95 ***(978-0-8075-1177-0(3))*** Whitman, Albert & Co.

Lomas Garza, Carmen. Magic Windows (Ventanas Magicas) Lomas Garza, Carmen, illus. 1999. (ENG & SPA., Illus.). 32p. (J). (gr. 1-4). 15.95 (978-0-89239-157-8(X)) Children's Bk. Pr.

Lowery, Linda. Cinco de Mayo. Knutson, Barbara, illus. 2005. (On My Own Holidays Ser.). 48p. (J). (gr. k-3). pap. 5.95 (978-1-57505-764-4(6)); (gr. 2-4). 25.26 (978-1-57505-654-8(2)) Lerner Publishing Group.

—Day of the Dead. Knutson, Barbara, illus. 2004. (On My Own Holidays Ser.). 48p. (J). (gr. 2-4). lib. bdg. 25.26 (978-0-87614-914-0(X)) Lerner Publishing Group.

—Day of the Dead. 2004. (gr. k-3). lib. bdg. 14.10 (978-0-613-79241-7(6)) Tandem Library Bks.

MacMillan, Dianne M. Mexican Independence Day & Cinco de Mayo. 2nd ed. 2008. (Best Holiday Books Ser.). 48p. (J). (gr. 3-4). lib. bdg. 23.93 ***(978-0-7660-3044-2(X))*** Enslow Pubs., Inc.

Mattern, Joanne. Celebrate Cinco de Mayo. 2006. (Celebrate Holidays Ser.). (Illus.). 104p. (J). lib. bdg. 31.93 (978-0-7660-2579-0(9)) Enslow Pubs., Inc.

McCulloch, Julie. Mexico. (Illus.). 48p. (J). 2002. (gr. 4-6). pap. (978-1-58810-390-1(0) , 91140); 2001. (gr. 3-5). lib. bdg. 25.64 (978-1-58810-088-7(X)) Heinemann Library.

McDaniel, Jan. The Food of Mexico. 2002. (Encyclopedia of Mexico Ser.). (Illus.). 64,80p. (YA). (gr. 5 up). lib. bdg. (978-1-59084-085-6(2)) Mason Crest Pubs.

Murray, Julie. Cinco de Mayo. 2005. (Buddy Book Ser.). (Illus.). 24p. (J). (gr. k-4). lib. bdg. 21.35 (978-1-59197-586-1(7)) ABDO Publishing Co.

Nobleman, Marc Tyler. Cinco de Mayo. 2004. (Let's See Ser.). 24p. (J). (gr. 1 up). lib. bdg. 19.93 (978-0-7565-0768-8(5)) Compass Point Bks.

Parker, Victoria. Mexico. 2005. (We're from Ser.). (Illus.). 32p. (J). (gr. 3-7). lib. bdg. 24.21 (978-1-4034-5787-5(5)) Heinemann.

—We're from Mexico. 2005. (We're from Ser.). (Illus.). 32p. (J). pap. 7.25 (978-1-4034-5794-3(8)) Heinemann.

Peppas, Lynn. Life in Ancient Mesoamerica. 2004. (Peoples of the Ancient World Ser.). (Illus.). 32p. (J). (978-0-7787-2039-3(X)) Crabtree Publishing Co.

Ross, Michael Elsohn. Mexican Christmas. Rigau, Felix, illus. Rigau, Felix, photos by. 2002. (Photo Bks.). 40p. (J). (gr. k-3). lib. bdg. 23.93 (978-0-87614-601-9(9) , Carolrhoda Bks.) Lerner Publishing Group.

San Vicente, Luis. The Festival of Bones, el Festival de las Calaveras: The Little-Bitty Book for the Day of the Dead. Byrd, John Williams & Byrd, Bobby, trs. San Vicente, Luis, illus. 2002. (SPA & ENG., Illus.). 32p. (J). (gr. k-5). 14.95 (978-0-938317-67-8(9)) Cinco Puntos Pr.

Schaefer, Lola M. Cinco de Mayo. Saunders-Smith, Gail, ed. 2000. (Holidays & Celebrations Ser.). (Illus.). 24p. (J). (gr. k-1). lib. bdg. 15.95 (978-0-7368-0661-9(X) , Pebble Bks.) Capstone Pr., Inc.

—Cinco de Mayo, Vol. 2. 2005. (One World, Many Cultures Ser.). 24p. (YA). (gr. k-3). pap. (978-0-7368-9430-2(6) , Pebble Bks.) Capstone Pr., Inc.

Stevenson, Monica. Tradiciones Mexicanas para Ninos. 2006. (SPA.). 136p. (YA). (gr. 4-7). pap. (978-968-403-934-6(4)) Selector, S.A. de C.V.

Tabor, Nancy Maria Grande. Celebrations/Celebraciones: Holidays of the United States of America & Mexico/ Dias Feriados de los Estados Unidos y Mexico. Tabor, Nancy Maria Grande, illus. 2004. (SPA & ENG., Illus.). 32p. (J). pap. 7.95 (978-1-57091-550-5(4)) Charlesbridge Publishing, Inc.

Tait, Leia. Cinco de Mayo. 2006. (J). (978-1-59036-460-4(0)); (978-1-59036-463-5(5)) Weigl Pubs., Inc.

Turck, Mary C. Mexico & Central America: A Fiesta of Cultures, Crafts, & Activities for Ages 8-12. 2004. (Illus.). 160p. (J). pap. 16.95 (978-1-55652-525-4(7)) Chicago Review Pr., Inc.

Urrutia, Maria Cristina & Orozco, Rebeca. Cinco de Mayo: Yesterday & Today. 2006. (SPA., Illus.). 29p. (J). (gr. 4-8). reprint ed. 16.00 (978-1-4223-5464-3(4)) DIANE Publishing Co.

Vasquez, Sarah. Cinco de Mayo. 1999. (World of Holidays Ser.). (Illus.). 32p. (J). (gr. 2-5). lib. bdg. 25.70 (978-0-8172-5562-6(1)) Raintree.

—Cinco de Mayo. 2000. (Illus.). (J). (978-0-606-18478-6(3)) Tandem Library Bks.

Wade, Mary Dodson. Cinco de Mayo. 2003. (Rookie Read-About Holidays Ser.). (Illus.). 32p. (J). (gr. 1-2). pap. 5.95 (978-0-516-27489-8(9) , Children's Pr.) Scholastic Library Publishing.

—Cinco de Mayo. 2003. (gr. k-3). lib. bdg. 14.10 (978-0-613-59594-0(7)) Tandem Library Bks.

—El Dia de los Muertos. 2002. (Rookie Read-About Holidays Ser.).Tr. of Day of the Dead. (Illus.). 32p. (J). (gr. 1-2). pap. 20.50 (978-0-516-22493-0(X) , Children's Pr.) Scholastic Library Publishing.

Williams, Colleen Madonna Flood. The Festivals of Mexico. 2002. (Encyclopedia of Mexico Ser.). (Illus.). 64,80p. (YA). (gr. 5 up). lib. bdg. (978-1-59084-078-8(X)) Mason Crest Pubs.

MNO

—The People of Mexico. 2002. (Mexico Ser.). (Illus.). 64,80p. (J). (gr. 5 up). lib. bdg. (978-1-59084-077-1(1)) Mason Crest Pubs.

Wood, Ira. A Mexican Feast: The Food & Recipes of Mexico. 2002. (Reading Room Collection). (Illus.). 24p. (J). lib. bdg. 18.75 (978-0-8239-3736-3(4)) Rosen Publishing Group, Inc., The.

Zocchi, Judy. In Mexico. Brodie, Neale, illus. 2005. (Global Adventures I Ser.). 32p. (J). lib. bdg. 20.65 (978-1-59646-002-7(4)) Dingles & Co.

—In Mexico/en México. Brodie, Neale, illus. 2005. (Global Adventures I Ser.).Tr. of En México. (ENG & SPA.). 32p. (J). pap. 9.95 (978-1-59646-137-6(3)); lib. bdg. 20.65 (978-1-59646-003-4(2)) Dingles & Co.

MEXICO, GULF OF

Green, Jen. Caribbean Sea & Gulf of Mexico. 2006. (Illus.). 48p. (J). pap. (978-0-8368-6280-5(5) , World Almanac Library) Stevens, Gareth Inc.

Mitchell, Mark. Raising la Belle. Mitchell, Mark, illus. (Professor Wigglestix & the Weather Ser.). (Illus.). 112p. 10.95 (978-1-57168-703-6(3)) Eakin Pr.

Petersen, David. The Gulf of Mexico. 2001. (True Bks.). (Illus.). 48p. (J). (gr. 3-5). pap. 6.95 (978-0-516-27317-4(5) , Children's Pr.) Scholastic Library Publishing.

Peterson, David. The Gulf of Mexico. 2001. (Geography Ser.). (Illus.). 48p. (J). (gr. 3-5). 25.00 (978-0-516-21665-2(1) , Children's Pr.) Scholastic Library Publishing.

Zollman, Pam. Gulf of Mexico. 2006. 32p. (gr. 1-2). (YA). pap. 5.95 (978-0-516-29711-8(2)); (Illus.). (J). 20.50 (978-0-516-25035-9(3)) Scholastic Library Publishing. (Children's Pr.).

MIAMI DOLPHINS (FOOTBALL TEAM)

Kennedy, Nick. Dan Marino: Star Quarterback. 1998. (Sports Reports). (Illus.). 112p. (YA). (gr. 4-10). lib. bdg. 26.60 (978-0-89490-933-7(9)) Enslow Pubs., Inc.

Leboutillier, Nate. Miami Dolphins. 2005. (Super Bowl Champions Ser.). (Illus.). 24p. (gr. 1-4). 16.95 (978-1-58341-385-2(5) , Creative Education) Creative Co., The.

Miami Dolphins. Miami Dolphins. CWC Sports Inc., ed. 1998. (NFL Team Yearbooks Ser.). (J). (gr. 1-12). pap. 9.99 (978-1-891613-13-5(8)) Everett Sports Publishing & Marketing.

Schmalzbauer, Adam. The History of the Miami Dolphins. 2004. (NFL Today Ser.). (Illus.). 32p. 18.95 (978-1-58341-302-9(2) , Creative Education) Creative Co., The.

Stewart, Mark. Miami Dolphins. 2006. (Team Spirit Ser.). (Illus.). 48p. (J). lib. bdg. 25.27 (978-1-59953-065-9(1)) Norwood Hse. Pr.

MICE

Carle, Eric. Do You Want to Be My Friend? Carle, Eric, illus. 2002. (Illus.). (J). 15.49 (978-0-7587-8917-4(3)) Book Wholesalers, Inc.

Coppendale, Jean. Mice. 2004. (QEB You & Your Pet Ser.). (Illus.). 32p. (J). lib. bdg. 18.95 (978-1-59566-056-5(9)) QEB Publishing Inc.

DK Publishing. Mouse: See How They Grow. 2008. (See How They Grow Ser.). 1p. (J). (ps-k). pap. 3.99 (***978-0-7566-3764-4(3)***) Dorling Kindersley Publishing, Inc.

Group/McGraw-Hill, Wright. The Mouse Mapper: Level I, 6 vols. (Take Twostm Ser.). 16p. 29.95 (978-0-322-08967-9(0)) Wright Group, The.

Gunson, Dave, illus. Mice 6 Packs. First Wave Satellite. (Sails Literacy Ser.). 16p. (gr. k up). 27.00 (978-0-7578-6877-1(0)) Rigby Education.

Head, Honor. Rats & Mice. Burton, Jane, photos by. 2000. (My Pet Ser.). (Illus.). 32p. (J). (gr. 3-5). lib. bdg. 25.69 (978-0-7398-2889-2(4)) Raintree.

—Rats & Mice. 2000. (My Pet Ser.). (Illus.). 32p. (J). (gr. 3-5). pap. 8.95 (978-0-7398-3014-7(7)) Steck-Vaughn.

Hipp, Andrew. The Life Cycle of a Mouse. Kuhn, Dwight, photos by. 2002. (Life Cycles Library). (Illus.). 24p. (J). lib. bdg. 18.75 (978-0-8239-5866-5(3)) Rosen Publishing Group, Inc., The.

Jacobs, Lee. Mouse. 2003. (Wild America Ser.). (Illus.). 24p. (J). 22.45 (978-1-56711-569-7(1) , Blackbirch Pr., Inc.) Thomson Gale.

Leavitt, Amie. Care for a Pet Mouse. 2007. (How to Convince Your Parents You Can ... Ser.). (Illus.). 32p. (J). (gr. 1-4). lib. bdg. 25.70 (***978-1-58415-606-2(6)***) Mitchell Lane Pubs., Inc.

Loves, June. Mice & Rats. 2003. (Pets Ser.). (Illus.). 32p. (gr. 2-4). 23.00 (978-0-7910-7551-7(6) , Chelsea Hse.) Facts On File, Inc.

Lupo, Tamar. Caring for Your Mouse. 2006. (J). (978-1-59036-472-7(4)); (978-1-59036-473-4(2)) Weigl Pubs., Inc.

Mice. (Animals Ser.). 32p. (J). 6.95 (978-0-7368-8067-1(4)) Capstone Pr., Inc.

Mice, 6 vols. (gr. 2-5). 36.95 (978-0-7368-8177-7(8)) Red Brick Learning.

Mice at School: Individual Title Six-Packs. (Story Steps Ser.). (gr. k-2). 32.00 (978-0-7635-9825-9(9)) Rigby Education.

Morris Mouse: Individual Title Six-Pack. (Story Steps Ser.). (gr. k-2). 23.00 (978-0-7635-9827-3(5)) Rigby Education.

Morris, Ting. Harvest Mouse. Rosewarne, Graham, illus. 2005. 32p. (J). (gr. 3-7). lib. bdg. 27.10 (978-1-58340-523-9(2)) Smart Apple Media.

Nice Mice! Long Vowel i, CVCe Pattern: Level B, 6 vols. (Wright Skills Ser.). 16p. (gr. k-3). 17.95 (978-0-322-03102-9(8)) Wright Group, The.

Pascoe, Elaine & Kuhn, Dwight. Mice. 2005. (Nature Close-up Ser.). (Illus.). 48p. (J). (ps-7). lib. bdg. 24.95 (978-1-4103-0537-4(6) , Blackbirch Pr., Inc.) Thomson Gale.

Savage, Stephen. Mouse. 2003. (Animal Neighbours Ser.). (Illus.). 32p. (978-0-7502-4474-9(7) , Hodder Wayland) Hodder Children's Division.

Sjonger, Rebecca & Kalman, Bobbie. Mice. Crabtree, Marc, illus. Crabtree, Marc, photos by. 2004. (Pet Care Ser.). 32p. (J). pap. (978-0-7787-1786-7(0)); (978-0-7787-1754-6(2)) Crabtree Publishing Co.

Spilsbury, Louise & Spilsbury, Richard. Mice. 2006. (Keeping Pets Ser.). (Illus.). 48p. (J). (978-1-4034-7704-0(3)) Heinemann Library.

Vidner, Bradley. All about Your... Mouse. 1998. (All about Your...Ser.). (Illus.). 64p. 2.95 (978-1-86054-066-0(X)) Ringpress Bks., Ltd. GBR. *Dist:* 7 Hills Bk. Distributors.

Waters, Jo. The Wild Side of Mice & Rats. 2004. (Raintree Perspectives Ser.). (Illus.). 32p. (J). pap. (978-1-4109-1412-5(7)) Harcourt Schl. Pubs.

—The Wild Side of Pet Mice & Rats. 2005. (Raintree Perspectives Ser.). (Illus.). 32p. (J). (ps-ps). lib. bdg. 27.50 (978-1-4109-1406-4(2)) Harcourt Schl. Pubs.

Watts, Barrie. Mouse. 2004. (Illus.). 32p. (J). (ps-17). lib. bdg. 24.25 (978-1-58340-231-3(4)) Smart Apple Media.

The Wild Side of Mice & Rats. 2004. pap. (978-1-4109-1418-7(6)) Harcourt Schl. Pubs.

MICE—FICTION

Ada, Alma Flor & Campoy, F. Isabel. A New Job for Perez, the Mouse. (Gateways to the Sun). 32p. (J). (gr. k-6). pap. 13.95 (978-1-58105-962-5(0)) Santillana USA Publishing Co., Inc.

Adamson, Bobby R. The Field Mice of Deer Park. 2002. 96p. (YA). (gr. 7-12). 6.95 (978-0-9720631-0-4(2)) Adamson, Bobby R.

Adventures of Danny Meadow Mouse. 2000. mass mkt. 3.99 (978-1-55902-946-9(3) , Aerie) Doherty, Tom Assocs., LLC.

Aesop. Lion & the Mouse PB. 2007. (Illus.). (J). pap. 6.95 (978-0-7358-2129-3(1)) North-South Bks., Inc.

—The Town Mouse & the Country Mouse. Watts, Bernadette, illus. 1998. 32p. (J). (ps-3). 16.50 (978-1-55858-988-9(0)) North-South Bks., Inc.

Aesop. Town Mouse Country Mouse Sha. Hays, Ethel, illus. 2007. 14p. (J). (ps-3). pap. 9.95 (***978-1-59583-192-7(4)*** , Green Tiger Pr.) Laughing Elephant.

Aigner-Clark, Julie. Baby Einstein: La casa de Violet Violet's House, Spanish-Language Edition. Zaidi, Nadeem, illus. 2005. (Baby Einstein: Libros de Carton Ser.). (SPA.). 10p. (J). bds. 9.95 (978-970-718-305-6(5) , Silver Dolphin en Español) Advanced Marketing, S. de R. L. de C. V. MEX. *Dist:* Perseus Distribution.

—Violet's House: A Giant Touch-and-Feel Book. Zaidi, Nadeem, illus. 2003. 10p. (ps-17). 9.99 (978-0-7868-1872-3(7)) Disney Pr.

—What Does Violet See? Birds & Nests. Zaidi, Nadeem, illus. 2002. (Baby Einstein Ser.). 16p. (ps-ps). 5.99 (978-0-7868-0874-8(8)) Disney Pr.

—What Does Violet See? Raindrops & Puddles. Zaidi, Nadeem, illus. 2002. (Baby Einstein Ser.). 16p. (ps-ps). 5.99 (978-0-7868-0871-7(3)) Disney Pr.

—What Does Violet See? Sand & Sea. Zaidi, Nadeem, illus. 2002. (Baby Einstein Ser.). 16p. (ps-ps). 5.99 (978-0-7868-0873-1(X)) Disney Pr.

—What Does Violet See? Snowflakes & Icicles. Zaidi, Nadeem, illus. 2002. (Baby Einstein Ser.). 16p. (ps-ps). 5.99 (978-0-7868-0872-4(1)) Disney Pr.

Alborough, Jez. Watch Out! Big Bro's Coming! Alborough, Jez, illus. 1998. (Illus.). 32p. (J). (ps-3). pap. 6.99 (978-0-7636-0584-1(0)) Candlewick Pr.

Alfred Oscar Valentine: Tales from Spoon Creek: New Beginnings. 2006. (J). 12.00 (978-0-9766894-5-4(6)) Stanley, Donna Lacy.

Allan, Nicholas. Que Animales! Mayobre, Maria Francisca, tr. from ENG. Allan, Nicholas, illus. 2001. (Coleccion Primeras Lecturas). (SPA., Illus.). 28p. (J). pap. 7.50 (978-980-257-264-9(0)) Ekare, Ediciones VEN. *Dist:* AIMS International Bks., Inc., Lectorum Pubns., Inc.

Alter, Anna. Don't Eat a Mouse with a Spoon. 2001. (Illus.). 24p. (J). (ps up). 14.89 (978-0-688-17883-3(9)) HarperCollins Pubs.

Andrews, Miriam. The Butterfly's Last Journey. 2001. pap. (***978-1-889733-10-4(5)***) Precious Life Bks., Inc.

Anfousse, Ginette. Polo et L'anniversaire. Sarrazin, Marisol, tr. 2003. (Polo Baby Board Bks.). (FRE., Illus.). 16p. (J). (-ps). bds. (978-2-89021-656-3(X)) Diffusion du livre Mirabel.

Anzola, Rosario. El Son Del Raton y Otras Canciones. Fuenmayor, Morella, illus. (SPA.). (J). pap. 6.00 (978-980-01-0693-8(6)) Monte Avila Editores Latinoamericana CA VEN. *Dist:* Lectorum Pubns., Inc.

Archambault, John. Boom Chicka Rock. Chitwood, Suzanne Tanner, illus. 2004. 36p. (J). (ps-2). 15.99 (978-0-399-23587-0(6) , Philomel) Penguin Group (USA) Inc.

Archer, Mike. Looking after Little Ellie. Archer, Dosh, illus. 2005. 300p. (J). 15.95 (978-1-58234-971-8(1)) Bloomsbury Publishing.

Aremds, Donald L. Norm the Ninja River Mouse. 2006. (J). (978-0-9768880-1-7(7)) Mission Manuscripts, Inc.

Arengo, Sue. The Town Mouse & the Country Mouse Beginner Level 2. 1999. (Illus.). 24p. (J). 5.50 (978-0-19-422021-7(4)) Oxford Univ. Pr., Inc.

Arenstam, Peter. Nicholas: A Massachusetts Tale. Holman, Karen Busch, illus. 2007. (J). 14.95 (***978-1-58726-519-8(2)*** , Mitten Pr.) Ann Arbor Media Group, LLC.

Arnosky, Jim. Mouse Colors: A Very First Book. Arnosky, Jim, illus. 2001. (Illus.). 48p. (J). (gr. k-ps). tchr. ed. 5.95 (978-0-618-01521-4(3) , Clarion Bks.) Houghton Mifflin Co. Trade & Reference Div.

—Mouse Shapes: A Very First Book. Arnosky, Jim, illus. 2001. (Illus.). 48p. (J). (gr. k-ps). tchr. ed. 5.95 (978-0-618-01522-1(1) , Clarion Bks.) Houghton Mifflin Co. Trade & Reference Div.

Asch, Frank. Battle in a Bottle. Kanzler, John, illus. 2004. (Class Pets Ser.: No. 2). 96p. (J). (gr. 2-6). pap. 3.99 (978-0-689-84654-0(1) , Aladdin) Simon & Schuster Children's Publishing.

Asch, Frank. Mrs. Marlowe's Mice. Asch, Devin, illus. 2007. 32p. (J). (gr. k-4). (***978-1-55453-022-9(9)***) Kids Can Pr., Ltd.

Asch, Frank & Asch, Devin. Mr. Maxwell's Mouse. Asch, Frank & Asch, Devin, illus. 2005. (Illus.). 32p. (J). (gr. k-4). (978-1-55337-486-2(X)) Kids Can Pr., Ltd.

Aston, Dianna Hutts. Bless This Mouse: A Soft-to-Touch Book. 2004. (Illus.). 24p. (J). 14.95 (978-1-59354-050-0(7)) Handprint Bks.

Avi. Poppy. Floca, Brian, illus. 1999. (Poppy Stories Ser.). 192p. (J). (gr. 3-7). pap. 5.99 (978-0-380-72769-8(2) , Harper Trophy) HarperCollins Pubs.

—Poppy & Rye. Floca, Brian, illus. (Poppy Bks.). (J). (gr. 3-7). 1999. 240p. pap. 5.99 (978-0-380-79717-2(8) , Harper Trophy); 1998. 192p. 16.99 (978-0-380-97638-6(2)) HarperCollins Pubs.

—Poppy & Rye, unabr. ed. 2000. (J). (gr. 8). pap., stu. ed. 50.24 incl. audio (978-0-7887-3185-3(8) , 40920E5) Recorded Bks., LLC.

—Poppy & Rye. Floca, Brian, illus. 1999. 182p. (J). (ps-7). per. 14.15 (978-0-613-17447-3(X)) Tandem Library Bks.

—Poppy & Rye. 1999. (978-0-606-16352-1(2)) Tandem Library Bks.

—Poppy's Return. Floca, Brian, illus. 2005. (Poppy Stories Ser.). 240p. (J). 15.99 (978-0-06-000012-7(0)) HarperCollins Pubs.

—Ragweed. Howard, E., ed. Floca, Brian, illus. 2000. (Tales from Dimwood Forest Ser.). 224p. (J). (gr. 3-7). pap. 5.99 (978-0-380-80167-1(1)) HarperCollins Pubs.

—Ragweed. Floca, Brian, illus. 1999. (Avon Camelot Bks.). 192p. (J). (gr. 3-7). 16.99 (978-0-380-97690-4(0)) HarperCollins Pubs.

—Ragweed. 2000. (978-0-606-18714-5(6)); (gr. 3-6). lib. bdg. 14.15 (978-0-613-26699-4(4)) Tandem Library Bks.

Aylesworth, Jim. Little Bitty Mousie. Hague, Michael, illus. 2007. 32p. (J). 17.85 (***978-0-8027-9638-7(9));*** 16.95 (***978-0-8027-9637-0(0)***) Walker & Co.

Baglio, Ben M. The Midnight Mouse. Ellis, Andy, illus. 2003. 59p. (J). (978-0-439-41916-1(6)) Scholastic, Inc.

Bailey, Scott Arthur. Tale of Dickie Deer Mouse. 2006. pap. 33.99 (***978-1-4280-4928-4(2)***) IndyPublish.com.

Baisa, Marie. Mirabelle Mouse Bakes Cookies. 2005. (ENG.). 36p. per. 21.75 (978-1-4208-2043-0(5)) AuthorHouse.

Baker, Keith. Hickory Dickory Dock. 2007. (Illus.). 32p. (J). (ps-2). 16.00 (978-0-15-205818-0(4)) Harcourt Trade Pubs.

Balian, Lorna. Mother's Mother's Day. 2004. (Illus.). 40p. (J). 8.95 (978-1-932065-39-8(3)) Star Bright Bks., Inc.

Ballinger. The Great Cheese Squeeze. 2002. (Illus.). 40p. (J). pap. 14.99 (978-0-310-70506-2(1)) Zondervan.

Balloon Books Staff, ed. Max Mouse Learns First Words. 2000. (Plush Learning Bks.). (Illus.). 12p. (J). bds. 4.95 (978-0-8069-2919-4(7) , Balloon Bks.) Sterling Publishing Co., Inc.

Barbaresi, Nina. Firemouse. Barbaresi, Nina, illus. 2004. (Illus.). 40p. (J). (gr. k-3). pap. 6.99 (978-0-553-11177-4(9) , Dragonfly Bks.) Random Hse. Children's Bks.

Barbey, Beatrice. Meow Said the Mouse. Ames, Philippe, illus. 2005. 40p. (J). 15.00 (978-1-888375-49-7(3)) Parallax Pr.

Barkan, Joanne. There's A Mouse in My House! 2006. (Illus.). 10p. (J). bds. 14.99 (978-0-7944-1138-1(X)) Reader's Digest Assn., Inc., The.

Barnes, Peter W. Maestro Mouse: And the Mystery of the Missing Baton. Barnes, Cheryl Shaw, illus. 2005. 32p. (J). 16.95 (978-1-893622-17-3(7) , VSP Bks.) Vacation Spot Publishing.

—Woodrow for President: A Tail of Voting, Campaigns & Elections. Barnes, Cheryl Shaw, illus. 1999. 32p. (J). (gr. 3-6). 16.95 (978-1-893622-01-2(0) , VSP Bks.) Vacation Spot Publishing.

—Woodrow, the White House Mouse. Barnes, Cheryl Shaw, illus. 2nd rev. ed. 1998. 32p. (J). (gr. 1-3). (978-0-9637688-9-6(1)) Vacation Spot Publishing.

Barnes, Peter W. & Barnes, Cheryl Shaw. Woodrow, the White House Mouse. 2000. 32p. (J). (gr. k-3). pap. 5.99 (978-0-439-12952-7(4)) Scholastic, Inc.

Barns, Peter & Barns, Cheryl. Woodrow, the White House Mouse. 2000. (978-0-606-18617-9(4)) Tandem Library Bks.

Bauer, Elizabeth. The Happy Forest: Animal Adventures in the Forest. Bauer, Elizabeth, illus. l.t. ed. 2001. 130p. (J). per. incl. cd-rom (978-0-9630409-7-8(9)) Galaxy Publishing Hse.

Bauer, Marion Dane. Christmas in the Forest. Hearn, Diane Dawson, illus. (Holiday House Reader Ser.). 48p. (J). (gr. k-3). tchr. ed. 15.95 (978-0-8234-1371-3(3)) Holiday Hse., Inc.

Baum, Louis. The Mouse Who Braved Bedtime. Hellard, Sue, illus. 2006. 32p. (J). 16.95 (978-1-58234-691-5(7) , Bloomsbury Children) Bloomsbury Publishing.

Beaton, Clare. One Moose, Twenty Mice. Beaton, Clare, illus. (Illus.). 32p. (J). (gr. k-2). 2002. pap. 6.99 (978-1-84148-129-6(7)); 2000. reprint ed. bds. 6.99 (978-1-84148-285-9(4)) Barefoot Bks., Inc.

—One Moose, Twenty Mice. 2000. (ps-2). lib. bdg. 14.15 (978-0-613-26485-3(1)) Tandem Library Bks.

Becker, Bonny. A Visitor for Bear. Denton, Kady MacDonald, illus. 2008. (J). (***978-0-7636-2807-9(7)***) Candlewick Pr.

Beckler, Bruce. The Secrets of the Green Mansion. l.t. ed. 2004. (Illus.). 240p. (J). per. 13.99 (978-0-9745210-1-5(9)) Myers Publishing Co.

Beeke, Tiphanie. Roar Like a Lion! A First Book about Sounds. 2001. (Illus.). 16p. (J). (978-1-86233-143-3(X) , Gullane Children's Bks.) Pinwheel.

Benjamin, A. Hunaka Ma Hua Aswaa: It Could Have Been Worse. 2005. 32p. pap. 12.00 (978-977-6171-07-7(9) , 706-006) Al-Balsam Pubng. Hse. EGY. *Dist:* Bookworld Trade, Inc.

Benjamin, A. H. It Could Have Been Worse. Warnes, Tim, illus. 1998. 32p. (J). (ps-2). 14.95 (978-1-888444-26-1(6) , 21024) Little Tiger Pr.

—Little Mouse & the Big Red Apple. Williamson, Gwyneth, illus. 2001. 32p. (J). pap. 5.95 (978-1-58925-358-2(2) , tiger tales) ME Media LLC.

Bennett, John, illus. The Mice: Individual Title Six-Packs. (Sails Literacy Ser.). 16p. (gr. k up). 27.00 (978-0-7635-4432-4(9)) Rigby Education.

Benson, Laura. The Mouse's Picnic. Adams Marks, Elizabeth, illus. 2002. (Two Can Read Ser.). 16p. (J). 2.99 (978-1-56472-667-4(3)) Edupress, Inc.

Berkeley, Jon. Chopsticks. 2005. (Illus.). 32p. (J). (ps-3). 16.95 (978-0-375-83309-0(9) , Random Hse. Bks. for Young Readers) Random Hse. Children's Bks.

Big Hungry Bear Storysack. (J). 50.00 (978-0-85953-684-4(X)) Child's Play-International.

Big Mouse, Little Mouse: Individual Title Six-Packs. (Sails Literacy Ser.). (gr. 1-2). 36.00 (978-0-7578-6710-1(3)) Rigby Education.

Billingsley, Franny. Big Bad Bunny. Karas, G. Brian, illus. 2008. 40p. (J). 16.95 (***978-1-4169-0601-8(0)***) Simon & Schuster Children's Publishing.

Bishop, Dorothy S., et al. Leonardo el Leon y Ramon el Raton. 2001. Tr. of Lion & the Mouse. (SPA & ENG., Illus.). 64p. (J). 6.95 (978-0-8442-7445-4(3) , NT268) McGraw-Hill/Contemporary.

Blair, Eric. El Flautista de Hamelin. Peterson, Ben, illus. 2006. (Read-It! Readers en Espanol Ser.).Tr. of Pied Piper. (SPA.). 32p. (J). (ps-3). 19.95 (978-1-4048-1651-0(8)) Picture Window Bks.

—El Raton de Campo y el Raton de Ciudad: Version de la Fabula de Esopo. Silverman, Dianne, illus. 2006. (Read-It! Readers en Espanol Ser.).Tr. of Country Mouse & the City Mouse: A Retelling of Aesop's Fable. (SPA.). 32p. (J). (ps-3). 19.95 (978-1-4048-1617-6(8)) Picture Window Bks.

Blanchard, Patricia & Suhr, Joanne. There Was a Mouse. Gorbachev, Valeri, illus. 2003. 16p. (J). pap. 20.00 net. (978-1-57274-702-9(1) , BB2210) Owen, Richard C. Pubs., Inc.

Bloess, Herman E., Jr. Winter Adventures of Danny Deermouse & Friends. Martinez, Mike Louis, illus. l.t. ed. 2001. 86p. (J). per. 17.95 (978-0-9716744-0-0(X)) Bloess, Herman E.

Bloom, Becky. Mice Make Trouble. Biet, Pascal, illus. 2000. 32p. (J). (gr. k-2). pap. 15.95 (978-0-531-30253-8(9) , Orchard Bks.) Scholastic, Inc.

Bloom, Becky & Biet, Pascal. Crackers. 2001. (Illus.). (J). lib. bdg. (978-0-531-33326-6(4) , Orchard Bks.) Scholastic, Inc.

—Mice Make Trouble. 2000. (Illus.). 32p. (J). (ps-2). 16.99 (978-0-531-33253-5(5) , Orchard Bks.) Scholastic, Inc.

Boegehold, Betty. A Pet for Pippa Mouse. 2000. (Illus.). (J). 2.99 (978-0-679-89340-0(7) , Random Hse. Bks. for Young Readers) Random Hse. Children's Bks.

—A Pet for Pippa Mouse. 1999. (J). lib. bdg. 7.99 (978-0-679-99340-7(1)) Random Hse., Inc.

Bogacki, Tomek. Cat & Mouse in the Snow. Bogacki, Tomek, illus. 1999. (Illus.). 26p. (J). (gr. 2-4). reprint ed. 16.00 (978-0-7567-6125-7(5)) DIANE Publishing Co.

Bogart, Jo Ellen & Bogart, Jill. Out & about with the Big Tree Gang. Griffiths, Dean, illus. 2006. 64p. (J). pap. 4.99 (978-1-55143-603-6(5)) Orca Bk. Pubs. USA.

Boling, Ruth. Mouse Tales Vol. 1: Advent-Christmas-Epiphany. Carrier, Tracy, illus. 2005. 80p. (J). 14.95 (978-0-664-22705-0(8)) Westminster John Knox Pr.

Bonnell, Kris. Mmm, Apples. 2006. (J). 3.95 (***978-1-933727-22-6(5)***) Reading Reading Bks., LLC.

Bottner, Barbara & Kruglik, Gerald. Wallace's Lists. Landstrom, Olof, illus. 2004. 40p. (J). (ps-2). lib. bdg. 16.89 (978-0-06-000225-1(5)) HarperCollins Pubs.

—Wallace's Lists. Landstrom, Olof, Landstrom, Olof, illus. 2004. 40p. (J). (ps-2). 16.99 (978-0-06-000224-4(7) , Tegen, Katherine Bks) HarperCollins Pubs.

Brady, Charles A. The Church Mouse of Saint Nicholas. 2004. (Illus.). 48p. (J). 16.00 (978-1-930873-97-1(2)) Neumann Pr., The.

Brandreth, Gyles. Amanda Mouse & the Birthday Cake. 2000. (Illus.). 32p. (J). 9.99 (978-0-233-99574-8(9)) Andre Deutsch GBR. *Dist:* Independent Pubs. Group.

—Jack Mouse & the Scarecrow. 2000. (Illus.). 32p. (J). 9.99 (978-0-233-99577-9(3)) Andre Deutsch GBR. *Dist:* Trafalgar Square Publishing.

—Matt Mouse And The Big Surprise. 2000. (Illus.). 32p. (J). 8.99 (978-0-233-99575-5(7)) Andre Deutsch GBR. *Dist:* Independent Pubs. Group.

—Myrtle Mouse & the Naughty Twins. 2000. (Tales from Mouse Village Ser.). 32p. (J). 8.99 (978-0-233-99576-2(5)) Andre Deutsch GBR. *Dist:* Independent Pubs. Group.

—Welcome to Mouse Village. Hall, Mary, illus. 1999. 36p. (J). 15.99 (978-0-233-99380-5(0)) Andre Deutsch GBR. *Dist:* Independent Pubs. Group.

Bratun, Katy. Gingerbread Mouse. Bratun, Katy, illus. 32p. (J). 2007. pap. 6.99 (***978-0-06-009082-1(0)*** , Harper Trophy); 2003. (Illus.). lib. bdg. 13.89 (978-0-06-009081-4(2)) HarperCollins Pubs.

Brave Little Mouse: Individual Title Six-Packs. (Story Steps Ser.). (gr. k-2). 32.00 (978-0-7635-9831-0(3)) Rigby Education.

Brenner, Barbara. Too Many Mice. Cymerman, John E., illus. 1998. (Bank Street Reader Collection). 48p. (J). (gr. 1-3). lib. bdg. 22.60 (978-0-8368-1771-3(0)) Stevens, Gareth Inc.

Brightwood, Laura, illus. Lion & Mousie. Brightwood, Laura, . 2007. (J). DVD ***(978-1-934409-00-8(6))*** 3-C Institute for Social Development.

Brooks, Nigel & Horner, Abigail. Country Mouse Cottage: How We Lived One Hundred Years Ago. Brooks, Nigel & Horner, Abigail, illus. 2000. (Illus.). 32p. (J). (ps-3). 15.95 (978-0-8027-8752-1(5)) Walker & Co.

—Mouse Tales. 2004. (Illus.). 126p. (978-0-09-189358-3(5)) Random Hse. Children's Bks.

—Town Mouse House: How We Lived One Hundred Years Ago. 2000. (Illus.). 32p. (J). (gr. k-3). 15.95 (978-0-8027-8732-3(0)) Walker & Co.

Broome, Errol. Magnus Maybe. 2002. (gr. 3-6). lib. bdg. 13.00 (978-0-613-62526-5(9)) Tandem Library Bks.

—Missing Mem. 2003. (gr. 3-6). lib. bdg. 13.00 (978-0-613-61801-4(7)) Tandem Library Bks.

Brown, Jamie B. Angelo & the Master. 2006. (Illus.). 32p. (J). 19.99 (978-1-59715-018-7(5)) Chapel Hill Pr.

Brown, Janet Allison. Hello, Mr. Snowman. Chaffey, Samantha, illus. 2005. (Holidays In 3D Ser.). 8p. (J). bds. 4.95 (978-0-7641-5832-2(5)) Barron's Educational Series, Inc.

Bunting, Eve. Mouse Island. Catalano, Dominic, illus. 2008. (J). ***(978-1-59078-447-1(2))*** Boyds Mills Pr.

Burgess, Thornton W. The Adventures of Danny Meadow Mouse. (J). 18.95 (978-0-8488-0377-3(9)) Amereon LTD.

—Whitefoot the Wood Mouse. (J). 18.95 (978-0-8488-0395-7(7)) Amereon LTD.

—Whitefoot the Wood Mouse. 2006. (Dover Children's Thrift Classics Ser.). 112p. (J). pap. 2.00 (978-0-486-44944-9(0)) Dover Pubns., Inc.

Burgess, W. Thornton. Whitefoot the Wood Mouse. 2006. 24.99 ***(978-1-4280-4184-4(2));*** pap. 18.99 ***(978-1-4280-4180-6(X))*** IndyPublish.com.

Burningham, John. Trubloff, el Raton Que Queria Tocar la Balalaica. 2001. Tr. of Trubloff, the Mouse Who Wanted to Play the Balalaika. (SPA.). 32p. (J). 16.76 (978-84-355-0436-2(0)) Minon, S.A. ESP. *Dist:* Lectorum Pubns., Inc.

Burton, Katherine. One Gray Mouse. Fernandes, Kim, illus. 2006. 24p. 6.95 (978-1-55453-026-7(1)) Kids Can Pr., Ltd. CAN. *Dist:* Wybel Marketing Group.

—One Grey Mouse. Fernandes, Kim, illus. 2002. (Little Mice Ser.).Tr. of Souris Grise. 24p. (J). (ps-k). (978-1-55074-324-1(4)) Kids Can Pr., Ltd.

Burton, Katherine & Fernandes, Kim. Une Souris Grise.Tr. of Souris Grise. (FRE., Illus.). 24p. (J). pap. 6.99 (978-0-590-16023-0(0)) Scholastic, Inc.

Bush, Robert Quacken. The Return of Pete Pack Rat. Bush, Robert Quacken, ed. rev. deluxe ed. 2005. (Illus.). 64p. (J). (gr. 2-4). reprint ed. 12.95 (978-0-9712757-1-3(8)); pap. 6.95 (978-0-9712757-2-0(6)) Quackenbush, Robert Studios.

Butler, Stephen. The Mouse & the Apple. 2000. (Illus.). 32p. (J). (ps-k). pap. 7.99 (978-0-7112-0856-8(5)) Lincoln, Frances Ltd. GBR. *Dist:* Transition Vendor.

Bynum, Janie. Nutmeg & Barley: A Budding Friendship. Bynum, Janie, illus. 2006. (Illus.). 32p. (J). (ps-2). 15.99 (978-0-7636-2382-1(2)) Candlewick Pr.

Calmenson, Stephanie. Birthday at the Panda Palace. Cushman, Doug, illus. 2007. 32p. (J). (ps-1). 15.99 (978-0-06-052663-4(7)); lib. bdg. 16.89 (978-0-06-052664-1(5)) HarperCollins Pubs.

Carlson, Nancy. I Don't Like to Read! Carlson, Nancy, illus. 2007. (Illus.). 32p. (J). (gr. k-2). 15.99 (978-0-670-06191-4(3) , Viking Juvenile) Penguin Group (USA) Inc.

Carlson, Nancy L. First Grade, Here I Come! 2006. (Illus.). (J). ***(978-1-4156-8114-5(7)*** , Viking Adult) Penguin Group (USA) Inc.

Carlstrom, Nancy White. I'M Not Moving, Mama. 1999. (gr. k-3). lib. bdg. 14.15 (978-0-613-21751-4(9)) Tandem Library Bks.

—I'm Not Moving, Mama. Wickstrom, Thor, illus. 1999. 32p. (J). (ps-3). pap. 6.99 (978-0-689-82881-2(0) , Aladdin) Simon & Schuster Children's Publishing.

Carman, Debby. I'm Maximum Cat That's a Fact. 2006. (J). (978-0-9777340-2-3(1)) Faux Paw Media Group.

Carpino, Nancy. The Tenor Mouse - Topo Tenori. McNeilis, Jessica, illus. 1999. 20p. (J). (gr. k-4). pap. 8.95 (978-1-928675-01-3(8)) Carpino Bks.

Carter, David & Carter, Noelle. Little Mouse & Daddy: Little Mouse Series. Carter, David & Carter, Noelle, illus. 2005. (Little Mouse Ser.). (Illus.). 12p. (J). 7.95 (978-1-58117-223-2(0) , Intervisual/Piggy Toes) Dalmatian Pr.

—Little Mouse & Mommy: Little Mouse Series. Carter, David & Carter, Noelle, illus. 2005. (Little Mouse Ser.). (Illus.). 12p. (J). 7.95 (978-1-58117-224-9(9) , Intervisual/Piggy Toes) Dalmatian Pr.

—Little Mouse Plays Peek-a-Boo: Little Mouse Series. Carter, David & Carter, Noelle, illus. 2005. (Little Mouse Ser.). (Illus.). 12p. (J). 7.95 (978-1-58117-225-6(7) , Intervisual/Piggy Toes) Dalmatian Pr.

—Little Mouse's Christmas: Little Mouse Series. Carter, David & Carter, Noelle, illus. 2005. (Little Mouse Ser.). (Illus.). 12p. (J). 7.95 (978-1-58117-226-3(5) , Intervisual/Piggy Toes) Dalmatian Pr.

Cartlidge, Michelle. The Mouse Christmas House: A Press-Out Model Book. (Illus.). 32p. (J). (978-1-904613-67-1(5) , Buster Bks.) O'Mara, Michael Bks., Ltd.

Cast, John. Little Mouse. 1999. (ps-1). 6.99 (978-0-85953-694-3(7)) Child's Play International Ltd. GBR. *Dist:* Child's Play-International.

—Magic Mouse. 1999. (Let's Play Ser.). (Illus.). 24p. (J). (ps-3). pap. 3.99 (978-0-85953-568-7(1)) Child's Play-International.

Chandler, Paul. Mouse of Commons - Mouse of Lords. 2006. 186p. pap. 14.99 (978-1-4116-8447-8(8)) Lulu.com.

Chang, Monica. Mousebride. 2000. (J). (KOR & ENG.). 18.95 (978-957-32-2153-1(5)); (TAG & ENG.). 18.95 (978-957-32-2154-8(3)); (THA & ENG.). 18.95 (978-957-32-2152-4(7)); (VIE & ENG.). 18.95 (978-957-32-2151-7(9)) Yuan-liou Publishing Co., Ltd. TWN. *Dist:* AIMS International Bks., Inc.

Charles, Faustin. The Selfish Crocodile. Terry, Michael, illus. 1999. 32p. (J). (gr. k-2). 14.95 (978-1-888444-56-8(8)) Little Tiger Pr.

Charlie Church Mouse Bible Adventures! Early Elementary. 2003. (J). cd-rom 19.98 (978-0-9714753-1-1(8)) Life-Line Studios, Inc.

Chato Y Su Cena. 2004. (J). pap. 32.75 incl. audio (978-1-55592-342-6(9)) Weston Woods Studios, Inc.

Chato's Kitchen. 2004. (J). 24.95 incl. audio (978-0-7882-0696-2(6)); pap. 18.95 incl. audio compact disk (978-1-55592-386-0(0)); pap. 18.95 incl. audio compact disk (978-1-55592-389-1(5)); pap. 38.75 incl. audio compact disk (978-1-55592-388-4(7)); pap. 38.75 incl. audio compact disk (978-1-55592-390-7(9)); pap. 32.75 incl. audio (978-1-55592-202-3(3)); pap. 32.75 incl. audio (978-1-55592-203-0(1)); (SPA.). pap. 14.95 incl. audio (978-0-7882-0134-9(4)); pap. 14.95 incl. audio (978-0-7882-0697-9(4)) Weston Woods Studios, Inc.

Chinnery, Karen. Secret Agent Squirrel. 2006. (ENG.). 48p. per. 12.95 ***(978-1-4241-5459-3(6))*** PublishAmerica, Inc.

Christian, Cheryl, Matty & Patty. Sampson, Pamela, illus. 1998. (Domino Readers Ser.). 24p. (J). (ps-1). pap. 5.95 (978-1-887734-30-1(9)) Star Bright Bks., Inc.

Christian, Peggy. The Bookstore Mouse. Lippincott, Gary A., illus. 2002. 144p. (YA). (gr. 3-7). pap. 6.95 (978-0-15-204564-7(3) , Harcourt Paperbacks) Harcourt Children's Bks.

—Bookstore Mouse. 2002. (gr. 3-6). lib. bdg. 14.10 (978-0-613-56250-8(X)) Tandem Library Bks.

Chrysanthemum. 2004. (J). (SPA.). 24.95 incl. audio (978-1-55592-162-0(0)); pap. 18.95 incl. audio compact disk (978-1-55592-395-2(X)); pap. 18.95 incl. audio compact disk (978-1-55592-398-3(4)); pap. 38.75 incl. audio compact disk (978-1-55592-397-6(6)); pap. 38.75 incl. audio compact disk (978-1-55592-399-0(2)); pap. 32.75 incl. audio (978-1-55592-208-5(2)); pap. 32.75 incl. audio (978-1-55592-209-2(0)); pap. 32.75 incl. audio (978-0-7882-0248-3(0)); pap. 14.95 incl. audio (978-1-55592-654-0(1)) Weston Woods Studios, Inc.

Clairmont, Patsy. Basil & Parsley. 2007. (Tails from the Pantry Ser.). 32p. (J). 9.99 ***(978-1-4003-1039-5(3))*** Nelson, Thomas Inc.

—Meatball. 2005. (Tails from the Pantry Ser.). (Illus.). 32p. (J). 9.99 (978-1-4003-0561-2(6)) Nelson, Thomas Inc.

—Spud. 2006. (Tails from the Pantry Ser.). (Illus.). 32p. (J). 9.99 (978-1-4003-0802-6(X)) Nelson, Thomas Inc.

—Stinky. Oeltjenbruns, Joni, illus. 2006. (Tails from the Pantry Ser.). 32p. (J). 9.99 (978-1-4003-0803-3(8)) Nelson, Thomas Inc.

Clairmont, Patsy. 5 Cheesy Stories: About Friendship, Bravery, Bullying, & More. 2007. (Tails from the Pantry Ser.). 144p. (J). 14.99 ***(978-1-4003-1042-5(3))*** Nelson, Thomas Inc.

Clark, Lance. There Is an Old Mouse Who Lives in My House. Hughes, Jeff, illus. 2001. 32p. (J). 16.95 (978-0-9707491-0-9(4)) Clark, Lance Publishing.

Cleary, Beverly. La Escapada de Ralph. (SPA., Illus.). 128p. (YA). (gr. 5-8). (978-84-279-3424-5(6)) Noguer y Caralt Editores, S. A. ESP. *Dist:* Lectorum Pubns., Inc.

—Lucky Chuck. Higginbottom, J. Winslow, illus. 2002. 48p. (J). pap. 7.99 (978-0-06-008239-0(9) , Harper Trophy) HarperCollins Pubs.

—The Mouse & the Motorcycle: El ratoncito de la Moto. Darling, Louis, illus. 2003. (SPA.). 144p. (J). 15.99 (978-0-06-000056-1(2) , Rayo) HarperCollins Pubs.

—The Ralph Mouse Collection. 2001. (Cleary Reissue Ser.). 592p. (J). pap. 14.99 (978-0-06-441004-5(8) , Harper Trophy) HarperCollins Pubs.

—Ralph S. Mouse. 160p. (J). (gr. 3-5). pap. 4.95 (978-0-8072-1476-3(0) , Listening Library) Random Hse. Audio Publishing Group.

—El Ratoncito de la Moto. Netto, Lydia, tr. Darling, Louis, illus. 2003. Tr. of Mouse & the Motorcycle. (SPA.). 144p. pap. 5.99 (978-0-06-000057-8(0) , Rayo) HarperCollins Pubs.

—El Ratoncito de la Moto. 2003. Tr. of Mouse & the Motorcycle. (SPA.). (gr. 3-6). lib. bdg. 14.15 (978-0-613-67220-7(8)) Tandem Library Bks.

Collicott, Sharleen. Mildred & Sam & Their Babies. Collicott, Sharleen, illus. (I Can Read Bks.). 48p. (J). 2007. pap. 3.99 ***(978-0-06-058113-8(1)*** , Harper Trophy); 2005. (Illus.). 15.99 (978-0-06-058111-4(5) , Geringer, Laura Book); 2005. (Illus.). lib. bdg. 16.89 (978-0-06-058112-1(3) , Geringer, Laura Book) HarperCollins Pubs.

Collicott, Sharleen. Mildred & Sam Go to School. Collicott, Sharleen, illus. (I Can Read Bks.). (J). 2008. 64p. 16.99 (978-0-06-058114-5(X) , Geringer, Laura Book); 2008. (Illus.). 64p. lib. bdg. 17.89 (978-0-06-058115-2(8) , Geringer, Laura Book); 2004. (Illus.). 48p. pap. 3.99 (978-0-06-000200-8(X) , Harper Trophy); 2003. (Illus.). 48p. 15.99 (978-0-06-026681-3(3)) HarperCollins Pubs.

—Mildred & Sam Go to School. 2004. (gr. k-3). lib. bdg. 11.80 (978-0-613-82531-3(4)) Tandem Library Bks.

Como los ratones robaron el Fuego: Aventuras (Adventure Books) 2000. (Aventuras A Traves Del Tiempo Ser.). (ENG & SPA.). (gr. 4 up). (978-0-02-148709-7(X)) Macmillan/McGraw-Hill Schl. Div.

Cook, Sherry & Johnson, Terri. Mary Motion. 2006, 26 vols. Kuhn, Jesse, illus. l.t. ed. 2006. (Quirkles—Exploring Phonics through Science Ser.: 13). 32p. (J). 7.99 (978-1-933815-12-1(4) , Quirkles, The) Creative 3, LLC.

Coons, Susan. The Lighthouse Mouse. 2006. 19.99 ***(978-0-9721410-1-7(4))*** Vinland Pr.

Copp, Raymond. Tales of a Milford Mouse: Genevieve Sara Deglise. 2003. 83p. pap. 14.95 (978-1-59286-908-4(4)) PublishAmerica, Inc.

Cosgrove, Stephen. Little Mouse on the Prairie. James, Robin, illus. 2001. (Serendipity Bks.). 32p. (J). (ps-3). pap. 4.99 (978-0-8431-7632-2(6) , Price Stern Sloan) Penguin Group (USA) Inc.

—Little Mouse on the Prairie. 2000. (gr. k-3). lib. bdg. 13.00 (978-0-613-33657-4(7)) Tandem Library Bks.

Country Mouse & City Mouse. 2002. (Classic Tales Mini Bks.). (Illus.). 32p. (J). (978-1-59069-037-6(0) , T1006); incl. audio compact disk (978-1-59069-104-5(0) , T1106) Studio Mouse LLC.

Coursen, H. R. Pim Pim the Mouse. 1999. (J). 15.95 (978-0-8050-6095-9(2) , Holt, Henry & Co. Bks. For Young Readers) Holt, Henry & Co.

Cousins, Lucy. A Maisy le Gusta Conducir. 2002. (Illus.). (J). (CAT.). 14p. bds. 7.95 (978-84-95040-90-9(5)); (SPA., 64p. 8.99 (978-84-95040-89-3(1) , RR6349) Serres, Ediciones, S. L. ESP. *Dist:* Lectorum Pubns., Inc.

— A Maisy le Gusta Jugar. 2002. (Illus.). (J). (CAT.). 14p. bds. 7.95 (978-84-95040-88-6(3)); (SPA., 64p. 7.99 (978-84-95040-87-9(5) , RR6586) Serres, Ediciones, S. L. ESP. *Dist:* Lectorum Pubns., Inc.

—El Autobus de Maisy. (Illus.). 24p. (J). 2002. (SPA.). 10.95 (978-84-95040-69-5(7) , RR5867); 2000. (CAT., 10.95 (978-84-95040-70-1(0)) Serres, Ediciones, S. L. ESP. *Dist:* Lectorum Pubns., Inc.

—El Coche de Bomberos de Maisy. 2002. (Illus.). 14p. (J). (SPA.). 7.95 (978-84-8488-044-8(3) , RR31039); (CAT., bds. 7.95 (978-84-8488-045-5(1)) Serres, Ediciones, S. L. ESP. *Dist:* Lectorum Pubns., Inc.

—Los Colores de Maisy. 2001. (Illus.). (J). (ps). (CAT.). 16p. 10.95 (978-84-95040-60-2(3)); (SPA., 24p. 15.95 (978-84-95040-75-6(1) , RR7142) Serres, Ediciones, S. L. ESP. *Dist:* Lectorum Pubns., Inc., Lectorum Pubns., Inc., Libros Sin Fronteras.

—Las Cosas Favoritas de Maisy. 2000. (Maisy Bks.).Tr. of Maisy's Favorite Things. (SPA., Illus.). 16p. (J). (ps). 8.95 (978-84-95040-12-1(3)) Lectorum Pubns., Inc.

—Count with Maisy. Cousins, Lucy, illus. 2nd ed. 1999. (Maisy Bks.). (Illus.). 24p. (J). (gr. k-ps). bds. 5.99 (978-0-7636-0234-5(5)) Candlewick Pr.

—Diviertete y Aprende con Maisy. 2002. (Illus.). 12p. (J). (CAT.). bds. 16.95 (978-84-8488-019-6(2)); (SPA., 16.95 (978-84-8488-018-9(4) , RR7668) Serres, Ediciones, S. L. ESP. *Dist:* Lectorum Pubns., Inc.

—Donde Esta el Panda de Maisy? 1999. (Maisy Bks.). (Illus.). 16p. (J). (ps). (CAT.). 10.95 (978-84-95040-08-4(5)); (SPA., 11.50 (978-84-95040-07-7(7) , RR4459) Serres, Ediciones, S. L. ESP. *Dist:* Lectorum Pubns., Inc.

—Donde Se Esconde Maisy? 1999. (Maisy Bks.). (Illus.). 16p. (J). (ps). (CAT.). 10.95 (978-84-95040-06-0(9)); (SPA., 10.99 (978-84-95040-05-3(0) , RR4499) Serres, Ediciones, S. L. ESP. *Dist:* Lectorum Pubns., Inc.

—Donde Vive Maisy? 2000. (Maisy Bks.). (Illus.). 16p. (J). (ps). (CAT.). 10.95 (978-84-95040-47-3(6)); (SPA., 11.50 (978-84-95040-46-6(8)) Serres, Ediciones, S. L. ESP. *Dist:* Lectorum Pubns., Inc.

—Feliz Cumpleanos, Maisy. 1999. (Maisy Bks.). (Illus.). 16p. (J). (ps). (CAT.). 16.95 (978-84-88061-95-9(1)); (SPA., 17.99 (978-84-88061-96-6(X) , RR3371) Serres, Ediciones, S. L. ESP. *Dist:* Lectorum Pubns., Inc.

—Fun with Maisy. 2002. (ps-2). lib. bdg. 11.80 (978-0-613-74761-5(5)) Tandem Library Bks.

—La Granja de Maisy. 2001. (Illus.). (J). (SPA.). 8p. 26.95 (978-84-8488-007-3(9)); (CAT., 16p. 26.95 (978-84-8488-011-0(7)) Serres, Ediciones, S. L. ESP. *Dist:* Lectorum Pubns., Inc.

—Ha, Ha, Maisy! Cousins, Lucy, illus. 2005. (Illus.). 14p. (J). (gr. k-k). bds. 4.99 (978-0-7636-2633-4(3)) Candlewick Pr.

—Happy Birthday, Maisy: Mini Edition. 2004. (Maisy Ser.). (Illus.). 14p. (J). (gr. k-k). 4.99 (978-0-7636-2454-5(3)) Candlewick Pr.

—Jugando con Maisy. 2002. (Illus.). 16p. (J). (SPA.). (978-84-95040-44-2(1) , RR8303); (CAT., 10.95 (978-84-95040-45-9(X)) Serres, Ediciones, S. L. ESP. *Dist:* Lectorum Pubns., Inc.

—Maisy Big, Maisy Small. Cousins, Lucy, illus. 2007. (Illus.). 56p. (J). (ps-k). 15.99 ***(978-0-7636-3406-3(9))*** Candlewick Pr.

—Maisy Cleans Up. 2002. (Maisy Ser.). (Illus.). 24p. (J). (ps-k). pap. 3.99 (978-0-7636-1712-7(1)) Candlewick Pr.

—Maisy Cleans Up. 2002. (ps-2). lib. bdg. 11.00 (978-0-613-51315-9(0)) Tandem Library Bks.

—Maisy Dresses Up. Cousins, Lucy, illus. 1999. (Maisy Bks.). (Illus.). 24p. (J). (gr. k-k). pap. 3.99 (978-0-7636-0909-2(9)) Candlewick Pr.

—Maisy Dresses Up. 1999. (gr. k-3). lib. bdg. 11.00 (978-0-613-21952-5(X)) Tandem Library Bks.

—Maisy Drives the Bus. Cousins, Lucy, illus. 2000. (Maisy Bks.). (Illus.). 24p. (J). (gr. k-k). pap. 3.99 (978-0-7636-1085-2(2)) Candlewick Pr.

—Maisy Drives the Bus. 2000. (ps-2). lib. bdg. 11.00 (978-0-613-27961-1(1)) Tandem Library Bks.

—Maisy en la Granja. 1999. (Maisy Bks.). (Illus.). (J). (ps). (CAT.). 16p. 16.95 (978-84-88061-94-2(3)); (SPA., 24p. 17.88 (978-84-88061-97-3(8) , RR3457) Serres, Ediciones, S. L. ESP. *Dist:* Lectorum Pubns., Inc.

—Maisy Goes Camping. Cousins, Lucy, illus. 2004. (Maisy Ser.). (Illus.). 32p. (J). (gr. k-k). 12.99 (978-0-7636-2369-2(5)) Candlewick Pr.

—Maisy Goes Shopping. Cousins, Lucy, illus. 2001. (Maisy Bks.). (Illus.). 24p. (J). (gr. k-k). pap. 3.99 (978-0-7636-1503-1(X)) Candlewick Pr.

—Maisy Goes to the Library. Cousins, Lucy, illus. 2005. (Illus.). 32p. (J). (gr. k-k). 12.99 (978-0-7636-2669-3(4)) Candlewick Pr.

—Maisy Likes Music. Cousins, Lucy, illus. 2002. (Maisy Ser.). (Illus.). 12p. (J). (ps-k). bds. 6.99 (978-0-7636-1915-2(9)) Candlewick Pr.

—Maisy Loves You. 2004. (Illus.). 10p. (J). (gr. k-k). bds. 4.99 (978-0-7636-2687-7(2)) Candlewick Pr.

—Maisy Loves You. Cousins, Lucy, illus. 2003. (Maisy Ser.). (Illus.). 10p. (J). (gr. k-k). bds. 5.99 (978-0-7636-2065-3(3)) Candlewick Pr.

—Maisy Makes Lemonade. 2002. (Maisy Ser.). (Illus.). 24p. (J). (ps-k). pap. 3.99 (978-0-7636-1729-5(6)) Candlewick Pr.

—Maisy Makes Lemonade. 2002. (ps-2). lib. bdg. 11.00 (978-0-613-51316-6(9)) Tandem Library Bks.

—Maisy Se Bana. 2002. (Illus.). 24p. (J). (CAT.). 10.95 (978-84-95040-72-5(7)); (SPA., 10.95 (978-84-95040-71-8(9) , RR3035) Serres, Ediciones, S. L. ESP. *Dist:* Lectorum Pubns., Inc.

—Maisy Se Va a Nadar. 2000. (Maisy Bks.). (SPA., Illus.). 24p. (J). (ps). 16.95 (978-84-88061-32-4(3) , RR7052) Serres, Ediciones, S. L. ESP. *Dist:* Lectorum Pubns., Inc.

—Maisy Takes a Bath. Cousins, Lucy, illus. 2000. (Maisy Bks.). (Illus.). 24p. (J). (gr. k-k). pap. 3.99 (978-0-7636-1084-5(4)) Candlewick Pr.

—Maisy y Sus Amigos. 1999. (Maisy Bks.). (Illus.). 16p. (J). (ps). (CAT & SPA.). 16.95 (978-84-95040-03-9(4)); (SPA., 17.99 (978-84-95040-02-2(6) , RR2456) Serres, Ediciones, S. L. ESP. *Dist:* Lectorum Pubns., Inc.

—Maisy's Amazing Big Book of Words. Cousins, Lucy, illus. 2007. (Maisy Ser.). (Illus.). 64p. (J). (ps-k). 14.99 (978-0-7636-0794-4(0)) Candlewick Pr.

—Maisy's Bedtime. Cousins, Lucy, illus. 1999. (Maisy Bks.). (Illus.). 24p. (J). pap. 3.99 (978-0-7636-0908-5(0)) Candlewick Pr.

—Maisy's Colors. Cousins, Lucy, illus. 2nd ed. 1999. (Maisy Bks.). (Illus.). 24p. (J). (gr. k-ps). bds. 5.99 (978-0-7636-0237-6(X)) Candlewick Pr.

—Maisy's Favorite Things. Cousins, Lucy, illus. 2001. (Maisy Bks.). (Illus.). 22p. (J). (gr. k-k). bds. 3.99 (978-0-7636-1574-1(9)) Candlewick Pr.

—Maisy's Fire Engine. Cousins, Lucy, illus. 2002. (Maisy Bks.). (Illus.). 16p. (J). (gr. k-k). bds. 4.99 (978-0-7636-1780-6(6)) Candlewick Pr.

—Maisy's Pool. Cousins, Lucy, illus. 1999. (Maisy Bks.). (Illus.). 24p. (J). pap. 3.99 (978-0-7636-0907-8(2)) Candlewick Pr.

—Maisy's Rainbow Dream. Cousins, Lucy, illus. 2003. (Maisy Ser.). (Illus.). 32p. (J). (ps up). 16.99 (978-0-7636-2195-7(1)) Candlewick Pr.

—Maisy's Seasons. 2002. (Maisy Ser.). (Illus.). 12p. (J). (gr. k-k). bds. 8.99 (978-0-7636-1914-5(0)) Candlewick Pr.

—Maisy's Snowy Christmas Eve. Cousins, Lucy, illus. 2003. (Maisy Ser.). (Illus.). 32p. (J). (gr. k-k). 12.99 incl. audio compact disk (978-0-7636-2196-4(X)) Candlewick Pr.

—Maisy's Train. Cousins, Lucy, illus. 2002. (Maisy Noisy Board Bks.). (Illus.). 16p. (J). (gr. k-k). bds. 4.99 (978-0-7636-1781-3(4)) Candlewick Pr.

—More Fun with Maisy. Cousins, Lucy, illus. 2005. (Illus.). 14p. (J). (gr. k-k). bds. 4.99 (978-0-7636-2632-7(5)) Candlewick Pr.

—La Nochebuena de Maisy. 2004. (SPA., Illus.). 32p. (J). 16.99 (978-84-8488-106-3(7)) Serres, Ediciones, S. L. ESP. *Dist:* Lectorum Pubns., Inc.

—Playtime, Maisy! Cousins, Lucy, illus. 2001. (Maisy Bks.). (Illus.). 6p. (J). (gr. k-ps). pap. 6.99 (978-0-7636-1602-1(8)) Candlewick Pr.

—Pool. 1999. (gr. k-3). lib. bdg. 11.00 (978-0-613-22206-8(7)) Tandem Library Bks.

—Que Hora Es, Maisy? 2002. (Illus.). (J). (SPA.). 12p. (978-84-8488-048-6(6)); (CAT., 14p. (978-84-8488-049-3(4)) Serres, Ediciones, S. L. ESP. *Dist:* Lectorum Pubns., Inc.

—Snacktime, Maisy! Cousins, Lucy, illus. 2001. (Maisy Bks.). (Illus.). 6p. (J). (gr. k-ps). pap. 6.99 (978-0-7636-1603-8(6)) Candlewick Pr.

—Stop & Go Maisy. Cousins, Lucy, illus. 2005. (Illus.). 16p. (J). (gr. k-k). 9.99 (978-0-7636-2668-6(6)) Candlewick Pr.

—Sueños de Colores. 2004. (SPA., Illus.). 32p. (J). 18.99 (978-84-8488-108-7(3)) Serres, Ediciones, S. L. ESP. *Dist:* Lectorum Pubns., Inc.

—Sweet Dreams, Maisy. Cousins, Lucy, illus. 2005. (Illus.). 16p. (J). (ps-k). 12.99 (978-0-7636-2874-1(3)) Candlewick Pr.

—El Tren de Maisy. 2002. (Illus.). 14p. (J). (SPA.). 7.95 (978-84-8488-042-4(7) , RR31040); (CAT., bds. 7.95 (978-84-8488-043-1(5)) Serres, Ediciones, S. L. ESP. *Dist:* Lectorum Pubns., Inc.

—What Are You Doing, Maisy? Cousins, Lucy, illus. 2003. (Lift-the-Flap Bks.). (Illus.). 14p. (J). (gr. k-k). 7.99 (978-0-7636-2171-1(4)) Candlewick Pr.

—Where Are You Going, Maisy? Cousins, Lucy, illus. 2003. (Lift-the-Flap Bks.). (Illus.). 14p. (J). (gr. k-ps). 7.99 (978-0-7636-2172-8(2)) Candlewick Pr.

—Where Is Maisy? A Lift-the-Flap Book. Cousins, Lucy, illus. 1999. (Maisy Bks.). (Illus.). 12p. (J). (gr. k-k). bds. 4.99 (978-0-7636-0752-4(5)) Candlewick Pr.

—Where Is Maisy's Panda? A Lift-the-Flap Book. Cousins, Lucy, illus. 1999. (Maisy Bks.). (Illus.). 14p. (J). (gr. k-k). bds. 4.99 (978-0-7636-0753-1(3)) Candlewick Pr.

Cousins, Lucy. With Love from Maisy: Mini Edition. Cousins, Lucy, illus. 2007. (Maisy Ser.). (Illus.). 16p. (J). (ps). 4.99 ***(978-0-7636-3539-8(1))*** Candlewick Pr.

Cox, Judy. One Is a Feast for Mouse. Ebbeler, Jeffrey, illus. 2008. (J). ***(978-0-8234-1977-7(0))*** Holiday Hse., Inc.

Cox, Phil Roxbee. Mouse Moves House. Cartwright, Stephen, illus. rev. ed. 2006. 16p. (J). pap. 6.99 (978-0-7945-1507-2(X) , Usborne) EDC Publishing.

M N O

Cox, Phil Roxbee & Cartwright, Stephen. Mouse Moves House. 2004. (Easy Words to Read Ser.). (Illus.). 16p. (J). (gr. 1 up). pap. 6.95 (978-0-7945-0367-3(5), Usborne) EDC Publishing.

Crackers. abr. ed. 2002. (J). (gr. k-3). 26.90 incl. audio (978-0-8045-6886-9(3)) Spoken Arts, Inc.

Craig, Helen. Angelina on Stage. 2006. 32p. (J). 12.99 (978-0-670-06058-0(5), Viking Juvenile) Penguin Group (USA) Inc.

Craig, Helen, illus. Angelina's Halloween. 2007. 32p. (J). (***978-0-670-91162-2(3)**, Viking Juvenile) Penguin Group (USA) Inc.

Crawford, Joanne Sneed. Respectfully Yours Buford: Program on Respect. Norcross, Harry, illus. 1999. 31p. (J). (ps-2). pap. 6.95 (978-1-57543-076-8(2)) MAR*CO Products, Inc.

Crimi, Carolyn. Tessa's Tip-Tapping Toes. Carrington, Marsha Gray, illus. 2002. 32p. (J). (ps-2). pap. 16.95 (978-0-439-31768-9(1), Orchard Bks.) Scholastic, Inc.

Currey, Anna. Truffle Goes to Town. Currey, Anna, illus. 2003. (Illus.). 32p. (YA). (978-1-85602-429-7(6)) Chrysalis Children's Bks.

—Truffle's Christmas. 2000. (Illus.). (J). (978-0-531-30289-7(X), Orchard Bks.) Scholastic, Inc.

Daddy. Daddy There's a Mouse in the House. 2006. (J). 10.00 (978-0-9762839-1-1(3)) Elizabooks.

D'Agnese, Joseph. Gauss, a Mouse & Me. Date not set. (J). (978-0-8050-6613-5(6), Holt, Henry & Co. Bks. For Young Readers) Holt, Henry & Co.

Dahl, Roald. The Witches. 2002. (J). pap. 29.95 incl. audio (978-0-7540-6247-9(3)) BBC Audiobooks America.

—The Witches. Blake, Quentin, illus. 208p. (J). 2007. (gr. 2). 6.99 (***978-0-14-241011-0(X)**, Puffin); 1999. (gr. 3-7). pap. 3.95 (978-0-14-031730-5(9), Viking Juvenile) Penguin Group (USA) Inc.

—The Witches. 1999. (J). (gr. 3-6). lib. bdg. 14.15 (978-0-8085-7491-0(4)) Tandem Library Bks.

Dalmatian Press Staff. Disney Mickey Mouse & All His Friends: 400 Pages of Coloring Fun. 2006. 400p. pap. 5.99 (978-1-4037-1967-6(5)) Dalmatian Pr.

Danby, Aaron. Jazzmin's Jamboree. Martin, M. J., illus. 2005. 40p. 13.95 (978-0-9730583-3-8(1)) Lion & Mouse Tales, Inc. CAN. *Dist:* Hushion Hse. Publishing, Ltd.

Daniels, Lucy & Baglio, Ben M. Mouse Magic. Howard, Paul, illus. 1999. (Animal Ark Pets Ser.: No. 5). 128p. (J). (gr. 3-6). pap. 3.99 (978-0-439-05162-0(2)) Scholastic, Inc.

A Dark, Dark Tale. 2004. (J). pap. 18.95 incl. audio compact disk (978-1-55592-804-9(8)); pap. 38.75 incl. audio compact disk (978-1-55592-821-6(8)); pap. 32.75 incl. audio (978-1-55592-192-7(2)) Weston Woods Studios, Inc.

Das, Christina. Munchy Mouse. l.t. ed. 2005. (Illus.). 32p. (J). 15.95 (978-0-9763082-0-1(7), A JuneOne Production) JuneOne Publishing Hub.

Dashney, John. The Adventures of Walter the Weremouse; the Adventures of Mishka the Mousewere. Somerville, Sheila, illus. 2005. 202p. (J). pap. (978-0-9633236-7-5(9)) Storm Peak Pr.

Davidson, Susanna. Town Mouse & the Country Mouse. East, Jacqueline, illus. 2007. (First Reading Level 4 Ser.). 48p. (J). 8.99 (***978-0-7945-1613-0(0)**, Usborne) EDC Publishing.

Davis, Jim. Die Feldmaus und die Stadtmaus: Opposites, Means of Transport, Utensils, Prepositions. 1999. (Lesen Leicht Gemacht Ser.).Tr. of Country Mouse & the City Mouse. (GER., Illus.). 24p. (J). (ps-5). pap. 4.95 (978-88-8148-247-4(9)) European Language Institute ITA. *Dist:* Midwest European Pubns.

Davis, L. Mitchell. Mouse Adventures: The Tale of Micah Mouse. 2007. 32p. per. 13.99 (***978-1-59886-655-1(9)**) Tate Publishing & Enterprises, L.L.C.

Davis, Ruth Barton. A Story from Home Featuring the House Mice. 2000. (Illus.). 33p. (J). (978-0-9623785-2-2(6)) Pilgrim Way Pr., The.

Davis, Tim. Mice of the Herring Bone, 2 vols., Set. 2000. (Illus.). (J). (ps-5). pap. 14.98 incl. audio (978-0-89084-907-1(2), 100263) Jones, Bob Univ. Pr.

—Mice of the Nine Lives, 2 vols., Set. 2000. (Illus.). (J). (ps-5). pap. 14.98 incl. audio (978-1-57924-089-9(5), 115048) Jones, Bob Univ. Pr.

Davoll, Barbara. Christopher & His Family. Hockerman, Dennis, illus. 2003. (Christopher Churchmouse Ser.). 128p. (J). 14.99 (978-0-8423-5735-7(1)) Tyndale Hse. Pubs.

—Christopher & His Friends. Hockerman, Dennis, illus. 2003. (Christopher Churchmouse Ser.). 128p. (J). 14.99 (978-0-8423-5734-0(3)) Tyndale Hse. Pubs.

—A Churchmouse Christmas. 1999. (Christopher Churchmouse Classics Ser.). (Illus.). 25p. (J). (ps-3). 9.99 (978-0-8024-5394-5(5)) Moody Pubs.

—Saved by the Bell. Hockerman, Dennis, illus. 1999. (Christopher Churchmouse Classics Ser.). 24p. (J). (ps-3). 7.99 (978-0-8024-4934-4(4)) Moody Pubs.

—To London to See the Queen. Hockerman, Dennis, illus. 1999. (New Christopher Churchmouse Adventures Ser.: Vol. 4). 24p. (J). (ps-3). 9.99 (978-0-8024-5399-0(6)) Moody Pubs.

De Long, Robert & De Long, Janice. Redwall Study Guide. 2003. ring bd. 14.99 (978-1-58609-196-5(4)) Progeny Pr.

Deem, Saitofi Anne. Myrtle Teachable Moments Series, 16 vols. Incl. Myrtle Learns about Asthma. 8p. pap. 7.95 (978-1-930694-00-2(8)); Myrtle Learns about Dangerous Situations. 8p. pap. 7.95 (978-1-930694-03-3(2)); Myrtle Learns about Diabetes. 12p. pap. 7.95 (978-1-930694-04-0(0)); Myrtle Learns about Hygiene. 8p. pap. 7.95 (978-1-930694-09-5(1)); Myrtle Learns about Lice. 12p. pap. 7.95 (978-1-930694-11-8(3)); Myrtle Learns about Medicine. 8p. pap. 7.95 (978-1-930694-12-5(1)); Myrtle Learns about Safety. 8p. pap. 7.95 (978-1-930694-13-2(X)); Myrtle Learns about Seizures. 8p. pap. 7.95 (978-1-930694-14-9(8)); Myrtle Learns How You Catch an Illness. 8p. pap. 7.95 (978-1-930694-10-1(5)); Myrtle Learns to Eat Well. 12p. pap. 7.95 (978-1-930694-05-7(9)); Myrtle Learns to Get Along. 8p. pap. 7.95 (978-1-930694-08-8(3)); Myrtle Learns to Make Friends. 8p. pap. 7.95 (978-1-930694-07-1(5)); Myrtle Learns to Take Care of Boo Boos. 12p. pap. 7.95 (978-1-930694-01-9(6)); Myrtle Learns Why Exercise Is Important. 8p. pap. 7.95 (978-1-930694-06-4(7)); Myrtle Makes a Choice. 8p. pap. 7.95 (978-1-930694-02-6(4)); Myrtle's Friend Is Very Sick. 8p. pap. 7.95 (978-1-930694-15-6(6)); (J). (ps-3). 1998. (Illus.). Set pap. 114.48 (978-1-930694-16-3(4)) Myrtle Learns.

Deer Mouse at Old Farm Road. 2005. (Smithsonian's Backyard Ser.). (Illus.). 32p. (J). (ps-2). 6.95 (978-1-59249-195-7(2), S5015) Soundprints.

Deer Mouse Family. 2002. (Backyard Mini Bks.). (Illus.). 32p. (J). (978-1-59069-020-8(6), H2009) Studio Mouse LLC.

Delaney, Ned. Two Strikes, Four Eyes. Date not set. (J). pap. (978-0-679-84172-2(5)); lib. bdg. (978-0-679-94172-9(X)) Random Hse. Children's Bks. (Random Hse. Bks. for Young Readers).

Delval, Marie-Helene. Mama Pata Cuenta a Sus Pequeqos. Courtin, Thierry, illus. 2002. (Palabras Menudas Ser.).Tr. of Mother Duck Counts to Her Young. (SPA.). 14p. (ps). 4.95 (978-84-7864-516-9(0)) Combel Editorial, S.A. ESP. *Dist:* Independent Pubs. Group.

Demas, Corinne. Two Christmas Mice. Roth, Stephanie, illus. 32p. (J). (ps). 16.95 (978-0-8234-1785-8(9)) Holiday Hse., Inc.

DePrisco, Dorothea. Country Mouse & City Mouse. 2006. 10p. 10.95 (978-1-58117-479-3(9), Intervisual/Piggy Toes) Dalmatian Pr.

Deru, Myriam, illus. Little Mouse. 2001. (Little Pebbles Ser.). 32p. (J). (ps-3). 6.95 (978-0-7892-0692-3(7)) Abbeville Pr., Inc.

deRubertis, Barbara. Bouncy Mouse. Cockrille, Eva V., illus. 1998. (Let's Read Together Ser.). 32p. (J). (ps-3). pap. 4.95 (978-1-57565-043-2(6)); pap. 8.95 incl. audio (978-1-57565-048-7(7)) Kane Pr., The.

DeSantis, Anthony John & Namorato, Carmine, Jr. Vincent Van Mouse. 2001. 32p. (J). per. 16.50 (978-0-9712994-0-5(4)) Black Cat Pubns., Inc.

Devetach, Laura. El Raton Que Queria Comerse la Luna. 2002. (SPA.). 32p. (J). pap. 8.95 (978-1-4000-0027-2(0)) Random Hse., Inc.

DiCamillo, Kate. The Tale of Despereaux. Ering, Timothy Basil, illus. 2003. 272p. (J). (gr. 2-7). 17.99 (978-0-7636-1722-6(9)) Candlewick Pr.

—The Tale of Despereaux. 2004. (J). (gr. 3-4). stu. ed. 11.95 (978-1-58130-524-1(9)) Novel Units, Inc.

—The Tale of Despereaux. Ering, Timothy B., illus. l.t. ed. 2004. 255p. 23.95 (978-0-7862-6578-7(7), Large Print Pr.) Thorndike Pr.

—The Tale of Despereaux: Being the Story of a Mouse, a Princess, Some Soup & a Spool of Thread. Ering, Timothy Basil, illus. 2006. 272p. (J). (gr. 2-7). reprint ed. pap. 7.99 (978-0-7636-2529-0(9)) Candlewick Pr.

Dietl, Erhard. Max Mouse at the Zoo. 2007. (Illus.). 12p. (J). bds. 12.95 (978-0-7358-2103-3(8)) North-South Bks., Inc.

Dijkstra, Lida. Little Mouse. Grobler, Piet, illus. 2004. 32p. (J). 15.95 (978-1-932425-06-2(3), Lemniscaat) Boyds Mills Pr.

Disney Book Club Staff. Country Mouse, City Mouse. 1999. (J). lib. bdg. (978-0-394-94026-7(1), Random Hse. Bks. for Young Readers) Random Hse. Children's Bks.

Dobbie, Geraldine, illus. Country Mouse. 1999. (Patchwork Mice Ser.). 10p. (J). bds. 5.95 (978-1-57717-108-9(X)) New Line Bks.

—Farm Mouse. 1999. (Patchwork Mice Ser.). 10p. (J). bds. 5.95 (978-1-57717-111-9(X)) New Line Bks.

—House Mouse. 1999. (Patchwork Mice Ser.). 10p. (J). bds. 5.95 (978-1-57717-109-6(8)) New Line Bks.

Doctor de Soto. 2004. (J). 24.95 incl. audio (978-0-89719-770-0(4)) Weston Woods Studios, Inc.

Doctor Desoto. 2004. (J). pap. 18.95 incl. audio compact disk (978-0-7882-0950-5(7)); pap. 32.75 incl. audio (978-1-55592-219-1(8)); pap. 32.75 incl. audio (978-1-55592-220-7(1)); pap. 14.95 incl. audio (978-1-55592-937-4(0)) Weston Woods Studios, Inc.

Dolan, Penny. Eight Enormous Elephants. Bradley, Leo, illus. 2004. (Read-It! Readers Ser.). 32p. (C). (gr. k-3). 18.60 (978-1-4048-0054-0(9)) Picture Window Bks.

—Roly-Poly Rice Ball. Mayo, Diana, illus. 2004. (Read-It! Readers Ser.). 32p. (C). (gr. k-3). 18.60 (978-1-4048-0914-7(7)) Picture Window Bks.

Donaldson, Julia. El Grufalo. Scheffler, Axel, illus. 2003. (SPA.). 32p. (J). (gr. k-2). 7.96 (978-84-233-3145-1(8), DS4478) Ediciones Destino ESP. *Dist:* Lectorum Pubns., Inc.

—The Gruffalo. 2006. 32p. (J). pap. 5.99 (978-0-14-240387-7(3), Puffin) Penguin Group (USA) Inc.

—The Gruffalo's Child. Scheffler, Axel, illus. 2005. 32p. (J). (ps). 16.99 (978-0-8037-3009-0(8), Dial) Penguin Group (USA) Inc.

Donofrio, Beverly. Mary & the Mouse, the Mouse & Mary. McClintock, Barbara, illus. 2007. 32p. (J). (ps-2). 16.99 (***978-0-375-83609-1(8)**); lib. bdg. 19.99 (***978-0-375-93609-8(2)**) Random Hse. Children's Bks. (Schwartz & Wade Bks.).

Douglas, Babette. Miss Evonne: And the Mice of Nice! 2005. (Illus.). (J). 9.99 (978-1-890343-19-4(6)) Kiss A Me Productions, Inc.

Downes, Alice. Soccer Season. 2002. (ps-2). lib. bdg. 10.95 (978-0-613-50501-7(8)) Tandem Library Bks.

Drew, James. Rackstraw: The Magical Thoughts & Adventures of A Brilliant Young Art Mouse. George, Mary G., ed. Drew, James, illus. 2000. (Illus.). 168p. (J). (gr. 2-9). 18.95 (978-0-9625023-9-2(1)) Artistry Pr. International.

Driscoll, Laura. Stuart Little: A Little Mess. 2004. (ps-2). lib. bdg. 11.80 (978-0-613-71374-0(5)) Tandem Library Bks.

—Stuart Little: A Little Too Fast. 2004. (ps-2). lib. bdg. 11.80 (978-0-613-71373-3(7)) Tandem Library Bks.

—Stuart Little Bk. 2: Think Big, Vote Little! 2003. (gr. k-3). lib. bdg. 11.80 (978-0-613-69199-4(7)) Tandem Library Bks.

Duckworth, Liz. Ragtail Remembers. Barnes, Jeff, illus. 2002. (J). (978-1-56123-163-8(0)) Centering Corp.

Duke, Kate. Aunt Isabel Makes Trouble. 1999. (Illus.). (J). (978-0-606-20557-3(8)) Tandem Library Bks.

—The Tale of Pip & Squeak. 2007. 32p. (J). (ps). 16.99 (978-0-525-47777-8(2), Dutton Juvenile) Penguin Group (USA) Inc.

Dunbar. Happy Days for Mouse & Mole. 2000. (Illus.). 28p. (J). pap. 6.95 (978-0-552-52978-5(8)) Transworld Publishers Ltd. GBR. *Dist:* Trafalgar Square Publishing.

—Mouse & Mole. 2000. (Illus.). 25p. (J). 15.95 (978-0-385-40198-2(1)) Transworld Publishers Ltd. GBR. *Dist:* Trafalgar Square Publishing.

—Very Special Mouse & Mole. 2000. (Illus.). 28p. (J). pap. 6.95 (978-0-552-52977-8(X)) Transworld Publishers Ltd. GBR. *Dist:* Trafalgar Square Publishing.

Dunbar, Joyce. Hip-Dip-Dip with Mouse & Mole. de Vere, Alison, illus. 2002. 62p. pap. 7.99 (978-0-552-54673-7(9), Corgi) Transworld Publishers Ltd. GBR. *Dist:* Trafalgar Square Publishing.

—Mouse & Mole Have a Party. Mayhew, James, illus. 2000. 32p. (J). pap. 6.95 (978-0-552-54557-0(0)) Transworld Publishers Ltd. GBR. *Dist:* Trafalgar Square Publishing.

—Where's My Sock? Rescek, Sanja, illus. 2006. 32p. (J). pap. 15.99 (978-0-439-74831-5(3), Chicken Hse., The) Scholastic, Inc.

Dunbar, Joyce & de Vere, Alison. The Ups & Downs of Mouse & Mole. 2002. (Illus.). 63p. pap. 7.99 (978-0-552-54674-4(7), Corgi) Transworld Publishers Ltd. GBR. *Dist:* Trafalgar Square Publishing.

Duncan, Sharyn. The Mouse House & other Stories: You Are the Artist. 2004. 40p. (J). 9.95 (978-1-933002-04-0(2)) PublishingWorks.

Dunn, Diane E. The Adventures of a Harp Mouse. Endres, Linda Carollo, illus. 2005. (J). 14.95 (978-0-9742174-3-7(3)) Heart & Harp LLC.

Dunphy, Joan S. The Mouse Family's Most Terrible, Terrifying Day: Helping Children Cope with Terrorism Fears. DePrince, Erik & Volinski, Jessica, illus. 2002. (Let's Talk Ser.). 48p. (J). pap. 12.95 (978-0-88282-227-3(6)) New Horizon Pr. Pubs., Inc.

Dyan, Penelope. The Warrior Mouse of Forest Hollow. 2005. (J). per. 5.95 (978-0-9771916-5-9(6)) Bellissima Publishing, LLC.

Eady, Ellen. Pardon Me. . . Is That the Grand Ole Opry? Brown, Emily, illus. 2001. 28p. (J). 15.95 (978-0-9679065-2-2(0)) Majestic Publishing.

—Pardon Me, Is That the Chattanooga Choo-Choo? Guhne, Kelly, illus. 2000. (J). pap. 9.95 (978-0-9679065-1-5(2)) Majestic Publishing.

Edwards, Julie Andrews. The Great American Mousical. Walton, Tony, illus. 2007. 160p. (J). pap. 5.99 (***978-0-06-057920-3(X)**, Harper Trophy) HarperCollins Pubs.

Edwards, Julie Andrews & Hamilton, Emma Walton. The Great American Mousical. Walton, Tony, illus. 2006. (Julie Andrews Collection). 160p. (J). 15.99 (978-0-06-057918-0(8), Julie Andrews Collection); lib. bdg. 16.89 (978-0-06-057919-7(6)) HarperCollins Pubs.

Edwards, Pamela Duncan. Livingstone Mouse. Cole, Henry, illus. 1998. 32p. (J). (ps-2). pap. 6.99 (978-0-06-443508-6(3), Harper Trophy) HarperCollins Pubs.

—Livingstone Mouse II. 2005. 32p. (J). pap. (978-0-7868-1171-7(4)) Hyperion Bks. for Children.

—Livingstone Mouse II. 1998. (978-0-606-13577-1(4)) Tandem Library Bks.

Edwards, Pamela Duncan & Cole, Henry. Bravo, Livingstone Mouse! 2000. (Illus.). 32p. (gr. k-4). 16.49 (978-0-7868-2247-8(3)) Hyperion Bks. for Children.

Eggleton, Jill. Brave Mouse. Taylor, Clive, illus. (Sails Literacy Ser.). 24p. (gr. 1 up). 27.00 (978-0-7635-5933-5(4)); Pack. 57.00 (978-0-7578-3205-5(9)) Rigby Education.

—Brave Mouse: 6 Small Books. Taylor, Clive, illus. (Sails Literacy Ser.). 24p. (gr. 1 up). 25.00 (978-0-7578-3181-2(8)) Rigby Education.

Egielski, Richard. Slim & Jim. Egielski, Richard, illus. 2005. (Illus.). 37p. (J). (gr. k-4). reprint ed. 16.00 (978-0-7567-8936-7(2)) DIANE Publishing Co.

Ehrlich, F. M. Does a Mouse Have a Mommy? 2004. (Early Experiences Ser.). (Illus.). 32p. 10.95 (978-1-59354-034-0(5)) Blue Apple Bks.

Ellwand, David. Midas Mouse. 2000. (J). lib. bdg. 14.89 (978-0-06-029225-6(3)) HarperCollins Pubs.

Emond, Landis J. Caruso the Mouse. 2nd rev. ed. 2007. 44p. (J). pap. 9.99 (978-1-59092-204-0(2), Little Blue Works) Windstorm Creative.

Engelbreit, Mary. Mary Engelbreit's A Merry Little Christmas: Celebrate from A to Z. Engelbreit, Mary, illus. 2006. (Illus.). 40p. (J). lib. bdg. 17.89 (978-0-06-074159-4(7)) HarperCollins Pubs.

—Mary Engelbreit's a Merry Little Christmas: Celebrate from A to Z. Engelbreit, Mary, illus. 2006. (Illus.). 40p. (J). 16.99 (978-0-06-074158-7(9)) HarperCollins Pubs.

Erdogan, Buket & Thompson, Lauren. Mouse's First Valentine. 2004. (Classic Board Bks.). (Illus.). 34p. (J). 7.99 (978-0-689-85585-6(0), Little Simon) Simon & Schuster Children's Publishing.

Ernest & Celestine. 2004. (J). pap. 14.95 incl. audio (978-1-56008-039-8(6)) Weston Woods Studios, Inc.

Ernest & Celestine's Picnic. 2004. 24.95 incl. audio (978-1-56008-198-2(8)); (J). pap. 14.95 incl. audio (978-1-56008-199-9(6)) Weston Woods Studios, Inc.

Esbaum, Jill. Estelle Takes a Bath. DePalma, Mary Newell, illus. rev. ed. 2006. 32p. (J). 16.95 (978-0-8050-7741-4(3)) Holt, Henry & Co.

Evelyn. Lucy the Elephant & Sami the Mouse: A Bedtime Story. Conforti, John W., tr. Conforti, John W., illus. 2003. (J). (978-0-9740115-0-9(9)) WeBeANS Corp.

—Lucy the Elephant & Sami the Mouse: The Birthday Party. Conforti, John W., illus. 2004. (J). (978-0-9740115-1-6(7)) WeBeANS Corp.

Fagan, Cary. Ten Old Men & a Mouse. Clement, Gary, illus. 2007. 32p. (J). (ps-2). 18.95 (978-0-88776-716-6(8)) Tundra Bks., Inc./Livres Toundra, Inc. CAN. *Dist:* Random Hse., Inc.

Farland, David. Of Mice & Magic. Lyon, Howard, illus. 2005. (Ravenspell Ser.: Bk. 1). 276p. (J). 16.95 (978-1-57734-918-1(0)) Covenant Communications, Inc.

Faulkner, Keith. The Mouse Who Ate Bananas. Tyger, Rory, illus. 2001. 32p. (J). (ps-k). 10.95 (978-0-531-30312-2(8), Orchard Bks.) Scholastic, Inc.

Fearnley, Jan. Just Like You. Fearnley, Jan, illus. 2003. (Illus.). 32p. (J). (ps-1). pap. 6.99 (978-0-7636-2207-7(9)) Candlewick Pr.

—Just Like You. 2004. (ps-2). lib. bdg. 15.30 (978-0-613-74824-7(7)) Tandem Library Bks.

—Watch Out! Fearnley, Jan, illus. 2004. (Illus.). 40p. (J). (ps-2). 15.99 (978-0-7636-2318-0(0)) Candlewick Pr.

Fernandes, Eugenie. Busy Little Mouse. Fernandes, Kim, illus. unabr. ed. 2002. (Little Mice Ser.). 24p. (J). (ps-k). (978-1-55074-776-8(2)) Kids Can Pr., Ltd.

—Busy Little Mouse. Fernandes, Kim, illus. 2006. 24p. 6.95 (978-1-55453-027-4(X)) Kids Can Pr., Ltd. CAN. *Dist:* Wybel Marketing Group.

—Busy Little Mouse. Fernandes, Kim, illus. 2004. 20p. (ps-ps). lib. bdg. 12.75 (978-0-606-31383-4(4)) Tandem Library Bks.

—Sleepy Little Mouse. Fernandes, Kim, illus. 2000. (Little Mice Ser.). 24p. (J). (ps-k). (978-1-55074-701-0(0)) Kids Can Pr., Ltd.

—Sleepy Little Mouse. Ferandes, Kim, illus. unabr. ed. 2002. (Little Mice Ser.). 24p. (J). (ps-k). (978-1-55074-703-4(7)) Kids Can Pr., Ltd.

—Sleepy Little Mouse. 2002. (ps-2). lib. bdg. 14.10 (978-0-613-81789-9(3)) Tandem Library Bks.

Fernandes, Eugenie & Fernandes, Kim. Big Week for Little Mouse. Fernandes, Eugenie & Fernandes, Kim, illus. (Little Mice Ser.). (Illus.). 24p. (J). (gr. k up). 2005. (978-1-55337-170-0(4)); 2004. (978-1-55337-665-1(X)) Kids Can Pr., Ltd.

Fernandes, Eugenie & Fernandes, Kim, illus. Busy Little Mouse. 2004. (Little Mice Ser.). 24p. (J). (ps-k). (978-1-55074-778-2(9)) Kids Can Pr., Ltd.

Ferraby, Sue. Run! Fiorin, Fabiano, illus. 2004. (Read-It! Readers Ser.). 32p. (C). (gr. k-3). 18.60 (978-1-4048-0552-1(4)) Picture Window Bks.

Finkelstein, Ruth. Mendel the Mouse. Bk. 1. (Illus.). (J). 10.00 (978-0-914131-43-4(5), D350); Bk. 2. 2002. 10.00 (978-0-914131-44-1(3), D350) Torah Umesorah Pubns.

Finklea, Ernest. Little One. 2006. (Illus.). 32p. (J). 12.99 (978-1-57921-849-2(0)) WinePress Publishing.

Fiore, Michael. The Mouse, the Computer, & the Mouse. 1999. (Illus.). 32p. (J). (gr. k-3). pap. 6.75 (978-0-8059-4604-8(7)) Dorrance Publishing Co., Inc.

Fischer, Rusty. Dear Mouse. 2003. (YA). pap. 10.95 (978-1-931095-57-0(4)) Silver Lake Publishing.

Fitch, Sheree. There's a Mouse in My House! braille ed. 2004. (Illus.). (J). (gr. k-3). spiral bd. (978-0-616-07234-9(1)); spiral bd. (978-0-616-07235-6(X)) Canadian National Institute for the Blind/Institut National Canadien pour les Aveugles.

—There's a Mouse in My House! 1999. (ps-2). lib. bdg. 15.25 (978-0-613-27220-9(X)) Tandem Library Bks.

Fleming, David. Miss Mouse's House. Storms, Samantha Ivey, illus. l.t. ed. 2001. 36p. (J). 15.00 (978-0-9643003-2-3(X)) Country Place Bks.

Fleming, Denise. Alphabet under Construction. 2006. (Illus.). 32p. (J). reprint ed. pap. 7.95 (978-0-8050-8112-1(7), Holt, Henry & Co. Bks. For Young Readers) Holt, Henry & Co.

—Alphabet under Construction. Fleming, Denise, illus. rev. ed. 2002. (Illus.). 32p. (J). (ps-2). 16.95 (978-0-8050-6848-1(1), Holt, Henry & Co. Bks. For Young Readers) Holt, Henry & Co.

—Lunch. Fleming, Denise, illus. 2002. (Illus.). (J). 15.49 (978-0-7587-3054-1(3)) Book Wholesalers, Inc.

—Lunch. Fleming, Denise, illus. rev. ed. 1998. (Illus.). 32p. (J). (ps-k). bds. 6.95 (978-0-8050-5696-9(3), Holt, Henry & Co. Bks. For Young Readers) Holt, Henry & Co.

Fleming, Maria. Chicken Soup with Rice & Mice. Sasaki, Ellen Joy, illus. 2002. (Word Family Tales Ser.). 16p. (ps-2). pap. 2.95 (978-0-439-26259-0(3)) Scholastic, Inc.

Fontes, Justine. Signs of Spring. Hefferan, Rob, illus. 2002. 24p. (J). pap. (978-1-59034-180-3(5)); 14.95 (978-1-59034-189-6(9)) Mondo Publishing.

Fox, Diane & Fox, Christyan. Raton, Que Te Pilla el Gato! 2003. (ENG & SPA., Illus.). 20p. pap. 11.95 (978-84-7864-693-7(0)) Combel Editorial, S.A. ESP. *Dist:* Independent Pubs. Group.

Fraser, Mary Ann. I.Q. Gets Fit. Fraser, Mary Ann, illus. 2007. (Illus.). 32p. (J). (gr. k-2). 15.95 (978-0-8027-9558-8(7)); 16.85 (978-0-8027-9559-5(5)) Walker & Co.

Frederick, Heather Vogel. The Black Paw. Comport, Sally Wern, illus. 2006. (Spy Mice Ser.). 256p. (J). pap. 5.99 (978-1-4169-2770-9(0)); pap. 2.99 (978-1-4169-2502-6(3)) Simon & Schuster Children's Publishing. (Aladdin).

—For Your Paws Only. Comport, Sally Wern, illus. (Spy Mice Ser.). 272p. (J). 2006. pap. 5.99 (978-1-4169-4025-8(1) , Aladdin); 2005. (gr. 4-6). 9.95 (978-1-4169-0573-8(1)) Simon & Schuster Children's Publishing.

—Goldwhiskers. Comport, Sally Wern, illus. 2007. (Spy Mice Ser.). 256p. (J). pap. 5.99 (978-1-4169-1442-6(0) , Simon & Schuster Children's Publishing) Simon & Schuster Children's Publishing.

Freedman, Claire. New Kid in Town. Stephenson, Kristina, illus. 2006. 28p. (J). 16.00 (978-1-56148-547-5(0)) Good Bks.

French & Currey. Squeaky Cleaners: In a Stew. (Illus.). 64p. pap. 7.99 (978-0-340-72666-2(0) , Hodder & Stoughton) Hodder General Publishing Division GBR. *Dist:* Trafalgar Square Publishing.

Galvin, Laura. Deer Mouse at Old Farm Road. Bratun, Katy, illus. 1998. (Smithsonian's Backyard Ser.). 32p. (J). (ps-2). 15.95 (978-1-56899-516-8(4) , B5015); Incl. large toy. 32.95 (978-1-56899-520-5(2)); Micro bk. 4.95 (978-1-56899-517-5(2) , B5065); Micro bk., incl. small toy. 9.95 (978-1-56899-521-2(0) , PB5065) Soundprints.

Galvin, Laura Gates. Deer Mouse at Old Farm Road. 2005. (Smithsonian's Backyard Ser.). (Illus.). 32p. (J). (ps-2). 8.95 incl. audio (978-1-59249-223-7(1) , SC5015) Soundprints.

—Deer Mouse at Old Farm Road. Bratun, Katy, illus. 1998. (Smithsonian's Backyard Ser.). 32p. (J). (ps-2). 19.95 incl. reel tape (978-1-56899-518-2(0) , BC5015) Soundprints.

Gardner, Sally. Boolar's Big Day Out. 2003. (Tales from the Box Ser.: Vol. 2). (Illus.). 128p. (J). 14.95 (978-1-58234-833-9(2) , Bloomsbury Children) Bloomsbury Publishing.

—The Countess's Calamity: Tales from the Box. Gardner, Sally, illus. 2003. (Tales from the Box Ser.). (Illus.). 160p. (J). (gr. 1-6). 14.95 (978-1-58234-812-4(X)); pap. 6.95 (978-1-58234-855-1(3)) Bloomsbury Publishing. (Bloomsbury Children).

Garland, Michael. Hooray Jose! 2007. (Illus.). 32p. (J). 14.99 ***(*978-0-7614-5345-1(8))*** Cavendish, Marshall Corp.

—How Many Mice? 2007. (Illus.). 32p. (J). (gr. k-2). 15.99 (978-0-525-47833-1(7) , Dutton Juvenile) Penguin Group (USA) Inc.

—The Mouse Before Christmas. Garland, Michael, illus. 2001. (Illus.). 32p. (J). pap. 6.99 (978-0-14-230005-3(5) , Puffin) Penguin Group (USA) Inc.

—Mouse Before Christmas. 2001. (gr. k-3). lib. bdg. 15.30 (978-0-613-71585-0(3)) Tandem Library Bks.

Garland, Michael, illus. Hooray José! 2007. (J). ***(*978-1-4287-3591-0(7)*** , Cavendish Children's Bks.) Cavendish, Marshall Corp.

Gauthier, Lance C., text. The One-Eared Mouse of Pasture Hill. 2003. 55p. (J). per. 6.95 (978-1-884540-70-7(8)) Haley's.

Gelman, Rita Golden. Hello, Cat, You Need a Hat. 1999. (Hello Reader! Ser.). (Illus.). (J). (978-0-606-18557-8(7)) Tandem Library Bks.

—Pizza Pat. 1999. (Step into Reading Ser.). (978-0-606-16891-5(5)) Tandem Library Bks.

George, Lindsay Barrett. Inside Mouse, Outside Mouse. George, Lindsay Barrett, illus. (Illus.). 40p. (J). 2004. 15.99 (978-0-06-000466-8(5)); 2004. lib. bdg. 16.89 (978-0-06-000467-5(3)); 2006. reprint ed. pap. 6.99 (978-0-06-000468-2(1) , Harper Trophy) HarperCollins Pubs.

Gerritsen, Paula. Nuts. 2006. 32p. (J). 15.95 (978-1-932425-66-6(7) , Lemniscaat) Boyds Mills Pr.

Ghigna, Charles. Mice Are Nice. Goodell, Jon, illus. 2002. (J). 11.91 (978-0-7587-6201-6(1)) Book Wholesalers, Inc.

—Mice Are Nice. 1999. (Step into Reading Step 1 Bks.). (Illus.). 32p. (J). (ps-1). lib. bdg. 11.99 (978-0-679-98929-5(3) , Random Hse. Bks. for Young Readers) Random Hse. Children's Bks.

—Mice Are Nice. Goodell, Jon, illus. 1999. (Step into Reading Step 1 Bks.). 32p. (J). (ps-1). pap. 3.99 (978-0-679-88929-8(9) , Random Hse. Bks. for Young Readers) Random Hse. Children's Bks.

—Mice Are Nice. Goodell, Jon, illus. 1999. 32p. (J). (ps-ps). lib. bdg. 11.80 (978-0-613-16154-1(8)) Tandem Library Bks.

—Mice Are Nice. 1999. (J). (978-0-606-16838-0(9)) Tandem Library Bks.

Gibbs, Kimberly B. Herman the Mouse. Clark, Jarrod C. & Bova, Shawna, illus. 2002. (J). (978-0-945069-19-5(7)) Freedom Pr. Assocs.

Gibbs, Lynne. Quiet as a Mouse. Mitchell, Melanie, illus. 2003. (Growing Pains Ser.). 32p. (J). pap. 4.95 (978-1-57768-928-7(3)); 12.95 (978-1-57768-481-7(8)) School Specialty Publishing. (Gingham Dog Pr.).

Gillis, Jennifer B. Two Nice Mice. 2006. (Reader's Clubhouse Set B Ser.). (Illus.). 24p. (J). pap. 3.99 (978-0-7641-3295-7(4)) Barron's Educational Series, Inc.

Gleason, Anne V. Mouse. Hardystoehr, Chastine, illus. 1999. 40p. (J). (ps-k). mass mkt. 19.95 (978-0-9673900-0-0(1)) Gleason, Anne V.

Glitz, Angelika. A Monster under Alex's Bed. Kerntke, Felix, tr. from GER. Sonnichsen, Imke, illus. 2002. 32p. (J). pap. 5.95 (978-1-58925-373-5(6) , tiger tales) ME Media LLC.

—Monster under Alex's Bed. 2002. (gr. k-3). lib. bdg. 14.10 (978-0-613-62803-7(9)) Tandem Library Bks.

Godon, Ingrid. In, Out & Other Places. 2000. (Nelly & Caesar Picture Bks.). (Illus.). 24p. (J). 6.95 (978-0-7641-5255-9(6)) Barron's Educational Series, Inc.

—Jump, Dance & Other Adventures. 2000. (Nelly & Caesar Picture Bks.). (Illus.). 24p. (J). 6.95 (978-0-7641-5257-3(2)) Barron's Educational Series, Inc.

—Neli y Gus: Tocar, Probar y Otras Sensaciones. (SPA.). 96p. (J). (978-84-246-8834-9(1)) La Galera, S.A. Editorial ESP. *Dist:* Lectorum Pubns., Inc.

Golden Books Staff. Mickey & Friends: Animal Kingdom. 1999. (Disney Ser.). 40p. (J). (ps-3). pap. 1.09 (978-0-307-21123-1(1) , 21123, Golden Bks.) Random Hse. Children's Bks.

Golds, Cassandra. Clair de Lune. Blackall, Sophie, illus. 2006. 208p. (J). (gr. 5). 15.95 (978-0-375-83395-3(1)); lib. bdg. 17.99 (978-0-375-93395-0(6)) Random Hse. Children's Bks. (Knopf Bks. for Young Readers).

—Clair de Lune. Blackall, Sophie, illus. 2007. 208p. (J). (gr. 4-7). 5.99 (978-0-440-42089-7(X) , Yearling) Random Hse. Children's Bks.

Goldsboro, Bobby. Jonah & the Whale/Daniel & the Lion's Den, Vol. 2. Stewart, Toni D., illus. 2003. (Adventures of Cheze & Kwackers Ser.: Bk. 2). 48p. (J). (gr. k-3). pap. 8.95 (978-1-889658-28-5(6)) New Canaan Publishing Co. LLC.

—Noah & the Ark/David & Goliath. Stewart, Toni D., illus. 2003. (Adventures of Cheze & Kwackers Ser.: Bk. 1). 48p. (J). (gr. k-3). pap. 8.95 (978-1-889658-27-8(8)) New Canaan Publishing Co. LLC.

Goodings, Christina. Bartimouse Aboard the Ark. Dorsey, Maxwell Lawrence, illus. 2003. 32p. (J). 14.99 (978-0-7459-3959-9(7) , Lion) Lion Hudson plc GBR. *Dist:* Independent Pubs. Group.

Goodrich, Carter & Moore, Clement Clarke. A Creature Was Stirring. Goodrich, Carter, illus. 2006. (Illus.). 40p. (J). 16.95 (978-0-689-86399-8(3) , Simon & Schuster Children's Publishing) Simon & Schuster Children's Publishing.

Gorbachev, Valeri. Dragon Is Coming! 2008. (J). ***(*978-0-15-205196-9(1))*** Harcourt Trade Pubs.

Graves, Damien. The Deadly Catch. 2008. (Midnight Library: Vol. 8). 176p. (J). pap. 5.99 ***(*978-0-439-89395-4(X)*** , Scholastic Paperbacks) Scholastic, Inc.

Greene, Stephanie. Christmas at Stony Creek. Sheban, Chris, illus. 2007. 96p. (J). (gr. 2-7). 14.99 ***(*978-0-06-121486-8(8));*** lib. bdg. 15.89 ***(*978-0-06-121487-5(6))*** HarperCollins Pubs. (Greenwillow Bks.).

Griffin, Daniel. The Adventures of Merlin the Mouse, 2005. (Illus.). 44p. (J). (978-0-9768348-0-9(4)) DiGuiseppi, Joseph.

Gutman, Anne. Gaspard et Lisa au Musee. (FRE.). pap. 19.95 (978-2-01-224132-9(8)) Hachette Groupe Livre FRA. *Dist:* Distribooks, Inc.

Guy, Geoffrey. Hannibal's Rat. 2003. (Illus.). mass mkt. (978-0-340-85485-3(5) , Hodder Children's Books) Hodder Children's Division.

Haber, Melissa. Heroic Adventures of Hercules Amsterdam. 2004. 224p. (J). (gr. 5). pap. 5.99 (978-0-14-240216-0(8) , Puffin) Penguin Group (USA) Inc.

Hall, Nancy Christensen. Mouse at Night. Erdogan, Buket, illus. 2000. 32p. (J). (ps-1). pap. 14.95 (978-0-531-30260-6(1) , Orchard Bks.) Scholastic, Inc.

Haller, Reese. Fred the Mouse: Making Friends, 2. Galasterer, Lynne, illus. 2nd ed. 2006. 112p. (J). 4.97 (978-0-9772321-0-9(7)) Personal Power Pr.

—Fred the Mouse: Rescuing Freedom. Haller, Thomas, illus. 3rd ed. 2006. 108p. (J). 4.97 (978-0-9772321-3-0(1)) Personal Power Pr.

—Fred the Mouse: The Adventures Begin. 2005. (Illus.). 108p. (J). lib. bdg. 4.97 (978-0-9616046-8-4(9)) Personal Power Pr.

Hanna, William. It's Always a Mice Day. 1999. (Magical Library). (J). (ps-3). (978-1-894155-34-2(3)) Cethial & Bossche Co.

Harcourt School Publishers Staff. Frisby & the Rats. 1999. (Reader's Choice Bks.). (Illus.). pap. 20.00 (978-0-15-314421-9(1)) Harcourt Schl. Pubs.

—Mouse Mess: Little Book. 2000. (Collections Ser.). (Illus.). (J). pap. 10.20 (978-0-15-314501-8(3)) Harcourt Schl. Pubs.

—Wait for Me, Captain! On Level. 3rd ed. 2002. (Trophies Reading Program Ser.). (Illus.). pap. 5.10 (978-0-15-323099-8(1)) Harcourt Schl. Pubs.

Harms, Jeanine, illus. Boss Mouse Coloring Book & Theme Song. 2006. (J). 4.00 (978-1-4276-0118-6(6)) Aardvark Global Publishing.

Harper, Jessica. I'm Not Going to Chase the Cat Today! 2000. (Illus.). 32p. (J). (ps-3). 15.89 (978-0-688-17637-2(2)) HarperCollins Pubs.

—I'm Not Going to Chase the Cat Today! Dupont, Lindsay Harper, illus. 2000. 32p. (J). (ps-3). 15.95 (978-0-688-17636-5(4)) HarperCollins Pubs.

HarperCollins Staff, ed. Stuart's New Brother. 2000. (gr. k-3). lib. bdg. 11.80 (978-0-613-31764-1(5)) Tandem Library Bks.

Harris, Robie H. Adios, Ratoncito. Rioja, Alberto Jiménez, tr. Ormerod, Jan, illus. (SPA.). (J). (gr. k-2). 16.00 (978-1-930332-34-8(3) , LC8567) Lectorum Pubns., Inc.

—Goodbye Mousie. Ormerod, Jan, illus. 2004. 32p. (J). reprint ed. 6.99 (978-0-689-87134-4(1) , Aladdin) Simon & Schuster Children's Publishing.

Hart, Melissa. Tale of Despereaux Literature Unit. 2005. 48p. pap. 7.99 (978-1-4206-3164-7(0)) Teacher Created Resources, Inc.

Head, Honor. Direction. Stower, Adam, illus. 1998. (Ed Mouse Finds Out about Ser.). 32p. (J). (ps-2). 19.98 (978-0-8172-5200-7(2)) Raintree.

—Direction. Stower, Adam, illus. 1998. (Ed Mouse Finds Out about Ser.). 32p. (J). (ps-2). pap. 5.95 (978-0-8172-8100-7(2)) Steck-Vaughn.

—Opposites. Stower, Adam, illus. 1998. (Ed Mouse Finds Out about Ser.). 32 p. (J). (ps-2). 19.98 (978-0-8172-5202-1(9)) Raintree.

—Size & Shape. Stower, Adam, illus. 1998. (Ed Mouse Finds Out about Ser.). 32p. (J). (ps-2). 19.98 (978-0-8172-5201-4(0)) Raintree.

—Times of Day. Stower, Adam, illus. 1999. (Ed Mouse Finds Out about Ser.). 32p. (J). (ps-2). 19.98 (978-0-8172-5203-8(7)) Raintree.

Heling, Kathryn. Mouse Makes Magic: Phonics Reader. 2002. (gr. k-3). lib. bdg. 11.80 (978-0-613-87817-3(5)) Tandem Library Bks.

—Mouse Makes Words: A Phonics Reader. 2002. (ps-2). lib. bdg. 11.80 (978-0-613-83542-8(5)) Tandem Library Bks.

—Mouse's Hide-and-Seek Words: A Phonics Reader. 2003. (ps-2). lib. bdg. 11.80 (978-0-613-89790-7(0)) Tandem Library Bks.

Heling, Kathryn & Hembrook, Deborah. Mouse Makes Magic. Joseph, Patrick & O'Malley, Kevin, illus. 2002. (Early Step into Reading Ser.). 32p. (J). (ps-1). lib. bdg. 11.99 (978-0-375-92184-1(2) , Random Hse. Bks. for Young Readers) Random Hse. Children's Bks.

—Mouse Makes Magic: A Phonics Reader. O'Malley, Kevin, illus. 2002. (Early Step into Reading Ser.). 32p. (J). (ps-1). pap. 3.99 (978-0-375-82184-4(8) , Random Hse. Bks. for Young Readers) Random Hse. Children's Bks.

—Mouse Makes Words: A Phonics Reader. Joseph, Patrick, illus. 2002. (Early Step into Reading Ser.). 32p. (J). (ps-1). pap. 3.99 (978-0-375-81399-3(3) , Random Hse. Bks. for Young Readers) Random Hse. Children's Bks.

—Mouse's Hide-and-Seek Words. Joseph, Patrick, illus. 2003. (Early Step into Reading Ser.: Vol. 1). 32p. (J). (ps-1). pap. 3.99 (978-0-375-82185-1(6) , Random Hse. Bks. for Young Readers) Random Hse. Children's Bks.

—Mouse's Hide-and-Seek Words: A Phonics Reader. Joseph, Patrick, illus. 2003. (Early Step into Reading Ser.). 32p. (J). (ps-1). lib. bdg. 11.99 (978-0-375-92185-8(0) , Random Hse. Bks. for Young Readers) Random Hse. Children's Bks.

Helmer, Marilyn. Three Cat & Mouse Tales. Masse, Josee, illus. 2004. (Once-upon-a-Time Ser.). 32p. (J). (gr. k-3). (978-1-55074-943-4(9)) Kids Can Pr., Ltd.

Hendry, Diana. Que Noche Mas Ruidosa! Chapman, Jane, illus. 2003. (SPA.). 28p. (J). (gr. k-2). 16.95 (978-84-488-0865-5(7) , BS3550) Beascoa, Ediciones S.A. ESP. *Dist:* Lectorum Pubns., Inc.

—Very Noisy Night. 2001. (gr. k-3). lib. bdg. 14.15 (978-0-613-44427-9(2)) Tandem Library Bks.

Hendry, Diana. The Very Snowy Christmas. Chapman, Jane, illus. 32p. (J). 2007. pap. 6.95 ***(*978-1-58925-406-0(6));*** 2005. 15.95 (978-1-58925-051-2(6)) ME Media LLC. (tiger tales).

Henkes, Kevin. Chester's Way. (Illus.). 25.95 incl. audio (978-1-59112-968-4(0)); 28.95 incl. audio compact disk (978-1-59112-972-1(9)); pap. 33.95 incl. audio (978-1-59112-969-1(9)); pap. 35.95 incl. audio compact disk (978-1-59112-973-8(7)) Live Oak Media.

—Chrysanthemum. unabr. ed. 1998. (J). (ps-2). 24.95 incl. audio (978-0-7882-0672-6(9) , HRA369); pap. 14.95 incl. audio (978-0-7882-0675-7(3) , PRA369) Weston Woods Studios, Inc.

—Lilly's Big Day. Henkes, Kevin, illus. 2006. (Illus.). 40p. (J). 16.99 (978-0-06-074236-2(4)); lib. bdg. 17.89 (978-0-06-074237-9(2)) HarperCollins Pubs.

—Lilly's Purple Plastic Purse. Henkes, Kevin, illus. 10th anniv. ed. 2006. (Illus.). 40p. (J). (ps-3). 16.99 (978-0-688-12897-5(1)) HarperCollins Pubs.

—Lilly's Purple Plastic Purse. Henkes, Kevin, illus. (Illus.). pap. incl. audio (978-0-87499-688-3(0)); pap. 18.95 incl. audio compact disk (978-1-59112-347-7(X)); pap. incl. audio compact disk (978-1-59112-557-0(X)); pap. 16.95 incl. audio (978-0-87499-686-9(4)); 2000. (J). pap. 28.95 incl. audio compact disk (978-1-59112-348-4(8)) Live Oak Media.

—Lilly's Sticker & Storybook Fun. 2000. (Illus.). 16p. (YA). (ps-3). pap. 7.95 (978-0-688-17710-2(7)) HarperCollins Pubs.

—Lily y Su Bolso de Plastico Morado. 2001. (SPA., Illus.). (J). (ps-4). pap. 16.95 incl. audio (978-0-87499-811-5(5)) Live Oak Media.

—Owen. Gil-Toresano, Maria Luz Castela, tr. 2006. (SPA., Illus.). 24p. (J). 8.99 ***(*978-84-241-1519-7(8))*** Everest de Ediciones y Distribucion, S.L. ESP. *Dist:* Lectorum Pubns., Inc.

—Sheila Rae, the Brave. Henkes, Kevin, illus. (Illus.). 9.95 (978-1-59112-865-6(X)); 2002. 28.95 incl. audio compact disk (978-1-59112-550-1(2)); 2002. pap. 35.95 incl. audio compact disk (978-1-59112-549-5(9)) Live Oak Media.

—Sheila Rae, the Brave. 2002. (Illus.). (J). pap., tchr.'s planning gde. ed. 33.95 incl. audio (978-0-87499-954-9(5)); 25.95 incl. audio (978-0-87499-953-2(7)) Live Oak Media.

—Wemberly Worried. Henkes, Kevin, illus. 2000. (Illus.). 32p. (J). (ps-3). 16.99 (978-0-688-17027-1(7)); lib. bdg. 17.89 (978-0-688-17028-8(5)) HarperCollins Pubs.

—Wemberly Worried. Henkes, Kevin, illus. (Illus.). pap. 16.95 incl. audio (978-0-87499-806-1(9)); pap. incl. audio (978-0-87499-808-5(5)); pap. 18.95 incl. audio compact disk (978-1-59112-359-0(3)); pap. incl. audio compact disk (978-1-59112-561-7(8)) Live Oak Media.

—Wemberly Worried. unabr. ed. 2001. (Illus.). (J). (ps-2). 25.95 incl. audio (978-0-87499-807-8(7)) Live Oak Media.

Herman, Gail. The Lion & the Mouse. McCue, Lisa, illus. 1998. 28p. lib. bdg. 10.79 (978-0-606-15973-9(8)) Tandem Library Bks.

Herman, Gail & Aesop. The Lion & the Mouse. McCue, Lisa, illus. 1998. (Step into Reading Ser.). 32p. (J). (ps-k). lib. bdg. 11.99 (978-0-679-98674-4(X) , Random Hse. Bks. for Young Readers) Random Hse. Children's Bks.

Herman, R. A. The Littlest Pumpkin. Ogden, Betina, illus. 2001. 32p. (J). (ps-2). 3.99 (978-0-439-29544-4(0)) Scholastic, Inc.

—Littlest Pumpkin. 2001. (ps-2). lib. bdg. 11.25 (978-0-613-86020-8(9)) Tandem Library Bks.

—Littlest Pumpkin - Library. 2006. (J). 18.95 (978-0-439-89837-9(4)) Scholastic, Inc.

—Littlest Pumpkin Read Along. 2006. (J). 9.95 (978-0-439-89555-2(3)) Scholastic, Inc.

Herrera De Fernandez, Maria Victoria. All Because of a Mouse. 2005. pap. 7.95 (978-0-533-15000-7(0)) Vantage Pr., Inc.

Heurtelou, Maude. Istwa Chat ak Sourit. Louissaint, Louis, illus. 1999. Tr. of Cat & Mouse. (CRP.). 24p. (J). (gr. 3-5). pap. 19.00 incl. audio (978-1-881839-90-3(7)) Educa Vision.

Higginson, Sheila. Are We There Yet? Disney Storybook Artists Staff, illus. 2007. 24p. (J). (ps-k). pap. 3.99 ***(*978-1-4231-0648-7(2))*** Disney Pr.

—Over the River & Through the Woods. Disney Storybook Artists Staff, illus. 2007. 24p. (J). (ps-k). pap. 3.99 ***(*978-1-4231-0649-4(0))*** Disney Pr.

Higginson, Sheila Sweeny. Minnie's Valentine. rev. ed. 2007. 24p. (J). (ps-1). pap. 4.99 ***(*978-1-4231-0746-0(2))*** Disney Pr.

Hill, Susan. Stuart at the Fun House. Halverson, Lydia, illus. 2001. (I Can Read Bks.). 32p. (J). (ps-1). pap. 3.99 (978-0-06-444304-3(3) , Harper Trophy); Bk. 1. 15.89 (978-0-06-029635-3(6)); Bk. 1. 15.99 (978-0-06-029539-4(2)) HarperCollins Pubs.

—Stuart at the Fun House. 2001. (gr. k-3). lib. bdg. 11.80 (978-0-613-35575-9(X)); (Illus.). (J). (978-0-606-21470-4(4)) Tandem Library Bks.

—Stuart at the Library. Halverson, Lydia, illus. 2001. (I Can Read Bks.). 32p. (J). (ps-1). pap. 3.99 (978-0-06-444303-6(5) , Harper Trophy); Bk. 1. 15.99 (978-0-06-029538-7(4)); Bk. 1. 15.89 (978-0-06-029632-2(1)) HarperCollins Pubs.

—Stuart at the Library. 2001. (gr. k-3). lib. bdg. 11.80 (978-0-613-35576-6(8)); (Illus.). (J). (978-0-606-21471-1(2)) Tandem Library Bks.

—Stuart Hides Out. Halverson, Lydia, illus. 2001. (I Can Read Bks.). 32p. (J). (ps-3). pap. 3.99 (978-0-06-444301-2(9) , Harper Trophy); Bk. 1. 14.95 (978-0-06-029536-3(8)); Bk. 1. 14.89 (978-0-06-029634-6(8)) HarperCollins Pubs.

—Stuart Hides Out. 2001. (gr. k-3). lib. bdg. 11.80 (978-0-613-35577-3(6)) Tandem Library Bks.

—The Stuart Little I Can Read Library Box Set: Stuart Hides Out; Stuart at the Library; Stuart at the Fun House. Halverson, Lydia, illus. 2003. (I Can Read Bks.). (J). (gr. k-3). pap. 11.99 (978-0-06-053915-3(1) , Harper Trophy) HarperCollins Pubs.

—Stuart Sets Sail. Halverson, Lydia, illus. 2001. (I Can Read Bks.). 32p. (J). (ps-3). pap. 3.99 (978-0-06-444302-9(7) , Harper Trophy); Bk. 1. 14.95 (978-0-06-029537-0(6)) HarperCollins Pubs.

—Stuart Sets Sail. 2001. (gr. k-3). lib. bdg. 11.80 (978-0-613-35578-0(4)) Tandem Library Bks.

Hoberman, Mary Ann. The Two Sillies. Cravath, Lynne W., illus. 2004. 28p. (J). (ps-2). reprint ed. 16.00 (978-0-7567-7869-9(7)) DIANE Publishing Co.

Hockerman, Dennis, illus. The Country Mouse & the City Mouse: A Tale of Tolerance. 2006. (J). 6.99 (978-1-59939-003-1(5) , Reader's Digest Young Families, Inc.) Reader's Digest Children's Publishing, Inc.

—The Lion & the Mouse: A Tale about Being Helpful. 2006. (J). 6.99 (978-1-59939-007-9(8)) Reader's Digest Young Families, Inc.

Hockinson, Liz. Marcello the Movie Mouse. Otoshi, Kathryn, illus. 2005. 40p. (J). 16.95 (978-0-9723946-2-8(1)) KO Kids Bks.

Hoeye, Michael. Una Cuestion de Tiempo. (SPA.). 304p. (J). (gr. 6-8). 17.56 (978-84-8441-167-3(2) , MO1007) Grijalbo Mondadori, S.A.-Montena ESP. *Dist:* Lectorum Pubns., Inc.

—No Time Like Show Time. 2007. 304p. (J). pap. 7.99 ***(*978-0-14-240982-4(0)*** , Puffin) Penguin Group (USA) Inc.

—No Time Like Show Time: A Hermux Tantamoq Adventure. 2004. (Illus.). 288p. (J). (ps). 14.99 (978-0-399-23880-2(8) , Putnam Juvenile) Penguin Group (USA) Inc.

—The Sands of Time. (J). 2007. 304p. (gr. 1). pap. 7.99 ***(*978-0-14-240983-1(9)*** , Puffin); 2002. (Hermux Tantamoq Adventure Ser.: Bk. 2). (Illus.). 288p. (gr. 5-8). 14.99 (978-0-399-23879-6(4) , Putnam Juvenile) Penguin Group (USA) Inc.

—The Sands of Time. 2001. (Hermux Tantamoq Adventure Ser.: Bk. 2). (Illus.). 300p. (YA). (gr. 5-8). pap. 12.95 (978-0-9675111-2-2(7)) Terfle Bks.

—The Sands of Time: A Hermux Tantamoq AdventureTM. 2004. 288p. (J). (gr. 5-9). pap. 40.00 incl. audio (978-1-4000-9016-7(4) , Listening Library) Random Hse. Audio Publishing Group.

—The Sands of Time: A New Hermux Tantamoq Adventure. 2003. 288p. pap. 6.99 (978-0-14-250176-4(X) , Puffin) Penguin Group (USA) Inc.

—Time Stops for No Mouse. 272p. 2007. (J). pap. 7.99 ***(*978-0-14-240984-8(7));*** 2003. (Hermux Tantamoq Adventure Ser.: Bk. 1). (Illus.). (YA). (gr. 5-8). pap. 7.99 (978-0-698-11991-8(6)) Penguin Group (USA) Inc. (Puffin).

—Time Stops for No Mouse. 2003. (Illus.). 250p. (J). (ps-7). per. 16.45 (978-0-613-62122-9(0)) Tandem Library Bks.

—Time Stops for No Mouse. 2000. (Hermux Tantamoq Adventure Ser.: Bk. 1). (Illus.). 288p. (YA). (gr. 5-8). pap. 12.95 (978-0-9675111-1-5(9)) Terfle Bks.

—Time Stops for No Mouse: A Hermux Tantamoq Adventure. 2002. (Hermux Tantamoq Adventure Ser.: Bk. 1). (Illus.). 288p. (J). (gr. 5-8). 14.99 (978-0-399-23878-9(6) , Putnam Juvenile) Penguin Group (USA) Inc.

—Time Stops for No Mouse: A Hermux Tantamoq AdventureTM. 2004. 272p. (J). (gr. 5-9). pap. 40.00 incl. audio (978-0-8072-2280-5(1) , Listening Library) Random Hse. Audio Publishing Group.

Hoffman, Elizabeth. Miss Renee's Mice Go to an Exhibition. Peterson, Dawn, illus. 2003. (Miss Rene's Mice Ser.: No. 2). 32p. (gr. k-2). 15.95 (978-0-89272-581-6(8)) Down East Bks.

Hoffman, Elizabeth Stokes. Miss Renee's Mice. Peterson, Dawn, illus. 2001. (Miss Rene's Mice Ser.: No. 1). 32p. (ps-3). 15.95 (978-0-89272-505-2(2)) Down East Bks.

Holabird, Katharine. All Dancers on Deck. Craig, Helen, illus. 2006. (Angelina Ballerina Ser.). 32p. (J). (ps-1). 3.99 (978-0-448-44388-1(0) , Grosset & Dunlap) Penguin Group (USA) Inc.

—Angelina & Alice. 2006. (Angelina Ballerina Ser.). 32p. (J). (ps). 12.99 (978-0-670-06125-9(5) , Viking Juvenile) Penguin Group (USA) Inc.

—Angelina & Henry. Craig, Helen, illus. 2006. 32p. (J). pap. 5.99 (978-0-14-240590-1(6) , Puffin) Penguin Group (USA) Inc.

—Angelina & the Princess. Craig, Helen, illus. 2006. 32p. (J). (ps). 13.99 (978-0-670-06085-6(2) , Viking Juvenile) Penguin Group (USA) Inc.

—Angelina & the Rag Doll. Craig, Helen, illus. 2006. (Angelina Ballerina Ser.). 24p. (J). (ps-1). 3.99 (978-0-448-44331-7(7) , Grosset & Dunlap) Penguin Group (USA) Inc.

—Angelina at the Fair. Craig, Helen, illus. 2007. 32p. (J). 12.99 (978-0-670-06234-8(0) , Viking Juvenile) Penguin Group (USA) Inc.

—Angelina at the Fair. 2006. (Illus.). 32p. (J). pap. 5.99 (978-0-14-240591-8(4) , Puffin) Penguin Group (USA) Inc.

—Angelina Ballerina. Craig, Helen, illus. 2006. (Angelina Ballerina Ser.). 32p. (J). (ps). 13.99 (978-0-670-06026-9(7) , Viking Juvenile) Penguin Group (USA) Inc.

—Angelina Ballerina: The Costume Ball. Craig, Helen, illus. 2006. (Angelina Ballerina Ser.). 24p. (J). (ps-1). 3.99 (978-0-448-44334-8(1) , Grosset & Dunlap) Penguin Group (USA) Inc.

—Angelina Ballerina Book & Doll Set. Craig, Helen, illus. 2006. (Angelina Ballerina Ser.). 32p. (J). 27.99 (978-0-670-06088-7(7) , Viking Juvenile) Penguin Group (USA) Inc.

—Angelina Has the Hiccups! Craig, Helen, illus. 2006. (Angelina Ballerina Ser.). 32p. (J). (ps-1). pap. 3.99 (978-0-448-44389-8(9) , Grosset & Dunlap) Penguin Group (USA) Inc.

—Angelina Ice Skates. Craig, Helen, illus. 32p. (J). (ps). 2007. 13.99 (*978-0-670-06237-9(5)) , Viking Juvenile); 2006. pap. 6.99 (978-0-14-240658-8(9) , Puffin) Penguin Group (USA) Inc.

—Angelina in the Wings. Craig, Helen, illus. 2006. (Angelina Ballerina Ser.). 24p. (J). (ps-1). 3.99 (978-0-448-44471-0(2) , Grosset & Dunlap) Penguin Group (USA) Inc.

—Angelina Takes the Stage. Craig, Helen, illus. 2006. (Angelina Ballerina Ser.). 16p. (J). (ps-1). 4.99 (978-0-448-44018-7(0) , Grosset & Dunlap) Penguin Group (USA) Inc.

—Angelina's Baby Sister. Craig, Helen, illus. 2006. (Angelina Ballerina Ser.). 32p. (J). (ps). 12.99 (978-0-670-06146-4(8) , Viking Juvenile) Penguin Group (USA) Inc.

—Angelina's Ballet Class. Craig, Helen, illus. 2006. (Angelina Ballerina Ser.). 24p. (J). (ps-2). pap. 5.99 (978-0-448-44013-2(X) , Grosset & Dunlap) Penguin Group (USA) Inc.

—Angelina's Birthday. Craig, Helen, illus. 2006. 32p. (J). (ps). 12.99 (978-0-670-06057-3(7) , Viking Juvenile) Penguin Group (USA) Inc.

—Angelina's Christmas. Craig, Helen, illus. 2006. 32p. (J). (ps). 12.99 (978-0-670-06103-7(4) , Viking Juvenile) Penguin Group (USA) Inc.

—Angelina's Diary. Craig, Helen, illus. 2006. (Angelina Ballerina Ser.). 80p. (J). (gr. 1-3). 3.99 (978-0-448-44016-3(4) , Grosset & Dunlap) Penguin Group (USA) Inc.

—The Angelina's Diary No. 4. Craig, Helen, illus. 2006. (Angelina Ballerina Ser.). 80p. (J). (gr. 1-3). 3.99 (978-0-448-44386-7(4) , Grosset & Dunlap) Penguin Group (USA) Inc.

—Angelina's Halloween. Craig, Helen, illus. 2006. (Angelina Ballerina Ser.). 32p. (J). (ps). pap. 5.99 (978-0-14-240621-2(X) , Puffin) Penguin Group (USA) Inc.

—Angelina's Invitation to the Ballet. Craig, Helen, illus. 2007. 32p. (J). (ps). 16.99 (*978-0-670-06201-0(4)) , Viking Juvenile) Penguin Group (USA) Inc.

—Angelina's Lucky Penny. Craig, Helen, illus. 2006. (Angelina Ballerina Ser.). 24p. (J). (ps-1). 3.99 (978-0-448-44449-9(6) , Grosset & Dunlap) Penguin Group (USA) Inc.

—Angelina's Silly Little Sister: Station Stop 1. Craig, Helen, illus. 2007. (Angelina Ballerina Ser.). 32p. (J). pap. 3.99 (978-0-448-44468-0(2) , Grosset & Dunlap) Penguin Group (USA) Inc.

—Christmas in Mouseland. Craig, Helen, illus. 2007. (Angelina Ballerina Ser.). 24p. (J). (ps-1). 6.99 (*978-0-448-44663-9(4)) , Grosset & Dunlap) Penguin Group (USA) Inc.

—Miss Lilly Is Leaving. Craig, Helen, illus. 2006. (Angelina Ballerina Ser.). 24p. (J). (ps-1). 3.99 (978-0-448-44473-4(9) , Grosset & Dunlap) Penguin Group (USA) Inc.

—Mouse of the Year. Craig, Helen, illus. 2006. (Angelina Ballerina Ser.). 24p. (J). (ps-1). 3.99 (978-0-448-44474-1(7) , Grosset & Dunlap) Penguin Group (USA) Inc.

—The Nutcracker—Sticker Stories. Craig, Helen, illus. 2007. 16p. (J). (ps-1). pap. 5.99 (*978-0-448-44681-3(2)) , Grosset & Dunlap) Penguin Group (USA) Inc.

—Places, Everyone! Craig, Helen, illus. 2006. (Angelina Ballerina Ser.). 64p. (J). 5.99 (978-0-448-44021-7(0) , Grosset & Dunlap) Penguin Group (USA) Inc.

—The Silver Locket. Craig, Helen, illus. 2006. (Angelina Ballerina Ser.). 24p. (J). (ps-1). 3.99 (978-0-448-44472-7(0) , Grosset & Dunlap) Penguin Group (USA) Inc.

—Two Mice in a Boat. Craig, Helen, illus. 2006. (Angelina Ballerina Ser.). 24p. (J). 3.99 (978-0-448-44450-5(X) , Grosset & Dunlap) Penguin Group (USA) Inc.

—A Very Special Secret: Angelina Young Readers. Craig, Helen, illus. 2006. (Angelina Ballerina Ser.: No. 3). 80p. (J). (gr. 1-3). 3.99 (978-0-448-44332-4(5) , Grosset & Dunlap) Penguin Group (USA) Inc.

Holabird, Katharine & Lever, Sally-Ann. Angelina & the Butterfly. Craig, Helen, illus. 2006. (Angelina Ballerina Ser.). 24p. (J). (ps-2). 3.99 (978-0-448-44015-6(6) , Grosset & Dunlap) Penguin Group (USA) Inc.

Holabird, Katharine & Mason, James. Dance of Friendship. Craig, Helen, illus. 2006. (Angelina Ballerina Ser.). 24p. (J). (ps-2). 3.99 (978-0-448-44115-3(2) , Grosset & Dunlap) Penguin Group (USA) Inc.

Hollander, Barbara S. Henry the Great's First Adventure. 2004. 56p. pap. 12.95 (978-1-4137-3500-0(2)) PublishAmerica, Inc.

Holm & Hamel. The Postman Always Brings Mice. 2005. (Stink Files Ser.). (Illus.). 144p. pap. 4.99 (978-0-06-052981-9(4) , Harper Trophy) HarperCollins Pubs.

Holm, Jennifer L. & Holm, Matthew. Beach Babe! 2006. (Babymouse Ser.). (Illus.). 96p. (J). (gr. 2-5). pap. 5.95 (978-0-375-83231-4(9)); lib. bdg. 12.99 (978-0-375-93231-1(3)) Random Hse. Children's Bks. (Random Hse. Bks. for Young Readers).

—Camp Babymouse. 2007. (Babymouse Ser.: No. 6). 96p. (J). (gr. 2-5). pap. 5.99 (978-0-375-83988-7(7)); lib. bdg. 12.99 (978-0-375-93988-4(1)) Random Hse. Children's Bks. (Random Hse. Bks. for Young Readers).

—Heartbreaker. 2006. (Babymouse Ser.: No. 5). (Illus.). 96p. (J). (gr. 2-5). lib. bdg. 12.99 (978-0-375-93798-9(6) , Random Hse. Bks. for Young Readers) Random Hse. Children's Bks.

—Our Hero. 2005. (Babymouse Ser.). (Illus.). 96p. (J). (gr. 2-5). pap. 5.95 (978-0-375-83230-7(0)); lib. bdg. 12.99 (978-0-375-93230-4(5)) Random Hse. Children's Bks. (Random Hse. Bks. for Young Readers).

—Queen of the World! 2005. (Babymouse Ser.). (Illus.). 96p. (J). (gr. 2-5). pap. 5.95 (978-0-375-83229-1(7)); lib. bdg. 12.99 (978-0-375-93229-8(1)) Random Hse. Children's Bks. (Random Hse. Bks. for Young Readers).

—Rock Star! Holm, Jennifer L. & Holm, Matthew, illus. 2006. (Babymouse Ser.). (Illus.). 96p. (J). (gr. 1-5). pap. 5.95 (978-0-375-83232-1(7) , Random Hse. Bks. for Young Readers) Random Hse. Children's Bks.

—Rock Star! 2006. (Babymouse Ser.). (Illus.). 96p. (J). (gr. 1-5). lib. bdg. 12.99 (978-0-375-93232-8(1) , Random Hse. Bks. for Young Readers) Random Hse. Children's Bks.

Horacek, Petr. A New House for Mouse. Horacek, Petr, illus. 2004. (Illus.). 32p. (J). (ps-k). 12.99 (978-0-7636-2517-7(5)) Candlewick Pr.

—Run, Mouse, Run! Horacek, Petr, illus. 2005. (Illus.). 16p. (J). (gr. k-ps). bds. 5.99 (978-0-7636-2824-6(7)) Candlewick Pr.

Houdek, Andi. Mice in My Tummy. 2006. (J). per. 16.95 (978-0-9771939-9-8(3) , 012) New World Publishing.

Howe, James. Horace & Morris & Dolores. Walrod, Amy, illus. 2009. 32p. (J). 16.99 (978-0-689-83940-5(5) , Atheneum) Simon & Schuster Children's Publishing.

—Horace & Morris but Mostly Delores. Walrod, Amy, illus. 2002. (J). 25.11 (978-0-7587-2749-7(6)) Book Wholesalers, Inc.

—Horace & Morris but Mostly Dolores. Walrod, Amy, illus. 1999. 32p. (J). (ps-3). 16.00 (978-0-689-31874-0(X) , Atheneum) Simon & Schuster Children's Publishing.

—Horace & Morris, but Mostly Delores. 2003. (Live Oak Readalong Ser.). (Illus.). (J). pap. 16.95 incl. audio (978-1-59112-241-8(4)) Live Oak Media.

—Horace & Morris, but Mostly Dolores. 1999. (gr. k-3). lib. bdg. 15.30 (978-0-613-61776-5(2)) Tandem Library Bks.

—Horace & Morris, but Mostly Dolores. Waldrod, Amy, illus. 2003. 28.95 incl. audio compact disk (978-1-59112-342-2(9)); pap. 39.95 incl. audio compact disk (978-1-59112-538-9(3)); (J). pap. 18.95 incl. audio compact disk (978-1-59112-341-5(0)); pap. 37.95 incl. audio (978-1-59112-243-2(0)) Live Oak Media.

—Horace & Morris Join the Chorus. Waldrod, Amy, illus. pap. 16.95 incl. audio (978-1-59112-447-4(6)); pap. incl. audio (978-1-59112-449-8(2)); pap. 18.95 incl. audio compact disk (978-1-59112-907-3(9)); pap. incl. audio compact disk (978-1-59112-909-7(5)); 2005. (J). 25.95 incl. audio (978-1-59112-448-1(4)); 2005. (J). 28.95 incl. audio compact disk (978-1-59112-908-0(7)) Live Oak Media.

—Horace & Morris Join the Chorus: But What about Dolores? Walrod, Amy, illus. 2002. 32p. (J). (ps-2). 16.95 (978-0-689-83939-9(1) , Atheneum) Simon & Schuster Children's Publishing.

—Horace & Morris Join the Chorus (but what about Dolores?) Walrod, Amy, illus. 2005. 32p. (J). 6.99 (978-1-4169-0616-2(9) , Aladdin) Simon & Schuster Children's Publishing.

Hughes, Monica. Little Mouse Deer & the Crocodile. Moricuchi, Mique, illus. 2004. 24p. (J). lib. bdg. 22.65 (*978-1-59646-684-5(7)) Dingles & Co.

Hunter, Jana Novotny. I Have Feelings. Porter, Sue, illus. 2002. (J). 25p. pap. (978-1-59034-193-3(7)); 32p. 15.95 (978-1-59034-196-4(1)) Mondo Publishing.

Hurd, Thacher. Little Mouse's Big Valentine. Hurd, Thacher, illus. 2002. (Illus.). (J). 14.43 (978-0-7587-3010-7(1)) Book Wholesalers, Inc.

—Santa Mouse & the Ratdeer. (Illus.). 40p. (J). (ps-1). 2000. pap. 5.95 (978-0-06-443709-7(4) , Harper Trophy); 1998. 14.95 (978-0-06-027694-2(0)) HarperCollins Pubs.

—Santa Mouse & the Ratdeer. 2000. (Illus.). (J). (978-0-606-22063-7(1)) Tandem Library Bks.

I Am a Painter: Individual Title, 6 Packs. (Sails Literacy Ser.). 16p. (gr. k up). 27.00 (978-0-7635-4410-2(8)) Rigby Education.

I Can: Individual Title Six-Packs. (Sails Literacy Ser.). 16p. (gr. k up). 27.00 (978-0-7635-4396-9(9)) Rigby Education.

I Like Boxes: Individual Title, 6 Packs. (Sails Literacy Ser.). 16p. (gr. k up). 27.00 (978-0-7635-4442-3(6)) Rigby Education.

I Like Riding: Individual Title, 6 Packs. (Sails Literacy Ser.). 16p. (gr. k up). 27.00 (978-0-7635-4400-3(0)) Rigby Education.

Inteli, Nancy. Tutter Family Reunion. 2001. (gr. k-3). lib. bdg. 14.15 (978-0-613-51327-2(4)) Tandem Library Bks.

Irving, John. A Sound Like Someone Trying Not to Make a Sound. Hauptmann, Tatjana, illus. 2004. 40p. (J). (ps). 15.95 (978-0-385-74680-9(6) , Doubleday Bks. for Young Readers) Random Hse. Children's Bks.

Jacques, Brian. The Bellmaker. 2004. (Redwall Ser.). (gr. 3-6). lib. bdg. 16.45 (978-0-613-71573-7(X)) Tandem Library Bks.

—Friend & Foe. 2000. (Redwall Ser.). (Illus.). 16p. (J). (gr. 4-7). 8.99 (978-0-399-23589-4(2) , Philomel) Penguin Group (USA) Inc.

—The Great Redwall Feast. Denise, Christopher, illus. 2000. (Redwall Ser.). 64p. (J). (gr. 4-8). pap. 6.99 (978-0-698-11876-8(6) , Putnam Juvenile) Penguin Group (USA) Inc.

—The Great Redwall Feast. Denise, Christopher, illus. 2000. (Redwall Ser.). 64p. (J). (ps-3). lib. bdg. 13.79 (978-0-606-20360-9(5)) Tandem Library Bks.

—The Great Redwall Feast. 2000. (Redwall Ser.). (J). (gr. 4-8). (978-0-606-20236-7(6)) Tandem Library Bks.

—The Legend of Luke. 2005. (Redwall Ser.). (Illus.). 384p. (YA). (gr. k-3). pap. 7.99 (978-0-14-250109-2(3) , Puffin) Penguin Group (USA) Inc.

—The Legend of Luke. Baker, Chris, illus. (Redwall Ser.). (gr. 4-8). 2000. 384p. (J). 23.99 (978-0-399-23490-3(X) , Philomel); 2001. 368p. reprint ed. mass mkt. 7.99 (978-0-441-00773-8(2) , Ace Bks.) Penguin Group (USA) Inc.

—The Legend of Luke. 2001. (J). (978-0-606-20880-2(1)) Tandem Library Bks.

—Mariel of Redwall. Chalk, Gary, illus. 2003. (Redwall Ser.). 400p. (YA). (gr. 5). pap. 8.99 (978-0-14-230239-2(2) , Puffin) Penguin Group (USA) Inc.

—Mariel of Redwall. 2000. (Redwall Ser.). (Illus.). 384p. (gr. 4-8). mass mkt. 7.99 (978-0-441-00694-6(9) , Ace Bks.) Penguin Group (USA) Inc.

—Mariel of Redwall. 2003. (Redwall Ser.). (gr. 5-8). lib. bdg. 16.45 (978-0-613-59976-4(4)) Tandem Library Bks.

—Marlfox. Baker, Chris, illus. 1998. (Redwall Ser.). 400p. (J). (gr. 4-8). 22.99 (978-0-399-23307-4(5) , Philomel) Penguin Group (USA) Inc.

—Martin the Warrior. Chalk, Gary, illus. 2004. (Redwall Ser.). 376p. (YA). 8.99 (978-0-14-240055-5(6) , Puffin) Penguin Group (USA) Inc.

—Martin the Warrior. 2004. (Redwall Ser.). (gr. 3-6). lib. bdg. 16.45 (978-0-613-71583-6(7)) Tandem Library Bks.

—Mattimeo. Chalk, Gary, illus. 2003. (Redwall Ser.). 448p. (J). pap. 8.99 (978-0-14-230240-8(6) , Puffin) Penguin Group (USA) Inc.

—Mattimeo. 1999. (Redwall Ser.). (Illus.). 448p. (gr. 4-8). mass mkt. 7.99 (978-0-441-00610-6(8) , Ace Bks.) Penguin Group (USA) Inc.

—Mattimeo. (Redwall Ser.). (gr. 5-8). 2003. lib. bdg. 16.45 (978-0-613-64193-7(0)); 1999. lib. bdg. 15.30 (978-0-8335-8134-1(1)) Tandem Library Bks.

—Die Mauer. pap. 19.95 (978-3-570-26021-0(6)) Bertelsman, Verlagsgruppe C. GmbH DEU. *Dist:* Distribooks, Inc.

—Mice. 2004. 32p. (J). (gr. 3-5). pap. 8.99 (978-0-399-24283-0(X) , Philomel) Penguin Group (USA) Inc.

—Mossflower. 2002. (Redwall Ser.). (Illus.). 432p. pap. 8.99 (978-0-14-230238-5(4) , Puffin) Penguin Group (USA) Inc.

—Mossflower. Elliott, David W., illus. collector's ed. 2004. (Redwall Ser.). 432p. (YA). (gr. 4). 30.00 (978-0-399-24031-7(4) , Philomel) Penguin Group (USA) Inc.

—Mossflower. 1998. (Redwall Ser.). (Illus.). 384p. (gr. 4-8). reprint ed. mass mkt. 7.99 (978-0-441-00576-5(4) , Ace Bks.) Penguin Group (USA) Inc.

—Redwall. 2002. (Redwall Ser.). (Illus.). 352p. (J). pap. 8.99 (978-0-14-230237-8(6) , Puffin) Penguin Group (USA) Inc.

—Redwall. Howell, Troy, illus. 2000. (Redwall Ser.). 352p. (J). (gr. 4-8). pap. 12.99 (978-0-399-23629-7(5) , Philomel) Penguin Group (USA) Inc.

—Redwall. (Redwall Ser.). 352p. 10th anniv. ed. 1998. (Illus.). (gr. 4-8). mass mkt. 7.99 (978-0-441-00548-2(9) , Ace Bks.); 20th anniv. ed. 2007. (YA). (gr. 5). 23.99 (*978-0-399-24794-1(7)) , Philomel) Penguin Group (USA) Inc.

—Redwall. (Redwall Ser.). 2002. (gr. 3-6). lib. bdg. 16.45 (978-0-613-71581-2(0)); 2000. (gr. 3-6). lib. bdg. 22.25 (978-0-613-89563-7(0)); 1998. (J). (gr. 4-8). (978-0-606-13734-8(3)) Tandem Library Bks.

—Redwall. Chalk, Gary, illus. l.t. ed. 2002. (Redwall Ser). (J). 25.95 (978-0-7862-3858-3(5)) Thomson Gale.

—Redwall Map & Riddle Book: Includes the Redwall Riddler! Baker, Chris & Curless, Allan, illus. 1998. (Redwall Ser.). (J). (gr. 4-8). 9.99 (978-0-399-23248-0(6) , Philomel) Penguin Group (USA) Inc.

—A Redwall Winter's Tale. Denise, Christopher, illus. 2001. (Redwall Ser.). 80p. (J). (gr. 4-8). 18.99 (978-0-399-23346-3(6) , Philomel) Penguin Group (USA) Inc.

—Seven Strange & Ghostly Tales. 1999. (Illus.). 144p. (J). (gr. 4-7). pap. 5.99 (978-0-698-11808-9(1) , Putnam Juvenile) Penguin Group (USA) Inc.

Jaffrey, Madhur. Robi Dobi: The Marvellous Adventures of an Indian Elephant. Hall, Amanda, illus. 2001. 64p. (YA). (gr. 1 up). pap. 13.00 (978-1-86205-160-7(7) , Pavilion Bks., Ltd.) Anova Bks. GBR. *Dist:* Trafalgar Square Publishing.

Jareckie, Ellen. A House-Mouse Christmas: House-Mouse Tales. 4th ed. 2004. (Illus.). 22p. (J). (ps-k). bds. 6.99 (978-0-316-73806-4(9)) Little, Brown Bks. for Young Readers.

Jarvis, Robin. The Crystal Prison. (Deptford Mice Ser.: Bk. 2). (Illus.). 256p. (YA). 2002. pap. 6.95 (978-1-58717-161-1(9)); 2001. (gr. 5 up). 17.95 (978-1-58717-107-9(4)) Chronicle Bks. LLC. (SeaStar Bks.).

—Crystal Prison. 2002. (gr. 5-8). lib. bdg. 15.25 (978-0-613-56295-9(X)) Tandem Library Bks.

—The Dark Portal. 2001. (Deptford Mice Ser.). (Illus.). 240p. (YA). (gr. 5 up). pap. 6.95 (978-1-58717-112-3(0) , SeaStar Bks.) Chronicle Bks. LLC.

—Dark Portal. 2000. (gr. 5-8). lib. bdg. 15.25 (978-0-613-44356-2(X)) Tandem Library Bks.

—The Final Reckoning. 2003. (Deptford Mice Ser.). (Illus.). 304p. (YA). pap. 6.95 (978-1-58717-244-1(5) , SeaStar Bks.) Chronicle Bks. LLC.

—Thomas. 2006. 400p. (J). 17.95 (978-0-8118-5412-2(4)) Chronicle Bks. LLC.

Jaskiewicz, A. E. Hickory & the Big Clock. 2006. (ENG.). 56p. per. 12.95 (*978-1-4241-6024-2(3)) PublishAmerica, Inc.

Jeffs, Stephanie. Christmas Mouse. Thorne, Jenny, illus. 2005. 30p. pap. 11.95 (978-1-59325-054-6(1)) Word Among Us Pr.

Jeffs, Stephanie, et al. Llygoden y Nadolig. 2005. (WEL., Illus.). 30p. (978-1-85994-497-4(3)) Cyhoeddiadau'r Gair.

Jenkins, Amanda. The Lion & the Mouse Shoot Hoops. 2006. spiral bd. 42.00 (*978-1-4108-7173-2(8)) Benchmark Education Co.

Jennings, Sharon. Priscilla's Paw de Deux. Hendry, Linda, illus. 2002. 36p. (J). (ps-2). (978-1-55041-718-0(5)) Fitzhenry & Whiteside, Ltd.

Jeram, Anita. All Together Now. Jeram, Anita, illus. 2005. (Illus.). 40p. (J). (gr. k-k). reprint ed. pap. 5.99 (978-0-7636-2690-7(2)) Candlewick Pr.

Jerome, Kate Boehm. Miniature Golf Madness. 2005. (Illus.). 32p. (J). 15.95 (978-0-9769087-3-9(5)) Vertical Connect Pr.

Jeswald, Mary J. The Crazy Adventure of Nicholas Mouse. Trimble, Anne M., illus. 2004. 32p. (J). 14.99 (978-0-9760651-0-4(X)) OrangeFoot Publishing Co.

Johnson, Donna. Gavendy the Little Red Mouse. 1999. (Illus.). 20p. (J). (ps-3). pap. 6.95 (978-1-881524-54-0(X)) Milligan Bks., Inc.

Johnson, Kimberly P. The Adventures of the Itty Bitty Spider & the Itty Bitty Mouse. 2004. (Illus.). 31p. (gr. k-2). 14.95 (978-1-57197-236-1(6)) Pentland Pr., Inc.

Johnson, Spencer. Who Moved My Cheese? An A-Mazing Way to Change & Win! for Kids. Pileggi, Steve, illus. 2003. 64p. (J). (ps-3). 20.99 (978-0-399-24016-4(0) , Putnam Juvenile) Penguin Group (USA) Inc.

Johnston-Brown, A. M. The Chronicles of Pleasant Grove. 2006. (J). pap. 12.95 (978-0-9760718-5-3(1)) Retriever Pr.

—The Chronicles of Pleasant Grove (Glossary of Terms) 2006. (J). pap. 1.95 (978-0-9760718-6-0(X)) Retriever Pr.

Jones, Brenda. The Adventures of Murphy the Mouse. Moore, Dwain, illus. 2007. (J). per. 12.99 (*978-1-59712-069-2(3)) Catawba Publishing Co.

Kakugawa, Frances H. Wordsworth Dances the Waltz. DeSica, Melissa, illus. 2007. 32p. 10.95 (*978-0-9790647-3-9(2)) Watermark Publishing, LLC.

Kakugawa, Frances H. Wordsworth the Poet. Goto, Scott, illus. 2004. 32p. (J). 10.95 (978-0-9742672-0-3(1)) Watermark Publishing, LLC.

Kampmann, Durten. Adventures of moxie Mouse. Kampmann, Durten, illus. 2006. (Illus.). 32p. 9.95 (978-1-57188-389-6(4) , MM) Amato, Frank Pubns., Inc.

Kawai, Ritsuko. Hamtaro Gets Lost & Other Stories Vol. 2. Kawai, Ritsuko, illus. 2003. (Adventures of Hamtaro Ser.). (Illus.). 92p. (YA). (gr. 1-3). 9.95 (978-1-56931-817-1(4)) Viz Media.

—Hamtaro, Let's Play! Vol. 4: A Playground for Ham-Ham. Kawai, Ritsuko, illus. 2003. (Hamtaro Ser.). 16p. (YA). (gr. 1-3). pap. 7.95 (978-1-56931-821-8(2)) Viz Media.

—The Little Lost Caterpillar, Vol. 3. Kawai, Ritsuko, illus. 2003. (Hamtaro Ser.). (Illus.). 16p. (YA). pap. 7.95 (978-1-56931-816-4(6)) Viz Media.

Keffer, Lois. Mercury Mouse Slows down in the House. 1999. (J). 9.99 (978-1-57673-437-7(4)) Zondervan.

Kelley, True. Blabber Mouse. Kelley, True, illus. 2001. (Illus.). 32p. (J). (ps-2). 15.99 (978-0-525-46742-7(4) , Dutton Juvenile) Penguin Group (USA) Inc.

—The Blabber Report. Kelley, True, illus. 2007. (Illus.). 32p. (J). (gr. k-4). 15.99 (978-0-525-47809-6(4) , Dutton Juvenile) Penguin Group (USA) Inc.

Kenny, Michael. The Misadventures of Mocha the Mouse. 2000. 160p. (J). (gr. 4-7). pap. 10.95 (978-0-595-13472-4(6)) iUniverse, Inc.

Kilner, Dorothy. The Life & Perambulations of a Mouse. 2005. 26.95 (978-1-4218-0923-6(0) , 1st World Library - Literary Society) 1st World Publishing, Inc.

—The Life & Perambulations of a Mouse. 2006. (ENG.). pap. (*978-1-4250-2656-1(7)) Assistedreadingbooks.com Inc.

—Life & Perambulations of a Mouse. 2005. 96p. pap. 10.95 (978-1-59540-623-1(9) , 1st World Library - Literary Society) 1st World Publishing, Inc.

—The Life & Perambulations of a Mouse. 2004. reprint ed. pap. 15.95 (978-1-4191-6941-0(6)) Kessinger Publishing, LLC.

—The Life & Perambulations of A Mouse. 2004. reprint ed. pap. 1.99 (978-1-4192-6941-7(0)) Kessinger Publishing, LLC.

King, Daren. Mouse Noses on Toast. Roberts, David, illus. 2008. 128p. (J). (gr. 3). 15.99 (***978-0-399-25037-8(9)*** , Putnam Juvenile) Penguin Group (USA) Inc.

King-Smith, Dick. How Green Was My Mouse. 1999. (Illus.). 112p. (J). (978-0-14-038807-7(9) , Puffin) Penguin Group (USA) Inc.

—Martin's Mice. Alborough, Jez, illus. 1998. 128p. (J). (gr. 3-7). 5.50 (978-0-679-89098-0(X) , Yearling) Random Hse. Children's Bks.

—Martin's Mice. 1998. (978-0-606-13598-6(7)) Tandem Library Bks.

—A Mouse Called Wolf. Goodell, Jon, illus. 1999. 112p. (gr. k-3). pap. 5.50 (978-0-375-80066-5(2) , Yearling) Random Hse. Children's Bks.

—A Mouse Called Wolf. Goodell, Jon, illus. 1999. 98p. (J). (ps-k). lib. bdg. 13.00 (978-0-613-17058-1(X)) Tandem Library Bks.

—A Mouse Called Wolf. 1999. (J). (978-0-606-16571-6(1)) Tandem Library Bks.

—The School Mouse. Fisher, Cynthia, illus. 1999. 124p. pap. 4.99 (978-0-7868-1156-4(0)) Disney Pr.

—Three Terrible Trins. 105p. (J). pap. 4.99 (978-0-8072-1482-4(5) , Listening Library) Random Hse. Audio Publishing Group.

Kirk, Daniel. Library Mouse. 2007. (Illus.). 32p. (J). (ps-3). 15.95 (***978-0-8109-9346-4(5)*** , Abrams Bks. for Young Readers) Abrams, Harry N. , Inc.

Kirk, David, illus. Little Mouse, Biddle Mouse. 2002. (Biddle Bks.). 32p. (J). pap. 9.95 (978-0-439-28051-8(6) , Scholastic Pr.) Scholastic, Inc.

Kirkpatrick, June. The Little Church Mouse of the Loretto Chapel. Brokaw, Michele, illus. 2nd ed. 2000. 40p. (J). (gr. k-3). reprint ed. pap. 10.95 (978-0-9708940-5-2(8)) Gently Worded Bks., LLC.

Kirkpatrick, June & Brokaw, Michele. The Little Church Mouse of the Loretto Chapel. l.t. ed. 2000. (Illus.). 40p. (J). (gr. k-5). 16.50 (978-1-929115-02-0(4)) Azro Pr., Inc.

Kline, Trish & Donev, Mary. Don¿t Frown, Clown! KA Reader 9. 2007. (Illus.). 32p. (J). per. 20.00 (***978-1-934307-02-1(5)***) Ghost Hunter Productions.

Knight, Hilary. A Firefly in a Fir Tree: A Carol for Mice. Knight, Hilary, illus. 2004. (Illus.). 32p. (J). (ps-3). lib. bdg. 15.89 (978-0-06-000992-2(6) , Tegen, Katherine Bks) HarperCollins Pubs.

Kraus, Robert. Mouse in Love. Aruego, Jose & Dewey, Ariane, illus. 2000. 32p. (J). (ps-2). 16.99 (978-0-531-33297-9(7) , Orchard Bks.) Scholastic, Inc.

—Viens Jouer avec Moi, Petit Souris. 2000. Tr. of Come Out & Play, Little Mouse. (FRE.). (J). pap. 14.95 (978-2-211-03723-5(2)) Archimede Editions FRA. *Dist:* Distribooks, Inc.

—Whose Mouse Are You? Aruego, Jose, illus. 2000. 40p. (J). (ps-2). 17.95 (978-0-689-84052-4(7)) Simon & Schuster Children's Publishing.

—Whose Mouse Are You? Aruego, Jose, illus. 2005. (Stories to Go! Ser.). 40p. (J). 4.99 (978-1-4169-0311-6(9) , Aladdin) Simon & Schuster Children's Publishing.

Krensky, Stephen. Case of the Missing Mice: A Simon Mystery. 2003. (Illus.). 14.95 (978-1-59319-022-4(0)) LeapFrog Enterprises, Inc.

Kroll, Steven. The Biggest Easter Basket Ever. 2008. 32p. pap. 4.99 (***978-0-545-01702-2(5)*** , Cartwheel Bks.) Scholastic, Inc.

—Biggest Pumpkin Ever. Bassett, Jeni, illus. 2007. 32p. (J). pap. 4.99 (***978-0-439-92946-2(6)***) Scholastic, Inc.

—The Biggest Snowman Ever. Bassett, Jeni, illus. 2005. 32p. (J). (ps-3). pap. 3.99 (978-0-439-62768-9(0) , Cartwheel Bks.) Scholastic, Inc.

—The Biggest Valentine Ever. Bassett, Jeni, illus. 2006. 32p. (J). pap. 3.99 (978-0-439-76419-3(X)) Scholastic, Inc.

Krupinski, Loretta. Pirate Treasure. Krupinski, Loretta, illus. 2006. (Illus.). 32p. (J). (gr. k). 15.99 (978-0-525-47579-8(6) , Dutton Juvenile) Penguin Group (USA) Inc.

La Fontaine, Jean De. El Leon y el Raton. (Coleccion Pequenos Clasicos). (SPA.). 24p. (J). (gr. k-3). (978-84-246-2533-7(1) , GL7988) La Galera, S.A. Editorial ESP. *Dist:* Lectorum Pubns., Inc.

LaDeane, Symone. Momma, Where Will You Be? 2007. (J). pap. 6.99 (***978-1-60247-120-7(7)***) Tate Publishing & Enterprises, L.L.C.

Lakin, Patricia. Clarence the Copy Cat. Manders, John, illus. 2007. 32p. (J). (ps-3). pap. 6.99 (978-0-440-41725-5(2) , Dragonfly Bks.) Random Hse. Children's Bks.

Landa, Norbert. The Secret House of Papa Mouse. Turk, Hanne, illus. 2004. 30p. (J). lib. bdg. 24.67 (978-0-8368-4106-0(9)) Stevens, Gareth Inc.

Lang, Andrew. The Queen & the Mouse: A Story about Friendship. Lohmann, Renate, illus. 2006. (J). (978-1-59939-081-9(7) , Reader's Digest Young Families, Inc.) Reader's Digest Children's Publishing, Inc.

Lawson, Robert. Ben & Me: An Astonishing Life of Benjamin Franklin by His Good Mouse Amos. (J). (ps-5). 2005. pap. 6.99 (978-0-316-01636-0(5)); 1999. (978-0-316-52533-6(2)); 1999. pap. (978-0-316-52520-6(0)) Little Brown & Co.

Layman, Richard. The Halloween Mouse. Clark, Alan M., illus. 2001. 36p. 25.00 (978-1-58767-047-3(X)) Cemetery Dance Pubns.

Le Guin, Ursula K. Tom Mouse. ed. 2004. (Illus.). (J). (gr. k-3). spiral bd. (978-0-616-14584-5(5)) Canadian National Institute for the Blind/Institut National Canadien pour les Aveugles.

—Tom Mouse & Ms. Howe. Downing, Julie, illus. 1999. (J). (978-0-7894-2554-6(8)) Dorling Kindersley Publishing, Inc.

LeapFrog Staff, compiled by. Cake & Mice Cream. 2002. (J). (ps-2). spiral bd. 14.99 (978-1-58605-743-5(X)) LeapFrog Enterprises, Inc.

Learning Wrap-Ups: The Sky Is Falling, The City Mouse & The Country Mouse. 2006. 66p. (J). 12.99 (978-1-59204-202-9(3)) Learning Wrap-Ups.

Lecaye, Olga. El Ratoncito Perez. (SPA.). 40p. 18.95 (978-84-95150-03-5(4)); 2005. 24p. (J). 9.95 (978-84-8470-051-7(8)) Corimbo, Editorial S.L. ESP. *Dist:* Distribooks, Inc., Iaconi, Mariuccia Bk. Imports.

Lee, P. Janet. Ella Elephant: And Her Fear of Mice. 2007. (ENG., Illus.). 36p. (J). per. 15.95 (***978-1-59800-713-8(0)***) Outskirts Press, Inc.

Leeson, Christine. Just for You! Ellis, Andy, illus. 2004. 32p. (J). tchr. ed. 15.95 (978-1-58925-042-0(7) , tiger tales) ME Media LLC.

—The Magic of Christmas. Hansen, Gaby, illus. 2001. 32p. (J). tchr. ed. 14.95 (978-1-58925-011-6(7) , tiger tales) ME Media LLC.

—Molly & the Storm. Hansen, Gaby, illus. 2003. 32p. (J). (gr. k-2). tchr. ed. 15.95 (978-1-58925-027-7(3) , tiger tales) ME Media LLC.

Leeson, Christine. Snow Angel. Chapman, Jane, illus. 2007. 32p. (J). (ps-2). 15.95 (***978-1-58925-068-0(0)*** , tiger tales) ME Media LLC.

El leon y el Raton: Individual Title Six-Packs. (Coleccion Pm Ser.).Tr. of Lion & the Mouse. (SPA.). 16p. (gr. 1 up). 26.00 (978-0-7578-3019-8(6)) Rigby Education.

Leonard, Nellie M. Grand Daddy Whiskers, M. D. 2004. reprint ed. pap. 15.95 (978-1-4191-2227-9(4)); pap. 1.99 (978-1-4192-2227-6(9)) Kessinger Publishing, LLC.

Lias, Joe. The Wood Rats Dragging Their Long Tales. 2005. 183p. pap. 19.95 (978-1-4137-5900-6(9)) PublishAmerica, Inc.

Lin, Grace. Robert's Snow. 2004. (Illus.). 40p. (J). (ps). 15.99 (978-0-670-05911-9(0) , Viking Juvenile) Penguin Group (USA) Inc.

The Lion & the Mouse, Vol. 2. 2005. (Fluent Library). (YA). (ps-3). 29.34 (978-0-8215-8968-7(7)) Sadlier, William H. Inc.

Lionni, Leo. A Busy Year. 2004. (Illus.). 26p. (J). (gr. k-ps). bds. 6.99 (978-0-375-82737-2(4) , Knopf Bks. for Young Readers) Random Hse. Children's Bks.

—Frederic. (FRE.). (J). pap. 14.95 (978-2-211-06589-4(9)) Archimede Editions FRA. *Dist:* Distribooks, Inc.

—The Greentail Mouse. 2003. (Illus.). 32p. (J). (ps-3). 15.95 (978-0-375-82399-2(9) , Knopf Bks. for Young Readers) Random Hse. Children's Bks.

—Leo Lionni's Little Mice Tales, 4 vols. 2003. (Illus.). (J). (978-0-375-82618-4(1)); (978-0-375-82616-0(5)); (978-0-375-82619-1(X)); (978-0-375-82617-7(3)) Knopf, Alfred A. Inc.

—Leo Lionni's Little Mice Tales Box Set, 4 vols. 2003. (Illus.). 32p. (J). (ps-3). 15.95 (978-0-375-82615-3(7) , Knopf Bks. for Young Readers) Random Hse. Children's Bks.

—Let's Play. 2003. (Illus.). 28p. (J). (gr. k-ps). bds. 6.99 (978-0-375-82528-6(2) , Knopf Bks. for Young Readers) Random Hse. Children's Bks.

—Nicolas, Where Have You Been? 2007. 32p. (J). (ps-3). 16.99 (978-0-375-84550-8(3)); lib. bdg. 19.99 (978-0-375-94450-5(8)) Random Hse. Children's Bks. (Knopf Bks. for Young Readers).

—El Sueno de Matias. (SPA.). (J). (gr. 1-3). 32p. 13.56 (978-84-264-3675-7(7) , LM4689); 1998. (Illus.). 42p. 10.95 (978-84-264-3718-1(4) , LUM7184) Editorial Lumen ESP. *Dist:* Lectorum Pubns., Inc.

Listening with Zachary. (J). pap. 13.75 (978-0-8136-4655-8(3)) Modern Curriculum Pr.

Litchmore, Michael. The MB Force: Heroes at the Best! 2007. 56p. pap. 9.00 (***978-0-8059-7399-0(0)***) Dorrance Publishing Co., Inc.

Lithgow, John. Mahalia Mouse Goes to College. Oleynikov, Igor, illus. 2007. 40p. (J). 17.99 (978-1-4169-2715-0(8) , Simon & Schuster Children's Publishing) Simon & Schuster Children's Publishing.

Lobel, Arnold. Historias de Ratones. 2003. (SPA.). 64p. (978-84-95123-95-4(9) , KA7695) Kalandraka Editora, S.L. ESP. *Dist:* Lectorum Pubns., Inc.

—Sopa de Raton. 2004. (SPA., Illus.). 66p. (J). (gr. 1-3). pap. 7.99 (978-980-257-286-1(1)) Ekare, Ediciones VEN. *Dist:* Lectorum Pubns., Inc., Iaconi, Mariuccia Bk. Imports.

Lobel, Gillian. For Everyone to Share. Howarth, Daniel, illus. 2008. (J). (***978-1-56148-598-7(5)***) Good Bks.

London, Jonathan. The Gruffalo's Child. Moore, Margie, illus. 2007. 32p. (J). pap. 5.99 (978-0-14-240754-7(2) , Puffin) Penguin Group (USA) Inc.

Louthain, J. A. Ame the Elephant: Terrorized by Evil Mice. Eberbach, Andrea, illus. 2nd l.t. ed. 2003. 48p. (J). 12.97 (978-0-9679416-2-2(8) , 0-9679416-2-8) Alexie Bks.

Low, Alice. Blueberry Mouse. Friend, David Michael, tr. Friend, David Michael, illus. 2004. (J). 15.95 (978-1-59336-111-2(4)); pap. (978-1-59336-112-9(2)) Mondo Publishing.

Low, Joseph. Mice Twice. Low, Joseph, illus. 2nd ed. 2005. (Stories to Go! Ser.). (Illus.). 32p. (J). 4.99 (978-0-689-87832-9(X) , Aladdin) Simon & Schuster Children's Publishing.

Loyd, Mark. Big Ben: A Little Known Story. Loyd, Mark, illus. ed. 2005. (J). (978-0-9773317-1-0(7)) Too Fun Publshing.

Ludy, Mark. The Flower Man. 2005. (Illus.). 24p. (J). (ps-k). 16.95 (978-0-9664276-4-6(5)) Green Pastures Publishing, Inc.

Luke, Deanna. Chris Mouse & the Christmas House. Woytek, Joann A., illus. 2001. 40p. (J). (gr. 2-4). 14.95 (978-1-928777-04-5(X) , BOW Bks.) Blessing Our World, Inc.

—Chris Mouse & the Christmas House Audio Story Book. 2001. (J). cd-rom 5.95 (978-1-928777-35-9(X) , BOW Bks.) Blessing Our World, Inc.

—Marky & the Mouse. Chambers, Lynne, illus. 2000. (Marky Ser.: Vol. No. 1). 32p. (J). (gr. 2-6). 8.95 (978-1-928777-05-2(8) , BOW Bks.) Blessing Our World, Inc.

—Marky & the Mouse Vol. 1: Story Book. 2001. (Marky Ser.: Vol. 1). (J). cd-rom 5.95 (978-1-928777-20-5(1) , BOW Bks.) Blessing Our World, Inc.

—Marky & the Mouse Electronic Coloring Book. Chambers, Lynne, illus. 2001. (Marky Ser.: Vol. 1). (J). cd-rom 3.95 (978-1-928777-14-4(7) , BOW Bks.) Blessing Our World, Inc.

MacDonald, Alan. Scaredy Mouse. Warnes, Tim, illus. (J). (ps-k). 2007. 18p. bds. 6.95 (***978-1-58925-827-3(4);*** 2002. 32p. tchr. ed. 14.95 (978-1-58925-018-5(4)) ME Media LLC. (tiger tales).

MacDonald, Alan. Wilfred to the Rescue. Sanders, Lizzie, illus. 2006. 32p. (J). (ps-1). 15.95 (978-1-4169-0901-9(X) , Atheneum) Simon & Schuster Children's Publishing.

MacDonald, Margaret Read. Mabela the Clever. Coffey, Tim, illus. 2006. 32p. (J). pap. 6.95 (978-0-8075-4903-2(7)) Whitman, Albert & Co.

Maitland, Barbara. Bookstore Burglar. 2001. (gr. k-3). lib. bdg. 11.80 (978-0-613-35609-1(8)) Tandem Library Bks.

—Bookstore Valentine. 2002. (gr. k-3). lib. bdg. 11.80 (978-0-613-64398-6(4)) Tandem Library Bks.

Makinson, Robert. Horace Morris II. Makinson, Robert, ed. Paduano, Joseph, illus. 2000. 17p. (J). (ps-5). spiral bd. 6.00 (978-0-9654228-7-1(9)) Makinson, R. B.

Mantovani, Maria & Barsotti, Renzo, illus. Classic Fairy Tales - Town Mouse & Country Mouse. 32p. 7.95 (978-1-904668-53-4(4)) Mercury Bks. Ltd. GBR. *Dist:* International Publishers Marketing.

Marlow, Herb & Marlow, Lynn. Max the School House Mouse. Newberry, Loretta, illus. l.t. ed. 1998. (Max Ser.). 32p. (J). (gr. k-5). lib. bdg. 14.95 (978-0-9666858-5-5(7)) Four Seasons Bks., Inc.

—Max the Skydiving Mouse. Newberry, Loretta, illus. l.t. ed. 2002. 28p. (J). lib. bdg. 14.95 (978-1-893595-19-4(6)) Four Seasons Bks., Inc.

Marlow, Herb & Marlowe, Lynn. Max the Rodeo Mouse. Newburry, Loretta, illus. l.t. ed. 2000. (Max Ser.). 32p. (J). (gr. k-6). lib. bdg. 14.95 (978-1-893595-07-1(2)) Four Seasons Bks., Inc.

Martin, Bill, Jr. A Beasty Story. Kellogg, Steven, illus. 2002. 40p. (J). (gr. k-2). pap. 7.00 (978-0-15-216560-4(6) , Voyager Bks./Libros Viajeros) Harcourt Children's Bks.

—A Beasty Story. Kellogg, Steven, illus. 1999. 40p. (J). (ps-2). 17.00 (978-0-15-201683-8(X) , Silver Whistle) Harcourt Trade Pubs.

Martin, Bill. Beasty Story. 2002. (gr. k-3). lib. bdg. 15.30 (978-0-613-53796-4(3)) Tandem Library Bks.

Martin, Bill, Jr. Fire! Fire! Said Mrs. Mcguire. Radunsky, Vladimir, illus. 2006. 32p. (J). 16.00 (978-0-15-205725-1(0) , Gulliver Bks.) Harcourt Children's Bks.

Martin, David. All for Pie, Pie for All. Gorbachev, Valeri, illus. 2006. 32p. (J). (ps-k). 15.99 (978-0-7636-2393-7(8)) Candlewick Pr.

Massman-Wardzala, Joan. The Story of LittleMouse: LittleMouse Finds Tools for the Adventure of Life. Massman, Marjorie, ed. Wardzala, Phillip, illus. l.t. ed. 1999. (J). (gr. k-4). pap. 6.95 (978-0-9669902-0-1(X)) MassAward Publishing, Inc.

Matsutani, Miyoko. Peek-a-Boo. Segawa, Yasuo, illus. 2006. 20p. (J). 10.95 (978-1-74126-047-2(7)) R.I.C. Pubns. AUS. *Dist:* SCB Distributors.

Mayer, Mercer. The Little Drummer Mouse. 2006. (Illus.). 40p. (J). (ps). 16.99 (978-0-8037-3147-9(7) , Dial) Penguin Group (USA) Inc.

Mayerhofer, Felix. Horace the Great Harmonica King. MacFarlane, John, illus. 2006. 31p. (J). per. 16.95 (***978-1-60002-255-5(3)*** , 4313, Airleaf Publishing) Airleaf Publishing & Bookselling.

McBratney, Sam. The Dark at the Top of the Stairs. 2002. (Illus.). (J). 14.47 (978-0-7587-2347-5(4)) Book Wholesalers, Inc.

McBratney, Sam. Yes We Can! Fuge, Charles, illus. 2007. 32p. (J). (ps-1). 16.99 (***978-0-06-121515-5(5)***) HarperCollins Pubs.

McBride, Earvin, Jr. The American Blonds. McBride, Earvin, Jr., illus. unabr. ed. 2002. (Earvin MacBride's Fun Fun Lovable Cartoons Ser.). (Illus.). 123p. (J). (gr. 7-12). pap. 4.95 (978-1-892511-01-0(0)) MacBride, E. J. Pubn., Inc.

McCully, Emily Arnold. First Snow. McCully, Emily Arnold, illus. 2004. (Illus.). 32p. (J). (ps-k). 16.99 (978-0-06-623852-4(8)); lib. bdg. 17.89 (978-0-06-623853-1(6)) HarperCollins Pubs.

—Monk Camps Out. McCully, Emily Arnold, illus. 2000. (Illus.). 32p. (J). (ps-4). pap. 15.95 (978-0-439-09976-9(5) , Levine, Arthur A. Bks.) Scholastic, Inc.

—Monk Camps Out. 2000. (Illus.). (J). (978-0-439-09977-6(3)) Scholastic, Inc.

—Mouse Practice. 1999. (J). (Illus.). pap. 16.95 (978-0-590-68267-1(9)); (978-0-439-07055-3(4)) Scholastic, Inc.

—Picnic. McCully, Emily Arnold, illus. 2003. (Illus.). 32p. (J). (ps-k). 16.89 (978-0-06-623855-5(2)); 16.99 (978-0-06-623854-8(4)) HarperCollins Pubs.

—School. McCully, Emily Arnold, illus. 2005. (Illus.). 32p. (J). 15.99 (978-0-06-623856-2(0)); lib. bdg. 16.89 (978-0-06-623857-9(9)) HarperCollins Pubs.

McElreath, Kim. Mikey the Schoolhouse Mouse. 2006. (J). 13.95 (978-0-9769271-1-2(X)) McElreath, K.M.

McFarland, Lyn Rossiter. Mouse Went Out to Get a Snack. McFarland, Jim, illus. 2005. 32p. (J). 16.00 (978-0-374-37672-7(7) , Farrar, Straus & Giroux (BYR)) Farrar, Straus & Giroux.

McGrath, Meggan. My Grapes. McGrath, Meggan, illus. 2001. (Illus.). 48p. (J). (ps-1). pap. 16.95 (978-0-439-09259-3(0)) Scholastic, Inc.

McKinley, Cheryl. The Mouse in the Bathtub. Alexander, Colin, illus. 2005. (ENG.). 32p. (J). (ps). per. 18.00 (978-1-4208-2555-8(0)) AuthorHouse.

McLeod, Edythe B. The Mouse Tale: A Christmas Mouse. Groesser, Debra J., illus. unabr. ed. 1998. 24p. (J). (gr. 1-6). pap. 9.95 (978-0-9666869-0-6(X)) Brooks Bks.

McMillan, Bruce. Mouse Views: What the Class Pet Saw. McMillan, Bruce, illus. 2002. (Illus.). (J). 15.49 (978-0-7587-3182-1(5)) Book Wholesalers, Inc.

McMullan, Kate. Pearl & Wagner: Three Secrets. Alley, R. W., illus. 2004. (Easy-to-Read, Dial Ser.). 48p. (J). (gr. 2). 14.99 (978-0-8037-2574-4(4) , Dial) Penguin Group (USA) Inc.

—Pearl & Wagner: Two Good Friends. Alley, R. W., illus. 2003. (Easy-to-Read Ser.). 48p. (J). (gr. k-3). 13.99 (978-0-8037-2573-7(6) , Dial) Penguin Group (USA) Inc.

McQuinn, Austin. This Will Take Forever... 2003. (Mimi Mouse Book Ser.). (Illus.). 24p. (J). 9.95 (978-1-84089-199-7(8) , Zero to Ten, Limited) Evans Publishing Group GBR. *Dist:* Independent Pubs. Group.

The Meadow Mouse Treasury: Stories, Poems, Pictures from Canada's Finest Authors & Illustrators. (Illus.). (J). 9.99 (978-0-88899-249-9(1)) Groundwood Bks. CAN. *Dist:* Transition Vendor.

Meek, Jeffrey/K. Nimble the Thimble Mouse, 1. Dungey, Thomas, illus. 2007. 21p. (J). 9.95 (***978-0-9794522-0-8(1)***) Thimble Mouse Publishing, Inc.

Mice & Other Stories: Individual Title Six-Pack. (Story Steps Ser.). (gr. k-2). 48.00 (978-0-7635-9823-5(2)) Rigby Education.

Mice on Ice: KinderReaders Individual Title Six-Packs. (Kinderstarters Ser.). 8p. (ps-1). 21.00 (978-0-7635-8664-5(1)) Rigby Education.

Mickey & Friends. 1999. (Super Coloring Book Ser.). (J). pap. 2.29 (978-0-307-03156-3(X) , 03156, Golden Bks.) Random Hse. Children's Bks.

Mickey, Mouse Clubhouse. Minnies Rainbow. rev. ed. 2008. 24p. pap. 3.99 (***978-1-4231-0743-9(8)***) Disney Pr.

Milbourne, A. & Wells, R. Mouse on the Moon. 2004. (Touchy-Feely Board Bks.). (Illus.). 10p. (J). (ps up). 4.95 (978-0-7945-0163-1(X) , Usborne) EDC Publishing.

Milgrim, David. See Pip Point. Milgrim, David, illus. 2004. (Adventures of Otto Ser.). (Illus.). 32p. (J). pap. 3.99 (978-0-689-85140-7(5) , Aladdin) Simon & Schuster Children's Publishing.

Milway, Alex. The Mouse Hunter. 2007. 384p. (J). pap. 5.99 (***978-0-316-02455-6(4)***) Little, Brown Bks. for Young Readers.

Miracle Mouse Cranky's Miracle. ed. 2006. (J). lib. bdg. 19.95 (978-1-934017-00-5(0)) Hignites, Tom Miracle Studio.

Mitchard, Jacquelyn. Starring Prima! The Mouse of the Ballet Jolie. Tusa, Tricia, illus. 2004. 160p. (J). (gr. 3 up). 15.99 (978-0-06-057356-0(2)); 16.89 (978-0-06-057357-7(0)) HarperCollins Pubs.

Mitchell, Carolyn. The Tale of the Pumpkin Seed Squad. 2006. (ENG.). 40p. per. 16.99 (***978-1-4259-7004-8(4)***) AuthorHouse.

Mitchell, Gloria. The Mouse That Went to Find Christmas. Johnson, Jerome A., illus. (J). pap. (978-0-9706186-0-3(3)) Fourth Generation Pubs.

Mitchell, Peggie C. Lara & the Field Mice. 1998. (Illus.). 51p. (J). (978-0-7541-0251-9(3)) Minerva Pr. GBR. *Dist:* Unity Distribution.

Modesitt, Jeanne. Mouse's Halloween Party. Spowart, Robin, illus. 2004. 32p. (J). (ps up). 13.95 (978-1-56397 950-7(0)) Boyds Mills Pr.

Mollel, Tololwa M. Kitoto the Mighty. Frost, Kristi, illus. 1998. 28p. (J). (gr. k-3). 14.95 (978-0-7737-3019-9(2)) Stoddart Kids CAN. *Dist:* Fitzhenry & Whiteside, Ltd.

Montardre, Helene. Elephant & Mouse. 2004. (Turn & Learn Ser.). (Illus.). 8p. (J). (ps up). bds. 7.95 (978-1-58728-482-3(0) , Two Can Publishing) T&N Children's Publishing.

Moore, Lilian. Don't Be Afraid, Amanda. 2001. (Ready-for-Chapters Ser.). (Illus.). (J). (978-0-606-21154-3(3)) Tandem Library Bks.

—I'll Meet You at the Cucumbers. Wooding, Sharon, illus. 2001. (Ready-for-Chapters (Library) Ser.). 63p. (J). (gr. 2-6). lib. bdg. 11.80 (978-0-613-90800-9(7)) Tandem Library Bks.

—I'll Meet You at the Cucumbers. 2001. (Ready-for-Chapters Ser.). (Illus.). (J). 10.79 (978-0-606-21326-4(0)) Tandem Library Bks.

Moran, Alex. Sam & Jack: Three Stories. 2001. (gr. k-3). lib. bdg. 11.80 (978-0-613-64590-4(1)) Tandem Library Bks.

Moranville, Sharelle Byars. The Purple Ribbon. Alter, Anna, illus. rev. ed. 2003. 80p. (J). (gr. 1-4). 17.95 (978-0-8050-6659-3(4) , Holt, Henry & Co. Bks. For Young Readers) Holt, Henry & Co.

Morgan, Mary. Sleep Tight, Little Mouse. Morgan, Mary, illus. 2003. (Illus.). 32p. (J). (ps-1). 12.95 (978-0-375-82308-4(5)); lib. bdg. 14.99 (978-0-375-92308-1(X)) Random Hse. Children's Bks. (Knopf Bks. for Young Readers).

Morgan, Michaela. Brave, Brave Mouse. Cartlidge, Michelle, illus. 2004. 32p. (J). (ps-2). 15.95 (978-0-8075-0869-5(1)) Whitman, Albert & Co.

—Dear Bunny. 2007. 32p. (J). pap. 5.99 (978-0-439-74834-6(8) , Scholastic Paperbacks) Scholastic, Inc.

—Dear Bunny. Jayne Church, Caroline, illus. 2006. 32p. (J). pap. 15.99 (978-0-439-74833-9(X) , Chicken Hse., The) Scholastic, Inc.

Morgan, Michaela. Mouse with No Name. Mikhail, Jess, illus. 2004. 24p. (J). lib. bdg. 22.65 (***978-1-59646-682-1(0)***) Dingles & Co.

Mosely, Keith. Beauty Mouse & The Beast. 1999. (Illus.). 4p. (J). pap. 8.95 (978-90-76048-24-6(X)) Van Der Meer Tennis Univ.

—Cindy Mouse. 1999. (Illus.). 4p. (J). pap. 8.95 (978-90-76048-25-3(8)) Van Der Meer Tennis Univ.

—Robinson Mouse. 1999. (Illus.). 4p. (J). pap. 8.95 (978-90-76048-26-0(6)) Van Der Meer Tennis Univ.

—Snow Mouse & The Seven Moles. 1999. (Illus.). 4p. (J). pap. 8.95 (978-90-76048-23-9(1)) Van Der Meer Tennis Univ.

Moser, Erwin. Manuel y Didi y el Coche de Maiz. (Manuel & Didi Ser.).Tr. of Manuel & Didi & the Corn Car. (SPA., Illus.). 48p. (J). (978-84-392-8721-6(6)) Gaviota Ediciones ESP. *Dist:* Lectorum Pubns., Inc.

Moss, Miriam. I'll Be Your Friend, Smudge! Chapman, Lynne, illus. 2002. 24p. (J). (ps-2). (978-1-86233-207-2(X) , Gullane Children's Bks.) Pinwheel.

—Smudge's Grumpy Day. 2006. (Illus.). 10p. (J). bds. 12.95 (978-0-7696-4639-8(5) , Gingham Dog Pr.) School Specialty Publishing.

Moulton, Mark Kimball. One Enchanted Evening. Crouch, Karen Hillard, illus. 2003. 32p. (J). 14.95 (978-0-8249-5480-2(7)) Ideals Pubns.

—One Enchanted Evening. Crouch, Karen Hillard, illus. 2000. 32p. (J). (gr. k-3). 18.00 (978-0-7412-0439-4(8)) Lang Graphics, Ltd.

Moulton, Mark Kimball. A Royal Wedding. Good, Karen Hillard, illus. 2007. 32p. (J). (gr. k-3). 14.99 (***978-0-8249-8677-3(6)***) Ideals Pubns.

The Mouse & the Grouse. 2006. (J). lib. bdg. (978-0-9787826-0-3(7)) Happy Bks. Pr.

Mouse & the Motorcycle. 1999. (J). 9.95 (978-1-56137-274-4(9)) Novel Units, Inc.

A Mouse Named Sam. 2006. pap. 13.95 (***978-1-59526-381-0(0)***) Media Creations, Inc.

A Mouse on the Moon. Date not set. 5.95 (978-0-89868-347-9(5)) ARO Publishing Co.

Mouse Works Staff. Mickey Mouse. 1998. (Friendly Tales Ser.). (Illus.). 10p. (J). (ps-k). 6.99 (978-1-57082-929-1(2)) Mouse Works.

—Mickey Mouse's Christmas. 1999. 64p. 6.99 (978-0-7364-0126-5(1)) Mouse Works.

—Mickey's Christmas Surprise. 1998. (J). 2.98 (978-0-7364-0006-0(0)) Mouse Works.

—Mickey's Friendly Tale, Vol. 1. 1999. (Disney's Friendly Tales Ser.). (Illus.). 10p. (J). (ps-k). 6.99 (978-0-7364-0176-0(8)) Mouse Works.

—Mickey's Toon Town. 1999. (Illus.). (J). bds. (978-0-7364-0063-3(X)) Mouse Works.

—Minnie Mouse. 1998. (Friendly Tales Ser.). (Illus.). 10p. (J). (ps). 6.99 (978-1-57082-930-7(6)) Mouse Works.

—Noodle Dance! Chunky Roly Poly. 1999. (P B & J Otter Noodle Stories Ser.). (Illus.). 16p. (J). bds. 3.50 (978-0-7364-0011-4(7)) Mouse Works.

—Santa Mickey Friendly Tales. 1998. (J). 6.99 (978-1-57082-974-1(8)) Mouse Works.

Mr. Cheesehead Goes for a Ride... 2nd rev. ed. 2005. (Illus.). 32p. (J). 12.99 (978-0-9764463-1-6(6)) Vertigo Publishing.

Myers, Walter Dean. The Mouse Rap. 2002. (Illus.). (J). 14.43 (978-0-7587-4824-9(8)) Book Wholesalers, Inc.

Nakagawa, Rieko. Guri & Gura. Howlett, Peter & McNamara, Richard B., trs. from JPN. Yamawaki, Yuriko, illus. 2003. (Guri & Gura Ser.). 32p. (gr. k-3). 10.95 (978-0-8048-3352-3(4)) Tuttle Publishing.

—Guri & Gura Cd Edition. 2006. (Illus.). 32p. (J). 12.95 (978-0-8048-3782-8(1)) Tuttle Publishing.

—Guri & Gura's Seaside Adventure. Yamawaki, Yuriko, illus. 2003. (Guri & Gura Ser.). 32p. 10.95 (978-0-8048-3354-7(0)) Tuttle Publishing.

—Guri & Gura's Songs of the Seasons, Vol. 9. Macnamara, Richard & Howlett, Peter, trs. from JPN. 2004. (Tuttle for Kids Ser.). (Illus.). 28p. 12.95 (978-0-8048-3588-6(8)) Tuttle Publishing.

Napoli, Donna Jo & Casale, Paul. Breath. 2005. (Illus.). 272p. (YA). pap. 5.99 (978-0-689-86177-2(X) , Simon Pulse) Simon & Schuster Children's Publishing.

Ned Visits New York. ed. 2006. (J). 15.95 (978-0-9789384-0-6(2)) Kip Kids of New York.

Newell, Jeff. Skimper-Scamper. Hranilovich, Barbara J., illus. 2005. (Green Light Readers Level 2 Ser.). 24p. (J). 12.95 (978-0-15-205166-2(X)); pap. 3.95 (978-0-15-205165-5(1)) Harcourt Children's Bks. (Green Light Readers).

Nibble, Nibble, Nibble: KinderConcepts Individual Title Six-Packs. (Kinderstarters Ser.). 8p. (ps-1). 21.00 (978-0-7635-8716-1(8)) Rigby Education.

Nimmo, Jenny & Rivers, Ruth. Matty Mouse. 2006. (Blue Bananas Ser.). (Illus.). (J). 48p. pap. (978-0-7787-0898-8(5)); 47p. (978-0-7787-0852-0(7)) Crabtree Publishing Co.

Nivola, Claire A. El Bosque. 2002. (SPA.). 32p. (J). (978-84-261-3255-0(3)) Juventud, Editorial.

Norton, Miriam. The Kitten Who Thought He Was a Mouse. 2008. (Little Golden Book Ser.). (Illus.). 24p. (J). (gr. k-k). 2.99 (***978-0-375-84822-3(3)*** , Golden Bks.) Random Hse. Children's Bks.

Novak, Matt. Mouse TV. 1998. (Illus.). 32p. (J). (ps-1). pap. 6.95 (978-0-531-07099-4(9) , Orchard Bks.) Scholastic, Inc.

Numeroff, Laura. Merry Christmas, Mouse! Bond, Felicia, illus. 2007. (If You Give... Ser.). 24p. (J). (ps). pap. 6.99 (***978-0-06-134499-2(0)*** , Harper Festival) HarperCollins Pubs.

Numeroff, Laura Joffe. The Best Mouse Cookie. Bond, Felicia, illus. (If You Give... Ser.). 24p. (J). 2006. 9.99 (978-0-06-113760-0(X) , Geringer, Laura Book); 1999. 6.99 (978-0-694-01270-1(X) , Harper Festival) HarperCollins Pubs.

—If You Give a Mouse a Cookie. ed. 2004. (Illus.). (J). (gr. k-3). spiral bd. (978-0-616-01751-7(0)); spiral bd. (978-0-616-01752-4(9)) Canadian National Institute for the Blind/Institut National Canadien pour les Aveugles.

—If You Give a Mouse a Cookie. Bond, Felicia, illus. Date not set. 32p. (J). (ps-2). 4.95 (978-0-06-443166-8(5)) HarperCollins Pubs.

—If You Take a Mouse to School. ed. 2004. (Illus.). (J). (gr. k-3). spiral bd. (978-0-616-14593-7(4)); spiral bd. (978-0-616-14594-4(2)) Canadian National Institute for the Blind/Institut National Canadien pour les Aveugles.

—If You Take a Mouse to School. Bond, Felicia, illus. 2002. (If You Give... Ser.). 32p. (J). (ps-2). 15.99 (978-0-06-028328-5(9) , Geringer, Laura Book) HarperCollins Pubs.

—If You Take a Mouse to School: Si llevas un raton a la Escuela. Bond, Felicia, illus. 2003. (If You Give... Ser.). (SPA.). 32p. (J). (ps-2). 15.99 (978-0-06-052340-4(9) , Rayo) HarperCollins Pubs.

—If You Take a Mouse to the Movies. ed. 2004. (Illus.). (J). (gr. k-3). spiral bd. (978-0-616-11128-4(2)); spiral bd. (978-0-616-11129-1(0)) Canadian National Institute for the Blind/Institut National Canadien pour les Aveugles.

—If You Take a Mouse to the Movies. Mlawer, Teresa, tr. Bond, Felicia, illus. 2001. (If You Give... Ser.). (SPA.). 40p. (J). (ps-2). 16.99 (978-0-06-623802-9(1) , HC6271) HarperCollins Pubs.

—If You Take a Mouse to the Movies. Bond, Felicia, illus. 2000. (If You Give... Ser.). (J). (ps-2). 40p. 15.99 (978-0-06-027867-0(6) , Geringer, Laura Book); 9.95 (978-0-694-01531-3(8) , Harper Festival); 40p. lib. bdg. 16.89 (978-0-06-027868-7(4) , Geringer, Laura Book) HarperCollins Pubs.

—If You Take a Mouse to the Movies: Book & Doll. Bond, Felicia, illus. 2001. (J). (ps-2). 19.95 (978-0-694-01427-9(3)) HarperCollins Pubs.

—A Mouse Cookie First Library. Bond, Felicia, illus. 2007. (If You Give... Ser.). (J). 15.99 (***978-0-06-117479-7(3)*** , Harper Festival) HarperCollins Pubs.

—Mouse Cookies & More: A Treasury. Bond, Felicia, illus. 2006. (If You Give... Ser.). 224p. 24.99 (978-0-06-113763-1(4) , Geringer, Laura Book) HarperCollins Pubs.

—Mouse's Family Album. Date not set. 32p. (J). 10.99 (978-0-06-028561-6(3) , Geringer, Laura Book) HarperCollins Pubs.

Numeroff, Laura Joffe & Bond, Felicia. If You Give a Mouse a Cookie. l.t. ed. (FRE.). (J). bds. 29.99 (978-0-590-71930-8(0)) Scholastic, Inc.

Nunez, Ralph. Cooper's Tale. Madeline, Simon, illus. 2000. (J). per. 5.95 (978-0-9641784-7-2(8)) Homes for the Homeless, Inc.

Oakley, Graham. Church Mice Take a Break. (Illus.). 25p. (J). 17.99 (978-0-340-73254-0(7) , Hodder & Stoughton) Hodder General Publishing Division GBR. *Dist:* Trafalgar Square Publishing.

O'Brien, Robert C. Mrs. Frisby & the Rats of Nimh. Bernstein, Zena, illus. 2002. (J). 13.94 (978-0-7587-0205-0(1)) Book Wholesalers, Inc.

—Mrs. Frisby & the Rats of Nimh. Bernstein, Zena, illus. l.t. ed. 2000. (Rats of NIMH Ser.). 300p. (J). (gr. 4-7). lib. bdg. 29.95 (978-1-58118-056-5(X) , 23470) LRS.

O'Brien, Robert C. & Pryne, Jane. Mrs. Frisby & the Rats of Nimh. 1998. (Literature Unit Ser.). (Illus.). 48p. pap., tchr. ed. 7.99 (978-1-55734-523-3(6) , TCA0523) Teacher Created Materials, Inc.

Ocker, Christ Holder. A Mouse Without a House. 2006. (J). per. (***978-1-59872-711-1(7)***) Instantpublisher.com.

O'Connell, Fabian. Alpha's Baseball Field. 2004. 42p. pap. 19.95 (978-1-4137-0301-6(1)) PublishAmerica, Inc.

Oh, Jiwon. Mr. Monkey's Classroom. Oh, Jiwon, illus. 2005. (Illus.). 32p. (J). (ps-2). lib. bdg. 15.89 (978-0-06-055722-5(2)) HarperCollins Pubs.

O'Malley, Kevin. Herbert Fieldmouse, Secret Agent. 2003. (Illus.). 32p. (J). pap. (978-1-59336-043-6(6)); (gr. 1-6). 15.95 (978-1-59336-042-9(8)) Mondo Publishing.

Oram, Hiawyn. The Giant Surprise: A Narnia Story. Humphries, Tudor, illus. 2005. (Step into Narnia Ser.). 40p. (J). (ps-2). lib. bdg. 16.89 (978-0-06-001360-8(5)) HarperCollins Pubs.

—Mr Strongmouse & the Baby. Chapman, Lynne, illus. 2006. 32p. (J). pap. (***978-1-84362-588-9(1)*** , Orchard Bks.) Scholastic, Inc.

Oram, Hiawyn. Princess Chamomile Gets Her Way. 2001. (Illus.). (J). (978-0-606-21386-8(4)) Tandem Library Bks.

Oram, Hiawyn & Lewis, C. S. The Giant Surprise: A Narnia Story. Humphries, Tudor, illus. 2005. (Step into Narnia Ser.). 40p. (J). (ps-2). 15.99 (978-0-06-008361-8(1)) HarperCollins Pubs.

Ormerod, Jan. Miss Mouse's Day. Ormerod, Jan, illus. 2002. (Illus.). (J). 24.00 (978-0-7587-6481-2(2)) Book Wholesalers, Inc.

Ottolenghi, Carol. Tip the Mouse Can't Sleep. Campanella, Marco, illus. 2005. (Tip the Mouse Ser.). 32p. (J). (ps-ps). 10.95 (978-0-7696-4299-4(3) , Gingham Dog Pr.) School Specialty Publishing.

—Tip the Mouse Runs Away. Campanella, Marco, illus. 2005. (Tip the Mouse Ser.). 32p. (J). (ps-ps). 10.95 (978-0-7696-4298-7(5) , Gingham Dog Pr.) School Specialty Publishing.

Owhonda, John. Musa the Mouse. Stidom, Damon, illus. l.t. ed. 1999. 27p. (J). (gr. 1-4). 19.95 (978-0-9650505-3-1(X)) CGS Communications.

Owl & Mouse in the House: Individual Title Six-Packs. (Sails Literacy Ser.). (gr. 1-2). 36.00 (978-0-7578-4016-6(7)) Rigby Education.

Packard, Albert. Cavern of Babel. Boyles, Shawn, illus. 2006. (J). per. 14.95 (***978-0-9790652-0-0(8)***) Diamond Triple C Ranch.

Packard, Mary. Sleep-over Mouse. 2004. (My First Reader Ser.). (J). (gr. k-1). pap. 3.95 (978-0-516-24638-3(0) , Children's Pr.) Scholastic Library Publishing.

—Sleep-over Mouse. Wilburn, Kathy, illus. 2003. (My First Reader Ser.). 32p. (J). 18.50 (978-0-516-22936-2(2) , Children's Pr.) Scholastic Library Publishing.

Pantin, Yolanda. Raton y Vampiro en el Castillo. Cabrera, Marcela, illus. (SPA.). (J). pap. 7.96 (978-980-01-0881-9(5)) Monte Avila Editores Latinoamericana CA VEN. *Dist:* Lectorum Pubns., Inc.

—Raton y Vampiro Se Concen. Cabrera, Marcela, illus. (SPA.). (J). pap. 6.00 (978-980-01-0480-4(1)) Monte Avila Editores Latinoamericana CA VEN. *Dist:* Lectorum Pubns., Inc.

Parker, Ant. Wake up, Ginger. Parker, Ant, illus. 2001. (Illus.). 32p. (J). (ps-1). pap. 5.95 (978-1-58653-853-8(5)) Mondo Publishing.

Paul, Brian. Julio & Maria Raise the Rook: Gift Set. Marrero, J., illus. 2002. Tr. of Julio y Maria Levantan la Azotea. (SPA & ENG.). (J). per. 15.99 (978-1-893108-91-2(0)) Neighborhood Pr. Publishing.

Percy, Graham, illus. El Raton de Ciudad y el Raton de Campo. l.t. ed. 2001. Tr. of City Mouse & the Country Mouse. (SPA.). 28p. (J). (ps-3). incl. audio (978-84-86154-52-3(9)) Peralt Montagut.

Perry, Phyllis J. The Secrets of the Rock. Lipking, Ron, illus. 2004. (Fribble Mouse Library Mystery Ser.). 96p. (J). 16.95 (978-1-932146-22-6(9)) Highsmith Inc.

Peterson, John. The Littles Go Around the World, No. 2. Rogers, Jacqueline, illus. 2000. (Littles Ser.). 32p. (J). (gr. 1-5). pap. 3.99 (978-0-439-20300-5(7)) Scholastic, Inc.

Petricic, Dusan, illus. The Enormous potato. 1998. 32p. (J). (gr. k-3). (978-1-55074-386-9(4)) Kids Can Pr., Ltd.

Pierre, Dana. Mousey, Mousey Finds Cheese? Illustrated by Wellon Pierre. 2006. 17.00 (978-0-8059-9867-2(5)) Dorrance Publishing Co., Inc.

Pilkey, Dav. Dogzilla. Pilkey, Dav, illus. 2002. (Illus.). (J). 14.04 (978-0-7587-2405-2(5)) Book Wholesalers, Inc.

—Dogzilla. 2003. (Illus.). 32p. (J). 14.00 (978-0-15-204948-5(7)); pap. 5.95 (978-0-15-204949-2(5) , Harcourt Paperbacks) Harcourt Children's Bks.

—Giant Robot vs. the Mutant Mosquitoes from Mercury. Ontiveros, Martin, illus. 2000. (Ricky Ricotta Ser.: No. 2). 128p. (J). (ps-3). pap. 16.95 (978-0-590-30721-5(5) , Blue Sky Pr., The) Scholastic, Inc.

—Kat Kong. Pilkey, Dav, illus. 2002. (Illus.). (J). 14.04 (978-0-7587-2923-1(5)) Book Wholesalers, Inc.

—Kat Kong. 2003. (Illus.). 32p. (J). 14.00 (978-0-15-204951-5(7)); pap. 5.95 (978-0-15-204950-8(9) , Harcourt Paperbacks) Harcourt Children's Bks.

—Kat Kong. 2003. (gr. k-3). lib. bdg. 12.95 (978-0-613-71635-2(3)) Tandem Library Bks.

—Mighty Robot vs. the Jurassic Jackrabbits from Jupiter. Ontiveros, Martin, illus. 2002. (Ricky Ricotta Ser.: No. 5). 128p. (J). (ps-3). pap. 16.95 (978-0-439-37642-6(4) , Blue Sky Pr., The); pap. 3.99 (978-0-439-37643-3(2)) Scholastic, Inc.

—Mighty Robot vs. the Jurassic Jackrabbits from Jupiter. 2002. (Ricky Ricotta Ser.: No. 5). (ps-2). lib. bdg. 11.80 (978-0-613-50493-5(3)) Tandem Library Bks.

—Mighty Robot vs. the Uranium Unicorns from Uranus. Ontiveros, Martin, illus. 2005. (Ricky Ricotta Ser.: Bk. 7). 128p. (J). pap. 16.99 (978-0-439-37646-4(7) , Blue Sky Pr., The) Scholastic, Inc.

—Ricky Ricotta Y el Poderoso Robot Contra Los Mecamonos de Marte. 2007. (Ricky Ricotta Ser.: No. 4). 144p. (J). pap. 3.99 (978-0-439-85105-3(X) , Scholastic en Espanol) Scholastic, Inc.

—Ricky Ricotta Y el Poderoso Robot Contra Los Mecamonos de Marte. Ontiveros, Martin, illus. 2002. (Ricky Ricotta Ser.: No. 4). 144p. (gr. 2-4). pap. 3.99 (978-0-439-25296-6(2)); (J). (ps-3). pap. 16.95 (978-0-439-25295-9(4)) Scholastic, Inc. (Blue Sky Pr., The).

—Ricky Ricotta Y el Poderoso Robot Contra Los Mecamonos de Marte. 2002. (Ricky Ricotta Ser.: No. 4). (ps-2). lib. bdg. 11.80 (978-0-613-45613-5(0)) Tandem Library Bks.

—Ricky Ricotta's Giant Robot. Ontiveros, Martin, illus. 2000. (Ricky Ricotta Ser.: Bk. 1). (ps-3). 111p. (J). pap. 16.95 (978-0-590-30719-2(3)); 112p. mass mkt. 3.99 (978-0-590-30720-8(7)) Scholastic, Inc. (Blue Sky Pr., The).

—Ricky Ricotta's Giant Robot vs. the Mutant Mosquitoes from Mercury. Ontiveros, Martin, illus. 2000. (Ricky Ricotta Ser.: No. 2). (J). (ps-3). pap. 47.88 (978-0-439-21522-0(6)) Scholastic, Inc.

—Ricky Ricotta's Giant Robot vs. the Mutant Mosquitoes from Mercury. Ontiveros, Martin, illus. 2000. (Ricky Ricotta Ser.: Bk. 2). 127p. (J). (ps). per. 11.80 (978-0-613-26747-2(8)) Tandem Library Bks.

—Ricky Ricotta's Giant Robot vs. the Mutant Mosquitoes from Mercury. 2000. (Ricky Ricotta Ser.: No. 2). (J). (ps-3). (978-0-606-19604-8(8)) Tandem Library Bks.

—Ricky Ricotta's Giant Robot vs. the Voodoo Vultures from Venus. Ontiveros, Martin, illus. 2001. (Ricky Ricotta Ser.: No. 3). 128p. (J). (ps-3). pap. 16.95 (978-0-439-23624-9(X)) Scholastic, Inc.

—Ricky Ricotta's Mighty Robot Collection: Ricky Ricotta's Mighty Robot; Ricky Ricotta's Mighty Robot vs. the Mutant Mosquito from Mercury; Ricky Ricotta's Mighty Robot vs. the Voodoo Vultures from Venus; Ricky Ricotta's Mighty Robot vs. the Mechamonkeys from Mars, 4 vols. Ontiveros, Martin, illus. 2002. (Ricky Ricotta Ser.: Bks. 1-4). 128p. (J). 15.96 (978-0-439-43522-2(6) , Blue Sky Pr., The) Scholastic, Inc.

—Ricky Ricotta's Mighty Robot vs. the Mutant Mosquitoes from Mercury. Ontiveros, Martin, illus. 2000. (Ricky Ricotta Ser.: No. 2). 128p. (J). (ps-3). pap. 3.99 (978-0-590-30722-2(3)) Scholastic, Inc.

—Ricky Ricotta's Mighty Robot vs. the Stupid Stinkbugs from Saturn. Ontiveros, Martin, illus. 2003. (Ricky Ricotta Ser.: No. 6). 128p. (J). pap. 16.95 (978-0-439-37644-0(0) , Blue Sky Pr., The) Scholastic, Inc.

Pistinier, Caroline. La Noche Del Ratoncito Perez. 2004. (SPA.). 40p. (J). 19.99 (978-84-8470-055-5(0)) Corimbo, Editorial S.L. ESP. *Dist:* Lectorum Pubns., Inc.

Pogo the Clown. A Little Gray Mouse: Harley's Great Adventures. Miller, Richard D., illus. 2005. (J). 12.95 (978-0-9755253-7-1(9)) Chiliric Pubns.

Potter, Beatrix. El Cuento de Juanito Raton de Ciudad. 1999. (Beatrix Potter Ser.).Tr. of Tale of Johnny Town-Mouse. (SPA., Illus.). 60p: 6.95 (978-84-7444-558-9(2)) Debate, Editorial ESP. *Dist:* Libros Sin Fronteras.

—The Tailor of Gloucester. Jorgensen, David, illus. 2007. (J). 25.65 (978-1-59961-312-3(3)) ABDO Publishing Co.

—The Tale of Johnny Town-Mouse. Potter, Beatrix, illus. 2002. (Illus.). (J). 15.23 (978-0-7587-4501-9(X)) Book Wholesalers, Inc.

—The Tale of Johnny Town-Mouse, Vol. 13. 2002. (Illus.). 64p. (J). 6.99 (978-0-7232-4782-1(X) , Warne) Penguin Group (USA) Inc.

—The Tale of Mrs. Tittlemouse. Potter, Beatrix, illus. 2002. (Illus.). (J). 15.23 (978-0-7587-3750-2(5)) Book Wholesalers, Inc.

—The Tale of Mrs. Tittlemouse. 2002. (Illus.). 64p. (J). 6.99 (978-0-7232-4780-7(3) , Warne) Penguin Group (USA) Inc.

—The Tale of Two Bad Mice. Potter, Beatrix, illus. 2002. (Illus.). (J). 15.23 (978-0-7587-3758-8(0)) Book Wholesalers, Inc.

—A Tale of Two Bad Mice. McClintock, Barbara, illus. 2007. (J). 25.65 (978-1-59961-314-7(X)) ABDO Publishing Co.

—The Tale of Two Bad Mice, Vol. 5. 2002. (Illus.). 64p. (J). 6.99 (978-0-7232-4774-6(9) , Warne) Penguin Group (USA) Inc.

Powell, Richard. Quiet as a Mouse: A Moving Picture Storybook. Hendra, Sue, illus. 2003. 16p. (J). 7.95 (978-1-58925-678-1(6) , tiger tales) ME Media LLC.

Powell, Richard & Davis, Caroline. Mouse's Tail. 2003. (Animal Tails Ser.). (Illus.). 10p. (J). 3.95 (978-1-58925-675-0(1) , tiger tales) ME Media LLC.

Powers, Paul. Tales of the Swamp Creatures. 2003. 71p. pap. 11.95 (978-1-4137-0160-9(4)) PublishAmerica, Inc.

Preller, James. Wake Me in Spring. Scherer, Jeffrey, illus. 2004. 32p. (J). lib. bdg. 15.00 (978-1-59054-397-9(1)) Fitzgerald Bks.

Prentice-Hall Staff. Of Mice & Men. 2nd ed. (J). stu. ed. (978-0-13-717018-0(1)) Prentice Hall (Schl. Div.).

Price, Kathryn. The Mouse & the Buddha. Price, Traer, illus. 2006. 36p. (J). 14.95 (978-0-9773812-0-3(X)) Little Hse. Pr.

Pryor, Bonnie. The Porcupine Mouse. Begin, Mary Jane, illus. 2002. 32p. (J). (ps-4). 15.95 (978-1-58717-185-7(6) , SeaStar Bks.) Chronicle Bks. LLC.

—Porcupine Mouse. rev. ed. 2002. (gr. k-3). lib. bdg. 14.10 (978-0-613-70724-4(9)) Tandem Library Bks.

The Pumpkin House, 6 Packs. (Literatura 2000 Ser.). (gr. 2-3). 33.00 (978-0-7635-0182-2(4)) Rigby Education.

Rabley, Stephen. Maisie & the Dolphin. 2002. (Illus.). 16p. pap. (978-0-582-40283-6(2) , Putnam Juvenile) Penguin Group (USA) Inc.

—Marcel & the Mona Lisa. 2002. (Illus.). 16p. pap. (978-0-582-40173-0(9) , Putnam Juvenile) Penguin Group (USA) Inc.

Ralph S. Mouse. 1999. (J). 9.95 (978-1-56137-173-0(4)) Novel Units, Inc.

Randall, Ronne. The Hanukkah Mice. Kneen, Maggie, illus. 2002. 20p. (J). (ps-1). 15.95 (978-0-8118-3623-4(1)) Chronicle Bks. LLC.

Ranieri, Nik. The Great Elephant. Ranieri, Nik, illus. 2005. (Illus.). 46p. (J). (ps-7). 19.95 (978-1-57921-780-8(X)) WinePress Publishing.

Ratnayake, Kumari/Keiko. Monsieur Bagel's War. Ratnayake, Kumari/Keiko, illus. 2007. (Illus.). 25p. (J). spiral bd. 15.00 net. (***978-0-9797015-1-1(1)***) Augustana College Geology Dept. Pr.

Rau, Dana Meachen. Sweet Pea: Escape in the Garden. Hannon, Holly, illus. 2006. (J). (***978-1-58987-200-4(2)***) Kindermusik International.

Read, Miss. The Christmas Mouse. Goodall, John S., illus. (J). lib. bdg. 14.95 (978-0-8488-1452-6(5)) Amereon LTD.

Reed, Patricia. Mousetrap. 2005. pap. 15.99 (978-1-4196-0540-6(2)) BookSurge, LLC.

Reid, Barbara. The Subway Mouse. Reid, Barbara, illus. 2005. (Illus.). 40p. (J). 15.95 (978-0-439-72827-0(4)) Scholastic, Inc.

—The Subway Mouse. 2005. (Illus.). (J). (978-0-439-77430-7(6)) Scholastic, Inc.

Reitman, Andrea. Mouse in the House: Pop-Up Playset. Bell, Karen, illus. 2001. 3p. (J). (ps-k). 16.95 (978-1-58117-156-3(0) , Intervisual/Piggy Toes) Dalmatian Pr.

Rider, Cynthia. The Greedy Mouse. 2000. (Cambridge Reading Ser.). (Illus.). 12p. (ps-1). pap. 5.00 (978-0-521-77699-8(6)) Cambridge Univ. Pr.

Rigby Education Staff. Baby Kangaroo. (Sails Literacy Ser.). (Illus.). 16p. (gr. k-1). 27.00 (978-0-7635-9879-2(8) , 698798C99) Rigby Education.

—House for Mouse. (Sails Literacy Ser.). (Illus.). 16p. (gr. 1-2). 27.00 (978-0-7635-9893-8(3)) Rigby Education.

—A Mouse Manual. (Sails Literacy Ser.). (Illus.). 16p. (gr. 2-3). 27.00 (978-0-7635-9942-3(5) , 699425C99) Rigby Education.

Riley, Linnea A. Mouse Mess. Riley, Linnea A., illus. 2002. (Illus.). (J). 25.06 (978-0-7587-3179-1(5)) Book Wholesalers, Inc.

Rip Squeak & His Friends. 2003. Tr. of Rip Squeak y Sus Amigos. (J). 16.95 (978-0-9672422-4-8(X)) Rip Squeak, Inc.

Rip Squeak & His Friends Discover the Treasure. 2003. Tr. of Rip Squeak y Sus Amigos Descubren un Tesoro. per. 16.95 (978-0-9672422-5-5(8)) Rip Squeak, Inc.

Risco, Elle D. Magnificent Mouse. Disney Storybook Artists Staff, illus. 2007. 14p. (J). (ps-3). 15.99 (***978-1-4231-0477-3(3)***) Disney Pr.

Robbins, Maria Polushkin. Mother, Mother, I Want Another. Goodell, Jon, illus. 2005. 32p. (J). (ps-1). 14.95 (978-0-375-82588-0(6)); lib. bdg. 16.99 (978-0-375-92588-7(0)) Random Hse. Children's Bks. (Knopf Bks. for Young Readers).

Roberts, Bethany. Birthday Mice! Cushman, Doug, illus. 2002. 32p. (J). (gr. k-ps). tchr. ed. 13.00 (978-0-618-07772-4(3) , Clarion Bks.) Houghton Mifflin Co. Trade & Reference Div.

—Christmas Mice. Cushman, Doug, illus. 2000. 32p. (J). (gr. k-ps). tchr. ed. 13.00 (978-0-395-91204-1(0) , Clarion Bks.) Houghton Mifflin Co. Trade & Reference Div.

—Christmas Mice. Cushman, Doug, illus. 2004. 32p. (J). (gr. k-ps). 5.95 (978-0-618-48601-4(1) , Clarion Bks.) Houghton Mifflin Co. Trade & Reference Div.

—Easter Mice! Cushman, Doug, illus. 2003. 32p. (J). (gr. k-ps). tchr. ed. 13.00 (978-0-618-16455-4(3) , Clarion Bks.) Houghton Mifflin Co. Trade & Reference Div.

—Fourth of July Mice! Cushman, Doug, illus. 2004. (Holiday Mice Ser.). 32p. (J). (gr. k-ps). 13.00 (978-0-618-31366-2(4) , Clarion Bks.) Houghton Mifflin Co. Trade & Reference Div.

—Fourth of July Mice ! 2004. (Illus.). 32p. (J). (ps-1). tchr. ed. 13.00 (978-0-618-31367-9(2) , Clarion Bks.) Houghton Mifflin Co. Trade & Reference Div.

—Thanksgiving Mice! Cushman, Doug, illus. 32p. (J). (ps-k). 2005. 5.95 (978-0-618-60486-9(3)); 2001. tchr. ed. 13.00 (978-0-618-12040-6(8)) Houghton Mifflin Co. Trade & Reference Div. (Clarion Bks.).

—Valentine Mice! Cushman, Doug, illus. 2001. 32p. (J). (gr. k-3). pap. 5.95 (978-0-618-05152-6(X) , Clarion Bks.) Houghton Mifflin Co. Trade & Reference Div.

—Valentine Mice! 2001. (ps-2). lib. bdg. 14.10 (978-0-613-31854-9(4)); (Illus.). (J). (978-0-606-20967-0(0)) Tandem Library Bks.

Roberts, Smith. A House for a Mouse. Roberts, Smith, illus. 2003. (Illus.). 56p. (J). per. 16.00 (978-0-9727315-3-9(9)) Prospero's Pr.

Robertson, Ivan T. Jack & the Leprechaun. Bratun, Katy, illus. 2000. (Pictureback Ser.). 24p. (J). (gr. k-3). pap. 3.99 (978-0-375-80328-4(9) , Random Hse. Bks. for Young Readers) Random Hse. Children's Bks.

—Jack & the Leprechaun. 2000. (gr. k-3). lib. bdg. 10.95 (978-0-613-21788-0(8)) Tandem Library Bks.

Robleda, Margarita. Ramon y Su Raton. Suarez, Maribel, illus. (Rana, Rema, Rimas Ser.). (SPA.). 16p. (J). (gr. k-3). 7.95 (978-1-59437-818-8(5)) Santillana USA Publishing Co., Inc.

Rockas, Leo. Mice Make War. 2007. 53p. 12.95 (***978-1-4241-5708-2(0)***) PublishAmerica, Inc.

Roddie, Shen. You're Too Small! Lavis, Steve, illus. 2004. 32p. (J). 6.95 (978-1-58925-385-8(X)); tchr. ed. 15.95 (978-1-58925-038-3(9)) ME Media LLC. (tiger tales).

Rohmann, Eric. My Friend Rabbit. Rohmann, Eric, illus. rev. ed. 2002. (Illus.). 32p. (J). (ps-3). 16.95 (978-0-7613-1535-3(7)) Roaring Brook Pr.

—My Friend Rabbit. Rohmann, Eric, illus. 2007. (Illus.). 32p. (J). pap. 6.95 (***978-0-312-36752-7(X)***) Square Fish.

Root, Phyllis. Mouse Goes Out. Croft, James, illus. 2002. (Brand New Readers Ser.). (J). (ps-2). 48p. 12.99 (978-0-7636-1351-8(7)); 32p. pap. 5.99 (978-0-7636-1352-5(5)) Candlewick Pr.

—Mouse Has Fun. Croft, James, illus. 2002. (Brand New Readers Ser.). 32p. (J). (ps-2). pap. 5.99 (978-0-7636-1358-7(4)) Candlewick Pr.

Rose, Gerald. The Lion & the Mouse. 2002. (Illus.). 16p. pap. 0.40 (978-0-521-01515-8(4)) Cambridge Univ. Pr.

—The Lion & the Mouse ELT Edition. 2001. (Cambridge Storybooks Ser.). (Illus.). 16p. pap. 5.00 (978-0-521-00724-5(0)) Cambridge Univ. Pr.

Ross, Tony. Silly Silly. 1999. (Illus.). 29p. (J). pap. 9.99 (978-0-86264-904-3(8)) Andersen GBR. *Dist:* Independent Pubs. Group.

Roth, Susan L. Hanukkah, Oh Hanukkah. Roth, Susan L., illus. 2006. 24p. (J). (ps). pap. 5.99 (978-0-14-240701-1(1) , Puffin) Penguin Group (USA) Inc.

—Mi Amor Por Ti/My Love for You. 2003. (ENG & SPA., Illus.). 24p. (J). (ps). bds. 5.99 (978-0-8037-2944-5(8) , Dial) Penguin Group (USA) Inc.

Rourke, Janet W. The New Baby: Featuring Marta the Mouse. 2004. (Illus.). 20p. (J). 7.99 (978-0-9729583-1-8(2)) Hale Publishing.

Rowland, Patty. Marvelous Max, the Mansion Mouse. Rasmussen, Wendy, tr. Rasmussen, Wendy, illus. 2003. 32p. (J). 17.95 (978-0-9649934-4-0(9)) Norfleet Pr., Inc.

Rubin, Bruce Joel & Michaels, Julie. Stuart Little 2 Vol. 2: El Libro de la Pelicula. 2003. (SPA., Illus.). 60p. (J). (gr. 3-5). 14.95 (978-84-204-6503-6(8)) Santillana USA Publishing Co., Inc.

Ryan, Pam Muñoz. Arroz con Frijoles y unos Amables Ratones. Cepeda, Joe, illus. 2002. (SPA.). 32p. (J). (gr. k-2). pap. 5.99 (978-0-439-31737-5(1) , SO30909, Scholastic en Espanol) Scholastic, Inc.

—Arroz con Frijoles y unos Amables Ratones. 2001. (SPA.). (ps-2). lib. bdg. 14.15 (978-0-613-45519-0(3)) Tandem Library Bks.

—Mice & Beans. Cepeda, Joe, illus. 2001. 32p. (J). (ps-2). pap. 16.95 (978-0-439-18303-1(0) , Levine, Arthur A. Bks.) Scholastic, Inc.

Rylant, Cynthia. The Eagle. McDaniels, Preston, illus. 2004. (Lighthouse Family Ser.). 64p. (J). 14.95 (978-0-689-86243-4(1)) Simon & Schuster Children's Publishing.

—The Eagle. McDaniels, Preston, illus. 2005. (Lighthouse Family Ser.). 64p. (J). pap. 3.99 (978-0-689-86311-0(X) , Aladdin) Simon & Schuster Children's Publishing.

—The Octopus. McDaniels, Preston, illus. 2005. (Lighthouse Family Ser.). 64p. (J). 15.99 (978-0-689-86246-5(6)) Simon & Schuster Children's Publishing.

Sabuda, Robert. Uh-Oh Leonardo! 2003. (Illus.). 48p. (J). 16.95 (978-0-689-81160-9(8) , Atheneum) Simon & Schuster Children's Publishing.

Sacre, Antonio. The Barking Mouse. Aguirre, Alfredo, illus. 2003. 32p. (J). (gr. k-3). 15.95 (978-0-8075-0571-7(4)) Whitman, Albert & Co.

Said Mouse to Mole. 2005. (J). per. 8.95 (978-1-59566-139-5(5)) QEB Publishing Inc.

Salmassian, Jennifer. Sally Saves the Mice. 2007. (J). per. 0.01 net. (***978-1-60402-115-8(2)***) Independent Pub.

San Souci, Robert D. Zigzag. Czernecki, Stefan, illus. 2005. 32p. (gr. 9). 16.95 (978-0-87483-764-3(2)) August Hse. Pubs., Inc.

Sargent, Dave & Sargent, Pat. Big Jake: I'm Very Curious, 56 vols., Vol. 12. Huff, Jeane, illus. 2nd rev. ed. 2003. (Animal Pride Ser.: 12). 42p. (J). lib. bdg. 19.95 (978-1-56763-781-6(7)) Ozark Publishing.

—Ginny Giraffe: High Standards, 56 vols., Vol. 46. Lenoir, Jane, illus. 2001. (Animal Pride Ser.: Vol. 46). 36p. (J). lib. bdg. 19.95 (978-1-56763-533-1(4)) Ozark Publishing.

Sargent, Dave, et al. Ginny Giraffe: High Standards, 17 bks, Vol. 46. 2000. (Animal Pride Ser.: 46). (Illus.). (J). pap. 6.95 (978-1-56763-534-8(2)) Ozark Publishing.

Savary, Fabien. Caillou Peek-a-Boo! 2007. (Pull-tab Ser.). 12p. (J). bds. 4.95 (***978-2-89450-621-9(X)***) Chouette Publishing CAN. *Dist:* Independent Pubs. Group.

Scagliotti, Loti. They Say He Said She Said. 2006. (Silly Word & Number Stories Ser.). (Illus.). 28p. (J). 12.95 (978-9974-7925-0-0(9)) Hardenville SA URY. *Dist:* Independent Pubs. Group.

Scam, Busta. The Kingdom of Nome. 2006. (Illus.). 44p. pap. 12.95 (978-1-59663-516-6(9) , Castle Keep Pr.) Rock, James A. & Co. Pubs.

Scarry, Richard. Christmas Mice. Scarry, Richard, illus. 2004. (Illus.). 26p. (J). (gr. k-k). bds. 4.99 (978-0-375-83004-4(9) , Golden Bks.) Random Hse. Children's Bks.

—Richard Scarry's Christmas Mice. Scarry, Richard, illus. 2004. (Illus.). 23p. (J). (gr. k-4). reprint ed. (978-0-7567-7752-4(6)) DIANE Publishing Co.

Scheer, Ruth D. The Mouse & the Angel. 2003. (J). lib. bdg. 15.95 (978-0-9671761-3-0(1)) Scheer Delight Publishing.

Schmidt, Hans-Christian & Bieber, Hartmut. The Wondrous Day. 2004. (Illus.). 18p. (J). 10.99 (978-1-59384-047-1(0)) Parklane Publishing.

Schneider, Richard H. Zeek, the Christmas Tree Mouse. Davies, Florence S., illus. 2004. 18.00 (978-0-687-09465-3(8)) Abingdon Pr.

Schoenherr, Ian. Pip & Squeak. Schoenherr, Ian, illus. 2007. (Illus.). 32p. (J). (ps-1). 16.99 (978-0-06-087253-3(5)); lib. bdg. 17.89 (978-0-06-087254-0(3)) HarperCollins Pubs.

School Zone Publishing Company Staff & Hoenecke, Karen. Mouse Finds a House. 2000. (Start to Read Board Bks.). (Illus.). 10p. (J). (ps-k). bds. 4.99 (978-0-88743-807-3(5) , 06803) School Zone Publishing Co.

Schubert, Ingrid & Schubert, Dieter. My Hero. 2005. (Illus.). 40p. (J). (gr. 1-3). (978-1-932425-10-9(1) , Lemniscaat) Boyds Mills Pr.

Schumacher, Claire, illus. Little Mouse Meets Santa. 2005. 16p. (J). (ps-ps). pap. 5.95 (978-1-4027-2848-8(4)) Sterling Publishing Co., Inc.

Schwabauer, Daniel. Runt the Hunted. 2007. (Illus.). 304p. (J). 17.99 (***978-0-9742972-3-1(2)***) Clear Water Pr.

Schwartz, Corey Rosen & Klein, Tali. Hop! Plop! Dunrea, Olivier, illus. 2006. 32p. (J). 16.85 (978-0-8027-8057-7(1)); 15.95 (978-0-8027-8056-0(3)) Walker & Co.

Schwartz, Roslyn. The Mole Sisters & the Piece of Moss. Schwartz, Roslyn, illus. 2001. (Mole Sisters Ser.). (Illus.). 32p. (J). (ps-k). lib. bdg. 14.95 (978-1-55037-583-1(0)) Annick Pr., Ltd. CAN. *Dist:* Firefly Bks., Ltd.

Scott, Nathan Kumar. Mangoes & Bananas. Balaji, T., illus. 2006. 32p. 16.95 (978-81-86211-06-9(3)) Consortium Bk. Sales & Distribution.

Selden, George. The Cricket in Times Square. Williams, Garth, illus. 2008. 144p. (J). pap. 6.99 (***978-0-312-38003-8(8)***) Square Fish.

Selden, George. Harry Kitten & Tucker Mouse. Williams, Garth, illus. 2001. (Chester Cricket Ser.). 80p. (J). (gr. 3-6). reprint ed. pap. 5.95 (978-0-374-42895-2(6) , Sunburst) Farrar, Straus & Giroux.

—Harry Kitten & Tucker Mouse. 2001. (gr. 3-6). lib. bdg. 14.10 (978-0-613-85136-7(6)) Tandem Library Bks.

Sharp, Margery. Miss Bianca. Williams, Garth, illus. 2006. 160p. (J). 15.99 (978-0-316-00056-7(6)) Little Brown & Co.

Sheehan, Irene. Mitsie the Meekest Mouse. Sheehan, Irene, illus. 2001. 40p. (J). 7.95 (978-0-9711768-9-8(2) , 28281) Red Reef Publishing, Inc.

Sheila Rae, the Brave. 2003. (Illus.). (J). (ps-2). 18.95 (978-1-59112-326-2(7)) Live Oak Media.

Shepard, Aaron. The Adventures of Mouse Deer. Gamble, Kim, illus. 2005. 56p. (J). pap. 6.00 (978-0-938497-32-5(4) , Skyhook Pr.) Shepard Pubns.

—The Adventures of Mouse Deer: Tales of Indonesia & Malaysia (or Indonesian & Malaysian Folktales) Gamble, Kim, illus. 2006. 56p. (J). lib. bdg. 15.00 (978-0-938497-31-8(6) , Skyhook Pr.) Shepard Pubns.

Shook, Babs. A House for Mouse, Level 1. Couri, Kathy, illus. 2000. (All-Star Readers Ser.). 32p. (J). (ps-1). pap. 3.99 (978-1-57584-383-4(8) , Reader's Digest Children's Bks.) Reader's Digest Children's Publishing, Inc.

Shook-Hazen, Barbara. House for Mouse. 2000. (ps-2). lib. bdg. 11.80 (978-0-613-25577-6(1)) Tandem Library Bks.

Shope, Ray & Shope, Lois. Sandy Claws & Chris Mouse. White, Michael, illus. 2005. 30p. (J). 13.95 (978-0-9714734-0-9(4)) Flutter-By Productions.

Sierra, Judy. Twas the Fright Before Christmas. Hillenbrand, Will, illus. 2005. 32p. (J). (ps-ps). reprint ed. pap., pap. 7.00 (978-0-15-205640-7(8) , Voyager Bks./Libros Viajeros) Harcourt Children's Bks.

Siete Ratones Ciegos. 1999. (SPA.). (J). mass mkt. 4.95 (978-0-590-48525-8(3) , SO5874) Scholastic, Inc.

Singer, Marilyn. A Dog's Gotta Do What a Dog's Gotta Do: Dogs at Work. rev. ed. 2000. (Illus.). 96p. (J). (gr. 2-5). 16.00 (978-0-8050-6074-4(X) , Holt, Henry & Co. Bks. For Young Readers) Holt, Henry & Co.

Sizer, Paul. Dream of the Ghost: Little White Mouse: Collection 1. 2004. (Illus.). 143p. pap. 12.95 (978-1-888429-56-5(9)) Blue Line Pro.

Skinner, Daphne, adapted by. The Adventures of Stuart Little. 1999. (Stuart-Little Ser.). (Illus.). 64p. (J). (gr. 2 up). pap. 3.99 (978-0-06-440827-1(2)) HarperCollins Pubs.

Slanina, Anne M. The Adventures of Annie Mouse: Baby Brother Goes to the Hospital. Agnew, Alicia, illus. 2007. 28p. (J). 16.99 (***978-0-9793379-1-8(7)***); per. 9.99 (***978-0-9793379-0-1(9)***) Annie Mouse Bks.

Slim, Lillian. Casrar-am Neqai. Sparck, Carole C., illus. l.t. ed. 1999. Tr. of Mouse Food. (ESK.). 12p. (J). (gr. k-3). pap. 17.00 (978-1-58084-109-2(0)) Lower Kuskokwim Schl. District.

—Mouse Food. Sparck, Carole C., illus. l.t. ed. 1999. 12p. (J). (gr. k-3). pap. 17.00 (978-1-58084-068-2(X)) Lower Kuskokwim Schl. District.

—Uugnaraam Neqkai. Sparck, Carole C., illus. l.t. ed. 1999. Tr. of Mouse Food. (ESK.). 12p. (J). (gr. k-3). pap. 17.00 (978-1-58084-069-9(8)) Lower Kuskokwim Schl. District.

—Uuqnaraam Negkia. Sparck, Carole C., illus. l.t. ed. 1999. Tr. of Mouse Food. (ESK.). 12p. (J). (gr. k-3). pap. 17.00 (978-1-58084-122-1(8)) Lower Kuskokwim Schl. District.

—Uuqnaraam Negkia (Mouse Food) Sparck, Carole C., illus. l.t. ed. 1999. (ESK.). 12p. (J). (gr. k-3). pap. 17.00 (978-1-58084-129-0(5)); pap. 17.00 (978-1-58084-143-6(0)) Lower Kuskokwim Schl. District.

Smith, Callie. Bud's Prairietown Holiday. Skinner, R. Carol, illus. 2000. 64p. (J). (gr. 1-9). 16.95 (978-0-9703951-0-8(8)) Conner Prairie Pr.

Smith, Jane Davis. Mousie. 2007. 56p. (J). pap. 14.95 (***978-1-58909-401-7(8)***) Bookstand Publishing.

Sommer, Carl. If Only I Were. . . , 1 bk. 2003. (Another Sommer-Time Story Ser.). (Illus.). 48p. (J). 16.95 incl. audio compact disk (978-1-57537-502-1(8)); (gr. 1-4). 16.95 incl. audio (978-1-57537-551-9(6)) Advance Publishing, Inc.

—Noise! Noise! Noise! 2003. (Another Sommer-Time Story Ser.). (Illus.). 48p. (J). (gr. 1-4). 16.95 incl. audio compact disk (978-1-57537-519-9(2)); 16.95 incl. audio (978-1-57537-568-7(0)) Advance Publishing, Inc.

—Noise! Noise! Noise! James, Kennon, illus. 2003. (J). 9.95 (978-1-57537-020-0(4)); lib. bdg. 16.95 (978-1-57537-069-9(7)) Advance Publishing, Inc.

—Noise! Noise! Noise! Read-along. 2003. (Another Sommer-Time Story Ser.). (Illus.). 48p. (J). lib. bdg. 23.95 incl. audio (978-1-57537-769-8(1)) Advance Publishing, Inc.

Sorenson, Margo. Ambrose & the Cathedral Dream. Szegedi, Katalin, illus. 2006. 30p. (J). (978-0-8146-3004-4(9)) Liturgical Pr

—Ambrose & the Princess. Szegedi, Katalin, illus. 2005. 30p. (J). (ps-3). 16.95 (978-0-8146-3043-3(X)) Liturgical Pr.

Soto, Gary. Chato's Kitchen. 2002. (Live Oak Readalong Ser.). (Illus.). (J). pap. 16.95 incl. audio (978-1-59112-205-0(8)); pap. 18.95 incl. audio compact disk (978-1-59112-336-1(4)) Live Oak Media.

—Chato's Kitchen. Guevara, Susan, illus. 2002. 25.95 incl. audio (978-1-59112-206-7(6)); 28.95 incl. audio compact disk (978-1-59112-528-0(6)); pap. 37.95 incl. audio (978-1-59112-207-4(4)); pap. 39.95 incl. audio compact disk (978-1-59112-527-3(8)) Live Oak Media.

—Chato's Kitchen; Chato Y Su Cena. Guevara, Susan, illus. 2002. pap. 33.95 incl. audio (978-1-59112-208-1(2)) Live Oak Media.

Souricette. 2000. (FRE., Illus.). 32p. (J). 13.95 (978-2-09-202107-1(9)) Nathan, Fernand FRA. *Dist:* Distribooks, Inc.

Spangenberg, Greg. A Christmas Eve Victory: The Adventures of Churchy Church Mouse & His Cousin Tootsie. Lodwick, Sarah, illus. l.t. ed. 2006. 34p. (J). 16.99 (978-1-59879-140-2(0)) Lifevest Publishing, Inc.

—Churchy & the Light on Christmas Eve. Lodwick, Sarah, illus. l.t. ed. 2005. 38p. (J). 14.99 (978-1-59879-017-7(X)) Lifevest Publishing, Inc.

Spence, Rebecca. Little Mouse. Block, Kat, illus. 2001. (J). pap. (978-0-9702406-0-6(0)) Little Iris Pr.

Spinelli, Eileen. Now It Is Winter. DePalma, Mary Newell, illus. 2004. 32p. (J). 16.00 (978-0-8028-5244-1(0)) Eerdmans, William B. Publishing Co.

—Three Pebbles & a Song. Schindler, S. D., illus. 2003. 32p. (J). (gr. k). 16.99 (978-0-8037-2528-7(0) , 53666302, Dial) Penguin Group (USA) Inc.

Spires, Elizabeth. The Mouse of Amherst. 2001. (Illus.). (J). (978-0-606-20812-3(7)) Tandem Library Bks.

—The Mouse of Amherst: A Tale of Young Readers. Nivola, Claire A., illus. 2001. (Sunburst Bks.). 64p. (J). (gr. 3-7). pap. 5.95 (978-0-374-45411-1(6) , Sunburst) Farrar, Straus & Giroux.

Spowart, Robin. Inside, Outside Christmas. 1998. (Illus.). 24p. (J). (ps-k). tchr. ed. 15.95 (978-0-8234-1370-6(5)) Holiday Hse., Inc.

Stadler, John. Big & Little. 2007. (Illus.). 32p. (J). (ps-1). 9.99 (978-0-375-84175-0(X) , Robin Corey Bks.) Random Hse. Children's Bks.

Stansfield, David. The Amazing Adventures of Boogie One Shoe & Munch the Mouse. 2006. 48p. pap. 12.95 (978-1-4241-2404-6(2)) PublishAmerica, Inc.

Stapler, Jeannie. Cheesey the Mouse. 1998. mass mkt. 10.95 (978-1-889131-21-4(0)) Janson Media Group.

Steig, William. Abel's Island. 2007. (Illus.). 128p. (J). pap. 5.99 (***978-0-312-37143-2(8)***) Square Fish.

—Amos & Boris. 1999. (J). 13.75 (978-0-606-16476-4(6)) Tandem Library Bks.

—Doctor De Soto. 2003. (Picture Books Collection). (SPA.). 32p. (J). (gr. k-3). 16.95 (978-84-372-6616-9(5)) Altea, Ediciones, S.A. - Grupo Santillana ESP. *Dist:* Santillana USA Publishing Co., Inc.

—Doctor De Soto. Steig, William, illus. 2002. (Illus.). (J). 14.43 (978-0-7587-0256-2(6)) Book Wholesalers, Inc.

—Doctor De Soto. ed. 2004. (J). (gr. k-3). spiral bd. (978-0-616-01784-5(7)); spiral bd. (978-0-616-01785-2(5)) Canadian National Institute for the Blind/Institut National Canadien pour les Aveugles.

—Doctor De Soto. Steig, William, illus. 1998. (Illus.). pap. 39.95 incl. audio compact disk (978-1-59519-161-8(5)); (SPA., (J). pap. 18.95 incl. audio compact disk (978-1-59519-160-1(7)) Live Oak Media.

—Doctor De Soto. Puncel, María, tr. 1998. (SPA., Illus.). pap., tchr. ed. 37.95 incl. audio (978-0-87499-459-9(4)); (J). pap. 16.95 incl. audio (978-0-87499-458-2(6)) Live Oak Media.

—Doctor De Soto. 2004. (J). (gr. k-5). pap. 14.95 incl. audio (978-0-89719-771-7(2) , PRA284) Weston Woods Studios, Inc.

Steven, Kenneth. The Sea Mice & the Stars. Ho, Louise, illus. 2005. 28p. (J). 16.00 (978-1-56148-490-4(3)) Good Bks.

Stevenson, James. The Castaway. Stevenson, James, illus. 2002. (Illus.). 32p. (J). (gr. 2 up). 15.95 (978-0-688-16965-7(1)) HarperCollins Pubs.

Stewart, Amber. Birthday Countdown. Marlow, Layn, illus. 2007. 20p. (J). (ps-k). bds. 12.95 (***978-0-7696-5352-5(9)***, Gingham Dog Pr.) School Specialty Publishing.

Stilton, Geronimo. All Because of a Cup of Coffee. 2004. (Geronimo Stilton Ser.: No. 10). (Illus.). 128p. (J). mass mkt. 6.99 (978-0-439-55972-0(3) , Scholastic Paperbacks) Scholastic, Inc.

—All Because of a Cup of Coffee. 2004. (Geronimo Stilton Ser.: No. 10). (Illus.). 112p. (J). (gr. 2-5). lib. bdg. 13.94 (978-0-606-33273-6(1)) Tandem Library Bks.

—Attack of the Bandit Cats. Wolf, Matt, illus. 2004. (Geronimo Stilton Ser.: No. 8). 115p. (J). lib. bdg. 10.00 (***978-1-4242-0277-5(9)***) Fitzgerald Bks.

—Cat & Mouse in a Haunted House. Wolf, Matt & Keys, Larry, illus. 2004. (Geronimo Stilton Ser.: No. 3). 128p. (J). pap. 6.99 (978-0-439-55965-2(0) , Scholastic Paperbacks) Scholastic, Inc.

—Cat & Mouse in a Haunted House. 2004. (Geronimo Stilton Ser.: No. 3). (gr. 3-6). lib. bdg. 14.15 (978-0-613-72224-7(8)) Tandem Library Bks.

—Christmas Catastrophe. ed. 2007. (Geronimo Stilton Ser.). 128p. (J). pap. 6.99 (***978-0-545-00902-7(2)*** , Scholastic Paperbacks) Scholastic, Inc.

—The Christmas Toy Factory. 2006. (Geronimo Stilton Ser.: No. 27). (Illus.). (J). 128p. pap. 6.99 (978-0-439-84118-4(6) , Scholastic Paperbacks); 95p. (***978-1-4156-8969-1(5)***) Scholastic, Inc.

—The Curse of the Cheese Pyramid. Wolf, Matt, illus. 2004. (Geronimo Stilton Ser.: No. 2). 113p. (J). lib. bdg. 10.00 (***978-1-4242-0696-4(0)***) Fitzgerald Bks.

—The Curse of the Cheese Pyramid. Wolf, Matt & Keys, Larry, illus. 2004. (Geronimo Stilton Ser.: No. 2). 128p. (J). pap. 5.99 (978-0-439-55964-5(2)) Scholastic, Inc.

—The Curse of the Cheese Pyramid. 2004. (Geronimo Stilton Ser.: No. 2). (gr. 3-6). lib. bdg. 14.15 (978-0-613-72223-0(X)) Tandem Library Bks.

—A Fabumouse Vacation for Geronimo. 2004. (Geronimo Stilton Ser.: No. 9). (Illus.). 113p. (J). (gr. 2-5). lib. bdg. 13.94 (978-0-606-33272-9(3)) Tandem Library Bks.

—Field Trip to Niagara Falls. 2006. (Geronimo Stilton Ser.: No. 24). 128p. (J). pap. 6.99 (978-0-439-69146-8(X) , Scholastic Paperbacks) Scholastic, Inc.

—Four Mice Deep in the Jungle. Wolf, Matt & Keys, Larry, illus. 2004. (Geronimo Stilton Ser.: No. 5). 128p. (J). pap. 6.99 (978-0-439-55967-6(7) , Scholastic Paperbacks) Scholastic, Inc.

—Geronimo & the Gold Medal Mystery. 2008. (Geronimo Stilton Ser.). 128p. (J). 6.99 (***978-0-545-02133-3(2)*** , Scholastic Paperbacks) Scholastic, Inc.

—Geronimo Stilton. 2005. (J). (978-0-439-79161-8(8)) Scholastic, Inc.

—I'm Too Fond of My Fur! Wolf, Matt, illus. 2004. (Geronimo Stilton Ser.: No. 4). 116p. (J). lib. bdg. 10.00 (***978-1-4242-0698-8(7)***) Fitzgerald Bks.

—I'm Too Fond of My Fur! Wolf, Matt & Keys, Larry, illus. 2004. (Geronimo Stilton Ser.: No. 4). 128p. (J). pap. 6.99 (978-0-439-55966-9(9) , Scholastic Paperbacks) Scholastic, Inc.

—I'm Too Fond of My Fur! 2004. (Geronimo Stilton Ser.: No. 4). (gr. 3-6). lib. bdg. 14.15 (978-0-613-72225-4(6)) Tandem Library Bks.

—It's Halloween, You 'Fraidy Mouse! Wolf, Matt, illus. 2004. 113p. (J). lib. bdg. 10.00 (***978-1-4242-0280-5(9)*** Fitzgerald Bks.

—It's Halloween, You 'Fraidy Mouse! 2004. (Geronimo Stilton Ser.: No. 11). (Illus.). 128p. (J). (gr. 2-3). pap. 5.99 (978-0-439-55973-7(1) , Scholastic Paperbacks) Scholastic, Inc.

—It's Halloween, You 'Fraidy Mouse! 2004. (Geronimo Stilton Ser.: No. 11). (Illus.). 113p. (J). (gr. 2-5). lib. bdg. 13.94 (978-0-606-33274-3(X)) Tandem Library Bks.

—Lost Treasure of the Emerald Eye. Wolf, Matt, illus. 2004. (Geronimo Stilton Ser.: No. 1). 116p. (J). lib. bdg. 10.00 (***978-1-4242-0695-7(2)*** Fitzgerald Bks.

—Lost Treasure of the Emerald Eye. 2007. (Geronimo Stilton Ser.: No. 1). 128p. (J). pap. 2.99 (***978-0-545-01032-0(2)*** , Scholastic Paperbacks) Scholastic, Inc.

—Lost Treasure of the Emerald Eye. Wolf, Matt & Keys, Larry, illus. 2004. (Geronimo Stilton Ser.: No. 1). 128p. (J). (gr. 2-5). pap. 6.99 (978-0-439-55963-8(4) , Scholastic Paperbacks) Scholastic, Inc.

—Merry Christmas, Geronimo! 2004. (Geronimo Stilton Ser.: No. 12). (Illus.). 128p. (J). (gr. 2-5). pap. 6.99 (978-0-439-55974-4(X) , Scholastic Paperbacks) Scholastic, Inc.

—The Mona Mousa Code. Wolf, Matt, illus. 2005. (Geronimo Stilton Ser.: No. 15). 113p. (J). lib. bdg. 10.00 (***978-1-4242-0284-3(1)*** Fitzgerald Bks.

—The Mona Mousa Code. Wolf, Matt, illus. 2005. (Geronimo Stilton Ser.: No. 15). 113p. (J). (ps-k). lib. bdg. 13.54 (978-0-606-33278-1(2)) Tandem Library Bks.

—The Mouse Island Marathon. 2007. (Geronimo Stilton Ser.: No. 30). 128p. (J). pap. 6.99 (***978-0-439-84121-4(6)*** , Scholastic Paperbacks) Scholastic, Inc.

—The Mummy with No Name. 2006. (Geronimo Stilton Ser.: No. 26). 128p. (J). pap. 6.99 (978-0-439-84117-7(8) , Scholastic Paperbacks) Scholastic, Inc.

—My Name Is Stilton, Geronimo Stilton. 2005. (Geronimo Stilton Ser.: No. 19). (Illus.). 128p. (J). pap. 5.99 (978-0-439-69142-0(7) , Scholastic Paperbacks) Scholastic, Inc.

—Paws off, Cheddarface! Wolf, Matt & Keys, Larry, illus. 2004. (Geronimo Stilton Ser.: No. 6). 128p. (J). mass mkt. 6.99 (978-0-439-55968-3(5)) Scholastic, Inc.

—The Phantom of the Subway. Wolf, Matt, illus. 2004. (Geronimo Stilton Ser.: No. 13). 112p. (J). lib. bdg. 10.00 (***978-1-4242-0282-9(5)*** Fitzgerald Bks.

—The Phantom of the Subway. 2004. (Geronimo Stilton Ser.: No. 13). (Illus.). 128p. (J). (gr. 2-5). pap. 5.99 (978-0-439-66162-1(5) , Scholastic Paperbacks) Scholastic, Inc.

—The Phantom of the Subway. 2004. (Geronimo Stilton Ser.: No. 13). (Illus.). 112p. (J). (gr. 2-5). lib. bdg. 13.94 (978-0-606-33276-7(6)) Tandem Library Bks.

—Red Pizzas for a Blue Count. Wolf, Matt & Keys, Larry, illus. 2004. (Geronimo Stilton Ser.: No. 7). 128p. (J). pap. 6.99 (978-0-439-55969-0(3)) Scholastic, Inc.

—The Search for Sunken Treasure. Wolf, Matt, illus. 2006. (Geronimo Stilton Ser.: No. 25). 111p. (J). lib. bdg. 10.00 (***978-1-4242-1519-5(6)*** Fitzgerald Bks.

—The Secret of Cacklefur Castle. 2005. (Geronimo Stilton Ser.: No. 22). (Illus.). 128p. (ps-k). pap. 6.99 (978-0-439-69145-1(1) , Scholastic Paperbacks) Scholastic, Inc.

—The Secret of Cacklefur Castle. 2005. (Geronimo Stilton Ser.: No. 22). (Illus.). 111p. (J). (gr. 2-5). lib. bdg. 13.04 (978-0-606-33833-2(0)) Tandem Library Bks.

—Surf's up Geronimo! 2005. (Geronimo Stilton Ser.: No. 20). (Illus.). 109p. (J). (gr. 2-5). per. 13.94 (978-0-606-33812-7(8)) Tandem Library Bks.

—Surf's up, Geronimo! 2005. (Geronimo Stilton Ser.: No. 20). (Illus.). 109p. (J). (978-1-4156-0622-3(6)) Scholastic, Inc.

—The Temple of the Ruby of Fire. Wolf, Matt, illus. 2004. (Geronimo Stilton Ser.: No. 14). 109p. (J). lib. bdg. 10.00 (***978-1-4242-0283-6(3)*** Fitzgerald Bks.

—The Temple of the Ruby of Fire. 2004. (Geronimo Stilton Ser.: No. 14). (Illus.). 128p. (J). (gr. 2-5). pap. 6.99 (978-0-439-66163-8(3) , Scholastic Paperbacks) Scholastic, Inc.

—The Temple of the Ruby of Fire. 2004. (Geronimo Stilton Ser.: No. 14). (Illus.). 106p. (J). (gr. 2-5). lib. bdg. 13.94 (978-0-606-33277-4(4)) Tandem Library Bks.

—Valentine's Day Disaster. Keys, Larry et al, illus. 2006. (Geronimo Stilton Ser.: No. 23). 122p. (J). lib. bdg. 18.46 (***978-1-4242-0292-8(2)*** Fitzgerald Bks.

—Valentine's Day Disaster. 2006. (Geronimo Stilton Ser.: No. 23). (Illus.). (J). 91p. (978-1-4156-4780-6(1)); 128p. pap. 5.99 (978-0-439-69147-5(8) , Scholastic Paperbacks) Scholastic, Inc.

—Valley of the Giant Skeletons. 2008. (Geronimo Stilton Ser.: No. 32). 128p. (J). pap. 6.99 (***978-0-545-02132-6(4)*** , Scholastic Paperbacks) Scholastic, Inc.

—Watch Your Whiskers, Stilton! 2005. (Geronimo Stilton Ser.: No. 17). (Illus.). 111p. (J). (978-1-4155-8205-3(X)) Scholastic, Inc.

—Watch Your Whiskers, Stilton! 2005. (Geronimo Stilton Ser.: No. 17). (Illus.). 111p. (J). (gr. 2-5). lib. bdg. 13.94 (978-0-606-33292-7(8)) Tandem Library Bks.

—Wedding Crasher. 2007. (Geronimo Stilton Ser.: No. 28). 128p. (J). pap. 6.99 (978-0-439-84119-1(4) , Scholastic Paperbacks) Scholastic, Inc.

Stilton, Geronimo. The Wild, Wild West. Stilton, Geronimo et al, illus. 2005. (Geronimo Stilton Ser.: No. 21). 121p. (J). lib. bdg. 18.46 (***978-1-4242-0290-4(6)*** Fitzgerald Bks.

Stilton, Geronimo, text. A Cheese-Colored Camper. 2005. (Geronimo Stilton Ser.: No. 16). (Illus.). 111p. (J). (ps-k). lib. bdg. 12.64 (978-0-606-33281-1(2)) Tandem Library Bks.

Stilton, Geronimo & Wolf, Matt. All Because of a Cup of Coffee. 2004. (Geronimo Stilton Ser.: No. 10). (Illus.). 112p. (J). lib. bdg. 10.00 (***978-1-4242-0279-9(5)*** Fitzgerald Bks.

Streep, Meryl, narrated by. Chrysanthemum. unabr. ed. 1998. (SPA.). (J). (ps-2). pap. 14.95 incl. audio (978-0-7882-0126-4(3) , PRA369SP) Weston Woods Studios, Inc.

Suarez, Maribel, illus. Klaus & His Mouse. (Rowing Frog's Rhymes Ser.). 16p. (J). (gr. k-3). 7.95 (978-1-59437-839-3(8)) Santillana USA Publishing Co., Inc.

Summers, Kate. Milly & Tilly: The Story of a Town Mouse & a Country Mouse. 2000. (978-0-606-18433-5(3)) Tandem Library Bks.

Swanson, Maggie, illus. The Tale of Two Bad Mice. 2006. (J). 6.99 (978-1-59939-030-7(2)) Reader's Digest Young Families, Inc.

Sweeney, Jacqueline. Critter Sitters. 2001. (We Can Read! Ser.). (Illus.). 32p. (J). 21.36 (978-0-7614-1122-2(4) , Benchmark Bks.) Cavendish, Marshall Corp.

—Molly's Store. Hart, G. K. & Empey, Mark, illus. 2000. (We Can Read! Ser.). 32p. (J). (gr. 1-2). lib. bdg. 21.36 (978-0-7614-1116-1(X) , Benchmark Bks.) Cavendish, Marshall Corp.

Talbot, Amy. Deer & Friends: A Folktale from India. 2006. 23.00 (***978-1-4108-6173-3(2)*** Benchmark Education Co.

Tara, Stephanie Lisa. Little Library Mouse. Walton, Alex, illus. 2006. (J). 16.95 (978-1-933285-39-9(7)) Brown Bks. Publishing Group.

Tashiro, Chisato. Five Nice Mice. Uchida, Sayako, tr. from JPN. Tashiro, Chisato, illus. 2007. 36p. (J). (ps-2). 16.99 (***978-0-698-40058-0(5)*** , Minedition) Penguin Group (USA) Inc.

Testa, F. Cat & Mouse & Something to Do. 1998. (Illus.). 25p. (J). 19.99 (978-0-86264-799-5(1)) Andersen GBR. *Dist:* Independent Pubs. Group.

Thompson, Lauren. Mouse's First Christmas. Erdogan, Buket, illus. 2002. (Classic Board Bks.). 34p. (J). (ps-1). 7.99 (978-0-689-85141-4(3) , Little Simon) Simon & Schuster Children's Publishing.

—Mouse's First Christmas. 2003. (ps-2). lib. bdg. 14.15 (978-0-613-91039-2(7)) Tandem Library Bks.

—Mouse's First Halloween. Erdogan, Buket, illus. 2000. 32p. (J). (ps-3). 12.95 (978-0-689-83176-8(5)) Simon & Schuster Children's Publishing.

—Mouse's First Halloween. Erdogan, Buket, illus. 2003. (Classic Board Bks.). 34p. (J). 7.99 (978-0-689-85584-9(2) , Little Simon) Simon & Schuster Children's Publishing.

—Mouse's First Spring. Erdogan, Buket, illus. 2005. 32p. (J). 12.95 (978-0-689-85838-3(8) , Simon & Schuster Children's Publishing) Simon & Schuster Children's Publishing.

—Mouse's First Summer. Erdogan, Buket, illus. 2004. 32p. (J). 12.95 (978-0-689-85835-2(3)) Simon & Schuster Children's Publishing.

Thompson, Lauren & Erdogan, Buket. Mouse's First Christmas. 2003. (Illus.). 32p. (J). pap. 5.99 (978-0-689-86348-6(9) , Aladdin) Simon & Schuster Children's Publishing.

—Mouse's First Fall. 2006. 32p. (J). (ps-1). 12.95 (978-0-689-85837-6(X) , Simon & Schuster Children's Publishing) Simon & Schuster Children's Publishing.

—Mouse's First Snow. 2005. (Illus.). 32p. (J). 12.95 (978-0-689-85836-9(1)) Simon & Schuster Children's Publishing.

Thompson, Lauren, et al. Mouse's First Day of School. 2003. (Illus.). 32p. (J). (ps-1). 12.95 (978-0-689-84727-1(0)) Simon & Schuster Children's Publishing.

Titus, Eve. Anatole. 2006. 40p. (J). (gr. k-4). 14.95 (978-0-375-83901-6(1) , Knopf Bks. for Young Readers) Random Hse. Children's Bks.

—Anatole. Galdone, Paul, illus. 2006. 40p. (J). (gr. k-4). 16.99 (978-0-375-93901-3(6) , Knopf Bks. for Young Readers) Random Hse. Children's Bks.

—Anatole & the Cat. 2006. 40p. (J). (gr. k-4). 14.95 (978-0-375-83902-3(X) , Knopf Bks. for Young Readers) Random Hse. Children's Bks.

—Anatole & the Cat. Galdone, Paul, illus. 2006. 40p. (J). (gr. k-4). 16.99 (978-0-375-93902-0(4) , Knopf Bks. for Young Readers) Random Hse. Children's Bks.

Tolan, Stephanie S. Bartholomew's Blessing. Moore, Margie, illus. 2004. 32p. (J). (ps-3). lib. bdg. 16.89 (978-0-06-001198-7(X)) HarperCollins Pubs.

Tomos, Angharad. Cosyn. 2005. (WEL., Illus.). 24p. pap. (978-0-86243-566-0(8)) Y Lolfa.

Tompert, Ann. The Pied Piper of Peru. Kasparavicius, Kestutis, illus. 2003. 32p. (YA). (gr. k-2). 15.95 (978-1-56397-949-1(7)) Boyds Mills Pr.

Toms, Kate. Twinkle, Twinkle, Little Star. 2007. (Illus.). 26p. (ps). bds. 7.99 (***978-1-84610-485-5(8)*** Make Believe Ideas GBR. *Dist:* Ingram Pub. Services.

Top That Publishing Staff, ed. Mr. Mouse Needs House. 2005. (Illus.). 8p. (978-1-84510-128-2(6)) Top That! Publishing PLC.

Il Topo di Citta e il Topo di Campagna. 1999. (ITA., Illus.). 24p. (J). (ps-5). pap. 7.95 (978-88-8148-257-3(6)) European Language Institute ITA. *Dist:* Distribooks, Inc., Midwest European Pubns.

Town Mouse & Country Mouse. 2005. (J). (978-1-58453-303-0(X)) Pioneer Valley Educational Pr., Inc.

Town Mouse & Country Mouse: Individual Title Six-Packs. (Story Steps Ser.). (gr. k-2). 32.00 (978-0-7635-9826-6(7)); 32p. (gr. 2 up). 37.00 (978-0-7635-9222-6(6)) Rigby Education.

Turley, Sandy. The Clock & the Mouse: A Teaching Rhyme about Time. Peterson, Sara & Lindstrom, Brita, illus. 2006. (J). 16.95 (***978-0-9778548-0-6(9)*** Turley, Sandy.

Twinn, Michael. Giant Mouse. 1998. (Great Pals Ser.). (Illus.). 12p. (J). (ps-1). bds. 8.99 (978-0-85953-993-7(8)) Child's Play-International.

Van-Leeuwen, Jan. Lost Treasures Bk. 4: The Great Cheese Conspiracy. 2001. 96p. (J). 13.49 (978-0-7868-2555-4(3)) Hyperion Pr.

Vaniko, K. L. Why the Dog Chases the Cat & the Cat C. 2006. 30.99 (***978-1-59926-863-7(9)*** Xlibris Corp.

Vaswani, Navina. A Wonderful Christmas. 2004. (YA). per. (978-0-9754818-5-1(1)) Creative Bk. Pubs.

Vere, Ed. The Getaway. Vere, Ed, illus. 2007. 34p. (J). (gr. k-2). 16.99 (***978-1-4169-4789-9(2)*** , McElderry, Margaret K.) Simon & Schuster Children's Publishing.

Villeneuve, Marie-Paule & Audet, Patrice. Qui a Enleve Polka? 2004. (FRE., Illus.). 122p. (J). 8.95 (978-2-922565-81-2(5)) Editions de la Paix CAN. *Dist:* World of Reading, Ltd.

Vulliamy, Clara. Small. 2002. (Illus.). 32p. (J). (gr. k-ps). 15.00 (978-0-618-19459-9(2) , Clarion Bks.) Houghton Mifflin Co. Trade & Reference Div.

Waber, Bernard. The Mouse That Snored. 2004. (Illus.). 32p. (J). (gr. k-3). 5.95 (978-0-618-43954-6(4) , Walter Lorraine) Houghton Mifflin Co. Trade & Reference Div.

Waddell, Martin. Tiny's Big Adventure. Lawrence, John, illus. 2004. 32p. (J). (ps-1). 15.99 (978-0-7636-2170-4(6)) Candlewick Pr.

Wagener, Gerda. Hay un Raton en Casa! 2002. Tr. of There's a Mouse in the House!. (SPA.). (gr. k-3). lib. bdg. 14.10 (978-0-613-73551-3(X)) Tandem Library Bks.

Wagner, Karen. Bravo, Mildred & Ed! Pedersen, Janet, illus. 2000. 32p. (J). (gr. k-3). 16.95 (978-0-8027-8734-7(7)); lib. bdg. 17.85 (978-0-8027-8735-4(5)) Walker & Co.

—A Friend Like Ed. Pedersen, Janet, illus. 1998. 32p. (J). (gr. k-3). 15.95 (978-0-8027-8662-3(6)) Walker & Co.

Wahl, Jan. Pleasant Fieldmouse. Sendak, Maurice, illus. 2007. (Sendak Reissues Ser.). 72p. (J). 15.95 (978-0-06-029725-1(5)) HarperCollins Pubs.

Wallace, Karen. Bed for the Winter. 2000. (gr. k-3). lib. bdg. 11.80 (978-0-613-32318-5(1)) Tandem Library Bks.

Wallace, Nancy Elizabeth & Friedlaender, Linda. Look! Look! Look! Wallace, Nancy Elizabeth & Friedlaender, Linda, illus. 2006. (Illus.). 40p. (J). 16.95 (978-0-7614-5282-9(6)) Cavendish, Marshall Corp.

Walsh, Ellen Stoll. Dot & Jabber & the Big Bug Mystery. 2003. (Dot & Jabber Ser.). (Illus.). 40p. (J). 15.00 (978-0-15-216518-5(5)) Harcourt Trade Pubs.

—Mouse Count. Walsh, Ellen Stoll, illus. 2002. (Illus.). (J). 12.77 (978-0-7587-3177-7(9)) Book Wholesalers, Inc.

—Mouse Count: Lap-Sized Board Book. 2006. (Illus.). 30p. (J). bds. 10.95 (978-0-15-205699-5(8) , Red Wagon Bks.) Harcourt Children's Bks.

—Mouse Paint. 2006. (Illus.). 30p. (J). bds. 10.95 (978-0-15-205533-2(9) , Red Wagon Bks.) Harcourt Children's Bks.

—Mouse Shapes. Walsh, Ellen Stoll, illus. 2007. (Illus.). 40p. (J). (ps-2). 16.00 (978-0-15-206091-6(X)) Harcourt Trade Pubs.

—Pintura de Raton. Campoy, F. Isabel, tr. 2006. (Illus.). 30p. (J). bds. 6.95 (978-0-15-205743-5(9) , Voyager Bks./Libros Viajeros) Harcourt Children's Bks.

Walton, Rick. Around the House, the Fox Chased the Mouse: A Prepositional Tale. Bradshaw, Jim, illus. 2006. 32p. (J). 15.95 (978-1-4236-0006-0(1)) Gibbs Smith, Publisher.

Ward, Nick. Farmer George & the Fieldmice. 2001. (Illus.). 32p. (J). (ps-k). pap. 8.99 (978-1-86205-413-4(4) , Pavilion Bks., Ltd.) Anova Bks. GBR. *Dist:* Independent Pubs. Group.

Wargin, Kathy-Jo. Minn from Minnesota. Holman, Karen Busch, illus. 2006. 141p. (J). 14.95 (978-1-58726-304-0(1) , Mitten Pr.) Ann Arbor Media Group, LLC.

—Mitt & Minn at the Wisconsin Cheese Jamboree. Busch Holman, Karen, illus. 2007. 144p. (J). 14.95 (***978-1-58726-305-7(X)*** , Mitten Pr.) Ann Arbor Media Group, LLC.

—Mitt & Minn's Illinois Adventure. Holman, Karen Busch, illus. 2007. 144p. (J). 14.95 (***978-1-58726-306-4(8)*** , Mitten Pr.) Ann Arbor Media Group, LLC.

Wargin, Kathy-Jo. Mitt the Michigan Mouse. 2006. (Illus.). 144p. (J). 14.95 (978-1-58726-303-3(3) , Mitten Pr.) Ann Arbor Media Group, LLC.

Warnes, Tim. Chalk & Cheese. 2008. (J). (***978-1-4169-1378-8(5)*** , Simon & Schuster Children's Publishing) Simon & Schuster Children's Publishing.

Waters, Tony. Cinnamon's Busy Year. Guevara, Linda L. & Merrill, Libby, eds. Waters, Tony, illus. 2003. (Illus.). 32p. (J). (ps-3). pap. 5.95 (978-0-9710278-2-4(X)) All About Kids Publishing.

Watkins, Greg. Brendon Mouses Big Idea to save the Bad Bird Bunch. 2006. 30p. 14.95 (978-0-9761318-0-9(3)) Cute & Cuddly Productions, Inc.

—Brendon Mouse's Big Idea to Save the Bad Bird Bunch. 2007. 32p. (J). 15.95 (978-1-58980-449-4(X)) Pelican Publishing Co., Inc.

Watson, Louise. The Mouse in Our House. 2005. (J). pap. 8.00 (978-0-8059-6719-7(2)) Dorrance Publishing Co., Inc.

Watt, Fiona. Christmas Eve Board Book. 2007. (Luxury Touchy-Feely Board Bks). 10p. (J). bds. 11.99 (***978-0-7945-1478-5(2)*** , Usborne) EDC Publishing.

—Christmas Mice. 2004. (Big Touchy Feely Board Bks.). (Illus.). 10p. (J). 11.95 (978-0-7945-0482-3(5) , Usborne) EDC Publishing.

—That's Not My Kitten. Wells, Rachel, illus. rev. ed. 2006. 10p. (J). bds. 7.99 (978-0-7945-1266-8(6) , Usborne) EDC Publishing.

Weale, David. The True Meaning of Crumbfest. McNevin, Dale, illus. 28p. pap. 5.95 (978-0-9698606-4-8(1)) Acorn Pr., The CAN. *Dist:* Goose Lane Editions.

The Wedding of the Mouse: An Asian Folktale. 2006. (J). 17.95 (***978-0-9790033-0-1(X)*** Playground Pr.

A Weekend with Wendell. 2004. 29.95 incl. cd-rom (978-1-55592-129-3(9)); (J). 24.95 incl. audio (978-1-56008-003-9(5)); (J). pap. 18.95 incl. audio compact disk (978-1-55592-116-3(7)); (J). pap. 32.75 incl. audio (978-1-55592-329-7(1)) Weston Woods Studios, Inc.

A Weekend with Wendell. 2004. (J). pap. 38.75 incl. audio compact disk (978-1-55592-647-2(9)) Weston Woods Studios, Inc.

Weeks, Sarah. Drip Drop. 2002. (gr. k-3). lib. bdg. 11.80 (978-0-613-44518-4(X)) Tandem Library Bks.

—Pip Squeak. Manning, Jane, illus. 2007. (I Can Read Bks.). 32p. (J). lib. bdg. 16.89 (978-0-06-075637-6(3)); 15.99 (978-0-06-075635-2(7)) HarperCollins Pubs. (Geringer, Laura Book).

Welling, Peter J. Darlene Halloween & the Great Chicago Fire. Welling, Peter J., illus. 2007. 32p. (J). (gr. k-3). 15.95 (***978-1-58980-479-1(1)*** Pelican Publishing Co., Inc.

Wells, Rosemary. Julieta, Estate Quieta! (SPA.). 43p. (J). 5.50 (978-84-372-1523-5(4)) Santillana USA Publishing Co., Inc.

—The Secret Birthday. Nez, John & Wheeler, Jody, illus. 2002. (Yoko & Friends School Days Ser.: No. 7). 32p. (gr. k-2). 9.99 (978-0-7868-0729-1(6)) Hyperion Bks. for Children.

—Shy Charles. 2001. (J). (978-0-606-21432-2(1)); lib. bdg. 14.15 (978-0-613-36076-0(1)) Tandem Library Bks.

Weninger, Brigitte. A Ball for All. Tharlet, Eve, illus. 2006. 32p. (J). (ps-3). 16.99 (978-0-698-40049-8(6) , Minedition) Penguin Group (USA) Inc.

Wheeler, Lisa. One Dark Night. Bates, Ivan, illus. 2006. 32p. (J). reprint ed. pap. 6.00 (978-0-15-205888-3(5) , Voyager Bks./Libros Viajeros) Harcourt Children's Bks.

Wherry, Alwyn. The Hungry Little Mouse. 2006. 17p. (J). 12.08 (978-1-4116-8056-2(1)) Lulu.com.

White, E. B. Le Avventure di Stuart Little.Tr. of Stuart Little. (ITA.). pap. 17.95 (978-88-451-2736-6(2)); 2000. (J). pap. 15.95 (978-88-452-3861-1(X)) Fabbri - RCS Libri ITA. *Dist:* Distribooks, Inc.

—Charlotte's Web/Stuart Little Slipcase, Set. Williams, Garth, illus. collector's gif. ed. 2004. (J). 49.99 (978-0-06-073940-9(1)) HarperCollins Pubs.

—Stuart Little. Date not set. 141p. 18.95 (978-0-8488-2602-4(7)) Amereon LTD.

—Stuart Little. Williams, Garth, illus. 2001. (SPA.). 144p. (gr. 3-5). 22.90 (978-84-204-4669-1(6)) Harcourt Schl. Pubs.

—Stuart Little. Williams, Garth, illus. 2006. (Charming Classics). 144p. (J). pap. 6.99 (978-0-06-082334-4(8) , Harper Festival) HarperCollins Pubs.

—Stuart Little. Williams, Garth & Wells, Rosemary, illus. 60th anniv. ed. 2001. (Stuart-Little Ser.). 144p. (J). (gr. 5 up). pap. 8.99 (978-0-06-441092-2(7)) HarperCollins Pubs.

—Stuart Little. Williams, Garth, illus. 60th collector's anniv. ed. 1999. (Stuart-Little Ser.). 144p. (J). (gr. 4-7). 24.95 (978-0-06-028297-4(5)) HarperCollins Pubs.

—Stuart Little. Williams, Garth, illus. l.t. ed. 2000. (LRS Large Print Cornerstone Ser.). 175p. (J). (gr. 2-8). lib. bdg. 27.95 (978-1-58118-064-0(0) , 23655) LRS.

—Stuart Little. 131p. (J). pap. 5.95 (978-0-8072-8333-2(9)); 2004. (gr. 3-7). pap. 29.00 incl. audio (978-0-8072-8332-5(0) , YA165SP) Random Hse. Audio Publishing Group. (Listening Library).

—Stuart Little. Williams, Garth, illus. (SPA.). 144p. (J). (gr. 3-5). pap. 9.95 (978-1-59437-554-5(2)) Santillana USA Publishing Co., Inc.

—Stuart Little. 2001. (gr. 3-6). lib. bdg. 17.60 (978-0-613-83865-8(3)) Tandem Library Bks.

—Stuart Little: Read-Aloud Edition. Williams, Garth, illus. 1999. (Stuart-Little Ser.). 144p. (J). (gr. 7 up). 19.95 (978-0-06-028334-6(3)) HarperCollins Pubs.

Whose Mouse Are You? 2004. (J). 24.95 incl. audio (978-0-7882-0560-6(9)); pap. 14.95 incl. audio (978-0-7882-0627-6(3)) Weston Woods Studios, Inc.

Whybrow, Ian. Miss Wire's Christmas Surprise. Clark, E., illus. 2007. 48p. (J). (ps-3). pap. 3.95 (***978-0-7534-6136-5(6)*** , Kingfisher) Houghton Mifflin Co. Trade & Reference Div.

Wienski, Vera. Erkuleese & Tobias. 2002. (J). per. 7.99 (978-1-930200-98-2(6)) Martell Publishing Co.

The Wild, Wild West. 2005. (Illus.). 106p. (J). (978-1-4156-0684-1(6)) Scholastic, Inc.

Wilkins, Ken. Marvin's Mansion. 1998. (Illus.). 128p. (J). (ps-1). pap. 10.95 (978-1-57921-129-5(1)) WinePress Publishing.

Williams, G. Walton. Of Mice & Bells. Kollock, John, illus. unabr. ed. 1999. 674p. (J). (gr. k-3). pap. 6.95 (978-0-9703570-1-4(X)) Barksdale Hse. Pr.

Williams, Juliet. Mouse House: An Extravagant Lift-the-Flap Hide-and-Seek Adventure. 2005. (Illus.). 7p. (J). bds. 9.95 (978-1-59354-082-1(5)) Handprint Bks.

Willis, Jeanne. Cottonball Colin. Ross, Tony, illus. 2008. (J). (***978-0-8028-5331-8(5)*** , Eerdmans Bks For Young Readers) Eerdmans, William B. Publishing Co.

Wilsdon, Christina. An Alligator Adventure in Florida. Mayo, Frank, illus. 2006. 26p. (J). 7.99 (978-1-59939-010-9(8) , Reader's Digest Young Families, Inc.) Reader's Digest Children's Publishing, Inc.

—An Amusement Park Mystery in Ohio. Ebert, Len, illus. 2006. 26p. (J). 7.99 (978-1-59939-013-0(2) , Reader's Digest Young Families, Inc.) Reader's Digest Children's Publishing, Inc.

—Lights! Action! California! Hockerman, Dennis, illus. 2006. 26p. (J). 7.99 (978-1-59939-009-3(4) , Reader's Digest Young Families, Inc.) Reader's Digest Children's Publishing, Inc.

—A New York Sailing Adventure. Hockerman, Dennis, illus. 2006. 26p. (J). 7.99 (978-1-59939-014-7(0) , Reader's Digest Young Families, Inc.) Reader's Digest Children's Publishing, Inc.

—On the Trail of Bigfoot in Washington. McCreary, Jane, illus. 2006. 26p. (J). 7.99 (978-1-59939-012-3(4) , Reader's Digest Young Families, Inc.) Reader's Digest Children's Publishing, Inc.

—A Wild Ride in Texas. Jaekel, Susan, illus. 2006. 26p. (J). 7.99 (978-1-59939-011-6(6) , Reader's Digest Young Families, Inc.) Reader's Digest Children's Publishing, Inc.

Wilson, Karma. Mortimer's Christmas Manger. Chapman, Jane, illus. 2005. 40p. (J). 15.95 (978-0-689-85511-5(7) , McElderry, Margaret K.) Simon & Schuster Children's Publishing.

Wilson, Rosalee. Meet Mushy Mouse. 2003. 27 p. pap. 14.95 (978-1-4137-0714-4(9)) PublishAmerica, Inc.

Wise, William. Christopher Mouse. Benson, Patrick, illus. 2006. 160p. (J). pap. 5.95 (978-1-58234-708-0(5) , Bloomsbury Children) Bloomsbury Publishing.

—Christopher Mouse. 2004. (J). (978-1-58234-961-9(4)) Bloomsbury Publishing.

—Christopher Mouse: The Tale of a Small Traveler. Benson, Patrick, tr. Benson, Patrick, illus. 2004. 154p. (J). (gr. 2-5). 15.95 (978-1-58234-878-0(2) , Bloomsbury Children) Bloomsbury Publishing.

Wisniewski, David. Sumo Mouse. Wisniewski, David, illus. 2002. (Illus.). 32p. (J). (ps-3). 16.95 (978-0-8118-3492-6(1)) Chronicle Bks. LLC.

—Sumo Mouse. Wisniewski, David, illus. 2004. (Illus.). 26p. (J). (gr. k-4). reprint ed. 17.00 (978-0-7567-8506-2(5)) DIANE Publishing Co.

Wolf, Jackie. Picture Me Peek-A-Boo Farm. 2002. (Peek-a-Boo Ser.). (Illus.). 10p. (J). (ps up). bds. 4.99 (978-1-57151-595-7(X)) Playhouse Publishing.

Wolkstein, Diane. Little Mouse's Painting. 2002. (gr. k-3). lib. bdg. 14.10 (978-0-613-63049-8(1)) Tandem Library Bks.

Wood, Don. The Little Mouse, the Red Ripe Strawberry & the Big Hungry Bear. Wood, Don, illus. 2002. (Illus.). 14.79 (978-1-4046-0467-4(7)) Book Wholesalers, Inc.

Wood, Don & Wood, Audrey. Merry Christmas: Big Hungry Bear! Wood, Don, illus. 2002. (Illus.). 48p. (J). (gr. k-2). pap. 15.95 (978-0-439-32092-4(5) , Blue Sky Pr., The) Scholastic, Inc.

Wood, Robert E. The Mouse Who Wanted to Stay in the Trap. 1999. (Illus.). 28p. (J). (ps-7). 16.95 (978-1-892458-04-9(7)) Life's Footprints, Inc.

Wormell, Christopher. George & the Dragon. 2006. (Illus.). 32p. (J). (gr. k-3). 16.95 (978-0-375-83315-1(3) , Knopf Bks. for Young Readers) Random Hse. Children's Bks.

Wormell, Christopher. George, the Dragon & the Princess: 2008. (Illus.). 32p. (J). 16.95 (***978-0-224-07072-0(X)***) Transworld Publishers Ltd. GBR. *Dist:* Independent Pubs. Group.

Wright, Al & Clarke, Roger. Do Mice Eat Rice? 2005. (Illus.). 32p. (J). 12.95 (978-0-8048-3643-2(4)) Tuttle Publishing.

Wynne-Jones, Tim. Ned Mouse Breaks Away. Petricic, Dusan, illus. 2003. 68p. (J). (gr. 3 up). 14.95 (978-0-88899-474-5(5)) Groundwood Bks. CAN. *Dist:* Perseus Distribution.

Wynne-Jones, Tim & Petricic, Dusan. Ned Mouse Breaks Away. 2004. (Illus.). 68p. (J). pap. 5.95 (978-0-88899-594-0(6)) Groundwood Bks. CAN. *Dist:* Perseus Distribution.

Yamada, Utako. The Story of Cherry the Pig. Yamada, Utako, illus. 2007. (Illus.). 32p. (J). 15.95 (978-1-933605-25-8(1) , 05258) Kane/Miller Bk. Pubs., Inc.

Yang, Stella, illus. My Family: Individual Title Six-Packs. (Sails Literacy Ser.). 16p. (gr. k up). 27.00 (978-0-7635-4393-8(4)) Rigby Education.

Yarbrough, Elizabeth. The World of J. J. Mouse. Ragsdale, Cathy, illus. 2001. (J). (gr. k-5). lib. bdg. 14.95 (978-0-9705727-5-2(1)) Coastal Publishing Carolina, Inc.

Yee, Brenda Shannon. Hide & Seek. Tilley, Debbie, illus. 2001. 32p. (J). (ps). pap. 15.95 (978-0-531-30302-3(0) , Orchard Bks.) Scholastic, Inc.

Yee, Wong Herbert. Abracadabra! Magic with Mouse & Mole. 2007. 48p. (J). (gr. k-3). 15.00 (***978-0-618-75926-2(3)***) Houghton Mifflin Co.

—Here Come Train Mice! 2000. (Illus.). 9p. (J). (gr. k ps). bds. 4.95 (978-0-395-98401-7(7)) Houghton Mifflin Co. Trade & Reference Div.

—Hooray for Truckmice! 2000. (Illus.). 8p. (J). (gr. k-ps). bds. 4.95 (978-0-395-98404-8(1)) Houghton Mifflin Co. Trade & Reference Div.

—Upstairs Mouse, Downstairs Mole. 2005. (Illus.). 48p. (J). (gr. k-3). 15.00 (978-0-618-47313-7(0)) Houghton Mifflin Co. Trade & Reference Div.

Yee, Wong Herbert. Upstairs Mouse Downstairs Mole. 12th ed. 2007. (Illus.). 48p. (J). (gr. 1-5). 3.99 (***978-0-618-91586-6(9)***) Houghton Mifflin Co. Trade & Reference Div.

Yeoman, John A. Mouse Trouble. (Illus.). 32p. (J). 19.95 (978-0-241-02248-1(7) , Hamilton, Hamish) Penguin Bks., Ltd. GBR. *Dist:* Trafalgar Square Publishing.

Yolen, Jane. Beneath the Ghost Moon. 2001. (J). pap. 16.90 incl. audio (978-0-8045-6833-3(2) , 6833) Spoken Arts, Inc.

Yost-Filgate, Susan. Rip Squeak & His Friends. Filgate, Leonard, illus. 2005. 32p. (J). (ps-3). 14.99 (978-0-9747825-0-8(5)) Rip Squeak, Inc.

—Rip Squeak & His Friends: An Introduction to the Roaring Adventures of Rip Squeak. Filgate, Leonard, illus. 2nd deluxe collector's gif. ed. 1999. (GER.). 64p. 35.00 (978-0-9672422-0-0(7)) Rip Squeak, Inc.

—Rip Squeak & His Friends Discover the Treasure. Filgate, Leonard, illus. 2005. 32p. (J). 16.95 (978-0-9672422-2-4(3)) Rip Squeak, Inc.

Young, Ed. Siete Ratones Ciegos. Uribe, Veronica, tr. Young, Ed, illus. 2001. (SPA., Illus.). 40p. (J). pap. (978-980-257-255-7(1)) Ekare, Ediciones.

Ziefert, H. & Bolam, Emily. Sometimes Buzzy Shares. 2005. (Illus.). 24p. 9.95 (978-1-59354-069-2(8)) Blue Apple Bks.

Ziefert, Harriet. The Best Smelling Christmas Book Ever: 9 Scents to Scratch & Sniff! Rader, Laura, illus. 2004. 18p. (J). (gr. k-4). reprint ed. 13.00 (978-0-7567-7600-8(7)) DIANE Publishing Co.

—Presents for Santa. Rader, Laura, illus. 2000. (Easy-to-Read Ser.). 32p. (J). (gr. k-3). 13.89 (978-0-670-88390-5(5) , Viking Juvenile) Penguin Group (USA) Inc.

—What Is Mother's Day? Schumacher, Claire, illus. 2006. 16p. pap. 5.95 (978-1-4027-2398-8(9)) Sterling Publishing Co., Inc.

—What's a Vacation? Schumacher, Claire, illus. 2006. 16p. pap. 5.95 (978-1-4027-2400-8(4)) Sterling Publishing Co., Inc.

MICHELANGELO BUONARROTI, 1475-1564

Carvalho de Magalhaes, Roberto. Michelangelo. 2005. (Great Artists Ser.). (Illus.). 40p. (J). (gr. 4-7). pap. 7.95 (978-1-59270-049-3(7)) Enchanted Lion Bks., LLC.

Connolly, Sean & Michelangelo Buonarroti. Michelangelo. 2004. (Lives of the Artists Ser.). (Illus.). 48p. (J). (gr. 5 up). pap. 29.26 (978-0-8368-5605-7(8)); lib. bdg. 30.00 (978-0-8368-5600-2(7)) Stevens, Gareth Inc. (World Almanac Library).

Cook, Diane. Michelangelo: Renaissance Artist. 2002. (Great Names Ser.). (Illus.). 32p. (J). (gr. 3 up). lib. bdg. (978-1-59084-156-3(5)) Mason Crest Pubs.

De Salvia, Maria Siponta. Michelangelo. 2003. (Great Artists Ser.). (Illus.). 40p. (J). 15.95 (978-1-59270-008-0(X)) Enchanted Lion Bks., LLC.

Di Cagno, Gabriela. Miguel Angel: Los Desafios del Genio. 2000. (Maestros del Arte Ser.).Tr. of Michael Angelo. (SPA., Illus.). 64p. (J). (gr. 4-7). 22.95 (978-84-88061-79-9(X)) Serres, Ediciones, S. L. ESP. *Dist:* Lectorum Pubns., Inc.

Di Cagno, Gabriella. Michelangelo. 2008. (YA). lib. bdg. 24.95 net. (***978-1-934545-01-0(5)***) Oliver Pr., Inc.

Hart, Tony. Michelangelo. Hellard, Susan, illus. 2002. (Ninos Famosos Ser.). (SPA & ENG.). 24p. (gr. 1-5). pap. 6.95 (978-85-7416-165-5(9)) Callis Editora Ltda BRA. *Dist:* Independent Pubs. Group.

Langley, Andrew. Michelangelo. 2003. (Raintree Biographies Ser.). (Illus.). 32p. (J). (ps-ps). pap. 7.50 (978-1-4109-0070-8(3)); lib. bdg. 25.70 (978-0-7398-6864-5(0)) Raintree.

—Michelangelo. 2003. (gr. 3-6). lib. bdg. 15.90 (978-0-613-78166-4(X)) Tandem Library Bks.

Mattern, Joanne. Michelangelo. 2005. (Checkerboard Biography Library). (Illus.). 32p. (J). (gr. k-6). lib. bdg. 22.78 (978-1-59197-845-9(9)) ABDO Publishing Co.

McNeese, Tim. Michelangelo: Painter, Sculptor & Architect. 2005. (Makers of the Middle Ages & Renaissance Ser.). (Illus.). 148p. (J). (gr. 4-8). lib. bdg. 30.00 (978-0-7910-8627-8(5) , Chelsea Hse.) Facts On File, Inc.

Nichols, Catherine. Michelangelo Buonarroti. 2006. (Primary Source Library of Famous Artists). (Illus.). 32p. (J). 21.95 (978-1-4042-2763-7(6) , PowerKids Pr.) Rosen Publishing Group, Inc., The.

Quill, Charles G. Michelangelo: His Life & Art. 2002. (Reading Room Collection). (Illus.). 24p. (J). lib. bdg. 18.75 (978-0-8239-3749-3(6)) Rosen Publishing Group, Inc., The.

Rebman, Renee C. The Sistine Chapel. 2000. (Building History Ser.). (Illus.). 96p. (YA). (gr. 6-9). 28.70 (978-1-56006-640-8(7) , Lucent Bks.) Thomson Gale.

Richard Tames. Michelangelo Buonarroti. 2nd ed. 2006. (Heinemann First Library). (Illus.). 32p. (J). pap. (***978-1-4034-8505-2(4)***) Heinemann Library.

Richmond, Robin. Introducing Michelangelo. 2002. (Introducing Painters Ser.). (Illus.). 32p. (J). lib. bdg. 24.25 (978-1-931983-43-3(7)) Chrysalis Education.

Sateren, Shelley Swanson. Michaelangelo. 2002. (Masterpieces). (Illus.). 24p. (J). (gr. 2-3). lib. bdg. 18.60 (978-0-7368-1125-5(7) , Bridgestone Bks.) Capstone Pr., Inc.

Somervill, Barbara A. Michelangelo: Sculptor & Painter. 2004. (Signature Lives Ser.). (Illus.). 112p. (J). 30.60 (978-0-7565-0814-2(2)) Compass Point Bks.

Stanley, Diane. Michelangelo. Stanley, Diane, illus. (Illus.). 48p. (J). 2003. (gr. 2 up). pap. 6.99 (978-0-06-052113-4(9)); 2000. (gr. 3 up). 17.99 (978-0-688-15085-3(3)) HarperCollins Pubs.

—Michelangelo. 2003. (gr. 3-6). lib. bdg. 15.30 (978-0-613-65700-6(4)) Tandem Library Bks.

Tames, Richard. Michelangelo Buonarroti. 2000. (Life & Work of. . . Ser.). (Illus.). 32p. (J). (gr. k-2). pap. 21.36 (978-1-57572-343-3(3)) Heinemann Library.

Tames, Richard. Michelangelo Buonarroti. 2006. (Heinemann First Library). (Illus.). 32p. (J). lib. bdg. (***978-1-4034-8494-9(5)***) Heinemann Library.

Whiting, Jim. Michelangelo. 2007. (Art Profiles for Kids Ser.). (Illus.). 48p. (J). lib. bdg. 29.95 (***978-1-58415-562-1(0)***) Mitchell Lane Pubs., Inc.

Wilkinson, Philip. Michelangelo: The Young Artist Who Dreamed of Perfection. 2006. (Illus.). 64p. (J). (gr. 3-7). 27.90 (978-0-7922-5534-5(8)); 17.95 (978-0-7922-5533-8(X)) National Geographic Society. (National Geographic Children's Bks.).

MICHELANGELO BUONARROTI, 1475-1564—FICTION

Brezina. Who Can Open Michelangelo's Seven Seals? (Illus.). 112p. (***978-3-7913-3555-1(3)***) Prestel Verlag, Germany.

Hi-stories presents Michelangelo Bunnyrroti. 2006. (J). bds. 14.99 (978-0-9763233-2-7(X)) Little Germ That Could-...Creations, Inc., The.

Jacobson, Rick. The Master's Apprentice. Jacobson, Rick & Fernandez, Laura, illus. 2008. 32p. 18.95 (***978-0-88776-783-8(4)***) Tundra Bks., Inc./Livres Toundra, Inc. CAN. *Dist:* Random Hse. of Canada, Ltd.

MICHIGAN

Abramowski, Christina. Something Special. (Illus.). 32p. (J). (gr. 2-4). 9.95 (978-0-9634927-0-8(5)) Junior League of Grand Rapids Michigan, Inc.

Appleford, Annie. M Is for Mitten: A Michigan Alphabet. Monroe, Michael G., illus. 1999. 40p. (J). (ps-3). 16.95 (978-1-886947-73-3(2)) Sleeping Bear Pr.

Aretha, David. Michigan: A MyReportLinks.com Book. 2003. (States Ser.). (Illus.). 48p. (J). lib. bdg. 25.26 (978-0-7660-5154-6(4) , MyReportLinks.com Bks.) Enslow Pubs., Inc.

Arrathoon, Leigh A. Holland, Michigan. pap. (978-1-893047-03-7(2)) Paint Creek Pr., Ltd.

Arrathoon, Leigh A. & Davio, John. Jody's Travelbooks for Kids Vol. I: Frankenmuth, Michigan. Morris, Jeanne L., illus. 48p. (J). (gr. 2-6). pap. 4.95 (978-0-9648564-7-9(6)) Paint Creek Pr., Ltd.

—Jody's Travelbooks for Kids Vol. II: Holland, Michigan. Morris, Jeanne L., illus. 48p. (J). (gr. 2-6). pap. 4.95 (978-0-9648564-8-6(4)) Paint Creek Pr., Ltd.

—Jody's Travelbooks for Kids Vol. III: Mackinaw, Michigan. Morris, Jeanne L., illus. 48p. (J). (gr. 2-6). pap. 4.95 (978-0-9648564-9-3(2)) Paint Creek Pr., Ltd.

Barenblat, Rachel. Michigan: The Wolverine State. 2002. (World Almanac Library of the States). (Illus.). 48p. (J). (gr. 5 up). pap. 14.95 (978-0-8368-5287-5(7)); lib. bdg. 30.00 (978-0-8368-5117-5(X)) Stevens, Gareth Inc. (World Almanac Library).

—Michigan: The Wolverine State. 2002. (gr. 5-8). lib. bdg. 24.15 (978-0-613-52445-2(4)) Tandem Library Bks.

Binstadt, Chari Yost. Up North in Michigan. Scott, Ken, photos by. 2002. 48p. (J). (ps-5). reprint ed. 19.95 (978-0-9712904-0-2(7)) Duneside Pr.

—Up North in Michigan. Scott, Ken, photos by. 2000. (Illus.). 32p. (J). (ps-7). 19.95 (978-0-9662399-7-3(0)) Petunia Pr., Inc.

Bower, Gary. I'm a Michigan Kid! Bower, Jan, illus. 2005. 48p. (J). 17.99 (978-0-9704621-6-9(6)) Storybook Meadow Publishing.

Brill, Marlene Targ. Michigan. (Celebrate the States Ser.). 1998. (Illus.). 144p. (gr. 4-8). lib. bdg. 37.07 (978-0-7614-0418-7(X)); 2nd ed. 2007. (J). lib. bdg. 39.93 (978-0-7614-2351-5(6)) Cavendish, Marshall Corp. (Benchmark Bks.).

Brown, Jonatha A. & DuBois, Muriel L. Michigan. 2005. (Portraits of the States Ser.). (Illus.). 32p. (J). (ps-17). lib. bdg. 23.33 (978-0-8368-4627-0(3)) Stevens, Gareth Inc.

Brown, Michael S., Jr. Berrien County Michigan - Photos & Memories. 2002. (Illus.). 50p. (J). 14.95 (978-0-9661776-1-9(4)) Bluebird Meadows.

Capstone Press Staff, contrib. by. Michigan. rev. ed. 2002. (One Nation Ser.). (Illus.). 48p. (J). (gr. 3-4). lib. bdg. 22.60 (978-0-7368-1246-7(6) , Bridgestone Bks.) Capstone Pr., Inc.

Craats, Rennay. A Guide to Michigan. 2001. (American States Ser.). 32p. (J). lib. bdg. 16.95 (978-1-930954-64-9(6)) Weigl Pubs., Inc.

Dubois, Muriel L. & Brown, Jonatha A. Michigan. 2005. (Portraits of the States Ser.). (Illus.). 32p. (J). pap. (978-0-8368-4646-1(X)) Stevens, Gareth Inc.

Fix, Alexandra. All Around Michigan: Regions & Resources. 2003. (Heinemann State Studies). (Illus.). 48p. (J). 27.07 (978-1-4034-0658-3(8)) Heinemann Library.

Georgiady, Nicholas P., et al. Michigan Historical Sights, Vol. 4. Merritt, Bernard E., Jr., illus. 2nd rev. ed. 1998. 30p. (J). (gr. 4-8). pap. 4.50 (978-0-917961-10-6(2)) Argee Pubs.

—Michigan Men, Vol. 2. Schimmels, John H., illus. 2nd ed. 1998. 32p. (J). (gr. 4-8). reprint ed. pap. 4.50 (978-0-917961-07-6(2)) Argee Pubs.

—Michigan Women, Vol. 1. Nixon, Buford, illus. 2nd rev. ed. 1998. 32p. (J). (gr. 4-8). pap. 4.50 (978-0-917961-08-3(0)) Argee Pubs.

—Michigan's First Settlers: The Indians - Native Americans, Vol. 3. Nixon, Buford, illus. 2nd rev. ed. 1998. 31p. (J). (gr. 4-8). pap. 4.50 (978-0-917961-09-0(9)) Argee Pubs.

Haney, Johannah. Michigan. 2005. (It's My State! Ser.). (Illus.). 79p. (J). 27.07 (978-0-7614-1861-0(X) , Benchmark Bks.) Cavendish, Marshall Corp.

Heinrichs, Ann. Massachusetts. 2003. (This Land Is Your Land Ser.). (Illus.). 48p. (J). (gr. 3 up). lib. bdg. 22.60 (978-0-7565-0323-9(X)) Compass Point Bks.

—Michigan. 2003. (This Land Is Your Land Ser.). (Illus.). 48p. (J). (gr. 3 up). lib. bdg. 22.60 (978-0-7565-0314-7(0)) Compass Point Bks.

Henry, Ragene. The Time of the Shining Rocks: A Time Travel Adventure into Upper Michigan History. 1999. (Illus.). 100p. (J). (gr. 4-6). pap. 9.95 (978-0-9670743-0-6(4)) Chickadee Pr.

Johnson, Elizabeth M. Michigan. 2002. (From Sea to Shining Sea Ser.: 2). (Illus.). 80p. (J). (gr. 3-5). 30.50 (978-0-516-22316-2(X) , Children's Pr.) Scholastic Library Publishing.

Kammeraad, Kevin. A Curious Glimpse of Michigan. 2004. (Illus.). (J). 19.95 (978-0-9712692-9-3(7)) EDCO Publishing, Inc.

Kammeraad, Kevin & Kammeraad, Stephanie. A Curious Glimpse of Michigan. Kammeraad, Kevin & Hipp, Ryan, illus. 2006. (J). per. 9.95 (***978-0-9749412-9-5(8)***) EDCO Publishing, Inc.

Knox, Barbara. Michigan. 2003. (Land of Liberty Ser.). (Illus.). 64p. (J). (gr. 3-4). lib. bdg. 23.93 (978-0-7368-1590-1(2) , Bridgestone Bks.) Capstone Pr., Inc.

L Is for Ludington: An alphabet book about Ludington, MI created by Children. 2006. (J). pap. 10.00 (978-0-9786128-0-1(9)) Bosse, Andre Ctr.

Lewis, Anne Margaret & Campbell, Janis. Hidden Michigan. Popko, Wendy, illus. 2006. 40p. (J). (978-1-934133-01-9(9)) Mackinac Island Pr., Inc.

Mader, Jan. Michigan. 2003. (Rookie Read-About Geography Ser.). (gr. 1-2). pap. 5.95 (978-0-516-27781-3(2)); (Illus.). 32p. (J). 20.50 (978-0-516-22736-8(X)) Scholastic Library Publishing. (Children's Pr.).

—Michigan. 2003. (gr. k-3). lib. bdg. 14.10 (978-0-613-67914-5(8)) Tandem Library Bks.

Marsh, Carole. The Magnificent Michigan Coloring Book. 2004. (Michigan Experience! Ser.). (Illus.). 32p. (J). (gr. k-2). pap. 3.95 (978-0-7933-9567-5(4)) Gallopade International.

—Michigan Classic Christmas Trivia. 2002. (Carole Marsh Michigan Bks.). (Illus.). 32p. pap. 6.95 (978-0-635-01411-5(4) , 14114); lib. bdg. 21.95 (978-0-635-01412-2(2) , 14122) Gallopade International. (Marsh, Carole Bks.).

—Michigan Current Events Projects: 30 Cool, Activities, Crafts, Experiments & More for Kids to Do to Learn about Your State! 2003. (Michigan Experience Ser.). 32p. (gr. k-8). pap. 5.95 (978-0-635-02041-3(6) , Marsh, Carole Bks.) Gallopade International.

—The Michigan Experience Library State: Resoruce Set. 2001. (Illus.). (J). (gr. k-8). pap. 100.20 incl. cd-rom (978-0-635-00475-8(5)) Gallopade International.

—The Michigan Experience Pocket Guide. 2004. (Michigan Experience! Ser.). (Illus.). 96p. (J). (gr. 3-8). pap. 6.95 (978-0-7933-9562-0(3)) Gallopade International.

—Michigan Geography Projects: 30 Cool, Activities, Crafts, Experiments & More for Kids to Do to Learn about Your State! 2003. (Michigan Experience Ser.). 32p. (gr. k-5). pap. 5.95 (978-0-635-01841-0(1) , Marsh, Carole Bks.) Gallopade International.

—Michigan Government Projects: 30 Cool, Activities, Crafts, Experiments & More for Kids to Do to Learn about Your State! 2003. (Michigan Experience Ser.). 32p. (gr. k-5). pap. 5.95 (978-0-635-01941-7(8) , Marsh, Carole Bks.) Gallopade International.

—Michigan Jeopardy! Answers & Questions about Our State! 2004. (Michigan Experience! Ser.). (Illus.). 32p. (J). (gr. 3-8). pap. 7.95 (978-0-7933-9564-4(X)) Gallopade International.

—Michigan "Jography" A Fun Run Thru Our State! 2004. (Michigan Experience! Ser.). (Illus.). 32p. (J). (gr. 3-8). pap. 7.95 (978-0-7933-9565-1(8)) Gallopade International.

—Michigan Millionaire: Game Book. 2001. (Carole Marsh Michigan Bks.). (Illus.). 32p. (J). (gr. 3-8). pap., act. bk. ed. 9.95 (978-0-635-00060-6(1)) Gallopade International.

—Michigan People Projects: 30 Cool, Activities, Crafts, Experiments & More for Kids to Do to Learn about Your State! 2003. (Michigan Experience Ser.). 32p. (gr. k-5). pap. 5.95 (978-0-635-01991-2(4) , Marsh, Carole Bks.) Gallopade International.

—Michigan Survivor: Game Book. 2001. (Carole Marsh Michigan Bks.). (Illus.). 32p. (J). (gr. 3-8). pap., act. bk. ed. 9.95 (978-0-635-00543-4(3)) Gallopade International.

—Michigan Symbols & Facts Projects: 30 Cool, Activities, Crafts, Experiments & More for Kids to Do to Learn about Your State! 2003. (Michigan Experience Ser.). 32p. (gr. k-5). pap. 5.95 (978-0-635-01891-5(8) , Marsh, Carole Bks.) Gallopade International.

—Michigan's Big Activity Book. 2004. (Michigan Experience! Ser.). (Illus.). 96p. (J). (gr. 2-6). pap. 9.95 (978-0-7933-9566-8(6)) Gallopade International.

—My First Book about Michigan. 2004. (Michigan Experience! Ser.). (Illus.). 32p. (J). (gr. k-4). pap. 7.95 (978-0-7933-9563-7(1)) Gallopade International.

—The Survivor: A Class Challenge. 2001. (Carole Marsh Michigan Bks.). lib. bdg. 29.95 (978-0-635-00668-4(5)) Gallopade International.

—Texas's Big Activity Book. 2004. (Texas Experience! Ser.). (Illus.). 96p. (J). (gr. 2-6). pap. 9.95 (978-0-7933-9465-4(1)) Gallopade International.

McAuliffe, Emily. Michigan Facts & Symbols. (States & Their Symbols Ser.). 24p. (J). 1998. (Illus.). (gr. 2-3). lib. bdg. 18.60 (978-0-7368-0083-9(2) , Bridgestone Bks.); 2003. lib. bdg. 19.93 (978-0-7368-2252-7(6)) Capstone Pr., Inc.

McConnell, David B. Our Michigan Adventure. McConnell, Stella M., ed. 1998. (Illus.). 282p. (J). (gr. 3-4). 30.95 (978-0-910726-35-1(3) , 35-3) Hillsdale Educational Pubs., Inc.

McNamara, Connie. My First Michigan State Words GO STATE. 2004. (J). bds. 11.95 (978-0-9743244-3-2(4)) Shamrock Publishing, Inc.

—My First Michigan Words. 2004. (J). bds. 11.95 (978-0-9743244-6-3(9)) Shamrock Publishing, Inc.

Michigan. 2000. (Switched on Schoolhouse Ser.). (Illus.). (YA). (gr. 7-12). pap. 24.95 incl. cd-rom (978-0-7403-0274-9(4) , SOSMI) Alpha Omega Pubns., Inc.

Michigan - Eastern Upper Penninsula Fishing Map Guide: Lake Maps & Fishing Information for over 250 Lakes Plus Great Lake Coverage Including the Following Counties: Alger, Chippewa, Delta, Luce, Mackinac, Marquette & Schoolcraft. 2002. (Illus.). 208p. (YA). spiral bd. 21.95 (978-1-885010-56-8(7)) Sportsman's Connection.

Michigan - Northwestern Fishing Map Guide: Lake Maps & Fisihing Information for over 130 Lakes Plus Lake Huron & Lake Michigan Covering the Counties of Antrim, Benzie, Charlevoix, Cheboygan, Emmet, Grand Traverse, Kalkaska, Leelanau & Otesgo. 2002. (Illus.). 184p. (YA). spiral bd. 21.95 (978-1-885010-54-4(0)) Sportsman's Connection.

Michigan - Southeastern Fishing Map Guide: Lake Maps & Fishing Information for about 200 Lakes Plus Lake Erie, Detroit & St. Claire Rivers Covering the Counties of Clinton, Genesee Hillsdale, Ingham, Jackson, Lapeer, Lenawee, Livingston, Macomb, Oakland, St. Clair, Washtenaw & Wayne. 2002. (Illus.). 200p. (YA). spiral bd. 21.95 (978-1-885010-51-3(6)) Sportsman's Connection.

Michigan - Southwestern Fishing Map Guide: Lake Maps & Fishing Information for over 180 Lake Plus Lake Michigan Covering the Counties of Ionia, Kent, Manistee, Mason, Mecosta, Missaukee, Muskegon, Newaygo, Oceana, Osceola & Wexford. 2002. (Illus.). 192p. (YA). spiral bd. 21.95 (978-1-885010-50-6(8)) Sportsman's Connection.

Michigan - West Central Fishing Map Guide. 2002. (Illus.). 192p. (YA). spiral bd. 21.95 (978-1-885010-52-0(4)) Sportsman's Connection.

Michigan - Western Upper Penninsula Fishing Map Guide. 2002. (Illus.). (YA). spiral bd. 21.95 (978-1-885010-55-1(9)) Sportsman's Connection.

Murray, Julie. Michigan. 2006. (Buddy Book Ser.). (Illus.). 32p. (J). (gr. k-4). lib. bdg. 22.78 (978-1-59197-681-3(2) , Buddy Bks.) ABDO Publishing Co.

Obregon, Jose Maria. Michigan. Brusca, Maria Cristina, tr. 2005. (Bilingual Library of the United States of America: Set 1). (ENG & SPA., Illus.). 32p. (J). (gr. 2-5). lib. bdg. 22.50 (978-1-4042-3087-3(4) , Buenas Letra) Rosen Publishing Group, Inc., The.

Raatma, Lucia. Michigan. 2007. (America the Beautiful, Third Ser.). (Illus.). 144p. (YA). (gr. 5-8). lib. bdg. 38.00 (***978-0-531-18562-9(1)*** , Children's Pr.) Scholastic Library Publishing.

Riggs, Kate. Michigan. 2008. (J). (***978-1-58341-647-1(1)*** , Creative Education) Creative Co., The.

Schonberg, Marcia. All Around Michigan. 2003. (Heinemann State Studies). (Illus.). 48p. (J). 8.50 (978-1-4034-2676-5(7)) Heinemann Library.

—Michigan Plants & Animals. 2003. (Heinemann State Studies). (Illus.). 48p. (J). 27.07 (978-1-4034-0662-0(6)); pap. 8.50 (978-1-4034-2679-6(1)) Heinemann Library.

—Uniquely Michigan. 2003. (Heinemann State Studies). (Illus.). 48p. (J). pap. 8.50 (978-1-4034-2681-9(3)) Heinemann Library.

Sirvaitis, Karen. Michigan. 2nd rev. exp. ed. 2002. (Hello U. S. A. Ser.). (Illus.). 84p. (J). (gr. 3-6). lib. bdg. 25.26 (978-0-8225-4085-4(1)) Lerner Publishing Group.

—Michigan. rev. ed. 2002. (gr. 3-6). lib. bdg. 15.25 (978-0-613-46089-7(8)) Tandem Library Bks.

Stewart, Jacqueline. The Glaciers' Treasure Trove: A Field Guide to the Lake Michigan Riviera. 2003. (Illus.). 155p. spiral bd. 19.95 (978-0-9727484-7-6(4)) Lexicus Pr.

Thieda, Nichole. Uniquely Michigan. 2003. (Heinemann State Studies). (Illus.). 48p. (J). 27.07 (978-1-4034-0663-7(4)) Heinemann Library.

Wargin, Kathy-Jo. Look & See with Me: Michigan. 2007. (J). 13.95 (***978-1-58536-323-0(5)***) Sleeping Bear Pr.

MICHIGAN—FICTION

Arthur M. Winfi Staff. Rover Boys on the Great Lakes or the Sec. 2006. 63.99 (***978-1-4219-9685-1(5)***) IndyPublish.com.

Aryal, Aimee. Let's Go Blue! Perez, Gerry, illus. 2004. (J). (978-1-932888-19-5(5)) Mascot Bks., Inc.

Baumer, Dawn McVay, creator. Dune Daze: Silver Lake. 2004. (Illus.). (J). (978-0-9754960-0-8(X)) Butters Pr.

Bellairs, John. The House with a Clock in Its Walls. Gorey, Edward, illus. 2004. (Lewis Barnavelt Ser.). 192p. (J). pap. 5.99 (978-0-14-240257-3(5) , Puffin) Penguin Group (USA) Inc.

—The House with a Clock in Its Walls. 179p. (J). (gr. 4-6). pap. 4.50 (978-0-8072-1423-7(X) , Listening Library) Random Hse. Audio Publishing Group.

Bury, Laurie D. The Adventures of Dalbert Juan: Enjoying Michigan. Gallo, Karen A., illus. 2000. (J). 12.95 (978-0-9702319-1-8(1)) Rhette Enterprises, Inc.

Carr, Annie Roe. Nan Sherwoods Winter Holidays or Rescuin. 2007. pap. (***978-1-4065-1296-0(6)***) Dodo Pr.

Comerford, Kevin. Halcyon. 2003. 158p. pap. 19.95 (978-1-4137-0675-8(4)) PublishAmerica, Inc.

Cory, Kim Delmar. Home to Mackinac: The Tale of Young Jack Murphy's Discovery of Loyalty, Family & Forgiveness. Evans, Laura, illus. 2007. 175p. (J). pap. 9.95 (978-0-911872-87-3(6)) Mackinac State Historic Parks.

—Lilly's Way. Austin, Jane G., ed. 1998. 187p. (YA). (gr. 4-6). 9.99 (978-0-88092-363-7(6) , 3636) Royal Fireworks Publishing Co.

Costello, Emily. Calling the Shots. 1999. (Soccer Stars Ser.: No. 7). (J). (gr. 3-7). (978-0-606-17152-6(5)) Tandem Library Bks.

Curtis, Christopher Paul. Bucking the Sarge. (YA). (gr. 7). 2004. 272p. lib. bdg. 17.99 (978-0-385-90159-8(3) , Lamb, Wendy); 2006. 288p. reprint ed. mass mkt. 6.50 (978-0-440-41331-8(1) , Laurel Leaf) Random Hse. Children's Bks.

—Bucking the Sarge. l.t. ed. 2005. 325p. 23.95 (978-0-7862-7148-1(5) , Large Print Pr.) Thorndike Pr.

—Bud, Not Buddy. 1999. (Illus.). 256p. (J). (gr. 4-7). 16.95 (978-0-385-32306-2(9) , Delacorte Bks. for Young Readers) Random Hse. Children's Bks.

—Bud, Not Buddy. l.t. ed. 2000. (Illus.). 279p. (J). (gr. 8-12). 22.95 (978-0-7862-2574-3(2)) Thorndike Pr.

—Mr. Chickee's Funny Money. 160p. (J). (gr. 4-7). 6.50 (978-0-440-22919-3(7) , Yearling); 2005. (Illus.). (J). (gr. 3-7). 15.95 (978-0-385-32772-5(2) , Lamb, Wendy); 2005. (Illus.). (J). (gr. 3-7). lib. bdg. 17.99 (978-0-385-90936-5(5) , Lamb, Wendy) Random Hse. Children's Bks.

—Mr. Chickee's Funny Money. l.t. ed. 2006. 190p. 23.95 (978-0-7862-8670-6(9)) Thorndike Pr.

—Mr. Chickee's Messy Mission. 240p. (J). (gr. 4-7). 2008. 6.50 (***978-0-440-22922-3(7)*** , Yearling); 2007. (Illus.). 15.99 (978-0-385-32775-6(7) , Lamb, Wendy) Random Hse. Children's Bks.

Curtis, Christopher Paul. The Watsons Go to Birmingham - 1963. 2002. (Illus.). (J). 14.47 (978-0-7587-0328-6(7)) Book Wholesalers, Inc.

—The Watsons Go to Birmingham - 1963. 1998. 15p. pap., stu. ed., tchr.'s training gde. ed. 15.95 (978-1-58303-068-4(9)) Pathways Publishing.

—The Watsons Go to Birmingham - 1963. 210p. (YA). (gr. 5 up). pap. 5.50 (978-0-8072-8336-3(3)); 2004. (J). (gr. 4 up). pap. 38.00 incl. audio (978-0-8072-8335-6(5) , YA166SP) Random Hse. Audio Publishing Group. (Listening Library).

—The Watsons Go to Birmingham - 1963. 2000. 224p. (YA). (gr. 5-7). pap. 6.50 (978-0-440-22800-4(X) , Laurel Leaf) Random Hse. Children's Bks.

—The Watsons Go to Birmingham - 1963. 2000. (gr. 5-8). lib. bdg. 14.15 (978-0-613-85111-4(0)) Tandem Library Bks.

—The Watsons Go to Birmingham - 1963. l.t. ed. 2004. 254p. pap. 10.95 (978-0-7862-6406-3(3)) Thorndike Pr.

Day, Karen. No Cream Puffs. 2008. 160p. (J). (gr. 5). 15.99 (***978-0-375-83775-3(2)***); lib. bdg. 18.99 (***978-0-375-93775-0(7)***) Random Hse. Children's Bks. (Lamb, Wendy).

Giff, Patricia Reilly. Willow Run. 160p. (J). (gr. 4-7). 2007. pap. 5.99 (978-0-440-23801-0(3) , Yearling); 2005. 15.95 (978-0-385-73067-9(5) , Lamb, Wendy); 2005. lib. bdg. 17.99 (978-0-385-90096-6(1) , Lamb, Wendy) Random Hse. Children's Bks.

Hahn, Cathe. Step Up! Artley, Bob, illus. 2005. 32p. (J). 15.95 (978-1-58980-214-8(4)) Pelican Publishing Co., Inc.

Holt, Rinehart and Winston Staff. The Watsons Go to Birmingham: With Connections. 1998. pap., stu. ed. 13.20 (978-0-03-054049-3(6)) Holt, Rinehart & Winston.

Howard, Ellen. The Log Cabin Wedding. Himler, Ronald, illus. 2006. 64p. (J). 15.95 (978-0-8234-1989-0(4)) Holiday Hse., Inc.

Jones, Patrick. Chasing Tail Lights. 2007. 304p. (YA). (gr. 9 up). 16.95 (***978-0-8027-9628-8(1)***) Walker & Co.

—Cheated. 2008. 208p. (YA). 16.95 (***978-0-8027-9699-8(0)***) Walker & Co.

Langley, Jan. Captain & Harry Haunting Tail. 2004. pap. (978-0-9724777-0-3(5)) Langley, Jan.

Lewis, Anne Margaret. What Am I? Michigan. DeWildt, Jim, illus. 2007. 32p. (J). 9.95 (978-0-9749145-6-5(8)) Mackinac Island Pr., Inc.

Lytle, Robert A. Three Rivers Crossing. 2000. 161p. (J). pap. 8.95 (978-0-938682-60-8(1)); (gr. 4-8). 15.95 (978-0-938682-55-4(5)) River Road Pubns., Inc.

Martin, Terri L. A Family Trait. 1999. 160p. (J). (gr. 4-6). tchr. ed. 15.95 (978-0-8234-1467-3(1)) Holiday Hse., Inc.

Murray, Anna. Sarah's Page. 1998. (Illus.). 144p. (J). (gr. 4-7). 14.00 (978-1-886947-58-0(9)) Sleeping Bear Pr.

Noble, Trinka Hakes. The Legend of Michigan. Frankenhuyzen, Gijsbert van, illus. 2006. 48p. (J). 17.95 (978-1-58536-278-3(6)) Sleeping Bear Pr.

Oneill, Elizabeth. Alfred Visits Michigan. 2006. 24p. pap. 12.00 (978-0-9771836-6-1(1)) Funny Bone Bks.

Otten, Charlotte. Home in a Wilderness Fort: Copper Harbor 1844. 2006. (J). pap. 14.95 (978-0-9766104-5-8(0)) Arbutus Pr.

Panagopoulos, Janie Lynn. A Castle at the Straits. Evans, Laura, illus. 2003. 48p. (J). (gr. 1-6). (978-0-911872-83-5(3)) Mackinac State Historic Parks.

—A Place Called Home: Michigan's Mill Creek Story. van Frankenhuyzen, Gijsbert, illus. 2001. 48p. (J). 18.95 (978-1-58536-054-3(6)) Sleeping Bear Pr.

Polacco, Patricia. Mrs. Mack. 2001. (J). (978-0-606-20813-0(5)); lib. bdg. 15.30 (978-0-613-33714-4(X)) Tandem Library Bks.

—The Trees of the Dancing Goats. Polacco, Patricia, illus. 2002. (Illus.). (J). 25.11 (978-0-7587-3858-5(7)) Book Wholesalers, Inc.

—The Trees of the Dancing Goats. Polacco, Patricia, illus. 2000. (Illus.). 32p. (J). (gr. k-3). 7.99 (978-0-689-83857-6(3) , Aladdin) Simon & Schuster Children's Publishing.

—The Trees of the Dancing Goats. 2000. (J). (978-0-606-20094-3(0)) Tandem Library Bks.

—Trees of the Dancing Goats. 2000. (gr. k-3). lib. bdg. 15.30 (978-0-613-30164-0(1)) Tandem Library Bks.

Rand, Jonathan. Dinosaurs Destroy Detroit. 2001. (Michigan Chillers: Vol. 8). 215p. (YA). pap. 5.99 (978-1-893699-14-4(5)) AudioCraft Publishing, Inc.

Smucker, Anna Egan. To Keep the South Manitou Light. 2004. (J). pap. 19.95 (978-0-8143-3236-8(6)); (Illus.). 144p. 23.95 (978-0-8143-3235-1(8) , Painted Turtle) Wayne State Univ. Pr.

Tromp, Janyre. That Sinking Feeling: Blue Water Mysteries. 2006. 128p. (J). pap. (978-0-8254-3887-5(X)) Kregel Pubns.

Van Frankenhuyzen, Robbyn Smith. Kelly of Hazel Ridge. van Frankenhuyzen, Gijsbert, illus. 3rd rev. ed. 2006. 48p. (J). (gr. k-5). 17.95 (978-1-58536-268-4(9)) Sleeping Bear Pr.

Wagner, Jerri. Jako's Vacation. 2001. 58p. pap. 9.95 (978-0-7414-0704-7(3)) Infinity Publishing.

Walter, Debbie. Introducing Russell. Walter, Debbie, illus. 2007. (Illus.). 68p. (J). per. 6.95 (***978-0-9766315-2-1(0)***) Moose Run Productions.

Wargin, Kathy-Jo. The Michigan Reader for Boys & Girls. Darnell, K. L., illus. 2001. 96p. (J). 12.95 (978-1-58536-042-0(2)) Sleeping Bear Pr.

—Mitt the Michigan Moose. 2006. (Illus.). 144p. (J). 14.95 (978-1-58726-303-3(3) , Mitten Pr.) Ann Arbor Media Group, LLC.

Whelan, Gloria. Farewell to the Island. 208p. (gr. 4 up). 1999. (Illus.). (YA). pap. 5.99 (978-0-06-440821-9(3) , Harper Trophy); 1998. (J). 16.95 (978-0-06-027751-2(3)) HarperCollins Pubs.

—Forgive the River, Forgive the Sky. 2004. 96p. (J). pap. 8.00 (978-0-8028-5256-4(4)) Eerdmans, William B. Publishing Co.

—Forgive the River, Forgive the Sky. 2003. (gr. 5-8). lib. bdg. 16.45 (978-0-613-75512-2(X)) Tandem Library Bks.

—Mackinac Bridge: The Five-Mile Poem. van Frankenhuyzen, Gijsbert, illus. 2006. 40p. (J). 17.95 (978-1-58536-283-7(2)) Sleeping Bear Pr.

—The Pathless Woods: Ernest Hemingway's Sixteenth Summer in Northern Michigan. Wolff, Glenn, illus. 2nd rev. ed. 1998. (J). (gr. 6-10). 16.95 (978-1-882376-63-6(3)); 176p. (gr. 7-12). pap. 11.95 (978-1-882376-44-5(7)) Thunder Bay Pr.

—Return to the Island. 192p. (J). (gr. 4-7). 2002. pap. 5.95 (978-0-06-440761-8(6)); 2000. 15.89 (978-0-06-028254-7(1)) HarperCollins Pubs.

White, Ruth. Memories of Summer. 2000. 144p. (J). (gr. 7-10). 17.00 (978-0-374-34945-5(2) , Farrar, Straus & Giroux (BYR)) Farrar, Straus & Giroux.

Winfield, Arthur M. The Rover Boys on the Great Lakes. 2004. reprint ed. pap. 22.95 (978-1-4191-8119-1(X)) Kessinger Publishing, LLC.

Winfield, Arthur M. The Rover Boys on the Great Lakes. 2004. reprint ed. pap. 1.99 (978-1-4192-8119-8(4)) Kessinger Publishing, LLC.

Winston, Sherri. Acting: A Novel. 2004. 256p. (YA). 15.95 (978-0-7614-5173-0(0)) Cavendish, Marshall Corp.

MICHIGAN—HISTORY

Bernard-Nollins, Sonya M. Here I Stand: A Musical History of African Americans in Battle Creek, Michigan. 2003. (Illus.). (YA). pap. 15.00 (978-0-9741611-0-5(1)) Fortitude Graphic Design & Printing.

Bush, Karen Elizabeth. Marie-Therese Guyon, Mme. Cadillac: First Lady of Detroit. 2001. (Detroit Biography Series for Young Readers). (Illus.). 191p. (J). (gr. 5 up). 27.95 (978-0-8143-2983-2(7) , Great Lakes Bks.) Wayne State Univ. Pr.

Deinard, Jenny. How to Draw Michigans Sights & Symbols. 2002. (Kids Guide to Drawing America Ser.). 32p. (J). lib. bdg. 25.25 (978-0-8239-6078-1(1) , PowerKids Pr.) Rosen Publishing Group, Inc., The.

Frank, David. The Kids & Sites of Kalamazoo. 2004. 80p. (978-0-9758971-0-2(1)) Artstreet LLC.

Glupker, Dianne. Great Tastes of Michigan. Delsi, Dawna, illus. 2006. (J). per. 9.95 (978-0-9769846-1-0(X)) Harambee Pr.

Heinrichs, Ann. Michigan. 2005. (Welcome to the USA Ser.). (Illus.). 40p. (J). (gr. 1-5). 27.07 (978-1-59296-377-5(3)) Child's World, Inc.

Hoffman, Mary Hramiec. Elizabeth Whitney Williams & the Little Traverse Light. 2004. (Illus.). 38p. (J). 17.95 (978-0-9746901-0-0(4)) Hramiec Hoffman Publishing.

Killingbeck, Dale. Michigan Triumphs & Tragedies, 2005. (Illus.). 160p. per. 9.95 (978-0-9762758-0-0(5)) Killingbeck, Dale.

Marsh, Carole. Michigan History Projects: 30 Cool, Activities, Crafts, Experiments & More for Kids to Do to Learn about Your State! 2003. (Michigan Experience Ser.). 32p. (gr. k-5). pap. 5.95 (978-0-635-01791-8(1) , Marsh, Carole Bks.) Gallopade International.

—My First Pocket Guide Michigan. 2000. (Michigan Experience! Ser.). (Illus.). 96p. (J). (gr. 3-8). 12.95 (978-0-635-01312-5(6) , 13126) Gallopade International.

Nishnawbe: A Story of Indians in Michigan. pap., tchr. ed. (978-0-938682-59-2(8)) River Road Pubns., Inc.

Peckham, Linda R. & Heuft, Lori E. Saw Mills & Sleigh Bells. 1999. (Illus.). xv, 103p. (J). (gr. 2-5). pap. 11.95 (978-0-9671616-1-7(4)) Catalpa Pubns.

Pena, Evelyn. Fun Facts & Games: Michigan. Dieterichs, Shelley, illus. 2000. (Fun Facts & Games Activity Book Ser.). 64p. (J). (gr. 1-5). pap. 5.95 (978-1-892920-48-5(4)) GHB Publishers, LLC.

Schonberg, Marcia. Michigan History. 2003. (Heinemann State Studies). (Illus.). 48p. (J). 27.07 (978-1-4034-0659-0(6)); pap. 8.50 (978-1-4034-2677-2(5)) Heinemann Library.

—People of Michigan. 2003. (Heinemann State Studies). (Illus.). 48p. (J). pap. 8.50 (978-1-4034-2680-2(5)); 27.07 (978-1-4034-0661-3(8)) Heinemann Library.

Smucker, Anna Egan. To Keep the South Manitou Light. 2004. (J). pap. 19.95 (978-0-8143-3236-8(6)) Wayne State Univ. Pr.

Wagenaar, Larry J. & Trap, Paul, eds. Michigan History Directory of Historical Societies, Museums, Archives, Agencies & Commissions. 2004. 19.95 net. (978-1-880311-04-2(6)) Historical Society of Michigan, The.

Wells, Sherry A. Father, Ford, $5 a Day: The Mullers from Missouri. Bulla, Randy, illus. 2003. 128p. lib. bdg. 14.00 (978-0-934981-11-8(6)) Lawells Publishing.

MICHIGAN, LAKE

Ylvisaker, Anne. Lake Michigan. 2003. (Fact Finders Ser.). (Illus.). 32p. (J). lib. bdg. 22.60 (978-0-7368-2210-7(0) , Bridgestone Bks.) Capstone Pr., Inc.

MICHIGAN, LAKE—FICTION

Bergel, Colin. Mail by the Pail. Koenig, Mark, illus. 2000. (Great Lakes Bks.). (J). pap. 16.95 (978-0-8143-2891-0(1)); 32p. (gr. 1-4). 18.95 (978-0-8143-2890-3(3) , Great Lakes Bks.) Wayne State Univ. Pr.

Caszatt-Allen, Wendy. Last Voyage of the Griffon. 2007. (Illus.). 140p. (J). pap. 6.95 (***978-1-934133-08-8(6)***) Mackinac Island Pr., Inc.

Snell, J. Roy. Curlie Carson Listens In. 2007. (ENG.). 136p. 41.99 (***978-1-4280-7269-5(1)***); per. 34.99 (***978-1-4280-7273-2(X)***) IndyPublish.com.

MICKEY MOUSE (FICTITIOUS CHARACTER)—FICTION

Abracadabra. 2001. (Mickey Mysteries Ser.: No. 4). (Illus.). 96p. (gr. 2-5). pap. 4.99 (978-0-7868-4452-4(3)) Disney Pr.

Barks, Carl, et al. Walt Disney's Christmas Parade #5. 2007. 80p. pap. 10.50 (***978-1-60360-005-7(1)***) Gemstone Publishing, Inc.

—Walt Disney's Comics & Stories #686. 2007. 64p. pap. 7.99 (***978-1-888472-97-4(9)***) Gemstone Publishing, Inc.

Braybrooks, Ann. Mickey's ABC. 2005. 32p. (J). (978-0-7868-3088-6(3)) Disney Pr.

Dalmatian Press Staff. Disney Vintage Mickey Mouse & his Friends. 2006. 16p. (J). pap. 3.99 (978-1-4037-2336-9(2)) Dalmatian Pr.

—Mickey's Alphbet BK. 2006. 32p. pap. 11.99 (978-1-4037-2188-4(2)) Dalmatian Pr.

—Mickey's Fire Brigade. 2006. 68p. pap. 11.99 (978-1-4037-2189-1(0)) Dalmatian Pr.

Disney Press Staff, contrib. by. Mystery in Midair. 2001. (Mickey Mysteries Ser.: No. 1). (Illus.). 96p. (J). (gr. 2-5). reprint ed. pap. 4.99 (978-0-7868-4449-4(3)) Disney Pr.

Disney Staff. Mickey Mouse & Minnie Mouse: Story & Illustrations. deluxe ed. 1999. (Illus.). 32p. (J). (ps-3). reprint ed. pap. 100.00 (978-1-55709-215-1(X)) Applewood Bks.

—The Story of Mickey Mouse. 2004. (Illus.). 92p. (J). (ps-3). 100.00 incl. audio compact disk (978-1-55709-352-3(0)) Applewood Bks.

Erickson, Byron, et al. Mickey Mouse Adventures, Vol. 9. 2006. (Illus.). 128p. (YA). pap. 7.95 (978-1-888472-10-3(3)) Gemstone Publishing, Inc.

Erickson, Byron, et al. Walt Disney's Comics & Stories #687. 2007. 64p. pap. 7.99 (***978-1-888472-98-1(7)***) Gemstone Publishing, Inc.

Gemstone Publishing, creator. Mickey Mouse Adventures, Vol. 6. 2005. (Illus.). 128p. (YA). pap. 7.95 (978-0-911903-71-3(2)) Gemstone Publishing, Inc.

Gerstein, David. Mickey & the Gang: Classic Stories in Verse. 2005. 360p. pap. 29.99 (978-1-888472-06-6(5)) Gemstone Publishing, Inc.

Gilbert, Michael T., et al. Mickey Mouse Adventures, Vol. 8. 2006. 128p. (YA). pap. 7.95 (978-1-888472-09-7(X)) Gemstone Publishing, Inc.

Gutman, Dan. Mickey & Me: A Baseball Card Adventure. 2003. (Baseball Card Adventures Ser.). (Illus.). 160p. (J). (gr. 4-6). 15.99 (978-0-06-029247-8(4)); lib. bdg. 16.89 (978-0-06-029248-5(2)) HarperCollins Pubs.

Higginson, Sheila Sweeny. 5+1 Makes More Fun. rev. ed. 2007. 10p. (J). (ps-1). 12.99 (***978-1-4231-0744-6(6)***) Disney Pr.

McGreal, Pat, et al. Mickey Mouse Adventures, Vol. 10. 2006. (Illus.). 128p. (YA). pap. 7.95 (978-1-888472-32-5(4)) Gemstone Publishing, Inc.

Mickey Mouse Adventures, Vol. 5. 2005. 128p. (YA). pap. 7.95 (978-0-911903-70-6(4)) Gemstone Publishing, Inc.

Mickey, Mouse Clubhouse. Go Goofy Go. rev. ed. 2008. 24p. pap. 3.99 (***978-1-4231-0742-2(X)***) Disney Pr.

—Mickeys Easter Hunt. rev. ed. 2007. 16p. pap. 4.99 (***978-1-4231-0747-7(0)***) Disney Pr.

—MYST of Missing Muffins. rev. ed. 2008. 24p. pap. 3.99 (***978-1-4231-0741-5(1)***) Disney Pr.

Mouse Works Staff. Goofy. 1998. (Friendly Tales Ser.). (Illus.). 10p. (J). (ps). 6.99 (978-1-57082-928-4(4)) Mouse Works.

Muldrow, Diane. Mickey Big Book. 2000. 48p. (J). 12.99 (978-0-7364-1018-2(X)) Disney Pr.

Mystery of the Secret Treasure. 2001. (Mickey Mysteries Ser.: No. 2). (Illus.). 96p. (gr. 2-5). reprint ed. pap. 4.99 (978-0-7868-4450-0(7)) Disney Pr.

North Bedford, Annie. Mickey Mouse Flies the Christmas Mail. Walt Disney Company, illus. 2007. (Little Golden Book Ser.). 24p. (J). (gr. k-k). 2.99 (***978-0-7364-2424-0(5)*** , Golden/Disney) Random Hse. Children's Bks.

Onish, Liane B. Mickey Mouse Stories. 2000. (Illus.). (J). 12.99 (978-0-7868-3326-9(2)) Disney Pr.

Petrucha, Stefan, et al. Mickey Mouse Adventures, Vol. 7. 2006. 128p. (YA). pap. 7.95 (978-0-911903-92-8(5)) Gemstone Publishing, Inc.

Salas, Macarena, ed. Baby Mickey Finds a Friend/Bebé Mickey Encuentra un Amigo: A Book about Action Words/Un Libro Sobre Palabras de Accion. 2005. (Disney Bil Ser.). (SPA & ENG., Illus.). 10p. (J). bds. 3.99 (978-0-439-66363-2(6) , Scholastic en Espanol) Scholastic, Inc.

Silver Dolphin en Español Editors, ed. Tesoros Para Llevar: Mickey Mouse. 2006. (Illus.). 24p. (J). bds. 12.95 (978-970-718-357-5(8) , Silver Dolphin en Español) Advanced Marketing, S. de R. L. de C. V. MEX. *Dist:* Perseus Distribution.

Tieman, Robert. The Mickey Mouse Treasures. 2007. 64p. (ps-17). 60.00 (***978-1-4231-0641-8(5)*** , Disney Editions) Disney Pr.

Weiss, Ellen. Mickey's Neighborhood Discovery. 2000. (Lift the Flaps Bks.). 12p. (J). 6.99 (978-0-7364-1035-9(X)) Mouse Works.

MICROBES

see Bacteriology; Microorganisms; Viruses

MICROBIOLOGY

see also Bacteriology; Microorganisms; Microscopes

Alphin, Elaine Marie. Germ Hunter: A Story about Louis Pasteur. Verstraete, Elaine, illus. 2003. 64p. (J). 6.95 (978-0-87614-929-4(8) , Carolrhoda Bks.) Lerner Publishing Group.

—Germ Hunter: A Story about Louis Pasteur. 2003. (gr. 3-6). lib. bdg. 14.10 (978-0-613-77207-5(5)) Tandem Library Bks.

Armentrout, David & Armentrout, Patricia. Louis Pasteur. 2002. (Discover Someone Who Made a Difference Discovery Library Ser.). (Illus.). 24p. (gr. 2-5). 14.95 (978-1-58952-056-1(4)) Rourke Publishing, LLC.

—Louis Pasteur. Sarfatti, Esther & de la Vega, Eida, trs. 2001. (Personas que Cambiaron la Historia Ser.). (SPA., Illus.). 24p. (J). (gr. 1-4). lib. bdg. 19.27 (978-1-58952-170-4(6) , RK5237) Rourke Publishing, LLC.

Bank Street Staff & Jakab, E. A. M. Louis Pasteur: Hunting Killer Germs. 2000. (Ideas on Trial Ser.). (Illus.). 122p. (C). (gr. 5-10). pap. 8.95 (978-0-07-134334-3(2) , 9780071343343) McGraw-Hill Cos., The.

Claybourne, Anna. From Amoebas to Protozoa. 2004. (Science Answers Ser.). (Illus.). 32p. (J). pap. 7.50 (978-1-4034-5514-7(7)) Heinemann Library.

—Microlife: From Amoebas to Viruses. 2004. (Science Answers Ser.). (Illus.). 32p. (J). lib. bdg. 24.22 (978-1-4034-4768-5(3)) Heinemann Library.

Cole, Joanna. Giant Germ. 2000. (gr. 3-6). lib. bdg. 11.80 (978-0-613-35806-4(6)) Tandem Library Bks.

Cole, Joanna & Krulik, Nancy E. The Magic School Bus in a Pickle: A Book about Microbes. Degan, Bruce & Ostrum, Bob, illus. 1998. (Magic School Bus Ser.). 32p. (J). (gr. 1-4). pap. 3.50 (978-0-590-39377-5(4)) Scholastic, Inc.

Farrell, Jeanette. Invisible Allies: Microbes That Shape Our Lives. 2005. (Illus.). 176p. (YA). 17.00 (978-0-374-33608-0(3) , Farrar, Straus & Giroux (BYR)) Farrar, Straus & Giroux.

Feinstein, Stephen. Louis Pasteur: The Father of Microbiology. 2008. (Inventors Who Changed the World Ser.). 128p. (J). (gr. 6 up). lib. bdg. 33.27 (***978-1-59845-078-1(6)*** , MyReportLinks.com Bks.) Enslow Pubs., Inc.

Harcourt School Publishers Staff. Harcourt Science: How Does a Plant Grow Reader. 1999. (Illus.). (gr. 2). pap. 3.10 (978-0-15-314863-7(2)) Harcourt Schl. Pubs.

Kornberg, Arthur. Germ Stories. Alaniz, Adam, illus. Kolter, Roberto, photos by. 2007. (J). (gr. 1-7). 22.50 (***978-1-891389-51-1(3)***) University Science Bks.

Krulik, Nancy E. The Magic School Bus in a Pickle: A Book about Microbes. 1998. (Magic School Bus Ser.). (Illus.). (J). (gr. 1-4). (978-0-606-13590-0(1)) Tandem Library Bks.

Latta, Sara L. The Good, the Bad, the Slimy: The Secret Life of Microbes. 2006. (Prime Ser.). (Illus.). 128p. (J). (gr. 4-9). lib. bdg. 31.93 (978-0-7660-1294-3(8)) Enslow Pubs., Inc.

Micro-Life Complete Materials Package. 2001. (Illus.). (YA). tchr. ed., ring bd. (978-1-887725-34-7(2)) Lab-Aids, Inc.

Mitchell, Melanie. Killing Germs. 2006. (Pull Ahead Bks.). (Illus.). 32p. (J). (ps). 22.60 (978-0-8225-2450-2(3) , Lerner Pubns.) Lerner Publishing Group.

—Matar los Germenes. 2005. (Libros para Avanzar (Pull Ahead Bks.)). (SPA., Illus.). 32p. (J). (gr. 3-7). lib. bdg. 22.60 (978-0-8225-3144-9(5) , Ediciones Lerner) Lerner Publishing Group.

Orr, Tamra. Public Health Microbiologist. 2008. (J). pap. 7.95 (***978-1-60279-082-7(5)***); lib. bdg. 25.26 (***978-1-60279-053-7(1)***) Cherry Lake Publishing.

Rainis, Kenneth G. Cell & Microbe Science Fair Projects Using Microscopes, Mold, & More. 2005. (Biology! Best Science Projects Ser.). (Illus.). 128p. (J). (gr. 6-12). lib. bdg. 26.60 (978-0-7660-2369-7(9)) Enslow Pubs., Inc.

Solway, Andrew. What's Living in Your Backyard? 2004. (Hidden Life Ser.). (Illus.). 32p. (J). pap. 7.50 (978-1-4034-5482-9(5)); lib. bdg. (978-1-4034-4843-9(4)) Heinemann Library.

—What's Living in Your Bedroom? 2004. (Hidden Life Ser.). (Illus.). 32p. (J). pap. 7.50 (978-1-4034-5484-3(1)); lib. bdg. 25.64 (978-1-4034-4845-3(0)) Heinemann Library.

—What's Living in Your Classroom? 2004. (Hidden Life Ser.). (Illus.). 32p. (J). pap. 7.50 (978-1-4034-5485-0(X)); lib. bdg. 25.64 (978-1-4034-4846-0(9)) Heinemann Library.

—What's Living in Your Kitchen? 2004. (Hidden Life Ser.). (Illus.). 32p. (J). pap. 7.50 (978-1-4034-5483-6(3)); lib. bdg. 25.64 (978-1-4034-4844-6(2)) Heinemann Library.

Taylor-Butler, Christine. Tiny Life in the Air. (J). 2006. 32p. (gr. 1-2). pap. 4.95 (978-0-516-25476-0(6)); 2005. (Illus.). 31p. (ps-ps). 20.50 (978-0-516-25273-5(9)) Scholastic Library Publishing. (Children's Pr.).

Trumbauer, Lisa. Tiny Life in Your Home. (J). 2006. 32p. (gr. 1-2). pap. 4.95 (978-0-516-25477-7(4)); 2005. (Illus.). 31p. (ps-ps). 20.50 (978-0-516-25274-2(7)) Scholastic Library Publishing. (Children's Pr.).

Walker, Richard. Microscopic Life. 2004. (Kingfisher Knowledge Ser.). (Illus.). 64p. (J). (gr. 5-9). 12.95 (978-0-7534-5778-8(4) , Kingfisher) Houghton Mifflin Co. Trade & Reference Div.

Ward, Brian R. Microscopic Life in Your Food. 2004. (Illus.). 32p. (J). lib. bdg. (978-1-58340-471-3(6)) Smart Apple Media.

—Microscopic Life in Your Home. 2004. (Illus.). 32p. (J). lib. bdg. (978-1-58340-472-0(4)) Smart Apple Media.

MICROCOMPUTERS

Bennington, Stephen & Fisher, Paul. All about Computers. 2002. (All about Ser.). (Illus.). 64p. pap. 7.99 (978-1-84215-711-4(6) , Southwater) Anness Publishing GBR. *Dist:* National Bk. Network.

Kazunas, Thomas & Kazunas, Charnan. Personal Computers. rev. ed. 2000. (True Bks.). (Illus.). 48p. (J). (gr. 3-5). 25.00 (978-0-516-21938-7(3) , Children's Pr.) Scholastic Library Publishing.

Rooney, Anne. Communicate Online. 2004. (QEB Learn Computing Ser.). (Illus.). 32p. (J). lib. bdg. 18.95 (978-1-59566-043-5(7)) QEB Publishing Inc.

—Fact Factory. 2004. (QEB Learn Computing Ser.). (Illus.). 32p. (J). lib. bdg. 18.95 (978-1-59566-042-8(9)) QEB Publishing Inc.

Roza, Greg. The Incredible Story of Computers & the Internet. 2004. (Kid's Guide to Incredible Technology Ser.). (Illus.). 24p. (J). lib. bdg. 19.95 (978-0-8239-6717-9(4) , PowerKids Pr.) Rosen Publishing Group, Inc., The.

Sherman, Josepha. The History of Personal Computer. 2003. (Watts Library Ser.). 64p. (J). (gr. 5-7). pap. 8.95 (978-0-531-16213-2(3) , Watts, Franklin) Scholastic Library Publishing.

Steinhauser, Peggy L. Mousetracks: A Kid's Computer Idea Book. Steinhauser, Peggy L., illus. 2004. (Illus.). 104p. (gr. k-5). pap. 12.95 (978-1-883672-48-5(1) , Tricycle Pr.) Ten Speed Pr.

Stevens, Cara J., et al. The Kid's Guide to E-Mail. Gilligan, Paul, illus. 2000. 80p. (J). (gr. 3-7). pap. 6.95 (978-0-7373-0352-0(2) , 03522W, Roxbury Park Juvenile) Lowell Hse. Juvenile.

Weber, Sandra. Personal Computer. 2003. (Transforming Power of Technology Ser.). (Illus.). 112p. (J). (gr. 9-13). 30.00 (978-0-7910-7450-3(1) , Chelsea Hse.) Facts On File, Inc.

MICROELECTRONICS

Charlton, Windsor. The Invention of the Silicon Chip: A Revolution in Daily Life. 2002. (Point of Impact Ser.). (Illus.). 32p. (J). (gr. 5-7). lib. bdg. 25.64 (978-1-58810-554-7(7)); pap. 7.50 (978-1-4034-0073-4(3) , 91553) Heinemann Library.

Gilliland, Matt. Microcontroller Application Cookbook, with BS-2 Homework Board, Vol. 2. 2002. (Illus.). 248p. per. 64.95 (978-0-9720159-2-9(2)) Woodglen Pr.

MICROGRAPHIC ANALYSIS

see Microscopes

MICROMINIATURE ELECTRONIC EQUIPMENT

see Microelectronics

MICROMINIATURIZATION (ELECTRONICS)

see Microelectronics

MICRONESIA

Department of Chamorro Affairs, Division of Research, Publication and Training Staff. I Manfayi Vol. I: Who's Who in Chamorro History. (Hale'-ta Ser.). 250p. (J). (gr. 6-7). pap. 30.00 (978-1-883488-04-8(4)) Dept. of Chamorro Affairs.

—I Manfayi Vol. II: Who's Who in Chamorro History. Date not set. 250p. (J). (gr. 6-7). pap. 25.00 (978-1-883488-06-2(0)) Dept. of Chamorro Affairs.

Millhoff, Brian L. The Micronesian Coloring Book. 2nd l.t. ed. 2006. (Illus.). 68p. (J). per. 6.50 net. (***978-0-9790111-0-8(8)***) M-m-mauleg Publishing.

Tinkham, Tom. Island English for Micronesia. Miranda, Roland, illus. 2001. 256p. 19.95 (978-1-57306-131-5(X)) Bess Pr., Inc.

MICROORGANISMS

see also Bacteriology; Microbiology; Microscopes; Protozoa; Viruses

Anderson, Rodney P. The Invisible ABCs: Exploring the World of Microbes. 2006. (Illus.). 64p. (J). 19.95 (978-1-55581-386-4(0)) ASM Pr.

Bailey, Jill. Life in the Human Body. 2003. (Illus.). (J). pap. 7.50 (978-1-4109-0351-8(6)); 32p. lib. bdg. 24.28 (978-0-7398-6803-4(9)) Raintree.

Benchmark Education Staff, compiled by. Organisms. 2006. spiral bd. 279.00 (***978-1-4108-7122-0(3)***) Benchmark Education Co.

—Organisms: Past & Present. 2005. (English Explorers Ser.). (J). spiral bd. 265.00 (***978-1-4108-5758-3(1)***) Benchmark Education Co.

—Organisms Past & Present. 2006. spiral bd. 330.00 (***978-1-4108-7016-2(2)***) Benchmark Education Co.

Breidahl, Harry. Extremophiles: Life in Extreme Environments. 2001. (Life in Strange Places Ser.). (Illus.). 32p. (J). (gr. 4 up). 28.00 (978-0-7910-6617-1(7) , 011004, Chelsea Hse.) Facts On File, Inc.

Claybourne, Anna. From Amoebas to Protozoa. 2004. (Science Answers Ser.). (Illus.). 32p. (J). pap. 7.50 (978-1-4034-5514-7(7)) Heinemann Library.

—Microlife: From Amoebas to Viruses. 2004. (Science Answers Ser.). (Illus.). 32p. (J). lib. bdg. 24.22 (978-1-4034-4768-5(3)) Heinemann Library.

—World's Worst Germs. 2005. (Illus.). 32p. (J). (978-1-4109-1972-4(2)) Steck-Vaughn.

—World's Worst Germs: Microorganisms & Disease. 2005. (Illus.). 32p. (J). (gr. 3-5). lib. bdg. 28.21 (978-1-4109-1941-0(2)) Steck-Vaughn.

Cole, Joanna. El Autobus Magico se Descompone. 1998. (Magic School Bus Ser.).Tr. of Magic School Bus in a Pickle. (SPA.). 116p. (J). (gr. 1-4). pap. 3.50 (978-0-590-76126-0(9)) Scholastic, Inc.

—Giant Germ. 2000. (gr. 3-6). lib. bdg. 11.80 (978-0-613-35806-4(6)) Tandem Library Bks.

Cole, Joanna & Krulik, Nancy E. The Magic School Bus in a Pickle: A Book about Microbes. Degan, Bruce & Ostrum, Bob, illus. 1998. (Magic School Bus Ser.). 32p. (J). (gr. 1-4). pap. 3.50 (978-0-590-39377-5(4)) Scholastic, Inc.

Drake, Jane & Love, Ann. Alien Invaders: Species That Threaten Our World. Thurman, Mark, illus. 2008. 56p. 19.95 (***978-0-88776-798-2(2)***) Tundra Bks., Inc./Livres Toundra, Inc. CAN. *Dist:* Random Hse. of Canada, Ltd.

Farrell, Jeanette. Invisible Allies: Microbes That Shape Our Lives. 2005. (Illus.). 176p. (YA). 17.00 (978-0-374-33608-0(3) , Farrar, Straus & Giroux (BYR)) Farrar, Straus & Giroux.

Germ Warfare: Individual Title Six-Packs. (Bookweb Ser.). 32p. (gr. 5 up). 34.00 (978-0-7635-3798-2(5)) Rigby Education.

Gunzi, Christiane. Mini Beasts. 2007. (Feels Real Ser.). 10p. (J). 4.99 (***978-0-7641-6052-3(4)***) Barron's Educational Series, Inc.

Harrison, Paul. Micro Bugs. 2007. (Up Close Ser.). (Illus.). 24p. (J). (gr. 3-5). lib. bdg. 23.95 (***978-1-4042-3760-5(7)*** , PowerKids Pr.) Rosen Publishing Group, Inc., The.

Holt, Rinehart and Winston Staff. Holt Science & Technology Chapter 11: Life Science: Protists & Fungi. 5th ed. 2004. (Illus.). pap. 12.86 (978-0-03-030211-4(0)) Holt, Rinehart & Winston.

—Holt Science & Technology 2002 Bk. A: Microorganisms. 2nd ed. 2002. 18.60 (978-0-03-064772-7(X)) Holt, Rinehart & Winston.

—Microorganisms. (Holt Science & Technology Ser.: Vol. A). 5th ed. 2003. 19.33 (978-0-03-025533-5(3)); Vol. A. 3rd ed. 2002. (SPA.). 18.60 (978-0-03-069239-0(3)) Holt, Rinehart & Winston.

Krulik, Nancy E. The Magic School Bus in a Pickle: A Book about Microbes. 1998. (Magic School Bus Ser.). (Illus.). (J). (gr. 1-4). (978-0-606-13590-0(1)) Tandem Library Bks.

Latta, Sara L. The Good, the Bad, the Slimy: The Secret Life of Microbes. 2006. (Prime Ser.). (Illus.). 128p. (J). (gr. 4-9). lib. bdg. 31.93 (978-0-7660-1294-3(8)) Enslow Pubs., Inc.

Lindstrom, Karin. Tiny Life on Plants. (J). 2006. 32p. (gr. 1-2). pap. 4.95 (978-0-516-25478-4(2)); 2005. (Illus.). 31p. (ps-ps). 20.50 (978-0-516-25297-1(6)) Scholastic Library Publishing. (Children's Pr.).

Marsh, Carole. A Kid's Official Guide to Germs! 2002. (Here & Now Ser.). 32p. (YA). (gr. 2-8). pap. 9.95 (978-0-635-01082-7(8)) Gallopade International.

May, Suellen. Invasive Microbes. 2007. (Invasive Species Ser.). (Illus.). 112p. (J). (gr. 6-12). 30.00 (978-0-7910-9131-9(7) , Chelsea Hse.) Facts On File, Inc.

Maynard, Christopher. Micromonsters: Life under the Microscope. 1999. (Eyewitness Readers). (Illus.). 48p. (J). (ps-3). 12.99 (978-0-7894-4757-9(6)); pap. 3.99 (978-0-7894-4756-2(8)) Dorling Kindersley Publishing, Inc.

—Micromonsters: Life under the Microscope. 1999. (Eyewitness Readers Ser.). (978-0-606-17810-5(4)); (gr. 3-6). lib. bdg. 11.80 (978-0-613-28383-0(X)) Tandem Library Bks.

Micro-Life Complete Materials Package. 2001. (Illus.). (YA). tchr. ed., stu. ed., ring bd. (978-1-887725-55-2(5)) Lab-Aids, Inc.

Millican, Julie. What If All Germs Were Purple? 2001. pap. 11.95 (978-1-58909-080-4(2)) Bookstand Publishing.

Morgan, Sally. Germ Killers: Fighting Disease. (Science at the Edge Ser.). 64p. 8.95 (978-1-4034-4121-8(9)); 2002. (Illus.). (J). (gr. 6-8). lib. bdg. 27.86 (978-1-58810-699-5(3)) Heinemann Library.

Nardo, Don. Germs. 2003. (Great Medical Discoveries Ser.). (Illus.). 128p. (J). 29.95 (978-1-59018-255-0(3) , Lucent Bks.) Thomson Gale.

Oetting, Judy & Herr, Tad. Germs. 2006. (Illus.). 32p. (YA). pap. 4.95 (978-0-516-24995-7(9) , Children's Pr.) Scholastic Library Publishing.

Parker, Steve. Microlife That Helps Us. 2005. (J). pap. (978-1-4109-1850-5(5)); lib. bdg. (978-1-4109-1845-1(9)) Steck-Vaughn.

—Microlife That Makes Us Ill. 2005. (978-1-4109-1847-5(5)); pap. (978-1-4109-1852-9(1)) Steck-Vaughn.

Pascoe, Elaine. Single-Celled Organisms. 2003. (Kids Guide to the Classification of Living Things Ser.). (Illus.). 32p. (J). lib. bdg. 21.25 (978-0-8239-6312-6(8)) Rosen Publishing Group, Inc., The.

Sian revision Microworlds. 2004. (J). (978-1-59242-045-2(1)) Delta Education, LLC.

Sian revision sm Wonders. 2004. (J). (978-1-59242-067-4(2)) Delta Education, LLC.

Silverstein, Alvin. What Are Germs? 2002. (gr. 3-6). lib. bdg. 15.25 (978-0-613-59556-8(4)) Tandem Library Bks.

Silverstein, Alvin, et al. What Are Germs? 2003. (My Health Ser.). 48p. (J). (gr. 3-5). pap. 6.95 (978-0-531-16640-6(6) , Watts, Franklin) Scholastic Library Publishing.

Simione, Ruth. The Return of Mike the Microbe. Simione, Allen, illus. 2000. 39p. (J). (gr. 4-8). pap. 15.00 (978-1-877960-26-0(8)) Kemtec Educational Corp.

Solway, Andrew. Hidden Life, 6 bks. 2004. (J). (gr. 4-6). lib. bdg. 166.71 (978-1-4034-4849-1(3)) Heinemann Library.

—What's Living Inside Your Body? 2004. (Hidden Life Ser.). (Illus.). 32p. (J). pap. 7.50 (978-1-4034-5486-7(8)); lib. bdg. (978-1-4034-4847-7(7)) Heinemann Library.

—What's Living on Your Body? 2004. (Hidden Life Ser.). (Illus.). 32p. (J). pap. 7.50 (978-1-4034-5487-4(6)); lib. bdg. (978-1-4034-4848-4(5)) Heinemann Library.

Townsend, John. Rotters!/John Townsend. 2005. (Illus.). 32p. (978-1-4109-1971-7(4)); (978-1-4109-1940-3(4)) Steck-Vaughn.

Wade, Mary Dodson. Tiny Life on the Ground. 2006. (Rookie Read-About Science Ser.). (Illus.). 32p. (J). (gr. 1-2). pap. 4.95 (978-0-516-25479-1(0) , Children's Pr.) Scholastic Library Publishing.

Ward, Brian R. Microscopic Life in the Garden. 2004. (Illus.). 32p. (J). lib. bdg. (978-1-58340-473-7(2)) Smart Apple Media.

—Microscopic Life in Your Body. 2004. (J). lib. bdg. (978-1-58340-470-6(8)) Smart Apple Media.

—Microscopic Life in Your Food. 2004. (Illus.). 32p. (J). lib. bdg. (978-1-58340-471-3(6)) Smart Apple Media.

Ward, Pat & Ward, Barb. Microorganisms. 1998. (Illus.). 64p. (YA). (gr. 5). pap. 8.95 (978-1-58037-080-6(2)) Twain, Mark Media, Inc. Pubs.

MICROSCOPE AND MICROSCOPY

see Microscopes; Microscopy

MICROSCOPES

Here are entered works on microscopes in general as well as works specifically on light or optical microscopes.

Bender, Lionel. Magnification: A Closer Look. Davis, Jon, illus. 2007. (Amazing Science Ser.). (J). 23.93 (978-1-4048-2196-5(1)) Picture Window Bks.

Bergethon, Peter R. The Microscope: Technology, Lenses & Light, Student Science Journal. 2000. (Illus.). 137p. (YA). (gr. 6-8). pap. (978-1-58447-047-2(X)) Symmetry Learning Systems.

Bullock, Linda. Looking Through a Microscope. (Rookie Read-About Science Ser.). (Illus.). (J). 2004. 31p. (gr. 1-2). pap. 4.95 (978-0-516-27912-1(2)); 2003. 32p. 20.50 (978-0-516-22872-3(2)) Scholastic Library Publishing. (Children's Pr.).

Doak, Robin S. The Telescope & Microscope. 2005. (Great Inventions Ser.). (Illus.). 48p. (J). lib. bdg. 30.00 (978-0-8368-5880-8(8) , World Almanac Library) Stevens, Gareth Inc.

Gikow, Louise. Up Close: A Chapter Book. 2004. (True Tales Ser.). (Illus.). 48p. (J). 22.50 (978-0-516-23729-9(2) , Children's Pr.) Scholastic Library Publishing.

Gikow, Louise A. Up Close: A Chapter Book. 2005. (True Tales Ser.). (Illus.). 48p. (J). (gr. 2-4). pap. 4.95 (978-0-516-24690-1(9) , Children's Pr.) Scholastic Library Publishing.

Greg's Microscope. 2003. 22.95 (978-0-673-75918-4(0)) Celebration Pr.

Kramer, Stephen. Hidden Worlds: Looking Through a Scientist's Microscope. Kunkel, Dennis, photos by. 2003. (Scientists in the Field Ser.). (Illus.). 64p. (J). (gr. 4-6). pap. 6.95 (978-0-618-35405-4(0)) Houghton Mifflin Co. Trade & Reference Div.

—Hidden Worlds: Looking Through a Scientist's Microscope. 2003. (gr. k-3). lib. bdg. 14.10 (978-0-613-88665-9(8)) Tandem Library Bks.

Kramer, Stephen P. Hidden Worlds: Looking Through a Scientist's Microscope. Kunkel, Dennis, photos by. 2001. (Scientists in the Field Ser.). (Illus.). 64p. (J). (gr. 4-6). tchr. ed. 16.00 (978-0-618-05546-3(0)) Houghton Mifflin Co. Trade & Reference Div.

Levine, Shar & Johnstone, Leslie. The Ultimate Guide to Your Microscope. 2008. (Illus.). 144p. (J). pap. 9.95 (***978-1-4027-4329-0(7)***) Sterling Publishing Co., Inc.

Petersen, Christine. The Microscope. 2006. 80p. (gr. 5-8). pap. 9.95 (978-0-531-13902-8(6)); (Illus.). (J). 30.50 (978-0-531-12408-6(8)) Scholastic Library Publishing. (Watts, Franklin).

Rainis, Kenneth G. Microscope Science Projects & Experiments: Magnifying the Hidden World. 2003. (Science Fair Success Ser.). (Illus.). 128p. (J). lib. bdg. 26.60 (978-0-7660-2090-0(8)) Enslow Pubs., Inc.

Richardson, Adele D. Microscopes. 2004. (First Facts Ser.). (Illus.). 24p. (J). 15.95 (978-0-7368-2517-7(7)) Capstone Pr., Inc.

Rivera, Sheila. Microscope. 2007. (First Step Nonfiction Ser.). (Illus.). 8p. (J). lib. bdg. (978-0-8225-6853-7(5)) Lerner Publishing Group.

Rodgers, Kirsteen. El Gran Libro del Microscopio. 2004. (Complete Bks.).Tr. of Complete Book of the Microscope. (SPA., Illus.). 96p. (J). (gr. 3 up). pap. 14.95 (978-0-7460-3901-4(8) , EU31323); lib. bdg. 22.95 (978-1-58086-317-9(5) , EU31324) EDC Publishing.

—El Gran Libro del Microscopio. 2001. Tr. of Complete Book of the Microscope. (SPA.). (gr. 3-6). lib. bdg. 24.55 (978-0-613-74460-7(8)) Tandem Library Bks.

Rogers, K. Complete Book of the Microscope. 2004. (Complete Bks.). (SPA., Illus.). 96p. (J). lib. bdg. 22.95 (978-1-58086-384-1(1)) EDC Publishing.

Rogers, Kirsteen. Compl Bk of the Microscope - Internet Linked. rev. ed. 2006. 96p. (J). pap. 14.99 (978-0-7945-1558-4(4) , Usborne) EDC Publishing.

Rogers, Kirsteen, ed. The Usborne Complete Book of the Microscope. 1999. (Complete Bks.). (Illus.). 96p. (YA). (gr. 3 up). lib. bdg. 22.95 (978-1-58086-162-5(8)) EDC Publishing.

See & Learn Science: A Curriculum Guide for Using Your Digital Microscope. 2007. (J). (***978-1-933229-69-0(1)***) APTE, Inc.

Simon, Seymour. Out of Sight: Pictures of Hidden World. 2000. (gr. 3-6). lib. bdg. 15.25 (978-0-613-44470-5(1)) Tandem Library Bks.

Slade, Suzanne. Scientific Instruments for Studying Atoms & Molecules. 2007. (Library of Physical Sciences). (Illus.). 24p. (J). (978-1-4042-2356-1(8)); pap. (978-1-4042-2166-6(2)); lib. bdg. (978-1-4042-3419-2(5)) Rosen Publishing Group, Inc., The. (PowerKids Pr.).

Stefoff, Rebecca. Microscopes & Telescopes. 2006. (Great Inventions Ser.). (Illus.). 128p. (J). lib. bdg. 39.93 (978-0-7614-2230-3(7) , Benchmark Bks.) Cavendish, Marshall Corp.

Using a Microscope, 6 Packs. (Rigby Focus Ser.). 16p. (gr. 1 up). 30.00 (978-0-7578-5550-4(4)) Rigby Education.

Using a Microscope: Individual Title Six-Packs. (Rigby Focus Ser.). 16p. (gr. 1 up). 28.00 (978-0-7578-5318-0(8)) Rigby Education.

VanCleave, Janice Pratt. Janice VanCleave's Microscopes & Magnifying Lenses: Mind-Boggling Chemistry & Biology Experiments You Can Turn into Science Fair Projects. 2002. (Janice Vancleave Ser.). (Illus.). (J). 19.72 (978-0-7587-4631-3(8)) Book Wholesalers, Inc.

Woog, Adam. The Microscope. 2003. (Great Medical Discoveries Ser.). (Illus.). 128p. (J). 29.95 (978-1-59018-302-1(9) , Lucent Bks.) Thomson Gale.

Yount, Lisa. Antoni Van Leeuwenhoek: First to See Microscopic Life. 2008. (J). (***978-0-7660-3012-1(1)***) Enslow Pubs., Inc.

MICROSCOPIC ANALYSIS

see Microscopy

MNO

MICROSCOPIC ORGANISMS

see Microorganisms

MICROSCOPY

Here are entered works on microscopy in general as well as works specifically on light or optical microscopy.

Cobb, Vicki. Blood & Gore, Like You've Never Seen. 1998. (Like You've Never Seen! Ser.). 32p. (J). (gr. 3-7). pap. 4.99 (978-0-590-92665-2(9)) Scholastic, Inc.

Early, Bobbi. Tiny Life in a Puddle. (J). 2006. 32p. (gr. 1-2). pap. 4.95 (978-0-516-25475-3(8)); 2005. (Illus.). 31p. (ps-ps). 20.50 (978-0-516-25272-8(0)) Scholastic Library Publishing. (Children's Pr.).

Kramer, Stephen. Hidden Worlds: Looking Through a Scientist's Microscope. Kunkel, Dennis, photos by. 2003. (Scientists in the Field Ser.). (Illus.). 64p. (J). (gr. 4-6). pap. 6.95 (978-0-618-35405-4(0)) Houghton Mifflin Co. Trade & Reference Div.

—Hidden Worlds: Looking Through a Scientist's Microscope. 2003. (gr. k-3). lib. bdg. 14.10 (978-0-613-88665-9(8)) Tandem Library Bks.

Kramer, Stephen P. Hidden Worlds: Looking Through a Scientist's Microscope. Kunkel, Dennis, photos by. 2001. (Scientists in the Field Ser.). (Illus.). 64p. (J). (gr. 4-6). tchr. ed. 16.00 (978-0-618-05546-3(0)) Houghton Mifflin Co. Trade & Reference Div.

Levine, Shar & Johnstone, Leslie. The Ultimate Guide to Your Microscope. 2008. (Illus.). 144p. (J). pap. 9.95 (***978-1-4027-4329-0(7)***) Sterling Publishing Co., Inc.

Rogers, Kirsteen. Compl Bk of the Microscope - Internet Linked. rev. ed. 2006. 96p. (J). pap. 14.99 (978-0-7945-1558-4(4) , Usborne) EDC Publishing.

Simon, Seymour. Out of Sight: Pictures of Hidden Worlds. 2002. (Illus.). 48p. (J). (gr. k up). 6.95 (978-1-58717-149-9(X) , SeaStar Bks.) Chronicle Bks. LLC.

MICROSOFT SOFTWARE

Bill Gates. rev. ed. 2007. (Biography Ser.). 112p. (J). (gr. 6-12). 29.27 (***978-0-8225-7363-0(6)*** , Twenty-First Century Bks.) Lerner Publishing Group.

Brocklehurst, R. An Introduction to Powerpoint. rev. ed. 2002. (Computer Guides). 32p. (J). pap. 8.95 (978-1-58086-498-5(8)) EDC Publishing.

MIDDLE AGES

see also Art, Medieval; Chivalry; Civilization, Medieval; Knights and Knighthood; Literature, Medieval; Renaissance

Adams, Simon. The Kingfisher Atlas of the Medieval World. Maddison, Kevin, illus. 2007. 48p. (J). (gr. 5-9). 15.95 (978-0-7534-5946-1(9) , Kingfisher) Houghton Mifflin Co. Trade & Reference Div.

The Age of Castles, 4 bks., Set. 2000. (Illus.). (J). (978-0-7398-4214-0(5)) Raintree.

Bailey, Linda. Adventures in the Middle Ages. 2000. (gr. 3-6). lib. bdg. 16.40 (978-0-613-81239-9(5)) Tandem Library Bks.

Bailey, Linda & Slavin, Bill. Adventures in the Middle Ages. 2004. (Good Times Travel Agency Ser.). (Illus.). 48p. (J). (gr. 4-6). (978-1-55074-540-5(9)); (978-1-55074-538-2(7)) Kids Can Pr., Ltd.

Barron's Educational Editorial Staff. Life in the Middle Ages. 1998. (Megascope Ser.). (Illus.). 64p. (J). (gr. 3-7). 6.95 (978-0-7641-5094-4(4)) Barron's Educational Series, Inc.

—Middle Ages. 1999. (Bravo Ser.). (Illus.). 124p. (J). (gr. 6 up). pap. 8.95 (978-0-7641-0948-5(0)) Barron's Educational Series, Inc.

Barter, James. Life in a Medieval Village. 2003. (Way People Live Ser.). (Illus.). 96p. (J). 29.95 (978-1-59018-266-6(9) , Lucent Bks.) Thomson Gale.

Bauer, Susan Wise. The Middle Ages. 2003. (Story of the World: Vol. 2). (Illus.). 275p. (J). pap., act. bk. ed. 29.95 (978-0-9714129-4-1(4) , AB2) Peace Hill Pr.

—The Middle Ages Vol. 2: From the Fall of Rome to the Rise of the Renaissance. 2003. (Story of the World: Vol. 2). (Illus.). 21.95 (978-0-9714129-8-9(7)); 336p. (J). pap. 21.95 (978-0-9714129-3-4(6) , SOTW2) Peace Hill Pr.

Benduhn, Tea. Middle Ages. 2006. (Illus.). 24p. (J). pap. (***978-0-8368-7789-2(6)***); lib. bdg. (***978-0-8368-7784-7(5)***) Stevens, Gareth Inc. (Weekly Reader Early Learning Library).

Bergin, Mark. Warfare in the Ancient World. Battle Zones Staff, ed. 2003. (Battle Zones Ser.). (Illus.). 48p. (J). 18.95 (978-1-57768-595-1(4) , Bedrick, Peter Bks.) School Specialty Publishing.

Bingham, Jane. Medieval world - internet Linked. Firenze, Inklink, illus. rev. ed. 2004. 96p. (J). pap. 14.95 (978-0-7945-0815-9(4) , Usborne) EDC Publishing.

Bingham, Marjorie. An Age of Empires, 1200-1750. 2006. 32.95 (978-0-19-522268-5(7)) Oxford Univ. Pr., Inc.

Bingham, Marjorie Wall. An Age of Empires, 1200-1750. 2005. (Medieval & Early Modern World Ser.). (Illus.). 160p. (YA). 32.95 (978-0-19-517839-5(4)) Oxford Univ. Pr., Inc.

—Student Study Guide to an Age of Empires, 1200-1750. 2005. (Medieval & Early Modern World Ser.). 60p. (YA). 9.95 (978-0-19-522341-5(1)) Oxford Univ. Pr., Inc.

Carlson, Laurie M. Days of Knights & Damsels: An Activity Guide. 2003. (Kid's Guide Ser.). (Illus.). 184p. (J). (gr. k-7). pap. 14.95 (978-1-55652-291-8(6)) Chicago Review Pr., Inc.

Caselli, Giovanni. The Middle Ages. Caselli, Giovanni, illus. 2nd ed. 1998. (History of Everyday Things Ser.). (Illus.). 48p. (YA). (gr. 5-9). reprint ed. pap. 10.95 (978-0-87226-263-8(4) , 62634B, Bedrick, Peter Bks.) School Specialty Publishing.

Chrisp, Peter. The Middle Ages. rev. ed. 2004. (Come & Discover My World Ser.). (Illus.). 32p. (gr. 2-5). (J). pap. 7.95 (978-1-58728-069-6(8)); 14.95 (978-1-58728-063-4(9)) T&N Children's Publishing. (Two Can Publishing).

—The Middle Ages. 2000. (My World Ser.). (Illus.). (J). (978-0-606-21950-1(1)) Tandem Library Bks.

—Town & Country Life. 2004. (J). (gr. 7-10). 29.95 (978-1-59018-536-0(6) , Lucent Bks.) Thomson Gale.

Corbishley, Mike. The Middle Ages. (Cultural Atlas for Young People Ser.). (Illus.). 96p. 2nd rev. ed. 2003. (J). (gr. 4-9). 35.00 (978-0-8160-5150-2(X)); 3rd rev. ed. 2007. (YA). (gr. 5-8). 35.00 (***978-0-8160-6825-8(9)*** , Chelsea Hse.) Facts On File, Inc.

Corrick, James A. The Early Middle Ages. 2005. (World History Ser.). (Illus.). 96-128p. (J). (gr. 7-10). 32.45 (978-1-59018-652-7(4) , Lucent Bks.) Thomson Gale.

Cosman, Madeline Pelner & Jones, Linda G. Handbook to Life in the Medieval World, 3 Vols., Set. Facts on File, Inc. Staff, ed. 2008. (Handbook to Life Ser.). 960 for setp. (gr. 9). 210.00 (978-0-8160-4887-8(8)) Facts On File, Inc.

Cox, Reg. The Seven Wonders of the Medieval World. 2000. (Wonders of the World Ser.). (Illus.). 32p. (J). (gr. 4-7). 21.95 (978-0-7910-6047-6(0) , Chelsea Hse.) Facts On File, Inc.

Daly-Weir, Catherine. Knights. Crosby, Jeff, illus. 1998. (All Aboard Reading Ser.). 48p. (J). (gr. 1-3). pap. 3.99 (978-0-448-41857-5(6) , Grosset & Dunlap) Penguin Group (USA) Inc.

Dawson, Imogene. Clothes & Crafts in the Middle Ages. 2000. (Clothes & Crafts in History Ser.). (Illus.). 32p. (J). (gr. 4 up). lib. bdg. 24.67 (978-0-8368-2736-1(8)) Stevens, Gareth Inc.

Deary, Terry. Measly Middle Ages. 1998. (Horrible Histories Ser.). (J). (gr. 7-12). pap. 4.50 (978-0-590-49848-7(7)) Scholastic, Inc.

DK Publishing. Medieval Life. 2008. (DK Eyewitness Bks.). 48p. (J). (gr. 2-8). pap. 9.99 (***978-0-7566-3783-5(X)***) Dorling Kindersley Publishing, Inc.

DK Publishing Staff. Castle. 2007. (Experience Ser.). 64p. (J). (gr. 3-8). 15.99 (978-0-7566-2838-3(5)) Dorling Kindersley Publishing, Inc.

Douglas, Vincent & School Specialty Publishing Staff. The Middle Ages. 2001. (History of the World Ser.). (Illus.). 48p. (J). (gr. 3 up). 18.95 (978-1-57768-952-2(6) , Bedrick, Peter Bks.) School Specialty Publishing.

Eastwood, Kay. The Life of a Knight. 2003. (Medieval World Ser.). (Illus.). 32p. (J). (gr. 5). (978-0-7787-1342-5(3)) Crabtree Publishing Co.

—Medieval Society. 2003. (Medieval World Ser.). (Illus.). 32p. (J). (gr. 5). (978-0-7787-1345-6(8)); pap. (978-0-7787-1377-7(6)) Crabtree Publishing Co.

—Women & Girls in the Middle Ages. 2003. (Medieval World Ser.). (Illus.). 32p. (J). (gr. 5). pap. (978-0-7787-1378-4(4)) Crabtree Publishing Co.

English Heritage Staff. My Life as a Knight. 2005. (Illus.). 32p. pap. 19.95 (978-1-85074-985-1(X)) English Heritage GBR. *Dist:* Brown, David Bk. Co., The.

—My Life as a Princess. 2005. (Illus.). 32p. pap. 19.95 (978-1-85074-984-4(1)) English Heritage GBR. *Dist:* Brown, David Bk. Co., The.

Farman, John. The Short & Bloody History of Knights. 2005. (Short & Bloody Histories Ser.). (Illus.). 96p. (gr. 6-12). lib. bdg. 19.93 (978-0-8225-0841-0(9)) Lerner Publishing Group.

—Short & Bloody History of Knights. 2002. (gr. 5-8). lib. bdg. 14.10 (978-0-613-52497-1(7)) Tandem Library Bks.

Freeman, Cathy, et al. Middle Ages. 2000. (Students' Active Interdisciplinary Learning Ser.). (YA). (gr. 1 up). pap. 20.00 (978-1-893413-07-8(1)) Univ. Schl. at the Univ. of Tulsa.

George, Linda S. 800 A. D. 2001. (Around the World Ser.). (Illus.). 96p. (J). 29.93 (978-0-7614-1085-0(6) , Benchmark Bks.) Cavendish, Marshall Corp.

Grant, Neil. Medieval Europe. 2003. (Uncovering History Ser.). 46p. (J). lib. bdg. 28.50 (978-1-58340-254-2(3)) Smart Apple Media.

Grolier Educational Staff. Medieval World, 10 vols. 2001. (Illus.). (J). (978-0-7172-5530-6(1) , Grolier) Scholastic Library Publishing.

Grolier Educational Staff, contrib. by. Medieval World, 10 vols. 2001. (Illus.). (J). (978-0-7172-5521-4(2)); (978-0-7172-5522-1(0)); (978-0-7172-5523-8(9)); (978-0-7172-5524-5(7)); (978-0-7172-5525-2(5)); (978-0-7172-5526-9(3)); (978-0-7172-5527-6(1)); (978-0-7172-5528-3(X)); (978-0-7172-5529-0(8)) Scholastic Library Publishing. (Grolier).

Hanawalt, Barbara. The European World, 400-1450. (Illus.). 2006. 189p. 32.95 (978-0-19-522267-8(9)); 2005. 192p. (YA). 32.95 (978-0-19-517844-9(0)) Oxford Univ. Pr., Inc.

Hanawalt, Barbara A. The Middle Ages: An Illustrated History. 1999. (Oxford Illustrated Histories Ser.). (Illus.). 160p. (YA). (gr. 5). 35.00 (978-0-19-510359-5(9)) Oxford Univ. Pr., Inc.

Harding, Samuel B. The Story of the Middle Ages (Yesterday's Classics) 2006. (Illus.). 228p. (YA). per. 10.95 (978-1-59915-157-1(X)) Yesterday's Classics.

Hart, Avery & Mantell, Paul. Knights & Castles: 50 Hands-On Activities to Experience the Middle Ages. 1998. (Kaleidoscope Kids Bks.: Vol. 2). (Illus.). 96p. (J). (gr. 2-8). pap. 12.95 (978-1-885593-17-7(1) , Williamson Bks.) Ideals Pubns.

Hazen, Walter. Middle Ages. 2005. (Illus.). 92p. (J). (gr. 6-9). pap. 12.95 (978-1-59647-059-0(3)) Good Year Bks.

Hazen, Walter A., ed. Medieval Times. 2000. (Illus.). (YA). (gr. 6-9). pap. 4.95 (978-1-55708-674-7(5) , MCR539) McDonald Publishing Co.

Hindley, Judy, et al. Time Traveler: Visit Medieval Times, the Viking Age, the Roman World & Ancient Egypt. rev. ed. 2004. (Time Travelers Bks.). (Illus.). 130p. (J). (gr. 3-6). 22.95 (978-0-7460-3365-4(6)) EDC Publishing.

Jane Shuter. The Middle Ages. 2nd ed. 2007. (Illus.). 32p. (J). pap. (***978-1-4034-8820-6(7)***) Heinemann Library Bks.

Jess, Denise & Shepherd-Wundrow, Debra. Travels with a Troubadour: A Journey Through the Middle Ages: An Interactive Curriculum Unit for Social Studies. 2nd ed. 2001. (J). (978-1-885360-25-0(8)) Demco, Inc.

Jovinelly, Joann. The Crafts & Culture of a Medieval Guild. 2006. (Illus.). 48p. (J). lib. bdg. (978-1-4042-0757-8(0)) Rosen Publishing Group, Inc., The.

Jovinelly, Joann & Netelkos, Jason. The Crafts & Culture of a Medieval Castle. 2006. (Illus.). 47p. (J). (978-1-4042-0760-8(0)) Rosen Publishing Group, Inc., The.

—The Crafts & Culture of a Medieval Cathedral. 2006. (Illus.). 28p. (J). lib. bdg. (978-1-4042-0758-5(9)) Rosen Publishing Group, Inc., The.

—The Crafts & Culture of a Medieval Manor. 2006. (Illus.). 48p. (J). lib. bdg. (978-1-4042-0756-1(2)) Rosen Publishing Group, Inc., The.

—The Crafts & Culture of a Medieval Town. 2006. (Crafts & Culture of the Middle Ages Ser.). (Illus.). 48p. (J). (gr. 4-8). lib. bdg. 29.25 (978-1-4042-0761-5(9)) Rosen Publishing Group, Inc., The.

Kenney, Karen Latchana. Harsh or Heroic? The Middle Ages. 2007. (Shockwave: History & Politics Ser.). 36p. (J). pap. 6.95 (***978-0-531-18794-4(2)***); (Illus.). (gr. 4-6). lib. bdg. 25.00 (***978-0-531-17754-9(8)***) Scholastic Library Publishing. (Children's Pr.).

Koestler-Grack, Rachel A. Eleanor of Aquitaine: Heroine of the Middle Ages. 2005. (Makers of the Middle Ages & Renaissance Ser.). (Illus.). 158p. (J). (gr. 4-8). lib. bdg. 30.00 (978-0-7910-8633-9(X) , Chelsea Hse.) Facts On File, Inc.

Lilly, Melinda. Blacksmith. 2002. (Illus.). 32p. (J). lib. bdg. 26.60 (978-1-58952-226-8(5)) Rourke Publishing, LLC.

—Minstrel. 2002. (Illus.). 32p. (J). lib. bdg. 26.60 (978-1-58952-228-2(1)) Rourke Publishing, LLC.

—Peasant. 2002. (People of the Middle Ages Ser.). (Illus.). 32p. (J). lib. bdg. 26.60 (978-1-58952-229-9(X)) Rourke Publishing, LLC.

—People of the Middle Ages. 2002. 159.60 (978-1-58952-225-1(7)) Rourke Publishing, LLC.

—Pilgrim. 2002. (People of the Middle Ages Ser.). (Illus.). 32p. (J). lib. bdg. 26.60 (978-1-58952-230-5(3)) Rourke Publishing, LLC.

Macdonald, Fiona. Monarchs in the Middle Ages. 2005. (World Almanac Library of the Middle Ages). (Illus.). 48p. pap. (978-0-8368-5905-8(7) , World Almanac Library) Stevens, Gareth Inc.

MacDonald, Fiona. Monarchs in the Middle Ages. 2005. (World Almanac' Library of the Middle Ages). (Illus.). 48p. (YA). (gr. 10-12). lib. bdg. 30.00 (978-0-8368-5896-9(4) , World Almanac Library) Stevens, Gareth Inc.

—Women in Medieval Times. 2000. (Other Half of History Ser.). (Illus.). 48p. (J). (gr. 3 up). 17.95 (978-0-87226-569-1(2) , 65692B, Bedrick, Peter Bks.) School Specialty Publishing.

Marshall, Chris. Warfare in the Medieval World. 1999. (History of Warfare Ser.). (Illus.). 80p. (YA). (gr. 7-12). lib. bdg. 29.97 (978-0-8172-5443-8(9)) Raintree.

McNeil, Niki, et al. HOCPP 1054 Middle Ages. 2006. spiral bd. 21.00 (***978-1-60308-054-5(6)***) In the Hands of a Child.

McNeil, Sarah. The Middle Ages. 1998. (Spotlights Ser.). (Illus.). 46p. (YA). (gr. 4-6). 12.95 (978-0-19-521394-2(7)) Oxford Univ. Pr., Inc.

Medieval Africa DBA. 2003. spiral bd. 16.95 (978-1-56004-170-2(6)) Social Studies Schl. Service.

Medieval China DBA. 2002. spiral bd. 16.95 (978-1-56004-141-2(2)) Social Studies Schl. Service.

Medieval Europe DBA. 2002. spiral bd. 16.95 (978-1-56004-138-2(2)) Social Studies Schl. Service.

Medieval World, 6 bks. Incl. Life in a Castle. Eastwood, Kay. pap. (978-0-7787-1343-2(1)); Life of a Knight. Eastwood, Kay. (978-0-7787-1342-5(3)); Medieval Society. Eastwood, Kay. (978-0-7787-1345-6(8)); Medieval Warfare. Steele, Tara. (978-0-7787-1344-9(X)); Places of Worship in the Middle Ages. Eastwood, Kay. (978-0-7787-1347-0(4)); Women & Girls in the Middle Ages. Eastwood, Kay. (978-0-7787-1346-3(6)); 32p. (J). (gr. 5). 2003. (Illus.). 2003. (978-0-7787-1341-8(5)) Crabtree Publishing Co.

Middle Ages: Fun Projects for World History. 2006. cd-rom 29.95 net. (978-1-56004-252-5(4)) Social Studies Schl. Service.

Olmstead, Jennifer. Art of the Middle Ages. 2001. (Art in History Ser.). (Illus.). 32p. (J). (gr. 5-7). pap. 6.95 (978-1-4034-4019-8(0)) Heinemann Library.

Pianini, Michele. Life in a Medieval Castle. Mesturini, Cristina, illus. 2004. 40p. (J). bds. 9.99 (978-0-7641-5751-6(5)) Barron's Educational Series, Inc.

Plain, Nancy. Eleanor of Aquitaine & the High Middle Ages. 2005. (Rulers & Their Times Ser.). (Illus.). 96p. (J). (gr. 3-7). lib. bdg. 29.93 (978-0-7614-1834-4(2) , Benchmark Bks.) Cavendish, Marshall Corp.

Quigley, Mary. The Middle Ages. 2003. (Understanding People in the Past Ser.). (Illus.). 64p. (J). (gr. 4-6). pap. 28.50 (978-1-4034-0387-2(2)); pap. 8.95 (978-1-4034-0607-1(3)) Heinemann Library.

Reid, Struan. Castle under Seige. 1998. (Age of Castles Ser.). (Illus.). 48 p. (J). (gr. 3-7). lib. bdg. 25.69 (978-0-8172-5120-8(0)) Raintree.

Schaffer, David. Viking Conquest. 2002. (World History Ser.). (Illus.). 112p. (YA). (gr. 8-11). lib. bdg. 32.45 (978-1-56006-322-3(X) , LML00902-177714, Lucent Bks.) Thomson Gale.

Shuter, Jane. The Middle Ages. 2007. (Illus.). 32p. (J). (***978-1-4034-8813-8(4)***) Heinemann Library.

Smith, Bonnie G., ed. The Medieval & Early Modern World, 7 vols., Set. 2005. (Medieval & Early Modern World Ser.). (Illus.). 1232p. (YA). 230.00 (978-0-19-522157-2(5)) Oxford Univ. Pr., Inc.

Smith, Bonnie G. & Kelley, Donald R. The Medieval & Early Modern World: Primary Sources & Reference Volume. 2006. 32.95 (978-0-19-522300-2(4)) Oxford Univ. Pr., Inc.

—Primary Sources & Reference Volume. 2005. (Medieval & Early Modern World Ser.). (Illus.). 176p. (YA). 32.95 (978-0-19-517848-7(3)); (978-0-19-523081-9(7)) Oxford Univ. Pr., Inc.

Stefoff, Rebecca. The Medieval World. 2003. (Illus.). 48p. (J). 27.07 (978-0-7614-1642-5(0) , Benchmark Bks.) Cavendish, Marshall Corp.

Stevens, Catrin, et al. Yr Oesoedd Canol. 2005. (WEL., Illus.). 144p. 4.99 (978-1-84323-423-4(8)) Gomer Pr. GBR. *Dist:* Gomer Pr.

Streissguth, Thomas. The Middle Ages. 2003. (A to Z Encyclopedias Ser.). (Illus.). 332p. (J). 77.45 (978-0-7377-0793-9(3) , Greenhaven Pr., Inc.) Thomson Gale.

Student Study Guide to the European World, 400-1450. 2005. (Medieval & Early Modern World Ser.). 48p. (YA). 9.95 (978-0-19-522336-1(5)) Oxford Univ. Pr., Inc.

Tartaglino, Anna Cazzini & Torcellan, Nanda. Medieval Paris. 2001. (Journey to the Past Ser.). (Illus.). 56p. (J). (gr. 6-8). lib. bdg. 27.12 (978-0-7398-1956-2(9)) Raintree.

Trembinski, Donna. Famous People of the Middle Ages. 2005. (Medieval World Ser.). (Illus.). 32p. (J). (gr. 4-9). (978-0-7787-1356-2(3)) Crabtree Publishing Co.

Weisner-Hanks, Merry E. Teaching Guide to an Age of Voyages, 1450-1600. 2005. (Medieval & Early Modern World Ser.). 122p. (YA). 19.95 (978-0-19-522344-6(6)) Oxford Univ. Pr., Inc.

Whitfield, Cathy. History Odyssey, Middle Ages - Level One. 2006. (J). ring bd. 31.00 (***978-0-9766057-7-5(5)***) Pandia Pr.

Wiesner-Hanks, Merry E. An Age of Voyages, 1350-1600. 2005. (Medieval & Early Modern World Ser.). (Illus.). 192p. (YA). (gr. 7 up). 32.95 (978-0-19-517672-8(3)) Oxford Univ. Pr., Inc.

Wiesner, Merry E. An Age of Voyages, 1450-1600. 2006. (Illus.). 189p. 32.95 (978-0-19-522264-7(4)) Oxford Univ. Pr., Inc.

Woog, Adam. A Medieval Knight. 2003. (Daily Life Ser.). (Illus.). 48p. (J). (gr. 4-6). 26.20 (978-0-7377-0992-6(8) , Kidhaven) Thomson Gale.

World Almanac Library of the Middle Ages, 8. 240.00 (978-0-8368-5891-4(3)) Stevens, Gareth Inc.

MIDDLE AGES—BIOGRAPHY

Dixon, Darla, illus. What Really Happened During the Middle Ages: A Collection of Historical Biographies. 2006. 222p. per. 15.95 (***978-1-933596-47-1(3)***) Morgan James Publishing, LLC.

Johnson, Terri, compiled by. What Really Happened During the Middle Ages: A Collection of Historical Biographies, 4. 2005. (Illus.). 224p. (J). per. 15.95 (***978-1-932786-22-4(8)***) Knowledge Quest.

Trembinski, Donna. Famous People of the Middle Ages. 2005. (Medieval World Ser.). (Illus.). 32p. (J). (gr. 4-9). pap. (978-0-7787-1388-3(1)) Crabtree Publishing Co.

MIDDLE AGES—FICTION

Abbott, Tony. Kringle. Call, Greg, illus. 2005. 304p. (J). (gr. 4-7). pap. 14.99 (978-0-439-74942-8(5) , Scholastic Pr.) Scholastic, Inc.

Ardagh, Philip. The Green Men of Gressingham. Phillips, Mike, illus. 2006. 72;88p. (J). (gr. 2-3). lib. bdg. (978-1-59889-000-6(X)) Stone Arch Bks.

Avi. The Book Without Words: A Fable of Medieval Magic. 2006. 224p. (gr. 5-9). reprint ed. pap. 5.99 (978-0-7868-1659-0(7)) Hyperion Pr.

—The Book Without Words: A Fable of Medieval Magic. l.t. ed. 2005. 220p. (YA). 23.95 (978-0-7862-7940-1(0)) Thorndike Pr.

—Crispin: La Cruz de Plomo. 2004. Tr. of Crispin: The Cross of Lead. (SPA., Illus.). (YA). pap. 7.99 (978-84-348-9601-7(X)) SM Ediciones ESP. *Dist:* Lectorum Pubns., Inc.

—Crispin: The Cross of Lead. 2002. 256p. (gr. 5-9). 16.49 (978-0-7868-2647-6(9)) Disney Pr.

—Crispin: The Cross of Lead. 2002. (Illus.). 272p. (gr. 5-9). 15.99 (978-0-7868-0828-1(4)) Hyperion Bks. for Children.

—Crispin: The Cross of Lead. 2004. 320p. (J). (gr. 3-7). reprint ed. pap. 6.99 (978-0-7868-1658-3(9)) Hyperion Paperbacks for Children.

—Crispin: The Cross of Lead. 2004. (gr. 3-6). lib. bdg. 15.30 (978-0-613-74965-7(0)) Tandem Library Bks.

—Crispin: The Cross of Lead. 2003. 303p. (J). 25.95 (978-0-7862-5501-6(3)) Thorndike Pr.

Avi Staff. Crispin: At the Edge of the World. 2nd rev. ed. 2006. 240p. (gr. 5-9). 16.99 (978-0-7868-5152-2(X)) Hyperion Pr.

Banks, Steven. Lost in Time. The Artifact Group, illus. 2006. 22p. (J). lib. bdg. 15.00 (***978-1-4242-0977-4(3)***) Fitzgerald Bks.

—Lost in Time. 2007. 24p. (J). 21.35 (***978-1-59961-367-3(0)***) Spotlight.

Barrett, Tracy. Anna of Byzantium. 2000. (Illus.). 224p. (YA). (gr. 7-12). pap. 5.99 (978-0-440-41536-7(5) , Laurel Leaf) Random Hse. Children's Bks.

—Anna of Byzantium. 2000. (J). 11.64 (978-0-606-19742-7(7)); (gr. 7-12). lib. bdg. 12.40 (978-0-613-28364-9(3)) Tandem Library Bks.

M N O

Bulla, Clyde Robert. The Sword in the Tree. 2000. (gr. 3-6). lib. bdg. 12.10 (978-0-613-27147-9(5)) Tandem Library Bks.

Cadnum, Michael. Book of the Lion. 2001. (gr. 7-12). lib. bdg. 14.15 (978-0-613-44378-4(0)) Tandem Library Bks.

—Daughter of the Wind. 2003. 272p. (J). pap. 17.95 (978-0-439-35224-6(X) , Orchard Bks.) Scholastic, Inc.

—The Dragon Throne. 2005. 224p. (YA). (gr. 7). 16.99 (978-0-670-03631-8(5) , Viking Juvenile) Penguin Group (USA) Inc.

—Forbidden Forest: The Story of Little John & the Robin Hood. 2002. 224p. (J). (gr. 7 up). pap. 17.95 (978-0-439-31774-0(6) , Orchard Bks.) Scholastic, Inc.

—The Leopard Sword. 2002. 224p. (YA). (gr. 7 up). 15.99 (978-0-670-89908-1(9) , Viking Juvenile) Penguin Group (USA) Inc.

Clement-Davies, David. Fell. 2007. 542p. (YA). (gr. 7-17). 19.95 ***978-0-8109-1185-7(X)*** Abrams, Harry N. , Inc.

Clement-Davies, David. The Sight. 2002. (gr. 7-12). lib. bdg. 16.45 (978-0-613-68285-5(8)) Tandem Library Bks.

Comrie, Margaret S. The Heroes of Castle Bretten. 2003. (Illus.). 229p. (J). (978-1-894666-65-7(8)) Inheritance Pubns.

Crossley-Holland, Kevin. At the Crossing Places. 2002. (Arthur Trilogy: Bk. 2). 416p. (J). (gr. 9 up). 17.95 (978-0-439-26598-0(3) , Levine, Arthur A. Bks.) Scholastic, Inc.

—At the Crossing-Places. 2004. (Illus.). 394p. (YA). (gr. 7-12). lib. bdg. 13.64 (978-0-606-32761-9(4)) Tandem Library Bks.

—At the Crossing Places. 2004. (Arthur Trilogy: Bk. 2). 416p. (J). (gr. 4-7). reprint ed. pap. 7.99 (978-0-439-26599-7(1) , Levine, Arthur A. Bks.) Scholastic, Inc.

—King of the Middle March. 432p. (J). 2006. pap. 7.99 (978-0-439-26601-7(7)); Book 3. 2004. (gr. 7 up). 17.95 (978-0-439-26600-0(9) , Levine, Arthur A. Bks.) Scholastic, Inc.

—The Seeing Stone. 2002. (Arthur Trilogy: Vol. 1). 368p. (J). (gr. 5 up). mass mkt. 6.99 (978-0-439-43524-6(2) , Levine, Arthur A. Bks.) Scholastic, Inc.

—Seeing Stone. 2002. (gr. 7-12). lib. bdg. 15.30 (978-0-613-50642-7(1)) Tandem Library Bks.

Cushman, Karen. Catherine, Called Birdy. 2002. (Illus.). (J). 15.00 (978-0-7587-0246-3(9)) Book Wholesalers, Inc.

—Matilda Bone. 2002. 13.94 (978-1-4046-1906-7(2)) Book Wholesalers, Inc.

—Matilda Bone. 2000. (Illus.). 176p. (J). (gr. 5-9). tchr. ed. 15.00 (978-0-395-88156-9(0) , Clarion Bks.) Houghton Mifflin Co. Trade & Reference Div.

—Matilda Bone. unabr. ed. 2004. (Middle Grade Cassette Librariestm Ser.). 176p. (J). (gr. 5-9). pap. 36.00 incl. audio (978-0-8072-1725-2(5) , S YA 252 SP, Listening Library) Random Hse. Audio Publishing Group.

—Matilda Bone. 2002. 176p. (J). (gr. 5-7). reprint ed. 5.99 (978-0-440-41822-1(4) , Yearling) Random Hse. Children's Bks.

—Matilda Bone. 2002. 167p. (J). (gr. 4-7). lib. bdg. 13.55 (978-0-613-45343-1(3)) Tandem Library Bks.

—The Midwife's Apprentice. 2002. (Illus.). (J). 14.47 (978-0-7587-0202-9(7)) Book Wholesalers, Inc.

De Angeli, Marguerite. The Door in the Wall. 1998. (Illus.). 128p. (J). (gr. 5-9). reprint ed. pap. 4.99 (978-0-440-22779-3(8) , Laurel Leaf) Random Hse. Children's Bks.

—The Door in the Wall. 1998. 11.64 (978-0-606-13344-9(5)) Tandem Library Bks.

Decker, Timothy. Run Far, Run Fast. Decker, Timothy, illus. 2007. (Illus.). 40p. (J). (gr. 5 up). 17.95 ***(978-1-59078-469-3(3)*** , Front Street) Boyds Mills Pr.

French, Jackie. My Dad the Dragon. King, Stephen Michael, illus. 2007. (Funny Families Ser.). (J). (gr. 2-4). 107p. pap. 7.95 ***(978-1-59889-436-3(6));*** 112p. lib. bdg. 22.60 ***(978-1-59889-343-4(2))*** Stone Arch Bks.

Gilman, Laura Anne. The Camelot Spell. 2006. (Grail Quest Trilogy Ser.: No. 1). 304p. (J). 10.99 (978-0-06-077279-6(4)); lib. bdg. 14.89 (978-0-06-077280-2(8)) HarperCollins Pubs.

—Morgain's Revenge. 2006. (Grail Quest Trilogy Ser.: No. 2). 288p. (J). lib. bdg. 14.89 (978-0-06-077283-3(2)) HarperCollins Pubs.

Goussett, Catherine. The Perfect Knight. Negrin, Fabian, tr. from FRE. Negrin, Fabian, illus. 2004. (Books for Young Readers Ser.). 22p. 5.95 (978-0-89236-739-9(3)) Oxford Univ. Pr., Inc.

Grant, K. M. Blood Red Horse. 2006. 288p. (J). pap. 7.95 (978-0-8027-7734-8(1)) Walker & Co.

Gray, Elizabeth Janet. Adam of the Road. Lawson, Robert, illus. 2006. (Puffin Modern Classics Ser.). 320p. (J). (gr. 3). pap. 6.99 (978-0-14-240659-5(7) , Puffin) Penguin Group (USA) Inc.

Hardinge, Frances. Fly by Night. 2006. 496p. (J). (gr. 5-9). 16.99 (978-0-06-087627-2(1)) HarperCollins Pubs.

Hartman, Rachel. Amy Unbounded: Belondweg Blossoming. 2002. 208p. (J). pap. 16.95 (978-0-9717900-0-1(0)) Pug House Pr.

Jinks, Catherine. Pagan in Exile. 2004. (Pagan Chronicles Ser.: Bk. 2). (Illus.). 336p. (J). (gr. 7 up). 15.99 (978-0-7636-2020-2(3)) Candlewick Pr.

—Pagan's Daughter. 2008. (YA). ***(978-0-7636-3650-0(9))*** Candlewick Pr.

—Pagan's Scribe. 2006. (Pagan Chronicles Ser.: Bk. 4). 368p. (YA). (gr. 7). pap. 6.99 (978-0-7636-2973-1(1)) Candlewick Pr.

—Pagan's Vows. 2005. (Pagan Chronicles Ser.: Bk. 3). 336p. (YA). (gr. 7 up). pap. 6.99 (978-0-7636-2754-6(2)) Candlewick Pr.

—Pagan's Vows. De Seve, Peter, illus. 2004. (Pagan Chronicles Ser.: Bk. 3). 336p. (J). (gr. 7 up). 16.99 (978-0-7636-2021-9(1)) Candlewick Pr.

Jordan, Sherryl. The Hunting of the Last Dragon. 2002. 192p. (J). (gr. 7 up). 15.99 (978-0-06-028902-7(3)); 15.89 (978-0-06-028903-4(1)) HarperCollins Pubs.

Keller, John E. The Emperor's Elephant. 2006. 127p. (YA). per. 12.95 (978-0-942566-45-1(9)) LinguaText, Ltd.

Krensky, Stephen. We Just Moved! Di Fiori, Lawrence, illus. 1998. (Hello Reader! Ser.). 32p. (J). pap. 3.99 (978-0-590-33127-2(2)) Scholastic, Inc.

Lamprey, L. Masters of the Guild. l.t. ed. 2006. 168p. pap. 14.99 (978-1-4264-2076-4(5)) BiblioBazaar.

Levitin, Sonia. The Cure. 1999. 192p. (YA). (gr. 5 up). 16.00 (978-0-15-201827-6(1) , Silver Whistle) Harcourt Trade Pubs.

—The Cure. 2000. 272p. (J). (gr. 7 up). pap. 6.99 (978-0-380-73298-2(X) , Harper Trophy) HarperCollins Pubs.

—The Cure. 2000. (J). 12.64 (978-0-606-19967-4(5)) Tandem Library Bks.

—Cure. 2000. (gr. 5-8). lib. bdg. 14.15 (978-0-613-29918-3(3)) Tandem Library Bks.

Love, D. Anne. The Puppeteer's Apprentice. 192p. (J). 2003. 16.95 (978-0-689-84424-9(7) , McElderry, Margaret K.); 2004. (Illus.). reprint ed. pap. 4.99 (978-0-689-84425-6(5) , Aladdin) Simon & Schuster Children's Publishing.

Malone, Patricia. Lady Ilena: Way of the Warrior. 2007. 176p. (YA). (gr. 7-11). mass mkt. 5.99 ***(978-0-440-23901-7(X)*** , Laurel Leaf) Random Hse. Children's Bks.

Malone, Patricia. The Legend of Lady Ilena. 2003. (Illus.). 240p. (YA). (gr. 7). mass mkt. 5.50 (978-0-440-22909-4(X) , Laurel Leaf) Random Hse. Children's Bks.

—The Legend of Lady Ilena. 2003. (gr. 7-12). lib. bdg. 13.55 (978-0-613-72280-3(9)) Tandem Library Bks.

McMullan, Kate. Countdown to the Year 1000. Basso, Bill, illus. 2003. (Dragon Slayers' Academy Ser.: No. 8). 112p. (J). pap. 4.99 (978-0-448-43508-4(X) , Grosset & Dunlap) Penguin Group (USA) Inc.

—Countdown to the Year 1000. 2003. (Dragon Slayers' Academy Ser.: No. 8). (gr. 3-6). lib. bdg. 13.00 (978-0-613-72562-0(X)) Tandem Library Bks.

Morris, Gerald. The Lioness & Her Knight. 2005. (Squire's Tales Ser.). 352p. (J). (gr. 5-7). 16.00 (978-0-618-50772-6(8)) Houghton Mifflin Co. Trade & Reference Div.

Napoli, Donna Jo. Breath. 2003. (Illus.). 272p. (YA). 17.95 (978-0-689-86174-1(5) , Atheneum) Simon & Schuster Children's Publishing.

—Breath. l.t. ed. 2005. 251p. 21.95 (978-0-7862-7420-8(4) , Large Print Pr.) Thorndike Pr.

Napoli, Donna Jo. Hush: An Irish Princess' Tale. 2007. 320p. (YA). (gr. 7 up). 16.99 ***(978-0-689-86176-5(1))*** Simon & Schuster Children's Publishing.

Nunes, Rachel Ann. The Secret of the King. Ward, Jay Bryant, illus. 2005. 32p. (J). (ps-ps). 17.95 (978-1-59038-241-7(2) , Shadow Mountain) Deseret Bk. Co.

Osborne, Mary Pope. The Knight at Dawn. unabr. ed. 2004. (Magic Tree House Ser. : No. 2). 66p. (J). (gr. k-3). pap. 17.00 incl. audio (978-0-8072-0331-6(9) , Listening Library) Random Hse. Audio Publishing Group.

Osborne, Mary Pope. The Knight at Dawn Book & CD. Murdocca, Sal, illus. 2008. (Stepping Stone Book(TM) Ser.). (J). (gr. k-3). 9.99 ***(978-0-375-84406-5(6)*** , Random Hse. Bks. for Young Readers) Random Hse. Children's Bks.

Platt, Richard. Castle Diary: The Journal of Tobias Burgess. Riddell, Chris, illus. 2003. 128p. (J). (gr. 4). 6.99 (978-0-7636-2164-3(1)) Candlewick Pr.

—Castle Diary: The Journal of Tobias Burgess. 2003. (gr. 3-6). lib. bdg. 15.30 (978-0-613-74821-6(2)) Tandem Library Bks.

—Castle Diary: The Journal of Tobias Burgess, Page. 2001. (J). (978-0-606-22543-4(9)) Tandem Library Bks.

Pringle, Eric. Big George & the Seventh Knight. Paine, Colin, illus. 2002. 208p. pap. 10.99 (978-0-7475-5539-1(7)) Bloomsbury Publishing Plc GBR. *Dist:* Independent Pubs. Group.

—Big George & the Winter King. Paine, Colin, illus. 2004. 208p. pap. 12.99 (978-0-7475-6341-9(1)) Bloomsbury Publishing Plc GBR. *Dist:* Independent Pubs. Group.

Quindlen, Anna. Happily Ever After. 1999. (gr. 3-6). lib. bdg. 13.00 (978-0-613-17806-8(8)) Tandem Library Bks.

Rautenberg, Karen Rita. Lady Lucy's Gallant Knight. 2007. 156p. (J). pap. 7.95 (978-1-933255-22-4(6)) DNA Pr.

Santillo, LuAnn. Medieval Magic, 6 vols. Santillo, LuAnn, ed. 2003. (Half-Pint Kids Readers Ser.). (Illus.). 42p. (J). (ps-1). pap. 6.99 (978-1-59256-049-3(0)) Half-Pint Kids, Inc.

Sauerwein, Leigh. Song for Eloise. 2004. 136p. (YA). 15.95 (978-1-886910-90-4(1) , Lemniscaat) Boyds Mills Pr.

Shire, Poppy. Brightheart the Knight's Pony. Berg, Ron, illus. 2007. (Magic Pony Carousel Ser.: No. 2). 96p. (J). pap. 3.99 (978-0-06-083782-2(9)); 14.99 (978-0-06-083780-8(2)) HarperCollins Pubs. (Harper Trophy).

Shulevitz, Uri. The Travels of Benjamin of Tudela: Through Three Continents in the Twelfth Century. 2005. (Illus.). 48p. (J). 17.00 (978-0-374-37754-0(5) , Farrar, Straus & Giroux (BYR)) Farrar, Straus & Giroux.

Skurzynski, Gloria. The Minstrel in the Tower. Heller, Julek, illus. 2004. (Stepping Stone Bks.). 64p. (J). (gr. 4-7). pap. 3.99 (978-0-394-89598-7(3) , Random Hse. Bks. for Young Readers) Random Hse. Children's Bks.

Springer, Nancy. Lionclaw. 2002. (Tales of Rowan Hood Ser.: No. 2). 160p. (YA). (gr. 4-7). 16.99 (978-0-399-23716-4(X) , Philomel) Penguin Group (USA) Inc.

—Rowan Hood: Outlaw Girl of Sherwood Forest. 2002. (Tales of Rowan Hood Ser.: No. 1). 192p. (J). (ps-7). pap. 5.99 (978-0-698-11972-7(X) , Putnam Juvenile) Penguin Group (USA) Inc.

—Rowan Hood: Outlaw Girl of Sherwood Forest. 2002. (Tales of Rowan Hood Ser.: No. 1). (gr. 5-8). lib. bdg. 14.15 (978-0-613-53860-2(9)) Tandem Library Bks.

—Wild Boy: A Tale of Rowan Hood. 2004. (Tales of Rowan Hood Ser.: No. 4). 128p. (YA). (gr. 5-7). 16.99 (978-0-399-24015-7(2) , Philomel) Penguin Group (USA) Inc.

Sturt, M. The Canterbury Pilgrims (Being Chaucer's. 2006. 94.99 ***(978-1-4280-0313-2(4));*** pap. 88.99 ***(978-1-4280-0309-5(6))*** IndyPublish.com.

Thal, Lilli. Mimus. Brownjohn, John, tr. from GER. 2005. 398p. (YA). (gr. 7-10). 19.95 (978-1-55037-925-9(9)) Annick Pr., Ltd. CAN. *Dist:* Firefly Bks., Ltd.

—Mimus. Brownjohn, John, tr. from GER. 2005. 398p. (YA). (gr. 7-10). pap. 9.95 (978-1-55037-924-2(0)) Annick Pr., Ltd. CAN. *Dist:* Firefly Bks., Ltd.

Tomlinson, Theresa. Child of the May. 1998. (Illus.). 128p. (YA). (gr. 5-9). pap. 15.95 (978-0-531-30118-0(4) , Orchard Bks.) Scholastic, Inc.

Warkentin, Karla. Mystery in Medieval Castle. 2004. (Time Stone Travelers Ser.). 144p. (J). pap., pap. 6.99 (978-0-7814-4025-7(4) , 0781440254) Cook, David C. Publishing Co.

Williams, Laura E. Executioner's Daughter. 2007. 144p. (YA). pap. 6.95 ***(978-0-8050-8186-2(0)*** , Holt, Henry & Co. Bks. For Young Readers) Holt, Henry & Co.

MIDDLE ATLANTIC STATES

see Atlantic States

MIDDLE CLASS—FICTION

Kytle, Calvin. Like a Tree. 2007. 430p. 28.95 ***(978-1-58838-220-7(6)*** , NewSouth Bks.) NewSouth, Inc.

MIDDLE EARTH (IMAGINARY PLACE)—FICTION

Tolkien, J. R. R. The Hobbit. 2002. 16.60 (978-0-7587-7961-8(5)) Book Wholesalers, Inc.

—The Hobbit. 1999. (YA). 9.95 (978-1-56137-253-9(6)) Novel Units, Inc.

—The Hobbit. 2001. (gr. 7-12). lib. bdg. 18.80 (978-0-613-88165-4(6)) Tandem Library Bks.

—El Hobbit. 2003. (Lord of the Rings Ser.). (SPA.). 320p. (YA). 17.95 (978-84-450-7141-0(6) , MQ9001) Minotauro Ediciones ESP. *Dist:* Distribooks, Inc., Lectorum Pubns., Inc., Planeta Publishing Corp.

—The Hobbit. adapted ed. 2001. (J). 23.50 (978-0-606-21234-2(5)) Tandem Library Bks.

—Hobbit: An Illustrated Edition of the Fantasy Classic. Wenzel, David, illus. 2001. 144p. reprint ed. pap. 17.95 (978-0-345-44560-5(0) , Del Rey) Random House Publishing Group.

—Hobbit: An Illustrated Edition of the Fantasy Classic. abr. ed. 2001. (gr. 5-8). lib. bdg. 24.60 (978-0-613-53684-4(3)) Tandem Library Bks.

—Hobbit: Or There & Back Again. 1999. (gr. 3-6). lib. bdg. 21.10 (978-0-613-87066-5(2)) Tandem Library Bks.

—The Hobbit: Or There & Back Again. 2002. (Illus.). 365p. (YA). (gr. 5). pap. 10.00 (978-0-618-26030-0(7)) Houghton Mifflin Co. Trade & Reference Div.

—The Hobbit: Or There & Back Again. Sis, Peter, illus. 2001. 320p. (YA). (gr. 7 up). pap. 10.00 (978-0-618-15082-3(X)) Houghton Mifflin Co. Trade & Reference Div.

—The Hobbit: Or There & Back Again. 1999. (Illus.). 320p. pap. 12.00 (978-0-618-00221-4(9)) Houghton Mifflin Co. Trade & Reference Div.

—The Hobbit: Or, There & Back Again. 2001. (Illus.). 330p. (YA). (gr. 7 up). 18.00 (978-0-618-16221-5(6)) Houghton Mifflin Co. Trade & Reference Div.

—Hobbit, or, There & Back Again. 2002. (gr. 5-8). lib. bdg. 18.80 (978-0-613-90725-5(6)) Tandem Library Bks.

—The Lord of the Rings. unabr. ed. 2000. 1216p. (YA). pap. 80.00 incl. audio (978-0-8072-8344-8(4) , LL0187, Listening Library) Random Hse. Audio Publishing Group.

—The Return of the King. 2002. (J). 16.60 (978-0-7587-5212-3(1)) Book Wholesalers, Inc.

—Senhor dos Aneis. pap. 36.95 (978-85-336-1337-9(7)) Livraria Martins Editora BRA. *Dist:* Distribooks, Inc.

MIDDLE EAST

Here are entered works on the region consisting of Asia west of Pakistan, northeastern Africa, and occasionally Greece and Pakistan. Works treating collectively the Arabic-speaking countries of Asia and Africa, or of Asia only, are entered under Arab Countries.

Arab Community Center for Economic and Social Services Staff. Arab American Encyclopedia. Ameri, Anan & Ramey, Dawn, eds. 2000. (Arab American Reference Library). (Illus.). 260p. (J). (gr. 4-7). 67.00 (978-0-7876-2952-6(9) , GML00502-112523, UXL) Thomson Gale.

Bowden, Rob. The Middle East & North Africa. 2007. (J). ***(978-1-4034-9902-8(0));*** (Illus.). 64p. (gr. 4-7). pap. ***(978-1-4034-9911-0(X))*** Heinemann Library.

Brimson, Samuel. Sierra Leone-United Arab Emirates, 8 vols. 2003. (Nations of the World Ser.: Vol. 7). (Illus.). 64p. (J). (gr. 5 up). lib. bdg. 30.00 (978-0-8368-5491-6(8) , World Almanac Library) Stevens, Gareth Inc.

Downing, David. Geography & Resources of the Middle East. 2006. (World Almanac Library of the Middle East). (Illus.). 48p. (J). pap. (978-0-8368-7341-2(6)); lib. bdg. (978-0-8368-7334-4(3)) Stevens, Gareth Inc. (World Almanac Library).

—Governments & Leaders of the Middle East. 2006. (World Almanac Library of the Middle East). (Illus.). 48p. (J). pap. (978-0-8368-7342-9(4)); lib. bdg. (978-0-8368-7335-1(1)) Stevens, Gareth Inc. (World Almanac Library).

Eboch, Chris. Yemen. 2003. (Modern Nations of the World Ser.). (Illus.). 112p. (J). 29.95 (978-1-59018-240-6(5) , Lucent Bks.) Thomson Gale.

Gelletly, LeeAnne. Kurds. 2005. (Growth & Influence of Islam in the Nations of Asia & Central Asia Ser.). (Illus.). 128p. (J). lib. bdg. 25.95 (978-1-59084-837-1(3)) Mason Crest Pubs.

Gottfried, Ted. The Israelis & Palestinians: Small Steps to Peace. 2000. (Headliners Ser.). (Illus.). 64p. (gr. 5-8). lib. bdg. 25.90 (978-0-7613-1859-0(3) , Millbrook Pr.) Lerner Publishing Group.

Gritzner, Jeffrey A. & Gritzner, Charles F. North Africa & the Middle East. 2006. (Modern World Cultures Ser.). (Illus.). 128p. (J). (gr. 6-12). 30.00 (978-0-7910-8145-7(1) , Chelsea Hse.) Facts On File, Inc.

Gunderson, Cory Gideon. Countries of the Middle East. 2004. (World in Conflict-the Middle East Ser.). (Illus.). 48p. (J). (gr. 4-8). lib. bdg. 25.65 (978-1-59197-419-2(4)) ABDO Publishing Co.

—Religions of the Middle East. 2004. (World in Conflict-the Middle East Ser.). (Illus.). 48p. (J). (gr. 4-8). lib. bdg. 25.65 (978-1-59197-412-3(7)) ABDO Publishing Co.

Hall, Loretta & Hall, Bridget K. Arab American Biography, 2 vols. 1999. (Arab American Reference Library). (Illus.). 528p. (J). (gr. 4-7). 120.00 (978-0-7876-2953-3(7) , GML00502-112524, UXL) Thomson Gale.

Hestler, Anna. Yemen. 1999. (Cultures of the World Ser.). (Illus.). 128p. (gr. 5-12). lib. bdg. 37.07 (978-0-7614-0956-4(4) , Benchmark Bks.) Cavendish, Marshall Corp.

Johnson, Julia. United Arab Emirates. 1999. (Major World Nations Ser.). (Illus.). 144p. (J). (gr. 4-7). 29.95 (978-0-7910-5402-4(0) , Chelsea Hse.) Facts On File, Inc.

King, David C. The United Arab Emirates. 2008. (Cultures of the World Ser.). (J). lib. bdg. ***(978-0-7614-2565-6(9)*** , Benchmark Bks.) Cavendish, Marshall Corp.

King, John. Making of the Middle East. 2005. (Middle East Ser.). (Illus.). 56p. (J). (978-1-4109-1620-4(0)); pap. (978-1-4109-1626-6(X)) Steck-Vaughn.

—Oil in the Middle East. 2005. (Middle East Ser.). (Illus.). 56p. (J). (978-1-4109-1624-2(3)); pap. (978-1-4109-1630-3(8)) Steck-Vaughn.

Kort, Michael. The Handbook of the Middle East. 2007. lib. bdg. ***(978-0-8225-7143-8(9))*** Twenty First Century Bks.

Kort, Michael G. The Handbook of the Middle East. 2002. (Single Titles Ser.). (Illus.). 304p. (gr. 7 up). lib. bdg. 39.90 (978-0-7613-1611-4(6) , Twenty-First Century Bks.) Lerner Publishing Group.

McCoy, Lisa. Facts & Figures about the Middle East. 2003. (Modern Middle East Nations & Their Strategic Place in the World Ser.). (Illus.). 112,128p. (J). (gr. 7 up). lib. bdg. (978-1-59084-528-8(5)) Mason Crest Pubs.

Miller, Debra A. Middle East. 2007. (Current Controversies Ser.). (Illus.). 240p. (gr. 10-12). 36.20 ***(978-0-7377-3960-2(6));*** pap. 24.95 ***(978-0-7377-3961-9(4))*** Thomson Gale. (Greenhaven Pr., Inc.).

Miller, Debra A. U.S. Involvement in the Middle East: Inciting Conflict. 2004. (Lucent Library of Conflict in the Middle East). (Illus.). 112p. (J). (gr. 7-10). 29.95 (978-1-59018-494-3(7) , Lucent Bks.) Thomson Gale.

National Geographic Atlas of the Middle East. 2003. (gr. 7-12). lib. bdg. 30.35 (978-0-613-70599-8(8)) Tandem Library Bks.

Sammis, Fran. Europe & the Middle East. 1998. (Mapping Our World Ser.). (Illus.). 64p. (J). (gr. 4-8). lib. bdg. 27.07 (978-0-7614-0370-8(1) , Benchmark Bks.) Cavendish, Marshall Corp.

Senker, Cath. Saudi Arabia. 2007. (J). ***(978-1-84234-465-1(X))*** Cherrytree Pubns., Inc.

Stacey, Gill. Religions of the Middle East. 2006. (World Almanac Library of the Middle East). (Illus.). 48p. (J). pap. (978-0-8368-7345-0(9)); lib. bdg. (978-0-8368-7338-2(6)) Stevens, Gareth Inc. (World Almanac Library).

Steele, Philip. The Middle East. 2006. (Kingfisher Knowledge Ser.). (Illus.). 64p. (J). (gr. 5-9). 12.95 (978-0-7534-5984-3(1) , Kingfisher) Houghton Mifflin Co. Trade & Reference Div.

Willis, Terri. Qatar. 2004. (Enchantment of the World, Second Ser.). (Illus.). 144p. (J). (gr. 5-9). 36.00 (978-0-516-24254-5(7) , Children's Pr.) Scholastic Library Publishing.

Yancey, Diane. The Middle East: An Overview. 2004. (Lucent Library of Conflict in the Middle East). (Illus.). 112p. (J). (gr. 7-10). 29.95 (978-1-59018-492-9(0) , Lucent Bks.) Thomson Gale.

MIDDLE EAST—ANTIQUITIES

Allen, T. R. Allen. Antiquus: Ephesus. Allen, T. R. Allen & Kubiak, Mike, photos by. 2002. (Antiquus). cd-rom 12.00 (978-1-931792-20-2(8)) E-Digital Bks., LLC.

Hunter, Erica C. D. & Corbishley, Mike. First Civilizations. 2nd rev. ed. 2003. (Cultural Atlas for Young People Ser.). (Illus.). 96p. (J). (gr. 4-9). 35.00 (978-0-8160-5149-6(6)) Facts On File, Inc.

Osborne, Rick. Bible Fortresses, Temples & Tombs. 2003. (gr. 3-6). lib. bdg. 16.45 (978-0-613-71764-9(3)) Tandem Library Bks.

Osborne, Rick & Wooding, Marnie. Bible Fortresses, Temples & Tombs. 2003. (2:52 Soul Gear Ser.). (Illus.). 128p. (J). pap. 7.99 (978-0-310-70483-6(9)) Zonderkidz.

Tubb, Jonathan N. & Dorling Kindersley Publishing Staff. Bible Lands. 2000. (Eyewitness Bks.). (Illus.). 64p. (J). (gr. 4-7). lib. bdg. 19.99 (978-0-7894-6579-5(5)) Dorling Kindersley Publishing, Inc.

MIDDLE EAST—DESCRIPTION AND TRAVEL

Dorling Kindersley Publishing Staff. Mundo Antiguo de Egipto. 2004. (Eyewitness Books). 72p. (J). lib. bdg. 19.99 (978-0-7566-0793-7(0)) Dorling Kindersley Publishing, Inc.

Due, Andrea. Atlas del Mundo Biblico.Tr. of Atlas of the Bible Lands. (SPA.). 61p. (YA). (gr. 5-8). 21.56 (978-84-207-9008-4(7)) Grupo Anaya, S.A. ESP. *Dist:* Lectorum Pubns., Inc.

Feiler, Bruce S. Walking the Bible: A Journey by Land Through the Five Books of Moses. 2002. (gr. 7-12). lib. bdg. 24.55 (978-0-613-62166-3(2)) Tandem Library Bks.

M
N
O

—Walking the Bible: An Illustrated Journey for Kids Through the Greatest Stories Ever Told. Meret, Sasha, illus. ed. 2005. 112p. (J). pap. 7.99 (978-0-06-051119-7(2) , Harper Trophy) HarperCollins Pubs.

—Walking the Bible: An Illustrated Journey for Kids Through the Greatest Stories Ever Told. Meret, Sasha, tr. Meret, Sasha, illus. ed. 2004. 112p. (J). (gr. 2 up). 16.99 (978-0-06-051117-3(6)) HarperCollins Pubs.

Groner, Judyth & Wikler, Madeline. Let's Visit Israel. Nathan, Cheryl, illus. 2004. 12p. (J). (ps up). 5.95 (978-1-58013-087-5(9)) Kar-Ben Publishing.

Wagner, Heather Lehr. Gertrude Bell: Explorer of the Middle East. 2004. (Women Explorers Ser.). (Illus.). 120p. 30.00 (978-0-7910-7711-5(X) , Chelsea Hse.) Facts On File, Inc.

Yanofsky, Tsivia. Take Me to the Holy Land: A Youngster's Tour of Eretz Yisrael. 2000. (ArtScroll Youth Ser.). (Illus.). 96p. (J). 19.99 (978-1-57819-495-7(4) , TAKH) Mesorah Pubns., Ltd.

MIDDLE EAST—FICTION

Alexander, Lloyd. The Jedera Adventure. 2001. (Vesper Holly Ser.). (Illus.). 160p. (J). (gr. 5-9). pap. 5.99 (978-0-14-131238-5(6) , Puffin) Penguin Group (USA) Inc.

Alrawi, Karim. The Girl Who Lost Her Smile. Czernecki, Stefan, illus. 2000. 32p. (J). (ps-3). 16.95 (978-1-890817-17-6(1)) Winslow Pr.

Alrawi, Karim & Czernecki, Stefan. The Girl Who Lost Her Smile. 2000. (Illus.). 30p. (J). 6.95 (978-1-896580-15-9(7)) Tradewind Bks. CAN. *Dist:* Orca Bk. Pubs. USA.

Balaguae, Lin & Long, Robert, contrib. by. Alai Babaa y los 40 Ladrones: Ali Baba & the 40 Thieves. 2000. (Cuentos y Leyendas Bilingues Ser.). (ENG & SPA.). (J). 21.20 (978-0-658-01023-1(9) , National Textbook Co.) McGraw-Hill/Contemporary.

Balague, Lin & Long, Robert. Ali Baba y los 40 Ladrones (Ali Baba & the 40 Thieves) 2000. (Cuentos y Leyendas Bilingues Ser.). (SPA & ENG., Illus.). (J). 17.68 (978-0-658-01024-8(7)) McGraw-Hill/Contemporary.

Center for Learning Staff. Habibi/Seven Daughters & Seven Sons: Novel Curriculum Unit. 2004. (Novel Ser.). 73p. (YA). tchr. ed., spiral bd. 19.95 (978-1-56077-770-0(2)) Ctr. for Learning, The.

Climo, Shirley. The Persian Cinderella. Florczak, Robert, illus. 2001. 32p. (J). (gr. k-4). pap. 6.99 (978-0-06-443853-7(8) , Harper Trophy) HarperCollins Pubs.

Cooper, Patrick. I Is Someone Else. 304p. (YA). 2007. (gr. 7-11). mass mkt. 6.50 (978-0-440-23919-2(2) , Laurel Leaf); 2006. (Illus.). (gr. 9). 16.95 (978-0-385-73269-7(4) , Delacorte Bks. for Young Readers); 2006. (Illus.). (gr. 9). lib. bdg. 18.99 (978-0-385-90286-1(7) , Delacorte Bks. for Young Readers) Random Hse. Children's Bks.

Fables of Bah Ya Bah. 2002. 40p. (J). pap., tchr. ed. 10.00 (978-1-932008-11-1(X)) Fine Media Group.

Fletcher, Susan. Alphabet of Dreams. 2006. (Illus.). 304p. (YA). (gr. 7 up). 16.95 (978-0-689-85042-4(5) , Atheneum) Simon & Schuster Children's Publishing.

Hancock, H. Irving. The Young Engineers on the Gulf. rev. ed. 2006. 216p. 27.95 (978-1-4218-1752-1(7)); pap. 12.95 (978-1-4218-1852-8(3)) 1st World Publishing, Inc. (1st World Library - Literary Society).

Jolin, Paula. In the Name of God. 2007. 208p. (YA). (gr. 9 up). 16.95 (978-1-59643-211-6(X)) Roaring Brook Pr.

Kyuchukov, Hristo. My Name Was Hussein. Eitzen, Allan, illus. 2004. 32p. (YA). (gr. 2-4). pap. 15.95 (978-1-56397-964-4(0)) Boyds Mills Pr.

Luedke, Robert James. Eye Witness: A Fictional Tale of Absolute Truth. 2004. (Illus.). 96p. 24.99 (978-0-9758924-1-1(X)); pap. 13.99 (978-0-9758924-0-4(1)) Head Pr. Publishing.

Marston, Elsa. Figs & Fate: Stories about Growing up in the Arab World Today. 2005. 146p. (J). 22.50 (978-0-8076-1551-5(X)); pap. 15.95 (978-0-8076-1554-6(4)) Braziller, George Inc.

Matze, Claire Sidhom. The Stars in My Geddoh's Sky. Farnsworth, Bill, illus. 1999. (Concept Book Ser.). 32p. (J). (gr. k-3). pap. 14.95 (978-0-8075-5332-9(8)) Whitman, Albert & Co.

Mitchell, Stephen. Genies, Meanies, & Magic Rings: Three Tales from the 1001 Nights. Pohrt, Tom & Campbell Pearson, Tracey, illus. 2007. 192p. (J). 16.95 ***(978-0-8027-9639-4(7))*** Walker & Co.

Osborne, Mary Pope. Season of the Sandstorms. 2006. (Magic Tree House Ser.: No. 34). 144p. (J). (gr. k-3). pap. 4.99 (978-0-375-83032-7(4) , Random Hse. Bks. for Young Readers) Random Hse. Children's Bks.

Pirotta, Saviour & Marks, Alan. The Glass Palace. 2007. (J). ***(978-1-59771-078-7(4))*** Sea-To-Sea Pubns.

Reiche, Dietlof. Freddy's Final Quest Book Five in Golden Hamster. 2008. 208p. pap. 5.99 ***(978-0-439-87415-1(7)*** , Scholastic Paperbacks) Scholastic, Inc.

Reiche, Dietlof & Brownjohn, John. Freddy's Final Quest. Cepeda, Joe, illus. 2007. (Golden Hamster Saga Ser.: Bk. 5). 304p. (J). pap. 16.99 (978-0-439-87414-4(9) , Scholastic Pr.) Scholastic, Inc.

Serafin, Mike. 7 Stories from Baghdad. 2005. 50p. pap. 12.95 (978-1-4137-8808-2(4)) PublishAmerica, Inc.

Shah, Idries. The Silly Chicken. Jackson, Jeff, illus. 2005. 32p. (J). pap. 6.99 (978-1-883536-50-3(2) , Hoopoe Bks.) ISHK.

—The Silly Chicken/el Pollo Bobo. Wirkala, Rita, tr. Jackson, Jeff, illus. 2005. 32p. (J). (ps-ps). 18.00 (978-1-883536-37-4(5) , Hoopoe Bks.) ISHK.

Smith, Chris. One City, Two Brothers: The Story of Jerusalem. Fronty, Aurélia, illus. 2007. 32p. (J). (ps-5). 16.99 ***(978-1-84686-042-3(3))*** Barefoot Bks., Inc.

Sorrells, Walter. First Shot. 2007. 279p. (YA). (gr. 7-12). 16.99 ***(978-0-525-47801-0(9)*** , Dutton Juvenile) Penguin Group (USA) Inc.

Temple, Frances. The Beduins' Gazelle. Bowers, David, illus. 1998. (Harper Trophy Bks.). 160p. (J). (gr. 7 up). pap. 5.99 (978-0-06-440669-7(5) , Harper Trophy) HarperCollins Pubs.

Thomas, Jerry D. The Red Hat Mystery. Odell, Lad, illus. 2003. (Detective Zack Ser.). 132p. (J). pap., pap. 6.99 (978-0-7814-3802-5(0) , 0781438020) Cook, David C. Publishing Co.

—The Secrets in the Sand. Odell, Lad, illus. 2003. (Detective Zack Ser.). 132p. (J). pap., pap. 6.99 (978-0-7814-3803-2(9) , 0781438039) Cook, David C. Publishing Co.

Tunnell, Michael O. Moon Without Magic. 2007. 240p. (YA). (gr. 7). 17.99 ***(978-0-525-47729-7(2)*** , Dutton Juvenile) Penguin Group (USA) Inc.

Whelan, Gloria. Parade of Shadows. 2007. 304p. (J). (gr. 5 up). 15.99 ***(978-0-06-089028-5(2));*** lib. bdg. 16.89 ***(978-0-06-089029-2(0))*** HarperCollins Pubs.

MIDDLE EAST—HISTORY

Ahmed, Akbar, intro. Creation of the Modern Middle East, Set. 2005. (Illus.). 112 - 144p. (YA). (gr. 6-12). pap. 420.00 (978-0-7910-6503-7(0)) Facts On File, Inc.

Barr, Gary. History & Activities of the Islamic Empire. 2006. (Hands-On Ancient History Ser.). (Illus.). 32p. (J). pap. (978-1-4034-7934-1(8)) Heinemann Library.

Bodnarchuk, Kari J. Kurdistan: Region under Siege. 2000. (World in Conflict Ser.). (Illus.). 104p. (YA). (gr. 7-12). 25.26 (978-0-8225-3556-0(4) , Lerner Pubns.) Lerner Publishing Group.

Cheshire, Gerard & Hammond, Paula. The Middle East. 2002. (Cultures & Costumes Ser.). (Illus.). 64p. (J). (gr. 7 up). lib. bdg. (978-1-59084-434-2(3)) Mason Crest Pubs.

Coletti, Sharon. Everything You Need to Teach the Middle East. 2005. (YA). ring bd. 149.95 (978-1-933558-04-2(0)) InspirEd Educators.

Crisp, Peter. Mesopotamia: Iraq in Ancient Times. 2004. (Picturing the Past Ser.). (Illus.). 32p. (J). 15.95 (978-1-59270-024-0(1)) Enchanted Lion Bks., LLC.

Davenport, John. A Brief Political & Geographic History of the Middle East: Where Are Persia, Babylon, & the Ottoman Empire? 2007. (Places in Time Ser.). (Illus.). 112p. (YA). (gr. 5-10). lib. bdg. 37.10 ***(978-1-58415-622-2(8))*** Mitchell Lane Pubs., Inc.

Downing, David. Conflicts of the Middle East. 2006. (World Almanac Library of the Middle East). (Illus.). 48p. (J). pap. (978-0-8368-7340-5(8)); lib. bdg. (978-0-8368-7333-7(5)) Stevens, Gareth Inc. (World Almanac Library).

—History of the Middle East. 2006. (World Almanac Library of the Middle East). (Illus.). 48p. (J). pap. (978-0-8368-7343-6(2)); lib. bdg. (978-0-8368-7336-8(X)) Stevens, Gareth Inc. (World Almanac Library).

Frank, Mitch. Understanding the Holy Land: Answering Questions about the Israeli-Palestinian Conflict. 2005. (Illus.). 160p. (YA) (gr. 6). 17.99 (978-0-670-06032-0(1) , Viking Juvenile) Penguin Group (USA) Inc.

Hampton, Wilborn. War in the Middle East: A Reporter's Story: Black September & the Yom Kippur War. 2007. (Illus.). 128p. (YA). (gr. 5 up). 19.99 ***(978-0-7636-2493-4(4))*** Candlewick Pr.

Hancock, Ian & Kyuchukov, Hristo. A History of the Romani People. 2005. (Illus.). 32p. (J). (gr. 4-7). 19.95 (978-1-56397-962-0(4)) Boyds Mills Pr.

Hunter, Erica C. D. & Corbishley, Mike. First Civilizations. 2nd rev. ed. 2003. (Cultural Atlas for Young People Ser.). (Illus.). 96p. (J). (gr. 4-9). 35.00 (978-0-8160-5149-6(6)) Facts On File, Inc.

LoBaido, Anthony C., et al. The Kurds of Asia. 2005. (First Peoples Ser.). (Illus.). 48p. (gr. 4-8). lib. bdg. 23.95 (978-0-8225-0664-5(5)) Lerner Publishing Group.

Macaulay, David. Mosque. Macaulay, David, illus. 2003. (Illus.). 96p. (YA). (gr. 5 up). 18.00 (978-0-618-24034-0(9) , Walter Lorraine) Houghton Mifflin Co. Trade & Reference Div.

Maury, Rob. Immigration from the Middle East. 2004. (Changing Face of North America Ser.). (Illus.). 112p. (J). lib. bdg. (978-1-59084-695-7(8)) Mason Crest Pubs.

Pendergast, Tom, et al. The Middle East Conflict. 2005. (Middle East Conflict Reference Library). (Illus.). (J). lxvii, 267p. 67.00 (978-0-7876-9456-2(8)); xlii, 238p. 67.00 (978-0-7876-9458-6(4)) Thomson Gale. (UXL).

—The Middle East Conflict: Biographies. 2005. (Middle East Conflict Reference Library). (Illus.). li, 282p. (J). 67.00 (978-0-7876-9457-9(6) , UXL) Thomson Gale.

Perliger, Arie, et al. Terrorism in the Middle East. 2006. (Roots of Terrorism Ser.). (Illus.). 120p. (J). (gr. 6-12). 35.00 (978-0-7910-8309-3(8) , Chelsea Hse.) Facts On File, Inc.

Podany, Amanda H. & McGee, Marni. The Ancient near Eastern World. 2005. (World in Ancient Times Ser.). (Illus.). 176p. (YA). 32.95 (978-0-19-516159-5(9)) Oxford Univ. Pr., Inc.

Raintree Steck-Vaughn Staff, ed. New Perspectives. 1999. (J). 179.82 (978-0-7398-2793-2(6)) Raintree.

Rubin, Barry M. The Middle East in the Age of Uncertainty, 1991-Present. 2007. (J). ***(978-1-4222-0176-3(7))*** Mason Crest Pubs.

Schomp, Virginia. Ancient Mesopotamia. 2004. (People of the Ancient World Ser.). (J). 29.50 (978-0-531-11818-4(5) , Watts, Franklin) Scholastic Library Publishing.

Senker, Cath. The Arab-Israeli Conflict. 2007. (J). ***(978-1-84193-725-0(8))*** Smart Apple Media.

Stefoff, Rebecca. The Ancient Near East. 2004. (World Historical Atlases Ser.). (J). 27.07 (978-0-7614-1639-5(0) , Benchmark Bks.) Cavendish, Marshall Corp.

Wagner, Heather Lehr. The Division of the Middle East: The Treaty of Sevres. 2004. (Arbitrary Borders Ser.). (Illus.). 120p. (gr. 9-13). 35.00 (978-0-7910-7831-0(0) , Chelsea Hse.) Facts On File, Inc.

Wallenfels, Ronald, ed. The Ancient Near East: An Encyclopedia for Students, 4 vols. 2000. (Illus.). 852p. (J). 460.00 (978-0-684-80597-9(9) , GML00502-170634, Charles Scribner's Sons) Thomson Gale.

Wallenfels, Ronald & Sasson, Jack M., eds. The Ancient Near East: An Encyclopedia for Students, Vol. 4. 2000. (Illus.). (J). vii, 216p. 60.00 (978-0-684-80596-2(0)); vii, 216p. 60.00 (978-0-684-80594-8(4)); vii, 216p. 60.00 (978-0-684-80595-5(2)); xix, 204p. 60.00 (978-0-684-80589-4(8)) Thomson Gale. (Macmillan Reference USA).

Williamson, Joanne S. Hittite Warrior. 1999. (Living History Library). (Illus.). xvii, 237p. (J). (gr. 6-12). reprint ed. pap. 13.95 (978-1-883937-38-6(8) , 98-73485) Bethlehem Bks.

Women in the Ancient Near East: Stories & Primary Sources from the Sumerians through the Early Israelites. l.t. ed. 1999. 94p. (YA). spiral bd. 16.95 net. (978-1-890380-07-6(5)) Women in World History Curriculum.

World in Conflict-the Middle East. 2004. (J). (gr. 4-8). lib. bdg. 307.80 (978-1-59197-409-3(7) , ABDO & Daughters) ABDO Publishing Co.

Young Voices from the Arab World: The Lives & Times of Five Teenagers. 2004. 139p. (YA). (gr. 5 up). tchr. ed. 35.00 incl. VHS (978-0-913957-15-8(1)) AMIDEAST.

Zerbonia, Ralph. Middle East Conflict Cumulative Index. 2005. (Middle East Conflict Reference Library). 16p. (J). 5.00 (978-0-7876-9459-3(2) , UXL) Thomson Gale.

MIDDLE EAST—POLITICS AND GOVERNMENT

Carey Sabbah, Ann. Kurds. 1999. (Endangered Cultures Ser.). (Illus.). 32p. (J). (gr. 4-7). lib. bdg. 16.95 (978-1-887068-92-5(9)) Smart Apple Media.

Einfeld, Jann, ed. Can Democracy Succeed in the Middle East? 2006. (At Issue Ser.). (Illus.). 128p. (YA). (gr. 6 up). pap. 21.20 (978-0-7377-3394-5(2)); lib. bdg. 29.95 (978-0-7377-3393-8(4)) Thomson Gale. (Greenhaven Pr., Inc.).

Foreign Policy Research Institute Staff, ed. Modern Middle East Nations & Their Strategic Places in the World, 25 vols., Set. 2003. (Illus.). 112,128p. (YA). (gr. 7 up). lib. bdg. (978-1-59084-504-2(8)) Mason Crest Pubs.

Gunderson, Cory Gideon. The Need for Oil. 2004. (World in Conflict-the Middle East Ser.). (Illus.). 48p. (J). (gr. 4-8). lib. bdg. 25.65 (978-1-59197-417-8(8)) ABDO Publishing Co.

Harmon, Daniel E. Turkey. 2003. (Modern Middle East Nations & Their Strategic Place in the World Ser.). (Illus.). 112,128p. (YA). (gr. 7 up). lib. bdg. (978-1-59084-524-0(2)) Mason Crest Pubs.

Miller, Debra A. U.S. Involvement in the Middle East: Inciting Conflict. 2004. (Lucent Library of Conflict in the Middle East). (Illus.). 112p. (J). (gr. 7-10). 29.95 (978-1-59018-494-3(7) , Lucent Bks.) Thomson Gale.

Petersen, Christine. The Iran-Contra Scandal. 2004. (Cornerstones of Freedom Ser.). (Illus.). 48p. (J). 26.00 (978-0-516-24228-6(8) , Children's Pr.) Scholastic Library Publishing.

Wagner, Heather Lehr. Anwar Sadat & Menachem Begin: Negotiating Peace in the Middle East. 2007. (Modern Peacemakers Ser.). (Illus.). 128p. (J). (gr. 9 up). 30.00 ***(978-0-7910-9000-8(0)*** , Chelsea Hse.) Facts On File, Inc.

MIDDLE STATES

see Atlantic States

MIDDLE WEST

Here are entered works on the region of the United States between the Rocky Mountains and the Allegheny Mountains and north of the Ohio River and the southern border of Missouri and Kansas, generally including the states of Ohio, Indiana, Michigan, Illinois, Wisconsin, Minnesota, Iowa, Missouri, Kansas, Nebraska, South Dakota and North Dakota.

Benchmark Education Staff. The Midwest Region. 2005. 2.00 ***(978-1-4108-4653-2(9))*** Benchmark Education Co.

Curry, Jud & Curry, Elizabeth. The Midwest. 2006. (Regions of the USA Ser.). (Illus.). 56p. (J). (978-1-4109-2311-0(8)); pap. (978-1-4109-2319-6(3)) Steck-Vaughn.

Geisert, Bonnie. Prairie Town. Geisert, Arthur, illus. 1998. (Small Town U. S. A. Ser.). 32p. (J). (gr. k-3). tchr. ed. 16.00 (978-0-395-85907-0(7) , Walter Lorraine) Houghton Mifflin Co. Trade & Reference Div.

Katzin, Nathan. Dust Bowl. 2002. (Instant Social Studies Activities Folders Ser.). (Illus.). 6p. (gr. 4-8). 3.95 (978-0-439-37085-1(X)) Scholastic, Inc.

Leonardo, Victoria. The Midwest Region. 2005. 39.00 ***(978-1-4108-4605-1(9))*** Benchmark Education Co.

National Geographic Society Staff, contrib. by. The Midwest Today. 2004. (Illus.). 32p. (J). pap. (978-0-7922-4534-6(2)) National Geographic Society.

Schaeffer, Julia. The Midwest States. 2006. (Navigators Ser.). (J). pap. 42.00 ***(978-1-4108-6253-2(4))*** Benchmark Education Co.

Weber, Valerie & Mcnamara, Valerie J. Fun in Grandma's Day. 1999. (In Grandma's Day Ser.). (Illus.). 32p. (J). (gr. 2-4). lib. bdg. 21.27 (978-1-57505-325-7(X) , Carolrhoda Bks.) Lerner Publishing Group.

Williams, Colleen Madonna Flood. My Adventure in the Midwest: Advanced My Adventure. 2007. 44p. (J). pap. 8.99 (978-1-59092-564-5(5) , Orchard Academy Pr.) Windstorm Creative.

MIDDLE WEST—FICTION

Hammond, John, as told by. Lucky in Life. 2003. 150p. (YA). per. 13.95 (978-1-885631-76-3(6)) Hutchison, G.F. Pr.

Klause, Annette Curtis. Freaks: Alive, on the Inside! 2006. 336p. (YA). 16.95 (978-0-689-05143-2(3) , McElderry, Margaret K.) Simon & Schuster Children's Publishing.

L'Allier, Peter. Rotten Robbie & the Legend of Wanibinoo. 2006. (Illus.). (YA). 18.95 (978-0-9724022-8-6(4)) Dr. Todd, LLC.

MacLachlan, Patricia. Caleb's Story. 2001. (Sarah, Plain & Tall Ser.). 128p. (J). (gr. 3-5). 16.99 (978-0-06-023605-2(1) , Cotler, Joanna Books) HarperCollins Pubs.

Peck, Richard. The Ghost Belonged to Me. 2005. 176p. (YA). 21.00 (978-0-8446-7275-5(0) , 3590) Smith, Peter Pub., Inc.

Rapp, Adam. 33 Snowfish. Ering, Timothy Basil, illus. 2006. 192p. (YA). (gr. 10). pap. 6.99 (978-0-7636-2917-5(0)) Candlewick Pr.

Sheth, Kashmira. Blue Jasmine. 2004. 192p. (gr. 4-7). 15.99 (978-0-7868-1855-6(7)) Hyperion Bks. for Children.

Townsend, Wendy. Lizard Love. 2008. (J). ***(978-1-932425-34-5(9)*** , Front Street) Boyds Mills Pr.

Wargin, Kathy-Jo. Mitt & Minn at the Wisconsin Cheese Jamboree. Busch Holman, Karen, illus. 2007. 144p. (J). 14.95 ***(978-1-58726-305-7(X)*** , Mitten Pr.) Ann Arbor Media Group, LLC.

—Mitt & Minn's Illinois Adventure. Holman, Karen Busch, illus. 2007. 144p. (J). 14.95 ***(978-1-58726-306-4(8)*** , Mitten Pr.) Ann Arbor Media Group, LLC.

Weber, Richard D. Elvis & Me. 2004. 511p. (YA). per. 17.41 (978-1-4116-0549-7(7)) Lulu.com.

Wilder, Laura Ingalls. A Little House Birthday. Ettlinger, Doris, illus. 1998. (My First Little House Bks.). 40p. (J). (ps-3). pap. 6.99 (978-0-06-443494-2(X)) HarperCollins Pubs.

—A Little Prairie House. Graef, Renée, illus. 1999. (My First Little House Bks.). 32p. (J). (ps-3). pap. 6.99 (978-0-06-443526-0(1) , Harper Trophy) HarperCollins Pubs.

Wright, Timothy. Childish Things. 2006. 163p. pap. 11.49 (978-1-4116-6987-1(8)) Lulu.com.

MIDDLE WEST—HISTORY

Brannon, Barbara. Discover the Midwest Region. 2005. 39.00 ***(978-1-4108-5151-2(6))*** Benchmark Education Co.

Doherty, Kieran. Voyageurs, Lumberjacks & Farmers: Pioneers of the Midwest. 2003. (Shaping America Ser.: Vol. 5). (Illus.). 176p. (gr. 7 up). lib. bdg. 22.95 (978-1-881508-54-0(4)) Oliver Pr., Inc.

Katz, William Loren. Black Pioneers: An Untold Story. 1999. (Illus.). 208p. (YA). (gr. 7 up). 21.99 (978-0-689-81410-5(0) , Atheneum) Simon & Schuster Children's Publishing.

MIDGETS

see Dwarfs

MIDWAY, BATTLE OF, 1942

McGowan, Tom. Battle of Midway. 2001. (gr. 3-6). lib. bdg. 14.10 (978-0-613-51621-1(4)) Tandem Library Bks.

White, Steve. The Battle of Midway: The Destruction of the Japanese Fleet. 2007. (Graphic Battles of World War II Ser.). (Illus.). 48p. ***(978-1-4042-7425-9(1));*** pap. ***(978-1-4042-7424-2(3))*** Rosen Publishing Group, Inc., The.

—The Battle of Midway: The Destruction of the Japanese Fleet. Elson, Richard, illus. 2007. (Graphic Battles of World War II Ser.). 48p. (gr. 5-8). lib. bdg. 29.25 (978-1-4042-0783-7(X)) Rosen Publishing Group, Inc., The.

—The Empire Falls: Battle of Midway. Erskine, Gary & Elson, Richard, illus. 2006. (Graphic History Ser.). 48p. (J). (gr. 3). pap. 9.95 (978-1-84603-058-1(7)) Osprey Publishing, Ltd. GBR. *Dist:* Random Hse., Inc.

MIDWEST

see Middle West

MIDWIFERY

see Childbirth

MIGRANT LABOR

Here are entered works dealing with casual or seasonal workers who move from place to place in search of employment. Works on the movement of population within a country for permanent settlement are entered under Migration, Internal.

Atkin, S. Beth. Voices from the Fields: Children of Migrant Farmworkers Tell Their Stories. 2000. (Illus.). 96p. (J). (gr. 5-17). pap. 14.99 (978-0-316-05620-5(0)) Little Brown & Co.

—Voices from the Fields: Children of Migrant Farmworkers Tell Their Stories. 2000. (978-0-606-17851-8(1)) Tandem Library Bks.

Gillis, Jennifer Blizin. Dolores Huerta. 2005. (Illus.). 32p. (J). (978-1-4034-6980-9(6)); pap. (978-1-4034-6987-8(3)) Heinemann Library.

Herrera, Juan Felipe. Calling the Doves. 2001. Tr. of El Canto De Las Palomos. (SPA.). (gr. 3-6). lib. bdg. 16.40 (978-0-613-34098-4(1)) Tandem Library Bks.

—El Canto de las Palomas/Calling the Doves. ed. 2004. (ENG & SPA., Illus.). (J). (gr. 3-6). spiral bd. (978-0-616-14607-1(8)) Canadian National Institute for the Blind/Institut National Canadien pour les Aveugles.

Kent, Deborah. Migrant Farmworkers: Hoping for a Better Life. 2005. (Proud Heritage: the Hispanic Library Ser.). (Illus.). 40p. (J). (gr. 3-7). 28.50 (978-1-59296-386-7(2)) Child's World, Inc.

Ouellette, Jeannine. A Day Without Immigrants: Rallying Behind America's Newcomers. 2007. (J). lib. bdg. ***(978-0-7565-2498-2(9))*** Compass Point Bks.

Thatcher, Rebecca. Dolores Huerta. 2002. (Latinos in American History). (Illus.). 56p. (gr. 4-8). lib. bdg. 29.95 (978-1-58415-155-5(2)) Mitchell Lane Pubs., Inc.

MIGRANT LABOR—FICTION

Altman, Linda Jacobs. El Camino de Amelia. ed. 2004. (SPA., Illus.). (J). (gr. k-3). spiral bd. (978-0-616-14603-3(5)) Canadian National Institute for the Blind/Institut National Canadien pour les Aveugles.

Bridgers, Sue E. Home Before Dark. 1998. 186p. (J). reprint ed. lib. bdg. 29.95 (978-0-7351-0053-4(5)) Replica Bks.

Fitzgerald, Joanne. Yum! Yum! Delicious Nursery Rhymes. 2007. (Illus.). 32p. (J). (ps-1). (***978-1-55041-888-0(2)***) Fitzhenry & Whiteside, Ltd.

Gates, Doris. Blue Willow. 2000. (J). (gr. 3-7). 21.25 (978-0-8446-7143-7(6)) Smith, Peter Pub., Inc.

Jiménez, Francisco. The Christmas Gift. Cotts, Claire B., illus. 2000. Tr. of Regalo de Navidad. (SPA & ENG.). 32p. (J). (gr. k-3). tchr. ed. 16.00 (978-0-395-92869-1(9)) Houghton Mifflin Co. Trade & Reference Div.

Keep, Linda Lowery. Truth & Salsa. 2006. 176p. (J). 14.95 (978-1-56145-366-5(8) , Peachtree Junior) Peachtree Pubs., Ltd.

Literature Connections English: ... & the Earth Did Not Devour Him. 2004. (gr. 6-12). (978-0-395-77139-6(0) , 2-70217) McDougal Littell Inc.

McDonald, Joyce. Devil on My Heels. 272p. (YA). (gr. 7 up). 2005. pap. 6.50 (978-0-440-23829-4(3) , Laurel Leaf); 2004. 15.95 (978-0-385-73107-2(8) , Delacorte Bks. for Young Readers) Random Hse. Children's Bks.

Montgomery, Bobbie. Fruit Tramp Kids. 2000. (Pathfinder Junior Book Club Ser.). 143p. (J). (gr. 4-7). pap. 6.99 (978-0-8280-1422-9(1)) Review & Herald Publishing Assn.

Mora, Pat. Tomas & the Library Lady. Colon, Raul, illus. 2000. 40p. (J). (gr. k-3). pap. 6.99 (978-0-375-80349-9(1) , Dragonfly Bks.) Random Hse. Children's Bks.

—Tomas & the Library Lady. 2000. (978-0-606-18093-1(1)); lib. bdg. 15.30 (978-0-613-28362-5(7)) Tandem Library Bks.

—Tomas y la Senora de la Biblioteca. ed. 2004. (SPA., Illus.). (J). (gr. k-3). spiral bd. (978-0-616-03092-9(4)) Canadian National Institute for the Blind/Institut National Canadien pour les Aveugles.

Perez, L. King. First Day in Grapes. Casilla, Robert, illus. 2002. 32p. (J). (gr. 1-3). 16.95 (978-1-58430-045-8(0)) Lee & Low Bks., Inc.

Rio, Adam del & Arroyo, David. Vines of the Earth. Rio, Adam del & Arroyo, David, illus. 2006. (SPA & ENG., Illus.). 27p. (***978-0-9772852-7-3(8)***); pap. (***978-0-9772852-6-6(X)***) Lectura Bks.

Smothers, Ethel Footman. The Hard-Times Jar. Holyfield, John, illus. 2003. 32p. (J). 16.00 (978-0-374-32852-8(8) , Farrar, Straus & Giroux (BYR)) Farrar, Straus & Giroux.

Williams, Sherley Anne. Working Cotton. Byard, Carole, illus. 2002. (J). 14.04 (978-0-7587-0168-8(3)) Book Wholesalers, Inc.

MIGRANT LABOR—UNITED STATES

Ancona, George. Harvest. 2001. 48p. (J). (gr. 3-7). 15.95 (978-0-7614-5086-3(6) , Cavendish Children's Bks.) Cavendish, Marshall Corp.

Atkin, S. Beth. Voices from the Fields: Children of Migrant Farm Workers Tell Their Stories. 2000. (gr. 5-8). lib. bdg. 21.95 (978-0-613-27432-6(6)) Tandem Library Bks.

Brown, Jonatha A. Cesar Chavez. (People We Should Know Ser.). (J). 2006. 24p. pap. 5.95 (978-0-8368-4766-6(0)); 2006. 24p. lib. bdg. 19.33 (978-0-8368-4759-8(8)); 2005. (Illus.). 24p. pap. (978-0-8368-4752-9(0)); 2005. (Illus.). 24p. lib. bdg. 19.33 (978-0-8368-4745-1(8)); 2004. (Illus.). 48p. (gr. 5 up). pap. 11.95 (978-0-8368-5257-8(5) , World Almanac Library); 2004. (Illus.). 48p. (gr. 5 up). lib. bdg. 30.00 (978-0-8368-5097-0(1) , World Almanac Library) Stevens, Gareth Inc.

Cruz, Barbara C. Cesar Chavez: A Voice for Farmworkers. 2005. (Latino Biography Library). (Illus.). 128p. (J). (gr. 6-13). lib. bdg. 31.93 (978-0-7660-2489-2(X)) Enslow Pubs., Inc.

Davis, Lucile. Cesar Chavez. Schon, Isabel, ed. Ferrer, Martín Luis Guzman, tr. from ENG. 1998. (Biografias Ilustradas con Fotografias Ser.). (SPA., Illus.). 24p. (J). (gr. 2-3). lib. bdg. 18.60 (978-1-56065-808-5(8) , CAP2791, Bridgestone Bks.) Capstone Pr., Inc.

Feinstein, Stephen. Lee sobre César Chavez/Read about Cesar Chavez. 2006. (I Like Biographies! Bilingual Ser.). (ENG & SPA., Illus.). 24p. (J). (gr. 1-3). lib. bdg. 21.26 (978-0-7660-2744-2(9) , Enslow Elementary) Enslow Pubs., Inc.

Gaines, Ann Graham. Cesar E. Chavez: The Fight for Farm Workers' Rights. 2003. (Proud Heritage-The Hispanic Library). (Illus.). 40p. (J). (gr. 3-7). 28.50 (978-1-56766-209-2(9)) Child's World, Inc.

Hovius, Christopher. Latino Migrant Workers: America's Harvesters. 2005. (Illus.). 112p. (J). (ps-7). lib. bdg. (978-1-59084-937-8(X)) Mason Crest Pubs.

Krull, Kathleen. Cosechando Esperanza: La Historia de Cesar Chavez. Campoy, F. Isabel & Ada, Alma Flor, trs. Morales, Yuyi, illus. 2004. (SPA). 48p. (J). pap. 7.00 (978-0-15-205169-3(4) , Voyager Bks./Libros Viajeros) Harcourt Children's Bks.

—Harvesting Hope: The Story of Cesar Chavez. Morales, Yuyi, illus. 2003. 48p. (J). (gr. 3-6). 17.00 (978-0-15-201437-7(3)) Harcourt Children's Bks.

Krull, Kathleen & Morales, Yuyi. Cosechando Esperanza: La Historia de Cesar Chavez. Ada, Alma Flor & Campoy, F. Isabel, trs. from ENG. Morales, Yuyi, illus. 2003. (SPA., Illus.). 48p. (J). 17.00 (978-0-15-204755-9(7) , Voyager Bks./Libros Viajeros) Harcourt Children's Bks.

Marcovitz, Hal. Cesar Chavez. 2003. (Great Hispanic Heritage Ser.). (Illus.). 112p. (gr. 6-12). 30.00 (978-0-7910-7253-0(3)); pap. 30.00 (978-0-7910-7515-9(X)) Facts On File, Inc. (Chelsea Hse.).

Matthews, J. L. & Rasinski, Timothy V. Cesar Chavez: Fighter in the Fields. 2002. (High Five Reading Ser.). (Illus.). 48p. (J). (gr. 2-3). lib. bdg. 22.60 (978-0-7368-9550-7(7) , Capstone High-Interest Bks.); pap. 16.95 (978-0-7368-9528-6(0)) Capstone Pr., Inc.

McLeese, Don. Cesar E. Chavez. 2003. (Rourke Discovery Library). (Illus.). 24p. (gr. 2-5). 14.95 (978-1-58952-285-5(0)) Rourke Publishing, LLC.

Rinaldo, Denise. Cesar Chavez: With a Discussion of Compassion. 2003. (Values in Action Ser.). (J). (978-1-59203-064-4(5)) Learning Challenge, Inc.

Roman, Michelle. Becoming Cesar Chavez. Ballis, George, photos by. 2002. (ENG & SPA., Illus.). 48p. (J). (gr. 1-6). pap. 8.95 (978-0-938911-21-0(X)) Individualized Education Systems/Poppy Lane Publishing.

Schaefer, Lola M. Cesar Chavez. Saunders-Smith, Gail, ed. 1998. (Famous Americans Ser.). (Illus.). 24p. (J). (gr. k-1). lib. bdg. 15.93 (978-0-7368-0109-6(X) , Pebble Bks.) Capstone Pr., Inc.

Seidman, David. Cesar Chavez: Labor Leader. 2004. (Great Life Stories Ser.). (Illus.). 127p. (J). 30.50 (978-0-531-12319-5(7) , Watts, Franklin) Scholastic Library Publishing.

Shea, Kitty. Cesar Chavez: Leader of Migrant Farm Workers. 2004. (Compass Point Early Biographies Ser.). (Illus.). 32p. (J). (gr. 1-3). lib. bdg. 21.26 (978-0-7565-0793-0(6)) Compass Point Bks.

Slade, Suzanne. Cesar Chavez: Champion & Voice of Farmworkers. Thompson, Jeffrey, illus. 2007. (J). lib. bdg. (***978-1-4048-3724-9(8)***) Picture Window Bks.

Soto, Gary. Cesar Chavez: A Hero for Everyone. Lohstoeter, Lori, illus. 2003. (Milestone Ser.). 80p. (J). pap. 3.99 (978-0-689-85922-9(8) , Aladdin) Simon & Schuster Children's Publishing.

—Cesar Chavez: A Hero for Everyone. 2003. (gr. 3-6). lib. bdg. 11.80 (978-0-613-90718-7(3)) Tandem Library Bks.

Wheeler, Jill C. Cesar Chavez. 2003. (Breaking Barriers Ser.). (Illus.). 64p. (J). (gr. 3-8). lib. bdg. 25.65 (978-1-57765-905-1(8)) ABDO Publishing Co.

Zannos, Susan. Cesar Chavez. 1998. (Real-Life Reader Biographies Ser.). (Illus.). 32p. (J). (gr. 4-7). lib. bdg. 15.95 (978-1-883845-71-1(8)) Mitchell Lane Pubs., Inc.

MIGRATION

see Emigration and Immigration

MIGRATION, INTERNAL

Haskins, Jim. The Geography of Hope: Black Exodus from the South after Reconstruction. 1999. (Single Titles Ser.: up). (Illus.). 144p. (gr. 7 up). lib. bdg. 31.90 (978-0-7613-0323-7(5) , Millbrook Pr.) Lerner Publishing Group.

Price, Sean. The Dirty Thirties: Documenting the Dust Bowl. 2006. (American History Through Primary Sources Ser.). (Illus.). 32p. (J). (978-1-4109-2416-2(5)); pap. (978-1-4109-2427-8(0)) Steck-Vaughn.

Sioux, Tracee. Immigrants, Migration, & the Growth of the American City. 2004. (Primary Sources of Immigration & Migration in America Ser.). (Illus.). 24p. (J). lib. bdg. 19.95 (978-0-8239-6828-2(6) , PowerKids Pr.) Rosen Publishing Group, Inc., The.

—Immigrants, Migration, & the Industrial Revolution. 2004. (Primary Sources of Immigration & Migration in America Ser.). (Illus.). 24p. (J). lib. bdg. 19.95 (978-0-8239-6826-8(X) , PowerKids Pr.) Rosen Publishing Group, Inc., The.

—Immigration, Migration, & the Growth of the American City. 2004. (Primary Sources of Immigration & Migration in America Ser.). (Illus.). 24p. (J). lib. bdg. (978-0-8239-8954-6(2) , PowerKids Pr.) Rosen Publishing Group, Inc., The.

—Immigration, Migration, & the Industrial Revolution. 2004. (Primary Sources of Immigration & Migration in America Ser.). (Illus.). 24p. (J). lib. bdg. (978-0-8239-8998-0(4) , PowerKids Pr.) Rosen Publishing Group, Inc., The.

MIGRATION OF ANIMALS

see Animals—Migration

MIGRATION OF BIRDS

see Birds—Migration

MIGRATORY WORKERS

see Migrant Labor

MILITARY AERONAUTICS

see Aeronautics, Military

MILITARY AIRPLANES

see Airplanes, Military

MILITARY ART AND SCIENCE

see also Aeronautics, Military; Armies; Arms and Armor; Battles; Disarmament; Fortification; Guerrilla Warfare; Ordnance; Signals and Signaling; Soldiers; Spies; War also headings beginning with the word Military

Alvarez, Jose E. Beast War Transformers: The Unofficial Guide. 2002. (Illus.). 176p. (gr. 10-13). pap. 29.95 (978-0-7643-1512-1(9)) Schiffer Publishing, Ltd.

Baker, David. Infiltration & Spying. 2006. (Fighting Terrorism Ser.). (Illus.). 48p. (gr. 4-8). 20.95 (978-1-59515-486-6(8)) Rourke Publishing, LLC.

—M2A2 Bradley Fighting Vehicle. 2007. (Fighting Forces on Land Ser.). (Illus.). 32p. (J). (978-1-60044-249-0(8)) Rourke Publishing, LLC.

Barron's Educational Editorial Staff. Weapons & Warfare. 1998. (History Ser.). (Illus.). 32p. (J). (gr. 5). pap. 5.95 (978-0-7641-0534-0(5)) Barron's Educational Series, Inc.

Bergin, Mark & Robertshaw, Andrew. Warfare in the 16th-19th Centuries: The Age of Empires. Bergin, Mark, illus. 2003. (Battle Zones Ser.). (Illus.). 48p. (J). (gr. 5-8). 18.95 (978-1-57768-593-7(8) , Bedrick, Peter Bks.) School Specialty Publishing.

Black, Michael A. Tank: The M1A1 Abrams. 2000. (High Interest Bks.). (Illus.). 48p. (YA). (gr. 7-12). 24.00 (978-0-516-23342-0(4) , Children's Pr.) Scholastic Library Publishing.

Calkhoven, Laurie. Flash, Boom, Blast! Amazing Inventions from the War Front. 2004. (Illus.). 72p. (J). pap. (978-0-439-68357-9(2)) Scholastic, Inc.

Caraccilo, Dominic J. Military Intelligence Technology of the Future. 2005. (Library of Future Weaponry). (Illus.). 64p. (J). lib. bdg. (978-1-4042-0528-4(4)) Rosen Publishing Group, Inc., The.

Chapman, Caroline. Battles & Weapons: Exploring History Through Art. 2007. (Picture That! Ser.). 64p. (gr. 3-7). 19.95 (***978-1-58728-588-2(6)*** , Two Can Publishing) T&N Children's Publishing.

Cooper, Jason. U. S. Special Operations. 2003. (Illus.). 32p. (J). 28.50 (978-1-58952-711-9(9)) Rourke Publishing, LLC.

Derkins, Susie. The Irish Republican Army. 2005. (Inside the World's Most Infamous Terrorist Organizations Ser.). (Illus.). 64p. (YA). (gr. 7-12). lib. bdg. 26.50 (978-0-8239-3822-3(0)) Rosen Publishing Group, Inc., The.

Donovan, Sandy. U. S. Navy Special Forces. 2005. (U. S. Armed Forces Ser.). (Illus.). 64p. (J). (gr. 4-7). lib. bdg. 26.60 (978-0-8225-1650-7(0)) Lerner Publishing Group.

Felber, Bill. The Horse in War. (Horse Library). (Illus.). 64p. (J). 2005. pap. 200.00 (978-0-7910-6650-8(9)); 2001. 25.00 (978-0-7910-6651-5(7)) Facts On File, Inc. (Chelsea Hse.).

Ferguson, Amanda. SAS: British Special Air Service. 2003. (Inside Special Operations Ser.). (Illus.). 64p. (YA). (gr. 5-8). lib. bdg. 26.50 (978-0-8239-3810-0(7) , Rosen Central) Rosen Publishing Group, Inc., The.

Fowler, William. Modern Weapons: Discover the Technology of War from 1700 to the Present Day. 2003. (History Detectives Ser.). (Illus.). 64p. (gr. 3-7). pap. 7.99 (978-1-84215-782-4(5) , Southwater) Anness Publishing GBR. *Dist:* National Bk. Network.

Fridell, Ron. Military Technology. 2007. (Cool Science Ser.). 48p. (J). (gr. 4-8). lib. bdg. 26.60 (978-0-8225-6769-1(5) , Lerner Pubns.) Lerner Publishing Group.

Gilbert, Adrian. Going to War in Ancient Greece. 2001. (gr. 3-6). lib. bdg. 15.25 (978-0-613-54518-1(4)) Tandem Library Bks.

Gonzalez, Lissette. Bomb Squads in Action. 2008. lib. bdg. (***978-1-4042-3781-0(X)*** , PowerKids Pr.) Rosen Publishing Group, Inc., The.

Green, Michael. Military Police. 2000. (Serving Your Country Ser.). (Illus.). 48p. (J). (gr. 3-4). lib. bdg. 21.26 (978-0-7368-0473-8(0) , Capstone High-Interest Bks.) Capstone Pr., Inc.

Guinta, Peter & Cribbs, Randy. Illumination Rounds. 2004. (Illus.). 192p. (YA). per. (978-0-9725796-4-3(8) , 9051945) OCRS, Inc.

Hamilton, John. Special Forces. 2007. (Defending the Nation Ser.). (Illus.). 32p. (J). (gr. 3-5). lib. bdg. 22.78 (978-1-59679-759-8(2) , Checkerboard Library) ABDO Publishing Co.

—Weapons of War. 2002. (War on Terrorism Ser.). (Illus.). 64p. (J). (gr. 4-8). lib. bdg. 25.65 (978-1-57765-673-9(3) , ABDO & Daughters) ABDO Publishing Co.

—Weapons of World War I. 2004. (World War I Ser.). (Illus.). 32p. (J). (gr. 4-8). lib. bdg. 24.21 (978-1-57765-917-4(1)) ABDO Publishing Co.

Holmes, Richard. Battle. 2000. (Eyewitness Bks.). (Illus.). 64p. (J). (gr. 4-7). 15.99 (978-0-7894-6032-5(7)) Dorling Kindersley Publishing, Inc.

Hopkins, Ellen H. United States Special Forces. 2003. (Heinemann Know It Ser.). (Illus.). 48p. (J). pap. 7.95 (978-1-4034-0449-7(6)) Heinemann Library.

Inside Special Operations, 6 bks. Incl. Army Rangers : Surveillance & Reconnaissance for the U. S. Army. Poolos, J. (YA). lib. bdg. 26.50 (978-0-8239-3805-6(0)); British Royal Marines : Amphibious Division of the United Kingdom's Royal Navy. Scheppler, Bill. (YA). lib. bdg. 26.50 (978-0-8239-3806-3(9)); Delta Force : Counterterrorism Unit of the U. S. Army. Burnett, Betty. (J). lib. bdg. 26.50 (978-0-8239-3807-0(7)); Green Berets : The U. S. Army Special Forces. Goldberg, Jan. (YA). lib. bdg. 26.50 (978-0-8239-3808-7(5)); Navy SEALs : Special Operations for the U. S. Navy. Payment, Simone. (YA). lib. bdg. 26.50 (978-0-8239-3809-4(3)); SAS : British Special Air Service. Ferguson, Amanda. (YA). lib. bdg. 26.50 (978-0-8239-3810-0(7)); 64p. (gr. 5-8). 2003. (Illus.). 2002. Set lib. bdg. 159.00 (978-0-8239-4083-7(7) , Rosen Central) Rosen Publishing Group, Inc., The.

Kaelberer, Angie Peterson. U. S. Army Special Operations. 2005. (Blazers—The U.S. Armed Forces Ser.). (Illus.). 32p. (J). 19.93 (978-0-7368-3795-8(7)) Capstone Pr., Inc.

Levine, Herbert M. Chemical & Biological Weapons in Our Times. 2000. (Single Titles Ser.). (Illus.). 128p. (J). (gr. 9-12). 24.00 (978-0-531-11852-8(5) , Watts, Franklin) Scholastic Library Publishing.

Lorenz Books Staff & Fowler, Will. Modern Weapons & Warfare: The Technology of War from 1700 to the Present Day. 2000. (Exploring History Ser.). (Illus.). 64p. (gr. 3-7). 12.95 (978-0-7548-0453-6(4)) Anness Publishing, Inc.

MacDonald, Fiona. So You Want to Be a Roman Soldier. Hewetson, Nicholas, illus. 1999. (So You Want to Be... Ser.). 32p. (gr. 3-6). lib. bdg. 21.90 (978-0-7613-1421-9(0) , Twenty-First Century Bks.) Lerner Publishing Group.

—Warfare in the Middle Ages. 2003. (Battle Zones Ser.). (Illus.). 48p. (J). 18.95 (978-1-57768-596-8(2) , Bedrick, Peter Bks.) School Specialty Publishing.

Malam, John. War & Weapons. 2002. (People in the Past Ser.). (Illus.). 48p. (J). pap. (978-1-4034-0516-6(6)) Heinemann Library.

Margulies, Phillip. Strategic Defense Systems of the Future. 2005. (Library of Future Weaponry). (Illus.). 64p. (YA). (978-1-4042-0527-7(6)) Rosen Publishing Group, Inc., The.

Marx, Christy. Battlefield Command Systems of the Future. 2005. (Library of Future Weaponry). (Illus.). 64p. (J). (978-1-4042-0521-5(7)) Rosen Publishing Group, Inc., The.

Maybury, Richard J. World War II: The Rest of the Story & How It Affects You Today, 1930 to September 11 2001. Williams, Jane A., ed. rev. ed. 2003. ("Uncle Eric" Bk.). 349p. (YA). pap. 19.95 (978-0-942617-43-6(6)) Bluestocking Pr.

McGowen, Tom. Assault from the Sea: Amphibious Invasions of the Twentieth Century. 2002. (Military Might Ser.). (Illus.). 64p. (gr. 5-8). lib. bdg. 26.90 (978-0-7613-1811-8(9) , Twenty-First Century Bks.) Lerner Publishing Group.

—Assault from the Sky: Airborne Infantry of World War II. 2002. (Military Might Ser.). (Illus.). 64p. (J). (gr. 5-8). lib. bdg. 26.90 (978-0-7613-1809-5(7) , Twenty-First Century Bks.) Lerner Publishing Group.

McNab, Chris. Martial Arts for the Special Forces. 2002. (Martial & Fighting Arts Ser.). (Illus.). 96p. (J). (gr. 7 up). lib. bdg. (978-1-59084-400-7(9)) Mason Crest Pubs.

Millard, Anne. Going to War in Ancient Egypt. Bergin, Mark, illus. 2001. (Armies of the Past Ser.). 32p. (J). (gr. 3-6). 25.50 (978-0-531-14589-0(1) , Watts, Franklin) Scholastic Library Publishing.

Nardo, Don. Ancient Egypt. 2002. (History of Weapons & Warfare Ser.). (Illus.). 112p. (J). 27.45 (978-1-59018-066-2(6) , Lucent Bks.) Thomson Gale.

—Life of a Roman Soldier. 2000. (Way People Live Ser.). (Illus.). 112p. (J). (gr. 7-10). 27.45 (978-1-56006-679-8(2) , LML00902-178031, Lucent Bks.) Thomson Gale.

Poolos, J. Army Rangers: Surveillance & Reconnaissance for the U. S. Army. 2003. (Inside Special Operations Ser.). (Illus.). 64p. (YA). (gr. 5-8). lib. bdg. 26.50 (978-0-8239-3805-6(0) , Rosen Central) Rosen Publishing Group, Inc., The.

Reavis, Tracey. Stealth Jet Fighter: The F-117A. 2000. (High-Tech Military Weapons Ser.). (Illus.). 48p. (YA). (gr. 7-12). 24.00 (978-0-516-23341-3(6) , Children's Pr.) Scholastic Library Publishing.

Richie, Jason. Weapons: Designing the Tools of War. 2000. (Innovators Ser.). (Illus.). 144p. (gr. 5 up). lib. bdg. 21.95 (978-1-881508-60-1(9)) Oliver Pr., Inc.

Ripley, Tim. Weapon Technology. 2004. (History of Invention Ser.). (Illus.). 96p. (YA). (gr. 6-12). 35.00 (978-0-8160-5438-1(X)) Facts On File, Inc.

Rivera, Sheila. Weapons of Mass Destruction. 2004. (World in Conflict-the Middle East Ser.). (Illus.). 48p. (J). (gr. 4-8). lib. bdg. 25.65 (978-1-59197-421-5(6)) ABDO Publishing Co.

Roberts, Jeremy. U. S. Air Force Special Forces. 2005. (U. S. Armed Forces Ser.). (Illus.). 64p. (J). (gr. 4-7). lib. bdg. 26.60 (978-0-8225-1644-6(6)) Lerner Publishing Group.

Ross, Nancy. Joan of Arc. 1999. (gr. 3-6). lib. bdg. 14.15 (978-0-613-21810-8(8)) Tandem Library Bks.

Scheppler, Bill. British Royal Marines: Amphibious Division of the United Kingdom's Royal Navy. 2003. (Inside Special Operations Ser.). (Illus.). 64p. (YA). (gr. 5-8). lib. bdg. 26.50 (978-0-8239-3806-3(9) , Rosen Central) Rosen Publishing Group, Inc., The.

Schmidt, Roderic D. Land Warfare of the Future. 2005. (Library of Future Weaponry). (Illus.). 64p. (J). lib. bdg. (978-1-4042-0524-6(1)) Rosen Publishing Group, Inc., The.

Somervill, Barbara A. Samurai, Shoguns, & Soldiers: The Rise of the Japanese Military. 2007. (Lucent Library of Historical Eras:Twentieth-Century Japan Ser.). (Illus.). 128p. (gr. 7-10). 31.20 (***978-1-4205-0030-1(9)*** , Lucent Bks.) Thomson Gale.

Steele, Tara. Medieval Warfare. 2003. (Medieval World Ser.). (Illus.). 32p. (J). (gr. 5). pap. (978-0-7787-1376-0(8)) Crabtree Publishing Co.

Tools of War. (Illus.). 192p. (J). (978-0-7835-0154-3(4)) Time-Life Education, Inc.

Warfare & Weapons, 9 bks. Incl. SWAT Teams. Green, Michael. 2000. lib. bdg. 21.26 (978-1-56065-758-3(8)); U. S. Air Force Special Forces : Combat Controllers. Covert, Kim. 1999. lib. bdg. 21.26 (978-0-7368-0334-2(3)); U. S. Air Force Special Forces : Pararescue. Covert, Kim. 1999. lib. bdg. 21.26 (978-0-7368-0335-9(1)); U. S. Air Force Special Forces : Special Operations Wings. Boraas, Tracey. 1999. lib. bdg. 21.26 (978-0-7368-0336-6(X)); U. S. Army Special Operations Command : Night Stalkers-Special Operations Aviation. Weiser, Andrea L. 1999. lib. bdg. 21.26 (978-0-7368-0338-0(6)); U. S. Army Special Operations Forces : Airborne Rangers. Burgan, Michael. 1999. lib. bdg. 21.26 (978-0-7368-0337-3(8)); U. S. Marine Corps Special Forces : Recon Marines. Voeller, Edward A. 1999. lib. bdg. 21.26 (978-0-7368-0339-7(4)); U. S. Navy Special Forces : SEAL Teams. Burgan, Michael. 1999. lib. bdg. 21.26 (978-0-7368-0340-3(8)); U. S. Navy Special Forces : Special Boat Units. Burgan, Michael. 1999. lib. bdg. 21.26 (978-0-7368-0341-0(6)); 48p. (J). (gr. 3-4). (Illus.). 2001. Set lib. bdg. 170.08 (978-0-7368-0465-3(X) , Capstone High-Interest Bks.) Capstone Pr., Inc.

Weapons & Warfare. 2003. (Illus.). 32p. (YA). pap. (978-1-904516-31-6(9)) Chrysalis Children's Bks.

Williams, Brian. Ancient Roman War & Weapons. 2002. (People in the Past Ser.). (Illus.). 48p. (J). pap. 8.50 (978-1-4034-0521-0(2)) Heinemann Library.

MILITARY ART AND SCIENCE—HISTORY

Anon. Tudor War. (Illus.). 32p. pap. (978-0-7502-3742-0(2) , Hodder Wayland) Hodder Children's Division.

Barron's Educational Editorial Staff. Weapons & Warfare. 1998. (History Ser.). (Illus.). 32p. (J). (gr. 5). pap. 5.95 (978-0-7641-0534-0(5)) Barron's Educational Series, Inc.

M
N
O

Bergin, Mark. Warfare in the Ancient World. Battle Zones Staff, ed. 2003. (Battle Zones Ser.). (Illus.). 48p. (J). 18.95 (978-1-57768-595-1(4) , Bedrick, Peter Bks.) School Specialty Publishing.

Brewer, Paul. Warfare in the Ancient World. 1999. (History of Warfare Ser.). (Illus.). 80p. (YA). (gr. 7-12). lib. bdg. 29.97 (978-0-8172-5442-1(0)) Raintree.

—Warfare in the Renaissance World. 1999. (History of Warfare Ser.). (Illus.). 80p. (YA). (gr. 7-12). lib. bdg. 29.97 (978-0-8172-5444-5(7)) Raintree.

Butterfield, Moira. Going to War in Roman Times. 2001. (Armies of the Past Ser.). (Illus.). 32p. (J). (gr. 3-6). 25.50 (978-0-531-14591-3(3) , Watts, Franklin) Scholastic Library Publishing.

Chrisp, Peter. Warfare. 2004. (Medieval Realms Ser.). (J). (gr. 7-10). 29.95 (978-1-59018-537-7(4) , Lucent Bks.) Thomson Gale.

Farndon, John. Religion, Science, Medicine & Warfare. 2001. (Illustrated Encyclopedia Ser.). (Illus.). 256p. (gr. 3-7). pap. 19.95 (978-1-84215-518-9(0) , Southwater) Anness Publishing GBR. *Dist:* National Bk. Network.

Gilbert, Adrian. Going to War in Ancient Greece. Bergin, Mark, illus. 2001. (Armies of the Past Ser.). 32p. (J). (gr. 3-6). pap. 6.95 (978-0-531-16351-1(2) , Watts, Franklin) Scholastic Library Publishing.

Heaton, Colin D. German Anti-Partisan Warfare in Europe: 1939-1945. 2001. (Schiffer Military History Ser.). (Illus.). 480p. (gr. 10-13). 29.95 (978-0-7643-1395-0(9)) Schiffer Publishing, Ltd.

MacDonald, Fiona. Knights, Castles, & Warfare in the Middle Ages. 2005. (World Almanac Library of the Middle Ages). (Illus.). 48p. (J). pap. (978-0-8368-5904-1(9)); lib. bdg. 30.00 (978-0-8368-5895-2(6)) Stevens, Gareth Inc. (World Almanac Library).

Malam, John. Ancient Egyptian War & Weapons. 2003. (People in the Past Ser.). (Illus.). 48p. (J). (gr. 4-6). lib. bdg 27.07 (978-1-4034-0312-4(0)) Heinemann Library.

—Ancient Egyptian War & Weapons. 2002. (gr. 3-6). lib. bdg. 17.05 (978-0-613-85908-0(1)) Tandem Library Bks.

—You Wouldn't Want to Be a Roman Gladiator! Gory Things You'd Rather Not Know. Antram, David, illus. 2001. (You Wouldn't Want to Ser.). 32p. (J). (gr. 2-5). pap. 9.95 (978-0-531-16204-0(4) , Watts, Franklin) Scholastic Library Publishing.

—You Wouldn't Want to Be a Roman Gladiator! Gory Things You'd Rather Not Know! Antram, David & Salariya, David, illus. 2001. (You Wouldn't Want to Ser.). 32p. (J). (gr. 2-5). 28.50 (978-0-531-14598-2(0) , Watts, Franklin) Scholastic Library Publishing.

Marshall, Chris. Warfare in the Medieval World. 1999. (History of Warfare Ser.). (Illus.). 80p. (YA). (gr. 7-12). lib. bdg. 29.97 (978-0-8172-5443-8(9)) Raintree.

Middleton, Haydn. Ancient Greek War & Weapons. 2002. (People in the Past Ser.). (Illus.). 48p. (J). (gr. 4-6). lib. bdg. 27.07 (978-1-58810-635-3(7)) Heinemann Library.

—Ancient Greek War & Weapons. 2002. (gr. 3-6). lib. bdg. 17.05 (978-0-613-87483-0(8)) Tandem Library Bks.

Middleton, Haydn & Tames, Richard. Ancient Greek War & Weapons. 2002. (People in the Past Ser.). 64p. (J). (gr. 4-7). pap. 8.50 (978-1-4034-0134-2(9) , 91639) Heinemann Library.

Miles, Elizabeth & Noon, Steve. Warrior Masks. 2001. (Big Book of... Ser.). (Illus.). 24p. (J). pap. 9.95 (978-1-901323-16-0(1)) Orpheus Bks., Ltd. GBR. *Dist:* CPG Publishing, Inc.

Millard, Anne. Going to War in Ancient Egypt. Bergin, Mark, illus. 2001. (Armies of the Past Ser.). 32p. (J). (gr. 3-6). pap. 6.95 (978-0-531-16350-4(4) , Watts, Franklin) Scholastic Library Publishing.

—Going to War in Ancient Egypt. 2001. (gr. 3-6). lib. bdg. 15.25 (978-0-613-54517-4(6)) Tandem Library Bks.

Morgan, Sally & Morgan, Adrian. Warfare in a Hi-Tech Age. 2005. (Science at the Edge Ser.). (Illus.). 64p. (J). (978-1-4034-7765-1(5)) Heinemann Library.

Nardo, Don. The Native Americans. 2002. (History of Weapons & Warfare Ser.). (Illus.). 112p. (J). 29.95 (978-1-59018-070-9(4) , Lucent Bks.) Thomson Gale.

Ripley, Tim. Weapon Technology. 2004. (History of Invention Ser.). (Illus.). 96p. (YA). (gr. 6-12). 35.00 (978-0-8160-5438-1(X)) Facts On File, Inc.

Southwater Books Staff. Ancient Weapons. 2002. (History Detectives Ser.). (Illus.). 64p. (gr. 3-7). pap. 7.95 (978-1-84215-628-5(4) , Southwater) Anness Publishing GBR. *Dist:* National Bk. Network.

Steele, Tara. Medieval Warfare. 2003. (Medieval World Ser.). (Illus.). 32p. (J). (gr. 5). (978-0-7787-1344-9(X)) Crabtree Publishing Co.

Westwell, Ian. Warfare in the 18th Century. 1999. (History of Warfare Ser.). (Illus.). 80p. (YA). (gr. 7-12). lib. bdg. 29.97 (978-0-8172-5445-2(5)) Raintree.

Williams, Brian. Ancient Roman War & Weapons. 2003. (People in the Past Ser.). (Illus.). 48p. (J). (gr. 4-6). lib. bdg. 27.07 (978-1-58810-630-8(6)) Heinemann Library.

Woods, Mary B. & Woods, Michael. Ancient Warfare: From Clubs to Catapults. 2005. (Ancient Technology Ser.). (Illus.). 96p. (gr. 6-12). 25.26 (978-0-8225-2999-6(8)) Lerner Publishing Group.

Worth, Richard. Gunpowder. 2003. (Transforming Power of Technology Ser.). (Illus.). 112p. (J). (gr. 9-13). 30.00 (978-0-7910-7448-0(X) , Chelsea Hse.) Facts On File, Inc.

MILITARY ART AND SCIENCE—STUDY AND TEACHING

see Military Education

MILITARY BIOGRAPHY

see Generals

MILITARY COSTUME

see Uniforms, Military

MILITARY EDUCATION

see also names of military schools, e.g. United States Military Academy, West Point; etc.

Long, Barbara. United States vs. Virginia: Virginia Military Institute Accepts Women. 2000. (Landmark Supreme Court Cases Ser.). (Illus.). 128p. (YA). (gr. 6-12). lib. bdg. 20.95 (978-0-7660-1342-1(1)) Enslow Pubs., Inc.

Mace, Nancy. In the Company of Men: A Woman at the Citadel. 2002. (gr. 7-12). lib. bdg. 16.45 (978-0-613-51841-3(1)) Tandem Library Bks.

Wehrertuchtigungslager der Hitler-Jugend, 1942-1945. (GER.). (978-3-928379-00-7(3)) Verein zur Fordenrung der Umweltforschung.

MILITARY FORCES

see Armies

MILITARY HISTORY

see also Battles; Naval History

also names of countries with the subdivision Army or History, Military

Barron's Educational Editorial Staff. Weapons & Warfare. 1998. (History Ser.). (Illus.). 32p. (J). (gr. 5). pap. 5.95 (978-0-7641-0534-0(5)) Barron's Educational Series, Inc.

Bergin, Mark. Warfare in the Ancient World. Battle Zones Staff, ed. 2003. (Battle Zones Ser.). (Illus.). 48p. (J). 18.95 (978-1-57768-595-1(4) , Bedrick, Peter Bks.) School Specialty Publishing.

Brewer, Paul. Warfare in the Ancient World. 1999. (History of Warfare Ser.). (Illus.). 80p. (YA). (gr. 7-12). lib. bdg. 29.97 (978-0-8172-5442-1(0)) Raintree.

—Warfare in the Renaissance World. 1999. (History of Warfare Ser.). (Illus.). 80p. (YA). (gr. 7-12). lib. bdg. 29.97 (978-0-8172-5444-5(7)) Raintree.

Brownlie, Ali & Mason, Chris. Why Do People Fight Wars? 2002. (Exploring Tough Issues Ser.). (Illus.). 48p. (J). lib. bdg. 25.69 (978-0-7398-4961-3(1)) Raintree.

Cawthorne, Nigel. Military Commanders: The 100 Greatest Throughout History. 2004. (Illus.). 208p. 18.95 (978-1-59270-029-5(2)) Enchanted Lion Bks., LLC.

Chrisp, Peter. Warfare. 2004. (Medieval Realms Ser.). (J). (gr. 7-10). 29.95 (978-1-59018-537-7(4) , Lucent Bks.) Thomson Gale.

Crompton, Samuel Willard. 100 Military Leaders Who Changed the World. 2003. (People Who Changed the World Ser.). (Illus.). 112p. (J). (gr. 5 up). lib. bdg. 30.00 (978-0-8368-5470-1(5) , World Almanac Library) Stevens, Gareth Inc.

Eldridge, Jim. Warriors! True Stories of Combat, Skill & Courage. 2001. (J). (978-0-606-21509-1(3)) Tandem Library Bks.

Griehl, Manfred. Arado Ar 234, Vol. 15. 2001. (Luftwaffe Profile Ser.: Vol. 15). (Illus.). 48p. (gr. 10-13). pap. 14.95 (978-0-7643-1431-5(9)) Schiffer Publishing, Ltd.

Hargrove, Julia. Tomb of the Unknowns. 2003. (Illus.). 48p. (J). pap. 6.95 (978-1-57310-405-0(1)) Teaching & Learning Co.

Hull, Robert. Trade & Warfare. 2006. (World of Ancient Greece Ser.). (Illus.). 32p. (J). (978-1-59771-062-6(8)) Sea-To-Sea Pubns.

Jentz, Thomas L. Germany's Tiger Tanks Series Tigers at the Front: A Photo Study Compiled by Thomas L. Jentz. 2001. (Germany's Tiger Tanks Ser.). (Illus.). 208p. (gr. 10-13). 29.95 (978-0-7643-1339-4(8)) Schiffer Publishing, Ltd.

Kubert, Joe. Fax from Sarajevo. Kubert, Joe, illus. 2002. (Illus.). 25.21 (978-1-4046-0889-4(3)) Book Wholesalers, Inc.

MacDonald, Fiona. Warfare in the Middle Ages. 2003. (Battle Zones Ser.). (Illus.). 48p. (J). 18.95 (978-1-57768-596-8(2) , Bedrick, Peter Bks.) School Specialty Publishing.

MacDonald, Fiona, et al. Warfare in the 20th Century: The Age of Global Conflict. 2004. (Battle Zones Ser.). (Illus.). 48p. (J). (gr. 5-8). 18.95 (978-1-57768-594-4(6) , Bedrick, Peter Bks.) School Specialty Publishing.

Marshall, Chris. Warfare in the Medieval World. 1999. (History of Warfare Ser.). (Illus.). 80p. (YA). (gr. 7-12). lib. bdg. 29.97 (978-0-8172-5443-8(9)) Raintree.

McGowen, Tom. Military Might, 6 vols. 2004. (History & Social Studies Ser.). (Illus.). 64p. (YA). (gr. 5-8). (978-0-7613-3138-4(7) , Twenty-First Century Bks.) Lerner Publishing Group.

McManners, Hugh. Ultimate Special Forces. 2003. (Illus.). 192p. 30.00 (978-0-7894-9973-8(8)) Dorling Kindersley Publishing, Inc.

Nardo, Don. The Native Americans. 2002. (History of Weapons & Warfare Ser.). (Illus.). 112p. (J). 29.95 (978-1-59018-070-9(4) , Lucent Bks.) Thomson Gale.

Nusbacher, Aryeh S. War & Conflict. 2003. (Face the Facts Ser.). (Illus.). 56p. (J). lib. bdg. 28.56 (978-0-7398-6435-7(1)) Raintree.

—War & Conflict. 2003. (gr. 5-8). lib. bdg. 17.60 (978-0-613-78128-2(7)) Tandem Library Bks.

On the Front Lines, 4 bks. Incl. U. S. Air Force at War. Dougherty, Terri. lib. bdg. 21.26 (978-0-7368-0921-4(X)); U. S. Army at War. Dougherty, Terri. lib. bdg. 21.26 (978-0-7368-0922-1(8)); U. S. Marine Corps at War. Abramovitz, Melissa. lib. bdg. 21.26 (978-0-7368-0923-8(6)); U. S. Navy at War. Abramovitz, Melissa. lib. bdg. 21.26 (978-0-7368-0924-5(4)); 32p. (J). (gr. 3-4). 2001. (Illus.). Set lib. bdg. 85.04 (978-0-7368-1005-0(6) , Capstone High-Interest Bks.) Capstone Pr., Inc.

Pickels, Dwayne E. Ancient Warriors. 1998. (Costume, Tradition & Culture). (Illus.). 64p. (YA). 19.75 (978-0-7910-5166-5(8) , Chelsea Hse.) Facts On File, Inc.

Sieges That Changed the World. 2005. (Illus.). 100+p. (gr. 6-12). pap. 180.00 (978-0-7910-7099-4(9) , Chelsea Hse.) Facts On File, Inc.

Steele, Tara. Medieval Warfare. 2003. (Medieval World Ser.). (Illus.). 32p. (J). (gr. 5). pap. (978-0-7787-1376-0(8)) Crabtree Publishing Co.

Westwell, Ian. Revolutionary & Napoleonic Wars. 1999. (History of Warfare Ser.). (Illus.). 80p. (YA). (gr. 7-12). lib. bdg. 29.97 (978-0-8172-5446-9(3)) Raintree.

—Warfare in the 18th Century. 1999. (History of Warfare Ser.). (Illus.). 80p. (YA). (gr. 7-12). lib. bdg. 29.97 (978-0-8172-5445-2(5)) Raintree.

Williams, Jack S. The California Presidios. 2004. (American Forts & Their Strategic Importance Ser.). (J). (978-1-59084-711-4(3)) Mason Crest Pubs.

The World Wars Series, 10 bks., Set. 2003. 285.60 (978-0-7398-5484-6(4)); (Illus.). 114.24 (978-0-7398-5483-9(6)) Raintree.

The World Wars Series, 6 bks., Set. Incl. Great Battles of World War II. Hansen, Ole Steen. lib. bdg. 27.12 (978-0-7398-2757-4(X)); Leaders of World War II. Ross, Stewart. lib. bdg. 27.12 (978-0-7398-2756-7(1)); World War I : Armistice 1918. Grant, R. G. lib. bdg. 27.12 (978-0-7398-2753-6(7)); World War I : War in the Trenches. Hansen, Ole Steen. lib. bdg. 27.12 (978-0-7398-2752-9(9)); World War II : Allied Victory. Sheehan, Sean. lib. bdg. 27.12 (978-0-7398-2755-0(3)); World War II : Germany & Japan Attack. Sheehan, Sean. Sloan, Frank, ed. lib. bdg. 27.12 (978-0-7398-2754-3(5)); 64p. (J). (gr. 5). (Illus.). 2001. Set lib. bdg. 171.36 (978-0-7398-2758-1(8)) Raintree.

MILITARY LIFE

see Soldiers; United States—Army—Military Life

MILITARY MUSIC—HISTORY

Farmer, Henry George. The Rise & Development of Military Music. 2001. 156p. (YA). reprint ed. 88.00 (978-0-7222-5178-2(5)) Library Reprints, Inc.

War Office Staff. Trumpet & Bugle Sounds. 2001. (YA). reprint ed. 150.00 (978-0-7222-6070-8(9)) Library Reprints, Inc.

MILITARY POWER

see Armies; Disarmament; Military Art and Science; Sea Power

MILITARY SCHOOLS

see Military Education

MILITARY SCIENCE

see Military Art and Science

MILITARY SERVICE, COMPULSORY

George Milite. Military Draft. 2006. (Illus.). 244p. (J). (gr. 7-10). 33.70 (978-0-7377-3601-4(1) , Greenhaven Pr., Inc.) Thomson Gale.

MILITARY SERVICE—VOCATIONAL GUIDANCE

Ferry, Monica. Search & Rescue Specialist & Careers in FEMA. 2006. (Homeland Security & Counterterrorism Careers Ser.). (Illus.). 128p. (J). lib. bdg. 31.93 (978-0-7660-2650-6(7)) Enslow Pubs., Inc.

MILITARY SIGNALING

see Signals and Signaling

MILITARY TRAINING

see Military Education

MILITARY UNIFORMS

see Uniforms, Military

MILITARY VEHICLES

see Vehicles, Military

MILK

Aliki. Milk from Cow to Carton. 1999. (Illus.). (J). (gr. k-3). lib. bdg. 14.10 (978-0-8335-9083-1(9)) Tandem Library Bks.

Benduhn, Tea. Milk & Cheese. 2007. (J). pap. (***978-0-8368-8260-5(1)***); 24p. lib. bdg. 19.93 (***978-0-8368-8253-7(9)***) Stevens, Gareth Inc. (Weekly Reader Early Learning Library).

—Milk & Cheese: Leche y Queso. 2007. (SPA & ENG.). (J). pap. (***978-0-8368-8464-7(7)*** , Weekly Reader Early Learning Library) Stevens, Gareth Inc.

—Milk & Cheese/Leche y Queso. 2007. (Find Out about Food/Conoce la Comida Ser.). (SPA & ENG.). 24p. (J). (gr. k-2). lib. bdg. 19.93 (***978-0-8368-8457-9(4)*** , Weekly Reader Early Learning Library) Stevens, Gareth Inc.

Bentley, Joyce. Milk. 2005. (Illus.). 32p. (J). (gr. 2 up). lib. bdg. 27.10 (978-1-59389-216-6(0)) Chrysalis Education.

The Book Carton, 6 vols. (Let's Read about... Ser.). (Illus.). 10p. (J). (978-2-7643-0028-2(X)) Phidal Publishing, Inc./Editions Phidal, Inc.

Dawson, Susan H. & Norton, Susan R. Pyramid Pal - Milk: Eating Should Always Be Fun for a Kid. O'Hare, Mark, illus. 2000. (Adventures in Eating with the Nutrition Champion of Kids Ser.). 16p. (J). pap. 3.00 (978-1-58000-067-3(3)) Griffin Publishing Group.

Heurtelou, Maude. Mwen Pito Bwe Let. Hippolyte, Johanne & Corbett, Kecia, illus. 2001. (Big Book Ser.).Tr. of I Prefer to Drink Milk. (CRP.). 14p. (J). (gr. k-2). 19.50 (978-1-58432-084-5(2)) Educa Vision.

Kalz, Jill. Dairy Products. 2003. 24p. (J). lib. bdg. 21.35 (978-1-58340-297-9(7)) Smart Apple Media.

Klingel, Cynthia Fitterer & Noyed, Robert B. Milk & Cheese. Andersen, Gregg, photos by. 2002. (Weekly Reader Early Learning Library). 24p. (J). (ps up). pap. 5.95 (978-0-8368-3148-1(9)); lib. bdg. 19.33 (978-0-8368-3059-0(8)) Stevens, Gareth Inc. (Weekly Reader Early Learning Library).

Leeper, Angela. The Dairy. 2004. (Field Trip! Ser.). (Illus.). 24p. (J). pap. 5.75 (978-1-4034-5166-8(4)) Heinemann Library.

—To a Dairy. 2004. (Field Trip! Ser.). (Illus.). 24p. (J). lib. bdg. (978-1-4034-5160-6(5)) Heinemann Library.

Llewellyn, Claire. Milk. 2005. (Illus.). 24p. (YA). (gr. 1 up). lib. bdg. 22.80 (978-1-932889-41-3(8)) Sea-To-Sea Pubns.

Mayo, Gretchen Will. Milk. 2004. (Weekly Reader Early Learning Library). (Illus.). 24p. (gr. 2 up). (J). pap. 5.95 (978-0-8368-4074-2(7)); (YA). lib. bdg. 19.33 (978-0-8368-4067-4(4)) Stevens, Gareth Inc. (Weekly Reader Early Learning Library).

Murray, Julie. Grass to Milk. 2007. (Beginning to End Ser.). (Illus.). 24p. (J). (gr. k-3). lib. bdg. 21.35 (978-1-59679-837-3(8) , Buddy Bks.) ABDO Publishing Co.

—Milk to Ice Cream. 2007. (Beginning to End Ser.). (Illus.). 24p. (J). (gr. k-3). lib. bdg. 21.35 (978-1-59679-838-0(6) , Buddy Bks.) ABDO Publishing Co.

Schaefer, Lola M. Milk. 2007. (J). (***978-1-4329-0145-5(1)***); pap. (***978-1-4329-0152-3(4)***) Heinemann Library.

Sloan, Peter. From Grass to Milk. 1999. (gr. k-3). lib. bdg. 11.80 (978-0-613-30418-4(7)) Tandem Library Bks.

Spilsbury, Louise. Milk. 2001. (Food in Focus Ser.). (Illus.). 32p. (J). (gr. k-2). lib. bdg. 21.36 (978-1-58810-147-1(9)) Heinemann Library.

Taus-Bolstad, Stacy. From Grass to Milk. 2004. (Start to Finish Ser.). (Illus.). 24p. (J). 18.60 (978-0-8225-4664-1(7) , Lerner Pubns.) Lerner Publishing Group.

MILKWEED

Holland, Mary. Milkweed Visitors. Holland, Mary, photos by. 2006. (Illus.). 32p. (J). per. 10.95 (***978-0-9657472-4-0(7)***) Bas Relief Publishing.

MILL, JOHN STUART, 1806-1873

Mill, Stuart John. Autobiography. 2006. 95.99 (***978-1-4280-0368-2(1)***); pap. 89.99 (***978-1-4280-0369-9(X)***) Indy-Publish.com.

MILL AND FACTORY BUILDINGS

see Factories

MILLIPEDES

Greenaway, Theresa. Centipedes & Millipedes. Fairclough, Chris, illus. 1999. (Minipets Ser.). 32p. (J). (gr. 1-5). lib. bdg. 25.69 (978-0-7398-1829-9(5)) Raintree.

—Centipedes & Millipedes. 2000. (Minipets Ser.). (Illus.). 32p. (J). (gr. 1-5). pap. 7.95 (978-0-7398-2194-7(6)) Steck-Vaughn.

—Centipedes & Millipedes. 2000. (gr. 3-6). lib. bdg. 17.85 (978-0-613-74066-1(1)) Tandem Library Bks.

Landau, Elaine. Minibeasts as Pets. 1998. (True Bks.). (Illus.). 48p. (J). (gr. 3-5). pap. 6.95 (978-0-516-26268-0(8) , Children's Pr.) Scholastic Library Publishing.

Ross, Michael Elsohn. Millipedeology. Erickson, Darren, illus. Grogan, Brian, photos by. 2005. (Backyard Buddies Ser.). 48p. (gr. 3-6). lib. bdg. 19.93 (978-1-57505-398-1(5)) Lerner Publishing Group.

Schaffer, Donna. Millipedes. 1999. (Life Cycles Ser.). (Illus.). 24p. (J). (gr. 2-3). lib. bdg. 18.60 (978-0-7368-0210-9(X) , Bridgestone Bks.) Capstone Pr., Inc.

MILLIPEDES—FICTION

Ross, Bakthi. Millipede Curl. 2007. 17.00 (***978-0-8059-8820-8(3)***) Dorrance Publishing Co., Inc.

MILNE, A. A. (ALAN ALEXANDER), 1882-1956

Ward, S. Meet A. A. Milne. 2001. (About the Author Ser.). (Illus.). 24p. (J). (gr. 3). lib. bdg. 18.75 (978-0-8239-5708-8(X) , PowerKids Pr.) Rosen Publishing Group, Inc., The.

Wheeler, Jill C. A. A. Milne. 2005. (Children's Authors Ser.). (Illus.). 24p. (J). (gr. k-6). lib. bdg. 21.35 (978-1-59197-607-3(3)) ABDO Publishing Co.

MILWAUKEE (WIS.)

Ancona, George. Mis Abuelos/My Grandparents. 32p. (J). 2006. (SPA.). (gr. 1-3). pap. 8.95 (978-0-516-25495-1(2)); 2005. (ENG & SPA.). 21.00 (978-0-516-25294-0(1)) Scholastic Library Publishing. (Children's Pr.).

Milwaukee Sold C 2005. 2004. 580p. (YA). pap. 15.00 (978-1-58553-958-1(9) , 05GC0016) Entertainment Publications, Inc.

Ruebartsch, John, photos by. All about Wisconsin: Todo Acerca de Wisconsin. 2007. Tr. of Todo Acerca de Wisconsin. (ENG & SPA., Illus.). 84p. (J). pap. 16.00 (978-0-9770816-3-9(X)) SHARP Literacy, Inc.

MILWAUKEE (WIS.)—FICTION

Wilkins, Celia. Little City by the Lake. Andreasen, Dan, illus. 2003. (Little House Ser.). 320p. (J). (gr. 5 up). pap. 6.99 (978-0-06-440735-9(7)) HarperCollins Pubs.

—Little City by the Lake. 2003. (gr. 3-6). lib. bdg. 14.15 (978-0-613-66981-8(9)) Tandem Library Bks.

Wimmer, Mary. Reaching Shore. 2007. 280p. (YA). per. 14.95 (***978-1-59598-063-2(6)***) Goblin Fern Pr., Inc.

MILWAUKEE (WIS.)—HISTORY

Weber, Valerie & Crawford, Beverly. Shopping in Grandma's Day. Lafford, Stuart, illus. 1999. (In Grandma's Day Ser.). 32p. (J). (ps-3). lib. bdg. 21.27 (978-1-57505-324-0(1) , Carolrhoda Bks.) Lerner Publishing Group.

MILWAUKEE BREWERS (BASEBALL TEAM)

Frisch, Aaron. Milwaukee Brewers. 2002. (Baseball Ser.). (Illus.). 32p. (J). (978-1-58341-213-8(1) , Creative Education); pap. 5.95 (978-0-89812-347-0(X) , Creative Paperbacks) Creative Co., The.

Gilbert, Sara. The Story of the Milwaukee Brewers. 2007. (***978-1-58341-492-7(4)*** , Creative Education) Creative Co., The.

Rambeck, Richard. The History of the Milwaukee Brewers. 1998. (Baseball, the Great American Game Ser.). (Illus.). 32p. (YA). (gr. 3-12). pap. 21.30 (978-0-88682-913-1(5) , Creative Education) Creative Co., The.

MIND

see Intellect; Psychology

MIND AND BODY

see also Dreams; Nervous System; Psychoanalysis; Psychology, Pathological; Sleep

Atkins, Adrianne. I Am Who I Think I Am... 2002. 28p. (978-0-9720647-1-2(0) , 166-001) Inner Peace Publishing.

Chobanian, Elizabeth. Real Spirit: Fun Ideas for Refreshing, Relaxing, & Staying Strong. Yoshizumi, Carol, illus. 2005. (American Girl Library). 64p. (J). (gr. 4-7). pap. 9.95 (978-1-58485-730-3(7) , American Girl) American Girl Publishing, Inc.

Chopra, Deepak. Teens Ask Deepak: All the Right Questions. Barchowsky, Damien, illus. 2005. 208p. (YA). pap. 12.95 (978-0-689-86218-2(0) , Simon Pulse) Simon & Schuster Children's Publishing.

Cook, David Fuller, compiled by. A Balanced Approach to Long Life & Vitality, Signature Edition: As Used in Fitness, Wellness, Clinical Weight Loss, & Cardiac Rehabilitation Programs. 2003. (Illus.). 80p. spiral bd. 31.95 (978-0-9741629-0-4(6)) Cook, David.

Esherick, Joan. Diet & Your Emotions: The Comfort Food Falsehood. 2004. (Obesity Ser.). (Illus.). 104p. (J). (ps-7). lib. bdg. 23.95 (978-1-59084-950-7(7)) Mason Crest Pubs.

Fisher, Beverly. Level One Workbook: Getting Started, 2004. (Illus.). pap. 9.99 (978-0-9745066-2-3(1)) Sports In Mind.

Fitzhugh, Karla. Body Image. 2004. (Health Issues Ser.). (Illus.). 64p. (J). 32.79 (978-0-7398-6891-1(8)) Harcourt Schl. Pubs.

Jaha, Niambi. Project Butterfly: Supporting Young Women & Girls of African Descent Through the Transitions of Life. 2003. 360p. (YA). per. 19.95 (978-0-9720854-1-0(6)) Perfect Bks.

Laskey, Elizabeth. Giant & Teeny. 2004. (Heinemann Infosearch Ser.). (Illus.). 32p. (J). lib. bdg. (978-1-4034-4957-3(0)) Heinemann Library.

Lee, Ilchi. Home Massage Therapy Book 1: Heal Yourself & Your Loved Ones, 2 vols. 2004. (Dahnhak, the Way to Perfect Health Ser.: Vol. 2). (Illus.). 148p. pap. 17.95 (978-0-9720282-9-5(3)) Healing Society, Inc.

Mattern, Joanne. Famous Mystics & Psychics. 2004. (gr. 7-10). 27.45 (978-1-59018-558-2(7)) Thomson Gale.

Steps to Healthy Touching: Activities to Help Kids Understand & Control Their Problems with Touching. 2nd ed. 2003. (Illus.). 128p. (J). per. 12.95 (978-1-55864-138-9(6)) JIST Publishing.

Townsend. Mysteries of the Body & Mind. 2004. (Out There Ser.). (Illus.). pap. 8.95 (978-1-4109-0961-9(1)) Raintree.

—Mysteries of the Body & Mind 6-Pack. 2004. (Out There Ser.). lib. bdg. 48.30 (978-1-4109-0970-1(0)) Raintree.

Wells, Rosemary. El Mundo Que Nos Rodea. Fernandez, Leire Amigo, tr. Koelsch, Michael, illus. 2004. (SPA.). 29p. (J). 13.95 (978-84-241-8711-8(3)) Everest de Ediciones y Distribucion, S.L. ESP. *Dist:* Lectorum Pubns., Inc.

MIND CURE

see Christian Science; Mind and Body

MINERAL INDUSTRIES

see Mines and Mineral Resources

MINERAL LANDS

see Mines and Mineral Resources

MINERAL OIL

see Petroleum

MINERAL RESOURCES

see Mines and Mineral Resources

MINERALOGY

see also Gems; Precious Stones

Benchmark Education Staff, compiled by. Rocks & Minerals. 2006. spiral bd. 199.00 (***978-1-4108-7135-0(5)***) Benchmark Education Co.

—Rocky Tales & Earth Systems. 2005. spiral bd. 225.00 (***978-1-4108-5819-1(7)***) Benchmark Education Co.

Bingham, Caroline. Rocks & Minerals. 2003. (Eye Wonder Ser.). (Illus.). 48p. (J). 9.99 (978-0-7894-9760-4(3)) Dorling Kindersley Publishing, Inc.

Blashfield, Jean F. Calcium. 1999. (Sparks of Life Ser.). (Illus.). 64p. (YA). (gr. 7-8). lib. bdg. 27.12 (978-0-8172-5040-9(9)) Raintree.

—Carbon. 1999. (Sparks of Life Ser.). (Illus.). 64p. (YA). (gr. 7-8). lib. bdg. 27.12 (978-0-8172-5041-6(7)) Raintree.

—Sodium. 1999. (Sparks of Life Ser.). (Illus.). 64p. (YA). (gr. 7-8). lib. bdg. 27.12 (978-0-8172-5042-3(5)) Raintree.

—Sulfur. 2001. (Sparks of Life Ser.). (Illus.). 64p. (J). (gr. 7-8). lib. bdg. 27.12 (978-0-7398-3452-7(5)) Raintree.

Bown, Deni & Dorling Kindersley Publishing Staff. Rocks & Minerals. 2003. (Ultimate Sticker Bks.). (Illus.). 16p. (J). (ps-3). pap. 6.99 (978-0-7894-0007-9(3)) Dorling Kindersley Publishing, Inc.

Brinkman, Patricia. Discover Minerals. 2006. pap. 39.00 (***978-1-4108-6495-6(2)***) Benchmark Education Co.

—Minerals. 2006. pap. 39.00 (***978-1-4108-6492-5(8)***) Benchmark Education Co.

Carson, Mary Kay & Stewart, Melissa. Extreme Rocks & Minerals! Q&A. 2007. 48p. (J). (gr. k-4). 16.99 (***978-0-06-089982-0(4)***); (Illus.). pap. 6.99 (***978-0-06-089981-3(6)***) HarperCollins Pubs.

Cefrey, Holly. Gems. 2003. (Reading Power Ser.). (Illus.). 24p. (J). lib. bdg. 17.25 (978-0-8239-6467-3(1) , PowerKids Pr.) Rosen Publishing Group, Inc., The.

—Minerals. 2003. (Reading Power Ser.). (Illus.). 24p. (J). lib. bdg. 17.25 (978-0-8239-6468-0(X) , PowerKids Pr.) Rosen Publishing Group, Inc., The.

Chasek, Ruth. Rocks & Minerals. 2000. (High Interest Bks.). (Illus.). 48p. (YA). (gr. 7-12). 24.00 (978-0-516-23333-8(5) , Children's Pr.) Scholastic Library Publishing.

Christian, Spencer & Felix, Antonia. Is There a Dinosaur in Your Backyard: The World's Most Fascinating Fossils, Rocks, & Minerals. 1998. (Spencer Christians World of Wonders: Vol. 12). (Illus.). 120p. (gr. 4-7). pap. 12.95 (978-0-471-19616-7(9) , Wiley) Wiley, John & Sons, Inc.

Crump, Irving, ed. Investigating Science - Rocks & Minerals. 2000. 48p. 9.95 (978-1-56234-445-0(5) , Mailbox Bks., The) Education Ctr., Inc.

Dayton, Connor. Crystals. 2007. (Rocks & Minerals Ser.). (Illus.). 24p. (J). (gr. 2-5). lib. bdg. 21.25 (***978-1-4042-3687-5(2)*** , PowerKids Pr.) Rosen Publishing Group, Inc., The.

—Minerals. 2007. (Rocks & Minerals Ser.). (Illus.). 24p. (J). (gr. 2-5). lib. bdg. 21.25 (***978-1-4042-3691-2(0)*** , PowerKids Pr.) Rosen Publishing Group, Inc., The.

—Rocks & Minerals, 6 bks., Set. Incl. Crystals. lib. bdg. 21.25 (***978-1-4042-3687-5(2)***); Fossils. lib. bdg. 21.25 (***978-1-4042-3689-9(9)***); Gemstones. lib. bdg. 21.25 (***978-1-4042-3686-8(4)***); Minerals. lib. bdg. 21.25 (***978-1-4042-3691-2(0)***); Rock Formations. lib. bdg. 21.25 (***978-1-4042-3690-5(2)***); Volcanic Rocks. lib. bdg. 21.25 (***978-1-4042-3688-2(0)***); (Illus.). 24p. (J). (gr. 2-5). 2007. 2007. Set lib. bdg. 127.50 (***978-1-4042-3610-3(4)*** , PowerKids Pr.) Rosen Publishing Group, Inc., The.

DK Publishing. Rocks & Minerals. 2008. 48p. (J). (gr. 2-8). pap. 9.99 (***978-0-7566-3822-1(4)***) Dorling Kindersley Publishing, Inc.

Dorling Kindersley Publishing Staff & Fuller, Sue. Rocks & Minerals. 2nd rev. ed. 2003. (DK Pockets Ser.). (Illus.). 160p. (J). pap. 6.99 (978-0-7894-9587-7(2)) Dorling Kindersley Publishing, Inc.

Dunlop, Jenna. Minerals. 2004. (Rocks, Minerals, & Resources Ser.). (Illus.). 32p. (J). (978-0-7787-1415-6(2)); pap. (978-0-7787-1447-7(0)) Crabtree Publishing Co.

Eid, Alain. 1000 Photos of Minerals & Fossils. Viard, Michel, illus. 2003. (One Thousand Photos Ser.). 128p. (YA). (gr. 5 up). pap. 24.95 (978-0-7641-5218-4(1)) Barron's Educational Series, Inc.

Farndon, John. Rock & Mineral. 2007. (Dk Online Ser.). 96p. (J). (gr. 3-8). pap. 9.99 (***978-0-7566-3136-9(X)***) Dorling Kindersley Publishing, Inc.

Farndon, John, et al. Rocks & Minerals. 2005. (Google E Guides). (Illus.). 96p. (J). 17.99 (978-0-7566-1140-8(7)) Dorling Kindersley Publishing, Inc.

Faulkner, Rebecca. Minerals. 2007. (J). (***978-1-4109-2750-7(4)***); (***978-1-4109-2758-3(X)***) Steck-Vaughn.

Fuller, Sue. Backpack Books: 1,001 Facts about Rocks & Minerals. 2003. (gr. 3-6). lib. bdg. 17.60 (978-0-613-55690-3(9)) Tandem Library Bks.

—Rocks & Minerals. 2003. (gr. 3-6). lib. bdg. 15.30 (978-0-613-75184-1(1)) Tandem Library Bks.

Fuller, Sue & Maynard, Christopher. 1,001 Facts about Rocks & Minerals. Grabham, Sue, ed. 2002. (Backpack-Books). (Illus.). 192p. (J). (gr. k-3). pap. 8.99 (978-0-7894-9043-8(9)) Dorling Kindersley Publishing, Inc.

Gallant, Roy A. Minerals. 2000. (Kaleidoscope Ser.). (Illus.). 48p. (J). (gr. 3 up). lib. bdg. 25.64 (978-0-7614-1039-3(2) , Benchmark Bks.) Cavendish, Marshall Corp.

Gardner, Robert. Smashing Science Projects about Earth's Rocks & Minerals. LaBaff, Tom, illus. 2007. (Rockin' Earth Science Experiments Ser.). 48p. (J). (gr. 3-4). lib. bdg. 23.93 (978-0-7660-2731-2(7) , Enslow Elementary) Enslow Pubs., Inc.

Goldman, Phyllis B., ed. Monkeyshines on Rocks & Minerals. (Illus.). 148p. (J). (ps-7). reprint ed. pap. 26.95 (978-1-888325-14-0(3)) Allosaurus Pubs.

Group/McGraw-Hill, Wright. Materials Que Hay en la Tierra, 6 vols. (First Explorers. Primeros Exploradores Nonfiction Sets Ser.). (SPA.). (gr. 1-2). 29.95 (978-0-7699-1468-8(3)) Shortland Pubns. (U. S. A.) Inc.

Halls, Kelly Milner. Rocks & Minerals. 2006. (Illus.). 48p. (J). (978-1-4034-7911-2(9)) Heinemann Library.

Hantula, Richard. Rocks & Fossils. 2006. (J). pap. (***978-0-8368-7876-9(0)***) Stevens, Gareth Inc.

Hirschmann, Kris. Rocks & Minerals. 2004. (World Discovery Science Readers Ser.). (Illus.). 31p. (J). pap. (978-0-439-56630-8(4)) Scholastic, Inc.

Hodge, Judith. Las riquezas de la tierra & Riches from Earth. 2005. spiral bd. 84.00 (***978-1-4108-5716-3(6)***) Benchmark Education Co.

Holt, Rinehart and Winston Staff. Holt Science & Technology Chptr. 7: Minerals of the Earth: Chapter Resources - Tennessee Edition. 3rd ed. 2003. (YA). (gr. 8). pap. 11.40 (978-0-03-069166-9(4)) Holt, Rinehart & Winston.

—Holt Science & Technology Chptr. 8: Rocks & Minerals: Chapter Resources - Tennessee Edition. 3rd ed. 2003. (YA). pap. 11.40 (978-0-03-069167-6(2)) Holt, Rinehart & Winston.

Hunter, Rebecca M. Rocks, Minerals & Fossils. 2001. (Discovering Science Ser.). (Illus.). 32p. (J). (gr. 4-7). lib. bdg. 25.69 (978-0-7398-3250-9(6)) Raintree.

Instructional Fair. Rocks & Minerals. 1999. (Ready Reference Cards Ser.). 12p. (J). (gr. 5-12). ring bd. 11.50 (978-0-7424-0777-0(2) , IF676R) School Specialty Publishing.

Jones, Robert W. & Discovery Books Staff. Rocks & Minerals. 1999. (Explore Your World Ser.). (Illus.). 192p. (J). pap. 13.95 (978-1-56331-803-0(2)) Discovery Bks.

Lorenz Books Staff, et al. Rocks & Minerals. 2000. (Investigations Ser.). (Illus.). 64p. (gr. 3-7). 12.95 (978-0-7548-0457-4(7) , Lorenz Bks.) Anness Publishing, Inc.

Mattern, Joanne. Minerals & the Rock Cycle. 2006. (J). lib. bdg. (978-1-4042-3199-3(4) , PowerKids Pr.) Rosen Publishing Group, Inc., The.

Miles, Lisa. Rocas y Minerales. 2004. (Spotter's Guides Sticker Bks.). (SPA., Illus.). 24p. (J). (gr. 2 up). pap. 7.95 (978-0-7460-3642-6(6)) EDC Publishing.

—Rocks & Minerals Sticker Book. rev. ed. 2006. 16p. (J). pap. 8.99 (978-0-7945-1413-6(8) , Usborne) EDC Publishing.

Miller-Schroeder, Patricia. Minerals. 2004. (Science Matters Ser.). (Illus.). 24p. (J). lib. bdg. 24.45 (978-1-59036-214-3(4)) Weigl Pubs., Inc.

Minerals. (Exploring the Earth Ser.). 24p. (J). 6.95 (978-0-7368-3366-0(8)) Capstone Pr., Inc.

Minerals: Individual Title Six-Packs. (On Deck Ser.: Vol. 2). 24p. (gr. 4-5). 35.00 (978-0-7578-5821-5(X)) Rigby Education.

Morris, Neil. Rocks & Minerals. 1998. (Wonders of Our World Ser.). (Illus.). 32p. (J). (gr. 3-4). lib. bdg. (978-0-86505-833-4(0)); pap. (978-0-86505-847-7(4)) Crabtree Publishing Co.

Oceanor Staff. Mineralogia - Atlas Visual. 1999. (SPA.). (gr. 3-6). lib. bdg. 20.00 (978-0-613-80884-2(3)) Tandem Library Bks.

O'Daly, Anne. Sodium. 2001. (Elements Ser.). (Illus.). 32p. (J). (gr. 3-5). lib. bdg. 25.64 (978-0-7614-1271-7(9) , Benchmark Bks.) Cavendish, Marshall Corp.

O'Donoghue, Michael. Rocks & Minerals of the World. 2004. (World Book's Science & Nature Guides Ser.). (Illus.). 80p. (J). (978-0-7166-4217-6(4)) World Bk., Inc.

Oetting, Judy. Fun Facts & Games: Missouri's Rocks & Minerals. Nolte, Larry, illus. 2000. (Fun Facts & Games Ser.). 64p. (J). (ps-3). pap. 5.95 (978-1-892920-24-9(7)) GHB Publishers, LLC.

—"M" Is for Missouri's Rocks & Minerals. Dorenkamp, Michelle, illus. 2000. (Alpha Flight Bks.). 60p. (J). (ps-3). 17.95 (978-1-892920-29-4(8)) GHB Publishers, LLC.

Parker, Steve. Rocks & Minerals. 2002. (Science Files Ser.). (Illus.). 32p. (J). (gr. 3 up). lib. bdg. 24.67 (978-0-8368-3085-9(7)) Stevens, Gareth Inc.

Pellant, Chris. The Best Book of Fossils, Rocks & Minerals. 2007. (Best Book of... Ser.). 32p. (J). (gr. k-3). pap. 6.95 (978-0-7534-6081-8(5) , Kingfisher) Houghton Mifflin Co. Trade & Reference Div.

Pellant, Chris & Pellant, Helen. Quartz & Other Minerals. 2006. (J). lib. bdg. (***978-0-8368-7908-7(2)***) Stevens, Gareth Inc.

Pellant, Chris & Perrault, Chris. The Best Book of Fossils, Rocks & Minerals. Grinaway, Ray & Forsey, Chris, illus. 2000. (Best Book of... Ser.). 32p. (J). (gr. k-3). tchr. ed. 12.95 (978-0-7534-5274-5(X) , Kingfisher) Houghton Mifflin Co. Trade & Reference Div.

Phelan, Glen. Rocks & Minerals. 2004. (National Geographic Reading Expeditions Ser.). (Illus.). 32p. (J). pap. (978-0-7922-4571-1(7)) National Geographic Society.

Pinet, Michele. Be Your Own Rock & Mineral Expert. Greenbaum, Fay, tr. from FRE. Korkos, Alain, illus. 2003. 40p. (J). (gr. 5-7). 14.95 (978-0-8069-9580-9(7)) Sterling Publishing Co., Inc.

Powell, Darryl. Minerals, A to Z: Games & Coloring Fun for Kids. 2000. (Illus.). 32p. (J). (gr. k-6). pap. 1.95 (978-0-9678163-1-9(9)) Diamond Dan Pubns.

Prokos, Anna. Rocks & Minerals. 2004. (Discovery Channel School Science Ser.). (Illus.). 32p. (J). (gr. 5 up). lib. bdg. 24.67 (978-0-8368-3384-3(8)) Stevens, Gareth Inc.

Ricciuti, Edward R. Rocks & Minerals. 2001. (Scholastic Science Readers Ser.). (Illus.). 48p. (J). pap. (978-0-439-26993-3(8)) Scholastic, Inc.

Ricciuti, Edward R., et al. Rocks & Minerals. 1998. (Audubon Society First Field Guide Ser.). (Illus.). 160p. (YA). (gr. 3-7). pap. 17.95 (978-0-590-05463-8(5)) Scholastic, Inc.

Richardson, Adele D. Minerals. 2001. (Bridgestone Science Library). (Illus.). 24p. (J). (gr. 2-3). lib. bdg. 18.60 (978-0-7368-0952-8(X) , Bridgestone Bks.) Capstone Pr., Inc.

Rocks & Minerals. 2005. 48p. (J). per. 6.99 (978-1-59441-202-8(2) , CD-104110) Carson-Dellosa Publishing Co., Inc.

Rocks & Minerals. 2002. 32p. (J). 7.95 (978-0-7525-7243-7(1)) Parragon, Inc.

Rocks & Minerals. 2002. (Super Science Activities Ser.). 48p. (J). (gr. 2-5). 7.99 (978-0-7439-3666-8(3) , 3666) Teacher Created Materials, Inc.

Royston, Angela. Vitamins & Minerals for a Healthy Body. 2003. (Illus.). 48p. (J). pap. 7.99 (978-1-4034-3313-8(5)); lib. bdg. 27.07 (978-1-4034-0758-0(4)) Heinemann Library.

Science & Technology for Children BOOKS: Rocks & Minerals Set. 2007. (J). 127.60 (***978-1-933008-44-8(X)***) National Science Resources Ctr.

Science stories foss spanish earth materials ea Cr05. 2005. (J). (978-1-59242-590-7(9)) Delta Education, LLC.

Sheen, Martin, contrib. by. Rocks & Minerals. 2007. 16p. (J). (gr. 3-8). pap. 29.99 (***978-0-7566-3132-1(7)***) Dorling Kindersley Publishing, Inc.

Squire, Ann O. Rocks & Minerals. 2002. (True Bks.). (Illus.). 48p. (J). (gr. 3-5). pap. 6.95 (978-0-516-26985-6(2) , Children's Pr.) Scholastic Library Publishing.

—Rocks & Minerals. 2002. (gr. 3-6). lib. bdg. 15.25 (978-0-613-54328-6(9)) Tandem Library Bks.

Stamper, Judith Bauer. Rocks & Minerals. Gangloff, Hope, illus. 2004. (Magic School Bus Ser.). 96p. (J). (gr. 3 up). pap. 4.99 (978-0-439-56053-5(5) , Scholastic Paperbacks) Scholastic, Inc.

Stewart, Melissa. Crystals. 2002. (Rocks & Minerals Ser.). (Illus.). 32p. (J). (gr. 4-6). lib. bdg. 24.22 (978-1-58810-254-6(8)); pap. 7.50 (978-1-4034-0090-1(3) , 91657) Heinemann Library.

—Minerals. 2002. (Rocks & Minerals Ser.). (Illus.). 32p. (J). (gr. 4-6). lib. bdg. 24.22 (978-1-58810-258-4(0)); pap. 7.50 (978-1-4034-0094-9(6) , 91661) Heinemann Library.

Stille, Darlene R. Minerals: From Apatite to Zinc. 2004. (Exploring Science Ser.). (Illus.). 48p. 25.27 (978-0-7565-0855-5(X)) Compass Point Bks.

Symes, R. F. Rock & Mineral. 2008. (DK Eyewitness Bks.). 72p. (J). (gr. 3-8). 15.99 (***978-0-7566-3777-4(5)***) Dorling Kindersley Publishing, Inc.

Symes, R. F. Rocks & Minerals. 2004. (Dk Eyewitness Books Ser.). (Illus.). 72p. (ps-12). 15.99 (978-0-7566-0719-7(1)) Dorling Kindersley Publishing, Inc.

Symes, R. F., et al. Rocks & Minerals. Keates, Colin & Einsiedel, Andreas, illus. 2004. (Eyewitness Books). 72p. (J). lib. bdg. 19.99 (978-0-7566-0718-0(3)) Dorling Kindersley Publishing, Inc.

Tocci, Salvatore. Experiments with Rocks & Minerals. 2002. (True Bks.). (Illus.). 48p. (J). (gr. 3-5). pap. 6.95 (978-0-516-26995-5(X) , Children's Pr.) Scholastic Library Publishing.

—Experiments with Rocks & Minerals. 2002. (gr. 3-6). lib. bdg. 15.25 (978-0-613-54212-8(6)) Tandem Library Bks.

Trueit, Trudi Strain. Rocks, Gems, & Minerals. 2003. (Watts Library). 64p. (gr. 5-7). pap. 8.95 (978-0-531-16241-5(9)); (Illus.). (J). 25.50 (978-0-531-12195-5(X)) Scholastic Library Publishing. (Watts, Franklin).

—Rocks, Gems, & Minerals. 2003. (gr. 5-8). lib. bdg. 17.60 (978-0-613-67665-6(3)) Tandem Library Bks.

VanCleave, Janice Pratt. Janice VanCleave's Rocks & Minerals: Mind-Boggling Experiments You Can Turn into Science Fair Projects. 2002. (Janice Vancleave Ser.). (Illus.). (J). 19.72 (978-0-7587-4633-7(4)) Book Wholesalers, Inc.

Walker, Sally M. Minerals. 2007. (Early Bird Earth Science Ser.). (Illus.). 48p. (J). 25.26 (978-0-8225-5946-7(3)); pap. (***978-0-8225-6620-5(6)***) Lerner Publishing Group. (Lerner Pubns.).

Walshaw, R. Rocks & Minerals. 2002. (All about Ser.). (Illus.). 64p. (gr. 3-7). pap. 7.95 (978-1-84215-629-2(2) , Southwater) Anness Publishing GBR. *Dist:* National Bk. Network.

West, Krista. Hands-On Projects about Rocks, Minerals & Fossils. 2002. (Great Earth Science Projects Ser.). (Illus.). 24p. (J). lib. bdg. 19.95 (978-0-8239-5842-9(6) , PowerKids Pr.) Rosen Publishing Group, Inc., The.

Woolley, A. Rocks & Minerals. 2004. (Spotter's Guides). (Illus.). 64p. (J). lib. bdg. 13.95 (978-1-58086-309-4(4)) EDC Publishing.

—Rocks & Minerals Spotter's Guide - Internet Referenced. rev. ed. 2007. 64p. (J). pap. 5.99 (978-0-7945-1304-7(2) , Usborne) EDC Publishing.

Zim, Herbert S. & Shaffer, Paul R. Rocks, Gems & Minerals: A Guide to Familiar Minerals, Gems, Ores & Rocks. Perlman, Raymond, illus. rev. ed. 2001. (Golden Guides Ser.). 160p. pap. 6.95 (978-1-58238-132-9(1) , Golden Guides from Saint Martin's Pr.) St. Martin's Pr.

MINERALS

see Mineralogy

MINERS

Harcourt School Publishers Staff. Trofeos On Level: Viaje Al Pasado. 3rd ed. 2002. (SPA., Illus.). pap. 6.80 (978-0-15-324094-2(6)) Harcourt Schl. Pubs.

MINERS—FICTION

Blackwater Mine, 6 Pack. (Bookweb Ser.). 32p. (gr. 6 up). 34.00 (978-0-7578-0893-7(X)) Rigby Education.

Harcourt School Publishers Staff. A Trip to the Past On Level. 3rd ed. 2002. (Trophies Reading Program Ser.). (Illus.). pap. 5.10 (978-0-15-323183-4(1)) Harcourt Schl. Pubs.

Hope, Laura Lee. Outdoor Girls in the Saddle or the Girl. 2007. 95.99 (***978-1-4280-5359-5(X)***); pap. 88.99 (***978-1-4280-5368-7(9)***) IndyPublish.com.

Perez, Norah A. Breaker. 2002. (Pitt Golden Triangle Bks.). 216p. pap. 9.95 (978-0-8229-5778-2(7) , Golden Triangle Bks.) Univ. of Pittsburgh Pr.

St John, Patricia. A Home for Virginia. Smith, Helen, illus. 2005. 24p. (J). (ps-7). per. (978-1-85792-961-4(6) , Christian Focus) Christian Focus Pubns.

Varonka, Steve. Hard Coal Times: Pennsylvania Anthracite Stories, Vol. 1. 2003. (Illus.). 40p. (J). 4.72 (978-0-9709630-2-4(5)) Coal Hole Productions.

Whale Watch, 6 Packs. (Bookweb Ser.). 32p. (gr. 6 up). 34.00 (978-0-7578-0895-1(6)) Rigby Education.

Wiseman, David. Jeremy Visick. 2005. 176p. (YA). (gr. 5 up). 21.25 (978-0-8446-7271-7(8) , 3594) Smith, Peter Pub., Inc.

MINES AND MINERAL RESOURCES

see also Mineralogy; Mining Engineering; Prospecting

also specific types of mines and mining, e.g. Coal Mines and Mining; etc.

Crowther, Robert. Deep down under Ground: A Pop-up Book of Amazing Facts & Feats. Crowther, Robert, illus. 2004. (Illus.). 18p. (J). (gr. 3-8). reprint ed. pap. 22.00 (978-0-7567-7179-9(X)) DIANE Publishing Co.

Graham, Ian. Minerals: A Resource Our World Depends On. 2004. (J). pap. 7.50 (978-1-4034-5624-3(0)); lib. bdg. 24.22 (978-1-4034-5616-8(X)) Heinemann Library.

Holt, Rinehart and Winston Staff. Environmental Science Chptr. 16: Mining & Mineral Resources. 4th ed. 2004. pap. 11.20 (978-0-03-068077-9(8)) Holt, Rinehart & Winston.

Hopkins, Ellen H. Tarnished Legacy: The Story of the Comstock Lode. 2001. (Cover-to-Cover Bks.). (Illus.). 64p. (J). pap. (978-0-7891-1003-9(2)); (gr. 4-7). lib. bdg. 17.95 (978-0-7807-9702-4(7)) Perfection Learning Corp.

Love, Ann & Drake, Jane. Mining: Canada at Work. Cupples, Pat, illus. 2001. (Canada at Work Ser.). 32p. (J). (gr. 2-5). (978-1-55074-920-5(X)) Kids Can Pr., Ltd.

M
N
O

Miles, Lisa. Rocks & Minerals. 2003. (Usborne Hotshots Ser.). (Illus.). 32p. (YA). (gr. 2 up). pap. 2.95 (978-0-7460-2790-5(7)) EDC Publishing.

Whyman, Kathryn. Rocks & Minerals & the Environment. 2004. (J). lib. bdg. (978-1-932799-36-1(2)) Stargazer Bks.

Zronik, John Paul. Metals. 2004. (Rocks, Minerals, & Resources Ser.). (Illus.). 32p. (J). (978-0-7787-1418-7(7)); pap. (978-0-7787-1450-7(0)) Crabtree Publishing Co.

MINES AND MINERAL RESOURCES—FICTION

Breaker. 2002. (gr. 7-12). lib. bdg. 18.75 (978-0-613-46050-7(2)) Tandem Library Bks.

Burkhard, Daryl. Riddle in the Mountain. Riccio, Frank, illus. 2005. 240p. 16.95 (978-0-9668289-5-5(X)) Nomad Pr.

Duey, Kathleen & Bale, Karen A. Cave-In, St. Claire, Pennsylvania, 1859. 1998. (Survival! Ser.: No. 7). 160p. (J). (gr. 4-7). pap. 3.99 (978-0-689-82350-3(9) , Simon Pulse) Simon & Schuster Children's Publishing.

Ferris, Jean. Much Ado about Grubstake. 2006. (Illus.). 272p. (YA). 17.00 (978-0-15-205706-0(4)) Harcourt Children's Bks.

Hamilton, Morse. The Garden of Eden Motel. 1999. (Illus.). 160p. (J). (gr. 5 up). 16.00 (978-0-688-16814-8(0)) HarperCollins Pubs.

Murphy, Claire Rudolf & Golden Books Staff. Gold Rush Winter. 2002. (Road to Reading Ser.). (Illus.). 48p. (J). (gr. 2-4). pap. 3.99 (978-0-307-26413-8(0) , Random Hse. Bks. for Young Readers) Random Hse. Children's Bks.

Stellinga, Mark. Buster Boogernose & the Copper Mine. 2007. (J). per. 9.95 (*978-0-9796421-3-5(2)) Stellinga, Mark.

Winfield, M. Arthur. The Rover Boys Out West or the Search Fo. 2006. 63.99 (*978-1-4280-1837-2(9)) IndyPublish.com.

MINIATURE CAMERAS

see Cameras

MINIATURE OBJECTS

see Dollhouses; Models and Modelmaking; Toys

see names of objects with the subdivision Models, e.g. Airplanes—Models

MINING

see Mines and Mineral Resources; Mining Engineering

MINING ENGINEERING

Love, Ann. Mining. 2002. (gr. 3-6). lib. bdg. 14.10 (978-0-613-84414-7(9)) Tandem Library Bks.

Love, Ann & Drake, Jane. Mining. Cupples, Pat, illus. 2002. (America at Work Ser.). 32p. (J). (gr. k-3). (978-1-55337-424-4(X)); (978-1-55074-508-5(5)) Kids Can Pr., Ltd.

MINISTERS (DIPLOMATIC AGENTS)

see Diplomats

MINISTERS OF THE GOSPEL

see Clergy

MINKS

Gray, Susan H. American Mink. 2008. (J). lib. bdg. 25.26 (*978-1-60279-114-5(7)) Cherry Lake Publishing.

MINKS—FICTION

Burgess, Thornton W. Billy Mink. (J). 18.95 (978-0-8488-0397-1(3)) Amereon LTD.

Elliott, David. Evangeline Mudd & the Great Mink Escapade. Wesson, Andrea, illus. 2006. 192p. (J). (gr. 2-5). 15.99 (978-0-7636-2295-4(8)) Candlewick Pr.

Kink the Mink: KinderReaders Individual Title Six-Packs. (Kinderstarters Ser.). 8p. (ps-1). 21.00 (978-0-7635-8652-2(8)) Rigby Education.

Sargent, Dave & Sargent, Pat. Mad Jack: I Throw Fits, 15 vols., 16. Huff, Jeane, illus. 2nd rev. ed. 2003. (Animal Pride Ser.: 16). 42p. (J). pap. 6.95 (978-1-56763-790-8(6)); lib. bdg. 19.95 (978-1-56763-789-2(2)) Ozark Publishing.

—Patty Panda: Disposition, 56 vols., 54. Lenoir, Jane, illus. 2000. (Cherokee Indian Legend Ser.: Vol. 54). 36p. (J). lib. bdg. 19.95 (978-1-56763-549-2(0)) Ozark Publishing.

MINNESOTA

Ash, Stephanie Wilbur. Uniquely Minnesota. 2003. (State Studies). (Illus.). 48p. (J). pap. 8.50 (978-1-4034-4509-4(5)); lib. bdg. 27.07 (978-1-4034-4494-3(3)) Heinemann Library.

Brown, Vanessa. Minnesota. Brusca, Maria Cristina, tr. 2005. (Bilingual Library of the United States of America: Set 1). (ENG & SPA., Illus.). 32p. (J). (gr. 2-5). lib. bdg. 22.50 (978-1-4042-3088-0(2) , Buenas Letra) Rosen Publishing Group, Inc., The.

Capstone Press Staff, contrib. by. Minnesota. rev. ed. 2002. (One Nation Ser.). (Illus.). 48p. (J). (gr. 3-4). lib. bdg. 22.60 (978-0-7368-1247-4(4) , Bridgestone Bks.) Capstone Pr., Inc.

Dolan, Sean. Minnesota. 2006. 32p. (J). (gr. 1-2). pap. 5.95 (978-0-516-25158-5(9) , Children's Pr.) Scholastic Library Publishing.

Dolan, Sean J. Minnesota. 2005. (Rookie Read-About Geography Ser.). (Illus.). 31p. (J). (ps-ps). 20.50 (978-0-516-25257-5(7) , Children's Pr.) Scholastic Library Publishing.

Dykstra, Mary. Minnesota. 2006. (Portraits of the States Ser.). (Illus.). 32p. (J). (gr. 1 up). lib. bdg. 23.33 (978-0-8368-4669-0(9)) Stevens, Gareth Inc.

Feinstein, Stephen. Minnesota: A MyReportLinks.com Book. 2003. (States Ser.). (Illus.). 48p. (J). (gr. 4-10). lib. bdg. 25.26 (978-0-7660-5096-9(3) , MyReportLinks.com Bks.) Enslow Pubs., Inc.

Gedatus, Gustav Mark. Minnesota. 2006. (Portraits of the States Ser.). (Illus.). 32p. (J). pap. 8.95 (978-0-8368-4688-1(5)) Stevens, Gareth Inc.

Glaser, Rebecca Stromstad. Minnesota. 2003. (Land of Liberty Ser.). (Illus.). 64p. (J). (gr. 3-4). lib. bdg. 23.93 (978-0-7368-1591-8(0) , Bridgestone Bks.) Capstone Pr., Inc.

Hasday, Judy L. Minnesota. 2003. (From Sea to Shining Sea Ser.: 2). (Illus.). 80p. (J). 30.50 (978-0-516-22478-7(6) , Children's Pr.) Scholastic Library Publishing.

Heinrichs, Ann. Minnesota. 2005. (Welcome to the USA Ser.). 40p. (J). (gr. 1-5). 27.07 (978-1-59296-474-1(5)) Child's World, Inc.

—Minnesota. 2003. (This Land Is Your Land Ser.). (Illus.). 48p. (J). (gr. 3 up). lib. bdg. 22.60 (978-0-7565-0315-4(9)) Compass Point Bks.

Luecke, John C. Northern Pacific in Minnesota. 2003. (Illus.). 400p. 75.00 (978-0-9621020-5-9(9)) Grenadier Pubns.

Marsh, Carole. The Big Minnesota Reproducible Activity Book. 2001. (Carole Marsh Minnesota Bks.). (Illus.). 96p. (J). (gr. 2-6). pap. 9.95 (978-0-7933-9946-8(7)) Gallopade International.

—Minnesota Classic Christmas Trivia. 2002. (Carole Marsh Minnesota Bks.). (Illus.). 32p. pap. 14.95 (978-0-635-01413-9(0) , 14130); lib. bdg. 21.95 (978-0-635-01414-6(9) , 14149) Gallopade International. (Marsh, Carole Bks.).

—Minnesota Current Events Projects: 30 Cool, Activities, Crafts, Experiments & More for Kids to Do to Learn about Your State! 2003. (Minnesota Experience Ser.). 32p. (gr. k-8). pap. 5.95 (978-0-635-02042-0(4) , Marsh, Carole Bks.) Gallopade International.

—The Minnesota Experience Library State: Resource Set. 2001. (Illus.). (J). (gr. k-8). pap. 100.20 incl. cd-rom (978-0-635-00476-5(3)) Gallopade International.

—The Minnesota Experience Pocket Guide. 2001. (Carole Marsh Minnesota Bks.). (Illus.). 96p. (J). (gr. 3-8). pap. 6.95 (978-0-7933-9917-8(3)) Gallopade International.

—Minnesota Geography Projects: 30 Cool, Activities, Crafts, Experiments & More for Kids to Do to Learn about Your State! 2003. (Minnesota Experience Ser.). 32p. (gr. k-5). pap. 5.95 (978-0-635-01842-7(X) , Marsh, Carole Bks.) Gallopade International.

—Minnesota Government Projects: 30 Cool, Activities, Crafts, Experiments & More for Kids to Do to Learn about Your State! 2003. (Minnesota Experience Ser.). 32p. (gr. k-5). pap. 5.95 (978-0-635-01942-4(6) , Marsh, Carole Bks.) Gallopade International.

—Minnesota "Jography" A Fun Run Thru Our State! 2001. (Carole Marsh Minnesota Bks.). (Illus.). 32p. (J). (gr. 3-8). pap. 7.95 (978-0-7933-9830-0(4)) Gallopade International.

—Minnesota Millionaire: Game Book. 2001. (Carole Marsh Minnesota Bks.). (Illus.). 32p. (J). (gr. 3-8). pap., act. bk. ed. 9.95 (978-0-635-00062-0(8)) Gallopade International.

—Minnesota People Projects: 30 Cool, Activities, Crafts, Experiments & More for Kids to Do to Learn about Your State! 2003. (Minnesota Experience Ser.). 32p. (gr. k-5). pap. 5.95 (978-0-635-01992-9(2) , Marsh, Carole Bks.) Gallopade International.

—Minnesota Survivor: Game Book. 2001. (Carole Marsh Montana Bks.). (Illus.). 32p. (J). (gr. 3-8). pap., act. bk. ed. 9.95 (978-0-635-00544-1(1)) Gallopade International.

—Minnesota Symbols & Facts Projects: 30 Cool, Activities, Crafts, Experiments & More for Kids to Do to Learn about Your State! 2003. (Minnesota Experience Ser.). 32p. (gr. k-5). pap. 5.95 (978-0-635-01892-2(6) , Marsh, Carole Bks.) Gallopade International.

—My First Book about Minnesota. 2001. (Carole Marsh Minnesota Bks.). (Illus.). 32p. (J). (gr. k-4). pap. 7.95 (978-0-7933-9888-1(6)) Gallopade International.

—The Survivor: A Class Challenge. 2001. (Carole Marsh Minnesota Bks.). lib. bdg. 29.95 (978-0-635-00669-1(3)) Gallopade International.

—Who Wants to Be a Millionaire? 2001. (Carole Marsh Minnesota Bks.). lib. bdg. 29.95 (978-0-635-00063-7(6)) Gallopade International.

Marsh, Carole & Marsh, Michael. Let's Discover Minnesota! 2001. (Illus.). (J). (gr. 2-8). cd-rom 14.95 (978-0-7933-9975-8(0)) Gallopade International.

Maruca, Mary. A Kid's Guide to Exploring Great Sand Dunes National Monument & Preserve. 2002. (Illus.). 12p. (J). pap. 1.00 (978-1-58369-023-9(9)) Western National Parks Assn.

McAuliffe, Bill. Minnesota: Facts & Symbols. 1999. (J). lib. bdg. 14.00 (978-0-531-11803-0(7)) Capstone Pr., Inc.

—Minnesota Facts & Symbols. (States & Their Symbols Ser.). 24p. (J). 1999. (Illus.). (gr. 2-3). lib. bdg. 18.60 (978-0-7368-0219-2(3) , Bridgestone Bks.); 2003. lib. bdg. 19.93 (978-0-7368-2253-4(4)) Capstone Pr., Inc.

Minneapolis Sold C 2005. 2004. 420p. (YA). pap. 17.00 (978-1-58553-959-8(7) , 05GC0026) Entertainment Publications, Inc.

Minnesota. 2000. (Switched on Schoolhouse Ser.). (Illus.). (YA). (gr. 7-12). pap. 24.95 incl. cd-rom (978-0-7403-0275-6(2) , SOSMN) Alpha Omega Pubns., Inc.

Moore, Dave, compiled by. A Few People: Tracing Our Hmong Roots. 2nd ed. 2003. (ENG., Illus.). 144p. (J). per. 14.95 (978-1-888194-42-5(1)) Master Communications, Inc.

Murray, Julie. Minnesota. 2006. (Illus.). 32p. (J). (gr. k-4). lib. bdg. 22.78 (978-1-59197-682-0(0) , Buddy Bks.) ABDO Publishing Co.

Paulsen, Gary. Woodsong. unabr. ed. 2004. 132p. (J). (gr. 6 up). pap. 29.00 incl. audio (978-0-8072-0460-3(9) , Listening Library) Random Hse. Audio Publishing Group.

—Woodsong. 2007. 144p. (J). pap. 5.99 (*978-1-4169-3939-9(3) , Aladdin) Simon & Schuster Children's Publishing.

—Woodsong. 2000. (J). (gr. 6 up). 20.25 (978-0-8446-7152-9(5)) Smith, Peter Pub., Inc.

Peterson, Sheryl. Minnesota. 2008. (J). (*978-1-58341-648-8(X) , Creative Education) Creative Co., The.

Pollock, Miriam Heddy & Jaffe, Peter. Minnesota. 2002. (World Almanac Library of the States). (Illus.). 48p. (J). pap. 14.60 (978-0-8368-5308-7(3)); lib. bdg. 30.00 (978-0-8368-5138-0(2)) Stevens, Gareth Inc. (World Almanac Library).

Porter, A. P. Minnesota. 2nd rev. exp. ed. (Hello U. S. A. Ser.). (Illus.). 84p. (J). (gr. 3-6). 2003. pap. 6.95 (978-0-8225-4149-3(1)); 2002. 25.26 (978-0-8225-4059-5(2) , Lerner Pubns.) Lerner Publishing Group.

—Minnesota. 2001. (gr. 3-6). lib. bdg. 15.25 (978-0-613-81865-0(2)) Tandem Library Bks.

Purslow, Neil. A Guide to Minnesota. (American States Ser.). 32p. (J). 2002. (Illus.). (gr. 4-7). lib. bdg. 16.95 (978-1-930954-85-4(9)); 2001. per. 7.95 (978-1-930954-72-4(7)) Weigl Pubs., Inc.

Schwabacher, Martin & Kummer, Patricia K. Minnesota. 2nd ed. 2008. (Celebrate the States Ser.). (J). lib. bdg. 39.93 (*978-0-7614-2716-2(3) , Benchmark Bks.) Cavendish, Marshall Corp.

Wargin, Kathy-Jo. V Is for Viking: A Minnesota Alphabet. Latham, Karen & Latham, Rebecca, illus. 2003. 40p. (J). 17.95 (978-1-58536-125-0(9)) Sleeping Bear Pr.

MINNESOTA—FICTION

Allosso, Dan. Outside the Box. 2007. 148p. 21.95 (*978-0-595-68621-6(4)); per. 11.95 (*978-0-595-44295-9(1)) iUniverse, Inc.

Applegate, Katherine. Home of the Brave. 2007. 256p. (J). (gr. 5-9). 16.95 (*978-0-312-36765-7(1)) Feiwel & Friends.

Bauer, Marion Dane. Land of the Buffalo Bones: The Diary of Mary Elizabeth Rodgers, an English Girl in Minnesota. 2003. (Dear America Ser.). (Illus.). 224p. (J). pap. 12.95 (978-0-439-22027-9(0)) Scholastic, Inc.

Bender, Carrie. Birch Hollow Schoolmarm. 1999. (gr. 7-12). lib. bdg. 17.60 (978-0-613-81313-6(8)) Tandem Library Bks.

Blume, Lesley M. M. The Rising Star of Rusty Nail. 2007. 288p. (J). (gr. 3-7). 15.99 (978-0-375-83524-7(5) , Knopf Bks. for Young Readers) Random Hse. Children's Bks.

—The Rising Star of the Rusty Nail. 2007. 288p. (J). (gr. 3-7). lib. bdg. 18.99 (978-0-375-93524-4(X) , Knopf Bks. for Young Readers) Random Hse. Children's Bks.

Brummer, Sandy. Bound for Minnesota. 2004. (YA). per. 9.95 (978-1-931945-14-1(4) , et al Publishing) Expert Publishing, Inc.

Bull, Emma. War for the Oaks. 2001. (gr. 7-12). lib. bdg. 23.40 (978-0-613-60631-8(0)) Tandem Library Bks.

Casanova, Mary. Trouble in Pembrook. Rayyan, Omar, illus. 2006. 117p. (J). (*978-1-4156-7757-5(3) , Aladdin) Simon & Schuster Children's Publishing.

Delton, Judy. Wild, Wild West. 1999. (Pee Wee Scouts Ser.: No. 37). (J). (gr. 2-5). (978-0-606-16585-3(1)) Tandem Library Bks.

Dines, Carol. Talk to Me: Stories & a Novella. 1999. (978-0-606-16451-1(0)) Tandem Library Bks.

Duey, Kathleen & Bale, Karen A. Forest Fire, Hinckley, Minnesota, 1894. 1999. (Survival! Ser.: No. 10). (J). (gr. 4-7). (978-0-606-16301-9(8)) Tandem Library Bks.

Durbin, William. Song of Sampo Lake. 2004. 224p. (J). (gr. 5). reprint ed. pap. 5.50 (978-0-440-22899-8(9) , Yearling) Random Hse. Children's Bks.

—Song of Sampo Lake. 2004. (gr. 5-8). lib. bdg. 13.55 (978-0-613-85112-1(9)) Tandem Library Bks.

Edwards, Michelle. Zero Grandparents. 2005. (Jackson Friends Ser.). (Illus.). 64p. (J). (ps-ps). pap., pap. 5.95 (978-0-15-205754-1(4) , Harcourt Paperbacks) Harcourt Children's Bks.

Ellsworth, Loretta. Shrouding Woman. 2007. 160p. (YA). pap. 6.95 (*978-0-8050-8185-5(2) , Holt, Henry & Co. Bks. For Young Readers) Holt, Henry & Co.

Ellsworth, Loretta. The Shrouding Woman. rev. ed. 2002. 160p. (J). (gr. 5-8). 16.95 (978-0-8050-6651-7(9) , Holt, Henry & Co. Bks. For Young Readers) Holt, Henry & Co.

Fleck, Earl. Chasing Fire: Danger in Canoe Country. 2002. (Illus.). 160p. pap. 12.95 (978-0-930100-53-7(0)) Holy Cow! Pr.

Freeland, Alan W. Pursuit up North. 2000. 120p. (gr. 4-7). pap. 9.95 (978-0-595-12901-0(3)) iUniverse, Inc.

Harbo, Gary. The Northern Woods Adventure: Advanced Reader, 6 vols. Harbo, Gary, illus. l.t. ed. 2004. (If You Want to Succeed, You Need to Read! Ser.: 6). (Illus.). 33p. (J). per. 10.95 (978-1-884149-15-3(4)) Kutie Kari Bks., Inc.

Kirtland, William F. Billy: A Story of a Minnesota Boy Growing Up. Kirtland, Lucy M., ed. Udave, Consuelo, illus. rev. ed. 2000. 206p. (YA). (gr. 5-10). pap. 10.00 (978-0-9679086-0-1(4)) Idaho Bk. & Schl. Supply.

—Billy Remembers: Fishbones, Crows & Other Woes. Kirtland, Lucy M., ed. Karstens, Kevin & Kidwell, Stan, illus. 2000. 222p. (YA). (gr. 5-10). pap. 10.00 (978-0-9679086-1-8(2)) Idaho Bk. & Schl. Supply.

Lane, Rose Wilder. Young Pioneers. Andreasen, Dan, illus. 1998. (Little House Ser.). 192p. (J). (gr. 3 up). pap. 6.99 (978-0-06-440698-7(9) , Harper Trophy) HarperCollins Pubs.

Lasky, Kathryn. Marven of the Great North Woods. Hawkes, Kevin, illus. 2002. 48p. (J). (gr. 1-4). pap. 7.00 (978-0-15-216826-1(5) , Voyager Bks./Libros Viajeros) Harcourt Children's Bks.

Lee, Marie G. Necessary Roughness. 1998. 240p. (J). (gr. 7 up). pap. 6.50 (978-0-06-447169-5(1) , Harper Trophy) HarperCollins Pubs.

—Necessary Roughness. 1998. (J). (978-0-606-13000-4(4)) Tandem Library Bks.

Lewis, Anne Margaret. What Am I? Minnesota. DeWildt, Jim, illus. 2007. 32p. (J). 9.95 (*978-1-934133-18-7(3)) Mackinac Island Pr., Inc.

Lorbiecki, Marybeth. Paul Bunyan's Sweetheart. Graef, Renee, illus. rev. ed. 2007. 32p. (J). (gr. 1-4). 16.95 (*978-1-58536-289-9(1)) Sleeping Bear Pr.

Lovelace, Maud Hart. Carney's House Party. 2000. (gr. 3-6). lib. bdg. 15.25 (978-0-613-31046-8(2)) Tandem Library Bks.

Marvin, Isabel R. A Bride for Anna's Papa. 2004. (Historical Fiction for Young Readers Ser.). (Illus.). 144p. (J). pap. 6.95 (978-1-57131-650-9(7)) Milkweed Editions.

—A Bride for Anna's Papa. Sather, Kay, illus. 2004. 136p. (J). (ps-7). per. 13.60 (978-0-606-33218-7(9)) Tandem Library Bks.

—The Tenth Rifle. Costner, Howard, illus. Date not set. 128p. (Orig.). (J). (gr. 3-8). pap. 9.95 (978-0-89896-109-6(2)) Larksdale.

McColley, Kevin. Pecking Order. 2000. 224p. (YA). (gr. 12 up). pap. 4.95 (978-0-06-440516-4(8)) HarperCollins Pubs.

Miller-Burke, Jude. Snowball, Come Home! 2005. (Illus.). 32p. (J). bds. 16.95 (978-1-59298-093-2(7)) Beaver's Pond Pr., Inc.

Nixon, Joan Lowery. Land of Dreams. l.t. ed. 2001. (Ellis Island Stories Ser.). 153p. (J). (gr. 4 up). lib. bdg. 23.33 (978-0-8368-2810-8(0)) Stevens, Gareth Inc.

O'Brien, Tim. Tomcat in Love. 1999. (gr. 7-12). lib. bdg. 22.25 (978-0-613-62863-1(2)) Tandem Library Bks.

Paulsen, Gary. Dancing Carl. 2007. 144p. (J). pap. 5.99 (*978-1-4169-3938-2(5) , Aladdin) Simon & Schuster Children's Publishing.

Paulsen, Gary. Foxman. l.t. ed. 2004. (YA). (gr. 6-12). 27.95 (978-1-58118-112-8(4)) LRS.

Perry, Marie. A Gift for Sadia. Perry, Marie, illus. l.t. ed. 2005. (Illus.). 32p. (J). lib. bdg. 15.95 (978-0-9755675-1-7(9)) Buttonweed Pr., L.L.C.

Pixley, Marcella. Freak. 2007. 144p. (YA). (gr. 7 up). 16.00 (*978-0-374-32453-7(0)) Farrar, Straus & Giroux.

Qualey, Marsha. Too Big a Storm. 2004. 256p. (J). (gr. 9). 16.99 (978-0-8037-2839-4(5) , Dial) Penguin Group (USA) Inc.

Rempel, Leah. Hey, Hmong Girl, Whassup? The Journal of Choua Vang. 2004. (Illus.). v, 138p. (YA). pap. (*978-0-9723721-5-2(6)) Hamline Univ. Pr.

Rylant, Cynthia. Old Town in the Green Groves: Laura Ingalls Wilder's Lost Little House Years. 2007. (Little House Ser.). 192p. (J). pap. 6.99 (978-0-06-088546-5(7) , Harper Trophy) HarperCollins Pubs.

—Old Town in the Green Groves: Laura Ingalls Wilder's Lost Little House Years. LaMarche, Jim, illus. (Little House Ser.). 176p. (J). 2004. pap. 5.99 (978-0-06-440990-2(2) , Harper Trophy); 2002. 15.99 (978-0-06-029561-5(9)) HarperCollins Pubs.

Sandin, Joan. At Home in a New Land. 2007. (I Can Read Bks.). 64p. (J). (ps-3). lib. bdg. 16.89 (*978-0-06-058078-0(X)) HarperCollins Pubs.

—At Home in a New Land. Sandin, Joan, illus. 2007. (I Can Read Bks.). (Illus.). 64p. (J). (ps-3). 15.99 (*978-0-06-058077-3(1)) HarperCollins Pubs.

Schultz, Jan Neubert. Firestorm. 2003. (Adventures in Time Ser.). 204p. (YA). (gr. 4-7). 15.95 (978-0-87614-276-9(5) , Carolrhoda Bks.) Lerner Publishing Group.

—Horse Sense: The Story of Will Sasse, His Horse Star & the Outlaw Jesse James. (Adventures in Time Ser.). (J). 2005. (Illus.). 180p. (gr. 4-8). 15.95 (978-1-57505-998-3(3)); 2001. lib. bdg. 6.95 (978-1-57505-999-0(1) , Carolrhoda Bks.) Lerner Publishing Group.

Siemsen, Nancy. The Girl Who Loved Jupiter. 2005. 151p. pap. 19.95 (978-1-4137-9004-7(6)) PublishAmerica, Inc.

Sommerdorf, Norma. Red River Girl. 2006. (Illus.). 192p. (J). 16.95 (978-0-8234-1903-6(7)) Holiday Hse., Inc.

Tavares, Matt. Mudball. Tavares, Matt, illus. 2005. (Illus.). 32p. (J). (gr. 1-5). 15.99 (978-0-7636-2387-6(3)) Candlewick Pr.

Walters, T. E. Power Play. 2000. (gr. 7-12). lib. bdg. 18.75 (978-0-613-88312-2(8)) Tandem Library Bks.

—Power Play. 2000. 116p. (gr. 7-12). pap. 9.95 (978-0-595-09876-7(2) , Writers Club Pr.) iUniverse, Inc.

Wargin, Kathy-Jo. The Legend of Minnesota. Geister, David, illus. 2006. 40p. (J). (gr. k-5). 17.95 (978-1-58536-262-2(X)) Sleeping Bear Pr.

—Minn from Minnesota. Holman, Karen Busch, illus. 2006. 141p. (J). 14.95 (978-1-58726-304-0(1) , Mitten Pr.) Ann Arbor Media Group, LLC.

Weaver, Will. Claws. 240p. (J). 2003. lib. bdg. 16.89 (978-0-06-009474-4(5)); 2004. reprint ed. pap. 6.99 (978-0-06-009475-1(3) , HarperTeen) HarperCollins Pubs.

—Claws. 2004. lib. bdg. 15.30 (978-0-613-71445-7(8)) Tandem Library Bks.

—Defect. 2007. 208p. (YA). (gr. 7 up). 16.00 (*978-0-374-31725-6(9) , Farrar, Straus & Giroux (BYR)) Farrar, Straus & Giroux.

—Farm Team. 1999. 288p. (J). (gr. 6 up). pap. 7.99 (978-0-06-447118-3(7) , Harper Trophy) HarperCollins Pubs.

—Farm Team. 1999. (J). 12.64 (978-0-606-15860-2(X)); (gr. 5-8). lib. bdg. 14.10 (978-0-613-11530-8(9)) Tandem Library Bks.

—Hard Ball. (gr. 6 up). 1999. 256p. (J). pap. 5.99 (978-0-06-447208-1(6) , Harper Trophy); 1998. 240p. (YA). 15.89 (978-0-06-027122-0(1)); 1998. 240p. (YA). 15.95 (978-0-06-027121-3(3)) HarperCollins Pubs.

—Hard Ball. 1999. (J). 12.64 (978-0-606-16706-2(4)); (gr. 7-12). lib. bdg. 14.15 (978-0-613-18254-6(5)) Tandem Library Bks.

—Hard Ball: A Billy Baggs Novel. l.t. ed. 2000. (Illus.). 270p. (YA). (gr. 8-12). 20.95 (978-0-7862-2752-5(4)) Thorndike Pr.

Weaver, Will. Saturday Night Dirt. 2008. (Motor Novel Ser.). 176p. (YA). 14.95 (*978-0-374-35060-4(4)) Farrar, Straus & Giroux.

Wells, Rosemary. Wingwalker. Selznick, Brian, illus. 2002. 80p. (gr. 2-5). 15.99 (978-0-7868-0397-2(5)); 16.49 (978-0-7868-2347-5(X)) Hyperion Bks. for Children.

Wilder, Laura Ingalls. On the Banks of Plum Creek. Williams, Garth, illus. 2004. (Little House Ser.). 352p. (J). pap. 8.99 (978-0-06-058183-1(2) , Harper Trophy) HarperCollins Pubs.

—On the Banks of Plum Creek. l.t. ed. 2002. (LRS Large Print Cornerstone Ser.). (Illus.). (J). lib. bdg. 35.95 (978-1-58118-099-2(3) , 25531) LRS.

—On the Banks of Plum Creek. 2003. (gr. 3-6). lib. bdg. 14.15 (978-0-613-71423-5(7)) Tandem Library Bks.

Ylvisaker, Anne. Dear Papa. (Illus.). 192p. (J). (gr. 4). 2007. pap. 5.99 ***978-0-7636-3402-5(6));*** 2002. 15.99 (978-0-7636-1618-2(4)) Candlewick Pr.

MINNESOTA—HISTORY

Anderson, Debby L. Minnesota for Mini-Sotans. 2004. (Illus.). spiral bd. 24.95 (978-0-9759281-0-3(4)) Busy Bee Bks.

Bruun, Erik & Peterson, Rick. Minnesota. 2001. (Illus.). 48p. (J). (gr. 3-7). 9.95 (978-1-57912-168-6(3) , 81168) Black Dog & Leventhal Pubs., Inc.

Davis, W. Harry. Changemaker: W. Harry Davis. Sturdevant, Lori, ed. 2004. (Illus.). 136p. (J). pap. 17.95 (978-1-890434-60-1(4)) Afton Historical Society Pr.

Graham, Joan Claire. Minnesota Memories 3. 2003. (Illus.). 192p. per. 13.95 (978-0-9711971-2-1(1)) Megyeri, Graham Bks.

Graham, JoanClaire, compiled by. Minnesota Memories 4. 2004. 208p. per. 13.95 (978-0-9711971-3-8(X)) Megyeri, Graham Bks.

Kallas, Randi & Dougherty, Mike, eds. Rochester, Minnesota: A Visual & Historic Journey. 2003. (Illus.). 136p. pap. 24.95 (978-0-9659875-3-0(1)) Riggott, Dean Photography.

Kallen, Stuart A. Minnesota. 2001. (Seeds of a Nation Ser.). (Illus.). 48p. (J). (gr. 3-5). 26.20 (978-0-7377-1021-2(7) , LML00902-178630, Kidhaven) Thomson Gale.

Kenney, Dave, et al. Northern Lights: The Stories of Minnesota's Past. 2nd ed. 2003. (Illus.). 352p. 50.00 (978-0-87351-440-8(8) , Borealis Bk.) Minnesota Historical Society Pr.

Kuedee, Jaycee. How to Draw Minnesotas Sights & Symbols. 2002. (Kids Guide to Drawing America Ser.). 32p. (J). lib. bdg. 25.25 (978-0-8239-6079-8(X) , PowerKids Pr.) Rosen Publishing Group, Inc., The.

Marsh, Carole. Minnesota History Projects: 30 Cool, Activities, Crafts, Experiments & More for Kids to Do to Learn about Your State! 2003. (Minnesota Experience Ser.). 32p. (gr. k-5). pap. 5.95 (978-0-635-01792-5(X) , Marsh, Carole Bks.) Gallopade International.

—My First Pocket Guide Minnesota. 2000. (Minnesota Experience Ser.). (Illus.). 96p. (J). (gr. 3-8). 12.95 (978-0-635-01313-2(4) , 13134) Gallopade International.

Murphy, Nora & Murphy-Gnatz, Mary, contrib. by. Meet African Americans in Minnesota: Telling Our Own Stories. 2000. (Illus.). 88p. (J). (gr. 3-7). pap. 12.95 (978-0-87351-380-7(0) , 380-0, Borealis Bk.) Minnesota Historical Society Pr.

Riggott, Dean. Life on the Farm: A Pictorial Journey of Minnesota's Farmland & Its People. 100th l.t. ed. 2001. 124p. pap. 24.95 (978-0-9659875-2-3(3)) Riggott, Dean Photography.

Sateren, Shelley Swanson. A Civil War Drummer Boy: The Diary of William Bircher, 1861-1865. 1999. (Diaries, Letters & Memoirs Ser.). (Illus.). 32p. (J). (gr. 2-7). pap. 21.00 (978-0-516-21850-2(6) , Children's Pr.) Scholastic Library Publishing.

Urdahl, Dean. Lives Lived Large: Minnesotans in the Public Eye. 2001. 200p. pap. 15.00 (978-0-87839-164-6(9)) North Star Pr. of St. Cloud.

MINNESOTA VIKINGS (FOOTBALL TEAM)

Frisch, Aaron. The History of the Minnesota Vikings. 2004. (NFL Today Ser.). (Illus.). 32p. 18.95 (978-1-58341-303-6(0) , Creative Education) Creative Co., The.

Grabowski, John F. The Minnesota Vikings. 2002. (Great Sports Teams in History Ser.). (Illus.). 112p. (J). 29.95 (978-1-56006-943-0(0) , Lucent Bks.) Thomson Gale.

Minnesota Vikings Staff. Minnesota Vikings. CWC Sports Inc., ed. 1998. (NFL Team Yearbooks Ser.). (Illus.). (J). (gr. 1-12). pap. 9.99 (978-1-891613-14-2(6)) Everett Sports Publishing & Marketing.

MINORITIES

see also Discrimination; Race Relations

Anderson, Sonya, et al, eds. Facing Racism in Education. 3rd ed. 2005. (Harvard Educational Review Ser.: No. 39). (Illus.). 315p. (YA). pap. 29.95 (978-0-916690-42-7(3)) Harvard Educational Review.

Ansary, Mir Tamim. People of California. 2003. (Heinemann State Studies). (Illus.). 48p. (J). (gr. 3-5). lib. bdg. (978-1-4034-0342-1(2)) Heinemann Library.

Bauchner, Elizabeth. Teen Minorities in Rural North America: Growing up Different. 2008. (Youth in Rural North America Ser.). (J). (978-1-4222-0014-8(0)) Mason Crest Pubs.

Bode, Janet. The Colors of Freedom: Immigrant Stories. (Single Titles Social Studies Ser.). (Illus.). 144p. (YA). (gr. 8-12). 2000. pap. 9.95 (978-0-531-15961-3(2)); 1999. 26.00 (978-0-531-11530-5(5)) Scholastic Library Publishing. (Watts, Franklin).

—Colors of Freedom: Immigrant Stories. 2000. (Illus.). (J). (978-0-606-18146-4(6)); 1999. (gr. 7-12). lib. bdg. 18.75 (978-0-613-29211-5(1)) Tandem Library Bks.

Cha, Dia. Dia's Story Cloth: The Hmong People's Journey of Freedom. Cha, Chue & Cha, Nhia Thao, illus. 1998. 24p. (J). (gr. 1 up). 6.95 (978-1-880000-63-2(6)) Lee & Low Bks., Inc.

Engelbert, Phillis. American Civil Rights: Biographies. 1999. (American Civil Rights Reference Library). (Illus.). xl, 203p. (J). (gr. 4-7). 67.00 (978-0-7876-3173-4(6) , GML00402-112774, UXL) Thomson Gale.

Fleming, Thomas. Everybody's Revolution: A New Look at the People Who Won America's Freedom. 2006. (Illus.). 96p. (J). (gr. 4-7). pap. 19.99 (978-0-439-63404-5(0) , Scholastic Nonfiction) Scholastic, Inc.

Gayle-Evans, Guda. An Annotated Bibliography of Multi-Cultural Literature for Children Three to Ten Years. 2004. (Mellen Studies in Children's Literature: Vol. 6). (Illus.). 204p. 109.95 (978-0-7734-6474-2(3)) Mellen, Edwin Pr., The.

Hansen-Krening, Nancy, et al, eds. Kaleidoscope: A Multicultural Booklist for Grades K-8. 4th ed. 2003. (NCTE Bibliography Ser.). (Illus.). 118p. (J). pap. 30.95 (978-0-8141-2539-7(5) , 25395) National Council of Teachers of English.

Hermann, Spring. The Struggle for Equality: Women & Minorities in America. 2006. (American Saga Ser.). (Illus.). 128p. (J). lib. bdg. 31.93 (978-0-7660-2573-8(X)) Enslow Pubs., Inc.

Hiber, Amanda. Is the United States Ready for a Minority President? (New Title) 2007. (At Issue Ser.). (Illus.). 128p. (gr. 10-12). 28.70 ***(978-0-7377-3878-0(2));*** pap. 19.95 ***(978-0-7377-3879-7(0))*** Thomson Gale. (Greenhaven Pr., Inc.).

Hunter, Miranda. Story Of Latino Civil Rights: Fighting for Justice. 2005. (Illus.). 112p. (J). lib. bdg. (978-1-59084-934-7(5)) Mason Crest Pubs.

Lehman, Jeffrey, ed. Gale Encyclopedia of Multicultural America Set: Primary Documents, 2 vols. 1999. (Illus.). xiv, 820p. (YA). (gr. 9 up). 225.00 (978-0-7876-3990-7(7) , GML00502-113793, Gale Research International, Ltd.) Thomson Gale.

Marcovitz, Hal. Race Relations. 2006. (Gallup Major Trends & Events Ser.). 112p. (J). (gr. 7 up). lib. bdg. (978-1-59084-968-2(X)) Mason Crest Pubs.

McGuinn, Taro. East Timor: Island in Turmoil. 1998. (World in Conflict Ser.). (Illus.). 104p. (YA). (gr. 7-12). 25.26 (978-0-8225-3555-3(6) , Lerner Pubns.) Lerner Publishing Group.

Nelson, Teresa. Affirmative Action. 2007. (Essential Viewpoints Ser.). (ENG., Illus.). 112p. (YA). (gr. 7-9). lib. bdg. 32.79 ***(*978-1-59928-857-4(5)*** , Essential Library) ABDO Publishing Co.

Peoples of North America, 10 vols. 2003. (Illus.). (J). 359.00 (978-0-7172-5777-5(0) , Grolier) Scholastic Library Publishing.

Perrin, Pat. Getting Started-America's Melting Pot. 2004. (Illus.). (J). (978-1-932663-04-4(5)) History Compass, LLC.

—Getting Started-Our 50 United States. 2004. (Illus.). (J). (978-1-932663-03-7(7)) History Compass, LLC.

—Getting Started-Our Government. 2004. (Illus.). (J). (978-1-932663-02-0(9)) History Compass, LLC.

Pobst, Sandy. The Newest Americans, 5 vols. 2003. (Middle School Reference Ser.). (Illus.). 144p. (gr. 6-8). 209.95 (978-0-313-32553-3(7) , MS2553, Middle School Reference) Greenwood Publishing Group, Inc.

Radzilowski, John. Ukrainian Americans. 2007. (New Immigrants Ser.). (Illus.). 128p. (J). (gr. 6-12). 27.95 (978-0-7910-8789-3(1) , Chelsea Hse.) Facts On File, Inc.

Smith, Carter & Lindroth, David, eds. Ethnic Minorities in America, 3 vols., Set. 2000. (Illus.). 172p. (YA). (gr. 6-12). ring bd. 420.00 (978-0-8160-3952-4(6)) Facts On File, Inc.

Stanek, Muriel. We Came from Vietnam. McMahon, Wm. Franklin, photos by. 2004. (Illus.). 46p. (J). (gr. k-4). reprint ed. (978-0-7567-7795-1(X)) DIANE Publishing Co.

Steward, Mark. People of New York. 2003. (Heinemann State Studies). (Illus.). 48p. (J). (gr. 3-5). lib. bdg. (978-1-4034-0355-1(4)) Heinemann Library.

Williams, Mary E., ed. Discrimination. 2002. (Illus.). 200p. (J). 36.20 (978-0-7377-1226-1(0) , Greenhaven Pr., Inc.) Thomson Gale.

Wright, John D. Race & Crime. 2002. (Crime & Detection Ser.). (Illus.). 96p. (J). (gr. 7 up). lib. bdg. (978-1-59084-378-9(9)) Mason Crest Pubs.

MINTS

see also Coinage

Morrison, Taylor. The Buffalo Nickel. Morrison, Taylor, illus. 2006. (Illus.). 32p. (J). (gr. 4-8). reprint ed. 16.00 ***(*978-1-4223-5858-0(5))*** DIANE Publishing Co.

—The Buffalo Nickel. 2002. (Illus.). 32p. (J). (gr. 1-5). 16.00 (978-0-618-10855-8(6) , Walter Lorraine) Houghton Mifflin Co. Trade & Reference Div.

MIRACLE PLAYS

see Mysteries and Miracle Plays

MIRRORS

Aigner-Clark, Julie. Mirror Me! Zaidi, Nadeem, illus. 2002. (Baby Einstein Ser.). 12p. (J). bds. 6.99 (978-0-7868-0843-4(8)) Hyperion Bks. for Children.

Bahrampour, Ali. Otto, the Story of a Mirror. 2002. (Illus.). (J). (978-0-374-35663-7(7)) Farrar, Straus & Giroux.

Farmer, Karen. When I Look at Me: What do I See? 2007. (Illus.). 14p. (J). (gr. 1-5). bds. 8.95 ***(*978-1-59125-809-4(X)*** , Penton Kids) Penton Overseas, Inc.

Lowkie-Wanamaker, Tamanu. What Do You See in the Mirror: Love, Pain, Living & Learning. 1998. (Broken Chains Ser.: Vol. II). 36p. (J). pap. 10.00 (978-0-9661959-2-7(2)) Nu-Nu & You.

Raintree Steck-Vaughn Staff. Mirror Magic: Level B. 2000. (Read All about It Ser.). (Illus.). (J). pap. 4.95 (978-0-8114-3769-1(8)) Steck-Vaughn.

Strom, Laura Layton. Mirror Power. 2007. (Shockwave: Technology & Manufacturing Ser.). 36p. (J). pap. 6.95 ***(*978-0-531-18772-2(1));*** (Illus.). (gr. 4-6). lib. bdg. 25.00 ***(*978-0-531-17588-0(X))*** Scholastic Library Publishing. (Children's Pr.).

Witkowski, Dan. Funhouse Mirrors: The Science & Illusion of Reflection. Foote, Christopher Bailey, illus. 2000. 28p. (J). (gr. 1-2). reprint ed. 15.00 (978-0-7881-9359-0(7)) DIANE Publishing Co.

Zubrowski, Bernie. Mirrors: Finding Out about the Properties of Light. 2001. 59p. spiral bd. 9.00 (978-1-58651-903-2(4)) Pitsco/Pitsco LEGO Dacta.

MISDEMEANORS (LAW)

see Criminal Law

MISS NELSON (FICTITIOUS CHARACTER)—FICTION

Allard, Harry G. La Senorita Nelson Ha Desaparecido! Marshall, James, illus. 1998. (Miss Nelson Ser.). (SPA.). 32p. (J). (gr. k-3). 16.00 (978-0-395-90009-3(3)) Houghton Mifflin Co. Trade & Reference Div.

Marshall, James, illus. Miss Nelson Has a Field Day. 2002. (Miss Nelson Ser.). (J). 13.79 (978-0-7587-3145-6(0)) Book Wholesalers, Inc.

—Miss Nelson Is Missing! 2002. (Miss Nelson Ser.). (J). 13.79 (978-0-7587-3147-0(7)) Book Wholesalers, Inc.

MISS SPIDER (FICTITIOUS CHARACTER)—FICTION

Kirk, David. All Around Sunny Patch. 2006. (Miss Spider Ser.). 24p. (J). (ps-1). pap. 4.99 (978-0-448-44110-8(1) , Grosset & Dunlap) Penguin Group (USA) Inc.

—Ant-tuition. 2006. (Miss Spider Ser.). (Illus.). 24p. (J). (ps-ps). pap. 3.99 (978-0-448-44411-6(9) , Grosset & Dunlap) Penguin Group (USA) Inc.

—Flower Power. 2007. (Miss Spider Ser.). 32p. (J). 6.99 (978-0-448-44504-5(2)) Callaway Editions, Inc.

—Giddy up Bugs! 2007. (Miss Spider Ser.). 32p. (J). 6.99 (978-0-448-44505-2(0)) Callaway Editions, Inc.

—Little Miss Spider. (Miss Spider Ser.). (J). 2003. (Illus.). 32p. pap. 5.99 (978-0-439-54315-6(0)); 1999. 155.40 (978-0-439-11737-1(2)) Scholastic, Inc.

—Little Miss Spider. Kirk, David, illus. 1999. (Miss Spider Ser.). (Illus.). 32p. (J). (ps-2). pap. 12.95 (978-0-439-08389-8(3)) Scholastic, Inc.

—Little Miss Spider at Sunny Patch School. Kirk, David, illus. (Miss Spider Ser.). (Illus.). 32p. (J). 2003. pap. 5.99 (978-0-439-54316-3(9)); 2000. pap. 12.95 (978-0-439-08727-8(9)) Scholastic, Inc.

—Little Miss Spider at Sunnypatch School. Kirk, David, illus. 2002. (Little Miss Spider Ser.). (Illus.). (J). 21.85 (978-0-7587-3008-4(X)) Book Wholesalers, Inc.

—Little Miss Spider's Christmas Wish: A Christmas Wish. Kirk, David, illus. 2001. (Miss Spider Ser.). (Illus.). 32p. (J). (ps-2). pap. 12.95 (978-0-439-31463-3(1) , Levine, Arthur A. Bks.) Scholastic, Inc.

—Miss Spider Boxset: The Counting Book; New Car; ABC. 2003. (Illus.). (J). 12.95 (978-0-439-54317-0(7)) Scholastic, Inc.

—Miss Spider Treasury. 2006. (Miss Spider Ser.). 144p. (J). pap. 22.99 (978-0-439-85740-6(6) , Scholastic) Scholastic, Inc.

—Miss Spider's Abc. Kirk, David, illus. 2002. (Little Miss Spider Ser.). (Illus.). (J). 26.11 (978-0-7587-3149-4(3)) Book Wholesalers, Inc.

—Miss Spider's ABC. Kirk, David, illus. 1998. (Miss Spider Ser.). (Illus.). 32p. (J). (ps-2). pap. 16.95 (978-0-590-28279-6(4)) Scholastic, Inc.

—Miss Spider's ABC: New Board Book Edition. Kirk, David, illus. 2000. (Miss Spider Ser.). (Illus.). 32p. (J). (ps-2). bds. 8.95 (978-0-439-13747-8(0) , Scholastic Reference) Scholastic, Inc.

—Miss Spider's New Car. 2006. (Scholastic Reader Level 2 Ser.). (Illus.). 32p. (J). pap. 3.99 (978-0-439-83306-6(X) , Cartwheel Bks.) Scholastic, Inc.

—Miss Spider's New Car. Kirk, David, illus. 1999. (Miss Spider Ser.). (Illus.). 32p. (J). (ps-2). bds. 8.95 (978-0-439-04675-6(0)) Scholastic, Inc.

—Miss Spider's Tea Party. 32p. (J). 2007. pap. 5.99 (978-0-439-91817-6(0)); 2006. (Illus.). pap. 3.99 (978-0-439-83305-9(1) , Cartwheel Bks.) Scholastic, Inc.

Kirk, David & Scholastic, Inc. Staff. Miss Spider's Sunny Patch Kids. Rees, Jenifer, ed. 2004. (Illus.). 40p. (J). pap. 14.95 (978-0-439-40870-7(9) , Scholastic Pr.) Scholastic, Inc.

MISSILES, GUIDED

see Guided Missiles

MISSING PERSONS

Gordon, Olivia. Cold Case File: Murder in the Mountains. 2008. (J). lib. bdg. ***(*978-1-59716-547-1(6))*** Bearport Publishing Co., Inc.

Herbst, Judith. Vanished. (Unexplained Ser.). (Illus.). 48p. (J). 2005. (gr. 5-12). lib. bdg. 26.60 (978-0-8225-1631-6(4)); 2004. pap. 7.95 (978-0-8225-2404-5(X) , Lerner Pubns.) Lerner Publishing Group.

Hyde, Margaret O. Missing & Murdered Children. 1998. (Impact Bks.). (Illus.). 112p. (YA). (gr. 9-12). 25.00 (978-0-531-11384-4(1) , Watts, Franklin) Scholastic Library Publishing.

Townsend. Mysterious Disappearances. 2004. (Out There Ser.). (Illus.). pap. 8.95 (978-1-4109-0962-6(X)) Raintree.

Townsend, John. Mysterious Disappearances. 2004. (Out There Ser.). (Illus.). 56p. 28.56 (978-1-4109-0561-1(6)) Raintree.

MISSING PERSONS—FICTION

Agbodza, Ena and Kwami. The Bad Ices Man & the Girl Who Saved Christmas. 2006. (Illus.). 45p. (J). per. 9.95 (978-1-59453-782-0(8) , Airleaf Publishing) Airleaf Publishing & Bookselling.

Aiken, Joan. Black Hearts in Battersea. 2004. (Illus.). 259p. (J). pap. 10.95 (978-0-09-945639-1(7) , Red Fox) Random Hse. Children's Bks. GBR. *Dist:* Random Hse. of Canada, Ltd.

Alphin, Elaine Marie. Picture Perfect. 2003. (Illus.). 252p. (J). (gr. 7 up). 15.95 (978-0-8225-0535-8(5)) Lerner Publishing Group.

Ashley, Bernard. A Present for Paul. Mitchell, David, illus. 2004. 28p. (J). (ARA, CHI, BEN, GUJ & ENG.). (978-1-85269-359-6(2)); (CHI, ARA, BEN, GUJ & ENG.). (978-1-85269-360-2(6)) Mantra Publishing, Ltd.

Auer, Chris. Molly & the Good Shepherd. Wummer, Amy, illus. 2005. 40p. (J). 12.99 (978-0-310-70826-1(5)) Zonderkidz.

Ballantyne, R. M. Silver Lake. 2004. reprint ed. pap. 15.95 (978-1-4191-4729-6(3)); pap. 1.99 (978-1-4192-4729-3(8)) Kessinger Publishing, LLC.

Balmer, Fred. Festus & the Stranger. Miller, Callie, ed. Newcomb, Kristene, illus. 2007. 30p. (J). per. 7.00 ***(*978-0-9760790-4-0(6))*** Folsom Fallies Pr.

Banim, Lisa. Case of the Missing She-Geek. 2004. 125p. (J). lib. bdg. 16.92 ***(*978-1-4242-0683-4(9))*** Fitzgerald Bks.

Beckham, David. Charlie Barker & the Secret of the Deep Dark Woods. 2006. 570p. pap. ***(*978-1-4120-9264-7(7))*** Trafford Publishing.

Bessen, Luc. Arthur & the Minimoys. Sowchek, Ellen, tr. from FRE. 2005. 240p. (J). 15.99 (978-0-06-059623-1(6)) HarperCollins Pubs.

Besson, Luc. Arthur & the Invisibles. movie tie-in ed. 2006. 416p. (J). pap. 7.99 (978-0-06-122726-4(9)) HarperCollins Pubs.

—Arthur & the Minimoys. (Illus.). (J). 2006. 256p. pap. 6.99 (978-0-06-059625-5(2) , Harper Trophy); 2005. 240p. lib. bdg. 16.89 (978-0-06-059624-8(4)) HarperCollins Pubs.

Birch, Beverley. Rift. 2008. (Illus.). 224p. (YA). pap. 9.95 ***(*978-1-4052-1589-3(5))*** Egmont Bks., Ltd. GBR. *Dist:* Independent Pubs. Group.

Borntrager, Mary Christner. Daniel. l.t. ed. 2000. (Christian Fiction Ser.). 191p. 23.95 (978-0-7862-2859-1(8)) Thorndike Pr.

Brown, Jo. Where's My Mommy? Brown, Jo, illus. 2006. (Illus.). 18p. (J). bds. 6.95 (978-1-58925-795-5(2) , tiger tales) ME Media LLC.

Capeci, Anne. Missing! Casale, Paul, illus. 2005. 144p. (J). 12.95 (978-1-56145-334-4(X)) Peachtree Pubs., Ltd.

Carlson, Melody. Bad Connection. 2006. 256p. pap. 11.99 (978-1-59052-692-7(9) , Multnomah) WaterBrook Pr.

Carroll, Jenny, pseud. Code Name Cassandra. 2007. (1-800-Where-R-You Ser.: No. 2). 272p. (YA). mass mkt. 6.99 (978-1-4169-2704-4(2) , Simon Pulse) Simon & Schuster Children's Publishing.

—When Lightning Strikes. 2007. (1-800-Where-R-You Ser.: No. 1). 272p. (YA). mass mkt. 6.99 (978-1-4169-2705-1(0) , Simon Pulse) Simon & Schuster Children's Publishing.

Cate, Annette LeBlanc. The Magic Rabbit. Cate, Annette LeBlanc, illus. 2007. (Illus.). 32p. (J). (ps-3). 15.99 ***(*978-0-7636-2672-3(4))*** Candlewick Pr.

Chan, Ching. Mystery of the Black Sun: Songs of the Unicorn. 2006. (Anime Sticker Stories Ser.). 16p. (J). (ps-1). 4.99 (978-0-448-44340-9(6) , Grosset & Dunlap) Penguin Group (USA) Inc.

Charles, Veronika Martenova. Stretch, Swallow & Stare. Charles, Veronika Martenova, illus. l.t. ed. 1999. (Illus.). 31p. (J). (ps-3). 16.95 (978-0-7737-3098-4(2)) Stoddart Kids CAN. *Dist:* Fitzhenry & Whiteside, Ltd.

Coben, Harlan. Tell No One. 2002. (gr. 7-12). lib. bdg. 15.30 (978-0-613-60443-7(1)) Tandem Library Bks.

Coburn, Ann. Glint. 2007. 432p. (J). (gr. 6-8). 17.99 (978-0-06-084723-4(9)); lib. bdg. 18.89 (978-0-06-084724-1(7)) HarperCollins Pubs.

Collins, Suzanne. Gregor & the Prophecy of Bane. 2003. 320p. (J). (gr. 3-6). 16.95 (978-0-439-43536-9(6)) Scholastic, Inc.

Collins, Terry. Spike Speaks! The Rugrats Meet the Wild Thornberrys. 2003. (gr. k-3). lib. bdg. 11.80 (978-0-613-66385-4(3)) Tandem Library Bks.

Couloumbis, Audrey. Say Yes. 2003. 208p. (J). pap. 6.99 (978-0-14-250186-3(7) , Puffin) Penguin Group (USA) Inc.

Coutu, Raymond & Jones, Dawn L. Poker & the Cupcake Chase. Graef, Renee, illus. 2001. (J). pap. (978-0-9712840-7-4(5)) Boyds Collection Ltd., The.

Crawford, Ann Fears. Vangie: The Ghost of the Pines. 2002. 142p. (J). 17.95 (978-1-57168-710-4(6) , Eakin Pr.) Eakin Pr.

Croggon, Alison. The Crow. 2007. (Pellinor Ser.: Bk. 3). (Illus.). 528p. (YA). (gr. 7 up). 18.99 ***(*978-0-7636-3409-4(3))*** Candlewick Pr.

Cross, Gillian. The Nightmare Game. 2007. 272p. (J). (gr. 7). 18.99 ***(*978-0-525-47923-9(6)*** , Dutton Juvenile) Penguin Group (USA) Inc.

Cutbill, Andy. The Beast of Baloddan. 2003. (Hotel Chronicles). (Illus.). 208p. pap. (978-0-340-86570-5(9) , Hodder Children's Books) Hodder Children's Division.

Czekaj, Jef. Grampa & Julie: Shark Hunters. 2004. (Illus.). 128p. pap. 14.95 (978-1-891830-52-5(X)) Top Shelf Productions.

Danziger, Paula. It's a Fair Day, Amber Brown. Ross, Tony, illus. 2003. 28.95 incl. audio compact disk (978-1-59112-565-5(0)); pap. 31.95 incl. audio compact disk (978-1-59112-564-8(2)) Live Oak Media.

Decker, Wendy. The Bedazzling Bowl. 2006. pap. 13.99 ***(*978-1-60034-468-8(2))*** Xulon Pr., Inc.

Deskis, Jane. Arianna & the Missing Princess. 2002. 84p. pap. 14.95 (978-1-59129-556-3(4)) PublishAmerica, Inc.

Dixon, Franklin W. Pushed. 2007. (Hardy Boys (All New) Undercover Brothers Ser.). 154p. (J). (gr. 3-7). per. 4.99 ***(*978-1-4169-4802-5(3)*** , Aladdin) Simon & Schuster Children's Publishing.

Doro, Ann. The Missing Canary. l.t. ed. 2005. 93p. 12.95 (978-0-9745052-2-0(6) , Peeper & Friends) Tree Of Life Publishing.

MNO

Dowd, Siobhan. The London Eye Mystery. 2008. 336p. (J). (***978-0-375-84976-3(9)***); lib. bdg. (***978-0-375-94976-0(3)***) Random Hse. Children's Bks. (Fickling, David Bks.).

DuQuette, Keith. Little Monkey Lost. DuQuette, Keith, illus. 2007. 32p. (J). (ps). 15.99 (978-0-399-24294-6(5), Putnam Juvenile) Penguin Group (USA) Inc.

Dver, Alyssa. When Whizzly Wanders. 2005. 15p. 6.78 (978-1-4116-4667-4(3)) Lulu.com.

Eden, Alexandra. To Oz & Back: A Bones & the Duchess Mystery. 2002. 151p. (J). 16.00 (978-1-888310-22-1(7)) Knoll, Allen A. Pubs.

Edwards, Julie Andrews & Hamilton, Emma Walton. Dumpy to the Rescue! Walton, Tony, illus. 2004. (My First I Can Read Bks.). 32p. (J). (ps up). 14.99 (978-0-06-052689-4(0)); pap. 3.99 (978-0-06-052691-7(2)); lib. bdg. 15.89 (978-0-06-052690-0(4)) HarperCollins Pubs.

Eige, Lillian. Dangling. 2003. (gr. 3-6). lib. bdg. 13.00 (978-0-613-90716-3(7)) Tandem Library Bks.

Emerson, Alice B. Ruth Fielding at Snow Camp: Or, Lost in the Backwoods. 2006. 134p. pap. 10.99 (***978-1-4264-5024-2(9)***); 144p. pap. 13.99 (***978-1-4264-5325-0(6)***) BiblioBazaar.

Feehan-Vileria, Elaine. The Legend of Old Mr. Clarke. 2004. 58p. per. 17.95 (978-1-4116-1523-6(9)) Lulu.com.

Fickey, Brenda. Whispering Darkness. 2007. (ENG.). 136p. per. 19.95 (***978-1-4241-6932-0(1)***) PublishAmerica, Inc.

Fishbone, Greg. The Penguins of Doom. 2007. (From the Desk of Septina Nash Ser.). (Illus.). 192p. (J). (gr. 3-9). 13.95 (***978-1-933831-03-9(0)***) Blooming Tree Pr.

French, Jackie. My Uncle the Werewolf. King, Stephen Michael, illus. 2007. (J). 112p. (***978-1-59889-346-5(7)***); 107p. pap. (***978-1-59889-439-4(0)***) Stone Arch Bks.

Godwin, Jane. Falling from Grace. 2007. 204p. (YA). (gr. 6 up). 16.95 (***978-0-8234-2105-3(8)***) Holiday Hse., Inc.

Goobie, Beth. Flux. 2004. 224p. (J). (gr. 7-12). lib. bdg. 16.95 (978-1-55143-314-1(1)) Orca Bk. Pubs. USA.

Greenburg, Dan. Claws. 208p. (YA). 2007. (gr. 3-7). 5.99 (978-0-375-83411-0(7), Yearling); 2006. (gr. 5). lib. bdg. 17.99 (978-0-375-93410-0(3), Random Hse. Bks. for Young Readers) Random Hse. Children's Bks.

Guest, Elissa Haden. Iris & Walter & the Field Trip. Davenier, Christine, illus. 2007. (Iris & Walter Ser.). 44p. (J). pap. 5.95 (***978-0-15-205370-3(0)***, Harcourt Paperbacks) Harcourt Children's Bks.

Hapka, Cathy. Over the Top. 2005. 140p. (J). (978-1-4155-7730-1(7), Aladdin) Simon & Schuster Children's Publishing.

Hartnett, Sonya. What the Birds See. 208p. (YA). (gr. 9). 2007. (Illus.). pap. 7.99 (***978-0-7636-3680-7(0)***); 2003. 15.99 (978-0-7636-2092-9(0)) Candlewick Pr.

Hunt, Elizabeth Singer. The Mystery of the Mona Lisa. 2007. (Secret Agent Jack Stalwart Ser.). 128p. (J). (gr. 1-4). pap. 4.99 (***978-1-60286-001-8(7)***) Weinstein Bks.

—The Search for the Sunken Treasure. 2007. (Secret Agent Jack Stalwart Ser.). 128p. (J). (gr. 1-4). pap. 4.99 (***978-1-60286-002-5(5)***) Weinstein Bks.

Hutt, Sarah. Missing. 2004. 64p. (YA). per. 3.95 (978-1-56254-824-7(7), SP8247) Saddleback Educational Publishing.

Jenisch, Betty. Rennie. 2007. 9.00 (***978-0-8059-8947-2(1)***) Dorrance Publishing Co., Inc.

Jenkins, Jerry B. & Fabry, Chris. Phantom Writer. 2005. (Red Rock Mysteries Ser.). 256p. (J). pap. 5.99 (978-1-4143-0145-7(6)) Tyndale Hse. Pubs.

—Windy City Danger. 2006. (Red Rock Mysteries Ser.). 246p. (J). pap. 5.99 (978-1-4143-0150-1(2)) Tyndale Hse. Pubs.

Jeram, Anita. Bunny My Honey. Jeram, Anita, illus. 2006. (Illus.). 32p. (J). (ps). reprint ed. pap. 4.99 (978-0-7636-3217-5(1)) Candlewick Pr.

Johnson, Kathleen Jeffrie. A Fast & Brutal Wing. 2007. 208p. (YA). pap. 6.99 (***978-0-312-37148-7(9)***) Square Fish.

Kaaberbol, Lene. Heartbreak Island. 2005. (W. I. T. C. H. Adventures Ser. : Bk. 3). (Illus.). 105p. (J). lib. bdg. 11.00 (***978-1-4242-0786-2(X)***) Fitzgerald Bks.

Kasischke, Laura. Feathered. 2008. 272p. (J). 16.99 (***978-0-06-081317-8(2)***); lib. bdg. 17.89 (***978-0-06-081318-5(0)***) HarperCollins Pubs. (HarperTeen).

Kidd, Rob & Ching, Jacqueline. Pirates of the Caribbean: The Missing Pirate. Disney Storybook Artists Staff, illus. 2007. 32p. (gr. k-2). pap. 3.99 (***978-1-4231-0621-0(0)***) Disney Pr.

Kilgras, Heidi. Peanut. Reed, Mike, illus. 2003. (Step into Reading Ser.). 32p. (J). (ps-2). pap. 3.99 (978-0-375-80618-6(0), Random Hse. Bks. for Young Readers) Random Hse. Children's Bks.

Kir-On, Calanitte. The Adventures of the Gimmel Gang I: The Fake Mezuza. 2002. 75p. (YA). pap. 8.95 (978-1-931681-21-6(X)) Israel Bk. Shop.

Klim, Christopher. Firecracker Jones Is on the Case. 2006. (Illus.). 116p. (J). lib. bdg. 19.95 (978-1-933435-11-4(9)) Hopewell Pubns., LLC.

Klise, Kate. Regarding the Sink: Where, Oh Where, Did Waters Go? Klise, M. Sarah, illus. 2006. (Regarding The ... Ser.). 144p. (J). pap. 5.95 (978-0-15-205544-8(4), Harcourt Paperbacks) Harcourt Children's Bks.

Leeson, Robert. Liar. 128p. (J). 9.95 (978-0-14-130143-3(0)) Penguin Bks., Ltd. GBR. *Dist:* Trafalgar Square Publishing.

Lewis, C. S. The Silver Chair. Baynes, Pauline, illus. 2006. (Narnia Ser.). 256p. (J). 11.99 (978-0-06-112528-7(8)) HarperCollins Pubs.

Linamen, Karen Scalf. Princess Madison & the Whispering Woods. 2006. (Princess Madison Trilogy Ser.). (Illus.). 32p. 12.99 (978-0-8007-1842-8(9)) Revell.

Littke, Lael. Lake of Secrets. rev. ed. 2002. 208p. (YA). (gr. 7-9). 16.95 (978-0-8050-6730-9(2), Holt, Henry & Co. Bks. For Young Readers) Holt, Henry & Co.

Lorimer, Janet. An Eye for an Eye. 2001. (PageTurner Spy Ser.). 80p. (YA). per. 3.95 (978-1-56254-137-8(4), SP 1374) Saddleback Educational Publishing.

MacGregor, Roy. The Secret of the Deep Woods. 2003. 128p. (J). (gr. 4 up). mass mkt. 4.95 (978-0-7710-5646-8(X), Screech Owls) McClelland & Stewart CAN. *Dist:* Random Hse. of Canada, Ltd., Random Hse., Inc.

MacIntyre, R. P. Revved. 2005. 220p. pap. 11.95 (978-1-894345-46-0(0)) Thistledown Pr., Ltd. CAN. *Dist:* Literary Pr. Group of Canada.

Maguire, Gregory. A Couple of April Fools. Clayton, Elaine, illus. 2004. (Hamlet Chronicles Ser.). 192p. (J). (gr. 3-5). tchr. ed. 16.00 (978-0-618-27474-1(X), Clarion Bks.) Houghton Mifflin Co. Trade & Reference Div.

Mancusi, Mari. Girls That Growl. 2007. 249p. (YA). (gr. 12-12). per. 9.99 (***978-0-425-21716-0(7)***, Berkley Trade) Penguin Group (USA) Inc.

Marks, Graham. Missing in Tokyo. 2006. 256p. (YA). 16.95 (978-1-58234-907-7(X), Bloomsbury Children) Bloomsbury Publishing.

Marsh, Carole. The Mystery of the Vanished Player. 2006. 96p. (gr. 2-4). pap. 4.99 (***978-0-635-06231-4(3)***) Gallopade International.

Maselli, Christopher P. N. The Runaway Mission. 2004. 104p. (***978-1-57562-805-9(8)***) Copeland, Kenneth Pubns.

McBride, Anthony & McBride, Autumn. The Lost Cat. 2007. (Illus.). pap. 11.00 (***978-1-56411-540-9(2)***, CB Publishing & Design) UBUS Communications Systems.

McDonald, Megan. When the Library Lights Go Out. Tillotson, Katherine, tr. Tillotson, Katherine, illus. 2005. 40p. (J). 16.95 (978-0-689-86170-3(2), Atheneum/Richard Jackson Bks.) Simon & Schuster Children's Publishing.

McMillan, Frank. Cezanne Is Missing. 2006. 323p. (YA). pap. 14.95 (978-0-9711359-4-9(0)) Cambridge Hse. Publishing Co., LLC.

McMillon, LaToya. Bad News! 2006. (ENG.). 28p. per. 14.99 (***978-1-4259-3563-4(X)***) AuthorHouse.

Miklowitz, Gloria D. The Enemy Has a Face. 2004. 143p. (YA). pap. 8.00 (978-0-8028-5261-8(0)) Eerdmans, William B. Publishing Co.

The Missing Man & the Twenty Dragons. 2005. (Illus.). 204p. (J). per. (978-0-9760045-1-6(8), Reluctant Reader Bks.) e-Pluribus Unum Publishing Co.

Mitchell, Todd. The Traitor King. 2007. 368p. (J). (gr. 4-7). pap. 16.99 (978-0-439-82788-1(4), Scholastic Pr.) Scholastic, Inc.

Moore, James A. Newbies. 2004. (YA). mass mkt. 5.99 (978-0-8439-5474-6(4)) Dorchester Publishing Co., Inc.

Moore, Ulysses. Isle of Masks. 2008. (Ulysses Moore Book Ser.). 256p. (J). 5.99 (***978-0-439-77671-4(6)***, Scholastic Paperbacks) Scholastic, Inc.

Mowry, Jess. Tyger Tales. 2007. 280p. (YA). pap. 14.99 (978-1-59092-358-0(8), Blue Works) Windstorm Creative.

Narsimhan, Mahtab. The Third Eye. 2007. 240p. (YA). pap. 11.99 (***978-1-55002-750-1(6)***, Boardwalk Bks.) Dundurn Group, The CAN. *Dist:* Univ. of Toronto Pr.

Norton, Mary. Borrowers Aloft: Plus the Short Tale, Poor Stainless. 2003. (gr. 3-6). lib. bdg. 14.10 (978-0-613-66944-3(4)) Tandem Library Bks.

Orndorff, John C. Princess Mary & the Prophet. 2002. (J). per. 6.95 (978-1-893213-02-9(1)) Pensive Bks.

Pattison, Darcy. Searching for Oliver K. Woodman. Cepeda, Joe, illus. 2005. 56p. (J). 16.00 (978-0-15-205184-6(8)) Harcourt Children's Bks.

Peet, Mal. The Penalty. 2007. (Illus.). 272p. (YA). (gr. 9). 16.99 (***978-0-7636-3399-8(2)***) Candlewick Pr.

Perry, Naresha S. Zora's Valentine. 2005. (J). per. 13.00 (***978-0-9767189-0-1(1)***) Better Day Publishing Co.

Pfister, Marcus. Perdido en el Mar with Sticker. 2002. Tr. of Lost at Sea. (SPA.). (gr. k-3). lib. bdg. 11.80 (978-0-613-85239-5(7)) Tandem Library Bks.

Plum-Ucci, Carol. The Body of Christopher Creed. 2000. 256p. (YA). (gr. 7-12). 17.00 (978-0-15-202388-1(7)) Harcourt Children's Bks.

—The Body of Christopher Creed. 2001. 331p. (YA). (gr. 7-17). pap. 6.99 (978-0-7868-1641-5(4), Volo) Hyperion Bks. for Children.

—The Body of Christopher Creed. 2001. 13.39 (978-0-606-22569-4(2)); (gr. 7-12). lib. bdg. 15.00 (978-0-613-49392-5(3)) Tandem Library Bks.

—The Body of Christopher Creed. l.t. ed. 2001. 352p. (YA). 23.95 (978-0-7862-3509-4(8)) Thorndike Pr.

Polak, Monique. Flip Turn. 2004. (Sports Stories Ser.). 104p. (J). (gr. 3-13). (***978-1-55028-819-3(9)***); 7.95 (978-1-55028-818-6(0)) Lorimer, James & Co., Ltd., Pubs. CAN. *Dist:* Casemate Pubs. & Bk. Distributors, LLC.

Prévost, Guillaume & Rodarmor, William. The Book of Time. 2007. (J). (***978-0-439-88379-5(2)***); 224p. (gr. 4-7). pap. 16.99 (***978-0-439-88375-7(X)***) Scholastic, Inc. (Levine, Arthur A. Bks.).

Rabb, M. E. Missing Persons Vol. 1: The Rose Queen. 2004. (Missing Persons Ser.). 192p. (YA). pap. 5.99 (978-0-14-250041-5(0), Puffin) Penguin Group (USA) Inc.

Rene, Richard. The Nightmare Tree. 2007. 240p. (YA). (gr. 5-8). 8.95 (***978-1-55050-363-0(4)***) Coteau Bks. CAN. *Dist:* Fitzhenry & Whiteside, Ltd.

Richardson, E. E. Devil's Footsteps. 192p. 2006. (YA). (gr. 9). mass mkt. 5.99 (978-0-440-23916-1(8), Laurel Leaf); 2005. (J). (gr. 7 up). lib. bdg. 17.99 (978-0-385-90279-3(4), Delacorte Bks. for Young Readers); 2005. (YA). (gr. 7 up). 15.95 (978-0-385-73263-5(5), Delacorte Bks. for Young Readers) Random Hse. Children's Bks.

Roach, Joyce Gibson, tr. Cowgirl of the Rocking R. 2003. (J). (978-0-9726573-0-3(4)) Crosswinds Bks.

Rodgers, Frank. Little T & the Dragon's Tooth. 2007. (Read-It! Chapter Books). (J). 21.26 (978-1-4048-2727-1(7)) Picture Window Bks.

Rouse, Marisa K. Hildigarde of Willow Hollow. 2007. 64p. pap. 9.95 (***978-1-4327-0127-7(4)***) Outskirts Press, Inc.

Rushford, Patricia H. Secrets of Ghost Island. 2007. (J). (***978-88-02-46255-4(0)***) Moody Pubs.

Salley, Coleen. Epossumondas Saves the Day. Stevens, Janet, illus. 2006. 48p. (J). 16.00 (978-0-15-205701-5(3)) Harcourt Trade Pubs.

Sargent, Dave & Sargent, Pat. Young Dike: Teamwork!, 5. Woodward, Elaine, illus. 2003. (Young Animal Pride Ser.: 5). 24p. (J). pap. 6.95 (978-1-56763-872-1(4)); lib. bdg. 19.95 (978-1-56763-871-4(6)) Ozark Publishing.

Schmidt, Werner. The Forests of Adventure. 2005. 137p. pap. 12.50 (978-1-4116-4721-3(1)) Lulu.com.

Schmidtfranz, Theone. Rules Are for Safety. 2007. (ENG.). 16p. (J). per. 19.99 (***978-1-4141-0887-2(7)***) Pleasant Word.

Schraff, Anne. Lost & Found. Langan, Paul, ed. 2002. (Bluford Ser.: 1). 133p. (J). mass mkt. 4.95 (978-0-944210-02-4(3)) Townsend Pr.

—Where's Dudley? 2001. (PageTurner Mystery Ser.). 80p. (YA). per. 3.95 (978-1-56254-177-4(3), SP 1773) Saddleback Educational Publishing.

—Where's Dudley? 2001. (gr. 7-12). lib. bdg. 11.80 (978-0-613-33240-8(7)) Tandem Library Bks.

Sherrard, Valerie. Chasing Shadows: A Shelby Belgarden Mystery. 2004. 200p. pap. 9.99 (978-1-55002-502-6(3)) Dundurn Group, The CAN. *Dist:* Univ. of Toronto Pr.

Smith, Michael & Smith, Debbie. Where's Whitney? 2000. 32p. 12.99 (978-0-310-20717-7(7)) Zondervan.

Snyder, Laurel. Up & down the Scratchy Mountains, or, the Search for a Suitable Princess. Dorman, Brandon, illus. 2008. (J). (***978-0-375-84719-6(7)***); lib. bdg. (***978-0-375-94719-3(1)***) Random Hse., Inc.

Sparks, Beatrice. Finding Katie: The Diary of Anonymous, a Teenager in Foster Care. 2005. (Illus.). 192p. (J). pap. 5.99 (978-0-06-050721-3(7)) HarperCollins Pubs.

Springer, Nancy. The Case of the Bizarre Bouquets: An Enola Holmes Mystery. 2008. 192p. (YA). (gr. 4). 14.99 (***978-0-399-24518-3(9)***, Philomel) Penguin Group (USA) Inc.

Springer, Nancy. The Case of the Missing Marquess: An Enola Holmes Mystery. (J). 2007. 224p. (gr. 3). 6.99 (***978-0-14-240933-6(2)***, Puffin); 2006. 208p. (gr. 4). 10.99 (978-0-399-24304-2(6), Philomel) Penguin Group (USA) Inc.

Steck-Vaughn Staff. Kim's Wish/What Is Missing. 1999. (Take Me Home Ser.). (Illus.). (J). pap. (978-0-7398-2674-4(3)) Steck-Vaughn.

Steig, William. Sylvester & the Magic Pebble. Steig, William, illus. 2006. (Stories to Go! Ser.). 32p. (J). 4.99 (978-1-4169-1857-8(4), Aladdin) Simon & Schuster Children's Publishing.

Stephenson, Beth Mitchell. The Angel's Song. unabr. ed. 2002. 106p. (Orig.). pap. 7.95 (978-1-930980-93-8(0), 80930) Granite Publishing & Distribution.

Stone, David Lee. The Ratastrophe Catastrophe. Lea, Bob, illus. 2004. (Illmoor Chronicles Ser.: Bk. 1). 288p. (gr. 5-9). 16.99 (978-0-7868-5128-7(7)) Hyperion Bks. for Children.

Straight, Susan. The Friskative Dog. 2007. 160p. (J). (gr. 3-7). 14.99 (978-0-375-83777-7(9)); lib. bdg. 17.99 (978-0-375-93777-4(3)) Random Hse. Children's Bks. (Knopf Bks. for Young Readers).

Taylor, Jeannie. Am I Praying? 2003. (Illus.). 32p. (J). 12.99 (978-0-8254-3723-6(7)) Kregel Pubns.

Theo. Oscar & Hoo. 2003. (Illus.). 32p. (J). pap. 8.95 (978-0-00-710794-0(3), HarperSport) HarperCollins Pubs. Ltd. GBR. *Dist:* Trafalgar Square Publishing.

—Oscar & Hoo. Dudok de Wit, Michael, illus. 2003. 32p. (J). (ps-2). 17.99 (978-0-00-710793-3(5)) HarperCollins Pubs. Ltd. GBR. *Dist:* Trafalgar Square Publishing.

Torres, Laura. Crossing Montana, Grade 7. 2002. 128p. (J). (gr. 7 up). tchr. ed. 16.95 (978-0-8234-1643-1(7)) Holiday Hse., Inc.

Tucker, Mark. Super Phil & the Missing Mom. Patete, Christine, illus. 2003. 24p. (J). 4.50 (978-1-882440-01-6(3)) God's World Pubns. Inc.

Ure, Jean. Is Anybody There? Seeing Is Believing. 2004. (Diary Ser.). (Illus.). 192p. (J). pap. 8.99 (978-0-00-716136-2(0), Collins) HarperCollins Pubs. Ltd. GBR. *Dist:* Independent Pubs. Group.

Valentine, Jenny. Me, the Missing, & the Dead. 2008. 208p. (J). 16.99 (***978-0-06-085068-5(X)***); lib. bdg. 17.89 (***978-0-06-085069-2(8)***) HarperCollins Pubs.

Valverde, Mikel. Paula en Nueva York. Valverde, Mikel, illus. 2005. (SPA., Illus.). 32p. (J). 14.99 (978-1-933032-15-3(4)) Lectorum Pubns., Inc.

Vogelaar, Alie. A Shot Through the Window. Bazen, Edith, tr. from DUT. Visser, Rino, illus. 2000. Orig. Title: Een Schot Door Het Raam. 107p. lib. bdg. 8.95 (978-0-9670728-1-4(6)) Early Foundations Pubs.

Vrettos, A. M. Sight. 2007. 272p. (YA). (gr. 7 up). 16.99 (***978-1-4169-0657-5(6)***, McElderry, Margaret K.) Simon & Schuster Children's Publishing.

Walter, Lee. The Gifts That Are Forgotten. 2006. 60p. pap. 12.95 (978-1-4137-9070-2(4)) PublishAmerica, Inc.

Warner, Gertrude Chandler. The Vanishing Passenger. 2006. (Boxcar Children Mysteries Ser.: 106). (Illus.). 128p. (J). 14.95 (978-0-8075-1066-7(1)); pap. 4.50 (978-0-8075-1067-4(X)) Whitman, Albert & Co.

Weatherly, Lee. Missing Abby. 208p. 2006. (YA). (gr. 7). mass mkt. 5.99 (978-0-553-49488-4(0), Laurel Leaf); 2004. (J). (gr. k-7). lib. bdg. 17.99 (978-0-385-75053-0(6), Fickling, David Bks.); 2004. (J). (gr. 7). 15.95 (978-0-385-75052-3(8), Fickling, David Bks.) Random Hse. Children's Bks.

Westerfeld, Scott. So Yesterday. 240p. (gr. 7-12). 2004. (J). 16.99 (978-1-59514-000-5(X)); 2005. (YA). reprint ed. pap. 7.99 (978-1-59514-032-6(8)) Penguin Group (USA) Inc. (Razorbill).

Weston, Carrie. If a Chicken Stayed for Supper. Fatus, Sophie, illus. 2007. 32p. (J). (ps-3). 16.95 (978-0-8234-2067-4(1)) Holiday Hse., Inc.

Wheeler, Lisa. Where, Oh Where, Is Santa Claus? Bates, Ivan, illus. 2007. 32p. (J). (ps-2). 16.00 (978-0-15-216408-9(1)) Harcourt Trade Pubs.

Wilson, Eric. Kootenay Kidnapper. 2001. (gr. 3-6). lib. bdg. 13.00 (978-0-613-54818-2(3)) Tandem Library Bks.

Wilson, N. D. Leepike Ridge. 2007. (Illus.). 240p. (J). (gr. 3-7). 15.99 (978-0-375-83873-6(2)); lib. bdg. 18.99 (978-0-375-93873-3(7)) Random Hse. Children's Bks. (Random Hse. Bks. for Young Readers).

—Leepike Ridge. 2007. (Illus.). 224p. (J). pap. (978-0-375-83874-3(0)) Random Hse., Inc.

Yolen, Jane & Stemple, Adam. Pay the Piper: A Rock 'n' Roll Fairy Tale. 2006. 192p. (J). 5.99 (978-0-7653-5041-1(6), Starscape) Doherty, Tom Assocs., LLC.

MISSIONARIES

Alex, Ben. Hudson Taylor. Rava, Giuseppe, illus. 1998. (Heroes of Faith & Courage Ser.). 50p. (gr. 3-12). pap. 7.99 (978-1-884543-14-2(6)) Authentic Media.

—William Carey. Rava, Giuseppe, illus. 1998. (Heroes of Faith & Courage Ser.). 50p. (gr. 3-12). reprint ed. pap. 7.99 (978-1-884543-15-9(4)) Authentic Media.

Anderson, Dick. African Adventures. (Illus.). 96p. (J). pap. 5.99 (978-1-85792-807-5(5), Christian Focus) Christian Focus Pubns. GBR. *Dist:* Riverside.

Bagley, Val Chadwick. My Missionary Book. 2004. pap. 3.95 (978-1-57734-518-3(5), 01114182) Covenant Communications, Inc.

Benge, Janet. Eric Liddell: Something Greater Than Gold. 1998. (gr. 5-8). lib. bdg. 15.30 (978-0-613-83686-9(3)) Tandem Library Bks.

Benge, Janet & Benge, Geoff. Florence Young: Mission Accomplished. 2005. (Christian Heroes, Then & Now Ser.). 185p. (J). (978-1-57658-313-5(9)) YWAM Publishing.

—Ida Scudder, Healing Bodies, Touching Hearts. 2003. (Christian Heroes, Then & Now Ser.). (Illus.). 192p. pap. 8.99 (978-1-57658-285-5(X)) YWAM Publishing.

—John Williams, Messenger of Peace. 2002. (Christian Heroes, Then & Now Ser.). (Illus.). 208p. pap. 8.99 (978-1-57658-256-5(6)) YWAM Publishing.

—Lillian Trasher: The Greatest Wonder in Egypt. 2003. (Christian Heroes, Then & Now Ser.). 190p. (J). pap. 8.99 (978-1-57658-305-0(8)) YWAM Publishing.

Benge, Janet Hazel & Benge, Geoffrey Francis. Nate Saint: On a Wing & a Prayer. 1998. (Christian Heroes Ser.). (Illus.). 208p. (gr. 5-9). pap. 8.99 (978-1-57658-017-2(2)) YWAM Publishing.

Caughey, Ellen. Eric Liddell: Gold Medal Missionary. (Heros of the Faith Ser.). 2006. 208p. pap. 2.97 (978-1-59789-115-8(0)); 2000. (Illus.). 224p. (J). (gr. 3-7). pap. 1.39 (978-1-57748-721-0(4)) Barbour Publishing, Inc.

Crouch, Howard E. Brother Dutton of Molokai. 2000. (Illus.). 160p. (J). 10.95 (978-0-9606330-6-7(5)) Damien-Dutton Society for Leprosy Aid, Inc.

Dakos, Kalli & Karas, G. Brian. Don't Read This Book, Whatever You Do! More Poems about School. 1998. (Illus.). 64p. (J). (gr. 2-4). pap. 3.99 (978-0-689-82132-5(8), Aladdin) Simon & Schuster Children's Publishing.

Demi. Mother Teresa. 2005. (Illus.). 40p. (J). (gr. 1-4). 19.95 (978-0-689-86407-0(8), McElderry, Margaret K.) Simon & Schuster Children's Publishing.

Dils, Tracy. Mother Theresa. 2001. (Women of Achievement Ser.). (Illus.). 112p. (J). pap. 9.95 (978-0-7910-5888-6(3)); (gr. 4-7). 30.00 (978-0-7910-5887-9(5)) Facts On File, Inc. (Chelsea Hse.).

Durango, Julia. Pedro Claver, Patron Saint of Slaves. 2002. (ENG & SPA., Illus.). 32p. 8.95 (978-0-8091-6697-8(6), 6697-6) Paulist Pr.

Farmer, Lucile. A Willing Heart. 246p. (Orig.). (YA). pap. 7.95 (978-1-877917-10-3(9)) Alpha Bible Pubns.

Fitzpatrick, Anne. Mother Teresa. 2005. (Genius Ser.). (Illus.). 48p. (gr. 5-9). 21.95 (978-1-58341-330-2(8), Creative Education) Creative Co., The.

Freedman, Frances. David Livingstone. (Great Explorers Ser.). (Illus.). 48p. (J). (gr. 5 up). 2002. pap. 14.60 (978-0-8368-5175-5(7)); 2001. lib. bdg. 30.00 (978-0-8368-5015-4(7)) Stevens, Gareth Inc. (World Almanac Library).

Glavich, Mary Kathleen. Blessed Teresa of Calcutta: Missionary of Charity. Kiwak, Barbara, tr. Kiwak, Barbara, illus. 2003. (Encounter the Saints Ser.: Vol. 17). 136p. (J). pap. 7.95 (978-0-8198-1160-8(2), 332-024) Pauline Bks. & Media.

Hambrick, Sharon. Adoniram Judson: God's Man in Burma. 2001. (Illus.). 143p. (J). 6.49 (978-1-57924-625-9(7)) Jones, Bob Univ. Pr.

Harness, Cheryl. The Tragic Tale of Narcissa Whitman & a Faithful History of the Oregon Trail. Harness, Cheryl, illus. 2006. (Illus.). 144p. (J). (gr. 5-9). 16.95 (978-0-7922-5920-6(3), National Geographic Children's Bks.) National Geographic Society.

Howat, Irene. Jim Elliot: He Is No Fool... 2005. 153p. mass mkt. (978-1-84550-064-1(4), Christian Focus) Christian Focus Pubns.

Jackson, Dave & Jackson, Neta. Hero Tales. 2005. (Illus.). 192p. (J). (gr. 1-7). pap. 12.99 (978-0-7642-0079-3(8)); pap. 12.99 (978-0-7642-0080-9(1)) Bethany Hse. Pubs.

Jacobs, William J. Mother Teresa: Helping the Poor. rev. ed. 1998. (Gateway Biography Ser.). (Illus.). 48p. (gr. 2-4). lib. bdg. 23.90 (978-1-56294-020-1(1), Millbrook Pr.) Lerner Publishing Group.

Johnson, Emma. Mother Teresa. 2003. (20th Century History Makers Ser.). (Illus.). 112p. (J). lib. bdg. 32.85 (978-0-7398-6143-1(3)) Raintree.

M N O

Joiner, Barbara. Not Simply with Words: The Story of Susan Ingouf Lafferty. 1998. 118p. (YA). (gr. 9-12). pap. 7.95 (978-1-56309-234-3(4) , W986103) Woman's Missionary Union.

Klaus, Sandra. Surrounded by Headhunters. Date not set. (ARA.). (J). (gr. 2-7). pap. (978-1-890940-03-4(8)) Gospel Missionary Union.

—Surrounded by Headhunters. Ra, David, tr. Espe, Marvin, illus. 1998. (KOR.). 10p. (J). (gr. 2-7). pap. (978-1-890940-01-0(1)) Gospel Missionary Union.

Langley, Judy. God's World & Me from A to Z. Coker, Carla, illus. 2004. 32p. (ps). 8.99 (978-1-56309-367-8(7)) New Hope Pubs.

Leidenfrost, Lisa. At the Edge of the Village: Musings of a Missionary Wife. 2004. Orig. Title: African Sketches. (Illus.). 212p. (YA). per. 12.00 (978-1-59128-017-0(6)) Canon Pr.

The Lottie & Annie Upside-down Book. 2003. 8.99 (978-1-56309-627-3(7)) Woman's Missionary Union.

Lovelace, Braken & Lovelace, Brooklyn. It's Fun to Be an MK. Turrentine, Jan, ed. 2001. 24p. (J). (gr. k-2). pap. 8.99 (978-1-56309-523-8(8)) Woman's Missionary Union.

Mattews, Basil. Livingstone: The Pathfinder. 2003. 112p. (YA). pap. 8.95 (978-0-923309-86-2(1)) Hartland Pubns.

McNeil, Niki, et al. HOCPP 1096 Missionaries to Know. 2006. spiral bd. 21.00 ***(*978-1-60308-096-5(1))*** In the Hands of a Child.

Middleton, Haydn. Mother Teresa. 2000. (Profiles Ser.). (Illus.). 56p. (J). (gr. 4-6). lib. bdg. 24.22 (978-1-57572-227-6(5)) Heinemann Library.

Miller, William. Tales of Persia: Missionary Stories from Islamic Iran. Van Patten, Bruce, illus. 2005. 163p. pap. 9.99 (978-0-87552-615-7(2)) P & R Publishing.

Morgan, Nina. Mother Teresa: Saint of the Poor. 1998. (Illus.). 48p. (gr. 4-7). pap. 7.95 (978-0-8172-7848-9(6)) Steck-Vaughn.

Morris, Brenda. First Steps in Missions, Vol. 7. Reeves, Rhonda, ed. 2001. 96p. (J). (ps). pap. 13.00 (978-1-56309-506-1(8)) Woman's Missionary Union.

Nelson, Robin. Mother Teresa: A Life of Caring. 2007. (Pull Ahead Books). (Illus.). 32p. (J). 22.60 (978-0-8225-6384-6(3) , Lerner Pubns.) Lerner Publishing Group.

Otfinoski, Steven. David Livingstone: Deep in the Heart of Africa. 2006. (Great Explorations Ser.). (Illus.). 80p. (YA). (gr. 5-9). lib. bdg. 32.79 (978-0-7614-2226-6(9) , Benchmark Bks.) Cavendish, Marshall Corp.

Papademetriou, Dorrie. North Star: St. Herman of Alaska. 2000. (Illus.). 32p. (J). 17.00 (978-0-88141-223-9(6)) St. Vladimir's Seminary Pr.

Petrie, Kristin. Marquette & Jolliet. 2007. (Illus.). 32p. (J). 22.78 (978-1-59679-745-1(2)) ABDO Publishing Co.

Ransom, Candice F. Mother Teresa. Verstraete, Elaine, illus. 2000. (On My Own Biographies Ser.). 48p. (J). (gr. 1-3). 23.93 (978-1-57505-441-4(8) , Carolrhoda Bks.) Lerner Publishing Group.

Reymond, Robert L. Paul Missionary Theologian: A Survey of His Missionary Labours & Theology. 2000. (Illus.). 640p. (978-1-85792-497-8(5) , Mentor) Christian Focus Pubns.

Rice, Tanya. Mother Teresa. 1999. (Life & Times of Ser.). (Illus.). 48p. (YA). (gr. 5 up). 12.95 (978-0-7910-4637-1(0) , Chelsea Hse.) Facts On File, Inc.

Robinson, Virgil E. Curse of the Cannibals. 2005. (Illus.). 126p. (J). per. 10.95 (978-1-57258-355-9(X)) TEACH Services, Inc.

—Mighty Mary: The Story of Mary Slessor. 2000. (Illus.). 121p. (YA). (gr. 8 up). reprint ed. per. 8.95 (978-1-57258-159-3(X) , 945-6019) TEACH Services, Inc.

Ross, Stewart. The Story of Mother Teresa. 2001. (Illus.). 48p. (J). lib. bdg. 24.25 (978-1-930643-21-5(7)) Chrysalis Education.

Ruth, Amy. Mother Teresa. 1999. (Biography Ser.). (Illus.). 112p. (YA). (gr. 6-12). lib. bdg. 27.93 (978-0-8225-4943-7(3) , Lerner Pubns.) Lerner Publishing Group.

Schaefer, Lola M. Mother Teresa. Saunders-Smith, Gail, ed. 2003. (First Biographies Ser.). (Illus.). 24p. (J). (gr. k-1). lib. bdg. 15.93 (978-0-7368-1646-5(1) , Pebble Bks.) Capstone Pr., Inc.

—Mother Teresa, Vol. 2. 2005. (First Biographies Ser.). 24p. (YA). (gr. k-3). pap. (978-0-7368-3381-3(1) , Pebble Bks.) Capstone Pr., Inc.

Slavicek, Louise Chipley. Mother Teresa: Caring for the World's Poor. 2007. (Modern Peacemakers Ser.). (Illus.). 120p. (YA). (gr. 9 up). 30.00 ***(*978-0-7910-9433-4(2)*** , Chelsea Hse.) Facts On File, Inc.

Stone, Elaine Murray. Mother Teresa: A Life of Love. 1999. (Illus.). 128p. (gr. 5-9). 7.95 (978-0-8091-6651-0(8) , 6651-8) Paulist Pr.

Sullivan, Anne Marie. Mother Theresa: Religious Humanitarian. 2002. (Great Names Ser.). (Illus.). 32p. (J). (gr. 3 up). lib. bdg. (978-1-59084-142-6(5)) Mason Crest Pubs.

Tan, Joyce. Finding the Lord's ELect: How Missionaries can Tract Fruitfully. 2004. per. 12.95 (978-0-9746016-0-1(8)) Eclectic Dragon Pr.

Tilton, Rafael. Mother Teresa. 1999. (Importance of Ser.). (Illus.). 120p. (YA). (gr. 7-10). 27.45 (978-1-56006-565-4(6) , Lucent Bks.) Thomson Gale.

Valentine, Emily. Mother Teresa: With a Discussion of Compassion. 2004. (Values in Action Ser.). (J). (978-1-59203-070-5(X)) Learning Challenge, Inc.

Walsh, Kay. John Paton, a South Sea Island Rescue. 160p. (J). mass mkt. 5.99 (978-1-85792-852-5(0) , Christian Focus) Christian Focus Pubns. GBR. *Dist:* Riverside.

Wellman, Sam. David Livingstone: Missionary & Explorer. 1999. (Heroes of the Faith Ser.). (Illus.). 208p. (YA). (gr. 4-7). 14.95 (978-0-7910-5038-5(6) , Chelsea Hse.) Facts On File, Inc.

—Mother Teresa: Missionary of Charity. 1999. (Heroes of the Faith Ser.). 208p. (YA). (gr. 4-7). 14.95 (978-0-7910-5033-0(5) , Chelsea Hse.) Facts On File, Inc.

—Mother Teresa: Missionary of Charity. Lt. ed. 2001. (Thorndike Christian Fiction Ser.). 274p. (J). 24.95 (978-0-7862-3250-5(1)) Thorndike Pr.

Wheeler, Jill C. Mother Teresa. 2002. (Breaking Barriers Ser.). (Illus.). 64p. (J). (gr. 3-8). lib. bdg. 25.65 (978-1-57765-315-8(7) , ABDO & Daughters) ABDO Publishing Co.

Wilder, M. L. Missionary Annuls: Memoir of Robert Moffat. 2003. 64p. (YA). pap. 7.95 (978-0-923309-88-6(8)) Hartland Pubns.

Woronoff, Kristen. Mother Teresa: Helper of the Poor. 2002. (Famous Women Juniors Ser.). (Illus.). 32p. (J). (gr. 3-5). 23.70 (978-1-56711-591-8(8) , Blackbirch Pr., Inc.) Thomson Gale.

MISSIONARIES, CANADIAN

Benge, Janet & Benge, Geoff. Rowland Bingham: Into Africa's Interior. 2003. (Christian Heroes, Then & Now Ser.). (Illus.). 192p. pap. 8.99 (978-1-57658-282-4(5)) YWAM Publishing.

Harkins, Susan and William. The Life & Times of Father Jacques Marquette. 2007. (Profiles in American History Ser.). (J). lib. bdg. ***(*978-1-58415-528-7(0))*** Mitchell Lane Pubs., Inc.

MISSIONARIES—FICTION

Barth, Jeff. The Missionary Adventures of Bob & Arty Vol. 3: Mission Alaska. Barth, Marge, ed. 1998. (Illus.). 293p. (J). (gr. 4-12). pap. 10.00 (978-0-9624067-8-2(3)) Barth Family Ministries.

—The Missionary Adventures of Bob & Arty Vol. 4: The Storm! Barth, Marge, ed. 1999. (Illus.). 392p. (J). (gr. 4-12). pap. 10.00 (978-1-891484-01-8(X)) Barth Family Ministries.

Berry, Eileen. Roses on Baker Street. Roberts, John, illus. 1998. 48p. (J). (gr. k-4). pap. 5.49 (978-0-89084-934-7(X) , 106401) Jones, Bob Univ. Pr.

Boonstra, Jean Elizabeth. Going Home. 2004. 95p. (J). (978-0-8163-2019-6(5)) Pacific Pr. Publishing Assn.

—Secrets & Friends. 2004. 95p. (J). (978-0-8163-2021-9(7)) Pacific Pr. Publishing Assn.

Carlson, Melody. Diary of a Teenage Girl - It's My Life: Diary Number 2. 2002. (gr. 7-12). lib. bdg. 22.25 (978-0-613-88463-1(9)) Tandem Library Bks.

Dewey, Jennifer Owings. Minik's Story. 2003. (Illus.). 160p. (YA). 15.95 (978-0-7614-5134-1(X)) Cavendish, Marshall Corp.

Eby, Wes. Jungle Jeopardy. 2006. 56p. 7.75 (978-0-8341-2228-4(6)) Beacon Hill Pr. of Kansas City.

Farnes, Catherine. Out of Hiding. 2000. 174p. (YA). (gr. 9 up). pap. 6.49 (978-1-57924-329-6(0) , 122085) Jones, Bob Univ. Pr.

—Out of Hiding. 2000. (gr. 7-12). lib. bdg. 14.70 (978-0-613-83927-3(7)) Tandem Library Bks.

Gostick, Adrian R. Jessica's Search: The Secret of Ballycater Cove. 1998. (J). 1.99 (978-1-57345-436-0(2)) Deseret Bk. Co.

Haislip, Phyllis Hall. Lottie's Courage: A Contraband Slave's Story. 2003. (Illus.). 120p. (J). pap. 7.95 (978-1-57249-311-7(9) , White Mane Kids) White Mane Publishing Co., Inc.

Hardy, LeAnne. Between Two Worlds: A Novel. 2003. 160p. pap. 6.99 (978-0-8254-2793-0(2)) Kregel Pubns.

—The Wooden Ox: A Novel. 2002. 192p. (gr. 4-8). pap. 6.99 (978-0-8254-2794-7(0)) Kregel Pubns.

Hernandez, Natalie. Las Aventuras con Padre Serra. Hernandez, Tony Y., tr. Nolan, Claudia, illus. 1999. (ENG & SPA.). 112p. (Orig.). (J). (gr. 3-8). pap. 9.95 (978-0-9644386-1-3(5)) Santa Ines Pubns.

Hilderbrand, Barbara. Paul's Missionary Adventure. 2003. (Pencil Fun Bks.: Vol. 10). 16p. (J). (ps-3). pap., pap. 9.90 (978-1-55513-270-5(7) , 1555132707) Cook, David C. Publishing Co.

Hutchens, Paul. The White Boat Rescue. 1998. (gr. 3-6). lib. bdg. 13.00 (978-0-613-90326-4(9)) Tandem Library Bks.

Jackson, Dave. Sinking the Dayspring: John G. Paton. 2001. (gr. 3-6). lib. bdg. 14.15 (978-0-613-82919-9(0)) Tandem Library Bks.

Johnson, Lissa Halls & Wierenga, Kathy. Croutons for Breakfast, Vol. 7. 2005. (Brio Girls Ser.). (Illus.). 192p. (YA). (gr. 6-11). pap. 7.99 (978-1-58997-080-9(2)) Focus on the Family Publishing.

Little, Jean. His Banner over Me. 1999. 224p. (J). mass mkt. 6.99 (978-0-14-037761-3(1)) Penguin Group (USA) Inc.

McDaniel, Lurlene. Angel of Hope. 2000. (Mercy Trilogy). 240p. (YA). (gr. 7-12). pap. 4.99 (978-0-553-57148-6(6) , Laurel Leaf) Random Hse. Children's Bks.

—Angel of Hope. 2000. (Mercy Trilogy). (gr. 7-12). lib. bdg. 13.00 (978-0-613-24184-7(3)); (Illus.). (J). 11.64 (978-0-606-17991-1(7)) Tandem Library Bks.

—Angel of Mercy. 2001. (Mercy Trilogy). (gr. 7-12). lib. bdg. 13.00 (978-0-613-90625-8(X)); 11.64 (978-0-606-21031-7(8)) Tandem Library Bks.

Moffett, Slyvia. The Missionary Kids Adventure Series: Bo. 2006. 48p. pap. 12.95 (978-1-4241-2854-9(4)) PublishAmerica, Inc.

Oliva, Nephi. Elder Teddy & His First Companion. Maruyama, Jerrod, illus. 2005. 32p. (J). per. 4.95 (978-1-886249-30-1(X)) WindRiver Publishing.

Palmer, Viola. The Man in the Green Jeep. 2006. (ENG.). 144p. pap. (978-0-929292-61-8(8) , 800-747-0738) Hannibal Bks.

Repp, Gloria. Charlie. 2002. (Illus.). 147p. (J). (gr. 4-7). 7.49 (978-1-57924-817-8(9)) Jones, Bob Univ. Pr.

—Mik-Shrok. 1998. 133p. (J). (gr. 4-7). pap. 7.49 (978-1-57924-069-1(0) , 113902) Jones, Bob Univ. Pr.

—Zebra 77. Schuppert, David, illus. 2002. (Adventures of an Arctic Missionary Ser.). 156p. (J). (gr. 4-7). 7.49 (978-1-57924-930-4(2)) Jones, Bob Univ. Pr.

Riordan, Robert. Medicine for Wildcat: A Story of the Friendship between a Menominee Indian & Frontier Priest Samuel Mazzuchelli. 2006. (Illus.). 132p. (YA). per. 14.95 (978-0-9774934-0-1(7)) Sinsinawa Dominicans, Inc.

Singleton, Linda Joy. Melissa's Mission Impossible/Mail Order Monster: Twin Spins. 2005. (Twin Spins Ser.: 10). (ENG.). 168p. (YA). per. 10.95 (978-0-7599-1009-6(X)) Hard Shell Word Factory.

Smith, Goerky. Danger Follows. 1999. 98p. (YA). (gr. 7 up). pap. 6.49 (978-1-57924-070-7(4) , 109835) Jones, Bob Univ. Pr.

St. John, Patricia. Secret of the Fourth Candle. rev. ed. 2003. (Illus.). 94p. 6.49 (978-1-85999-511-2(X)) Scripture Union GBR. *Dist:* Gabriel Resources.

—Star of Light. 2002. (Illus.). 160p. (YA). pap. 6.99 (978-0-8024-6577-1(3)) Moody Pubs.

Stewart, Jennifer J. Close Encounters of a Third World Kind. 2004. 128p. (J). (gr. 4-6). tchr. ed. 16.95 (978-0-8234-1850-3(2)) Holiday Hse., Inc.

Tada, Joni Eareckson. Mission Adventure. 2001. (gr. 3-6). lib. bdg. 14.15 (978-0-613-89086-1(8)) Tandem Library Bks.

Tada, Joni Eareckson & Jensen, Steve. The Mission Adventure. 2005. (Darcy & Friends Ser.). 143p. (gr. 3-6). pap. 5.99 (978-1-58134-257-4(8) , Crossway Bibles) Crossway Bks.

Van Dyke, Tony & Van Dyke, Tracey. Ricky & Friends Go to Africa. Perry, Craig Rex & Preston, Felicia, illus. 2003. (Encouraging African-Americans in Their Walk Ser.). 64p. (J). pap. 5.99 (978-0-8024-0902-7(4)) Moody Pubs.

Wilson, Heather Gemmen. Lydia Barnes & the Blood Diamond Treasure. 2007. (J). ***(*978-0-89827-350-2(1))*** Wesleyan Publishing Hse.

YKids Staff. Mother Teresa. 2008. (Great Figures in History Ser.). 144p. (J). pap. 14.95 ***(*978-981-05-7552-6(1))*** Youngjin (Singapore) Pte Ltd. SGP. *Dist:* Independent Pubs. Group.

Youngberg, Norma R. Jungle Thorn. 2000. (Illus.). 112p. (J). reprint ed. per. 8.95 (978-1-57258-157-9(3) , 945-6024) TEACH Services, Inc.

Zaugg, Sandra L. Alice Says Goodbye. 2005. (Illus.). 95p. (J). pap. (978-0-8163-2049-3(7)) Pacific Pr. Publishing Assn.

—Hidden Notes & High Seas. 2005. (Illus.). 95p. (J). (978-0-8163-2052-3(7)) Pacific Pr. Pubns.

—The Man in the Blue Skirt. 2005. (Illus.). 95p. (J). pap. (978-0-8163-2055-4(1)) Pacific Pr. Pubns.

—A Prayer for Mother. 2005. (Illus.). 95p. (J). (978-0-8163-2056-1(X)) Pacific Pr. Pubns.

MISSIONS

see also Missionaries

also names of churches, denominations, religious orders, etc. with the subdivision Missions, e.g. Catholic Church—Missions; etc.

Abbink, Emily. Missions of the Monterey Bay Area: San Carlos Borromeo de Carmelo, San Juan Bautista, Santa Cruz. 1999. (California Missions Ser.). (Illus.). 80p. (gr. 4-7). pap., lib. bdg. 23.93 (978-0-8225-9835-0(3)) Lerner Publishing Group.

Abbink, Emily. Monterey Bay Area Missions. 2007. (Exploring California Missions Ser.). (J). 27.93 ***(*978-0-8225-0887-8(7)*** , Lerner Pubns.) Lerner Publishing Group.

Anderson, Dale. The California Missions. 2002. (Landmark Events in American History Ser.). (Illus.). 48p. (J). (gr. 5 up). lib. bdg. 30.00 (978-0-8368-5339-1(3)); pap. 14.60 (978-0-8368-5353-7(9)) Stevens, Gareth Inc. (World Almanac Library).

Anderson, Gerald. Biographical Dictionary of Christian Missions. 1999. (gr. 7-12). lib. bdg. 65.20 (978-0-613-64653-6(3)) Tandem Library Bks.

Baldridge, Carol. Texas Missions Fact Cards. Tamminga, Jean, illus. 1998. 86p. (J). (gr. 4-8). ring bd. 34.00 (978-1-884925-58-0(8)) Toucan Valley Pubns., Inc.

Behrens, June. Central Coast Missions in California. 2007. (Exploring California Missions Ser.). (J). 27.93 ***(*978-0-8225-0897-7(4)*** , Lerner Pubns.) Lerner Publishing Group.

Behrens, June. Missions of the Central Coast: Santa Barbara, Santa Ines, la Purisima Concepcion. 1999. (California Missions Ser.). (Illus.). 80p. (J). (gr. 4-7). pap. (978-0-8225-9832-9(9) , Lerner Pubns.) Lerner Publishing Group.

Bert, Ruth J. Everyone Called Her Sister Sarah. 2004. (ENG., Illus.). 32p. (J). pap. 4.99 (978-1-928915-62-1(0)) Evangel Publishing Hse.

Bial, Raymond. Missions & Presidios. 2004. (American Community Ser.). (Illus.). 48p. (J). (gr. 2-5). 29.00 (978-0-516-23708-4(X) , Children's Pr.) Scholastic Library Publishing.

Binns, Tristan Boyer. Mission San Juan Capistrano. 2002. (Visiting the Past Ser.). (Illus.). 32p. (J). (gr. 5-7). pap. 6.95 (978-1-58810-410-6(9) , 91183) Heinemann Library.

—San Juan Capistrano. 2001. (Visiting the Past Ser.). (Illus.). 32p. (J). (gr. 5-7). lib. bdg. 24.22 (978-1-58810-272-0(6)) Heinemann Library.

Blackwell, Jodi. Fundamentals: Secret Mission Children's Pack. (J). (gr. 1-6). (978-0-633-05795-4(9)) LifeWay Christian Resources.

Brower, Pauline. Inland Valley Missions in California. 2007. (Exploring California Missions Ser.). (J). 27.93 ***(*978-0-8225-0899-1(0)*** , Lerner Pubns.) Lerner Publishing Group.

Brower, Pauline. Missions of the Inland Valleys: San Luis Obispo de Tolosa, San Miguel Arcangel, San Antonio de Padua, Nuestra Senora de la Soledad. 1999. (California Missions Ser.). (Illus.). 80p. (gr. 4-7). pap., lib. bdg. 23.93 (978-0-8225-9833-6(7)) Lerner Publishing Group.

Bushor, Mark. Mission Mania: A Can-Do Guide for Youth. 2000. 64p. (J). tchr. ed. 10.00 (978-0-687-03299-0(7)) Abingdon Pr.

—Mission Mania: Crazy to Serve. 2004. 32p. (gr. 8-12). stu. ed. 2.50 (978-0-687-03289-1(X)) Abingdon Pr.

California Missions Fact Cards. 2nd rev. ed. 1998. (Illus.). 48p. (J). (gr. 3-6). ring bd. 24.00 (978-1-884925-05-4(7)) Toucan Valley Pubns., Inc.

Ching, Jacqueline. Mission San Fernando Rey de Espana. (Missions of California Ser.). 64p. (J). 2004. lib. bdg. 25.50 (978-0-8239-5893-1(0)); 2000. (Illus.). (gr. 4). lib. bdg. 25.50 (978-0-8239-5503-9(6)) Rosen Publishing Group, Inc., The. (PowerKids Pr.).

—Mission San Rafael Arcangel. 2000. (Missions of California Ser.). (Illus.). 64p. (J). (gr. 4). lib. bdg. 25.50 (978-0-8239-5506-0(0) , PowerKids Pr.) Rosen Publishing Group, Inc., The.

—Mission Santa Ines. (Missions of California Ser.). 64p. (J). 2004. lib. bdg. 25.50 (978-0-8239-5894-8(9)); 2000. (Illus.). (gr. 4). lib. bdg. 25.50 (978-0-8239-5505-3(2)) Rosen Publishing Group, Inc., The. (PowerKids Pr.).

Clere, Jodi Rae. Youth on Mission Vol. 6: Beyond Belief! 2000. 128p. (YA). (gr. 11-12). pap. 15.99 (978-1-56309-345-6(6)) Woman's Missionary Union.

Dorr, Donal. Mission in Today's World. 2000. (Illus.). 308p. (YA). pap. 25.00 (978-1-57075-339-8(3)) Orbis Bks.

Draper, Allison Stark. Mission San Francisco de Solano. 2000. (Missions of California Ser.). (Illus.). 64p. (J). (gr. 4). lib. bdg. 25.50 (978-0-8239-5507-7(9) , PowerKids Pr.) Rosen Publishing Group, Inc., The.

—Mission San Juan Bautista. (Missions of California Ser.). 64p. (J). 2004. lib. bdg. 25.50 (978-0-8239-5879-5(5)); 2000. (Illus.). (gr. 4). lib. bdg. 25.50 (978-0-8239-5501-5(X)) Rosen Publishing Group, Inc., The. (PowerKids Pr.).

Edgar, Kathleen J. & Edgar, Nancy A. Mission San Miguel Arcangel. 2000. (Missions of California Ser.). (Illus.). 64p. (J). (gr. 4). lib. bdg. 25.50 (978-0-8239-5502-2(8) , PowerKids Pr.) Rosen Publishing Group, Inc., The.

Edgar, Kathleen J. & Edgar, Susan E. Mission San Carlos Borromeo del Rio Carmela. 2000. (Missions of California Ser.). (Illus.). 64p. (J). (gr. 4). lib. bdg. 25.50 (978-0-8239-5488-9(9) , PowerKids Pr.) Rosen Publishing Group, Inc., The.

—Mission San Diego de Alcala. (Missions of California Ser.). 64p. (J). 2004. lib. bdg. 25.50 (978-0-8239-5885-6(X)); 2000. (Illus.). (gr. 4). lib. bdg. 25.50 (978-0-8239-5487-2(0)) Rosen Publishing Group, Inc., The. (PowerKids Pr.).

—Mission San Francisco de Asis. 2000. (Missions of California Ser.). (Illus.). 64p. (J). (gr. 4). lib. bdg. 25.50 (978-0-8239-5492-6(7) , PowerKids Pr.) Rosen Publishing Group, Inc., The.

—Mission San Juan Capistrano. 2000. (Missions of California Ser.). (Illus.). 64p. (J). (gr. 4). lib. bdg. 25.50 (978-0-8239-5493-3(5) , PowerKids Pr.) Rosen Publishing Group, Inc., The.

—Mission San Luis Obispo de Tolosa. 2000. (Missions of California Ser.). (Illus.). 64p. (J). (gr. 4). lib. bdg. 25.50 (978-0-8239-5491-9(9) , PowerKids Pr.) Rosen Publishing Group, Inc., The.

—Mission San Miguel Arcangel. 2004. (Missions of California Ser.). 64p. (J). lib. bdg. 25.50 (978-0-8239-5896-2(5) , PowerKids Pr.) Rosen Publishing Group, Inc., The.

Gaines, Ann Graham. The Alamo: The Fight over Texas. 2003. (Proud Heritage-The Hispanic Library). (Illus.). 40p. (J). (gr. 3-7). 28.50 (978-1-56766-173-6(4)) Child's World, Inc.

Hare, Eric B. Jungle Heroes & Other Stories. 2005. (Illus.). 106p. (J). (978-0-8163-2063-9(2)) Pacific Pr. Publishing Assn.

Heinrichs, Ann. The California Missions. 2002. (We the People Ser.). (Illus.). 48p. (J). (gr. 4 up). lib. bdg. 22.60 (978-0-7565-0208-9(X)) Compass Point Bks.

Henley, Karyn. Missions: The Foundation for Sharing God. Koehler, Ed, illus. 2002. (Foundations Curriculum). 96p. (J). (gr. 3-6). 12.99 (978-0-7847-1367-9(7) , 42068) Standard Publishing.

Herrera, Matthew D. History Guide to Old Mission San Luis Obispo de Tolosa. 2003. (Illus.). 77p. 9.95 (978-0-9723720-1-5(6)) Tixlini Scriptorium, Inc.

I Can Do It! 2003. 9.99 (978-1-56309-626-6(9)) Woman's Missionary Union.

Isaacs, Sally Senzell. Life in a California Mission. (Picture the Past Ser.). (Illus.). 32p. (J). 2002. (gr. k-3). pap. 7.50 (978-1-58810-414-4(1) , 91187); 2001. (gr. 2-4). lib. bdg. 21.36 (978-1-58810-249-2(1)) Heinemann Library.

Jingling, Kathy, ed. Bernabe y su Gran Mision pro Cristo. Oyola, Milta, tr. from ENG. Tobar, Malena, illus. 2003. Tr. of Barnabas & his Great Mission for Christ. (SPA.). 191p. (J). spiral bd. 8.00 (978-1-931984-41-6(7) , 2002-00S1) RDM.

Johnson, Kevin. Mission Trip Prep Student Journal: A Student Journal for Capturing the Experience. 2003. (Evangelism Ser.). (Illus.). 112p. pap., stu. ed. 8.99 (978-0-310-24021-1(2) , 140005) Zondervan.

Keremitsis, Eileen. Life in a California Mission. 2002. (Way People Live Ser.). (Illus.). 112p. (J). (gr. 7-10). 29.95 (978-1-59018-159-1(X) , Lucent Bks.) Thomson Gale.

Langley, Judy. God's World & Me from A to Z. Coker, Carla, illus. 2004. 32p. (ps). 8.99 (978-1-56309-367-8(7)) New Hope Pubs.

M N O

Lemke, Nancy. Southern Coast Missions in California. 2007. (Exploring California Missions Ser.). (J). 27.93 (***978-0-8225-1935-5(6)***, Lerner Pubns.) Lerner Publishing Group.

Linse, Barbara B. Live Again Our Mission Past for Kids. Kuska, George & Clark, Cynthia, illus. 2000. (California Mission Ser.). (SPA.). 108p. (J). (gr. 4-7). pap. (978-1-878079-26-8(3)) Arts Pubns.

MacMillan, Dianne. Missions of the Los Angeles Area: San Gabriel Arcangel, San Fernando Rey de Espana, San Buenaventura. 1999. (California Missions Ser.). (Illus.). 80p. (gr. 4-7). pap., lib. bdg. 23.93 (978-0-8225-9834-3(5)) Lerner Publishing Group.

MacMillan, Dianne M. Los Angeles Area Missions. 2007. (Exploring California Missions Ser.). (J). 27.93 (***978-0-8225-0898-4(2)***, Lerner Pubns.) Lerner Publishing Group.

Margaret, Amy. Mission San Jose de Guadalupe. (Missions of California Ser.). 64p. (J). 2004. lib. bdg. 25.50 (978-0-8239-5897-9(3)); 2000. (Illus.). (gr. 4). lib. bdg. 25.50 (978-0-8239-5495-7(1)) Rosen Publishing Group, Inc., The. (PowerKids Pr.).

—Mission Santa Barbara. 2000. (Missions of California Ser.). (Illus.). 64p. (J). (gr. 4). lib. bdg. 25.50 (978-0-8239-5497-1(8), PowerKids Pr.) Rosen Publishing Group, Inc., The.

Marsh, Carole. Father Claude Allouez. 2002. (One Thousand Readers Ser.). (Illus.). 12p. (J). (gr. k-4). 2.95 (978-0-635-01535-8(8), 15358) Gallopade International.

Maruca, Mary. A Kid's Guide to Exploring San Antonio Missions. 2000. (Illus.). 12p. (J). (gr. 3-6). pap. 1.00 (978-1-58369-002-4(6), E1018) Western National Parks Assn.

McGinty, Alice B. Mission San Gabriel Arcangel. 2000. (Missions of California Ser.). (Illus.). 64p. (J). (gr. 4). lib. bdg. 25.50 (978-0-8239-5490-2(0), PowerKids Pr.) Rosen Publishing Group, Inc., The.

La Mision (The Mission) Quarter 2, Level 3. (Caminando con Jesus (Walking with Jesus) Series A). (SPA.). (J). stu. ed. 3.50 (978-0-570-05150-3(9)) Concordia Publishing Hse.

Missions of the Southwest. 2001. (J). pap. 4.95 (978-0-88388-204-7(3)) Bellerophon Bks.

Morris, Brenda. First Steps in Missions, Vol. 7. Reeves, Rhonda, ed. 2001. 96p. (J). (ps). pap. 13.00 (978-1-56309-506-1(8)) Woman's Missionary Union.

Munson, Jared. Courageous Witness: A Teenager Shares Jesus. 2003. (Illus.). 88p. 8.95 (978-0-8309-1069-4(7)) Herald Publishing Hse.

Nelson Libby. California Mission Projects & Layouts. Cornell, Kari, illus. 2007. (Exploring California Missions Ser.). (J). 27.93 (***978-0-8225-7950-2(2)***, Lerner Pubns.) Lerner Publishing Group.

Old Father's Long Journey. 2nd ed. 2001. 150p. (J). pap. 9.95 (978-1-930702-04-2(3), Wisdom Bks.) Literary Assocs. Pr.

Onwu, Jackie. Children of Africa: Restoring the Village. 2000. (Illus.). 142p. (J). pap. 6.95 (978-1-890569-28-0(3)) General Board of Global Ministries, The United Methodist Church.

Ostrow, Kim. Mission la Purisima Concepcion. 2000. (Missions of California Ser.). (Illus.). 64p. (J). (gr. 4). lib. bdg. 25.50 (978-0-8239-5498-8(6), PowerKids Pr.) Rosen Publishing Group, Inc., The.

—Mission Santa Cruz. (Missions of California Ser.). 64p. (J). 2004. lib. bdg. 25.50 (978-0-8239-5878-8(7)); 2000. (Illus.). (gr. 4). lib. bdg. 25.50 (978-0-8239-5499-5(4)) Rosen Publishing Group, Inc., The. (PowerKids Pr.).

Our Mission Past for Kids. 2000. (J). pap. 10.95 (978-1-878079-25-1(5)) Arts Pubns.

Price, Sean. The Birth of a State: California Missions. 2007. (J). (***978-1-4109-2694-4(X)***); pap. (***978-1-4109-2705-7(9)***) Steck-Vaughn.

Primeros pasitos misioneros (First Steps, Spanish) 2004. pap. 12.99 (978-1-56309-930-4(6)) Woman's Missionary Union.

Quasha, Jennifer. Mission San Luis Rey de Francia. (Missions of California Ser.). 64p. (J). 2004. lib. bdg. 25.50 (978-0-8239-5895-5(7)); 1999. (Illus.). (gr. 4). lib. bdg. 25.50 (978-0-8239-5504-6(4)) Rosen Publishing Group, Inc., The. (PowerKids Pr.).

Reeves, Rhonda. God's Beautiful World. 2001. (Missions & Me Ser.). 16p. (J). (ps). 7.99 (978-1-56309-375-3(8)) Woman's Missionary Union.

—Myself. 2001. (Missions & Me Ser.). 16p. (J). (ps). 7.99 (978-1-56309-360-9(X)) Woman's Missionary Union.

Rice, Tanya. Mother Teresa. 1999. (Life & Times of Ser.). (Illus.). 48p. (YA). (gr. 5 up). 12.95 (978-0-7910-4637-1(0), Chelsea Hse.) Facts On File, Inc.

Scarbrough, Mary Hertz. A California Mission. 2005. (Daily Life Ser.). (J). (978-0-7377-3090-6(0), Greenhaven Pr., Inc.) Thomson Gale.

Serafin, Kim. Mission San Antonio de Padua. 2000. (Missions of California Ser.). (Illus.). 64p. (J). (gr. 4). lib. bdg. 25.50 (978-0-8239-5489-6(7), PowerKids Pr.) Rosen Publishing Group, Inc., The.

Skelton, Cindy & Anderson, Vickie. Children in Action Vol. 1: Special Assignments. 2001. 144p. (J). (gr. 4-7). pap. 24.99 (978-1-56309-524-5(6)) Woman's Missionary Union.

Staeger, Rob. The Spanish Missions of California. 2002. (History of the Old West Ser.). (Illus.). 64p. (J). (gr. 5 up). lib. bdg. (978-1-59084-059-7(3)) Mason Crest Pubs.

Swinford, Betty. Missionary Stories from Around the World. 2005. (Illus.). 187p. (J). (ps-7). pap. (978-1-84550-042-9(3), Christian Focus) Christian Focus Pubns.

Tamminga, Jean, illus. Inside the Missions: California Missions Fact Cards, No. 2. 2000. 52p. (J). (gr. 4-6). ring bd. 24.00 (978-1-884925-75-7(8)) Toucan Valley Pubns., Inc.

Thompson, Gare. Missions & Ranchos: Early California Life. 2004. (National Geographic Reading Expeditions Ser.). (Illus.). 40p. (J). pap. (978-0-7922-4548-3(2)) National Geographic Society.

—When the Mission Padre Came to the Rancho: The Early California Adventures of Rosalinda & Simon Delgado. 2004. (I Am American Ser.). (Illus.). 40p. (J). (gr. 3-7). pap. 6.99 (978-0-7922-6945-8(4), National Geographic Children's Bks.) National Geographic Society.

Van Steenwyk, Elizabeth. The California Missions. 1998. (Illus.). 63p. (J). (gr. 4-7). lib. bdg. 15.25 (978-0-613-53978-4(8)) Tandem Library Bks.

Weber, Valerie J. & Anderson, Dale. The California Missions. 2002. (Events That Shaped America Ser.). (Illus.). 32p. (J). (gr. 3 up). lib. bdg. 24.67 (978-0-8368-3223-5(X)) Stevens, Gareth Inc.

White, Tekla N. Missions of the San Francisco Bay Area: Santa Clara de Asis, San Jose, San Francisco de Asis, San Rafael Arcangel, San Francisco Solano. 1999. (California Missions Ser.). (Illus.). 80p. (J). (gr. 4-7). pap. (978-0-8225-9836-7(1), Lerner Pubns.) Lerner Publishing Group.

White, Tekla N. San Francisco Bay Area Missions. 2007. (Exploring California Missions Ser.). (J). 27.93 (***978-0-8225-0900-4(8)***, Lerner Pubns.) Lerner Publishing Group.

Wilkinson, Brenda. Under the Baobob Tree: Children of Africa. Feelings, Tom, illus. 2000. 35p. (J). pap. 4.00 (978-1-890569-19-8(4), 2872) General Board of Global Ministries, The United Methodist Church.

Williams, Jack S. & Davis, Thomas L. Padres of the California Mission Frontier. 2004. (People of the California Missions Ser.). (Illus.). 64p. (J). lib. bdg. 25.50 (978-0-8239-6283-9(0), PowerKids Pr.) Rosen Publishing Group, Inc., The.

—Soldiers & Their Families of the California Mission Frontier. 2004. (People of the California Missions Ser.). (Illus.). 64p. (J). lib. bdg. 25.50 (978-0-8239-6285-3(7)) Rosen Publishing Group, Inc., The.

—Townspeople & Ranchers of the California Mission Frontier. 2004. (People of the California Missions Ser.). (Illus.). 64p. (J). lib. bdg. 25.50 (978-0-8239-6284-6(9), PowerKids Pr.) Rosen Publishing Group, Inc., The.

WorldVenture 1 Activity Book for Girls in Action Grade 1. 2004. pap. 4.99 (978-1-56309-628-0(5)) Woman's Missionary Union.

WorldVenture 2 Activity Book for Girls in Action Grade 2. 2003. pap. 4.99 (978-1-56309-629-7(3)) Woman's Missionary Union.

WorldVenture 3 Activity Book for Girls in Action Grade 3. 2003. pap. 4.99 (978-1-56309-630-3(7)) Woman's Missionary Union.

WorldVenture 4 Activity Book for Girls in Action Grade 4. 2003. pap. 4.99 (978-1-56309-631-0(5)) Woman's Missionary Union.

WorldVenture 5 Activity Book for Girls in Action Grade 5. 2003. pap. 4.99 (978-1-56309-632-7(3)) Woman's Missionary Union.

WorldVenture 6 Activity Book for Girls in Action Grade 6. 2003. pap. 4.99 (978-1-56309-633-4(1)) Woman's Missionary Union.

WorldVenture Guide for Leaders of Grades 1-6. 2003. pap. 8.99 (978-1-56309-634-1(X)) Woman's Missionary Union.

Worsham, Tammie. First Steps in Missions, 2000-2001. Reeves, Rhonda, ed. 2000. 96p. (J). (ps). pap. 13.00 (978-1-56309-324-1(3)) Woman's Missionary Union.

Yenne, Bill. The Missions of California. 2002. (Illus.). 48p. (J). (gr. 3-6). pap. 9.95 (978-1-58728-416-8(2)); 18.95 (978-1-58728-415-1(4)) T&N Children's Publishing. (Two Can Publishing).

Young, Robert. A Personal Tour of la Purisima. 1999. (How It Was Ser.). (Illus.). 64p. (J). (gr. 4-6). lib. bdg. (978-0-8225-3576-8(9), Lerner Pubns.) Lerner Publishing Group.

MISSISSIPPI

Brown, Jonatha A. & Ruffin, Frances E. Mississippi. 2006. (Portraits of the States Ser.). (Illus.). 32p. (J). pap. 8.95 (978-0-8368-4689-8(3)); lib. bdg. 23.33 (978-0-8368-4670-6(2)) Stevens, Gareth Inc.

Brown, Vanessa. Mississippi. Brusca, Maria Cristina, tr. 2005. (Bilingual Library of the United States of America: Set 2). (ENG & SPA., Illus.). 32p. (J). (gr. 2-5). lib. bdg. 22.50 (978-1-4042-3089-7(0), Buenas Letra) Rosen Publishing Group, Inc., The.

Deady, Kathleen W. Mississippi. 2003. (Land of Liberty Ser.). (Illus.). 64p. (J). lib. bdg. 25.26 (978-0-7368-2182-7(1)) Capstone Pr., Inc.

Dell, Pamela. Mississippi. 2007. (America the Beautiful, Third Ser.). (Illus.). 144p. (YA). (gr. 5-8). lib. bdg. 38.00 (***978-0-531-18563-6(X)***, Children's Pr.) Scholastic Library Publishing.

Figueroa, Acton. Mississippi: The Magnolia State. 2003. (World Almanac Library of the States). (Illus.). 48p. (J). (gr. 5 up). pap. 14.95 (978-0-8368-5323-0(7)); lib. bdg. 30.00 (978-0-8368-5152-6(8)) Stevens, Gareth Inc. (World Almanac Library).

Foran, Jill. A Guide to Mississippi. (American States Ser.). 32p. (J). 2001. per. 7.95 (978-1-930954-52-6(2)); 2000. (Illus.). (gr. 4-7). lib. bdg. 16.95 (978-1-930954-70-0(0)) Weigl Pubs., Inc.

Gaines, Ann. Mississippi. 2007. (J). (***978-0-7614-2214-3(5)***) Cavendish, Marshall Bks., Ltd.

Gibson, Karen Bush. Mississippi Facts & Symbols. (States & Their Symbols Ser.). 24p. (J). 2000. (Illus.). (gr. 2-3). lib. bdg. 18.60 (978-0-7368-0640-4(7), Bridgestone Bks.); 2003. lib. bdg. 19.93 (978-0-7368-2254-1(2)) Capstone Pr., Inc.

Heinrichs, Ann. Mississippi. 2005. (Welcome to the USA Ser.). 40p. (J). (gr. 1-5). 27.07 (978-1-59296-446-8(X)) Child's World, Inc.

—Mississippi. 2003. (This Land Is Your Land Ser.). (Illus.). 48p. (J). (gr. 3 up). lib. bdg. 22.60 (978-0-7565-0355-0(8)) Compass Point Bks.

Kummer, Patricia K. Mississippi. rev. ed. 2002. (One Nation Ser.). (Illus.). 48p. (J). (gr. 3-4). lib. bdg. 22.60 (978-0-7368-1248-1(2), Bridgestone Bks.) Capstone Pr., Inc.

Marsh, Carole. The Magnificent Mississippi Coloring Book. 2004. (Mississippi Experience! Ser.). (Illus.). 32p. (J). (gr. k-2). pap. 3.95 (978-0-7933-9559-0(3)) Gallopade International.

—Mississippi Big Activity Book. 2004. (Mississippi Experience! Ser.). (Illus.). 96p. (J). (gr. 2-6). pap. 9.95 (978-0-7933-9558-3(5)) Gallopade International.

—Mississippi Classic Christmas Trivia. 2002. (Carole Marsh Mississippi Bks.). (Illus.). 32p. pap. 6.95 (978-0-635-01415-3(7), 14157); lib. bdg. 21.95 (978-0-635-01416-0(5), 14165) Gallopade International. (Marsh, Carole Bks.).

—Mississippi Current Events Projects: 30 Cool, Activities, Crafts, Experiments & More for Kids to Do to Learn about Your State! 2003. (Mississippi Experience Ser.). 32p. (gr. k-8). pap. 5.95 (978-0-635-02043-7(2), Marsh, Carole Bks.) Gallopade International.

—The Mississippi Experience Library State: Resource Set. 2001. (Illus.). (J). (gr. k-8). pap. 100.20 incl. cd-rom (978-0-635-00477-2(1)) Gallopade International.

—The Mississippi Experience Pocket Guide. 2004. (Mississippi Experience! Ser.). (Illus.). 96p. (J). (gr. 3-8). pap. 6.95 (978-0-7933-9554-5(2)) Gallopade International.

—Mississippi Geography Projects: 30 Cool, Activities, Crafts, Experiments & More for Kids to Do to Learn about Your State! 2003. (Mississippi Experience Ser.). 32p. (gr. k-5). pap. 5.95 (978-0-635-01843-4(8), Marsh, Carole Bks.) Gallopade International.

—Mississippi Government Projects: 30 Cool, Activities, Crafts, Experiments & More for Kids to Do to Learn about Your State! 2003. (Mississippi Experience Ser.). 32p. (gr. k-5). pap. 5.95 (978-0-635-01943-1(4), Marsh, Carole Bks.) Gallopade International.

—Mississippi Jeopardy. 2004. (Mississippi Experience! Ser.). (Illus.). 32p. (J). (gr. 3-8). pap. 7.95 (978-0-7933-9556-9(9)) Gallopade International.

—Mississippi "Jography" A Fun Run Thru Our State! 2004. (Mississippi Experience! Ser.). (Illus.). 32p. (J). (gr. 3-8). pap. 7.95 (978-0-7933-9557-6(7)) Gallopade International.

—Mississippi Millionaire: Game Book. 2001. (Carole Marsh Mississippi Bks.). (Illus.). 32p. (J). (gr. 3-8). pap., act. bk. ed. 9.95 (978-0-635-00064-4(4)) Gallopade International.

—Mississippi People Projects: 30 Cool, Activities, Crafts, Experiments & More for Kids to Do to Learn about Your State! 2003. (Mississippi Experience Ser.). 32p. (gr. k-5). pap. 5.95 (978-0-635-01993-6(0), Marsh, Carole Bks.) Gallopade International.

—Mississippi Symbols & Facts Projects: 30 Cool, Activities, Crafts, Experiments & More for Kids to Do to Learn about Your State! 2003. (Mississippi Experience Ser.). 32p. (gr. k-5). pap. 5.95 (978-0-635-01893-9(4), Marsh, Carole Bks.) Gallopade International.

—My First Book about Mississippi. 2004. (Mississippi Experience! Ser.). (Illus.). 32p. (J). (gr. k-4). pap. 7.95 (978-0-7933-9555-2(0)) Gallopade International.

—The Survivor: A Class Challenge. 2001. (Carole Marsh Mississippi Bks.). lib. bdg. 29.95 (978-0-635-00670-7(7)) Gallopade International.

Mississippi. 2000. (Switched on Schoolhouse Ser.). (Illus.). (YA). (gr. 7-12). pap. 24.95 incl. cd-rom (978-0-7403-0276-3(0), SOSMS) Alpha Omega Pubns., Inc.

Murray, Julie. Mississippi. 2006. (Illus.). 32p. (J). (gr. k-4). lib. bdg. 22.78 (978-1-59197-683-7(9), Buddy Bks.) ABDO Publishing Co.

Naden, Corinne J. & Blue, Rose. Mississippi: A MyReportLinks.com Book. 2003. (States Ser.). (Illus.). 48p. (J). lib. bdg. 25.26 (978-0-7660-5144-7(7), MyReportLinks.com Bks.) Enslow Pubs., Inc.

Parker, Laurie. Mississippi Alphabet. 1998. (Illus.). 32p. (ps-3). 15.95 (978-0-937552-92-6(5)) Quail Ridge Pr., Inc.

Ready, Anna. Mississippi. (Hello U. S. A. Ser.). (Illus.). (J). (gr. 3-6). 2000. 72p. pap. 5.95 (978-0-8225-9788-9(8), First Avenue Editions); 2nd exp. rev. ed. 2003. 84p. 25.26 (978-0-8225-4109-7(2), Lerner Pubns.) Lerner Publishing Group.

—Mississippi. rev. ed. 2003. (gr. 3-6). lib. bdg. 15.25 (978-0-613-52446-9(2)) Tandem Library Bks.

Shirley, David. Mississippi. 1999. (Celebrate the States Ser.). (Illus.). 144p. (gr. 4-8). lib. bdg. 37.07 (978-0-7614-0664-8(6), Benchmark Bks.) Cavendish, Marshall Corp.

Shirley, David & Kummer, Patricia K. Mississippi. 2nd ed. 2008. (Celebrate the States Ser.). (J). lib. bdg. 39.93 (***978-0-7614-2717-9(1)***, Benchmark Bks.) Cavendish, Marshall Corp.

Shofner, Shawndra. Mississippi. 2008. (J). (***978-1-58341-649-5(8)***, Creative Education) Creative Co., The.

Siebert, Diane. Mississippi. Harlin, Greg, illus. 2001. 40p. (J). (gr. 3 up). 16.95 (978-0-688-16445-4(5)); lib. bdg. 17.89 (978-0-688-16446-1(3)) HarperCollins Pubs.

Somervill, Barbara A. Mississippi. 2003. (From Sea to Shining Sea Ser.: 2). (Illus.). 80p. (J). 30.50 (978-0-516-22392-6(5), Children's Pr.) Scholastic Library Publishing.

Trueit, Trudi Strain. Mississippi. 2007. (Rookie Read-about' Geography: States Ser.). 32p. (J). pap. 5.95 (***978-0-531-16813-4(1)***); (Illus.). (gr. 1-2). 20.50 (978-0-531-12572-4(6)) Scholastic Library Publishing. (Children's Pr.).

Wescovich Dill, Pamela. Katrina's Rainbow: The Miracle of the Storm Crosses. 2006. (Illus.). 46p. (J). 17.99 (***978-1-59879-302-4(0)***) Lifevest Publishing, Inc.

Wilson, Cristi. Just Because. Wilson, Cristi, illus. l.t. ed. 2006. (Illus.). 24p. (J). per. 10.99 (***978-1-59879-251-5(2)***) Lifevest Publishing, Inc.

Wilson, Martin. Uniquely Mississippi. 2004. (Heinemann State Studies). (Illus.). 48p. (J). pap. (978-1-4034-4725-8(X)); lib. bdg. 27.07 (978-1-4034-4656-5(3)) Heinemann Library.

MISSISSIPPI—FICTION

Altsheler, Joseph A. The Free Rangers: A Story of the Early D. 2006. pap. (***978-1-4065-0811-6(X)***) Dodo Pr.

Applegate, Stan. The Devil's Highway. Watling, James, illus. 1998. 224p. (J). (gr. 3-7). pap. 8.95 (978-1-56145-184-5(3), Q21196) Peachtree Pubs., Ltd.

Armistead, John. The Return of Gabriel. Gregory, Fran, illus. 2002. 240p. (J). (gr. 3-8). 17.95 (978-1-57131-637-0(X)); pap. 6.95 (978-1-57131-638-7(8)) Milkweed Editions.

Boone, Jack W. Billy Box. 2000. 367p. (YA). pap. 14.95 (978-1-880719-07-7(X), Grafco Bks.) Grafco Productions, Inc.

Coleman, Evelyn. White Socks Only. Geter, Tyrone, illus. 2004. (Prairie Paperback Bks.). 32p. (J). (gr. k-4). pap. 6.95 (978-0-8075-8956-4(X)) Whitman, Albert & Co.

Crowe, Chris. The Mississippi Trial, 1955. 2003. 240p. (YA). pap. 5.99 (978-0-14-250192-4(1), Puffin) Penguin Group (USA) Inc.

—The Mississippi Trial, 1955. 2003. (gr. 7-12). lib. bdg. 14.15 (978-0-613-86522-7(7)) Tandem Library Bks.

Curry, Kenneth. The Legend of the Dancing Trees: An African American Folk Tale. 2007. 111p. (J). per. 14.95 (***978-0-9798364-0-4(9)***) Curry Brothers Publishing.

Curry, Kenneth, et al. The Legend of the Dancing Tees Teachers Resource: The Legend of the Dancing Trees. 2007. Tr. of Teachers Resource. per. 19.95 (***978-0-9798364-1-1(7)***) Curry Brothers Publishing.

Ernst, Kathleen. Ghosts of Vicksburg. 2003. (White Main Kids Ser.: 13). (Illus.). 180p. (J). pap. 8.95 (978-1-57249-322-3(4), White Mane Kids) White Mane Publishing Co., Inc.

Fountain of Ecstasy. 2000. (YA). spiral bd. 19.95 (978-0-9740227-0-3(5)) Kendrick, G. David Properties.

Greenberg, Polly. Oh Lord, I Wish I Was a Buzzard. Aliki, illus. 2002. 32p. (J). (gr. k-3). 15.95 (978-1-58717-122-2(8), SeaStar Bks.) Chronicle Bks. LLC.

Johnson, Angela & Long, Loren. I Dream of Trains. 2003. (Illus.). 32p. (J). (gr. k-2). 17.99 (978-0-689-82609-2(5)) Simon & Schuster Children's Publishing.

Lees, Stewart. Runaway Jack. 2004. (Illus.). 32p. (J). 14.95 (978-0-7641-5712-7(4)) Barron's Educational Series, Inc.

Literature Connections English: Roll of Thunder, Hear My Cry. 2004. (gr. 6-12). (978-0-395-77530-1(2), 2-80099) McDougal Littell Inc.

Literature Connections Spanish: Lloro por la Tierra (Roll of Thunder, Hear My Cry) 2004. (gr. 6-12). (978-0-395-80048-5(X), 2-70467) McDougal Littell Inc.

Littlesugar, Amy. Freedom School, Yes! Cooper, Floyd, illus. 2001. 1p. (J). (ps-3). 16.99 (978-0-399-23006-6(8), Philomel) Penguin Group (USA) Inc.

Mandrake the Wild Mallard Duck. 2000. (Illus.). 133p. (YA). (gr. 10 up). pap. 13.95 (978-0-9616701-0-8(X)) Oak Hill Bks.

Masters, Susan Rowan. Night Journey to Vicksburg. Killcoyne, Hope L., ed. Smith, Duane A., illus. 2003. (Adventures in America Ser.). 74p. (J). 14.95 (978-1-893110-30-4(3)) Silver Moon Pr.

Matas, Carol. The War Within: A Novel of the Civil War. l.t. ed. 2003. (J). 22.95 (978-0-7862-5499-6(8)) Thorndike Pr.

McMullan, Margaret. How I Found the Strong. 2004. 144p. (J). (gr. 5-9). tchr. ed. 15.00 (978-0-618-35008-7(X)) Houghton Mifflin Co. Trade & Reference Div.

—How I Found the Strong. 2006. 144p. (YA). (gr. 7). reprint ed. mass mkt. 5.50 (978-0-553-49492-1(9), Laurel Leaf) Random Hse. Children's Bks.

McMullan, Margaret. When I Crossed No-Bob. 2007. 224p. (J). (gr. 5-9). 16.00 (***978-0-618-71715-6(3)***) Houghton Mifflin Co. Trade & Reference Div.

Peters, Nancy L. Wishmagic. 1998. 24p. (J). (gr. k-4). pap. 6.00 (978-0-8059-4304-7(8)) Dorrance Publishing Co., Inc.

Plummer, Joseph. Listening to Crickets. 2006. pap. 10.49 (***978-1-4259-5697-4(1)***) AuthorHouse.

Robinet. Mississippi Chariot. 1998. (J). pap. 3.99 (978-0-87628-571-8(X)) Ctr. for Applied Research in Education, The.

Rodman, Mary Ann. Yankee Girl. 2004. (Illus.). 224p. (J). 17.00 (978-0-374-38661-0(7), Farrar, Straus & Giroux (BYR)) Farrar, Straus & Giroux.

Romeu, Emma. A Mississippi por el Mar. 2003. (SPA., Illus.). 150p. (J). (gr. 5-8). pap. 11.95 (978-968-19-0554-5(7)) Santillana USA Publishing Co., Inc.

Rubright, Lynn. Mama's Window. Smith, Duane, illus. 2005. 89p. (J). 16.95 (978-1-57480-160-6(0)) Lee & Low Bks., Inc.

Skates, Craig. Mississippi Stories for Young People: A Look at the Past. 1999. 112p. (YA). pap. 6.95 (978-1-893062-07-8(4)) Quail Ridge Pr., Inc.

Spears, Britney. Mother's Gift. 2003. (gr. 5-8). lib. bdg. 14.15 (978-0-613-72254-4(X)) Tandem Library Bks.

Taulbert, Clifton L. Little Cliff & the Porch People. Kane, Cindy, ed. Lewis, Earl, illus. 1999. 32p. (J). (ps-3). 16.99 (978-0-8037-2174-6(9), Dial) Penguin Group (USA) Inc.

Taylor, Mildred D. The Friendship. Ginsberg, Max, illus. 1998. 56p. (gr. 2-6). pap. 4.99 (978-0-14-038964-7(4), Puffin) Penguin Group (USA) Inc.

—The Friendship. 1998. 11.79 (978-0-606-12938-1(3)) Tandem Library Bks.

—Mississippi Bridge. 2002. (J). 12.87 (978-0-7587-9586-1(6)) Book Wholesalers, Inc.

—Mississippi Bridge. Ginsburg, Max, illus. 2000. 64p. (J). (gr. 4-7). pap. 4.99 (978-0-14-130817-3(6) , Puffin) Penguin Group (USA) Inc.

—Mississippi Bridge. 2002. (J). (gr. 2-6). 21.00 (978-0-8446-7213-7(0)) Smith, Peter Pub., Inc.

—Mississippi Bridge. 2000. (978-0-606-18434-2(1)) Tandem Library Bks.

—Roll of Thunder, Hear My Cry. 2004. 276p. (gr. 4-8). reprint ed. pap. 10.00 (978-0-7567-7955-9(3)) DIANE Publishing Co.

—Roll of Thunder, Hear My Cry. l.t. ed. 2000. (LRS Large Print Cornerstone Ser.). 348p. (YA). (gr. 5-12). lib. bdg. 32.95 (978-1-58118-057-2(8) , 23471) LRS.

—Roll of Thunder, Hear My Cry. 1999. (Masterpiece Series Access Editions). xvii, 205p. (J). pap. 10.95 (978-0-8219-1985-9(7) , 35335) Paradigm Publishing, Inc.

—Roll of Thunder, Hear My Cry. Pinkney, Jerry, illus. 25th anniv. ed. 2001. 296p. (J). (gr. 5 up). 17.99 (978-0-8037-2647-5(3) , Dial) Penguin Group (USA) Inc.

—Roll of Thunder, Hear My Cry. 1999. 60p. (J). (gr. 6-8). stu. ed., ring bd. 12.99 (978-1-58609-152-1(2)) Progeny Pr.

—Roll of Thunder, Hear My Cry. 1998. (J). (gr. 5). pap. 3.95 (978-0-439-04476-9(6)) Scholastic, Inc.

Tingle, Tim. Crossing Bok Chitto: A Choctaw Tale of Friendship & Freedom. Bridges, Jeanne Rorex, illus. 2006. (SPA & ENG.). 40p. (J). 17.95 (978-0-938317-77-7(6)) Cinco Puntos Pr.

Twain, Mark. The Adventures of Tom Sawyer. 2007. (Oxford Children's Classics). 304p. (YA). 9.95 (*978-0-19-271999-7(8)) Oxford Univ. Pr., Inc.

Twain, Mark. The Adventures of Tom Sawyer. Corvino, Lucy, illus. 2005. (Classic Starts Ser.). 160p. 4.95 (978-1-4027-1216-6(2)) Sterling Publishing Co., Inc.

Vander Zee, Ruth. Mississippi Morning. Cooper, Floyd, illus. 2004. 32p. (J). 16.00 (978-0-8028-5211-3(4)) Eerdmans, William B. Publishing Co.

Wiles, Deborah. The Aurora County All-Stars. 2007. (Illus.). 256p. (J). (gr. 5 up). 16.00 (*978-0-15-206068-8(5)) Harcourt Children's Bks.

Wiles, Deborah. Love, Ruby Lavender. (Illus.). (J). 2001. 200p. (gr. 3-7). 16.00 (978-0-15-202314-0(3)); 2005. 228p. reprint ed. pap. 5.95 (978-0-15-205478-6(2)) Harcourt Children's Bks. (Gulliver Bks.).

—Love, Ruby Lavender. 2004. 216p. (J). (gr. 3-7). pap. 36.00 incl. audio (978-0-8072-2096-2(5) , Listening Library) Random Hse. Audio Publishing Group.

MISSISSIPPI—HISTORY

Akin, Edward N. & Bolton, Charles C. Mississippi: An Illustrated History. 2002. (Illus.). 220p. 32.95 (978-1-892724-33-5(2)) American Historical Pr.

Aretha, David. Freedom Summer. 2007. (J). (*978-1-59935-059-2(9)) Reynolds, Morgan Inc.

Arrigo, Joe. Coloring Historic Mississippi. 2000. 32p. (J). (gr. 4-7). pap. 3.95 (978-1-893062-18-4(X)) Quail Ridge Pr., Inc.

Banks, James A. Mississippi: Adventures in Time & Place. 1999. (Illus.). (J). (978-0-02-148265-8(9) , Aladdin) Simon & Schuster Children's Publishing.

Fiorelli, June Estep. Fannie Lou Hamer: A Voice for Freedom. 2004. (Avisson Young Adult Ser.). (Illus.). 117p. (J). pap. 19.95 (978-1-888105-62-9(3)) Avisson Pr., Inc.

Fischer, Laura. Life in a Mississippi River Town. 2003. (Picture the Past Ser.). (Illus.). 32p. (J). lib. bdg. 24.22 (978-1-4034-3797-6(1)); pap. 7.50 (978-1-4034-4283-3(5)) Heinemann Library.

Kuedee, Jaycee. How to Draw Mississippis Sights & Symbols. 2002. (Kids Guide to Drawing America Ser.). 32p. (J). lib. bdg. 25.25 (978-0-8239-6080-4(3) , PowerKids Pr.) Rosen Publishing Group, Inc., The.

Lichter, Nick. The Road of Souls: Reflections on the Mississippi. 2004. (Illus.). 150p. per. 14.95 (978-0-9758615-0-9(6)) Wing Dam Pr.

Marsh, Carole. Mississippi History Projects: 30 Cool, Activities, Crafts, Experiments & More for Kids to Do to Learn about Your State! 2003. (Mississippi Experience Ser.). 32p. (gr. k-5). pap. 5.95 (978-0-635-01793-2(8) , Marsh, Carole Bks.) Gallopade International.

—My First Pocket Guide Mississippi. 2000. (Mississippi Experience! Ser.). (Illus.). 96p. (J). (gr. 3-8). 12.95 (978-0-635-01314-9(2) , 13142) Gallopade International.

Shoulders, Michael. 1 Mississippi 2 Mississippi: A Mississippi Number Book. Anderson, Rick, illus. 2004. 40p. (J). 16.95 (978-1-58536-188-5(7)) Sleeping Bear Pr.

St. Lawrence, Genevieve. Medgar Evers. 2003. (gr. 3-6). lib. bdg. 18.20 (978-0-613-78291-3(7)) Tandem Library Bks.

Thompson, Linda. The Mississippi & the West. 2004. (Expansion of America Ser.). 48p. pap. 7.95 (978-1-59515-327-2(6)) Rourke Publishing, LLC.

MISSISSIPPI RIVER

Adil, Janeen R. The Mississippi River. (Natural Wonders of the U. S. A. Ser.). (Illus.). 32p. (J). 2004. pap. 7.95 (978-1-59036-163-4(6)); 2003. lib. bdg. 16.95 (978-1-59036-041-5(9)) Weigl Pubs., Inc.

Bauer, Marion Dane. The Mighty Mississippi. Wallace, John, illus. 2007. (Ready-To-Read Ser.). 32p. (J). pap. 3.99 (978-0-689-86950-1(9)); lib. bdg. 11.89 (978-0-689-86951-8(7)); (*978-1-4287-2059-6(6)) Simon & Schuster Children's Publishing. (Aladdin).

Bechtold, Phyliss. Seymour Bluffs & the Legend of the Piasa Bird. 2007. 26p. 9.95 (*978-0-9728532-8-6(6)) New Horizons Christian Ctr.

Bowden, Rob. Settlements of the Mississippi River. (Rivers Through Time Ser.). 48p. (J). 2005. pap. 8.50 (978-1-4034-5724-0(7)); 2004. (Illus.). lib. bdg. 29.93 (978-1-4034-5719-6(0)); 2004. (Illus.). pap. (978-1-4034-6250-3(X)) Heinemann Library.

Englar, Mary. Sieur de la Salle. 2004. (Fact Finders Ser.). (Illus.). 32p. (J). lib. bdg. 22.60 (978-0-7368-2666-2(1)) Capstone Pr., Inc.

Fowler, Allan. The Mississippi River. (Rookie Read-About Geography Ser.). (Illus.). 32p. (J). (gr. 1-2). 2000. pap. 5.95 (978-0-516-26556-8(3)); 1999. 20.50 (978-0-516-21557-0(4)) Scholastic Library Publishing. (Children's Pr.).

—The Mississippi River. 1999. (gr. k-3). lib. bdg. 14.10 (978-0-613-54025-4(5)) Tandem Library Bks.

Green, Jen. The Mississippi River. 2003. (Rivers of North America Ser.). (Illus.). 32p. (J). (gr. 3 up). lib. bdg. 24.67 (978-0-8368-3757-5(6)) Stevens, Gareth Inc.

Harcourt School Publishers Staff. The Mighty Mississippi. 3rd ed. 2002. (Horizons Ser.). (Illus.). (J). pap. 7.30 (978-0-15-333551-8(3)) Harcourt Schl. Pubs.

Harkins, Susan and William. The Life & Times of Father Jacques Marquette. 2007. (Profiles in American History Ser.). (J). lib. bdg. (*978-1-58415-528-7(0)) Mitchell Lane Pubs., Inc.

Kent, Deborah. The Great Mississippi Flood of 1927. 2006. (Cornerstones of Freedom Ser.). (Illus.). 48p. (J). (978-0-516-23628-5(8)) Children's Pr., Ltd.

Kline, Trish. Robert la Salle. 2002. (Discover the Life of an Explorer Ser.). (Illus.). 24p. (gr. 2-5). 14.95 (978-1-58952-069-1(6)) Rourke Publishing, LLC.

Larson, Paul Cliff & Larson, Pamela All. Mississippi Escapade: Reliving the Grand Excursion Of 1854. 2004. (Illus.). 128p. (J). (gr. 3-7). pap. 17.95 (978-1-890434-64-9(7)) Afton Historical Society Pr.

Lourie, Peter. Mississippi River: A Journey down the Father of Waters. 2003. (Illus.). 48p. (YA). (gr. 4-6). 17.95 (978-1-56397-756-5(7)) Boyds Mills Pr.

—Mississippi River: A Journey down the Father of Waters. Lourie, Peter, photos by. 2003. (River Ser.). (Illus.). 48p. (YA). (gr. 4-6). pap. 11.95 (978-1-59078-044-2(2)) Boyds Mills Pr.

McNeese, Tim. The Mississippi River. 2004. (Rivers in American Life & Times Ser.). (Illus.). 120p. (gr. 9-13). 30.00 (978-0-7910-7723-8(3) , Chelsea Hse.) Facts On File, Inc.

Milligan, Simon & Curtis, Martin. The Mississippi. 2003. (River Journey Ser.). (Illus.). 48p. (J). lib. bdg. 28.56 (978-0-7398-6071-7(2)) Raintree.

The Mississippi River. 2003. (Crossing America Ser.). 48p. (YA). (gr. 5-8). pap. 5.99 (978-1-56822-652-1(7) , IF6020-E4, Instructional Fair) Schaffer, Frank Pubns.

Mudd-Ruth, Maria. The Mississippi River. 2001. (Ecosystems of North America Ser.). (Illus.). 64p. (J). (gr. 6 up). lib. bdg. 28.50 (978-0-7614-0934-2(3) , Benchmark Bks.) Cavendish, Marshall Corp.

Olson, Nathan. The Mississippi River. 2004. (Fact Finders Ser.). (Illus.). 32p. (J). 16.95 (978-0-7368-2483-5(9) , Bridgestone Bks.) Capstone Pr., Inc.

Petrie, Kristin. Marquette & Jolliet. 2007. (Illus.). 32p. (J). 22.78 (978-1-59679-745-1(2)) ABDO Publishing Co.

—La Salle. 2007. (Illus.). 32p. (J). 22.78 (978-1-59679-750-5(9)) ABDO Publishing Co.

Prevost, John F. Mississippi River. 2002. (Rivers & Lakes Ser.). (Illus.). 24p. (J). (gr. k-6). lib. bdg. 21.35 (978-1-57765-102-4(2) , Checkerboard Library) ABDO Publishing Co.

Simon, Charnan. The Mighty Mississippi. 2004. (Geography of the World Ser.). 32p. (J). (gr. 2-6). 27.07 (978-1-59296-339-3(0)) Child's World, Inc.

Telford, Carole & Theodorou, Rod. Down a River. 2006. (Illus.). 32p. (J). (*978-1-4034-8789-6(8)) Heinemann Library.

—Down a River. 2nd ed. 2006. (Illus.). 32p. (J). pap. (*978-1-4034-8796-4(0)) Heinemann Library.

Vieira, Linda. The Mighty Mississippi: The Life & Times of America's Greatest River. Bond, Higgins, illus. 2005. (J). 32p. 17.85 (978-0-8027-8944-0(7)); 32p. 16.95 (978-0-8027-8943-3(9)); (978-7-80802-789-7(8)) Walker & Co.

Walsh, Kieran. The Mississippi. 2003. (Great Rivers of the World Ser.). (Illus.). 48p. (gr. 5 up). (J). pap. 14.95 (978-0-8368-5451-0(9)); (YA). lib. bdg. 30.00 (978-0-8368-5444-2(6)) Stevens, Gareth Inc. (World Almanac Library).

Youngblood, Wayne. Mark Twain along the Mississippi. 2006. (In the Footsteps of American Heroes Ser.). (Illus.). 64p. (J). pap. (978-0-8368-6435-9(2)); lib. bdg. 32.67 (978-0-8368-6430-4(1)) Stevens, Gareth Inc. (World Almanac Library).

Zelenyi, Alexander. Marquette & Jolliet: Quest for the Mississippi. 2006. (In the Footsteps of Explorers Ser.). (Illus.). 32p. (J). (gr. 3-9). (978-0-7787-2431-5(X)); pap. (978-0-7787-2467-4(0)) Crabtree Publishing Co.

Zronik, John Paul. Sieur de La Salle: New World Adventurer. 2005. (In the Footsteps of Explorers Ser.). (Illus.). 32p. (J). (gr. 3-9). (978-0-7787-2413-1(1)); pap. (978-0-7787-2449-0(2)) Crabtree Publishing Co.

MISSISSIPPI RIVER—FICTION

The Adventures of Tom Sawyer. 2004. (Classic Retelling Ser.). (gr. 6-12). (978-0-618-12053-6(X) , 2-00218) McDougal Littell Inc.

The Adventures of Tom Sawyer. 1998. 44p. (YA). stu. ed. 11.95 (978-1-56137-528-8(4) , NU5284SP) Novel Units, Inc.

The Adventures of Tom Sawyer. 2004. (Literature Units Ser.). (Illus.). 48p. 7.99 (978-1-57690-637-8(X)) Teacher Created Materials, Inc.

Clements, Bruce. I Tell a Lie Every So Often. 2001. (Sunburst Ser.). 160p. (J). (gr. 7 up). pap. 5.95 (978-0-374-43539-4(1) , Sunburst) Farrar, Straus & Giroux.

Crawford, Robert, illus. Tom Sawyer. 1998. 32p. (J). (gr. 1-3). 12.99 (978-1-929174-00-3(4)) Oshkosh B'Gosh, Inc.

Duey, Kathleen & Bale, Karen A. Flood: Mississippi 1927. 1998. (Survival! Ser.: No. 5). 176p. (J). (gr. 4-7). pap. 4.99 (978-0-689-82116-5(6) , Aladdin) Simon & Schuster Children's Publishing.

—Flood, Mississippi, 1927. 1998. (Survival! Ser.: No. 5). (J). (gr. 4-7). 10.64 (978-0-606-13829-1(3)) Tandem Library Bks.

Esbaum, Jill. Ste-e-e-e-eamboat A-Comin'! Rex, Adam, illus. 2005. 40p. (J). 16.00 (978-0-374-37236-1(5) , Farrar, Straus & Giroux (BYR)) Farrar, Straus & Giroux.

Gray, Dianne E. Tomorrow, the River. Cooper, Stephanie, illus. 2006. 240p. (J). (gr. 5-9). 16.00 (978-0-618-56329-6(6)) Houghton Mifflin Co.

Harcourt School Publishers Staff. Old Mr. Muddy On Level. 3rd ed. 2002. (Trophies Reading Program Ser.). (Illus.). pap. 5.10 (978-0-15-323440-8(7)) Harcourt Schl. Pubs.

Helgerson, Joseph. Horns & Wrinkles. Ceccoli, Nicoletta, illus. 2006. 368p. (J). (gr. 4-6). 16.00 (978-0-618-61679-4(9)) Houghton Mifflin Co.

Helgerson, Joseph. Horns & Wrinkles. Ceccoli, Nicoletta, illus. 2008. 240p. (J). (gr. 5-9). pap. 4.95 (*978-0-618-98178-6(0)) Houghton Mifflin Co. Trade & Reference Div.

Howard, Annabelle. Keelboat Annie: An AMER Tall Tale. 2006. 42.00 (*978-1-4108-6169-6(4)) Benchmark Education Co.

Jennings, Richard W. Ferret Island. 2007. 192p. (J). (gr. 4-6). 16.00 (*978-0-618-80632-4(6) , Walter Lorraine) Houghton Mifflin Co. Trade & Reference Div.

Kenny, Kathryn. The Mystery on the Mississippi. 2006. (Illus.). 256p. (J). (gr. 3-7). lib. bdg. 9.99 (978-0-375-93055-3(8)); (Trixie Belden Ser.: No. 15). 6.99 (978-0-375-83055-6(3)) Random Hse. Children's Bks. (Random Hse. Bks. for Young Readers).

Lorenz, Albert & Schleh, Joy. Journey to Cahokia: A Boy's Visit to the Great Mound City. 2004. (Illus.). 32p. (J). (gr. k-4). 17.95 (978-0-8109-5047-4(2)) Abrams, Harry N. , Inc.

Meigs, Cornelia & Holm, Jennifer. Swift Rivers. 2004. (Newbery Honor Roll Ser.). 288p. (J). pap. 6.95 (978-0-8027-7703-4(1)) Walker & Co.

Meyer, L. A. Mississippi Jack: Being an Account of the Further Waterborne Adventures of Jacky Faber, Midshipman, Fine Lady, & Lily of the West. 2007. (Bloody Jack Adventures Ser.). (Illus.). 624p. (YA). (gr. 7 up). 17.00 (*978-0-15-206003-9(0)) Harcourt Trade Pubs.

Singer, Marilyn. Monday on the Mississippi. Lessac, Frane, illus. rev. ed. 2005. 32p. (J). 16.95 (978-0-8050-7208-2(X) , Holt, Henry & Co. Bks. For Young Readers) Holt, Henry & Co.

Stevermer, Caroline & Collin, Frances. River Rats. 2005. (Illus.). 320p. (YA). (gr. 7-12). pap. 6.95 (978-0-15-205554-7(1) , Magic Carpet Bks.) Harcourt Children's Bks.

Twain, Mark. The Adv. of Tom Sawyer: #1 A Song for Aunt Polly. 2007. (Easy Reader Classics Ser.). 32p. (J). (ps-3). 21.35 (*978-1-59961-334-5(4)) Spotlight.

—The Adventures of Huckleberry Finn. Pablo Marcos Studio Staff, illus. 2002. (Great Illustrated Classics Ser.). 240p. (J). (gr. 3-8). 21.35 (978-1-57765-676-0(8) , ABDO & Daughters) ABDO Publishing Co.

—The Adventures of Huckleberry Finn. 2001. (J). pap. 7.95 (978-0-8010-1220-4(1)) Baker Bks.

—The Adventures of Huckleberry Finn. (Great Classics for Children Ser.). (Illus.). (J). 192p. 5.99 (978-1-4037-0594-5(1)); 2002. 180p. 4.99 (978-1-57759-553-3(X)) Dalmatian Pr.

—The Adventures of Huckleberry Finn. 96p. (J). pap. 4.95 (978-0-7910-4108-6(5) , Chelsea Hse.) Facts On File, Inc.

—The Adventures of Huckleberry Finn. 2004. (Classic Retelling Ser.). (Illus.). 235p. (J). (gr. 6-12). (978-0-618-00374-7(6) , 2-00111) McDougal Littell Inc.

—The Adventures of Huckleberry Finn. 2002. (Classics Ser.). (Illus.). 368p. (gr. 12). pap. 7.00 (978-0-14-243717-9(4) , Penguin Classics) Penguin Group (USA) Inc.

—The Adventures of Huckleberry Finn. 2007. (Children's Classics Ser.). (Illus.). 256p. (J). 6.99 (978-0-517-22999-6(4) , Gramercy) Random Hse. Value Publishing.

—The Adventures of Huckleberry Finn. 1999. 10.64 (978-0-606-17508-1(3)) Tandem Library Bks.

—The Adventures of Huckleberry Finn. Fischer, Victor et al, eds. Kemble, E. W. & Harley, John, illus. 2001. (Mark Twain Library). 596p. 55.00 (978-0-520-22806-1(5)); pap. 14.95 (978-0-520-22838-2(3)) Univ. of California Pr.

—The Adventures of Huckleberry Finn. Andreasen, Dan, illus. 2006. (Classic Starts Ser.). 160p. 4.95 (978-1-4027-2499-2(3)) Sterling Publishing Co., Inc.

—The Adventures of Huckleberry Finn. 1999. reprint ed. pap. 28.00 (978-1-4047-1118-1(X)) Classic Textbooks.

—The Adventures of Huckleberry Finn. Green, John, illus. abr. ed. 1998. (Dover Children's Thrift Classics Ser.). 64p. (J). (gr. 3-6). pap. 1.50 (978-0-486-40349-6(1)) Dover Pubns., Inc.

—The Adventures of Huckleberry Finn. Redondo, Francisco, illus. 2nd ed. 1998. (Illustrated Classic Book Ser.). 61p. (J). (gr. 3 up). reprint ed. pap. 4.95 (978-1-56767-255-8(8)) Educational Insights, Inc.

—The Adventures of Huckleberry Finn. unabr. ed. 2002. (YA). pap. incl. audio compact disk (978-1-58472-261-8(4) , In Audio) Sound Room Pubs., Inc.

—The Adventures of Huckleberry Finn. 1999. 230p. (YA). reprint ed. pap. 9.95 (978-1-57002-098-8(1)) University Publishing Hse., Inc.

—The Adventures of Huckleberry Finn: With a Discussion of Friendship. Lauter, Richard, tr. Lauter, Richard, illus. 2003. (Values in Action Illustrated Classics Ser.). (J). (978-1-59203-042-2(4)) Learning Challenge, Inc.

—The Adventures of Tom Sawyer. 2005. 264p. 28.95 (978-1-4218-0768-3(8) , 1st World Library - Literary Society) 1st World Publishing, Inc.

—The Adventures of Tom Sawyer. Pablo Marcos Studio Staff, illus. 2002. (Great Illustrated Classics Ser.). 240p. (J). (gr. 3-8). 21.35 (978-1-57765-679-1(2) , ABDO & Daughters) ABDO Publishing Co.

—The Adventures of Tom Sawyer. 1999. reprint ed. pap. 28.00 (978-1-4047-1117-4(1)) Classic Textbooks.

—The Adventures of Tom Sawyer. (Great Classics for Children Ser.). (Illus.). 192p. (J). 5.99 (978-1-4037-0598-3(4)) Dalmatian Pr.

—The Adventures of Tom Sawyer. Fletcher, Claire, illus. 2002. (Kingfisher Classics Ser.). 352p. (J). (gr. k-3). tchr. ed. 15.95 (978-0-7534-5478-7(5) , Kingfisher) Houghton Mifflin Co. Trade & Reference Div.

—The Adventures of Tom Sawyer. 2004. reprint ed. pap. 1.99 (978-1-4192-5166-5(X)) Kessinger Publishing, LLC.

—The Adventures of Tom Sawyer. (Young Collector's Illustrated Classics Ser.). (Illus.). 192p. (J). (gr. 3-7). 9.95 (978-1-56156-453-8(2)) Kidsbooks, Inc.

—The Adventures of Tom Sawyer. (J). (978-0-448-41455-3(4) , Putnam Juvenile); 2006. 272p. (gr. 12). pap. 7.00 (978-0-14-303956-3(3) , Penguin Classics) Penguin Group (USA) Inc.

—The Adventures of Tom Sawyer. 2001. (Paperback Classics Ser.). (Illus.). 304p. pap. 6.95 (978-0-375-75681-8(7) , Modern Library) Random House Publishing Group.

—The Adventures of Tom Sawyer. 2006. (Scholastic Classics Ser.). (Illus.). vi, 219p. (J). (gr. 9-12). 25.00 (978-0-531-16978-0(2) , Watts, Franklin) Scholastic Library Publishing.

—The Adventures of Tom Sawyer. 2001. (Aladdin Classics Ser.). 272p. (J). (gr. 4-7). pap. 4.99 (978-0-689-84224-5(4) , Aladdin) Simon & Schuster Children's Publishing.

—The Adventures of Tom Sawyer. Williams, True W., illus. 2nd rev. ed. 2002. (Mark Twain Library). 288p. pap. 15.95 (978-0-520-23575-5(4)) Univ. of California Pr.

—The Adventures of Tom Sawyer. 2001. 184p. pap. 9.95 (978-1-57002-169-5(4)) University Publishing Hse., Inc.

—The Adventures of Tom Sawyer: With a Discussion of Imagination. Butterfield, Ned, illus. 2003. (Values in Action Illustrated Classics Ser.). 190p. (J). (978-1-59203-027-9(0)) Learning Challenge, Inc.

—The Adventures of Tom Sawyer; Adventures of Huckleberry Finn. 2002. 544p. mass mkt. 5.95 (978-0-451-52864-3(6) , Signet Classics) Penguin Group (USA) Inc.

—Mark Twain/the Adventures of Huckleberry Finn. Redondo, Frank, illus. 2005. 48p. (gr. 5-8). 25.50 (978-0-7910-9101-2(5)) Facts On File, Inc.

—Mark Twain/the Adventures of Tom Sawyer. Cruz, E. R., illus. 2005. 48p. (gr. 5-8). 25.50 (978-0-7910-9102-9(3)) Facts On File, Inc.

—Tom Sawyer. Cruz, E. R., illus. 2nd ed. 1998. (Illustrated Classic Book Ser.). 61p. (J). (gr. 3 up). reprint ed. pap. 4.95 (978-1-56767-263-3(9)) Educational Insights, Inc.

—Tom Sawyer. adapted ed. (YA). (gr. 5-12). pap. 8.50 (978-0-8359-0212-0(9)) Globe Fearon Educational Publishing.

—Tom Sawyer. (Coleccion Clasicos de la Juventud). (SPA., Illus.). 220p. (J). 12.95 (978-84-7189-029-0(1) , ORT310) Ortells, Alfredo Editorial S.L. ESP. *Dist:* Continental Bk. Co., Inc.

—Tom Sawyer. 1999. (Illus.). 336p. (J). (gr. 4-7). pap. 4.99 (978-0-439-09940-0(4)) Scholastic, Inc.

—Tom Sawyer. unabr. ed. 2002. (YA). pap. incl. audio compact disk (978-1-58472-341-7(6) , In Audio) Sound Room Pubs., Inc.

—Tom Sawyer Abroad. 1999. reprint ed. pap. 28.00 (978-1-4047-1125-9(2)) Classic Textbooks.

—Tom Sawyer Abroad & Tom Sawyer, Detective. l.t. ed. 1999. (Large Print Heritage Ser.). 265p. (YA). (gr. 7-12). lib. bdg. 29.95 (978-1-58118-046-6(2) , 22315) LRS.

—Tom Sawyer & Huckleberry Finn. unabr. ed. 1998. (Wordsworth Classics Ser.). (YA). (gr. 6-12). 5.27 (978-0-89061-011-4(8) , R0118WW) Jamestown.

Twain, Mark & Olmos. The Adventures of Huckleberry Finn. 2004. (SPA.). 360p. pap. 17.95 (*978-84-263-5252-1(9)) Vives, Luis Editorial (Edelvives) ESP. *Dist:* Lectorum Pubns., Inc.

MISSISSIPPI VALLEY

see also Middle West

Blue, Rose. Exploring Mississippi River Valley. 2003. (Exploring America Ser.). (Illus.). 64p. pap. 9.50 (978-1-4109-0043-2(6)) Raintree.

Bowden, Rob. Settlements of the Mississippi River. (Rivers Through Time Ser.). 48p. (J). 2005. pap. 8.50 (978-1-4034-5724-0(7)); 2004. (Illus.). lib. bdg. 29.93 (978-1-4034-5719-6(0)) Heinemann Library.

Englar, Mary. Sieur de la Salle. 2004. (Fact Finders Ser.). (Illus.). 32p. (J). lib. bdg. 22.60 (978-0-7368-2666-2(1)) Capstone Pr., Inc.

Walsh, Kieran. The Mississippi. 2003. (Great Rivers of the World Ser.). (Illus.). 48p. (gr. 5 up). (J). pap. 14.95 (978-0-8368-5451-0(9)); (YA). lib. bdg. 30.00 (978-0-8368-5444-2(6)) Stevens, Gareth Inc. (World Almanac Library).

MISSISSIPPI VALLEY—HISTORY

Blue, Rose & Naden, Corinne J. Exploring the Mississippi River Valley. 2003. (Illus.). 64p. (J). lib. bdg. 28.56 (978-0-7398-4949-1(2)) Raintree.

Larson, Paul Cliff & Larson, Pamela All. Mississippi Escapade: Reliving the Grand Excursion Of 1854. 2004. (Illus.). 128p. (J). (gr. 3-7). pap. 17.95 (978-1-890434-64-9(7)) Afton Historical Society Pr.

MISSOURI

Alter, Judy. Missouri: A MyReportLinks.com Book. 2003. (States Ser.). (Illus.). 48p. (J). (gr. 4-10). lib. bdg. 25.26 (978-0-7660-5127-0(7) , MyReportLinks.com Bks.) Enslow Pubs., Inc.

Bennett, M. Missouri. 2001. (Celebrate the States Ser.). (Illus.). 144p. (gr. 4-8). lib. bdg. 37.07 (978-0-7614-1063-8(5) , Benchmark Bks.) Cavendish, Marshall Corp.

Boekhoff, P. M. Missouri. 2005. (Portraits of the States Ser.). (Illus.). 32p. (J). pap. (978-0-8368-4647-8(8)); lib. bdg. 23.33 (978-0-8368-4628-7(1)) Stevens, Gareth Inc.

Discover the Missouri River KIDS Activity Booklet. 2003. (J). pap. (978-1-888631-20-3(1)) Watercourse, The.

Dodd, Monroe & Serda, Daniel. Journeys Through Time: A Young Traveler's Guide to Kansas City History. 2000. (Illus.). vi, 121p. (J). (978-0-9679519-0-4(9)) Kansas City Star Bks.

Evdokimoff, Natasha. A Guide to Missouri. 2001. (American States Ser.). (Illus.). 32p. (J). lib. bdg. 16.95 (978-1-930954-43-4(3)); per. 7.95 (978-1-930954-86-1(7)) Weigl Pubs., Inc.

Greene, Carol. "M" Is for Missouri. Dorenkamp, Michelle, illus. 2000. (Alpha Flight Bks.). 60p. (J). (ps-3). 17.95 (978-1-892920-26-3(3)) GHB Publishers, LLC.

Heinrichs, Ann. Missouri. 2005. (Welcome to the USA Ser.). 40p. (J). (gr. 1-5). 27.07 (978-1-59296-447-5(8)) Child's World, Inc.

—Missouri. 2003. (This Land Is Your Land Ser.). (Illus.). 48p. (J). (gr. 3 up). lib. bdg. 22.60 (978-0-7565-0329-1(9)) Compass Point Bks.

Hodgkins, Fran. Missouri. 2003. (Land of Liberty Ser.). (Illus.). 64p. (J). lib. bdg. 25.26 (978-0-7368-2183-4(X)) Capstone Pr., Inc.

Ingram, W. Scott. Missouri: The Show Me State. 2002. (World Almanac Library of the States). (Illus.). 48p. (J). (gr. 5 up). lib. bdg. 30.00 (978-0-8368-5139-7(0)); pap. 14.95 (978-0-8368-5309-4(1)) Stevens, Gareth Inc. (World Almanac Library).

Kansas City Sold C 2005. 2004. 420p. (YA). pap. 15.00 (978-1-58553-957-4(0) , 05GC0022) Entertainment Publications, Inc.

Kummer, Patricia K. Missouri. rev. ed. 2002. (One Nation Ser.). (Illus.). 48p. (J). (gr. 3-4). lib. bdg. 22.60 (978-0-7368-1249-8(0) , Bridgestone Bks.) Capstone Pr., Inc.

LaDoux, Rita C. Missouri. 2nd exp. rev. ed. (Hello U. S. A. Ser.). (Illus.). 84p. (J). (gr. 3-6). 2003. pap. 6.95 (978-0-8225-4140-0(8)); 2002. 25.26 (978-0-8225-4069-4(X) , Lerner Pubns.) Lerner Publishing Group.

—Missouri. 2001. (gr. 3-6). lib. bdg. 15.25 (978-0-613-84026-2(7)) Tandem Library Bks.

Lago, Mary Ellen & Karnovsky, Susan. Missouri. 2003. (From Sea to Shining Sea Ser.: 2). (Illus.). 80p. (J). 30.50 (978-0-516-22390-2(9) , Children's Pr.) Scholastic Library Publishing.

Lowe, Pamela Fleming. Missouri Then & Now Activity Book. 2004. (Illus.). (J). 184p. pap., tchr. ed., act. bk. ed. 19.95 (978-0-8262-1539-0(4)); 240p. pap., stu. ed., act. bk. ed. 12.95 (978-0-8262-1540-6(8)) Univ. of Missouri Pr.

Marsh, Carole. The Big Missouri Reproducible Big Activity Book. 2004. (Missouri Experience! Ser.). (Illus.). 128p. (J). (gr. 2-6). per. 9.95 (978-0-7933-9574-3(7)) Gallopade International.

—The Magnificant Missouri Coloring Book. 2004. (Missouri Experience! Ser.). (Illus.). 32p. (J). (gr. k-2). pap. 3.95 (978-0-7933-9575-0(5)) Gallopade International.

—Missouri Classic Christmas Trivia. 2002. (Carole Marsh Missouri Bks.). (Illus.). 32p. pap. 6.95 (978-0-635-01417-7(3) , 14173); lib. bdg. 21.95 (978-0-635-01418-4(1) , 14181) Gallopade International. (Marsh, Carole Bks.).

—Missouri Current Events Projects: 30 Cool, Activities, Crafts, Experiments & More for Kids to Do to Learn about Your State! 2003. (Missouri Experience Ser.). 32p. (gr. k-8). pap. 5.95 (978-0-635-02044-4(0) , Marsh, Carole Bks.) Gallopade International.

—The Missouri Experience Library State: Resource Set. 2001. (Illus.). (J). (gr. k-8). pap. 100.20 incl. cd-rom (978-0-635-00478-9(X)) Gallopade International.

—The Missouri Experience Pocket Guide. 2004. (Missouri Experience! Ser.). (Illus.). 96p. (J). (gr. 3-8). pap. 6.95 (978-0-7933-9570-5(4)) Gallopade International.

—Missouri Geography Projects: 30 Cool, Activities, Crafts, Experiments & More for Kids to Do to Learn about Your State! 2003. (Missouri Experience Ser.). 32p. (gr. k-5). pap. 5.95 (978-0-635-01844-1(6) , Marsh, Carole Bks.) Gallopade International.

—Missouri Government Projects: 30 Cool, Activities, Crafts, Experiments & More for Kids to Do to Learn about Your State! 2003. (Missouri Experience Ser.). 32p. (gr. k-5). pap. 5.95 (978-0-635-01944-8(2) , Marsh, Carole Bks.) Gallopade International.

—Missouri Jeopardy! Answers & Questions about Our State! 2004. (Missouri Experience! Ser.). (Illus.). 32p. (J). (gr. 3-8). pap. 7.95 (978-0-7933-9572-9(0)) Gallopade International.

—Missouri "Jography" A Fun Run Thru Our State! 2004. (Missouri Experience! Ser.). (Illus.). 32p. (J). (gr. 3-8). pap. 7.95 (978-0-7933-9573-6(9)) Gallopade International.

—Missouri Millionaire: Game Book. 2001. (Carole Marsh Missouri Bks.). (Illus.). 32p. (J). (gr. 3-8). pap., act. bk. ed. 9.95 (978-0-635-00066-8(0)) Gallopade International.

—Missouri People Projects: 30 Cool, Activities, Crafts, Experiments & More for Kids to Do to Learn about Your State! 2003. (Missouri Experience Ser.). 32p. (gr. k-5). pap. 5.95 (978-0-635-01994-3(9) , Marsh, Carole Bks.) Gallopade International.

—Missouri Survivor: Game Book. 2001. (Carole Marsh Missouri Bks.). (Illus.). 32p. (J). (gr. 3-8). pap., act. bk. ed. 9.95 (978-0-635-00546-5(8)) Gallopade International.

—Missouri Symbols & Facts Projects: 30 Cool, Activities, Crafts, Experiments & More for Kids to Do to Learn about Your State! 2003. (Missouri Experience Ser.). 32p. (gr. k-5). pap. 5.95 (978-0-635-01894-6(2) , Marsh, Carole Bks.) Gallopade International.

—My First Book about Missouri. 2004. (Missouri Experience! Ser.). (Illus.). 32p. (J). (gr. k-4). pap. 7.95 (978-0-7933-9571-2(2)) Gallopade International.

McAuliffe, Emily. Missouri: Facts & Symbols. 1999. (States & Their Symbols Ser.). (Illus.). 24p. (J). (gr. k-3). pap. 15.00 (978-0-531-12003-3(1) , Watts, Franklin) Scholastic Library Publishing.

Missouri. 2000. (Switched on Schoolhouse Ser.). (YA). (gr. 7-12). pap. 24.95 incl. cd-rom (978-0-7403-0277-0(9) , SOSMO) Alpha Omega Pubns., Inc.

Murray, Julie. Missouri. 2006. (Buddy Book Ser.). (Illus.). 32p. (J). (gr. k-4). lib. bdg. 22.78 (978-1-59197-684-4(7) , Buddy Bks.) ABDO Publishing Co.

Obregon, Jose M. Missouri. Brusca, Maria Cristina, tr. 2005. (Bilingual Library of the United States of America: Set 2). (ENG & SPA., Illus.). 32p. (J). (gr. 2-5). lib. bdg. 22.50 (978-1-4042-3090-3(4) , Buenas Letra) Rosen Publishing Group, Inc., The.

Oetting, Judy. Fun Facts & Games: Missouri's Rocks & Minerals. Nolte, Larry, illus. 2000. (Fun Facts & Games Ser.). 64p. (J). (ps-3). pap. 5.95 (978-1-892920-24-9(7)) GHB Publishers, LLC.

Owens, Lisa. Uniquely Missouri. 2004. (Heinemann State Studies). (Illus.). 48p. (J). pap. 8.50 (978-1-4034-4510-0(9)); lib. bdg. 27.07 (978-1-4034-4495-0(1)) Heinemann Library.

Sanders, Doug. Missouri. 2004. (It's My State! Ser.). (Illus.). 80p. (J). 27.07 (978-0-7614-1822-1(9) , Benchmark Bks.) Cavendish, Marshall Corp.

Saunders, Lesley. When We Were the Toast of Black Kansas City. Pulliam, Henry, ed. Blair, Leola, illus. Clark, Ken, photos by. 1999. 175p. (YA). (gr. 6-12). pap. 15.95 (978-0-9676736-0-8(7)) Les-Man Pubns.

Taylor-Butler, Christine. Missouri. (J). 2006. 32p. (gr. 1-2). pap. 5.95 (978-0-516-25193-6(7)); 2005. (Illus.). 31p. (ps-ps). 20.50 (978-0-516-25258-2(5)) Scholastic Library Publishing. (Children's Pr.).

—The Missouri River. 2006. 32p. (gr. 1-2). (YA). pap. 5.95 (978-0-516-29796-5(1)); (Illus.). (J). 20.50 (978-0-516-25037-3(X)) Scholastic Library Publishing. (Children's Pr.).

Wimmer, Teresa. Missouri. 2008. (J). ***978-1-58341-650-1(1)** , Creative Education) Creative Co., The.

Young, Judy. S Is for Show Me: A Missouri Alphabet. Young, Ross B., illus. 2004. 40p. (J). pap. 7.95 (978-1-58536-248-6(4)) Sleeping Bear Pr.

—S Is for Show Me: A Missouri Alphabet. Young, Ross, illus. 2001. 40p. (J). 17.95 (978-1-58536-026-0(0)) Sleeping Bear Pr.

Young, Judy & Young, Ross B. Missouri Number. rev. ed. 2007. (State Counting Ser.). 40p. (J). 17.95 (***978-1-58536-156-4(9)**) Sleeping Bear Pr.

MISSOURI—FICTION

The Adventures of Tom Sawyer. 2004. (Classic Retelling Ser.). (gr. 6-12). (978-0-618-12053-6(X) , 2-00218) McDougal Littell Inc.

The Adventures of Tom Sawyer. 1998. 44p. (YA). stu. ed. 11.95 (978-1-56137-528-8(4) , NU5284SP) Novel Units, Inc.

The Adventures of Tom Sawyer. 2004. (Literature Units Ser.). (Illus.). 48p. 7.99 (978-1-57690-637-8(X)) Teacher Created Materials, Inc.

Blackwood, Gary L. Moonshine. 1999. (Accelerated Reader Bks.). 160p. (J). (gr. 3-7). 14.95 (978-0-7614-5056-6(4) , Cavendish Children's Bks.) Cavendish, Marshall Corp.

Bornstein, Ruth Lercher. Butterflies & Lizards, Beryl & Me. 2002. (Illus.). 160p. (J). (gr. 3-7). 14.95 (978-0-7614-5118-1(8) , Cavendish Children's Bks.) Cavendish, Marshall Corp.

Byers, Stephen P. Lost River Bridge. Mack, Greg, illus. 2001. 165p. (J). pap. 12.95 (978-1-929663-02-6(1)) Books By Byers.

Ciocca, Donna. Tavern Tales. 2005. 136p. per. 14.95 (978-0-9747361-3-6(9)) Oak Manor Publishing, Inc.

Clements, Bruce. I Tell a Lie Every So Often. 2001. (Sunburst Ser.). 160p. (J). (gr. 7 up). pap. 5.95 (978-0-374-43539-4(1) , Sunburst) Farrar, Straus & Giroux.

Copeland, Colene. My Favorite Hobo. 2001. (Priscilla Pig Ser.: 8). 172p. (J). per. 4.95 (978-0-939810-25-3(5) , M) Jordan Valley Heritage Hse.

Crawford, Robert, illus. Tom Sawyer. 1998. 32p. (J). (gr. 1-3). 12.99 (978-1-929174-00-3(4)) Oshkosh B'Gosh, Inc.

Crofford, Emily. When the River Ran Backward. (Adventures in Time Ser.). (gr. 4-8). 2005. (Illus.). 84p. 15.95 (978-1-57505-305-9(5)); 2003. 80p. (J). pap. 6.95 (978-1-57505-488-9(4)) Lerner Publishing Group.

Doty, Kathryn Adams. Wild Orphan. 2006. 144p. pap. 14.95 (978-1-889020-20-4(6)) Edinborough Pr.

Fleischner, Jennifer. Nobody's Boy. 2006. (Illus.). 96p. (J). pap. 12.95 (978-1-883982-58-4(8)) Missouri Historical Society Pr.

Ford, Laura. Buster Brown & Tige in Misfit Heroes. 2004. (Illus.). 320p. 19.95 (978-1-881554-28-8(7)) Skyward Publishing Co.

Garrity, Jennifer Johnson. Bushwhackers: A Civil War Adventure. 1999. (gr. 3-6). lib. bdg. 17.60 (978-0-613-24444-2(3)) Tandem Library Bks.

Gilbert, Sheri. The Legacy of Gloria Russell. 2004. 224p. (J). (gr. 3-7). 15.95 (978-0-375-82823-2(0) , Knopf Bks. for Young Readers) Random Hse. Children's Bks.

Grippando, James. Leapholes. 2006. 176p. 15.95 (978-1-59031-666-5(5)) American Bar Assn.

Grove, Vicki. Reaching Dustin. 2000. (Illus.). 208p. (J). (gr. 4-9). pap. 6.99 (978-0-698-11839-3(1) , Putnam Juvenile) Penguin Group (USA) Inc.

—Reaching Dustin. 2000. (978-0-606-18844-9(4)); (gr. 5-8). lib. bdg. 14.15 (978-0-613-28619-0(7)) Tandem Library Bks.

H., Yves & Hermann. Manhattan Beach 1957. 2003. (Illus.). 56p. (YA). (gr. 11 up). 12.95 (978-1-931724-23-4(7)) Diamond Select Toys & Collectibles.

Harness, Cheryl. Just for You to Know. 2008. (J). pap. (***978-0-06-078315-0(X)**) HarperCollins Pubs.

Hill, Pamela Smith. A Voice from the Border. 2000. (J). (978-0-606-20004-2(5)) Tandem Library Bks.

Hoffman, Allen. Big League Dreams. 1999. (Small Worlds Ser.). 296p. 12.95 (978-0-7892-0583-4(1)) Abbeville Pr., Inc.

Horvath, Polly. The Happy Yellow Car. 2004. (Illus.). 128p. (J). pap. 5.95 (978-0-374-42879-2(4) , Sunburst) Farrar, Straus & Giroux.

Hughes, Dean. As Wide As the River. 2005. 156p. (J). pap. (978-1-59038-450-3(4)) Deseret Bk. Co.

—Facing the Enemy. 2005. (Illus.). 153p. (J). pap. (978-1-59038-449-7(0)) Deseret Bk. Co.

—Under the Same Stars. 2005. viii, 152p. (J). pap. (978-1-59038-448-0(2)) Deseret Bk. Co.

Hughes, Pat. Guerrilla Season. 2003. 336p. (J). 18.00 (978-0-374-32811-5(0) , Farrar, Straus & Giroux (BYR)) Farrar, Straus & Giroux.

Kenny, Kathryn. The Mystery on the Mississippi. 2006. (Illus.). 256p. (J). (gr. 3-7). lib. bdg. 9.99 (978-0-375-93055-3(8)); (Trixie Belden Ser.: No. 15). 6.99 (978-0-375-83055-6(3)) Random Hse. Children's Bks. (Random Hse. Bks. for Young Readers).

Loesch, Joe. The Pony Express. Hutchinson, Cheryl, ed. Cox, Brian T., illus. unabr. ed. 2000. (Backyard Adventure Ser.). 56p. (J). (gr. k-5). reprint ed. 16.95 incl. audio compact disk (978-1-932332-04-9(9)) Toy Box Productions.

MacBride, Roger Lea. The Adventures of Rose & Swiney. Ettlinger, Doris, illus. 2000. (Little House Chapter Bks.: No. 4). 80p. (J). (gr. 2-5). 14.89 (978-0-06-028553-1(2)) HarperCollins Pubs.

—The Adventures of Rose & Swiney. Ettlinger, Doris, illus. 2000. (Little House Chapter Bks.). (J). (978-0-606-19996-4(9)) Tandem Library Bks.

—Little Farm in the Ozarks Bk. 2: The Rose Years. 2007. (Little House Ser.). 176p. (J). pap. 5.99 (***978-0-06-114810-1(5)** , Harper Trophy) HarperCollins Pubs.

—Little House on Rocky Ridge. 2007. (Little House Ser.). 176p. (J). pap. 5.99 (***978-0-06-114809-5(1)** , Harper Trophy) HarperCollins Pubs.

—Missouri School Days. Ettlinger, Doris, illus. 2001. (Little House Chapter Bks.). 80p. (J). (gr. 2-5). 14.89 (978-0-06-028555-5(9)); pap. 4.25 (978-0-06-442110-2(4) , Harper Trophy) HarperCollins Pubs.

—Rose & Alva. 1999. (Little House Chapter Bks.). (J). (gr. 2-5). (978-0-606-18718-3(9)) Tandem Library Bks.

MacBride, Roger Lea & Ettlinger, Doris, illus. Rose & Alva. 2000. (Little House Chapter Bks.: No. 3). 80p. (J). (gr. 2-5). 14.89 (978-0-06-028158-8(8)) HarperCollins Pubs.

McJunkin, Jehu David & Wethern, Amelia. A Missouri River Tale. l.t. ed. 2005. (ENG., Illus.). 47p. (J). 12.95 (978-0-9766124-0-7(2)) Ap Amelia Pr.

Moonshower, Candie. The Legend of Zoey. 2007. 224p. (J). (gr. 4-7). 5.99 (***978-0-440-23924-6(9)** , Yearling) Random Hse. Children's Bks.

Mulford, Carolyn. The Feedsack Dress. 2007. (YA). per. 7.95 (***978-0-9713497-4-2(6)**) Cave Hollow Pr.

Sargent, Daina. Missouri: Teamwork. Lenoir, Jane, illus. l.t. ed. 2004. (Double Trouble Ser.). 48p. (J). pap. 6.95 (978-1-59381-127-3(6)); lib. bdg. 22.60 (978-1-59381-126-6(8)) Ozark Publishing.

Simmons, Marc. Millie Cooper's Ride: A True Story from History. Kil, Ronald R., illus. 2002. 56p. (J). 16.95 (978-0-8263-2925-7(X)) Univ. of New Mexico Pr.

Smiley, Jane. The All-True Travels & Adventures of Lidie Newton: A Novel. 1999. (gr. 7-12). lib. bdg. 23.45 (978-0-613-17077-2(6)) Tandem Library Bks.

Smith, Ozzie. Hello, Fredbird! de Angel, Miguel, illus. 2006. 30p. (J). 17.95 (***978-1-932888-83-6(7)**) Mascot Bks., Inc.

Tate, Eleanora E. The Minstrel's Melody. 2001. (American Girl Collection). (Illus.). (J). (978-0-606-21331-8(7)) Tandem Library Bks.

Twain, Mark. The Adv. of Tom Sawyer: #1 A Song for Aunt Polly. 2007. (Easy Reader Classics Ser.). 32p. (J). (ps-3). 21.35 (***978-1-59961-334-5(4)**) Spotlight.

—The Adventures of Huckleberry Finn. Pablo Marcos Studio Staff, illus. 2002. (Great Illustrated Classics Ser.). 240p. (J). (gr. 3-8). 21.35 (978-1-57765-676-0(8) , ABDO & Daughters) ABDO Publishing Co.

—The Adventures of Huckleberry Finn. 2001. (J). pap. 7.95 (978-0-8010-1220-4(1)) Baker Bks.

—The Adventures of Huckleberry Finn. 1999. reprint ed. pap. 28.00 (978-1-4047-1118-1(X)) Classic Textbooks.

—The Adventures of Huckleberry Finn. (Great Classics for Children Ser.). (Illus.). (J). 192p. 5.99 (978-1-4037-0594-5(1)); 2002. 180p. 4.99 (978-1-57759-553-3(X)) Dalmatian Pr.

—The Adventures of Huckleberry Finn. Green, John, illus. abr. ed. 1998. (Dover Children's Thrift Classics Ser.). 64p. (J). (gr. 3-6). pap. 1.50 (978-0-486-40349-6(1)) Dover Pubns., Inc.

—The Adventures of Huckleberry Finn. Redondo, Francisco, illus. 2nd ed. 1998. (Illustrated Classic Book Ser.). 61p. (J). (gr. 3 up). reprint ed. pap. 4.95 (978-1-56767-255-8(8)) Educational Insights, Inc.

—The Adventures of Huckleberry Finn. 2004. (Classic Retelling Ser.). (Illus.). 235p. (J). (gr. 6-12). (978-0-618-00374-7(6) , 2-00111) McDougal Littell Inc.

—The Adventures of Huckleberry Finn. 2002. (Classics Ser.). (Illus.). 368p. (gr. 12). pap. 7.00 (978-0-14-243717-9(4) , Penguin Classics) Penguin Group (USA) Inc.

—The Adventures of Huckleberry Finn. 2007. (Children's Classics Ser.). (Illus.). 256p. (J). 6.99 (978-0-517-22999-6(4) , Gramercy) Random Hse. Value Publishing.

—The Adventures of Huckleberry Finn. unabr. ed. 2002. (YA). pap. incl. audio compact disk (978-1-58472-261-8(4) , In Audio) Sound Room Pubs., Inc.

—The Adventures of Huckleberry Finn. 1999. 10.64 (978-0-606-17508-1(3)) Tandem Library Bks.

—The Adventures of Huckleberry Finn. Fischer, Victor et al, eds. Kemble, E. W. & Harley, John, illus. 2001. (Mark Twain Library). 596p. 55.00 (978-0-520-22806-1(5)); pap. 14.95 (978-0-520-22838-2(3)) Univ. of California Pr.

—The Adventures of Huckleberry Finn: With a Discussion of Friendship. Lauter, Richard, tr. Lauter, Richard, illus. 2003. (Values in Action Illustrated Classics Ser.). (J). (978-1-59203-042-2(4)) Learning Challenge, Inc.

—The Adventures of Tom Sawyer. 2005. 264p. 28.95 (978-1-4218-0768-3(8) , 1st World Library - Literary Society) 1st World Publishing, Inc.

—The Adventures of Tom Sawyer. Pablo Marcos Studio Staff, illus. 2002. (Great Illustrated Classics Ser.). 240p. (J). (gr. 3-8). 21.35 (978-1-57765-679-1(2) , ABDO & Daughters) ABDO Publishing Co.

—The Adventures of Tom Sawyer. 2002. 12.17 (978-0-7587-7968-7(2)) Book Wholesalers, Inc.

—The Adventures of Tom Sawyer. (Great Classics for Children Ser.). (J). (Illus.). 192p. 5.99 (978-1-4037-0598-3(4)); 2003. 182p. 4.99 (978-1-57759-556-4(4)) Dalmatian Pr.

—The Adventures of Tom Sawyer. Fletcher, Claire, illus. 2002. (Kingfisher Classics Ser.). 352p. (J). (gr. k-3). tchr. ed. 15.95 (978-0-7534-5478-7(5) , Kingfisher) Houghton Mifflin Co. Trade & Reference Div.

—The Adventures of Tom Sawyer. (Young Collector's Illustrated Classics Ser.). (Illus.). 192p. (J). (gr. 3-7). 9.95 (978-1-56156-453-8(2)) Kidsbooks, Inc.

—The Adventures of Tom Sawyer. 2006. 272p. (gr. 12). pap. 7.00 (978-0-14-303956-3(3) , Penguin Classics) Penguin Group (USA) Inc.

—The Adventures of Tom Sawyer. 2001. (Paperback Classics Ser.). (Illus.). 304p. pap. 6.95 (978-0-375-75681-8(7) , Modern Library) Random House Publishing Group.

—The Adventures of Tom Sawyer. 2006. (Scholastic Classics Ser.). (Illus.). vi, 219p. (J). (gr. 9-12). 25.00 (978-0-531-16978-0(2) , Watts, Franklin) Scholastic Library Publishing.

—The Adventures of Tom Sawyer. 2001. (Aladdin Classics Ser.). 272p. (J). (gr. 4-7). pap. 4.99 (978-0-689-84224-5(4) , Aladdin) Simon & Schuster Children's Publishing.

—The Adventures of Tom Sawyer. Corvino, Lucy, illus. 2005. (Classic Starts Ser.). 160p. 4.95 (978-1-4027-1216-6(2)) Sterling Publishing Co., Inc.

—The Adventures of Tom Sawyer. 1999. reprint ed. pap. 28.00 (978-1-4047-1117-4(1)) Classic Textbooks.

—The Adventures of Tom Sawyer. 2004. reprint ed. pap. 1.99 (978-1-4192-5166-5(X)) Kessinger Publishing, LLC.

—The Adventures of Tom Sawyer. Williams, True W., illus. 2nd rev. ed. 2002. (Mark Twain Library). 288p. pap. 15.95 (978-0-520-23575-5(4)) Univ. of California Pr.

—The Adventures of Tom Sawyer: With a Discussion of Imagination. Butterfield, Ned, illus. 2003. (Values in Action Illustrated Classics Ser.). 190p. (J). (978-1-59203-027-9(0)) Learning Challenge, Inc.

—The Adventures of Tom Sawyer; Adventures of Huckleberry Finn. 2002. 544p. mass mkt. 5.95 (978-0-451-52864-3(6) , Signet Classics) Penguin Group (USA) Inc.

—Mark Twain/the Adventures of Huckleberry Finn. Redondo, Frank, illus. 2005. 48p. (gr. 5-8). 25.50 (978-0-7910-9101-2(5)) Facts On File, Inc.

—Mark Twain/the Adventures of Tom Sawyer. Cruz, E. R., illus. 2005. 48p. (gr. 5-8). 25.50 (978-0-7910-9102-9(3)) Facts On File, Inc.

—The Spelling Bee. Bates, Amy, illus. 2007. (Adventures of Tom Sawyer Ser.: Bk. 4). 32p. (J). pap. 3.95 (978-1-4027-4269-9(X)) Sterling Publishing Co., Inc.

—Tom Sawyer. Cruz, E. R., illus. 2nd ed. 1998. (Illustrated Classic Book Ser.). 61p. (J). (gr. 3 up). reprint ed. pap. 4.95 (978-1-56767-263-3(9)) Educational Insights, Inc.

—Tom Sawyer. adapted ed. (YA). (gr. 5-12). pap. 8.50 (978-0-8359-0212-0(9)) Globe Fearon Educational Publishing.

—Tom Sawyer. (Coleccion Clasicos de la Juventud). (SPA., Illus.). 220p. (J). 12.95 (978-84-7189-029-0(1) , ORT310) Ortells, Alfredo Editorial S.L. ESP. *Dist:* Continental Bk. Co., Inc.

—Tom Sawyer. 2003. (Timeless Classics Ser.). (SPA., Illus.). 95p. (J). (gr. 5-8). pap. 12.95 (978-84-372-2235-6(4)) Santillana USA Publishing Co., Inc.

—Tom Sawyer. 1999. (Illus.). 336p. (J). (gr. 4-7). pap. 4.99 (978-0-439-09940-0(4)) Scholastic, Inc.

—Tom Sawyer. unabr. ed. 2002. (YA). pap. incl. audio compact disk (978-1-58472-341-7(6) , In Audio) Sound Room Pubs., Inc.

—Tom Sawyer Abroad. 1999. reprint ed. pap. 28.00 (978-1-4047-1125-9(2)) Classic Textbooks.

—Tom Sawyer Abroad & Tom Sawyer, Detective. l.t. ed. 1999. (Large Print Heritage Ser.). 265p. (YA). (gr. 7-12). lib. bdg. 29.95 (978-1-58118-046-6(2) , 22515) LRS.

—Tom Sawyer & Huckleberry Finn. unabr. ed. 1998. (Wordsworth Classics Ser.). (YA). (gr. 6-12). 5.27 (978-0-89061-011-4(8) , R0118WW) Jamestown.

Twain, Mark & Olmos. The Adventures of Huckleberry Finn. 2004. (SPA.). 360p. pap. 17.95 (***978-84-263-5252-1(9)**) Vives, Luis Editorial (Edelvives) ESP. *Dist:* Lectorum Pubns., Inc.

Walter, Mildred Pitts. Justin & the Best Biscuits in the World. Stock, Catherine, illus. 2002. (J). 13.40 (978-0-7587-0371-2(6)) Book Wholesalers, Inc.
—Justin & the Best Biscuits in the World. 1999. (Illus.). 128p. (J). (gr. 3-5). pap. 4.99 (978-0-679-89448-3(9)) Knopf, Alfred A. Inc.

MISSOURI—HISTORY

Bank One Community Writers Staff. Sand Dollar $ucce$$ Crisp, John T., Jr., illus. l.t. ed. 1998. (WeWrite Kids! Ser.: No. 40). 45p. (J). (gr. 2-5). pap. 3.95 (978-1-57635-022-5(3)) WeWrite LLC.
Jackson, Robert. Meet Me in St. Louis: A Trip to the 1904 World's Fair. 2004. (Illus.). 144p. (J). (gr. 3 up). 17.99 (978-0-06-009267-2(X)) HarperCollins Pubs.
Kuedee, Jaycee. How to Draw Missouris Sights & Symbols. 2002. (Kids Guide to Drawing America Ser.). 32p. (J). lib. bdg. 25.25 (978-0-8239-6081-1(1) , PowerKids Pr.) Rosen Publishing Group, Inc., The.
Marsh, Carole. Missouri History Projects: 30 Cool, Activities, Crafts, Experiments & More for Kids to Do to Learn about Your State! 2003. (Missouri Experience Ser.). 32p. (gr. k-5). pap. 5.95 (978-0-635-01794-9(6) , Marsh, Carole Bks.) Gallopade International.
—The Missouri Survivor: A Class Challenge. 2001. (Carole Marsh Missouri Bks.). (J). lib. bdg. 29.95 (978-0-635-00671-4(5)) Gallopade International.
—My First Pocket Guide Missouri. 2000. (Missouri Experience! Ser.). (Illus.). 96p. (J). (gr. 3-8). 12.95 (978-0-635-01315-6(0) , 13150) Gallopade International.
—Wheel of Fortune. 2001. (Missouri Bks.). (J). lib. bdg. 29.95 (978-0-7933-9667-2(0)) Gallopade International.
—Who Wants to Be a Millionaire? 2001. (Carole Marsh Missouri Bks.). (J). lib. bdg. 29.95 (978-0-635-00067-5(9)) Gallopade International.
McCandless, Perry & Foley, William E. Missouri: Then & Now. 2nd enl. ed. 2001. (Illus.). 392p. (J). 29.95 (978-0-8262-1352-5(9)) Univ. of Missouri Pr.
Royals, Susan. Fun Facts & Games: Missouri. Nolte, Larry, illus. 2000. (Fun Facts & Games Ser.). 64p. (J). (gr. 1-5). pap. 5.59 (978-1-892920-21-8(2)) GHB Publishers, LLC.
Schultz, James Willard. Floating on the Missouri: 100 Years after Lewis & Clark. 2003. 152p. per. 14.95 (978-1-931832-15-1(3) , 18667872363) Riverbend Publishing.
St. Louis Union Station: A City Within a City. 2003. 19.95 (978-0-9748109-0-4(8)) Market 1 Group Inc.
Susan Ann Rhoades: A Story of Early Raytown, Missouri. 1999. (Illus.). 44p. (J). (gr. 3-5). pap. 6.00 (978-0-9700112-1-3(0)) Bonnewitz, Roberta L.

MISSOURI VALLEY

McNeese, Tim. The Missouri River. 2004. (Rivers in American Life & Times Ser.). (Illus.). 120p. (gr. 9-13). 30.00 (978-0-7910-7724-5(1)); pap. 13.25 (978-0-7910-8007-8(2)) Facts On File, Inc. (Chelsea Hse.).

MITCHELL, MARIA, 1818-1889

Anderson, Dale. Maria Mitchell. 2003. (Women in Science Ser.). (Illus.). 112p. (gr. 6-12). 30.00 (978-0-7910-7249-3(5) , Chelsea Hse.) Facts On File, Inc.
Gormley, Beatrice. Maria Mitchell: The Soul of an Astronomer. 2004. (Illus.). 166p. (J). pap. 12.00 (978-0-8028-5264-9(5)) Eerdmans, William B. Publishing Co.

MITCHELL, WILLIAM, 1879-1936

Miller, Roger G. Billy Mitchell: Evangelist of Airpower. 2007. (Illus.). 152p. (YA). (gr. 10 up). lib. bdg. 25.95 ***(978-1-59556-025-4(4))*** OTTN Publishing.

MIXED MARRIAGE

see Intermarriage

MOBILES (SCULPTURE)

French, Cathy. Haz un movil de animales & Make an Animal Mobile. 2005. spiral bd. 66.00 ***(978-1-4108-5619-7(4))*** Benchmark Education Co.
Mobile Magic: Discovering Birds. 2002. (Illus.). (J). (gr. 4-6). pap. (978-1-876367-88-6(1)) Wizard Bks.
Mobile Magic: Discovering Fish. 2002. (Illus.). (J). (gr. 4-6). pap. (978-1-876367-89-3(X)) Wizard Bks.

MOBS

see Riots

MODEL CAR RACING

DK Publishing Staff. Pinewood Derby Design Secrets. 2007. 12.95 ***(978-0-7566-3262-5(5))*** Dorling Kindersley Publishing, Inc.

MODELING

see also Sculpture—Technique

Boase, Petra & Smith, Thomasina. Magic Modelling. 2004. (Fun Factory Ser.). (Illus.). 64p. (gr. k-2). pap. 9.99 (978-1-84215-927-9(5) , Southwater) Anness Publishing GBR. *Dist:* National Bk. Network.
Carlson, Maureen. Clay Characters for Kids. 2003. (Illus.). 64p. (J). pap. 12.99 (978-1-58180-286-3(2) , 32161) F & W Pubns., Inc.
Dean, Irene Semanchuk. Polymer Clay: 30 Terrific Projects to Roll, Mold & Squish. (Illus.). 112p. (ps-7). 2005. (J). pap., pap. 9.95 (978-1-57990-755-6(5)); 2003. 19.95 (978-1-57990-350-3(9)) Lark Bks.
Fernandes, Kim. Gifts to Make with Crayola Model Magic, Incl. modelling material.Tr. of Surprises a Modeler avec Model Magic de Crayola. (FRE., Illus.). 32p. (J). 12.99 (978-0-590-24760-3(3)) Scholastic, Inc.
Fitzgerald-Scales, Sam. Play Clay. 2002. 64p. (J). pap. 9.98 (978-0-7525-6296-4(7)) Parragon, Inc.
Kohl, MaryAnn F. Mudworks: Creative Clay, Dough, & Modeling Experiences. Kerr, Kathleen, illus. 2003. (Bright Ideas for Learning Ser.: Vol. 2). 152p. (J). (ps-6). pap. 18.95 (978-0-935607-02-4(1)) Bright Ring Publishing, Inc.
—Mudworks: Experiencias Creativas con Arcilla, Masa y Modelado. Viglione, Renata, tr. Kerr, Kathleen, illus. 2001. (Bright Ideas for Learning Ser.: Vol. 7). (SPA & ENG.). 152p. (ps-7). pap. 14.95 (978-0-935607-17-8(X)) Bright Ring Publishing, Inc.
Morris, Ting & Morris, Neil. Dinosaurs. Levy, Ruth & Cowne, Joanne, illus. 2007. 32p. (J). ***(978-1-59771-029-9(6))*** Sea-To-Sea Pubns.
Newell, Keith. Models. 2005. (Illus.). 32p. (J). (gr. 3-7). lib. bdg. 27.10 (978-1-932889-85-7(X) , 1247657) Sea-To-Sea Pubns.
Nicholson, Libby & Lau, Yvonne. Creating with Fimo Acrylic Clay. Walker, Tracy, illus. 1999. (Kids Can Do It Ser.). (J). (gr. 4-6). 158p. (978-1-55074-274-9(4)); 350p. (978-1-55074-310-4(4)) Kids Can Pr., Ltd.
Reid, Barbara. Fun with Modeling Clay. Reid, Barbara, illus. 1998. (Kids Can Do It Ser.). (Illus.). 134p. (J). (gr. 4-6). (978-1-55074-510-8(7)) Kids Can Pr., Ltd.
Schecter, Deborah. Shape, Sculpt, & Roll: [with Crayola Model Magic]. 2001. (Illus.). 32p. (J). (978-0-439-33617-8(1)) Scholastic, Inc.
Speechley, Greta. Clay Modeling. 2000. (Step-by-Step Ser.). (Illus.). 32p. (J). (gr. 3-5). lib. bdg. 24.22 (978-1-57572-326-6(3)) Heinemann Library.
—Clay Modeling. 2002. (gr. 3-6). lib. bdg. 16.40 (978-0-613-86421-3(2)) Tandem Library Bks.
—Step-by-Step Clay Modelling. 2004. (Step-by-Step Children's Crafts Ser.). (Illus.). 32p. pap. 7.95 (978-0-85532-914-3(9) , 9149) Search Pr., Ltd. GBR. *Dist:* Search Pr. USA.

MODELS (PERSONS)

Berne, Emma Carlson. Paris & Nicky Hilton. 2007. (J). ***(978-1-4222-0204-3(6))*** Mason Crest Pubs.
Jones, Jen. Fashion Modeling: Being Beautiful, Selling Clothes. 2007. (Illus.). 32p. (J). pap. ***(978-0-7368-7884-5(X)*** , 1264961) Capstone Pr., Inc.
Levin, Pam. Tyra Banks. 1999. (Black Americans of Achievement Ser.). (Illus.). (YA). (gr. 4 up). pap. 9.95 (978-0-7910-4962-4(0) , Chelsea Hse.) Facts On File, Inc.
Naomi Campbell. 2000. (Black Americans of Achievement Ser.). (Illus.). (YA). (gr. 4 up). 19.95 (978-0-7910-4961-7(2) , Chelsea Hse.) Facts On File, Inc.
Torres, Jennifer. Paris Hilton. 2005. (Blue Banner Biography Ser.). (Illus.). 32p. (J). (gr. 4-8). lib. bdg. 25.70 (978-1-58415-382-5(2)) Mitchell Lane Pubs., Inc.
Woodcock, Sandra & Basic Skills Agency Staff. Livewire. 2005. (Illus.). 32p. pap. (978-0-340-74716-2(1)) Cambridge Univ. Pr.

MODELS (PERSONS)—FICTION

Blacker, Terence. Ms Wiz, Supermodel. Ross, Tony, illus. 2003. 58p. (J). pap. 6.99 (978-0-330-35312-0(8) , Pan) Pan Macmillan GBR. *Dist:* Trafalgar Square Publishing.
Clarke, Nicole. French Twist. 2007. (Flirt Ser.: Vol. 8). 224p. (YA). pap. 6.99 (978-0-448-44463-5(1) , Grosset & Dunlap) Penguin Group (USA) Inc.
—Model Behavior, No. 10. 2007. 224p. (J). pap. 6.99 (978-0-448-44562-5(X) , Grosset & Dunlap) Penguin Group (USA) Inc.
Dessen, Sarah. Just Listen. 2008. 384p. (YA). (gr. 7). pap. 8.99 ***(978-0-14-241097-4(7)*** , Puffin) Penguin Group (USA) Inc.
Farrell, Mame. Bradley & the Billboard. 2002. 224p. (J). pap. 5.95 (978-0-374-40912-8(9) , Sunburst) Farrar, Straus & Giroux.
—Bradley & the Billboard. 1999. (YA). pap., stu. ed. 58.00 incl. audio (978-0-7887-3060-3(6) , 40894) Recorded Bks., LLC.
Johnson, Catherine. Face Value. 2006. 256p. (YA). 16.95 (978-0-8027-8920-4(X)) Walker & Co.
The Model, 6 vols., Pack. (Chiquilibros Ser.). (gr. k-1). 23.00 (978-0-7635-0426-7(2)) Rigby Education.
Myers, Walter Dean. Crystal. 2002. 208p. (YA). (gr. 7 up). reprint ed. pap. 6.50 (978-0-06-447312-5(0) , Harper Trophy) HarperCollins Pubs.
—Crystal. 2001. (gr. 5-8). lib. bdg. 14.10 (978-0-613-59802-6(4)) Tandem Library Bks.
Rayban, C. Models Move on to Starring Roles. 137p. pap. (978-0-340-71428-7(X) , Hodder & Stoughton) Hodder General Publishing Division.
—Skin Deep, Vol. 2. 138p. pap. (978-0-340-71429-4(8) , Hodder & Stoughton) Hodder General Publishing Division.
Rue, Nancy N. Here's Lily! 2000. (gr. 7-12). lib. bdg. 10.65 (978-0-613-71716-8(3)) Tandem Library Bks.
Walker, Melissa. Violet by Design. 2008. 224p. pap. 9.99 ***(978-0-425-21940-9(2)*** , Berkley Trade) Penguin Group (USA) Inc.
—Violet on the Runway. 2007. 240p. (YA). (gr. 12 up). pap. 9.99 ***(978-0-425-21704-7(3)*** , Berkley Trade) Penguin Group (USA) Inc.

MODELS (PERSONS)—VOCATIONAL GUIDANCE

Franks, Katie. I Want to Be a Supermodel. 2007. (Dream Jobs Ser.). (Illus.). 24p. (J). (gr. 3-5). lib. bdg. 21.25 (978-1-4042-3620-2(1) , PowerKids Pr.) Rosen Publishing Group, Inc., The.
Jones, Jen. Fashion Modeling: Being Beautiful, Selling Clothes. 2007. (Illus.). 32p. (J). (978-0-7368-6830-3(5) , 1264961) Capstone Pr., Inc.
O'Donnell, Kerri. Careers in Modeling. 2005. (Career Resource Library). (Illus.). 192p. (YA). (gr. 7-12). lib. bdg. 26.50 (978-0-8239-3183-5(8)) Rosen Publishing Group, Inc., The.
Prescott, Sheri. How to Be a Super Model: A Guide to Inner Beauty. 2004. 237p. (YA). per. 14.99 (978-1-58930-129-0(3)) Selah Publishing Group, LLC.
Tauber, Michelle. Make Me a Supermodel. Phibes, A. V., illus. 2005. 96p. (J). pap. 7.99 (978-0-316-01192-1(4)) Little Brown & Co.
Tobey, Cheryl. Choosing a Career as a Model. 2005. (World of Work Ser.). (Illus.). 64p. (YA). (gr. 7-12). lib. bdg. 25.25 (978-0-8239-3243-6(5)) Rosen Publishing Group, Inc., The.

MODELS, FASHION

see Models (Persons)

MODELS AND MODELMAKING

see also subdivision Models under types of objects, e.g. Automobiles—Models; Machinery—Models; and phrase headings for types of models

Ashman, Iain. Egyptian Mummy. 2004. (Cut-Out Models Ser.). (Illus.). 32p. (J). pap. 9.95 (978-0-7945-0255-3(5) , Usborne) EDC Publishing.
Beck, Esther. I'm on the Trail to Learn about Scale! 2006. (Illus.). 24p. (J). (978-1-59928-593-1(2)) ABDO Publishing Co.
Bliss, Helen & Thomson, Ruth. Models. 1998. (Craft Workshop Ser.). (Illus.). 32p. (J). (gr. 3). pap. (978-0-86505-788-3(5)); lib. bdg. (978-0-86505-778-4(8)) Crabtree Publishing Co.
Campadonica, Carol. How to Build a California Mission: San Juan Capistiano, 20 vols. Mueller, Bondell et al, eds. Anderson, Bill, illus. Sousa, Jay, photos by. 1998. (How to Build a California Mission Ser.). (J). (gr. 4-5). pap. (978-0-9648488-8-7(0)) Buzzard Pr. International.
Campodonica, Carol A. How Congress Works. Miller, Bondell, ed. Anderson, Bill, illus. Uni Photo Picture Agency Staff, photos by. Date not set. (J). (gr. 4-5). pap. (978-0-9648488-9-4(9)) Buzzard Pr. International.
—How to Build a California Mission: Santa Barbara, 20 vols. Wardup, Shirley et al, eds. Sousa, Jay, photos by. Date not set. (How to Build a California Mission Ser.). (Illus.). (J). (gr. 4-5). pap. (978-0-9648488-3-2(X)) Buzzard Pr. International.
—How to Build a California Mission: Santa Cruz, 20 vols. Weber, Francis J. et al, eds. Anderson, Bill, illus. Anderson, Jay, photos by. Date not set. (How to Build a California Mission Ser.). (J). (gr. 4-5). pap. (978-0-9648488-5-6(6)) Buzzard Pr. International.
—How to Build the White House, Vol. 3. Scouten, Rex et al, eds. Anderson, Bill, illus. White House Historical Society Staff, photos by. 1998. 40p. (J). (gr. 4-5). pap. 19.95 (978-0-9648488-6-3(4)) Buzzard Pr. International.
Doudna, Kelly. I'm on the Trail to Learn about Scale. 2007. (Illus.). 24p. (J). 19.93 (978-1-59928-592-4(4) , Sand-Castle) ABDO Publishing Co.
Farrington, Karen. Make Your Own Solar System. 1998. (Illus.). (J). (gr. 1 up). pap. 7.95 (978-0-688-16330-3(0)) HarperCollins Pubs.
Farshtey, Greg. Bionicle Encyclopedia (Updated) 2007. 160p. (J). pap. 6.99 ***(978-0-439-91640-0(2))*** Scholastic, Inc.
Fox, Mark & Fox, Olga. Model Magic: Discovering Minibeasts (Insects) 2002. (Illus.). 86p. (J). (gr. 4-6). (978-1-876367-95-4(4)) Wizard Bks.
French, Cathy. Haz una isla & Make an Island. 2005. spiral bd. 66.00 ***(978-1-4108-5632-6(1))*** Benchmark Education Co.
Goossens, Linda. Micro Minis: Create Teeny Tiny Rooms with Your Own Style & Flair! 2004. (Americangirl Library(R) Ser.). (Illus.). 48p. (J). (gr. 4 up). 17.95 (978-1-58485-872-0(9)) American Girl Publishing, Inc.
Holt, Rinehart and Winston Staff. Holt Science & Technology Chptr. 6: Maps & Models: Chapter Resources - Tennessee Edition. 3rd ed. 2003. (YA). pap. 11.40 (978-0-03-069164-5(8)) Holt, Rinehart & Winston.
Kerley, Barbara. The Dinosaurs of Waterhouse Hawkins: An Illuminating History of Mr. Warehouse Hawkins, Artist & Lecturer. Selznick, Brian, illus. 2001. 48p. (J). (gr. 2-5). pap. 16.95 (978-0-439-11494-3(2) , Levine, Arthur A. Bks.) Scholastic, Inc.
Models. (Jump Ser.). (Illus.). 36p. (J). (gr. 2-6). pap. (978-1-882210-36-7(0)) Action Publishing, Inc.
NASCAR Micro Cars: Start Your Engines! 2002. 18p. (J). (978-0-439-45567-1(7)) Scholastic, Inc.
Nelson Libby. California Mission Projects & Layouts. Cornell, Kari, illus. 2007. (Exploring California Missions Ser.). (J). 27.93 ***(978-0-8225-7950-2(2)*** , Lerner Pubns.) Lerner Publishing Group.
Newell, Keith. Models. 1999. (Arts & Crafts Skills Ser.). (Illus.). 32p. (gr. 3-6). pap. 6.95 (978-0-516-26451-6(6) , Children's Pr.) Scholastic Library Publishing.
Quigley, Sebastian, illus. Mars Mission Masterbuilders. 2000. (LEGO Masterbuilders Ser.). (J). (ps-3). 19.99 (978-1-903276-16-7(0)) Lego Media International, Inc.
Schaefer, Lola M. Models. 2000. (Yellow Umbrella Books). (Illus.). 16p. (J). (gr. 1). lib. bdg. 14.60 (978-0-7368-0731-9(4) , Pebble Bks.) Capstone Pr., Inc.
Stillinger, Doug. Klutz Building Cards - How to Build Pirate Ships. 2006. (Illus.). 30p. (YA). spiral bd. 12.95 (978-1-57054-228-2(7)) Klutz.
Troughton, Lester, illus. Busy City Masterbuilders. 2000. (LEGO Masterbuilders Ser.). 47p. (J). (ps-3). pap. 19.99 (978-1-903276-13-6(6)) Lego Media International, Inc.
Zuravicky, Orli. Exploring Pyramids Around the World: Making Models of Geometric Solids. 2004. (PowerMath Ser.). (Illus.). 32p. (J). lib. bdg. (978-0-8239-8908-9(9)); lib. bdg. 22.50 (978-0-8239-8992-8(5)) Rosen Publishing Group, Inc., The. (PowerKids Pr.).

MODERN CIVILIZATION

see Civilization, Modern

MODERN HISTORY

see History, Modern

MODERN PHILOSOPHY

see Philosophy, Modern

MODERNISM (ART)

Fitzpatrick, Anne. Late Modernism. 2005. (Movements in Art Ser.). (Illus.). 48p. (gr. 5-9). 21.95 (978-1-58341-348-7(0) , Creative Education) Creative Co., The.
Knapp, Ruthie & Lehmberg, Janice. Modern Art. 2001. (Off the Wall Museum Guides for Kids). (ENG., Illus.). 72p. (J). (gr. 2-5). pap. 10.95 (978-0-87192-548-0(6)) Davis Pubns., Inc.
Marotske, Michelle R. & Yoakum, Kimberly H. Modernism. Marotske, Michelle R. & Yoakum, Kimberly H., illus. 1998. (Illus.). 20p. (J). (gr. 1-6). pap. (978-1-893397-03-3(3)) Painted in the Corner Productions, L.L.C.
Minond, Edgardo. Drac, Tell Us about Modernism. (SPA.). 80p. (978-84-96137-13-4(9)) Asppan, A., S.L. Distribuidora Internacional de Libros y Revistas.

MOGUL EMPIRE

Ganeri, Anita. India under the Mughal Empire, 1526-1858. 1999. (Looking Back Ser.). (J). 19.98 (978-0-8172-5432-2(3)) Raintree.

MOGUL EMPIRE—FICTION

Lasky, Kathryn. Jahanara: Princess of Princesses, India, 1627. 2002. (Royal Diaries Ser.). 192p. (J). (gr. 4-8). pap. 10.95 (978-0-439-22350-8(4) , Scholastic Pr.) Scholastic, Inc.

MOHAMMED, PROPHET, D. 632

see Muhammad, Prophet, d. 632

MOHAMMEDAN ART

see Art, Islamic

MOLDS (BOTANY)

Pascoe, Elaine. Slime, Molds & Fungi. Kuhn, Dwight, photos by. 1998. (Nature Close-Up Ser.). (Illus.). 48p. (J). (gr. 4-8). 23.70 (978-1-56711-182-8(3) , Blackbirch Pr., Inc.) Thomson Gale.
Silverman, Buffy. Molds & Fungi. 2004. (Kidhaven Science Library). (Illus.). 48p. (J). (gr. 4-7). 26.20 (978-0-7377-2075-4(1) , Greenhaven Pr., Inc.) Thomson Gale.

MOLECULAR BIOCHEMISTRY

see Molecular Biology

MOLECULAR BIOLOGY

Marx, Christy. Watson & Crick & DNA. 2004. (Primary Sources of Revolutionary Scientific Discoveries & Theories Ser.). (Illus.). 64p. (J). lib. bdg. 29.25 (978-1-4042-0312-9(5)) Rosen Publishing Group, Inc., The.
Phelan, Glen. Double Helix: The Quest to Uncover the Structure of DNA. 2006. (Science Quest Ser.). (Illus.). 64p. (J). (gr. 5-9). 17.95 (978-0-7922-5541-3(0)); lib. bdg. 25.90 (978-0-7922-5542-0(9)) National Geographic Society. (National Geographic Children's Bks.).
Senker, Cath. Rosalind Franklin. 2002. (Scientists Who Made History Ser.). (Illus.). 48p. (J). 27.12 (978-0-7398-5226-2(4)) Raintree.

MOLECULAR BIOPHYSICS

see Molecular Biology

MOLECULES

Claybourne, Anna. Microworlds: Unlocking the Secrets of Atoms & Molecules. 2008. (J). ***(978-1-60044-606-1(X))*** Rourke Publishing, LLC.
Clowes, Martin. Atoms & Molecules. 2004. (Routes of Science Ser.). (J). pap. 11.20 (978-1-4103-0324-0(1) , Blackbirch Pr., Inc.) Thomson Gale.
Gish, Melissa. Temperature. 2005. (My First Look at Science Ser.). (Illus.). 24p. (gr. k-3). 15.95 (978-1-58341-375-3(8) , Creative Education) Creative Co., The.
Juettner, Bonnie. Molecules. 2004. (Kidhaven Science Library). (Illus.). 48p. (J). (gr. 4-7). 26.20 (978-0-7377-2076-1(X)) Thomson Gale.
Manning, Phillip. Atoms, Molecules, & Compounds. 2007. (Essential Chemistry Ser.). 144p. (gr. 6-12). 35.00 ***(978-0-7910-9534-8(7)*** , Chelsea Hse.) Facts On File, Inc.
Mebane, Robert C. & Rybolt, Thomas R. Adventures with Atoms & Molecules: Chemistry Experiments for Young People. 1998. (Adventures with Science Ser.). (Illus.). 96p. (YA). (gr. 4-9). Bk. III. pap. 11.93 (978-0-7660-1226-4(3)); Bk. IV. pap. 11.93 (978-0-7660-1227-1(1)); Bk. V. pap. 11.93 (978-0-7660-1228-8(X)) Enslow Pubs., Inc.
Saunders, N. Atoms & Molecules. 2007. (J). lib. bdg. ***(978-1-4042-3750-6(X)*** , Rosen Central) Rosen Publishing Group, Inc., The.
Science Kids Publishing Staff. What's the Matter? The Story of Atoms & Molecules. 1999. (J). (gr. 2-6). pap. 6.95 (978-1-891418-14-3(9)) Science Kids.
Slade, Suzanne. Scientific Instruments for Studying Atoms & Molecules. 2007. (Library of Physical Sciences). (Illus.). 24p. (J). (978-1-4042-2356-1(8)); pap. (978-1-4042-2166-6(2)); lib. bdg. (978-1-4042-3419-2(5)) Rosen Publishing Group, Inc., The. (PowerKids Pr.).
—States of Matter. 2007. (Library of Physical Sciences). (J). (978-1-4042-2353-0(3)); (Illus.). 24p. pap. (978-1-4042-2163-5(8)) Rosen Publishing Group, Inc., The. (PowerKids Pr.).
Spilsbury, Louise & Spilsbury, Richard. Atoms & Molecules. 2007. (Illus.). 32p. (J). (978-1-4034-9341-5(3)); lib. bdg. (978-1-4034-9336-1(7)) Heinemann Library.
Stille, Darlene R. Atoms & Molecules: Building Blocks of the Universe. 2006. (Illus.). 48p. (J). (978-0-7565-1960-5(8)) Compass Point Bks.

MOLES (ANIMALS)

George, Jean Craighead. Winter Moon. 2003. (J). (gr. 3-7). 20.75 (978-0-8446-7244-1(0)) Smith, Peter Pub., Inc.
—Winter Moon. 2001. (gr. 3-6). lib. bdg. 14.10 (978-0-613-50525-3(5)) Tandem Library Bks.
Lockwood, Sophie. Sea Otters. 2005. (World of Mammals Ser.). 40p. (J). (gr. 2-6). 29.93 (978-1-59296-500-7(8)) Child's World, Inc.
Miller, Sara Swan. Moles & Hedgehogs: What They Have in Common. 2001. (Animals in Order Ser.). (Illus.). 48p. (J). (gr. 4-6). pap. 6.95 (978-0-531-13957-8(3) , Watts, Franklin) Scholastic Library Publishing.

—Moles & Hedgehogs: What They Have in Common. 2001. (Illus.). 48p. (J). (gr. 4-7). lib. bdg. 15.25 (978-0-613-37463-7(0)) Tandem Library Bks.

Morris, Ting. Mole. Rosewarne, Graham, illus. 2005. 32p. (J). (gr. 3-7). lib. bdg. 27.10 (978-1-58340-525-3(9)) Smart Apple Media.

Pfister, Marcus. Holey Moley. James, J. Alison, tr. from GER. 2006. (Illus.). 32p. (J). (ps-2). 16.95 (978-0-7358-2064-7(3)) North-South Bks., Inc.

Whitehouse, Patricia. Moles. 2003. (Heinemann Read & Learn Ser.). (Illus.). 24p. (J). pap. 5.25 (978-1-4034-4326-7(2)); lib. bdg. 18.50 (978-1-4034-4317-5(3)) Heinemann Library.

—Los Topos/Patricia Whitehouse ; Traduccion de Patricia Abello. 2003. (ENG & SPA.). (J). 12.95 (978-1-4034-4343-4(2)); pap. 5.25 (978-1-4034-4351-9(3)) Heinemann Library.

MOLES (ANIMALS)—FICTION

Addabbo, Carole. Dina the Deaf Dinosaur. Valentine, illus. 1998. 32p. (J). (ps-5). 19.95 (978-1-889262-04-8(8)) Hannacroix Creek Bks., Inc.

Bailey, Arthur Scott. The Tale of Grandfather Mole. 2005. reprint ed. pap. 20.95 (978-0-7661-9549-3(X)) Kessinger Publishing, LLC.

Caballero, Erica. Mount Mole. 2006. pap. 10.00 (***978-1-4257-2301-9(2)*** Xlibris Corp.

Delessert, Etienne. Alert! 2007. (Illus.). 32p. (J). (gr. k-3). 17.00 (978-0-618-73474-0(0)) Houghton Mifflin Co.

Duffie, Charles. The Mole & the Owl: A Romantic Fable about Braving the Wide World for Love. 1998. (Illus.). 120p. 18.95 (978-1-57174-082-3(1)) Hampton Roads Publishing Co., Inc.

Dunbar. Happy Days for Mouse & Mole. 2000. (Illus.). 28p. (J). pap. 6.95 (978-0-552-52978-5(8)) Transworld Publishers Ltd. GBR. *Dist:* Trafalgar Square Publishing.

—Mouse & Mole. 2000. (Illus.). 25p. (J). 15.95 (978-0-385-40198-2(1)) Transworld Publishers Ltd. GBR. *Dist:* Trafalgar Square Publishing.

—Very Special Mouse & Mole. 2000. (Illus.). 28p. (J). pap. 6.95 (978-0-552-52977-8(X)) Transworld Publishers Ltd. GBR. *Dist:* Trafalgar Square Publishing.

Dunbar, Joyce. Hip-Dip-Dip with Mouse & Mole. de Vere, Alison, illus. 2002. 62p. pap. 7.99 (978-0-552-54673-7(9) , Corgi) Transworld Publishers Ltd. GBR. *Dist:* Trafalgar Square Publishing.

—Mouse & Mole Have a Party. Mayhew, James, illus. 2000. 32p. (J). pap. 6.95 (978-0-552-54557-0(0)) Transworld Publishers Ltd. GBR. *Dist:* Trafalgar Square Publishing.

Dunbar, Joyce & de Vere, Alison. The Ups & Downs of Mouse & Mole. 2002. (Illus.). 63p. pap. 7.99 (978-0-552-54674-4(7) , Corgi) Transworld Publishers Ltd. GBR. *Dist:* Trafalgar Square Publishing.

Dunrea, Olivier. Essie & Myles. 2005. (J). (978-0-374-39991-7(3) , Farrar, Straus & Giroux (BYR)) Farrar, Straus & Giroux.

Ehlert, Lois. Mole's Hill: A Woodland Tale. 1998. (Illus.). 36p. (J). (ps-3). pap. 7.00 (978-0-15-201890-0(5) , Harcourt Paperbacks) Harcourt Children's Bks.

Emmett, Jonathan. Diamond in the Snow. Cabban, Vanessa, illus. 2006. 32p. (J). (ps-1). 15.99 (978-0-7636-3117-8(5)) Candlewick Pr.

—No Place Like Home. Cabban, Venessa, illus. 2005. 32p. (J). (ps-1). 15.99 (978-0-7636-2554-2(X)) Candlewick Pr.

Gates, Susan. Mole Who was Scared of the Dark. Breakespeare, Andrew, illus. 2005. 24p. (J). lib. bdg. 22.65 (***978-1-59646-710-1(X)*** Dingles & Co.

Grahame, Kenneth. Open Road Bk. 2. Iosa, Ann, illus. 2006. (Easy Reader Classics Ser.). 32p. (J). pap. 3.95 (978-1-4027-3294-2(5)) Sterling Publishing Co., Inc.

—The Wind in the Willows Bk. 1: The Riverbank. Iosa, Ann, illus. 2006. (Easy Reader Classics Ser.). 32p. (J). pap. 3.95 (978-1-4027-3293-5(7)) Sterling Publishing Co., Inc.

Hillenbrand, Jane. What a Treasure! Hillenbrand, Will, illus. 24p. (J). (ps-1). 16.95 (978-0-8234-1896-1(0)); pap. 6.95 (***978-0-8234-2077-3(9)*** Holiday Hse., Inc.

Holzwarth, Werner. Little Mole Pop up. 2008. (Illus.). 24p. (J). 14.95 (***978-1-84365-095-9(9)*** Anova Bks. GBR. *Dist:* Independent Pubs. Group.

Holzwarth, Werner & Erlbruch, Wolf. The Story of the Little Mole Who Went in Search of Whodunit. 2007. (J). (ps-5). 24p. 14.95 (***978-0-8109-1641-8(X)*** , Abrams Bks. for Young Readers); 22p. 9.95 (***978-0-8109-4457-2(X)*** , Abrams Image) Abrams, Harry N. , Inc.

Honigsberg, Peter Jan. Armful of Memories. Morse, Tony, illus. 2004. 32p. 17.95 (978-1-57143-089-2(X)) RDR Bks.

—Pillow of Dreams. Morse, Tony, illus. 2004. 32p. (gr. k-4). 17.95 (978-1-57143-076-2(8)) RDR Bks.

Hooper, Mary & McAllister, Angela. Take a Kiss to School. Hellard, Sue, illus. 2006. 32p. (J). 15.95 (978-1-58234-702-8(6) , Bloomsbury Children) Bloomsbury Publishing.

Jenkins, Amanda. Why Mole Lives Underground: A Folktale from Peru. 2006. spiral bd. 23.00 (***978-1-4108-7160-2(6)*** Benchmark Education Co.

Jonell, Lynne. Bravemole. ed. 2004. (Illus.). (J). (gr. k-3). spiral bd. (978-0-616-14579-1(9)) Canadian National Institute for the Blind/Institut National Canadien pour les Aveugles.

Koller, Jackie French. Mole & Shrew Are Two. Reas, Anne, illus. 2000. (J). (978-0-606-19903-2(9)) Tandem Library Bks.

—Mole & Shrew Have Jobs to Do. 2001. (Stepping Stone Bks.). (Illus.). (J). (978-0-606-21335-6(X)) Tandem Library Bks.

McPhail, David M. Mole Music. McPhail, David M., illus. 2002. (Illus.). (J). 25.38 (978-0-7587-3152-4(3)) Book Wholesalers, Inc.

—Mole Music. rev. ed. (Illus.). 32p. (J). (ps-3). 2001. pap. 7.95 (978-0-8050-6766-8(3)); 1999. 16.95 (978-0-8050-2819-5(6)) Holt, Henry & Co. (Holt, Henry & Co. Bks. For Young Readers).

—Mole Music. McPhail, David M., illus. 2001. (Illus.). 28.95 incl. audio compact disk (978-1-59112-429-0(8)); pap. 37.95 incl. audio (978-0-87499-749-1(6)); pap. 39.95 incl. audio compact disk (978-1-59112-606-5(1)); (J). pap. 16.95 incl. audio (978-0-87499-747-7(X)); (J). pap. 18.95 incl. audio compact disk (978-1-59112-406-1(9)) Live Oak Media.

—Mole Music. 2001. (gr. k-3). lib. bdg. 15.25 (978-0-613-78380-4(8)); (978-0-606-22641-7(9)) Tandem Library Bks.

Mole Follows the Christmas Star. 2002. (J). bds. 3.98 (978-1-84250-587-8(4) , Bright Sparks) Parragon, Inc.

Mosely, Keith. Snow Mouse & The Seven Moles. 1999. (Illus.). 4p. (J). pap. 8.95 (978-90-76048-23-9(1)) Van Der Meer Tennis Univ.

Newman, Marjorie. Mole & the Baby Bird. Benson, Patrick, illus. 2002. 32p. (J). (gr. k-3). 16.95 (978-1-58234-784-4(0) , Bloomsbury Children) Bloomsbury Publishing.

Oram, Hiawyn. Badger's Bad Mood. Varley, Susan, illus. 32p. (J). (ps-3). 2002. pap. 5.99 (978-0-590-21693-7(7)); 1998. pap. 15.95 (978-0-590-18920-0(4)) Scholastic, Inc.

Owen, Chris. Hairy Mole the Pirate 1. 2007. (Hairy Mole the Pirate Ser.). (Illus.). 82p. pap. 7.95 (***978-1-84167-562-6(8)*** Ransom Publishing Ltd. GBR. *Dist:* International Publishers Marketing.

Pearce, Philippa. The Little Gentleman. Pohrt, Tom, illus. 2004. 208p. (J). (gr. 3 up). 15.99 (978-0-06-073160-1(5)); lib. bdg. 16.89 (978-0-06-073161-8(3)) HarperCollins Pubs.

Pearce, Philippa & Pearl, Matthew. The Little Gentleman. unabr. ed. 2005. (J). 56.64 incl. audio (978-1-4193-3601-0(0) , 42047) Recorded Bks., LLC.

Pochocki, Ethel. The Mushroom Man. Moser, Barry, illus. 2006. (J). reprint ed. pap. (978-0-88448-278-9(2)) Tilbury Hse. Pubs.

Said Mouse to Mole. 2005. (J). per. 8.95 (978-1-59566-139-5(5)) QEB Publishing Inc.

Santillo, LuAnn. Mole. Santillo, LuAnn, ed. 2003. (Half-Pint Kids Readers Ser.). (Illus.). 7p. (J). (ps-1). pap. (978-1-59256-111-7(X)) Half-Pint Kids, Inc.

—Rose. Santillo, LuAnn, ed. 2003. (Half-Pint Kids Readers Ser.). (Illus.). 7p. (J). (ps-1). pap. (978-1-59256-101-8(2)) Half-Pint Kids, Inc.

Sargent, Dave & Sargent, Pat. Molly's Journey: I'm Getting Older, 15 vols., 19. Huff, Jeane, illus. 2nd rev. ed. 2003. (Animal Pride Ser.: 19). 42p. (J). pap. 6.95 (978-1-56763-796-0(5)); lib. bdg. 19.95 (978-1-56763-795-3(7)) Ozark Publishing.

—Polly Platypus: Unique, 56 vols., 55. Lenoir, Jane, illus. 2000. (Animal Pride Ser.: Vol. 55). 36p. (J). lib. bdg. 19.95 (978-1-56763-551-5(2)) Ozark Publishing.

Sargent, Dave, et al. Polly Platypus: Unique, 17, 55. 2000. (Animal Pride Ser.: 55). (Illus.). 42p. (J). pap. 6.95 (978-1-56763-552-2(0)) Ozark Publishing.

Schwartz, Roslyn. The Complete Adventures of the Mole Sisters. Schwartz, Roslyn, illus. 2004. (Mole Sisters Ser.). (Illus.). 168p. (J). (ps-k). 19.95 (978-1-55037-883-2(X)) Annick Pr., Ltd. CAN. *Dist:* Firefly Bks., Ltd.

—The Mole Sisters & the Blue Egg. Schwartz, Roslyn, illus. 2001. (Mole Sisters Ser.). (Illus.). 32p. (J). (ps-k). pap. 4.95 (978-1-55037-704-0(3)); lib. bdg. 14.95 (978-1-55037-705-7(1)) Annick Pr., Ltd. CAN. *Dist:* Firefly Bks., Ltd.

—The Mole Sisters & the Busy Bees. Schwartz, Roslyn, illus. 2000. (Mole Sisters Ser.). (Illus.). 32p. (J). (ps-k). pap. 4.95 (978-1-55037-662-3(4)); lib. bdg. 14.95 (978-1-55037-663-0(2)) Annick Pr., Ltd. CAN. *Dist:* Firefly Bks., Ltd.

—Mole Sisters & the Busy Bees. 2000. (ps-2). lib. bdg. 12.95 (978-0-613-78377-4(8)) Tandem Library Bks.

—The Mole Sisters & the Cool Breeze. Schwartz, Roslyn, illus. 2002. (Mole Sisters Ser.). (Illus.). 32p. (J). (ps-k). pap. 4.95 (978-1-55037-770-5(1)); lib. bdg. 14.95 (978-1-55037-771-2(X)) Annick Pr., Ltd. CAN. *Dist:* Firefly Bks., Ltd.

—The Mole Sisters & the Fairy Ring. Schwartz, Roslyn, illus. 2003. (Mole Sisters Ser.). (Illus.). 32p. (J). (ps-k). pap. 4.95 (978-1-55037-818-4(X)); lib. bdg. 14.95 (978-1-55037-819-1(8)) Annick Pr., Ltd. CAN. *Dist:* Firefly Bks., Ltd.

—The Mole Sisters & the Moonlit Night. Schwartz, Roslyn, illus. 2001. (Mole Sisters Ser.). (Illus.). 32p. (J). (ps-k). pap. 4.95 (978-1-55037-702-6(7)); lib. bdg. 14.95 (978-1-55037-703-3(5)) Annick Pr., Ltd. CAN. *Dist:* Firefly Bks., Ltd.

—The Mole Sisters & the Piece of Moss. Schwartz, Roslyn, illus. 2001. (Mole Sisters Ser.). (Illus.). 32p. (J). (ps-k). pap. 4.95 (978-1-55037-582-4(2)); lib. bdg. 14.95 (978-1-55037-583-1(0)) Annick Pr., Ltd. CAN. *Dist:* Firefly Bks., Ltd.

—The Mole Sisters & the Question. Schwartz, Roslyn, illus. 2002. (Mole Sisters Ser.). (Illus.). 32p. (J). (ps-k). pap. 4.95 (978-1-55037-768-2(X)); lib. bdg. 14.95 (978-1-55037-769-9(8)) Annick Pr., Ltd. CAN. *Dist:* Firefly Bks., Ltd.

—The Mole Sisters & the Rainy Day. Schwartz, Roslyn, illus. 2001. (Mole Sisters Ser.). (Illus.). 32p. (J). (ps-k). pap. 4.95 (978-1-55037-610-4(1)); lib. bdg. 14.95 (978-1-55037-611-1(X)) Annick Pr., Ltd. CAN. *Dist:* Firefly Bks., Ltd.

—Mole Sisters & the Rainy Day. 2001. (ps-2). lib. bdg. 12.95 (978-0-613-78347-7(6)) Tandem Library Bks.

—The Mole Sisters & the Wavy Wheat. Schwartz, Roslyn, illus. 2000. (Mole Sisters Ser.). (Illus.). 32p. (J). (ps-k). pap. 4.95 (978-1-55037-660-9(8)); lib. bdg. 14.95 (978-1-55037-661-6(6)) Annick Pr., Ltd. CAN. *Dist:* Firefly Bks., Ltd.

—The Mole Sisters & the Way Home. Schwartz, Roslyn, illus. 2003. (Mole Sisters Ser.). (Illus.). 32p. (J). (ps-k). pap. 4.95 (978-1-55037-820-7(1)); lib. bdg. 14.95 (978-1-55037-821-4(X)) Annick Pr., Ltd. CAN. *Dist:* Firefly Bks., Ltd.

Segal, Lore. More Mole Stories & Little Gopher, Too. Ruzzier, Sergio, illus. 2005. 40p. (J). 16.00 (978-0-374-35026-0(4) , Farrar, Straus & Giroux (BYR)) Farrar, Straus & Giroux.

Twinn, Michael. Here We Go Round the Mulberry Bush. 2001. (Illus.). 16p. (J). 19.99 (978-0-85953-893-0(1)) Child's Play-International.

Wheeler, Lisa. One Dark Night. Bates, Ivan, illus. 2006. 32p. (J). reprint ed. pap. 6.00 (978-0-15-205888-3(5) , Voyager Bks./Libros Viajeros) Harcourt Children's Bks.

Yee, Wong Herbert. Abracadabra! Magic with Mouse & Mole. 2007. 48p. (J). (gr. k-3). 15.00 (***978-0-618-75926-2(3)*** Houghton Mifflin Co.

—Upstairs Mouse, Downstairs Mole. 2005. (Illus.). 48p. (J). (gr. k-3). 15.00 (978-0-618-47313-7(0)) Houghton Mifflin Co. Trade & Reference Div.

Yee, Wong Herbert. Upstairs Mouse Downstairs Mole. 12th ed. 2007. (Illus.). 48p. (J). (gr. 1-5). 3.99 (***978-0-618-91586-6(9)*** Houghton Mifflin Co. Trade & Reference Div.

MOLLUSKS

see also Shells

Blaxland, Beth. Mollusks: Snails, Clams, & Their Relatives. 2002. (Invertebrates Ser.). (Illus.). 32p. (gr. 4-8). 28.00 (978-0-7910-6997-4(4) , Chelsea Hse.) Facts On File, Inc.

Cassie, Brian. Shells. 2000. (National Audubon Society First Field Guides). (Illus.). 160p. (J). (gr. 3 up). pap. 8.95 (978-0-590-64258-3(8)) Scholastic, Inc.

—Shells. 2000. (National Audubon Society First Field Guide Ser.). (J). (978-0-606-19583-6(1)) Tandem Library Bks.

Cassie, Brian & National Audubon Society Staff. Shells. 2000. (National Audubon Society First Field Guides). (Illus.). 159p. (J). (gr. 3 up). pap. 17.95 (978-0-590-64233-0(2)) Scholastic, Inc.

Chanell, Jim & Greenaway, Theresa. Slugs & Snails. 1999. (Minipets Ser.). (Illus.). 32p. (J). (gr. 1-5). lib. bdg. 25.69 (978-0-8172-5587-9(7)) Raintree.

Fowler, Allan. Shellfish Aren't Fish. 1999. (Illus.). 31p. (J). (gr. 1-2). lib. bdg. 12.95 (978-0-613-37536-8(X)) Tandem Library Bks.

Fredericks, Anthony D. Slugs. Ellis, Gerry, photos by. 2000. (Early Bird Nature Bks.). (Illus.). 48p. (J). (gr. 2-4). lib. bdg. 25.26 (978-0-8225-3041-1(4) , Lerner Pubns.) Lerner Publishing Group.

Garrow, Linda, illus. Young Naturalist Field Guides, 5 bks. Incl. Berries, Nuts & Seeds. Burns, Diane L. 2000. lib. bdg. 24.67 (978-0-8368-2144-0(0)); Frogs, Toads & Turtles. Burns, Diane L. 1999. lib. bdg. 24.67 (978-0-8368-2145-1(9)); Rabbits, Squirrels & Chipmunks. Boring, Mel. 1999. lib. bdg. 24.67 (978-0-8368-2146-8(7)); Tracks, Scats & Signs. Dendy, Leslie. 1999. lib. bdg. 24.67 (978-0-8368-2147-5(5)); Wildflowers, Blooms & Blossoms. Burns, Diane L. 2000. lib. bdg. 24.67 (978-0-8368-2148-2(3)); 40p. (J). (gr. 3 up). (Illus.). Set lib. bdg. 123.35 (978-0-8368-2658-6(2)) Stevens, Gareth Inc.

Gilpin, Daniel. Snails, Shellfish & Other Mollusks. 2006. (Animal Kingdom Classification Ser.). (Illus.). 48p. (J). (gr. 4-6). 26.60 (978-0-7565-1613-0(7) , 1253127) Compass Point Bks.

Greenaway, Theresa. Slugs & Snails. 1999. (Minipets Ser.). (Illus.). 32p. (gr. 1-5). pap. 7.95 (978-0-8172-4207-7(4)) Steck-Vaughn.

Holt, Rinehart and Winston Staff. Biology: Mollusks & Annelids: Resources for Chapter 29. 4th ed. 2004. pap. 9.20 (978-0-03-069963-4(0)) Holt, Rinehart & Winston.

Lewis, Brenda Ralph. Crabs & Mollusks. 2006. (Nature's Monsters Ser.). (Illus.). 32p. (J). lib. bdg. 23.33 (978-0-8368-6176-1(0)) Stevens, Gareth Inc.

Llewellyn, Claire. Slugs & Snails. 2001. (gr. k-3). lib. bdg. 12.95 (978-0-613-54357-6(2)) Tandem Library Bks.

McNeil, Niki, et al. HOCPP 1103 Mollusks. 2006. spiral bd. 19.00 (***978-1-60308-103-0(8)*** In the Hands of a Child.

Miller, Ruth. Mollusks. 2004. (Illus.). 48p. (J). 32.79 (978-1-4109-1051-6(2)); pap. 9.50 (978-1-4109-1347-0(3)) Harcourt Schl. Pubs.

Morgan, Sally. Slugs & Snails. 2000. (Looking at Minibeasts Ser.). (Illus.). 32p. (J). (gr. 1-4). lib. bdg. 16.95 (978-1-929298-81-5(1)) Chrysalis Education.

Murray, Peter. Mollusks & Crustaceans. 2004. (Science Around Us Ser.). 32p. (J). (gr. 2-6). 27.07 (978-1-59296-217-4(3)) Child's World, Inc.

Ofinoski, Steven A. Snails & Other Mollusks. World Book, Inc. Staff, ed. 2002. (World Book's Animals of the World Ser.: Set 3). (Illus.). 64p. (J). (978-0-7166-1232-2(1)) World Bk., Inc.

Richardson, Adele D. Seashells. 1998. (Let's Investigate Ser.: Vol. 12). (Illus.). 32p. (J). (ps-3). lib. bdg. (978-0-88682-996-4(8) , Creative Education) Creative Co., The.

Richardson, Joy. Mollusks. 2005. (Illus.). 32p. (J). lib. bdg. 23.33 (978-0-8368-4507-5(2)) Stevens, Gareth Inc.

Robb, Jackie & Stringle, Berny. The Story of Slug. Duncan, Karen & Stringle, Sam, illus. 2004. (Bang on the Door Ser.). 32p. (YA). pap. (978-1-85602-317-7(6)) Chrysalis Children's Bks.

Salzmann, Mary Elizabeth. What Has a Shell? 2007. (Creature Features Ser.). (ENG., Illus.). 24p. (J). (ps-3). lib. bdg. 24.21 (***978-1-59928-871-0(0)*** , Super SandCastle) ABDO Publishing Co.

Sill, Cathryn P. & Sill, John. About Mollusks. Sill, Cathryn P. & Sill, John, illus. 2005. (Illus.). 40p. (J). 15.95 (978-1-56145-331-3(5)) Peachtree Pubs., Ltd.

Townsend, John. Incredible Molluscs. 2005. (J). 56p. (978-1-4109-1718-8(5)); (978-1-4109-1709-6(6)) Steck-Vaughn.

Zoehfeld, Kathleen Weidner. What Lives in a Shell? 2001. 24.75 (978-0-06-000305-0(7)) HarperCollins Pubs.

MONACO

Hintz, Martin. Monaco. 2004. (Enchantment of the World, Second Ser.). (Illus.). 144p. (YA). (gr. 5-9). 36.00 (978-0-516-24251-4(2) , Children's Pr.) Scholastic Library Publishing.

King, David C. Monaco. 2008. (Cultures of the World Ser.). (J). lib. bdg. (***978-0-7614-2567-0(5)*** , Benchmark Bks.) Cavendish, Marshall Corp.

MONARCHS

see Kings, Queens, Rulers, etc.; Queens

MONASTERIES

see also Monasticism and Religious Orders

Anderson, Dale. Monks & Monasteries in the Middle Ages. 2005. (World Almanac Library of the Middle Ages). (J). pap. (978-0-8368-5906-5(5)); (Illus.). 48p. (YA). (gr. 10-12). lib. bdg. 30.00 (978-0-8368-5897-6(2)) Stevens, Gareth Inc. (World Almanac Library).

Cowie, Sarah. The Abbot & I (As Told by Josie the Cat) Selby, Sarah, illus. 2002. 24p. pap. 8.95 (978-1-888212-25-9(X) , 005197) Conciliar Pr.

Jovinelly, Joann & Netelkos, Jason. The Crafts & Culture of a Medieval Monastery. 2006. (Crafts & Culture of the Middle Ages Ser.). (Illus.). 48p. (J). (gr. 4-8). lib. bdg. 29.25 (978-1-4042-0759-2(7)) Rosen Publishing Group, Inc., The.

McAleavy, Tony. Life in a Medieval Abbey. 2003. (English Heritage (Series)). (Illus.). 64p. (J). (gr. 6-12). 22.00 (978-1-59270-006-6(3)) Enchanted Lion Bks., LLC.

MONASTIC ORDERS

see Monasticism and Religious Orders

MONASTICISM AND RELIGIOUS ORDERS

see also Monasteries

Anderson, Dale. Monks & Monasteries in the Middle Ages. 2005. (World Almanac Library of the Middle Ages). (J). pap. (978-0-8368-5906-5(5)); (Illus.). 48p. (YA). (gr. 10-12). lib. bdg. 30.00 (978-0-8368-5897-6(2)) Stevens, Gareth Inc. (World Almanac Library).

Barter, James. A Medieval Monk. 2003. (Working Life Ser.). (Illus.). 112p. (J). 29.95 (978-1-59018-478-3(5) , Lucent Bks.) Thomson Gale.

Cels, Marc. Life in a Medieval Monastery. 2004. (Medieval World Ser.). (Illus.). 32p. (J). pap. (978-0-7787-1384-5(9)) Crabtree Publishing Co.

—Life in a Medieval Monastery: The Medieval World. 2004. (Medieval World Ser.). (Illus.). 32p. (J). (978-0-7787-1352-4(0)) Crabtree Publishing Co.

Crompton, Samuel Willard. Thomas Merton. 2004. (Spiritual Leaders & Thinkers Ser.). (Illus.). 120p. (gr. 9-13). 30.00 (978-0-7910-7862-4(0) , Chelsea Hse.) Facts On File, Inc.

Holderness, Ginny W. & Palmer, Forrest C. Career & Calling: A Guide for Counselors, Youth & Young Adults. 2000. (Illus.). 176p. (YA). 21.95 (978-0-664-22232-1(3)) Westminster John Knox Pr.

O'Keefe, Susan Heyboer. What Does a Priest Do? What Does a Nun Do? 2002. (Illus.). 32p. 7.95 (978-0-8091-6698-5(4) , 6698-4) Paulist Pr.

Young, Patricia A. The Holy Monks of Mt. Athos. Young, Patricia A., illus. l.t. ed. 2005. (Illus.). 28p. (J). 20.00 (978-0-913026-24-3(7)); 10.00 (978-0-913026-49-6(2)) St. Nectarios Pr.

MONASTICISM AND RELIGIOUS ORDERS—FICTION

Coles Notes Staff. Canterbury Tales. 1999. (YA). 9.95 (978-1-56137-919-4(0)); (J). 11.95 (978-1-56137-920-0(4)) Novel Units, Inc.

DePaolo, Audrey F. Rebel Nun. 2000. 260p. (YA). pap. 13.95 (978-1-891929-34-2(8)) Four Seasons Pubs.

Harrison, Cora. The Secret of the Seven Crosses. 1998. (Drumshee Timeline Ser.: Bk. 2). (Illus.). 128p. (J). (gr. 4-8). pap. 6.95 (978-0-86327-616-3(4)) Wolfhound Pr. IRL. *Dist:* Irish American Bk. Co.

Jordan, Sherryl. The Hunting of the Last Dragon. 2002. 192p. (J). (gr. 7 up). 15.99 (978-0-06-028902-7(3)); 15.89 (978-0-06-028903-4(1)) HarperCollins Pubs.

Miller, Walter. Saint Leibowitz & the Wild Horse Woman. 2000. (gr. 7-12). lib. bdg. 24.55 (978-0-613-22295-2(4)) Tandem Library Bks.

Trottier, Maxine. Little Dog Moon. Fernandez, Laura & Jacobson, Rick, illus. 2000. 20p. (J). (ps-3). 14.95 (978-0-7737-3220-9(9)) Stoddart Kids CAN. *Dist:* Fitzhenry & Whiteside, Ltd.

Whitesel, Cheryl Aylward. Rebel: A Tibetan Odyssey. 2000. 208p. (J). (gr. 5 up). 16.99 (978-0-688-16735-6(7)) HarperCollins Pubs.

Ziefert, Harriet. Presents for Santa. 2000. (Easy-to-Read Ser.). (J). (978-0-606-20250-3(1)) Tandem Library Bks.

MONDAY, ANTHONY (FICTITIOUS CHARACTER)—FICTION

Bellairs, John. The Mansion in the Mist. Gorey, Edward, illus. 2004. (Anthony Monday Ser.). 176p. (J). pap. 5.99 (978-0-14-240262-7(1) , Puffin) Penguin Group (USA) Inc.

MONET, CLAUDE, 1840-1926

Carvalho de Magalhaes, Roberto. Claude Monet. 2005. (Great Artists Ser.). (Illus.). 40p. (J). (gr. 5). pap. 7.95 (978-1-59270-050-9(0)) Enchanted Lion Bks., LLC.

Connolly, Sean. Claude Monet. 2006. (Heinemann First Library). (Illus.). 32p. (J). lib. bdg. (***978-1-4034-8489-5(9)*** Heinemann Library.

Connolly, Sean, contrib. by. Claude Monet. 1999. (Life & Work of. . . Ser.). (Illus.). 32p. (J). (gr. k-2). lib. bdg. 21.36 (978-1-57572-956-5(3)) Heinemann Library.

Connolly, Sean & Monet, Claude. Claude Monet. 2004. (Lives of the Artists Ser.). (Illus.). 48p. (J). pap. (978-0-8368-5655-2(4)); lib. bdg. 30.00 (978-0-8368-5650-7(3)) Stevens, Gareth Inc. (World Almanac Library).

Consuelo, Sanchez. Claudet Monet. 2005. 132p. pap. (978-958-30-1869-5(4)) Panamericana Editorial.

De Magalhaes, Roberto Carvalho. Claude Monet. 2003. (Great Artists Ser.). (Illus.). 40p. (J). 15.95 (978-1-59270-009-7(8)) Enchanted Lion Bks., LLC.

Dorling Kindersley Publishing Staff & Welton, Jude. Monet. 1999. (Eyewitness Art Ser.). (Illus.). 64p. (J). (gr. 3-7). 15.99 (978-0-7894-4880-4(7)) Dorling Kindersley Publishing, Inc.

Hodge, Susie. Claude Monet. 2002. (Artists in Their Time Ser.). (J). (gr. 5-7). pap. 6.95 (978-0-531-16619-2(8)); (Illus.). 48p. pap. 23.50 (978-0-531-12226-6(3)) Scholastic Library Publishing. (Watts, Franklin).

—Claude Monet. 2002. (gr. 5-8). lib. bdg. 15.25 (978-0-613-54133-6(2)) Tandem Library Bks.

Kelley, True. Claude Monet: Sunshine & Waterlilies. Kelley, True, illus. 2001. (Smart about Art Ser.). (Illus.). 32p. (J). (gr. k-4). pap. 5.99 (978-0-448-42522-1(X) , Grosset & Dunlap) Penguin Group (USA) Inc.

—Claude Monet: Sunshine & Waterlilies. 2001. (gr. k-3). lib. bdg. 14.15 (978-0-613-45253-3(4)) Tandem Library Bks.

Klein, Adam G. & Monet, Claude. Claude Monet. 2007. (Illus.). 32p. (J). 22.78 (978-1-59679-732-1(0)) ABDO Publishing Co.

Merberg, Julie & Bober, Suzanne. A Picnic with Monet. 2003. (Illus.). 22p. (J). bds. 6.95 (978-0-8118-4046-0(8)) Chronicle Bks. LLC.

Muhlberger, Richard. What Makes a Monet a Monet? 2002. (Illus.). 48p. (YA). 16.99 (978-0-670-03570-0(X) , Viking Juvenile) Penguin Group (USA) Inc.

Nichols, Catherine. Claude Monet. 2006. (Primary Source Library of Famous Artists). (Illus.). 32p. (J). 21.95 (978-1-4042-2761-3(X) , PowerKids Pr.) Rosen Publishing Group, Inc., The.

Northeast, Brenda V. Claude con Amor. 2001. Tr. of For the Love of Claude. (CAT., Illus.). 32p. (J). (gr. 1-4). 14.95 (978-84-95040-93-0(X)) Serres, Ediciones, S. L. ESP. *Dist:* Lectorum Pubns., Inc.

—Claude con Amor. Mendo, Miguel Angel, tr. 2001. Tr. of For the Love of Claude. (SPA., Illus.). 32p. (J). (gr. 1-4). 14.95 (978-84-95040-92-3(1)) Serres, Ediciones, S. L. ESP. *Dist:* Lectorum Pubns., Inc.

Prestel. Coloring Book Claude Monet. 2006. (Illus.). 32p. 8.95 (978-3-7913-3713-5(0)) Prestel Publishing.

Sateren, Shelley Swanson. Monet. 2001. (Masterpieces). (Illus.). 24p. (J). (gr. 2-3). lib. bdg. 18.60 (978-0-7368-1123-1(0) , Bridgestone Bks.) Capstone Pr., Inc.

Welton, Jude & Dorling Kindersley Publishing Staff. Monet. 2000. (Eyewitness Bks.). (Illus.). 64p. (J). (gr. 4-7). lib. bdg. 19.99 (978-0-7894-6815-4(8)) Dorling Kindersley Publishing, Inc.

Whiting, Jim. Claude Monet. 2007. (Art Profiles for Kids Ser.). (Illus.). 48p. (J). lib. bdg. 29.95 (***978-1-58415-563-8(9)***) Mitchell Lane Pubs., Inc.

MONET, CLAUDE, 1840-1926—FICTION

Anholt, Laurence. The Magical Garden of Claude Monet. (Anholt's Artists Books for Children Ser.). 32p. (J). (ps-3). 2007. pap. 7.99 (***978-0-7641-3855-3(3));*** 2003. (Illus.). 14.95 (978-0-7641-5574-1(1)) Barron's Educational Series, Inc.

MONETARY QUESTION

see Money

MONEY

see also Banks and Banking; Coinage; Coins; Credit; Gold; Mints; Paper Money

Aboff, Marcie. The Lemonade Standoff. Olin, Troy, illus. 2007. (J). lib. bdg. (***978-1-4048-3668-6(3)***) Picture Window Bks.

Algonzzine, Kate. Time & Money. 1998. (Basic Skills Ser.). (Illus.). 32p. (J). (gr. k-1). pap. 4.95 (978-0-88724-466-7(1) , CD-2134) Carson-Dellosa Publishing Co., Inc.

American Education Publishing Staff. Time & Money. 2003. (Brighter Child Learning Flash Cards Ser.). (Illus.). 36p. (J). 2.99 (978-1-56189-467-3(2) , 31050, American Education Publishing) School Specialty Publishing.

American Education Publishing Staff & Douglas, Vincent. Time & Money: Grade 2. 2001. (Together We Learn Ser.). (Illus.). 32p. (C). (gr. 2). pap. 2.99 (978-1-56189-629-5(2) , 31325-629, American Education Publishing) School Specialty Publishing.

American Education Publishing Staff, et al. The Complete Book of Time & Money. 2000. (Complete Book Ser.). (Illus.). 352p. (J). (gr. k-6). pap. 14.95 (978-1-56189-500-7(8) , 31133, American Education Publishing) School Specialty Publishing.

Anderson, Jon. Money a Rich History. Wickstrom, Thor, illus. 2003. (Smart about History Ser.). 32p. (J). (gr. k-5). pap. 5.99 (978-0-448-43205-2(6) , Grosset & Dunlap) Penguin Group (USA) Inc.

—Smart about History: Money. 2003. (gr. k-3). lib. bdg. 14.15 (978-0-613-72510-1(7)) Tandem Library Bks.

Ayers, Amy. Using Money at the Lemonade Stand. 2007. pap. (***978-0-8368-8481-4(7));*** 24p. (J). (gr. 1-3). lib. bdg. 19.93 (***978-0-8368-8472-2(8)***) Stevens, Gareth Inc. (Weekly Reader Early Learning Library).

Bailey, Gerry & Law, Felicia. Common Cents: The Money in Your Pocket. Phillips, Mike & Brooks, Rosie, illus. 2006. (My Money Ser.). 24p. (J). (gr. 4-6). 27.93 (978-0-7565-1671-0(4)) Compass Point Bks.

—What's It All Worth? The Value of Money. Phillips, Mike & Brooks, Rosie, illus. 2006. (My Money Ser.). 24p. (J). (gr. 4-6). 27.93 (978-0-7565-1673-4(0)) Compass Point Bks.

Basel, Roberta. Checks, Credit, & Debit Cards. 2006. (First Facts Ser.). (Illus.). 24p. (J). (978-0-7368-5394-1(4)) Capstone Pr., Inc.

Bateman, Katherine R. The Young Investor: Projects & Activities for Making Your Money Grow. 2001. (Illus.). 144p. (J). (gr. 6-9). pap. 14.95 (978-1-55652-396-0(3)) Chicago Review Pr., Inc.

Benchmark Education Staff, compiled by. Money. 2006. spiral bd. 95.00 (***978-1-4108-7077-3(4)***) Benchmark Education Co.

Berger, Melvin & Berger, Gilda. Round & Round the Money Goes: What Money Is & How We Use It. McCreary, Jane, illus. 1999. (Discovery Readers Ser.). 48p. (J). (gr. 4-7). lib. bdg. 15.95 (978-0-7910-5066-8(1) , Chelsea Hse.) Facts On File, Inc.

Berne, Stanley. Legal Tender - Or - It's All About Money! 2003. 160p. (YA). pap. 40.00 (978-0-913844-27-4(6)) Rising Tide Pr.

Berry, Joy Wilt. Earning an Allowance: A Kid's Money Book About. Bartholomew & Pace, Don, illus. rev. ed. 2000. (Living Skills Ser.: Vol. 1). 48p. (J). (gr. 1-7). pap. 4.95 (978-1-58634-140-4(5)) Goldstar Publishing, Inc.

Berry, Rob & Duey, Kathleen. The Smart Kids Allowance System: Step-by-Step Money Management Guidebook. Bartholomew, illus. Date not set. (Family Skill Builders Ser.). (J). (gr. k-6). pap. 9.95 (978-1-883761-34-9(4)) Family Life Productions.

Bochner, Arthur Berg & Berg, Adriane G. The Totally Awesome Money Book for Kids. 2nd ed. 2002. (Childcare/Parenting Guides Ser.). 160p. 12.95 (978-1-55704-493-8(7)) Newmarket Pr.

Boritzer, Etan. What Is Money. 2006. pap. 6.95 (***978-0-9762743-3-9(7)***) Lane, Veronica Bks.

—What Is Money? 2006. (What Is? Ser.). 14.95 (***978-0-9762743-2-2(9)***) Lane, Veronica Bks.

Burkett, Larry. All about Money. Locke, Gary, illus. 2003. (All about Ser.). 32p. (J). pap., pap. 7.99 (978-0-7814-3786-8(5) , 0781437865) Cook, David C. Publishing Co.

—All about Talent: Discovering Your Gifts & Personality. 2003. (All about Ser.). 32p. (J). pap., pap. 7.99 (978-0-7814-3787-5(3) , 0781437873) Cook, David C. Publishing Co.

—Money Matters for Teens. 2001. (gr. 7-12). lib. bdg. 22.25 (978-0-613-90343-1(9)) Tandem Library Bks.

Burkett, Larry, et al. Money Matters for Kids. 2001. 64p. (gr. 1-7). pap. 10.99 (978-0-8024-4635-0(3)) Moody Pubs.

—Money Matters for Teens. rev. ed. 2001. 160p. (gr. 8-12). pap. 12.99 (978-0-8024-4636-7(1)) Moody Pubs.

Burton, Margie & French, Tammy, Cathy - Jones. Clasificar mi dinero & Sorting My Money. 2005. spiral bd. 66.00 (***978-1-4108-5630-2(5)***) Benchmark Education Co.

Burton, Margie, et al. Our Money. Adams, Alison, ed. 1999. (Early Connections Ser.). 16p. (J). (gr. k-2). pap. 4.50 (978-1-58344-076-6(3)) Benchmark Education Co.

—Travel Money, U. S. A. Adams, Alison, ed. 1999. (Early Connections Ser.). 16p. (J). (gr. k-2). pap. 4.50 (978-1-58344-083-4(6)) Benchmark Education Co.

Cernek, Kim. Build-a-Skill Instant Books Time & Money. Faulkner, Stacey, ed. Campbell, Jenny & Tom, Darcy, illus. 2007. (J). 4.99 (***978-1-59198-417-7(3)***) Creative Teaching Pr., Inc.

Check It Out! Money Workbook. 2001. (J). pap. 4.95 (978-1-56911-724-8(1)) Learning Resources, Inc.

Cipriano, Jeri S. Haciendo Dinero. 2005. Tr. of Making Money. (SPA., Illus.). 16p. (J). (gr. 1 up). lib. bdg. 15.93 (978-0-7368-4178-8(4)) Capstone Pr., Inc.

Cooper, Jason. How Coins & Bills are Made. 2003. (Money Power Discovery Library Ser.). (Illus.). 24p. (J). (gr. 3-6). 14.95 (978-1-58952-211-4(7)) Rourke Publishing, LLC.

—Keeping Money Safe. 2003. (Rourke Discovery Library). (Illus.). 24p. (J). (gr. 3-6). 14.95 (978-1-58952-214-5(1)) Rourke Publishing, LLC.

—Money Around the World. 2003. (Rourke Discovery Library). (Illus.). 24p. (J). (gr. 3-6). 14.95 (978-1-58952-212-1(5)) Rourke Publishing, LLC.

—Paying Without Money. 2003. (Rourke Discovery Library). (Illus.). 24p. (J). (gr. 3-6). 14.95 (978-1-58952-213-8(3)) Rourke Publishing, LLC.

Counting Money. 2004. (Illus.). (J). pap. 3.95 (978-0-8225-1289-9(0)) Lerner Publishing Group.

Counting Money. 2003. (Illus.). 48p. (J). (gr. k-2). suppl. ed. 8.99 (978-1-56451-371-7(8) , ID7522) School Specialty Publishing.

Cribb, Joe & Buller, Laura. Money. 2005. (Dk eyewitness Bks.). 72p. (J). lib. bdg. 19.99 (978-0-7566-1398-3(1)); (Illus.). (gr. 4-7). 15.99 (978-0-7566-1389-1(2)) Dorling Kindersley Publishing, Inc.

Dalmatian Press Staff. Money, Time & Fractions: Chalkboard Book. 2003. (Home Learning Tools Ser.). 10p. (J). (gr. 2 up). pap. 3.99 (978-1-4037-0331-6(0)) Dalmatian Pr.

Dalton, Julie. Counting Money. (J). 2006. 32p. (gr. 1-2). pap. 5.95 (978-0-516-25361-9(1)); 2005. (Illus.). 31p. (ps-ps). 20.50 (978-0-516-25260-5(7)) Scholastic Library Publishing. (Children's Pr.).

—Making Change at the Fair. 2006. 32p. (gr. 1-2). (YA). pap. 5.95 (978-0-516-21224-1(9)); (Illus.). (J). 20.50 (978-0-516-24960-5(6)) Scholastic Library Publishing. (Children's Pr.).

Daniels, Kathryn. A Bluestocking Guide - the Money Mystery: Based on Richard J. Maybury's book the Money Mystery. Williams, Jane A., ed. 2004. (Bluestocking Guide Ser.). 31p. (YA). pap. 8.95 (978-0-942617-49-8(5)) Bluestocking Pr.

DK Publishing. Show Me the Money. 2008. 96p. (J). (gr. 2-5). 15.99 (***978-0-7566-3762-0(7)***) Dorling Kindersley Publishing, Inc.

Dollars & Cents, Set. 2002. (J). (ps-3). lib. bdg. 119.58 (978-1-57765-909-9(0)); lib. bdg. 119.58 (978-1-57765-910-5(4)); lib. bdg. 119.58 (978-1-57765-883-2(3)) ABDO Publishing Co.

Dollars & Sense. 2003. 96p. (gr. 5-8). 9.99 (978-1-56822-547-0(4) , IF2527) School Specialty Publishing.

Donovan, Sandy. Budgeting. 2006. (How Economics Works). (Illus.). 48p. (J). (gr. 3-7). 25.26 (978-0-8225-2665-0(4) , Lerner Pubns.) Lerner Publishing Group.

Doudna, Kelly. Let's Add Bills. 2003. (Dollars & Cents Ser.). (Illus.). 23p. (J). (ps-3). lib. bdg. 19.93 (978-1-57765-898-6(1)) ABDO Publishing Co.

—Let's Add Coins. 2003. (Dollars & Cents Ser.). (Illus.). 23p. (J). (ps-3). lib. bdg. 19.93 (978-1-57765-896-2(5)) ABDO Publishing Co.

—Let's Add Money. 2003. (Dollars & Cents Ser.). (Illus.). 23p. (J). (ps-3). lib. bdg. 19.93 (978-1-57765-900-6(7)) ABDO Publishing Co.

—Let's Subtract Bills. 2003. (Dollars & Cents Ser.). (Illus.). 23p. (J). (ps-3). lib. bdg. 19.93 (978-1-57765-899-3(X)) ABDO Publishing Co.

—Let's Subtract Coins. 2003. (Dollars & Cents Ser.). (Illus.). 23p. (J). (ps-3). lib. bdg. 19.93 (978-1-57765-897-9(3)) ABDO Publishing Co.

—Let's Subtract Money. 2003. (Dollars & Cents Ser.). (Illus.). 23p. (J). (ps-3). lib. bdg. 19.93 (978-1-57765-901-3(5)) ABDO Publishing Co.

Douglas, Vincent. Math, Time, & Money. 2004. (Flash Card Collection). 324p. (C). 16.95 (978-1-58845-663-2(3)) School Specialty Publishing.

—Money. 2000. (Spectrum Flash Cards Ser.). (Illus.). 50p. (J). (gr. k-3). 2.99 (978-1-57768-150-2(9) , Learning Materials) School Specialty Publishing.

Douglas, Vincent & School Specialty Publishing Staff. My Little Showcase of Getting Ready for School. 2005. (My Little Showcase Ser.). (Illus.). 100p. (J). bds. 14.95 (978-1-58845-652-6(8) , Brighter Child) School Specialty Publishing.

Duey, Kathleen & Berry, Ron. The Smart Kids Allowance System: Tool Kit. 2000. (Illus.). (J). (gr. 1-6). pap. 14.95 incl. audio (978-1-891100-68-0(8)) Smart Kids Publishing.

Dyer, Wayne W. & Tracy, Kristina. It's Not What You've Got: Lessons for Kids on Money & Abundance. Budnick, Stacy Heller, illus. 2007. 32p. (J). (ps-3). 15.95 (***978-1-4019-1850-7(6)***) Hay Hse., Inc.

Ehrlich, Fred. You Can't Buy a Dinosaur with Dime. 2007. (Illus.). 32p. pap. 6.95 (***978-1-59354-591-8(6)***) Blue Apple Bks.

Ekblad, Linda. Contemos las monedas: Metro Math Readers Yellow Level. 2000. (Metro Math Readers Yellow Level Ser.). (J). (gr. 1-2). 3.75 (978-1-58120-474-2(4)) Metropolitan Teaching & Learning Co.

—Money. 2000. (Metro Math Readers Yellow Level Ser.). (J). (gr. 1-2). 49.95 (978-1-58830-101-7(X)) Metropolitan Teaching & Learning Co.

Endres, Hollie J. How Much Money? (J). (gr. k-2). 2006. (Illus.). 16p. 15.93 (978-0-7368-5859-5(8) , Yellow Umbrella Bks.); 2005. (978-0-7368-5325-5(1)); 2005. (Illus.). 16p. (978-0-7368-5289-0(1)) Capstone Pr., Inc.

Fetty, Maurice A. Theme Pack: Money. 2002. (Pair-It Bks.). (Illus.). (J). pap. (978-0-7398-6378-7(9)) Steck-Vaughn.

Firestone, Mary. Earning Money. 2004. (Learning about Money Ser.). (Illus.). 24p. (J). lib. bdg. 21.26 (978-0-7368-2639-6(4)) Capstone Pr., Inc.

—Spending Money. 2004. (Learning about Money Ser.). (Illus.). 24p. (J). lib. bdg. 21.26 (978-0-7368-2641-9(6)) Capstone Pr., Inc.

—What Is Money? 2004. (Learning about Money Ser.). 24p. (J). lib. bdg. 21.26 (978-0-7368-2642-6(4)) Capstone Pr., Inc.

Forte, Imogene. Ready to Learn Time & Money. 2003. (Illus.). 64p. per. 7.95 (978-0-86530-592-2(7)) Incentive Pubns., Inc.

Freeman, Cynthia & Wilson, Clifford. Money Does Grow on Trees! Kids Learn How to Earn, Spend, Save & Invest Your Money. Cicetti, Kim, illus. 2000. 165p. (J). (978-0-9673735-0-8(6)) Magic Penny Publishing Co., The.

Geist, Ellen, retold by. Not for Me. 2002. (Illus.). 16p. (J). (978-0-439-35081-5(6)) Scholastic, Inc.

Giesecke, Ernestine. Dollars & Sense: Managing Your Money. 2003. (Everyday Economics Ser.). (Illus.). 48p. (J). (gr. 2-5). lib. bdg. 27.07 (978-1-58810-492-2(3)) Heinemann Library.

—From Seashells to Smart Cards: Money & Currency. 2003. (Everyday Economics Ser.). (Illus.). 48p. (J). (gr. 3-5). lib. bdg. 27.07 (978-1-58810-491-5(5)) Heinemann Library.

Gill, Shelley & Tobola, Deborah. The Big Buck Adventure. Lin, Grace, illus. 2000. 32p. (J). (gr. k-4). 15.95 (978-0-88106-294-6(4)) Charlesbridge Publishing, Inc.

Giesecke, Ernestine. Dollars & Sense: Managing Your Money. 2002. (Everyday Economics Ser.). 48p. (J). (gr. 3-5). pap. 8.50 (978-1-58810-955-2(0) , 91584) Heinemann Library.

—Everyday Banking: Consumer Banking. 2002. (Everyday Economics Ser.). 48p. (J). (gr. 3-5). pap. 8.50 (978-1-58810-952-1(6) , 91585) Heinemann Library.

—From Seashells to Smart Cards: Money & Currency. 2002. (Everyday Economics Ser.). 48p. (J). (gr. 3-5). pap. 8.50 (978-1-58810-954-5(2) , 91586) Heinemann Library.

—Money Business: Banks & Banking. 2002. (Everyday Economics Ser.). 48p. (J). (gr. 3-5). pap. 8.50 (978-1-58810-953-8(4) , 91587) Heinemann Library.

Godfrey, Neale S. A Money Adventure: Earning, Saving, Spending, Sharing: Primary Home-School Kit. 2003. (One & Only Common Sense/ents Ser.). 44.50 (978-0-7652-2451-4(8)) Modern Curriculum Pr.

Goldman, Phyllis B., ed. Monkeyshines on Math, Money & Banking. 2002. (Illus.). 183p. (J). pap. 32.95 (978-1-888325-21-8(6)) Allosaurus Pubs.

Greenes, Carol, et al. Time & Money. 2003. (Illus.). 60p. (J). (ps-3). 16.95 (978-0-7690-0004-6(5)) Seymour, Dale Pubns.

Greenes, Carole, et al. Money & Time. 2003. (Illus.). (J). (gr. 3). 16.95 (978-0-7690-0834-9(8)) Seymour, Dale Pubns.

Guy, Pauline. Let's Count. 2004. 24p. (J). (ps). 15.99 (978-0-9744205-6-1(5)) Golden Eagle Publishing Hse., Inc.

Harcourt School Publishers Staff. Count Your Change. 3rd ed. 2002. (Trophies English Language Learners Ser.). (Illus.). pap. 5.10 (978-0-15-327714-6(9)) Harcourt Schl. Pubs.

—Money, Money. 3rd ed. 2002. (Illus.). pap. 5.10 (978-0-15-327768-9(8)) Harcourt Schl. Pubs.

—Money, Money, Money. 3rd ed. 2002. (Trophies English Language Learners Ser.). (Illus.). pap. 5.10 (978-0-15-327828-0(5)) Harcourt Schl. Pubs.

—What Is Money: Take-Home Book. 1999. (Collections Ser.). (Illus.). (J). pap. 1.90 (978-0-15-317314-1(9)) Harcourt Schl. Pubs.

Harman, Hollis Page. Money Sense for Kids. 2nd ed. 2004. (Illus.). 192p. (J). pap. 10.95 (978-0-7641-2894-3(9)) Barron's Educational Series, Inc.

Haugen, Janie. Money Calc Worksheet Program. Britt, Melissa, ed. 1999. (Illus.). 100p. (J). ring bd. 39.95 (978-1-884074-75-2(8) , PCI 914) PCI Educational Publishing.

Haydon, Julie. Making Coins & Bills. 2006. (Money Ser.). (Illus.). 32p. (J). (978-1-58340-784-4(7)) Smart Apple Media.

High, Q. Money. 1998. (Orig.). pap. 2.99 (978-0-7681-0029-7(1) , McClanahan Bk.) Learning Horizons, Inc.

Hill, Mary. Dollars. 2005. (Welcome Bks.). (Illus.). 24p. (J). (ps-2). pap. 4.95 (978-0-516-25170-7(8) , Children's Pr.) Scholastic Library Publishing.

The History of Money. pap. 12.95 (978-89-314-3702-7(1)) Youngjin.com Publishing Co., Ltd. KOR. *Dist:* Transition Vendor.

Howard, Constance A. All about Money, a Youth's Guide to Money Matters. 2000. (J). (gr. 4-6). pap. 11.95 (978-0-9705781-0-5(5)) Savannah Butterfly Bks.

HSP. Time & Money, Bk. E. 2nd ed. 2002. (First-Place Math Ser.). (gr. 1 up). pap. 12.60 (978-0-15-334613-2(2)); (gr. 2 up). pap. 12.60 (978-0-15-334619-4(1)) Harcourt Schl. Pubs.

Hunt, Darleen L. Dog's Dollars: Patterns. Komarck, Michael, illus. 2003. (Sherman's Math Corner Ser.). (J). (ps-3). (978-1-929591-08-4(X)) Reading Rock, Inc.

If You Made a Million. 2004. pap. 18.95 incl. audio compact disk (978-1-55592-178-1(7)); pap. 38.75 incl. audio compact disk (978-1-55592-634-2(7)); pap. 32.75 incl. audio (978-1-55592-365-5(8)); pap. 32.75 incl. audio (978-1-55592-364-8(X)); pap. 14.95 incl. audio (978-1-55592-166-8(3)); (J). 29.95 incl. cd-rom (978-1-55592-134-7(5)); (J). 24.95 incl. audio (978-1-55592-096-8(9)); (J). pap. 14.95 incl. audio (978-1-55592-097-5(7)); (J). pap. 18.95 incl. audio compact disk (978-1-55592-136-1(1)) Weston Woods Studios, Inc.

Jackson, Abby. Making Money. 2003. (Yellow Umbrella Books for Early Readers). (Illus.). 17p. (J). 15.93 (978-0-7368-2928-1(8)); pap. (978-0-7368-2887-1(7)) Yellow Umbrella Pr.

Kompelien, Tracy. I Know about Money, It Is so Funny! 2007. (Math Made Fun Ser.). (Illus.). 24p. (J). 19.93 (978-1-59928-527-6(4) , SandCastle) ABDO Publishing Co.

—I Know about Money, It Is So Funny! 2006. (Math Made Fun Ser.). (Illus.). 24p. (J). (978-1-59928-528-3(2)) ABDO Publishing Co.

Kravitz, Robert J. A Collector's Guide to Fractional Currency: The Pocket Change of the Union Soldier. collector's ed. 2003. (Illus.). 262p. pap. 29.95 (978-0-918501-46-2(6) , RK-2003, Archives Pr.) Media Assocs.

Kummer, Patricia K. Currency. (Inventions That Shaped the World Ser.). (J). 2005. (Illus.). 80p. (gr. 5-8). pap. 9.95 (978-0-531-16734-2(8)); 2004. 30.50 (978-0-531-12341-6(3)) Scholastic Library Publishing. (Watts, Franklin).

Learning about Money. (First Facts Ser.). (Illus.). (J). (gr. 1-2). lib. bdg. 85.04 (978-0-7368-2755-3(2)) Capstone Pr., Inc.

Leatherdale, Linda. Money Is a Kid's Best Friend. 2000. 256p. (J). pap. 22.95 (978-0-13-018878-6(6)) Prentice Hall PTR.

Leedy, Loreen. Follow the Money! 2005. (Illus.). 32p. (Orig.). (J). (gr. k-3). tchr. ed. 17.95 (978-0-8234-1587-8(2)) Holiday Hse., Inc.

Lewin, Ted. How Much? Visiting Markets Around the World. Lewin, Ted, illus. 2006. (Illus.). 40p. (J). 16.99 (978-0-688-17552-8(X)) HarperCollins Pubs.

Loewen, Nancy. In the Money: A Book about Banking. Fitzpatrick, Brad, illus. 2004. (J). (978-1-4048-0950-5(3)) Picture Window Bks.

Loewen, Nancy & Fitzgerald, Brad. Cash, Credit Cards, or Check? A Book about Payment Methods. 2004. (Money Matters Ser.). (Illus.). 24p. (J). 22.60 (978-1-4048-0951-2(1)) Picture Window Bks.

Long, Lynette. One Dollar: My First Book about Money. 1998. (Illus.). 32p. (J). (ps-2). bds. 8.95 (978-0-7641-0319-3(9)); bds. 13.95 (978-0-7641-7132-1(1)) Barron's Educational Series, Inc.

Marks, Jenny L. Sorting Money. 2007. (Sorting Ser.). (Illus.). 32p. (J). (gr. k-3). lib. bdg. 23.93 (978-0-7368-6738-2(4)) Capstone Pr., Inc.

Marsh, Carole. Who Wants to Be a Florida Millionaire? 2001. (Carole Marsh Florida Bks.). lib. bdg. 29.95 (978-0-635-00035-4(0)) Gallopade International.

Mayr, Diane. Everything Kids' Money Book: From Saving to Spending to Investing-Learn All Abou. 2000. (gr. 3-6). lib. bdg. 15.25 (978-0-613-51247-3(2)) Tandem Library Bks.

—Kids' Everything Money: From Saving to Spending to Investing - Learn All about Money! 2000. (Everything Kids Ser.). 144p. (gr. 4-7). pap. 6.95 (978-1-58062-685-9(8)) Adams Media Corp.

—Kids' Money Book. 2000. (978-0-606-22488-8(2)) Tandem Library Bks.

McGillian, Jamie Kyle. The Kids' Money Book. Phillips, Ian, illus. 2006. 96p. (J). (gr. 4-8). reprint ed. 18.00 (978-0-7567-9900-7(7)) DIANE Publishing Co.

—The Kids' Money Book: Earning * Saving * Spending * Investing * Donating. 2004. (Illus.). 96p. pap. 5.95 (978-1-4027-1765-9(2)) Sterling Publishing Co., Inc.

Molter, Carey. A Dime = 10 Cents. 2003. (Dollars & Cents Ser.). (Illus.). 23p. (J). (ps-3). lib. bdg. 19.93 (978-1-57765-884-9(1)) ABDO Publishing Co.

—A Dollar = $1.00. 2003. (Dollars & Cents Ser.). (Illus.). 23p. (J). (ps-3). lib. bdg. 19.93 (978-1-57765-885-6(X)) ABDO Publishing Co.

—A Half-Dollar = 50 Cents. 2003. (Dollars & Cents Ser.). (Illus.). 23p. (J). (ps-3). lib. bdg. 19.93 (978-1-57765-886-3(8)) ABDO Publishing Co.

—How Much Is $1.00? 2003. (Dollars & Cents Ser.). (Illus.). 23p. (J). (ps-3). lib. bdg. 19.93 (978-1-57765-892-4(2)) ABDO Publishing Co.

—How Much Is $100.00? 2003. (Dollars & Cents Ser.). (Illus.). 23p. (J). (ps-3). lib. bdg. 19.93 (978-1-57765-893-1(0)) ABDO Publishing Co.

—How Much Is $20.00? 2003. (Dollars & Cents Ser.). (Illus.). 23p. (J). (ps-3). lib. bdg. 19.93 (978-1-57765-895-5(7)) ABDO Publishing Co.

—How Much Is $5.00? 2003. (Dollars & Cents Ser.). (Illus.). 23p. (J). (ps-3). lib. bdg. 19.93 (978-1-57765-891-7(4)) ABDO Publishing Co.

—How Much Is $50.00? 2003. (Dollars & Cents Ser.). (Illus.). 23p. (J). (ps-3). lib. bdg. 19.93 (978-1-57765-890-0(6)) ABDO Publishing Co.

—How Much Is Ten Dollars. 2003. (Dollars & Cents Ser.: Level Ii). (Illus.). 23p. (J). (ps-3). lib. bdg. 19.93 (978-1-57765-894-8(9)) ABDO Publishing Co.

—A Nickel = 5 Cents. 2003. (Dollars & Cents Ser.). (Illus.). 23p. (J). (ps-3). lib. bdg. 19.93 (978-1-57765-887-0(6)) ABDO Publishing Co.

—A Penny = 1 Cent. 2003. (Dollars & Cents Ser.). (Illus.). 23p. (J). (ps-3). lib. bdg. 19.93 (978-1-57765-888-7(4)) ABDO Publishing Co.

—A Quarter. 2003. (Dollars & Cents Ser.: Level I). (J). (ps-3). lib. bdg. 19.93 (978-1-57765-889-4(2)) ABDO Publishing Co.

Money. (Illus.). 24p. (J). (gr. k-2). pap. 6.95 (978-1-55254-044-2(8) , BV25002) Brighter Vision Pubns.

Money. ldr.'s ed. 1998. (Cross Training Ser.: Vol. 4). 64p. (YA). (gr. 10-12). pap. 15.00 incl. VHS (978-1-57405-033-2(8)) CharismaLife Pubs.

Money. 2004. (Illus.). lib. bdg. 7.95 (978-0-8225-5257-4(4)) Lerner Publishing Group.

Money - Set 2: Dollars that Add Up. 2005. (J). spiral bd. 19.90 (978-0-9770248-5-8(7)) Sidedoor Publishing LLC.

Money Adventure. deluxe ed. 1998. (Neale Godfrey Money Program Ser.). (J). (978-0-8136-4218-5(3)); incl. cd-rom (978-0-8136-4219-2(1)) Modern Curriculum Pr.

Money & Banks, 6 Vols. 115.98 (978-0-8368-4867-0(5)) Stevens, Gareth Inc.

Money & Values, Grades 7-12: What Is Wealth? 2001. (YA). pap., tchr. ed. 89.00 incl. VHS (978-0-917159-11-4(X)) Learning Seed Co.

Money Matters. 2005. (C). (gr. 1-3). 67.80 (978-1-4048-0992-5(9)) Picture Window Bks.

Money, Money. 96p. 9.99 (978-0-7424-0197-6(9) , LL80001) School Specialty Publishing.

Money, Money, Money! Individual Title Six-Packs. (Bookweb Ser.). 32p. (gr. 5 up). 34.00 (978-0-7635-3796-8(9)) Rigby Education.

Money Set D, 6 vols. (Phonics Readers Ser.). (gr. k-2). 28.95 (978-0-7368-4052-1(4)) Red Brick Learning.

Moriarty, J. T. The Birth of American Capitalism: The Rise of the American Bank. 2003. (America's Industrial Society in the 19th Century Ser.). (Illus.). 32p. (J). pap. (978-0-8239-4280-0(5)) Rosen Publishing Group, Inc., The.

Morrison, Taylor. The Buffalo Nickel. 2002. (Illus.). 32p. (J). (gr. 1-5). 16.00 (978-0-618-10855-8(6) , Walter Lorraine) Houghton Mifflin Co. Trade & Reference Div.

Mototsune, Kat. Money: Pay the Price. Geoffroi, Remie, illus. 2007. (Deal with It Ser.). 32p. (J). (gr. 4-8). pap., pap. 12.95 (*978-1-55028-958-9(6)*) Lorimer, James & Co., Ltd., Pubs. CAN. *Dist:* Casemate Pubs. & Bk. Distributors, LLC.

Murphy, Debbie & Murphy, Frank. Time & Money. 2002. (Best-Ever Activities for Grades 2-3 Ser.). (Illus.). 48p. (J). (gr. 2-3). 10.95 (978-0-439-29648-9(X)) Scholastic, Inc.

Murphy, Patricia J. Earning Money. 2006. (How Economics Works). (Illus.). 48p. (J). (ps-7). 25.26 (978-0-8225-2149-5(0) , Lerner Pubns.) Lerner Publishing Group.

My Book of Money: Dollars & Cents. 2007. (J). per. 6.95 (*978-1-933241-43-2(8)*) Kumon Publishing North America, Inc.

My First Book of Money: Counting Coins. 2007. (J). per. 6.95 (*978-1-933241-42-5(X)*) Kumon Publishing North America, Inc.

Nathan, Amy. The Kids' Allowance Book. Palen, Debbie, illus. 1998. 128p. (J). (gr. 3-7). 15.95 (978-0-8027-8651-7(0)) Walker & Co.

Osborne, J. E. The Money Book. Date not set. (Early Math Big Bks.). (Illus.). 16p. (J). (ps-2). pap. 16.95 (978-1-58273-141-4(1)) Sundance/Newbridge Educational Publishing.

Practice Power Flip & Learn Money. 2000. (Illus.). 16p. (J). (gr. k-2). spiral bd. (978-1-930355-25-5(4)) Greenbrier/Scentex.

Practice Power Practice Book Money. 2001. (Illus.). 18p. (J). (gr. k-2). spiral bd., wbk. ed. (978-1-930355-36-1(X)) Greenbrier/Scentex.

Prior, Jennifer. Math Games to Master Basic Skills: Time & Money: 14 Reproducible Games That Help Struggling Learners Practice & Really Master Basic Time & Money Skills & Concepts. 2007. 48p. pap. 10.99 (978-0-439-55414-5(4) , Teaching Resources) Scholastic, Inc.

Quin, Caroline. Shopping. 2004. (Activities for 3-5 Year Olds Ser.). (Illus.). 32p. pap. 11.00 (978-1-897675-58-8(5)) Brilliant Pubns. GBR. *Dist:* Parkwest Pubns., Inc.

Rau, Dana Meachen. Spending Money. 2005. (Money & Banks Ser.). (Illus.). 24p. (J). pap. (978-0-8368-4879-3(9)); lib. bdg. 19.33 (978-0-8368-4872-4(1)) Stevens, Gareth Inc.

Realtime Associates and Mazer Corporation Staff & LeapFrog Staff, compiled by. Name & Know the Value of Money. 2002. (J). (gr. 2). 66.75 (978-1-58605-339-0(6) , LeapFrog Schl. Hse.) LeapFrog Enterprises, Inc.

Reeves, Diane Lindsey. Career Ideas for Kids Who Like Math & Money. 2nd rev. ed. (Career Ideas for Kids Ser.). 208p. (J). (gr. 4-9). pap. 16.95 (*978-0-8160-6546-2(2)* , Checkmark Bks.); 2007. 32.95 (*978-0-8160-6545-5(4)* , Ferguson Publishing Co.) Facts On File, Inc.

Richardson, Adele D. Money. 1999. (Let's Investigate Economics Ser.). (Illus.). 32p. (J). (gr. 2 up). lib. bdg. (978-0-88682-555-3(5) , Creative Education) Creative Co., The.

Roberson, Erin. All about Money. (Rookie Read-About Math Ser.). (J). 2005. (Illus.). 32p. (gr. 1-2). pap. 5.95 (978-0-516-24672-7(0)); 2004. 31p. 20.50 (978-0-516-24420-4(5)) Scholastic Library Publishing. (Children's Pr.).

Roderick, Stacey & Warwick, Ellen. Centsibility: The Planet Girl Guide to Money. Melnychuk, Monika, illus. 2008. 80p. (*978-1-55453-208-7(6)*) Kids Can Pr., Ltd.

Rosinsky, Natalie M. All about Money. 2003. (Let's See Library). (Illus.). 24p. (J). (gr. 1 up). 19.93 (978-0-7565-0482-3(1)) Compass Point Bks.

—Earning Money. 2003. (Let's See Library). (Illus.). 24p. (J). (gr. 1 up). 19.93 (978-0-7565-0483-0(X)) Compass Point Bks.

—Saving Money. 2003. (Let's See Library). (Illus.). 24p. (J). (gr. 1 up). 19.93 (978-0-7565-0484-7(8)) Compass Point Bks.

—Spending Money. 2003. (Let's See Library). (Illus.). 24p. (J). (gr. 1 up). 19.93 (978-0-7565-0485-4(6)) Compass Point Bks.

Round & Round the Money Goes. (Discovery Readers Ser.). 48p. (J). pap. 3.95 (978-0-8249-5310-2(X) , Ideals Children's Bks.) Ideals Pubns.

Roy, Jennifer Rozines & Roy, Gregory. Money at the Store. 2006. (Math All Around Ser.). (Illus.). 32p. (J). lib. bdg. 28.50 (978-0-7614-2264-8(1) , Benchmark Bks.) Cavendish, Marshall Corp.

Saving Money. 2004. (Illus.). pap. 3.95 (978-0-8225-1291-2(2)) Lerner Publishing Group.

School Specialty Publishing. I Can Tell Time & Count Money. 2006. (Brighter Child I Can... Ser.). 128p. (J). pap. 3.95 (978-0-7696-4907-8(6) , Brighter Child) School Specialty Publishing.

—Learning about Money, Grades 1-2. 2006. 48p. (C). pap. 6.99 (*978-0-7682-3451-0(4)* , Schaffer, Frank) Schaffer, Frank Pubns.

—Learning about Money, Grades 3-4. 2006. 48p. (C). pap. 6.99 (*978-0-7682-3453-4(0)* , Schaffer, Frank) Schaffer, Frank Pubns.

—Money. 1999. (Flip-Flashtm Math Ser.). 160p. (J). (gr. 1 up). pap. 7.99 (978-1-56451-349-6(1) , ID7873, Ideal School Supply) Schaffer, Frank Pubns.

—Time & Money. 2006. (Brighter Child Flash Cards Ser.). 54p. (J). 2.99 (978-0-7696-6480-4(6) , Brighter Child) School Specialty Publishing.

School Zone Interactive Staff. Time, Money & Fractions. rev. ed. 2003. (On-Track Software Ser.). 64p. (J). (gr. k-2). pap. 15.99 incl. cd-rom (978-1-58947-832-9(0)) School Zone Publishing Co.

School Zone Publishing Company Staff. Money. 2000. (Mats Ser.). (Illus.). (J). 3.29 (978-0-88743-723-6(0) , 03112) School Zone Publishing Co.

School Zone Publishing Interactive Staff. Time, Money & Fractions. 2001. (On-Track Software Ser.). (Illus.). 32p. (J). pap. 13.99 incl. cd-rom (978-0-88743-954-4(3) , 08830) School Zone Publishing Co.

School Zone Staff. Time & Money. 2004. 56p. (J). 2.79 (978-1-58947-990-6(4)) School Zone Publishing Co.

School Zone Staff, ed. Time & Money. 2005. 26p. (J). (gr. 1-2). pap. 3.79 (978-1-58947-788-9(X)) School Zone Publishing Co.

—Time, Money & Fractions. 2003. (J). (gr. 1-2). cd-rom 19.99 (978-1-58947-930-2(0)) School Zone Publishing Co.

Schott, Jane A. Children of a New Century. 1999. (Picture the American Past Ser.). (Illus.). 48p. (gr. 2-5). lib. bdg. 22.60 (978-1-57505-220-5(2)) Lerner Publishing Group.

Seuling, Barbara. Ancient Coins Were Shaped Like Hams: And Other Freaky Facts about Coins, Bills, & Counterfeiting. Skeens, Matthew, illus. 2007. (J). lib. bdg. (*978-1-4048-3750-8(7)*) Picture Window Bks.

Somervill, Barbara A. The History of Money. 2006. (Timeline Library Ser.). (Illus.). 32p. (J). (gr. 2-6). 27.07 (978-1-59296-439-0(7)) Child's World, Inc.

Sparks, Candi. Can I Have Some Money? Of Course You Can! Educating Children about Money. Graf, William, illus. 2006. (*978-0-9789445-0-6(X)*) Sparks Fly.

Spending Money. 2004. (Illus.). pap. 3.95 (978-0-8225-1292-9(0)) Lerner Publishing Group.

SpongeBob Money. 2007. (J). 2.95 (*978-1-59545-104-0(8)*) Learning Horizons, Inc.

Steck-Vaughn Staff. At-Home Workbooks: Money. 2004. (Illus.). pap., wbk. ed. 5.99 (978-0-7398-8537-6(5)) Steck-Vaughn.

Sterling, Kristin. Money. 2008. (J). pap. (*978-0-8225-8848-1(X)*) Lerner Publishing Group.

The Story of Money: Third Grade Guided Reading Level I. (On Our Way to English Ser.). (gr. 3 up). 34.50 (978-0-7578-7116-0(X)) Rigby Education.

Studio 2B Focus - On the Money. 2004. (YA). (978-0-88441-687-6(9)) Girl Scouts of the USA.

Swain, Cynthia. I Have a Coin. 2006. (Early Explorers Ser.). (J). 30.00 (*978-1-4108-6040-8(X)*) Benchmark Education Co.

Tattersall, Clare. The Young Zillionaire's Guide to Money & Banking. 2000. (Be a Zillionaire Ser.). (Illus.). 48p. (YA). (gr. 5-8). lib. bdg. 23.95 (978-0-8239-3262-7(1) , ZIMOBA, Rosen Central) Rosen Publishing Group, Inc., The.

Thayer, Tanya. Counting Money. 2005. (First Step Nonfiction Ser.). (Illus.). 24p. (gr. k-2). lib. bdg. 17.27 (978-0-8225-1258-5(0)) Lerner Publishing Group.

Thomas, Keltie. The Kids Guide to Money Cent$ MacEachern, Stephen, tr. MacEachern, Stephen, illus. 2004. 56p. (J). (gr. 4-6). (978-1-55337-389-6(8)); (978-1-55337-390-2(1)) Kids Can Pr., Ltd.

Thouin, Juanita. Get Your Wallet On: The Money Quiz for High School Grads. 2003. 97p. (YA). per. 6.49 (978-0-9740641-0-9(6)) Daisy Publishing.

Time & Money. (Basics First Ser.). 32p. (gr. k up). 4.99 (978-0-7647-0048-4(0) , FS30090); (gr. 1 up). 4.99 (978-0-7647-0049-1(9) , FS30091); (gr. 2 up). 4.99 (978-0-7647-0075-0(8) , FS30092); (gr. 3 up). 4.99 (978-0-7647-0076-7(6) , FS30093) Schaffer, Frank Pubns.

Time & Money. (Homework Booklets Ser.). 80p. (gr. 1 up). 2.99 (978-1-56822-834-1(1) , IF0357); (gr. 3 up). 2.99 (978-1-56822-836-5(8) , IF0359) School Specialty Publishing.

TNT Stone and Associates Staff & Petertil Design Partners Staff, illus. Counting Money. 1998. (Powertools for Kids Ser.: No. 13). 4p. (J). (gr. 1-3). pap., wbk. ed. 4.95 (978-1-58220-012-5(2) , 32503, PowerTools for Kids) Navigator Systems, Inc.

Tobias. The Only Investment Guide Teens Will Ever Need. 2003. (YA). pap. (978-0-15-600711-5(8)) Harcourt Trade Pubs.

Understanding Money in Business Made Easy. 2002. per. 14.99 (978-0-9657083-4-0(9)) ANUP Research & Multimedia LP.

Vinyl Children's Savings Bank. 2004. 5.95 (978-1-59156-126-2(4)) Covenant Communications, Inc.

Walsh, Kieran. Money Math. 2003. (Illus.). 48p. (J). 29.93 (978-1-58952-381-4(4)) Rourke Publishing, LLC.

Waters, Jennifer. Money. 2002. (Spyglass Books). (Illus.). 24p. (J). (gr. 1 up). lib. bdg. 18.60 (978-0-7565-0374-1(4)) Compass Point Bks.

Williams, Rozanne Lanczak. Learning about Coins. Jarrett, Michael, photos by. 2004. (I Can Do Math Ser.). (Illus.). 24p. (J). (gr. 1 up). lib. bdg. 20.67 (978-0-8368-4110-7(7)) Stevens, Gareth Inc.

Work with Time & Money. 2004. (Math "How To" Ser.). (Illus.). 48p. (J). 7.99 (978-1-57690-967-6(0)) Teacher Created Materials, Inc.

Worth, Bonnie. One Cent, Two Cent, Old Cent, New Cent: All about Money. Ruiz, Aristides & Mathieu, Joseph, illus. 2008. (J). (*978-0-375-82881-2(8)*); lib. bdg. (*978-0-375-92881-9(2)*) Random Hse., Inc.

2-Sided Math Puzzles: Money. 2002. (J). 15.95 (978-1-930820-23-4(2)) Garlic Pr.

MONEY—FICTION

Adebayo, Yinka. Ragga to Riches. 1999. 187p. (J). (978-1-874509-69-1(7)) X Pr., The.

Allen, Nancy K. Once upon a Dime: A Math Adventure. Doyle, Adam, illus. 2004. (Math Adventures Ser.). 32p. (J). pap. 6.95 (978-1-57091-161-3(4)) Charlesbridge Publishing, Inc.

Auseon, Andrew. Funny Little Monkey. 2006. 312p. (YA). pap. 6.95 (978-0-15-205413-7(8)) Harcourt Trade Pubs.

Bank One Community Writers Staff. Sand Dollar $ucce$$ Crisp, John T., Jr., illus. l.t. ed. 1998. (WeWrite Kids! Ser.: No. 40). 45p. (J). (gr. 2-5). pap. 3.95 (978-1-57635-022-5(3)) WeWrite LLC.

Belgue, Nancy. Casey Little: Yo-Yo Queen. 2005. (Orca Young Readers Ser.). (Illus.). 144p. (J). (gr. 3-6). pap. 5.95 (978-1-55143-357-8(5)) Orca Bk. Pubs. USA.

Berenstain, Stan & Berenstain, Jan. The Berenstain Bears & the Big Blooper. Klimo, Kate, ed. 2000. (Berenstain Bears First Time Bks.). (Illus.). 32p. (J). (gr. k-3). pap. 3.25 (978-0-679-88962-5(0) , Random Hse. Bks. for Young Readers) Random Hse. Children's Bks.

—The Berenstain Bears & the Big Blooper. 2000. (Berenstain Bears First Time Bks.). (J). (gr. k-2). 10.05 (978-0-606-19887-5(3)); lib. bdg. 10.95 (978-0-613-32320-8(3)) Tandem Library Bks.

—The Berenstain Bears' Dollars & Sense. 2001. (Berenstain Bears First Time Bks.). (Illus.). 32p. (J). (gr. k-3). pap. 3.99 (978-0-375-81124-1(9) , Random Hse. Bks. for Young Readers) Random Hse. Children's Bks.

—The Berenstain Bears' Dollars & Sense. 2001. (Berenstain Bears First Time Bks.). (J). (gr. k-3). 10.79 (978-0-606-22793-3(8)); (gr. 3-6). lib. bdg. 10.95 (978-0-613-32322-2(X)) Tandem Library Bks.

Blume, Judy. Double Fudge. (Fudge Ser.). 224p. 2007. (J). (gr. 2). 5.99 (*978-0-14-240878-0(6)* , Puffin); 2002. (gr. 3-7). 15.99 (978-0-525-46926-1(5) , Dutton Juvenile) Penguin Group (USA) Inc.

—Double Fudge. 2004. (Fudge Ser.). 160p. (J). (gr. 3-7). pap. 36.00 incl. audio (978-0-8072-2036-8(1) , Listening Library) Random Hse. Audio Publishing Group.

Brandeis, Batsheva. Faiga Finds the Way. Levitas, Alexander, illus. 2005. (Fun to Read Book Ser.). 120p. (J). pap. 8.95 (978-1-929628-28-5(5)) Hachai Publishing.

Bricker, Chris. The Leaping Frogs of Calameris County. 2006. 48p. pap. 12.95 (978-1-4241-2408-4(5)) PublishAmerica, Inc.

Burkett, Larry. A Home for the Hamsters. 2000. (Great Smoky Mountain Storybook Ser.). (Illus.). 32p. (J). (ps-3). 7.99 (978-0-8024-0982-9(2)) Moody Pubs.

Chad Borrows Money. l.t. ed. 2003. (Illus.). 16p. (J). ring bd. 15.95 (978-0-9722829-6-3(3)) Red Carpet Publishing.

Chorao, Kay. Pig & Crow. rev. ed. (Illus.). (J). 2005. 40p. reprint ed. pap. 6.95 (978-0-8050-7261-7(6)); 2000. 32p. 16.95 (978-0-8050-5863-5(X)) Holt, Henry & Co. (Holt, Henry & Co. Bks. For Young Readers).

Cosby, Bill. The Day I Was Rich. Honeywood, Varnette P., illus. 1999. (Little Bill Books for Beginning Readers Ser.). 40p. (J). (gr. k-3). pap. 15.95 (978-0-590-52172-7(1) , Cartwheel Bks.) Scholastic, Inc.

—The Day I Was Rich. 1999. (Little Bill Books for Beginning Readers Ser.). (J). (gr. k-3). 10.64 (978-0-606-16932-5(6)) Tandem Library Bks.

Curtis, Christopher Paul. Mr. Chickee's Funny Money. 160p. 2007. (gr. 4-7). 6.50 (978-0-440-22919-3(7) , Yearling); 2005. (Illus.). (J). (gr. 3-7). 15.95 (978-0-385-32772-5(2) , Lamb, Wendy); 2005. (Illus.). (J). (gr. 3-7). lib. bdg. 17.99 (978-0-385-90936-5(5) , Lamb, Wendy) Random Hse. Children's Bks.

—Mr. Chickee's Funny Money. l.t. ed. 2006. 190p. 23.95 (978-0-7862-8670-6(9)) Thorndike Pr.

The Darling of Wall Street. 2005. (J). pap. (978-0-9744863-1-4(0)) Paulus Publishing.

deRubertis, Barbara. Deena's Lucky Penny. 1999. (Math Matters Ser.). (Illus.). (J). 11.75 (978-0-606-18218-8(7)) Tandem Library Bks.

—Deena's Lucky Penny. Holub, Joan & Fisher, Cynthia, illus. 1999. 32p. (J). (ps-ps). lib. bdg. 12.95 (978-0-613-17168-7(3)) Tandem Library Bks.

—Deena's Lucky Penny: Math Concept: Money. Holub, Joan & Fisher, Cynthia, illus. 1999. (Math Matters Ser.). 32p. (J). (ps-1). pap. 4.95 (978-1-57565-091-3(6)) Kane Pr., The.

Driscoll, Laura. Sally's Big Save. Wummer, Amy, illus. 2006. 32p. (J). lib. bdg. 20.00 (*978-1-4242-1116-6(6)*) Fitzgerald Bks.

—Sally's Big Save. Wummer, Amy, illus. 2006. (Social Studies Connects). 32p. (J). pap. 4.99 (978-1-57565-164-4(5)) Kane Pr., The.

Durham, Kathryn. Mom Can You Buy Me This? 2000. (Illus.). 70p. (YA). (gr. 4-10). pap. 9.95 (978-0-9703876-0-8(1)) Pen & Paper Publishing.

Dussling, Jennifer. Fair Is Fair! Palmisciano, Diane, illus. 2003. (Math Matters Ser.). 32p. (J). (gr. 1-3). pap. 4.99 (978-1-57565-131-6(9)) Kane Pr., The.

—Fair Is Fair! 2003. (gr. k-3). lib. bdg. 12.95 (978-0-613-79279-0(3)) Tandem Library Bks.

Earnest Took It with Him. 2005. (J). 12.95 (978-0-9762679-0-4(X)) Birdsall, Bonnie Thomas.

Endicott, Jodi. I Had a Dollar in Hawaii: A Story of One Dollar That Traveled Hawaii. Loffel, Hans, ed. 1999. (Illus.). 32p. (J). (gr. 1-5). 9.95 (978-0-9674183-0-8(5)) Palila Bks.

—I Had a Dollar in Hawaii: A Story of One Dollar That Traveled Hawaii. Loffel, Hans & Nehmad, Debbie, illus. 1999. 32p. (J). (ps-3). 8.95 (978-0-9621280-7-3(4)) Words & Pictures Publishing, Inc.

Flake, Sharon G. Money Hungry. (J). 2003. 208p. (gr. 5-17). pap. 5.99 (978-0-7868-1503-6(5)); 2001. 192p. (gr. 3-7). 15.99 (978-0-7868-0548-8(X) , Jump at the Sun) Hyperion Bks. for Children.

Foster, Kinsley. Wild Abandon Vol. 3: How to Grow a Snowball. 2000. (YA). pap. 10.95 (978-0-9667634-7-8(5)) What's Inside Pr.

Fuller, Matthew. Smart Little Saver. 2000. (J). 14.95 (978-0-9675849-0-4(6)) Fuller, Matt.

Fusillo, Archimede. Let It Rip! David & Nick Have the Smelliest Plan of All! 2006. (Bites Ser.). (Illus.). 84p. (J). (gr. 2-5). pap. 3.95 (978-0-7624-2622-5(5) , Running Pr. Kids) Running Pr. Bk. Pubs.

Glass, Julie. A Dollar for Penny. Allen, Joy, illus. 2000. (Step into Reading Ser.: No. 3). 32p. (J). (gr. k-3). pap. 3.99 (978-0-679-88973-1(6) , Random Hse. Bks. for Young Readers) Random Hse. Children's Bks.

—A Dollar for Penny. Allen, Joy, illus. 2000. 32p. (J). (ps-ps). lib. bdg. 11.80 (978-0-613-07631-9(1)) Tandem Library Bks.

—A Dollar for Penny. 2000. (Illus.). (J). 10.79 (978-0-606-18492-2(9)) Tandem Library Bks.

Great Paint Problem. 2000. (gr. k-3). lib. bdg. 11.80 (978-0-613-35614-5(4)) Tandem Library Bks.

Greene, Stephanie. Owen Foote, Money Man. Weston, Martha, illus. 96p. (J). 2003. (gr. k-3). pap. 4.95 (978-0-618-37837-1(5)); 2000. (gr. 5-9). tchr. ed. 15.00 (978-0-618-02369-1(0)) Houghton Mifflin Co. Trade & Reference Div. (Clarion Bks.).

Grove, Vicki. Destiny. 2001. 12.64 (978-0-606-22525-0(0)) Tandem Library Bks.

Gutman, Dan. The Million Dollar Goal. 2003. (Illus.). 176p. (gr. 3-7). 15.99 (978-0-7868-1883-9(2) , Disney Editions) Disney Pr.

—The Million Dollar Goal. 2005. 176p. (gr. 3-7). pap. 5.99 (978-0-7868-5494-3(4)) Hyperion Bks. for Children.

Haesche, Richard P., Sr. Jason & the Money Tree. Switzer, Cheryle, illus. aut. ed. 2000. 170p. (J). pap. 11.99 (978-1-929381-71-5(9) , Third Millennium Publishing) Sci Fi-Arizona, Inc.

Harcourt School Publishers Staff. Benny's Pennies: Library Book. 1999. (Collections Ser.). (Illus.). pap. 14.90 (978-0-15-313412-8(7)) Harcourt Schl. Pubs.

—The Greatest Treasure: Reader's Choice Book. 2001. (Collections Ser.). (Illus.). pap. 12.10 (978-0-15-314357-1(6)) Harcourt Schl. Pubs.

—Kids Can Earn Money: Take-Home Book. 1999. (Signatures Ser.). (Illus.). (J). pap. 1.90 (978-0-15-313902-4(1)) Harcourt Schl. Pubs.

—Ten, Twenty, Thirty... 3rd ed. 2002. (Trophies English Language Learners Ser.). (Illus.). pap. 5.10 (978-0-15-327639-2(8)) Harcourt Schl. Pubs.

Harris, Richard T. If I Had a Penny... Harris, Richard Craig, illus. 2001. 32p. (J). 14.95 (978-0-9704504-0-1(0)) RTH ENT.

Harris, Ted. Catney Reid Who Needs Money? (978-0-9744597-5-2(5)) Brown Bks. Publishing Group.

Haskins, Lori. No Money? No Problem! Nez, John A., illus. 2004. (Social Studies Connects). 32p. (J). (gr. k-2). pap. 4.99 (978-1-57565-141-5(6)) Kane Pr., The.

Hoban, Lillian. Arthur's Funny Money. Hoban, Lillian, illus. 2002. (Arthur the Chimpanzee Ser.). (Illus.). (J). 12.34 (978-0-7587-5985-6(1)) Book Wholesalers, Inc.

In Business with Mallory. 2007. 160p. (J). (gr. 2-6). pap. 5.95 (***978-0-8225-6561-1(7)*** , First Avenue Editions) Lerner Publishing Group.

Inkpen, Mick. Great Pet Sale. 1999. (Illus.). 16p. (J). (ps-1). pap. 14.95 (978-0-531-30130-2(3) , Orchard Bks.) Scholastic, Inc.

Jorisch, Stephane, illus. The Trial of the Stone: A Folk Tale. 2000. 32p. (J). (ps-1). pap. 6.95 (978-1-55037-646-3(2)) Annick Pr., Ltd. CAN. *Dist:* Firefly Bks., Ltd.

Kowitt, Holly. Cold Hard Cash. 2003. (gr. k-3). lib. bdg. 11.80 (978-0-613-72169-1(1)) Tandem Library Bks.

Krulik, Nancy E. New Girl. 2008. (How I Survived Middle School Ser.: No. 4). 112p. (J). pap. 4.99 (***978-0-545-01303-1(8)*** , Scholastic Paperbacks) Scholastic, Inc.

Lee, Kathy. Phoebe's Fortune. 2003. 128p. 6.49 (978-1-85999-700-0(7)) Scripture Union GBR. *Dist:* Gabriel Resources.

Leedy, Loreen. The Monster Money Book. Leedy, Loreen, illus. 2005. (Illus.). 32p. (J). (gr. k-3). pap. 6.95 (978-0-8234-1558-8(9)) Holiday Hse., Inc.

Little, Robert. Jamaal's Lucky Day. Fitzpatrick, Audrey, illus. 2003. 32p. (J). (gr. 2-6). 15.95 (978-0-9701863-4-8(7)) Relde Publishing.

The Lost Money. 2005. (J). (978-1-932570-37-3(3)) Literacy Footprints Inc.

Lowry, Brigid. Things You Either Hate or Love. 2005. 179p. (YA). 16.95 (978-0-8234-2004-9(3)) Holiday Hse., Inc.

—Things You Either Hate or Love. 2007. 192p. (YA). (gr. 4-7). pap. 8.95 (978-0-312-36308-6(7) , St. Martin's Griffin) St. Martin's Pr.

Maccarone, Grace & Burns, Marilyn. Monster Money. 1998. (Hello Reader! Math Ser.: Level 1). (Illus.). 32p. (J). (ps-3). pap. 3.99 (978-0-590-12007-4(7)) Scholastic, Inc.

Mackey, Lori. Money Mama & the Three Little Pigs. 2004. (Illus.). 48p. (J). 19.95 (978-0-9744570-2-4(7)) P4K Publishing.

Milway, Katie Smith. One Hen: How One Small Loan Made a Big Difference. Fernandes, Eugenie, illus. 2008. 32p. (***978-1-55453-028-1(8)***) Kids Can Pr., Ltd.

Mollel, Tololwa M. My Rows & Piles of Coins. Lewis, Earl, illus. 2002. (J). 22.45 (978-0-7587-0385-9(6)) Book Wholesalers, Inc.

—My Rows & Piles of Coins. Lewis, E. B., illus. 1999. 32p. (J). (gr. k-3). tchr. ed. 16.00 (978-0-395-75186-2(1) , Clarion Bks.) Houghton Mifflin Co. Trade & Reference Div.

The Moneybag: a Tale from Korea: Small Versions of Big Books. (On Our Way to English Ser.). (gr. 3 up). 35.50 (978-0-7578-7247-1(6)) Rigby Education.

The Moneybag: a Tale from Korea: Third Grade Big Books. (On Our Way to English Ser.). (gr. 3 up). 29.95 (978-0-7578-4214-6(3)) Rigby Education.

El Mono Azul. (Fantasmas de Fear Street Coleccion). (SPA.). (YA). (gr. 5-8). pap. 7.95 (978-950-04-2022-8(8) , EM10965) Emecé Editores S.A. ARG. *Dist:* Lectorum Pubns., Inc., Planeta Publishing Corp.

Mooney, E. S. Snow Fun. 2002. (gr. k-3). lib. bdg. 11.80 (978-0-613-58168-4(7)) Tandem Library Bks.

Moonjar, ed. Noom & Raj Start Business. 2005. 36p. 19.95 (978-0-9724282-2-4(4)); 9.95 (978-0-9724282-5-5(9)) Moonjar, LLC.

Moore, Allan. Lottery Winner. 2001. 32p. (YA). (gr. 6-12). pap. (978-0-8224-1456-8(2)) Globe Fearon Educational Publishing.

Morgan, Allen. Matthew & the Midnight Money Van. Martchenko, Michael, illus. 2003. 24p. (J). (ps-2). pap. 4.95 (978-0-920303-72-6(2)); lib. bdg. 14.95 (978-0-920303-75-7(7)); (Annikins Ser.: Vol. 11). pap. 0.99 (978-1-55037-194-9(0)) Annick Pr., Ltd. CAN. *Dist:* Firefly Bks., Ltd.

Myers, Bill. My Life as a Walrus Whoopee Cushion, Vol. 16. 1999. (Incredible Worlds of Wally McDoogle Ser.: No. 16). 128p. (J). (gr. 3-7). pap. 6.99 (978-0-8499-4025-5(7)) Nelson, Thomas Inc.

Naylor, Phyllis Reynolds. Girls Rule! 2004. 160p. (gr. 4-7). 15.95 (978-0-385-73139-3(6) , Delacorte Bks. for Young Readers) Random Hse. Children's Bks.

Neuschwander, Cindy. The Chocolate Champs. Ong, Cristina, illus. 2002. (Hello Math Reader Ser.). 32p. (J). pap. (978-0-439-24230-1(4)) Scholastic, Inc.

No Pay, No Way. 2002. (Illus.). (J). pap. (978-0-7398-5065-7(2)) Steck-Vaughn.

Oakley, Graham. Humphrey Hits the Jackpot. 1998. (Illus.). 25p. (J). (978-0-340-67079-8(7) , Hodder & Stoughton) Hodder General Publishing Division.

Pascal, Francine. Dinero Desaparecido. Orig. Title: Jessica & the Money Mix-Up. (SPA.). (J). 6.95 (978-84-272-3600-4(X)) Molino, Editorial ESP. *Dist:* AIMS International Bks., Inc.

Paulsen, Gary. The Tent. 2006. (Illus.). 96p. (J). pap. 5.95 (978-0-15-205833-3(8) , Harcourt Paperbacks) Harcourt Children's Bks.

Pritchard, J. J. Quest for the Pillars of Wealth: A Children's Guide to Growing Rich. 2000. 256p. (YA). (gr. 5-9). 14.95 (978-0-9703433-0-7(2)) Lantern Pr.

Ramsey, Dave. Careless at the Carnival: Junior Discovers Spending. Ramsey, Marshall, illus. 2003. 26p. (J). 9.99 (978-0-9726323-1-7(X)) Lampo Group Inc., The.

—Dave Ramsey's 6 Kids Books Boxed Set. 2005. (J). 59.99 (978-0-9774895-8-9(2)) Lampo Group Inc., The.

—My Fantastic Fieldtrip: Junior Discovers Saving. Ramsey, Marshall, illus. 2003. 26p. (J). 9.99 (978-0-9726323-3-1(6)) Lampo Group Inc., The.

Rocklin, Joanne. The Case of the Shrunken Allowance, Level 4. Van Wright, Cornelius & Hu, Ying-Hwa, illus. 1999. (Hello Reader! Math Ser.). 48p. (J). (gr. 2-4). pap. 3.99 (978-0-590-12006-7(9)) Scholastic, Inc.

Rouillard, Wendy W. A Penny for Barnaby. l.t. ed. 1998. (Illus.). 32p. (J). (gr. 1-3). 15.95 (978-0-9642836-7-1(0)) Barnaby & Co.

Roy, Ron. The Talking T. Rex. Gurney, John Steven, illus. 2003. (A to Z Mysteries Ser.: No. 20). (J). (gr. 3-6). lib. bdg. 11.80 (978-0-613-85127-5(7)) Tandem Library Bks.

—Trouble at the Treasury. Bush, Timothy, illus. 2006. (Capital Mysteries Ser.: No. 7). 96p. (J). (gr. 2-4). pap. 3.99 (978-0-375-83969-6(0) , Random Hse. Bks. for Young Readers) Random Hse. Children's Bks.

Sadler, Marilyn & Bollen, Roger. Money, Money, Honey Bunny! 2006. (Bright & Early Bks.). (Illus.). 36p. (J). 8.99 (978-0-375-83370-0(6)); lib. bdg. 12.99 (978-0-375-93370-7(0)) Random Hse. Children's Bks. (Random Hse. Bks. for Young Readers).

Santillo, LuAnn. Digging for Clams. Santillo, LuAnn, ed. 2003. (Half-Pint Kids Readers Ser.). (Illus.). 7p. (J). (ps-1). pap. (978-1-59256-092-9(X)) Half-Pint Kids, Inc.

Scraper, Katherine. Tag Sale Today. 2005. 40.00 (***978-1-4108-4210-7(X)***) Benchmark Education Co.

Seuling, Barbara. Robert Flip Book, No. 2. 2004. (Illus.). 128p. (J). (gr. 2-5). pap. 4.50 (978-0-439-61387-3(6) , Scholastic Paperbacks) Scholastic, Inc.

Shoup, Barbara. Everything You Want. 2008. 312p. (J). 16.95 (***978-0-7387-1227-7(2)*** , Flux) Llewellyn Pubns.

Skinner, Daphne. Tightwad Tod. Nez, John, illus. 2005. (Math Matters Ser.). 32p. (gr. 1-3). pap. 4.95 (978-1-57565-109-5(2)) Kane Pr., The.

—Tightwad Tod. 2001. (gr. k-3). lib. bdg. 12.95 (978-0-613-39368-3(6)) Tandem Library Bks.

Slater, Jean M. Monkey Business: At the Market. Slater, Jean M., illus. 2003. (Illus.). 10p. (J). bds. 16.00 (978-0-9743149-4-5(3)) Slater Software. Inc.

Slater, Teddy. Max's Money. Lewis, Anthony, illus. 1999. (Hello Reader! Math Ser.: Level 4). 32p. (J). (gr. 2-4). pap. 3.99 (978-0-590-12010-4(7) , Cartwheel Bks.) Scholastic, Inc.

Standish, Burt L. Dick Merriwell's Marked Money. Rudman, Jack, ed. 2003. (Frank Merriwell Ser.). pap. 9.95 (978-0-8373-9100-7(8)) Merriwell, Frank Inc.

Stewart, Sarah. The Money Tree. Small, David, illus. 2004. (J). (ps-ps). lib. bdg. 14.15 (978-0-606-29981-7(5)) Tandem Library Bks.

Strasser, Todd. For Money & Love. 2007. (Mob Princess Ser.). 208p. (YA). (gr. 9 up). pap. 8.99 (***978-1-4169-3533-9(9)*** , Simon Pulse) Simon & Schuster Children's Publishing.

Townson, Hazel. The One-Day Millionaires. l.t. ed. 1998. (Illus.). 79p. (J). pap. 16.95 (978-0-7540-6017-8(9) , Galaxy Children's Large Print) BBC Audiobooks America.

—The One Day Millionaires: An Arthur Venger Story. McKee, David, illus. 1998. 80p. (J). (gr. 2-6). pap. 8.99 (978-0-86264-835-0(1)) Andersen GBR. *Dist:* Independent Pubs. Group.

Tyrrell, Helen. Nora & the Dancing Horse. 2003. 231p. (J). pap. 14.95 (978-0-7414-1349-9(3)) Infinity Publishing.

Viorst, Judith. Alexander, Who Used to Be Rich Last Sunday. Cruz, Ray, illus. 2002. (J). 14.47 (978-0-7587-1919-5(1)) Book Wholesalers, Inc.

—Alexander, Who Used to Be Rich Last Sunday. 1999. (Alexander Ser.). (J). (gr. k-3). pap. 24.24 incl. audio (978-0-7887-3634-6(5) , 40999) Recorded Bks., LLC.

—Alexander, Who Used to Be Rich Last Sunday. Cruz, Ray, illus. 1999. (Alexander Ser.). (J). (gr. k-3). lib. bdg. 14.15 (978-0-8085-2752-7(5)) Tandem Library Bks.

Wells, Rosemary. Bunny Money. Wells, Rosemary, illus. 2002. (Max the Bunny Ser.). (Illus.). (J). 13.19 (978-0-7587-5446-2(9)) Book Wholesalers, Inc.

—Bunny Money. 2000. (Max & Ruby Ser.). (Illus.). 32p. (J). (gr. k-3). pap. 5.99 (978-0-14-056750-2(X) , Puffin) Penguin Group (USA) Inc.

—Bunny Money. 1999. (Max & Ruby Ser.). (Illus.). 32p. (J). (gr. k-2). 15.99 (978-0-670-88688-3(2) , Viking Juvenile) Penguin Group (USA) Inc.

—Bunny Money. 2000. (Max & Ruby Ser.). (gr. k-2). (J). (978-0-606-20226-8(9)); (J). 12.79 (978-0-606-20352-4(4)); lib. bdg. 14.15 (978-0-613-33681-9(X)) Tandem Library Bks.

Wesley, Valerie Wilson. How to Lose Your Cookie Money. Roos, Maryn, illus. 2004. 105p. (J). lib. bdg. 15.00 (***978-1-4242-0644-5(8)***) Fitzgerald Bks.

—How to Lose Your Cookie Money. Roos, Maryn, illus. 3rd rev. ed. 2004. (Willimena Rules! Ser.: Bk. 3). 112p. (gr. 2-5). pap. 3.99 (978-0-7868-5146-1(5) , Jump at the Sun) Hyperion Bks. for Children.

WeWrite Kids Staff. A Goo Idea! Brodland, Rita, ed. Freeman, Troy, illus. 2002. (WeWrite Kids! Ser.). 64p. (J). (gr. k-4). pap. 8.95 (978-1-57635-058-4(4)) WeWrite LLC.

Zimelman, Nathan. The Dollar. Zemke, Deborah, illus. 1999. (Books for Young Learners). 16p. (J). (gr. k-2). pap. 5.00 (978-1-57274-242-0(9) , A2446) Owen, Richard C. Pubs., Inc.

MONEY—HISTORY

Bailey, Gerry & Law, Felicia. Cowries, Coins, Credit: The History of Money. Phillips, Mike & Brooks, Rosie, illus. 2006. (My Money Ser.). 24p. (J). 27.93 (978-0-7565-1676-5(5)) Compass Point Bks.

Basel, Roberta. The History of Money. 2006. (First Facts Ser.). (Illus.). 24p. (J). (978-0-7368-5396-5(0)) Capstone Pr., Inc.

Cooper, Jason. American Coins & Bills. 2003. (Money Power Discovery Library Ser.). (Illus.). 24p. (gr. 3-6). 14.95 (978-1-58952-209-1(5)) Rourke Publishing, LLC.

—Money Power Discovery Library. 2003. (Money Power Discovery Ser.). (gr. 3-6). 89.70 (978-1-58952-208-4(7)) Rourke Publishing, LLC.

—Money Through the Ages. 2003. (Money Power Discovery Library Ser.). (Illus.). 24p. (gr. 3-6). 14.95 (978-1-58952-210-7(9)) Rourke Publishing, LLC.

Hall, Margaret. Money. 2nd ed. 2007. (J). (***978-1-4034-9815-1(6)***); pap. (***978-1-4034-9820-5(2)***) Heinemann Library.

Harcourt School Publishers Staff. Many Kinds of Money. 3rd ed. 2002. (Horizons Ser.). (Illus.). (J). pap. 3.70 (978-0-15-333180-0(1)) Harcourt Schl. Pubs.

—On the Money. 3rd ed. 2002. (Horizons Ser.). (Illus.). (J). pap. 3.70 (978-0-15-333135-0(6)) Harcourt Schl. Pubs.

—What Is Money? Below Level. 3rd ed. 2002. (Trophies Reading Program Ser.). (Illus.). pap. 5.10 (978-0-15-323155-1(6)) Harcourt Schl. Pubs.

Haydon, Julie. The History of Money. 2006. (Illus.). 32p. (J). (978-1-58340-780-6(4)) Smart Apple Media.

Loewen, Nancy. That Costs Two Cowries: A Book about the History of Money. Fitzpatrick, Brad, illus. 2004. (J). (978-1-4048-0953-6(8)) Picture Window Bks.

—That Costs Two Shells: The History of Money. Jensen, Brian, illus. 2005. (Money Matters Ser.). 24p. (J). (ps). lib. bdg. 22.60 (978-1-4048-1159-1(1)) Picture Window Bks.

Modern Curriculum Press Staff. Why Money Was Invented. 2001. (gr. k-3). lib. bdg. 15.90 (978-0-613-74852-0(2)) Tandem Library Bks.

Rau, Dana Meachen. The History of Money. 2005. (Money & Banks Ser.). (Illus.). 24p. (J). pap. (978-0-8368-4876-2(4)); lib. bdg. 19.33 (978-0-8368-4869-4(1)) Stevens, Gareth Inc.

Samuel, Charlie. Money & Finance in Colonial America. 2003. (Primary Sources of Everyday Life in Colonial America Ser.). (Illus.). 24p. (J). lib. bdg. 21.25 (978-0-8239-6602-8(X) , PowerKids Pr.) Rosen Publishing Group, Inc., The.

Spies, Karen Bornemann. Our Money. rev. ed. 2001. (I Know America Ser.). 48p. (gr. 2-7). pap. 9.95 (978-0-7613-1641-1(8)); (Illus.). lib. bdg. 24.90 (978-0-7613-2620-5(0)) Lerner Publishing Group. (Millbrook Pr.).

Tiner, John. The Story of in God We Trust: Discovering Our Nations Heritage. 2003. (Discovering Our Nation's Heritage Ser.). (Illus.). 48p. (J). 9.99 (978-0-89051-392-7(9) , 303-090) Master Bks.

MONEY-MAKING PROJECTS FOR CHILDREN

see Moneymaking Projects

MONEY, PAPER

see Paper Money

MONEY RAISING

see Fund Raising

MONEYMAKING PROJECTS

Bochner, Arthur & Bochner, Rose. The New Totally Awesome Business Book for Kids. 3rd rev. ed. 2007. 160p. (J). pap. 9.95 (***978-1-55704-757-1(X)***) Newmarket Pr.

Erlbach, Arlene. The Kids' Business Book. 1998. (Kids' Ventures Ser.). (Illus.). 64p. (J). (gr. 3-6). (978-0-8225-2413-7(9)); pap. (978-0-8225-9821-3(3)) Lerner Publishing Group. (Lerner Pubns.).

Firestone, Mary. Earning Money. 2004. (Learning about Money Ser.). (Illus.). 24p. (J). lib. bdg. 21.26 (978-0-7368-2639-6(4)) Capstone Pr., Inc.

Goldish, Meish. Kids & Co. Pellaton, Karen E., illus. 2002. 16p. (J). (978-0-439-35179-9(0)) Scholastic, Inc.

Haydon, Julie. Fundraising. 2006. (Illus.). 32p. (J). (978-1-58340-785-1(5)) Smart Apple Media.

Kiefer, Jeanne. Jobs for Kids: A Smart Kid's Q & A Guide. Green, Anne Canevari, illus. 2003. (Single Titles Ser.). 112p. (gr. 5-8). lib. bdg. 25.90 (978-0-7613-2611-3(1) , Millbrook Pr.) Lerner Publishing Group.

Linecker, Adelia Cellini. What Color Is Your Piggy Bank? Entrepreneurial Ideas for Self-Starting Kids. Lamb, Sandra, illus. 2004. 144p. (J). pap. 10.95 (978-1-894222-82-2(2)) Lobster Pr. CAN. *Dist:* Univ. of Toronto Pr.

Mazer, Anne. Have Wheels, Will Travel. 2001. (Amazing Days of Abby Hayes Ser.: No. 4). (Illus.). (J). 11.15 (978-0-606-21229-8(9)) Tandem Library Bks.

Murphy, Patricia J. Earning Money. 2006. (How Economics Works). (Illus.). 48p. (J). (ps-7). 25.26 (978-0-8225-2149-5(0) , Lerner Pubns.) Lerner Publishing Group.

Murphy, Stuart J. Sluggers' Car Wash. Saltzberg, Barney, illus. 2002. (MathStart Ser.).). 40p. (J). (gr. 2 up). pap. 5.99 (978-0-06-446248-8(X)) HarperCollins Pubs.

Rancic, Bill. Beyond the Lemonade Stand. 2006. 176p. (J). (gr. 5-9). 5.99 (978-1-59514-111-8(1) , Razorbill) Penguin Group (USA) Inc.

Rosinsky, Natalie M. Earning Money. 2003. (Let's See Library). (Illus.). 24p. (J). (gr. 1 up). 19.93 (978-0-7565-0483-0(X)) Compass Point Bks.

Tangerine Press Staff & Scholastic, Inc. Staff, contrib. by. Kid Biz. 2004. (Illus.). 62p. (J). (978-0-439-69986-0(X)) Scholastic, Inc.

Thayer, Tanya. Earning Money. 2005. (First Step Nonfiction Ser.). (Illus.). 24p. (gr. k-2). lib. bdg. 17.27 (978-0-8225-1259-2(9)) Lerner Publishing Group.

MONEYMAKING PROJECTS—FICTION

Adler, David A. The Babe & I. Widener, Terry, illus. 1999. 32p. (J). (gr. k-4). 17.00 (978-0-15-201378-3(4) , Gulliver Bks.) Harcourt Children's Bks.

Banim, Lisa. In the Doghouse. 2005. 124p. (J). lib. bdg. 16.92 (***978-1-4242-0685-8(5)***) Fitzgerald Bks.

Best, Cari & Davenier, Christine. Sally Jean, the Bicycle Queen. 2006. (Illus.). 32p. (J). (gr. k-2). 16.00 (978-0-374-36386-4(2) , Nelanie Kroupa Bks.) Farrar, Straus & Giroux.

Brown, Marc. Arthur's TV Trouble. Brown, Marc, illus. 2002. (Arthur Adventure Ser.). (Illus.). (J). 13.15 (978-0-7587-1990-4(6)) Book Wholesalers, Inc.

—Arthur's TV Trouble. Brown, Marc, illus. 1999. (Arthur Adventure Ser.). (Illus.). 32p. (J). (ps-3). 9.95 (978-0-316-11594-0(0)) Little, Brown Bks. for Young Readers.

Buchanan, Paul & Randall, Rod. The Monopoly, Vol. 10. 1998. (Misadventures of Willie Plummett Ser.: Vol. 10). 128p. (J). (gr. 3-7). 5.99 (978-0-570-05089-6(8)) Concordia Publishing Hse.

Clements, Andrew. Lunch Money. Selznick, Brian, illus. 2007. 240p. (J). (gr. 3-7). pap. 5.99 (***978-0-689-86685-2(2)*** , Aladdin) Simon & Schuster Children's Publishing.

—Lunch Money. Selznick, Brian, illus. l.t. ed. 2005. 231p. (J). (gr. 3-7). 21.95 (978-0-7862-8036-0(0) , Large Print Pr.) Thorndike Pr.

Conford, Ellen. A Job for Jenny Archer. 2006. (Illus.). 80p. (J). (gr. 1-4). pap. 3.99 (978-0-316-01484-7(2)) Little Brown & Co.

—What's Cooking, Jenny Archer? Palmisciano, Diane, illus. 2006. 80p. (J). (gr. 1-4). pap. 3.99 (978-0-316-01488-5(5)) Little Brown & Co.

Cosby, Bill. Money Troubles. Honeywood, Varnette P., illus. 1998. (Little Bill Books for Beginning Readers Ser.). 40p. (J). (gr. k-3). pap. 13.95 (978-0-590-16402-3(3)) Scholastic, Inc.

—Money Troubles. Honeywood, Varnette P., illus. 1998. (Little Bill Books for Beginning Readers Ser.). (J). (gr. k-3). (978-0-606-13615-0(0)) Tandem Library Bks.

—Money Troubles, Level. 3. Honeywood, Varnette P., illus. 1998. (Little Bill Books for Beginning Readers Ser.: No. 6). 40p. (J). (gr. k-3). pap. 3.99 (978-0-590-95623-9(X)) Scholastic, Inc.

Davies, Jacqueline. The Lemonade War. 2007. 192p. (J). (gr. 3-5). 16.00 (***978-0-618-75043-6(6)***) Houghton Mifflin Co.

Einspruch, Andrew. Dunkin' Dazza's Daring Dribble. 1999. (gr. 3-6). lib. bdg. 12.60 (978-0-613-30370-5(9)) Tandem Library Bks.

Ferraro, Tina. How to Hook a Hottie. 2008. 208p. (J). pap. (***978-0-385-73438-7(7)*** , Delacorte Pr.) Dell Publishing.

—How to Hook a Hottie. 2008. 208p. (YA). (gr. 7). lib. bdg. 11.99 (***978-0-385-90444-5(4)*** , Delacorte Bks. for Young Readers) Random Hse. Children's Bks.

Fletcher, Ralph J. Tommy Trouble & the Magic Marble. Caldwell, Benjamin H., Jr., illus. rev. ed. 2000. 64p. (J). (gr. 2-5). 16.00 (978-0-8050-6387-5(0) , Holt, Henry & Co. Bks. For Young Readers) Holt, Henry & Co.

Foland, Constance M. Flying High, Pogo! 2002. (gr. 3-6). lib. bdg. 14.10 (978-0-613-89603-0(3)) Tandem Library Bks.

Friedman, Laurie B. In Business with Mallory. Pollak, Barbara, illus. 2006. 159p. (J). 15.95 (978-1-57505-925-9(8) , Carolrhoda Bks.) Lerner Publishing Group.

Glass, Julie. A Dollar for Penny. Allen, Joy, illus. 2000. (Step into Reading Ser.: No. 3). 32p. (J). (gr. k-3). pap. 3.99 (978-0-679-88973-1(6) , Random Hse. Bks. for Young Readers) Random Hse. Children's Bks.

—A Dollar for Penny. Allen, Joy, illus. 2000. 32p. (J). (ps-ps). lib. bdg. 11.80 (978-0-613-07631-9(1)) Tandem Library Bks.

—A Dollar for Penny. 2000. (Illus.). (J). 10.79 (978-0-606-18492-2(9)) Tandem Library Bks.

Graff, Lisa. Bernetta Wallflower: A Novel. 2008. 256p. (J). 16.99 (***978-0-06-087592-3(5)***); lib. bdg. 17.89 (***978-0-06-087593-0(3)***) HarperCollins Pubs. (Geringer, Laura Book).

Gutman, Dan. The Get Rich Quick Club. 128p. (J). 2006. pap. 5.99 (978-0-06-053442-4(7) , Harper Trophy); 2004. 15.99 (978-0-06-053440-0(0)); 2004. lib. bdg. 16.89 (978-0-06-053441-7(9)) HarperCollins Pubs.

Hambrick, Sharon. Tommy's Race. Manning, Maurie, illus. 2004. (Fig Street Kids Ser.). 95p. (J). (gr. 1-2). 7.49 (978-1-59166-286-0(9)) Jones, Bob Univ. Pr.

Haugaard, Kay. No Place. Peterson-Albandoz, Michelle, illus. 1999. 175p. (J). (gr. 3-8). 15.95 (978-1-57131-616-5(7)) Milkweed Editions.

—No Place. 2nd ed. 2007. (Illus.). 140p. pap. 6.95 (***978-1-57131-675-2(2)***) Milkweed Editions.

—No Place. 1999. (J). (978-0-606-19034-3(1)) Tandem Library Bks.

Honeywood, Varnette P., illus. Money Troubles. 2002. (Little Bill Ser.). (J). 11.91 (978-0-7587-1452-7(1)) Book Wholesalers, Inc.

In Business with Mallory. 2007. 160p. (J). (gr. 2-6). pap. 5.95 (***978-0-8225-6561-1(7)*** , First Avenue Editions) Lerner Publishing Group.

Kennedy, Fran. The Pickle Patch Bathtub. Aldridge, Sheila, illus. 2004. 32p. (J). 14.95 (978-1-58246-112-0(0) , Tricycle Pr.) Ten Speed Pr.

Klein, Abby. Ready, Freddy! 2006. (Illus.). 96p. (J). pap. 3.99 (978-0-439-78458-0(1) , Blue Sky Pr., The) Scholastic, Inc.

—Yikes! Bikes! McKinley, John, illus. 2006. (Ready, Freddy! Ser.: No. 7). 96p. (J). pap. 3.99 (978-0-439-78456-6(5) , Blue Sky Pr., The) Scholastic, Inc.

M N O

Masterman-Smith, Virginia. First Mate Tate. 2000. (Illus.). 160p. (J). (gr. 5-9). 14.95 (978-0-7614-5075-7(0) , Cavendish Children's Bks.) Cavendish, Marshall Corp.

Mayer, Mercer. New Fire Truck. 2001. (gr. k-3). lib. bdg. 11.80 (978-0-613-67652-6(1)) Tandem Library Bks.

—The New Fire Truck, Vol. 2. 2002. (Little Critter First Readers Ser.). (Illus.). 24p. (J). (gr. k-1). pap. 3.95 (978-1-57768-843-3(0)) School Specialty Publishing.

Moss, Marissa. Amelia Works It Out. 2000. (Amelia - American Girl Ser.). (J). 12.75 (978-0-606-20544-3(6)) Tandem Library Bks.

Nesbit, E. Story of the Treasure Seekers. 2006. pap. (*978-1-4068-3507-6(2)) Echo Library.

Nesbit, E. The Story of the Treasure Seekers: Being the Adventures of the Bastable Children in Search of A Fortune. l.t. ed. 2005. 288p. pap. (978-1-84637-207-0(0)) Echo Library.

Nolen, Jerdine. Pitching in for Eubie. Lewis, E. B., illus. 2007. 32p. (J). lib. bdg. 17.89 (*978-0-06-056960-0(3)); 16.99 (*978-0-688-14917-8(0)) HarperCollins Pubs. (Amistad).

Olson, Gretchen. Call Me Hope. 2007. 288p. (J). (gr. 3-7). 15.99 (*978-0-316-01236-2(X)) Little Brown & Co.

—Call Me Hope: A Novel. 2007. 272p. (J). (*978-1-4287-4131-7(3)) Little Brown & Co.

Orme, Helen. Who's Who? 2008. (Siti's Sisters Ser.). 36p. pap. 7.95 (*978-1-84167-687-6(X)) Ransom Publishing Ltd. GBR. Dist: International Publishers Marketing.

Scraper, Katherine. The Yard Sale. 2006. (Early Explorers Ser.). (J). 30.00 (*978-1-4108-6043-9(4)) Benchmark Education Co.

Sharmat, Marjorie Weinman. Hollywood Hound. 2000. (Illus.). (J). 10.79 (978-0-606-18493-9(7)) Tandem Library Bks.

Stanley, George Edward. The Secret Ingredient. 1999. (Katie Lynn Cookie Company Ser.). (Illus.). (J). (978-0-606-18500-4(3)) Tandem Library Bks.

Weston, Martha. Owen Foote, Money Man. 2003. (gr. k-3). lib. bdg. 12.95 (978-0-613-73020-4(8)) Tandem Library Bks.

Willson, Sarah. Cookie Crisis! Bergman, Shannon & Ross, Sharon, illus. 2005. (Ready-To-Read Ser.). 32p. (J). (ps-ps). pap. 3.99 (978-0-689-86646-3(1) , Simon Spotlight/ Nickelodeon) Simon & Schuster Children's Publishing.

—Pet Peeves! Nez, John A., illus. 2005. (Social Studies Connects). 32p. (J). pap. 4.99 (978-1-57565-149-1(1)) Kane Pr., The.

Willson, Sarah. Pet Peeves. Nez, John, illus. 2005. 32p. (J). lib. bdg. 20.00 (*978-1-4242-1114-2(X)) Fitzgerald Bks.

MONGOLIA

Cheng-Pang, G. Mongolia. 1999. (Cultures of the World Ser.). (Illus.). 128p. (gr. 5-12). lib. bdg. 37.07 (978-0-7614-0954-0(8) , Benchmark Bks.) Cavendish, Marshall Corp.

Fisher, Frederick. Mongolia. 1999. (Festivals of the World Ser.). (Illus.). 32p. (J). (gr. 3 up). lib. bdg. 24.67 (978-0-8368-2024-9(X)) Stevens, Gareth Inc.

Grolier Educational Staff, contrib. by. Mongolia. 2003. (Illus.). 32p. (J). (978-0-7172-5796-6(7) , Grolier) Scholastic Library Publishing.

Harper, Judith. Unique Places. 2005. (Real Deal - Green Plus Ser.). (Illus.). 32p. (gr. 4-8). 19.00 (978-0-7910-8903-3(7)) Facts On File, Inc.

Harper, Judith E. Unique Places. 2005. (Real Deal Ser.). (Illus.). 32p. (J). pap. (978-0-7608-9635-8(6)) Sundance/ Newbridge Educational Publishing.

Lassieur, Allison. Mongolia. 2007. (Enchantment of the World, Second Ser.). (Illus.). 144p. (J). (gr. 5-9). 36.00 (978-0-516-24903-2(7) , Children's Pr.) Scholastic Library Publishing.

MONGOLIA—FICTION

Aldridge, James. The Marvellous Mongolian. 2003. 144p. (J). (gr. 4-7). pap. (978-1-55041-820-0(3)) Fitzhenry & Whiteside, Ltd.

Wilson, Diane Lee. I Rode a Horse of Milk White Jade. 1999. (Illus.). 288p. (J). (gr. k-9). lib. bdg. 15.30 (978-0-613-20158-2(2)) Tandem Library Bks.

—Rode a Horse of Milk White Jade. 1999. 14.64 (978-0-606-17306-3(4)) Tandem Library Bks.

MONGOLISM

see Down Syndrome

MONGOLS

Greenblatt, Miriam. Genghis Khan & the Mongol Empire. 2001. (Rulers & Their Times Ser.). (Illus.). 80p. (J). (gr. 6-8). lib. bdg. 29.93 (978-0-7614-1027-0(9) , Benchmark Bks.) Cavendish, Marshall Corp.

Kent, Zachary. Genghis Khan: Invincible Ruler of the Mongol Empire. 2007. (Rulers of the Middle Ages Ser.). (Illus.). 160p. (YA). (gr. 6). lib. bdg. 34.60 (*978-0-7660-2715-2(5)) Enslow Pubs., Inc.

Reynolds, Jan. Mongolia: Vanishing Cultures. 2007. 32p. (J). (*978-1-60060-145-3(6)); (*978-1-60060-130-9(8)) Lee & Low Bks., Inc.

Rice, Earle, Jr. Empire in the East: The Story of Genghis Khan. 2005. (World Leaders Ser.). (Illus.). 160p. (J). (ps-7). per. 26.95 (978-1-931798-62-4(1)) Reynolds, Morgan Inc.

Watson, Galadriel Findlay. Mongols. (Indigenous Peoples Ser.). 32p. 2005. pap. 7.95 (978-1-59036-257-0(8)); 2004. (Illus.). (J). lib. bdg. 26.00 (978-1-59036-220-4(9)) Weigl Pubs., Inc.

Zelenyj, Alexander. Marco Polo: Overland to China. 2005. (In the Footsteps of Explorers Ser.). (Illus.). 32p. (J). (gr. 3-9). (978-0-7787-2417-9(4)); pap. (978-0-7787-2453-7(0)) Crabtree Publishing Co.

MONGOLS—FICTION

McCaughrean, Geraldine. The Kite Rider. 2003. (Illus.). 320p. (J). (gr. 7 up). pap. 6.99 (978-0-06-441091-5(9)) HarperCollins Pubs.

—The Kite Rider. 2002. (gr. 7-12). lib. bdg. 15.30 (978-0-613-68440-8(0)) Tandem Library Bks.

MONGOLS—HISTORY

Burgan, Michael. Empire of the Mongols. 2005. (Great Empires of the Past Ser.). (Illus.). 128p. (J). (gr. 6-12). 35.00 (978-0-8160-5563-0(7)) Facts On File, Inc.

Nardo, Don. The Mongol Empire. 2005. (Life During the Great Civilizations Ser.). (Illus.). 48p. (J). (gr. 5-7). lib. bdg. 24.95 (978-1-4103-0585-5(6) , Blackbirch Pr., Inc.) Thomson Gale.

Streissguth, Thomas. Genghis Khan's Mongol Empire. 2005. (Lost Civilizations Ser.). (Illus.). 112p. (J). (gr. 5-8). lib. bdg. 29.95 (978-1-59018-436-3(X) , Lucent Bks.) Thomson Gale.

Whiting, Jim. The Life & Times of Genghis Khan. 2005. (Biography from Ancient Civilizations Ser.). (Illus.). 48p. (J). (gr. 4-8). lib. bdg. 29.95 (978-1-58415-348-1(2)) Mitchell Lane Pubs., Inc.

Worth, Richard. The Great Empire of China & Marco Polo in World History. 2003. (In World History Ser.). (Illus.). 112p. (J). lib. bdg. 26.60 (978-0-7660-1939-3(X)) Enslow Pubs., Inc.

MONGOOSES

Halfmann, Janet. Mongoose. 2004. (Nature's Predators Ser.). (Illus.). 48p. (J). 26.20 (978-0-7377-2622-0(9) , Greenhaven Pr., Inc.) Thomson Gale.

Meerkat Chat, 6 vols., Pack. (Story Steps Ser.). (gr. k-2). 32.00 (978-0-7635-9850-1(X)) Rigby Education.

MONGOOSES—FICTION

Bannerman, Helen. The Story of Little Black Mingo (Illustr. 2006. pap. (*978-1-4065-0770-6(9)) Dodo Pr.

Corry, Beatrice J. Old Friends. 2002. (Babu the Buffalo, Tales of India Ser.: Bk. 1). (Illus.). 21p. (J). (978-0-9722880-0-2(7)); pap. (978-0-9722880-1-9(5)) Babu Bks.

Footloose the Mongoose & His Ohana. 2001. (J). 10.99 (978-0-89610-422-8(2)) Island Heritage Publishing.

Harcourt School Publishers Staff. Rikki-Tikki-Tavi Level D Library. 2001. (Vamos de Fiesta Ser.). (SPA., Illus.). 79p. (gr. 8-12). 28.10 (978-84-03-60277-9(4)) Harcourt Schl. Pubs.

Kipling, Rudyard. Rikki Tikki Tavi. Jones, Chuck, illus. 2006. 32p. (J). 8.95 (978-0-8249-6597-6(3) , Ideals Children's Bks.) Ideals Pubns.

—Rikki-Tikki-Tavi. Pinkney, Jerry, illus. 2004. 48p. (J). (ps-3). reprint ed. pap. 6.99 (978-0-06-058785-7(7) , Harper Trophy) HarperCollins Pubs.

—Rikki Tikki Tavi & the Mystery in the Garden. Madsen, Jim, illus. 2006. (Easy Reader Classics Ser.: No. 2). 32p. (J). pap. 3.95 (978-1-4027-3290-4(2)) Sterling Publishing Co., Inc.

—Rikki Tikki Tavi Moves In No. 1, No. 1. Madsen, Jim, illus. 2006. (Easy Reader Classics Ser.). 32p. (J). pap. 3.95 (978-1-4027-3289-8(9)) Sterling Publishing Co., Inc.

Miller, Mark. Meerkats Don't Fly. Butterfield, Cathy, illus. 2007. (J). (*978-0-9794393-0-8(2)) Good Turn Publishing.

Mongoose, Mongoose, Stop! Don't Run. 2004. (J). 8.99 (978-0-931548-65-9(9)) Island Heritage Publishing.

Pinkney, Jerry. Rikki-Tikki-Tavi. 2004. (gr. k-3). lib. bdg. 15.30 (978-0-613-83560-2(3)) Tandem Library Bks.

MONITOR (IRONCLAD)

Abnett, Dan. The Monitor vs. the Merrimac: Ironclads at War! 2007. (Graphic Battles of the Civil War Ser.). (Illus.). 48p. (J). lib. bdg. (978-1-4042-0778-3(3)) Rosen Publishing Group, Inc., The.

Brager, Bruce L. The Monitor vs. the Merrimack. (Great Battles Through the Ages Ser.). (Illus.). 112p. (gr. 6-12). 2004. pap. 13.25 (978-0-7910-7792-4(6)); 2003. 30.00 (978-0-7910-7439-8(0)) Facts On File, Inc. (Chelsea Hse.).

Burgan, Michael. The Battle of the Ironclads. 2006. (Illus.). 48p. (J). (gr. 4-6). 23.93 (978-0-7565-1628-4(5)) Compass Point Bks.

O'Brien, Patrick. Duel of the Ironclads: The Monitor vs. the Virginia. 2003. (Illus.). 40p. (J). (gr. 1-5). 17.95 (978-0-8027-8842-9(4)); 18.85 (978-0-8027-8843-6(2)) Walker & Co.

Thompson, Gare. Monitor: The Iron Warship That Changed the World. Day, Larry, illus. 2003. (All Aboard Reading Ser.). 48p. (J). (gr. 4-4). pap. 3.99 (978-0-448-43245-8(5) , Grosset & Dunlap) Penguin Group (USA) Inc.

—Monitor: The Iron Warship That Changed the World. 2003. (gr. k-3). lib. bdg. 11.80 (978-0-613-72533-0(6)) Tandem Library Bks.

—The Monitor: The Iron Warship That Changed the World. Day, Larry, illus. 2003. (All Aboard Reading Ser.). 48p. (J). 13.89 (978-0-448-43283-0(8) , Grosset & Dunlap) Penguin Group (USA) Inc.

MONITOR (IRONCLAD)—FICTION

Sappey, Maureen S. Dreams of Ships, Dreams of Julia: At Sea with the Monitor & the Merrimack-Virginia, 1862. 1998. (Young American Ser.: Vol. 2). (Illus.). 140p. (YA). (gr. 4-7). 5.99 (978-1-57249-134-2(5)) White Mane Publishing Co., Inc.

MONKEYS

see also Baboons

Aloian, Molly & Kalman, Bobbie. Endangered Monkeys. 2007. (Earth's Endangered Animals Ser.). (Illus.). 32p. (J). (gr. 1-7). (*978-0-7787-1862-8(X)); pap. (*978-0-7787-1908-3(1)) Crabtree Publishing Co.

Banks, Martin. How Monkeys "Talk" 1998. (Nature's Mysteries Ser.). (Illus.). 32p. (J). (gr. 3-5). lib. bdg. 22.79 (978-0-7614-0858-1(4) , Benchmark Bks.) Cavendish, Marshall Corp.

Braun, Eric & Donovan, Sandy. Tamarins. 2001. (Animals of the Rain Forest Ser.). (Illus.). 32p. (YA). lib. bdg. 22.83 (978-0-7398-4684-1(1)) Raintree.

Canizares, Susan & Chanko, Pamela. Monkeys: Monos. 2002. (Science Emergent Readers Ser.). (ENG & SPA., Illus.). (J). pap. (978-0-439-41159-2(9)) Scholastic, Inc.

Costain, Meredith. Golden Lion Tamarin Monkeys. 2000. (gr. k-3). lib. bdg. 11.80 (978-0-613-30439-9(X)) Tandem Library Bks.

Crawford, Tracey. Monkeys. 2006. (Illus.). 24p. (J). (978-1-4034-8455-0(4)); pap. (978-1-4034-8462-8(7)) Heinemann Library.

Dennard, Deborah. Apes & Monkeys. McGee, John F., illus. 2004. (Our Wild World Ser.). 192p. (J). (gr. 2-5). ring bd. 16.95 (978-1-55971-863-9(3) , NorthWord Bks. for Young Readers) T&N Children's Publishing.

—Monkeys. McGee, John F., illus. 2004. (Our Wild World Ser.). 48p. (J). (gr. 2-5). ring bd. 10.95 (978-1-55971-850-9(1)); pap. 7.95 (978-1-55971-849-3(8)) T&N Children's Publishing. (NorthWord Bks. for Young Readers).

—Monkeys. 2003. (gr. 3-6). lib. bdg. 16.40 (978-0-613-67972-5(5)) Tandem Library Bks.

Donovan, Sandy. Howler Monkeys. 2003. (Animals of the Rain Forest Ser.). (Illus.). 32p. (J). lib. bdg. 24.28 (978-0-7398-6836-2(5)) Raintree.

Eckart, Edana. Woolly Monkey. 2005. (Welcome Bks.). (Illus.). 24p. (ps-2). (J). pap. 4.95 (978-0-516-25168-4(6)); 18.00 (978-0-516-25055-7(8)) Scholastic Library Publishing. (Children's Pr.).

Gikow, Louise. Ripley's Apes & Monkeys. 2004. (Illus.). 60p. (J). (978-0-439-63364-2(8)) Scholastic, Inc.

Grolier Educational Staff, contrib. by. New World Monkeys. 2001. (Nature's Children Ser.). (Illus.). 48p. (J). (978-0-7172-5540-5(9) , Grolier) Scholastic Library Publishing.

Hewett, Richard, illus. & photos by. A Monkey Baby Grows Up. Hewett, Richard, photos by. Hewett, Joan, photos by. 2004. (Baby Animals Ser.). 32p. (J). (gr. k-3). lib. bdg. 21.27 (978-1-57505-199-4(0)) Lerner Publishing Group.

Hoff, Mary King. Monkeys. 2005. (Illus.). 32p. (gr. 2-5). 18.95 (978-1-58341-352-4(9) , Creative Education) Creative Co., The.

Horak, Steven A. Baboons & Other Old World Monkeys, Vol. 1. World Book, Inc. Staff, ed. 2002. (World Book's Animals of the World Ser.: Set 3). (Illus.). 64p. (J). (978-0-7166-1224-7(0)) World Bk., Inc.

Jackson, Tom. Monkeys: Nature Watch. 2003. (Nature Watch Ser.). (Illus.). 64p. 14.99 (978-0-7548-1073-5(9) , Lorenz Bks.) Anness Publishing GBR. Dist: National Bk. Network.

—Nature Factfile: Monkeys, 90 vols. 2005. (Illus.). 64p. pap. 8.99 (978-1-84476-061-9(8) , Southwater) Anness Publishing GBR. Dist: National Bk. Network.

Jeunesse, Gallimard. Monkeys & Apes. Prunier, James, illus. 1999. (First Discovery Book Ser.). 24p. (J). (ps-2). 12.95 (978-0-590-87610-0(4)) Scholastic, Inc.

Macken, JoAnn Early. Monkeys. 2002. (Weekly Reader Early Learning Library). (Illus.). 24p. (J). (ps up). pap. 5.95 (978-0-8368-3285-3(X)); lib. bdg. 19.33 (978-0-8368-3272-3(8)) Stevens, Gareth Inc. (Weekly Reader Early Learning Library).

—Monkeys: Los Monos. 2004. (ENG & SPA., Illus.). 24p. (J). pap. (978-0-8368-4388-0(6)); lib. bdg. 19.33 (978-0-8368-4383-5(5)) Stevens, Gareth Inc.

Martin, Patricia. Monkeys from Asia & Africa. 2000. (gr. 3-6). lib. bdg. 15.25 (978-0-613-37467-5(3)) Tandem Library Bks.

—Monkeys from Central & South America. 2000. (gr. 3-6). lib. bdg. 15.25 (978-0-613-37468-2(1)) Tandem Library Bks.

Miller-Schroeder, Patricia. Japanese Macaques. 2001. (Untamed World Ser.). (Illus.). 64p. (J). lib. bdg. 28.54 (978-0-8172-4576-4(6)) Raintree.

Molter, Carey. Monkeys. l.t. ed. 2001. (Zoo Animals Ser.). (Illus.). 24p. (J). (ps-3). lib. bdg. 19.93 (978-1-57765-561-9(3) , SandCastle) ABDO Publishing Co.

Monkey. 2004. (Peek-A-Boo Coloring Pads Ser.). 48p. (J). act. bk. ed. 3.99 (978-1-85997-393-6(0)) Byeway Bks.

Monkey. (Buggy Buddies Ser.). (Illus.). (J). (ps). bds. (978-1-56021-353-6(1) , 204) W.J. Fantasy, Inc.

Moore, Heidi. A Mob of Meerkats. 2004. 32p. (J). pap. 6.95 (978-1-4034-5418-8(3)); (Illus.). lib. bdg. 24.22 (978-1-4034-4694-7(6)) Heinemann Library.

Murray, Julie. Monkeys. 2005. (Animal Kingdom Set Ii Ser.). (Illus.). 24p. (J). (gr. k-4). lib. bdg. 21.35 (978-1-59197-326-3(0)) ABDO Publishing Co.

Parramon Staff. Gorilas. 2006. (SPA.). 32p. (J). (gr. 2-3). 10.40 (978-84-342-2733-0(9) , PR33932) Parramon Ediciones S.A. ESP. Dist: Lectorum Pubns., Inc.

Pfloog, Jan. Monkey Book. 1999. (ps-2). lib. bdg. 11.00 (978-0-613-87570-7(2)) Tandem Library Bks.

Presnall, Judith Janda. Capuchin Monkeys. 2003. (Animals with Jobs Ser.). (Illus.). 48p. (J). (gr. 3-5). 26.20 (978-0-7377-1788-4(2) , Kidhaven) Thomson Gale.

Redmond, Ian. Gorilas. Anderson, Peter & Brightling, Geoff, illus. 2003. (SPA.). 64p. 14.95 (978-84-372-2323-0(7)) Altea, Ediciones, S.A. - Grupo Santillana ESP. Dist: Santillana USA Publishing Co., Inc.

—Gorilla. 2000. (Eyewitness Bks.). (Illus.). 64p. (J). (gr. 4-7). 15.99 (978-0-7894-6036-3(X)) Dorling Kindersley Publishing, Inc.

Redmond, Ian & Dorling Kindersley Publishing Staff. Gorilla. 2000. (Eyewitness Bks.). (Illus.). 64p. (J). (gr. 4-7). lib. bdg. 19.99 (978-0-7894-6613-6(9)) Dorling Kindersley Publishing, Inc.

Reid, Mary Ebeltoft. Howlers & Other New World Monkeys, Vol. 5. World Book, Inc. Staff, ed. 2002. (World Book's Animals of the World Ser.: Set 1). 64p. (J). (978-0-7166-1242-1(9)) World Bk., Inc.

Stewart, Melissa. New World Monkeys. 2007. (Nature Watch Ser.). 48p. (J). (gr. 4-8). lib. bdg. 26.60 (*978-0-8225-6765-3(2) , Lerner Pubns.) Lerner Publishing Group.

Stonehouse, Bernard. Monkeys & Apes: A Visual Introduction to Monkeys & Apes. Camm, Martin & Orr, Richard, illus. (Animal Watch Ser.). 48p. (J). (gr. 4-9). 16.95 (978-0-8160-3927-2(5) , Checkmark Bks.) Facts On File, Inc.

Taylor, Barbara. Apes & Monkeys. (Science Kids Ser.). (Illus.). 48p. (J). 2007. pap. 6.95 (*978-0-7534-6163-1(3)); 2004. 9.95 (978-0-7534-5760-3(1)) Houghton Mifflin Co. Trade & Reference Div. (Kingfisher).

Taylor, Barbara & Jackson, Tom. Apes & Monkeys. 2004. (Illus.). 128p. pap. 17.99 (978-1-84215-955-2(0) , Southwater) Anness Publishing GBR. Dist: National Bk. Network.

Where Are the Monkeys? Second Grade Guided Reading Level F. (On Our Way to English Ser.). (gr. 2 up). 34.50 (978-0-7578-7074-3(0)) Rigby Education.

Wildlife Education, Ltd. Staff. Old World Monkeys. Orr, Richard, illus. 2000. (Zoobooks Ser.). (J). 24p. 15.95 (978-0-937934-92-0(5)); 18p. pap. 2.95 (978-0-937934-69-2(0)) Wildlife Education, Ltd.

Wildlife Education, Ltd Staff, contrib. by. Monkeys. 2006. (Critters Up Close Ser.). (Illus.). (J). bds. 5.95 (*978-1-932396-15-7(2)) Wildlife Education, Ltd.

Wilsdon, Christina. Monkeys. 2007. (J). (*978-1-59939-134-2(1) , Reader's Digest Young Families, Inc.) Reader's Digest Children's Publishing, Inc.

Woods, Mae. Monkeys, Set Incl. Baboons. lib. bdg. 21.35 (978-1-56239-596-4(3)); Chimpanzees. lib. bdg. 21.35 (978-1-56239-597-1(1)); Gibbons. lib. bdg. 21.35 (978-1-56239-598-8(X)); Gorillas. lib. bdg. 21.35 (978-1-56239-599-5(8)); Orangutans. lib. bdg. 21.35 (978-1-56239-600-8(5)); Snow Monkeys. lib. bdg. 21.35 (978-1-56239-601-5(3)); 24p. (J). (gr. k-6). 1998. (Illus.). 1998. Set lib. bdg. 128.10 (978-1-56239-933-7(0) , Checkerboard Library) ABDO Publishing Co.

Zabludoff, Marc. Monkeys. 2007. (Animalways Ser.). 112p. (J). lib. bdg. 34.21 (*978-0-7614-2535-9(7) , Benchmark Bks.) Cavendish, Marshall Corp.

MONKEYS—FICTION

Ackerman, Arlene. Glimmer de Gloop de Monkey Face: The Elf Named Pee-U & What He Knew. 2003. pap. 8.00 (978-0-8059-6031-0(7)) Dorrance Publishing Co., Inc.

Adiccabandhu & Padmasri. The Monkey King. Adiccabandhu, illus. 2004. (Illus.). 32p. (gr. k-3). pap. 10.95 (978-1-899579-09-9(5)) Windhorse Pubns. GBR. Dist: Consortium Bk. Sales & Distribution.

Aikins, Dave, illus. At the Carnival. 2005. (J). (*978-1-4156-0769-5(9) , Simon Spotlight/Nickelodeon) Simon & Schuster Children's Publishing.

Alborough, Jez. Hug. Alborough, Jez, illus. 2005. (Illus.). 32p. (J). (gr. k-ps). bds. 9.99 (978-0-7636-2893-2(X)) Candlewick Pr.

—Tall. Alborough, Jez, illus. 2005. (Illus.). 40p. (J). (ps up). 15.99 (978-0-7636-2784-3(4)) Candlewick Pr.

—Tall. Alborough, Jez, illus. 2007. (Illus.). 34p. (J). (gr. k-ps). bds. 6.99 (978-0-7636-3328-8(3)) Candlewick Pr.

Allen, Jonathan. Banana! Allen, Jonathan, illus. 2006. (Illus.). 32p. (J). pap. (*978-1-905417-02-5(0)) Boxer Bks., Ltd.

—Banana! 2006. (Illus.). 32p. (J). 12.95 (978-1-905417-07-0(1)) Boxer Bks., Ltd. GBR. Dist: Sterling Publishing Co., Inc.

Anderson, Bob. Obo. Anderson, Bob, illus. 1999. (Illus.). 48p. (J). (ps-5). bds. 16.00 (978-1-57174-124-0(0)) Hampton Roads Publishing Co., Inc.

Anderson, R. P., et al. Curious George at the Aquarium. Hines, Anna Grossnickle, illus. 2007. 24p. (J). (ps-k). 12.95 (*978-0-618-80067-4(0)); pap. 3.95 (*978-0-618-80068-1(9)) Houghton Mifflin Co.

Anholt, Catherine & Anholt, Laurence. Happy Birthday Chimp & Zee. 2006. (Chimp & Zee Ser.). (Illus.). 32p. (J). 15.95 (978-1-84507-507-1(2)) Lincoln, Frances Ltd. GBR. Dist: Perseus Distribution.

—Monkey about with Chimp & Zee. 2006. (Chimp & Zee Ser.). (Illus.). 8p. (J). bds. 6.95 (978-1-84507-508-8(0)) Lincoln, Frances Ltd. GBR. Dist: Perseus Distribution.

Arrington, H. J. Friends Again? Kitchel, JoAnn E., illus. 2001. 32p. (J). 15.95 (978-1-56554-834-3(5)) Pelican Publishing Co., Inc.

Aylesworth, Jim. Naughty Little Monkeys. Cole, Henry, illus. (J). (ps). 2003. 40p. 16.99 (978-0-525-46940-7(0) , Dutton Juvenile); 2006. 32p. reprint ed. pap. 6.99 (978-0-14-240562-8(0) , Puffin) Penguin Group (USA) Inc.

Bailey, Arthur. The Tale of Major Monkey. 2002. 136p. pap. 19.95 (978-1-932080-53-7(8)) Ross & Perry, Inc.

Bailey, Scott Arthur. The Tale of Major Monkey. 2006. pap. 33.99 (*978-1-4280-4050-2(1)) IndyPublish.com.

Banana-Tail. 2003. lib. bdg. 13.95 (978-0-9727681-0-8(6)) Active Media Publishing, LLC.

Banks, Kate. Baboon. Hallensleben, Georg, illus. 2004. 32p. (J). reprint ed. pap. 6.95 (978-0-374-40473-4(9) , Sunburst) Farrar, Straus & Giroux.

Barber, Antonia & So, Meilo. The Monkey & the Panda. 1999. (Illus.). 32p. (J). (ps-4). pap. 7.99 (978-0-7112-1085-1(3)) Lincoln, Frances Ltd. GBR. Dist: Transition Vendor.

Bell, Cece. Sock Monkey Boogie-Woogie: A Friend Is Made. Bell, Cece, illus. 2004. (Illus.). 32p. (J). (ps-2). 14.99 (978-0-7636-2392-0(X)) Candlewick Pr.

—Sock Monkey Goes to Hollywood: A Star Is Bathed. Bell, Cece, illus. 2003. (Illus.). 32p. (J). (ps). 13.99 (978-0-7636-1962-6(0)) Candlewick Pr.

Beobi & the Magic Coloring Book A Visit to the Doctor. 2005. (J). 3.99 (978-0-9743847-3-3(9)) Cohn, Tricia.

Beobi & the Magic Coloring Book Funland. 2006. (Illus.). 24p. (J). 3.99 (978-0-9743847-1-1(1)) Cohn, Tricia.

Berenstain, Jan. The Berenstain Bears' Baby Easter Bunny. Berenstain, Jan, illus. 2008. (Berenstain Bears Ser.). 16p. (J). 6.99 (*978-0-06-057420-8(8) , Harper Festival) HarperCollins Pubs.

Brimner, Larry Dane. Monkey Math. Kulka, Joe, illus. 2006. (Rookie Reader Skill Set Ser.). 32p. (J). (gr. k-2). 19.50 (978-0-531-12463-5(0) , Children's Pr.) Scholastic Library Publishing.

Browne, Paula. El Cumpleanos de la Mona. Isabel, Isaias, tr. Browne, Paula, illus. 2004. (Paca, la Macaca Ser.). (SPA., Illus.). 20p. pap. 4.95 (978-85-7416-214-0(0)) Callis Editora Ltda BRA. *Dist:* Independent Pubs. Group.

—Paca, la macaca en la Cocina. Isabel, Isaias, tr. Browne, Paula, illus. 2004. (Paca, la Macaca Ser.). (SPA., Illus.). 20p. pap. 4.95 (978-85-7416-210-2(8)) Callis Editora Ltda BRA. *Dist:* Independent Pubs. Group.

—Paca, la Macaca va al Mercado. Isabel, Isaias, tr. Browne, Paula, illus. 2004. (Paca, la Macaca Ser.). (Illus.). 20p. pap. 4.95 (978-85-7416-215-7(9)) Callis Editora Ltda BRA. *Dist:* Independent Pubs. Group.

—Que Desbarajuste, Paca. Isabel, Isaias, tr. Browne, Paula, illus. 2004. (Paca, la Macaca Series Ser.). (Illus.). 20p. pap. 6.95 (978-85-7416-211-9(6)) Callis Editora Ltda BRA. *Dist:* Independent Pubs. Group.

Campbell, Carole R. The Powder Monkey. 1999. (Young American Ser.: Vol. 4). (Illus.). vii, 108p. (J). (ps up). pap. 5.99 (978-1-57249-170-0(1) , White Mane Kids) White Mane Publishing Co., Inc.

Canetti, Yanitzia, tr. from ENG. Jorge el Curioso y el Conejito. Rey, H. A., illus. 2002. (SPA.). 26p. (J). (gr. k-ps). bds. 5.95 (978-0-618-20316-1(8)) Houghton Mifflin Co. Trade & Reference Div.

Carle, Eric. What's for Lunch? Carle, Eric, illus. 1998. (Play-and-Read Book Ser.). (Illus.). 12p. (J). (ps). bds. 6.95 (978-0-590-32842-5(5)) Scholastic, Inc.

Carr, Jon & Carr, Debra. Maurice the Monkey in a Lesson on Prayer. 2000. 13p. 6.00 (978-1-885072-37-5(6)) Creflo Dollar Ministries Pubns.

Cassidy, Anne. The Sassy Monkey. Smith, Lisa, illus. 2004. (Read-It! Readers Ser.). 32p. (C). (gr. k-3). 18.60 (978-1-4048-0058-8(1)) Picture Window Bks.

Chen, Debby. Monkey King Wreaks Havoc in Heaven. 2001. (Adventures of Monkey King Ser.: Vol. 2). (CHI.). 32p. (J). (gr. 1). 16.95 (978-1-57227-070-1(5)) Pan Asia Pubns. (USA), Inc.

—Monkey King Wreaks Havoc in Heaven. Ma, Wenhai, illus. 2001. (Adventures of Monkey King Ser.: Vol. 2). 32p. (J). (gr. 1-7). 16.95 (978-1-57227-068-8(3)) Pan Asia Pubns. (USA), Inc.

—Monkey King Wreaks Havoc in Heaven. de la Vega, Eida, tr. Ma, Wenhai, illus. 2001. (Adventures of Monkey King Ser.: Vol. 2). (SPA.). 32p. (J). (gr. 1-7). 16.95 (978-1-57227-069-5(1)) Pan Asia Pubns. (USA), Inc.

—Monkey King Wreaks Havoc in Heaven. Nguyen, Ngoc Ngan, tr. Ma, Wenhai, illus. 2001. (Adventures of Monkey King Ser.: Vol. 2). (VIE.). 32p. (J). (gr. 1-7). 16.95 (978-1-57227-071-8(3)) Pan Asia Pubns. (USA), Inc.

Chojnowski, Bryan. Muffin Time: Origins. 2005. 98p. pap. 25.01 (978-1-4116-4440-3(9)) Lulu.com.

Christelow, Eileen. Cinco Monitos Brincando en la Cama: Five Little Monkeys Jumping on the Bed. Ortiz, Victoria, tr. 2005. (SPA & ENG., Illus.). 28p. (J). (gr. k-ps). bds. 5.95 (978-0-618-56442-2(X) , Clarion Bks.) Houghton Mifflin Co. Trade & Reference Div.

—Don't Wake up Mama! Christelow, Eileen, illus. 2002. (Illus.). (J). 13.79 (978-0-7587-2410-6(1)) Book Wholesalers, Inc.

—En un Arbol Estan los Cinco Monitos / Five Little Monkeys Sitting in a Tree. 2007. Tr. of Five Little Monkeys Sitting in a Tree. (ENG & SPA., Illus.). 28p. (J). (gr. k-ps). bds. 5.95 (978-0-618-75248-5(X) , Clarion Bks.) Houghton Mifflin Co. Trade & Reference Div.

—Five Little Monkeys Bake a Birthday Cake. 2005. (Five Little Monkeys Ser.). (Illus.). (J). (gr. k-ps). 32p. 15.00 (978-0-618-49647-1(5)); 28p. pap. 5.95 (978-0-618-49648-8(3)) Houghton Mifflin Co. Trade & Reference Div. (Clarion Bks.).

—Five Little Monkeys Bake a Birthday Cake. Christelow, Eileen, illus. 2004. (Illus.). 28p. (J). (gr. k-ps). bds. 5.95 (978-0-618-46264-3(3) , Clarion Bks.) Houghton Mifflin Co. Trade & Reference Div.

—Five Little Monkeys Go Shopping. Christelow, Eileen, illus. 2007. (Illus.). 40p. (J). (ps-k). 16.00 ***978-0-618-82161-7(9)*** , Clarion Bks.) Houghton Mifflin Co. Trade & Reference Div.

—Five Little Monkeys Jumping on the Bed. Christelow, Eileen, illus. 2002. (Illus.). (J). 14.66 (978-0-7587-2511-0(6)) Book Wholesalers, Inc.

—Five Little Monkeys Jumping on the Bed. 1998. (Five Little Monkeys Ser.). (Illus.). 14p. (J). (gr. k-ps). bds. 5.95 (978-0-395-90023-9(9) , Clarion Bks.) Houghton Mifflin Co. Trade & Reference Div.

—Five Little Monkeys Jumping on the Bed. 2000. (Illus.). (J). 12.75 (978-0-606-18041-2(9)) Tandem Library Bks.

—Five Little Monkeys Jumping on the Bed Big Book. 2006. 32p. (J). (ps-k). 25.00 (978-0-618-83682-6(9)) Houghton Mifflin Co. Trade & Reference Div.

—Five Little Monkeys Play Hide-and-Seek. 2004. (Illus.). 40p. (J). (ps-k). tchr. ed. 16.00 (978-0-618-40949-5(1) , Clarion Bks.) Houghton Mifflin Co. Trade & Reference Div.

—Five Little Monkeys Sitting in a Tree. Christelow, Eileen, illus. 2002. (Illus.). (J). 13.79 (978-0-7587-2512-7(4)) Book Wholesalers, Inc.

—Five Little Monkeys Sitting in a Tree. Christelow, Eileen, illus. 1999. (Five Little Monkeys Ser.). (Illus.). 28p. (J). (gr. k-ps). bds. 5.95 (978-0-395-98033-0(X) , Clarion Bks.) Houghton Mifflin Co. Trade & Reference Div.

—Five Little Monkeys Wash the Car. (Illus.). 40p. (J). (ps-1). 2004. 5.95 (978-0-618-48602-1(X)); 2000. tchr. ed. 15.00 (978-0-395-92566-9(5)) Houghton Mifflin Co. Trade & Reference Div. (Clarion Bks.).

—Five Little Monkeys with Nothing to Do. Christelow, Eileen, illus. 2002. (Five Little Monkeys Ser.). (Illus.). 28p. (J). (gr. k-ps). bds. 5.95 (978-0-618-24615-1(0) , Clarion Bks.) Houghton Mifflin Co. Trade & Reference Div.

—Five Little Monkeys with Nothing to Do. 2000. (Five Little Monkeys Ser.). (Illus.). 40p. (J). (gr. k-3). pap. 5.95 (978-0-618-04032-2(3) , Clarion Bks.) Houghton Mifflin Co. Trade & Reference Div.

—Five Little Monkeys with Nothing to Do. 2000. (ps-2). lib. bdg. 14.10 (978-0-613-28487-5(9)); (Illus.). (J). 12.75 (978-0-606-18042-9(7)) Tandem Library Bks.

Christie, Michael G. The Amazing Crumpet. Grimes, Tammy, illus. 2003. 46p. (gr. 3-6). pap. 6.95 (978-1-889658-31-5(6)) New Canaan Publishing Co. LLC.

Chronicle Books LLC Staff. Paul Frank Picturebook 1. 2008. (J). 12.95 (978-0-8118-6024-6(8)) Chronicle Bks. LLC.

Cleveland, Robert. Clever Monkey. Hoffmire, Baird, illus. 2006. 32p. (J). pap. 3.95 (978-0-87483-801-5(0)) August Hse. Pubs., Inc.

Climo, Shirley. Monkey Business: Stories from Around the World. Brooks, Erik, illus. rev. ed. 2005. 128p. (J). 18.95 (978-0-8050-6392-9(7) , Holt, Henry & Co. Bks. For Young Readers) Holt, Henry & Co.

Cohn, Tricia L. Beobi & the Magic Coloring Book ABC First Words. 2003. (J). (978-0-9743847-0-2(4)) Cohn, Tricia.

Corke, Estelle. Monkey Tale. 2001. (Bendy Tales Ser.). 8p. (J). (ps). bds. 4.95 (978-0-7641-5371-6(4)) Barron's Educational Series, Inc.

Cornell, Kevin. Mojo the Sock Monkey. 2005. 48p. (YA). pap. 15.99 (978-1-4116-5713-7(6)) Lulu.com.

Curious, George & Brazelton, T. Berry. George Was Here. 2007. (Curious George Ser.). 224p. (J). (ps-1). 4.99 (***978-1-4169-4847-6(3)*** , Simon Scribbles) Simon & Schuster Children's Publishing.

—Monkey Around. Obrero, Rudy, illus. 2007. (Curious George Ser.). 48p. (J). (ps-1). 3.99 (***978-1-4169-4846-9(5)*** , Simon Scribbles) Simon & Schuster Children's Publishing.

Curious George Rides a Bike. 2004. (J). pap. 18.95 incl. audio compact disk (978-1-55592-802-5(1)); pap. 18.95 incl. audio compact disk (978-1-55592-770-7(X)); pap. 38.75 incl. audio compact disk (978-1-55592-819-3(6)); pap. 38.75 incl. audio compact disk (978-1-55592-785-1(8)); pap. 32.75 incl. audio (978-1-55592-213-9(9)); pap. 32.75 incl. audio (978-1-55592-214-6(7)); pap. 14.95 incl. audio (978-1-56008-096-1(5)); pap. 14.95 incl. audio (978-1-55592-721-9(1)) Weston Woods Studios, Inc.

Curry, Kenneth. Priscilla & the Talking Monkey. 2007. (Illus.). 22p. (J). 10.95 (***978-0-9798364-6-6(8)*** Curry Brothers Publishing.

Dahl, Roald. The Giraffe, the Pelly & Me. Blake, Quentin, illus. 1998. 80p. (Orig.). (J). (gr. 2-6). pap. 5.99 (978-0-14-130228-7(3) , Puffin) Penguin Group (USA) Inc.

Dalmatian Press Staff. Curious George Everybody's Favorite Monkey: Big Best Book to Color. rev. ed. 2005. (Big Best Book to Color Ser.). (Illus.). 80p. (J). pap. 2.99 (978-1-4037-0724-6(3)) Dalmatian Pr.

Dalmatian Press Staff, creator. Ten Little Monkeys. 2003. (Talking Book Ser.). 14p. (J). 16.99 (978-0-7948-1338-3(0)) Dalmatian Pr.

de Brunhoff, Jean. Babar & Zephir. de Brunhoff, Jean, illus. 2005. (Illus.). 38p. (J). (gr. k-4). reprint ed. 16.00 (978-0-7567-8935-0(4)) DIANE Publishing Co.

DePalma, Mary Newell. The Strange Egg. 2001. (Illus.). 32p. (J). (gr. k-3). tchr. ed. 15.00 (978-0-618-09507-0(1)) Houghton Mifflin Co. Trade & Reference Div.

Deutsch, David. In Search of the Little People. l.t. ed. 2005. (Illus.). 60p. (J). per. 13.95 (978-1-59879-013-9(7)) Lifevest Publishing, Inc.

Diakite, Baba Wague. The Hatseller & the Monkeys. Diakite, Baba Wague, illus. 1999. (Illus.). 32p. (J). (ps-2). pap. 16.95 (978-0-590-96069-4(5)) Scholastic, Inc.

Dickins, Rosie. Monkey King. Ovani, Germano, illus. 2007. (Young Reading Series 1 Gift Bks). 48p. (J). 8.99 (***978-0-7945-1593-5(2)*** , Usborne) EDC Publishing.

Dixon, Chuck. Way of the Rat Traveler, Vol. 1. 2003. (Way of the Rat Traveler Ser.). (Illus.). 160p. (YA). pap. 9.95 (978-1-59314-032-8(0)) CrossGeneration Comics, Inc.

Do, Kim-Thu, tr. Tang Monk Disciples Monkey King: English/Vietnamese. Ma, Wenhai, illus. 2005. (Adventures of Monkey King Ser.: No. 3). (ENG & VIE.). 32p. (J). 16.95 (978-1-57227-087-9(X)) Pan Asia Pubns. (USA), Inc.

Donahue, Jill L. Cass the Monkey. Muehlenhardt, Amy Bailey, illus. 2006. (Read-It! Readers Ser.). (J). 19.93 (978-1-4048-2407-2(3)) Picture Window Bks.

Donaldson, Julia. Night Monkey, Day Monkey. (Illus.). 32p. (J). pap. 9.99 (978-0-7497-4893-7(1)) Egmont Bks., Ltd. GBR. *Dist:* Trafalgar Square Publishing.

—Night Monkey, Day Monkey. Richards, Lucy, illus. braille ed. 2006. 26p. (J). 8.99 (978-1-4052-2430-7(4)) Egmont Bks., Ltd. GBR. *Dist:* Independent Pubs. Group.

Donaldson, Julia. Where's My Mom? Scheffler, Axel, illus. 2008. 32p. (J). (ps). 16.99 (***978-0-8037-3228-5(7)*** , Dial) Penguin Group (USA) Inc.

Don't Let the Monkey Drive! 2004. (J). 10.95 (978-0-9761350-1-2(9)) Blue Zebra Entertainment, INc.

Dower, Laura. Monkey See, Doggy Do. 2000. (ps-2). lib. bdg. 11.25 (978-0-613-32842-5(6)) Tandem Library Bks.

Dowswell, Paul. Powder Monkey: The Adventures of Sam Witchall. 2005. (Illus.). 200p. (YA). (gr. 4-7). 16.95 (978-1-58234-675-5(5) , Bloomsbury Children) Bloomsbury Publishing.

Driscoll, Laura, et al. Curious George at the Baseball Game. Hines, Anna Grossnickle, illus. 2006. 24p. (J). (ps-k). 12.95 (978-0-618-66374-3(6)); pap. 3.95 (978-0-618-66375-0(4)) Houghton Mifflin Co.

Duckett, Brenda. Jeffrey & the blue Monkey. 2005. 32p. (J). spiral bd. 14.99 (978-1-4116-5504-1(4)) Lulu.com.

DuQuette, Keith. Little Monkey Lost. DuQuette, Keith, illus. 2007. 32p. (J). (ps). 15.99 (978-0-399-24294-6(5) , Putnam Juvenile) Penguin Group (USA) Inc.

Durango, Julia. Cha-Cha Chimps. Taylor, Eleanor, illus. 2006. 32p. (J). (ps-1). 15.95 (978-0-689-86456-8(6)) Simon & Schuster Children's Publishing.

Durant, Alan. I Love You Little Monkey. 2003. 32p. (J). (978-0-7534-5555-5(2)) Kingfisher Publications, plc.

—I Love You, Little Monkey. McEwen, Katharine, illus. 2007. 32p. (J). 15.95 (978-1-4169-2481-4(7)) Simon & Schuster Children's Publishing.

Edwards, Leo. Monkey's Paw. 2000. 21.95 (978-0-8488-2763-2(5)) Amereon LTD.

Edwards, Richard. Little Monkey's One Safe Place. Winter, Susan, illus. 2005. 32p. (J). 15.95 (978-1-84507-291-9(X)) Lincoln, Frances Ltd. GBR. *Dist:* Perseus Distribution.

—Un Lugar Seguro para Pequeno Mono/Little Monkey's One Safe Place. Sarfatti, Esther, tr. Winter, Susan, illus. 2006. (ENG & SPA.). 32p. (J). (ps-1). 15.95 (978-1-84507-736-5(9)) Lincoln, Frances Ltd. GBR. *Dist:* Perseus Distribution.

Eggleton, Jill. Monkey's Tail: Emergent Level Satellite Individual Title Six-Packs. Webb, Philip, illus. (Sails Literacy Ser.). (gr. k-1). 27.00 (978-0-7578-7919-7(5)) Rigby Education.

Elboz, Stephen. Clever Monkeys. Bowman, Pete, illus. 2006. (Read-It! Chapter Books). 64p. (J). (***978-1-4048-3115-5(0)*** , 1265802) Picture Window Bks.

Elliott, George. The Boy Who Loved Bananas. Krystoforski, Andrei, illus. 2006. 32p. (978-1-55453-119-6(5)) Kids Can Pr., Ltd.

—The Boy Who Loved Bananas. Krystoforski, Andrej, illus. 2005. 32p. (J). (ps-2). (978-1-55337-744-3(3)) Kids Can Pr., Ltd.

Emerson, Carl. Speed up, Sammy the Tree Sloth! Trover, Zachary, illus. 2007. (Animal Underdogs Ser.). 32p. (J). (ps-4). lib. bdg. 27.07 (***978-1-60270-019-2(2)*** , Looking Glass Library) Magic Wagon.

Erickson, John R. The Case of the Monkey Burglar. Holmes, Gerald L., illus. 2006. (Hank the Cowdog Ser.: NMo. 48). 129p. (J). lib. bdg. 17.00 (***978-1-4242-1604-8(4)***) Fitzgerald Bks.

—The Case of the Monkey Burglar. Holmes, Gerald L., illus. 2006. (Hank the Cowdog Ser.: No. 48). 144p. (J). (gr. 3). 4.99 (978-0-14-240636-6(8) , Puffin); 15.99 (978-0-670-06098-6(4) , Viking Juvenile) Penguin Group (USA) Inc.

—Hank the Cowdog & Monkey Business. Holmes, Gerald L., illus. 1999. (Hank the Cowdog Ser.: No. 14). (J). (gr. 3-6). lib. bdg. 13.00 (978-0-8335-6827-4(2)) Tandem Library Bks.

—Monkey Business. Holmes, Gerald L., illus. 1998. (Hank the Cowdog Ser.: No. 14). 144p. (J). (gr. 2-5). 14.99 (978-0-670-88421-6(9) , Viking Juvenile); Vol. 14. pap. 4.99 (978-0-14-130390-1(5) , Puffin) Penguin Group (USA) Inc.

Faulkner, Keith. Ten Little Monkeys: A Counting Story Book. Lambert, Jonathan, illus. 2004. 12p. (J). reprint ed. 20.00 (978-0-7567-8203-0(1)) DIANE Publishing Co.

Feely, Jenny. Little Monkey. 1999. (gr. k-3). lib. bdg. 11.80 (978-0-613-19387-0(3)) Tandem Library Bks.

Find the Monkey. 2005. (J). (978-0-9767179-2-8(1)) ABC Development, Inc.

Fitch, Sheree. There Were Monkeys in My Kitchen! braille ed. 2004. (Illus.). (J). (gr. k-3). spiral bd. (978-0-616-01639-8(5)) Canadian National Institute for the Blind/Institut National Canadien pour les Aveugles.

Five Monkeys. 8p. (J). (978-0-8136-3516-3(0)) Modern Curriculum Pr.

Foreman, Michael. Can't Catch Me! 2006. (Illus.). 32p. (J). pap. 8.99 (978-1-84270-474-5(5)) Andersen GBR. *Dist:* Independent Pubs. Group.

Franklin. When the Monkeys Came Back: Spanish. 1999. (J). 4.95 (978-0-689-31951-8(7) , Atheneum) Simon & Schuster Children's Publishing.

Freeman, Tina. Ten Little Monkeys: Jumping on the Bed. 2001. (gr. k-3). lib. bdg. 15.30 (978-0-613-77001-9(3)) Tandem Library Bks.

Freeman, Tina, illus. Ten Little Monkeys. 2005. (J). bds. 12.99 (978-0-85953-450-5(2)) Child's Play-International.

Galloway, Ginger. Jasper. Zemke, Deborah, illus. 2003. (Books for Young Learners). 16p. (J). pap. 5.00 net. (978-1-57274-539-1(8) , 2457) Owen, Richard C. Pubs., Inc.

Garis, Howard Roger. Curly & Floppy Twistytail. 2005. 26.95 (978-1-4218-1461-2(7)); 164p. pap. 11.95 (978-1-4218-1561-9(3)) 1st World Publishing, Inc. (1st World Library - Literary Society).

—Curly & Floppy Twistytail. 2004. reprint ed. pap. 19.95 (978-1-4191-1479-3(4)); pap. 1.99 (978-1-4192-1479-0(9)) Kessinger Publishing, LLC.

—Umboo, the Elephant. 2005. 132p. pap. 10.95 (978-1-59540-656-9(5) , 1st World Library - Literary Society) 1st World Publishing, Inc.

Gates, Josephine Scribner. Nannette & the baby Monkey. 2007. (Illus.). 50p. (J). lib. bdg. 59.00 (***978-1-60304-020-4(X)***) Dollworks.

Greban, Quentin. Nestor. 2001. (Illus.). 27p. (J). pap. 15.95 (978-1-59034-012-7(4)) Mondo Publishing.

—Nestor. Greban, Quentin, illus. 2001. (Illus.). 27p. (J). (ps-4). 15.95 (978-1-58653-855-2(1)) Mondo Publishing.

—Nestor. (Buenas Noches Coleccion). (SPA., Illus.). (J). (gr. k-3). 8.95 (978-958-04-6032-9(9)) Norma S.A. COL. *Dist:* Distribuidora Norma, Inc., Lectorum Pubns., Inc.

Greco, Francesca. Cyril the Mandrill. 2004. (Illus.). 40p. (J). (ps-ps). 16.95 (978-1-932065-92-3(X)) Star Bright Bks., Inc.

Greene, Josh. Hanuman. 2004. (Illus.). 40p. (J). 7.95 (978-1-58246-125-0(2) , Tricycle Pr.) Ten Speed Pr.

Gunson, Dave, illus. Naughty Monkey: First Wave Satellite Individual Title Six-Packs. (Sails Literacy Ser.). 16p. (gr. k up). 27.00 (978-0-7578-6848-1(7)) Rigby Education.

Hamilton, Linda. The Big-Hearted Monkey & the Crocodile. 2005. (J). (978-1-933248-01-1(7)) World Quest Learning.

Hammerslough, Jane. Langur Monkey's Day. Buelt, Laura, illus. 2005. (Wild Reading Adventures! Ser.). (J). (ps-2). 32p. 2.95 (978-1-59249-143-8(X) , S7156); 36p. 9.95 (978-1-59249-144-5(8) , PS7156); 32p. 19.95 incl. audio (978-1-59249-221-3(5) , BC7106) Soundprints.

—Langur Monkey's Day. Buelt, Laura, tr. Buelt, Laura, illus. 2005. (Wild Reading Adventures! Ser.). 36p. (J). (ps-2). 15.95 (978-1-59249-141-4(3) , B7106); pap. 6.95 (978-1-59249-142-1(1) , S7106) Soundprints.

Hana's Year: Evaluation Guide. 2006. (J). (978-1-55942-408-0(7)) Marsh Media.

Hanson, Anders. Monkey Business. Chawla, Neena, illus. 2006. (Fact & Fiction Ser.). 24p. (J). 21.35 (978-1-59679-951-6(X) , SandCastle); pap. (978-1-59679-952-3(8)) ABDO Publishing Co.

Hapka, Cathy, et al. Curious George's Dinosaur Discovery. Hines, Anna Grossnickle, illus. 2006. 24p. (J). (ps-k). 12.95 (978-0-618-66376-7(2)); pap. 3.95 (978-0-618-66377-4(0)) Houghton Mifflin Co.

—Merry Christmas, Curious George. Young, Mary O'Keefe, illus. 2006. 32p. (J). (ps-k). 16.00 (978-0-618-69237-8(1)) Houghton Mifflin Co.

Harcourt School Publishers Staff. Around the Zoo with Baboon: On Level. 3rd ed. 2002. (Trophies Reading Program Ser.). (Illus.). pap. 5.10 (978-0-15-323006-6(1)) Harcourt Schl. Pubs.

—Baboon's Park: Below Level. 3rd ed. 2002. (Trophies Reading Program Ser.). (Illus.). (J). pap. 4.10 (978-0-15-322972-5(1)) Harcourt Schl. Pubs.

—Baboon's Park 5-Pack, Below Level. 3rd ed. 2002. (Illus.). (gr. 1). pap. 20.10 (978-0-15-326822-9(0)) Harcourt Schl. Pubs.

—Monkey Fun: Take-Home Book. 1999. (Collections Ser.). (Illus.). (J). pap. 1.90 (978-0-15-317216-8(9)) Harcourt Schl. Pubs.

—So Say the Little Monkeys: LIbrary Book. 1999. (Collections Ser.). (Illus.). pap. 14.90 (978-0-15-313405-0(4)) Harcourt Schl. Pubs.

Hascamp, Steve, illus. Eight Silly Monkeys. 2005. 18p. (J). 9.95 (978-1-58117-186-0(2) , Intervisual/Piggy Toes) Dalmatian Pr.

Haskamp, Steve, illus. Five Silly Monkeys. 2005. 12p. (J). 14.95 (978-1-58117-264-5(8) , Intervisual/Piggy Toes) Dalmatian Pr.

Heck, Ed. Monkey Lost. 2005. (Illus.). 32p. (J). 15.95 (978-0-689-04633-9(2)); 15.95 (978-1-59687-187-8(3)) ibooks, Inc. (Milk & Cookies).

Hood, Sue. Monkey Business. Chapman, Susan, illus. 2005. (J). bds. (978-1-890647-17-9(9)) RC2 Corp.

Hoosier, Wanda M. Princess Mandisa. McCabe, Pat, illus. 1999. 34p. (J). 15.00 (978-1-56469-070-8(9)) Harmony Hse. Pubs.

Hope, Laura Lee. The Story of a Monkey on a Stick. 2006. pap. 87.99 (***978-1-4280-0316-3(9)***) IndyPublish.com.

Horowitz, Dave. A Monkey among Us. Horowitz, Dave, illus. 2004. (Illus.). 40p. (J). (ps-1). 14.99 (978-0-06-054335-8(3) , Harper Festival) HarperCollins Pubs.

Houghton Mifflin Company Editors. Curious George Discovery Day. 2007. (Illus.). 14p. (J). (gr. k-ps). bds. 13.95 (***978-0-618-73761-1(8)***) Houghton Mifflin Co. Trade & Reference Div.

Houghton Mifflin Company Staff. Bigger & Smaller. 2009. (Illus.). 12p. (J). (ps-k). bds. 6.99 (***978-0-618-73760-4(X)***) Houghton Mifflin Co. Trade & Reference Div.

Houghton Mifflin Company Staff & Rey, Margret. Curious George the Movie: A Junior Novel. 2006. (Illus.). 128p. (J). (gr. k-3). pap. 4.99 (978-0-618-60591-0(6)) Houghton Mifflin Co. Trade & Reference Div.

Howell, Gill. Tortoise & the Baboon. Woody, illus. 2004. 16p. (J). lib. bdg. 22.65 (***978-1-59646-686-9(3)***) Dingles & Co.

Hudson, Charlotte & Gormley, Greg. Monkey Words. 2003. (Illus.). 32p. 19.99 (978-0-370-32636-8(9)) Random Hse. GBR. *Dist:* Independent Pubs. Group.

Hutcheson, John C. Tom Finch's Monkey. 2004. reprint ed. pap. 15.95 (978-1-4191-9041-4(5)); pap. 1.99 (978-1-4192-9041-1(X)) Kessinger Publishing, LLC.

Jaffrey, Saeed. The Monkey King. 1998. (Karadi Tales Ser.). (Illus.). 24p. (YA). (gr. 1 up). 9.99 incl. audio (978-81-86838-12-9(0)) APG Sales and Fulfillment.

Jarrell, Pamela R. Michael Monkey Pretends. Linke, Don, Jr., illus. l.t. ed. 1999. (Cuddle Bks.). 7p. (J). (ps-k). pap. 10.95 (978-1-57332-128-0(1)) HighReach Learning, Inc.

Jiang, Ji-Li. The Magical Monkey King: Mischief in Heaven. Su-Kennedy, Hui Hui, illus. 2002. 128p. (J). (gr. 2-6). lib. bdg. 14.89 (978-0-06-029544-8(9)) HarperCollins Pubs.

—The Magical Monkey King: Mischief in Heaven. Tang, You-shan, illus. 2004. 124p. (J). 14.95 (978-1-885008-24-4(4)); pap. 8.95 (978-1-885008-25-1(2)) Shen's Bks.

Johnston, Fellows An. The Story of Dago. 2006. pap. 33.99 (***978-1-4280-0198-5(0)***) IndyPublish.com.

Jones, David. Baboon: A Novel. 2007. 171p. (J). (gr. 5-9). 21.95 (***978-1-55451-054-2(6)***); pap. 11.95 (***978-1-55451-053-5(8)***) Annick Pr., Ltd. CAN. *Dist:* Firefly Bks., Ltd.

Jordan, Mark. Courage the Monkey. 2006. (Illus.). 40p. (J). 13.95 (978-0-9717013-7-3(7)) Decere Publishing.

M N O

Juliette, the Modern Art Monkey: Individual Title Six-Packs. (Bookweb Ser.). 32p. (gr. 5 up). 34.00 (978-0-7635-3776-0(4)) Rigby Education.

Kaczman, James. Lucky Monkey, Unlucky Monkey. 2008. 32p. (J). (gr. 3-5). 16.00 (*978-0-618-63153-7(4)) Houghton Mifflin Co. Trade & Reference Div.

Kamau, G. How Porcupine Got His Spines. 2004. (Illus.). 22p. 13.95 (978-9966-25-168-8(5)) Heinemann Kenya, Limited (East African Educational Publishers Ltd E.A.E.P.) KEN. *Dist:* Michigan State Univ. Pr.

Kitunga, Demere. Lupompo & the Baby Monkey. 2004. (Illus.). 36p. pap. (978-9987-411-21-4(5)) E & D Ltd.

Knife & Packer. Captain Fact: Space Adventure. 2004. (Illus.). 103p. (J). (*978-1-4156-0561-5(0)) Hyperion Bks. for Children.

Koller, Jackie French. One Monkey Too Many. Munsinger, Lynn, illus. 2003. 32p. (J). (ps-2). pap. 7.00 (978-0-15-204764-1(6) , Voyager Bks./Libros Viajeros) Harcourt Children's Bks.

—One Monkey Too Many. Munsinger, Lynn, illus. 1999. 28p. (J). (ps-2). lib. bdg. 14.15 (978-0-613-70500-4(9)) Tandem Library Bks.

—Seven Spunky Monkeys. Munsinger, Lynn M., illus. 2005. 32p. (J). (ps-ps). 16.00 (978-0-15-202519-9(7)) Harcourt Trade Pubs.

Krailing, Tessa. Monkey Puzzle: Vacation Special. Lewis, Jan & Eastwood, John, illus. 1999. (Petsitters Club Ser.). 96p. (J). (gr. 1-4). pap. 3.95 (978-0-7641-0737-5(2)) Barron's Educational Series, Inc.

Krasner, Steven. Have a Nice Nap, Humphrey. Griffis, Sandy, illus. 1998. 36p. (J). (gr. k-5). pap. 12.95 (978-0-9642721-2-5(1)) Gorilla Productions.

Kraus, Robert & Chen, Debby. The Making of Monkey King. Moua, Xe Susane, tr. Ma, Wenhai, illus. 1998. (Adventures of Monkey King Ser.). (ACE.). 34p. (J). (gr. 3-6). 16.95 (978-1-57227-047-3(0)) Pan Asia Pubns. (USA), Inc.

—The Making of Monkey King. Ngan, Nguyen N., tr. Ma, Wenhai, illus. 1998. (Adventures of Monkey King Ser.: No. 1). 34p. (J). (gr. 2-5). 16.95 (978-1-57227-043-5(8)) Pan Asia Pubns. (USA), Inc.

—The Making of Monkey King. Kobylinski, Pauling, tr. Ma, Wenhai, illus. 1998. (Adventures of Monkey King Ser.: No. 1). (ENG & SPA.). 32p. (J). (gr. 3-6). 16.95 (978-1-57227-044-2(6)) Pan Asia Pubns. (USA), Inc.

—The Making of Monkey King. Ngan, Nguyen N., tr. Ma, Wenhai, illus. 1998. (Adventures of Monkey King Ser.: No. 1). 34p. (J). (gr. 3-6). (CHI & ENG.). 16.95 (978-1-57227-045-9(4)); (ENG & VIE.). 16.95 (978-1-57227-046-6(2)) Pan Asia Pubns. (USA), Inc.

Kurtz, Jane & Kurtz, Christopher. Water Hole Waiting. Christiansen, Lee, illus. 2002. 32p. (J). (gr. 5 up). 16.99 (978-0-06-029850-0(2)); (gr. 7 up). lib. bdg. 18.89 (978-0-06-029851-7(0)) HarperCollins Pubs.

Laird, Elizabeth & Davidson, Roz. Jungle School. Sim, David, illus. 2006. (Green Bananas Ser.). 48p. (J). (gr. k-2). pap. (978-0-7787-1042-4(4)); (978-0-7787-1026-4(2)) Crabtree Publishing Co.

Landstrom, Lena. A Hippo's Tale. Sandin, Joan, tr. from SWE. 2007. (Illus.). 32p. (J). (ps-1). 15.00 (*978-91-29-66603-8(1)) R & S Bks. SWE. *Dist:* Macmillan.

LaReau, Kara. Rocko & Spanky Call It Quits. LaReau, Jenna, illus. 2008. (Rocko & Spanky Ser.). 40p. (J). 16.00 (978-0-15-216611-3(4)) Harcourt Children's Bks.

LaReau, Kara & LaReau, Jenna. Rocko & Spanky Have Company. LaReau, Kara & LaReau, Jenna, illus. 2006. (Rocko & Spanky Ser.). (Illus.). 40p. (J). 16.00 (978-0-15-216618-2(1)) Harcourt Trade Pubs.

Laske, Ernest. Life in Monkey Town. 2005. 174p. per. 12.95 (978-1-59886-010-8(0)) Tate Publishing & Enterprises, L.L.C.

Lawrence, David L. The First Adventure of Geoffrey & Chongo. 2006. (ENG.). 40p. per. 16.99 (*978-1-4259-6473-3(7)) AuthorHouse.

Leatham, Alan D. Four Cats, Five Monkeys, Absurd Birds & Other Fanciful Stuff. 2006. 108p. pap. 16.95 (*978-1-4241-0692-9(3)) PublishAmerica, Inc.

Lindgren, Astrid. Do You Know Pippi Longstocking? Dyssegaard, Elisabeth Kallick, tr. Nyman, Ingrid, illus. 2005. 32p. (J). pap. 4.95 (978-91-29-66203-0(6)) R & S Bks. SWE. *Dist:* Macmillan.

—Pippi Calzaslargas. 2003. (SPA., Illus.). 137p. (J). (gr. 3-5). (978-84-261-3192-8(1) , JV30550) Juventud, Editorial ESP. *Dist:* Lectorum Pubns., Inc.

Lloyd, Sam. Yummy Yummy! Food for My Tummy. Tickle, Jack, illus. 2004. 32p. (J). tchr. ed. 15.95 (978-1-58925-035-2(4) , tiger tales) ME Media LLC.

Lonczak, Heather Suzanne. Mookey the Monkey Gets over Being Teased. Ramsey, Marcy Dunn, illus. 2006. 32p. (J). (gr. k-2). 14.95 (978-1-59147-479-1(5)); pap. 8.95 (978-1-59147-480-7(9)) American Psychological Assn. (Magination Pr.).

Lyon, Justice. Little Monkey Smarty. 2002. 16p. (J). 4.95 (978-0-9716596-1-2(3) , GWS-02) 7 Heads Publishing.

Ma, Wenhai, illus. Tang Monk Disciples Monkey King. 2005. (Adventures of Monkey King Ser.: No. 3). 32p. (J). 16.95 (978-1-57227-084-8(5)) Pan Asia Pubns. (USA), Inc.

—Tang Monk Disciples Monkey King: English/Chinese. 2005. (Adventures of Monkey King Ser.: No. 3). (ENG & CHI.). 32p. (J). 16.95 (978-1-57227-086-2(1)) Pan Asia Pubns. (USA), Inc.

Mackall, Dandi Daley. No, No, Noah! Kucharik, Elena, illus. 2002. (I'm Not Afraid Ser.). 24p. (J). (ps-2). 6.99 (978-0-8499-7750-3(9)) Nelson, Thomas Inc.

Mackall, Dandi Daley. No, No Noah! 2007. 26p. (J). bds. 6.99 (*978-1-4003-1007-4(5)) Nelson, Thomas Inc.

Mangan, Anne. The Monkey Who Wanted the Moon. Walters, Catherine, illus. 2000. 32p. (J). (gr. k-3). 15.95 (978-1-56656-376-5(3)) Interlink Publishing Group, Inc.

Margaret. Curious George im Schokolade. 20.95 (978-3-8157-2329-6(9)) Coppenrath, F. Verlag KG DEU. *Dist:* Distribooks, Inc.

—Curious George und der Lastwa. 20.95 (978-3-8157-2327-2(2)) Coppenrath, F. Verlag KG DEU. *Dist:* Distribooks, Inc.

—Curious George und der Seltsa. 20.95 (978-3-8157-2330-2(2)) Coppenrath, F. Verlag KG DEU. *Dist:* Distribooks, Inc.

—Curious George und die Hundelb. 20.95 (978-3-8157-2328-9(0)) Coppenrath, F. Verlag KG DEU. *Dist:* Distribooks, Inc.

Martin, David. Monkey Business. Nash, Scott, illus. 2000. (Brand New Readers Ser.). 32p. (J). (ps-2). pap. 5.99 (978-0-7636-0773-9(8)) Candlewick Pr.

—Monkey Trouble. 2000. (Brand New Readers Ser.). (Illus.). 1p. (J). (ps-2). pap. 5.99 (978-0-7636-0771-5(1)) Candlewick Pr.

Matthews, Stuart. How Does It Work?, 4 vols., Set. 2001. (Illus.). (J). (gr. 2-7). lib. bdg. 85.20 (978-1-58340-069-2(9)) Smart Apple Media.

McIntyre, Pat Henican. ?Oh Freddie!? Richie, Rebecca, illus. 2002. 48p. (J). (978-1-55306-382-7(1) , Epic Pr.) Essence Publishing.

McKenna, Mark, creator. Banana Tail's Tales & Activities. 2006. (J). 4.95 (978-0-9727681-1-5(4)) McKenna, Mark.

McKenna, Mark, et al, illus. Banana Tail. 2003. 32p. (J). 12.95 (978-0-9727681-3-9(0)) Active Media Publishing, LLC.

McNeil, Niki, et al. HOCPP 1069 Curious George Rides a Bike. 2006. spiral bd. 15.50 (*978-1-60308-069-9(4)) In the Hands of a Child.

Meek, Nora. Sniffing for Democracy. 2004. (J). per. (978-0-9753852-0-3(8)) PM, INK.

Milgrim, David. Swing Otto Swing! Milgrim, David, illus. 2004. (Adventures of Otto Ser.). (Illus.). 32p. (J). 14.95 (978-0-689-85564-1(8) , Atheneum) Simon & Schuster Children's Publishing.

Miller, Wiley. The Extraordinary Adventures of Ordinary Basil Vol. 2: Island of the Volcano Monkeys. 2008. (Extraordinary Adventures of Ordinary Bas Ser.). 128p. (J). pap. 14.99 (*978-0-439-86132-8(2) , Blue Sky Pr., The) Scholastic, Inc.

Millionaire, Tony. Sock Monkey: the Inches Incident: The Inches Incident. 2007. 88p. (J). pap. 12.95 (*978-1-59307-842-3(0)) Dark Horse Comics.

Millionaire, Tony. That Darn Yarn. 2005. (Illus.). 40p. (J). (ps-17). 7.95 (978-1-59582-009-9(4)) DH Pr.

Miserable Monkey. 2000. 14p. (J). bds. 7.95 (978-0-7525-4605-6(8)) Parragon, Inc.

Mlawer, Teresa, tr. Se Venden Gorras. unabr. ed. 1999. (SPA., Illus.). (J). (gr. k-3). pap., tchr. ed. 37.95 incl. audio (978-0-87499-514-5(0)) Live Oak Media.

—Se Venden Gorras. Slobodkina, Esphyr, illus. unabr. ed. 1999. (SPA.). (J). (gr. k-3). 25.95 incl. audio (978-0-87499-513-8(2)); pap. 16.95 incl. audio (978-0-87499-512-1(4) , LK3259) Live Oak Media.

Monkey Business. 2005. (J). 4.95 (978-1-59792-015-5(0)) F.A.S.T. Learning LLLC.

Monkeys: Individual Title, 6 packs. (Sails Literacy Ser.). 16p. (gr. k up). 27.00 (978-0-7635-4405-8(1)) Rigby Education.

Monkeys Can't Cook! 2004. (J). 10.95 (978-0-9761350-3-6(5)) Blue Zebra Entertainment, INc.

Monkeys Can't Fly! 2004. (J). 10.95 (978-0-9761350-2-9(7)) Blue Zebra Entertainment, INc.

Monkeys, Diverse Animals: MainSails Individual Title Six-Packs. (Sails Literacy Ser.). (gr. 5 up). 37.00 (978-0-7578-8043-8(6)) Rigby Education.

Monkey's Friends: Individual Title Six-Packs. (Literatura 2000 Ser.). (gr. 1-2). 28.00 (978-0-7635-0098-6(4)) Rigby Education.

Monkey's Miserable Monday. 2001. (ps-2). lib. bdg. 9.80 (978-0-613-32843-2(4)) Tandem Library Bks.

Monkey's Ride: Individual Title Six-Packs. (Sails Literacy Ser.). (gr. 1-2). 36.00 (978-0-7578-6720-0(0)) Rigby Education.

Monkey's Shoes: 3-in-1 Package. (Sails Literacy Ser.). 24p. (gr. k up). 57.00 (978-0-7578-3201-7(6)) Rigby Education.

Monkey's Shoes: 6 Small Books. (Sails Literacy Ser.). 24p. (gr. k up). 25.00 (978-0-7578-3177-5(X)) Rigby Education.

Monkey's Shoes: Big Book Only. (Sails Literacy Ser.). 24p. (gr. k up). 27.00 (978-0-7635-6987-7(9)) Rigby Education.

El mono y la Banana 11: Leveled Books. 2001. (McGraw-Hill. Lectura Ser.). (ENG & SPA.). (gr. 4 up). (978-0-02-188156-7(1)) Macmillan/McGraw-Hill Schl. Div.

Monroe, Chris. Monkey with a Tool Belt. 2008. (J). lib. bdg. (*978-0-8225-7631-0(7)) Univ. of Minnesota Pr.

Morrow, Tara Jaye. Just Mommy & Me. Bratun, Katy, illus. 2004. 32p. (J). 13.89 (978-0-06-000725-6(7)) HarperCollins Pubs.

Murphy, Cary. Meeko the Monkey's A-Z Animal Band. Victoria, Arody, illus. 2006. 32p. (J). (978-0-9778546-0-8(4)) Lucky Dog Publishing.

Murphy, Stuart J. Spunky Monkeys on Parade. Cravath, Lynne W., illus. 1999. (MathStart Ser.). 40p. (J). (gr. 1 up). pap. 5.99 (978-0-06-446727-8(9) , Harper Trophy) HarperCollins Pubs.

—Spunky Monkeys on Parade. 1999. (MathStart Ser.). (Illus.). 40p. (YA). (gr. 1 up). 15.95 (978-0-06-028014-7(X)) HarperCollins Pubs.

—Spunky Monkeys on Parade. 1999. (Math Start Ser.). (978-0-606-17496-1(6)); lib. bdg. 13.00 (978-0-613-22430-7(2)) Tandem Library Bks.

Myers, Martha. Nibbles, the Mostly Mischievous Monkey. 2003. (Julius & Friends Ser.: Vol. 10). (Illus.). 91p. (J). 6.99 (978-0-8163-1947-3(2)) Pacific Pr. Publishing Assn.

Napoli, Donna Jo & Johnston, Shelagh. Hotel Jungle. Spengler, Kenneth, tr. Spengler, Kenneth, illus. 2004. 33p. (J). 15.95 (978-1-59336-002-3(9)); pap. (978-1-59336-003-0(7)) Mondo Publishing.

Nelson, Theresa. Empress of Elsewhere. 2000. (Illus.). (J). 12.64 (978-0-606-18836-4(3)) Tandem Library Bks.

Nonan, Sammi. The Monkey That Could Fly. l.t. ed. 2001. 24p. (J). 2.99 (978-0-9704868-5-1(5)) Be-Mused Pubns.

Ochiltree, Dianne. Ten Monkey Jamboree. Lanquetin, Anne-Sophie, illus. 2001. 32p. (J). (ps-2). 16.95 (978-0-689-83402-8(0) , McElderry, Margaret K.) Simon & Schuster Children's Publishing.

Ocho Monitos. 2005. Tr. of Eight Silly Monkeys. (SPA.). 18p. (J). 9.95 (978-1-58117-334-5(2) , Intervisual/Piggy Toes) Dalmatian Pr.

Olshan, Matthew. The Flown Sky, 1. 2007. (Illus.). 352p. 19.95 (978-0-9789391-0-6(7)) Chacmool Pr.

Pankratz, Justin, illus. Blue Monkey. 2003. (J). 5.95 (978-0-9742637-0-0(2)) Pankratz Creations.

Papineau, Lucie. Bamboo at Jungle School. Jolin, Dominique, illus. 2005. (Read-It! Readers Ser.). 32p. (J). (gr. k-3). 18.60 (978-1-4048-1036-5(6)) Picture Window Bks.

—Bamboo at the Beach. Jolin, Dominique, illus. 2005. (Read-It! Readers Ser.). 32p. (C). (gr. k-3). 18.60 (978-1-4048-1035-8(8)) Picture Window Bks.

—Gilda the Giraffe & Marvin the Marmoset. Sarrazin, Marisol, illus. 2005. (Gilda the Giraffe Ser.). 32p. (J). (ps-3). lib. bdg. 22.60 (978-1-4048-1516-2(3)) Picture Window Bks.

Papineau, Lucie, et al. Bamboo at the Beach. 2000. (Illus.). 32p. (J). (gr. 1-4). pap. (978-1-894363-38-9(8)) Dominique & Friends.

Paul, Ann Whitford & Walker, David. Little Monkey Says Good Night. 2003. (Illus.). 32p. (J). 16.00 (978-0-374-34609-6(7) , Farrar, Straus & Giroux (BYR)) Farrar, Straus & Giroux.

Perez, Monica & Saric, Lazar. Curious George Roller Coaster. 2007. (Illus.). 24p. (J). (ps-k). pap. 3.99 (*978-0-618-80040-7(9)) Houghton Mifflin Co.

Perez, Monica, et al. Curious George & the Kite: Early Reader. 2007. (Illus.). 24p. (J). (gr. k-3). 3.99 (978-0-618-72396-6(X)) Houghton Mifflin Co.

—Curious George Builds a Home. 2006. (Illus.). 24p. (J). (gr. k-3). 3.99 (978-0-618-72395-9(1)) Houghton Mifflin Co.

—Dog Show: Early Reader. 2007. (Curious George Ser.). (Illus.). 24p. (J). (gr. k-3). 3.99 (978-0-618-72397-3(8)) Houghton Mifflin Co.

—The Donut Delivery. 2007. (Curious George Ser.). (Illus.). 24p. (J). (gr. k-3). 3.99 (978-0-618-73757-4(X)) Houghton Mifflin Co.

Phillips, Betty Lou. Emily Goes Wild. Watts, Sharon, illus. 2nd ed. 2003. 32p. (J). (ps-3). reprint ed. 16.95 (978-1-58685-268-9(X)) Gibbs Smith, Publisher.

—Emily Works Out. Watts, Sharon, illus. 2005. 12p. (J). (ps). bds. 6.95 (978-1-58685-458-4(5)) Gibbs Smith, Publisher.

—Emily's Manners. Watts, Sharon, illus. 2005. 12p. (J). (ps). bds. 6.95 (978-1-58685-457-7(7)) Gibbs Smith, Publisher.

Piggy Toes Press Staff & Haskamp, Steve. Five Silly Monkeys: With Handpuppet. 2006. (Illus.). 12p. (J). bds. 12.95 (978-1-58117-460-1(8) , Intervisual/Piggy Toes) Dalmatian Pr.

Pilkey, Dav. Ricky Ricotta Y el Poderoso Robot Contra Los Mecamonos de Marte. 2002. (Ricky Ricotta Ser.: No. 4). (ps-2). lib. bdg. 11.80 (978-0-613-45613-5(0)) Tandem Library Bks.

Popper, Garry. Scary Monkeys: Going Ape. Forshaw, John, illus. 2004. 48p. 9.00 (978-1-84161-014-6(3)) Ravette Publishing, Ltd. GBR. *Dist:* Parkwest Pubns., Inc.

Powell, Richard. Mandy Monkey. Rhodes, Katie, illus. 2004. (Fuzzy Friends Ser.). 10p. (J). 7.95 (978-1-58925-720-7(0) , tiger tales) ME Media LLC.

Prap, Lila. Why? 2005. Orig. Title: Zakaj?. (Illus.). 32p. (J). (ps-ps). 14.95 (978-1-929132-80-5(8)) Kane/Miller Bk. Pubs., Inc.

Priddy, Roger. Funny Faces Charlie Monkey. 2007. 24p. (J). bds. 14.95 (*978-0-312-49892-4(6) , Priddy Bks.) St. Martin's Pr.

Priddy, Roger. Funny Faces Touch & Feel: Charlie Monkey. rev. ed. 2006. (Illus.). 10p. (J). bds. 9.95 (978-0-312-49692-0(3) , Priddy Bks.) St. Martin's Pr.

Ralph, Brian. Crum Bums. 2007. (Illus.). 208p. (YA). pap. 15.00 (*978-1-60309-002-5(9)) Top Shelf Productions.

Randall, Ronne. Don't Be Pesky, Little Monkey! Church, Caroline Jayne, illus. 2002. (Little Friends Ser.). 14p. (J). (ps-1). 12.95 (978-1-57145-771-4(2) , Silver Dolphin Bks.) Advantage Pubs. Group.

Rathmann, Peggy. Buenas Noches, Gorila. Mayobre, Maria Francisca, tr. from ENG. Rathmann, Peggy, illus. 2001. (SPA., Illus.). 36p. (J). 18.95 (978-980-257-265-6(9)) Ekare, Ediciones VEN. *Dist:* AIMS International Bks., Inc., Lectorum Pubns., Inc.

Rawls, Wilson. Summer of the Monkeys. 1998. 288p. (J). (gr. 5-9). pap. 5.99 (978-0-440-41580-0(2) , Yearling) Random Hse. Children's Bks.

—Summer of the Monkeys. 1998. (gr. 5-8). lib. bdg. 14.15 (978-0-613-83533-6(6)) Tandem Library Bks.

Regan, Dana. Monkey See, Monkey Do. Regan, Dana, illus. 2000. (All Aboard Reading Ser.). (Illus.). 32p. (J). (ps-3). pap. 3.99 (978-0-448-42299-2(9) , Grosset & Dunlap) Penguin Group (USA) Inc.

Rey. George O Curioso. pap. 23.95 (978-85-336-0916-7(7)) Livraria Martins Editora BRA. *Dist:* Distribooks, Inc.

Rey, H. A. Coco der Neugierige Affe. 1999. Orig. Title: Curious George. (GER., Illus.). 44p. (J). pap. (978-3-257-00816-6(3)) Diogenes Verlag AG CHE. *Dist:* International Bk. Import Service, Inc.

—Curious George & Firefighters. Rey, Margret, illus. 2007. 24p. (J). (ps-k). bds. 9.95 (*978-0-618-89194-8(3)) Houghton Mifflin Co. Trade & Reference Div.

—Curious George & Puppies. Rey, Margret, illus. 2007. 24p. (J). (ps-k). pap. 9.95 incl. audio compact disk (*978-0-618-80065-0(4)) Houghton Mifflin Co. Trade & Reference Div.

—Curious George Feeds the Animals. 1998. (Illus.). 24p. (J). (gr. k-3). tchr. ed. 12.95 (978-0-395-91904-0(5)) Houghton Mifflin Co. Trade & Reference Div.

—Curious George Flies a Kite. Rey, H. A., illus. 2002. (Curious George Picture Bks.). (Illus.). (J). 13.79 (978-0-7587-2314-7(8)) Book Wholesalers, Inc.

—Curious George Flies a Kite. ed. 2004. (J). (gr. k-3). spiral bd. (978-0-616-01770-8(7)); spiral bd. (978-0-616-01771-5(5)) Canadian National Institute for the Blind/Institut National Canadien pour les Aveugles.

—Curious George Goes to the Hospital. Rey, H. A., illus. 2002. (Curious George Picture Bks.). (J). 13.79 (978-0-7587-2319-2(9)) Book Wholesalers, Inc.

—Curious George in the Big City. Weston, Martha, illus. 2001. (Curious George Ser.). 24p. (J). (ps-2). 7.95 (978-0-618-15253-7(9)) Houghton Mifflin Co.

—Curious George Learns the Alphabet. Rey, H. A., illus. 2002. (Curious George Picture Bks.). (Illus.). (J). 13.79 (978-0-7587-2318-5(0)) Book Wholesalers, Inc.

—Curious George Takes a Job. Rey, H. A., illus. 2002. (Curious George Picture Bks.). (Illus.). (J). 13.79 (978-0-7587-2322-2(9)) Book Wholesalers, Inc.

—Curious George Takes a Job. Rey, Margret, illus. 2007. 48p. (J). (ps-k). pap. 9.95 incl. audio compact disk (*978-0-618-72406-2(0)) Houghton Mifflin Co. Trade & Reference Div.

—Jorge el Curioso Encuentra Trabajo. 2003. (SPA.). (gr. k-3). lib. bdg. 14.10 (978-0-613-62962-1(0)) Tandem Library Bks.

—Jorge el Curioso Monta en Bicicleta. Canetti, Yanitzia, tr. 2002. Tr. of Curious George Rides a Bike. (SPA., Illus.). 48p. (J). (gr. k-3). pap. 6.95 (978-0-618-19677-7(3)); tchr. ed. 14.95 (978-0-618-21615-4(4)) Houghton Mifflin Co. Trade & Reference Div.

—Jorge el Curioso Monta en Bicicleta. 2002. Tr. of Curious George Rides a Bike. (SPA.). (gr. k-3). lib. bdg. 14.10 (978-0-613-60749-0(X)) Tandem Library Bks.

Rey, H. A., illus. Cecily G. & the 9 Monkeys. 2007. (Curious George Ser.). 48p. (J). (gr. 3-5). 16.00 (*978-0-618-80066-7(2)) Houghton Mifflin Co.

Rey, H. A. & Rey, Margret. CG TV Curious George Plants a Seed Spanish Bilingual Edition. 2007. 24p. (J). (gr. k-3). mass mkt. 3.99 (*978-0-618-89688-2(0)) Houghton Mifflin Co. Trade & Reference Div.

—The Complete Adventures of Curious George. 2005. (J). (ps-k). 30.00 (978-0-618-64550-3(0)) Houghton Mifflin Co. Trade & Reference Div.

—Curious George & the Puppies. 2006. (Curious George Ser.). (Illus.). 24p. (J). (ps-k). bds. 9.95 (978-0-618-77241-4(3)) Houghton Mifflin Co. Trade & Reference Div.

—Curious George Gets a Medal. gif. ed. 2005. (Illus.). 48p. (J). (gr. k-3). 9.95 (978-0-618-54906-1(4)) Houghton Mifflin Co. Trade & Reference Div.

—Curious George Goes to the Beach. 1999. (Curious George Ser.). (Illus.). (J). (gr. k-3). 24p. tchr. ed. 12.95 (978-0-395-97834-4(3)); 32p. pap. 3.95 (978-0-395-97838-2(6)) Houghton Mifflin Co. Trade & Reference Div.

—Curious George's First Day of School. 2005. (Illus.). 24p. (J). (gr. k-3). 12.95 (978-0-618-60563-7(0)) Houghton Mifflin Co. Trade & Reference Div.

—Jorge el Curioso Encuentra Trabajo. Canetti, Yanitzia, tr. 2003. (SPA., Illus.). 48p. (J). (gr. k-3). 14.95 (978-0-618-33601-2(X)); pap. 6.95 (978-0-618-33600-5(1)) Houghton Mifflin Co. Trade & Reference Div.

—The New Adventures of Curious George 2006. 2006. (Illus.). 208p. (J). (ps-k). 10.99 (978-0-618-66373-6(8)) Houghton Mifflin Co. Trade & Reference Div.

—The Original Curious George. Rey, H. A., illus. 1998. (Curious George Ser.). (Illus.). 64p. (J). (gr. k-3). tchr. ed. 25.00 (978-0-395-92272-9(0)) Houghton Mifflin Co. Trade & Reference Div.

Rey, H. A. & Rey, Margret, creators. Opuestos con Jorge el Curioso. 2002. (SPA., Illus.). 8p. (J). (gr. k-ps). bds. 5.95 (978-0-618-20317-8(6)) Houghton Mifflin Co. Trade & Reference Div.

Rey, H. A. & Rey, Margret, illus. Curious George's ABCs. 2003. (J). bds. 9.95 (978-0-618-27708-7(0)) Houghton Mifflin Co. Trade & Reference Div.

—Curious George's Are You Curious? 2003. (J). bds. 9.95 (978-0-618-27710-0(2)) Houghton Mifflin Co. Trade & Reference Div.

—Curious George's Opposites. 2003. (J). bds. 9.95 (978-0-618-27709-4(9)) Houghton Mifflin Co. Trade & Reference Div.

Rey, H. A. & Vipah Interactive Staff. Curious George Goes to a Chocolate Factory. 1998. (Curious George Ser.). (Illus.). 24p. (J). (gr. k-3). pap. 3.95 (978-0-395-91214-0(8)) Houghton Mifflin Co.

Rey, Margret. Curious George & the Dinosaur. Rey, Margret, illus. 2002. (Curious George TV Bks.). (Illus.). (J). 11.87 (978-0-7587-2311-6(3)) Book Wholesalers, Inc.

—Curious George & the Pizza. Rey, Margret, illus. 2002. (Curious George TV Bks.). (Illus.). (J). 11.87 (978-0-7587-2312-3(1)) Book Wholesalers, Inc.

—Curious George Goes to a Costume Party. Vipah Interactive Staff, illus. 2001. (Curious George Ser.). 24p. (J). (gr. k-3). tchr. ed. 12.95 (978-0-618-06564-6(4)) Houghton Mifflin Co. Trade & Reference Div.

—Curious George Goes to a Costume Party. 2001. (gr. k-3). lib. bdg. 11.80 (978-0-613-35499-8(0)) Tandem Library Bks.

—Curious George Goes to the Aquarium. Rey, Margret, illus. 2002. (Curious George TV Bks.). (Illus.). (J). 11.87 (978-0-7587-2317-8(2)) Book Wholesalers, Inc.

—Curious George in the Big City. Weston, Martha, illus. 2001. (Curious George Ser.). 24p. (J). (gr. k-3). pap. 3.95 (978-0-618-15240-7(7)) Houghton Mifflin Co. Trade & Reference Div.

—Curious George in the Big City. 2001. (gr. k-3). lib. bdg. 11.80 (978-0-613-35500-1(8)) Tandem Library Bks.

—Curious George Visits the Zoo. Rey, Margret, illus. 2002. (Curious George TV Bks.). (Illus.). (J). 11.87 (978-0-7587-2323-9(7)) Book Wholesalers, Inc.

Rey, Margret & Rey, H. A. Curious George & the Bunny. 1998. (Curious George Ser.). (Illus.). 12p. (J). (gr. k-ps). bds. 5.95 (978-0-395-89922-9(2)) Houghton Mifflin Co. Trade & Reference Div.

—Curious George & the Dumptruck. 1999. (Curious George Ser.). (Illus.). 24p. (J). (gr. k-3). tchr. ed. 12.95 (978-0-395-97832-0(7)) Houghton Mifflin Co. Trade & Reference Div.

—Curious George & the Dumptruck. Vipah Interactive Staff, illus. 1999. (Curious George Ser.). 24p. (J). (gr. k-3). pap. 3.95 (978-0-395-97836-8(X)) Houghton Mifflin Co. Trade & Reference Div.

—Curious George & the Hot Air Balloon. 1998. (Curious George Ser.). (Illus.). 24p. (J). (gr. k-3). tchr. ed. 12.95 (978-0-395-91918-7(5)) Houghton Mifflin Co. Trade & Reference Div.

—Curious George & the Hot Air Balloon. Vipah Interactive Staff, illus. 1998. (Curious George Ser.). 24p. (J). (gr. k-3). pap. 3.95 (978-0-395-91909-5(6)) Houghton Mifflin Co. Trade & Reference Div.

—Curious George & the Puppies. 1998. (Curious George Ser.). (Illus.). 24p. (J). (gr. k-3). pap. 3.95 (978-0-395-91215-7(6)); tchr. ed. 12.95 (978-0-395-91217-1(2)) Houghton Mifflin Co. Trade & Reference Div.

—Curious George at the Parade. 1999. (Curious George Ser.). (Illus.). 24p. (J). (gr. k-3). pap. 3.95 (978-0-395-97837-5(8)); tchr. ed. 12.95 (978-0-395-97833-7(5)) Houghton Mifflin Co. Trade & Reference Div.

—Curious George Feeds the Animals. 1998. (Curious George Ser.). (Illus.). 24p. (J). (gr. k-3). pap. 3.95 (978-0-395-91910-1(X)) Houghton Mifflin Co. Trade & Reference Div.

—Curious George Goes Camping. 1999. (Curious George Ser.). (Illus.). 24p. (J). (gr. k-3). tchr. ed. 12.95 (978-0-395-97831-3(9)) Houghton Mifflin Co. Trade & Reference Div.

—Curious George Goes Camping. Interactive, Vipah, illus. 1999. (Curious George Ser.). 32p. (J). (gr. k-3). pap. 3.95 (978-0-395-97835-1(1)) Houghton Mifflin Co. Trade & Reference Div.

—Curious George Goes to a Chocolate Factory. 1998. (Curious George Ser.). (Illus.). 24p. (J). (gr. k-3). tchr. ed. 12.95 (978-0-395-91216-4(4)) Houghton Mifflin Co. Trade & Reference Div.

—Curious George Goes to a Movie. 1998. (Curious George Ser.). (Illus.). 24p. (J). (gr. k-3). pap. 3.95 (978-0-395-91906-4(1)); tchr. ed. 12.95 (978-0-395-91901-9(0)) Houghton Mifflin Co. Trade & Reference Div.

—Curious George in the Snow. 1998. (Curious George Ser.). (Illus.). 24p. (J). (gr. k-3). tchr. ed. 12.00 (978-0-395-91902-6(9)) Houghton Mifflin Co. Trade & Reference Div.

—Curious George Learns Phonics & Spelling. 1998. (Curious George Ser.). (J). (ps-2). 24.72 (978-0-395-85431-0(8)) Houghton Mifflin Co.

—Curious George Makes Pancakes. 1998. (Curious George Ser.). (Illus.). 24p. (J). (gr. k-3). tchr. ed. 12.95 (978-0-395-91903-3(7)) Houghton Mifflin Co. Trade & Reference Div.

—Curious George Makes Pancakes. Interactive, Vipah, illus. 1998. (Curious George Ser.). 24p. (J). (gr. k-3). pap. 3.95 (978-0-395-91908-8(8)) Houghton Mifflin Co. Trade & Reference Div.

—Curious George Visits a Toy Store. Weston, Martha, illus. 2002. 24p. (J). (gr. k-3). tchr. ed. 12.00 (978-0-618-06398-7(6)) Houghton Mifflin Co. Trade & Reference Div.

—Curious George's ABCs. Rey, H. A., illus. 1998. (Curious George Ser.). (Illus.). 12p. (J). (gr. k-ps). bds. 5.95 (978-0-395-89925-0(7)) Houghton Mifflin Co. Trade & Reference Div.

—Curious George's Are You Curious? Rey, H. A., illus. 1998. (Curious George Ser.). (Illus.). 16p. (J). (gr. k-ps). bds. 5.95 (978-0-395-89924-3(9)) Houghton Mifflin Co. Trade & Reference Div.

—Curious George's Dream. 1998. (Curious George Ser.). (Illus.). 24p. (J). (gr. k-3). tchr. ed. 12.95 (978-0-395-91905-7(3)) Houghton Mifflin Co. Trade & Reference Div.

—Curious George's Dream. Vipah Interactive Staff, illus. 1998. (Curious George Ser.). 24p. (J). (gr. k-3). pap. 3.95 (978-0-395-91911-8(8)) Houghton Mifflin Co. Trade & Reference Div.

—Curious George's First Day of School. Hines, Anna Grossnickle, illus. 2005. 24p. (J). (gr. k-3). pap. 3.95 (978-0-618-60564-4(9)) Houghton Mifflin Co. Trade & Reference Div.

—Curious George's Opposites. 1998. (Curious George Ser.). (Illus.). 16p. (J). (gr. k-ps). bds. 5.95 (978-0-395-89923-6(0)) Houghton Mifflin Co. Trade & Reference Div.

Rey, Margret & Rey, H. A., creators. Curious George Goes Fishing. 2001. (Curious George Ser.). (Illus.). 24p. (J). (gr. k-ps). bds. 5.95 (978-0-618-12071-0(8)) Houghton Mifflin Co. Trade & Reference Div.

Rey, Margret, et al. Curious George Goes to a Costume Party. Weston, Martha, illus. 2001. (Curious George Ser.). 24p. (J). (gr. k-3). pap. 3.95 (978-0-618-06569-1(5)) Houghton Mifflin Co. Trade & Reference Div.

Ricci, Christine. Dora's Costume Party! Saunders, Zina, illus. 2005. 24p. (J). lib. bdg. 9.00 (***978-1-4242-0978-1(1)***) Fitzgerald Bks.

Ricci, Christine. Dora's Costume Party. 2006. (J). (ps-2). 21.35 (978-1-59961-071-9(X)) Spotlight.

Riccio, Nina M. Five Kids & a Monkey, 3 vols., Set. Blair, Beth L., illus. (J). (gr. 2-6). 23.85 (978-0-9653955-3-3(7)) Creative Attic, Inc., The.

Risk, Mary & Jansen, Jacqueline. I Want My Banana: English-French Version: Je Veux Ma Banane. De Wolf, Alex, illus. 1998. (I Can Read Bks.). (ENG & FRE.). (J). (ps up). pap. 9.95 incl. audio (978-0-7641-7190-1(9)) Barron's Educational Series, Inc.

Rosano, John. Molly Monkey. 2008. (Illus.). (J). 14.95 (***978-1-60131-013-2(7)***) Big Tent Bks.

Rosario, Joann. Bitty Witty Witty Witty Witty Monkey! Rosario, Joann, illus. 2004. (Illus.). 10p. (J). pap. 10.00 (978-0-9758746-9-1(1) , 1246169) J.G.R. Enterprises.

Roy, Ron. Mystery at the Washington Monument. Bush, Timothy, illus. 2007. (J). (Capital Mysteries Ser.: No. 8). 96p. (gr. 2-6). 3.99 (978-0-375-83970-2(4) , Random Hse. Bks. for Young Readers); (Capital Mysteries Ser.: No. 8). 96p. (gr. 2-6). lib. bdg. 11.99 (978-0-375-93970-9(9) , Random Hse. Bks. for Young Readers); 87p. (***978-1-4287-4577-3(7)***) Random Hse. Children's Bks.

Rylant, Cynthia. The Case of the Missing Monkey. Karas, G. Brian, illus. (High-Rise Private Eyes Ser.: No. 1). 48p. (J). 2001. (ps-3). pap. 3.99 (978-0-06-444306-7(X) , Harper Trophy); 2000. (gr. 1 up). 14.95 (978-0-688-16306-8(8)) HarperCollins Pubs.

—The Case of the Missing Monkey. Karas, G. Brian, illus. 2003. (High-Rise Private Eyes Ser.: No. 1). (J). 25.95 incl. audio (978-1-59112-194-7(9)); pap. 29.95 incl. audio (978-1-59112-195-4(7)); pap. 18.95 incl. audio compact disk (978-1-59112-614-0(2)); pap. 16.95 incl. audio (978-1-59112-193-0(0)) Live Oak Media.

—The Case of the Missing Monkey. Karas, G. Brian, illus. 2002. (High-Rise Private Eyes Ser.: No. 1). 46p. (J). (ps-17). lib. bdg. 11.80 (978-0-613-44194-0(X)) Tandem Library Bks.

—The Case of the Missing Monkey. 2001. (High-Rise Private Eyes Ser.: No. 1). (J). 10.79 (978-0-606-22319-5(3)) Tandem Library Bks.

—El Caso del Mono Extraviado. (SPA.). (J). 7.95 (978-958-04-6866-0(4)) Norma S.A. COL. *Dist:* Distribuidora Norma, Inc.

Santamaria, Benjamin. Tales of the Monkey King. Deines, Brian, illus. 2005. 32p. (J). (gr. 1-3). 15.95 (978-0-88776-684-8(6)) Tundra Bks., Inc./Livres Toundra, Inc. CAN. *Dist:* Random Hse., Inc.

Santat, Dan. The Guild of Geniuses. 2004. (Illus.). (J). pap. (978-0-439-29810-0(5) , Levine, Arthur A. Bks.) Scholastic, Inc.

Sargent, Dave & Sargent, Pat. Manny Monkey: Friendship, 56 vols., 52. Lenoir, Jane, illus. 2001. (Animal Pride Ser.: Vol. 52). 36p. (J). lib. bdg. 19.95 (978-1-56763-545-4(8)) Ozark Publishing.

Sargent, Dave, et al. Manny Monkey: Friendship, 17, 52. 2001. (Animal Pride Ser.: 52). (Illus.). 42p. (J). lib. bdg. 19.95 (978-1-56763-546-1(6)) Ozark Publishing.

Sayles, Kristi. Jacob's Monkey-the Trouble with Lying. 2005. 38p. (J). pap. 10.29 (978-1-4116-6429-6(9)) Lulu.com.

Schade, Susan. Bungee Baboon Rescue. Buller, Jon, illus. 2002. (Danger Joe Show Ser.: No. 2). 112p. (J). pap. 3.99 (978-0-439-40976-6(4) , Scholastic Paperbacks) Scholastic, Inc.

—Bungee Baboon Rescue. 2002. (gr. k-3). lib. bdg. 11.80 (978-0-613-72067-0(9)) Tandem Library Bks.

Schindel, John & Marigo, Luiz Claudio. Busy Monkeys. 2004. (Illus.). 20p. (J). bds. 6.95 (978-1-58246-082-6(5) , Tricycle Pr.) Ten Speed Pr.

Schuyer, Silvia. Noticias de un Mono. Bernalene, Poly, illus. 2001. Tr. of News from a Monkey. (SPA.). 24p. (J). 12.50 (978-950-08-2571-9(6)) Atlantida ARG. *Dist:* AIMS International Bks., Inc.

Scott, Nathan Kumar. Mangoes & Bananas. Balaji, T., illus. 2006. 32p. 16.95 (978-81-86211-06-9(3)) Consortium Bk. Sales & Distribution.

Shah, Naseeruddin. The Monkey & the Crocodile. 1998. (Karadi Tales Ser.). (Illus.). 24p. (YA). (gr. 1 up). 9.99 incl. audio (978-81-86838-35-8(X)) APG Sales and Fulfillment.

Shaky Monkey. alt. ed. 2002. (J). (978-1-931312-97-4(4)) SoftPlay, Inc.

Shepard, Aaron. The Monkey King: A Superhero Tale of China, Retold from the Journey to the West. 2008. (Ancient Fantasy Ser.: 4). 50p. (J). lib. bdg. 15.00 (***978-0-938497-40-0(5)***); lib. bdg. 6.00 (***978-0-938497-41-7(3)***) Shepard Pubns. (Skyhook Pr.).

Sierra, Judy. Counting Crocodiles. Hillenbrand, Will, illus. 2001. 40p. (J). (gr. k-2). pap. 7.00 (978-0-15-216356-3(5) , Voyager Bks./Libros Viajeros) Harcourt Children's Bks.

—Counting Crocodiles. 2001. (ps-2). lib. bdg. 15.30 (978-0-613-82223-7(4)); 13.80 (978-0-606-22596-0(X)) Tandem Library Bks.

—What Time Is It, Mr. Crocodile? Cushman, Doug, illus. 2007. 32p. (J). pap. 7.00 (978-0-15-205850-0(8) , Voyager Bks./Libros Viajeros) Harcourt Children's Bks.

—What Time Is It, Mr. Crocodile? Cushman, Doug, tr. Cushman, Doug, illus. 2004. 32p. (J). 16.00 (978-0-15-216445-4(6) , Gulliver Bks.) Harcourt Children's Bks.

Silverhardt, Lauryn. Boots. Thompson Brothers Staff, illus. 2003. (Dora the Explorer Ser.). (SPA & ENG.). 12p. (J). bds. 7.99 (978-0-689-85485-9(4) , Simon Spotlight/Nickelodeon) Simon & Schuster Children's Publishing.

Slobodkina, Esphyr. Caps for Sale. 2000. (J). pap. 19.97 incl. audio (978-0-7366-9218-2(5)) Books on Tape, Inc.

—Caps for Sale. 2005. (Illus.). (J). pap. 18.95 incl. audio compact disk (978-1-59112-697-3(5)) Live Oak Media.

—Caps for Sale. Slobodkina, Esphyr, illus. (Illus.). (J). (gr. k-3). 2005. pap. 16.95 incl. audio (978-0-87499-058-4(0)); 2000. 25.95 incl. audio (978-0-87499-059-1(9)) Live Oak Media.

—Caps for Sale, 2 bks. Mlawer, Teresa, tr. Slobodkina, Esphyr, illus. unabr. ed. 1999. (ENG & SPA., Illus.). (J). (gr. k-3). pap. 33.95 incl. audio (978-0-87499-562-6(0)) Live Oak Media.

—Caps for Sale. 2004. (J). 24.95 incl. audio (978-0-89719-863-9(8) , HRA012) Weston Woods Studios, Inc.

—Caps for Sale: A Tale of a Peddler, Some Monkeys, & Their Monkey Business. 2000. (978-0-606-20342-5(7)) Tandem Library Bks.

—Caps for Sale Board Book: A Tale of a Peddler, Some Monkeys & Their Monkey Business. Slobodkina, Esphyr, illus. 2008. 32p. (J). 8.99 (***978-0-06-147453-8(3)*** , Harper Festival) HarperCollins Pubs.

Slobodkina, Esphyr. Se Venden Gorras. Slobodkina, Esphyr, illus. 1999. (Illus.). 28.95 incl. audio compact disk (978-1-59519-195-3(X)); pap. 39.95 incl. audio compact disk (978-1-59519-194-6(1)); (SPA., (J). pap. 18.95 incl. audio compact disk (978-1-59519-193-9(3)) Live Oak Media.

Smalley, Roger, adapted by. The Big-Hearted Monkey & the Lion. 2005. (J). (978-1-933248-02-8(5)) World Quest Learning.

Smith, Dana C. Monkey Learns to Potty. 2005. (Illus.). 8p. pap. 7.95 (978-0-9762877-2-8(2) , 2500) PottyMD LLC.

Smith, Mariza A. Monkey & Turtle. Calamug, Cynthia & Calamug, Christine, illus. 1999. 18p. (J). (gr. 2-5). pap. 7.95 (978-0-9674241-0-1(0)) IZA Publishing Co.

Smith, Todd Aaron. The Average Monkey. Smith, Todd Aaron, illus. 2003. (Higby the Monkey Ser.). (Illus.). 32p. (J). pap. 4.97 (978-1-58660-857-6(6)) Barbour Publishing, Inc.

—Higby Throws a Fit. Smith, Todd Aaron, illus. 2003. (Higby the Monkey Ser.). (Illus.). 32p. (J). pap. 4.97 (978-1-58660-858-3(4)) Barbour Publishing, Inc.

Snyder, Vicki & West, Lois. Lighten up Lenny. Karn, Mike, illus. 2005. (J). (978-0-9773187-0-4(2)) Snyder, Vicki.

Thomasson, Clarissa. Hattie to the Rescue. 2001. (Little Green Monkey Stories Ser.). (Illus.). 14p. (J). (gr. k-3). pap. 6.95 (978-1-929202-15-7(6)) Salt Marsh Pubns.

—Jocko Pays a Visit. 2001. (Little Green Monkey Ser.). 14p. (J). (gr. k-8). pap. 6.95 (978-1-929202-17-1(2)) Salt Marsh Pubns.

—A Lost Tail. 2001. (Little Green Monkey Stories Ser.). (Illus.). 14p. (J). (gr. k-8). pap. 6.95 (978-1-929202-14-0(8)) Salt Marsh Pubns.

—Where's Eddie? 2001. (Little Green Monkey Ser.). (Illus.). 14p. (J). (gr. k-3). pap. 6.95 (978-1-929202-18-8(0)) Salt Marsh Pubns.

—Who's a Friend? 2001. (Little Green Monkey Stories Ser.). (Illus.). 14p. (J). (gr. k-3). pap. 6.95 (978-1-929202-16-4(4)) Salt Marsh Pubns.

Thottam, Meena, adapted by. Monkey Do as Monkey Does. 2006. (J). 3.95 (978-0-9776917-0-8(5) , Curcumin Bks.) Davlaw Press.

Tiger & Monkey: Early Level Satellite Individual Title Six-Packs. (Sails Literacy Ser.). 16p. (gr. 1-2). 27.00 (978-0-7578-2923-9(6)) Rigby Education.

Tigre, Tigre, 6, Pack. (Coleccion Pm Ser.).Tr. of Tiger, Tiger. (SPA.). 16p. (gr. 1 up). 26.00 (978-0-7578-2963-5(5)) Rigby Education.

Ufer, David A. The Giraffe Who Was Afraid of Heights. Carlson, Kirsten, illus. (J). 2007. 1p. 8.95 (***978-1-934359-05-1(X)***); 2006. 32p. 15.95 (978-0-9768823-0-5(2)) Sylvan Dell Pubng.

Valdes, Leslie. At the Carnival. Roper, Robert, illus. 2005. 24p. (J). lib. bdg. 9.00 (***978-1-4242-0982-8(X)***) Fitzgerald Bks.

van Kampen, Vlasta, illus. Monkey Tales. 1998. 40p. (J). (gr. k-3). pap. 6.95 (978-1-55037-530-5(X)); lib. bdg. 18.95 (978-1-55037-531-2(8)) Annick Pr., Ltd. CAN. *Dist:* Firefly Bks., Ltd.

Veldkamp, Tjibbe. Little Monkey's Big Peeing Circus. de Boer, Kees, illus. 2006. 32p. (J). (ps-1). 12.95 (978-0-8109-3949-3(5) , Abrams Bks. for Young Readers) Abrams, Harry N. , Inc.

Viselman, Kenn. I Love You Bunches. 2004. (Illus.). 28p. 14.98 (978-0-9722361-0-2(4)) Viselman, Kenn Presents...

Wang, Margaret. Monkey Tumbles. 2006. 10p. 9.95 (978-1-58117-501-1(9) , Intervisual/Piggy Toes) Dalmatian Pr.

Ward, Nick. No Hay Quien Gane a un Leopardo! Rubies, Carlota, tr. Ward, Nick, illus. 2001. (SPA., Illus.). 32p. (J). (gr. k-3). (978-84-480-1668-5(8) , TM30405) Timun Mas, Editorial S.A. ESP. *Dist:* Lectorum Pubns., Inc.

Wax, Wendy & Zucker, Zoey. Clean up This Mess! Obrero, Rudy, illus. 2007. (Curious George Ser.). 32p. (J). 3.99 (***978-1-4169-3376-2(X)*** , Simon Scribbles) Simon & Schuster Children's Publishing.

Weare, Tim. I'm a Little Monkey. 2004. (Illus.). 7p. (J). (ps-3). bds. 7.95 (978-1-904613-35-0(7) , Buster Bks.) O'Mara, Michael Bks., Ltd. GBR. *Dist:* Independent Pubs. Group.

West, Tracey. Yu-Gi-Oh Gx Reader #3 Rescue Duel. 2008. 32p. pap. 3.99 (***978-0-439-88840-0(9)*** , Scholastic) Scholastic, Inc.

Weston, Martha. Curious George Goes to a Costume Party. 2001. (Curious George Ser.). (Illus.). (J). 10.75 (978-0-606-21931-0(5)) Tandem Library Bks.

—Curious George in the Big City. 2001. (Curious George Ser.). (Illus.). (J). 10.75 (978-0-606-21932-7(3)) Tandem Library Bks.

—Curious George Takes a Train. 2002. (ps-2). lib. bdg. 11.80 (978-0-613-50553-6(0)) Tandem Library Bks.

—Curious George Visits a Toy Store. 2002. (ps-2). lib. bdg. 11.80 (978-0-613-50554-3(9)) Tandem Library Bks.

Weston, Martha, illus. Curious George in the Big City. 2001. (Curious George Ser.). 24p. (J). (gr. k-3). tchr. ed. 12.95 (978-0-618-15252-0(0)) Houghton Mifflin Co. Trade & Reference Div.

—Curious George Takes a Train. 2002. 24p. (J). (gr. k-3). pap. 3.95 (978-0-618-06567-7(9)); tchr. ed. 12.00 (978-0-618-06566-0(0)) Houghton Mifflin Co. Trade & Reference Div.

—Curious George Visits a Toy Store. 2002. 24p. (J). (gr. k-3). pap. 3.95 (978-0-618-06570-7(9)) Houghton Mifflin Co. Trade & Reference Div.

Whitfield, Peter. Zen Tails up & Down. Bevington, Nancy, illus. 2005. (Zen Tails Ser.). 28p. (J). (gr. 1-17). 15.95 (978-1-894965-22-4(1)) Simply Read Bks. CAN. *Dist:* Perseus Distribution.

Wiley. The Extraordinary Adventures of Ordinary Basil: Island of the Volcano Monkeys. 2007. (J). pap. (***978-0-439-86133-5(0)***) Blue Sky Pr.

Williams, Rozanne Lanczak. Monkey in the Story Tree. Maio, Barbara & Faulkner, Stacey, eds. Hanke, Karen, illus. 2006. (Learn to Write Ser.). (J). 8p. pap. 1.99 (978-1-59198-282-1(0) , 6176); per. 4.99 (***978-1-59198-333-0(9)***) Creative Teaching Pr., Inc.

Williams, Suzanne. Ten Naughty Little Monkeys. Watts, Suzanne, illus. 2007. 32p. (J). (ps-k). 16.99 (978-0-06-059904-1(9)); lib. bdg. 17.89 (978-0-06-059905-8(7)) HarperCollins Pubs.

Willis & Ross. Manky Monkey. 2002. (Illus.). 32p. (J). 17.99 (978-1-84270-051-8(0)) Andersen GBR. *Dist:* Independent Pubs. Group.

Willis, Jeanne & Ross, Tony. Manky Monkey. 2004. (Illus.). 32p. pap. 11.00 (978-1-84270-329-8(3)) Andersen GBR. *Dist:* Independent Pubs. Group.

Wilson, Budge & LaFave, Kim. Duff's Monkey Business. 2000. (New First Novels Ser.). (Illus.). 63p. (gr. 1-5). 4.95 (978-0-88780-498-4(5)); (978-0-88780-499-1(3)) Formac Publishing Co., Ltd. CAN. *Dist:* Casemate Pubs. & Bk. Distributors, LLC.

Winburn, William B., photos by. Sock Monkeys: Do the Monkey Monkey! 2005. (Illus.). 24p. (J). 9.95 (978-1-4027-2849-5(2)) Sterling Publishing Co., Inc.

Winter, Barbara. Monkey Business. 2002. (Amazing Dictionary Ser.). (Illus.). 64p. pap. 4.95 (***978-0-921156-94-9(4)***) Rubicon Publishing, Inc. CAN. *Dist:* International Publishers Marketing.

Wood, Deanna Plummer. Whenever Monkeys Move Next Door, 1 volume. 2005. (Illus.). 24p. (J). pap. 8.50 (978-0-9762935-1-4(X)) Perkins Crawford.

Woodward, Joanie. Seven Little Monkeys. Woodward, Joanie, illus. 2005. (Illus.). 40p. (J). per. (978-0-9754676-4-0(6)) Yeoman Hse.

Yerrid, Gable. Marley's Treasure. Fitzgerald, Jennifer, illus. 2007. 28p. (J). 15.95 (***978-0-9767442-6-9(0)***) Yorkville Pr.

Zanimo & Perkes, Carolyn. My Day. 2000. (Maki's Words Ser.). (Illus.). 24p. (J). (ps-k). pap. (978-1-894363-54-9(X)) Dominique & Friends.

Ziefert, Harriet. Monkey's Noisy Jungle. Newton, Jill, illus. 2007. bds. 7.95 (978-1-59354-598-7(3)) Blue Apple Bks.

—10 Little Sock Monkeys. Winburn, William B., illus. 2005. 24p. (J). 9.95 (978-1-4027-1944-8(2)) Sterling Publishing Co., Inc.

Zoehfeld, Kathleen Weidner. Curious You: You're on Your Way! Rey, H. A., illus. 2008. 32p. (gr. k). 12.95 (***978-0-618-91975-8(9)***) Houghton Mifflin Co.

MONKS

see Monasticism and Religious Orders

MONOLOGUES

Here are entered collections of monologues.

Bolton, Martha. Humorous Monologues. Behr, Joyce, illus. 2003. 128p. (J). (gr. 2-7). 19.00 (978-0-8069-6750-9(1)) Sterling Publishing Co., Inc.

Dabrowski, Kristen. 111 One-Minute Monologues: The Ultimate Monologue Book for Middle School Actors, Vol. 3. 2004. (Ultimate Monologue Book for Middle School Actors Ser.: Vol. 1). 136p. (J). pap. 11.95 (978-1-57525-419-7(0)) Smith and Kraus Publishers, Incorporated.

Ellis, Roger, ed. Audition Monologs for Student Actors: Selections from Contemporary Plays. 1999. 137p. (gr. 9 up). pap. 15.95 (978-1-56608-055-2(X) , N-B232) Meriwether Publishing, Ltd.

Haehnel, Alan. Remotely Related: Comedy Monologue. 2003. (YA). pap. 4.50 (978-1-932404-05-0(8) , 273) Brooklyn Pubs.

Harvey, Anne, ed. The Methuen Book of Monologues for Young Actors. 2004. 192p. pap. 13.95 (978-0-413-77279-4(9)) Methuen Publishing Ltd. GBR. *Dist:* Consortium Bk. Sales & Distribution.

Henderson, Heather. Flip Side: 64 Point-of-View Monologs for Teens. 1998. (gr. 7-12). lib. bdg. 24.55 (978-0-613-86860-0(9)) Tandem Library Bks.

Henderson, Heather H. The Flip Side: 64 Point-of-View Monologs for Teens. Zapel, Theodore O., ed. 1998. 138p. (gr. 6-12). pap. 14.95 (978-1-56608-045-3(2) , N-B221) Meriwether Publishing, Ltd.

Howard, Vernon. Monologues for Teens. Landes, William-Allan, ed. unabr. ed. 2003. (Illus.). 120p. (J). pap. 15.00 (978-0-88734-666-8(9)) Players Pr., Inc.

Jelliroll. Echo Booming Monologues. 2007. per. 11.95 net. (***978-1-60402-529-3(8)***) Independent Pub.

Johansen, Mila. 50 Scenes to Go: And 20 Monologues to Show. 2003. (Illus.). 160p. (YA). (gr. 4-12). pap. 22.00 (978-0-88734-933-1(1)) Players Pr., Inc.

MNO

Karshner, Roger. Teenage Mouth. 2000. (Illus.). 64p. (J). (gr. 8-12). pap. 9.95 (978-0-940669-17-8(X) , D-12) Dramaline Pubns.

Keller, Amanda. Andrea's Reflection: A Ten-Minute Comedy Monologue. 2001. (YA). (gr. 7-12). pap. 4.50 (978-1-931000-88-8(3) , 252) Brooklyn Pubs.

Lamedman, Debbie. The Ultimate Audition Book for Teens Vol. II: 111 Monologues from Classical Theater, 2 Minutes & Under. 2006. 11.95 (978-1-57525-458-6(1)) Smith and Kraus Publishers, Incorporated.

—The Ultimate Audition Book for Teens Vol. III: 111 Monologues from Classical Literature, 2 Minutes & Under. 2006. 11.95 (978-1-57525-459-3(X)) Smith and Kraus Publishers, Incorporated.

—The Ultimate Audition Book for Teens Vol. IX: 111 Monologues from Contemporary Literature, 2 Minutes & Under. 2006. 11.95 (978-1-57525-460-9(3)) Smith and Kraus Publishers, Incorporated.

—The Ultimate Audition Book for Teens IV: 111 One Minute Monologues. 2003. (Ultimate Audition Book for Teens Ser.: Vol. 4). viii, 117p. (J). 11.95 (978-1-57525-353-4(4)) Smith and Kraus Publishers, Incorporated.

Lindsay, David & Marlow, Jean. Satire of the Three Estates. McDiarmid, Matthew & Kemp, Robert, eds. 2000. 144p. (J). 17.95 (978-0-87830-114-0(3) , Theatre Arts Bks.) Routledge.

Maddox, Deborah. Audition Monologues: Power Pieces for Kids & Teens. 2002. (ENG.). 80p. (J). per. 12.95 (978-0-9716827-0-2(4)) Lucid Solutions.

McCullough, L. E. The Ultimate Audition Book for Teens Vol. II: III One-Minute Monologues for Teens. 2000. (Young Actors Ser.). 128p. (J). pap. 11.95 (978-1-57525-237-7(6)) Smith and Kraus Publishers, Incorporated.

—Wild & Wacky Characters for Kids: 60 One-Minute Monologues. 2001. 63p. (J). 11.95 (978-1-57525-305-3(4)) Smith and Kraus Publishers, Incorporated.

Meadows, Kelly. The Dating Game: Comedy Monologue. 2003. (YA). pap. 4.50 (978-1-932404-06-7(6) , 274) Brooklyn Pubs.

Milstein, Janet B. Cool Characters for Kids: 60 One-Minute Monologues. 2001. xii, 78p. (J). (gr. k-6). 11.95 (978-1-57525-306-0(2)) Smith and Kraus Publishers, Incorporated.

Pierce, J. P. Killer Monologues: Highly Actable Monologues & Performance Tips to Give You an Almost Unfair Advantage in the Auditioning Game. 1998. 128p. (YA). (gr. 9-12). pap. 39.95 incl. VHS (978-1-892553-00-3(7)) Impact Films.

Pomerance, Susan. Monologues for Teenage Girls: Contemporary Scene-Study Pieces for Young Actresses. 1998. 60p. (gr. 9). pap. 9.95 (978-0-940669-39-0(0) , D-45) Dramaline Pubns.

—More Monologues for Teenage Girls. 2002. 58p. (J). pap. 9.95 (978-0-940669-53-6(6)) Dramaline Pubns.

Rabushka, Jerry. Truck Stop Incident: Comedy Monologue. 2002. (YA). pap. 4.50 (978-1-931805-54-4(7) , 259) Brooklyn Pubs.

Roddy, Ruth Mae. Minute Monologues for Kids. 2000. 64p. (J). (gr. 4-7). pap. 9.95 (978-0-940669-45-1(5)) Dramaline Pubns.

—Minute Monologues for Kids. 2000. (gr. 3-6). lib. bdg. 18.75 (978-0-613-77781-0(6)) Tandem Library Bks.

—More Minute Monologues for Kids: Contemporary Scene-Study Pieces for Kids. 2005. 57p. (J). pap. 9.95 (978-0-940669-57-4(9)) Dramaline Pubns.

Stevens, Chambers. Magnificent Monologues for Kids. 1999. (gr. 3-6). lib. bdg. 23.40 (978-0-613-80203-1(9)) Tandem Library Bks.

—Magnificent Monologues for Kids: The Kids' Monologue Source for Every Occasion! Rolle-Whatley, Renee, ed. 1999. (Hollywood 101 Ser.: Vol. 1). 80p. (J). (gr. k-7). per. 13.95 (978-1-883995-08-9(6)) Sandcastle Publishing.

MONOPLANES

see Airplanes

MONROE, JAMES, 1758-1831

Gross, Miriam. How to Draw the Life & Times of James Monroe. 2006. (Kid's Guide to Drawing the Presidents of the United States of America Ser.). (J). 25.25 (978-1-4042-2982-2(5) , PowerKids Pr.) Rosen Publishing Group, Inc., The.

Kallen, Stuart A. John Marshall. 2001. (Founding Fathers Ser.). (Illus.). 64p. (J). (gr. 3-8). lib. bdg. 25.65 (978-1-57765-016-4(6) , ABDO & Daughters) ABDO Publishing Co.

Kelley, Brent P. James Monroe. 2000. (Revolutionary War Leaders Ser.). (Illus.). 80p. (J). (gr. 4-7). pap. 8.95 (978-0-7910-6129-9(9)); (gr. 8-12). 27.50 (978-0-7910-5971-5(5)) Facts On File, Inc. (Chelsea Hse.).

—James Monroe: American Statesman. 2001. (gr. 5-8). lib. bdg. 17.60 (978-0-613-32705-3(5)) Tandem Library Bks.

Levy, Debbie. James Monroe. 2005. (Presidential Leaders Ser.). (Illus.). 112p. (J). 29.27 (978-0-8225-0824-3(9) , Lerner Pubns.) Lerner Publishing Group.

Lusted, Marcia Amidon. Revolution & the New Nation. 2007. (978-1-59036-739-1(1)); (*978-1-59036-740-7(5)) Weigl Pubs., Inc.

Marcovitz, Hal. James Monroe. 2003. (Childhoods of the Presidents Ser.). (Illus.). 48p. (J). (gr. 4 up). lib. bdg. (978-1-59084-283-6(9)) Mason Crest Pubs.

Marsh, Carole. James Monroe. 2002. (One Thousand Readers Ser.). (Illus.). 12p. (J). (gr. k-4). 2.95 (978-0-635-01482-5(3) , 14823) Gallopade International.

—The Virginia Reader: James Monroe. 2001. (Virginia Experience! Ser.). 12p. (J). (gr. k-5). pap. 2.95 (978-0-635-00508-3(5)) Gallopade International.

Old, Wendie C. James Monroe. 1998. (United States Presidents Ser.). (Illus.). 128p. (YA). (gr. 5-12). lib. bdg. 26.60 (978-0-89490-941-2(X)) Enslow Pubs., Inc.

O'Shei, Tim & Marren, Joe. James Monroe: A MyReportLinks.com Book. 2002. (Presidents Ser.). (Illus.). 48p. (J). (gr. 4-10). lib. bdg. 25.26 (978-0-7660-5076-1(9)) Enslow Pubs., Inc.

Santella, Andrew. James Monroe. 2003. (Encyclopedia of Presidents Ser.). (Illus.). 110p. (J). 34.00 (978-0-516-24200-2(8) , Children's Pr.) Scholastic Library Publishing.

Teitelbaum, Michael. James Monroe. 2002. (Profiles of the Presidents Ser.). (Illus.). 64p. (J). (gr. 4 up). lib. bdg. 23.93 (978-0-7565-0253-9(5)) Compass Point Bks.

Venezia, Mike. James Monroe. Venezia, Mike, illus. 2005. (Getting to Know the U. S. Presidents Ser.). (Illus.). 32p. (J). (gr. 3-4). pap. 7.95 (978-0-516-27479-9(1) , Children's Pr.) Scholastic Library Publishing.

Venezia, Mike, tr. & illus. James Monroe. Venezia, Mike, illus. 2004. (Gtk Us Presidents Ser.). (J). 27.00 (978-0-516-22610-1(X) , Children's Pr.) Scholastic Library Publishing.

Welsbacher, Anne. James Monroe. 1999. (United States Presidents Ser.). (Illus.). 32p. (J). (gr. k-6). lib. bdg. 22.78 (978-1-56239-810-1(5) , Checkerboard Library) ABDO Publishing Co.

MONROE DOCTRINE

Alagna, Magdalena. The Monroe Doctrine: An End to European Colonies in America. 2003. (Life in the New American Nation Ser.). (Illus.). 32p. (YA). pap. 6.50 (978-0-8239-4258-9(9)) Rosen Publishing Group, Inc., The.

Burgan, Michael. The Monroe Doctrine. 2006. (Illus.). 48p. (J). lib. bdg. (*978-0-7565-2028-1(2)) Compass Point Bks.

Renehan, Edward J. The Monroe Doctrine: The Cornerstone of American Foreign Policy. 2007. (Milestones in American History Ser.). 128p. (gr. 6-12). 35.00 (*978-0-7910-9353-5(0) , Chelsea Hse.) Facts On File, Inc.

MONSTERS

see also Dragons; Dwarfs; Giants

Aunt Darla. There's a Monster under the Captain's Bed!!! Erik's Monster. Petersen, Darla & Shields, Erik P., illus. Date not set. 32p. 16.00 (978-0-9658926-1-2(1)) Poet Tree Pubns.

Barr, Steve. 1-2-3 Draw Cartoon Monsters: A Step-by-Step Guide. 2004. (Illus.). 64p. pap. 8.99 (978-0-939217-74-8(0)) Peel Productions, Inc.

Brassey, Richard. Nessie the Loch Ness Monster. 2003. (Illus.). 24p. (J). pap. 7.99 (978-1-85881-309-7(3)) Orion Bks. Ltd. GBR. *Dist:* Trafalgar Square Publishing.

Coleman, Loren. Cryptozoology from a to Z: The Encyclopedia of Loch Monsters, Sasquatch, Chupaca. 1999. (gr. 7-12). lib. bdg. 23.45 (978-0-613-33996-4(7)) Tandem Library Bks.

Copeland, Peter F. Sea Monsters Coloring Book. 1998. (Illus.). 32p. (J). pap. 3.95 (978-0-486-40562-9(1)) Dover Pubns., Inc.

Deary, Terry. True Monster Stories. Wyatt, David, illus. l.t. ed. 1999. 216p. (J). pap. (978-0-7540-6062-8(4) , CLP 261) BBC Audio.

Dinosaurs & Monsters. Date not set. (Illus.). 64p. (J). 2.98 (978-1-4054-0448-8(5)) Parragon, Inc.

Dorling Kindersley Publishing Staff. Glow in the Dark Night Creatures. 2004. (Ultimate Sticker Bks.). 16p. (J). pap. 6.99 (978-0-7566-0218-5(1)) Dorling Kindersley Publishing, Inc.

Draw 50 Beasties & Yugglies & Turnover Uglies & Things That Go Bump in the Night. 2002. (Draw 50 Ser.). (Illus.). (J). 17.60 (978-0-7587-4704-4(7)) Book Wholesalers, Inc.

Draw 50 Monsters, Creeps, Superheroes, Demons, Dragons, Nerds, Dirts, Ghouls, Giants, Vampires, Zombies, & Other Curiosa!. 2002. (Draw 50 Ser.). (Illus.). (J). 17.60 (978-0-7587-4166-0(9)) Book Wholesalers, Inc.

Edwards, Katie. Myths & Monsters: Secrets Revealed. Mendez, Simon, illus. 2004. 29p. (J). 16.95 (978-1-57091-581-9(4)); pap. 6.95 (978-1-57091-582-6(2)) Charlesbridge Publishing, Inc.

Emberley, Ed. Ed Emberley's Drawing Book of Weirdos. 2005. (Illus.). 32p. (J). (gr. 2-17). pap. 6.99 (978-0-316-78971-4(2)) Little, Brown Bks. for Young Readers.

Famous Movie Monsters, 8 Bks., Set. 2005. (YA). 212.00 (978-1-4042-0377-8(X)) Rosen Publishing Group, Inc., The.

Fisher, Enid Broderick. True-Life Monsters of the Prehistoric Seas. Grant, Richard, illus. 1999. (World of Dinosaurs Ser.). 32p. (J). (gr. 4 up). lib. bdg. 21.26 (978-0-8368-2293-9(5)) Stevens, Gareth Inc.

—True-Life Monsters of the Prehistoric Skies. Grant, Richard, illus. 1999. (World of Dinosaurs Ser.). 32p. (J). (gr. 4 up). lib. bdg. 21.26 (978-0-8368-2294-6(3)) Stevens, Gareth Inc.

Funston, Sylvia. Monsters. Weissmann, Joe, illus. 2001. (Strange Science Ser.: Vol. 2). 40p. (J). (gr. 3-7). 19.95 (978-1-894379-17-5(9)) Maple Tree Pr. CAN. *Dist:* Firefly Bks., Ltd.

Gilpin, Rebecca. Monster Things to Make & Do. Harrison, Erica Et Al, illus. 2006. 32p. (J). pap. 6.99 (978-0-7945-1354-2(9) , Usborne) EDC Publishing.

Gorman, Jacqueline Laks. The Loch Ness Monster. 2002. (X Science Ser.). (Illus.). 24p. (YA). (gr. 2 up). lib. bdg. 22.00 (978-0-8368-3200-6(0)) Stevens, Gareth Inc.

Gray, Peter C. How to Draw Manga Monsters. 2006. (Kid's Guide to Drawing Ser.). (Illus.). 32p. (J). lib. bdg. 25.25 (978-1-4042-3331-7(8) , PowerKids Pr.) Rosen Publishing Group, Inc., The.

Halls, Kelly Milner & Young, Roxanne K. Tales of the Cryptids: Mysterious Creatures That May or May Not Exist. Spears, Rick, illus. 2006. 72p. (J). (gr. 6 up). 18.95 (978-1-58196-049-5(2)) Darby Creek Publishing.

Hamilton, Sue L. Creatures of Abyss. 2007. (Unsolved Mysteries Ser.). (ENG., Illus.). 32p. (J). (gr. 4-8). lib. bdg. 25.65 (*978-1-59928-836-9(2) , ABDO & Daughters) ABDO Publishing Co.

—Monsters. 2007. (ENG., Illus.). 32p. (YA). lib. bdg. 24.21 (*978-1-59928-771-3(4) , ABDO & Daughters) ABDO Publishing Co.

—Monsters of Mystery. 2007. (Unsolved Mysteries Ser.). (ENG., Illus.). 32p. (J). (gr. 4-8). lib. bdg. 25.65 (*978-1-59928-835-2(4) , ABDO & Daughters) ABDO Publishing Co.

Harcourt School Publishers Staff. Making Monsters: Take-Home Book. 2001. (Collections Ser.). (Illus.). (J). pap. 1.90 (978-0-15-319561-7(4)) Harcourt Schl. Pubs.

Hart, Christopher. Kids Draw Manga Monsters! 2007. (Illus.). 64p. (J). pap. 11.95 (*978-0-8230-9840-8(0)) Watson-Guptill Pubns., Inc.

Herbst, Judith. Monsters. (Unexplained Ser.). (Illus.). 48p. (J). 2005. (gr. 5-12). lib. bdg. 26.60 (978-0-8225-1626-2(8)); 2004. pap. 7.95 (978-0-8225-2408-3(2) , Lerner Pubns.) Lerner Publishing Group.

How to Draw 101 Monsters. 2004. (How to Draw... Ser.). (Illus.). 48p. (J). pap. (978-1-84229-742-1(2)) Top That! Publishing PLC.

Innes, Brian. Water Monsters. 1999. (Unsolved Mysteries Ser.). (Illus.). 48p. (YA). (gr. 3 up). lib. bdg. 25.69 (978-0-8172-5479-7(X)) Raintree.

—Water Monsters. 1998. (Unsolved Mysteries Ser.). (Illus.). 48p. (gr. 3-7). pap. 8.05 (978-0-8172-4276-3(7)) Steck-Vaughn.

—Water Monsters. 1999. (gr. 3-6). lib. bdg. 15.25 (978-0-613-76291-5(6)) Tandem Library Bks.

Jennings, Linda & Gardener, Louise. Monsters. 1999. (Spooky Pop-Ups Ser.). (Illus.). 12p. (J). 4.95 (978-1-899607-19-8(6)) Sterling Publishing Co., Inc.

Krensky, Stephen. The Bogeymen. 2007. (Monster Chronicles Ser.). 48p. (J). (gr. 4-8). lib. bdg. 26.60 (*978-0-8225-6760-8(1) , Lerner Pubns.) Lerner Publishing Group.

—Creatures from the Deep. 2007. (Monster Chronicles Ser.). 48p. (J). (gr. 4-8). lib. bdg. 26.60 (*978-0-8225-6761-5(X) , Lerner Pubns.) Lerner Publishing Group.

Krensky, Stephen. Frankenstein. 2007. (Monster Chronicles Ser.). (Illus.). 48p. (J). (gr. 4-8). lib. bdg. 26.60 (978-0-8225-5923-8(4)) Lerner Publishing Group.

Lehner, Ernst & Lehner, Johanna. Big Book of Dragons, Monsters, & Other Mythical Creatures. 2004. (Pictorial Archive Ser.). (Illus.). 192p. pap. 16.95 (978-0-486-43512-1(1)) Dover Pubns., Inc.

Lichtenheld, Tom. Everything I Know about Monsters. Lichtenheld, Tom, illus. 2002. (Illus.). 40p. (J). (gr. k-3). 17.95 (978-0-689-84381-5(X)) Simon & Schuster Children's Publishing.

Lynette, Rachel. The Abominable Snowman. 2007. (Monsters Ser.). 48p. (J). (gr. 4-8). 23.70 (*978-0-7377-3448-5(5) , Kidhaven) Thomson Gale.

MacDonald, Fiona. World of Monsters. 2003. (World Of... Ser.). (Illus.). 64p. pap. 7.99 (978-1-84215-712-1(4) , Southwater) Anness Publishing GBR. *Dist:* National Bk. Network.

—World of Monsters. 2003. (gr. 3-6). lib. bdg. 16.45 (978-0-613-82087-5(8)) Tandem Library Bks.

MacDonald, Fiona & Shuker, Karl. Monsters. 2003. (Illus.). 64p. 14.99 (978-0-7548-1248-7(0)) Anness Publishing GBR. *Dist:* National Bk. Network.

Macken, JoAnn Early. Gila Monsters: Monstruos de Gila. 2005. (ENG & SPA., Illus.). 24p. (J). pap. (978-0-8368-4848-9(9)); lib. bdg. 19.33 (978-0-8368-4841-0(1)) Stevens, Gareth Inc.

Mason. Monsters. 2003. (Mysteries of the Past Ser.). (Illus.). 32p. pap. 7.95 (978-1-4109-0063-0(0)) Raintree.

Mason, Paul. Monsters. 2001. (Young Library - Mysteries of the Past). (Illus.). 32p. (J). lib. bdg. 25.69 (978-0-7398-4339-0(7)) Raintree.

—Monsters. 2005. (Illus.). 32p. (J). (gr. 4-7). lib. bdg. 27.10 (978-1-58340-774-5(X)) Smart Apple Media.

—Monsters. 2003. (gr. 3-6). lib. bdg. 16.40 (978-0-613-78228-9(3)) Tandem Library Bks.

McAllister, Angela. Monster. Middleton, Charlotte, illus. 2005. 32p. (J). pap. (*978-0-689-86139-0(7)) Simon & Schuster.

McKerley, Jennifer Guess. The Kraken. 2007. (Monsters Ser.). 48p. (J). (gr. 4-8). 23.70 (*978-0-7377-3531-4(7) , Kidhaven) Thomson Gale.

McNab, Chris. Mythical Monsters: The Scariest Creatures from Legends, Books, & Movies. 2006. (Illus.). 95p. (J). (*978-0-439-85479-5(2)) Scholastic, Inc.

Miles, Elizabeth & Montgomery, Lee. Horror Masks. 2001. (Big Book of... Ser.). (Illus.). 24p. (J). pap. 9.95 (978-1-901323-14-6(5)) Orpheus Bks., Ltd. GBR. *Dist:* CPG Publishing, Inc.

Monsters. Date not set. (Illus.). 40p. (J). 3.98 (978-1-4054-0175-3(3)) Parragon, Inc.

Moran, Paul, illus. World's Scariest Monster Games & Stories. 2003. (World's Ser.). 112p. (J). pap. 3.99 (978-0-603-56103-0(9)) Egmont Bks., Ltd. GBR. *Dist:* Independent Pubs. Group.

My Big Creepy Sticker. 2003. (Illus.). 48p. (J). 5.98 (978-1-4054-1218-6(6)) Parragon, Inc.

Namm, Diane. Monsters! Chambliss, Maxie, illus. 2003. (My First Reader Ser.). 32p. (J). 18.50 (978-0-516-22933-1(8) , Children's Pr.) Scholastic Library Publishing.

Nardo, Don. Martians. 2007. (Monsters Ser.). 48p. (gr. 4-8). 23.70 (*978-0-7377-3639-7(9) , Kidhaven) Thomson Gale.

Nathan, Cheryl. Funny Monsters Activity Book. 2003. (Illus.). 48p. (J). (gr. 4-7). pap., act. bk. ed. 3.95 (978-0-486-43060-7(X)) Dover Pubns., Inc.

Nichols, Catherine. Mysterious Creatures. 2006. (True Tales Ser.). (Illus.). 48p. (J). (gr. 2-4). pap. 4.95 (978-0-516-25452-4(9) , Children's Pr.) Scholastic Library Publishing.

—Mysterious Creatures: A Chapter Book. 2005. (True Tales Ser.). (Illus.). 48p. (J). (ps-ps). 22.50 (978-0-516-25182-0(1) , Children's Pr.) Scholastic Library Publishing.

Perry, Janet & Gentle, Victor. Manmade Monsters. 1999. (Imagination Library). (Illus.). 24p. (J). (gr. 2 up). lib. bdg. 22.00 (978-0-8368-2439-1(3)) Stevens, Gareth Inc.

Pipe, Jim. Monsters. 2007. (Illus.). 32p. (J). lib. bdg. 25.27 (978-1-59716-204-3(3)) Bearport Publishing Co., Inc.

Priest, Grace E. The Great Winged Monster of the Piasa Valley: The Legend of the Piasa. 1998. (Illus.). 123p. (YA). (gr. 4-12). 17.00 (978-0-9678461-0-1(2)); pap. 15.00 (978-0-9678461-1-8(0)) Alton Museum of History & Art, Inc.

Ross, Dave. The Not-so-Scary Monster Handbook: Halloween. Ross, Dave, illus. 2003. (Illus.). (J). 135.44 (978-0-06-055492-7(4)) HarperCollins Pubs.

Ross, Kathy. Make Yourself a Monster! A Book of Creepy Crafts. 1999. (978-0-606-17240-0(8)) Tandem Library Bks.

—Make Yourself A Monster! A Book of Creepy Crafts. Vargo, Sharon Hawkins, illus. 1999. (Books for Halloween & Thanksgiving Ser.). 48p. (J). (gr. k-2). 7.95 (978-0-7613-1049-5(5) , Millbrook Pr.) Lerner Publishing Group.

Sautter, Aaron. How to Draw Grotesque Monsters. Bascle, Brian, illus. 2008. (J). (*978-1-4296-1300-2(9)) Capstone Pr., Inc.

Schulte, Mary. The Sirens. 2007. (Monsters Ser.). (Illus.). 48p. (gr. 4-8). 23.70 (*978-0-7377-3451-5(5) , Kidhaven) Thomson Gale.

Sertori, J. M. Monsters. 2006. (Illus.). 36p. (J). lib. bdg. 24.67 (978-0-8368-6266-9(X)) Stevens, Gareth Inc.

Sievert, Terri. The Loch Ness Monster. 2004. (Edge Books, the Unexplained). (Illus.). 32p. (J). lib. bdg. 22.60 (978-0-7368-2716-4(1)) Capstone Pr., Inc.

Sloan, Peter. Making an Ooze Monster. 1999. (gr. k-3). lib. bdg. 11.80 (978-0-613-30587-7(6)) Tandem Library Bks.

Smith, Jared. Usagi Yojimbo: Monsters. Sakai, Stan, illus. 2000. 48p. (J). pap. 12.00 (978-1-890305-09-3(X) , U101, Gold Rush Games) Gold Rush Entertainment.

Stephens, Jay. Monsters! Draw Your Own Mutants, Freaks & Creeps. 2007. (Illus.). 64p. (J). pap. 5.95 (*978-1-60059-178-5(7)) Lark Bks.

Streissguth, Thomas. The Loch Ness Monster. 2002. (Mystery Library). (Illus.). 112p. (J). (gr. 4-12). 27.45 (978-1-56006-772-6(1) , Lucent Bks.) Thomson Gale.

Top That Publishing Staff, ed. Funny Monsters. 2005. 12p. (978-1-84510-734-5(9)) Top That! Publishing PLC.

Townsend. Mysterious Monsters. 2004. (Out There Ser.). (Illus.). pap. 8.95 (978-1-4109-0965-7(4)) Raintree.

—Mysterious Monsters 6-Pack. 2004. (Out There Ser.). lib. bdg. 48.30 (978-1-4109-0974-9(3)) Raintree.

Townsend, John. Mysterious Monsters. 2004. (Illus.). 56p. (J). lib. bdg. 28.56 (978-1-4109-0564-2(0)) Raintree.

Vallejo-Nagera, Alejandra. Los Cazadores de Monstruos. Guerrero, Andrés, illus. (SPA.). 31p. (J). (gr. k-1). 8.95 (978-1-58986-549-5(9)) Santillana USA Publishing Co., Inc.

Vosberg, Barbra. The Great Sphinx. 2007. (Monsters Ser.). 48p. (gr. 4-8). 23.70 (*978-0-7377-3633-5(X) , Kidhaven) Thomson Gale.

Yorke, Malcolm & Davis, Lee. Beastly Tales: Big Foot, Yeti & the Loch Ness Monster. 1998. (Eyewitness Readers). (Illus.). 48p. (J). (gr. 2-3). pap. 3.99 (978-0-7894-2962-9(4) , 0-7894-4754-1) Dorling Kindersley Publishing, Inc.

MONSTERS—FICTION

Abbott, Tony. The Sleeping Giant of Goll. Jessell, Tim, illus. 2000. (Secrets of Droon Ser.: No. 6). 112p. (gr. 2-5). pap. 3.99 (978-0-590-10844-7(1) , Scholastic Paperbacks) Scholastic, Inc.

Aboff, Marcie & Funke, Cornelia. Shrek: Classic Shrek Halloween. 2006. (Shrek Ser.). (Illus.). 16p. (J). pap. 5.99 (978-0-439-82817-8(1) , Scholastic) Scholastic, Inc.

Ahlberg, Allan. The Improbable Cat. Bailey, Peter, illus. 2004. 128p. (gr. 5). 9.95 (978-0-385-73186-7(8) , Delacorte Bks. for Young Readers) Random Hse. Children's Bks.

Alcock, Vivien. The Monster Garden. 2000. 176p. (J). (gr. 5-9). pap. 4.95 (978-0-618-00337-2(1)) Houghton Mifflin Co. Trade & Reference Div.

—Monster Garden. 2000. (gr. 3-6). lib. bdg. 12.95 (978-0-8335-4263-2(5)) Tandem Library Bks.

Amis, Yana. The Adventurers of Crystal Lake. 1998. (978-0-921252-85-6(4)) LEGAS.

Anaya, Rudolfo. Curse of the ChupaCabra. 2006. 174p. (YA). 24.95 (978-0-8263-4114-3(4)) Univ. of New Mexico Pr.

Anderson, Al. Pegasus: Adventures with Bingo Borden. Kurzyca, Krystyna Emilia, illus. 2006. 77p. (J). per. 19.50 (*978-1-887250-46-7(8)) Agora Pubns., Inc.

Anholt, Laurence. Billy Beast. 2004. (Illus.). 64p. (C). (gr. 3-5). 13.26 (978-0-7565-0628-5(X)) Compass Point Bks.

Armenteros, Sarah. Emma & the Mashed Potato Monster. 2007. 44p. (J). 16.99 (978-1-59092-384-9(7) , Little Blue Works) Windstorm Creative.

Arnold, Caroline. The Terrible Hodag & the Animal Catchers. Sandford, John, illus. 2006. 32p. (J). 15.95 (978-1-59078-166-1(X)) Boyds Mills Pr.

Arnold, Tedd. Huggly & the Toy Monster. Arnold, Tedd, illus. 1999. (Monster under the Bed Ser.). (Illus.). 32p. (J). (ps-3). pap. 3.25 (978-0-590-91821-3(4) , Cartwheel Bks.) Scholastic, Inc.

—Huggly & the Toy Monster. 1998. (Monster under the Bed Ser.). (J). pap. 3.50 (978-0-590-11761-6(0)) Scholastic, Inc.

—Huggly Gets Dressed. (Huggly Ser.). (Illus.). 24p. (J). (ps-1). 1999. pap. 3.25 (978-0-439-10268-1(5)); 1998. pap. 8.95 (978-0-590-91819-0(2) , Cartwheel Bks.) Scholastic, Inc.

—Huggly Takes a Bath. (Huggly Ser.). (Illus.). (ps-1). 1999. 24p. pap. 3.25 (978-0-439-10269-8(3)); 1999. 32p. (J). pap. 15.95 (978-0-590-91820-6(6)); 1998. 24p. (J). pap. 2.99 (978-0-590-11760-9(2)) Scholastic, Inc.

Arnold, Tedd, et al. Five Ugly Monsters. Arnold, Tedd, illus. 2003. 28p. (J). bds. 6.99 (978-0-439-52465-0(2) , Cartwheel Bks.) Scholastic, Inc.

Arnosky, Jim. Little Champ. Arnosky, Jim, illus. 2001. (J). pap. 6.95 (978-0-9657144-5-7(4)) Onion River Pr.

Atkinson, Robert. Daddy Monster Does the Silliest Things. Atkinson, Robert, illus. 2001. (J). spiral bd. 16.95 (978-0-9700615-8-4(7)) WordWright.biz, Inc.

—Daddy Monster Eats (Around) the World! Atkinson, Robert, illus. 2001. (J). spiral bd. 16.95 (978-0-9717868-5-1(2)) WordWright.biz, Inc.

—Daddy Monster Tells the Tale of the Teddy Bear. Atkinson, Robert, illus. 2001. (J). spiral bd. 16.95 (978-0-9717868-6-8(0)) WordWright.biz, Inc.

Austin, M. O. Boy Named Joe. 2006. pap. 12.99 (***978-1-4259-6217-3(3)***) AuthorHouse.

Babbitt, Natalie. El Cerro del Abismo. 2003. (SPA., Illus.). 128p. (J). (gr. 3-5). (978-84-236-3420-0(5) , ED0964) Edebé ESP. *Dist:* Lectorum Pubns., Inc.

Bader, Bonnie. 100 Monsters in My School, Vol. 2. Hendrix, Bryan, illus. 2002. (All Aboard Math Reader Ser.). 48p. (J). pap. 3.99 (978-0-448-42859-8(8) , Grosset & Dunlap) Penguin Group (USA) Inc.

—100 Monsters in My School. 2002. (gr. k-3). lib. bdg. 11.80 (978-0-613-64089-3(6)) Tandem Library Bks.

Baggette, Susan K. Jonathan Goes to the Library. Moriarty, William J., photos by. 1998. (Jonathan Adventures Ser.). (Illus.). 16p. (J). (ps-k). bds. 5.95 (978-0-9660172-3-6(4)) Brookfield Reader, Inc., The.

Bailey City Monsters. 2005. (J). (978-1-59564-798-6(8)) Steps To Literacy, LLC.

Baker, Ken. Brave Little Monster. Hayes, Geoffrey, illus. 2001. 32p. (J). (ps-3). 15.99 (978-0-06-028698-9(9)); 14.89 (978-0-06-028699-6(7)) HarperCollins Pubs.

—Brave Little Monster. 1999. (Illus.). 32p. (J). (ps-3). pap. 5.95 (978-0-06-443625-0(X)) HarperCollins Pubs.

Baldwin, Neil. Tracking the Plumed Serpent. 1999. (978-0-7868-6146-0(0)) Disney Pr.

Balian, Lorna. The Aminal. Balian, Lorna & Balian, Lecia, illus. 2005. 56p. (J). 17.95 (978-1-59572-006-1(5)) Star Bright Bks., Inc.

—Leprechauns Never Lie. Balian, Lorna, illus. 2004. (Illus.). 40p. (J). 14.95 (978-1-932065-37-4(7)) Star Bright Bks., Inc.

Ballman, Swanee. The Monster of Boggy Creek. 2002. (Illus.). 32p. (YA). 4.95 (978-1-59094-012-9(1) , 1590940121) Jawbone Publishing Corp.

Balmer, Fred. Festus & the Monster. Newcomb, Kristene, illus. 2004. 27p. (J). per. 6.95 (978-0-9760790-2-6(X)) Folsom Fallies Pr.

Baumgarten, Josephine & Baumgarten, Michael. My Baby Monsters & I went to the Park. 2005. 32p. pap. 14.99 (978-1-4116-6348-0(9)) Lulu.com.

Bazaldua, Charles. Disney's Monsters Inc. 2001. (Illus.). 48p. (J). pap. 4.95 (978-1-56971-670-0(6)) Dark Horse Comics.

Beast Quest 6 & Blade, Adam. Beast Quest #6 Epos the Winged Flame. 2008. (Beast Quest Ser.). 96p. (J). pap. 4.99 (***978-0-439-02458-7(7)*** , Scholastic Paperbacks) Scholastic, Inc.

Beck, Scott. Happy Birthday, Monster! 2007. (Illus.). 32p. (J). (ps-2). 14.95 (***978-0-8109-9363-1(5)*** , Abrams Bks. for Young Readers) Abrams, Harry N. , Inc.

Beeke, Jemma. The Brand New Creature. 1999. (Illus.). 32p. (J). (ps-2). pap. 6.95 (978-1-86233-037-5(9)) Sterling Publishing Co., Inc.

Beeke, Jemma, et al. The Brand New Creature. 1998. (Illus.). 32p. (J). (ps-3). 14.95 (978-1-899607-66-2(8)) Sterling Publishing Co., Inc.

Bennett, Veronica. Angelmonster. 2006. 240p. (YA). (gr. 9). 15.99 (978-0-7636-2994-6(4)) Candlewick Pr.

Bentley, Nancy. The Case of the Garden Monster. Borlasca, Hector, illus. 2003. 32p. (J). (978-0-439-47470-2(1)) Scholastic, Inc.

Benton, Jim. Lunch Walks among Us. Benton, Jim, illus. (Franny K. Stein, Mad Scientist Ser.: Bk. 2). (Illus.). 112p. (J). 2004. (gr. 2-5). mass mkt. 3.99 (978-0-689-86295-3(4) , Aladdin); 2003. 15.99 (978-0-689-86291-5(1)) Simon & Schuster Children's Publishing.

Benz, Derek & Lewis, J. S. The Fall of the Templar. 2008. (Grey Griffins Ser.). 304p. (J). 12.99 (***978-0-439-83776-7(6)*** , Orchard Bks.) Scholastic, Inc.

Benz, Derek & Lewis, J. S. The Rise of the Black Wolf. 2007. (Grey Griffins Ser.: No. 2). 320p. (J). (gr. 4-7). pap. 12.99 (978-0-439-83774-3(X) , Orchard Bks.) Scholastic, Inc.

Berglin, Ruth. Dear Big, Mean, Ugly Monster. 2005. (Illus.). 40p. (J). 14.95 (978-1-58760-072-2(2) , Child & Family Pr.) Child Welfare League of America, Inc.

Bicknell, Joanna. Tickle Monsters. 2007. (Finger Puppet Books Ser.). (Illus.). 12p. (ps). bds. 12.99 (***978-1-84610-427-5(0)***) Make Believe Ideas GBR. *Dist:* Ingram Pub. Services.

Bienert, Kristin, ed. Monster Nation Jr. 2007. 32p. (J). pap. 6.99 (***978-0-696-23688-4(5)***) Meredith Bks.

Binder, Helga, illus. Wild Wicked Winifred & the Sea Serpent. 1999. (J). (978-0-7608-3204-2(8)) Sundance/Newbridge Educational Publishing.

Birchall, Mark. What Kind of Monster. 2003. (Illus.). 32p. (J). 17.99 (978-1-84270-177-5(0)) Andersen GBR. *Dist:* Independent Pubs. Group.

—What Kind of Monster? 2004. (Illus.). 32p. (J). pap. 9.99 (978-1-84270-318-2(8)) Andersen GBR. *Dist:* Independent Pubs. Group.

Biro, Val. Gumdrop & the Monster. (Illus.). 32p. (J). (978-0-340-71446-1(8) , Hodder & Stoughton) Hodder General Publishing Division.

—Gumdrop & the Monster. (Illus.). 32p. (J). pap. 11.99 (978-0-340-71447-8(6) , Hodder & Stoughton) Hodder General Publishing Division GBR. *Dist:* Trafalgar Square Publishing.

—The Hobyahs. Biro, Val, illus. 1998. (Illus.). 32p. (J). (gr. k-3). pap. 4.99 (978-1-887734-44-8(9)) Star Bright Bks., Inc.

Blade, Adam. Sepron the Sea Serpent. 2007. (Beast Quest Ser.: No. 2). 80p. (J). pap. 4.99 (978-0-439-90654-8(7) , Scholastic Paperbacks) Scholastic, Inc.

Blade, Adam. Tagus the Night Horse. 2007. (Beast Quest Ser.: No. 4). 80p. (J). pap. 4.99 (***978-0-439-02456-3(0)*** , Scholastic Paperbacks) Scholastic, Inc.

Blance, Ellen. Monstruo, 12 bks., Set. Incl. Monstruo Compre un Animalito. Cook, Ann. 1.98 (978-0-8372-3482-3(4)); Monstruo Encuentra Trabajo. Cook. 1.98 (978-0-8372-3485-4(9)); Monstruo, la Senorita Monstruo y el Paseo en Bicicleta. Cook. 1.98 (978-0-8372-3488-5(3)); Monstruo Recorre la Ciudad. Cook. 1.98 (978-0-8372-3490-8(5)); Monstruo Va a la Playa. Cook. 1.98 (978-0-8372-3479-3(4)); Monstruo Va Al Circo. Cook. 1.98 (978-0-8372-3483-0(2)); Monstruo Va Al Hospital. Cook. 1.98 (978-0-8372-3489-2(1)); Monstruo y el Muro. Cook. 1.98 (978-0-8372-3487-8(5)); Monstruo y la Galleta de Sorpresa. Cook. 1.98 (978-0-8372-3486-1(7)); Monstruo y la Liquidacion de Juguetes. Cook. 1.98 (978-0-8372-3480-9(8)); Plan de la Senorita Monstruo. Cook. 1.98 (978-0-8372-3481-6(6)); Senorita Monstruo Ayuda. Cook. 1.98 (978-0-8372-3484-7(0)); (J). (Illus.). Set pap. 215.00 (978-0-8372-3493-9(X)) Bowmar/Noble Pubs.

Blance, Ellen & Cook. Lady Monster Has a Plan. Date not set. (Illus.). 40p. pap. 129.15 (978-0-582-19312-3(5)) Addison-Wesley Longman, Ltd. GBR. *Dist:* Trans-Atlantic Pubns., Inc.

—Lady Monster Helps Out. Date not set. (Illus.). 32p. pap. 129.15 (978-0-582-19302-4(8)) Addison-Wesley Longman, Ltd. GBR. *Dist:* Trans-Atlantic Pubns., Inc.

—Monster & Magic Umbrella. Date not set. (Illus.). 16p. pap. 129.15 (978-0-582-18593-7(9)) Addison-Wesley Longman, Ltd. GBR. *Dist:* Trans-Atlantic Pubns., Inc.

—Monster & Surprise Cookie. Date not set. (Illus.). 38p. pap. 129.15 (978-0-582-19308-6(7)) Addison-Wesley Longman, Ltd. GBR. *Dist:* Trans-Atlantic Pubns., Inc.

—Monster at School. Date not set. (Illus.). 24p. pap. 129.15 (978-0-582-18597-5(1)) Addison-Wesley Longman, Ltd. GBR. *Dist:* Trans-Atlantic Pubns., Inc.

—Monster Buys a Pet. Date not set. (Illus.). 40p. pap. 129.15 (978-0-582-19311-6(7)) Addison-Wesley Longman, Ltd. GBR. *Dist:* Trans-Atlantic Pubns., Inc.

—Monster Cleans His House. Date not set. (Illus.). 16p. pap. 129.15 (978-0-582-18590-6(4)) Addison-Wesley Longman, Ltd. GBR. *Dist:* Trans-Atlantic Pubns., Inc.

—Monster Comes to the City. Date not set. (Illus.). 16p. pap. 129.15 (978-0-582-18588-3(2)) Addison-Wesley Longman, Ltd. GBR. *Dist:* Trans-Atlantic Pubns., Inc.

—Monster Gets a Job. Date not set. (Illus.). 40p. pap. 129.15 (978-0-582-19307-9(9)) Addison-Wesley Longman, Ltd. GBR. *Dist:* Trans-Atlantic Pubns., Inc.

—Monster Goes Around Town. Date not set. (Illus.). 38p. pap. 129.15 (978-0-582-19309-3(5)) Addison-Wesley Longman, Ltd. GBR. *Dist:* Trans-Atlantic Pubns., Inc.

—Monster Goes to Circus. Date not set. (Illus.). 32p. pap. 129.15 (978-0-582-19304-8(4)) Addison-Wesley Longman, Ltd. GBR. *Dist:* Trans-Atlantic Pubns., Inc.

—Monster Goes to School. Date not set. (Illus.). 24p. pap. 129.15 (978-0-582-18596-8(3)) Addison-Wesley Longman, Ltd. GBR. *Dist:* Trans-Atlantic Pubns., Inc.

—Monster Goes to the Beach. Date not set. (Illus.). 40p. pap. 129.15 (978-0-582-19306-2(0)) Addison-Wesley Longman, Ltd. GBR. *Dist:* Trans-Atlantic Pubns., Inc.

—Monster Goes to the Hospital. Date not set. (Illus.). 40p. pap. 129.15 (978-0-582-19305-5(2)) Addison-Wesley Longman, Ltd. GBR. *Dist:* Trans-Atlantic Pubns., Inc.

—Monster Goes to the Zoo. Date not set. (Illus.). 24p. pap. 129.15 (978-0-582-18599-9(8)) Addison-Wesley Longman, Ltd. GBR. *Dist:* Trans-Atlantic Pubns., Inc.

—Monster Looks for a House. Date not set. (Illus.). 16p. pap. 129.15 (978-0-582-18589-0(0)) Addison-Wesley Longman, Ltd. GBR. *Dist:* Trans-Atlantic Pubns., Inc.

—Monster Looks for Friend. Date not set. (Illus.). 16p. pap. 129.15 (978-0-582-18591-3(2)) Addison-Wesley Longman, Ltd. GBR. *Dist:* Trans-Atlantic Pubns., Inc.

—Monster Meets Lady Monster. Date not set. (Illus.). 16p. pap. 129.15 (978-0-582-18592-0(0)) Addison-Wesley Longman, Ltd. GBR. *Dist:* Trans-Atlantic Pubns., Inc.

—Monster on the Bus. Date not set. (Illus.). 24p. pap. 129.15 (978-0-582-18595-1(5)) Addison-Wesley Longman, Ltd. GBR. *Dist:* Trans-Atlantic Pubns., Inc.

—Monstruo Encuentra Trabajo. (J). 1.98 (978-0-8372-3485-4(9)) Bowmar/Noble Pubs.

—Monstruo, la Senorita Monstruo y el Paseo en Bicicleta. (J). 1.98 (978-0-8372-3488-5(3)) Bowmar/Noble Pubs.

—Monstruo Recorre la Ciudad. (J). 1.98 (978-0-8372-3490-8(5)) Bowmar/Noble Pubs.

—Monstruo Va a la Playa. (J). 1.98 (978-0-8372-3479-3(4)) Bowmar/Noble Pubs.

—Monstruo Va Al Circo. (J). 1.98 (978-0-8372-3483-0(2)) Bowmar/Noble Pubs.

—Monstruo Va Al Hospital. (J). 1.98 (978-0-8372-3489-2(1)) Bowmar/Noble Pubs.

—Monstruo y el Muro. (J). 1.98 (978-0-8372-3487-8(5)) Bowmar/Noble Pubs.

—Monstruo y la Galleta de Sorpresa. (J). 1.98 (978-0-8372-3486-1(7)) Bowmar/Noble Pubs.

—Monstruo y la Liquidacion de Juguetes. (J). 1.98 (978-0-8372-3480-9(8)) Bowmar/Noble Pubs.

—El Plan de la Senorita Monstruo. (J). 1.98 (978-0-8372-3481-6(6)) Bowmar/Noble Pubs.

—La Senorita Monstruo Ayuda. (J). 1.98 (978-0-8372-3484-7(0)) Bowmar/Noble Pubs.

Blance, Ellen & Cook, Ann. Monstruo Compre un Animalito. (J). 1.98 (978-0-8372-3482-3(4)) Bowmar/Noble Pubs.

Blume, Rebecca. A Really, Really, Scary Monster Story! Koji, Jeanette, illus. l.t. ed. 2006. 32p. (J). 24.95 (978-0-9785427-0-2(3)) Liberty Artists Management.

Bonniol, Magali. El Ogro De Mariuchi. 2003. (SPA.). 40p. (978-84-8470-112-5(3)) Corimbo, Editorial S.L.

Bottner, Barbara. Pish & Posh Wish for Fairy Wings. Bottner, Barbara, illus. 2007. (I Can Read Bks.). 48p. (J). pap. 3.99 (***978-0-06-051421-1(3)*** , Harper Trophy) HarperCollins Pubs.

Bottner/Kruglik. Pish & Posh. Bottner, Barbara, illus. 2004. 48p. (J). lib. bdg. 13.85 (***978-1-4242-0513-4(1)***) Fitzgerald Bks.

Brami, Elisabeth. Sweet Dreams, Scary Monsters. McGowan, Siobhan, tr. from FRE. Bertrand, Philippe, illus. 1999. 32p. (J). (ps-3). 14.95 (978-1-55670-945-6(5)) Stewart, Tabori & Chang.

Brandle, Bine. FLUSI: The Sock Monster. Brandle, Bine, illus. 2004. (Illus.). 32p. (J). (ps-1). 15.95 (978-1-929132-69-0(7)) Kane/Miller Bk. Pubs., Inc.

Branson, Dave. The Monster Encyclopedia. Bartimole, Tom, illus. 1998. 40p. (J). (gr. k-3). 16.95 (978-1-880851-35-7(0)) Greene Bark Pr., Inc.

Brege K. B. Mick Morris Myth Solver All Isn't Well in Roswell! No. 1. 2005. (Mick Morris Myth Solver Ser.: No. 1). (Illus.). 188p. (J). pap. 6.99 (978-0-9774119-0-0(7)) Team B Creative LLC.

Brewster, Joy. Roller-Ghoster: Junior Chapter Book. del Sur, Duendes, illus. 2004. (Scooby-Doo Ser.). 48p. (J). mass mkt. 3.99 (978-0-439-55710-8(0) , Scholastic Paperbacks) Scholastic, Inc.

Bright, Paul. I'm Not Going Out There! Cort, Ben, illus. 2006. 28p. (J). (ps-2). 16.00 (978-1-56148-535-2(7)) Good Bks.

—Under the Bed. Cort, Ben, illus. 2004. 32p. (J). 16.00 (978-1-56148-436-2(9)) Good Bks.

Brittain. The Wizards & the Monster. Date not set. 96p. (J). (gr. 2-5). pap. 4.25 (978-0-06-442003-7(5)) HarperCollins Pubs.

Brooks, Felicity. Jason & the Argonauts. Humphreys, Graham, illus. 2005. 144p. (J). pap. 4.95 (978-0-7945-0275-1(X) , Usborne) EDC Publishing.

Brouwer, Sigmund. Creature of the Mists. 2003. (Accidental Detectives Ser.). (Illus.). 144p. (J). pap. 5.99 (978-0-7642-2569-7(3)) Bethany Hse. Pubs.

—Creature of the Mists. 2003. (gr. 3-6). lib. bdg. 14.15 (978-0-613-84508-3(0)) Tandem Library Bks.

Brown, Marcy & Haley, Dennis. We Both Read-the Well-Mannered Monster. Raglin, Tim, illus. 2006. (We Both Read Ser.). 48p. (J). 7.99 (978-1-891327-65-0(8)); pap. 3.99 (978-1-891327-66-7(6)) Treasure Bay, Inc.

Browne, N. M. Basilisk. 2006. 320p. (YA). pap. 7.95 (978-1-58234-910-7(X) , Bloomsbury Children) Bloomsbury Publishing.

Bruchac, Joseph. The Dark Pond. Comport, Sally Wern, illus. 160p. (J). (gr. 5 up). 2005. pap. 5.99 (978-0-06-052998-7(9) , Harper Trophy); 2004. lib. bdg. 16.89 (978-0-06-052997-0(0)) HarperCollins Pubs.

—Heroes & Heroines, Monsters & Magic: Native American Legends & Folktales. Burgevin, Daniel, illus. 2004. 200p. (gr. 3-7). reprint ed. pap. 12.95 (978-0-89594-995-0(4) , Crossing Pr., Inc.) Ten Speed Pr.

Buckley, Michael. The Fairy Tale Detectives. Ferguson, Peter, illus. 2007. (Sisters Grimm Ser.: Bk. 1). 312p. (J). (gr. 2-8). pap. 5.95 (***978-0-8109-9322-8(8)*** , Amulet Bks.) Abrams, Harry N. , Inc.

Buckley, Michael. The Problem Child. Ferguson, Peter, illus. 2006. (Sisters Grimm Ser.: Bk. 3). 320p. (J). (gr. 3-7). 14.95 (978-0-8109-4914-0(8) , Amulet Bks.) Abrams, Harry N. , Inc.

Buluma, M. O. Cheche & Taaka. 2000. 65p. pap. (978-9970-02-048-5(X)) Fountain Pubs. Ltd.

Burch, Sharon. Freddie the Frog & the Bass Clef Monster: 2nd Adventure: Bass Clef Monster. Harris, Tiffany, illus. 2006. (J). 23.95 (978-0-9747454-8-0(0)) Mystic Publishing.

Burfoot, Ella. Louie & the Monsters. Burfoot, Ella, illus. 2005. (Illus.). 32p. (J). (ps-ps). 6.95 (978-1-58925-395-7(7) , tiger tales) ME Media LLC.

Burger, E. Maze of Monsters. 2005. 52p. pap. 12.95 (978-1-4137-6301-0(4)) PublishAmerica, Inc.

Butterworth, MyLinda. The Monster Run. Day, Linda S., ed. Mercer, Matthew, illus. l.t. ed. 2004. 32p. (J). (ps-3). 14.95 (978-1-890905-23-1(2)) Day to Day Enterprises.

Cazet, Denys. Minnie & Moo Meet Frankenswine. Cazet, Denys, illus. 2002. (Minnie & Moo Ser.). (Illus.). 12.34 (978-1-4046-1308-9(0)) Book Wholesalers, Inc.

—Minnie & Moo Meet Frankenswine. Cazet, Denys, illus. (I Can Read Bks.: Bk. 3). (Illus.). 48p. (J). 2002. pap. 3.99 (978-0-06-444311-1(6)); 2001. 15.89 (978-0-06-623749-7(1)); 2001. 14.95 (978-0-06-623748-0(3)) HarperCollins Pubs.

—Minnie & Moo Meet Frankenswine. Cazet, Denys, illus. (Readalongs for Beginning Readers Ser.). (Illus.). 2005. (J). pap. 16.95 incl. audio (978-1-59112-261-6(9)); 2005. (J). pap. 18.95 incl. audio compact disk (978-1-59112-875-5(7)); 2004. 28.95 incl. audio compact disk (978-1-59112-876-2(5)); 2004. (J). 25.95 incl. audio (978-1-59112-262-3(7)); 2004. (J). pap. 29.95 incl. audio (978-1-59112-263-0(5)); 2004. (J). pap. 31.95 incl. audio compact disk (978-1-59112-877-9(3)) Live Oak Media.

—Minnie & Moo Meet Frankenswine. 2002. (gr. k-3). lib. bdg. 11.80 (978-0-613-62183-0(2)) Tandem Library Bks.

Cerasini, Marc. Godzilla Saves America: A Monster Showdown In 3-D! Morgan, Tom & Mounts, Paul, illus. 2006. 20p. (J). (gr. k-4). reprint ed. 12.00 (978-1-4223-5409-4(1)) DIANE Publishing Co.

Charlesworth, Liza. Word Family Tales: Dine with Nine Messy Monsters. Phillips, Matt, illus. 2002. (Word Family Tales Ser.). 16p. (ps-2). pap. 2.95 (978-0-439-26250-7(X)) Scholastic, Inc.

Chartrand, Lili. Taming Horrible Harry. Ouriou, Susan, tr. from FRE. Rogé, illus. 2006. 32p. (J). (ps-3). 16.95 (978-0-88776-772-2(9)) Tundra Bks., Inc./Livres Toundra, Inc. CAN. *Dist:* Random Hse., Inc.

Cherry, Lynne. The Dragon & the Unicorn. 1998. (Illus.). 36p. (J). (gr. 1-5). pap. 7.00 (978-0-15-201888-7(3) , Harcourt Paperbacks) Harcourt Children's Bks.

Christian, Mary Blount. Swamp Monsters. Brown, Marc, illus. 48p. (J). (gr. 1-2). pap. 3.99 (978-0-8072-1355-1(1) , Listening Library) Random Hse. Audio Publishing Group.

Ciencin, Scott. Vengance. 2002. (gr. 7-12). lib. bdg. 14.15 (978-0-613-63240-9(0)) Tandem Library Bks.

Cioffi, Dom, illus. Digby & the Lake Monster. l.t. ed. 2003. 36p. (J). per. (978-0-9745931-0-4(9)) Vermont Bookworks.

Clancy, Tom. Gameprey. 2000. (gr. 7-12). lib. bdg. 13.00 (978-0-613-81160-6(7)) Tandem Library Bks.

Clarke, Judith & Egan, Caroline, illus. Monsters Inc. 2001. (J). 15.98 (978-0-7853-4861-0(1)) Publications International, Ltd.

Claybourne, Anna. Adventures of Ulysses. 2005. 144p. (J). pap. 4.95 (978-0-7945-0322-2(5) , Usborne) EDC Publishing.

Coleman, Joanna. Monster Manners. Lee, Jared D., illus. 2004. 48p. (J). lib. bdg. 15.00 (978-1-59054-406-8(4)) Fitzgerald Bks.

Constantin, Pascale, illus. I'm Going to Read (Level 1): Little Monster. 2007. (I'm Going to Read Ser.). 80p. (J). pap. 3.95 (***978-1-4027-2078-9(5)***) Sterling Publishing Co., Inc.

Cooper, Susan. The Boggart & the Monster. Rayyan, Omar, illus. 2004. 192p. (J). pap. 5.99 (978-0-689-86931-0(2) , Aladdin) Simon & Schuster Children's Publishing.

Corentin, Philippe. Papa! (SPA.). 32p. (978-84-95150-38-7(7)) Corimbo, Editorial S.L.

Cornish, D. M. Foundling, Bk. 1. 2007. (Monster Blood Tattoo Ser.). 448p. (YA). (gr. 7 up). 8.99 (***978-0-14-240913-8(8)*** , Puffin) Penguin Group (USA) Inc.

—Lamplighter: Monster Blood Tattoo, Book 2: Monster Blood Tattoo, Bk. 2. 2008. 400p. (YA). (gr. 7). 18.99 (***978-0-399-24639-5(8)*** , Putnam Juvenile) Penguin Group (USA) Inc.

Cornish, D. M. Monster Blood Tattoo: Foundling. 2006. 404p. (YA). (gr. 4 up). 18.99 (978-0-399-24638-8(X) , Putnam Juvenile) Penguin Group (USA) Inc.

Cosgrove, Stephen. Snugg N. Flitter: Facing Your Fears. Arroyo, Fian, illus. 2004. (J). (978-1-58804-377-1(0)) PCI Educational Publishing.

Cote, Denis. La Trahison du Vampire. 2002. (Roman Jeunesse Ser.). (FRE., Illus.). 96p. (YA). (gr. 4-7). pap. (978-2-89021-238-1(6)) Diffusion du livre Mirabel.

Cote, Denis & Poulin, Stephane. La Nuit du Vampire. 2001. (FRE., Illus.). 96p. (J). pap. (978-2-89021-469-9(9)) Diffusion du livre Mirabel.

Court-Kaemon, Amy. Shrek 3: The Photo Novel. 2007. (Shrek 3 Ser.). 96p. (J). pap. 7.99 (978-0-06-122953-4(9)) HarperCollins Pubs.

Courtney, Richard, illus. The Monster under the Shed. 2001. (Pictureback Bk.). 24p. (J). (ps-3). pap. 3.25 (978-0-375-81371-9(3) , Random Hse. Bks. for Young Readers) Random Hse. Children's Bks.

Coville, Bruce. The Mischief Monster. Coville, Katherine, illus. 2007. (Moongobble & Me Ser.). 80p. (J). 15.99 (978-1-4169-0807-4(2) , Simon & Schuster Children's Publishing) Simon & Schuster Children's Publishing.

—The Monsters of Morley Manor. 2003. (gr. 3-6). lib. bdg. 14.10 (978-0-613-56926-2(1)) Tandem Library Bks.

—The Monster's Ring. Coville, Katherine, illus. anniv. exp. ed. 2002. (Magic Shop Bks.). 128p. (YA). (gr. 3-7). 16.00 (978-0-15-204618-7(6)) Harcourt Children's Bks.

—The Monster's Ring. Coville, Katherine, illus. 2003. (Magic Shop Bks.). 128p. mass mkt. 5.99 (978-0-689-85692-1(X) , Aladdin) Simon & Schuster Children's Publishing.

—The Monster's Ring. 2003. (gr. 3-6). lib. bdg. 13.00 (978-0-613-73386-1(X)) Tandem Library Bks.

Cowan, Bianca. Monster is Hiding (El Monstruo Escondido) 1999. (SPA & ENG., Illus.). 32p. (J). per. 7.95 (978-0-9669645-3-0(5) , AlterLingo Bks.) O'Hollow Publishing.

Cranch, Christopher. The Last of the Huggermuggers. 2004. reprint ed. pap. 15.95 (978-1-4191-6876-5(2)) Kessinger Publishing, LLC.

Cranch, Christopher Pierce. The Last of the Huggermuggers. 2004. reprint ed. pap. 1.99 (978-1-4192-6876-2(7)) Kessinger Publishing, LLC.

Crassy the Crude Beastie. 2001. (Beastie Buddies Ser.). (Illus.). 32p. (J). 6.95 (978-1-891100-86-4(6)) Smart Kids Publishing.

Crew, Gary. The Kraken. McBride, Marc, illus. 2002. 32p. (YA). (978-0-7344-0182-3(5) , Lothian Bks.) Hachette Livre Australia.

M N O

Crilley, Mark. Billy Clikk: Creatch Battler. 2006. (Illus.). 246p. (J). (*978-1-4156-5030-1(6), Yearling) Random Hse. Children's Bks.

Crilley, Mark. Rogmasher Rampage. 2007. (Billy Clikk Ser.). 224p. (J). (gr. 4-7). 5.99 (978-0-440-41955-6(7), Yearling) Random Hse. Children's Bks.

Crimi, Carolyn. Boris & Bella. Grimly, Gris, illus. 32p. (J). 2004. 15.00 (978-0-15-202528-1(6)); 2006. reprint ed. pap. 6.00 (978-0-15-205900-2(8), Voyager Bks./Libros Viajeros) Harcourt Children's Bks.

Cummings, Pat. Ananse & the Monster. (Illus.). (YA). (978-0-8050-7782-7(0)) Holt, Henry & Co.

Cunliffe, John. Postman Pat & the Beast of Greendale, Bk. 12. (Illus.). 32p. (J). (978-0-340-67816-9(X), Hodder & Stoughton) Hodder General Publishing Division.

Curtis, Patricia Gregory. A Secret from the Deep. 2004. 154p. pap. 19.95 (978-1-4137-2293-2(8)) PublishAmerica, Inc.

Cuyler, Margery. Monster Mess! Schindler, S. D., illus. 2008. (J). (978-0-689-86405-6(1), McElderry, Margaret K.) Simon & Schuster Children's Publishing.

Dadey, Debbie. Swamp Monster in Third Grade. 2003. (Illus.). 96p. (J). (gr. 2-5). pap. 3.99 (978-0-439-42441-7(0), Scholastic Paperbacks) Scholastic, Inc.

Dadey, Debbie & Jones, Marcia Thornton. Ghouls Don't Scoop Ice Cream. 1998. (Adventures of the Bailey School Kids Ser.: No. 31). (J). (gr. 2-4). 10.79 (978-0-606-13426-2(3)) Tandem Library Bks.

—Monsters Don't Scuba Dive. (Adventures of the Bailey School Kids Ser.: No. 14). (FRE., Illus.). 80p. (J). (gr. 2-4). pap. 5.99 (978-0-590-24550-0(3)) Scholastic, Inc.

—Mrs. Jeepers' Scariest Halloween Ever. Gurney, John Steven, illus. 2005. 103p. (J). (978-1-4156-2066-3(0)) Scholastic, Inc.

—Robots Don't Catch Chicken Pox. (Bailey School Kids Ser.). 2001. (Illus.). (J). (978-0-606-21402-5(X)); 2000. (gr. 3-6). lib. bdg. 11.80 (978-0-613-35743-2(4)) Tandem Library Bks.

—Sea Monsters Don't Ride Motorcycles. 2000. (Bailey School Kids Ser.: No.40). (gr. 3-6). lib. bdg. 11.80 (978-0-613-26864-6(4)) Tandem Library Bks.

—Vikings Don't Wear Wrestling Belts. 2001. (Adventures of the Bailey School Kids Ser.). (Illus.). (J). (978-0-606-21504-6(2)) Tandem Library Bks.

—Wolfmen Don't Hula Dance. 1999. (Adventures of the Bailey School Kids Ser.: No. 36). (J). (gr. 2-4). (978-0-606-16938-7(5)); (Bailey School Kids Ser.: No.36). (gr. 3-6). lib. bdg. 11.80 (978-0-613-17044-4(X)) Tandem Library Bks.

D'Agata, Tabatha Jean. Marvin Monster's Big Date. Newmann, Ed, illus. 2007. 32p. (J). pap. 6.95 (*978-0-9792371-4-0(9), Moo Pr.) Keene Publishing.

D'Agata, Tabatha Jean. Marvin Monster's Teacher Jitters. Newmann, Ed, illus. 2006. 48p. pap. 6.95 (978-0-9766805-3-6(X)) Keene Publishing.

Dague, Paige A. ScribbleMonster & the Crunchy, Crunchy Carrots. Dague, James, illus. 2001. (J). (ps). pap. 5.50 (978-0-9706406-0-4(9)) ScribbleBooks Co., The.

Dague, Paige A. & Dague, James. ScribbleMonster & the Broken TV. 2001. (Illus.). 32p. (J). (ps). pap. 5.50 (978-0-9706406-1-1(7)) ScribbleBooks Co., The.

—ScribbleMonster Takes a Bath. 2001. (Illus.). 32p. (J). (ps). pap. 5.50 (978-0-9706406-2-8(5)) ScribbleBooks Co., The.

Dahl, Michael. The Beast Beneath the Stairs. Garvey, Brann, illus. 2007. (J). 40p. (*978-1-59889-323-6(8)); 33p. pap. (*978-1-59889-418-9(8)) Stone Arch Bks.

Daisy, April. The Monster's in My Room. Daisy, April, illus. 2005. (Illus.). (J). per. 7.95 (978-1-59466-048-1(4), Little Ones) Port Town Publishing.

David, Lawrence. The Cupcaked Crusader. Gott, Barry, illus. 2002. (Horace Splattly Ser.: Vol. 1). 144p. (J). pap. 4.99 (978-0-14-230021-3(7), Puffin) Penguin Group (USA) Inc.

—Horace Splattly: The Cupcaked Crusader. (gr. 3-6). 2003. lib. bdg. 13.00 (978-0-613-61708-6(8)); 2002. lib. bdg. 13.00 (978-0-613-45274-8(7)); 2002. lib. bdg. 13.00 (978-0-613-45275-5(5)) Tandem Library Bks.

—Invasion of the Shag Carpet Creature. 2004. (Horace Splattly Ser.). (Illus.). 160p. (J). pap. 4.99 (978-0-14-240042-5(4), Puffin) Penguin Group (USA) Inc.

—To Catch a Clownosaurus. Gott, Barry, tr. Gott, Barry, illus. 2003. (Horace Splattly Ser.). 160p. (J). pap. 4.99 (978-0-14-250135-1(2), Puffin) Penguin Group (USA) Inc.

Davis, Daniel M. & Davis, Dawna Jo. Klawberry: Good Girl. Bad World. McClellan, Sara, ed. ltd. ed. 2007. per. 20.00 (*978-0-9774173-3-9(6)) Steam Crow Pr.

Dayan, Linda Marcos. El Monstruo Glotopeo. Nepomniachi, Leonid, illus. (Barril Sin Fondo Ser.). (SPA.). (J). (gr. 3-5). pap. (978-968-6465-60-0(X)) Casa de Estudios de Literatura y Talleres Artisticos Amaquemecan A.C. MEX. Dist: Lectorum Pubns., Inc.

Deary, Terry. The Fire Thief Fights Back. 2007. (Fire Thief Ser.). 224p. (J). (gr. 5-7). 9.95 (978-0-7534-5970-6(1), Kingfisher) Houghton Mifflin Co. Trade & Reference Div.

deGroat, Diane. Annie Pitts, Swamp Monster. 2001. (978-0-606-22334-8(7)) Tandem Library Bks.

Del Negro, Janice. Lucy Dove. 2001. (gr. 3-6). lib. bdg. 15.25 (978-0-613-75135-3(3)) Tandem Library Bks.

Del Negro, Janice & Dorling Kindersley Publishing Staff. Lucy Dove. Gore, Leonid, illus. 2001. 32p. (J). (gr. 3-6). pap. 6.95 (978-0-7894-8084-2(0)) Dorling Kindersley Publishing, Inc.

Desrosiers, Sylvie. Mefiez-Vous des Monstres Marins. 2002. (Roman Jeunesse Ser.). (FRE.). 96p. (YA). (gr. 4-7). pap. (978-2-89021-146-9(0)) Diffusion du livre Mirabel.

Dewin, Howie. Monsters Unleashed: Book of Monsters. 2004. (Scooby-Doo Ser.). (Illus.). 48p. (J). 5.99 (978-0-439-56756-5(4), Scholastic Paperbacks) Scholastic, Inc.

—Sand Hassle. 2001. (gr. k-3). lib. bdg. 11.80 (978-0-613-43877-3(9)) Tandem Library Bks.

—Sleeping Ugly. 2004. (Shrek 2 Ser.). 64p. (J). 3.99 (978-0-439-59716-6(1)) Scholastic, Inc.

Dezago, Todd. Fantastic Four: The Menace of Monster Isle! 2006. (Spider-Man Team up Ser.). (Illus.). (J). (gr. 2-6). 21.35 (978-1-59961-006-1(X)) Spotlight.

—Kitty Pryde: Down with the Monsters! 2006. (Spider-Man Team up Ser.). (Illus.). (J). (gr. 2-6). 21.35 (978-1-59961-002-3(7)) Spotlight.

Dhami, Narinder. Monster under the Stairs. Spoor, Mike, illus. 2005. 24p. (J). lib. bdg. 22.65 (*978-1-59646-718-7(5)) Dingles & Co.

Dickerson, Sharon. Jessica & the Tangle Monster. 2003. (J). pap. 9.00 (978-0-8059-5991-8(2)) Dorrance Publishing Co., Inc.

Dickinson, Rebecca. Over in the Hollow. Britt, Stephanie, illus. 2008. (J). 15.95 (978-0-8118-5035-3(8)) Chronicle Bks. LLC.

Dickinson, Rebecca, tr. & illus. Over in the Hollow. Dickinson, Rebecca, illus. 2002. (J). (978-0-385-74620-5(2), Doubleday Bks. for Young Readers) Random Hse. Children's Bks.

Dinan, Carolyn. Goodnight, Monster. (Illus.). 32p. (J). 13.95 (978-0-241-13021-6(2), Hamilton, Hamish); pap. 7.95 (978-0-14-038281-5(X)) Penguin Bks., Ltd. GBR. Dist: Trafalgar Square Publishing.

DiPucchio, Kelly S. Monster Makeovers. Pham, LeUyen, illus. 2006. (J). (978-0-7868-5181-2(3)) Hyperion Bks. for Children.

Disney/Pixar: Finding Nemo CD Read-Along. 2007. 48p. (ps-2). 12.99 (978-1-4231-0270-0(3)) Disney Pr.

Dodd, Lynley. Zachary Quack Minimonster. 2006. (Gold Star First Readers Ser.). (Illus.). 31p. (J). 22.00 (978-0-8368-6187-7(6)) Stevens, Gareth Inc.

Donaldson, Julia. The Gruffalo. Scheffler, Axel, illus. 2003. 24p. (J). pap. 11.99 (978-0-333-71093-7(2)) Macmillan Publishers Ltd. GBR. Dist: Trafalgar Square Publishing.

—The Gruffalo. Scheffler, Axel, illus. 2005. 24p. (J). (ps). bds. 6.99 (978-0-8037-3047-2(0), Dial) Penguin Group (USA) Inc.

Donato, Cindy. Monsters! Monsters! 2004. 33p. pap. 17.95 (978-1-4137-3221-4(6)) PublishAmerica, Inc.

Dower, Laura. Powerpuff Girls Save Halloween. 2002. (gr. k-3). lib. bdg. 14.15 (978-0-613-50497-3(6)) Tandem Library Bks.

—Shrek & Fiona's Slide Show Projector Book. 2004. (Shrek 2 Ser.). (Illus.). 32p. (J). pap. 21.99 (978-0-439-57631-4(8)) Scholastic, Inc.

—Three Girls & a Monster. 2002. (gr. k-3). lib. bdg. 11.25 (978-0-613-43964-0(3)) Tandem Library Bks.

Downey, Lynn. Most Loved Monster. Davis, Jack E., illus. 2004. 32p. (J). (ps). 16.99 (978-0-8037-2728-1(3), Dial) Penguin Group (USA) Inc.

Doyle, Malachy. Hungry! Hungry! Hungry! Hess, Paul, illus. 2001. 28p. (J). (ps-3). 15.95 (978-1-56145-241-5(6)) Peachtree Pubs., Ltd.

Dracula. (J). 9.95 (978-1-56156-373-9(0)) Kidsbooks, Inc.

Drescher, Henrik. Simon's Book. Drescher, Henrik, illus. 2006. (Illus.). 32p. (J). 14.95 (978-1-59692-135-1(8)) MacAdam/Cage Publishing, Inc.

Druitt, Tobias. Corydon & the Fall of Atlantis. 2007. 352p. (J). (gr. 5). 15.99 (978-0-375-83383-0(8)); lib. bdg. 18.99 (978-0-375-93383-7(2)) Random Hse. Children's Bks. (Knopf Bks. for Young Readers).

—Corydon & the Island of Monsters. 304p. (J). (gr. 3-7). 2007. 6.50 (*978-0-440-42173-3(X), Yearling); 2006. 15.95 (978-0-375-83382-3(X), Knopf Bks. for Young Readers); 2006. lib. bdg. 17.99 (978-0-375-93382-0(4), Knopf Bks. for Young Readers) Random Hse. Children's Bks.

Duchesne, Christiane. Nox & Archimusse in the Monsters' Feast. Perkes, Carolyn, tr. Jorisch, Stephane, illus. 2000. (J). (ps-3). pap. (978-1-894363-20-4(5)) Dominique & Friends.

Duey, Kathleen. Boogeyman in the Basement! 2000. (Alone in the Dark Ser.). (Illus.). 32p. (J). pap. 3.95 (978-1-891100-12-3(2)) Smart Kids Publishing.

—Nowhere to Run, Nowhere to Hide! 2000. (Alone in the Dark Ser.). (Illus.). 32p. (J). pap. 3.95 (978-1-891100-14-7(9)) Smart Kids Publishing.

Duey, Kathleen & Berry, Ron. Crassy the Crude Beastie. Sharp, Chris & Currant, Gary, illus. 2000. (Beastie Buddies Ser.). 32p. (J). (ps-3). pap. 3.95 (978-1-891100-28-4(9)) Smart Kids Publishing.

—Glumby the Grumbling Beastie. Sharp, Chris & Currant, Gary, illus. 2000. (Beastie Buddies Ser.). 32p. (J). (ps-3). mass mkt. 3.95 (978-1-891100-27-7(0)) Smart Kids Publishing.

Duncan, Jane. Janet Reachfar & the Kelpie. Hedderwick, Mairi, illus. 2002. 32p. (J). (gr. k-3). pap. 7.95 (978-1-84158-210-8(7)) Birlinn, Ltd. GBR. Dist: Interlink Publishing Group, Inc.

Durant, Alan. Creepe Hall for Ever! l.t. ed. 2005. (Illus.). 112p. (J). pap. (978-0-7540-6142-7(6), CLP 333) BBC Audio.

Dyer, Sarah. Five Little Fiends. Dyer, Sarah, illus. 2002. (Illus.). 32p. (J). 15.95 (978-1-58234-751-6(4), Bloomsbury Children) Bloomsbury Publishing.

Eaton Deborah. Canciones de monstruos (Monster Songs) 2007. (Lecturas para niños de verdad - Nivel 2 (Real Kids Readers - Level 2) Ser.). (J). pap. 5.95 (*978-0-8225-7803-1(4), Ediciones Lerner) Lerner Publishing Group.

Eaton, Deborah. Monster Songs. Handelman, Dorothy, photos by. 1999. (Real Kids Readers Ser.). (Illus.). 32p. (gr. k-2). (J). pap. 4.99 (978-0-7613-2079-1(2)); lib. bdg. 18.90 (978-0-7613-2054-8(7)) Lerner Publishing Group. (Millbrook Pr.).

—Monster Songs. 1999. (J). (978-0-606-19162-3(3)); lib. bdg. 11.80 (978-0-613-16767-3(8)) Tandem Library Bks.

Edwards, Jason. Will Allen & the Great Monster Detective. l.t. ed. 2007. (Illus.). 96p. (J). per. 5.95 (*978-0-9789512-0-7(4)) Rogue Bear Pr.

Ekaitis, Joe. Collinsfort Village. 2005. (Illus.). 161p. (J). per. 9.95 (978-1-886249-21-9(0)) WindRiver Publishing.

Elmo & the Monsters. 2001. (J). (978-1-931312-39-4(7)) SoftPlay, Inc.

Emberley, Ed. Bye-Bye, Big Bad Bullybug. Emberley, Ed, illus. 2007. (Illus.). 32p. (J). (ps-1). 10.99 (978-0-316-01762-6(0)) Little Brown & Co.

—Go Away, Big Green Monster! Make the Monster Disappear! 2005. 32p. (J). 10.99 (978-0-316-01104-4(5)) Little Brown & Co.

Emberley, Edward R. Go Away, Big Green Monster! 2005. (Illus.). 32p. (J). (ps-1). reprint ed. 10.99 (978-0-316-23653-9(5)) Little Brown & Co.

Emmett, Jonathan. Ten Little Monsters. 2001. (Illus.). 12p. (J). (gr. k-ps). tchr. ed. 10.95 (978-0-7534-5333-9(9), Kingfisher) Houghton Mifflin Co. Trade & Reference Div.

—Ten Little Monsters. Parker, Ant, illus. 2000. 12p. (J). (ps). tchr. ed. (978-0-7534-0452-2(4)) Kingfisher Publications, plc.

Erenberger, Timothy D. Abacar the Wizard Book One: A Tale of Magic, War, Elves, Goblins, Orcs, Monsters, Fantasy, & Adventure. 2001. 210p. pap. 14.95 (978-0-595-21261-3(1), Writer's Showcase Pr.) iUniverse, Inc.

Ering, Timothy Basil. The Story of Frog Belly Rat Bone. Ering, Timothy Basil, illus. 2003. (Illus.). 48p. (J). (ps-2). 16.99 (978-0-7636-1382-2(7)) Candlewick Pr.

Escondete y Grita, Vol. II. (Fantasmas de Fear Street Coleccion: No. 1). (SPA.). (J). (gr. 4-7). pap. 7.95 (978-950-04-1999-4(8), EM4474) Emecé Editores S.A. ARG. Dist: Lectorum Pubns., Inc., Planeta Publishing Corp.

Espinosa, Laura & Espinosa, Leo. Otis & Rae & the Grumbling Splunk. Espinosa, Laura & Espinosa, Leo, illus. 2008. 32p. (J). (ps-3). 12.95 (*978-0-618-98206-6(X)) Houghton Mifflin Co.

Excuse Me, Are You a Dragon? 2002. (Illus.). 32p. (J). (gr. k-3). reprint ed. 16.95 (978-1-880851-34-0(2)) Greene Bark Pr., Inc.

Farber, Erica. The Swamp Thing. Mayer, Mercer, illus. 2006. (Critter Kids Adventure Ser.). 32p. (J). (gr. 2-5). pap. 4.95 (978-0-7696-4762-3(6), Gingham Dog Pr.) School Specialty Publishing.

Farshtey, Greg. Web of Shadows. 2005. 139p. (J). (978-1-4156-0699-5(4)) Scholastic, Inc.

Faulkner, Keith. The Monster Who Loved Books. Lambert, Jonathan, illus. 2002. 16p. (J). (ps-k). pap. 10.95 (978-0-439-34099-1(3), Orchard Bks.) Scholastic, Inc.

La Fiesta Monstruosa, 6 Pks. (Chiquilibros Ser.). (SPA.). (gr. k-1). 23.00 (978-0-7635-8600-3(5)) Rigby Education.

Fleetwood, Tamela. Nellie Jelly & the Jelly Well, No. 1. 2000. 32p. (J). lib. bdg. 10.95 (978-0-9702128-0-1(1)) Odditeas, Inc.

Flesh, Chris P. Me So Pretty! 2007. (Pretty Freekin Scary Ser.: No. 2). 176p. (J). (gr. 3). pap. 4.99 (*978-0-448-44683-7(9), Grosset & Dunlap) Penguin Group (USA) Inc.

—You Smell Dead. 2007. (Pretty Freekin Scary Ser.: No. 1). 176p. (J). (gr. 3). pap. 4.99 (*978-0-448-44682-0(0), Grosset & Dunlap) Penguin Group (USA) Inc.

Flynn, Kieran. Monster Jam. 1998. (Screammates Ser.: Vol. 3). (J). pap. 3.99 (978-0-590-09896-0(9), Scholastic Paperbacks) Scholastic, Inc.

Fred, Anthony. Meet Heinie Goblins. Primavera, Elise, illus. rev. ed. 2008. 128p. 14.99 (*978-0-7868-3681-9(4)) Hyperion Bks. for Children.

Fred, Anthony & Primavera, Elise. Meet Heinie Goblins. Primavera, Elise, illus. rev. ed. 2008. 128p. pap. 4.99 (*978-0-7868-3682-6(2)) Hyperion Bks. for Children.

Freidman, Mel. The Blue Moon Effect. Smith, Eric, illus. gif. ed. 2005. 96p. (J). (gr. 2-5). per. 3.99 (978-1-57791-178-4(4)) Brighter Minds Children's Publishing.

French, Vivian. The Snow Dragon. 2003. (Illus.). 32p. (J). pap. 11.99 (978-0-552-54595-2(3)) Transworld Publishers Ltd. GBR. Dist: Trafalgar Square Publishing.

Friedman, Rainey L. Monsters in Your Bed... Monsters in Your Head. Dill, Betsy, illus. 1999. 32p. (J). 15.95 (978-0-9666199-1-1(9)) DreamDog Pr.

Friendly Frosty Monster. 2007. 24p. pap. 3.50 (*978-1-4037-3612-3(X)) Dalmatian Pr.

Funke, Cornelia. Ghosthunters & the Muddy Monster of Doom! 2007. (Ghosthunters Ser.: No. 4). 176p. (J). (gr. 2-5). pap. 16.99 (978-0-439-86268-4(X), Chicken Hse., The) Scholastic, Inc.

—Muddy Monster of Doom. 2007. (Ghosthunters Ser.: No. 4). 176p. (J). pap. 4.99 (978-0-439-86269-1(8), Chicken Hse., The) Scholastic, Inc.

Gaiman, Neil. Dangerous Alphabet. Grimly, Gris, illus. 2008. 32p. (J). 17.99 (*978-0-06-078333-4(8)); lib. bdg. 18.89 (*978-0-06-078334-1(6)) HarperCollins Pubs.

Galouchko, Annouchka. Sho & the Demons of the Deep. Galouchko, Annouchka, illus. 1998. (Illus.). 32p. (J). (gr. 2-3). pap. 6.95 (978-1-55037-393-6(5)) Annick Pr., Ltd. CAN. Dist: Firefly Bks., Ltd.

Gardner, Brandy. Monster Spray. Gardner, Greg, ed. Gardner, Greg, illus. 1998. 20p. (J). (ps-2). pap. 4.95 (978-0-9667770-0-0(X)) New Horizons Pr.

Garmon, Larry Mike. Bride of Frankenstein: Vow of Vengence. 2002. (gr. 5-8). lib. bdg. 12.40 (978-0-613-72087-8(3)) Tandem Library Bks.

—Creature from the Black Lagoon: Black Water Horror. 2002. (Illus.). 192p. (J). pap. 4.50 (978-0-439-40228-6(X)) Scholastic, Inc.

—The Wolf Man: Blood Moon Rising. 2001. (Universal Monsters Ser.: No. 2). 160p. (J). (gr. 5 up). pap. 4.50 (978-0-439-20847-5(5)) Scholastic, Inc.

Garza, Xavier & Villarroel, Carolina. Juan & the Chupacabras: Juan y la Chupacabras. Ward, April, illus. 2006. (ENG & SPA.). 32p. (J). 15.95 (978-1-55885-454-3(1), Piñata Books) Arte Publico Pr.

Gelsey, James. Scooby-Doo! & the Hoopster Horror. 2005. (Illus.). 61p. (J). lib. bdg. 15.00 (*978-1-4242-0305-5(8)) Fitzgerald Bks.

—Scooby-Doo & the Monster Menace. 2006. (Scooby-Doo Mysteries Ser.: No. 34). (Illus.). 64p. (J). pap. 3.99 (978-0-439-81417-1(0), Scholastic) Scholastic, Inc.

—Scooby-Doo & the Snow Monster. 1999. (Scooby-Doo Mysteries Ser.: No. 3). (Illus.). 57p. (J). (ps-3). 3.99 (978-0-590-81914-5(3), Scholastic Paperbacks) Scholastic, Inc.

—Scooby-Doo & the Snow Monster. 1999. (gr. 3-6). lib. bdg. 11.80 (978-0-613-12085-2(X)) Tandem Library Bks.

Geoghegan, Adrienne. There's a Wardrobe in My Monster! Johnson, Adrian, illus. 2003. (Picture Bks.). 32p. (J). (ps-3). 15.95 (978-1-57505-414-8(0), Carolrhoda Bks.) Lerner Publishing Group.

Gerth, Melanie & Bilgrami, Shaheen. Mega Motors: Heavy Duty Dump Truck. 2005. (Illus.). 64p. (J). pap. 19.95 (978-0-7624-2094-0(4), Running Pr. Kids) Running Pr. Bk. Pubs.

Gilmour, H. B. Godzilla: A Junior Novelization. novel ed. 1998. (Godzilla Ser.). 88p. (J). (gr. 1-4). pap. 3.99 (978-0-590-68091-2(9)) Scholastic, Inc.

Glumby the Grumbling Beastie. 2001. (Beastie Buddies Ser.). (Illus.). 32p. (J). 6.95 (978-1-891100-85-7(8)) Smart Kids Publishing.

Godfrey, Martyn. More Monsters in School. Mardon, John, illus. 1999. (First Flight Ser.). 64p. (J). pap. (978-1-55041-506-3(9)) Fitzhenry & Whiteside, Ltd.

—More Monsters in School. 1999. (gr. 3-6). lib. bdg. 11.80 (978-0-613-88774-8(3)) Tandem Library Bks.

Golden, Christopher. Monster Book. 2000. (gr. 7-12). lib. bdg. 26.85 (978-0-613-63322-2(9)) Tandem Library Bks.

Gollub, Matthew. Ten Oni Drummers. Stone, Kazuko G., illus. 2000. (JPN & ENG.). 32p. (J). (ps-3). 15.95 (978-1-58430-011-3(6)) Lee & Low Bks., Inc.

Gomez Cerda, Alfredo. El Monstruo y la Bibliotecaria. 4th ed. (SPA., Illus.). 62p. (J). (gr. 3-5). (978-84-279-3456-6(4), NG1580) Noguer y Caralt Editores, S. A. ESP. Dist: Lectorum Pubns., Inc.

Goode, Molly. How the Grinch Got So Grinchy. 2000. (Step into Reading Step 2 Bks.). (Illus.). (J). pap. 3.99 (978-0-375-81226-2(1)) Random Hse., Inc.

Gordon, Wendy. I'm Safe! from Monsters. Gordon, Paul, illus. 1999. (I'm Safe! Ser.). 32p. (J). (ps-3). pap. 6.95 (978-1-891596-02-5(0)) BackYard Bks.

—I'm Safe! from Monsters. 1999. 24p. (ps-3). pap., act. bk. ed. 2.95 (978-1-891596-03-2(9)) Backyard Pub. Co., Inc.

Gorey, Edward. The Wuggly Ump. Gorey, Edward, illus. 2007. 32p. 12.95 (*978-0-7649-4192-4(5), A142) Pomegranate Communications, Inc.

Grabis, Bettina. Bobbo the Basement Monster. Durr, Gisela, illus. 1999. Tr. of Bobbo das Kellermonster. 108p. (gr. 2-4). pap. 6.95 (978-1-889658-09-4(X)) New Canaan Publishing Co. LLC.

Graham, Alastair. Full Moon Soup. 2007. (Illus.). 32p. (J). 12.95 (*978-1-905417-54-4(3)) Boxer Bks., Ltd. GBR. Dist: Sterling Publishing Co., Inc.

Graham, Richard. Jack y el Monstruo. Varley, Susan, illus. (Cotton Cloud Ser.). (SPA.). 32p. (J). (gr. 1-3). (978-84-7722-680-2(6)) Timun Mas, Editorial S.A. ESP. Dist: Lectorum Pubns., Inc.

Graves, Keith. Frank Was a Monster Who Wanted to Dance. 1999. (Illus.). 32p. (J). (ps-3). 13.95 (978-0-8118-2169-8(2)) Chronicle Bks. LLC.

Gray, Kes. Nelly the Monstersitter. Ross, Tony, illus. 2006. 48p. (J). lib. bdg. (*978-1-4048-3124-7(X)) Picture Window Bks.

Gresko, Marcia S. Monster Stew, Vol. 4474. Kupperstein, Joel, ed. Dunne, Kathleen, illus. 1998. (Learn to Read Math Ser.). 16p. (J). pap. 2.75 (978-1-57471-381-7(7), 4474) Creative Teaching Pr., Inc.

Grindley, Sally. Perfect Monster. Waters, Erica-Jane, illus. 2005. (I Am Reading Ser.). 48p. (J). (gr. k-3). pap. 3.95 (978-0-7534-5858-7(6), Kingfisher) Houghton Mifflin Co. Trade & Reference Div.

Groves. Pond Monster, Bk. 5A. Date not set. (Illus.). 16p. (J). pap. 129.15 (978-0-582-18796-2(6)) Addison-Wesley Longman, Ltd. GBR. Dist: Trans-Atlantic Pubns., Inc.

Haggarty, Holly. Summer Dragons. 2007. 144p. (J). (gr. 3 up). pap. 7.98 (*978-1-894917-52-0(9)) Napoleon Publishing/Rendezvous Pr. CAN. Dist: AtlasBooks Distribution.

Hagiwara, Kazushi. Bastard!!, Vol. 12. Hagiwara, Kazushi, illus. 2006. (Bastard!! Ser.). 208p. (YA). pap. 9.99 (978-1-4215-0434-6(0)) Viz Media.

Halfmann, Janet. Ogre Hunter No. 2: With Stencils. Karl, Linda, illus. 2004. (Shrek 2 Ser.). 32p. (J). act. bk. ed. 3.99 (978-0-439-57633-8(4)) Scholastic, Inc.

Hall, Starr. Jopalbers & Goodles: Face Your Fears. Hall, Grady, ed. Gage, Carl, illus. 1998. (Doom Ser.). 62p. (J). (gr. k-4). 19.95 (978-0-9651678-9-5(5)) Simply Angels Creative Pr. & Design.

Hamilton, John. Mission to Mars, 6 bks. Incl. Future Missions to Mars. lib. bdg. 24.21 (978-1-56239-832-3(6)); Mariner Missions to Mars. lib. bdg. 24.21 (978-1-56239-828-6(8)); Mars Myths & Legends. lib. bdg. 24.21 (978-1-56239-827-9(X)); Pathfinder Mission to Mars. lib. bdg. 24.21 (978-1-56239-831-6(8)); Search for Life on Mars. lib. bdg. 24.21 (978-1-56239-830-9(X)); Viking Missions to Mars. lib. bdg. 24.21 (978-1-56239-829-3(6)); 32p. (J). (gr. 5). 1998. (Illus.). Set lib. bdg. 136.68 (978-1-57765-258-8(4), ABDO & Daughters) ABDO Publishing Co.

Hapka, Catherine. Shrek the Third: A Good King Is Hard to Find. Gordon, Steven E., illus. 2007. (I Can Read Bks.: Bk. 2). 32p. (J). pap. 3.99 (978-0-06-122866-7(4) , Harper Trophy) HarperCollins Pubs.

—Shrek the Third: Friends & Foes. 2007. (I Can Read Bks.: Bk. 1). 32p. (J). pap. 3.99 (978-0-06-122865-0(6) , Harper Trophy) HarperCollins Pubs.

Hardgrove, Micheal. The Ogre & the Angel: To Go & Tell Somebody. Hardgrove, J. Franklin, ed. Hardgrove, Micheal, illus. 1998. (Illus.). 32p. (J). (ps-6). pap. 12.95 (978-0-9660797-2-2(8) , OAA) Tiwinke Publishing, Inc.

Harper, Charise Mericle. The Monster Show: Everything You Never Knew about Monsters. 2004. (Illus.). 32p. (J). (gr. k-3). tchr. ed. 15.00 (978-0-618-38797-7(8)) Houghton Mifflin Co. Trade & Reference Div.

Harrington, Sean P. Patterson & the Great Green Greedy Galumpus. 2000. (Illus.). 20p. (J). (gr. k-4). pap. 10.95 (978-0-9672290-2-7(2)) Harrington, Denis J. Pub.

Harris, Christine. Undercover Girl #5: Twisted. 2007. 136p. (J). per. 10.95 (****978-1-59594-151-0(7)*** , Wingspan Pr.) WingSpan Publishing.

Harris, Emma. Bedtime, Little Monsters! Cherrill, Paul, illus. 2002. 20p. (J). tchr. ed. 14.95 (978-1-58925-689-7(1) , tiger tales) ME Media LLC.

Harris, Joe. Halloween Ball. 2008. (J). (****978-0-375-84975-6(0)); (*978-0-375-84373-0(6));*** lib. bdg. (****978-0-375-94975-3(5))*** Random Hse., Inc.

Hart, J. J. Zombie Monkey Monster Jamboree. Meugniot, Will, illus. 2006. 141p. (J). 12.95 (978-1-933925-07-3(8) , Actionopolis) Komikwerks, LLC.

Hart, Tessa & Sergi, Frank. The Snarth Goes to School. Freeman, Pietri, illus. 2000. 48p. (J). (gr. k-5). 18.95 (978-0-9660172-0-5(X)) Brookfield Reader, Inc., The.

Hawkins, Colin & Hawkins, Jacqui. Snap! Snap! 2005. (Illus.). 32p. (J). pap. 7.99 (978-1-4052-1099-7(0)) Egmont Bks., Ltd. GBR. *Dist:* Trafalgar Square Publishing.

Hawley, Kelvin, illus. My Things, 6 Packs. (Sails Literacy Ser.). 16p. (gr. k up). 27.00 (978-0-7635-4395-2(0)) Rigby Education.

—The Vacation: Individual Title Six-Packs. (Sails Literacy Ser.). 16p. (gr. k up). 27.00 (978-0-7635-4434-8(5)) Rigby Education.

Hawthorn, Phillip & Tyler, Jenny. There's A Monster in My House. 2007. 16p. (J). 9.99 (978-0-7945-1567-6(3) , Usborne) EDC Publishing.

Hayes, Fiona. Don't Say Boo! 2007. (Illus.). 10p. (J). 4.95 (978-1-4027-4477-8(3)) Sterling Publishing Co., Inc.

Hazen, Barbara Shook. Who Is Your Favorite Monster, Mama? Kovalski, Maryann, illus. 2006. 32p. (ps-2). 15.99 (978-0-7868-1810-5(7)) Hyperion Pr.

Hee-Joon, Son. PhD Vol. 3: Phantasy Degree. Hee-Joon, Son, illus. 2005. (Illus.). pap. 9.99 (978-1-59532-319-4(8) , Tokyopop Adult) TOKYOPOP, Inc.

Heimberg, Justin. Shrek Scratch n' Stink Storybook. 2002. (Illus.). pap. 7.99 (978-0-525-46937-7(0) , Dutton Juvenile) Penguin Group (USA) Inc.

Heller, Nicholas. Ogres! Ogres! Ogres! A Feasting Frenzy from A to Z. Smith, Joseph A., illus. 1999. 32p. (J). (gr. k-3). 16.89 (978-0-688-16987-9(2)) HarperCollins Pubs.

Hemingway, Edward. Bump in the Night. 2008. 32p. (J). (ps-k). 15.99 (****978-0-399-24761-3(0)*** , Putnam Juvenile) Penguin Group (USA) Inc.

Herman, Gail. Boo on the Loose! 2002. (gr. k-3). lib. bdg. 11.80 (978-0-613-73662-6(1)) Tandem Library Bks.

—The Racecar Monster. del Sur, Duendes, illus. 2001. (Scooby-Doo Ser.: No. 8). 32p. (J). (ps-3). pap. 3.99 (978-0-439-24236-3(3)) Scholastic, Inc.

—Scooby-Doo: Racecar Monster. 2001. (gr. k-3). lib. bdg. 11.80 (978-0-613-43872-8(8)) Tandem Library Bks.

—Scooby Doo: Sea Monster Scare. 2002. (gr. k-3). lib. bdg. 11.80 (978-0-613-51324-1(X)) Tandem Library Bks.

Heusler, Marianna. Annabelle's Monsters. 2005. 190p. pap. 19.95 (978-1-4137-6451-2(7)) PublishAmerica, Inc.

Hicks, Barbara Jean. Jitterbug Jam: A Monster Tale. Deacon, Alexis, illus. 2005. 40p. (J). 16.00 (978-0-374-33685-1(7) , Farrar, Straus & Giroux) Farrar, Straus & Giroux.

Hiebert, Elfrieda H. & Juel, Connie. My Monster & Me. (Little Book Practice Reader). (J). (978-0-8136-0677-4(2)) Modern Curriculum Pr.

Ho, Jason, illus. Frankenstein. 2007. (Graphic Horror Ser.). 32p. (YA). (gr. 5-8). lib. bdg. 27.07 (****978-1-60270-059-8(1)*** , Graphic Planet) Magic Wagon.

Holden, Anthony. One Hungry Monster. 2001. (Illus.). 1p. (J). 5.95 (978-0-316-64185-2(5)) Little Brown & Co.

Holder, Nancy. Long Way Home. 2001. (gr. 7-12). lib. bdg. 15.30 (978-0-613-63316-1(4)) Tandem Library Bks.

Holub, Joan. Happy Monster Day! Holub, Joan, illus. 1999. (Read with Me Ser.). (Illus.). 32p. (J). (ps-2). pap. 3.25 (978-0-439-06753-9(7) , Cartwheel Bks.) Scholastic, Inc.

—Happy Monster Day! 1999. (Illus.). (J). (978-0-606-18555-4(0)) Tandem Library Bks.

Hook. Wrinkled Crinkled Grapes: A Purple Monster. 2007. 52p. per. 8.95 (****978-0-595-42310-1(8))*** iUniverse, Inc.

Hooks, William H. Mr. Monster. Meisel, Paul, illus. 1998. (Bank Street Reader Collection). 48p. (J). (gr. 2-4). lib. bdg. (978-0-8368-1774-4(5)) Stevens, Gareth Inc.

Hopper, Karyn. There's a Monster in My Opu. 2006. (Illus.). 24p. (J). mass mkt. 11.95 (978-1-57306-244-2(8)) Bess Pr., Inc.

Howe, David J. Doctor Who - A Book of Monsters: Meet the Monster & Their Makers. 1999. (Doctor Who Ser.). (Illus.). 118p. (J). (978-0-563-40562-7(7)) BBC Worldwide.

Howe, John. Beowulf: A Tale of Blood, Heat, & Ashes. 2007. (Illus.). 96p. (J). (gr. 5). 18.99 (****978-0-7636-3647-0(9))*** Candlewick Pr.

Howie, Betsy. The Block Mess Monster. Decker, Cynthia B., illus. 2008. 32p. (J). 16.95 (****978-0-8050-7940-1(8))*** Holt, Henry & Co.

Hutchins, Pat. Favorite Author Collection: Pat Hutchins, 3 bks., Set. unabr. ed. 1999. (Illus.). (J). (ps-3). pap. 42.95 incl. audio (978-0-87499-485-8(3)) Live Oak Media.

—Ten Red Apples. Hutchins, Pat, illus. 2000. (Illus.). 32p. (J). (ps up). lib. bdg. 17.89 (978-0-688-16798-1(5)) HarperCollins Pubs.

Huws, Emily. Anghenfil o Joc. 2005. (WEL., Illus.). 24p. (978-0-86174-164-9(1)) Drake Educational Assocs. Ltd.

I Am Working, 6 Packs. (Sails Literacy Ser.). 16p. (gr. k up). 27.00 (978-0-7635-4407-2(8)) Rigby Education.

I Like Jam: Individual Title, 6 Packs. (Sails Literacy Ser.). 16p. (gr. k up). 27.00 (978-0-7635-4440-9(X)) Rigby Education.

If You're Gonna be a Monster do it Right. 2005. (YA). per. (978-1-59872-088-4(0)) Instantpublisher.com.

Impey, Rose. The Ankle Grabber. Kemp, Moira, illus. 1998. (Creepies Ser.). 48p. (J). (gr. 1-3). lib. bdg. 22.60 (978-1-57505-296-0(2)); pap. 6.95 (978-1-57505-313-4(6)) Lerner Publishing Group. (Carolrhoda Bks.).

—The Flat Man. Kemp, Moira, illus. 1998. (Creepies Ser.). 48p. (J). (gr. k-3). pap. 6.95 (978-1-57505-314-1(4) , Carolrhoda Bks.) Lerner Publishing Group.

—Jumble Joan. Kemp, Moira, illus. 1998. (Creepies Ser.). 48p. (J). (gr. 1-3). pap. 6.95 (978-1-57505-315-8(2) , Carolrhoda Bks.) Lerner Publishing Group.

—Scare Yourself to Sleep. Kemp, Moira, illus. 1998. (Creepies Ser.). 48p. (J). (gr. 1-3). pap. 6.95 (978-1-57505-316-5(0) , Carolrhoda Bks.) Lerner Publishing Group.

In the Mud, Pk. 6. (Sails Literacy Ser.). 16p. (gr. k up). 27.00 (978-0-7635-4428-7(0)) Rigby Education.

Irving, John. A Sound Like Someone Trying Not to Make a Sound. Hauptmann, Tatjana, illus. 2004. 40p. (J). (ps). 15.95 (978-0-385-74680-9(6) , Doubleday Bks. for Young Readers) Random Hse. Children's Bks.

Jablonsky, Alice. Mane Event. 2002. (gr. k-3). lib. bdg. 11.25 (978-0-613-50466-9(6)) Tandem Library Bks.

Jacques, Brian. The Ribbajack & Other Curious Yarns. (J). 2006. 176p. (gr. 3). pap. 6.99 (978-0-14-240378-5(4) , Puffin); 2004. 128p. (gr. 4). 16.99 (978-0-399-24220-5(1) , Philomel) Penguin Group (USA) Inc.

Jane, Pamela. Monster Countdown: A Spooky Counting Book. Zarin-Ackerman, Nick, illus. 2001. (J). (ps-2). 14.95 (978-1-58653-857-6(8)) Mondo Publishing.

Jarvis, Robin. Thorn Ogres of Hagwood. 2002. (Hagwood Books: Bk. 1). (Illus.). 256p. (YA). (gr. 5 up). 16.00 (978-0-15-216752-3(8) , Silver Whistle) Harcourt Trade Pubs.

Jennings, Sharon. No Monsters Here. Ohi, Ruth, illus. 2004. 32p. (J). (gr. k-1). (978-1-55041-787-6(8)) Fitzhenry & Whiteside, Ltd.

JJ Rabbit & the Monster: Level K, 6 vols. 128p. (gr. 2-3). 49.95 (978-0-7699-0981-3(7)) Shortland Pubns. (U. S. A.) Inc.

Johnson, Vickey L. The Monster Mix-Up. 2003. (Illus.). (J). pap. 9.00 (978-0-8059-6125-6(9)) Dorrance Publishing Co., Inc.

Johnston, Tony. Bigfoot Cinderrrrrella. Warhola, James, illus. 2000. 32p. (J). (ps-3). pap. 6.99 (978-0-698-11871-3(5) , Putnam Juvenile) Penguin Group (USA) Inc.

—Bigfoot Cinderrrrrella. 2000. 13.79 (978-0-606-20348-7(6)); lib. bdg. 15.30 (978-0-613-33673-4(9)) Tandem Library Bks.

Jones, Marcia Thornton & Dadey, Debbie. Double Trouble Monsters. 1999. (Bailey City Monsters Ser.: No. 5). (Illus.). 80p. (J). (gr. 2-4). pap. 3.99 (978-0-439-05870-4(8)) Scholastic, Inc.

—Double Trouble Monsters. 1999. (Bailey City Monsters Ser.: No. 5). (J). (gr. 2-4). (978-0-606-16604-1(1)) Tandem Library Bks.

—The Hauntlys' Hairy Surprise. 1999. (Bailey City Monsters Super Special Ser.: No. 1). (Illus.). 112p. (J). (gr. 2-4). pap. 3.99 (978-0-590-04302-1(1)) Scholastic, Inc.

—The Hauntlys' Hairy Surprise. 1999. (Bailey City Monsters Super Special Ser.: No. 1). (J). (gr. 2-4). (978-0-606-19911-7(X)) Tandem Library Bks.

—Howling at the Hauntlys' Gurney, John Steven, illus. 1998. (Bailey City Monsters Ser.: No.2). (J). (gr. 2-4). pap. 3.99 (978-0-590-10845-4(X)) Scholastic, Inc.

—Kilmer's Pet Monster. 1999. (Bailey City Monsters Ser.: No. 4). (Illus.). 72p. (J). (gr. 2-4). pap. 3.99 (978-0-590-10847-8(6)) Scholastic, Inc.

—The Monsters Next Door. Gurney, John Steven, illus. 1998. (Bailey City Monsters Ser.: No. 1). 71p. (J). (gr. 2-4). pap. 3.99 (978-0-590-10787-7(9)) Scholastic, Inc.

—Mrs. Jeepers' Scariest Halloween Ever. 2005. (Adventures of the Bailey School Kids Ser.: Bk. 7). (Illus.). 112p. mass mkt. 3.99 (978-0-439-77527-4(2) , Scholastic Paperbacks) Scholastic, Inc.

—Snow Monster Mystery. 1999. (Bailey City Monsters Ser.: No. 8). (Illus.). (J). (gr. 2-4). (978-0-606-18514-1(3)) Tandem Library Bks.

—Spooky Spells. 1999. (Bailey City Monsters Ser.: No. 6). (Illus.). 80p. (J). (gr. 2-4). pap. 3.99 (978-0-439-05871-1(6)) Scholastic, Inc.

—Spooky Spells. 1999. (Bailey City Monsters Ser.: No. 6). (J). (gr. 2-4). (978-0-606-16656-0(4)) Tandem Library Bks.

—Vampire Baby. 1999. (Bailey City Monsters Ser.: No. 7). (Illus.). 80p. (J). (gr. 2-4). pap. 3.99 (978-0-439-05872-8(4)) Scholastic, Inc.

—Vampire Baby. 1999. (Bailey City Monsters Ser.: No. 7). (J). (gr. 2-4). (978-0-606-17059-8(6)) Tandem Library Bks.

—Vampire Trouble. 1998. (Bailey City Monsters Ser.: No. 3). (Illus.). 80p. (J). (gr. 2-4). pap. 3.99 (978-0-590-10846-1(8)) Scholastic, Inc.

Jungman, Ann. Vlad the Drac Returns. 2006. (Vlad the Drac Ser.). (Illus.). 123p. (J). pap. 6.95 (978-1-903015-34-6(0)) Barn Owl Bks, London GBR. *Dist:* Independent Pubs. Group.

—Vlad the Drac Superstar. unabr. ed. 1998. (J). pap. 24.95 incl. audio (978-0-7540-6202-8(3)) BBC Audiobooks America.

—Vlad the Drac Superstar. 2006. (Vlad the Drac Ser.). (Illus.). 123p. (J). pap. 6.95 (978-1-903015-45-2(6)) Barn Owl Bks, London GBR. *Dist:* Independent Pubs. Group.

Kasza, Keiko. Los Secretos de Abuelo Sapo. (SPA., Illus.). (J). (gr. 1-3). 8.95 (978-958-04-3624-9(X) , NR7688) Norma S.A. COL. *Dist:* Distribuidora Norma, Inc., Lectorum Pubns., Inc.

Katz, Welwyn Wilton. Beowulf. Gal, Laszlo, illus. 2nd ed. 2007. 96p. (J). (gr. 5 up). 17.95 (978-0-88899-807-1(4)) Groundwood Bks. CAN. *Dist:* Perseus Distribution.

Keller, Bill. Beowulf. McLean, J., illus. 2007. (Kingfisher Epics Ser.). 176p. (J). (gr. 5-9). pap. 7.95 (****978-0-7534-6134-1(X)*** , Kingfisher) Houghton Mifflin Co. Trade & Reference Div.

Kennen, Ally. Beast. 2007. 224p. (J). pap. 7.99 (****978-0-439-86550-0(6))*** Scholastic, Inc.

Kennis, Don. Monsters Have Big Feet. Gowens, Kyle & Richmond, Bob, illus. 2006. (J). per. 8.95 (978-0-9788553-0-7(2)) Guppy Publishing LLC.

Kerr, Judith. Mog in the Garden. Kerr, Judith, illus. 2003. (Illus.). 16p. (J). pap. 6.99 (978-0-00-137476-8(1)) HarperCollins Pubs. Ltd. GBR. *Dist:* Independent Pubs. Group.

Kessler, Liz. Emily Windsnap & the Monster from the Deep. Gibb, Sarah, illus. 2007. (Emily Windsnap Ser.). 240p. (J). (gr. 3-7). 5.99 (****978-0-7636-3301-1(1))*** Candlewick Pr.

Kibuishi, Kazu. Amulet: Book 1. 2008. 192p. (J). pap. 9.99 (****978-0-439-84681-3(1)*** , Graphix) Scholastic, Inc.

King-Smith, Dick. Water Horse. 2000. (gr. 3-6). lib. bdg. 13.00 (978-0-613-24003-1(0)) Tandem Library Bks.

Klemer, Amy Wade. The Scary Snake Monster. 2003. (Illus.). 16p. (J). pap. 8.00 (978-0-9729216-1-9(3)) ABCDMoon Publishing.

Klevin, Elisa. Monster in the House. 2001. (Illus.). (J). (978-0-606-20808-6(9)) Tandem Library Bks.

Klug, Eric. The Monster in My Closet. Klug, Eric, illus. 2007. (Illus.). 32p. (J). 15.95 (978-1-60108-007-3(7)) Red Cygnet Pr.

Knight. The Monster in the Loch. (Thumbprint Mysteries Ser.). 32.86 (978-0-8092-0411-3(8)) McGraw-Hill/Contemporary.

Koller, Jackie. No Such Thing. Lewin, Betsy, illus. 2003. 32p. (J). (gr. k-2). 15.95 (978-1-56397-490-8(8)) Boyds Mills Pr.

Krailing, Tessa. Beastly Basil. Phillips, Mike, illus. 2006. 48p. (J). lib. bdg. (****978-1-4048-3113-1(4))*** Picture Window Bks.

—Disgusting Denzil. Phillips, Mike, illus. 2006. 48p. (J). lib. bdg. (****978-1-4048-3117-9(7))*** Picture Window Bks.

Kubler, Annie. Wheels on the Bus. 2005. (Illus.). 16p. (J). (ENG & ARA.). bds. 9.95 (978-1-84444-970-5(X)); (ENG & BEN., bds. 9.95 (978-1-84444-971-2(8)); (ENG & CHI., bds. 9.95 (978-1-84444-972-9(6)); (ENG & CHI., bds. 9.95 (978-1-84444-973-6(4)); (ENG & FRE., bds. 9.95 (978-1-84444-974-3(2)); (ENG & GUJ., bds. 9.95 (978-1-84444-975-0(0)); (ENG & PAN., bds. 9.95 (978-1-84444-976-7(9)); (POR & ENG., bds. 9.95 (978-1-84444-977-4(7)); (ENG & SOM., bds. 9.95 (978-1-84444-978-1(5)); (ENG & SPA., bds. 9.95 (978-1-84444-979-8(3)); (ENG & TUR., bds. 9.95 (978-1-84444-980-4(7)); (ENG & URD., bds. 9.95 (978-1-84444-981-1(5)) Mantra Lingua GBR. *Dist:* Mantra Publishing, Ltd.

—Wheels on the Bus. 2001. (gr. k-3). lib. bdg. 15.30 (978-0-613-77000-2(5)) Tandem Library Bks.

Kudalis, Eric. Classic Monster Stories, 4 bks. Incl. Dracula & Other Vampire Stories. lib. bdg. 21.26 (978-1-56065-212-0(8)); Frankenstein & Other Stories of Man-Made Monsters. lib. bdg. 21.26 (978-1-56065-213-7(6)); Stories of Mummies & the Living Dead. lib. bdg. 21.26 (978-1-56065-214-4(4)); Werewolves & Stories about Them. lib. bdg. 21.26 (978-1-56065 215-1(2)); 48p. (J). (gr. 3-4). 1994. (Illus.). Set lib. bdg. 85.04 (978-1-56065-652-4(2) , Capstone High-Interest Bks.) Capstone Pr., Inc.

Kutner, Merrily. The Zombie Nite Cafe. Long, Ethan, illus. 2007. 32p. (J). (ps-3). 16.95 (978-0-8234-1963-0(0)) Holiday Hse., Inc.

Labatt, Mary. Sam Finds a Monster. 2003. (gr. k-3). lib. bdg. 11.80 (978-0-613-82321-0(4)) Tandem Library Bks.

Lagonegro, Melissa. Monsters Get Scared of the Dark, Too. Harchy, Atelier Philippe, illus. 2003. (Disney Books in Pictureback). 16p. (J). (ps-2). pap. 3.99 (978-0-7364-2162-1(9) , 53528995, RH/Disney) Random Hse. Children's Bks.

Lagonegro, Melissa & Random House Disney Staff. Monsters Get Scared of School, Too. Harchy, Atelier Philippe, illus. 2004. (Random House Pictureback Book Ser.). 16p. (J). (ps-2). pap. 3.99 (978-0-7364-2245-1(5) , RH/Disney) Random Hse. Children's Bks.

Lai-Ma. The Monster of Palapala Mountain. 2006. (Illus.). 44p. (J). 17.95 (978-0-9762056-5-4(3)) Heryin Publishing Corp.

L'Allier, Peter. Rotten Robbie & the Legend of Wanibinoo. 2006. (Illus.). (YA). 18.95 (978-0-9724022-8-6(4)) Dr. Todd, LLC.

Lane, Barbara Donnelly. The Monster Boring. McMahon, Melissa M., illus. 2001. 14p. (J). (ps-4). pap. 7.95 (978-0-9702985-0-8(1)) Shamrock Hse., The.

Langrish, Katherine. Troll Fell. 2004. (Illus.). 272p. (J). (gr. 5 up). lib. bdg. 16.89 (978-0-06-058305-7(3)) HarperCollins Pubs.

LaRose, Linda. Jessica Takes Charge. 1999. (gr. k-3). lib. bdg. 14.10 (978-0-613-29826-1(8)) Tandem Library Bks.

Larsen, Wendy. After Dark. Larsen, Wendy, illus. 1999. (Illus.). 19p. (J). (ps-3). pap. 10.99 (978-0-9665699-0-2(3)) Chase Pubns.

Lavette, Lavaille. The Adventures of Roopster Roux: The Monster All-Stars. Mitchell, Louis H., illus. 1998. (Adventures of Roopster Roux Ser.). 32p. (J). (ps-3). pap. 5.95 (978-1-56554-362-1(9)) Pelican Publishing Co., Inc.

Laybourn, Emma. Monster Shoes. Overwater, Georgien, illus. 2000. 63p. (J). pap. 7.99 (978-0-552-54634-8(8)) Transworld Publishers Ltd. GBR. *Dist:* Trafalgar Square Publishing.

Layne, Steven L. My Brother Dan's Delicious. Galey, Chuck, illus. 2004. 32p. 15.95 (978-1-58980-071-7(0)) Pelican Publishing Co., Inc.

Leedy, Loreen. The Monster Money Book. Leedy, Loreen, illus. 2005. (Illus.). 32p. (J). (gr. k-3). pap. 6.95 (978-0-8234-1558-8(9)) Holiday Hse., Inc.

Lemmens, Riske. A Box Full of Monsters. 2004. (URD, SOM, ALB, CHI & ARA., Illus.). 26p. (J). (978-1-85269-827-0(6)); (978-1-85269-832-4(2)); (978-1-85269-837-9(3)); (978-1-85269-842-3(X)); (978-1-85269-847-8(0)); (978-1-85269-852-2(7)); (978-1-85269-857-7(8)) Mantra Publishing, Ltd.

Lemmens, Riske & Dutta, Kunal, texts. A Box Full of Monsters: Kutia Plot Me Monstra. 2004. (URD, SOM, ALB, CHI & ARA., Illus.). 25p. (J). (978-1-85269-822-5(5)) Mantra Publishing, Ltd.

Leon McCann, Jesse. Haunted Halloween: Sticker Storybook. del Sur, Duendes, illus. 2004. (Scooby-Doo Ser.). 24p. (J). pap. 5.99 (978-0-439-60699-8(3) , Scholastic Paperbacks) Scholastic, Inc.

Leuck, Laura. Goodnight Baby Monster. Date not set. 32p. (J). (ps-1). pap. 4.99 (978-0-06-443723-3(X)) HarperCollins Pubs.

—Goodnight, Baby Monster. 2002. (Illus.). 32p. (J). (ps-1). 14.99 (978-0-06-029151-8(6)); 16.89 (978-0-06-029152-5(4)) HarperCollins Pubs.

—Jeepers Creepers: A Monstrous ABC. Parkins, David, illus. 2003. 32p. (J). 15.95 (978-0-8118-3509-1(X) , 53408263) Chronicle Bks. LLC.

—My Creature Teacher. Nash, Scott, illus. 2004. 32p. (J). (ps-1). 15.99 (978-0-06-029694-0(1)) HarperCollins Pubs.

—My Monster Mama Loves Me So. Buehner, Mark, illus. 24p. (J). (ps-3). 2002. pap. 6.99 (978-0-06-008860-6(5) , Harper Trophy); 1999. 15.89 (978-0-688-16867-4(1)); 1999. 15.99 (978-0-688-16866-7(3)) HarperCollins Pubs.

—My Monster Mama Loves Me So. 2002. (gr. k-3). lib. bdg. 14.15 (978-0-613-53844-2(7)) Tandem Library Bks.

—Santa Claws: A Scary Christmas to All. Grimly, Gris, illus. 2006. 32p. (J). 16.95 (978-0-8118-4992-0(9)) Chronicle Bks. LLC.

Lewin, Betsy. Wiley Learns to Spell. Lewin, Betsy, illus. 1998. (Hello Reader! Ser.). (Illus.). 32p. (J). (ps-1). pap. 3.99 (978-0-590-10835-5(2)) Scholastic, Inc.

—Wiley Learns to Spell. 1998. (Hello Reader! Ser.). (J). (978-0-606-13916-8(8)) Tandem Library Bks.

Lijewski, Christy. Next Exit, Vol. 1. 2006. (Illus.). 168p. (YA). pap. 12.95 (978-1-59362-037-0(3)) Slave Labor Bks.

Little Monster Becomes an Author. 2006. (Learn to Write Ser.). (Illus.). 16p. (J). pap. 2.99 (978-1-59198-300-2(2) , 6192) Creative Teaching Pr., Inc.

The Little Monster Who Lived in the Brushpile. 2002. (J). lib. bdg. 14.95 (978-1-931650-12-0(8)) Coastal Publishing Carolina, Inc.

Lively, Penelope. Dragon Trouble. Rowland, Andrew, illus. 2002. (Yellow Bananas Ser.). 48p. (J). (gr. 3-4). pap. (978-0-7787-0987-9(6)); lib. bdg. (978-0-7787-0941-1(8)) Crabtree Publishing Co.

Lodge, Bernard. How Scary! Who Scares Who from One to Ten. 2001. (Illus.). 32p. (J). (gr. k-ps). tchr. ed. 15.00 (978-0-618-11547-1(1) , Walter Lorraine) Houghton Mifflin Co. Trade & Reference Div.

Lonely Sea Monster. 2007. per. (****978-1-59916-155-6(9))*** Printing Systems.

Look Out for Space Monster. 2003. (J). (978-1-932570-04-5(7)) Literacy Footprints Inc.

Louise, T. Paula. The Baggage Comes to Town. 2002. (Illus.). 32p. (J). (gr. 1-5). pap. 7.99 (978-0-9719775-0-1(X)) Idea & Design Works, LLC.

Lubar, David. Gloomy Ghost, 4. 1998. (Accidental Monsters Ser.). (978-0-606-13108-7(6)) Tandem Library Bks.

Lund, Deb. Monsters on Machines. Neubecker, Robert, illus. 2008. (J). (****978-0-15-205365-9(4))*** Harcourt Trade Pubs.

Lundgren, Mary Beth. Seven Scary Monsters. Fine, Howard, illus. 2003. 32p. (J). (gr. k-3). tchr. ed. 15.00 (978-0-395-88913-8(8) , Clarion Bks.) Houghton Mifflin Co. Trade & Reference Div.

Lunge-Larsen, Lise. The Troll with No Heart in His Body. Bowen, Betsy, illus. 1999. 96p. (J). (gr. 4-6). tchr. ed. 18.00 (978-0-395-91371-0(3)) Houghton Mifflin Co. Trade & Reference Div.

Lynn, Erin. Demon Envy. 2007. 192p. (gr. 12 up). 9.99 (****978-0-425-21737-5(X)*** , Berkley Trade) Penguin Group (USA) Inc.

Maccarone, Grace. Monster Math. Hartelius, Margaret A., illus. 2002. (J). 11.91 (978-0-7587-1457-2(2)) Book Wholesalers, Inc.

—Monster Math Picnic. 1998. (J). (978-0-606-13617-4(7)) Tandem Library Bks.

Maccarone, Grace & Burns, Marilyn. Monster Money. 1998. (Hello Reader! Math Ser.: Level 1). (Illus.). 32p. (J). (ps-3). pap. 3.99 (978-0-590-12007-4(7)) Scholastic, Inc.

Maccarone, Grace, et al. Monster Math Picnic. Hartelius, Margaret A., illus. 1998. (Hello Reader! Math Ser.). 32p. (J). (ps-4). pap. 3.99 (978-0-590-37127-8(4)) Scholastic, Inc.

MacDonald, Alan. Snarlyhissopus. Voce, Louise, illus. 2002. 32p. (J). pap. 5.95 (978-1-58925-370-4(1)); tchr. ed. 14.95 (978-1-58925-021-5(4)) ME Media LLC. (tiger tales).

—Snarlyhissopus. 2002. (ps-2). lib. bdg. 14.10 (978-0-613-53314-0(3)) Tandem Library Bks.

MacKall, Dandi Daley. The Cinnamon Lake-Ness Monster. 1998. (Cinnamon Lake Mysteries Ser.: Vol. 7). 80p. (J). (gr. 1-4). 5.99 (978-0-570-05336-1(6) , 12-3384) Concordia Publishing Hse.

Mann, Paul. Meet My Monster. 1999. (gr. k-3). lib. bdg. 11.80 (978-0-613-26180-7(1)) Tandem Library Bks.

Marijanovic, Stanislav. A Manual of House Monsters. Marijanovic, Stanislav, illus. 1999. (Manual of House Monsters Ser.: Vol. 1). (Illus.). 32p. (J). (gr. 2-6). 15.95 (978-1-57255-718-5(4)) Mondo Publishing.

—A Manual of House Monsters II. 2000. (Illus.). (J). pap. 15.95 (978-1-58653-181-2(6)) Mondo Publishing.

—A Manual of House Monsters II. Marijanovic, Stanislav, illus. 2000. (Manual of House Monsters Ser.: Vol. 2). (Illus.). 32p. (J). (gr. 2-6). 15.95 (978-1-58653-171-3(9)) Mondo Publishing.

Marshall, Paula, ed. Shrek the Third. 2007. (I Can Find It Ser.). 22p. (J). 7.99 (978-0-696-23382-1(7)) Meredith Bks.

—Shrek the Third: Deluxe Sound Storybook. 2007. 22p. (J). 15.95 (978-0-696-23381-4(9)) Meredith Bks.

Martin, Nicole. The Werewolf. 2006. 146p. pap. (*978-1-4120-8802-2(X)) Trafford Publishing.

Martin, Paul. Frankie Rocks the House. 2003. (gr. 3-6). lib. bdg. 13.00 (978-0-613-68236-7(X)) Tandem Library Bks.

—Sally Gets Silly. Boisteau, Manu, illus. 7th rev. ed. 2004. (Monster Manor Ser.: Bk. 7). 96p. (gr. 2-5). pap. 4.99 (978-0-7868-0984-4(1)) Hyperion Pr.

Mason, Tom & Danko, Dan. Dj's Notebook. 2006. (Monster House Ser.). 24p. (J). pap. 3.99 (978-1-4169-1816-5(7) , Simon Spotlight) Simon & Schuster Children's Publishing.

—Shrek 2: The Movie Storybook. Koelsch Studios Staff, illus. movie tie-in ed. 2004. (Shrek 2 Ser.). 56p. (J). (gr. 3-6). pap. 8.99 (978-0-439-53849-7(1)) Scholastic, Inc.

Maxwell, Mimi. Monster Mash. 1998. (J). pap. 6.99 (978-0-9680678-8-8(3)) Tumbleweed Pr.

Mayer, Mercer. One Monster after Another. 2001. (gr. k-3). lib. bdg. 14.10 (978-0-613-84263-1(4)) Tandem Library Bks.

—There Are Monsters Everywhere. 2005. (Illus.). 32p. (YA). (ps-2). 15.99 (978-0-8037-0621-7(9) , Dial) Penguin Group (USA) Inc.

—There's a Nightmare in My Closet. Mayer, Mercer, illus. 2002. (Illus.). (J). 14.04 (978-0-7587-3783-0(1)) Book Wholesalers, Inc.

Mayer, Meyer. Il y a un cauchemar dans Mon. pap. 16.95 (978-2-07-054814-9(7)) Gallimard, Editions FRA. *Dist:* Distribooks, Inc.

McCann, Jesse Leon. Scooby-Doo! & the Eerie Ice Monster. 2000. (gr. k-3). lib. bdg. 14.15 (978-0-613-54351-4(3)) Tandem Library Bks.

—Scooby-Doo & the Tiki's Curse. 2004. (Scooby-Doo Ser.). (Illus.). 24p. (J). 3.50 (978-0-439-54604-1(4) , Scholastic Paperbacks) Scholastic, Inc.

—Scooby-Doo! & You. del Sur, Duendes, illus. 2001. (Collect the Clues Mystery Ser.). 60p. (J). (978-0-439-23156-5(6)) Scholastic, Inc.

—Scooby-Doo!TM & the Eerie Ice Monster. 2000. (Scooby-Doo Ser.). (Illus.). 24p. (J). (ps-3). 5.99 (978-0-439-20667-9(7)) Scholastic, Inc.

McCann, Jesse Leon, adapted by. Scooby-DooTM 2: Monsters Unleashed. movie tie-in ed. 2004. (Scooby-Doo Ser.). (Illus.). 32p. (J). 3.50 (978-0-439-57862-2(0) , Scholastic Paperbacks) Scholastic, Inc.

McConnell, Robert. Norbert Nipkin & the Magic Riddle Stone. Pilcher, Steve, illus. 2nd anniv. ed. 2004. 42p. (J). 20.95 (978-0-929141-79-4(2)) Napoleon Publishing/ Rendezvous Pr. CAN. *Dist:* AtlasBooks Distribution.

McCurry, Meryl. The Seamonster's Back. 2005. (J). per. 8.99 (978-0-9764690-4-9(9)) Milligan Bks., Inc.

McCurry, Meryl Alyse. The Sea Monster's Darkest Night. McCurry, Meryl Alyse, illus. 1999. (Illus.). 34p. (J). (ps-3). pap. 7.99 (978-1-881524-67-0(1)) Milligan Bks., Inc.

McDonald, Ann-Eve. There are No Such Thing as Monsters. 2004. (J). (978-0-9770158-4-9(X)) BeachWalk Bks. Inc.

McDonald, Megan. Bedbugs. Johnson, Paul Brett, illus. 1999. 32p. (J). (ps-1). 16.99 (978-0-531-33193-4(8) , Orchard Bks.) Scholastic, Inc.

McGee, Warner, illus. Monster Halloween Party. 2007. (Backyardigans Ser.). 14p. (J). bds. 6.99 (*978-1-4169-3435-6(9) , Simon Spotlight/Nickelodeon) Simon & Schuster Children's Publishing.

McGrath, Raymond, illus. The Moon: Individual Title Six-Packs. (Sails Literacy Ser.). 16p. (gr. k up). 27.00 (978-0-7635-4426-3(4)) Rigby Education.

McKee. Two Monsters. Date not set. 25p. (J). pap. (978-0-05-004546-6(6)) Addison-Wesley Longman, Inc.

McKee, David. The Monster & the Teddy Bear. 1998. (Illus.). 32p. (J). (ps-1). pap. 9.95 (978-0-86264-762-9(2)) Andersen GBR. *Dist:* Trafalgar Square Publishing.

—Not Now, Bernard. 2005. (Illus.). 32p. (J). 6.99 (978-1-84270-456-1(7)) Trafalgar Square Publishing.

—Three Monsters. 2007. 32p. (J). 15.50 (978-1-59354-131-6(7)); 15.95 (978-1-59354-121-7(X)) Handprint Bks.

—Tres Monstruos. Dearden, Carmen Diana & Mayobre, Maria Francisca, trs. 2005. (SPA., Illus.). (978-980-257-317-2(5)) Ekare, Ediciones.

McKissack, Patricia C. & Moss, Onawumi Jean. Precious & the Boo Hag. Brooker, Kyrsten, illus. 2005. 40p. (J). (ps-3). 17.99 (978-0-689-85194-0(4) , Atheneum/Anne Schwartz Bks.) Simon & Schuster Children's Publishing.

McMahon, Kara. The Mud Monster: A Bath Book. Lo Raso, Carlo, illus. 2007. (Backyardigans Ser.). 8p. (J). 6.99 (978-1-4169-3979-5(2) , Simon Spotlight/Nickelodeon) Simon & Schuster Children's Publishing.

McQueen, John Troy. A World Full of Monsters. Brown, Marc, illus. 2001. 32p. (J). (gr. 5 up). 15.89 (978-0-06-029770-1(0)); (ps up). 15.95 (978-0-06-029769-5(7)) HarperCollins Pubs.

McShane, Pol. Return to Animal Land: The Adventures of Johnny & Joey. 2007. 132p. (J). per. 10.95 (*978-0-595-45804-2(1)) iUniverse, Inc.

Meganck, Glenn. Big Deal at the Center of the Earth. 1999. (Illus.). 67p. 11.99 (978-1-892339-02-7(1)); (gr. 4-7). pap. 4.99 (978-1-892339-03-4(X)) Beachfront Publishing.

Meomi. The Octonauts & the Only Lonely Monster. 2006. (Illus.). 36p. (J). (ps-3). 15.95 (978-1-59702-005-3(2)) Immedium.

Meredith Books Staff & Marvel Books Staff. The Brotherhood of Monsters. Curry, Don, ed. 2006. (X-Men Ser.). 24p. (J). pap. 3.99 (978-0-696-22984-8(6)) Meredith Bks.

Meredith, Randy & Simonson, Louise, creators. Extreme Monsters Graphic Storybook. gif. ed. 2009. (Illus.). 62p. (J). 15.95 (978-1-57791-180-7(6)) Brighter Minds Children's Publishing.

Metz, Lorijo. Floridius Bloom & the Planet of Gloom. Phelan, Matt, illus. 2007. 32p. (J). (gr. 1-3). 16.99 (978-0-8037-3084-7(5) , Dial) Penguin Group (USA) Inc.

Metzenthen, David. Bay Boys: Big Wave Day, Adrian over the Top, Adrian Goes Out There! 2005. (Triple Play-Yellow Ser.). (Illus.). 48p. (gr. 4-8). 41.85 (978-0-7910-9080-0(9)) Facts On File, Inc.

Mick Morris MyM Solver No. 2: Bigfoot... Big Trouble! 2006. (J). mass mkt. 6.99 (978-0-9774119-1-7(5)) Team B Creative LLC.

Miglis Sandvik, Jenny. Smellyweds. Bahr, Beth Lazor, illus. 2004. (Shrek 2 Ser.). 32p. (J). 4.99 (978-0-439-63402-1(4)) Scholastic, Inc.

—Who Are You Calling Ugly? Karl, Linda, illus. 2004. (Shrek 2 Ser.). 32p. (J). act. bk. ed. 3.99 (978-0-439-57632-1(6)) Scholastic, Inc.

Mills, Lauren A. The Dog Prince. Mills, Lauren A. & Nolan, Dennis, illus. 2001. 32p. (J). (gr. 1-3). 15.95 (978-0-316-57417-4(1)) Little, Brown Bks. for Young Readers.

Milton, Joyce. Monster Hunters. 1998. (J). pap. 3.99 (978-0-679-88575-7(7)); lib. bdg. 11.99 (978-0-679-98575-4(1)) Random Hse. Children's Bks. (Random Hse. Bks. for Young Readers).

Miranda, Anne. Monster Math. Powell, Polly, illus. 2002. 32p. (J). (ps-2). pap. 7.00 (978-0-15-216530-7(4) , Voyager Bks./Libros Viajeros) Harcourt Children's Bks.

—Monster Math. 2002. (ps-2). lib. bdg. 14.15 (978-0-613-53840-4(4)) Tandem Library Bks.

Mitchell, Mark S. The Curious Kingship of Sir George, 5 vols. 1998. (Chronicles of the House of Chax Ser.: Bk. 3). 89p. (J). (gr. 3-6). 9.99 (978-0-88092-355-2(5) , 3555) Royal Fireworks Publishing Co.

Mitter, Matt. Hungry Monsters: A Book about Colors. Brown, Jo, illus. 2008. 10p. (J). 7.99 (*978-0-7944-1305-7(6)) Reader's Digest Assn., Inc., The.

Mitter, Matt. I'm Going to Eat You. 2006. (Pop-up Flap Book Ser.). (Illus.). 10p. (J). pap. 10.99 (978-0-7944-0767-4(6)) Reader's Digest Assn., Inc., The.

The Model Monster. 2001. (Animal Shelf Ser.). 24p. pap. 3.50 (978-0-439-31794-8(0)) Scholastic, Inc.

Moffatt, Julia. Mi dentista no es un Monstruo. Axworthy, Anni, illus. 2005. (Lightning Readers Ser.). 32p. (J). (gr. k-1). pap. 3.95 (978-0-7696-4070-9(2) , Gingham Dog Pr.) School Specialty Publishing.

—My Dentist Is Not a Monster. Axworthy, Anni, illus. 2005. (Lightning Readers Ser.). 32p. (J). (gr. k-1). pap. 3.95 (978-0-7696-4030-3(3) , Gingham Dog Pr.) School Specialty Publishing.

A Monster House: Individual Title Six-Packs. (Sails Literacy Ser.). 16p. (gr. k up). 27.00 (978-0-7635-4385-3(3)) Rigby Education.

The Monster in the Cave: Individual Title Six-Pack Pouch - Level K. (Lighthouse Ser.). 16p. (gr. 2 up). 28.00 (978-0-7578-0873-9(5)) Rigby Education.

The Monster of Mirror Mountain: Individual Title Six-Packs. (Literatura 2000 Ser.). (gr. 2-3). 33.00 (978-0-7635-0231-7(6)) Rigby Education.

Monster Party: Individual Title Six-Packs. (Chiquilibros Ser.). (gr. k-1). 23.00 (978-0-7635-0422-9(X)) Rigby Education.

Monster Stories. 256p. (J). 2003. 5.98 (978-1-4054-1008-3(6)); 2002. 25.95 (978-0-7525-5673-4(8)) Parragon, Inc.

The Monster Truck. 2002. 32p. (J). (ps-2). 12.95 (978-1-930758-68-1(5) , Yeva Kids) Yeva Corp.

The Monster's Clothes: Individual Title Six-Packs. (Sails Literacy Ser.). 16p. (gr. k up). 27.00 (978-0-7635-4391-4(8)) Rigby Education.

Monsters Inc. Read Along. 2001. (J). pap. 9.98 incl. audio compact disk (978-0-7634-1828-1(5)) Walt Disney Records.

El monstruo de Montespejo: Individual Title Six-Packs. (Literatura 2000 Ser.). (SPA.). (gr. 2-3). 33.00 (978-0-7635-1265-1(6)) Rigby Education.

El monstruo Verde 16: Leveled Books. 2001. (McGraw-Hill. Lectura Ser.). (ENG & SPA.). (gr. 1 up). (978-0-02-187969-4(9)) Macmillan/McGraw-Hill Schl. Div.

Montoya, Martha, creator. Cenando con el Monstruo: Take-Home. 2005. (Los Kitos Ser.). (SPA.). (YA). (gr. 1-3). 15.00 (978-0-8215-8813-0(3)) Sadlier, William H. Inc.

Moodie, Fiona. Noko & the Night Monster. Moodie, Fiona, illus. 2001. (Illus.). 32p. (J). (gr. k-3). 15.95 (978-0-7614-5093-1(9) , Cavendish Children's Bks.) Cavendish, Marshall Corp.

Moogie the Messy Beastie. 2000. (Beastie Buddies Ser.). (Illus.). 32p. (J). (gr. k-3). pap. 3.95 (978-1-891100-26-0(2)) Smart Kids Publishing.

Moon, Nicola. J. J. Rabbit & the Monster. Parker, Ant, illus. 2005. (I Am Reading Ser.). 48p. (J). (gr. k-3). pap., pap. 3.95 (978-0-7534-5855-6(1) , Kingfisher) Houghton Mifflin Co. Trade & Reference Div.

Mooney, E. S. Powerpuff Girls Save the Easter Bunny. 2002. (gr. k-3). lib. bdg. 14.15 (978-0-613-50489-8(5)) Tandem Library Bks.

Morpurgo, Michael. Beowulf. Foreman, Michael, illus. 2006. 96p. (J). (gr. 3-7). 17.99 (978-0-7636-3206-9(6)) Candlewick Pr.

—Gentle Giant. Foreman, Michael, illus. 2006. 28p. (J). (gr. k-4). reprint ed. pap. 12.00 (978-1-4223-5667-8(1)) DIANE Publishing Co.

—Red Eyes at Night. (Illus.). 64p. (J). pap. 7.99 (978-0-340-68753-6(3) , Hodder & Stoughton) Hodder General Publishing Division GBR. *Dist:* Trafalgar Square Publishing.

Morris, Garvin. Dump Dog. Morris, Garvin, illus. 2007. 32p. (J). (ps-2). 15.95 (*978-1-60108-012-7(3)) Red Cygnet Pr.

Morrissey, Dean. The Monster Trap. Morrissey, Dean, illus. 2006. (Illus.). 40p. (J). reprint ed. pap. 6.99 (978-0-06-052500-2(2) , Harper Trophy) HarperCollins Pubs.

Morrissey, Dean & Krensky, Stephen. The Monster Trap. Morrissey, Dean, illus. 2004. (Illus.). 40p. (J). lib. bdg. 17.89 (978-0-06-052499-9(5)) HarperCollins Pubs.

Mosel, Arlene. The Funny Little Woman. Lent, Blair, illus. 2002. (J). 13.19 (978-0-7587-0033-9(4)) Book Wholesalers, Inc.

Moser, Lisa. The Monster in the Backpack. Jones, Noah, illus. 2006. 48p. (J). (gr. k-2). 14.99 (978-0-7636-2390-6(3)) Candlewick Pr.

—The Monster in the Backpack: Candlewick Sparks. Jones, Noah Z., illus. 2007. (Candlewick Sparks Ser.). 48p. (J). (gr. k-2). pap. 4.99 (978-0-7636-3307-3(0)) Candlewick Pr.

Mullins, Denvil. Soapy-Dope: The Monster Who Lived in a Chuckhole. 2001. 32p. (J). (ps-3). 9.95 (978-1-57072-163-2(7)) Overmountain Pr.

Murphy, Jill. All for One. ed. 2004. (Illus.). (J). (ps-2). spiral bd. (978-0-616-14591-3(8)); spiral bd. (978-0-616-14592-0(6)) Canadian National Institute for the Blind/ Institut National Canadien pour les Aveugles.

Murrietta, Celena. The Big Green Hairy Monster. 2004. (Illus.). 23p. (J). spiral bd. 15.95 (978-1-932373-31-8(4) , Cedar Hill Pr.) Cedar Hill Publishing.

Muzzy, Kirk. The Monster Tots: Opening Day at Loretta's Day Care Center. 1999. (Illus.). (J). (ps-5). 14.95 (978-1-880015-31-5(5)) Petra Publishing Corp.

My Monster Friends, 6 Packs. (Literatura 2000 Ser.). (gr. 1-2). 28.00 (978-0-7635-0102-0(6)) Rigby Education.

Myers, Bill & Wimbish, Dave. Fangs for the Memories. 1999. (Bloodhounds, Inc. Ser.: Vol. 5). 128p. (J). (gr. 3-8). mass mkt. 5.99 (978-1-55661-489-7(6)) Bethany Hse. Pubs.

Myers, Walter Dean. Monster. l.t. ed. 2004. 231p. 22.95 (978-0-7862-7093-4(4)) Thorndike Pr.

—Monster. l.t. ed. 2005. 231p. pap. 10.95 (978-0-7862-7363-8(1) , Large Print Pr.) Thorndike Pr.

Namm, Diane. Monsters! 2004. (My First Reader Ser.). 29p. (J). (gr. k-1). pap. 3.95 (978-0-516-24635-2(6) , Children's Pr.) Scholastic Library Publishing.

Napoli, Donna Jo. Little Creatures. Klementz-Harte, Lauren, illus. 1999. (Angelwings Ser.: No. 2). 96p. (J). (gr. 2-5). pap. 7.95 (978-0-689-82695-5(8) , Aladdin) Simon & Schuster Children's Publishing.

—Little Creatures. 1999. (Angelwings Ser.: No. 2). (Illus.). (J). (978-0-606-17905-8(4)) Tandem Library Bks.

Napp, Daniel. Professor Bumble & the Monster of the Deep. 2008. 32p. (J). 15.95 (*978-0-8109-9484-3(4) , Abrams Bks. for Young Readers) Abrams, Harry N. , Inc.

Neebe, Charles A. The Cave Monster. DiSalvo, Len, illus. 2007. (J). 15.95 (*978-1-933872-32-2(2)) Lima Bear Pr LLC, The.

Neubecker, Robert. Beasty Bath. 2005. (Illus.). 32p. (J). (ps-1). pap. 14.99 (978-0-439-64000-8(8) , Orchard Bks.) Scholastic, Inc.

Niles, Steve, et al. Marvel Monsters. 2006. (Illus.). 224p. 20.99 (978-0-7851-2141-1(2)) Marvel Enterprises, Inc.

Nolan, Lucy. The Lizard Man of Crabtree County. Kastner, Jill, illus. 32p. (J). 2005. pap. 5.95 (978-0-7614-5144-0(7)); 1999. 15.95 (978-0-7614-5049-8(1) , Cavendish Children's Bks.) Cavendish, Marshall Corp.

Norac, Carl. Monster, Don't Eat Me! Amado, Elisa, tr. from DUT. Cneut, Carll, illus. 2007. 32p. (J). (ps-1). 18.95 (978-0-88899-800-2(7)) Groundwood Bks. CAN. *Dist:* Perseus Distribution.

Numeroff, Laura Joffe. Laura Numeroff's 10-Step Guide to Living with Your Monster. Evans, Nate, illus. 2002. 32p. (J). (ps-2). 16.99 (978-0-06-623822-7(6) , Geringer, Laura Book) HarperCollins Pubs.

O'Connor, George. Sally & the Some-Thing. O'Connor, George, illus. 2006. (Illus.). 32p. (J). 16.95 (978-1-59643-141-6(5)) Roaring Brook Pr.

O'Connor, Jane. Sir Small & the Sea Monster. O'Brien, John, illus. 2005. (Step into Reading Ser.). 32p. (J). (gr. k-2). pap. 3.99 (978-0-375-82565-1(7) , Random Hse. Bks. for Young Readers) Random Hse. Children's Bks.

O'Keefe, Susan Heyboer. Hungry Monster ABC: An Alphabet Book. Munsinger, Lynn, illus. 2007. 32p. (J). (ps-1). 12.99 (978-0-316-15574-8(8)) Little Brown & Co.

—More Hungry Monsters. 2004. (Illus.). 32p. (J). 15.95 (978-0-316-61061-2(5)) Little Brown & Co.

—One Hungry Monster: A Counting Book in Rhyme. Munsinger, Lynn, illus. 2001. 10p. (J). (ps-k). bds. 6.99 (978-0-316-60804-6(1)) Little Brown & Co.

Olander, Johan, illus. A Field Guide to Monsters: Googly-Eyed Wart Floppers, Shadow-Casters, Toe-Eaters, & Other Creatures. 2007. 64p. (J). (gr. 4-7). 14.99 (*978-0-7614-5359-8(8)) Cavendish, Marshall Corp.

Onion Head Monster Attacks. 2007. (YA). per. 12.95 (*978-0-9793676-0-1(3)) Friedrich, Paul.

Onion Head Monster Attacks (XL) 2006. per. 19.99 (*978-0-9793676-3-2(8)) Friedrich, Paul.

Onion Head Monster Bombastic. 2007. (YA). per. 12.95 (*978-0-9793676-1-8(1)) Friedrich, Paul.

Onion Head Monster Catastrophic. 2007. per. 12.95 (*978-0-9793676-2-5(X)) Friedrich, Paul.

Orlev, Uri. El Monstruo de la Oscuridad. (Barco de Vapor). (SPA.). 90p. (YA). (gr. 5-8). 7.50 (978-84-348-5327-0(2) , SM7480) SM Ediciones ESP. *Dist:* Lectorum Pubns., Inc.

Orme, David. Monster Planet. Savage, Paul, illus. 2008. (J). pap. (*978-1-59889-900-9(7)); 32p. (YA). (gr. 5-9). lib. bdg. 21.26 (*978-1-59889-848-4(5)) Stone Arch Bks.

Orme, David. Something Evil. Savage, Paul, illus. 2006. 40p. (J). (gr. 2-3). lib. bdg. (978-1-59889-017-4(4)) Stone Arch Bks.

Otoshi, Kathryn. Simon & the Sock Monster. 2004. (Illus.). 36p. 16.95 (978-0-9723946-1-1(3)) KO Kids Bks.

Otto, Carolyn B. Mighty Joe Young. 1998. (Junior Novelization Ser.). (Illus.). 96p. (J). (gr. 3-7). pap. 4.95 (978-0-7868-4137-0(0)) Disney Pr.

Page, Terry. The Saddest Centaur. Page, Terry, illus. (Illus.). 24p. (J). (gr. 2-6). pap. 4.00 (978-1-887864-68-8(7)); lib. bdg. 7.00 (978-1-887864-36-7(9)) Boo Bks., Inc.

Pantuso, Mike & Henson, Jim. 1,2,3 by Elmo. 2001. (Illus.). (J). lib. bdg. (978-0-375-91390-7(4) , Random Hse. Bks. for Young Readers) Random Hse. Children's Bks.

Parish, Peggy. No More Monsters for Me! 2003. 22.95 (978-0-673-75926-9(1)) Celebration Pr.

Park, Barbara. Junie B. Jones Has a Monster under Her Bed. unabr. ed. 2004. (Junie B. Jones Ser.: No. 8). 69p. (J). (gr. k-3). pap. 17.00 incl. audio (978-0-8072-0644-7(X) , Listening Library) Random Hse. Audio Publishing Group.

—Junie B. Jones Has a Monster under Her Bed. Brunkus, Denise, illus. 2006. (Junie B. Jones Ser.: No. 8). (SPA.). 80p. (J). (gr. k-3). pap. 3.99 (978-0-439-66123-2(4) , Scholastic en Espanol) Scholastic, Inc.

—Psssst! It's Me... the Bogeyman. Kroninger, Stephen, illus. 1999. 32p. (J). (gr. k-3). per. 16.00 (978-0-689-82742-6(3) , Simon & Schuster Children's Publishing) Simon & Schuster Children's Publishing.

—Psssst! It's Me... the Bogeyman. 2001. (gr. k-3). lib. bdg. 15.30 (978-0-613-73372-4(X)) Tandem Library Bks.

Parnell, Fran. The Barefoot Book of Monsters. Fatus, Sophie, illus. 2003. 64p. (J). pap. 19.99 (978-1-84148-178-4(5)) Barefoot Bks., Inc.

The Party, 6 Packs. (Sails Literacy Ser.). 16p. (gr. k up). 27.00 (978-0-7635-4414-0(0)) Rigby Education.

Paterson, Brian, illus. Zigby & the Monster. 2005. 32p. (J). (ps). pap. 8.99 (978-0-00-717423-2(3) , HarperCollins Children's Bks.) HarperCollins Pubs. Ltd. GBR. *Dist:* Independent Pubs. Group.

Peacock, David. The Sea Serpent of Grenadier Pond. Peacock, David, illus. 2004. (Illus.). 32p. 9.99 (978-0-88882-086-0(0) , Hounslow Pr.) Dundurn Group, The CAN. *Dist:* Univ. of Toronto Pr.

Peck, Richard. Monster Night at Grandma's House. Freeman, Don, illus. 2003. 32p. (J). (gr. k-3). reprint ed. 12.99 (978-0-8037-2904-9(9) , Dial) Penguin Group (USA) Inc.

Penton Overseas, Inc. Staff. Hogger the Hoarding Beastie. 2001. (Beastie Buddies Ser.). (Illus.). 32p. (J). 6.95 (978-1-891100-83-3(1)) Smart Kids Publishing.

—Moogie the Messy Beastie. 2001. (Beastie Buddies Ser.). (Illus.). 32p. (J). 6.95 (978-1-891100-84-0(X)) Smart Kids Publishing.

Peretti, Frank E. The Cooper Kids Adventure Series. 2004. (Cooper Kids Adventure Ser.). (gr. 5-7). 23.96 (978-0-89107-901-9(7)) Crossway Bks.

Perro Monstruoso. (Fantasmas de Fear Street Coleccion). (SPA.). (YA). (gr. 5-8). pap. 7.95 (978-950-04-1930-7(0) , EM0316) Emecé Editores S.A. ARG. *Dist:* Lectorum Pubns., Inc., Planeta Publishing Corp.

Perry, Janet & Gentle, Victor. Aliens. 1999. (Imagination Library). (Illus.). 24p. (J). (gr. 2 up). lib. bdg. 22.00 (978-0-8368-2435-3(0)) Stevens, Gareth Inc.

—Giants & Wild, Hairy Monsters. 1999. (Imagination Library). (Illus.). 24p. (J). (gr. 2 up). lib. bdg. 22.00 (978-0-8368-2437-7(7)) Stevens, Gareth Inc.

—Manmade Monsters. 1999. (Imagination Library). (Illus.). 24p. (J). (gr. 2 up). lib. bdg. 22.00 (978-0-8368-2439-1(3)) Stevens, Gareth Inc.

—Monsters, 9 bks. Incl. Aliens. lib. bdg. 22.00 (978-0-8368-2435-3(0)); Dragons & Dinosaurs. lib. bdg. 22.00 (978-0-8368-2436-0(9)); Giants & Wild, Hairy Monsters. lib. bdg. 22.00 (978-0-8368-2437-7(7)); Mad Scientists. lib. bdg. 22.00 (978-0-8368-2438-4(5)); Manmade Monsters. lib. bdg. 22.00 (978-0-8368-2439-1(3)); Monsters of the Deep. lib. bdg. 22.00 (978-0-8368-2440-7(7)); Morph Monsters. lib. bdg. 22.00 (978-0-8368-2441-4(5)); Vampires. lib. bdg. 22.00 (978-0-8368-2442-1(3)); Zombies. lib. bdg. 22.00 (978-0-8368-2443-8(1)); 24p. (J). (gr. 2 up). 1999. (Illus.). Set lib. bdg. 198.00 (978-0-8368-2434-6(2)) Stevens, Gareth Inc.

—Monsters of the Deep. 1999. (Imagination Library). (Illus.). 24p. (J). (gr. 2 up). lib. bdg. 22.00 (978-0-8368-2440-7(7)) Stevens, Gareth Inc.

—Morph Monsters. 1999. (Imagination Library). (Illus.). 24p. (J). (gr. 2 up). lib. bdg. 22.00 (978-0-8368-2441-4(5)) Stevens, Gareth Inc.

Petrucha, Stefan & Pendleton, Thomas. Tom. 2007. (Wicked Dead Ser.: No. 2). 224p. (YA). (gr. 7 up). pap. 7.99 (***978-0-06-113850-8(9)***, HarperTeen) HarperCollins Pubs.

Pike, Christopher, pseud. The Creepy Creature. 1998. (Spooksville Ser.: No. 22). (J). (gr. 4-6). 10.64 (978-0-606-13798-0(X)) Tandem Library Bks.

—Monstre de l'Armoire.Tr. of Spooksville. (FRE.). (J). pap. 12.95 (978-2-266-08418-5(6)) Presses Pocket FRA. *Dist:* Distribooks, Inc.

Pilkey, Dav. Dogzilla. Pilkey, Dav, illus. 2002. (Illus.). (J). 14.04 (978-0-7587-2405-2(5)) Book Wholesalers, Inc.

—Dogzilla. 2003. (Illus.). 32p. (J). 14.00 (978-0-15-204948-5(7)); pap. 5.95 (978-0-15-204949-2(5) , Harcourt Paperbacks) Harcourt Children's Bks.

Plaza, José María. David y el Monstruo Que No Sabia Jugar (David & the Monster Who Didn't Know How to Play) Julius, illus. 3rd ed. 2001. (Barco de Vapor Ser.: No. 85). (SPA.). 64p. (J). 4.95 (978-84-348-7764-1(3)) SM Ediciones ESP. *Dist:* AIMS International Bks., Inc.

Pollack, P. & Belviso, M. Challenge of Super. 2007. (Foster's Home for Imaginary Friends Ser.: No. 2). 24p. (J). pap. 3.99 (978-0-439-89949-9(4)) Scholastic, Inc.

Pratchett, Terry. A Hat Full of Sky. 2004. (Discworld Ser.). 288p. (J). (gr. 7 up). 16.99 (978-0-06-058660-7(5)) HarperCollins Pubs.

Preller, James. Case of the Marshmallow Monster. 2000. (gr. 3-6). lib. bdg. 11.80 (978-0-613-32379-6(3)) Tandem Library Bks.

—Godzilla Deluxe Storybook. 1998. (Godzilla Ser.). 48p. (J). (gr. 2-5). pap. 5.98 (978-0-590-57213-2(X)) Scholastic, Inc.

Prince, Sarah. Monsters. 1999. (ps-2). lib. bdg. 11.55 (978-0-613-30611-9(2)) Tandem Library Bks.

Proctor, Darrell. The Cigarette Monster. 2006. (J). pap. 8.00 (978-0-8059-6790-6(7)) Dorrance Publishing Co., Inc.

Punter, Russell. Monsters, Stories Of. 2004. (Young Reading Series One Ser.). 48p. (J). (gr. 2 up). pap. 5.95 (978-0-7945-0757-2(3) , Usborne) EDC Publishing.

The Race Car: Individual Title Six-Packs. (Sails Literacy Ser.). 16p. (gr. k up). 27.00 (978-0-7635-4438-6(8)) Rigby Education.

Radford, Sheri. Penelope & the Monsters. Tripp, Christine, illus. 2005. (Penelope Ser.). 32p. (J). (ps-2). 15.95 (978-1-894222-94-5(6)) Lobster Pr. CAN. *Dist:* Univ. of Toronto Pr.

Ramos, Mario. A La Cama, Monstruito! (SPA.). 32p. (J). 16.95 (978-84-8470-007-4(0)) Corimbo, Editorial S.L. ESP. *Dist:* Distribooks, Inc., Lectorum Pubns., Inc.

Random House Disney Staff. Beauty & the Beast. 2004. (Illus.). 24p. (J). (gr. k-k). bds. 4.99 (978-0-7364-2248-2(X) , RH/Disney) Random Hse. Children's Bks.

Random House Staff & Monster, Cookie. Food! by Cookie Monster. Pantuso, Mike, illus. 2006. 32p. (J). (gr. k-ps). bds. 6.99 (978-0-375-83509-4(1) , Random Hse. Bks. for Young Readers) Random Hse. Children's Bks.

Ravishankar, Anushka. The Fivetongued, Firefanged, Folkadotted Dragon Snake. Roy, Indrapramit & Ramanathan, Rathna, illus. 1999. 50p. (J). pap. (978-81-86211-26-7(8)) Tara Publishing.

—Moin & the Monster. 2006. 196p. (J). pap. 6.99 (978-0-14-333515-3(4) , Penguin Global) Penguin Group (USA) Inc.

Reed, Don C. The Kraken. Hunt, Judith, illus. 2003. 224p. (YA). (gr. 5-9). pap. 7.95 (978-1-56397-693-3(5)) Boyds Mills Pr.

Regan, Dian Curtis. Monster of the Month Club, unabr. ed. 1998. (J). 38.24 incl. audio (978-0-7887-2239-4(5) , 40723); (gr. 4). 89.70 incl. audio (978-0-7887-2544-9(0) , 46714) Recorded Bks., LLC.

—Monsters in the Attic. Cornell, Laura, illus. 1999. 178p. (J). (gr. 4-6). reprint ed. 15.00 (978-0-7881-6676-1(X)) DIANE Publishing Co.

Reidy, Hannah. Crazy Creature Colors. Mackie, Clare, illus. 2003. (Crazy Creatures Ser.). 26p. (J). pap. (978-1-84089-221-5(8) , Zero to Ten, Limited) Evans Publishing Group.

—Crazy Creatures Counting. Mackie, Clare, illus. 2003. (Crazy Creatures Ser.). 26p. (J). pap. (978-1-84089-220-8(X) , Zero to Ten, Limited) Evans Publishing Group.

Reimer, Ramon. Irene & the Big Red Monster. Schroeder, Maurice, illus. 2000. (J). (gr. k-5). lib. bdg. 14.95 (978-0-9705727-0-7(0)) Coastal Publishing Carolina, Inc.

Reiner, Carl. Tell Me a Scary Story: ... But Not Too Scary. Bennett, James, illus. rev. ed. 2007. 32p. (J). (ps-1). pap. 7.99 (***978-0-316-00260-8(7)*** Little, Brown Bks. for Young Readers.

Reiner, Carl. Tell Me a Scary Story... but Not Too Scary! Bennett, James, illus. 2003. 32p. (J). (ps-17). 18.95 incl. audio (978-0-316-83329-5(0)) Little Brown & Co.

Rennie, Gordon. Glimmer Rats. 2002. 64p. pap. 14.95 (978-1-56971-698-4(6)) Dark Horse Comics.

Rex, Michael. Goodnight Goon. 2008. 32p. (J). (ps-k). 14.99 (***978-0-399-24534-3(0)*** , Putnam Juvenile) Penguin Group (USA) Inc.

Ricci, Christine. Legend Hunters! McGee, Warner, illus. 2007. (Backyardigans Ser.). 24p. (J). pap. 3.99 (978-1-4169-4058-6(8) , Simon Spotlight/Nickelodeon) Simon & Schuster Children's Publishing.

Richards, Justin. The Death Collector. 336p. (YA). 2007. (gr. 7 up). pap. 7.95 (***978-1-59990-148-0(X)***); 2006. 16.95 (978-1-58234-721-9(2)) Bloomsbury Publishing. (Bloomsbury Children).

—The Invisible Detective: Ghost Soldiers. 2006. 160p. (J). (gr. 4). 11.99 (978-0-399-24500-8(6) , Putnam Juvenile) Penguin Group (USA) Inc.

—The Invisible Detective: Shadow Beast. 2005. 160p. (YA). (gr. 4). 10.99 (978-0-399-24314-1(3) , Putnam Juvenile) Penguin Group (USA) Inc.

Riddell, Chris. The Emperor of Absurdia. 2006. (Illus.). 32p. (J). (***978-1-4050-5061-6(6)*** , Macmillan Children's Bks.) Pan Macmillan.

Ridley, R. W. Dèlon City: Book Two of the Oz Chronicles. 2006. (YA). per. 14.99 (***978-0-9792067-0-2(7)***) Middleburry Hse. Publishing.

Riordan, Rick. The Sea of Monsters. 2nd rev. ed. 2006. (Percy Jackson & the Olympian Ser.: Bk. 2). 288p. (gr. 5-17). 17.95 (978-0-7868-5686-2(6)) Miramax Bks.

Riordan, Rick. The Titan's Curse. 3rd rev. ed. 2007. (Percy Jackson & the Olympians Ser.: Bk. 3). 320p. (gr. 5 up). 17.95 (***978-1-4231-0145-1(6)***) Miramax Bks.

Roberts, Chris. A Mcspooky Halloween. 2006. (J). pap. 9.00 (***978-0-8059-7196-5(3)***) Dorrance Publishing Co., Inc.

Rodda, Emily. The Deltora Book of Monsters. McBride, Marc, illus. 2002. (Deltora Quest Ser.). 48p. (J). (gr. 3-7). pap. 7.99 (978-0-439-39084-2(2)) Scholastic, Inc.

—The Deltora Book of Monsters. 2002. (gr. 5-8). lib. bdg. 16.45 (978-0-613-50600-7(6)) Tandem Library Bks.

—Tales of Deltora. 2006. (Illus.). 176p. (J). pap. 14.99 (978-0-439-87785-5(7)); pap. 7.99 (978-0-439-82909-0(7) , Scholastic Paperbacks) Scholastic, Inc.

Rogers, Amy. All Chalked Up. 2000. (gr. k-3). lib. bdg. 11.80 (978-0-613-24133-5(9)) Tandem Library Bks.

Rosoff, Meg. Jumpy Jack & Googily. Blackall, Sophie, illus. 2008. 32p. (J). 16.95 (***978-0-8050-8066-7(X)***) Holt, Henry & Co.

S. I. International Staff & George, Chris, illus. The Green Monster. 2004. (Teenage Mutant Ninja Turtles Ser.). 32p. (J). pap. 3.99 (978-0-689-86902-0(9) , Simon Spotlight) Simon & Schuster Children's Publishing.

Sage, James & Ayto, Russell. Mr. Beast. Ayto, Russell, illus. 2005. (Illus.). 32p. (J). 16.95 (978-0-8050-7730-8(8)) Holt, Henry & Co.

Sampson, Fay. Pangur Ban, the White Cat, Vol. 2. 2002. 160p. (J). (gr. 5-8). pap. 7.99 (978-0-7459-4763-1(8) , Lion) Lion Hudson plc GBR. *Dist:* Independent Pubs. Group.

Sanschagrin, Joceline. La Marque du Dragon. 2002. (Roman Jeunesse Ser.). (Illus.). 96p. (YA). (gr. 4-7). pap. (978-2-89021-355-5(2)) Diffusion du livre Mirabel.

Sargent, Dave, et al. Grubby: (Smutty Olive Grullo) Have a Good Disposition, 30, 31. 2003. (Saddle Up Ser.: Vol. 31). (Illus.). 42p. (J). lib. bdg. 22.60 (978-1-56763-691-8(8)) Ozark Publishing.

Satrapi, Marjane. Monsters Are Afraid of the Moon. 2006. (Illus.). 32p. (J). 15.95 (978-1-58234-744-8(1) , Bloomsbury Children) Bloomsbury Publishing.

Schaefer, Lola M. Frankie Stein. Atteberry, Kevan, illus. 2007. 32p. (J). (ps-2). 16.99 (***978-0-7614-5358-1(X)***) Cavendish, Marshall Corp.

Schaefer, Lola M. Out of the Night. Gilbert, Rob, illus. 1999. 32p. (ps-k). pap. 6.95 (978-1-58089-023-6(7)) Charlesbridge Publishing, Inc.

Schecter, Ellen. Murky Monster's Birthday Bash. Ulrich, George, illus. 1999. (Bank Street Ready-to-Read Ser.). (J). trans. 20.01 (978-0-553-37588-6(1)) Bantam Bks.

Schnitzlein, Danny. The Monster Who Ate My Peas. Faulkner, Matt, illus. 2001. 32p. (J). (gr. k-3). 15.95 (978-1-56145-216-3(5) , Q32689) Peachtree Pubs., Ltd.

Schnitzlein, Danny. The Monster Who Did My Math. Mayer, Bill, illus. 2007. 32p. (J). (gr. 1-5). 16.95 (***978-1-56145-420-4(6)*** , Peachtree Junior) Peachtree Pubs., Ltd.

Scholastic, Inc. Staff. Attack of the Baby Godzillas No. 2: Picture Book. 1998. (Godzilla Ser.). (Illus.). 32p. (J). (gr. k-3). pap. 3.50 (978-0-590-68112-4(5)) Scholastic, Inc.

—Eduardo Goes Extreme. 2007. (Foster's Home for Imaginary Friends Ser.: No. 1). 24p. (J). pap. 3.99 (***978-0-439-88560-7(4)***) Scholastic, Inc.

—Godzilla: A Novelization. novel ed. 1998. (Godzilla Ser.). (Illus.). 152p. (J). (gr. 3-7). pap. 3.99 (978-0-590-28243-7(3)) Scholastic, Inc.

—Godzillas Scrapbook. 1998. (Godzilla Ser.). 32p. (J). (gr. 2-5). pap. 7.98 (978-0-590-57239-2(3)) Scholastic, Inc.

—Picture Book No. 1. 1998. (Godzilla Ser.). 32p. (J). (gr. k-3). pap. 3.50 (978-0-590-57212-5(1)) Scholastic, Inc.

—Shrek Color & Activity: (Bilingual) Salas, Macarena, ed. 2004. (Shrek Ser.). (SPA.). 80p. (J). 2.99 (978-0-439-63201-0(3) , Scholastic en Espanol) Scholastic, Inc.

Scholastic, Inc. Staff. Snow Fun. 2007. (Care Bears Ser.). 24p. (J). pap. 3.99 (***978-0-545-01310-9(0)***) Scholastic, Inc.

Scholastic, Inc. Staff & Dewin, Howie. Sleeping Ugly. 2004. (Shrek Ser.). (SPA., Illus.). 64p. (J). pap. 3.99 (978-0-439-63199-0(8) , Scholastic en Espanol) Scholastic, Inc.

Schooley, Bob. Kim Possible Cine-Manga: Sink or Swim & Number One, 9 vols., Vol. 6. McCorkle, Mark, illus. 2004. 96p. pap. 7.99 (978-1-59182-569-2(5) , Tokyopop Kids) TOKYOPOP, Inc.

Seabrooke, Brenda. The Vampire in My Bathtub. 1999. 160p. (J). (gr. 4-6). tchr. ed. 16.95 (978-0-8234-1505-2(8)) Holiday Hse., Inc.

The Secret of the Monster Book, 6 vols., Vol. 2. (Woodland Mysteriestm Ser.). 133p. (gr. 3-7). 42.50 (978-0-7802-7933-9(6)) Wright Group, The.

Selick, Henry. Moongirl: With DVD. Chan, Peter & Booker, Courtney, illus. gif. ed. 2006. 48p. (J). (ps-2). 22.99 incl. DVD (978-0-7636-3068-3(3)) Candlewick Pr.

Selznick, Brian. Boy of a Thousand Faces. 2000. (gr. 3-6). lib. bdg. 15.30 (978-0-613-44191-9(5)) Tandem Library Bks.

Sendak, Maurice. Donde Viven los Monstruos. 2003. (SPA., Illus.). 40p. (J). (gr. k-3). 12.95 (978-84-372-2185-4(4)) Altea, Ediciones, S.A. - Grupo Santillana ESP. *Dist:* Santillana USA Publishing Co., Inc.

—Donde Viven los Monstruos. Mlawer, Teresa, tr. 2001. (SPA., Illus.). (J). 7.96 net. (978-1-56137-544-8(6) , NU5725) Novel Units, Inc.

—Monsters in Space. 2003. (gr. k-3). lib. bdg. 11.80 (978-0-613-68264-0(5)) Tandem Library Bks.

—Where the Wild Things Are. Sendak, Maurice, illus. 2002. (Illus.). (J). 16.60 (978-0-7587-0028-5(8)) Book Wholesalers, Inc.

—Where the Wild Things Are. 1998. (J). 16.95 (978-0-06-028223-3(1)) HarperCollins Pubs.

—Where the Wild Things Are. 1999. (J). 9.95 (978-1-56137-022-1(3)) Novel Units, Inc.

—Where the Wild Things Are. (J). pap. 12.95 incl. audio Weston Woods Studios, Inc.

—Wo die Wilden Kerle Wohnen. 2000. Tr. of Where the Wild Things Are. (GER.). (J). pap. 15.95 (978-3-257-25105-0(X)) Diogenes Verlag AG CHE. *Dist:* Distribooks, Inc.

Sensel, Joni. The Garbage Monster. Bivins, Christopher, illus. 2003. 24p. (J). (ps up). 14.95 (978-0-9701195-2-0(6)) Dream Factory Bks.

Sesame Street Staff & Stone, Jon. The Monster at the End of This Book. Smollin, Michael, illus. 2003. (Popular Characters/Author Collection). 24p. (J). (gr. k-k). 2.99 (978-0-307-01085-8(6) , Golden Bks.) Random Hse. Children's Bks.

Sesame Street Storybook COLL 2. 2007. 10.99 (***978-1-4037-3614-7(6)***) Dalmatian Pr.

Sesame Workshop Staff & SoftPlay (Firm) Staff, contrib. by. Happy Families in Elmo's World. 2002. (Elmo's World Ser.). (Illus.). (J). (978-1-931312-47-9(8)) SoftPlay, Inc.

Sfar, Joann. Little Vampire Does Kung Fu! Sfar, Joann, illus. 2003. (Illus.). 40p. (J). 12.95 (978-0-689-85769-0(1)) Simon & Schuster Children's Publishing.

Shannon, Margaret. Gullible's Troubles. (Illus.). 32p. (J). (gr. k-3). 2000. pap. 5.95 (978-0-618-07033-6(8)); 1998. tchr. ed. 15.00 (978-0-395-83933-1(5)) Houghton Mifflin Co. Trade & Reference Div.

—Gullible's Troubles. 2000. (J). (978-0-606-19424-2(X)) Tandem Library Bks.

Sharkey, Niamh. Ravenous Beast. 2003. (Illus.). 32p. (J). (ps-1). 17.99 (978-0-7636-2182-7(X)) Candlewick Pr.

Sharmat, Marjorie Weinman. Nate the Great & the Monster Mess. Weston, Martha, illus. 2001. (Nate the Great Ser.). 80p. (J). (gr. 1-4). pap. 4.50 (978-0-440-41662-3(0) , Yearling) Random Hse. Children's Bks.

—Nate the Great & the Monster Mess. 2001. (978-0-606-22399-7(1)); (gr. 3-6). lib. bdg. 12.40 (978-0-613-36847-6(9)) Tandem Library Bks.

Shelley, Mary Wollstonecraft. Frankenstein. Pablo Marcos Studio Staff, illus. 2002. (Great Illustrated Classics Ser.). 240p. (J). (gr. 3-8). 21.35 (978-1-57765-686-9(5) , ABDO & Daughters) ABDO Publishing Co.

—Frankenstein. Cruz, Nardo, illus. 2005. 48p. (gr. 5-8). 25.50 (978-0-7910-9100-5(7)) Facts On File, Inc.

—Frankenstein. 1999. (Saddleback Classics). (Illus.). (J). 13.75 (978-0-606-21551-0(4)) Tandem Library Bks.

—Frankenstein. Akib, Jamel, illus. 2006. (Classic Starts Ser.). 160p. (J). 4.95 (978-1-4027-2666-8(X)) Sterling Publishing Co., Inc.

—Frankenstein: Or the Modern Prometheus. Joseph, M. K., ed. 1998. (Oxford World's Classics Ser.). 260p. (gr. 7 up). 7.95 (978-0-19-283487-4(8)) Oxford Univ. Pr., Inc.

—Frankenstein: With a Discussion of Tolerance. Clift, Eva, tr. Clift, Eva, illus. 2003. (Values in Action Illustrated Classics Ser.). (J). (978-1-59203-048-4(3)) Learning Challenge, Inc.

Shelley, Mary Wollstonecraft & Grant, J. Frankenstein. 144p. (J). lib. bdg. 12.95 (978-1-58086-667-5(0) , Usborne) EDC Publishing.

Sherrill, Rusty & Miers, Doug. Kid Nitro & the Sinister Slorp. Sherrill, Cathy, ed. Sherrill, Rusty, illus. 2007. (Illus.). 273p. (YA). per. 14.95 (***978-0-9787729-0-1(3)***) RS Art Studio.

Shi, Sharon. Monsters Get Scared Too. Jensen, Keli, illus. rev. ed. 2000. 24p. (J). mass mkt. 4.99 (978-0-9678636-8-9(6) , B009, Tattooties Bks.) Tattoo Manufacturing.

Shook, Karl. The Family Thing. 2004. 166p. (YA). pap. 12.95 (978-0-595-31121-7(0)) iUniverse, Inc.

Shopping, 6 Packs. (Sails Literacy Ser.). 16p. (gr. k up). 27.00 (978-0-7635-4422-5(1)) Rigby Education.

Shortsleeve, Kevin. 13 Monsters Who Should Be Avoided. Austin, Michael, illus. 1998. 32p. (J). (gr. 1-5). 16.95 (978-1-56145-146-3(0)) Peachtree Pubs., Ltd.

Sierra, Judy. The Gruesome Guide to World Monsters. Drescher, Henrik, illus. 2005. 64p. (J). (gr. 1-ps). 18.99 (978-0-7636-1727-1(X)) Candlewick Pr.

—The House That Drac Built. Hillenbrand, Will, illus. 1998. 32p. (J). (ps-2). pap. 7.00 (978-0-15-201879-5(4) , Harcourt Paperbacks) Harcourt Children's Bks.

—The House That Drac Built. Hillenbrand, Will, illus. 1998. (J). (ps-ps). lib. bdg. 14.15 (978-0-613-09949-3(4)) Tandem Library Bks.

—Thelonius Monster's Sky-High Fly-Pie. Koren, Edward, illus. 2006. 40p. (J). (ps-3). 16.95 (978-0-375-83218-5(1)); lib. bdg. 18.99 (978-0-375-93218-2(6)) Random Hse. Children's Bks. (Knopf Bks. for Young Readers).

Simone, Gail. Gus Beezer with the Hulk. 2006. (Marvelous Adventures of Gus Beezer Ser.). (Illus.). (J). (gr. 2-6). 21.35 (978-1-59961-049-8(3)) Spotlight.

Simonson, Louise. Extreme Monsters Battling Bigfoot. Elston, James W., illus. 2007. 96p. (J). (gr. 2-5). pap. 3.99 (978-1-57791-275-0(6) , Penny Candy Pr.) Brighter Minds Children's Publishing.

—Extreme Monsters Chapter, Vol. 3. Elston, James W., illus. gif. ed. 2006. 96p. (J). per. 3.99 (978-1-57791-255-2(1)) Brighter Minds Children's Publishing.

—What's with Wulf? Elston, James W., illus. gif. ed. 2005. 96p. (J). (gr. 2-5). per. 3.99 (978-1-57791-179-1(2)) Brighter Minds Children's Publishing.

Slade, Arthur G. Monsterology: The Fabulous Lives of the Creepy, the Revolting, & the Undead. Mah, Derek, illus. 2005. 96p. (J). (gr. 4-7). pap. 8.95 (978-0-88776-714-2(1)) Tundra Bks., Inc./Livres Toundra, Inc. CAN. *Dist:* Random Hse., Inc.

Slater, Dashka & Chien, Catia. The Sea Serpent & Me. Slater, Dashka & Chien, Catia, illus. 2008. 40p. (J). (gr. 3-5). 17.00 (***978-0-618-72394-2(3)***) Houghton Mifflin Co.

Smith, Todd Aaron. Riley O'Smiley. 2006. (Illus.). 32p. (J). 12.99 (978-1-4003-0818-7(6)) Nelson, Thomas Inc.

Sniegoski, Thomas E. Leviathan. 2003. (gr. 7-12). lib. bdg. 14.15 (978-0-613-66516-2(3)) Tandem Library Bks.

Snow, Alan. Here Be Monsters! Snow, Alan, illus. (Ratbridge Chronicles Ser.). 544p. (J). (gr. 3-9). 2007. pap. 8.99 (978-0-689-87048-4(5) , Aladdin); 2006. (Illus.). 17.95 (978-0-689-87047-7(7) , Atheneum) Simon & Schuster Children's Publishing.

Snow, Jeff. Beasts in the Closet. Snow, Jeff, illus. 2006. (Illus.). 32p. (J). 17.95 (978-1-932362-11-4(8)) Snowbound Pr., Inc.

Something Is There & Other Stories: Individual Title Six-Pack. (Story Steps Ser.). (gr. k-2). 48.00 (978-0-7635-9828-0(3)) Rigby Education.

Space Monster Saves the Day. 2007. (J). per. (***978-1-932570-61-8(6)***) Literacy Footprints Inc.

Space Monster's Birthday Party. 2005. (J). (978-1-932570-30-4(6)) Literacy Footprints Inc.

Spaht-Gill, Janie. Monster Stew. Reese, Bob, illus. (J). 5.95 (978-0-89868-307-3(6)) ARO Publishing Co.

Spencely, Annabel, illus. The Kingfisher Treasury of Monster Stories, Vol. 7. 2003. (Kingfisher Treasury of Stories Ser.). 164p. (J). (gr. k-3). pap. 5.95 (978-0-7534-5667-5(2) , Kingfisher) Houghton Mifflin Co. Trade & Reference Div.

Spinelli, Eileen. Wanda's Monster. Hayashi, Nancy, illus. 2002. 32p. (J). (gr. k-3). 15.95 (978-0-8075-8656-3(0)); pap. 6.95 (978-0-8075-8657-0(9)) Whitman, Albert & Co.

Spinner, Stephanie. Monster in the Maze: The Story of the Minotaur. 2000. (All Aboard Reading Ser.). (Illus.). (J). (978-0-606-20404-0(0)) Tandem Library Bks.

Springer, Nancy. Dusssie. 2007. 176p. (J). (gr. 5-9). 16.95 (***978-0-8027-9649-3(4)***) Walker & Co.

St-Aubin, Bruno. My Favorite Monster. 2005. (Read-It! Readers Ser.). (Illus.). 32p. (J). (gr. k-3). 18.60 (978-1-4048-1029-7(3)) Picture Window Bks.

St. Aubin, Bruno & Homel, David. My Favourite Monster. 2000. (Illus.). 32p. (J). (gr. 1-4). pap. (978-1-894363-41-9(8)) Dominique & Friends.

Stamper, Judith Bauer. Monster Phonics: Monster Town. 1998. (Hello Reader! Ser.). (J). (gr. 1-2). (978-0-606-13619-8(3)) Tandem Library Bks.

Stamper, Judith Bauer & Blevins, Wiley. Monster Town Fair. Evans, Nate, illus. 1998. (Hello Reader! Ser.). 160p. (J). (gr. 1-2). pap. 3.99 (978-0-590-76268-7(0)) Scholastic, Inc.

Staunton, Ted. The Monkey Mountain Monster. Lafontaine, Roger, illus. 2004. (Monkey Mountain Bks.). 64p. (J). (gr. 2-5). pap. 4.95 (978-0-88995-206-5(X)) Red Deer Pr. CAN. *Dist:* Fitzhenry & Whiteside, Ltd.

Steer, Dugald. Snappy Little Halloween. Matthews, Derek, illus. 2004. 20p. (J). (gr. k-4). reprint ed. 13.00 (978-0-7567-7403-5(9)) DIANE Publishing Co.

Steig, William. Shrek! Steig, William, illus. 2002. (Illus.). (J). 14.43 (978-0-7587-3617-8(7)) Book Wholesalers, Inc.

—Shrek! Steig, William, illus. (Illus.). 2005. (J). pap. 18.95 incl. audio compact disk (978-1-59112-328-6(3)); 1998. pap. 35.95 incl. audio compact disk (978-1-59112-551-8(0)) Live Oak Media.

—Shrek! 1998. (Illus.). pap., tchr. ed. 33.95 incl. audio (978-0-87499-456-8(X)); (J). pap. 16.95 incl. audio (978-0-87499-454-4(3)) Live Oak Media.

Stein, David Ezra. Monster Hug! 2007. (Illus.). 40p. (J). (ps-2). 15.99 (***978-0-399-24637-1(1)*** , Putnam Juvenile) Penguin Group (USA) Inc.

Stein, Mathilde. Monstersong. Linden, Gerdien van der, illus. 2007. 32p. (J). 15.95 (978-1-932425-90-1(X) , Lemniscaat) Boyds Mills Pr.

Stevenson, Robert Louis. Dr. Jekyll & Mr. Hyde: And Other Stories of the Supernatural. 2006. (Scholastic Classics Ser.). iv, 143p. (J). (gr. 9-12). 25.00 (978-0-531-16985-8(5) , Watts, Franklin) Scholastic Library Publishing.

Stewart, Joel. Dexter Bexley & the Big Blue Beastie. Stewart, Joel, illus. 2007. (Illus.). 32p. (J). (ps-3). 16.95 (***978-0-8234-2068-1(X)***) Holiday Hse., Inc.

Stimson, James. Thirteen O'Clock. 2005. (Illus.). 40p. (J). 15.95 (978-0-8118-4839-8(6)) Chronicle Bks. LLC.

Stine, R. L. The Blob That Ate Everyone. 2006. (Goosebumps Ser.). 144p. (J). pap. 4.99 (978-0-439-79619-4(9) , Scholastic Paperbacks) Scholastic, Inc.

—Como Matar a un Monstruo. 2004. (Goosebumps Ser.).Tr. of How to Kill a Monster. (SPA.). 128p. (gr. 4-7). mass mkt. 4.99 (978-0-439-67052-4(7) , Scholastic Paperbacks) Scholastic, Inc.

—The Girl Who Cried Monster. 2005. 137p. (J). (ps-7). 12.04 (978-0-606-33299-6(5)) Tandem Library Bks.

—Goosebumps: The Girl Who Cried Monster. 2005. (Goosebumps Ser.). 144p. pap. 4.99 (978-0-439-69353-0(5) , Scholastic Paperbacks) Scholastic, Inc.

—How to Kill a Monster. 2005. (Goosebumps Ser.). 144p. (J). pap. 1.99 (978-0-439-79629-3(6) , Scholastic Paperbacks) Scholastic, Inc.

—Monster Blood. 2003. (Goosebumps Ser.). 144p. (J). pap. 4.99 (978-0-439-56839-5(0) , 53655433, Scholastic Paperbacks) Scholastic, Inc.

—Monster Blood. 2003. (gr. 3-6). lib. bdg. 13.00 (978-0-613-67466-9(9)) Tandem Library Bks.

M N O

—Monster Blood II. rev. ed. 2004. (Goosebumps Ser.). 144p. (J). (gr. 4-7). 4.99 (978-0-439-66988-7(X) , Scholastic Paperbacks) Scholastic, Inc.
—Monster Blood III. 2007. (Goosebumps Ser.). 144p. (J). pap. 4.99 (978-0-439-89112-7(4)) Scholastic, Inc.
—The Werewolf in the Living Room. 1999. (Goosebumps Series 2000: No. 17). 112p. (J). (gr. 3-7). pap. 3.99 (978-0-590-68521-4(X)) Scholastic, Inc.
—You Can't Scare Me! 2005. (Goosebumps Ser.). 144p. (J). pap. 1.99 (978-0-439-79636-1(9) , Scholastic Paperbacks) Scholastic, Inc.
Stone, Jon. Another Monster at the End of This Book. Smollin, Michael, illus. 2000. (Big Bird's Favorites Board Bks.). 24p. (J). (gr. k-ps). bds. 4.99 (978-0-375-80562-2(1) , Random Hse. Bks. for Young Readers) Random Hse. Children's Bks.
—The Monster at the End of This Book. Smollin, Michael, illus. 2004. 32p. (J). (gr. k-k). 8.99 (978-0-375-82913-0(X)); lib. bdg. 10.99 (978-0-375-92913-7(4)) Random Hse. Children's Bks. (Golden Bks.).
—The Monster at the End of This Book: Starring Lovable, Furry Old Grover. Smollin, Mike, illus. 2000. (Big Bird's Favorites Board Bks.). 24p. (J). (gr. k-ps). bds. 4.99 (978-0-375-80561-5(3) , Random Hse. Bks. for Young Readers) Random Hse. Children's Bks.
Stowell, Louie. Beauty & the Beast. Tavares, Victor, illus. 2007. 64p. (J). 8.99 (978-0-7945-1456-3(1) , Usborne) EDC Publishing.
Strachan, Linda. Serach for Loch Ness Monster. 2005. (Illus.). 32p. pap. 9.00 (978-0-9546701-5-3(9)) GW Publishing GBR. *Dist:* Wilson & Assocs.
Stuby, Tim, illus. Extreme Monsters Joke Book. gif. ed. 2005. 96p. (J). (gr. 2-5). per. 3.99 (978-1-57791-181-4(4)) Brighter Minds Children's Publishing.
Suarez, Sergio Lopez. Huakala! a los Miedos. Suarez, Sergio Lopez, illus. 2003. (SPA., Illus.). 32p. (J). (gr. k-3). 9.95 (978-968-19-0556-9(3)) Aguilar, Altea, Taurus, Alfaguara, S.A. de C.V MEX. *Dist:* Santillana USA Publishing Co., Inc.
—Huakala! a los Miedos. 2000. (SPA.). 32p. (J). (ps-3). 15.95 (978-84-204-4936-4(9)) Alfaguara, Ediciones, S.A.- Grupo Santillana ESP. *Dist:* Santillana USA Publishing Co., Inc.
Svendsen, Mark. Circus Carnivore. Redlich, Ben, illus. 2006. 40p. (J). (gr. 3-5). 16.00 (978-0-618-56328-9(8)) Houghton Mifflin Co. Trade & Reference Div.
Sweeney, Jacqueline. Pond Monster. 2001. (We Can Read! Ser.). (Illus.). 32p. (J). (gr. 1-2). lib. bdg. 21.36 (978-0-7614-1123-9(2) , Benchmark Bks.) Cavendish, Marshall Corp.
Tadjo, Veronique. Mamy Wata & the Monster. (Illus.). 24p. 2005. (ARA, ENG, VIE, CHI & BEN.). pap. 9.95 (978-1-84059-264-1(8)); 2000. (GER, ENG, VIE, CHI & ARA., (J). pap. 9.95 (978-1-84059-268-9(0)); 2000. (GUJ, ENG, VIE, CHI & ARA., (J). pap. 9.95 (978-1-84059-269-6(9)); 2000. (SOM, ENG, VIE, CHI & ARA., (J). pap. 9.95 (978-1-84059-270-2(2)); 2000. (TUR, ENG, VIE, CHI & ARA., (J). pap. 9.95 (978-1-84059-271-9(0)); 2000. (J). pap. 7.95 (978-1-84059-263-4(X)); 2000. (BEN, ENG, VIE, CHI & ARA., (J). pap. 9.95 (978-1-84059-265-8(6)); 2000. (CHI, ENG, VIE, ARA & BEN., (J). pap. 9.95 (978-1-84059-266-5(4)) Milet Publishing.
—Mamy Wata & the Monster. Iqbal, Gulshan, tr. 2000. (Veronique Tadjo Ser.). (URD, ENG, VIE, CHI & ARA., Illus.). 24p. (J). pap. 9.95 (978-1-84059-272-6(9)) Milet Publishing.
—Mamy Wata & the Monster. Wood, Kim Marie, tr. 2000. (Veronique Tadjo Ser.). (VIE, ENG, CHI, ARA & BEN., Illus.). 24p. (J). pap. 9.95 (978-1-84059-273-3(7)) Milet Publishing.
Tagg, Christine. Who Will You Meet on Scary Street? Nine Pop-up Nightmares! Fuge, Charles, illus. 2004. 20p. (J). reprint ed. 15.00 (978-0-7567-8003-6(9)) DIANE Publishing Co.
Takada, Yuzo. Curse of the Gesu. 2nd ed. 2003. (3 X 3 Eyes Ser.). (Illus.). 152p. (YA). (gr. 12 up). pap. 14.95 (978-1-56971-931-2(4)) Dark Horse Comics.
Takahashi, Kazuki. Monster World. Takahashi, Kazuki, illus. 2004. (Illus.). 200p. lib. bdg. 18.55 (978-1-4176-5898-5(3)) Tandem Library Bks.
Taylor, Sean. When a Monster Is Born. Sharratt, Nick, illus. 2007. 32p. (J). (ps-1). 16.95 (*978-1-59643-254-3(3)) Roaring Brook Pr.
Teague, Mark. Field Beyond the Outfield. 2006. (Illus.). 40p. (J). pap. 5.99 (978-0-439-81215-3(1) , Scholastic Pr.) Scholastic, Inc.
Thach, James Otis. A Child's Guide to Common Household Monsters. Udovic, David, illus. 2007. 32p. (J). (ps-1). 16.95 (*978-1-932425-58-1(6) , Front Street) Boyds Mills Pr.
Thaler, Mike. The Halloween Party from the Black Lagoon. Lee, Jared D., illus. 2004. (Little Apple Ser.). 64p. (J). pap. (978-0-439-68075-2(1)) Scholastic, Inc.
—Teacher from the Black Lagoon. Lee Jared, illus. 2006. (Scholastic Reader Collection Level 3 Ser.). 144p. (J). pap. 6.99 (978-0-439-84803-9(2) , Cartwheel Bks.) Scholastic, Inc.
—The Teacher from the Black Lagoon. Lee, Jared D., illus. unabr. ed. 2006. (J). 9.95 (978-0-439-87590-5(0)) Scholastic, Inc.
Thaler, Mike. Valentine's Day from the Black Lagoon. Lee, Jared D., illus. 2006. 64p. (J). lib. bdg. 15.00 (*978-1-4242-2263-6(X)) Fitzgerald Bks.
There's a Monster under the Sheets. 2004. (J). pap. 8.00 (978-0-8059-6461-5(4)) Dorrance Publishing Co., Inc.
Thomas, Frances. Little Monster's Book of Numbers. Collins, Ross, illus. 2005. 10p. (J). (ps-k). bds. 5.95 (978-1-58234-979-4(7)) Bloomsbury Publishing.
—Little Monster's Book of Opposites. Collins, Ross, illus. 2005. 10p. (J). (ps-k). bds. 5.95 (978-1-58234-980-0(0)) Bloomsbury Publishing.
Thomassie, Tynia. Feliciana Feydra LeRoux Meets d'Loup Garou: A Cajun Tall Tale. Smith, Cat Bowman, illus. 1998. 32p. (J). (ps-3). 15.95 (978-0-316-84133-7(1)) Little Brown & Co.
—Feliciana Meets D'Loup Garou: A Cajun Tall Tale. Bowman Smith, Cat, illus. 2005. 32p. (J). (ps-3). 15.95 (978-1-58980-287-2(X)) Pelican Publishing Co., Inc.
Thompson, B. B. Strangetales: A Book of Beginning. Cuce, Thomas A. & Sutphin, Eric, illus. 2002. (Strangetales Ser.). 172p. pap. 4.95 (978-0-9725614-0-2(4)) Tricorner Publishing.
Thompson, Jill. Scary Godmother. 2005. (Illus.). 48p. pap. 9.95 (978-1-57989-070-4(9)) Sirius Entertainment, Inc.
—Scary Godmother: The Revenge of Jimmy. 2006. (Illus.). 48p. pap. 9.95 (978-1-57989-071-1(7)) Sirius Entertainment, Inc.
Thompson, Jill, creator. Scary Godmother: The Mystery Date. 2004. (Illus.). 48p. pap. 9.95 (978-1-57989-072-8(5)) Sirius Entertainment, Inc.
Tich, Jan. Quien es ese monstruo? y ese Otro? Bilotti, Viviana, illus. 2005. (SPA.). 28p. (J). 14.95 (978-84-96448-00-1(2)) Hardenville SA URY. *Dist:* Independent Pubs. Group.
—Who Is That Monster? And That One? McGrail, Efe, tr. 2006. (Illus.). 28p. (J). pap. 12.95 (978-9974-7925-1-7(7)) Hardenville SA URY. *Dist:* Independent Pubs. Group.
Todd, Barbara. Roger Gets Carried Away. Roge, illus. 2005. 32p. (J). (ps-2). pap. 7.95 (978-1-55037-898-6(8)); lib. bdg. 19.95 (978-1-55037-899-3(6)) Annick Pr., Ltd. CAN. *Dist:* Firefly Bks., Ltd.
Top That Publishing Staff, ed. Mini Monsters. 2005. (Illus.). 24p. pap. (978-1-84510-159-6(6)) Top That! Publishing PLC.
Torres, J. Mucho Monsters. Benton, Jim, illus. 2006. (Franny K. Stein, Mad Scientist Ser.). 64p. (J). pap. 3.99 (978-1-4169-2528-6(7) , Simon Scribbles) Simon & Schuster Children's Publishing.
Torrey, Michele. Doyle & Fossey Science Detectives: Case of the Mossy Lake Monster. Newman, Barbara, illus. 2002. 112p. (J). (gr. 3-6). 14.99 (978-0-525-46815-8(3) , Dutton Juvenile) Penguin Group (USA) Inc.
Toy Box Innovations Staff, creator. Disney Pixar: Finding Nemo/A Bug's Life/Monsters, Inc. unabr. abr. ed. 2005. (Disney's Read along Collection). (J). audio compact disk 14.99 (978-0-7634-1151-0(5)) Walt Disney Records.
ToyBox Innovations, creator. Disney's Monsters Inc. 2006. (Disney's Read Along Ser.). (Illus.). 24p. (J). audio, audio compact disk 7.99 (978-0-7634-2175-5(8)) Walt Disney Records.
Trayer, Edward H. Struggles of Felicity Brady: Articulus Quest. 2005. (YA). per. 14.95 (978-1-59571-091-8(4)) Word Association Pubs.
Trondheim, Lewis. Harum Scarum: The Spiffy Adventures of McConey, Vol. 1. (Illus.). 48p. (gr. 10 up). pap. 10.95 (978-1-56097-288-4(2)) Fantagraphics Bks.
Tunnell, Michael O. Halloween Pie. Highlights Staff, ed. Omalley, Kevin, illus. 2004. 32p. (J). (gr. k-2). pap. 9.95 (978-1-59078-250-7(X)) Boyds Mills Pr.
Tyrrell, Melissa. Beauty & the Beast. McMullen, Nigel, illus. 2005. (Fairytale Friends Ser.). 12p. (J). bds. 5.95 (978-1-58117-153-2(6) , Intervisual/Piggy Toes) Dalmatian Pr.
Uram, Maggie. Good Night Good Knight. 2004. (Illus.). 39p. (J). per. (978-1-932077-38-4(3)) Athena Pr.
Urasawa, Naoki. Naoki Urasawa's Monster. 2006. (Naoki Urasawa's Monster Ser.). (YA). 208p. pap. 9.99 (978-1-4215-0255-7(0)); Vol. 2. 216p. pap. 9.99 (978-1-4215-0112-3(0)); Vol. 4. 208p. pap. 9.99 (978-1-4215-0385-1(9)) Viz Media.
—Naoki Urasawa's Monster, Volume 1 Vol. 1: Herr Dr Tenma. Urasawa, Naoki, illus. 2006. (Monster Ser.). 224p. (YA). pap. 9.99 (978-1-59116-641-2(1)) Viz Media.
Ure, Jean. Monster in the Mirror. 2000. (Illus.). 64p. (J). pap. 7.99 (978-0-00-675531-9(3) , Collins) HarperCollins Pubs. Ltd. GBR. *Dist:* Independent Pubs. Group.
Vallejo-Nagera, Alejandra. Los Cazadores de Monstruos. (SPA.). 32p. (J). 10.95 (978-84-204-4955-5(5)) Alfaguara, Ediciones, S.A.- Grupo Santillana ESP. *Dist:* Santillana USA Publishing Co., Inc.
Van der Meer, Mara. How Many Monsters? A Monster Counting Book. (Illus.). (J). (ps-3). 2001. 24p. pap. 8.99 (978-0-7112-1500-9(6)); 2000. 35p. 19.99 (978-0-7112-1499-6(9)) Lincoln, Frances Ltd. GBR. *Dist:* Transition Vendor, Antique Collectors' Club.
Van Leeuwen, Jean. Amanda Pig & the Awful, Scary Monster. Schweninger, Ann, illus. 2003. (Easy-to-Read Ser.: Vol. 2). 48p. (J). (ps). 13.99 (978-0-8037-2766-3(6) , Dial) Penguin Group (USA) Inc.
Vestergaard, Hope. What Do You Do— When a Monster Says Boo? Smith, Maggie, illus. 2006. 32p. (J). (ps-1). 15.99 (978-0-525-47737-2(3) , Dutton Juvenile) Penguin Group (USA) Inc.
Wackwitz, Winnie. The Creature of Lost Bayou. 2004. (YA). pap. 12.95 (978-1-58752-107-2(5)) Timberwolf Pr., Inc.
Waldron, Jan L. John Pig's Halloween. 2001. (gr. 3-6). lib. bdg. 15.30 (978-0-613-58416-6(3)) Tandem Library Bks.
Warren, Celia. A Big Surprise, 4 vols. 2005. (Illus.). 24p. (J). (gr. 1-4). lib. bdg. 15.95 (978-1-59566-092-3(5)) QEB Publishing Inc.
Washer, S. N. The Wingate Adventures: Our New Friends. 2006. 164p. pap. 11.95 (978-1-59800-510-3(3)) Outskirts Press, Inc.
Wasserman, Robin. Unfabulous: Meltdown. 2006. (Teenick Ser.). 128p. (J). pap. 4.99 (978-0-439-84873-2(3)) Scholastic, Inc.
Watson, T. E. The Monster in the Mailbox. Lancaster, Mari & Lancaster, Linus, illus. 2002. 32p. (J). (gr. 2-6). 16.95 (978-1-58478-011-3(8) , Paw Prints Pr.) Heather & Highlands Publishing.
Weare, Tim. Hide-and-Seek with Leo. 2001. (Hand Puppet Board Bks.). (Illus.). 10p. (J). (ps). pap., bds. 14.95 (978-0-439-29719-6(2) , Cartwheel Bks.) Scholastic, Inc.
Webb, Philip, illus. The Monster Town: Individual Title Six-Packs. (Sails Literacy Ser.). 16p. (gr. k up). 27.00 (978-0-7635-4419-5(1)) Rigby Education.
Weinberg, Larry. Frankenstein. 2000. (Golden Star Reader Ser.). (Illus.). (J). 10.79 (978-0-606-18854-8(1)) Tandem Library Bks.
Wellington, Stanley. Where Monsters Hide. 2003. 223p. (YA). per. 16.95 (978-1-59196-384-4(2)); 2nd ed. 2004. 237p. per. 17.95 (978-1-59196-481-0(4)) Instantpublisher.com.
West, Tracey. Bubblevision. 2001. (gr. k-3). lib. bdg. 11.25 (978-0-613-43799-8(3)) Tandem Library Bks.
—Pop Goes the Monster! Alger, Bill, illus. 2001. (Powerpuff Girls Ser.). 6p. (J). (gr. 4). 12.95 (978-0-439-30548-8(9)) Scholastic, Inc.
Westerfeld, Scott. The Last Days. 2007. 304p. (YA). (gr. 9-12). pap. 8.99 (978-1-59514-128-6(6) , Razorbill) Penguin Group (USA) Inc.
Weyn, Suzanne. Monsters Unleashed: Junior Novelization. movie tie-in novel ed. 2004. (Scooby-Doo Ser.). (Illus.). 128p. (J). pap. 4.99 (978-0-439-56755-8(6) , Scholastic Paperbacks) Scholastic, Inc.
Where the Wild Things Are. 2005. (J). (978-1-59564-831-0(3)) Steps To Literacy, LLC.
Whitfield, Dwight K. King Shaka's Fierce Battle on the Little Umkosi. Whitfield, Joseph, illus. 2000. 32p. (J). (gr. 1-7). pap. (978-0-9706671-0-6(8)) Sandwight Publishing Co.
Wickstrom, Lois June & Lorrah, Jean. Nessie & the Living Stone. Strand, Sara Silvestri, illus. 2001. (J). pap. 13.80 (978-1-58338-616-3(5) , CrossroadsPub.Org) CrossroadsPub.com.
Willems, Mo. Leonardo, the Terrible Monster. 2005. (Illus.). 44p. (J). (ps-1). 16.99 (978-0-7868-5294-9(1)) Hyperion Pr.
Williams, Harland. The Kid with Too Many Nightmares. 2006. (Illus.). 32p. (J). (ps-2). pap. 3.99 (978-0-448-44365-2(1) , Grosset & Dunlap) Penguin Group (USA) Inc.
Williams, Harland, illus. The Kid with Too Many Nightmares. 2004. (J). (978-0-8431-1582-6(3) , Price Stern Sloan) Penguin Group (USA) Inc.
Williams, Rozanne Lanczak. Little Monster Becomes an Author. Maio, Barbara, ed. Hefferan, Rob, illus. 2006. (J). per. 6.99 (*978-1-59198-349-1(5)) Creative Teaching Pr., Inc.
Willis, Jeanne. The Monster Bed. Varley, Susan, illus. 2007. 32p. (J). pap. 9.95 (978-1-84270-222-2(X)) Andersen GBR. *Dist:* Independent Pubs. Group.
—Monster Bed. 1999. (J). (978-0-606-17392-6(7)) Tandem Library Bks.
—La Tormenta Monstruosa. (Cotton Cloud Ser.). (SPA.). (J). (gr. 1-3). pap. (978-84-480-0180-3(X)) Timun Mas, Editorial S.A. ESP. *Dist:* Lectorum Pubns., Inc.
Willis, Jeanne & Varley, Susan. The Monster Bed. 1999. (Illus.). 32p. (J). (ps-3). mass mkt. 5.95 (978-0-688-16707-3(1) , Harper Trophy) HarperCollins Pubs.
Willis, Meredith Sue. Marco's Monster. 2nd ed. 2001. 118p. (J). pap. 7.95 (978-0-9674477-5-9(5)) Montemayor Pr.
Wilson, F. Paul. The Christmas Thingy. Clark, Alan M., illus. 2000. 32p. (J). 20.00 (978-1-58767-031-2(3)) Cemetery Dance Pubns.
Windsor, Jo. The Monsters of Burwood: Individual Title Six-Packs. Hoit, Richard, illus. (Sails Literacy Ser.). 20p. (gr. 2-3). 27.00 (978-0-7578-0723-7(2)) Rigby Education.
Wing, Natasha. Go to Bed, Monster! Kantorovitz, Sylvie, illus. 2007. 40p. (J). (ps-2). 16.00 (978-0-15-205775-6(7)) Harcourt Trade Pubs.
Winters, Kay. Teeny Tiny Ghost & the Monster. Munsinger, Lynn, illus. 2006. 32p. (J). pap. 6.99 (978-0-06-443662-5(4) , Harper Trophy) HarperCollins Pubs.
Winthrop, Elizabeth. Maggie & the Monster. DePaola, Tomie, illus. 2007. 32p. (J). 16.99 (978-0-399-24711-8(4) , Putnam Juvenile) Penguin Group (USA) Inc.
Wisniewski, David & Wisniewski, David. The Wave of the Sea-Wolf. Wisniewski, David, illus. 1999. (Illus.). 32p. (J). (gr. k-3). pap. 6.95 (978-0-395-96892-5(5) , Clarion Bks.) Houghton Mifflin Co. Trade & Reference Div.
Wong, Angi Ma. Who Ate My Socks? 2005. (Illus.). 32p. (J). 11.98 (978-1-928753-00-1(0)) Pacific Heritage Bks.
Woo, Soo Jung. Legend Volume 3. 2007. 200p. (YA). pap. 10.95 (*978-89-527-4712-9(7)) ICE Kunion KOR. *Dist:* Diamond Bk. Distributors.
—Legend Volume 4. 2007. 200p. (YA). pap. 10.95 (*978-89-527-4871-3(9)) ICE Kunion KOR. *Dist:* Diamond Bk. Distributors.
—Legend Volume 5. 2007. 200p. (YA). pap. 10.95 (*978-89-527-4883-6(2)) ICE Kunion KOR. *Dist:* Diamond Bk. Distributors.
Wood, David. Under the Bed. Fowler, Richard, illus. 2006. 18p. (J). 9.99 (978-0-7641-5926-8(7)) Barron's Educational Series, Inc.
Wormell, Christopher. The Big Ugly Monster & the Little Stone Rabbit. 2004. (Illus.). 32p. (J). (gr. k-3). 15.95 (978-0-375-82891-1(5) , Knopf Bks. for Young Readers) Random Hse. Children's Bks.
—The Sea Monster. (Illus.). 32p. 2006. pap. 8.99 (978-0-09-945147-1(6) , Red Fox); 2005. (J). 16.99 (978-0-224-07025-6(8) , Jonathan Cape) Random Hse. Children's Bks. GBR. *Dist:* Trafalgar Square Publishing.
Wright, Terry. The One-Eyed Monster. 2006. 48p. pap. 12.95 (978-1-4241-3696-4(2)) PublishAmerica, Inc.
Wynne-Jones, Tim. On Tumbledown Hill. Petricic, Dusan, illus. 1998. (Northern Lights Books for Children Ser.). 32p. (ps-3). 15.95 (978-0-88995-186-0(1)) Red Deer Pr. CAN. *Dist:* Fitzhenry & Whiteside, Ltd.
Yaccarino, Dan. The Lima Bean Monster. McCauley, Adam, illus. 32p. (J). (ps-2). 2002. 16.85 (978-0-8027-8777-4(0)); 2001. 15.95 (978-0-8027-8776-7(2)) Walker & Co.
Yagi, Norihiro. Claymore. 2006. (Claymore Ser.). 208p. (YA). Vol. 2. pap. 7.99 (978-1-4215-0619-7(X)); Vol. 3. pap. 7.99 (978-1-4215-0620-3(3)) Viz Media.
Yolen, Jane. Here There Be Dragons. 1998. 19.55 (978-0-606-13477-4(8)); (gr. 5-8). lib. bdg. 21.10 (978-0-613-71566-9(7)) Tandem Library Bks.
Yoon, Salina. Monsters. 2004. (Illus.). 12p. (J). (ps-1). bds. 5.99 (978-0-8431-1079-1(1) , Price Stern Sloan) Penguin Group (USA) Inc.
Yorinks, Arthur. Maurice Sendak's Seven Little Monsters: Hide & Seek. 6th rev. ed. 2004. 24p. (J). pap. 3.99 (978-0-7868-1780-1(1)) Hyperion Pr.
—Maurice Sendak's Seven Little Monsters: Take a Hike. 5th rev. ed. 2004. 24p. (J). pap. 3.99 (978-0-7868-1779-5(8)) Hyperion Pr.
—Mommy? Sendak, Maurice, illus. 2006. 32p. (J). pap. 24.95 (978-0-439-88050-3(5) , Di Capua, Michael) Scholastic, Inc.
Zappa, Ahmet. The Monstrous Memoirs of a Mighty McFearless. 2006. (Illus.). 224p. (J). (gr. 3-7). 12.95 (978-0-375-83287-1(4) , Random Hse. Bks. for Young Readers) Random Hse. Children's Bks.
Zatz, Lia. Mamita Monstruo. Guevara, Angeles Godinez, tr. Furnari, Eva, illus. 2003. (ENG & SPA.). 32p. pap. 6.95 (978-85-7416-173-0(X)) Callis Editora Ltda BRA. *Dist:* Independent Pubs. Group.
Zimet, Sara Goodman. The Monster Solution. Parish, Shannon, illus. 2005. 32p. (J). 16.95 (978-0-9645159-1-8(1) , 1245168) Discovery Pr. Pubns., Inc.
Zindel, Paul. Loch. 2005. 224p. (gr. 5-9). pap. 5.99 (978-0-7868-5150-8(3)) Hyperion Bks. for Children.
—Night of the Bat. 144p. (gr. 5-9). 2003. pap. 5.99 (978-0-7868-1226-4(5)); 2001. 15.99 (978-0-7868-0340-8(1)) Hyperion Bks. for Children.
—Reef of Death. 1998. (Illus.). 192p. (J). (gr. 3 up). 15.95 (978-0-06-024728-7(2)); (gr. 6-10). lib. bdg. 15.89 (978-0-06-024733-1(9)) HarperCollins Pubs.
—Reef of Death. 1999. (978-0-606-16669-0(6)) Tandem Library Bks.
Zornow, Jeff. Werewolf. Zornow, Jeff, illus. 2007. (Graphic Horror Ser.). (Illus.). 32p. (YA). (gr. 5-8). lib. bdg. 27.07 (*978-1-60270-062-8(1) , Graphic Planet) Magic Wagon.
Zucker, Jonny. Creature Chase. Troiano, Enzo, illus. 2007. 33p. (J). pap. (*978-1-59889-424-0(2)); 40p. (YA). (gr. 5-9). 21.26 (*978-1-59889-336-6(X)) Stone Arch Bks.
—A Deck of Monsters. Williams, Anthony, illus. 2008. (J). pap. (*978-1-59889-898-9(1)); 33p. (YA). (gr. 5-9). lib. bdg. 21.26 (*978-1-59889-846-0(9)) Stone Arch Bks.
Zuckerman, Heather. A Monster Named Criney Who Makes Kids Whiney. Delice, Shelly Meredith, illus. 2005. 32p. (ps-7). 15.95 (978-0-9744307-0-6(6)) Merry Lane Pr.

MONSTROSITIES

see Monsters

MONTANA

Alt, David D. & Hyndman, Donald W. Roadside Geology of Montana. rev. ed. (Roadside Geology Ser.). (Illus.). 435p. (J). (gr. 4). pap. 20.00 (978-0-87842-202-9(1) , 212) Mountain Pr. Publishing Co., Inc.
Alter, Judy. Montana: A MyReportLinks.com Book. 2003. (States Ser.). (Illus.). 48p. (J). lib. bdg. 25.26 (978-0-7660-5136-2(6) , MyReportLinks.com Bks.) Enslow Pubs., Inc.
Bakker, Robert T. Raptor Pack. Skrepnick, Michael William, illus. 2003. (Step into Reading Ser.). 48p. (J). (gr. 2-4). 3.99 (978-0-375-82303-9(4)); lib. bdg. 11.99 (978-0-375-92303-6(9)) Random Hse. Children's Bks. (Random Hse. Bks. for Young Readers).
Bennett, Clayton. Montana. 2001. (Celebrate the States Ser.). (Illus.). 144p. (gr. 4-8). lib. bdg. 37.07 (978-0-7614-1312-7(X)); (J). lib. bdg. 35.64 (978-0-7614-1068-3(6)) Cavendish, Marshall Corp. (Benchmark Bks.).
Boone, Mary. Uniquely Montana. 2003. (Heinemann State Studies). (Illus.). 48p. (J). pap. 8.50 (978-1-4034-4717-3(9)); lib. bdg. 27.07 (978-1-4034-4648-0(2)) Heinemann Library.
Brown, Jonatha A. Montana. 2006. (Portraits of the States Ser.). (J). pap. (978-0-8368-4719-2(9)); lib. bdg. (978-0-8368-4702-4(4)) Stevens, Gareth Inc.
Brown, Vanessa. Montana. 2006. (Bilingual Library of the United States of America: Set 2). (ENG & SPA., Illus.). 32p. (J). (gr. 3-6). lib. bdg. 22.50 (978-1-4042-3091-0(2) , Buenas Letra) Rosen Publishing Group, Inc., The.
Bruchac, Joseph. Buffalo Song. Farnsworth, Bill, illus. 2008. (J). Lee & Low Bks., Inc.
Collard, Sneed B., III. B Is for Big Sky Country: A Montana Alphabet. Yardley, Joanna, illus. 2003. 40p. (J). 17.95 (978-1-58536-098-7(8)) Sleeping Bear Pr.
George, Charles & George, Linda. Montana. 2000. (America the Beautiful, Second Ser.). (Illus.). 144p. (J). (gr. 5-8). 36.00 (978-0-516-21092-6(0) , Children's Pr.) Scholastic Library Publishing.
Graf, Mike. Montana. 2003. (Land of Liberty Ser.). (Illus.). 64p. (J). lib. bdg. 25.26 (978-0-7368-2184-1(8)) Capstone Pr., Inc.
A Guide to Montana. 2001. (American States Ser.). 32p. (J). per. 7.95 (978-1-930954-83-0(2)) Weigl Pubs., Inc.
Heinrichs, Ann. Montana. 2005. (Welcome to the USA Ser.). 40p. (J). (gr. 1-5). 27.07 (978-1-59296-475-8(3)) Child's World, Inc.

—Montana. 2003. (This Land Is Your Land Ser.). (Illus.). 48p. (J). (gr. 3 up). lib. bdg. 22.60 (978-0-7565-0334-5(5)) Compass Point Bks.

Hirschmann, Kris. Montana: The Treasure State. 2003. (World Almanac Library of the States). (Illus.). 48p. (J). (gr. 5 up). pap. 14.95 (978-0-8368-5324-7(5)); lib. bdg. 30.00 (978-0-8368-5153-3(6)) Stevens, Gareth Inc. (World Almanac Library).

Hood, Karen Jean Matsko. Montana State: Educational Activity & Coloring Book Series. 2003. 15.95 (978-1-930948-66-2(2)) Whispering Pine Pr., Inc.

Kummer, Patricia K. Montana. rev. ed. 2002. (One Nation Ser.). (Illus.). 48p. (J). (gr. 3-4). lib. bdg. 22.60 (978-0-7368-1250-4(4) , Bridgestone Bks.) Capstone Pr., Inc.

LaDoux, Rita C. Montana. 2nd exp. rev. ed. 2003. (Hello U. S. A. Ser.). (Illus.). 84p. (J). (gr. 3-6). 25.26 (978-0-8225-4092-2(4) , Lerner Pubns.) Lerner Publishing Group.

—Montana. rev. ed. 2003. (gr. 3-6). lib. bdg. 15.25 (978-0-613-52448-3(9)) Tandem Library Bks.

Lawson, Cheri. Chip the Buffalo: Based on a True Story. Lawson, J., illus. Beerntsen, Tammy, photos by. 2006. 32p. (J). lib. bdg. 14.95 (978-1-930580-61-9(4) , Luminary Media Group) Pine Orchard, Inc.

Marsh, Carole. The Big Montana Reproducible Activity Book. 2001. (Carole Marsh Montana Bks.). 96p. (J). (gr. 2-6). pap. 9.95 (978-0-7933-9947-5(5)) Gallopade International.

—Montana Classic Christmas Trivia. 2002. (Carole Marsh Montana Bks.). (Illus.). 32p. pap. 6.95 (978-0-635-01419-1(X) , 1419X); lib. bdg. 21.95 (978-0-635-01420-7(3) , 14203, Marsh, Carole Bks.) Gallopade International.

—Montana Current Events Projects: 30 Cool, Activities, Crafts, Experiments & More for Kids to Do to Learn about Your State! 2003. (Montana Experience Ser.). 32p. (gr. k-5). pap. 5.95 (978-0-635-02045-1(9) , Marsh, Carole Bks.) Gallopade International.

—The Montana Experience Library State: Resource Set. 2001. (Illus.). (J). (gr. k-8). cd-rom 100.20 (978-0-635-00479-6(8)) Gallopade International.

—The Montana Experience Pocket Guide. 2001. (Carole Marsh Montana Bks.). (Illus.). 96p. (J). (gr. 3-8). pap. 6.95 (978-0-7933-9918-5(1)) Gallopade International.

—Montana Geography Projects: 30 Cool, Activities, Crafts, Experiments & More for Kids to Do to Learn about Your State! 2003. (Montana Experience Ser.). 32p. (gr. k-5). pap. 5.95 (978-0-635-01845-8(4) , Marsh, Carole Bks.) Gallopade International.

—Montana Government Projects: 30 Cool, Activities, Crafts, Experiments & More for Kids to Do to Learn about Your State! 2003. (Montana Experience Ser.). 32p. (gr. k-5). pap. 5.95 (978-0-635-01945-5(0) , Marsh, Carole Bks.) Gallopade International.

—Montana Jeopardy! Answers & Questions about Our State! 2001. (Carole Marsh Montana Bks.). 32p. (J). (gr. 3-8). pap. 7.95 (978-0-7933-9802-7(9)) Gallopade International.

—Montana "Jography" A Fun Run Thru Our State! 2001. (Carole Marsh Montana Bks.). 32p. (J). (gr. 3-8). pap. 7.95 (978-0-7933-9831-7(2)) Gallopade International.

—Montana People Projects: 30 Cool, Activities, Crafts, Experiments & More for Kids to Do to Learn about Your State! 2003. (Montana Experience Ser.). 32p. (gr. k-5). pap. 5.95 (978-0-635-01995-0(7) , Marsh, Carole Bks.) Gallopade International.

—Montana Symbols & Facts Projects: 30 Cool, Activities, Crafts, Experiments & More for Kids to Do to Learn about Your State! 2003. (Montana Experience Ser.). 32p. (gr. k-5). pap. 5.95 (978-0-635-01895-3(0) , Marsh, Carole Bks.) Gallopade International.

—My First Book about Montana. 2001. (Carole Marsh Montana Bks.). 32p. (J). (gr. k-4). pap. 7.95 (978-0-7933-9889-8(4)) Gallopade International.

—Who Wants to Be a Millionaire? 2001. (Carole Marsh Mississippi Bks.). lib. bdg. 29.95 (978-0-635-00065-1(2)) Gallopade International.

McLuskey, Krista. A Guide to Montana. 2001. (American States Ser.). (Illus.). 32p. (J). lib. bdg. 16.95 (978-1-930954-92-2(1)) Weigl Pubs., Inc.

Montana. 2000. (Switched on Schoolhouse Ser.). (Illus.). (YA). (gr. 7-12). pap. 24.95 incl. cd-rom (978-0-7403-0278-7(7) , SOSMT) Alpha Omega Pubns., Inc.

Murray, Julie. Montana. 2006. (Buddy Book Ser.). (Illus.). 32p. (J). (gr. k-4). lib. bdg. 22.78 (978-1-59197-685-1(5) , Buddy Bks.) ABDO Publishing Co.

Trumbauer, Lisa. Montana. (Rookie Read-About Geography Ser.). (Illus.). (J). 2004. 31p. (gr. 1-2). pap. 5.95 (978-0-516-23606-3(7)); 2003. 32p. 20.50 (978-0-516-22737-5(8)) Scholastic Library Publishing. (Children's Pr.).

Williams, Judith M. Montana. 2002. (From Sea to Shining Sea Ser.: 2). (Illus.). 80p. (J). (gr. 3-5). 30.50 (978-0-516-22479-4(4) , Children's Pr.) Scholastic Library Publishing.

MONTANA—FICTION

Beth, Hodder. The Ghost of Schafer Meadows. 2007. (J). per. 7.99 (***978-0-9793963-0-4(1)***) Grizzly Ridge Publishing.

Bowen, Asta. Wolf: The Journey Home. 2005. 288p. (J). 16.95 (978-1-58234-689-2(5) , Bloomsbury Children) Bloomsbury Publishing.

Brammer, Deb. Moose. 2006. (YA). (***978-1-59166-722-3(4)***) Jones, Bob Univ. Pr.

Campbell, Joanna. Star's Chance. 2001. (Thoroughbred Ser.: No. 45). 176p. (gr. 4-7). mass mkt. 4.99 (978-0-06-106669-6(9) , Harper Entertainment) HarperCollins Pubs.

—Star's Chance. 2001. (gr. 3-6). lib. bdg. 12.40 (978-0-613-67227-6(5)) Tandem Library Bks.

Collard, Sneed. Flash Point. 2006. 256p. (J). 15.95 (978-1-56145-385-6(4) , Peachtree Junior) Peachtree Pubs., Ltd.

Collard, Sneed B., III. Dog Sense. 2005. 192p. (J). 14.95 (978-1-56145-351-1(X)) Peachtree Pubs., Ltd.

Eberhard, Phyllis Lunde Brees. Little Miss Neat-As-A-Pin. Jacoby, Nickolina Dye, illus. 2007. (J). (***978-0-9722741-7-3(0)***) Publishing Factory, The.

Ellison, Laura. Hard Rock, Hard Times: Coming of Age in Butte Montana, 1911-1917. 2005. 195p. (YA). per. (978-0-9722217-7-1(8)) Horse Creek Pubns.

Farnes, Catherine. Over the Divide. 2001. 146p. (J). (gr. 7-12). 6.49 (978-1-57924-646-4(X)) Jones, Bob Univ. Pr.

—Over the Divide. 2001. (gr. 7-12). lib. bdg. 14.70 (978-0-613-85517-4(5)) Tandem Library Bks.

—Snowblind. 2004. 108p. (J). (978-1-59166-329-4(6)) Jones, Bob Univ. Pr.

Ficklin, Jonene H. Orinoco Intrigue. 2005. (YA). 14.95 (978-0-9761188-1-7(5)) Victor's Crown Publishing.

Gavila, Robert. Nisha: Montana. 2004. (YA). 2.25 (978-0-9748466-0-6(0)) Crossover Comics.

A Gift to Share. 2005. (J). 17.00 (978-0-9721457-1-8(0)) Silent Moon Bks.

Gilliland, Hap. Alone in the Wilderness. 2003. (Illus.). 160p. (YA). (gr. 6-10). pap. 14.95 (978-0-87961-257-3(6)) Naturegraph Pubs., Inc.

Harmon, Michael B. The Last Exit to Normal. 2008. (YA). (***978-0-375-84098-2(2)***); lib. bdg. (***978-0-375-94098-9(7)***) Knopf, Alfred A. Inc.

Hill, Janet Muirhead. Danny's Dragon: A Story of Wartime Loss. Lehmkuhl, Pat & Ore, Peter, illus. 2006. 192p. (J). per. 10.00 (978-0-9772525-0-3(7)) Raven Publishing Inc. of Montana.

—Starlight Comes Home: (the Starlight Books, 6) Lehmkuhl, Pat, illus. 2004. (Starlight Bks.). 236p. (YA). per. 9.00 (978-0-9714161-6-1(8)) Raven Publishing Inc. of Montana.

—Starlight's Shooting Star: The Starlight Books, 4. Lehmkuhl, Pat, illus. 2003. (Starlight Bks.). 192p. (J). (gr. 3-8). per. 9.00 (978-0-9714161-3-0(3)) Raven Publishing Inc. of Montana.

Ingold, Jeanette. The Big Burn. 2003. (Illus.). 320p. (YA). pap. 6.95 (978-0-15-204924-9(X) , Harcourt Paperbacks) Harcourt Children's Bks.

—The Big Burn. 2003. (gr. 5-8). lib. bdg. 15.25 (978-0-613-55148-9(6)) Tandem Library Bks.

—Hitch. 288p. (YA). 2006. (Illus.). pap. 6.95 (978-0-15-205619-3(X) , Harcourt Paperbacks); 2005. (gr. 7-12). 17.00 (978-0-15-204747-4(6)) Harcourt Children's Bks.

—Mountain Solo. 320p. (YA). 2005. (gr. 7-17). pap. 6.95 (978-0-15-205358-1(1) , Harcourt Paperbacks); 2003. 17.00 (978-0-15-202670-7(3)) Harcourt Children's Bks.

Katschke, Judy. The Case of the Wild Wolf River. 1998. (New Adventures of Mary-Kate & Ashley Ser.). 87p. (J). (gr. 2-7). pap. 3.99 (978-0-590-29401-0(6)) Scholastic, Inc.

Larson, Kirby. Hattie Big Sky. 2006. 304p. (J). (gr. 7). 15.95 (978-0-385-73313-7(5)); lib. bdg. 17.99 (978-0-385-90332-5(4)) Random Hse. Children's Bks. (Delacorte Bks. for Young Readers).

—Hattie Big Sky. l.t. ed. 2007. 400p. (YA). 23.95 (***978-0-7862-9697-2(6)***) Thorndike Pr.

Lewis, Randolph. Alanis Obomsawin: The Vision of a Native Filmmaker. 2006. (American Indian Lives Ser.). (Illus.). 262p. 45.00 (978-0-8032-2963-1(1)) Univ. of Nebraska Pr.

Long, Ben. Great Montana Bear Stories. 2002. (gr. 5-8). lib. bdg. 22.20 (978-0-613-61489-4(5)) Tandem Library Bks.

Martin, Nora. A Perfect Snow. (J). 2004. 144p. pap. 6.95 (978-1-58234-925-1(8)); 2002. 250p. 16.95 (978-1-58234-788-2(3)) Bloomsbury Publishing. (Bloomsbury Children).

—A Perfect Snow. 2004. 144p. (YA). (gr. 7-17). lib. bdg. 14.00 (978-0-606-32848-7(3)) Tandem Library Bks.

Maynard, Joyce. The Cloud Chamber. 288p. (YA). 2006. (gr. 9). pap. 7.99 (978-1-4169-2699-3(2) , Simon Pulse); 2005. (gr. 6-9). 16.95 (978-0-689-87152-8(X) , Atheneum) Simon & Schuster Children's Publishing.

Mercer, Gary. Justin Flowers & the Orb of Time. 2003. 147p. pap. 16.95 (978-1-59286-530-7(5)) PublishAmerica, Inc.

Miller, Paula. One-Eyed Jack. Forrest, Chris, illus. 144p. (J). 2007. per. 8.95 (978-0-9769417-0-5(8)); 2006. 13.95 (978-0-9718348-8-0(1)) Blooming Tree Pr.

Mills, Charles. Stranger in the Shadows. 1998. (Shadow Creek Ranch Ser.: Vol. 11). 151p. (Orig.). (J). (gr. 4-7). pap. 5.99 (978-0-8280-1316-1(0)) Review & Herald Publishing Assn.

Patchin, Gee Frank. The Pony Rider Boys in Montana. 2006. 63.99 (***978-1-4280-1132-8(3)***); pap. 57.99 (***978-1-4280-1126-7(9)***) IndyPublish.com.

Piper, William Bowman. Giraffe of Montana, Volume I, 1. Megenhardt, William, illus. ed. 2005. 152p. (J). 19.95 (978-0-9763359-4-8(8) , 0-9763359) Little Pemberley Pr.

Place, Marian T. Mystery of the Wild Horse Trap. 2004. (Classic Ser.). (Illus.). 212p. (gr. 4-7). pap. 15.95 (978-0-87004-411-3(7)) Caxton Pr.

Porter, Pamela. Sky. Gerber, Mary Jane, illus. 2005. 88p. (J). (gr. 4-7). pap. 5.95 (978-0-88899-607-7(1) , Libros Tigrillo) Groundwood Bks. CAN. *Dist:* Perseus Distribution.

Sargent, Dave & Sargent, Pat. Sweetpea: (Purple Corn Welsh) Be Happy, 30, 58. Lenoir, Jane, illus. 2003. (Saddle Up Ser.: Vol. 58). 42p. (J). pap. 6.95 (978-1-56763-816-5(3)); lib. bdg. 22.60 (978-1-56763-815-8(5)) Ozark Publishing.

Schaaf, Ron. BearClaw: Finding Courage Within. 2007. (J). (***978-0-9787555-1-5(0)***) Hickory Tales Publishing.

Schofield, S. M. Race to Eagle Mountain. 2007. (ENG.). 184p. (J). per. 16.99 (***978-1-4141-0814-8(1)***) Pleasant Word.

Simmons, Marc. Billy Blackfeet in the Rockies: A Story from History. Kil, Ronald R., illus. 2006. 56p. (J). 18.95 (978-0-8263-4105-1(5)) Univ. of New Mexico Pr.

Thomas, Jane Resh. Blind Mountain. 2006. 128p. (J). (gr. 4-6). 15.00 (978-0-618-64872-6(0) , Clarion Bks.) Houghton Mifflin Co. Trade & Reference Div.

Tighe, Bridget M. Traveling Wildflower: Treasure in Time. 2006. 109p. pap. 16.95 (978-1-4137-7959-2(X)) PublishAmerica, Inc.

Wallace, Bill. Eye of the Great Bear. 1999. 176p. (J). (gr. 3-6). pap. 9.95 (978-0-671-02502-1(3) , Aladdin) Simon & Schuster Children's Publishing.

—Eye of the Great Bear. 1999. (J). 11.64 (978-0-606-19050-3(3)); (gr. 3-6). lib. bdg. 13.00 (978-0-613-21509-1(5)) Tandem Library Bks.

Yep, Laurence. When the Circus Came to Town. Wang, Suling, illus. 2001. 128p. (J). (ps-1). 14.99 (978-0-06-029325-3(X)); lib. bdg. 15.89 (978-0-06-029326-0(8)) HarperCollins Pubs.

—When the Circus Came to Town. 2004. (gr. 3-6). lib. bdg. 14.15 (978-0-613-86716-0(5)) Tandem Library Bks.

Yep, Laurence & Yep, Laurence. When the Circus Came to Town. Wang, Suling, illus. 2004. 128p. (J). (ps-k). pap. 5.99 (978-0-06-440965-0(1) , Harper Trophy) HarperCollins Pubs.

MONTANA—HISTORY

Cohn, Janice. The Christmas Menorahs: How a Town Fought Hate. 2000. (J). 13.75 (978-0-606-19688-8(9)) Tandem Library Bks.

Jones, Donald M., photos by. Buffalo Country: America's National Bison Range. 2005. (Illus.). 72p. per. 13.95 (978-1-931832-56-4(0) , 8667872363) Riverbend Publishing.

Kuedee, Jaycee. How to Draw Montanas Sights & Symbols. 2002. (Kids Guide to Drawing America Ser.). 32p. (J). lib. bdg. 25.25 (978-0-8239-6082-8(X) , PowerKids Pr.) Rosen Publishing Group, Inc., The.

Marsh, Carole. Montana History Projects: 30 Cool, Activities, Crafts, Experiments & More for Kids to Do to Learn about Your State! 2003. (Montana Experience Ser.). 32p. (gr. k-5). pap. 5.95 (978-0-635-01795-6(4) , Marsh, Carole Bks.) Gallopade International.

—Montana Millionaire. 2001. (GameBook Ser.). 32p. (J). (gr. 3-8). pap., act. bk. ed. 9.95 (978-0-635-00068-2(7)) Gallopade International.

—Montana Survivor. 2001. (GameBook Ser.). 32p. (J). (gr. 3-8). pap., act. bk. ed. 9.95 (978-0-635-00547-2(6)) Gallopade International.

—The Montana Survivor: A Class Challenge. 2001. (Carole Marsh Montana Bks.). (J). lib. bdg. 29.95 (978-0-635-00672-1(3)) Gallopade International.

—Montana Wheel of Fortune. 2001. (GameBook Ser.). 32p. (J). (gr. 3-8). pap., act. bk. ed. 9.95 (978-0-7933-9668-9(9)) Gallopade International.

—My First Pocket Guide Montana. 2000. (Montana Experience Ser.). (Illus.). 96p. (J). (gr. 3-8). 12.95 (978-0-635-01316-3(9) , 13169) Gallopade International.

—Wheel of Fortune. 2001. (Carole Marsh Montana Bks.). (J). lib. bdg. 29.95 (978-0-7933-9669-6(7)) Gallopade International.

Merrill-Maker, Andrea. Montana: People & Their Stories. 2004. (Illus.). 371p. (J). 32.09 (978-0-913205-28-0(1)) Sage Hill Pubs., LLC.

Montana History Notebook Map. 2004. (J). (978-0-9759433-6-6(7)) Maps For Kids Inc.

Solberg, Jessica L. First Dog: Unleashed in the Montana Capitol. Rath, Robert, illus. 2007. (J). (***978-1-56037-419-0(5)***) Farcountry Pr.

MONTEREY (CALIF.)

Abbink, Emily. Monterey Bay Area Missions. 2007. (Exploring California Missions Ser.). (J). 27.93 (***978-0-8225-0887-8(7)*** , Lerner Pubns.) Lerner Publishing Group.

MONTEREY (CALIF.)—FICTION

Collins, Yvonne & Rideout, Sandy. The Black Sheep. 2007. 352p. (gr. 5 up). 15.99 (***978-1-4231-0156-7(1)***) Hyperion Pr.

MONTEZUMA II, EMPEROR OF MEXICO, 1480-1520

Flowers, Charles. Cortes & the Conquest of the Aztec Empire in World History. 2001. (In World History Ser.). (Illus.). 128p. (J). (gr. 5-12). lib. bdg. 26.60 (978-0-7660-1395-7(2)) Enslow Pubs., Inc.

Kimmel, Eric A. Montezuma & the Fall of the Aztecs. San Souci, Daniel, illus. 2000. 32p. (J). (gr. 4-6). tchr. ed. 16.95 (978-0-8234-1452-9(3)) Holiday Hse., Inc.

Reid, Struan. Montezuma. 2003. 32p. pap. 7.50 (978-1-4034-0101-4(2)) Heinemann Library.

MONTEZUMA, CARLOS, 1866-1923

Capaldi, Gina, illus. A Boy Named Beckoning: The True Story of Dr. Carlos Montezuma, Native American Hero. 2008. (Exceptional Social Studies Titles for Intermediate Grades Ser.). (J). lib. bdg. 16.95 (***978-0-8225-7644-0(9)*** , Carolrhoda Bks.) Lerner Publishing Group.

MONTGOMERY, L. M. (LUCY MAUD), 1874-1942

Gillen, Mollie. Lucy Maud Montgomery. 1999. (Canadians Ser.). (Illus.). 64p. (J). pap. (978-1-55041-461-5(5)) Fitzhenry & Whiteside, Ltd.

—Lucy Maud Montgomery. 1999. (gr. 3-6). lib. bdg. 15.25 (978-0-613-90270-0(X)) Tandem Library Bks.

Kjelle, Marylou Morano. L. M. Montgomery. 2005. (Who Wrote That? Ser.). (Illus.). 124p. (J). (gr. 6-12). lib. bdg. 30.00 (978-0-7910-8234-8(2) , Chelsea Hse.) Facts On File, Inc.

Langille, J. H. L. M. Montgomery. 2001. (J). reprint ed. pap. (978-0-920427-54-5(5)) Four East Pubns.

MacLeod, Elizabeth. Lucy Maud Montgomery. Mantha, John, illus. 2008. 32p. pap. (***978-1-55453-056-4(3)***) Kids Can Pr., Ltd.

MacLeod, Elizabeth. Lucy Maud Montgomery: A Writer's Life. 2004. (Snapshots Ser.). (Illus.). 32p. (J). (gr. 4-6). (978-1-55074-489-7(5)); (978-1-55074-487-3(9)) Kids Can Pr., Ltd.

—Lucy Maud Montgomery: A Writer's Life. 2001. (gr. 3-6). lib. bdg. 15.25 (978-0-613-36490-4(2)) Tandem Library Bks.

Wallner, Alexandra. Lucy Maud Montgomery: The Author of Anne of Green Gables. Wallner, Alexandra, illus. 2006. (Illus.). 32p. (J). 16.95 (978-0-8234-1549-6(X)) Holiday Hse., Inc.

MONTGOMERY (ALA.)—RACE RELATIONS

Adler, David A. A Picture Book of Rosa Parks. Casilla, Robert, illus. 2004. (J). (ps-3). audio compact disk 18.95 (978-1-59112-761-1(0)) Live Oak Media.

Baker, Courtney. Let's Read About— Rosa Parks. Hunt, Robert, illus. 2004. (Scholastic First Biographies Ser.). 29p. (J). pap. (978-0-439-56413-7(1) , Cartwheel Bks.) Scholastic, Inc.

Banting, Erinn. Rosa Parks. 2005. (Great African American Women for Kids Ser.). (Illus.). 24p. (J). (ps-7). pap. 6.95 (978-1-59036-342-3(6)); lib. bdg. 26.00 (978-1-59036-336-2(1)) Weigl Pubs., Inc.

Bjornlund, Lydia. Rosa Parks & the Montgomery Bus Boycott. 2007. (Lucent Library of Black History Ser.). (Illus.). 128p. (J). (gr. 7-10). 28.70 (***978-1-4205-0010-3(4)*** , Lucent Bks.) Thomson Gale.

Brandt, Keith & Mattern, Joanne. Rosa Parks: Freedom Rider. Griffith, Gershom, illus. 2006. 54p. (J). pap. (***978-0-439-66045-7(9)***) Scholastic, Inc.

Brown, Jonatha A. Rosa Parks. 2005. (Illus.). 24p. (J). (ENG & SPA.). pap. (978-0-8368-4769-7(5)); (ENG & SPA., lib. bdg. 19.33 (978-0-8368-4762-8(8)); pap. (978-0-8368-4755-0(5)); lib. bdg. 19.33 (978-0-8368-4748-2(2)) Stevens, Gareth Inc.

Crewe, Sabrina & Walsh, Frank. The Montgomery Bus Boycott. 2003. (Events That Shaped America Ser.). (Illus.). 32p. (J). (gr. 3 up). lib. bdg. 24.67 (978-0-8368-3394-2(5)) Stevens, Gareth Inc.

DeGezelle, Terri. Life in the Time of Rosa Parks & the Civil Rights Movement. 2007. (J). (***978-1-4034-9671-3(4)***); pap. (***978-1-4034-9679-9(X)***) Heinemann Library.

Donovan, Sandy. Rosa Parks. 2003. (Illus.). 64p. (J). (gr. 4-7). pap. 9.50 (978-1-4109-0320-4(6)); lib. bdg. 28.56 (978-0-7398-7032-7(7)) Raintree.

Dubois, Muriel L. Rosa Parks. 2003. (Photo-Illustrated Biographies Ser.). (Illus.). 24p. (J). (gr. 2-3). lib. bdg. 18.60 (978-0-7368-1607-6(0) , Bridgestone Bks.) Capstone Pr., Inc.

Dubowski, Cathy East. Rosa Parks: Don't Give In! 2005. (Defining Moments Ser.). (Illus.). 32p. (J). lib. bdg. 25.27 (978-1-59716-078-0(4)) Bearport Publishing Co., Inc.

Edwards, Pamela Duncan. The Bus Ride That Changed History: The Story of Rosa Parks. Shanahan, Danny, illus. 2005. 32p. (J). (gr. k-3). 16.00 (978-0-618-44911-8(6)) Houghton Mifflin Co. Trade & Reference Div.

Fine, Edith Hope. Rosa Parks: Meet a Civil Rights Hero. 2004. (Meeting Famous People Ser.). (Illus.). 32p. (J). lib. bdg. 22.60 (978-0-7660-2099-3(1)) Enslow Pubs., Inc.

Freedman, Russell. Freedom Walkers: The Story of the Montgomery Bus Boycott. 2006. (Illus.). 112p. (J). (gr. 3-7). 18.95 (978-0-8234-2031-5(0)) Holiday Hse., Inc.

Giovanni, Nikki. Rosa. Collier, Bryan, illus. rev. ed. 2005. 40p. (J). (gr. 4-7). 16.95 (978-0-8050-7106-1(7) , Holt, Henry & Co. Bks. For Young Readers) Holt, Henry & Co.

—Rosa. Collier, Bryan, illus. 2007. 40p. (J). pap. 7.99 (***978-0-312-37602-4(2)***) Square Fish.

Greenfield, Eloise. Rosa Parks. Ashby, Gil, illus. 2002. 12.62 (978-0-7587-0755-0(X)) Book Wholesalers, Inc.

Hull, Mary, et al. Rosa Parks: Civil Rights Leader. 2nd rev. ed. 2006. (Black Americans of Achievement Ser.). 128p. (J). (gr. 6-12). 30.00 (***978-0-7910-9523-2(1)*** , Chelsea Hse.) Facts On File, Inc.

Hull, Mary E. Rosa Parks: Civil Rights Leader. (Black Americans of Achievement Ser.). (Illus.). 112p. (J). (gr. 6-12). 2005. pap. 13.25 (978-0-7910-8338-3(1)); 2004. 30.00 (978-0-7910-8164-8(8)) Facts On File, Inc. (Chelsea Hse.).

Kelso, Richard. Walking for Freedom: The Montgomery Bus Boycott. (Nonfiction Bookbag Ser.). (J). (gr. 5-6). 2001. per. 8.45 (978-1-58830-202-1(4)); 2002. per. (978-1-58120-806-1(5)) Metropolitan Teaching & Learning Co.

Kishel, Ann-Marie. Rosa Parks: A Life of Courage. 2006. (Pull Ahead Books). (Illus.). 32p. (J). 22.60 (978-0-8225-3478-5(9) , Lerner Pubns.) Lerner Publishing Group.

—Rosa Parks: Una Vida de Valentía. 2006. (Libros para Avanzar Ser.). (ENG & SPA.). 32p. (J). lib. bdg. 22.60 (978-0-8225-6239-9(1)) Lerner Publishing Group.

Kudlinski, Kathleen V. Rosa Parks. Henderson, Meryl, illus. 2001. (Childhood of Famous Americans Ser.). 224p. (gr. 3-7). mass mkt. 5.99 (978-0-689-83925-2(1) , Aladdin) Simon & Schuster Children's Publishing.

Mara, Wil. Rosa Parks. (Rookie Biographies Ser.). (Illus.). (J). 2004. 31p. (gr. 1-2). pap. 4.95 (978-0-516-27916-9(5)); 2003. 32p. 19.50 (978-0-516-25876-8(1)) Scholastic Library Publishing. (Children's Pr.).

McLeese, Don. Rosa Parks. 2002. (Rourke Discovery Library). (Illus.). 24p. (J). lib. bdg. 20.64 (978-1-58952-287-9(7)) Rourke Publishing, LLC.

Miller, Jake. The Montgomery Bus Boycott: Integrating Public Buses. 2004. (Library of the Civil Rights Movement Ser.). (Illus.). 24p. (J). lib. bdg. 19.95 (978-0-8239-6251-8(2) , PowerKids Pr.) Rosen Publishing Group, Inc., The.

Morris, Roz. Rosa Parks: Mother of the Civil Rights Movement. 2003. (Alabama Roots Biography Ser.). (Illus.). 109p. (J). (978-1-878561-57-2(X)) Seacoast Publishing, Inc.

Nobleman, Marc Tyler. Rosa Parks. 2002. (Trailblazers of the Modern World Ser.). (Illus.). 48p. (J). (gr. 5 up). pap. 14.95 (978-0-8368-5231-8(1)); lib. bdg. 30.00 (978-0-8368-5071-0(8)) Stevens, Gareth Inc. (World Almanac Library).

—Rosa Parks. 2002. (gr. 3-6). lib. bdg. 19.90 (978-0-613-76804-7(3)) Tandem Library Bks.

O'Hern, Kerri & Walsh, Frank. The Montgomery Bus Boycott. 2006. (Graphic Histories Ser.). (Illus.). (J). pap. (978-0-8368-6257-7(0) , World Almanac Library) Stevens, Gareth Inc.

Parks, Rosa. I Am Rosa Parks. 2000. (gr. k-3). lib. bdg. 11.80 (978-0-613-22996-8(7)); (Illus.). (J). 10.79 (978-0-606-18410-6(4)) Tandem Library Bks.

—Rosa Parks: My Story. 1999. (Illus.). 200p. (YA). (gr. 5-9). pap. 6.99 (978-0-14-130120-4(1) , Puffin) Penguin Group (USA) Inc.

—Rosa Parks: My Story. 1999. (978-0-606-15995-1(9)); (gr. 5-8). lib. bdg. 15.30 (978-0-613-15120-7(8)) Tandem Library Bks.

Parks, Rosa & Haskins, Jim. I Am Rosa Parks. Clay, Wil, illus. 1999. (Easy-to-Read Ser.). 48p. (J). (gr. 1-3). pap. 3.99 (978-0-14-130710-7(2) , Puffin) Penguin Group (USA) Inc.

Rinaldo, Denise. Rosa Parks: With a Discussion of Courage. 2003. (Values in Action Ser.). (J). (978-1-59203-061-3(0)) Learning Challenge, Inc.

Ringgold, Faith. If a Bus Could Talk: The Story of Rosa Parks. Ringgold, Faith, illus. (Illus.). 32p. (J). 2003. (gr. k-4). pap. 7.99 (978-0-689-85676-1(8) , Aladdin); 1999. (gr. 1-4). 16.00 (978-0-689-81892-9(0)) Simon & Schuster Children's Publishing.

—If a Bus Could Talk: The Story of Rosa Parks. 2003. (gr. k-3). lib. bdg. 15.30 (978-0-613-61633-1(2)) Tandem Library Bks.

Schaefer, Lola M. Rosa Parks. Saunders-Smith, Gail, ed. 2002. (First Biographies Ser.). (Illus.). 24p. (J). (gr. k-1). lib. bdg. 15.93 (978-0-7368-1176-7(1) , Pebble Bks.) Capstone Pr., Inc.

Schraff, Anne E. Rosa Parks: Tired of Giving In. 2005. (African-American Biography Library). (Illus.). 128p. (J). (gr. 6-12). lib. bdg. 31.93 (978-0-7660-2463-2(6)) Enslow Pubs., Inc.

Shone, Rob. Rosa Parks: The Life of a Civil Rights Heroine. Spender, Nik, illus. 2006. 48p. (J). (978-1-4042-0926-8(3)); pap. (978-1-4042-0927-5(1)); (gr. 3-8). lib. bdg. 29.95 (978-1-4042-0864-3(X)) Rosen Publishing Group, Inc., The.

Shores, Erika L. Rosa Parks: Civil Rights Poineer. 2005. (Fact Finders Ser.). (Illus.). 32p. (J). (ps-7). lib. bdg. 22.60 (978-0-7368-3746-0(9)) Capstone Pr., Inc.

Steele, Phillip. Rosa Parks & Her Protest for Civil Rights. 2002. (Dates with History Ser.). (Illus.). 31p. (J). lib. bdg. 24.25 (978-1-58340-215-3(2)) Smart Apple Media.

Tieck, Sarah. Rosa Parks. 2007. (Buddy Book Ser.). (Illus.). 32p. (J). 22.78 (978-1-59679-788-8(6)) ABDO Publishing Co.

Vaughn, Wally G. & Davis, Mattie Campbell, eds. The Selma Campaign, 1963-1965: The Decisive Battle of the Civil Rights Movement. 2006. 261p. pap. 19.95 (978-0-912469-44-7(7)) Majority Pr., Inc., The.

Walsh, Frank. The Montgomery Bus Boycott. 2003. (Landmark Events in American History Ser.). (Illus.). 48p. (J). (gr. 5 up). pap. 14.95 (978-0-8368-5403-9(9)); lib. bdg. 30.00 (978-0-8368-5375-9(X)) Stevens, Gareth Inc. (World Almanac Library).

Weidt, Maryann N. Rosa Parks. 2003. (History Maker Bios Ser.). (Illus.). 47p. (J). 26.60 (978-0-8225-4673-3(6) , Lerner Pubns.) Lerner Publishing Group.

Wheeler, Jill C. Rosa Parks, Set II. 2003. (Breaking Barriers Ser.). (Illus.). 64p. (J). (gr. 3-8). lib. bdg. 25.65 (978-1-57765-640-1(7)) ABDO Publishing Co.

Whiting, Jim. Rosa Parks. 2007. (What's So Great About... ? Ser.). (J). lib. bdg. 25.70 (*978-1-58415-573-7(6)) Mitchell Lane Pubs., Inc.

Wilson, Cammie. Rosa Parks: From the Back of the Bus to the Front of a Movement. 2001. (Scholastic Biography Ser.). (Illus.). 88p. (J). (gr. 3-7). pap. 4.50 (978-0-439-16330-9(7)) Scholastic, Inc.

MONTHS

Brode, Robyn. April. 2003. (Weekly Reader Early Learning Library). (Illus.). 24p. (J). (ps-2). pap. 7.93 (978-0-8368-3615-8(4)); lib. bdg. 19.33 (978-0-8368-3579-3(4)) Stevens, Gareth Inc. (Weekly Reader Early Learning Library).

—August. 2003. (Weekly Reader Early Learning Library). (Illus.). 24p. (J). (ps-2). pap. 7.93 (978-0-8368-3619-6(7)); lib. bdg. 19.33 (978-0-8368-3583-0(2)) Stevens, Gareth Inc. (Weekly Reader Early Learning Library).

—December. 2003. (Illus.). 24p. (J). pap. (978-0-8368-3623-3(5)); lib. bdg. 19.33 (978-0-8368-3587-8(5) , Weekly Reader Early Learning Library) Stevens, Gareth Inc.

—February. 2003. (Weekly Reader Early Learning Library). (Illus.). 24p. (J). (ps-2). pap. 7.93 (978-0-8368-3613-4(8)); lib. bdg. 19.33 (978-0-8368-3577-9(8)) Stevens, Gareth Inc. (Weekly Reader Early Learning Library).

—January. 2003. (Weekly Reader Early Learning Library). (Illus.). 24p. (J). (ps-2). pap. 7.93 (978-0-8368-3612-7(X)); lib. bdg. 19.33 (978-0-8368-3576-2(X)) Stevens, Gareth Inc. (Weekly Reader Early Learning Library).

—July. 2003. (Weekly Reader Early Learning Library). (Illus.). 24p. (J). (ps-2). pap. 7.93 (978-0-8368-3618-9(9)); lib. bdg. 19.33 (978-0-8368-3582-3(4)) Stevens, Gareth Inc. (Weekly Reader Early Learning Library).

—June. 2003. (Weekly Reader Early Learning Library). (Illus.). 24p. (J). (ps-2). pap. 7.93 (978-0-8368-3617-2(0)); lib. bdg. 19.33 (978-0-8368-3581-6(6)) Stevens, Gareth Inc. (Weekly Reader Early Learning Library).

—March. (Months of the Year Ser.). (Illus.). 24p. (J). (ps up). lib. bdg. 19.33 (978-0-8368-3578-6(6)); 2003. pap. 7.93 (978-0-8368-3614-1(6)) Stevens, Gareth Inc. (Weekly Reader Early Learning Library).

—May. 2003. (Weekly Reader Early Learning Library). (Illus.). 24p. (J). (ps-2). pap. 7.93 (978-0-8368-3616-5(2)); lib. bdg. 19.33 (978-0-8368-3580-9(8)) Stevens, Gareth Inc. (Weekly Reader Early Learning Library).

—Months of the Year, 12 bks. Incl. April. 2003. lib. bdg. 19.33 (978-0-8368-3579-3(4)); August. 2003. lib. bdg. 19.33 (978-0-8368-3583-0(2)); December. 2003. lib. bdg. 19.33 (978-0-8368-3587-8(5)); February. 2003. lib. bdg. 19.33 (978-0-8368-3577-9(8)); January. 2003. lib. bdg. 19.33 (978-0-8368-3576-2(X)); July. 2003. lib. bdg. 19.33 (978-0-8368-3582-3(4)); June. 2003. lib. bdg. 19.33 (978-0-8368-3581-6(6)); March. lib. bdg. 19.33 (978-0-8368-3578-6(6)); May. 2003. lib. bdg. 19.33 (978-0-8368-3580-9(8)); November. 2003. lib. bdg. 19.33 (978-0-8368-3586-1(7)); October. 2003. lib. bdg. 19.33 (978-0-8368-3585-4(9)); September. 2003. lib. bdg. 19.33 (978-0-8368-3584-7(0)); 24p. (J). (ps up). (Illus.). Set lib. bdg. 231.96 (978-0-8368-3575-5(1)); pap. (978-0-8368-3611-0(1)) Stevens, Gareth Inc. (Weekly Reader Early Learning Library).

—November. 2003. (Illus.). 24p. (J). pap. (978-0-8368-3622-6(7)); lib. bdg. 19.33 (978-0-8368-3586-1(7) , Weekly Reader Early Learning Library) Stevens, Gareth Inc.

—October. 2003. (Illus.). 24p. (J). pap. (978-0-8368-3621-9(9)); lib. bdg. 19.33 (978-0-8368-3585-4(9) , Weekly Reader Early Learning Library) Stevens, Gareth Inc.

—September. 2003. (Illus.). 24p. (J). pap. (978-0-8368-3620-2(0)); lib. bdg. 19.33 (978-0-8368-3584-7(0) , Weekly Reader Early Learning Library) Stevens, Gareth Inc.

Brown, Angela McHaney. Months of the Year. 2005. (Talking about Time Ser.). (Illus.). 24p. (J). (978-1-4109-1642-6(1)); pap. (978-1-4109-1648-8(0)) Steck-Vaughn.

Cernek, Kim & Howley, Ronda. July - August No. 2374: Celebrate the Months. Johnson, Kristine, ed. Tom, Darcy, illus. 1999. (Celebrate the Months Ser.). 96p. (J). (gr. k-3). pap. 9.98 (978-1-57471-539-2(9)) Creative Teaching Pr., Inc.

—June No. 2373: Celebrate the Months. Johnson, Kristine, ed. Tom, Darcy, illus. 1999. (Celebrate the Months Ser.). 96p. (J). (gr. k-3). pap. 9.98 (978-1-57471-538-5(0)) Creative Teaching Pr., Inc.

Clarke, Jacqueline. Fresh & Fun May: Dozens of Instant & Irresistible Ideas & Activities from Creative Teachers Across the Country. 2001. (Fresh & Fun Ser.). 32p. pap. 8.95 (978-0-439-21609-8(5)) Scholastic, Inc.

—March. 2001. 32p. pap. 8.95 (978-0-439-21606-7(0)) Scholastic, Inc.

Douglas, Vincent & School Specialty Publishing Staff. My Little Showcase of Zoo Animals. 2005. (My Little Showcase Ser.). (Illus.). 100p. (J). bds. 14.95 (978-1-58845-648-9(X) , Brighter Child) School Specialty Publishing.

Hunt, Darleen L. Bob's Busy Year: Months of the Year. Komarck, Michael, illus. 2003. (Sherman's Math Corner Ser.). (J). (ps-3). (978-1-929591-03-9(9)) Reading Rock, Inc.

Jackson, Ellen B. August. DeWitt, Robin & DeWitt, Pat, illus. 2004. (It Happens in the Month of... Ser.). 32p. (YA). 8.95 (978-0-88106-921-1(3)) Charlesbridge Publishing, Inc.

—January. DeWitt, Pat & DeWitt, Robin, illus. 2004. (It Happens in the Month of... Ser.). 32p. (YA). (gr. k-3). 8.95 (978-0-88106-995-2(7)) Charlesbridge Publishing, Inc.

—July. DeWitt, Pat & DeWitt, Robin, illus. 2004. (It Happens in the Month of... Ser.). 32p. (YA). 8.95 (978-0-88106-920-4(5)) Charlesbridge Publishing, Inc.

—June. Life, Kay, illus. 2004. (It Happens in the Month of... Ser.). 32p. (YA). 8.95 (978-0-88106-919-8(1)) Charlesbridge Publishing, Inc.

—March. Life, Kay, illus. 2004. (It Happens in the Month of... Ser.). 32p. (YA). 8.95 (978-0-88106-905-1(1)) Charlesbridge Publishing, Inc.

—May. Life, Kay, illus. 2004. (It Happens in the Month of... Ser.). 32p. (YA). 8.95 (978-0-88106-918-1(3)) Charlesbridge Publishing, Inc.

—November. DeWitt, Pat & DeWitt, Robin, illus. 2004. (It Happens in the Month of... Ser.). 32p. (YA). 8.95 (978-0-88106-927-3(2)) Charlesbridge Publishing, Inc.

—October. DeWitt, Robin & DeWitt, Pat, illus. 2004. (It Happens in the Month of... Ser.). 32p. (YA). (gr. 2-3). 8.95 (978-0-88106-923-5(X)) Charlesbridge Publishing, Inc.

—September. DeWitt, Robin & DeWitt, Pat, illus. 2004. (It Happens in the Month of... Ser.). 32p. (YA). 8.95 (978-0-88106-922-8(1)) Charlesbridge Publishing, Inc.

Krech, Bob. December. 2001. (Fresh & Fun Ser.). 32p. (J). pap. 8.95 (978-0-439-21574-9(9)) Scholastic, Inc.

Lieberman, M. Coloring Books on Events of the Jewish Months: Kislev, Teves, Shevat, Adar. 2002. (Learn As You Color Series 2). 6.00 (978-0-914131-85-4(0) , D711) Torah Umesorah Pubns.

Murphy, Patricia J. Months. 2005. (Calendar Ser.). (Illus.). 24p. (J). 15.93 (978-0-7368-3628-9(4) , Pebble Bks.) Capstone Pr., Inc.

—Months. (Calendar Ser.). 24p. (J). pap. 5.95 (978-0-7368-5075-9(9)) Capstone Pr., Inc.

Nelson, Robin. Months. 2005. (First Step Nonfiction Ser.). (Illus.). 24p. (gr. k-2). 17.27 (978-0-8225-0179-4(1)) Lerner Publishing Group.

Novelli, Joan. February. 2001. (Fresh & Fun Ser.). 32p. (J). pap. 8.95 (978-0-439-21605-0(2)) Scholastic, Inc.

Provensen, Alice. Year at Maple Hill Farm. 2001. (ps-2). lib. bdg. 15.30 (978-0-613-90198-7(3)) Tandem Library Bks.

Randolph, Joanne. All about the Months. 2008. lib. bdg. (*978-1-4042-3769-8(0) , PowerKids Pr.) Rosen Publishing Group, Inc., The.

Rondeau, Amanda. Months. l.t. ed. 2001. (Capital Letters Ser.). (Illus.). 24p. (J). (ps-3). lib. bdg. 19.93 (978-1-57765-612-8(1) , SandCastle) ABDO Publishing Co.

Updike, John. A Child's Calendar. Hyman, Trina Schart, illus. 1999. (Caldecott Honor Book Ser.). 36p. (J). (gr. k-3). tchr. ed. 16.95 (978-0-8234-1445-1(0)) Holiday Hse., Inc.

MONTHS—FICTION

Barner, Bob. Parade Day: Marching Through the Calendar Year. 2003. (Illus.). 32p. (J). (gr. k-3). tchr. ed. 16.95 (978-0-8234-1690-5(9)) Holiday Hse., Inc.

Blackstone, Stella. Jump into January. Carluccio, Maria, illus. 2004. 32p. (J). 15.99 (978-1-84148-629-1(9)) Barefoot Bks., Inc.

—Skip through the Seasons. Carluccio, Maria, illus. 2006. 32p. (J). (ps-2). pap. 6.99 (978-1-905236-71-8(9)) Barefoot Bks., Inc.

Day, Nancy Raines. A Kitten's Year. Mortimer, Anne, illus. 2002. (J). 23.98 (978-0-7587-2937-8(5)) Book Wholesalers, Inc.

—A Kitten's Year. Mortimer, Anne, illus. 32p. (J). (ps-4). 2001. pap. 5.95 (978-0-06-443863-6(5) , Harper Trophy); 2000. 16.99 (978-0-06-027230-2(9)) HarperCollins Pubs.

Degen, Bruce, illus. How Do You Say It Today, Jesse Bear? 2002. (Jesse Bear Ser.). (J). 14.47 (978-0-7587-2760-2(7)) Book Wholesalers, Inc.

Freeman, Don. Rhymes & Riddles with Corduroy. 2002. (gr. k-3). lib. bdg. 11.25 (978-0-613-51510-8(2)) Tandem Library Bks.

Gosline, Andrea Alban. January's Child: The Birthday Month Book. Bossi, Lisa Burnett, illus. 2007. 32p. (J). (ps-3). pap. 12.99 (978-0-439-67268-9(6) , Scholastic Pr.) Scholastic, Inc.

Hubbell, Patricia. Rabbit Moon: A Book of Holidays & Celebrations. Watson, Wendy, illus. 2002. 32p. (J). (ps-3). 15.95 (978-0-7614-5103-7(X) , Cavendish Children's Bks.) Cavendish, Marshall Corp.

Katz, Karen. Twelve Hats for Lena: A Book of Months. Katz, Karen, illus. 2002. (Illus.). 34p. (J). (ps-3). 17.99 (978-0-689-84873-5(0) , McElderry, Margaret K.) Simon & Schuster Children's Publishing.

Lesser, Carolyn. What a Wonderful Day to Be a Cow. 1999. (Illus.). (J). (978-0-606-16958-5(X)) Tandem Library Bks.

Lionni, Leo. A Busy Year. 2004. (Illus.). 26p. (J). (gr. k-ps). bds. 6.99 (978-0-375-82737-2(4) , Knopf Bks. for Young Readers) Random Hse. Children's Bks.

Lobel, Anita. One Lighthouse, One Moon. Lobel, Anita, illus. 2000. (Illus.). 48p. (J). (ps up). 16.99 (978-0-688-15539-1(1)) HarperCollins Pubs.

Martin. The Turning of the Year. Shed, Greg, illus. 2007. 28p. (J). pap. 6.00 (978-0-15-204555-5(4) , Voyager Bks./Libros Viajeros) Harcourt Children's Bks.

Martin, Bill, Jr. The Turning of the Year. Shed, Greg, illus. 1998. 28p. (J). (ps-3). 15.00 (978-0-15-201085-0(8)) Harcourt Children's Bks.

Parker, Sandy. What Month Is It? Hofher, Cathy, illus. l.t. ed. 2004. 32p. 15.95 (978-0-9643462-5-3(7) , Just Think Bks.) Canary Connect Pubns.

Rylant, Cynthia & Siegel, Mark, Long Night Moon. 2004. (Illus.). 40p. (J). 16.95 (978-0-689-85426-2(9)) Simon & Schuster Children's Publishing.

Scelsa, Greg. Months of the Year. Faulkner, Stacey, ed. Fulcher, Roz, illus. 2006. (J). pap. 2.99 (*978-1-59198-320-0(7)) Creative Teaching Pr., Inc.

Spinelli, Eileen. Here Comes the Year. Narahashi, Keiko, illus. rev. ed. 2002. 32p. (J). (ps-3). 16.95 (978-0-8050-6685-2(3) , Holt, Henry & Co. Bks. For Young Readers) Holt, Henry & Co.

Tafuri, Nancy. Snowy Flowy Blowy: A Twelve Months Rhyme. 1999. (Illus.). (J). pap. (978-0-590-18974-3(3)) Scholastic Reading Counts.

Tanen, Sloane. Coco All Year Round. Hagen, Stefan, photos by. 2006. (Illus.). 32p. (J). 15.95 (978-1-58234-709-7(3) , Bloomsbury Children) Bloomsbury Publishing.

Tudor, Tasha. Around the Year. Tudor, Tasha, illus. 64p. (J). 2004. pap. 6.99 (978-0-689-87350-8(6) , Aladdin); 2001. (Illus.). 17.99 (978-0-689-82847-8(0)) Simon & Schuster Children's Publishing.

White-Carlstrom, Nancy. How Do You Say it Today, Jesse Bear? 1999. (J). (978-0-606-16941-7(5)) Tandem Library Bks.

MONTHS—POETRY

Chicken Soup with Rice. 2004. (J). 24.95 incl. audio (978-0-89719-865-3(4)); pap. 18.95 incl. audio compact disk (978-1-55592-801-8(3)); pap. 18.95 incl. audio compact disk (978-1-55592-769-1(6)); pap. 38.75 incl. audio compact disk (978-1-55592-818-6(8)); pap. 38.75 incl. audio compact disk (978-1-55592-784-4(X)); pap. 32.75 incl. audio (978-1-55592-206-1(6)); pap. 32.75 incl. audio (978-1-55592-207-8(4)); pap. 14.95 incl. audio (978-1-56008-049-7(3)); pap. 14.95 incl. audio (978-1-55592-720-2(3)) Weston Woods Studios, Inc.

Coleridge, Sara. The Months: Fun with Friends All Year 'Round! Weller, Kathy, illus. 2007. (Read Me a Poem Ser.). 32p. (J). (ps-1). 17.95 (*978-1-897073-67-4(4)) Lobster Pr. CAN. *Dist:* National Bk. Network.

—Les P'tits Amis Découvrent les Mois. Weller, Kathy, illus. 2007. (FRE.). 28p. (J). pap. 9.95 (*978-2-922435-17-7(2)) Lobster Pr. CAN. *Dist:* National Bk. Network.

Livingston, Myra Cohn. Calendar. Hillenbrand, Will, illus. 2007. 32p. (J). (ps-k). 16.95 (978-0-8234-1725-4(5)) Holiday Hse., Inc.

MONTICELLO (VA.)

Bober, Natalie S. Thomas Jefferson: Draftsman of a Nation. 2007. 352p. (YA). (gr. 7 up). 22.95 (*978-0-8139-2632-2(7)) Univ. Pr. of Virginia.

Burgan, Michael. Monticello. 2003. (We the People Ser.). (Illus.). 48p. (J). (gr. 4 up). lib. bdg. 22.60 (978-0-7565-0491-5(0)) Compass Point Bks.

Mohrman, Gary, illus. Monticello. 2005. (Historic Monuments Ser.). 48p. (J). pap. 6.95 (978-1-57310-442-5(6)) Teaching & Learning Co.

Young, Robert. A Personal Tour of Monticello. 1999. (How It Was Ser.). (Illus.). 64p. (J). (gr. 4-6). lib. bdg. (978-0-8225-3575-1(0) , Lerner Pubns.) Lerner Publishing Group.

MONTREAL (QUEBEC)

Mattern, Joanne. Montreal. 2006. (J). (978-1-59679-717-8(7)) ABDO Publishing Co.

Rogers, Stillman D. Montreal. 2000. (Cities of the World Ser.). (Illus.). 64p. (YA). (gr. 4). pap. 9.95 (978-0-516-27038-8(9) , Children's Pr.) Scholastic Library Publishing.

—Montreal. 2000. (gr. 5-8). lib. bdg. 18.75 (978-0-613-54615-7(6)) Tandem Library Bks.

Rowe, Percy & Coster, Patience. Montreal. 2004. (Great Cities of the World Ser.). (Illus.). 48p. (J). pap. (978-0-8368-5199-1(4)); (YA). lib. bdg. 30.00 (978-0-8368-5039-0(4)) Stevens, Gareth Inc. (World Almanac Library).

Symon, John. The Lobster Kids' Guide to Exploring Montreal: 12 Months of Fun. Kirner, Bob, ed. Battuz, Christine, illus. 2nd rev. ed. 2000. (Lobster Kids' City Explorers Ser.). 232-272p. (J). (ps up). pap. 12.95 (978-1-894222-09-9(1)) Lobster Pr. CAN. *Dist:* Univ. of Toronto Pr.

MONTREAL (QUEBEC)—FICTION

Bayle, B. J. Perilous Passage. 2007. 176p. (YA). pap. 11.99 (*978-1-55002-689-4(5) , Sandcastle Bks.) Dundurn Group, The CAN. *Dist:* Univ. of Toronto Pr.

Frechette, Carole. In the Key of Do. Ouriou, Susan, tr. from FRE. 2004. 96p. (YA). (gr. 8 up). pap. 9.95 (978-0-88995-254-6(X)) Red Deer Pr. CAN. *Dist:* Fitzhenry & Whiteside, Ltd.

—In the Key of Do. 2003. (gr. 7-12). lib. bdg. 16.40 (978-0-613-82355-5(9)) Tandem Library Bks.

Gamble, Adam. Good Night Montreal. Kelly, Cooper, illus. 2007. (Good Night Our World Ser.). 20p. (J). bds. 9.95 (*978-1-60219-012-2(7)) Our World of Books.

Goodwin, Catherine. Seeking Shelter. 2006. 154p. (J). pap. (*978-1-55380-033-0(8)) Ronsdale Pr.

Gutman, Dan. The Million Dollar Goal. 2nd ed. 2006. 176p. (J). (gr. 3-7). pap. 5.99 (978-1-4231-0083-6(2)) Hyperion Pr.

King, Donna. Double Twist. 2007. 144p. (J). (gr. 4-6). pap. 5.95 (978-0-7534-6023-8(8) , Kingfisher) Houghton Mifflin Co. Trade & Reference Div.

Polak, Monique. Finding Elmo. 2007. (Orca Currents Ser.). 112p. (YA). (gr. 5 up). pap. (*978-1-55143-686-9(8)); lib. bdg. (*978-1-55143-688-3(4)) Orca Bk. Pubs.

Schwartz, Ellen. Yossi's Goal. 2006. (Illus.). 144p. (J). pap. 5.95 (978-1-55143-492-6(X)) Orca Bk. Pubs. USA.

MONUMENTS

see also Pyramids

Binns, Tristan Boyer. The Lincoln Memorial. (Symbols of Freedom Ser.). (Illus.). 32p. (J). (gr. k-2). 2002. pap. 6.95 (978-1-58810-404-5(4) , 91146); 2001. lib. bdg. 21.36 (978-1-58810-120-4(7)) Heinemann Library.

Capstone Press. Stonehenge. 2007. (Edge Books, the Unexplained). (Illus.). 32p. (J). (*978-0-7368-6762-7(7) , 1265023) Capstone Pr., Inc.

Harcourt School Publishers Staff. World Monuments. 3rd ed. 2002. (Horizons Ser.). (Illus.). (J). pap. 5.50 (978-0-15-333316-3(2)) Harcourt Schl. Pubs.

Hargrove, Julia. Bostons Trail to Freedom. 2003. (Historic Monuments Ser.). (Illus.). 48p. (J). (gr. 4-8). pap. 6.95 (978-1-57310-403-6(5)) Teaching & Learning Co.

—Fort Knox Bullion Depository. 2003. (Historic Monuments Ser.). (Illus.). 48p. (J). (gr. 4-8). pap. 6.95 (978-1-57310-404-3(3)) Teaching & Learning Co.

—Wounded Knee Historic Site. Mohrman, Gary, illus. 2004. (Historic Monuments Ser.). 48p. (J). pap. 6.95 (978-1-57310-431-9(0) , 1238117) Teaching & Learning Co.

Hill, Lee Sullivan. Monuments Help Us Remember. 2000. (Building Block Bks.). (Illus.). 32p. (J). (gr. k-3). lib. bdg. (978-1-57505-475-9(2) , Carolrhoda Bks.) Lerner Publishing Group.

Lace, William W. Stonehenge. 2003. (Mystery Library). (Illus.). 104p. (J). 29.95 (978-1-59018-131-7(X) , Lucent Bks.) Thomson Gale.

Malam, John. Super Structures. 2000. (J). (978-0-606-19796-0(6)) Tandem Library Bks.

Mason, Paul. Mysterious Monuments. 2005. (Illus.). 32p. (J). (gr. 4 up). lib. bdg. 27.10 (978-1-58340-771-4(5)) Smart Apple Media.

Patriotic Monuments & Memorials. 2004. (Patriotic Activities Ser.). 48p. (J). 7.99 (978-0-7439-3598-2(5)) Teacher Created Materials, Inc.

Putnam, Jeff. National Monuments: Events & Times. 2004. (Illus.). iii, 75p. (J). pap. (*978-0-7367-1787-8(0)) Zaner-Bloser, Inc.

Savage, Andrea. Famous Structures. 2005. (X-Zone Ser.). (Illus.). 30p. (gr. 4-8). 23.00 (978-0-7910-8976-7(2)) Facts On File, Inc.

Scholastic, Inc. Staff & Keenan, Sheila. O, Say Can You See? America's Symbols, Landmarks, & Important Words. 2007. 64p. (J). pap. 5.99 (*978-0-439-59360-1(3) , Scholastic Nonfiction) Scholastic, Inc.

Silate, Jennifer. The Statue of Liberty. 2005. (Illus.). 24p. (J). lib. bdg. (978-1-4042-2696-8(6)) Rosen Publishing Group, Inc., The.

M N O

Weatherly, Myra. Taj Mahal. 2002. (Building History Ser.). (Illus.). 112p. (J). (gr. 6-9). 32.45 (978-1-56006-723-8(3) , Lucent Bks.) Thomson Gale.

MONUMENTS, NATURAL

see Natural Monuments

MONUMENTS—UNITED STATES

Armentrout, David & Armentrout, Patricia. Historic Sites & Monuments. 2002. (Guides to State Symbols). (Illus.). 48p. (gr. 3-8). 20.95 (978-1-58952-085-1(8)) Rourke Publishing, LLC.

Ashley, Susan. Mount Rushmore. 2004. (Weekly Reader Early Learning Library). (Illus.). 24p. (J). (gr. 2 up). pap. 5.95 (978-0-8368-4149-7(2)); lib. bdg. 19.33 (978-0-8368-4142-8(5)) Stevens, Gareth Inc. (Weekly Reader Early Learning Library).

—The Statue of Liberty. 2004. (Weekly Reader Early Learning Library). (Illus.). 24p. (J). (gr. 2 up). pap. 5.95 (978-0-8368-4150-3(6)); lib. bdg. 19.33 (978-0-8368-4143-5(3)) Stevens, Gareth Inc. (Weekly Reader Early Learning Library).

—The Washington Monument. 2004. (Weekly Reader Early Learning Library). (Illus.). 24p. (J). (gr. 2 up). pap. 5.95 (978-0-8368-4151-0(4)); lib. bdg. 19.33 (978-0-8368-4144-2(1)) Stevens, Gareth Inc. (Weekly Reader Early Learning Library).

Britton, Tamara L. Devil's Tower. 2005. (Illus.). 32p. (J). (gr. k-6). lib. bdg. 22.78 (978-1-59197-833-6(5)) ABDO Publishing Co.

—Symbols, Landmarks, & Monuments Set II. 2004. (Illus.). (J). (gr. k-6). lib. bdg. 136.68 (978-1-59197-517-5(4) , Checkerboard Library) ABDO Publishing Co.

De Capua, Sarah. The Vietnam Memorial. 2003. (Cornerstones of Freedom, 2ND Ser.). (Illus.). 48p. (J). 26.00 (978-0-516-24223-1(7) , Children's Pr.) Scholastic Library Publishing.

DeGezelle, Terri. The Thomas Jefferson Memorial. 2004. (Fact Finders Ser.). (Illus.). 24p. (J). 15.95 (978-0-7368-2531-3(2)) Capstone Pr., Inc.

Ferry, Joseph. The Jefferson Memorial. 2002. (American Symbols & Their Meanings Ser.). (Illus.). 48p. (YA). (gr. 4 up). lib. bdg. (978-1-59084-034-4(8)) Mason Crest Pubs.

—The Vietnam Veterans Memorial. 2002. (American Symbols & Their Meanings Ser.). (Illus.). 48p. (YA). (gr. 4 up). lib. bdg. (978-1-59084-039-9(9)) Mason Crest Pubs.

Foran, Jill. Statues & Monuments. 2004. (American Symbols Ser.). (J). pap. 6.95 (978-1-59036-178-8(4)) Weigl Pubs., Inc.

Healy, Nick. The Statue of Liberty. 2003. (J). pap. (978-1-58417-117-1(0)); lib. bdg. (978-1-58417-054-9(9)) Lake Street Pubs.

Jango-Cohen, Judith. Mount Rushmore. 2004. (Pull Ahead Bks.). (Illus.). 32p. (J). (gr. k-3). lib. bdg. 22.60 (978-0-8225-3801-1(6)) Lerner Publishing Group.

Kasson, Joseph E. The Making of the Star of Texas. 2003. (Illus.). 32p. (J). lib. bdg. 14.95 (978-0-9729435-8-1(7)) Kasson Publishing.

Lavelett, Lucille. Through the Years at Monument, Colorado, 1 Vol. 5th ed. 2004. (Illus.). 168p. (YA). per. (978-0-9755989-0-0(2)) Palmer Lake Historical Society.

Nash, Gary B. Landmarks of the American Revolution. 2003. (American Landmarks Ser.). (Illus.). 160p. (YA). 32.00 (978-0-19-512849-9(4)) Oxford Univ. Pr., Inc.

National Landmarks, 4 bks. Incl. Lincoln Memorial. Deady, Kathleen W. lib. bdg. 18.60 (978-0-7368-1114-9(1)); Statue of Liberty. Deady, Kathleen W. lib. bdg. 18.60 (978-0-7368-1115-6(X)); Vietnam Veterans Memorial. Dubois, Muriel L. lib. bdg. 18.60 (978-0-7368-1116-3(8)); Washington Monument. Dubois, Muriel L. lib. bdg. 18.60 (978-0-7368-1117-0(6)); 24p. (J). (gr. 2-3). 2002. (Illus.). Set lib. bdg. 74.40 (978-0-7368-1158-3(3) , Bridgestone Bks.) Capstone Pr., Inc.

Nelson, Kristin L. The Lincoln Memorial. 2004. (Pull Ahead Bks.). (Illus.). 32p. (J). (gr. k-3). lib. bdg. 22.60 (978-0-8225-3690-1(0)) Lerner Publishing Group.

Nobleman, Marc Tyler. The Lincoln Memorial. 2004. (Let's See Library). (Illus.). 24p. (J). (gr. 1 up). lib. bdg. 19.93 (978-0-7565-0618-6(2)) Compass Point Bks.

Silber, Nina. Landmarks of the Civil War. 2003. (American Landmarks Ser.). (Illus.). 144p. (YA). 30.00 (978-0-19-512920-5(2)) Oxford Univ. Pr., Inc.

Stein, R. Conrad. The Oklahoma City National Memorial. 2003. (Cornerstones of Freedom). (Illus.). 48p. (J). (gr. 4-6). 26.00 (978-0-516-24205-7(9) , Children's Pr.) Scholastic Library Publishing.

Stone, Lynn M. America's Monuments. 2003. (Land of Liberty Ser.). (Illus.). 24p. (gr. 2-5). 17.95 (978-1-58952-312-8(1)) Rourke Publishing, LLC.

Torpie, Kate. Our National Treasures. 2002. (Illus.). 32p. (J). pap. 6.00 (978-1-59034-042-4(6)); (gr. 1-5). 15.95 (978-1-59034-191-9(0)) Mondo Publishing.

Trumbauer, Lisa. Set in Stone. 2005. (Yellow Umbrella Ser.). (J). (978-0-7368-5308-8(1)); (Illus.). 17p. (978-0-7368-5272-2(7)) Capstone Pr., Inc.

Wachtel, Roger. The Tomb of the Unknown Soldier. 2003. (Cornerstones of Freedom, 2ND Ser.). (Illus.). 48p. (J). 26.00 (978-0-516-24215-6(6) , Children's Pr.) Scholastic Library Publishing.

MOODY, DWIGHT LYMAN, 1837-1899

Harvey, Bonnie C. D. L. Moody. 1999. (Young Reader's Christian Library). (Illus.). 220p. (J). (gr. 3-7). pap. 1.39 (978-1-57748-652-7(8)) Barbour Publishing, Inc.

MOODY, JUDY (FICTITIOUS CHARACTER)—FICTION

McDonald, Megan. Doctora Judy Moody. Reynolds, Peter H., illus. 2005. (SPA.). 175p. (J). (gr. 3-5). pap. 7.95 (978-1-59820-034-8(8)) Santillana USA Publishing Co., Inc.

—Judy Moody. Reynolds, Peter H., illus. (Judy Moody Ser.: No. 1). (J). (gr. 1-5). 2002. 160p. pap. 5.99 (978-0-7636-1231-3(6)); 2000. 196p. 15.99 (978-0-7636-0685-5(5)) Candlewick Pr.

—Judy Moody. Reynolds, Peter H., illus. 2002. (Judy Moody Ser.: No. 1). 160p. (J). (ps-7). per. 14.15 (978-0-613-56467-0(7)) Tandem Library Bks.

—Judy Moody Around the World in 8 1/2 Days. Reynolds, Peter H., illus. 2006. (Judy Moody Ser.: No. 7). 176p. (J). (gr. 1-4). 15.99 (978-0-7636-2832-1(8)) Candlewick Pr.

—Judy Moody Declares Independence. Reynolds, Peter H., illus. 2005. (Judy Moody Ser.: No. 6). 160p. (J). (gr. 1-4). 15.99 (978-0-7636-2361-6(X)) Candlewick Pr.

—Judy Moody Esta de Mal Humor, de Muy Mal Humor. Mendoza Garcia, Isabel, tr. Reynolds, Peter H., illus. (SPA.). 168p. (J). (gr. 3-5). pap. 7.95 (978-1-59437-816-4(9)) Santillana USA Publishing Co., Inc.

—Judy Moody Gets Famous! Reynolds, Peter H., illus. (Judy Moody Ser.: No. 2). 144p. (J). (gr. 1-5). 2003. pap. 5.99 (978-0-7636-1931-2(0)); 2001. 15.99 (978-0-7636-0849-1(1)) Candlewick Pr.

—Judy Moody Gets Famous! 2003. (Judy Moody Ser.: No. 2). (gr. 3-6). lib. bdg. 14.15 (978-0-613-62107-6(7)) Tandem Library Bks.

—Judy Moody Predicts the Future. Reynolds, Peter H., illus. 2003. (Judy Moody Ser.: No. 4). 160p. (J). (gr. 1-5). 15.99 (978-0-7636-1792-9(X)) Candlewick Pr.

—Judy Moody Predicts the Future. Reynolds, Peter, illus. 2005. (Judy Moody Ser.: No. 4). 160p. (J). (gr. 1-5). reprint ed. pap. 5.99 (978-0-7636-2343-2(1)) Candlewick Pr.

—Judy Moody Saves the World! Reynolds, Peter H., illus. (Judy Moody Ser.: No. 3). 160p. (J). (gr. 1-5). 2004. pap. 5.99 (978-0-7636-2087-5(4)); 2002. 15.99 (978-0-7636-1446-1(7)) Candlewick Pr.

—Judy Moody se Vuelve Famosa! Mendoza Garcia, Isabel, tr. Reynolds, Peter H., illus. (SPA.). 144p. (J). (gr. 3-5). pap. 7.95 (978-1-59437-817-1(7)) Santillana USA Publishing Co., Inc.

MOON, LOTTIE, 1840-1912

Benge, Janet Hazel & Benge, Geoffrey Francis. Lottie Moon. 2000. (Christian Heroes Ser.). 208p. (gr. 5-9). pap. 8.99 (978-1-57658-188-9(8)) YWAM Publishing.

The Lottie & Annie Upside-down Book. 2003. 8.99 (978-1-56309-627-3(7)) Woman's Missionary Union.

Lottie Moon. (Christian Heroes Ser.). 64p. 8.99 (978-1-57658-209-1(4)) YWAM Publishing.

Meloche, Renee. Lottie Moon: A Generous Offering. Pollard, Bryan, illus. 2004. (Heroes for Young Readers Ser.). 32p. (J). 6.99 (978-1-57658-243-5(4)) YWAM Publishing.

MOON

see also Tides

Adamson, Thomas K. The Moon. 2007. (J). (978-0-7368-6745-0(7)) Capstone Pr., Inc.

Ashby, Ruth. The Earth & Its Moon. 2003. (New Solar System Ser.). (J). lib. bdg. 28.50 (978-1-58340-287-0(X)) Smart Apple Media.

Asimov, Isaac. The Solar System: The Moon. 2004. (Isaac Asimov's 21st Century Library of the Universe). (Illus.). 32p. 14.00 (978-1-59102-123-0(5)) Prometheus Bks., Pubs.

Asimov, Isaac & Hantula, Richard. La Luna. Porras, Carlos & D'Andrea, Patricia, trs. 2003. (Isaac Asimov's Biblioteca del Universo del Siglo XXI). (SPA., Illus.). 32p. (J). (gr. 3 up). lib. bdg. 24.67 (978-0-8368-3855-8(6)); pap. 8.95 (978-0-8368-3868-8(8) , Weekly Reader Early Learning Library) Stevens, Gareth Inc.

—The Moon. 2003. (Isaac Asimov's 21st Century Library of the Universe). (Illus.). 32p. (gr. 3 up). (J). pap. (978-0-8368-3942-5(0) , Weekly Reader Early Learning Library); (YA). lib. bdg. 24.67 (978-0-8368-3238-9(8)) Stevens, Gareth Inc.

Atcheson, Dan. Puppy Dog Moon. Grubbs, Kent, illus. 2002. 14p. (J). (ps-5). pap. (978-0-9613202-7-0(3)) Norseman Publishing Co.

Bailey, Jacqui. Sun Up, Sun Down: The Story of Day & Night. Lilly, Matthew, illus. 2004. (Science Works Ser.). 32p. (J). (gr. 3-6). 23.93 (978-1-4048-0567-5(2)) Picture Window Bks.

Birch, Robin. Earth, Sun, & Moon. 2002. (Space Ser.). (Illus.). 32p. (gr. k-2). 23.00 (978-0-7910-6970-7(2) , Chelsea Hse.) Facts On File, Inc.

—The Moon. 2004. (Solar System Ser.). (Illus.). 32p. (gr. 3-5). 23.00 (978-0-7910-7929-4(5) , Chelsea Hse.) Facts On File, Inc.

Bourgeois, Paulette. The Moon. Slavin, Bill, illus. unabr. ed. 1999. (Starting with Space Ser.). 40p. (J). (gr. 4-6). (978-1-55074-332-6(5)) Kids Can Pr., Ltd.

Branley, Franklyn M. What the Moon Is Like. Kelley, True, illus. 2000. (Let's-Read-and-Find-Out Science Ser.). 40p. (J). (gr. k-4). 15.89 (978-0-06-027993-6(1)); pap. 5.99 (978-0-06-445185-7(2) , Harper Trophy) HarperCollins Pubs.

Bredeson, Carmen. La Luna. 2004. (Rookie Readers - Spanish Ser.). (J). 19.50 (978-0-516-24447-1(7) , Watts, Franklin) Scholastic Library Publishing.

—La Luna: The Moon. 2005. (Rookie Espanol: Ciencias Ser.). (SPA., Illus.). 32p. (J). (gr. k-2). pap. 5.95 (978-0-516-24696-3(8) , Children's Pr.) Scholastic Library Publishing.

—The Moon. (Rookie Read-About Science Ser.). (Illus.). (J). 2003. 32p. (gr. 1-2). 20.50 (978-0-516-22864-8(1) , Children's Pr.); 1998. 64p. (gr. 5-7). pap. 6.95 (978-0-531-15911-8(6) , Watts, Franklin); 1998. 64p. (gr. 4-6). 23.00 (978-0-531-20308-8(5) , Watts, Franklin) Scholastic Library Publishing.

—Moon. 2003. (gr. k-3). lib. bdg. 12.95 (978-0-613-67916-9(4)) Tandem Library Bks.

Bredeson, Carmen. What Is the Moon? 2008. (I Like Space! Ser.). (Illus.). 32p. (J). (gr. 1-3). lib. bdg. 22.60 ***(*978-0-7660-2946-0(8)*** , Enslow Elementary) Enslow Pubs., Inc.

Brinkman, Patricia. Discover the Moon. 2006. pap. 39.00 ***(*978-1-4108-6478-9(2))*** Benchmark Education Co.

—The Moon. 2006. pap. 39.00 ***(*978-1-4108-6475-8(8))*** Benchmark Education Co.

Carroll, Jillian. Zoom Around a Moon. 2003. (J). pap. (978-1-58417-241-3(X)); lib. bdg. (978-1-58417-240-6(1)) Lake Street Pubs.

Carruthers, Margaret W. The Moon. (Watts Library). (J). 2004. (gr. 5-7). pap. 8.95 (978-0-531-16373-3(3)); 2003. (Illus.). 64p. 25.50 (978-0-531-12281-5(6)) Scholastic Library Publishing. (Watts, Franklin).

Chrismer, Melanie. The Moon. (Scholastic News Nonfiction Readers: Space Science Ser.). 24p. (J). 2008. pap. 6.95 ***(*978-0-531-14764-1(9));*** 2007. (Illus.), (gr. 1-2). lib. bdg. 20.00 ***(*978-0-531-14699-6(5))*** Scholastic Library Publishing. (Children's Pr.).

Cole, Michael D. The Moon: Earth's Companion in Space. 2001. (Countdown to Space Ser.). (Illus.). 48p. (YA). (gr. 4-10). lib. bdg. 23.93 (978-0-7660-1510-4(6)) Enslow Pubs., Inc.

Dubarle-Bossy, Philippe. Hello, Moon! Moon, Jo, illus. 2005. 8p. (J). 9.95 (978-1-4027-2624-8(4) , Sterling/Pinwheel) Sterling Publishing Co., Inc.

Eckart, Edana. Watching the Moon. 2004. (Wel-Watching Nature Ser.). (Illus.). 24p. (J). 18.00 (978-0-516-27598-7(4)); pap. 4.95 (978-0-516-25936-9(9)) Scholastic Library Publishing. (Children's Pr.).

Feinstein, Stephen. The Moon: A MyReportLinks. com Book. 2005. (Solar System Ser.). (Illus.). 48p. (J). lib. bdg. 25.26 (978-0-7660-5306-9(7) , MyReportLinks.com Bks.) Enslow Pubs., Inc.

Frank, Marjorie Slavick, et al. Science Instant Readers Bk. 7: The Moon. 1999. (Harcourt Science Ser.). (gr. 2 up). pap. 15.50 (978-0-15-316217-6(1)) Harcourt Schl. Pubs.

Galat, Joan Marie. Stories of the Moon. Bennett, Lorna, illus. 2004. (Dot to Dot in the Sky Ser.). 64p. (J). (gr. 2-6). pap. 12.95 (978-1-55285-610-9(0)) Whitecap Bks., Ltd. CAN. *Dist:* Firefly Bks., Ltd.

Gardner, Robert. Far-Out Science Projects about Earth's Sun & Moon. LaBaff, Tom, illus. 2007. (Rockin' Earth Science Experiments Ser.). 48p. (J). (gr. 3-6). lib. bdg. 23.93 (978-0-7660-2736-7(8) , Enslow Elementary) Enslow Pubs., Inc.

Goldstein, Margaret J. The Moon. 2005. (Pull Ahead Bks.). (Illus.). 32p. (gr. 2-4). lib. bdg. 22.60 (978-0-8225-4658-0(2)) Lerner Publishing Group.

Graham, Ian. The Best Book of the Moon. 2005. (Best Book of... Ser.). (Illus.). 32p. (J). (gr. k-3). pap. 5.95 (978-0-7534-5902-7(7) , Kingfisher) Houghton Mifflin Co. Trade & Reference Div.

—The Best Book of the Moon. Grinaway, Ray & Stewart, Roger, illus. 1999. (Best Book of... Ser.). 32p. (J). (gr. k-3). tchr. ed. 12.95 (978-0-7534-5174-8(3) , Kingfisher) Houghton Mifflin Co. Trade & Reference Div.

—The Moon. 2007. (J). ***(*978-1-59920-070-5(8))*** Smart Apple Media.

Graham, Ian. My Book of Space. 2001. (My Book of... Ser.). (Illus.). 48p. (J). (ps-k). tchr. ed. 14.95 (978-0-7534-5399-5(1) , Kingfisher) Houghton Mifflin Co. Trade & Reference Div.

Harcourt School Publishers Staff. The Moon: Science Reader. 1999. (SPA., Illus.). (J). pap. 3.70 (978-0-15-316122-3(1)) Harcourt Schl. Pubs.

—Moon Days. 3rd ed. 2002. (Trophies English Language Learners Ser.). (Illus.). pap. 51.00 (978-0-15-327897-6(8)) Harcourt Schl. Pubs.

—Our Moon On Level. 3rd ed. 2002. (Trophies Reading Program Ser.). (Illus.). pap. 5.10 (978-0-15-323190-2(4)) Harcourt Schl. Pubs.

—Trofeos On Level: La Luna. 3rd ed. 2002. (SPA., Illus.). pap. 6.80 (978-0-15-324101-7(2)) Harcourt Schl. Pubs.

HB Staff. Moon Changes Shape. 95th ed. 1998. (gr. 1). pap. 11.80 (978-0-15-303633-0(8)) Harcourt Schl. Pubs.

Hutson, Matt. The Inside Story of the Moon. 2006. (J). 7.80 (978-1-933798-05-9(X)) Sally Ride Science.

Kerrod, Robin. Moon-Earth's Neighbor. 1999. (J). (978-1-57505-362-2(4) , Carolrhoda Bks.) Lerner Publishing Group.

—The Sun & the Moon. 2001. (Exploring the Universe Ser.). (Illus.). 48p. (J). lib. bdg. 27.12 (978-0-7398-2818-2(5)) Raintree.

Kosek, Jane Kelly. What's Inside the Moon? 1999. (What's Inside Library). 24p. (J). (gr. k-4). lib. bdg. 18.75 (978-0-8239-5282-3(7) , PowerKids Pr.) Rosen Publishing Group, Inc., The.

Krupp, Edwin C. The Moon & You. 2000. (Illus.). 32p. (J). (gr. k-3). pap. 5.95 (978-0-688-17818-5(9)) HarperCollins Pubs.

Landau, Elaine. The Moon. (True Booktrade;: Space Ser.). 48p. (J). 2008. pap. 6.95 ***(*978-0-531-14792-4(4));*** 2007. (Illus.). (gr. 3-5). lib. bdg. 26.00 ***(*978-0-531-12562-5(9))*** Scholastic Library Publishing. (Children's Pr.).

Lassieur, Allison. The Moon. 2001. (True Bks.). (Illus.). 48p. (J). (gr. 3-5). pap. 6.95 (978-0-516-27186-6(5) , Children's Pr.) Scholastic Library Publishing.

—The Moon Exposed. 2006. (Illus.). 32p. (J). pap. (978-1-4109-2604-3(4)); lib. bdg. (978-1-4109-2575-6(7)) Steck-Vaughn.

Lilly, Melinda. Sun & Moon. 2006. (Rourke Discovery Library). (Illus.). 24p. (gr. 1-4). 14.95 (978-1-59515-405-7(1) , 1244276) Rourke Publishing, LLC.

Lipschultz, Wes. All about the Moon. 2002. (Reading Room Collection). (Illus.). 24p. (J). lib. bdg. 18.75 (978-0-8239-3742-4(9)) Rosen Publishing Group, Inc., The.

Llewellyn, Claire. The Moon. 2003. (Starters Ser.). 24p. (J). lib. bdg. 21.35 (978-1-58340-260-3(8)) Smart Apple Media.

Lucas, Debra. Our Moon. (Illus.). (J). (gr. k-2). 2006. 16p. 15.93 (978-0-7368-5830-4(X) , Yellow Umbrella Bks.); 2005. 17p. (978-0-7368-5296-8(4)); 2005. 17p. (978-0-7368-5260-9(3)) Capstone Pr., Inc.

Malam, John. Man Walks on the Moon. 2003. (Dates with History Ser.). 45p. (J). lib. bdg. 28.50 (978-1-58340-407-2(4)) Smart Apple Media.

McNeil, Niki, et al. HOCPP 1100 the Moon. 2006. spiral bd. 16.50 ***(*978-1-60308-100-9(3))*** In the Hands of a Child.

McNulty, Faith. If You Decide to Go to the Moon. Kellogg, Steven, illus. 2005. 48p. (J). (ps-3). pap. 16.99 (978-0-590-48359-9(5) , Scholastic Pr.) Scholastic, Inc.

Milbourne, Anna. On the Moon. 2004. (On the Moon Ser.). 24p. (J). 9.95 (978-0-7945-0617-9(8) , Usborne) EDC Publishing.

Miller, Heather L. The Moon. 2007. (KidHaven Science Library Ser.). (Illus.). 48p. (J). (gr. 4-8). 23.70 ***(*978-0-7377-3777-6(8)*** , Kidhaven) Thomson Gale.

Miller, Ron. Earth & the Moon. 2003. (Worlds Beyond Ser.). (Illus.). 96p. (gr. 7 up). lib. bdg. (978-0-7613-2358-7(9) , Twenty-First Century Bks.) Lerner Publishing Group.

Mist, Rosalind. Will the Sun Ever Burn Out? Earth, Sun, & Moon. 2006. (Stargazers Guides Ser.). (Illus.). 48p. (J). (978-1-4034-7707-1(8)); pap. (978-1-4034-7714-9(0)) Heinemann Library.

Mitchell, Melanie S. Moon. 2004. (First Step Nonfiction Ser.). (Illus.). 24p. (J). (gr. k-2). lib. bdg. 18.60 (978-0-8225-0188-6(0)) Lerner Publishing Group.

—The Moon. 2003. (First Step Nonfiction Ser.). (Illus.). 22p. (J). pap. 3.95 (978-0-8225-3591-1(2) , Lerner Pubns.) Lerner Publishing Group.

The Moon, 6 vols. 2005. (Earth & Outer Space Ser.). (gr. k-2). 28.95 (978-0-7368-3259-5(9)) Red Brick Learning.

The Moon: Individual Title Six-Packs. (Rigby Focus Ser.). 16p. (gr. k up). 26.00 (978-0-7578-5289-3(0)); 28.00 (978-0-7578-5523-8(7)) Rigby Education.

The Moon in 12 Phases Journal. 2002. 14.95 (978-0-7893-0775-0(8)) Universe Publishing.

Murphy, Patricia J. Why Does the Moon Change. 2004. (Library of Why?). (Illus.). 24p. (J). lib. bdg. 18.75 (978-0-8239-6234-1(2)) Rosen Publishing Group, Inc., The.

Nardo, Don. The Moon. 2002. (Eyes on the Sky Ser.). (Illus.). 48p. (J). (gr. 3-5). 23.70 (978-0-7377-1291-9(0) , Kidhaven) Thomson Gale.

Nuestro Satelite: La Luna. (SPA.). (J). 10.00 (978-84-342-1811-6(9)) Parramon Ediciones S.A. ESP. *Dist:* Distribuidora Norma, Inc.

Olaondo, Susana. Una Luna. Olaondo, Susana, illus. (SPA., Illus.). 32p. (J). (gr. k-3). pap. 7.95 (978-1-58105-635-8(4)) Santillana USA Publishing Co., Inc.

Olien, Rebecca. Exploring the Moon. 2007. (Objects in the Sky Ser.). (Illus.). 24p. (J). pap. (978-1-4042-2174-1(3)); (gr. 4-6). lib. bdg. 21.25 (978-1-4042-3466-6(7)) Rosen Publishing Group, Inc., The. (PowerKids Pr.).

Olson, Gillia M. Las Fases de la Luna: Phases of the Moon. 2008. (ENG & SPA.). (J). ***(*978-1-4296-0044-6(6))*** Capstone Pr., Inc.

Olson, Gillia M. The Phases of the Moon. 2007. (Pebble Plus Ser.). (Illus.). 24p. (J). 19.93 (978-0-7368-6340-7(0)) Capstone Pr., Inc.

Orme, Helen & Orme, David. Let's Explore the Moon. 2006. (J). pap. ***(*978-0-8368-8128-8(1));*** lib. bdg. ***(*978-0-8368-7943-8(0))*** Stevens, Gareth Inc.

Oxlade, Chris. The Earth & Its Moon. 2007. (J). lib. bdg. ***(*978-1-4042-3734-6(8)*** , Rosen Central) Rosen Publishing Group, Inc., The.

Phelan, Glen. Earth, Sun, Moon. 2004. (National Geographic Reading Expeditions Ser.). (Illus.). 32p. (J). pap. (978-0-7922-4573-5(3)) National Geographic Society.

Prinja, Raman. The Moon. 2003. (Universe Ser.). (Illus.). 32p. (J). (gr. 3-5). lib. bdg. 22.79 (978-1-58810-914-9(3)); pap. 7.50 (978-1-4034-0615-6(4)) Heinemann Library.

—The Sun. 2003. (Universe Ser.). (Illus.). 32p. (J). pap. (978-1-4034-0618-7(9)) Heinemann Library.

Rau, Dana Meachen. Moon. 2003. (Our Solar System Ser.). (Illus.). 32p. (J). (gr. 3 up). lib. bdg. 21.26 (978-0-7565-0438-0(4)) Compass Point Bks.

—Night Light: A Book about the Moon. Shea, Denise, illus. 2005. (Amazing Science Ser.). 24p. (J). (ps-k). lib. bdg. 22.60 (978-1-4048-1136-2(2)) Picture Window Bks.

Riley, Peter D. Earth, Moon & Sun. 2007. (J). ***(*978-1-59920-025-5(2))*** Smart Apple Media.

Rushworth, Gary. Our Solar System: The Moon. 2006. (Navigators Ser.). (J). pap. 38.00 ***(*978-1-4108-6221-1(6))*** Benchmark Education Co.

Rustad, Martha E. H. The Moon. Saunders-Smith, Gail, ed. 2002. (Out in Space Ser.). (Illus.). 24p. (J). (gr. k-1). lib. bdg. 15.93 (978-0-7368-1177-4(X) , Pebble Bks.) Capstone Pr., Inc.

Ryback, Carol. The Moon. 2006. (Illus.). 24p. (J). pap. (978-0-8368-6348-2(8)); lib. bdg. 19.33 (978-0-8368-6343-7(7)) Stevens, Gareth Inc.

Scholastic, Inc. Staff & Cole, Joanna. Magic School Bus Takes a Moonwalk. 2007. (Msb Science Reader Ser.). 32p. (J). pap. 3.99 ***(*978-0-439-68400-2(5))*** Scholastic, Inc.

Seymour, Arlene. The Moon Book: A Lunar Pop-up Celebration. Seymour, Arlene, illus. 2004. (Illus.). 14p. (YA). (gr. k-4). reprint ed. 22.00 (978-0-7567-7645-9(7)) DIANE Publishing Co.

Simon, Seymour. The Moon. rev. ed. 2003. (Illus.). 32p. (J). 18.99 (978-0-689-83563-6(9)) Simon & Schuster Children's Publishing.

Slade, Suzanne. Lunar Cycles. 2007. (Illus.). 24p. (J). (978-1-4042-2387-5(8)); pap. (978-1-4042-2197-0(2)) Rosen Publishing Group, Inc., The. (PowerKids Pr.).

M N O

Sneider, Cary I. Earth, Moon & Stars. Bergman, Lincoln & Fairwell, Kay, eds. Baker, Lisa H. et al, illus. Sneider, Cary I., photos by. rev. ed. 1998. (Great Explorations in Math & Science Ser.). 100p. (YA). (gr. 5-8). pap. 13.50 (978-0-924886-05-8(6) , GEMS) Univ. of California, Berkeley, Lawrence Hall of Science.

Spangenburg, Ray. Look at Moons. 2000. (gr. 5-8). lib. bdg. 24.55 (978-0-613-54740-6(3)) Tandem Library Bks.

Sparrow, Giles. Moon. (Exploring the Solar System Ser.). (Illus.). (J). (gr. 4-6). 2002. 40p. pap. 7.95 (978-1-58810-963-7(1) , 91446); 2001. 39p. lib. bdg. 24.22 (978-1-57572-390-7(5)) Heinemann Library.

Stefoff, Rebecca. Earth & the Moon. 2001. (Blastoff! Ser.). (Illus.). 64p. (J). (gr. 5 up). lib. bdg. 28.50 (978-0-7614-1235-9(2) , Benchmark Bks.) Cavendish, Marshall Corp.

Stewart, Melissa. Why Does the Moon Change Shape? 2008. (J). (*978-0-7614-2921-0(2)) Cavendish, Marshall Bks., Ltd.

Taylor, Joanne. Full Moon Rising. Tooke, Susan, illus. 2002. 32p. (J). (gr. k-3). 16.95 (978-0-88776-548-3(3)) Tundra Bks., Inc./Livres Toundra, Inc. CAN. *Dist:* Random Hse., Inc.

Tocci, Salvatore. Experiments with the Sun & the Moon. 2003. (True Bks.). (gr. 3-5). pap. 6.95 (978-0-516-27469-0(4)); (Illus.). 48p. (J). 25.00 (978-0-516-22605-7(3)) Scholastic Library Publishing. (Children's Pr.).

—Experiments with the Sun & the Moon. 2003. (gr. 3-6). lib. bdg. 15.25 (978-0-613-67892-6(3)) Tandem Library Bks.

Tomecek, Steve. Moon. Guida, Liisa C., illus. 2005. (Jump into Science Ser.). 32p. (J). (ps-3). 16.95 (978-0-7922-5123-1(7)); 25.90 (978-0-7922-8304-1(X)) National Geographic Society. (National Geographic Children's Bks.).

Turnbull, Stephanie. Sun, Moon & Stars (Level 2) - Internet Referenced. 2006. 32p. (J). 4.99 (978-0-7945-1399-3(9) , Usborne) EDC Publishing.

Twist, Clint. The Moon. 2006. (Stories of the Sun). 28p. (J). (gr. 3-8). 14.95 (978-0-7696-4490-5(2)) School Specialty Publishing.

Whitehouse, Patricia. Moon. 2004. (J). lib. bdg. 24.21 (978-1-4034-5152-1(4)) Heinemann Library.

—The Moon. 2004. (J). pap. 7.25 (978-1-4034-5656-4(9)) Heinemann Library.

Willis, Shirley. Dime por Que Cambia de Forma la Luna. 1999. (Coleccion los Estupendos). (SPA., Illus.). 32p. (J). (gr. 2-4). 20.00 (978-0-531-11847-4(9) , OD30025, Watts, Franklin) Scholastic Library Publishing.

—Dime Por Que Cambia de Forma la Luna. 2000. Tr. of Tell Me Why the Moon Changes Shape. (SPA.). (gr. k-3). lib. bdg. 14.10 (978-0-613-72669-6(3)) Tandem Library Bks.

—Dime por Que la Luna Cambia de Forma. 2000. (Estupendos Ser.).Tr. of Tell Me Why the Moon Changes Shape. (J). 12.75 (978-0-606-20149-0(1)) Tandem Library Bks.

—Tell Me Why the Moon Changes Shape. 2000. (Whiz Kids Ser.). (Illus.). 32p. (J). (gr. 1-3). pap. 5.95 (978-0-531-15980-4(9) , Watts, Franklin) Scholastic Library Publishing.

Winrich, Ralph. The Moon. (J). 2008. (*978-1-4296-0725-4(4)); 2005. (Illus.). 24p. 21.26 (978-0-7368-3691-3(8)) Capstone Pr., Inc.

World Book, contrib. by. Earth & Earth's Moon. 2nd ed. 2007. (World Book's Solar System & Space Exploration Library). (Illus.). 64p. (J). (*978-0-7166-9512-7(X)) World Bk., Inc.

World Book, Inc Staff, contrib. by. Earth & Earth's Moon. 2006. (World Book's Solar System & Space Exploration Library). 63p. (J). (978-0-7166-9503-5(0)) World Bk., Inc.

York, Pat. The Moon. 2002. (Science Matters Ser.). (Illus.). 24p. (J). lib. bdg. 17.10 (978-1-59036-088-0(5)) Weigl Pubs., Inc.

MOON—EXPLORATION

Bredeson, Carmen. The Moon. 1998. (First Bks.). (Illus.). 64p. (J). (gr. 4-6). 23.00 (978-0-531-20308-8(5) , Watts, Franklin) Scholastic Library Publishing.

Caruso, Kevin M. Back to the Moon: Mankind Returns to the Lunar Surface. 2001. (Illus.). xxx, 282p. (J). (gr. 7-12). per. 35.00 (978-0-9705150-0-1(6)) Aerospace 1 Pubns.

Cole, Michael D. Moon Base: First Colony in Space. 1999. (Countdown to Space Ser.). (Illus.). 48p. (YA). (gr. 4-10). lib. bdg. 23.93 (978-0-7660-1118-2(6)) Enslow Pubs., Inc.

Dyson, Marianne J. Home on the Moon: Living on a Space Frontier. 2003. (Illus.). 64p. (J). (gr. 3-7). 18.95 (978-0-7922-7193-2(9) , National Geographic Children's Bks.) National Geographic Society.

Glatzer, Jenna. The Exploration of the Moon. 2002. (Exploration & Discovery Ser.). (Illus.). 64p. (J). (gr. 5 up). lib. bdg. (978-1-59084-048-1(8)) Mason Crest Pubs.

Jefferis, David. Return to the Moon. 2007. (Illus.). 32p. (J). (gr. 3-7). (*978-0-7787-3103-0(0)); pap. (*978-0-7787-3117-7(0)) Crabtree Publishing Co.

Kemnitz, Tom, Jr. Winning the Race to the Moon: Space. 2001. (Adventures on the American Frontiers Ser.). (Illus.). 80p. (J). (gr. 3-6). pap. 9.99 (978-0-89824-319-2(X) , 319x) Royal Fireworks Publishing Co.

Landmark Events in American History: The First Moon Landing; Lexington & Concord; The Terrorist Attacks of September 11, 2001; The Trail of Tears; The Transcontinental Railroad; The Triangle Shirtwaist Factory Fire, 6 bks. 2003. (Illus.). (J). (gr. 5 up). lib. bdg. 175.60 (978-0-8368-5377-3(6) , World Almanac Library) Stevens, Gareth Inc.

Man Walks on the Moon. 2002. (History in the Headlines Ser.). 32p. (gr. 6-8). 6.99 (978-0-7682-0472-8(0) , GA131697) School Specialty Publishing.

Marcovitz, Hal. Reaching for the Moon: The Apollo Astronauts. 2000. (Explorers of the New World Ser.). (Illus.). (J). 63p. (gr. 4-7). pap. 25.00 (978-0-7910-6167-1(1)); 64p. (gr. 8-12). 25.00 (978-0-7910-5957-9(X)) Facts On File, Inc. (Chelsea Hse.).

—Reaching for the Moon: The Apollo Astronauts. 2001. (gr. 3-6). lib. bdg. 17.60 (978-0-613-32989-7(9)) Tandem Library Bks.

Shearer, Deborah A. Walking on the Moon. 2002. (Explore Space! Ser.). (Illus.). 24p. (J). (gr. 1-2). lib. bdg. 18.60 (978-0-7368-1145-3(1) , Bridgestone Bks.) Capstone Pr., Inc.

Tucker, Mary. Moon Walk. Mitchell, Judy, ed. Hierstein, Judith, illus. 2002. (History - Hands On! Ser.). 32p. (J). (gr. 1-4). pap., tchr. ed. 6.95 (978-1-57310-329-9(2)) Teaching & Learning Co.

Vogt, Gregory L. Apollo Moonwalks: The Amazing Lunar Missions. 2000. (Countdown to Space Ser.). (Illus.). 48p. (YA). (gr. 4-10). lib. bdg. 23.93 (978-0-7660-1306-3(5)) Enslow Pubs., Inc.

Woodford, Chris. Moon Missions. 2004. (History of Space Exploration Ser.). (Illus.). 48p. (J). pap. (978-0-8368-5713-9(5)); (YA). lib. bdg. 30.00 (978-0-8368-5706-1(2)) Stevens, Gareth Inc. (World Almanac Library).

MOON—EXPLORATION—FICTION

Anderson, M. T. Feed. 2004. 320p. (YA). (gr. 9 up). pap. 7.99 (978-0-7636-2259-6(1)) Candlewick Pr.

—Feed. 2004. 320p. (J). (gr. 7 up). pap. 38.00 incl. audio (978-1-4000-9022-8(9) , Listening Library) Random Hse. Audio Publishing Group.

Bennett, Jeffrey. Max Goes to the Moon. Okamoto, Alan, illus. 2003. (Science Adventures with Max the Dog Ser.). 32p. (J). (ps-7). 16.95 (978-0-9721819-0-7(3)) Big Kid Science.

Hickam, Homer H., Jr. Back to the Moon. 2000. (gr. 7-12). lib. bdg. 15.30 (978-0-613-27720-4(1)) Tandem Library Bks.

Montgomery, Anson. Moon Quest: Choose Your Own Adventure #25 - Moon Quest. 2008. (Choose Your Own Adventure Ser.: 25). (Illus.). 144p. (J). per. 5.99 (*978-1-933390-25-3(5)) Chooseco LLC.

Ralles, H. J. Darok 9. 2002. 229p. pap. 9.95 (978-1-929976-10-2(0)) Top Pubns., Ltd.

Yaccarino, Dan. Zoom! Zoom! Zoom! I'm off to the Moon. 2001. (978-0-606-22251-8(0)) Tandem Library Bks.

MOON—FICTION

Allen, Page. Madison's Descent: A Child's Journey. (J). 2006. pap. 25.00 (*978-0-9752516-2-1(7)); 2004. lib. bdg. 60.00 (*978-0-9752516-1-4(9)) Otis & Randolph Pr.

Alonzo, Debra. To the Moon & Back. 2001. (J). pap. 10.00 (978-0-8059-5297-1(7)) Dorrance Publishing Co., Inc.

Andersen, D. R. Why the Moon Changes in the Night Sky. 2005. 40.00 (*978-1-4108-4190-2(1)) Benchmark Education Co.

Armstrong, Jennifer. Sunshine, Moonshine. 2003. (Early Step into Reading Ser.). (Illus.). 32p. (J). (ps-1). 11.99 (978-0-679-96442-1(8) , Random Hse. Bks. for Young Readers) Random Hse. Children's Bks.

Asch, Frank. Happy Birthday, Moon. Asch, Frank, illus. 2002. (Moonbear Ser.). (Illus.). (J). 15.53 (978-0-7587-2686-5(4)) Book Wholesalers, Inc.

—Happy Birthday, Moon. Asch, Frank, illus. (Stories to Go! Ser.). (Illus.). 32p. (J). 2005. 4.99 (978-1-4169-0307-9(0)); 2000. pap. 6.99 (978-0-689-83544-5(2)) Simon & Schuster Children's Publishing. (Aladdin).

—Happy Birthday, Moon. 2005. (Stories to Go! Ser.). (Illus.). (J). (*978-1-4156-0411-3(8) , Aladdin) Simon & Schuster Children's Publishing.

—Mooncake. Asch, Frank, illus. 2002. (Moonbear Ser.). (Illus.). (J). 14.47 (978-0-7587-6749-3(8)) Book Wholesalers, Inc.

—Mooncake. Asch, Frank, illus. 2000. (Moonbear Ser.). 32p. (J). (ps-k). 6.99 (978-0-689-83517-9(5) , Aladdin) Simon & Schuster Children's Publishing.

—Mooncake. 1999. (ps-2). lib. bdg. 15.30 (978-0-613-37191-9(7)) Tandem Library Bks.

—Moondance. Asch, Frank, illus. 2002. (Moonbear Ser.). (Illus.). 13.83 (978-1-4046-0169-7(4)) Book Wholesalers, Inc.

—Moongame. Asch, Frank, illus. 2002. (Moonbear Ser.). (Illus.). (J). 14.47 (978-0-7587-6424-9(3)) Book Wholesalers, Inc.

—Moongame. Asch, Frank, illus. 2000. (Moonbear Ser.). (Illus.). 32p. (J). (ps-k). 6.99 (978-0-689-83518-6(3) , Aladdin) Simon & Schuster Children's Publishing.

—Moongame. (Moonbear Ser.). (ps-k). 2000. (J). (978-0-606-18896-8(7)); 1999. lib. bdg. 15.30 (978-0-613-60907-4(7)) Tandem Library Bks.

Asch, Frank & Asch, Frank. Happy Birthday, Moon. 1999. (Illus.). 28p. (J). (ps-3). lib. bdg. 15.30 (978-0-613-63293-5(1)) Tandem Library Bks.

Avery, Terry. Moon Rabbit Builds a Fine House. l.t. ed. 2000. (Illus.). 32p. (J). (ps-3). 17.95 (978-1-929115-00-6(8)) Azro Pr., Inc.

Baggette, Susan K. The Night the Moon Slept. Saunders, Ward, illus. 2000. 32p. (J). (ps-3). (978-0-9660172-8-1(5)) Brookfield Reader, Inc., The.

Balzola, Asun. Munia y la Luna. 2001. (SPA.). 32p. (J). (978-84-233-1199-6(6)) Ediciones Destino ESP. *Dist:* Lectorum Pubns., Inc.

Banks, Kate. And If the Moon Could Talk. Hallensleben, Georg, illus. 2002. (J). 24.36 (978-0-7587-1943-0(4)) Book Wholesalers, Inc.

—And If the Moon Could Talk. Hallensleben, Georg, illus. 32p. (J). (ps-k). 1998. 15.00 (978-0-374-30299-3(5) , Farrar, Straus & Giroux (BYR)); 2005. reprint ed. pap. 5.95 (978-0-374-43558-5(8) , Sunburst) Farrar, Straus & Giroux.

—And If the Moon Could Talk. Hallensleben, Georg, illus. 2001. (J). (gr. k-2). 25.95 incl. audio (978-0-8045-6867-8(7) , 6867) Spoken Arts, Inc.

Berger, Barbara Helen. A Lot of Otters. Berger, Barbara Helen, illus. 32p. (J). (ps). 2008. bds. 7.99 (*978-0-399-25015-6(8) , Philomel); 2000. (Illus.). pap. 6.99 (978-0-698-11863-8(4) , Putnam Juvenile) Penguin Group (USA) Inc.

Berggren, Jeff. My Moon Lagoon. Hansen, Tammy A., ed. Berggren, Jeff, illus. 2007. (J). per. 14.95 (*978-0-9755033-1-7(6)) Deep Dish Design.

Black Moon. 2004. 176p. (YA). per. 15.00 (978-0-9747017-2-1(6)) Neshee Pubn.

Black, Robert A. Lunar Pioneers. 2008. 280p. (YA). pap. 14.99 (978-1-59092-397-9(9) , Blue Works) Windstorm Creative.

Bonnell, Kris. The Happy Moon. 2006. (J). 3.95 (*978-1-933727-30-1(6)) Reading Reading Bks., LLC.

Branson, Terri. Tyler on the Moon. Taylor, Chet, illus. l.t. ed. 24p. (J). 2005. lib. bdg. 24.95 (978-0-9765786-2-8(X)); 2004. 18.99 (978-0-9755888-2-6(6)) Dragonfly Publishing, Inc.

Brenner, Barbara. Moon Boy. Gabau, Jesus, illus. 1999. (Bank Street Reader Collection). 48p. (J). (gr. 1-3). lib. bdg. 18.60 (978-0-8368-1778-2(8)) Stevens, Gareth Inc.

Bronn, Charles Heil. The Sun, the Moon, & the Gardener's Son. Kami, Y. Z., illus. 2006. 30p. (J). (gr. 4-12). reprint ed. 16.00 (978-1-4223-5222-9(6)) DIANE Publishing Co.

Brooks. Mary Will Not Watch Moon. Date not set. 32p. (J). (ps-1). 14.99 (978-0-06-024491-0(7)) HarperCollins Pubs.

—Mary Will Not Watch the Moon. Date not set. 32p. (J). (ps-1). lib. bdg. 15.89 (978-0-06-024492-7(5)) HarperCollins Pubs.

Brown, Margaret. Over the Moon: A Collection of First Books: Goodnight Moon, the Runaway Bunny, & My World. Hurd, Clement, illus. 2006. 108p. (J). 19.99 (978-0-06-076162-2(8)) HarperCollins Pubs.

Brown, Margaret Wise. Goodnight Moon. Hurd, Clement, illus. 2001. 38p. (J). (ps-1). pap. 6.95 (978-0-9629298-7-8(5) , MHC-7-5) Minnesota Humanities Commission.

—Goodnight Moon 123 Board Book: A Counting Book. Hurd, Clement, illus. 2008. 30p. (J). 8.99 (*978-0-06-112597-3(0) , Harper Festival) HarperCollins Pubs.

—Goodnight Moon Board Book & Slippers. Hurd, Clement, illus. 2007. 34p. (J). 19.99 (*978-0-06-123902-1(X) , Harper Festival) HarperCollins Pubs.

Bunting, Eve. Moonstick: The Seasons of the Sioux. Sandford, John B., illus. 2000. (Trophy Picture Bk.). 32p. (J). (gr. k-4). pap. 6.99 (978-0-06-443619-9(5) , Harper Trophy) HarperCollins Pubs.

—Moonstick: The Seasons of the Sioux. 2000. (978-0-606-18706-0(5)); (gr. 3-6). lib. bdg. 14.10 (978-0-613-34014-4(0)) Tandem Library Bks.

Byng, Georgia. Molly Moon, Micky Minus, & the Mind Machine. 2007. 416p. (J). (gr. 3-7). 16.99 (*978-0-06-075036-7(7)); lib. bdg. 17.89 (*978-0-06-075037-4(5)) HarperCollins Pubs.

Byrne, Barbara. Megan's Moon. 2004. 18p. 14.87 (978-1-4116-1008-8(3)) Lulu.com.

Carle, Eric. Coccinelle Mal Lune. pap. 18.95 (978-2-87142-287-7(7)) Mijade Editions BEL. *Dist:* Distribooks, Inc.

Casado, Alicia & Casado, Dami. La Luna. 2005. (SPA., Illus.). 14p. (J). per. 8.99 (978-84-272-7386-3(X)) Molino, Editorial ESP. *Dist:* Santillana USA Publishing Co., Inc.

Castelli, Jeanette. The cats on the Moon / Los gatos en la Luna. 2005. 48p. pap. (978-958-30-1767-4(1)) Panamericana Editorial.

Cazet, Denys. Minnie & Moo Go to the Moon. Cazet, Denys, illus. 2002. (Minnie & Moo Ser.). (Illus.). (J). 11.32 (978-0-7587-1444-2(0)) Book Wholesalers, Inc.

—Minnie & Moo Go to the Moon. 2001. (Live Oak Readalong Ser.). (Illus.). (J). (ps-4). pap. 16.95 incl. audio (978-0-87499-717-0(8)) Live Oak Media.

Cazet, Denys & Dorling Kindersley Publishing Staff. Minnie & Moo Go to the Moon. 1998. (Minnie & Moo Ser.: Vol. 1). (Illus.). 48p. (J). (gr. 1-3). pap. 3.99 (978-0-7894-2537-9(8)) Dorling Kindersley Publishing, Inc.

Chaikin, Miriam & Fieser, Stephen. Alexandra's Scroll: The Story of the First Hanukkah. rev. ed. 2002. (Illus.). 128p. (J). (gr. 4-7). 18.95 (978-0-8050-6384-4(6) , Holt, Henry & Co. Bks. For Young Readers) Holt, Henry & Co.

Choldenko, Gennifer. Moonstruck: The True Story of the Cow Who Jumped over the Moon. 1999. (978-0-606-17169-4(X)) Tandem Library Bks.

Christenson, Lisa & Christenson, Emme Jo. Who Ate the Moon? Christenson, Lisa & Christenson, Emme Jo, illus. 2006. (J). per. (978-0-9725311-2-2(2)) Pickled Eggs Pr.

Craft, Mahlon. Christmas Moon. Craft, K. Y., illus. 2003. 32p. (J). 15.95 (978-1-58717-056-0(6)); lib. bdg. (978-1-58717-057-7(4)) Chronicle Bks. LLC. (SeaStar Bks.).

Crews, Nina. I'll Catch the Moon. 1999. (Metro Reading Program Ser.). (J). (gr. k). 29.95 (978-1-58120-105-5(2)); 7.98 (978-1-58120-968-6(1)); 45.95 (978-1-58830-014-0(5)) Metropolitan Teaching & Learning Co.

Crook, Connie Brummel. Maple Moon. Cameron, Scott, illus. unabr. ed. 1998. 32p. (YA). (ps-2). (978-0-7737-3017-5(6)) Stoddart Kids.

—Maple Moon. 2000. (Illus.). 30p. (J). (ps-3). 6.95 (978-0-7737-6098-1(9)) Stoddart Kids CAN. *Dist:* Fitzhenry & Whiteside, Ltd.

Cross, Nicholas. The Boy & the Dog Who Walked to the Moon. 2000. (Illus.). 160p. (J). (gr. 3 up). pap. (978-0-86315-314-3(3)) Floris Bks. GBR. *Dist:* SteinerBooks, Inc.

Cummings, Jean. Luna. Cummings, Jean, illus. 2001. (SPA., Illus.). 32p. (J). (ps-3). pap. (978-1-59134-002-7(0)) Maval Publishing, Inc.

Curtis, Carolyn. I Took the Moon for a Walk. Jay, Alison, illus. 2004. 32p. (J). 16.99 (978-1-84148-611-6(6)) Barefoot Bks., Inc.

Danziger, Paula. This Place Has No Atmosphere. 2006. (J). 176p. (gr. 5). 5.99 (978-0-14-240680-9(5)); 156p. (*978-1-4156-7492-5(2)) Penguin Group (USA) Inc. (Puffin).

de Brunhoff, Laurent. Babar Raconte la Course a la Lune. (Babar Ser.). (FRE., Illus.). 48p. (J). (ps-3). 19.95 (978-0-7859-8820-5(3)) French & European Pubns., Inc.

De Lint, Charles. Wolf Moon. 2004. (Illus.). 256p. (Orig.). (YA). pap. 6.99 (978-0-14-240077-7(7) , Puffin) Penguin Group (USA) Inc.

Desimini, Lisa. The Sun & Moon: A Giant Love Story. 1999. (Illus.). 40p. (YA). (ps-3). pap. 16.95 (978-0-590-18720-6(1) , Blue Sky Pr., The) Scholastic, Inc.

Devries, Karen. Peekaboo, Pearly Moon. Myers, Stan, illus. 2004. 32p. (ps-2). 12.99 (978-0-8254-2448-9(8)) Kregel Pubns.

Dillon, Jana. Lucky O'Leprechaun in School. 2003. (Illus.). 32p. 15.95 (978-1-58980-035-9(4)) Pelican Publishing Co., Inc.

DiTerlizzi, Tony. Jimmy Zangwow's Out-of-This-World Moon-Pie Adventure. 2003. (gr. k-3). lib. bdg. 15.30 (978-0-613-61784-0(3)) Tandem Library Bks.

Duffy, Carol Ann. The Tear Thief. Ceccoli, Nicoletta, illus. 2007. 32p. (J). (ps-5). 16.99 (*978-1-84686-045-4(8)) Barefoot Bks., Inc.

Dwyer, Tom. What the Man in the Moon Saw. Buziak, Cari, illus. 2000. (J). cd-rom 9.95 (978-1-58338-701-6(3)) CrossroadsPub.com.

Ehlert, Lois. Moon Rope. 2003. Tr. of Lazo A La Luna. (SPA.). (gr. k-3). lib. bdg. 15.30 (978-0-613-70661-2(7)) Tandem Library Bks.

Ellis, Kiersten. Do Planets Hang on Strings? 2006. 24p. (J). per. 11.99 (*978-1-59886-688-9(5)); 14.99 (*978-1-59886-992-7(2)) Tate Publishing & Enterprises, L.L.C.

Farias, Juan. Los Caminos de la Luna. (SPA., Illus.). 96p. (J). (978-84-207-8293-5(9)) Grupo Anaya, S.A. ESP. *Dist:* Lectorum Pubns., Inc.

Fitch, Sheree. If I Were the Moon. Watts, Leslie Elizabeth, illus. 1999. 32p. (J). 14.00 (978-0-385-25744-2(9) , Doubleday Can) Doubleday Canada, Ltd. CAN. *Dist:* Random Hse., Inc.

Fleischman, Sid. Bandit's Moon. 2002. (Illus.). (J). 13.38 (978-0-7587-6511-6(8)) Book Wholesalers, Inc.

—Bandit's Moon. Smith, Jos A., illus. 2000. 144p. (J). (gr. 4-7). pap. 5.50 (978-0-440-41586-2(1) , Yearling) Random Hse. Children's Bks.

—Bandit's Moon. 2000. 11.64 (978-0-606-17891-4(0)); (gr. 3-6). lib. bdg. 13.00 (978-0-613-28411-0(9)) Tandem Library Bks.

Fletcher, Ralph J. Hello, Harvest Moon. Kiesler, Kate, illus. 2003. 32p. (J). (gr. k-3). 16.00 (978-0-618-16451-6(0) , Clarion Bks.) Houghton Mifflin Co. Trade & Reference Div.

García, Cristina. The Dog Who Loved the Moon. Serra, Sebastia, illus. 2008. 32p. (J). 15.99 (*978-1-4169-1836-3(1)) Simon & Schuster Children's Publishing.

Gauthier, Bertrand. Les Griffes de la Pleine Lune. 2002. (Roman Jeunesse Ser.). (FRE.). 96p. (YA). (gr. 4-7). pap. (978-2-89021-188-9(6)) Diffusion du livre Mirabel.

Gay, Marie-Louise. Mademoiselle Moon. Gay, Marie-Louise, illus. 2006. (Illus.). 32p. pap. 7.95 (978-1-55005-134-6(2)) Fitzhenry & Whiteside, Ltd. CAN. *Dist:* F & W Pubns., Inc.

—Midnight Mimi. 2001. (Illus.). 32p. (J). (ps-2). 6.95 (978-0-7737-6203-9(5)) Stoddart Kids CAN. *Dist:* Fitzhenry & Whiteside, Ltd.

Geras, Adele. Little Elephant's Moon. (Illus.). 32p. (J). 13.95 (978-0-241-11729-3(1) , Hamilton, Hamish) Penguin Bks., Ltd. GBR. *Dist:* Trafalgar Square Publishing.

Gershator, David & Gershator, Phillis. Moon Rooster. Halsey, Megan, illus. 2001. 32p. (J). (gr. k-3). 15.95 (978-0-7614-5092-4(0) , Cavendish Children's Bks.) Cavendish, Marshall Corp.

Gerstein, Mordecai. Carolinda Clatter! unabr. ed. 2007. (Illus.). (J). (ps-2). 28.95 incl. audio compact disk (*978-1-59519-958-4(6)) Live Oak Media.

Gerstein, Mordicai. Carolinda Clatter! 2005. (Illus.). 40p. (J). 16.95 (978-1-59643-063-1(X)) Roaring Brook Pr.

Gillmor, Don. Yuck, a Love Story. Gay, Marie-Louise, illus. 2001. 26p. (ps-3). (J). 15.95 (978-0-7737-3218-6(7)); 7.95 (978-0-7737-6209-1(4)) Stoddart Kids CAN. *Dist:* Fitzhenry & Whiteside, Ltd.

Glassman, Peter. The Magical Land of Noom. 1998. (Books of Wonder). (Illus.). 192p. (J). (gr. 3-7). reprint ed. 22.00 (978-0-688-14117-2(X)) HarperCollins Pubs.

Goldberg, Myla. Catching the Moon. Sheban, Chris, illus. 2007. 40p. (J). (ps-3). pap. 16.99 (978-0-439-57686-4(5) , Levine, Arthur A. Bks.) Scholastic, Inc.

Gollub, Matthew. Gobble, Quack, Moon. Love, Judy, illus. 2002. 32p. (J). (ps-3). 18.95 incl. audio compact disk (978-1-889910-20-8(1)) Tortuga Pr.

—Moon Was at a Fiesta. 2002. (gr. k-3). lib. bdg. 15.25 (978-0-613-70980-4(2)) Tandem Library Bks.

Graham, Alistair. Full Moon Afloat. Graham, Alistair, illus. 2003. (Full Moon Soup & Full Moon Afloat Ser.). (Illus.). 32p. (YA). pap. (978-1-85602-217-0(X)) Chrysalis Children's Bks.

Gralley, Jean. The Moon Came down on Milk Street. rev. ed. 2004. (Illus.). 32p. (J). 16.95 (978-0-8050-7266-2(7) , Holt, Henry & Co. Bks. For Young Readers) Holt, Henry & Co.

Guess What the Moon Saw? Individual Title Six-Packs. (ps-2). 23.00 (978-0-7635-8807-6(5)) Rigby Education.

Hale, Bruce. How the Gecko Lost His Tail. Hale, Bruce, illus. 1999. (Moki the Gecko Ser.). Orig. Title: The Adventures of Space Gecko. (Illus.). 32p. (J). (gr. k-6). 8.95 (978-0-9621280-8-0(2)) Words & Pictures Publishing, Inc.

Hanson, Anders. Night Owl. Haberstroh, Anne, illus. 2006. (Fact & Fiction Ser.). 24p. (J). 21.35 (978-1-59679-953-0(6) , SandCastle); pap. (978-1-59679-954-7(4)) ABDO Publishing Co.

Happy Birthday, Moon. 2004. (J). 24.95 incl. audio (978-1-56008-031-2(0)) Weston Woods Studios, Inc.

Happy Birthday Moon. 2004. 29.95 incl. cd-rom (978-1-55592-842-1(0)); pap. 32.75 incl. audio (978-1-55592-236-8(8)); (J). pap. 18.95 incl. audio compact disk (978-1-55592-805-6(6)); (J). pap. 18.95 incl. audio compact disk (978-1-55592-773-8(4)); (J). pap. 38.75 incl. audio compact disk (978-1-55592-822-3(6)); (J). pap. 38.75 incl. audio compact disk (978-1-55592-788-2(2)); (J). pap. 32.75 incl. audio (978-1-55592-237-5(6)); (J). pap. 14.95 incl. audio (978-1-55592-657-1(6)) Weston Woods Studios, Inc.

Harcourt School Publishers Staff. Sky Tales Advanced Level. 3rd ed. 2002. (Trophies Reading Program Ser.). (Illus.). pap. 5.10 (978-0-15-323220-6(X)) Harcourt Schl. Pubs.

Hargrove, Linda J. Wings Across the Moon. Un-Kim, Joung, illus. 2001. (Growing Tree Ser.). 24p. (J). (ps up). 9.95 (978-0-694-01280-0(7) , Harper Festival) HarperCollins Pubs.

Harley, Bill. Bear's All-Night Party. Ferreira, Melissa, illus. 2001. 32p. (J). (ps-2). 15.95 (978-0-87483-572-4(0)) August Hse. Pubs., Inc.

Harris, Jay M. The Moon Is la Luna: A Fun & Easy Way to Learn 55 Spanish Words. Cordell, Matthew, illus. 2007. 32p. (J). (gr. 3-5). 15.00 ***(978-0-618-64645-6(0))*** Houghton Mifflin Co.

Hébert, Marie-Francine & Perkes, Carolyn. Daddy, Can I Have the Moon? Pratt, Mylene, illus. 2001. 32p. (J). (ps up). pap. (978-1-894363-79-2(5)) Dominique & Friends.

Heller, Janet Ruth. How the Moon Regained Her Shape. Hodson, Ben, illus. (J). 2007. 1p. 8.95 ***(978-1-934359-02-0(5));*** 2006. 32p. 15.95 (978-0-9764943-4-8(5)) Sylvan Dell Pubng.

Heller, Nicholas. Elwood & the Witch. Smith, Jos. A., illus. 2000. 32p. (J). (gr. k-3). 15.89 (978-0-688-16946-6(5)) HarperCollins Pubs.

—Elwood & the Witch. Smith, Jos. A., illus. 2000. 32p. (J). (gr. k-3). 15.95 (978-0-688-16945-9(7)) HarperCollins Pubs.

Henkes, Kevin. Kitten's First Full Moon. Henkes, Kevin, illus. 2004. (Illus.). 40p. (J). (ps-k). 16.99 (978-0-06-058828-1(4)); lib. bdg. 16.89 (978-0-06-058829-8(2)) HarperCollins Pubs.

—La Primera Luna Llena de Gatita. Henkes, Kevin, illus. 2006. Orig. Title: Kitten's First Full Moon. (SPA.). 32p. (J). 16.99 (978-0-06-087223-6(3)) HarperCollins Pubs.

Herbauts, Anne. La Luna. Rubio, Esther, tr. from FRE. Herbauts, Anne, illus. 2000. (SPA., Illus.). (J). (ps-2). 18.95 (978-84-88342-24-9(1) , KK5295) S.A. Kokinos ESP. *Dist:* Lectorum Pubns., Inc.

Hergé. Destination Moon.Tr. of Objectif Lune. (J). (gr. 3-8). ring bd. 19.95 (978-0-8288-5026-1(7)); (Illus.). 62p. 19.95 (978-0-8288-5027-8(5)) French & European Pubns., Inc.

—Objectif Lune.Tr. of Destination Moon. (FRE., Illus.). (J). (gr. 7-9). ring bd. 19.95 (978-0-8288-5051-3(8)) French & European Pubns., Inc.

—On a Marche sur la Lune. (Tintin Ser.).Tr. of Explorers on the Moon. (FRE.). (J). pap. 21.95 (978-2-203-00116-9(X)) Casterman, Editions FRA. *Dist:* Distribooks, Inc.

—On a Marche sur la Lune.Tr. of Explorers on the Moon. (FRE., Illus.). (J). (gr. 7-9). ring bd. 19.95 (978-0-8288-5053-7(4)) French & European Pubns., Inc.

Hija del Sol y de Luna (Daughter of Sun & Moon) (SPA.). 24p. (J). 4.95 (978-84-246-1610-6(3)) La Galera, S.A. Editorial ESP. *Dist:* AIMS International Bks., Inc.

Hoffman, Mary. Cuentos del Sol, la Luna y las Estrellas: Mitos, Leyendas y Tradiciones de Todas las Culturas. Ray, Jane, illus. 2002. (SPA & ENG.). 80p. (gr. 1-7). 19.95 (978-84-89396-52-4(3)) Blume ESP. *Dist:* Independent Pubs. Group.

Holland, Trish. Lasso the Moon. Petrone, Valeria, illus. 2005. 24p. (J). (gr. k-k). 2.99 (978-0-375-83289-5(0) , Golden Bks.) Random Hse. Children's Bks.

Horacek, Petr. When the Moon Smiled. 2004. (Illus.). 32p. (J). (ps-k). 14.99 (978-0-7636-2209-1(5)) Candlewick Pr.

Hunter, Anne. Possum's Harvest Moon. Hunter, Anne, illus. 2002. (Illus.). (J). 14.74 (978-0-7587-3441-9(7)) Book Wholesalers, Inc.

—Possum's Harvest Moon. 1998. (Illus.). 32p. (J). (gr. k-3). pap. 6.95 (978-0-395-91824-1(3)) Houghton Mifflin Co. Trade & Reference Div.

Inkpen, Mick. Blue Nose Island Ploo & the Terrible Gnobbler. 2006. (Blue Nose Island Ser.: Bk. 1). (Illus.). (J). (ps). pap. 9.99 (978-0-340-87900-9(9) , Hodder & Stoughton) Hodder General Publishing Division GBR. *Dist:* Trafalgar Square Publishing.

—Ploo & the Terrible Gnobbler. 2006. (Blue Nose Island Ser.: Bk. 1). (Illus.). (J). (ps). 19.99 (978-0-340-85573-7(8) , Hodder & Stoughton) Hodder General Publishing Division GBR. *Dist:* Trafalgar Square Publishing.

Isadora, Rachel. Mr. Moon. Date not set. (J). 15.99 (978-0-06-029821-0(9)); lib. bdg. 16.89 (978-0-06-029822-7(7)) HarperCollins Pubs.

Jeffers, Oliver. The Way Back Home. Jeffers, Oliver, illus. 2008. 32p. (J). (ps). 16.99 ***(978-0-399-25074-3(3)*** , Philomel) Penguin Group (USA) Inc.

Keehn, Sally M. Magpie Gabbard & the Quest for the Buried Moon. 2007. 208p. (YA). (gr. 5-8). 16.99 (978-0-399-24340-0(2) , Philomel) Penguin Group (USA) Inc.

—Moon of Two Dark Horses. 2002. (Illus.). 240p. (YA). (gr. 5-9). pap. 6.99 (978-0-698-11949-9(5) , Putnam Juvenile) Penguin Group (USA) Inc.

—Moon of Two Dark Horses. 2002. (gr. 3-6). lib. bdg. 14.15 (978-0-613-45344-8(1)) Tandem Library Bks.

Kemble, Mai. The Moon & the Night Sweeper. Kemble, Mai, illus. 2007. 32p. (J). (ps-2). 15.95 ***(978-1-60108-013-4(1))*** Red Cygnet Pr.

Kenrick, Joanna & Weir, Doffy. Moondance. 2004. (Illus.). 32p. (J). 19.99 (978-1-84270-324-3(2)) Andersen GBR. *Dist:* Independent Pubs. Group.

King, Thomas. Coyote Sings to the Moon. Wales, Johnny, illus. 2002. 40p. (YA). (gr. 1-3). 15.95 (978-1-55868-642-7(8) , West Winds Pr.) Graphic Arts Ctr. Publishing Co.

King, Thomas. Coyote Sings to the Moon. Wales, Johnny, illus. 2008. 36p. pap. 9.95 ***(978-1-55263-868-2(5))*** Key Porter Bks. CAN. *Dist:* Perseus Distribution.

Kirk, Daniel. Moondogs. 1999. (Illus.). 1p. (J). (ps-3). 16.99 (978-0-399-23128-5(5) , Putnam Juvenile) Penguin Group (USA) Inc.

Kitze, Carrie A. We See the Moon. l.t. ed. 2003. (Illus.). 32p. (J). lib. bdg. 16.95 (978-0-9726244-0-4(6)) EMK Pr.

Kline, Suzy. Horrible Harry Goes to the Moon. Remkiewicz, Frank, illus. 2000. (Horrible Harry Ser.: No. 12). 64p. (J). (gr. 2-4). 13.99 (978-0-670-88764-4(1) , Viking Juvenile) Penguin Group (USA) Inc.

Lamar, Gail Renfroe. Moon of the Wishing Night. Mask, Cynthia, illus. 2004. 32p. (J). 17.95 (978-1-57966-047-5(9) , River City Kids) River City Publishing.

Landry, Leo. Space Boy. 2007. 32p. (J). (gr. k-3). 16.00 ***(978-0-618-60568-2(1))*** Houghton Mifflin Co.

Lascurain, Anna. Apollo in the Moon House. 2006. Orig. Title: The Moonboy. (J). per. 7.99 (978-0-9769612-3-9(7) , Pixiefire) Darker Intentiona Pr.

Law, Felicia. The Moon. Evans, Nicola, illus. 2005. (Bamboo & Friends Ser.). 24p. (J). (ps-3). lib. bdg. 22.60 (978-1-4048-1282-6(2)) Picture Window Bks.

LeapFrog Staff, compiled by. Leap to the Moon: MFLP. 2001. (J). (ps-2). spiral bd. 12.99 (978-1-58605-110-5(5)) LeapFrog Enterprises, Inc.

Lemieux, Jean. Toby Shoots for Infinity. Cummins, Sarah, tr. from FRE. Casson, Sophie, illus. 2005. (First Novel Ser.). 64p. (J). (gr. 2-5). ***(978-0-88780-685-8(6));*** 4.95 (978-0-88780-684-1(8)) Formac Publishing Co., Ltd. CAN. *Dist:* Casemate Pubs. & Bk. Distributors, LLC.

Lobel, Gillian. Little Honey Bear & the Smiley Moon. Warnes, Tim, illus. 2006. 28p. (J). 16.00 (978-1-56148-533-8(0)) Good Bks.

London, Jonathan. I See the Moon & the Moon Sees Me. 1998. 13.79 (978-0-606-13509-2(X)) Tandem Library Bks.

MacDonald, George. The Wind & the Moon. rev. ed. 2002. 32p. (J). 15.95 (978-0-8050-4127-9(3) , Holt, Henry & Co. Bks. For Young Readers) Holt, Henry & Co.

MacGregor, Rob. Hawk Moon. 1998. (J). (978-0-606-13469-9(7)) Tandem Library Bks.

Mack, Lizzie. Catch a Ride to the Moon: Whimsical Rhymes to Read & Sing. G Studios, illus. 2007. (Land of Milk & Honey Ser.). 30p. (J). (ps). 10.99 ***(978-1-4169-2764-8(6)*** , Little Simon Inspirations) Simon & Schuster Children's Publishing.

Mackin, Joan Marie. It's Just the Moon. 2004. (J). pap. 9.00 (978-0-8059-6315-1(4)) Dorrance Publishing Co., Inc.

Madison's Descent: A Child's Journey. collector's ed. 2004. (J). 75.00 ***(978-0-9752516-0-7(0))*** Otis & Randolph Pr.

Maher, Mickle Brandt. Master Stitchum & the Moon. Dousias, Spiro, illus. 2003. (J). 19.99 (978-1-932188-01-1(0)) Bollix Bks.

McCarty, Peter. Moon Plane. 2006. (Illus.). 40p. (J). 16.95 (978-0-8050-7943-2(2)) Holt, Henry & Co.

McClure, Brian D. The Sun & the Moon. 2006. (Illus.). 36p. (J). 14.95 (978-1-933426-09-9(8)) Universal Flag Publishing.

McGough, Roger. Moonthief. Dann, Penny, illus. 2003. 32p. (J). (ps-k). tchr. ed. 15.00 (978-0-7534-5481-7(5) , Kingfisher) Houghton Mifflin Co. Trade & Reference Div.

Milbourne, A. & Wells, R. Mouse on the Moon. 2004. (Touchy-Feely Board Bks.). (Illus.). 10p. (J). (ps up). 4.95 (978-0-7945-0163-1(X) , Usborne) EDC Publishing.

Mills, Nancy Libbey. The Knight the Moon & the Stars Got Stuck. Thieves, Sam, illus. 2000. 32p. (J). (ps-4). 15.95 (978-1-893815-01-8(3)) Pie in the Sky Publishing, LLC.

Mindler, Jason. Giralon. 2003. 122p. (YA). 20.95 (978-0-595-74854-9(6)); pap. 10.95 (978-0-595-28581-5(3)) iUniverse, Inc. (Writers Club Pr.).

Mitchell, Joni. Chelsea Morning. Froud, Brian, illus. 2004. 32p. (J). (978-0-689-03593-7(4) , Milk & Cookies) ibooks, Inc.

Moon Stories. 2004. (YA). 11.95 (978-0-9752801-1-9(2)) Beres, Nancy.

Mora, Pat. The Night the Moon Fell. Domi, illus. 2000. (J). (ps-3). (978-0-88899-398-4(6)) Groundwood Bks.

Morrissey, Dean. The Crimson Comet. Morrissey, Dean, illus. 2006. (Illus.). 32p. (J). lib. bdg. 17.89 (978-0-06-008070-9(1)) HarperCollins Pubs.

Morrissey, Dean & Krensky, Stephen. The Crimson Comet. Morrissey, Dean, illus. 2006. (Illus.). 32p. (J). 16.99 (978-0-06-008068-6(X)) HarperCollins Pubs.

—The Moon Robber. 2001. (Magic Door Ser.). (Illus.). 64p. (J). (gr. 2-5). pap. 5.95 (978-0-06-442113-3(9) , Harper Trophy) HarperCollins Pubs.

Murray, Joe. Who Asked the Moon to Dinner? 1999. (Illus.). 32p. (gr. 4-7). 16.95 (978-0-9676061-8-7(7)) Tallfellow Pr.

Murray, Marjorie D. Little Wolf & the Moon. Schuett, Stacey, illus. 2002. 32p. (J). (ps-2). 16.95 (978-0-7614-5100-6(5)) Cavendish, Marshall Corp.

My Trip to the Moon. 2004. (J). ring bd. 4.50 (978-0-9762740-0-1(0) , Flat Kids) Smart Smiles Co., The.

Nash, Deborah. The Little Star. Morgan, Richard, illus. 2004. (Read-It! Readers Ser.). 32p. (C). (gr. k-3). 18.60 (978-1-4048-0065-6(4)) Picture Window Bks.

Nishimura, Kae. Bunny Lune. Nishimura, Kae, illus. 2007. (Illus.). 32p. (J). (gr. k-3). 15.00 (978-0-618-71606-7(8) , Clarion Bks.) Houghton Mifflin Co. Trade & Reference Div.

Oddo, Joanne. The Strawberry Moon. 2004. (Illus.). 24.99 (978-1-4134-5075-0(X)) Xlibris Corp.

Olker, Constance. The Punctuation Pals Go to the Moon. 2005. (Illus.). (J). 64p. per. 24.95 (978-1-933449-13-5(6)); per. 19.95 (978-0-9761289-6-0(9)) Nightengale Pr.

Oppenheim, Shulamith Levey. What Is the Full Moon Full Of? Moore, Cyd, illus. 2003. 32p. (J). (ps up). 14.95 (978-1-56397-479-3(7)) Boyds Mills Pr.

—What Is the Moon Full Of? 2000. (978-0-606-18793-0(6)) Tandem Library Bks.

Oramas, Rafael Rivero. El Hombre, el Tigre, y la Luna. Areco, Amelie, illus. (SPA.). (J). pap. 7.96 (978-980-01-0482-8(0)) Monte Avila Editores Latinoamericana CA VEN. *Dist:* Lectorum Pubns., Inc.

Ormerod, Jan. Moonlight. 2004. (Illus.). 32p. (J). 15.95 (978-1-84507-049-6(6)) Lincoln, Frances Ltd. GBR. *Dist:* Perseus Distribution.

Papineau, Lucie. Gontrand & the Crescent Moon. Homel, David, tr. from FRE. Reno, Alain, illus. 1999. 32p. (J). (ps-4). pap. (978-1-894363-15-0(9)) Dominique & Friends.

Peirce-Bale, Mary. Noah's Moon. 2006. (J). spiral bd. 10.90 (978-0-9773990-2-4(8)) Mother's Hse. Publishing.

Pierson, Judith. The Always Moon. Brooks, Karen S., illus. 1998. 24p. (J). (gr. k-2). 13.95 (978-1-890326-17-3(8)) First Story Pr.

Pinkney, Brian. Cosmo & the Robot. 2000. (Illus.). 32p. (J). (ps up). 15.95 (978-0-688-15940-5(0)) HarperCollins Pubs.

—Cosmo & the Robot. Pinkney, Brian, illus. 2000. (Illus.). 32p. (J). (ps up). lib. bdg. 16.89 (978-0-688-15941-2(9)) HarperCollins Pubs.

Pla Valencia, Nancy. Under Bright Rays & Sparkling Stars. Pla Valencia, Nancy, illus. 1999. (J). (978-1-56492-283-0(9)) Laredo Publishing Co., Inc.

Pyle, Howard. The Garden Behind the Moon. 2002. (gr. 3-6). lib. bdg. 14.15 (978-0-613-57052-7(9)) Tandem Library Bks.

Ragnar. Izzy's Very Important Job. Ragnar, illus. 2005. (Illus.). 32p. 9.00 (978-0-9729388-2-2(6)) Baby Tattoo Bks.

Raintree Steck-Vaughn Staff. El Hombre en la Luna. 1999. (SPA.). (J). pap., stu. ed. 31.05 (978-0-7398-0762-0(5)) Steck-Vaughn.

Raschka, Chris. Can't Sleep. Raschka, Chris, illus. 1999. (Illus.). (J). (ps-1). 32p. 15.99 (978-0-531-08779-4(4)); 16p. bds. 6.95 (978-0-531-30201-9(6)); 32p. pap. 14.95 (978-0-531-09479-2(0)) Scholastic, Inc. (Orchard Bks.).

Remkiewicz, Frank, illus. Horrible Harry Goes to the Moon. 2002. (Horrible Harry Ser.). (J). 11.49 (978-0-7587-9216-7(6)) Book Wholesalers, Inc.

Robertson, M. P. Seven Ways to Catch the Moon. 2004. (Illus.). 32p. (J). pap. 7.95 (978-1-84507-231-5(6)) Lincoln, Frances Ltd. GBR. *Dist:* Perseus Distribution.

Robertson, Mark. Seven Ways to Catch the Moon. 1999. (Illus.). 36p. (J). (ps-1). (978-0-7112-1417-0(4)) Lincoln, Frances Ltd.

—Seven Ways to Catch the Moon. 2001. (Illus.). 36p. (J). (ps-3). pap. 8.99 (978-0-7112-1413-2(1)) Lincoln, Frances Ltd. GBR. *Dist:* Transition Vendor.

Robledo, Honorio. Nico Visita la Luna. Robledo, Honorio, illus. 2001. (SPA., Illus.). 32p. (J). 15.95 (978-0-938317-62-3(8)) Cinco Puntos Pr.

—Nico Visits the Moon. Robledo, Honorio, illus. 2001. (Illus.). 32p. (J). (gr. k-2). 15.95 (978-0-938317-57-9(1)) Cinco Puntos Pr.

Rosario, Joann. Where Did Sabrina Go? Rosario, Joann, illus. 2004. (Illus.). 13p. (J). (ps-5). pap. 10.00 (978-0-9758746-1-5(6)) J.G.R. Enterprises.

Ross, Andrea. Chester Goes to the Moon. 1999. (Chester Earth Ant Ser.). (Illus.). 25p. (J). (gr. k-3). pap. 7.95 (978-1-887683-08-1(9)) Storybook Pr. & Productions.

Rylant, Cynthia & Siegel, Mark. Long Night Moon. 2004. (Illus.). 40p. (J). 16.95 (978-0-689-85426-2(9)) Simon & Schuster Children's Publishing.

Rymond, Lynda Gene. Oscar & the Mooncats. Ceccoli, Nicoletta, illus. 2007. 40p. (J). (gr. k-3). 16.00 ***(978-0-618-56316-6(4))*** Houghton Mifflin Co.

Satrapi, Marjane. Monsters Are Afraid of the Moon. 2006. (Illus.). 32p. (J). 15.95 (978-1-58234-744-8(1) , Bloomsbury Children) Bloomsbury Publishing.

Schaefer, Carole Lexa. The Full Moon Barnyard Dance. Davenier, Christine, illus. 2003. 32p. (J). (ps-1). 15.99 (978-0-7636-1878-0(0)) Candlewick Pr.

—Sometimes Moon. 2001. (Illus.). (J). (978-0-606-21438-4(0)) Tandem Library Bks.

Scillian, Devin. Cosmo's Moon. Braught, Mark, illus. 2003. 40p. (J). (gr. k-5). 15.95 (978-1-58536-123-6(2)) Sleeping Bear Pr.

Seeley, Laura L. The Magical Moonballs. Seeley, Laura L., illus. 1998. (Illus.). 48p. (J). (ps-3). reprint ed. pap. 7.95 (978-1-56145-189-0(4)) Peachtree Pubs., Ltd.

Selick, Henry. Moongirl: With DVD. Chan, Peter & Booker, Courtney, illus. gif. ed. 2006. 48p. (J). (ps-2). 22.99 incl. DVD (978-0-7636-3068-3(3)) Candlewick Pr.

Seuss, Dr. & Rabe, Tish. On Beyond Bugs! All about Insects. Ruiz, Aristides, illus. 1999. (Cat in the Hat's Learning Library). 48p. (J). (gr. k-3). 8.99 (978-0-679-87303-7(1) , Random Hse. Bks. for Young Readers) Random Hse. Children's Bks.

Shea, Pegi Deitz. New Moon. Falwell, Cathryn, illus. 2003. 32p. (J). (ps up). pap. 8.95 (978-1-56397-922-4(5)) Boyds Mills Pr.

—New Moon. 2000. (gr. k-3). lib. bdg. 17.60 (978-0-613-36929-9(7)) Tandem Library Bks.

Shulman, Lisa. The Moon Might Be Milk. Hillenbrand, Will, illus. 2007. (J). (ps-k). 32p. 16.99 (978-0-525-47647-4(4)); ***(978-1-4287-3291-9(8))*** Penguin Group (USA) Inc. (Dutton Juvenile).

Singh, Rina. Moon Tales. Lush, Debbie, illus. 2001. 80p. (J). pap. 16.99 (978-0-7475-4795-2(5)) Bloomsbury Publishing Plc GBR. *Dist:* Trafalgar Square Publishing.

Sinke, Janet Mary. Priscilla McdoodleNutMcDoodleMcMae Asks Why. Penington, Craig, illus. 2007. 40p. (J). 17.95 (978-0-9742732-8-0(7)) My Grandma & Me Pubs.

Smith. When the Moon Fell Down. Date not set. 32p. (J). (ps up). pap. 4.99 (978-0-06-443550-5(4)) HarperCollins Pubs.

Snyder, Midori. New Moon. 2005. (Queen's Quarter Ser.: Bk. 1). 288p. (YA). (gr. 7). pap. 7.99 (978-0-14-240349-5(0) , Puffin) Penguin Group (USA) Inc.

Snyder, Olympia. That Man in the Moon. 2002. (J). 6.99 (978-1-930200-97-5(8)) Martell Publishing Co.

The Spotted Moon & Deputy KC: Chase the Big Orange Ball. 2008. (J). spiral bd. ***(978-0-9793930-3-7(5))*** Dandelion Publishing.

Spurling, Margaret. Bilby Moon. Snell, Danny, illus. 2001. 32p. (J). (ps-4). 14.95 (978-1-929132-06-5(9)) Kane/Miller Bk. Pubs., Inc.

St. Romain, Rose Anne. Moon's Cloud Blanket. Waites, Joan C., illus. 2003. 32p. (J). 15.95 (978-1-56554-922-7(8)) Pelican Publishing Co., Inc.

Steadman, Ralph. Flowers for the Moon. 2004. (Illus.). 42p. 100.00 (978-0-9760742-0-5(6)) Sylph Pubns.

Steck-Vaughn Staff. Folktales & Legends: Moon, Sun. 1998. (Illus.). (J). pap. (978-0-8172-8646-0(2)) Steck-Vaughn.

—How the Moon Tricked the Sun. 1998. (Illus.). pap. (978-0-8172-8699-6(3)) Steck-Vaughn.

Steinmann, Donna. Hello, Grand Mamoon! Guion, Tamara, illus. 2005. 32p. (J). 16.95 (978-0-9663286-4-6(7)) EarthTime Pubns.

Suen, Anastasia. Man on the Moon. 2002. (Illus.). 32p. (J). pap. 6.99 (978-0-14-056598-0(1) , Puffin) Penguin Group (USA) Inc.

—Man on the Moon. 2002. (gr. k-3). lib. bdg. 15.30 (978-0-613-83555-8(7)) Tandem Library Bks.

Tan, Amy. The Moon Lady. 1998. (J). pap. 5.95 (978-0-87628-573-2(6)) Ctr. for Applied Research in Education, The.

Tanemura, Arina. Full Moon, Vol. 5. 2006. (Full Moon o Sagashite Ser.). 200p. (YA). pap. 8.99 (978-1-4215-0266-3(6)) Viz Media.

Tara, Stephanie. I'll Follow the Moon. Fodi, Lee Edward, illus. 2005. 40p. (J). 20.95 (978-1-933285-13-9(3)) Brown Bks. Publishing Group.

Thurber, James. Many Moons. Simont, Marc, illus. 2002. (J). 14.79 (978-0-7587-0084-1(9)) Book Wholesalers, Inc.

—Many Moons. Simont, Marc, illus. 1998. 48p. (J). (ps-3). pap. 7.00 (978-0-15-201895-5(6) , Harcourt Paperbacks) Harcourt Children's Bks.

Torgerson, Scotty Delray. Jacob Goes to the Moon. 2nd l.t. ed. 2005. (Illus.). 32p. (J). 10.00 (978-0-9767116-0-5(5)) Torgerson Meadows Publishing.

Udry, Janice May. The Moon Jumpers. Sendak, Maurice, illus. 2003. (Sendak Reissues Ser.). 32p. (J). (ps-1). 15.95 (978-0-06-028460-2(9)) HarperCollins Pubs.

Ungerer, Tomi. El Hombre de la Luna. (SPA., Illus.). 40p. (J). (gr. k-2). 7.95 (978-84-204-3746-0(8) , AF0456) Santillana USA Publishing Co., Inc.

—El Hombre de la Luna. Ungerer, Tomi, illus. 2003. (Picture Books Collection). (SPA., Illus.). 40p. (J). (gr. k-3). pap. 10.95 (978-968-19-0661-0(6)) Santillana USA Publishing Co., Inc.

—Moon Man. 1998. (Illus.). 40p. (J). (ps-1). pap. 6.95 (978-1-57098-207-1(4)) Rinehart, Roberts Pubs.

Vail, Rachel. Over the Moon. Nash, Scott, illus. 1998. 32p. (J). (ps-2). 16.99 (978-0-531-33068-5(0)); pap. 15.95 (978-0-531-30068-8(4)) Scholastic, Inc. (Orchard Bks.).

Van Steenhoven, Tom. Moon Adventure. 1999. (Billy Bks.). (Illus.). (J). 15.99 (978-0-9672652-0-9(7)) Nation of Imagi, LLC, The.

Viola, Karen & Reader's Digest Staff. Good Night Sun, Hello Moon. Chung, Chi, illus. 2004. 16p. (J). bds. 12.99 (978-0-7944-0356-0(5) , Reader's Digest Children's Bks.) Reader's Digest Children's Publishing, Inc.

Wahl, Jan. Cabbage Moon. Johnson-Petrov, Arden, illus. 1998. 32p. (J). (ps-1). 15.95 (978-1-56397-584-4(X)) Boyds Mills Pr.

Ward, Helen. Little Moon Dog. Anderson, Wayne, illus. 2007. 32p. (J). (ps-3). 16.99 (978-0-525-47727-3(6) , Dutton Juvenile) Penguin Group (USA) Inc.

Ward, Helen. Moon Dog. 2005. (Illus.). 40p. (J). ***(978-1-84011-864-3(4))*** Templar Publishing, Dorking.

Wartko, Karen J. I Know My Daddy Works on the Moon. 2004. (J). lib. bdg. 17.95 (978-0-9748979-0-5(6)) Spreeda Publishing.

Wynne-Jones, Tim. Architect of the Moon. Wallace, Ian, illus. 1998. (J). (ps-2). pap. 5.95 (978-0-88899-150-8(9) , Libros Tigrillo) Groundwood Bks. CAN. *Dist:* Transition Vendor.

—Architect of the Moon. 1998. (ps-2). lib. bdg. 14.10 (978-0-613-88548-5(1)) Tandem Library Bks.

Yorinks, Arthur & Yorinks, Adrienne, illus. Quack! There's a Duck on the Moon! 2002. 40p. (J). 9.95 (978-1-58837-021-1(6)) Winslow Pr.

Young, Selina. Big Dog & Little Dog Visit the Moon. Young, Selina, illus. 2001. (Blue Bananas Ser.). (Illus.). 48p. (J). (gr. 1-2). (978-0-7787-0849-0(7)); pap. (978-0-7787-0895-7(0)) Crabtree Publishing Co.

—Big Dog & Little Dog Visit the Moon. 2002. (gr. k-3). lib. bdg. 12.95 (978-0-613-52811-5(5)) Tandem Library Bks.

Zaugh, Robert. Teddy Bear Goes to the Moon. Peterson, Mary, illus. 1998. 32p. (J). (gr. k-3). pap. 7.95 (978-1-892071-00-2(2)) Dillingham Publishing.

Ziefert, Harriet. Moon Ride. Chwast, Seymour, illus. 2000. 32p. (J). (gr. k-3). tchr. ed. 15.00 (978-0-618-00229-0(4) , Walter Lorraine) Houghton Mifflin Co. Trade & Reference Div.

—Scare the Moon. Karas, G. Brian, illus. 2004. 16p. (J). 9.95 (978-1-4027-1702-4(4)) Sterling Publishing Co., Inc.

MOON, VOYAGES TO

see Space Flight to the Moon

MOON PROBES

see Lunar Probes

MOONBEAR (FICTITIOUS CHARACTER)—FICTION

Asch, Frank. Happy Birthday, Moon. Asch, Frank, illus. 2002. (Moonbear Ser.). (Illus.). (J). 15.53 (978-0-7587-2686-5(4)) Book Wholesalers, Inc.

—Happy Birthday, Moon. Asch, Frank, illus. 2000. (Illus.). 32p. (J). (ps-k). pap. 6.99 (978-0-689-83544-5(2) , Aladdin) Simon & Schuster Children's Publishing.

—Moonbear's Bargain. Asch, Frank, illus. 2002. (Moonbear Ser.). (Illus.). (YA). 14.47 (978-1-4046-0166-6(X)) Book Wholesalers, Inc.

—Moonbear's Bargain. (Moonbear Ser.). (ps-k). 2000. (J). (978-0-606-18624-7(7)); 1999. lib. bdg. 14.15 (978-0-8335-2711-0(8)) Tandem Library Bks.

—Moonbear's Dream. Asch, Frank, illus. 2002. (Illus.). 32p. (J). (ps-1). pap. 6.99 (978-0-689-85310-4(6) , Aladdin) Simon & Schuster Children's Publishing.

—Moonbear's Pet. Asch, Frank, illus. 2002. (Moonbear Ser.). (Illus.). (J). 14.47 (978-1-4046-0167-3(8)) Book Wholesalers, Inc.

—Moonbear's Shadow. Asch, Frank, illus. 2002. (Moonbear Ser.). (Illus.). (J). 14.47 (978-0-7587-6647-2(5)) Book Wholesalers, Inc.

—Moonbear's Shadow. Asch, Frank, illus. 2000. (Moonbear Ser.). 32p. (J). (ps-k). 6.99 (978-0-689-83519-3(1) , Aladdin) Simon & Schuster Children's Publishing.

—Moonbear's Shadow. 2000. (978-0-606-18625-4(5)); 1999. lib. bdg. 15.30 (978-0-8335-2452-2(6)) Tandem Library Bks.

—Mooncake. Asch, Frank, illus. 2002. (Moonbear Ser.). (Illus.). (J). 14.47 (978-0-7587-6749-3(8)) Book Wholesalers, Inc.

—Mooncake. Asch, Frank, illus. 2000. (Moonbear Ser.). 32p. (J). (ps-k). 6.99 (978-0-689-83517-9(5) , Aladdin) Simon & Schuster Children's Publishing.

—Mooncake. 1999. (ps-2). lib. bdg. 15.30 (978-0-613-37191-9(7)) Tandem Library Bks.

—Moondance. Asch, Frank, illus. 2002. (Moonbear Ser.). (Illus.). 13.83 (978-1-4046-0169-7(4)) Book Wholesalers, Inc.

—Moongame. Asch, Frank, illus. 2002. (Moonbear Ser.). (Illus.). (J). 14.47 (978-0-7587-6424-9(3)) Book Wholesalers, Inc.

—Moongame. Asch, Frank, illus. 2000. (Moonbear Ser.). (Illus.). 32p. (J). (ps-k). 6.99 (978-0-689-83518-6(3) , Aladdin) Simon & Schuster Children's Publishing.

—Moongame. (Moonbear Ser.). (ps-k). 2000. (J). (978-0-606-18896-8(7)); 1999. lib. bdg. 15.30 (978-0-613-60907-4(7)) Tandem Library Bks.

Asch, Frank & Asch, Frank. Happy Birthday, Moon. 1999. (Illus.). 28p. (J). (ps-3). lib. bdg. 15.30 (978-0-613-63293-5(1)) Tandem Library Bks.

MOORE, HENRY, 1898-1986

Connolly, Sean. Henry Moore. 2006. (Heinemann First Library). (Illus.). 32p. (J). lib. bdg. (***978-1-4034-8491-8(0)***) Heinemann Library.

Connolly, Sean. The Life & Work of Henry Moore, Set 2. 2002. (Illus.). 32p. (J). (gr. k-2). pap. 6.50 (978-1-4034-0003-1(2) , 91621) Heinemann Library.

Oliver, Clare. Henry Moore. 2003. (gr. 5-8). lib. bdg. 15.25 (978-0-613-59496-7(7)) Tandem Library Bks.

Oliver, Clare & O'Reilly, Sally. Henry Moore. 2003. (Artists in Their Time Ser.). (Illus.). 48p. (J). (gr. 5-7). pap. 6.95 (978-0-531-16643-7(0) , Watts, Franklin) Scholastic Library Publishing.

O'Reilly, Sally. Henry Moore. 2003. (Artists in Their Time Ser.). (Illus.). 48p. (J). 23.50 (978-0-531-12241-9(7) , Watts, Franklin) Scholastic Library Publishing.

Wallis, Jeremy. Henry Moore. 2001. (Creative Lives Ser.). (J). 26.50 (978-1-58810-204-1(1)) Heinemann Library.

MOORISH ART

see Art, Islamic

MOORS (PEOPLE)

see Muslims

MOOSE

Creative Publishing international Editors. Forest Animals. 2004. (Our Wild World Ser.). (Illus.). 192p. (J). (gr. 2-5). ring bd. 16.95 (978-1-55971-708-3(4) , NorthWord Bks. for Young Readers) T&N Children's Publishing.

DuTemple, Lesley A. North American Moose. 2000. (Nature Watch Ser.). (Illus.). 48p. (J). (gr. 3-6). lib. bdg. 25.26 (978-1-57505-426-1(4) , Carolrhoda Bks.) Lerner Publishing Group.

Estigarribia, Diana. Moose. 2005. (Animals Animals Ser.). (Illus.). 48p. (J). (gr. 3-7). lib. bdg. (978-0-7614-1870-2(9) , Benchmark Bks.) Cavendish, Marshall Corp.

Fraggalosch, Audrey. Northern Refuge: A Story of a Canadian Boreal Forest. Forest, Crista, illus. 1999. (Habitat Ser.: Vol. 12). (J). (gr. 1-4). 32p. 15.95 (978-1-56899-678-3(0) , B7012); 32p. 19.95 incl. reel tape (978-1-56899-680-6(2) , BC7012); 36p. pap. 26.95 (978-1-56899-682-0(9)); 36p. 31.95 incl. audio (978-1-56899-684-4(5)); 32p. pap. 6.95 (978-1-56899-679-0(9) , S7012); 36p. pap. 19.95 incl. audio (978-1-56899-681-3(0)); 36p. pap. 19.95 incl. audio (978-1-56899-685-1(3)) Soundprints.

Fredericks, Anthony D. Moose. McGee, John F., illus. 2004. (Our Wild World Ser.). 48p. (J). (gr. 2-5). pap. 7.95 (978-1-55971-744-1(0) , NorthWord Bks. for Young Readers) T&N Children's Publishing.

—Moose. 2000. (gr. 3-6). lib. bdg. 16.40 (978-0-613-26271-2(9)) Tandem Library Bks.

Gannij, Joan & Beaton, Clare. Elusive Moose. 2006. (Illus.). (J). (978-1-905236-75-6(1)) Barefoot Bks., Inc.

Harvard, Christian. The Moose: Gentle Giant. Blachas, Michel & Piche, Carole, illus. Blachas, Michel & Piche, Carole, photos by. 2002. (Animal Close-Ups Ser.). 28p. (J). pap. 6.95 (978-1-57091-505-5(9)) Charlesbridge Publishing, Inc.

Hemstock, Annie. The Moose. 1998. (Wildlife of North America Ser.). (Illus.). 48p. (J). (gr. 3-4). lib. bdg. 21.26 (978-0-7368-0030-3(1) , Capstone High-Interest Bks.) Capstone Pr., Inc.

Hodge, Deborah. Deer, Moose, Elk & Caribou. 1999. (J). 12.75 (978-0-606-19013-8(9)) Tandem Library Bks.

—Deer, moose, elk & caribou. 2004. (Kids Can Press Wildlife Ser.). (Illus.). 32p. (J). (gr. k-3). (978-1-55074-667-9(7)) Kids Can Pr., Ltd.

—Deer, moose, elk & caribou. Stephens, Pat, illus. 1998. (Kids Can Press Wildlife Ser.). 32p. (J). (gr. k-3). (978-1-55074-435-4(6)) Kids Can Pr., Ltd.

Leach, Michael. Moose/Buffalo/Bison. 2003. (Natural World Ser.). (Illus.). 48p. (J). lib. bdg. 27.14 (978-0-7398-6055-7(0)) Raintree.

Love, Pamela. A Moose's Morning. Sochor, Lesia, illus. 2007. 32p. (gr. k-3). 15.95 (978-0-89272-733-9(0)) Down East Bks.

Macken, JoAnn Early. Moose. 2005. (Illus.). 24p. (J). pap. (978-0-8368-4489-4(0)); (YA). lib. bdg. 19.33 (978-0-8368-4482-5(3)) Stevens, Gareth Inc.

The Moose. (Wildlife of North America Ser.). 48p. (YA). 7.95 (978-0-7368-8488-4(2)) Capstone Pr., Inc.

The Moose, 6 vols. (gr. 4 up). 39.95 (978-0-7368-8500-3(5)) Red Brick Learning.

Rodgers, Art. Moose. rev. ed. 2001. (WorldLife Library). (Illus.). 72p. (J). (gr. 5 up). pap. 17.95 (978-0-89658-521-8(2)) Voyageur Pr., Inc.

Squire, Ann. Moose. 2006. (True Book Ser.). (Illus.). 47p. (J). (978-0-516-25471-5(5)) Children's Pr., Ltd.

—Moose. 2006. (True Book Ser.). (Illus.). 47p. (J). (978-0-516-22824-2(2) , Children's Pr.) Scholastic Library Publishing.

Stewart, Anne. I Saw a Moose Today. Spink, Brent, illus. 2007. (J). (***978-0-9766264-6-6(2)***); pap. (***978-0-9766264-7-3(0)***) Raven Productions, Inc.

Wrobel, Scott. Moose. 2000. (Northern Trek Ser.). (Illus.). 24p. (J). (gr. 2-7). lib. bdg. 15.95 (978-1-58340-034-0(6)) Smart Apple Media.

MOOSE—FICTION

Bailey, Elinor Peace. Ross T. Moose. Bailey, Elinor Peace, illus. 2002. (J). 9.50 (978-0-9716586-9-1(2)) Fairfield Processing Corp.

Beaton, Clare. One Moose, Twenty Mice. Beaton, Clare, illus. (Illus.). 32p. (J). (gr. k-2). 2002. pap. 6.99 (978-1-84148-129-6(7)); 2000. reprint ed. bds. 6.99 (978-1-84148-285-9(4)) Barefoot Bks., Inc.

—One Moose, Twenty Mice. 2000. (ps-2). lib. bdg. 14.15 (978-0-613-26485-3(1)) Tandem Library Bks.

Beck, Ana. Elliot Digs for Treasure. 2001. (ps-2). lib. bdg. 14.10 (978-0-613-53183-2(3)) Tandem Library Bks.

—Elliot's Bath. 2001. lib. bdg. 14.10 (978-0-613-36327-3(2)) Tandem Library Bks.

—Elliot's Shipwreck. 2000. (gr. 3-6). lib. bdg. 14.10 (978-0-613-36328-0(0)) Tandem Library Bks.

Beck, Andrea. Elliot Bakes a Cake. Beck, Andrea, illus. 2004. (Elliot Moose Ser.). (Illus.). 32p. (J). (gr. k-3). (978-1-55074-696-9(0)) Kids Can Pr., Ltd.

—Elliot Bakes a Cake. 2004. (Elliot Moose Ser.). (Illus.). 32p. (J). (gr. k-3). (978-1-55074-443-9(7)) Kids Can Pr., Ltd.

—Elliot Bakes a Cake. 2000. (J). (978-0-606-19014-5(7)) Tandem Library Bks.

—Elliot Digs for Treasure. Beck, Andrea, illus. 2004. (Elliot Moose Ser.). (Illus.). 32p. (J). (gr. k-3). (978-1-55074-806-2(8)); (978-1-55074-808-6(4)) Kids Can Pr., Ltd.

—Elliot Gets Stuck. Beck, Andrea, illus. 2004. (Elliot Moose Ser.). (Illus.). 32p. (J). (gr. k-3). (978-1-55337-010-9(4)); (978-1-55337-014-7(7)) Kids Can Pr., Ltd.

—Elliot's Bath. 2004. (Elliot Moose Story Ser.). (Illus.). 32p. (J). (gr. k-3). (978-1-55074-802-4(5)) Kids Can Pr., Ltd.

—Elliot's Emergency. 2004. (Elliot Moose Ser.). (Illus.). 32p. (J). (gr. k-3). (978-1-55074-687-7(1)) Kids Can Pr., Ltd.

—Elliot's Emergency. Beck, Andrea, illus. 1998. (Elliot Moose Ser.). (Illus.). 32p. (J). (gr. k-3). (978-1-55074-441-5(0)) Kids Can Pr., Ltd.

—Elliot's Emergency. 1999. (J). (978-0-606-17371-1(4)) Tandem Library Bks.

—Elliot's Noisy Night. Beck, Andrea, illus. 2004. (Elliot Moose Ser.). (Illus.). 32p. (J). (gr. k-3). (978-1-55337-654-5(4)); (978-1-55337-011-6(2)) Kids Can Pr., Ltd.

—Elliot's Shipwreck. Beck, Andrea, illus. 2004. (Elliot Moose Ser.). (Illus.). 32p. (J). (gr. k-3). (978-1-55074-700-3(2)); reprint ed. (978-1-55074-698-3(7)) Kids Can Pr., Ltd.

Beck, Andrea, illus. Elliot's Christmas Surprise. 2004. (Elliot Moose Ser.). 32p. (J). (gr. k-3). (978-1-55337-661-3(7)); (978-1-55337-474-9(6)) Kids Can Pr., Ltd.

—Elliot's Great Big. 2003. (Elliot Moose Ser.). 12p. (J). (gr. k-3). (978-1-55337-373-5(1)) Kids Can Pr., Ltd.

Beckhorn, Susan Williams. Moose Eggs or, Why Moose Has Flat Antlers. Stevens, Helen, illus. 2007. 32p. (gr. k-3). 15.95 (***978-0-89272-689-9(X)***) Down East Bks.

Bloxam, Frances. Antlers Forever! Sollers, Jim, illus. 2001. 32p. pap. 9.95 (978-0-89272-550-2(8)); 15.95 (978-0-89272-512-0(5)) Down East Bks.

—Antlers Forever! 2003. (ps-2). lib. bdg. 18.75 (978-0-613-77412-3(4)) Tandem Library Bks.

Bourgeois, Paulette. Franklin's New Friend. ed. 2004. (Illus.). (J). (gr. k-3). spiral bd. (978-0-616-01590-2(9)); spiral bd. (978-0-616-01591-9(7)) Canadian National Institute for the Blind/Institut National Canadien pour les Aveugles.

—Franklin's New Friend. Clark, Brenda, illus. (Franklin Ser.). 96p. (J). (ps-3). (978-1-55074-363-0(5)) Kids Can Pr., Ltd.

Bourgeois, Paulette & Clark, Brenda. Franklin's New Friend. 1999. (Franklin Ser.). (Illus.). 180p. (J). (ps-3). (978-1-55074-797-3(5)) Kids Can Pr., Ltd.

Bowdish, Lynea. Preguntas Tontitas. 2002. (SPA.). lib. bdg. 12.95 (978-0-613-54300-2(9)) Tandem Library Bks.

Brightwood, Laura, illus. Red Hat / Blue Hat. Brightwood, Laura, . 2006. (J). (978-0-9779290-5-4(1)) 3-C Institute for Social Development.

Bunting, Eve. A Turkey for Thanksgiving. 2002. (Illus.). (J). 13.79 (978-0-7587-3875-2(7)) Book Wholesalers, Inc.

Carlson, Amanda. Sultenfuss Moose's Lost Slipper. 2006. 26p. 18.03 (978-1-4116-7729-6(3)) Lulu.com.

Casanova, Mary. Moose Tracks. l.t. ed. 2004. (LRS Large Print Cornerstone Ser.). 117p. (J). lib. bdg. 27.95 (978-1-58118-117-3(5)) LRS.

The Chocolate Moose. 2007. (Illus.). 48p. (J). per. 13.00 (***978-0-9767189-5-6(2)***) Better Day Publishing Co.

Clark, Brenda, illus. Franklin's New Friend. 2002. (Franklin Ser.). 12.40 (978-1-4046-0327-1(1)) Book Wholesalers, Inc.

Cook, Sherry & Johnson, Terri. Mary Motion, 26 vols. Kuhn, Jesse, illus. l.t. ed. 2006. (Quirkles—Exploring Phonics through Science Ser.: 13). 32p. (J). 7.99 (978-1-933815-12-1(4) , Quirkles, The) Creative 3, LLC.

Derrick, Patricia. Montgomery the Moose. 2007. 32p. 18.95 (978-1-933818-18-4(2)) Animalations.

Dixon, Karen S. Alexander the Moose. Crouch, Frances, illus. 2004. 23p. pap. 14.95 (978-1-4137-3626-7(2)) PublishAmerica, Inc.

Dubowski, Cathy East. Adventures of Rocky & Bullwinkle. 2000. (gr. 3-6). lib. bdg. 11.80 (978-0-613-24090-1(1)) Tandem Library Bks.

Egan, Tim. The Trial of Cardigan Jones. 2004. (Illus.). 32p. (J). (gr. k-3). tchr. ed. 16.00 (978-0-618-40237-3(3)) Houghton Mifflin Co. Trade & Reference Div.

Foote, Catherine. A Goose, a Moose, & a Caboose. 1999. (J). (gr. k-2). pap. 6.95 (978-0-533-12985-0(0)) Vantage Pr., Inc.

Fraggalosch, Audrey. Let's Explore, Moose! Forest, Crista, illus. 2005. (Soundprints' Read-and-Discover Ser.). 32p. (J). (ps-1). pap. 3.95 (978-1-59249-151-3(0) , S2017) Soundprints.

—Northern Refuge: A Story of A Canadian Boreal Forest. 1999. (gr. 3-6). lib. bdg. 15.25 (978-0-613-56929-3(6)) Tandem Library Bks.

Greene, Stephanie. Moose Crossing. Mathieu, Joe, illus. 2005. 56p. (J). (gr. 1-4). per. 14.95 (978-0-7614-5233-1(8)) Cavendish, Marshall Corp.

—Moose's Big Idea. Matthieu, Joe, illus. 2005. 51p. (J). (gr. 1-3). 14.95 (978-0-7614-5212-6(5)) Cavendish, Marshall Corp.

—Not Just Another Moose. Wallace, Andrea, illus. 2000. (Accelerated Reader Bks.). 32p. (J). (gr. 1-5). 15.95 (978-0-7614-5061-0(0) , Cavendish Children's Bks.) Cavendish, Marshall Corp.

—Pig Pickin' Mathieu, Joseph, illus. 2006. (Marshall Cavendish Chapter Book Ser.). 64p. (J). 14.99 (978-0-7614-5324-6(5)) Cavendish, Marshall Corp.

Greene, Stephanie. The Show-Off. Mathieu, Joseph, illus. 2007. (Moose & Hildy Ser.). 64p. (J). (gr. 1-4). 14.99 (***978-0-7614-5374-1(1)***) Cavendish, Marshall Corp.

Guthrie, Arlo & Brock, Alice. Mooses Come Walking. Brock, Alice, illus. 2004. (Illus.). 32p. (J). (ps-1). 13.95 (978-0-8118-1051-7(8)) Chronicle Bks. LLC.

Haseley, Dennis. The Invisible Moose. Kellogg, Steven, illus. 40p. (J). (ps). 2008. pap. 6.99 (***978-0-14-241066-0(7)*** , Puffin); 2006. 16.99 (978-0-8037-2892-9(1) , Dial) Penguin Group (USA) Inc.

Have You Ever Seen a Moose Taking a Bath? 2000. (J). pap. 12.95 (978-0-9709533-0-8(5)) JAFS, Inc.

Lakeshore Learning Materials Staff, contrib. by. If You Give a Moose a Muffin Packet. 2000. (J). pap. 36.95 (978-1-929255-46-7(2)) Lakeshore Learning Materials.

Lansing, Richard D., Jr. The Blue Moose. Lansing, Randy, illus. 1999. 48p. (J). (ps-4). mass mkt. 6.00 (978-0-9661844-5-7(9)) Purple Gorilla, LLC, The.

Larsen, Jill. There's a Moose on the Loose Coloring Book. 2004. (J). pap. 4.99 (978-0-9755200-0-0(8)) Kids, Critters & Country Publishing.

Macy-Mills, Phyllis. Murphy Moose & Garrett Goose. Russell, Kay, illus. 2003. (J). spiral bd. (978-1-932303-48-3(0) , Llumina Pr.) Media Creations, Inc.

Majestic's Search. 2004. (J). (978-0-615-12544-2(1)) Jadenaila Publishing.

Marshall, James. The Guest. 2001. (gr. k-3). lib. bdg. 12.95 (978-0-613-35523-0(7)) Tandem Library Bks.

McClaine, Jamie. Have You Ever Seen a Moose Brushing His Teeth? Willy, April, illus. 2003. 30p. (J). 18.95 (978-0-9709533-2-2(1)) JAFS, Inc.

—Have You Ever Seen a Moose Taking a Bath? Willy, April, illus. 2003. 28p. (J). per. 18.95 (978-0-9709533-1-5(3)) JAFS, Inc.

Messy Moose. 2005. (Emergent Library: Vol. 2). (YA). (ps-1). 23.94 (978-0-8215-8921-2(0)) Sadlier, William H. Inc.

Messy Moose: Take-Home Book. 2005. (Emergent Library: Vol. 2). (YA). (ps-1). 12.60 (978-0-8215-7251-1(2)) Sadlier, William H. Inc.

Mooney, Silk Waters. Puka the Moose. 2006. (YA). 24.95 (***978-0-9776608-1-0(8)***) Silk Waters Mooney.

Murray, Martine. A Moose Called Mouse. (Illus.). 32p. (J). 2003. 12.95 (978-1-86508-495-4(6)); 2002. pap. 6.95 (978-1-86508-494-7(8)) Allen & Unwin AUS. *Dist:* Independent Pubs. Group.

Numeroff, Laura Joffe. If You Give a Moose a Matzoh. Date not set. (J). pap. (978-0-06-443558-1(X)) HarperCollins Pubs.

—If You Give a Moose a Muffin. Bond, Felicia, illus. Date not set. (J). bds. 6.99 (978-0-694-01426-2(5)) HarperCollins Pubs.

—If You Give a Moose a Muffin: Book & Doll. Bond, Felicia, illus. Date not set. (J). 19.99 (978-0-694-01421-7(4)) HarperCollins Pubs.

—Moose Stroller Songs. Bond, Felicia, illus. Date not set. (J). 9.99 (978-0-694-01424-8(9)) HarperCollins Pubs.

Orme, David. El Alce Que Tenia Sed. Gordon, Mike, illus. 2005. (Lightning Readers Ser.). 32p. (J). (gr. k-1). pap. 3.95 (978-0-7696-4090-7(7) , Gingham Dog Pr.) School Specialty Publishing.

—The Thirsty Moose. Gordon, Mike, illus. 2005. (Lightning Readers Ser.). 32p. (J). (gr. k-1). pap. 3.95 (978-0-7696-4050-1(8) , Gingham Dog Pr.) School Specialty Publishing.

Palatini, Margie. Mooseltoe. Cole, Henry, illus. 2000. 32p. (ps-3). 15.99 (978-0-7868-0567-9(6)) Hyperion Bks. for Children.

—Moosestache. 32p. pap. (978-0-7868-1497-8(7)) Hyperion Bks. for Children.

—Moosetache. Cole, Henry, illus. 1999. 32p. (ps-2). pap. 5.99 (978-0-7868-1170-0(6)) Hyperion Bks. for Children.

—Moosetache. 1999. (ps-2). lib. bdg. 14.15 (978-0-613-74986-2(3)) Tandem Library Bks.

Parent, Nancy. Orange You Glad? 2000. (Captain Kangaroo Ser.). 32p. (J). (gr. k-1). pap. 3.99 (978-0-06-107157-7(9) , Harper Entertainment) HarperCollins Pubs.

Plourde, Paulette. Smitty Moose, Petey & Me - Episode One, the Witch. Golen, Jessica, illus. l.t. ed. 2005. 32p. (J). per. 9.95 (978-1-59879-038-2(2)) Lifevest Publishing, Inc.

Rea, Monique. Toulouse the Moose. 2003. (J). 3.50 (978-1-891030-30-7(2)) Paragon Agency, The.

Rea, Monique F. The Original Story of Toulouse the Moose & His Friends: Book & CD. 2007. (J). (***978-0-9788926-2-3(3)***) Trails of Discovery.

—Toulouse the Moose Coloring Book. 2007. (J). (***978-0-9788926-3-0(1)***) Trails of Discovery.

Robinson, Fiona. The Useful Moose: A Truthful, Moose-Full Tale. 2004. (Illus.). 32p. (J). (ps-3). 14.95 (978-0-8109-4925-6(3)) Abrams, Harry N. , Inc.

Root, Phyllis. Looking for a Moose. Cecil, Randy, illus. 2006. 40p. (J). (ps-k). 15.99 (978-0-7636-2005-9(X)) Candlewick Pr.

Sargent, Dave & Sargent, Pat. Jack Moose: I Need Help, 56 vols., 29. Huff, Jeane, illus. 2001. (Animal Pride Ser.: Vol. 29). 36p. (J). lib. bdg. 19.95 (978-1-56763-374-0(9)) Ozark Publishing.

Segal, John. The Lonely Moose. rev. ed. 2007. 40p. (ps-2). 15.99 (***978-1-4231-0173-4(1)***) Hyperion Pr.

Simon and Schuster Children's Staff, ed. Rocky & Bullwinkle & the Jet Fuel Formula. 2000. pap. 3.99 (978-0-689-82478-4(5) , Simon Spotlight) Simon & Schuster Children's Publishing.

—Rocky & Bullwinkle & the Rue Brittania. 1999. pap. 3.99 (978-0-689-82479-1(3) , Simon Spotlight) Simon & Schuster Children's Publishing.

Stihler, Cherie B. The Cabin That Moose Built: An Alaskan Tale. Trammell, Jeremiah, illus. 2006. 32p. (J). pap. 10.95 (978-1-57061-446-0(6)) Sasquatch Bks.

Stong, Phil. Honk the Moose. Wiese, Kurt, illus. 2001. 80p. (J). (gr. 4-7). 18.95 (978-1-930650-36-7(1)) Trellis Publishing, Inc.

Tetro, Marc. A Barbecue for Charlotte. 1999. (Illus.). 32p. 19.95 (978-1-55278-112-8(7)) McArthur & Co. CAN. *Dist:* National Bk. Network.

Van Laan, Nancy. Busy, Busy Moose. Rusch, Amy, illus. 2003. 48p. (J). (gr. k-3). tchr. ed. 15.00 (978-0-395-96091-2(6)) Houghton Mifflin Co. Trade & Reference Div.

—Busy, Busy Moose. Rusch, Amy, illus. 2007. 48p. (J). (gr. k-3). 6.95 (***978-0-618-80907-3(4)***) Houghton Mifflin Co. Trade & Reference Div.

Van Laan, Nancy. Moose Tales. Rusch, Amy, illus. 1999. 48p. (J). (gr. k-3). tchr. ed. 15.00 (978-0-395-90863-1(9)) Houghton Mifflin Co. Trade & Reference Div.

—Moose Tales. 2004. (Illus.). (J). (978-0-606-21337-0(6)); 2001. lib. bdg. 14.10 (978-0-613-35539-1(3)) Tandem Library Bks.

Van, Vonnie. The Purple Moose: A Children's Story in Verse with Pictures to be Colored. Ashford, Jenny, illus. 1998. 28p. (gr. 2 up). 4.95 (978-1-891232-08-4(8)) Crane, Robert Publishing.

Wallace, Carol & Wallace, Bob. Bub, Snow, & the Burly Bear Scare. 2003. (gr. 3-6). lib. bdg. 13.00 (978-0-613-70870-8(9)) Tandem Library Bks.

Wilson, Karma. Moose Tracks! Davis, Jack E., illus. 2006. 32p. (J). (ps-2). 16.95 (978-0-689-83437-0(3) , McElderry, Margaret K.) Simon & Schuster Children's Publishing.

Wiseman, Bernard. Morris & Boris at the Circus. Wiseman, Bernard, illus. 2002. (Illus.). (J). 12.34 (978-0-7587-5557-5(0)) Book Wholesalers, Inc.

Yellowstone Moose. 2004. (Illus.). (J). spiral bd. 9.95 (978-0-9754913-1-7(8) , Gap Tooth Publishing) Charles River Pr.

MORAL EDUCATION

Aguilera, Dana, et al. Character in Motion! Real Life Stories Series 5th Grade Student Workbook. 2006. 68p. (J). per. 5.95 (978-0-9765722-8-2(1)) Positively for Kids, Inc.

Bakhtiar, Laleh. Islamic Ethics: An Interfaith Perspective: Grade 2: the Moral Education Series. 2005. 32p. (J). pap., pupil's gde. ed. 4.95 net. (978-1-56744-722-4(8)) Kazi Pubns., Inc.

—Islamic Ethics: An Interfaith Perspective: Grade 3: the Moral Education Textbook Series. 2005. 32p. (J). 4.95 net. (978-1-56744-723-1(6)) Kazi Pubns., Inc.

—Islamic Ethics: An Interfaith Perspective: the Moral Education Textbook Series. 2005. (Islamic Books for Children). 32p. (J). pupil's gde. ed. 4.95 net. (978-1-56744-721-7(X)) Kazi Pubns., Inc.

Bergstrom, Amy, et al. The Seventh Generation: Native Students Speak about Finding the Good Path. 2003. 300p. (YA). (gr. 7-12). pap. 25.00 (978-1-880785-25-6(0)) ERIC Clearinghouse on Rural Education & Small Schls.

Boritzer, Etan. What Is Right? l.t. ed. 2004. (What Is? Ser.). (Illus.). 32p. 6.95 (978-0-9762743-0-8(2)) Lane, Veronica Bks.

Brooks, Diane L. Readings & Activities for Character Education. 220p. (YA). (gr. 4 up). ring bd. 69.95 (978-0-8126-7550-4(9)) Cricket Bks.

Building Character, Set. 2002. (J). (ps-3). lib. bdg. 119.58 (978-1-57765-824-5(8)) ABDO Publishing Co.

Building Christian Character. 2002. (Christian Bks.). 144p. (J). (gr. k-4). 14.99 (978-0-7439-7103-4(5) , 7103) Teacher Created Materials, Inc.

Burch, Regina G. Everyone Is Special & Unique Vol. 3133: Learning about Acceptance K-3. Hamaguchi, Carla, ed. Jarrett, Michael, photos by. 2002. (Character Education Readers). (Illus.). 16p. (J). (ps-3). pap. 1.99 (978-1-57471-834-8(7)) Creative Teaching Pr., Inc.

—Following the Rules: Learning about Respect. Hamaguchi, Carla, ed. Ember, Kathi, illus. 2002. (Character Education Readers Ser.: Vol. 3128). 16p. (J). (gr. k-3). pap. 2.99 (978-1-57471-829-4(0) , CTP 3128) Creative Teaching Pr., Inc.

—Never Give Up: Learning about Perseverance. Hamaguchi, Carla, ed. Harris, Jennifer Beck, illus. 2002. (Character Education Readers). 16p. (J). (gr. k-3). pap. 2.99 (978-1-57471-828-7(2) , CTP 3127) Creative Teaching Pr., Inc.

—Sharing Is Caring Vol. 3131: Learning about Generosity K-3. Hamaguchi, Carla, ed. Jarrett, Michael, photos by. 2002. (Character Education Readers). (Illus.). 16p. (J). (ps). pap. 1.99 (978-1-57471-832-4(0)) Creative Teaching Pr., Inc.

—Show You Understand Vol. 3134: Learning about Compassion & Caring K-3. Hamaguchi, Carla, ed. Jarrett, Michael, photos by. 2002. (Character Education Readers). (Illus.). 16p. (J). (ps-3). pap. 1.99 (978-1-57471-835-5(5)) Creative Teaching Pr., Inc.

—Working Together Vol. 3130: Learning about Cooperation & Citizenship K-3. Hamaguchi, Carla, ed. Nobens, Cheryl A., illus. 2002. (Character Education Readers). 16p. (J). (ps-3). pap. 1.99 (978-1-57471-831-7(2)) Creative Teaching Pr., Inc.

—Would It Be Right? Learning about Good Judgement. Hamaguchi, Carla, ed. Allen, Joy, illus. 2002. (Character Education Readers). 16p. (J). (gr. k-3). pap. 2.99 (978-1-57471-825-6(8) , CTP 3124) Creative Teaching Pr., Inc.

—You Can Count on Me Vol. 3129: Learning about Responsiblity K-3. Hamaguchi, Carla, ed. Burris, Priscilla, illus. 2002. (Character Education Readers). 16p. (J). (ps-3). pap. 1.99 (978-1-57471-830-0(4)) Creative Teaching Pr., Inc.

Character Counts, Set. 2002. (J). (gr. k-6). lib. bdg. 136.68 (978-1-57765-868-9(X)) ABDO Publishing Co.

Character Ed Says Courtesy Is Contagious. 2006. (J). 4.95 (978-1-55548-055-4(1) , 676) Human Relations Media.

Character Ed Says Honesty Counts. 2006. (J). 4.95 (978-1-55548-057-8(8) , 678) Human Relations Media.

Character Ed Says Keep Your Cool. 2006. (J). 4.95 (978-1-55548-056-1(X) , 677) Human Relations Media.

Character Education. 2004. 96p. (J). per. 9.99 (978-0-88724-244-1(8) , CD-0072) Carson-Dellosa Publishing Co., Inc.

Character Education, 12 vols.s. (Illus.). 2003. pap. 81.00 (978-1-4109-0430-0(X)); Set,6 Pack. 2004. pap. 486.00 (978-1-4109-1247-3(7)) Raintree.

Character Education Series, 6 bks., Set. (Illus.). 145.56 (978-0-7398-5783-0(5)) Raintree.

Clifford, Kathleen & Uy, Meqan Black. Great Lives, Vital Lessons: A Character Education Curriculum Resource for Grades 5-8. Bohlin, Karen E. & Lerner, Bernice, eds. 2005. (gr. 5-8). pap. 19.95 (978-1-892056-41-2(0)) Character Development Publishing.

Daily Character Education Activities 2-3. 2004. 64p. (J). pap. 7.99 (978-0-88724-206-9(5) , CD-0066) Carson-Dellosa Publishing Co., Inc.

Daily Character Education Activities 4-5. 2004. 64p. (J). pap. 7.99 (978-0-88724-207-6(3) , CD-0067) Carson-Dellosa Publishing Co., Inc.

Daily Character Education Activities K-1. 2004. 64p. (J). pap. 7.99 (978-0-88724-205-2(7) , CD-0065) Carson-Dellosa Publishing Co., Inc.

Daniel, Thesina C. How to Succeed Through Your Teenage Years: And Avoid Yielding to Drugs, Teen Pregnancy, Suicide & Serving Time in Jail. Bookmasters, Inc. Staff, ed. 2000. 130p. (YA). (gr. 8 up). per. 9.95 (978-0-9678621-1-8(6)) Gardenia Publishing.

Deroche, Ed, et al. Character: A Guide for Middle Grade Students. 176p. pap. 9.95 (978-1-55864-152-5(1) , JIST Life) JIST Publishing.

Dunagan, Cindy. Journaling Toward Moral Excellence Volume Four for Young Adults: A Character Building Workbook of 100 Thought-Provoking Questions to Help the Young Discover the Value of Moral Strength. 2004. (Journaling Toward Moral Excellence Ser.: Vol. 4). 107p. (YA). (gr. 11 up). 11.95 (978-0-9759871-3-1(5)) Straight Paths Pr.

—Journaling Toward Moral Excellence Volume One for Young Writers. 2004. (Journaling Toward Moral Excellence Ser.: Vol. 1). 107p. (J). (gr. 1-4). 11.95 (978-0-9759871-0-0(0)) Straight Paths Pr.

—Journaling Toward Moral Excellence Volume Three for Teenagers: A Character Building Workbook of 100 Thought-Provoking Questions to Help the Young Discover the Value of Moral Strength. 2004. (Journaling Toward Moral Excellence Ser.: Vol. 3). 107p. (YA). (gr. 8-10). 11.95 (978-0-9759871-2-4(7)) Straight Paths Pr.

—Journaling Toward Moral Excellence Volume Two for Pre-Teens Vol. 2: A Character Building Workbook of 100 Thought-Provoking Questions to Help the Young Discover the Value of Moral Strength. 2004. (Journaling Toward Moral Excellence Ser.: Vol. 2). 107p. (J). (gr. 5-7). 11.95 (978-0-9759871-1-7(9)) Straight Paths Pr.

Erlbach, Arlene. Real Kids Taking the Right Risks: Plus, How You Can, Too! 1998. Orig. Title: Worth the Risk: True Stories about Risk Takers: Plus How You Can Be One, Too. (Illus.). 136p. (YA). (gr. 5-10). pap. 12.95 (978-1-57542-051-6(1)) Free Spirit Publishing, Inc.

Everyday Character Education, 12 vols., Set. 2005. (Illus.). (J). 191.40 (978-0-7368-4410-9(4)) Capstone Pr., Inc.

Findlay, Diane. Characters with Character: Using Children's Literature in Character Education. 2001. (Illus.). 88p. (J). (gr. k-5). pap. 16.95 (978-1-57950-064-1(1) , Upstart Bks.) Highsmith Inc.

Forrest, Donna B. 180 Days of Character. Madden, Elizabeth, illus. 1998. 180p. (J). (gr. k-12). pap. 8.95 (978-1-889636-10-8(X) , B002) Youthlight, Inc.

Gater, Jean Star. Supa Dupa Babee & Friends "Best of Friends" Bryant, Sanders & Wilson, Ralph, illus. 2000. (J). (ps-1). pap., act. bk. ed. 3.50 (978-0-9706907-0-8(3)) Castleberry Toys, Inc.

Handley, Rod, et al. Team Studies on Character: Inspiration for Life & Sports. 2004. (YA). pap. 6.99 (978-1-929478-65-1(8)) Cross Training Publishing.

Hirschhorn, Vera. America's Young Heroes: A Journal for You: Learn about Yourself, Learn the Lessons of the Civil War. 2nd rev. ed. 2002. 117p. (YA). (gr. 5-10). pap. 24.95 (978-0-9718197-0-2(X)) America's Young Heroes Pubns.

Hodge, Aleta S. The Value Book. 2002. 230p. 13.95 (978-0-9648316-3-6(5)) Money Counsel, Inc.

Jordan, Denise. Now It's Your Turn. 2003. (Heinemann Read & Learn Ser.). (Illus.). 24p. (J). pap. 5.25 (978-1-4034-4411-0(0)) Heinemann Library.

Karges-Bone, Linda. Christian Character Building Stories for Middle Grade Students, Grades 5-8. 2003. (Illus.). 64p. (J). (gr. 5-8). pap. 10.99 (978-0-7647-0952-4(6) , In Celebration) Schaffer, Frank Pubns.

Keuss, Jeff & Sloth, Lia. Character in Motion! Athlete Series. 2006. (Illus.). 136p. (YA). per. 5.95 (978-0-9765722-0-6(6)) Positively for Kids, Inc.

Koehler, Michael D. & Royer, Karen E. First Class Character Education Activities Program: Ready-to-Use Lessons & Activities for Grades 7-12. 2001. 432p. (gr. 7-12). pap. 29.95 (978-0-13-042586-7(9) , Jossey-Bass) Wiley, John & Sons, Inc.

Lang, Carol, et al. Character in Motion! Real Life Stories Series 3rd Grade Student Workbook. 2006. 63p. (J). per. 5.95 (978-0-9765722-9-9(X)) Positively for Kids, Inc.

Lewis, Barbara A. What Do You Stand for? for Kids: A Guide to Building Character. 2005. (Illus.). 176p. (J). (gr. 2-7). pap. 14.95 (978-1-57542-174-2(7)) Free Spirit Publishing, Inc.

Little Lesson's from the Hundred-Acre Wood. 2000. (Illus.). 24p. (J). 16.99 (978-0-7868-3284-2(3)) Disney Pr.

MacAdam, Lea. You & the Rules in Your Family. 2005. (Family Matters Ser.). (Illus.). 48p. (YA). (gr. 5-8). lib. bdg. 23.95 (978-0-8239-3350-1(4)) Rosen Publishing Group, Inc., The.

Making Good Moral Choices, 6 booklets. 1998. (Illus.). (YA). (gr. 7-10). stu. ed. 6.95 (978-0-89837-217-5(8)) Pflaum Publishing Group.

Martenz, Arden. Character Building Classroom Guidance: Focusing on Character Education. Norcross, Harry, illus. 2001. 175p. (YA). (gr. 4-8). pap. 21.95 (978-1-57543-095-9(9)) MAR*CO Products, Inc.

Munroe, Terri, et al. Rachel's Challenge: A Columbine Legacy Student Workbook. 2006. (YA). per. 5.95 (978-0-9765722-4-4(9)) Positively for Kids, Inc.

Murray, Amy. The Character & Career Connection. 2005. (Illus.). 76p. (J). per. 19.95 (978-1-931636-45-2(1)) National Center For Youth Issues.

Peacefulness. (Character Education Ser.). 24p. (J). 6.95 (978-0-7368-9154-7(4)) Capstone Pr., Inc.

Perez, Claire M. & Fox, Mary. Peacemakers: The New Generation Practical Group Activities for Grades 6-8. 2003. (Illus.). 78p. (YA). (gr. 6-8). 20.00 (978-1-893757-32-5(3)) Needer, E.T. Publishing.

Raintree IL Staff. Connections: Character Education. 2003. (Illus.). pap. 5.95 (978-1-4109-0794-3(5)) Raintree.

Rogers, Kathy. Biographies That Build Character. Rogers, Kathy, ed. 2001. 64p. (J). per. 8.95 (978-1-56472-343-7(7)) Edupress, Inc.

Shail, Linda. Reading for Character: 40 Lessons for Middle School Classrooms Based on the Book of Virtues. 2002. 121p. (J). per. 20.00 (978-1-892056-11-5(9)) Character Development Publishing.

Small, Mary. Caring: A Book about Caring. Previn, Stacey, illus. 2005. (Way to Be! Ser.). 24p. (J). (ps). lib. bdg. 22.60 (978-1-4048-1049-5(8)) Picture Window Bks.

Speigler. Matter for Judgment. 2001. (J). pap. 13.50 (978-0-87065-284-4(2)) Globe Fearon Educational Publishing.

Stephens, Wayne. Building Character Through Music - Elementary Song Book. 2004. spiral bd. 39.95 (978-1-892056-32-0(1)) Character Development Publishing.

—Building Character Through Music - High School Song Book. 2004. (YA). spiral bd. 39.95 (978-1-892056-36-8(4)) Character Development Publishing.

Thayer, Eva. The MeLand 3: Songs & Raps for 3-4-5 Year Olds. 2001. (J). 12.95 incl. audio compact disk (978-1-931228-02-2(7)) Tes Publishing Co.

Tracy, Jean. Character Building on BackTalk Street. 2004. 110p. (J). spiral bd. 25.00 (978-0-9749244-0-3(7)) Tracy, Jean A.

Turner, Dale. Free to Be. Summer, Angel, ed. Smart, Ross, illus. 2003. 112p. (J). (gr. k-5). 16.95 (978-1-892696-28-1(2)) High Tide Pr.

Who You are on the Inside. 2002. (Illus.). (J). pap. 5.43 (978-0-7398-5932-2(3)) Steck-Vaughn.

Wiley, Lori. Character Education Activities. 2004. (Illus.). 176p. (J). per. 9.95 (978-1-55864-154-9(8) , K1548, KIDSRIGHTS) JIST Publishing.

MORAL EDUCATION—FICTION

Alger, Horatio. Making His Way: Or, Frank Courtneys Struggle. 2006. 96.99 ***(978-1-4280-2109-9(4))***; pap. 89.99 ***(978-1-4280-2133-4(7))*** IndyPublish.com.

Clark, Kenneth L. The Adventures in Nit Picky: Home of the Fighting Tomcats. 2002. (Illus.). 162p. pap. 11.95 (978-0-9720043-0-5(0)) Clark, Kenneth L.

Cosgrove, Stephen. Nitter Pitter. James, Robin, illus. ed. 2002. (Serendipity Ser.). 32p. (J). reprint ed. pap. 4.99 (978-0-8431-4870-1(5) , Price Stern Sloan) Penguin Group (USA) Inc.

Ferrin, Wendy Wakefield. Germs on Their Fingers! Tono, Lucia, tr. Broyles, Beverly Ashley, illus. 2003. Tr. of Germenes en Tus Manos!. (SPA & ENG.). 64p. (J). (gr. 1-7). 17.95 (978-0-9703632-1-3(4)); pap. 12.95 (978-0-9703632-0-6(6)) Wakefield Connection, The.

Hamilton, Elizabeth L. Christopher Cat's Character Club. 2003. (Character Critters Ser.: No. 1). (Illus.). 32p. (J). (ps-3). per. 5.95 (978-0-9713749-2-8(9) , Character-in-Action) Quiet Impact, Inc.

—Cubby Bear's Big Responsibility. 2004. (Character Critters Ser.: No. 8). (Illus.). 32p. (J). per. 5.95 (978-0-9754629-4-2(6) , Character-in-Action) Quiet Impact, Inc.

—Date with Responsibility. 2004. (Character-in-Action Ser.: No. 2). (Illus.). 384p. (YA). per. 19.95 (978-0-9713749-0-4(2) , Character-in-Action) Quiet Impact, Inc.

—Georgey Giraffe's Giant Respect: Character Critter Series #6. 2004. (Character Critters Ser.: No. 6). (Illus.). 32p. (J). per. 5.95 (978-0-9754629-1-1(1) , Character-in-Action) Quiet Impact, Inc.

—Jeremy Rabbit's Honesty Pie. 2003. (Character Critters Ser.: No. 2). (Illus.). 32p. (J). (ps-3). per. 5.95 (978-0-9713749-5-9(3) , Character-in-Action) Quiet Impact, Inc.

—Little Zoh's Submissive Trunk. 2003. (Character Critters Ser.: No. 3). (Illus.). 32p. (J). (ps-3). per. 5.95 (978-0-9713749-9-7(6) , Character-in-Action) Quiet Impact, Inc.

—Lost on Superstition Mountain. 2004. (Character Mystery Ser.: No. 3). (Illus.). 144p. (J). per. 9.95 (978-0-9754629-5-9(4) , Character-in-Action) Quiet Impact, Inc.

—Mystery at Lake Cachuma. 2003. (Character Mystery Ser.: No. 1). (Illus.). 114p. (J). (gr. 3-6). per. 9.95 (978-0-9713749-4-2(5) , Character-in-Action) Quiet Impact, Inc.

—Pandora Puppy's Caring Circle. 2004. (Character Critters Ser.: No. 5). (Illus.). 32p. (J). per. 5.95 (978-0-9754629-0-4(3) , Character-in-Action) Quiet Impact, Inc.

—Pansy Pig's Patience Pit. 2004. (Character Critters Ser.: No. 7). (Illus.). 32p. (J). per. 5.95 (978-0-9754629-3-5(8) , Character-in-Action) Quiet Impact, Inc.

—Passport to Courage. 2002. (Character-in-Action Ser.: No. 1). (Illus.). 384p. (YA). per. 19.95 (978-0-9713749-3-5(7) , Character-in-Action) Quiet Impact, Inc.

—Stinky Skunk's Self-Control. 2004. (Character Critters Ser.: No. 4). (Illus.). 32p. (J). (ps-3). per. 5.95 (978-0-9713749-6-6(1) , Character-in-Action) Quiet Impact, Inc.

—Surprise at Pearl Harbor. 2004. (Character Mystery Ser.: No. 2). (Illus.). 144p. (J). per. 9.95 (978-0-9754629-2-8(X) , Character-in-Action) Quiet Impact, Inc.

Henry, Heather French. What Freedom Means to Me: A Flag Day Story. Henry, Heather French, illus. 2004. (Claire's Holiday Adventures Ser.). (Illus.). 32p. (gr. k-4). (J). pap. 8.95 (978-0-9706341-9-1(6)); 15.95 (978-0-9706341-2-2(9) , 1231611) Cubbie Blue Publishing.

Kahn, Sheryl. Disney's Family Story Collection. 1999. 192p. (J). 19.99 (978-0-7868-3255-2(X)) Disney Pr.

Montgomery, Arch. Hank. 2003. 171p. (YA). 19.95 (978-1-890862-22-0(3)) Bancroft Pr.

Nicholetti, Terry & Campbell, Annie. Noralee's Adventures on Planet Ifwee. 2002. pap. 10.95 (978-0-9716488-0-7(8)) Goldstar Magic.

Norfolk, Bobby & Norfolk, Sherry. The Moral of the Story: Folktales for Character Development. 1999. 176p. 24.95 (978-0-87483-542-7(9)) August Hse. Pubs., Inc.

Prien, Margaret S. Character Links. Cory, Beverly, ed. Re Bane, Kaja & English, Kevin, illus. 1999. 140p. (J). (ps-3). pap. 49.95 (978-0-9673095-0-7(6)) Paw Impressions, Inc.

Sdoia-Satz, Phyllis & Satz, Barry. The Husky Gang Tales. 2002. 21.95 incl. audio compact disk (978-0-7579-9918-5(2) , Warner Bros. Pubns.) Alfred Publishing Co., Inc.

Silverstein, Shel. La Parte que Falta. 2000. (SPA., Illus.). 96p. (J). pap. 17.95 (978-84-7808-351-0(0) , SJ30292) Sirio, Editorial S.A. ESP. *Dist:* Lectorum Pubns., Inc.

—La Parte que Falta Conoce a la O Grande. 2000. (SPA., Illus.). 96p. (J). pap. 17.95 (978-84-7808-352-7(9) , SJ30291) Sirio, Editorial S.A. ESP. *Dist:* Lectorum Pubns., Inc.

Urdaneta, Josefina. Pequeno Zambo. 2000. 7.95 (978-980-6437-13-5(6)) Baker & Taylor Bks.

MORAL PHILOSOPHY

see Ethics

MORALITY

see Ethics

MORALS

see Behavior; Ethics

MORE, THOMAS, SIR, SAINT, 1478-1535

Crompton, Samuel Willard. Thomas More: And His Struggles of Conscience. 2005. (Makers of the Middle Ages & Renaissance Ser.). (Illus.). 140p. (J). (gr. 4-8). lib. bdg. 30.00 (978-0-7910-8636-0(4) , Chelsea Hse.) Facts On File, Inc.

MORGAN, DANIEL, 1736-1802

Gallagher, Jim. Daniel Morgan: Fighting Frontiersman. 2006. (J). pap. (978-1-59556-020-9(3)); (Illus.). 88p. (gr. 5-11). lib. bdg. 23.95 (978-1-59556-015-5(7)) OTTN Publishing.

MORGAN, HENRY, SIR, 1635-1688

Hamilton, Sue L. Henry Morgan. 2007. (Pirates! Ser.). (ENG., Illus.). 32p. (J). (gr. 3-6). 24.21 ***(978-1-59928-760-7(9)*** , ABDO & Daughters) ABDO Publishing Co.

MORMONS AND MORMONISM

Bagley, Val. Gospel Truths from the Book of Mormon. 2004. (Seek & Ye Shall Find Flap Book Ser.). (Illus.). (J). bds. 13.95 (978-1-59156-279-5(1)) Covenant Communications, Inc.

—Hidden Treasures of the Book of Mormon. 2004. 13.95 (978-1-57734-759-0(5)) Covenant Communications, Inc.

Bagley, Val Chadwick. New Star in Heaven. 2004. (Seek & Ye Shall Find Flap Book Ser.). (Illus.). bds. 13.95 (978-1-57734-902-0(4)) Covenant Communications, Inc.

Bagley, Val Chadwick, illus. I Will Follow God's Plan for Me. 2004. (J). (978-1-59156-579-6(0)) Covenant Communications.

Barnes, Kathleen H. & Pearce, Virginia H. I Love to See the Temple. Marsh, Dilleen, illus. 2002. (J). 10.95 (978-1-57008-792-9(X) , Bookcraft, Inc.) Deseret Bk. Co.

Bernice, Janet. Tiny Talks: I Will Follow God's Plan for Me, Vol. 5. 2004. (YA). pap. 7.95 (978-1-55517-815-4(4) , Cedar Fort, Inc.) Cedar Fort, Inc./CFI Distribution.

Bial, Raymond. Nauvoo: Mormon City on the Mississippi River. 2006. (Illus.). 48p. (J). (gr. 4-6). 17.00 (978-0-618-39685-6(3)) Houghton Mifflin Co.

Bowman, David. Who's Your Hero? Vol. 2: Book of Mormon Stories Applied to Children. Bowman, David, illus. 2006. 80p. (J). pap. 14.95 (978-1-59038-691-0(4)) Deseret Bk. Co.

—Who's Your Hero? Vol. 2: Book of Mormon Stories Applied to Children. 2006. (Illus.). 74p. (J). pap. (978-1-59038-573-9(X)) Deseret Bk. Co.

Bowman, Kimberly Jensen. Junior Book of Mormon. Stucki, Joy Burch, illus. 2002. 171p. (YA). 12.95 (978-1-55517-507-8(4) , Bonneville Bks.) Cedar Fort, Inc./CFI Distribution.

Brown, Susan C. Book of Mormon Activity Book. 1999. (Activity Bks.). (Illus.). 76p. (J). pap. 8.95 (978-1-57665-060-8(X)) Muggli Graphics.

Brown, Toni Sorenson. Heroes of the Book of Mormon. 2004. bds. 10.95 (978-1-59156-056-2(X)) Covenant Communications, Inc.

Bushman, Claudia Lauper & Bushman, Richard. Mormons in America. 1998. (Religion in America Ser.). (Illus.). 144p. (YA). 30.00 (978-0-19-510677-0(6)) Oxford Univ. Pr., Inc.

Bytheway, John. Are Your Standards Fences or Guardrails? 2003. (Illus.). xiv, 97p. (J). pap. (978-1-57008-990-9(6)) Deseret Bk. Co.

Cannon, Elaine. Baptized & Confirmed: Your Lifeline to Heaven. 2001. 96p. (J). pap. 9.95 (978-1-57345-915-0(1) , SKU 4128992, Bookcraft, Inc.) Deseret Bk. Co.

Craner, Ben, tr. & illus. I Can Be a Missionary, Too. Craner, Ben, illus. 2003. (J). (978-1-57008-965-7(5)) Deseret Bk. Co.

Daybell, Chad. The Aaronic Priesthood: Seven Principles That Will Make This Power a Part of Your Daily Life. Murray, Rhett E., illus. 2003. 100p. (J). pap. 8.95 (978-1-55517-717-1(4) , 77174) Cedar Fort, Inc./CFI Distribution.

—Book of Mormon Numbers. Bonham, Bob, illus. 2004. (J). bds. 8.95 (978-1-55517-755-3(7) , 77557) Cedar Fort, Inc./CFI Distribution.

Daybell, Chad & Daybell, Tammy. Tiny Talks Vol. 3: Volume 3: the Church of Jesus Christ. Murray, Rhett E., illus. 2002. 80p. (J). pap. 7.95 (978-1-55517-672-3(0)) Cedar Fort, Inc./CFI Distribution.

Daybell, Tammy & Daybell, Chad. Tiny Talks Vol. 1: Volume 1: Temples. Ford, Adam, illus. 2002. 78p. (J). pap. 7.95 (978-1-55517-612-9(7) , 76127) Cedar Fort, Inc./CFI Distribution.

—Tiny Talks Vol. 2: The Savior, Vol. 2. Daybell, Tammy, illus. 2002. 801p. (J). pap. 7.95 (978-1-55517-617-4(8)) Cedar Fort, Inc./CFI Distribution.

Durrant, George D. Seven Years Old & Preparing for Baptism. 2007. (Illus.). 68p. (J). pap. 7.95 ***(978-1-932898-74-3(3))*** Spring Creek Bk. Co.

Gowans, Floyd W. Covenant Verses: The Book of Mormon. 2004. 276p. (YA). per. 19.95 (978-1-58982-160-6(2) , Millennial Mind Publishing) American Bk. Publishing Group.

Hawkins, Chad S. Youth & the Temple. 2002. (Illus.). vii, 136p. (J). pap. 12.95 (978-1-57008-846-9(2)) Scribbulations LLC.

Landau, Elaine. The Mormon Trail. 2006. (True Book - Westward Expansion Ser.). (Illus.). 48p. (J). (gr. 3-5). 25.00 (978-0-516-25872-0(9) , Children's Pr.) Scholastic Library Publishing.

Marsh, Dilleen, tr. & illus. What Happens When People Die? Marsh, Dilleen, illus. 2003. (J). 12.95 (978-1-57008-954-1(X)) Deseret Bk. Co.

Millett, Melanie. Teeny Tiny Talks: Junior Primary: I Will Follow God's Plan for Me, Vol. 1. Millett, Melanie, illus. 2004. (J). per. 12.95 (978-1-55517-778-2(6) , Cedar Fort, Inc.) Cedar Fort, Inc./CFI Distribution.

The Mormon Pioneer Trail: Individual Title Six-Packs. (On Deck Ser.: Vol. 2). 24p. (gr. 4-5). 35.00 (978-0-7578-5811-6(2)) Rigby Education.

Morton, William A. From Plowboy to Mormon Prophet Being a Short History of Joseph Smith for Children. Ramsey, L. A., illus. 2004. reprint ed. pap. 30.95 (978-1-4179-6860-2(5)) Kessinger Publishing, LLC.

Muggli, Glorianne. Church of Jesus Christ Activity Book. 2005. (J). pap. 9.95 (978-1-57665-124-7(X)) Muggli Graphics.

—Classroom Activity Book: Book of Mormon. 1999. (Classroom Activity Book Ser.). (Illus.). 96p. (J). pap. 8.95 (978-1-57665-062-2(6)) Muggli Graphics.

Mullins, Amy. I'm Reverent When- Bagley, Val Chadwick, illus. 2005. ("Move-About" Book Ser.). (J). (978-1-59156-951-0(6)) Covenant Communications.

My Very First LDS Word Book. 2005. 18p. (J). 11.95 (978-1-59038-495-4(4)) Deseret Bk. Co.

Naden, Corinne J. & Blue, Rose. Mormonism. 2004. (Illus.). 112p. (J). 29.95 (978-1-59018-452-3(1) , Lucent Bks.) Thomson Gale.

Nash, Carol Rust. The Mormon Trail & the Latter-Day Saints in American History. 1999. (In American History Ser.). (Illus.). 128p. (YA). (gr. 5-12). lib. bdg. 26.60 (978-0-89490-988-7(6)) Enslow Pubs., Inc.

Newell, Karmel H. Come Follow Me: A Child's Guide to Faith, Hope, & Charity. Smith, Mary Ann Free, illus. 2003. (J). 16.95 (978-1-57008-809-4(8)) Scribbulations LLC.

Oaks, Robert C. Believe! Helping Youth Learn to Trust in the Lord. 2003. (Illus.). xiii, 126p. (J). pap. 14.95 (978-1-59038-203-5(X)) Deseret Bk. Co.

Perry, Janice Kapp. I Love to See the Temple. Muir, Michael, tr. Muir, Michael, illus. 2004. (J). 17.95 (978-1-57734-997-6(0)) Covenant Communications, Inc.

Rich, J. Milton. Heavenly Fathers Plan of Salvation Coloring Book. Knaupp, Andrew & Koford, Adam, illus. 2003. 108p. (J). per. 7.95 (978-0-9726670-2-9(4)) Rich Publishing.

Robinson, Timothy M. Nauvoo Temple Stone. Barrett, Robert, illus. 2002. 32p. (J). 16.95 (978-1-57008-776-9(8)) Scribbulations LLC.

—A Night Without Darkness. Madsen, Jim, illus. 1999. (J). 15.95 (978-1-57345-504-6(0)) Deseret Bk. Co.

Robison, Lynda C. Boys Who Became Prophets. Mann, Paul & Harston, Jerry, illus. 1998. (J). 14.95 (978-1-57345-083-6(9)) Deseret Bk. Co.

Rostrom, Laura Lee. My Book of Mormon. 1999. 32p. (J). (ps-5). pap. 2.99 (978-1-55517-425-5(6)) Cedar Fort, Inc./CFI Distribution.

Rowley, Deborah Pace. White Dresses: A Baptism Keepsake for Girls. Hodson, Jewel, illus. 2006. 32p. (J). 14.95 (978-1-59038-632-3(9)) Deseret Bk. Co.

—White Shirts: A Baptism Keepsake for Boys. Call, Brian, illus. 2006. 32p. (J). 14.95 (978-1-59038-633-0(7)) Deseret Bk. Co.

Setzer, Lee Ann. I Am Ready for Baptism. 2006. 30p. (J). 4.99 (978-1-55517-944-1(4) , Cedar Fort, Inc.) Cedar Fort, Inc./CFI Distribution.

—Tiny Talks #6: I will Trust in Heavenly Father & His Son, Jesus Christ-Their Promises are Sure, Vol. 6. 2005. (YA). pap. 7.99 (978-1-55517-889-5(8) , Cedar Fort, Inc.) Cedar Fort, Inc./CFI Distribution.

Simon, Charnan. Brigham Young: Mormon & Pioneer. 1998. (Community Builders Ser.). (Illus.). 48p. (J). (gr. 3-5). 25.00 (978-0-516-20392-8(4) , Children's Pr.) Scholastic Library Publishing.

Sonneborn, Liz. The Mormon Trail. 2005. (Watts Library). (Illus.). 63p. (J). (gr. 5-8). 25.50 (978-0-531-12317-1(0) , Watts, Franklin) Scholastic Library Publishing.

Turley, Richard E. & Littke, Lael. Stories from the Life of Joseph Smith. 2003. (Illus.). viii, 184p. (J). (978-1-57008-915-2(9)) Deseret Bk. Co.

Wa, Kaye Mangum, illus. & retold by. A Prophet in My Pocket - Nephi. Wa, Kaye Mangum, retold by. 2002. 10p. (J). pap. 2.49 (978-0-9726557-1-2(9)) ldscrafts.com.

Wallace, Kaye Mangum, illus. & retold by. A Prophet in My Pocket - Abinadi. Wallace, Kaye Mangum, retold by. 2002. 10p. (J). pap. 2.49 (978-0-9726557-3-6(5)) ldscrafts.com.

—A Prophet in My Pocket - Ammon. Wallace, Kaye Mangum, retold by. 2002. 10p. (J). pap. 2.49 (978-0-9726557-4-3(3)) ldscrafts.com.

—A Prophet in My Pocket - Benjamin. Wallace, Kaye Mangum, retold by. 2002. 10p. (J). pap. 2.49 (978-0-9726557-2-9(7)) ldscrafts.com.

—A Prophet in My Pocket - Ether. Wallace, Kaye Mangum, retold by. 2002. 10p. (J). pap. 2.49 (978-0-9726557-5-0(1)) ldscrafts.com.

—A Prophet in My Pocket - Lehi. Wallace, Kaye Mangum, retold by. 2002. 10p. (J). pap. 2.49 (978-0-9726557-0-5(0)) ldscrafts.com.

—Six Pocket-Sized Stories of Book of Mormon Prophets & Heroes: Packet #1 - Lehi, Nephi, King Benjamin, Abinadi, Ammon, Ether, 6 bks. Wallace, Kaye Mangum, retold by. 2002. 60p. (J). pap. 12.95 (978-0-9726557-6-7(X)) ldscrafts.com.

Wallis, MaryAlice Lloyd & Lindstrom, C. G. LDS Puzzle Pals. 2007. (J). (***978-1-55517-994-6(0)***) Cedar Fort, Inc./CFI Distribution.

Wells, Anita. Nephi, Nephi, the Scriptures Are True. Anderson, Neal, illus. 2004. 32p. (J). (ps-2). 17.95 (978-1-59038-307-0(9)) Deseret Bk. Co.

Whelan, Shane LeGrande. More Than One: Plural Marriage - A Sacred Heritage, a Promise for Tomorrow. 2nd rev. ed. 2002. (Illus.). 262p. pap. 16.95 (978-0-9717704-2-3(5)) Zion Pubs.

Wise, Gayla. I Am a Latter-Day Saint. 1999. (Religions of the World Ser.). 24p. (J). (gr. k-4). lib. bdg. 18.75 (978-0-8239-5259-5(2)) Rosen Publishing Group, Inc., The.

Wright, Dennis A. & Huntington, Ray L. The LDS Children's Encyclopedia. 2002. (Illus.). ix, 213p. (J). 24.95 (978-1-57345-897-9(X) , Bookcraft, Inc.) Deseret Bk. Co.

MORMONS AND MORMONISM—FICTION

Andersen, C. B. The Book of Mormon Sleuth Vol. 3: The Hidden Path. 2003. ix, 214p. (J). pap. (978-1-57008-988-6(4)) Deseret Bk. Co.

—The Forgotten Treasure. 2004. 215p. (J). pap. (978-1-59038-314-8(1)) Deseret Bk. Co.

Anderson, Launi K. Clarissa's Heart. 1998. (Latter-Day Daughters Ser.). 5.95 (978-1-57345-416-2(8)) Deseret Bk. Co.

—Jillian's Discovery. 1999. (Choose the Right Ser.: Bk. 3). 60p. (J). pap. (978-1-57008-673-1(7)) Scribbulations LLC.

Bateman, Anya. The Makeover of James Orville Wickenbee. 2007. 262p. (J). pap. (***978-1-59038-707-8(4)***) Deseret Bk. Co.

Bell, Michele Ashman. Dragon's Jaw: A Heart-Pounding Adventure. 2005. 241p. (J). (978-1-59156-880-3(3)) Covenant Communications.

Bessey, Sian Ann. Uprising in Samoa: A Novel. 2004. 178p. (J). (978-1-59156-890-2(0)) Covenant Communications.

Bowman, David. Who's Your Hero? BK of Mormon Stories Applied to Children, Vol. 3. 2007. 80p. pap. 14.95 (***978-1-59038-759-7(7)***) Deseret Bk. Co.

Brown, Toni Sorenson. I Can't Go to Church. Jolley, Mack, illus. 2005. (J). (978-1-59156-270-2(8)) Covenant Communications.

Call, Brian D., tr. & illus. Sarah's Cloud. Call, Brian D., illus. 2003. (J). 15.95 (978-1-57008-955-8(8)) Deseret Bk. Co.

Condie, Allyson. First Day. 2007. 304p. (YA). pap. 15.95 (***978-1-59038-775-7(9)***) Deseret Bk. Co.

Condie, Allyson B. Yearbook. 2006. 208p. (YA). pap. 14.95 (978-1-59038-690-3(6)) Deseret Bk. Co.

Durrant, George D. Shakespeare's Best Work: A Novel of Unexpected Family Ties & Uncommon Faith. 2003. 130p. (YA). pap. 10.95 (978-1-55517-709-6(3) , 77093, Bonneville Bks.) Cedar Fort, Inc./CFI Distribution.

Embry-Litchman, Kristin. All Is Well. 1999. (J). (978-0-606-16714-7(5)) Tandem Library Bks.

Evans, Lauralee. The King's Heir. 2006. (YA). (***978-1-55517-865-9(0)*** , Bonneville Bks.) Cedar Fort, Inc./CFI Distribution.

Ficklin, Jonene H. The Garden Gate. 2005. (YA). 14.95 (978-0-9761188-2-4(3)) Victor's Crown Publishing.

Gostick, Adrian R. Jessica's Search: The Secret of Ballycater Cove. 1998. (J). 1.99 (978-1-57345-436-0(2)) Deseret Bk. Co.

Heimerdinger, Chris. Kingdoms & Conquerors: A Novel. 2005. 434p. (YA). (***978-1-59156-740-0(8)***) Covenant Communications.

Heimerdinger, Chris. Tower of Thunder Vol. 9: A Novel. 2004. (Tennis Shoes Adventure Ser.). 406p. pap. 14.95 (978-1-59156-177-4(9)) Covenant Communications, Inc.

Heuston, Kimberley Burton. Book of Jude. 2008. (J). (***978-1-932425-26-0(8)*** , Front Street) Boyds Mills Pr.

—The Shakeress. 2008. (J). pap. (***978-1-59078-575-1(4)*** , Calkins Creek) Boyds Mills Pr.

Heuston, Kimberly. The Shakeress. 2004. 208p. (YA). pap. 6.99 (978-0-14-240054-8(8) , Puffin) Penguin Group (USA) Inc.

Hopkins, Ellen. Burned. 2007. 544p. (YA). pap. 9.99 (***978-1-4169-0355-0(0)*** , Simon Pulse) Simon & Schuster Children's Publishing.

Hughes, Dean. As Wide As the River. 2005. 156p. (J). pap. (978-1-59038-450-3(4)) Deseret Bk. Co.

—Under the Same Stars. 2005. viii, 152p. (J). pap. (978-1-59038-448-0(2)) Deseret Bk. Co.

Hulme, Joy N. Through the Open Door. 2000. 176p. (J). (gr. 4-6). 14.95 (978-0-380-97870-0(9)) HarperCollins Pubs.

Johnson-Choong, Shelly. A Light to Come Home By. 2nd unabr. ed. 2004. 212p. (C). reprint ed. pap. 12.95 (978-1-932280-52-4(9) , 80529) Granite Publishing & Distribution.

Kearns, Ann. Dell's Discovery. 2006. 108p. (YA). per. 9.95 (978-0-9710696-6-4(2)) Jorlan Publishing, Inc.

Levitin, Sonia. Clem's Chances. 2001. (Illus.). 208p. (J). (gr. 2-7). pap. 17.95 (978-0-439-29314-3(6) , Orchard Bks.) Scholastic, Inc.

Littke, Lael. Searching for Selene. 2003. 203p. (J). pap. 13.95 (978-1-59038-179-3(3)) Deseret Bk. Co.

Mangum, Kay Lynn. When the Bough Breaks. 2007. 352p. (YA). pap. 15.95 (***978-1-59038-748-1(1)***) Deseret Bk. Co.

Norton, Tamra. Molly Mormon? Myth or Me? 2002. (Illus.). 170p. (J). pap. 12.95 (978-1-55517-606-8(2) , Bonneville Bks.) Cedar Fort, Inc./CFI Distribution.

Peck, Lisa J. A Challenge for Brittany. 1999. (Choose the Right Ser.: Bk. 2). 60p. (J). pap. (978-1-57008-664-9(8)) Scribbulations LLC.

Rich, J. Milton. The Book of Mormon on Trial. Koford, Adam & Knaupp, Andrew, illus. 2nd ed. 2002. 400p. lib. bdg. 29.95 (978-0-9726670-0-5(8)) Rich Publishing.

Rostrom, Laura Lee. My Book of Mormon Storybook: 90 Favorite Stories. Rostrom, Laura Lee, photos by. 1999. (Illus.). (J). (ps-6). 19.95 (978-1-55517-352-4(7)) Cedar Fort, Inc./CFI Distribution.

Rowley, B. J. My Body Fell Off! 2000. (Light Traveler Adventure Ser.: Vol. 1). 206p. (YA). (gr. 6-12). pap. 11.95 (978-0-9700103-1-5(1)) Golden Wings Enterprises.

—Silver Hawk's Revenge. 2000. (Light Traveler Adventure Ser.: Vol. 2). 256p. (YA). (gr. 6-12). pap. 12.95 (978-0-9700103-2-2(X)) Golden Wings Enterprises.

Sebra, Diane. Making Mountains Out of Moles. 2003. 120p. (YA). pap. 9.95 (978-1-55517-712-6(3) , 77123, Bonneville Bks.) Cedar Fort, Inc./CFI Distribution.

Sume, Lori Anne, illus. Sorry, Sorry, Sorry: Learning to Choose the Right. 2004. (J). bds. 9.95 (978-1-59156-298-6(8)) Covenant Communications, Inc.

Thomasma, Kenneth. Doe Sia: Bannock Girl & the Handcart Pioneer. 1999. (Amazing Indian Children: 8). (J). (gr. 3-8). pap. 7.99 (978-1-880114-20-9(8)); 12.99 (978-1-880114-21-6(6)) Grandview Publishing Co.

—Doe Sia: Bannock Girl & the Handcart Pioneers. 1999. (Illus.). (J). 14.64 (978-0-606-21884-9(X)) Tandem Library Bks.

Wiles, Patricia. Early-Morning Cemetery: A Novel. 2006. 243p. (YA). pap. (978-1-59811-077-7(2)) Covenant Communications.

Williams, Carol Lynch. Victoria's Courage. 1998. (Latter-Day Daughters Ser.). (J). 5.95 (978-1-57345-434-6(6)) Deseret Bk. Co.

Yates, Alma J. Sammy's Song: A Novel. 2005. 272p. (J). (***978-1-59156-945-9(1)***) Covenant Communications.

Yates, Dan. An Angel in the Family: A Novel. 1999. (Illus.). 188 p. pap. 12.95 (978-1-57734-282-3(8) , 01113461) Covenant Communications, Inc.

MOROCCO

Beardsley, Kurt. Under Saharan Skies. 2004. (Illus.). 96p. per. 25.00 (978-0-9761103-0-9(X) , 1000) International Vaquero Productions.

Blauer, Ettagale & Laure, Jason. Morocco. 1999. (Enchantment of the World, Second Ser.). (Illus.). 144p. (YA). (gr. 5-9). 36.00 (978-0-516-20961-6(2) , Children's Pr.) Scholastic Library Publishing.

Cassanos, Lynda Cohen. Morocco. 2003. (Modern Middle East Nations & Their Strategic Place in the World Ser.). (Illus.). 112,128p. (YA). (gr. 7 up). lib. bdg. (978-1-59084-515-8(3)) Mason Crest Pubs.

Chelsea House Publishing Staff. Morocco. 1999. (Major World Nations Ser.). (Illus.). 144p. (gr. 4-7). 29.95 (978-0-7910-5389-8(X) , Chelsea Hse.) Facts On File, Inc.

Delgado, Kevin. Morocco. 2005. (Modern Nations of the World Ser.). (Illus.). 96-144p. (J). (gr. 7-10). 29.95 (978-1-59018-625-1(7) , 1244585, Lucent Bks.) Thomson Gale.

Ferro, Jennifer. Moroccan Foods & Culture. 1999. (Festive Foods & Celebrations Ser.). (Illus.). 48p. (J). (gr. 3-6). lib. bdg. 27.93 (978-1-57103-304-8(1)) Rourke Publishing, LLC.

Fordyce, Deborah. Welcome to Morocco. 2004. (Welcome to My Country Ser.). (Illus.). 48p. (J). (gr. 2 up). lib. bdg. 26.00 (978-0-8368-2561-9(6)) Stevens, Gareth Inc.

Habeeb, Mark. Morocco. 2002. (Countries of the World Ser.). (Illus.). 96p. (J). (gr. 6 up). lib. bdg. 30.00 (978-0-8368-2361-5(3)) Stevens, Gareth Inc.

McCulloch, Susan H. Morocco. 2003. (World Tour Ser.). (Illus.). 48p. (J). lib. bdg. 25.70 (978-0-7398-6813-3(6)) Raintree.

Merrick, Patrick. Morocco. 2000. (Countries: Faces & Places Ser.). (Illus.). 32p. (J). (gr. 1-5). 25.64 (978-1-56766-737-0(6)) Child's World, Inc.

Raabe, Emily. Morocco, a Primary Source Guide. 2005. (Countries of the World, a Primary Source Journey Ser.). (Illus.). 24p. (J). 19.95 (978-1-4042-2755-2(5) , PowerKids Pr.) Rosen Publishing Group, Inc., The.

Ryan, Marla Felkins. Into Wild Moracco. 2004. (Jeff Corwin Experience Ser.). (Illus.). 48p. (J). 11.20 (978-1-4103-0236-6(9)); (gr. 4-7). 24.95 (978-1-4103-0235-9(0)) Thomson Gale. (Blackbirch Pr., Inc.).

Seward, Pat & Hargraves, Orin. Morocco. 2nd ed. 2006. (Cultures of the World Ser.). (J). (978-0-7614-2051-4(7) , Benchmark Bks.) Cavendish, Marshall Corp.

U. S. A. Global Investment Center Staff. Morocco Customs, Trade Regulations & Procedures Handbook. 2003. (World Investment & Business Library). pap. 99.95 (978-0-7397-5590-7(0)) International Business Pubns., USA.

MOROCCO—FICTION

Alalou, Elizabeth & Alalou, Ali. The Butter Man. Essakalli, Julie Klear, illus. 2008. (J). (***978-1-58089-127-1(6)***) Charlesbridge Publishing, Inc.

Bellamy, Richard. Saharan Boy. 2002. (gr. 7-12). lib. bdg. 24.00 (978-0-613-78103-9(1)) Tandem Library Bks.

Coatsworth, Elizabeth Jane. The White Horse. Sewell, Helen, illus. 2005. 169p. (J). pap. 11.95 (978-1-883937-86-7(8)) Bethlehem Bks.

Geis, Patricia. Pequena Tamazigh. 2005. (Ninos y ninas del mundo Ser.). (SPA., Illus.). 32p. (J). 5.95 (978-84-7864-882-5(8)) Combel Editorial, S.A. ESP. *Dist:* Independent Pubs. Group.

Ichikawa, Satomi. My Father's Shop. Ichikawa, Satomi, illus. 2006. (Illus.). 40p. (J). (gr. k-2). 15.95 (978-1-929132-99-7(9)) Kane/Miller Bk. Pubs., Inc.

Jackson, Dave & Jackson, Neta. Risking the Forbidden Game: Maude Cary. Gavitt, Anne, illus. 2002. (Trailblazers Ser.). 160p. (J). (gr. 3-7). pap. 6.99 (978-0-7642-2234-4(1)) Bethany Hse. Pubs.

Klaus, Sandra. Mustafas Geheimnis: Ein Moslemischer Junge auf der Suche nach Gott. Date not set. Tr. of Mustapha's Secret - A Muslim Boy's Search to Know God. (GER., Illus.). (J). (gr. 2-7). pap. (978-0-9617490-6-4(7)) Gospel Missionary Union.

—Tainata na Mustapha. Date not set. Tr. of Mustapha's Secret. (BUL.). (J). (gr. 2-7). pap. (978-1-890940-04-1(6)) Gospel Missionary Union.

Lewin, Ted. The Storytellers. 1998. (Illus.). 40p. (J). (gr. k-3). 16.00 (978-0-688-15178-2(7)) HarperCollins Pubs.

St. John, Patricia. Star of Light. 2002. (Illus.). 160p. (YA). pap. 6.99 (978-0-8024-6577-1(3)) Moody Pubs.

MOROCCO—HISTORY

Binns, Tristan Boyer. La Casa Blanca. 2003. (Simbolos de Libertad Ser.).Tr. of White House. (SPA., 32p. (J). Illus.). lib. bdg. 22.79 (978-1-4034-2998-8(7)); pap. 6.95 (978-1-4034-3021-2(7)) Heinemann Library.

—La Casa Blanca. 2003. Tr. of White House. (SPA.). (gr. k-3). lib. bdg. 14.75 (978-0-613-89946-8(6)) Tandem Library Bks.

Italia, Bob. Morocco. 2000. (Countries Ser.). (Illus.). 40p. (J). (gr. k-6). lib. bdg. 22.78 (978-1-57765-393-6(9) , Checkerboard Library) ABDO Publishing Co.

MORPHOLOGY

see Anatomy; Anatomy, Comparative; Biology

MORRISON, TONI, 1931-

Bloom, Harold. Toni Morrison. 1999. (Bloom's Major Novelists Ser.). 120p. (YA). (gr. 8 up). 31.95 (978-0-7910-5258-7(3) , 039959, Chelsea Hse.) Facts On File, Inc.

Bloom, Harold, ed. Toni Morrison. 2002. (Bloom's BioCritiques Ser.). (Illus.). 112p. (gr. 9-13). 35.00 (978-0-7910-6180-0(9) , 000861, Chelsea Hse.) Facts On File, Inc.

Blue. Toni Morrison. 2004. (African-American Biographies Ser.). 64p. pap. 9.50 (978-1-4109-1120-9(9)) Raintree.

Burton, Zisca. Bloom's How to Write about Toni Morrison. 2007. (Bloom's How to Write about Literature Ser.). 256p. (YA). (gr. 9 up). 45.00 (***978-0-7910-9548-5(7)*** , Chelsea Hse.) Facts On File, Inc.

Colson, Mary. The Story Behind Toni Morrison's the Bluest Eye. 2006. (History in Literature Ser.). 56p. (J). (gr. 7 up). lib. bdg. 32.86 (978-1-4034-8212-9(8)) Heinemann Library.

Haskins, Jim. Toni Morrison: Telling a Tale Untold. 2002. (Techies Ser.). (Illus.). 144p. (gr. 7 up). lib. bdg. 26.90 (978-0-7613-1852-1(6) , Twenty-First Century Bks.) Lerner Publishing Group.

—Toni Morrison: The Magic of Words. 2001. (Gateway Biography Ser.). (Illus.). 48p. (J). (gr. 2-4). lib. bdg. 23.90 (978-0-7613-1806-4(2) , Millbrook Pr.) Lerner Publishing Group.

Naden, Corinne J. & Blue, Rose. Toni Morrison. 2004. (African-American Biographies Ser.). (Illus.). 64p. (J). (gr. 4-7). 32.86 (978-1-4109-1043-1(1)) Raintree.

Rhodes, Lisa Renee. Toni Morrison: Great American Writer. 2001. (Book Report Biographies Ser.). (Illus.). 100p. (YA). (gr. 6-8). pap. 6.95 (978-0-531-15555-4(2) , Watts, Franklin) Scholastic Library Publishing.

Watson, Galadriel Findlay. Toni Morrison. 2005. (Great African American Women for Kids Ser.). (Illus.). 24p. (J). (ps-7). pap. 6.95 (978-1-59036-340-9(X)); lib. bdg. 26.00 (978-1-59036-334-8(5)) Weigl Pubs., Inc.

MORSE, SAMUEL FINLEY BREESE, 1791-1872

Alter, Judy. Samuel F. B. Morse: Inventor & Code Creator. 2003. (Spirit of America: Our People Ser.). (Illus.). 32p. (J). (gr. 2-6). 27.07 (978-1-56766-446-1(6)) Child's World, Inc.

Hall, Margaret. Samuel Morse. 2004. (J). pap. 6.50 (978-1-4034-5337-2(3)); lib. bdg. 22.79 (978-1-4034-5329-7(2)) Heinemann Library.

Kerby, Mona. Frederick Douglass & Samuel Morse. 2001. (Illus.). 132p. (gr. 4-7). pap. 10.95 (978-0-595-18574-0(6)) iUniverse, Inc.

Quackenbush, Robert. Two Slapstick Biographies: Once upon a Time! A Story of the Brothers Grimm & Quick, Annie, Give Me a Catchy Line! A Story of Samuel F. B. Morse. 1999. (Two Slapstick Biographies Ser.: Vol. 1). (Illus.). 64p. (YA). (gr. 3 up). reprint ed. pap. 5.95 (978-0-9612518-1-9(6)) Quackenbush, Robert Studios.

Seidman, David. Samuel Morse & the Telegraph. 2007. 32p. (J). (978-0-7368-6846-4(1)) Capstone Pr., Inc.

Zannos, Susan. Samuel Morse & the Telegraph. 2004. (Uncharted, Unexplored, & Unexplained Ser.). (Illus.). 48p. (J). (gr. 4-8). lib. bdg. 29.95 (978-1-58415-269-9(9)) Mitchell Lane Pubs., Inc.

MORTON, JULIUS STERLING, 1832-1902

Beaty, Sandy & Wilkerson, J. L. Champion of Arbor Day: J. Sterling Morton. Parkison, Jami, ed. 1999. (Great Heartlanders Ser.). (Illus.). 130p. (YA). (gr. 4-12). pap. 8.95 (978-0-9664470-1-9(8)) Acorn Bks.

MORTUARY CUSTOMS

see Funeral Rites and Ceremonies

MOSAICS

Casey, Dennis John. Mosaics - Prairie Art Glass Patterns: From the Designs of Frank Lloyd Wright. 1999. (Illus.). 27p. 16.50 (978-0-9724559-3-0(0) , BK-4) Prairie Designs of California.

Freixenet, Anna. Creating with Mosaics. 2000. (Crafts for All Seasons Ser.). (Illus.). 32p. (J). (gr. 3-8). lib. bdg. 23.70 (978-1-56711-440-9(7) , Blackbirch Pr., Inc.) Thomson Gale.

Powell, Michelle. Mosaics. (Step-by-Step Ser.). (Illus.). 32p. 2003. (YA). pap. 7.95 (978-1-4034-0710-8(X)); 2001. (J). (gr. 3-5). lib. bdg. 24.22 (978-1-57572-332-7(8)) Heinemann Library.

—Mosaics. 2001. (Step-by-Step Children's Crafts Ser.). (Illus.). 32p. (J). pap. 7.95 (978-0-85532-909-9(2) , 9092) Search Pr., Ltd. GBR. *Dist:* Independent Pubs. Group.

—Mosaics. 2001. (gr. k-3). lib. bdg. 17.60 (978-0-613-76977-8(5)) Tandem Library Bks.

MOSBY, JOHN SINGLETON, 1833-1916

Beller, Susan Provost. Mosby & His Rangers: Adventures of the Gray Ghost. 2000. (Illus.). 108p. (gr. 4-7). pap. 9.95 (978-0-595-00788-2(0) , Backinprint.com) iUniverse, Inc.

MOSCOW (RUSSIA)

Corona, Laurel. Life in Moscow. 2000. (Way People Live Ser.). (Illus.). 112p. (J). (gr. 7-10). 28.70 (978-1-56006-795-5(0) , LML00902-178132, Lucent Bks.) Thomson Gale.

Fowler, Allan. Moscow. 1999. (Rookie Read-About Geography Ser.). (Illus.). 32p. (J). (gr. 1-2). 20.50 (978-0-516-21558-7(2) , Children's Pr.) Scholastic Library Publishing.

—Moscow. 2000. (Illus.). 31p. (J). (ps-3). lib. bdg. 14.10 (978-0-613-54029-2(8)) Tandem Library Bks.

Hatt, Christine. Moscow. 1999. (World Cities Ser.). (Illus.). 48p. (J). (gr. 2-6). lib. bdg. 16.95 (978-1-929298-25-9(0)) Chrysalis Education.

Holmes, Burton. Moscow. Schlesinger, Arthur M., Jr. & Isreal, Fred L., eds. 1999. (World 100 Years Ago Ser.). (Illus.). 144p. (YA). (gr. 4-7). 29.95 (978-0-7910-4658-6(3) , Chelsea Hse.) Facts On File, Inc.

Mattern, Joanne. Moscow. 2006. (J). (978-1-59679-718-5(5)) ABDO Publishing Co.

Steele, Philip. Moscow. 2003. (Great Cities of the World Ser.). (Illus.). 48p. (J). (gr. 5 up). pap. 11.95 (978-0-8368-5184-7(6)); lib. bdg. 30.00 (978-0-8368-5024-6(6)) Stevens, Gareth Inc. (World Almanac Library).

Toht, Patricia. Daily Life in Ancient & Modern Moscow. Moulder, Bob, illus. 2005. (Cities Through Time Ser.). 64p. (J). (gr. 5-12). 25.26 (978-0-8225-3220-0(4)) Lerner Publishing Group.

MOSCOW (RUSSIA)—FICTION

Evans, Cornelia. Sasha & Babushka: A Story of Russia. (Make Friends Around the World Ser.). (Illus.). 32p. (J). (gr. k-3). 19.95 incl. audio (978-1-59249-445-3(5) , BC8007); 8.95 incl. audio (978-1-59249-446-0(3) , SC8007); 2006. 15.95 (978-1-59249-443-9(9) , B8007) Soundprints.

Evans, Cornilia. Sasha & Babushka: A Story of Russia. 2006. (Make Friends Around the World Ser.). (Illus.). 32p. (J). (gr. k-3). pap. 6.95 (978-1-59249-444-6(7) , S8007) Soundprints.

Kravetz, Nathan. Moscow, Farewell! A Russian Boy's Adventure in Times Past. 2000. (gr. 7-12). lib. bdg. 31.55 (978-0-613-73907-8(8)) Tandem Library Bks.

Riser, Winifred. Max Goes to Moscow. 2006. (Illus.). 40p. (J). (ps-1). 15.95 (978-1-84507-482-1(3)) Lincoln, Frances Ltd. GBR. *Dist:* Perseus Distribution.

Spirin, Gennady. Martha. Spirin, Gennady, illus. 2005. (Illus.). 32p. (J). (ps-3). 14.99 (978-0-399-23980-9(4) , Philomel) Penguin Group (USA) Inc.

Thompson, Kay & Knight, Hilary. Eloise in Moscow. 40th ed. 2000. (Illus.). 80p. (J). (ps-3). 17.00 (978-0-689-83211-6(7)) Simon & Schuster Children's Publishing.

MOSES (BIBLICAL LEADER)

The Adventures of Moses: A Bible Story to Color. (Illus.). 16p. (J). pap. 1.50 (978-0-87162-849-7(X) , E6023) Warner Pr. Pubs.

Auld, Mary. Exodus from Egypt. 2000. (Bible Stories Ser.). (Illus.). 32p. (J). pap. 7.95 (978-0-531-15437-3(8) , Watts, Franklin) Scholastic Library Publishing.

—Exodus from Egypt. Mayo, Diana, illus. 2000. 31p. (J). (ps-3). lib. bdg. 16.40 (978-0-613-62460-2(2)) Tandem Library Bks.

Auld, Mary & Mayo, Diana. Moses in the Bulrushes. 2000. (Bible Stories Ser.). (Illus.). 32p. (J). (gr. 2-4). pap. 7.95 (978-0-531-15387-1(8) , Watts, Franklin) Scholastic Library Publishing.

Baby Moses in a Basket. 2006. 16p. (J). pap. 1.99 (978-0-7847-1710-3(9) , 04171) Standard Publishing.

Barron, Sharon. Moses & Judaism. 2002. (Great Religious Leaders Ser.). (Illus.). 48p. (J). lib. bdg. 28.50 (978-1-58340-219-1(5)) Smart Apple Media.

Beneduce, Ann. Moses: The Long Road to Freedom. Spirin, Gennady, illus. 2004. 32p. (J). pap. 16.95 (978-0-439-35225-3(8)) Scholastic, Inc.

Blyton, Enid. El Bebe Entre los Juncos. 1999. (Historias Biblicas Ilustradas; Illustrated Bible Stories Ser.). (SPA., Illus.). 32p. (ps-3). pap. 4.99 (978-0-8254-1063-5(0) , Editorial Portavoz) Kregel Pubns.

—El Bebe Entre los Juncos. 1999. (SPA.). (gr. k-3). lib. bdg. 13.00 (978-0-613-76710-1(1)) Tandem Library Bks.

Bostrom, Kathleen Long. Green Plagues & Lamb: The Story of Moses & Pharaoh. McKinsey, Dennis, illus. 2003. 48p. 12.95 (978-0-664-22635-0(3)) Westminster John Knox Pr.

Chaikin, Miriam. Angels Sweep the Desert Floor: Bible Legends about Moses in the Wilderness. Koshkin, Alexander, illus. 2002. 112p. (J). (gr. 3-5). 19.00 (978-0-395-97825-2(4) , Clarion Bks.) Houghton Mifflin Co. Trade & Reference Div.

Chariot Victor Publishing Staff. Moses. 2000. (Shadowbox Bks.). (J). (978-0-7814-3421-8(1)) Cook, David C. Publishing Co.

Curren, Joan E. Moses' Dry Feet. Wheeler, Ron, illus. 1998. (Arch Bks.). (ENG.). 16p. (J). (gr. k-4). 1.99 (978-0-570-07545-5(9)) Concordia Publishing Hse.

Dalmatian Press Staff. Moses Baby in the Bulrushes. 2000. (Illus.). (J). (ps-3). pap. 4.97 incl. audio (978-1-888567-36-6(8)) Dalmatian Pr.

De Graaf, Anne. Moses. Montero, Jose Perez, illus. 1999. (Little Children's Bible Bks.). 38p. (J). (gr. k-1). 5.99 (978-0-8054-1900-9(4)) B&H Publishing Grp.

Dietrich, Julie. Tiny Baby Moses. Clark, Bill, illus. 2003. (Arch Bks.). (ENG.). 16p. (J). (gr. k-4). 1.99 (978-0-570-07581-3(5)) Concordia Publishing Hse.

Fernandez, Francisco. Moises. Osorio, Sergio, illus. 2005. (Historia de la Biblia Ser.). (SPA.). 64p. (J). pap. 4.70 (978-970-643-875-1(0)) Selector, S.A. de C.V. MEX. *Dist:* Lectorum Pubns., Inc.

Fogle, Robin. Baby Moses Coloring Book. 2007. (Illus.). 16p. (J). pap. 1.89 (***978-1-59317-189-6(7)***) Warner Pr. Pubs.

Frank, Penny. Let My People Go! (Illus.). 24p. 2.99 (978-0-7459-4108-0(7) , Lion) Lion Hudson plc GBR. *Dist:* Trafalgar Square Publishing.

—The Princess & the Baby. (Illus.). 24p. 2.99 (978-0-7459-4107-3(9) , Lion) Lion Hudson plc GBR. *Dist:* Trafalgar Square Publishing.

Gamblin, Rose Tooley. Baby Moses. 2007. (J). (***978-0-8127-0466-2(5)***) Autumn Hse. Publishing Co.

Hodges, Margaret. Moses. Wimmer, Mike & Moser, Barry, illus. 2006. 32p. (J). (gr. 3-5). 16.00 (978-0-15-200946-5(9)) Harcourt Children's Bks.

Koralek, Jenny. The Moses Basket. Baynes, Pauline, illus. 2004. 32p. (J). 16.00 (978-0-8028-5251-9(3)) Eerdmans, William B. Publishing Co.

Martin, Oscar, Jr., creator. The Story of Moses, l.t. ed. 2003. (Illus.). 25p. (J). E-Book 19.95 incl. cd-rom (978-0-9748416-2-5(5)) Build Your Story.

Metaxas, Eric. A to Z: The Prince of Egypt. 1998. (Prince of Egypt Ser.). (Illus.). 32p. (J). (ps-1). 9.99 (978-0-8499-5850-2(4)) Nelson, Thomas Inc.

Moises (Moses) (Divertidas Historias Biblicas para Ninos Ser.). (SPA.). (J). 3.49 (978-0-7899-0597-0(3) , 496644) Editorial Unilit.

Morin, Theresa. Moses Parts the Sea. 2000. (Little Bible Bks.). (Illus.). 24p. (J). (ps-3). 1.99 (978-1-57748-686-2(2)) Barbour Publishing, Inc.

Morris, Neil & Foglia, Enrico. The Life of Moses. 2003. (Art Revelations Ser.). (Illus.). 32p. (J). (gr. 6-9). 18.95 (978-1-59270-001-1(2)) Enchanted Lion Bks., LLC.

Moses. 2004. (Junior Bible Ser.: Vol. 3). 36p. pap. 5.95 (978-1-58516-131-7(4)) American Bible Society.

Moses Bible Sticker Book. 2003. (Illus.). 16p. (J). 2.98 (978-1-4054-1557-6(6)) Parragon, Inc.

Moses: God's Man of the Hour—Activity Book. 2005. pap. 1.69 (978-1-59317-109-4(9)) Warner Pr. Pubs.

Nederveld, Patricia L. I'll Do It! The Story of Moses & the Burning Bush. 1998. (God Loves Me Ser.). (Illus.). 24p. (J). (ps-3). pap. 2.95 (978-1-56212-281-2(9) , 001212, Faith Alive Christian Resources) CRC Pubns.

—Safe at Last! The Story of Moses & the Red Sea. 1998. (God Loves Me Ser.). (Illus.). 24p. (J). (ps-3). pap. 2.95 (978-1-56212-282-9(7) , 001213, Faith Alive Christian Resources) CRC Pubns.

—Safe in a Basket: The Story of Baby Moses. 1998. (God Loves Me Ser.). (Illus.). 24p. (J). (ps-3). pap. 2.95 (978-1-56212-280-5(0) , 001211, Faith Alive Christian Resources) CRC Pubns.

New Leaf Press Staff, contrib. by. Moses: The Deliverance of Israel & God's Commands. 2000. (Awesome Adventure Bible Stories Ser.). (Illus.). 40p. (J). (gr. 2-7). pap. 5.99 (978-0-89051-325-5(2)) Master Bks.

Pakulak, Eric. At the Side of Moses: A Multiple-Ending Bible Adventure. Fielding, David, illus. 2000. (J). pap. 6.95 (978-0-8198-0770-0(2)) Pauline Bks. & Media.

Parker, Victoria. Moses & the 10 Commandments. 2002. (Illus.). 64p. pap. 7.95 (978-1-84215-631-5(4)) Anness Publishing GBR. *Dist:* National Bk. Network.

Pingry, Patricia A. The Story of Miriam & Baby Moses. Venturi-Pickett, Stacy, illus. 2000. 26p. (J). (ps-3). bds. 6.95 (978-0-8249-4180-2(2) , Candy Cane Pr.) Ideals Pubns.

—The Story of the Ten Commandments. Venturi-Pickett, Stacy, illus. 2007. 32p. pap. 3.99 (***978-0-8249-5554-0(4)*** , Ideals Children's Bks.) Ideals Pubns.

—The Story of the Ten Commandments. 2006. (Illus.). 26p. (J). bds. 10.95 (978-0-8249-6656-0(2) , Candy Cane Pr.) Ideals Pubns.

Roberts, Catrin, et al. Mawredd Mawr Moses! 16 Sesiwn Beiblaidd Ar Gyfer Clwb Plant Neu'r Ysgol Sul. 2005. (WEL., Illus.). 73p. (978-1-85994-034-1(X)) Cyhoeddiadau'r Gair.

Round, Graham. Historia de Moises (The Story of Moses) 1999. (SPA.). (J). (ps-3). pap. (978-0-7899-0722-6(4) , 498776) Editorial Unilit.

—Moses. 2001. (Your Favorite Bible Stories Ser.). 16p. (J). (ps-5). pap. 4.99 (978-0-8254-7220-6(2)) Kregel Pubns.

Schwartz, Stephen. Through Heaven's Eyes: Prince of Egypt. 1998. (Illus.). 32p. (J). (gr. k-3). 14.99 (978-0-8499-5897-7(0)) Nelson, Thomas Inc.

Sobel, Ileene Smith. Moses & the Angels. Podwal, Mark, illus. rev. ed. 2003. 64p. (J). (gr. 4-8). 17.00 (978-0-7567-6835-5(7)) DIANE Publishing Co.

The Story of the Ten Commandments/la Historia de Los Diez Mandamientos. 2002. (SPA & ENG., Illus.). 28p. (J). pap. 3.95 (978-0-8249-4205 2(1)) Ideals Pubns.

Stowell, Gordon, et al. Y Ddihangfa Anhygoel! Llyfr Drysfa Beiblaidd. 2005. (WEL., Illus.). 12p. (978-1-85994-469-1(8)) Cyhoeddiadau'r Gair.

Van Der Veer, Andrew. Bible Lessons for Juniors, Book 1: Creation through Moses. 2007. (J). (***978-1-60178-012-6(5)***) Reformation Heritage Bks.

Whiting, Jim. The Life & Times of Moses. 2005. (Biography from Ancient Civilizations Ser.). (Illus.). 48p. (J). (ps-7). lib. bdg. 29.95 (978-1-58415-340-5(7)) Mitchell Lane Pubs., Inc.

Wildsmith, Brian. Exodus. Wildsmith, Brian, illus. 1998. (Illus.). 24p. (gr. k-4). 20.00 (978-0-8028-5175-8(4)) Eerdmans, William B. Publishing Co.

Yolen, Jane. The Prince of Egypt: Classic Edition. 1998. (Prince of Egypt Ser.). (Illus.). 80p. (J). (ps-4). 8.99 (978-0-8499-5894-6(6)) Nelson, Thomas Inc.

Zobel-Nolan, Allia. Moses' Big Adventure: A Lift-the-Flap Bible Book. Cox, Steve, illus. 2004. 12p. (J). bds. 10.99 (978-0-8254-5521-6(9)) Kregel Pubns.

MOSES (BIBLICAL LEADER)—FICTION

Adams, Anne Tyra. Songbird of the Nile: The Diary of Miriam's Best Friend, Egypt, 1527 B. C. -1526 B. C. 2004. (Promised Land Diaries). (Illus.). 192p. (J). 10.99 (978-0-8010-4525-7(8)) Baker Bks.

Adler, David A. Brothers in Egypt. abr. ed. (Prince of Egypt Ser.). 64p. pap. (978-0-582-36482-0(5)) Addison-Wesley Longman, Inc.

Baby Moses. 2005. (J). bds. 5.99 (978-0-9753127-9-7(0)) Family Bks. at Home.

Booth, Bradley. Plagues in the Palace. 2006. 159p. (J). (978-0-8163-2143-8(4)) Pacific Pr. Publishing Assn.

Rothero, C. Moses in the Bulrushes. 2005. (Illus.). 20p. (J). 5.95 (978-965-483-008-9(6) , Devora Publishing) Pitspopany Pr.

Sproul, R. C., Jr. Quothe the Prophet. Bustard, Ned, illus. 2000. per. 3.00 (978-1-930710-47-4(X)) Veritas Pr., Inc.

MOSES, GRANDMA, 1860-1961

Klein, Adam G. & Moses. Grandma Moses. 2007. (Illus.). 32p. (J). 22.78 (978-1-59679-737-6(1)) ABDO Publishing Co.

Nikola-Lisa, W. & Moses, Grandma. The Year with Grandma Moses. rev. ed. 2000. (Illus.). 32p. (J). (ps-5). 20.00 (978-0-8050-6243-4(2) , Holt, Henry & Co. Bks. For Young Readers) Holt, Henry & Co.

Schaefer, A. R. Grandma Moses. (Life & Work of. . . Ser.). (Illus.). 32p. (J). (gr. k-2). 2003. lib. bdg. 22.79 (978-1-4034-0289-9(2)); 2002. pap. 6.50 (978-1-4034-0495-4(X)) Heinemann Library.

Venezia, Mike. Grandma Moses. (Getting to Know the World's Greatest Artists Ser.). (J). 2004. (gr. 3-4). pap. 6.95 (978-0-516-27913-8(0)); 2003. (Illus.). 32p. 27.00 (978-0-516-22027-7(6)) Scholastic Library Publishing. (Children's Pr.).

MOSLEM ART

see Art, Islamic

MOSQUITOES

Ada, Alma Flor. The Song of the Teeny-Tiny Mosquito. (Stories for the Telling Ser.). (Illus.). 16p. (J). (gr. k-3). pap. 6.95 (978-1-58105-230-5(8)) Santillana USA Publishing Co., Inc.

Bailey, Jill. Mosquito. (Illus.). 32p. (J). 2006. (***978-1-4034-8300-3(0));*** 2002. pap. 6.95 (978-1-57572-459-1(6) , 90449) Heinemann Library.

—El Mosquito. 2003. (Los Insectos Ser.). (SPA.). 32p. (J). pap. 6.95 (978-1-4034-3034-2(9)) Heinemann Library.

—El Mosquito. 2003. (SPA.). (gr. k-3). lib. bdg. 14.75 (978-0-613-67105-7(8)) Tandem Library Bks.

Bailey, Jill. Mosquito. 2nd ed. 2006. (Illus.). 32p. (J). pap. (***978-1-4034-8313-3(2)***) Heinemann Library.

Barraclough, Sue. Mosquitoes. 2005. (Raintree Sprouts Ser.). (Illus.). 24p. (J). pap. (978-1-4109-1512-2(3)); lib. bdg. (978-1-4109-1507-8(7)) Steck-Vaughn.

Birch. Mosquitoes up Close, 6 Pack. 2004. pap. 40.50 (978-1-4109-1155-1(1)) Harcourt Schl. Pubs.

Birch, Robin. Mosquitoes. 2004. (J). 26.36 (978-1-4109-1141-4(1)); pap. 7.50 (978-1-4109-1148-3(9)) Harcourt Schl. Pubs.

Day, Nancy. Malaria, West Nile & Other Mosquito-Borne Diseases. 2001. (Diseases & People Ser.). (Illus.). 128p. (YA). (gr. 6-12). lib. bdg. 26.60 (978-0-7660-1597-5(1)) Enslow Pubs., Inc.

DiConsiglio, John. Blood Suckers! Deadly Mosquito Bites! 2007. (24/7 - Science Behind the Scenes Ser.). 64p. (YA). (gr. 8-12). 26.00 (978-0-531-12070-5(8) , Watts, Franklin) Scholastic Library Publishing.

DiConsiglio, John. Blood Suckers! Deadly Mosquito Bites. 2007. (24/7: Science Behind the Scenes: Medical Files Ser.). 64p. (J). pap. 7.95 (***978-0-531-17529-3(4)*** , Watts, Franklin) Scholastic Library Publishing.

Flying Mosquitoes. (Pull Ahead Books-Animals Ser.). (J). 2007. 22.60 (978-0-8225-5932-0(3) , Lerner Pubns.); 2006. pap. 5.95 (978-0-8225-6508-6(0) , First Avenue Editions) Lerner Publishing Group.

Hall, Margaret. Mosquitoes. 2006. (Illus.). 24p. (J). (978-0-7368-5351-4(0)) Capstone Pr., Inc.

Harcourt School Publishers Staff. Mosquitoes & Wrigglers Advanced Level. 3rd ed. 2002. (Trophies Reading Program Ser.). (Illus.). pap. 5.10 (978-0-15-323208-4(0)) Harcourt Schl. Pubs.

—Trofeos On Level: Querido Diario. 3rd ed. 2002. (SPA., Illus.). pap. 6.80 (978-0-15-324089-8(X)) Harcourt Schl. Pubs.

Kalman, Bobbie. El Ciclo de Vida del Mosquito. 2005. (Serie Ciclos de Vida Ser.). (SPA., Illus.). 32p. (J). (ps-7). pap. (978-0-7787-8713-6(3)); (978-0-7787-8667-2(6)) Crabtree Publishing Co.

—The Life Cycle of a Mosquito. 2004. (Life Cycle Ser.). (Illus.). 32p. (J). (978-0-7787-0665-6(6)); pap. (978-0-7787-0695-3(8)) Crabtree Publishing Co.

Kalman, Bobbie & Brière, Marie-Josée. Les Moustiques: Life Cycle of a Mosquito. 2006. (FRE., Illus.). 32p. pap. (978-2-89579-077-8(9)) Crabtree Publishing Co.

Kravetz, Jonathan. Mosquitoes. 2006. (Illus.). 24p. (J). lib. bdg. (978-1-4042-3044-6(0) , PowerKids Pr.) Rosen Publishing Group, Inc., The.

Loewen, Nancy. Bzzz, Bzzz! Mosquitoes in Your Backyard. Peterson, Rick, illus. 2005. (Backyard Bugs Ser.). 24p. (J). (ps). lib. bdg. 22.60 (978-1-4048-1140-9(0)) Picture Window Bks.

Markle, Sandra. Mosquitoes: Tiny Insect Troublemakers. 2008. (Insect World Ser.). (J). lib. bdg. 27.93 (***978-0-8225-7299-2(0)*** , Lerner Pubns.) Lerner Publishing Group.

Meister, Cari. Mosquitoes. 2001. (Insects Ser.). (Illus.). 24p. (J). (gr. k-6). lib. bdg. 21.35 (978-1-57765-464-3(1) , Checkerboard Library) ABDO Publishing Co.

Miller, Heather. Mosquito. 2004. (Bugs Ser.). (J). 24.95 (978-0-7377-1772-3(6) , Greenhaven Pr., Inc.) Thomson Gale.

Morgan, Sally. Flies & Mosquitoes. 2001. (Illus.). 32p. (J). lib. bdg. 24.25 (978-1-930643-12-3(8)) Chrysalis Education.

Murray, Julie. Mosquitos. 2002. (Buddy Book Ser.). (Illus.). 24p. (J). (gr. k-4). lib. bdg. 21.35 (978-1-57765-723-1(3)) ABDO Publishing Co.

Rustad, Martha E. H. Mosquitoes. 2007. (Illus.). 24p. (J). lib. bdg. 19.95 (978-1-60014-078-5(5)) Bellwether Media.

Scott, Jane Beecher. The Amazing Mosquito Bridge Secret. Scott, Jane Beecher, ed. Scott, Jane Beecher, illus. Scott, Jane Beecher, photos by. 5th ed. 2004. (Illus.). 32p. (J). (gr. k-12). 12.95 (978-0-9763077-0-9(7)) Beecher Scott.

Siy, Alexandra. Mosquito Bite. Kunkel, Dennis, illus. 2005. 32p. (J). pap. 6.95 (978-1-57091-592-5(X)); (gr. 3-5). 15.95 (978-1-57091-591-8(1)) Charlesbridge Publishing, Inc.

Somervill, Barbara A. Mosquitoes: Hungry for Blood. 2008. (J). lib. bdg. (***978-1-4042-3802-2(6)*** , PowerKids Pr.) Rosen Publishing Group, Inc., The.

Whitehouse, Patricia. El Mosquito. Abello, Patricia, tr. 2003. (Los Insectos Ser.). (SPA & ENG., Illus.). 32p. (J). lib. bdg. 23.40 (978-1-4034-3011-3(X)) Heinemann Library.

MOTELS

see Hotels, Motels, etc.

MOTHER AND CHILD

see also Mothers and Daughters; Mothers and Sons

Bolam, Emily & Ehrlich, Fred. Does a Mouse Have a Mommy? Early Experiences. 2007. (Illus.). 28p. pap. 5.95 (978-1-59354-589-5(4)) Blue Apple Bks.

Elkus, Julie. Cuando Mi Mama Me Lee. Nunez, Jose Luis, illus. 2005. (SPA & ENG.). 24p. pap. 8.95 (978-1-933197-06-7(4)) Orange Frazer Pr.

Huss, Sally. I Love You with All My Hearts. 2007. 24p. (J). bds. 7.99 (978-1-4003-0986-3(7)) Nelson, Thomas Inc.

Liles, Rebecca. My Mommy's a Soldier, 2 bks. 2003. (Illus.). 16p. (J). 4.99 (978-0-9744346-1-2(2)) Rebecca's Bks.

Lindsay, Jeanne Warren & Brunelli, Jean. Nurturing Your Newborn: Young Parents' Guide to Baby's First Month. 2nd ed. 2006. (Illus.). 96p. (J). pap. 7.95 (978-1-932538-38-0(0)) Morning Glory Pr., Inc.

Maloney, Alison. For the Mom Who's Best at Everything. 2008. (Moms' Book Ser.). 128p. (J). 9.99 (***978-0-545-04211-6(9)*** , Scholastic) Scholastic, Inc.

Miller, Jake. Decoding Mom: Making Sense of Her Moods, Her Methods, & Her Madness. Ketelhut, Linda, illus. 2007. 80p. (J). pap. 9.95 (***978-0-9772660-4-3(4)*** , Zest Bks.) Orange Avenue Publishing.

Richmond, Marianne. Thank You Mom. 2004. (Illus.). 40p. (YA). 7.95 (978-0-9741465-6-0(0)) Marianne Richmond Studios, Inc.

Richmond, Marianne R. The DIY Guide to Mommy Sanity. 2004. (Illus.). 40p. (YA). 7.95 (978-0-9753528-4-7(9)) Marianne Richmond Studios, Inc.

Sirett, Dawn & Parfitt, Rachael. Mommy Loves Me. 2006. (Illus.). 16p. (J). bds. 5.99 (978-0-7566-1725-7(1)) Dorling Kindersley Publishing, Inc.

Snead, Kathi. My Mom Has a Job. Grove, Christine, illus. 2004. (J). (978-0-9747385-0-5(6)) City of Manassas Department of Social Services.

MOTHER AND CHILD—FICTION

Alcantara, Ignacio, illus. My Very Breast Friend. 2005. 40p. (J). 17.00 (978-0-9659538-5-6(8)) Soul Vision Works Publishing.

Anastas, Margaret. Mommy's Best Kisses Board Book. Winter, Susan, illus. 2008. 34p. (J). 6.99 (***978-0-06-124130-7(X)*** , Harper Festival) HarperCollins Pubs.

Appelt, Kathi. Oh My Baby, Little One. Dyer, Jane, illus. 2006. 32p. (J). pap. 3.99 (978-0-15-206031-2(6) , Voyager Bks./Libros Viajeros) Harcourt Children's Bks.

Ashburn, Boni. Hush, Little Dragon. Murphy, Kelly, illus. 2008. 32p. (J). 15.95 (***978-0-8109-9491-1(7)*** , Abrams Bks. for Young Readers) Abrams, Harry N. , Inc.

Aston, Dianna Hutts. Mama Outside, Mama Inside. Gaber, Susan, illus. rev. ed. 2006. 32p. (J). 15.95 (978-0-8050-7716-2(2)) Holt, Henry & Co.

Averbeck, Jim. In a Blue Room. Tusa, Tricia, illus. 2008. 32p. (J). 16.00 (***978-0-15-205992-7(X)***) Harcourt Trade Pubs.

Baker, Liza. I Love You Because You're You. 2008. (Scooby-Doo Ser.). 24p. (J). bds. 8.99 (***978-0-545-02931-5(7)*** , Cartwheel Bks.) Scholastic, Inc.

—I Love You Because You're You. McPhail, David M., illus. 2001. 32p. (J). (ps-k). pap. 9.95 (978-0-439-20638-9(3) , Cartwheel Bks.) Scholastic, Inc.

Bateman, Teresa. Will You Be My Valenswine? Stephenson, Kristina, illus. 2005. 24p. (J). (ps-2). lib. bdg. 15.95 (978-0-8075-9195-6(5)) Whitman, Albert & Co.

Bedford, David. Little Otter's Big Journey. Winter, Susan, illus. 2006. 28p. (J). 16.00 (978-1-56148-548-2(9)) Good Bks.

Bergren, Lisa Tawn. How Big Is God? Bryant, Laura J., illus. 2008. (HarperBlessings Ser.). 32p. (J). 10.99 (***978-0-06-113174-5(1)***) HarperCollins Pubs.

Billingsley, Franny. Big Bad Bunny. Karas, G. Brian, illus. 2008. 40p. (J). 16.95 (***978-1-4169-0601-8(0)***) Simon & Schuster Children's Publishing.

Bloom, Susan & Bertram, Debbie. The Best Place to Read. Garland, Michael, illus. 2007. 32p. (J). (ps-3). pap. 6.99 (978-0-375-83757-9(4) , Dragonfly Bks.) Random Hse. Children's Bks.

Bonnell, Kris. Presents for Mom. 2007. (J). 3.95 (***978-1-933727-61-5(6)***) Reading Reading Bks., LLC.

Boynton, Sandra. What's Wrong, Little Pookie? 2007. (Illus.). 18p. (J). (ps). bds. 5.99 (***978-0-375-84552-9(6)*** , Robin Corey Bks.) Random Hse. Children's Bks.

Brown, Jo. Where's My Mommy? Brown, Jo, illus. 2006. (Illus.). 18p. (J). bds. 6.95 (978-1-58925-795-5(2) , tiger tales) ME Media LLC.

Brown, Margaret Wise. The Runaway Bunny. Hurd, Clement, illus. abr. ed. 2007. (Share a Story Ser.). 36p. (J). 9.99 (978-0-06-114271-0(9) , Harper Festival) HarperCollins Pubs.

Brown, Margaret Wise. The Runaway Bunny Big Book. Hurd, Clement, illus. 2008. 48p. (J). pap. 24.99 (***978-0-06-111976-7(8)*** , Harper Festival) HarperCollins Pubs.

M
N
O

Brown, Toni Sorenson. I Can't Go to Church. Jolley, Mack, illus. 2005. (J). (978-1-59156-270-2(8)) Covenant Communications.

Browne, Anthony. My Mom. 2005. (Illus.). 32p. (J). 16.00 (978-0-374-35098-7(1) , Farrar, Straus & Giroux) Farrar, Straus & Giroux.

Calloway, Troy. Clarence. 2007. 44p. (J). 16.99 (978-1-59092-377-1(4) , Little Blue Works) Windstorm Creative.

Campbell, Bebe Moore. Sometimes My Mommy Gets Angry. Lewis, E. B., illus. 2005. 32p. (J). pap. 5.99 (978-0-14-240359-4(8) , Puffin) Penguin Group (USA) Inc.

Carlisle, Kelly. My Mommy Is A Rocker. 2007. (Illus.). 21p. (J). lib. bdg. (***978-0-9795046-2-4(7)***) Kwist, Karla.

Carpenter, Donna. A Triple Treat. 2007. (Illus.). 20p. (J). 14.95 (***978-0-9793987-0-4(3)***) DFC Pubs.

Carrick, Carol. Mothers Are Like That. Carrick, Paul, illus. 2007. 32p. (J). (gr. k-ps). pap. 5.95 (978-0-618-75241-6(2) , Clarion Bks.) Houghton Mifflin Co. Trade & Reference Div.

Cartwheel Books Staff & Maccarone, Grace. Keepsake Story Collection. 2008. (I Love My Mommy Ser.). 96p. (J). pap. 7.99 (***978-0-545-01168-6(X)*** , Cartwheel Bks.) Scholastic, Inc.

Castle, Caroline. Snip, Snap, Croc. 2007. (J). lib. bdg. 16.95 (***978-1-59566-367-2(3)***) QEB Publishing Inc.

Choclate-Brown, Honey. Mama never told Me. 2005. (J). 9.95 (978-0-9765467-0-2(1)) Creative Bk. Pubs.

Cote, Genevieve. With You Always, Little Monday. 2007. (Illus.). 32p. (J). (ps-2). 16.00 (978-0-15-205997-2(0)) Harcourt Children's Bks.

Cousins, Lucy. Hooray for Fish! Cousins, Lucy, illus. 2005. (Illus.). 40p. (J). (gr. k-k). 14.99 (978-0-7636-2741-6(0)) Candlewick Pr.

Crumbaugh, David. The Primrose Kids. 2006. 81p. pap. 14.95 (978-1-4241-3250-8(9)) PublishAmerica, Inc.

Crumpacker, Bunny. Alexander's Great Pretending Day. Andersen, Dan, illus. 2005. 32p. (J). (ps). 15.99 (978-0-525-46936-0(2) , Dutton Juvenile) Penguin Group (USA) Inc.

Daley Mackall, Dandi. I Love You Mommy. Lee Schmidt, Karen, illus. 2005. (I Love You Ser.). 20p. (J). bds. 7.99 (978-0-7847-1815-5(6) , 04137) Standard Publishing.

Darling, Helen. Hide-n-seek Monday. Glickstein, Jennifer, ed. Sona and Jacob, illus. 2007. (J). 10.00 (***978-0-9797674-0-1(7)***) My Darling-Tots Pubns.

Demas, Corinne. Valentine Surprise. Alley, R. W., illus. (J). 2008. lib. bdg. (***978-0-8027-9665-3(5)***); 2007. 32p. 12.95 (***978-0-8027-9664-6(8)***) Walker & Co.

DePrisco, Dorothea & Summers, Lesley. Back in My Arms. 2006. (Illus.). 12p. (J). 9.95 (978-1-58117-459-5(4) , Intervisual/Piggy Toes) Dalmatian Pr.

Dewdney, Anna. Llama Llama Mad at Mama. Dewdney, Anna, illus. 2007. (Illus.). 40p. (J). (ps-k). 15.99 (***978-0-670-06240-9(5)*** , Viking Juvenile) Penguin Group (USA) Inc.

Doman, Regina. Angel in the Waters. Hatke, Ben, illus. 2004. 48p. (J). (ps-3). pap. 6.95 (978-1-928832-81-2(4)) Sophia Institute Pr.

Doman, Regina. Mi Angelito en las aquas. 2006. (SPA.). 46p. pap. 6.95 (***978-1-933184-22-7(1)***) Sophia Institute Pr.

Edwards, Julie Andrews & Hamilton, Emma Walton. Thanks to You: Wisdom from Mother & Child. 2007. (Illus.). 40p. 14.99 (978-0-06-124002-7(8)) HarperCollins Pubs.

Elya, Susan Middleton. Bebé Goes to the Beach. Salerno, Steven, illus. 2008. (ENG & SPA.). (J). (***978-0-15-206000-8(6)***) Harcourt Trade Pubs.

Famoriyo, Olusegun. The Handkerchief. 2005. 111p. pap. 16.95 (978-1-4137-2162-1(0)) PublishAmerica, Inc.

Finley, Martha. Elsies Motherhood. 2006. 79.99 (***978-1-4280-2607-0(X)***) IndyPublish.com.

Fleuriel, Allison. Are You Done Sleeping? 2006. (J). pap. 16.00 (978-0-8059-7115-6(7)) Dorrance Publishing Co., Inc.

George, Lindsay Barrett. Alfred Digs. 2008. 40p. (J). 16.99 (***978-0-06-078760-8(0)***); lib. bdg. 17.89 (***978-0-06-078761-5(9)***) HarperCollins Pubs. (Greenwillow Bks.).

Golden Books Staff. Mommy Loves Me. Butcher, Samuel J., illus. 2006. (Precious Moments Ser.). 24p. (J). (gr. k-k). 2.99 (978-0-375-83214-7(9) , Golden Bks.) Random Hse. Children's Bks.

Gray, Rita. Mama Mine, Mama Mine. Goembel, Ponder, illus. 2008. 32p. (J). (ps). 15.99 (***978-0-525-47206-3(1)*** , Dutton Juvenile) Penguin Group (USA) Inc.

Green, Jose. Castro's Diary. 2004. 174p. pap. 19.95 (978-1-4137-4556-6(3)) PublishAmerica, Inc.

Griffune, Donna L. I Love You with My Heart. 2007. 44p. (J). pap. 8.99 (978-1-59092-391-7(X) , Little Blue Works) Windstorm Creative.

Gummelt, Donna & Melchiorre, Dondino. Your Name Is Mud. Wall, Randy Hugh, ed. Varela, Carmen, tr. Varela, Juan D., illus. l.t. ed. 2006. Tr. of Tu nombre es Mud. 34p. (J). 14.95 (978-0-9764798-3-3(4)) Story Store Collection Publishing.

Hague, Kathleen. Good Night Fairies. Hague, Michael, illus. 2006. 40p. (J). pap. 6.95 (978-0-8118-5762-8(X)) Chronicle Bks. LLC.

Hallinan, P. K. My Mommy & I. 2006. (Illus.). 32p. (J). pap. 3.95 (978-0-8249-5520-5(X) , Ideals Children's Bks.) Ideals Pubns.

Hample, Stoo. I Will Kiss You (Lots & Lots & Lots!) 2006. (Illus.). 32p. (J). (ps up). 15.99 (978-0-7636-2787-4(9)) Candlewick Pr.

Hanson, P. H. My Mommy's Tote. 2007. (Illus.). 16p. (J). bds. 16.95 (***978-0-7611-4767-1(5)***) Workman Publishing Co., Inc.

Harper, Josephin & Harper, Jo. Teresa's Journey. 2006. 192p. (YA). pap. 17.95 (978-0-89672-591-1(X)) Texas Tech Univ. Pr.

Harris, Sue. The Little Seal. Boey, Stephanie, illus. 2007. 28p. (J). (ps). pap. 15.99 (***978-0-525-47839-3(6)*** , Dutton Juvenile) Penguin Group (USA) Inc.

Henkes, Kevin. Words of Stone. 2005. (J). 152p. (***978-1-4156-2647-4(2)***); 160p. reprint ed. pap. 5.99 (978-0-06-078230-6(7)) HarperCollins Pubs. (Harper Trophy).

Hudson, Charlotte. In a Little While. 2007. (Illus.). 32p. (J). 19.95 (***978-0-370-32656-6(3)***) Transworld Publishers Ltd. GBR. *Dist:* Independent Pubs. Group.

I'm Glad I'm Your Mother. 2006. 16p. (J). pap. 1.99 (978-0-7847-1687-8(0) , 02989) Standard Publishing.

Jacobs, Julie. My Heart Is a Magic House. Pons, Bernadette, illus. 2007. 32p. (J). (ps-1). 15.95 (978-0-8075-5335-0(2)) Whitman, Albert & Co.

Jenkins, Emily. Love You When You Whine. Ruzzier, Sergio, illus. 2006. 32p. (J). 15.00 (978-0-374-34652-2(6)) Farrar, Straus & Giroux.

Jeram, Anita. Bunny My Honey. Jeram, Anita, illus. 2006. (Illus.). 32p. (J). (ps). reprint ed. pap. 4.99 (978-0-7636-3217-5(1)) Candlewick Pr.

Katz, Karen. Mommy Hugs. Katz, Karen, illus. (Classic Board Bks.). 32p. (J). 2007. bds. 7.99 (978-1-4169-4121-7(5) , Little Simon); 2006. (Illus.). 12.95 (978-0-689-87772-8(2) , McElderry, Margaret K.) Simon & Schuster Children's Publishing.

—Where Is Baby's Mommy? Katz, Karen, illus. 2001. (Illus.). 14p. (J). (ps-k). bds. 5.99 (978-0-689-83561-2(2) , Little Simon) Simon & Schuster Children's Publishing.

Killion, Bette. Just Think. 2001. (Growing Tree Ser.). (Illus.). 24p. (J). (ps). 9.95 (978-0-694-01315-9(3) , Harper Festival) HarperCollins Pubs.

Kindermans, Martine. You & Me. Quinton, Sasha, tr. from GER. Kindermans, Martine, illus. 2006. (Illus.). 32p. (J). (ps-3). 15.99 (978-0-399-24471-1(9) , Philomel) Penguin Group (USA) Inc.

Kingsbury, Karen. Let's Go on a Mommy Date. Andreasen, Dan, illus. 2008. 32p. (J). (978-0-310-71214-5(9)) Zonderkidz.

Kuskin, Karla. A Boy Had a Mother Who Bought Him Hat. 2008. (J). (***978-0-06-075330-6(7)***); (***978-0-06-075331-3(5)***) HarperCollins Pubs. (Geringer, Laura Book).

LaDeane, Symone. Momma, Where Will You Be? 2007. (J). pap. 6.99 (***978-1-60247-120-7(7)***) Tate Publishing & Enterprises, L.L.C.

LaLumiere, Michael & Messinger, Kim. Birthday Snow. 2006. (Illus.). 32p. (J). 14.95 (***978-0-9791006-1-1(5)***) Stagger Lee Bks.

—Princess Caitlin's Tiara. 2006. (J). 14.95 (***978-0-9791006-0-4(7)***) Stagger Lee Bks.

The Land Beyond Forever. 2006. 25.00 (***978-0-9785570-0-3(X)***) Three Sisters Publishing Hse., Ltd.

Lawson-Miller, Barb. I Love Mommy Because... 2004. (Illus.). 14p. bds. (978-0-9688553-1-7(8)) Barbamel Bks., Inc.

Lee, Spike & Lee, Tonya Lewis. Please, Baby, Please. Nelson, Kadir, illus. 2007. (Classic Board Bks.). 32p. (J). bds. 7.99 (***978-1-4169-4911-4(9)*** , Little Simon) Simon & Schuster Children's Publishing.

Lee, Tae-Joon. Waiting for Mama. Chun, Eun Hee, tr. Kim, Dong-Sung, illus. 2007. (KOR & ENG.). 32p. (J). (ps-2). 16.95 (***978-0-7358-2143-9(7)***) North-South Bks., Inc.

Less, Emma. My Day with Mommy. Ledger, Bill, illus. 2006. 14p. bds. 5.95 (978-1-4027-2176-2(5)) Sterling Publishing Co., Inc.

Lewis, Gill. The Most Precious Thing. Ho, Louise, illus. 2006. (J). 16.00 (978-1-56148-534-5(9)) Good Bks.

The Little Saguaro. 2007. (YA). pap. 15.95 (***978-1-886679-37-5(1)***) Arizona Sonora Desert Museum Pr.

London, Jonathan. Count the Ways, Little Brown Bear. Moore, Margie, illus. 2004. 32p. (J). (ps-3). lib. bdg. 14.19 (978-0-606-30362-0(6)) Tandem Library Bks.

Looper, Grace W. Great-Grandpa's Hidden Treasure. 2006. (YA). pap. (***978-1-933523-18-7(2)***) Bella Rosa Bks.

Love, Judy. Praise Be & Rainbows. 2006. 51p. pap. 12.95 (978-1-4241-0333-1(9)) PublishAmerica, Inc.

Ltd Mommy Loves/Mommy Kisses. 2005. (J). bds. 11.90 (978-0-8118-9934-5(9)) Chronicle Bks. LLC.

MacLachlan, Patricia. Two Novels: Baby/Journey. 2007. 224p. (J). (gr. 4-7). 16.99 (978-0-385-73423-3(9)); lib. bdg. 19.99 (978-0-385-90436-0(3)) Random Hse. Children's Bks. (Delacorte Bks. for Young Readers).

Martin, Bill, Jr. Baby Bear, Baby Bear, What Do You See? Carle, Eric, illus. 2007. 32p. (J). (ps-3). 16.95 (***978-0-8050-8336-1(7)*** , Holt, Henry & Co. Bks. For Young Readers) Holt, Henry & Co.

The Mary & Little Jesus, Beginner's Biblereg; 2007. 24p. (J). 5.99 (978-0-8297-5010-2(X)) Vida Pubs.

McAllister, Angela. Trust Me, Mom! Collins, Ross, illus. 2005. 32p. (J). (ps-2). 16.95 (978-1-58234-955-8(X)) Bloomsbury Publishing.

McCourt, Lisa. Happy Halloween, Stinky Face. Moore, Cyd, illus. 2007. 32p. (J). (ps-3). pap. 15.99 (978-0-439-77977-7(4)) Scholastic, Inc.

McDonnell, Patrick. Art. 2006. (Illus.). 44p. (J). (ps-1). 14.99 (978-0-316-11491-2(X)) Little Brown & Co.

McGhee, Alison. Someday. Reynolds, Peter H., illus. 2007. 40p. (J). (ps-2). 14.99 (978-1-4169-2811-9(1) , Atheneum) Simon & Schuster Children's Publishing.

McGinty, Alice B. Eliza's Kindergarten Surprise. Speir, Nancy, illus. 2007. (J). (ps-k). 14.99 (978-0-7614-5351-2(2)) Cavendish, Marshall Corp.

Meade, L. A Little Mother to the Others. 2006. pap. 36.99 (***978-1-4219-7036-3(8)***) IndyPublish.com.

Mitchell, Melanie. Mommy & Baby: Jungle. 2006. (Illus.). 8p. (J). bds. 6.95 (978-0-8027-8979-2(X)) Walker & Co.

—Mommy & Baby: Pets. 2006. (Illus.). 8p. (J). bds. 6.95 (978-0-8027-8982-2(X)) Walker & Co.

Mommy You're My Hero. 2nd ed. 2005. (J). bds. 12.99 (978-0-9729264-3-0(7) , Books for Brats) Little Redhaired Girl Publishing, Inc.

Moore, Rita M. Big Bell Goes Shopping. 2005. (J). pap. 8.00 (978-0-8059-6514-8(9)) Dorrance Publishing Co., Inc.

Morris, C. J. The Stone Children. 2005. (YA). per. 13.95 (978-1-58597-314-9(9)) Leathers Publishing.

Moses, Antoinette. The Girl at the Window: Starter/Beginner. 2007. (Cambridge English Readers Ser.). 32p. pap. 5.00 (***978-0-521-70585-1(1)***) Cambridge Univ. Pr.

—The Girl at the Window Book: Starter/Beginner. 2007. (Cambridge English Readers Ser.). (Illus.). 32p. pap. 9.00 (***978-0-521-70586-8(X)***) Cambridge Univ. Pr.

Nash, Sarah. The Snuggliest Snuggle in the World. Howarth, Daniel, illus. 2006. 10p. (J). bds. 12.95 (978-0-7696-4649-7(2) , Gingham Dog Pr.) School Specialty Publishing.

Nolan, Allia Zobel. I Love You the World. Mitchell, Susan, illus. 2006. 20p. (J). (ps-1). bds. 10.99 (978-0-7944-1218-0(1)) Reader's Digest Assn., Inc., The.

Norac, Carl. My Mommy Is Magic. Godon, Ingrid, illus. 2007. 32p. (J). (ps-k). 16.00 (978-0-618-75766-4(X) , Clarion Bks.) Houghton Mifflin Co. Trade & Reference Div.

O'Connor, Crystal Ball. Gift/ Book Combo. Hollinger, Valerie Bunch, illus. 2005. (J). 25.00 (978-0-9774038-0-6(7)) Monarch Pubs.

—Jake & the Migration of the Monarch. Hollinger, Valerie Bunch, illus. 2005. 32p. (J). 17.95 (978-0-615-12659-3(6)) Monarch Pubs.

—Jake y la Migraci'on de la Monarca. Brenes-Sotela, Guillermo J. & Quave, Gloria Martinez, trs. from ENG. Hollinger, Valerie Bunch, illus. 2005. (SPA.). (J). 17.95 (978-0-9774038-2-0(3)) Monarch Pubs.

Ottolenghi, Carol. I Love You, My Little One! Campanella, Marco, illus. 2006. (Tell Me a Story Ser.). 36p. (J). (gr. k-k). bds. 14.95 (978-0-7696-4814-9(2) , Gingham Dog Pr.) School Specialty Publishing.

—Mother Loves Her Little One. Campanella, Marco, illus. 2006. (Tell Me a Story Ser.). 36p. (J). (gr. k-k). bds. 14.95 (978-0-7696-4812-5(6) , Gingham Dog Pr.) School Specialty Publishing.

Paratore, Coleen. Catching the Sun. Catalanotto, Peter, illus. 2008. (J). (***978-1-57091-720-2(5)***) Charlesbridge Publishing, Inc.

Penn, Audrey. A Pocket Full of Kisses. Gibson, Barbara Leonard, illus. 2004. (New Child & Family Press Titles Ser.). 32p. (ps-1). 16.95 (978-0-87868-894-4(3) , 8943, Child & Family Pr.) Child Welfare League of America, Inc.

—A Pocket Full of Kisses. Gibson, Barbara, illus. 2006. 32p. 16.95 (978-1-933718-02-6(1)) Tanglewood Pr.

Polacco, Patricia. Mommies Say Shh! Polacco, Patricia, illus. 2007. 32p. (J). (ps). 5.99 (978-0-399-24720-0(3) , Philomel) Penguin Group (USA) Inc.

Porter-Gaylord, Laurel. I Love My Mommy Because. Wolff, Ashley, illus. 2004. (SPA.). 24p. (J). bds. 6.99 (978-0-525-47248-3(7) , Dutton Juvenile) Penguin Group (USA) Inc.

Propaganda, Amanda. People Flavors. 2006. (J). 6.00 (978-1-60149-000-1(3)) Punkin Pr.

Quintart, Natalie. Mama Bear. Blanchart, Stephanie, illus. 2005. 32p. (J). (ps-ps). 6.95 (978-1-58925-394-0(9) , tiger tales) ME Media LLC.

Rao, Sandhya. My Mother's Sari. Sabnani, Nina, illus. 2006. 28p. (J). (gr. k-2). 14.95 (978-0-7358-2101-9(1)) North-South Bks., Inc.

Root, Phyllis. Big Momma Makes the World. Oxenbury, Helen, illus. 2007. 48p. (J). (ps-3). pap. 6.99 (978-0-7636-2600-6(7)) Candlewick Pr.

Roth, Carol. Who Will Tuck Me in Tonight Sp. 2007. (J). 16.50 (978-0-7358-2108-8(9)); (Illus.). pap. 6.95 (978-0-7358-2107-1(0)) North-South Bks., Inc.

Ryder, Joanne. Bear of My Heart. Moore, Margie, illus. 32p. (J). 2010. bds. 8.99 (***978-1-4169-5472-9(4)*** , Little Simon Inspirations); 2006. 12.95 (978-0-689-85947-2(3) , Simon & Schuster Children's Publishing) Simon & Schuster Children's Publishing.

Schad, Kristine. Do You Love Me Best? Timmons, Gayle, illus. 2007. 40p. (J). lib. bdg. 23.95 (***978-1-58374-156-6(9)***) Chicago Spectrum Pr.

Schlein, Miriam. Little Raccoon's Big Question. Schoenherr, Ian, illus. 2004. 32p. (J). 15.99 (978-0-06-052116-5(3)); lib. bdg. 16.89 (978-0-06-052117-2(1)) HarperCollins Pubs.

Scholastic, Inc. Staff. Cars & Trucks. 2008. (Littlest Pet Shop Ser.). (SPA.). 24p. (J). pap. 3.99 (***978-0-545-02728-1(4)*** , Scholastic en Espanol) Scholastic, Inc.

Scholastic, Inc. Staff & Baker, Liza. Keepsake Storybook Collection. 2008. (I Love You Ser.). (SPA.). 112p. (J). pap. 7.99 (***978-0-545-03941-3(X)*** , Scholastic en Espanol) Scholastic, Inc.

Schulz, Kathy. I Need a Little Help. Iosa, Ann, illus. 2004. 24p. lib. bdg. 12.15 (978-0-606-30160-2(7)) Tandem Library Bks.

Scott, Ann Herbert. En Las Piernas de Mama: On Mother's Lap. Coalson, Glo, illus. 2007. 14p. (J). (gr. k-ps). bds. 5.95 (978-0-618-75247-8(1) , Clarion Bks.) Houghton Mifflin Co. Trade & Reference Div.

Senderak, Carol Hunt. Mommy in My Pocket. Nakata, Hiroe, illus. 2006. 32p. (ps-1). 12.99 (978-0-7868-5596-4(7)) Hyperion Pr.

Sheehy-Culhane, Roisin. WHEN MAMA GOES to WORK: DEVIN's STORY. 2006. (ENG.). 32p. per. 19.99 (***978-1-4257-0596-1(0)***) Xlibris Corp.

Sherwood, Mary Marth. The History of Lucy Clare. 2004. reprint ed. pap. 15.95 (978-1-4191-6620-4(4)) Kessinger Publishing, LLC.

Sherwood, Mary Martha. The History of Lucy Clare. 2004. reprint ed. pap. 1.99 (978-1-4192-6620-1(9)) Kessinger Publishing, LLC.

Smith, Joye. What Does It Mean to Be Poor? 2005. (Illus.). 30p. (J). 8.99 (978-1-56309-880-2(6)) Woman's Missionary Union.

Spinelli, Eileen. I Like Noisy, Mom Likes Quiet. Halverson, Lydia, illus. 2006. 32p. (J). 8.95 (978-0-8249-5517-5(X) , 1256103, Ideals Children's Bks.) Ideals Pubns.

—When Mama Comes Home Tonight. Dyer, Jane, illus. 2001. (Classic Board Bks.). 30p. (J). (ps-k). bds. 7.99 (978-0-689-84220-7(1) , Little Simon) Simon & Schuster Children's Publishing.

Spohn, Kate. Mommies! 2008. (Illus.). 14p. (J). (gr. k-ps). bds. 4.99 (***978-0-375-84277-1(2)*** , Random Hse. Bks. for Young Readers) Random Hse. Children's Bks.

Strelitski, Mies & Hartog, Arnold. Woobie Dreams Hc. 2006. (Illus.). 32p. (J). 16.95 (978-1-59249-554-2(0)) Soundprints.

Summer, Laura LeClair. Mommy will always come Home. White, Kathy, illus. 2006. 35p. (J). per. 24.95 (978-1-4276-0158-2(5)) Aardvark Global Publishing.

Sutherland, Eileen & Sutherland, Maggie. Mom & the Polka-Dot Boo-Boo. 2007. 32p. 14.95 (***978-0-944235-87-4(5)*** , 9780944235874) American Cancer Society, Inc.

Swain, Cynthia. The Birthday Flowers. 2006. (Early Explorers Ser.). (J). 30.00 (***978-1-4108-6025-5(6)***) Benchmark Education Co.

Tafuri, Nancy. Five Little Chicks. Tafuri, Nancy, illus. 2006. (Illus.). 32p. (J). (ps-k). 14.95 (978-0-689-87342-3(5)) Simon & Schuster Children's Publishing.

—Whose Chick Are You? Tafuri, Nancy, illus. 2007. (Illus.). 40p. (J). (ps-k). 16.99 (978-0-06-082514-0(6)); lib. bdg. 17.89 (978-0-06-082515-7(4)) HarperCollins Pubs.

Testa, Maria. Almost Forever. 2007. 80p. (J). (gr. 4-8). pap. 5.99 (978-0-7636-3366-0(6)) Candlewick Pr.

Thomas, Pam. Mamarswpial. 2005. (WEL., Illus.). 128p. pap. (978-0-86243-360-4(6)) Y Lolfa.

Tomey, Ingrid. The Queen of Dreamland. 2004. 179p. (YA). (gr. 6-10). reprint ed. 15.00 (978-0-7567-7151-5(X)) DIANE Publishing Co.

Toms, Kate. I Udderly Love You. 2007. (Illus.). 25p. (ps). per., bds. 7.95 (978-1-84610-460-2(2)) Make Believe Ideas GBR. *Dist:* Ingram Pub. Services.

Top That Publishing Staff, ed. Who's My Mommy. 2005. 12p. bds. (978-1-84510-067-4(0)) Top That! Publishing PLC.

Vail, Rachel & Bjorkman, Steve. Halloween Knight. 2004. (Illus.). (J). (ps-2). lib. bdg. 12.19 (978-0-606-29858-2(4)) Tandem Library Bks.

van Genechten, Guido. Because I Love you So Much: A Pop-up Book. van Genechten, Guido, illus. 2006. (Illus.). 12p. (J). 15.95 (978-1-58925-794-8(4) , tiger tales) ME Media LLC.

Velde, Marie. Laundry Day. 2007. (J). bds. 22.95 (***978-1-933156-17-0(1)*** , Visikid Bks.) GSVQ Publishing.

Walsh, Ann. Horse Power. 2007. (Orca Currents Ser.). 112p. lib. bdg. (***978-1-55143-883-2(6)***); (YA). (gr. 5 up). pap. (***978-1-55143-881-8(X)***) Orca Bk. Pubs.

Walters, Clare & Kemp, Jane. Time to Say I Love You. Dale, Penny, illus. 2006. 32p. (J). 15.95 (978-1-84507-449-4(1)) Lincoln, Frances Ltd. GBR. *Dist:* Perseus Distribution.

White, Ellen Emerson. The President's Daughter. 2008. (YA). pap. 8.99 (***978-0-312-37488-4(7)***) Feiwel & Friends.

Wild, Margaret. Kiss Kiss! Strevens-Marzo, Bridget, illus. ed. 2006. 24p. (J). 6.99 (978-1-4169-3440-0(5)) Simon & Schuster Children's Publishing.

Wilson, Karma. Mama Always Comes Home. Dyer, Brooke, illus. 2007. 32p. (J). pap. 6.99 (978-0-06-057507-6(7) , Harper Trophy) HarperCollins Pubs.

Wingfield, David. Little Goose. Apple, Margot, illus. 2007. (J). (***978-1-58246-190-8(2)*** , Tricycle Pr.) Ten Speed Pr.

Ziefert, Harriet. Surprise! Brown, Richard Eric, illus. 2006. (I'm Going to Read Ser.). 24p. (J). (ps-1). pap. 3.95 (978-1-4027-3410-6(7)) Sterling Publishing Co., Inc.

Ziefert, Harriet. When Mommy Travels. Bolam, Emily, illus. 2007. 16p. (J). pap. 5.95 (***978-1-4027-4803-5(5)***) Sterling Publishing Co., Inc.

MOTHER GOOSE

Addams, Charles. The Charles Addams Mother Goose. Addams, Charles, illus. 2002. (Illus.). 64p. (J). 19.95 (978-0-689-84874-2(9)) Simon & Schuster Children's Publishing.

Foreman, Michael, illus. Michael Foreman's Mother Goose. 1999. (Reading Together Ser.). (J). pap. (978-0-7636-0855-2(6)) Candlewick Pr.

Here & There & Everywhere with Mother Goose & Friends. l.t. ed. 1999. (Illus.). 20p. (J). pap. 19.00 (978-1-893467-05-7(8)) Spedial Editions Pr.

Hysom, Dennis Joe & Walker, Christine. Wooleycat's Musical Rhyme Time Theater. 2003. (Wooleycat's Favorite Nursery Rhymes Ser.). (Illus.). (J). pap. (978-1-889910-26-0(0)) Tortuga Pr.

—Wooleycat's Musical Theater. Walker, Christine, illus. 2003. (Wooleycat's Favorite Nursery Rhymes Ser.). (Illus.). 32p. (J). (ps-2). 18.95 incl. audio compact disk (978-1-889910-25-3(2)) Tortuga Pr.

Lansky, Bruce. Peter Peter Pizza Eater. 2006. (Illus.). 32p. (J). 15.95 (978-0-684-03166-8(3)) Meadowbrook Pr.

Long, Sylvia. Mother Goose Block Books, 16 vols. Long, Sylvia, illus. 2002. (Illus.). 12p. (J). bds. 24.95 (978-0-8118-3574-9(X)) Chronicle Bks. LLC.

McDonald, Jill, illus. Finger Puppet Storybook: Mother Goose Rhymes. rev. ed. 2007. (Alex Toys Ser.). 10p. (J). (ps-1). 11.99 (***978-0-316-06524-5(2)***) Little, Brown Bks. for Young Readers.

MNO

Opie, Iona, ed. Here Comes Mother Goose. Wells, Rosemary, illus. 1999. (Mother Goose Ser.). 108p. (J). (ps-1). 22.99 (978-0-7636-0683-1(9)) Candlewick Pr.

Sabuda, Robert. The Movable Mother Goose. Sabuda, Robert, illus. 1999. (Illus.). 12p. (J). (ps-3). 21.99 (978-0-689-81192-0(6) , Little Simon) Simon & Schuster Children's Publishing.

Scarry, Richard, illus. Best Mother Goose Ever! 1999. (Richard Scarry's Ser.). 96p. (J). (ps-2). 14.99 (978-0-307-15578-8(1) , 15578, Golden Bks.) Random Hse. Children's Bks.

MOTHER GOOSE—SONGS AND MUSIC

Beall, Pamela Conn & Nipp, Susan Hagen. Wee Sing Mother Goose. Guida, Liisa & Klein, Nancy, illus. 2006. (Wee Sing Ser.). 64p. (J). (ps-2). 9.99 (978-0-8431-0485-1(6) , Price Stern Sloan) Penguin Group (USA) Inc.

Lobel, Arnold, illus. The Arnold Lobel Book of Mother Goose: A Treasury of More Than 300 Classic Nursery Rhymes. unabr. ed. 2003. Orig. Title: The Random House Book of Mother Goose. 176p. (J). (gr. k-k). reprint ed. 19.95 (978-0-679-88736-2(9) , Knopf Bks. for Young Readers) Random Hse. Children's Bks.

MOTHERS

Auld, Mary. Mi Mama. 2004. (Conoce la Familia Ser.). (SPA., Illus.). 24p. (J). (gr. 1 up). lib. bdg. 20.67 (978-0-8368-3932-6(3)) Stevens, Gareth Inc.

—My Mom. 2004. (Meet the Family Ser.). (Illus.). 24p. (J). (gr. 1 up). lib. bdg. 20.67 (978-0-8368-3927-2(7)) Stevens, Gareth Inc.

Barbara, Diane & Donnier, Christine. Mom & Me: A Special Book for You & Your Mom to Fill in Together & Share with Each Other. 2004. (Illus.). 48p. (J). (ps-3). 16.95 (978-0-8109-4820-4(6)) Abrams, Harry N. , Inc.

Bell, Arlene. Teen Parenthood: It's Not What You Think It Is. 2001. 20p. (YA). pap. 2.95 (978-0-9636426-5-3(0)) Windham Pr.

Dalmatian Press Staff. Mommy Loves Me. (J). 2005. 8p. 4.99 (978-1-4037-1987-4(X)); 2000. (Illus.). 20p. bds. 2.99 (978-1-57759-373-7(1)) Dalmatian Pr.

Durrant, Jolene. Never Never Never Will She Stop Loving You: The Adoption Love Story of Angel Annie. Allred, Steve, photos by. rev. ed. 1999. (Illus.). 40p. (YA). (gr. k up). pap. 6.95 (978-0-9663567-9-3(9)) JoBiz!, Inc.

Ericsson, Jennifer A. She Did It! Westcott, Nadine Bernard, illus. 2002. 32p. (J). (ps-3). 16.00 (978-0-374-36776-3(0) , Farrar, Straus & Giroux (BYR)) Farrar, Straus & Giroux.

Greive, Bradley Trevor & Easton, Samantha. Querida Mama' (Dear Mom Spanish) Gracias por Todo. 2007. 80p. 9.95 (978-0-7407-6543-8(4)) Andrews McMeel Publishing.

Macmillan Children's Books Staff. The Little Guide to Mums. 2000. (Little Guides Ser.). (Illus.). 24p. (J): (ps-3). (978-0-333-73419-3(X) , Macmillan Children's Bks.) Pan Macmillan.

Mama, 6 Packs. (Coleccion Pm Ser.: Vol. 1). Tr. of Mom. (SPA.). 16p. (gr. k-1). 26.00 (978-0-7578-0659-9(7)) Rigby Education.

Manning, Mick. Supermom. Granstrom, Brita, illus. 2001. 32p. (J). (ps-3). 16.95 (978-0-8075-7666-3(2)) Whitman, Albert & Co.

Moore, M. Meet My Mom: Learning the M Sound. 2002. (PowerPhonics Ser.). (Illus.). 24p. (J). (gr. 1). lib. bdg. 18.00 (978-0-8239-5913-6(9) , PowerKids Pr.) Rosen Publishing Group, Inc., The.

Moore, Sharon. Meet My Mom: Learning the M Sound. 2002. (PowerPhonics Ser.). (Illus.). 23p. (J). lib. bdg. (978-0-8239-8258-5(0) , PowerKids Pr.) Rosen Publishing Group, Inc., The.

Mothers. 7.50 (978-0-8054-5972-2(3)) B&H Publishing Grp.

Numeroff, Laura Joffe. What Mommies Do Best/What Daddies Do Best. Munsinger, Lynn, illus. 2006. (Stories to Go! Ser.). 40p. (J). pap. 4.99 (978-0-689-84218-4(X) , Aladdin) Simon & Schuster Children's Publishing.

Rabinovici, Schoschana. Thanks to My Mother: An Unforgettable True Story. Skofield, James, tr. 2000. (Illus.). 256p. (J). (gr. 7-12). pap. 8.99 (978-0-14-130596-7(7) , Puffin) Penguin Group (USA) Inc.

Roche, Hannah. My Mom Is Magic. 1998. (Science Made Simple Ser.). (Illus.). 24p. (J). (ps-k). pap. (978-1-84089-012-9(6) , 868235Q, Zero to Ten, Limited) Evans Publishing Group.

Running Press Staff. Bear Hugs for Moms. 2003. (Inspirio/ Zondervan Miniature Editionstm Ser.). (Illus.). 128p. 4.95 (978-0-7624-1673-8(4) , Running Pr. Minature Editions) Running Pr. Bk. Pubs.

Ruth, Angie. My Mommy: Early My Adventure. 2007. 44p. (J). 8.99 (978-1-59092-483-9(5) , Orchard Academy Pr.) Windstorm Creative.

—My Step-Mom: Early My Adventure. 2007. 44p. (J). 8.99 (978-1-59092-486-0(X) , Orchard Academy Pr.) Windstorm Creative.

Santiago, Esmeralda. Mamis: Favorite Latino Authors Remember Their Mothers. 2001. (gr. 7-12). lib. bdg. 21.10 (978-0-613-33933-9(9)) Tandem Library Bks.

Schaefer, Lola M. Mothers. Saunders-Smith, Gail, ed. 1999. (Families Ser.). (Illus.). 24p. (J). (gr. k-1). lib. bdg. 15.93 (978-0-7368-0259-8(2) , Pebble Bks.) Capstone Pr., Inc.

—Mothers, 6 vols. Saunders-Smith, Gail, ed. (gr. k-2). 28.95 (978-0-7368-8270-5(7)) Red Brick Learning.

Sim, David. Cos You're My Mum. 2001. (Illus.). 32p. (J). pap. 6.99 (978-0-7459-4543-9(0) , Lion) Lion Hudson plc GBR. *Dist:* Independent Pubs. Group.

To Honor Thy Mother. 2003. (YA). mass mkt. 21.95 (978-0-9744027-0-3(2)) Cahill Publishing.

Watson, Michael C. & Gallery of Diamonds Jewelers Staff. Why Mom Deserves a Diamond' -1998: 2002 Essay Contest Winners For 1998. 1998. (Illus.). 96p. (J). pap. 24.95 (978-1-891665-26-4(X)) Gallery of Diamonds Publishing.

MOTHERS—FICTION

A. B. Publishing Staff. Come Home Mother. 1998. (J). (gr. 4-7). pap. 6.95 (978-1-881545-92-7(X)) A B Publishing.

Alexander, Sue. One More Time, Mama. Soman, David, illus. 1999. (Accelerated Reader Bks.). 32p. (J). (ps-k). 15.95 (978-0-7614-5051-1(3) , Cavendish Children's Bks.) Cavendish, Marshall Corp.

Anderson, Laurie Halse. No Time for Mother's Day. 2001. (978-0-606-21356-1(2)); 1999. lib. bdg. 15.25 (978-0-613-37020-2(1)) Tandem Library Bks.

Andreae, Giles. Mama Tiene una Casa en la Barriga. Cabban, Vanessa, illus. 2002. (SPA.). 102p. (J). (gr. k-2). 14.95 (978-84-488-1101-3(1) , BS30460) Beascoa, Ediciones S.A. ESP. *Dist:* Lectorum Pubns., Inc.

Arno, Iris H. I Love You, Mom. 1998. (978-0-606-13508-5(1)) Tandem Library Bks.

Ashman, Linda. Mama's Day. Ormerod, Jan, illus. 2006. 32p. (J). (ps-1). 15.95 (978-0-689-83475-2(6)) Simon & Schuster Children's Publishing.

Bailey, Debbie. Mi Mama. Huszar, Susan, photos by. 2003. (Hablemos Ser.). (SPA., Illus.). 14p. (J). (ps). bds. 5.95 (978-1-55037-264-9(5)) Annick Pr., Ltd. CAN. *Dist:* Firefly Bks., Ltd.

Balian, Lorna. Mother's Mother's Day. 2004. (Illus.). 40p. (J). 8.95 (978-1-932065-39-8(3)) Star Bright Bks., Inc.

Banks, Kate. Close Your Eyes. Hallensleben, Georg, illus. 2002. 40p. (J). (ps-1). 16.95 (978-0-374-31382-1(2) , Farrar, Straus & Giroux (BYR)) Farrar, Straus & Giroux.

—Mama's Coming Home. Bogacki, Tomek, illus. 2003. 32p. (J). (ps-1). 16.00 (978-0-374-34747-5(6) , Farrar, Straus & Giroux (BYR)) Farrar, Straus & Giroux.

Banting, Celia. I Only Said I Didn't Want You Because I Was Terrified. 2006. (I Only Said Ser.: 4). 240p. (YA). pap. 14.99 (***978-0-9786648-3-1(3)***) Wighita Pr.

Barber, Barbara E. Saturday at the New You. Rich, Anna, illus. 2002. (J). 14.66 (978-0-7587-3566-9(9)) Book Wholesalers, Inc.

Barkow, Henriette. That's My Mum. Brazell, Derek, illus. 2004. (J). (ALB & ENG.). 24p. (978-1-85269-595-8(1)); (ENG & YOR.). (978-1-84444-381-9(7)) Mantra Publishing, Ltd.

Baskin, Nora Raleigh. What Every Girl. 2002. (gr. 5-8). lib. bdg. 13.00 (978-0-613-89779-2(X)) Tandem Library Bks.

Bauer, Marion Dane. My Mother Is Mine. Elwell, Peter, illus. 40p. (J). (ps-k). 2001. 13.00 (978-0-689-82267-4(7)); 2004. reprint ed. pap. 6.99 (978-0-689-86695-1(X) , Aladdin) Simon & Schuster Children's Publishing.

—My Mother Is Mine. 2004. (ps-2). lib. bdg. 14.15 (978-0-613-88067-1(6)) Tandem Library Bks.

Bell, Caroline. I Love My Mom. Bell, Caroline, illus. 2000. 18p. (J). (978-0-88902-292-8(5)) Fitzhenry & Whiteside, Ltd.

Belle Prater's Boy. 1999. (Pathways to Critical Thinking Ser.). 32p. (YA). pap., stu. ed., tchr.'s training gde. ed. 19.95 (978-1-58303-081-3(6)) Pathways Publishing.

Berenstain, Stan & Berenstain, Jan. The Berenstain Bears & the Mama's Day Surprise. 2004. (Berenstain Bears First Time Bks.). (Illus.). 32p. (J). (gr. k-3). pap. 3.99 (978-0-375-81132-6(X)); lib. bdg. 10.99 (978-0-375-91132-3(4)) Random Hse. Children's Bks. (Random Hse. Bks. for Young Readers).

Bergman, Tamar. Where Is? Modan, Rutu, illus. 2002. 24p. (J). (gr. k-3). tchr. ed. 15.00 (978-0-618-09539-1(X) , Walter Lorraine) Houghton Mifflin Co. Trade & Reference Div.

A Big Surprise for Mom. 2005. (J). per. (978-0-9765950-1-4(X)) Carlson, Debra R.

Black, Frank M. A Visit with Mommy. Moses, Robin, photos by. 1999. (Illus.). 20p. (J). pap. 6.95 (978-1-929157-01-3(0)) Inside-OUT Corp.

—Una Visita a Mami. Moses, Robin, photos by. 1999. (SPA., Illus.). 20p. (J). pap. 6.95 (978-1-929157-03-7(7)) Inside-OUT Corp.

Bonnell, Kris. Mother Animals. 2007. (J). 3.95 (***978-1-933727-49-3(7)***) Reading Reading Bks., LLC.

Book, Rita. My Soccer Mom from Mars. Wummer, Amy, illus. 2001. (All Aboard Reading Ser.). 48p. (J). pap. 3.99 (978-0-448-42599-3(8) , Grosset & Dunlap) Penguin Group (USA) Inc.

—My Soccer Mom from Mars. 2001. (gr. k-3). lib. bdg. 11.80 (978-0-613-64077-0(2)) Tandem Library Bks.

Bourgeois, Paulette. Franklin Says I Love You. Clark, Brenda & Southern, Shelley, illus. ed. 2005. (Franklin Picture Books II). 30p. (J). lib. bdg. 15.00 (978-1-59054-700-7(4)) Fitzgerald Bks.

Boyd, Lizi. The Not-So-Wicked Stepmother. 1999. (Illus.). 32p. (J). pap. 6.99 (978-0-14-054080-2(6) , N A L Trade) Penguin Group (USA) Inc.

Bradby, Marie. Momma, Where Are You From? Soentpiet, Chris K., illus. 2000. 32p. (J). 17.99 (978-0-531-33105-7(9) , Orchard Bks.) Scholastic, Inc.

—Momma, Where Are You From. Soentpiet, Chris K., illus. 2000. 32p. (J). (ps-2). pap. 16.95 (978-0-531-30105-0(2) , Orchard Bks.) Scholastic, Inc.

Brami, Elisabeth. Mommy Time. Tschiegg, Anne-Sophie, illus. 2002. 48p. (J). (gr. k up). 9.95 (978-1-929132-22-5(0)) Kane/Miller Bk. Pubs., Inc.

Brandt, Amy. Benjamin Comes Back. de la Vega, Eida, tr. Porter, Janice Lee, illus. 2004. (Child Care Bks. for Kids).Tr. of Benjamin Regresa. (ENG & SPA.). 32p. (J). (ps-3). pap. 11.95 (978-1-884834-79-0(5) , 709801) Redleaf Pr.

Braun, Sebastien. I Love My Mommy. Braun, Sebastien, illus. 2004. (Illus.). 32p. (J). (ps-2). 15.99 (978-0-06-054310-5(8)) HarperCollins Pubs.

Breathed, Berkeley. Mars Needs Moms! Breathed, Berkeley, illus. 2007. 48p. (J). (ps). 16.99 (978-0-399-24736-1(X) , Philomel) Penguin Group (USA) Inc.

Brez, Lisa. Hickerdoodle Gets Lost. l.t. ed. 2003. (Illus.). 32p. (J). per. 6.99 (978-0-9743758-4-7(5)) Red Engine Pr.

Bridges, Margaret Park. If I Were Your Mother. Denton, Kady MacDonald, illus. 1999. 32p. (J). (ps-3). 15.95 (978-0-688-15190-4(6)) HarperCollins Pubs.

Bridwell, Norman. Clifford's Happy Mother's Day. (ps-2). 2001. lib. bdg. 11.25 (978-0-613-35665-7(9)); 2000. (Illus.). (J). 10.30 (978-0-606-21114-7(4)) Tandem Library Bks.

Brinkerhoff, Shirley. Tangled Web. 2000. (Nikki Sheridan Ser.: Vol. 5). 176p. (J). (gr. 9-12). pap. 5.99 (978-1-56179-737-0(5)) Bethany Hse. Pubs.

—Tangled Web. 2000. (gr. 7-12). lib. bdg. 14.15 (978-0-613-84406-2(8)) Tandem Library Bks.

Brisson, Pat. Mama Loves Me From Away. Caple, Laurie, illus. 2004. 32p. (YA). (gr. 2-4). 15.95 (978-1-56397-966-8(7)) Boyds Mills Pr.

Brooks, Martha. Mistik Lake. 2007. 224p. (J). (gr. 9 up). 16.00 (***978-0-374-34985-1(1)*** , Farrar, Straus & Giroux (BYR)) Farrar, Straus & Giroux.

Browne, Anthony. My Mom. 2005. (Illus.). 32p. (J). 16.00 (978-0-374-35098-7(1) , Farrar, Straus & Giroux) Farrar, Straus & Giroux.

Brugman, Alyssa. Being Bindy. 2006. 208p. (YA). (gr. 7). 15.95 (978-0-385-73294-9(5)); lib. bdg. 17.99 (978-0-385-90315-8(4)) Random Hse. Children's Bks. (Delacorte Bks. for Young Readers).

Buller, Jon & Schade, Susan. I Love You, Good Night. Pons, Bernadette, illus. 2005. 28p. (J). 7.99 (978-0-689-86212-0(1) , Little Simon) Simon & Schuster Children's Publishing.

Butterworth, Nick. Mi Mama es Fantastica. 2000. (SPA., Illus.). 32p. (J). (ps-k). (978-84-207-9266-8(7) , GS7682); 5th ed. 11.95 (978-84-207-3848-2(4)) Grupo Anaya, S.A. ESP. *Dist:* Lectorum Pubns., Inc., Distribooks, Inc., Lectorum Pubns., Inc.

—My Mom Is Excellent. Butterworth, Nick, illus. 2003. (Illus.). 32p. (J). (ps-3). 5.99 (978-0-7636-2050-9(5)) Candlewick Pr.

Capdevila, Roser. El Loby Y Los Siete Cabritos. 2002. (SPA.). (gr. k-3). lib. bdg. 14.10 (978-0-613-64537-9(5)) Tandem Library Bks.

Capucilli, Alyssa Satin. Only My Mom & Me. Beeke, Tiphanie, illus. 2003. 16p. (J). (ps up). pap. 6.99 (978-0-694-52585-0(5) , Harper Festival) HarperCollins Pubs.

Carabine, Sue. Mom's Night Before Christmas. Kawasaki, Shauna Mooney, illus. 2002. 60p. 5.95 (978-1-58685-166-8(7)) Gibbs Smith, Publisher.

Carle, Eric. Hal Lil Kangar Aidan Un? Does a Kangaroo Have a Mother Too? 2005. 32p. pap. 12.00 (978-977-6171-05-3(2) , 706-003) Al-Balsam Pubng. Hse. EGY. *Dist:* Bookworld Trade, Inc.

Carlstrom, Nancy White. I'M Not Moving, Mama. 1999. (gr. k-3). lib. bdg. 14.15 (978-0-613-21751-4(9)) Tandem Library Bks.

—I'm Not Moving, Mama. Wickstrom, Thor, illus. 1999. 32p. (J). (ps-3). pap. 6.99 (978-0-689-82881-2(0) , Aladdin) Simon & Schuster Children's Publishing.

Carrick, Carol. Mothers Are Like That. Carrick, Paul, illus. 2000. 32p. (J). (gr. k-ps). tchr. ed. 15.00 (978-0-395-88351-8(2) , Clarion Bks.) Houghton Mifflin Co. Trade & Reference Div.

Casey, Dawn. The Children of Lir: A Celtic Legend. Mayo, Diana, illus. 2004. 32p. (J). (TAM, CZE, VIE, SPA & IRI.). pap. (978-1-85269-818-8(7)); (TAM, CZE, VIE, SPA & IRI.). pap. (978-1-85269-823-2(3)); (TAM, CZE, VIE, SPA & IRI.). pap. (978-1-85269-828-7(4)); (TAM, CZE, VIE, SPA & IRI.). pap. (978-1-85269-838-6(1)); (TAM, CZE, VIE, SPA & IRI.). pap. (978-1-85269-843-0(8)); (TAM, CZE, VIE, SPA & IRI.). pap. (978-1-85269-848-5(9)); (TAM, CZE, VIE, SPA & IRI.). pap. (978-1-85269-853-9(5)); (TAM, CZE, VIE, SPA & IRI.). pap. (978-1-85269-858-4(6)); (TAM, CZE, VIE, SPA & IRI.). pap. (978-1-85269-863-8(2)); (TAM, CZE, VIE, SPA & IRI.). pap. (978-1-85269-867-6(5)); (TAM, CZE, VIE, IRI & SPA.). pap. (978-1-85269-868-3(3)); (TAM, CZE, VIE, SPA & IRI.). pap. (978-1-85269-872-0(1)); (CZE, TAM, VIE, SPA & IRI.). pap. (978-1-85269-873-7(X)); (TAM, CZE, VIE, SPA & IRI.). pap. (978-1-85269-877-5(2)); (TAM, CZE, VIE, SPA & IRI.). pap. (978-1-85269-878-2(0)); (TAM, CZE, VIE, SPA & IRI.). pap. (978-1-85269-882-9(9)); (TAM, CZE, VIE, SPA & IRI.). pap. (978-1-85269-883-6(7)); (TAM, CZE, VIE, SPA & IRI.). pap. (978-1-85269-887-4(X)); (TAM, CZE, SPA, IRI & VIE.). pap. (978-1-85269-888-1(8)); (TAM, CZE, VIE, SPA & IRI.). pap. (978-1-85269-892-8(6)); (TAM, CZE, VIE, SPA & IRI.). pap. (978-1-85269-897-3(7)) Mantra Publishing, Ltd.

Cave, Patrick. Number 99. 2001. 176p. (978-0-19-271878-5(9)) Oxford Univ. Pr., Inc.

Celcer, Irene. The Gift of Surrogacy. Gatto, Horacio, illus. 2007. (Hope & Will Have a Baby Ser.). 32p. (J). (gr. k-3). pap. 19.95 (978-0-9755810-4-9(X) , 9780975581049) Graphite Pr.

A Chair for My Mother. 1998. (J). 3.95 (978-0-439-04431-8(6)) Scholastic, Inc.

Church, Caroline Jayne. Who Is My Mommy? 1999. (Illus.). 11p. (J). bds. 11.98 (978-1-58048-068-0(3)) Sandvik Publishing.

Cleary, Beverly. Emily's Runaway Imagination. 2002. (J). 13.83 (978-0-7587-9141-2(0)) Book Wholesalers, Inc.

—Emily's Runaway Imagination. 221p. (J). (gr. 2-4). pap. 4.95 (978-0-8072-1416-9(7) , Listening Library) Random Hse. Audio Publishing Group.

Cohen, Caron Lee. Happy to You! Litzinger, Rosanne, illus. 2001. 40p. (J). (gr. k-ps). tchr. ed. 15.00 (978-0-618-04229-6(6) , Clarion Bks.) Houghton Mifflin Co. Trade & Reference Div.

Cole, Babette. The Trouble with Mum. 2005. (Illus.). 32p. (J). pap. 3.99 (978-1-4052-1121-5(0)) Egmont Bks., Ltd. GBR. *Dist:* Trafalgar Square Publishing.

Cole, Brock. The Facts Speak for Themselves. 2000. (Illus.). (J). (978-0-606-18403-8(1)) Tandem Library Bks.

Colfer, Eoin. The Arctic Incident. 2003. (Artemis Fowl Ser.: Bk. 2). 288p. (J). (ps-17). pap. 7.99 (978-0-7868-1708-5(9)) Hyperion Bks. for Children.

—Artemis Fowl. (Artemis Fowl Ser.: Bk. 1). (FRE.). pap. 34.95 (978-2-07-054681-7(0)) Gallimard, Editions FRA. *Dist:* Distribooks, Inc.

—Artemis Fowl. 2003. (Artemis Fowl Ser.: Bk. 1). (Illus.). 416p. (ps-17). pap. 5.99 (978-0-7868-1787-0(9)) Hyperion Bks. for Children.

—Artemis Fowl. 2002. (Artemis Fowl Ser.: Bk. 1). 304p. (J). (ps-17). pap. 7.99 (978-0-7868-1707-8(0)) Hyperion Paperbacks for Children.

—Artemis Fowl. 2001. (Artemis Fowl Ser.: Bk. 1). 288p. (gr. 8-17). 16.95 (978-0-7868-0801-4(2)) Miramax Bks.

—Artemis Fowl. abr. ed. 2001. (Artemis Fowl Ser.: Bk. 1). (Illus.). 2p. (J). (gr. 3-6). cd-rom (978-0-14-180286-2(3) , Penguin AudioBooks) Penguin Group (USA) Inc.

—Artemis Fowl. (Artemis Fowl Ser.: Bk. 1). 2003. (gr. 7-12). lib. bdg. 14.15 (978-0-613-75035-6(7)); 2002. (gr. 5-8). lib. bdg. 16.15 (978-0-613-60637-0(X)) Tandem Library Bks.

—Artemis Fowl. l.t. ed. 2001. (Artemis Fowl Ser.: Bk. 1). 312p. (J). (gr. 3-6). 28.95 (978-1-58724-092-8(0) , Wheeler Publishing, Inc.) Thomson Gale.

Connor, Leslie. Waiting for Normal. 2008. 304p. (J). 16.99 (***978-0-06-089088-9(6)***); lib. bdg. 17.89 (***978-0-06-089089-6(4)***) HarperCollins Pubs.

Corbett, Sue. 12 Again. 2007. 240p. (J). (gr. 5 up). pap. 5.99 (978-0-14-240729-5(1) , Puffin) Penguin Group (USA) Inc.

Cordes, Jayne A. The Hope Star. Allen, Gwynne L., illus. 1999. 32p. (YA). (ps up). 16.95 (978-0-9662670-1-3(X)) J. Kid Productions, Ltd.

Cowell, Cressida. Don't Do That Kitty Kilroy! Cowell, Cressida, illus. 2000. (Illus.). 32p. (J). (ps-2). 15.95 (978-0-531-30209-5(1) , Orchard Bks.) Scholastic, Inc.

Curtis, Christopher Paul. Bucking the Sarge. 2006. 288p. (YA). (gr. 7). reprint ed. mass mkt. 6.50 (978-0-440-41331-8(1) , Laurel Leaf) Random Hse. Children's Bks.

Curtis, Jamie Lee. My Mommy Hung the Moon. Date not set. 32p. (J). (ps-3). 16.99 (978-0-06-029016-0(1)); pap. 6.99 (978-0-06-443696-0(9)); lib. bdg. 17.89 (978-0-06-029017-7(X)) HarperCollins Pubs.

Dannhauss, Dianne. My Mom, the Professional. Bowen, Debbie, ed. Alexander, I. L., illus. 1998. 23p. (J). (gr. 1-4). lib. bdg. 19.95 (978-1-56763-147-0(9)) Ozark Publishing.

de Beer, Hans. Where Is Mother? 2004. (Little Polar Bear Story Ser.). (Illus.). 22p. (J). pap. 3.95 (978-1-4027-1634-8(6)) Sterling Publishing Co., Inc.

De Palma, Toni. Under the Banyan Tree. 2007. 192p. (YA). (gr. 7 up). 16.95 (978-0-8234-1965-4(7)) Holiday Hse., Inc.

Deem, James M. 3 NBs of Julian Drew. 2004. 208p. (YA). (gr. 7 up). pap. 6.99 (978-0-618-43907-2(2) , Graphia) Houghton Mifflin Co. Trade & Reference Div.

Delton, Judy. Angel's Mother's Boyfriend. Weber, Jill, illus. 1999. 176p. (J). (gr. 4-6). pap. 4.95 (978-0-395-97913-6(7)) Houghton Mifflin Co. Trade & Reference Div.

—Angel's Mother's Boyfriend. 1999. (J). 11.60 (978-0-606-17363-6(3)); (gr. 3-6). lib. bdg. 12.95 (978-0-613-22810-7(3)) Tandem Library Bks.

Desrosiers, Sylvie. Ma Mère Est un Extraterrestre. Franson, Leanne, illus. 2002. (Premier Roman Ser.). (FRE.). 64p. (J). (gr. 1-4). pap. (978-2-89021-561-0(X)) Diffusion du livre Mirabel.

Dickinson, Peter. Mana's Story. 1999. (Kin Ser.). (978-0-606-17678-1(0)) Tandem Library Bks.

Dodd, Christina. Back to School Mom, 18 Copies. 2003. mass mkt. 128.88 (978-0-06-056267-0(6)) HarperCollins Pubs.

Dowley, Ruth. Hard Rock. 2006. 160p. (J). pap. 9.99 (***978-1-84270-467-7(2)***) Andersen GBR. *Dist:* Independent Pubs. Group.

Downing, Julie. Where Is My Mommy? Downing, Julie, illus. 2003. (Illus.). 32p. (J). (ps up). 15.99 (978-0-688-17824-6(3)) HarperCollins Pubs.

Doyle, Roddy. Wilderness. 2007. (J). (***978-0-439-02357-3(2)***); 224p. (gr. 7 up). pap. 16.99 (***978-0-439-02356-6(4)***) Scholastic, Inc. (Levine, Arthur A. Bks.).

Duncan, Alice Faye. Honey Baby Sugar Child. Keeter, Susan, illus. 2005. 32p. (J). 15.95 (978-0-689-84678-6(9)) Simon & Schuster Children's Publishing.

Eastman, P. D. Are You My Mother? Eastman, P. D., illus. l.t. ed. 1998. (Bright & Early Board Bks.). (Illus.). 24p. (J). (gr. k-ps). bds. 4.99 (978-0-679-89047-8(5) , Random Hse. Bks. for Young Readers) Random Hse. Children's Bks.

Ehrlich, H. M. Gotcha, Louie! Bolam, Emily, illus. 2002. 32p. (J). (gr. k-3). 15.00 (978-0-618-19549-7(1) , Walter Lorraine) Houghton Mifflin Co. Trade & Reference Div.

Ellis, Sarah. Pick-up Sticks. 2001. (gr. 3-6). lib. bdg. 14.10 (978-0-613-90977-8(1)) Tandem Library Bks.

Evans, Edie. I Love You, Mommy. Fletcher, Rusty, illus. 1999. (Little Golden Bks.). 16p. (J). (gr. k-k). 2.99 (978-0-307-99507-0(0) , Golden Bks.) Random Hse. Children's Bks.

Farrell, Sue. To the Pool with Mama. Lewis, Robin Baird, illus. 2000. 24p. (J). (gr. k-ps). pap. 5.95 (978-1-55037-620-3(9)); lib. bdg. 15.95 (978-1-55037-621-0(7)) Annick Pr., Ltd. CAN. *Dist:* Firefly Bks., Ltd.

Feldman, Thea. Mummy with the Golden Mask. 2003. (gr. k-3). lib. bdg. 11.80 (978-0-613-71493-8(8)) Tandem Library Bks.

MNO

Finley, Martha. Elsie's Motherhood, Vol. 5. (Elsie Bks.: Bk. 5). 320p. (gr. 7-12). pap. 5.95 (978-1-58182-068-3(2)) Cumberland Hse. Publishing.

—Elsie's Motherhood. 1998. (Elsie Bks.: Vol. 5). 256p. (J). (gr. 7-12). pap. 6.99 (978-1-888306-38-5(6) , Full Quart Pr.) Holly Hall Pubns., Inc.

Ford, Miela. Mom & Me. Ford, Miela, photos by. 1998. (Illus.). 24p. (J). (ps-3). 15.00 (978-0-688-15889-7(7)) HarperCollins Pubs.

Franklin, Emily. Labor of Love: The Principles of Love. 2007. 256p. (gr. 12 up). pap. 9.99 (*978-0-451-22211-4(3)) , N A L Trade) Penguin Group (USA) Inc.

Freed, Shirley Ann & Moon, Louise. The Prayed for Baby. Morelan, Bill, ed. Butler, Steven, illus. l.t. ed. 2002. 24p. (J). (gr. 6). pap. 3.99 (978-1-58938-039-4(8)) Concerned Communications.

Friedrich, Molly. You're Not My Real Mother! Hale, Christy, tr. Hale, Christy, illus. 2004. 32p. (J). (ps-3). 15.99 (978-0-316-60553-3(0) , Tingley, Megan Bks.) Little, Brown Bks. for Young Readers.

Fruisen, Catherine Myler. My Mother's Pearls. Fruisen, Catherine Myler, illus. 2000. (Illus.). 32p. (J). (ps-3). 12.95 (978-0-7683-2177-7(8)) CEDCO Publishing.

—My Mother's Pearls. 2005. (Illus.). 32p. (J). pap. 5.95 (978-1-59572-005-4(7)) Star Bright Bks., Inc.

Fry, Sonali. A Day with Mom. Workman, Lisa, illus. 2007. (Holly Hobbie & Friends Ser.). 24p. (J). 8.99 (978-1-4169-3579-7(7) , Little Simon) Simon & Schuster Children's Publishing.

Fusco, Kimberly Newton. Tending to Grace. 2004. 176p. (YA). (gr. 7). 14.95 (978-0-375-82862-1(1) , Knopf Bks. for Young Readers) Random Hse. Children's Bks.

Gabriel, Andrea. My Favorite Bear. Gabriel, Andrea, illus. 2004. (Illus.). 32p. (J). pap. 6.95 (978-1-58089-039-7(3)) Charlesbridge Publishing, Inc.

—My Favorite Bear. 2003. (Illus.). 32p. (J). 15.95 (978-1-58089-038-0(5)) Charlesbridge Publishing, Inc.

Gaines, Isabel. World's Best Mama. 2000. (Winnie the Pooh Ser.). (Illus.). 37p. (J). (ps-3). pap. 3.99 (978-0-7868-4368-8(3)) Disney Pr.

Gantos, Jack. The Love Curse of the Rumbaughs. 2006. 192p. (YA). (gr. 7 up). 17.00 (978-0-374-33690-5(3) , Farrar, Straus & Giroux (BYR)) Farrar, Straus & Giroux.

—The Love Curse of the Rumbaughs. 2008. 208p. (YA). pap. 7.99 (*978-0-312-38052-6(6)) Square Fish.

Gay, Michel. El Cochecito. 2003. (SPA.). 68p. (978-84-8470-084-5(4)) Corimbo, Editorial S.L.

Geller, Nancy Jewell. Sailor Song. Vitale, Stefano, illus. 1999. 32p. (J). (gr. k-3). tchr. ed. 13.00 (978-0-395-82511-2(3) , Clarion Bks.) Houghton Mifflin Co. Trade & Reference Div.

Genechten, Guido van. Porque Te Quiero Tanto. 2003. (SPA., Illus.). 28p. (J). (gr. k-3). 15.95 (978-970-29-0912-5(0)) Santillana USA Publishing Co., Inc.

Gibbons, Alan. The Lost Boys' Appreciation Society. 2006. 176p. (J). pap. 11.99 (*978-1-84255-095-3(0)) Orion Publishing Group, Ltd. GBR. *Dist:* Independent Pubs. Group.

Gibbons, Faye. Mama & Me & the Model T. 1999. (Illus.). 40p. (J). (ps-3). 15.89 (978-0-688-15299-4(6)) HarperCollins Pubs.

—Mama & Me & the Model T. Rand, Ted, illus. 1999. 40p. (J). (ps-3). 16.95 (978-0-688-15298-7(8)) HarperCollins Pubs.

Goobie, Beth. Flux. 2004. 224p. (J). (gr. 7-12). lib. bdg. 16.95 (978-1-55143-314-1(1)) Orca Bk. Pubs. USA.

Gray, Kes & Milgrim, David. My Mum Goes to Work. 2006. (Illus.). 32p. (J). (ps). 15.99 (978-0-340-88368-6(5) , Hodder & Stoughton) Hodder General Publishing Division GBR. *Dist:* Trafalgar Square Publishing.

Gray, Libba Moore. My Mama Had a Dancing Heart. 2001. (Illus.). (J). pap. 18.95 incl. audio compact disk (978-1-59112-320-0(8)) Live Oak Media.

—My Mama Had a Dancing Heart. Colon, Raul, illus. 2001. pap. 35.95 incl. audio compact disk (978-1-59112-543-3(X)) Live Oak Media.

—My Mama Had a Dancing Heart. abr. ed. 2001. (Illus.). (J). (ps-2). 25.95 incl. audio (978-0-87499-740-8(2)); pap. 33.95 incl. audio (978-0-87499-741-5(0)) Live Oak Media.

—My Mama Had a Dancing Heart. Colon, Raul, illus. abr. ed. 2001. (J). (ps-2). pap. 16.95 incl. audio (978-0-87499-739-2(9)) Live Oak Media.

—My Mama Had a Dancing Heart. Colon, Raul, illus. 1999. 32p. (J). (ps-3). pap. 6.99 (978-0-531-07142-7(1) , Orchard Bks.) Scholastic, Inc.

—My Mama Had a Dancing Heart. 1999. (978-0-606-18334-5(5)) Tandem Library Bks.

Gray, Nigel. My Dog, My Cat, My Mama, & Me! Graham, Bob, illus. 2007. 24p. (J). (gr. k-ps). 8.99 (*978-0-7636-3639-5(8)) Candlewick Pr.

Greban, Quentin. Mommy, I Love You. 2005. (Illus.). 28p. (ps-3). 9.95 (978-1-59687-184-7(9) , Milk & Cookies) ibooks, Inc.

Greene, Stephanie. Owen Foote, Frontiersman. Weston, Martha, illus. 2002. 96p. (J). (gr. k-3). pap. 4.95 (978-0-618-24620-5(7) , Clarion Bks.) Houghton Mifflin Co. Trade & Reference Div.

—Owen Foote, Frontiersman. 2002. (gr. k-3). lib. bdg. 12.95 (978-0-613-72910-9(2)) Tandem Library Bks.

Greenfield, Giles. The World of Mother Goose. 2008. (Illus.). 56p. (J). 9.98 (978-0-7624-2312-5(9)) Running Pr. Bk. Pubs.

Gutman, Anne. Mommy Hugs. Hallensleben, Georg, illus. 2003. 14p. (J). bds. 5.95 (978-0-8118-3916-7(8)) Chronicle Bks. LLC.

Haddix, Margaret Peterson. Escape from Memory. (YA). 2005. 288p. (gr. 7-12). mass mkt. 6.99 (978-1-4169-0338-3(0) , Simon Pulse); 2003. (Illus.). 224p. 16.95 (978-0-689-85421-7(8)) Simon & Schuster Children's Publishing.

Hale, Chaika P. Mama Is Hapai. Asato, Dennis, illus. l.t. ed. 1998. 32p. (J). (gr. 1-6). 14.00 (978-0-9653971-2-4(2)) Anoai Pr.

Hall, Barbara. The Noah Confessions. 2007. 224p. (YA). (gr. 7). lib. bdg. 18.99 (978-0-385-90346-2(4)); 15.99 (978-0-385-73328-1(3)) Random Hse. Children's Bks. (Delacorte Bks. for Young Readers).

Hallinan, P. K. We're Very Good Friends, My Mother & I. 24p. (J). 7.95 (978-0-8249-5373-7(8) , Ideals); 5.95 (978-0-8249-5374-4(6)) Ideals Pubns.

Hancock, Greg. My Hugger Is Empty. Morrison, Melody, illus. l.t. ed. 1999. 24p. (J). (ps-3). pap. (978-1-894303-14-9(8)) Raven Rock Publishing.

Harris, Robie H. Happy Birth Day! Emberley, Michael, illus. 2002. (J). 24.94 (978-0-7587-2684-1(8)) Book Wholesalers, Inc.

—Happy Birth Day! Emberley, Michael, illus. 2002. (J). (ps-ps). lib. bdg. 15.30 (978-0-613-74733-2(X)) Tandem Library Bks.

Harvey, Jacqueline. The Sound of the Sea. Crossett, Warren, illus. 2005. 32p. (J). (*978-0-7344-0742-9(4) , Lothian Bks.) Hachette Livre Australia.

Hernandez, Mary L. Mama Me Dio. Maval Publishing Inc. Staff, illus. 2001. Tr. of Mommy Gave Me. (SPA.). 32p. (J). (gr. k-3). pap. 7.50 (978-1-59134-005-8(5)); pap. 7.50 (978-1-884083-03-7(X)) Maval Publishing, Inc.

Hesse, Karen. Come on, Rain! 1999. (J). (ps up). (978-0-439-06015-8(X)) Scholastic, Inc.

Hest, Amy. You Can Do It, Sam. Jeram, Anita, illus. 2003. 32p. (J). (ps). 15.99 (978-0-7636-1934-3(5)) Candlewick Pr.

Hicks, Betty. Busted ! 2008. 192p. (J). pap. 6.99 (*978-0-312-38053-3(4)) Square Fish.

Hilbrecht, Kirk. My Mommy Is an Airman. 2005. 32p. pap. 6.95 (978-1-889658-39-1(1)) New Canaan Publishing Co. LLC.

Hill, Sandi. Celebrating Mother's Day: Mom's Memory Box. 1999. (ps-2). lib. bdg. 10.65 (978-0-613-34122-6(8)) Tandem Library Bks.

Hundal, Nancy. I Heard My Mother Call My Name. Fernandez, Laura, illus. 1998. 24p. (J). (ps-3). pap. 6.95 (978-0-00-647496-8(9) , Harper San Francisco) HarperCollins Pubs.

Igus, Toyomi. Two Mrs Gibsons. 2001. (gr. k-3). lib. bdg. 16.40 (978-0-613-65372-5(6)) Tandem Library Bks.

Jacobson, Jennifer Richard. Moon Sandwich Mom. Huang, Benrei, illus. 2004. 24p. (J). (ps-1). pap. 6.95 (978-0-8075-4072-5(2)) Whitman, Albert & Co.

Jahn-Clough, Lisa. Country Girl, City Girl. 2004. 192p. (YA). (gr. 5). tchr. ed. 15.00 (978-0-618-44791-6(1) , Walter Lorraine) Houghton Mifflin Co. Trade & Reference Div.

Jarrell, Pamela R. A Gift for Mother. Metzger, Jeanne, illus. l.t. ed. 1998. (Cuddle Bks.). 7p. (J). (ps-k). pap. 10.95 (978-1-57332-130-3(3)) HighReach Learning, Inc.

Jennings, Sharon. Into My Mother's Arms. Ohi, Ruth, illus. 2000. 32p. (J). (ps-k). (978-1-55041-533-9(6)) Fitzhenry & Whiteside, Ltd.

—Into My Mother's Arms: With Sticker & Card. Ohi, Ruth, illus. 2001. 32p. (J). (ps-k). (978-1-55041-669-5(3)) Fitzhenry & Whiteside, Ltd.

Jimenez, Angeles. Macarena la Anguila. Gil, Sabina, illus. 2004. 26p. pap. 8.00 (978-84-931888-0-1(8)) Editorial Brief ESP. *Dist:* Independent Pubs. Group.

Johansson, Cecilia, illus. Just Like Mommy. 2006. 16p. (J). bds. 6.99 (978-1-4169-1218-7(5) , Little Simon) Simon & Schuster Children's Publishing.

Johnson, Dolores. My Mom Is My Show-and-Tell. 1999. (Accelerated Reader Bks.). (Illus.). 32p. (J). (gr. k-3). 15.95 (978-0-7614-5041-2(6) , Cavendish Children's Bks.) Cavendish, Marshall Corp.

Johnson, Paul Brett. The Goose Who Went off in a Huff. Johnson, Paul Brett, illus. 2001. (Illus.). 40p. (J). (ps-1). pap. 15.95 (978-0-531-30317-7(9) , Orchard Bks.) Scholastic, Inc.

Jones, Kelly. Mama. Kewley, Ken, illus. 2004. 32p. (J). (978-0-9745930-0-5(1)) Stunt Publishing.

Joosse, Barbara M. Mama, Do You Love Me? Lavallee, Barbara, illus. 2002. (J). 23.98 (978-0-7587-3082-4(9)) Book Wholesalers, Inc.

—Mama, Do You Love Me? Nesting Blocks. Lavallee, Barbara, illus. 2001. -1p. (J). 19.95 (978-0-8118-3259-5(7)) Chronicle Bks. LLC.

Jordan, Deloris & Jordan, Roslyn. Did I Tell You I Love You Today? Evans, Shane, tr. Evans, Shane, illus. 2004. 32p. (J). 16.95 (978-0-689-85271-8(1)) Simon & Schuster Children's Publishing.

Kasza, Keiko. A Mother for Choco. Kasza, Keiko, illus. 2002. (Illus.). (J). 13.19 (978-0-7587-3173-9(6)) Book Wholesalers, Inc.

—A Mother for Choco. 2003. 32p. (J). (ps-1). bds. 6.99 (978-0-399-24191-8(4) , Putnam Juvenile) Penguin Group (USA) Inc.

Kehret, Peg. I'm Not Who You Think I Am. 2001. 160p. (J). (gr. 5-9). pap. 5.99 (978-0-14-131237-8(8) , Puffin) Penguin Group (USA) Inc.

—I'm Not Who You Think I Am. 2001. (J). (978-0-606-20717-1(1)); (gr. 5-8). lib. bdg. 13.00 (978-0-613-35962-7(3)) Tandem Library Bks.

Koss, Amy Goldman. Smoke Screen. 2000. (978-0-606-21791-0(6)) Tandem Library Bks.

Kranendonk, Anke. Espera un Momento! (Los Especiales de A la Orilla Del Viento Ser.). (SPA., Illus.). 28p. (J). 13.99 (978-968-16-5716-1(0)) Fondo de Cultura Economica USA.

Krauss, Ruth. You're Just What I Need. Noonan, Julia, illus. 1998. 40p. (J). (ps-2). 15.95 (978-0-06-027514-3(6)) HarperCollins Pubs.

Kroll, Virginia L. Motherlove. Washburn, Lucia, illus. 1998. 32p. (J). (ps-3). 16.95 (978-1-883220-81-5(5)); pap. 7.95 (978-1-883220-80-8(7)) Dawn Pubns.

Lachtman, Ofelia Dumas. Tina & the Scarecrow Skins/Tina y las pieles de Espantapajaros. Colin, Jose Juan, tr. De-Lange, Alex Pardo, illus. 2002. (ENG & SPA.). 32p. (J). 14.95 (978-1-55885-373-7(1) , Piñata Books) Arte Publico Pr.

Lasky, Kathryn. Before I Was Your Mother. Pham, Le Uyen, illus. 2005. 30p. (J). (gr. k-4). reprint ed. 16.00 (978-0-7567-8541-3(3)) DIANE Publishing Co.

—Before I Was Your Mother. Pham, LeUyen, illus. 2003. 40p. (J). 16.00 (978-0-15-201464-3(0)) Harcourt Children's Bks.

—Mommy's Hands. 2001. 32p. (J). pap. 4.99 (978-0-7868-1437-4(3)) Hyperion Bks. for Children.

Lee, Marie Myung-Ok. Somebody's Daughter. 2006. 280p. pap. 14.00 (978-0-8070-8389-5(5)) Beacon Pr.

Leuck, Laura. My Monster Mama Loves Me So. Buehner, Mark, illus. 24p. (J). (ps-3). 2002. pap. 6.99 (978-0-06-008860-6(5) , Harper Trophy); 1999. 15.89 (978-0-688-16867-4(1)); 1999. 15.99 (978-0-688-16866-7(3)) HarperCollins Pubs.

—My Monster Mama Loves Me So. 2002. (gr. k-3). lib. bdg. 14.15 (978-0-613-53844-2(7)) Tandem Library Bks.

Levine, Phyllis. At the Skylight: With Matilda. 2003. pap. 12.95 (978-1-891429-45-3(0)) Armadillo Publishing Corp.

Lewis, Carolyn. Hairy Beary Book Two Bk. 2,Vol. 2: The Great Waterfall, 3 bks. DeVince, James, ed. Porcheron, Tammy, illus. 2003. (Hairy Beary Ser.: 2). 42p. (J). pap. 9.95 (978-0-9712641-1-3(2)) J M D's Business Services.

Lowell, Pamela. Returnable Girl. 2006. 240p. (YA). 16.99 (978-0-7614-5317-8(2)) Cavendish, Marshall Corp.

Ly, Many. Home Is East. 304p. 2007. (YA). (gr. 7-11). mass mkt. 6.50 (*978-0-440-23900-0(1) , Laurel Leaf); 2005. (J). (gr. 5 up). lib. bdg. 17.99 (978-0-385-73223-9(6) , Delacorte Bks. for Young Readers) Random Hse. Children's Bks.

Mac, Carrie. Charmed. 2004. 112p. (J). (gr. 7-12). pap. 7.95 (978-1-55143-321-9(4)) Orca Bk. Pubs. USA.

MacKall, Dandi Daley. Home Is Where Your Horse Is, Vol. 6. 2000. (Horsefeathers Ser.: Vol. 6). (Illus.). 192p. (J). (gr. 7-11). 5.99 (978-0-570-07087-0(2)) Concordia Publishing Hse.

—Home Is Where Your Horse Is. 2000. (gr. 7-12). lib. bdg. 14.15 (978-0-613-72790-7(8)) Tandem Library Bks.

MacLachlan, Patricia. More Perfect than the Moon. 2004. (Sarah, Plain & Tall Ser.). 96p. (J). 14.99 (978-0-06-027558-7(8) , Cotler, Joanna Books) HarperCollins Pubs.

Martin, Ann M. Here Today. (J). 2005. 336p. (gr. 5-9). pap. 5.99 (978-0-439-57945-2(7) , Scholastic Paperbacks); 2004. 320p. (gr. 4-7). pap. 16.95 (978-0-439-57944-5(9) , Scholastic Pr.) Scholastic, Inc.

Martin, David. Monkey Trouble. 2000. (Brand New Readers Ser.). (Illus.). 1p. (J). (ps-2). pap. 5.99 (978-0-7636-0771-5(1)) Candlewick Pr.

Marzollo, Jean. Mama Mama. Regan, Laura, illus. 1999. (Growing Tree Ser.). 16p. (J). (ps up). 5.99 (978-0-694-01245-9(9) , Harper Festival) HarperCollins Pubs.

Massicotte, Sylvie & Faniel, Lucie. C'est la Vie, Pitchounette. 2001. (Premier Roman Ser.). (FRE.). 64p. (J). (gr. 1-4). pap. (978-2-89021-434-7(6)) Diffusion du livre Mirabel.

Mayer, Mercer. Just for You. Mayer, Mercer, illus. 1998. (Little Critter Ser.). (Illus.). 24p. (J). (gr. k-k). pap. 3.99 (978-0-307-11838-7(X) , 11838, Random Hse. Bks. for Young Readers) Random Hse. Children's Bks.

—Just Me & My Mom. Mayer, Mercer, illus. 2001. (Little Critter Ser.). (Illus.). 24p. (J). (gr. k-k). pap. 3.29 (978-0-307-12584-2(X) , 12584, Random Hse. Bks. for Young Readers) Random Hse. Children's Bks.

McCourt, Lisa. I Love You, Stinky Face. Moore, Cyd, illus. (J). 2004. 32p. pap. 15.95 (978-0-439-63571-4(3)); 2004. 16p. bds. 6.99 (978-0-439-63572-1(1)); 2003. 32p. 5.99 (978-0-439-63469-4(5)) Scholastic, Inc.

—It's Time for School, Stinky Face. Moore, Cyd, illus. 2004. 32p. (J). pap. 15.95 (978-0-439-63574-5(8)); pap. 5.99 (978-0-439-63575-2(6)) Scholastic, Inc.

McDaniel, Lurlene. Mother, Please Don't Die. 2005. 128p. (Orig.). (J). (gr. 5-8). pap. 4.99 (978-1-58196-028-0(X)) Darby Creek Publishing.

McLellan, Stephanie Simpson. The Chicken Cat. Cassidy, Sean, illus. 2001. (gr. k-3). 36p. (J). (978-1-55041-531-5(X)); 40p. (J). pap. (978-1-55041-673-2(1)); 40p. (978-1-55041-677-0(4)) Fitzhenry & Whiteside, Ltd.

McMullan, Kate. If You Were My Bunny. McPhail, David M., illus. 2002. 15.70 (978-0-7587-2831-9(X)) Book Wholesalers, Inc.

—If You Were My Bunny. McPhail, David M., illus. 1998. (Hello Reader! Ser.). 26p. (J). reprint ed. bds. 6.99 (978-0-590-34126-4(X)) Scholastic, Inc.

Meckley, Stephanie R., et al. Just Like Mom. 1998. (Illus.). 24p. (J). (gr. k-2). pap. 3.00 (978-1-892464-03-3(9)) Meckley Publishing Co.

Melmed, Laura Krauss. I Love You as Much... Sorensen, Henri, illus. 1998. 11p. (J). (ps-2). bds. 7.99 (978-0-688-15978-8(8)) HarperCollins Pubs.

—I Love You As Much... Sorensen, Henri, illus. 2001. 22p. (J). (ps-2). 12.99 (978-0-06-001011-9(8) , Harper Festival) HarperCollins Pubs.

—I Love You As Much... 2001. (Illus.). 32p. (J). (ps up). pap. 6.95 (978-0-688-16806-3(X)) HarperCollins Pubs.

—I Love You As Much... Board Book & Picture Frame. 2003. (Illus.). 22p. (J). (ps-2). 12.99 (978-0-06-008659-6(9) , Harper Festival) HarperCollins Pubs.

Mendes, Valerie. Coming of Age. 2004. 224p. (YA). pap. 8.99 (978-0-689-83772-2(0)) Simon & Schuster, Ltd. GBR. *Dist:* Independent Pubs. Group.

Miller, Kathryn Ann. Did My First Mother Love Me? A Story for an Adopted Child. Moffett, Jamie, illus. 2003. 48p. (J). (ps-3). 12.95 (978-0-930934-85-9(7)); pap. 5.95 (978-0-930934-84-2(9)) Morning Glory Pr., Inc.

Minarik, Else Holmelund. Mother Bear's Picnic. 2003. (gr. k-3). lib. bdg. 11.80 (978-0-613-67212-2(7)) Tandem Library Bks.

Minsky, Terri, creator. When Moms Attack & Misadventures in Babysitt, 4 vols., Vol. 3. 2003. (Lizzie McGuire Ser.: Vol. 3). (Illus.). 192p. pap. 7.99 (978-1-59182-245-5(9) , Tokyopop Kids) TOKYOPOP, Inc.

Modesitt, Jeanne. Mama, If You Had a Wish. 1999. (J). (978-0-606-16286-9(0)) Tandem Library Bks.

Molk, Laurel. Good Job, Oliver! 2001. (Illus.). (J). (978-0-606-20679-2(5)) Tandem Library Bks.

Mom Dresses Up. 2003. (J). (978-1-58453-254-5(8)) Pioneer Valley Educational Pr., Inc.

Mom's Bag: Individual Title Six-Packs. (Sails Literacy Ser.). (gr. 1-2). 36.00 (978-0-7578-3998-6(3)) Rigby Education.

Moore, Karen. Mommy Loves Me. Stanley, Mandy, illus. gif. ed. 2005. 20p. (J). (ps-ps). per. 6.99 (978-1-57791-182-1(2)) Brighter Minds Children's Publishing.

Mora, Pat. Rainbow Tulip. 2003. (gr. k-3). lib. bdg. 15.30 (978-0-613-61653-9(7)) Tandem Library Bks.

—Uno, Dos, Tres: One, Two, Three. Lavallee, Barbara, illus. 2000. (SPA.). 43p. (ps-ps). lib. bdg. 15.25 (978-0-613-28687-9(1)) Tandem Library Bks.

Morris, Clarine. Mommie Star. Bamford, Daneen, illus. 2000. (J). (ps-10). pap. 3.00 (978-0-9650312-3-3(3)) Cosmo Starr Bks.

Morse-Travis, Heidi. And Mommy's On Her Side. Hoffmann, Mark, illus. 2000. 28p. (J). 14.95 (978-0-9650848-3-3(3) , A Place to Remember) deRuyter-Nelson Pubns., Inc.

Moss, Miriam. Don't Forget I Love You. Currey, Anna, illus. 2003. 32p. (J). (ps-2). 15.99 (978-0-8037-2920-9(0) , Dial) Penguin Group (USA) Inc.

Mouse Works Staff. I Love You, Mama! 1999. (Disney's Pooh Ser.). (Illus.). 10p. (J). (ps). bds. 6.99 (978-1-57082-985-7(3)) Mouse Works.

Munsch, Robert. I'm So Embarrassed! Martchenko, Michael, illus. 2006. 32p. (J). pap. 4.99 (978-0-439-83578-7(X) , Cartwheel Bks.) Scholastic, Inc.

—Love You Forever. McGraw, Sheila, illus. gif. ed. 2000. 32p. (J). (ps-1). 19.95 (978-1-55209-109-8(0)) Firefly Bks., Ltd.

My Mom Is Great. 2002. (Great Relatives Ser.). 32p. (J). 11.95 (978-1-84250-577-9(7) , Bright Sparks) Parragon, Inc.

My Mommy Works. 2001. 16p. 6.99 (978-0-9716113-0-6(0)) Achievers Technology Resource, Inc.

My Mother's Cup. (J). (978-0-02-538388-3(4) , Scribner) Simon & Schuster.

My Stepmother: Individual Title Six-Packs. (ps-2). 27.00 (978-0-7635-9466-4(0)) Rigby Education.

Naylor, Phyllis Reynolds. Polo's Mother. Daniel, Alan, illus. (Cat Pack Ser.). 176p. (J). 2006. pap. 5.99 (978-0-689-87404-8(9) , Aladdin); 2005. 15.95 (978-0-689-86555-8(4) , Atheneum) Simon & Schuster Children's Publishing.

Newman, Leslea. Heather Has Two Mommies. Souza, Diana, illus. 2003. 32p. reprint ed. pap. 8.95 (978-1-55583-180-6(X)) Alyson Pubns.

—Heather Has Two Mommies. 2000. (gr. k-3). lib. bdg. 19.90 (978-0-613-78719-2(6)) Tandem Library Bks.

Nolen, Jerdine. In My Momma's Kitchen. Nolen, Jerdine & Bootman, Colin, illus. 2001. (Amistad Ser.). 32p. (J). (gr. k up). reprint ed. pap. 6.99 (978-0-06-443786-8(8) , Amistad) HarperCollins Pubs.

—In My Momma's Kitchen. 2001. (gr. k-3). lib. bdg. 14.10 (978-0-613-34780-8(3)) Tandem Library Bks.

Numeroff, Laura Joffe & Munsinger, Lynn. What Mommies Do Best: What Daddies Do Best. 1998. (Illus.). 40p. (J). (ps-3). 13.95 (978-0-689-80577-6(2)) Simon & Schuster Children's Publishing.

Oke, Janette. Pordy's Prickly Problem. Munger, Nancy, illus. rev. ed. 2001. (Animal Friends Ser.). 80p. (J). (gr. 1-5). pap. 6.99 (978-0-7642-2458-4(1)) Bethany Hse. Pubs.

Old Mother Hubbard: 6 Small Books. (gr. k-2). 23.00 (978-0-7635-8496-2(7)) Rigby Education.

Olsen, Sylvia. The Girl with a Baby. 2004. 208p. (J). pap. 7.95 (978-1-55039-142-8(9)) Sono Nis Pr. CAN. *Dist:* Orca Bk. Pubs. USA.

Olshan, Matthew. Finn. 2001. 245p. (YA). (gr. 8-12). 19.95 (978-1-890862-13-8(4)); pap. 14.95 (978-1-890862-14-5(2)) Bancroft Pr.

Orloff, Karen Kaufman. If Mom Had Three Arms. Whitehead, Pete, illus. 2006. 32p. 14.95 (978-1-4027-2356-8(3)) Sterling Publishing Co., Inc.

Ostrow, Kim. Gem of a Mom. 2002. (gr. 3-6). lib. bdg. 11.80 (978-0-613-51304-3(5)) Tandem Library Bks.

Otterman, Lynn. Fluffy Bunny. Fletcher, Rusty, illus. 2002. (Animal Snuggles Ser.). 8p. (J). bds. 7.95 (978-0-8069-8403-2(5)) Sterling Publishing Co., Inc.

Paratore, Coleen. Catching the Sun. 2010. (J). (978-0-618-45780-9(1)) Houghton Mifflin Co.

Parr, Todd. The Mommy Book. Parr, Todd, illus. 2002. (Illus.). 32p. (J). (ps-1). 15.99 (978-0-316-60827-5(0)) Little, Brown Bks. for Young Readers.

Paschalis, Juli. Druan o Mam! 2005. (WEL., Illus.). 16p. (978-0-86174-149-6(8)) Drake Educational Assocs. Ltd.

Potter, Beatrix. Peter Rabbit's I Love My Mommy. 2005. (Illus.). 10p. (J). (ps). 6.99 (978-0-7232-5367-9(6) , Warne) Penguin Group (USA) Inc.

Price, Mathew. My Mommy. Claverie, Jean, illus. 2003. (Peekaboo Board Bks.). 10p. (J). bds. 4.99 (978-0-7696-3155-4(X) , Gingham Dog Pr.) School Specialty Publishing.

Prince, Sarah. Lost Mother. 1999. (ps-2). lib. bdg. 11.80 (978-0-613-30569-3(8)) Tandem Library Bks.

Pullman, Philip. Sally y el Tigre en el Pozo. Miquel, Isabel de, tr. 2004. (SPA.). 512p. (978-84-95618-49-8(4) , Umbriel) Ediciones Urano S. A.

Quarles, Heather. A Door Near Here. 2000. 11.64 (978-0-606-17796-2(5)) Tandem Library Bks.

—Door near Here. 2000. (gr. 7-12). lib. bdg. 13.00 (978-0-613-22981-4(9)) Tandem Library Bks.

—A Door near Here. 2000. (Illus.). 240p. (YA). (gr. 7 up). pap. 5.50 (978-0-440-22761-8(5) , Laurel Leaf) Random Hse. Children's Bks.

Rach, Nikki. Dear Mommy. 1999. (Illus.). 64p. (J). 10.99 (978-0-570-05364-4(1) , 12-3415GJ) Concordia Publishing Hse.

Rahaman, Vashanti. Read for Me, Mama. McElrath-Eslick, Lori, illus. 2003. 32p. (J). (gr. 2-4). 15.95 (978-1-56397-313-0(8)) Boyds Mills Pr.

Reinhardt, Dana. A Brief Chapter in My Impossible Life. 2007. 256p. (YA). (gr. 7). pap. 8.99 (***978-0-375-84691-5(3)*** , Lamb, Wendy) Random Hse. Children's Bks.

Reiser, Lynn W. Cherry Pies & Lullabies. Reiser, Lynn W., illus. 1998. (Illus.). 40p. (J). (ps-3). 18.99 (978-0-688-13391-7(6)) HarperCollins Pubs.

—Cherry Pies & Lullabies. 1998. (Illus.). 40p. (J). (ps-3). 16.89 (978-0-688-13392-4(4)) HarperCollins Pubs.

Rich, Scharlotte. I Love My Mommy. 2001. 96p. (J). 7.99 (978-0-310-70103-3(1)) Zondervan.

Richter, Bernd & Richter, Susan. The Little Bear Who Didn't Want to Hibernate. Green, Sue, illus. 2003. 42p. pap. 9.95 (978-1-931353-10-6(7)) Saddle Pal Creations, Inc.

Richter, Jutta. The Summer of the Pike. Brailovsky, Anna, tr. from GER. Buchholz, Quint, illus. 2006. 132p. (J). pap. 6.95 (978-1-57131-672-1(8)); 16.95 (978-1-57131-671-4(X)) Milkweed Editions.

Rigby Education Staff. Old Mother Big Book. (gr. k-2). 21.00 (978-0-7635-2408-1(5)) Rigby Education.

Ringgold, Robyn. My Mom Hugs Trees. Vasudevan, Vidya, illus. 2006. 24p. (J). per. 15.95 (978-0-9785326-1-1(9)) Solar Publishing LLC.

Ripslinger, Jon. Derailed. 2006. 288p. (J). pap. 8.95 (978-0-7387-0888-1(7) , Flux) Llewellyn Pubns.

Rushton, Rosie. Just Don't Make a Scene, Mum! 2005. 224p. (J). pap. 5.99 (978-0-7868-5186-7(4)) Hyperion Bks. for Children.

Russell, Barbara Timberlake. The Remembering Stone. Peck, Beth, illus. 1999. (J). (978-0-7894-2583-6(1)) Dorling Kindersley Publishing, Inc.

Russell, James. Fabulous America: Romantic Comedy Screenplay. 2001. 108p. (YA). pap. 12.95 (978-0-916367-33-6(9)) Russell, James.

Russo, Marisabina. Mama Talks Too Much. 1999. (Illus.). (J). lib. bdg. (978-0-688-16412-6(9)) HarperCollins Pubs.

—Mama Talks Too Much. Russo, Marisabina, illus. 1999. (Illus.). 288p. (J). (ps-3). 16.00 (978-0-688-16411-9(0)) HarperCollins Pubs.

—When Mama Gets Home. Russo, Marisabina, illus. 1998. (Illus.). 24p. (J). (ps-3). 16.99 (978-0-688-14985-7(5)) HarperCollins Pubs.

Salan, Felipe Lopez, illus. Jack & the Beanstalk. 2006. 32p. (J). 15.95 (978-1-933327-11-2(1)) Purple Bear Bks., Inc.

Sautereau, Francois. La Extrana Navidad de Jonas.Tr. of Jonas's Extraordinary Christmas. (SPA.). 92p. (YA). (gr. 5-8). (978-84-279-3163-3(8) , NG3472) Noguer y Caralt Editores, S. A. ESP. *Dist:* Lectorum Pubns., Inc.

—La Extrana Navidad de Jonas. 2000. Tr. of Jonas's Extraordinary Christmas. (SPA.). (gr. 5-8). lib. bdg. 18.20 (978-0-613-80653-4(0)) Tandem Library Bks.

Say, Allen. Tree of Cranes. Say, Allen, illus. 2002. (Illus.). 25.28 (978-0-7587-3857-8(9)) Book Wholesalers, Inc.

Schlein, Miriam. The Way Mothers Are. 2000. (978-0-606-18777-0(4)) Tandem Library Bks.

—The Way Mothers Are. Lasker, Joe, illus. 2003. (Concept Book Ser.). 32p. (J). (ps-2). pap. 6.95 (978-0-8075-8690-7(0)) Whitman, Albert & Co.

—Way Mothers Are. 2000. (ps-2). lib. bdg. 15.25 (978-0-613-28691-6(X)) Tandem Library Bks.

Schlessinger, Laura. Why Do You Love Me? 2001. (gr. k-3). lib. bdg. 14.10 (978-0-613-36029-6(X)) Tandem Library Bks.

Schlessinger, Laura & Lambert, Martha. Why Do You Love Me? McFeeley, Daniel, illus. 2001. 40p. (J). (ps-2). pap. 6.99 (978-0-06-443654-0(3) , Harper Trophy) HarperCollins Pubs.

Scott, Ann Herbert. On Mother's Lap. Coalson, Glo, illus. 2002. (J). 14.74 (978-0-7587-3318-4(6)) Book Wholesalers, Inc.

—On Mother's Lap. Coalson, Glo, illus. 2000. 14p. (J). (gr. k-ps). bds. 5.95 (978-0-618-05159-5(7) , Clarion Bks.) Houghton Mifflin Co. Trade & Reference Div.

Sendak, Maurice. We Love You, Mama! 2003. (gr. k-3). lib. bdg. 11.80 (978-0-613-68299-2(8)) Tandem Library Bks.

Senderak, Carol Hunt. Mommy in My Pocket. Nakata, Hiroe, illus. 2006. 32p. (ps-1). 12.99 (978-0-7868-5596-4(7)) Hyperion Pr.

Setterington, Ken. Mom & Mum Are Getting Married. Priestley, Alice, illus. 2005. 24p. (J). 11.95 (978-1-896764-84-9(3)) Second Story Pr. CAN. *Dist:* Orca Bk. Pubs. USA.

Shahan, Sherry. Death Mountain. 2005. 176p. (J). 15.95 (978-1-56145-353-5(6)) Peachtree Pubs., Ltd.

Shanahan, Lisa & Guthridge, Bettina. My Mom Tarzan. 2007. (J). bds. 12.95 (***978-1-59692-239-6(7)***) MacAdam/Cage Publishing, Inc.

Shaw, Susan. Safe. 2007. 208p. (J). (gr. 9). 16.99 (***978-0-525-47829-4(9)*** , Dutton Juvenile) Penguin Group (USA) Inc.

Simmons, Jane. Come on, Daisy! (Illus.). (Orig.). 2005. (ARA, ENG, VIE, CHI & BEN.). 32p. 11.95 (978-1-84059-217-7(6)); 2005. (URD, ENG, VIE, CHI & ARA., 32p. 11.95 (978-1-84059-182-8(X)); 2005. (VIE, ENG, CHI, ARA & BEN., 32p. 11.95 (978-1-84059-183-5(8)); 2000. (BEN, ENG, VIE, CHI & ARA., 36p. (J). pap. 11.95 (978-1-84059-177-4(3)); 2000. (GUJ, ENG, VIE, CHI & ARA., 36p. (J). pap. 11.95 (978-1-84059-179-8(X)); 2000. (TUR, ENG, VIE, CHI & ARA., 36p. (J). pap. 11.95 (978-1-84059-181-1(1)) Milet Publishing.

Simpson, Kathie. Libby. 2003. 192p. per. 14.95 (978-1-59453-025-8(4) , 1688) Airleaf Publishing & Bookselling.

Slater, Teddy. Un Minuto! 2000. Tr. of Just a Minute!. (SPA.). (gr. k-3). lib. bdg. 10.90 (978-0-613-72012-0(1)) Tandem Library Bks.

Snead, Kathi. My Mom Has a Job. Christine, Grove, illus. 2004. (J). (978-0-9747385-1-2(4)) City of Manassas Department of Social Services.

Sollinger, Emily. Kisses for Mommy. Hathon, Elizabeth, photos by. 2002. (Illus.). 14p. (J). bds. 5.99 (978-0-448-42547-4(5) , Grosset & Dunlap) Penguin Group (USA) Inc.

Spinelli, Eileen. When Mama Comes Home Tonight. Dyer, Jane, illus. 1998. 32p. (J). (ps-k). 14.00 (978-0-689-81065-7(2)) Simon & Schuster Children's Publishing.

Springer, Nancy. The Case of the Missing Marquess: An Enola Holmes Mystery. 2006. 208p. (J). (gr. 4). 10.99 (978-0-399-24304-2(6) , Philomel) Penguin Group (USA) Inc.

St. Anthony, Jane. Grace above All. 2007. 176p. (J). (gr. 5-8). 16.00 (978-0-374-39940-5(9) , Farrar, Straus & Giroux (BYR)) Farrar, Straus & Giroux.

Staub, Wendy Corsi. Lily Dale: Awakening. 2007. 240p. (YA). (gr. 7 up). 15.95 (***978-0-8027-9654-7(0)***) Walker & Co.

Stauffacher, Sue. Harry Sue. 2005. 304p. (J). (gr. 3-7). 15.95 (978-0-375-83274-1(2)); lib. bdg. 17.99 (978-0-375-93274-8(7)) Random Hse. Children's Bks. (Knopf Bks. for Young Readers).

Stewart, Maddie. Peg. Willey, Bee, illus. 2001. (Blue Bananas Ser.). 48p. (J). (gr. 1-2). (978-0-7787-0841-4(1)); pap. (978-0-7787-0887-2(X)) Crabtree Publishing Co.

—Peg. 2002. (gr. k-3). lib. bdg. 12.95 (978-0-613-52895-5(6)) Tandem Library Bks.

Symes, Ruth. The Mum Trap. 2000. (Illus.). 128p. (J). pap. 8.99 (978-0-86264-933-3(1)) Andersen GBR. *Dist:* Independent Pubs. Group.

Tafuri, Nancy. I Love You, Little One. 2000. (Illus.). 15p. (J). (ps-k). bds. 7.99 (978-0-439-13746-1(2) , Scholastic Reference) Scholastic, Inc.

Tamaro, Susanna. Castello Dei Sogni Storie Che. pap. 18.95 (978-88-04-50610-2(5)) Mondadori ITA. *Dist:* Distribooks, Inc.

Tan, Amy H. My Mommy's an Angel! Tan, Mariam, illus. l.t. ed. 2002. (Angel Ser.). 20p. (J). 18.95 incl. audio compact disk (978-0-9717299-0-2(5)) JeaMei Publishing.

Tattum, Stephan. Mom. 2005. (J). 4.95 (978-1-59792-006-3(1)) F.A.S.T. Learning LLLC.

Thiesing, Lisa. Me & You: A Mother-Daughter Album. 2000. (ps-2). lib. bdg. 13.00 (978-0-613-31466-4(2)) Tandem Library Bks.

Thompson, Jill. Scary Godmother, Vol. 1. 2003. (Illus.). 48p. 19.95 (978-1-57989-015-5(6)) Sirius Entertainment, Inc.

Tolan, Stephanie S. Listen! 2006. 208p. (J). 15.99 (978-0-06-057935-7(8)); lib. bdg. 16.89 (978-0-06-057936-4(6)) HarperCollins Pubs.

Trebi-Ollennu, Flora. Shogologo Babies. Vandenberg, Jan, illus. 2002. 64p. pap. (***978-1-894718-03-5(8)***) Amerley Treb Bks.

Tucker, Mark. Super Phil & the Missing Mom. Patete, Christine, illus. 2003. 24p. (J). 4.50 (978-1-882440-01-6(3)) God's World Pubns. Inc.

Valdes, Leslie. Happy Mother's Day, Mami! Fruchter, Jason, illus. 2003. (Dora the Explorer Ser.: Vol. 3). 24p. (J). pap. 3.99 (978-0-689-85233-6(9) , Simon Spotlight/ Nickelodeon) Simon & Schuster Children's Publishing.

—Happy Mother's Day, Mami! 2003. (ps-2). lib. bdg. 11.80 (978-0-613-73353-3(3)) Tandem Library Bks.

Vestergaard, Hope. Wake up, Mama! Courtin, Thierry, illus. 2003. 24p. (J). 6.99 (978-0-525-47030-4(1) , Dutton Juvenile) Penguin Group (USA) Inc.

Waber, Bernard. Funny, Funny Lyle. Waber, Bernard, illus. 2002. (Lyle the Crocodile Ser.). (Illus.). (J). 14.74 (978-0-7587-2559-2(0)) Book Wholesalers, Inc.

—Lyle Finds His Mother. Waber, Bernard, illus. 2002. (Lyle the Crocodile Ser.). (Illus.). (J). 14.74 (978-0-7587-3060-2(8)) Book Wholesalers, Inc.

Waddell, Martin. Owl Babies. 2002. (Illus.). (J). 13.83 (978-1-4046-3008-6(2)) Book Wholesalers, Inc.

—Owl Babies. 2003. (Illus.). 22p. (J). 12.99 (978-0-7636-2157-5(9)) Candlewick Pr.

—Owl Babies. Benson, Patrick, illus. 32p. (J). (ps-2). 2002. pap. 5.99 (978-0-7636-1710-3(5)); 2000. pap. 19.99 (978-0-7636-1283-2(9)) Candlewick Pr.

—Owl Babies. (Illus.). 25p. (J). (CHI, ENG, URD, TUR & VIE.). (978-1-85430-343-1(0) , 93441); (ENG, VIE, URD, TUR & CHI., (978-1-85430-348-6(1) , 93442) Magi Pubns.

—Owl Babies. 2002. (ps-2). lib. bdg. 14.15 (978-0-613-74780-6(1)) Tandem Library Bks.

—Webster J. Duck. Parkins, David, illus. 2001. 32p. (J). (gr. k-ps). 13.99 (978-0-7636-1506-2(4)) Candlewick Pr.

Wallace, Nancy Elizabeth, illus. Shells! Shells! Shells! 2006. 32p. (J). 16.99 (978-0-7614-5332-1(6)) Cavendish, Marshall Corp.

Webster, Michelle B. The Christmas of Miracles. 2004. 136p. per. 12.95 (978-0-9753117-0-7(0)) Four Sonkist Angels.

Weeks, Sarah. Mama. 2001. 32p. (J). (ps-2). 15.95 (978-0-06-027507-5(3)) HarperCollins Pubs.

Weiss, Ellen & de Brunhoff, Laurent. Babar: A Gift for Mother. Gibert, Jean Claude & Gray, Judith, illus. 2004. 24p. (J). (ps-1). 9.95 (978-0-8109-4837-2(0)) Abrams, Harry N. , Inc.

Wells, Rosemary. La Estupenda Mama de Roberta. (SPA.). (J). 16.95 (978-84-372-1612-6(5)) Santillana USA Publishing Co., Inc.

—La Estupenda Mama de Roberta. Wells, Rosemary, illus. 2001. (Picture Books Collection). (SPA., Illus.). 32p. (J). (gr. k-3). pap. 9.95 (978-84-372-2187-8(0)) Santillana USA Publishing Co., Inc.

White, Ruth. Belle Prater's Boy. unabr. ed. 2004. 196p. (J). (gr. 5-9). pap. 38.00 incl. audio (978-0-8072-8682-1(6) , YA234SP, Listening Library) Random Hse. Audio Publishing Group.

—Belle Prater's Boy. 1998. (YA). 12.15 (978-0-606-12610-6(4)) Tandem Library Bks.

—Belle Prater's Boy. l.t. ed. 2000. (Illus.). 221p. (YA). (gr. 4-7). 21.95 (978-0-7862-2885-0(7)) Thorndike Pr.

Wild, Margaret. One Night. 2006. 240p. (YA). (gr. 7). mass mkt. 5.99 (978-0-553-49434-1(1) , Laurel Leaf) Random Hse. Children's Bks.

Williams. Heeey Ma. Date not set. (Illus.). 40p. (J). (ps-1). pap. 5.99 (978-0-06-443601-4(2)) HarperCollins Pubs.

Williams, Jacklyn. Happy Valentine's Day, Gus! Cushman, Doug, illus. 2005. (Read-It! Readers Ser.). 32p. (J). (gr. k-3). 18.60 (978-1-4048-0962-8(7)) Picture Window Bks.

Williams, Lori Aurelia. Broken China. 2005. 272p. (YA). (gr. 7 up). 16.95 (978-0-689-86878-8(2) , Simon & Schuster Children's Publishing) Simon & Schuster Children's Publishing.

Williams, Vera B. Un Sillon para Mi Mama. Williams, Vera B., illus. unabr. ed. 2004. (SPA., Illus.). (J). (gr. k-2). pap. 16.95 incl. audio (978-0-87499-335-6(0) , LK6260) Live Oak Media.

Wilson, Jacqueline. The Mum-Minder. 2000. (Corgi Yearling Ser.). 32p. (J). 8.99 (978-0-440-86302-1(3) , Corgi) Transworld Publishers Ltd. GBR. *Dist:* Trafalgar Square Publishing.

Wolff, Virginia Euwer. Make Lemonade. 2006. 208p. (YA). pap. 6.95 (978-0-8050-8070-4(8) , Holt, Henry & Co. Bks. For Young Readers) Holt, Henry & Co.

—Make Lemonade. l.t. ed. 2004. 257p. pap. 10.95 (978-0-7862-6358-5(X)) Thorndike Pr.

Wolfgram, Barbara. I Know My Mommy Loves Me. McAuley, Marlene, illus. 1998. 32p. (J). (ps-1). 6.99 (978-0-570-05049-0(9) , 56-1873GJ) Concordia Publishing Hse.

Wood, Douglas. What Moms Can't Do. Cushman, Doug, illus. (J). (ps-3). 2001. 32p. 14.00 (978-0-689-83358-8(X)); 2005. 24p. 6.95 (978-1-4169-0198-3(1)) Simon & Schuster Children's Publishing.

Woodson, J. L. Superwoman's Child: Son of a Single Mother. Malone, Susan Mary, ed. 2005. 204p. pap. 14.95 (978-0-9754130-8-1(2)) Macro Publishing Group.

Wynne-Jones, Tim. A Thief in the House of Memory. 2005. 224p. (YA). 17.00 (978-0-374-37478-5(3) , Nelanie Kroupa Bks.) Farrar, Straus & Giroux.

—A Thief in the House of Memory. l.t. ed 2006. 235p. (YA). 21.95 (978-0-7862-9022-2(6)) Thorndike Pr.

Yates, Sharon Murphy. The Busy Mom. 2001. (Illus.). 32p. 16.95 (978-0-87868-789-3(0) , 7890, Child & Family Pr.) Child Welfare League of America, Inc.

Young, Andrew. The Giving Mother. 2006. (J). (***978-1-933554-36-5(3)***) Primordia.

Youngberg, Norma R. Miracle of the Song. 2000. (Illus.). 188p. (J). (gr. 3-6). reprint ed. per. 11.95 (978-1-57258-187-6(5) , 945-6049) TEACH Services, Inc.

Zatz, Lia. Mamita Monstruo. Guevara, Angeles Godinez, tr. Furnari, Eva, illus. 2003. (ENG & SPA.). 32p. pap. 6.95 (978-85-7416-173-0(X)) Callis Editora Ltda BRA. *Dist:* Independent Pubs. Group.

Ziefert, Harriet. Just Like Mommy! Brown, Erik, illus. 2005. 16p. (J). bds. 6.95 (978-1-4027-1788-8(1)) Sterling Publishing Co., Inc.

—Mommies Are for Counting Stars. Jabar, Cynthia, illus. 1999. (Lift-the-Flap Bks.). 16p. (J). (ps-1). pap. 6.99 (978-0-14-056552-2(3) , Puffin) Penguin Group (USA) Inc.

—Mommy, Where Are You? 1999. (Illus.). 20p. pap. 4.95 (978-0-14-050899-4(6) , N A L Trade) Penguin Group (USA) Inc.

—31 Uses for a Mom. Doughty, Rebecca, illus. 2003. 32p. (J). (ps). 12.99 (978-0-399-23862-8(X) , Putnam Juvenile) Penguin Group (USA) Inc.

Zolotow, Charlotte. This Quiet Lady. Lobel, Anita, illus. 2000. 24p. (J). (ps-3). pap. 6.99 (978-0-688-17527-6(9) , Harper Trophy) HarperCollins Pubs.

—This Quiet Lady. 2000. (ps-2). lib. bdg. 14.10 (978-0-613-27232-2(3)) Tandem Library Bks.

MOTHERS—POETRY

Micklos, John, Jr. Mommy Poems. McElrath-Eslick, Lori, illus. 2003. 32p. (YA). (gr. 2-4). 16.95 (978-1-56397-849-4(0)) Boyds Mills Pr.

Micklos, John, Jr., ed. Mommy Poems. McElrath-Eslick, Lori, illus. 2003. 32p. (YA). (gr. 2-4). pap. 9.95 (978-1-56397-908-8(X)) Boyds Mills Pr.

Purple Ronnie. Purple Ronnie's Little Book for a Lovely Mom. 2008. 64p. 8.95 (***978-0-7407-7117-0(5)***) Andrews McMeel Publishing.

Sones, Sonya. What My Mother Doesn't Know. 2003. (gr. 7-12). lib. bdg. 15.30 (978-0-613-61828-1(9)) Tandem Library Bks.

MOTHERS AND DAUGHTERS

McDonald, Stacy. Raising Maidens of Virtue: A Study of Feminine Loveliness for Mothers & Daughters. 2004. (Illus.). 226p. (YA). 18.00 (978-0-9743390-1-6(6)) Books on the Path.

Shirk, Rohrer Lynette. The Mother Daughter Cookbook: Recipes to Nourish Relationships. Houshyar, Azadeh, illus. 2007. 128p. (J). pap. 14.95 (978-0-9772660-6-7(0)) Orange Avenue Publishing.

Sim, David. Cos You're My Mum. 2001. (Illus.). 32p. (J). pap. 6.99 (978-0-7459-4543-9(0) , Lion) Lion Hudson plc GBR. *Dist:* Independent Pubs. Group.

MOTHERS AND DAUGHTERS—FICTION

Abbott, Candy. Gavin Goodfellow: The Lure of Burnt Swamp. 2007. 368p. pap. 14.95 (***978-1-886068-03-2(8)***) Fruitbearer Publishing.

The Adventures of Molly. 2004. pap. 13.95 (***978-1-59526-180-9(X)***) Media Creations, Inc.

Ain, Beth Levine. The Portrait. 2008. (J). (***978-0-7636-3396-7(8)***) Candlewick Pr.

Alegria, Malin. Estrella's Quinceañera. 2007. 288p. (YA). (gr. 7 up). pap. 8.99 (978-0-689-87810-7(9) , Simon Pulse) Simon & Schuster Children's Publishing.

—Estrellas Quinceanera. 2006. (Illus.). 272p. (YA). 15.99 (978-0-689-87809-1(5)) Simon & Schuster Children's Publishing.

Alfonsi, Alice, adapted by. 'Rents: Lizzie Mcguire. 2005. 134p. (J). lib. bdg. 16.92 (***978-1-4242-0689-6(8)***) Fitzgerald Bks.

Amesse, Susan. Kissing Brendan Callahan. 2005. 160p. (J). (gr. 5-8). 15.95 (978-1-59643-015-0(X)) Roaring Brook Pr.

Anselmo, Robert Louis. We're All Different & yet Still the Same. l.t. ed. 2006. (Illus.). 22p. (J). 14.99 (978-1-59879-107-5(9)); per. 9.99 (978-1-59879-088-7(9)) Lifevest Publishing, Inc.

Apperley, Dawn. Princess Rosebud: Perfectly Perfect Princess. 2007. 32p. (J). (gr. k-1). 14.99 (978-0-7641-6033-2(8)) Barron's Educational Series, Inc.

Arrington, Aileen. Paper Heart. 2006. 113p. (J). 16.95 (978-1-932425-61-1(6) , Lemniscaat) Boyds Mills Pr.

Atwell, Debby. The Warthog's Tail. 2005. (Illus.). 32p. (J). (gr. k-3). 16.00 (978-0-618-50781-8(7) , Walter Lorraine) Houghton Mifflin Co. Trade & Reference Div.

Banks, Lynne Reid. Alice-by-Accident. 2000. (Avon Camelot Bks.). 144p. (J). (gr. 4-7). 14.95 (978-0-380-97865-6(2)) HarperCollins Pubs.

Baratz-Logsted, Lauren. Secrets of My Suburban Life. 2008. 240p. (YA). pap. 7.99 (***978-1-4169-2525-5(2)*** , Simon Pulse) Simon & Schuster Children's Publishing.

Barkow, Henriette & Finlay, Lizzie, illus. Buri & the Marrow: An Indian Folk Tale: Un Conte Traditionnel Indien = Buri et la Courge. 2004. (TAM, VIE, SPA, GUJ & PER.). 24p. (J). pap. (978-1-85269-583-5(8)) Mantra Publishing, Ltd.

Bateson, Catherine. The Boyfriend Rules of Good Behavior. 2006. 192p. (YA). 16.95 (978-0-8234-2026-1(4)) Holiday Hse., Inc.

Becker, Shelly. Mine! Mine! Mine! Takahashi, Hideko, illus. 2006. 32p. (J). 14.95 (978-1-4027-2538-8(8)) Sterling Publishing Co., Inc.

Bell, Clare. Ratha's Challenge: The Fourth Book of the Named. 2007. 272p. (YA). (gr. 7). 8.99 (***978-0-14-240915-2(4)*** , Puffin) Penguin Group (USA) Inc.

Berger, Samantha. Word Family Tales: Please Don't Tell about Mom's Bell. Brown, Rick, illus. 2002. (Word Family Tales Ser.). 16p. (ps-2). pap. 2.95 (978-0-439-26258-3(5)) Scholastic, Inc.

Blume, Lesley M. M. Tennyson. 2008. 240p. (J). (gr. 3-7). 15.99 (***978-0-375-84703-5(0)*** , Knopf Bks. for Young Readers) Random Hse. Children's Bks.

Bonnell, Kris. We Like the Beach. 2007. (J). 3.95 (***978-1-933727-55-4(1)***) Reading Reading Bks., LLC.

Bonnett-Rampersaud, Louise. Bubble & Squeak. Banta, Susan, illus. 2006. 24p. (J). 14.99 (978-0-7614-5310-9(5)) Cavendish, Marshall Corp.

Bowers, Laura. Beauty Shop for Rent: ... Fully Equipped, Inquire Within. 2007. (Illus.). 336p. (J). (gr. 6-10). 17.00 (978-0-15-205764-0(1)) Harcourt Trade Pubs.

Bowers, Laura. Beauty Shop for Rent: ... fully equipped, inquire Within. 2008. (Illus.). 336p. (J). pap. 6.95 (***978-0-15-206385-6(4)*** , Harcourt Paperbacks) Harcourt Children's Bks.

Bowsher, Melodie. My Lost & Found Life. (YA). 2007. 320p. pap. 7.95 (***978-1-59990-155-8(2)***); 2006. 350p. 16.95 (978-1-58234-736-3(0)) Bloomsbury Publishing. (Bloomsbury Children).

Brooks, Bruce. Midnight Hour Encores. 2000. (978-0-606-19987-2(X)) Tandem Library Bks.

Bruha, Ginger. Lilly's Breakfast Time. 2004. 20p. pap. 14.95 (978-1-4137-3133-0(3)) PublishAmerica, Inc.

Buckley, Michael. Once upon a Crime. Ferguson, Peter, illus. 2007. (Sisters Grimm Ser.: Bk. 4). 288p. (J). (gr. 2-8). 14.95 (***978-0-8109-1610-4(X)*** , Amulet Bks.) Abrams, Harry N. , Inc.

Butcher, Nancy. Beauty. 2005. 168p. (YA). (gr. 7-12). lib. bdg. 15.60 (978-1-4176-6053-7(8)) Tandem Library Bks.

Byrd, Sandra. Red Velvet. 2005. (Friends for a Season Ser.). 256p. (J). (gr. 8-12). pap. 10.99 (978-0-7642-0022-9(4)) Bethany Hse. Pubs.

Campbell-Fells. Blue Ribbon Girls. 2005. 145p. pap. 13.95 (978-0-7414-2593-5(9)) Infinity Publishing.

Campbell, Terry. Harlem & Momma: A Short Children Story. 2005. 42p. (J). pap. 10.00 (978-0-9761560-0-0(8)) Sweet T. C. Campbell.

Capone, Deb. Families Are Forever. 2004. (J). 16.95 (***978-0-9728666-6-8(3))*** As Simple As That Publishing.

Carey, Janet Lee. Dragon's Keep. (Illus.). 320p. (YA). 2008. pap. 7.95 (***978-0-15-206401-3(X)*** , Magic Carpet Bks.); 2007. (gr. 6-10). 17.00 (978-0-15-205926-2(1)) Harcourt Children's Bks.

—Dragon's Keep. 2007. 302p. (J). (***978-1-4287-3929-1(7))*** Harcourt Trade Pubs.

Cassidy, Cathy. Dizzy. 2004. 224p. (J). pap. (978-0-14-131785-4(X) , Puffin) Penguin Group (USA) Inc.

Chappas, Bess. Kiki & the Red Shoes. 2007. (J). 17.99 (***978-1-60131-012-5(9))*** Big Tent Bks.

Charles, Bob. A una visita al mercado & Trip to the Market. 2005. spiral bd. 66.00 (***978-1-4108-5642-5(9))*** Benchmark Education Co.

Clay, Margaret. Double Identity. 2007. 276p. (YA). pap. 12.95 (***978-0-9792328-6-2(4))*** Helm Publishing.

Cohen, Tish. The Invisible Rules of the Zoe Lama. 2007. 208p. (J). (gr. 4-7). 15.99 (978-0-525-47810-2(8) , Dutton Juvenile) Penguin Group (USA) Inc.

Cohn, Rachel. Shrimp. 2006. 288p. (YA). (gr. 7 up). reprint ed. pap. 6.99 (978-0-689-86613-5(5) , Simon Pulse) Simon & Schuster Children's Publishing.

Cole, Brock. Facts Speak for Themselves. 2006. 184p. (YA). 8.95 (978-1-932425-71-0(3) , Lemniscaat) Boyds Mills Pr.

Collins, Yvonne & Rideout, Sandy. Introducing Vivien Leigh Reid: Daughter of the Diva. 2005. 240p. pap. 9.95 (978-0-312-33837-4(6) , St. Martin's Griffin) St. Martin's Pr.

—The New & Improved Vivien Leigh Reid: Diva in Control. 2007. 240p. (gr. 7-10). pap. 9.95 (978-0-312-35828-0(8) , St. Martin's Griffin); 231p. (YA). (***978-1-4287-1928-6(8))*** St. Martin's Pr.

—Now Starring Vivien Leigh Reid: Diva in Training. 2006. 256p. pap. 9.95 (978-0-312-33839-8(2) , St. Martin's Griffin) St. Martin's Pr.

Coman, Carolyn. Tell Me Everything. 2006. 160p. (YA). pap. 6.95 (978-0-374-40005-7(9) , Farrar, Straus & Giroux (BYR)) Farrar, Straus & Giroux.

Connors, Faith Raymond. Love, Midgie. 2007. (J). pap. 14.95 (***978-0-9640138-1-0(9))*** BelleAire Pr.

Conway, Celeste. The Melting Season. (YA). (gr. 7). 2008. 224p. mass mkt. 6.50 (***978-0-440-23953-6(2)*** , Laurel Leaf); 2006. 288p. 15.95 (978-0-385-73339-7(9) , Delacorte Bks. for Young Readers); 2006. 288p. 17.99 (978-0-385-90357-8(X) , Delacorte Bks. for Young Readers) Random Hse. Children's Bks.

Coté, Geneviève, illus. The Magic Beads. 2007. 32p. (J). (gr. 2 up). 16.95 (***978-1-894965-47-7(7))*** Simply Read Bks. CAN. *Dist:* Perseus Distribution.

Cunningham, Laura Shaine. The Midnight Diary of Zoya Blume. 176p. (J). 2006. pap. 5.99 (978-0-06-072261-6(4) , Harper Trophy); 2005. (gr. 3 up). 15.99 (978-0-06-072259-3(2) , Geringer, Laura Book) HarperCollins Pubs.

Czech, Jan. Grace Happens. 2007. 160p. (YA). pap. 6.99 (978-0-14-240752-3(6) , Puffin) Penguin Group (USA) Inc.

Dalton, Annie & Dalton, Maria. Invisible Threads. 2006. 208p. (YA). (gr. 9). 15.95 (978-0-385-73286-4(4)); lib. bdg. 17.99 (978-0-385-90303-5(0)) Random Hse. Children's Bks. (Delacorte Bks. for Young Readers).

Danziger, Paula. Amber Brown Wants Extra Credit. Ross, Tony, illus. 2008. (Amber Brown Ser.: No. 4). 128p. (J). (gr. 2-6). 4.99 (***978-0-14-241049-3(7)*** , Puffin) Penguin Group (USA) Inc.

Dao, Cindy. Mama? 2005. (Illus.). 36p. (J). per. 8.99 (978-1-932338-79-9(9)) Lifevest Publishing, Inc.

Davenport, Jennifer. Anna Begins. 2007. 21.95 (***978-0-930773-83-0(7))*** Black Heron Pr.

Davis, Deborah. Not Like You. 2007. 272p. (YA). (gr. 7 up). 16.00 (***978-0-618-72093-4(6)*** , Clarion Bks.) Houghton Mifflin Co. Trade & Reference Div.

Delaney, Mark. Pepperland. 2007. 224p. pap. 7.95 (***978-1-56145-402-0(8)*** , Peachtree Junior) Peachtree Pubs., Ltd.

Desplechin, Marie. Poor Little Witch Girl. Rosner, Gillian, tr. 2007. 144p. (J). pap. 6.95 (***978-1-59990-128-2(5)*** , Bloomsbury Children) Bloomsbury Publishing.

Donahue, Jill L. Bliss, Blueberries, & the Butterfly. Ice, D. C., illus. 2006. 32p. (J). lib. bdg. (***978-1-4048-3206-0(8))*** Picture Window Bks.

—Bliss, Blueberries, & the Butterfly. 2006. (Illus.). 32p. (J). (***978-1-4048-1222-2(9))*** Picture Window Bks.

Doty, Kathryn Adams. Wild Orphan. 2006. 144p. pap. 14.95 (978-1-889020-20-4(6)) Edinborough Pr.

Dreidemy, Joelle, illus. Bath Time, Beth! 2006. 24p. 9.99 (978-1-84643-024-4(0)) Child's Play-International.

Duble, Kathleen Benner. The Sacrifice. 2007. 224p. (J). pap. 5.99 (***978-0-689-87651-6(3)*** , Aladdin) Simon & Schuster Children's Publishing.

Durst, Sarah. Into the Wild. 2007. 272p. (J). (gr. 5-7). 15.99 (978-1-59514-156-9(1) , Razorbill) Penguin Group (USA) Inc.

Elliott, Louise. Dangerous Redheads. 114p. pap. 11.95 (978-0-7022-2631-1(9)) Univ. of Queensland Pr. AUS. *Dist:* International Specialized Bk. Services.

Emesse, Tea. Yumi Talks the Talk. 2006. (Star Sisterztm Ser.: Bk. 6). 144p. (YA). pap. 4.99 (978-0-7869-3992-3(3) , Mirrorstone) Wizards of the Coast.

Erb, Sharlyne. A hug from Daddy. 2005. 43p. pap. 12.97 (978-1-4116-5576-8(1)) Lulu.com.

Erlich, Bev. Pink Roses Everywhere. gif. ed. 2004. (Illus.). 64p. (J). 14.95 (978-0-9743913-0-4(1)) Snojoy Publishing.

Ferguson, Alane. The Circle of Blood. 2008. 256p. (YA). (gr. 7). 15.99 (***978-0-670-06056-6(9)*** , Viking Juvenile) Penguin Group (USA) Inc.

Findon, Joanne. When Night Eats the Moon. 2004. 175p. (YA). (gr. 7-12). per. 16.60 (978-0-613-93942-3(5)) Tandem Library Bks.

Flinn, Alex. Diva. 2007. 288p. (J). pap. 7.99 (***978-0-06-056846-7(1));*** 2006. 272p. (YA). 16.99 (978-0-06-056843-6(7)); 2006. 272p. (YA). lib. bdg. 17.89 (978-0-06-056845-0(3)) HarperCollins Pubs. (HarperTeen).

Forde, Catherine. Tug of War: Two Mums, One Girl, One Choice. 2007. 304p. (J). pap. 9.95 (***978-1-4052-2005-7(8))*** Egmont Bks., Ltd. GBR. *Dist:* Independent Pubs. Group.

Frederick, Heather Vogel. The Mother-Daughter Book Club. 2007. 256p. (J). (gr. 4-7). 15.99 (978-0-689-86412-4(4)) Simon & Schuster Children's Publishing.

Gardner, Sally. I, Coriander. 2007. 288p. (J). (gr. 5 up). pap. 6.99 (978-0-14-240763-9(1) , Puffin) Penguin Group (USA) Inc.

Garland, Sarah. Doing the Garden. 2008. (Illus.). 32p. (J). 9.95 (***978-1-84507-721-1(0))*** Lincoln, Frances Ltd. GBR. *Dist:* Perseus Distribution.

Gephart, Donna. As If Being 12 3/4 Isn't Bad Enough, My Mother Is Running for President! 2008. (J). (gr. 3-7). 240p. 15.99 (***978-0-385-73481-3(6));*** 192p. lib. bdg. 18.99 (***978-0-385-90479-7(7))*** Random Hse. Children's Bks. (Delacorte Bks. for Young Readers).

Gillis, Jennifer B. What Do You Say? 2006. (Reader's Clubhouse Set B Ser.). (Illus.). 24p. (J). pap. 3.99 (978-0-7641-3298-8(9)) Barron's Educational Series, Inc.

Glassman, Peter. My Working Mom. Arnold, Tedd, illus. 2001. 32p. (J). (ps-3). pap. 5.95 (978-0-06-441033-5(1) , Harper Trophy) HarperCollins Pubs.

Glocke, Robin. Tiny Fish. 2006. 56p. pap. 12.95 (978-1-4241-3777-0(2)) PublishAmerica, Inc.

Goldblatt, Stacey. Stray. 2007. 288p. (YA). (gr. 7-10). 15.99 (978-0-385-73443-1(3)); lib. bdg. 18.99 (978-0-385-90448-3(7)) Random Hse. Children's Bks. (Delacorte Bks. for Young Readers).

Gomes, Filomena. My Mom Loves Me More Than Sushi. Spires, Ashley, illus. 2006. 24p. (J). pap. (***978-1-897187-13-5(0))*** Second Story Pr.

—My Mom Loves Me More Than Sushi. Spires, Ashley, illus. 2006. 32p. (J). 12.95 (978-1-897187-09-8(2)) Second Story Pr. CAN. *Dist:* Orca Bk. Pubs. USA.

Gray, Dianne. Holding up the Earth. 2006. 224p. (J). (gr. 5-9). pap. 6.95 (978-0-618-73747-5(2)) Houghton Mifflin Co. Trade & Reference Div.

Gray, Kes. Eat Your Peas: A Daisy Book. Sharratt, Nick, illus. 2006. 32p. (J). (ps-1). 10.95 (978-0-8109-5974-3(7)) Abrams, Harry N. , Inc.

Gray, Kes. 006 & a Half: A Daisy Book. Sharratt, Nick, illus. 2007. 32p. (J). (ps-1). 10.95 (***978-0-8109-1719-4(X)*** , Abrams Bks. for Young Readers) Abrams, Harry N. , Inc.

Gray, Libba Moore. My Mama Had a Dancing Heart. Colon, Raul, illus. 2001. pap. 35.95 incl. audio compact disk (978-1-59112-543-3(X)) Live Oak Media.

Grove, Vicki. Rhiannon. 2007. 224p. (YA). (gr. 5). 18.99 (***978-0-399-23633-4(3)*** , Putnam Juvenile) Penguin Group (USA) Inc.

Guest, Jacqueline. Dream Racer. 2006. (SideStreets Ser.). 136p. (YA). (gr. 7-12). (***978-1-55028-945-9(4));*** 7.95 (***978-1-55028-942-8(X))*** Lorimer, James & Co., Ltd., Pubs. CAN. *Dist:* Casemate Pubs. & Bk. Distributors, LLC.

Hacker, Randi. Life As I Knew It. 2006. 240p. (J). pap. 6.99 (978-1-4169-0995-8(8) , Simon Pulse) Simon & Schuster Children's Publishing.

Hagood, Kawanna. Chores to Do. 2007. 11.95 (***978-1-59526-684-2(4))*** Media Creations, Inc.

Hahn, Mary Downing. Deep & Dark & Dangerous: A Ghost Story. 2007. 192p. (J). (gr. 5-9). 16.00 (***978-0-618-66545-7(5)*** , Clarion Bks.) Houghton Mifflin Co. Trade & Reference Div.

Hahn, Mary Downing. Tallahassee Higgins. 2007. 192p. (J). pap. 6.95 (978-0-618-75246-1(3) , Clarion Bks.) Houghton Mifflin Co. Trade & Reference Div.

Hamilton, Deborah E. Why are You my Mother? A Mother's Response to Her Adopted Daughter. Andrules, Jamie L., illus. 2006. (J). 9.99 net. (978-0-9789202-0-3(1)) Dreams Due Media Group, Inc.

Harmel, Kristin. When You Wish. 2008. 288p. (J). (***978-0-385-73475-2(1)*** , Delacorte Pr.) Dell Publishing.

Hasquet, DeAnn. The Teeny Tiny Penny. 2000. 10p. (J). pap. 8.99 (978-1-930673-00-7(0)) Childhood Friends, Inc.

Haydel, Catherine. Uno the Cat & Hurricane Katrina. 2006. 18.00 (978-0-8059-7341-9(9)) Dorrance Publishing Co., Inc.

Hayes-Knoll, Carolyn. Ista Cante. 2004. (Illus.). 32p. (J). (978-0-9755646-6-0(8)) Westview Publishing Co., Inc.

Headley, Justina Chen. Nothing but the Truth (And a Few White Lies) 2006. 256p. (J). (gr. 5-9). 16.99 (978-0-316-01128-0(2)) Little Brown & Co.

—Nothing but the Truth (And a Few White Lies) 2007. 256p. (J). (gr. 7 up). pap. 7.99 (***978-0-316-01131-0(2))*** Little, Brown Bks. for Young Readers.

Henig, Sherry. Sara Makes Her Mother Proud & Learns Good Behavior: A Children's Book. 2nd ed. 2006. per. 6.95 (978-0-9777203-2-3(2)) Brenner Publishing, LLC.

Hernandez, Jo Ann Yolanda. The Throw-Away Piece. 246p. (Orig.). (YA). pap. 9.95 (978-1-55885-353-9(7) , Piñata Books) Arte Publico Pr.

Hines, Thomas, illus. The Bubble Machine. l.t. ed. 2003. 26p. (J). per. (978-1-887636-02-5(1)) Creative Writing & Publishing Co.

Hoffman, Alice. The Foretelling. (J). (gr. 8-17). 2005. 176p. 16.99 (978-0-316-01018-4(9)); 2006. 192p. reprint ed. pap. 7.99 (978-0-316-15409-3(1)) Little Brown & Co.

—The Foretelling. l.t. ed. 2006. 156p. 23.95 (978-0-7862-8285-2(1)) Thorndike Pr.

Howie, Betsy. The Block Mess Monster. Decker, Cynthia B., illus. 2008. 32p. (J). 16.95 (***978-0-8050-7940-1(8))*** Holt, Henry & Co.

Hysen, Sylvia. A Very Dairy Christmas. 2005. 312p. (YA). 24.95 (978-0-9763365-6-3(1)) 1st Impression Publishing.

Ibbotson, Eva. The Star of Kazan. 2006. (Illus.). 416p. (J). (gr. 3). reprint ed. 6.99 (978-0-14-240582-6(5) , Puffin) Penguin Group (USA) Inc.

Jacobs, John. I Wanna Be. 2006. (Illus.). 144p. 9.95 (978-0-9774659-6-5(9)) Cameo Pubns., LLC.

Jahn-Clough, Lisa. Me, Penelope. 2007. 208p. (YA). (gr. 7 up). 16.00 (***978-0-618-77366-4(5)*** , Walter Lorraine) Houghton Mifflin Co. Trade & Reference Div.

Jalonen, Riitta. Tundra Mouse Mountain. Ledgard, J. M., tr. Louhi, Kristiina, illus. 2006. (Picture books from around the World Seri Ser.). 56p. (J). 19.95 (978-1-905341-05-4(9)) WingedChariot Pr. GBR. *Dist:* Independent Pubs. Group.

Jocelyn, Marthe. How It Happened in Peach Hill. 2007. 240p. (J). (gr. 7 up). 15.99 (978-0-375-83701-2(9)); lib. bdg. 18.99 (978-0-375-93701-9(3)) Random Hse. Children's Bks. (Lamb, Wendy).

Johns, Linda. Hannah West & the Belltown Towers. 2006. (Hannah West Mystery Ser.). 176p. (J). (gr. 5). pap. 5.99 (978-0-14-240637-3(6) , Puffin) Penguin Group (USA) Inc.

Johnson, Catherine. Face Value. 2006. 256p. (YA). 16.95 (978-0-8027-8920-4(X)) Walker & Co.

Johnson, D. C. & Turner, Sandra. Let's Be Friends. Johnson, D. C. & Johnson, Darnell, illus. 2007. (J). per. 9.95 (***978-1-933556-66-6(8))*** Publishers' Graphics, L.L.C.

Jones, Patrick. Things Change. 2006. 228p. (J). reprint ed. pap. 7.95 (978-0-8027-7746-1(5)) Walker & Co.

Katies Choice. 2005. (YA). per. (978-1-59872-217-8(4)) Instantpublisher.com.

Katschke, Judy. I Love My Mami! Aikins, Dave, illus. 2006. (Dora the Explorer Ser.: No. 9). 24p. (J). pap. 3.99 (978-1-4169-0650-6(9) , Simon Spotlight/Nickelodeon) Simon & Schuster Children's Publishing.

Klam, Cheryl. Learning to Swim. 2007. 224p. (YA). (gr. 7). pap. 8.99 (978-0-385-73372-4(0)); lib. bdg. 13.99 (978-0-385-90387-5(1)) Random Hse. Children's Bks. (Delacorte Bks. for Young Readers).

Knight. Dead Beckoning. (Thumbprint Mysteries Ser.). 32.86 (978-0-8092-0421-2(5)) McGraw-Hill/Contemporary.

Koja, Kathe. The Blue Mirror. 2006. 128p. (YA). (gr. 8). pap. 6.99 (978-0-14-240693-9(7) , Puffin) Penguin Group (USA) Inc.

Komaiko, Leah. Malibu Carmie. 2007. 256p. (YA). (gr. 7-11). mass mkt. 5.99 (978-0-440-42014-9(8) , Laurel Leaf) Random Hse. Children's Bks.

Korelitz, Jean Hanff. Interference Powder. 2006. 144p. (J). pap. 5.95 (978-0-7614-5275-1(3)) Cavendish, Marshall Corp.

Krisher, Trudy B. Kinship. 1999. (J). (978-0-606-16170-1(8)) Tandem Library Bks.

Krosoczka, Jarrett J. Giddy up Cowgirl. 2006. (Illus.). 40p. (J). 15.99 (978-0-670-06050-4(X) , Viking Juvenile) Penguin Group (USA) Inc.

LaLumiere, Michael & Messinger, Kim. Princess Caitlin's Tiara. 2006. 21.81 (***978-1-4116-0926-6(3))*** Lulu.com.

Lappin, Amber. My, You Have Your Hands Full! Galey, Chuck, illus. 2000. 16p. (J). pap. 5.95 (978-1-891846-21-2(3)) Business Word, The.

Lasky, Kathryn. Before I Was Your Mother. Pham, LeUyen, illus. 2007. 40p. (J). pap. 6.00 (978-0-15-205842-5(7) , Voyager Bks./Libros Viajeros) Harcourt Children's Bks.

Lautanen, Michelle. Mom, What If I Swallowed an Icecube? A Humorous Tale of Worst Aid. l.t. ed. 2006. (Illus.). 25p. (J). per. 14.95 (978-1-933324-38-8(4)) Cedar Hill Publishing.

Leavitt, Caroline. Girls in Trouble: A Novel. 2005. 368p. pap. 13.95 (978-0-312-33973-9(9) , St. Martin's Paperbacks) St. Martin's Pr.

Lee, P. Janet. Ella Elephant: And Her Fear of Mice. 2007. (ENG., Illus.). 36p. (J). per. 15.95 (***978-1-59800-713-8(0))*** Outskirts Press, Inc.

Leonard Marcia. Mi día de campamento (My Camp-Out) 2007. (Lecturas para niños de verdad - Nivel 1 (Real Kids Readers - Level 1) Ser.). (J). pap. 5.95 (***978-0-8225-7798-0(4)*** , Ediciones Lerner) Lerner Publishing Group.

Love, D. Anne. Semiprecious. 2006. 304p. (J). (gr. 5-9). 16.95 (978-0-689-85638-9(5) , McElderry, Margaret K.) Simon & Schuster Children's Publishing.

Lyon, George Ella. No Dessert Forever! Catalanotto, Peter, illus. 2006. 40p. (J). (gr. k-4). 16.95 (978-1-4169-0385-7(2) , Atheneum/Richard Jackson Bks.) Simon & Schuster Children's Publishing.

MacCready, Robin. Buried. 2006. 208p. (YA). (gr. 9). 16.99 (978-0-525-47724-2(1) , Dutton Juvenile) Penguin Group (USA) Inc.

Mackall, Dandi Daley. Grace under Pressure. 2007. (Faithgirlz!#8482; / Blog On! Ser.). 128p. (J). pap. 6.99 (978-0-310-71263-3(7)) Zonderkidz.

Madison, Bennett. Lulu Dark & the Summer of the Fox. 2007. 208p. (YA). (gr. 7-12). 5.99 (978-1-59514-154-5(5) , Razorbill) Penguin Group (USA) Inc.

Mahy, Margaret. The Catalogue of the Universe. Hopes, illus. 2002. 192p. (YA). pap. 7.99 (978-0-689-85353-1(X) , Simon Pulse) Simon & Schuster Children's Publishing.

Makhijani, Pooja. Mama's Saris. Gomez, Elena, illus. 2007. 32p. (J). (ps-1). 16.99 (978-0-316-01105-1(3)) Little Brown & Co.

Marlow, Herb. A Long Way Home. l.t. ed. 2003. (Illus.). 14p. (J). 19.95 (978-1-893595-35-4(8)) Four Seasons Bks., Inc.

Mathews, Eleanor. The Linden Tree. 2007. 224p. (J). pap. 6.95 (***978-1-57131-674-5(4));*** (gr. 3-6). 16.95 (***978-1-57131-673-8(6))*** Milkweed Editions.

Maury, Inez. My Mother the Mail Carrier - Mi Mama la Cartera. Alemany, Norah, tr. from SPA. McCrady, Lady, illus. 2004. (ENG & SPA.). 32p. (ps-4). pap. 7.95 (978-0-935312-23-2(4)) Feminist Pr. at The City Univ. of New York.

Mazer, Norma Fox. Missing Pieces. 2007. (Illus.). 160p. (YA). pap. 6.95 (978-0-15-206271-2(8) , Harcourt Paperbacks) Harcourt Children's Bks.

McDonald, Janet. Off-Color. 2007. 176p. (YA). (gr. 7 up). 16.00 (***978-0-374-37196-8(2))*** Farrar, Straus & Giroux.

McElreath, Kim. Pouring in Love. l.t. ed. 2005. (Illus.). 30p. (J). 13.95 (978-0-9769271-0-5(1)) McElreath, K.M.

McElroy, Lisa Tucker. Love, Lizzie: Letters to a Military Mom. Paterson, Diane, illus. 2005. 32p. (J). (gr. k-3). lib. bdg. 15.95 (978-0-8075-4777-9(8)) Whitman, Albert & Co.

McFarlane, Sheryl. The Smell of Paint. 2006. 192p. (YA). (gr. 7 up). pap. (***978-1-55041-457-8(7))*** Fitzhenry & Whiteside, Ltd.

McGrath, Liz & Quick, Barbara. Even More/Todavía Mas. de la Vega, Eida, tr. McGrath, Liz, illus. 2004. Tr. of Todavía Mas. (SPA & ENG., Illus.). 34p. (J). (gr. k-3). 16.95 (978-0-9720192-8-6(6) , 626999) Raven Tree Pr.

Melling, O. R. The Light-Bearer's Daughter. 2007. (Chronicles of Faerie Ser.). (Illus.). 304p. (J). (gr. 2-8). 16.95 (***978-0-8109-0781-2(X)*** , Amulet Bks.) Abrams, Harry N. , Inc.

Mooney, Bel, selected by. You Never Did Learn to Knock: 14 Stories about Girls & Their Mothers. 2006. 256p. (J). (gr. 5-9). pap. 7.95 (978-0-7534-5877-8(2) , Kingfisher) Houghton Mifflin Co. Trade & Reference Div.

Morales, Yuyi. Little Night. 2007. (Illus.). 32p. (J). (ps-3). 16.95 (978-1-59643-088-4(5)) Roaring Brook Pr.

Morales, Yuyi. Nochecita. 2007. (SPA., Illus.). 32p. (J). (ps-3). 16.95 (***978-1-59643-232-1(2))*** Roaring Brook Pr.

Myers, Anna. Confessions from the Principal's Chair. 2006. 192p. 16.95 (978-0-8027-9560-1(9)) Walker & Co.

Na, An. Wait for Me. 2007. 192p. (YA). (gr. 7 up). 7.99 (***978-0-14-240918-3(9)*** , Puffin) Penguin Group (USA) Inc.

Napoli, Donna Jo. Zel. 2005. 240p. (J). (gr. 5-9). 21.00 (978-0-8446-7278-6(5) , 3593) Smith, Peter Pub., Inc.

Nation, Kay. Jamie Learns to Love. 2006. pap. 10.00 (***978-1-4257-0534-3(0))*** Xlibris Corp.

Nelson, R. A. Breathe My Name. 2007. 288p. (J). (gr. 7). 16.99 (***978-1-59514-094-4(8)*** , Razorbill) Penguin Group (USA) Inc.

Nickles, Clay & Ayres, Ella. Ali's Treasure. l.t. ed. 2005. (Illus.). 38p. (J). per. 16.95 (978-1-59879-006-1(4)) Lifevest Publishing, Inc.

Nimmo, Jenny. Griffin's Castle. 2007. 288p. (J). 16.99 (***978-0-439-02554-6(0)*** , Orchard Bks.) Scholastic, Inc.

Noble, Sheilagh. More! 2000. (Toddler Ser.). (Illus.). 24p. (J). (ps up). 9.95 (978-1-84089-127-0(0) , Zero to Ten, Limited) Evans Publishing Group GBR. *Dist:* Independent Pubs. Group.

Noyes, Deborah. Angel & the Apostle. 2006. 304p. pap. 14.95 (978-1-932961-29-4(1)) Unbridled Bks.

O'Brien, Claudia Moore. My Mom's Apron. Friar, Joanne, illus. 2005. 12p. (J). pap. 5.00 (978-1-57274-753-1(6) , 2772, Bks. for Young Learners) Owen, Richard C. Pubs., Inc.

Olsen, Roberta. Royal Pains 2: The Seventh Dwarf. 2002. pap. 10.95 (978-1-59088-968-8(1)) Wings ePress, Inc.

Olson, Gretchen. Call Me Hope. 2007. 288p. (J). (gr. 3-7). 15.99 (***978-0-316-01236-2(X))*** Little Brown & Co.

—Call Me Hope: A Novel. 2007. 272p. (J). (***978-1-4287-4131-7(3))*** Little Brown & Co.

One Last Garden. 2006. (J). per. 10.95 (978-1-933505-20-6(6)) Authors' Pr., The.

Paratore, Coleen Murtagh. The Wedding Planner's Daughter. 2006. (Wedding Planner's Daughter Ser.). 208p. (J). reprint ed. pap. 5.99 (978-1-4169-1854-7(X) , Aladdin) Simon & Schuster Children's Publishing.

Pascal, Francine. Falsas Apariencias. Orig. Title: Jumping to Conclusions. (SPA., Illus.). 128p. (J). 6.95 (978-84-272-3794-0(4)) Molino, Editorial ESP. *Dist:* AIMS International Bks., Inc.

Paul, Dominique. The Possibility of Fireflies. 224p. 2007. (YA). pap. 8.99 (***978-1-4169-1311-5(4)*** , Simon Pulse); 2006. (J). 15.95 (978-1-4169-1310-8(6)) Simon & Schuster Children's Publishing.

Pearce, Emily Smith. Isabel & the Miracle Baby. 2007. 144p. (YA). (gr. 3 up). 15.95 (***978-1-932425-44-4(6)*** , Front Street) Boyds Mills Pr.

Porter, James G. Edge of the Rainforest. (Illus.). 180p. pap. 11.95 (978-0-7022-2350-1(6)) Univ. of Queensland Pr. AUS. *Dist:* International Specialized Bk. Services.

Poston, Karen. A Baby for Mabel & Frederick. 2005. 20p. (J). 11.28 (978-1-4116-6024-3(2)) Lulu.com.

Pullman, Philip. Le Miroir d'Ambre. (FRE.). pap. 18.95 (978-2-07-054376-2(5)) Gallimard, Editions FRA. *Dist:* Distribooks, Inc.

Rahlens, Holly-Jane. Prince William, Maximilian Minsky, & Me. (YA). (gr. 7-11). 2007. 320p. pap. 7.99 (***978-0-7636-3299-1(6));*** 2005. 160p. 16.99 (978-0-7636-2704-1(6)) Candlewick Pr.

Rayban, Chloë. Hollywood Bliss: My Life So Far. 2007. 288p. (J). 16.95 (***978-1-59990-093-3(9))*** Bloomsbury Publishing.

Rayban, Chloe. Hollywood Bliss: My Life Starring Mum. 2007. 304p. (J). pap. 7.95 (***978-1-59990-097-1(1)*** , Bloomsbury Children) Bloomsbury Publishing.

Rayban, Chloe. My Life Starring Mum. 2006. 250p. (J). 16.95 (978-1-58234-713-4(1) , Bloomsbury Children) Bloomsbury Publishing.

Robberecht, Thierry. Back into Mommy's Tummy. Goossens, Philippe, illus. 2005. 32p. (J). (ps-k). 15.00 (978-0-618-58106-1(5) , Clarion Bks.) Houghton Mifflin Co. Trade & Reference Div.

Rodgers, Mary. Freaky Friday. 2005. 176p. (YA). (gr. 5-9). 21.25 (978-0-8446-7273-1(4) , 3588) Smith, Peter Pub., Inc.

Ryder, Joanne. My Mother's Voice. Catalanotto, Peter, illus. 2006. 32p. (J). 15.99 (978-0-06-029509-7(0)); lib. bdg. 17.89 (978-0-06-029510-3(4)) HarperCollins Pubs.

Satterfield, Barbara. Answer Why for Mee Mee. 2004. (Illus.). 32p. (J). pap. 11.50 (978-0-9748715-1-6(6) , 314-004) Vision Harmony Publishing.

Sauer, Tammi. Dear Jack. 2004. 164p. (YA). mass mkt. 6.99 ***(978-0-9753367-0-0(3))*** Onstage Publishing, LLC.

Sharenow, Robert. My Mother the Cheerleader. 2007. 304p. (gr. 7 up). (J). lib. bdg. 17.89 (978-0-06-114897-2(0)); (YA). 16.99 (978-0-06-114896-5(2)) HarperCollins Pubs. (Geringer, Laura Book).

Shaw, Susan. Black-Eyed Suzie. 2007. 176p. (YA). pap. 9.95 ***(978-1-59078-533-1(9)*** , Front Street) Boyds Mills Pr.

Siebold, Jan. My Nights at the Improv. 2005. 98p. (YA). (gr. 6-9). lib. bdg. 14.95 (978-0-8075-5630-6(0)) Whitman, Albert & Co.

Silverthorne, Judith. The Secret of the Stone House. 2006. (From Many Peoples Ser.). (Illus.). 192p. (J). pap. 7.95 (978-1-55050-325-8(1)) Coteau Bks. CAN. *Dist:* F & W Pubns., Inc.

Simner, Janni Lee. Secret of the Three Treasures. 2005. 160p. (J). 16.95 (978-0-8234-1914-2(2)) Holiday Hse., Inc.

Snyder, Laurel. Up & down the Scratchy Mountains, or, the Search for a Suitable Princess. Dorman, Brandon, illus. 2008. (J). ***(978-0-375-84719-6(7))***; lib. bdg. ***(978-0-375-94719-3(1))*** Random Hse., Inc.

Sorrells, Walter. Club Dread. (Hunted Ser.). 272p. (YA). 2007. (gr. 7). 7.99 ***(978-0-14-240904-6(9)*** , Puffin); 2006. (gr. 6-10). 10.99 (978-0-525-47618-4(0) , Dutton Juvenile) Penguin Group (USA) Inc.

—Fake ID. 2005. (Hunted Ser.: 1). 192p. (YA). (gr. 6). 12.99 (978-0-525-47514-9(1) , Dutton Juvenile) Penguin Group (USA) Inc.

—Fake ID: A Mystery. 2007. (Hunted Ser.). 336p. (YA). (gr. 7 up). pap. 6.99 (978-0-14-240762-2(3) , Puffin) Penguin Group (USA) Inc.

Springer, Nancy. Dusssie. 2007. 176p. (J). (gr. 5-9). 16.95 ***(978-0-8027-9649-3(4))*** Walker & Co.

Sproule, Gail. Singing in Dark. Lott, Sheena, illus. 2006. 32p. pap. 7.95 (978-1-55041-348-9(1)) Fitzhenry & Whiteside, Ltd. CAN. *Dist:* F & W Pubns., Inc.

Stauffacher, Sue. Harry Sue. 2007. 304p. (J). (gr. 3-7). pap. 6.50 (978-0-440-42064-4(4) , Yearling) Random Hse. Children's Bks.

Stone, Jade. Whispering Willow Woods. 2005. 73p. pap. 14.95 (978-1-4137-4264-0(5)) PublishAmerica, Inc.

Stratton Porter, Gene. A Girl of the Limberlost. 2006. 336p. (YA). 21.95 ***(978-1-934169-30-8(7))***; pap. 10.95 ***(978-1-934169-31-5(5))*** Norilana Bks.

Stratton-Porter, Gene. A Girl of the Limberlost. Benda, Wladyslaw T., illus. 2005. reprint ed. pap. 38.95 (978-0-7661-9424-3(8)) Kessinger Publishing, LLC.

Sweeney, Joyce. Waiting for June. 2006. 160p. 5.99 (978-0-7614-5329-1(6)) Cavendish, Marshall Corp.

Taylor-Butler, Christine. A Mom Like No Other. Devard, Nancy, illus. 2004. 32p. (J). lib. bdg. 15.00 ***(978-1-4242-0227-0(2))*** Fitzgerald Bks.

Toten, Teresa. Bright Red Kisses. Betteridge, Deirdre, illus. 2005. 32p. (J). (ps-k). pap. 7.95 (978-1-55037-908-2(9)); lib. bdg. 19.95 (978-1-55037-909-9(7)) Annick Pr., Ltd. CAN. *Dist:* Firefly Bks., Ltd.

Tracey, Rhian. True Colours. 2007. 272p. (J). pap. 11.95 ***(978-0-7475-8941-9(0))*** Bloomsbury Publishing Plc GBR. *Dist:* Independent Pubs. Group.

Train, Mary. Time for the Fair. Hayes, Karel, illus. 2005. (ps). 15.95 (978-0-89272-694-3(6)) Down East Bks.

Triana, Gaby. Cubanita. 2006. 208p. (J). pap. 7.99 (978-0-06-056022-5(3)) HarperCollins Pubs.

Trotter, Deborah W. How Do You Know? Downing, Julie, illus. 2006. 32p. (J). (ps-k). 16.00 (978-0-618-46343-5(7) , Clarion Bks.) Houghton Mifflin Co. Trade & Reference Div.

Trueit, Trudi. Julep O' Toole: Miss Independent. 2006. (Illus.). 160p. (J). (gr. 3). 15.99 (978-0-525-47637-5(7) , Dutton Juvenile) Penguin Group (USA) Inc.

—Julep O' Toole: Miss Independent: Miss Independent. 2007. 176p. (J). 5.99 (978-0-14-240829-2(8) , Puffin) Penguin Group (USA) Inc.

—Julep O'Toole: What I Really Want to Do Is Direct. 2007. 160p. (J). (gr. 3 up). 16.99 (978-0-525-47781-5(0) , Dutton Juvenile) Penguin Group (USA) Inc.

Tuminelly, Nancy. Horse Shoes. Nobens, C. A., illus. 2006. (Fact & Fiction Ser.). 24p. (J). pap. (978-1-59679-944-8(7)) ABDO Publishing Co.

V., Patti. My Na Na Stories. 2005. 18.00 (978-0-8059-9806-1(3)) Dorrance Publishing Co., Inc.

Van Draanen, Wendelin. Sammy Keyes & the Hollywood Mummy. VanDraanen, Wendelin, illus. 2001. (Sammy Keyes Ser.: Bk. 6). pap. 36.95 incl. audio (978-0-87499-800-9(X)); pap. 54.95 incl. audio compact disk (978-0-87499-868-9(9)) Live Oak Media.

Van Etten, David. Likely Story (Book 1) 2008. (Likely Story Ser.). 208p. (J). (gr. 7). 15.99 ***(978-0-375-84676-2(X))***; lib. bdg. 18.99 ***(978-0-375-94676-9(4))*** Random Hse. Children's Bks. (Knopf Bks. for Young Readers).

van Genechten, Guido. Kangaroo Christine. van Genechten, Guido, illus. 2006. (Illus.). 32p. (J). 6.95 (978-1-58925-396-4(5) , tiger tales) ME Media LLC.

Vande Velde, Vivian. The Book of Mordred. 2005. (Illus.). 352p. (YA). (gr. 7-7). 18.00 (978-0-618-50754-2(X)) Houghton Mifflin Co. Trade & Reference Div.

Vander Zee, Ruth. Always with You. Himler, Ronald, illus. 2008. (J). ***(978-0-8028-5295-3(5)*** , Eerdmans Bks For Young Readers) Eerdmans, William B. Publishing Co.

Vejjajiva, Jane. The Happiness of Kati. Borthwick, Prudence, tr. from THA. 2006. 144p. (J). (gr. 6-8). 15.95 (978-1-4169-1788-5(8) , Atheneum) Simon & Schuster Children's Publishing.

Velde, Vivian Vande. The Book of Mordred. 2007. 352p. (YA). (gr. 7). pap. 8.99 ***(978-0-618-80916-5(3)*** , Graphia) Houghton Mifflin Co. Trade & Reference Div.

Vescovi, Laura A. Good Morning Sleepyhead. 2004. 15.95 (978-0-9763219-0-3(4)) Vescori, Laura.

Vidal, Clara. Like a Thorn. Maudet, Y., tr. 2008. 128p. (J). (gr. 9). 14.99 ***(978-0-385-73564-3(2)*** , Delacorte Bks. for Young Readers) Random Hse. Children's Bks.

Vita. Head in the Clouds. 2004. (Illus.). 108p. pap. 44.50 (978-0-9760062-0-6(0)) Magic Woman Pubns.

Wargin, Kathy-Jo. A Mother's Wish. Roman, Irena, illus. 2006. 32p. (J). 15.99 (978-0-06-057170-2(5)); lib. bdg. 16.89 (978-0-06-057171-9(3)) HarperCollins Pubs.

Weatherly, Lee. Breakfast at Sadie's. 208p. (gr. 7). 2008. (YA). mass mkt. 6.99 ***(978-0-440-24069-3(7)*** , Laurel Leaf); 2006. (J). 15.95 (978-0-385-75094-3(3) , Fickling, David Bks.); 2006. (J). lib. bdg. 17.99 (978-0-385-75095-0(1) , Fickling, David Bks.) Random Hse. Children's Bks.

Weber, Lori. Tattoo Heaven. 2005. (SideStreets Ser.). 168p. (YA). (gr. 7-12). ***(978-1-55028-903-9(9))***; 7.95 (978-1-55028-902-2(0)) Lorimer, James & Co., Ltd., Pubs. CAN. *Dist:* Casemate Pubs. & Bk. Distributors, LLC.

Weeks, Sarah. So B. It. 2005. 272p. (J). pap. 6.99 (978-0-06-441047-2(1) , Harper Trophy) HarperCollins Pubs.

Wells, Christine. Scandal's Daughter. 2007. 304p. (YA). (gr. 12). pap. 6.99 ***(978-0-425-21832-7(5)*** , Berkley) Penguin Group (USA) Inc.

Wels, Barbara. Finwood & Lisa. 144p. pap. 11.95 (978-0-7022-2502-4(9)) Univ. of Queensland Pr. AUS. *Dist:* International Specialized Bk. Services.

Westerlund, Kate. Sharing Christmas. Tharlet, Eve, illus. 2007. 32p. (J). (ps). 16.99 ***(978-0-698-40074-0(7)*** , Minedition) Penguin Group (USA) Inc.

White, Ellen Emerson. White House Autumn. 2008. (YA). pap. 8.99 ***(978-0-312-37489-1(5))*** Feiwel & Friends.

Whittenberg, Allison. Life Is Fine. 2008. 192p. (YA). (gr. 7). 15.99 ***(978-0-385-73480-6(8)*** , Delacorte Bks. for Young Readers) Random Hse. Children's Bks.

Williams, Dar. Lights, Camera, Amalee. 2006. (Amalee Ser.: No. 2). 192p. (J). pap. 16.99 (978-0-439-80352-6(7) , Scholastic Pr.) Scholastic, Inc.

Williams, Lori Aurelia. Broken China. 2006. 336p. (YA). (gr. 7 up). reprint ed. mass mkt. 5.99 (978-1-4169-1618-5(0) , Simon Pulse) Simon & Schuster Children's Publishing.

Williams, Rozanne Lanczak. How Can I Get a Pet? Maio, Barbara & Faulkner, Stacey, eds. Reid, Mick, illus. 2006. (Learn to Write Ser.). (J). 8p. pap. (978-1-59198-290-6(1) , 6184); per. 4.99 ***(978-1-59198-363-7(0))*** Creative Teaching Pr., Inc.

Wilson, Jacqueline. The Illustrated Mum. 2006. 288p. (gr. 4-7). reprint ed. 5.50 (978-0-440-42043-9(1) , Yearling) Random Hse. Children's Bks.

Wittlinger, Ellen. Blind Faith. (YA). 2007. 304p. pap. 8.99 ***(978-1-4169-4906-0(2)*** , Simon Pulse); 2006. 288p. (gr. 7 up). 16.99 (978-1-4169-0273-7(2) , Simon & Schuster Children's Publishing) Simon & Schuster Children's Publishing.

Wollman, Jessica. Switched. 2007. 256p. (gr. 7). (J). lib. bdg. 18.99 (978-0-385-90410-0(X)); (YA). 15.99 (978-0-385-73396-0(8)) Random Hse. Children's Bks. (Delacorte Bks. for Young Readers).

Woodson, Jacqueline. Show Way. Talbott, Hudson, illus. 2005. 48p. (J). (ps). 16.99 (978-0-399-23749-2(6) , Putnam Juvenile) Penguin Group (USA) Inc.

Ye, Ting-Xing. Throwaway Daughter. 2004. 320p. mass mkt. 5.99 (978-0-7704-2921-8(1) , Seal Bks) Doubleday Canada, Ltd. CAN. *Dist:* Random Hse., Inc.

Zimmerman, Mary Joyce. Just Four. 2005. (Illus.). 32p. (ps-5). 2.70 (978-0-7399-2340-5(4) , 2779) Rod & Staff Pubs., Inc.

Zirin, David. My Name Is Erica Montoya de la Cruz. White, Deborah, illus. 2005. 16p. (J). pap. 5.00 (978-1-57274-732-6(3) , 2779, Bks. for Young Learners) Owen, Richard C. Pubs., Inc.

1. 2. 3 Happy Family. 2005. (J). bds. (978-0-9769910-2-1(0)) Terrific Twins LLC.

MOTHERS AND SONS

Mobley, Tracy. I Remember When. l.t. ed. 2006. (ENG., Illus.). 34p. (J). per. 7.95 (978-1-933300-04-7(3)) Wandering Sage Bookstore & More, LLC.

Sawyer, Louise. Jimmy. 2002. (YA). 6.95 (978-0-9719842-6-4(3)) Martin & Brothers.

—Jr @ the Cobbler Shop. 2001. (YA). spiral bd. 9.95 (978-0-9719842-7-1(1)) Martin & Brothers.

—Snakes & Hot Dogs. 2002. (YA). 7.95 (978-0-9719842-5-7(5)) Martin & Brothers.

MOTHERS AND SONS—FICTION

Alger, Horatio. Herbert Carter's Legacy. 2006. pap. ***(978-1-4065-0710-2(5))*** Dodo Pr.

Alger Jr. Horatio Staff. Andy Grants Pluck. rev. ed. 2006. 312p. 29.95 (978-1-4218-1762-0(4)); pap. 14.95 (978-1-4218-1862-7(0)) 1st World Publishing, Inc. (1st World Library - Literary Society).

—Do & Dare. rev. ed. 2006. 272p. 28.95 (978-1-4218-1757-6(8)); pap. 13.95 (978-1-4218-1857-3(4)) 1st World Publishing, Inc. (1st World Library - Literary Society).

—Herbert Carter's Legacy. rev. ed. 2006. 264p. 28.95 (978-1-4218-1756-9(X)); pap. 13.95 (978-1-4218-1856-6(6)) 1st World Publishing, Inc. (1st World Library - Literary Society).

Anderson, Jane. Inspector Insector. 2005. 22.00 ***(978-1-4108-4196-4(0))*** Benchmark Education Co.

Avi. Poppy's Return. Floca, Brian, illus. 2005. (Poppy Stories Ser.). 240p. (J). 15.99 (978-0-06-000012-7(0)) HarperCollins Pubs.

Banerjee, Anjali. The Silver Spell. Fiegenshuh, Emily, illus. 2005. (Knights of the Silver Dragon Ser.: Bk. 8). 174p. (J). ***(978-1-4156-1645-1(0)*** , Mirrorstone) Wizards of the Coast.

Beechen, Adam. Wish upon A Mom. Lapadula, Tom, illus. ed. 2005. (Fairly Odd Parents Ser.: 3). 24p. (J). lib. bdg. 15.00 (978-1-59054-807-3(8)) Fitzgerald Bks.

Bingham, Janet. Mommy's Little Star. 2008. (Barbie Fairytopia Ser.). 32p. (J). pap. 9.99 ***(978-0-545-03408-1(6)*** , Cartwheel Bks.) Scholastic, Inc.

Blackaby, Susan. Greg Gets a Hint. Trover, Zachary, illus. 2006. (Read-It! Readers Ser.). (J). 19.93 (978-1-4048-2411-9(1)) Picture Window Bks.

—New to Drew. Yi, Hye Won, illus. 2006. (Read-It! Readers Ser.). (J). 19.93 (978-1-4048-2417-1(0)) Picture Window Bks.

Blake, Jocelyn. Mama Is on an Airplane. Blake, Jocelyn, illus. ed. 2006. (Illus.). (J). per. 9.99 ***(978-0-9790572-0-5(5))*** Kreativ Kaos.

Bridwell, Norman. Clifford's Bedtime. 2008. (Naked Brothers Band Ser.). 10p. (J). pap. 6.99 ***(978-0-545-03513-2(9)*** , Cartwheel Bks.) Scholastic, Inc.

Broach, Elise. When Dinosaurs Came with Everything. Small, David, illus. 2007. (Junior Library Guild Selection Ser.). 40p. (J). (ps-2). 16.99 (978-0-689-86922-8(3)) Simon & Schuster Children's Publishing.

Cali, Davide. Piano Piano. Rivers, Randi, tr. from FRE. Héliot, Eric, illus. 2007. 28p. (J). (gr. 1-3). 15.95 ***(978-1-58089-191-2(8))*** Charlesbridge Publishing, Inc.

Cardenas, Teresa. Old Dog. Unger, David, tr. from SPA. 2007. 144p. (YA). (gr. 7 up). 16.95 ***(978-0-88899-757-9(4))*** Groundwood Bks. CAN. *Dist:* Perseus Distribution.

—Perro Viejo. Unger, David, tr. 2007. (SPA.). 144p. (gr. 7 up). 16.95 ***(978-0-88899-758-6(2))*** Groundwood Bks. CAN. *Dist:* Perseus Distribution.

Cole, Kenneth. No Bad News. Ruebartsch, John, photos by. 2001. (Illus.). 40p. (J). (gr. 2-6). pap. 7.95 (978-0-8075-5693-1(9)) Whitman, Albert & Co.

Coleman, Candace. Zubie the Lightning Bug - I Want to Remember Your Thoughts. ed. 2006. (J). 15.99 (978-0-9774998-0-9(4)) Parent Brigade Company, The.

Colfer, Eoin. Artemis Fowl: The Graphic Novel. Rigano, Giovanni & Lamanna, Paolo, illus. 2007. (Artemis Fowl Ser.). 112p. (gr. 5 up). 18.99 ***(978-0-7868-4881-2(2))*** Miramax Bks.

—Artemis Fowl: The Graphic Novel. Lamanna, Paolo, illus. 2007. (Artemis Fowl Ser.). 112p. (gr. 5 up). pap. 9.99 ***(978-0-7868-4882-9(0))*** Miramax Bks.

—Artemis Fowl Encuentro en el Artico: Encuentro en el Artico. 2005. (SPA., Illus.). 320p. (J). pap. 13.95 (978-0-307-34310-9(3) , Montena) Random House Mondadori ESP. *Dist:* Random Hse., Inc.

—El Cubo B. 2005. (Artemis Fowl Ser.: No. 3). (SPA., Illus.). 352p. (J). pap. 13.95 (978-0-307-34311-6(1) , Montena) Random House Mondadori ESP. *Dist:* Random Hse., Inc.

Corbett, Sue. Free Baseball. 160p. (J). (gr. 3). 2008. 5.99 ***(978-0-14-241080-6(2)*** , Puffin); 2006. 15.99 (978-0-525-47120-2(0) , Dutton Juvenile) Penguin Group (USA) Inc.

Cornish, Linda Sowa Young. Pong's Birthday Journey. 2006. (J). pap. 15.00 (978-0-8059-6993-1(4)) Dorrance Publishing Co., Inc.

D'Agata, Tabatha. Storm Tunes. Lineberger, Judy, illus. 2006. (Yes, I Can Read! Ser.: Bk. 2). 30p. (J). 6.95 ***(978-1-934138-02-1(9))*** Bouncing Ball Bks., Inc.

Deary, Terry. The Fire Thief Fights Back. 2007. (Fire Thief Ser.). 224p. (J). (gr. 5-7). 9.95 (978-0-7534-5970-6(1) , Kingfisher) Houghton Mifflin Co. Trade & Reference Div.

DeJong, Jennifer Bailey. Say Cheese! Loopstra, Esther Dawn, illus. 2006. 24p. (J). lib. bdg. ***(978-1-4048-2400-3(6))*** Picture Window Bks.

—Say Cheese ! 2007. (Illus.). 24p. (J). ***(978-1-4048-2430-0(8))*** Picture Window Bks.

DiCamillo, Jennifer. Big Boys Playing with Babies. 2007. 52p. (J). 10.00 ***(978-0-615-14240-1(0))*** Tree Pr.

Dodd, Emma. What Pet to Get? 2008. 32p. (J). pap. 16.99 ***(978-0-545-03570-5(8)*** , Levine, Arthur A. Bks.) Scholastic, Inc.

Donahue, Jill L. Rudy Helps Out. Previn, Stacey, illus. 2006. (Read-It! Readers Ser.). (J). 19.93 (978-1-4048-2420-1(0)) Picture Window Bks.

Downing, Julie. No Hugs till Saturday. 2008. (J). ***(978-0-618-91078-6(6)*** , Clarion Bks.) Houghton Mifflin Co. Trade & Reference Div.

Duksta, Laura. I Love You More. Keesler, Karen, illus. 2007. 34p. (J). (gr. 4-7). 16.99 ***(978-1-4022-1126-3(0)*** , Sourcebooks Jabberwocky) Sourcebooks, Inc.

Dye, Stacey. Twinship Is in Your Heart. Stubbs, Charles, illus. 2001. 16p. (J). pap. 5.95 (978-1-891846-24-3(8)) Business Word, The.

Edwards, Carol. Jacy Meets Betsy: Jacy's Search for Jesus Book II. Frey, Daniel, illus. 2006. 32p. (J). 15.95 (978-0-9755314-1-9(7)) Majestic Publishing, LLC.

Edwards, Richard. Un Lugar Seguro para Pequeno Mono/ Little Monkey's One Safe Place. Sarfatti, Esther, tr. Winter, Susan, illus. 2006. (ENG & SPA.). 32p. (J). (ps-1). 15.95 (978-1-84507-736-5(9)) Lincoln, Frances Ltd. GBR. *Dist:* Perseus Distribution.

Feiffer, Jules. I'm Not Bobby! Feiffer, Jules, illus. 2006. (Illus.). 28p. (J). (gr. k-4). reprint ed. 16.00 (978-0-7567-9853-6(1)) DIANE Publishing Co.

Fisher, Catherine. Corbenic. 2006. 288p. (J). 16.99 (978-0-06-072470-2(6) , Greenwillow Bks.) HarperCollins Pubs.

Fitch, Sheree. One More Step. 2006. (Orca Soundings Ser.). 112p. (YA). lib. bdg. 14.95 (978-1-55143-554-1(3)) Orca Bk. Pubs. USA.

Fogg, K. L. Serpent Tide. 2006. 16.95 (978-1-59156-861-2(7)) Covenant Communications, Inc.

Ford, J. One in Four. 2007. pap. ***(978-1-84747-173-4(0))*** Chipmunkapublishing.

French, Jackie. My Mom the Pirate. King, Stephen Michael, illus. 2007. (Funny Families Ser.). (J). (gr. 2-4). 107p. pap. 7.95 ***(978-1-59889-438-7(2))***; 112p. lib. bdg. 22.60 ***(978-1-59889-345-8(9))*** Stone Arch Bks.

Fullerton, Alma. Walking on Glass. 2007. 144p. (J). (gr. 9 up). 15.99 (978-0-06-077851-4(2)); lib. bdg. 16.89 (978-0-06-077852-1(0)) HarperCollins Pubs. (HarperTeen).

Goode, Diane. The Most Perfect Spot. Goode, Diane, illus. 2006. (Illus.). 32p. (J). lib. bdg. 17.89 (978-0-06-072698-0(9)); 16.99 (978-0-06-072697-3(0)) HarperCollins Pubs.

Grambling, Lois G. My Mom Is a Firefighter. Manning, Jane, illus. 2007. 32p. (J). (ps-3). 16.99 ***(978-0-06-058640-9(0))*** HarperCollins Pubs.

Gruber, Michael. The Witch's Boy. (gr. 6-9). 2006. 400p. (J). pap. 7.99 (978-0-06-076167-7(9)); 2005. 384p. (YA). 16.99 (978-0-06-076164-6(4)) HarperCollins Pubs. (HarperTeen).

—The Witch's Boy. l.t. ed. 2006. 448p. (YA). 22.95 (978-0-7862-8580-8(X)) Thorndike Pr.

Gutman, Dan. Abner & Me. 2007. (Baseball Card Adventures Ser.). 176p. (J). pap. 5.99 (978-0-06-053445-5(1) , Harper Trophy) HarperCollins Pubs.

Hall, Kirsten. At the Carnival. Rader, Laura, illus. 2003. 32p. (J). pap. 3.99 (978-0-439-59427-1(8) , Scholastic, Inc.) Scholastic, Inc.

Halpin, Brendan. How Ya Like Me Now. 2007. 208p. (YA). (gr. 7 up). 16.00 (978-0-374-33495-6(1)) Farrar, Straus & Giroux.

Halvorson, Marilyn. Let It Go. 2004. 224p. (YA). (gr. 7-9). (978-1-55005-105-6(9)) Fitzhenry & Whiteside, Ltd.

Hanington, John G. The Adventures of Quick Fox. 2006. 80p. pap. 9.95 ***(978-0-7414-3223-0(4))*** Infinity Publishing.

Hest, Amy. Don't You Feel Well, Sam? Jeram, Anita, illus. 2007. 32p. (J). (ps). pap. 4.99 (978-0-7636-2408-8(X)) Candlewick Pr.

Hill, Eric. Spot Loves His Mommy. Hill, Eric, illus. 2006. 12p. (J). (ps-k). bds. 5.99 (978-0-399-24511-4(1) , Putnam Juvenile) Penguin Group (USA) Inc.

Hiris, Monica. Just Like Mom. Sierra, Holly, illus. 2005. (J). pap. 4.95 (978-1-57874-088-8(6)) Kaeden Corp.

Hudson, Charlotte & McQuillan, Mary. Get Well Soon. Hudson, Charlotte & McQuillan, Mary, illus. 2007. (Illus.). 32p. (J). pap. 10.95 ***(978-0-09-943945-5(X)*** , Red Fox) Random Hse. Children's Bks. GBR. *Dist:* Independent Pubs. Group.

Hunter, S.C. The Little Cow in Valle Grande: El Becerrito en Valle Grande. Ritthaler, Sarah Pilcher, tr. from ENG. Sundstrom, Mary, illus. 2006. (SPA & ENG.). 32p. (J). (978-0-8263-4044-3(X)) Univ. of New Mexico Pr.

Jasper, J. J. When I Grow Up. Bullock, Brad, illus. 2003. 16p. (J). (978-0-9727279-8-3(1)) Pine Hill Graphics.

Jonell, Lynne. Mommy Go Away! 2000. (Illus.). (J). (978-0-606-22033-0(X)) Tandem Library Bks.

Jones, Christianne C. Caleb's Race. 2007. (Illus.). 24p. (J). ***(978-1-4048-1224-6(5))*** Picture Window Bks.

Judd, Christopher M. Bearable Moments. 2005. (J). 18.95 (978-0-9766666-1-5(8)) Arcadian Hse.

Judd-Leisten, Betty. Tell It for a Toll, Toll It for a Tale. 2005. 102p. per. 7.95 (978-1-59824-057-3(9)) E-BookTime LLC.

Karnowski, Anthony. Cameron & the Grim. 2006. 176p. pap. 13.95 (978-1-59113-919-5(8)) Booklocker.com, Inc.

Katz, Welwyn W. Out of the Dark. 2001. 185p. (J). (gr. 4) pap. 5.95 (978-0-88899-262-8(9)) Groundwood Bks. CAN. *Dist:* Perseus Distribution.

Kelley, Maria Felicia. Buz Words: Discovering Words in Pairs. Kelley, Maria Felicia, illus. 2006. (Illus.). 32p. (J). 14.95 (978-0-9650918-1-7(3)) April Arts Press & Productions.

Kern, Noris & Baronian, Jean-Baptiste. I Love You with All My Heart. 1998. (Illus.). 32p. (J). (ps-1). 15.95 (978-0-8118-2031-8(9)) Chronicle Bks. LLC.

King, Jennifer. A Bear for Breakfast. King, Jennifer, illus. 2007. (Illus.). 22p. (J). bds. 12.95 ***(978-0-7696-5258-0(1)*** , Gingham Dog Pr.) School Specialty Publishing.

Koertge, Ronald. Confess-O-Rama. 1998. (978-0-606-13291-6(0)) Tandem Library Bks.

—Where the Kissing Never Stops. 2005. 256p. (YA). (gr. 9 up). pap. 6.99 (978-0-7636-2696-9(1)); 2nd ed. 16.99 (978-0-7636-2543-6(4)) Candlewick Pr.

Landstrom, Olof & Landstrom, Lena. Will Goes to the Beach. Wilberg, Carla, tr. from SWE. Landstrom, Olof & Landstrom, Lena, illus. 2001. (Illus.). 28p. (J). (ps-1). pap. 4.95 (978-91-29-65305-2(3)) R & S Bks. SWE. *Dist:* Macmillan.

Lawrence, David L. The First Adventure of Geoffrey & Chongo. 2006. (ENG.). 40p. per. 16.99 ***(978-1-4259-6473-3(7))*** AuthorHouse.

Layefsky, Virginia. Impossible Things. 1998. (Accelerated Reader Bks.). 208p. (J). (gr. 5-9). 14.95 (978-0-7614-5038-2(6) , Cavendish Children's Bks.) Cavendish, Marshall Corp.

Lee, Huy Voun, ed. In the Snow. rev. ed. 2000. (Illus.). 32p. (J). (ps). pap. 7.95 (978-0-8050-6579-4(2) , Holt, Henry & Co. Bks. For Young Readers) Holt, Henry & Co.

Lee, Huy Youn, ed. In the Snow. 2000. (Illus.). (J). (ps-ps). lib. bdg. 15.25 (978-0-613-30516-7(7)) Tandem Library Bks.

Leonard, Marcia. Pantalones Nuevos, No! Handelman, Dorothy, photos by. 2005. Tr. of No New Pants!. (ENG & SPA., Illus.). 32p. (J). (ps-1). pap. 4.99 (978-0-8225-3297-2(2)) Lerner Publishing Group.

—Pantalones Nuevos, ¡No! Handelman, Dorothy, photos by. 2005. (Lecturas para Niños de Verdad (Real Kids Readers) Ser.). (SPA., Illus.). 32p. (J). (ps-1). pap. 4.99 (978-0-8225-3296-5(4) , Ediciones Lerner) Lerner Publishing Group.

Licciardi, Paula. Wasting Calvin's Time. 2006. 9.00 (978-0-8059-8138-4(1)) Dorrance Publishing Co., Inc.

Marcotte, David A. Be Wary of Strangers. 2005. (ENG., Illus.). 36p. per. 14.95 (978-1-932672-47-3(8)) Outskirts Press, Inc.

Marshall, Peter, et al. Nate Donovan: Revolutionary Spy. 2007. 208p. (J). pap. 9.99 (*978-0-8054-4394-3(0) , B&H Bks.) B&H Publishing Grp.

Masterson, Rebecca. Jesus & the Great Garbage War. 2008. 120p. (YA). pap. 14.99 (978-1-59092-393-1(6) , Blue Works) Windstorm Creative.

McClure, Brian D. The Bubble. 2006. (Illus.). 64p. (J). 14.95 (978-1-933426-05-1(5)) Universal Flag Publishing.

McKinty, Adrian. The Lighthouse Land. 2006. (Illus.). 200p. (YA). (gr. 6-10). 16.95 (978-0-8109-5480-9(X)) Abrams, Harry N. , Inc.

Mendes, Valerie. Coming of Age. 2004. 224p. (YA). pap. 8.99 (978-0-689-83772-2(0)) Simon & Schuster, Ltd. GBR. *Dist:* Independent Pubs. Group.

Miller, Lisa K. The Range of Light. 2005. (Illus.). 112p. (YA). pap. 11.95 (978-1-58736-538-6(3)) Wheatmark.

Millman, Selena. The Prince & Me. 2006. 146p. (YA). per. 11.20 (*978-1-4243-2353-1(3)) Independent Publisher Services.

Minarik, Else Holmelund. Osito. Sendak, Maurice, illus. 2003. (SPA.). 60p. (J). (gr. k-3). pap. 8.95 (978-84-204-3044-7(7) , AF1346) Santillana USA Publishing Co., Inc.

Mitchell, Mary Esther. The Adventures of Timmy Gills. 2005. (J). pap. 20.00 (978-0-8059-9660-9(5) , RoseDog Bks.) Dorrance Publishing Co., Inc.

Moon, Adam. The Fuzzle. 2007. (J). per. 7.95 (*978-1-934345-28-3(8)) SouthWest Pubns.

Morgenroth, Kate. Jude. 2006. (Illus.). 288p. (YA). reprint ed. mass mkt. 5.99 (978-1-4169-1267-5(3) , Simon Pulse) Simon & Schuster Children's Publishing.

Mowry, Jess. Skeleton Key. 2007. 280p. (YA). pap. 14.99 (978-1-59092-353-5(7) , Blue Works) Windstorm Creative.

—When All Goes Bright. 2007. 280p. (YA). pap. 14.99 (978-1-59092-361-0(8) , Blue Works) Windstorm Creative.

Neitzel, Shirley. I'm Taking a Trip on My Train. Parker, Nancy Winslow, illus. 1999. 40p. (J). (ps-3). 14.89 (978-0-688-15834-7(X)) HarperCollins Pubs.

Newton, Robert. Runner. 2007. 224p. (J). (gr. 5). lib. bdg. 18.99 (978-0-375-93744-6(7) , Knopf Bks. for Young Readers) Random Hse. Children's Bks.

Nicolas, Stephanie. A Forged Report Card. 2004. (J). pap. 8.00 (978-0-8059-6420-2(7)) Dorrance Publishing Co., Inc.

Olvera, Jillann. Christian's Lullaby. 2006. 29p. pap. 14.95 (978-1-4241-1909-7(X)) PublishAmerica, Inc.

Padwe, Phil. Mommy Has A Tattoo. Padwe, Phil, illus. 2006. (GER, ITA & SPA., Illus.). 22p. (J). 16.95 (978-0-9770232-7-1(3)) Mommy Has Tattoos.

Parazette, Joan. Aldo! Nascimbene, Yan, illus. 2006. (J). (978-1-56846-197-7(6) , Creative Editions) Creative Co., The.

Paulsen, Gary. The Glass Cafe: Or the Stripper & the State; How My Mother Started a War with the System That Made Us Kind of Rich & a Little Bit Famous. 2004. 112p. (J). (gr. 5). pap. 5.99 (978-0-440-23843-0(9) , Laurel Leaf) Random Hse. Children's Bks.

Penn, Audrey. Un Beso en Mi Mano. 2006. (SPA.). 32p. 16.95 (978-1-933718-01-9(3)) Tanglewood Pr.

Penn, Audrey. The Kissing Hand. 2007. 32p. (ps-3). 28.95 (*978-1-933718-07-1(2)); (J). pap. 9.95 incl. audio compact disk (*978-1-933718-10-1(2)) Tanglewood Pr.

Peters, Julie Anne. Between Mom & Jo. 2006. 240p. (J). (gr. 7-17). 16.99 (978-0-316-73906-1(5)) Little Brown & Co.

Powell, Randy. Tribute to Another Dead Rock Star. 224p. (YA). 2003. pap. 5.95 (978-0-374-47968-8(2) , Sunburst); 1999. (gr. 7-12). 17.00 (978-0-374-37748-9(0) , Farrar, Straus & Giroux (BYR)) Farrar, Straus & Giroux.

—Tribute to Another Dead Rock Star. l.t. ed. 2000. 224p. (J). 21.95 (978-0-7862-2191-2(7)) Thorndike Pr.

Price, Charlie. Lizard People. 2007. 192p. (YA). (gr. 7 up). 16.95 (*978-1-59643-190-4(3)) Roaring Brook Pr.

Prince Apple Head Humpledink. 2006. 38p. (J). 13.68 (978-1-4116-7232-1(1)) Lulu.com.

Ramthun, Bonnie. The White Gates. 2008. (J). (*978-0-375-84554-3(2)); pap. (*978-0-375-84555-0(0)); lib. bdg. (*978-0-375-94554-0(7)) Random Hse., Inc.

Richardson, Tom. Dominic Is Strong. 2005. (Illus.). 26p. (J). lib. bdg. 16.95 (978-1-932338-99-7(3)) Lifevest Publishing, Inc.

Ryan, Pam Muñoz. Yo, Naomi Leon. 2005. (SPA.). 272p. (J). (gr. 4-7). pap. 4.99 (978-0-439-75572-6(7) , Scholastic en Espanol) Scholastic, Inc.

Rylant, Cynthia. A Kindness. Date not set. (Sky Bks.). 104p. pap. 54.75 (978-0-582-08106-2(8)) Addison-Wesley Longman, Ltd. GBR. *Dist:* Trans-Atlantic Pubns., Inc.

Salan, Felipe Lopez, illus. Jack & the Beanstalk. 2006. 32p. (J). 16.50 (978-1-933327-12-9(X)) Purple Bear Bks., Inc.

Samuel, Lynette M. Mommy's Hat. Capps, Leigh, illus. 2005. (J). per. (978-0-9727703-3-0(X)) P.R.A. Publishing.

Sargent, Dave. Say You Love Me. Bowen, Debbie, ed. Lenoir, Jane, illus. 1998. 31p. (J). (gr. k-6). lib. bdg. 6.00 (978-1-56763-130-2(4)) Ozark Publishing.

Sawyer, Louise. The Barking Baby. 2001. (YA). spiral bd. 9.95 (978-0-9719842-2-6(0)) Martin & Brothers.

—Mother's Storybook Signs, Vol. 1. 2004. (YA). spiral bd. 19.95 (978-0-9719842-0-2(4)) Martin & Brothers.

Scraper, Katherine. The Yard Sale. 2006. (Early Explorers Ser.). (J). 30.00 (*978-1-4108-6043-9(4)) Benchmark Education Co.

Selfors, Suzanne. To Catch a Mermaid. Chien, Catia, illus. rev. ed. 2007. 254p. (J). (gr. 3-7). 14.99 (*978-0-316-01816-6(3)) Little, Brown Bks. for Young Readers.

Shaskan, Trisha Speed. Camden's Game. 2007. (Illus.). 24p. (J). (*978-1-4048-1226-0(1)) Picture Window Bks.

—Camden's Game. Yilmaz, Necdet, illus. 2006. 24p. (J). (*978-1-4048-3136-0(3)) Picture Window Bks.

Sidjanski, Brigitte. Mama's Favorite. Burg, Sarah, illus. 2008. 32p. (J). (ps-k). 16.99 (*978-0-698-40076-4(3) , Minedition) Penguin Group (USA) Inc.

Silberberg, Alan. Pond Scum. 2007. 288p. (gr. 3-7). pap. 5.99 (978-0-7868-5635-0(1)) Hyperion Pr.

Smith, Stephen D. & Caldwell, Lise. High Hurdles. 2006. 128p. (J). pap. 5.99 (978-0-7847-1439-3(8) , 42144) Standard Publishing.

Sullivan, Paula. Todd's Box. Westcott, Nadine Bernard, illus. 2004. 24p. (J). lib. bdg. 10.00 (*978-1-4242-0188-4(8)) Fitzgerald Bks.

Swain, Cynthia. No, Tim. 2006. (Early Explorers Ser.). (J). 30.00 (*978-1-4108-6029-3(9)) Benchmark Education Co.

Sweeney, Joyce. Headlock. 2006. 224p. (YA). 16.95 (978-0-8050-8018-6(X) , Holt, Henry & Co. Bks. For Young Readers) Holt, Henry & Co.

Thomas, Alease Allen. Bobby Jones of Beardsley Terrace. 2006. 18.00 (978-0-8059-9829-0(2)) Dorrance Publishing Co., Inc.

Thompson, Kate. Fourth World: Book One in the Missing Link Trilogy. 2006. 336p. (YA). pap. 7.95 (978-1-58234-897-1(9) , Bloomsbury Children) Bloomsbury Publishing.

Tinkham, Kelly. Hair for Mama. Bates, Amy June, illus. 2007. 32p. (J). (ps-3). 16.99 (978-0-8037-2955-1(3) , Dial) Penguin Group (USA) Inc.

Truly Blessed Ink. I Know You Won't Forget. Jordan, Carol, illus. 2007. (ENG.). 40p. (J). 16.95 (*978-0-9789066-1-0(6)) Square Circle Pr. LLC.

Trupin/Nascimbeni, Nick/Barbara. Sorry Sam. 2006. (Illus.). 32p. (J). lib. bdg. 9.00 (*978-1-4242-0884-5(X)) Fitzgerald Bks.

Turpin, Nick. Samuel, lo siento, Level P. NASCIMBENI, Barbara, illus. 2006. (Lightning Readers Ser.). 32p. (J). pap. 3.95 (978-0-7696-4216-1(0) , Gingham Dog Pr.) School Specialty Publishing.

Underwood, Deborah. Pirate Mom. Gilpin, Stephen, illus. 2006. (Step into Reading Ser.). 48p. (J). (gr. 1-3). lib. bdg. 11.99 (978-0-375-93323-3(9)); 3.99 (978-0-375-83323-6(4)) Random Hse. Children's Bks. (Random Hse. Bks. for Young Readers).

Ungerer, Tomi. Keine Kuss fur Mutler. 2000. Tr. of No Kiss for Mother. (GER.). (J). pap. 15.95 (978-3-257-25018-3(5)) Diogenes Verlag AG CHE. *Dist:* Distribooks, Inc.

Wahl, Mats. The Invisible. Tucker, Katarina E., tr. from SWE. 2007. 192p. (YA). (gr. 7 up). 16.00 (978-0-374-33609-7(1) , Farrar, Straus & Giroux (BYR)) Farrar, Straus & Giroux.

Walters, Celeste. Deception. 2005. 288p. (YA). pap. 18.95 (978-0-7022-3527-6(X)) Univ. of Queensland Pr. AUS. *Dist:* International Specialized Bk. Services.

Ward Appleton's Pancakes a Special Way. 2005. 10.95 (*978-0-9754779-6-0(X)) Chosen Word Publishing.

Weatherall, Barry. Jay & the Worm Save the Day. 2005. 40p. 14.28 (978-1-4116-4717-6(3)) Lulu.com.

Weiner, Brian. Toad Catchers' Creek. Weintraub, Claudia & Frederick, Robin, eds. Cannon, Martin, illus. 2005. 40p. (J). lib. bdg. 17.99 (978-1-932949-58-2(5)) Illusion Factory, The.

Williamson, Jennifer. Timmy the Tow Truck, 6 vols. Williamson, Alan, 8th, illus. 2005. 28p. (J). pap. (978-0-9771678-1-4(X)) Theee Hole Punch Publishing.

Willis, Jeanne. Cottonball Colin. Ross, Tony, illus. 2008. (J). (*978-0-8028-5331-8(5) , Eerdmans Bks For Young Readers) Eerdmans, William B. Publishing Co.

Wilson, N. D. Leepike Ridge. 2007. (Illus.). 240p. (J). (gr. 3-7). 15.99 (978-0-375-83873-6(2)); lib. bdg. 18.99 (978-0-375-93873-3(7)) Random Hse. Children's Bks. (Random Hse. Bks. for Young Readers).

—Leepike Ridge. 2007. (Illus.). 224p. (J). pap. (978-0-375-83874-3(0)) Random Hse., Inc.

Woodson, Jacqueline. From the Notebooks of Melanin Sun. 2003. 160p. (J). (gr. 7 up). pap. 5.99 (978-0-590-45881-8(7) , Scholastic Paperbacks) Scholastic, Inc.

Zobel-Nolan, Allia. My Nasty Backpack. 2006. 16p. (J). pap. 10.99 (978-0-7944-0921-0(0)) Reader's Digest Assn., Inc., The.

MOTHER'S DAY

All New Crafts for Mother's Day & Father's Day. 2007. 48p. (J). (gr. k-4). pap. 7.95 (*978-0-8225-6368-6(1) , First Avenue Editions) Lerner Publishing Group.

DK Publishing Staff. I Love You Mom. 2007. 10p. (J). (ps-1). bds. 8.99 (978-0-7566-2930-4(6)) Dorling Kindersley Publishing, Inc.

Erlbach, Arlene & Erlbach, Herbert. Mother's Day Crafts. 2005. (Fun Holiday Crafts Kids Can Do Ser.). (Illus.). 32p. (J). lib. bdg. 22.60 (978-0-7660-2348-2(6) , Enslow Elementary) Enslow Pubs., Inc.

Gilpin, Rebecca. Things to Make for Mother's Day. Figg, Non, illus. 2004. 32p. (J). pap. 8.95 (978-0-7945-0693-3(3) , Usborne) EDC Publishing.

Heinrichs, Ann. Mother's Day. Alley, R. W., illus. 2006. (Holidays, Festivals, & Celebrations Ser.). 32p. (J). (gr. k-4). 22.79 (978-1-59296-579-3(2)) Child's World, Inc.

Hill, Sandi. Celebrating Mother's Day No. 4528: Mom's Memory Box. Kupperstein, Joel, ed. Banta, Susan, illus. 1999. 16p. (J). (ps-2). pap. 2.99 (978-1-57471-573-6(9)) Creative Teaching Pr., Inc.

Honoring Mothers. 7.50 (978-0-8054-5928-9(6)) B&H Publishing Grp.

Ross, Kathy. All New Crafts for Mother's Day & Father's Day. Holm, Sharon Lane, illus. 2007. (All New Holiday Crafts for Kids Ser.). 48p. (J). (gr. k-3). lib. bdg. 25.26 (978-0-8225-6367-9(3) , Millbrook Pr.) Lerner Publishing Group.

Watson, Michael C., frwd. Why Mom Deserves a Diamond' -Twelve Years of Love: Twelve Years of Love. 2005. 144p. (YA). lib. bdg. 29.95 (978-1-891665-35-6(9)) Gallery of Diamonds Publishing.

Williams, Colleen Madonna Flood. My Adventure on Mother's Day. 2007. 44p. (J). 8.99 (978-1-59092-552-2(1) , Orchard Academy Pr.) Windstorm Creative.

MOTHER'S DAY—FICTION

De Groat, Diane. Mother, You're the Best! (but Sister, You're a Pest!) 2008. 32p. (J). 16.99 (*978-0-06-123899-4(6)); lib. bdg. 17.89 (*978-0-06-123900-7(3)) HarperCollins Pubs.

Gonzalez, Rigoberto & Alvarez, Cecilia Concepcion. Antonio's Card. 2005. (ENG & SPA., Illus.). 32p. (J). 16.95 (978-0-89239-204-9(5)) Children's Bk. Pr.

Grambling, Lois G. Rex Helps Out on Mothers Day. 2008. 32p. (J). 16.99 (978-0-06-053126-3(6)); lib. bdg. 17.89 (978-0-06-053127-0(4)) HarperCollins Pubs. (Tegen, Katherine Bks).

Hillert, Margaret. Happy Mother's Day, Dear Dragon. 2004. (Illus.). 32p. (J). (978-1-59577-023-3(2)) Starfall Education.

Knudsen, Michelle. Mother's Day Ribbons. Wallace, John, illus. 2005. 12p. (J). bds. 6.99 (978-0-689-86381-3(0) , Little Simon) Simon & Schuster Children's Publishing.

Lukas, Catherine. Hooray for Mother's Day! 2003. (gr. k-3). lib. bdg. 14.15 (978-0-613-63298-0(2)) Tandem Library Bks.

Martin, Ann M. Karen's Gift. 2000. (Baby-Sitters Little Sister Ser.: No. 121). 80p. (J). (gr. 3-7). pap. 3.99 (978-0-590-52527-5(1)) Scholastic, Inc.

Mother's Day: A Book for Little Catholics to Color & Keep. 2005. (J). pap. 6.00 (978-0-911845-12-9(7)) Neumann Pr., The.

Random House Disney Staff. I Love You, Mama. 2002. (gr. k-3). lib. bdg. 11.80 (978-0-613-73727-2(X)) Tandem Library Bks.

Rylant, Cynthia. Henry & Mudge & the Funny Lunch. Bracken, Carolyn, illus. 2005. (Henry & Mudge Ser.). 40p. (J). (gr. k-2). lib. bdg. 12.10 (978-1-4176-7107-6(6)) Tandem Library Bks.

Spinelli, Eileen. I Like Noisy, Mom Likes Quiet. Halverson, Lydia, illus. 2006. 32p. (J). 8.95 (978-0-8249-5517-5(X) , 1256103, Ideals Children's Bks.) Ideals Pubns.

Temple, Bob. The Day Mom Finally Snapped. Harpster, Steve, illus. 2006. (Graphic Sparks Ser.). 33p. (J). 19.93 (978-1-59889-038-9(7)) Stone Arch Bks.

Umansky, Kaye. Sophie & the Mother's Day Card. Currey, Anna, illus. 2005. 30p. (J). 3.95 (978-1-56148-481-2(4)); 9.95 (978-1-56148-479-9(2)) Good Bks.

Valdes, Leslie. Happy Mother's Day, Mami! Fruchter, Jason, illus. ed. 2005. (Dora the Explorer Ser.: No. 3). 22p. (J). lib. bdg. 15.00 (978-1-59054-798-4(5)) Fitzgerald Bks.

Ziefert, Harriet. Hey Irma! It's Mother's Day. 2004. (Illus.). 36p. pap. 7.95 (978-1-59354-027-2(2)) Blue Apple Bks.

—What Is Mother's Day? Schumacher, Claire, illus. 2006. 16p. pap. 5.95 (978-1-4027-2398-8(9)) Sterling Publishing Co., Inc.

MOTHS

see also Butterflies; Caterpillars; Silkworms

Berkowitz, Henry. Butterflies & Moths: An Educational Coloring Book. Berkowitz, Henry, illus. 2001. (Illus.). 32p. (J). (ps-3). pap. 4.95 (978-0-932855-66-4(0)) Winner Enterprises.

Brimner, Larry Dane. Butterflies & Moths. 1999. (gr. 3-6). lib. bdg. 15.25 (978-0-613-37303-6(0)) Tandem Library Bks.

Farndon, John. Butterflies & Moths. 2004. (Illus.). 32p. (J). 23.70 (978-1-4103-0123-9(0) , Blackbirch Pr., Inc.) Thomson Gale.

Frost, Helen. Moths. Saunders-Smith, Gail, ed. 2001. (Insects Ser.). (Illus.). 24p. (J). (gr. k-1). lib. bdg. 15.93 (978-0-7368-0852-1(3) , Pebble Bks.) Capstone Pr., Inc.

Helget, Nicole Lea. Moths. 2007. (J). (978-1-58341-543-6(2) , Creative Education) Creative Co., The.

Himmelman, John. A Luna Moth's Life. Stewart, Melissa, ed. Himmelman, John, illus. 1998. (Nature Upclose Ser.). (Illus.). 32p. (J). (gr. k-2). pap. 6.95 (978-0-516-26354-0(4) , Children's Pr.) Scholastic Library Publishing.

Howard, Fran. Moths. 2005. (Pebble Plus: Bugs, Bugs, Bugs! Ser.). (Illus.). 24p. (J). 19.93 (978-0-7368-3644-9(6)) Capstone Pr., Inc.

List, Ilka Katherine. Moths & Butterflies of North America. Gonzales, Jose & Savage, Steve, illus. 2002. (Animals in Order Ser.). 48p. (J). (gr. 4-6). 26.50 (978-0-531-11597-8(6) , Watts, Franklin) Scholastic Library Publishing.

Lockwood, Sophie. Moths. 2007. (World of Insects Ser.). 40p. (J). (gr. 2-6). 29.93 (*978-1-59296-824-4(4)) Child's World, Inc.

Loewen, Nancy. Night Flyers: Moths in Your Backyard. Reibeling, Brandon, illus. 2004. (Backyard Bugs Ser.). 24p. (C). (gr. k-3). 22.60 (978-1-4048-0144-8(8)) Picture Window Bks.

Markle, Sandra. Luna Moths: Masters of Change. 2008. (Insect World Ser.). (J). lib. bdg. 27.93 (*978-0-8225-7302-9(4) , Lerner Pubns.) Lerner Publishing Group.

McEvey, Shane F. Moths & Butterflies. 2001. (Insects & Spiders Ser.). (Illus.). (J). (gr. 4 up). 16.95 (978-0-7910-6598-3(7) , 010555, Chelsea Hse.) Facts On File, Inc.

Morgan, Sally. Butterflies & Moths. 2000. (Looking at Minibeasts Ser.). (Illus.). 32p. (J). (gr. 1-4). lib. bdg. 16.95 (978-1-929298-80-8(3)) Chrysalis Education.

Moths. (Bugs, Bugs, Bugs! Ser.). 24p. (J). 6.95 (978-0-7368-5102-2(X)); Vol. 2. 2005. (YA). (978-0-7368-9087-8(4) , Pebble Bks.) Capstone Pr., Inc.

Moths, 6 vols. (gr. k-2). 28.95 (978-0-7368-9108-0(0)) Red Brick Learning.

Night Fliers. (Backyard Bugs Ser.). 24p. (J). 7.95 (978-1-4048-0446-3(3)) Picture Window Bks.

Preston-Mafham, Rod. Butterflies & Moths. 2002. (Secret World Of... Ser.). (Illus.). 48p. (J). lib. bdg. 27.12 (978-0-7398-4984-2(0)) Raintree.

Richardson, Adele D. Moths. 1998. (Bugs Ser.). (Illus.). 32p. (YA). (gr. 3-12). lib. bdg. 16.95 (978-1-887068-36-9(8)) Smart Apple Media.

Rustad, Martha E. H. Moths. 2007. (Illus.). 24p. (J). lib. bdg. 19.95 (978-1-60014-107-2(2)) Bellwether Media.

Taylor, Barbara & Dorling Kindersley Publishing Staff. Butterflies & Moths. 2nd ed. 2004. (Pocket Guides Ser.). (Illus.). 160p. (J). pap. 6.99 (978-0-7566-0204-8(1)) Dorling Kindersley Publishing, Inc.

Upgrade kit dsm-3 Butterflies&moths. (J). 2004. (978-1-59242-526-6(7)); 2003. (978-1-59242-409-2(0)) Delta Education, LLC.

Webber, Hiltrud M. Collecting Butterflies & Moths. l.t. ed. 1999. (Ozarkae Ser.: Vol. 2). (Illus.). 35p. (J). spiral bd. 10.95 (978-0-9652173-2-3(9)) HMW Pubns.

Whalley, Paul. Butterfly & Moth. 2000. (Eyewitness Bks.). (Illus.). 64p. (J). (gr. 4-7). 15.99 (978-0-7894-5832-2(2)) Dorling Kindersley Publishing, Inc.

Whalley, Paul & Dorling Kindersley Publishing Staff. Butterfly & Moth. 2000. (Eyewitness Bks.). (Illus.). 64p. (J). (gr. 4-7). lib. bdg. 19.99 (978-0-7894-6556-6(6)) Dorling Kindersley Publishing, Inc.

MOTION

see also Force and Energy; Mechanics; Speed

Barraclough, Sue. Fast & Slow. 2006. (Illus.). 24p. (J). (978-1-4109-2266-3(9)); (978-1-4109-2261-8(8)) Steck-Vaughn.

—Straight & Curving. 2006. (Illus.). 24p. (J). (978-1-4109-2260-1(X)); pap. (978-1-4109-2270-0(7)) Steck-Vaughn.

Benchmark Education Staff. Newton & His Laws. 2005. 2.00 (*978-1-4108-4670-9(9)) Benchmark Education Co.

—Objects in Motion. 2005. 2.00 (*978-1-4108-4663-1(6)) Benchmark Education Co.

—The Three Laws of Motion. 2005. 2.00 (*978-1-4108-4677-8(6)) Benchmark Education Co.

Benchmark Education Staff, compiled by. Bodies in Motion & Body Systems. 2005. spiral bd. 225.00 (*978-1-4108-5824-5(3)) Benchmark Education Co.

—Forces & Motion. 2006. spiral bd. 330.00 (*978-1-4108-7014-8(6)); 2006. spiral bd. 165.00 (*978-1-4108-7030-8(8)); 2006. spiral bd. 169.00 (*978-1-4108-7146-6(0)); 2005. (J). spiral bd. 265.00 (*978-1-4108-5760-6(3)) Benchmark Education Co.

—Science Theme: Forces & Motion. 2005. spiral bd. 115.00 (*978-1-4108-5312-7(8)) Benchmark Education Co.

Brannon, Barbara. Discover Motion. 2005. 39.00 (*978-1-4108-5126-0(5)) Benchmark Education Co.

—Discover the Laws of Motion. 2005. 39.00 (*978-1-4108-5128-4(1)) Benchmark Education Co.

Bryant-Mole, Karen & Ansary, Mir Tamim. Moving. 2002. (Science All Around Me Ser.). (Illus.). 24p. (J). (gr. 1-3). pap. 6.50 (978-1-4034-0054-3(7) , 91498) Heinemann Library.

Bug, Amy L. Forces & Motion. 2007. (Physics in Action Ser.). 128p. (gr. 9). 30.00 (*978-0-7910-8931-6(2) , Chelsea Hse.) Facts On File, Inc.

Burnett, Betty. The Laws of Motion: Understanding Uniform & Accelerated Motion. 2004. (Illus.). 48p. (J). lib. bdg. 25.25 (978-1-4042-0335-8(4)) Rosen Publishing Group, Inc., The.

Cheshire, Gerard. Forces & Motion. 2006. (Fundamental Physics Ser.). (Illus.). 48p. (J). (978-1-58340-995-4(5)) Smart Apple Media.

Cobb, Allan B. Super Science Projects about Energy & Motion. 2005. (Psyched for Science Ser.). (Illus.). 48p. (YA). (gr. 5-8). lib. bdg. 23.95 (978-0-8239-3116-3(1) , SCENMO) Rosen Publishing Group, Inc., The.

Cobb, Vicki. Whirlers & Twirlers: Science Fun with Spinning. Haefele, Steve, illus. 2001. (Science Fun with Vicki Cobb Ser.). 64p. (gr. 3-6). lib. bdg. 24.90 (978-0-7613-1573-5(X) , Millbrook Pr.) Lerner Publishing Group.

Dalton, Cindy Devine. Force & Motion. 2001. (How Can I Experiment With? Ser.). (Illus.). 32p. (J). (gr. 1-4). lib. bdg. 28.50 (978-1-58952-012-7(2)) Rourke Publishing, LLC.

Dixon, Malcolm & Smith, Karen. Forces & Movement. 1998. (Young Scientists Ser.). (Illus.). 32p. (J). (ps-3). lib. bdg. 16.95 (978-1-887068-68-0(6)) Smart Apple Media.

DK Publishing Staff. On the Move. 2007. 32p. (J). 14.99 (978-0-7566-2945-8(4)); pap. 3.99 (978-0-7566-2944-1(6)) Dorling Kindersley Publishing, Inc.

Dreier, David Louis. Forces & Motion. 2007. (J). (*978-1-4034-9923-3(3)); pap. (*978-1-4034-9931-8(4)) Heinemann Library.

Farndon, John. Motion. 2002. (Science Experiments Ser.). (Illus.). 32p. (J). 25.64 (978-0-7614-1471-1(1) , Benchmark Bks.) Cavendish, Marshall Corp.

Frank, Marjorie Slavick, et al. Science Instant Readers Bk. 11: Motion. 1999. (Harcourt Science Ser.). (gr. 2 up). pap. 15.50 (978-0-15-316221-3(X)) Harcourt Schl. Pubs.

Fredericks, Anthony D. Weird Walkers. 2000. (gr. 3-6). lib. bdg. 16.40 (978-0-613-27488-3(1)) Tandem Library Bks.

Frisch, Joy. Motion & Movement. 2008. (J). (***978-1-58341-578-8(5)*** , Creative Education) Creative Co., The.

—Motion & Movement. 2002. (Illus.). 32p. (J). lib. bdg. 24.25 (978-1-58340-160-6(1)) Smart Apple Media.

Funk, Tara. Newton & His Laws. 2005. 39.00 (***978-1-4108-4622-8(9)***) Benchmark Education Co.

—Objects in Motion. 2005. 39.00 (***978-1-4108-4615-0(6)***) Benchmark Education Co.

—The Three Laws of Motion. 2005. 42.00 (***978-1-4108-4629-7(6)***) Benchmark Education Co.

Gianopoulos, Andrea. Isaac Newton & the Laws of Motion. 2007. 32p. (J). (978-0-7368-6847-1(X)) Capstone Pr., Inc.

Glover, David. Forces & Movement. 2001. (Experiments in Science Ser.). (Illus.). (J). (978-0-7894-7463-6(8)) Dorling Kindersley Publishing, Inc.

Gold-Dworkin, Heidi. Learning about the Way Things Move. 2001. (gr. 3-6). lib. bdg. 22.20 (978-0-613-27931-4(X)) Tandem Library Bks.

Goodstein, Madeline. Science Fair Success Using Newton's Laws of Motion. 2002. (Science Fair Success Ser.). (Illus.). 128p. (YA). (gr. 6-12). lib. bdg. 26.60 (978-0-7660-1628-6(5)) Enslow Pubs., Inc.

—Sports Science Projects: The Physics of Balls in Motion. 1999. (Science Fair Success Ser.). (Illus.). 128p. (YA). (gr. 6-12). lib. bdg. 26.60 (978-0-7660-1174-8(7)) Enslow Pubs., Inc.

Graham, John. Forces & Motion: Over 40 Fantastic Experiments. 2001. (Hands-On Science Ser.). (Illus.). (J). 13.75 (978-0-606-21194-9(2)) Tandem Library Bks.

Graham, John & Angliss, Sarah. Forces & Motion: Over 40 Fantastic Experiments. 2001. (Hands-On Science Ser.). (Illus.). 40p. (J). (gr. 3-5). pap. 6.95 (978-0-7534-5348-3(7) , Kingfisher) Houghton Mifflin Co. Trade & Reference Div.

Haber-Schaim, Uri, et al. Force, Motion, & Energy Assessment Package. 2003. pap. (978-1-882057-15-3(5) , SCI-777-3393) Science Curriculum, Inc.

Halls, Kelly Milner. Forces & Motion. 2006. (Science Fair Projects Ser.). (Illus.). 48p. (YA). (gr. 6-9). lib. bdg. 30.00 (978-1-4034-7910-5(0)) Heinemann Library.

Hands on Science: Forces & Motion. 1999. (J). 58.43 (978-0-7398-1710-0(8)) Raintree.

Harcourt School Publishers Staff. Motion: Science Reader. 1999. (SPA., Illus.). (J). pap. 3.70 (978-0-15-316126-1(4)) Harcourt Schl. Pubs.

Hewitt, Sally. Amazing Forces & Movement. 2007. 32p. pap. (***978-0-7787-3625-7(3)***) Crabtree Publishing Co.

—Fly Like a Superhero? 2001. (Why Can't I Ser.). (Illus.). 30p. (J). lib. bdg. 24.25 (978-1-930643-03-1(9)) Chrysalis Education.

—Forces & Motion. (Illus.). 32p. (YA). (gr. 2 up). lib. bdg. 27.10 (978-1-932333-32-9(0)) Chrysalis Education.

Holt, Rinehart and Winston Staff. Holt Science & Technology Chapter 5: Physical Science: Matter in Motion. 5th ed. 2004. (Illus.). pap. 12.86 (978-0-03-030376-0(1)) Holt, Rinehart & Winston.

—Holt Science & Technology Chptr. 16: Matter & Motion: Chapter Resources - Tennessee Edition. 3rd ed. 2003. (YA). pap. 11.40 (978-0-03-069177-5(X)) Holt, Rinehart & Winston.

Hunter, Rebecca. The Facts about Forces & Motion. 2004. (Science the Facts Ser.). (Illus.). 32p. (J). lib. bdg. (978-1-58340-451-5(1)) Smart Apple Media.

Juettner, Bonnie. Motion. 2004. (KidHaven Science Library). (Illus.). 48p. (J). (gr. 4-7). 26.20 (978-0-7377-1536-1(7) , Greenhaven Pr., Inc.) Thomson Gale.

Kelly, Lynne. Simple Concepts in Physics: Motion. (Illus.). (J). (gr. 3-6). pap. (978-1-875739-35-6(1)) Wizard Bks.

Knight, Tim. Magnificent Movers. 2003. (Amazing Nature Ser.). 32p. (J). pap. 6.95 (978-1-4034-3259-9(7)) Heinemann Library.

Lauw, Darlene. Motion. 2002. (gr. 3-6). lib. bdg. 16.40 (978-0-613-52883-2(2)) Tandem Library Bks.

Lauw, Darlene & Puay, Lim Cheng. Motion. 2002. (Science Alive! Ser.). (Illus.). 32p. (J). (gr. 4-5). pap. (978-0-7787-0604-5(4)); lib. bdg. (978-0-7787-0558-1(7)) Crabtree Publishing Co.

Lawrence, Debbie & Lawrence, Richard. Machines & Motion: God's Design for the Physical World. 2005. (Illus.). 160p. per. (978-0-9725365-9-2(0)) R & D Educational Ctr.

Lee, Quinlan B. Barney Follow Me. McKee, Darren, illus. 2004. (Barney Ser.). 6p. (J). bds. 5.99 (978-0-439-62496-1(7)) Scholastic, Inc.

Llewellyn, Claire. And Everyone Shouted, "Pull!" A First Look at Forces & Motion. Abel, Simone, illus. 2004. (First Look Science Ser.). 32p. (C). (gr. k-3). 22.60 (978-1-4048-0656-6(3)) Picture Window Bks.

—Forces & Movement. 2005. (Illus.). 24p. (J). (gr. 1-4). lib. bdg. (978-1-84234-335-7(1) , Cherrytree Books) Evans Publishing Group.

Madgwick, Wendy. On the Move. 1999. (Science Starters Ser.). (Illus.). 32p. (J). (gr. k-4). 25.70 (978-0-8172-5333-2(5)) Raintree.

—On the Move. 1999. (Science Starters Ser.). (Illus.). 32 p. (gr. k-4). 7.95 (978-0-8172-5884-9(1)) Steck-Vaughn.

Mason, Adrienne. Move It! Motion, Forces & You. Davila, Claudia, illus. 2005. (Primary Physical Science Ser.). 32p. (J). (ps-ps). (978-1-55337-758-0(3)) Kids Can Pr., Ltd.

—Move It! Movement, Forces & You. Davila, Claudia, illus. 2005. (Primary Physical Science Ser.). 32p. (J). (gr. k-2). (978-1-55337-759-7(1)) Kids Can Pr., Ltd.

Mason, Paul. The Extreme Zone: Forces & Motion. 2005. (Illus.). 32p. (J). (978-1-4109-1950-2(1)); lib. bdg. (978-1-4109-1919-9(6)) Steck-Vaughn.

—Roller Coaster! 2006. (Illus.). 32p. (J). pap. (978-1-4109-2616-6(8)); lib. bdg. (978-1-4109-2587-9(0)) Steck-Vaughn.

McGraw-Hill Staff. Glencoe Science: Motion, Forces, & Energy. 2001. stu. ed. 20.64 (978-0-07-825607-3(0) , 9780078256073) Glencoe/McGraw-Hill.

Motion & Force: Integrated Physics & Chemistry / Algebra I Instructional Unit. 2003. (Region IV ESC Resources for Mathematics & Science Ser.). stu. ed., per. (978-1-932524-69-7(X)) Region IV Education Service Ctr.

Murphy, Brian. Movement. 2004. (Experiment with Ser.). (SPA., Illus.). 32p. (J). (gr. 2-5). 9.95 (978-1-58728-248-5(8)); pap. 5.95 (978-1-58728-116-7(3)) T&N Children's Publishing. (Two Can Publishing).

Murphy, Patricia. Back & Forth. 2002. (gr. k-3). lib. bdg. 12.95 (978-0-613-53339-3(9)) Tandem Library Bks.

—Up & Down. 2002. (gr. k-3). lib. bdg. 12.95 (978-0-613-54372-9(6)) Tandem Library Bks.

Murphy, Patricia J. Around & Around. 2002. (Rookie Read-About Science Ser.). (Illus.). 32p. (J). (gr. 1-2). 20.50 (978-0-516-22550-0(2) , Children's Pr.) Scholastic Library Publishing.

—Back & Forth. 2002. (Rookie Read-About Science Ser.). (Illus.). 32p. (J). (gr. 1-2). pap. 4.95 (978-0-516-26865-1(1)); 20.50 (978-0-516-22552-4(9)) Scholastic Library Publishing. (Children's Pr.).

—Up & Down. 2002. (Rookie Read-About Science Ser.). (Illus.). 32p. (J). (gr. 1-2). 20.50 (978-0-516-22553-1(7) , Children's Pr.) Scholastic Library Publishing.

Murray, Julie. Motion. 2007. (Illus.). 24p. (J). 21.35 (978-1-59679-829-8(7) , Buddy Bks.) ABDO Publishing Co.

Nardo, Don. Kinetic Energy: The Energy of Motion. Schultz, Ashlee & Hossain, Farhana, illus. 2007. (J). lib. bdg. (***978-0-7565-3378-6(3)***) Compass Point Bks.

Nelson, Robin. Como Se Mueven las Cosas (Ways Things Move) 2007. (Mi Primer Paso al Mundo Real - Fuerzas y Movimiento (First Step Nonfiction - Forces & Motion) Ser.). (SPA.). 24p. (J). (gr. k-2). lib. bdg. 18.60 (***978-0-8225-7811-6(5)*** , Ediciones Lerner) Lerner Publishing Group.

Nelson, Robin. Ways Things Move. (Forces & Motion Ser.). (Illus.). (J). 2005. 22p. pap. (978-0-8225-5300-7(7)); 2004. 24p. lib. bdg. 18.60 (978-0-8225-5136-2(5)) Lerner Publishing Group.

Nsrc. Science & Technology for Children Books, Motion & Design: Motion & Design. 2004. (Illus.). 64p. (J). (978-1-933008-03-5(2)) National Science Resources Ctr.

O'Daley, Anne. Motion. 2003. (Illus.). 24p. (J). 22.45 (978-1-4103-0082-9(X) , Blackbirch Pr., Inc.) Thomson Gale.

O'Donnell, Kerri. Sir Isaac Newton: Using the Laws of Motion to Solve Problems. 2006. (Math for the Real World Ser.). (Illus.). 32p. (J). pap. (978-1-4042-6079-5(X)); lib. bdg. (978-1-4042-3363-8(6)) Rosen Publishing Group, Inc., The.

Olien, Rebecca. Motion. 2004. (First Facts Ser.). 24p. (J). lib. bdg. 21.26 (978-0-7368-2618-1(1)) Capstone Pr., Inc.

O'Neil, Sarah. Going Fast. 2001. (gr. k-3). lib. bdg. 11.65 (978-0-613-33370-2(5)) Tandem Library Bks.

Parker, Steve. Forces & Movement. 2004. (Science View Ser.). (Illus.). 32p. (J). (gr. 4-8). 28.00 (978-0-7910-8211-9(3) , Chelsea Hse.) Facts On File, Inc.

Phelan, Glen. Forces & Motion in Sports. 2005. (Navigators Ser.). (J). pap. 44.00 (***978-1-4108-5088-1(9)***) Benchmark Education Co.

—Forces & Motion on Earth. 2005. (Navigators Ser.). (J). pap. 44.00 (***978-1-4108-5087-4(0)***) Benchmark Education Co.

—Introduction to Energy. 2004. (Illus.). 32p. (J). pap. (978-0-7922-4580-3(6)) National Geographic Society.

—Invisible Force: The Quest to Define the Laws of Motion. 2006. (Science Quest Ser.). (Illus.). 64p. (J). (gr. 5-9). 17.95 (978-0-7922-5539-0(9) , National Geographic Children's Bks.) National Geographic Society.

—An Invisible Force: The Quest to Define the Laws of Motion. 2006. (Illus.). 64p. (J). (gr. 5-9). 25.90 (978-0-7922-5540-6(2) , National Geographic Children's Bks.) National Geographic Society.

—Newton's Laws. 2004. (National Geographic Reading Expeditions Ser.). (Illus.). 32p. (J). pap. (978-0-7922-4584-1(9)) National Geographic Society.

Pipe, Jim. Movement: Things That Go. 2005. (Science Starters Ser.). (Illus.). 32p. (J). (gr. 1-4). lib. bdg. 27.10 (978-1-59604-018-2(1)) Stargazer Bks.

Riley, Peter D. Forces & Motion. 1999. (Science Topics Ser.). 32p. (YA). (gr. 6-8). lib. bdg. 24.22 (978-1-57572-772-1(2)) Heinemann Library.

—Forces & Movement. 2005. (Illus.). 32p. (J). (gr. 4-7). lib. bdg. 27.10 (978-1-58340-712-7(X)) Smart Apple Media.

Roberts, Jeremy. How Do We Know the Laws of Motion? 2001. (Great Scientific Questions & the Scientists Who Answered Them Ser.). (Illus.). 112p. (YA). (gr. 4-6). lib. bdg. 26.50 (978-0-8239-3383-9(0)) Rosen Publishing Group, Inc., The.

Rosinsky, Natalie M. Sir Isaac Newton: Brilliant Mathematician & Scientist. 2007. (Signature Lives Ser.). (J). lib. bdg. 31.93 (***978-0-7565-2209-4(9)***) Compass Point Bks.

Royston, Angela. Forces & Motion. (My World of Science Ser.). (Illus.). 32p. (J). (gr. k-2). 2002. pap. 6.95 (978-1-4034-0039-0(3) ; 91483); 2001. lib. bdg. 21.36 (978-1-58810-240-9(8)) Heinemann Library.

—Fuerzas y Movimiento. 2006. (ENG & SPA., Illus.). 32p. (J). pap. (978-1-4034-9115-2(1)); lib. bdg. 25.36 (978-1-4034-9108-4(9)) Heinemann Library.

Royston, Angela. Looking at Forces & Motion: How Do Things Move? 2008. (Looking at Science: How Things Change Ser.). 32p. (J). (gr. 1-3). lib. bdg. 22.60 (***978-0-7660-3089-3(X)***) Enslow Pubs., Inc.

Schaefer, Lola M. Back & Forth. Saunders-Smith, Gail, ed. 1999. (Way Things Move Ser.). (Illus.). 24p. (J). (gr. k-1). lib. bdg. 15.93 (978-0-7368-0398-4(X) , Pebble Bks.) Capstone Pr., Inc.

—Back & Forth. 1999. pap. 13.25 (978-0-516-21921-9(9) , Children's Pr.) Scholastic Library Publishing.

School Specialty Publishing. Force & Motion. 2005. (Science Search Lab Ser.). (J). (gr. 3-5). pap. 24.95 (978-0-7682-2833-5(6) , Ideal School Supply) Schaffer, Frank Pubns.

Science & Technology for Children Books, Motion & Design Set, 8 vols. 2004. (Illus.). 64p. (J). (978-1-933008-15-8(6)) National Science Resources Ctr.

Science Stories Foss Spanish Balance & Motion EA CR05. 2005. (J). (978-1-59242-582-2(8)) Delta Education, LLC.

Sheehan, Thomas F. Ciencia en el Parque (Playground Science) Sarfatti, Esther, tr. from ENG. 2005. (Ciencia Citadina Ser.). (SPA., Illus.). 24p. (J). (ps-3). lib. bdg. 21.36 (978-1-59515-667-9(4)) Rourke Publishing, LLC.

—Playground Science. 2006. (City Science Ser.). (Illus.). 24p. (gr. k-3). 14.95 (978-1-59515-410-1(8)) Rourke Publishing, LLC.

Sohn, Emily. A Crash Course in Forces & Motion with Max Axiom, Super Scientist. Erwin, Steve & Barnett, Charles, illus. 2007. (Graphic Library). 32p. (J). (***978-0-7368-6837-2(2)*** , 1264931) Capstone Pr., Inc.

Solway, Andrew. Forces & Motion. 2007. (J). lib. bdg. (***978-1-4042-3747-6(X)*** , Rosen Central) Rosen Publishing Group, Inc., The.

Spilsbury, Richard & Spilsbury, Louise. What Are Forces & Motion? Exploring Science with Hands-On Activities. 2008. (In Touch with Basic Science Ser.). 32p. (J). (gr. 3-4). lib. bdg. 22.60 (***978-0-7660-3095-4(4)***) Enslow Pubs., Inc.

Stewart, Melissa. Energy in Motion. 2006. (Rookie Read-About Science Ser.). (Illus.). 32p. (J). (gr. 1-2). 20.50 (978-0-516-24956-8(8) , Children's Pr.) Scholastic Library Publishing.

—Motion. 2003. (Simply Science Ser.). (Illus.). 32p. (J). (gr. 3 up). lib. bdg. 19.93 (978-0-7565-0443-4(0)) Compass Point Bks.

Stille, Darlene R. Motion. 2004. (Science Around Us Ser.). 32p. (J). (gr. 2-6). 27.07 (978-1-59296-224-2(6)) Child's World, Inc.

—Motion: Push & Pull, Fast & Slow. Boyd, Sheree, tr. Boyd, Sheree, illus. 2004. (Amazing Science Ser.). 24p. (J). (gr. k-4). 22.60 (978-1-4048-0250-6(9)) Picture Window Bks.

Tabak, John. Science in Motion. 2002. (J). (978-0-531-11890-0(8) , Watts, Franklin) Scholastic Library Publishing.

Tocci, Salvatore. Experiments with Motion. 2003. (True Book Ser.). (gr. 3-5). pap. 6.95 (978-0-516-27467-6(8)); (Illus.). 48p. (J). 25.00 (978-0-516-22603-3(7)) Scholastic Library Publishing. (Children's Pr.).

—Experiments with Motion. 2003. (gr. 3-6). lib. bdg. 15.25 (978-0-613-67889-6(3)) Tandem Library Bks.

Two-Can Publishing Ltd. Staff. Experiment with Movement. 2001. (gr. 3-6). lib. bdg. 14.10 (978-0-613-84873-2(X)) Tandem Library Bks.

Wadsworth, Pamela. Golwg Gyntaf Ar Bethau'n Symud. 2005. (WEL., Illus.). 24p. pap. (978-1-85596-252-1(7)) Dref Wen.

Waters, Jennifer. Move It! McEwen, Rebecca & Auch, Alison, eds. 2002. (Spyglass Books). (Illus.). 24p. (J). (gr. 1 up). lib. bdg. 18.60 (978-0-7565-0238-6(1)) Compass Point Bks.

Welch, Catherine A. Forces & Motion: A Question & Answer Book. 2006. (Fact Finders Ser.). (Illus.). 32p. (978-0-7368-5445-0(2)) Capstone Pr., Inc.

What Makes It Move? KinderFacts Individual Title Six-Packs. (Kinderstarters Ser.). 8p. (ps-1). 21.00 (978-0-7635 8755 0(9)) Rigby Education.

Wheeler, Jill C. Move It! A Book about Motion. 1998. (Kid Physics Ser.). (J). lib. bdg. 13.98 (978-1-56239-631-2(5)) ABDO Publishing Co.

Whirlers & Twirlers: Science Fun with Spinning. 2007. (J). pap. 7.95 (***978-0-8225-7025-7(4)*** , First Avenue Editions) Lerner Publishing Group.

Whitehouse, Patricia. Maquinas Que Se Mueven. 2007. (SPA & ENG., Illus.). 24p. (J). (***978-1-60044-277-3(3)***) Rourke Publishing, LLC.

—Moving Machines. 2007. (J). (978-1-60044-192-9(0)) Rourke Publishing, LLC.

—Rolling. 2003. (Illus.). 24p. (J). pap. (978-1-4034-3470-8(0)); lib. bdg. 18.50 (978-1-4034-0907-2(2)) Heinemann Library.

Willis, Shirley. Dime Que Tan Rapidamente Va. 2000. (Los Estupendos Whiz Kids, Spanish Edition Ser.). (SPA., Illus.). 32p. (J). (gr. 1-3). pap. 5.95 (978-0-531-15993-4(0) , OD30044, Watts, Franklin) Scholastic Library Publishing.

—Dime Que Tan Rapidamente Va. 2000. (gr. k-3). (SPA.). lib. bdg. 14.10 (978-0-613-72673-3(1)); (J). 12.75 (978-0-606-20154-4(8)) Tandem Library Bks.

MOTION PICTURE CARTOONS

see Animated Films

MOTION PICTURE INDUSTRY

Albert, Lisa Rondinelli. So You Want to Be a Film or TV Actor? 2008. (Careers in Film & Television Ser.). (Illus.). 128p. (J). (gr. 6 up). lib. bdg. 31.93 (***978-0-7660-2741-1(4)***) Enslow Pubs., Inc.

Brown, Don. Mack Made Movies. 2005. (Illus.). 32p. (J). (ps-ps). reprint ed. pap. 6.95 (978-1-59643-091-4(5)) Roaring Brook Pr.

—Mack Made Movies. Brown, Don, illus. rev. ed. 2003. (Illus.). 32p. (J). (ps-4). 16.95 (978-0-7613-1538-4(1)) Roaring Brook Pr.

Gosling, Maureen, et al. You Can Be a Woman Movie Maker. 1.t. ed. 2003. (Illus.). 80p. (J). 19.95 incl. DVD (978-1-880599-64-8(3)); pap. 14.95 incl. DVD (978-1-880599-63-1(5)) Cascade Pass, Inc.

Harcourt School Publishers Staff. Making Monsters: Take-Home Book. 2001. (Collections Ser.). (Illus.). (J). pap. 1.90 (978-0-15-319561-7(4)) Harcourt Schl. Pubs.

Horn, Geoffrey M. Steven Spielberg. 2002. (Trailblazers of the Modern World Ser.). (Illus.). 48p. (J). (gr. 5 up). pap. 14.95 (978-0-8368-5240-0(0)); lib. bdg. 30.00 (978-0-8368-5080-2(7)) Stevens, Gareth Inc. (World Almanac Library).

Johnson, Marlys H. Careers in the Movies. 2005. (Careers Ser.). (Illus.). 192p. (YA). (gr. 7-12). lib. bdg. 26.50 (978-0-8239-3186-6(2)) Rosen Publishing Group, Inc., The.

LeapFrog Staff, compiled by. Time for Kids: Making Movies. 2002. (J). (gr. 3-5). spiral bd. 14.99 (978-1-58605-062-7(1)) LeapFrog Enterprises, Inc.

Roca, Nuria. Que Es el Arte? Cine. 2004. (Libros Que Es el Arte? Ser.).Tr. of What Is Art? Movies. (SPA.). 36p. (J). pap. 6.95 (978-0-7641-2707-6(1)) Barron's Educational Series, Inc.

—What Is Art? Movies. 2004. (What Is Art? Bks.). (Illus.). 36p. (J). pap. 6.95 (978-0-7641-2703-8(9)) Barron's Educational Series, Inc.

Svitil, Torene & Dunkleberger, Amy. So You Want to Work in Set Design, Costuming, or Make-up? 2008. (Careers in Film & Television Ser.). (Illus.). 128p. (J). (gr. 6 up). lib. bdg. 31.93 (***978-0-7660-2740-4(6)***) Enslow Pubs., Inc.

Wormser, Richard. To the Young Filmmaker: Conversations with Working Filmmakers. 2002. (To the Young Ser.). (Illus.). 128p. (YA). (gr. 8-10). pap. 24.00 (978-0-531-11727-9(8) , Watts, Franklin) Scholastic Library Publishing.

MOTION PICTURE INDUSTRY—FICTION

Ackerman, Karen. Bean's Big Day. Mombourquette, Paul, tr. Mombourquette, Paul, illus. 2004. 32p. (J). (gr. k-3). (978-1-55337-444-2(4)) Kids Can Pr., Ltd.

Castellucci, Cecil. Boy Proof. 208p. (YA). (gr. 9 up). 2005. 15.99 (978-0-7636-2333-3(4)); 2006. reprint ed. pap. 7.99 (978-0-7636-2796-6(8)) Candlewick Pr.

Hare, Mimi & Naylor, Clare. The First Assistant: A Continuing Tale from Behind the Hollywood Curtain. 2007. 288p. pap. 14.00 (978-0-452-28836-2(3) , Plume) Penguin Group (USA) Inc.

Kennedy, Mary. Tales of a Hollywood Gossip Queen. 2006. 256p. (YA). (gr. 12). pap. 9.99 (978-0-425-20993-6(8) , Berkley Trade) Penguin Group (USA) Inc.

Lee, Tanith. Indigara: Firebird Novella. 2007. 192p. (YA). (gr. 7 up). 11.99 (***978-0-14-240922-0(7)*** , Puffin) Penguin Group (USA) Inc.

McCann, Jesse Leon. Shrek 2 Movie Novelization. 2004. (Shrek 2 Ser.). (Illus.). 120p. (J). pap. 4.99 (978-0-439-53847-3(5)) Scholastic, Inc.

Morgan, Allen. Matthew & the Midnight Movie. Martchenko, Michael, illus. 2002. (Matthew's Midnight Adventures Ser.). 32p. (YA). 6.99 (978-0-7737-6273-2(6)) Stoddart Kids CAN. *Dist:* Fitzhenry & Whiteside, Ltd.

Roter, Jordan. Girl in Development. 2008. 320p. (YA). (gr. 7). pap. 7.99 (***978-0-14-240822-3(0)*** , Puffin) Penguin Group (USA) Inc.

Roter, Jordan. Girl of Development (Splashproof Ed) 2007. 1p. (YA). (gr. 7). pap. 7.99 (978-0-14-240838-4(7) , Puffin) Penguin Group (USA) Inc.

Wilcox, Mary. Truth or Dare. 2008. (J). (***978-0-385-90514-5(9)***); pap. (***978-0-385-73528-5(6)***) Dell Publishing. (Delacorte Pr.).

MOTION PICTURE MUSIC

Hal Leonard Corp., creator. The Big Book of Children's Movie Songs. 2001. 312p. pap. 17.95 (978-0-634-02907-3(X) , 063402907X) Leonard, Hal Corp.

—Children's Movie Songs. 2001. 96p. pap. 10.95 (978-0-634-02910-3(X) , 063402910X) Leonard, Hal Corp.

Horn, Geoffrey M. Movie Soundtracks & Sound Effects. 2006. (Making Movies Ser.). (Illus.). 32p. (J). (gr. 4-6). lib. bdg. 23.93 (978-0-8368-6839-5(0)) Stevens, Gareth Inc.

Movie Title Hits. 2000. 13.95 incl. audio compact disk (978-1-85909-704-5(9) , Warner Bros. Pubns.) Alfred Publishing Co., Inc.

MOTION PICTURE PLAYS

Millar, Mark. Civil War Script Book TPB. 2007. (Illus.). 208p. pap. 17.99 (***978-0-7851-2794-9(1)***) Marvel Enterprises, Inc.

Mitter, Matt. Create Your Own Horror Movies. Zalme, Ron, illus. 2001. 32p. (J). (978-0-439-35562-9(1)) Scholastic, Inc.

Scholastic, Inc. Staff. Godzilla Danger Zone: The Ultimate Movie Fact Book. 1998. (Godzilla Ser.). (J). (gr. 3-7). pap. 4.98 (978-0-590-78627-0(X)) Scholastic, Inc.

MOTION PICTURES

Abraham, Philip. Television & Movies. 2004. (High-American Pop Culture Ser.). (Illus.). 48p. (J). 24.00 (978-0-516-24074-9(9) , Watts, Franklin); (gr. 7-12). pap. 6.95 (978-0-516-25946-8(6) , Children's Pr.) Scholastic Library Publishing.

Adair, Gene. Alfred Hitchcock: Filming Our Fears. 2002. (Oxford Portraits Ser.). (Illus.). 160p. (YA). (gr. 7-10). 28.00 (978-0-19-511967-1(3)) Oxford Univ. Pr., Inc.

At the Movies, 6, Packs. (Bookweb Ser.). 32p. (gr. 3 up). 34.00 (978-0-7635-3944-3(9)) Rigby Education.

Auerbach, Annie & Heiss, Lori. Lilo & Stitch. 2003. (DMA Learn to Draw Ser.). (Illus.). 32p. (J). pap. 5.95 (978-1-56010-045-4(1)) Foster, Walter Publishing, Inc.

Baker, Frank. Coming Distractions: Questioning Movies. 2007. (Fact Finders Ser.). (Illus.). 32p. (J). (*978-0-7368-7862-3(9)* , 1264910) Capstone Pr., Inc.

Baker, Frank W. Coming Distractions: Questioning Movies. 2007. (Fact Finders Ser.). (Illus.). 32p. (J). (gr. 4-7). lib. bdg. 22.60 (978-0-7368-6766-5(X) , 1264910, Fact Finders) Capstone Pr., Inc.

Barker, Martin & Austin, Thomas. From Antz to Titanic: Reinventing Film Analysis. 2000. (Illus.). 240p. 65.00 (978-0-7453-1584-3(4)) Pluto Pr. GBR. *Dist:* Univ. of Michigan Pr.

Bednarz, Robert, et al. TIME for Kids Readers: From Silents to Talkies. 3rd ed. 2002. (Harcourt Horizons Ser.). (gr. k-7). pap. 38.10 (978-0-15-335296-6(5)) Harcourt Schl. Pubs.

Beecroft, Simon. Inside the Worlds of Star Wars': Attack of the ClonesTM. Chasemore, Richard & Jenssen, Hans, illus. 2003. (Star Wars Ser.). 40p. (J). 19.99 (978-0-7894-9227-2(X)) Dorling Kindersley Publishing, Inc.

Beecroft, Simon, ed. Inside the Worlds of Star Wars Attack of the Clones. Jenssen, Hans & Chasemore, Richard, illus. 2004. 40p. (978-0-7513-6516-0(5)) Dorling Kindersley.

Behind the Camera, 6 vols., Set. 2005. (Illus.). 112p. (YA). (gr. 6-12). pap. 180.00 (978-0-7910-6711-6(4) , Chelsea Hse.) Facts On File, Inc.

Bergmann, Michael. Trifling with Fate How to Make a Digital Video Feature Film. 2001. 264p. per. 18.95 (978-0-9712872-0-4(1) , Separate Star Publishing) Separate Star, Inc.

Branch, Muriel M. Film & Theater: America in the King Years 1963-65. 2003. (African-American Arts Ser.). 80p. (J). lib. bdg. (978-0-7613-1867-5(4) , Twenty-First Century Bks.) Lerner Publishing Group.

A Brief Guide for the High School Moviemaker. 2003. 56p. (YA). per. (978-0-9753076-0-1(6)) Kerr, Alex.

Brighton, Catherine. Keep Your Eye on the Kid: The Early Years of Buster Keaton. 2008. 32p. (J). 16.95 (*978-1-59643-158-4(X)*) Roaring Brook Pr.

Brodie, Ian. Cameras in Narnia: How the Lion, the Witch & the Wardrobe Came to Life. 2005. (Illus.). 72p. pap. 14.95 (978-0-06-088595-3(5) , Harper San Francisco) HarperCollins Pubs.

Buckley, Annie. Making Movies. 2006. (Girls Rock! Ser.). (Illus.). 32p. (J). (gr. 1-5). 24.21 (978-1-59296-746-9(9)) Child's World, Inc.

Byrum, R. T. Film. 2006. (Careers for the Twenty-First Century Ser.). (J). (978-1-59018-668-8(0) , Lucent Bks.) Thomson Gale.

Chambers, Catherine. Movies. 2001. (Behind Media Ser.). (Illus.). 48p. (J). (gr. 6-8). lib. bdg. 24.22 (978-1-58810-031-3(6)) Heinemann Library.

El Cine. (Coleccion Biblioteca Visual).Tr. of Cinema. (SPA.). (YA). (gr. 5-8). (978-84-372-3767-1(X)) Altea, Ediciones, S.A. - Grupo Santillana.

Clements, J. M. Kid's Guide to Movies. 2002. (gr. 3-6). lib. bdg. 13.00 (978-0-613-67557-4(6)) Tandem Library Bks.

Cocoro Books Staff, creator. Silver Screen Samurai: The Best of Japan's Samurai Movie Posters. 2004. (Illus.). 112p. 19.95 (978-0-9723124-3-1(9)) DH Publishing, Inc.

Cole, Steve & Dorling Kindersley Publishing Staff. Madagascar Essential Guide. 2005. (Illus.). 48p. (J). 12.99 (978-0-7566-1175-0(X)) Dorling Kindersley Publishing, Inc.

Collins, Terry. E T: The Extra-Terrestrial. 2002. (gr. 3-6). lib. bdg. 13.00 (978-0-613-87769-5(1)) Tandem Library Bks.

—King Kong. 2006. (Monsters Ser.). (Illus.). 48p. (J). (gr. 4-8). 26.20 (978-0-7377-3585-7(6) , Kidhaven) Thomson Gale.

Conor, William. Titan a E How to Draw. 2000. (gr. 3-6). lib. bdg. 15.30 (978-0-613-82378-4(8)) Tandem Library Bks.

Cottringer, Anne. Movie Magic. 1999. (Eyewitness Readers Ser.). (J). (978-0-606-19384-9(7)) Tandem Library Bks.

Cottringer, Anne & Dorling Kindersley Publishing Staff. Movie Magic. 1999. (Eyewitness Readers). (Illus.). 48p. (J). (ps-4). 12.99 (978-0-7894-4009-9(1)) Dorling Kindersley Publishing, Inc.

Cottringer, Anne, et al. Movie Magic. 1999. (Eyewitness Readers Ser.). (Illus.). 48p. (J). (ps-4). pap. 3.99 (978-0-7894-4008-2(3)) Dorling Kindersley Publishing, Inc.

DC Comics Staff, et al. Flight. 3rd ed. 2002. (Smallville Ser.: No. 3). 192p. (J). (gr. 7-17). mass mkt. 5.99 (978-0-316-17468-8(8)) Little, Brown Bks. for Young Readers.

DK Publishing Staff. Shrek: The Complete Guide. 2007. 64p. (J). 12.99 (978-0-7566-2988-5(8)) Dorling Kindersley Publishing, Inc.

Dorling Kindersley Publishing Staff. Disney Princess Ultimate Sticker Book. 2003. (Disney Princess Ser.). (Illus.). 16p. (J). (ps-12). pap. 6.99 (978-0-7894-9747-5(6)) Dorling Kindersley Publishing, Inc.

Dorling Kindersley Publishing Staff, ed. The Incredibles. 2004. (Ultimate Sticker Bks.). (Illus.). 16p. (J). pap. 6.99 (978-0-7566-0588-9(1)) Dorling Kindersley Publishing, Inc.

—The Incredibles: The Essential Guide. 2004. (Illus.). 48p. (J). 12.99 (978-0-7566-0551-3(2)) Dorling Kindersley Publishing, Inc.

—Star Wars Classic. 2004. (Ultimate Sticker Bks.). 16p. (J). pap. 6.99 (978-0-7566-0764-7(7)) Dorling Kindersley Publishing, Inc.

Dorling Kindersley Publishing Staff & Karney, Robin, eds. Cinema Year by Year 1894-2004. 2004. 1024p. 50.00 (978-0-7566-0508-7(3)) Dorling Kindersley Publishing, Inc.

Dougall, Alastair. James Bond: The Secret World of 007. Worrall, Dave, ed. Stewart, Roger, illus. 2000. 144p. (J). 19.99 (978-0-7894-6691-4(0)) Dorling Kindersley Publishing, Inc.

Dunham, M. L. Disney's Junior Encyclopedia of Animated Characters: Including Characters from Your Favorite Disney Pixar Films. 2004. (Illus.). 192p. (gr. 2-6). 17.99 (978-0-7868-3434-1(X) , Disney Editions) Disney Pr.

Dunkleberger, Amy. So You Want to Be a Film or TV Director? 2007. (Careers in Film & Television Ser.). (Illus.). 128p. (YA). (gr. 5-10). lib. bdg. 31.93 (978-0-7660-2738-1(4)) Enslow Pubs., Inc.

—So You Want to Be a Film or TV Screenwriter? 2007. (Careers in Film & Television Ser.). (Illus.). 128p. (YA). (gr. 5-10). lib. bdg. 31.93 (978-0-7660-2645-2(0)) Enslow Pubs., Inc.

England, Tamara, ed. Lights! Camera! Felicity! the Making of the Felicity Movie. 2005. (American Girls Collection). (Illus.). (J). pap. 9.95 (978-1-59369-062-5(2) , American Girl) American Girl Publishing, Inc.

Fernandes, Lindsay, ed. Princess: The Essential Guide. 2003. (Disney Princess Ser.). (Illus.). 48p. (J). pap. 12.99 (978-0-7894-9830-4(8)) Dorling Kindersley Publishing, Inc.

Film. 2001. (Finditquick Ser.). (Illus.). 32p. (J). pap. 6.99 (978-0-307-10537-0(7) , Golden Bks.) Random Hse. Children's Bks.

Fiscus, James W. Meet King Kong. 2004. (Famous Movie Monsters Ser.). (Illus.). 48p. lib. bdg. 26.50 (978-1-4042-0270-2(6)) Rosen Publishing Group, Inc., The.

Foster, Walter, ed. Finding Nemo. 2003. (Disney's How to Draw Classic Character Ser.). (Illus.). 32p. (J). pap. 5.95 (978-1-56010-689-0(1)) Foster, Walter Publishing, Inc.

Franks, Katie. I Want to Be a Movie Star. 2007. (Dream Jobs Ser.). (Illus.). 24p. (J). (gr. 3-5). lib. bdg. 21.25 (978-1-4042-3619-6(8)) Rosen Publishing Group, Inc., The.

Gifford, Clive. So You Think You Know James Bond. 2007. 140p. pap. 8.95 (*978-0-340-93198-1(1)*) Hodder Children's Division GBR. *Dist:* Independent Pubs. Group.

Glencoe McGraw-Hill Staff. Understanding the Film. 5th ed. 2001. 51.32 (978-0-8442-2349-0(2)) Glencoe/McGraw-Hill.

Golden Books Staff. Hold Your Sea Horses! 2004. (Illus.). 64p. (J). (ps-2). pap. 3.99 (978-0-375-82895-9(8) , Golden Bks.) Random Hse. Children's Bks.

Green, Naima. Meet Frankenstein. 2004. (Famous Movie Monsters Ser.). (Illus.). 48p. lib. bdg. 26.50 (978-1-4042-0268-9(4)) Rosen Publishing Group, Inc., The.

Greenberger, Robert. Meet Godzilla. 2004. (Famous Movie Monsters Ser.). (Illus.). 48p. lib. bdg. 26.50 (978-1-4042-0269-6(2)) Rosen Publishing Group, Inc., The.

Gregory, Deborah. The Cheetah Girls Supa-Star Scrapbook. 2005. (Illus.). (J). (*978-1-4155-9670-8(0)* , Jump at the Sun) Hyperion Bks. for Children.

Harland, Joan & Timmons, Nick. As Film Studies. 2006. (Illus.). 234p. (YA). pap. 49.50 (978-0-7487-9030-2(6)) Nelson Thornes Ltd. GBR. *Dist:* Trans-Atlantic Pubns., Inc.

Hess, Jared & Hess, Jerusha. Napoleon Dynamite: Flippin' Sweet! Simon and Schuster Children's Staff, ed. 2005. (Illus.). 176p. 3.99 (978-1-4169-1914-8(7)) Simon & Schuster Children's Publishing.

High Interest Books: Backstage Pass. 2004. (Illus.). 100.00 (978-0-516-29632-6(9)) Scholastic Library Publishing.

Higman, Anita. Lights! Camera! Action! A Fun Look at the Movies. 1999. (Cover-to-Cover Bks.). (Illus.). 56p. (J). pap. (978-0-7891-2866-9(7)); (gr. 4-7). lib. bdg. 17.95 (978-0-7807-7837-5(5) , Covercraft) Perfection Learning Corp.

Hill, Mary. Let's Go to a Movie. 2004. (Welcome Bks.). (J). (ps-2). pap. 4.95 (978-0-516-25917-8(2) , Children's Pr.) Scholastic Library Publishing.

Hofer, Charles. Meet Dracula. 2004. (Famous Movie Monsters Ser.). 26.50 (978-1-4042-0267-2(6)) Rosen Publishing Group, Inc., The.

Horn, Geoffrey M. Writing, Producing, & Directing Movies. 2006. (Illus.). 32p. (J). lib. bdg. (978-0-8368-6841-8(2)) Stevens, Gareth Inc.

Hughes, Morgan. Entertainment Hall of Fame. 2000. (Halls of Fame Ser.). (Illus.). 24p. (J). (gr. 2-6). lib. bdg. 23.93 (978-1-55916-267-8(8)) Rourke Publishing, LLC.

Hurley, Joe. Screen Scene. 2001. (Celebrity Quiz O-Rama Ser.: No. 3). (Illus.). 104p. (J). (gr. 2-6). pap. 3.99 (978-0-439-24410-7(2)) Scholastic, Inc.

Hyland, Tony. Film & Fiction Robots. 2007. (J). (*978-1-59920-120-7(8)*) Smart Apple Media.

The Island of the Skog. 2004. 24.95 incl. audio (978-0-89719-883-7(2)); pap. 32.75 incl. audio (978-1-55592-249-8(X)); pap. 14.95 incl. audio (978-1-56008-057-2(4)) Weston Woods Studios, Inc.

Jones, Sarah. Film. 2003. (Media Wise Ser.). (Illus.). 64p. (J). lib. bdg. 28.50 (978-1-58340-256-6(X)) Smart Apple Media.

Kenworthy, Christopher. Christopher Kenworthy: The World of Cinema. 2000. (World of Ser.). (Illus.). 96p. (gr. 5 up). 27.50 (978-0-237-52038-0(9) , Evans Brothers, Limited) Evans Publishing Group GBR. *Dist:* Independent Pubs. Group.

King, Viki. How to Write a Movie in 21 Days. 2001. (gr. 7-12). lib. bdg. 24.60 (978-0-613-64732-8(7)) Tandem Library Bks.

Kramer, Peter & Paul Willetts. American Film: An A-Z Guide. 2003. (Watts Reference Ser.). (Illus.). 128p. (J). 34.00 (978-0-531-12313-3(8) , Watts, Franklin) Scholastic Library Publishing.

Lekich, John. Reel Adventures: The Savvy Teens' Guide to Great Movies. 2002. 176p. (YA). (gr. 12). pap. 8.95 (978-1-55037-735-4(3)) Annick Pr., Ltd. CAN. *Dist:* Firefly Bks., Ltd.

—Reel Adventures: The Savvy Teens' Guide to Great Movies. 2002. (gr. 7-12). lib. bdg. 17.60 (978-0-613-78437-5(5)) Tandem Library Bks.

Little Sparrow. 2004. pap. 9.99 (978-0-307-14298-6(1)) Random Hse., Inc.

Luceno, James. Star Wars: Revenge of the Sith: The Visual Dictionary. Ivanov, Alex, photos by. 2005. (Star Wars Ser.). (Illus.). 64p. (J). 19.99 (978-0-7566-1128-6(8) , 1241618) Dorling Kindersley Publishing, Inc.

Luceno, James & Dorling Kindersley Publishing Staff. Inside the World of Star Wars Trilogy: The Ultimate Guide to the Incredible Locations of Episodes (IV, V & VI) Chasemore, Richard & Jenssen, Hans, illus. 2004. 48p. (J). 19.99 (978-0-7566-0307-6(2)) Dorling Kindersley Publishing, Inc.

Lund, Kristin, et al. Star Wars Complete Locations: Inside the Worlds of Episodes I-VI. Chasemore, Richard, illus. 2005. 176p. (J). (ps-7). 39.99 (978-0-7566-1419-5(8)) Dorling Kindersley Publishing, Inc.

McAlpine, Margaret. Working in Film & Television. 2004. (My Future Career Ser.). (Illus.). 64p. (J). lib. bdg. 26.00 (978-0-8368-4237-1(5)) Stevens, Gareth Inc.

McCracken, Kristin. Freddie Prinze, Jr. 2001. (gr. 7-12). lib. bdg. 15.25 (978-0-613-52058-4(0)) Tandem Library Bks.

Morina, Barbara. Films a Movie Lovers Journal. Morina, Barbara, ed. 2003. (Write It down Ser.). (Illus.). 202p. 19.95 (978-1-892033-34-5(8)) Journals Unlimited, Inc.

Munyon, Russ. Twelve Angry Men. 2000. (Literary Companion to American Literature Ser.). (Illus.). 156p. (YA). (gr. 9 up). 36.20 (978-0-7377-0314-6(8) , Greenhaven Pr., Inc.) Thomson Gale.

Murdico, Suzanne J. Meet the Blob. 2004. (Famous Movie Monsters Ser.). (Illus.). 48p. lib. bdg. 26.50 (978-1-4042-0271-9(4)) Rosen Publishing Group, Inc., The.

Norwich, Grace. Daniel Radcliffe: No Ordinary Wizard. 2005. (Illus.). 128p. (J). pap. 4.99 (978-1-4169-1390-0(4) , Simon Spotlight) Simon & Schuster Children's Publishing.

O'Brien, Lisa. Lights, Camera, Action! Making Movies & TV from the Inside Out. MacEachern, Stephen, illus. 2nd ed. 2007. 64p. (J). (gr. 3-7). 21.95 (978-1-897066-88-1(0)); pap. 10.95 (978-1-897066-89-8(9)) Maple Tree Pr. CAN. *Dist:* Perseus Distribution.

Parish, James Robert. Steven Spielberg, Filmmaker. 2003. (Ferguson Career Biographies Ser.). (Illus.). 160p. (J). (gr. 6-12). 25.00 (978-0-8160-5481-7(9) , Ferguson Publishing Co.) Facts On File, Inc.

Pelusey, Michael & Pelusey, Jane. Film & Television (Media) 2005. (Media Ser.). (Illus.). 32p. (J). (ps-8). lib. bdg. 21.95 (978-0-7910-8802-9(2) , Chelsea Hse.) Facts On File, Inc.

Platt, Richard. Film. 2000. (Eyewitness Bks.). (Illus.). 64p. (J). (gr. 4-7). 15.99 (978-0-7894-5587-1(0)) Dorling Kindersley Publishing, Inc.

Platt, Richard & Dorling Kindersley Publishing Staff. Film. 2000. (Eyewitness Bks.). (Illus.). 64p. (J). (gr. 4-7). lib. bdg. 19.99 (978-0-7894-6583-2(3)) Dorling Kindersley Publishing, Inc.

Pope, Marcia & McRoberts, Richard. Gattaca. 2003. (Wizard Study Guides Ser.). 64p. pap., stu. ed. 6.00 (978-0-521-53615-8(4)) Cambridge Univ. Pr.

Poteet, Michael. The Lord of the Rings: The Two Towers Study Guide. 2002. 110p. (YA). ring bd. 14.99 (978-1-58609-190-3(5)) Progeny Pr.

Preller, James. Mummy Scrapbook. 1999. 48p. pap. 5.50 (978-0-439-05016-6(2)) Scholastic, Inc.

Rau, Dana Meachen. George Lucas: Creator of Star Wars. 1999. (Illus.). (J). (978-0-606-18149-5(0)) Tandem Library Bks.

Reynolds, David West. Attack of the Clones': The Visual DictionaryTM. Ivanov, Alex, photos by. 2002. (Star Wars Ser.). (Illus.). 64p. (J). (gr. 4-7). 19.99 (978-0-7894-8588-5(5)) Dorling Kindersley Publishing, Inc.

—Star Wars: Incredible Cross-Sections. Jenssen, Hans & Chasemore, Richard, illus. 1998. (Star Wars Ser.). 32p. (J). 19.95 (978-0-7894-3480-7(6)) Dorling Kindersley Publishing, Inc.

—Star Wars': The Visual Dictionary. Ivanov, Alexander, photos by. 1998. (Star Wars Ser.). (Illus.). 64p. (J). 19.99 (978-0-7894-3481-4(4)) Dorling Kindersley Publishing, Inc.

Richards, Andrea. Girl Director: A How-to Guide for the First-Time, Flat-Broke Film & Video Maker. McCallie, Elizabeth, illus. rev. ed. 2005. 121p. pap., pap. 17.95 (978-1-58008-675-2(6)) Ten Speed Pr.

—Girl Director: A How-to-Guide for the First-Time, Flat-Broke Filmaker (and Videomaker) (Illus.). 106p. (YA). pap. 17.95 (978-1-931497-00-8(1)) Girl Pr., Inc.

Richardson, Adele. Manners at the Movies. 2006. (First Facts Ser.). (978-0-7368-4294-5(2)) Capstone Pr., Inc.

Roca, Nuria. Que Es el Arte? Cine. 2004. (Libros Que Es el Arte? Ser.).Tr. of What Is Art? Movies. (SPA.). 36p. (J). pap. 6.95 (978-0-7641-2707-6(1)) Barron's Educational Series, Inc.

—What Is Art? Movies. 2004. (What Is Art? Bks.). (Illus.). 36p. (J). pap. 6.95 (978-0-7641-2703-8(9)) Barron's Educational Series, Inc.

Saunders, Catherine. Chicken Little: The Essential Guide. 2005. (Illus.). 48p. (J). (gr. 4-7). 12.99 (978-0-7566-1169-9(5)) Dorling Kindersley Publishing, Inc.

Scholastic, Inc. Staff. Making of the Naked Brothers Band. 2007. (Naked Brothers Band Ser.). 48p. (J). pap. 5.99 (*978-0-545-02071-8(9)*) Scholastic, Inc.

Scully, Michael. Reaching Teens Through Film & Music. Cannizzo, Karen A., ed. 2001. (Jesus in Modern Media Ser.: Vol. 2001-2002). 96p. (YA). pap. 19.95 (978-0-89837-176-5(7)) Pflaum Publishing Group.

—Reaching Teens Through Film & Music. 1999. (Jesus in Modern Media Ser.: Vol. 2000). 128p. (YA). pap. 19.95 (978-0-937997-60-4(9) , 3700) Pflaum Publishing Group.

Segall, Miriam. Career Building Through Digital Moviemaking. 2007. (J). (*978-1-4042-1945-8(5)*) Rosen Publishing Group, Inc., The.

Seibert, Brian. Jerome Robbins. 2005. (Library of American Choreographers). (Illus.). 48p. (J). (ps-ps). lib. bdg. 23.95 (978-1-4042-0448-5(2)) Rosen Publishing Group, Inc., The.

Singer, Michael. Bring Me That Horizon. Shaner, Timothy, illus. 2007. 176p. (ps-17). pap. 24.95 (*978-1-4231-0319-6(X)* , Disney Editions) Disney Pr.

Smith, Kath. Let's Make a Movie. Dodd, Emma, illus. 2003. 32p. (J). 16.95 (978-1-84089-190-4(4) , Zero to Ten, Limited) Evans Publishing Group GBR. *Dist:* Independent Pubs. Group.

Somervill, Barbara A. The History of the Motion Picture. 2006. (Timeline Library Ser.). (Illus.). 32p. (J). (gr. 2-6). 27.07 (978-1-59296-440-6(0)) Child's World, Inc.

Sublette, Guen. Here's Lookin' at Lizzie. (978-0-312-32669-2(6)) St. Martin's Pr.

Surrell, Jason. Haunted Mansion: From the Magic Kingdom to the Movies. 2003. (gr. 3-6). lib. bdg. 30.35 (978-0-613-89733-4(1)) Tandem Library Bks.

The Swiss Family Robinson. 2006. (Saddleback's Illustrated Classics). (J). (978-1-56254-938-1(3)) Saddleback Educational Publishing.

Die Theatre der Welt.Tr. of Theater of the World. (GER., Illus.). (YA). 31.95 (978-3-411-09061-7(8)) Bibliographisches Institut & F. A. Brockhaus AG DEU. *Dist:* Continental Bk. Co., Inc.

Thompson, Frank. Tim Burton's Nightmare Before Christmas: The Film, the Art, the Vision. 2002. (Illus.). 192p. pap. 17.95 (978-0-7868-5378-6(6)) Disney Pr.

Tolkien, J. R. R. Como Se Hizo el Senor de los Anillos. 2003. (Lord of the Rings Ser.). (SPA., Illus.). 192p. (J). 14.95 (978-84-450-7414-5(8)) Minotauro Ediciones ESP. *Dist:* Planeta Publishing Corp.

—Guia de Fotos. 2003. (Lord of the Rings Ser.). (SPA., Illus.). 48p. (J). 7.95 (978-84-450-7415-2(6)) Minotauro Ediciones ESP. *Dist:* Planeta Publishing Corp.

Tolkien, J. R. R. & Brawn, David. The Lord of the Rings: The Two Towers Creatures. 2002. (Illus.). 48p. (gr. 3-6). pap. 8.95 (978-0-618-25811-6(6)) Houghton Mifflin Co. Trade & Reference Div.

Trailblazers of the Modern World: Neil Armstrong; Bob Dylan; Bill Gates; Nelson Mandela; Eleanor Roosevelt; Steven Spielberg, 6 bks. 2002. (Illus.). (J). (gr. 5 up). pap. 87.60 (978-0-8368-5234-9(6) , World Almanac Library) Stevens, Gareth Inc.

Triumph Books Staff. Hilary Duff: Total Hilary, Metamorphosis, Lizzie McGuire. . . & More. 2003. (Illus.). 80p. pap. 9.95 (978-1-57243-625-1(5)) Triumph Bks.

Valentine, Emily. Steven Spielberg: With a Discussion of Imagination. 2004. (Values in Action Biographies Ser.). (J). (978-1-59203-072-9(6)) Learning Challenge, Inc.

Vander Hook, Sue. Film. 1999. (Making Contact Ser.). (Illus.). 32p. (YA). (gr. 4 up). lib. bdg. 16.95 (978-1-887068-65-9(1)) Smart Apple Media.

Vaz, Mark Cotta. Mythic Vision: The Making of Eragon. 2006. (Mythic Vision Ser.). 144p. (YA). (gr. 7). pap. 12.95 (978-0-375-83917-7(8) , Knopf Bks. for Young Readers) Random Hse. Children's Bks.

Wessling, Katherine. Backstage at a Movie Set. 2003. (High Interest Bks.). (Illus.). 48p. (YA). (gr. 7-12). pap. 6.95 (978-0-516-24387-0(X) , Children's Pr.) Scholastic Library Publishing.

—Backstage at a Movie Set. 2003. (gr. 7-12). lib. bdg. 15.25 (978-0-613-59577-3(7)) Tandem Library Bks.

White. Search & Find Columbia Tristar. 2000. 48p. (J). pap. 0.95 (978-0-06-444294-7(2)) HarperCollins Pubs.

Whos Who at the Zoo. 2004. pap. 9.99 (978-0-307-14272-6(8)) Random Hse., Inc.

Willian, Michael. The Essential It's a Wonderful Life Film Guidebook: A scene by scene look at a holiday Classic. 2004. (Illus.). 140p. per. 15.95 (978-0-9762429-0-1(7)) Kerpluggo Bks. LLC.

Wilshin, Mark. A Cinematic History of Gangsters & Detectives. 2005. (Illus.). 32p. (978-1-4109-2009-6(7)) Steck-Vaughn.

Windham, Ryder. Star Wars: The Ultimate Visual Guide. 2007. 176p. (J). 24.99 (*978-0-7566-3052-2(5)*) Dorling Kindersley Publishing, Inc.

Windham, Ryder. Star Wars: Episode I: Adventures. 1999. 108p. (J). (978-0-439-12987-9(7)) Scholastic, Inc.

Woog, Adam. Frankenstein. 2005. 48p. (gr. 4-8). 26.20 (978-0-7377-3164-4(8) , Greenhaven Pr., Inc.) Thomson Gale.

—Godzilla. 2004. (Illus.). 48p. (J). (gr. 4-7). 26.20 (978-0-7377-2616-9(4) , Greenhaven Pr., Inc.) Thomson Gale.

Wooley, John & Price, Michael H. The Big Book of Biker Flicks: 40 of the Best Motorcycle Movies of All Times, 1. 2005. (Illus.). 168p. pap. 24.95 (978-1-930709-45-4(5)) HAWK Publishing Group.

Wormser, Richard. To the Young Filmmaker: Conversations with Working Filmmakers. 2002. (To the Young Ser.). (Illus.). 128p. (YA). (gr. 8-10). pap. 24.00 (978-0-531-11727-9(8) , Watts, Franklin) Scholastic Library Publishing.

Wright, Greg. Peter Jackson in Perspective: The Power Behind Cinema's the Lord of the Rings: A Look at Hollywood's Take on Tolkien's Epic Tale. 2004. 212p. per. 13.95 (978-0-9759577-0-7(8)) Hollywood Jesus Bks.

MOTION PICTURES—BIOGRAPHY

see also Actors and Actresses

Ada, Alma Flor & Campoy, F. Isabel, contrib. by. Pasos. (Literature Collection of Puertas Al Sol Ser.). (SPA.). 32p. (J). (gr. k-6). pap. 13.95 (978-1-59437-704-4(9)) Santillana USA Publishing Co., Inc.

—Voces. (Literature Collection of Puertas Al Sol Ser.). (SPA.). 32p. (J). (gr. k-6). pap. 13.95 (978-1-59437-707-5(3)) Santillana USA Publishing Co., Inc.

Alter, Judy. Christopher Reeve: Triumph over Tragedy. 2000. (Book Report Biographies Ser.). (Illus.). 112p. (YA). (gr. 6-8). pap. 6.95 (978-0-531-16455-6(1) , Watts, Franklin) Scholastic Library Publishing.

Aronson, Virginia. Drew Barrymore. (Overcoming Adversity Ser.). (Illus.). (YA). 2000. 112p. 30.00 (978-0-7910-5306-5(7)); 1999. 128p. pap. 30.00 (978-0-7910-5307-2(5)) Facts On File, Inc. (Chelsea Hse.).

—Drew Barrymore. 2000. (gr. 5-8). lib. bdg. 18.75 (978-0-613-21469-8(2)) Tandem Library Bks.

Blue, Rose & Naden, Corinne J. Halle Berry. 2001. (Black Americans of Achievement Ser.). (Illus.). 103p. (J). (gr. 8-12). pap. 30.00 (978-0-7910-5803-9(4) , Chelsea Hse.) Facts On File, Inc.

Brown, Jonatha A. Steven Spielberg. 19.33 (978-0-8368-4585-3(4)); 2005. (Illus.). 24p. (J). pap. (978-0-8368-4476-4(9)); 2005. (Illus.). 24p. (YA). lib. bdg. 19.33 (978-0-8368-4469-6(6)) Stevens, Gareth Inc.

Brown, Lauren. Emma Roberts: Simply Fabulous! 2007. 128p. (J). pap. 5.99 (978-1-4169-0822-7(6) , Simon Spotlight) Simon & Schuster Children's Publishing.

Chapman, Ferguson. Spike Lee. 1998. (Ovations Ser.). (Illus.). 32p. (YA). (gr. 4-7). lib. bdg. (978-0-88682-697-0(7) , Creative Education) Creative Co., The.

Dempsey, Amy. Brad Pitt. 1999. (Superstars of Film Ser.). (Illus.). 48p. (YA). (gr. 5 up). lib. bdg. 18.65 (978-0-7910-4649-4(4) , Chelsea Hse.) Facts On File, Inc.

Dougherty, Terri. Hillary Duff. 2007. (People in the News Ser.). (Illus.). 128p. (gr. 7-10). 31.20 (***978-1-4205-0012-7(0)*** , Lucent Bks.) Thomson Gale.

—Jennifer Lopez. 2007. (Twentieth Century Most Influential Hispanics Ser.). (Illus.). 128p. (J). (gr. 7-10). 31.20 (***978-1-4205-0021-9(X)*** , Lucent Bks.) Thomson Gale.

Dougherty, Terri. Orlando Bloom. 2005. (People in the News Ser.). (Illus.). 112p. (YA). (gr. 7-10). lib. bdg. 32.45 (978-1-59018-714-2(8) , Lucent Bks.) Thomson Gale.

Edge, Laura Bufano. Steven Spielberg: Director of Blockbuster Films. 2008. (J). (***978-0-7660-2888-3(7)***) Enslow Pubs., Inc.

Epstein, Dwayne. Hilary Swank. 2006. 112p. (gr. 7-10). 32.45 (978-1-59018-856-9(X) , Lucent Bks.) Thomson Gale.

Ferber, Elizabeth. Steven Spielberg. 2000. (Pop Culture Legends Ser.). (978-0-606-19355-9(3)) Tandem Library Bks.

Ford, Carin T. Walt Disney: Meet the Cartoonist. 2003. (Meeting Famous People Ser.). (Illus.). 32p. (J). (gr. 1-4). lib. bdg. 22.60 (978-0-7660-1857-0(1)) Enslow Pubs., Inc.

Galaxy of Superstars. 2005. pap. 925.00 (978-0-7910-9145-6(7) , Chelsea Hse.) Facts On File, Inc.

Gish, Melissa. Steven Spielberg. 1999. (Ovations Ser.). (Illus.). 32p. (YA). (gr. 4-7). 15.95 (978-0-88682-832-5(5) , Creative Education) Creative Co., The.

Gogerly, Liz. Halle Berrry. 2004. (Star Files Ser.). (Illus.). 48p. 29.93 (978-1-4109-1085-1(7)) Harcourt Schl. Pubs.

Gonzalez, Juan Carlos. Francois Truffaut -una vida hecha Cine. 2005. 150p. pap. (978-958-30-1686-8(1)) Panamericana Editorial.

Gosling, Maureen, et al. You Can Be a Woman Movie Maker. l.t. ed. 2003. (Illus.). 80p. (J). 19.95 incl. DVD (978-1-880599-64-8(3)); pap. 14.95 incl. DVD (978-1-880599-63-1(5)) Cascade Pass, Inc.

Gottfried, Ted. Steven Spielberg. 2000. (gr. 5-8). lib. bdg. 15.25 (978-0-613-54690-4(3)) Tandem Library Bks.

—Steven Spielberg: From Reels to Riches. 2000. (Book Report Biographies Ser.). (Illus.). 112p. (YA). (gr. 6-8). pap. 6.95 (978-0-531-16493-8(4) , Watts, Franklin) Scholastic Library Publishing.

Graziano, Jim. Johnny Depp. 2007. (J). (***978-1-4222-0200-5(3)***) Mason Crest Pubs.

Hasday, Judy L. Extraordinary People in the Movies. 2003. (Extraordinary People Ser.). (Illus.). 208-288p. (J). (gr. 6 up). 40.00 (978-0-516-22348-3(8) , Children's Pr.) Scholastic Library Publishing.

Hawes, Esme. Pamela Anderson Lee. 1999. (Superstars of Film Ser.). (Illus.). 48p. (YA). (gr. 5 up). lib. bdg. 18.65 (978-0-7910-4647-0(8) , Chelsea Hse.) Facts On File, Inc.

Hill, Anne E. Cameron Diaz. 1999. (Galaxy of Superstars Ser.). (Illus.). 64p. (YA). (gr. 3 up). pap. 25.00 (978-0-7910-5334-8(2)); 25.00 (978-0-7910-5234-1(6)) Facts On File, Inc. (Chelsea Hse.).

—Cameron Diaz. 2000. (gr. 5-8). lib. bdg. 17.60 (978-0-613-21283-0(5)) Tandem Library Bks.

—Denzel Washington: Actor. 1999. (Black Americans of Achievement Ser.). (Illus.). 96p. (J). (gr. 4-7). pap. 9.95 (978-0-7910-4693-7(1)); 32.00 (978-0-7910-4692-0(3)) Facts On File, Inc. (Chelsea Hse.).

Hughes, Mary. Jim Carrey. 1999. (Overcoming Adversity Ser.). (Illus.). 128p. (YA). (gr. 5 up). pap. 9.95 (978-0-7910-4699-9(0) , Chelsea Hse.) Facts On File, Inc.

Koopmans, Andy. Filmmakers. 2005. (History Makers Ser.). (Illus.). 112p. (YA). (gr. 7-10). lib. bdg. 29.95 (978-1-59018-598-8(6) , Lucent Bks.) Thomson Gale.

Kramer, Barbara. Ron Howard: Child Star & Hollywood Director. 1998. (People to Know Ser.). (Illus.). 112p. (YA). (gr. 6-12). lib. bdg. 26.60 (978-0-89490-981-8(9)) Enslow Pubs., Inc.

Latinos in the Limelight. 2005. pap. 357.50 (978-0-7910-8728-2(X) , Chelsea Hse.) Facts On File, Inc.

Lynette, Rachel. Tim Burton, Filmmaker. 2006. (Inventors & Creators Ser.). 48p. (gr. 4-8). 27.45 (978-0-7377-3556-7(2) , Greenhaven Pr., Inc.) Thomson Gale.

Mara, Wil. Steven Spielberg. 2005. (Rookie Biographies(R) Ser.). (Illus.). (gr. 1-2). 31p. (J). pap. 4.95 (978-0-516-25821-8(4)); 32p. 20.50 (978-0-516-21842-7(5)) Scholastic Library Publishing. (Children's Pr.).

Marcovitz, Hal. Ron Howard. 2002. (Behind the Camera Ser.). (Illus.). 112p. (YA). (gr. 6-12). 30.00 (978-0-7910-6716-1(5) , Chelsea Hse.) Facts On File, Inc.

McAvoy, Jim. Tom Hanks. 1999. (Galaxy of Superstars Ser.). (Illus.). 64p. (YA). 25.00 (978-0-7910-5235-8(4) , Chelsea Hse.) Facts On File, Inc.

McDaniel, Melissa. Spike Lee: On His Own Terms. 1999. (Book Report Biographies Ser.). (Illus.). 112p. (YA). (gr. 6-8). pap. 6.95 (978-0-531-15935-4(3) , Watts, Franklin) Scholastic Library Publishing.

McMeans, Bonnie. James Cameron. 2002. (Behind the Camera Ser.). (Illus.). 112p. (J). (gr. 6-12). 30.00 (978-0-7910-6713-0(0) , Chelsea Hse.) Facts On File, Inc.

Moerbeek, Kees. Alfred Hitchcock: The Master of Suspense: A Pop-Up Book. 2006. (Illus.). 16p. 29.95 (978-0-689-87595-3(9) , Little Simon) Simon & Schuster Children's Publishing.

Noble, Sandy. Mel Gibson. 1999. (Superstars of Film Ser.). (Illus.). 48p. (J). (gr. 4-7). lib. bdg. 18.65 (978-0-7910-4643-2(5) , Chelsea Hse.) Facts On File, Inc.

Parish, James Robert. Jim Henson: Puppeteer & Filmmaker. 2006. 144p. (gr. 6-12). 25.00 (978-0-8160-5834-1(2) , Ferguson Publishing Co.) Facts On File, Inc.

Powell, Elfreda. Robert De Niro. 1999. (Superstars of Film Ser.). (Illus.). 48p. (YA). (gr. 5 up). 12.95 (978-0-7910-4645-6(1) , Chelsea Hse.) Facts On File, Inc.

Powers, Tom. Steven Spielberg. (Just the Facts Biographies Ser.). (Illus.). 112p. (J). (gr. 6-12). 2005. 27.93 (978-0-8225-2473-1(2)); 2003. pap. 7.95 (978-0-8225-9694-3(6)) Lerner Publishing Group.

Preszler, June. Walt Disney. 2003. (Photo-Illustrated Biographies Ser.). (Illus.). 24p. (J). lib. bdg. 19.93 (978-0-7368-2226-8(7) , Bridgestone Bks.) Capstone Pr., Inc.

Richardson, Adele D. The Story of Disney. 2003. (Built for Success Ser.). (Illus.). 48p. (J). 19.95 (978-1-58340-291-7(8)) Smart Apple Media.

Riehecky, Janet. George Lucas: An Unauthorized Biography. 2001. (Profiles Ser.). (Illus.). 56p. (J). (gr. 4-6). lib. bdg. 24.22 (978-1-58810-057-3(X)) Heinemann Library.

Sandison, David. Sharon Stone. 1999. (Superstars of Film Ser.). (Illus.). 48p. (YA). (gr. 5 up). 12.95 (978-0-7910-4650-0(8) , Chelsea Hse.) Facts On File, Inc.

Schoell, William. Magic Man: The Life & Films of Steven Spielberg. 1998. (Illus.). 128p. (J). (gr. 4-7). 18.95 (978-0-936389-57-8(5)) Tudor Pubs., Inc.

Schuman, Michael. Halle Berry: Beauty Is Not Just Physical. 2006. (African-American Biography Library). (Illus.). 112p. (YA). lib. bdg. 31.93 (978-0-7660-2467-0(9)) Enslow Pubs., Inc.

Seibert, Brian. Jerome Robbins. 2005. (Library of American Choreographers). (Illus.). 48p. (J). (ps-ps). lib. bdg. 23.95 (978-1-4042-0448-5(2)) Rosen Publishing Group, Inc., The.

Shields, Charles J. Georges Lucas. 2002. (Behind the Camera Ser.). (Illus.). 112p. (J). (gr. 6-12). 30.00 (978-0-7910-6712-3(2) , Chelsea Hse.) Facts On File, Inc.

—Spike Lee. 2002. (Behind the Camera Ser.). (Illus.). 112p. (J). (gr. 6-12). 30.00 (978-0-7910-6715-4(7) , Chelsea Hse.) Facts On File, Inc.

Simon, Charnan. Walt Disney: Creator of Magical Worlds. 2000. (Community Builders Ser.). (Illus.). 48p. (J). (gr. 3-5). pap. 6.95 (978-0-516-26515-5(6) , Children's Pr.) Scholastic Library Publishing.

Sirimarco, Elizabeth. Steven Spielberg. 2002. (Behind the Camera Ser.). (Illus.). 112p. (J). (gr. 6-12). 30.00 (978-0-7910-6714-7(9) , Chelsea Hse.) Facts On File, Inc.

Snyder, Gail. Jake Gyllenhaal. 2007. (J). (***978-1-4222-0203-6(8)***) Mason Crest Pubs.

Spears, Britney & Culotta, Felicia. Britney Spears' Crossroads Diary. movie tie-in ed. 2002. (Illus.). 48p. (J). (gr. 4-7). pap. 5.99 (978-0-439-39745-2(6)) Scholastic, Inc.

Steven Spielberg. 2006. (People We Should Know Ser.). (SPA.). (J). (gr. 3-4). 4.76 (978-0-8368-4592-1(7) , GHS33828) Stevens, Gareth Inc.

Stone, Amy. Jackie Chan. 2006. (Today's Superstars). (Illus.). 32p. (J). (gr. 5 up). lib. bdg. 23.93 (***978-0-8368-7648-2(2)***) Stevens, Gareth Inc.

—Jim Carrey. 2007. (Today's Superstars). 32p. (J). (gr. 5 up). lib. bdg. 23.93 (***978-0-8368-8197-4(4)***) Stevens, Gareth Inc.

Taliadoros, Jenny, ed. Alice Faye: Glamorous Movie Star Paper Dolls & Costumes. Mingo, Norman & Ernst, Clara, illus. 2007. 8p. pap. 12.00 (***978-0-9795053-0-0(5)***) Paper Studio Pr.

—Bette Davis Paper Dolls. Mingo, Norman & Ernst, Clara, illus. 2007. 8p. (J). pap. 12.00 (***978-0-9790668-2-5(4)***) Paper Studio Pr.

—Betty Grable Paper Dolls. 2007. 8p. pap. 12.00 (***978-0-9790668-7-0(5)***) Paper Studio Pr.

—Deanna Durbin Paper Dolls. Mingo, Norman & Ernst, Clara, illus. 2007. 8p. pap. 12.00 (***978-0-9790668-5-6(9)***) Paper Studio Pr.

—Doris Day Paper Dolls. 2007. 8p. pap. 12.00 (***978-0-9790668-4-9(0)***) Paper Studio Pr.

—Greer Garson Paper Dolls. Madan, Fredric & Ernst, Clara, illus. 2007. 8p. pap. 12.00 (***978-0-9790668-6-3(7)***) Paper Studio Pr.

—Judy Garland Cut-Out Dolls. 2007. (Illus.). 8p. pap. 12.00 (***978-0-9790668-9-4(1)***) Paper Studio Pr.

—Lana Turner Paper Dolls. Valliant, Regina & Meixner, Jo Hedwig, illus. 2007. 8p. (J). pap. 12.00 (***978-0-9790668-1-8(6)***) Paper Studio Pr.

—Rita Hayworth Paper Doll: Dancing Star Dolls & Clothes. Mingo, Norman & Ernst, Clara, illus. 2007. 8p. (J). pap. 12.00 (***978-0-9790668-0-1(8)***) Paper Studio Pr.

Thomas, William David. Johnny Depp. 2006. (Today's Superstars). (Illus.). 32p. (J). (gr. 5 up). lib. bdg. 23.93 (***978-0-8368-7650-5(4)***) Stevens, Gareth Inc.

Tracy, Kathleen. Johnny Depp. 2007. (Blue Banner Biography Ser.). (Illus.). 32p. (J). (gr. 4-8). lib. bdg. 25.70 (***978-1-58415-614-7(7)***) Mitchell Lane Pubs., Inc.

Watts, Franklin, et al. George Lucas: Creator of Star Wars. 1999. (Book Report Bios Ppbk Ser.). (Illus.). 112p. (YA). pap. 6.95 (978-0-531-15951-4(5) , Watts, Franklin) Scholastic Library Publishing.

Weber, Terri Smith. Halle Berry: Fighting for First. 2003. (J). pap. (978-0-9740180-8-9(2)); lib. bdg. (978-0-9740180-7-2(4)) Panda Publishing, L.L.C. (Bios for Kids).

Wellman, Sam. Ben Affleck. 1999. (Galaxy of Superstars Ser.). (Illus.). 64p. (YA). (gr. 4-7). pap. 25.00 (978-0-7910-5331-7(8)); (J). (gr. 10). 25.00 (978-0-7910-5231-0(1)) Facts On File, Inc. (Chelsea Hse.).

—Ben Affleck. 2000. (Galaxy of the Superstars Ser.). (gr. 5-8). lib. bdg. 17.60 (978-0-613-21191-8(X)) Tandem Library Bks.

Westbrook, Caroline. Leonardo DiCaprio: The Illustrated Story. rev. ed. 2000. (Illus.). 76p. (YA). (978-0-600-59883-1(7) , Hamlyn) Octopus Publishing Group.

Wheeler, Jill C. Jim Carrey. 2001. (Star Tracks Ser.). (Illus.). 64p. (J). (gr. 3-8). lib. bdg. 25.65 (978-1-57765-556-5(7) , ABDO & Daughters) ABDO Publishing Co.

—Julia Roberts. 2001. (Star Tracks Ser.). (Illus.). 64p. (J). (gr. 3-8). lib. bdg. 25.65 (978-1-57765-555-8(9) , ABDO & Daughters) ABDO Publishing Co.

—Tom Cruise. 2001. (Star Tracks Ser.). (Illus.). 64p. (J). (gr. 3-8). lib. bdg. 25.65 (978-1-57765-553-4(2) , ABDO & Daughters) ABDO Publishing Co.

—Tom Hanks. 2001. (Star Tracks Ser.). (Illus.). 64p. (J). (gr. 3-8). lib. bdg. 25.65 (978-1-57765-554-1(0) , ABDO & Daughters) ABDO Publishing Co.

Woog, Adam. Steven Spielberg. 1998. (People in the News Ser.). (Illus.). 112p. (YA). (gr. 6-9). 27.45 (978-1-56006-361-2(0) , Lucent Bks.) Thomson Gale.

MOTION PICTURES—FICTION

Abela, Deborah. Mission: Hollywood. O'Connor, George, illus. 2006. (Spy Force Ser.). 240p. (J). 9.95 (978-0-689-87360-7(3)) Simon & Schuster Children's Publishing.

Abela, Deborah. Mission: Hollywood. O'Connor, George, illus. 2007. (Spy Force Ser.). 240p. (J). pap. 5.99 (***978-1-4169-3969-6(5)*** , Aladdin) Simon & Schuster Children's Publishing.

Appleton, Victor. The Moving Picture Boys on the Coast or Showing up the Perils of the Deep. 2004. reprint ed. pap. 24.95 (978-1-4179-1612-2(5)) Kessinger Publishing, LLC.

Appleton, Victor. Tom Swift & His Wizard Camera or Thril. 2006. pap. (***978-1-4065-0912-0(4)***) Dodo Pr.

Bell, Cece. Sock Monkey Rides Again. Bell, Cece, illus. 2006. (Illus.). 32p. (J). (ps-2). 13.99 (978-0-7636-3089-8(6)) Candlewick Pr.

Berenstain, Stan & Berenstain, Jan. The Berenstain Bears Go Hollywood. 1999. (Berenstain Bears Big Chapter Bks.). (J). (gr. 2-6). (978-0-606-17264-6(5)) Tandem Library Bks.

Block, Francesca Lia. Violet & Claire. 2000. (J). (978-0-606-20003-5(7)) Tandem Library Bks.

Brunelle, Lynn. Elmo's Movie Star Diary. Walz, Richard, illus. Bridges, James, photos by. 1999. (J). 7.99 (978-0-375-80132-7(4) , Random Hse. Bks. for Young Readers) Random Hse. Children's Bks.

Buchanan, Paul & Randall, Rod. Shooting Stars, Vol. 8. 1998. (Misadventures of Willie Plummett Ser.: Vol. 8). (Illus.). 128p. (J). (gr. 3-7). 5.99 (978-0-570-05087-2(1)) Concordia Publishing Hse.

Butcher, Nancy. Lights! Camera! Action Dog! l.t. ed. 2000. (Wishbone Mysteries Ser.: No. 11). (Illus.). 139p. (J). (gr. 4 up). lib. bdg. 23.33 (978-0-8368-2694-4(9)) Stevens, Gareth Inc.

Castellucci, Cecil. Boy Proof. 208p. (YA). (gr. 9 up). 2005. 15.99 (978-0-7636-2333-3(4)); 2006. reprint ed. pap. 7.99 (978-0-7636-2796-6(8)) Candlewick Pr.

Decary, Marie & Beshwaty, Steve. Le Bon Roi Adam. 2002. (Premier Roman Ser.). (FRE., Illus.). 64p. pap. (978-2-89021-534-4(2)) Diffusion du livre Mirabel.

deGroat, Diane. Annie Pitts, Swamp Monster. 2001. (978-0-606-22334-8(7)) Tandem Library Bks.

DK Publishing Staff. Ratatouille: The Guide to Remy's World. 2007. 48p. (J). (gr. 1-4). 12.99 (978-0-7566-2991-5(8)) Dorling Kindersley Publishing, Inc.

Donkin, Andrew & Dorling Kindersley Publishing Staff. Terrorcon Attack. 2005. (Dk Readers Ser.). (Illus.). 48p. (J). (ps-k). 14.99 (978-0-7566-1149-1(0)) Dorling Kindersley Publishing, Inc.

Donkin, Andrew, et al. Terrorcon Attack. 2005. (Dk Readers Ser.). (Illus.). 48p. (J). (ps-7). pap. 3.99 (978-0-7566-1150-7(4)) Dorling Kindersley Publishing, Inc.

Durkee, Sarah. Over the Hedge: Movie Storybook. 2006. (Over the Hedge Ser.). (Illus.). 56p. (J). pap. 8.99 (978-0-439-80145-4(1)) Scholastic, Inc.

Dussling, Jennifer. Creep Show. Spackman, Jeff, illus. 1999. (Eek! Stories to Make You Shriek Ser.). (J). (978-0-606-19883-7(0)) Tandem Library Bks.

Emerson, B. Alice. Ruth Fielding in Moving Pictures or Help. 2006. 32.99 (***978-1-4280-2942-2(7)***) IndyPublish.com.

Farshtey, Greg. Legends of Metru Nui. 2004. (Bionicle Adventures Ser.: No. 4). (Illus.). 144p. (J). (gr. 4-7). 4.99 (978-0-439-62747-4(8)) Scholastic, Inc.

Fox, Hugh. Wobbley Zombies. 2004. 64p. (J). per. 5.95 (978-1-930648-80-7(4)) Goose River Pr.

Gaiman, Neil. MirrorMask. McKean, Dave, illus. ed. 2005. 80p. (J). 16.99 (978-0-06-082110-4(8)) ; lib. bdg. 17.89 (978-0-06-082110-4(8)) HarperCollins Pubs.

Gorgas, Paula Blais. Little Lost Leprechaun. 2006. (Illus.). 24p. (J). lib. bdg. 24.95 (978-0-9778651-4-7(2)) Dragonfly Publishing, Inc.

Hartinger, Brent. Split Screen: Attack of the Soul-Sucking Brain Zombies/Bride of the Soul-Sucking Brain Zombies. 2007. 304p. (J). (gr. 9 up). 16.99 (978-0-06-082408-2(5)); lib. bdg. 17.89 (978-0-06-082409-9(3)) HarperCollins Pubs. (HarperTeen).

Hope, Laura Lee. Moving Picture Girls or First Appearance. 2007. 41.99 (***978-1-4280-5187-4(2)***); pap. 35.99 (***978-1-4280-5159-1(7)***) IndyPublish.com.

Inches, Alison. Barbie: Super Spy. Wolcott, Karen, illus. 2005. (Starring Barbie Ser.: Vol. 4). (J). (***978-1-4155-7688-5(2)*** , Golden Bks.) Random Hse. Children's Bks.

Jordan, Apple. Color & Activity No. 2: Suburban Invasion. Simpson, Fiona, ed. 2006. (Over the Hedge Ser.). (Illus.). 48p. (J). pap. 3.99 (978-0-439-80148-5(6) , Scholastic) Scholastic, Inc.

Kaplan-Taylor, Maeve. At the Movies with Maeve. 2004. (Illus.). 36p. (J). 3.99 (978-0-9746587-4-2(X) , Beacon Street Girls) B*tween Productions, Inc.

Kendall, Jane. Miranda & the Movies. 1999. (Illus.). (J). (978-0-606-22059-0(3)) Tandem Library Bks.

Kido, Yukiko. Who's at the Movies? 2006. (I'm Going to Read Ser.). (Illus.). 32p. (J). pap. 3.95 (978-1-4027-3340-6(2)) Sterling Publishing Co., Inc.

Klise, Kate. Far from Normal. 2006. 240p. (J). pap. 16.99 (978-0-439-79447-3(1) , Scholastic Pr.) Scholastic, Inc.

Koeppel, Ruth. Nick Jr. Dora & Friends Movie Theater Storybook & Movie Projector. 2005. (Nick Jr. Movie Theater Ser.). (Illus.). 48p. (J). 24.99 (978-0-7944-0783-4(8)) Reader's Digest Assn., Inc., The.

Kowitt, Holly, adapted by. Batman Begins: Training Bruce Wayne. 2005. (Batman Begins Ser.). (Illus.). 32p. (J). (ps-ps). 3.99 (978-0-439-74112-5(2)) Scholastic, Inc.

Krulik, Nancy E. It's Snow Joke, No. 22. John and Wendy Staff, illus. 2006. (Katie Kazoo, Switcheroo Ser.: No. 22). 80p. (J). (gr. 2-5). pap. 3.99 (978-0-448-44396-6(1) , Grosset & Dunlap) Penguin Group (USA) Inc.

—Quiet on the Set!, No. 10. 2003. (Katie Kazoo, Switcheroo Ser.: No. 10). (gr. 3-6). lib. bdg. 11.80 (978-0-613-72524-8(7)) Tandem Library Bks.

Lantz, Francess L. Lights, Camera, Love! 2000. (gr. 3-6). lib. bdg. 11.80 (978-0-613-21906-8(6)) Tandem Library Bks.

Lloyd, Tanya. Jared Lester, Fifth Grade Jester. Newbigging, Martha, illus. 2006. 74p. (J). (gr. 3-5). 18.95 (978-1-55451-026-9(0)); pap. 7.95 (978-1-55451-025-2(2)) Annick Pr., Ltd. CAN. *Dist:* Firefly Bks., Ltd.

Martin, Ann M. Stacey's Movie. 1999. (Baby-Sitters Club Ser.: No. 130). 124p. (J). (gr. 3-7). pap. 4.50 (978-0-590-50389-1(8)) Scholastic, Inc.

Mitchelhill, Barbara. The Case of the Disappearing Daughter. Ross, Tony, illus. 2007. 72p. (J). (***978-1-59889-269-7(X)***) Stone Arch Bks.

Myers, Bill. My Life as Alien Monster Bait. Mangiat, Jeff, illus. 2005. (Incredible Worlds of Wally McDoogle Ser.: Vol. 2). 128p. (J). (ps-7). 9.99 (978-1-4003-0572-8(1)) Nelson, Thomas Inc.

Pfeffer, Susan Beth. Revenge of the Aztecs. 2004. 118p. (J). lib. bdg. 16.92 (***978-1-4242-0763-3(0)***) Fitzgerald Bks.

Poulsen, David A. The Hunk Machine No. 2: The Salt & Pepper Chronicles. 2nd rev. ed. 2007. 160p. pap. 6.95 (***978-1-55263-723-4(9)***) Key Porter Bks. CAN. *Dist:* Perseus Distribution.

Read along with Blue! 2005. (Blue's Clues Ser.). (Illus.). 128p. (J). pap. 7.99 (978-1-4169-0626-1(6) , Simon Spotlight/Nickelodeon) Simon & Schuster Children's Publishing.

Rey. Vive le Cinema. 16.95 (978-2-09-250166-5(6)) Nathan, Fernand FRA. *Dist:* Distribooks, Inc.

Rey, Margret & Rey, H. A. Curious George Goes to a Movie. 1998. (Curious George Ser.). (Illus.). 24p. (J). (gr. k-3). pap. 3.95 (978-0-395-91906-4(1)); tchr. ed. 12.95 (978-0-395-91901-9(0)) Houghton Mifflin Co. Trade & Reference Div.

Salas, Macarena, ed. Suburban Invasion/Invasion en las Afueras. 2006. (Over the Hedge Ser.: No. 2). (ENG & SPA., Illus.). 48p. (J). pap. 3.99 (978-0-439-80904-7(5) , Scholastic en Espanol) Scholastic, Inc.

Scholastic, Inc. Staff & Gikow, Louise. Shark Tale. 2004. (Shark Tale Ser.). (Illus.). 96p. (J). (gr. 2-5). pap. 4.99 (978-0-439-64144-9(6)) Scholastic, Inc.

Selzer, Adam. Pirates of the Retail Wasteland. 2008. 208p. (YA). (gr. 7). 15.99 (***978-0-385-73482-0(4)*** , Delacorte Bks. for Young Readers) Random Hse. Children's Bks.

Shan, Darren, pseud. Slawter. 2006. (Demonata Ser.: No. 3). 240p. (J). (gr. 10-17). 16.99 (978-0-316-01387-1(0)) Little Brown & Co.

—Slawter. 2007. (Demonata Ser.: No. 3). 240p. (J). (gr. 10-17). pap. 8.99 (***978-0-316-01388-8(9)***) Little, Brown Bks. for Young Readers.

Sheldon, Dyan. Confessions of a Teenage Hollywood Star. 2007. (Illus.). 208p. (YA). (gr. 7 up). pap. 7.99 (***978-0-7636-3408-7(5)***) Candlewick Pr.

Sordo, Maria Luisa Rodriguez. El Senor de Alfoz. 1998. (SPA.). (gr. 7-12). lib. bdg. 14.10 (978-0-613-80663-3(8)) Tandem Library Bks.

Sortland, Bjorn. The Dream Factory Starring Anna & Henry. Christianson, Emily V. & Hedin, Robert, trs. from NOR. Elling, Lars, illus. 2003. (Picture Bks.). 40p. (J). (ps-3). 15.95 (978-0-87614-009-3(6) , Carolrhoda Bks.) Lerner Publishing Group.

Stem, J. David & Weiss, David. Eloise in Hollywood. Enik, Ted, illus. 2006. (Eloise Ser.). 70p. (J). 17.95 (978-0-689-84289-4(9) , Simon & Schuster Children's Publishing) Simon & Schuster Children's Publishing.

Stolarz, Laurie Faria. Project 17. rev. ed. 2007. 256p. (gr. 7 up). 15.99 (***978-0-7868-3856-1(6)***) Hyperion Bks. for Children.

Vaughan, Christina. Artie Goes to Hollywood. 2000. (Artie Stories Ser.: Vol. 2). (Illus.). 34p. (J). (gr. 1-5). spiral bd. 18.95 (978-0-9641697-6-0(2) , You-Draw-It Bks.) Castlebrook Pubns.

Viz Communications Staff. Art of Pokemon: The Third Movie. 2001. (gr. 3-6). lib. bdg. 22.20 (978-0-613-79060-4(X)) Tandem Library Bks.

Weyn, Suzanne. Sleepover. novel ed. 2004. (Illus.). 104p. (J). pap. 4.99 (978-0-439-65787-7(3) , Scholastic Paperbacks) Scholastic, Inc.

Williams, Dar. Lights, Camera, Amalee. 2006. (Amalee Ser.: No. 2). 192p. (J). pap. 16.99 (978-0-439-80352-6(7) , Scholastic Pr.) Scholastic, Inc.

Wilsdon, Christina. Lights! Action! California! Hockerman, Dennis, illus. 2006. 26p. (J). 7.99 (978-1-59939-009-3(4) , Reader's Digest Young Families, Inc.) Reader's Digest Children's Publishing, Inc.

Wilson, Bob. Stanley Bagshaw & the Frantic Film Fiasco. (Illus.). 64p. (J). 7.95 (978-0-14-038024-8(8)) Penguin Bks., Ltd. GBR. *Dist:* Trafalgar Square Publishing.

Windham, Ryder. Hunt the Sun Runner Game Book. 2002. 108p. (J). (978-0-439-45908-2(7)) Scholastic, Inc.

MOTION PICTURES—PLAY WRITING

see Motion Picture Plays

MOTOR BOATS

see Motorboats

MOTOR BUSES

see Buses

MOTOR CARS

see Automobiles

MOTOR COURTS

see Hotels, Motels, etc.

MOTOR CYCLES

see Motorcycles

MOTOR SPORTS

see also Automobile Racing

2004. (Machines at Work Ser.). 24p. (J). (ps-3). lib. bdg. 21.36 Child's World, Inc.

Budd, E. S. ATVs. 2004. (Machines at Work Ser.). 24p. (J). (ps-3). 21.36 (978-1-59296-160-3(6)) Child's World, Inc.

Crawford, Cindy. Drag Racing Basics: Christmas Tree to Finish Line Has Something for All Drag Racing Enthusiasts. 2003. (Illus.). 168p. pap. 24.95 (978-0-929758-22-0(6)) Beeman Jorgensen, Inc.

Jeffries. Race Cars. 2003. (Monster Machines Ser.). (Illus.). 32p. (J). pap. 7.95 (978-1-4109-0057-9(6)) Raintree.

Maurer, Tracy. Moto Freestyle. 2002. (Radsports Guides). (Illus.). 48p. (gr. 4-8). 20.95 (978-1-58952-101-8(3)) Rourke Publishing, LLC.

Mezzanotte, Jim. Supermoto. 2006. (Illus.). 24p. (J). lib. bdg. 22.00 (978-0-8368-6426-7(3)) Stevens, Gareth Inc.

MotorSports, 16 bks. Incl. ATV Racing. McAuliffe, Bill. 1998. lib. bdg. 21.26 (978-0-7368-0024-2(7)); Demolition Derby. Savage, Jeff. 1995. lib. bdg. 21.26 (978-1-56065-259-5(4)); Drag Racing. Smith, Jay H. 1995. lib. bdg. 21.26 (978-1-56065-230-4(6)); Indianapolis 500. Dregni, Michael. 1994. lib. bdg. 21.26 (978-1-56065-205-2(5)); Kart Racing. Smith, Jay H. 1995. lib. bdg. 21.26 (978-1-56065-229-8(2)); Monster Truck Racing. Johnston, Scott. 1994. lib. bdg. 21.26 (978-1-56065-204-5(7)); Monster Truck Wars. Savage, Jeff. 1995. lib. bdg. 21.26 (978-1-56065-258-8(6)); Motocross Racing. Young, Jesse. 1995. lib. bdg. 21.26 (978-1-56065-228-1(4)); Motorcycle Racing. Dregni, Michael. 1994. lib. bdg. 21.26 (978-1-56065-207-6(1)); Mud Racing. Savage, Jeff. 1995. lib. bdg. 21.26 (978-1-56065-257-1(8)); Off-Road Truck Racing. McAuliffe, Bill. 1998. lib. bdg. 21.26 (978-0-7368-0026-6(3)); Powerboat Racing. Smith, Jay H. 1995. lib. bdg. 21.26 (978-1-56065-231-1(4)); Pro Stock Car Racing. Mara, W. P. 1998. lib. bdg. 21.26 (978-0-7368-0025-9(5)); Snowmobile Racing. Mara, W. P. 1998. lib. bdg. 21.26 (978-0-7368-0027-3(1)); Stock Car Racing. Dregni, Michael. 1994. lib. bdg. 21.26 (978-1-56065-206-9(3)); Truck & Tractor Pulling. Savage, Jeff. 1995. lib. bdg. 21.26 (978-1-56065-260-1(8)); 48p. (J). (gr. 3-4). (Illus.). Set lib. bdg. 255.20 (978-0-7368-0127-0(8) , Capstone High-Interest Bks.) Capstone Pr., Inc.

MotorSports Classroom Library. (gr. 4 up). lib. bdg. 24.95 (978-0-7368-8965-0(5)) Red Brick Learning.

MotorSports Complete Unit. (gr. 4 up). 142.95 (978-0-7368-8966-7(3)) Red Brick Learning.

New Action Sports, 6 bks. Incl. In-Line Skating Basics. Savage, Jeff. lib. bdg. 21.26 (978-1-56065-400-1(7)); Learning Martial Arts. Potts, Steve. lib. bdg. 21.26 (978-1-56065-403-2(1)); Mastering Martial Arts. Potts, Steve. lib. bdg. 21.26 (978-1-56065-404-9(X)); Skateboarding Basics. Jay, Jackson. lib. bdg. 21.26 (978-1-56065-374-5(4)); Snowboarding Basics. Jay, Jackson. lib. bdg. 21.26 (978-1-56065-401-8(5)); Wrestling Basics. Savage, Jeff. lib. bdg. 21.26 (978-1-56065-402-5(3)); 48p. (J). (gr. 3-4). 1996. (Illus.). Set lib. bdg. 127.56 (978-1-56065-654-8(9) , Capstone High-Interest Bks.) Capstone Pr., Inc.

Schuette, Sarah L. Drift Cars. 2008. (***978-1-4296-0826-8(9)***) Capstone Pr., Inc.

Schwartz, Tina P. Motocross Freestyle. 2004. (Edge Books, Dirt Bikes). (Illus.). 32p. (J). 16.95 (978-0-7368-2436-1(7)) Capstone Pr., Inc.

Sievert, Terri. Motocross Racing. 2004. (Edge Books, Dirt Bikes). (Illus.). 32p. (J). 16.95 (978-0-7368-2437-8(5)) Capstone Pr., Inc.

Tyson, Carolee. Factory Ride. 2004. 198p. (YA). per. 6.99 (978-0-9754459-0-7(1)) Pumpkin Ridge Publishing.

Weil, Ann. BMX Racing. 2004. (Edge Books, X-Sports). (Illus.). 32p. (J). lib. bdg. 22.60 (978-0-7368-2709-6(9)) Capstone Pr., Inc.

MOTOR TRUCKS

see Trucks

MOTORBOATS

Beyer, Mark. Speed Boat. 2001. (Built for Speed Ser.). (Illus.). 48p. (gr. 7-12). (J). 24.00 (978-0-516-23162-4(6)); (YA). pap. 6.95 (978-0-516-23265-2(7)) Scholastic Library Publishing. (Children's Pr.).

—Speed Boat. 2001. (gr. 7-12). lib. bdg. 15.25 (978-0-613-52185-7(4)) Tandem Library Bks.

Bullard, Lisa. Powerboats. 2004. (Pull Ahead Bks.). (Illus.). 32p. (J). (gr. k-2). lib. bdg. 22.60 (978-0-8225-0744-4(7)) Lerner Publishing Group.

Cooper, Jason. Power Boats. 1999. (Boats & Ships Discovery Library). (Illus.). 24p. (J). (gr. 1-4). lib. bdg. 19.27 (978-0-86593-564-8(5)) Rourke Publishing, LLC.

Graham, Ian. Superboats. 2003. 32p. pap. 7.50 (978-1-4034-3361-9(5)); (Illus.). (J). 24.22 (978-1-4034-0774-0(6)) Heinemann Library.

A History of Powered Ships. 2005. (Moving People, Things, & Ideas Ser.). (Illus.). 48p. (J). (ps-7). lib. bdg. 24.95 (978-1-4103-0660-9(7) , Blackbirch Pr., Inc.) Thomson Gale.

Jefferis. Speedboats. 2004. (Mean Machines Ser.). (Illus.). 64p. (J). pap. 8.95 (978-1-4109-0831-5(3)) Harcourt Schl. Pubs.

—Speedboats 6-Pack. 2004. (Illus.). (J). pap. 48.35 (978-1-4109-0836-0(4)) Harcourt Schl. Pubs.

Morris, Mark. Boats. 2004. (Mean Machines Ser.). (Illus.). 64p. (J). (gr. 6-8). lib. bdg. 32.79 (978-1-4109-0557-4(8)) Harcourt Schl. Pubs.

Parker, Steve. The Inside & Out Guide to Speed Machines. 2006. (Illus.). 32p. (J). (978-1-4034-9089-6(9)); pap. (978-1-4034-9096-4(1)) Heinemann Library.

Pike, Dag. Practical Motor Cruising. 2003. (Illus.). 192p. 22.95 (978-0-229-11827-4(5)) A & C Black GBR. *Dist:* MBI Distribution Services.

Sautter, Aaron. Hovercrafts. 2007. (Blazers—Horsepower Ser.). (Illus.). 32p. (J). (978-0-7368-6782-5(1) , 1264928) Capstone Pr., Inc.

—Speedboats. 2007. (Blazers—Horsepower Ser.). (Illus.). 32p. (J). (978-0-7368-6783-2(X) , 1264930) Capstone Pr., Inc.

Savage, Jeff. Hydroplane Boats. 2004. (Wild Rides! Ser.). (Illus.). 32p. (J). lib. bdg. 16.95 (978-0-7368-2430-9(8)) Capstone Pr., Inc.

Werther, Scott P. Lanchas Motorizadas. 2004. (Maquinas Extremas Ser.). (SPA & ENG., Illus.). 24p. (J). (gr. 3-6). lib. bdg. 17.25 (978-0-8239-6890-9(1) , Buenas Letra) Rosen Publishing Group, Inc., The.

—Lanchas Motorizadas 6 Packs. Individual Title. (On Deck en Espanol Ser.).Tr. of Powerboats. (SPA.). 24p. (gr. 4-5). 35.00 (978-0-7578-6419-3(8)) Rigby Education.

—Powerboats. 2002. (Reading Power Ser.). (Illus.). 24p. (J). (gr. 1). lib. bdg. 17.25 (978-0-8239-5957-0(0) , PowerKids Pr.) Rosen Publishing Group, Inc., The.

—Powerboats: Individual Title Six-Packs. (On Deck Ser.). 24p. (gr. 4-5). 35.00 (978-0-7578-1044-2(6)) Rigby Education.

MOTORCYCLES

Armentrout, D. Choppers. 2005. 24p. pap. 5.45 (978-1-59515-766-9(2)) Rourke Publishing, LLC.

—Dirt Bikes. 2005. 24p. pap. 5.45 (978-1-59515-767-6(0)) Rourke Publishing, LLC.

—Drag Bikes. 2005. 24p. pap. 5.45 (978-1-59515-768-3(9)) Rourke Publishing, LLC.

—Speedway Bikes. 2005. 24p. pap. 5.45 (978-1-59515-769-0(7)) Rourke Publishing, LLC.

—Sport Bikes. 2005. 24p. pap. 5.45 (978-1-59515-770-6(0)) Rourke Publishing, LLC.

—Touring Bikes. 2005. 24p. pap. 5.45 (978-1-59515-771-3(9)) Rourke Publishing, LLC.

Armentrout, David & Armentrout, Patricia. Bike Rallies. 2008. (J). (***978-1-60044-586-6(1)***) Rourke Publishing, LLC.

—Dirt Bikes. 2006. (Motorcycle Mania Ser.). (Illus.). 24p. (gr. 3-6). 17.95 (978-1-59515-453-8(1) , 1244371) Rourke Publishing, LLC.

—Drag Bikes. 2006. (Motorcycle Mania Ser.). (Illus.). 24p. (gr. 3-6). 17.95 (978-1-59515-454-5(X) , 1244372) Rourke Publishing, LLC.

—Motorcycle Gear. 2008. (J). (***978-1-60044-588-0(8)***) Rourke Publishing, LLC.

—Motorcycle Races. 2008. (J). (***978-1-60044-589-7(6)***) Rourke Publishing, LLC.

—On the Tracks. 2008. (J). (***978-1-60044-590-3(X)***) Rourke Publishing, LLC.

—Speedway Bikes. 2006. (Motorcycle Mania Ser.). (Illus.). 24p. (gr. 3-6). 17.95 (978-1-59515-455-2(8) , 1244373) Rourke Publishing, LLC.

—Sportbikes. 2006. (Motorcycle Mania Ser.). (Illus.). 24p. (gr. 3-6). 17.95 (978-1-59515-456-9(6) , 1244375) Rourke Publishing, LLC.

—Stunts, Tricks, & Jumps. 2008. (J). (***978-1-60044-591-0(8)***) Rourke Publishing, LLC.

—Touring Bikes. 2006. (Motorcycle Mania Ser.). (Illus.). 24p. (gr. 3-6). 17.95 (978-1-59515-457-6(4) , 1244376) Rourke Publishing, LLC.

—Travis Pastrana. 2005. (Discover the Life of a Sports Star Ser.). (Illus.). 24p. (gr. 1-4). 14.95 (978-1-59515-133-9(8)) Rourke Publishing, LLC.

Bailey, Katharine. Sport Bikes. 2007. (Illus.). 32p. (J). (gr. 2-9). (***978-0-7787-3013-2(1));*** pap. (***978-0-7787-3035-4(2)***) Crabtree Publishing Co.

Barnes, Pete. Harley & the Davidsons: Motorcycle Legends. 2007. (Badger Biographies Ser.). (Illus.). 112p. (J). pap. 12.95 (978-0-87020-380-0(0)) Wisconsin Historical Society.

Bender, Lionel. Cars & Motorcycles. 2006. (J). (978-1-59389-262-3(4)) Chrysalis Education.

Beyer, Mark. Motocicletas Del Pasado. 2004. (Transporte Ayer y Hoy Ser.). (SPA & ENG., Illus.). 24p. (J). (gr. 3-6). lib. bdg. 17.25 (978-0-8239-6854-1(5) , Buenas Letra) Rosen Publishing Group, Inc., The.

—Motorcycles of the Past. 2002. (Reading Power Ser.). (Illus.). 24p. (J). (gr. 1). lib. bdg. 17.25 (978-0-8239-5987-7(2) , PowerKids Pr.) Rosen Publishing Group, Inc., The.

Blackbirch. Motorcycles. 2001. (gr. 3-6). lib. bdg. 18.75 (978-0-613-89919-2(9)) Tandem Library Bks.

BMX Bikes, 6 vols. (gr. 4 up). 39.95 (978-0-7368-9288-9(5)) Red Brick Learning.

BMX Extreme. (Illus.). (J). (gr. 3-4). lib. bdg. 90.40 (978-0-7368-2549-8(5)) Capstone Pr., Inc.

Budd, E. S. BMX Bicycles. 2004. (Machines at Work Ser.). 24p. (J). (ps-3). 21.36 (978-1-59296-161-0(4)) Child's World, Inc.

Bullard, Lisa. Supercross Motorcycles. 2006. (Pull Ahead Books). (Illus.). 32p. (J). pap. 5.95 (978-0-8225-5898-9(X) , First Avenue Editions) Lerner Publishing Group.

Case, Jeremy. Scooters! The Ultimate Guide to the Coolest Ride! 2001. (gr. 3-6). lib. bdg. 11.80 (978-0-613-73330-4(4)) Tandem Library Bks.

David, Jack. Choppers. 2007. (Illus.). 24p. (J). lib. bdg. 19.95 (***978-1-60014-131-7(5)***) Bellwether Media.

—Choppers. 2007. (Torque: Motorcycles Ser.). (Illus.). 24p. (J). (gr. 3-7). lib. bdg. 20.00 (***978-0-531-18476-9(5)*** , Children's Pr.) Scholastic Library Publishing.

—Cruisers. 2007. (Illus.). 24p. (J). lib. bdg. 19.95 (***978-1-60014-132-4(3)***) Bellwether Media.

—Cruisers. 2007. (Torque: Motorcycles Ser.). (Illus.). 24p. (J). (gr. 3-7). lib. bdg. 20.00 (***978-0-531-18478-3(1)*** , Children's Pr.) Scholastic Library Publishing.

—Dirt Bikes. 2008. (Illus.). 24p. (J). lib. bdg. 19.95 (***978-1-60014-147-8(1)***) Bellwether Media.

—Enduro Motorcycles. 2007. (Illus.). 24p. (J). lib. bdg. 19.95 (***978-1-60014-133-1(1)***) Bellwether Media.

—Enduro Motorcycles. 2007. (Torque: Motorcycles Ser.). (Illus.). 24p. (J). (gr. 3-7). lib. bdg. 20.00 (***978-0-531-18479-0(X)*** , Children's Pr.) Scholastic Library Publishing.

—Harley Davidson Motorcycles. 2007. (Illus.). 24p. (J). lib. bdg. 19.95 (***978-1-60014-134-8(X)***) Bellwether Media.

—Harley Davidson Motorcycles. 2007. (Torque: Motorcycles Ser.). (Illus.). 24p. (J). (gr. 3-7). lib. bdg. 20.00 (***978-0-531-18480-6(3)*** , Children's Pr.) Scholastic Library Publishing.

—Moto-X Freestyle. 2007. (Illus.). 24p. (J). lib. bdg. 19.95 (978-1-60014-125-6(0)) Bellwether Media.

—Motocross Cycles. 2008. (Illus.). 24p. (J). lib. bdg. 19.95 (***978-1-60014-152-2(8)***) Bellwether Media.

—Motocross Racing. 2007. (Illus.). 24p. (J). lib. bdg. 19.95 (978-1-60014-124-9(2)) Bellwether Media.

—Sport Bikes. 2007. (Illus.). 24p. (J). lib. bdg. 19.95 (***978-1-60014-135-5(8)***) Bellwether Media.

—Sport Bikes. 2007. (Torque: Motorcycles Ser.). (Illus.). 24p. (J). (gr. 3-7). lib. bdg. 20.00 (***978-0-531-18682-4(2)*** , Children's Pr.) Scholastic Library Publishing.

—Touring Motorcycles. 2007. (Illus.). 24p. (J). lib. bdg. 19.95 (***978-1-60014-136-2(6)***) Bellwether Media.

—Touring Motorcycles. 2007. (Torque: Motorcycles Ser.). (Illus.). 24p. (J). (gr. 3-7). lib. bdg. 20.00 (***978-0-531-18683-1(0)*** , Children's Pr.) Scholastic Library Publishing.

David West. Motorcycle. 2006. (Illus.). 32p. (J). pap. (978-1-4109-2561-9(7)) Steck-Vaughn.

Davidson, Jean. My Daddy Makes the Best Motorcycles in the Whole Wide World, the Harley-Davidson. Hammerquist, Theresa, illus. 2004. (J). 16.95 (978-1-930596-26-9(X)) Amherst Pr.

Davidson, Jean & Oeflein, Jon Davidson. Riding Back in Time. Bauknecht, Julie, illus. 2006. (J). (978-1-930596-47-4(2)) Amherst Pr.

Dirt Bikes. (Horsepower Ser.). 32p. (YA). 7.95 (978-0-7368-5216-6(3)); 2005. (Illus.). (J). (gr. 3-4). lib. bdg. 180.80 (978-0-7368-4427-7(9)) Capstone Pr., Inc.

Doeden, Matt. Choppers. 2008. (Motor Mania Ser.). (J). lib. bdg. 26.60 (***978-0-8225-7288-6(5)*** , Lerner Pubns.) Lerner Publishing Group.

Doeden, Matt. Dirt Bikes. 2004. (Horsepower Ser.). (Illus.). 149p. (J). 19.93 (978-0-7368-2733-1(1)) Capstone Pr., Inc.

Dowds, Alan. High-Speed Superbikes. 2006. (Cool Wheels Ser.). (J). lib. bdg. (978-0-8368-6826-5(9)) Stevens, Gareth Inc.

Dubowski, Mark. Superfast Motorcycles. 2005. (Ultimate Speed Ser.). (Illus.). 32p. (J). lib. bdg. 25.27 (978-1-59716-081-0(4)) Bearport Publishing Co., Inc.

Eagen, Rachel. Street Bikes. 2007. (Illus.). 32p. (J). (gr. 2-9). (***978-0-7787-3014-9(X));*** pap. (***978-0-7787-3036-1(0)***) Crabtree Publishing Co.

Endres, Hollie. Mountain Biking. 2007. (Torque: Action Sports Ser.). (Illus.). 24p. (J). (gr. 3-7). lib. bdg. 20.00 (***978-0-531-18493-6(5)*** , Children's Pr.) Scholastic Library Publishing.

Fiske, Brian D. BMX Design & Equipment. 2004. (Edge Books BMX Extreme). (Illus.). 32p. (J). 16.95 (978-0-7368-2432-3(4)) Capstone Pr., Inc.

—BMX Events. 2004. (Edge Books BMX Extreme). (Illus.). 32p. (J). 16.95 (978-0-7368-2433-0(2)) Capstone Pr., Inc.

—BMX Greats. 2004. (Edge Books BMX Extreme). (Illus.). 32p. (J). 16.95 (978-0-7368-2434-7(0)) Capstone Pr., Inc.

—BMX History. 2004. (Edge Books BMX Extreme). (Illus.). 32p. (J). 16.95 (978-0-7368-2435-4(9)) Capstone Pr., Inc.

Franks, Katie. Choppers. 2007. (Motorcycles Ser.). (Illus.). 24p. (J). (gr. k-5). lib. bdg. 21.25 (978-1-4042-3654-7(6)) Rosen Publishing Group, Inc., The.

—Cool Bikes. 2007. (Motorcycles Ser.). (Illus.). 24p. (J). (gr. k-5). lib. bdg. 21.25 (978-1-4042-3655-4(4)) Rosen Publishing Group, Inc., The.

—Dirt Bikes. 2007. (Motorcycles Ser.). (Illus.). 24p. (J). (gr. k-5). lib. bdg. 21.25 (978-1-4042-3652-3(X)) Rosen Publishing Group, Inc., The.

—Motorcylces: Made for Speed, 6 bks., Set. Incl. Choppers. lib. bdg. 21.25 (978-1-4042-3654-7(6)); Cool Bikes. lib. bdg. 21.25 (978-1-4042-3655-4(4)); Dirt Bikes. lib. bdg. 21.25 (978-1-4042-3652-3(X)); Street Bikes. lib. bdg. 21.25 (978-1-4042-3656-1(2)); Superbikes. lib. bdg. 21.25 (978-1-4042-3653-0(8)); Tricks with Bikes. lib. bdg. 21.25 (978-1-4042-3657-8(0)); (Illus.). 24p. (J). (gr. k-5). 2007. 2007. Set lib. bdg. 127.50 (***978-1-4042-3604-2(X)***) Rosen Publishing Group, Inc., The.

—Street Bikes. 2007. (Motorcycles Ser.). (Illus.). 24p. (J). (gr. k-5). lib. bdg. 21.25 (978-1-4042-3656-1(2)) Rosen Publishing Group, Inc., The.

—Superbikes. 2007. (Motorcycles Ser.). (Illus.). 24p. (J). (gr. k-5). lib. bdg. 21.25 (978-1-4042-3653-0(8)) Rosen Publishing Group, Inc., The.

Freeman, Gary. Motocross. 2002. (Radical Sports Ser.). (Illus.). 32p. (J). (gr. 5-7). lib. bdg. 25.64 (978-1-58810-627-8(6)); pap. 7.50 (978-1-4034-0105-2(5) , 91653) Heinemann Library.

—Motocross. 2001. (To the Limit Ser.). (Illus.). 32p. (J). (gr. 4-7). lib. bdg. 25.69 (978-0-7398-3275-2(1)) Raintree.

Frisch, Aaron. Motorcross. 2002. (Illus.). 32p. (J). 24.25 (978-1-58340-164-4(4)) Smart Apple Media.

Gibbs, Lynne. Mega Book of Motorcycles. 2003. (Illus.). 32p. (YA). pap. (978-1-903954-57-7(6)) Chrysalis Children's Bks.

Goodman, Susan E. Motorcycles! Doolittle, Michael J., illus. 2007. (Step into Reading Ser.). 48p. (J). (gr. k-3). lib. bdg. 11.99 (***978-0-375-94116-0(9));*** per. 3.99 (***978-0-375-84116-3(4)***) Random Hse. Children's Bks. (Random Hse. Bks. for Young Readers).

Graham, Ian. Motorbikes. 2005. (World's Greatest Ser.). (Illus.). 32p. (J). (978-1-4109-2084-3(4)); pap. (978-1-4109-2091-1(7)) Steck-Vaughn.

—Motorcycles. 1999. (Built for Speed Ser.). (Illus.). 32p. (J). (gr. 3-7). lib. bdg. 25.69 (978-0-8172-4223-7(6)) Raintree.

—Motorcycles. 1998. (Worldwise Ser.). (Illus.). 40p. (J). (gr. 3-5). 23.00 (978-0-531-14464-0(X) , Watts, Franklin) Scholastic Library Publishing.

—Motorcycles. Connell, Tom, illus. 1998. (Built for Speed Ser.). 32p. (J). (gr. 3-7). pap. 7.95 (978-0-8172-8074-1(X)) Steck-Vaughn.

—Super Bikes. Hewetson, Nicholas, illus. 2001. (Fast Forward Ser.). 32p. (J). (gr. 4-8). 29.00 (978-0-531-14617-0(0)); pap. 9.95 (978-0-531-14809-9(2)) Scholastic Library Publishing. (Watts, Franklin).

—Super Bikes. 2001. (gr. 3-6). lib. bdg. 18.75 (978-0-613-54694-2(6)) Tandem Library Bks.

—Superbikes. 2003. 32p. pap. 7.50 (978-1-4034-3362-6(3)); (Illus.). (J). 24.22 (978-1-4034-0773-3(8)) Heinemann Library.

Hanson, Anders. Let's Go by Motorcycle. 2007. (Let's Go! Ser.). (ENG., Illus.). 24p. (J). (ps-3). lib. bdg. 19.93 (***978-1-59928-901-4(6)*** , SandCastle) ABDO Publishing Co.

Hatter, Hilda E. Bananas & Balloons: Inspirational Stories of Motorcycling Adventures. 2004. 307p. (YA). per. 15.99 (978-0-9761167-0-7(7)) TIGO & Co.

Hedrickson, Steve. Enduro Racing. 2000. (Motorcycles Ser.). (Illus.). 48p. (J). (gr. 3-4). lib. bdg. 21.26 (978-0-7368-0477-6(3) , Capstone High-Interest Bks.) Capstone Pr., Inc.

—Land Speed Racing. 2000. (Motorcycles Ser.). (Illus.). 48p. (J). (gr. 3-4). lib. bdg. 21.26 (978-0-7368-0476-9(5) , Capstone High-Interest Bks.) Capstone Pr., Inc.

—Supercross Racing. 2000. (Motorcycles Ser.). (Illus.). 48p. (J). (gr. 3-4). lib. bdg. 21.26 (978-0-7368-0479-0(X) , Capstone High-Interest Bks.) Capstone Pr., Inc.

Henshaw, Peter. The Encyclopedia of Motorcycles, 5 vols. 2000. (Illus.). (J). (978-0-7910-6053-7(5)); (978-0-7910-6054-4(3)); (978-0-7910-6055-1(1)); (978-0-7910-6056-8(X)); 96p. (gr. 4-7). 180.00 (978-0-7910-6052-0(7)); Set. (978-0-7910-6057-5(8)) Facts On File, Inc. (Chelsea Hse.).

Herran, Joe & Thomas, Ron. Motocross. 2003. (Action Sports Ser.). (Illus.). 32p. (J). (gr. 4-8). 28.00 (978-0-7910-7536-4(2) , Chelsea Hse.) Facts On File, Inc.

—Motorcycle Grand Prix Racing. 2002. (Action Sports Ser.). (Illus.). 32p. (gr. 4-8). 28.00 (978-0-7910-7001-7(8) , Chelsea Hse.) Facts On File, Inc.

Hill, Lee Sullivan. Motorcycles. 2004. (Pull Ahead Bks.). (Illus.). 32p. (J). (gr. k-2). 5.95 (978-0-8225-9924-1(4)); lib. bdg. 22.60 (978-0-8225-0695-9(5)) Lerner Publishing Group.

Jefferis. Motorbikes. 2004. (Mean Machines Ser.). (Illus.). 64p. (J). pap. 8.95 (978-1-4109-0832-2(1)) Harcourt Schl. Pubs.

—Superbikes. 2004. (Mean Machines Ser.). (Illus.). 64p. (J). 32.79 (978-1-4109-0558-1(6)) Harcourt Schl. Pubs.

—Superbikes 6-Pack. 2004. (Illus.). (J). pap. 48.35 (978-1-4109-0837-7(2)) Harcourt Schl. Pubs.

Jefferis, David. Super Bikes. (Monster Machines Ser.). (Illus.). 32p. (J). (ps-ps). 2003. pap. 7.95 (978-1-4109-0059-3(2)); 2001. lib. bdg. 25.69 (978-0-7398-2882-3(7)) Raintree.

—Super Bikes. 2003. (gr. 3-6). lib. bdg. 16.40 (978-0-613-78223-4(2)) Tandem Library Bks.

Kimber, David & Newland, Richard. Motorcycle-Mania! 2003. (Vehicle-Mania! Ser.). (Illus.). 32p. (J). (gr. 2 up). lib. bdg. 23.33 (978-0-8368-3783-4(5)) Stevens, Gareth Inc.

LeapFrog Staff, compiled by. The Bike Race. 2001. (J). (ps-2). spiral bd. 13.95 (978-1-58605-024-5(9)) LeapFrog Enterprises, Inc.

M N O

Levy, Janey. Freestyle Motocross. 2007. (Motocross Ser.). (Illus.). 32p. (J). (gr. 4-6). lib. bdg. 23.95 ***(978-1-4042-3694-3(5)***, PowerKids Pr.) Rosen Publishing Group, Inc., The.

—Motocross. 2007. (Motocross Ser.). (Illus.). 32p. (J). (gr. 4-6). lib. bdg. 23.95 ***(978-1-4042-3692-9(9)***, PowerKids Pr.) Rosen Publishing Group, Inc., The.

—Motocross, 6 bks., Set. Incl. Freestyle Motocross. lib. bdg. 23.95 ***(978-1-4042-3694-3(5)***); lib. bdg. 23.95 ***(978-1-4042-3692-9(9)***); Motocross Races. lib. bdg. 23.95 ***(978-1-4042-3696-7(1)***); Motocross Superstars. lib. bdg. 23.95 ***(978-1-4042-3695-0(3)***); Motocross Tricks. lib. bdg. 23.95 ***(978-1-4042-3697-4(X)***); Supercross. lib. bdg. 23.95 ***(978-1-4042-3693-6(7)***); (Illus.). 32p. (J). (gr. 4-6). 2007., PowerKids Pr. 2007. Set lib. bdg. 143.70 ***(978-1-4042-3611-0(2))*** Rosen Publishing Group, Inc., The.

—Motocross Races. 2007. (Motocross Ser.). (Illus.). 32p. (J). (gr. 4-6). lib. bdg. 23.95 ***(978-1-4042-3696-7(1)***, PowerKids Pr.) Rosen Publishing Group, Inc., The.

—Motocross Superstars. 2007. (Motocross Ser.). (Illus.). 32p. (J). (gr. 4-6). lib. bdg. 23.95 ***(978-1-4042-3695-0(3)***, PowerKids Pr.) Rosen Publishing Group, Inc., The.

—Motocross Tricks. 2007. (Motocross Ser.). (Illus.). 32p. (J). (gr. 4-6). lib. bdg. 23.95 ***(978-1-4042-3697-4(X)***, PowerKids Pr.) Rosen Publishing Group, Inc., The.

—Supercross. 2007. (Motocross Ser.). (Illus.). 32p. (J). (gr. 4-6). lib. bdg. 23.95 ***(978-1-4042-3693-6(7)***, PowerKids Pr.) Rosen Publishing Group, Inc., The.

Louck, Cheryl. The ABC's of Motocross. Zielinski, Dave, photos by. 2003. (Illus.). 24p. (J). per. 14.95 (978-0-9744230-0-5(9)) Louck, Cheryl.

Loves, June. Bicycles & Motorcycles. 2001. (Database Transportation Ser.). (Illus.). 32p. (J). (gr. 4 up). 22.95 (978-0-7910-6591-4(X), 010502, Chelsea Hse.) Facts On File, Inc.

Macken, JoAnn Early. Bike Riding. 2005. (Illus.). 24p. (J). pap. (978-0-8368-4519-8(6)); (YA). lib. bdg. 19.33 (978-0-8368-4512-9(9)) Stevens, Gareth Inc.

Mahaney, Ian F. Travis Pastrana: Motorcross Champion. 2005. (Extreme Sports Biographies Ser.). (Illus.). 24p. (J). 19.95 (978-1-4042-2748-4(2), PowerKids Pr.) Rosen Publishing Group, Inc., The.

Marx, Mandy. Motocross. 2006. (Blazers—To the Extreme Ser.). (Illus.). 32p. (J). (978-0-7368-5462-7(2)) Capstone Pr., Inc.

Marx, Mandy & Fox, Barbara J. Choppers. 2005. (Blazers—Horsepower Ser.). (Illus.). 32p. (J). (978-0-7368-4388-1(4)) Capstone Pr., Inc.

—Superbikes. 2005. (Blazers—Horsepower Ser.). (Illus.). 32p. (J). (978-0-7368-4391-1(4)) Capstone Pr., Inc.

Mattern, Joanne. Staying Safe on My Bike. 2006. (Illus.). 24p. (J). pap. ***(978-0-8368-7801-1(9)***); lib. bdg. ***(978-0-8368-7794-6(2))*** Stevens, Gareth Inc. (Weekly Reader Early Learning Library).

—Staying Safe on My Bike: La Seguridad en Mi Bicicleta. 2006. (Illus.). 24p. pap. ***(978-0-8368-8066-3(8)***); lib. bdg. ***(978-0-8368-8059-5(5))*** Stevens, Gareth Inc. (Weekly Reader Early Learning Library).

Maurer, Tracy. Moto Freestyle. 2002. (Radsports Guides). (Illus.). 48p. (gr. 4-8). 20.95 (978-1-58952-101-8(3)) Rourke Publishing, LLC.

McClellan, Ray. SuperMoto. 2008. (Illus.). 24p. (J). lib. bdg. 19.95 ***(978-1-60014-144-7(7))*** Bellwether Media.

Mezzanotte, Jim. Motocross. 2006. (Illus.). 24p. (J). pap. 5.95 (978-0-8368-6572-1(3)); lib. bdg. 22.00 (978-0-8368-6423-6(9)) Stevens, Gareth Inc.

—Superbike. 2006. (Illus.). 24p. (J). pap. 5.95 (978-0-8368-6573-8(1)); lib. bdg. 22.00 (978-0-8368-6424-3(7)) Stevens, Gareth Inc.

—Supercross. 2006. (J). lib. bdg. 22.00 (978-0-8368-6425-0(5)) Stevens, Gareth Inc.

—Supermoto. 2006. (Illus.). 24p. (J). pap. (978-0-8368-6575-2(8)) Stevens, Gareth Inc.

Milan, Garth. Freestyle Motocross II: Air Sickness. 2002. (gr. 5-8). lib. bdg. 30.35 (978-0-613-60556-4(X)) Tandem Library Bks.

Miller, Heather. Motocicletas. (Ruedas, Alas y Agua Ser.).Tr. of Motorcycles. 24p. pap. 5.25 (978-1-4034-3534-7(0)); 2003. (SPA., Illus.). (J). lib. bdg. 18.50 (978-1-4034-0918-8(8)) Heinemann Library.

—Motocicletas. 2003. Tr. of Motorcycles. (SPA.). (gr. k-3). lib. bdg. 13.30 (978-0-613-67423-2(5)) Tandem Library Bks.

—Motorcycles. 2003. (Wheels, Wings, & Water Ser.). (Illus.). 24p. (J). lib. bdg. 18.50 (978-1-4034-0881-5(5)); pap. (978-1-4034-3621-4(5)) Heinemann Library.

Morse, Jenifer Corr. Motorcycles. 2001. (J). 9.95 (978-1-56711-454-6(7)); (Illus.). 24p. (gr. 3-6). 21.20 (978-1-56711-470-6(9), Blackbirch Pr., Inc.) Thomson Gale.

Motocicletas del Pasado: Individual Title Six-Packs. (On Deck en Espanol Ser.).Tr. of Motorcycles of the Past. (SPA.). 24p. (gr. 4-5). 35.00 (978-0-7578-6427-8(9)) Rigby Education.

Motocross Cycles, 6 vols. (gr. 4 up). 39.95 (978-0-7368-9293-3(1)) Red Brick Learning.

Motocross Freestyle. (To the Extreme Ser.). 32p. (YA). 7.95 (978-0-7368-5225-8(5)) Capstone Pr., Inc.

Motor Bike. 2004. (Press-Out & Build Ser.). (Illus.). 24p. (J). per. (978-1-84229-724-7(4)) Top That! Publishing PLC.

Motorcycles of the Past: Individual Title Six-Packs. (On Deck Ser.). 24p. (gr. 4-5). 35.00 (978-0-7578-1052-7(7)) Rigby Education.

Mr Mcdoodle & His Scooter: 3-in-1 Package. (Sails Literacy Ser.). 24p. (gr. 2 up). 57.00 (978-0-7578-6831-3(2)) Rigby Education.

Mr Mcdoodle & His Scooter: 6 Small Books. (Sails Literacy Ser.). 24p. (gr. 2 up). 25.00 (978-0-7578-6827-6(4)) Rigby Education.

Mr Mcdoodle & His Scooter: Big Book Only. (Sails Literacy Ser.). 24p. (gr. 2 up). 27.00 (978-0-7578-6819-1(3)) Rigby Education.

Nix, Harvey. How to Ride a Bike: My Very First Learn-To Book. 2006. 92p. 14.95 (978-0-944353-22-6(3)) Rivendell Bk. Factory.

Norman, Tony. Motorbike Racing. 2006. (Illus.). 32p. (J). 24.67 (978-0-8368-6368-0(2)) Stevens, Gareth Inc.

O'Shei, Tim. Supercross Racing. 2006. (Edge Books, Dirt Bikes). (Illus.). 32p. (J). (978-0-7368-4366-9(3)) Capstone Pr., Inc.

Oxlade, Chris. Motorbikes. 2001. (Transportation Around the World Ser.). (Illus.). 32p. (J). (gr. k-2). lib. bdg. 21.36 (978-1-57572-305-1(0)) Heinemann Library.

—Motorcycles. (J). 2007. ***(978-1-59920-041-5(4))***; 2006. (Illus.). 31p. (978-1-58340-919-0(X), 1262374) Smart Apple Media.

Preszler, Eric. Harley-Davidson Motorcycles. 2004. (Wild Rides! Ser.). (Illus.). 32p. (J). lib. bdg. 16.95 (978-0-7368-2429-3(4)) Capstone Pr., Inc.

Raby, Philip. Motorbikes. 1999. (gr. 5-8). lib. bdg. 16.40 (978-0-613-84023-1(2)) Tandem Library Bks.

Raby, Philip & Nix, Simon. Motorbikes. 2005. (Need for Speed Ser.). (Illus.). 32p. (gr. 3-5). 23.93 (978-0-8225-9854-1(X)) Lerner Publishing Group.

Raby, Phillip. Motorbikes. 1999. (978-0-606-18824-1(X)) Tandem Library Bks.

Riggs, Kate. Motorcycles. 2007. (J). (978-1-58341-528-3(9), Creative Education) Creative Co., The.

Roberts, Cynthia. Motorcycles. 2007. (Machines at Work Ser.). 24p. (J). 22.79 (978-1-59296-833-6(3)) Child's World, Inc.

Sautter, Aaron. How to Draw Amazing Motorcycles. Smith, Tod, illus. 2008. (J). ***(978-1-4296-0073-6(X))*** Capstone Pr., Inc.

Savage, Jeff. Motorcycles. collector's ed. 2005. (Race Car Legends Ser.). (Illus.). 73p. (J). (gr. 4-8). lib. bdg. 25.00 (978-0-7910-8695-7(X), Chelsea Hse.) Facts On File, Inc.

—Travis Pastrana. 2006. (Illus.). (J). pap. 5.95 (978-0-8225-3433-4(9), First Avenue Editions) Lerner Publishing Group.

Schaefer, A. R. Extreme Freestyle Motocross Moves. 2003. (Behind the Moves Ser.). (Illus.). 32p. (J). (gr. 3-4). lib. bdg. 21.26 (978-0-7368-1512-3(0), Capstone High-Interest Bks.) Capstone Pr., Inc.

Schuette, Sarah L. Harley-Davidson Motorcycles. 2007. (Blazers—Horsepower Ser.). (Illus.). 32p. (J). 19.93 (978-0-7368-6449-7(0)) Capstone Pr., Inc.

Schwartz, Tina P. Motocross Freestyle. 2004. (Edge Books, Dirt Bikes). (Illus.). 32p. (J). 16.95 (978-0-7368-2436-1(7)) Capstone Pr., Inc.

Sherman, Josepha. The Story of Harley-Davidson. 2005. (Robbie Reader Ser.). (Illus.). 32p. (J). (gr. 1-4). lib. bdg. (978-1-58415-358-0(X), 1244893) Mitchell Lane Pubs., Inc.

Shofner, Shawndra. How It Happens at the Motorcycle Plant. Wolfe, Bob & Wolfe, Diane, photos by. 2006. (How It Happens Ser.). (Illus.). 32p. (J). (gr. 2-5). lib. bdg. 19.95 (978-1-881508-99-1(4)) Oliver Pr., Inc.

Sievert, Terri. Dirt Bike History. 2004. (Edge Books, Dirt Bikes). (Illus.). 32p. (J). 16.95 (978-0-7368-2439-2(1)) Capstone Pr., Inc.

—Motocross Racing. 2004. (Edge Books, Dirt Bikes). (Illus.). 32p. (J). 16.95 (978-0-7368-2437-8(5)) Capstone Pr., Inc.

—The World's Fastest Superbikes. 2002. (Built for Speed Ser.). (Illus.). 48p. (J). (gr. 3-4). lib. bdg. 21.26 (978-0-7368-1060-9(9), Capstone High-Interest Bks.) Capstone Pr., Inc.

Sloan, Peter. Parts of a Bike. 1999. (gr. k-3). lib. bdg. 11.80 (978-0-613-30663-8(5)) Tandem Library Bks.

Smedman, Lisa. From Boneshakers to Choppers: The Rip-Roaring History of Motorcycles. 2007. (Illus.). 120p. (YA). (gr. 7-12). 24.95 ***(978-1-55451-016-0(3)***; pap. 14.95 ***(978-1-55451-015-3(5))*** Annick Pr., Ltd. CAN. *Dist:* Firefly Bks., Ltd.

Stille, Darlene R. Motorcycles. 2004. (Illus.). 32p. (J). (gr. 1 up). 21.26 (978-0-7565-0607-0(7)) Compass Point Bks.

Streissguth, Thomas. Mini Bikes. 2008. (Illus.). 24p. (J). lib. bdg. 19.95 ***(978-1-60014-155-3(2))*** Bellwether Media.

—Off-Road Motorcycles. 2008. (Illus.). 24p. (J). lib. bdg. 19.95 ***(978-1-60014-156-0(0))*** Bellwether Media.

—Pocket Bikes. 2008. (Illus.). 24p. (J). lib. bdg. 19.95 ***(978-1-60014-157-7(9))*** Bellwether Media.

—Scooters. 2008. (Illus.). 24p. (J). lib. bdg. 19.95 ***(978-1-60014-158-4(7))*** Bellwether Media.

—Standard Motorcycles. 2008. (Illus.). 24p. (J). lib. bdg. 19.95 ***(978-1-60014-159-1(5))*** Bellwether Media.

Stuart, Dee. Motorcycles. 2001. (Transportation & Communication Ser.). (Illus.). 48p. (J). (gr. 1-4). lib. bdg. 23.93 (978-0-7660-1648-4(X)) Enslow Pubs., Inc.

Super Bikes. (Horsepower Ser.). 32p. (YA). 7.95 (978-0-7368-6172-4(6)) Capstone Pr., Inc.

Tiner, John Hudson. Motorcycles. (Illus.). 32p. 2004. pap. 8.95 (978-0-89812-389-0(5), Creative Paperbacks); 2003. (J). lib. bdg. 18.95 (978-1-58341-285-5(9), Creative Education) Creative Co., The.

West, David. Motorcycle. 2006. (Why Things Don't Work Ser.). (Illus.). 32p. (J). (gr. 4-6). lib. bdg. 29.29 (978-1-4109-2554-1(4)) Raintree.

Wilson, Hugo. The Ultimate Harley-Davidson Book. 2003. (Illus.). 208p. 25.00 (978-0-7894-9974-5(6)) Dorling Kindersley Publishing, Inc.

Windsor, Jo. Bikes: Early Level Satellite Individual Title Six-Packs. (Sails Literacy Ser.). 16p. (gr. 1-2). 27.00 (978-0-7578-6501-5(1)) Rigby Education.

Youngblood, Ed. Dirt Track Racing. 2000. (Motorcycles Ser.). (Illus.). 48p. (J). (gr. 3-4). lib. bdg. 21.26 (978-0-7368-0474-5(9), Capstone High-Interest Bks.) Capstone Pr., Inc.

—Hillclimbing. 2000. (Motorcycles Ser.). (Illus.). 48p. (J). (gr. 3-4). lib. bdg. 21.26 (978-0-7368-0475-2(7), Capstone High-Interest Bks.) Capstone Pr., Inc.

MOTORCYCLES—FICTION

Appleton, Victor. Tom Swift & His Motor Cycle. 2004. (Tom Swift Original Ser.: No. 1). 206p. (J). (ps-3). 17.95 (978-1-55709-175-8(7)) Applewood Bks.

—Tom Swift & His Motor Cycle. 2004. reprint ed. pap. 1.99 (978-1-4192-8459-5(2)) Kessinger Publishing, LLC.

—Tom Swift & His Motor Cycle. 2000. (Tom Swift Original Ser.: Vol. No. 1). 114p. (gr. 3-7). 19.95 (978-1-57646-353-6(2)); 114p. (gr. 3-7). pap. 7.95 (978-1-57646-201-0(3)); 180p. pap. 12.99 (978-1-57646-354-3(0)) Quiet Vision Publishing.

—Tom Swift & His MotorCycle. 2006. pap. ***(978-1-4068-0727-1(3))*** Echo Library.

—Tom Swift & His MotorCycle. 2006. 18.99 ***(978-1-4280-3267-5(3))*** IndyPublish.com.

—Tom Swift & His MotorCycle or Fun and. 2006. pap. ***(978-1-4065-0905-2(1))*** Dodo Pr.

Bike Safe! Life Safety Coloring/Activity Book. 2007. (Illus.). (J). ***(978-1-933934-31-0(X))*** Educational Adventures.

Blake, Quentin. Mrs. Armitage: Queen of the Road. Blake, Quentin, illus. 2003. (Illus.). 32p. (J). (gr. k-3). 15.95 (978-1-56145-287-3(4)) Peachtree Pubs., Ltd.

—Mrs. Armitage Queen of the Road. 2003. (Illus.). 32p. (978-0-224-06472-9(X), Jonathan Cape) Random Hse. Children's Bks. GBR. *Dist:* Random Hse. of Canada, Ltd.

Brown, Marc. The Mystery of the Stolen Bike. ed. 2005. (Arthur Chapter Bks.: Bk. 8). (Illus.). 59p. (J). lib. bdg. 15.00 (978-1-59054-745-8(4)) Fitzgerald Bks.

Bryant, Raymond. At the Races. 2004. (Funtime Rhymes Ser.). (Illus.). 10p. (J). bds. 4.95 (978-0-7641-5717-2(5)) Barron's Educational Series, Inc.

Carney, Charles. Harley-Davidson Great Rides. Eberhart, Donald G., illus. 2002. (J). 15.98 (978-0-7853-7043-7(9)) Publications International, Ltd.

Christopher, Matt. Dirt Bike Racer. 2007. lib. bdg. ***(978-1-59953-113-7(5))*** Norwood Hse. Pr.

Dad & the Bike Race, 6 Packs. (Sails Literacy Ser.). (gr. 1-2). 36.00 (978-0-7578-4003-6(5)) Rigby Education.

Dadey, Debbie & Jones, Marcia Thornton. Sea Monsters Don't Ride Motorcycles. 2000. (Bailey School Kids Ser.: No.40). (gr. 3-6). lib. bdg. 11.80 (978-0-613-26864-6(4)) Tandem Library Bks.

Davidson, Jean. My Grandma Rides a Harley: She's Cool! Bauknecht, Julie, illus. 2007. (J). ***(978-1-930596-79-5(0))*** Amherst Pr.

Davis, Terry. If Rock & Roll Were a Machine: A Novel. 2003. 174p. (YA). pap. 15.95 (978-0-910055-86-4(6)) Eastern Washington Univ. Pr.

Guest, Jacqueline. Lightning Rider. 2000. (SideStreets Ser.). (gr. 7-12). 168p. 7.95 (978-1-55028-720-2(6)); 162p. (YA). (978-1-55028-721-9(4)) Lorimer, James & Co., Ltd., Pubs. CAN. *Dist:* Casemate Pubs. & Bk. Distributors, LLC.

—Lightning Rider. 2001. (gr. 7-12). lib. bdg. 13.00 (978-0-613-78316-3(6)); (gr. 3-6). lib. bdg. 13.00 (978-0-613-54819-9(1)) Tandem Library Bks.

Harcourt School Publishers Staff. The Big Bike Race Level D: Reader. 2001. (Collections Ser.). (Illus.). (J). 6.90 (978-0-15-314372-4(X)) Harcourt Schl. Pubs.

Link, C. Edward. The Little Motorcycle. Serfass, Jim, illus. 2004. (J). 9.95 (978-0-9749615-0-7(7)) Roadracing World Publishing, Inc.

Maddox, Jake. Motorcross Double-Cross. Tiffany, Sean, illus. 2008. (J). pap. ***(978-1-59889-897-2(3)***; lib. bdg. ***(978-1-59889-845-3(0))*** Univ. of Minnesota Pr.

Mount, Jill. The Mystery of the Dirty Bike. 2005. 9.00 (978-0-8059-9778-1(4)) Dorrance Publishing Co., Inc.

Nelson, Scott. Patch the Porcupine & the Bike Shop Job. Nelson, Scott, illus. 2004. (Illus.). 28p. (J). 14.95 (978-0-9745715-3-9(9)) KRBY Creations, LLC.

Paulsen, Gary. Zero to Sixty: The Motorcycle Journey of a Lifetime. 1999. (gr. 7-12). lib. bdg. 21.10 (978-0-613-16042-1(8)) Tandem Library Bks.

Prince, Alison. A Biker's Ghost. 2002. (Illus.). 16p. pap. (978-0-582-42653-5(7), Putnam Juvenile) Penguin Group (USA) Inc.

Quigley, Daniel. A Face Full of Wind. 2003. 106p. (YA). pap. 10.95 (978-0-7414-1798-5(7)) Infinity Publishing.

Siebert, Diane. Motorcycle Song. Jenkins, Leonard, illus. 32p. (J). (ps-3). Date not set. 5.99 (978-0-06-443632-8(2)); 2002. 16.89 (978-0-06-028733-7(0)) HarperCollins Pubs.

St. George, Mark. The Wolfpack. 2001. 240p. (J). pap. 18.95 (978-0-9620541-3-6(5)) Proteus.

Strange, David. Why Grandpa Rides a Harley. 2005. 16.95 (978-0-9772771-0-0(0)) Cherry Tree Pr. LLC.

Townsend, John. The Omen & the Ghost. Cunningham, Kelley, illus. 2007. (J). 80p. ***(978-1-59889-353-3(X)***; 71p. pap. ***(978-1-59889-448-6(X))*** Stone Arch Bks.

Walters, Celeste. The Glass Mountain. 2003. 280p. (YA). pap. 17.00 (978-0-7022-3297-8(1)) Univ. of Queensland Pr. AUS. *Dist:* International Specialized Bk. Services.

Ward, Michael. Mike & the Bike. 2005. 32p. (J). per. 16.99 (978-1-59441-498-5(X), C04040) Carson-Dellosa Publishing Co., Inc.

MOTORING

see Automobile Travel

MOTORS

see Electric Motors; Engines

MOTT, LUCRETIA, 1793-1880

Davis, Lucile. Lucretia Mott. 1998. (Read-and-Discover Biographies Ser.). (J). pap. 14.00 (978-0-516-21272-2(9), Children's Pr.) Scholastic Library Publishing.

De Angelis, Gina. Lucretia Mott: Woman Suffragist. 2000. (Women of Achievement Ser.). (Illus.). 112p. (J). (gr. 4-7). 30.00 (978-0-7910-5295-2(8), Chelsea Hse.) Facts On File, Inc.

Sterling, Dorothy. Lucretia Mott. 3rd ed. 2004. (Illus.). 240p. (gr. 4-7). pap. 12.95 (978-1-55861-217-4(3)) Feminist Pr. at The City Univ. of New York.

MOUNDS AND MOUND BUILDERS

see also Excavations (Archaeology)

Kavasch, E. Barrie. The Mound Builders of Ancient America. 2003. (J). lib. bdg. (978-0-7613-2368-6(6), Twenty-First Century Bks.) Lerner Publishing Group.

McGowen, Tom. Giant Stones & Earth Mounds. 2000. (Women at War Ser.). (Illus.). 80p. (gr. 5-8). lib. bdg. 25.90 (978-0-7613-1372-4(9), Twenty-First Century Bks.) Lerner Publishing Group.

Rosebrough, Amy & Malone, Bobbie. Water Panthers, Bears, & Thunderbirds: Exploring the Effigy Mounds of Wisconsin. 2003. (New Badger History Ser.). (Illus.). 32p. (J). pap. 9.95 (978-0-87020-357-2(6)) Wisconsin Historical Society.

MOUNT RUSHMORE NATIONAL MEMORIAL (S.D.)

Ashley, Susan. Mount Rushmore. 2004. (Weekly Reader Early Learning Library). (Illus.). 24p. (J). (gr. 2 up). pap. 5.95 (978-0-8368-4149-7(2)); lib. bdg. 19.33 (978-0-8368-4142-8(5)) Stevens, Gareth Inc. (Weekly Reader Early Learning Library).

Bauer, Marion Dane. Mount Rushmore. Wallace, John, illus. 2007. (Wonders of America Ser.). 32p. (J). pap. 3.99 (978-1-4169-3477-6(4), Aladdin); lib. bdg. 13.89 (978-1-4169-3478-3(2), Aladdin Library) Simon & Schuster Children's Publishing.

Curlee, Lynn. Rushmore. (J). (gr. 3-5). (978-0-439-06013-4(3)) Scholastic, Inc.

—Rushmore: Monument for the Ages. 1998. 48p. (J). pap. 16.95 (978-0-590-22201-3(5)) Scholastic, Inc.

Jango-Cohen, Judith. Mount Rushmore. 2004. (Pull Ahead Bks.). (Illus.). 32p. (J). (gr. k-3). lib. bdg. 22.60 (978-0-8225-3801-1(6)) Lerner Publishing Group.

Koestler-Grack, Rachel A. Mount Rushmore. 2005. (American Moments Ser.). (Illus.). 48p. (J). (gr. 4-8). lib. bdg. 25.65 (978-1-59197-936-4(6)) ABDO Publishing Co.

Marcovitz, Hal. Mount Rushmore. 2002. (American Symbols & Their Meanings Ser.). (Illus.). 48p. (YA). (gr. 4 up). lib. bdg. (978-1-59084-027-6(5)) Mason Crest Pubs.

Murray, Julie. Mount Rushmore. 2005. (Buddy Book Ser.). (Illus.). 24p. (J). (gr. k-4). lib. bdg. 21.35 (978-1-57765-667-8(9)) ABDO Publishing Co.

Patrick, Jean L. S. Who Carved the Mountain? The Story of Mount Rushmore. Graef, Renee, illus. 2005. 37p. (J). 16.99 (978-0-9752617-4-3(6)) Mount Rushmore History Assn.

Rau, Dana Meachen. Mount Rushmore. 2002. (Let's See Library). (Illus.). 24p. (J). (gr. 1 up). lib. bdg. 19.93 (978-0-7565-0141-9(5)) Compass Point Bks.

Santella, Andrew. Mount Rushmore. 1999. (Cornerstones of Freedom Ser.). 32p. (gr. 4-6). pap. 5.95 (978-0-516-26459-2(1), Children's Pr.) Scholastic Library Publishing.

—Mount Rushmore. 1999. (gr. 3-6). lib. bdg. 14.10 (978-0-613-52148-2(X)) Tandem Library Bks.

Schaefer, Lola M. Mount Rushmore. (Symbols of Freedom Ser.). (Illus.). 32p. (J). (gr. k-2). 2002. pap. 6.95 (978-1-58810-397-0(8), 91192); 2001. lib. bdg. (978-1-58810-176-1(2)) Heinemann Library.

—Mount Rushmore. 2002. (gr. k-3). lib. bdg. 14.75 (978-0-613-68165-0(7)) Tandem Library Bks.

The Seasons of Mount Rushmore Coloring Book. 2006. (J). (978-0-9752617-7-4(0)) Mount Rushmore History Assn.

Sorensen, Lynda. El Monte Rushmore. Palacios, Argentina, tr. 2002. (Simbolos Americanos Ser.). (SPA., Illus.). 24p. mass mkt. 5.95 (978-1-58952-272-5(9), RK0023) Rourke Publishing, LLC.

MOUNT VERNON (VA. : ESTATE)

Santella, Andrew. Mount Vernon. 2004. (Illus.). 48p. (J). (gr. 4 up). lib. bdg. 22.60 (978-0-7565-0682-7(4)) Compass Point Bks.

MOUNTAIN CLIMBING

see Mountaineering

MOUNTAIN LIFE—SOUTHERN STATES

Fowler, Allan. Living in the Mountains. 2000. (gr. k-3). lib. bdg. 14.10 (978-0-613-54734-5(9)) Tandem Library Bks.

Santella, Andrew. Mountain Men. 2003. (Cornerstones of Freedom, 2ND Ser.). (Illus.). 48p. (J). 26.00 (978-0-516-24216-3(4), Children's Pr.) Scholastic Library Publishing.

MOUNTAIN LIFE—SOUTHERN STATES—FICTION

Collier, James Lincoln. Wild Boy. 2002. 160p. (YA). (gr. 4-7). 15.95 (978-0-7614-5126-6(9)) Cavendish, Marshall Corp.

Crum, Shutta. My Mountain Song. Rand, Ted, tr. Rand, Ted, illus. 2004. 32p. (J). (gr. k-3). tchr. ed. 16.00 (978-0-618-15970-3(3), Clarion Bks.) Houghton Mifflin Co. Trade & Reference Div.

Harshman, Marc & Collins, Bonnie. Rocks in My Pockets. Goffe, Toni, illus. 2002. 36p. (J). per. 6.95 (978-1-891852-23-7(X)) Quarrier Pr.

Heidi. 2006. 64p. (J). 8.99 (978-0-7945-1237-8(2), Usborne) EDC Publishing.

Henson, Heather. Angel Coming. Gaber, Susan, illus. 2005. 40p. (J). 15.95 (978-0-689-85531-3(1), Atheneum) Simon & Schuster Children's Publishing.

Johnston, Tony. Amber on the Mountain. Duncan, Robert, illus. 1998. (Picture Puffin Ser.). 32p. (J). (ps-3). pap. 6.99 (978-0-14-056408-2(X), Puffin) Penguin Group (USA) Inc.

—Amber on the Mountain. 1998. (Picture Puffin Ser.). (J). 13.79 (978-0-606-13119-3(1)) Tandem Library Bks.

M
N
O

Parker, Gary. Highland Hopes. 2001. (gr. 5-8). lib. bdg. 22.25 (978-0-613-55605-7(4)) Tandem Library Bks.

MOUNTAINEERING

Anderson, Jameson. A Day in the Life of a Mountain Rescue Team. 2006. (Illus.). 32p. (J). (978-1-4109-2510-7(2)); pap. (978-1-4109-2515-2(3)) Steck-Vaughn.

Armentrout, David. Climbing. 1998. (Outdoor Adventures Ser.). (Illus.). 24p. (J). (gr. 2-6). lib. bdg. 23.93 (978-1-57103-203-4(7)) Rourke Publishing, LLC.

Billings, Henry & Billings, Melissa. Climbing the World's Highest Mountains. 1999. (Livewire Investigates Ser.). (Illus.). 32p. pap. (978-0-340-74777-3(3) , Hodder Arnold) Hodder Education.

Boy Scouts of America Staff. Climbing. 1999. (Merit Badge Ser.). (Illus.). 96p. (YA). (gr. 6-12). pap. 2.90 (978-0-8395-5001-3(4)) Boy Scouts of America.

—Topping Out: A BSA Climbing - Rappelling Manual. 1999. (Illus.). 160p. (J). pap. 14.95 (978-0-8395-3207-1(5)) Boy Scouts of America.

Chapman, Simon. In the Himalayas. Chapman, Simon, illus. 2005. (Illus.). 103p. (J). lib. bdg. 20.00 (***978-1-4242-0626-1(X)***) Fitzgerald Bks.

Chester, Jonathan. Young Adventurers' Guide to Everest: From Avalanche to Zopkio. 2005. (Illus.). 48p. (J). 7.95 (978-1-58246-151-9(1) , Tricycle Pr.) Ten Speed Pr.

Deady, Kathleen W. Extreme Rock Climbing Moves. 2003. (Behind the Moves Ser.). (Illus.). 32p. (J). (gr. 3-4). lib. bdg. 21.26 (978-0-7368-1514-7(7) , Capstone High-Interest Bks.) Capstone Pr., Inc.

Dean, Cynthia A. & Rasinski, Timothy V. Rock Climbing: Making It to the Top. 2005. (High Five Reading Ser.). (Illus.). 48p. (978-0-7368-5745-1(1)); 17.95 (978-0-7368-5735-2(4)) Capstone Pr., Inc.

Doeden, Matt. Mountaineering Adventures. 2000. (Dangerous Adventures Ser.). (Illus.). 48p. (J). (gr. 3-4). lib. bdg. 21.26 (978-0-7368-0575-9(3) , Capstone High-Interest Bks.) Capstone Pr., Inc.

Doeden, Matt. Trapped in a Canyon! Aron Ralston's Story of Survival. 2007. (Illus.). 32p. (J). (***978-0-7368-6775-7(9)***) Capstone Pr., Inc.

Donkin, Andrew. Danger on the Mountain: Scaling the World's Highest Peaks. Martin, Linda, ed. 2001. (Readers Ser.). (Illus.). 48p. (J). (gr. 4-7). pap. 3.99 (978-0-7894-7385-1(2)) Dorling Kindersley Publishing, Inc.

—Danger on the Mountain: Scaling the World's Highest Peaks. 2001. (gr. k-3). lib. bdg. 11.80 (978-0-613-35094-5(4)); (Illus.). (J). 10.75 (978-0-606-21136-9(5)) Tandem Library Bks.

Donkin, Andrew & Dorling Kindersley Publishing Staff. Danger on the Mountain: Scaling the World's Highest Peaks. 2001. (Readers Ser.). (Illus.). 48p. (J). (gr. 4-7). 14.99 (978-0-7894-7386-8(0)) Dorling Kindersley Publishing, Inc.

Endres, Hollie. Rock Climbing. 2007. (Illus.). 24p. (J). lib. bdg. 19.95 (978-1-60014-127-0(7)) Bellwether Media.

—Rock Climbing. 2007. (Torque: Action Sports Ser.). (Illus.). 24p. (J). (gr. 3-7). lib. bdg. 20.00 (***978-0-531-18494-3(3)*** , Children's Pr.) Scholastic Library Publishing.

Fandel, Jennifer. Rock Climbing. 2007. (J). (978-1-58341-468-2(1) , Creative Education) Creative Co., The.

Follett, Katherine. One Giant Leap. ed. 2004. (Reader's Theater Ser.). (J). pap. 22.00 (978-1-4108-1147-9(6)) Benchmark Education Co.

Gammelgaard, Lene. Climbing High: A Woman's Account of Surviving the Everest Tragedy. 2000. (Illus.). (J). (978-0-606-18683-4(2)) Tandem Library Bks.

Graf, Mike. Rock Climbing. 2004. (Illus.). 56p. (J). pap. (978-0-7891-6043-0(9)); (gr. 4-7). lib. bdg. 17.95 (978-0-7569-1385-4(3)) Perfection Learning Corp.

Harcourt School Publishers Staff. Climbing High. 3rd ed. 2002. (Horizons Ser.). (Illus.). (J). pap. 7.30 (978-0-15-333638-6(2)) Harcourt Schl. Pubs.

Hirschmann, Kris. The Highest Mountain. 2002. (Extreme Places Ser.). (Illus.). 48p. (J). (gr. 3-5). 26.20 (978-0-7377-1373-2(9) , Kidhaven) Thomson Gale.

Jefferis, David. Rock Climbing & Mountaineering. 2001. (Young Library - Super Sports). (Illus.). 32p. (J). lib. bdg. 25.69 (978-0-7398-4346-8(X)) Raintree.

Jenkins, Steve. The Top of the World: Climbing Mount Everest. Jenkins, Steve, illus. 2002. (Illus.). 32p. (J). (gr. k-3). pap. 6.95 (978-0-618-19676-0(5)) Houghton Mifflin Co. Trade & Reference Div.

—The Top of the World: Climbing Mount Everest. 1999. (Illus.). 32p. (J). (gr. k-3). tchr. ed. 16.00 (978-0-395-94218-5(7)) Houghton Mifflin Co. Trade & Reference Div.

—Top of the World: Climbing Mount Everest. 1999. (gr. 3-6). lib. bdg. 15.25 (978-0-613-60732-2(5)) Tandem Library Bks.

Kaelberer, Angie Peterson. Ice Climbing. 2006. (Blazers—To the Extreme Ser.). (Illus.). 32p. (J). (978-0-7368-4398-0(1)) Capstone Pr., Inc.

Kalman, Bobbie & Crossingham, John. Extreme Climbing. 2004. (Extreme Sports No Limits! Ser.). (Illus.). 32p. (J). (978-0-7787-1671-6(6)); pap. (978-0-7787-1717-1(8)) Crabtree Publishing Co.

Kerr, James. Hillary & Norgay's Mount Everest Adventure. 2007. (J). (***978-1-4034-9755-0(9)***) Heinemann Library.

Klingel, Cynthia Fitterer. Art of the Aztecs. 2003. (Scribbles Institute : Art in Ancient Civilizations Ser.). 32p. (J). (gr. 1-5). 21.36 (978-1-56766-552-9(7)) Child's World, Inc.

Mason, Paul. Rock Climbing & Rappeling. 2007. (J). (***978-1-59920-132-0(1)***) Smart Apple Media.

Mountain Biking Bald Eagle State Forest: Pennsylvania State Forest Series, 1. 2002. (Illus.). 206p. per. 14.95 (978-0-9719681-0-3(1)) Griz Innovations.

Mountaineering Adventures, 6 vols. (gr. 4 up). 39.95 (978-0-7368-9029-8(7)) Red Brick Learning.

Nichols, John. Sport Climbing. 2001. (Extreme Sports Ser.). (Illus.). 48p. (J). (gr. 3-6). lib. bdg. 24.26 (978-0-7398-4691-9(4)) Raintree.

O'Shei, Tim. Stranded! Amy Racina's Story of Survival. 2008. (J). (***978-1-4296-0088-0(8)***) Capstone Pr., Inc.

Oxlade, Chris. Rock Climbing. 2005. (Extreme Sports Ser.). (Illus.). 32p. (J). (gr. 3-6). lib. bdg. 22.60 (978-0-8225-1240-0(8)) Lerner Publishing Group.

Preszler, Eric. Mountainboarding. 2005. (X-Sports Ser.). (Illus.). 32p. (J). (ps-ps). lib. bdg. 22.60 (978-0-7368-3781-1(7)) Capstone Pr., Inc.

Roberts, Jeremy. Rock & Ice Climbing! Top the Tower. 2000. (Extreme Sports Collection). (Illus.). 64p. (YA). (gr. 5-8). lib. bdg. 26.50 (978-0-8239-3009-8(2) , EXROIC, Rosen Central) Rosen Publishing Group, Inc., The.

—Rock & Ice Climbing! Top the Tower. 2000. (Illus.). 64p. (YA). per. 9.95 (978-1-56254-301-3(6) , SP 3016) Saddleback Educational Publishing.

Ryan, Pat. Rock Climbing. 2000. (World of Sports Ser.). (Illus.). 32p. (J). (gr. 4 up). lib. bdg. 16.95 (978-1-887068-57-4(0)) Smart Apple Media.

Salkeld, Audrey. Climbing Everest: Tales of Triumph & Tragedy on the World's Highest Mountain. 2003. (Illus.). 128p. (J). (gr. 5). 21.00 (978-0-7922-5105-7(9) , National Geographic Children's Bks.) National Geographic Society.

—Mystery on Everest: A Photobiography of George Mallory. 2000. (Illus.). 64p. (J). (gr. 5-8). 17.95 (978-0-7922-7222-9(6) , National Geographic Children's Bks.) National Geographic Society.

Schindler, John. Rock Climbing. 2005. (Illus.). 24p. (J). pap. (978-0-8368-4548-8(X)); (YA). lib. bdg. 22.00 (978-0-8368-4541-9(2)) Stevens, Gareth Inc.

Seddon, Tony. Big Book of Climbing Mount Everest. 2000. (Cambridge Reading Routes Ser.). (Illus.). 24p. pap. 12.40 (978-0-521-77888-6(3)) Cambridge Univ. Pr.

Seeberg, Timothy J. Rock Climbing. 2004. (Complete Guides Ser.). (Illus.). 32p. (J). (gr. 1-5). 25.64 (978-1-59296-033-0(2)) Child's World, Inc.

Skreslet, Laurie. To the Top of Everest. 2003. (gr. 3-6). lib. bdg. 17.60 (978-0-613-84973-9(6)) Tandem Library Bks.

Skreslet, Laurie & MacLeod, Elizabeth. To the Top of Everest. (Illus.). 56p. (J). (gr. 4-6). 2003. (978-1-55074-814-7(9)); 2001. (978-1-55074-721-8(5)) Kids Can Pr., Ltd.

Takeda, Pete. Climb! Your Guide to Bouldering, Sport Climbing, Trad Climbing, Ice Climbing, Alpinism, & More. Dickason, Jack, illus. 2002. (Extreme Sports Ser.). 64p. (J). (gr. 4-9). pap. 8.95 (978-0-7922-6744-7(3) , National Geographic Children's Bks.) National Geographic Society.

Teitelbaum, Michael. Rock Climbing. 2008. (J). pap. 7.95 (***978-1-60279-088-9(4));*** lib. bdg. 25.26 (***978-1-60279-014-8(0)***) Cherry Lake Publishing.

Tomljanovic, Tatiana. Rock Climbing. 2007. (J). (***978-1-59036-667-7(0)); (978-1-59036-668-4(9))*** Weigl Pubs., Inc.

Weintraub, Aileen. Mount Everest: The Highest Mountain. 2001. (Great Record Breakers in Nature Ser.). (Illus.). 24p. (J). lib. bdg. 18.75 (978-0-8239-5636-4(9) , PowerKids Pr.) Rosen Publishing Group, Inc., The.

—Rock Climbing. 2003. (High Interest Bks.). (Illus.). 48p. (J). 24.00 (978-0-516-24319-1(5) , Children's Pr.); (YA). (gr. 7-12). pap. 6.95 (978-0-516-24381-8(0) , Watts, Franklin) Scholastic Library Publishing.

—Rock Climbing. 2003. (gr. 7-12). lib. bdg. 15.25 (978-0-613-59712-8(5)) Tandem Library Bks.

Werther, Scott P. Jon Krakauer's Adventure on Mount Everest. 2002. (gr. 7-12). lib. bdg. 15.25 (978-0-613-58780-8(4)) Tandem Library Bks.

—Jon Krakauer's Adventure on Mt. Everest. 2002. (High Interest Bks.). (Illus.). 48p. (YA). (gr. 7-12). pap. 6.95 (978-0-516-23488-5(9) , Children's Pr.) Scholastic Library Publishing.

Whiting, Jim. Ultra Running with Scott Jurek. 2006. (Extreme Sports Ser.). (Illus.). 32p. (J). (gr. 1-4). lib. bdg. (978-1-58415-484-6(5)) Mitchell Lane Pubs., Inc.

Wickwire, Jim. Addicted to Danger. 1999. (gr. 7-12). lib. bdg. 24.55 (978-0-613-28718-0(5)) Tandem Library Bks.

Willett, Edward. Rock Sport Climbing. 2005. (Rad Sports Techniques & Tricks Ser.). (Illus.). 48p. (YA). (gr. 5-8). lib. bdg. 26.50 (978-0-8239-3847-6(6)) Rosen Publishing Group, Inc., The.

Wurdinger, Scott D. & Rapparlie, Leslie. Rock Climbing. 2006. (Illus.). 48p. (J). 21.95 (978-1-58341-394-4(4) , Creative Education) Creative Co., The.

MOUNTAINEERING—BIOGRAPHY

Elish, Dan. Edmund Hillary: First to the Top. 2007. (Great Explorations Ser.). (Illus.). 80p. (YA). (gr. 5-9). lib. bdg. 32.79 (***978-0-7614-2224-2(2)*** , Benchmark Bks.) Cavendish, Marshall Corp.

O'Shei, Tim. Left for Dead! Lincoln Hall's Story of Survival. 2008. (J). (***978-1-4296-0090-3(X)***) Capstone Pr., Inc.

Weihenmayer, Erik. Touch the Top of the World. 2002. (gr. 7-12). lib. bdg. 23.45 (978-0-613-56864-7(8)) Tandem Library Bks.

Werther, Scott P. Jon Krakauer's Adventure on Mt. Everest. 2002. (Survivors Ser.). (Illus.). 48p. (YA). (gr. 7-12). 24.00 (978-0-516-23902-6(3) , Children's Pr.) Scholastic Library Publishing.

Whipple, Heather. Hillary & Norgay: To the Top of Mount Everest. 2007. (Illus.). 32p. (J). (gr. 3-9). (***978-0-7787-2418-6(2));*** pap. (***978-0-7787-2454-4(9)***) Crabtree Publishing Co.

MOUNTAINEERING—FICTION

Arnosky, Jim. Climbing Crinkle Mountain. 2004. (J). mass mkt. 5.99 (978-0-689-81601-7(4) , Aladdin) Simon & Schuster Children's Publishing.

Bailie, Helen. The Azura Stones. 2007. 212p. (YA). per. 18.00 (***978-1-58982-374-7(5)*** , Bedside Bks.) American Bk. Publishing Group.

Barron, T. A. High As a Hawk: A Brave Girl's Historic Climb. Lewin, Ted, tr. Lewin, Ted, illus. 2004. 32p. (J). (ps-3). 16.99 (978-0-399-23704-1(6) , Philomel) Penguin Group (USA) Inc.

Becker, Shari. Maxwell's Mountain. Wong, Nicole, illus. 32p. (J). (ps-2). 2007. pap. 6.95 (***978-1-58089-212-4(4));*** 2006. 15.95 (978-1-58089-047-2(4)) Charlesbridge Publishing, Inc.

Brin, Susannah. Climb. 2000. (gr. 5-8). lib. bdg. 11.80 (978-0-613-51205-3(7)) Tandem Library Bks.

Brouillet, Chrystine. La Montagne Noire. Brochard, Philippe, illus. 2001. (Roman Jeunesse Ser.). (FRE.). 96p. (J). (gr. 4-7). pap. (978-2-89021-472-9(9)) Diffusion du livre Mirabel.

Burgess, Robert F. Where Condors Fly. 2000. (Illus.). 196p. (gr. 4-7). pap. 12.95 (978-0-595-00347-1(8) , Backinprint.com) iUniverse, Inc.

Doyle, Bill. Iced! The 2007 Journal of Nick Fitzmorgan. Simpson, Philomena, illus. 2006. 133p. (J). lib. bdg. 18.46 (***978-1-4242-1734-2(2)***) Fitzgerald Bks.

Doyle, Malachy. Owen & the Mountain. 2001. (Illus.). 32p. (J). pap. 12.99 (978-0-7475-5093-8(X)) Bloomsbury Publishing Plc GBR. *Dist:* Independent Pubs. Group.

—Owen & the Mountain. 2002. (gr. k-3). lib. bdg. 18.75 (978-0-613-70955-2(1)) Tandem Library Bks.

George, Jean Craighead. Cliff Hanger. Minor, Wendell, illus. 2002. (Outdoor Adventures Ser.). 32p. (J). (ps-4). 15.99 (978-0-06-000260-2(3)) HarperCollins Pubs.

—Frightful's Mountain. 1999. (YA). (gr. 5-9). 5.99 (978-0-525-46303-0(8) , Dutton Juvenile); 1999. (Illus.). 272p. (J). (gr. 4-7). 15.99 (978-0-525-46166-1(3) , Dutton Juvenile); 2001. (Illus.). 272p. (YA). (gr. 4-7). reprint ed. pap. 6.99 (978-0-14-131235-4(1) , Puffin) Penguin Group (USA) Inc.

—Frightful's Mountain. 2001. 12.64 (978-0-606-21203-8(5)); (gr. 3-6). lib. bdg. 14.15 (978-0-613-35948-1(8)) Tandem Library Bks.

Johnson, D. B. Henry Climbs a Mountain. Johnson, D. B., illus. 2003. (Illus.). 32p. (J). (gr. k-3). 15.00 (978-0-618-26902-0(9)) Houghton Mifflin Co. Trade & Reference Div.

Keller, Jeff, Jr. Ricky Climbs Pikes Peak. 2006. (J). 8.95 (978-0-9773990-9-3(5)) Mother's Hse. Publishing.

Korman, Gordon. The Climb. 2002. (Everest Ser.: Bk. 2). 160p. (J). (gr. 3-7). pap. 4.99 (978-0-439-40506-5(8)) Scholastic, Inc.

—The Contest. 2002. (Everest Ser.: Bk. 1). 146p. (gr. 3-8). pap. 4.99 (978-0-439-40139-5(9)) Scholastic, Inc.

—The Contest. 2002. (Everest Ser.: Bk. 1). (gr. 3-6). lib. bdg. 12.40 (978-0-613-58945-1(9)) Tandem Library Bks.

—The Summit, Vol. 3. 2002. (Everest Ser.: Bk. 3). 160p. (J). (gr. 3-7). pap. 4.99 (978-0-439-41137-0(8)) Scholastic, Inc.

Kusugak, Michael Arvaarluk. Who Wants Rocks? Krykorka, Vladyana Langer, illus. 1999. 24p. (J). (ps-2). lib. bdg. 17.95 (978-1-55037-589-3(X)) Annick Pr., Ltd. CAN. *Dist:* Firefly Bks., Ltd.

—Who Wants Rocks? 1999. (gr. k-3). lib. bdg. 15.25 (978-0-613-27556-9(X)) Tandem Library Bks.

Lawrie, Robin & Lawrie, Christine, illus. Fear 3.1. 2007. 32p. (J). pap. (***978-1-59889-443-1(9)***) Stone Arch Bks.

Mantell, Paul. Mountain Bike Mania. ed. 2005. (Sports Classics IV Ser.). 151p. (J). lib. bdg. 15.00 (978-1-59054-764-9(0)) Fitzgerald Bks.

Monroy, Eva. Little Mountain. 2004. (J). pap. 8.00 (978-0-8059-6535-3(1)) Dorrance Publishing Co., Inc.

Montgomery, R. A. The Abominable Snowman, 2006. (Choose Your Own Adventure Ser.: No. 1). (Illus.). 144p. (J). mass mkt. 5.99 (978-1-933390-01-7(8) , CHCL01) Chooseco LLC.

Murphy, Claire Rudolf. To the Summit. 1998. 208p. pap. 3.99 (978-0-380-79537-6(X)) HarperCollins Pubs.

Murray, W. Mountain Adventure. (Key Words Readers Ser.: B Series, No. 641-12b). (Illus.). 56p. (J). (ps-5). 3.50 (978-0-7214-0024-2(8) , Dutton Juvenile) Penguin Group (USA) Inc.

Neale, Jonathan. Himalaya. 2004. 160p. (J). (gr. 5-9). tchr. ed. 16.00 (978-0-618-41200-6(X)) Houghton Mifflin Co. Trade & Reference Div.

Newman, Gwill York. Bingo Bear Was Here: A Toy Bear's Climb to the Top of Africa's Highest Mountain. Babcock, Jeff, illus. 2003. 48p. (J). pap. 8.95 (978-0-86534-395-5(0)) Sunstone Pr.

Orme, Helen. Wet! 2008. (Siti's Sisters Ser.). 36p. pap. 7.95 (***978-1-84167-688-3(8)***) Ransom Publishing Ltd. GBR. *Dist:* International Publishers Marketing.

Patneaude, David. A Piece of the Sky. 2007. 194p. (J). 15.95 (978-0-8075-6536-0(9)) Whitman, Albert & Co.

Paulsen, Gary & Roberts, Esyllt Nest. Craig y Diafol. 2005. (WEL.). 62p. (978-0-86381-684-0(3)) Gwasg Carreg Gwalch.

Raintree Steck-Vaughn Staff. Mountain Hike. 2000. (Read All about It Ser.). (Illus.). (J). pap. 4.95 (978-0-8114-3793-6(0)) Steck-Vaughn.

Rau, Dana Meachen. Climb up a Mountain. 2000. (Adventurers Ser.). (Illus.). 24p. (J). (gr. k-2). lib. bdg. 19.27 (978-1-57103-317-8(3)) Rourke Publishing, LLC.

Retana, Maria L. Tall Tails from a Mountain Slope. Retana, Guillermo, tr. Weaver, Marian, illus. 1999. Tr. of Rabos Altos de la Ladera. (SPA.). 32p. (Orig.). (J). (gr. k-3). pap. 6.95 (978-0-9652920-0-9(2)) High Desert Productions.

Rylant, Cynthia. When I Was Young in the Mountains. 2002. (Illus.). (J). 14.04 (978-0-7587-0164-0(0)) Book Wholesalers, Inc.

Selman, Marty. This Rocks! Weizman, Daniel, ed. 2000. (Jersey Ser.: 4). (Illus.). 128p. (gr. 3-7). pap. 4.99 (978-0-7868-4424-1(8)) Disney Pr.

—This Rocks! 2000. (Jersey Ser.). (Illus.). (J). (978-0-606-20739-3(2)) Tandem Library Bks.

Smith, Roland. Peak. 2008. (Illus.). 272p. (YA). pap. 6.95 (***978-0-15-206268-2(8)*** , Harcourt Paperbacks) Harcourt Children's Bks.

Stilton, Geronimo. I'm Too Fond of My Fur! Wolf, Matt, illus. 2004. (Geronimo Stilton Ser.: No. 4). 116p. (J). lib. bdg. 10.00 (***978-1-4242-0698-8(7)***) Fitzgerald Bks.

Stone Arch Books (Firm : Afton, Minn.) Staff. Fear 3.1. Lawrie, Robin & Lawrie, Christine, illus. 2007. (Ridge Riders Ser.). 40p. (J). (gr. 2-6). lib. bdg. 21.26 (***978-1-59889-348-9(3)***) Stone Arch Bks.

Thomas, Jane Resh. Blind Mountain. 2006. 128p. (J). (gr. 4-6). 15.00 (978-0-618-64872-6(0) , Clarion Bks.) Houghton Mifflin Co. Trade & Reference Div.

To Reach the Top. 2002. (Illus.). (J). pap. (978-0-7398-5101-2(2)) Steck-Vaughn.

Yates, Elizabeth. American Haven. 2002. (Illus.). 112p. (J). (gr. 4-7). 7.49 (978-1-57924-896-3(9)) Jones, Bob Univ. Pr.

MOUNTAINS

see also Mountaineering; Volcanoes

also names of mountain ranges, e.g. Rocky Mountains; etc.

Aldridge, Janet. The Meadow-Brook Girls in the Hills: Or the Missing Pilot of the White Mountains. 2006. 95.99 (***978-1-4280-1513-5(2)***); pap. 89.99 (***978-1-4280-1528-9(0)***) IndyPublish.com.

Aleshire & Peter. Mountains. 2008. (Extreme Earth Ser.). 176p. (J). (gr. 6-12). 35.00 (978-0-8160-5918-8(7)) Facts On File, Inc.

Anderson, Sheila. Mountain. 2008. (First Step Nonfiction - Landforms Ser.). (J). lib. bdg. 18.60 (***978-0-8225-8590-9(1)*** , Lerner Pubns.) Lerner Publishing Group.

Baker, Lucy. Vida en las Montanas. 2000. Tr. of Life in the Mountains. (Illus.). (J). (978-0-606-20971-7(9)) Tandem Library Bks.

Baldwin, Carol. Living on a Mountain. 2003. (Living Habitats Ser.). (Illus.). 32p. (J). pap. (978-1-4034-3233-9(3)) Heinemann Library.

Banting, Erinn. Mountains. 2006. (J). (978-1-59036-444-4(9)); (978-1-59036-445-1(7)) Weigl Pubs., Inc.

Barber, Nicola. Mountain Home. 2007. 32p. (gr. 7-10). pap. (***978-0-7787-3557-1(5)***) Crabtree Publishing Co.

Barnes, Julia. 101 Facts about Mountains. 2003. (One Hundred One Facts about Our World Ser.). (Illus.). 32p. (J). (gr. 3 up). lib. bdg. 23.33 (978-0-8368-3708-7(8)) Stevens, Gareth Inc.

Benduhn, Tea. Living in Mountains. 2007. (J). pap. (***978-0-8368-8347-3(0));*** 24p. (gr. 2-4). lib. bdg. 19.93 (***978-0-8368-8342-8(X)***) Stevens, Gareth Inc. (Weekly Reader Early Learning Library).

Bevan, Finn. Mighty Mountains. 1998. (Landscapes of Legend Ser.). (Illus.). 32p. (J). (gr. 4-8). pap. 6.95 (978-0-516-26299-4(8) , Children's Pr.) Scholastic Library Publishing.

BHB International Staff. Mountains. 1998. (Here We Go Round Ser.). (J). (978-2-215-06180-9(4)) Editions Fleurus.

Bodden, Valerie. Mountains. 2006. (Our World Ser.). (Illus.). 24p. 16.95 (978-1-58341-463-7(0) , Creative Education) Creative Co., The.

Bradley, Catherine. Life in the Mountains: Animals, People, Plants. 2000. (gr. 3-6). lib. bdg. 15.25 (978-0-613-43344-0(0)) Tandem Library Bks.

Brimner, Larry Dane. Mountains. (True Bks.). (Illus.). 48p. (J). (gr. 3-5). 2001. pap. 6.95 (978-0-516-27192-7(X)); 2000. 25.00 (978-0-516-21568-6(X)) Scholastic Library Publishing. (Children's Pr.).

—Mountains. 2000. (gr. 3-6). lib. bdg. 15.25 (978-0-613-54031-5(X)) Tandem Library Bks.

Casado, Dami & Casado, Alicia. Las Montanas. 2005. (SPA., Illus.). 14p. (J). per. 8.99 (978-84-272-7388-7(6)) Molino, Editorial ESP. *Dist:* Santillana USA Publishing Co., Inc.

Chambers, Catherine & Lapthorn, Nicholas. Mountains. 2nd ed. 2007. (***978-1-4034-9602-7(1));*** pap. (***978-1-4034-9612-6(9)***) Heinemann.

Cheshire, Gerard. Nature Unfolds Mountains & Deserts. Barrett, Peter, illus. 2002. (Nature Unfolds Ser.). 40p. (J). (gr. 4). pap. (978-0-7787-0323-5(1)); lib. bdg. (978-0-7787-0311-2(8)) Crabtree Publishing Co.

Claybourne, Anna. Mountains. 2004. (Geography Fact Files Ser.). (Illus.). (J). lib. bdg. 28.50 (978-1-58340-426-3(0)) Smart Apple Media.

Cole, Melissa S. Mountain. 2003. (Wild America Habitats Ser.). (Illus.). 24p. (J). 21.20 (978-1-56711-806-3(2) , Blackbirch Pr., Inc.) Thomson Gale.

Doeden, Matt. Mountains. Sloan, Frank, ed. 2001. (Biomes Ser.). (Illus.). 32p. (J). (gr. 4-7). lib. bdg. 15.98 (978-0-7398-3563-0(7)) Raintree.

Dorling Kindersley Publishing Staff. Mountain. 2006. (Dk 24 Hours Ser.). (Illus.). 48p. (J). 12.99 (978-0-7566-2215-2(8)) Dorling Kindersley Publishing, Inc.

Dwyer, Jacqueline, et al, contrib. by. Mountains. 2001. (PowerKids Readers Ser.). (Illus.). 24p. (J). (gr. 1). lib. bdg. 16.00 (978-0-8239-5680-7(6) , PKMNTN, PowerKids Pr.) Rosen Publishing Group, Inc., The.

Gaff, Jackie. I Wonder Why Mountains Have Snow on Top: And Other Questions about Mountains. 2004. (I Wonder Why Ser.). 32p. (J). (gr. k-3). pap. 6.95 (978-0-7534-5763-4(6) , Kingfisher) Houghton Mifflin Co. Trade & Reference Div.

—I Wonder Why Mountains Have Snow on Top: And Other Questions about Mountains. Gaff, Jackie, illus. 2001. (I Wonder Why Ser.). (Illus.). 32p. (J). (gr. k-3). tchr. ed. 12.95 (978-0-7534-5344-5(4) , Kingfisher) Houghton Mifflin Co. Trade & Reference Div.

Galko, Francine. Mountain Animals. 2003. (Animals in Their Habitats Ser.). (Illus.). 32p. (J). (gr. k-2). lib. bdg. 21.36 (978-1-4034-0180-9(2)); pap. 6.95 (978-1-4034-0437-4(2)) Heinemann Library.

—Mountain Animals. 2003. (gr. k-3). lib. bdg. 14.75 (978-0-613-45799-6(4)) Tandem Library Bks.

Gill, Shelley. Up on Denali: Alaska's Wild Mountain. Cartwright, Shannon, illus. 2006. 32p. (J). 16.95 (978-1-57061-366-1(4)); pap. 10.95 (978-1-57061-365-4(6)) Sasquatch Bks.

Gordon, Sharon. At Home on the Mountain. 2005. (Bookworms Ser.). (ENG & SPA., Illus.). 32p. (J). (gr. 3-7). lib. bdg. (978-0-7614-1961-7(6) , Benchmark Bks.) Cavendish, Marshall Corp.

—At Home on the Mountain (Mi Casa en la Montaña) 2006. (Bookworms Ser.). (ENG & SPA.). 32p. (J). lib. bdg. 22.79 (978-0-7614-2455-0(5)) Cavendish, Marshall Corp.

—Mi Casa en la Montaña. 2006. (Bookworms Ser.). (SPA & ENG.). 32p. (J). lib. bdg. 22.79 (978-0-7614-2376-8(1)) Cavendish, Marshall Corp.

Gray, Susan Heinrichs. Mountains. 2000. (First Reports). (Illus.). 48p. (J). (gr. 3 up). lib. bdg. 21.26 (978-0-7565-0021-4(4)) Compass Point Bks.

Green, Emily K. Mountains. 2006. (Blastoff! Readers Ser.). (Illus.). 24p. (J). lib. bdg. 16.95 (978-1-60014-038-9(6)) Bellwether Media.

Green, Jen. People of the Mountains. 1998. (Wide World Ser.). (Illus.). 48 p. (J). (gr. 3-7). 18.98 (978-0-8172-5062-1(X)) Raintree.

Harcourt School Publishers Staff. Making Mountains On Level. 3rd ed. 2002. (Trophies Reading Program Ser.). (Illus.). pap. 5.10 (978-0-15-323446-0(6)) Harcourt Schl. Pubs.

Harris. Mountains & Highlands. 2003. (Biomes Atlas Ser.). (Illus.). 64p. pap. 9.50 (978-1-4109-0012-8(6)) Raintree.

—Mountains Highlands. 2003. (Biomes Atlas Ser.). pap. 48.30 (978-1-4109-0247-4(1)) Raintree.

Harris, Tim. Mountains & Highlands. 2002. (Biomes Atlases Ser.). (Illus.). 64p. (J). lib. bdg. 31.42 (978-0-7398-5511-9(5)) Raintree.

—Mountains & Highlands. 2003. (gr. 5-8). lib. bdg. 18.20 (978-0-613-78181-7(3)) Tandem Library Bks.

Harrison, David L. Mountains: The Tops of the World. Nathan, Cheryl, illus. 2005. (Earthworks Ser.). 28p. (J). (gr. 1-3). 16.95 (978-1-59078-326-9(3)) Boyds Mills Pr.

Hodge, Susie. Mountain Survival. 2007. (Extreme Habitats Ser.). 32p. (J). (gr. 4-6). lib. bdg. 25.27 (***978-0-8368-8246-9(6)***) Stevens, Gareth Inc.

Holland, Gini. I Live in the Mountains. 2004. (Weekly Reader Early Learning Library). (Illus.). 24p. (gr. k up). (J). pap. (978-0-8368-4088-9(7)); (YA). lib. bdg. 19.33 (978-0-8368-4081-0(X)) Stevens, Gareth Inc. (Weekly Reader Early Learning Library).

—I Live in the Mountains/Vivo en las Montañas. Coffey, Colleen & Carrillo, Consuelo, trs. 2004. (Weekly Reader Early Learning Library). (ENG & SPA., Illus.). 24p. (J). (gr. k up). pap. 5.95 (978-0-8368-4136-7(0)); lib. bdg. 19.33 (978-0-8368-4129-9(8)) Stevens, Gareth Inc. (Weekly Reader Early Learning Library).

Howard, Fran. Mountains. 2007. (Habitats Ser.). (Illus.). 32p. (J). (gr. k-4). lib. bdg. 22.78 (978-1-59679-780-2(0)) ABDO Publishing Co.

Hynes, Margaret. Mountains. 2007. (Kingfisher Young Knowledge Ser.). (Illus.). 48p. (J). (gr. k-3). 9.95 (978-0-7534-6037-5(8) , Kingfisher) Houghton Mifflin Co. Trade & Reference Div.

Jennings, Terry. Mountains. 2002. (Restless Earth Ser.). (Illus.). 32p. (J). lib. bdg. 24.25 (978-1-931983-19-8(4)) Chrysalis Education.

Karecki, Jason, illus. The Adventures of Drake Montana Vol. 2: Asian Mountains. 1998. 24p. (J). (gr. k-5). (978-1-890716-08-0(1)) K&M International.

Kelsey, Michael R. Climber's & Hiker's Guide to the World's Mountains & Volcanos. 4th ed. 2001. (Illus.). 1248p. (YA). pap. 36.95 (978-0-944510-18-6(3)) Kelsey Publishing.

Le Tord, Bijou. A Mountain Is to Climb. Le Tord, Bijou, illus. Date not set. (Illus.). 40p. (J). 5.99 (978-0-06-443591-8(1)) HarperCollins Pubs.

—A Mountain Is to Climb. 2001. 40p. (J). 15.95 (978-0-06-028514-2(1)) HarperCollins Pubs.

Levete, Sarah. Geography. 2006. (Illus.). 32p. (J). (978-1-59604-099-1(8)) Stargazer Bks.

Levy, Janey. Discovering Mountains. 2008. (J). lib. bdg. (***978-1-4042-3785-8(2)*** , PowerKids Pr.) Rosen Publishing Group, Inc., The.

Lovell, Scarlett. Exploring Mountain Habitats. 1999. (gr. 3-6). lib. bdg. 12.95 (978-0-613-17211-0(6)) Tandem Library Bks.

Lovell, Scarlett, et al. Exploring Mountain Habitats. Noreika, Robert & Katin, Miriam, illus. 1999. (Mondo's Exploring Ser.). 24p. (J). (gr. 1-5). pap. 4.95 (978-1-57255-164-0(X)) Mondo Publishing.

Lynch, Emma. Mountain. 2004. (Raintree Sprouts Ser.). (Illus.). 24p. (J). pap. 5.50 (978-1-4109-0873-5(9)); lib. bdg. 18.56 (978-1-4109-0868-1(2)) Raintree.

Macken, JoAnn Early. Montañas. 2006. (ENG & SPA., Illus.). 24p. (J). pap. 5.95 (978-0-8368-6553-0(7)); lib. bdg. 19.33 (978-0-8368-6546-2(4)) Stevens, Gareth Inc.

—Mountains. 2006. (Illus.). 24p. (J). pap. (978-0-8368-6402-1(6)); lib. bdg. 19.33 (978-0-8368-6395-6(X)) Stevens, Gareth Inc.

Marsico, Katie. A Home on the Tundra. 2006. (Scholastic News Nonfiction Readers Ser.). (Illus.). 24p. (J). (gr. 1-3). 19.00 (978-0-516-25345-9(X) , Children's Pr.) Scholastic Library Publishing.

Mayer, Cassie. Mountains. 2006. (Illus.). 24p. (J). (978-1-4034-8435-2(X)); pap. (978-1-4034-8441-3(4)) Heinemann Library.

Maynard, Charles W. The Appalachians. 2004. (Great Mountain Ranges of the World Ser.). (Illus.). 24p. (J). lib. bdg. 21.25 (978-0-8239-6695-0(X) , PowerKids Pr.) Rosen Publishing Group, Inc., The.

—The Ural Mountains. 2004. (Great Mountain Ranges of the World Ser.). (Illus.). 24p. (J). lib. bdg. 21.25 (978-0-8239-6699-8(2) , PowerKids Pr.) Rosen Publishing Group, Inc., The.

McCurry, Kristen. Mountain Babies. McCurry, Kristen, ed. 2006. (Illus.). 22p. (J). bds. 5.95 (978-1-55971-940-7(0) , NorthWord Bks. for Young Readers) T&N Children's Publishing.

Morris, Neil. Earth's Changing Mountains. 2003. (Illus.). (J). pap. 7.50 (978-1-4109-0345-7(1)); 32p. lib. bdg. 25.70 (978-1-4109-0174-3(2)) Raintree.

—Earth's Changing Mountains. 2003. (gr. 3-6). lib. bdg. 15.90 (978-0-613-78239-5(9)) Tandem Library Bks.

—Living in the Mountains. 2004. (J). lib. bdg. (978-1-58340-484-3(8)) Smart Apple Media.

Mountain 6-Pack. 2004. (Illus.). (J). pap. 29.70 (978-1-4109-0878-0(X)) Raintree.

Mountains Learning about the Earth. 2006. (Illus.). 24p. (J). (gr. k-2). 18.50 (***978-0-531-17890-4(0)***) Scholastic Library Publishing.

Nadeau, Isaac. Mountains. 2006. (Illus.). 24p. (J). lib. bdg. (978-1-4042-3127-6(7)) Rosen Publishing Group, Inc., The.

Owen, Andy, et al. Mountains. 2002. (Illus.). 32p. (J). (gr. k-2). pap. 6.95 (978-1-58810-976-7(3) , 91459) Heinemann Library.

Oxlade, Chris. Mountains. 2003. (Science Files Ser.). (Illus.). 32p. (J). (gr. 3 up). lib. bdg. 24.67 (978-0-8368-3569-4(7)) Stevens, Gareth Inc.

Parker, Jane & Parker, Steve. Mountains. 1998. (Take 5 Geography Ser.). (Illus.). 32p. (J). (gr. 3-5). 21.00 (978-0-531-14457-2(7) , Watts, Franklin) Scholastic Library Publishing.

Price, Martin F. Mountains: Geology, Natural History, & Ecosystems. rev. ed. 2002. (WorldLife Library Ser.). (Illus.). 72p. (J). pap. 17.95 (978-0-89658-251-4(5)) Voyageur Pr., Inc.

Pyers. Mountain Explorer. 2004. (Illus.). (J). pap. 7.50 (978-1-4109-0838-4(0)) Raintree.

—Mountain Explorer 6-Pack. 2004. (Illus.). (J). lib. bdg. 40.50 (978-1-4109-0844-5(5)) Raintree.

Raintree Steck-Vaughn Staff. True Tales from the Mountains. 1999. (Illus.). (J). pap. 13.00 (978-0-7398-0854-2(0)) Steck-Vaughn.

Rotter, Charles. Mountains. 2002. (LifeViews Ser.). (J). (978-0-89812-375-3(5) , Creative Paperbacks) Creative Co., The.

—Mountains: The Towering Sentinels. 2002. (LifeViews Ser.). (Illus.). 32p. (J). lib. bdg. (978-1-58341-123-0(2) , Creative Education) Creative Co., The.

Royston, Angela. Mountains. 2004. (My World of Geography Ser.). (J). 24.21 (978-1-4034-5592-5(9)) Heinemann Library.

—Mountains. (Extreme Survival Ser.). (Illus.). 32p. (J). 2004. pap. 7.95 (978-1-4109-0360-0(5)); 2003. lib. bdg. 25.70 (978-1-4109-0001-2(0)) Raintree.

Salzmann, Mary Elizabeth. On a Mountain. l.t. ed. 2001. (What Do You See? Ser.). (Illus.). 24p. (J). (ps-3). lib. bdg. 19.93 (978-1-57765-566-4(4) , SandCastle) ABDO Publishing Co.

Saunders-Smith, Gail, ed. Earth Features, 8 bks. Incl. What Are Caves? Schuh, Mari C. 2002. lib. bdg. 15.93 (978-0-7368-1169-9(9)); What Are Deserts? Trumbauer, Lisa. 2001. lib. bdg. 15.93 (978-0-7368-0987-0(2)); What Are Forests? Trumbauer, Lisa. 2001. lib. bdg. 15.93 (978-0-7368-0988-7(0)); What Are Lakes? Schuh, Mari C. 2002. lib. bdg. 15.93 (978-0-7368-1170-5(2)); What Are Mountains? Trumbauer, Lisa. 2001. lib. bdg. 15.93 (978-0-7368-0989-4(9)); What Are Oceans? Trumbauer, Lisa. 2001. lib. bdg. 15.93 (978-0-7368-0990-0(2)); What Are Rivers? Schuh, Mari C. 2002. lib. bdg. 15.93 (978-0-7368-1171-2(0)); What Are Volcanoes? Schuh, Mari C. 2002. lib. bdg. 15.93 (978-0-7368-1172-9(9)); 24p. (J). (gr. k-1). (Illus.). 2001. Set lib. bdg. 127.44 (978-0-7368-1198-9(2) , Pebble Bks.) Capstone Pr., Inc.

Sheehan, Thomas F. Mountain Ranges. 2008. (J). (***978-1-60044-547-7(0)***) Rourke Publishing, LLC.

Snedden, Robert. Mountains. 2004. (Illus.). 32p. (J). lib. bdg. (978-1-58340-384-6(1)) Smart Apple Media.

—Protecting Mountain Habitats. 2005. (Protecting Habitats Ser.). (Illus.). 32p. (J). lib. bdg. 24.67 (978-0-8368-4991-2(4)) Stevens, Gareth Inc.

Somervill, Barbara A. The Timeworn Urals. 2004. (Geography of the World Ser.). (Illus.). 32p. (J). (gr. 2-6). 27.07 (978-1-59296-335-5(8)) Child's World, Inc.

Staub, Frank. America's Mountains. 2003. (Illus.). 48p. (J). (gr. 2-6). 16.95 (978-1-59034-870-3(2)); (978-1-59034-872-7(9)) Mondo Publishing.

Stronach, Neil. Mountains. 2001. (People & Places in Peril Ser.). (Illus.). 48p. 19.99 (978-0-7451-5216-5(3) , Cherrytree Books) Evans Publishing Group GBR. *Dist:* Independent Pubs. Group.

Taylor, Barbara. Mountains & Volcanoes: Geography Facts & Experiments. 2002. (Young Discoverers Ser.). (Illus.). 32p. (J). (gr. k-3). pap. 7.95 (978-0-7534-5507-4(2) , Kingfisher) Houghton Mifflin Co. Trade & Reference Div.

—Mountains & Volcanoes: Geography Facts & Experiments. 2002. (gr. k-3). lib. bdg. 16.40 (978-0-613-90354-7(4)) Tandem Library Bks.

Tidmarsh, Celia. Mountains. 2004. (Geography First Ser.). (J). 23.70 (978-1-4103-0110-9(9) , Blackbirch Pr., Inc.) Thomson Gale.

Trumbauer, Lisa. What Are Mountains? Saunders-Smith, Gail, ed. 2001. (Earth Features Ser.). (Illus.). 24p. (J). (gr. k-1). lib. bdg. 15.93 (978-0-7368-0989-4(9) , Pebble Bks.) Capstone Pr., Inc.

Tull, Mary. Mountains. 2004. (Illus.). 32p. (J). pap. (978-0-7922-4562-9(8)) National Geographic Society.

Weatherly, Myra. The Lure of Mountain Peaks. 2004. (Geography of the World Ser.). (Illus.). 32p. (J). (gr. 2-6). 27.07 (978-1-59296-333-1(1)) Child's World, Inc.

Webster, Christine. Hills. 2005. (Illus.). 24p. (J). 21.26 (978-0-7368-3712-5(4)) Capstone Pr., Inc.

—Mountains. 2005. (Illus.). 24p. (J). 21.26 (978-0-7368-3714-9(0)) Capstone Pr., Inc.

Weil, Ann. Mountain Disasters. 2003. (Illus.). 64p. (YA). per. 3.95 (978-1-56254-658-8(9) , SP6589) Saddleback Educational Publishing.

What Are Mountains?, 6 vols., Vol. 2. 2005. (Earth & Outer Space Ser.). (gr. k-2). 28.95 (978-0-7368-3277-9(7)) Red Brick Learning.

Williams, Brenda. Hills & Mountains. 1998. (Geography Starts Here Ser.). (Illus.). 32p. (J). (gr. 1-4). 25.69 (978-0-8172-5112-3(X)) Raintree.

Winne, Joanne. Living on a Mountain. 2000. (Welcome Bks.). (Illus.). 24p. (J). (ps-2). 17.00 (978-0-516-23303-1(3) , Children's Pr.) Scholastic Library Publishing.

—Living on a Mountain. 2000. (gr. k-3). lib. bdg. 12.95 (978-0-613-52133-8(1)) Tandem Library Bks.

Zolty, Howard. Mountain View A through Z. A Colorful Reader for Children of All Ages. 2006. 28p. 14.99 (978-1-4116-5708-3(X)) Lulu.com.

MOUNTIES

see Royal Canadian Mounted Police

MOURNING CUSTOMS

see Funeral Rites and Ceremonies

MOUSE

see Mice

MOUTH ORGAN

see Harmonica

MOVIES

see Motion Pictures

MOVING, HOUSEHOLD

Amos, Janine. Moving. Green, Gwen, illus. Hampton, Angela, photos by. 2002. (Separations Ser.). 32p. (J). (gr. 3 up). lib. bdg. 23.33 (978-0-8368-3092-7(X)) Stevens, Gareth Inc.

Davis, Gabriel. The Moving Book: A Kids' Survival Guide. Dennen, Sue, illus. 2003. (J). spiral bd. 20.95 (978-0-912301-52-5(X)) First Bks.

—The Moving Book: A Kid's Survival Guide. Dennen, Sue, illus. 2002. 120p. (J). (gr. 2-5). reprint ed. pap. 17.00 (978-0-7567-5839-4(4)) DIANE Publishing Co.

Helmer, Diana Star. Let's Talk about Moving to a New Place. 1999. (Let's Talk Library). (Illus.). 24p. (J). (gr. 3). lib. bdg. 18.75 (978-0-8239-5194-9(4) , PowerKids Pr.) Rosen Publishing Group, Inc., The.

Hunter, Rebecca. Moving House. Fairclough, Chris, photos by. 2007. (First Times Ser.). (Illus.). 24p. (J). pap. 10.95 (***978-0-237-52696-2(4)*** , Evans Brothers, Limited) Evans Publishing Group GBR. *Dist:* Independent Pubs. Group.

Murphy, Patricia J. Moving. 2008. (J). (***978-1-4034-9776-5(1)*** ***);*** pap. (***978-1-4034-9781-9(8)***) Heinemann Library.

A New House. 2004. (J). pap. 6.95 (978-0-9760646-0-2(X)) Grape Elephant MarketPr.

Schubeck, Carol M. Let's Move Together. Clanuwat, Rinna, illus. 2000. 52p. (J). (ps-6). pap. 15.95 (978-0-9675567-0-3(8)) Suitcase Pr.,The.

Sportelli-Rehak, Angela. Moving Again Mom! Hinlicky, Gregg, illus. (J). (ps-7). 2004. (Uncle Sam's Kids Ser.: Bk. 2). 40p. pap. 7.95 (978-0-9714515-0-6(8)); 2003. pap. (978-0-9714515-3-7(2)) Abidenme Bks.

—Uncle Sam's Kids: Moving Again Mom. Hinlicky, Gregg, illus. 2004. (Uncle Sam's Kids Ser.: Bk. 2). 40p. (gr. k-6). 16.95 (978-0-9714515-2-0(4)) Abidenme Bks.

Thomas, Lyn. My New Home & Me: A Memory Scrapbook for Kids. Ritchie, Scot, illus. unabr. ed. 2001. (Memory Scrapbks. for Kids). 32p. (J). (gr. k-3). (978-1-55074-894-9(7)) Kids Can Pr., Ltd.

Willson, Sarah. How to Make Moving Less Miserable. 2003. (Nick Reference Ser.). (Illus.). 48p. (J). pap. 5.99 (978-0-689-84560-4(X) , Simon Spotlight/Nickelodeon) Simon & Schuster Children's Publishing.

MOVING, HOUSEHOLD—FICTION

Acampora, Paul. Defining Dulcie. 2006. 176p. (J). (gr. 7). 16.99 (978-0-8037-3046-5(2) , Dial) Penguin Group (USA) Inc.

Adee, Donna J. Miriam & Timothy Face Life, Vol. 3. Babcock, Marci, illus. 2000. 384p. (J). pap. 12.95 (978-0-9654272-3-4(4)) Harvest Pubns.

Almond, David. Skellig. 2001. (Illus.). 208p. (gr. 5). mass mkt. 6.50 (978-0-440-22908-7(1) , Laurel Leaf) Random Hse. Children's Bks.

—Skellig. Wojtyla, Karen, ed. 2000. (Illus.). 192p. (gr. 5-7). 6.50 (978-0-440-41602-9(7) , Yearling) Random Hse. Children's Bks.

—Skellig. 1999. 192p. (gr. 5 up). 16.95 (978-0-385-32653-7(X) , Delacorte Bks. for Young Readers) Random Hse. Children's Bks.

—Skellig. 2001. (gr. 5-8). lib. bdg. 14.15 (978-0-613-84565-6(X)); 2000. (J). (978-0-606-19192-0(5)); 2000. (gr. 5-8). lib. bdg. 13.00 (978-0-613-28330-4(9)) Tandem Library Bks.

Anderson, Laurie Halse. Time to Fly. 2003. (Wild at Heart Ser.). (Illus.). 113p. (J). (gr. 4 up). lib. bdg. 23.33 (978-0-8368-3262-4(0)) Stevens, Gareth Inc.

Arnold, Marsha Diane & Pelzel, Vernise Elaine. Hugs on the Wind. Warnick, Elsa, illus. 2006. 32p. (J). (ps-1). 15.95 (978-0-8109-5968-2(2)) Abrams, Harry N. , Inc.

Atkinson, Beth. From Alice to Zen & Everyone in Between: A Novel. 2008. (Exceptional Reading & Language Arts Titles for Intermediate Grades Ser.). (J). 15.95 (***978-0-8225-7271-8(0)*** , Carolrhoda Bks.) Lerner Publishing Group.

Ballard, Mignon F. Aunt Matilda's Ghost. 2000. (Illus.). vii, 136p. (J). 22.50 (978-1-57072-116-8(5)); pap. 12.50 (978-1-57072-132-8(7)) Overmountain Pr.

Barnes, Jennifer Lynn. Golden. 2006. 256p. (YA). (gr. 7). pap. 7.95 (978-0-385-73311-3(9)); lib. bdg. 9.99 (978-0-385-90330-1(8)) Random Hse. Children's Bks. (Delacorte Bks. for Young Readers).

Barrett, Tracy. Cold in Summer. rev. ed. 2003. (Illus.). 208p. (YA). (gr. 5-9). 16.95 (978-0-8050-7052-1(4) , Holt, Henry & Co. Bks. For Young Readers) Holt, Henry & Co.

Bateson, Catherine. Rain May & Captain Daniel. 2002. 144p. (YA). pap. 15.50 (978-0-7022-3337-1(4)) Univ. of Queensland Pr. AUS. *Dist:* International Specialized Bk. Services.

Bateson, Catherine. Stranded in Boringsville. 144p. (gr. 5-9). (J). 16.95 (978-0-8234-1969-2(X)); 2007. (YA). pap. 6.95 (***978-0-8234-2113-8(9)***) Holiday Hse., Inc.

Bauer, Marion Dane. The Secret of the Painted House. Gore, Leonid, illus. 2007. (Stepping Stone Bks.). 112p. (J). (gr. 1-4). 11.99 (***978-0-375-84079-1(6)*** ***);*** lib. bdg. 14.99 (***978-0-375-94079-8(0)***) Random Hse. Children's Bks. (Random Hse. Bks. for Young Readers).

Beake, Lesley. Home Now. Littlewood, Karin, illus. 2007. 32p. (J). (gr. k-3). 16.95 (978-1-58089-162-2(4)); pap. 6.95 (***978-1-58089-163-9(2)***) Charlesbridge Publishing, Inc.

Bennett, Cherie & Gottesfeld, Jeff. A Heart Divided. 2004. 320p. (YA). (gr. 7). 15.95 (978-0-385-32749-7(8) , Delacorte Bks. for Young Readers) Random Hse. Children's Bks.

Benson, Linda. Finding Chance. Lane, Nancy, illus. 2006. 112p. (J). (978-1-59336-696-4(5)) Mondo Publishing.

Berry, Eileen. Roses on Baker Street. Roberts, John, illus. 1998. 48p. (J). (gr. k-4). pap. 5.49 (978-0-89084-934-7(X) , 106401) Jones, Bob Univ. Pr.

Berry, Eileen M. Looking for Home. 2005. 75p. (J). (978-1-59166-493-2(4)) Jones, Bob Univ. Pr.

Blackaby, Susan. Moving Day. Haugen, Ryan, illus. 2005. (Read-It! Readers Ser.). 32p. (J). (gr. k-3). 18.60 (978-1-4048-1006-8(4)) Picture Window Bks.

—Mudanza. Haugen, Ryan, illus. 2006. (Read-It! Readers en Espanol Ser.).Tr. of Moving Day. (SPA.). 32p. (J). (ps-3). 19.95 (978-1-4048-1686-2(0)) Picture Window Bks.

Blades, Ann. Too Small. Blades, Ann, illus. 2000. (Illus.). 32p. (J). (ps-3). 15.95 (978-0-88899-400-4(1)) Groundwood Bks. CAN. *Dist:* Perseus Distribution.

Bottner, Barbara. Rosa's Room. Spiegel, Beth, tr. Spiegel, Beth, illus. 2004. 32p. (J). (gr. 1-2). 15.95 (978-1-56145-302-3(1)) Peachtree Pubs., Ltd.

Bourgeois, Paulette. Franklin Tiene un Mal Dia. Varela, Alejandra Lopez, tr. from ENG. Clark, Brenda, illus. 1999. (Franklin Ser.). (SPA.). (J). (ps-3). pap. 5.95 (978-1-880507-52-0(8) , LC8141) Lectorum Pubns., Inc.

Boutwell, Florence. Teresa of Northwood Prairie: An Historical Adventure Story for Young & Old. Haff, Monica, illus. 1998. 175p. (J). 17.95 (978-0-87062-284-7(6) , Clark, Arthur H. Co., The) Univ. of Oklahoma Pr.

Bowers, Tim. A New Home. 2003. (Green Light Readers Level 1 Ser.). (Illus.). 24p. (J). 11.95 (978-0-15-204808-2(1)); pap. 3.95 (978-0-15-204848-8(0)) Harcourt Children's Bks. (Green Light Readers).

—New Home. 2002. (gr. k-3). lib. bdg. 11.80 (978-0-613-63169-3(2)) Tandem Library Bks.

Bowman, Crystal. Boxes, Boxes Everywhere. Schettle, Jane, illus. (J). 2004. 20p. 4.99 (978-0-310-70815-5(X)); 2001. 24p. 6.99 (978-0-310-70062-3(0)) Zonderkidz.

—Everyboxes, Boxes. 2004. (ps-2). lib. bdg. 13.00 (978-0-613-71757-1(0)) Tandem Library Bks.

Brandon, Anthony G. Moving Day. Yee, Wong Herbert, illus. 2005. (Green Light Readers Level 2 Ser.). 32p. (J). (ps-ps). 12.95 (978 0-15-205646-9(7)); pap. 3.95 (978-0-15-205652-0(1)) Harcourt Trade Pubs.

Brezenoff, Steven. Alley of Shadows. Martin, Cynthia, illus. 2008. (J). pap. (***978-1-59889-922-1(8)*** ***);*** (YA). (gr. 5-9). lib. bdg. 17.95 (***978-1-59889-856-9(6)***) Stone Arch Bks.

Bullard, Lisa. My Neighborhood: Places & Faces. Wesley, Omarr, illus. 2004. (All about Me Ser.). 24p. (C). (gr. k-1). 21.26 (978-1-4048-0047-2(6)) Picture Window Bks.

—Trick-or-Treat on Milton Street. Oeltjenbruns, Joni, illus. (Carolrhoda Picture Books Ser.). 32p. (J). (ps-3). 2004. pap. 6.95 (978-1-57505-793-4(X)); 2003. 15.95 (978-1-57505-158-1(3) , Carolrhoda Bks.) Lerner Publishing Group.

Burgoyne, Tom. The Phillie Phanatics Moving Day. Epstein, Len, illus. 2005. 32p. (J). pap. (978-0-9705804-8-1(7)) Middle Atlantic Pr.

Butler, Dori Hillestad. Sliding into Home. Casale, Paul, illus. 2003. (Peachtree Junior Publication Ser.). 192p. (J). 14.95 (978-1-56145-222-4(X)) Peachtree Pubs., Ltd.

Carbone, Elisa. Starting School with an Enemy. 1999. (978-0-606-16568-6(1)) Tandem Library Bks.

Carey, Janet Lee. The Double Life of Zoe Flynn. 2004. (Illus.). 240p. (J). 16.95 (978-0-689-85604-4(0) , Atheneum) Simon & Schuster Children's Publishing.

Carlson, Nancy. My Best Friend Moved Away. Carlson, Nancy, illus. 2003. (Illus.). 32p. (J). (gr. k-2). pap. 5.99 (978-0-14-250067-5(4) , Puffin) Penguin Group (USA) Inc.

—My Best Friend Moved Away. 2003. (gr. k-3). lib. bdg. 14.15 (978-0-613-67291-7(7)) Tandem Library Bks.

Carlstrom, Nancy White. I'M Not Moving, Mama. 1999. (gr. k-3). lib. bdg. 14.15 (978-0-613-21751-4(9)) Tandem Library Bks.

M N O

—I'm Not Moving, Mama. Wickstrom, Thor, illus. 1999. 32p. (J). (ps-3). pap. 6.99 (978-0-689-82881-2(0) , Aladdin) Simon & Schuster Children's Publishing.

Cassidy, Cathy. Indigo Blue. 2006. 240p. (J). (gr. 5). pap. 5.99 (978-0-14-240703-5(8) , Puffin) Penguin Group (USA) Inc.

Charles, Norma M. Sophie Sea to Sea: Star Girl's Cross-Canada Adventures! 2005. 152p. (YA). (gr. 3-8). pap., tchr. ed. (978-0-88878-404-9(X) , Sandcastle Bks.) Dundurn Group, The.

Cheng, Andrea. Honeysuckle House. 2004. 136p. (YA). 16.95 (978-1-886910-99-7(5) , Lemniscaat) Boyds Mills Pr.

—The Key Collection. Choi, Yangsook, illus. rev. ed. 2003. 128p. (J). (gr. 3-6). 16.95 (978-0-8050-7153-5(9) , Holt, Henry & Co. Bks. For Young Readers) Holt, Henry & Co.

Christopher, Matt. One Smooth Move. Koelsch, Michael, illus. 2004. (Extreme Team Ser.: Vol. 1). 64p. (J). (gr. 2-4). pap. 4.99 (978-0-316-73749-4(6)) Little Brown & Co.

Citra, Becky. Ellie's New Home. 1999. (Young Reader Ser.). (Illus.). 82p. (J). (gr. 3-6). pap. 4.99 (978-1-55143-164-2(5)) Orca Bk. Pubs. USA.

—Ellie's New Home. 1999. (gr. 3-6). lib. bdg. 13.00 (978-0-613-29608-3(7)) Tandem Library Bks.

Civardi, Anne. Moving House. Bates, Michelle, ed. Cartwright, Stephen, illus. rev. ed. 2005. 16p. (J). (ps-17). pap. 4.95 (978-0-7945-1009-1(4) , Usborne) EDC Publishing.

Clark, Brenda, illus. Franklin's Bad Day. 2002. (Franklin Ser.). 12.40 (978-1-4046-0321-9(2)) Book Wholesalers, Inc.

Clark, Eleanor. Katie Sue: Heading West. 2007. (Eleanor Jo Ser.). (J). pap. 14.99 (978-0-9788726-0-1(6)) HonorNet.

Clark, Sherryl. Knock It Off! 2000. (gr. 7-12). lib. bdg. 12.25 (978-0-613-28919-1(6)) Tandem Library Bks.

—Prove It! 2000. (gr. 7-12). lib. bdg. 12.25 (978-0-613-29023-4(2)) Tandem Library Bks.

Clausen, Andrew. In the Year of the Boar & Jackie Robinson. 1999. 66p. (J). (gr. 4-6). stu. ed., ring bd. 12.99 (978-1-58609-135-4(2)) Progeny Pr.

Collard, Sneed B., III. Dog Sense. 2005. 192p. (J). 14.95 (978-1-56145-351-1(X)) Peachtree Pubs., Ltd.

Cork, Barbara & Cork, Barbara Taylor. Lucy's New House. Dodds, Siobhan, illus. 2002. (First Experiences Ser.). 32p. (J). (gr. k-2). 15.00 (978-1-57768-988-1(7) , Waterbird Bks.) School Specialty Publishing.

Cosgrove, Stephen. Bee Double Bopp: Respecting Others. Arroyo, Fian, illus. 2004. (J). (978-1-58804-350-4(9)) PCI Educational Publishing.

Cox, Phil Roxbee. Mouse Moves House. Cartwright, Stephen, illus. rev. ed. 2006. 16p. (J). pap. 6.99 (978-0-7945-1507-2(X) , Usborne) EDC Publishing.

Creel, Ann Howard. Nowhere, Now Here. 2000. (J). (978-0-606-21789-7(4)); (gr. 5-8). lib. bdg. 14.10 (978-0-613-31532-6(4)) Tandem Library Bks.

Crimi, Carolyn. The Louds Move In! Dunnick, Regan, illus. 2006. 32p. (J). 14.95 (978-0-7614-5221-8(4)) Cavendish, Marshall Corp.

Crist-Evans, Craig. North of Everything. 2004. (Illus.). 80p. (J). (gr. 5-9). 14.99 (978-0-7636-2098-1(X)) Candlewick Pr.

Cumbie, Patricia. Where People Like Us Live. 2008. 224p. (J). 16.99 (*978-0-06-137597-2(7)*); lib. bdg. 17.89 (*978-0-06-137598-9(5)*) HarperCollins Pubs. (Geringer, Laura Book).

Daly, Niki. Where's Jamela? 2004. (Jamela Ser.). (Illus.). 36p. (J). 16.00 (978-0-374-38324-4(3) , Farrar, Straus & Giroux (BYR)) Farrar, Straus & Giroux.

D'Amico, Carmela & D'Amico, Steven. Ella the Elegant Elephant. 2004. (Illus.). 56p. (J). (ps-3). pap. 16.95 (978-0-439-62792-4(3) , Levine, Arthur A. Bks.) Scholastic, Inc.

Danziger, Paula. Amber Brown Is Green with Envy. Ross, Tony, illus. 2003. (Amber Brown Ser.: No. 9). 160p. (J). (gr. 2-5). 15.99 (978-0-399-23181-0(1) , Putnam Juvenile) Penguin Group (USA) Inc.

—Amber Brown Is Green with Envy. Ross, Tony, illus. 2004. (Amber Brown Ser.: No. 9). 160p. (J). (gr. 3-6). pap. 4.99 (978-0-439-07171-0(2) , Scholastic Paperbacks) Scholastic, Inc.

—Amber Brown Is Not a Crayon. Ross, Tony, illus. 2006. (Amber Brown Ser.: No. 1). 80p. (J). (gr. 2-6). pap. 4.99 (978-0-14-240619-9(8) , Puffin) Penguin Group (USA) Inc.

—Amber Brown Is Not a Crayon. (Amber Brown Ser.: No. 1). 80p. (J). (gr. 3-6). pap. 3.50 (978-0-8072-1289-9(X) , Listening Library) Random Hse. Audio Publishing Group.

—P. S. Longer Letter Later: A Novel in Letters. 1999. (gr. 5-8). lib. bdg. 13.00 (978-0-613-18271-3(5)) Tandem Library Bks.

—Seguiremos Siendo Amigos.Tr. of Amber Brown Is Not a Crayon. (J). (gr. 4-5). 8.95 (978-970-29-0185-3(5) , AF33034) Santillana, S.A. de C.V., Editorial MEX. *Dist:* Santillana USA Publishing Co., Inc.

—This Place Has No Atmosphere. 2006. (J). 176p. (gr. 5). 5.99 (978-0-14-240680-9(5)); 156p. (*978-1-4156-7492-5(2)*) Penguin Group (USA) Inc. (Puffin).

Danziger, Paula & Martin, Ann M. P. S. Longer Letter Later: A Novel in Letters. 2004. 240p. (J). (gr. 3-5). pap. 4.99 (978-0-8072-1537-1(6) , Listening Library) Random Hse. Audio Publishing Group.

—P. S. Longer Letter Later: A Novel in Letters. 240p. 2006. (J). pap. 5.99 (978-0-439-83884-9(3) , Scholastic Paperbacks); 1999. (gr. 3-7). 6.99 (978-0-590-21311-0(3)); 1998. (J). (gr. 5-8). pap. 16.95 (978-0-590-21310-3(5)) Scholastic, Inc.

Davies, Sally J. K. When William Went Away. Davies, Sally J. K., illus. 1998. (Picture Bks.). (Illus.). 32p. (J). (ps-3). lib. bdg. 15.95 (978-1-57505-303-5(9) , Carolrhoda Bks.) Lerner Publishing Group.

De Guzman, Michael. Beekman's Big Deal. 2004. 224p. (J). 16.00 (978-0-374-30672-4(9) , Farrar, Straus & Giroux (BYR)) Farrar, Straus & Giroux.

Dellasega, Cheryl. Nugrl90 (Sadie) LaPierre, Karina, illus. 2007. (Bloggrls Ser.). (YA). (gr. 7 up). 200p. 15.99 (*978-0-7614-5375-8(X)*); 190p. per. 6.99 (*978-0-7614-5396-3(2)*) Cavendish, Marshall Corp.

Delton, Judy. Angel Bites the Bullet. Weber, Jill, illus. 2003. 144p. (J). (gr. 3-5). pap. 4.95 (978-0-618-36920-1(1)) Houghton Mifflin Co. Trade & Reference Div.

Deriso, Christine Hurley. Do-Over. 2006. 192p. (J). (gr. 4-7). 15.95 (978-0-385-73333-5(X)); lib. bdg. 17.99 (978-0-385-90350-9(2)) Random Hse. Children's Bks. (Delacorte Bks. for Young Readers).

Deriso, Christine Hurley. Do-over. 2007. 160p. (J). (gr. 4-7). 5.99 (*978-0-440-42119-1(5)* , Yearling) Random Hse. Children's Bks.

DiCerto, Joseph. The Wall People. 2006. 19.95 (978-1-58752-112-6(1)) Timberwolf Pr., Inc.

Duckett, Brenda. Summit Lane. 2005. 79p. pap. 10.99 (978-1-4116-3897-6(2)) Lulu.com.

Dyahnne. Sweetie's Place: A Moving Adventure. 2004. 26p. (J). per. 7.99 (978-1-4116-0760-6(0)) Lulu.com.

Eager, Edward. Magic or Not? Bodecker, N. M., illus. 1999. (Odyssey Classics). 208p. (J). (gr. 3-7). pap. 7.00 (978-0-15-202080-4(2) , Odyssey Classics) Harcourt Children's Bks.

—Magic or Not? 1999. (J). (978-0-606-19001-5(5)) Tandem Library Bks.

Ellis, Sarah. Pick-Up Sticks. 2001. 124p. (J). (gr. 4-7). pap. 5.95 (978-0-88899-162-1(2)) Groundwood Bks. CAN. *Dist:* Perseus Distribution.

—Pick-up Sticks. 2001. (gr. 3-6). lib. bdg. 14.10 (978-0-613-90977-8(1)) Tandem Library Bks.

Emerman, Ellen. Just Right: The Story of a Jewish Home. Rosenfeld, Dina, ed. Kranz, Sarah, illus. 1999. 32p. (J). (ps-1). 9.95 (978-0-922613-91-5(5)) Hachai Publishing.

Emmer, E. R. Me, Minerva & the Flying Flora. Huerta, Catherine, illus. 2nd rev. ed. 2003. (Going to Ser.). Orig. Title: Me, Minera & the Flying Car. 136p. (gr. 4-8). pap. 6.95 (978-1-893577-10-7(4)) Four Corners Publishing Co., Inc.

Engel, Christiane. Louis & Bobo. 2007. (Illus.). 28p. (J). pap. 6.99 (*978-1-84458-375-1(9)*) Anova Bks. GBR. *Dist:* Independent Pubs. Group.

Enright, Elizabeth. The Four-Story Mistake. Enright, Elizabeth, illus. rev. ed. 2002. (Melendy Quartet Ser.: Bk. 2). (Illus.). 208p. (J). (gr. 3-7). 16.95 (978-0-8050-7061-3(3) , Holt, Henry & Co. Bks. For Young Readers) Holt, Henry & Co.

Esckilsen, Erik E. Offsides. 2004. 176p. (YA). (gr. 5-9). tchr. ed. 15.00 (978-0-618-46284-1(8) , Walter Lorraine) Houghton Mifflin Co. Trade & Reference Div.

Fast, Natalie. The Secret Apartment. 2007. 192p. (gr. 4-7). 5.99 (978-0-553-48794-7(9) , Yearling) Random Hse. Children's Bks.

Fenner, Carol. Yolonda's Genius. Colon, Raul, illus. 2002. (J). 14.47 (978-0-7587-0333-0(3)) Book Wholesalers, Inc.

Figueredo, D. H. Mundo Nuevo. 1999. (SPA.). (gr. 3-6). lib. bdg. 15.25 (978-0-613-32852-4(3)) Tandem Library Bks.

Fleming, Candace. Lowji Discovers America. 2005. (Illus.). 160p. (J). 15.95 (978-0-689-86299-1(7) , Atheneum) Simon & Schuster Children's Publishing.

Fletcher, Ralph. Spider Boy. 1998. 183p. (J). (ps-7). per. 13.00 (978-0-613-08798-8(4)) Tandem Library Bks.

Fletcher, Ralph J. Moving Day. Emery, Jennifer, illus. (J). (gr. 3-7). 17.95 (978-1-59078-339-9(5)) Boyds Mills Pr.

—Spider Boy. 1998. 192p. (J). (gr. 4-7). 5.99 (978-0-440-41483-4(0) , Yearling) Random Hse. Children's Bks.

—Spider Boy. 1998. (978-0-606-13794-2(7)) Tandem Library Bks.

Freeman, Martha. The Trouble with Babies. Smith, Cat Bowman, illus. 2002. 80p. (J). (gr. 4-6). tchr. ed. 15.95 (978-0-8234-1698-1(4)) Holiday Hse., Inc.

—The Year My Parents Ruined My Life. 1999. (978-0-606-16453-5(7)) Tandem Library Bks.

Friedman, Aimee. Year My Sister Got Lucky. 2008. 384p. (J). pap. 16.99 (*978-0-439-92227-2(5)*) Scholastic, Inc.

Friedman, Laurie. Mallory Se Muda (Mallory on the Move) Anaya, Josefina, tr. Schmitz, Tamara, illus. 2007. (Mallory en español (Mallory in Spanish) Ser.). (SPA.). (J). (gr. 2-6). pap. 5.95 (*978-0-8225-7493-4(4)* , Ediciones Lerner) Lerner Publishing Group.

Friedman, Laurie B. Back to School, Mallory. Schmitz, Tamara, illus. (J). 2005. 175p. (ps-7). pap. 5.95 (978-1-57505-865-8(0)); 2004. 160p. (gr. 2-5). 15.95 (978-1-57505-658-6(5)) Lerner Publishing Group.

—Mallory on the Move. Schmitz, Tamara, tr. Schmitz, Tamara, illus. 2004. (Middle Grade Fiction Ser.). 160p. (J). 15.95 (978-1-57505-538-1(4)) Lerner Publishing Group.

Friel, Maeve. Felix on the Move. Blake, Beccy, illus. 2004. (Read-It! Readers Ser.). 32p. (C). (gr. k-3). 18.60 (978-1-4048-0055-7(7)) Picture Window Bks.

Friend, Natasha. Bounce. 2007. 192p. (YA). (gr. 6-8). pap. 16.99 (*978-0-439-85350-7(8)* , Scholastic Pr.) Scholastic, Inc.

Fuqua, Jonathon Scott. Catie & Josephine. Parke, Steven, illus. 2003. 72p. (J). (gr. 3-5). 16.00 (978-0-618-39403-6(6)) Houghton Mifflin Co. Trade & Reference Div.

Gantos, Jack. Jack Adrift: Fourth Grade Without a Clue. 2003. (Jack Henry Ser.). (Illus.). 208p. (J). 16.00 (978-0-374-39987-0(5) , Farrar, Straus & Giroux (BYR)) Farrar, Straus & Giroux.

—Jack Adrift: Fourth Grade Without a Clue. l.t. ed. 2004. 226p. (J). 22.95 (978-0-7862-6387-5(3)) Thorndike Pr.

—Jack on the Tracks: Four Seasons of Fifth Grade. (Jack Henry Ser.). 192p. (J). (gr. 5 up). 2001. pap. 6.95 (978-0-374-43717-6(3) , Sunburst); 1999. (Illus.). 16.00 (978-0-374-33665-3(2) , Farrar, Straus & Giroux (BYR)) Farrar, Straus & Giroux.

—Jack on the Tracks: Four Seasons of Fifth Grade. 2001. (gr. 5-8). lib. bdg. 14.10 (978-0-613-85137-4(4)) Tandem Library Bks.

—Jack on the Tracks: Four Seasons of Fifth Grade. l.t. ed. 2002. 210p. (J). 22.95 (978-0-7862-4394-5(5)) Thorndike Pr.

Garcia-Clairac, Santiago. El Libro Invisible (The Invisible Book) Flores, Enrique, illus. 10th ed. 2001. (SPA.). 140p. (J). (gr. 4-6). (978-84-348-6556-3(4)) SM Ediciones.

Giff, Patricia Reilly. Horas de Sol. 2000. Tr. of Sunny Side Up. (SPA.). (YA). (gr. 1 up). 3.95 (978-0-922852-48-2(0)) AIMS International Bks., Inc.

Giffard, Hannah. Red Fox on the Move. (Illus.). 36p. pap. (978-0-7112-2159-8(6)) Lincoln, Frances Ltd. GBR. *Dist:* Transition Vendor.

Gleeson, Libby. Half a World Away. Blackwood, Freya, illus. (J). pap. (978-0-439-88978-0(2)); 2007. 40p. pap. 15.99 (978-0-439-88977-3(4)) Scholastic, Inc. (Levine, Arthur A. Bks.).

Goldstein, Gary. The Mythfits. 2005. 280p. (YA). (ps-7). pap. 14.99 (978-1-59092-125-8(9) , Blue Works) Windstorm Creative.

Gonzalez, Gabriela & Triana, Gaby. Backstage Pass. 2004. (Illus.). 224p. (J). (gr. 7 up). 15.99 (978-0-06-056017-1(7)); lib. bdg. 16.89 (978-0-06-056018-8(5)) HarperCollins Pubs.

Gorman, Carol. Dork in Disguise. 2000. (J). 12.64 (978-0-606-20049-3(5)) Tandem Library Bks.

Grabenstein, Chris. The Crossroads. 2008. 368p. (J). (gr. 4-7). 16.99 (*978-0-375-84697-7(2)* , Random Hse. Bks. for Young Readers) Random Hse. Children's Bks.

Graff, Nancy Price. A Long Way Home. 2001. 208p. (J). (gr. 5-9). tchr. ed. 15.00 (978-0-618-12042-0(4) , Clarion Bks.) Houghton Mifflin Co. Trade & Reference Div.

Greene, Stephanie. Falling into Place. 128p. (J). (gr. 4-6). 2006. pap. 5.95 (978-0-618-68928-6(1)); 2002. (Illus.). tchr. ed. 15.00 (978-0-618-17744-8(2)) Houghton Mifflin Co. Trade & Reference Div. (Clarion Bks.).

Greenfield, Eloise. Grandmama's Joy. 1999. (J). 12.79 (978-0-606-16847-2(8)) Tandem Library Bks.

Gunn, Robin Jones. Only You, Sierra. 1998. (Sierra Jensen Ser.: Bk. 1). 176p. (J). (gr. 7-11). pap. 6.99 (978-1-56179-370-9(1)) Bethany Hse. Pubs.

Gunnery, Sylvia. Out of Bounds. 2004. (Sports Stories Ser.). 104p. (J). (gr. 3-8). 7.95 (978-1-55028-826-1(1)); (*978-1-55028-827-8(X)*) Lorimer, James & Co., Ltd., Pubs. CAN. *Dist:* Casemate Pubs. & Bk. Distributors, LLC.

Hale, Marian. The Truth about Sparrows. rev. ed. 2004. (Illus.). 272p. (J). 16.95 (978-0-8050-7584-7(4) , Holt, Henry & Co. Bks. For Young Readers) Holt, Henry & Co.

—The Truth about Sparrows. 2007. 288p. (J). pap. 6.99 (*978-0-312-37133-3(0)*) Square Fish.

Hall, Kirsten. My New Town. Suzan, Gerardo, illus. (J). (gr. k-1). 2006. 32p. pap. 3.95 (978-0-516-24972-8(X)); 2005. 31p. 18.50 (978-0-516-24877-6(4)) Scholastic Library Publishing. (Children's Pr.).

Harcourt School Publishers Staff. Goodbye, Hello: Library Book. 1999. (Collections Ser.). (Illus.). pap. 14.90 (978-0-15-313411-1(9)) Harcourt Schl. Pubs.

—Over the Gate: Take-Home Book. 1999. (Collections Ser.). (Illus.). (J). pap. 1.90 (978-0-15-317209-0(6)) Harcourt Schl. Pubs.

—P. Bunyan Moves Out: Take-Home Book. 1999. (Collections Ser.). (Illus.). (J). pap. 1.90 (978-0-15-317308-0(4)) Harcourt Schl. Pubs.

Harper, Jessica. I Like Where I Am. Osborn, Kathy & Karas, G. Brian, illus. 2004. 32p. (J). (ps-3). 15.99 (978-0-399-23479-8(9) , Putnam Juvenile) Penguin Group (USA) Inc.

Harper, Jo. Como los Perros de la Pradera. 2000. (SPA.). (gr. k-3). lib. bdg. 17.60 (978-0-613-32422-9(6)) Tandem Library Bks.

Harper, Jo & Harper, Josephine. Prairie Dog Pioneers. Spearing, Craig, illus. 48p. (J). (ps-3). 2000. pap. 8.95 (978-1-890515-23-2(X)); 1998. (SPA.). 16.95 (978-1-890515-10-2(8)) Turtle Bks.

Harper, Jo & Harper, Josephine L. Prairie Dog Pioneers. Spearing, Craig, illus. 2000. 44p. (J). (ps-3). lib. bdg. 17.60 (978-0-613-32966-8(X)) Tandem Library Bks.

Harrington, Janice N. & Lagarrigue, Jerome. Going North. 2004. (Illus.). 40p. (J). 16.00 (978-0-374-32681-4(9) , Farrar, Straus & Giroux (BYR)) Farrar, Straus & Giroux.

Harris, Joan. Moving Day: An Alfie & Roxy Adventure. Santeramo, Rich, illus. 2007. 16p. (J). 12.95 (*978-0-9796994-9-8(5)*) TRIAD Publishing Group.

Harrison, Cora. Milleniumdrumshee. 1999. (Drumshee Timeline Ser.). (Illus.). 143p. (J). (978-0-86327-715-3(2)) Wolfhound Pr.

Harvey, Brett. Cassie's Journey: Going West in the 1960s. Ray, Deborah Kogan, illus. 1998. 40p. (J). (ps-3). pap. 6.95 (978-0-8234-1172-6(9)) Holiday Hse., Inc.

Haskins, Lori. Butterfly Fever. Smath, Jerry, illus. 2004. 31p. (J). lib. bdg. 20.00 (*978-1-4242-1087-9(9)*) Fitzgerald Bks.

—Butterfly Fever. Smath, Jerry, tr. Smath, Jerry, illus. 2004. (Science Solves It! Ser.). (J). pap. 4.99 (978-1-57565-134-7(3)) Kane Pr., The.

Havill, Juanita. Jamaica's Blue Marker. O'Brien, Anne Sibley, illus. 2003. 32p. (J). (gr. k-3). pap. 6.95 (978-0-618-36917-1(1)) Houghton Mifflin Co. Trade & Reference Div.

Hees, Miriam. The Adventures of Jilly & Brad: Noises in the Attic. Kinneman, D. Michael, illus. 2003. 128p. (J). pap. 5.95 (978-0-9718348-4-2(9)) Blooming Tree Pr.

Herman, Gail. New Dog in Town. Nez, John, illus. 2006. 32p. (J). lib. bdg. 20.00 (*978-1-4242-1110-4(7)*) Fitzgerald Bks.

—New Dog in Town. Nez, John A., illus. 2006. (Social Studies Connects). 32p. (J). pap. 4.99 (978-1-57565-165-1(3)) Kane Pr., The.

Heuston, Kimberley Burton. Book of Jude. 2008. (J). (*978-1-932425-26-0(8)* , Front Street) Boyds Mills Pr.

Hickey, Caroline. Cassie Was Here. 2007. 192p. (J). (gr. 4-7). 16.95 (*978-1-59643-205-5(5)*) Roaring Brook Pr.

Hill, Janet Muirhead. Danny's Dragon: A Story of Wartime Loss. Lehmkuhl, Pat & Ore, Peter, illus. 2006. 192p. (J). per. 10.00 (978-0-9772525-0-3(7)) Raven Publishing Inc. of Montana.

Hobbs, Valerie. How Far Would You Have Gotten If I Hadn't Called You Back? 2003. 320p. (J). pap. 5.99 (978-0-439-58396-1(9) , Scholastic Paperbacks) Scholastic, Inc.

Hobbs, William. Leaving Protection. 2004. 192p. (J). (gr. 5 up). lib. bdg. 16.89 (978-0-06-051632-1(1)) HarperCollins Pubs.

Hoffman, Alice. Aquamarine. 112p. (J). 2002. (gr. 4-7). pap. 4.99 (978-0-439-09864-9(5) , Scholastic Pr.); 2001. (gr. 5-9). pap. 16.95 (978-0-439-09863-2(7)) Scholastic, Inc.

Hogan, Mary. The Serious Kiss. 2005. 256p. (J). pap. 7.99 (978-0-06-072208-1(8) , Harper Trophy); (YA). (gr. 7 up). 16.99 (978-0-06-072206-7(1)) HarperCollins Pubs.

Holt, Kimberly Willis. Piper Reed, Navy Brat. Davenier, Christine, illus. 2007. 160p. (J). (gr. 3-6). 14.95 (*978-0-8050-8197-8(6)* , Holt, Henry & Co. Bks. For Young Readers) Holt, Henry & Co.

—Piper Reed, Navy Brat. Davenier, Christine, illus. 2008. 176p. (J). pap. 6.99 (*978-0-312-38020-5(8)*) Square Fish.

Hurst, Carol Otis. The Wrong One. 2003. 160p. (YA). (gr. 4-6). tchr. ed. 15.00 (978-0-618-27599-1(1) , Walter Lorraine) Houghton Mifflin Co. Trade & Reference Div.

Jenkins, A. M. Beating Heart: A Ghost Story. 2006. 256p. (YA). 16.99 (978-0-06-054607-6(7)); (Illus.). (J). lib. bdg. 16.89 (978-0-06-054608-3(5)) HarperCollins Pubs.

Johnson, Angela. Maniac Monkeys on Magnolia Street. Ward, John, illus. 2000. 97p. (J). (ps-7). 12.04 (978-0-606-19829-5(6)) Tandem Library Bks.

Johnson-Choong, Shelly. The Jewelry Box. 2nd ed. 2004. (YA). reprint ed. pap. 10.95 (978-1-932280-40-1(5) , 80405) Granite Publishing & Distribution.

Johnson, Lindsay Lee. Worlds Apart. 2005. 176p. (J). (gr. 5). 16.95 (978-1-932425-28-4(4) , Lemniscaat) Boyds Mills Pr.

Joosse, Barbara M. Ghost Trap. Truesdell, Sue, illus. 1998. (Wild Willie Mystery Ser.). 80p. (J). (gr. 4-6). tchr. ed. 15.00 (978-0-395-66587-9(6) , Clarion Bks.) Houghton Mifflin Co. Trade & Reference Div.

Jordan, Sarah Clark. The BossQueen, Little BigBark, & the Sentinel Pup. 2004. (Illus.). 144p. (J). 14.95 (978-1-58246-115-1(5) , Tricycle Pr.) Ten Speed Pr.

Kehret, Peg. The Stranger Next Door. (J). 2003. (Illus.). 176p. (gr. 3-7). pap. 5.99 (978-0-14-250178-8(6) , Puffin); 2002. 160p. (gr. 4-8). 15.99 (978-0-525-46829-5(3) , Dutton Juvenile) Penguin Group (USA) Inc.

—The Stranger Next Door. 2003. (gr. 5-8). lib. bdg. 14.15 (978-0-613-82994-6(8)) Tandem Library Bks.

Kelly, Katy. Lucy Rose: Here's the Thing about Me. Rex, Adam, illus. (J). (gr. 3-7). 2004. 144p. 12.95 (978-0-385-73203-1(1) , Delacorte Bks. for Young Readers); 2004. 144p. lib. bdg. 14.99 (978-0-385-90234-2(4) , Delacorte Bks. for Young Readers); 2006. 160p. reprint ed. 5.99 (978-0-440-42026-2(1) , Yearling) Random Hse. Children's Bks.

Kennedy, Pamela. Moving Day for Sam. Petrov, Anton, illus. 2007. 32p. (J). (gr. k-3). 8.99 (*978-0-8249-5558-8(7)* , GPKids) Ideals Pubns.

Kittinger, Jo S. Moving Day. Richard, Ilene, illus. 2003. (Rookie Reader Skill Set Ser.). (J). (gr. k-2). pap. 4.95 (978-0-516-27784-4(7)); 24p. 19.50 (978-0-516-22846-4(3)) Scholastic Library Publishing. (Children's Pr.).

—Moving Day. 2003. (gr. k-3). lib. bdg. 12.95 (978-0-613-67645-8(9)) Tandem Library Bks.

Kline, Suzy. Herbie Jones Moves On. 2003. 80p. (J). (gr. 2-5). 14.99 (978-0-399-23635-8(X) , Putnam Juvenile) Penguin Group (USA) Inc.

Klise, Kate. Deliver Us from Normal. 2005. 240p. (YA). (gr. 5-9). 16.95 (978-0-439-52322-6(2)) Scholastic, Inc.

—Deliver Us from Normal: Read-Along/Homework Pack. unabr. ed. 2005. (YA). (gr. 5-8). 65.70 incl. audio (978-1-4193-3619-5(3) , 42050) Recorded Bks., LLC.

Koponen, Libby. Blow Out the Moon. 2006. 224p. (gr. 8-17). pap. 15.99 (978-0-316-01480-9(X) , Tingley, Megan Bks.) Little, Brown Bks. for Young Readers.

Koss, Amy Goldman. The Ashwater Experiment. 2001. (J). (978-0-606-21046-1(6)) Tandem Library Bks.

—The Ashwater Experiment. l.t. ed. 2000. 188p. (YA). (gr. 8-12). 20.95 (978-0-7862-2686-3(2)) Thorndike Pr.

Krensky, Stephen. We Just Moved! DiFiori, Larry, illus. 2004. 32p. (J). lib. bdg. 15.00 (978-1-59054-384-9(X)) Fitzgerald Bks.

—We Just Moved! Di Fiori, Lawrence, illus. 1998. (Hello Reader! Ser.). 32p. (J). pap. 3.99 (978-0-590-33127-2(2)) Scholastic, Inc.

—We Just Moved! 1998. (Hello Reader! Ser.). (J). (978-0-606-13891-8(9)) Tandem Library Bks.

Krishnaswami, Uma. The Closet Ghosts. Bhabha, Shiraaz, illus. 2005. 32p. (J). 16.95 (978-0-89239-208-7(8)) Children's Bk. Pr.

Krulik, Nancy E. Drat! You Copycat, No. 7. 2003. (Katie Kazoo, Switcheroo Ser.: No. 7). (gr. 3-6). lib. bdg. 11.80 (978-0-613-62943-0(4)) Tandem Library Bks.

—Drat! You Copycat!, No. 7. 2003. (Katie Kazoo, Switcheroo Ser.: No. 7). (Illus.). 80p. (J). (gr. 2-4). pap. 3.99 (978-0-448-43171-0(8) , Grosset & Dunlap) Penguin Group (USA) Inc.

—Tommy's Last Stand. 1999. (gr. 3-6). lib. bdg. 11.80 (978-0-613-16014-8(2)) Tandem Library Bks.

Lachtman, Ofelia Dumas. The Summer of El Pintor. 2001. (Illus.). 240p. (J). (gr. 11 up). pap. 9.95 (978-1-55885-327-0(8) , Piñata Books) Arte Publico Pr.

—Summer of el Pintor. 2001. (gr. 5-8). lib. bdg. 18.75 (978-0-613-59023-5(6)) Tandem Library Bks.

Law, Felicia. Rumble the Dragon's Cave. 2005. (Read-It! Readers Ser.). (Illus.). 32p. (J). (ps-k). lib. bdg. 18.60 (978-1-4048-1353-3(5)) Picture Window Bks.

The League of Super Movers: My Moving Adventure. 2001. 16p. (J). 5.95 (978-1-888891-33-1(5)) BR Anchor Publishing.

Lears, Laurie. Megan's Birthday Tree: A Story about Open Adoption. Farnsworth, Bill, illus. 2005. 32p. (J). (ps-3). 15.95 (978-0-8075-5036-6(1)) Whitman, Albert & Co.

Levy, Kimberley M. Chelsea's New Home. Herman, Terry, illus. 2001. 32p. (J). 15.95 (978-0-9706531-2-3(3)) Printstar Bks.

Lewis, Beverly. Good-Bye, Dressel Hills. 2002. (Holly's Heart Ser.: Bk. 7). 160p. (YA). pap. 6.99 (978-0-7642-2506-2(5)) Bethany Hse. Pubs.

Lewis, Maggie. Morgy Makes His Move. Chesworth, Michael, illus. 80p. (J). 2002. (gr. 1-4). pap. 4.95 (978-0-618-19680-7(3)); 1999. (gr. 4-6). tchr. ed. 15.00 (978-0-395-92284-2(4)) Houghton Mifflin Co. Trade & Reference Div.

—Morgy Makes His Move. 1999. (gr. 3-6). lib. bdg. 12.95 (978-0-613-60698-1(1)) Tandem Library Bks.

Lindbergh, Anne M. The People in Pineapple Place. 2003. (Illus.). 192p. (J). (gr. 3-7). pap. 5.99 (978-0-7636-1739-4(3)) Candlewick Pr.

—People in Pineapple Place. Frazee, Marla, illus. 2003. 192p. (J). (gr. 3-7). 16.99 (978-0-7636-2131-5(5)) Candlewick Pr.

Ling, Bettina. The Big City. Ong, Cristina, illus. 1999. (Scholastic At-Home Phonics Reading Program Ser.: Vol. 32). 24p. (J). (978-0-590-68780-5(8)) Scholastic, Inc.

Lobel, Anita. Nini Here & There. Lobel, Anita, illus. 2007. 32p. (J). (ps-2). 16.99 (978-0-06-078767-7(8)); (Illus.). lib. bdg. 17.89 (978-0-06-078768-4(6)) HarperCollins Pubs.

Lock, Deborah. A Trip to the Library. 2004. (Illus.). 32p. (J). (ps-ps). lib. bdg. 10.79 (978-0-606-30871-7(7)) Tandem Library Bks.

Lough, Loree. Dream Seekers: Roger William's Stand for Freedom. 1999. (American Adventure Ser.: No. 3). (Illus.). 144p. (J). (gr. 3-7). lib. bdg. 15.95 (978-0-7910-5043-9(2) , Chelsea Hse.) Facts On File, Inc.

Lowry, Lois. Anastasia de Nuevo. 2003. (Juvenil Ser.: Vol. 77). Tr. of Anastasia Again. (SPA., Illus.). 112p. (J). (gr. 5-7). 9.95 (978-84-239-9047-4(8)) Espasa Calpe, S.A. ESP. *Dist:* Lectorum Pubns., Inc., Planeta Publishing Corp.

Lynch, Chris. The Gravedigger's Cottage. 2004. 208p. (J). (gr. 7 up). 15.99 (978-0-06-623940-8(0)) HarperCollins Pubs.

MacBride, Roger Lea. Missouri Bound. 1999. (Little House Chapter Bks.: No. 1). (J). (gr. 3-6). (978-0-606-18717-6(0)) Tandem Library Bks.

Maddox, Jake. Board Rebel. Tiffany, Sean, illus. 2007. (J). 72p. (***978-1-59889-319-9(X)***); 65p. pap. (***978-1-59889-414-1(5)***) Stone Arch Bks.

Maisner, Heather. We're Moving! Stephenson, Kristina, illus. 2004. (First Time Stories Ser.). 24p. (J). (gr. k-ps). pap. 3.95 (978-0-7534-5739-9(3) , Kingfisher) Houghton Mifflin Co. Trade & Reference Div.

Major, Kevin. The House of Wooden Santas. George, Imelda, illus. Pratt, Ned, photos by. 2004. 96p. (J). 24.95 (978-0-88995-166-2(7)) Red Deer Pr. CAN. *Dist:* Fitzhenry & Whiteside, Ltd.

—The House of Wooden Santas. Pratt, Ned, photos by. gif. ed. 2004. (Illus.). 96p. (J). 34.95 (978-0-88995-249-2(3)) Red Deer Pr. CAN. *Dist:* Fitzhenry & Whiteside, Ltd.

Marsden, Carolyn. Bird Springs. 2007. 128p. (J). (gr. 3 up). 14.99 (978-0-670-06193-8(X) , Viking Juvenile) Penguin Group (USA) Inc.

—The Gold-Threaded Dress. 2006. 80p. (J). (gr. 2-4). reprint ed. pap. 5.99 (978-0-7636-2993-9(6)) Candlewick Pr.

Marsden, Carolyn & Mackler, Carolyn. The Gold-Threaded Dress. 2002. 80p. (J). (gr. 2-4). 14.99 (978-0-7636-1569-7(2)) Candlewick Pr.

Martin, Ann M. Karen's Big Move. 1998. (Baby-Sitters Little Sister Ser.: No. 96). (Illus.). (J). (gr. 3-7). pap. 3.50 (978-0-590-06594-8(7) , Scholastic Paperbacks) Scholastic, Inc.

—Karen's Big Move. 1998. (Baby-Sitters Little Sister Ser.: No. 96). (J). (gr. 3-7). (978-0-606-13172-8(8)) Tandem Library Bks.

Martin, Ann M. Welcome to Camden Falls. 2007. (Main Street Ser.: No. 1). 192p. (J). (gr. 4-7). pap. 6.99 (***978-0-439-86879-2(3)*** , Scholastic Paperbacks) Scholastic, Inc.

Martin, Rebella. Joanna's Journey. Yoder, Laura, illus. 2006. 168p. (YA). pap. 10.99 (978-1-933753-01-0(3)) Carlisle Pr.- Walnut Creek.

Matas, Carol. Sparks Fly Upward. 2002. 192p. (YA). (gr. 5-9). 15.00 (978-0-618-15964-2(9) , Clarion Bks.) Houghton Mifflin Co. Trade & Reference Div.

Mazer, Anne. Home Is Where the Heart Is. 2006. (Amazing Days of Abby Hayes Ser.: no. 17). 118p. (J). lib. bdg. 16.92 (***978-1-4242-1518-8(8)***) Fitzgerald Bks.

Mazer, Norma Fox. What I Believe. 176p. 2007. (Illus.). (J). pap. 6.95 (978-0-15-206283-5(1) , Harcourt Paperbacks); 2005. (YA). (gr. 5-9). 16.00 (978-0-15-201462-9(4) , Harcourt Children's Bks) Harcourt Children's Bks.

McDonald, Joyce. Comfort Creek. 1998. 10.64 (978-0-606-13289-3(9)) Tandem Library Bks.

McDonough, Alison. Do the Hokey Pokey. Urbanovic, Jackie, illus. 2001. 112p. (J). (gr. 3-7). 14.95 (978-0-8126-2699-5(0)) Cricket Bks.

Medearis, Angela Shelf. With Friends Like These, Who Needs Enemies? Papp, Robert, illus. 2003. 153p. (J). (978-0-439-52326-4(5)) Scholastic, Inc.

Meltzer, Amy. A Mezuzah on the Door. Fried, Janice, illus. 2007. (Jewish Identity Ser.). 32p. (J). (ps-2). 17.95 (***978-1-58013-249-7(9)***); pap. 7.95 (***978-1-58013-251-0(0)***) Kar-Ben Publishing.

Michelin, Linda. Zuzu's Wishing Cake. Johnson, D. B., illus. 2006. 32p. (J). (gr. k-3). 16.00 (978-0-618-64640-1(X)) Houghton Mifflin Co. Trade & Reference Div.

Miller, Elizabeth I. Just Like Home: Como en Mi Tierra. Reisberg, Mira, illus. 2004. 32p. (J). (gr. 1-3). pap. 6.95 (978-0-8075-4069-5(2)) Whitman, Albert & Co.

Mills, Elizabeth. Belle. 2007. (Stablemates Ser.). 48p. (J). pap. 4.99 (***978-0-439-88336-8(9)***) Scholastic, Inc.

Moore, Stephanie Perry. True Friends. 2005. (Carmen Browne Ser.). 128p. (YA). pap. 5.99 (978-0-8024-8172-6(8)) Moody Pubs.

Morgan, Nicola. Chicken Friend. 2005. 160p. (J). (gr. 4-7). 15.99 (978-0-7636-2735-5(6)) Candlewick Pr.

Morris, Joyce. Sweet Annie. 2006. pap. 14.99 (***978-1-4259-7159-5(8)***) AuthorHouse.

Moss, Alexandra. Ellie's Chance to Dance, No. 1. 2005. (Royal Ballet School Diaries Ser.: Bk. 1). 144p. (J). (gr. 4-8). mass mkt. 4.99 (978-0-448-43535-0(7) , Grosset & Dunlap) Penguin Group (USA) Inc.

Moss, Marissa. Amelia's Notebook. Moss, Marissa, illus. 2006. (Amelia's Notebooks). (Illus.). 40p. (J). 9.95 (978-1-4169-0905-7(2)) Simon & Schuster Children's Publishing.

—Amelia's Notebook. Moss, Marissa, illus. 2006. (Amelia's Notebooks). (J). 5.99 (978-1-4169-1286-6(X)) Simon & Schuster, Inc.

—Amelia's Notebook. 1999. (Amelia's Notebooks). (Illus.). (J). (gr. 3-5). 12.75 (978-0-606-18353-6(1)) Tandem Library Bks.

Moss, Miriam. A New House for Smudge. Chapman, Lynne, illus. 2002. 24p. (J). (ps-2). (978-1-86233-202-7(9) , Gullane Children's Bks.) Pinwheel.

Munro, Sandie. Karlee's Other Family. 2006. 84p. pap. 8.95 (***978-1-60126-000-0(8)***) Masthof Pr.

Mustapha, G. Haole Girl. 2002. (J). pap. 4.95 (978-0-89610-358-0(7)) Island Heritage Publishing.

My Neighborhood. (All about Me Ser.). 24p. (J). 6.95 (978-1-4048-0162-2(6)) Picture Window Bks.

Myers, Robert J. When the Monarchs Fly. McGehee, Cricket, illus. 2005. 64p. 11.95 (978-0-945582-76-2(5)) Down The Shore Publishing.

Myracle, Lauren. TTFN (Ta-Ta for Now) (Internet Girls Ser.). 2007. 256p. (J). (gr. 2-8). pap. 6.95 (***978-0-8109-9279-5(5)***); 2006. 240p. (YA). (gr. 9-17). 15.95 (978-0-8109-5971-2(2)) Abrams, Harry N. , Inc. (Amulet Bks.).

Napoli, Donna Jo. Friends Everywhere. 1999. (Angelwings Ser.: No. 1). (Illus.). (J). 10.79 (978-0-606-17904-1(6)) Tandem Library Bks.

—Partners. 2001. (Angelwings Ser.: No. 15). 80p. (J). (gr. 2-5). pap. 7.95 (978-0-689-83972-6(3) , Aladdin) Simon & Schuster Children's Publishing.

Napoli, Donna Jo & Ben-Ami, Doron. Friends Everywhere. Klementz-Harte, Lauren, illus. 1999. (Angelwings Ser.: No. 1). 96p. (J). (gr. 2-5). pap. 7.95 (978-0-689-82694-8(X) , Aladdin) Simon & Schuster Children's Publishing.

O'Dell, Kathleen. Ophie Out of Oz. 2005. 192p. (J). (gr. 3). pap. 5.99 (978-0-14-240394-5(6) , Puffin) Penguin Group (USA) Inc.

Oldham, Mary. No Fire, No Candle. 2001. 217p. (YA). pap. 12.95 (978-1-85902-945-9(0)) Beekman Bks., Inc.

Penner, Lucille Recht. X Marks the Spot. Smath, Jerry, illus. 2002. (Math Matters Ser.). 32p. (J). pap. 4.95 (978-1-57565-111-8(4)) Kane Pr., The.

—X Marks the Spot! Smath, Jerry, illus. 2002. 32p. (J). (gr. 4-7). lib. bdg. 12.95 (978-0-613-53585-4(5)) Tandem Library Bks.

Petty, Kate. Moving Day. 2007. (J). (***978-1-59604-157-8(9)***) Stargazer Bks.

Pevsner, Stella. Would My Fortune Cookie Lie? 1999. (978-0-606-14369-1(6)) Tandem Library Bks.

Pfeiffer, Joseph R. & Pfeiffer, Robert J. Billy's Unusual Adventure. Pfeiffer, Joseph R., illus. l.t. ed. 1998. (Illus.). 32p. (J). (gr. k-4). 11.95 (978-0-9659772-1-0(8)); pap. 5.95 (978-0-9659772-2-7(6)) Chessmore Publishing.

Pinkwater, Daniel M. Looking for Bobowicz: A Hoboken Chicken Story. Pinkwater, Jill, illus. (J). 2006. 224p. pap. 5.99 (978-0-06-053556-8(3) , Harper Trophy); 2004. 208p. 15.99 (978-0-06-053554-4(7)) HarperCollins Pubs.

—Mush, a Dog from Space. Pinkwater, Jill, illus. 2002. (Ready-for-Chapters Ser.). 64p. (J). (gr. 1-4). lib. bdg. 11.89 (978-0-689-84801-8(3) , Aladdin Library) Simon & Schuster Children's Publishing.

Polacco, Patricia. The Graves Family. Gauch, Patricia Lee, ed. 2003. (Illus.). 48p. (J). (ps-5). 16.99 (978-0-399-24034-8(9) , Philomel) Penguin Group (USA) Inc.

Prestine, Joan Singleton. Moving Is Hard. Kylberg, Virginia, illus. 2002. 32p. (J). pap. 6.95 (978-1-57768-654-5(3)) School Specialty Publishing.

Raintree Steck-Vaughn Staff. Simon's Big Challenge. 1999. (Illus.). (J). pap. 35.60 (978-0-7398-0909-9(1)) Steck-Vaughn.

Ramthun, Bonnie. The White Gates. 2008. (J). (***978-0-375-84554-3(2)***); pap. (***978-0-375-84555-0(0)***); lib. bdg. (***978-0-375-94554-0(7)***) Random Hse., Inc.

Ransom, Candice. Seeing Sky-Blue Pink. 2007. (Exceptional Reading & Language Arts Titles for Intermediate Grades Ser.). 128p. (J). (gr. 3-6). 16.95 (***978-0-8225-7142-1(0)*** , Carolrhoda Bks.) Lerner Publishing Group.

Ray, Karen. The T. F. Letters. 2000. (978-0-606-22349-2(5)) Tandem Library Bks.

Rehfuss, Mary E. The Pottsville Chronicles: A New Beginning. 2005. 102p. (YA). per. 9.95 (978-1-933290-49-2(8)) Tate Publishing & Enterprises, L.L.C.

Reiss-Weimann, Elayne. I'm Different. Yeagle, Dean, illus. 2002. (Read-To-Me Ser.). 25p. (J). (978-0-7665-1224-5(X)) Abrams, Harry N. , Inc.

Rizzo, Kay D. Old Friends & New. 2003. 96p. (J). (978-0-8163-1975-6(8)) Pacific Pr. Publishing Assn.

Roberts, Diane. Puppet Pandemonium. 128p. (J). (gr. 3-7). 2007. 5.99 (***978-0-440-42096-5(2)*** , Yearling); 2006. 15.95 (978-0-385-73309-0(7) , Delacorte Bks. for Young Readers); 2006. lib. bdg. 17.99 (978-0-385-90328-8(6) , Delacorte Bks. for Young Readers) Random Hse. Children's Bks.

Roman, Beverly D. Let's Move Overseas: The International Edition of Let's Make a Move! Bickel, Dalene, ed. Cadieux, Michael J., illus. 2000. 32p. (J). (gr. 2-6). mass mkt. 8.45 (978-1-888891-16-4(5)) BR Anchor Publishing.

Rosensweig, Jay B. & Repka, Janice. The Stupendous Dodgeball Fiasco. Dibley, Glin, illus. 2004. 192p. (J). (gr. 3-6). 16.99 (978-0-525-47346-6(7) , Dutton Juvenile) Penguin Group (USA) Inc.

Ross, Tony. I Want to Go Home! 2006. (Illus.). 32p. (J). (978-1-84270-585-8(7)) Andersen.

Rostoker-Gruber, Karen. Bandit. Nguyen, Vincent, illus. 2008. (J). (***978-0-7614-5382-6(2)***) Cavendish, Marshall Corp.

Roth, Susan L. It's a Dog's New York. 2001. (Illus.). 32p. (J). (gr. 5-3). 16.95 (978-0-7922-7054-6(1) , National Geographic Children's Bks.) National Geographic Society.

Rowland, Patty. Marvelous Max, the Mansion Mouse. Rasmussen, Wendy, tr. Rasmussen, Wendy, illus. 2003. 32p. (J). 17.95 (978-0-9649934-4-0(9)) Norfleet Pr., Inc.

Rue, Nancy N. & Youth Specialties Staff. New Girl in Town. 2004. (Invert / 'Nama Beach High Ser.: No. 1). 176p. (J). pap. 6.99 (978-0-310-24399-1(8)) Zondervan.

Rylant, Cynthia. Henry & Mudge & Annie's Good Move. Stevenson, Sucie, illus. 2002. (Henry & Mudge Ser.). (J). 11.91 (978-0-7587-1260-8(X)) Book Wholesalers, Inc.

—Henry & Mudge & Annie's Good Move. Stevenson, Sucie, illus. 2002. (Henry & Mudge Ser.). 28.95 incl. audio compact disk (978-1-59112-648-5(7)); pap. 31.95 incl. audio compact disk (978-1-59112-647-8(9)); (J). pap. 18.95 incl. audio compact disk (978-1-59112-646-1(0)); (J). 25.95 incl. audio (978-0-87499-965-5(0)); (J). pap. 16.95 incl. audio (978-0-87499-964-8(2)) Live Oak Media.

—Henry & Mudge & Annie's Good Move. Stevenson, Sucie, illus. (Henry & Mudge Ser.). (J). (gr. k-3). 2000. 48p. pap. 3.99 (978-0-689-83284-0(2) , Aladdin); 1998. 40p. 15.95 (978-0-689-81174-6(8)) Simon & Schuster Children's Publishing.

Salisbury, Linda G. The Wild Women of Lake Anna: A Bailey Fish Adventure. 2005. (Illus.). 159p. (J). (978-1-881539-37-7(7)) Tabby Hse. Bks.

Schmidt, Gary D. Lizzie Bright & the Buckminster Boy. (gr. 5). 2008. 240p. (YA). mass mkt. 6.99 (***978-0-375-84169-9(5)*** , Laurel Leaf); 2006. 224p. (J). reprint ed. pap. 6.50 (978-0-553-49495-2(3) , Yearling) Random Hse. Children's Bks.

Schultz, Jan Neubert. Firestorm. 2003. (Adventures in Time Ser.). 204p. (YA). (gr. 4-7). 15.95 (978-0-87614-276-9(5) , Carolrhoda Bks.) Lerner Publishing Group.

Seckar, Alvena Vajdak. Misko. Merwin, Decie, illus. 1999. 159p. (J). 19.00 (978-0-86516-465-9(7)) Bolchazy-Carducci Pubs.

Sedita, Francesco. Miss Popularity. 2007. (Candy Apple Ser.: No. 3). 144p. (J). pap. 4.99 (***978-0-439-88814-1(X)*** , Scholastic Paperbacks) Scholastic, Inc.

Shreve, Susan Richards. Blister. 2003. (Illus.). 176p. (J). (gr. 3-7). pap. 4.99 (978-0-439-19314-6(1) , Scholastic Paperbacks) Scholastic, Inc.

Siebold, Jan. My Nights at the Improv. 2005. 98p. (YA). (gr. 6-9). lib. bdg. 14.95 (978-0-8075-5630-6(0)) Whitman, Albert & Co.

Silberberg, Alan. Pond Scum. 2007. 288p. (gr. 3-7). pap. 5.99 (978-0-7868-5635-0(1)) Hyperion Pr.

Simpson, Lesley. The Purim Surprise. Church, Peter, illus. 2004. (Purim Ser.). 32p. (J). (ps-3). pap. 6.95 (978-1-58013-090-5(9)) Kar-Ben Publishing.

Sleator, William. The Boxes. 2000. 208p. (J). (gr. 3-7). pap. 5.99 (978-0-14-130810-4(9) , Puffin) Penguin Group (USA) Inc.

Sonenklar, Carol. My Own Worst Enemy. 2001. 160p. (J). (gr. 3-7). pap. 4.50 (978-0-439-17518-0(6)) Scholastic, Inc.

Sones, Sonya. One of Those Hideous Books Where the Mother Dies. 272p. (YA). 2004. (Illus.). 16.95 (978-0-689-85820-8(5)); 2005. (gr. 7-12). reprint ed. pap. 6.99 (978-1-4169-0788-6(2) , Simon Pulse) Simon & Schuster Children's Publishing.

Spalding, Andrea. Me & Mr Mah. 2001. (gr. k-3). lib. bdg. 16.40 (978-0-613-88504-1(X)) Tandem Library Bks.

Spietz, Heidi A. Natalie's New Home. Henderson, Frances, ed. l.t. ed. 1998. (Illus.). 27p. (J). (gr. 1-2). pap. 5.00 (978-0-929487-12-0(5)) American Montessori Consulting.

Spinelli, Eileen. Where I Live. 2007. (Illus.). 112p. (J). (gr. 2-4). 16.99 (978-0-8037-3122-6(1) , Dial) Penguin Group (USA) Inc.

Stahler, David, Jr. Gathering of Shades. 2006. pap. (978-0-06-052296-4(8)) HarperCollins Canada, Ltd.

—A Gathering of Shades. 2005. 304p. (J). 15.99 (978-0-06-052294-0(1)); lib. bdg. 16.89 (978-0-06-052295-7(X)) HarperCollins Pubs. (HarperTeen).

Stanley, George Edward. Ghost Horse. Barrow, Ann, illus. 1999. (Stepping Stones Ser.). 80p. (J). (gr. 1-4). pap. 3.99 (978-0-307-26500-5(5) , Random Hse. Bks. for Young Readers) Random Hse. Children's Bks.

—Ghost Horse. 2000. (Road to Reading Ser.). (Illus.). (J). 10.79 (978-0-606-20436-1(9)) Tandem Library Bks.

Steck-Vaughn Staff. Simon's Big Challenge/Over-Comming Challenges: The Life of Charles F. Bolden Jr. 1999. (Take Me Home Ser.). (J). pap. 11.30 (978-0-7398-0944-0(X)) Steck-Vaughn.

Stewart, Jennifer. If That Breathes Fire, We're Toast! 1999. 128p. (J). (gr. 4-6). tchr. ed. 15.95 (978-0-8234-1430-7(2)) Holiday Hse., Inc.

Sumpolec, Sarah Anne. The Masquerade. 2003. (Becoming Beka Ser.). 224p. (YA). pap. 12.99 (978-0-8024-6451-4(3)) Moody Pubs.

Tapp, Kathy Kennedy. Deadbolts & Dinkles. 2000. (gr. 3-6). lib. bdg. 11.80 (978-0-613-27788-4(0)) Tandem Library Bks.

Tildes, Phyllis Limbacher. The Garden Wall. Tildes, Phyllis Limbacher, illus. 2006. (Illus.). (J). 16.95 (978-1-57091-467-6(2) , 1258423); pap. 7.95 (978-1-57091-468-3(0) , 1258423) Charlesbridge Publishing, Inc.

Tocher, Timothy. Long Shot. 2001. (J). 137p. (978-0-88166-395-2(6)); 144p. pap. 4.95 (978-0-689-84331-0(3)) Meadowbrook Pr.

Trebi-Ollennu, Flora. Sweetie Awo Goes to Boarding School. Darko, Anima A., illus. 2001. 119p. pap. (***978-1-894718-02-8(X)***) Amerley Treb Bks.

Ullman, Barb Bentler. The Fairies of Nutfolk Wood. 2008. 256p. (J). pap. 5.99 (***978-0-06-134563-0(6)*** , Harper Trophy) HarperCollins Pubs.

Valgardson, W. D. Garbage Creek: And Other Stories. 1998. (Illus.). 136p. (J). (gr. 3-7). 5.95 (978-0-88899-339-7(0)) Groundwood Bks. CAN. *Dist:* Perseus Distribution.

Villeneuve, Marie-Paule & Audet, Patrice. Qui a Enleve Polka? 2004. (FRE., Illus.). 122p. (J). 8.95 (978-2-922565-81-2(5)) Editions de la Paix CAN. *Dist:* World of Reading, Ltd.

Viorst, Judith. Alexander, Who's Not (Do You Hear Me? I Mean It!) Going to Move. Glasser, Robin Preiss, illus. 1998. (Alexander Ser.). 32p. (J). (gr. k-3). pap. 6.99 (978-0-689-82089-2(5) , Aladdin) Simon & Schuster Children's Publishing.

Waber, Bernard. Ira Says Goodbye. Waber, Bernard, illus. unabr. ed. 2005. (Illus.). (J). (gr. k-3). pap. 16.95 incl. audio (978-0-87499-138-3(2)) BBC Audiobooks America.

Wallace, Bill. Aloha Summer. 2000. (J). 10.64 (978-0-606-19487-7(8)) Tandem Library Bks.

Wallace, Ian. Mr. Kneebone's New Digs. Wallace, Ian, illus. (Illus.). (J). 16.95 (978-0-88899-143-0(6)) Groundwood Bks. CAN. *Dist:* Transition Vendor.

Wallace, Rich. Southpaw. 2006. 105p. (J). lib. bdg. 15.38 (***978-1-4242-2166-0(8)***) Fitzgerald Bks.

—Southpaw. (Winning Season Ser.: Vol. 6). 128p. (J). 2007. pap. 4.99 (978-0-14-240785-1(2) , Puffin); 2006. (gr. 4). 14.99 (978-0-670-06053-5(4) , Viking Juvenile) Penguin Group (USA) Inc.

Waugh, Sylvia. Mennyms Alive. 1999. 224p. (J). (gr. 3-7). pap. 4.50 (978-0-380-72943-2(1) , Harper Trophy) HarperCollins Pubs.

Weber, Jill. Angel Bites the Bullet. 2003. (gr. 3-6). lib. bdg. 12.95 (978-0-613-88088-6(9)) Tandem Library Bks.

Weeks, Jan. The Marathon Runner. Harrison, Paul, illus. 2006. (Read-It! Chapter Books). 64p. (J). (gr. 2-4). 19.95 (978-1-4048-1669-5(0)) Picture Window Bks.

Weinheimer, Beckie. Converting Kate. 2007. 288p. (YA). (gr. 7 up). 16.99 (978-0-670-06152 5(2) , Viking Juvenile) Penguin Group (USA) Inc.

West, Tracey. Liz on the Move. Ostrom, Bob, illus. 1999. (Magic School Bus Ser.). 24p. (J). (gr. 1-4). pap. 3.50 (978-0-590-66236-9(8)) Scholastic, Inc.

WeWrite Kids Staff. We're Moving! Fisher, Suzanne, ed. Freeman, Troy, illus. l.t. ed. 1999. (WeWrite Kids! Ser.: Vol. 44). 45p. (J). (gr. 2-6). pap. 3.95 (978-1-57635-052-2(5)) WeWrite LLC.

Whelan, Gloria. Time to Keep Silent. 2003. (gr. 5-8). lib. bdg. 16.45 (978-0-613-75511-5(1)) Tandem Library Bks.

White, Ruth. Memories of Summer. 2000. 144p. (J). (gr. 7-10). 17.00 (978-0-374-34945-5(2) , Farrar, Straus & Giroux (BYR)) Farrar, Straus & Giroux.

Wigington, Patti. Summer's Ashes. 2007. 208p. (YA). pap. 15.00 (***978-0-9766805-9-8(9)***) Keene Publishing.

Williams, Tara. Benji Martin Is Bashful. Lenoir, Jane, illus. 2001. 36p. (J). (gr. 1-6). lib. bdg. 14.95 (978-0-9705727-1-4(9)) Coastal Publishing Carolina, Inc.

Wittlinger, Ellen. Razzle. 2001. (Illus.). 256p. (J). (gr. 7-10). 17.00 (978-0-689-83565-0(5)) Simon & Schuster Children's Publishing.

—Razzle. 2003. (gr. 7-12). lib. bdg. 16.45 (978-0-613-61811-3(4)) Tandem Library Bks.

Wolfe, Jacqueline A. Megan Has to Move. Kouse, Patrick, illus. 2006. (Read-It! Readers Ser.). 32p. (J). (ps-3). 18.60 (978-1-4048-1613-8(5)) Picture Window Bks.

Wong, Janet S. Homegrown House. Lewis, Earl B, illus. 2008. (J). (***978-0-689-84718-9(1)*** , McElderry, Margaret K.) Simon & Schuster Children's Publishing.

Woodruff, Elvira. The Ghost of Lizard Light. Clayton, Elaine, illus. 2001. 192p. (gr. 3-7). pap. 4.99 (978-0-440-41655-5(8) , Yearling) Random Hse. Children's Bks.

Wynne-Jones, Tim. Rex Zero & the End of the World. 2007. (J). (Illus.). 192p. (gr. 3-7). 16.00 (978-0-374-33467-3(6)); 186p. (*978-1-4287-3318-3(3)) Farrar, Straus & Giroux.

Yee, Lisa. So Totally Emily Ebers. 2008. 304p. (J). 5.99 (978-0-439-83848-1(7) , Levine, Arthur A. Bks.) Scholastic, Inc.

—So Totally Emily Embers. 2007. 304p. (J). (gr. 4-7). pap. 16.99 (978-0-439-83847-4(9) , Levine, Arthur A. Bks.) Scholastic, Inc.

Yee, Wong Herbert. Did You See Chip? Ovresat, Laura, illus. 2004. (Green Light Readers Level 2 Ser.). 24p. (J). 12.95 (978-0-15-205095-5(7)); pap. 3.95 (978-0-15-205096-2(5)) Harcourt Children's Bks. (Green Light Readers).

—Did You See Chip? 2004. (gr. k-3). lib. bdg. 11.80 (978-0-613-81965-7(9)) Tandem Library Bks.

Zack's Moving Day Surprise. 2001. (J). (978-1-58453-166-1(5)) Pioneer Valley Educational Pr., Inc.

Zagwyn, Deborah Turney. The Winter Gift. 2004. (Illus.). 32p. (J). (gr. k-3). 15.95 (978-1-883672-93-5(7) , Tricycle Pr.) Ten Speed Pr.

Ziefert, Harriet. One Smart Skunk. Cohen, Santiago, illus. 2004. 40p. (gr. k-3). 15.95 (978-1-59354-064-7(7)) Blue Apple Bks.

Ziegler, Jennifer. How Not to Be Popular. 2008. 224p. (YA). (gr. 7). 15.99 (*978-0-385-73465-3(4)); lib. bdg. 18.99 (*978-0-385-90463-6(0)) Random Hse. Children's Bks. (Delacorte Bks. for Young Readers).

Zinnen, Linda. Holding at Third. 2006. 160p. (YA). (gr. 4). pap. 5.99 (978-0-14-240554-3(X) , Puffin) Penguin Group (USA) Inc.

Zoehfeld, Kathleen Weidner. Tigger's Moving Day. 1999. (My Very First Winnie the Pooh Ser.). (Illus.). 32p. (J). (ps-k). 11.99 (978-0-7868-3225-5(8)) Disney Pr.

MOWGLI (FICTITIOUS CHARACTER)—FICTION

Dalmation Press. Jungle Book: Mowgli. 2007. 48p. 3.99 (*978-1-4037-3604-8(9)) Dalmatian Pr.

Greene, Janice. Jungle Book. abr. ed. 2001. (gr. 7-12). lib. bdg. 15.25 (978-0-613-36449-2(X)) Tandem Library Bks.

Kipling, Rudyard. The Jungle Book. Alexander, Gregory, illus. 1999. (Classics Ser.).Tr. of 192. 160p. (J). 12.95 (978-0-7892-0558-2(0)); pap. 7.95 (978-0-7892-0548-3(3)) Abbeville Pr., Inc. (Abbeville Kids).

—The Jungle Book.Tr. of 192. (J). reprint ed. lib. bdg. 24.95 (978-0-88411-819-0(3)) Amereon LTD.

—The Jungle Book. 2000. (Dover Juvenile Classics Ser.).Tr. of 192. 160p. (J). (gr. 4-7). pap. 2.50 (978-0-486-41024-1(2)) Dover Pubns., Inc.

—The Jungle Book. 1998. (Children's Classics).Tr. of 192. (ENG., Illus.). 192p. (J). (gr. 4-7). pap. (978-1-85326-119-0(X) , 119XWW) Wordsworth Editions, Ltd.

—The Jungle Book: Mowgli Knows Best, No. 4. Hale, Nathan, illus. 2007. (Easy Reader Classics Ser.). 32p. (J). pap. 3.95 (978-1-4027-4125-8(1)) Sterling Publishing Co., Inc.

—The Jungle Book by Rudyard Kipling: Digital Classics. 2002. cd-rom 5.00 (978-1-931457-07-1(7)) Stargate Electronic Library, Inc.

—El Libro de la Selva. Alfonso Lopez, Javier, tr. 2005. (Clasicos de la literatura Ser.). (SPA., Illus.). 376p. pap. 5.95 (978-84-9764-492-1(1)) Edimat Libros, S. A. ESP. *Dist:* Independent Pubs. Group.

—El Libro de la Selva. 2000. (SPA.). lib. bdg. 10.55 (978-0-613-83762-0(2)) Tandem Library Bks.

Kipling, Rudyard & Hedge, Tricia. The Jungle Book, Level 2. 2nd abr. ed. 2000. (Bookworms Ser.).Tr. of 192. (Illus.). 64p. 6.50 (978-0-19-422977-7(7)) Oxford Univ. Pr., Inc.

Mason, Jane B. & Hines Stephens, Sarah. Jungle Book. 2004. 128p. (J). pap. 3.99 (978-0-439-57424-2(2) , Scholastic Paperbacks) Scholastic, Inc.

MOZART, WOLFGANG AMADEUS, 1756-1791

Allman, Barbara. Musical Genius: A Story about Wolfgang Amadeus Mozart. Hamlin, Janet, illus. 2004. (Creative Minds Biographies Ser.). 64p. (J). pap. 6.95 (978-1-57505-637-1(2)); 22.60 (978-1-57505-604-3(6)) Lerner Publishing Group.

Baby's First Classics/mozart. 2001. (Baby's First Ser.). (J). 24.95 (978-1-56015-720-5(8)) Penton Overseas, Inc.

Breakspeare, Eustace J. Mozart. 2001. 299p. (YA). reprint ed. 98.00 (978-0-7222-5475-2(X)) Library Reprints, Inc.

Brighton, Catherine. Mozart. 2004. (Illus.). 30p. (J). pap. 7.95 (978-1-84507-212-4(X)) Lincoln, Frances Ltd. GBR. *Dist:* Transition Vendor.

—Mozart: Scenes from the Childhood of the Great Composer. 2000. (Illus.). 30p. (J). (gr. 1 up). pap. 9.99 (978-0-7112-1604-4(5)) Lincoln, Frances Ltd. GBR. *Dist:* Transition Vendor.

Cencetti, Greta. Mozart. 2002. (World of Composers Ser.). (Illus.). 40p. (J). (gr. 1-5). 18.95 (978-1-58845-471-3(1) , Bedrick, Peter Bks.) School Specialty Publishing.

—Mozart. 2002. (Classic Composers Ser.). (Illus.). 40p. (J). incl. audio compact disk (978-1-59069-097-0(4) , T2107) Studio Mouse LLC.

—Mozart: Getting to Know Your Classical Composers. 2002. (Classic Composers Ser.). (Illus.). 32p. (978-1-59069-030-7(3) , T2007) Studio Mouse LLC.

Cook, Diane. Wolfgang Amadeus Mozart: World-Famous Composer. 2002. (Great Names Ser.). (Illus.). 32p. (J). (gr. 3 up). lib. bdg. (978-1-59084-159-4(X)) Mason Crest Pubs.

Dunn, Mary. My Adventure with Mozart. 2006. 44p. (J). 8.99 (978-1-59092-459-4(2) , Orchard Academy Pr.) Windstorm Creative.

Ekker, Ernst A. Mozart: A Musical Picture Book. Eisenburger, Doris, illus. 2006. 32p. (J). 20.00 incl. audio compact disk (978-0-7358-2056-2(2)) North-South Bks., Inc.

—W. A. Mozart: Un Album Musical. Eisenburger, Doris, illus. 2nd ed. 2002. (Coleccion Joven Musica).Tr. of W. A. Mozart: Un Album Musical. (SPA.). 36p. (YA). 20.76 incl. audio compact disk (978-84-89804-28-9(1)) Loguez Ediciones ESP. *Dist:* Lectorum Pubns., Inc.

Gehring, Franz E. Mozart. 2001. 131p. (YA). reprint ed. 88.00 (978-0-7222-5195-9(5)) Library Reprints, Inc.

Hussey, Dyneley. Wolfgang Amadeus Mozart. 2001. 368p. (YA). reprint ed. 98.00 (978-0-7222-6316-7(3)) Library Reprints, Inc.

Isadora, Rachel. Young Mozart. 1999. (978-0-606-16807-6(9)) Tandem Library Bks.

Jahn, Otto. Life of Mozart, 3 vols., set. 2001. (YA). reprint ed. 375.00 (978-0-7222-5479-0(2)) Library Reprints, Inc.

Levin, Judy. Wolfgang Amadeus Mozart: Virtuoso of the Classical Form. 2006. (Lives & Times of the Great Composers of the World Ser.). (J). lib. bdg. (978-1-4042-0722-6(8)) Rosen Publishing Group, Inc., The.

McDonough, Yona Zeldis. Who Was Wolfgang Amadeus Mozart? Robbins, Carrie, illus. 2003. (Who Was...? Ser.). 112p. (J). (gr. 3-7). pap. 4.99 (978-0-448-43104-8(1) , Grosset & Dunlap) Penguin Group (USA) Inc.

—Who Was Wolfgang Amadeus Mozart? 2003. (gr. 3-6). lib. bdg. 13.00 (978-0-613-61669-0(3)) Tandem Library Bks.

Pancella, Peggy. Wolfgang Amadeus Mozart. 2005. (J). pap. (978-1-4034-6755-3(2)); (Illus.). 32p. (978-1-4034-6747-8(1)) Heinemann Library.

Rachlin, Ann. Mozart. 2002. (Ninos Famosos Ser.). (ENG & SPA.). 24p. 6.95 (978-85-7416-080-1(6)) Callis Editora Ltda BRA. *Dist:* Independent Pubs. Group.

Rau, Herlbert. The Tone King: A Romance of the Life of Mozart. 2001. 387p. (YA). reprint ed. 98.00 (978-0-7222-5482-0(2)) Library Reprints, Inc.

Riggs, Kate. Wolfgang Amadeus Mozart. 2008. (J). (*978-1-58341-664-8(1) , Creative Education) Creative Co., The.

Ross, Stewart. The Story of Wolfgang Amadeus Mozart. (Lifetimes Ser.). (Illus.). 48p. (J). lib. bdg. 28.50 (978-1-931983-14-3(3)) Chrysalis Education.

—Wolfgang Amadeus Mozart: Musical Genius. 2004. (Famous Lives Ser.). (Illus.). 48p. (J). (gr. 3). lib. bdg. 29.93 (978-0-7398-6627-6(3)) Raintree.

Sis, Peter. Play, Mozart, Play! Sis, Peter, illus. 2006. (Illus.). 32p. (J). 16.99 (978-0-06-112181-4(9)); lib. bdg. 17.89 (978-0-06-112182-1(7)) HarperCollins Pubs. (Greenwillow Bks.).

Summerer, Eric Michael. Wolfgang Amadeus Mozart. 2006. (Primary Source Library of Famous Composers). (Illus.). 32p. (J). 21.95 (978-1-4042-2772-9(5) , PowerKids Pr.) Rosen Publishing Group, Inc., The.

Turner, Barrie Carson. Mozart. 2003. (Famous Childhoods Ser.). (Illus.). (J). lib. bdg. 24.25 (978-1-59389-115-2(6)) Chrysalis Education.

Vernon, Roland. Mozart: Introducing. 2000. (Introducing Composers Ser.). (Illus.). 32p. (J). (gr. 4-7). 21.95 (978-0-7910-6041-4(1) , Chelsea Hse.) Facts On File, Inc.

Walcker, Yann. Wolfgang Amadeus Mozart. 2007. (Descubrimos a los Musicos Ser.). (Illus.). 24p. (J). 14.95 (*978-84-7864-958-7(1)) Combel Editorial, S.A. ESP. *Dist:* Independent Pubs. Group.

Weeks, Marcus. Mozart: The Boy Who Changed the World with His Music. 2007. (World History Biographies Ser.). (Illus.). 64p. (J). (gr. 3-7). 17.95 (978-1-4263-0002-8(6)); lib. bdg. 27.90 (978-1-4263-0003-5(4)) National Geographic Society. (National Geographic Children's Bks.).

MOZART, WOLFGANG AMADEUS, 1756-1791—FICTION

Costanza, Stephen. Mozart Finds a Melody. rev. ed. 2004. (Illus.). 40p. (J). 17.95 (978-0-8050-6627-2(6) , Holt, Henry & Co. Bks. For Young Readers) Holt, Henry & Co.

Moerike, Eduard. Mozart Auf der Reise Nach Prag. 2006. (GER.). pap. (*978-1-4068-0825-4(3)) Echo Library.

Muir, Sabine. Meeting Wolfie: A Story about Mozart. 2006. 129p. pap. 16.95 (978-1-4241-3968-2(6)) PublishAmerica, Inc.

Nickel, Barbara Kathleen. The Secret Wish of Nannerl Mozart. 2004. 208p. pap. (978-1-894549-08-0(2)) Sumach Pr.

MUDGE (FICTITIOUS CHARACTER)—FICTION

Henry & Mudge Book Set 800925, 6 vols. 2005. (J). pap. (978-1-59794-090-0(9)) Environments, Inc.

Rylant, Cynthia. Henry & Mudge & a Very Merry Christmas. Stevenson, Sucie, illus. 2004. (Henry & Mudge Ser.). 40p. (J). (gr. k-3). 14.95 (978-0-689-81168-5(3)) Simon & Schuster Children's Publishing.

—Henry & Mudge & Annie's Good Move. 2002. (Henry & Mudge Ser.). (Illus.). (J). (ps-3). pap., tchr.'s planning gde. ed. 29.95 incl. audio (978-0-87499-966-2(9)) Live Oak Media.

—Henry & Mudge & Annie's Good Move. Stevenson, Sucie, illus. (Henry & Mudge Ser.). (J). (gr. k-3). 2000. 48p. pap. 3.99 (978-0-689-83284-0(2) , Aladdin); 1998. 40p. 15.95 (978-0-689-81174-6(8)) Simon & Schuster Children's Publishing.

—Henry & Mudge & Annie's Good Move. 2000. (Henry & Mudge Ser.). (gr. k-3). lib. bdg. 11.80 (978-0-613-28519-3(0)); (J). 10.79 (978-0-606-17826-6(0)) Tandem Library Bks.

—Henry & Mudge & Annie's Perfect Pet. Stevenson, Sucie, illus. 2001. (Henry & Mudge Ser.). 40p. (J). (gr. k-3). pap. 3.99 (978-0-689-83443-1(8) , Aladdin) Simon & Schuster Children's Publishing.

—Henry & Mudge & Mrs. Hopper's House. Bracken, Carolyn, illus. 2003. (Henry & Mudge Ser.). 40p. (J). pap. 3.99 (978-0-689-83446-2(2) , Aladdin); 14.95 (978-0-689-81153-1(5)) Simon & Schuster Children's Publishing.

—Henry & Mudge & the Big Sleepover. Stevenson, Sucie, illus. (Henry & Mudge Ser.). 40p. (J). 2007. pap. 3.99 (978-0-689-83451-6(9) , Aladdin); 2006. 14.95 (978-0-689-81171-5(3) , Simon & Schuster Children's Publishing) Simon & Schuster Children's Publishing.

—Henry & Mudge & the Careful Cousin. Stevenson, Sucie, illus. 2000. (Henry & Mudge Ser.). (J). (gr. k-3). pap. 19.97 incl. audio (978-0-7366-9183-3(9)) Books on Tape, Inc.

—Henry & Mudge & the Careful Cousin. Stevenson, Sucie, illus. (Henry & Mudge Ser.). 2005. (J). pap. 18.95 incl. audio compact disk (978-1-59112-370-5(4)); 1999. 28.95 incl. audio compact disk (978-1-59112-571-6(5)); 1999. pap. 31.95 incl. audio compact disk (978-1-59112-570-9(7)); 1999. (J). pap. 29.95 incl. audio (978-0-87499-530-5(2)); 1999. (J). 25.95 incl. audio (978-0-87499-529-9(9)); 1999. (J). pap. 16.95 incl. audio (978-0-87499-528-2(0)) Live Oak Media.

—Henry & Mudge & the Careful Cousin. Stevenson, Sucie, illus. 1999. (Henry & Mudge Ser.). 48p. (J). (gr. k-3). 15.99 (978-0-689-81007-7(5)) Simon & Schuster Children's Publishing.

—Henry & Mudge & the Forever Sea. Stevenson, Sucie, illus. 2000. (Henry & Mudge Ser.). (J). (gr. k-3). pap. 19.97 incl. audio (978-0-7366-9187-1(1)) Books on Tape, Inc.

—Henry & Mudge & the Forever Sea. Stevenson, Sucie, illus. (Henry & Mudge Ser.). (J). 2005. pap. 18.95 incl. audio compact disk (978-1-59112-374-3(7)); 2000. 25.95 incl. audio (978-0-87499-606-7(6)); 2000. pap. 16.95 incl. audio (978-0-87499-605-0(8)); 2000. pap., tchr. ed. 29.95 incl. audio (978-0-87499-607-4(4)) Live Oak Media.

—Henry & Mudge & the Great Grandpas. Stevenson, Sucie, illus. 2005. (Henry & Mudge Ser.). 40p. (J). (gr. k-2). 14.95 (978-0-689-81170-8(5) , Simon & Schuster Children's Publishing) Simon & Schuster Children's Publishing.

—Henry & Mudge & the Long Weekend. Stevenson, Sucie, illus. unabr. ed. 2000. (Henry & Mudge Ser.). (J). pap. 29.95 incl. audio (978-0-87499-603-6(1)); 25.95 incl. audio (978-0-87499-602-9(3)); pap. 16.95 incl. audio (978-0-87499-601-2(5)) Live Oak Media.

—Henry & Mudge & the Sneaky Crackers. 2002. (Henry & Mudge Ser.). (Illus.). (J). pap., tchr.'s planning gde. ed. 29.95 incl. audio (978-0-87499-958-7(8)) Live Oak Media.

—Henry & Mudge & the Sneaky Crackers. Stevenson, Sucie, illus. 2002. (Henry & Mudge Ser.). 28.95 incl. audio compact disk (978-1-59112-639-3(8)); pap. 31.95 incl. audio compact disk (978-1-59112-640-9(1)); (J). pap. 18.95 incl. audio compact disk (978-1-59112-638-6(X)) Live Oak Media.

—Henry & Mudge & the Sneaky Crackers. abr. ed. 2002. (Henry & Mudge Ser.). (Illus.). (J). pap. 16.95 incl. audio (978-0-87499-956-3(1)) Live Oak Media.

—Henry & Mudge & the Sneaky Crackers. Stevenson, Sucie, illus. abr. ed. 2002. (Henry & Mudge Ser.). (J). 25.95 incl. audio (978-0-87499-957-0(X)) Live Oak Media.

—Henry & Mudge & the Sneaky Crackers. Stevenson, Sucie, illus. 1999. (Henry & Mudge Ser.). 48p. (J). (gr. k-3). pap. 3.99 (978-0-689-82525-5(0) , Aladdin) Simon & Schuster Children's Publishing.

—Henry & Mudge & the Sneaky Crackers. 1999. (Henry & Mudge Ser.). (gr. k-3). lib. bdg. 11.80 (978-0-613-11622-0(4)); (J). 10.79 (978-0-606-15925-8(8)) Tandem Library Bks.

—Henry & Mudge & the Snowman Plan. 2002. (Henry & Mudge Ser.). (Illus.). (J). pap., tchr.'s planning gde. ed. 29.95 incl. audio (978-0-87499-970-9(7)) Live Oak Media.

—Henry & Mudge & the Snowman Plan. Stevenson, Sucie, illus. 2002. (Henry & Mudge Ser.). (J). pap. 18.95 incl. audio compact disk (978-1-59112-650-8(9)) Live Oak Media.

—Henry & Mudge & the Snowman Plan. abr. ed. 2002. (Henry & Mudge Ser.). (Illus.). (J). 25.95 incl. audio (978-0-87499-969-3(3)); pap. 16.95 incl. audio (978-0-87499-968-6(5)) Live Oak Media.

—Henry & Mudge & the Snowman Plan. Stevenson, Sucie, illus. (Henry & Mudge Ser.). 40p. (J). (gr. k-3). 2000. pap. 3.99 (978-0-689-83449-3(7) , Aladdin); 1999. 15.95 (978-0-689-81169-2(1)) Simon & Schuster Children's Publishing.

—Henry & Mudge & the Snowman Plan. 2000. (Henry & Mudge Ser.). (gr. k-3). lib. bdg. 11.80 (978-0-613-29977-0(9)); (J). 10.79 (978-0-606-19711-3(7)) Tandem Library Bks.

—Henry & Mudge & the Starry Night. Stevenson, Sucie, illus. 2002. (Henry & Mudge Ser.). 28.95 incl. audio compact disk (978-1-59112-643-0(6)); pap. 31.95 incl. audio compact disk (978-1-59112-644-7(4)); (J). pap. 18.95 incl. audio compact disk (978-1-59112-642-3(8)) Live Oak Media.

—Henry & Mudge & the Starry Night. abr. ed. 2002. (Henry & Mudge Ser.). (Illus.). (J). 25.95 incl. audio (978-0-87499-961-7(8)); pap. 16.95 incl. audio (978-0-87499-960-0(X)); pap., tchr.'s planning gde. ed. 29.95 incl. audio (978-0-87499-962-4(6)) Live Oak Media.

—Henry & Mudge & the Starry Night. Stevenson, Sucie, illus. 1999. (Henry & Mudge Ser.). 48p. (J). (gr. k-3). pap. 3.99 (978-0-689-82586-6(2) , 076714003996, Aladdin) Simon & Schuster Children's Publishing.

—Henry & Mudge & the Starry Night. 1999. (Henry & Mudge Ser.). (gr. k-3). lib. bdg. 11.80 (978-0-613-18179-2(4)); (J). 10.79 (978-0-606-16305-7(0)) Tandem Library Bks.

—Henry & Mudge & the Wild Goose Chase. Bracken, Carolyn, illus. 2004. (Henry & Mudge Ser.). 40p. (J). pap. 3.99 (978-0-689-83450-9(0) , Aladdin) Simon & Schuster Children's Publishing.

—Henry & Mudge Get the Cold Shivers. Stevenson, Sucie, illus. 2000. (Henry & Mudge Ser.). (J). (gr. k-3). pap. 19.97 incl. audio (978-0-7366-9186-4(3)) Books on Tape, Inc.

—Henry & Mudge Get the Cold Shivers. Stevenson, Sucie, illus. (Henry & Mudge Ser.). 2005. (J). pap. 18.95 incl. audio compact disk (978-1-59112-372-9(0)); 1999. 28.95 incl. audio compact disk (978-1-59112-573-0(1)); 1999. pap. 31.95 incl. audio compact disk (978-1-59112-572-3(3)); 1999. (J). pap. 29.95 incl. audio (978-0-87499-526-8(4)); 1999. (J). 25.95 incl. audio (978-0-87499-525-1(6)); 1999. (J). pap. 16.95 incl. audio (978-0-87499-524-4(8)) Live Oak Media.

—Henry & Mudge in Puddle Trouble. Stevenson, Sucie, illus. 2000. (Henry & Mudge Ser.). (J). (gr. k-3). pap. 19.97 incl. audio (978-0-7366-9192-5(8)) Books on Tape, Inc.

—Henry & Mudge in the Family Trees. Stevenson, Sucie, illus. 1998. (Henry & Mudge Ser.). 40p. (J). (gr. k-3). pap. 3.99 (978-0-689-82317-6(7) , Aladdin) Simon & Schuster Children's Publishing.

—Henry & Mudge in the Green Time. Stevenson, Sucie, illus. 2000. (Henry & Mudge Ser.). (J). (gr. k-3). pap. 19.97 incl. audio (978-0-7366-9191-8(X)) Books on Tape, Inc.

—Henry & Mudge in the Green Time. Stevenson, Sucie, illus. (Henry & Mudge Ser.). 2005. (J). pap. 18.95 incl. audio compact disk (978-1-59112-378-1(X)); 1999. 28.95 incl. audio compact disk (978-1-59112-579-2(0)); 1999. pap. 31.95 incl. audio compact disk (978-1-59112-578-5(2)); 1999. (J). 25.95 incl. audio (978-0-87499-422-3(5)); 1999. (J). pap. 16.95 incl. audio (978-0-87499-421-6(7)); 1999. (J). pap., tchr. ed. 29.95 incl. audio (978-0-87499-423-0(3)) Live Oak Media.

—Henry & Mudge in the Sparkle Days. Stevenson, Sucie, illus. 2000. (Henry & Mudge Ser.). (J). (gr. k-3). pap. 19.97 incl. audio (978-0-7366-9185-7(5)) Books on Tape, Inc.

—Henry & Mudge in the Sparkle Days. Stevenson, Sucie, illus. (Henry & Mudge Ser.). 2005. (J). pap. 18.95 incl. audio compact disk (978-1-59112-382-8(8)); 1999. 28.95 incl. audio compact disk (978-1-59112-583-9(9)); 1999. pap. 31.95 incl. audio compact disk (978-1-59112-582-2(0)); 1999. (J). pap. 29.95 incl. audio (978-0-87499-501-5(9)); 1999. (J). 25.95 incl. audio (978-0-87499-500-8(0)); 1999. (J). pap. 16.95 incl. audio (978-0-87499-499-5(3)) Live Oak Media.

—Henry & Mudge under the Yellow Moon. Stevenson, Sucie, illus. 2000. (Henry & Mudge Ser.). (J). (gr. k-3). pap. 19.97 incl. audio (978-0-7366-9184-0(7)) Books on Tape, Inc.

—Henry & Mudge under the Yellow Moon. Stevenson, Sucie, illus. (Henry & Mudge Ser.). 2005. (J). pap. 18.95 incl. audio compact disk (978-1-59112-384-2(4)); 1998. 28.95 incl. audio compact disk (978-1-59112-585-3(5)); 1998. pap. 31.95 incl. audio compact disk (978-1-59112-584-6(7)); 1998. (J). pap., tchr. ed. 29.95 incl. audio (978-0-87499-447-6(0)); 1998. (J). 25.95 incl. audio (978-0-87499-446-9(2)); 1998. (J). pap. 16.95 incl. audio (978-0-87499-445-2(4)) Live Oak Media.

—Henry y Mudge: El Primer Libro de Sus Aventuras. Stevenson, Sucie, illus. 1999. (Henry & Mudge Ser.). (SPA.). (J). (gr. k-3). 13.00 (978-0-689-80685-8(X) , Atheneum) Simon & Schuster Children's Publishing.

—Puppy Mudge Finds a Friend. Stevenson, Sucie, illus. 2005. (Puppy Mudge Ser.). (J). (*978-1-4156-3675-6(3) , Aladdin) Simon & Schuster Children's Publishing.

Rylant, Cynthia. Seasons with Henry & Mudge. Stevenson, Sucie, illus. 2000. (Henry & Mudge Ser.). pap. 68.95 incl. audio compact disk (978-1-59112-855-7(2)) Live Oak Media.

Rylant, Cynthia & Bracken, Carolyn. Henry & Mudge & the Funny Lunch. 2004. (Henry & Mudge Ser.). (Illus.). 40p. (J). (gr. k-3). 14.95 (978-0-689-81178-4(0)) Simon & Schuster Children's Publishing.

—Henry & Mudge & the Tall Tree House. 2002. (Henry & Mudge Ser.). (Illus.). 40p. (J). (gr. k-3). 15.95 (978-0-689-81173-9(X)) Simon & Schuster Children's Publishing.

—Henry & Mudge & the Tumbling Trip. Stevenson, Sucie, illus. 2005. (Henry & Mudge Ser.). 40p. (J). (gr. k-3). 14.95 (978-0-689-81180-7(2)) Simon & Schuster Children's Publishing.

—Henry & Mudge & the Wild Goose Chase. 2003. (Henry & Mudge Ser.). (Illus.). 40p. (J). (gr. k-3). 14.95 (978-0-689-81172-2(1)) Simon & Schuster Children's Publishing.

Rylant, Cynthia & Mones, Isidre. Puppy Mudge Has a Snack. 2004. (Puppy Mudge Ser.). (Illus.). 32p. (J). pap. 3.99 (978-0-689-86995-2(9) , Aladdin) Simon & Schuster Children's Publishing.

MUHAMMAD, PROPHET, D. 632

Aziz, Abdullah. Muhammad's Believe It or Else!, Bk. 3. 2001. 23p. (YA). mass mkt. 3.95 (978-1-931230-01-8(3) , Crescent Moon Pubns.) Christian Scholar's Pr.

Azzam, Leila & Gouverneur, Aisha. The Life of the Prophet Muhammad. 1999. (Illus.). 136p. (Orig.). (gr. 10 up). pap. 27.95 (978-0-946621-02-6(0)) Islamic Texts Society GBR. *Dist:* Independent Pubs. Group.

Caglaroglu, Nurefsan. Awaiting the Prophet. 2008. 96p. (J). pap. 34.95 (*978-1-59784-126-9(9)) Light, Inc., The.

Ganeri, Anita. The Great Night Journey & Other Stories: Muslim Stories. 2007. (J). lib. bdg. 19.95 (*978-1-59566-375-7(4)) QEB Publishing Inc.

Gulen, Fethullah. Prophet Muhammad As Commander. 1998. 126p. (J). pap. 5.95 (978-975-7388-46-3(7) , Fountain, The) Light, Inc., The.

Ismail, Imam Vehbi. Muhammad, the Last Prophet. 2001. (Illus.). 167p. (J). 9.95 (978-0-915957-58-3(2)) amana pubns.

Marston, Elsa. Muhammad of Mecca: Prophet of Islam. 2001. (Book Report Biographies Ser.). (Illus.). 100p. (YA). (gr. 6-8). pap. 6.95 (978-0-531-15554-7(4) , Watts, Franklin) Scholastic Library Publishing.

MUHAMMAD ALI, 1942-

see Ali, Muhammad, 1942-

MUIR, JOHN, 1838-1914

Armentrout, David. John Muir. 2002. (SPA.). (gr. k-3). lib. bdg. 14.10 (978-0-613-79836-5(8)) Tandem Library Bks.

Armentrout, David & Armentrout, Patricia. John Muir. 2002. (Discover Someone Who Made a Difference Discovery Library Ser.). (Illus.). 24p. (gr. 2-5). 14.95 (978-1-58952-055-4(6)) Rourke Publishing, LLC.

—John Muir. Sarfatti, Esther & de la Vega, Eida, trs. 2001. (Personas que Cambiaron la Historia Ser.). (SPA., Illus.). 24p. (J). (gr. 1-4). lib. bdg. 19.27 (978-1-58952-168-1(4) , RK7725) Rourke Publishing, LLC.

Dunham, Montrew. John Muir: Young Naturalist. Fiorentino, Al, illus. 1998. (Childhood of Famous Americans Ser.). 192p. (J). (gr. 3-7). pap. 10.95 (978-0-689-81996-4(X) , Aladdin) Simon & Schuster Children's Publishing.

Dunlap, Julie & Lorbiecki, Marybeth. John Muir & the Stickeen: An Icy Adventure with a No Good Dog. Farnsworth, Bill, illus. 2004. 32p. (gr. k-3). 16.95 (978-1-55971-903-2(6) , NorthWord Bks. for Young Readers) T&N Children's Publishing.

Kiely Miller, Barbara. John Muir. 2007. (J). pap. (***978-0-8368-8325-1(X)** , Weekly Reader Early Learning Library) Stevens, Gareth Inc.

Koehler-Pentacoff, Elizabeth. John Muir & Stickeen: An Alaskan Adventure. 2003. (Single Titles Ser.). 32p. lib. bdg. 23.90 (978-0-7613-2769-1(X) , Millbrook Pr.) Lerner Publishing Group.

—John Muir & Stickeen: An Alaskan Adventure. Swanson, Karl W., illus. 2003. (Single Titles Ser.). 32p. (J). 14.95 (978-0-7613-1997-9(2) , Millbrook Pr.) Lerner Publishing Group.

Lasky, Kathryn. John Muir: America's First Environmentalist. Fellows, Stan, illus. 2006. 48p. (J). (gr. 1-5). 16.99 (978-0-7636-1957-2(4)) Candlewick Pr.

—John Muir: America's First Environmentalist. Fellows, Stanley, illus. 2006. 41p. (J). (978-1-4156-7115-3(X)) Candlewick Pr.

Locker, Thomas. John Muir: America's Naturalist. (Illus.). 32p. (gr. 4). 17.95 (978-1-55591-393-9(8)) Fulcrum Publishing.

Mara, Wil. John Muir. (Rookie Biographies Ser.). (Illus.). 32p. (J). (gr. 1-2). 2003. pap. 4.95 (978-0-516-27342-6(6)); 2002. 20.50 (978-0-516-22515-9(4)) Scholastic Library Publishing. (Children's Pr.).

—John Muir. 2002. (gr. k-3). lib. bdg. 12.95 (978-0-613-59504-9(1)) Tandem Library Bks.

Marsh, Carole. John Muir. 2002. (One Thousand Readers Ser.). (Illus.). 12p. (J). (gr. k-4). 2.95 (978-0-635-01508-2(0) , 15099) Gallopade International.

Maruca, Mary. A Kid's Guide to Exploring John Muir. 1999. (Illus.). 16p. (J). (gr. 3-7). pap. 1.00 (978-1-877856-98-3(3) , E1003) Western National Parks Assn.

Maynard, Charles W. John Muir: Naturalist & Explorer. 2003. (Famous Explorers of the American West Ser.). (Illus.). 24p. (J). lib. bdg. 18.75 (978-0-8239-6291-4(1) , PowerKids Pr.) Rosen Publishing Group, Inc., The.

Miller, Barbara Kiely. John Muir. 2007. (Great Americans Ser.). 24p. (J). (gr. 2-4). lib. bdg. 19.93 (***978-0-8368-8318-3(7)** , Weekly Reader Early Learning Library) Stevens, Gareth Inc.

Muir, John. John Muir: My Life with Nature. 2000. lib. bdg. 17.60 (978-0-613-56465-6(0)) Tandem Library Bks.

—Stickeen: John Muir & the Brave Little Dog. Canyon, Christopher, illus. 1998. 32p. (YA). (ps-7). 16.95 (978-1-883220-79-2(3)); pap. 7.95 (978-1-883220-78-5(5)) Dawn Pubns.

Topp, Patricia. Call Him Father Nature: The Story of John Muir. 2001. (Illus.). 97p. (J). (gr. 4-7). pap. 8.95 (978-1-57733-047-9(1)) Blue Dolphin Publishing, Inc.

Warrick, Karen Clemens. John Muir: Crusader for the Wilderness. 2002. (Historical American Biographies Ser.). (Illus.). 128p. (YA). (gr. 6-12). lib. bdg. 26.60 (978-0-7660-1622-4(6)) Enslow Pubs., Inc.

MULES—FICTION

Grovet, Heather. Sarah Lee & a Mule Named Maybe. 2003. 136p. (J). pap. 7.99 (978-0-8280-1725-1(5) , 191-530) Review & Herald Publishing Assn.

Hodges, Meredith. Jasper: The Story of a Mule. Shields, Bonnie, illus. 2003. 245p. (J). (gr. k-7). 39.95 (978-0-9702309-8-0(2)) Lucky 3 Ranch, Inc.

Hopkinson, Deborah. From Slave to Soldier: Based on a True Civil War Story. Floca, Brian, illus. (Ready-to-Reads Ser.). 48p. (J). 2007. pap. 3.99 (978-0-689-83966-5(9) , Aladdin); 2005. 14.95 (978-0-689-83965-8(0) , Atheneum) Simon & Schuster Children's Publishing.

Huston, Donna. Mr. O'Toole, the Diabetic Mule. 2006. (J). spiral bd. 19.95 (978-0-9771192-2-6(X)) Shayne Publishing.

Jasper: A Christmas Caper. 2004. (Illus.). 85p. (J). 24.95 (978-1-928624-20-2(0)) Lucky 3 Ranch, Inc.

King-Smith, Dick. Traffic. 2003. (Illus.). (gr. 3-6). lib. bdg. 11.80 (978-0-613-88820-2(0)) Tandem Library Bks.

Rawlinson, Julia. Mule School. Chapman, Lynne, illus. 2008. (J). (***978-1-56148-597-0(7)**) Good Bks.

Schmauss, Judy Kentor. Luke's Mule. 2006. (Reader's Clubhouse Set B Ser.). (Illus.). 24p. (J). pap. 3.99 (978-0-7641-3297-1(0)) Barron's Educational Series, Inc.

Skeeter: Individual Chapter Book Title Six-Pack. Vol. 29. 32p. (gr. 5 up). 44.00 (978-0-7578-0973-6(1)) Rigby Education.

MULTICULTURAL EDUCATION

Braman, Arlette. Kids Around the World Create! the Best Crafts & Activities from Many Lands. 1999. (gr. 3-6). lib. bdg. 22.20 (978-0-613-16520-4(9)) Tandem Library Bks.

Dwight, Laura, photos by. We Are All Alike... We Are All Different. 2002. (Illus.). 32p. (J). 15.95 (978-0-439-41780-8(5)) Scholastic, Inc.

Gainer, Cindy. I'm Like You, You're Like Me: A Child's Book about Understanding & Celebrating Each Other. Gainer, Cindy, illus. 1998. (Illus.). 48p. (J). (ps-3). 12.95 (978-1-57542-039-4(2)) Free Spirit Publishing, Inc.

Pugliano-Martin, Carol. Artesanías del mundo & Making Crafts from Around the World. 2005. spiral bd. 77.00 (***978-1-4108-5674-6(7)**) Benchmark Education Co.

Schuman, Jo Miles. Art from Many Hands: Multicultural Art Projects. rev. ed. 2003. (ENG., Illus.). 304p. (J). pap. 29.95 (978-0-87192-593-0(1)) Davis Pubns., Inc.

MULTICULTURALISM

Here are entered works on policies or programs that foster the preservation of different cultural identities, including customs, languages, and beliefs, within a unified society such as a state or nation.

Ajmera, Maya, et al. Ser Niño. 2004. (SPA., Illus.). 32p. (J). (ps-3). pap. 6.95 (978-0-88106-136-9(0)) Charlesbridge Publishing, Inc.

Fox, Mem. Quienquiera Que Seas. 2002. (SPA.). (ps-2). lib. bdg. 15.30 (978-0-613-83224-3(8)) Tandem Library Bks.

Fox, Mem & Staub, Leslie. Whoever You Are. 2007. (Illus.). 28p. (J). (ps). bds. 6.95 (***978-0-15-206066-4(9)** , Red Wagon Bks.) Harcourt Children's Bks.

Ganeri, Anita. Journey's End: Death & Mourning. 1999. (Life Times Ser.). (Illus.). 30p. (YA). (gr. 2 up). 15.95 (978-0-87226-289-8(8) , 62898B, Bedrick, Peter Bks.) School Specialty Publishing.

—Wedding Days: Celebrations of Marriage. 1999. (Life Times Ser.). (Illus.). 32p. (J). 15.95 (978-0-87226-288-1(X) , 6288XB, Bedrick, Peter Bks.) School Specialty Publishing.

Holman, Sandy Lynne. We All Have a Heritage. Kowetiawi, Lela, illus. l.t. ed. 2002. (People Ser.: Pt. II). 35p. (J). (gr. k-6). 18.95 (978-0-9644655-2-7(3)) Culture C.O.-O.P., The.

Hull, Bunny. Peace in Our Land: Children Celebrating Diversity. Saint-James, Synthia, illus. 2002. 24p. pap. 10.95 incl. audio (978-0-9673762-9-5(7) , BH105pkg or ISBN) BrassHeart Music.

Kerley, Barbara. A Cool Drink of Water. 2006. 32p. (J). (gr. 5 up). 7.95 (978-0-7922-5489-8(9) , National Geographic Children's Bks.) National Geographic Society.

Loonin, Meryl. Multicultural America. 2004. (Lucent Overview Ser.). (Illus.). 112p. (J). 29.95 (978-1-56006-766-5(7) , Lucent Bks.) Thomson Gale.

Milord, Susan. Tales Alive! Donato, Michael A., illus. 2007. 128p. pap. 16.99 (***978-0-8249-6804-5(2)** , Williamson Bks.) Ideals Pubns.

Schramm, Linda Anette. Don't Let the Ziglers into the Zoo! 2004. 31p. pap. 17.95 (978-1-4137-1541-5(9)) PublishAmerica, Inc.

Teichmann, Iris. A Multicultural World. 2006. (Understanding Immigration Ser.). (Illus.). 44p. (YA). (gr. 5-8). lib. bdg. 31.35 (978-1-58340-969-5(6)) Smart Apple Media.

Tomlin, Carolyn. More Alike Than Different. Reeves, Rhonda, ed. 2000. (Illus.). 32p. (J). (ps). 9.99 (978-1-56309-351-7(0)) Woman's Missionary Union.

MULTICULTURALISM—FICTION

Gomes, Linda Nunes. Special Words: A Story about Multicultural Families & Their Pets. Levine, Lenora D., illus. 2007. (YA). per. 12.99 (***978-1-934400-02-9(5)**) Rock Village Publishing.

Hammond, John. A Martian Named Zoom. McConnon, Michael, illus. 2001. (J). (gr. k-5). lib. bdg. 14.95 (978-0-9705727-4-5(3)) Coastal Publishing Carolina, Inc.

hooks, bell. Skin Again. Raschka, Chris, illus. 2004. 32p. (ps-3). 16.99 (978-0-7868-0825-0(X)) Hyperion Bks. for Children.

Hughes, Monica. Jan's Awesome Party. Freire, Carlos, illus. 2001. (First Novels Ser.: Vol. 18). 57p. (gr. 1-5). (J). (978-0-88780-533-2(7)); 4.95 (978-0-88780-532-5(9)) Formac Publishing Co., Ltd. CAN. *Dist:* Casemate Pubs. & Bk. Distributors, LLC.

Iyengar, Malathi. Romina's Rangoli/By Malathi Michelle Iyengar ; Illustrated by Jennifer Wanardi. Wanardi, Jennifer, illus. 2007. (J). (***978-1-885008-32-9(5)**) Shen's Bks.

Leedom, Tim C. The Light Side. l.t. ed. 2002. 80p. (J). per. 21.95 (978-0-9646885-1-3(4)) Manoa Valley Publishing Co., The.

Rodari, Gianni. One & Seven. Anglin, David, tr. from ITA. Alemagna, Beatrice, illus. 2005. (SPA.). 26p. (J). (gr. k-3). 17.95 (978-0-9628720-6-8(7)) Iaconi, Mariuccia Bk. Imports.

Russell, Ching Yeung. Water Ghost. Zhang, Christopher Zhong-Yuan, illus. 2003. 192p. (YA). (gr. 4-6). pap. 10.95 (978-1-59078-045-9(0)) Boyds Mills Pr.

Selected Children's Stories - Multi Cultural, 3 bks. (Illus.). (J). lib. bdg. 38.85 (978-1-56674-906-0(9)) Forest Hse. Publishing Co., Inc.

Sparrow, L. T. All My Relations, a Prayer. 2000. (Illus.). 32p. (YA). (gr. 3 up). 16.95 (978-0-9670171-0-5(6)) Sparrow, L.T. Publishing.

Sykes, Marsha F. The Village of Spence Hill: A Multicultural Bedtime Story. Sykes, Johnnie F., illus. 2002. 20p. (J). (ps-6). pap. 6.00 (978-0-9720816-0-3(7)) M & JP Publishing.

Theo & the Sisters of Sage: From the Creator of We Are All the Same Inside. 2003. (We Are All the Same Inside Ser.: Vol. 3). (Illus.). 32p. (J). pap. 7.95 (978-0-9718232-1-1(9)) T.I.M.M.-E. Co., Inc.

Winkler, Henry & Oliver, Lin. Holy Enchilada! Heyer, Carol & Watson, Jesse Joshua, illus. 2004. (Hank Zipzer Ser.: No. 6). 160p. (J). (gr. 3-8). pap. 4.99 (978-0-448-43353-0(2) , Grosset & Dunlap) Penguin Group (USA) Inc.

—Holy Enchilada!, No. 6. Watson, Jesse Joshua, illus. 2004. (Hank Zipzer Ser.: No. 6). 160p. (J). (gr. 3-7). 13.99 (978-0-448-43554-1(3) , Grosset & Dunlap) Penguin Group (USA) Inc.

—Holy Enchilada! 2006. (Hank Zipzer Ser.: No. 6). (J). (gr. 3-8). 24.21 (978-1-59961-105-1(8)) Spotlight.

—Holy Enchilada! 2003. (Hank Zipzer Ser.: No. 6). (gr. 3-6). lib. bdg. 13.00 (978-0-613-72546-0(8)) Tandem Library Bks.

—The Zippity Zinger. 2003. (Hank Zipzer Ser.: No. 4). (Illus.). 160p. (J). (gr. 3-8). mass mkt. 4.99 (978-0-448-43193-2(9) , Grosset & Dunlap) Penguin Group (USA) Inc.

—The Zippity Zinger. Heyer, Carol, illus. 2003. (Hank Zipzer Ser.: No. 4). 160p. (J). 13.99 (978-0-448-43287-8(0) , Grosset & Dunlap) Penguin Group (USA) Inc.

MUMMIES

Ashman, Iain. Egyptian Mummy. 2004. (Cut-Out Models Ser.). (Illus.). 32p. (J). pap. 9.95 (978-0-7945-0255-3(5) , Usborne) EDC Publishing.

Bampton, Claire. The Amazing Pop-up Pull-Out Mummy Book. Hawcock, David & Watton, Nick, illus. 2004. 15p. (gr. 4-10). reprint ed. 20.00 (978-0-7567-7290-1(7)) DIANE Publishing Co.

Berger, Melvin & Berger, Gilda. Mummies of the Pharaohs: Exploring the Valley of the Kings. 2001. (Illus.). 64p. (J). (gr. 3-7). 17.95 (978-0-7922-7223-6(4) , National Geographic Children's Bks.) National Geographic Society.

Besel, Jennifer M. Mummies. 2007. (Blazers Ser.). (Illus.). 32p. (J). 19.93 (978-0-7368-6441-1(5)) Capstone Pr., Inc.

Buell, Janet. Ancient Horsemen of Siberia. 1998. (Time Travelers Ser.: 8). (Illus.). 64p. (gr. 5-8). lib. bdg. 25.90 (978-0-7613-3005-9(4) , Twenty-First Century Bks.) Lerner Publishing Group.

—Greenland Mummies. 1998. (Time Travelers Ser.: 8). (Illus.). 64p. (gr. 5-8). lib. bdg. 25.90 (978-0-7613-3004-2(6) , Twenty-First Century Bks.) Lerner Publishing Group.

Burgan, Michael. The Valley of the Kings: Egypt's Greatest Mummies. 2005. (Mummies Ser.). (Illus.). 32p. (J). 22.60 (978-0-7368-3772-9(8)) Capstone Pr., Inc.

Chrisp, Peter. Mummy. 2007. (Dk Online Ser.). (Illus.). 96p. (J). pap. 9.99 (978-0-7566-2295-4(6)) Dorling Kindersley Publishing, Inc.

Chrisp, Peter & Dorling Kindersley Publishing Staff. Mummy. 2004. (Google E Guides). 96p. (J). 17.99 (978-0-7566-0760-9(4)) Dorling Kindersley Publishing, Inc.

Cooper, Terry, ed. Pyramids & Mummies. 2001. (Instant Internet Activities Folder Ser.). 6p. pap. 3.95 (978-0-439-30956-1(5)) Scholastic, Inc.

Davis, Kenneth C. Don't Know Much about Mummies. Date not set. 48p. (J). pap. 5.99 (978-0-06-443645-8(4)) HarperCollins Pubs.

—Don't Know Much about Mummies. Schindler, S. D., illus. 2005. (Don't Know Much About Ser.: No. 8). 48p. (J). (gr. 1-4). lib. bdg. 16.89 (978-0-06-028782-5(9)); (ps). 15.99 (978-0-06-028781-8(0)) HarperCollins Pubs.

Dineen, Jacqueline. Lift the Lid on Mummies: Unravel the Mysteries of Egyptian Tombs, & Make Your Own Mummy! 1998. (Lift the Lid Ser.). (Illus.). 24p. (gr. 4-7). pap. 22.95 (978-0-7624-0208-3(3) , Running Pr. Kids) Running Pr. Bk. Pubs.

Dorling Kindersley Publishing Staff, ed. Mummy. 2004. (Dk Eyewitness Books Ser.). (Illus.). 72p. (J). 15.99 (978-0-7566-0707-4(8)) Dorling Kindersley Publishing, Inc.

Fleury, Kevin. Mummies. 2007. (Up Close Ser.). (Illus.). 24p. (J). (gr. 3-5). lib. bdg. 23.95 (***978-1-4042-3761-2(5)** , PowerKids Pr.) Rosen Publishing Group, Inc., The.

Funston, Sylvia. Mummies. Weissmann, Joe, illus. 2000. (Strange Science Ser.). 40p. (J). (gr. 3-7). pap. 9.95 (978-1-894379-04-5(7)); 19.95 (978-1-894379-03-8(9)) Maple Tree Pr. CAN. *Dist:* Firefly Bks., Ltd.

—Mummies. 2000. (gr. 3-6). lib. bdg. 18.75 (978-0-613-50348-8(1)) Tandem Library Bks.

Ganeri, Anita. Mummies & Ancient Egypt. 2005. (First Look at History Ser.). (Illus.). 24p. (J). lib. bdg. 22.00 (978-0-8368-4527-3(7)) Stevens, Gareth Inc.

Garmon, Larry Mike. The Mummy: Book of the Dead. 2002. (Universal Monsters Ser.: No. 4). 192p. (J). (gr. 5 up). pap. 4.50 (978-0-439-30346-0(X)) Scholastic, Inc.

Griffey, Harriet. Secrets of the Mummies. 1998. (Eyewitness Readers). (Illus.). 48p. (J). (gr. 5-5). pap. 3.99 (978-0-7894-3442-5(3)) Dorling Kindersley Publishing, Inc.

Halls, Kelly Milner. Mysteries of the Mummy Kids. 2007. (Illus.). 72p. (J). (gr. 4-8). 18.95 (***978-1-58196-059-4(X)**) Darby Creek Publishing.

Hawass, Zahi. The Curse of the Pharaohs: My Adventures with Mummies. 2004. (Illus.). 160p. (J). (gr. 5). 19.95 (978-0-7922-6665-5(X)); 29.90 (978-0-7922-6963-2(2)) National Geographic Society. (National Geographic Children's Bks.).

Hussain Iqbal. Freaky Facts about Mummies. 2006. (Freaky Facts Ser.). (Illus.). 32p. (J). 8.95 (978-1-58728-538-7(X) , Two Can Publishing) T&N Children's Publishing.

Hussain, Iqbal. Freaky Facts about Mummies. 2006. (Freaky Facts Ser.). (Illus.). 32p. 13.95 (978-1-58728-537-0(1) , Two Can Publishing) T&N Children's Publishing.

Keyes, Anna. Faraones, pirámides y momias & Pharaohs, Pyramids & Mummies. 2005. spiral bd. 88.00 (***978-1-4108-5732-3(8)**) Benchmark Education Co.

Krensky, Stephen. The Mummy. 2007. (Monster Chronicles Ser.). (Illus.). 48p. (J). (gr. 4-8). lib. bdg. 26.60 (978-0-8225-5924-5(2) , Lerner Pubns.) Lerner Publishing Group.

Kudalis, Eric. Ice Mummies: Frozen in Time. 2002. (Mummies Ser.). (Illus.). 32p. (J). (gr. 3-4). lib. bdg. 21.26 (978-0-7368-1307-5(1) , Capstone High-Interest Bks.) Capstone Pr., Inc.

—The Royal Mummies: Remains from Ancient Egypt. 2002. (Mummies Ser.). (Illus.). 32p. (J). (gr. 3-4). lib. bdg. 21.26 (978-0-7368-1308-2(X) , Capstone High-Interest Bks.) Capstone Pr., Inc.

Kunhardt, Edith. Mummies. 2000. (Road to Reading Ser.). (Illus.). (J). (978-0-606-20445-3(8)) Tandem Library Bks.

MacDonald, Fiona. Amazing World of Mummies. 2005. (Illus.). 64p. 15.99 (978-0-7548-1469-6(6) , Lorenz Bks.) Anness Publishing GBR. *Dist:* National Bk. Network.

—Mysterious Mummies. 2003. (History Hunters Ser.). (Illus.). 32p. (J). (gr. 3 up). lib. bdg. 24.67 (978-0-8368-3742-1(8)) Stevens, Gareth Inc.

MacDonald, Fiona & Millard, Anne. Mummies & Tombs. 2000. (World Of... Ser.). (Illus.). 64p. (gr. 3-7). pap. 7.95 (978-1-84215-231-7(9) , Southwater) Anness Publishing GBR. *Dist:* National Bk. Network.

Malam, John. Mummies. (Kingfisher Knowledge Ser.). (Illus.). 64p. (J). (gr. 4-6). 2007. pap. 8.95 (***978-0-7534-6122-8(6));** 2003. tchr. ed. 12.95 (978-0-7534-5623-1(0)) Houghton Mifflin Co. Trade & Reference Div. (Kingfisher).

—Mummies. 2007. (J). (***978-1-59920-106-1(2)**) Smart Apple Media.

Malam, John. See-Through Mummies. Malam, John, illus. 2000. (See-Through Ser.). (Illus.). 32p. (J). 15.95 (978-0-7624-1586-1(X) , Running Pr. Kids) Running Pr. Bk. Pubs.

Markle, Sandra. Outside & Inside Mummies. 2005. (Illus.). 40p. (J). 18.85 (978-0-8027-8967-9(6)); 17.95 (978-0-8027-8966-2(8)) Walker & Co.

Mason. Mummies. 2003. (Mysteries of the Past Ser.). (Illus.). 32p. pap. 7.95 (978-1-4109-0064-7(9)) Raintree.

—Mummies - Mysteries of the Past. 2004. pap. 48.30 (978-1-4109-0283-2(8)) Harcourt Schl. Pubs.

Mason, Paul. Mummies. 2001. (Young Library - Mysteries of the Past). (Illus.). 32p. (J). lib. bdg. 25.69 (978-0-7398-4338-3(9)) Raintree.

—Mummies. 2005. (Marvels & Mysteries Ser.). (Illus.). 32p. (J). (gr. 4-7). lib. bdg. 27.10 (978-1-58340-786-8(3)) Smart Apple Media.

—Mummies. 2003. (gr. 3-6). lib. bdg. 16.40 (978-0-613-78230-2(5)) Tandem Library Bks.

McCall, Henrietta. Egyptian Mummies. 2000. (Fast Forward Ser.). (Illus.). 32p. (J). (gr. 4-8). pap. 9.95 (978-0-531-16443-3(8) , Watts, Franklin) Scholastic Library Publishing.

—Egyptian Mummies. 2000. (J). 16.75 (978-0-606-19782-3(6)); (gr. 3-6). lib. bdg. 18.75 (978-0-613-34692-4(0)) Tandem Library Bks.

McNeil, Niki, et al. HOCPP 1064 Egyptian Mummies. 2006. spiral bd. 12.50 (***978-1-60308-064-4(3)**) In the Hands of a Child.

Momias. 2003. (Megabites Ser.). (SPA., Illus.). (J). pap. 8.95 (978-0-9715256-6-5(8)) Planeta Publishing Corp.

Mummies. 2005. (Illus.). (J). (gr. 3-4). lib. bdg. 180.50 (978-0-7368-3821-4(X)) Capstone Pr., Inc.

Mummies, 4 bks. Incl. Animal Mummies : Preserved Through the Ages. Wilcox, Charlotte. lib. bdg. 21.26 (978-0-7368-1305-1(5)); Bog Mummies : Preserved in Peat. Wilcox, Charlotte. lib. bdg. 21.26 (978-0-7368-1306-8(3)); Ice Mummies : Frozen in Time. Kudalis, Eric. lib. bdg. 21.26 (978-0-7368-1307-5(1)); Royal Mummies : Remains from Ancient Egypt. Kudalis, Eric. lib. bdg. 21.26 (978-0-7368-1308-2(X)); 32p. (J). (gr. 3-4). 2002. (Illus.). 2002. Set lib. bdg. 85.04 (978-0-7368-1309-9(8) , Capstone High-Interest Bks.) Capstone Pr., Inc.

Mummy Sticker Book. 2003. (Illus.). 16p. (J). 2.98 (978-1-84273-122-2(X)) Parragon, Inc.

Newstead, Keith. Mummies. 2002. (Moving Model Bks.). (Illus.). 32p. (J). (gr. 3 up). pap. 8.99 (978-0-439-38820-7(1)) Scholastic, Inc.

Nobleman, Marc Tyler. Mummies. 2006. (Atomic (Chicago, Ill.) Ser.). (Illus.). 32p. (J). (978-1-4109-2481-0(5)); pap. (978-1-4109-2486-5(6)) Steck-Vaughn.

Ollhoff, Jim. Mummies. 2007. (ENG., Illus.). 32p. (YA). lib. bdg. 24.21 (***978-1-59928-772-0(2)** , ABDO & Daughters) ABDO Publishing Co.

Orme, David. Mummies. 2007. (Trailblazers Ser.). (Illus.). 36p. pap. 7.95 (***978-1-84167-427-8(3)**) Ransom Publishing Ltd. GBR. *Dist:* International Publishers Marketing.

Osborne, Mary Pope & Osborne, Will. Mummies & Pyramids: A Nonfiction Companion to Mummies in the Morning. Murdocca, Sal, illus. 2001. (Magic Tree House Research Guide Ser.: No. 3). 128p. (J). (gr. k-3). lib. bdg. 11.99 (978-0-375-90298-7(8) , Random Hse. Bks. for Young Readers) Random Hse. Children's Bks.

Osborne, Will & Osborne, Mary Pope. Mummies & Pyramids: A Nonfiction Companion to Mummies in the Morning. Murdocca, Sal, illus. 2001. (Magic Tree House Research Guide Ser.: No. 3). 128p. (J). (gr. k-3). pap. 4.99 (978-0-375-80298-0(3) , Random Hse. Bks. for Young Readers) Random Hse. Children's Bks.

—Mummies & Pyramids: A Nonfiction Companion to Mummies in the Morning. Murdocca, Salvatore, illus. 2001. (Magic Tree House Research Guide Ser.: No. 3). 119p. (J). (gr. k-3). per. 13.00 (978-0-613-33837-0(5)) Tandem Library Bks.

Patent, Dorothy Hinshaw. Secrets of the Ice Man. 1999. (Frozen in Time Ser.). (Illus.). 72p. (J). (gr. 5-9). lib. bdg. 28.50 (978-0-7614-0782-9(0) , Benchmark Bks.) Cavendish, Marshall Corp.

Patton, Geoff. Mummies. 2005. (X-Zone Ser.). (Illus.). 30p. (gr. 4-8). 23.00 (978-0-7910-8993-4(2)) Facts On File, Inc.

Pemberton. Egyptian Mummies. 2000. 48p. 27.14 (978-0-7398-3949-2(7)) Raintree.

Polk, Milbry. Egyptian Mummies. Stewart, Roger & Seminario, Jose R., illus. 2004. 8p. (J). (gr. k-4). reprint ed. 20.00 (978-0-7567-8329-7(1)) DIANE Publishing Co.

Preller, James. Mummy Scrapbook. 1999. 48p. pap. 5.50 (978-0-439-05016-6(2)) Scholastic, Inc.

Prior, Natalie Jane. The Encyclopedia of Preserved People: Pickled, Frozed, & Mummified Corpses from Around the World. 2003. (Illus.). 64p. (J). (gr. 2-7). 16.99 (978-0-375-92287-9(3) , Crown Books For Young Readers) Random Hse. Children's Bks.

Raleigh, Richard. Mummies: Secrets of the Dead. 2005. (High Interest Books Ser.). (Illus.). 48p. (J). (ps-7). 24.00 (978-0-516-25596-5(7)); (Illus.). 48p. (YA). (gr. 7-12). pap. 6.95 (978-0-516-25094-6(9)); (J). lib. bdg. (978-0-516-25125-7(2)) Scholastic Library Publishing. (Children's Pr.).

Simon, Seymour. Pyramids & Mummies. 2004. (See More Readers). (Illus.). 40p. (J). 14.50 (978-1-58717-240-3(2)); Vol. 3. pap. 3.95 (978-1-58717-241-0(0)) Chronicle Bks. LLC. (SeaStar Bks.).

—Seemore Pyramids & Mummies. 2006. 40p. (J). pap. 3.95 (978-0-8118-5497-9(3)) Chronicle Bks. LLC.

Skillet, Helen. Mummies! Unwrapping the Secrets of Ancient Egypt. 2005. (YA). cd-rom (978-1-4105-0411-1(5)) Johnston, Don Inc.

Steele, Philip. The Best Book of Mummies. (Best Book of... Ser.). 32p. (J). (gr. k-3). 2005. pap. 5.95 (978-0-7534-5873-0(X)); 1998. (Illus.). 12.95 (978-0-7534-5132-8(8)) Houghton Mifflin Co. Trade & Reference Div. (Kingfisher).

Stewart, David. You Wouldn't Want to Be an Egyptian Mummy! 2000. (gr. 3-6). lib. bdg. 18.75 (978-0-613-36765-3(0)) Tandem Library Bks.

—You Wouldn't Want to Be an Egyptian Mummy! Disgusting Things You'd Rather Not Know. Antram, David & Salariya, David, illus. 2001. (You Wouldn't Want to Ser.). 32p. (J). (gr. 2-5). 28.50 (978-0-531-14597-5(2) , Watts, Franklin) Scholastic Library Publishing.

—You Wouldn't Want to Be an Egyptian Mummy! Disgusting Things You'd Rather Not Know. Antram, David, illus. 2001. (You Wouldn't Want to Ser.). 32p. (J). (gr. 2-5). pap. 9.95 (978-0-531-16206-4(0) , Watts, Franklin) Scholastic Library Publishing.

Strom, Laura Layton. The Egyptian Science Gazette. 2007. (Shockwave: Science in Practice Ser.). (Illus.). 36p. (J). (gr. 4-6). lib. bdg. 25.00 (*978-0-531-17582-8(0) , Children's Pr.) Scholastic Library Publishing.

Tanaka, Shelley. Secrets of the Mummies: Uncovering the Bodies of Ancient Egyptians. 2001. (I Was There Bk.). (Illus.). (J). (978-0-606-20900-7(X)) Tandem Library Bks.

Taplin, Sam. Mummies & Pyramids. 2004. (Discovery Program Ser.). (Illus.). 48p. (J). pap. 8.95 (978-0-7945-0317-8(9) , Usborne); lib. bdg. 16.95 (978-1-58086-479-4(1)) EDC Publishing.

Taylor, Barbara & MacDonald, Fiona. Mummies & Tombs. 2000. (Discovery Ser.). (Illus.). 64p. (gr. 3-7). 14.95 (978-0-7548-0505-2(0) , Lorenz Bks.) Anness Publishing GBR. Dist: National Bk. Network.

Trumble, Kelly. Cat Mummies. Kubinyi, Laszlo, illus. 1999. 64p. (J). (gr. 4-6). pap. 7.95 (978-0-395-96891-8(7) , Clarion Bks.) Houghton Mifflin Co. Trade & Reference Div.

Weinberger, Kimberly. Mummies Unwrapped. 2001. (gr. k-3). lib. bdg. 11.80 (978-0-613-63558-5(2)) Tandem Library Bks.

Wilcox, Charlotte. Animal Mummies: Preserved Through the Ages. 2002. (Mummies Ser.). (Illus.). 32p. (J). (gr. 3-4). lib. bdg. 21.26 (978-0-7368-1305-1(5) , Capstone High-Interest Bks.) Capstone Pr., Inc.

—Mummies, Bones & Body Parts. 2000. (Photo Bks.). (Illus.). 64p. (J). (gr. 4-7). 25.26 (978-1-57505-428-5(0) , Carolrhoda Bks.) Lerner Publishing Group.

MUMMIES—FICTION

Bellairs, John. The Mummy, the Will, & the Crypt. 2001. (J). (gr. 4-8). 21.75 (978-0-8446-7170-3(3)) Smith, Peter Pub., Inc.

Bradman, Tony. The Magnificent Mummies. Chatterton, Martin, illus. 2001. (Blue Bananas Ser.). 48p. (J). (gr. 1-2). (978-0-7787-0843-8(8)); pap. (978-0-7787-0889-6(6)) Crabtree Publishing Co.

—Magnificent Mummies. 2002. (gr. k-3). lib. bdg. 12.95 (978-0-613-52878-8(6)) Tandem Library Bks.

—Midnight in Memphis. Chatterton, Martin & Chatterton, Ann, illus. 2001. (Blue Bananas Ser.). 48p. (J). (gr. 1-2). (978-0-7787-0848-3(9)); pap. (978-0-7787-0894-0(2)) Crabtree Publishing Co.

—Midnight in Memphis. 2002. (gr. k-3). lib. bdg. 12.95 (978-0-613-52881-8(6)) Tandem Library Bks.

—The Surprise Party. 2005. (Red Bananas Ser.). (Illus.). 48p. (J). (ps). pap. (978-0-7787-1084-4(X)) Crabtree Publishing Co.

Bradman, Tony & Chatterton, Martin. The Mummy Family Finds Fame. 2006. (Illus.). 46p. (J). (978-0-7787-1076-9(9)) Crabtree Publishing Co.

Bunting, Eve. I Am the Mummy Heb-Nefert. Christiana, David, illus. 2000. 32p. (J). (ps-3). pap. 7.00 (978-0-15-202464-2(6) , Harcourt Paperbacks) Harcourt Children's Bks.

Chatterton, Martin. The Surprise Party. Chatterton, Martin, illus. 2005. (Red Bananas Ser.). (Illus.). 48p. (J). (978-0-7787-1068-4(8)) Crabtree Publishing Co.

Costain, Meredith. The Mummy's Curse. 1999. (Brains & Parker McGoohan Ser.). 64 p. (978-0-7608-1938-8(6)) Sundance/Newbridge Educational Publishing.

—Mummy's Curse. 1999. (gr. 3-6). lib. bdg. 12.60 (978-0-613-18975-0(2)) Tandem Library Bks.

Deary, Terry. The Magic & the Mummy. Flook, Helen, illus. 2005. (Read-It! Chapter Bks.). 64p. (J). (ps-k). lib. bdg. 19.95 (978-1-4048-1271-0(7)) Picture Window Bks.

Duey, Kathleen. Mummy. Epstein, Eugene, illus. Gould, Robert, photos by. 2005. (Time Soldiers Ser.: 5). (J). 48p. 15.95 (978-1-929945-50-4(7)); 96p. pap. 5.95 (978-1-929945-57-3(4)) Big Guy Bks., Inc.

Gelsey, James. Scooby-Doo y la Maldicion de la Momia. 2003. (Scooby-Doo Mysteries Ser.: No. 2). (SPA., Illus.). 64p. (J). (gr. 2-4). pap. 3.99 (978-0-439-40985-8(3) , Scholastic en Espanol) Scholastic, Inc.

—Scooby-Doo y la Maldicion de la Momia. 2003. (SPA.). (gr. k-3). lib. bdg. 11.80 (978-0-613-87302-4(5)) Tandem Library Bks.

Hawksley, Gerald. Mommies & Mummies & Babies on the Farm. Calitri, Susan, illus. 2004. (J). bds. 11.99 (978-1-890647-11-7(X)) RC2 Corp.

Herman, Gail. Mummies at the Mall. del Sur, Duendes, illus. 2002. (Scooby-Doo! Reader Ser.: Vol. 11). 32p. (J). (ps-3). pap. 3.99 (978-0-439-34114-1(0)) Scholastic, Inc.

—Scooby Doo: Mummies at the Mall. 2002. (gr. k-3). lib. bdg. 11.80 (978-0-613-51319-7(3)) Tandem Library Bks.

Howe, James. Howie Monroe & the Screaming Mummies of the Pharoah's Tomb II. 2004. (Tales from the House of Bunnicula Ser.). 112p. (J). (gr. 3-6). pap. 17.00 incl. audio (978-1-4000-8635-1(3) , Listening Library) Random Hse. Audio Publishing Group.

Irbinskas, Heather & King, Andra. Morgan the Dog: An Egyptian Adventure. 2002. 33p. 14.95 (978-0-9711970-2-2(4)) Morgan Hse. Publishing.

Johnston, Tony. Mummy's Mother. 2003. (Illus.). 160p. (J). pap. 15.95 (978-0-439-32462-5(9) , Blue Sky Pr., The) Scholastic, Inc.

Labatt, Mary. Mummy Lives! 2002. (gr. 3-6). lib. bdg. 12.95 (978-0-613-62530-2(7)) Tandem Library Bks.

Lantz, Francess L. The Case of the Missing Mummy. 1998. (New Adventures of Mary-Kate & Ashley Ser.). (Illus.). 82p. (J). (gr. 2-7). pap. 3.99 (978-0-590-29404-1(0)) Scholastic, Inc.

Laybourn, Emma. Mummy Mania. 2002. 128p. (J). pap. 8.99 (978-1-84270-167-6(3)) Andersen GBR. Dist: Independent Pubs. Group.

Levithan, David. The Mummy, Level 2. 2001. 48p. (C). pap. 9.00 (978-0-582-45193-3(0)) Longman Publishing Group.

Myers, Bill & Wimbish, Dave. I Want My Mummy. 2000. (Bloodhounds, Inc. Ser.: Vol. 8). (Illus.). 128p. (J). (gr. 3-8). pap. 5.99 (978-1-55661-492-7(6)) Bethany Hse. Pubs.

Osborne, Mary Pope. Una Momia en la Manana. 2004. (Coleccion la Casa Del Arbol the Magic Tree House Ser.). (SPA.). (J). pap. 4.95 (978-1-930332-51-5(3)) Lectorum Pubns., Inc.

—Una Momia en la Manana. 2003. (SPA.). (gr. 3-6). lib. bdg. 12.95 (978-0-613-64609-3(6)) Tandem Library Bks.

—Mummies in the Morning, Vol. 3. unabr. ed. 2004. (Magic Tree House Ser. : No. 3). 65p. (J). (gr. k-5). pap. 17.00 incl. audio (978-0-8072-0332-3(7) , Listening Library) Random Hse. Audio Publishing Group.

Pollack, Pamela. Curse of Beetenkaumun. 2000. (gr. 3-6). lib. bdg. 13.00 (978-0-613-31101-4(9)) Tandem Library Bks.

Preller, James. The Case of the Mummy Mystery. Alley, R. W., illus. 2001. (Jigsaw Jones Mystery Ser.: No. 6). 80p. (J). (gr. 1-4). pap. 3.99 (978-0-439-08094-1(0)) Scholastic, Inc.

—The Case of the Mummy Mystery. 2000. (Jigsaw Jones Mystery Ser.: No. 6). (Illus.). (J). (gr. 1-4). 10.79 (978-0-606-18528-8(3)) Tandem Library Bks.

—Case of the Mummy Mystery. 1999. (gr. 3-6). lib. bdg. 11.80 (978-0-613-17901-0(3)) Tandem Library Bks.

Ross, Jil. Foster, the Dummy (Mummy) Another Installment in the Shenanigan's Series. Pruitt, Gwendolyn, illus. 2004. 58p. (J). pap. 6.95 (978-1-932373-94-3(2)) Cedar Hill Publishing.

Ross, Pat. M & M & the Mummy Mess. Hafner, Marylin, illus. 1999. (Puffin Chapters Ser.). 48p. (J). (gr. 2-5). pap. 4.99 (978-0-14-130654-4(8) , Puffin) Penguin Group (USA) Inc.

—M & M & the Mummy Mess. 1999. (Illus.). (J). (978-0-606-18424-3(4)) Tandem Library Bks.

Roy, Ron. The Missing Mummy. Gurney, John Steven, illus. 2001. (A to Z Mysteries Ser.: No. 13). 96p. (J). (gr. k-3). 11.99 (978-0-375-90268-0(6)); pap. 3.99 (978-0-375-80268-3(1)) Random Hse. Children's Bks. (Random Hse. Bks. for Young Readers).

Schachner, Judy. Skippyjon Jones in Mummy Trouble. Schachner, Judy, illus. 2006. (Illus.). 36p. (J). (ps). 16.99 (978-0-525-47754-9(3) , Dutton Juvenile) Penguin Group (USA) Inc.

Simon, Francesca. Horrid Henry & the Mummy's Curse. l.t. ed. 2001. (Illus.). 88p. (J). 16.95 (978-0-7540-6166-3(3) , Galaxy Children's Large Print) BBC Audiobooks America.

Sommers, Stephen. The Mummy. novel ed. 1999. (Illus.). 172p. (J). pap. 3.99 (978-0-439-05015-9(4)) Scholastic, Inc.

Stilton, Geronimo. The Mummy with No Name. 2006. (Geronimo Stilton Ser.: No. 26). 128p. (J). pap. 6.99 (978-0-439-84117-7(8) , Scholastic Paperbacks) Scholastic, Inc.

Strong, Jeremy. Let's Do the Pharaoh. 2005. (Illus.). (J). pap. 24.95 incl. audio (978-0-7540-6283-7(X) , Chivers Children's Audio Bks.) BBC Audiobooks America.

Thompson, Bart A. Mummy. Miroglio, Brian, illus. 2007. (Graphic Horror Ser.). 32p. (YA). (gr. 5-8). lib. bdg. 27.07 (*978-1-60270-061-1(3) , Graphic Planet) Magic Wagon.

Warner, Gertrude Chandler. Mystery of the Mummy's Curse. 2002. (gr. 3-6). lib. bdg. 11.80 (978-0-613-58377-0(9)) Tandem Library Bks.

—The Mystery of the Mummy's Curse, Vol. 88. 2004. (Boxcar Children Ser.: Vol. 88). 128p. (J). pap. 4.50 (978-0-8075-5504-0(5)) Whitman, Albert & Co.

Wilding. Secret Diaries 4 - Egyptian. 2008. (Illus.). 160p. (J). pap. 7.95 (*978-1-4052-1840-5(1)) Egmont Bks., Ltd. GBR. Dist: Independent Pubs. Group.

Yates, Philip. Ten Little Mummies: An Egyptian Counting Book. Karas, G. Brian, illus. 2005. 40p. (J). pap. 6.99 (978-0-14-240367-9(9) , Puffin) Penguin Group (USA) Inc.

Yorinks, Arthur. Mommy? 2006. (J). 24.95 (978-0-439-89526-2(X)) Scholastic, Inc.

MUMPS

Laskey, Elizabeth. Mumps. 2003. (It's Catching Ser.). (Illus.). 32p. (J). (gr. k-2). lib. bdg. 22.79 (978-1-4034-0275-2(2)) Heinemann Library.

MUNICIPAL ADMINISTRATION

see Municipal Government

MUNICIPAL EMPLOYEES

see Civil Service; Municipal Government

MUNICIPAL ENGINEERING

see also Refuse and Refuse Disposal; Water-Supply

Levy, Matthys & Panchyk, Richard. Engineering the City: How Infrastructure Works - Projects & Principles for Beginners. 2000. (Illus.). 144p. (J). (gr. 4 up). pap. 14.95 (978-1-55652-419-6(6)) Chicago Review Pr., Inc.

MUNICIPAL GOVERNMENT

see also Cities and Towns; Public Administration

also names of cities with the subdivision Politics and Government, e.g. New York (City)—Politics and Government; etc.

Attebury, Nancy Garhan. Out & about at City Hall. Trover, Zachary, illus. 2005. (Field Trips Ser.). 24p. (J). (ps). lib. bdg. 23.93 (978-1-4048-1146-1(X)) Picture Window Bks.

DeGezelle, Terri. The City Council. 2005. (First Facts Ser.). (Illus.). 24p. (J). 21.26 (978-0-7368-3684-5(5)) Capstone Pr., Inc.

—The City Mayor. 2005. (First Facts Ser.). (Illus.). 24p. (J). 21.26 (978-0-7368-3685-2(3)) Capstone Pr., Inc.

Harris, Nancy. What's a City Council? 2007. (J). (*978-1-4034-9509-9(2)); pap. (*978-1-4034-9515-0(7)) Heinemann Library.

—What's a Mayor? 2007. (J). (*978-1-4034-9507-5(6)); pap. (*978-1-4034-9513-6(0)) Heinemann Library.

Muschal, Frank. Local Action. 2008. (J). lib. bdg. 25.26 (*978-1-60279-061-2(2)) Cherry Lake Publishing.

Silate, Jennifer. Your Mayor: Local Government in Action. 2003. (Primary Source Library of American Citizenship). (Illus.). 32p. (J). pap. (978-1-4042-5095-6(6)) Rosen Publishing Group, Inc., The.

MUNICIPALITIES

see Cities and Towns; Municipal Government

MUNOZ MARIN, LUIS, 1898-1980

George, Linda. Luis Munoz Marin: Father of Modern Puerto Rico. 1999. (gr. 3-6). lib. bdg. 15.25 (978-0-613-54744-4(6)) Tandem Library Bks.

George, Linda & George, Charles. Luis Munoz Marin: Father of Modern Puerto Rico. 1999. (Community Builders Ser.). (Illus.). 48p. (J). (gr. 3-5). 25.00 (978-0-516-21586-0(8) , Children's Pr.) Scholastic Library Publishing.

MURAL PAINTING AND DECORATION

see Cave Drawings; Mosaics

MURDER

see also Assassination

Blohn, Craig. The D. C. Sniper Shootings. 2006. 112p. (J). (gr. 7-10). 32.45 (978-1-59018-926-9(4) , Lucent Bks.) Thomson Gale.

Dowswell, Paul. Investigating Murder Mysteries. 2004. (Forensic Files Ser.). (Illus.). 48p. (J). pap. 8.50 (978-1-4034-5471-3(X)) Heinemann Library.

—Murder Mysteries. 2004. (Forensic Files Ser.). (Illus.). 48p. (J). lib. bdg. 27.07 (978-1-4034-4831-6(0)) Heinemann Library.

Gordon, Olivia. Cold Case File: Murder in the Mountains. 2008. (J). lib. bdg. (*978-1-59716-547-1(6)) Bearport Publishing Co., Inc.

Koopmans, Andy. The Leopold & Loeb Case. 2003. (Famous Trials Ser.). (Illus.). 112p. (J). 29.95 (978-1-59018-227-7(8) , Lucent Bks.) Thomson Gale.

Loker, Aleck. The Murder of Joseph Henry Ching: A Legend Examined. 2003. (Illus.). 28p. 6.00 (978-1-928874-04-1(5)) Solitude Pr.

Margolis, Jeffrey A. Everything You Need to Know about Teens Who Kill. 1999. (Need to Know Library). (Illus.). 64p. (YA). (gr. 7-12). lib. bdg. 25.25 (978-0-8239-2883-5(7) , NTTEKI) Rosen Publishing Group, Inc., The.

Mayell, Mark. The Lindbergh Kidnapping. 2003. (Famous Trials Ser.). (Illus.). 112p. (J). 29.95 (978-1-59018-267-3(7) , Lucent Bks.) Thomson Gale.

—Saskatchewan. 2003. (Illus.). 128p. (J). 29.95 (978-1-59018-052-5(6) , Lucent Bks.) Thomson Gale.

Nicholson, Edward. Murder File: A Killer's Manual. 2008. (J). lib. bdg. (*978-1-59716-549-5(2)) Bearport Publishing Co., Inc.

Pellowski, Michael J. The O. J. Simpson Murder Trial: A Headline Court Case. 2001. (Headline Court Cases Ser.). (Illus.). 104p. (J). (gr. 6-12). lib. bdg. 26.60 (978-0-7660-1480-0(0)) Enslow Pubs., Inc.

Powell, Phelan. Major Unsolved Crimes. Sarat, Austin, ed. 1999. (Crime, Justice & Punishment Ser.). (Illus.). 80p. (J). (gr. 7-12). 30.00 (978-0-7910-4277-9(4) , Chelsea Hse.) Facts On File, Inc.

Rosinsky, Natalie M. Jack the Ripper. 2004. (Illus.). 112p. (J). 29.95 (978-1-59018-444-8(0) , Lucent Bks.) Thomson Gale.

Sitford, Mikaela. Serial Killer File: The Doctor of Death Investigation. 2008. (J). lib. bdg. (*978-1-59716-551-8(4)) Bearport Publishing Co., Inc.

Townsend, John. Kidnappers & Assassins. 2006. 48p. (J). pap. 8.90 (978-1-4109-1432-3(1)) Raintree.

Worth, Richard. Children, Violence & Murder. Sarat, Austin, ed. 2001. (Crime, Justice & Punishment Ser.). (Illus.). 80p. (J). (gr. 7-12). 30.00 (978-0-7910-5154-2(4) , Chelsea Hse.) Facts On File, Inc.

Worth, Richard. Massacre at Virginia Tech: Disaster & Survival. 2008. (Deadly Disasters Ser.). (Illus.). 48p. (gr. 5-9). lib. bdg. 23.93 (*978-0-7660-3274-3(4)) Enslow Pubs., Inc.

Yancey, Diane. Murder: Inside the Crime Lab. 2006. (Inside the Crime Lab Ser.). (Illus.). 112p. (J). (gr. 7-10). 32.45 (978-1-59018-619-0(2) , Lucent Bks.) Thomson Gale.

MURDER—FICTION

Abbott, Wes, illus. & creator. Dogby Walks Alone. Abbott, Wes, creator. 2006. 192p. pap. 9.99 (978-1-59816-582-1(8) , Tokyopop Adult) TOKYOPOP, Inc.

Abrahams, Peter. Down the Rabbit Hole: An Echo Falls Mystery. (Echo Falls Ser.). (J). 2005. 384p. (gr. k-17). 16.99 (978-0-06-073701-6(8) , Geringer, Laura Book); 2005. 384p. (gr. 5 up). lib. bdg. 17.89 (978-0-06-073702-3(6) , Geringer, Laura Book); 2006. 448p. reprint ed. pap. 6.99 (978-0-06-073703-0(4) , Harper Trophy) HarperCollins Pubs.

Abrahams, Peter. Into the Dark: An Echo Falls Mystery. 2008. (Echo Falls Ser.). 304p. (J). 15.99 (*978-0-06-073708-5(5)); lib. bdg. 16.89 (*978-0-06-073709-2(3)) HarperCollins Pubs. (Geringer, Laura Book).

Alphin, Elaine Marie. Counterfeit Son. 2002. 192p. (YA). pap. 5.99 (978-0-14-230147-0(7) , Puffin) Penguin Group (USA) Inc.

—Counterfeit Son. 2002. (gr. 7-12). lib. bdg. 14.15 (978-0-613-45254-0(2)) Tandem Library Bks.

—The Perfect Shot. 2005. 360p. (YA). (gr. 7-13). per. 16.95 (978-1-57505-862-7(6) , Carolrhoda Bks.) Lerner Publishing Group.

Asesinato Por Encargo. 2001. lib. bdg. (978-0-9747787-0-9(2)) Sepulveda, Wilfredo.

Ballantyne, Michael. Blown to Bits or the Lonely Man of Rakat. 2006. 36.99 (*978-1-4280-4221-6(0)); pap. 30.99 (*978-1-4280-4226-1(1)) IndyPublish.com.

Ballantyne, R. M. Blown to Bits; or, the Lonely Man of Rak. 2006. pap. (*978-1-4065-0515-3(3)) Dodo Pr.

Barrett. Lethal Delivery, Postage Prepaid. (Thumbprint Mysteries Ser.). 32.86 (978-0-8092-0425-0(8)) McGraw-Hill/Contemporary.

Boaz, Ashley. The Mystery of the Midnight Blaze. 2005. (J). (978-0-9761033-6-3(2)) Waldenhouse Pub., Inc.

Braun, Lilian Jackson. The Cat Who Robbed a Bank. 2001. (gr. 5-8). lib. bdg. 15.30 (978-0-613-51483-5(1)) Tandem Library Bks.

Brooks, Kevin. The Road of the Dead. (J). (gr. 7 up). 2007. 368p. pap. 7.99 (978-0-439-78624-9(X) , PUSH); 2006. 352p. pap. 16.99 (978-0-439-78623-2(1) , Chicken Hse., The) Scholastic, Inc.

Brooks, Kevin. Road of the Dead. rev. l.t. ed. 2007. 353p. (YA). 22.95 (*978-0-7862-9550-0(3)) Thorndike Pr.

Burke, Morgan. Get It Started. 2005. (Party Room Ser.: No. 1). 272p. (YA). (gr. 11 up). pap. 5.99 (978-0-689-87225-9(9) , Simon Pulse) Simon & Schuster Children's Publishing.

Burr, Daniela. Murder in Hollywood Hills. 2007. (Nancy Drew Movie Ser.). 128p. (J). pap. 5.99 (978-1-4169-3899-6(0) , Simon Spotlight) Simon & Schuster Children's Publishing.

Byars, Betsy. Death's Door. 2006. (Herculeah Jones Mystery Ser.). 144p. (J). (gr. 3). pap. 5.99 (978-0-14-240565-9(5) , Puffin) Penguin Group (USA) Inc.

—The King of Murder: A Herculeah Jones Mystery. 2006. 80p. (J). (gr. 4). 10.99 (978-0-670-06065-8(8) , Viking Juvenile) Penguin Group (USA) Inc.

Carroll, Jenny, pseud & Cabot, Meg. Young Blood. 4th ed. 2005. (Mediator Ser.: No. 4). 336p. (J). (gr. 7 up). pap. 7.99 (978-0-06-072514-3(1)) HarperCollins Pubs.

Cassidy, Anne. Looking for JJ. 2007. (Illus.). 336p. (YA). (gr. 9 up). 17.00 (*978-0-15-206190-6(8)) Harcourt Children's Bks.

—Looking for JJ. 2005. (Point Ser.). 304p. (J). pap. (*978-0-439-97717-3(7)) Scholastic, Inc.

Catran, Ken. Blue Murder. 2002. 208p. (YA). pap. (978-0-7344-0389-6(5) , Lothian Bks.) Hachette Livre Australia.

Chadwick, Robert. Vengeful Impulse. 2003. (gr. 7-12). lib. bdg. 17.60 (978-0-613-83499-5(2)) Tandem Library Bks.

—Vengeful Impulse. 2003. 70p. pap. 8.95 (978-0-595-27876-3(0)) iUniverse, Inc.

Christie, Agatha. Asesinato en el Orient. 2002. (gr. 7-12). lib. bdg. 17.60 (978-0-613-63579-0(5)) Tandem Library Bks.

Clancy, Tom. Virtual Vandals. 1999. (gr. 7-12). lib. bdg. 13.00 (978-0-613-33500-3(7)) Tandem Library Bks.

Connor, Leslie. Dead on Town Line. Triplett, Gina, illus. 2006. 144p. (YA). (gr. 6). pap. 6.99 (978-0-14-240697-7(X) , Puffin) Penguin Group (USA) Inc.

Cormier, Robert. Rag & Bone Shop. 2003. lib. bdg. 14.15 (978-0-613-62220-2(0)) Tandem Library Bks.

Crawford, Ann Fears. Keechee: The Witch of the Woods. 2005. (J). (978-1-931823-21-0(9)) Halcyon Pr.

M N O

Crew, Gary. Mama's Babies: A Novel. 2002. 160p. (J). (gr. 5-9). pap. 6.95 (978-1-55037-724-8(8)); lib. bdg. 18.95 (978-1-55037-725-5(6)) Annick Pr., Ltd. CAN. *Dist:* Firefly Bks., Ltd.

—Mama's Babies: A Novel. 2002. (gr. 5-8). lib. bdg. 15.25 (978-0-613-58241-4(1)) Tandem Library Bks.

Dane, James. Hyde & Seek. 2001. iii, 207p. (YA). pap. 14.95 (978-0-9712798-0-3(2)) James Dane Bks.

Day, Marlis. Curriculum Murders: A Margo Brown Mystery. 2004. 192p. 12.95 (978-1-56315-316-7(5)) Sterling-House Pubs., Inc.

Deaver, Julie Reece. Night I Disappeared. 2002. 242p. (J). (ps-7). per. 14.15 (978-0-613-60586-1(1)) Tandem Library Bks.

Dike, Tina. His Greatest Challenge. Schulman, Cory & Johnstone, Sandy, eds. 2000. 125p. (YA). (gr. 7-9). pap. 9.95 (978-0-9642997-1-9(2)) Best Seller Pubns., Inc.

Dixon, Franklin W. Top Ten Ways to Die. 2006. 169p. (J). lib. bdg. 16.92 (*978-1-4242-0390-1(2)) Fitzgerald Bks.

Donnelly, Jennifer. A Northern Light. (YA). 2003. (Illus.). 400p. (gr. 9 up). 17.00 (978-0-15-216705-9(6)); 2004. 408p. reprint ed. pap. 8.95 (978-0-15-205310-9(7) , Harcourt Paperbacks) Harcourt Children's Bks.

Dowell, Frances O'Roark. Dovey Coe. 192p. (J). 2001. (Illus.). pap. 5.99 (978-0-689-84667-0(3) , Aladdin); 2000. (gr. 4-7). 16.99 (978-0-689-83174-4(9) , Atheneum) Simon & Schuster Children's Publishing.

—Dovey Coe. 2001. 11.64 (978-0-606-22127-6(1)); (gr. 5-8). lib. bdg. 13.00 (978-0-613-55445-9(0)) Tandem Library Bks.

—Dovey Coe. l.t. ed. 2001. 171p. (J). 22.95 (978-0-7862-3590-2(X)) Thorndike Pr.

Doyle, Arthur Conan. A Study in Scarlet. 2001. (gr. 7-12). lib. bdg. 15.30 (978-0-613-64328-3(3)) Tandem Library Bks.

Electric Chair or Taser Fried: Malicious Murder; Good Cop, Bad Cop. 2004. (YA). per. 25.00 (978-0-9760909-0-8(2)) Yost-Haynes, Melissa.

Emerson, Scott. The Brotherhood of the Moon: From the Notebooks of Edward R. Smithfield, D.V.M. Glasauer, Willi, illus. 2005. (J). 9.95 (978-0-689-87630-1(0) , Simon & Schuster Children's Publishing) Simon & Schuster Children's Publishing.

Ewing, Lynne. Party Girl. 1999. 128p. (YA). (gr. 9-11). pap. 5.50 (978-0-375-80210-2(X) , Laurel Leaf) Random Hse. Children's Bks.

—Party Girl. 1999. (978-0-606-17373-5(0)); (gr. 7-12). lib. bdg. 13.00 (978-0-613-23023-0(X)) Tandem Library Bks.

Ferguson, Alane. The Angel of Death. 2006. (Forensic Mystery Ser.). 272p. (YA). (gr. 7). 15.99 (978-0-670-06055-9(0) , Viking Adult) Penguin Group (USA) Inc.

Ferguson, Alane. Angel of Death. 2008. (Forensic Mystery Ser.). 272p. (YA). (gr. 7). pap. 6.99 (*978-0-14-241087-5(X) , Puffin) Penguin Group (USA) Inc.

Fiedler, Lisa. Dating Hamlet: Ophelia's Story. rev. ed. 2002. 176p. (YA). (gr. 7 up). 17.95 (978-0-8050-7054-5(0) , Holt, Henry & Co. Bks. For Young Readers) Holt, Henry & Co.

Fisher, Linda C. A Will of Her Own. 2006. (YA). pap. (978-0-88092-641-6(4)); lib. bdg. (978-0-88092-640-9(6)) Royal Fireworks Publishing Co.

Flinn, Alex. Nothing to Lose. 2005. 304p. (J). (gr. 8-12). pap. 6.99 (978-0-06-051752-6(2)) HarperCollins Pubs.

Forrest. Sign of Blood. (Thumbprint Mysteries Ser.). 32.86 (978-0-8092-0408-3(8)) McGraw-Hill/Contemporary.

Gerritsen, Tess. The Apprentice. 2003. (gr. 7-12). lib. bdg. 16.45 (978-0-613-65524-8(9)) Tandem Library Bks.

Giles, Gail. Playing in Traffic. 2006. (Illus.). 176p. (YA). reprint ed. pap. 6.99 (978-1-4169-0926-2(5) , Simon Pulse) Simon & Schuster Children's Publishing.

Giles, Gail. Right Behind You. 2007. 304p. (YA). (gr. 10 up). 15.99 (*978-0-316-16636-2(7)) Little, Brown Bks. for Young Readers.

Godfrey. Murder in the Shadows. (Thumbprint Mysteries Ser.). 32.86 (978-0-8092-0418-2(5)) McGraw-Hill/ Contemporary.

Gratz, Alan M. Something Rotten: A Horatio Wilkes Mystery. 2007. 208p. (J). (gr. 6). 16.99 (*978-0-8037-3216-2(3) , Dial) Penguin Group (USA) Inc.

Green. Not a Chance. (Thumbprint Mysteries Ser.). 32.86 (978-0-8092-0422-9(3)) McGraw-Hill/Contemporary.

Groot, De. Clifton: Black Moon. Spear, Luke, tr. from FRE. Rodrigue, illus. 2007. 48p. pap. 9.99 (*978-1-905460-30-4(9)) CineBook GBR. *Dist:* Biblio Distribution.

Hansen, Lynne & Bosco, Sally. AltDeath.com. 2004. 152p. (YA). pap. 9.00 (978-0-7599-4572-2(1)) Hard Shell Word Factory.

Harris, Loretta. A Gangsta's Life. 2006. (YA). (*978-0-9786681-4-3(6)) Children's Heart Publishing Co.

Harrison, Cora. Murder at Drumshee. 2002. (Drumshee Timeline Ser.). 144p. (J). (gr. 3-9). pap. 6.95 (978-0-86327-832-7(9)) Wolfhound Pr. IRL. *Dist:* Interlink Publishing Group, Inc.

Heisel, Sharon E. Precious Gold, Precious Jade. 2000. 192p. (J). (gr. 7 up). tchr. ed. 16.95 (978-0-8234-1432-1(9)) Holiday Hse., Inc.

Henn, Pamela. Nick & Slim: The Legend of the Falcon Mine. 2006. (Illus.). 472p. (YA). 19.95 (978-0-9760654-0-1(1)) White Wolf Studio, Inc.

Heyes, Eileen. O'Dwyer & Grady Starring In: Acting Innocent. Carver, Steve, illus. 2002. 176p. (J). (gr. 4-7). pap. 4.99 (978-0-689-84911-4(7) , Aladdin) Simon & Schuster Children's Publishing.

—O'Dwyer & Grady Starring in Acting Innocents. 2002. (gr. 3-6). lib. bdg. 13.00 (978-0-613-57433-4(8)) Tandem Library Bks.

—O'Dwyer & Grady Starring in Tough Act to Follow. 2003. (gr. 3-6). lib. bdg. 13.00 (978-0-613-66465-3(5)) Tandem Library Bks.

Hockenberger, Henry. The Gold Case. 2006. (YA). pap. 15.95 (978-1-58736-584-3(7)) Wheatmark.

Hoffman, Mary. The Falconer's Knot: A Story of Friars, Flirtation & Foul Play. 2007. (Illus.). 288p. (YA). (gr. 7 up). 16.95 (978-1-59990-056-8(4) , Bloomsbury Children) Bloomsbury Publishing.

Holder, Nancy. Evil That Men Do. 2000. (gr. 7-12). lib. bdg. 15.30 (978-0-613-27810-2(0)) Tandem Library Bks.

Hurst, Carol Otis & Otis, Rebecca. A Killing in Plymouth Colony. 2003. 160p. (YA). (gr. 5-9). tchr. ed. 15.00 (978-0-618-27597-7(5) , Walter Lorraine) Houghton Mifflin Co. Trade & Reference Div.

Jones, Patrick. Cheated. 2008. 208p. (YA). 16.95 (*978-0-8027-9699-8(0)) Walker & Co.

Jorda, Jordi Suris. La Chica de los Zapatos Verdes. 1998. (SPA.). (gr. 7-12). lib. bdg. 14.10 (978-0-613-80705-0(7)) Tandem Library Bks.

Julian, B. T. Mirror Me This. 2006. 172p. per. 12.95 (978-1-59886-056-6(9)) Tate Publishing & Enterprises, L.L.C.

Karbo, Karen. Minerva Clark Gets a Clue. 2006. 256p. (J). pap. 6.95 (978-1-58234-747-9(6) , Bloomsbury Children) Bloomsbury Publishing.

Klein, Lisa & Shakespeare, William. Ophelia. 2006. 336p. (YA). 16.95 (978-1-58234-801-8(4)) Bloomsbury Publishing.

Klise, Kate. Trial by Journal. Klise, M. Sarah, illus. 256p. (J). 2002. (gr. 3-6). pap. 6.99 (978-0-380-81672-9(5)); 2001. (gr. 4-6). 15.95 (978-0-380-97880-9(6)); 2001. (gr. 4-6). 16.89 (978-0-06-029541-7(4)) HarperCollins Pubs.

—Trial by Journal. 2002. (gr. 5-8). lib. bdg. 15.30 (978-0-613-60649-3(3)) Tandem Library Bks.

Kollar, J. P. Three Tomato Brand. 2005. 127p. per. 12.95 (978-1-59879-076-4(5)) Lifevest Publishing, Inc.

Koontz, Dean. Watchers. 2003. (gr. 7-12). lib. bdg. 16.45 (978-0-613-57487-7(7)) Tandem Library Bks.

Kyi, Tanya Lloyd. Truth. 2003. (YA). (gr. 7 up). pap. 7.95 (978-1-55143-235-9(8)) Orca Bk. Pubs. USA.

—Truth. 2003. (gr. 7-12). lib. bdg. 16.40 (978-0-613-70627-8(7)) Tandem Library Bks.

Lawrence, Caroline. The Assassins of Rome, Vol. 4. 2005. (Illus.). 176p. (J). (gr. 3-7). pap. 5.99 (978-0-14-240214-6(1) , Puffin) Penguin Group (USA) Inc.

Lawrence, Iain. The Convicts Book I: The Curse of the Jolly Stone Trilogy. 2006. 208p. (YA). (gr. 7). pap. 5.99 (978-0-440-41932-7(8) , Laurel Leaf) Random Hse. Children's Bks.

Lester, Julius. When Dad Killed Mom. 2003. (YA). 216p. pap. 6.95 (978-0-15-204698-9(4)); (gr. 7-12). mass mkt. 6.95 (978-0-15-524698-0(4)) Harcourt Trade Pubs. (Silver Whistle).

—When Dad Killed Mom. 2003. (gr. 7-12). lib. bdg. 15.25 (978-0-613-59932-0(2)) Tandem Library Bks.

Libby, Alisa. The Blood Confession. 2006. 360p. (YA). (gr. 9). 18.99 (978-0-525-47732-7(2) , Dutton Juvenile) Penguin Group (USA) Inc.

MacGregor, Roy. The Complete Screech Owls, Vol. 4. 2006. 488p. (J). pap. 15.95 (978-0-7710-5491-4(2) , Screech Owls) McClelland & Stewart CAN. *Dist:* Random Hse., Inc.

—Murder at the Winter Games. 2004. (Screech Owls Ser.: No. 18). (Illus.). 128p. (YA). mass mkt. 4.95 (978-0-7710-5647-5(8) , Screech Owls) McClelland & Stewart CAN. *Dist:* Random Hse., Inc.

Margolin, Phillip. El Asociado. 2002. (SPA.). 412p. 34.95 (978-84-666-0658-5(0) , EB13952) Ediciones B ESP. *Dist:* Lectorum Pubns., Inc.

Mason, Lynn. Disappeared. 2003. (Illus.). 208p. (YA). (gr. 7). mass mkt. 5.99 (978-0-553-49400-6(7) , Bantam Bks. for Young Readers) Random Hse. Children's Bks.

Mathews-Danzer, R. & Mathews, Rinaldo. Murder at Fort Christmas: The Duck Did It. Kipnis, Libby, ed. 2002. (Provost Files Ser.). 200p. 14.95 (978-1-888417-50-0(1)) Dimefast, Ltd.

Matthews. Death in the Desert. (Thumbprint Mysteries Ser.). 32.86 (978-0-8092-0416-8(9)) McGraw-Hill/ Contemporary.

McDaniel, Lurlene. Holly's Story. 2005. (Angels in Pink Ser.). 224p. (gr. 7). (YA). 10.95 (978-0-385-73158-4(2)); (J). lib. bdg. 12.99 (978-0-385-90195-6(X)) Random Hse. Children's Bks. (Delacorte Bks. for Young Readers).

—Raina's Story. 2006. (Angels in Pink Ser.). 208p. (YA). (gr. 7). pap. 6.50 (978-0-440-23866-9(8) , Laurel Leaf) Random Hse. Children's Bks.

McNamee, Graham. Acceleration. 2003. 224p. (YA). (gr. 7). lib. bdg. 17.99 (978-0-385-90144-4(5) , Lamb, Wendy) Random Hse. Children's Bks.

Meyer, Adam. The Last Domino. 2005. 272p. (YA). (gr. 6). 16.99 (978-0-399-24332-5(1) , Putnam Juvenile) Penguin Group (USA) Inc.

Miller, Sue. While I Was Gone. 2000. (gr. 3-6). lib. bdg. 23.45 (978-0-613-45855-9(9)) Tandem Library Bks.

Morrison, Ellen M. Murder's Take: The First Adventure of Sam & Sam. 2000. 108p. (gr. 4-7). pap. 9.95 (978-0-595-16322-9(X)) iUniverse, Inc.

Mussi, Sarah. The Door of No Return. 2008. (YA). (*978-1-4169-1550-8(8) , McElderry, Margaret K.) Simon & Schuster Children's Publishing.

Myers, Walter Dean. Monster. Myers, Christopher A., illus. 1999. (Amistad Ser.). 288p. (J). (gr. 7 up). 16.99 (978-0-06-028077-2(8)) HarperCollins Pubs.

—Monster. Myers, Christopher, illus. (Newbery Honor Roll Ser.). (J). 1999. 288p. (gr. 7 up). lib. bdg. 17.89 (978-0-06-028078-9(6)); 2001. 304p. reprint ed. pap. 7.99 (978-0-06-440731-1(4) , Amistad) HarperCollins Pubs.

Naylor, Phyllis Reynolds. Saving Shiloh. unabr. ed. 2004. 137p. (J). (gr. 3-7). pap. 29.00 incl. audio (978-0-8072-0456-6(0) , Listening Library) Random Hse. Audio Publishing Group.

Nelson, Blake. Paranoid Park. 2006. 176p. (YA). (gr. 7). 15.99 (978-0-670-06118-1(2) , Viking Juvenile) Penguin Group (USA) Inc.

Nelson, R. A. Breathe My Name. 2007. 288p. (J). (gr. 7). 16.99 (*978-1-59514-094-4(8) , Razorbill) Penguin Group (USA) Inc.

Nixon & Brush. Champagne with a Corpse. (Thumbprint Mysteries Ser.). 32.86 (978-0-8092-0420-5(7)) McGraw-Hill/Contemporary.

Nixon, Joan Lowery. Laugh till You Cry. 2004. 112p. (J). (gr. 5). lib. bdg. 17.99 (978-0-385-90186-4(0) , Delacorte Bks. for Young Readers) Random Hse. Children's Bks.

—Murdered, My Sweet. 2004. (Illus.). 208p. (J). (gr. 5). pap. 4.99 (978-0-440-41988-4(3) , Yearling) Random Hse. Children's Bks.

—Nightmare. 2003. 176p. (YA). (gr. 7). 15.95 (978-0-385-73026-6(8)); lib. bdg. 17.99 (978-0-385-90151-2(8)) Random Hse. Children's Bks. (Delacorte Bks. for Young Readers).

—Nightmare. l.t. ed. 2004. 200p. 22.95 (978-0-7862-6911-2(1) , Large Print Pr.) Thorndike Pr.

Nordin, Ruth Ann. Witness to a Murder. 2007. 140p. per. 11.95 (*978-0-595-45089-3(X)) iUniverse, Inc.

Oates, Joyce Carol. Freaky Green Eyes. 2003. 352p. (J). 16.99 (978-0-06-623759-6(9) , HarperTeen); 2003. 352p. (J). lib. bdg. 17.89 (978-0-06-623757-2(2) , HarperTeen); 2003. tchr. ed. (978-0-06-056885-6(2)); 2005. 368p. (YA). reprint ed. pap. 7.99 (978-0-06-447348-4(1) , HarperTeen) HarperCollins Pubs.

O'Leary, Edward J. Murder in the I. R. S. 2003. (YA). per. 18.95 (978-0-9708590-9-9(0)) First Word Publishing, The.

Pagliarulo, Antonio. The Celebutantes: In the Club. 2008. (YA). (*978-0-385-73473-8(5)); 12.99 (*978-0-385-90472-8(X)) Dell Publishing. (Delacorte Pr.).

Pagliarulo, Antonio. On the Avenue. 2007. (Celebutantes Ser.). 352p. (YA). (gr. 9 up). pap. 9.99 (978-0-385-73404-2(2)); lib. bdg. 12.99 (978-0-385-90415-5(0)) Random Hse. Children's Bks. (Delacorte Bks. for Young Readers).

Pennington, Kate. Nightingale's Song. 2007. 284p. (YA). (gr. 7 up). pap. 9.95 (*978-0-340-87875-0(4)) Hodder Children's Division GBR. *Dist:* Independent Pubs. Group.

Perkins, TJ. Fantasies Are Murder: A Kim & Kelly Mystery. novel ed. 2005. (Illus.). 148p. (YA). 10.99 (978-0-9777538-0-2(8)) GumShoe Press.

Powers, J. L. The Confessional. 2007. 304p. (gr. 9). (J). 16.99 (*978-0-375-83872-9(4)); (YA). lib. bdg. 19.99 (*978-0-375-93872-6(9)) Random Hse. Children's Bks. (Knopf Bks. for Young Readers).

Price, Charlie. Dead Connection. 2006. 240p. (YA). 16.95 (978-1-59643-114-0(8)) Roaring Brook Pr.

—Dead Connection. 2008. 256p. (YA). pap. 7.99 (*978-0-312-37966-7(8)) Square Fish.

Priestley, Chris. Death & the Arrow. l.t. ed. 2005. (J). pap. (978-0-7540-7899-9(X) , CLP 467) BBC Audio.

—Death & the Arrow. 2005. 176p. (YA). (gr. 7). pap. 5.50 (978-0-440-23811-9(0) , Laurel Leaf) Random Hse. Children's Bks.

—Death & the Arrow. 2007. (Tom Marlowe Serie Ser.). (Illus.). 230p. (J). (gr. 4-6). 9.99 (*978-0-552-55475-6(8) , Corgi) Transworld Publishers Ltd. GBR. *Dist:* Independent Pubs. Group.

Prophet, John M. Body in the Salt Marsh Boatyard: A Casey Miller Mystery. 2004. 162p. (YA). pap. 13.95 (978-0-595-30991-7(7) , Mystery & Suspense Pr.) iUniverse, Inc.

Qualey, Marsha. Close to a Killer. 2000. 11.64 (978-0-606-20499-6(7)) Tandem Library Bks.

Richards, Zackary. Frostie the Deadman. 2004. 222p. (J). pap. 14.95 (978-0-9713069-8-1(2)) Burns, Nicholas K. Publishing.

Riise, Torben. Emily & the Arabic Letter. 2001. 164p. (YA). pap. 11.95 (978-0-595-17399-0(3) , Writers Club Pr.) iUniverse, Inc.

Roberts, Willo Davis. Twisted Summer. 1998. (978-0-606-13089-6(0)) Tandem Library Bks.

Rose, Malcolm. The Alibi: The Perfect Murder... l.t. ed. 2000. (Illus.). 302p. (J). pap. (978-0-7540-6099-4(3) , CLP 297) BBC Audio.

—Double Check. 2007. (Traces Ser.). 224p. (J). (gr. 5). pap. 5.95 (978-0-7534-6004-7(1) , Kingfisher) Houghton Mifflin Co. Trade & Reference Div.

—Lost Bullet. 2007. (Traces Ser.). 212p. (J). (gr. 5-9). pap. 5.95 (978-0-7534-5980-5(9) , Kingfisher) Houghton Mifflin Co. Trade & Reference Div.

—Roll Call. 2007. (Traces Ser.). 224p. (J). (gr. 5-9). pap. 5.95 (978-0-7534-5981-2(7) , Kingfisher) Houghton Mifflin Co. Trade & Reference Div.

Sanders, Scott Russell. Bad Man Ballad. 2004. (Library of Indiana Classics). (J). reprint ed. 256p. 32.95 (978-0-253-34414-4(X)); 192p. 14.95 (978-0-253-34408-3(5)) Indiana Univ. Pr.

Schraff, Anne. The Case of the Cursed Chalet: PageTurner Detective. 2002. 80p. (YA). per. 3.95 (978-1-56254-387-7(3) , SP 3873) Saddleback Educational Publishing.

—The Case of the Dead Duck. 2002. (PageTurner Detective Ser.). 80p. (YA). per. 3.95 (978-1-56254-388-4(1) , SP 3881) Saddleback Educational Publishing.

Schunk, Laurel. Black & Secret Midnight. 1998. 238p. (gr. 6-8). 24.99 (978-0-9661879-0-8(3) , SKP98-41) St Kitts Pr.

Simmons, Michael. Finding Lubchenko. 2006. 304p. (YA). (gr. 7-12). pap. 8.99 (978-1-59514-075-3(1) , Razorbill) Penguin Group (USA) Inc.

Singer, Nicky. The Innocent's Story. 2007. 224p. (YA). (gr. 7 up). 16.95 (*978-0-8234-2082-7(5)) Holiday Hse., Inc.

Singleton, Linda Joy. Fatal Charm. 2007. 384p. pap. 6.99 (*978-0-7387-1153-9(5) , Flux) Llewellyn Pubns.

Smiley, Jane. The All-True Travels & Adventures of Lidie Newton: A Novel. 1999. (gr. 7-12). lib. bdg. 23.45 (978-0-613-17077-2(6)) Tandem Library Bks.

Snicket, Lemony, pseud & Stookey, Nathaniel. The Composer Is Dead. Ellis, Carson, illus. 2008. (J). (*978-0-06-123627-3(6)); lib. bdg. (*978-0-06-123628-0(4)) HarperCollins Pubs.

Snyder, Zilpha Keatley. The Egypt Game. 2002. (Illus.). (J). 14.47 (978-0-7587-0259-3(0)) Book Wholesalers, Inc.

Sorrells, Walter. Club Dread. (Hunted Ser.). 272p. (YA). 2007. (gr. 7). 7.99 (*978-0-14-240904-6(9) , Puffin); 2006. (gr. 6-10). 10.99 (978-0-525-47618-4(0) , Dutton Juvenile) Penguin Group (USA) Inc.

—Fake ID. 2005. (Hunted Ser.: 1). 192p. (YA). (gr. 6). 12.99 (978-0-525-47514-9(1) , Dutton Juvenile) Penguin Group (USA) Inc.

—Fake ID: A Mystery. 2007. (Hunted Ser.). 336p. (YA). (gr. 7 up). pap. 6.99 (978-0-14-240762-2(3) , Puffin) Penguin Group (USA) Inc.

Soto, Gary. The Afterlife: A Novel. 2003. 176p. (J). (gr. 6 up). 17.00 (978-0-15-204774-0(3) , 53597422) Harcourt Children's Bks.

Staples, Suzanne Fisher. Dangerous Skies. 1998. 12.64 (978-0-606-13312-8(7)) Tandem Library Bks.

Steiner. Murder Takes a Fast Track. (Thumbprint Mysteries Ser.). 32.86 (978-0-8092-0417-5(7)) McGraw-Hill/ Contemporary.

Stine, R. L., ed. Midnight Games. 2005. 183p. (YA). (978-1-4156-1074-9(6) , Simon Pulse) Simon & Schuster Children's Publishing.

Stine, R.L. The Confession. 2005. 150p. (J). lib. bdg. 13.00 (*978-1-4242-1000-8(3)) Fitzgerald Bks.

—Midnight Games. 2005. 183p. (YA). lib. bdg. 20.00 (*978-1-4242-1119-7(0)) Fitzgerald Bks.

Tamura, Yumi. Basara. 2006. (Basara Ser.). 208p. (YA). Vol. 18. pap. 9.99 (978-1-4215-0528-2(2)); Vol. 19. pap. 9.99 (978-1-4215-0529-9(0)) Viz Media.

Tosal, Oscar. Asesinato en el Barrio Gotico Level 2. 1998. (SPA.). (gr. 7-12). lib. bdg. 14.10 (978-0-613-80706-7(5)) Tandem Library Bks.

Urasawa, Naoki. Naoki Urasawa's Monster, Vol. 7. 2007. (Naoki Urasawa's Monster Ser.). 216p. (YA). pap. 9.99 (978-1-4215-0500-8(2)) Viz Media.

Vande Velde, Vivian. Magic Can Be Murder. 2000. (Illus.). 208p. (YA). (gr. 7-12). 17.00 (978-0-15-202665-3(7)) Harcourt Children's Bks.

—Witch Dreams. 2005. 128p. (J). (gr. 5-9). 15.95 (978-0-7614-5235-5(4)) Cavendish, Marshall Corp.

Velde, Vivian V. Magic Can Be Murder. 2002. 208p. (J). pap. 6.99 (978-0-14-230210-1(4) , Puffin) Penguin Group (USA) Inc.

Volponi, Paul. Rucker Park Setup. 2007. 208p. (J). 15.99 (978-0-670-06130-3(1) , Viking Juvenile) Penguin Group (USA) Inc.

Walter, Virginia. Making up Megaboy. 1999. (978-0-606-17215-8(7)) Tandem Library Bks.

Weber, Richard D. Elvis & Me. 2004. 511p. (YA). per. 17.41 (978-1-4116-0549-7(7)) Lulu.com.

Werlin, Nancy. Black Mirror. 2003. 256p. (YA). (gr. 7-12). pap. 6.99 (978-0-14-250028-6(3) , Puffin) Penguin Group (USA) Inc.

—Black Mirror. Nielsen, Cliff, illus. 2001. 244p. (YA). (gr. 7 up). 16.99 (978-0-8037-2605-5(8) , Dial) Penguin Group (USA) Inc.

—Black Mirror. 2003. (gr. 7-12). lib. bdg. 15.30 (978-0-613-61606-5(5)) Tandem Library Bks.

—The Killer's Cousin. 2000. 240p. (YA). (gr. 9-12). mass mkt. 5.99 (978-0-440-22751-9(8) , Laurel Leaf) Random Hse. Children's Bks.

—The Killer's Cousin. 2000. (978-0-606-17820-4(1)) Tandem Library Bks.

—Killer's Cousin. 2000. (gr. 7-12). lib. bdg. 13.00 (978-0-613-23909-7(1)) Tandem Library Bks.

—The Killer's Cousin. l.t. ed. 1999. 277p. (YA). (gr. 9-12). 21.95 (978-0-7862-2188-2(7)) Thorndike Pr

Wilcox. The Hidden Men. (Thumbprint Mysteries Ser.). 32.86 (978-0-8092-0415-1(0)) McGraw-Hill/ Contemporary.

Wilson, Linda Miller. A Few Days Journey. 1998. 124p. (YA). (gr. 4-8). 9.99 (978-0-88092-402-3(0) , 4020) Royal Fireworks Publishing Co.

Wittlinger, Ellen. The Long Night of Leo & Bree. 2003. (Illus.). 128p. (YA). pap. 6.99 (978-0-689-86335-6(7) , Simon Pulse) Simon & Schuster Children's Publishing.

Wynne-Jones, Tim. The Boy in the Burning House. braille ed. 2003. (J). (gr. 2). spiral bd. (978-0-616-15275-1(2)) Canadian National Institute for the Blind/Institut National Canadien pour les Aveugles.

—The Boy in the Burning House. 2000. (J). (978-0-7894-5621-2(4)) Dorling Kindersley Publishing, Inc.

—The Boy in the Burning House. 2003. 224p. (J). pap. 6.95 (978-0-374-40887-9(4) , Sunburst) Farrar, Straus & Giroux.

—The Boy in the Burning House. pap. 8.95 (978-0-88899-500-1(8)) Groundwood Bks. CAN. *Dist:* Transition Vendor.

—The Boy in the Burning House. 2001. (gr. 7-12). lib. bdg. 14.10 (978-0-613-69045-4(1)) Tandem Library Bks.

—The Boy in the Burning House. l.t. ed. 2002. 332p. (J). 23.95 (978-0-7862-4435-5(6)) Thorndike Pr.

Zindel, Paul. The Square Root of Murder. 2002. (P. C. Hawke Mysteries Ser.: Vol. 5). (Illus.). 144p. (gr. 3-7). pap. 4.99 (978-0-7868-1588-3(4) , Volo) Hyperion Bks. for Children.

MURRY FAMILY (FICTITIOUS CHARACTER)—FICTION

L'Engle, Madeleine. Many Waters. 2002. (Illus.). (J). 15.00 (978-0-7587-9605-9(6)) Book Wholesalers, Inc.

MNO

—Many Waters. Sis, Peter & Nelson, Cliff, illus. anniv. rev. ed. 1998. 336p. (J). (gr. 5-8). pap. 5.99 (978-0-440-22770-0(4) , Laurel Leaf) Random Hse. Children's Bks.

—Many Waters. 2007. 224p. (J). 6.99 (978-0-312-36861-6(5)); pap. 6.99 (978-0-312-36857-9(7)) Square Fish.

—Many Waters. 1998. (J). (978-0-606-13596-2(0)); (gr. 5-8). lib. bdg. 14.15 (978-0-613-72320-6(1)) Tandem Library Bks.

—A Swiftly Tilting Planet. 228p. (YA). (gr. 5 up). pap. 5.50 (978-0-8072-1495-4(7) , Listening Library) Random Hse. Audio Publishing Group.

—A Swiftly Tilting Planet. 2007. 224p. (J). 6.99 (978-0-312-36860-9(7)); pap. 6.99 (978-0-312-36856-2(9)) Square Fish.

—A Swiftly Tilting Planet. 1998. (978-0-606-13831-4(5)) Tandem Library Bks.

—A Wind in the Door. 211p. (YA). (gr. 5 up). pap. 5.50 (978-0-8072-1466-4(3) , Listening Library) Random Hse. Audio Publishing Group.

—A Wind in the Door. 2007. 224p. (J). 6.99 (978-0-312-36859-3(3)); pap. 6.99 (978-0-312-36854-8(2)) Square Fish.

—A Wrinkle in Time. 2002. (J). 15.00 (978-0-7587-6754-7(4)) Book Wholesalers, Inc.

—A Wrinkle in Time, 2 vols., Set. 20.00 (978-0-89064-014-2(9)) National Assn. for Visually Handicapped.

—A Wrinkle in Time. 211p. (YA). (gr. 5 up). pap. 5.99 (978-0-8072-1460-2(4) , Listening Library) Random Hse. Audio Publishing Group.

—A Wrinkle in Time. l.t. ed. 2005. 273p. pap. 10.95 (978-0-7862-7335-5(6) , Large Print Pr.); 1998. 208p. (J). (gr. 4-7). 24.95 (978-0-7838-8371-7(4)) Thorndike Pr.

MUSA, SULTAN OF MALI, FL. 1324

Supples, Kevin. Mali. 2004. (Civilizations Past to Present Ser.). (Illus.). 24p. (J). pap. (978-0-7922-4539-1(3)) National Geographic Society.

MUSA, SULTAN OF MALI, FL. 1324—FICTION

Burns, Khephra. Mansa Musa: The Lion of Mali. Dillon, Leo & Dillon, Diane, illus. 2001. 56p. (J). (gr. 3-5). 18.00 (978-0-15-200375-3(4) , Gulliver Bks.) Harcourt Children's Bks.

MUSCLES

Angliss, Sarah. Movers & Shapers: Muscle & Bones. 1999. (Human Machine Ser.). (Illus.). 32p. (J). lib. bdg. 16.95 (978-1-929298-18-1(8)) Chrysalis Education.

Ballard, Carol. Muscles. 2003. (Body Focus Ser.). (Illus.). 48p. (J). lib. bdg. 27.07 (978-1-4034-0752-8(5)); pap. (978-1-4034-3300-8(3)) Heinemann Library.

—The Skeleton & Muscles. 2005. (Exploring the Human Body Ser.). (Illus.). 32p. (J). (gr. 4-7). lib. bdg. 24.95 (978-0-7377-3022-7(6) , Greenhaven Pr., Inc.) Thomson Gale.

Bellamy, Rufus. How We Move. 2004. (Body Science Ser.). (J). lib. bdg. (978-1-58340-458-4(9)) Smart Apple Media.

Berger, Melvin & Berger, Gilda. Your Muscles. 2005. (Illus.). pap. (978-0-439-77371-3(7)) Scholastic, Inc.

Brynie, Faith Hickman. 101 Questions about Muscles: To Stretch Your Mind & Flex Your Brain. 2007. (101 Questions... Ser.). (Illus.). 176p. (YA). (gr. 7). lib. bdg. (***978-0-8225-6380-8(0)***) Twenty First Century Bks.

Buckley, James. Incredible Hulk's Book of Strength. 2003. (gr. k-3). lib. bdg. 11.80 (978-0-613-62434-3(3)) Tandem Library Bks.

Buckley, James, Jr. The Incredible Hulk's Book of Strength. 2003. (DK Readers Ser.). (Illus.). 48p. pap. 3.99 (978-0-7894-9263-0(6)) Dorling Kindersley Publishing, Inc.

Buckley, James & Dorling Kindersley Publishing Staff. The Incredible Hulk's Book of Strength. 2003. (DK Readers Ser.). (Illus.). 48p. (J). 12.99 (978-0-7894-9543-3(0)) Dorling Kindersley Publishing, Inc.

Creative Media Applications Staff. The Human Body & Environment: Skeletal & Muscular Systems, 4 vols., Vol. 1. 2003. (Middle School Reference Ser.). (Illus.). (J). (gr. 4-8). 160.00 (978-0-313-32559-5(6)) Greenwood Publishing Group, Inc.

Fitzpatrick, Anne. The Muscles. 2003. (Illus.). 24p. (J). lib. bdg. 21.35 (978-1-58340-309-9(4)) Smart Apple Media.

Frost, Helen. The Muscular System. Saunders-Smith, Gail, ed. 2000. (Human Body Systems Ser.). (Illus.). 24p. (J). (gr. k-1). lib. bdg. 15.93 (978-0-7368-0650-3(4) , Pebble Bks.) Capstone Pr., Inc.

—The Muscular System. (Human Body Systems Ser.). 24p. (J). pap. 5.95 (978-0-7368-8778-6(4)) Capstone Pr., Inc.

Ganeri, Anita. Your Muscles & Bones. Shott, Steve, photos by. 2003. (How Your Body Works). (Illus.). 32p. (J). (gr. 2 up). lib. bdg. 23.33 (978-0-8368-3635-6(9)) Stevens, Gareth Inc.

Goode, Katherine. Skeleton & Muscles. 2000. (Bodyworks Ser.). (Illus.). 32p. (J). (gr. 3-6). 23.70 (978-1-56711-498-0(9) , Blackbirch Pr., Inc.) Thomson Gale.

Gray, Susan Heinrichs. The Muscular System. 2003. (Body Systems Ser.). (Illus.). 32p. (J). (gr. 2-6). 27.07 (978-1-59296-038-5(3)) Child's World, Inc.

Green, Jen. Muscles. 2005. (Illus.). 32p. (J). (gr. 4-7). lib. bdg. 27.10 (978-1-59604-056-4(4)) Stargazer Bks.

Houghton, Gillian. The Muscular System. 2007. (How Your Body Works). (Illus.). 24p. (J). (978-1-4042-2374-5(6)); pap. (978-1-4042-2184-0(0)); lib. bdg. (978-1-4042-3475-8(6)) Rosen Publishing Group, Inc., The. (PowerKids Pr.).

Jakab, Cheryl. The Muscular System. 2006. (Illus.). 32p. (J). (978-1-58340-734-9(0)) Smart Apple Media.

Johansson, Philip. Carpal Tunnel Syndrome & Other Repetitive Strain Injuries. 1999. (Diseases & People Ser.). (Illus.). 128p. (YA). (gr. 6-12). lib. bdg. 26.60 (978-0-7660-1184-7(4)) Enslow Pubs., Inc.

Johnson, Rebecca L. Bones & Muscles. 2004. (National Geographic Reading Expeditions Ser.). (Illus.). 32p. (J). pap. (978-0-7922-4585-8(7)) National Geographic Society.

—The Muscular System. 2005. (Early Bird Body Systems Ser.). (Illus.). 48p. (J). (gr. 2-4). lib. bdg. 25.26 (978-0-8225-1248-6(3)) Lerner Publishing Group.

—Muscular System. 2005. (Illus.). 48p. (YA). pap. (978-0-8225-2520-2(8) , Lerner Pubns.) Lerner Publishing Group.

—El Sistema Muscular. 2006. (Libros Sobre el Cuerpo Humano para Madrugadores Ser.). (ENG & SPA.). 48p. (J). 25.26 (978-0-8225-6254-2(5)) Lerner Publishing Group.

LeVert, Suzanne. Bones & Muscles. 2001. (Kaleidoscope Ser.). (Illus.). 48p. (J). (gr. 3 up). lib. bdg. 25.64 (978-0-7614-1309-7(X) , Benchmark Bks.) Cavendish, Marshall Corp.

Lindeen, Carol. My Muscles. 2007. 24p. (J). (***978-0-7368-6695-8(7)*** , Pebble Bks.) Capstone Pr., Inc.

Llamas, Andreu. Muscles & Bones. Rizo, Luis, illus. 1998. (Human Body Ser.). 32p. (J). (gr. 5 up). lib. bdg. 24.67 (978-0-8368-2112-3(2)) Stevens, Gareth Inc.

Mason, Paul. Are You Tough Enough? 2005. (Illus.). 32p. (J). (gr. 6-9). lib. bdg. 28.21 (978-1-4109-1932-8(3)) Steck-Vaughn.

—Are You Tough Enough? Body Systems. 2005. (Illus.). 32p. (J). (gr. 3-5). 7.85 (978-1-4109-1963-2(3)) Steck-Vaughn.

Muscles. 2001. (Human Anatomy Ser.). (J). (gr. k-12). vinyl bd. 4.95 (978-1-58845-087-6(2)) School Specialty Publishing.

El Musculo, Organo de la Fuerza. (Coleccion Mundo Invisible).Tr. of How Are Muscles Work. (SPA.). (YA). (gr. 5-8). pap. 8.00 (978-958-04-3225-8(2)) Norma S.A. COL. *Dist:* Distribuidora Norma, Inc., Lectorum Pubns., Inc.

Nettleton, Pamela Hill. Bend & Stretch: Learning about Your Bones & Muscles. Shipe, Becky, illus. 2004. (Amazing Body Ser.). 24p. (C). (gr. k-3). 22.60 (978-1-4048-0256-8(8)) Picture Window Bks.

Parker, Steve. Move Your Body! Bones & Muscles. 2006. (Illus.). 48p. (J). pap. (978-1-4109-1884-0(X)); lib. bdg. (978-1-4109-1877-2(7)) Steck-Vaughn.

—The Skeleton & Muscles. 2004. (Our Bodies Ser.). (Illus.). 48p. (J). lib. bdg. 28.56 (978-0-7398-6622-1(2)) Raintree.

—Skin, Muscles, & Bones. 2004. (Understanding the Human Body Ser.). (Illus.). 32p. (J). lib. bdg. 24.67 (978-0-8368-4207-4(3)) Stevens, Gareth Inc.

Petrie, Kristin. The Muscular System. 2007. (Checkerboard Science Library). (Illus.). 32p. (J). 22.78 (978-1-59679-711-6(8)) ABDO Publishing Co.

Rau, Dana Meachen. Huesos y Musculos. 2006. (Bookworms Ser.). (SPA & ENG., Illus.). 32p. (J). lib. bdg. 22.79 (978-0-7614-2401-7(6)) Cavendish, Marshall Corp.

—My Bones & Muscles. 2004. (Bookworms Ser.). (ENG & SPA., Illus.). 31p. (J). 21.36 (978-0-7614-1777-4(X) , Benchmark Bks.) Cavendish, Marshall Corp.

—My Bones & Muscles (Huesos y Musculos) 2006. (Bookworms Ser.). (ENG & SPA., Illus.). 32p. (J). lib. bdg. 22.79 (978-0-7614-2479-6(2)) Cavendish, Marshall Corp.

Ross, Veronica. The Muscles. 2004. (J). lib. bdg. 27.10 (978-1-59389-166-4(0)) Chrysalis Education.

Royston, Angela. Why Do Bones Break? And Other Questions about Bones & Muscles. 2003. (Body Matters Ser.). (Illus.). 32p. (J). pap. 7.50 (978-1-4034-0456-5(9)) Heinemann Library.

Rushworth, Gary. Body Systems: Skeletal & Muscular. 2005. (Navigators Ser.). (J). pap. 42.00 (***978-1-4108-5085-0(4)***) Benchmark Education Co.

Simon, Seymour. Muscles: Our Muscular System. 2000. (Illus.). 32p. (J). (ps-17). pap. 6.99 (978-0-688-17720-1(4) , Harper Trophy) HarperCollins Pubs.

—Muscles: Our Muscular System. 2000. (Illus.). (J). (ps-ps). lib. bdg. 15.30 (978-0-613-30040-7(8)) Tandem Library Bks.

El sistema muscular (the Muscular System) 2007. (J). pap. 7.95 (978-0-8225-6650-2(8) , Ediciones Lerner) Lerner Publishing Group.

Taylor, Barbara. The Muscular System. 2001. (Insider's Guide to the Body Ser.). (Illus.). 48p. (YA). (gr. 5-8). lib. bdg. 23.95 (978-0-8239-3340-2(7) , Rosen Central) Rosen Publishing Group, Inc., The.

Thames, Susan. Our Muscles. 2008. (J). (***978-1-60044-512-5(8)***) Rourke Publishing, LLC.

Treays, Rebecca. Understanding Your Muscles & Bone - Internet Link. rev. ed. 2004. 32p. (J). pap. 7.99 (978-0-7945-0813-5(8) , Usborne) EDC Publishing.

Vv. Musculo, Organo de la Fuerza. (SPA.). 88p. (J). 10.00 (978-84-342-1740-9(6)) Parramon Ediciones S.A. ESP. *Dist:* Distribuidora Norma, Inc.

Ylvisaker, Anne. Your Muscles. 2002. (Bridgestone Science Library). (Illus.). 24p. (J). (gr. 1-2). lib. bdg. 18.60 (978-0-7368-1150-7(8) , Bridgestone Bks.) Capstone Pr., Inc.

Your Muscles. (Your Body Ser.). 24p. (J). 6.95 (978-0-7368-3354-7(4)) Capstone Pr., Inc.

MUSEUMS

see also Art Museums

also names of countries, cities, etc. with the subdivision Galleries and Museums (e.g. United States—Galleries and Museums; etc.); and names of galleries and museums, e.g. New York Metropolitan Museum of Art

Bromley, Robin. At Work in a Museum. Stewart, Arvis L., illus. 2002. 16p. (J). pap. (978-0-439-35110-2(3)) Scholastic, Inc.

Canizares, Susan & McVeigh, Mark. Museum. 2000. (Illus.). (J). (978-0-439-15375-1(1)) Scholastic, Inc.

Cooper, Jason. U. S. Holocaust Memorial Museum. 2000. (Historic Landmarks Ser.). (Illus.). 24p. (J). (gr. 1-4). lib. bdg. 20.64 (978-1-55916-330-9(5)) Rourke Publishing, LLC.

Davis, Rebecca & Sprinkle, Karen. Riverside's History from Its First People to the Present: Third Grade Student Edition. Tobias, Martin & Pratt, Jan, illus. 1998. 141p. (J). (gr. 3-6). pap., stu. ed. 5.00 (978-0-935661-29-3(8)) Riverside Museum Pr.

Foley, Cate. Let's Go to the Museum. 2001. (Weekend Fun Ser.). (Illus.). 24p. (J). (ps-2). 17.00 (978-0-516-23193-8(6)); pap. 4.95 (978-0-516-29583-1(7)) Scholastic Library Publishing. (Children's Pr.).

—Let's Go to the Museum. 2001. (gr. k-3). lib. bdg. 12.95 (978-0-613-58988-8(2)) Tandem Library Bks.

Gietzen, Georgia, et al. Penrod's New Home: A Story about the Grand Rapids Children's Museum. Tanis, Joel, illus. 2000. 32p. (J). (ps-5). 15.95 (978-0-9703346-0-2(5)) Park Street Pr., LLC.

Gillis, Jennifer Blizin. Museums: Field Trip. 2008. (J). (***978-1-60044-561-3(6)***) Rourke Publishing, LLC.

Gorman, Jacqueline Laks. The Museum. 2004. (I Like to Visit Ser.). (Illus.). 24p. (J). pap. (978-0-8368-4460-3(2)); (YA). lib. bdg. 19.93 (978-0-8368-4453-5(X)) Stevens, Gareth Inc.

—The Museum: El Museo. 2005. (ENG & SPA., Illus.). 24p. (J). pap. (978-0-8368-4604-1(4)) Stevens, Gareth Inc.

—The Museum/El Museo. Acosta, Tatiana & Gutiérrez, Guillermo, trs. 2005. (I Like to Visit/Me Gusta Visitar Ser.). (SPA & ENG., Illus.). 24p. (J). lib. bdg. 19.33 (978-0-8368-4597-6(8)) Stevens, Gareth Inc.

Harcourt School Publishers Staff. At the Museum. 3rd ed. 2002. (Horizons Ser.). (Illus.). (J). pap. 3.70 (978-0-15-333220-3(4)) Harcourt Schl. Pubs.

—Mr. Peale's Amazing Museum. 3rd ed. 2002. (Horizons Ser.). (Illus.). (J). pap. 7.30 (978-0-15-333573-0(4)) Harcourt Schl. Pubs.

Hill, Mary. Let's Go to a Science Center. 2004. (Weekend Fun Ser.). (J). 18.00 (978-0-516-23996-5(1)); pap. 4.95 (978-0-516-25920-8(2)) Scholastic Library Publishing. (Children's Pr.).

Hughes, Morgan. Entertainment Hall of Fame. 2000. (Halls of Fame Ser.). (Illus.). 24p. (J). (gr. 2-6). lib. bdg. 23.93 (978-1-55916-267-8(8)) Rourke Publishing, LLC.

—History & Americana Hall of Fame. 2001. (Illus.). 24p. (J). (gr. 2-6). lib. bdg. 23.93 (978-1-55916-268-5(6)) Rourke Publishing, LLC.

—Music Hall of Fame. 2000. (Halls of Fame Ser.). (Illus.). 24p. (J). (gr. 2-6). lib. bdg. 23.93 (978-1-55916-269-2(4)) Rourke Publishing, LLC.

—Science & Technology Hall of Fame. 2000. (Illus.). 24p. (J). (gr. 2-6). lib. bdg. 23.93 (978-1-55916-270-8(8)) Rourke Publishing, LLC.

—Women's Hall of Fame. 2000. (Halls of Fame Ser.). (Illus.). 24p. (J). (gr. 2-6). lib. bdg. 23.93 (978-1-55916-272-2(4)) Rourke Publishing, LLC.

Koelsch, Patrice. Museums. 2001. (Designing the Future Ser.). (Illus.). 32p. (J). (978-1-58341-132-2(1) , Creative Education) Creative Co., The.

Leeper, Angela. The Nature Museum. 2004. (Field Trip! Ser.). (Illus.). 24p. (J). pap. (978-1-4034-5170-5(2)) Heinemann Library.

—To a Natural Science Museum. 2004. (Field Trip! Ser.). (Illus.). 24p. (J). lib. bdg. (978-1-4034-5164-4(8)) Heinemann Library.

Macdonald, Sharon. Behind the Scenes at the Science Museum. 2002. (Materializing Culture Ser.). (Illus.). 224p. pap. 30.95 (978-1-85973-571-8(1)) Berg Pubs. GBR. *Dist:* Macmillan.

Margaret, Amy. George Bush Presidential Library. 2004. (Presidential Libraries Ser.). (Illus.). 24p. (J). lib. bdg. 18.75 (978-0-8239-6273-0(3) , PowerKids Pr.) Rosen Publishing Group, Inc., The.

—Gerald R. Ford Library & Museum. 2004. (Presidential Libraries Ser.). (Illus.). 24p. (J). lib. bdg. 18.75 (978-0-8239-6270-9(9) , PowerKids Pr.) Rosen Publishing Group, Inc., The.

Mark, Jan. The Museum Book: A Guide to Strange & Wonderful Collections. Holland, Richard & Holland, Richard, illus. 2007. 51p. (J). (gr. 4-7). 18.99 (978-0-7636-3370-7(4)) Candlewick Pr.

Mattern, Joanne. Museums. 2002. (Illus.). 23p. (J). 21.35 (978-1-58340-149-1(0)) Smart Apple Media.

Metropolitan Museum of Art Staff. Museum ABC. 2002. (Illus.). 60p. (J). (ps-17). 16.99 (978-0-316-07170-3(6)) Little, Brown Bks. for Young Readers.

Munro, Roxie. The Inside-Outside Book of Texas. 2001. (Illus.). 48p. (J). (ps-4). 17.50 (978-1-58717-051-5(5) , SeaStar Bks.) Chronicle Bks. LLC.

Out & about at the Science Center. (Field Trips Ser.). 24p. (J). 8.95 (978-1-4048-0202-5(9)) Picture Window Bks.

Poulakidas, Georgene. The Guggenheim Museum Bilbao: Transforming a City. 2004. (High Interest Bks.). (Illus.). 48p. (J). (gr. 7-12). pap. 6.95 (978-0-516-25907-9(5) , Children's Pr.) Scholastic Library Publishing.

Shea, Kitty. Out & About at the Science Center. Shipe, Becky, illus. 2004. (Field Trips Ser.). 24p. (C). (gr. k-3). 23.93 (978-1-4048-0297-1(5)) Picture Window Bks.

Smithsonian American Art Museum Staff, compiled by. Scenes of American Life: Treasures from the Smithsonian American Art Museum. 2000. (YA). pap. 75.00 net. incl. 3/4" U-Matic, sl. (978-1-56290-229-2(6)) Crystal Productions.

Somervill, Barbara A. The Holocaust Museum. 2007. (J). lib. bdg. (***978-0-7565-3357-1(0)***) Compass Point Bks.

What Is a Museum? Set F, 6 vols. (Phonics Readers Ser.). (gr. k-2). 28.95 (978-0-7368-4076-7(1)) Red Brick Learning.

Yenawine, Philip. Places. 2006. (Illus.). 22p. (J). (gr. 4-8). reprint ed. 15.00 (978-1-4223-5407-0(5)) DIANE Publishing Co.

MUSEUMS—FICTION

Adler, David A. Bones & the Dinosaur Mystery. Newman, Barbara Johansen, illus. 2005. (Jeffrey Bones Mystery Ser.: No. 4). 32p. (J). (978-0-670-05970-6(6) , Viking Adult) Penguin Group (USA) Inc.

Albee, Sarah & Mathieu, Joe. Sesame Street Field Trip! Book & Finger Puppets. 2007. 12p. (J). bds. 14.99 (978-0-7944-1233-3(5)) Reader's Digest Assn., Inc., The.

Armstrong-Ellis, Carey. Prudy's Problem & How She Solved It. Armstrong-Ellis, Carey, illus. 2002. (Illus.). 32p. (J). (ps-3). 14.95 (978-0-8109-0569-6(8)) Abrams, Harry N., Inc.

Auer, Chris. The Chinese Puzzle Box. 2005. 128p. (J). pap. 4.99 (978-0-310-70872-8(9)) Zonderkidz.

—Hidden in Plain Sight. 2005. (Illus.). 128p. (J). pap. 4.99 (978-0-310-70870-4(2)) Zonderkidz.

—Molly & the Good Shepherd. Wummer, Amy, illus. 2005. 40p. (J). 12.99 (978-0-310-70826-1(5)) Zonderkidz.

—A Stranger, a Thief & a Pack of Lies. 2005. (Illus.). 128p. (J). pap. 4.99 (978-0-310-70871-1(0)) Zonderkidz.

Bailer, Darice. The Pony Express. Antonishak, Tom, illus. 3rd ed. 2005. (Soundprints' Read-and-Discover Ser.). 48p. (J). (gr. 2-4). pap. 3.95 (978-1-59249-019-6(0) , S2008) Soundprints.

Baker, Sharon. A Nickel, a Trolley, a Treasure House. Peck, Beth, illus. 2007. 32p. (J). (gr. k-5). 16.99 (978-0-670-05982-9(X) , Viking Juvenile) Penguin Group (USA) Inc.

Banks, Steven. In Search of Reptar. 2002. (gr. 3-6). lib. bdg. 11.80 (978-0-613-50538-3(7)) Tandem Library Bks.

Berenstain, Stan & Berenstain, Jan. The Berenstain Bears & the Escape of the Bogg Brothers. 2000. (Berenstain Bears Ser.). (J). (gr. k-3). (978-0-606-20272-5(2)) Tandem Library Bks.

—The Berenstain Bears & the Wax Museum. 1999. (Berenstain Bears Big Chapter Bks.). (J). (gr. 2-6). (978-0-606-16943-1(1)) Tandem Library Bks.

Bernheimer, Kate. The Girl in the Castle Inside the Museum. Ceccoli, Nicoletta, illus. 2008. 40p. (J). (***978-0-375-83606-0(3)*** , Schwartz & Wade Bks.) Random Hse. Children's Bks.

Boehm, Arlene P. Jack in Search of Art. Boehm, Arlene P., illus. (Illus.). 32p. (ps-3). 2001. pap. 7.95 (978-1-57098-234-7(1)); 1998. 16.95 (978-1-57098-244-6(9)) Rinehart, Roberts Pubs.

Bourgeois, Paulette. Franklin en el Museo. Clark, Brenda, illus. 1999. (Franklin Ser.). (SPA.). (J). (ps-3). pap. 5.95 (978-1-880507-57-5(9) , LC2801) Lectorum Pubns., Inc.

—Franklin's Class Trip. Clark, Brenda, illus. (Franklin Ser.). (J). (ps-3). 1999. 30p. (978-1-55074-472-9(0)); 2004. 32p. (978-1-55074-470-5(4)) Kids Can Pr., Ltd.

—Franklin's Class Trip. Clark, Brenda, illus. 1999. (Franklin Ser.). 32p. (J). (ps-3). pap. 4.50 (978-0-590-13002-8(1)) Scholastic, Inc.

Brochu, Lisa. Who Cleans the Museum? Loomis, Monica, illus. 2000. (Books for Young Learners). 12p. (J). pap. 5.00 (978-1-57274-274-1(7)) Owen, Richard C. Pubs., Inc.

Brown, Marc. Arthur Lost in the Museum. 2005. (Arthur Ser.). (Illus.). 24p. (J). (gr. 1-3). pap. 3.99 (978-0-375-82973-4(3)); lib. bdg. 11.99 (978-0-375-92973-1(8)) Random Hse. Children's Bks. (Random Hse. Bks. for Young Readers).

Bruna, Dick. Miffy at the Museum. 1998. (Miffy Ser.). (Illus.). 28p. (J). (ps-k). 4.95 (978-1-56836-270-0(6)) Kodansha America, Inc.

Bunting, Eve. I Am the Mummy Heb-Nefert. unabr. ed. 2001. (J). pap. 16.95 incl. audio (978-0-8045-6849-4(9) , 6849) Spoken Arts, Inc.

—I Am the Mummy Heb-Nefert. 2000. 12.80 (978-0-606-20326-5(5)); (gr. 3-6). lib. bdg. 14.15 (978-0-613-29983-1(3)) Tandem Library Bks.

Clark, Brenda, illus. Franklin's Class Trip. 2002. (Franklin Ser.). 12.40 (978-1-4046-0325-7(5)) Book Wholesalers, Inc.

Clement, Rod. Frank's Great Museum Adventure. Clement, Rod, illus. 1999. (Illus.). 32p. (J). (ps-3). 14.95 (978-0-06-027673-7(8)) HarperCollins Pubs.

Comella, Maria Angeles, et al. Buenos Dias, Senor Tapies! 2001. Tr. of Good Day, Mr. Tapies!. (Illus.). 32p. (J). (CAT.). (gr. k-2). 14.95 (978-84-95040-97-8(2)); (SPA., (gr. 2-5). 14.95 (978-84-95040-96-1(4)) Serres, Ediciones, S. L. ESP. *Dist:* Lectorum Pubns., Inc.

Costain, Meredith. The Mummy's Curse. 1999. (Brains & Parker McGoohan Ser.). 64 p. (978-0-7608-1938-6(6)) Sundance/Newbridge Educational Publishing.

—Mummy's Curse. 1999. (gr. 3-6). lib. bdg. 12.60 (978-0-613-18975-0(2)) Tandem Library Bks.

Cummings, Pat. Harvey Moon Museum Boy. Cummings, Pat, illus. 2008. (Illus.). 32p. (J). 16.99 (978-0-688-17889-5(8)) HarperCollins Pubs.

—Harvey Moon Museum Boy. 2008. (Illus.). 32p. (J). lib. bdg. 17.89 (978-0-06-057861-9(0)) HarperCollins Pubs.

Czernecki, Stefan. Mystery at Midnight Museum. Date not set. 32p. (J). 14.99 (978-0-06-026199-3(4)) HarperCollins Pubs.

David Wiggles: Individual Title Six-Packs. (ps-2). 27.00 (978-0-7635-9445-9(8)) Rigby Education.

de Brunhoff, Laurent. Babar's Museum of Art. 2003. (Illus.). 48p. (J). (ps-17). 17.95 (978-0-8109-4597-5(5)) Abrams, Harry N. , Inc.

Delaney, Mark. The Vanishing Chip. 1998. (Misfits, Inc. Ser.: No. 1). 240p. (J). (gr. 7-11). pap. 5.95 (978-1-56145-176-0(2) , Q21568) Peachtree Pubs., Ltd.

Estes, Eleanor. The Moffat Museum. 2001. (Odyssey Classics). (Illus.). 256p. (gr. 3 up). pap. 6.00 (978-0-15-202553-3(7) , Odyssey Classics) Harcourt Children's Bks.

—The Moffat Museum. 2001. (J). (978-0-606-20805-5(4)); (gr. 3-6). lib. bdg. 14.15 (978-0-613-35463-9(X)) Tandem Library Bks.

Fearnley, Jan. Colin & the Curly Claw. Fearnley, Jan, illus. 2001. (Blue Bananas Ser.). (Illus.). 48p. (J). (gr. 1-2). (978-0-7787-0840-7(3)); pap. (978-0-7787-0886-5(1)) Crabtree Publishing Co.

—Colin & the Curly Claw. 2002. (gr. k-3). lib. bdg. 12.95 (978-0-613-52821-4(2)) Tandem Library Bks.

Finchler, Judy & O'Malley, Kevin. Miss Malarkey's Field Trip. 2006. (Illus.). 32p. (J). pap. 6.95 (978-0-8027-8917-4(X)) Walker & Co.

—Miss Malarkey's Field Trip. O'Malley, Kevin, illus. 2004. (Illus.). 32p. (J). 16.95 (978-0-8027-8912-9(9)) Walker & Co.

Floca, Brian. The Frightful Story of Harry Walfish. Floca, Brian, illus. 2004. (Illus.). 26p. (J). (gr. k-4). reprint ed. pap. (978-0-7567-7852-1(2)) DIANE Publishing Co.

Garcia, Marina. Mateo de Paseo Por el Museo Del Prado. 2004. (SPA.). 42p. (J). 18.99 (978-84-8488-070-7(2)) Serres, Ediciones, S. L. ESP. *Dist:* Lectorum Pubns., Inc.

Gayle, Sharon Shavers. Emma's Escape: A Story of America's Underground Railroad. Velasquez, Eric, illus. 3rd ed. 2005. (Soundprints' Read-and-Discover Ser.). 48p. (J). (gr. 2-4). pap. 3.95 (978-1-59249-021-9(2) , S2009) Soundprints.

Geisert, Arthur. Mystery. Geisert, Arthur, illus. 2003. (Illus.). 32p. (J). (gr. k-3). 16.00 (978-0-618-27293-8(3) , Walter Lorraine) Houghton Mifflin Co. Trade & Reference Div.

Glintenkamp, Pamela. Sarah McSleuth's Coloring Casebook: Mystery in the Museum. Stern, Steven, ed. Glintenkamp, Pamela, illus. 1999. (Illus.). 32p. (J). (gr. 2-7). pap. 4.95 (978-1-892572-01-1(X)) Zen Comics, Inc.

Greenburg, Dan. Trapped in the Museum of Unnatural History, Vol. 25. Davis, Jack E., illus. 2002. (Zack Files Ser.: No. 25). 64p. (J). pap. 4.99 (978-0-448-42632-7(3) , Grosset & Dunlap) Penguin Group (USA) Inc.

—Trapped in the Museum of Unnatural History. 2002. (gr. 3-6). lib. bdg. 13.00 (978-0-613-50089-0(X)) Tandem Library Bks.

Gutman, Anne. Gaspard & Lisa at the Museum. Hallensleben, Georg, illus. 2001. 32p. (J). (ps-3). 9.95 (978-0-375-81117-3(6) , Knopf Bks. for Young Readers) Random Hse. Children's Bks.

Hooper, Meredith. Celebrity Cat: With Paintings from Art Galleries Around the World. Willey, Bee, illus. 2006. 40p. 15.95 (978-1-84507-290-2(1)) Lincoln, Frances Ltd. GBR. *Dist:* Perseus Distribution.

—Dog's Night. Curless, Allan, illus. 32p. (gr. k-3). 2002. pap. (978-0-7613-1649-7(3)); 2000. lib. bdg. 22.90 (978-0-7613-1824-8(0)) Lerner Publishing Group. (Millbrook Pr.).

Hooper, Meredith & Curless, Allan. Dogs' Night. Burgess, Mark, illus. 2006. 36p. pap. 7.95 (978-1-84507-688-7(5)) Lincoln, Frances Ltd. GBR. *Dist:* Perseus Distribution.

Hunt, Elizabeth Singer. The Escape of the Deadly Dinosaur. 2007. (Secret Agent Jack Stalwart Ser.). 128p. (J). (gr. 1-4). pap. 4.99 (***978-1-60286-004-9(1)***) Weinstein Bks.

—The Mystery of the Mona Lisa. 2007. (Secret Agent Jack Stalwart Ser.). 128p. (J). (gr. 1-4). pap. 4.99 (***978-1-60286-001-8(7)***) Weinstein Bks.

Jaggi, Harleen. Mystery at the Book Store. 2007. (J). per. (***978-0-9790896-0-2(3)***) Booksmart Pubns.

James, B. J., et al. Supertwins Meet the Dangerous Dino-Robots, No. 3. Demarest, Chris L., illus. 2003. (Scholastic Reader Ser.). 32p. (J). pap. 3.99 (978-0-439-46625-7(3) , Cartwheel Bks.) Scholastic, Inc.

Jane, Pamela. Winky Blue Goes Wild! Tilley, Debbie, illus. 2003. 64p. (J). 13.95 (978-1-59034-588-7(6)); pap. (978-1-59034-589-4(4)) Mondo Publishing.

Kapper, Jon. Bow Wow Blast Off: Little Lucy & Friends. Ottinger, Jon, illus. Zaidan, Rick, photos by. 2001. (Little Lucy & Friends Ser.). 24p. (J). (gr. k-3). 9.99 (978-1-57151-702-9(2)) Playhouse Publishing.

Kapper, R. Jon & D'Andrea, Deborah. Bow Wow Blast Off: Little Lucy & Friends. Ottinger, Jon & Zaidan, Rick illus. 2001. (Little Lucy & Friends Ser.). 24p. (J). pap. 4.99 (978 1-57151-707-4(3)) Playhouse Publishing.

Kellogg, Steven. Prehistoric Pinkerton! 2002. (gr. k-3). lib. bdg. 15.30 (978-0-613-85725-3(9)) Tandem Library Bks.

Kelly, Katherine, text. Albert Bear & the Big Celebration. 2005. (J). 12.95 (978-0-9773481-0-7(5)) Pink Hyacinth Pr.

Kenah, Katharine. The Best Seat in Second Grade. Carter, Abby, illus. (I Can Read Bks.). 48p. (J). 2006. pap. 3.99 (978-0-06-000736-2(2) , Harper Trophy); 2005. 16.99 (978-0-06-000734-8(6)); 2005. lib. bdg. 17.89 (978-0-06-000735-5(4)) HarperCollins Pubs.

Kerr, P. B. The Day of the Djinn Warriors. 2008. (Scholastic First Discovery Ser.). 400p. (J). pap. 17.99 (***978-0-439-93214-1(9)*** , Orchard Bks.) Scholastic, Inc.

Konigsburg, E. L. From the Mixed-Up Files of Mrs. Basil E. Frankweiler. 35th anniv. ed. 2002. (gr. 5-8). lib. bdg. 14.15 (978-0-613-73358-8(4)) Tandem Library Bks.

—From the Mixed-Up Files of Mrs. Basil E. Frankweiler. l.t. ed. 2005. 186p. pap. 10.95 (978-0-7862-7358-4(5)); (Illus.). 205p. (J). 22.95 (978-0-7862-7297-6(X)) Thorndike Pr. (Large Print Pr.).

Krulik, Nancy E. No Bones about It, No. 12. John and Wendy Staff, illus. 2004. (Katie Kazoo, Switcheroo Ser.: No. 12). 80p. (J). (gr. 2-6). pap. 3.99 (978-0-448-43358-5(3) , Grosset & Dunlap) Penguin Group (USA) Inc.

—No Bones about It. 2004. (Katie Kazoo, Switcheroo Ser.: Vol. 12). (gr. 3-6). lib. bdg. 11.80 (978-0-613-72571-2(9)) Tandem Library Bks.

LaFevers, R. L. Theodosia & the Serpents of Chaos. Tanaka, Yoko, illus. 2007. 368p. (J). (gr. 5-7). 16.00 (***978-0-618-75638-4(8)***) Houghton Mifflin Co. Trade & Reference Div.

Lantz, Francess L. The Case of the Missing Mummy. 1998. (New Adventures of Mary-Kate & Ashley Ser.). (Illus.). 82p. (J). (gr. 2-7). pap. 3.99 (978-0-590-29404-1(0)) Scholastic, Inc.

Lattimore, Deborah Nourse. Mystery at Midnight Museum. Date not set. 32p. (J). 15.89 (978-0-06-026202-0(8)) HarperCollins Pubs.

Lavette, Lavaille. That's Not Punny. Kuon, Vuthy, illus. 2007. (Steve Harvey Presents the Adventures of Roopster Roux Ser.: Vol. 5). 32p. (J). 16.95 (***978-1-58980-483-8(X)***) Pelican Publishing Co., Inc.

Lehman, Barbara. Museum Trip. 2006. (Illus.). 32p. (J). (gr. k-3). 15.00 (978-0-618-58125-2(1)) Houghton Mifflin Co.

Lerangis, Peter. Smiler's Bones. 2007. 176p. (J). pap. 4.99 (978-0-439-34488-3(3) , Scholastic Paperbacks) Scholastic, Inc.

Liotta, Colin J. The Boy Werewolf: Curse of the Golden Statue. 2004. 190p. pap. 19.95 (978-1-4137-3484-3(7)) PublishAmerica, Inc.

Lithgow, John. The Carnival of the Animals. Kulikov, Boris, illus. 2004. 40p. (J). (ps-3). 17.95 (978-0-689-86721-7(2)) Simon & Schuster Children's Publishing.

—Micawber. Payne, C. F., illus. 2002. 44p. (J). (gr. k-3). 17.95 incl. audio compact disk (978-0-689-83341-0(5)) Simon & Schuster Children's Publishing.

—Micawber. Payne, C. F., illus. 2005. 40p. (J). reprint ed. pap. 6.99 (978-0-689-83542-1(6) , Aladdin) Simon & Schuster Children's Publishing.

Magoon, Scott. Hugo & Miles In: I've Painted Everything! 2007. (Illus.). (J). (***978-1-4287-3565-1(8)***) Houghton Mifflin Co.

Magoon, Scott. Hugo & Miles in I've Painted Everything! 2007. (Illus.). 40p. (J). (gr. 3-5). 16.00 (978-0-618-64638-8(8)) Houghton Mifflin Co.

Margolis, Leslie Goldman. Night at the Museum: A Junior Novelization. 2006. (Illus.). 128p. (J). mass mkt. 4.99 (978-0-7641-3576-7(7)) Barron's Educational Series, Inc.

Matyas, Diane. The Terrible Captain Jack Visits the Museum: Or A Guide of Museum Manners for Incorrigible Pirates & the Like. ed. 2008. (Illus.). 24p. (J). (***978-0-9623017-2-8(8)***) Noble Maritime Collection, The.

Mayer, Mercer. Class Trip, Vol. 3. 2002. (Little Critter First Readers Ser.). (Illus.). 24p. (J). (gr. 1-2). pap. 3.95 (978-1-57768-845-7(7)) School Specialty Publishing.

—Class Trip. 2001. (gr. k-3). lib. bdg. 11.80 (978-0-613-67604-5(1)) Tandem Library Bks.

Mayhew, James. Carlota y las Semillas de Girasol. 2001. (CAT.). 38p. (J). (ps-3). 14.95 (978-84-95040-83-1(2)) Serres, Ediciones, S. L. ESP. *Dist:* Lectorum Pubns., Inc.

—Katie & the Sunflowers. 2001. (Illus.). 32p. (J). (ps-2). pap. 16.95 (978-0-531-30325-2(X) , Orchard Bks.) Scholastic, Inc.

—Katie Meets the Impressionists. 2007. 32p. (J). pap. 5.99 (***978-0-439-93508-1(3)***) Scholastic, Inc.

—Katie Meets the Impressionists. Mayhew, James, illus. 1999. (Illus.). 32p. (J). (ps-2). pap. 16.95 (978-0-531-30151-7(6) , Orchard Bks.) Scholastic, Inc.

—Katie's Sunday Afternoon. 2005. (Illus.). 32p. (J). pap. 16.95 (978-0-439-60678-3(0) , Orchard Bks.) Scholastic, Inc.

McMullan, Kate. Fluffy Meets the Dinosaurs. Smith, Mavis, illus. 2004. 40p. (J). lib. bdg. 15.00 (978-1-59054-459-4(5)) Fitzgerald Bks.

—Fluffy Meets the Dinosaurs. 2000. (Hello Reader! Ser.). (Illus.). (J). 10.79 (978-0-606-18545-5(3)) Tandem Library Bks.

Meredith-Markowitz, Susan. Charlie's Museum Adventure. ed. 2003. (Early Connections Ser.). (J). pap. 33.00 (978-1-4108-1367-1(3)) Benchmark Education Co.

Monica, Carol. Fisher Price Let's Go on a Class Trip Lift the Flap. SI Artists, illus. 2007. 10p. (J). bds 8.99 (***978-0-7944-1291-3(2)***) Reader's Digest Assn., Inc., The.

Nolan, Han. When We Were Saints. (YA). 2005. 312p. pap. 6.95 (978-0-15-205322-2(0) , Harcourt Paperbacks); 2003. (Illus.). 304p. 17.00 (978-0-15-216371-6(9) , 53586153) Harcourt Children's Bks.

O'Connor, Jane. Fancy Nancy at the Museum. Glasser, Robin Preiss & Enik, Ted, illus. 2008. (I Can Read Bks.). 32p. (J). 16.99 (***978-0-06-123608-2(X)***) HarperCollins Pubs.

—Fancy Nancy at the Museum. Glasser, Robin Preiss, illus. 2008. (I Can Read Bks.). 32p. (J). pap. 3.99 (***978-0-06-123607-5(1)*** , Harper Trophy) HarperCollins Pubs.

O'neal, Katherine Pebley. The Fume in the Tomb. Collins, Daryl, illus. 2004. 68p. (J). lib. bdg. 15.00 (***978-1-4242-0901-9(3)***) Fitzgerald Bks.

O'Neil, Amy. I'm Glad I Asked. Silver, Pattie, illus. 2002. (Read-to-Me Ser.). 24p. (J). (978-0-7665-1217-7(7)) Letter People, The.

Parish, Herman. Amelia Bedelia's Masterpiece. Sweat, Lynn, illus. 2007. 64p. (J). 15.99 (978-0-06-084355-7(1)); lib. bdg. 16.89 (978-0-06-084356-4(X)) HarperCollins Pubs.

Parsons, Tom. Pinky the Rat at the Brussels Sprout Museum. 2007. 194p. 27.76 (***978-1-4303-1538-4(5)***) Lulu.com.

Prime, D. Van al Museo. (Serie Sara y Pablo - Sarah & Paul Ser.: No. 5). Tr. of Go to the Museum. (SPA.). (J). 2.99 (978-0-7899-0499-7(3) , 498899) Editorial Unilit.

Rabley, Stephen. Marcel & the Mona Lisa. 2002. (Illus.). 16p. pap. (978-0-582-40173-0(9) , Putnam Juvenile) Penguin Group (USA) Inc.

Rau, Dana Meachen. Moon Walk. Buchs, Thomas, illus. 3rd ed. 2005. (Soundprints' Read-and-Discover Ser.). 48p. (J). (gr. 2-4). pap. 3.95 (978-1-59249-015-8(8) , S2006) Soundprints.

Reid, Kathleen. Magical Mondays at the Art Museum. Reifsnider, Robin, illus. 2000. iii, 26p. (J). (978-0-9702653-0-2(1)); pap. (978-0-9702653-1-9(X)) Phoenix Color Corp.

Rosen, Michael. You're Thinking about Doughnuts. Tisdall, Sarah, illus. 2006. 90p. (J). pap. 6.95 (978-1-903015-03-2(0)) Barn Owl Bks, London GBR. *Dist:* Independent Pubs. Group.

Ross, Pat. M & M & the Mummy Mess. 1999. (Illus.). (J). (978-0-606-18424-3(4)) Tandem Library Bks.

Ruzzier, Sergio. The Room of Wonders. 2006. (Illus.). 40p. (J). 16.00 (978-0-374-36343-7(9) , Frances Foster Bks.) Farrar, Straus & Giroux.

Sally's Picture: Individual Title Six-Packs. (Literatura 2000 Ser.). (gr. 1-2). 28.00 (978-0-7635-0108-2(5)) Rigby Education.

Saunders, Zina, illus. Secret Agents. 2006. (Backyardigans Ser.). 24p. (J). pap. 3.99 (978-1-4169-1226-2(6) , Simon Spotlight/Nickelodeon) Simon & Schuster Children's Publishing.

Scieszka, Jon. 2095. (Time Warp Trio Ser.: No. 5). (SPA.). (J). (gr. 2). 7.95 (978-958-04-5638-4(0) , NR31192) Norma S.A. COL. *Dist:* Distribuidora Norma, Inc., Lectorum Pubns., Inc.

—2095. Smith, Lane, illus. 2004. (Time Warp Trio Ser.: No. 5. 5). 80p. (J). (gr. 2-6). pap. 4.99 (978-0-14-240044-9(0) , Puffin) Penguin Group (USA) Inc.

Scieszka, Jon & Smith, Lane. Seen Art? 2005. (Illus.). (J). (978-1-4155-7784-4(6)) Museum of Modern Art.

Stine, R. L. Goosebumps: Night of the Living Dummy III. 2005. (Goosebumps Ser.). 144p. (J). 4.99 (978-0-439-66989-4(8) , Scholastic Paperbacks) Scholastic, Inc.

Thompson, Kay & McClatchy, Lisa. Eloise & the Dinosaurs. Lyon, Tammie, illus. 2007. (Ready-to-Reads Ser.). 32p. (J). pap. 3.99 (978-0-689-87453-6(7) , Aladdin) Simon & Schuster Children's Publishing.

Torres, J. Machina Ex Deus. 2003. (Jason & the Argobots Ser.: Vol. 2). (Illus.). 88p. pap. 11.95 (978-1-929998-56-2(2)) Oni Pr., Inc.

Trenc, Milan. The Night at the Museum. 2006. 32p. (J). pap. 6.99 (978-0-7641-3631-3(3)) Barron's Educational Series, Inc.

Tunnell, Michael O. The Joke's on George. Osborn, Kathy, illus. 2003. 32p. (J). (gr. k-2). 9.95 (978-1-56397-970-5(5)) Boyds Mills Pr.

Waite, Judy. Digging for Dinosaurs. Parsons, Garry, illus. (Flying Foxes Ser.). 32p. (J). 2004. pap. (978-0-7787-1529-0(9)); 2003. (978-0-7787-1483-5(7)) Crabtree Publishing Co.

Wax, Wendy. Secret Agents. 2007. 24p. (J). 21.35 (***978-1-59961-161-7(9)***) Spotlight.

Weitzman, Jacqueline Preiss. You Can't Take a Balloon into the Metropolitan Museum. Bonnell, J., ed. Glasser, Robin Preiss, illus. 2001. 40p. (J). (ps-3). pap. 6.99 (978-0-14-056816-5(6) , Puffin) Penguin Group (USA) Inc.

—You Can't Take a Balloon into the Metropolitan Museum. Glasser, Robin, illus. 1998. 40p. (J). (gr. k-3). 18.99 (978-0-8037-2301-6(6) , Dial) Penguin Group (USA) Inc.

—You Can't Take a Balloon into the Metropolitan Museum. 2000. (gr. k-3). lib. bdg. 15.30 (978-0-613-33742-7(5)) Tandem Library Bks.

—You Can't Take a Balloon into the Museum of Fine Arts. Glasser, Robin Preiss, illus. 2002. 40p. (J). (gr. k-4). 18.99 (978-0-8037-2570-6(1) , Dial) Penguin Group (USA) Inc.

—You Can't Take a Balloon into the National Gallery. Glasser, Robin Preiss, illus. 2002. 40p. (J). pap. 7.99 (978-0-14-230131-9(0) , Puffin) Penguin Group (USA) Inc.

—You Can't Take a Balloon into the National Gallery. 2002. (ps-2). lib. bdg. 16.45 (978-0-613-83550-3(6)) Tandem Library Bks.

Wheatley, Nadia & Ottley, Matt. Luke's Way of Looking. 2001. (Illus.). 36p. (J). (gr. k up). 15.95 (978-1-929132-18-8(2)) Kane/Miller Bk. Pubs., Inc.

Whybrow, Ian. Harry & the Dinosaurs at the Museum. Reynolds, Adrian, illus. 2005. 32p. (J). (ps-2). 15.95 (978-0-375-83338-0(2) , Random Hse. Bks. for Young Readers) Random Hse. Children's Bks.

Willson, Sarah. Picture Perfect Tommy. 2001. (gr. k-3). lib. bdg. 11.80 (978-0-613-43949-7(X)) Tandem Library Bks.

Wyse, Lois, et al. How to Take Your Grandmother to the Museum. 1998. (Illus.). 48p. (J). (gr. k-3). 12.95 (978-0-7611-0990-7(0) , 10990) Workman Publishing Co., Inc.

Zindel, Paul. The Scream Museum. l.t. ed. 2002. (Illus.). 175p. (J). 22.95 (978-0-7862-4473-7(9)) Thorndike Pr.

MUSEUMS—VOCATIONAL GUIDANCE

L'Hommedieu, Arthur John. Working at a Museum. (Working Here Ser.). (Illus.). 32p. (J). (gr. 2-4). 1999. pap. 6.95 (978-0-516-20590-8(0)); 1998. 23.50 (978-0-516-20748-3(2)) Scholastic Library Publishing. (Children's Pr.).

MUSHROOMS

see also Fungi

Fowler, Allan. Good Mushrooms & Bad Toadstools. 1998. (Rookie Read-About Science Ser.). (Illus.). 32p. (J). (gr. 1-2). 19.50 (978-0-516-20808-4(X) , Children's Pr.) Scholastic Library Publishing.

Mushroom. 2003. stu. ed. 36.95 (978-0-8136-9261-6(X)) Modern Curriculum Pr.

Nelson, Cyndi. Rocky Mountain Mushrooms: Edible & Poisonous. Miller, Millie, illus. 2nd rev. ed. 2007. 42p. pap. 7.95 (***978-1-55566-404-6(0)***) Johnson Bks.

Royston, Angela. Life Cycle of a Mushroom. 2000. (Life Cycle of a... Ser.). (Illus.). 32p. (J). (gr. k-2). lib. bdg. 21.36 (978-1-57572-210-8(0)) Heinemann Library.

MUSIC

see also Church Music; Concerts; Jazz; Musicians; Singing; Sound

also Orchestral Music; Organ Music; Piano music; etc. and headings beginning with the words Music and Musical

Abbado, Claudio. Yo Sere Director de Orquesta. 2007. 48p. (J). (gr. 2-5). 19.95 (***978-84-8470-052-4(6)***) Corimbo, Editorial S.L. ESP. *Dist:* Lectorum Pubns., Inc.

Adolphe, Bruce. Red Dogs & Pink Skies: Paul Gauguin on Painting & Music. 2002. (Illus.). 24p. (J). 18.95 (978-0-9701249-1-3(0)) PollyRhythm Productions.

Aksomitis, Linda. Downloading Music 2007. 2007. (Issues that Concern You Ser.). 144p. (gr. 7-10). 33.70 (***978-0-7377-3646-5(1)*** , Greenhaven Pr., Inc.) Thomson Gale.

Alberto & Aitor. Comision: Cambiando la Historia. 2001. Tr. of Commission: "Changing History". (SPA.). (YA). 7.99 (978-0-8254-1158-8(0)) Kregel Pubns.

Allman, Toney. Downloading Music. 2007. (Ripped from the Headlines Ser.). 64p. (J). (gr. 5). 23.95 (***978-1-60217-006-3(1)***) Erickson Pr.

Amery, Heather. The Usborne Children's Songbook. Cartwright, Stephen, illus. 2nd rev. ed. 1998. (Songbooks Ser.). 64p. (J). (ps-3). pap. 10.95 (978-0-7460-2981-7(0)) EDC Publishing.

Ancona, George. Mi Musica/My Music. 2005. (Somos Latinos (We Are Latinos) Ser.). (ENG & SPA.). 32p. (J). 21.00 (978-0-516-25295-7(X) , Children's Pr.) Scholastic Library Publishing.

Aranda, Alfredo. My First Music Book: Mi Primer Libro de Musica. 2003. per. 14.95 (978-1-932637-00-7(1)) Escuela de Musica.

Archuleta, Michael, concept. Mariachi Method Book for Vihuela. 2nd ed. 2005. (YA). 24.95 (978-0-9675951-3-9(4)) Mixta Publishing Co.

Ardley, Neil. La Musica.Tr. of Music. (SPA.). 64p. (YA). (gr. 5-8). (978-84-372-3711-4(4)) Altea, Ediciones, S.A. - Grupo Santillana.

Ardley, Neil & Dorling Kindersley Publishing Staff. Music. 2004. (Eyewitness Books). (Illus.). 72p. (J). (ps-7). lib. bdg. 19.99 (978-0-7566-0708-1(6)) Dorling Kindersley Publishing, Inc.

Arnott. Three-Choir Festivals. 2001. (YA). reprint ed. 150.00 (978-0-7222-5126-3(2)) Library Reprints, Inc.

Arpeggio Hand Puppet. 2000. (ps up). suppl. ed. 30.00 (978-0-382-34711-5(0)) Silver, Burdett & Ginn, Inc.

Axford, Elizabeth C. & Perry, Phyllis J. The Musical ABC. 2001. 30p. (J). spiral bd. 14.95 (978-0-9673325-6-7(7) , PP1007) Piano Pr.

Baby Einstein, creator. Baby Einstein Music Is Fun. 2005. (Illus.). 14p. (J). (ps-ps). per. 15.98 (978-1-4127-3357-1(X) , 7250100) Publications International, Ltd.

Bach, Johann Sebastian. Organ Works, 20 vols., set. 2001. (YA). reprint ed. 2500.00 (978-0-7222-5312-0(5)) Library Reprints, Inc.

Bach, Sebastian. Baby Bach. 2000. (J). 9.98 (978-1-892309-11-2(4)) Baby Einstein Co., LLC, The.

Balakirev, Mily, et al. Islamey & Other Favorite Russian Piano Works. 2000. 160p. pap. 15.95 (978-0-486-41160-6(5)) Dover Pubns., Inc.

Band-in-a-Box. 2002. (gr. 2-8). cd-rom 88.00 (978-0-382-34878-5(8)); cd-rom 88.00 (978-0-382-34877-8(X)) Silver, Burdett & Ginn, Inc.

Bangs, Lawrence Bailey. Math & Music. 2000. (Bigger World Ser.: Vol. 2). (YA). incl. cd-rom (978-1-59106-013-0(3)) Wildridge Software, Inc.

Barber Adagio for Strings, Vol. 26. 1998. (J). ring bd. 60.00 (978-1-928908-26-5(8)) Classical Connections.

Barber, Nicola. Music: An A-Z Guide. 2001. (Watts Reference Ser.). (Illus.). 128p. (YA). (gr. 6-8). 34.00 (978-0-531-11898-6(3) , Watts, Franklin) Scholastic Library Publishing.

Bass Schule. 2004. (GER.). (YA). cd-rom (978-1-891155-18-5(0)) EMedia Corp.

Beethoven Ode to Joy, Vol. 27. 1998. (J). ring bd. 60.00 (978-1-928908-27-2(6)) Classical Connections.

Beethoven Pastoral Symphony, Vol. 14. 1998. (J). ring bd. 60.00 (978-1-928908-14-2(4)) Classical Connections.

Ben-Hur, Roni Amos. Talk Jazz Guitar: A Comprehensive Collection of Be Bop Studies for the Aspiringand Professional Jazz Guitarist. 2004. 268p. (YA). pap. 34.00 net. (978-0-9744943-1-9(3)) Bohobza Music.

Bennett, Paul. The Seven Harmonies of Music: A Field Guide, 1. 2004. (Illus.). 80p. ring bd. 19.95 (978-0-9753599-0-7(8)) Music Awareness.

Bergerac. My First Book of Classical Music: 20 Themes by Beethoven, Mozart, Chopin & Other Great Composers. 2000. (Illus.). 48p. pap. 4.95 (978-0-486-41092-0(7)) Dover Pubns., Inc.

Bernard, Yves & Fredette, Nathalie. Le Guide de la Musique du Monde. 2004. (FRE., Illus.). 230p. (J). pap. (978-2-89021-662-4(4)) Diffusion du livre Mirabel.

Bernstein West Side Story, Vol. 20. 1998. (J). ring bd. 60.00 (978-1-928908-20-3(9)) Classical Connections.

Between the Lions - Early Literacy Kit - Zoop! Zoop!, 1 cass., 1 bk. 2005. (Between the Lions Ser.). 36p. (J). VHS 29.95 (978-1-59375-287-3(3) , WG38653) WGBH Boston Video.

Big Book. 2002. (Big Book Ser.). (gr. k up). stu. ed. 364.00 (978-0-382-34343-8(3)); (gr. 1 up). stu. ed. 397.00 (978-0-382-34344-5(1)) Silver, Burdett & Ginn, Inc.

Binns, Tricia. Funstation Music Works, 5 vols., Set. 1998. (Funstations Ser.). (Illus.). 48p. (J). (gr. 3-7). 17.95 (978-1-57145-347-1(4) , Silver Dolphin Bks.) Advantage Pubs. Group.

Birthday Party Songs. (Early Learning Ser.). (J). incl. audio. 7.98 incl. audio NewSound, LLC.

Bissinger, Wendy & Wendy Bissinger. Sequenced Scale Studies for Cello. 2004. (Illus.). 108p. (J). spiral bd. (978-0-9755624-0-6(1)) Boshu Pr.

Bizet Carmen, Vol. 1. 1998. (J). ring bd. 60.00 (978-1-928908-01-2(2)) Classical Connections.

Black, Dave. Alfred's Kid's Drum Course 1 Bk & Cd & Drum. 2005. 64p. 24.95 (978-0-7390-3742-3(0)) Alfred Publishing Co., Inc.

Blair, Cathy. Music Baseball: Name That Style. 2005. act. bk. ed., instr.'s gde. ed. 29.95 (978-0-89328-174-8(3) , 30/2006H) Heritage Music Pr.

—Rhythm Rally! Level 1, Grades 3-5: Six Fun & Fast-Paced Rhythm Games in One! 2004. act. bk. ed. 29.95 (978-0-89328-176-2(X) , 30/1908H) Heritage Music Pr.

—Rhythm Rally! Level 2, Grades 5-7: Six Fun & Fast-Paced Rhythm Games in One! 2004. act. bk. ed. 29.95 (978-0-89328-177-9(8) , 30/1909H) Heritage Music Pr.

—Rhythms of the World: Discovering the Indigenous Rhythms of Africa, India, Cuba, & Brazil; Grades 5-8. 2005. 34.95 (978-0-89328-173-1(5) , 30/1989H) Heritage Music Pr.

Blending Music Styles Videotape: Videotape Packages. 2003. (Share the Music Ser.). (gr. 4-8). (978-0-02-295486-4(4)) Macmillan/McGraw-Hill Schl. Div.

Bliss, Phil, et al, illus. Silly Songs Sing-Along. 2002. (J). (978-0-7853-7500-5(7)) Publications International, Ltd.

Blue's Clues: Blue's Big Musical Playset. 2002. (J). pap. 19.98 incl. audio compact disk (978-0-7379-0144-3(6) , 79846) Rhino Entertainment Co, A Warner Music Group Co.

Bodenmann, Hans & Pahlen, Kurt, contrib. by. El ABC de la Flauta Dulce. (SPA.). (J). 10.00 (978-0-7692-9925-9(3) , Warner Bros. Pubns.) Alfred Publishing Co., Inc.

Boytim, Joan Frey. Daffodils, Violets & Snowflakes: 24 Classical Songs for Young Women, Ages 10 to Mid-Teens. 2003. 88p. (gr. 5 up). pap. 14.95 incl. audio compact disk (978-0-634-06181-3(X) , 063406181X) Leonard, Hal Corp.

—Daffodils, Violets & Snowflakes: 24 Classical Songs for Young Women, Ages Ten to Mid-Teens. 2003. 88p. pap. 14.95 incl. audio compact disk (978-0-634-06212-4(3) , 0634062123) Leonard, Hal Corp.

Bracken, Carolyn. Music Maker. Durk, Jim, illus. 2002. (Fisher-Price Little People Ser.). (J). 15.98 (978-0-7853-6476-4(5)) Publications International, Ltd.

Brahms Lullaby Hungarian Dance No. 6, Vol. 2. 1998. (J). ring bd. 60.00 (978-1-928908-02-9(0)) Classical Connections.

Brannon, Tom, illus. Elmo's Rock Star Guitar. 2002. (Sesame Street Ser.). (J). 16.98 (978-0-7853-7006-2(4)) Publications International, Ltd.

British Museum Staff. Catalogue of Manuscript Music in the British Museum, 3 Vols., Set. 2001. (YA). reprint ed. 375.00 (978-0-7222-5003-7(7)) Library Reprints, Inc.

—Catalogue of Printed Music, 2 vols., set. 2001. (YA). reprint ed. 250.00 (978-0-7222-5001-3(0)) Library Reprints, Inc.

Bruckner, Anton. Drei kleine Stucke. 2005. 5p. pap. 5.95 (978-1-4234-0292-3(8) , 1423402928) Schott Musik International GmbH & Co. KG DEU. *Dist:* Leonard, Hal Corp.

Bryant, Anne. Keyclub Pupils, Vol. 1. 2000. (Illus.). 49p. 6.95 (978-1-85909-589-8(5) , Warner Bros. Pubns.) Alfred Publishing Co., Inc.

Burch, Lynda S. Meet Me at the Park! Burch, Lynda S., photos by. 2005. (Illus.). 64p. (J). E-Book 6.00 incl. cd-rom (978-1-933090-15-3(4)) Guardian Angel Publishing, Inc.

—Wicky Wacky Things that Go! Airplanes 1. Roberts, MarySue, photos by. 2004. (Illus.). 28p. (J). E-Book 9.95 incl. cd-rom (978-1-933090-07-8(3)) Guardian Angel Publishing, Inc.

—Wicky Wacky Things that Go! Tractors. Burch, Lynda S., photos by. 2004. (Illus.). 28p. (J). E-Book 9.95 incl. cd-rom (978-1-933090-09-2(X)) Guardian Angel Publishing, Inc.

—Wicky Wacky Things that Go! Trains 1. Burch, Lynda S., photos by. 2004. (Illus.). 16p. (J). E-Book 9.95 incl. cd-rom (978-1-933090-02-3(2)) Guardian Angel Publishing, Inc.

—Wicky Wacky Things That Go! Trucks. Burch, Lynda S., photos by. 2004. (Illus.). 28p. (J). E-Book 9.95 incl. cd-rom (978-1-933090-11-5(1)) Guardian Angel Publishing, Inc.

—Zoom Zoom Zoom Come Count with Me! Burch, Lynda S., photos by. 2005. (Illus.). 20p. (J). E-Book 6.00 incl. cd-rom (978-1-933090-14-6(6)) Guardian Angel Publishing, Inc.

Burrows, John, ed. Classical Music. 2005. (Eyewitness Companions Ser.). (Illus.). 512p. pap. 30.00 (978-0-7566-0958-0(5)) Dorling Kindersley Publishing, Inc.

Buttwinick, Marty. How to Rehearse: To Make the Most of Your Time. Lamont, Daveda, ed. 2001. (Musician's How-To Ser.). 20p. 7.00 (978-0-9642529-3-6(7)) Sonata Publishing.

—What Do I Play? The Basics of Jamming. Lamont, Daveda, ed. 2001. (Musician's How-To Ser.). 20p. 7.00 (978-0-9642529-2-9(9)) Sonata Publishing.

Casterline, L. C. The Sounds of Music. Yerkes, Lane, illus. 2004. 16p. (J). (gr. 1 up). lib. bdg. 19.33 (978-0-8368-4100-8(X)) Stevens, Gareth Inc.

Cathcart, Cynthia. From My Music Stand: Arrangements for the Wire Strung Harp. 2001. 42p. spiral bd. 18.00 (978-0-9743126-1-3(4) , HCM61) Highland Circle Publishing.

—Traditional Beginnings for the Harp. 2001. 74p. spiral bd. 22.00 (978-0-9743126-0-6(6) , HCM12) Highland Circle Publishing.

Cefrey, Holly. Backstage at a Music Video. 2003. (High Interest Bks.). (Illus.). 48p. (YA). (gr. 7-12). pap. 6.95 (978-0-516-24386-3(1) , Children's Pr.) Scholastic Library Publishing.

—Backstage at a Music Video. 2003. (Illus.). 48p. (YA). (gr. 8-12). lib. bdg. 15.25 (978-0-613-59578-0(5)) Tandem Library Bks.

Celia, Shannon Casey. Nature's Music. 2003. (Illus.). 12p. (J). spiral bd. 10.95 (978-1-931844-07-9(0) , PP1019) Piano Pr.

Cherician, David. Juguetes de Palabras. (SPA.). 56p. (J). (gr. k-3). (978-958-30-0402-5(2)) Panamericana Editorial COL. *Dist:* Lectorum Pubns., Inc.

Chorus: Individual Title Six-Packs. (On Deck Ser.). 24p. (gr. 4-5). 35.00 (978-0-7578-1025-1(X)) Rigby Education.

Christ Church Oxford Staff. Catalogue of Manuscript Music in Library. 2001. (YA). reprint ed. 150.00 (978-0-7222-5005-1(3)) Library Reprints, Inc.

Classical Connections: Complete Program, 31 vols., Set. Incl. Vol. 1. Bizet Carmen. ring bd. 60.00 (978-1-928908-01-2(2)); Vol. 2. Brahms Lullaby Hungarian Dance No. 6. ring bd. 60.00 (978-1-928908-02-9(0)); Vol. 3. Rimsky-Korsakov Flight of the Bumblebee. ring bd. 60.00 (978-1-928908-03-6(9)); Vol. 4. Rodgers/Hammerstein Oklahoma! ring bd. 60.00 (978-1-928908-04-3(7)); Vol. 5. Tchaikovsky Nutcracker. ring bd. 60.00 (978-1-928908-05-0(5)); Vol. 6. Prokofiev Cinderella Suite. ring bd. 60.00 (978-1-928908-06-7(3)); Vol. 7. Dukas Sorcerer's Apprentice. ring bd. 60.00 (978-1-928908-07-4(1)); Vol. 8. Grieg Peer Gynt. ring bd. 60.00 (978-1-928908-08-1(X)); Vol. 9. Menotti Amahl & the Night Visitors. ring bd. 60.00 (978-1-928908-09-8(8)); Vol. 10. Rossini William Tell. ring bd. 60.00 (978-1-928908-10-4(1)); Vol. 11. Sousa Marches. ring bd. 60.00 (978-1-928908-11-1(X)); Vol. 12. Willson Music Man. ring bd. 60.00 (978-1-928908-12-8(8)); Vol. 13. Tchaikovsky Sleeping Beauty. ring bd. 60.00 (978-1-928908-13-5(6)); Vol. 14. Beethoven Pastoral Symphony. ring bd. 60.00 (978-1-928908-14-2(4)); Vol. 15. Debussy La Mer. ring bd. 60.00 (978-1-928908-15-9(2)); Vol. 16. Humperdinck Hansel & Gretel. ring bd. 60.00 (978-1-928908-16-6(0)); Vol. 17. Lowe/Lerner Camelot. ring bd. 60.00 (978-1-928908-17-3(9)); Vol. 18. Strauss Waltzes. ring bd. 60.00 (978-1-928908-18-0(7)); Vol. 19. Webber Cats. ring bd. 60.00 (978-1-928908-19-7(5)); Vol. 20. Bernstein West Side Story. ring bd. 60.00 (978-1-928908-20-3(9)); Vol. 21. Copland Appalachian Spring. ring bd. 60.00 (978-1-928908-21-0(7)); Vol. 22. Dvorak New World Symphony. ring bd. 60.00 (978-1-928908-22-7(5)); Vol. 23. Joplin Maple Leaf Rag : Entertainer. ring bd. 60.00 (978-1-928908-23-4(3)); Vol. 24. Rinsky-Korsakov Scheherazade. ring bd. 60.00 (978-1-928908-24-1(1)); Vol. 25. Tchaikovsky Romeo & Juliet. ring bd. 60.00 (978-1-928908-25-8(X)); Vol. 26. Barber Adagio for Strings. ring bd. 60.00 (978-1-928908-26-5(8)); Vol. 27. Beethoven Ode to Joy. ring bd. 60.00 (978-1-928908-27-2(6)); Vol. 28. Gershwin Rhapsody in Blue. ring bd. 60.00 (978-1-928908-28-9(4)); Vol. 29. Ravel Bolero. ring bd. 60.00 (978-1-928908-29-6(2)); Vol. 30. Schonberg/Boubil Les Miserables. ring bd. 60.00 (978-1-928908-30-2(6)); Vol. 31. Verdi Aida. ring bd. 60.00 (978-1-928908-31-9(4)); (J). 1998. Set ring bd. 1600.00 (978-1-928908-00-5(4)) Classical Connections.

Coll, Ivar Da, illus. El Libro de Anton Pirulero. (SPA.). 72p. (J). (gr. k-3). (978-958-30-0474-2(X)) Panamericana Editorial COL. *Dist:* Lectorum Pubns., Inc.

Compact Disc Package. 2002. (gr. k up). stu. ed. 384.00 (978-0-382-34445-9(6)); (gr. 2 up). stu. ed. 480.00 (978-0-382-34447-3(2)); (gr. 3 up). 496.00 (978-0-382-34448-0(0)); (gr. 4 up). 516.00 (978-0-382-34449-7(9)); (gr. 5 up). 516.00 (978-0-382-34450-3(2)); (gr. 6 up). 550.00 (978-0-382-34451-0(0)) Silver, Burdett & Ginn, Inc.

Compact Disc Staff. Classical Music. 1998. (Growing Minds with Music Ser.). (J). audio compact disk 12.99 (978-1-57583-071-1(X)) Twin Sisters Productions, LLC.

Compact Discs. 2003. (Share the Music Ser.). (gr. 2 up). (978-0-02-295437-6(6)); (gr. 3 up). (978-0-02-295438-3(4)); (gr. 4 up). (978-0-02-295439-0(2)); (gr. 5 up). (978-0-02-295440-6(6)); (gr. 7 up). (978-0-02-295442-0(2)) Macmillan/McGraw-Hill Schl. Div.

Congratulations - Grade 1 Alto Sax & Piano. (YA). 9.95 (978-1-85909-666-6(2) , Warner Bros. Pubns.) Alfred Publishing Co., Inc.

Conrad, Jeffrey & Stein, David, illus. CareBears: Songs from Care-A-Lot. 2002. (J). (978-0-7853-7222-6(9)) Publications International, Ltd.

Copland Appalachian Spring, Vol. 21. 1998. (J). ring bd. 60.00 (978-1-928908-21-0(7)) Classical Connections.

Creating Musical Moods Videotape: Videotape Packages. 2003. (Share the Music Ser.). (gr. 3-6). (978-0-02-295484-0(8)) Macmillan/McGraw-Hill Schl. Div.

Cumulated Dramatic Index, 1909-1949: A Cumulation of the F.W. Faxon Company's Dramatic Index, 2 vols., set. 2001. (YA). reprint ed. 250.00 (978-0-7222-6295-5(7)) Library Reprints, Inc.

Dale, Monica. Eurhythmics for Young Children: Six Lessons for Winter. 2001. (Illus.). 108p. pap. 24.95 (978-0-9701416-1-3(0)) MusiKinesis.

Day, Eileen. Soy Bueno para la Musica. 2003. (SPA.). 24p. pap. 5.25 (978-1-4034-3579-8(0)) Heinemann Library.

Debussy La Mer, Vol. 15. 1998. (J). ring bd. 60.00 (978-1-928908-15-9(2)) Classical Connections.

Delaney, Mary Ann. Black to Basics. Barge, John, III, illus. Langie, Kenneth Alan, photos by. 2001. (YA). (gr. 6 up). pap. 12.95 (978-0-9706776-0-0(X)) De'Languille Music & Poetry.

Dembska, Anna & Harkness, Joan. You've Got Rhythm Vol. 1: Read Music Better by Feeling the Beat. 2000. 56p. (YA). (gr. 3 up). pap. 9.95 (978-1-930664-00-5(1)) Flying Leap Music.

—You've Got Rhythm Vol. 2: Read Music Better by Feeling the Beat. 2000. 56p. (YA). (gr. 3 up). pap. 9.95 (978-1-930664-01-2(X)) Flying Leap Music.

—You've Got Rhythm Vol. 3: Read Music Better by Feeling the Beat. 2000. 56p. (YA). (gr. 3 up). pap. 9.95 (978-1-930664-02-9(8)) Flying Leap Music.

Deva, Jeannie. The Contemporary Vocalist Improvement Course: The Deva Method, a Non-Classical Approach for Singers. Lieberman, Julie Lyonn, ed. Rouelle, Trish, illus. 2001. 174p. per. 59.95 incl. audio compact disk (978-1-882224-09-8(4)) Jeannie Deva Enterprises, Inc.

Diamond, Eileen. Let's Make Music Fun! Songs to Sing, Action Songs, Rounds & Songs with Percussion Instruments. (Let's Make Music Fun Ser.). 14.95 (978-1-85909-417-4(1) , Warner Bros. Pubns.) Alfred Publishing Co., Inc.

Dickey, Christa, ed. Fans of the Millennium: The Backstreet Boys. 2001. 640p. (YA). 44.95 (978-1-886161-16-0(X)) Millennium Marketing & Publishing.

District License Package: Technology: Music with MIDI. 2003. (Share the Music Ser.). (gr. 1 up). (978-0-02-295470-3(8)); (gr. 2 up). (978-0-02-295471-0(6)); (gr. 3 up). (978-0-02-295472-7(4)); (gr. 4 up). (978-0-02-295473-4(2)); (gr. 5 up). (978-0-02-295474-1(0)); (gr. 6 up). (978-0-02-295475-8(9)); (gr. 7 up). (978-0-02-295298-3(5)); (gr. 8 up). (978-0-02-295299-0(3)) Macmillan/McGraw-Hill Schl. Div.

Dixon, Malcolm & Smith, Karen. Sound & Music. 1998. (Young Scientists Ser.). (Illus.). 32p. (J). (ps-3). lib. bdg. 16.95 (978-1-887068-72-7(4)) Smart Apple Media.

Domnauer, Teresa & Lithgow, John. Sing, Strum, & Beat the Drum!, Level 4: A Musical Adventure. 2005. (Lithgow Palooza Readers Ser.). (Illus.). 32p. (J). (gr. 2-3). pap. 3.95 (978-0-7696-4224-6(1)) School Specialty Publishing.

Dorling Kindersley Publishing Staff, ed. Music. 2004. (Dk Eyewitness Books Ser.). (Illus.). 72p. (J). 15.99 (978-0-7566-0709-8(4)) Dorling Kindersley Publishing, Inc.

Doug Smith's Classical Guitar Method, Reading Book 1: Introduction to the Natural Notes in the First Position. 2004. (J). 24.95 (978-0-9729879-1-2(6)) Musictech College Pr.

Dukas Sorcerer's Apprentice, Vol. 7. 1998. (J). ring bd. 60.00 (978-1-928908-07-4(1)) Classical Connections.

Dunleavy, Deborah. The Jumbo Book of Music. 2001. (Illus.). (J). 21.60 (978-0-606-21280-9(9)) Tandem Library Bks.

Dvorak New World Symphony, Vol. 22. 1998. (J). ring bd. 60.00 (978-1-928908-22-7(5)) Classical Connections.

Dworsky, Alan & Sansby, Betsy. Slap Happy: How to Play World-Beat Rhythms with Just Your Body & a Buddy. 2002. 72p. (gr. 3-6). 19.95 incl. audio compact disk (978-0-9638801-7-8(9)) Dancing Hands Music.

Easterling, Lisa. Music. 2007. (Illus.). 24p. (J). ***(978-1-4034-9406-1(1))***; pap. ***(978-1-4034-9415-3(0))*** Heinemann Library.

Eisen, Ann M. & Robertson, Lamar. My Fourth Grade Music Book. Ritchie, Ann, illus. 1999. (My Music Book Ser.: Vol. 4). 102p. (J). (gr. 4-7). pap., wbk. ed. 40.00 (978-1-889967-02-8(5)) Sneaky Snake Pubns.

EMedia Fortgeschrittene Gitarren Schule. 2004. (GER.). (YA). cd-rom (978-1-891155-16-1(4)) EMedia Corp.

Emmer, Rae. Banda. 2004. (Actividades Escolares Ser.). (SPA & ENG., Illus.). 24p. (J). lib. bdg. 17.25 (978-0-8239-6902-9(9) , 1213143, Buenas Letra) Rosen Publishing Group, Inc., The.

—Coro. 2004. (Actividades Escolares Ser.). (SPA & ENG., Illus.). 24p. (J). lib. bdg. 17.25 (978-0-8239-6903-6(7) , 1213163, Buenas Letra) Rosen Publishing Group, Inc., The.

Feierabend, John M. The Book of Beginning Circle Games: Let's Make a Circle. 2004. (First Steps in Music Ser.). (Illus.). 84p. (J). pap. 11.95 (978-1-57999-266-8(8) , G-5878) GIA Pubns., Inc.

Feierabend, John M. & Kahan, Jane. The Book of Movement Exploration: Can You Move Like This? 2004. (First Steps in Music Ser.). (Illus.). 66p. (J). pap. 11.95 (978-1-57999-264-4(1) , G-5876) GIA Pubns., Inc.

Feldman, Jean. Nursery Rhymes: 12 Delightful Nursery Rhyme Songs with Sing-Along Mini-Books That Build Early Literacy Skills. 2002. (Teaching Tunes Audio Cd & Mini-books S Ser.). (Illus.). 48p. pap. 11.95 (978-0-439-30586-0(1) , Teaching Resources) Scholastic, Inc.

Feldstein, Sandy. Rhythm Party Guide. 2004. audio compact disk 24.95 (978-1-932895-16-2(7)) PlayinTime Productions, Inc.

Feldstein, Sandy & Clark, Larry. Antiphony. 2004. (YA). pap. 40.00 (978-1-932895-03-2(5)) PlayinTime Productions, Inc.

—Fanfare Minuet - Trombone/Baritone/Basson Solo with Piano Acc. 2005. (YA). pap. 9.95 incl. audio compact disk (978-1-932895-53-7(1)) PlayinTime Productions, Inc.

—Fanfare Minuet -Trumpet/Baritone Solo with Piano Acc. 2005. (YA). pap. 9.95 incl. audio compact disk (978-1-932895-51-3(5)) PlayinTime Productions, Inc.

—The Fifers. 2005. (YA). pap. 10.95 (978-1-932895-81-0(7)) PlayinTime Productions, Inc.

—Honor March. 2005. (YA). pap. 40.00 (978-1-932895-99-5(X)) PlayinTime Productions, Inc.

—Jupiter. 2004. (YA). pap. 40.00 (978-1-932895-00-1(0)) PlayinTime Productions, Inc.

—Jupiter - Conductor's Score. 2004. (YA). pap. 6.00 (978-1-932895-01-8(9)) PlayinTime Productions, Inc.

—Outback Rhapsody. 2004. (YA). pap. 40.00 (978-1-932895-06-3(X)) PlayinTime Productions, Inc.

—Outback Rhapsody - Conductor's Score. 2004. (YA). pap. 8.00 (978-1-932895-07-0(8)) PlayinTime Productions, Inc.

—Scherzando - Alto Sax/Bari. Sax Solo with Piano Acc. W/CD. 2005. (YA). pap. 9.95 (978-1-932895-28-5(0)) PlayinTime Productions, Inc.

—Scherzando - Keyboard Percussion Solo with piano acc. W/CD. 2005. (YA). pap. 9.95 (978-1-932895-34-6(5)) PlayinTime Productions, Inc.

—Scherzando - Snare Drum Solo with Piano Acc. W/CD. 2005. (YA). pap. 9.95 (978-1-932895-35-3(3)) PlayinTime Productions, Inc.

—Scherzando - Trombone/Baritone/Bassoon Solo with Piano Acc. W/CD. 2005. (YA). pap. 9.95 (978-1-932895-32-2(9)) PlayinTime Productions, Inc.

—Scherzando - Tuba Solo with Piano Acc. W/CD. 2005. (YA). pap. 9.95 (978-1-932895-33-9(7)) PlayinTime Productions, Inc.

—Scherzando -Trumpet/Baritone Solo with Piano Acc. w/ CD. 2005. (YA). pap. 9.95 (978-1-932895-30-8(2)) PlayinTime Productions, Inc.

—Scherzando Tenor Sax Solo with Piano Acc. W/CD. 2005. (YA). pap. 9.95 (978-1-932895-29-2(9)) PlayinTime Productions, Inc.

—Sentinel. 2004. (YA). pap. 40.00 (978-1-932895-10-0(8)) PlayinTime Productions, Inc.

—Sentinel - conductor's Score. 2004. (YA). pap. 6.00 (978-1-932895-11-7(6)) PlayinTime Productions, Inc.

Feldstein, Sandy & Firth, Vic. Vic Firth/SandyFeldstein Percussion Series - complete Score. 2004. (YA). 24.95 (978-1-932895-12-4(4)) PlayinTime Productions, Inc.

First Book of the Recorder Kid Kit. 64p. (J). 22.95 (978-1-58086-453-4(8)) EDC Publishing.

Galashan, Kathy. Starting a Band. 2nd rev. ed. 2005. (Illus.). 32p. pap. (978-0-340-81125-2(0)) Cambridge Univ. Pr.

—Starting a Band. 2001. (Livewire Ser.). (Illus.). 32p. pap. (978-0-340-80075-1(5) , Hodder Arnold) Hodder Education.

Gameplan - Grade One: An Active Music Curriculum for Children. 2005. spiral bd. 80.00 net. (978-0-9767650-0-4(4)) KiD Sounds.

Gardner, Janet. School Daze, 5, Pack. 1998. 160p. (J). pap. 22.50 (978-0-7390-0942-0(7) , 16981) Alfred Publishing Co., Inc.

—School Daze - Performance Pack. 1998. 368p. (J). pap. 54.95 (978-0-7390-0944-4(3) , 16983) Alfred Publishing Co., Inc.

George-Warren, Holly. Honky-Tonk Heroes & Hillbilly Angels: The Pioneers of Country & Western Music. Levine, Laura, illus. 2006. 32p. (J). (gr. 3-5). 16.00 (978-0-618-19100-0(3)) Houghton Mifflin Co.

Gershwin Rhapsody in Blue, Vol. 28. 1998. (J). ring bd. 60.00 (978-1-928908-28-9(4)) Classical Connections.

Gitarren Einstieg. 2004. (GER.). (YA). cd-rom (978-1-891155-21-5(0)) EMedia Corp.

Godula, Ellen Kjelgaard & Godula, Brian. Queen Mab, Musical Verses Volume 3. 2007. (J). audio compact disk 16.99 ***(978-0-9764109-3-5(1))*** Pillar Rock Publishing.

Gordon, Edwin E. Am I Musical? Discover Your Musical Potential (Adults & Children Ages 7 & Up) 2004. (Illus.). 40p. pap. 18.95 (978-1-57999-222-4(6) , G-6092) GIA Pubns., Inc.

Grade: Gr 7 Te Share the Music 2000. 2003. (Share the Music Ser.). (gr. 7 up). (978-0-02-295393-5(0)) Macmillan/McGraw-Hill Schl. Div.

Grade: Gr 8 CDs Share the Music 2000. 2003. (Share the Music Ser.). (gr. 8 up). (978-0-02-295443-7(0)) Macmillan/McGraw-Hill Schl. Div.

Grade: Gr 8 Te Share the Music 2000. 2003. (Share the Music Ser.). (gr. 8 up). (978-0-02-295394-2(9)) Macmillan/McGraw-Hill Schl. Div.

Gray, Alan. The Book of Descants: Organ Education. 2001. (YA). reprint ed. 150.00 (978-0-7222-6131-6(4)) Library Reprints, Inc.

Gray, Susan H. Zebra Mussel. 2008. (J). lib. bdg. 25.26 ***(978-1-60279-111-4(2))*** Cherry Lake Publishing.

The Grey House Performing Arts Directory. 4th ed. 2004. 1,500p. 185.00 (978-1-59237-023-8(3) , Universal Reference Pubns.) Grey Hse. Publishing.

Grieg Peer Gynt, Vol. 8. 1998. (J). ring bd. 60.00 (978-1-928908-08-1(X)) Classical Connections.

Hal Leonard Corp., creator. The Charlie Brown Songbook: Recorder Fun. 2003. (Style Collections). (Illus.). 32p. (J). pap. 9.95 (978-0-634-05598-0(4) , 0634055984) Leonard, Hal Corp.

—Children's TV Songs. 2003. 48p. pap. 10.95 (978-0-634-06695-5(1) , 0634066951) Leonard, Hal Corp.

—Disney Movie Hits: Alto Sax. 2003. 20p. pap. 12.95 incl. audio compact disk (978-0-634-00095-9(0) , 0634000950) Leonard, Hal Corp.

—Disney Movie Hits: Cello. 2003. 20p. pap. 12.95 incl. audio compact disk (978-0-634-00101-7(9) , 0634001019) Leonard, Hal Corp.

—Disney Movie Hits: Clarinet. 2003. 16p. pap. 12.95 (978-0-634-00094-2(2) , 0634000942) Leonard, Hal Corp.

—Disney Movie Hits: French Horn. 2003. 16p. pap. 12.95 incl. audio compact disk (978-0-634-00097-3(7) , 0634000977) Leonard, Hal Corp.

—Disney Movie Hits: Trombone. 2003. 20p. pap. 12.95 incl. audio compact disk (978-0-634-00098-0(5) , 0634000985) Leonard, Hal Corp.

—Disney Movie Hits: Trumpet. 2003. 20p. pap. 12.95 incl. audio compact disk (978-0-634-00096-6(9) , 0634000969) Leonard, Hal Corp.

—Disney Movie Hits: Viola. 2003. 20p. pap. 12.95 incl. audio compact disk (978-0-634-00100-0(0) , 0634001000) Leonard, Hal Corp.

—Easy Disney Favorites. 2000. 16p. pap. 12.95 incl. audio compact disk (978-0-634-00606-7(1) , 0634006061) Leonard, Hal Corp.

—My First Hymnal: Recorder Fun. 2003. (Recorder Fun! Ser.). 16p. (J). pap. 9.95 (978-0-634-05672-7(7) , 0634056727) Leonard, Hal Corp.

Hapka, Catherine. Together We Can Do It. 2004. (Star Power Ser.: Vol. 4). 160p. (J). pap. 4.99 (978-0-689-86790-3(5) , Aladdin) Simon & Schuster Children's Publishing.

Harcourt School Publishers Staff. Around the World with Music Below Level. 3rd ed. 2002. (Trophies Reading Program Ser.). (Illus.). pap. 5.10 (978-0-15-323402-6(4)) Harcourt Schl. Pubs.

—Como Rueda la Rueda: Take Home Book. 1999. (Vamos Ser.). (SPA., Illus.). (J). pap. 2.50 (978-0-15-318815-2(4)) Harcourt Schl. Pubs.

—Music Makes Joy: Take-Home Book. 1999. (Collections Ser.). (Illus.). (J). pap. 1.90 (978-0-15-317316-5(5)) Harcourt Schl. Pubs.

Hemperly, Ilona K. & Nanni, Lyn. Koa'e Kea. (Illus.). (J). pap. 11.95 (978-0-9639279-0-3(6)) Sunset Beach Music.

Hogg, Karen. Guitar Made Easy. 2001. (Made Easy). 48p. per. incl. audio compact disk (978-1-929395-26-2(4)) Workshop Arts, Inc.

Howerton, Mari & Sorensen, Karen. Sing & Hum Bumblebee. 2005. (Illus.). 32p. (J). 16.95 (978-1-57197-428-0(8)) Pentland Pr., Inc.

Hugo, Victor. The Hunchback of Notre-Dame. Hugo, Victor, illus. 2006. (Illus.). 56p. (C). pap. 9.00 (***978-0-582-81986-3(5)**) Pearson ESL.

Hull, Arthur E. & Hull, Moore. International Library of Music. 2001. (YA). reprint ed. 98.00 (978-0-7222-6365-5(1)) Library Reprints, Inc.

Hull, Bunny. Dream a World: A Child's Journey to Self-Discovery Dreamer's Activity Kit. Saint-James, Synthia, illus. 2004. 24p. (J). 16.95 incl. cd-rom (978-0-9721478-3-5(7)) BrassHeart Music.

Humperdinck Hansel & Gretel, Vol. 16. 1998. (J). ring bd. 60.00 (978-1-928908-16-6(0)) Classical Connections.

Hyde, Heidi Smith. Mendel's Accordion: The Story of the Klezmorim. Van der Sterre, Johanna, illus. 2007. 32p. (J). (gr. k-4). spiral bd. 16.95 (978-1-58013-212-1(X)) Kar-Ben Publishing.

Im Kindergarten. 2005. (GER.). (J). pap. 14.25 (978-3-411-09841-5(4)) Langenscheidt Pubs Inc.

Introduction to the Computer in Music Videotape: Videotape Packages. 2003. (Share the Music Ser.). (gr. 3-8). (978-0-02-295492-5(9)) Macmillan/McGraw-Hill Schl. Div.

Joplin Maple Leaf Rag: Entertainer, Vol. 23. 1998. (J). ring bd. 60.00 (978-1-928908-23-4(3)) Classical Connections.

Kallen, Stuart A. The History of Country Music. 2002. (Illus.). 112p. (J). 32.45 (978-1-59018-124-9(7) , Lucent Bks.) Thomson Gale.

Keefe, Patricia. Baby's First Jingle. unabr. ed. 1999. (Illus.). 14p. (J). 14.95 (978-0-9705088-1-2(6)) Playful Harmonies, Inc.

Kelley, Kristin. Keyboard Made Easy. 2001. (Made Easy). 48p. pap. 17.45 incl. audio compact disk (978-1-929395-30-9(2)) Workshop Arts, Inc.

Keyboard Accompaniment Book. 2002. (Keyboard Accompaniment Book Ser.). (gr. k up). tchr. ed. 43.40 (978-0-382-34483-1(9)); (gr. 1 up). tchr. ed. 43.40 (978-0-382-34484-8(7)); (gr. 2 up). tchr. ed. 43.40 (978-0-382-34485-5(5)); (gr. 3 up). tchr. ed. 43.40 (978-0-382-34486-2(3)); (gr. 4 up). tchr. ed. 43.40 (978-0-382-34487-9(1)); (gr. 5 up). tchr. ed. 43.40 (978-0-382-34488-6(X)); (gr. 6 up). tchr. ed. 49.50 (978-0-382-34489-3(8)) Silver, Burdett & Ginn, Inc.

Klavier und Keyboard Einstieg. 2004. (GER.). (YA). cd-rom (978-1-891155-22-2(9)) EMedia Corp.

Koopmans, Andy. The History of the Blues. 2005. (Music Library). 96-128p. (J). (gr. 7-10). 32.45 (978-1-59018-767-8(9) , Lucent Bks.) Thomson Gale.

Krull, Kathleen. M Is for Music. Innerst, Stacy, illus. 2003. 56p. (J). (ps-3). 17.00 (978-0-15-201438-4(1)) Harcourt Children's Bks.

Lach, William & Metropolitan Museum of Art Staff. Can You Hear It? 2006. (Illus.). 40p. (J). (ps-5). 18.95 (978-0-8109-5721-3(3) , Abrams Bks. for Young Readers) Abrams, Harry N. , Inc.

Laing, Robin. The Whisky Muse: Collected & Introduced by Robin Laing. Dewar, Bob, illus. 2nd ed. 2004. (ENG.). 224p. per. 14.95 (978-1-84282-041-4(9)) Luath Pr. Ltd. GBR. *Dist:* Ingram Pub. Services.

Larousse Kingfisher Chambers Staff. Kingfisher Young People's Book of Music. 1999. (gr. 5-8). lib. bdg. 22.20 (978-0-613-88045-9(5)) Tandem Library Bks.

Lauw, Darlene. Sound. 2002. (gr. 3-6). lib. bdg. 16.40 (978-0-613-52910-5(3)) Tandem Library Bks.

Lauw, Darlene & Puay, Lim Cheng. Sound. 2002. (Science Alive! Ser.). (Illus.). 32p. (J). (gr. 4-5). pap. (978-0-7787-0608-3(7)); lib. bdg. (978-0-7787-0562-8(5)) Crabtree Publishing Co.

LeapFrog Staff, compiled by. Hit It Maestro. 2001. (J). (ps-1). spiral bd. 14.99 (978-1-58605-077-1(X)) LeapFrog Enterprises, Inc.

Learn to Play the Recorder. 2004. (Fun Kits Ser.). (Illus.). 48p. (J). (978-1-84229-730-8(9)) Top That! Publishing PLC.

Learning to Play the Recorder. 2001. 36p. (YA). pap. (978-0-9623694-2-1(X)) JR Pubs.

Listening Map Transparencies. 2003. (Share the Music Ser.). (gr. k up). (978-0-02-295494-9(5)); (gr. 1 up). (978-0-02-295495-6(3)); (gr. 2 up). (978-0-02-295496-3(1)); (gr. 3 up). (978-0-02-295497-0(X)); (gr. 4 up). (978-0-02-295498-7(8)); (gr. 5 up). (978-0-02-295499-4(6)); (gr. 6 up). (978-0-02-295500-7(3)) Macmillan/McGraw-Hill Schl. Div.

Lock, Deborah. Let's Make Music. 2005. (Dk Readers Ser.). (Illus.). 32p. (J). (gr. 4-7). 14.99 (978-0-7566-1423-2(6)); pap. 3.99 (978-0-7566-1422-5(8)) Dorling Kindersley Publishing, Inc.

Lorenz, Geoff, et al, creators. The Ultimate Music Game Book: Grades K-6+ 2005. (Illus.). 96p. spiral bd. 29.95 (978-0-89328-031-4(3) , 30/2013H) Heritage Music Pr.

Lorenz, Geoff & Vogt, Janet, creators. Music Out of a Hat, Grades 4-6: 7 Card Games for Classroom Fun! 2005. act. bk. ed. 39.95 (978-0-89328-025-3(9) , 30/2008H) Heritage Music Pr.

—Music Out of a Hat, Grades K-3: 7 Card Games for Classroom Fun! 2005. act. bk. ed. 39.95 (978-0-89328-024-6(0) , 30/2007H) Heritage Music Pr.

Lowe, Marilyn, et al. Music Moves for Two. 2004. (J). Bk. 1. 15.95 (978-1-57999-347-4(8) , G-6443); Bk. 2. 22p. 7.95 (978-1-57999-348-1(6) , G-6444) GIA Pubns., Inc.

Lowe/Lerner Camelot, Vol. 17. 1998. (J). ring bd. 60.00 (978-1-928908-17-3(9)) Classical Connections.

Macken, JoAnn Early. Music Lessons. 2005. (Illus.). 24p. (J). pap. (978-0-8368-4522-8(6)) Stevens, Gareth Inc.

Madrigals by English Composers of the Close of the Fifteenth Century. 2001. 39p. (YA). reprint ed. 88.00 (978-0-7222-6145-3(4)) Library Reprints, Inc.

Making More Music. 2002. (gr. k-6). cd-rom 43.42 (978-0-382-34706-1(4)) Silver, Burdett & Ginn, Inc.

Making Music. 2002. (gr. k-4). tchr. ed. 43.42 incl. cd-rom (978-0-382-34319-3(0)); (gr. k up). tchr. ed. 64.25 (978-0-382-34353-7(0)); (gr. 1 up). tchr. ed. 64.25 (978-0-382-34354-4(9)); (gr. 1 up). stu. ed. 43.95 (978-0-382-34345-2(X)); (gr. 2 up). tchr. ed. 75.70 (978-0-382-34355-1(7)); (gr. 2 up). stu. ed. 46.95 (978-0-382-34346-9(8)); (gr. 3 up). tchr. ed. (978-0-382-34356-8(5)); (gr. 3 up). stu. ed. 46.95 (978-0-382-34347-6(6)); (gr. 4 up). tchr. ed. 75.70 (978-0-382-34357-5(3)); (gr. 4 up). stu. ed. 46.95 (978-0-382-34348-3(4)); (gr. 5 up). tchr. ed. 80.10 (978-0-382-34358-2(1)); (gr. 5 up). stu. ed. 49.95 (978-0-382-34349-0(2)); (gr. 6 up). tchr. ed. 83.50 (978-0-382-34359-9(X)); (gr. 6 up). stu. ed. 49.95 (978-0-382-34350-6(6)) Silver, Burdett & Ginn, Inc.

Making Music Videotape: Videotape Packages. 2003. (Share the Music Ser.). (gr. 4-8). (978-0-02-295487-1(2)) Macmillan/McGraw-Hill Schl. Div.

Making Music with MIDI. 2000. (gr. 1 up). tchr.'s training gde. ed. 99.00 incl. cd-rom (978-0-382-36864-6(9)); (gr. 2 up). tchr.'s training gde. ed. 99.00 incl. cd-rom (978-0-382-36865-3(7)); (gr. 3 up). 99.00 incl. cd-rom (978-0-382-36866-0(5)); (gr. 4 up). tchr.'s training gde. ed. 99.00 incl. cd-rom (978-0-382-36867-7(3)); (gr. 5 up). 99.00 incl. cd-rom (978-0-382-36868-4(1)); (gr. 6 up). tchr.'s training gde. ed. 99.00 incl. cd-rom (978-0-382-36869-1(X)) Silver, Burdett & Ginn, Inc.

Manz Simon, Mary. Goodnight Angel. (Illus.). 13p. (J). (ps-1). pap. 9.99 incl. audio (978-0-570-04966-1(0) , 56-1839) Concordia Publishing Hse.

Marchant, A. W. Five Hundred Fugue Subjects & Answers. 2001. (YA). reprint ed. 150.00 (978-0-7222-5698-5(1)) Library Reprints, Inc.

Martin, Oscar, Jr., creator. History of Music, l.t. ed. 2003. (Illus.). 25p. (J). E-Book 19.95 incl. cd-rom (978-0-9748416-7-0(6)) Build Your Story.

Martyr, Paula, illus. Join the Band. 1999. (My First Piano Ser.). 8p. (J). (ps-3). bds. 7.95 (978-1-57717-113-3(6)) New Line Bks.

Mason, Antony. Music. 2003. (Culture Encyclopedia Ser.). (Illus.). 40p. (J). (gr. 5 up). lib. bdg. (978-1-59084-479-3(3)) Mason Crest Pubs.

Matthews. The Violin Music of Beethoven. 2001. (YA). reprint ed. 150.00 (978-0-7222-5339-7(7)) Library Reprints, Inc.

McAlpine, Margaret. Working in Music & Dance. 2005. (My Future Career Ser.). (Illus.). 54p. (J). lib. bdg. 26.00 (978-0-8368-4777-2(6)) Stevens, Gareth Inc.

McGrath, Bob & Davidson, Marilyn Copeland. Music for Fun: McGrath. 2000. 32p. (J). (ps). stu. ed. 3.95 (978-0-7692-9482-7(0) , Warner Bros. Pubns.) Alfred Publishing Co., Inc.

McGraw-Hill Staff. Essential Elements for Choir: Musicianship. 2001. Level 1. (C). pap., stu. ed. 27.96 (978-0-07-826085-8(X) , 9780078260858); Level 2. stu. ed. 25.96 (978-0-07-826039-1(6) , 9780078260391) Glencoe/McGraw-Hill.

—Essential Elements for Choir Pt. 2 & 3: Beginning Level 1, Repertoire. 2001. (C). stu. ed. 29.96 (978-0-07-826037-7(X) , 9780078260377) Glencoe/McGraw-Hill.

—Essential Elements for Choir, Intermediate Level 3 Repertoire, Mixed. 2001. stu. ed. 29.96 (978-0-07-826049-0(3) , 9780078260490) Glencoe/McGraw-Hill.

—Essential Elements for Choir, Intermediate Level 3, Repertoire, Tenor-Bass. 2001. stu. ed. 29.96 (978-0-07-826053-7(1) , 9780078260537) Glencoe/McGraw-Hill.

—Essential Elements for Choir, Intermediate Level 3, Repertoire, Treble. 2001. (C). stu. ed. 29.96 (978-0-07-826051-3(5) , 9780078260513) Glencoe/McGraw-Hill.

—Essential Elements for Choir Level 2 Repertoire, Mixed, Student Edition. 2001. 29.96 (978-0-07-826041-4(8) , 9780078260414) Glencoe/McGraw-Hill.

—Essential Elements for Choir Level 2 Repertoire, Tenor-Bass. 2001. stu. ed. 29.96 (978-0-07-826045-2(0) , 9780078260452) Glencoe/McGraw-Hill.

—Essential Elements for Choir Level 4 Repertoire, Mixed, Student Edition. 2001. 29.96 (978-0-07-826057-5(4) , 9780078260575) Glencoe/McGraw-Hill.

—Essential Elements for Choir Level 4 Repertoire, Tenor-Bass, Student Edition. 2001. (C). 29.96 (978-0-07-826061-2(2) , 9780078260612) Glencoe/McGraw-Hill.

—Essential Elements for Choir Level 4 Repertoire, Treble, Student Edition. 2001. 29.96 (978-0-07-826059-9(0) , 9780078260599) Glencoe/McGraw-Hill.

—Essential Elements for Choir Repertoire, Treble, Level 2. 2001. (C). stu. ed. 29.96 (978-0-07-826043-8(4) , 9780078260438) Glencoe/McGraw-Hill.

—Experiencing Choral Music, Advanced Mixed Voices. 2004. (C). pap., stu. ed. 29.32 (978-0-07-861129-2(6) , 9780078611292) Glencoe/McGraw-Hill.

—Experiencing Choral Music, Beginning Unison 2-Part/3-Part. 2004. pap., stu. ed. 29.32 (978-0-07-861104-9(0) , 9780078611049) Glencoe/McGraw-Hill.

—Experiencing Choral Music, Intermediate Mixed Voices. 2004. pap., stu. ed. 29.32 (978-0-07-861108-7(3) , 9780078611087) Glencoe/McGraw-Hill.

—Experiencing Choral Music, Intermediate Tenor Bass Voices. 2004. pap., stu. ed. 29.32 (978-0-07-861114-8(8) , 9780078611148) Glencoe/McGraw-Hill.

—Experiencing Choral Music, Intermediate Treble Voices. 2004. pap., stu. ed. 29.32 (978-0-07-861111-7(3) , 9780078611117) Glencoe/McGraw-Hill.

—Experiencing Choral Music, Proficient Mixed Voices. 2004. pap., stu. ed. 29.32 (978-0-07-861119-3(9) , 9780078611193) Glencoe/McGraw-Hill.

—Experiencing Choral Music, Proficient Tenor Bass Voices. 2004. pap., stu. ed. 29.32 (978-0-07-861125-4(3) , 9780078611254) Glencoe/McGraw-Hill.

—Experiencing Choral Music, Proficient Treble Voices. 2004. pap., stu. ed. 29.32 (978-0-07-861122-3(9) , 9780078611223) Glencoe/McGraw-Hill.

—Grade: Gr 4-8 Sound Perc. Video Share Music 2000. 2003. (Share the Music Ser.). (gr. 4-8). (978-0-02-295485-7(6)) Macmillan/McGraw-Hill Schl. Div.

—Grade: Gr 6 Playing Guitar Share Music 2000. 2003. (Share the Music Ser.). (gr. 6 up). (978-0-02-295406-2(6)) Macmillan/McGraw-Hill Schl. Div.

—Grade: Gr K CDs Share the Music 2000. 2003. (Share the Music Ser.). (gr. k up). (978-0-02-295435-2(X)) Macmillan/McGraw-Hill Schl. Div.

—Grade: Gr1 Cd(8) Share the Music 2000 Ed. 2003. (Share the Music Ser.). (gr. 1 up). (978-0-02-295436-9(8)) Macmillan/McGraw-Hill Schl. Div.

—Videocassette: Video Gr 3-6 Signing Share Music 2000. 2003. (Share the Music Ser.). (gr. 3-6). (978-0-02-295480-2(5)) Macmillan/McGraw-Hill Schl. Div.

Me & My Bean Bag. 2001. (J). 10.95 incl. audio (978-0-937124-21-5(4) , KIM 9111C) Kimbo Educational.

Menotti Amahl & the Night Visitors, Vol. 9. 1998. (J). ring bd. 60.00 (978-1-928908-09-8(8)) Classical Connections.

Meredith-Markowitz, Susan. Around the World with Music. 2003. (Early Connections Ser.). (J). pap. 33.00 (978-1-4108-1081-6(X)) Benchmark Education Co.

Michael, Judah Israel. The New Music. 2004. 60p. (YA). per. 12.95 (978-1-59196-665-4(5)) Instantpublisher.com.

MiDisaurus. 2003. (Share the Music Ser.). (gr. 1-3). (978-0-02-295528-1(3)); (978-0-02-295557-1(7)) Macmillan/McGraw-Hill Schl. Div.

The Mischievous Bugs. 2003. (J). pap., tchr. ed., act. bk. ed. 17.95 (978-0-9722673-2-8(8)) Audrey Productions.

Mitchell, Loretta. Ready-to-Use Music Reading Activities Kit: A Complete Sequential Program for Use with Mallet & Keyboard Instruments. 2003. (Illus.). 228p. pap. 29.95 (978-0-89328-156-4(5) , 30/1801H) Heritage Music Pr.

Morgan, Sally & Laler, Pauline. Music. 2001. (Behind Media Ser.). (Illus.). 48p. (YA). (gr. 6-8). lib. bdg. 24.22 (978-1-58810-030-6(8)) Heinemann Library.

Mueller, Todd & Boland, Hank. Soup du Jour (mus) 2003. (YA). (gr. 10). pap. 7.50 (978-1-58342-179-6(3) , SH7) Dramatic Publishing Co.

Music. Gr 1 Share the Music Pe. 2003. (Share the Music Ser.). (gr. 1 up). (978-0-02-295563-2(1)) Macmillan/McGraw-Hill Schl. Div.

—Gr 6 Share the Music Pe. 2003. (Share the Music Ser.). (gr. 6 up). (978-0-02-295568-7(2)) Macmillan/McGraw-Hill Schl. Div.

—Gr K-3 Stm Music & Moveme. 2003. (Share the Music Ser.). (gr. k-3). (978-0-02-295482-6(1)) Macmillan/McGraw-Hill Schl. Div.

—Instrmnts of the Orch(Cd- 2003. (Share the Music Ser.). (gr. 1-8). (978-0-02-295594-6(1)) Macmillan/McGraw-Hill Schl. Div.

—Instrmnts of the World(Cd. 2003. (Share the Music Ser.). (gr. 3-8). (978-0-02-295595-3(X)) Macmillan/McGraw-Hill Schl. Div.

—Instrumental Sounds. 2003. (Share the Music Ser.). (gr. 1-8). incl. audio compact disk (978-0-02-295596-0(8)) Macmillan/McGraw-Hill Schl. Div.

—Share the Music Big Book Grade 1. 2003. (Share the Music Ser.). (gr. 1 up). (978-0-02-295384-3(1)) Macmillan/McGraw-Hill Schl. Div.

—Share the Music Big Book Grade 2. 2003. (Share the Music Ser.). (gr. 2 up). (978-0-02-295385-0(X)) Macmillan/McGraw-Hill Schl. Div.

Music Ace. 2003. (Technology: Music Ser.). (978-0-02-295318-8(3)); (978-0-02-295319-5(1)); (978-0-02-295320-1(5)); (978-0-02-295321-8(3)); (978-0-02-295327-0(2)); (978-0-02-295328-7(0)) Macmillan/McGraw-Hill Schl. Div.

Music Ace 2. 2003. (Technology: Music Ser.). (978-0-02-295333-1(7)); (978-0-02-295334-8(5)); (978-0-02-295335-5(3)); (978-0-02-295336-2(1)); (978-0-02-295344-7(2)) Macmillan/McGraw-Hill Schl. Div.

Music Alive Magazine Classroom Set. 2003. (Share the Music Ser.). (gr. 6-8). (978-0-02-295618-9(2)) Macmillan/McGraw-Hill Schl. Div.

Music & Poetry. 2004. (Literacy Activities for Circle Time Ser.). 96p. (J). pap. 10.99 (978-1-57029-478-5(X) , WPH99039, Totline Pubns.) Schaffer, Frank Pubns.

Music Express Magazine Classroom Set. 2003. (Share the Music Ser.). (gr. k-6). (978-0-02-295671-4(9)) Macmillan/McGraw-Hill Schl. Div.

Music, Music, Music! Individual Title, 6 packs. (Rigby Infoquest Ser.). (gr. 6 up). 37.00 (978-0-7578-8001-8(0)) Rigby Education.

Music Time. 1.85 (978-0-7673-6158-3(X)); 2005. 1.95 (978-0-633-17857-4(8)); 2005. 1.95 (978-0-633-17659-4(1)); 2004. 1.95 (978-0-633-17464-4(5)); 2004. 1.95 (978-0-633-08665-7(7)); 2004. 1.95 (978-0-633-08415-8(8)); 2004. 1.95 (978-0-633-08163-8(9)); 2003. 1.95 (978-0-633-07791-4(7)) LifeWay Christian Resources.

Music Time. 2003. (Technology: Music Ser.). (978-0-02-295245-7(4)); (978-0-02-295243-3(8)) Macmillan/McGraw-Hill Schl. Div.

Musica para todos Handbook: Additional Components. 2003. (Share the Music Ser.). (gr. k-2). (978-0-02-295444-4(9)); (gr. 3-6). (978-0-02-295445-1(7)) Macmillan/McGraw-Hill Schl. Div.

Musical Expression Videotape: Videotape Packages. 2003. (Share the Music Ser.). (gr. 3-6). (978-0-02-295483-3(X)) Macmillan/McGraw-Hill Schl. Div.

Musical Max. 2004. 24.95 incl. audio (978-1-56008-092-3(2)); pap. 14.95 incl. audio (978-1-56008-068-8(X)) Weston Woods Studios, Inc.

Musik. 3rd ed. (Duden-Schuelerduden Ser.). (GER.). 504p. (YA). (978-3-411-05393-3(3)) Bibliographisches Institut & F. A. Brockhaus AG DEU. *Dist:* International Bk. Import Service, Inc.

Musser, Bill & Musser, Gloria. International Method for Band Bk. 1: Flute. 2001. 32p. stu. ed. 6.95 (978-1-58918-000-0(3)) Pocono Mountain Music Publishing, Inc.

—International Method for Band Bk. 2: Flute. 2001. 32p. stu. ed. 6.95 (978-1-58918-002-4(X)) Pocono Mountain Music Publishing, Inc.

—International Method for Band Bk. 3: Flute. 2001. 32p. stu. ed. 6.95 (978-1-58918-004-8(6)) Pocono Mountain Music Publishing, Inc.

—International Method for Band Bk. 3: Trumpet. 2001. 32p. (J). stu. ed. 6.95 (978-1-58918-049-9(6)) Pocono Mountain Music Publishing, Inc.

Myers, Gary E. Understanding & Using Chords & Chord Progressions. 2001. (Illus.). 110p. 12.95 (978-0-9643073-5-3(9)) MusicGem.

Naji, Jamilla. Musical Storyland: A Sing-A-Long Book with Musical Disc. l.t. ed. 2004. (Illus.). 32p. (J). per. 19.99 (978-0-9745568-0-2(7)) Worlds In Ink Publishing, Inc.

Neelly, Linda Page, et al, eds. Start the Music Strategies. 2000. (Illus.). 32p. pap. 6.00 (978-1-56545-144-5(9)) MENC - The National Assn. for Music Education.

Ng, Henry, illus. Rock'n'roll Guitar. 2002. 10p. (J). bds. (978-0-7853-7150-2(8)) Publications International, Ltd.

The Nutcracker Music Game. 2004. (J). (gr. 2-8). 24.95 incl. audio (978-1-55592-175-0(2)) Weston Woods Studios, Inc.

Ochs, Bill. The Clarke Learn-to-Play Tin Whistle Set: Includes Clarke Original D Tin Whistle on Blister Card: Book, Whistle & Compact Disc. 2003. (Illus.). 80p. audio compact disk 29.95 (978-0-9727516-0-5(2)) Pennywhistler's Pr.

—The Clarke Tin Whistle: Includes Clarke Sweetone D. Whistle. deluxe ed. 2000. 80p. pap. 24.95 incl. audio compact disk (978-0-9623456-8-5(7)) Pennywhistler's Pr.

Oesterlein, Nikolaus. Katalog Einer Richard Wagner-Bibliothek, 4 vols., set. 2001. (YA). reprint ed. 500.00 (978-0-7222-5562-9(4)) Library Reprints, Inc.

Orchestrations for Orff Instruments. 2003. (Share the Music Ser.). (gr. 1 up). (978-0-02-295407-9(4)); (gr. 2 up). (978-0-02-295408-6(2)); (gr. 3 up). (978-0-02-295409-3(0)); (gr. 4 up). (978-0-02-295410-9(4)); (gr. 5 up). (978-0-02-295411-6(2)); (gr. 6 up). (978-0-02-295412-3(0)) Macmillan/McGraw-Hill Schl. Div.

Osterling, Eric. Overture for Youth, No. 1. 1999. (YA). 30.00 (978-0-7692-8197-1(4) , Warner Bros. Pubns.) Alfred Publishing Co., Inc.

Paker, Josephine. I Wonder Why Mice Are Musical: Mice Are Musical. Kingfisher Editors, ed. 2007. (I Wonder Why Ser.). (Illus.). 32p. (J). (gr. k-3). pap. 6.95 (978-0-7534-6084-9(X) , Kingfisher) Houghton Mifflin Co. Trade & Reference Div.

Parker, Steve. The Science of Sound: Projects & Experiments with Music & Sound Waves. 2005. (Tabletop Scientist Ser.). (Illus.). 32p. (J). (gr. 4-7). lib. bdg. 29.29 (978-1-4034-7281-6(5)) Heinemann Library.

—The Science of Sound: Projects with Experiments with Music & Sound Waves. 2005. (Illus.). 32p. (J). pap. (978-1-4034-7288-5(2)) Heinemann Library.

Parry, Charles H. H. College Addresses Delivered to Pupils of the Royal College of Music. 2001. 301p. (YA). reprint ed. 98.00 (978-0-7222-5832-3(1)) Library Reprints, Inc.

Patrick, Chris. Beyoncé & Destiny's Child. 2005. (Illus.). 122p. (J). (978-0-439-80832-3(4)) Scholastic, Inc.

Penton. Masterpieces Set. 2003. (Baby's First Ser.). (J). 23.95 (978-1-59125-335-8(7)) Penton Overseas, Inc.

—Sleep Little Baby Set. 2003. (Relaxation Ser.). (J). 23.95 (978-1-59125-336-5(5)) Penton Overseas, Inc.

Performance Supplement Kit: Additional Components. 2003. (Share the Music Ser.). (gr. k up). (978-0-02-295664-6(6)); (gr. 1 up). (978-0-02-295665-3(4)); (gr. 2 up). (978-0-02-295666-0(2)); (gr. 3 up). (978-0-02-295667-7(0)); (gr. 4 up). (978-0-02-295668-4(9)); (gr. 5 up). (978-0-02-295669-1(7)); (gr. 6 up). (978-0-02-295670-7(0)) Macmillan/McGraw-Hill Schl. Div.

Perucca, Nancy Call & Evans, Renee Call. Sea Notes on the Keyboard: The Fast & Fun Way to Learn the Notes on the Keyboard! Perucca, Nancy Call, illus. 2004. (Illus.). 32p. (J). pap. 9.95 (978-0-9748074-1-6(9)) Nancy's Artworks.

Playing the Recorder. 2003. (Share the Music Ser.). (gr. 3 up). (978-0-02-295402-4(3)); (gr. 4 up). (978-0-02-295403-1(1)); (gr. 5 up). (978-0-02-295404-8(X)); (gr. 6 up). (978-0-02-295405-5(8)) Macmillan/McGraw-Hill Schl. Div.

Potter, Giselle, illus. C'mon an' Swing in My Tree! 2005. 14p. (J). bds. 16.95 incl. audio compact disk (978-0-9763012-0-2(2)) Cow Heard Records.

Presley. Can't Help Falling in Love. Date not set. 32p. 15.99 (978-0-06-027796-3(3)) HarperCollins Pubs.

Pressnall, Debra Olson. The Big Book of Music Games. 1999. (Illus.). 320p. (J). (gr. 1-5). pap. 22.99 (978-1-56822-673-6(X) , IF20453) School Specialty Publishing.

Prokofiev Cinderella Suite, Vol. 6. 1998. (J). ring bd. 60.00 (978-1-928908-06-7(3)) Classical Connections.

Pupil Edition. 2003. (Share the Music Ser.). (gr. 2 up). (978-0-02-295564-9(X)); (gr. 3 up). (978-0-02-295565-6(8)); (gr. 4 up). (978-0-02-295566-3(6)); (gr. 5 up). (978-0-02-295567-0(4)) Macmillan/McGraw-Hill Schl. Div.

Radabaugh, Melinda Beth. Going to a Concert. 2004. (Heinemann Read & Learn Ser.). (Illus.). 24p. (J). pap. 5.75 (978-1-4034-3882-9(X)); lib. bdg. 18.50 (978-1-4034-3867-6(6)) Heinemann Library.

Rands, Bernard. Concerto, No. 1. 2006. 92p. pap. 100.00 (978-1-4234-0305-0(3) , 1423403053) Schott Musik International GmbH & Co. KG DEU. *Dist:* Leonard, Hal Corp.

Ravel Bolero, Vol. 29. 1998. (J). ring bd. 60.00 (978-1-928908-29-6(2)) Classical Connections.

Reynolds, Peter H. The North Star Musical Journey. 2000. (Illus.). 88p. (J). ring bd. 79.00 (978-1-891405-12-9(8)) FableVision Pr.

Ridgeley, Sara. The Shiniest Star (Nativity) (Illus.). (J). 25.95 incl. audio compact disk (978-1-85909-656-7(5) , Warner Bros. Pubns.) Alfred Publishing Co., Inc.

Ridgley, Sara & Mole, Gavin. Sing It & Say - France. (Illus.). 124p. 10.95 (978-1-85909-301-6(9) , Warner Bros. Pubns.) Alfred Publishing Co., Inc.

Ridgley, Sara, et al. Sing It & Say - Festivals. (Illus.). 128p. 10.95 (978-1-85909-304-7(3) , Warner Bros. Pubns.) Alfred Publishing Co., Inc.

Rigby. Tuned in to Shared Reading & Music. 2001. (Illus.). pap. (978-0-7635-7342-3(6)) Steck-Vaughn.

Rigby Education Staff. Bingo. (Illus.). (J). suppl. ed. 20.00 (978-0-7635-6473-5(7) , 764737C99) Rigby Education.

Riley, Athelstan. A Collection of Faux-Bourdons & Descants. 2001. (YA). reprint ed. 150.00 (978-0-7222-6132-3(2)) Library Reprints, Inc.

Rimsky-Korsakov Flight of the Bumblebee, Vol. 3. 1998. (J). ring bd. 60.00 (978-1-928908-03-6(9)) Classical Connections.

Rinsky-Korsakov Scheherazade, Vol. 24. 1998. (J). ring bd. 60.00 (978-1-928908-24-1(1)) Classical Connections.

Roca, Nuria. Que Es el Arte? Musica. 2004. (Libros Que Es el Arte? Ser.).Tr. of What Is Art? Music. (SPA.). 36p. (J). pap. 6.95 (978-0-7641-2706-9(3)) Barron's Educational Series, Inc.

Roca, Nuria. What Is Art? Music. 2004. (gr. k-3). lib. bdg. 15.25 (978-0-613-81361-7(8)) Tandem Library Bks.

Roca, Nuria. What Is Art? Music. 2004. (What Is Art? Bks.). (Illus.). 36p. (J). pap. 6.95 (978-0-7641-2702-1(0)) Barron's Educational Series, Inc.

Rodgers/Hammerstein Oklahoma!, Vol. 4. 1998. (J). ring bd. 60.00 (978-1-928908-04-3(7)) Classical Connections.

Rodrigo, Joaquin. Concierto de Aranjuez. 2005. 80p. pap. 27.95 (978-1-4234-0287-9(1) , 1423402871) Schott Musik International GmbH & Co. KG DEU. *Dist:* Leonard, Hal Corp.

Rossini William Tell, Vol. 10. 1998. (J). ring bd. 60.00 (978-1-928908-10-4(1)) Classical Connections.

Saint-Saens, Camille. The Aquarium: Hands-on Music: an iconic listening experience in Felt. 2005. (UND., Illus.). 18p. (J). 35.00 (978-0-9763194-1-2(1)) MusicWorks.

—The Aquarium (Craft Kit) Hands-on Music: An Iconic Listening Experience in Felt. 2005. (UND., Illus.). 18p. (J). 30.00 (978-0-9763194-0-5(3)) MusicWorks.

Sands, Ginger. The Gift of Make-Believe. Brittingham, Geoffrey et al, illus. 1999. (J). (ps). pap. 15.99 incl. audio compact disk (978-0-9674849-0-7(1) , 061496) Laughing Sun Productions.

Scarlatti, Alessandro. Harpsichord & Organ Music, 12 vols., set. 2001. (YA). reprint ed. 1500.00 (978-0-7222-5987-0(5)) Library Reprints, Inc.

Scholastic, Inc. Staff. Clifford Musical Memory Games. 2004. (J). cd-rom 9.99 (978-0-439-44355-5(5)) Scholastic, Inc.

Schonberg/Boubil Les Miserables, Vol. 30. 1998. (J). ring bd. 60.00 (978-1-928908-30-2(6)) Classical Connections.

Schwartz, Bettina. Baby Loves Beethoven Vol. 3: Introducing Classical Music to Your Child. Devine, Sheila K., illus. 1998. 16p. (Orig.). (J). (ps). pap. 5.95 (978-0-9640303-6-7(5)) Addington Publishing.

Schwartz, Betty Ann. What Makes Music? A Magic Ribbon Book. Turner, Dona, illus. 2005. (Stories to Share Ser.). 16p. (J). (ps-3). act. bk. ed. 11.95 (978-1-58117-139-6(0) , Intervisual/Piggy Toes) Dalmatian Pr.

Scully, Michael. Reaching Teens Through Film & Music. Cannizzo, Karen A., ed. 2001. (Jesus in Modern Media Ser.: Vol. 2001-2002). 96p. (YA). pap. 19.95 (978-0-89837-176-5(7)) Pflaum Publishing Group.

—Reaching Teens Through Film & Music. 1999. (Jesus in Modern Media Ser.: Vol. 2000). 128p. (YA). pap. 19.95 (978-0-937997-60-4(9) , 3700) Pflaum Publishing Group.

Sdoia-Satz, Phyllis & Leon, Alfredo, Jr. Husky Gang: My Playing Book. 2001. (Illus.). 48p. (J). (ps-3). pap. 7.95 (978-0-7579-7891-3(6) , Warner Bros. Pubns.) Alfred Publishing Co., Inc.

—Husky Gang: My Song & Story Book. 2001. (Illus.). 120p. (J). (ps-3). pap. 16.95 incl. audio compact disk (978-0-7579-7889-0(4) , Warner Bros. Pubns.) Alfred Publishing Co., Inc.

—Husky Gang: My Working Book. 2001. (Illus.). 48p. (J). (ps-3). pap. 7.95 (978-0-7579-7890-6(8) , Warner Bros. Pubns.) Alfred Publishing Co., Inc.

Sesame Street Makes Music. 2002. (Play-A-Song Ser.). (Illus.). 12p. (J). 15.98 (978-0-7853-6064-3(6)) Publications International, Ltd.

Shady Bizzness: Life As Marshall Mathers' Body Guard in An Industry of Paper Gangsters. 2nd collector's ed. 2000. 176p. (YA). mass mkt. (978-0-9703881-0-0(1)) Big Willz Records.

Share Caribbean Music: Additional Components. 2003. (Share the Music Ser.). (gr. 3-5). incl. audio compact disk (978-0-02-295598-4(4)) Macmillan/McGraw-Hill Schl. Div.

Share the Music Big Book. 2003. (Share the Music Ser.). (gr. k up). (978-0-02-295366-9(3)) Macmillan/McGraw-Hill Schl. Div.

Signing for Primary Grades Videotape: Videotape Packages. 2003. (Share the Music Ser.). (gr. k-2). (978-0-02-295479-6(1)) Macmillan/McGraw-Hill Schl. Div.

Silver Burdett Making Music Music Connection: Compact Disc Package. 2002. (gr. 1 up). (978-0-382-34446-6(4)) Silver, Burdett & Ginn, Inc.

Sing a Song Set 800867, 3 vols. 2005. (J). pap. (978-1-59794-052-8(6)) Environments, Inc.

Site License Package: Technology: Music with MIDI. 2003. (Share the Music Ser.). (gr. 4 up). (978-0-02-295467-3(8)); (gr. 7 up). (978-0-02-295237-2(3)); (gr. 8 up). (978-0-02-295238-9(1)) Macmillan/McGraw-Hill Schl. Div.

Smith, Douglas W. Doug Smith's Classical Guitar Method, Reading Book 2: Beginning Pieces for the First Position. 2004. (J). 24.95 (978-0-9729879-2-9(4)) Musictech College Pr.

Sousa Marches, Vol. 11. 1998. (J). ring bd. 60.00 (978-1-928908-11-1(X)) Classical Connections.

Sra. Grade: Gr 6 CDs Share the Music. 2003. (Share the Music Ser.). (gr. 6 up). (978-0-02-295441-3(4)) Macmillan/McGraw-Hill Schl. Div.

Standard Package: Technology: Music with MIDI. 2003. (Share the Music Ser.). (gr. 4 up). (978-0-02-295461-1(9)); (gr. 7 up). (978-0-02-295231-0(4)); (gr. 8 up). (978-0-02-295232-7(2)) Macmillan/McGraw-Hill Schl. Div.

Stephens, Wayne. Building Character Through Music - Elementary Song Book. 2004. spiral bd. 39.95 (978-1-892056-32-0(1)) Character Development Publishing.

—Building Character Through Music - High School Song Book. 2004. (YA). spiral bd. 39.95 (978-1-892056-36-8(4)) Character Development Publishing.

Sternal, Mark John. The 12 Notes of Music: Ear Training & Interval Study Course. 2004. (Illus.). 18p. 7.95 (978-0-9762917-2-5(X)) MJS Music Pubns.

Storms, Jerry B. 101 More Music Games for Children: More Fun & Learning with Rhythm & Song. Bowman, Cecilia, illus. 2001. (SmartFun Activity Bks.). 176p. (J). (ps up). pap. 14.95 (978-0-89793-298-1(6)) Hunter Hse., Inc.

The Story of Music, 10 vols. 2000. (Illus.). 800p. (J). (gr. 5-10). lib. bdg. 329.00 (978-0-7172-9559-3(1) , Grolier) Scholastic Library Publishing.

Story of Music, 10 vols. 2000. (Illus.). (J). (978-0-7172-9569-2(9)); (978-0-7172-9560-9(5)); (978-0-7172-9562-3(1)); (978-0-7172-9563-0(X)); (978-0-7172-9564-7(8)); (978-0-7172-9565-4(6)); (978-0-7172-9566-1(4)); (978-0-7172-9567-8(2)); (978-0-7172-9568-5(0)) Scholastic Library Publishing. (Grolier).

Strauss, Alix & Pearl, A. Hey Carson! Meet TRL's Carson Daly. 2000. (Illus.). 112p. (J). (gr. 7-12). pap. 4.99 (978-0-439-20759-1(2)) Scholastic, Inc.

Strauss Waltzes, Vol. 18. 1998. (J). ring bd. 60.00 (978-1-928908-18-0(7)) Classical Connections.

Taylor, Terilyn & Milleret, Toni. The Cello Handbook: A Reference Guide to Music Literacy. 2000. (Color Connection Ser.). (Illus.). 56p. (YA). (gr. 1 up). pap. 15.95 (978-0-9671719-8-2(9)) T&T Publishing.

Tchaikovsky Nutcracker, Vol. 5. 1998. (J). ring bd. 60.00 (978-1-928908-05-0(5)) Classical Connections.

Tchaikovsky Romeo & Juliet, Vol. 25. 1998. (J). ring bd. 60.00 (978-1-928908-25-8(X)) Classical Connections.

Tchaikovsky Sleeping Beauty, Vol. 13. 1998. (J). ring bd. 60.00 (978-1-928908-13-5(6)) Classical Connections.

Teacher, Matthew. On the Road Again: 25 Sing-Along Tunes to Make the Miles Fly By! 2005. (Illus.). 80p. pap. 12.95 incl. audio compact disk (978-0-7624-2210-4(6) , Running Pr. Kids) Running Pr. Bk. Pubs.

Television Themes Alto Sax. 13.95 incl. audio compact disk (978-1-85909-718-2(9) , Warner Bros. Pubns.) Alfred Publishing Co., Inc.

Television Themes Clarinet. 13.95 incl. audio compact disk (978-1-85909-717-5(0) , Warner Bros. Pubns.) Alfred Publishing Co., Inc.

Television Themes Flute. 13.95 incl. audio compact disk (978-1-85909-716-8(2) , Warner Bros. Pubns.) Alfred Publishing Co., Inc.

Theory for Young Musicians. (J). Bk. 1. (978-0-7390-0232-2(5) , 18513); Bk. 1. incl. audio compact disk (978-0-7390-0233-9(3) , 18514); Bk. 2. (978-0-7390-0235-3(X) , 18516); Bk. 2. incl. audio compact disk (978-0-7390-0236-0(8) , 18517) Alfred Publishing Co., Inc.

Theory for Young Musicians, Notespeller. (J). (978-0-7390-0231-5(7) , 18512) Alfred Publishing Co., Inc.

Thomas, Roger. Groups, Bands, & Orchestras. 2001. (Soundbites Ser.). (Illus.). 32p. (YA). (gr. 6-8). lib. bdg. 22.79 (978-1-58810-264-5(5)) Heinemann Library.

Thomson, Ryan J. Left Handed Fiddling for Beginners: A Teach Yourself Method, 1 bk, 1 CD. 2004. (Illus.). 22p. 22.95 (978-0-931877-44-5(X)) Captain Fiddle Pubns.

Tomaselli, Anthony. Play Guitar 1. 2003. cd-rom (978-0-9714299-5-6(2)) I Save A Tree.

Turnbull, Elizabeth, ed. Music from the Romantic Era: Violin & Piano. 2004. (gr. 4-7). 14.95 (978-0-8256-1843-7(6) , BOE005012) Music Sales Corp.

Turner, Gary. Progressive's Young Beginner Keyboard Giant Coloring Book. 2003. (Illus.). 36p. (J). pap. 23.95 incl. audio compact disk (978-1-86469-097-2(6)) Learntoplaymusic.com AUS. *Dist:* Bookworld Trade, Inc.

—Progressive's Young Beginner Recorder Giant Coloring Book. 2003. (Illus.). 36p. (J). pap. 23.95 incl. audio compact disk (978-1-86469-099-6(2)) Learntoplaymusic.com AUS. *Dist:* Bookworld Trade, Inc.

Upton, George P. Standard Concert Repertory & Other Concert Pieces: The Standard Overtures, Suites, Symphonic Poems, Rhapsodies, Fantasias. 2001. 449p. (YA). reprint ed. 98.00 (978-0-7222-5844-6(5)) Library Reprints, Inc.

Verdi Aida, Vol. 31. 1998. (J). ring bd. 60.00 (978-1-928908-31-9(4)) Classical Connections.

Video. Baby Bach (Music Video) 1999. (J). bds. 15.98 incl. VHS (978-1-892309-08-2(4)) Baby Einstein Co., LLC, The.

Visual MT. 2002. (gr. 1-8). cd-rom 99.05 (978-0-382-34441-1(3)) Silver, Burdett & Ginn, Inc.

Vv. ¡Musica! 2004. (SPA.). 48p. (J). 22.99 (978-84-261-3343-4(6)) Juventud, Editorial ESP. *Dist:* Lectorum Pubns., Inc.

Wadsworth, Pamela. Golwg Gyntaf Ar Sain a Cherddoriaeth. 2005. (WEL., Illus.). 24p. pap. (978-1-85596-247-7(0)) Dref Wen.

Walt Disney Records Staff, prod. More Silly Songs: Twenty More Simply Super Singable Silly Songs. 1998. (J). pap. 12.98 incl. audio compact disk (978-0-7634-0437-6(3)) Walt Disney Records.

Wargin, Kathy-Jo. M Is for Melody: A Music Alphabet. Larson, Katherine, illus. 2004. 40p. (J). 16.95 (978-1-58536-215-8(8)) Sleeping Bear Pr.

Wargin, Kathy-Jo. A Music Alphabet. rev. ed. 2007. 40p. pap. 7.95 ***(978-1-58536-332-2(4))*** Sleeping Bear Pr.

Warner, Dennis. Beads on One String. Unzelman, Alison, illus. 2004. 31p. (J). lib. bdg. 24.95 (978-0-9747147-7-6(1)) MK Publishing.

Waskiewicz, Alex, illus. Simply Music with Mr. Paul. 2000. spiral bd. (978-0-9716493-0-9(8) , 1) tunesntots.com.

Webber Cats, Vol. 19. 1998. (J). ring bd. 60.00 (978-1-928908-19-7(5)) Classical Connections.

Weber, Lou, ed. Jo Jo's Circus Little Music Note Book. 2004. 10p. (J). bds. 9.98 (978-1-4127-3496-7(7) , 7262700) Publications International, Ltd.

—Jo Jos Circus Little Sound Book. 2004. 10p. 9.98 (978-1-4127-3485-1(1)) Publications International, Ltd.

—Snow White Music in the Air. 2004. 10p. (J). bds. 9.98 (978-1-4127-3350-2(2) , 7249800) Publications International, Ltd.

—Spots Marching Band Interactive. 2005. 24p. (J). 15.98 (978-1-4127-3126-3(7) , 7231400) Publications International, Ltd.

—Spots Rainy Day Little Sound Book. 2004. 10p. 9.98 (978-1-4127-3108-9(9)) Publications International, Ltd.

—Tiggers Treasure Tunes Music Note Book. 2004. 10p. (J). bds. 9.98 (978-1-4127-3347-2(2) , 7249600) Publications International, Ltd.

—Wiggles Sing Play Drum Book. 2004. 14p. (J). bds. 15.98 (978-1-4127-3324-3(3) , 7246200) Publications International, Ltd.

Weeks, Sarah. Z Is for Zoe. Date not set. 32p. (J). (ps-3). 15.99 (978-0-06-028138-0(3)) HarperCollins Pubs.

Weingartner, Felix. On the Performance of Beethoven's Symphonies. 2001. 195p. (YA). reprint ed. 88.00 (978-0-7222-5352-6(4)) Library Reprints, Inc.

Weir, Albert E. Saxophone Pieces. 2001. (YA). reprint ed. 150.00 (978-0-7222-6069-2(5)) Library Reprints, Inc.

Whiting, Marilee. It's Wiggle Time! Futrell, Ashley, ed. Sharp, Jan, illus. 2005. 80p. (J). per. 10.99 (978-1-59441-041-3(0) , CD-104041) Carson-Dellosa Publishing Co., Inc.

Whittley, LuVonia. The Choir Member & the Music Ministry, 1 bk. 2001. 96p. (YA). stu. ed., per. (978-0-940955-66-0(0)) UMI (Urban Ministries, Inc.).

Willson Music Man, Vol. 12. 1998. (J). ring bd. 60.00 (978-1-928908-12-8(8)) Classical Connections.

Wilson, Robert. The Beginning. rev. ed. 1999. 72p. (YA). pap. 16.00 (978-0-9679829-0-8(1)) Wilson Publishing.

Wu, Miriam, et al. Scaling the Tenor Clef Dragon: A Tenor Clef Workbook for Cellists. 2004. 28p. (J). 8.95 (978-0-9755624-1-3(X)) Boshu Pr.

Yerkes, Lane. Sounds of Music, 2000. (Talking Pages Deluxe Ser.). (Illus.). (J). (ps-3). 11.00 (978-1-58224-130-2(9)) Futech Interactive Products, Inc.

Yes I Can Staff. A Mariachi I'll Be. (J). stu. ed. 12.95 (978-0-8136-4418-9(6)) Modern Curriculum Pr.

Zampino, Phil. The PAZ Method - Different Beats Rhythms & Styles on the Drum Set: (Latin, Jazz, Odd Time, Rock, Country) 2000. (YA). (gr. 5 up). Vol. 2. pap. 19.50 (978-0-942253-18-4(3)); Vol. 3. pap. 19.50 (978-0-942253-19-1(1)) PAZ Publishing.

Zoo-phonics Music that Teaches. 2004. (J). cd-rom 19.95 (978-1-886441-43-9(X)) Zoo-phonics, Inc.

Zweig, Stefan. Romain Rolland: The Man & His Work. 2001. 377p. (YA). reprint ed. 98.00 (978-0-7222-5499-8(7)) Library Reprints, Inc.

MUSIC, AMERICAN

Carlin, Richard, ed. American Popular Music, 8 vols., Set. 2005. (American Popular Music Ser.). 320-320p. (YA). (gr. 6-12). 469.00 (978-0-8160-5309-4(X)) Facts On File, Inc.

Elmer, Howard. Blues: Its Birth & Growth. 1999. (Library of African American Arts & Culture). (Illus.). 64p. (YA). (gr. 7-12). lib. bdg. 26.50 (978-0-8239-1853-9(X) , AABLUE) Rosen Publishing Group, Inc., The.

Elson, Louis C. The History of American Music. 2001. 380p. (YA). reprint ed. 98.00 (978-0-7222-5150-8(5)) Library Reprints, Inc.

Kuzma, Gregory. On the Field from Denver, Colorado... the Blue Knights! One Member's Experience of the 1994 Summer National Tour. 2004. 206p. (YA). pap. 17.95 (978-0-595-32278-7(6)) iUniverse, Inc.

Porte, John F. Edward Macdowell: A Great American Tone Poet, His Life & Music. 2001. 180p. (YA). reprint ed. 88.00 (978-0-7222-5457-8(1)) Library Reprints, Inc.

MUSIC—ANALYSIS, APPRECIATION

Antcliffe, Herbert. How to Enjoy Music. 2001. 165p. (YA). reprint ed. 88.00 (978-0-7222-5640-4(X)) Library Reprints, Inc.

Armstrong, Jennifer. What a Song Can Do: 12 Riffs on the Power of Music. 2004. 208p. (J). (gr. 5). lib. bdg. 17.99 (978-0-375-92499-6(X) , Knopf Bks. for Young Readers) Random Hse. Children's Bks.

Bell, Richard & Bell, Cathy. The Beginner's Guide to Understanding Music: Learn the Basics of Music Theory. 2002. (Illus.). 78p. (YA). (gr. 5 up). spiral bd. 19.95 (978-0-9716170-0-1(7)) Rosebird Publishing.

Bernard, Yves & Fredette, Nathalie. Le Guide de la Musique du Monde. 2004. (FRE., Illus.). 230p. (J). pap. (978-2-89021-662-4(4)) Diffusion du livre Mirabel.

Bresler, Lorraine. Music in Our World. 2000. (Cambridge Reading Routes Ser.). (Illus.). 24p. pap. 5.50 (978-0-521-77894-7(8)) Cambridge Univ. Pr.

Bridge, G. F. Musical Gestures. 2001. (YA). reprint ed. 150.00 (978-0-7222-5725-8(2)) Library Reprints, Inc.

Buchanan, Fannie R. Magic Music Story Interpretations. 2006. (Illus.). pap. 21.95 ***(978-1-4286-5945-2(5))*** Kessinger Publishing, LLC.

Clare, Eva. Musical Appreciation & the Studio Club. 2001. (YA). reprint ed. 150.00 (978-0-7222-5641-1(8)) Library Reprints, Inc.

Elterlein, Ernst von. Beethoven's Symphonies Explained. 2001. (YA). reprint ed. 150.00 (978-0-7222-5330-4(3)) Library Reprints, Inc.

Evans, Edwin. Beethoven's Nine Symphonies Fully Described & Analyzed, 2 vols., set. 2001. (YA). reprint ed. 250.00 (978-0-7222-5331-1(1)) Library Reprints, Inc.

Everly, Nita. Can You Listen with Your Eyes. 1999. 13p. (J). (gr. 2). pap. 20.00 (978-0-9667567-0-8(3)) Cherry Street Bks.

Fuller, Cheri. How to Grow a Young Music Lover: Helping Your Child Discover & Enjoy the World of Music. 2nd ed. 2002. (Illus.). 208p. pap. 12.99 (978-0-87788-370-8(X) , Shaw) WaterBrook Pr.

Fuller-Maitland, John A. The Spell of Music: An Attempt to Analyze the Enjoyment of Music. 2001. 108p. (YA). reprint ed. 88.00 (978-0-7222-5644-2(2)) Library Reprints, Inc.

Hadow, William H. Sonata Form. 2001. 184p. (YA). reprint ed. 88.00 (978-0-7222-5335-9(4)) Library Reprints, Inc.

Hamilton, Clarence G. Music Appreciation, Based upon Methods of Literary Criticism. 2001. 396p. (YA). reprint ed. 98.00 (978-0-7222-5647-3(7)) Library Reprints, Inc.

Hanslick, Eduard. The Beautiful in Music. 2001. 174p. (YA). reprint ed. 88.00 (978-0-7222-5648-0(5)) Library Reprints, Inc.

Lee, Ernest M. On Listening to Music. 2001. 159p. (YA). reprint ed. 88.00 (978-0-7222-5652-7(3)) Library Reprints, Inc.

Mason, Daniel G. The Appreciation of Music, Vol. 1. 2001. (YA). reprint ed. 150.00 (978-0-7222-5827-9(5)) Library Reprints, Inc.

Mendelssohn-Bartholdy, Felix. Letters from Italy & Switzerland. 2001. 356p. (YA). reprint ed. 98.00 (978-0-7222-5463-9(6)) Library Reprints, Inc.

Moyer, Dorothy T. Introduction to Music Appreciation & History. 2001. 137p. (YA). reprint ed. 88.00 (978-0-7222-5659-6(0)) Library Reprints, Inc.

Multicultural Music. 2003. 160p. (J). (gr. k-4). pap. 6.00 (978-0-7424-0444-1(7) , 24123CAS-E4, Instructional Fair) Schaffer, Frank Pubns.

Nye, Penny. Music. Eargle, Michele, illus. 2000. (Bookmates Ser.). 15p. (J). (ps-3). pap. 12.00 (978-1-890703-19-6(2) , Bookmates) Penny Laine Papers, Inc.

Persons, Marjorie Kiel. Themes to Remember, 3, Vol. 1. Nellis, Philip, illus. 2007. 124p. (J). lib. bdg. 31.95 incl. audio compact disk ***(978-0-9794947-0-3(2))*** Classical Magic, Inc.

—Themes to Remember. Nellis, Philip & Johnson, George Ann, illus. 2000. 128p. (J). Vol. 1. lib. bdg. 31.95 incl. audio compact disk (978-0-9675997-0-0(9)); Vol. 2. lib. bdg. 31.95 incl. audio compact disk (978-0-9675997-1-7(7)) Classical Magic, Inc.

—Themes to Remember, Volume 2, Vol. 2. Nellis, Philip & Johnson, George Ann, illus. rev. ed. 2004. 128p. (J). lib. bdg. 31.95 (978-0-9675997-5-5(X)) Classical Magic, Inc.

Rimington, Alexander W. Colour-Music: The Art of Mobile Colour. 2001. 184p. (YA). reprint ed. 88.00 (978-0-7222-5805-7(4)) Library Reprints, Inc.

Saperstein, Stella & Luey, Beth. The Harmonious Child: Every Parent's Guide to Musical Instruments, Teachers, & Lessons. 2004. (Illus.). 176p. pap. 12.95 (978-1-58761-171-1(6) , Celestial Arts Publishing Company) Ten Speed Pr.

Scholes, Percy Alfred. The Appreciation of Music by Means of the Duo-Art. 2001. (YA). reprint ed. 150.00 (978-0-7222-5983-2(2)) Library Reprints, Inc.

—The Listener's Guide to Music. 2001. 106p. (YA). reprint ed. 88.00 (978-0-7222-5663-3(9)) Library Reprints, Inc.

—Musical Appreciation in Schools: Why & How? 2001. 41p. (YA). reprint ed. 88.00 (978-0-7222-5664-0(7)) Library Reprints, Inc.

Sharma, Elizabeth. Strings: Live Music! 2000. (Illus.). 32p. (J). (gr. 5-7). reprint ed. lib. bdg. 16.00 (978-0-7881-9433-7(X)) DIANE Publishing Co.

Shinn, Frederick G. Musical Memory & Its Cultivation: An Investigation into the Forms of Memory Employed in Pianoforte Playing. 2001. 73p. (YA). reprint ed. 88.00 (978-0-7222-5763-0(5)) Library Reprints, Inc.

Sidgewick, Arthur H. The Promenade Ticket: A Lay Record of Concert Going. 2001. 183p. (YA). reprint ed. 88.00 (978-0-7222-5842-2(9)) Library Reprints, Inc.

Statham, Henry Heathcote. What Is Music? A Brief Analysis. 2001. (YA). reprint ed. 150.00 (978-0-7222-5624-4(8)) Library Reprints, Inc.

Storr, Muriel. Music for Children: First Steps in Appreciation. 2001. 195p. (J). reprint ed. 88.00 (978-0-7222-5667-1(1)) Library Reprints, Inc.

Turner, Walter J. Music & Life. 2001. 213p. (YA). reprint ed. 98.00 (978-0-7222-5839-2(9)) Library Reprints, Inc.

Wallace, William. The Musical Faculty, Its Origins & Processes. 2001. 228p. (YA). reprint ed. 98.00 (978-0-7222-5800-2(3)) Library Reprints, Inc.

MUSIC—APPRECIATION

see Music—Analysis, Appreciation

MUSIC—BIOGRAPHY

see Musicians

MUSIC—DICTIONARIES

Baughan, Edward A. Music & Musicians. 2001. 324p. (YA). reprint ed. 98.00 (978-0-7222-5224-6(2)) Library Reprints, Inc.

Bibliotheque Nationale Staff. Catalogue du Fonds de Musique Ancienne de la Bibliotheque Nationale, 8 vols., set. 2001. (YA). reprint ed. 1000.00 (978-0-7222-5000-6(2)) Library Reprints, Inc.

British Museum Staff. Catalogue of Music: Recent Acquisitions of Old Music Printed Before the Year 1800. 2001. 225p. (YA). reprint ed. 98.00 (978-0-7222-5002-0(9)) Library Reprints, Inc.

Brown, James Duff. Biographical Dictionary of Musicians. 2001. 637p. (YA). reprint ed. 128.00 (978-0-7222-5004-4(5)) Library Reprints, Inc.

Davison, James W. Mendelss: To Wagner. 2001. (YA). reprint ed. 150.00 (978-0-7222-5237-6(4)) Library Reprints, Inc.

Duncan, Edmondstoune. Encyclopedia of Musical Terms. 2001. (YA). reprint ed. 150.00 (978-0-7222-5016-7(9)) Library Reprints, Inc.

Gehrkens, Karl W. Music Notation & Terminology. 2001. 168p. (YA). reprint ed. 88.00 (978-0-7222-5773-9(2)) Library Reprints, Inc.

Hughes, Rupert. Music Lovers' Cyclopedia. 2001. 949p. (YA). reprint ed. 248.00 (978-0-7222-5213-0(7)) Library Reprints, Inc.

Hull, Arthur E. A Dictionary of Modern Music & Musicians. 2001. 543p. (YA). reprint ed. 98.00 (978-0-7222-5214-7(5)) Library Reprints, Inc.

—Library of Music & Musicians. 2001. (YA). reprint ed. 1410.00 (978-0-7222-6366-2(X)) Library Reprints, Inc.

Hull, Arthur E. & Hull, Moore. Music-Lover's Library. 2001. (YA). reprint ed. 1912.00 (978-0-7222-6372-3(4)) Library Reprints, Inc.

International Who's Who in Music: A Contemporary Biographical Dictionary & a Record of the World's Musical Activity. 2001. 861p. (YA). reprint ed. 198.00 (978-0-7222-5217-8(X)) Library Reprints, Inc.

Krull, Kathleen. M Is for Music. Innerst, Stacy, illus. 2003. 56p. (J). (ps-3). 17.00 (978-0-15-201438-4(1)) Harcourt Children's Bks.

Munoz, Miguel. Diccionario Juvenil de Musica.Tr. of Children's Music Dictionary. (SPA.). (J). (gr. 3-5). pap. 11.20 (978-958-33-1357-8(2)) Botero de Borrero, Beatriz & Martha Olga Botero de Gomez COL. *Dist:* Lectorum Pubns., Inc.

—Sonodiccionario: Asi Suenan los Instrumentos. (SPA.). (J). (gr. k-2). pap. 8.76 (978-958-33-1556-5(7)) Botero de Borrero, Beatriz & Martha Olga Botero de Gomez COL. *Dist:* Lectorum Pubns., Inc.

Musical Directory of United Kingdom. 2001. (YA). reprint ed. 150.00 (978-0-7222-5020-4(7)) Library Reprints, Inc.

New Library of Music. 2001. (YA). reprint ed. 294.00 (978-0-7222-6379-2(1)) Library Reprints, Inc.

O'Donoghue, D. J. Biographical Dictionary of Irish Artists & Musicians. 2001. (YA). reprint ed. 150.00 (978-0-7222-5303-8(6)) Library Reprints, Inc.

Riemann, Hugo. Dictionary of Music. 2001. 895p. (YA). reprint ed. 198.00 (978-0-7222-5216-1(1)) Library Reprints, Inc.

Scholes, Percy Alfred. Everybody's Guide to Broadcast Music. 2001. 237p. (YA). reprint ed. 98.00 (978-0-7222-5161-4(0)) Library Reprints, Inc.

Stainer, John. A Dictionary of Musical Terms. 2001. (YA). reprint ed. 96p. 88.00 (978-0-7222-6331-0(7)); 456p. 98.00 (978-0-7222-5018-1(5)) Library Reprints, Inc.

MUSIC, DRAMATIC

see Opera; Operetta

MUSIC—FICTION

The Adventures of Max & Millie: At the Pond. 2003. (Illus.). 32p. (J). 8.95 (978-0-9744427-0-9(4)) music bks. & games.

Agee, Jon. Elvis Lives! And Other Anagrams. 2004. (Illus.). 80p. (J). reprint ed. pap. 8.95 (978-0-374-42095-6(5) , Sunburst) Farrar, Straus & Giroux.

Alcamo, John. A Musical Mystery. 2004. 62p. pap. 12.95 (978-1-4137-3457-7(X)) PublishAmerica, Inc.

Anaya, Hector. Cuenta, Cuenta. Moreno, Sergio, illus. 2nd rev. ed. 2004. (Castillo de la Castillo Verde Ser.). (SPA.). 184p. (J). pap. 7.95 (978-970-20-0135-5(8)) Castillo, Ediciones, S. A. de C. V. MEX. *Dist:* Macmillan.

Anderson, Doug. Too Big to Dance. Anderson, Sara, illus. 2004. 32p. (J). 15.95 (978-1-59354-046-3(9)) Handprint Bks.

Arkin, Alan. Cassie Loves Beethoven. l.t. ed. 2003. (Children's Large Print Ser.). 28.95 (978-1-58118-108-1(6)) LRS.

Armstrong, Jennifer. What a Song Can Do: 12 Riffs on the Power of Music. 2006. 208p. (YA). (gr. 7-11). pap. 5.99 (978-0-440-23816-4(1) , Laurel Leaf) Random Hse. Children's Bks.

Ball, Marcia. Christmas Fais Do-Do. 2006. (Illus.). 36p. (J). per. 14.95 (*978-1-58939-972-3(2)) Virtualbookworm.com Publishing, Inc.

Bang-Campbell, Monika. Little Rat Makes Music. Bang, Molly, illus. 2007. (Little Rat Ser.). (J). (gr. 1-4). 15.00 (978-0-15-205305-5(0)) Harcourt Trade Pubs.

Banks, Steven. The Song That Never Ends. DePorter, Vince, illus. 2004. (Ready-to-Read Ser.: Vol. 4). 32p. (J). pap. 3.99 (978-0-689-86528-2(7) , Simon Spotlight/ Nickelodeon) Simon & Schuster Children's Publishing.

—Song That Never Ends. 2004. (gr. k-3). lib. bdg. 11.80 (978-0-613-73449-3(1)) Tandem Library Bks.

Barker, Cicely Mary. Flower Fairies Musical Treasure Chest. 2005. 1p. (J). pap. 12.99 (978-0-7232-5384-6(6) , Warne) Penguin Group (USA) Inc.

Barney Plays Piano. 2002. (Illus.). (J). 16.98 (978-0-7853-5234-1(1)) Publications International, Ltd.

Baron, Andrew, illus. El Pulpo Rex. 2003. (SPA.). (J). per. 17.95 (978-0-9760348-1-0(6)) BaHart Pubns. / Eight Legs Publishing.

Bartlett, T. C. Tuba Lessons. Felix, Monique, illus. 2004. 32p. pap. 9.95 (978-0-89812-522-1(7) , Creative Paperbacks) Creative Co., The.

Basore, Polly M. Santa's Stray in A Piano for Christmas. Williams, Carlene H., illus. 2005. 32p. (J). per. (978-0-9771749-1-1(3)) AngelBooks.

Bauer, A. C. E. No Castles Here. 2007. 288p. (J). (gr. 4-8). 15.99 (978-0-375-83921-4(6) , Random Hse. Bks. for Young Readers) Random Hse. Children's Bks.

Ben's Tune: Individual Chapter Book Title Six-Packs. Vol. 28. 32p. (gr. 4 up). 44.00 (978-0-7578-0603-2(1)) Rigby Education.

Bloom, Stephanie. The Drummer Who Lost His Beat. Keylon, Joe, illus. 2005. 40p. (J). lib. bdg. 16.95 (978-1-931969-47-5(7)) Bloom & Grow Bks.

Border, Rosemary & Hedge, Tricia. The Piano, Level 2. 2nd ed. 2000. (Bookworms Ser.). (Illus.). 64p. 6.50 (978-0-19-422982-1(3)) Oxford Univ. Pr., Inc.

Bourgeois, Paulette. Franklin's Music Lessons. 2002. (gr. k-3). lib. bdg. 11.80 (978-0-613-50568-0(9)) Tandem Library Bks.

Bowler, Tim. Firmament. 2004. (Illus.). 320p. (YA). 16.95 (978-0-689-86161-1(3) , McElderry, Margaret K.) Simon & Schuster Children's Publishing.

Bronson, Matthew Shane & Bronson, Tammy Carter. Kaleidonotes & the Mixed-up Orchestra. Bronson, Tammy Carter, illus. 2nd rev. ed. 2003. (Illus.). 24p. (J). lib. bdg. 12.99 (978-0-9678167-6-0(9)) Bookaroos Publishing, Inc.

Brown, Richard, illus. Street Music. 2006. (I'm Going to Read Ser.). 24p. (J). pap. 3.95 (978-1-4027-3073-3(X)) Sterling Publishing Co., Inc.

Bumpy Slide Books Staff. Blue's Rainy Day Music. Nickelodeon/Viacom International Staff, ed. 2000. (Blue's Clues: No. 2). (Illus.). 32p. (J). (ps-1). 3.49 (978-1-57973-068-0(X)) Advance Pubs. LLC.

Busse, Sarah Martin & Martin, Jacqueline Briggs. Banjo Granny. Root, Barry, illus. 2006. 32p. (J). (ps-k). 16.00 (978-0-618-33603-6(6)) Houghton Mifflin Co.

Canals, Sonia. Drum. 1999. (Music Time Ser.). (Illus.). 8p. (J). (ps). pap. 6.95 (978-1-899607-74-7(9)) Levinson Bks. Ltd. GBR. *Dist:* Sterling Publishing Co., Inc.

—Tambourine. 1999. (Music Time Ser.). (Illus.). 8p. (J). (ps). 6.95 (978-1-899607-73-0(0)) Sterling Publishing Co., Inc.

La Cancion de Roldan. (SPA., Illus.). 160p. (YA). 11.95 (978-84-7281-076-1(3) , AF1076) Auriga, Ediciones S.A. ESP. *Dist:* Continental Bk. Co., Inc.

Canciones Infantiles. 2001. Tr. of Children's Songs. (SPA.). 136p. (978-84-305-1746-6(4)) Lectorum Pubns., Inc.

Carr, Heather. The Jigglewonn. Carr, Greg, illus. ed. 2005. 18p. (J). 21.95 incl. audio compact disk (978-0-9768450-0-3(8) , Giggletins) Le Bk. Moderne, LLC.

Cattell, Bob & Agard, John. Butter-Finger. Smy, Pam, illus. 2006. 128p. pap. 7.95 (978-1-84507-376-3(2)) Lincoln, Frances Ltd. GBR. *Dist:* Perseus Distribution.

Cattell, Bob & Agard, John. Calypso Boy. Smy, Pam, illus. 2007. 96p. (J). pap. 7.95 (*978-1-84507-626-9(5)) Lincoln, Frances Ltd. GBR. *Dist:* Perseus Distribution.

Cattell, Bob, et al. Shine on Butterfinger. 2007. (Illus.). 96p. (J). 15.95 (*978-1-84507-773-0(3)) Lincoln, Frances Ltd. GBR. *Dist:* Perseus Distribution.

Celenza, Anna Harwell. Bach's Goldberg Variations. Kitchel, JoAnn E., illus. 2005. 32p. (J). 19.95 incl. audio compact disk (978-1-57091-510-9(5)) Charlesbridge Publishing, Inc.

—Pictures at an Exhibition. Kitchel, JoAnn, illus. 2006. 32p. (J). pap. 7.95 (978-1-57091-686-1(1)) Charlesbridge Publishing, Inc.

Chapin, Tom & reader. Mama Don't Allow. Chapin, Tom, reader. 2001. (Live Oak Readalong Ser.). (Illus.). (J). (ps-4). pap. 16.95 incl. audio (978-0-87499-743-9(7)) Live Oak Media.

Chaviano, Daina. Pais de Dragones. 2003. (Fables & Legends Ser.). (SPA., Illus.). 136p. (J). 9.95 (978-84-239-6346-1(2) , EC30627) Espasa Calpe, S.A. ESP. *Dist:* Lectorum Pubns., Inc., Planeta Publishing Corp.

Clark, Brenda, illus. Franklin's Music Lessons. 2002. (Franklin Ser.). 12.40 (978-1-4046-1981-4(X)) Book Wholesalers, Inc.

Clements, Andrew. The Last Holiday Concert. 2006. 176p. (J). pap. 5.99 (978-0-689-84525-3(1) , Aladdin) Simon & Schuster Children's Publishing.

—Things Hoped For. 176p. (gr. 5). 2008. (J). 6.99 (*978-0-14-241073-8(X) , Puffin); 2006. (YA). 16.99 (978-0-399-24350-9(X) , Philomel) Penguin Group (USA) Inc.

Cole, Barbara H. Wash Day. Himler, Ronald, illus. 2004. 40p. (J). 15.95 (978-1-932065-36-7(9) , 7187849112) Star Bright Bks., Inc.

Combel Editorial Staff. Los Musicos de Bremen. 2004. (Caballo alado clasicos-Al Galope Ser.). (SPA., Illus.). 24p. 6.95 (978-84-7864-783-5(X)) Combel Editorial, S.A. ESP. *Dist:* Independent Pubs. Group.

Cookson. Mrs. Flanagan's Trumpet. 2000. 189p. (J). 17.95 (978-0-385-40134-0(5)) Transworld Publishers Ltd. GBR. *Dist:* Trafalgar Square Publishing.

Coonan, Michelle. The Aldrich. 2005. 119p. pap. 16.95 (978-1-4137-8301-8(5)) PublishAmerica, Inc.

Cooner, Donna D. Barney Makes Music. Davis, Guy, ed. 1999. (Barney Ser.). (Illus.). 24p. (J). (ps-k). 4.95 (978-1-57064-461-0(6)) Scholastic, Inc.

Coveleskie, Sally & Goodrich, Peter. Henry the Steinway Tours the World. Friedman, Laura, illus. 2005. (Henry the Steinway Ser.: 3). 32p. (J). (ps-ps). 15.95 (978-0-9729427-8-2(5)) Yorkville Pr.

Coveleskie, Sally & Peter, Goodrich. Henry the Steinway a Star Is Born. Friedman, Laura, illus. 2003. (Henry the Steinway Ser.: Vol. 2). 32p. (J). (gr. k-3). (978-0-9729427-1-3(8)) Yorkville Pr.

Coveleskie, Sally, et al. Henry the Steinway & the Piano Recital. Friedman, Laura, illus. 2003. (Henry the Steinway Ser.: Vol. 1). 32p. (J). (gr. k-3). (978-1-931721-05-9(X)) Bright Sky Pr.

Cowley, Rich. Bang! Bang! Toot Toot. Cowley, Rich, illus. 2001. (Snappy Sounds Ser.: No. 3). (Illus.). 24p. (J). (gr. k-ps). reprint ed. bds. 3.95 (978-1-55209-034-3(5)) Annick Pr., Ltd. CAN. *Dist:* Firefly Bks., Ltd.

Cowling, Douglas. Vivaldi's Ring of Mystery. Fernandez, Laura & Jacobson, Rick, illus. 2004. 44p. (J). pap. (*978-0-439-96904-8(2) , North Winds Pr) Scholastic Canada, Ltd.

Crabtree, Sally & Mathieson, Roberta. Jungle Boogie. Jennings, Patti, illus. 2004. 12p. (J). bds. 7.99 (978-0-689-86184-0(2) , Little Simon) Simon & Schuster Children's Publishing.

Crew, Gary. Pig on the Titanic: A True Story. Whatley, Bruce, illus. 2005. (J). 32p. 15.99 (978-0-06-052305-3(0)); 40p. lib. bdg. 17.89 (978-0-06-052306-0(9)) HarperCollins Pubs.

Crouch, Cheryl Lynne. Chosen Girls/Backstage Pass. 2007. (Chosen Girls' Ser.). 144p. (J). pap. 3.99 (978-0-310-71267-1(X)) Zonderkidz.

Daddy Saved the Day: Six-Pack. (Greetings Ser.: Vol. 3). 24p. (gr. 2-3). 31.00 (978-0-7635-9417-6(2)) Rigby Education.

D'Allance, Mireille. No, No Y No! 2005. (SPA., Illus.). (J). 15.99 (978-84-8470-114-9(X)) Corimbo, Editorial S.L. ESP. *Dist:* Iaconi, Mariuccia Bk. Imports.

Davis, Terry. If Rock & Roll Were a Machine. 2003. (gr. 7-12). lib. bdg. 25.70 (978-0-613-77540-3(6)) Tandem Library Bks.

de Alcantara, Pedro. Befiddled. 2007. 192p. (J). (gr. 4-7). 5.99 (*978-0-440-42057-6(1) , Yearling) Random Hse. Children's Bks.

de Beer, Hans. El Pequeno Coco. 1999. Tr. of Little Coconut. (978-0-606-17554-8(7)) Tandem Library Bks.

de Varennes, Monique. The Jewel Box Ballerinas. Juan, Ana, illus. 2007. 40p. (J). (ps-3). lib. bdg. 19.99 (*978-0-375-93605-0(X) , Schwartz & Wade Bks.) Random Hse. Children's Bks.

Demas, Corinne. Nina's Waltz. Lanino, Deborah, illus. 2000. 32p. (J). (gr. k-4). pap. 16.95 (978-0-531-30281-1(4) , Orchard Bks.) Scholastic, Inc.

Demas, Corinne & Demas, Carole. Nina's Waltz. Lanino, Deborah, illus. 2000. 32p. (J). (gr. k-3). 17.99 (978-0-531-33281-8(0) , Orchard Bks.) Scholastic, Inc.

Desrosiers, Sylvie. Aimez-Vous la Musique? Sylvestre, Daniel, illus. 2004. (Roman Jeunesse Ser.). (FRE.). 96p. (J). (gr. 4-7). pap. (978-2-89021-709-6(4)) Diffusion du livre Mirabel.

Disney Press, ed. Disney High School Musical: Wildcats Box Set. rev. ed. 2007. (gr. 3-7). pap. 15.99 (*978-1-4231-1082-8(X)) Disney Pr.

Disney Press Staff & Alfonsi, Alice. House Party: Junior Novel. 17th rev. ed. 2006. 144p. (gr. 3-7). pap. 4.99 (978-0-7868-3837-0(X)) Disney Pr.

Disney Press Staff & Jones, Jasmine. Queen of Hearts. 18th rev. ed. 2006. 144p. (gr. 3-7). pap. 4.99 (978-0-7868-3838-7(8)) Disney Pr.

Dolan, Penny. Moo! Sharp, Melanie, illus. 2004. (Read-It! Readers Ser.). 32p. (C). (gr. k-3). 18.60 (978-1-4048-0643-6(1)) Picture Window Bks.

Domnauer, Teresa & Lithgow, John. Music Around the World Level 3: A Musical Adventure. 2005. (Lithgow Palooza Readers Ser.). (Illus.). 32p. (J). (gr. 1-2). pap. 3.95 (978-0-7696-4223-9(3)) School Specialty Publishing.

Drachman, Eric. Ellison the Elephant. Muscarello, James, illus. 2004. 32p. 18.95 (978-0-9703809-1-3(7)) Kidwick Bks.

Drake, Gillian. Rhian's Song. 1998. 160p. (J). (gr. 4-12). pap. 13.95 (978-0-8464-4906-5(4)) Beekman Bks., Inc.

EarTwiggle's Adventure 1: Twiggle Book. 2004. (J). 1.99 (978-0-9762573-1-8(9)) Ear Twiggles Productions, Inc.

Edelmann, Heinz. Yellow Submarine. Andreanelli, Fiona, illus. 2004. 40p. (J). (gr. k). 17.99 (978-0-7636-2440-8(3)) Candlewick Pr.

Elmo & Zoe: A Book of Opposites. 2003. (Busy Box Bks.). 14p. (J). bds. 15.98 (978-0-7853-7965-2(7) , 7175000) Publications International, Ltd.

Ewing, Lynne. Motown Anthology. 2003. 96p. (J). 22.99 (978-0-7868-0854-0(3)) Hyperion Pr.

Feltenberger, Myles. Mr. Everybody's Musical Apartment Bk. 3: A Note-Teaching Musical Story. Nakroshis, Estelle et al, illus. l.t. ed. 1999. 62p. (J). (ps-6). pap. 12.95 (978-0-9634218-2-1(4)) Myles Music Corp.

Fite, Anna. Ada y Max Aprenden Musica. 2002. (Ada y Max Series Ser.). (SPA & ENG., Illus.). 10p. 4.95 (978-84-7864-383-7(4)) Combel Editorial, S.A. ESP. *Dist:* Independent Pubs. Group.

Fixmer, Audrey M. Song of the Phoenix. 1998. 192p. (YA). (gr. 5 up). pap. 12.00 (978-0-9642672-2-0(5)) Write-on-Time Publishing.

Fogelin, Adrian. The Big Nothing. 2004. 224p. (J). 14.95 (978-1-56145-326-9(9)) Peachtree Pubs., Ltd.

—Big Nothing. 2006. 224p. (YA). pap. 6.95 (978-1-56145-388-7(9)) Peachtree Pubs., Ltd.

Franklin, Emily. The Principles of Love. 2005. 256p. (gr. 12-12). pap. 9.99 (978-0-451-21517-8(6) , N A L Trade) Penguin Group (USA) Inc.

—Summer of Love: The Principles of Love. 2007. 256p. (YA). pap. 9.99 (978-0-451-22040-0(4) , N A L Trade) Penguin Group (USA) Inc.

Freeman, Don. Manuelo, the Playing Mantis. McCue, Lisa, illus. 2004. 32p. (J). (ps-8). 15.99 (978-0-670-03684-4(6) , Viking Juvenile) Penguin Group (USA) Inc.

—Manuelo, the Playing Mantis. 2006. (Illus.). 32p. (J). reprint ed. pap. 5.99 (978-0-14-240560-4(4) , Puffin) Penguin Group (USA) Inc.

Friedman, D. Dina. Playing Dad's Song. 2006. 144p. (YA). 16.00 (978-0-374-37173-9(3)) Farrar, Straus & Giroux.

Friesel, Uwe. Tim, the Peacemaker. Wilkon, Jozef, illus. 32p. (J). (ps-3). 13.95 (978-0-87592-052-8(7)) Scroll Pr., Inc.

Gable, Paul. Love Flute. 2001. (J). (gr. k-3). pap. 16.95 incl. audio. pap. 16.95 incl. audio (978-0-8045-6843-2(X) , 6843) Spoken Arts, Inc.

Geras, Adèle. Ithaka. 2006. 368p. (YA). 17.00 (978-0-15-205603-2(3)) Harcourt Children's Bks.

—Ithaka. 2005. 416p. (J). (*978-0-385-60391-1(6) , Fickling, David Bks.) Random Hse. Children's Bks.

Gilbert, Barbara Snow. Broken Chords. 2001. (J). (978-0-606-21087-4(3)) Tandem Library Bks.

Givens, Steven J. The Violin Lesson & the Cross Street Band. Miller, Janet D., illus. 2002. 46p. (Orig.). (gr. 3-5). pap. 7.95 (978-1-889658-06-3(5)) New Canaan Publishing Co. LLC.

Godinez, Flory. The Adventures of Max & Millie: The Notable Orchard. 2004. (Illus.). 32p. (J). 9.95 (978-0-9744427-1-6(2)) music bks. & games.

Golden Books Staff. Bring on the Rock! Schigiel, Gregg, illus. 2004. 32p. (J). (ps). pap. 4.99 (978-0-375-82989-5(X) , Golden Bks.) Random Hse. Children's Bks.

Golden Books Staff. Little Boy with a Big Horn. Yaccarino, Dan, illus. 2008. (Golden Classic Ser.). 48p. (J). (gr. k-k). lib. bdg. 17.99 (*978-0-375-93903-7(2) , Golden Bks.) Random Hse., Inc.

Gordon, Amy. The Gorillas of Gill Park. 2003. 256p. (J). (gr. 4-6). tchr. ed. 16.95 (978-0-8234-1751-3(4)) Holiday Hse., Inc.

Grace, N. B. Battle of the Bands. 2007. (High School Musical Ser.: No. 1). 144p. (J). (gr. 3-7). pap. 4.99 (978-1-4231-0611-1(3)) Disney Pr.

—Broadway Dreams. rev. ed. 2007. (High School Musical Ser.: No. 5). 128p. (gr. 3-7). pap. 4.99 (*978-1-4231-0623-4(7)) Disney Pr.

—Crunch Time. Disney Press Staff, ed. 2007. (High School Musical Ser.: No. 4). 128p. (gr. 3-7). pap. 4.99 (*978-1-4231-0614-2(8)) Disney Pr.

—High School Musical No. 2: The Junior Novel. Disney Press Staff, ed. 2007. 144p. (J). (gr. 4-7). pap. 4.99 (*978-1-4231-0639-5(3)) Disney Pr.

Grace, N. B. & Alfonsi, Alice. Poetry in Motion. Disney Press Staff, ed. rev. ed. 2007. (High School Musical Ser.: No. 3). 128p. (J). (gr. 3-7). pap. 4.99 (*978-1-4231-0613-5(X)) Disney Pr.

Granfield, Linda. Silent Night: The Song from Heaven. Hofer, Nelly & Hofer, Ernst, illus. 2000. 24p. (J). (gr. 2 up). pap. 7.95 (978-0-88776-434-9(7)) Tundra Bks., Inc./Livres Toundra, Inc. CAN. *Dist:* Random Hse., Inc.

Gray, Libba Moore. When Uncle Took the Fiddle. Bloom, Lloyd, illus. 1999. 32p. (J). (ps-2). 16.99 (978-0-531-33137-8(7)); pap. 15.95 (978-0-531-30137-1(0)) Scholastic, Inc. (Orchard Bks.).

Grifalconi, Ann. Tiny's Hat. 2001. (J). (gr. k-3). 25.90 incl. audio (978-0-8045-6860-9(X) , 6860) Spoken Arts, Inc.

Griffin, Peni R. The Music Thief. rev. ed. 2002. 160p. (YA). (gr. 5-8). 16.95 (978-0-8050-7055-2(9) , Holt, Henry & Co. Bks. For Young Readers) Holt, Henry & Co.

—The Music Thief. l.t. ed. 2003. 190p. (J). 21.95 (978-0-7862-5606-8(0)) Thorndike Pr.

Grigg, Carol. The Singing Snowbear. Grigg, Carol, illus. 1999. (Illus.). 32p. (J). (gr. k-3). tchr. ed. 15.00 (978-0-395-94223-9(3)) Houghton Mifflin Co. Trade & Reference Div.

Gripe, Maria. Elvis Karlsson. Gripe, Harold, illus. 2003. (SPA.). 148p. (J). (gr. 3-5). pap. 9.95 (978-958-24-0181-8(8)) Santillana USA Publishing Co., Inc.

Haak, Harold H. The Mubox Bugs. l.t. ed. 2003. (Illus.). 20p. (J). 5.95 (978-1-931474-82-5(6)) Creative Teaching Assocs.

Hanson, Anders. Beetle Mania. Nobens, C. A., illus. (Fact & Fiction Ser.). 24p. (J). 2007. 21.35 (978-1-59928-432-3(4)); 2006. (978-1-59928-433-0(2)) ABDO Publishing Co.

Hapka, Catherine. Supernova. 2004. (Star Power Ser.: No. 1). 144p. (J). pap. 4.99 (978-0-689-86787-3(5) , Aladdin) Simon & Schuster Children's Publishing.

—Wildcat Spirit. rev. ed. 2007. (High School Musical Ser.: No. 2). 128p. (J). (gr. 3-7). pap. 4.99 (978-1-4231-0612-8(1)) Disney Pr.

Harcourt School Publishers Staff. The Junk Band: Take-Home Book. 1999. (Collections Ser.). (Illus.). (J). pap. 1.90 (978-0-15-317243-4(6)) Harcourt Schl. Pubs.

—Mi Mayor Deseo: Take-Home Book. 2001. (Vamos Ser.). (SPA., Illus.). (J). pap. 2.80 (978-0-15-319928-8(8)) Harcourt Schl. Pubs.

—Mine for a Song: Take-Home Book. 2001. (Collections Ser.). (Illus.). (J). pap. 1.90 (978-0-15-319564-8(9)) Harcourt Schl. Pubs.

M N O

—Mine for a Song Below Level. 3rd ed. 2002. (Trophies Reading Program Ser.). (Illus.). pap. 5.10 (978-0-15-323417-0(2)) Harcourt Schl. Pubs.

—Music Men: Take-Home Book. 1999. (Signatures Ser.). (Illus.). (J). pap. 1.90 (978-0-15-313943-7(9)) Harcourt Schl. Pubs.

—Practice Makes Perfect. 3rd ed. 2002. (Trophies English Language Learners Ser.). (Illus.). pap. 5.10 (978-0-15-327702-3(5)) Harcourt Schl. Pubs.

—Trofeos Advanced Level: La Nina Es Curiosa. 3rd ed. 2002. (SPA., Illus.). pap. 6.80 (978-0-15-324113-0(6)) Harcourt Schl. Pubs.

Harrison, Emma. High School Musical Yearbook. Disney Staff, ed. 2007. 56p. (J). (gr. 1-7). 10.99 (***978-1-4231-0596-1(6)***) Disney Pr.

Harrison, John. Fergal Onions. 2005. (Illus.). 32p. pap. 17.95 (978-0-7022-3481-1(8)) Univ. of Queensland Pr. AUS. *Dist:* International Specialized Bk. Services.

Hedderwick, Mairi. Katie Morag & the Grand Concert. 1999. (Katie Morag Stories Ser.). (Illus.). 32p. (J). pap. 10.99 (978-0-09-926275-6(4)) Random Hse. GBR. *Dist:* Independent Pubs. Group.

Helguera, Luis Ignacio. Gracias a Johannes. Morales, Judith, illus. 2003. (SPA.). (978-968-494-086-4(6) , CI5287) Centro de Informacion y Desarrollo de la Comunicacion y la Literatura MEX. *Dist:* Lectorum Pubns., Inc.

Henrie, Tanya. The Shaping. MacKessy, Kristine, illus. 1998. 60p. (J). (gr. 2-7). 17.95 (978-0-9667096-0-5(8)) Keeping Track of Time.

Hermes, Patricia. Sweet by & By. 2002. 208p. (J). (gr. 3-6). 15.99 (978-0-380-97452-8(5)) HarperCollins Pubs.

High School Musical: All-Access. rev. ed. 2007. 32p. (J). (gr. 2-7). 19.99 (***978-1-4231-1066-8(8)***) Disney Pr.

Hoff, Syd. Arturo's Baton. 2002. (Illus.). 32p. (J). (gr. k-3). pap. 6.95 (978-0-618-19597-8(1) , Clarion Bks.) Houghton Mifflin Co. Trade & Reference Div.

—Arturo's Baton. 2002. (gr. k-3). lib. bdg. 14.10 (978-0-613-65159-2(6)) Tandem Library Bks.

Hoffmann, Burton R. Millicent the Magnificent. du Houx, Emily C., illus. 2004. 64p. pap. 12.00 (978-1-882190-68-3(8)) Polar Bear & Co.

Hope Music. 2006. (J). per. 12.00 (***978-0-9773608-4-0(9)***) Shiny Red Ball Publishing.

Hulme, Joy N. The Whistling & Whittling Brigade. 1999. (J). (978-0-7868-0171-8(9)) Hyperion Pr.

Hyde, Judith Jensen. Rainy-Day Music. Abbott, Jason, illus. 2006. (Rookie Reader Skill Set Ser.). 32p. (J). (gr. k-2). 19.50 (978-0-516-24983-4(5) , Children's Pr.) Scholastic Library Publishing.

Hyde, Judith Jensen & Abbott, Jason. Rainy-day Music. 2006. (Illus.). 32p. (YA). pap. 4.95 (978-0-516-24998-8(3) , Children's Pr.) Scholastic Library Publishing.

Isadora, Rachel. Bring on That Beat. 2002. (Illus.). 32p. (J). (ps-3). 15.99 (978-0-399-23232-9(X) , Putnam Juvenile) Penguin Group (USA) Inc.

Jefferies, Cindy. Rivals!, No. 4. 2007. (Fame School Ser.). 144p. (YA). (gr. 5). 4.99 (978-0-14-240815-5(8) , Puffin) Penguin Group (USA) Inc.

Jennings, Sharon, et al. Franklin's Music Lessons. Southern, Shelley et al, illus. 2004. (Kids Can Read Ser.). 32p. (J). (gr. k-3). (978-1-55337-171-7(2)); (978-1-55337-172-4(0)) Kids Can Pr., Ltd.

Johns, Michael-Anne. Five: Backstage Pass. 1999. (Illus.). 48p. (gr. 5-9). pap. 5.99 (978-0-439-08797-1(X)) Scholastic, Inc.

—Five: Backstage Pass. 1999. (gr. 3-6). lib. bdg. 14.15 (978-0-613-16934-9(4)) Tandem Library Bks.

Joslin, Mary. The Minstrel's Tale. Patterson, Geoffrey, illus. 1999. 32p. (J). (ps-2). 17.95 (978-0-7459-3965-0(1) , Lion) Lion Hudson plc GBR. *Dist:* Trafalgar Square Publishing.

Kalman, Esther. Tchaikovski Descubre America. 2003. (SPA., Illus.). 38p. (J). (gr. 3-5). 10.95 (978-1-58105-123-0(9) , SAN1239) Santillana USA Publishing Co., Inc.

Karlins, Mark. Music over Manhattan. 1999. (J). (978-0-606-16712-3(9)) Tandem Library Bks.

Ketcham, Sallie. Bach's Big Adventure. Bush, Timothy, illus. 1999. 32p. (J). (gr. k-4). pap. 16.95 (978-0-531-30140-1(0) , Orchard Bks.) Scholastic, Inc.

King-Smith, Dick. A Mouse Called Wolf. Goodell, Jon, illus. 1999. 98p. (J). (ps-k). lib. bdg. 13.00 (978-0-613-17058-1(X)) Tandem Library Bks.

Knight, Hilary. A Firefly in a Fir Tree: A Carol for Mice. Knight, Hilary, illus. 2004. (Illus.). 32p. (J). (ps-3). lib. bdg. 15.89 (978-0-06-000992-2(6) , Tegen, Katherine Bks) HarperCollins Pubs.

Knutson, Kimberley. Jungle Jamboree. 1998. (Accelerated Reader Bks.). (Illus.). 32p. (J). (ps-3). 15.95 (978-0-7614-5032-0(7) , Cavendish Children's Bks.) Cavendish, Marshall Corp.

Krovatin, Christopher. Heavy Metal & You. 2005. 192p. (J). (gr. 7-12). pap. 16.95 (978-0-439-73648-0(X)) Scholastic, Inc.

Langham, Tony. Creepy Crawly Calypso. Harter, Debbie, illus. 2004. 32p. (J). 16.99 incl. audio compact disk (978-1-84148-699-4(X)) Barefoot Bks., Inc.

Langham, Tony & Harter, Debbie. Creepy Crawly Calypso. 2006. 32p. pap. 9.99 incl. cd-rom (978-1-902283-46-3(5)) Barefoot Bks., Inc.

Law, Felicia. Rumble Meets Eli Elephant. 2005. (Read-It! Readers Ser.). (Illus.). 32p. (J). (ps-k). lib. bdg. 18.60 (978-1-4048-1332-8(2)) Picture Window Bks.

Lems, Kristin. Piano Teacher's Daughter. Daoudi, Karima Lems & Daoudi, Kennan Lems, illus. 2002. pap. 18.00 (978-0-9637048-2-5(6)) Lems-Dworkin, Carol Pubs.

Lou Weber Staff, ed. Bubbly Beats. 2005. 14p. (J). (ps-ps). 15.98 (978-1-4127-3164-5(X) , 7232500) Publications International, Ltd.

Lyla & the New Piano. 2002. (978-1-58453-193-7(2)) Pioneer Valley Educational Pr., Inc.

MacHado, Ana Maria. Un Buen Coro. (Torre de Papel Ser.). (SPA., Illus.). (J). 7.95 (978-958-04-4525-8(7) , NR30643) Norma S.A. COL. *Dist:* Distribuidora Norma, Inc., Lectorum Pubns., Inc.

Madden, Kerry. Gentle's Holler. (YA). 2007. 272p. (gr. 4 up). 6.99 (978-0-14-240751-6(8) , Puffin); 2005. 256p. (gr. 5). 16.99 (978-0-670-05998-0(6) , Viking Juvenile) Penguin Group (USA) Inc.

Manz, L. B. Noshi's Special Gift. Yoshikawa, Sachiko, illus. 2003. (J). (978-0-9710278-9-3(7)) All About Kids Publishing.

The Marching Band. 1998. (P. B. Bear Ser.). (Illus.). 24p. (J). (ps). 6.95 (978-0-7894-3108-0(4)) Dorling Kindersley Publishing, Inc.

Mayerhofer, Felix. Horace the Great Harmonica King. MacFarlane, John, illus. 2006. 31p. (J). per. 16.95 (***978-1-60002-255-5(3)*** , 4313, Airleaf Publishing) Airleaf Publishing & Bookselling.

Mazer, Anne. It's Music to My Ears. 2004. (Amazing Days of Abby Hayes Ser.: No. 14). (Illus.). 110p. (J). lib. bdg. 16.92 (***978-1-4242-0745-9(2)***) Fitzgerald Bks.

McKenzie, Tim. Baxter Barret Brown's Cowboy Band. Atkinson, Elaine, illus. 2006. 24p. (J). 19.95 (978-1-931721-77-6(7)) Bright Sky Pr.

Mcmahon, Karen. Toe Tapping Fun. Albrecht, Jeff, illus. 2005. (Barney Ser.). 32p. (J). pap. 4.99 (978-0-439-74409-6(1)) Scholastic, Inc.

McNaughton, Colin. Once upon an Ordinary School Day. Kitamura, Satoshi, illus. 2005. 32p. (J). 16.00 (978-0-374-35634-7(3) , Farrar, Straus & Giroux (BYR)) Farrar, Straus & Giroux.

—When I Grow Up. McNaughton, Colin, illus. 2005. (Illus.). 40p. (J). (ps-1). 12.99 (978-0-7636-2675-4(9)) Candlewick Pr.

McPhail, David M. Mole Music. McPhail, David M., illus. 2002. (Illus.). (J). 25.38 (978-0-7587-3152-4(3)) Book Wholesalers, Inc.

—Mole Music. rev. ed. (Illus.). 32p. (J). (ps-3). 2001. pap. 7.95 (978-0-8050-6766-8(3)); 1999. 16.95 (978-0-8050-2819-5(6)) Holt, Henry & Co. (Holt, Henry & Co. Bks. For Young Readers).

—Mole Music. McPhail, David M., illus. 2001. (Illus.). 28.95 incl. audio compact disk (978-1-59112-429-0(8)); pap. 37.95 incl. audio (978-0-87499-749-1(6)); pap. 39.95 incl. audio compact disk (978-1-59112-606-5(1)); (J). pap. 16.95 incl. audio (978-0-87499-747-7(X)); (J). pap. 18.95 incl. audio compact disk (978-1-59112-406-1(9)) Live Oak Media.

—Mole Music. 2001. (gr. k-3). lib. bdg. 15.25 (978-0-613-78380-4(8)); (978-0-606-22641-7(9)) Tandem Library Bks.

Merveille, David. Jukebox. Merveille, David, illus. 2007. (Illus.). 44p. (J). 14.95 (***978-1-933605-72-2(3)***) Kane/Miller Bk. Pubs., Inc.

Miller, Sara Swan. My Pod: Libro de Cuentos y Reproductor Personal de Musica. 2007. (SPA., Illus.). 38p. (J). 24.95 (***978-970-718-495-4(7)*** , Silver Dolphin en Español) Advanced Marketing, S. de R. L. de C. V. MEX. *Dist:* Perseus Distribution.

Miller, Sarah. My Pod Storybook & Personal Music Player. 2006. (RD Innovative Book & Player Format Ser.). (Illus.). 40p. (J). 24.99 (978-0-7944-1130-5(4)) Reader's Digest Assn., Inc., The.

Mills, Claudia. Gus & Grandpa & the Piano Lesson. Stock, Catherine, illus. 2004. (Gus & Grandpa Ser.). 48p. (J). 15.00 (978-0-374-32814-6(5) , Farrar, Straus & Giroux (BYR)) Farrar, Straus & Giroux.

Mit musik geht alles Besser. pap. 12.95 (978-3-89748-676-8(8)) Dino Entertainment AG DEU. *Dist:* Distribooks, Inc.

Mitchel, Pratima. Petar's Song. Binch, Caroline, illus. 2004. 32p. (J). 15.95 (978-1-84507-266-7(9)) Lincoln, Frances Ltd. GBR. *Dist:* Perseus Distribution.

Mitchell, Pratima. Petar's Song. Binch, Caroline, illus. 2004. 32p. (J). pap. 7.95 (978-1-84507-352-7(5)) Lincoln, Frances Ltd. GBR. *Dist:* Perseus Distribution.

Mitchell, Pratima & Binch, Caroline. Petar's Song. (Illus.). 32p. (978-0-7112-2063-8(8)) Lincoln, Frances Ltd. GBR. *Dist:* Transition Vendor.

Modesitt, L. E., Jr. The Spellsong War. 1999. (Spellsong Cycle Ser.: Bk. 2). (gr. 7-12). lib. bdg. 15.30 (978-0-613-22421-5(3)) Tandem Library Bks.

Moss, Lloyd. Music Is. Petit-Roulet, Philippe, illus. 2003. 32p. (J). (ps-2). 14.99 (978-0-399-23336-4(9) , Putnam Juvenile) Penguin Group (USA) Inc.

—Zin! Zin! Zin! A Violin. Priceman, Marjorie, illus. 2002. (J). 15.53 (978-0-7587-0170-1(5)) Book Wholesalers, Inc.

—Zin! Zin! Zin! A Violin. Priceman, Marjorie, illus. (Stories to Go! Ser.). 32p. (J). 2005. 4.99 (978-1-4169-0838-8(2)); 2000. pap. 6.99 (978-0-689-83524-7(8)) Simon & Schuster Children's Publishing. (Aladdin).

Moulton, Mark Kimball. A Cricket's Carol. Blowers, Lisa, illus. 2004. 32p. (J). 14.95 (978-0-8249-5488-8(2)) Ideals Pubns.

—A Cricket's Carol. Blowers, Lisa, illus. 2000. 32p. (J). (gr. k-3). 18.00 (978-0-7412-0735-7(4)) Lang Graphics, Ltd.

Myers, Walter Dean. The Blues of Flats Brown. Laden, Nina, illus. 32p. (J). (gr. k-3). 2005. pap. 6.95 (978-0-8234-1679-0(8)); 2000. tchr. ed. 16.95 (978-0-8234-1480-2(9)) Holiday Hse., Inc.

—Blues of Flats Brown. 2002. (Live Oak Readalong Ser.). (Illus.). (J). pap. 18.95 incl. audio compact disk (978-1-59112-404-7(2)); pap. 16.95 incl. audio (978-0-87499-940-2(5)) Live Oak Media.

—The Blues of Flats Brown. Laden, Nina, illus. 2002. 28.95 incl. audio compact disk (978-1-59112-424-5(7)); pap. 39.95 incl. audio compact disk (978-1-59112-601-0(0)); (J). 25.95 incl. audio (978-0-87499-941-9(3)); (J). pap., tchr.'s planning gde. ed. 37.95 incl. audio (978-0-87499-942-6(1)) Live Oak Media.

Norman, Tyler & Perez, Jose S. The Banjoman/El Hombre del Banjo. Perez, Jose S., illus. 2004. (ENG & SPA., Illus.). 32p. (J). 12.95 (978-1-57072-292-9(7)) Overmountain Pr.

Nye, Ann Marie, ed. Basic Music. 2006. (Maya & Miguel Ser.). 32p. (J). pap. 3.99 (978-0-439-80901-6(0)) Scholastic, Inc.

—Papi Joins the Band. 2006. (Maya & Miguel Ser.). 32p. (J). pap. 3.99 (978-0-439-78959-2(1)) Scholastic, Inc.

O'Connor, Barbara. Beethoven in Paradise. 1999. (J). (978-0-606-17351-3(X)) Tandem Library Bks.

Okimoto, Jean Davies. Talent Night. 2000. (gr. 7-12). lib. bdg. 22.20 (978-0-613-83512-1(3)) Tandem Library Bks.

—Talent Night. 2000. 180p. (gr. 7-12). pap. 12.95 (978-0-595-00795-0(3) , Backinprint.com) iUniverse, Inc.

Paré, Roger. Plaisirs de Musique. 2002. (Plaisirs Ser.). (Illus.). 24p. (J). (ps). pap. (978-2-89021-394-4(3)) Diffusion du livre Mirabel.

Pattou, Edith. Hero's Song: The First Song of Eirren. 2005. (Illus.). 348p. (J). (gr. 7-17). pap. 7.95 (978-0-15-205542-4(8) , Magic Carpet Bks.) Harcourt Children's Bks.

Pelletier, Maryse. La Musique des Choses. 2002. (Roman + Ser.). (Illus.). 160p. (YA). (gr. 8 up). pap. (978-2-89021-319-7(6)) Diffusion du livre Mirabel.

Perelman-Bernstein, Helen. Heart to Heart. 6th rev. ed. 2007. (High School Musical Ser.: No. 6). 128p. (gr. 3-7). pap. 4.99 (***978-1-4231-0624-1(5)***) Disney Pr.

Perry, Michael. Turntable Timmy. Cunningham, Douglas, illus. 2005. 32p. (J). 18.95 incl. audio compact disk (978-0-86719-633-7(5)) Last Gasp of San Francisco.

Pinkney, Andrea Davis. Look at Me (Board Book Set) 1998. (Illus.). (J). bds. 25.80 (978-0-15-202176-4(0) , Red Wagon Bks.) Harcourt Children's Bks.

Plaka, Christina. Yonen Buzz. 2006. (Illus.). (YA). pap. 9.99 (978-1-59816-403-9(1) , Tokyopop Adult) TOKYOPOP, Inc.

Pooh Hundred Acre Music Maker. pap. 16.98 (978-0-7853-6068-1(9)) Publications International, Ltd.

Poulsen, David A. Jeremy's Song. 2004. 110p. (YA). pap. 3.99 (978-1-55305-027-8(4)) Cygnet Publishing Group, Inc./Coolreading.com CAN. *Dist:* Sea Bk. Pubs. USA.

Poupart, Jean-Marie. Des Pianos Qui S'Envolent. 2003. (Roman Jeunesse Ser.). (FRE.). 96p. (YA). (gr. 4-7). pap. (978-2-89021-173-5(8)) Diffusion du livre Mirabel.

Pritchett, Dylan. The First Music. Banks, Erin Bennett, illus. 2006. 32p. (ps-2). 16.95 (978-0-87483-776-6(6)) August Hse. Pubs., Inc.

Pugliano-Martin, Carol. The el rey malo & Very Mean King. 2005. spiral bd. 66.00 (***978-1-4108-5648-7(8)***) Benchmark Education Co.

Raney, Richard B., illus. A Dulcimer for Elspeth. 2002. 22p. (J). (gr. k-6). incl. audio compact disk (978-0-9718866-0-5(1)) Serene Sounds.

Reisfeld, Randi, ed. Romeo: Chapter Book. 2006. (Teenick Ser.). (Illus.). 96p. (J). pap. 4.99 (978-0-439-79667-5(9)) Scholastic, Inc.

Ring, Susan. Music of the Meadow. Zaidi, Nadeem et al, illus. 2006. (Disney's Little Einsteins Ser.). 32p. (ps-1). 6.99 incl. cd-rom (978-0-7868-5537-7(1)) Disney Pr.

Ring, Susan & Aigner-Clark, Julie. Baby Mozart: Music Is Everywhere. Zaidi, Nadeem, illus. 2004. (Baby Einstein Ser.). 16p. (ps-17). 7.99 (978-0-7868-5244-4(5)) Hyperion Bks. for Children.

Rollins, Barbara B. Syncopated Summer. unabr. ed. 2006. (ENG.). (J). per. 9.95 (978-1-932196-97-9(8)) Word-Wright.biz, Inc.

Romanelli, Serena. El Pequeno Coco. Lamas, Blanca Rosa, tr. from GER. de Beer, Hans, illus. 2004. (SPA.). 24p. (J). (gr. k-4). reprint ed. 16.00 (978-0-7567-7707-4(0)) DIANE Publishing Co.

Roth, Susan L. Do Re Mi: If You Can Read Music, Thank Guido D'Arezzo. 2007. (Illus.). 40p. (J). (gr. k-3). 17.00 (978-0-618-46572-9(3)) Houghton Mifflin Co.

Russell, D. Z. The Amazing Adventures of Andy Owl: A Children's Guide to Understanding Music. Stone, John, illus. 2003. 34p. (J). per. 7.95 (978-0-9725398-0-7(8)) World Famous Children's Bks.

Ryan, Margaret. Magic Music! Murfin, Teresa, illus. 2006. (Airy Fairy Bks.). 80p. (J). pap. 3.99 (978-0-7641-3427-2(2)) Barron's Educational Series, Inc.

Rylant, Cynthia. Mr. Putter & Tabby Toot the Horn. Howard, Arthur, illus. (Mr. Putter & Tabby Ser.). 44p. (J). 1999. (ps-3). pap. 5.95 (978-0-15-200247-3(2) , Harcourt Paperbacks); 1998. (gr. 1-5). 14.00 (978-0-15-200244-2(8)) Harcourt Children's Bks.

—Mr. Putter & Tabby Toot the Horn. Howard, Arthur, illus. 1999. (Mr. Putter & Tabby Ser.). (J). (ps). lib. bdg. 14.10 (978-0-613-22895-4(2)) Tandem Library Bks.

—Mr. Putter & Tabby Toot the Horn. 1999. (Mr. Putter & Tabby Ser.). (978-0-606-17489-3(3)) Tandem Library Bks.

Santillo, LuAnn. The Tune. Santillo, LuAnn, ed. 2003. (Half-Pint Kids Readers Ser.). (Illus.). 7p. (J). (ps-1). pap. (978-1-59256-102-5(0)) Half-Pint Kids, Inc.

Sarafati, Sonia. Tricot, Piano et Jeu Video. 2002. (Premier Roman Ser.). (FRE.). 64p. (J). (gr. 2-5). pap. (978-2-89021-181-0(9)) Diffusion du livre Mirabel.

Scholastic, Inc. Staff. Let's Make Some Noise! 2008. (Doodlebops Ser.). 96p. (J). 9.99 (***978-0-545-01328-4(3)***) Scholastic, Inc.

—Live in Concert. 2008. (Light of the World Ser.). 32p. (J). pap. 5.99 (***978-0-545-00791-7(7)***) Scholastic, Inc.

Schroeder, Alan. Satchmo's Blues. Cooper, Floyd, illus. 1999. 32p. (gr. 1-5). pap. 6.99 (978-0-440-41472-8(5) , Dragonfly Bks.) Random Hse. Children's Bks.

—Satchmo's Blues. 1999. (978-0-606-15897-8(9)) Tandem Library Bks.

—Satchmo's Blues. Cooper, Floyd, illus. 1999. (J). (ps-k). lib. bdg. 15.30 (978-0-613-13201-5(7)) Tandem Library Bks.

Schuch, Steve. A Symphony of Whales. Sylvada, Peter, illus. 2002. 32p. (J). (gr. 1-4). pap. 7.00 (978-0-15-216548-2(7) , Voyager Bks./Libros Viajeros) Harcourt Children's Bks.

—Symphony of Whales. 2002. (gr. k-3). lib. bdg. 14.15 (978-0-613-56636-0(X)) Tandem Library Bks.

Sesame Street Get up & Go Songs. 2003. (Illus.). 10p. (J). bds. 9.98 (978-0-7853-8280-5(1) , 7182400) Publications International, Ltd.

Shipton, Paul. Ghost in the Guitar. 2000. (Illus.). 48p. (C). pap. 9.00 (978-0-582-31913-4(7)) Longman Publishing Group.

Silse, Brenda & Akin, Galan. The Duet. 2000. (Illus.). viii, 47p. (J). pap. 5.95 (978-0-9686899-1-2(4)) Hodgepog Bks. CAN. *Dist:* Coteau Bks.

Simont, Marc, illus. Nate the Great & the Musical Note. 2002. (Nate the Great Ser.). (J). 12.87 (978-0-7587-0700-0(2)) Book Wholesalers, Inc.

Sis, Peter. Madlenka's Music. 2005. (J). (978-0-375-82855-3(9)); lib. bdg. (978-0-375-92855-0(3)) Random Hse., Inc.

Smith, Linda. Talisa's Song. 2006. 272p. (YA). pap. 8.95 (978-1-55050-327-2(8)) Coteau Bks. CAN. *Dist:* F & W Pubns., Inc.

Somerville, Oe. E. Mount Music. 2006. 80.99 (***978-1-4280-1970-6(7)***) IndyPublish.com.

Stadler, Alexander. Beverly Billingsly Takes a Bow. 2007. (Illus.). 32p. (J). (ps-2). pap. 6.00 (978-0-15-205861-6(3) , Voyager Bks./Libros Viajeros) Harcourt Children's Bks.

Staunton, Ted. Sounding Off. 2004. 184p. (J). pap. 7.95 (978-0-88995-293-5(0)) Red Deer Pr. CAN. *Dist:* Fitzhenry & Whiteside, Ltd.

Stone, Sadie. Jamal Martin & All That Jazz. Southivorarat, Sombat, illus. 2005. 71p. pap. 14.95 (978-1-4137-4768-3(X)) PublishAmerica, Inc.

Strelitski, Mies. Woobie Discovers Music: Uncle Jan's Visit. de Hartog, Arnold, illus. 2006. 32p. (J). (978-1-59249-647-1(4)) Soundprints.

Studio Mouse, ed. Sing with Your Baby. 2007. (Illus.). 36p. 12.99 incl. audio compact disk (978-1-59069-494-7(5) , 1P800) Studio Mouse LLC.

Swift, Louie. The Froggie Who Flunked Jumping School. 4 vols. 2000. (J). (ps-3). lib. bdg. 19.95 incl. audio (978-0-9675577-2-4(0)) Puddleduck Music & Publishing.

Tanner, Mike. Resurrection Blues. 2005. 200p. (YA). (gr. 10-12). 19.95 (978-1-55037-897-9(X)); pap. 9.95 (978-1-55037-896-2(1)) Annick Pr., Ltd. CAN. *Dist:* Firefly Bks., Ltd.

Taylor, Vincent. Cornbread Has a Bad Habit. 2007. (Illus.). 96p. (J). pap. 4.99 (***978-0-9704512-5-5(3)***) TriEclipse, Inc.

Thaler, Mike. The Music Teacher from the Black Lagoon. Lee, Jared D., illus. 2000. (Black Lagoon Ser.). 32p. (J). (ps-3). pap. 3.99 (978-0-439-18873-9(3)) Scholastic, Inc.

—The Music Teacher from the Black Lagoon. 2000. (Black Lagoon Ser.). (J). (ps-3). (978-0-606-18882-1(7)) Tandem Library Bks.

—Music Teacher from the Black Lagoon. 2000. (gr. 3-6). lib. bdg. 10.95 (978-0-613-24063-5(4)) Tandem Library Bks.

Thinking Publications. The Deciders Take on Concepts Mission I: Goobie Troubles. 2001. 27p. cd-rom 99.00 (978-1-888222-59-3(X)) Super Duper Pubns.

Thomas, Maria Jose. Bravo, Rosina. Munoz, Claudio, illus. 2006. Tr. of Bravo, Rosina!. (SPA.). (J). (gr. 4-5). 10.40 (978-980-257-242-7(X) , EK33833) Ekare, Ediciones VEN. *Dist:* Lectorum Pubns., Inc.

Thompson, Kate. The New Policeman. 2007. 448p. (gr. 7-10). (J). lib. bdg. 17.89 (978-0-06-117428-5(9)); (YA). 16.99 (978-0-06-117427-8(0) , Greenwillow Bks.) HarperCollins Pubs.

Thompson, Richard. There Is Music in a Pussy Cat. Hartmann, Barbara, illus. 1999. (First Flight Ser.). 32p. (J). pap. (978-1-55041-513-1(1)) Fitzhenry & Whiteside, Ltd.

Thorne, Donna Sloan & Felts, Marilyn Sloan. Buzz & Ollie's High, Low Adventure. Thorne, Donna Sloan & Felts, Marilyn Sloan, illus. 2002. (Illus.). 36p. (J). bds. 16.00 (978-0-9724147-0-8(3)) Sloan Publishing.

—Buzz & Ollie's Loud, Soft Adventure. Thorne, Donna Sloan & Felts, Marilyn Sloan, illus. 2002. (Illus.). 36p. (J). bds. 16.00 (978-0-9724147-1-5(1)) Sloan Publishing.

—Buzz & Ollie's Steady Beat Adventure. Thorne, Donna Sloan & Felts, Marilyn Sloan, illus. 2002. (Illus.). 36p. (J). bds. 16.00 (978-0-9724147-2-2(X)) Sloan Publishing.

Tibo, Gilles. Simon et la Musique. ed. 2004. Tr. of Simon Makes Music. (FRE.). (J). (ps-2). spiral bd. (978-0-616-01845-3(2)) Canadian National Institute for the Blind/Institut National Canadien pour les Aveugles.

—Simon Makes Music. ed. 2004. (J). (ps-2). spiral bd. (978-0-616-01792-0(8)); spiral bd. (978-0-616-01793-7(6)) Canadian National Institute for the Blind/Institut National Canadien pour les Aveugles.

Torres, J. Days Like This. 2003. (Illus.). 80p. (YA). pap. 8.95 (978-1-929998-48-7(1)) Oni Pr., Inc.

Tremain, Rose. Music & Silence. 2001. (gr. 7-12). lib. bdg. 24.55 (978-0-613-70861-6(X)) Tandem Library Bks.

Ungerer, Tomi. Tortoni Tremolo the Cursed Magician. Ungerer, Tomi, illus. 1998. (Illus.). 32p. (J). (gr. 1-5). 16.95 (978-1-57098-226-2(0)) Rinehart, Roberts Pubs.

van Holst Pellekaan, Karen. Coco Makes Music. De Backker, Vera, illus. 2000. (Coco the Koala Ser.). 29p. (J). (ps up). lib. bdg. 23.33 (978-0-8368-2730-9(9)) Stevens, Gareth Inc.

Varennes, Monique de. Bibi & the Sad Ballerinas. Juan, Ana, illus. 2006. (J). 16.95 (978-0-689-87665-3(3) , Atheneum) Simon & Schuster Children's Publishing.

Velasquez, Eric. Grandma's Records. Velasquez, Eric, illus. 2004. (Illus.). 32p. (J). pap. 7.95 (978-0-8027-7660-0(4)) Walker & Co.

—Grandma's Records. 2004. (Illus.). 32p. (J). (gr. k-3). 16.95 (978-0-8027-8760-6(6)); 17.85 (978-0-8027-8761-3(4)) Walker & Co.

Velasquez, Eric & de la Vega, Eida. Los Discos de Mi Abuela. 2002. (SPA., Illus.). (J). (gr. 1-3). 16.95 (978-1-930332-21-8(1) , LC7246) Lectorum Pubns., Inc.

Walters, Jennie. Michelle: Centre Stage. 2002. (Illus.). 128p. pap. 7.99 (978-0-340-85411-2(1) , Hodder & Stoughton) Hodder General Publishing Division GBR. *Dist:* Trafalgar Square Publishing.

Walton, O. F. Christie's Old Organ: A Little Boy's Journey to Find a Home of His Own. 1999. 176p. (J). (gr. 4-7). mass mkt. (978-1-85792-523-4(8) , Christian Heritage) Christian Focus Pubns.

Wasserman, Robin. Keepin' It Real! 2005. (Teenick Ser.: No. 1). (Illus.). 112p. (J). (gr. 4-7). pap. 4.99 (978-0-439-79666-8(0) , Scholastic Paperbacks) Scholastic, Inc.

Watts, Leander. Beautiful City of the Dead. 2007. 256p. (YA). (gr. 7). pap. 7.99 (***978-0-618-59499-3(X)***) Houghton Mifflin Co. Trade & Reference Div.

Weber, Lou. Strawberry Shortcake Little Music Note. 12p. 9.98 (978-1-4127-6209-0(X) , PIL Kids) Publications International, Ltd.

—Sweet Dreams Barney Musical Lullaby Treasury. 2005. 40p. 12.98 (978-1-4127-3780-7(X) , PIL Kids) Publications International, Ltd.

Weber, Lou, ed. Boohbah: Little Music Note. 2004. 10p. (J). 9.98 (978-1-4127-3242-0(5) , 7236200) Publications International, Ltd.

—The Incredibles Interactive Sound Book. 2004. 24p. (J). 15.98 (978-1-4127-3029-7(5) , 7226900) Publications International, Ltd.

Weidt, Maryann N. Daddy Played Music for the Cows. Sorensen, Henri, illus. 2nd ed. 2004. 32p. (J). pap. 7.95 (978-0-89317-060-8(7) , WW-0607, Windward Publishing) Finney Co., Inc.

Wells, Rosemary. Practice Makes Perfect. Wheeler, Jody, illus. 2002. (Yoko & Friends School Days Ser.: No. 10). 32p. (gr. k-2). 9.99 (978-0-7868-0725-3(3)) Disney Pr.

—Practice Makes Perfect. 2002. (gr. k-3). lib. bdg. 11.80 (978-0-613-74979-4(0)) Tandem Library Bks.

Wenberg, Michael. Elizabeth's Song. Van Wright, Cornelius, illus. 2002. 29p. (J). 15.95 (978-1-58270-069-4(9)) Beyond Words Publishing, Inc.

—Elizabeth's Song. Van Wright, Cornelius, illus. 2003. 32p. (J). (gr. 3 up). lib. bdg. 24.67 (978-0-8368-3572-4(7)) Stevens, Gareth Inc.

Wheeler, Lisa. Jazz Baby. Christie, Gregory R., illus. 2007. 40p. (J). (ps-2). 16.00 (978-0-15-202522-9(7)) Harcourt Trade Pubs.

Where's Henry?, 6 Pack. (gr. k-1). 23.00 (978-0-7635-8828-1(8)) Rigby Education.

Wieler, Diana. Drive. 2001. 246p. (J). (gr. 8-13). pap. 6.95 (978-0-88899-348-9(X)) Groundwood Bks. CAN. *Dist:* Perseus Distribution.

—Drive. 1999. (gr. 7-12). lib. bdg. 14.10 (978-0-613-28825-5(4)) Tandem Library Bks.

Williams, Sheron & Daly, Jude. Imani's Music. 2002. (Illus.). 40p. (J). (gr. 1-4). 17.00 (978-0-689-82254-4(5) , Atheneum) Simon & Schuster Children's Publishing.

Williams, Vera B. Algo Especial Para Mi. Williams, Vera B., illus. 2006. (SPA.). 32p. (J). pap. 6.99 (978-0-06-088707-0(9)) HarperCollins Pubs.

Willner-Pardo, Gina. Spider Storch's Music Mess. Sharratt, Nick, illus. 1998. 80p. (J). (gr. 2-5). lib. bdg. 11.95 (978-0-8075-7583-3(6)) Whitman, Albert & Co.

Wilson, Budge. A Fiddle for Angus. Tooke, Susan, illus. 2006. 32p. (J). (gr. 1-4). pap. 9.95 (978-0-88776-785-2(0) , Random Hse. Puzzles & Games) Random Hse. Information Group.

Winnie the Pooh Helping Songs. 2003. (Illus.). 10p. (J). bds. 9.98 (978-0-7853-8284-3(4) , 7182200) Publications International, Ltd.

Winter, Jonah. The 39 Apartments of Ludwig Van Beethoven. Blitt, Barry, illus. 2006. (J). (ps-4). 32p. lib. bdg. 17.99 (978-0-375-93602-9(5)), 40p. 15.95 (978-0-375-83602-2(0)) Random Hse. Children's Bks. (Schwartz & Wade Bks.).

Wolff, Virginia Euwer. The Mozart Season. 2000. (978-0-606-18579-0(8)) Tandem Library Bks.

Wood, Maryrose. My Life, the Musical. 2008. (YA). (***978-0-385-90297-7(2)*** , Delacorte Pr.) Dell Publishing.

Zimelman, Nathan. Evening Song. Morrison, Cathy, illus. 2003. (Books for Young Learners). 12p. (J). ring bd. 5.00 net. (978-1-57274-536-0(3) , 2741) Owen, Richard C. Pubs., Inc.

MUSIC—HISTORY AND CRITICISM

Aliki. Ah, Music! Aliki, illus. (Illus.). 48p. (J). 2005. pap. 6.99 (978-0-06-446236-5(6)); 2003. 17.99 (978-0-06-028719-1(5)); 2003. lib. bdg. 17.89 (978-0-06-028727-6(6)) HarperCollins Pubs.

Allen, Patrick. World of Music: Europe. 2007. (J). (***978-1-4034-9890-8(3)***) Heinemann Library.

Ancona, George. Mi Musica. 2006. Tr. of My Music. (SPA.). 32p. (J). (gr. 1-3). pap. 8.95 (978-0-516-25494-4(4) , Children's Pr.) Scholastic Library Publishing.

Anderton, H. Orsmond. Early English Music. 2001. (YA). reprint ed. 150.00 (978-0-7222-5103-4(3)) Library Reprints, Inc.

Antcliffe, Herbert. Short Studies in the Nature of Music. 2001. 245p. (YA). reprint ed. 98.00 (978-0-7222-5617-6(5)) Library Reprints, Inc.

Apthorp, William Foster. By the Way: A Collection of Short Essays on Music & Art in General, 2 vols., set. 2001. (YA). reprint ed. 250.00 (978-0-7222-5220-8(X)) Library Reprints, Inc.

—Musicians & Music-Lovers, & Other Essays. 5th ed. 2001. 346p. (YA). reprint ed. 98.00 (978-0-7222-5221-5(8)) Library Reprints, Inc.

Asirvatham, Sandy. The History of Blues. 2003. (American Mosaic Ser.). (Illus.). 112p. (gr. 6-12). 30.00 (978-0-7910-7266-0(5)); pap. 30.00 (978-0-7910-7490-9(0)) Facts On File, Inc. (Chelsea Hse.).

Auer, Leopold. My Long Life in Music. 2001. 377p. (YA). reprint ed. 98.00 (978-0-7222-5310-6(9)) Library Reprints, Inc.

Awmiller, Craig. This House on Fire: The Story of the Blues. 2004. (Illus.). 160p. (J). (gr. 4-8). reprint ed. pap. (978-0-7567-7826-2(3)) DIANE Publishing Co.

Bach, Albert B. The Art Ballad, Loewe & Schubert. 3rd ed. 2001. 215p. (YA). reprint ed. 98.00 (978-0-7222-5454-7(7)) Library Reprints, Inc.

Banister, Henry C. Interludes: Seven Lectures Delivered Between the Years 1891-1897. 2001. 229p. (YA). reprint ed. 98.00 (978-0-7222-5819-4(4)) Library Reprints, Inc.

Barlex, David & Wadsworth, Pamela. Rhagor Am Sain a Cherddoriaeth. 2005. (WEL., Illus.). 24p. pap. (978-1-85596-240-8(3)) Dref Wen.

—Sain a Cherddoriaeth. 2005. (WEL., Illus.). 24p. pap. (978-1-85596-239-2(X)) Dref Wen.

Barron's Educational Editorial Staff. Masters of Music Series Assortment. 1999. 239.20 (978-0-7641-7314-1(6)) Barron's Educational Series, Inc.

Bauer, Marion Dane. How Music Grew, from Prehistoric Times to the Present Day. 2001. 602p. (YA). reprint ed. 128.00 (978-0-7222-5021-1(5)) Library Reprints, Inc.

Beale, Thomas W. Light of Olden Days Seen Through Wrong End of Glass, 2 vols., set. 2001. (YA). reprint ed. 250.00 (978-0-7222-6268-9(X)) Library Reprints, Inc.

Beale, Willert. The Light of Other Days. 2001. (YA). reprint ed. 150.00 (978-0-7222-5225-3(0)) Library Reprints, Inc.

Beatty-Kingston, William. Music & Manners: Personal Reminiscences & Sketches of Character, 2 vols., set. 2001. (YA). reprint ed. 250.00 (978-0-7222-5263-5(3)) Library Reprints, Inc.

Berger, Francesco. Reminiscences, Impressions & Anecdotes. 2001. 227p. (YA). reprint ed. 98.00 (978-0-7222-5355-7(9)) Library Reprints, Inc.

Bertholf, Bret. The Long Gone Lonesome History of Country Music. 2007. (Illus.). 64p. (J). (gr. 1-5). 18.99 (978-0-316-52393-6(3)) Little Brown & Co.

Birkenshaw, Lois. Music for Fun, Music for Learning. 4th ed. 2006. (C). per. 46.00 (***978-1-891278-43-3(6)***) Barcelona Pubs.

Blue, Rose & Naden, Corinne J. The History of Gospel Music. 2001. (African American Achievers Ser.). (Illus.). (gr. 6-12). 112p. 30.00 (978-0-7910-5818-3(2)); 144p. pap. 30.00 (978-0-7910-5819-0(0)) Facts On File, Inc. (Chelsea Hse.).

Boughton, Rutland. Bach, the Master, a New Interpretation of His Genius. 2001. 303p. (YA). reprint ed. 98.00 (978-0-7222-6313-6(9)) Library Reprints, Inc.

Brasch, Nicolas. Classical Music & Opera. 2004. (J). lib. bdg. 27.10 (978-1-58340-547-5(X)) Smart Apple Media.

—Folk, Country & Reggae. 2004. (J). lib. bdg. 27.10 (978-1-58340-549-9(6)) Smart Apple Media.

—Jazz & Blues. 2004. (J). lib. bdg. 27.10 (978-1-58340-548-2(8)) Smart Apple Media.

—Pop & Rock Music. 2004. (J). lib. bdg. 27.10 (978-1-58340-546-8(1)) Smart Apple Media.

Bridge, Frederick. Twelve Good Musicians, from John Bull to Henry Purcell. 2001. 144p. (YA). reprint ed. 88.00 (978-0-7222-5230-7(7)) Library Reprints, Inc.

Brown, James Duff. British Musical Biography: A Dictionary of Musical Artists, Authors, & Composers Born in Britian & Its Colonies. 2001. 462p. (YA). reprint ed. 98.00 (978-0-7222-5297-0(8)) Library Reprints, Inc.

Buckland, Anne W. Anthropological Studies. 2001. 295p. (YA). reprint ed. 98.00 (978-0-7222-5060-0(6)) Library Reprints, Inc.

Bunting, Edward. Letters: In Young's Old Belfast 2001. 905p. (YA). reprint ed. 248.00 (978-0-7222-5373-1(7)) Library Reprints, Inc.

Burlin, Natalie C. Songs & Tales from the Dark Continent. 2001. 170p. (YA). reprint ed. 88.00 (978-0-7222-5068-6(1)) Library Reprints, Inc.

Burney, Charles. A General History of Music, from the Earliest Ages to the Present Period, 4 vols. 2001. (YA). reprint ed. 500.00 (978-0-7222-5022-8(3)) Library Reprints, Inc.

Burns, Robert. Notes on Scottish Song. 2001. 134p. (YA). reprint ed. 88.00 (978-0-7222-6198-9(5)) Library Reprints, Inc.

Calvocoressi, Michel D. The Principles & Methods of Musical Criticism. 2001. 148p. (YA). reprint ed. 88.00 (978-0-7222-5233-8(1)) Library Reprints, Inc.

Chappell, William. National English Airs: An Essay on Ancient English Minstrelsy, 2 vols., set. 2001. (YA). reprint ed. 250.00 (978-0-7222-5106-5(8)) Library Reprints, Inc.

Chassevant, Marie. Gibb. 2001. (YA). reprint ed. 150.00 (978-0-7222-5847-7(X)) Library Reprints, Inc.

Colles, Henry C. The Growth of Music: A Study in Musical History for Schools, 3 vols. 2001. (YA). reprint ed. 375.00 (978-0-7222-5024-2(X)) Library Reprints, Inc.

Coomaraswamy, Ananda Kentish. Indian Music. 2001. (YA). reprint ed. 150.00 (978-0-7222-5090-7(8)) Library Reprints, Inc.

Corder, Frederick. Modern Musical Composition: A Manual for Students. 2001. 98p. (YA). reprint ed. 88.00 (978-0-7222-5672-5(8)) Library Reprints, Inc.

Cowen, Frederic H. My Art & My Friends. 2001. 319p. (YA). reprint ed. 98.00 (978-0-7222-5396-0(6)) Library Reprints, Inc.

Cowling, George H. Music on the Shakespearian Stage. 2001. 116p. (YA). reprint ed. 88.00 (978-0-7222-5107-2(6)) Library Reprints, Inc.

Crowest, Frederick J. A Book of Musical Anecdote, 2 vols., set. 2001. (YA). reprint ed. 250.00 (978-0-7222-5235-2(8)) Library Reprints, Inc.

—Music Stories. 2001. (YA). reprint ed. 1620.00 (978-0-7222-6375-4(9)) Library Reprints, Inc.

—The Story of British Music. 2001. 396p. (YA). reprint ed. 98.00 (978-0-7222-5108-9(4)) Library Reprints, Inc.

Cummings, William H. Henry Purcell, 1658-1695. 2001. 124p. (YA). reprint ed. 88.00 (978-0-7222-5191-1(2)) Library Reprints, Inc.

Curwen, John S. Musical Statics. 2001. (YA). reprint ed. 150.00 (978-0-7222-5629-9(9)) Library Reprints, Inc.

Davey, Henry. History of English Music. 2nd ed. 2001. 505p. (YA). reprint ed. 98.00 (978-0-7222-5109-6(2)) Library Reprints, Inc.

De LaFontaine, Henry Cart. The King's Musick: A Transcript of Records Relating to Music & Musicians, 1460-1700. 2001. 522p. (YA). reprint ed. 98.00 (978-0-7222-5114-0(9)) Library Reprints, Inc.

Dell, Pamela. The Blues: Birth of an American Sound. 2005. (Journey to Freedom Ser.). (Illus.). 40p. (J). (gr. 3-7). 28.50 (978-1-59296-230-3(0)) Child's World, Inc.

Densmore, Frances. Northern U. T. E. Music. 2001. 213p. (YA). reprint ed. 98.00 (978-0-7222-5072-3(X)) Library Reprints, Inc.

Dickinson, Edward. Growth & Development of Music Described in Chapters on the Study of Musical History. 2001. 409p. (YA). reprint ed. 98.00 (978-0-7222-5025-9(8)) Library Reprints, Inc.

—The Spirit of Music: How to Find It & How to Share It. 2001. 218p. (YA). reprint ed. 98.00 (978-0-7222-5642-8(6)) Library Reprints, Inc.

Donovan, J. Aboriginal Union of Poetry & Song. 2001. (YA). reprint ed. 150.00 (978-0-7222-5061-7(4)) Library Reprints, Inc.

Dry, Wakeling. Music of the Masters. 2001. (YA). reprint ed. 362.00 (978-0-7222-6373-0(2)) Library Reprints, Inc.

Duncan, Edmondstoune. The Story of Minstrelsy. 2001. 336p. (YA). reprint ed. 98.00 (978-0-7222-6072-2(5)) Library Reprints, Inc.

Duncan, Walter E. Ultra-Modernism in Music. 2001. (YA). reprint ed. 150.00 (978-0-7222-5055-6(X)) Library Reprints, Inc.

Dunhill, Thomas Frederick. Chamber Music. 2001. 311p. (YA). reprint ed. 98.00 (978-0-7222-5162-1(9)) Library Reprints, Inc.

Dyson, George. The New Music. 2001. 151p. (YA). reprint ed. 88.00 (978-0-7222-5056-3(8)) Library Reprints, Inc.

Eclectic Library. 2001. (YA). reprint ed. 176.00 (978-0-7222-6363-1(5)) Library Reprints, Inc.

Edmunds, W. M. Sound & Rhythm. 2001. (YA). reprint ed. 150.00 (978-0-7222-5630-5(2)) Library Reprints, Inc.

Edwards, Frederick G. The History of Mendelssohn's Oratorio Elijah. 2001. 142p. (YA). reprint ed. 88.00 (978-0-7222-5467-7(9)) Library Reprints, Inc.

Edwards, Henry Sutherland. Personal Recollections. 2001. 280p. (YA). reprint ed. 98.00 (978-0-7222-5240-6(4)) Library Reprints, Inc.

Edwards, John H. God & Music. 2001. 319p. (YA). reprint ed. 98.00 (978-0-7222-5770-8(8)) Library Reprints, Inc.

Ellis, Alexander John. Speech in Song. 2001. 137p. (YA). reprint ed. 88.00 (978-0-7222-6162-0(4)) Library Reprints, Inc.

Ellis, W. Ashton. Glasenapp. 2001. (YA). reprint ed. 150.00 (978-0-7222-5568-1(3)) Library Reprints, Inc.

Elmer, Howard. Blues: Its Birth & Growth. 1999. (Library of African American Arts & Culture). (Illus.). 64p. (YA). (gr. 7-12). lib. bdg. 26.50 (978-0-8239-1853-9(X) , AABLUE) Rosen Publishing Group, Inc., The.

Elson, Arthur. The Book of Musical Knowledge: The History, Technique, & Appreciation of Music. 2001. 603p. (YA). reprint ed. 128.00 (978-0-7222-5820-0(8)) Library Reprints, Inc.

Elson, Louis C. Children in Music: Women in Music. 2001. 115p. (YA). reprint ed. 88.00 (978-0-7222-5244-4(7)) Library Reprints, Inc.

—Great Composers & Their Work. 2001. 302p. (YA). reprint ed. 98.00 (978-0-7222-5243-7(9)) Library Reprints, Inc.

—The History of American Music. 2001. 380p. (YA). reprint ed. 98.00 (978-0-7222-5150-8(5)) Library Reprints, Inc.

—The National Music of America & Its Source. rev. ed. 2001. 367p. (YA). reprint ed. 98.00 (978-0-7222-5151-5(3)) Library Reprints, Inc.

Engel, Carl. An Introduction to the Study of National Music: Comprising Researches into Popular Songs, Traditions & Customs. 2001. 435p. (YA). reprint ed. 98.00 (978-0-7222-5181-2(5)) Library Reprints, Inc.

—Music of the Most Ancient Nations, Particularly of the Assyrians, Egyptians, & Hebrews. 2001. 379p. (YA). reprint ed. 98.00 (978-0-7222-5062-4(2)) Library Reprints, Inc.

English Music, 1604 to 1904: English Music, Sixteen Hundred Four. 2001. 539p. (YA). reprint ed. 98.00 (978-0-7222-5117-1(3)) Library Reprints, Inc.

Evans, Edwin. Wagner's Teachings by Analogy: His Views on Absolute Music & of the Relations of Articulate & Tonal Speech. 2001. 79p. (YA). reprint ed. 88.00 (978-0-7222-5569-8(1)) Library Reprints, Inc.

Fairbanks, Arthur. A Study of the Greek Paan. 2001. 166p. (YA). reprint ed. 88.00 (978-0-7222-5081-5(9)) Library Reprints, Inc.

Fellowes, Edmund Horace. The English Madrigal School, 36 vols., set. 2001. (YA). reprint ed. 4500.00 (978-0-7222-6143-9(8)) Library Reprints, Inc.

—English Madrigal Verse, 1588-1632. 2001. 640p. (YA). reprint ed. 128.00 (978-0-7222-6144-6(6)) Library Reprints, Inc.

—The English School of Lutenist Song Writers, 17 vols., set. 2001. (YA). reprint ed. 2125.00 (978-0-7222-6140-8(3)) Library Reprints, Inc.

Finck, Henry Theophilus. Chopin & Other Musical Essays. 2001. 273p. (YA). reprint ed. 98.00 (978-0-7222-5379-3(6)) Library Reprints, Inc.

Ford, Robert. Song Histories. 2001. (YA). reprint ed. 150.00 (978-0-7222-6171-2(3)) Library Reprints, Inc.

Fridlander, Ernest D. Matthew Maris. 2001. 149p. (YA). reprint ed. 88.00 (978-0-7222-5460-8(1)) Library Reprints, Inc.

Galloway, William J. Musical England. 2001. 258p. (YA). reprint ed. 98.00 (978-0-7222-5111-9(4)) Library Reprints, Inc.

Gershenson, Harold P. America the Musical 1900-2000: A Nation's History Through Music. Chesworth, Michael, illus. 2006. (J). (***978-1-58987-201-1(0)***) Kindermusik International.

Gilman, Lawrence. The Music of To-Morrow, & Other Studies. 2001. 143p. (YA). reprint ed. 88.00 (978-0-7222-5823-1(2)) Library Reprints, Inc.

—Phases of Modern Music. 2001. 165p. (YA). reprint ed. 88.00 (978-0-7222-5824-8(0)) Library Reprints, Inc.

—Stories of Symphonic Music: A Guide to the Meaning of Important Symphonies, Overtures, & Tone-Poems from Beethoven to the Present Day. 2001. 358p. (YA). reprint ed. 98.00 (978-0-7222-5183-6(1)) Library Reprints, Inc.

Gish, D. L. Country Music. 2000. (J). (978-1-58341-066-0(X) , Creative Education) Creative Co., The.

—Country Music. 2001. (World of Music Ser.). (Illus.). 32p. (J). (gr. 2-7). lib. bdg. 22.60 (978-1-58340-020-3(6)) Smart Apple Media.

—Rock & Roll. 2001. (World of Music Ser.). (Illus.). 32p. (J). (gr. 2-7). lib. bdg. 15.95 (978-1-58340-060-9(5)) Smart Apple Media.

Gish, D. L. & Kirgiss, Crystal. World of Music, 6 vols., Set. 2001. (Illus.). (J). (gr. 2-7). lib. bdg. 135.60 (978-1-58340-017-3(6)) Smart Apple Media.

Glyn, Margaret H. The Evolution of Musical Form. 2001. 331p. (YA). reprint ed. 98.00 (978-0-7222-5714-2(7)) Library Reprints, Inc.

Goddard, Joseph. The Rise of Music, Being a Careful Enquiry into the Development of the Art from Its Primitive Puttings Forth in Egypt & Assyria to Its Triumphant Consummation in Modern Effect. 2001. 398p. (YA). reprint ed. 98.00 (978-0-7222-5027-3(4)) Library Reprints, Inc.

Godfrey, Dan. Memories & Music: Thirty-Five Years of Conducting. 2001. 327p. (YA). reprint ed. 98.00 (978-0-7222-5418-9(0)) Library Reprints, Inc.

Grace, Harvey. French Organ Music, Past & Present. 2001. 212p. (YA). reprint ed. 98.00 (978-0-7222-5910-8(7)) Library Reprints, Inc.

Gray, Cecil. A Survey of Contemporary Music. 2001. 261p. (YA). reprint ed. 98.00 (978-0-7222-5053-2(3)) Library Reprints, Inc.

Gutierrez, Peter. World of Music: Eastern Asia. 2007. (J). (***978-1-4034-9893-9(8)***) Heinemann Library.

Hadow, William H. A Croatian Composer. 2001. 96p. (YA). reprint ed. 88.00 (978-0-7222-5437-0(7)) Library Reprints, Inc.

—Studies in Modern Music, 2 vols., set. 9th ed. 2001. (YA). reprint ed. 250.00 (978-0-7222-5253-6(6)) Library Reprints, Inc.

Handyside, Chris. A History of Blues. 2006. (Illus.). 48p. (J). (978-1-4034-8148-1(2)) Heinemann Library.

—A History of Blues. 2006. (J). (978-1-4109-1811-6(4)) Steck-Vaughn.

—A History of Country. 2006. (Illus.). 48p. (J). (978-1-4034-8151-1(2)) Heinemann Library.

—A History of Country. 2006. (J). (978-1-4109-1814-7(9)) Steck-Vaughn.

—A History of Soul & R&B. 2006. (Illus.) 48p. (J). (978-1-4034-8153-5(9)) Heinemann Library.

—A History of Soul & R&B. 2006. (J). (978-1-4109-1816-1(5)) Steck-Vaughn.

Hanslick, Eduard. The Beautiful in Music. 2001. 174p. (YA). reprint ed. 88.00 (978-0-7222-5648-0(5)) Library Reprints, Inc.

Hargrave, Mary. The Earlier French Musicians, 1632-1834. 2001. 258p. (YA). reprint ed. 98.00 (978-0-7222-5305-2(2)) Library Reprints, Inc.

Harris, Clement A. The Story of British Music. 2001. 237p. (YA). reprint ed. 98.00 (978-0-7222-5112-6(2)) Library Reprints, Inc.

Haskins, James. Black Music in America: A History Through Its People. 2000. (Illus.). 200p. (J). pap. 12.95 (978-1-56649-133-4(9)) Welcome Rain Pubs.

Havergal, Francis T. Memorials of Frederick Arthur Gore Ouseley. 2001. (YA). reprint ed. 150.00 (978-0-7222-5490-5(3)) Library Reprints, Inc.

Haweis, Hugh R. Music & Morals. 2001. 556p. (YA). reprint ed. 98.00 (978-0-7222-5254-3(4)) Library Reprints, Inc.

Hawkins, John. A General History of the Science & Practice of Music, 3 vols. 2001. (YA). reprint ed. 375.00 (978-0-7222-5029-7(0)) Library Reprints, Inc.

—The Same: Medallion Portraits. 2001. (YA). reprint ed. suppl. ed. 150.00 (978-0-7222-5030-3(4)) Library Reprints, Inc.

Hayes, Malcolm. 20s & 30s: Between the Wars. 2002. (Twentieth Century Music Ser.). (Illus.). 32p. (J). (gr. 5 up). lib. bdg. 26.00 (978-0-8368-3032-3(6)) Stevens, Gareth Inc.

—20th Century Music, 6 bks. Incl. 20s & 30s : Between the Wars. lib. bdg. 26.00 (978-0-8368-3032-3(6)); 40s & 50s : From War to Peace. lib. bdg. 26.00 (978-0-8368-3033-0(4)); 80s & 90s : Different Paths. lib. bdg. 26.00 (978-0-8368-3036-1(9)); 1900-20 : New Horizons. lib.

bdg. 26.00 (978-0-8368-3031-6(8)); 1960s : Age of Rock. lib. bdg. 26.00 (978-0-8368-3034-7(2)); 1970s : Turbulent Times. lib. bdg. 26.00 (978-0-8368-3035-4(0)); 32p. (J). (gr. 5 up). (Illus.). 2002. Set lib. bdg. 156.00 (978-0-8368-3030-9(X)) Stevens, Gareth Inc.

—40s & 50s: From War to Peace. 2002. (Twentieth Century Music Ser.). (Illus.). 32p. (J). (gr. 5 up). lib. bdg. 26.00 (978-0-8368-3033-0(4)) Stevens, Gareth Inc.

—80s & 90s: Different Paths. 2002. (Twentieth Century Music Ser.). (Illus.). 32p. (J). (gr. 5 up). lib. bdg. 26.00 (978-0-8368-3036-1(9)) Stevens, Gareth Inc.

—1900-20: New Horizons. 2002. (Twentieth Century Music Ser.). (Illus.). 32p. (J). (gr. 5 up). lib. bdg. 26.00 (978-0-8368-3031-6(8)) Stevens, Gareth Inc.

—1960s: Age of Rock. 2002. (Twentieth Century Music Ser.). (Illus.). 32p. (J). (gr. 5 up). lib. bdg. 26.00 (978-0-8368-3034-7(2)) Stevens, Gareth Inc.

—1970s: Turbulent Times. 2002. (Twentieth Century Music Ser.). (Illus.). 32p. (J). (gr. 5 up). lib. bdg. 26.00 (978-0-8368-3035-4(0)) Stevens, Gareth Inc.

Helmore, Thomas. The Plain Song. 2001. 164p. (YA). reprint ed. 88.00 (978-0-7222-6155-2(1)) Library Reprints, Inc.

Hervey, Arthur. Alfred Bruneau. 2001. 86p. (YA). reprint ed. 88.00 (978-0-7222-5371-7(0)) Library Reprints, Inc.

Hewitt, Theodore B. Paul Gerhardt. 2001. 169p. (YA). reprint ed. 88.00 (978-0-7222-6137-8(3)) Library Reprints, Inc.

Hill, Edward B. Modern French Music. 2001. 406p. (YA). reprint ed. 98.00 (978-0-7222-5134-8(3)) Library Reprints, Inc.

Hirsch, William. Genius & Degeneration: A Psychological Study. 2001. 333p. (YA). reprint ed. 98.00 (978-0-7222-5581-0(0)) Library Reprints, Inc.

History of the Cardiff Festival. 2001. (YA). reprint ed. 150.00 (978-0-7222-5122-5(X)) Library Reprints, Inc.

Holbrooke, Joseph. Contemporary British Composers: Portraits & Facsimiles of Musical Examples. 2001. 324p. (YA). reprint ed. 98.00 (978-0-7222-5299-4(4)) Library Reprints, Inc.

Home, Ethel. Music As a Language: Lectures to Music Students. 2001. 82p. (YA). reprint ed. 88.00 (978-0-7222-5707-4(4)) Library Reprints, Inc.

Howes, Frank S. The Borderland of Music & Psychology. 2001. 244p. (YA). reprint ed. 98.00 (978-0-7222-5793-7(7)) Library Reprints, Inc.

Hueffer, Francis. Half a Century of Music in England, 1837-1887: Essays Towards a History. 2001. 240p. (YA). reprint ed. 98.00 (978-0-7222-5113-3(0)) Library Reprints, Inc.

—The Music of the Future. 2001. 333p. (YA). reprint ed. 98.00 (978-0-7222-5582-7(9)) Library Reprints, Inc.

Hull, Arthur E. Musical, Classical, Romantic & Modern. 2001. 473p. (YA). reprint ed. 98.00 (978-0-7222-5206-2(4)) Library Reprints, Inc.

Hullah, Frances R. Life of John Hullah. 2001. 298p. (YA). reprint ed. 98.00 (978-0-7222-5441-7(5)) Library Reprints, Inc.

Huneker, James. Ivory Apes & Peacocks. 2001. 328p. (YA). reprint ed. 98.00 (978-0-7222-5259-8(5)) Library Reprints, Inc.

—Melomaniacs. 2001. 350p. (YA). reprint ed. 98.00 (978-0-7222-5260-4(9)) Library Reprints, Inc.

Huneker, James G. Chopin: The Man & His Music. 2001. 415p. (YA). reprint ed. 98.00 (978-0-7222-5381-6(8)) Library Reprints, Inc.

Hunt, Bonavia H. G. A Concise History of Music: From the Commencement of the Christian Era to the Present Time for the Use of Students. 18th ed. 2001. 184p. (YA). reprint ed. 88.00 (978-0-7222-5036-5(3)) Library Reprints, Inc.

Hunt, Harry Ernest. Spirit & Music. 2001. 136p. (YA). reprint ed. 88.00 (978-0-7222-5794-4(5)) Library Reprints, Inc.

Hyde, Heidi Smith. Mendel's Accordion: The Story of the Klezmorim. Van der Sterre, Johanna, illus. 2007. 32p. (J). (gr. k-4). pap. 7.95 ***(*978-1-58013-214-5(6))*** Karben Publishing.

Jackman, Ian. Total Request Live: Behind the Scenes at MTV's Total Request Live. 2000. (gr. 5-8). lib. bdg. 22.20 (978-0-613-49379-6(0)) Tandem Library Bks.

Jameson, D. D. Colour Music. 2001. (YA). reprint ed. 150.00 (978-0-7222-5803-3(8)) Library Reprints, Inc.

Jean-Aubrey, Georges. French Music of Today & Musicians of Today, 2 vols. 2001. (YA). reprint ed. 98.00 (978-0-7222-5135-5(1)) Library Reprints, Inc.

Jones, F. O. A Handbook of American Music & Musicians. 2001. 182p. (YA). reprint ed. 88.00 (978-0-7222-5153-9(X)) Library Reprints, Inc.

Joyce, Frederick W. The Life of Reverend Ouseley. 2001. 276p. (YA). reprint ed. 98.00 (978-0-7222-5491-2(1)) Library Reprints, Inc.

Kallen, Stuart A. The History of Classical Music. 2002. (Illus.). 112p. (J). 32.45 (978-1-59018-123-2(9) , Lucent Bks.) Thomson Gale.

—The History of Latin Music. 2006. 112p. (J). (gr. 7-10). 32.45 (978-1-59018-737-1(7) , Lucent Bks.) Thomson Gale.

—The History of Reggae. 2005. (Music Library). (Illus.). 112p. (YA). (gr. 7-10). lib. bdg. 32.45 (978-1-59018-740-1(7) , Lucent Bks.) Thomson Gale.

—The History of World Music. 2006. (Illus.). 112p. (J). (gr. 7-10). 32.45 (978-1-59018-741-8(5) , Lucent Bks.) Thomson Gale.

Khanduri, Kamini. World of Music: Western Asia. 2007. (J). ***(*978-1-4034-9892-2(X))*** Heinemann Library.

Kilburn, Nicholas. The Story of Chamber Music. 2001. 251p. (YA). reprint ed. 98.00 (978-0-7222-5163-8(7)) Library Reprints, Inc.

Kirgiss, Crystal. Classical Music. 2001. (World of Music Ser.). (Illus.). 32p. (J). (gr. 2-7). lib. bdg. 22.60 (978-1-58340-019-7(2)) Smart Apple Media.

Klein, Hermann. Thirty Years of Musical Life in London, 1870-1900: More Than One Hundred Illustrations from Photographs. 2001. 483p. (YA). reprint ed. 98.00 (978-0-7222-5264-2(1)) Library Reprints, Inc.

—Unmusical New York: A Brief Criticism of Triumphs, Failures, & Abuses. 2001. 144p. (YA). reprint ed. 88.00 (978-0-7222-5159-1(9)) Library Reprints, Inc.

Knight, M. J. Sound Effects. 2005. (Musical Instruments of the World Ser.). (Illus.). 32p. (J). (gr. 3-7). lib. bdg. 27.10 (978-1-58340-413-3(9)) Smart Apple Media.

Krall, Emil. The Future of Musicians. 2001. (YA). reprint ed. 150.00 (978-0-7222-5864-4(X)) Library Reprints, Inc.

Lagerlof, Selma. The Queens of Kungahalla. 2001. 192p. (YA). reprint ed. 88.00 (978-0-7222-5186-7(6)) Library Reprints, Inc.

Lahee, Henry Charles. The Annals of Music in America: A Chronological Record of Significant Musical Events, from 1640 to the Present Day. 2001. 298p. (YA). reprint ed. 98.00 (978-0-7222-5154-6(8)) Library Reprints, Inc.

Lasserre, Pierre. The Spirit of French Music. 2001. 218p. (YA). reprint ed. 98.00 (978-0-7222-5137-9(8)) Library Reprints, Inc.

Lavignac, Albert. Music & Musicians: 94 Illustrations & 510 Examples in Musical Notation. 2001. 518p. (YA). reprint ed. 98.00 (978-0-7222-5268-0(4)) Library Reprints, Inc.

Lee, Ernest M. Brahms the Man & His Music. 2001. 185p. (YA). reprint ed. 88.00 (978-0-7222-5367-0(2)) Library Reprints, Inc.

Lilly, Melinda. Minstrel. 2002. (Illus.). 32p. (J). lib. bdg. 26.60 (978-1-58952-228-2(1)) Rourke Publishing, LLC.

Locke, Arthur W. Music & the Romantic Movement in France. 2001. 184p. (YA). reprint ed. 88.00 (978-0-7222-5138-6(6)) Library Reprints, Inc.

MacDonald, Fiona. Music & Dance. (Discovering World Cultures Ser.). (Illus.). 40p. (J). (gr. 4). 2001. pap. (978-0-7787-0249-8(9)); 2000. lib. bdg. (978-0-7787-0239-9(1)) Crabtree Publishing Co.

—Music & Dance. 2001. (gr. 3-6). lib. bdg. 17.60 (978-0-613-43477-5(3)) Tandem Library Bks.

MacDonald, John. Sound & Colour: Their Relations, Analogies & Harmonies. 2001. 86p. (YA). reprint ed. 88.00 (978-0-7222-5804-0(6)) Library Reprints, Inc.

MacDowell, Edward. Critical & Historical Essays: Lectures Delivered at Columbia University. 2001. 282p. (YA). reprint ed. 98.00 (978-0-7222-5270-3(6)) Library Reprints, Inc.

Macfarren, George A. Addresses & Lectures. 2001. (YA). reprint ed. 150.00 (978-0-7222-5826-2(7)) Library Reprints, Inc.

—Musical History, with a Roll of the Names of Musicians & the Times & Places of Their Births & Deaths. 2001. 220p. (YA). reprint ed. 98.00 (978-0-7222-5038-9(X)) Library Reprints, Inc.

Mackenzie, Morell. Essays. 2001. 306p. (YA). reprint ed. 98.00 (978-0-7222-6208-5(6)) Library Reprints, Inc.

MacKinlay, Malcolm S. Garcia the Centenarian & His Times: A Memoir of Manuel Garcia's Life & Labours for the Advancement of Music & Science. 2001. 335p. (YA). reprint ed. 98.00 (978-0-7222-5411-0(3)) Library Reprints, Inc.

MacPherson, Stewart. A Commentary on the Forty-Eight Preludes & Fugues, 2 vols., set. 2001. (YA). reprint ed. 250.00 (978-0-7222-6327-3(9)) Library Reprints, Inc.

Malam, John. Song & Dance. 2000. (Everyday History Ser.). (Illus.). 32p. (YA). (gr. 3-4). pap. 6.95 (978-0-531-15984-2(1) , Watts, Franklin) Scholastic Library Publishing.

—Song & Dance. 2000. (gr. 3-6). lib. bdg. 15.25 (978-0-613-54675-1(X)) Tandem Library Bks.

Manera, Alexandria. Bessie Smith. 2003. (African-American Biographies Ser.). (Illus.). 64p. pap. 8.95 (978-1-4109-0034-0(7)); (J). lib. bdg. 28.56 (978-0-7398-6875-1(6)) Raintree.

Mason, Daniel G. From Grieg to Brahms: Studies of Some Modern Composers & Their Art. 2001. 224p. (YA). reprint ed. 98.00 (978-0-7222-5271-0(4)) Library Reprints, Inc.

Mason, Daniel Gregory. The Romantic Composers. 2001. 353p. (YA). reprint ed. 98.00 (978-0-7222-5272-7(2)) Library Reprints, Inc.

Mee, John H. The Oldest Music Room in Europe. 2001. 215p. (YA). reprint ed. 98.00 (978-0-7222-5116-4(5)) Library Reprints, Inc.

Middleton, Edgar C. Banned by the Censor. 2001. 126p. (YA). reprint ed. 88.00 (978-0-7222-5187-4(4)) Library Reprints, Inc.

Modjeska, Helena. Memories & Impressions of Helena Modjeska: An Autobiography. 2001. 571p. (YA). reprint ed. 98.00 (978-0-7222-6289-4(2)) Library Reprints, Inc.

Monro, David Binning. The Modes of Ancient Greek Music. 2001. 145p. (YA). reprint ed. 88.00 (978-0-7222-5082-2(7)) Library Reprints, Inc.

Montagu-Nathan, Montagu. A History of Russian Music: An Account of the Rise & Progress of the Russian School of Composers. 2001. 346p. (YA). reprint ed. 98.00 (978-0-7222-5142-3(4)) Library Reprints, Inc.

—An Introduction to Russian Music. 2001. 71p. (YA). reprint ed. 88.00 (978-0-7222-5143-0(2)) Library Reprints, Inc.

Moore, Thomas. Moore's Irish Melodies with Symphonies & Accompaniments. 2001. 261p. (YA). reprint ed. 98.00 (978-0-7222-6196-5(9)) Library Reprints, Inc.

Moyer, Dorothy T. Introduction to Music Appreciation & History. 2001. 137p. (YA). reprint ed. 88.00 (978-0-7222-5659-6(0)) Library Reprints, Inc.

Mundy, Godfrey. The Birth of Music. 2001. (YA). reprint ed. 150.00 (978-0-7222-5063-1(0)) Library Reprints, Inc.

The Music Connection: Grade 5. 1999. tchr. ed. 80.10 (978-0-382-34568-5(1)) Silver, Burdett & Ginn, Inc.

Naumann, Emil. An Illustrated History of Music, 2 vols. 2001. (YA). reprint ed. 250.00 (978-0-7222-5040-2(1)) Library Reprints, Inc.

Naylor, Edward W. Shakespeare Music: Music of the Period. 2001. 66p. (YA). reprint ed. 88.00 (978-0-7222-5118-8(1)) Library Reprints, Inc.

Newcomb, Ethel. Leschetizky As I Knew Him. 2001. 295p. (YA). reprint ed. 98.00 (978-0-7222-5443-1(1)) Library Reprints, Inc.

Newman, Ernest. A Musical Motley. 2001. 326p. (YA). reprint ed. 98.00 (978-0-7222-5830-9(5)) Library Reprints, Inc.

Newmarch, Rosa H. Henry J. Wood. 2001. 100p. (YA). reprint ed. 88.00 (978-0-7222-5616-9(7)) Library Reprints, Inc.

—Living Masters of Music. 2001. (YA). reprint ed. 968.00 (978-0-7222-6367-9(8)) Library Reprints, Inc.

Newton, R. H. The Mysticism of Music. 2001. (YA). reprint ed. 150.00 (978-0-7222-5831-6(3)) Library Reprints, Inc.

Nicholls, Frederick. The Language of Music: Musical Expression & Characterization. 2001. 106p. (YA). reprint ed. 88.00 (978-0-7222-5709-8(0)) Library Reprints, Inc.

Niecks, Frederick. Programme Music in the Last Four Centuries: A Contribution to the History of Musical Expression. 2001. 548p. (YA). reprint ed. 98.00 (978-0-7222-5182-9(3)) Library Reprints, Inc.

Noble, Richard S. H. Shakespeare's Use of Song. 2001. 160p. (YA). reprint ed. 88.00 (978-0-7222-6172-9(1)) Library Reprints, Inc.

Obrien, Eileen. Story of Music. 2006. (Illus.). 32p. (J). pap. 7.99 (978-0-7945-1403-7(0) , Usborne) EDC Publishing.

Ogden, Robert M. Hearing. 2001. 351p. (YA). reprint ed. 98.00 (978-0-7222-5795-1(3)) Library Reprints, Inc.

Oliphant, W. Elwin. Story of German Song. 2001. (YA). reprint ed. 150.00 (978-0-7222-6200-9(0)) Library Reprints, Inc.

Otis, Philo A. Impressions of Europe, 1873-1874: Music, Art & History. 2001. 207p. (YA). reprint ed. 98.00 (978-0-7222-5275-8(7)) Library Reprints, Inc.

Our Musical Past, 16p. (YA). pap. 16.95 incl. audio (978-0-88432-403-4(6) , S11020) Norton, Jeffrey Pubs., Inc.

Paine, John K. Famous Composers & Their Works, 3 vols., set. 2001. (YA). reprint ed. 375.00 (978-0-7222-5276-5(5)) Library Reprints, Inc.

Paine, John Knowles. The History of Music to the Death of Schubert. 2001. 314p. (YA). reprint ed. 98.00 (978-0-7222-5042-6(8)) Library Reprints, Inc.

Palmer, Bessie. Musical Recollections. 2001. (YA). reprint ed. 150.00 (978-0-7222-5277-2(3)) Library Reprints, Inc.

Parry, Charles H. H. The Evolution of the Art & Music. 2001. 342p. (YA). reprint ed. 98.00 (978-0-7222-5043-3(6)) Library Reprints, Inc.

—Style in Musical Art. 2001. 438p. (YA). reprint ed. 98.00 (978-0-7222-5818-7(6)) Library Reprints, Inc.

—Summary of the History & Development of Mediaeval & Modern European Music. rev. ed. 2001. 143p. (YA). reprint ed. 88.00 (978-0-7222-6329-7(5)) Library Reprints, Inc.

Pazdirek, Franz. The Universal Handbook of Musical Literature, 12 vols., set. 2001. (YA). reprint ed. 1500.00 (978-0-7222-5011-2(8)) Library Reprints, Inc.

Pearce, Charles E. Sims Reeves: Fifty Years of Music in England. 2001. 315p. (YA). reprint ed. 98.00 (978-0-7222-6230-6(2)) Library Reprints, Inc.

Perlzweig, A. The Book of Esther: Text & Traditional Cantillation. 2001. (YA). reprint ed. 150.00 (978-0-7222-5098-3(3)) Library Reprints, Inc.

Piggott, Harry E. An Introduction to Music. 2001. 164p. (YA). reprint ed. 88.00 (978-0-7222-6301-3(5)) Library Reprints, Inc.

Pole, William. The Philosophy of Music. 5th ed. 2001. 328p. (YA). reprint ed. 98.00 (978-0-7222-5634-3(5)) Library Reprints, Inc.

Pougin, Arthur. A Short History of Russian Music. 2001. 331p. (YA). reprint ed. 98.00 (978-0-7222-5145-4(9)) Library Reprints, Inc.

Prentice, Ridley. The Musician. 2001. (YA). reprint ed. 150.00 (978-0-7222-5722-7(8)) Library Reprints, Inc.

Qualey, Marsha, ed. The Wheels on the Bus. D'Antonio, Sandra, illus. 2004. (Traditional Songs Ser.). 24p. (ps-2). 22.60 (978-1-4048-0154-7(5)) Picture Window Bks.

Quill, Charles G. The History of the Blues. 2003. (Reading Room Collection). (Illus.). 24p. (J). lib. bdg. 18.75 (978-0-8239-3706-6(2)) Rosen Publishing Group, Inc., The.

Reeves, Sims. My Jubilee: Fifty Years of Artistic Life. 2001. 280p. (YA). reprint ed. 98.00 (978-0-7222-6229-0(9)) Library Reprints, Inc.

Rice, William G. Carillons in Literature. 2001. 104p. (YA). reprint ed. 88.00 (978-0-7222-5131-7(9)) Library Reprints, Inc.

Riggs, Kate. Classical Music. 2008. (J). ***(*978-1-58341-564-1(5)*** , Creative Education) Creative Co., The.

—Country Music. 2008. (J). ***(*978-1-58341-565-8(3)*** , Creative Education) Creative Co., The.

—Folk Music. 2008. (J). ***(*978-1-58341-566-5(1)*** , Creative Education) Creative Co., The.

Rimbault, Edward F. Bibliotheca Madrigaliana: A Bibliographical Account of the Musical & Poetical Works Published in England During the Sixteenth & Seventeenth Centuries. 2001. 88p. (YA). reprint ed. 88.00 (978-0-7222-6141-5(1)) Library Reprints, Inc.

Ritter, Frederic Louis. Music in America. 2001. 423p. (YA). reprint ed. 98.00 (978-0-7222-5156-0(4)) Library Reprints, Inc.

—The Student's History of Music, 2 vols., Set. 2001. (YA). reprint ed. 250.00 (978-0-7222-5044-0(4)) Library Reprints, Inc.

Riviere, Jules. My Musical Life & Recollections. 2001. (YA). reprint ed. 150.00 (978-0-7222-5498-1(9)) Library Reprints, Inc.

Rockstro, William Smyth. A General History of Music from the Infancy of the Greek Drama to the Present Period. 3rd ed. 2001. 535p. (YA). reprint ed. 98.00 (978-0-7222-5045-7(2)) Library Reprints, Inc.

Rolland, Romain. John Christopher, 4 vols., set. 2001. (YA). reprint ed. 500.00 (978-0-7222-5834-7(8)) Library Reprints, Inc.

Ronald, Landon. Masters of Music. 2001. (YA). reprint ed. 970.00 (978-0-7222-6370-9(8)) Library Reprints, Inc.

Rorke, J. D. M. A Musical Pilgrim's Progress. 2001. 94p. (YA). reprint ed. 88.00 (978-0-7222-5282-6(X)) Library Reprints, Inc.

Rowbotham, John Frederick. A History of Music, 3 vols. 2001. (YA). reprint ed. 375.00 (978-0-7222-5064-8(9)) Library Reprints, Inc.

—A History of Music to the Time of the Troubadours. 2001. 419p. (YA). reprint ed. 98.00 (978-0-7222-5046-4(0)) Library Reprints, Inc.

Runciman, John F. Old Scores & New Readings: Discussions on Music & Certain Musicians. 2nd ed. 2001. 279p. (YA). reprint ed. 98.00 (978-0-7222-5286-4(2)) Library Reprints, Inc.

Ruskin, John. Ruskin on Music. 2001. 158p. (YA). reprint ed. 88.00 (978-0-7222-5835-4(6)) Library Reprints, Inc.

Russell, Henry. Cheer! Boys, Cheer: Memories of Men & Music. 2001. (YA). reprint ed. 150.00 (978-0-7222-6231-3(0)) Library Reprints, Inc.

Saint-Saens, Camille. Outspoken Essays on Music. 2001. 186p. (YA). reprint ed. 88.00 (978-0-7222-5287-1(0)) Library Reprints, Inc.

Salvador-Daniel, Francisco. The Music & Musical Instruments of the Arab. 2001. 272p. (YA). reprint ed. 98.00 (978-0-7222-5078-5(9)) Library Reprints, Inc.

Sayle, Charles E. In Praise of Music: An Anthology. 2001. 307p. (YA). reprint ed. 98.00 (978-0-7222-5841-5(0)) Library Reprints, Inc.

Scholes, Percy Alfred. Crotchets: A Few Short Musical Notes. 2001. 292p. (YA). reprint ed. 98.00 (978-0-7222-5836-1(4)) Library Reprints, Inc.

—Everyman & His Music: Simple Papers on Varied Subjects. 2001. 174p. (YA). reprint ed. 88.00 (978-0-7222-6322-8(8)) Library Reprints, Inc.

—The Listener's History of Music: A Book for Any Concert-Goer, Pianolist, Gramophonist, Or Radio Listener, 3 vols., set. 2nd ed. 2001. (YA). reprint ed. 375.00 (978-0-7222-5047-1(9)) Library Reprints, Inc.

Scott, Cyril. The Philosophy of Modernism in Its Connection with Music. 2001. 135p. (YA). reprint ed. 88.00 (978-0-7222-5058-7(4)) Library Reprints, Inc.

Sharma, Elizabeth. Strings: Live Music! 2000. (Illus.). 32p. (J). (gr. 5-7). reprint ed. lib. bdg. 16.00 (978-0-7881-9433-7(X)) DIANE Publishing Co.

The Sharpe Library of the Arts: Understanding Art; Music in the Twentieth Century; Lives & Works in the Arts, 14 vols., Set. 1999. 2302p. (YA). 775.00 (978-0-7656-8037-2(8)) Sharpe, M.E. Inc.

Shay, Frank. The Iron & Wooden Ships. 2001. 217p. (YA). reprint ed. 98.00 (978-0-7222-6115-6(2)) Library Reprints, Inc.

Sholes, Percy A. The Listener's History of Music: A Book for Any Concertgoer, Pianolist & Gramophonist, 3 vols., set. 2001. (YA). reprint ed. 375.00 (978-0-7222-5665-7(5)) Library Reprints, Inc.

Silverman, Jerry & Swan, Susan. Songs & Stories of the Civil War. 2002. (Single Titles Ser.). (Illus.). 96p. (gr. 5 up). lib. bdg. 29.90 (978-0-7613-2305-1(8) , Twenty-First Century Bks.) Lerner Publishing Group.

Simpson, Eugene E. America's Position in Music. 2001. (YA). reprint ed. 150.00 (978-0-7222-5157-7(2)) Library Reprints, Inc.

Smith, Hermann. The Making of Sound in Organ & Orchestra. 2001. (YA). reprint ed. 150.00 (978-0-7222-5897-2(6)) Library Reprints, Inc.

—The World's Earliest Music: Traced to Its Beginnings in Ancient Lands, by Collected Evidence of Relics, Records, History, & Musical Instruments from Greece, Etruria, Egypt, China, Through Assyria & Babylonia, to the Primitive Home. 2001. 362p. (YA). reprint ed. 98.00 (978-0-7222-5065-5(7)) Library Reprints, Inc.

Smyth, Ethel. Impressions That Remained, 2 vols., set. 2001. (YA). reprint ed. 250.00 (978-0-7222-5140-9(8)) Library Reprints, Inc.

Solway, Andrew. World of Music: Africa. 2007. (J). ***(*978-1-4034-9891-5(1))*** Heinemann Library.

—World of Music: Latin America & the Caribbean. 2007. (J). ***(*978-1-4034-9889-2(X))*** Heinemann Library.

Sombart, Elisabeth & Lafaye, Jean-Jacques. Doce Vidas para la Musica.Tr. of Twelve Composers. (SPA.). 118p. (J). 17.95 (978-84-261-3115-7(8) , JV11155) Juventud, Editorial ESP. *Dist:* Lectorum Pubns., Inc.

Sonneck, Oscar George Theodore. Miscellaneous Studies in the History of Music. 2001. 344p. (YA). reprint ed. 98.00 (978-0-7222-5048-8(7)) Library Reprints, Inc.

Spaeth, Sigmund G. The Common Sense of Music. 2001. 375p. (YA). reprint ed. 98.00 (978-0-7222-5838-5(0)) Library Reprints, Inc.

Stanbrook Abbey Staff. Gregorian Music. 2001. 97p. (YA). reprint ed. 88.00 (978-0-7222-6148-4(9)) Library Reprints, Inc.

Stanford, Charles V. A History of Music. 2001. 384p. (YA). reprint ed. 98.00 (978-0-7222-5049-5(5)) Library Reprints, Inc.

Statham, Henry Heathcote. The Organ & Its Position in Music Art. 2001. (YA). reprint ed. 150.00 (978-0-7222-5914-6(X)) Library Reprints, Inc.

Stone, W. H. Scientific Basis of Music. 2001. 71p. (YA). reprint ed. 88.00 (978-0-7222-6334-1(1)) Library Reprints, Inc.

Tapper, Thomas. Essentials in Music History. 2001. 365p. (YA). reprint ed. 98.00 (978-0-7222-5050-1(9)) Library Reprints, Inc.

Tenger, Miriam. Recollections of C's Theresa Brunswick. 2001. (YA). reprint ed. 150.00 (978-0-7222-5348-9(6)) Library Reprints, Inc.

Terry, Charles S. The Bach's Chorals, 3 vols., set. 2001. (YA). reprint ed. 375.00 (978-0-7222-6118-7(7)) Library Reprints, Inc.

Terry, Richard R. Mediaeval Music. 2001. (YA). reprint ed. 150.00 (978-0-7222-5102-7(5)) Library Reprints, Inc.

Thompson, Vance. The Life of Ethelbert Nevin. 2001. 247p. (YA). reprint ed. 98.00 (978-0-7222-5487-5(3)) Library Reprints, Inc.

Turner, Cherie. Everything You Need to Know about the Riot Grrrl Movement: The Feminism of a New Generation. 2001. (Need to Know Library). (Illus.). 64p. (YA). (gr. 4-6). lib. bdg. 25.25 (978-0-8239-3400-3(4)) Rosen Publishing Group, Inc., The.

Turner, Walter J. Variations on the Theme of Music. 2001. 315p. (YA). reprint ed. 98.00 (978-0-7222-5840-8(2)) Library Reprints, Inc.

Underwood, Deborah. World of Music: Australia, Hawaii, & the Pacific. 2007. (J). ***978-1-4034-9894-6(6)*** Heinemann Library.

Upton, George P. The Standard Concert Guide. 2001. 551p. (YA). reprint ed. 98.00 (978-0-7222-5843-9(7)) Library Reprints, Inc.

Van Aalst, J. A. An Account of Chinese Music. 2001. (YA). reprint ed. 150.00 (978-0-7222-5088-4(6)) Library Reprints, Inc.

Venables, Leonard C. Choral & Orchestral Societies. 2001. 273p. (YA). reprint ed. 98.00 (978-0-7222-6129-3(2)) Library Reprints, Inc.

Vernon, Roland. Vivaldi: Introducing. 2000. (Introducing Composers Ser.). (Illus.). 32p. (J). (gr. 4-7). 16.95 (978-0-7910-6044-5(6) , Chelsea Hse.) Facts On File, Inc.

Vibe Magazine Staff. Vibe History of Hip Hop. 1999. (YA). pap. 27.50 (978-0-609-89905-2(8) , Random Hse. Bks. for Young Readers) Random Hse. Children's Bks.

W. H. Hadow, 6 vols. 2001. (YA). reprint ed. 750.00 (978-0-7222-5041-9(X)) Library Reprints, Inc.

Walker, Ernest. A History of Music in England. 2nd ed. 2001. 386p. (YA). reprint ed. 98.00 (978-0-7222-5120-1(3)) Library Reprints, Inc.

Wargin, Kathy-Jo. M Is for Melody: A Music Alphabet. Larson, Katherine, illus. 2004. 40p. (J). 16.95 (978-1-58536-215-8(8)) Sleeping Bear Pr.

What Jazz & Blues Can I Play - Alto Sax. 20p. 6.95 (978-1-85909-426-6(0) , Warner Bros. Pubns.) Alfred Publishing Co., Inc.

Wheeler, Opal. Handel at the Court of Kings. 2006. (Illus.). 168p. (J). per. 12.95 (978-1-933573-03-8(1) , 4481) Zeezok Publishing.

—Robert Schumann & Mascot Ziff. 2006. (Illus.). (J). per. 12.95 (978-1-933573-06-9(6) , 4483) Zeezok Publishing.

Wheeler, Opal & Deucher, Sybil. Joseph Haydn, the Merry Little Peasant. Greenwalt, Mary, illus. 2005. 120p. (J). per. 10.95 (978-1-933573-00-7(7)) Zeezok Publishing.

Wilcox, Judy. Handel at the Court of Kings Study Guide. 2006. (Illus.). 32p. (J). 4.95 (978-1-933573-04-5(X) , 4482) Zeezok Publishing.

—Joseph Haydn, the Merry Little Peasant. 2006. (J). stu. ed. 4.95 (978-1-933573-01-4(5)) Zeezok Publishing.

—Robert Schumann & Mascot Ziff. 2006. (Illus.). (J). stu. ed. 4.95 (978-1-933573-07-6(4)) Zeezok Publishing.

Wincentsen, Edward. Yes, Phoenix Had Music in the Sixties! A Look at the Clubs, Bands & the Fans. 2002. (Illus.). 198p. pap. 18.95 (978-0-9648133-4-2(3)) Momentary Pleasures Pr.

Wood, Alexander. The Physical Basis of Music. 2001. 163p. (YA). reprint ed. 88.00 (978-0-7222-5637-4(X)) Library Reprints, Inc.

Wooldrigge, H. E. Musica Antiqua: Model Composition. 2001. (SPA.). (YA). reprint ed. 150.00 (978-0-7222-5678-7(7)) Library Reprints, Inc.

MUSIC, INDIAN

see Indians of North America—Music

MUSIC—INSTRUCTION AND STUDY

see Music—Study and Teaching

MUSIC—NOTATION

see Musical Notation

MUSIC, POPULAR

see Popular Music

MUSIC, SACRED

see Church Music

MUSIC—STUDY AND TEACHING

see also Conducting; Musical Form

Albrechtsberger, Johann G. Collected Works on Thorough-Bass, Harmony, & Composition, for Self-Instruction, 3 vols., set. 2001. (YA). reprint ed. 125.00 (978-0-7222-5726-5(0)) Library Reprints, Inc.

The Ants Go Marching. (Traditional Songs Ser.). 24p. (J). 7.95 (978-1-4048-0422-7(6)) Picture Window Bks.

Arnold, Bruce E. 1st Steps for a Beginning Guitarist: Chords & Chord Progressions. l.t. ed. 2001. (ENG.). 52p. (J). spiral bd. 23.99 (978-1-890944-90-2(4)) Muse Eek Publishing Co.

—1st Steps for a Beginning Guitarist: Chords & Chord Progressions for Guitar. 2001. 52p. per. 14.99 (978-1-890944-93-3(9)) Muse Eek Publishing Co.

Aruffo, Christopher, tr. We Hear & Play. 2005. (J). Vol. 1. 112p. ring bd. 44.95 (978-0-9761435-2-9(6)); Vol. 2. 112p. ring bd. 44.95 (978-0-9761435-3-6(4)); Vol. 3. ring bd. 49.95 (978-0-9761435-4-3(2)) Acoustic Learning Inc.

Bell, Richard & Bell, Cathy. The Beginner's Guide to Understanding Music: Learn the Basics of Music Theory. 2002. (Illus.). 78p. (YA). (gr. 5 up). spiral bd. 19.95 (978-0-9716170-0-1(7)) Rosebird Publishing.

Best, William T. The Art of Organ Playing, 2 vols., set. 2001. (YA). reprint ed. 250.00 (978-0-7222-5903-0(4)) Library Reprints, Inc.

Blair, Peter, compiled by. Concert Ensembles for Everyone: Works for Instrumental Ensembles with Limited or Non-Traditional Instrumentation, Grades 3-4 (Alto Saxophone - WW 3 And 4) 2006. 8.95 (978-0-89328-262-2(6)) Heritage Music Pr.

—Concert Ensembles for Everyone: Works for Instrumental Ensembles with Limited or Non-Traditional Instrumentation, Grades 3-4 (Bass - Tuba/Bass, Baritone Saxophone & Bass Clarinet) 2006. 8.95 (978-0-89328-268-4(5)) Heritage Music Pr.

—Concert Ensembles for Everyone: Works for Instrumental Ensembles with Limited or Non-Traditional Instrumentation, Grades 3-4 (Clarinet A - WW 1 And 2) 2006. 8.95 (978-0-89328-260-8(X)) Heritage Music Pr.

—Concert Ensembles for Everyone: Works for Instrumental Ensembles with Limited or Non-Traditional Instrumentation, Grades 3-4 (Clarinet B - WW 2 And 3) 2006. 8.95 (978-0-89328-261-5(8)) Heritage Music Pr.

—Concert Ensembles for Everyone: Works for Instrumental Ensembles with Limited or Non-Traditional Instrumentation, Grades 3-4 (F Horn - Brass 3 And 4) 2006. 8.95 (978-0-89328-266-0(9)) Heritage Music Pr.

—Concert Ensembles for Everyone: Works for Instrumental Ensembles with Limited or Non-Traditional Instrumentation, Grades 3-4 (Tenor Saxophone - WW 4 & Brass 4) 2006. 8.95 (978-0-89328-263-9(4)) Heritage Music Pr.

—Concert Ensembles for Everyone: Works for Instrumental Ensembles with Limited or Non-Traditional Instrumentation, Grades 3-4 (Trombone/Baritone B. C. /Bassoon - Brass 4 & Bass) 2006. 8.95 (978-0-89328-267-7(7)) Heritage Music Pr.

—Concert Ensembles for Everyone: Works for Instrumental Ensembles with Limited or Non-Traditional Instrumentation, Grades 3-4 (Trumpet A - Brass 1 And 2) 2006. 8.95 (978-0-89328-264-6(2)) Heritage Music Pr.

—Concert Ensembles for Everyone: Works for Instrumental Ensembles with Limited or Non-Traditional Instrumentation, Grades 3-4 (Trumpet B - Brass 2 And 3) 2006. 8.95 (978-0-89328-265-3(0)) Heritage Music Pr.

Bohm, Theobald. The Flute & Flute-Playing in Acoustical, Technical, & Artistic Aspects. 2001. 100p. (YA). reprint ed. 88.00 (978-0-7222-6057-9(1)) Library Reprints, Inc.

Brass, Alice. Orff Explorations: Classroom Projects in Music, Movement & Poetry. Sakhavarz, Nazy, illus. 2003. 80p. pap. 20.00 (978-1-896941-34-9(6)) Brass, Robin Studio, Inc. CAN. *Dist:* Midpoint Trade Bks., Inc.

Broadhouse, John. Student's Helmholtz. 2001. (YA). reprint ed. 150.00 (978-0-7222-5632-9(9)) Library Reprints, Inc.

Broadley, Arthur. Chats to Cello Students. 2001. 100p. (YA). reprint ed. 88.00 (978-0-7222-6020-3(2)) Library Reprints, Inc.

Bullock, Jack & Maiello, Anthony. Belwin 21st Century Band Method, Vol. 3. 1999. (J). (gr. 3). 10.95 incl. audio compact disk (978-0-7692-9349-3(2) , Warner Bros. Pubns.) Alfred Publishing Co., Inc.

Burton, Leon H. & Kudo, Takeo. SoundPlay: Understanding Music Through Creative Movement. 2000. (Illus.). 120p. 37.95 (978-1-56545-130-8(9) , 3003) Rowman & Littlefield Pubs., Inc.

Cain, Tim. Fanfare: Cambridge Primary Music. 1998. (Fanfare Ser.). (Illus.). 112p. pap., tchr. ed. 41.00 (978-0-521-45859-7(5)) Cambridge Univ. Pr.

Cavalier, Debbie. Learn & Play Kazoo. Lema, James, illus. 2002. spiral bd. 9.99 (978-0-9720533-0-3(1)) First Act, Inc.

—Learn & Play Recorder. Lema, James, illus. 2002. spiral bd. 9.99 (978-0-9720533-2-7(8)) First Act, Inc.

Celik, Vladislav. You Too Can Play Piano & Organ Without Teacher, Vol. 1. (Music Instructional Ser.). (Illus.). 96p. (J). pap. 12.95 incl. audio (978-0 9624062-1-8(X)) Music Institute of California.

Chaffin, L. G. Song-Writing & Song-Making. 2001. (YA). reprint ed. 150.00 (978-0-7222-6174-3(8)) Library Reprints, Inc.

Ciravolo, Tish. Girls Guitar Course 2: Everything a girl needs to know abut playing Guitar!, Vol. 2. 2003. 48p. pap. 14.95 incl. cd-rom (978-0-7390-3175-9(9) , 21971) Alfred Publishing Co., Inc.

Clements, Ernest. Introduction to the Study of Indian Music: An Attempt to Reconcile Modern Hindustani Music with Ancient Musical Theory & to Propound an Accurate & Comprehensive Method of Treatment of the Subject of Indian Musical Intonation. 2001. 104p. (YA). reprint ed. 88.00 (978-0-7222-5089-1(4)) Library Reprints, Inc.

Coates, Dan. The Kids' Music Collection, Vol. 2. 2005. 12.95 (978-0-7579-3763-7(2) , AFM0416, Warner Bros. Pubns.) Alfred Publishing Co., Inc.

Colles, Henry C. The Growth of Music: A Study in Musical History for Schools, 3 vols. 2001. (YA). reprint ed. 375.00 (978-0-7222-5024-2(X)) Library Reprints, Inc.

Concert Ensembles for Everyone: Works for Instrumental Ensembles with Limited or Non-Traditional Instrumentation, Grades 3-4 (Conductor's Score with CD) 2006. 29.95 (978-0-89328-258-5(8)) Heritage Music Pr.

Connors, Jerrold M. Jiminy Kokopo's Ukulele Sing & Strum Fun Book. Connors, Jerrold M., illus. 2002. (Illus.). 48p. (J). per. 9.95 (978-0-9721416-0-4(X)) Alligator Boogaloo.

Croft, J. B. Practical Plainsong. 2001. (YA). reprint ed. 150.00 (978-0-7222-6153-8(5)) Library Reprints, Inc.

Cumberland, Gerald. Memorizing Music. 2001. 127p. (YA). reprint ed. 88.00 (978-0-7222-6338-9(4)) Library Reprints, Inc.

Curwen, John S. Memorials of John Curwen. 2001. (YA). reprint ed. 150.00 (978-0-7222-5397-7(4)) Library Reprints, Inc.

—Tonic Sol-Fa. 2001. (YA). reprint ed. 150.00 (978-0-7222-6164-4(0)) Library Reprints, Inc.

—The Tonic Sol-Fa Method. 2001. (YA). reprint ed. 150.00 (978-0-7222-6163-7(2)) Library Reprints, Inc.

Dale, Monica. Eurhythmics for Young Children: Six Lessons for Spring. 2002. (Illus.). 108p. pap. 24.95 (978-0-9701416-2-0(9)) MusiKinesis.

Day, Eileen. I'm Good at Making Music. 2003. (Heinemann Read & Learn Ser.). (Illus.). 24p. (J). pap. 5.25 (978-1-4034-3447-0(6)); lib. bdg. 18.50 (978-1-4034-0900-3(5)) Heinemann Library.

—I'm Good at Making Music. 2003. (gr. k-3). lib. bdg. 13.30 (978-0-613-70658-2(7)) Tandem Library Bks.

Dembska, Anna & Harkness, Joan. You've Got Rhythm: Read Music Better by Feeling the Beat. 2002. 126p. (YA). (gr. 3 up). pap. 27.95 (978-1-930664-04-3(4)) Flying Leap Music.

Dolmetsch, Arnold. The Interpretation of the Music of the Seventeenth & Eighteenth Centuries Revealed by Contemporary Evidence. 2001. 493p. (YA). reprint ed. 98.00 (978-0-7222-5759-3(7)) Library Reprints, Inc.

Dorling Kindersley Publishing Staff & Ardely, Neil. Young Person's Guide to Music. rev. ed. 2004. 80p. (J). 24.99 incl. audio compact disk (978-0-7566-0540-7(7)) Dorling Kindersley Publishing, Inc.

Edwards, Linda Carol, et al. Music: A Way of Life for the Young Child. 5th ed. 2004. (Illus.). 288p. pap. 45.67 (978-0-13-111676-4(2)) Prentice Hall PTR.

Farnsworth, C. H. How to Study Music. 2001. (YA). reprint ed. 150.00 (978-0-7222-5850-7(X)) Library Reprints, Inc.

Feierabend, John M. The Book of Tapping & Clapping. 2000. (First Steps in Music Ser.). (Illus.). 48p. (J). (ps). pap. 7.95 (978-1-57999-054-1(1)) GIA Pubns., Inc.

—The Book of Wiggles & Tickles. 2000. (First Steps in Music Ser.). (Illus.). 48p. (J). (ps). pap. 7.95 (978-1-57999-053-4(3)) GIA Pubns., Inc.

—Conversational Solfege: Level 2. 2002. (J). stu. ed., spiral bd. 14.95 (978-1-57999-148-7(3) , G-5381S) GIA Pubns., Inc.

Fisher, Henry. Psychology for Music Teachers: The Laws of Thought Applied to Sounds & Their Symbols. 2001. 181p. (YA). reprint ed. 88.00 (978-0-7222-5792-0(9)) Library Reprints, Inc.

Fowles, Ernst. Musical Competition Festivals. 2001. (YA). reprint ed. 150.00 (978-0-7222-5123-2(8)) Library Reprints, Inc.

Fuller, Cheri. How to Grow a Young Music Lover: Helping Your Child Discover & Enjoy the World of Music. 2nd ed. 2002. (Illus.). 208p. pap. 12.99 (978-0-87788-370-8(X) , Shaw) WaterBrook Pr.

The Fundamental Guitar Method Book 2: The Science of Harmony. 2004. (YA). spiral bd. (978-0-9771357-1-4(3)) Sound Craft Designs.

Goddard, Joseph. Deeper Sources of Beauty & Expression in Music. 2001. (YA). reprint ed. 150.00 (978-0-7222-5645-9(0)) Library Reprints, Inc.

Grace, Harvey. The Complete Organist. 2001. 240p. (YA). reprint ed. 98.00 (978-0-7222-5909-2(3)) Library Reprints, Inc.

Greig, John. The Musical Educator: A Library of Musical Instruction by Eminent Specialists, 5 vols., set. 2001. (YA). reprint ed. 625.00 (978-0-7222-5853-8(4)) Library Reprints, Inc.

Hal Leonard Corp., creator. Pokemon. 1999. (Recorder Fun! Ser.). (Illus.). 16p. (J). (ps-3). pap. 9.95 (978-1-57560-324-7(1) , 1575603241) Cherry Lane Music Co.

Hal Leonard Corporation Staff. Toy Story Collection Recorder Fun! 2000. (Recorder Fun! Ser.). 16p. (gr. 4-7). pap. 9.95 (978-0-634-01650-9(4) , 0634016504) Leonard, Hal Corp.

Hammer, Jeff. Start Playing Easiest Keyboard. 2004. (Illus.). 48p. 9.95 (978-0-7119-8011-2(X) , AM958309) Music Sales Corp.

Harris & Brewe. Improve Sight-Singing Treble: Low to Medium Voice. 1998. 40p. (J). (gr. 1-5). 6.95 (978-0-571-51766-4(8)) Faber & Faber, Ltd. GBR. *Dist:* Leonard, Hal Corp.

Harris, P & Brewe. Improve Sight-Singing: High & Medium Voice. 1998. 40p. (J). (gr. 1-5). 6.95 (978-0-571-51733-6(1)) Faber & Faber, Ltd. GBR. *Dist:* Leonard, Hal Corp.

Home, Ethel. Ear-Training & Musical Education. 2001. (YA). reprint ed. 150.00 (978-0-7222-5854-5(2)) Library Reprints, Inc.

Hooper, Caroline. Learn Songwriting. 2004. (Learn to Play Ser.). (Illus.). 48p. (YA). (gr. 1 up). lib. bdg. 17.95 (978-1-58086-222-6(5)) EDC Publishing.

Hudson, Karen. Songwriter Journal. 2003. 128p. (J). 9.99 (978-0-439-42975-7(7)) Scholastic, Inc.

Hulbert, H. H. Eurhythm: Thought in Action. 2001. (YA). reprint ed. 150.00 (978-0-7222-5813-2(5)) Library Reprints, Inc.

Hunt, Harry Ernest. The Living Touch in Music & Education: A Manual for Musicians & Others. 2001. 224p. (YA). reprint ed. 98.00 (978-0-7222-6336-5(8)) Library Reprints, Inc.

Incentive Pieces for Guitar Students: For Beginner to Intermediate Fingerstyle Solos & Duets. 2001. 120p. (YA). (gr. 4-12). spiral bd., lab manual ed. 11.95 (978-0-9646652-7-9(1)) Anytime Pubns.

Kenyon, Charles F. How to Memorize Music. 5th ed. 2001. 56p. (YA). reprint ed. 88.00 (978-0-7222-5762-3(7)) Library Reprints, Inc.

Kleczynski, Jan. How to Play Chopin. 2001. (YA). reprint ed. 150.00 (978-0-7222-5387-8(7)) Library Reprints, Inc.

—The Works of Frederic Chopin: Their Proper Interpretation. 2001. 76p. (YA). reprint ed. 88.00 (978-0-7222-5386-1(9)) Library Reprints, Inc.

Kurz, Ron. The Inner Music Experience. l.t. ed. 2003. 124p. (YA). 75.00 (978-0-939829-07-1(X) , Item#3) Kurz, Ron.

Lavignac, Albert. Musical Education. 2001. 447p. (YA). reprint ed. 98.00 (978-0-7222-5855-2(0)) Library Reprints, Inc.

Lieberman, Julie L. Improvising Violin. rev. ed. 2003. (Illus.). 136p. (gr. 10 up). pap. 19.95 (978-1-879730-10-6(3) , 1879730103) Huiksi Music.

Lindo, Algernon H. The Art of Accompanying. 2001. 109p. (YA). reprint ed. 88.00 (978-0-7222-5957-3(3)) Library Reprints, Inc.

Lussy, Mathis. Musical Expression, Accents, Nuances, & Tempo, in Vocal & Instrumental Music. 2001. 236p. (YA). reprint ed. 98.00 (978-0-7222-5708-1(2)) Library Reprints, Inc.

Macken, JoAnn Early. Music Lessons. 2005. (After-School Fun Ser.). (Illus.). 24p. (YA). lib. bdg. 19.93 (978-0-8368-4515-0(3)) Stevens, Gareth Inc.

Manus, Ron & Harnsberger, L. C. Kids Guitar Course 1: The easiest guitar method Ever!, Vol. 1. Shelly, Jeff, illus. 2003. 48p. pap. 14.95 incl. cd-rom (978-0-88284-989-8(1) , 18451) Alfred Publishing Co., Inc.

—Kids Guitar Course 2: The easiest guitar method Ever!, Vol. 2. Shelly, Jeff, illus. 2005. 48p. pap. 14.95 incl. cd-rom (978-0-88284-987-4(5)) Alfred Publishing Co., Inc.

Marks, Anthony. Learn to Play Keyboards. 1999. (Learn to Play Ser.). (Illus.). 48p. (YA). (gr. 4 up). lib. bdg. 17.95 (978-0-88110-899-6(5)) EDC Publishing.

Mason, Jane B. & Hines Stephens, Sarah. Gymboree Music Play. rev. ed. 2007. (Illus.). 36p. (J). bds. 16.95 ***(978-1-55263-964-1(9))*** Key Porter Bks. CAN. *Dist:* Perseus Distribution.

McEwen, John B. The Thought in Music: An Enquiry into the Principles of Musical Rhythm, Phrasing & Expression. 2001. 233p. (YA). reprint ed. 98.00 (978-0-7222-5717-3(1)) Library Reprints, Inc.

Mister C's Beginning Drums, Vol. 1. 2004. (Illus.). (J). spiral bd. 14.99 (978-0-9755333-0-7(4)) Mister C Music.

Mitchell, Albert G. Public School Class Method for Cornet. 2001. (YA). reprint ed. 150.00 (978-0-7222-6056-2(3)) Library Reprints, Inc.

The Music Connection. 1999. (J). (gr. 4). stu. ed. 47.50 (978-0-382-34503-6(7)); (gr. 8). stu. ed. 53.45 (978-0-382-34507-4(X)) Silver, Burdett & Ginn, Inc.

The Music Connection: Grade 5. 1999. tchr. ed. 80.10 (978-0-382-34568-5(1)) Silver, Burdett & Ginn, Inc.

Music Primers. 2001. (YA). reprint ed. 3872.00 (978-0-7222-6374-7(0)) Library Reprints, Inc.

Musician's Handbooks. 2001. (YA). reprint ed. 764.00 (978-0-7222-6377-8(5)) Library Reprints, Inc.

Naylor, Edward W. An Elizabethan Virginal Book: A Critical Essay on the Contents of a Manuscript in the Fitzwilliam Museum at Cambridge. 2001. 220p. (YA). reprint ed. 98.00 (978-0-7222-5986-3(7)) Library Reprints, Inc.

Neelly, Linda Page. Musical ConverSings with Children. 2007. 79.00 ***(978-1-60021-708-1(7))*** Nova Science Pubs., Inc.

Nikola-Lisa, W., et al. Live Oak Music Maker Collection. Nikola-Lisa, W. et al, illus. 2001. pap. 106.95 incl. audio (978-0-87499-992-1(8)) Live Oak Media.

O'Brien, Eileen. First Book of the Piano. 1998. (gr. 3-6). lib. bdg. 19.90 (978-0-613-90708-8(6)) Tandem Library Bks.

—Introduction to Music. Alaverdy, Melissa, illus. 2004. 96p. (J). 7.95 (978-0-7945-0276-8(8) , Usborne) EDC Publishing.

Phillips, Sarah. Play It! Recorder. 2005. (Play It! Ser.). (Illus.). 24p. (J). (gr. k-3). 12.95 (978-1-905051-59-5(X)) Make Believe Ideas GBR. *Dist:* Ingram Pub. Services.

The Piano Bench of Golden Favorites. 2004. (Piano Bench Ser.). 400p. 27.95 (978-0-8256-1825-3(8) , AM967550, Schirmer Trade Bks.) Music Sales Corp.

Price, Melissa. Luke & Lori's Musical Journey: Learning the Basic Elements of Music. Keren Weaver Graphics, illus. 2003. 48p. (J). spiral bd. (978-0-9747792-0-1(2)) Luke & Lori Bks.

Purton, Michael. I Can Make Music: Simple-to-Make & Fun-to-Play Musical Instruments for Young Children. 2000. (Show Me How Ser.). (Illus.). 48p. (ps-2). pap. 7.95 (978-0-7548-0223-5(X) , Lorenz Bks.) Anness Publishing GBR. *Dist:* National Bk. Network.

Rink, C. H. Practical Organ School. 2001. (YA). reprint ed. 150.00 (978-0-7222-5912-2(3)) Library Reprints, Inc.

Rivera, Sophia. All-in-One Children's Music Curriculum. 2000. (Illus.). 100p. (J). (gr. 1-6). wbk. ed. (978-1-893853-00-3(4)) Anointed Pubns.

Roberts, Ellis. Manual of Instruments for Playing Welsh Harp. 2001. (YA). reprint ed. 150.00 (978-0-7222-6066-1(0)) Library Reprints, Inc.

Rowtham, C. B. Voice Training for Choirs & Schools. 2001. (YA). reprint ed. 150.00 (978-0-7222-6126-2(8)) Library Reprints, Inc.

Rutland, Jonathan. Abracadabra Clarinet: The Way to Learn Through Songs & Tunes. 2nd ed. 2002. (Illus.). 72p. pap., stu. ed. 11.95 (978-0-7136-6199-6(2)) A & C Black GBR. *Dist:* Consortium Bk. Sales & Distribution.

Saliba, Konnie. Hang on to the Big Balloon: Simple to Challenging Orff Instrumentals. 2005. 68p. (J). (gr. 1-8). 14.95 (978-0-7692-9986-0(5) , BMR08014, Warner Bros. Pubns.) Alfred Publishing Co., Inc.

Saperstein, Stella & Luey, Beth. The Harmonious Child: Every Parent's Guide to Musical Instruments, Teachers, & Lessons. 2004. (Illus.). 176p. pap. 12.95 (978-1-58761-171-1(6) , Celestial Arts Publishing Company) Ten Speed Pr.

Savidge, Wilbur M. & Vradenburg, Randy L. Everything about Playing Blues. 2004. (Illus.). 200p. 24.95 incl. audio compact disk (978-1-884848-09-4(5) , BS90001) Praxis Music Pubns., Inc.

Scholes, Percy Alfred. Musical Appreciation in Schools: Why & How? 2001. 41p. (YA). reprint ed. 88.00 (978-0-7222-5664-0(7)) Library Reprints, Inc.

Scott, Daniel. Classical Greats: Easy Playalong for Recorder. 2004. (Illus.). 32p. 12.95 incl. audio compact disk (978-0-7119-9144-6(8)) Music Sales Corp.

Seashore, Carl Emil. The Psychology of Musical Talent. 2001. 288p. (YA). reprint ed. 98.00 (978-0-7222-5797-5(X)) Library Reprints, Inc.

Snitkin, Harvey R. Practicing for Young Musicians: You Are Your Own Teacher!!! 2nd rev. ed. 2001. (Illus.). 151p. (Orig.). (J). (gr. 4 up). pap. 14.95 (978-1-888732-00-9(8)) HMS Pubns., Inc.

Step One: Teach Yourself Harmonica. 2004. (Illus.). 32p. DVD 14.95 (978-0-8256-1892-5(4) , AM971333, Schirmer Trade Bks.) Music Sales Corp.

Storr, Muriel. Music for Children: First Steps in Appreciation. 2001. 195p. (J). reprint ed. 88.00 (978-0-7222-5667-1(1)) Library Reprints, Inc.

Sullivan, Erin Ash. Calculos musicales & Music Counts. 2005. spiral bd. 77.00 (***978-1-4108-5675-3(5)***) Benchmark Education Co.

Suzuki, Shinichi. Note Reading for Violin. Selden, Kyoko, tr. from JPN. 1999. (Suzuki Viola School Ser.). (Illus.). 112p. (J). (gr. 1-6). reprint ed. 14.95 (978-0-87487-213-2(8) , Warner Bros. Pubns.) Alfred Publishing Co., Inc.

—Suzuki Viola School, Vol. 4. Preucil, Doris, ed. 1999. (Suzuki Viola School Ser.). 32p. (J). (gr. k-12). 6.95 (978-0-87487-244-6(8) , Warner Bros. Pubns.) Alfred Publishing Co., Inc.

Taylor, Sedley. System of Sight-Singing from Established Notations. 2001. (YA). reprint ed. 150.00 (978-0-7222-6167-5(5)) Library Reprints, Inc.

Terhume, A. M. Music-Study for Children. 2001. (YA). reprint ed. 150.00 (978-0-7222-5857-6(7)) Library Reprints, Inc.

Tischitanissohen. The Drum: A Training Aid for Ceremonial Teams. Tischitanissohen, illus. 10th rev. ed. 2002. (Illus.). 40p. (YA). (gr. 7 up). pap. 5.00 (978-0-9677560-0-4(6)) Dunbar, Doctor Jay.

Torr, Cecil. On the Interpretation of Greek Music. 2001. 26p. (YA). reprint ed. 88.00 (978-0-7222-5086-0(X)) Library Reprints, Inc.

Trotter, Henry Y. The Making of Musicians: The Rhythmic Method of Teaching Music. 2001. 143p. (YA). reprint ed. 88.00 (978-0-7222-5816-3(X)) Library Reprints, Inc.

Troutbeck, John. Church Choir Training. 2001. 52p. (YA). reprint ed. 88.00 (978-0-7222-6128-6(4)) Library Reprints, Inc.

Troutbeck, John & Troutbeck, Dale. Music Primer. 2001. (YA). reprint ed. 150.00 (978-0-7222-5625-1(6)) Library Reprints, Inc.

Venables, Leonard C. Ear-Training. 2001. (YA). reprint ed. 150.00 (978-0-7222-5858-3(5)) Library Reprints, Inc.

Wallace, William. The Threshold of Music: An Inquiry into the Development of the Musical Sense. 2001. 267p. (YA). reprint ed. 98.00 (978-0-7222-5801-9(1)) Library Reprints, Inc.

Weber, Fred. 1st Division Method 1 Trumpet. 1999. 32p. (YA). 5.95 (978-0-7692-1432-0(0) , FDL00012, Warner Bros. Pubns.) Alfred Publishing Co., Inc.

Wedgwood, Pamela. Up-Grade Flute: Light Relief Between Grades. 1998. 12p. (J). (gr. 2). 8.95 (978-0-571-51818-0(4)) Faber & Faber, Ltd. GBR. *Dist:* Leonard, Hal Corp.

Wood, Thomas. Music & Boyhood: Some Suggestions on the Possibilities of Music in Public, Preparatory & Other Schools. 2001. 66p. (YA). reprint ed. 88.00 (978-0-7222-5861-3(5)) Library Reprints, Inc.

Young. Music 3-5. 2008. 110.00 (***978-0-415-43056-2(9)***); pap. 26.95 (***978-0-415-43057-9(7)***) Routledge.

MUSIC—THEORY

see Music Theory

MUSIC—VOCATIONAL GUIDANCE

Dubois, Muriel L. I Like Music: What Can I Be? 2000. (What Can I Be? Ser.). (Illus.). 24p. (J). (gr. 1-2). lib. bdg. 18.60 (978-0-7368-0632-9(6) , Bridgestone Bks.) Capstone Pr., Inc.

Feierabend, John. First Steps in Music Vocal Development Kit. 2004. 21p. (J). 79.95 (978-1-57999-326-9(5) , G-6400) GIA Pubns., Inc.

Finck, Henry Theophilus. Success in Music & How Its Is Won. 2001. 471p. (YA). reprint ed. 98.00 (978-0-7222-5822-4(4)) Library Reprints, Inc.

Giacobello, John. Choosing a Career in Music. rev. ed. 1999. (World of Work Ser.). (Illus.). 64p. (YA). (gr. 7-12). lib. bdg. 25.25 (978-0-8239-3000-5(9) , WWMUSI) Rosen Publishing Group, Inc., The.

Harvey, M. A. Wannabes Pop Diva: For Girls Who Know What They Want to Be. 2004. (Illus.). 128p. (J). pap. (978-1-84458-049-1(0)) Chrysalis Children's Bks.

Hayward, Linda & Dorling Kindersley Publishing Staff. Jobs People Do: A Day in the Life of a Musician. 2001. (Readers Ser.). (Illus.). 32p. (J). (ps-3). 14.99 (978-0-7894-7952-5(4)); pap. 3.99 (978-0-7894-7953-2(2)) Dorling Kindersley Publishing, Inc.

Liebman, Daniel. I Want to Be a Musician. 2003. (I Want to Be Ser.). (Illus.). 24p. (J). (ps-2). pap. 3.99 (978-1-55297-759-0(5)); lib. bdg. 14.95 (978-1-55297-760-6(9)) Firefly Bks., Ltd.

—Quiero Ser Musico. 2003. (Quiero Ser.). (ENG & SPA., Illus.). 24p. (J). (ps-2). pap. 5.99 (978-1-55297-761-3(7)) Firefly Bks., Ltd.

Parks, Peggy J. Music. 2002. (Careers for the Twenty-First Century Ser.). (Illus.). 112p. (J). 27.45 (978-1-59018-223-9(5) , Lucent Bks.) Thomson Gale.

—Musician. 2003. (Illus.). 48p. (J). 26.20 (978-0-7377-2067-9(0) , Greenhaven Pr., Inc.) Thomson Gale.

Reeves, Diane Lindsey. Career Ideas for Kids Who Like Music & Dance. 2nd rev. ed. (Career Ideas for Kids Ser.). 208p. (J). (gr. 4-9). pap. 16.95 (***978-0-8160-6538-7(1)*** , Checkmark Bks.); 2007. 32.95 (***978-0-8160-6537-0(3)*** , Ferguson Publishing Co.) Facts On File, Inc.

Reeves, Diane Lindsey & Bryan, Gayle. Career Ideas for Kids Who Like Music & Dance. Bond, Nancy, illus. 2001. (Career Ideas for Kids Ser.). 192p. (J). (gr. 4-9). 23.00 (978-0-8160-4323-1(X)) Facts On File, Inc.

Schaefer, A. R. Equipping a Band. 2003. (Rock Music Library). (Illus.). 32p. (J). lib. bdg. 22.60 (978-0-7368-2145-2(7) , Capstone High/Low Bks.) Capstone Pr., Inc.

—Making a First Recording. 2003. (Rock Music Library). (Illus.). 32p. (J). lib. bdg. 22.60 (978-0-7368-2147-6(3) , Capstone High/Low Bks.) Capstone Pr., Inc.

Torres, John Albert. Careers in Music. 2001. (Latinos at Work Ser.). (Illus.). 96p. (gr. 5-12). lib. bdg. 32.75 (978-1-58415-085-5(8)) Mitchell Lane Pubs., Inc.

MUSIC APPRECIATION

see Music—Analysis, Appreciation

MUSIC CONDUCTORS

see Conductors (Music)

MUSIC THEORY

see also Counterpoint; Musical Form

Aristoxenus. The Harmonics of Aristoxenus. 2001. 303p. (YA). reprint ed. 98.00 (978-0-7222-5079-2(7)) Library Reprints, Inc.

Bevan, P. Harmonies in Japanese Music. 2001. (YA). reprint ed. 150.00 (978-0-7222-5096-9(7)) Library Reprints, Inc.

Bridge, Frederick. Double Counterpoint & Canon. 2001. 120p. (YA). reprint ed. 88.00 (978-0-7222-6323-5(6)) Library Reprints, Inc.

Clark, Frances, et al. The Music Tree: Students' Choice, Pt. 4. pap. 5.95 (978-1-58951-009-8(7) , 00970) Summy-Birchard, Inc.

Danes, E. Music Theory for Beginners. 2004. 48p. (J). lib. bdg. 16.95 (978-1-58086-562-3(3)); pap. 8.95 (978-0-7945-0389-5(6)) EDC Publishing.

Foote, Arthur. Modern Harmony in Its Theory & Practice. 2001. 254p. (YA). reprint ed. 98.00 (978-0-7222-5732-6(5)) Library Reprints, Inc.

Learning Wrap-Ups Music Theory. 2004. 34.99 (978-0-943343-56-3(9)) Learning Wrap-Ups.

McGraw-Hill Staff. Essential Elements for Choir: Level 3 Musicianship. 2001. stu. ed. 27.32 (978-0-07-826047-6(7) , 9780078260476) Glencoe/McGraw-Hill.

—Essential Elements for Choir: Level 4 Musicianship. 2001. (C). stu. ed. 27.32 (978-0-07-826055-1(8) , 9780078260551) Glencoe/McGraw-Hill.

O'Neill, Julia A. A Practical Guide to the Theory of Music. 2001. 96p. (YA). reprint ed. 150.00 (978-0-7222-6328-0(7)) Library Reprints, Inc.

Prout, Ebenezer. Double Counterpoint & Canon. 2001. 283p. (YA). reprint ed. 98.00 (978-0-7222-5703-6(1)) Library Reprints, Inc.

Sharp, M. Theory of Music for Young Musicians. 1999. 57p. reprint ed. pap. 28.00 (978-1-4047-9322-4(4)) Classic Textbooks.

Shaw, Martin. Principles of Church Music Composition. 2001. (YA). reprint ed. 150.00 (978-0-7222-5679-4(5)) Library Reprints, Inc.

Stainer, John. Harmony. 2001. Tr. of Modern Harmony in It's Theory & Practice. 124p. (YA). reprint ed. 88.00 (978-0-7222-6332-7(5)) Library Reprints, Inc.

—A Theory of Harmony Founded on the Tempered Scale. 2001. 126p. (YA). reprint ed. 88.00 (978-0-7222-5756-2(2)) Library Reprints, Inc.

Stanford, Charles V. Musical Composition: A Short Treatise for Students. 2001. 193p. (YA). reprint ed. 88.00 (978-0-7222-5675-6(2)) Library Reprints, Inc.

Warriner, John E. Transposition. 2001. 56p. (YA). reprint ed. 88.00 (978-0-7222-5817-0(8)) Library Reprints, Inc.

White, Robert T. Composition of Simple Melodies. 2001. (YA). reprint ed. 150.00 (978-0-7222-5677-0(9)) Library Reprints, Inc.

Williams, Charles F. A. The Aristoxenian Theory of Musical Rhythm. 2001. 191p. (YA). reprint ed. 88.00 (978-0-7222-5080-8(0)) Library Reprints, Inc.

Zampino, Phil. Music Theory, Scales & Chords for the Percussion Drum Student: Recommended for All Students & All Instruments. 1998. (Illus.). 130p. (YA). (gr. 4 up). spiral bd. 19.95 (978-0-942253-10-8(8)) PAZ Publishing.

MUSICAL APPRECIATION

see Music—Analysis, Appreciation

MUSICAL COMEDIES

see Musical Revues, Comedies, etc.

MUSICAL CRITICISM

see Music—History and Criticism

MUSICAL EDUCATION

see Music—Study and Teaching

MUSICAL FORM

see also Opera; Operetta

Anger, Joseph H. Form in Music: A Special Reference to the Bach Fugue & the Beethoven Sonata. 2001. 129p. (YA). reprint ed. 88.00 (978-0-7222-5712-8(0)) Library Reprints, Inc.

Harding, Henry A. Analysis of Form As Displayed in Beethoven's Thirty-Two Pianoforte Sonatas. 2001. 67p. (YA). reprint ed. 88.00 (978-0-7222-5715-9(5)) Library Reprints, Inc.

Kitson, Charles H. Studies in Fugue. 2001. 104p. (YA). reprint ed. 88.00 (978-0-7222-5695-4(7)) Library Reprints, Inc.

MacPherson, Stewart. Form in Music, with Special Reference to the Designs of Instrumental Music. 2001. 280p. (YA). reprint ed. 98.00 (978-0-7222-5719-7(8)) Library Reprints, Inc.

Pauer, Ernst. Musical Forms. 2001. 186p. (YA). reprint ed. 88.00 (978-0-7222-5721-0(X)) Library Reprints, Inc.

Prescott, Oliveria. Design in Music, Instrumental & Vocal. 2001. (YA). reprint ed. 150.00 (978-0-7222-5723-4(6)) Library Reprints, Inc.

Prout, Ebenezer. Musical Form. 5th ed. 2001. 244p. (YA). reprint ed. 98.00 (978-0-7222-5724-1(4)) Library Reprints, Inc.

MUSICAL INSTRUCTION

see Music—Study and Teaching

MUSICAL INSTRUMENTS

see also Orchestra

also groups of instruments, e.g. Percussion Instruments; Stringed Instruments; Wind Instruments; etc.; also names of musical instruments, e.g. Drum; etc.

Abbado, Claudio. Yo Sere Director de Orquesta. 2007. 48p. (J). (gr. 2-5). 19.95 (***978-84-8470-052-4(6)*** Corimbo, Editorial S.L. ESP. *Dist:* Lectorum Pubns., Inc.

Adam, Winky. Musical Instruments Stickers. 1999. (Illus.). 4p. (J). (ps-5). pap. 1.50 (978-0-486-40739-5(X)) Dover Pubns., Inc.

Amery, Heather. The Usborne Children's Songbook. Cartwright, Stephen, illus. 2nd rev. ed. 1998. (Songbooks Ser.). 64p. (J). (ps-3). pap. 10.95 (978-0-7460-2981-7(0)) EDC Publishing.

Archer, F. C. The Organ: A Theoretical & Practical Treatise. 2001. (YA). reprint ed. 150.00 (978-0-7222-5902-3(6)) Library Reprints, Inc.

Archibald, Paul. Playing the Trumpet & Brass. 2004. (Young Musician Ser.). (J). lib. bdg. 27.10 (978-1-932799-60-6(5)) Stargazer Bks.

Armstrong, Robert B. Musical Instruments, 2 vols., set. 2001. (YA). reprint ed. 250.00 (978-0-7222-5866-8(6)) Library Reprints, Inc.

Aylmore, Angela. Plucking. 2005. (Raintree Sprouts Ser.). (Illus.). 24p. pap. (978-1-4109-1611-2(1)); (J). (gr. 3-5). lib. bdg. 20.64 (978-1-4109-1606-8(5)) Steck-Vaughn.

Barber, Nicola. Should I Play the Flute? 2006. (Learning Musical Instruments Ser.). (Illus.). 32p. (J). (gr. 3-5). lib. bdg. 28.21 (978-1-4034-8187-0(3)) Heinemann Library.

Barrett, William A. Instrumentation. 2001. (YA). reprint ed. 150.00 (978-0-7222-5713-5(9)) Library Reprints, Inc.

Berlioz, Hector. A Treatise on Modern Instrumentation & Orchestration. 2001. 257p. (YA). reprint ed. 98.00 (978-0-7222-5775-3(9)) Library Reprints, Inc.

Blackwood, Alan. Playing the Piano & Keyboards. 2004. (Young Musician Ser.). (J). lib. bdg. (978-1-932799-59-0(1)) Stargazer Bks.

Blair, Peter, compiled by. Concert Ensembles for Everyone: Works for Instrumental Ensembles with Limited or Non-Traditional Instrumentation, Grades 3-4 (Flute/Oboe - WW 1 Ed) 2006. 8.95 (978-0-89328-259-2(6)) Heritage Music Pr.

Brett, H. The Cornet. 2001. (YA). reprint ed. 150.00 (978-0-7222-6055-5(5)) Library Reprints, Inc.

Brown, Mary E. A. Musical Instruments & Their Homes. 2001. 380p. (YA). reprint ed. 98.00 (978-0-7222-5867-5(4)) Library Reprints, Inc.

Casterline, L. C. The Sounds of Music. Yerkes, Lane, illus. 2004. 16p. (J). (gr. 1 up). lib. bdg. 19.33 (978-0-8368-4100-8(X)) Stevens, Gareth Inc.

Clarke, William H. Standard Organ Building. 2001. 219p. (YA). reprint ed. 98.00 (978-0-7222-5885-9(2)) Library Reprints, Inc.

Congratulations - Grade 1 Clarinet/Piano. (J). 9.95 (978-1-85909-667-3(0) , Warner Bros. Pubns.) Alfred Publishing Co., Inc.

Congratulations- Grade 2 Alto Sax/Piano. 9.95 (978-1-85909-816-5(9) , Warner Bros. Pubns.) Alfred Publishing Co., Inc.

Congratulations: Grade 2 Clarinet. (J). 9.95 (978-1-85909-814-1(2) , Warner Bros. Pubns.) Alfred Publishing Co., Inc.

Congratulations: Grade 2 Flute. 9.95 (978-1-85909-815-8(0) , Warner Bros. Pubns.) Alfred Publishing Co., Inc.

Coulthard, Emma. Recorder Wizard. 2005. 40p. pap. 8.95 incl. audio compact disk (978-0-8256-3338-6(9) , CH68575, Chester Music) Music Sales Corp.

Dale, William. Tschudi, the Harpsichord Maker. 2001. 91p. (YA). reprint ed. 88.00 (978-0-7222-5988-7(3)) Library Reprints, Inc.

Day, Eileen. I'm Good at Making Music. 2003. (Heinemann Read & Learn Ser.). (Illus.). 24p. (J). pap. 5.25 (978-1-4034-3447-0(6)); lib. bdg. 18.50 (978-1-4034-0900-3(5)) Heinemann Library.

—I'm Good at Making Music. 2003. (gr. k-3). lib. bdg. 13.30 (978-0-613-70658-2(7)) Tandem Library Bks.

Dearling, Robert. Encyclopedia of Musical Instruments, 5 vols., Set. 2005. (Illus.). 48p. (YA). (gr. 8 up). pap. 114.75 (978-0-7910-6090-2(X) , Chelsea Hse.) Facts On File, Inc.

—Keyboard Instruments & Ensembles. 2000. (Encyclopedia of Musical Instruments Ser.). (Illus.). 48p. (J). (gr. 4-7). 22.95 (978-0-7910-6094-0(2) , Chelsea Hse.) Facts On File, Inc.

—Non-Western & Obsolete Instruments. 2000. (Encyclopedia of Musical Instruments Ser.). (Illus.). 48p. (J). (gr. 4-7). 22.95 (978-0-7910-6095-7(0) , Chelsea Hse.) Facts On File, Inc.

—Percussion & Electronic Instruments. 2000. (Encyclopedia of Musical Instruments Ser.). (Illus.). 48p. (J). (gr. 4-7). 22.95 (978-0-7910-6093-3(4) , Chelsea Hse.) Facts On File, Inc.

—String Instruments. 2000. (Encyclopedia of Musical Instruments Ser.). (Illus.). 48p. (J). (gr. 4-7). 22.95 (978-0-7910-6092-6(6) , Chelsea Hse.) Facts On File, Inc.

—Woodwind & Brass Instruments. 2000. (Encyclopedia of Musical Instruments Ser.). (Illus.). 48p. (J). (gr. 4-7). 22.95 (978-0-7910-6091-9(8) , Chelsea Hse.) Facts On File, Inc.

Dickinson, Clarence. The Technique & Art of Organ Playing. 2001. 103p. (YA). reprint ed. 88.00 (978-0-7222-5907-8(7)) Library Reprints, Inc.

Doney, Meryl. Musical Instruments. 2004. (Crafts from Many Cultures Ser.). (Illus.). 32p. (J). (gr. 3 up). lib. bdg. 23.33 (978-0-8368-4045-2(3)) Stevens, Gareth Inc.

Drake, H. The Player-Piano Explained. 2001. (YA). reprint ed. 150.00 (978-0-7222-5979-5(4)) Library Reprints, Inc.

Ehrlich, D. J. History of the Flute from Ancient Times. 2001. (YA). reprint ed. 150.00 (978-0-7222-6058-6(X)) Library Reprints, Inc.

Elson, Arthur. Orchestral Instruments & Their Use. 2001. 340p. (YA). reprint ed. 98.00 (978-0-7222-5869-9(0)) Library Reprints, Inc.

Equipo Staff. Las lautas Tienen Agujeros. 2003. (Enciclopedia Me Pregunto Por Que). (SPA., Illus.). 102p. (J). (gr. 3-5). (978-84-241-1968-3(1) , EV2041) Everest de Ediciones y Distribucion, S.L. ESP. *Dist:* Lectorum Pubns., Inc.

Faine, Edward Allan. Bebop Babies. 2003. (Illus.). 22p. (J). bds. 5.95 (978-0-9716911-3-1(4)) IM Pr.

Fitzgibbon, Henry M. The Story of the Flute. 2001. 291p. (YA). reprint ed. 98.00 (978-0-7222-6059-3(8)) Library Reprints, Inc.

Flood, William H. G. The Story of the Bagpipe. 2001. 236p. (YA). reprint ed. 98.00 (978-0-7222-6050-0(4)) Library Reprints, Inc.

—The Story of the Harp. 2001. 207p. (YA). reprint ed. 98.00 (978-0-7222-6064-7(4)) Library Reprints, Inc.

Fraser, Alexander D. Some Reminiscences & the Bagpipe. 2001. 432p. (YA). reprint ed. 98.00 (978-0-7222-6052-4(0)) Library Reprints, Inc.

Froseth, James O. Alto Saxophone Home Helper First Lessons at School & at Home. 2005. 16p. 7.95 (978-1-57999-499-0(7) , M574) GIA Pubns., Inc.

—Baritone BC Home Helper First Lessons at School & at Home. 2005. 16p. 7.95 (978-1-57999-505-8(5) , M580) GIA Pubns., Inc.

—Bassoon Home Helper First Lessons at School & at Home. 2005. 16p. 7.95 (978-1-57999-498-3(9) , M573) GIA Pubns., Inc.

—Clarinet Home Helper First Lessons at School & at Home. 2005. 16p. 7.95 (978-1-57999-496-9(2) , M571) GIA Pubns., Inc.

Galpin, Francis W. Old English Instruments of Music, Their History & Character. 2001. 327p. (YA). reprint ed. 98.00 (978-0-7222-5871-2(2)) Library Reprints, Inc.

Gogerly, Liz. Musical Instruments. 2004. (Starters Ser.). (J). lib. bdg. (978-1-58340-567-3(4)) Smart Apple Media.

Green, John. Musical Instruments Stained Glass Coloring Book. 2006. (Dover Little Activity Bks.). 8p. (J). pap. 1.50 (978-0-486-44936-4(X)) Dover Pubns., Inc.

Grew, Sydney. The Art of the Player-Piano. 2001. 333p. (YA). reprint ed. 98.00 (978-0-7222-5981-8(6)) Library Reprints, Inc.

Harcourt School Publishers Staff. What Do You Play? 3rd ed. 2002. (Trophies English Language Learners Ser.). (Illus.). pap. 5.10 (978-0-15-327652-1(5)) Harcourt Schl. Pubs.

Harding, Henry A. Musical Instruments, Simply Explained. 5th ed. 2001. 37p. (YA). reprint ed. 88.00 (978-0-7222-5790-6(2)) Library Reprints, Inc.

Hasday, Judy L. Musical Instruments from Around the World. 1998. (Costume, Tradition & Culture). (Illus.). 64p. (YA). 19.75 (978-0-7910-5168-9(4) , Chelsea Hse.) Facts On File, Inc.

Helsby, Genevieve. Those Amazing Musical Instruments! 2007. 176p. (J). (gr. 3-7). 19.95 (***978-1-4022-0825-6(1)*** , Sourcebooks Jabberwocky) Sourcebooks, Inc.

Heron-Allen, Edward. De Fidiculis Bibliographia: An Attempt Towards a Bibliography of the Violin & All Other Instruments Played with a Bow in Ancient & Modern Times, 2 vols., set. 2001. (YA). reprint ed. 250.00 (978-0-7222-5989-4(1)) Library Reprints, Inc.

Hill, Arthur G. The Organ-Cases & Organs of the Middle Ages & Renaissance. 2001. 134p. (YA). reprint ed. 88.00 (978-0-7222-5887-3(9)) Library Reprints, Inc.

Hinton, John W. The Electric Organ. 2001. (YA). reprint ed. 150.00 (978-0-7222-5889-7(5)) Library Reprints, Inc.

Hipkins, Alfred J. A Description & History of the Pianoforte & of the Older Keyboard Stringed Instruments. 2001. 130p. (YA). reprint ed. 88.00 (978-0-7222-5935-1(2)) Library Reprints, Inc.

—The Selection: Musical Instruments, Historic, Rare & Unique. 2001. 123p. (YA). reprint ed. 88.00 (978-0-7222-5872-9(0)) Library Reprints, Inc.

Hopkins, Edward J. The Organ, Its History & Construction: A Comprehensive Treatise on the Structure & Capabilities of the Organ. 2001. 588p. (YA). reprint ed. 98.00 (978-0-7222-5890-3(9)) Library Reprints, Inc.

Kallen, Stuart A. The Instruments of Music. 2002. (Illus.). 112p. (J). 32.45 (978-1-59018-127-0(1) , Lucent Bks.) Thomson Gale.

King, Hall. The Harmonium. 2001. (YA). reprint ed. 150.00 (978-0-7222-5932-0(8)) Library Reprints, Inc.

M
N
O

Knight, M. J. Flutes. 2005. (Musical Instruments of the World Ser.). (Illus.). 32p. (J). (gr. 3-7). lib. bdg. 27.10 (978-1-58340-416-4(3)) Smart Apple Media.

—Keyboards. 2005. (Musical Instruments of the World Ser.). (Illus.). 32p. (J). (gr. 3-7). lib. bdg. 27.10 (978-1-58340-412-6(0)) Smart Apple Media.

Koscielniak, Bruce. Story of the Incredible Orchestra: An Introduction to Musical Instruments & Th. 2000. (gr. k-3). lib. bdg. 15.25 (978-0-613-60837-4(2)) Tandem Library Bks.

The Lac Hong Music Group: Six-Pack. (Greetings Ser.: Vol. 1). (gr. 3-5). 31.00 (978-0-7635-1750-2(X)) Rigby Education.

Lawson, Julia & Browne, Naima. Make Music! Millard, Peter, photos by. 2005. (Stepping Stones Ser.). (Illus.). 24p. (J). (ps). pap. 9.95 (978-0-237-52919-2(X) , Evans Brothers, Limited) Evans Publishing Group GBR. *Dist:* Independent Pubs. Group.

Levine, Robert T. & Hamilton, Meredith. The Story of the Orchestra: Listen While You Learn about the Instruments, the Music & the Composers Who Wrote the Music! 2000. (Illus.). 96p. (J). (gr. 4-7). tchr. ed. 19.95 (978-1-57912-148-8(9) , 81148) Black Dog & Leventhal Pubs., Inc.

Lovell, Sara. Cellotude. 2007. (Sara Lovell's Star Guides). (Illus.). 96p. pap. 15.95 (*978-1-905636-02-0(4)) Beautiful Bks. GBR. *Dist:* International Publishers Marketing.

Lynch, Wendy. Keyboard. 2001. (Musical Instruments Ser.). (Illus.). 32p. (J). (gr. k-2). lib. bdg. 21.36 (978-1-58810-234-8(3)) Heinemann Library.

Martin, Ian, illus. Complete Theory Fun Factory. 2004. 96p. pap. 14.95 (*978-0-85162-181-4(3) , 0851621813) Leonard, Hal Corp.

Matthews, J. The Organ Described. 2001. (YA). reprint ed. 150.00 (978-0-7222-5892-7(5)) Library Reprints, Inc.

Matthews, John. The Restoration of Organs. 2001. 124p. (YA). reprint ed. 88.00 (978-0-7222-5918-4(2)) Library Reprints, Inc.

McGraw-Hill Interactive Recorder. 2003. (Share the Music Ser.). (gr. 3-6). cd-rom (978-0-02-295529-8(1)) Macmillan/McGraw-Hill Schl. Div.

Miller, Randy. The Fiddler's Throne: A Selection of 375 Tunes for Contra Dances, Sessions, & House Parties, 2004. (Illus.). 246p. spiral bd. 25.00 (978-0-9770530-1-8(6)) Miller, Randy.

Mitchell, Albert G. Class Method for the Clarinet. 2001. 100p. (YA). reprint ed. 88.00 (978-0-7222-6054-8(7)) Library Reprints, Inc.

Morris, Ting & Morris, Neil. Music. Levy, Ruth, illus. 2006. 32p. (J). (978-1-59771-027-5(X)) Sea-To-Sea Pubns.

Music. Gr K-3 Stm Instrument Sou. 2003. (Share the Music Ser.). (gr. k-3). (978-0-02-295481-9(3)) Macmillan/McGraw-Hill Schl. Div.

Newman, Ernest. The Piano-Player & Its Music. 2001. 187p. (YA). reprint ed. 88.00 (978-0-7222-5982-5(4)) Library Reprints, Inc.

Niven, Felicia Lowenstein. Nifty Thrifty Music Crafts. 2007. (Nifty Thrifty Crafts for Kids Ser.). (Illus.). 32p. (J). (gr. 3-4). lib. bdg. 22.60 (978-0-7660-2784-8(8) , 1264783, Enslow Elementary) Enslow Pubs., Inc.

Norgaard, Martin. Jazz Cello/Bass Wizard Junior, Bk. 2. 2005. 64p. 17.95 (978-0-7866-6655-3(2) , 20869BCD) Mel Bay Pubns., Inc.

—Jazz Fiddle Wizard Junior, Book. 2. 2005. 64p. 17.95 (978-0-7866-6644-7(7) , 20726BCD) Mel Bay Pubns., Inc.

—Jazz Viola Wizard Junior, Bk. 2. 2005. 64p. 17.95 (978-0-7866-6653-9(6) , 20868BCD) Mel Bay Pubns., Inc.

O'Hara, Shelley. ICan iPod - the iPod Book for Kids. 2005. (Illus.). 160p. (J). pap. 7.99 (978-0-7897-3527-0(X)) Que.

Pitts, J. Recorder from the Beginning: Tunebook 1. 2004. (Illus.). 32p. 6.95 (978-0-7119-5073-3(3)) Music Sales Corp.

Pitts, John. Recorder from the Beginning. 2004. (Illus.). (gr. 2-6). Bk. 1. 40p. pap. 6.95 (978-0-7119-5079-5(2)); Bk. 2. 2nd ed. 47p. pap. 6.95 (978-0-7119-5080-1(6)); Vol. 3. 48p. pap. 6.95 (978-0-7119-5081-8(4)) Music Sales Corp.

—Recorder from the Beginning: Tunebook 2, Vol. 2. 2004. 32p. 6.95 (978-0-7119-5074-0(1)) Music Sales Corp.

—Recorder from the Beginning: Tunebook 3, Vol. 3. 2004. 32p. 6.95 (978-0-7119-5075-7(X)) Music Sales Corp.

Putnam, James & Dorling Kindersley Publishing Staff. Mummy. Hayman, Peter, illus. Hayman, Peter, photos by. 2004. (Eyewitness Books). 72p. (J). lib. bdg. 19.99 (978-0-7566-0706-7(X)) Dorling Kindersley Publishing, Inc.

Rau, Dana Meachen. Making Music, Level B. Fisher, Maureen Ivy, illus. 2001. (Compass Point Early Reader Ser.). 32p. (J). (gr. k up). lib. bdg. 18.60 (978-0-7565-0118-1(0)) Compass Point Bks.

Reinhardt, Donald S. Donald S. Reinhardt's Graduated Studies for the Brass Player for Trombone: Graduated Studies for the Brass Player for Trombone. 2004. 38p. (YA). 14.95 (978-0-9726185-9-5(7)) Boptism Music Publishing.

—Donald S. Reinhardt's Graduated Studies for the Brass Player for Trumpet: Beginning, Intermediate & Advanced Brass Method. 2004. Orig. Title: Donald S. Reinhardt's Trumpet for Beginners. 38p. (YA). 11.95 (978-0-9726185-8-8(9)) Boptism Music Publishing.

Roberts, Gregory. Chin Music. 2007. 208p. (J). pap. 12.99 (*978-0-14-305573-0(9)) Penguin Group (USA) Inc.

Robertson, Marvin L. How We Make Music. 2007. (Illus.). 24p. (J). (978-1-59515-991-5(6)) Rourke Publishing, LLC.

Rutland, Jonathan. Abracadabra Clarinet: The Way to Learn Through Songs & Tunes. 2nd ed. 2002. (Illus.). 72p. pap., stu. ed. 11.95 (978-0-7136-6199-6(2)) A & C Black GBR. *Dist:* Consortium Bk. Sales & Distribution.

Saliba, Konnie. Hang on to the Big Balloon: Simple to Challenging Orff Instruments. 2005. 68p. (J). (gr. 1-8). 14.95 (978-0-7692-9986-0(5) , BMR08014, Warner Bros. Pubns.) Alfred Publishing Co., Inc.

Schlesinger, Kathleen. The Instruments of the Modern Orchestra & Early Records of the Precursors of the Violin Family, 2 vols., set. 2001. (YA). reprint ed. 250.00 (978-0-7222-5873-6(9)) Library Reprints, Inc.

Scholastic Teacher Editors. Musical Instruments. 1998. (J). 12.95 (978-0-590-78800-7(0)) Scholastic, Inc.

School Specialty Publishing. Musical Instruments. 1999. (Learning Cards Ser.). 24p. (J). (gr. 3-8). 7.99 (978-0-7424-0649-0(0) , Instructional Fair) Schaffer, Frank Pubns.

Schwartz, Betty Ann. What Makes Music? A Magic Ribbon Book. Turner, Dona, illus. 2005. (Stories to Share Ser.). 16p. (J). (ps-3). act. bk. ed. 11.95 (978-1-58117-139-6(0) , Intervisual/Piggy Toes) Dalmatian Pr.

Sesame Workshop Staff, ed. My First Library Sesame Street: 12 Board Books. 2004. (Illus.). 120p. (J). bds. 10.98 (978-1-4127-0515-8(0) , 7224100) Publications International, Ltd.

Smith, A. G. Little Mandalas Stained Glass Coloring Book. 2006. (Dover Little Activity Bks.). 8p. (J). pap. 1.50 (978-0-486-44937-1(8)) Dover Pubns., Inc.

Smith, Melanie. Beginner Cello Theory for Children Book One. 2005. 84p. pap. 9.95 (978-0-7866-7088-8(6) , 20451) Mel Bay Pubns., Inc.

South Kensington Museum, London Staff. A Descriptive Catalogue of the Musical Instruments in the South Kensington Museum. 2nd ed. 2001. 402p. (YA). reprint ed. 98.00 (978-0-7222-5870-5(4)) Library Reprints, Inc.

Spilsbury, Richard. Should I Play the Clarinet? 2006. (Learning Musical Instruments Ser.). (Illus.). 32p. (J). (978-1-4034-8185-6(7)) Heinemann Library.

—Should I Play the Trumpet? 2006. (Learning Musical Instruments Ser.). (Illus.). 32p. (J). (978-1-4034-8190-0(3)) Heinemann Library.

Steinert, Morris. The M. Steinert Collection of Keyed & Stringed Instruments: Various Treatises on the History of These Instruments. 2001. 170p. (YA). reprint ed. 88.00 (978-0-7222-5875-0(5)) Library Reprints, Inc.

Stevens, Wallace. The Harmonium. 2001. 140p. (YA). reprint ed. 88.00 (978-0-7222-5933-7(6)) Library Reprints, Inc.

Suzuki, Shinichi. Suzuki Viola School Vol. 4: Piano Accompaniment. Preucil, Doris, ed. 2000. 64p. (J). (gr. k-12). 10.95 (978-0-87487-275-0(8) , Warner Bros. Pubns.) Alfred Publishing Co., Inc.

Thomas, Roger. Keyboards. 2001. (Soundbites Ser.). (Illus.). 32p. (YA). (gr. 6-8). lib. bdg. 22.79 (978-1-58810-263-8(7)) Heinemann Library.

Tours, Berthold. The Viola. 2001. (YA). reprint ed. 150.00 (978-0-7222-6018-0(0)) Library Reprints, Inc.

Turner, Barbara. Out & About at the Orchestra. McMullen, Anne, illus. 2004. (Field Trips Ser.). 24p. (C). (gr. k-3). 23.93 (978-1-4048-0040-3(9)) Picture Window Bks.

Turner, Barrie Carson. Flutes. 1998. (Musical Instruments of the World Ser.). (Illus.). 32p. (J). (gr. 1-5). lib. bdg. 16.95 (978-1-887068-45-1(7)) Smart Apple Media.

—Modern Instruments. 2000. (Musical Instruments of the World Ser.). (Illus.). 32p. (J). (ps-3). lib. bdg. 16.95 (978-1-58340-063-0(X)) Smart Apple Media.

—Musical Instruments, 8 vols., Set. 1999. (Illus.). 32p. (J). (gr. 1-5). lib. bdg. 135.60 (978-1-887068-50-5(3)) Smart Apple Media.

Van der Straeten, Edmund S. J. History of the Violoncello: The Viol Da Gamba, Their Precursors & Collateral Instruments, with Biographies of all the Most Eminent Players of Every Country, 2 vols., set. 2001. (YA). reprint ed. 250.00 (978-0-7222-6024-1(5)) Library Reprints, Inc.

Walton, Simon. Playing the Flute, Recorder, & Other Woodwinds. 2004. (Young Musician Ser.). (J). lib. bdg. 27.10 (978-1-932799-58-3(3)) Stargazer Bks.

Welch, Christopher Evan. History of the Boehm Flute. 2001. 504p. (YA). reprint ed. 98.00 (978-0-7222-6060-9(1)) Library Reprints, Inc.

—Six Lectures on the Recorder & Other Flutes in Relation to Literature. 2001. 457p. (YA). reprint ed. 98.00 (978-0-7222-6061-6(X)) Library Reprints, Inc.

Widor, Charles M. The Technique of the Modern Orchestra: A Manual of Practical Instrumentation. 2001. 200p. (YA). reprint ed. 98.00 (978-0-7222-5786-9(4)) Library Reprints, Inc.

Willey, Rich. Home Cookin' [97] 24 Dixie Jazz Duets for B-flat Instruments. 2002. 49p. (YA). 14.95 (978-0-9726185-4-0(6)) Boptism Music Publishing.

—Home Cookin' [97] 24 Dixie Jazz Duets for Bass Clef Instruments. 2002. 49p. (YA). 14.95 (978-0-9726185-5-7(4)) Boptism Music Publishing.

—I'd Rather Be Boppin' ¿ 24 Bop Duets for C Treble Clef Instruments. (YA). Vol. 1. 2002. 49p. 14.95 (978-0-9726185-1-9(1)); Vol. 2. 2004. 49p. 14.95 (978-0-9726185-2-6(X)); Vol. 3. 2004. 51p. 14.95 (978-0-9726185-3-3(8)) Boptism Music Publishing.

Wiseman, Ann Sayre & Langstaff, John. Making Music: Create & Play 70 Musical Instruments Using Stuff from Around Your House. 2003. (Illus.). 96p. (gr. 2-7). pap. 9.95 (978-1-58017-512-8(0) , 67512, Storey Kids) Storey Publishing, LLC.

Wiseman, Ann Sayre & Langstaff, John M. Making Music: Create & Play 70 Musical Instruments Using Stuff from Around Your House. Wiseman, Ann Sayre, illus. 2003. (Illus.). 96p. (gr. 2-7). tchr. ed. 19.95 (978-1-58017-513-5(9) , 67513, Storey Kids) Storey Publishing, LLC.

Zampino, Phil. The PAZ Method - Different Beats Rhythms & Styles on the Drum Set: (Funk, Soul, Reggae & More), Vol. 8. 2000. (YA). (gr. 5 up). pap. 19.50 (978-0-942253-26-9(4)) PAZ Publishing.

MUSICAL INSTRUMENTS—DICTIONARIES

Pulver, Jeffrey. A Dictionary of Old English Music & Musical Instruments. 2001. 247p. (YA). reprint ed. 98.00 (978-0-7222-5121-8(1)) Library Reprints, Inc.

MUSICAL INSTRUMENTS—FICTION

Adair, Amy. Jay Jay's Special Delivery. 2003. (Illus.). (J). 15.98 (978-0-7853-8625-4(4)) Publications International, Ltd.

Albee, Sarah. Max Can Fix That. Schick, Joel, illus. 2006. (Step-By-Step Readers Ser.). (J). pap. (978-1-59939-055-0(8) , Reader's Digest Young Families, Inc.) Reader's Digest Children's Publishing, Inc.

Bateman, Teresa. Red, White, Blue & Uncle Who? The Story Behind Some of America's Patriotic Symbols. O'Brien, John, illus. 2001. 64p. (J). (gr. 4-6). tchr. ed. 16.95 (978-0-8234-1285-3(7)) Holiday Hse., Inc.

Benator, Eileen. A Marching Band for Bears. Benator, Seth, illus. 2004. 32p. (J). lib. bdg. 15.95 (978-0-9748478-5-6(2)) Lion's Tale Press, L.L.C.

Ben's Tune: Individual Chapter Book Title Six-Packs. Vol. 28. 32p. (gr. 4 up). 44.00 (978-0-7578-0603-2(1)) Rigby Education.

Blumberg, Margie. Avram's Gift. McGaw, Laurie, illus. 48p. 2005. (YA). pap. 7.95 (978-0-9624166-3-7(0)); 2003. (J). (gr. 3 up). (978-0-9624166-2-0(2)) MB Publishing, LLC.

Cali, Davide. Piano Piano. Rivers, Randi, tr. from FRE. Héliot, Eric, illus. 2007. 28p. (J). (gr. 1-3). 15.95 (*978-1-58089-191-2(8)) Charlesbridge Publishing, Inc.

Carlson, Nancy. Loudmouth George & the Cornet. rev. ed. 2004. (Carolrhoda Picture Books Ser.). (Illus.). 32p. (J). (gr. k-2). pap. 6.95 (978-1-57505-725-5(5)) Lerner Publishing Group.

Child's Play, ed. Music Man Big Bk with Holes. 2006. (Illus.). 16p. 19.99 (978-1-84643-010-7(0)) Child's Play-International.

Currie, Susan. Basket of Beethoven. (J). 2002. 124p. pap. (978-1-55041-666-4(9)); 2001. 128p. (gr. 4-7). (978-1-55041-665-7(0)) Fitzhenry & Whiteside, Ltd.

Curtis, Gavin. The Bat Boy & His Violin. ed. 2004. (Illus.). (J). (gr. k-3). spiral bd. (978-0-616-07254-7(6)) Canadian National Institute for the Blind/Institut National Canadien pour les Aveugles.

Dem Bones. 2004. 24.95 incl. audio (978-1-55592-692-2(4)); 29.95 incl. cd-rom (978-1-55592-702-8(5)) Weston Woods Studios, Inc.

Falconer, Ian. Olivia Forms a Band. Falconer, Ian, illus. 2006. (Olivia Ser.). (Illus.). 50p. (J). (ps-2). 17.95 (978-1-4169-2454-8(X) , Atheneum) Simon & Schuster Children's Publishing.

Farmer, Zoe. Practice Makes Perfect. Farmer, Zoe, illus. 2007. (Illus.). 74p. (ps-k). pap. (978-1-58690-029-8(3)) Mould, Paul Publishing.

Free Kazoos. 2003. (978-0-375-88484-9(X)) Random Hse. Children's Bks.

Garriel, Barbara S. I Know a Shy Fellow Who Swallowed a Cello. O'Brian, John, illus. 2004. 32p. (J). (gr. k-2). 15.95 (978-1-59078-043-5(4)) Boyds Mills Pr.

Gingras, Charlotte. Emily's Piano. Ouriou, Susan, tr. from FRE. Jorisch, Stephane, illus. 2005. 64p. (J). (gr. 4-7). 18.95 (978-1-55037-913-6(5)); pap. 7.95 (978-1-55037-912-9(7)) Annick Pr., Ltd. CAN. *Dist:* Firefly Bks., Ltd.

Golden Books Staff. Little Boy with a Big Horn. Yaccarino, Dan, illus. 2008. (Golden Classic Ser.). 48p. (J). (gr. k-k). lib. bdg. 17.99 (*978-0-375-93903-7(2) , Golden Bks.) Random Hse., Inc.

Haley, Amanda, illus. Music Class. 2006. (I'm Going to Read Ser.). 32p. (J). pap. 3.95 (978-1-4027-3081-8(0)) Sterling Publishing Co., Inc.

Harcourt School Publishers Staff. The Bang-on-a-Can Band. 3rd ed. 2002. (Trophies English Language Learners Ser.). (Illus.). pap. 5.10 (978-0-15-327871-6(4)) Harcourt Schl. Pubs.

—Nosy Nina Advanced Level. 3rd ed. 2002. (Trophies Reading Program Ser.). (Illus.). pap. 5.10 (978-0-15-323202-2(1)) Harcourt Schl. Pubs.

—The Talking Drum Advance Level. 3rd ed. 2002. (Trophies Reading Program Ser.). (Illus.). pap. 5.10 (978-0-15-323123-0(8)) Harcourt Schl. Pubs.

—Trofeos On Level: La Pieza de Piano. 3rd ed. 2002. (SPA., Illus.). pap. 6.80 (978-0-15-324083-6(0)) Harcourt Schl. Pubs.

—The Violin Man, Level D. 2001. (Collections Ser.). (Illus.). (J). 6.90 (978-0-15-314405-9(X)) Harcourt Schl. Pubs.

—The Visit Advanced Level. 3rd ed. 2002. (Trophies Reading Program Ser.). (Illus.). pap. 5.10 (978-0-15-323294-7(3)) Harcourt Schl. Pubs.

Kenney, Cindy, et al. Frog Wars: A Lesson in Perseverance. 2005. (VeggieTown Values Ser.: Bk. 2). (Illus.). 32p. pap. 3.99 (978-0-310-70627-4(0)) Zonderkidz.

Landis, Leanne. Keaka & His Precious Pahu. 2002. 32p. (J). (ps-5). pap. 9.94 (978-0-9723707-1-4(4) , KPB01) White Door Publishing.

Landon, Kristen. Life in the Pit. Johnson, Regan, illus. 2007. 192p. (YA). (gr. 8-12). 16.95 (*978-1-933831-08-4(1)) Blooming Tree Pr.

Langham, Tony. Creepy Crawly Calypso. Harter, Debbie, illus. 2004. 32p. (J). 16.99 incl. audio compact disk (978-1-84148-699-4(X)) Barefoot Bks., Inc.

Langham, Tony & Harter, Debbie. Creepy Crawly Calypso. 2006. 32p. pap. 9.99 incl. cd-rom (978-1-902283-46-3(5)) Barefoot Bks., Inc.

Lithgow, John. The Remarkable Farkle McBride. Payne, C. F., illus. 2003. 40p. (J). pap. 7.99 (978-0-689-83541-4(8) , Aladdin) Simon & Schuster Children's Publishing.

—The Remarkable Farkle McBride: 52 Unexpected Ways to Make a Birthday, Holiday, or Any Day a Celebration. Payne, C. F., illus. 2000. 40p. (J). (ps-3). 16.00 (978-0-689-83340-3(7)) Simon & Schuster Children's Publishing.

Manning, Sarra. Guitar Girl. 2005. 240p. (YA). (gr. 9-12). reprint ed. pap. 6.99 (978-0-14-240318-1(0) , Puffin) Penguin Group (USA) Inc.

McPhail, David M. Mole Music. McPhail, David M., illus. 2001. (Live Oak Readalong Ser.). (Illus.). (J). pap. 16.95 incl. audio (978-0-87499-747-7(X)); pap. 18.95 incl. audio compact disk (978-1-59112-406-1(9)) Live Oak Media.

Miller, William. The Piano. Keeter, Susan, illus. 2000. 32p. (J). (ps up). 15.95 (978-1-880000-98-4(9)) Lee & Low Bks., Inc.

Montparker, Carol. Polly & the Piano. 2004. (Illus.). 40p. 19.95 incl. audio compact disk (978-1-57467-093-6(X) , 157467093X, Amadeus Press) Leonard, Hal Corp.

Parkinson, Siobhan. Second Fiddle: Or How to Tell a Blackbird from a Sausage. 2007. 192p. (J). (gr. 6-9). 16.95 (978-1-59643-122-5(9)) Roaring Brook Pr.

Raney, Richard B., illus. A Dulcimer for Elspeth. 2002. 22p. (J). (gr. k-6). incl. audio compact disk (978-0-9718866-0-5(1)) Serene Sounds.

Rau, Dana Meachen. Sounds Like Fun. 2004. (Compass Point Early Reader Ser.). (J). (978-0-7565-0570-7(4)) Compass Point Bks.

Richardson, Bill. The Aunts Come Marching. Nugent, Cynthia, illus. 2007. 32p. (J). 15.95 (*978-1-55192-990-3(2)) Raincoast Bk. Distribution CAN. *Dist:* Perseus Distribution.

Rovetch, Lissa. I Need a Kazoot! Castillon, Carly, illus. 2006. (J). (978-1-58987-055-0(7)) Kindermusik International.

Rumbley, Rose-Mary. Dear Santa: Thanks for the Piano. 2004. (Illus.). 46p. (J). pap. 8.95 (978-1-57168-466-0(2)) Eakin Pr.

Rylant, Cynthia. The Case of the Puzzling Possum. Karas, G. Brian, illus. (High-Rise Private Eyes Ser.: No. 3). (J). (ps-2). 2004. 48p. pap. 18.95 incl. audio compact disk (978-1-59112-618-8(5)); 2003. pap. 29.95 incl. audio (978-1-59112-199-2(X)); 2003. pap. 16.95 incl. audio (978-1-59112-197-8(3)); 2003. 25.95 incl. audio (978-1-59112-198-5(1)) Live Oak Media.

—The Case of the Puzzling Possum. 2002. (High-Rise Private Eyes Ser.: No. 3). (J). (gr. k-3). lib. bdg. 11.80 (978-0-613-44514-6(7)) Tandem Library Bks.

Shahan, Sherry. The Jazzy Alphabet. Thelen, Mary, illus. 2006. 30p. (J). (gr. k-4). reprint ed. 16.00 (978-1-4223-5730-9(9)) DIANE Publishing Co.

Shields, Carol Diggory, et al. Music. 2000. (Animagicals Ser.). (Illus.). 12p. (J). (ps-1). 9.95 (978-1-929766-05-5(X)) Handprint Bks.

Sis, Peter. Madlenka's Music. 2005. (J). (978-0-375-82855-3(9)); lib. bdg. (978-0-375-92855-0(3)) Random Hse., Inc.

Smith, John D. The Best Mariachi in the World/ el mejor mariachi del Mundo. de la Vega, Eida, tr. Jones, Dani, illus. 2008. (J). lib. bdg. 16.95 (978-0-9770906-1-7(2)) Raven Tree Pr.

Snicket, Lemony, pseud & Stookey, Nathaniel. The Composer Is Dead. Ellis, Carson, illus. 2008. (J). (*978-0-06-123627-3(6)); lib. bdg. (*978-0-06-123628-0(4)) HarperCollins Pubs.

Spyri, Johanna. Rico & Wiseli, Rico & Stineli, & H. 2006. 63.99 (*978-1-4280-3033-6(6)) IndyPublish.com.

Stewart, Kymberly M. Play It Again, Rachel. 2003. 74p. (J). pap. 10.95 (978-0-9740653-0-4(7)) Neema's Children Literature Assn., Inc.

Tripp, Paul. Tubby the Tuba. Cole, Henry, illus. 2006. 32p. (J). (ps). pap. 16.99 (978-0-525-47717-4(9) , Dutton Juvenile) Penguin Group (USA) Inc.

Urban, Linda. A Crooked Kind of Perfect. 2007. (Illus.). 224p. (J). (gr. 3-7). 16.00 (*978-0-15-206007-7(3)) Harcourt Children's Bks.

Wilson, Budge. A Fiddle for Angus. Tooke, Susan, illus. 2006. 32p. (J). (gr. 1-4). pap. 9.95 (978-0-88776-785-2(0) , Random Hse. Puzzles & Games) Random Hse. Information Group.

Wolff, Virginia Euwer. The Mozart Season. 2000. (978-0-606-18579-0(8)) Tandem Library Bks.

Zin Zin a Violin. 2004. pap. 14.95 incl. audio (978-1-55592-676-2(2)) Weston Woods Studios, Inc.

Zin! Zin! Zin! a Violin. 2004. 29.95 incl. cd-rom (978-1-55592-131-6(0)); pap. 29.95 incl. audio compact disk (978-1-55592-118-7(3)); pap. 38.75 incl. audio compact disk (978-1-55592-650-2(9)); pap. 32.75 incl. audio (978-1-55592-340-2(2)); pap. 32.75 incl. audio (978-1-55592-341-9(0)); pap. 14.95 incl. audio (978-1-55592-047-0(0)) Weston Woods Studios, Inc.

Zin!, Zin!, Zin!, a Violin. 2004. 24.95 incl. audio (978-1-56008-645-1(9)) Weston Woods Studios, Inc.

MUSICAL NOTATION

Collins, Kathleen. Music Math: Exploring Different Interpretations of Fractions. 2004. (Powermath Ser.). (Illus.). 32p. (J). lib. bdg. (978-0-8239-8877-8(5)); lib. bdg. 22.50 (978-0-8239-8984-3(4)) Rosen Publishing Group, Inc., The. (PowerKids Pr.).

Dembska, Anna & Harkness, Joan. You've Got Rhythm: Read Music Better by Feeling the Beat. 2002. 126p. (YA). (gr. 3 up). pap. 27.95 (978-1-930664-04-3(4)) Flying Leap Music.

Gehrkens, Karl W. Music Notation & Terminology. 2001. 168p. (YA). reprint ed. 88.00 (978-0-7222-5773-9(2)) Library Reprints, Inc.

Silver Burdett Making Music Music Connection: Technology. 2002. (gr. k-8). cd-rom (978-0-382-36553-9(4)); cd-rom (978-0-382-36552-2(6)) Silver, Burdett & Ginn, Inc.

Yazbeck, Peter & Castano, Clara. Learning Cards(tm), the ABCs of Keyboard Musicianship: Musical Symbols in Q&A Form- Secondary Level, 1. 2007. (Illus.). 130p. (J). 9.95 (***978-0-9785118-5-2(9)***) CCRiddles.

MUSICAL REVUES, COMEDIES, ETC.

Harling, Per. Fly, Pretty Angels, Fly! Piano/Vocal Book. 2002. (Illus.). 36p. (J). (gr. 1-8). pap. (978-1-890569-41-9(0) , GBGMusik) General Board of Global Ministries, The United Methodist Church.

—Fly, Pretty Angels, Fly: Singer's Edition. Kimbrough, S. T., Jr. & McGurty, Mark, eds. 2002. 24p. (J). (gr. 1-8). pap. (978-1-890569-52-5(6) , GBGMusik) General Board of Global Ministries, The United Methodist Church.

Jacobs, Peter & Jacobs, Hanneke, creators. I Witness News - Live from Bethlehem: A Christmas Musical for Children about God's Perfect Plan for Us. 2002. 136p. 7.99 (978-0-8341-7282-1(8) , MC-537) Lillenas Publishing Co.

Lantos, Jeff. Big Tush, Little Tush: Musical. 2002. 45p. (YA). pap. 6.95 (978-1-58342-138-3(6) , B07) Dramatic Publishing Co.

McMahon, James P. & Ryan, Nancy. Buttonbush. 2003. (Musicals Ser.). 55p. (Orig.). (J). (gr. k-7). pap. 10.00 (978-0-88734-526-5(3)) Players Pr., Inc.

Robinette, Joseph. The Just So Stories - Musical. 2002. 99p. (J). 6.95 (978-1-58342-103-1(3) , J03) Dramatic Publishing Co.

Son Seekers - Nation Vacation - Director's Resource Kit: A 60's Flavored Children's Musical Journey about Knowing & Growing with God! 2002. pap. 59.99 (978-0-8341-7363-7(8)) Lillenas Publishing Co.

MUSICIANS

see also African American Musicians; Composers; Conductors (Music); Pianists; Rap Musicians; Singers; Violinists

Abrams, Dennis. Eminem. 2007. (Hip-Hop Stars Ser.). 104p. (J). (gr. 6-12). 30.00 (***978-0-7910-9479-2(0)*** , Chelsea Hse.) Facts On File, Inc.

Adams, Michelle. Tim Mcgraw. 2006. (Blue Banner Biography Ser.). (Illus.). 32p. (J). (gr. 4-8). lib. bdg. 25.70 (978-1-58415-501-0(9)) Mitchell Lane Pubs., Inc.

Anderson, M. T. Handel, Who Knew What He Liked. Hawkes, Kevin, illus. 2004. 48p. (J). (gr. 3-7). reprint ed. pap. 6.99 (978-0-7636-2562-7(0)) Candlewick Pr.

Anderson, Marilyn D. Will Smith. 2002. (People in the News Ser.). (Illus.). 112p. (J). (gr. 6-9). 27.45 (978-1-59018-140-9(9) , Lucent Bks.) Thomson Gale.

Ashley, Susan. Yo-Yo Ma. 2004. (Trailblazers of the Modern World Ser.). (Illus.). 48p. (J). pap. 11.99 (978-0-8368-5266-0(4)); (YA). lib. bdg. 30.00 (978-0-8368-5497-8(7)) Stevens, Gareth Inc. (World Almanac Library).

Ball, Heather. Magnificent Women in Music: A Women's Hall of Fame Series Book. 2005. (Illus.). 100p. (YA). pap. 7.95 (978-1-897187-02-9(5)) Second Story Pr. CAN. *Dist:* Orca Bk. Pubs. USA.

Bankston, John. Jay-Z. 2004. (Blue Banner Biography Ser.). (Illus.). 32p. (J). (gr. 3-8). lib. bdg. 25.70 (978-1-58415-223-1(0)) Mitchell Lane Pubs., Inc.

—The Life & Times of Duke Ellington. 2004. (Masters of Music Ser.). (Illus.). 48p. (J). (gr. 4-8). lib. bdg. 20.95 (978-1-58415-248-4(6)) Mitchell Lane Pubs., Inc.

Bennett, James R. S. The Life of William Sterndale Bennett. 2001. 471p. (YA). reprint ed. 98.00 (978-0-7222-5354-0(0)) Library Reprints, Inc.

Blashfield, Jean F. Leonard Bernstein: Conductor & Composer. 2000. (Career Biographies Ser.). (Illus.). 128p. (YA). (gr. 6-12). 25.00 (978-0-89434-337-7(8) , F404, Ferguson Publishing Co.) Facts On File, Inc.

Blue Banner Biographies, 26 Bks, Set. (gr. 3-8). (Illus.). lib. bdg. (978-1-58415-323-8(7)); 2005. (J). lib. bdg. 745.80 (978-1-58415-412-9(8)) Mitchell Lane Pubs., Inc.

Boekhoff, P. M. & Kallen, Stuart A. Famous People - N'SYNC. 2002. (Famous People Ser.). (Illus.). 48p. (J). (gr. 3-5). 26.20 (978-0-7377-1460-9(3) , Kidhaven) Thomson Gale.

Bolden, Tonya. Take-Off! American All-Girl Bands During WW II. 2007. (Illus.). 80p. (J). (gr. 5-9). lib. bdg. 21.99 (978-0-375-92797-3(2) , Knopf Bks. for Young Readers) Random Hse. Children's Bks.

—Take-Off (Book & CD) American All-Girl Bands During World War II. 2007. (Illus.). 80p. (J). (gr. 5-9). 18.99 (978-0-375-82797-6(8) , Knopf Bks. for Young Readers) Random Hse. Children's Bks.

Boyes, Kate. Paul McCartney. 2003. (Importance of Ser.). (J). 32.45 (978-1-59018-283-3(9) , Lucent Bks.) Thomson Gale.

Brewster, Hugh. The Other Mozart: The Life of the Famous Chevalier de Saint-George. Velasquez, Eric, illus. 2006. 48p. (J). (gr. k-5). 18.95 (978-0-8109-5720-6(5) , Abrams Bks. for Young Readers) Abrams, Harry N. , Inc.

Brighton, Catherine. Mozart: Scenes from the Childhood of the Great Composer. 2000. (Illus.). 30p. (J). (gr. 1 up). pap. 9.99 (978-0-7112-1604-4(5)) Lincoln, Frances Ltd. GBR. *Dist:* Transition Vendor.

Britton, Tamara L. LeAnn Rimes. 1999. (Young Profiles Ser.). (Illus.). 32p. (J). (gr. k-6). lib. bdg. 22.78 (978-1-57765-325-7(4) , Checkerboard Library) ABDO Publishing Co.

Brower, Harriette M. Story-Lives of Master Musicians. 2001. 371p. (YA). reprint ed. 98.00 (978-0-7222-5231-4(5)) Library Reprints, Inc.

Brown, Gene. Duke Ellington: Jazz Master. 2001. (Giants of Art & Culture Ser.). (Illus.). 128p. (J). (gr. 5-8). 28.70 (978-1-56711-505-5(5) , Blackbirch Pr., Inc.) Thomson Gale.

Brown, Terrell. Alicia Keys. 2007. (Hip-Hop Ser.). (Illus.). 64p. (J). (gr. 5 up). 22.95 (978-1-4222-0120-6(1)) Mason Crest Pubs.

Buckley, Annie. Yo Yo Ma. 2008. (J). lib. bdg. 26.00 (***978-1-60279-077-3(9)***) Cherry Lake Publishing.

Burgan, Michael. Jim Morrison. 2004. (Edge Books, Rock Music Library). (Illus.). 32p. (J). lib. bdg. 22.60 (978-0-7368-2702-7(1)) Capstone Pr., Inc.

Burton, Frances. That's Me, Tyler! Thompson, Karmen, illus. 2002. 32p. (J). (ps-3). lib. bdg. 15.95 (978-0-9650769-2-0(X)) Stonehill Publishing.

Bustard, Anne. Buddy: The Story of Buddy Holly. Cyrus, Kurt, illus. 2005. 32p. (J). 16.95 (978-0-689-86667-8(4) , Simon & Schuster Children's Publishing) Simon & Schuster Children's Publishing.

B*Witched: Backstage Pass. 1999. (gr. 3-6). lib. bdg. 14.15 (978-0-613-21275-5(4)) Tandem Library Bks.

Chippendale, Lisa A. Yo-Yo Ma: A Cello Superstar Brings Music to the World. 2004. (People to Know Ser.). (Illus.). 112p. (J). lib. bdg. 26.60 (978-0-7660-2286-7(2)) Enslow Pubs., Inc.

Composers of Note Grades 5-8. 2000. 64p. (J). pap. 8.94 (978-1-889369-41-9(1)) Teaching Ink, Inc.

Cummings, William H. Biographical Dictionary of Musicians. rev. ed. 2001. 84p. (YA). reprint ed. 88.00 (978-0-7222-5210-9(2)) Library Reprints, Inc.

Da Coll, Ivar. Azucar! Da Coll, Ivar, illus. 2005. (SPA., Illus.). (J). 14.99 (978-1-930332-65-2(3)) Lectorum Pubns., Inc.

Diehl, Alice M. The True Story of My Life. 2001. (YA). reprint ed. 150.00 (978-0-7222-5402-8(4)) Library Reprints, Inc.

Doeden, Matt. Green Day: Keeping Punk Alive. 2007. (Gateway Biography Ser.). (Illus.). 48p. (J). 23.93 (978-0-8225-6390-7(8) , Lerner Pubns.) Lerner Publishing Group.

Dowswell, Paul. John Lennon. 2001. (Profiles Ser.). (Illus.). 56p. (J). (gr. 4-6). lib. bdg. 24.22 (978-1-58810-060-3(X)) Heinemann Library.

—Paul McCartney. 2001. (Profiles Ser.). (Illus.). 56p. (J). (gr. 4-6). lib. bdg. 24.22 (978-1-58810-062-7(6)) Heinemann Library.

Earls, Irene. Young Musicians in World History. 2002. (Illus.). 152p. 49.95 (978-0-313-31442-1(X) , MS1442, Greenwood Pr.) Greenwood Publishing Group, Inc.

Edward, Herman. Pink Floyd. 2008. (J). (***978-1-4222-0214-2(3)***) Mason Crest Pubs.

Elish, Dan. Louis Armstrong & the Jazz Age. 2005. (Cornerstones of Freedom Ser.). (Illus.). 48p. (J). (gr. 4-6). 26.00 (978-0-516-23629-2(6) , Children's Pr.) Scholastic Library Publishing.

Elvey, George J. Life & Reminiscences. 2001. (YA). reprint ed. 150.00 (978-0-7222-5408-0(3)) Library Reprints, Inc.

Flynn, Noa. The Who. 2008. (J). (***978-1-4222-0196-1(1)***) Mason Crest Pubs.

Forget, Thomas. The Rolling Stones. 2006. (Rock & Roll Hall of Famers Ser.). (Illus.). 112p. (YA). (gr. 5-8). lib. bdg. 29.25 (978-0-8239-3644-1(9)) Rosen Publishing Group, Inc., The.

Forkos, Heather. Tupac Shakur. 2000. (They Died Too Young Ser.). (Illus.). 48p. (J). (gr. 4-7). 21.95 (978-0-7910-5859-6(X) , Chelsea Hse.) Facts On File, Inc.

Fox, Charlotte M. Annals of the Irish Harpers. 2001. 320p. (YA). reprint ed. 98.00 (978-0-7222-6065-4(2)) Library Reprints, Inc.

Franks, Katie. I Want to Be a Rock Star. 2007. (Dream Jobs Ser.). (Illus.). 24p. (J). (gr. 3-5). lib. bdg. 21.25 (978-1-4042-3618-9(X) , PowerKids Pr.) Rosen Publishing Group, Inc., The.

Gallagher, Jim. The Beatles. 2008. (J). (***978-1-4222-0186-2(4)***) Mason Crest Pubs.

Gallagher, Jim. Shania Twain: Grammy Award-Winning Singer. 1999. (Real-Life Reader Biography Ser.). (Illus.). 32p. (gr. 3-8). lib. bdg. 15.95 (978-1-58415-000-8(9)) Mitchell Lane Pubs., Inc.

Galletti, Barbara. A Baltimore Symphony Chorus Retrospective. 2004. (Illus.). 56p. pap. 24.00 (978-0-9748737-0-1(5)) Galletti, Barbara.

George-Warren, Holly. Honky-Tonk Heroes & Hillbilly Angels: The Pioneers of Country & Western Music. Levine, Laura, illus. 2006. 32p. (J). (gr. 3-5). 16.00 (978-0-618-19100-0(3)) Houghton Mifflin Co.

Gloria Estefan. 1999. (SmartReader Ser.). (J). Level 1. pap., tchr. ed. 19.95 incl. audio (978-0-7887-1032-2(X) , 79338T3); Level 2. pap., tchr. ed. 19.95 incl. audio (978-0-7887-1036-0(2) , 79339T3) Recorded Bks., LLC.

Gogerly, Liz. John Lennon: Voice of a Generation. 2002. (Famous Lives Ser.). (Illus.). 48p. (J). lib. bdg. 27.12 (978-0-7398-5522-5(0)) Raintree.

Gourse, Leslie. Blowing on the Changes: The Art of the Jazz Horn Players. 1998. (Illus.). 144p. (YA). (gr. 8-12). lib. bdg. 17.60 (978-0-613-29202-3(2)) Tandem Library Bks.

—Timekeepers: The Great Jazz Drummers. 2000. (Art of Jazz Ser.). (Illus.). 144p. (J). (gr. 8-12). pap. 8.95 (978-0-531-16405-1(5) , Watts, Franklin) Scholastic Library Publishing.

Granados, Christine. Sheila E. 1999. (Real-Life Reader Biography Ser.). (Illus.). 32p. (J). (gr. 3-8). lib. bdg. 15.95 (978-1-58415-019-0(X)) Mitchell Lane Pubs., Inc.

The Great Musicians. 2001. (YA). reprint ed. 1516.00 (978-0-7222-6364-8(3)) Library Reprints, Inc.

Greene, Meg. Will Smith. 2001. (Galaxy of Superstars Ser.). (Illus.). 64p. (J). 25.00 (978-0-7910-6469-6(7) , Chelsea Hse.) Facts On File, Inc.

Gregory, Peter. The Allman Brothers Band. 2008. (J). (***978-1-4222-0188-6(0)***) Mason Crest Pubs.

—Queen. 2008. (J). (***978-1-4222-0193-0(7)***) Mason Crest Pubs.

Hampton, Wilborn. Up Close: Elvis Presley. 2007. 192p. (YA). (gr. 7 up). 16.99 (978-0-670-06166-2(2) , Viking Juvenile) Penguin Group (USA) Inc.

Hayward, Linda. Day in the Life of a Musician. 2001. (gr. k-3). lib. bdg. 11.80 (978-0-613-43927-5(9)) Tandem Library Bks.

Hayward, Linda & Dorling Kindersley Publishing Staff. Jobs People Do: A Day in the Life of a Musician. 2001. (Readers Ser.). (Illus.). 32p. (J). (ps-3). 14.99 (978-0-7894-7952-5(4)) Dorling Kindersley Publishing, Inc.

Hinman, Bonnie. Faith Hill. 2001. (Galaxy of Superstars Ser.). (Illus.). 64p. (YA). (gr. 5-9). 25.00 (978-0-7910-6471-9(9) , Chelsea Hse.) Facts On File, Inc.

Hoppus, Anne. Blink-182: Tales from Beneath Your Mom. 2001. (gr. 7-12). lib. bdg. 24.55 (978-0-613-49285-0(4)) Tandem Library Bks.

Horn, Geoffrey M. Bob Dylan. 2002. (Trailblazers of the Modern World Ser.). (Illus.). 48p. (J). (gr. 5 up). pap. 14.95 (978-0-8368-5236-3(2)); lib. bdg. 30.00 (978-0-8368-5076-5(9)) Stevens, Gareth Inc. (World Almanac Library).

—Usher. 2005. (Today's Superstars). (Illus.). 32p. (J). (gr. 5 up). lib. bdg. 23.93 (978-0-8368-4235-7(9)) Stevens, Gareth Inc.

Instrument Families, 6, Pack. (Bookweb Ser.). 32p. (gr. 3 up). 34.00 (978-0-7635-3945-0(7)) Rigby Education.

Joseph, Paul. Hanson. 1999. (Young Profiles Ser.). (Illus.). 32p. (J). (gr. k-6). lib. bdg. 22.78 (978-1-57765-321-9(1) , Checkerboard Library) ABDO Publishing Co.

—'N Sync. 2000. (Young Profiles Ser.). (Illus.). 32p. (J). (gr. k-6). lib. bdg. 22.78 (978-1-57765-430-8(7) , Checkerboard Library) ABDO Publishing Co.

—Will Smith. 1999. (Young Profiles Ser.). (Illus.). 32p. (J). (gr. k-6). lib. bdg. 22.78 (978-1-57765-320-2(3) , Checkerboard Library) ABDO Publishing Co.

Josephson, Judith Pinkerton. Louis Armstrong. 2008. (History Maker Biographies Ser.). (J). lib. bdg. 26.60 (***978-0-8225-7169-8(2)*** , Lerner Pubns.) Lerner Publishing Group.

Kimmel, Eric A. A Horn for Louis. 2005. (Illus.). 96p. (J). (gr. 1-4). 11.95 (978-0-375-83252-9(1)); lib. bdg. 13.99 (978-0-375-93252-6(6)) Random Hse. Children's Bks. (Random Hse. Bks. for Young Readers).

Klein, Hermann. Musicians & Mummers: With Twelve Halftone Plates. 2001. 340p. (YA). reprint ed. 98.00 (978-0-7222-5265-9(X)) Library Reprints, Inc.

Konieczny, Vladimir. Struggling for Perfection. 2007. 97p. pap. 15.95 (***978-1-894917-48-3(0)***) Napoleon Publishing/Rendezvous Pr. CAN. *Dist:* AtlasBooks Distribution.

Konieczny, Vladimir. Struggling for Perfection: The Story of Glenn Gould. 2004. (Illus.). 97p. (J). 16.95 (978-0-929141-13-8(X)) Napoleon Publishing/Rendezvous Pr. CAN. *Dist:* AtlasBooks Distribution.

Kraemer, Katie. Aaron Carter. l.t. ed. 2002. (Real Life Reader Biographies Ser.). (Illus.). 32p. (J). (gr. 3-8). lib. bdg. 15.95 (978-1-58415-126-5(9)) Mitchell Lane Pubs., Inc.

Krall, Emil. The Future of Musicians. 2001. (YA). reprint ed. 150.00 (978-0-7222-5864-4(X)) Library Reprints, Inc.

Kramer, Barbara. Mahalia Jackson: The Voice of Gospel & Civil Rights. 2003. (African-American Biographies Ser.). (Illus.). 128p. (J). lib. bdg. 26.60 (978-0-7660-2115-0(7)) Enslow Pubs., Inc.

Krull. Lives of The..., 2 bks. 2003. 41.98 (978-1-4109-0131-6(9)) Raintree.

Krull, Kathleen. The Book of Rock Stars: 24 Musical Icons That Shine Through History. Alcorn, Stephen, illus. 2003. 48p. (ps-17). 16.99 (978-0-7868-1950-8(2)) Hyperion Bks. for Children.

—Lives of the Musicians: Good Times, Bad Times. 2002. (gr. 3-6). lib. bdg. 21.10 (978-0-613-53829-9(3)) Tandem Library Bks.

—Lives of the Musicians: Good Times, Bad Times (And What the Neighbors Thought) Hewitt, Kathryn, illus. 2002. (Lives of... Ser.). 96p. (YA). (gr. 3-7). pap. 12.00 (978-0-15-216436-2(7) , Harcourt Paperbacks) Harcourt Children's Bks.

Lahee, Henry Charles. The Organ & Its Masters. 2001. 345p. (YA). reprint ed. 98.00 (978-0-7222-5928-3(X)) Library Reprints, Inc.

Lane, Stephanie. Eminem. 2004. 112p. (J). 32.45 (978-1-59018-449-3(1) , Lucent Bks.) Thomson Gale.

Leavitt, Amie. Keith Urban. 2007. (Blue Banner Biography Ser.). (Illus.). 32p. (J). (gr. 4-8). lib. bdg. 25.70 (***978-1-58415-619-2(8)***) Mitchell Lane Pubs., Inc.

Lester, Julius. The Blues Singers: Ten Who Rocked the World. Cohen, Lisa, illus. 2001. 48p. (gr. k-17). 16.49 (978-0-7868-2405-2(0) , Jump at the Sun) Hyperion Bks. for Children.

Liebman, Dan. Quiero Ser Musico. 2003. Tr. of I Want to Be a Musician. (SPA.). (gr. k-3). lib. bdg. 14.15 (978-0-613-78631-7(9)) Tandem Library Bks.

Liebman, Daniel. I Want to Be a Musician. 2003. (I Want to Be Ser.). (Illus.). 24p. (J). (ps-2). pap. 3.99 (978-1-55297-759-0(5)); lib. bdg. 14.95 (978-1-55297-760-6(9)) Firefly Bks., Ltd.

—Quiero Ser Musico. 2003. (Quiero Ser.). (ENG & SPA., Illus.). 24p. (J). (ps-2). pap. 5.99 (978-1-55297-761-3(7)) Firefly Bks., Ltd.

Lommel, Cookie. Beck. 2002. (Galaxy of Superstars Ser.). (Illus.). 64p. (J). 25.00 (978-0-7910-6767-3(X) , Chelsea Hse.) Facts On File, Inc.

Lommel, Cookie. Russell Simmons. 2007. (Hip-Hop Stars Ser.). 104p. (J). (gr. 6-12). 30.00 (***978-0-7910-9467-9(7)*** , Chelsea Hse.) Facts On File, Inc.

Lord, Michelle. A Song for Cambodia. Arihara, Shino, illus. 2008. (J). (***978-1-60060-139-2(1)***) Lee & Low Bks., Inc.

Lord, Raymond. Usher. 2007. (Hip-Hop Ser.). (Illus.). 64p. (YA). (gr. 5 up). 22.95 (978-1-4222-0131-2(7)) Mason Crest Pubs.

Magram, Clara. John Legend. 2007. (***978-1-4222-0076-6(0)***) Mason Crest Pubs.

Marin, Reva. Oscar: The Life & Music of Oscar Peterson. 2003. (Illus.). 144p. (J). (gr. 6 up). 16.95 (978-0-88899-537-7(7)) Groundwood Bks. CAN. *Dist:* Perseus Distribution.

Markel, Rita J. Jimi Hendrix. 2006. (Just the Facts Biographies Ser.). (Illus.). 112p. (J). 27.93 (978-0-8225-3532-4(7) , Lerner Pubns.) Lerner Publishing Group.

Martin, Michael. Kurt Cobain. 2004. (Edge Books, Rock Music Library). (Illus.). 32p. (J). lib. bdg. 22.60 (978-0-7368-2700-3(5)) Capstone Pr., Inc.

Matthews, Sheelagh. Bono. 2007. (J). (***978-1-59036-637-0(9)); (978-1-59036-638-7(7))*** Weigl Pubs., Inc.

McCracken, Kristin. LeAnn Rimes. 2001. (gr. 7-12). lib. bdg. 15.25 (978-0-613-52111-6(0)) Tandem Library Bks.

McDonough, Yona Zeldis. Who Was Louis Armstrong? O'Brien, John & Harrison, Nancy, illus. 2004. (Who Was...? Ser.). 112p. (J). 13.89 (978-0-448-43560-2(8)); (gr. 3-7). pap. 4.99 (978-0-448-43368-4(0)) Penguin Group (USA) Inc. (Grosset & Dunlap).

McIntosh, Kenneth. U2. 2008. (J). (***978-1-4222-0195-4(3)***) Mason Crest Pubs.

Mitchell Lane Publishers. Blue Banner Biographies-Child Stars. 2004. (Blue Banner Biography Ser.). (Illus.). (J). (gr. 3-8). lib. bdg. 179.90 (978-1-58415-354-2(7)) Mitchell Lane Pubs., Inc.

—Masters of Music: The World's Greatest Composers, 24 vols., Set. 2003. (Illus.). (gr. 4-8). lib. bdg. 502.80 (978-1-58415-318-4(0)) Mitchell Lane Pubs., Inc.

Mitten, Christopher. Shawn Fanning: Napster & the Music Revolution. 2002. (Techies Ser.). (Illus.). 80p. (gr. 5 up). lib. bdg. 23.90 (978-0-7613-2656-4(1) , Twenty-First Century Bks.) Lerner Publishing Group.

Morreale, Marie. Hangin' with Lil' Bow Wow. 2002. (Backstage Pass Ser.). (Illus.). 48p. (J). pap. 8.95 (978-0-439-37959-5(8)) Scholastic, Inc.

Morreale, Marie T. & Johns, Michael-Anne. Hanging with the Backstreet Boys: An Unauthorized Biography. rev. ed. 1998. 99p. (J). (gr. 4-7). pap. 3.99 (978-0-439-04532-2(0)) Scholastic, Inc.

N Sync: Backstage Pass. 1999. (gr. 3-6). lib. bdg. 14.15 (978-0-613-16983-7(2)) Tandem Library Bks.

Nathan, Amy. Meet the Musicians: From Prodigy (or not) to Pro. rev. ed. 2006. (Illus.). 176p. (J). 17.95 (978-0-8050-7743-8(X)) Holt, Henry & Co.

Neimark, Anne E. Johnny Cash. 2007. (Up Close Ser.). (Illus.). 208p. (J). (gr. 8 up). 15.99 (978-0-670-06215-7(4) , Viking Juvenile) Penguin Group (USA) Inc.

Neimark, Anne E. Johnny Cash: A Twentieth-Century Life. 2007. (Up Close Ser.). (Illus.). 207p. (J). (***978-1-4287-3958-1(0)*** , Viking Adult) Penguin Group (USA) Inc.

Neunzig, Hans A. Brahms. Mitchell, Mike, tr. from GER. 2005. (Life & Times Ser.). (Illus.). 192p. pap. 15.95 (978-1-904341-17-8(9)) Haus Publishing GBR. *Dist:* International Publishers Marketing.

Novello, Clara. Reminiscences. 2001. 216p. (YA). reprint ed. 98.00 (978-0-7222-5488-2(1)) Library Reprints, Inc.

Olmstead. Tito Puente. 2005. (Hispanic-American Biographies Ser.). pap. 9.50 (978-1-4109-1597-9(2)) Harcourt Schl. Pubs.

—Tito Puente 6-Pack. (Hispanic-American Biographies Ser.). 2005. pap. 34.20 (978-1-4109-1602-0(2)); 2004. (Illus.). pap. 51.30 (978-1-4109-1195-7(0)) Harcourt Schl. Pubs.

Olmstead, Mary. Tito Puente. 2004. (Hispanic-American Biographies Ser.). (Illus.). 64p. (J). pap. 9.50 (978-1-4109-0919-0(0)) Harcourt Schl. Pubs.

—Tito Puente. 2004. (Hispanic-American Biographies Ser.). (Illus.). 64p. (J). (gr. 4-6). 32.86 (978-1-4109-0713-4(9)) Raintree.

O'Mahony, John. Elton John. 2003. (World Musicmakers Ser.). (Illus.). 64p. (J). 26.20 (978-1-56711-972-5(7) , Blackbirch Pr., Inc.) Thomson Gale.

Parker, Robert Andrew. Piano Starts Here: The Young Art Tatum. 2008. (J). (***978-0-375-83965-8(8)*** , Schwartz & Wade Bks.) Random Hse. Children's Bks.

Parks, Peggy J. Musician. 2003. (Illus.). 48p. (J). 26.20 (978-0-7377-2067-9(0) , Greenhaven Pr., Inc.) Thomson Gale.

Patton, Julie. Maximizing Your Studio's Potential: the Student Log Book: Skill Assessment & Progress Management Tools for the College-Level Musician. 2004. 200p. (C). stu. ed., spiral bd. 24.95 (978-0-9762902-0-9(0)) Purple Lizard Pr. LLC.

Pearl, A. 'N Sync: Now & Forever. 2nd ed. 2000. (Backstage Pass Ser.). (Illus.). 48p. (J). (gr. 2-9). pap. 5.99 (978-0-439-22220-4(6)) Scholastic, Inc.

Pickels, Dwayne E. Shania Twain. 2001. (Overcoming Adversity Ser.). (Illus.). 112p. (J). 30.00 (978-0-7910-5901-2(4) , Chelsea Hse.) Facts On File, Inc.

Powell, Phelan. Garth Brooks: Award-Winning Country Music Star. 1999. (Real-Life Reader Biography Ser.). (Illus.). 32p. (J). (gr. 3-7). lib. bdg. 15.95 (978-1-58415-004-6(1)) Mitchell Lane Pubs., Inc.

Preszler, June. John Lennon. 2004. (Edge Books, Rock Music Library). (Illus.). 32p. (J). lib. bdg. 22.60 (978-0-7368-2701-0(3)) Capstone Pr., Inc.

Rappaport, Doreen. John's Secret Dreams: The Life of John Lennon. Collier, Bryan, illus. 2004. 48p. (ps-17). 16.99 (978-0-7868-0817-5(9)) Hyperion Bks. for Children.

Raschka, Chris. Charlie Parker Played Be Bop. Raschka, Chris, illus. 2000. (Live Oak Readalong Ser.). (Illus.). (J). pap. 18.95 incl. audio compact disk (978-1-59112-419-1(0)) Live Oak Media.

—Charlie Parker Played Be-Bop. Raschka, Chris, illus. 2000. (Illus.). 28.95 incl. audio compact disk (978-1-59112-425-2(5)); pap. 35.95 incl. audio compact disk (978-1-59112-602-7(9)) Live Oak Media.

—Mysterious Thelonious. Raschka, Chris, illus. (Illus.). pap. 18.95 incl. audio compact disk (978-1-59112-421-4(2)); 2000. 28.95 incl. audio compact disk (978-1-59112-422-1(0)) Live Oak Media.

M
N
O

Raso, Anne, ed. Backstreet Boys. 2000. (Celebrity Ser.: No. 20). (J). pap. 4.99 (978-0-88013-011-0(3)) Profile Entertainment, Inc.

Raum, Elizabeth. Louis Armstrong: Jazz Legend. 2006. (Fact Finders Ser.). (Illus.). 32p. (J). 22.60 (978-0-7368-6419-0(9)) Capstone Pr., Inc.

Ristori, Adelaide. Adelaide Ristori: Studies & Memoirs. 2001. 297p. (YA). reprint ed. 98.00 (978-0-7222-6291-7(4)) Library Reprints, Inc.

Rock & Roll Hall of Famers: Set 2, 6 bks. Incl. Aretha Franklin. Rivera, Ursula. lib. bdg. 29.25 (978-0-8239-3639-7(2)); Beach Boys. Holcomb, Mark. lib. bdg. 29.25 (978-0-8239-3643-4(0)); Billie Holiday. Alagna, Magdalena. lib. bdg. 29.25 (978-0-8239-3640-3(6)); Elton John. White, Katherine. lib. bdg. 29.25 (978-0-8239-3641-0(4)); Ray Charles. Beyer, Mark. lib. bdg. 29.25 (978-0-8239-3642-7(2)); Rolling Stones. Forget, Thomas. lib. bdg. 29.25 (978-0-8239-3644-1(9)); (YA). (gr. 5-8). (Illus.). 112p. 2006. Set lib. bdg. 175.50 (978-0-8239-3888-9(3)) Rosen Publishing Group, Inc., The.

The Rolling Stones. 2002. (Unseen Archives Ser.). 384p. (YA). 29.95 (978-0-7525-8971-8(7)) Parragon, Inc.

Rosenthal, Michele. Rock Rules! The Ultimate Rock Bandbook. 2000. (Illus.). 96p. (J). (gr. 3-7). pap. 5.99 (978-0-439-24380-3(7)) Scholastic, Inc.

Saint-Saens, Camille. Musical Memories. 2001. 282p. (YA). reprint ed. 98.00 (978-0-7222-5503-2(9)) Library Reprints, Inc.

Saucerman, Linda. Ozzy & Kelly Osbourne. 2004. (Famous Families Ser.). (Illus.). 48p. (J). lib. bdg. 25.25 (978-1-4042-0262-7(5)) Rosen Publishing Group, Inc., The.

Schlesinger, Ethan. Billy Joel. 2008. (J). (***978-1-4222-0185-5(6)***) Mason Crest Pubs.

—The Rolling Stones. 2008. (J). (***978-1-4222-0194-7(5)***) Mason Crest Pubs.

Schlessinger Media Staff, prod. My Family from Japan. 2003. (Families Around the World Ser.). (J). pap., tchr. ed. 19.95 incl. VHS (978-1-57225-644-6(3)) Schlessinger Media.

Schuman, Michael A. Bob Dylan: The Life & Times of an American Icon. 2003. (People to Know Ser.). (Illus.). 112p. (J). lib. bdg. 26.60 (978-0-7660-2108-2(4)) Enslow Pubs., Inc.

Schwimmer, Franciska. Great Musicians as Children. Murphy, M. Lois, illus. 2004. reprint ed. pap. 26.95 (978-1-4179-1579-8(X)) Kessinger Publishing, LLC.

Selfridge, John. John Coltrane: A Sound Supreme. 1999. (gr. 7-12). lib. bdg. 17.60 (978-0-613-29453-9(X)) Tandem Library Bks.

Seminara-Kennedy, Concetta. The Dixie Chicks. 2002. (Galaxy of Superstars Ser.). (Illus.). 64p. (J). 25.00 (978-0-7910-6768-0(8) , Chelsea Hse.) Facts On File, Inc.

Shady Bizzness: Life As Marshall Mathers' Body Guard in An Industry of Paper Gangsters. 2nd collector's ed. 2000. 176p. (YA). mass mkt. (978-0-9703881-0-0(1)) Big Willz Records.

Shipton, Alyn. Jazz Makers: Vanguards of Sound. 2002. (Oxford Profiles Ser.). (Illus.). 272p. (YA). (gr. 9 up). 50.00 (978-0-19-512689-1(0)) Oxford Univ. Pr., Inc.

Sierra I Fabra, Jordi. John Lennon - Imagina que esto fue Real. 2005. 168p. pap. (978-958-30-1702-5(7)) Panamericana Editorial.

Simons, Rae. Bruce Springsteen. 2008. (J). (***978-1-4222-0187-9(2)***) Mason Crest Pubs.

—The Doors. 2008. (J). (***978-1-4222-0190-9(2)***) Mason Crest Pubs.

Slavicek, Louise. Carlos Santana. 2006. (Great Hispanic Heritage Ser.). (Illus.). 120p. (J). 30.00 (978-0-7910-8844-9(8) , Chelsea Hse.) Facts On File, Inc.

Slick, Grace. Somebody to Love? a Rock-and-Roll Memoir. 1999. (gr. 7-12). lib. bdg. 16.45 (978-0-613-22403-1(5)) Tandem Library Bks.

Sloate, Susan. Ray Charles: Find Another Way! 2007. (Defining Moments Ser.). (Illus.). 32p. (J). lib. bdg. 25.27 (978-1-59716-267-8(1)) Bearport Publishing Co., Inc.

Smith Weber, Terri. Dixie Chicks. 2004. (J). pap. (978-0-9740180-9-6(0) , Bios for Kids) Panda Publishing, L.L.C.

Spears, Britney & Culotta, Felicia. Britney Spears' Crossroads Diary. movie tie-in ed. 2002. (Illus.). 48p. (J). (gr. 4-7). pap. 5.99 (978-0-439-39745-2(6)) Scholastic, Inc.

Stauffer, Stacey. Garth Brooks. 1999. (Galaxy of Superstars Ser.). (Illus.). 64p. (YA). (gr. 3). 31.00 (978-0-7910-5232-7(X)); pap. 25.00 (978-0-7910-5332-4(6)) Facts On File, Inc. (Chelsea Hse.).

—Garth Brooks. 2000. (gr. 5-8). lib. bdg. 17.60 (978-0-613-21579-4(6)) Tandem Library Bks.

Steinert, Morris. Reminiscences of Morris Steinert. 2001. 267p. (YA). reprint ed. 98.00 (978-0-7222-5876-7(3)) Library Reprints, Inc.

Strudwick, Leslie. Musicians. 1998. (Women in Profile Ser.). (Illus.). 48p. (J). (gr. 4). pap. (978-0-7787-0031-9(3)); lib. bdg. (978-0-7787-0009-8(7)) Crabtree Publishing Co.

Strutt, William M. The Reminiscences of a Musical Amateur. 2001. 172p. (YA). reprint ed. 88.00 (978-0-7222-5292-5(7)) Library Reprints, Inc.

Subset 2: Masters of Music. (Illus.). 9p. (gr. 4-8). lib. bdg. (978-1-58415-352-8(0)) Mitchell Lane Pubs., Inc.

Summerer, Eric Michael. Wolfgang Amadeus Mozart. 2006. (Primary Source Library of Famous Composers). (Illus.). 32p. (J). 21.95 (978-1-4042-2772-9(5) , PowerKids Pr.) Rosen Publishing Group, Inc., The.

Terrill, Richard. Duke Ellington. 2003. (African-American Biographies Ser.). (Illus.). 64p. (J). lib. bdg. 28.56 (978-0-7398-6869-0(1)) Raintree.

Tierney, Tom. Rock & Roll Legends of the 1950s Paper Dolls. 2007. 32p. (J). pap. 6.95 (***978-0-486-45660-7(9)***) Dover Pubns., Inc.

Trachtenberg, Martha P. Bono: Rock Star Activist. 2008. (People to Know Today Ser.). (Illus.). 112p. (J). (gr. 6 up). lib. bdg. 31.93 (***978-0-7660-2695-7(7)***) Enslow Pubs., Inc.

Tracy, Kathleen. Gwen Stefani. 2006. (Blue Banner Biography Ser.). (Illus.). 32p. (J). (gr. 4-8). lib. bdg. (978-1-58415-514-0(0)) Mitchell Lane Pubs., Inc.

—Mario: Hip-Hop Superstar. 2005. (Blue Banner Biography Ser.). (Illus.). 32p. (J). (gr. 3-8). lib. bdg. (978-1-58415-391-7(1)) Mitchell Lane Pubs., Inc.

Ungs, Tim. Paul McCartney & Stella McCartney. 2004. (Famous Families Ser.). (Illus.). 48p. (J). lib. bdg. 25.25 (978-1-4042-0263-4(3)) Rosen Publishing Group, Inc., The.

Walsh, Kimberly. Hangin' with Lil' Romeo. 2002. (Backstage Pass Ser.). (Illus.). 48p. (J). (gr. 2-6). pap. 5.99 (978-0-439-37958-8(X)) Scholastic, Inc.

Walsh, Kimberly. LFO: Backstage Pass. 1999. (J). (gr. 3-6). lib. bdg. 14.15 (978-0-613-21891-7(4)) Tandem Library Bks.

Waters, Rosa. Bob Marley & the Wailers. 2008. (J). (***978-1-4222-0192-3(9)***) Mason Crest Pubs.

Weatherly, Myra. Yo-Yo Ma: Internationally Acclaimed Cellist. 2006. (Illus.). 112p. (J). (***978-0-7565-1879-0(2)***) Compass Point Bks.

Westburg, John E. Cathedral Organists Past & Present: A Record of the Succession of Organists of the Cathedrals, Chapels Royal, & Principal Collegiate Churches of the United Kingdom. 2001. 176p. (YA). reprint ed. 88.00 (978-0-7222-5929-0(8)) Library Reprints, Inc.

Wheeler, Jill C. Faith Hill. 2003. (Star Tracks Ser.). (Illus.). 64p. (J). (gr. 3-8). lib. bdg. 25.65 (978-1-57765-771-2(3)) ABDO Publishing Co.

Wheeler, Opal & Deucher, Sybil. Sebastian Bach the Boy from Thuringia. l.t. ed. 2005. (Illus.). 128p. (J). per. 10.95 (978-0-9746505-1-7(X) , 4354) Zeezok Publishing.

Whiting, Jim. The Life & Times of Gilbert & Sullivan. 2004. (Masters of Music Ser.). (Illus.). 48p. (J). (gr. 4-8). lib. bdg. 20.95 (978-1-58415-276-7(1)) Mitchell Lane Pubs., Inc.

Wilds, Mary. Raggin' the Blues: Legendary Country, Blues & Ragtime Musicians. 2001. (Avisson Young Adult Ser.). (Illus.). 112p. (J). (gr. 7-12). pap. 19.95 (978-1-888105-47-6(X)) Avisson Pr., Inc.

Willett, Edward. Jimi Hendrix: Kiss the Sky. 2006. (American Rebels Ser.). (Illus.). 160p. (J). lib. bdg. 34.60 (978-0-7660-2449-6(0)) Enslow Pubs., Inc.

Winter, Jonah. Dizzy. Qualls, Sean, illus. 2006. (J). 48p. (gr. 3-8). pap. 16.99 (978-0-439-50737-0(5)); 16.99 (978-0-439-50736-3(7)) Scholastic, Inc. (Levine, Arthur A. Bks.).

Wood, Ramona. The Goat Woman of Smackover: An Arkansas Legend. Wood, Ramona, . 2006. (Illus.). 32p. (J). 11.00 (978-0-9758622-1-6(9)) ABC Pr.

Worth, Richard. Yo-Yo Ma. 2007. (Asian Americans of Achievement Ser.). (Illus.). 120p. (YA). (gr. 6-10). lib. bdg. 30.00 (978-0-7910-9270-5(4) , Chelsea Hse.) Facts On File, Inc.

Wren, Laura Lee. Garth Brooks: Country Music Superstar. 2002. (People to Know Ser.). (Illus.). 112p. (YA). (gr. 6-12). lib. bdg. 26.60 (978-0-7660-1672-9(2)) Enslow Pubs., Inc.

Wyborny, Sheila. Sting. 2004. (World Musicmakers Ser.). (Illus.). 64p. (J). 26.20 (978-1-56711-974-9(3) , Blackbirch Pr., Inc.) Thomson Gale.

Wyckoff, Edwin Brit. Electric Guitar Man: The Genius of les Paul. 2008. (Genius at Work! Great Inventor Biographies Ser.). (Illus.). 32p. (J). (gr. 3-4). lib. bdg. 22.60 (***978-0-7660-2847-0(X)*** , Enslow Elementary) Enslow Pubs., Inc.

Wyndham, Henry S. Who's Who in Music: A Biographical Record of Contemporary Musicians. 2001. 282p. (YA). reprint ed. 98.00 (978-0-7222-5218-5(8)) Library Reprints, Inc.

Young, Filson. Mastersingers: Appreciations of Music & Musicians. 2001. 201p. (YA). reprint ed. 98.00 (978-0-7222-5295-6(1)) Library Reprints, Inc.

Ziegler, Robert. Great Musicians. 2008. (DK Eyewitness Bks.). 72p. (J). (gr. 3-8). 15.99 (***978-0-7566-3774-3(0));*** lib. bdg. 19.99 (***978-0-7566-3773-6(2)***) Dorling Kindersley Publishing, Inc.

Zimmerman, Robert K. Switchfoot. 2006. (Contemporary Musicians & Their Music Ser.). (Illus.). 48p. (J). (978-1-4042-0709-7(0)) Rosen Publishing Group, Inc., The.

Zymet, Cathy Alder. Leann Rimes. 2000. (Illus.). 64p. (J). (ps-7). lib. bdg. 17.60 (978-0-613-17693-4(6)) Tandem Library Bks.

MUSICIANS, AFRICAN AMERICAN

see African American Musicians

MUSICIANS, AMERICAN

Abrams, Dennis. Eminem. (Hip-Hop Stars Ser.). 104p. (J). pap. 12.95 (***978-0-7910-9728-1(5)*** , Chelsea Hse.) Facts On File, Inc.

Adam, Michelle. Kenny Chesney. 2006. (Blue Banner Biography Ser.). (Illus.). 32p. (J). (gr. 4-8). lib. bdg. 25.70 (978-1-58415-502-7(7) , 1259607) Mitchell Lane Pubs., Inc.

Ayers, Samuel J. Buddy Holly: A Legacy of Music. l.t. ed. 1999. (Illus.). 32p. (J). (gr. 3-8). pap. 8.00 (978-0-9667681-1-4(6)) Hermosa Creations.

Bankston, John. The Life & Times of Scott Joplin. 2004. (Masters of Music Ser.). (Illus.). 48p. (gr. 4-8). lib. bdg. 20.95 (978-1-58415-270-5(2)) Mitchell Lane Pubs., Inc.

Breguet, Amy. Yellowcard. 2006. (Contemporary Musicians & Their Music Ser.). (Illus.). 48p. (J). (978-1-4042-0714-1(7)) Rosen Publishing Group, Inc., The.

Brown, Jim. Willie Nelson: Red Headed Stranger. 2001. (Illus.). 219p. (J). pap. 16.95 (978-1-55082-255-7(1)) Quarry Pr.

Dell, Pamela. Miles Davis: Jazz Master. 2005. (Journey to Freedom). (Illus.). 40p. (J). (gr. 3-7). 28.50 (978-1-59296-232-7(7)) Child's World, Inc.

Gabriel, Jan. Hanson Forever: Your Tay, Zac & Ike Keepsake Scrapbook. 1998. (Illus.). 48p. (gr. 2-9). pap. 5.99 (978-0-439-04530-8(4)) Scholastic, Inc.

Gelfand, Dale Evva. Sean Combs. 2008. (Hip-Hop Stars Ser.). 128p. (J). pap. 11.95 (***978-0-7910-9731-1(5)*** , Chelsea Hse.) Facts On File, Inc.

Glass, Eartha. 98 Degrees. 2001. (Pop People Ser.). (Illus.). 100p. (J). pap. (978-0-439-28662-6(X)) Scholastic, Inc.

Greenberg, Keith E. Madonna. 1999. (Illus.). 40p. (YA). (gr. 7-12). reprint ed. 15.00 (978-0-7881-6439-2(2)) DIANE Publishing Co.

Johns, Michael-Anne. Hanson: 101 Cool Questions. 2000. (Pop People Ser.). (Illus.). 76p. (J). (gr. 4-7). pap. 4.99 (978-0-439-23325-5(9)) Scholastic, Inc.

Kavanaugh, Lee Hill. Quincy Jones: Musician, Composer, Producer. 1998. (African-American Biographies Ser.). (Illus.). 128p. (YA). (gr. 6-12). lib. bdg. 20.95 (978-0-89490-814-9(6)) Enslow Pubs., Inc.

Markel, Rita J. Jimi Hendrix. 2003. (Biography Ser.). (Illus.). 112p. (YA). (gr. 6 up). pap. 7.95 (978-0-8225-9697-4(0) , Carolrhoda Bks.) Lerner Publishing Group.

Mathis, Sharon Bell. Ray Charles. Ford, George, illus. 2001. 32p. (J). (ps-5). 6.95 (978-1-58430-018-2(3)); 16.00 (978-1-58430-017-5(5)) Lee & Low Bks., Inc.

Matthews, Jill. Mmmbop to the Top. 1998. mass mkt. (978-0-671-02490-1(6) , Simon Pulse) Simon & Schuster Children's Publishing.

McIntosh, Kenneth. The Grateful Dead. 2008. (J). (***978-1-4222-0191-6(0)***) Mason Crest Pubs.

Neimark, Anne E. Up Close: Johnny Cash: Johnny Cash. 2008. (Up Close Ser.). 208p. (J). (gr. 6). pap. 6.99 (***978-0-14-241047-9(0)*** , Puffin) Penguin Group (USA) Inc.

Netter, Matt. Hanson Boxed Set. 1998. 320p. (J). (gr. 4-7). 11.97 (978-0-671-71384-3(1) , Simon Pulse) Simon & Schuster Children's Publishing.

Powell, Phelan. Hanson. 1999. (Galaxy of Superstars Ser.). (Illus.). 64p. (J). (gr. 3 up). pap. 25.00 (978-0-7910-5325-6(3) , Chelsea Hse.) Facts On File, Inc.

Tracy, Kathleen. Chris Daughtry. 2007. (Blue Banner Biography Ser.). (Illus.). 32p. (J). (gr. 4-8). lib. bdg. 25.70 (***978-1-58415-629-1(5)***) Mitchell Lane Pubs., Inc.

Venezia, Mike. John Philip Sousa. Venezia, Mike, illus. 1998. (Getting to Know the World's Greatest Composers Ser.). (Illus.). 32p. (J). (gr. 3-4). 27.00 (978-0-516-20761-2(X) , Children's Pr.) Scholastic Library Publishing.

Walker, Ida. Lynyrd Skynyrd. 2008. (J). (***978-1-4222-0213-5(5)***) Mason Crest Pubs.

Winter, Jonah. Once upon a Time in Chicago. Winter, Jeanette, illus. 2000. 32p. (ps-3). 15.49 (978-0-7868-2404-5(2)) Hyperion Bks. for Children.

—Once upon a Time in Chicago: The Story of Benny Goodman. 2000. 32p. (J). 14.99 (978-0-7868-0733-8(4)) Disney Pr.

—Once upon a Time in Chicago: The Story of Benny Goodman. 2000. (J). mass mkt. 16.00 (978-0-689-80342-0(7) , Simon & Schuster Children's Publishing) Simon & Schuster Children's Publishing.

MUSICIANS, BLACK

see African American Musicians

MUSICIANS—DICTIONARIES

Isaacson, Charles D. Face to Face with Great Musicians. 2001. 364p. (YA). reprint ed. 98.00 (978-0-7222-5262-8(5)) Library Reprints, Inc.

Rolland, Romain. Musicians of Today. 2001. 324p. (YA). reprint ed. 98.00 (978-0-7222-5280-2(3)) Library Reprints, Inc.

MUSICIANS—FICTION

Alexander, Lloyd. The Marvelous Misadventures of Sebastian. 2000. (gr. 3-6). lib. bdg. 14.15 (978-0-8335-8963-7(6)) Tandem Library Bks.

Alger, Horatio. Phil the Fiddler. rev. ed. 2006. (ENG.). 224p. 27.95 (978-1-4218-2091-0(9) , 1st World Library - Literary Society) 1st World Publishing, Inc.

—Phil the Fiddler. 2006. pap. (***978-1-4068-0667-0(6)***) Echo Library.

—The Young Musician. reprint ed. pap. 79.00 (978-1-4047-3629-0(8)) Classic Textbooks.

—The Young Musician. 2006. pap. (***978-1-4068-0673-1(0)***) Echo Library.

Appelt, Kathi. Piggies in a Polka. Pham, LeUyen, illus. 2003. 40p. (J). 16.00 (978-0-15-216483-6(9)) Harcourt Children's Bks.

Arrhenius, Peter. The Penguin Quartet. Peterson, Ingela, illus. 1998. (Picture Bks.). 28p. (J). (ps-3). 15.95 (978-1-57505-252-6(0) , Carolrhoda Bks.) Lerner Publishing Group.

Arterburn, Stephen & Hunt, Angela Elwell. Shane. 2004. (Young Believer on Tour Ser.). (J). pap. 3.99 (978-0-8423-8339-4(5)) Tyndale Hse. Pubs.

—Taz. 2004. (Young Believer on Tour Ser.). (J). pap. 3.99 (978-0-8423-8340-0(9)) Tyndale Hse. Pubs.

Base, Graeme. The Worst Band in the Universe: A Totally Cosmic Music Adventure. 1999. (Illus.). 46p. (YA). reprint ed. 20.00 (978-0-7567-6078-6(X)) DIANE Publishing Co.

Bateman, Teresa. Red, White, Blue & Uncle Who? The Story Behind Some of America's Patriotic Symbols. O'Brien, John, illus. 2001. 64p. (J). (gr. 4-6). tchr. ed. 16.95 (978-0-8234-1285-3(7)) Holiday Hse., Inc.

Battle-Lavert, Gwendolyn. The Music in Derrick's Heart. Bootman, Colin, illus. 2000. 32p. (J). (gr. k-3). tchr. ed. 16.95 (978-0-8234-1353-9(5)) Holiday Hse., Inc.

Blair, Eric. Los Musicos de Bremen: Version del Cuento de los Hermanos Grimm. Dickson, Bill, illus. 2006. (Read-It! Readers en Espanol Ser.).Tr. of Bremen Town Musicians: A Retelling of the Grimm's Fairy Tale. (SPA.). 32p. (J). (ps-3). 19.95 (978-1-4048-1628-2(3)) Picture Window Bks.

Blume, Lesley M. M. The Rising Star of Rusty Nail. 2007. 288p. (J). (gr. 3-7). 15.99 (978-0-375-83524-7(5) , Knopf Bks. for Young Readers) Random Hse. Children's Bks.

—The Rising Star of the Rusty Nail. 2007. 288p. (J). (gr. 3-7). lib. bdg. 18.99 (978-0-375-93524-4(X) , Knopf Bks. for Young Readers) Random Hse. Children's Bks.

Brooks, Walter R. Freddy the Pied Piper. Wiese, Kurt, illus. 2002. 253p. (J). (gr. 3). 23.95 (978-1-58567-226-4(2)) Overlook Pr., The.

Caletti, Deb. Wild Roses. (YA). (gr. 7 up). 2006. 320p. pap. 6.99 (978-0-689-86475-9(2) , Simon Pulse); 2005. 304p. 15.95 (978-0-689-86766-8(2)) Simon & Schuster Children's Publishing.

Calmenson, Stephanie. Jazzmatazz! Degen, Bruce, illus. 2008. 32p. (J). 16.99 (***978-0-06-077289-5(1));*** lib. bdg. 17.89 (***978-0-06-077290-1(5)***) HarperCollins Pubs.

Castellucci, Cecil. Beige. 2007. (Illus.). 304p. (YA). (gr. 9 up). 16.99 (***978-0-7636-3066-9(7)***) Candlewick Pr.

Child's Play, ed. Music Man Big Bk with Holes. 2006. (Illus.). 16p. 19.99 (978-1-84643-010-7(0)) Child's Play-International.

Chocolate, Debbi. The Piano Man. 2000. (978-0-606-17886-0(4)) Tandem Library Bks.

Chotjewitz, David & Orgel, Doris. Crazy Diamond. 2008. 272p. (YA). 17.99 (***978-1-4169-1176-0(6)***) Simon & Schuster Children's Publishing.

Cole, Babette. That's Why. 2007. (Illus.). 32p. (J). 17.95 (***978-0-224-07028-7(2)***) Transworld Publishers Ltd. GBR. *Dist:* Independent Pubs. Group.

Conover, Chris. Over the Hills & Far Away. 2004. (Illus.). 40p. (J). 16.00 (978-0-374-38043-4(0) , Farrar, Straus & Giroux (BYR)) Farrar, Straus & Giroux.

Constable, Kate. The Singer of All Songs. 2005. (Chanters of Tremaris Trilogy Ser.). 320p. (J). reprint ed. pap. 4.99 (978-0-439-55479-4(9) , Levine, Arthur A. Bks.) Scholastic, Inc.

—Singer of All Songs Bk. 1: In the Chanters of Tremaris Trilogy. 2004. (Chanters of Tremaris Trilogy Ser.). 304p. (J). pap. 16.95 (978-0-439-55478-7(0) , Levine, Arthur A. Bks.) Scholastic, Inc.

Cooner, Donna D. Barney Makes Music. Davis, Guy, ed. 1999. (Barney Ser.). (Illus.). 24p. (J). (ps-k). 4.95 (978-1-57064-461-0(6)) Scholastic, Inc.

Corbet, Robert. Fifteen Love. 2005. 192p. (YA). pap. 6.95 (978-0-8027-7714-0(7)) Walker & Co.

Cosgrove, Stephen. Cricket Clickett: Finding Your Talents. Arroyo, Fian, illus. 2004. (J). (978-1-58804-382-5(7)) PCI Educational Publishing.

Cowling, Douglas. Hallelujah Handel. Walker, Jason, illus. 2003. 48p. (J). pap. 16.95 (978-0-439-05850-6(3)) Scholastic, Inc.

Crow, Kristyn. Cool Daddy Rat. Lester, Mike, illus. 2008. 32p. (J). (ps). 16.99 (***978-0-399-24375-2(5)*** , Putnam Juvenile) Penguin Group (USA) Inc.

Cutler, Jane. The Cello of Mr. O. Couch, Greg, illus. 1999. 32p. (J). (gr. k-4). 15.99 (978-0-525-46119-7(1) , Dutton Juvenile) Penguin Group (USA) Inc.

Darden, Floyd. Drumdee makes a Drum. 2007. 15.95 (***978-1-59526-711-5(5)***) Media Creations, Inc.

Davol, Marguerite W. The Loudest, Fastest, Best Drummer in Kansas. Smith, Cat Bowman, illus. 2000. 32p. (J). (gr. k-4). 16.99 (978-0-531-33191-0(1)); pap. 15.95 (978-0-531-30191-3(5)) Scholastic, Inc. (Orchard Bks.).

Delaney, Mark. Growler's Horn. 2000. (Misfits, Inc. Ser.: No. 3). 192p. (J). (gr. 6-10). pap. 5.95 (978-1-56145-206-4(8)) Peachtree Pubs., Ltd.

—Growler's Horn. 2000. (gr. 7-12). lib. bdg. 14.10 (978-0-613-82661 8(7)); (Illus.). (J). 12.60 (978-0-606-18339-0(6)) Tandem Library Bks.

Dennis, Jeanne Gowen & Seifert, Sheila. Attack! Hohn, David, tr. Hohn, David, illus. 2003. (Strive to Thrive Ser.). 96p. (J). pap., pap. 5.99 (978-0-7814-3894-0(2) , 0781438942) Cook, David C. Publishing Co.

Dickson, Bill, illus. The Bremen Town Musicians: A Retelling of the Grimms' Fairy Tale. 2004. (Read-It! Readers Ser.). 32p. (C). (gr. k-3). 18.60 (978-1-4048-0310-7(6)) Picture Window Bks.

Disney. Boys & Beauty Blunders. 2007. (Hannah Montana Cine-manga Ser.: Vol. 3). 96p. pap. 7.99 (***978-1-4278-0785-4(X)*** , Tokyopop Kids) TOKYOPOP, Inc.

—Cars & Superstars. 2007. (Hannah Montana Cine-manga Ser.: Vol. 4). 96p. pap. 7.99 (***978-1-4278-0786-1(8)*** , Tokyopop Kids) TOKYOPOP, Inc.

Disney Staff. Crushes & Camping. 2007. (Hannah Montana Cine-manga Ser.: Vol. 2). 96p. pap. 7.99 (***978-1-4278-0282-8(3)*** , Tokyopop Kids) TOKYOPOP, Inc.

—Secrets & Super Sneaks, Vol. 1. 2007. (Hannah Montana Cine-manga Ser.: Vol. 1). pap. 7.99 (***978-1-4278-0281-1(5)*** , Tokyopop Kids) TOKYOPOP, Inc.

Durkee, Sarah. The Fruit Bowl Project. 2006. 160p. (J). (gr. 5-8). 14.95 (978-0-385-73289-5(9)); lib. bdg. 16.99 (978-0-385-90310-3(3)) Random Hse. Children's Bks. (Delacorte Bks. for Young Readers).

Durkee, Sarah. The Fruit Bowl Project: Fifty Ways to Tell a Story. 2007. 160p. (J). (gr. 5). 5.99 (***978-0-385-73385-4(2)*** , Yearling) Random Hse. Children's Bks.

Edwards, Julie Andrews. Simeon's Gift. 2003. (J). 169.90 (978-0-06-056905-1(0)); 169.90 (978-0-06-056906-8(9)) HarperCollins Pubs. (Julie Andrews Collection).

—Simeon's Gift. Spirin, Gennady, illus. 2006. 40p. (J). reprint ed. pap. 6.99 (978-0-06-008916-0(4) , Julie Andrews Collection) HarperCollins Pubs.

Edwards, Julie Andrews & Hamilton, Emma Walton. Simeon's Gift. Spirin, Gennady, illus. 2006. 30p. (J). (gr. 4-8). reprint ed. 17.00 (***978-1-4223-5855-9(0)***) DIANE Publishing Co.

—Simeon's Gift. Spirin, Gennady, illus. 2003. 40p. (J). 17.89 (978-0-06-008915-3(6)); 16.99 (978-0-06-008914-6(8)) HarperCollins Pubs. (Julie Andrews Collection).

Edwards, Pamela Duncan. The Leprechaun's Gold. Cole, Henry, illus. 2000. 40p. (J). reprint ed. pap. 6.99 (978-0-06-443878-0(3)) HarperCollins Pubs.

Ehrhardt, Karen. This Jazz Man. Roth, Robert, illus. 2006. 32p. (J). (ps-2). 16.00 (978-0-15-205307-9(7)) Harcourt Trade Pubs.

Eisenberg, Lisa. The Case of the Rock & Roll Mystery. 1998. (New Adventures of Mary-Kate & Ashley Ser.). 87p. (J). (gr. 2-7). pap. 3.99 (978-0-590-29402-7(4)) Scholastic, Inc.

Falconer, Ian. Olivia Forms a Band. Falconer, Ian, illus. 2006. (Olivia Ser.). (Illus.). 50p. (J). (ps-2). 17.95 (978-1-4169-2454-8(X) , Atheneum) Simon & Schuster Children's Publishing.

Fenner, Carol. Yolonda's Genius. Colon, Raul, illus. 2002. (J). 14.47 (978-0-7587-0333-0(3)) Book Wholesalers, Inc.

Fleming, Candace. Gabriella's Song. 2001. (gr. k-3). lib. bdg. 14.15 (978-0-613-34721-1(8)); (Illus.). (J). 12.79 (978-0-606-21206-9(X)) Tandem Library Bks.

Foreman, Michael. Rock-a-Doodle-Do! 2001. (Illus.). 32p. (J). (gr. k-3). 16.99 (978-0-86264-951-7(X)) Andersen GBR. *Dist:* Independent Pubs. Group.

Foster, Kinsley. Wild Abandon Vol. 4: Old Lang Sine. 2000. (YA). pap. 10.95 (978-0-9667634-5-4(9)) What's Inside Pr.

Fox, Paula. The Slave Dancer. Eros, Keith, illus. 2002. (J). 14.47 (978-0-7587-0214-2(0)) Book Wholesalers, Inc.

—The Slave Dancer. 1998. (Assessment Packs Ser.). 15p. pap., tchr.'s training gde. ed. 15.95 (978-1-58303-061-5(1)) Pathways Publishing.

—The Slave Dancer. unabr. ed. 2004. 152p. (J). (gr. 5-9). pap. 38.00 incl. audio (978-0-8072-0458-0(7) , Listening Library) Random Hse. Audio Publishing Group.

—The Slave Dancer. Keith, Eros, illus. 2001. 192p. (YA). 18.99 (978-0-689-84505-5(7) , Atheneum/Richard Jackson Bks.) Simon & Schuster Children's Publishing.

Francis, Panama, et al. David Gets His Drum. Velasquez, Eric, illus. 2002. 32p. (J). (gr. k-3). 16.95 (978-0-7614-5088-7(2)) Cavendish, Marshall Corp.

Frank, Lucy. Lucky Stars. (J). 2006. 240p. pap. 5.99 (978-0-689-85934-2(1) , Aladdin); 2005. (Illus.). 304p. 16.95 (978-0-689-85933-5(3) , Atheneum) Simon & Schuster Children's Publishing.

Garfinkle, Debra. The Band: Finding Love. 2007. 256p. (gr. 12 up). 9.99 (***978-0-425-21736-8(1)*** , Berkley Trade) Penguin Group (USA) Inc.

Garris, Bekah J. Maybe Later: One girl's struggle with time & her lack of control over It. 2004. 170p. pap. 19.95 (978-1-4137-3821-6(4)) PublishAmerica, Inc.

Gershenson, Harold P. Freddy Flamingo & the Kindertown Five. Mills, Christopher, illus. 2005. 27p. (J). (978-1-58987-070-3(0)) Kindermusik International.

Gibbons, Faye. Emma Jo's Song. Meidell, Sherry, illus. 2003. 32p. (J). (gr. k-2). 15.95 (978-1-56397-935-4(7)) Boyds Mills Pr.

Gillmor, Don. The Fabulous Song. Gay, Marie-Louise, illus. 2003. 32p. (J). pap. 7.95 (978-1-929132-48-5(4)) Kane/Miller Bk. Pubs., Inc.

—The Fabulous Song. Gay, Marie-Louise, illus. 2006. 36p. 16.95 (978-2-923163-17-8(6)) La Montagne Secrete CAN. *Dist:* National Bk. Network.

Going, K. L. Fat Kid Rules the World. (YA). 2004. (gr. 8-12). 17.99 (978-0-8037-2948-3(0) , Dial); 2003. 224p. (gr. 4 up). 17.99 (978-0-399-23990-8(1) , Putnam Juvenile); 2004. 192p. (gr. 6). reprint ed. pap. 6.99 (978-0-14-240208-5(7) , Puffin) Penguin Group (USA) Inc.

Gonzalez, Gabriela & Triana, Gaby. Backstage Pass. 2004. (Illus.). 224p. (J). (gr. 7 up). 15.99 (978-0-06-056017-1(7)); lib. bdg. 16.89 (978-0-06-056018-8(5)) HarperCollins Pubs.

Gregory, Deborah. Growl Power Forever! Bind-Up, Vol. 9-12. 2004. (Cheetah Girls Ser.: No. 3). 608p. (J). (gr. 3-7). pap. 9.99 (978-0-7868-5163-8(5)) Hyperion Bks. for Children.

Grimm. The Musicians of Bremen. Puttapipat, Niroot, illus. 2005. 32p. (J). (gr. k-3). 15.99 (978-0-7636-2758-4(5)) Candlewick Pr.

Grimm, Jacob W. The Bremen Town Musicians. 1998. 13.79 (978-0-606-13226-8(0)) Tandem Library Bks.

Grimm, Jacob W. & Grimm, Wilhelm K. The Bremen Town Musicians: A Tale about Working Together. Catalano, Dominic, illus. 2006. (Famous Fables Ser.). (J). (978-1-59939-039-0(6) , Reader's Digest Young Families, Inc.) Reader's Digest Children's Publishing, Inc.

Gutman, Dan. Mr. Hynde Is Out of His Mind! Paillot, Jim, illus. 2005. 97p. (J). (ps-k). lib. bdg. 10.64 (978-0-606-33934-6(5)) Tandem Library Bks.

Haas, Jessie. Keeping Barney. 1998. 160p. (J). (gr. 3 up). pap. 4.50 (978-0-688-15859-0(5)) HarperCollins Pubs.

Hanson, Anders. Beetle Mania. Nobens, C. A., illus. (Fact & Fiction Ser.). 24p. (J). 2007. 21.35 (978-1-59928-432-3(4)); 2006. (978-1-59928-433-0(2)) ABDO Publishing Co.

Harmel, Kristin. When You Wish. 2008. 288p. (J). (***978-0-385-73475-2(1)*** , Delacorte Pr.) Dell Publishing.

Harranth, Wolf. The Flute Concert. Candea, Romulus, illus. 1998. Tr. of Flotenkonzert. 32p. (J). (ps-3). 23.69 (978-1-56711-803-2(8) , Blackbirch Pr., Inc.) Thomson Gale.

Hillerman, Tony. Buster Mesquite's Cowboy Band (Reprint) 2006. (J). lib. bdg. 14.95 (***978-0-914001-12-6(4)***) Sidewinder Publishing LLC.

Hunt, Angela Elwell & Arterburn, Stephen. Josiah. 2004. (Young Believer on Tour Ser.). (J). pap. 3.99 (978-0-8423-8335-6(2)) Tyndale Hse. Pubs.

—Liane. 2004. (Young Believer on Tour Ser.). (J). pap. 3.99 (978-0-8423-8336-3(0)) Tyndale Hse. Pubs.

Hurd, Thacher. Mama Don't Allow. Hurd, Thacher, illus. 2001. (Illus.). pap. 33.95 incl. audio (978-0-87499-745-3(3)); pap. 35.95 incl. audio compact disk (978-1-59112-605-8(3)); (J). pap. 18.95 incl. audio compact disk (978-1-59112-135-0(3)) Live Oak Media.

James, Simon. Baby Brains Superstar: The Smartest Baby in the Whole World. James, Simon, illus. 2005. (Illus.). 32p. (J). (ps-3). 15.99 (978-0-7636-2894-9(8)) Candlewick Pr.

Johnson, Angela. Violet's Music. Huliska-Beith, Laura, illus. 2004. 32p. (J). (ps-3). 16.99 (978-0-8037-2740-3(2) , Dial) Penguin Group (USA) Inc.

Jones, Melanie Davis. Pigs Rock! 2003. (Illus.). 32p. (J). (ps-1). 15.99 (978-0-670-03581-6(5) , Viking Juvenile) Penguin Group (USA) Inc.

Kassirer, Sue. Math Fair Blues. Smath, Jerry, illus. 2005. (Math Matters Ser.). 32p. (J). (gr. k-2). pap. 4.95 (978-1-57565-104-0(1)) Kane Pr., The.

—Math Fair Blues. 2001. (gr. k-3). lib. bdg. 12.95 (978-0-613-39339-3(2)) Tandem Library Bks.

Kerner, Charlotte. Blueprint. Crawford, Elizabeth D., tr. from GER. 2003. (Young Adult Fiction Ser.). 192p. (YA). (gr. 9-12). 16.95 (978-0-8225-0080-3(9) , Carolrhoda Bks.) Lerner Publishing Group.

Ketcham, Sallie. Bach's Big Adventure. Bush, Timothy, illus. 1999. 32p. (J). (gr. k-4). 17.99 (978-0-531-33140-8(7)); pap. 16.95 (978-0-531-30140-1(0)) Scholastic, Inc. (Orchard Bks.).

Kitamura, Satoshi. Igor, the Bird Who Couldn't Sing. Kitamura, Satoshi, illus. 2005. (Illus.). 40p. (J). (ps-ps). 16.00 (978-0-374-33558-8(3) , Farrar, Straus & Giroux (BYR)) Farrar, Straus & Giroux.

Kogler, Jennifer Anne. Ruby Tuesday. 2005. 320p. (J). (gr. 7 up). 15.99 (978-0-06-073956-0(8)) HarperCollins Pubs.

Krosoczka, Jarrett. Punk Farm on Tour. 2007. 40p. (J). (gr. k-3). 15.99 (***978-0-375-83343-4(9)***); lib. bdg. 18.99 (***978-0-375-93343-1(3)***) Random Hse. Children's Bks. (Knopf Bks. for Young Readers).

Krosoczka, Jarrett J. Punk Farm. 2005. (Illus.). 40p. (J). (gr. k-3). 15.95 (978-0-375-82429-6(4)); lib. bdg. 17.99 (978-0-375-92429-3(9)) Random Hse. Children's Bks. (Knopf Bks. for Young Readers).

Kuper, Peter. Theo & the Blue Note. Kuper, Peter, illus. 2006. (Illus.). 32p. (J). (ps). 15.99 (978-0-670-06137-2(9) , Viking Juvenile) Penguin Group (USA) Inc.

Landis, Leanne. Keaka & His Precious Pahu. 2002. 32p. (J). (ps-5). pap. 9.94 (978-0-9723707-1-4(4) , KPB01) White Door Publishing.

LeFrak, Karen. Jake the Philharmonic Dog. Baranski, Marcin, illus. 2006. 32p. (J). 16.95 (978-0-8027-9552-6(8)) Walker & Co.

Lems, Kristin. Piano Teacher's Daughter. Daoudi, Karima Lems & Daoudi, Kennan Lems, illus. 2002. pap. 18.00 (978-0-9637048-2-5(6)) Lems-Dworkin, Carol Pubs.

Leonard, Marcia. Big Ben. Handelman, Dorothy, illus. 1998. (Real Kids Readers Ser.). 32p. (J). (gr. k-1). pap. 4.99 (978-0-7613-2038-8(5) , Millbrook Pr.) Lerner Publishing Group.

—Big Ben. Handelman, Dorothy, photos by. 1998. (Real Kids Readers Ser.). (Illus.). 32p. (ps-1). lib. bdg. 18.90 (978-0-7613-2013-5(X) , Millbrook Pr.) Lerner Publishing Group.

Leroux, Gaston. The Phantom of the Opera. Howell, Troy, illus. 2008. (Classic Starts Ser.). 160p. (J). 5.95 (***978-1-4027-4580-5(X)***) Sterling Publishing Co., Inc.

Levoy, Myron. Kelly 'n' Me. 2000. 212p. (YA). (gr. 7-12). pap. 13.95 (978-0-595-09356-4(6)) iUniverse, Inc.

Lithgow, John. The Remarkable Farkle McBride: 52 Unexpected Ways to Make a Birthday, Holiday, or Any Day a Celebration. Payne, C. F., illus. 2000. 40p. (J). (ps-3). 16.00 (978-0-689-83340-3(7)) Simon & Schuster Children's Publishing.

Littlesugar, Amy. Shake Rag: From the Life of Elvis Presley. 2001. (978-0-606-21428-5(3)) Tandem Library Bks.

MacLean, Mrs. Alistair, pseud. Hollywood. Milton, illus. l.t. ed. 1999. (Yesterday & Tomorrow Fantasy Cartoon Ser.). (FRE.). 75p. (YA). 10.00 (978-0-940178-89-2(3)) Sitare, Ltd.

Madison, Alan. Pecorino's First Concert. Cantone, Annalaura, illus. 2005. 40p. (J). (ps-ps). 15.95 (978-0-689-85952-6(X) , Atheneum/Anne Schwartz Bks.) Simon & Schuster Children's Publishing.

Malkin, Nina. 6x: The Uncensored Confessions. 2005. (6x Ser.). 224p. (YA). (gr. 7-12). 8.99 (978-0-439-72421-0(X) , Scholastic Paperbacks) Scholastic, Inc.

Marathon Team. Spies in Space. 4th rev. ed. 2007. (Totally Spies Ser.: No. 4). (Illus.). 112p. (J). 12.95 (978-1-59707-056-0(4)); pap. 7.95 (978-1-59707-055-3(6)) Papercutz.

Martin. The Maestro Plays. 2001. 13.95 (978-0-15-200259-6(6)) Harcourt Trade Pubs.

Martin, Bill. The Maestro Plays. 2002. (Illus.). (J). 26.47 (978-0-7587-6796-7(X)) Book Wholesalers, Inc.

Mayer, Mercer. The Little Drummer Mouse. 2006. (Illus.). 40p. (J). (ps). 16.99 (978-0-8037-3147-9(7) , Dial) Penguin Group (USA) Inc.

Mazer, Anne. It's Music to My Ears. Gesue, Lynn, illus. 2005. (Amazing Days of Abby Hayes Ser.: No. 14). 128p. (J). (gr. 5 up). 4.99 (978-0-439-68063-9(8) , Scholastic Paperbacks) Scholastic, Inc.

McKenzie, Tim A. Baxter Barret Brown's Bass Fiddle. 2004. (Illus.). 32p. (J). 19.95 incl. audio compact disk (978-1-931721-06-6(8)) Bright Sky Pr.

Millman, Isaac. Moses Goes to a Concert. Millman, Isaac, illus. (Moses Goes To Ser.). (Illus.). 40p. (J). 2002. pap. 6.95 (978-0-374-45366-4(7) , Sunburst); 1998. 17.00 (978-0-374-35067-3(1) , Farrar, Straus & Giroux (BYR)) Farrar, Straus & Giroux.

—Moses Goes to a Concert. 2002. (gr. k-3). lib. bdg. 14.10 (978-0-613-53841-1(2)) Tandem Library Bks.

Moerike, Eduard. Mozart Auf der Reise Nach Prag. 2006. (GER.). pap. (***978-1-4068-0825-4(3)***) Echo Library.

Montano, Josie. Pop Starlets. 2005. (Illus.). 142p. pap. (978-0-7344-0446-6(8) , Lothian Bks.) Hachette Livre Australia.

Morpurgo, Michael. The Mozart Question. Foreman, Michael, illus. 2008. (J). (gr. 1-4). 15.99 (***978-0-7636-3552-7(9)***) Candlewick Pr.

The Musicians of Bremen. 2004. 24.95 incl. audio (978-0-7882-0572-9(2)) Weston Woods Studios, Inc.

Mutchnick, Brenda & Casden, Ron. A Noteworthy Tale. Penney, Ian, illus. 2004. 30p. (J). (gr. k-4). reprint ed. 19.00 (978-0-7567-7654-1(6)) DIANE Publishing Co.

Myers, Walter Dean. Jazz. Myers, Christopher, illus. 2006. 48p. (J). (gr. 4-8). 18.95 (978-0-8234-1545-8(7)) Holiday Hse., Inc.

Napoli, Donna Jo. Changing Tunes. 2000. (Illus.). (J). (978-0-606-18394-9(9)) Tandem Library Bks.

Nelson, Blake. Rock Star, Superstar. 2004. 224p. (J). (gr. 7). 16.99 (978-0-670-05933-1(1) , Viking Juvenile) Penguin Group (USA) Inc.

—Rock Star Superstar Blake Nelson. 2006. 256p. (YA). (gr. 7). reprint ed. pap. 6.99 (978-0-14-240574-1(4) , Puffin) Penguin Group (USA) Inc.

Nickel, Barbara. Hannah Waters & the Daughter of Johann Sebastian Bach. 2007. (Illus.). 176p. (J). mass mkt. 6.99 (978-0-14-305079-7(6) , Penguin Global) Penguin Group (USA) Inc.

Nields, Nerissa. Plastic Angel. 2005. (Plastic Angel Ser.). 256p. (J). (ps-7). pap. 17.95 (978-0-439-70913-2(X) , Orchard Bks.) Scholastic, Inc.

Ornstein, Mike. The Daddy Longlegs Blues. Kopelke, Lisa, illus. 2008. (J). (***978-1-4027-4359-7(9)***) Sterling Publishing Co., Inc.

Ostrander, P. Martin. P Martin Ostrander's Dangerous Four Series: Book #1. 2007. 112p. 20.95 (***978-0-595-68250-8(2)***) iUniverse, Inc.

Ostrow, Kim. Rock-and-Roll Bob. Hot Animation Staff, Animation, illus. 2003. (Bob the Builder Ser.: Vol. 6). 24p. (J). pap. 3.99 (978-0-689-85832-1(9) , Simon Spotlight) Simon & Schuster Children's Publishing.

Percy, Graham, illus. The Pied Piper of Hamelin. l.t. ed. 2001. (SPA.). 28p. (ps-3). incl. audio compact disk (978-84-8214-085-8(X) , 1622) Peralt Montagut.

—The Pied Piper of Hamelin. l.t. ed. 2001. 28p. (J). (ps-3). 8.99 incl. audio (978-84-86154-38-7(3)) Peralt Montagut ESP. *Dist:* imaJen, Inc.

Pinkwater, Daniel M. Bongo Larry. Pinkwater, Jill, illus. 1998. (Accelerated Reader Bks.). 32p. (J). (ps up). 14.95 (978-0-7614-5020-7(3) , Cavendish Children's Bks.) Cavendish, Marshall Corp.

—Mush's Jazz Adventure. 2002. (gr. 3-6). lib. bdg. 11.80 (978-0-613-57577-5(6)) Tandem Library Bks.

Pinkwater, Daniel M. & Pinkwater, Jill. Mush's Jazz Adventure. 2002. (Ready-for-Chapters Ser.). (Illus.). 48p. (J). pap. 6.99 (978-0-689-84572-7(3) , Aladdin) Simon & Schuster Children's Publishing.

Plaka, Christina, illus. Yonen Buzz, Vol. 2. 2006. (YA). pap. 9.99 (978-1-59816-404-6(X) , Tokyopop Adult) TOKYOPOP, Inc.

Plume, Ilse. The Bremen-Town Musicians. 1998. (Illus.). 32p. (ps-3). reprint ed. pap. 6.99 (978-0-440-41456-8(3) , Dragonfly Bks.) Random Hse. Children's Bks.

Pratchett, Terry. The Amazing Maurice & His Educated Rodents. 2003. 368p. (YA). (gr. 7 up). pap. 6.99 (978-0-06-001235-9(8)) HarperCollins Pubs.

—The Amazing Maurice & His Educated Rodents. 2003. (gr. 5-8). lib. bdg. 15.30 (978-0-613-65757-0(8)) Tandem Library Bks.

Reisfeld, Randi, ed. Star Struck. 2006. (Teenick Ser.: Bk. 3). (Illus.). 120p. (J). pap. 4.99 (978-0-439-83157-4(1)) Scholastic, Inc.

—Unfabulous: Jinxed. 2006. (Teenick Ser.: Bk. 4). (Illus.). 120p. (J). pap. 4.99 (978-0-439-83158-1(X)) Scholastic, Inc.

Ritter, John H. Under the Baseball Moon. 2008. 320p. (J). (gr. 6). 6.99 (***978-0-14-241090-5(X)*** , Puffin); 2006. (Illus.). 224p. (YA). (gr. 5). 16.99 (978-0-399-23623-5(6) , Philomel) Penguin Group (USA) Inc.

Roy, Ron. The X'ed-Out X-Ray. Gurney, John Steven, illus. 2005. (A to Z Mysteries Ser.: No. 24). 96p. (J). (gr. k-3). pap. 3.99 (978-0-375-82481-4(2)); lib. bdg. 11.99 (978-0-375-92481-1(7)) Random Hse. Children's Bks. (Random Hse. Bks. for Young Readers).

—The X'ed-Out X-Ray. Gurney, John Steven, illus. 2005. (A to Z Mysteries Ser.: No. 25). 85p. (J). (gr. k-3). lib. bdg. 11.19 (978-0-606-33236-1(7)) Tandem Library Bks.

Sachar, Louis. Small Steps. 2008. 288p. (YA). (gr. 7). pap. 8.99 (***978-0-385-73315-1(1)*** , Delacorte Bks. for Young Readers) Random Hse. Children's Bks.

The Secret of the Elves Elite. 2001. Vol. First Run. per. 22.95 (978-0-9711234-0-3(3)) T F M Productions.

The Secret of the Elves Elite: With Elves Elite Hunting Kit. 2001. Vol. First Run. per. 22.95 (978-0-9711234-1-0(1)) T F M Productions.

Seeger, Pete & Jacobs, Paul DuBois. The Deaf Musicians. Christie, Gregory, illus. 2006. 32p. (J). (ps-3). 16.99 (978-0-399-24316-5(X)) Penguin Group (USA) Inc.

Seidler, Tor. Toes. Beddows, Eric, illus. 176p. (J). 2004. (gr. 3 up). 15.99 (978-0-06-054099-9(0) , Geringer, Laura Book); 2004. (gr. 3 up). lib. bdg. 16.89 (978-0-06-054100-2(8) , Geringer, Laura Book); 2006. reprint ed. pap. 5.99 (978-0-06-054101-9(6) , Harper Trophy) HarperCollins Pubs.

Shlasko, Robert. Molly & the Sword. Diamond, Donna, illus. 2004. 32p. (J). 15.95 (978-0-9745077-4-3(1)) Jane & Street Pubs. Ltd.

Smith, John D. The Best Mariachi in the World/ el mejor mariachi del Mundo. de la Vega, Eida, tr. Jones, Dani, illus. 2008. (J). lib. bdg. 16.95 (978-0-9770906-1-7(2)) Raven Tree Pr.

Sonnenblick, Jordan. Notes from the Midnight Driver. 2007. 288p. (J). pap. 6.99 (***978-0-439-75781-2(9)*** , Scholastic Paperbacks); 2006. 272p. (YA). pap. 16.99 (978-0-439-75779-9(7) , Scholastic Pr.) Scholastic, Inc.

Sorrells, Walter. Fake ID. 2005. (Hunted Ser.: 1). 192p. (YA). (gr. 6). 12.99 (978-0-525-47514-9(1) , Dutton Juvenile) Penguin Group (USA) Inc.

—Fake ID: A Mystery. 2007. (Hunted Ser.). 336p. (YA). (gr. 7 up). pap. 6.99 (978-0-14-240762-2(3) , Puffin) Penguin Group (USA) Inc.

Steele, Michael Anthony. Cry Wolff, Bk. 1. 2008. (Naked Brothers Band Ser.). 96p. (J). pap. 4.99 (***978-0-545-03838-6(3)***) Scholastic, Inc.

Stewart, Whitney. Blues Across the Bay. 2001. (Going to Ser.). (Illus.). 151p. (gr. 4-8). pap. 6.95 (978-1-893577-08-4(2)) Four Corners Publishing Co., Inc.

Stine, Catherine. Refugees. 288p. (gr. 7). 2006. (YA). pap. 5.99 (978-0-440-23876-8(5) , Laurel Leaf); 2005. (J). 15.95 (978-0-385-73179-9(5) , Delacorte Bks. for Young Readers); 2005. (YA). 17.99 (978-0-385-90216-8(6) , Delacorte Bks. for Young Readers) Random Hse. Children's Bks.

Tate, Eleanora E. The Minstrel's Melody. 2001. (American Girl Collection). (Illus.). (J). (978-0-606-21331-8(7)) Tandem Library Bks.

Taylor, Debbie. Sweet Music in Harlem. Morrison, Frank, tr. Morrison, Frank, illus. 2004. 32p. (J). 16.95 (978-1-58430-165-3(1)) Lee & Low Bks., Inc.

Thiesing, Lisa. The Aliens Are Coming. 2004. (Illus.). 32p. (J). (ps). 13.99 (978-0-525-47277-3(0) , Dutton Juvenile) Penguin Group (USA) Inc.

Townley, Roderick. Sky. 2004. (Illus.). 272p. (J). 16.95 (978-0-689-85712-6(8) , Atheneum/Richard Jackson Bks.) Simon & Schuster Children's Publishing.

Trine, Greg. The Grateful Fred. Montijo, Rhode, illus. 3rd rev. ed. 2006. (Melvin Beederman, Superhero Ser.). 144p. (J). 15.95 (978-0-8050-7921-0(1)) Holt, Henry & Co.

—The Grateful Fred. Montijo, Rhode, illus. 3rd rev. ed. 2006. (Melvin Beederman, Superhero Ser.). 144p. (J). pap. 5.99 (978-0-8050-7922-7(X)) Holt, Henry & Co.

Trout, Robert J. Drumbeat: The Story of a Civil War Drummer Boy. 2007. (J). pap. 12.95 (***978-1-57249-390-2(9)*** , White Mane Kids) White Mane Publishing Co., Inc.

Ungerer, Tomi. Tortoni Tremolo: The Cursed Musician. Ungerer, Tomi, illus. 2004. (Illus.). 28p. (J). (gr. k-4). reprint ed. 17.00 (978-0-7567-9047-9(6)) DIANE Publishing Co.

—Tortoni Tremolo the Cursed Magician. Ungerer, Tomi, illus. 1998. (Illus.). 32p. (J). (gr. 1-5). 16.95 (978-1-57098-226-2(0)) Rinehart, Roberts Pubs.

Voigt, Cynthia. Orfe. 2002. (Illus.). 160p. (YA). pap. 4.99 (978-0-689-84868-1(4) , Simon Pulse) Simon & Schuster Children's Publishing.

Wells, Helen. Cherry Ames, Private Duty Nurse. 2006. vi, 218p. (J). (978-0-8261-0398-7(7)) Springer.

Wheeler, Kathryn. Untitle. 2007. 32p. (J). pap. 3.99 (978-1-60095-246-3(1)) Cookie Jar.

Willett, Edward. The Dark Unicorn. 18th ed. 1998. 158p. (YA). (gr. 6 up). 9.99 (978-0-88092-414-6(4) , 4144) Royal Fireworks Publishing Co.

Willner-Pardo, Gina. Spider Storch's Music Mess. Sharratt, Nick, illus. 1998. 80p. (J). (gr. 2-5). lib. bdg. 11.95 (978-0-8075-7583-3(6)) Whitman, Albert & Co.

Wolff, Virginia Euwer. The Mozart Season. 2007. 272p. (J). pap. 6.99 (***978-0-312-36745-9(7)***) Square Fish.

—The Mozart Season. 2000. (978-0-606-18579-0(8)) Tandem Library Bks.

Yolen, Jane & Stemple, Adam. Troll Bridge. 2006. 240p. (J). 16.95 (978-0-7653-1426-0(6) , Starscape) Doherty, Tom Assocs., LLC.

Yolen, Jane & Stemple, Adam. Troll Bridge: A Rock 'n' Roll Fairy Tale. 2007. 240p. (J). 5.99 (***978-0-7653-5284-2(2)*** , Starscape) Doherty, Tom Assocs., LLC.

Yoo, Paula. Good Enough. 2008. 336p. (J). 16.99 (***978-0-06-079085-1(7)***); lib. bdg. 17.89 (***978-0-06-079089-9(X)***) HarperCollins Pubs. (HarperTeen).

Yoo, Paula & Dereske, Jo. Good Enough. 2008. 272p. mass mkt. 6.99 (***978-0-06-079086-8(5)*** , HarperTeen) HarperCollins Pubs.

MUSICIANS, NEGRO

see African American Musicians

MUSK-OX

Markle, Sandra. Musk Oxen. 2007. (Animal Prey Ser.). 40p. (J). (gr. 4-6). 25.26 (978-0-8225-6064-7(X) , Lerner Pubns.) Lerner Publishing Group.

MUSKRATS

Hall, Margaret. Muskrats. Saunders-Smith, Gail, ed. 2004. (Wetland Animals Ser.). (Illus.). 24p. (J). (gr. k-1). lib. bdg. 15.93 (978-0-7368-2066-0(3) , Pebble Bks.) Capstone Pr., Inc.

MUSKRATS—FICTION

Burgess, Thornton. The Adventures of Jerry Muskrat. 2006. pap. 9.95 (***978-1-59605-676-3(2)*** , Cosimo Classics) Cosimo, Inc.

Burgess, Thornton W. Jerry Muskrat at Home. (J). 18.95 (978-0-8488-0399-5(X)) Amereon LTD.

Burgess, W. Thornton. Adventures of Jerry Muskrat. 2006. pap. 87.99 (***978-1-4280-3662-8(8)**) IndyPublish.com.

Chaconas, Dori. Cork & Fuzz: Good Sports. McCue, Lisa, illus. 2007. (Viking Easy-To-Read Ser.). 32p. (J). (gr. k-2). 13.99 (978-0-670-06145-7(X) , Viking Adult) Penguin Group (USA) Inc.

—Cork & Fuzz: Short & Tall. McCue, Lisa, illus. 2006. (Viking Easy-To-Read Ser.). 32p. (J). (gr. k-3). 13.99 (978-0-670-05985-0(4) , Viking Adult) Penguin Group (USA) Inc.

Chaconas, Dori. Cork & Fuzz: The Collectors. McCue, Lisa, illus. 2008. 32p. (J). (ps-1). 13.99 (***978-0-670-06286-7(3)** , Viking Adult) Penguin Group (USA) Inc.

Chaconas, Doris J. Cork & Fuzz. McCue, Lisa, illus. 2005. (Viking Easy-To-Read Ser.). 32p. (J). (ps-3). 13.99 (978-0-670-03602-8(1) , Viking Juvenile) Penguin Group (USA) Inc.

Garis, Howard Roger. Sammie & Susie Littletail. 2006. 77.99 (***978-1-4142-5879-9(8)**); pap. 70.99 (***978-1-4142-5870-6(4)**) IndyPublish.com.

Savageau, Cheryl. Muskrat Will Be Swimming. Hynes, Robert, illus. 2006. 32p. (J). pap. (978-0-88448-280-2(4)) Tilbury Hse. Pubs.

MUSLIMS

Here are entered works on the community of believers in Islam. Works on the religion of which Muhammad is the prophet are entered under Islam.

Brown, Tricia. Salaam: A Muslim American Boy's Story. Cardwell, Kenneth, photos by. 2006. (Illus.). 40p. (J). (ps-3). 17.95 (978-0-8050-6538-1(5) , Holt, Henry & Co. Bks. For Young Readers) Holt, Henry & Co.

Demi. Muhammad. Demi, illus. 2004. (Illus.). 39p. (J). (gr. 2-5). reprint ed. (978-0-7567-7802-6(6)) DIANE Publishing Co.

—Muhammad. 2003. (Illus.). 48p. (J). 19.95 (978-0-689-85264-0(9) , McElderry, Margaret K.) Simon & Schuster Children's Publishing.

Hodges, Rick. What Muslims Think, & How They Live. 2003. (Introducing Islam Ser.). (Illus.). 112p. (YA). lib. bdg. 24.95 (978-1-59084-702-2(4)) Mason Crest Pubs.

Kemmetmueller, Donna Jean. My Muslim Friend: A Young Catholic Learns about Islam. Jacobsen, Laura, illus. 2006. 47p. (J). 15.95 (978-0-8198-4844-4(1)) Pauline Bks. & Media.

Khan, Saniyasnain. Tell Me about Hajj: What the Hajj Is, Why It Is So Important, & What It Teaches Me. Ravindran, K.M., illus. 2nd l.t. ed. 2001. (Tell Me about Ser.). 40p. pap. 6.50 (978-81-87570-90-5(3)) Goodword Bks. Pvt. Ltd. IND. *Dist:* Lodhia Ctr., The.

—Tell Me about Hajj: What the Hajj Is,Why It's So Important & What It Teaches Me. 2nd l.t. ed. 2001. (Tell Me About). (Illus.). 40p. per. 9.75 (978-81-87570-00-4(8)) Goodword Bks. Pvt. Ltd. IND. *Dist:* Lodhia Ctr., The.

Marchant, Kerena. Muhammad & Islam. 2002. (Great Religious Leaders Ser.). (Illus.). 48p. (J). lib. bdg. 28.50 (978-1-58340-217-7(9)) Smart Apple Media.

Marsh, Carole. What Is Islam? Who Are Muslims? 2002. (Here & Now Ser.). 32p. (YA). (gr. 2-8). pap. 9.95 (978-0-635-01080-3(1)) Gallopade International.

Marston, Elsa. Muhammad of Mecca: Prophet of Islam. 2001. (Book Report Biographies Ser.). (Illus.). 100p. (YA). (gr. 6-8). pap. 6.95 (978-0-531-15554-7(4) , Watts, Franklin) Scholastic Library Publishing.

Oliver, Marilyn Tower. Muhammad. 2003. (Importance of Ser.). (Illus.). 112p. (J). (gr. 7-10). 32.45 (978-1-59018-232-1(4) , Lucent Bks.) Thomson Gale.

Petrini, Catherine M. What Makes Me a Muslim? 2005. (What Makes Me A—? Ser.). (Illus.). 48p. (J). (ps-7). lib. bdg. 26.20 (978-0-7377-2265-9(7) , Greenhaven Pr., Inc.) Thomson Gale.

Sears, Evelyn. Muslims & the West. 2003. (Introducing Islam Ser.). (Illus.). 112p. (YA). lib. bdg. (978-1-59084-700-8(8)) Mason Crest Pubs.

Wolf, Bernard. Coming to America: A Muslim Family's Story. Wolf, Bernard, photos by. 2003. (Illus.). 48p. (J). (gr. k-8). 17.95 (978-1-58430-086-1(8)); pap. 7.95 (978-1-58430-177-6(5)) Lee & Low Bks., Inc.

—Coming to America: A Muslim Family's Story. 2003. (gr. 3-6). lib. bdg. 16.40 (978-0-613-67796-7(X)) Tandem Library Bks.

MUSLIMS, BLACK

see Black Muslims

MUSLIMS—FICTION

Abdel-Fattah, Randa. Does My Head Look Big in This? 2007. 368p. (J). (gr. 7 up). pap. 16.99 (***978-0-439-91947-0(9)*** , Orchard Bks.) Scholastic, Inc.

Clinton, Cathryn. Stone in My Hand. Johnson, Peter, illus. 2002. 192p. (YA). (gr. 6-12). 15.99 (978-0-7636-1388-4(6)) Candlewick Pr.

—Stone in My Hand. 2004. (Illus.). 208p. (YA). (gr. 6 up). reprint ed. pap. 5.99 (978-0-7636-2561-0(2)) Candlewick Pr.

Ellis, Deborah & Walters, Eric. Bifocal. 2007. 240p. (YA). (gr. 7 up). (***978-1-55455-036-4(X)***) Fitzhenry & Whiteside, Ltd.

Fama, Elizabeth. Overboard. 2002. (Illus.). 192p. (YA). (gr. 6-9). 15.95 (978-0-8126-2652-0(4)) Cricket Bks.

—Overboard. 2005. 160p. (YA). (gr. 7). pap. 5.50 (978-0-553-49436-5(8) , Laurel Leaf) Random Hse. Children's Bks.

Ghazi, A., ed. The First Ones: The Makkan Sahabah. Siddiqui, A. Sayeed, tr. 1999. (Stories of the Sahabah Ser.: Vol. II). (Illus.). 145p. (YA). (gr. 7-10). pap. 10.00 (978-1-56316-451-4(5)) IQRA International Educational Foundation.

—Those Promised Paradise. Siddiqui, M. Sayeed, tr. Siddiqui, M. Sayeed, illus. 1999. (Stories of the Sahabah Ser.: Vol. I). 256p. (YA). (gr. 7-10). pap. 10.00 (978-1-56316-374-6(8)) IQRA International Educational Foundation.

Grant, K. M. Blaze of Silver. 2007. 272p. 16.95 (978-0-8027-9625-7(7)) Walker & Co.

Hayes, Rosemary. Mixing It. 2007. 192p. (YA). (gr. 5 up). pap. 7.95 (***978-1-84507-495-1(5)***) Lincoln, Frances Ltd. GBR. *Dist:* Perseus Distribution.

Hingoro, Samira, creator. A Marriage Proposal. 2003. (YA). per. 12.95 (978-0-9743167-0-3(9)) Faith Pubns.

Ismail, Suzy. The BFF Sisters: Jennah's New Friends. 2001. 64p. (J). (978-1-59008-005-4(X)) amana pubns.

Jackson, Dave & Jackson, Neta. Risking the Forbidden Game: Maude Cary. Gavitt, Anne, illus. 2002. (Trailblazers Ser.). 160p. (J). (gr. 3-7). pap. 6.99 (978-0-7642-2234-4(1)) Bethany Hse. Pubs.

Jolin, Paula. In the Name of God. 2007. 208p. (YA). (gr. 9 up). 16.95 (978-1-59643-211-6(X)) Roaring Brook Pr.

Katz, Karen. My First Ramadan. 2007. (Illus.). 32p. (J). (ps-k). 14.95 (***978-0-8050-7894-7(0)***) Holt, Henry & Co.

Klaus, Sandra. Mustafas Geheimnis: Ein Moslemischer Junge auf der Suche nach Gott. Date not set. Tr. of Mustapha's Secret - A Muslim Boy's Search to Know God. (GER., Illus.). (J). (gr. 2-7). pap. (978-0-9617490-6-4(7)) Gospel Missionary Union.

—Tainata na Mustapha. Date not set. Tr. of Mustapha's Secret. (BUL.). (J). (gr. 2-7). pap. (978-1-890940-04-1(6)) Gospel Missionary Union.

Lat. Kampung Boy. Lat, illus. rev. ed. 2006. (Illus.). 144p. (J). (gr. 6-8). pap. 16.95 (978-1-59643-121-8(0) , First Second Bks.) Roaring Brook Pr.

Lipp, Frederick. Fatima. Lindmark, Margaret, illus. 2006. 32p. (J). pap. (978-1-59336-302-4(8)) Mondo Publishing.

McKeown, Adam & Shakespeare, William. Othello. Hundley, Sterling, illus. 2005. (Young Reader's Shakespeare Ser.). 80p. (J). 14.95 (978-1-4027-1115-2(8)) Sterling Publishing Co., Inc.

Nolan, Han. A Summer of Kings. 2006. (Illus.). 352p. (YA). 17.00 (978-0-15-205108-2(2)) Harcourt Children's Bks.

—A Summer of Kings. 2006. 334p. (J). (978-1-4156-7340-9(3)) Harcourt Trade Pubs.

Oppenheim, Shulamith Levey. Ali & the Magic Stew. Pels, Winslow, illus. 2003. 32p. (YA). (gr. k-2). 15.95 (978-1-56397-869-2(5)) Boyds Mills Pr.

Robert, Naima Bint. The Swirling Hijaab. Mistry, Nilesh, illus. 2004. 24p. (J). (TAM, CZE, VIE, SPA & GUJ.). (978-1-85269-119-6(0)); (TAM, CZE, VIE, SPA & GUJ.). (978-1-85269-143-1(3)); (TAM, CZE, VIE, SPA & GUJ.). (978-1-85269-160-8(3)); (TAM, CZE, VIE, SPA & GUJ.). (978-1-85269-161-5(1)); (TAM, CZE, VIE, SPA & GUJ.). (978-1-85269-163-9(8)); (TAM, CZE, VIE, SPA & GUJ.). (978-1-85269-165-3(4)); (TAM, CZE, VIE, SPA & GUJ.). (978-1-85269-167-7(0)); (TAM, CZE, VIE, SPA & GUJ.). (978-1-85269-178-3(6)); (TAM, CZE, VIE, SPA & GUJ.). (978-1-85269-179-0(4)); (TAM, CZE, VIE, SPA & GUJ.). (978-1-85269-180-6(8)); (TAM, CZE, VIE, SPA & GUJ.). (978-1-85269-181-3(6)); (TAM, CZE, VIE, SPA & GUJ.). (978-1-85269-182-0(4)); (CZE, TAM, VIE, SPA & GUJ.). (978-1-85269-188-2(3)); (TAM, CZE, VIE, SPA & GUJ.). (978-1-85269-189-9(1)); (TAM, CZE, VIE, SPA & GUJ.). (978-1-85269-629-0(X)); (TAM, CZE, VIE, SPA & GUJ.). (978-1-85269-669-6(9)); (TAM, CZE, VIE, SPA & GUJ.). (978-1-85269-910-9(8)) Mantra Publishing, Ltd.

Robert, Naima Bint & Mistry, Nilesh, trs. The Swirling Hijaab: Le Foulard Qui Tourbillonne. 2004. (TAM, CZE, VIE, SPA & GUJ., Illus.). 24p. (J). (978-1-85269-164-6(6)) Mantra Publishing, Ltd.

Sayres, Meghan Nuttall. Anahita's Woven Riddle. 2006. 368p. (YA). (gr. 5-9). 16.95 (978-0-8109-5481-6(8)) Abrams, Harry N. , Inc.

Schaenen, Inda. All the Cats of Cairo. 2007. 232p. (J). (gr. 5-10). pap. 8.95 (***978-0-9768126-5-4(7)***) Brown Barn Bks.

Stolz, Joelle. The Shadows of Ghadames. 128p. (gr. 3-7). 2006. 5.99 (978-0-440-41949-5(2) , Yearling); 2004. (J). 15.95 (978-0-385-73104-1(3) , Delacorte Bks. for Young Readers) Random Hse. Children's Bks.

Uddin, Asma Mobin. My Name Is Bilal. Kiwak, Barbara, illus. 2005. 32p. (J). (ps-17). 15.95 (978-1-59078-175-3(9)) Boyds Mills Pr.

Williams, Tad & Hoffman, Nina Kiriki. Child of an Ancient City. 1999. (J). (978-0-606-16882-3(6)) Tandem Library Bks.

Youree, Barbara. Senegal Sleuths. 2006. 56p. 7.75 (978-0-8341-2226-0(X)) Beacon Hill Pr. of Kansas City.

MUSSOLINI, BENITO, 1883-1945

Downing, David. Benito Mussolini. 2001. (Leading Lives Ser.). (Illus.). 64p. (J). (gr. 5-7). lib. bdg. 27.86 (978-1-58810-160-0(6)) Heinemann Library.

Haugen, Brenda. Benito Mussolini: Fascist Italian Dictator. (Illus.). 112p. (J). 2007. pap. (***978-0-7565-1988-9(8)***); 2006. (978-0-7565-1892-9(X)) Compass Point Bks.

Speaker-Yuan, Margaret. Benito Mussolini. 2005. (History's Villains Ser.). (J). (978-1-56711-899-5(2) , Blackbirch Pr., Inc.) Thomson Gale.

MUSTELIDAE

Klobuchar, Lisa. Badgers & Other Mustelids. 2005. (World Book's Animals of the World Ser.). (Illus.). 64p. (J). (978-0-7166-1265-0(8)) World Bk., Inc.

Morgan, Sally. The Weasel Family. 2004. (J). lib. bdg. (978-1-59389-173-2(3) , Cherrytree Books) Evans Publishing Group.

MUTATION (BIOLOGY)

see Evolution

MYCENAE (EXTINCT CITY)

Schlitz, Laura Amy. The Hero Schliemann: The Dreamer Who Dug up Troy. Byrd, Robert, illus. 2006. 80p. (J). (gr. 4-8). 17.99 (978-0-7636-2283-1(4)) Candlewick Pr.

MYCOLOGY

see Fungi

MYSTERIES AND MIRACLE PLAYS

Adams, Pam. Noah's Ark. l.t. ed. 1999. (Illus.). 12p. (J). (ps-1). bds. 8.99 (978-0-85953-586-1(X)) Child's Play-International.

Allen, Richard J. Parashah Plays: For Children of All Ages. 2000. 275p. (J). (gr. k-6). pap. 11.95 (978-0-86705-047-9(0)) Behrman Hse., Inc.

Christmas Bible Skits: Holidays. 2000. 48p. pap. (978-0-7647-0502-1(4)) School Specialty Publishing.

Duckworth, John. Instant Skits for Children's Ministry. 2004. (Illus.). 144p. (gr. k-6). pap. 16.99 (978-0-7644-2095-5(X) , Flagship Church Resources) Group Publishing, Inc.

Freeman, Kim. Bible Plays for Kids: A Visual Look at the Bible! 2003. 68p. (J). pap. 14.95 (978-0-9725827-0-4(3)) Keys For Kids Publishing Co.

Group Publishing Staff, contrib. by. The Humongous Book of Bible Skits for Children's Ministry. 2005. (Illus.). 208p. (J). pap. (978-0-7644-3083-1(1)) Group Publishing, Inc.

Kaplan, Gabrielle Suzanne. The Magic Tanach & Other Short Plays. 1999. (YA). (gr. 1-12). pap. 11.95 (978-0-86705-044-8(6)) Behrman Hse., Inc.

Ross, Alice E. Michael Meets a Special Friend: A Play about Angels. 1999. (Illus.). (J). (978-1-929486-05-2(7)) Son-Rises Bk. Publishing.

Sears, Donald J. & Senior High Sunday School Class Community Prebyterian Church of the Sand Hills Staff. The Trial of Jesus: A Drama in One Act, 12 vols. 2000. (Illus.). 24p. (YA). 99.50 (978-0-9678585-1-7(8)); pap. 9.95 (978-0-9678585-0-0(X)) Laurily Productions.

Wendt, Harry. The Divine Drama - Our Narrative. 4th rev. ed. 2004. (Illus.). 174p. per. 11.95 net. (978-1-891245-10-7(4) , 4872) Crossways International.

—The Divine Drama - the Biblical Narrative. 4th ed. 2004. (Illus.). 176p. per. 12.95 net. (978-1-891245-09-1(0) , 4871) Crossways International.

Williams, Guy. The Burning Fiery Furnace: Shadrach, Meshach, & Abednego. 2003. (More for Teens Ser.). 24p. (Orig.). (YA). (gr. 6-12). pap. 5.00 (978-0-88734-413-8(5)) Players Pr., Inc.

—Joseph & His Brothers. 2003. 24p. (J). (gr. 4-12). pap. 5.00 (978-0-88734-882-2(3)) Players Pr., Inc.

Willow Creek Association. 5-G Challenge Spring Quarter Bible Dramas: Doing Life with God in the Picture. 2004. (Promiseland Ser.). (J). pap. 34.99 (978-0-7441-4292-1(X)) Zonderkidz.

MYSTERIES AND MIRACLE PLAYS—COLLECTIONS

Twork, Carol Camp. "I Want to Be Jesus" Over 150 Easy-to-Use Gospel Plays for Children. 2003. 176p. tchr. ed. 17.95 (978-0-87793-691-6(9)) Ave Maria Pr.

MYSTERY AND DETECTIVE STORIES

Abbott, Tony. The Hidden Stairs & the Magic Carpet. Jessell, Tim, illus. 1999. (Secrets of Droon Ser.: No. 1). 80p. (J). (gr. 2-5). pap. 3.99 (978-0-590-10839-3(5)) Scholastic, Inc.

—The Hidden Stairs & the Magic Carpet. 1999. (Secrets of Droon Ser.: No. 1). (J). (gr. 2-5). 10.79 (978-0-606-18603-2(4)) Tandem Library Bks.

—The Mysterious Island. 1999. (gr. 3-6). lib. bdg. 11.80 (978-0-613-16982-0(4)) Tandem Library Bks.

—Stinky Business. 2000. (Don't Touch That Remote Ser.: No. 3). 160p. (J). (gr. 3-6). pap. 3.99 (978-0-671-02783-4(2) , Aladdin) Simon & Schuster Children's Publishing.

Aber, Linda Williams. The Clue in the Castle Wall. 2004. (Barbie Mystery Ser.: No. 6). 48p. (J). pap. 3.99 (978-0-439-55709-2(7) , Scholastic Paperbacks) Scholastic, Inc.

—The Haunted Mansion Mystery. 2002. (Barbie Mystery Files Ser.: No. 1). 64p. (J). (gr. 1-4). pap. 3.99 (978-0-439-37204-6(6)) Scholastic, Inc.

—The Mystery of the Jeweled Mask. 2002. (Barbie Mystery Files Ser.: No. 2). (Illus.). 80p. (J). (gr. 1-3). pap. 3.99 (978-0-439-37205-3(4)) Scholastic, Inc.

—The Mystery of the Lost Valentine. 2004. (Barbie Mystery Ser.). 48p. (J). pap. 3.99 (978-0-439-55708-5(9) , Scholastic Paperbacks) Scholastic, Inc.

—The Mystery of the Missing Stallion. 2003. (Barbie Mystery Files Ser.: No. 4). 80p. (J). pap. 3.99 (978-0-439-37207-7(0)) Scholastic, Inc.

The Abominable Snowman, 6 Vols., Pack. (Bookweb Ser.). 32p. (gr. 3 up). 34.00 (978-0-7635-3935-1(X)) Rigby Education.

The Abominable Snowman Doesn't Roast Marshmallows, 6 bks., Pack. 2005. 96p. (J). pap. 3.99 (978-0-439-86573-9(5)) Scholastic, Inc.

Abracadabra. 2001. (Mickey Mysteries Ser.: No. 4). (Illus.). 96p. (gr. 2-5). pap. 4.99 (978-0-7868-4452-4(3)) Disney Pr.

Abrahams, Peter. Behind the Curtain: An Echo Falls Mystery. (Echo Falls Ser.). (J). 2007. 400p. (gr. 5 up). pap. 6.99 (***978-0-06-073706-1(9)*** , Harper Trophy); 2006. 352p. 15.99 (978-0-06-073704-7(2) , Geringer, Laura Book); Bk. 2. 2006. 352p. lib. bdg. 16.89 (978-0-06-073705-4(0) , Geringer, Laura Book) HarperCollins Pubs.

—Down the Rabbit Hole: An Echo Falls Mystery. (Echo Falls Ser.). (J). 2005. 384p. (gr. k-17). 16.99 (978-0-06-073701-6(8) , Geringer, Laura Book); 2005. 384p. (gr. 5 up). lib. bdg. 17.89 (978-0-06-073702-3(6) , Geringer, Laura Book); 2006. 448p. reprint ed. pap. 6.99 (978-0-06-073703-0(4) , Harper Trophy) HarperCollins Pubs.

Abrahams, Peter. Into the Dark: An Echo Falls Mystery. 2008. (Echo Falls Ser.). 304p. (J). 15.99 (***978-0-06-073708-5(5)***); lib. bdg. 16.89 (***978-0-06-073709-2(3)***) HarperCollins Pubs. (Geringer, Laura Book).

Acker, Rick. The Case of the Autumn Rose. 2003. (Davis Detective Mysteries Ser.). 192p. pap. 7.99 (978-0-8254-2004-7(0)) Kregel Pubns.

—The Lost Treasure of Fernando Montoya, Vol. 2. 2003. (Davis Detective Mysteries Ser.). 192p. pap. 7.99 (978-0-8254-2005-4(9)) Kregel Pubns.

Adee, Ed & Adee, D. J. Jonathan & the Mystery in the Trunk. Babcock, Marci, illus. 2002. (Jonathan Ser.: No. 1). 216p. (J). pap. 9.95 (978-0-9654272-4-1(2)) Harvest Pubns.

Adeney, Anne. Skulduggery. Smith, Wendy, illus. l.t. ed. 2005. 256p. (J). pap. (978-0-7540-6195-3(7) , CLP 384) BBC Audio.

Adler, David A. Andy Russell, Not Wanted by the Police. Franson, Leanne, illus. (Andy Russell Ser.). 128p. 2005. (J). pap. 4.95 (978-0-15-216719-6(6)); 2001. (YA). (gr. 2-5). 15.00 (978-0-15-216474-4(X) , Gulliver Bks.) Harcourt Children's Bks.

—Andy Russell, Not Wanted by the Police. Franson, Leanne, illus. 2005. (Andy Russell Ser.). 118p. (J). (ps-k). per. 11.60 (978-0-606-33408-2(4)) Tandem Library Bks.

—Bones & the Big Yellow Mystery. Newman, Barbara, illus. 2008. (Jeffrey Bones Mystery Ser.: No. 1). 32p. (J). (gr. k). pap. 3.99 (***978-0-14-241042-4(X)*** , Puffin) Penguin Group (USA) Inc.

—Bones & the Big Yellow Mystery. Newman, Barbara Johansen, illus. 2004. (Jeffrey Bones Mystery Ser.: No. 1). 32p. (J). (gr. k-3). 13.99 (978-0-670-05947-8(1) , Viking Juvenile) Penguin Group (USA) Inc.

—Bones & the Birthday Mystery. Newman, Barbara Johansen, illus. 2007. (Jeffrey Bones Mystery Ser.: No. 5). 32p. (J). (gr. k). 13.99 (978-0-670-06164-8(6) , Viking Adult) Penguin Group (USA) Inc.

—Bones & the Cupcake Mystery. Newman, Barbara, illus. 2008. (Jeffrey Bones Mystery Ser.: No. 3). 32p. (J). (gr. 1-3). pap. 3.99 (***978-0-14-241147-6(7)*** , Puffin) Penguin Group (USA) Inc.

—Bones & the Cupcake Mystery. Newman, Barbara Johansen, illus. 2005. (Jeffrey Bones Mystery Ser.: No. 3). 32p. (J). (gr. k-3). 13.99 (978-0-670-05939-3(0) , Viking Juvenile) Penguin Group (USA) Inc.

—Bones & the Dinosaur Mystery. Newman, Barbara Johansen, illus. 2005. (Jeffrey Bones Mystery Ser.: No. 4). 32p. (J). (978-0-670-05970-6(6) , Viking Adult) Penguin Group (USA) Inc.

—Bones & the Dog Gone Mystery. Newman, Barbara, illus. 2008. (Jeffrey Bones Mystery Ser.: No. 2). 32p. (J). (gr. k). pap. 3.99 (***978-0-14-241043-1(8)*** , Puffin) Penguin Group (USA) Inc.

—Bones & the Dog Gone Mystery. Newman, Barbara Johansen, illus. 2004. (Jeffrey Bones Mystery Ser.: No. 2). 32p. (J). (gr. k-3). 13.99 (978-0-670-05948-5(X) , Viking Juvenile) Penguin Group (USA) Inc.

—Bones & the Math Test Mystery. Newman, Barbara Johansen, illus. 2008. 32p. (J). (gr. k). 13.99 (***978-0-670-06262-1(6)*** , Viking Adult) Penguin Group (USA) Inc.

—Cam Jansen & the Barking Treasure Mystery. Natti, Susanna, illus. (Cam Jansen Ser.: No. 19). 64p. (J). (gr. 2-4). 2005. pap. 3.99 (978-0-14-240319-8(9) , Puffin); 1999. 13.99 (978-0-670-88516-9(9) , Viking Juvenile) Penguin Group (USA) Inc.

—Cam Jansen & the Barking Treasure Mystery. 2001. (Cam Jansen Ser.: No. 19). 10.79 (978-0-606-22506-9(4)) Tandem Library Bks.

—Cam Jansen & the Birthday Mystery. Natti, Susanna, illus. (Cam Jansen Ser.: No. 20). 64p. (J). 2005. (gr. 2-4). pap. 3.99 (978-0-14-240354-9(7) , Puffin); 2000. (gr. 3-7). 13.99 (978-0-670-88877-1(X) , Viking Juvenile) Penguin Group (USA) Inc.

—Cam Jansen & the Catnapping Mystery. 1998. (Cam Jansen Ser.: No. 18). (Illus.). 64p. (J). (gr. 2-5). 13.99 (978-0-670-88044-7(2) , Viking Juvenile) Penguin Group (USA) Inc.

—Cam Jansen & the Catnapping Mystery. 2000. (Cam Jansen Ser.: No. 18). 10.79 (978-0-606-20353-1(2)); (J). (978-0-606-20227-5(7)) Tandem Library Bks.

—Cam Jansen & the First Day of School Mystery, Vol. 22. Natti, Susanna, illus. 2002. (Cam Jansen Ser.: No. 22). 80p. (J). 13.99 (978-0-670-03575-5(0) , Viking Juvenile) Penguin Group (USA) Inc.

—Cam Jansen & the Ghostly Mystery. Natti, Susanna, illus. 2005. (Cam Jansen Ser.: No. 16). 64p. (J). (gr. 2-4). pap. 3.99 (978-0-14-240287-0(7) , Puffin) Penguin Group (USA) Inc.

—Cam Jansen & the Mystery of Flight 54. 1999. (Cam Jansen Ser.: No. 12). (Illus.). (J). lib. bdg. 5.30 (978-0-15-314312-0(6)) Harcourt Schl. Pubs.

—Cam Jansen & the Mystery of the Babe Ruth Baseball. Natti, Susanna, illus. 2004. (Cam Jansen Ser.: No. 6). 64p. (J). (gr. 2-4). pap. 3.99 (978-0-14-240015-9(7) , Puffin) Penguin Group (USA) Inc.

—Cam Jansen & the Mystery of the Babe Ruth Baseball. (Cam Jansen Ser.: No. 6). 57p. (J). (gr. 2-4). pap. 3.99 (978-0-8072-1347-6(0) , Listening Library) Random Hse. Audio Publishing Group.

—Cam Jansen & the Mystery of the Babe Ruth Baseball. 1998. (Cam Jansen Ser.: No. 6). (J). 3.50 (978-0-439-04442-4(1)) Scholastic, Inc.

—Cam Jansen & the Mystery of the Dinosaur Bones. 2004. (Cam Jansen Ser.: No. 3). (Illus.). 64p. (J). (gr. 2-4). pap. 3.99 (978-0-14-240012-8(2) , Puffin) Penguin Group (USA) Inc.

—Cam Jansen & the Mystery of the Gold Coins. 2004. (Cam Jansen Ser.: No. 5). (Illus.). 64p. (YA). (gr. 2-4). 3.99 (978-0-14-240014-2(9) , Puffin) Penguin Group (USA) Inc.

MNO

—Cam Jansen & the Mystery of the Television Dog. 2004. (Cam Jansen Ser.: No. 4). (Illus.). 64p. (J). (gr. 2-4). pap. 3.99 (978-0-14-240013-5(0) , Puffin) Penguin Group (USA) Inc.

—Cam Jansen & the Mystery of the UFO. Natti, Susanna, illus. 2004. (Cam Jansen Ser.: No. 2). 64p. (J). (gr. 2-4). pap. 3.99 (978-0-14-240011-1(4) , Puffin) Penguin Group (USA) Inc.

—Cam Jansen & the Scary Snake Mystery. Natti, Susanna, illus. 2005. (Cam Jansen Ser.: No. 17). 64p. (J). (gr. 2-4). pap. 3.99 (978-0-14-240288-7(5) , Puffin) Penguin Group (USA) Inc.

—Cam Jansen & the Scary Snake Mystery. 1999. (Cam Jansen Ser.: No. 17). (J). 10.79 (978-0-606-17411-4(7)) Tandem Library Bks.

—Cam Jansen & the Secret Service Mystery. Natti, Susanna, illus. 2006. (Cam Jansen Ser.). 64p. (J). (gr. 2). 13.99 (978-0-670-06092-4(5) , Viking Juvenile) Penguin Group (USA) Inc.

—Cam Jansen & the Summer Camp Mysteries: A Super Special. Allen, Joy, illus. 2007. (Cam Jansen Ser.). 128p. (J). 4.99 (978-0-14-240742-4(9) , Puffin); 14.99 (978-0-670-06218-8(9) , Viking Adult) Penguin Group (USA) Inc.

—Cam Jansen & the Tennis Trophy Mystery. Natti, Susanna, tr. Natti, Susanna, illus. 2003. (Cam Jansen Ser.: No. 24). 64p. (J). 13.99 (978-0-670-03643-1(9) , Viking Juvenile) Penguin Group (USA) Inc.

—Cam Jansen Double Mystery: Cam Jansen & the Mystery of the Dinosaur Bones; Cam Jansen & the Mystery of the U.F.O. Natti, Susanna, illus. 2000. (Cam Jansen Ser.: Nos. 2-3). 128p. (J). (gr. 2-5). 5.99 (978-0-670-89365-2(X) , Viking Juvenile) Penguin Group (USA) Inc.

—The Catnapping Mystery. Natti, Susanna, illus. 2005. (Cam Jansen Ser.: No. 18). 64p. (J). (gr. 2-4). pap. 3.99 (978-0-14-240289-4(3) , Puffin) Penguin Group (USA) Inc.

—The Chocolate Fudge Mystery. Natti, Susanna, illus. 2004. (Cam Jansen Ser.: No. 14). 64p. (J). (gr. 2-4). pap. 3.99 (978-0-14-240211-5(7) , Puffin) Penguin Group (USA) Inc.

—The First Day of School Mystery. Natti, Susanna, illus. 2005. (Cam Jansen Ser.: No. 22). 64p. (J). (gr. 2-4). pap. 3.99 (978-0-14-240326-6(1) , Puffin) Penguin Group (USA) Inc.

—The Mystery of Flight 54. Natti, Susanna, illus. 2004. (Cam Jansen Ser.: No. 12). 64p. (J). (gr. 2-4). pap. 3.99 (978-0-14-240179-8(X) , Puffin) Penguin Group (USA) Inc.

—The Mystery of the Carnival Prize. 2004. (Cam Jansen Ser.: No. 9). (Illus.). 64p. (J). (gr. 2-4). pap. 3.99 (978-0-14-240018-0(1) , Puffin) Penguin Group (USA) Inc.

—The Mystery of the Circus Clown. 2004. (Cam Jansen Ser.: No. 7). (Illus.). 64p. (J). (gr. 2-4). pap. 3.99 (978-0-14-240016-6(5) , Puffin) Penguin Group (USA) Inc.

—The Mystery of the Monkey House. Natti, Susanna, illus. 2004. (Cam Jansen Ser.: No. 10). 64p. (J). (gr. 2-4). pap. 3.99 (978-0-14-240019-7(X) , Puffin) Penguin Group (USA) Inc.

—The Mystery of the Monster Movie. 2004. (Cam Jansen Ser.: No. 8). (Illus.). 64p. (J). (gr. 2-4). pap. 3.99 (978-0-14-240017-3(3) , Puffin) Penguin Group (USA) Inc.

—The Mystery of the Stolen Corn Popper. Natti, Susanna, illus. 2004. (Cam Jansen Ser.: No. 11). 64p. (J). (gr. 2-4). pap. 3.99 (978-0-14-240178-1(1) , Puffin) Penguin Group (USA) Inc.

—The Mystery of the Stolen Diamonds. Natti, Susanna, illus. 2004. (Cam Jansen Ser.: No. 1). 64p. (J). (gr. 2-4). pap. 3.99 (978-0-14-240010-4(6) , Puffin) Penguin Group (USA) Inc.

—The School Play Mystery, Vol. 21. Natti, Susanna, illus. 2005. (Cam Jansen Ser.: No. 21). 64p. (J). (gr. 2-4). pap. 3.99 (978-0-14-240355-6(5) , Puffin) Penguin Group (USA) Inc.

—The Secret Service Mystery. Natti, Susanna, illus. 2008. (Cam Jansen Ser.: No. 26). 64p. (J). (gr. 2). pap. 3.99 ***(978-0-14-241074-5(8)** , Puffin) Penguin Group (USA) Inc.

—The Snowy Day Mystery. Natti, Susanna, illus. 2005. (Cam Jansen Ser.: No. 24). 64p. (J). (gr. 2-4). pap. 3.99 (978-0-14-240417-1(9) , Puffin) Penguin Group (USA) Inc.

—The Triceratops Pops Mystery. Natti, Susanna, illus. 2004. (Cam Jansen Ser.: No. 15). 64p. (J). (gr. 2-6). pap. 3.99 (978-0-14-240206-1(0) , Puffin) Penguin Group (USA) Inc.

—The Valentine Baby Mystery. Natti, Susanna, illus. (Cam Jansen Ser.: No. 25). 80p. (J). 2006. (gr. 2). pap. 3.99 (978-0-14-240694-6(5) , Puffin); 2005. (gr. 3-7). 13.99 (978-0-670-06009-2(7) , Viking Juvenile) Penguin Group (USA) Inc.

—Young Cam Jansen & the Baseball Mystery. Moore, Lisa, ed. Natti, Susanna, illus. 2001. (Young Cam Jansen Ser.: No. 5). 32p. (J). pap. 3.99 (978-0-14-131106-7(1) , Puffin) Penguin Group (USA) Inc.

—Young Cam Jansen & the Baseball Mystery. Natti, Susanna, illus. 1999. (Young Cam Jansen Ser.: No. 5). 32p. (J). (gr. k-3). 14.99 (978-0-670-88481-0(2) , Viking Juvenile) Penguin Group (USA) Inc.

—Young Cam Jansen & the Dinosaur Game. Natti, Susanna, illus. 1998. (Young Cam Jansen Ser.: No. 1). 32p. (J). (gr. k-3). pap. 3.99 (978-0-14-037779-8(4) , Puffin) Penguin Group (USA) Inc.

—Young Cam Jansen & the Dinosaur Game. 1998. (Young Cam Jansen Ser.: No. 1). (J). (978-0-606-13934-2(6)) Tandem Library Bks.

—Young Cam Jansen & the Double Beach Mystery. Natti, Susanna, illus. (Young Cam Jansen Ser.: No. 8). 32p. (J). (gr. k-2). 2003. pap. 3.99 (978-0-14-250079-8(8) , Puffin); 2002. 13.99 (978-0-670-03531-1(9) , Viking Juvenile) Penguin Group (USA) Inc.

—Young Cam Jansen & the Double Beach Mystery. Natti, Susanna, illus. 2003. (Young Cam Jansen Ser.: No. 8). 30p. (J). (ps). lib. bdg. 11.80 (978-0-613-67477-5(4)) Tandem Library Bks.

—Young Cam Jansen & the Ice Skate Mystery. 2000. (Young Cam Jansen Ser.: No. 4). (Illus.). 32p. (J). (gr. k-3). pap. 3.99 (978-0-14-130012-2(4) , Puffin) Penguin Group (USA) Inc.

—Young Cam Jansen & the Ice Skate Mystery. 2000. (Young Cam Jansen Ser.: No. 4). (978-0-606-17776-4(0)); lib. bdg. 11.80 (978-0-613-22667-7(4)) Tandem Library Bks.

—Young Cam Jansen & the Library Mystery. Natti, Susanna, illus. (Young Cam Jansen Ser.: No. 7). 32p. (J). 2002. pap. 3.99 (978-0-14-230202-6(3) , Puffin); 2001. 14.99 (978-0-670-89281-5(5) , Viking Juvenile) Penguin Group (USA) Inc.

—Young Cam Jansen & the Library Mystery. 2002. (Young Cam Jansen Ser.: No. 7). (gr. k-3). lib. bdg. 11.80 (978-0-613-50582-6(4)) Tandem Library Bks.

—Young Cam Jansen & the Lions' Lunch Mystery. Natti, Susanna, illus. 2007. 32p. (J). 13.99 (978-0-670-06171-6(9) , Viking Juvenile) Penguin Group (USA) Inc.

—Young Cam Jansen & the Lost Tooth. Natti, Susanna, illus. 1999. (Young Cam Jansen Ser.: No. 3). 32p. (J). (gr. k-3). pap. 3.99 (978-0-14-130273-7(9) , Puffin) Penguin Group (USA) Inc.

—Young Cam Jansen & the Lost Tooth. 1999. (Young Cam Jansen Ser.: No. 3). (gr. k-3). lib. bdg. 11.80 (978-0-613-17895-2(5)) Tandem Library Bks.

—Young Cam Jansen & the Missing Cookie. Natti, Susanna, illus. 1998. (Young Cam Jansen Ser.: No. 2). 32p. (J). (gr. k-3). pap. 3.99 (978-0-14-038050-7(7) , Puffin) Penguin Group (USA) Inc.

—Young Cam Jansen & the Missing Cookie. 1998. (Young Cam Jansen Ser.: No. 2). (J). (978-0-606-13935-9(4)) Tandem Library Bks.

—Young Cam Jansen & the New Girl Mystery. Natti, Susanna, illus. 32p. (J). 2005. pap. 3.99 (978-0-14-240353-2(9) , Puffin); Vol. 10. 2004. 13.99 (978-0-670-05915-7(3) , Viking Juvenile) Penguin Group (USA) Inc.

—Young Cam Jansen & the Pizza Shop Mystery. Natti, Susanna, illus. 2001. (Young Cam Jansen Ser.: No. 6). 32p. (J). pap. 3.99 (978-0-14-230020-6(9) , Puffin) Penguin Group (USA) Inc.

—Young Cam Jansen & the Pizza Shop Mystery. 2001. (Young Cam Jansen Ser.: No. 6). (gr. k-3). lib. bdg. 11.80 (978-0-613-44435-4(3)) Tandem Library Bks.

—Young Cam Jansen & the Spotted Cat Mystery. (Young Cam Jansen Ser.). 32p. (J). (gr. k-3). 2007. 3.99 ***(978-0-14-241012-7(8)** , Puffin); 2006. (Illus.). 13.99 (978-0-670-06094-8(1) , Viking Juvenile) Penguin Group (USA) Inc.

—Young Cam Jansen & the Substitute Mystery. Natti, Susanna, illus. 2005. (Viking Easy-To-Read Ser.). 32p. (J). (gr. k-3). 13.99 (978-0-670-05988-1(9) , Viking Juvenile) Penguin Group (USA) Inc.

—Young Cam Jansen & the Zoo Note Mystery. Natti, Susanna, illus. (Young Cam Jansen Ser.). 32p. (J). 2004. pap. 3.99 (978-0-14-240204-7(4) , Puffin); 2003. 13.99 (978-0-670-03626-4(9) , Viking Juvenile) Penguin Group (USA) Inc.

Adone, Claudio. My Grandfather Jack the Ripper. 2000. Tr. of Mio Nonno Jack Lo Squartatore. (Illus.). 304p. (J). (gr. 7-10). 19.00 (978-1-928746-16-4(0)) Herodias.

Adorjan, Carol. The Cat Sitter Mystery. 2000. (Illus.). 116p. (gr. 4-7). pap. 9.95 (978-0-595-14087-9(4) , Backinprint.com) iUniverse, Inc.

—The Copy Cat Mystery. 2000. 128p. (gr. 4-7). pap. 9.95 (978-0-595-14491-4(8) , Backinprint.com) iUniverse, Inc.

Agbodza, Ena and Kwami. The Bad Ices Man & the Girl Who Saved Christmas. 2006. (Illus.). 45p. (J). per. 9.95 (978-1-59453-782-0(8) , Airleaf Publishing) Airleaf Publishing & Bookselling.

Aiken, Joan. Died on a Rainy Sunday. l.t. ed. 1999. (General Ser.). 192p. (YA). pap. 24.95 (978-0-7862-1962-9(9)); (978-0-7540-3811-5(4)) Thorndike Pr.

Alcorn, Steve. A Matter of Justice. 2003. (J). (978-1-59426-002-5(8)) Mundania Pr.

Alderink, Georgia. Who's Been Soaking in My Hot Tub? 2005. 50p. pap. 12.95 (978-1-4137-6077-4(5)) PublishAmerica, Inc.

Alexander, Fern. Hello, Hollywood. 2007. (Nancy Drew Movie Ser.). 32p. (J). pap. 3.99 (978-1-4169-3900-9(8) , Simon Spotlight) Simon & Schuster Children's Publishing.

Alexander, Heather. The Case of the Easter Egg Race. 2004. 84p. (J). (ps-17). 11.79 (978-0-606-32976-7(5)) Tandem Library Bks.

Alexander, Nina. The Case of the 202 Clues. 1998. (New Adventures of Mary-Kate & Ashley Ser.). (Illus.). 87p. (J). (gr. 2-7). pap. 3.99 (978-0-590-29307-5(9)) Scholastic, Inc.

Alfaya, Javier. Una Luz en la Marisma. 1998. (SPA., Illus.). 128p. (YA). (gr. 9-12). 12.95 (978-84-204-4806-0(0)) Alfaguara, Ediciones, S.A.- Grupo Santillana ESP. *Dist:* Santillana USA Publishing Co., Inc.

Alger, Horatio. The Store Boy. 2006. 170p. pap. 11.99 ***(978-1-4264-4359-6(5)**); 182p. pap. 14.99 ***(978-1-4264-4397-8(8))** BiblioBazaar.

—The Store Boy. 2006. pap. ***(978-1-4065-0722-5(9))** Dodo Pr.

Alison, Hart. Spy on Home Front, Molly Myste. Jean-P, Tibbles, illus. 2005. (American Girls Collection). 176p. (J). 10.95 (978-1-58485-996-3(2) , American Girl) American Girl Publishing, Inc.

Allen, Kathleen. Witch Hunter. 2005. 131p. pap. 19.95 (978-1-4137-7839-7(9)) PublishAmerica, Inc.

Allison, Jennifer. Gilda Joyce & the Ladies of the Lake. 2006. 352p. (J). (gr. 5). 15.99 (978-0-525-47693-1(8) , Dutton Juvenile) Penguin Group (USA) Inc.

Allison, Jennifer. The Ladies of the Lake: Gilda Joyce. 2007. 352p. (J). (gr. 5). 7.99 ***(978-0-14-240907-7(3)** , Puffin) Penguin Group (USA) Inc.

Aloha Bear - Footprint Detective. 2002. (J). pap. 8.99 (978-0-89610-290-3(4)) Island Heritage Publishing.

Alvarez, Julia. Las Huellas Secretas. Negrin, Fabin, illus. 2002. (SPA.). 40p. (J). (ps-2). pap. 6.99 (978-0-440-41764-4(3)); lib. bdg. 17.99 (978-0-385-90857-3(1)) Random Hse. Children's Bks. (Dragonfly Bks.).

Anastasio, Dina. The Case of the Grand Canyon Eagle. Saflund, Birgitta, illus. 2000. (Juliet Stone Mystery Ser.: No. 1). 73p. (Orig.). (gr. 5 up). pap. 6.95 (978-1-879373-84-6(X)) Rinehart, Roberts Pubs.

Anderson, Carolyn D. Granny¿s Favorite Tales. Anderson, Carolyn D. et al, illus. 2006. 156p. (J). per. 39.95 ***(978-1-60002-098-8(4)** , 3915, Airleaf Publishing) Airleaf Publishing & Bookselling.

Anderson, Janet. The Last Treasure. 2004. 272p. (J). (gr. 5). pap. 6.99 (978-0-14-240217-7(6) , Puffin) Penguin Group (USA) Inc.

Anderson, Jean & Lininger, Linda. Calistoga Candlestick Caper. 2000. 124p. (J). (gr. 4 up). pap. 14.95 (978-0-9678605-9-6(8)) InfoHi Publishing.

—Missing on Maui. 2002. (Hannah & Niki Mysteries Ser.: Vol. 3). (J). pap. 14.95 (978-0-9717849-1-8(4)) InfoHi Publishing.

Anderson, M. T. The Clue of the Linoleum Lederhosen: M. T. Anderson's Thrilling Tales. Cyrus, Kurt, illus. (M. T. Anderson's Thrilling Tales Ser.). 272p. (J). 2007. pap. 5.95 (978-0-15-205407-6(3) , Harcourt Paperbacks); 2006. 15.00 (978-0-15-205352-9(2)) Harcourt Children's Bks.

Anderson, M. T. Jasper Dash & the Flame-Pits of Delaware: M. T. Anderson's Thrilling Tales. Cyrus, Kurt, illus. 2008. (M. T. Anderson's Thrilling Tales Ser.). 300p. (J). 16.00 ***(978-0-15-205346-8(8))** Harcourt Children's Bks.

Anderson, Max Elliot. Mountain Cabin Mystery. 2004. 144p. pap. 10.95 (978-0-9729256-3-1(5) , Tweener Pr.) Baker Trittin Pr.

Andrews, Ted. Spirits, Ghosts & Guardians. Haugen, Diane, ed. 2001. (Young Person's School of Magic & Mystery Ser.: Vol. 5). (Illus.). 256p. (J). (gr. 7 up). 18.95 (978-1-888767-41-4(3)) Dragonhawk Publishing.

Anfousse, Ginette. Un Terrible Secret. 2001. (Roman + — Special Editions Ser.). (FRE.). 96p. (YA). (gr. 8). pap. (978-2-89021-513-9(X)) Diffusion du livre Mirabel.

Angello, Mary L. Rings of Power. 2001. 108p. (J). (gr. 4-7). pap. 9.95 (978-0-595-20231-7(4) , Writers Club Pr.) iUniverse, Inc.

Annette: The Desert Inn Mystery. 2003. (Illus.). pap. 15.99 (978-0-7868-4559-0(7)) Disney Pr.

Annette & the Mystery at Moonstone Bay. 2003. (Illus.). pap. 15.99 (978-0-7868-4560-6(0)) Disney Pr.

Annette & the Mystery at Smugglers' Cove. 2003. (Illus.). pap. 15.99 (978-0-7868-4558-3(9)) Disney Pr.

Anno, Masaichiro & Anno, Mitsumasa. Anno's Mysterious Multiplying Jar. 1999. (Illus.). 44p. (J). (gr. k-3). pap. 8.99 (978-0-698-11753-2(0) , Putnam Juvenile) Penguin Group (USA) Inc.

—Anno's Mysterious Multiplying Jar. 1999. (J). 15.79 (978-0-606-16852-6(4)); lib. bdg. 17.60 (978-0-613-14536-7(4)) Tandem Library Bks.

Anson-Weber, Joan. Snuffles Goes to Scotland Yard. Russell, Judith, illus. 2001. (J). 16.95 (978-0-87797-293-8(1)) Cherokee Publishing Co.

Anyone's Guess Teen Kits: A Murderous Melodrama. 2004. 39.95 (978-1-932146-26-4(1) , Upstart Bks.) Highsmith Inc.

Anza, Ana Luisa. El Misterio de la Casa Chueca (y el Bulto Color Mugre) Escobar, Antonio Rocha, illus. rev. ed. 2006. (Castillo de la Lectura Naranja Ser.). (SPA.). 120p. (J). pap. 7.95 (978-970-20-0200-0(1)) Castillo, Ediciones, S. A. de C. V. MEX. *Dist:* Macmillan.

Applegate, Katherine. Elfangor's Secret. 1999. (Animorphs Ser.: No. 3). (J). (gr. 3-7). 12.64 (978-0-606-16619-5(X)) Tandem Library Bks.

—The Suspicion. 1998. (Animorphs Ser.: No. 24). (J). (gr. 3-7). pap. 179.64 (978-0-590-63052-8(0)) Scholastic, Inc.

Appleton, Victor. Moving Picture Boys at Panama. 2006. pap. ***(978-1-4065-0890-1(X))** Dodo Pr.

—The Moving Picture Boys on the Coast or Showing up the Perils of the Deep. 2004. reprint ed. pap. 24.95 (978-1-4179-1612-2(5)) Kessinger Publishing, LLC.

—Moving Picture Boys on the War Front or. 2006. pap. ***(978-1-4065-0891-8(8))** Dodo Pr.

Appleton, Victor. On Top of the World. 2007. (Tom Swift, Young Inventor Ser.: No. 5). 160p. (J). pap. 4.99 (978-1-4169-3643-5(2) , Aladdin) Simon & Schuster Children's Publishing.

Ardagh, Philip. Heir of Mystery: The Second Unlikely Exploit. Roberts, David, illus. 2004. (Unlikely Exploits Ser.). 144p. (J). 9.95 (978-0-8050-7477-2(5) , Holt, Henry & Co. Bks. For Young Readers) Holt, Henry & Co.

Arensen, Shel. The Carjackers, Vol. 2. 2003. (Rugendo Rhino Ser.). 128p. pap. 5.99 (978-0-8254-2042-9(3)) Kregel Pubns.

—The Poison Arrow Tree. 2003. (Rugendo Rhino Ser.). (Illus.). 128p. (J). pap. 5.99 (978-0-8254-2041-2(5)) Kregel Pubns.

Arnold, Chirley. Double Trouble: A Novel. 160p. (YA). pap. 7.95 (978-1-56236-454-0(5)) Aspen Bks.

Arnold, Hap. The Secret of Council Hill. Wathen, Kieran, illus. 2000. (Council Hill Adventure Ser.: Vol. 1). viii, 136p. (J). (gr. 2-6). pap. 7.99 (978-0-9700809-0-5(5)) Pyxis Pr.

Arnold, Tedd. Rat Life. 2007. 208p. (YA). (gr. 7 up). 16.99 (978-0-8037-3020-5(9) , Dial) Penguin Group (USA) Inc.

Arrigan, Mary. The Spirits of the Attic. 2001. 128p. (J). pap. 9.95 (978-1-901737-27-1(6)) Anvil Bks., Ltd. IRL. *Dist:* Dufour Editions, Inc.

Asad, Megan Emily. The Juggler's Journey. 2005. 144p. pap. 9.95 (978-0-7599-4470-1(9)) Hard Shell Word Factory.

Ashby, Freya Katrina. Summer at the Dunes: A Deirdre Carlisle Mystery. 2007. 108p. per. 9.95 ***(978-0-595-43663-7(3))** iUniverse, Inc.

Ashley, Elana. Splunkunio Splunkey Detective & Peacemaker Detective y Pacificador: Case One: The Missing Friendship Bracelet Caso Primero: El Brazalete de la Amistad Desaparecido. Nikolov, Stefan V., tr. Ashley, Elana, photos by. 2005. (SPA & ENG., Illus.). 32p. (J). (gr. k-3). 17.95 (978-0-9744812-1-0(1)) Dream Image Pr., LLC.

Atanacio, Frank. Aggravating Factors: From the Nick Barnum Sealed Case File a Nick Barnum Novel II. 2003. 128p. (YA). pap. 10.95 (978-0-595-26985-3(0)) iUniverse, Inc.

Athkins, D. E. Swans in the Mist. 2006. 256p. (YA). (gr. 9 up). pap. 5.99 (978-1-4169-0047-4(0) , Simon Pulse) Simon & Schuster Children's Publishing.

Atkins, Ron. Abby & the Bicycle Caper. 2004. 48p. pap. 8.95 (978-0-595-30565-0(2)) iUniverse, Inc.

Atwater-Rhodes, Amelia. Midnight Predator. 256p. (YA). (gr. 7). 2003. pap. 5.99 (978-0-440-23797-6(1) , Laurel Leaf); 2002. 9.95 (978-0-385-32794-7(3) , Delacorte Bks. for Young Readers) Random Hse. Children's Bks.

—Midnight Predator. 2003. (gr. 7-12). lib. bdg. 13.55 (978-0-613-72270-4(1)) Tandem Library Bks.

Auer, Chris. The Chinese Puzzle Box. 2005. 128p. (J). pap. 4.99 (978-0-310-70872-8(9)) Zonderkidz.

—The Forgotten Room. 2005. 128p. (J). pap. 4.99 (978-0-310-70873-5(7)) Zonderkidz.

—Hidden in Plain Sight. 2005. (Illus.). 128p. (J). pap. 4.99 (978-0-310-70870-4(2)) Zonderkidz.

—A Stranger, a Thief & a Pack of Lies. 2005. (Illus.). 128p. (J). pap. 4.99 (978-0-310-70871-1(0)) Zonderkidz.

Ausbun, Nellie M. Skip & Meow. 2001. 22p. (J). per. 8.95 (978-0-7414-0613-2(6)) Infinity Publishing.

Avi. Midnight Magic. 2001. (978-0-606-22158-0(1)); (gr. 5-8). lib. bdg. 13.00 (978-0-613-54286-9(X)) Tandem Library Bks.

—The Traitors' Gate. Raude, Karina, illus. 2007. 368p. (J). (gr. 6-9). 17.99 (978-0-689-85335-7(1) , Atheneum/ Richard Jackson Bks.) Simon & Schuster Children's Publishing.

—Windcatcher. 1999. (J). (gr. 3-6). lib. bdg. 13.00 (978-0-8335-9328-3(5)) Tandem Library Bks.

Ayres, Katherine. Under Copp's Hill. 2000. (American Girl Collection). (Illus.). (J). (978-0-606-20963-2(8)) Tandem Library Bks.

—Voices at Whisper Bend. 1999. (American Girl Collection Ser.). (978-0-606-17521-0(0)) Tandem Library Bks.

Babbitt, Natalie. El Cerro del Abismo. 2003. (SPA., Illus.). 128p. (J). (gr. 3-5). (978-84-236-3420-0(5) , ED0964) Edebé ESP. *Dist:* Lectorum Pubns., Inc.

—Goody Hall. 2007. (Illus.). 192p. (J). pap. 6.99 ***(978-0-312-36983-5(2))** Square Fish.

—Kneeknock Rise. 2007. (Illus.). 144p. (J). pap. 6.99 ***(978-0-312-37009-1(1))** Square Fish.

Baccalario, Pierdomenico. The Door to Time. Dunfey, Beth, ed. Janeczko, Leah, tr. from ITA. Bruno, Iacopo, illus. 2006. (Ulysses Moore Ser.: No. 1). 240p. (J). (gr. 4-7). pap. 12.99 (978-0-439-77438-3(1)) Scholastic, Inc.

Backman, Aidel, illus. & adapted by. The Money in the Honey. Backman, Aidel, adapted by. 2003. 32p. (J). 13.95 (978-0-8266-0030-1(1)) Merkos L'Inyonei Chinuch.

Baglio, Ben M. The Dog with No Name. 2005. (Illus.). 148p. (J). (978-0-439-74617-5(5)) Scholastic, Inc.

—Horse in the House. Gregory, Jenny, illus. 2002. (Animal Ark Ser.: No. 26). 176p. (J). 3.99 (978-0-439-34387-9(9)) Scholastic, Inc.

—Looking for Lola. 2005. 141p. (J). (978-0-439-68885-7(X)) Scholastic, Inc.

—Max Is Missing. 2005. (Pet Finders Club Ser.: Vol. 2). (Illus.). 126p. (J). pap. ***(978-0-439-68884-0(1))** Scholastic, Inc.

—Rescuing Raisin. 2005. 136p. (J). (978-0-439-68886-4(8)) Scholastic, Inc.

Baglio, Ben M. Runaway Rascal. 2006. (Illus.). 157p. (J). ***(978-0-439-79250-9(9))** Scholastic, Inc.

Bailey, Linda. How Can I Be a Brilliant Detective Shine in the Dark? (Stevie Diamond Mystery Ser.). 200p. (YA). (gr. 13 up). 1999. (978-1-55074-750-8(9)); No. 6. 2004. (978-1-55074-896-3(3)) Kids Can Pr., Ltd.

—How Can I Be a Detective...? (Stevie Diamond Mysteries Ser.). 160p. (YA). (gr. 13 up). (978-1-55337-584-5(X)) Kids Can Pr., Ltd.

—How Come the Best Clues Are Always in the Garbage? 2004. (Stevie Diamond Mysteries Ser.). 176p. (YA). (gr. 13 up). (978-1-55337-583-8(1)) Kids Can Pr., Ltd.

—What's a Serious Detective Like Me Doing in Such a Silly Movie? (Stevie Diamond Mystery Ser.). 192p. (YA). 2004. (gr. 13 up). (978-1-55074-922-9(6)); 2004. (gr. 13 up). (978-1-55074-926-7(9)); 2003. (978-1-55337-639-2(0)) Kids Can Pr., Ltd.

Bailie, Helen. The Azura Stones. 2007. 212p. (YA). per. 18.00 ***(978-1-58982-374-7(5)** , Bedside Bks.) American Bk. Publishing Group.

Bajoria, Paul. The God of Mischief. Bertholf, Bret, illus. 2007. 400p. (J). (gr. 3-7). pap. 6.99 ***(978-0-316-01628-5(4))** Little, Brown Bks. for Young Readers.

The Baker Street Bunch & the Missing Honeybees Mystery. 2005. (J). per. (978-0-9754241-5-5(7)) MiMar Publishing.

Baldacci, David. Last Man Standing. 2002. (gr. 7-12). lib. bdg. 16.45 (978-0-613-60424-6(5)) Tandem Library Bks.

Baldwin, Rich & Jones, Sandie. The Detective Company. Dawn, Baumer, illus. 2004. 183p. (YA). pap. 9.95 (*978-0-9742920-0-7(1) , 2001) Buttonwood Pr.

Baldwin, Richard L. The Searing Mysteries, 3 in 1 vols. Garber, Gail, ed. 2001. 80p. (YA). (gr. 5-12). pap. (978-0-9660685-6-6(4)) Buttonwood Pr.

Balian, Lorna. Un Fiasco de Bruja. 2004. Tr. of Humbug Witch. (SPA., Illus.). 32p. (J). (ps). pap. 4.95 (978-1-59572-011-5(1)) Star Bright Bks., Inc.

Ballard, Mignon F. Aunt Matilda's Ghost. 2000. (Illus.). vii, 136p. (J). 22.50 (978-1-57072-116-8(5)); pap. 12.50 (978-1-57072-132-8(7)) Overmountain Pr.

Balliett, Blue. Chasing Vermeer. Helquist, Brett, illus. 272p. (J). 2004. (gr. 3-6). pap. 16.95 (978-0-439-37294-7(1)); 2005. reprint ed. 6.99 (978-0-439-37297-8(6)) Scholastic, Inc.

—The Wright 3. Helquist, Brett, illus. (J). 2007. 352p. (gr. 4-7). pap. 6.99 (*978-0-439-69368-4(3) , Scholastic Paperbacks); 2006. 272p. pap. 16.99 (978-0-439-69367-7(5) , Scholastic Pr.) Scholastic, Inc.

—The Wright 3. l.t. ed. 2006. 334p. (YA). 23.95 (978-0-7862-9024-6(2)) Thorndike Pr.

Balmer, Fred. Festus & the Hole in the Fence Gang. Newcomb, Kristene, illus. 2005. 33p. (J). per. 7.00 (*978-0-9760790-3-3(8)) Folsom Fallies Pr.

—Festus & the Missing Bag of Feed. Newcomb, Kristene, illus. 2004. 26p. (J). per. 7.00 (*978-0-9760790-0-2(3)) Folsom Fallies Pr.

Balouch, Kristen. Mystery Bottle. Balouch, Kristen, illus. 2006. (Illus.). 32p. (ps-3). 15.99 (978-0-7868-0999-8(X)) Hyperion Pr.

Banerjee, Anjali & Emesse, Tea. Rani & the Wedding Ghost. 2007. (Star Sisterz Ser.). 144p. (J). (gr. 3-7). pap. 4.99 (978-0-7869-4165-0(0) , Mirrorstone) Wizards of the Coast.

Banim, Lisa. Case at Camp Get-Me-Outie! Junior Novel. 2nd novel rev. ed. 2004. (Lizzie McGuire Original Mystery Ser.: No. 2). (Illus.). 128p. (gr. 3-7). pap. 4.99 (978-0-7868-4621-4(6) , Disney Editions) Disney Pr.

Banim, Lisa. In the Doghouse. 2005. 124p. (J). lib. bdg. 16.92 (*978-1-4242-0685-8(5)) Fitzgerald Bks.

Banim, Lisa & Minsky, Terri. The Case of the Kate Haters. 2005. (Illus.). 124p. (J). (*978-1-4156-3927-6(2)) Disney Pr.

Banjerji, Sujata. A Dark, Dark Tale. 2002. (BEN & ENG., Illus.). 29p. (J). 19.95 (978-1-85269-395-4(9)) Mantra Publishing, Ltd. GBR. *Dist:* AIMS International Bks., Inc.

Banks, Lynne Reid. The Mystery of the Cupboard. (Indian in the Cupboard Ser.: No. 4). 246p. (J). (gr. 4-7). pap. 4.99 (978-0-8072-1459-6(0) , Listening Library) Random Hse. Audio Publishing Group.

Banks, Steven. Catdog Undercover. 2000. (gr. 3-6). lib. bdg. 11.80 (978-0-613-21308-0(4)) Tandem Library Bks.

Banscherus, Jurgen. Detective's Duel. Baron, Daniel C., tr. from GER. Butschkow, Ralf, illus. 2007. 65p. (J). (gr. 3-6). lib. bdg. 22.60 (*978-1-59889-339-7(4)) Stone Arch Bks.

—The Great Snake Swindle. Baron, Daniel C., tr. from GER. Butschkow, Ralf, illus. 2007. 67p. (J). (gr. 3-6). lib. bdg. 22.60 (*978-1-59889-340-3(8)) Stone Arch Bks.

—Trouble under the Big Top. Baron, Daniel C., tr. from GER. Butschkow, Ralf, illus. 2007. 63p. (J). (gr. 3-5). lib. bdg. 22.60 (*978-1-59889-338-0(6)) Stone Arch Bks.

Banscherus, Jurgen & Baron, Daniel C. After School Ghosthunter. Butschkow, Ralf, illus. 2007. 63p. (J). (*978-1-59889-342-7(4)); pap. (*978-1-59889-441-7(2)) Stone Arch Bks.

—Clues in the Car Wash. Butschkow, Ralf, illus. 2007. (J). 40p. (*978-1-59889-337-3(8)); 67p. pap. (*978-1-59889-432-5(3)) Stone Arch Bks.

—Detective's Duel. Butschkow, Ralf, illus. 2007. 65p. (J). pap. (*978-1-59889-434-9(X)) Stone Arch Bks.

—The Great Snake Swindle. Butschkow, Ralf, illus. 2007. 67p. (J). pap. (*978-1-59889-435-6(8)) Stone Arch Bks.

—The Mysterious Mask. Butschkow, Ralf, illus. 2007. 65p. (J). (*978-1-59889-341-0(6)); pap. (*978-1-59889-440-0(4)) Stone Arch Bks.

—The Night of the Blue Heads. Butschkow, Ralf, illus. 2008. (J). pap. (*978-1-59889-910-8(4)); lib. bdg. (*978-1-59889-874-3(4)) Stone Arch Bks.

—The Puzzle of the Power Drain. Butschkow, Ralf, illus. 2008. (J). pap. (*978-1-59889-912-2(0)); lib. bdg. (*978-1-59889-876-7(0)) Stone Arch Bks.

—The Secret of the Flying Cows. Butschkow, Ralf, illus. 2008. (J). pap. (*978-1-59889-913-9(9)); lib. bdg. (*978-1-59889-877-4(9)) Stone Arch Bks.

—The Snarling Suspect. Butschkow, Ralf, illus. 2008. (J). pap. (*978-1-59889-911-5(2)); lib. bdg. (*978-1-59889-875-0(2)) Stone Arch Bks.

—Trouble under the Big Top. Butschkow, Ralf, illus. 2007. 63p. (J). pap. (*978-1-59889-433-2(1)) Stone Arch Bks.

Bar-el, Dan. Things Are Looking up Jack. 2003. (Orca Young Readers Ser.). (Illus.). 128p. (J). (gr. 3-6). pap. 4.99 (978-1-55143-278-6(1)) Orca Bk. Pubs. USA.

Barba, Rick. The Massively Multiplayer Mystery. Steccati, Eve, illus. 2006. (Spy Gear Adventures Ser.). 240p. (J). pap. 4.99 (978-1-4169-0888-3(9) , Aladdin) Simon & Schuster Children's Publishing.

—The Quantum Quandary. 2006. (Spy Gear Adventures Ser.). 208p. (J). pap. 4.99 (978-1-4169-0889-0(7) , Aladdin) Simon & Schuster Children's Publishing.

Barbo, Maria S. Catnapped Caper. del Sur, Duendes, illus. 2000. (Scooby-Doo! Picture Clue Book Ser.: No. 1). 32p. (J). (ps-3). pap. 3.99 (978-0-439-16010-0(3) , Scholastic Paperbacks) Scholastic, Inc.

Barker, Clive. Days of Magic, Nights of War. Barker, Clive, illus. 2005. (Abarat Ser.). 512p. (J). pap. 11.99 (978-0-06-440932-2(5) , Harper Trophy) HarperCollins Pubs.

Barklem, Jill. La Escalera Secreta.Tr. of Secret Staircase. (SPA.). 30p. (J). 8.95 (978-84-233-2765-2(5)) Ediciones Destino ESP. *Dist:* Planeta Publishing Corp.

Barnes, Creighton D. The Ghost Who Was Afraid of the Dark: The Ghost & the Flag. 2000. 148p. (gr. 4-7). pap. 8.95 (978-1-893652-92-7(0) , Writers Club Pr.) iUniverse, Inc.

Barnett, Angela. Mystic Grove. 2006. pap. 10.00 (*978-1-4257-1912-8(0)) Xlibris Corp.

Barr, Robert. The Clue of the Silver Spoons. 2004. reprint ed. pap. 15.95 (978-1-4191-5701-1(9)); pap. 1.99 (978-1-4192-5701-8(3)) Kessinger Publishing, LLC.

Barrett. Lethal Delivery, Postage Prepaid. (Thumbprint Mysteries Ser.). 32.86 (978-0-8092-0425-0(8)) McGraw-Hill/Contemporary.

Barth, Jeff. The Missionary Adventures of Bob & Arty Bk. 5: The Lighthouse Mystery. Barth, Marge, ed. 2001. (Illus.). 240p. (YA). (gr. 3-12). pap. (978-1-891484-03-2(6)) Barth Family Ministries.

Bartlett, Craig. The Mystery of the Bermuda Triangle. 2001. (Hey Arnold! Ser.: Bk. 6). (Illus.). 64p. (J). pap. 3.99 (978-0-689-83938-2(3) , Simon Spotlight) Simon & Schuster Children's Publishing.

The Baseball Heroes, 6 vols. (Woodland Mysteriestm Ser.). 133p. (gr. 3-7). 42.50 (978-0-7802-7931-5(X)) Wright Group, The.

Battersby, Alan R. East 43rd Street: Level 5. 2001. (English Readers Ser.). (Illus.). 96p. pap. 7.00 (978-0-521-78363-7(1)) Cambridge Univ. Pr.

Bauer, Joan. Peeled. 2008. 256p. (YA). (gr. 7). 16.99 (*978-0-399-23475-0(6) , Putnam Juvenile) Penguin Group (USA) Inc.

Beak, Nick Huckleberry & Boase, Petra. Crafty Detectives. Freeman, John, photos by. 2000. (Crafty Kids Ser.). (Illus.). 64p. (J). (gr. 3 up). lib. bdg. 26.00 (978-0-8368-2501-5(2)) Stevens, Gareth Inc.

Beake, Lesley. One Dark Night. Asenso, Okofo & Torgah, F. K. Atakpa Kple Edoh, trs. 2000. (EWE., Illus.). pap. 3.00 (978-0-521-79578-4(8)) Cambridge Univ. Pr.

—One Dark Night. Ablorh, Samuel Adjei, tr. 2000. (GAA., Illus.). pap. 3.00 (978-0-521-79588-3(5)) Cambridge Univ. Pr.

The Bear Lake Mystery. 2001. 200p. mass mkt. 5.99 (978-0-9708721-0-4(0)) Palmtree Publishing.

Beard, Elizabeth. Liza & the Mysteries. 2004. 70p. (J). per. (978-1-59196-640-1(X)) Instantpublisher.com.

Beatty, Scott. Murder in Mind, Vol. 4. Guice, Butch et al, illus. 2004. (Ruse Ser.: Vol. 4). 160p. (YA). pap. 15.95 (978-1-59314-047-2(9)) CrossGeneration Comics, Inc.

Bell, Albert A., Jr. The Secret of the Lonely Grave. 2007. 160p. pap. 8.95 (*978-1-932158-79-3(0) , Claystone Bks.) Ingalls Publishing Group, Inc.

Bell, Hilari. A Matter of Profit. 2001. 288p. (J). (gr. 7 up). 16.99 (978-0-06-029513-4(9)) HarperCollins Pubs.

—A Matter of Profit. 2003. (gr. 7-12). lib. bdg. 15.30 (978-0-613-60391-1(5)) Tandem Library Bks.

Bellairs, John. The Chessmen of Doom. Gorey, Edward, illus. 2000. (John Bellairs Ser.). 160p. (J). (gr. 3-7). pap. 5.99 (978-0-14-130697-1(1) , Puffin) Penguin Group (USA) Inc.

—The Chessmen of Doom. Gorey, Edward, illus. 2000. 155p. (J). (ps-7). per. 14.15 (978-0-8335-6637-9(7)) Tandem Library Bks.

—The Curse of the Blue Figurine. 2004. (Johnny Dixon Ser.). (Illus.). 208p. (J). pap. 5.99 (978-0-14-240258-0(3) , Puffin) Penguin Group (USA) Inc.

—The Curse of the Blue Figurine. 2000. (J). (gr. 4-8). 21.50 (978-0-8446-7138-3(X)) Smith, Peter Pub., Inc.

—The Eyes of the Killer Robot. 1998. (Johnny Dixon Mystery Ser.). 12.64 (978-0-606-13371-5(2)) Tandem Library Bks.

—The Mummy, the Will, & the Crypt. Gorey, Edward, illus. 2004. (Johnny Dixon Ser.). 176p. (J). pap. 5.99 (978-0-14-240263-4(X) , Puffin) Penguin Group (USA) Inc.

—The Mummy, the Will, & the Crypt. 2001. (J). (gr. 4-8). 21.75 (978-0-8446-7170-3(3)) Smith, Peter Pub., Inc.

—The Revenge of the Wizard's Ghost. 1999. (J). (gr. 3 up). 20.25 (978-0-8446-7010-2(3)) Smith, Peter Pub., Inc.

—The Spell of Sorcerer's Skull. Gorey, Edward, illus. 2004. (Johnny Dixon Ser.). 176p. (J). pap. 5.99 (978-0-14-240265-8(6) , Puffin) Penguin Group (USA) Inc.

—The Spell of the Sorcerer's Skull. 2002. (J). (gr. 3 up). 21.50 (978-0-8446-7206-9(8)) Smith, Peter Pub., Inc.

Belle Prater's Boy. 1999. (Pathways to Critical Thinking Ser.). 32p. (YA). pap., stu. ed., tchr.'s training gde. ed. 19.95 (978-1-58303-081-3(6)) Pathways Publishing.

Bellingham, Brenda. La Maldicion del Cofre de Plata. (SPA.). (YA). 8.95 (978-958-04-7079-3(0)) Norma S.A. COL. *Dist:* Distribuidora Norma, Inc.

Benjamin, David. Hangman. 2001. (Sixth Sense Ser.: Vol. 3). 160p. (J). (gr. 4-7). pap. 4.99 (978-0-439-20272-5(8)) Scholastic, Inc.

Benjamin, Ruth. The Lost Treasure of Chelton. 2004. viii, 170p. (J). 13.95 (978-1-932443-02-8(9)) Judaica Pr., Inc., The.

Benjamin, Ruth. The Mysterious Lighthouse of Chelton. 2006. (ENG.). 160p. (J). 14.95 (*978-1-932443-57-8(6)) Judaica Pr., Inc., The.

Bennett, Elizabeth. Night Is the Time. 2000. (J). 7.99 (978-0-375-90097-6(7)) Random Hse. Children's Bks.

Bennett, Jill. Playing Dead. l.t. ed. 2005. 320p. (J). pap. (978-0-7540-6138-0(8) , CLP 331) BBC Audio.

Bennett, Marcia Allen. Mystery at Saddlecreek. 2003. (Illus.). 162p. (J). pap. 12.95 (978-1-57168-494-3(8) , Eakin Pr.) Eakin Pr.

Bennett, Marcia Allen & Eckhardt, Jason C. Mystery at Saddlecreek. 2004. (Illus.). 162p. (J). 17.95 (978-1-57168-336-6(4) , Eakin Pr.) Eakin Pr.

Berenstain, Stan & Berenstain, Jan. The Berenstain Bear Scouts & the Missing Merit Badges. 1998. (Berenstain Bear Scouts Ser.). (Illus.). 32p. (J). (gr. 3-6). pap. 3.50 (978-0-590-56390-1(4)) Scholastic, Inc.

—The Berenstain Bear Scouts & the Missing Merit Badges. 1998. (Berenstain Bear Scouts Ser.). (J). (gr. 3-6). (978-0-606-13191-9(4)) Tandem Library Bks.

—The Berenstain Bear Scouts & the Search for Naughty Ned. 1998. (Berenstain Bear Scouts Ser.). (Illus.). 32p. (J). (gr. 3-6). pap. 3.50 (978-0-590-56509-7(5)) Scholastic, Inc.

—The Berenstain Bear Scouts & the Search for Naughty Ned. 1998. (Berenstain Bear Scouts Ser.). (J). (gr. 3-6). (978-0-606-13193-3(0)) Tandem Library Bks.

—The Berenstain Bear Scouts & the Stinky Milk Mystery. 1999. (Berenstain Bear Scouts Ser.). (Illus.). 32p. (J). (gr. 3-6). pap. 3.50 (978-0-590-56524-0(9) , Cartwheel Bks.) Scholastic, Inc.

—The Berenstain Bear Scouts & the Stinky Milk Mystery. 1999. (Berenstain Bear Scouts Ser.). (J). (gr. 3-6). (978-0-606-16597-6(5)) Tandem Library Bks.

—The Berenstain Bear Scouts & the White-Water Mystery. 1999. (Berenstain Bear Scouts Ser.). 32p. (J). (gr. 3-6). pap. 3.50 (978-0-590-56522-6(2)) Scholastic, Inc.

—The Berenstain Bear Scouts & the White-Water Mystery. 1999. (Berenstain Bear Scouts Ser.). (J). (gr. 3-6). (978-0-606-16598-3(3)) Tandem Library Bks.

—The Berenstain Bears & the Drug Free Zone. Berenstain, Stan & Berenstain, Jan, illus. 2002. (Berenstain Bears Big Chapter Bks.). (Illus.). (J). (gr. 2-6). 11.91 (978-0-7587-0941-7(2)) Book Wholesalers, Inc.

—The Berenstain Bears & the Escape of the Bogg Brothers. 2000. (Berenstain Bears Ser.). (J). (gr. k-3). (978-0-606-20272-5(2)) Tandem Library Bks.

—The Berenstain Bears & the Missing Watermelon Money. 2001. (Berenstain Bears Ser.). (Illus.). 48p. (J). (gr. 1-3). 11.99 (978-0-679-99230-1(8)); pap. 3.99 (978-0-679-89230-4(3)) Random Hse. Children's Bks. (Random Hse. Bks. for Young Readers).

—The Berenstain Bears & the Phantom of the Gymnasium. 2000. (Illus.). (J). pap. 3.99 (978-0-679-88949-6(3) , Random Hse. Bks. for Young Readers) Random Hse. Children's Bks.

—The Berenstain Bears & the Tic-Tac-Toe Mystery. (Berenstain Bears Ser.). (Illus.). 48p. (J). (gr. k-3). 2003. lib. bdg. 11.99 (978-0-679-99229-5(4)); 2001. pap. 3.99 (978-0-679-89229-8(X)) Random Hse. Children's Bks. (Random Hse. Bks. for Young Readers).

Berkeley, Laura, illus. The Spirit of the Maasai Man. 2000. 32p. (J). (gr. 3-7). 16.95 (978-1-902283-74-6(0)) Barefoot Bks., Inc.

Berlin, Eric. The Puzzling World of Winston Breen. 2007. (Illus.). 215p. (YA). (gr. 8-12). 16.99 (978-0-399-24693-7(2)) Penguin Group (USA) Inc.

Bern, Dave. Best Friends. 2006. 28p. pap. 9.95 (*978-1-4327-0036-2(7)) Outskirts Press, Inc.

Berner, Beth Engelman. The Superhero Dectectives. 2005. (Illus.). 10p. (J). (ps-7). 10.95 (978-1-58117-428-1(4) , Intervisual/Piggy Toes) Dalmatian Pr.

Berry, Connie Lee. The Criminal in the Caymans. 2007. (Incredible Journey Bks.). 85p. (J). pap. 3.95 (*978-0-9772848-0-1(8)) Kid's Fun Pr.

—Treasure in Tahiti. 2007. (Incredible Journey Bks.). 87p. (J). pap. 3.95 (*978-0-9772848-1-8(6)) Kid's Fun Pr.

Berry, Jeanine. The Graveyard Mystery. 2002. (YA). E-Book 9.95 incl. cd-rom (978-1-59201-003-5(2)) Bks. Unbound E-Publishing Co.

Bial, Raymond. Shadow Island: A Tale of Lake Superior. 2006. 176p. (J). (gr. 3-7). 18.95 (978-1-883953-37-9(5)); (gr. 4-7). pap. 12.95 (978-1-883953-36-2(7)) Midwest Traditions, Inc. (Blue Horse Bks.).

Bibee, John. The Home School Detectives Series, 8 vols., Set. Incl. Bk. 1. Mystery of the Homeless Treasure. 119p. (gr. 4-7). 1994. pap. 5.00 (978-0-8308-1911-9(8) , 1911); Bk. 3. Mystery of the Mexican Graveyard. 128p. (gr. 3-7). 1995. pap. 5.00 (978-0-8308-1913-3(4) , 1913); Bk. 4. Mystery of the Campus Crook. 123p. (gr. 4-7). 1996. pap. 4.99 (978-0-8308-1914-0(2) , 1914); Bk. 5. Mystery of the Vanishing Cave. (Illus.). 127p. (gr. 4-7). 1996. mass mkt. 5.00 (978-0-8308-1915-7(0) , 1915); Bk. 6. Mystery at the Broken Bridge. 128p. (gr. 5-7). 1997. pap. 5.00 (978-0-8308-1916-4(9) , 1916); (J). 1998. 39.92 (978-0-8308-1910-2(X) , 1910) InterVarsity Pr.

—The Mystery of the Widow's Watch. 1998. (Home School Detectives Ser.: Vol. 8). 123p. (J). (gr. 3-7). mass mkt. 5.00 (978-0-8308-1918-8(5) , 1918) InterVarsity Pr.

—The Mystery of the Widow's Watch Bk. 8. 1999. (Home School Detectives Ser.). (Illus.). (J). 18.99 (978-0-8308-8661-6(3)) InterVarsity Pr.

Bichoman Vuelve de la Tumba. (Fantasmas de Fear Street Coleccion). (SPA.). (YA). (gr. 5-8). pap. 7.95 (978-950-04-1718-1(9) , EM9292) Emecé Editores S.A. ARG. *Dist:* Lectorum Pubns., Inc., Planeta Publishing Corp.

Biggar, Joan R. Trapped at Haunted Canyon. 1998. (Megan Parnell Mysteries Ser.: Vol. 4). 160p. (J). (gr. 5-9). 5.99 (978-0-570-05069-8(3) , 56-1893) Concordia Publishing Hse.

Bikfalvy, Andrea. The Junkyard Club. 2002. 148p. pap. 15.00 (978-1-59146-055-8(7)) Crystal Dreams Publishing.

Bill Waite's Will. 2001. 32p. (YA). (gr. 6-12). pap. (978-0-8224-3466-5(0)) Globe Fearon Educational Publishing.

Bingley, Lori Derby. Lorelei. 2005. pap. 16.95 (978-1-59088-596-3(1)) Wings ePress, Inc.

Bingley, Margaret. Point Crime: Bored to Death. l.t. ed. 1999. 312p. (J). pap. (978-0-7540-6071-0(3) , CLP 278) BBC Audio.

Birch, Beverley. Rift. 2008. (Illus.). 224p. (YA). pap. 9.95 (*978-1-4052-1589-3(5)) Egmont Bks., Ltd. GBR. *Dist:* Independent Pubs. Group.

Bishop, Mary Harelkin. Tunnels of Tyranny: A Fourth Moose Jaw Adventure. 2005. (Juvenile Novel, Ser.). 312p. (J). (gr. 4-6). pap. 7.95 (978-1-55050-316-6(2)) Coteau Bks. CAN. *Dist:* Fitzhenry & Whiteside, Ltd.

Blackman, Malorie. Dangerous Reality. l.t. ed. 2000. (Illus.). 208p. 18.99 (978-0-7089-9531-0(4)) Ulverscroft Large Print Bks. GBR. *Dist:* Ulverscroft Large Print Bks., Ltd.

Blackwell-Burke, Melissa & Kunkel, Kristen. The Messy Mystery. 2003. (J). spiral bd. 14.95 (978-1-58605-958-3(0) , LeapFrog Schl. Hse.) LeapFrog Enterprises, Inc.

Blackwood, Gary L. Shakespeare's Spy, Vol. 3. 2003. (Shakespeare Stealer Ser.). 288p. (J). (gr. 4-6). 16.99 (978-0-525-47145-5(6) , Dutton Juvenile) Penguin Group (USA) Inc.

Bledsoe, Glen & Bledsoe, Karen, eds. Classic Mysteries Vol. II: A Collection of Mind-Bending Masterpieces. Kiwak, Barbara, illus. 1999. (Roxbury Park Bks.). 128p. (J). (gr. 4-7). pap. 5.95 (978-0-7373-0273-8(9) , 02739W, Roxbury Park) Lowell Hse.

Bloom, Carol Ann. The Secret of the Locked Trunk. 1998. (Magic Mansion Mystery Ser.: No. 1). 125p. (J). (ps-7). pap. 9.99 (978-0-88092-475-7(6) , 4756) Royal Fireworks Publishing Co.

Bloor, Edward. Crusader. 2001. (YA). 14.15 (978-0-606-21132-1(2)) Tandem Library Bks.

Blotcky, Mark. Cameron & Her Missing Shoes. 2006. 28p. pap. 9.95 (*978-1-4327-0035-5(9)) Outskirts Press, Inc.

—Erin & Her Shoe Laces. 2006. 28p. pap. 9.95 (*978-1-4327-0034-8(0)) Outskirts Press, Inc.

Bly, Stephen A. Mysterious Robbery on the Utah Plains. 2005. (Adventures of the American Frontier Ser.). 128p. pap. 6.99 (978-1-58134-473-8(2) , Crossway Bibles) Crossway Bks.

Blyton, Enid. The Adventure of the Strange Ruby. (Illus.). (J). pap. 5.95 (978-0-09-958230-4(9)) Random Hse. GBR. *Dist:* Trafalgar Square Publishing.

—Five Are Together Again. l.t. ed. 2000. 255p. (J). pap. (978-0-7540-6113-7(2) , CLP 308) BBC Audio.

—Five Have a Mystery to Solve. l.t. ed. 2000. (Famous Five Adventure Ser.). (Illus.). 263p. (J). pap. (978-0-7540-6094-9(2) , CLP 293) BBC Audio.

—Five on a Secret Trail. l.t. ed. 1998. (Illus.). 240p. (J). pap. 16.95 (978-0-7540-6024-6(1) , Galaxy Children's Large Print) BBC Audiobooks America.

—Fun for the Secret Seven. l.t. ed. 2005. 144p. (J). pap. (978-0-7540-6186-1(8) , CLP 376) BBC Audio.

—Fun for the Secret Seven. l.t. ed. 2003. (J). pap. 24.95 incl. audio (978-0-7540-6244-8(9) , Galaxy Children's Large Print) BBC Audiobooks America.

—Secret Seven. l.t. ed. 2000. (Illus.). 121p. (J). pap. 16.95 (978-0-7540-6098-7(5) , Galaxy Children's Large Print) BBC Audiobooks America.

—Secret Seven Win Through. l.t. ed. 1999. 167p. (J). pap. (978-0-7540-6068-0(3) , CLP 271) BBC Audio.

—Secret Seven Win Through. unabr. ed. 2000. (Read-Along Ser.). 120p. (J). pap. 24.95 incl. audio (978-0-7540-6221-9(X) , RA022, Chivers Children's Audio Bks.) BBC Audiobooks America.

—A Shock for the Secret Seven. l.t. ed. 2005. 160p. (J). pap. (978-0-7540-6152-6(3) , CLP 344) BBC Audio.

—Well Done, Secret Seven. l.t. ed. 1998. (Illus.). 104p. (J). pap. 16.95 (978-0-7540-6027-7(6) , Galaxy Children's Large Print) BBC Audiobooks America.

Boaz, Ashley. The Mystery of the Midnight Blaze. 2005. (J). (978-0-9761033-6-3(2)) Waldenhouse Pub., Inc.

Bollback, Anthony G. Rescue at Cripple Creek, Vol. 4. 1999. (Jack & Jill Mysteries Ser.). 135p. (J). pap. 7.95 (978-1-885729-18-7(9)) Toccoa Falls College Pr.

Bolte, Mary. Nate the Great: A Classroom Guide. 1998. (Literature Unit Ser.). (Illus.). 48p. (gr. k-3). pap., tchr. ed. 7.99 (978-1-57690-346-9(X) , TCA2346) Teacher Created Materials, Inc.

Bone, Ian. Blood on the Microphone. 2002. (Crime Waves Ser.). (Illus.). 160p. (YA). pap. (978-0-7344-0170-0(1) , Lothian Bks.) Hachette Livre Australia.

—Killer Plot. 2002. (Crime Waves Ser.). (Illus.). 96p. (YA). pap. (978-0-7344-0169-4(8) , Lothian Bks.) Hachette Livre Australia.

Bonner, Anne. Intrigue at Pine Haven: Civil War in Florida. Akridge, Bill, illus. 2006. 220p. (YA). 12.95 net. (978-1-878398-76-5(8) , Blue Note Bks.) Blue Note Pubns.

Bonsall, Crosby N. The Case of the Cat's Meow. Bonsall, Crosby N., illus. 2002. (Illus.). (J). 12.30 (978-0-7587-6045-6(0)) Book Wholesalers, Inc.

—The Case of the Double Cross. Bonsall, Crosby N., illus. 2002. (Illus.). (J). 12.34 (978-0-7587-6046-3(9)) Book Wholesalers, Inc.

—The Case of the Dumb Bells. Bonsall, Crosby N., illus. 2002. (Illus.). (J). 12.30 (978-0-7587-6047-0(7)) Book Wholesalers, Inc.

—The Case of the Hungry Stranger. Bonsall, Crosby N., illus. 2002. (Illus.). (J). 12.30 (978-0-7587-6048-7(5)) Book Wholesalers, Inc.

Boraks-Nemetz, Lillian. The Lenski File. 2001. (On Time's Wing Ser.). (Illus.). 176p. (YA). (gr. 9 up). pap. (978-1-896184-76-0(6)) Roussan Pubs., Inc./Roussan Editeur, Inc.

Borsky, Mary. Benny Bensky & the Perogy Palace. 2001. (978-0-606-22811-4(X)); (gr. 3-6). lib. bdg. 16.40 (978-0-613-50180-4(2)) Tandem Library Bks.

—Benny Bensky & the Perogy Palace. Hendry, Linda, illus. 2001. 128p. (J). (gr. 3-7). pap. 7.95 (978-0-88776-523-0(8)) Tundra Bks., Inc./Livres Toundra, Inc. CAN. *Dist:* Random Hse., Inc.

Bosch, Pseudonymous. The Name of This Book Is Secret. Ford, Gilbert, illus. rev. ed. 2007. 384p. (J). (gr. 3-7). 16.99 (*978-0-316-11366-3(2)) Little, Brown Bks. for Young Readers.

Bossley, Michele Martin. Cracked. 2007. (Orca Currents Ser.). 112p. (YA). (gr. 5 up). pap. (*978-1-55143-700-2(7)); lib. bdg. (*978-1-55143-702-6(3)) Orca Bk. Pubs.

Bossley, Michele Martin. Swiped. 2006. 112p. (J). lib. bdg. 14.95 (978-1-55143-652-4(3)); (gr. 5 up). pap. 8.95 (978-1-55143-646-3(9)) Orca Bk. Pubs. USA.

Boulden, Jim & Boulden, Joan. The Silver Dollar Mystery. Tate, Susan, ed. Prudhomme, Suzanne, illus. 1999. 24p. (J). (gr. 4-6). pap. 5.95 (978-1-892421-08-1(9), 08-9AB) Boulden Publishing.

Bow, James. Unwritten Girl. 2006. 180p. (J). pap. 12.99 (*978-1-55002-604-7(6), Boardwalk Bks.) Dundurn Group, The CAN. *Dist:* Univ. of Toronto Pr.

Bow, Patricia. The Spiral Maze. 2004. 192p. pap. (978-1-895449-68-6(5)) Thistledown Pr., Ltd.

Bowen, Gary. The Mare's Nest. Kimble, Warren, illus. 2001. 48p. (J). (gr. 1-5). 17.95 (978-0-06-028408-4(0)); (gr. 3-6). 17.89 (978-0-06-028407-7(2)) HarperCollins Pubs.

Bowkett, Stephen. Detective Files. Burroughs, Dave, illus. 2008. (J). (*978-1-59889-826-2(4)) Stone Arch Bks.

The Boxcar Children Paperback Bookcase. 2004. (J). pap. 17.95 (978-0-8075-0861-9(6)) Whitman, Albert & Co.

Boyd, David. Beware the Vikings. Rooth, Mike, illus. 2007. 48p. (J). lib. bdg. 23.08 (*978-1-4242-1624-6(9)) Fitzgerald Bks.

Boyer. The Mystery of the Medicine Woman's Cave. 2002. 187p. pap. 19.95 (978-1-59129-872-4(5)) PublishAmerica, Inc.

Braden, Richard. The Archer House Mystery. 2002. 128p. pap. 10.95 (978-0-595-21497-6(5), Writer's Showcase Pr.) iUniverse, Inc.

Bradman, Tony. Has Anyone Seen Jack? Chamberlain, Margaret, illus. 1999. 24p. (J). (ps-1). pap. 7.99 (978-0-7112-0728-8(3)) Lincoln, Frances Ltd. GBR. *Dist:* Transition Vendor.

—Sam the Detective, Vol. 5. 2000. (Illus.). 140p. (J). pap. 4.95 (978-0-440-86310-6(4)) Transworld Publishers Ltd. GBR. *Dist:* Trafalgar Square Publishing.

—Sam the Girl Detective. 2000. (Illus.). 96p. (J). pap. 4.95 (978-0-440-86212-3(4)); pap. 3.95 (978-0-440-86241-3(8)) Transworld Publishers Ltd. GBR. *Dist:* Trafalgar Square Publishing.

Brafman, Bonnie. Treasure in Marci's House. 2007. (J). pap. 8.00 (*978-0-8059-7418-8(0)) Dorrance Publishing Co., Inc.

Brannigan's Folly. 64p. (YA). (gr. 6-12). pap. (978-0-8224-2360-7(X)) Globe Fearon Educational Publishing.

Braun, Lilian Jackson. The Cat Who Robbed a Bank. 2001. (gr. 5-8). lib. bdg. 15.30 (978-0-613-51483-5(1)) Tandem Library Bks.

Brewster, Joy. The Roller Ghoster. del Sur, Duendes, illus. 2004. (Scooby-Doo Mysteries Ser.). 48p. (J). (gr. 1 up). pap. 3.99 (978-0-439-70128-0(7)) Scholastic, Inc.

—Snowman Snowdown. 2004. (Illus.). 46p. (J). (978-0-439-55712-2(7)) Scholastic, Inc.

Brewster, Joy & Gelsey, James. Mean Green Mystery Machine, Vol. 2. del Sur, Duendes, illus. 2004. (Scooby-Doo Mysteries Ser.). 48p. (J). (gr. 1 up). pap. 3.99 (978-0-439-70129-7(5)) Scholastic, Inc.

Brian, Kate. Inner Circle. 2007. (Private Ser.). 224p. (YA). (gr. 9 up). pap. 9.99 (*978-1-4169-5041-7(9), Simon Pulse) Simon & Schuster Children's Publishing.

Bricker, Sandra D. Freeze Frame. Taylor, Marjorie, illus. rev. ed. 1999. (Take Ten Ser.). 45p. (YA). (gr. 4-12). pap. 3.95 (978-1-58659-005-5(7)) Artesian Pr.

—Freeze Frame. 2000. (gr. 7-12). lib. bdg. 11.80 (978-0-613-51050-9(X)) Tandem Library Bks.

Bridges, Mitzi P. The Hoax Bk. II: The Delaney Family Mysteries. 2000. 108p. (gr. 4-7). pap. 9.95 (978-0-595-12914-0(5), Writers Club Pr.) iUniverse, Inc.

Bridges, Mitzi Pool. Fire Island. 2000. 116p. (gr. 4-7). pap. 9.95 (978-0-595-12757-3(6)) iUniverse, Inc.

—The Magic Star Book III: The Delaney Family Mysteries. 2001. 112p. pap. 9.95 (978-0-595-19145-1(2), Writers Club Pr.) iUniverse, Inc.

Brignole, Giancarla, tr. El Misterio del Condor. Polastri, Rosa Elena, illus. (Fabulas De Familia Ser.). (SPA.). 32p. (978-970-20-0270-3(2)) Castillo, Ediciones, S. A. de C. V.

Brin, Susannah. Timber. rev. ed. 1999. (Take Ten Ser.). 64p. (YA). (gr. 4-12). pap. 3.95 (978-1-58659-044-4(8)) Artesian Pr.

—Timber. 2000. (gr. 5-8). lib. bdg. 11.80 (978-0-613-51227-5(8)) Tandem Library Bks.

Broach, Elise. Shakespeare's Secret. 2007. 272p. (J). pap. 5.99 (*978-0-312-37132-6(2)) Square Fish.

Brockmeier, Kevin. Grooves: A Kind of Mystery. 2006. 208p. (J). 15.99 (978-0-06-073691-0(7)); lib. bdg. 16.89 (978-0-06-073692-7(5)) HarperCollins Pubs.

Brookes, Diane & Adler, David A. Cam Jansen & the Mystery of the Dinosaur Bones: Novel Study for Grades Two & Three. 1998. (J). pap., tchr. ed. (978-0-9683234-8-9(0)) Raven Rock Publishing.

Brooks, Dawn Marie. Cat-Ice. 2004. 175p. pap. 13.95 (978-0-7414-2240-8(9)) Infinity Publishing.

Brooks, Erik, illus. Octavius Bloom & the House of Doom. 2003. 32p. (J). (gr. 1-3). 15.95 (978-0-8075-5820-1(6)) Whitman, Albert & Co.

Brooks, Martha. Traveling on into the Light: And Other Stories. 160p. (J). reprint ed. 7.95 (978-0-88899-237-6(8)) Groundwood Bks. CAN. *Dist:* Transition Vendor.

Brooks, Walter R. Freddy & the IgnormOus. Wiese, Kurt, illus. 2001. 288p. (J). pap. 6.99 (978-0-14-230043-5(8), Puffin) Penguin Group (USA) Inc.

—Freddy & the Ignormus. 2001. (gr. 3-6). lib. bdg. 15.30 (978-0-613-43621-2(0)) Tandem Library Bks.

—Freddy Plays Football. Wiese, Kurt, illus. 2001. 265p. (J). (gr. 4-7). 23.95 (978-1-58567-133-5(9)) Overlook Pr., The.

—Freddy Plays Football. Wiese, Kurt, illus. 2002. 272p. (J). pap. 7.99 (978-0-14-230207-1(4), Puffin) Penguin Group (USA) Inc.

—Freddy Plays Football. 2002. (gr. 3-6). lib. bdg. 16.45 (978-0-613-54415-3(3)) Tandem Library Bks.

Brouillet, Chrystine. Mysteres de Chine. 2002. (Roman Jeunesse Ser.). (FRE.). 96p. (YA). (gr. 4-7). pap. (978-2-89021-189-6(4)) Diffusion du livre Mirabel.

—Un Rendez-Vous Troublant. 2001. (Roman + — Special Editions Ser.). (FRE., Illus.). 96p. (YA). (gr. 8). pap. (978-2-89021-491-0(5)) Diffusion du livre Mirabel.

Brouwer, Sigmund. Accidental Detective, Vols. 1-4. 2002. (Accidental Detectives Ser.). (J). pap. 23.99 (978-0-7642-8321-5(9)) Bethany Hse. Pubs.

—All-Star Pride. 2006. 144p. (J). pap. 8.95 (978-1-55143-635-7(3)) Orca Bk. Pubs. USA.

—Cobra Threat: Football. 2007. (Orca Sports Ser.). 176p. (YA). (gr. 5 up). pap. (*978-1-55143-725-5(2)) Orca Bk. Pubs.

—Hurricane Power. 2007. (Orca Sports Ser.). 176p. (YA). (gr. 5 up). pap. (*978-1-55143-865-8(8)) Orca Bk. Pubs.

—Legend of the Gilded Saber. 2002. (gr. 3-6). lib. bdg. 14.15 (978-0-613-89740-2(4)) Tandem Library Bks.

—Mystery Tribe of Camp Blackeagle. 2003. (gr. 5-8). lib. bdg. 14.15 (978-0-613-84509-0(9)) Tandem Library Bks.

—Phantom Outlaw at Wolf Creek. 2005. (Accidental Detectives Ser.). 144p. (J). pap. 5.99 (978-0-7642-2578-9(2)) Bethany Hse. Pubs.

—The Volcano of Doom. 2002. (Accidental Detectives). 144p. (J). pap. 5.99 (978-0-7642-2564-2(2)) Bethany Hse. Pubs.

—Volcano of Doom. 2002. (gr. 3-6). lib. bdg. 14.15 (978-0-613-87242-3(8)) Tandem Library Bks.

Brown, Ann. The Portal & the Key. 2001. 128p. (gr. 4-7). pap. 9.95 (978-0-595-15850-8(1), Writer's Showcase Pr.) iUniverse, Inc.

Brown, Gary. Sam's Mission Call. Tanner, Stephanie, illus. 24p. (J). 12.95 (978-0-910523-13-4(4)) Grandin Bk. Co.

Brown, Jeremy. Four-Minute Forensic Mysteries: Body of Evidence. 2006. (J). (Crime Files Ser.). 19.95 (978-0-439-89554-5(5)); (Crime Files: Four-Minute Forensic Mystery Ser.: Vol. 01). 208p. pap. 5.99 (978-0-439-76934-1(5), Scholastic Paperbacks) Scholastic, Inc.

—Shadow of a Doubt. 2006. (Crime Files Ser.). 224p. (J). pap. 5.99 (978-0-439-76935-8(3), Scholastic Paperbacks) Scholastic, Inc.

Brown, Marc. Arthur's Mystery Babysitter. Brown, Marc, illus. 2004. (Arthur's 8 x 8 Bks.). (Illus.). 24p. (J). (ps-3). pap. 3.99 (978-0-316-73394-6(6), Tingley, Megan Bks.) Little, Brown Bks. for Young Readers.

—The Mystery of the Stolen Bike. 8th ed. 1998. (Arthur Chapter Bks.: Bk. 8). (Illus.). 64p. (J). (gr. 2-4). pap. 4.25 (978-0-316-11571-1(1)) Little, Brown Bks. for Young Readers.

Brown, Ruth. A Dark, Dark Tale. 2004. (CHI, VIE, GUJ, ENG & SOM., Illus.). 27p. (J). (978-1-85269-457-9(2)) Mantra Publishing, Ltd.

—A Dark, Dark Tale. 2000. (Illus.). (J). (ARA & ENG.). 29p. 19.95 (978-1-85269-394-7(0)); (GUJ, ENG, VIE, CHI & SOM., 27p. 19.95 (978-1-85269-396-1(7)); (SOM, ENG, VIE, CHI & GUJ., 27p. 17.95 (978-1-85269-398-5(3)) Mantra Publishing, Ltd. GBR. *Dist:* AIMS International Bks., Inc.

—A Dark, Dark Tale. 2004. (Illus.). 32p. (J). pap. (978-0-09-987400-3(8), Red Fox) Random Hse. Children's Bks.

—A Dark, Dark Tale. 2004. (J). (gr. k-5). 24.95 incl. audio (978-0-89719-768-7(2), HRA275); pap. 14.95 incl. audio (978-0-89719-769-4(0), PRA275) Weston Woods Studios, Inc.

Brown, Ruth. The Old Tree: An Environmental Fable. Brown, Ruth, illus. 2007. (Illus.). 32p. (J). (ps-3). 16.99 (*978-0-7636-3461-2(1)) Candlewick Pr.

Brown, Ruth & Denham, Sylvia. A Dark, Dark Tale. 1998. (ENG & CHI., Illus.). 27p. (J). 19.95 (978-1-85269-399-2(1)) Mantra Publishing, Ltd. GBR. *Dist:* AIMS International Bks., Inc.

Bryant, Annie. Ghost Town. 2007. (Beacon Street Girls Ser.: Bk. 11). 250p. (J). (gr. 4-8). pap. 7.10 (*978-1-933566-09-2(4)) B*tween Productions, Inc.

Bryant, Megan E. The Great Valentine Mystery. Pierce, Mindy, illus. 2003. 24p. (J). (ps-1). pap. 4.99 (978-0-448-43281-6(1), Grosset & Dunlap) Penguin Group (USA) Inc.

Buchanan, Paul. Return of the Eagle. 2000. (gr. 5-8). lib. bdg. 11.80 (978-0-613-51222-0(7)) Tandem Library Bks.

—The Return of the Eagle. Taylor, Marjorie, illus. rev. ed. 1999. (Take Ten Ser.). 54p. (YA). (gr. 4-12). pap. 3.95 (978-1-58659-002-4(2)) Artesian Pr.

Buckeridge, Anthony. Jennings Follows a Clue. 2002. 212p. pap. (978-0-7551-1366-8(7)) House of Stratus, Inc.

Buckey, Sarah Masters. The Curse of Ravenscourt: A Samantha Mystery. 2005. (American Girls Collection). (Illus.). 192p. (YA). pap. 6.95 (978-1-58485-987-1(3), American Girl) American Girl Publishing, Inc.

—Enemy in the Fort. 2001. (American Girl Collection). (Illus.). (J). 12.60 (978-0-606-21180-2(2)) Tandem Library Bks.

—The Light in the Cellar: A Molly Mystery. 2007. 176p. (J). 10.95 (*978-1-59369-159-2(9)); pap. 6.95 (*978-1-59369-158-5(0)) American Girl Publishing, Inc.

Buckey, Sarah Masters. The Smuggler's Treasure. 1999. (American Girl Collection Ser.). (978-0-606-17520-3(2)) Tandem Library Bks.

Buckey, Sarah Masters & Ross, Peg. Stolen Sapphire: A Samantha Mystery. 2006. 192p. (J). 10.95 (978-1-59369-100-4(9)); pap. 6.95 (978-1-59369-099-1(1)) American Girl Publishing, Inc. (American Girl).

Buckley, Michael. The Fairy Tale Detectives. Ferguson, Peter, illus. 2005. (Sisters Grimm Ser.: Bk. 1). 288p. (J). (gr. 3-7). 14.95 (978-0-8109-5925-5(9)) Abrams Bks. for Young Readers) Abrams, Harry N., Inc.

—Magic & Other Misdemeanors. Ferguson, Peter, illus. 2007. (Sisters Grimm Ser.: Bk. 5). 304p. (YA). (gr. 3-7). 14.95 (*978-0-8109-9358-7(9), Amulet Bks.) Abrams, Harry N., Inc.

—Once upon a Crime. Ferguson, Peter, illus. 2007. (Sisters Grimm Ser.: Bk. 4). 288p. (J). (gr. 2-8). 14.95 (*978-0-8109-1610-4(X), Amulet Bks.) Abrams, Harry N., Inc.

—The Problem Child. Ferguson, Peter, illus. 2007. (Sisters Grimm Ser.: Bk. 3). 320p. (YA). (gr. 3-7). pap. 5.95 (*978-0-8109-9359-4(7)) Abrams, Harry N., Inc.

—The Unusual Suspects. Ferguson, Peter, illus. 2007. (Sisters Grimm Ser.: Bk. 2). 320p. (J). (gr. 2-8). pap. 5.95 (*978-0-8109-9323-5(6), Amulet Bks.) Abrams, Harry N., Inc.

Bullimore, Tom. Sherlock Holmes' Mini-Mysteries. 2005. (Illus.). 112p. pap. 6.95 (978-1-4027-2653-8(8)) Sterling Publishing Co., Inc.

Bunting, Eve. The Ghost Children. 2005. (J). 176p. (gr. 4-6). pap. 5.95 (978-0-618-60477-7(4)); 166p. (*978-1-4156-2991-8(9)) Houghton Mifflin Co. Trade & Reference Div. (Clarion Bks.).

—The Ghost Children. 2005. 166p. (J). (gr. 3-7). per. 13.00 (978-0-606-34237-7(0)) Tandem Library Bks.

Bunting, Eve. Man with the Red Bag. 2007. 240p. (J). (gr. 5 up). 15.99 (*978-0-06-081828-9(X)); lib. bdg. 16.89 (*978-0-06-081835-7(2)) HarperCollins Pubs. (Cotler, Joanna Books).

Burchett, Jan, et al. Exile. 2006. (Lady Grace Mysteries, from the Daybookes of Lady Grace Cavendish Ser.). 208p. (J). (gr. 3-7). 7.95 (978-0-385-73322-9(4)); lib. bdg. 9.99 (978-0-385-90341-7(3)) Random Hse. Children's Bks. (Delacorte Bks. for Young Readers).

Burgess, Robert F. The Mystery of Mound Key. 2000. (Illus.). 192p. (gr. 4-7). pap. 12.95 (978-0-595-00348-8(6), Backinprint.com) iUniverse, Inc.

The Buried Eye, 6 vols. (Woodland Mysteriestm Ser.). 133p. (gr. 3-7). 42.50 (978-0-7802-7932-2(8)) Wright Group, The.

Burke, Jan. Bones: An Irene Kelly Novel. 2001. (Signet Classics Ser.). (Illus.). (J). 13.64 (978-0-606-20575-7(6)) Tandem Library Bks.

Burke, Morgan. Get It Started. 2005. (Party Room Ser.: No. 1). 272p. (YA). (gr. 11 up). pap. 5.99 (978-0-689-87225-9(9), Simon Pulse) Simon & Schuster Children's Publishing.

Burkhard, Daryl. Riddle in the Mountain. Riccio, Frank, illus. 2005. 240p. 16.95 (978-0-9668289-5-5(X)) Nomad Pr.

Burns, Emily. Manitou Art Caper. 2003. (Rocky Mountain Mysteries Ser.: 2). 128p. (J). per. 4.95 (978-0-9723259-1-2(3), RMM2) Covered Wagon Publishing LLC.

—Marked Evidence. 2003. (Rocky Mountain Mysteries Ser.: 3). (J). per. 4.95 (978-0-9723259-2-9(1), RMM3) Covered Wagon Publishing LLC.

Burns, Emily R. Mystery on Rampart Hill. Breeding, John, illus. 2002. (Rocky Mountain Mysteries Ser.: 1). 113p. (J). per. 4.95 (978-0-9723259-0-5(5), RMM1) Covered Wagon Publishing LLC.

Burns, Laura J. & Metz, Melinda. The Case of the Nana-Napper, Vol. 2. 2005. (Wright & Wong Ser.: No. 2). 176p. (J). (gr. 3-7). pap. 5.99 (978-1-59514-015-9(8)) Penguin Group (USA) Inc.

—The Case of the Prank That Stank, Vol. 1. 2005. (Wright & Wong Ser.: No. 1). 192p. (J). (gr. 3-7). pap. 5.99 (978-1-59514-014-2(X)) Penguin Group (USA) Inc.

Burr, Daniela. Murder in Hollywood Hills. 2007. (Nancy Drew Movie Ser.). 128p. (J). pap. 5.99 (978-1-4169-3899-6(0), Simon Spotlight) Simon & Schuster Children's Publishing.

Burron, Arnold. One Man to Beat. 2002. 156p. (YA). (gr. 6-12). pap. 6.99 (978-0-9673697-2-3(X)) Diamond Peak Pr.

Burrus, Craig D. The Mystery of Shadow Lake. 2000. 124p. (YA). (gr. 4-7). pap. 9.95 (978-0-595-12542-5(5)) iUniverse, Inc.

Burt, Steve. Oddest Yet: Even More Stories to Chill the Heart. Hagerman, Jessica, illus. 2004. 144p. (gr. 5 up). pap. 14.95 (978-0-9741407-1-1(6)) Burt Creations.

Butcher, A. J. The Serpent Scenario. 2004. (Spy High Ser.: Vol. 3). 224p. (J). (gr. 5-8). pap. 6.99 (978-0-316-73766-1(6)) Little, Brown Bks. for Young Readers.

Butcher, Kristin. Summer of Suspense. 2002. (Science Squad Adventure Ser.). (Illus.). 160p. (J). (gr. 3-2). pap. 6.95 (978-1-55285-362-7(4)) Whitecap Bks., Ltd. CAN. *Dist:* Firefly Bks., Ltd.

Butcher, Nancy. Lights! Camera! Action Dog! l.t. ed. 2000. (Wishbone Mysteries Ser.: No. 11). (Illus.). 139p. (J). (gr. 4 up). lib. bdg. 23.33 (978-0-8368-2694-4(9)) Stevens, Gareth Inc.

Butler, Darren J. The Case of the Missing Locket: Abbie Girl Spy Mystery. Greer, Margaret, ed. Casteel, Kaye, illus. 2000. (Abbie, Girl Spy Ser.). 140p. (J). (gr. 3-9). lib. bdg. 12.99 (978-0-9700752-1-5(9)) Onstage Publishing, LLC.

—The Case of the Missing Locket: An Abbie Girl Spy Mystery. Greer, Margaret, ed. Casteel, Kaye, illus. 2000. (Abbie, Girl Spy Ser.). 140p. (J). (gr. 3-9). pap. 5.99 (978-0-9700752-0-8(0)) Onstage Publishing, LLC.

—The Ducks & Diamonds Mystery: Abbie Girl Spy Mystery. 2000. (Abbie, Girl Spy Ser.: 2). (J). 6.99 (978-0-9700752-8-4(6)) Onstage Publishing, LLC.

—The Ducks & Diamonds Mystery: Abbie Girl Spy Mystery. Greer, Margaret, ed. 2000. (Abbie, Girl Spy Ser.). 200p. (J). (gr. 3-7). lib. bdg. 16.95 (978-0-9700752-6-0(X)) Onstage Publishing, LLC.

—The Masterpiece: An Abbie Girl Spy Mystery. Casteel, Kay, illus. 2004. (Abbie, Girl Spy Ser.: 4). (ENG.). 278p. (J). mass mkt. 8.50 (978-0-9753367-3-1(8)) Onstage Publishing, LLC.

—The Secret of Crybaby Hollow. 2004. (YA). mass mkt. 6.99 (*978-0-9753367-5-5(4)) Onstage Publishing, LLC.

Butler, Darren J. The Secret of Crybaby Hollow: Abbie Girl Spy Mystery. Hamilton, Dianne & Greer, Margaret, eds. Casteel, Kaye, illus. 2002. (Abbie, Girl Spy Ser.: 3). 242p. (J). 16.95 (978-0-9700752-9-1(4)) Onstage Publishing, LLC.

Butler, Dori. Detective Cluck & the Missing Hens. 2005. 22.00 (*978-1-4108-4192-6(8)) Benchmark Education Co.

Butler, William S. Scraper Jones: Treasure Hunter. 2007. 320p. pap. 19.95 (*978-1-59663-770-2(6), Castle Keep Pr.) Rock, James A. & Co. Pubs.

Byars, Betsy. The Black Tower. (Herculeah Jones Ser.). 144p. (J). 2007. (gr. 3). 6.99 (*978-0-14-240937-4(5), Puffin); 2006. (gr. 4). 10.99 (978-0-670-06174-7(3), Viking Adult) Penguin Group (USA) Inc.

—The Blossoms & the Green Phantom. 146p. (J). (gr. 4-6). pap. 3.99 (978-0-8072-1443-5(4), Listening Library) Random Hse. Audio Publishing Group.

—The Dark Stairs. 2006. (Herculeah Jones Mystery Ser.). 160p. (J). pap. 5.99 (978-0-14-240592-5(2), Puffin) Penguin Group (USA) Inc.

—The Dark Stairs: A Herculeah Jones Mystery. (Herculeah Jones Mystery Ser.). 160p. (J). (gr. 3-5). pap. 4.99 (978-0-8072-1478-7(7), Listening Library) Random Hse. Audio Publishing Group.

—Dead Letter. 2006. (Herculeah Jones Mystery Ser.). 160p. (J). (gr. 3). pap. 5.99 (978-0-14-240564-2(7), Puffin) Penguin Group (USA) Inc.

—Dead Letter: A Herculeah Jones Mystery. 1998. (Herculeah Jones Mystery Ser.). 11.64 (978-0-606-13320-3(8)) Tandem Library Bks.

—Death's Door. 2006. (Herculeah Jones Mystery Ser.). 144p. (J). (gr. 3). pap. 5.99 (978-0-14-240565-9(5), Puffin) Penguin Group (USA) Inc.

—Death's Door: A Herculeah Jones Mystery. 2000. (Illus.). (J). 12.64 (978-0-606-18400-7(7)); 1999. (gr. 3-6). lib. bdg. 14.15 (978-0-613-17783-2(5)) Tandem Library Bks.

—Disappearing Acts. 2006. (Herculeah Jones Mystery Ser.). 144p. (J). (gr. 3). pap. 5.99 (978-0-14-240566-6(3), Puffin) Penguin Group (USA) Inc.

—Disappearing Acts. 1999. (Herculeah Jones Mystery Ser.). (Illus.). (J). 11.64 (978-0-606-18401-4(5)) Tandem Library Bks.

—King of Murder. 2007. (Herculeah Jones Mystery Ser.). 144p. (J). pap. 5.99 (978-0-14-240759-2(3), Puffin) Penguin Group (USA) Inc.

—The King of Murder: A Herculeah Jones Mystery. 2006. 80p. (J). (gr. 4). 10.99 (978-0-670-06065-8(8), Viking Juvenile) Penguin Group (USA) Inc.

—Tarot Says Beware. 2006. (Herculeah Jones Mystery Ser.). 160p. (J). (gr. 3). pap. 5.99 (978-0-14-240593-2(0), Puffin) Penguin Group (USA) Inc.

Calderon, Eduardo Caballero. Bolivar: Una Historia que Parece un Cuento. (SPA.). (J). 8.95 (978-958-04-7161-5(4)) Norma S.A. COL. *Dist:* Distribuidora Norma, Inc.

Call of the Selkie: Individual Title Six-Packs. (Action Packs Ser.). 104p. (gr. 3-5). 44.00 (978-0-7635-2991-8(5)) Rigby Education.

Cameron, Ann. Julian, Secret Agent. 2002. (Illus.). (J). 12.87 (978-0-7587-1353-7(3)) Book Wholesalers, Inc.

Campbell, Daniel. Bad to the Bone. 2000. (gr. 3-6). lib. bdg. 13.00 (978-0-613-30975-2(8)) Tandem Library Bks.

Campbell, Danny & Campbell, Kimberly. Bad to the Bone. 2000. (Doug: No. 6). (Illus.). 112p. (gr. 2-7). pap. 4.99 (978-0-7868-4412-8(4)) Disney Pr.

—True Graffiti. 2nd ed. 2000. (Doug: No. 2). (Illus.). 80p. (gr. 3-7). pap. 4.99 (978-0-7868-4383-1(7)) Disney Pr.

Campbell, Joanna. Melanie's Last Ride. 1998. (Thoroughbred Ser.: No. 29). 192p. (gr. 4-7). mass mkt. 4.99 (978-0-06-106531-6(5), Harper Entertainment) HarperCollins Pubs.

—Starstruck. 2004. (Thoroughbred Ser.: No. 63). (gr. 3-6). lib. bdg. 13.00 (978-0-613-71520-1(9)) Tandem Library Bks.

Campbell, Julie. The Gatehouse Mystery. 2003. (Trixie Belden Ser.: Vol. 3). (Illus.). 272p. (gr. 3-7). lib. bdg. 9.99 (978-0-375-92579-5(1), Random Hse. Bks. for Young Readers) Random Hse. Children's Bks.

—The Gatehouse Mystery. Stevens, Mary, illus. ed. 2003. (Trixie Belden Ser.: No. 3). 272p. (J). (gr. 3-7). 6.99 (978-0-375-82579-8(7), Random Hse. Bks. for Young Readers) Random Hse. Children's Bks.

—The Mysterious Visitor. 2003. (Trixie Belden Ser.: Vol. 4). (Illus.). 272p. (gr. 3-7). lib. bdg. 9.99 (978-0-375-92578-8(3), Random Hse. Bks. for Young Readers) Random Hse. Children's Bks.

—Mystery in Arizona, Vol. 6. Stevens, Mary, illus. 2004. (Trixie Belden Ser.: No. 6). 272p. (J). (gr. 3-7). 6.99 (978-0-375-82741-9(2), Random Hse. Bks. for Young Readers) Random Hse. Children's Bks.

—Mystery off Glen Road. 2004. (Trixie Belden Ser.: Vol. 5). (Illus.). 272p. (J). (gr. 3-7). 6.99 (978-0-375-82740-2(4), Random Hse. Bks. for Young Readers) Random Hse. Children's Bks.

—The Red Trailer Mystery. Stevens, Mary, illus. 2003. (Trixie Belden Ser.: No. 2). 272p. (J). (gr. 3-7). 6.99 (978-0-375-82411-1(1), Random Hse. Bks. for Young Readers) Random Hse. Children's Bks.

—The Secret of the Mansion. Stevens, Mary & Koelsch, Michael, illus. 2003. (Trixie Belden Ser.: Vol. 1). 272p. (gr. 3-7). lib. bdg. 9.99 (978-0-375-92412-5(4), Random Hse. Bks. for Young Readers) Random Hse. Children's Bks.

MNO

—The Secret of the Mansion. Stevens, Mary, illus. 2003. (Trixie Belden Ser.: No. 1). 272p. (J). (gr. 3-7). 6.99 (978-0-375-82412-8(X) , Random Hse. Bks. for Young Readers) Random Hse. Children's Bks.

—The Secret of the Mansion: Trixie Belden. 2004. 236p. (J). (gr. 3-7). pap. 29.00 incl. audio (978-1-4000-9000-6(8) , Listening Library) Random Hse. Audio Publishing Group.

—Trixie Belden, 3 bks., Bk. 1. 2004. (J). (gr. 3). 20.97 (978-0-375-83109-6(6) , Random Hse. Bks. for Young Readers) Random Hse. Children's Bks.

Campbell, Kim, et al. Invasion of the Judy Snatchers. 2000. (Doug: 1). (Illus.). 96p. (gr. 2-5). pap. 4.99 (978-0-7868-4382-4(9)) Disney Pr.

Capcom, et al, creators. Devil May Cry. 2006. pap. 7.99 (978-1-59816-450-3(3) , Tokyopop Adult) TOKYOPOP, Inc.

Capeci, Anne. The Cascade Mountain Railroad Mysteries: Danger! Dynamite! 2003. (Cascade Moutain Railroad Mystery Ser.: No. 1). (Illus.). 144p. (J). (gr. 1-5). 12.95 (978-1-56145-288-0(2)) Peachtree Pubs., Ltd.

—Case of the Cyber-Hacker. l.t. ed. 2000. (Wishbone Mysteries Ser.: No. 19). (Illus.). 141p. (J). (gr. 4 up). lib. bdg. 23.33 (978-0-8368-2702-6(3)) Stevens, Gareth Inc.

—Case of the Cyber-Hacker. 2000. (gr. 3-6). lib. bdg. 11.80 (978-0-613-27764-8(3)) Tandem Library Bks.

—Ghost Train, Vol. 3. Casale, Paul, illus. 2004. (Cascade Moutain Railroad Mystery Ser.: 3). 144p. (J). (gr. 2-5). 12.95 (978-1-56145-324-5(2)) Peachtree Pubs., Ltd.

—Key to the Golden Dog. l.t. ed. 1999. (Wishbone Mysteries Ser.: No. 8). 144p. (J). (gr. 4 up). lib. bdg. 23.33 (978-0-8368-2389-9(3)) Stevens, Gareth Inc.

—The Maltese Dog. l.t. ed. 1999. (Wishbone Mysteries Ser.: No. 6). 144p. (J). (gr. 4 up). lib. bdg. 23.33 (978-0-8368-2387-5(7)) Stevens, Gareth Inc.

—Missing! Casale, Paul, illus. 2005. 144p. (J). 12.95 (978-1-56145-334-4(X)) Peachtree Pubs., Ltd.

Capitol Mysteries. 2005. (J). (978-1-59564-732-0(5)) Steps To Literacy, LLC.

Carlotta & the Grand Island Mansion Mystery, 8 vols., Vol. 2. 2001. (DELTA MYSTERIES SERIES: Vol. 2). 54p. per. 14.95 (978-0-9703178-8-9(3) , Ramona's Bk. Co.) RBC Publishing Co., Inc.

Carlstone, Ed. Bubba's Big Banana Cream Crime: Resisting Temptation. 1998. (Quigley's Village Ser.: Vol. 8). (J). (ps-2). 12.99 incl. VHS (978-0-310-58319-6(5)) Zondervan.

Carlton, Bea. Mystery at Natural Bridge. 2002nd ed. 2002. 163p. (Orig.). (gr. 4-7). pap. 9.99 (978-0-9658103-2-6(1)) SonLife Publishing.

Carmichael, Claire. Leaving Simplicity. 2007. 256p. (J). (gr. 6-12). 21.95 (***978-1-55451-090-0(2)***); pap. 10.95 (***978-1-55451-089-4(9)***) Annick Pr., Ltd. CAN. *Dist:* Firefly Bks., Ltd.

Carpenter, Humphrey. Mr. Majeika Vanishes. 1998. (Illus.). 96p. (J). 7.95 (978-0-14-037840-5(5)) Penguin Group (USA) Inc.

Carpentieri, Tony & Mular, Paul. Hardy & Hardy Investigations. 3rd rev. ed. 1998. (Illus.). 620p. spiral bd. 56.95 (978-1-891388-00-2(2)) SynSine Pr.

Carr, Annie Roe. Nan Sherwood at Pine Camp or the Old Lum. 2007. pap. (***978-1-4065-1294-6(X)***) Dodo Pr.

—Nan Sherwood at Rose Ranch or the Old Me. 2007. pap. (***978-1-4065-1295-3(8)***) Dodo Pr.

—Nan Sherwoods Winter Holidays or Rescuin. 2007. pap. (***978-1-4065-1296-0(6)***) Dodo Pr.

Carr, Roe Annie. Nan Sherwood at Pine Camp (the Old Lumbe. 2006. 52.99 (***978-1-4219-7906-9(3)***); pap. 45.99 (***978-1-4219-7917-5(9)***) IndyPublish.com.

Carroll, Betty J. The Mystery of the Red-Brick House. 2002. 137p. pap. 10.95 (978-0-595-20562-2(3) , Writers Club Pr.) iUniverse, Inc.

Carroll, Jenny, pseud. Reunion. 2005. (Mediator Ser.: Bk. 3). 304p. (YA). (gr. 7 up). pap. 7.99 (978-0-06-072513-6(3)) HarperCollins Pubs.

—Safe House. 2007. (1-800-Where-R-You Ser.: No. 3). 272p. (YA). mass mkt. 6.99 (978-1-4169-2706-8(9) , Simon Pulse) Simon & Schuster Children's Publishing.

Carroll, Jenny, pseud & Cabot, Meg. Young Blood. 4th ed 2005. (Mediator Ser.: No. 4). 336p. (J). (gr. 7 up). pap. 7.99 (978-0-06-072514-3(1)) HarperCollins Pubs.

Carroll, Jenny, pseud & O'Neill, Jacquie. Sanctuary. 2007. (1-800-Where-R-You Ser.: No. 4). 240p. (YA). mass mkt. 6.99 (978-1-4169-2707-5(7) , Simon Pulse) Simon & Schuster Children's Publishing.

Carter, Alden R. Crescent Hoon. 2004. 153p. (YA). (gr. 6-9). reprint ed. 17.00 (978-0-7567-8336-5(4)) DIANE Publishing Co.

Casanova, Mary. Trouble in Pembrook. Rayyan, Omar, illus. 2006. 117p. (J). (***978-1-4156-7757-5(3)*** , Aladdin) Simon & Schuster Children's Publishing.

—The Turtle-Hatching Mystery. Rayyan, Omar, illus. 2008. (Dog Watch Ser.: No. 6). 144p. (J). pap. 4.99 (***978-1-4169-4783-7(3)*** , Aladdin) Simon & Schuster Children's Publishing.

Case, John. First Horseman. 1999. (gr. 7-12). lib. bdg. 15.30 (978-0-613-29244-3(8)) Tandem Library Bks.

Case, Linda. Brigits Day of Fun. 2006. 28p. pap. 9.95 (***978-1-4327-0001-0(4)***) Outskirts Press, Inc.

The Case of the Carnival Cash. 2002. (Illus.). (J). pap. (978-0-7398-5071-8(7)); pap. 28.35 (978-0-7398-5079-4(2)) Steck-Vaughn.

Cassels, Jean. The Mysterious Collection of Dr. David Harleyson. Cassels, Jean, illus. 2004. (Illus.). 32p. (J). 17.95 (978-0-8027-8916-7(1)) Walker & Co.

Cassidy, Anne. Patsy Kelly Investigates: A Family Affair. l.t. ed. 1998. 276p. (J). pap. (978-0-7540-6028-4(4) , CLP 231) BBC Audio.

Castleberry, Stephen B., Sr. & Castleberry, Susie. Footprints in the Barn. 2001. (Farm Mystery Ser.). 164p. (J). per. 8.50 (978-1-891907-11-1(5)) Castleberry Farms Pr.

—The History Mystery. 2005. (Farm Mystery Ser.). per. 8.50 (978-1-891907-16-6(6)) Castleberry Farms Pr.

—Where There's Smoke. 2004. (Farm Mystery Ser.). (J). per. 8.50 (978-1-891907-14-2(X)) Castleberry Farms Pr.

—Who, Me? 2001. (Farm Mystery Ser.). 176p. (J). per. 8.50 (978-1-891907-10-4(7)) Castleberry Farms Pr.

Castleberry, Stephen B. & Castleberry, Susie L. Midnight Sky. 1998. (Farm Mystery Ser.). 160p. (YA). per. 8.50 (978-1-891907-06-7(9)) Castleberry Farms Pr.

Castor, Daniel. Jam Sponge & Sneakers. (Illus.). 60p. (J). pap. 7.99 (978-0-340-63441-7(3) , Hodder & Stoughton) Hodder General Publishing Division GBR. *Dist:* Trafalgar Square Publishing.

Caswell, Brian. Double Exposure. 2005. 240p. (YA). pap. 18.95 (978-0-7022-3533-7(4)) Univ. of Queensland Pr. AUS. *Dist:* International Specialized Bk. Services.

Catran, Ken. Blue Murder. 2002. 208p. (YA). pap. (978-0-7344-0389-6(5) , Lothian Bks.) Hachette Livre Australia.

—Road Kill. 2002. (Crime Waves Ser.). (Illus.). 160p. (YA). pap. (978-0-7344-0258-5(9) , Lothian Bks.) Hachette Livre Australia.

—Road Kill. 2001. (gr. 7-12). lib. bdg. 18.75 (978-0-613-90374-5(9)) Tandem Library Bks.

Caudwell, Sarah. Sibyl in Her Grave. 2001. (gr. 7-12). lib. bdg. 14.15 (978-0-613-36875-9(4)) Tandem Library Bks.

Caughman, Roberta. A Lonesome Village near a Dark Mysterious-Looking Forest. 2002. 32p. pap. 9.00 (978-0-8059-5697-9(2)) Dorrance Publishing Co., Inc.

Caulfield, Annie. Katie Milk Solves Crimes & So On. 2006. 208p. (J). pap. 9.95 (***978-0-440-86686-2(3)***) Transworld Publishers Ltd. GBR. *Dist:* Independent Pubs. Group.

—Katie Milk Solves Reality TV Crimes. 2007. (Illus.). 208p. (J). pap. 9.95 (***978-0-440-86687-9(1)***) Transworld Publishers Ltd. GBR. *Dist:* Independent Pubs. Group.

Cavendish, Grace. Conspiracy. 2005. (Lady Grace Mysteries, from the Daybookes of Lady Grace Cavendish Ser.). 208p. (J). (gr. 3-7). 6.95 (978-0-385-73153-9(1) , Delacorte Bks. for Young Readers) Random Hse. Children's Bks.

—The Lady Grace Mysteries: Assassin. l.t. ed. 2006. pap. 16.95 (978-1-4056-6068-6(6)) BBC Audio GBR. *Dist:* BBC Audiobooks America.

Cebulash, Mel. Hot Like the Sun: A Terry Tyndale Mystery. 2000. 116p. (YA). (gr. 4-7). pap. 9.95 (978-0-595-09092-1(3)) iUniverse, Inc.

Cerasini, Marc, et al. The Getaway. Christmas, Lawrence & Johnson, Shane L., illus. 2007. (Sprouse Bros. 47 R. O. N. I. N. Ser.). 112p. (J). pap. 5.99 (***978-1-4169-3902-3(4)*** , Simon Spotlight) Simon & Schuster Children's Publishing.

—The Revelation. Pierandrei, Natalia & Christmas, Lawrence, illus. 2007. (Sprouse Bros. 47 R. O. N. I. N. Ser.). 128p. (J). (gr. 4-9). pap. 5.99 (978-1-4169-3607-7(6) , Simon Spotlight) Simon & Schuster Children's Publishing.

Cerasini, Marc, et al. The Siege. Christmas, Lawrence & Panosian, Dan, illus. 2007. (Sprouse Bros. 47 R. O. N. I. N. Ser.). 112p. (J). pap. 5.99 (***978-1-4169-3903-0(2)*** , Simon Spotlight) Simon & Schuster Children's Publishing.

Chan, Ching. Mystery of the Black Sun: Songs of the Unicorn. 2006. (Anime Sticker Stories Ser.). 16p. (J). (ps-1). 4.99 (978-0-448-44340-9(6) , Grosset & Dunlap) Penguin Group (USA) Inc.

Chan, Marty. The Mystery of the Frozen Brains. 2005. 112p. pap. 8.95 (978-1-894345-71-2(1)) Thistledown Pr., Ltd. CAN. *Dist:* Literary Pr. Group of Canada.

Chandler, Elizabeth. The Back Door of Midnight. 2004. (Dark Secrets Ser.). 224p. (YA). mass mkt. 5.99 (978-0-689-86642-5(9) , Simon Pulse) Simon & Schuster Children's Publishing.

—The Deep End of Fear. 2003. (gr. 7-12). lib. bdg. 13.00 (978-0-613-61757-4(6)) Tandem Library Bks.

—Legacy of Lies. 2000. (Dark Secrets Ser.: Vol. 1). (Illus.). 192p. (YA). (gr. 7-12). pap. 5.99 (978-0-7434-0028-2(3) , Simon Pulse) Simon & Schuster Children's Publishing.

—Legacy of Lies. 2000. (gr. 7-12). lib. bdg. 13.00 (978-0-613-74120-0(X)) Tandem Library Bks.

—No Time to Die. 2001. (gr. 5-8). lib. bdg. 13.00 (978-0-613-74122-4(6)) Tandem Library Bks.

Chandler, Elizabeth & Gottesfeld, Jeff. No Time to Die. 2001. (Dark Secrets Ser.: Vol. 3). 224p. (YA). (gr. 7-9). pap. 11.95 (978-0-7434-0030-5(5) , Simon Pulse) Simon & Schuster Children's Publishing.

Chapman, Brenda. Hiding in Hawk's Creek. 2006. 134p. (J). pap. 8.95 (978-1-894917-24-7(3)) Napoleon Publishing/Rendezvous Pr. CAN. *Dist:* AtlasBooks Distribution.

Charbonneau, Eileen. The Connor Emerald. Williams, Lori, ed. 1999. 170p. (YA). pap. 9.99 (978-1-58365-753-9(3) , Timeless Romance) Sierra Raconteur Publishing.

Charles, Norma M. Criss Cross, Double Cross: Sophie Alias Star Girl to the Rescue. 2005. 128p. (YA). pap. (978-0-88878-431-5(7) , Sandcastle Bks.) Dundurn Group, The.

Cheaney, J. B. The True Prince. 2004. (gr. 5-8). lib. bdg. 14.15 (978-0-613-89784-6(6)) Tandem Library Bks.

Cherrington, Janelle. Mystery at the Big Blue House. 2000. (gr. k-3). lib. bdg. 11.25 (978-0-613-26334-4(0)) Tandem Library Bks.

Cherrington, Janelle & Strader, P. Kevin. Mystery at the Big Blue House. Brannon, Tom, illus. 2000. (Bear in the Big Blue House Ser.). 24p. (J). pap. (978-0-7434-0843-1(8) , Simon & Schuster Children's Publishing) Simon & Schuster Children's Publishing.

Child, Lauren. Utterly Me, Clarice Bean. Child, Lauren, illus. 2003. (Illus.). 192p. (J). (gr. 3-7). 15.99 (978-0-7636-2186-5(2)) Candlewick Pr.

—Utterly Me, Clarice Bean. 2002. (Illus.). 160p. (J). 5.99 (978-1-84121-918-9(5) , Orchard Bks.) Scholastic, Inc.

Childress, David Hatcher & Shaver, Richard. Lost Continents & the Hollow Earth: I Remember Lemuria & the Shaver Mystery. 1998. (Illus.). 344p. 16.95 (978-0-932813-63-3(1)) Adventures Unlimited Pr.

Christelow, Eileen. Where's the Big Bad Wolf? Christelow, Eileen, illus. 2002. (Illus.). 40p. (J). (gr. k-3). tchr. ed. 16.00 (978-0-618-18194-0(6) , Clarion Bks.) Houghton Mifflin Co. Trade & Reference Div.

Christie, Agatha. Asesinato en el Orient. 2002. (gr. 7-12). lib. bdg. 17.60 (978-0-613-63579-0(5)) Tandem Library Bks.

—Asesinato en el Orient Expreso.Tr. of Murder on the Orient Express. (SPA.). 240p. (J). 7.95 (978-84-272-0005-0(6)) Molino, Editorial ESP. *Dist:* AIMS International Bks., Inc.

—The Body in the Library. 2001. (Illus.). (J). 12.64 (978-0-606-21077-5(6)) Tandem Library Bks.

—A Caribbean Mystery. 2000. (gr. 5-8). lib. bdg. 14.15 (978-0-613-57191-3(6)) Tandem Library Bks.

—Misterio del Guia. 2000. (gr. 7-12). lib. bdg. 17.60 (978-0-613-63631-5(7)) Tandem Library Bks.

—Mousetrap & Other Plays. 2000. (gr. 7-12). lib. bdg. 16.45 (978-0-613-62529-6(3)) Tandem Library Bks.

—Mrs. McGinty's Dead. 2000. (gr. 7-12). lib. bdg. 14.15 (978-0-613-46258-7(0)) Tandem Library Bks.

Christie, Amanda. Secrets. 2000. 176p. (YA). (gr. 5-8). pap. 4.99 (978-0-375-80340-6(8) , Random Hse. Bks. for Young Readers) Random Hse. Children's Bks.

—Secrets. rev. ed. 2000. (gr. 5-8). lib. bdg. 13.00 (978-0-613-44255-8(5)) Tandem Library Bks.

The Christmas Eve Caper. 1999. (SmartReader Ser.). (J). pap., tchr. ed. 19.95 incl. audio (978-0-7887-0118-4(5) , 79306T3) Recorded Bks., LLC.

Christopher, Matt. Skateboard Tough. 2007. (J). lib. bdg. (***978-1-59953-115-1(1)***) Norwood Hse. Pr.

Church, Lisa. Mystery on the Mayflower. 2001. (gr. 7-12). lib. bdg. 30.35 (978-0-613-84714-8(8)) Tandem Library Bks.

Ciencin, Scott. Green Gotham. Burchett, Rick, illus. 2005. (Scholastic Reader Ser.). 40p. (J). (ps-k). pap. 3.99 (978-0-439-47102-2(8) , Cartwheel Bks.) Scholastic, Inc.

Ciminera, Siobhan & Faulkner, Keith. A Yummy Mystery: A Scratch-and-Sniff Story. 2007. (Puppy Scooby-Doo Ser.). 16p. (J). pap. 5.99 (978-0-448-44406-2(2) , Grosset & Dunlap) Penguin Group (USA) Inc.

The Circus Mystery, 6 vols., Vol. 2. (Woodland Mysteriestm Ser.). 133p. (gr. 3-7). 42.50 (978-0-7802-7942-1(5)) Wright Group, The.

Cirrone, Dorian. The Big Scoop. Woodruff, Liza, illus. 2006. (Marshall Cavendish Chapter Book Ser.). 80p. (J). 14.99 (978-0-7614-5323-9(7)) Cavendish, Marshall Corp.

—The Missing Silver Dollar. Woodruff, Liza, illus. 2006. (Lindy Blues Ser.). 80p. (J). 14.95 (978-0-7614-5284-3(2)) Cavendish, Marshall Corp.

The Clamdollar Caper. 2002. (Rose Doolittle Mystery Ser.: 2). 260p. (J). per. 14.95 (978-0-9712971-1-1(8)) Creston Hall Pubns.

Clancy, Tom & Pieczenik, Steve. Tom Clancy's Net Force 01: Virtual Vandals. 1999. (Tom Clancy's Net Force Ser.). 384p. (gr. 12). mass mkt. 7.99 (978-0-425-16172-2(2) , Berkley) Penguin Group (USA) Inc.

Clark, Mary Higgins. Before I Say Good-Bye. 2001. (gr. 7-12). lib. bdg. 16.45 (978-0-613-33460-0(4)) Tandem Library Bks.

—Deck the Halls. 2001. (gr. 7-12). lib. bdg. 16.45 (978-0-613-50293-1(0)) Tandem Library Bks.

—Mientras Mi Preciosa Duerme. 2002. (SPA.). (gr. 7-12). lib. bdg. 19.90 (978-0-613-57319-1(6)) Tandem Library Bks.

Clasicos de Misterio. (Clasicos Juveniles Coleccion).Tr. of Classic Mystery Stories II. (SPA.). (YA). (gr. 5-8). pap. (978-950-11-1279-5(9) , SG4720) Sigmar ARG. *Dist:* Lectorum Pubns., Inc.

Clay, Margaret. Double Identity. 2007. 276p. (YA) pap. 12.95 (***978-0-9792328-6-2(4)***) Helm Publishing.

Clayton, John. Alexander Fox & the Amazing Mind Reader. Egan, Emily, illus. 1998. (Young Readers Ser.). 78p. (ps-3). pap. 16.00 (978-1-57392-221-0(8)) Prometheus Bks., Pubs.

Clement, Rod. Grandpa's Teeth. Clement, Rod, illus. 1998. (Illus.). 32p. (J). (ps-3). 16.99 (978-0-06-027671-3(1)) HarperCollins Pubs.

Clements, Andrew. Room One: A Mystery or Two. Blair, Chris, illus. 2006. 176p. (J). (gr. 3-7). 15.95 (978-0-689-86686-9(0)) Simon & Schuster Children's Publishing.

Clish, Marian L. J. P. Landers - Solve a Mystery, Bk. 1. 1999. (J). (gr. 2-7). 20.95 incl. cd-rom (978-1-928632-27-6(0)); (Illus.). 46p. reprint ed. 10.95 (978-0-516-01991-8(0)) Writers Marketplace:Consulting, Critiquing & Publishing.

—J. P. Landers - Solve a Mystery, Bk. 1. Crombie, Steven, illus. unabr. ed. 1999. (J). (gr. 2-7). 15.95 incl. audio (978-1-928632-26-9(2)) Writers Marketplace:Consulting, Critiquing & Publishing.

—J. P. Landers - Solve a Mystery, Bk. 2. 1999. (J). (gr. 2-7). 20.95 incl. cd-rom (978-1-928632-29-0(7)) Writers Marketplace:Consulting, Critiquing & Publishing.

—J. P. Landers - Solve a Mystery, Bk. 2. Crombie, Steven, illus. unabr. ed. 1999. (J). (gr. 2-7). 15.95 incl. audio (978-1-928632-28-3(9)) Writers Marketplace:Consulting, Critiquing & Publishing.

The Clue in the Castle, 6 vols., Vol. 2. (Woodland Mysteriestm Ser.). 133p. (gr. 3-7). 42.50 (978-0-7802-7935-3(2)) Wright Group, The.

Cofer, Amadeus. Mystery of the Golden Pearls: A Halloween Adventure in Clarkesville, 1. l.t. ed. 2004. (Illus.). 36p. (J). 14.00 (978-1-932957-02-0(2)) Legacy Pubs.

Cohen, Daniel. Conspiracy. 1998. (Alien Files Ser.: No. 2). (Illus.). 86p. (J). (gr. 3-7). pap. 3.99 (978-0-590-76342-4(3)) Scholastic, Inc.

—Conspiracy. 1999. (Illus.). (J). (978-0-606-15858-9(8)) Tandem Library Bks.

Cole, Joanna & Moore, Eva. The Search for the Missing Bones. 1999. (Magic School Bus Chapter Bks.: No. 2). (J). (gr. 1-4). (978-0-606-18575-2(5)) Tandem Library Bks.

Cole, Stephen. Prey. 2004. 256p. (YA). pap. (***978-0-7475-6503-1(1)***) Bloomsbury Pr.

Coleman, Evelyn. Circle of Fire. 2001. (American Girl Collection). (Illus.). (J). 12.60 (978-0-606-21249-6(3)) Tandem Library Bks.

—Mystery of the Dark Tower. 2000. (History Mysteries Ser.). (978-0-606-18356-7(6)) Tandem Library Bks.

Coleman, Evelyn. Shadows on Society Hill: An Addy Mystery. 2007. 192p. (J). 10.95 (***978-1-59369-163-9(7)***); pap. 6.95 (***978-1-59369-162-2(9)***) American Girl Publishing, Inc. (American Girl).

Coleman, Michael. Cyber Feud. 1998. (Internet Detectives Ser.). (978-0-606-13522-1(7)) Tandem Library Bks.

Coles, William E., Jr. Compass in the Blood: A Reissue of the Simon & Schuster Original Novel. 2004. (YA). per. 9.95 (978-1-59571-034-5(5)) Word Association Pubs.

Colfer, Eoin. Half-Moon Investigations. 304p. (gr. 5-17). 2007. pap. 7.99 (***978-0-7868-4960-4(6)***); 2006. 16.95 (978-0-7868-4957-4(6)) Miramax Bks.

Collier, Christine. Twelve Months of Mystery. 2003. 72p. pap. 8.95 (978-0-595-29943-0(1) , Mystery & Suspense Pr.) iUniverse, Inc.

Collier, James Lincoln. Me & Billy. 2004. 192p. (J). 15.95 (978-0-7614-5174-7(9)) Cavendish, Marshall Corp.

Conford, Ellen. A Case for Jenny Archer. Palmisciano, Diane, illus. 2nd ed. 2006. 64p. (J). (gr. 1-4). pap. 3.99 (978-0-316-01486-1(9)) Little Brown & Co.

Conly, Jane Leslie. While No One Was Watching. 2000. (978-0-606-18728-2(6)) Tandem Library Bks.

Conrad, Hy. Whodunit Crime Mysteries. 2003. (Illus.). 96p. (J). pap. 6.95 (978-1-4027-0646-2(4)) Sterling Publishing Co., Inc.

Conrad, Hy & LaFleur, Matt. The Little Giant Book of Whodunits. 1998. (Little Giant Bks.). (Illus.). 352p. pap. 6.95 (978-0-8069-0473-3(9)) Sterling Publishing Co., Inc.

Conrad, Hy, et al. Mensa Whodunits. 2004. (Official Mensa Puzzle Book Ser.). (Illus.). 286p. (J). pap. (978-1-4027-1643-0(5) , Sterling/Main St.) Sterling Publishing Co., Inc.

Conrad, Joseph & Snyder, John K., III. The Secret Agent: A Simple Tale. (Classics Illustrated Ser.). (Illus.). 52p. (YA). pap. 4.95 (978-1-57209-017-0(0)) Classics International Entertainment, Inc.

Conrique, Samantha. The Pod-Poppers. 2007. (J). pap. 8.00 (***978-0-8059-7200-9(5)***) Dorrance Publishing Co., Inc.

Cook, Gerri. Where the Buffalo Jump. Yu, Chao & Wang, Jue, illus. 2003. (Dinosaur Soup Ser.). 120p. (YA). (gr. 3-5). pap. 9.95 (978-1-895836-95-0(6)) River Bks. CAN. *Dist:* Fitzhenry & Whiteside, Ltd.

Cook, Vivian E. Alaska Adventure. Nelson, Grace I., illus. 1999. (Adventures of Spencer, Private Eye & His Psychic Sister, Tiffany Ser.: No. 6). 66p. (J). (gr. 3-5). pap. 8.95 (978-1-928659-05-1(5)) Two Sisters Publishing.

—Danger under the Big Top. Nelson, Grace I., illus. 1999. (Adventures of Spencer, Private Eye & His Psychic Sister, Tiffany Ser.: No. 4). 66p. (J). (gr. 3-5). pap. 8.95 (978-1-928659-03-7(9)) Two Sisters Publishing.

—The Journey Home. Nelson, Grace I., illus. 1999. (Adventures of Spencer, Private Eye & His Psychic Sister, Tiffany Ser.: No. 2). 50p. (J). (gr. 3-5). pap. 7.95 (978-1-928659-01-3(2)) Two Sisters Publishing.

—Rescue from Rapid Gully. Nelson, Grace I., illus. 1999. (Adventures of Spencer, Private Eye & His Psychic Sister, Tiffany Ser.: No. 3). 56p. (J). (gr. 3-5). pap. 7.95 (978-1-928659-02-0(0)) Two Sisters Publishing.

—The Search for Charming Carletta. Nelson, Grace I., illus. 1999. (Adventures of Spencer, Private Eye & His Psychic Sister, Tiffany Ser.: No. 1). 43p. (J). (gr. 3-5). pap. 7.95 (978-1-928659-00-6(4)) Two Sisters Publishing.

—Trapped in Haunted Castle. Nelson, Grace I., illus. 1999. (Adventures of Spencer, Private Eye & His Psychic Sister, Tiffany Ser.: No. 5). 58p. (J). (gr. 3-5). pap. 8.95 (978-1-928659-04-4(7)) Two Sisters Publishing.

Cool by the Pool: Coloring/Activity Book. 2005. (Illus.). (J). (978-0-9770455-2-5(8)) Educational Adventures.

Cool by the Pool: Picture Book (English) 2005. (Illus.). 47p. (J). (978-0-9770455-3-2(6)) Educational Adventures.

Cooney, Caroline B. Fatality. 2001. 11.64 (978-0-606-22171-9(9)) Tandem Library Bks.

—Terrorist. 1999. (978-0-606-17447-3(8)) Tandem Library Bks.

Cooper, Dolores Thome. The Story of the Knus. 2005. (Illus.). 64p. (J). pap. 9.95 (978-1-881539-38-4(5) , Strathmoor) Tabby Hse. Bks.

Cooper, Susan. The Boggart. 2005. 208p. (ps-7). pap. 2.99 (978-1-4169-0527-1(8) , Aladdin) Simon & Schuster Children's Publishing.

Coren, Alan. Railroad Arthur. 2004. (Illus.). 64p. (978-0-903895-92-7(7) , Robson Bks. Ltd.) Anova Bks.

Corirossi, Steven A. Angus & the Hidden Fort. 2003. 162p. pap. 9.95 (978-0-595-27540-3(0)) iUniverse, Inc.

—Angus & the Mysterious House. 2002. 172p. (J). pap. 9.95 (978-0-595-24025-8(9) , Writers Advantage Pr.) iUniverse, Inc.

Cormier, Robert. I Am the Cheese. l.t. ed. 2005. 255p. pap. 10.95 (978-0-7862-7336-2(4) , Large Print Pr.) Thorndike Pr.

—The Rag & Bone Shop. 2003. 176p. (YA). (gr. 7). mass mkt. 6.50 (978-0-440-22971-1(5) , Laurel Leaf) Random Hse. Children's Bks.

Corona, Sarah. El Misterio del Tiempo Robado. (Barril Sin Fondo Ser.). (SPA.). (J). (gr. 3-5). pap. (978-968-6465-16-7(2)) Casa de Estudios de Literatura y Talleres Artisticos Amaquemecan A.C. MEX. *Dist:* Lectorum Pubns., Inc.

Costain, Meredith. Mummy's Curse. 1999. (gr. 3-6). lib. bdg. 12.60 (978-0-613-18975-0(2)) Tandem Library Bks.

Cote, Denis. L' Idole des Inactifs. 2002. (Roman Plus Ser.). (FRE., Illus.). 160p. (YA). (gr. 8 up). pap. (978-2-89021-106-3(1)) Diffusion du livre Mirabel.

Coté, Denis. La Machination du Scorpion Noir. 2004. (Mon Roman Ser.). (FRE.). 160p. (J). (gr. 2). pap. (978-2-89021-667-9(5)) Diffusion du livre Mirabel.

Cote, Denis. Un Parfum de Mystere. 2003. (Premier Roman Ser.). (Illus.). 64p. (J). (gr. 2-5). pap. (978-2-89021-352-4(8)) Diffusion du livre Mirabel.

Cousineau-Peiffer, Trisha. Have You Ever Heard of a Rainbow Farm. Everett-Hawkes, Bonnie, illus. 2006. 32p. (J). 12.95 (***978-0-9792084-1-6(6)***) Dream Ridge Pr.

—Have You Ever Heard of a Rainbow Farm: The Missing Color Kittens. Everett-Hawkes, Bonnie, illus. 2007. 48p. (J). per. 15.95 (***978-0-9792084-2-3(4)***) Dream Ridge Pr.

Coutu, Raymond. Duke's First Case: Jessie & the Missing Yarn. Graef, Renee, illus. 2001. (J). (978-0-9712840-6-7(7) , Bear & Co.) Bear & Co.

Coutu, Raymond & Jones, Dawn L. Babette & the Apple Bandit. Graef, Renee, illus. 2001. (J). (978-0-9712840-8-1(3)) Boyds Collection Ltd., The.

—Poker & the Cupcake Chase. Graef, Renee, illus. 2001. (J). pap. (978-0-9712840-7-4(5)) Boyds Collection Ltd., The.

Cox, Judy. The Mystery of the Burmese Bandicoot. Rayyan, Omar, illus. 2007. (Tails of frederick & Ishbu Ser.). 256p. (YA). (gr. 5 up). 16.99 (***978-0-7614-5376-5(8)***) Cavendish, Marshall Corp.

Creary, Eve M. A Silent Witness in Harlem. O'Loughlin, Marianne, illus. 2002. (Mysteries in Time Ser.: Vol. 10). 96p. (J). (gr. 3-8). lib. bdg. 14.95 (978-1-893110-27-4(3)) Silver Moon Pr.

Cree, Ronald. Desert Blood 10pm/9c. 2006. (Illus.). 320p. (YA). pap. 7.99 (978-1-4169-1156-2(1) , Simon Pulse) Simon & Schuster Children's Publishing.

Crew, Gary. Cruel Nest. 2002. (Illus.). 160p. (YA). pap. (978-0-7344-0248-6(1) , Lothian Bks.) Hachette Livre Australia.

Crilley, Mark. Billy Clikk: Creatch Battler. 2006. (Illus.). 246p. (J). (***978-1-4156-5030-1(6)*** , Yearling) Random Hse. Children's Bks.

Cross, Gillian. Tightrope. 1999. 224p. (J). (gr. 7 up). 16.95 (978-0-8234-1512-0(0)) Holiday Hse., Inc.

—Tightrope. 1999. 210p. (YA). (978-0-19-271804-4(5)) Oxford Univ. Pr., Inc.

—Tightrope. 2001. (YA). (978-0-606-21489-6(5)) Tandem Library Bks.

Crossman, David A. The Mystery of the Black Moriah. 2002. (Bean & Ab Mystery Ser.: Vol. 2). (Illus.). 234p. 16.95 (978-0-89272-536-6(2)) Down East Bks.

—The Secret of the Missing Grave. 1999. (Bean & Ab Mystery Ser.). 184p. (YA). (gr. 4-10). 16.95 (978-0-89272-456-7(0)) Down East Bks.

—The Secret of the Missing Grave: Bean & Ab. 1999. (gr. 5 up). pap. 9.95 (978-0-89272-470-3(6)) Down East Bks.

Croteau-Fleury, Marie-Danielle & Back, Francis. La Prison de Verre. 1998. (Roman Jeunesse Ser.). (Illus.). 96p. (YA). (gr. 4-7). pap. (978-2-89021-330-2(7)) Diffusion du livre Mirabel.

Crowley, Bridget. Feast of Fools. 2005. (Illus.). (J). (gr. k-9). mass mkt. (978-0-340-85082-4(5) , Hodder Children's Books) Hodder Children's Division.

—Ship's Angel. 2005. (Illus.). (J). pap. (978-0-340-88155-2(0) , Hodder Children's Books) Hodder Children's Division.

Cummings, Patricia. The Secret in the Walnut Banister. 1998. 190p. (YA). (gr. 5-12). pap. 5.95 (978-0-9657962-2-4(1)) Blue Line Publishing.

Cunliffe, John. Postman Pat: Mystery Tour. 1999. (Postman Pat Ser.: Vol. 13). (Illus.). 32p. pap. 12.99 incl. audio (978-1-84032-007-7(9) , Hodder & Stoughton) Hodder General Publishing Division GBR. *Dist:* Trafalgar Square Publishing.

—Postman Pat & the Mystery Tour. (Postman Pat Ser.: Bk. 13). (Illus.). 32p. (J). pap. 8.99 (978-0-340-71333-4(X) , Hodder & Stoughton) Hodder General Publishing Division GBR. *Dist:* Trafalgar Square Publishing.

Cunning, Concord. Scripture Sleuth 3. 2004. pap. 8.95 (978-1-885904-39-3(8)) Focus Publishing.

Curry, Jane Louise. The Ice Ghosts Mystery. 2001. 220p. (gr. 4-7). pap. 15.95 (978-0-595-18000-4(0)) iUniverse, Inc.

Curtis, Christopher Paul. Mr. Chickee's Funny Money. 160p. 2007. (gr. 4-7). 6.50 (978-0-440-22919-3(7) , Yearling); 2005. (Illus.). (J). (gr. 3-7). 15.95 (978-0-385-32772-5(2) , Lamb, Wendy); 2005. (Illus.). (J). (gr. 3-7). lib. bdg. 17.99 (978-0-385-90936-5(5) , Lamb, Wendy) Random Hse. Children's Bks.

—Mr. Chickee's Funny Money. l.t. ed. 2006. 190p. 23.95 (978-0-7862-8670-6(9)) Thorndike Pr.

—Mr. Chickee's Messy Mission. 240p. (J). (gr. 4-7). 2008. 6.50 (***978-0-440-22922-3(7)*** , Yearling); 2007. (Illus.). 15.99 (978-0-385-32775-6(7) , Lamb, Wendy); 2007. (Illus.). lib. bdg. 18.99 (978-0-385-90942-6(X) , Lamb, Wendy) Random Hse. Children's Bks.

Curtis, Patricia. The Mysterious Intruder. 2005. 125p. pap. 17.95 (978-1-4137-5425-4(2)) PublishAmerica, Inc.

Cushman, Doug. Aunt Eater Loves a Mystery. Cushman, Doug, illus. 2002. (Aunt Eater Mysteries Ser.). (Illus.). (J). 12.30 (978-0-7587-5990-0(8)) Book Wholesalers, Inc.

—Aunt Eater's Mystery Christmas. Cushman, Doug, illus. 2002. (Aunt Eater Mysteries Ser.). (Illus.). (J). 12.30 (978-0-7587-5991-7(6)) Book Wholesalers, Inc.

—Aunt Eater's Mystery Halloween. Cushman, Doug, illus. 2002. (Aunt Eater Mysteries Ser.). (Illus.). (J). 11.91 (978-0-7587-5992-4(4)) Book Wholesalers, Inc.

—Aunt Eater's Mystery Halloween. Cushman, Doug, illus. 1999. (I Can Read Bks.). (Illus.). 64p. (J). (gr. k-3). pap. 3.99 (978-0-06-444266-4(7) , Harper Trophy) HarperCollins Pubs.

—Aunt Eater's Mystery Halloween. 1998. (I Can Read Bks.). (Illus.). (J). (gr. k-3). 64p. 14.95 (978-0-06-027803-8(X)); 40p. 14.89 (978-0-06-027804-5(8)) HarperCollins Pubs.

—Aunt Eater's Mystery Halloween. Cushman, Doug, illus. 1999. (I Can Read Bks.). (Illus.). 64p. lib. bdg. 10.79 (978-0-606-17301-8(3)) Tandem Library Bks.

—Aunt Eater's Mystery Halloween. 1999. (gr. k-3). lib. bdg. 11.80 (978-0-613-22814-5(6)) Tandem Library Bks.

—Aunt Eater's Mystery Vacation. Cushman, Doug, illus. 2002. (Aunt Eater Mysteries Ser.). (Illus.). (J). 12.30 (978-0-7587-5993-1(2)) Book Wholesalers, Inc.

—Dirk Bones & the Mystery of the Haunted House. Cushman, Doug, illus. 2006. (I Can Read Bks.). (Illus.). 32p. (J). 15.99 (978-0-06-073764-1(6)); lib. bdg. 16.89 (978-0-06-073765-8(4)) HarperCollins Pubs.

—Inspector Hopper. Cushman, Doug, illus. 2000. (I Can Read Bks.). (Illus.). 64p. (J). (gr. k-3). 14.95 (978-0-06-028382-7(3)) HarperCollins Pubs.

—Mystery at the Club Sandwich. 2004. (Illus.). 32p. (J). (gr. k-3). tchr. ed. 15.00 (978-0-618-41969-2(1) , Clarion Bks.) Houghton Mifflin Co. Trade & Reference Div.

—The Mystery of King Karfu. 1998. (978-0-606-13638-9(X)) Tandem Library Bks.

—The Mystery of the Monkey's Maze. Cushman, Doug, illus. 1999. (From the Casebook of Seymour Sleuth Ser.). (Illus.). 32p. (J). (gr. k-3). 15.95 (978-0-06-027719-2(X)); 15.89 (978-0-06-027720-8(3)) HarperCollins Pubs.

Cusick, Richie Tankersley. Walk of the Spirits. 2008. 336p. (YA). (gr. 7). pap. 8.99 (***978-0-14-241050-9(0)*** , Puffin) Penguin Group (USA) Inc.

Czernecki, Stefan. Mystery at Midnight Museum. Date not set. 32p. (J). 14.99 (978-0-06-026199-3(4)) HarperCollins Pubs.

Dabbs, Douglas, illus. The Legend's Granddaughter: Not Quite Super, Book 1. 2007. 281p. (J). pap. (***978-0-9793168-0-7(4)***) NQSBks.

Dadey, Debbie & Jones, Marcia Thornton. The Abominable Snowman Doesn't Roast Marshmallows. Gurney, John Steven, illus. 2005. (Little Apple Ser.). 73p. (J). (978-1-4155-8202-2(5)) Scholastic, Inc.

—The Abominable Snowman Doesn't Roast Marshmallows. Gurney, John Steven, illus. 2005. 73p. (J). (ps-k). lib. bdg. 10.79 (978-0-606-33290-3(1)) Tandem Library Bks.

—The Bride of Frankenstein Doesn't Bake Cookies. Gurney, John Steven, illus. 2000. (Adventures of the Bailey School Kids Ser.: No. 41). 80p. (J). (gr. 2-4). 3.99 (978-0-439-04400-4(6)) Scholastic, Inc.

—The Bride of Frankenstein Doesn't Bake Cookies. 2000. (Adventures of the Bailey School Kids Ser.: No. 41). (J). (gr. 2-4). 10.79 (978-0-606-19542-3(4)) Tandem Library Bks.

—Frankenstein Doesn't Start Food Fights. Gurney, John Steven, illus. 2003. (Adventures of the Bailey School Kids Ser.: No. 47). 80p. (J). 3.99 (978-0-439-55999-7(5) , Scholastic Paperbacks) Scholastic, Inc.

—Frankenstein Doesn't Start Food Fights. 2003. (gr. 3-6). lib. bdg. 11.80 (978-0-613-82754-6(6)) Tandem Library Bks.

—Hercules Doesn't Pull Teeth. Gurney, John Steven, illus. 1998. (Adventures of the Bailey School Kids Ser.: No. 30). 80p. (J). (gr. 2-4). pap. 3.99 (978-0-590-25809-8(5) , Scholastic Paperbacks) Scholastic, Inc.

—Sea Monsters Don't Ride Motorcycles. Gurney, John Steven, illus. 2000. (Adventures of the Bailey School Kids Ser.: No. 40). 80p. (J). (gr. 2-4). pap. 3.99 (978-0-439-04401-1(4) , Scholastic Paperbacks) Scholastic, Inc.

—Sea Monsters Don't Ride Motorcycles. 2000. (Adventures of the Bailey School Kids Ser.: No. 40). (J). (gr. 2-4). (978-0-606-18601-8(8)) Tandem Library Bks.

—Sea Serpents Don't Juggle Water Balloons. Gurney, John Steven, illus. 2002. (Bailey School Kids Ser.: Bk. 46). 80p. (J). 3.99 (978-0-439-36805-6(7) , Scholastic Paperbacks) Scholastic, Inc.

—Sea Serpents Don't Juggle Water Balloons. 2002. (gr. 3-6). lib. bdg. 11.80 (978-0-613-50498-0(4)) Tandem Library Bks.

Dadey, Debbie, et al. Ghouls Don't Scoop Ice Cream. Gurney, John Steven, illus. 1998. (Adventures of the Bailey School Kids Ser.: No. 31). 80p. (J). (gr. 2-4). 3.99 (978-0-590-25819-7(2) , Scholastic Paperbacks) Scholastic, Inc.

Dahl, Michael. The Horizontal M. A. N. 1999. 182p. (J). (ps-7). per. 11.64 (978-0-606-21622-7(7)) Tandem Library Bks.

—The Viking Claw. 2001. (Finnegan Zwake Ser.: Vol. 4). 192p. (YA). (gr. 4-7). pap. 4.99 (978-0-7434-1697-9(X) , Simon Pulse) Simon & Schuster Children's Publishing.

—Worm Tunnel. 1999. (Illus.). (J). (978-0-606-21798-9(3)) Tandem Library Bks.

Dahl, Roald. Volando Solo. 2000. (SPA.). 192p. (J). (978-84-204-4583-0(5)) Aguilar, S. A. de Ediciones-Grupo Santillana.

Dalmatian Press Staff. Clues on the Loose! Mystery Magnet Book. (Scooby-Doo! Ser.). 4p. (J). 9.99 (978-1-4037-0610-2(7)) Dalmatian Pr.

—Power Play: Glitter Paint Box Book. 2002. (Powerpuff Girls Ser.). (Illus.). 32p. (J). 3.99 (978-1-57759-870-1(9)) Dalmatian Pr.

—Scooby Doo Shadow Mystery: Window Board Book. 2003. (Scooby-Doo! Ser.). (Illus.). 14p. (J). bds. 7.99 (978-1-4037-0332-3(9)) Dalmatian Pr.

—Time to Save the World: Time Force. 2002. (Power Rangers Ninja Storm Ser.). (Illus.). 24p. (J). pap. 2.99 (978-1-57759-527-4(0)) Dalmatian Pr.

Dalton, Sheila. Trial by Fire. 1998. 208p. (YA). (gr. 9-12). pap. 6.95 (978-0-929141-63-3(6)) Napoleon Publishing/ Rendezvous Pr. CAN. *Dist:* AtlasBooks Distribution.

Daly, Joseph M. Strange Town Volume One: The Woods Behind Trevor Malone's House. 2007. 265p. (YA). pap. (***978-0-9779921-0-2(1)***) Wolfs Corner Publishing.

Danko, Dan. Scooby-Doo: The Complete Movie Scrapbook. 2002. (gr. k-3). lib. bdg. 14.15 (978-0-613-50741-7(X)) Tandem Library Bks.

Dark Hunger. 1999. (SmartReader Ser.). (J). pap., tchr. ed. 19.95 incl. audio (978-0-7887-0277-8(7) , 79317T3) Recorded Bks., LLC.

Davidson, Michele R. Stowaways to Smith Island: Hayden & Chloe's Enchanted Journey with the Nurses to Maryland's Mysterious Smith Island. Watjen, Laureen, illus. 2004. 128p. (J). pap. 8.95 (978-0-9754170-1-0(0)) Smith Island Foundation.

Davis, Olive McFate. Keeping Secrets: A Mystery. Davis, Olive McFate, illus. 2002. III, 181p. (J). (gr. 3-8). pap. 11.95 (978-0-9718472-0-0(7)) Bluebird Publishing.

De Grosbois, Paul. Un Mal Etrange. 2002. (Roman Plus Ser.). (FRE.). 160p. (YA). (gr. 8 up). pap. (978-2-89021-167-4(3)) Diffusion du livre Mirabel.

De Rosa, Mary. On Sacred Ground. 2005. 103p. pap. 14.95 (978-1-4137-5835-1(5)) PublishAmerica, Inc.

Deary, Terry. True Mystery Stories. unabr. ed. 2003. (Read-Along Ser.). (J). pap. 29.95 incl. audio (978-0-7540-6251-6(1) , Galaxy Children's Large Print) BBC Audiobooks America.

Death at the Border. 64p. (YA). (gr. 6-12). pap. (978-0-8224-2361-4(8)) Globe Fearon Educational Publishing.

Deathman Don't Follow Me. 2003. (J). pap. 2.95 (978-0-590-44006-6(3)) Scholastic, Inc.

Deaver, Jeffery. The Bone Collector: A Lincoln Rhyme Novel. 1999. (gr. 7-12). lib. bdg. 16.45 (978-0-613-23690-4(4)) Tandem Library Bks.

Deaver, Julie Reece. The Night I Disappeared. 2002. 256p. (YA). (gr. 6 up). pap. 5.99 (978-0-7434-3979-4(1) , Simon Pulse) Simon & Schuster Children's Publishing.

Decter, Ed. Expedition to Blue Cave. Yuen, Sammy, Jr., illus. 2007. (Outriders Ser.). 208p. (J). (gr. 3-7). pap. 4.99 (978-1-4169-1305-4(X) , Aladdin) Simon & Schuster Children's Publishing.

—Expedition to Willow Key, Vol. 2. Yuen, Sammy, Jr., illus. 2007. (Outriders Ser.). 224p. (J). (gr. 3-7). pap. 4.99 (978-1-4169-1306-1(8) , Aladdin) Simon & Schuster Children's Publishing.

DeFelice, Cynthia. The Ghost of Cutler Creek. 2006. (Ghost Mysteries Ser.). 192p. (J). pap. 5.95 (978-0-374-40004-0(0) , Farrar, Straus & Giroux (BYR)) Farrar, Straus & Giroux.

DeFelice, Cynthia. The Missing Manatee. 2008. 192p. (J). pap. 6.95 (***978-0-374-40020-0(2)*** , Farrar, Straus & Giroux (BYR)) Farrar, Straus & Giroux.

DeFelice, Cynthia C. Death at Devil's Bridge. 2002. (gr. 3-6). lib. bdg. 14.10 (978-0-613-82528-3(4)) Tandem Library Bks.

—The Ghost & Mrs. Hobbs. 2001. (Ghost Mysteries Ser.). (Illus.). 192p. (J). (gr. 3-7). 16.00 (978-0-374-38046-5(5) , Farrar, Straus & Giroux (BYR)) Farrar, Straus & Giroux.

—The Ghost & Mrs. Hobbs. 2003. 192p. (J). pap. 5.99 (978-0-06-001172-7(6) , Harper Trophy) HarperCollins Pubs.

—The Ghost & Mrs. Hobbs. 2003. (gr. 3-6). lib. bdg. 14.15 (978-0-613-85155-8(2)) Tandem Library Bks.

—The Ghost of Cutler Creek. 2004. (Ghost Mysteries Ser.). 192p. (J). 16.00 (978-0-374-38058-8(9)) Farrar, Straus & Giroux.

—The Missing Manatee. 2005. 192p. (J). 16.00 (978-0-374-31257-2(5) , Farrar, Straus & Giroux (BYR)) Farrar, Straus & Giroux.

—The Missing Manatee. l.t. ed. 2005. 183p. (J). 20.95 (978-0-7862-8178-7(2)) Thorndike Pr.

Deiss, A. The Sullivan Girls & the Mystery of Moonhouse. 2003. 104p. (Orig.). pap. 9.95 (978-0-595-29580-7(0)) iUniverse, Inc.

del Sur, Duendes. Catnapped Caper. 2000. (gr. k-3). lib. bdg. 11.80 (978-0-613-24507-4(5)) Tandem Library Bks.

—Search for Scooby Snacks. 2000. (gr. k-3). lib. bdg. 11.80 (978-0-613-26871-4(7)) Tandem Library Bks.

del Sur, Duendes, illus. Pizza Place Ghost. 2001. (Scooby-Doo! Picture Clue Book Ser.: No. 4). 32p. (J). (gr. 5). pap. 3.99 (978-0-439-20495-8(X)) Scholastic, Inc.

Delaney, Mark. Growler's Horn. 2000. (Misfits, Inc. Ser.: No. 3). 192p. (J). (gr. 6-10). pap. 5.95 (978-1-56145-206-4(8)) Peachtree Pubs., Ltd.

—Growler's Horn. 2000. (gr. 7-12). lib. bdg. 14.10 (978-0-613-82664-8(7)); (Illus.). (J). 12.60 (978-0-606-18339-0(6)) Tandem Library Bks.

—Heroes & Villains. 1999. (Misfits, Inc. Ser.). (978-0-606-17405-3(2)) Tandem Library Bks.

—Hit & Run. 2002. (Misfits, Inc. Ser.: No. 6). (Illus.). 224p. (J). (gr. 5-9). pap. 5.95 (978-1-56145-275-0(0)) Peachtree Pubs., Ltd.

—Hit & Run. 2002. (gr. 5-8). lib. bdg. 14.10 (978-0-613-82660-0(4)) Tandem Library Bks.

—The Kingfisher's Tale. 2000. (Misfits, Inc. Ser.: No. 4). 216p. (J). (gr. 7-11). pap. 5.95 (978-1-56145-226-2(2)) Peachtree Pubs., Ltd.

—The Kingfisher's Tale. 2000. (Misfits, Inc. Ser.). (J). (978-0-606-19862-2(8)) Tandem Library Bks.

—Kingfisher's Tale. 2000. (gr. 7-12). lib. bdg. 14.10 (978-0-613-85287-6(7)) Tandem Library Bks.

—Of Heroes & Villains. 1999. (Misfits, Inc. Ser.: No. 2). 207p. (J). (gr. 7-11). pap. 5.95 (978-1-56145-178-4(9) , 51789) Peachtree Pubs., Ltd.

—Of Heroes & Villains. 1999. (gr. 7-12). lib. bdg. 14.10 (978-0-613-85293-7(1)) Tandem Library Bks.

—The Protester's Song. 2001. (Misfits, Inc. Ser.: Vol. 5). (Illus.). 224p. (J). (gr. 7-11). pap. 5.95 (978-1-56145-244-6(0)) Peachtree Pubs., Ltd.

—Protester's Song. 2001. (gr. 7-12). lib. bdg. 14.10 (978-0-613-68378-4(1)) Tandem Library Bks.

—The Vanishing Chip. 1998. (Misfits, Inc. Ser.: No. 1). 240p. (J). (gr. 7-11). pap. 5.95 (978-1-56145-176-0(2) , Q21568) Peachtree Pubs., Ltd.

De'Leon, Lunden. Oops Loops. 2006. 28p. pap. 9.95 (***978-1-4327-0114-7(2)***) Outskirts Press, Inc.

Deming, Lynette. Day in Matthews Shoes. 2006. 28p. pap. 9.95 (***978-1-4327-0100-0(2)***) Outskirts Press, Inc.

DeMitchell, Terri. You Will Come Back. 2004. (Illus.). 176p. (J). pap. 14.95 (978-1-932278-02-6(8)) Mayhaven Publishing.

DeSio, Delores. Up a Tree with Mary Mcphee: A Mystery for Children. 2006. 86p. pap. 14.95 (978-1-4241-4309-2(8)) PublishAmerica, Inc.

Desrosiers, Sylvie & Sylvestre, Daniel. Le Mystere du Lac Carre. 2001. (FRE., Illus.). 96p. (J). pap. (978-2-89021-508-5(3)) Diffusion du livre Mirabel.

—Peut-On Dessiner un Souvenir? 2001. (FRE., Illus.). 96p. (J). pap. (978-2-89021-510-8(5)) Diffusion du livre Mirabel.

Detective Club: Mysteries for Young Thinkers. 2001. (J). per. 11.95 (978-0-88305-531-1(7)) Dandy Lion Pubns.

Detective Larue Standee. 2004. (J). 127.60 (978-0-439-68644-0(X) , Scholastic Pr.) Scholastic, Inc.

Detective Teacher's Resource Guide. 2002. (PageTurner Detective Ser.). 48p. (YA). tchr. ed. 9.95 (978-1-56254-391-4(1) , SP 3911) Saddleback Educational Publishing.

Devlin Affair. 64p. (YA). (gr. 6-12). pap. (978-0-8224-2362-1(6)) Globe Fearon Educational Publishing.

Devlin, Wende & Devlin, Harry. Cranberry Halloween. unabr. ed. 2001. (J). (gr. k-3). pap. 16.95 incl. audio (978-0-8045-6657-5(7) , 6552-A) Spoken Arts, Inc.

Dexter, Catherine. I Dream of Murder. 1999. 160p. (YA). (gr. 5-9). pap. 5.95 (978-0-688-16668-7(7)) HarperCollins Pubs.

—I Dream of Murder. 1999. (J). (978-0-606-16805-2(2)) Tandem Library Bks.

The Diamond Necklace. 1999. (SmartReader Ser.). (J). pap., tchr. ed. 19.95 incl. audio (978-0-7887-2853-2(9) , 79670T3) Recorded Bks., LLC.

The Diamond of Doom, 6 vols. (Woodland Mysteriestm Ser.). 133p. (gr. 3-7). 42.50 (978-0-7802-7927-8(1)) Wright Group, The.

Dickey, Janet. Anyone's Guess Jr: Who's a Fraidy Kat? 2003. 39.95 (978-1-57950-093-1(5) , Upstart Bks.) Highsmith Inc.

Dickson, Louise. Lu & Clancy's Crime Science. Cupples, Pat, illus. 1999. 40p. (J). (ps-k). lib. bdg. 14.10 (978-0-613-21938-9(4)) Tandem Library Bks.

—Vanishing Cat. 2002. (gr. 3-6). lib. bdg. 15.25 (978-0-613-53331-7(3)) Tandem Library Bks.

DiFiore, Frank R. Alias Doctor Webber. 2000. 634p. (J). pap. 15.00 (978-0-932896-09-4(X)) Westcliff Pubns.

Dillon, Eilis. Island of Horses. 2004. (New York Review Children's Collection). 224p. (J). pap. 17.95 (978-1-59017-102-8(0) , NYR Children's Collection) New York Review of Bks., Inc., The.

Disney Press Staff. Abracadabra. 2001. (gr. k-3). lib. bdg. 13.00 (978-0-613-75074-5(8)) Tandem Library Bks.

Disney Press Staff, contrib. by. Mystery in Midair. 2001. (Mickey Mysteries Ser.: No. 1). (Illus.). 96p. (J). (gr. 2-5). reprint ed. pap. 4.99 (978-0-7868-4449-4(3)) Disney Pr.

DiTocco, Robyn & DiTocco, Tony. Atlas' Revenge: Another Mad Myth Mystery. 2005. 234p. 19.95 (978-0-9723429-2-6(3)); pap. 11.95 (978-0-9723429-3-3(1)) Brainstorm Pubns., Inc.

Dixon, Franklin W. All Eyes on First Prize. 1999. (Hardy Boys Are: No. 14). (J). (gr. 2-4). (978-0-606-19046-6(5)) Tandem Library Bks.

—The Apeman's Secret. 2005. (Hardy Boys Ser.: No. 62). (Illus.). 192p. (J). (gr. 3-8). 5.99 (978-0-448-43699-9(X) , Grosset & Dunlap) Penguin Group (USA) Inc.

—Bayport Buccaneers. 2007. (Hardy Boys (All New) Undercover Brothers Ser.). 176p. (J). pap. 4.99 (***978-1-4169-3403-5(0)*** , Aladdin) Simon & Schuster Children's Publishing.

—The Best of the Hardy Boys' Classic Collection: The Tower Treasure; The Secret of the Old Mill; The Haunted Fort. 2004. (Hardy Boys Ser.). 546p. (J). (gr. 3-9). 12.99 (978-0-448-43627-2(2) , Grosset & Dunlap) Penguin Group (USA) Inc.

—The Best of the Hardy Boys' Classic Collection Vol. 2: The House on the Cliff, The Ghost on Skeleton Rock, The Sting of the Scorpion. 2004. (Hardy Boys Ser.: 2). 546p. (J). (gr. 3-9). 12.99 (978-0-448-43628-9(0) , Grosset & Dunlap) Penguin Group (USA) Inc.

—Blown Away. 2006. (Illus.). (J). (Hardy Boys (All New) Undercover Brothers Ser.: No. 10). 160p. pap. 4.99 (978-1-4169-1173-9(1)); 147p. (978-1-4156-7590-8(2)) Simon & Schuster Children's Publishing. (Aladdin).

—Boardwalk Bust. 2005. 164p. (J). lib. bdg. 16.92 (***978-1-4242-0385-7(6)***) Fitzgerald Bks.

—Boardwalk Bust, Vol. 3. 2005. (Hardy Boys Ser.). 176p. pap. 4.99 (978-1-4169-0004-7(7) , Aladdin) Simon & Schuster Children's Publishing.

—Burned. 2005. 154p. (J). lib. bdg. 16.92 (***978-1-4242-0391-8(0)***) Fitzgerald Bks.

—Burned. 2005. (Hardy Boys Ser.: No. 6). (Illus.). 160p. (J). pap. 4.99 (978-1-4169-0008-5(X) , Aladdin) Simon & Schuster Children's Publishing.

—The Caribbean Cruise Caper. 1999. (Hardy Boys Mystery Stories Ser.: No. 154). 160p. (J). (gr. 3-6). pap. 4.99 (978-0-671-02549-6(X) , Aladdin) Simon & Schuster Children's Publishing.

—The Case of the Psychic's Vision. 2003. (gr. 5-8). lib. bdg. 13.00 (978-0-613-61612-6(X)) Tandem Library Bks.

—The Castle Conundrum. 2002. (gr. 5-8). lib. bdg. 13.00 (978-0-613-63268-3(0)) Tandem Library Bks.

—The Dangerous Transmission. ed. 2005. (Hardy Boys II Ser.: No. 184). 147p. (J). lib. bdg. 15.00 (978-1-59054-850-9(7)) Fitzgerald Bks.

—Daredevils. l.t. ed. 2003. (Hardy Boys Mystery Ser.). 139p. (J). 21.95 (978-0-7862-5309-8(6)) Thorndike Pr.

—Death & Diamonds. 2007. (Hardy Boys (All New) Undercover Brothers Ser.: No. 15). 176p. (J). pap. 4.99 (978-1-4169-3402-8(2) , Aladdin) Simon & Schuster Children's Publishing.

—Disappearing Floor, No. 19. 2006. (Hardy Boys (Hardcover) Ser.). 228p. (J). (ps-3). 17.95 (978-1-55709-287-8(7)) Applewood Bks.

—The End of the Trail. 2000. (Hardy Boys Mystery Stories Ser.: No. 162). 144p. (J). (gr. 3-6). pap. 4.99 (978-0-671-04759-7(0) , Aladdin) Simon & Schuster Children's Publishing.

—The End of the Trail. 2000. (gr. 5-8). lib. bdg. 13.00 (978-0-613-27806-5(2)) Tandem Library Bks.

—Extreme Danger. 2005. 165p. (J). lib. bdg. 16.92 (***978-1-4242-0383-3(X)***) Fitzgerald Bks.

—Extreme Danger. 2005. (Hardy Boys Ser.). 172p. pap. 4.99 (978-1-4169-0002-3(0) , Aladdin) Simon & Schuster Children's Publishing.

—Farming Fear. ed. 2005. (Hardy Boys II Ser.: No. 188). 154p. (J). lib. bdg. 15.00 (978-1-59054-839-4(6)) Fitzgerald Bks.

—Feeding Frenzy. 2008. (Hardy Boys (All New) Undercover Brothers Ser.). 160p. (J). pap. 4.99 (***978-1-4169-5499-6(6)*** , Aladdin) Simon & Schuster Children's Publishing.

—Footprints under the Window. Gretta, J. Clemens, illus. 2001. (Hardy Boys Mystery Stories Ser.: No. 12). 218p. (J). (gr. 4-7). per. 14.95 (978-1-55709-270-0(2)) Applewood Bks.

—Foul Play. 2007. (Hardy Boys (All New) Undercover Brothers Ser.: No. 19). 192p. (J). pap. 4.99 (***978-1-4169-4977-0(1)*** , Aladdin) Simon & Schuster Children's Publishing.

—A Game Called Chaos. 2000. (Hardy Boys Ser.: No. 160). 160p. (J). (gr. 3-6). pap. 9.95 (978-0-671-03870-0(2) , Aladdin) Simon & Schuster Children's Publishing.

—A Game Called Chaos. 2000. (gr. 5-8). lib. bdg. 13.00 (978-0-613-27846-1(1)) Tandem Library Bks.

—The Great Airport Mystery. 2004. (Hardy Boys Mystery Stories Ser.: No. 9). 228p. (J). (gr. 4-7). 14.95 (978-1-55709-267-0(2)) Applewood Bks.

—The Hardy Boys, Vols. 1-6. 1998. (J). 22.98 (978-0-448-41671-7(9) , Grosset & Dunlap) Penguin Group (USA) Inc.

—The Hardy Boys. 75th collector's anniv. ed. 2002. (Hardy Boys Ser.). (Illus.). 464p. (J). pap. 7.99 (978-0-689-85620-4(2) , Aladdin) Simon & Schuster Children's Publishing.

—Hardy Boys Starter Set. 2007. (Hardy Boys Ser.). 128p. (J). lthr. 25.98 (***978-0-448-44820-6(3)*** , Grosset & Dunlap) Penguin Group (USA) Inc.

—Hazed. 2007. (Hardy Boys (All New) Undercover Brothers Ser.: No. 14). 160p. (J). pap. 4.99 (978-1-4169-1803-5(5) , Aladdin) Simon & Schuster Children's Publishing.

—The Hidden Harbor Mystery. Gretter, J. Clemens, illus. 2003. (Hardy Boys Mystery Stories Ser.). 219p. (J). (gr. 4-7). per. 14.95 (978-1-55709-272-4(9)) Applewood Bks.

—Hidden Mountain. ed. 2005. (Hardy Boys II Ser.: No. 186). 154p. (J). lib. bdg. 15.00 (978-1-59054-841-7(8)) Fitzgerald Bks.

—Hide & Sneak. 2002. (Hardy Boys Ser.: Vol. 174). 144p. (J). pap. 4.99 (978-0-7434-3758-5(6) , Aladdin) Simon & Schuster Children's Publishing.

—Hide & Sneak. 2002. (gr. 5-8). lib. bdg. 13.00 (978-0-613-45059-1(0)) Tandem Library Bks.

—Hunting for Hidden Gold. Rogers, Walter S., illus. 2004. (Hardy Boys Mystery Stories Ser.: No. 5). 210p. (J). (gr. 4-7). 17.95 (978-1-55709-148-2(X)) Applewood Bks.

—Hurricane Joe. 2006. (Hardy Boys (All New) Undercover Brothers Ser.: No.11). 160p. (J). pap. 4.99 (978-1-4169-1174-6(X) , Aladdin) Simon & Schuster Children's Publishing.

—In Plane Sight. ed. 2005. (Hardy Boys I Ser.: No. 176). 148p. (J). lib. bdg. 15.00 (978-1-59054-842-4(6)) Fitzgerald Bks.

—In Plane Sight. 2002. 148p. (gr. 5-8). lib. bdg. 13.00 (978-0-613-63303-1(2)) Tandem Library Bks.

—Kickoff to Danger. ed. 2005. (Hardy Boys I Ser.: No. 170). 149p. (J). lib. bdg. 15.00 (978-1-59054-843-1(4)) Fitzgerald Bks.

—Kidnapped at the Casino. 2007. (Hardy Boys Undercover Brothers: Super Mystery Ser.). 240p. (J). pap. 5.99 (978-1-4169-3923-8(7) , Aladdin) Simon & Schuster Children's Publishing.

—Line of Fire. (Illus.). (J). mass mkt. 2.95 (978-0-671-70492-6(3) , Simon Pulse) Simon & Schuster Children's Publishing.

—The London Deception. 1999. (Hardy Boys Mystery Stories Ser.: No. 158). (J). (gr. 3-6). (978-0-606-19052-7(X)) Tandem Library Bks.

—Martial Law. 2006. 152p. (J). lib. bdg. 16.92 (***978-1-4242-0389-5(9)***) Fitzgerald Bks.

—Martial Law. 2006. (Illus.). 152p. (J). (978-1-4156-6852-8(3) , Aladdin) Simon & Schuster Children's Publishing.

—The Missing Chums, No. 4. Rogers, Walter S., illus. 2004. (Hardy Boys Mystery Stories Ser.: No. 4). 210p. (J). (gr. 4-7). reprint ed. 17.95 (978-1-55709-147-5(1)) Applewood Bks.

—Motocross Madness. ed. 2005. (Hardy Boys II Ser.: No. 190). 154p. (J). lib. bdg. 15.00 (978-1-59054-844-8(2)) Fitzgerald Bks.

—The Mummy Case. 2005. (Hardy Boys Ser.: No. 63). (Illus.). 192p. (J). (gr. 3-8). 6.99 (978-0-448-43700-2(7) , Grosset & Dunlap) Penguin Group (USA) Inc.

—The Mummy's Curse. 2006. (Hardy Boys (All New) Undercover Brothers Ser.: No. 13). 176p. (J). pap. 4.99 (978-1-4169-1507-2(9) , Aladdin) Simon & Schuster Children's Publishing.

—Murder at the Mall. 2007. (Hardy Boys (All New) Undercover Brothers Ser.). 176p. (J). pap. 4.99 (***978-1-4169-3930-6(X)*** , Aladdin) Simon & Schuster Children's Publishing.

—The Mystery of Cabin Island, No. 8. Rogers, Walter S., illus. 2004. (Hardy Boys Mystery Stories Ser.: No. 8). 210p. (J). (gr. 4-7). 17.95 (978-1-55709-266-3(4)) Applewood Bks.

—Mystery of Smugglers Cove. 2005. (Hardy Boys Ser.: No. 64). (Illus.). 192p. (J). (gr. 3-8). 6.99 (978-0-448-43701-9(5) , Grosset & Dunlap) Penguin Group (USA) Inc.

—The Mystery of the Black Rhino. ed. 2005. (Hardy Boys I Ser.: No. 178). 151p. (J). lib. bdg. 15.00 (978-1-59054-851-6(5)) Fitzgerald Bks.

—The Mystery of the Black Rhino. 2003. (gr. 5-8). lib. bdg. 13.00 (978-0-613-61646-1(4)) Tandem Library Bks.

—Mystery of the Samurai Sword. 2005. (Hardy Boys Ser.: Vol. 60). (Illus.). 196p. (J). (gr. 3-8). pap. 5.99 (978-0-448-43697-5(3) , Grosset & Dunlap) Penguin Group (USA) Inc.

—The Mystery of the Silver Star, No. 86. 1999. pap. (978-0-671-70995-2(X) , Aladdin) Simon & Schuster Children's Publishing.

—Night of the Werewolf. 2005. (Hardy Boys Ser.: No. 59). (Illus.). 196p. (J). (gr. 3-8). pap. 5.99 (978-0-448-43696-8(5) , Grosset & Dunlap) Penguin Group (USA) Inc.

—No Way Out. ed. 2005. (Hardy Boys II Ser.: No. 187). 149p. (J). lib. bdg. 15.00 (978-1-59054-845-5(0)) Fitzgerald Bks.

—One False Step. ed. 2005. (Hardy Boys II Ser.: No. 189). 150p. (J). lib. bdg. 15.00 (978-1-59054-846-2(9)) Fitzgerald Bks.

—One False Step. 2005. 150p. (J). (978-1-4155-7722-6(6) , Aladdin) Simon & Schuster Children's Publishing.

—Passport to Danger. 2005. (Hardy Boys I Ser.: No. 179). 147p. (J). lib. bdg. 15.00 (978-1-59054-847-9(7)) Fitzgerald Bks.

—Passport to Danger. 2003. (gr. 5-8). lib. bdg. 13.00 (978-0-613-66466-0(3)) Tandem Library Bks.

—The Pentagon Spy. 2005. (Hardy Boys Ser.: No. 61). (Illus.). 192p. (J). (gr. 3-8). 5.99 (978-0-448-43698-2(1) , Grosset & Dunlap) Penguin Group (USA) Inc.

—Pushed. 2007. (Hardy Boys (All New) Undercover Brothers Ser.). 154p. (J). (gr. 3-7). per. 4.99 (***978-1-4169-4802-5(3)*** , Aladdin) Simon & Schuster Children's Publishing.

—Revenge of the Desert Phantom. (Hardy Boys Mystery Stories Ser.: No. 84). (J). (gr. 3-6). (978-0-671-49730-9(8) , Simon & Schuster Children's Publishing) Simon & Schuster Children's Publishing.

—Running on Fumes. 2005. 150p. (J). lib. bdg. 16.92 (***978-1-4242-0384-0(8)***) Fitzgerald Bks.

—Running on Fumes. 2005. (Illus.). 150p. (J). (***978-1-4156-0714-5(1)*** ***);*** Vol. 2. 160p. pap. 4.99 (978-1-4169-0003-0(9)) Simon & Schuster Children's Publishing. (Aladdin).

—The Secret of the Caves, No. 7. Rogers, Walter S., illus. 2004. (Hardy Boys Mystery Stories Ser.: No. 7). 228p. (J). (gr. 4-7). reprint ed. 14.95 (978-1-55709-150-5(1)) Applewood Bks.

—The Secret of the Soldier's Gold. ed. 2005. (Hardy Boys II Ser.: No. 182). 147p. (J). lib. bdg. 15.00 (978-1-59054-852-3(3)) Fitzgerald Bks.

—Secret Warning, No. 17. 2006. (Hardy Boys (Hardcover) Ser.). 228p. (J). (gr. 4-7). per. 17.95 (978-1-55709-285-4(0)) Applewood Bks.

—The Sinister Signpost, Vol. 15. 2004. (Hardy Boys(R) Mystery Ser.). 228p. (J). (gr. 4-7). 17.95 (978-1-55709-273-1(7)) Applewood Bks.

—Skin & Bones. ed. 2005. (Hardy Boys I Ser.: No. 164). 148p. (J). lib. bdg. 15.00 (978-1-59054-848-6(5)) Fitzgerald Bks.

—Slip, Slide & Slap Shot. 1999. (Hardy Boys Are: No. 15). (J). (gr. 2-4). (978-0-606-19063-3(5)) Tandem Library Bks.

—Speed Times Five. ed. 2005. (Hardy Boys I Ser.: No. 173). 150p. (J). lib. bdg. 15.00 (978-1-59054-849-3(3)) Fitzgerald Bks.

—Spy Set: Extreme Danger; Running on Fumes; Boardwalk Bust; Thrill Ride. 2005. (Hardy Boys Ser.). 672p. (J). pap. 17.95 (978-1-4169-1324-5(6) , Aladdin) Simon & Schuster Children's Publishing.

—The Stone Idol. 2005. (Hardy Boys Ser.: No. 65). (Illus.). 196p. (J). (gr. 3-8). pap. 6.99 (978-0-448-43702-6(3) , Grosset & Dunlap) Penguin Group (USA) Inc.

—The Test Case. l.t. ed. 2002. 169p. (J). 21.95 (978-0-7862-4657-1(X)) Thorndike Pr.

—Thrill Ride. 2005. (Illus.). 154p. (J). (978-1-4156-0585-1(8) , Aladdin) Simon & Schuster Children's Publishing.

—Top Ten Ways to Die. 2006. 169p. (J). lib. bdg. 16.92 (***978-1-4242-0390-1(2)***) Fitzgerald Bks.

—Training for Trouble. ed. 2005. (Hardy Boys I Ser.: No. 161). 147p. (J). lib. bdg. 15.00 (978-1-59054-853-0(1)) Fitzgerald Bks.

—Trick-or-Trouble. ed. 2005. (Hardy Boys I Ser.: No. 175). 154p. (J). lib. bdg. 15.00 (978-1-59054-854-7(X)) Fitzgerald Bks.

—Trouble in Paradise. 2006. (Hardy Boys (All New) Undercover Brothers Ser.: No. 12). 176p. (J). pap. 4.99 (978-1-4169-1178-4(2) , Aladdin) Simon & Schuster Children's Publishing.

—Trouble in Warp Space. ed. 2005. (Hardy Boys I Ser.: No. 172). 154p. (J). lib. bdg. 15.00 (978-1-59054-855-4(8)) Fitzgerald Bks.

—Trouble in Warp Space. 2002. (gr. 3-6). lib. bdg. 13.00 (978-0-613-45115-4(5)) Tandem Library Bks.

—Trouble in Warp Space. l.t. ed. 2002. 181p. (J). 21.95 (978-0-7862-4658-8(8)) Thorndike Pr.

—Typhoon Island. ed. 2005. (Hardy Boys II Ser.: No. 180). 148p. (J). lib. bdg. 15.00 (978-1-59054-857-8(4)) Fitzgerald Bks.

—Typhoon Island. 2003. (gr. 5-8). lib. bdg. 13.00 (978-0-613-66472-1(8)) Tandem Library Bks.

—The Vanishing Thieves. 2005. (Hardy Boys Ser.). (Illus.). 196p. (J). (gr. 3-8). pap. 6.99 (978-0-448-43703-3(1) , Grosset & Dunlap) Penguin Group (USA) Inc.

—Wanted. 2006. (Hardy Boys Undercover Brothers Ser.: No.1). 192p. (J). pap. 5.99 (978-1-4169-1258-3(4) , Aladdin) Simon & Schuster Children's Publishing.

—Warehouse Rumble. ed. 2005. (Hardy Boys II Ser.: No. 183). 152p. (J). lib. bdg. 15.00 (978-1-59054-858-5(2)) Fitzgerald Bks.

—What Happened at Midnight, No. 10. 2000. (Hardy Boys Mystery Stories Ser.: No. 10). (Illus.). 228p. (J). (gr. 4-7). 17.95 (978-1-55709-268-7(0)) Applewood Bks.

—While the Clock Ticked. Gretta, J. Cleme, illus. 2000. (Hardy Boys Mystery Stories Ser.: No. 11). 213p. (J). (gr. 4-7). per. 14.95 (978-1-55709-269-4(9)) Applewood Bks.

—A Will to Survive. 1999. (Hardy Boys Mystery Stories Ser.: No. 156). (J). (gr. 3-6). (978-0-606-19051-0(1)) Tandem Library Bks.

—Wreck & Roll. ed. 2005. (Hardy Boys II Ser.: No. 185). 153p. (J). lib. bdg. 15.00 (978-1-59054-859-2(0)) Fitzgerald Bks.

Dixon, Franklin W. & Walker, Jeff. The Mystery of the Black Rhino. 2003. (Hardy Boys Ser.). (Illus.). 160p. (J). pap. 4.99 (978-0-689-85598-6(2) , Aladdin) Simon & Schuster Children's Publishing.

—Passport to Danger, Vol. 179. 2003. (Hardy Boys Ser.). 160p. (J). pap. 4.99 (978-0-689-85779-9(9) , Aladdin) Simon & Schuster Children's Publishing.

—Typhoon Island, Vol. 180. 2003. (Hardy Boys Ser.). (Illus.). 160p. (J). pap. 4.99 (978-0-689-85884-0(1) , Aladdin) Simon & Schuster Children's Publishing.

Dobinson, Tony. The Crossing. 2006. 160p. pap. 10.00 (978-1-84427-003-3(3)) STL Distribution North America.

Dodds, Siobhan & Bentley, Dawn. Sherlock's Missing Bone. 1999. (Picture Puzzle Board Bks.). (Illus.). 12p. (J). bds. 6.95 (978-1-58117-032-0(7) , Intervisual/Piggy Toes) Dalmatian Pr.

Doder, Joshua. Grk & the Hotdog Trail. 2008. (J). (***978-0-385-73361-8(5)*** ***);*** (***978-0-385-90376-9(6)*** ***);*** pap. (***978-0-440-42150-4(0)***) Dell Publishing. (Delacorte Pr.).

Doerr, Bonnie J. Kenzie's Key. Aberle, Xylena Apotheloz, illus. 2003. 211p. (J). 16.95 (978-0-9619155-6-8(0)) Laurel & Herbert, Inc.

Donnell, Annie Hamilton. Four Girls & a Compact. 2005. 76p. pap. 10.95 (978-1-59540-606-4(9) , 1st World Library - Literary Society) 1st World Publishing, Inc.

—Four Girls & A Compact. 2005. 26.95 (978-1-4218-0906-9(0) , 1st World Library - Literary Society) 1st World Publishing, Inc.

—Four Girls & A Compact. 2004. reprint ed. pap. 15.95 (978-1-4191-2048-0(4)) ; pap. 1.99 (978-1-4192-2048-7(9)) Kessinger Publishing, LLC.

Doogan, Mike. Skeleton Lake. 2008. (gr. 8). 25.95 (***978-0-399-15492-8(2)*** , Putnam Adult) Penguin Group (USA) Inc.

Dorato, A. P. Arthur, Donna, & the Magic Crown of Tiabora. 2006. pap. 19.95 (978-1-4137-8898-3(X)) PublishAmerica, Inc.

Doro, Ann. The Missing Canary. l.t. ed. 2005. 93p. 12.95 (978-0-9745052-2-0(6) , Peeper & Friends) Tree Of Life Publishing.

Dorpinghaus, Penny. Fear Balls & Button Wads. 2006. 52p. pap. 12.95 (978-1-4241-2281-3(3)) PublishAmerica, Inc.

Dowd, Siobhan. The London Eye Mystery. 2008. 336p. (J). (***978-0-375-84976-3(9)*** ***);*** lib. bdg. (***978-0-375-94976-0(3)***) Random Hse. Children's Bks. (Fickling, David Bks.).

Dower, Laura. Caught in the Web. rev. ed. 2001. (From the Files of Madison Finn Ser.: Vol. 4). (Illus.). 176p. (J). (gr. 3-7). pap. 4.99 (978-0-7868-1556-2(6) , Volo) Hyperion Bks. for Children.

—Caught in the Web. 2001. (gr. 3-6). lib. bdg. 13.00 (978-0-613-74959-6(6)) Tandem Library Bks.

—Lost & Found. 6th rev. ed. 2002. (From the Files of Madison Finn Ser.: Vol. 6). (Illus.). 176p. (gr. 3-7). pap. 4.99 (978-0-7868-1558-6(2) , Volo) Hyperion Bks. for Children.

—Lost & Found. 2002. (gr. 3-6). lib. bdg. 13.00 (978-0-613-91012-5(5)) Tandem Library Bks.

—On the Case. 2004. 170p. (J). lib. bdg. 16.92 (***978-1-4242-0648-3(0)***) Fitzgerald Bks.

—On the Case, Bk. 17. rev. ed. 2004. (From the Files of Madison Finn Ser.: Vol. 17). 176p. (J). (gr. 3-7). pap. 4.99 (978-0-7868-0987-5(6) , Volo) Hyperion Bks. for Children.

—Play It Again. Powers, Stephanie, illus. 3rd rev. ed. 2001. (From the Files of Madison Finn Ser.: No. 3). 176p. (gr. 3-7). reprint ed. pap. 4.99 (978-0-7868-1555-5(8) , Volo) Hyperion Bks. for Children.

—Play It Again. 2001. (gr. 3-6). lib. bdg. 13.00 (978-0-613-75039-4(X)) Tandem Library Bks.

Downie, Mary Alice & Downie, John. Danger in Disguise. 2001. (On Time's Wing Ser.). (Illus.). 178p. (J). (gr. 4-7). pap. (978-1-896184-72-2(3)) Roussan Pubs., Inc./Roussan Editeur, Inc.

Doyle, Arthur Conan. The Adventure of the Speckled Band. Stemach, Jerry, ed. Letwenko, Michael, illus. 2000. 65.00 incl. audio, cd-rom (978-1-58702-338-5(5)); 2002. 104p. 150.00 (978-1-58702-041-4(6)); 2000. 104p. 50.00 (978-1-58702-496-2(9)) Johnston, Don Inc.

—The Adventures & Memoirs of Sherlock Holmes. 2001. (gr. 7-12). lib. bdg. 22.25 (978-0-613-64240-8(6)) Tandem Library Bks.

—Adventures of Sherlock Holmes. 1998. (Wordsworth Classics Ser.). (YA). (gr. 6-12). 5.27 (978-0-89061-033-6(9) , R0339WW) Jamestown.

—Adventures of Sherlock Holmes. 2004. (Illus.). 336p. (J). (gr. 4-8). pap. 3.99 (978-0-439-57428-0(5) , Scholastic Paperbacks) Scholastic, Inc.

—The Adventures of Sherlock Holmes: With a Discussion of Curiosity. Butterfield, Ned, tr. Butterfield, Ned, illus. 2003. (Values in Action Illustrated Classics Ser.). (J). (978-1-59203-045-3(9)) Learning Challenge, Inc.

—Las Aventuras de Sherlock Holmes. 2000. (SPA., Illus.). 339p. (978-84-206-3692-4(4)) Alianza Editorial, S. A.

—Favorite Sherlock Holmes Detective Stories. unabr. ed. 2000. (Dover Juvenile Classics Ser.). (Illus.). 208p. (J). (gr. 4-7). pap. 2.50 (978-0-486-41242-9(3)) Dover Pubns., Inc.

—The Hound of the Baskervilles. 2004. (Fast Track Classics Ser.). (Illus.). 48p. (J). pap. 8.99 (978-0-237-52402-9(3) , Evans Brothers, Limited) Evans Publishing Group GBR. *Dist:* Independent Pubs. Group.

—The Hound of the Baskervilles: Another Adventure of Sherlock Holmes. 2002. (YA). (gr. 5-12). pap. 6.50 (978-0-8359-0963-1(8)) Globe Fearon Educational Publishing.

—The Hound of the Baskervilles: Another Adventure of Sherlock Holmes, Level 4. abr. ed. 2000. (Bookworms Ser.). (Illus.). 6.50 (978-0-19-423035-3(X)) Oxford Univ. Pr., Inc.

—The Hound of the Baskervilles: Another Adventure of Sherlock Holmes. 2000. (Aladdin Classics Ser.). 256p. (J). (gr. 4-11). pap. 5.99 (978-0-689-83571-1(X) , Aladdin) Simon & Schuster Children's Publishing.

—The Hound of the Baskervilles: Another Adventure of Sherlock Holmes. 2001. (gr. 7-12). lib. bdg. 16.45 (978-0-613-64290-3(2)); 2001. (gr. 7-12). lib. bdg. 12.95 (978-0-613-37148-3(8)); 2001. (Illus.). (J). 13.75 (978-0-606-21554-1(9)); 2000. (gr. 3-6). lib. bdg. 11.80 (978-0-613-63203-4(6)) Tandem Library Bks.

—The Return of Sherlock Holmes. l.t. ed. 1998. (Large Print Heritage Ser.). 278p. (YA). (gr. 7-12). lib. bdg. 29.95 (978-1-58118-038-1(1)) LRS.

—El Sabueso de los Baskerville. 2nd ed. 2002. (Clover Ser.). (SPA., Illus.). 256p. (YA). (978-84-392-8024-8(6) , EV5542) Gaviota Ediciones ESP. *Dist:* Lectorum Pubns., Inc.

—Sherlock Holmes & the Case of the Hound of the Baskervilles. 2005. (Great Illustrated Classics Ser.). (Illus.). 237p. (J). (gr. 3-8). 21.35 (978-1-59679-250-0(7) , ABDO & Daughters) ABDO Publishing Co.

—Sherlock Holmes & the Case of the Hound of the Baskervilles. Vogel, Malvina G., ed. Marcos, Pablo, illus. 2006. 237p. (YA). (gr. 4-8). 10.00 (978-0-7567-9834-5(5)) DIANE Publishing Co.

—The Sign of Four. 2001. (gr. 7-12). lib. bdg. 15.30 (978-0-613-64324-5(0)) Tandem Library Bks.

—A Study in Scarlet. 2001. (gr. 7-12). lib. bdg. 15.30 (978-0-613-64328-3(3)) Tandem Library Bks.

Doyle, Arthur Conan. Adventures of Sherlock Holmes. Lynch, Brendan, illus. 2002. (Great Illustrated Classics Ser.). 240p. (J). (gr. 3-8). 21.35 (978-1-57765-678-4(4) , ABDO & Daughters) ABDO Publishing Co.

Doyle, Bill. Betrayed! The 1977 Journal of Zeke Moorie. Hoskins, Brian, illus. 2006. 139p. (J). lib. bdg. 18.46 (***978-1-4242-1733-5(4)***) Fitzgerald Bks.

—Betrayed! The 1977 Journal of Zeke Moorie. 4th ed. 2006. (Crime Through Time Ser.: No. 4). 144p. (J). (gr. 3-7). pap. 5.99 (978-0-316-05741-7(X)) Little Brown & Co.

—Iced! The 2007 Journal of Nick Fitzmorgan. Simpson, Philomena, illus. 2006. 133p. (J). lib. bdg. 18.46 (***978-1-4242-1734-2(2)***) Fitzgerald Bks.

—ICED: The 2007 Journal of Nick Fitzmorgan. 5th ed. 2006. (Crime Through Time Ser.: No. 5). (Illus.). 144p. (J). (gr. 3-7). pap. 5.99 (978-0-316-05753-0(3)) Little Brown & Co.

—Nabbed! The 1925 Journal of G. Codd Fitzmorgan. Lewis, Anthony, illus. 2006. 125p. (J). lib. bdg. 18.46 (***978-1-4242-1735-9(0)***) Fitzgerald Bks.

—Nabbed! The 1925 Journal of G. Codd Fitzmorgan. 2nd ed. 2006. (Crime Through Time Ser.: No. 2). (Illus.). 128p. (J). (gr. 3-7). pap. 5.99 (978-0-316-05737-0(1)) Little Brown & Co.

—Silenced! The 1969 Journal of Malcolm. Kelleher, Kathie, illus. 2006. 141p. (J). lib. bdg. 18.46 (***978-1-4242-1736-6(9)***) Fitzgerald Bks.

—Silenced! The 1969 Journal of Malcolm Moorie. 3rd ed. 2006. (Crime Through Time Ser.: No. 3). (Illus.). 144p. (J). (gr. 3-7). pap. 5.99 (978-0-316-05738-7(X)) Little Brown & Co.

—Swindled! The 1906 Journal of Fitz Morgan. Dow, Brian, illus. 2006. 138p. (J). lib. bdg. 18.46 (***978-1-4242-1737-3(7)***) Fitzgerald Bks.

—Swindled! The 1906 Journal of Fitz Morgan. 2006. (Crime Through Time Ser.: No. 1). (Illus.). 144p. (J). (gr. 3-7). pap. 5.99 (978-0-316-05736-3(3)) Little Brown & Co.

—Trapped: The 2031 Journal of Otis Fitzmorgan. 6th ed. 2006. (Crime Through Time Ser.: No. 6). 144p. (J). (gr. 3-7). pap. 5.99 (978-0-316-05754-7(1)) Little Brown & Co.

Doyle, Patrick H. T. Edgar Font's Hunt for a House to Haunt: Adventure Two: the Fakersville Power Station. 2007. (J). per. 7.99 (*978-0-9786132-1-1(X)) Armadillo Bks.

Doyle, Sir Arthur Canon. The Great Adventures of Sherlock Holmes. 2006. (Illus.). 61p. (J). lib. bdg. 30.77 (*978-1-4242-1327-6(4)) Fitzgerald Bks.

Drake, David. Secrets of the Hidden Valley: A Sons of Inu Adventure. 2001. 196p. (J). (gr. 4-9). pap. 13.99 (978-1-885631-05-3(7) , Family Of Man Pr., The) Hutchison, G.F. Pr.

Draper, Sharon M. The Backyard Animal Show. Watson, Jesse Joshua, illus. 2006. (Ziggy & the Black Dinosaurs Ser.). 128p. (J). pap. 4.99 (978-1-4169-0000-9(4) , Aladdin); lib. bdg. 11.89 (978-1-4169-2754-9(9) , Aladdin Library) Simon & Schuster Children's Publishing.

—The Buried Bones Mystery. Watson, Jesse Joshua, illus. 2006. (Ziggy & the Black Dinosaurs Ser.: Vol. 1). 112p. (J). pap. 4.99 (978-0-689-87910-4(5)) Simon & Schuster Children's Publishing.

Driggs, Scout. My Little Pony No. 4: Mystery Monster. Fletcher, Lyn, illus. 2005. (My Little Pony Ser.). 24p. (J). (ps-1). pap. 3.99 (978-0-06-074446-5(4) , Harper Festival) HarperCollins Pubs.

Dubowski, Cathy East. The Case of the High Seas Secret. 2001..(New Adventures of Mary-Kate & Ashley Ser.). (Illus.). (J). 11.15 (978-0-606-21919-8(6)) Tandem Library Bks.

—Family Reunion. 2000. (gr. 3-6). lib. bdg. 13.00 (978-0-613-25123-5(7)) Tandem Library Bks.

—Family Reunion: Junior Novel. Richardson, Julia, ed. 2000. (So Weird Ser.: No. 1). (Illus.). 144p. (gr. 3-7). pap. 4.99 (978-0-7868-1397-1(0)) Disney Pr.

Ducharme, Huguette. Enquete Tres Speciale. Caron, Romi, illus. 2004. (Collection des 6 Ans : Vol. 32). (FRE.). 68p. (YA). 7.95 (978-2-922565-94-2(7)) Editions de la Paix CAN. *Dist:* World of Reading, Ltd.

Duerst, Marilyn D. & Hill, John W. The Crimecracker Kids & the Bakeshop Break-In. Koch, Nora, illus. 1999. 53p. (YA). (gr. 4 up). pap. 10.95 (978-0-9678212-0-7(7)) Gravel Pit Pr.

Duey, Kathleen. Arthur. Epstein, Eugene, illus. Gould, Robert, photos by. 2005. (Time Soldiers Ser.: Vol. 4). 96p. (J). (gr. 3-4). pap. 5.95 (978-1-929945-56-6(6)) Big Guy Bks., Inc.

—Patch. Epstein, Eugene, illus. Gould, Robert, photos by. 2005. (Time Soldiers Ser.: Bk. 3). 96p. (J). (gr. 3-4). pap. 5.95 (978-1-929945-55-9(8)) Big Guy Bks., Inc.

Duffy, Daniel M., illus. Benny Goes into Business, Vol. 5. 1999. (Adventures of Benny & Watch: Vol. 5). 32p. (J). (ps-2). pap. 3.95 (978-0-8075-0637-0(0)) Whitman, Albert & Co.

—Benny's New Friend, Vol. 3. 1998. (Adventures of Benny & Watch: Vol. No. 3). 32p. (J). (ps-2). pap. 3.95 (978-0-8075-0649-3(4)) Whitman, Albert & Co.

—The Magic Show Mystery, Vol. 4. 1998. (Adventures of Benny & Watch: Vol. No. 4). 32p. (J). (ps-2). pap. 3.95 (978-0-8075-4939-1(8)) Whitman, Albert & Co.

—Meet the Boxcar Children. 1998. (Adventures of Benny & Watch: Vol. No. 1). 48p. (J). (ps-2). pap. 3.95 (978-0-8075-5034-2(5)) Whitman, Albert & Co.

—A Present for Grandfather, Vol. 2. 1998. (Adventures of Benny & Watch: Vol. No. 2). 32p. (J). (ps-2). pap. 3.95 (978-0-8075-6625-1(X)) Whitman, Albert & Co.

—Watch Runs Away, Vol. 6. 1999. (Adventures of Benny & Watch: Vol. No. 6). 32p. (J). (ps-2). pap. 3.95 (978-0-8075-8681-5(1)) Whitman, Albert & Co.

Duffy, Daniel Mark, illus. Benny's New Friend. 1998. (J). (ps-ps). lib. bdg. 11.80 (978-0-613-07332-5(0)) Tandem Library Bks.

Duffy, James. Desaparecida. (SPA.). 142p. (YA). (gr. 5-8). (978-84-279-3200-5(6) , NG4451) Noguer y Caralt Editores, S. A. ESP. *Dist:* Lectorum Pubns., Inc.

Dumas Lachtman, Ofelia. Looking for la Unica. 2004. (ENG & SPA., Illus.). 190p. (J). pap. 9.95 (978-1-55885-412-3(6) , Piñata Books) Arte Publico Pr.

Duncan, Lois. Gallows Hill. 1998. (Laurel-Leaf Bks.). 240p. (YA). (gr. 7-12). mass mkt. 5.99 (978-0-440-22725-0(9) , Laurel Leaf) Random Hse. Children's Bks.

—I Know What You Did Last Summer. 1999. 208p. (YA). (gr. 7-12). mass mkt. 5.99 (978-0-440-22844-8(1) , Laurel Leaf) Random Hse. Children's Bks.

—Killing Mr. Griffin. 223p. (YA). (gr. 7 up). pap. 4.50 (978-0-8072-1373-5(X) , Listening Library) Random Hse. Audio Publishing Group.

—Locked in Time. 2002. (Illus.). (J). 13.38 (978-0-7587-4791-4(8)) Book Wholesalers, Inc.

—Stranger with My Face. 2002. (Illus.). (J). 13.40 (978-0-7587-4793-8(4)) Book Wholesalers, Inc.

—Stranger with My Face. 235p. (YA). (gr. 7 up). pap. 4.99 (978-0-8072-1371-1(3) , Listening Library) Random Hse. Audio Publishing Group.

Dunlop, Ed. Sherlock Jones: The Assassination Plot. 2004. 116p. (J). (978-1-59166-315-7(6)) Jones, Bob Univ. Pr.

—Sherlock Jones: The Missing Diamond. 2004. 109p. (J). (978-1-59166-316-4(4)) Jones, Bob Univ. Pr.

—Sherlock Jones: The Willoughby Bank Robbery. 2004. 96p. (J). (978-1-59166-314-0(8)) Jones, Bob Univ. Pr.

E-Mail Intruder. 2000. 64p. (J). pap. 5.50 (978-0-8341-1859-1(9)) Beacon Hill Pr. of Kansas City.

East Edge Mystery, No. 6. 1999. 128p. (J). 11.99 (978-0-7814-1508-8(X)) Cook, David C. Publishing Co.

Eden, Alexandra. The Duchess to the Rescue: A Bones & the Duchess Mystery. 2006. (J). 16.00 (978-1-888310-55-9(3)) Knoll, Allen A. Pubs.

—Holy Smoke: A Bones & the Duchess Mystery. 2004. (Illus.). 117p. (J). 16.00 (978-1-888310-46-7(4)) ; 128p. (YA). pap. 8.00 (978-1-888310-47-4(2)) Knoll, Allen A. Pubs.

—To Oz & Back: A Bones & the Duchess Mystery. 2002. 151p. (J). 16.00 (978-1-888310-22-1(7)) Knoll, Allen A. Pubs.

Edwards, Byron. The Mystery of Melissa's First Date: Book One. 2001. 108p. pap. 9.95 (978-0-595-18836-9(2) , Writers Club Pr.) iUniverse, Inc.

—Mystery of Melissa's First Date: Book One. 2001. (gr. 7-12). lib. bdg. 18.75 (978-0-613-87284-3(3)) Tandem Library Bks.

Edwards, Jason. Will Allen & the Great Monster Detective. l.t. ed. 2007. (Illus.). 96p. (J). per. 5.95 (*978-0-9789512-0-7(4)) Rogue Bear Pr.

Edwards, Julie Andrews & Hamilton, Emma Walton. Dragon: Hound of Honor. 2005. 208p. (J). (gr. 4 up). pap. 5.99 (978-0-06-057121-4(7) , Julie Andrews Collection) HarperCollins Pubs.

Edwards, Leo. Monkey's Paw. 2000. 21.95 (978-0-8488-2763-2(5)) Amereon LTD.

Eggleton, Jill. The Mystery of Missing Big Wig. (Sails Literacy Ser.). 24p. (gr. 3 up). 27.00 (978-0-7578-6982-2(3)) Rigby Education.

—The Mystery of Missing Big Wig: 6 Small Books. (Sails Literacy Ser.). 24p. (gr. 3 up). 25.00 (978-0-7578-6990-7(4)) Rigby Education.

Eiselen, Claire. The Imagination Chronicles Pt. 1: The Wizard's Legacy. 2000. 116p. pap. 9.95 (978-0-595-13996-5(5) , Writers Club Pr.) iUniverse, Inc.

Eisenberg, Lisa. The Case of the Rock & Roll Mystery. 1998. (New Adventures of Mary-Kate & Ashley Ser.). 87p. (J). (gr. 2-7). pap. 3.99 (978-0-590-29402-7(4)) Scholastic, Inc.

Elise Broach. Shakespeare's Secret. l.t. ed. 2006. 350p. (J). 22.95 (978-0-7862-8735-2(7)) Thorndike Pr.

Elliott, Julia. Where Did God Come From? Elliott, Julia, illus. 2005. (J). 15.95 (978-0-9764129-0-8(X)) Rain Tree Bks.

Ellis, Deborah. Looking for X. 2001. 132p. (J). (gr. 4-7). pap. 5.95 (978-0-88899-382-3(X)) Groundwood Bks. CAN. *Dist:* Perseus Distribution.

—Looking for X. 2000. (gr. 5-8). lib. bdg. 14.10 (978-0-613-62637-8(0)) Tandem Library Bks.

Ellis, Sarah. Odd Man Out. 2008. 168p. (J). pap. 8.95 (*978-0-88899-703-6(5)); 2006. 160p. (gr. 4-7). 16.95 (978-0-88899-702-9(7)) Groundwood Bks. CAN. *Dist:* Perseus Distribution.

Emerson, B. Alice. Betty Gordon at Mountain Camp or the Mys. 2006. 77.99 (*978-1-4280-2604-9(5)) IndyPublish.com.

Emerson, Scott. The Brotherhood of the Moon: From the Notebooks of Edward R. Smithfield, D.V.M. Glasauer, Willi, illus. 2005. (J). 9.95 (978-0-689-87630-1(0) , Simon & Schuster Children's Publishing) Simon & Schuster Children's Publishing.

Encyclopedia Brown. 1999. (J). 9.95 (978-1-56137-282-9(X)) Novel Units, Inc.

Encyclopedia Brown & the Case of the Exploding Plumbing & Other Stories. 2003. (J). pap. 2.95 (978-0-590-44093-6(4)) Scholastic, Inc.

Enderle, Dotti. The Lost Girl. Nightingale, Kimberly, ed. 2002. (Fortune Tellers Club Ser.: Bk. 1). (Illus.). 144p. (gr. 4-6). pap. 4.99 (978-0-7387-0253-7(6)) Llewellyn Pubns.

—Lost Girl. 2002. (gr. 3-6). lib. bdg. 13.00 (978-0-613-90180-2(0)) Tandem Library Bks.

Enright, Elizabeth. The Four-Story Mistake. 2008. (Melendy Quartet Ser.). (Illus.). 224p. (J). pap. 6.99 (*978-0-312-37599-7(9)) Square Fish.

—Spiderweb for Two: A Melendy Maze. Enright, Elizabeth, illus. rev. ed. 2002. (Melendy Quartet Ser.: Bk. 4). (Illus.). 224p. (J). (gr. 3-7). 16.95 (978-0-8050-7063-7(X) , Holt, Henry & Co. Bks. For Young Readers) Holt, Henry & Co.

—Spiderweb for Two: A Melendy Maze. 2008. (Melendy Quartet Ser.). (Illus.). 240p. (J). pap. 6.99 (*978-0-312-37601-7(4)) Square Fish.

Ensor, Rod. Getting It. 2007. 216p. per. 14.95 (*978-0-595-44800-5(3)) iUniverse, Inc.

Erickson, John R. The Case of the Black-Hooded Hangmans. Holmes, Gerald L., illus. 1998. (Hank the Cowdog Ser.: No. 24). 144p. (J). (gr. 2-5). 15.99 (978-0-670-88431-5(6) , Viking Juvenile); Vol. 24. pap. 4.99 (978-0-14-130400-7(6) , Puffin) Penguin Group (USA) Inc.

—The Case of the Black-Hooded Hangmans. 1999. (Hank the Cowdog Ser.: No. 24). (gr. 3-6). lib. bdg. 13.00 (978-0-7857-6345-1(7)) Tandem Library Bks.

—The Case of the Booby-Trapped Pickup. Holmes, Gerald L., illus. 2007. (Hank the Cowdog Ser.: No. 49). 144p. (J). 4.99 (978-0-14-240755-4(0) , Puffin); 15.99 (978-0-670-06186-0(7) , Viking Juvenile) Penguin Group (USA) Inc.

—The Case of the Burrowing Robot, Vol. 42. Holmes, Gerald L., illus. 2003. (Hank the Cowdog Ser.: No. 42). 144p. (J). (gr. 3). 15.99 (978-0-670-03632-5(3) , Viking Juvenile); (gr. 4-6). pap. 4.99 (978-0-14-250063-7(1) , Puffin) Penguin Group (USA) Inc.

—The Case of the Burrowing Robot. 2003. (Hank the Cowdog Ser.: No. 42). (gr. 3-6). lib. bdg. 13.00 (978-0-613-66353-3(5)) Tandem Library Bks.

—The Case of the Car-Barkaholic Dog. Holmes, Gerald L., illus. 2000. (Hank the Cowdog Ser.: No. 17). 144p. (J). (gr. 2-5). 14.99 (978-0-670-88424-7(3) , Viking Juvenile) Penguin Group (USA) Inc.

—The Case of the Deadly Ha-Ha Game. Holmes, Gerald L., illus. 2001. (Hank the Cowdog Ser.: No. 37). 144p. (J). (gr. 2-5). 14.99 (978-0-670-89640-0(3) , Viking Juvenile) Penguin Group (USA) Inc.

—The Case of the Deadly Ha-Ha Game, Vol. 37. Gilson, K., ed. Holmes, Gerald L., illus. 2001. (Hank the Cowdog Ser.: No. 37). 144p. (J). (gr. 2-5). pap. 4.99 (978-0-14-131048-0(0) , Puffin) Penguin Group (USA) Inc.

—The Case of the Deadly Ha-Ha Game. 2001. (Hank the Cowdog Ser.: No. 37). 11.64 (978-0-606-20459-0(8)); (gr. 3-6). lib. bdg. 13.00 (978-0-613-33649-9(5)) Tandem Library Bks.

—The Case of the Fiddle-Playing Fox. Holmes, Gerald L., illus. 1998. (Hank the Cowdog Ser.: No. 12). 144p. (J). (gr. 2-5). 14.99 (978-0-670-88419-3(7) , Viking Juvenile); Vol. 12. pap. 4.99 (978-0-14-130388-8(3) , Puffin) Penguin Group (USA) Inc.

—The Case of the Fiddle-Playing Fox. Holmes, Gerald L., illus. 1999. (Hank the Cowdog Ser.: No. 12). 131p. (J). (gr. 3-6). lib. bdg. 13.00 (978-0-8335-6825-0(6)) Tandem Library Bks.

—The Case of the Garbage Monster from Outer Space. Holmes, Gerald L., illus. 1999. (Hank the Cowdog Ser.: No. 32). 144p. (J). (gr. 2-5). 13.99 (978-0-670-88488-9(X) , Viking Juvenile) Penguin Group (USA) Inc.

—The Case of the Halloween Ghost. Holmes, Gerald L., illus. 1998. (Hank the Cowdog Ser.: No. 9). 144p. (J). (gr. 2-5). 14.99 (978-0-670-88416-2(2) , Viking Juvenile); No. 9. pap. 4.99 (978-0-14-130385-7(9) , Puffin) Penguin Group (USA) Inc.

—The Case of the Kidnapped Collie. Holmes, Gerald L., illus. 1998. (Hank the Cowdog Ser.: No. 26). 144p. (J). (gr. 2-5). 14.99 (978-0-670-88433-9(2) , Viking Juvenile); Vol. 26. pap. 4.99 (978-0-14-130402-1(2) , Puffin) Penguin Group (USA) Inc.

—The Case of the Kidnapped Collie. 1999. (Hank the Cowdog Ser.: No. 26). (gr. 3-6). lib. bdg. 13.00 (978-0-7857-9075-4(6)) Tandem Library Bks.

—The Case of the Kidnapped Collie. Holmes, Gerald L., illus. 1999. (Hank the Cowdog Ser.: No. 26). (J). (gr. 2-5). 11.64 (978-0-606-09375-0(3)) Tandem Library Bks.

—The Case of the Midnight Rustler. Holmes, Gerald L., illus. 1998. (Hank the Cowdog Ser.: No. 19). 144p. (J). (gr. 2-5). 14.99 (978-0-670-88426-1(X) , Viking Juvenile); pap. 4.99 (978-0-14-130395-6(6) , Puffin) Penguin Group (USA) Inc.

—The Case of the Missing Bird Dog. 2002. (Hank the Cowdog Ser.: No. 40). (gr. 3-6). lib. bdg. 13.00 (978-0-613-50279-5(5)) Tandem Library Bks.

—The Case of the Monkey Burglar. Holmes, Gerald L., illus. 2006. (Hank the Cowdog Ser.: NMo. 48). 129p. (J). lib. bdg. 17.00 (*978-1-4242-1604-8(4)) Fitzgerald Bks.

—The Case of the Most Ancient Bone. Homes, Gerald L., illus. 2007. (Hank the Cowdog Ser.). 192p. (J). (gr. 3). 16.99 (978-0-670-06224-9(3) , Viking Juvenile) Penguin Group (USA) Inc.

—The Case of the Most Ancient Bone, No. 50. Holmes, Gerald L., illus. 2007. (Hank the Cowdog Ser.: No. 50). 256p. (J). (gr. 3). pap. 5.99 (978-0-14-240800-1(X) , Puffin) Penguin Group (USA) Inc.

—The Case of the One-Eyed Killer Stud Horse, Vol. 8. Holmes, Gerald L., illus. 1998. (Hank the Cowdog Ser.: No. 8). 144p. (gr. 2-5). pap. 4.99 (978-0-14-130384-0(0) , Puffin) Penguin Group (USA) Inc.

—The Case of the One-Eyed Killer Stud Horse. 1999. (Hank the Cowdog Ser.: No. 8). (J). (gr. 3-6). lib. bdg. 13.00 (978-0-8335-6821-2(3)) Tandem Library Bks.

—The Case of the Saddle House Robbery. Holmes, Gerald L., illus. 2000. (Hank the Cowdog Ser.: No. 35). 144p. (J). (gr. 2-5). 14.99 (978-0-670-88890-0(7) , Viking Juvenile); Vol. 35. pap. 4.99 (978-0-14-130678-0(5) , Puffin) Penguin Group (USA) Inc.

—The Case of the Saddle House Robbery. unabr. ed. 2000. (Hank the Cowdog Ser.: No. 35). (J). (gr. 2-5). pap. 23.00 incl. audio (978-0-8072-8376-9(2) , YA172SP, Listening Library) Random Hse. Audio Publishing Group.

—The Case of the Saddle House Robbery. 2000. (Hank the Cowdog Ser.: No. 35). (Illus.). (J). (gr. 2-5). 11.64 (978-0-606-18409-0(0)) Tandem Library Bks.

—The Case of the Tender Cheeping Chickies. Holmes, Gerald L., illus. 2005. (Hank the Cowdog Ser.: No. 47). 129p. (J). lib. bdg. 17.00 (*978-1-4242-1605-5(2)) Fitzgerald Bks.

—The Case of the Tricky Trap. Holmes, Gerald L., illus. 2005. (Hank the Cowdog Ser.: No. 46). 126p. (J). lib. bdg. 17.00 (*978-1-4242-1603-1(6)) Fitzgerald Bks.

—The Case of the Twisted Kitty, Vol. 43. Holmes, Gerald L., illus. 2004. (Hank the Cowdog Ser.: No. 43). 144p. (J). (gr. 3). 15.99 (978-0-670-03681-3(1) , Viking Juvenile) Penguin Group (USA) Inc.

—The Case of the Vampire Cat. Holmes, Gerald L., illus. 1998. (Hank the Cowdog Ser.: No. 21). 144p. (J). (gr. 2-5). 14.99 (978-0-670-88428-5(6) , Viking Juvenile); Vol. 21. pap. 4.99 (978-0-14-130397-0(2) , Puffin) Penguin Group (USA) Inc.

—The Case of the Vanishing Fishhook. Holmes, Gerald L., illus. 1999. (Hank the Cowdog Ser.: No. 31). (J). (gr. 2-5). 11.64 (978-0-606-16826-7(5)) Tandem Library Bks.

—The Curse of the Incredible Priceless Corncob. Holmes, Gerald L., illus. 1998. (Hank the Cowdog Ser.: No. 7). 144p. (J). (gr. 2-5). 14.99 (978-0-670-88414-8(6) , Viking Juvenile); Vol. 7. pap. 4.99 (978-0-14-130383-3(2) , Puffin) Penguin Group (USA) Inc.

—Discovery at Flint Springs. 2004. 192p. (J). (gr. 3-7). 16.99 (978-0-670-05946-1(3) , Viking Juvenile) Penguin Group (USA) Inc.

—The Further Adventures of Hank the Cowdog. Holmes, Gerald L., illus. (Hank the Cowdog Ser.: No. 2). 144p. (J). 1999. (gr. 2-5). pap. 4.99 (978-0-14-130378-9(6) , Puffin); 1998. (gr. 3-5). 14.99 (978-0-670-88409-4(X) , Viking Juvenile) Penguin Group (USA) Inc.

—The Further Adventures of Hank the Cowdog. Holmes, Gerald L., illus. 1999. (Hank the Cowdog Ser.: No. 2). (J). (gr. 2-5). lib. bdg. 13.00 (978-0-8335-6816-8(7)) Tandem Library Bks.

—The Garbage Monster from Outer Space, Vol. 32. Holmes, Gerald L., illus. 1999. (Hank the Cowdog Ser.: No. 32). 144p. (J). (gr. 2-5). pap. 4.99 (978-0-14-130422-9(7) , Puffin) Penguin Group (USA) Inc.

—The Garbage Monster from Outer Space. 1999. (Hank the Cowdog Ser.: No. 32). (J). (gr. 2-5). 11.64 (978-0-606-16827-4(3)); (gr. 3-6). lib. bdg. 13.00 (978-0-613-14748-4(0)) Tandem Library Bks.

—It's a Dog's Life. Holmes, Gerald L., illus. (Hank the Cowdog Ser.: No. 3). 100p. (J). (gr. 2-5). 9.95 (978-0-916941-04-8(3)) Maverick Bks., Inc.

—It's a Dog's Life. Holmes, Gerald L., illus. 1998. (Hank the Cowdog Ser.: No. 3). 144p. (J). (gr. 2-5). 14.99 (978-0-670-88410-0(3) , Viking Juvenile); pap. 4.99 (978-0-14-130379-6(4) , Puffin) Penguin Group (USA) Inc.

—Lost in the Dark Unchanted Forest, Vol. 11. Holmes, Gerald L., illus. 1998. (Hank the Cowdog Ser.: No. 11). 144p. (J). (gr. 2-5). pap. 4.99 (978-0-14-130387-1(5) , Puffin) Penguin Group (USA) Inc.

—Murder in the Middle Pasture. Holmes, Gerald L., illus. 1998. (Hank the Cowdog Ser.: No. 4). 144p. (J). (gr. 2-5). 14.99 (978-0-670-88411-7(1) , Viking Juvenile); Vol. 4. pap. 4.99 (978-0-14-130380-2(8) , Puffin) Penguin Group (USA) Inc.

—Murder in the Middle Pasture. Holmes, Gerald L., illus. 1999. (Hank the Cowdog Ser.: No. 4). (J). (gr. 3-6). lib. bdg. 13.00 (978-0-8335-6817-5(5)) Tandem Library Bks.

—Las Nuevas Aventuras de Hank el Perro Vaquero. 2000. (SPA., Illus.). (J). (978-0-606-18416-8(3)) Tandem Library Bks.

—The Original Adventures of Hank the Cowdog. Holmes, Gerald L., illus. 1998. (Hank the Cowdog Ser.: No. 1). 144p. (J). (gr. 2-5). pap. 4.99 (978-0-14-130377-2(8) , Puffin) Penguin Group (USA) Inc.

—The Original Adventures of Hank the Cowdog. Holmes, Gerald L., illus. 1999. (Hank the Cowdog Ser.: No. 1). (J). (gr. 3-6). lib. bdg. 13.00 (978-0-8335-6815-1(9)) Tandem Library Bks.

—The Phantom in the Mirror. Holmes, Gerald L., illus. (Hank the Cowdog Ser.: No. 20). 144p. (J). (gr. 2-5). 2000. 14.99 (978-0-670-88427-8(8) , Viking Juvenile); Vol. 20. 1998. pap. 4.99 (978-0-14-130396-3(4) , Puffin) Penguin Group (USA) Inc.

Erickson, R. C. The Mystery of Colborn's Treasure. 2007. 204p. pap. 13.95 (*978-0-615-15975-1(3)) Quool Publishing.

Ernst, Kathleen. Danger at the Zoo: A Kit Mystery. 2005. (American Girls Collection). (Illus.). 192p. (YA). pap. 6.95 (978-1-58485-989-5(X) , American Girl) American Girl Publishing, Inc.

—Midnight in Lonesome Hollow: A Kit Mystery. Tibbles, Jean-Paul, illus. 2007. 192p. (J). 10.95 (*978-1-59369-161-5(0)); pap. 6.95 (*978-1-59369-160-8(2)) American Girl Publishing, Inc. (American Girl).

Ernst, Kathleen. Trouble at Fort la Pointe. 2000. (American Girl Collection). (Illus.). (J). (978-0-606-20956-4(5)) Tandem Library Bks.

Erwin, Vicki B. Scooby-Doo! The Case of the Spinning Spider. 2001. (Collect the Clues Mystery Ser.). (Illus.). 59p. (J). pap. (978-0-439-23167-1(1)) Scholastic, Inc.

Erwin, Vicki Berger. Elizabeth Bryan Mysteries Set, 6 vols. (Elizabeth Bryan Mysteries Ser.). (J). 29.99 (978-0-7586-0008-0(9)) Concordia Publishing Hse.

Eskeland, N. L. Menace in the Walls: A Summer Project Turns Treacherous. 2004. (Joshua Keegan Mysteries Ser.). 142p. (J). per. 10.95 (978-0-9673811-6-9(9)) Science2Discover, Inc.

Estes, Eleanor. The Alley. Ardizzone, Edward, illus. 2003. 288p. pap. 5.95 (978-0-15-204918-8(5) , Odyssey Classics) Harcourt Children's Bks.

Ewart, Franzeska G. Sita Snake Queen of Speed. 2008. (Illus.). 96p. (J). 15.95 (*978-1-84507-779-2(2)); pap. 7.95 (*978-1-84507-748-8(2)) Lincoln, Frances Ltd. GBR. *Dist:* Perseus Distribution.

Fairchild, Simone. The Queen Bee Mystery Trilogy, 33 vols. Key, Pamela, illus. 2007. 126p. (J). per. 49.95 (978-0-9788985-6-4(7)) A Better Be Write Pub.

Fairchild, Simone. Queen Bee's Mystery in the Lilac Tree. Key, Pamela, illus. 2007. 42p. (J). per. 19.95 (*978-0-9788985-7-1(5)) A Better Be Write Pub.

Falconer, Ian. Olivia y el Juguete Desaparecido. Mlawer, Teresa, tr. from ENG. Falconer, Ian, illus. 2004. (Olivia Ser.). (SPA., Illus.). 30p. (J). 16.95 (978-1-930332-71-3(8)) Lectorum Pubns., Inc.

Fanning, Kieran. Trapdoor to Treachery. 2000. (Illus.). 128p. (J). (gr. 4-8). per. (978-1-84210-023-3(8)) Mentor Bks.

Farber, Erica. Golden Eagle. Mayer, Mercer, illus. 2006. (Critter Kids Adventure Ser.). 32p. (J). (gr. 2-5). pap. 4.95 (978-0-7696-4764-7(2) , Gingham Dog Pr.) School Specialty Publishing.

—Octopus Island. Mayer, Mercer, illus. 2006. (Critter Kids Adventure Ser.). 32p. (J). (gr. 2-5). pap. 4.95 (978-0-7696-4766-1(9) , Gingham Dog Pr.) School Specialty Publishing.

Fardell, John. The Seven Professors of the Far North. 2005. (Illus.). 192p. (YA). (gr. 3-7). 14.99 (978-0-399-24381-3(X) , Putnam Juvenile) Penguin Group (USA) Inc.

Farley, Terri. Mountain Mare. 2005. 214p. (J). lib. bdg. 16.92 (*978-1-4242-0834-0(3)) Fitzgerald Bks.

Farmer, Sylvia. The Bank Vault Mystery. Wise, Noreen, ed. Killeen, Dan, illus. 2001. (Gold Mixed Collection). 48p. (J). (gr. 1-6). pap. 6.95 (978-1-58584-407-4(1)) Huckleberry Pr.

Farren, Rick. Eliza's Wish. 2005. 154p. (J). per. 14.95 (978-0-9772078-0-0(3)) Journey Pubns., LLC.

Fast & Mysty. Shootout at Joe's. 2001. 32p. (YA). (gr. 6-12). pap. (978-0-8224-3462-7(8)) Globe Fearon Educational Publishing.

Fast, Natalie. The Secret Apartment. 2007. 192p. (gr. 4-7). 5.99 (978-0-553-48794-7(9) , Yearling) Random Hse. Children's Bks.

Feder, Harriet K. Death on Sacred Ground. 2003. (Young Adult Fiction Ser.). (Illus.). 192p. (J). (gr. 7 up). 14.95 (978-0-8225-0741-3(2) , Carolrhoda Bks.) Lerner Publishing Group.

Feehan-Vileria, Elaine. The Legend of Old Mr. Clarke. 2004. 58p. per. 17.95 (978-1-4116-1523-6(9)) Lulu.com.

Feinstein, John. Cover-up: Mystery at the Super Bowl. 2007. 304p. (J). (gr. 5). lib. bdg. 19.99 (***978-0-375-94247-1(5)*** , Knopf Bks. for Young Readers) Random Hse. Children's Bks.

—Cover-Up: Mystery at the Super Bowl. 2007. 304p. (J). (gr. 5 up). 16.99 (***978-0-375-84247-4(0)*** , Knopf Bks. for Young Readers) Random Hse. Children's Bks.

—Last Shot: A Final Four Mystery. (J). (gr. 6-10). 2005. 256p. 16.95 (978-0-375-83168-3(1) , Knopf Bks. for Young Readers); 2006. 272p. reprint ed. pap. 6.50 (978-0-553-49460-0(0) , Yearling) Random Hse. Children's Bks.

—Last Shot: A Final Four Mystery. l.t. ed. 2005. 366p. (YA). 22.95 (978-0-7862-7914-2(1) , Large Print Pr.) Thorndike Pr.

—Vanishing Act. 2008. 288p. (J). (gr. 5). 6.50 (***978-0-440-42125-2(X)*** , Yearling) Random Hse. Children's Bks.

—Vanishing Act: Mystery at the U. S. Open. 2006. 288p. (J). (gr. 5). lib. bdg. 18.99 (978-0-375-93592-3(4) , Knopf Bks. for Young Readers) Random Hse. Children's Bks.

—Vanishing Act: Mystery at the U.S. Open. 2006. 288p. (J). (gr. 5). 16.95 (978-0-375-83592-6(X) , Knopf Bks. for Young Readers) Random Hse. Children's Bks.

Felcoski, Victoria. Secret of the Scotchpottle Farm. 2006. 21.99 (***978-1-4259-8117-4(8)***); pap. 12.99 (***978-1-4259-8118-1(6)***) AuthorHouse.

Ferguson, Alane. The Angel of Death. 2006. (Forensic Mystery Ser.). 272p. (YA). (gr. 7). 15.99 (978-0-670-06055-9(0) , Viking Adult) Penguin Group (USA) Inc.

—Angel of Death. 2008. (Forensic Mystery Ser.). 272p. (YA). (gr. 7). pap. 6.99 (***978-0-14-241087-5(X)*** , Puffin) Penguin Group (USA) Inc.

—The Christopher Killer. (Forensic Mystery Ser.). 288p. (YA). (gr. 7). 2008. pap. 6.99 (978-0-14-240811-7(5) , Puffin); 2006. 15.99 (978-0-670-06008-5(9) , Viking Juvenile) Penguin Group (USA) Inc.

Ferguson, Alane. The Circle of Blood. 2008. 256p. (YA). (gr. 7). 15.99 (***978-0-670-06056-6(9)*** , Viking Juvenile) Penguin Group (USA) Inc.

Ferguson, Alane & Skurzynski, Gloria. Deadly Waters. 2007. (Illus.). 160p. (J). (gr. 3-7). 4.99 (***978-1-4263-0093-6(X)*** , National Geographic Children's Bks.) National Geographic Society.

Ferguson, Donald. Chums of Scranton High on the Cinder Pat. 2006. 40.99 (***978-1-4280-2658-2(4)***); pap. 34.99 (***978-1-4280-2660-5(6)***) IndyPublish.com.

Ferguson, Dwayne. Ghost Ranch: The Legend of Mad Jake, 2004. (Kid Caramel: Bk. 4). (J). pap. 4.50 (978-0-940975-17-0(3) , Sankofa Bks.) Just Us Bks., Inc.

Fevens, Irene. New Time New Place. 2000. 252p. (YA). mass mkt. (978-0-9686720-0-6(0)) Editions Odyssey.

Fickey, Brenda. Whispering Darkness. 2007. (ENG.). 136p. per. 19.95 (***978-1-4241-6932-0(1)***) PublishAmerica, Inc.

The Fiji Flood, 6 vols. (Woodland Mysteriestm Ser.). 133p. (gr. 3-7). 42.50 (978-0-7802-7925-4(5)) Wright Group, The.

Finding Conway: Seek the Truth. 2006. (YA). (978-0-9771114-1-1(5)) LIP Publishing LLC.

Finley, Mary Pearce. Little Fox's Secret: The Mystery of Bent's Fort. Spurlock, Martha J., illus. 2000. 60p. (J). (gr. 3-5). pap. 5.95 (978-0-86541-050-3(X)) Filter Pr., LLC.

Finney, Patricia & Cavendish, Grace. Assasin, No. 1. 2004. (Lady Grace Mysteries, from the Daybookes of Lady Grace Cavendish Ser.). 208p. (J). (gr. 3-7). lib. bdg. 12.99 (978-0-385-90189-5(5) , Delacorte Bks. for Young Readers) Random Hse. Children's Bks.

—Assassin, No. 1. 2004. (Lady Grace Mysteries, from the Daybookes of Lady Grace Cavendish Ser.). 208p. (J). (gr. 3-7). 9.95 (978-0-385-73151-5(5) , Delacorte Bks. for Young Readers) Random Hse. Children's Bks.

—Deception. 2005. (Lady Grace Mysteries, from the Daybookes of Lady Grace Cavendish Ser.). 224p. (J). (gr. 3-7). 7.95 (978-0-385-73321-2(6)); lib. bdg. 9.99 (978-0-385-90340-0(5)) Random Hse. Children's Bks. (Delacorte Bks. for Young Readers).

—Feud. 2006. (Lady Grace Mysteries, from the Daybookes of Lady Grace Cavendish Ser.). 192p. (J). (gr. 3-7). 7.95 (978-0-385-73323-6(2)); lib. bdg. 9.99 (978-0-385-90342-4(1)) Random Hse. Children's Bks. (Delacorte Bks. for Young Readers).

Firelight Secrets Vol. 28: Individual Chapter Book Title Six-Packs. Vol. 28. 32p. (gr. 4 up). 44.00 (978-0-7635-4499-7(X)) Rigby Education.

The Fishy, Flashy Fourth, 6 vols., Vol. 3. (Woodland Mysteriestm Ser.). 133p. (gr. 3-7). 42.50 (978-0-322-02373-4(4)) Wright Group, The.

Fisk, Nicholas. Snatched. (Illus.). 153p. mass mkt. 8.99 (978-0-330-33815-8(3) , Pan) Pan Macmillan GBR. *Dist:* Trafalgar Square Publishing.

Fitzgerald, John D. More Adventures of the Great Brain. Mayer, Mercer, illus. (Great Brain Ser.). 160p. (J). 2004. (gr. 3-7). pap. 4.99 (978-0-14-240065-4(3) , Puffin); 2000. (ps-3). 9.99 (978-0-8037-2591-1(4) , Dial) Penguin Group (USA) Inc.

—More Adventures of the Great Brain. 2004. (Great Brain Ser.). 142p. (J). (gr. 3-7). pap., tchr.'s training gde. ed. 36.00 incl. audio (978-0-8072-0860-1(4) , Listening Library) Random Hse. Audio Publishing Group.

—More Adventures of the Great Brain. 2004. (gr. 3-6). lib. bdg. 14.15 (978-0-613-83003-4(2)) Tandem Library Bks.

Fitzhugh, Louise. The Long Secret. unabr. ed. 2004. 224p. (J). (gr. 3-7). pap. 38.00 incl. audio (978-0-8072-0666-9(0) , LYA 303 SP, Listening Library) Random Hse. Audio Publishing Group.

—The Long Secret. Fitzhugh, Louise, illus. 2002. 288p. (J). (gr. 5-9). 6.50 (978-0-440-41819-1(4) , Yearling) Random Hse. Children's Bks.

—The Long Secret. 2001. (Illus.). 288p. (J). (gr. 5 up). 15.95 (978-0-385-32784-8(6) , Delacorte Bks. for Young Readers) Random Hse. Children's Bks.

Fleischman, Sid. Jim Ugly. Smith, Jos. A., illus. 2003. 144p. (J). (gr. 3-6). pap. 6.99 (978-0-06-052121-9(X) , Harper Trophy) HarperCollins Pubs.

Flesh, Chris P. The Mystery of the Mystery Meat #3. 2008. 176p. (J). (gr. 3). pap. 4.99 (***978-0-448-44811-4(4)*** , Grosset & Dunlap) Penguin Group (USA) Inc.

Flint, Garrison. The Butler Did It! A Raymond Masrters Mystery. 2003. (Raymond Masters Mystery: 10). 206p. per. 13.99 (978-1-885631-72-5(3)) Hutchison, G.F. Pr.

—The Case of the Clairvoyant Kid: A Raymond Masters Mystery. 2002. 180p. (gr. 7 up). pap. 13.99 (978-1-885631-58-9(8) , 588, Family Of Man Pr., The) Hutchison, G.F. Pr.

—The Case of the Cryptogram Murders: A Raymond Masters Mystery. 2002. (Raymond Masters Mystery: 8). 214p. per. 13.99 (978-1-885631-69-5(3)) Hutchison, G.F. Pr.

—The Murders at Terrapin Island: A Raymond Masters Mystery. 2002. (Raymond Masters Mystery: 9). 198p. per. 13.99 (978-1-885631-70-1(7)) Hutchison, G.F. Pr.

—Sanity in Search of Peter Alexander. 2003. 198p. (YA). per. 13.95 (978-1-885631-73-2(1)) Hutchison, G.F. Pr.

Fontenay, Charles L. Kipton & the Caves of Mars, 18 vols. 1998. (Kipton Chronicles Ser.: Bk. 11). (Illus.). 187p. (J). (ps-7). pap. 9.99 (978-0-88092-391-0(1) , 3911) Royal Fireworks Publishing Co.

—Kipton & the Delusions of Tante Else, 18 vols. 1999. (Kipton Chronicles Ser.: Bk. 17). 189p. (YA). (gr. 6-9). 9.99 (978-0-88092-456-6(X) , 456-X) Royal Fireworks Publishing Co.

—Kipton & the Monorail Murder, 18 vols. 1998. (Kipton Chronicles Ser.: Bk. 12). 185p. (YA). (gr. 5 up). 9.99 (978-0-88092-418-4(7) , 4187) Royal Fireworks Publishing Co.

—Kipton & the Riddle of Sandstone, 18 vols. 1999. (Kipton Chronicles Ser.: No. 18). 185p. (YA). (gr. 8-12). pap. 9.99 (978-0-88092-457-3(8) , 4578) Royal Fireworks Publishing Co.

—Kipton at the Martian Games, 18 vols. 1998. (Kipton Chronicles Ser.: Bk. 14). 187p. (J). (gr. k-8). pap. 9.99 (978-0-88092-396-5(2) , 3962) Royal Fireworks Publishing Co.

Forde, Catherine. Firestarter. 2006. 160p. (J). pap. 8.99 (***978-1-4052-1056-0(7)***) Egmont Bks., Ltd. GBR. *Dist:* Independent Pubs. Group.

The Forgotten Hiding Place, 6 vols., Vol. 3. (Woodland Mysteriestm Ser.). 133p. (gr. 3-7). 42.50 (978-0-322-02376-5(9)) Wright Group, The.

Forrest. Sign of Blood. (Thumbprint Mysteries Ser.). 32.86 (978-0-8092-0408-3(8)) McGraw-Hill/Contemporary.

Francis, Dick. Blood Sport. 1999. (gr. 7-12). lib. bdg. 15.30 (978-0-613-12525-3(8)) Tandem Library Bks.

Francis, Dorothy Brenner. Cody Smith & the Holiday Mysteries. Ersland, William, illus. 2001. (Cover-to-Cover Novel Ser.). 76p. (J). pap. (978-0-7891-5382-1(3)); (gr. 2-5). lib. bdg. 13.95 (978-0-7807-9743-7(4)) Perfection Learning Corp.

—The Jayhawk Horse Mystery. Ersland, William, illus. 2001. (Cover-to-Cover Novel Ser.). 80p. (J). pap. (978-0-7891-5349-4(1)); (gr. 2-5). lib. bdg. 13.95 (978-0-7807-9728-4(0)) Perfection Learning Corp.

Frankans, W. A. The Killings Tale: A Mystery. 2002. 96p. (YA). (gr. 7-12). pap. 6.00 (978-0-573-62790-3(8) , 13057) French, Samuel Inc.

Frankel, Aaron. A Jerusalem Mystery, Grades 7-9. 1998. (Illus.). 24p. (gr. 7-9). pap., tchr. ed. 15.00 (978-0-8074-0638-0(4) , 208046) URJ Pr.

Frazier, Janet. The Case of the Theme Park Cry. l.t. ed. 2004. 90p. (J). per. (978-1-59196-737-8(6)) Instantpublisher.com.

Frazier, Janet L. The Mysterious Mall Disapperance: P. K. Mystery Series # 2. 2004. 100p. (J). per. (978-1-59196-811-5(9)) Instantpublisher.com.

Freedom's Whisper. 2007. (J). (978-1-933343-52-5(4) , PONY) Stabenfeldt Inc.

Freeman, Martha. Who Stole Halloween? 224p. (J). (ps-7). 16.95 (978-0-8234-1962-3(2)) Holiday Hse., Inc.

Freese, Thomas, reader. Fog Swirler & 11 Other Ghost Stories. 2006. (J). Pt. 1. cd-rom 13.95 (***978-0-9789511-0-8(7)***); Pt. 2. cd-rom 13.95 (***978-0-9789511-1-5(5)***); Pt. 3. cd-rom 13.95 (***978-0-9789511-2-2(3)***) Illumination Pubns.

Frels, Merry Hassell. Simmering Secrets of Weeping Mary: A Deuteronomy Devilrow Mystery. Morgan, Dana Duvall, illus. l.t. ed. 2005. 130p. (J). pap. 9.95 (978-0-9714358-9-6(8)) Longhorn Creek Pr.

French, Jackie. My Uncle the Werewolf. King, Stephen Michael, illus. 2007. (J). 112p. (***978-1-59889-346-5(7)***); 107p. pap. (***978-1-59889-439-4(0)***) Stone Arch Bks.

French, Vivian. Detective Dan. Bartlett, Alison, illus. 2006. (Read-It! Chapter Books). 48p. (J). (gr. 2-4). 19.95 (978-1-4048-1659-6(3)) Picture Window Bks.

Frey, Hildegard G. The Camp Fire Girls Go Motoring. 2004. reprint ed. pap. 20.95 (978-1-4191-5583-0(3)); pap. 1.99 (978-1-4192-5583-0(5)) Kessinger Publishing, LLC.

Friedman, Kinky. Curse of the Missing Puppet Head. 2003. lib. bdg. 29.95 (978-0-9702383-6-8(3) , CMPH01) Vandam Pr., Inc.

Friedman, Mel. The Mystery of the Backlot Banshee: A ClueFinders Mystery Adventure. 2004. (Illus.). 96p. (J). pap. 4.99 (978-0-7630-7620-7(1)) Learning Co. Bks.

Friedman, Michael Jan. The Sirian Conspiracy. 1999. (Wishbone Mysteries Ser.: No. 16). (J). (gr. 2-5). (978-0-606-17768-9(X)) Tandem Library Bks.

—The Stolen Trophy. l.t. ed. 1999. (Wishbone Mysteries Ser.: No. 5). 144p. (J). (gr. 4 up). lib. bdg. 23.33 (978-0-8368-2386-8(9)) Stevens, Gareth Inc.

—The Stolen Trophy, 1998. (Wishbone Mysteries Ser.: No. 5). (J). (gr. 2-5). (978-0-606-12859-9(X)) Tandem Library Bks.

Friedman, Michael Jan, et al. The Sirian Conspiracy. l.t. ed. 2000. (Wishbone Mysteries Ser.: No. 16). (Illus.). 141p. (J). (gr. 4 up). lib. bdg. 23.33 (978-0-8368-2699-9(X)) Stevens, Gareth Inc.

Friedrich, Joachim. The Disappearing Bio Teacher, Bk. 2. 2001. (4 1/2 Friends Mysteries Ser.). (Illus.). 160p. (gr. 3-7). 14.99 (978-0-7868-0698-0(2) , Volo) Hyperion Bks. for Children.

—4 1/2 Friends: And the Disappearing Bio Teacher. Crawford, Elizabeth D., tr. from GER. 2001. 144p. (J). lib. bdg. 15.49 (978-0-7868-2588-2(X) , Volo) Hyperion Bks. for Children.

—4 1/2 Friends & the Secret Cave, Bk. 1. Crawford, Elizabeth D., tr. from GER. 2001. (Illus.). 160p. (gr. 3-7). 14.99 (978-0-7868-0648-5(6)) Hyperion Bks. for Children.

Fritz, Jean. Brendan the Navigator: A History Mystery about the Discovery of America. 1999. 32p. (J). (gr. 1-6). pap. 6.99 (978-0-698-11759-4(X) , Putnam Juvenile) Penguin Group (USA) Inc.

Fryer, Mary Beacock. Escape: Adventures of a Loyalist Family. 2006. (Illus.). 188p. (J). pap. 7.99 (978-1-895681-17-8(0) , Boardwalk Bks.) Dundurn Group, The CAN. *Dist:* Univ. of Toronto Pr.

Funke, Cornelia. El Señor de los Ladrones. Falco, Roberto, tr. Funke, Cornelia, illus. 2003. (Cornelia Funke Ser.). (SPA., Illus.). 368p. (J). 19.95 (978-84-233-3437-7(6)) Ediciones Destino ESP. *Dist:* Planeta Publishing Corp.

—The Thief Lord. l.t. ed. 2005. 483p. (J). (gr. 4-7). pap. 10.95 (978-0-7862-8092-6(1)) Thorndike Pr.

Gaetz, Dayle. Crossbow. 2007. (Orca Currents Ser.). 112p. (YA). (gr. 5 up). pap. (***978-1-55143-841-2(0)***); lib. bdg. (***978-1-55143-843-6(7)***) Orca Bk. Pubs.

Gaetz, Dayle. Something Suspicious in Saskatchewan. 2006. 208p. (J). pap. 7.95 (978-1-55143-565-7(9)) Orca Bk. Pubs. USA.

Gaetz, Dayle Campbell. Alberta Alibi. 2005. 176p. (J). (gr. 3-7). pap. 6.95 (978-1-55143-404-9(0)) Orca Bk. Pubs. USA.

Gallagher, Mary. The Legend of Lisnashee. 2006. (Illus.). 100p. pap. 9.95 (978-1-903464-71-7(4)) Collins Pr., The IRL. *Dist:* Dufour Editions, Inc.

Gallo, Donald R., ed. Time Capsule. 2001. 240p. (YA). (gr. 7). pap. 6.99 (978-0-440-22819-6(0) , Laurel Leaf) Random Hse. Children's Bks.

Gamer, Ron. Hidden Chance: Secrets of the Hermit¿s Hideaway. 2007. 240p. (YA). per. 8.95 (***978-1-59193-209-3(2)***) Adventure Pubns., Inc.

Gantt, Leticia. Phantom of the Video Store. l.t. ed. 2000. (Wishbone Mysteries Ser.: No. 18). (Illus.). 141p. (J). (gr. 4 up). lib. bdg. 23.33 (978-0-8368-2701-9(5)) Stevens, Gareth Inc.

Garcia-Huidobro, Beatriz. Misterio en el Campamento. 2002. (J). (978-956-240-348-1(3)) Arrayan Editores S.A.

Garfield, Valerie. Sergeant Sniff's Easter Egg Mystery. Durrell, Julie, illus. 2001. (Sergeant Sniff Scratch-and-Sniff Mystery Ser.). 16p. (J). (ps-k). 6.95 (978-0-694-01508-5(3) , Harper Festival) HarperCollins Pubs.

—Sergeant Sniff's Halloween Mystery Treat. 2000. (Sergeant Sniff Scratch-and-Sniff Mystery Ser.). (Illus.). 16p. (J). (ps-k). 6.95 (978-0-694-01513-9(X) , Harper Festival) HarperCollins Pubs.

—Sergeant Sniff's Secret Valentine Mystery. 2001. (Sergeant Sniff Scratch-and-Sniff Mystery Ser.). (Illus.). 16p. (J). (ps-k). 6.95 (978-0-694-01507-8(5) , Harper Festival) HarperCollins Pubs.

Garinger, Alan. Jeremiah Stokely, Inventor. 2002. (J). per. 14.95 (978-1-57860-105-9(3)) Emmis Bks.

Garmon, Larry Mike. The Calamari Code: an Agatha Pixie Mystery. 2007. 244p. pap. 15.49 (***978-0-615-15267-7(8)***) Zu Bks.

Garnet. The Handy Kap Kids in the Missing Link Mystery. 2002. 213p. pap. 14.95 (978-0-7414-1183-9(0)) Infinity Publishing.

Garretson, Jerri. The Secret of Whispering Springs. 2002. 208p. (J). per. 6.99 (978-0-9659712-4-9(4)) Ravenstone Pr.

Garthwaite, Lynn D. Dirkle Smat Inside Mount Flatbottom. Howarth, Craig, illus. 2006. 48p. (J). pap. 9.95 (978-1-59663-512-8(6) , Castle Keep Pr.) Rock, James A. & Co. Pubs.

Garton, Kevan. The Cockleton Mystery. 2006. 68p. pap. (***978-1-84401-788-1(5)***) Athena Pr.

Garvey, Dennis. Haunted House Hysteria. 2000. (gr. 3-6). lib. bdg. 13.00 (978-0-613-31295-0(3)) Tandem Library Bks.

Garvey, Dennis & Nichols, Tommy. Haunted House Hysteria. 2000. (Doug: No. 5). (Illus.). 112p. (gr. 2-5). pap. 4.99 (978-0-7868-4411-1(6)) Disney Pr.

Gates, Susan. Cry Wolf. l.t. ed. 2000. 151p. (J). pap. (978-0-7540-6105-2(1) , CLP 301) BBC Audio.

Gauch, Patricia Lee. Christina Katerina & the Box. Burn, Doris, illus. 1998. 32p. (J). (ps-3). pap. 7.99 (978-0-698-11676-4(3) , Putnam Juvenile) Penguin Group (USA) Inc.

Gauthier, Gail. Happy Kid! 2006. 192p. (YA). (gr. 3). 16.99 (978-0-399-24266-3(X)); 230p. (J). (***978-1-4156-6311-0(4)***) Penguin Group (USA) Inc. (Putnam Juvenile).

Gauthier, Gilles. Missing Mooch. Cummins, Sarah, tr. Deromer, Pierre-André, illus. 1999. (First Novels Ser.: Vol. 31). 61p. (J). (gr. 1-5). (978-0-88780-485-4(3)) Formac Publishing Co., Ltd. CAN. *Dist:* Casemate Pubs. & Bk. Distributors, LLC.

—Missing Mooch. Cummins, Sarah, tr. Derome, Pierre-Andre, illus. 1999. (First Novels Ser.: Vol. 31). 61p. (gr. 1-5). 4.95 (978-0-88780-484-7(5)) Formac Publishing Co., Ltd. CAN. *Dist:* Casemate Pubs. & Bk. Distributors, LLC.

Gee, Maurice. The Fire Raiser. 2007. 172p. (J). (gr. 4-6). pap. 6.95 (***978-0-618-75041-2(X)***) Houghton Mifflin Co. Trade & Reference Div.

Geiger, Lorraine Lynch. Trouble at the Blueberry Patch. 2002. 129p. pap. 17.95 (978-1-59129-771-0(0)) PublishAmerica, Inc.

Geisert, Arthur. Mystery. Geisert, Arthur, illus. 2003. (Illus.). 32p. (J). (gr. k-3). 16.00 (978-0-618-27293-8(3) , Walter Lorraine) Houghton Mifflin Co. Trade & Reference Div.

Geller, Beverly Mach. The Mystery of the Missing Pitom. Perel, Rivka-Lisa, illus. 2000. 24p. (J). (gr. 2-4). 12.95 (978-965-229-202-5(8)) Gefen Publishing Hse., Ltd ISR. *Dist:* Gefen Bks.

Gelsey, James. The Baseball Boogeyman. 2004. (Illus.). 44p. (J). (***978-0-439-55713-9(5)***) Scholastic, Inc.

—Chill-Out Scooby-Doo. 2007. (Scooby-Doo Video Tie-In Novelization Ser.). 64p. (J). pap. 3.99 (***978-0-439-91595-3(3)***) Scholastic, Inc.

—Deep Sea Diver. del Sur, Duendes, illus. 2003. (Scooby-Doo Mysteries Ser.: No. 26). 64p. (J). pap. 3.99 (978-0-439-42073-0(3) , Levine, Arthur A. Bks.) Scholastic, Inc.

—Deep Sea Diver. 2003. (gr. 3-6). lib. bdg. 11.80 (978-0-613-58165-3(2)) Tandem Library Bks.

—The Devilish Donut. 2007. (Scooby-Doo Case Files Ser.: No. 1). 80p. (J). pap. 3.99 (978-0-439-81418-8(9)) Scholastic, Inc.

—Scooby-Doo! & the Cactus Creature. 2005. (Illus.). 58p. (J). lib. bdg. 15.00 (***978-1-4242-0304-8(X)***) Fitzgerald Bks.

—Scooby-Doo! & the Cactus Creature. 2005. (Illus.). 58p. (J). (***978-1-4155-9742-2(1)***) Scholastic, Inc.

—Scooby-Doo & the Carnival Creeper. 1999. (Scooby-Doo Mysteries Ser.: No. 7). (Illus.). 64p. (J). (ps-3). 3.99 (978-0-439-11346-5(6)) Scholastic, Inc.

—Scooby-Doo & the Groovy Ghost. 8th ed. 2000. (Scooby-Doo Mysteries Ser.: No. 8). (Illus.). 64p. (J). (ps-3). pap. 3.99 (978-0-439-11347-2(4) , Scholastic Paperbacks) Scholastic, Inc.

—Scooby-Doo & the Groovy Ghost. 2000. (gr. 3-6). lib. bdg. 11.80 (978-0-613-22338-6(1)) Tandem Library Bks.

—Scooby-Doo! & the Gruesome Goblin. 2004. (Illus.). 60p. (J). lib. bdg. 15.00 (***978-1-4242-0303-1(1)***) Fitzgerald Bks.

—Scooby-Doo & the Haunted Castle. 1998. (Scooby-Doo Mysteries Ser.: No. 1). (Illus.). 64p. (ps-3). pap. 3.99 (978-0-590-81909-1(7)) Scholastic, Inc.

—Scooby-Doo & the Haunted Castle: Scooby-Doo Y el Castillo Hechizado. 2002. (Scooby-Doo Mysteries Ser.: No. 1). (SPA., Illus.). 64p. (J). (gr. 2-4). mass mkt. 3.99 (978-0-439-40984-1(5) , Scholastic en Espanol) Scholastic, Inc.

—Scooby-Doo & the Headless Horseman. 2002. (gr. 3-6). lib. bdg. 11.80 (978-0-613-58166-0(0)) Tandem Library Bks.

—Scooby-Doo & the Mummy's Curse. 1998. (Scooby-Doo Mysteries Ser.: No. 2). (Illus.). 64p. (ps-3). 3.99 (978-0-590-81910-7(0)) Scholastic, Inc.

—Scooby-Doo & the Scary Skateboarder. del Sur, Duendes, illus. 2006. (Scooby-Doo Mysteries Ser.). 64p. (J). pap. 3.99 (978-0-439-56117-4(5)) Scholastic, Inc.

—Scooby-Doo & the Snow Monster. 1999. (Scooby-Doo Mysteries Ser.: No. 3). (Illus.). 57p. (J). (ps-3). 3.99 (978-0-590-81914-5(3) , Scholastic Paperbacks) Scholastic, Inc.

—Scooby-Doo & the Spooky Strikeout. 2000. (gr. 3-6). lib. bdg. 11.80 (978-0-613-26854-7(7)) Tandem Library Bks.

—Scooby-Doo! & the Spooky Strikeout. del Sur, Duendes, illus. 2000. (Scooby-Doo Mysteries Ser.: No. 10). 64p. (J). (ps-3). 3.99 (978-0-439-11349-6(0)) Scholastic, Inc.

—Scooby-Doo & the Sunken Ship. 1999. (Scooby-Doo Mysteries Ser.: No. 4). (Illus.). 64p. (J). (ps-3). pap. 3.99 (978-0-590-81917-6(8)) Scholastic, Inc.

—Scooby-Doo & the Sunken Ship. 1999. (gr. 3-6). lib. bdg. 11.80 (978-0-613-17004-8(0)) Tandem Library Bks.

—Scooby Doo! & the Zombie's Treasure. 2000. (gr. 3-6). lib. bdg. 11.80 (978-0-613-27677-1(9)) Tandem Library Bks.

—Scooby-Doo! & You. del Sur, Duendes, illus. 2001. (Collect the Clues Mystery Ser.). 60p. (J). (978-0-439-23155-8(8)) Scholastic, Inc.

—Scooby-Doo! & You: The Case of Dr. Jenkins & Mr. Hyde. 2001. (Collect the Clues Mystery Ser.). (Illus.). 60p. (J). pap. (978-0-439-23157-2(4)) Scholastic, Inc.

—Scooby-Doo! & You: The Case of the Seaweed Monster. 2001. (Collect the Clues Mystery Ser.). (Illus.). 60p. (J). pap. (978-0-439-23153-4(1)) Scholastic, Inc.

—Scooby-Doo! & You: The Case of the Singing Ghost. 2001. (Collect the Clues Mystery Ser.). (Illus.). 61p. (J). pap. (978-0-439-23163-3(9)) Scholastic, Inc.

—Scooby-Doo y el Castillo Hechizado. 2002. Tr. of Scooby-Doo & the Haunted Castle. (SPA.). (gr. k-3). lib. bdg. 13.00 (978-0-613-82494-1(6)) Tandem Library Bks.

—Scooby-Doo!TM & the Fairground Phantom. del Sur, Duendes, illus. 2000. (Scooby-Doo Mysteries Ser.: No. 11). 64p. (J). (ps-3). 3.99 (978-0-439-10664-1(8)) Scholastic, Inc.

—Scooby-Doo!TM & the Headless Horseman. 2002. (Scooby-Doo Mysteries Ser.: No. 25). (Illus.). 64p. (J). (gr. 1-4). 3.99 (978-0-439-42072-3(5)) Scholastic, Inc.

—Seashore Slimer. del Sur, Duendes, illus. 2002. (Scooby-Doo Mysteries Ser.: No. 22). 64p. (J). (gr. 4-6). pap. 3.99 (978-0-439-28488-2(0)) Scholastic, Inc.

—The Summer Camp Cyclops. 2007. (Scooby-Doo Case Files Ser.: No. 2). 80p. (J). pap. 3.99 (***978-0-439-91592-2(9)***) Scholastic, Inc.

—Sunken Ship: Scooby-Doo y el Barco Hundido. 2004. (Scooby-Doo Ser.). (ENG & SPA.). 64p. (J). mass mkt. 3.99 (978-0-439-55116-8(1) , Scholastic en Espanol) Scholastic, Inc.

—Witch Doctor. del Sur, Duendes, illus. 2003. (Scooby Doo Mystery Ser.). 64p. (J). (gr. k-3). 3.99 (978-0-439-42075-4(X) , Scholastic Paperbacks) Scholastic, Inc.

—Witch Doctor. 2003. (gr. k-3). lib. bdg. 11.80 (978-0-613-72125-7(X)) Tandem Library Bks.

—The Zombie's Treasure. 2000. (Scooby-Doo Mysteries Ser.: No. 9). (Illus.). 64p. (J). (ps-3). pap. 3.99 (978-0-439-11348-9(2)) Scholastic, Inc.

Gelsey, James, et al. Chill-Out Scooby-Doo. 2007. (Scooby-Doo 8x8 Video Tie-In Ser.). 24p. (J). pap. 3.99 (***978-0-439-91597-7(X)***) Scholastic, Inc.

Gentile, Joe. Noir: The Mysterious Traveller. 2003. (Illus.). 48p. (gr. 12 up). pap. 5.50 (978-0-9721668-5-0(8)) Moonstone.

George, Jean Craighead. The Case of the Missing Cutthroats. Duranceau, Suzanne, illus. 1999. (Eco Mystery Ser.). 160p. (J). (gr. 3-7). pap. 5.99 (978-0-06-440647-5(4) , Harper Trophy) HarperCollins Pubs.

—The Case of the Missing Cutthroats. 1999. (J). 12.64 (978-0-606-16703-1(X)); (gr. 3-6). lib. bdg. 14.15 (978-0-613-18242-3(1)) Tandem Library Bks.

Geras, Adele. The Tower Room. 1998. (Egerton Hall Trilogy: Vol. 1). (J). (978-0-606-13860-4(9)) Tandem Library Bks.

Gerritsen, Tess. The Apprentice. 2003. (gr. 7-12). lib. bdg. 16.45 (978-0-613-65524-8(9)) Tandem Library Bks.

Gerwitz, Felice & Gerwitz, Christina. Dinosaur Quest at Diamond Peak, 3, Vol. 2. 2nd rev. ed. 2007. (Truth Seeker's Mystery Ser.). 208p. (YA). per. 8.99 (***978-1-931941-11-2(4)***) Media Angels, Inc.

—The Missing Link: Found, 3, Vol. 1. 2nd rev. ed. 2004. (Truth Seeker's Mystery Ser.). 208p. (YA). per. 8.99 (***978-1-931941-08-2(4)***) Media Angels, Inc.

Geshell, Carmen. Muffin's Makapu'u Adventure. 1998. (Illus.). 40p. (J). (gr. k-6). 8.95 (978-0-9665686-0-8(5)) Muffin & Co.

Gibbons, Alan. Defender. 2006. 192p. (J). pap. 11.99 (***978-1-84255-098-4(5)***) Orion Publishing Group, Ltd. GBR. *Dist:* Independent Pubs. Group.

Giff, Patricia Reilly. Eleven. 2008. 144p. (J). (***978-0-385-73069-3(1)*** , Delacorte Pr.) Dell Publishing.

—Kidnap at the Catfish Cafe. Cravath, Lynne W., illus. unabr. ed. 1999. (Adventures of Minnie & Max Ser.). (J). (gr. 4-7). pap. 23.95 incl. audio (978-0-87499-553-4(1)) Live Oak Media.

—Kidnap at the Catfish Cafe. Cravath, Lynne W., illus. 2000. (Adventures of Minnie & Max Ser.: Vol. 1). 80p. (J). (gr. 2-6). pap. 4.99 (978-0-14-130821-0(4) , Puffin) Penguin Group (USA) Inc.

—Kidnap at the Catfish Cafe. Cravath, Lynne, illus. 1998. 80p. (J). (gr. 2-6). 13.99 (978-0-670-88180-2(5) , Viking Juvenile) Penguin Group (USA) Inc.

—Kidnap at the Catfish Cafe. 2000. (gr. 3-6). lib. bdg. 13.00 (978-0-613-25875-3(4)); (Illus.). (J). 11.79 (978-0-606-18384-0(1)) Tandem Library Bks.

—Mary Moon Is Missing. Cravath, Lynne W., illus. 2000. (Adventures of Minnie & Max Ser.). (J). (gr. 4). pap. 23.95 incl. audio (978-0-87499-636-4(8)); (gr. 4-6). 30.95 incl. audio (978-0-87499-637-1(6)); pap., tchr. ed. 32.95 incl. audio (978-0-87499-638-8(4)) Live Oak Media.

—Mary Moon Is Missing. Cravath, Jill & Cravath, Lynne, illus. 2000. (Adventures of Minnie & Max Ser.: Vol. 2). 80p. (J). (gr. 2-6). pap. 4.99 (978-0-14-130823-4(0) , Puffin) Penguin Group (USA) Inc.

—Mary Moon Is Missing. 2000. (gr. 3-6). lib. bdg. 11.80 (978-0-613-26156-2(9)); (Illus.). (J). 10.79 (978-0-606-18385-7(X)) Tandem Library Bks.

—The Mystery of the Blue Ring. 73p. (J). (gr. 1-2). pap. 3.99 (978-0-8072-1272-1(5) , Listening Library) Random Hse. Audio Publishing Group.

—The Powder Puff Puzzle. 75p. (J). pap. 3.99 (978-0-8072-1275-2(X) , Listening Library) Random Hse. Audio Publishing Group.

—The Riddle of the Red Purse. 68p. (J). pap. 3.99 (978-0-8072-1273-8(3) , Listening Library) Random Hse. Audio Publishing Group.

—Secretos de Diciembre. 2000. (SPA.). (YA). (gr. 1 up). 3.95 (978-0-922852-43-7(X)) AIMS International Bks., Inc.

Gilbert, D. Hide & Seek: A Mystery Novel for Children. 2005. 187p. pap. 19.95 (978-1-4137-9748-0(2)) PublishAmerica, Inc.

Giles Chambers, Barbara. The Disappearance of Livvy. 2001. per. 9.95 (978-1-58630-088-3(1)) Word Wrangler Publishing, Inc.

Giles, Gail. Dead Girls Don't Write Letters. rev. ed. 2003. 144p. (YA). (gr. 7 up). 16.95 (978-0-7613-1727-2(9)) Roaring Brook Pr.

—Dead Girls Don't Write Letters. 2004. 128p. (YA). reprint ed. pap. 6.99 (978-0-689-86624-1(0) , Simon Pulse) Simon & Schuster Children's Publishing.

Gill, Janie S. What Could You See? Olson, Julie H., illus. 1999. 23p. 5.95 (978-0-89868-427-8(7)); pap. 3.95 (978-0-89868-426-1(9)) ARO Publishing Co.

—What Could You See? Olson, Julie Hansen, illus. 1999. (Predictable Word Bks.). 23p. (J). (ps-3). lib. bdg. 10.95 (978-0-89868-425-4(0)) ARO Publishing Co.

—Where Are My Glasses? Cantrell, Brook, illus. 1999. 23p. (J). 5.95 (978-0-89868-442-1(0)); pap. 3.95 (978-0-89868-441-4(2)); lib. bdg. 10.95 (978-0-89868-440-7(4)) ARO Publishing Co.

Gilligan, Shannon. The Case of the Silk King. 2005. 116p. (J). pap. (***978-0-7608-9702-7(6)***) Sundance/Newbridge Educational Publishing.

Gilligan, Shannon. The Case of the Silk King No. 14: Choose Your Own Adventure. 2006. (Choose Your Own Adventure Ser.). (Illus.). 144p. (J). mass mkt. 5.99 (978-1-933390-14-7(X) , CHCL14) Chooseco LLC.

Gilmour, H. B. & Reisfeld, Randi. Building a Mystery. 2001. (T*Witches Ser.: No. 2). 224p. (J). 4.99 (978-0-439-24071-0(9) , Scholastic Paperbacks) Scholastic, Inc.

—Dead Wrong. 2002. (T*Witches Ser.: No. 4). (Illus.). 176p. (J). pap. 4.99 (978-0-439-24073-4(5)) Scholastic, Inc.

Gilstrap, John. At All Costs. 1999. (gr. 7-12). lib. bdg. 15.90 (978-0-613-24254-7(8)) Tandem Library Bks.

Giovannoli, Renato. Misterio en Villa Jamaica. 2005. (SPA.). 122p. (J). (gr. 4-5). 7.95 (978-84-348-6713-0(3)) SM Ediciones ESP. *Dist:* Iaconi, Mariuccia Bk. Imports.

Gisbert, Joan M. La Mansion de los Ablsmos. 1999. Tr. of Mansion of the Abyss. (SPA.). (978-0-606-17685-9(3)) Tandem Library Bks.

Givens, Steven J. Stony Point: A Triangle Club Adventure. 2001. 106p. pap. 5.95 (978-1-889658-21-6(9)) New Canaan Publishing Co. LLC.

Givner, Joan. Ellen Fremedon: Journalist. 2006. 192p. pap. 6.95 (978-0-88899-691-6(8)) Groundwood Bks. CAN. *Dist:* Perseus Distribution.

Glaze, Dave. The Light-Fingered Gang. 2006. 196p. (YA). (gr. 4-7). pap. 7.95 (978-1-55050-326-5(X)) Coteau Bks. CAN. *Dist:* F & W Pubns., Inc.

Glintenkamp, Pamela. Sarah McSleuth's Coloring Casebook: Mystery in the Museum. Stern, Steven, ed. Glintenkamp, Pamela, illus. 1999. (Illus.). 32p. (J). (gr. 2-7). pap. 4.95 (978-1-892572-01-1(X)) Zen Comics, Inc.

Glover, Sandra. Foxcroft Files. 2003. (Illus.). 128p. (YA). pap. 9.99 (978-1-84270-279-6(3)) Andersen GBR. *Dist:* Independent Pubs. Group.

—Spiked! 2006. 176p. (J). pap. (978-1-84270-520-9(2)) Andersen.

Godfrey. Murder in the Shadows. (Thumbprint Mysteries Ser.). 32.86 (978-0-8092-0418-2(5)) McGraw-Hill/Contemporary.

Godfrey, Martyn. Mystery in the Frozen Lands. 2003. 132p. (YA). (gr. 3-8). 7.95 (978-1-55028-137-8(2)) Lorimer, James & Co., Ltd., Pubs. CAN. *Dist:* Casemate Pubs. & Bk. Distributors, LLC.

—Mystery in the Frozen Lands. 2003. (gr. 5-8). lib. bdg. 16.40 (978-0-613-78083-4(3)) Tandem Library Bks.

Golden Books Staff. Ghoul's Inn. 2000. (Scooby-Doo Ser.). (Illus.). 16p. (J). (ps-3). pap. 3.99 (978-0-307-15400-2(9) , 15400, Golden Bks.) Random Hse. Children's Bks.

—Mission: Marketropolis. 2007. (Illus.). 24p. (J). (ps-2). pap. 3.99 (978-0-375-83767-8(1) , Golden Bks.) Random Hse. Children's Bks.

—Top Dog. 2007. (Deluxe Coloring Book Ser.). (Illus.). 64p. (J). (ps-3). pap. 3.99 (978-0-375-83708-1(6) , Golden Bks.) Random Hse. Children's Bks.

—When Good Food Goes Bad. 2007. (Paint Box Book Ser.). (Illus.). 32p. (J). (ps-3). pap. 3.99 (978-0-375-83707-4(8) , Golden Bks.) Random Hse. Children's Bks.

Golden Books Staff, ed. Scooby-Doo & the Haunted Carnival. 2000. (Scooby-Doo Ser.). (Illus.). (J). (ps-3). pap. 3.99 (978-0-307-16612-8(0) , Golden Bks.) Random Hse. Children's Bks.

Golden, Christopher. Body Bags. 1999. (YA). 11.64 (978-0-606-20505-4(5)) Tandem Library Bks.

—Meets the Eye. 2000. (Body of Evidence Ser.: No. 4). 256p. (YA). (gr. 7 up). pap. 4.99 (978-0-671-03495-5(2) , Simon Pulse) Simon & Schuster Children's Publishing.

—Thief of Hearts. 1999. 245p. (YA). (gr. 8-12). per. 13.00 (978-0-613-73104-1(2)) Tandem Library Bks.

Goldsmith, Howard. The Twiddle Twins' Single Footprint Mystery. Jordan, Charles, illus. 1998. (Mondo Ser.). 40p. (J). (gr. 1-5). pap. 4.50 (978-1-57255-619-5(6)) Mondo Publishing.

Gonzalez, Eladia. El Misterio de las Damas Chinas. 2000. (SPA.). 30p. (J). (gr. 2-4). (978-968-494-094-9(7) , CI30454) Centro de Informacion y Desarrollo de la Comunicacion y la Literatura MEX. *Dist:* AIMS International Bks., Inc., Continental Bk. Co., Inc., Lectorum Pubns., Inc.

Goodman, David & Copp, Rick. Scooby-Doo & the Hex Files. 1999. (Scooby-Doo Movie Storybooks). (Illus.). 32p. (J). (ps-3). pap. 3.50 (978-0-439-08787-2(2)) Scholastic, Inc.

Gordon, Fran & Tischler, Faye. Dutch Double. 2007. (Illus.). 88p. pap. 15.95 (***978-1-59299-242-3(0)***) Inkwater Pr.

Gordon, Lawrence. Haunted High Vol. 2: The Ghost Chronicles. 2000. 162p. (YA). (gr. 6-9). pap. 11.95 (978-0-9653966-1-6(X)) Karmichael Pr.

Gosling, Gabby. The Top Secret Files of Mother Goose! Banks, Timothy, illus. 2003. 32p. (J). (gr. 2 up). lib. bdg. 24.67 (978-0-8368-3750-6(9)) Stevens, Gareth Inc.

Goswami, Hemesh. Boo-Boo Island: The Ghost-House & the Mystery of the Old Wooden House. l.t. ed. 2002. 108p. per. 4.95 (978-0-9718288-9-6(X)) Stylewriter Pubns.

Grant, Vicki. Pigboy. 2006. 112p. (J). pap. 8.95 (978-1-55143-643-2(4)); lib. bdg. 14.95 (978-1-55143-666-1(3)) Orca Bk. Pubs. USA.

Gratz, Alan M. Something Rotten: A Horatio Wilkes Mystery. 2007. 208p. (J). (gr. 6). 16.99 (***978-0-8037-3216-2(3)*** , Dial) Penguin Group (USA) Inc.

Great Expectations. 2004. (Literature Connections Ser.). (Illus.). (gr. 6-12). (978-0-395-87484-4(X) , 2-70843) McDougal Littell Inc.

The Great Paua Mystery: Kyss Series. 2003. (J). mass mkt. (978-1-932233-69-8(5)) Aurora Libris Corp.

Green. Not a Chance. (Thumbprint Mysteries Ser.). 32.86 (978-0-8092-0422-9(3)) McGraw-Hill/Contemporary.

Green, Jim. Shadows of the Moon... Dancing. 2007. (YA). pap. 14.95 (***978-1-59705-872-8(6)***) Wings ePress, Inc.

Greenaway, Elizabeth. Night Is the Time. Weston, Martha, illus. 1999. (Jellybean Bks.). 24p. (J). (ps-k). lib. bdg. 7.99 (978-0-375-99274-2(X) , Random Hse. Bks. for Young Readers) Random Hse. Children's Bks.

Greenburg, Dan. Now You See Me... Now You Don't. 1998. (Zack Files Ser.: No. 12). (J). (gr. 2-5). (978-0-606-12852-0(2)) Tandem Library Bks.

—The Shluffmuffin Boy Is History. Fischer, Scott M., illus. 2006. (Secrets of Dripping Fang Ser.: Bk. 5). 176p. (J). 9.95 (978-0-15-206035-0(9)) Harcourt Children's Bks.

—Trapped in the Museum of Unnatural History, Vol. 25. Davis, Jack E., illus. 2002. (Zack Files Ser.: No. 25). 64p. (J). pap. 4.99 (978-0-448-42632-7(3) , Grosset & Dunlap) Penguin Group (USA) Inc.

—Trapped in the Museum of Unnatural History. 2002. (gr. 3-6). lib. bdg. 13.00 (978-0-613-50089-0(X)) Tandem Library Bks.

Greene, Janice. Under Siege. 2001. (PageTurner Science Fiction Ser.). 80p. (YA). per. 3.95 (978-1-56254-134-7(X) , SP 134X) Saddleback Educational Publishing.

—Under Siege. 2001. (gr. 7-12). lib. bdg. 11.80 (978-0-613-34520-0(7)); (Illus.). (J). (978-0-606-21577-0(8)) Tandem Library Bks.

Greene, Michele Dominguez. Chasing the Jaguar. 240p. (J). 2008. pap. 7.99 (***978-0-06-076355-8(8)*** , Rayo); 2006. 15.99 (978-0-06-076353-4(1)) HarperCollins Pubs.

—Chasing the Jaguar. Greene, Michele Dominguez, illus. 2006. 240p. (J). lib. bdg. 16.89 (978-0-06-076354-1(X)) HarperCollins Pubs.

Greenwood, Kerry. The Three-Pronged Dagger. 2002. (Crime Waves Ser.). (Illus.). 160p. (YA). pap. (978-0-7344-0259-2(7) , Lothian Bks.) Hachette Livre Australia.

Gregory, Jillian Louise. Dobbs Dog Detective: Operation Fido & Fifi. 2003. 67p. pap. 11.95 (978-1-4137-0644-4(4)) PublishAmerica, Inc.

Gregory, Kristiana. Cabin Creek Mysteries #1 Secret of Rober's Cave. 2008. (Cabin Creek Mysteries Ser.). 192p. (J). pap. 4.99 (***978-0-439-92950-9(4)*** , Scholastic Paperbacks) Scholastic, Inc.

—Cabin Creek Mysteries #2 Clue at the Bottom Lake. 2008. (Cabin Creek Mysteries Ser.). 176p. (J). pap. 4.99 (***978-0-439-92951-6(2)*** , Scholastic Paperbacks) Scholastic, Inc.

Gregory, Nan. How Smudge Came. Lightburn, Ron, illus. 32p. (J). pap. (978-0-88995-161-7(6)) Red Deer Pr.

Gregory, Valiska. The Mystery of the Grindlecat. 2003. (Illus.). 32p. (J). 18.99 (978-1-57860-142-4(8)); pap. 9.99 (978-1-57860-141-7(X)) Emmis Bks.

Gresko, Marcia S. Measurement Mysteries, Vol. 4475. Kupperstein, Joel, ed. Jarrett, Michael, photos by. 1998. (Learn to Read Math Ser.). (Illus.). 16p. (J). pap. 2.75 (978-1-57471-382-4(5) , 4475) Creative Teaching Pr., Inc.

Griggs, Joyce. Imanis Good Deed. 2006. pap. 9.95 (***978-1-4327-0071-3(5)***) Outskirts Press, Inc.

Grigsby, Cynthia. Hollow Creek: A Haunted Beginning, 01. 2006. 163p. (J). 14.95 (978-0-9786840-0-6(1)) Grigsby, Cynthia.

Groot, Bob de & Turk. The Laughing Thief. 2007. (Illus.). 48p. pap. 9.99 (***978-1-905460-07-6(4)***) CineBook GBR. *Dist:* Biblio Distribution.

—My Dear Wilkinson. 2007. (Illus.). 48p. pap. 9.99 (***978-1-905460-06-9(6)***) CineBook GBR. *Dist:* Biblio Distribution.

Groot, De. Clifton: Black Moon. Spear, Luke, tr. from FRE. Rodrigue, illus. 2007. 48p. pap. 9.99 (***978-1-905460-30-4(9)***) CineBook GBR. *Dist:* Biblio Distribution.

Guest, Jacqueline. At Risk. 2004. (SideStreets Ser.). 192p. (YA). (gr. 7-12). 7.95 (978-1-55028-846-9(6)); (***978-1-55028-847-6(4)***) Lorimer, James & Co., Ltd., Pubs. CAN. *Dist:* Casemate Pubs. & Bk. Distributors, LLC.

Gutman, Dan. Back in Time. Thorkelson, illus. 2002. 208p. (J). pap. 5.99 (978-0-689-84125-5(6) , Aladdin) Simon & Schuster Children's Publishing.

—The Million Dollar Strike. 2006. 224p. (gr. 3-7). pap. 5.99 (978-0-7868-3751-9(9)) Hyperion Pr.

Gutman, Dan. Million Dollar Strike. 2004. 176p. (J). lib. bdg. 18.46 (***978-1-4242-2107-3(2)***) Fitzgerald Bks.

Guzaldo, Jessica. Murder & Betrayal, DeFalco, Julie & Cowhey, Dennis R., eds. Cowhey, Dennis E., illus. 2003. 72p. (YA). (gr. 7-8). pap. 9.95 (978-0-9642823-2-2(1)) Key Answer Products, Inc.

Haarsma, P. J. The Softwire: Virus on Orbis 1. 2008. (Illus.). 288p. (J). (gr. 5). 6.99 (***978-0-7636-3638-8(X)***) Candlewick Pr.

Haddix, Margaret Peterson. The House on the Gulf. (Illus.). 208p. (J). 2006. pap. 5.99 (978-1-4169-1406-8(4) , Aladdin); 2004. 15.95 (978-0-689-85422-4(6)) Simon & Schuster Children's Publishing.

Hadnot, Victor. The Wheels of God. 2003. 140p. (YA). pap. 11.95 (978-0-595-27507-6(9)) iUniverse, Inc.

Haidle, Helen. What Happens at Dawn. 1999. (Illus.). 18p. (J). (gr. k-2). 12.99 (978-1-57673-559-6(1) , Multnomah) WaterBrook Pr.

Hale, Bruce. The Big Nap. Hale, Bruce, illus. (Chet Gecko Mystery Ser.: No. 4). (Illus.) (J). 2002. 132p. (ps-7). pap. 4.95 (978-0-15-202479-6(4) , Harcourt Paperbacks); 2001. 128p. (gr. 3-7). 15.00 (978-0-15-202521-2(9)) Harcourt Children's Bks.

—The Big Nap. unabr. ed. 2004. (Chet Gecko, Private Eye Ser.: No. 4). 128p. (J). (gr. 3-6). pap. 17.00 incl. audio (978-0-8072-1707-8(7) , S FTR 272 SP, Listening Library) Random Hse. Audio Publishing Group.

—The Big Nap: From the Tattered Casebook of Chet Gecko, Private Eye. 2002. (Chet Gecko Mystery Ser.: No. 4). (J). (gr. 3-6). lib. bdg. 12.95 (978-0-613-50549-9(2)) Tandem Library Bks.

—The Chameleon Wore Chartreuse: A Chet Gecko Mystery. Hale, Bruce, illus. (Chet Gecko Mystery Ser.: No. 1). (Illus.). (J). 2000. 112p. (gr. 2-5). 14.00 (978-0-15-202281-5(3)); 2001. 120p. (gr. 3-7). reprint ed. pap. 4.95 (978-0-15-202485-7(9) , Harcourt Paperbacks) Harcourt Children's Bks.

—The Chameleon Wore Chartreuse: A Chet Gecko Mystery. 2001. (Chet Gecko Mystery Ser.: No. 1). (J). (gr. 3-6). lib. bdg. 12.95 (978-0-613-35450-9(8)); (Illus.). 11.60 (978-0-606-21105-5(5)) Tandem Library Bks.

—Farewell, My Lunchbag. unabr. ed. 2004. (Chet Gecko, Private Eye Ser.: No. 3). 128p. (J). (gr. 3-6). pap. 17.00 incl. audio (978-0-8072-1708-5(5) , S FTR 273 SP, Listening Library) Random Hse. Audio Publishing Group.

—Farewell, My Lunchbag: A Chet Gecko Mystery. 2002. (Chet Gecko Mystery Ser.: No. 3). (Illus.). 132p. (ps-7). pap. 4.95 (978-0-15-202629-5(0) , Harcourt Paperbacks) Harcourt Children's Bks.

—Farewell, My Lunchbag: A Chet Gecko Mystery. Hale, Bruce, illus. 2001. (Chet Gecko Mystery Ser.: No. 3). (Illus.). 128p. (J). (gr. 3-7). 15.00 (978-0-15-202275-4(9)) Harcourt Children's Bks.

—Farewell, My Lunchbag: A Chet Gecko Mystery. 2002. (Chet Gecko Mystery Ser.: No. 3). (J). (gr. 3-6). lib. bdg. 12.95 (978-0-613-49734-3(1)) Tandem Library Bks.

—Give My Regrets to Broadway: A Chet Gecko Mystery. (Chet Gecko Mystery Ser.: No. 9). (Illus.). (J). (gr. 3-6). 2005. 144p. pap. 4.95 (978-0-15-216730-1(7) , Harcourt Paperbacks); 2004. 136p. 15.00 (978-0-15-216700-4(5)) Harcourt Children's Bks.

—The Hamster of the Baskervilles: A Chet Gecko Mystery. (Chet Gecko Mystery Ser.: No. 5). (Illus.). (J). 2003. 144p. (gr. 3-7). pap. 4.95 (978-0-15-202509-0(X) , Harcourt Paperbacks); 2002. 132p. (gr. 4-7). 14.00 (978-0-15-202503-8(0)) Harcourt Children's Bks.

—The Hamster of the Baskervilles: A Chet Gecko Mystery. 2003. (Chet Gecko Mystery Ser.: No. 5). (J). (gr. 3-6). lib. bdg. 12.95 (978-0-613-59896-5(2)) Tandem Library Bks.

—Hiss Me Deadly: A Chet Gecko Mystery. Hale, Bruce, illus. 2007. (Chet Gecko Mystery Ser.: No. 13). (Illus.). 144p. (J). (gr. 3-7). 15.00 (***978-0-15-205482-3(0)***) Harcourt Children's Bks.

—Key Lardo: A Chet Gecko Mystery. Hale, Bruce, illus. 2007. (Chet Gecko Mystery Ser.: No. 12). (Illus.). 128p. (J). (gr. 3-7). pap. 4.95 (978-0-15-205235-5(6) , Harcourt Paperbacks) Harcourt Children's Bks.

—Key Lardo: A Chet Gecko Mystery. 2006. (Chet Gecko Mystery Ser.: No. 12). (Illus.). 128p. (J). (gr. 3-7). 14.00 (978-0-15-205074-0(4)) Harcourt Children's Bks.

—The Malted Falcon: A Chet Gecko Mystery. (Chet Gecko Mystery Ser.: No. 7). (Illus.). (J). (gr. 3-7). 2004. 132p. pap. 4.95 (978-0-15-216712-7(9) , Harcourt Paperbacks); 2003. 128p. 14.00 (978-0-15-216706-6(4)) Harcourt Children's Bks.

—The Malted Falcon: A Chet Gecko Mystery. 2004. (Chet Gecko Mystery Ser.: No. 7). (J). (gr. 3-6). lib. bdg. 12.95 (978-0-613-71645-1(0)) Tandem Library Bks.

—Murder, My Tweet: A Chet Gecko Mystery. (Chet Gecko Mystery Ser.: No. 10). (Illus.). (J). (gr. 3-6). 2005. 132p. pap. 4.95 (978-0-15-205219-5(4) , Harcourt Paperbacks); 2004. 136p. 15.00 (978-0-15-205012-2(4)) Harcourt Children's Bks.

—Murder, My Tweet: A Chet Gecko Mystery. 2004. (Illus.). 117p. (J). (gr. 3-7). per. 12.00 (978-0-606-33413-6(0)) Tandem Library Bks.

—The Mystery of Mr. Nice. Hale, Bruce, illus. 2001. (Chet Gecko Mystery Ser.: No. 2). (Illus.). 120p. (J). (gr. 3-7). pap. 4.95 (978-0-15-202515-1(4) , Harcourt Paperbacks) Harcourt Children's Bks.

—The Mystery of Mr. Nice. 2000. (Chet Gecko Mystery Ser.: No. 2). (Illus.). 112p. (J). (gr. 3-7). 14.00 (978-0-15-202271-6(6)) Harcourt Children's Bks.

—The Mystery of Mr. Nice. unabr. ed. 2004. (Chet Gecko, Private Eye Ser.: No. 2). 112p. (J). (gr. 3-6). pap. 17.00 incl. audio (978-0-8072-0343-9(2) , Listening Library) Random Hse. Audio Publishing Group.

—The Mystery of Mr. Nice. 2001. (Chet Gecko Mystery Ser.: No. 2). (J). (gr. 3-7). lib. bdg. 12.95 (978-0-613-35466-0(4)); (Illus.). (978-0-606-21344-8(9)) Tandem Library Bks.

—The Possum Always Rings Twice: A Chet Gecko Mystery. Hale, Bruce, illus. 2007. (Chet Gecko Mystery Ser.: No. 11). (Illus.). 144p. (J). (gr. 3-7). pap. 4.95 (978-0-15-205233-1(X) , Harcourt Paperbacks) Harcourt Children's Bks.

—The Possum Always Rings Twice: A Chet Gecko Mystery. 2006. (Chet Gecko Mystery Ser.: No. 11). (Illus.). 128p. (J). (gr. 3-7). 14.00 (978-0-15-205075-7(2)) Harcourt Children's Bks.

—This Gum for Hire: A Chet Gecko Mystery. (Chet Gecko Mystery Ser.: No. 6). (Illus.). (J). (gr. 3-7). 2003. 144p. pap. 4.95 (978-0-15-202497-0(2) , Harcourt Paperbacks); 2002. 136p. 15.00 (978-0-15-202491-8(3)) Harcourt Children's Bks.

—This Gum for Hire: A Chet Gecko Mystery. 2003. (Chet Gecko Mystery Ser.: No. 6). (J). (gr. 3-6). lib. bdg. 12.95 (978-0-613-59895-8(4)) Tandem Library Bks.

—Trouble Is My Beeswax: A Chet Gecko Mystery. 2004. (Chet Gecko Mystery Ser.: No. 8). (Illus.). 132p. (J). (gr. 3-6). pap. 4.95 (978-0-15-216724-0(2) , Harcourt Paperbacks) Harcourt Children's Bks.

—Trouble Is My Beeswax: A Chet Gecko Mystery. Weinman, Brad, illus. 2003. (Chet Gecko Mystery Ser.: No. 8). 128p. (J). (gr. 3-6). 14.00 (978-0-15-216718-9(8)) Harcourt Children's Bks.

—Trouble Is My Beeswax: A Chet Gecko Mystery. 2004. (Chet Gecko Mystery Ser.: No. 8). (J). (gr. 3-6). lib. bdg. 12.95 (978-0-613-71557-7(8)) Tandem Library Bks.

Halfmann, Janet. Mystery Mask Mix-Up. 2001. 32p. pap. 3.99 (978-0-307-21691-5(8) , Golden Bks.) Random Hse. Children's Bks.

Hall, John. The Casebook of Janet Moore, Vol. I. 2003. 265p. 18.95 (978-1-59286-403-4(1)) PublishAmerica, Inc.

Hallman, Ruth. Search Without Fear. 2000. (Illus.). 116p. (YA). (gr. 4-7). pap. 9.95 (978-0-595-09273-4(X) , Backinprint.com) iUniverse, Inc.

Halverson, Mathew. Concord Cunningham Returns: The Scripture Sleuth 2. pap. 8.95 (978-1-885904-25-6(8)) Focus Publishing.

Hamilton, Carol. Mystery of Black Mesa. Roberts, John, illus. 2002. 130p. (gr. 4-7). pap. 11.95 (978-0-595-22696-2(5) , Backinprint.com) iUniverse, Inc.

Hamilton, Elizabeth L. Mystery at Lake Cachuma. 2003. (Character Mystery Ser.: No. 1). (Illus.). 114p. (J). (gr. 3-6). per. 9.95 (978-0-9713749-4-2(5) , Character-in-Action) Quiet Impact, Inc.

—Surprise at Pearl Harbor. 2004. (Character Mystery Ser.: No. 2). (Illus.). 144p. (J). per. 9.95 (978-0-9754629-2-8(X) , Character-in-Action) Quiet Impact, Inc.

Hamilton, Virginia. The House of Dies Drear. 1998. 32p. (J). 9.95 (978-1-56137-516-5(0) , NU5168) Novel Units, Inc.

—The House of Dies Drear. 2001. (Assessment Packs Ser.). 15p. pap. 15.95 (978-1-58303-122-3(7)) Pathways Publishing.

—The House of Dies Drear. 8.97 (978-0-13-437491-8(6)) Prentice Hall PTR.

—The House of Dies Drear. 2006. 256p. (J). pap. 5.99 (978-1-4169-1405-1(6) , Aladdin) Simon & Schuster Children's Publishing.

Hancock, Irving H. Young Engineers on the Gulf or the Dread. 2006. 78.99 (***978-1-4280-2538-7(3)***) IndyPublish.com.

Haneberg, Janet. Moonlight Madness. 2004. 244p. pap. 19.95 (978-1-4137-4255-8(6)) PublishAmerica, Inc.

Hannah, Vickie. There's A Schnoozle in My Closet. 2004. (J). lib. bdg. 19.95 (***978-0-9754728-4-2(4)*** , Bear Hug Bks.) MidAmerica Publishing Co.

Hansen, Lynne & Bosco, Sally. AltDeath.com. 2004. 152p. (YA). pap. 9.00 (978-0-7599-4572-2(1)) Hard Shell Word Factory.

Hanson, Ed. Mystery at Bear Lake. 2004. 64p. (YA). per. 3.95 (978-1-56254-807-0(7) , SP8077) Saddleback Educational Publishing.

Hapka, Cathy. Clue School: The Case of the Missing Cat, Level 4. Torrey, Richard, illus. 2006. (innovativeKids readers ser.: level 4). 32p. (J). (gr. 2-17). pap., pap. 6.99 (978-1-58476-479-3(1) , IKIDS) Innovative Kids.

Happy Birthday, D. J. 2002. 80p. (J). 9.50 (978-0-9716704-2-6(0)) M & M Bk. Publishing Co.

Harcourt School Publishers Staff. Cam Jansen... Library Edition. 1999. (Collections Ser.). (Illus.). (J). lib. bdg. 5.30 (978-0-15-314326-7(6)) Harcourt Schl. Pubs.

—The Case of Derrick & the Mind-Benders On Level. 3rd ed. 2002. (Trophies Reading Program Ser.). (Illus.). pap. 5.10 (978-0-15-323355-5(9)) Harcourt Schl. Pubs.

—The Case of the Missing Fossils On Level. 3rd ed. 2002. (Trophies Reading Program Ser.). (Illus.). pap. 5.10 (978-0-15-323460-6(1)) Harcourt Schl. Pubs.

—The Case of the Red Bicycle. 3rd ed. 2002. (Trophies English Language Learners Ser.). (Illus.). pap. 5.10 (978-0-15-327766-5(1)) Harcourt Schl. Pubs.

—The Masterpiece Below Level. 3rd ed. 2002. (Trophies Reading Program Ser.). (Illus.). pap. 5.10 (978-0-15-323237-4(4)) Harcourt Schl. Pubs.

—The Missing Case On Level. 3rd ed. 2002. (Trophies Reading Program Ser.). (Illus.). pap. 5.10 (978-0-15-323163-6(7)) Harcourt Schl. Pubs.

—The Missing Case 5-Pack, On Level. 3rd ed. 2002. (Trophies Reading Program Ser.). (Illus.). (gr. 3). pap. 25.60 (978-0-15-327019-2(5)) Harcourt Schl. Pubs.

—The Mystery of Camp Owana! Take-Home Book. 1999. (Collections Ser.). (Illus.). (J). pap. 1.90 (978-0-15-317274-8(6)) Harcourt Schl. Pubs.

—A Summer Mystery On Level. 3rd ed. 2002. (Trophies Reading Program Ser.). (Illus.). (gr. 4). pap. 5.10 (978-0-15-323258-9(7)) Harcourt Schl. Pubs.

—The Thing That Visited Our Camp 5-Pack, Below Level. 3rd ed. 2002. (Trophies Reading Program Ser.). (Illus.). (gr. 1). pap. 20.10 (978-0-15-326818-2(2)) Harcourt Schl. Pubs.

—Trofeos Advanced Level: Las Dos Julias. 3rd ed. 2002. (SPA., Illus.). pap. 6.80 (978-0-15-324104-8(7)) Harcourt Schl. Pubs.

Hardcastle, Nick, illus. Detective Stories. 2003. (Red Hot Reads Ser.). 224p. (J). (gr. 4-8). pap. 6.95 (978-0-7534-5636-1(2) , Kingfisher) Houghton Mifflin Co. Trade & Reference Div.

Harper, Ben, adapted by. The Movie Storybook: Batman Begins. 2005. (Batman Begins Ser.). (Illus.). 48p. 6.99 (978-0-439-72506-4(2)) Scholastic, Inc.

Harrah, Madge. No Escape. 1998. 110p. (J). pap. 4.95 (978-1-57502-775-3(5) , PO2137) Morris Publishing.

—No Escape. 2001. 104p. reprint ed. pap. 7.95 (978-0-9709152-2-1(5)) Trailway Bks.

Harrington, Patty. Curiosity Shop: Young Detectives. 1998. 20p. 39.95 (978-1-878631-45-9(4)) Kovalik, Susan & Assocs.

Harris, Christine. Danger. 2006. (Undercover Girl Ser.: No. 4). 176p. (J). pap. 4.99 (978-0-439-76128-4(X) , Scholastic Paperbacks) Scholastic, Inc.

—Fugitive. 2005. (Undercover Girl Ser.: No. 2). (Illus.). 160p. (J). (gr. 3-7). pap. 4.99 (978-0-439-76126-0(3) , Scholastic Paperbacks) Scholastic, Inc.

—Nightmare. 2006. (Undercover Girl Ser.). 176p. (Orig.). (J). pap. 4.99 (978-0-439-76127-7(1) , Scholastic Paperbacks) Scholastic, Inc.

—Secrets. 2005. (Undercover Girl Ser.: No. 1). 128p. (Orig.). (J). (ps-7). pap. 4.99 (978-0-439-76125-3(5) , Scholastic Paperbacks) Scholastic, Inc.

Harris, Loretta. A Gangsta's Life. 2006. (YA). (***978-0-9786681-4-3(6)***) Children's Heart Publishing Co.

Harrison, Cora. Milleniumdrumshee. 1999. (Drumshee Timeline Ser.). (Illus.). 143p. (J). (978-0-86327-715-3(2)) Wolfhound Pr.

—Murder at Drumshee. 2002. (Drumshee Timeline Ser.). 144p. (J). (gr. 3-9). pap. 6.95 (978-0-86327-832-7(9)) Wolfhound Pr. IRL. *Dist:* Interlink Publishing Group, Inc.

Harrison, David L. The Purchase of Small Secrets. Henderson, Meryl, illus. 2003. 48p. (YA). 14.95 (978-1-56397-054-2(6)) Boyds Mills Pr.

Harshfield, James. Coaldon of Rocknee: Voices from the Outlast. 2000. 144p. (gr. 7-12). pap. 9.95 (978-0-595-01216-9(7) , Writer's Showcase Pr.) iUniverse, Inc.

Hart, Alison. Fires of Jubilee. 2003. (Aladdin Historical Fiction Ser.). (Illus.). 192p. (J). pap. 4.99 (978-0-689-85528-3(1) , Aladdin) Simon & Schuster Children's Publishing.

—Fires of Jubilee. 2003. (gr. 5-8). lib. bdg. 13.00 (978-0-613-90183-3(5)) Tandem Library Bks.

—A Spy on the Home Front: A Molly Mystery. 2005. (American Girls Collection). (Illus.). 176p. (YA). pap. 6.95 (978-1-58485-988-8(1) , American Girl) American Girl Publishing, Inc.

—A Spy on the Homefront: A Molly Mystery. 2005. (Illus.). 165p. (J). (gr. 4-7). per. 14.90 (978-0-606-33680-2(X)) Tandem Library Bks.

Hart, Anne. Roman Justice: Too Roman to Handle. 2003. 186p. (YA). pap. 13.95 (978-0-595-27282-2(7) , Mystery & Suspense Pr.) iUniverse, Inc.

Hart, Carolyn G. Sugarplum Dead. 2001. (Death on Demand Mysteries Ser.). 416p. mass mkt. 7.99 (978-0-380-80719-2(X)) HarperCollins Pubs.

Hart, Debbie L. The Fortune Teller Mystery. 1998. 24p. (J). (gr. 6-8). pap. 7.00 (978-0-8059-4179-1(7)) Dorrance Publishing Co., Inc.

Hartinger, Brent. Grand & Humble. 2006. 224p. (J). 15.99 (978-0-06-056727-9(9)); lib. bdg. 16.89 (978-0-06-056728-6(7) , HarperTeen) HarperCollins Pubs.

Hartley, Susan. Stephanie Investigates. ed. 2004. (Shared Connections Ser.). (J). pap. 27.00 (978-1-4108-1642-9(7)) Benchmark Education Co.

—Stephanie Investigates (Big Book) ed. 2004. (Shared Connections Ser.). (J). pap., instr.'s gde. ed. 27.00 (978-1-4108-1618-4(4)) Benchmark Education Co.

Hartnett, Sonya. What the Birds See. 2007. (Illus.). 208p. (YA). (gr. 9). pap. 7.99 (***978-0-7636-3680-7(0)***) Candlewick Pr.

Hartt-Snowbell, Sarah. Vivian Untangled. 2006. (Illus.). 128p. (J). pap. 8.95 (978-1-894917-25-4(1)) Napoleon Publishing/Rendezvous Pr. CAN. *Dist:* AtlasBooks Distribution.

Harvey, Bob, illus. The Hound of the Baskervilles. 2004. (Paperback Classics Ser.). 144p. (J). pap. 4.95 (978-0-7945-0574-5(0) , Usborne) EDC Publishing.

Harvey, M. A. Attack of the Jaguar: Dare to Take the Test. 2004. (Illus.). 128p. (J). pap. (978-1-84458-051-4(2)) Chrysalis Children's Bks.

—The Scorpion Secret: Dare to Take the Test. 2004. (Illus.). 128p. (J). pap. (978-1-84458-050-7(4)) Chrysalis Children's Bks.

Hautman, Pete. Snatched. 2007. 224p. (J). pap. 6.99 (978-0-14-240795-0(X) , Puffin) Penguin Group (USA) Inc.

Hautman, Pete & Logue, Mary. The Bloodwater Mysteries: Doppelganger: Doppelganger. 2008. 176p. (YA). (gr. 6). 16.99 (***978-0-399-24379-0(8)*** , Putnam Juvenile) Penguin Group (USA) Inc.

Hautman, Pete & Logue, Mary. Skullduggery. 2007. (Bloodwater Mysteries Ser.). 176p. (J). (gr. 5-9). 16.99 (978-0-399-24378-3(X) , Putnam Juvenile) Penguin Group (USA) Inc.

Hawke, Rosanne. A Kiss in Every Wave. 2002. 160p. (YA). pap. (978-0-7344-0267-7(8) , Lothian Bks.) Hachette Livre Australia.

—Sailmaker. (Illus.). 160p. pap. (978-0-7344-0318-6(6) , Lothian Bks.) Hachette Livre Australia.

Hawkins, Michelle Lee. The Case of the Cough. Wise, Noreen, ed. Porcaro, Susan Tait, illus. 2001. (Medical Mystery Ser.: Vol. 2). 64p. (J). (gr. 1-5). pap. 6.95 (978-1-58584-452-4(7)) Huckleberry Pr.

—The Mysterious Itch. Wise, Noreen, ed. Porcaro, Susan Tait, illus. 2001. (Medical Mystery Ser.: Vol. 1). 54p. (J). (gr. 1-5). pap. 6.95 (978-1-58584-450-0(0)) Huckleberry Pr.

Hayes, Eileen. O'Dwyer & Grady Starring in Tough Act to Follow. 2003. (Illus.). 144p. (J). (gr. 3-6). pap. 4.99 (978-0-689-84920-6(6) , Aladdin) Simon & Schuster Children's Publishing.

Hays, Anna Jane. The Secret of the Circle K Cave. Smath, Jerry, illus. 2006. (Science Solves It! Ser.). 32p. (J). (gr. k-3). pap. 4.99 (978-1-57565-189-7(0)) Kane Pr., The.

Hechtman, Betty Jacobson, Jr. & Brown Barn Books Staff. Blue Schwartz & Nefertiti's Necklace: A Mystery with Recipes. 2006. 152p. (J). (gr. 5-9). pap. 8.95 (978-0-9768126-3-0(0)) Brown Barn Bks.

Hees, Miriam. The Adventures of Jilly & Brad: Noises in the Attic. Kinneman, D. Michael, illus. 2003. 128p. (J). pap. 5.95 (978-0-9718348-4-2(9)) Blooming Tree Pr.

Heimerdinger, Chris. Daniel & Nephi. 2004. pap. 13.95 (978-1-57734-821-4(4)) Covenant Communications, Inc.

Henderson, Dianne. The Frightening Old Mansion. 2006. 116p. pap. 16.95 (978-1-4241-2486-2(7)) PublishAmerica, Inc.

Henderson, Lauren. Kiss Me Kill Me. 2008. 256p. (YA). (gr. 9). 15.99 (***978-0-385-73487-5(5)*** , Delacorte Bks. for Young Readers) Random Hse. Children's Bks.

Hendrickson-Foy, Alyssa. The Mysterious Garden of Maude M. Mcnutt. Bachand, Stephen, illus. 2002. 22p. (J). pap. 6.00 (978-1-928972-07-5(1)) Critter Pubns.

Hendry, Diana. Harvey Angell & the Ghost Child. 1999. 242p. (J). 16.95 (978-0-7540-6074-1(8) , Galaxy Children's Large Print) BBC Audiobooks America.

—Harvey Angell & the Ghost Child. 2002. (Harvey Angell Ser.: Vol. 2). (Illus.). 160p. (J). pap. 4.99 (978-0-7434-2829-3(3) , Aladdin) Simon & Schuster Children's Publishing.

—Harvey Angell & the Ghost Child. 2002. (gr. 3-6). lib. bdg. 13.00 (978-0-613-57904-9(6)) Tandem Library Bks.

Heneghan, James. The Grave. pap. 8.95 (978-0-88899-499-8(0)); 2000. (Illus.). (J). (gr. 7-10). pap. 7.95 (978-0-88899-414-1(1)) Groundwood Bks. CAN. *Dist:* Transition Vendor.

Henry, Ragene. The Barefoot Boys of Fayette. Stich, Carolyn R., illus. 2005. 184p. (YA). per. 9.95 (978-0-9749412-3-3(9)) EDCO Publishing, Inc.

Henry, Sue. Deadfall: An Alaska Mystery. 1999. (gr. 7-12). lib. bdg. 15.30 (978-0-613-29223-8(5)) Tandem Library Bks.

Henson, Heather, et al. The Vampire Bunny. Mack, Jeff, tr. Mack, Jeff, illus. 2004. (Bunnicula & Friends Ser.: Vol. 1). 48p. (J). 14.95 (978-0-689-85724-9(1) , Atheneum) Simon & Schuster Children's Publishing.

Herald, James M. Mystery Cave: Mystery Cave in Mystery Hill. 2000. (Illus.). 90p. (J). (gr. 1-7). pap. 15.00 (978-0-9648236-7-9(5)) Herald Source, Inc.

Herman, Gail. The Apple Thief. del Sur, Duendes, illus. 2002. (Scooby-Doo! Reader Ser.: Bk. 13). 32p. (J). 3.99 (978-0-439-34115-8(9)) Scholastic, Inc.

—The Big Red Detective. Cuddy, Robbin, illus. 2003. (Clifford Big Red Chapter Book Ser.: No. 1). 64p. (J). pap. 3.99 (978-0-439-47315-6(2)) Scholastic, Inc.

—Disappearing Donuts. del Sur, Duendes, illus. 2000. (Scooby-Doo! Reader Ser.: No. 2). 32p. (J). (ps-3). pap. 3.99 (978-0-439-16168-1(1)) Scholastic, Inc.

—Fall Fright. del Sur, Duendes, illus. 2005. (Hello Reader! Ser.). 32p. (J). pap. (978-0-439-78358-3(5)) Scholastic, Inc.

—Howling on the Playground. del Sur, Duendes, illus. 2000. (Scooby-Doo! Reader Ser.: No. 3). 32p. (J). (ps-3). 3.99 (978-0-439-16169-5(X)) Scholastic, Inc.

—Map in the Mystery Machine. del Sur, Duendes, illus. 2000. (Scooby-Doo! Reader Ser.: No. 1). 32p. (J). (ps-3). 3.99 (978-0-439-16167-1(3)) Scholastic, Inc.

—Mummies at the Mall. del Sur, Duendes, illus. 2002. (Scooby-Doo! Reader Ser.: Vol. 11). 32p. (J). (ps-3). pap. 3.99 (978-0-439-34114-1(0)) Scholastic, Inc.

—Scooby Doo: Mummies at the Mall. 2002. (gr. k-3). lib. bdg. 11.80 (978-0-613-51319-7(3)) Tandem Library Bks.

—Scooby-Doo: Racecar Monster. 2001. (gr. k-3). lib. bdg. 11.80 (978-0-613-43872-8(8)) Tandem Library Bks.

—Scooby Doo: Sea Monster Scare. 2002. (gr. k-3). lib. bdg. 11.80 (978-0-613-51324-1(X)) Tandem Library Bks.

—Scooby-Doo! Snack Snatcher. 2001. (gr. k-3). lib. bdg. 11.80 (978-0-613-36675-5(1)) Tandem Library Bks.

—Scooby Doo! The Haunted Ski Lodge. 2001. (gr. k-3). lib. bdg. 11.80 (978-0-613-43831-5(0)) Tandem Library Bks.

—Scooby-Doo & Aliens Too! del Sur, Duendes, illus. 2000. (Scooby-Doo Movie Storybooks). 32p. (J). (ps-3). 3.50 (978-0-439-17701-6(4)) Scholastic, Inc.

—Scooby-Doo & Aliens Too! 2000. (gr. k-3). lib. bdg. 11.25 (978-0-613-33034-3(X)) Tandem Library Bks.

—Scooby Doo! & the Football Fright. 2002. (gr. k-3). lib. bdg. 11.80 (978-0-613-58152-3(0)) Tandem Library Bks.

—Scooby Doo! & the Howling on the Playground. 2000. (gr. k-3). lib. bdg. 11.80 (978-0-613-32658-2(X)) Tandem Library Bks.

—Scooby-Doo on Zombie Island. 1998. (Scooby-Doo Movie Storybooks). (Illus.). 32p. (J). (ps-3). pap. 3.50 (978-0-590-38652-4(2)) Scholastic, Inc.

—Scooby Doo! Valentine's Day Dognapping. 2002. (gr. k-3). lib. bdg. 11.80 (978-0-613-54717-8(9)) Tandem Library Bks.

—Sea Monster Scare. del Sur, Duendes, illus. 2002. (Scooby-Doo! Reader Ser.: No. 12). 32p. (J). (gr. k-2). 3.99 (978-0-439-31831-0(9)) Scholastic, Inc.

—Thanksgiving Mystery. 2006. (Hello Reader! Ser.: No. 17). (Illus.). 32p. (J). pap. 3.99 (978-0-439-78359-0(3)) Scholastic, Inc.

Herman, Gail & del Sur, Duendes. Football Fright. 2002. (Scooby-Doo! Reader Ser.: No. 14). (Illus.). 32p. (J). (gr. k-3). pap. 3.99 (978-0-439-34116-5(7)) Scholastic, Inc.

Hermann. Blood Ties. 2000. 56p. (gr. 11 up). pap. 14.95 (978-1-56971-565-9(3)) Dark Horse Comics.

Hess, Joan. Murder@Maggody.com. 2001. (Arly Hanks Mystery Ser.). (gr. 7-12). lib. bdg. 15.30 (978-0-613-36535-2(6)) Tandem Library Bks.

Heusler, Marianna. Night the Penningtons Vanished. 2002. (gr. 7-12). lib. bdg. 24.60 (978-0-613-88682-6(8)) Tandem Library Bks.

Heyes, Eileen. O'Dwyer & Grady Starring In: Acting Innocent. Carver, Steve, illus. 2002. 176p. (J). (gr. 4-7). pap. 4.99 (978-0-689-84911-4(7) , Aladdin) Simon & Schuster Children's Publishing.

—O'Dwyer & Grady Starring in Acting Innocents. 2002. (gr. 3-6). lib. bdg. 13.00 (978-0-613-57433-4(8)) Tandem Library Bks.

—O'Dwyer & Grady Starring in Tough Act to Follow. 2003. (gr. 3-6). lib. bdg. 13.00 (978-0-613-66465-3(5)) Tandem Library Bks.

Hiaasen, Carl. Hoot. 2005. 304p. (gr. 5). 6.50 (978-0-440-41939-6(5) , Yearling) Random Hse. Children's Bks.

Hickey, Tony. Where's Jacko? Myler, Terry, illus. 2006. 64p. pap. 9.95 (978-1-901737-47-9(0)) Anvil Bks., Ltd. IRL. *Dist:* Dufour Editions, Inc.

Hickey, Tony & Myler, Terry. Flip 'n' Flop & the Movies. 1998. 112p. pap. 7.95 (978-1-901737-05-9(5)) Anvil Bks., Ltd. IRL. *Dist:* Dufour Editions, Inc.

Hicks, Clifford B. The Marvelous Inventions of Alvin Fernald. Geer, Charles, illus. 2006. 119p. (J). 16.95 (978-1-930900-21-9(X)) Purple Hse. Pr.

—The Marvelous Inventions of Alvin Fernald. unabr. ed. 1999. (YA). pap., stu. ed. 32.24 incl. audio (978-0-7887-3648-3(5) , 41014X4) Recorded Bks., LLC.

The Hidden Hand, 6 vols., Vol. 2. (Woodland Mysteriestm Ser.). 133p. (gr. 3-7). 42.50 (978-0-7802-7939-1(5)) Wright Group, The.

Higgins, Jack. The White House Connection. 2000. (gr. 7-12). lib. bdg. 16.45 (978-0-613-29382-2(7)) Tandem Library Bks.

Higman, Anita. The Living Darkness: Texas Caves. 2nd ed. 2003. (Illus.). xiii, 93p. (J). (978-1-57168-783-8(1) , Eakin Pr.) Eakin Pr.

Higson, Charlie. Blood Fever. 2nd rev. ed. 2007. (Young Bond Ser.). 368p. (gr. 7 up). pap. 7.99 (***978-1-4231-0029-4(8)***) Miramax Bks.

Hildick, E. W. Felicity Snell Mysteries Series. unabr. ed. 2000. (Illus.). (J). (gr. 4-7). (978-0-87499-709-5(7)) Live Oak Media.

—The Purloined Corn Popper: A Felicity Snell Mystery. unabr. ed. 2000. (Illus.). (J). (gr. 4-7). 38.95 incl. audio (978-0-87499-558-9(2)) Live Oak Media.

—The Serial Sneak Thief: A Felicity Snell Mystery. unabr. ed. 2000. (Illus.). (J). (gr. 4-7). 38.95 incl. audio (978-0-87499-648-7(1)) Live Oak Media.

Hill, Liz. Raven's Blood No.5: Twin Spins. 2002. Tr. of Web of Death: Twin Spins #5. (gr. 7-12). lib. bdg. 22.20 (978-0-613-74641-0(4)) Tandem Library Bks.

Hillerman, Tony. The Wailing Wind. 2003. 334p. (gr. 7-12). per. 16.45 (978-0-613-59827-9(X)) Tandem Library Bks.

Hilton, Nette. A Grave Catastrophe. 2005. (Illus.). 160p. (J). (ps-7). pap. (978-0-7344-0494-7(8) , Lothian Bks.) Hachette Livre Australia.

Hinson, Robert. Mystery on City Street. George, Cindy, illus. 1998. (YA). (gr. 6-12). pap. 5.95 (978-1-890424-05-3(6)) D-N Publishing.

Hirsch, Odo. Something's Fishy Hazel Green. 2005. 208p. (J). (gr. 3-6). 15.95 (978-1-58234-928-2(2) , Bloomsbury Children) Bloomsbury Publishing.

Hitchcock, Alfred. Alfred Hitchcock's Solve-Them-Yourself Mysteries. 1999. (J). 5.99 (978-0-679-89431-5(4) , Random Hse. Bks. for Young Readers) Random Hse. Children's Bks.

—Die Drei ??? Und die Spaete Rache. 2003. (GER.). 128p. pap. 15.00 (978-1-4000-3977-7(0) , New Media German Language) Random House Foreign Language Publishing.

—Misterio de la Arana de Plata. (Alfred Hitchcock y los Tres Investigadores Ser.). (SPA.). (YA). 8.95 (978-84-272-4908-0(X) , MO60) Molino, Editorial ESP. *Dist:* Continental Bk. Co., Inc.

—Misterio de la Calavera Parlante. (Alfred Hitchcock y los Tres Investigadores Ser.). (SPA.). (YA). 8.95 (978-84-272-4911-0(X) , MO63) Molino, Editorial ESP. *Dist:* Continental Bk. Co., Inc.

—Misterio de la Cueva de los Lamentos. (Alfred Hitchcock y los Tres Investigadores Ser.). (SPA.). 160p. (YA). 8.95 (978-84-272-4910-3(1) , MO62) Molino, Editorial ESP. *Dist:* Continental Bk. Co., Inc.

—Misterio de la Montana del Monstruo. (Alfred Hitchcock y los Tres Investigadores Ser.). (SPA.). (YA). 8.95 (978-84-272-4920-2(9) , MO72) Molino, Editorial ESP. *Dist:* Continental Bk. Co., Inc.

—Misterio de la Serpiente Susurrante. (Alfred Hitchcock y los Tres Investigadores Ser.). (SPA.). (YA). 8.95 (978-84-272-4917-2(9) , MO69) Molino, Editorial ESP. *Dist:* Continental Bk. Co., Inc.

—Misterio de Leon Mervioso. (Alfred Hitchcock y los Tres Investigadores Ser.). (SPA.). 192p. (YA). 8.95 (978-84-272-4916-5(0) , MO68) Molino, Editorial ESP. *Dist:* Continental Bk. Co., Inc.

—Misterio del Dragon. (Alfred Hitchcock y los Tres Investigadores Ser.). (SPA.). 176p. (YA). 8.95 (978-84-272-4914-1(4) , MO66) Molino, Editorial ESP. *Dist:* Continental Bk. Co., Inc.

—Misterio del Gato de Trapo. (Alfred Hitchcock y los Tres Investigadores Ser.). (SPA.). 152p. (YA). 8.95 (978-84-272-4913-4(6) , MO65) Molino, Editorial ESP. *Dist:* Continental Bk. Co., Inc.

—Misterio del Lago Fantasma. (Alfred Hitchcock y los Tres Investigadores Ser.). (SPA.). 173p. (YA). 8.95 (978-84-272-4919-6(5) , MO71) Molino, Editorial ESP. *Dist:* Continental Bk. Co., Inc.

—Misterio del Testamento Sorprendiente. (Alfred Hitchcock y los Tres Investigadores Ser.). (SPA.). (YA). 8.95 (978-84-272-4922-6(5) , MO74) Molino, Editorial ESP. *Dist:* Continental Bk. Co., Inc.

Hobbs, Valerie. Sweetie McGinnis Solves Them All. Date not set. (J). (978-0-374-37352-8(3) , Farrar, Straus & Giroux (BYR)) Farrar, Straus & Giroux.

Hock, Dan. The Birthday Bash 2 vols. An Iggy & Igor Mystery (#2) Hock, Dan, illus. l.t. ed. 2004. (Illus.). 51p. (J). per. 4.99 (978-0-9754046-1-4(X)) Anticipation Pr.

Hockenberger, Henry. The Gold Case. 2006. (YA). pap. 15.95 (978-1-58736-584-3(7)) Wheatmark.

Hodges, David. Flashpoint. 1999. pap. 9.95 (978-1-901442-04-5(7)) Pharaoh Pr. GBR. *Dist:* 7 Hills Bk. Distributors.

Hoeye, Michael. Una Cuestion de Tiempo. (SPA.). 304p. (J). (gr. 6-8). 17.56 (978-84-8441-167-3(2) , MO1007) Grijalbo Mondadori, S.A.-Montena ESP. *Dist:* Lectorum Pubns., Inc.

—No Time Like Show Time. 2007. 304p. (J). pap. 7.99 (*978-0-14-240982-4(0) , Puffin) Penguin Group (USA) Inc.

—No Time Like Show Time: A Hermux Tantamoq Adventure. 2004. (Illus.). 288p. (J). (ps). 14.99 (978-0-399-23880-2(8) , Putnam Juvenile) Penguin Group (USA) Inc.

—No Time Like Showtime. 2006. (Illus.). 288p. (YA). (gr. 7). pap. 7.99 (978-0-14-240563-5(9) , Puffin) Penguin Group (USA) Inc.

—The Sands of Time. (J). 2007. 304p. (gr. 1). pap. 7.99 (*978-0-14-240983-1(9) , Puffin); 2002. (Hermux Tantamoq Adventure Ser.: Bk. 2). (Illus.). 288p. (gr. 5-8). 14.99 (978-0-399-23879-6(4) , Putnam Juvenile) Penguin Group (USA) Inc.

—The Sands of Time. 2001. (Hermux Tantamoq Adventure Ser.: Bk. 2). (Illus.). 300p. (YA). (gr. 5-8). pap. 12.95 (978-0-9675111-2-2(7)) Terfle Bks.

—The Sands of Time: A Hermux Tantamoq AdventureTM. 2004. 288p. (J). (gr. 5-9). pap. 40.00 incl. audio (978-1-4000-9016-7(4) , Listening Library) Random Hse. Audio Publishing Group.

—The Sands of Time: A New Hermux Tantamoq Adventure. 2003. 288p. pap. 6.99 (978-0-14-250176-4(X) , Puffin) Penguin Group (USA) Inc.

—Time Stops for No Mouse. 272p. 2007. (J). pap. 7.99 (*978-0-14-240984-8(7)); 2003. (Hermux Tantamoq Adventure Ser.: Bk. 1). (Illus.). (YA). (gr. 5-8). pap. 7.99 (978-0-698-11991-8(6)) Penguin Group (USA) Inc. (Puffin).

—Time Stops for No Mouse. 2003. (Illus.). 250p. (J). (ps-7). per. 16.45 (978-0-613-62122-9(0)) Tandem Library Bks.

—Time Stops for No Mouse. 2000. (Hermux Tantamoq Adventure Ser.: Bk. 1). (Illus.). 288p. (YA). (gr. 5-8). pap. 12.95 (978-0-9675111-1-5(9)) Terfle Bks.

—Time Stops for No Mouse: A Hermux Tantamoq Adventure. 2002. (Hermux Tantamoq Adventure Ser.: Bk. 1). (Illus.). 288p. (J). (gr. 5-8). 14.99 (978-0-399-23878-9(6) , Putnam Juvenile) Penguin Group (USA) Inc.

—Time Stops for No Mouse: A Hermux Tantamoq AdventureTM. 2004. 272p. (J). (gr. 5-9). pap. 40.00 incl. audio (978-0-8072-2280-5(1) , Listening Library) Random Hse. Audio Publishing Group.

Hoffman, Mary. The Falconer's Knot: A Story of Friars, Flirtation & Foul Play. 2007. (Illus.). 288p. (YA). (gr. 7 up). 16.95 (978-1-59990-056-8(4) , Bloomsbury Children) Bloomsbury Publishing.

The Hole in the Hill: Individual Title Six-Packs. (Action Packs Ser.). 104p. (gr. 3-5). 44.00 (978-0-7635-2993-2(1)) Rigby Education.

Holl, Kristi D. Deadly Disguise. Miller, Amy Young, illus. 1999. (Carousel Mysteries Ser.: Vol. 3). 165p. (J). (gr. 3-7). pap. 7.50 (978-0-931209-83-3(8)) Mid-Prairie Bks.

—A Spin Out of Control. Miller, Amy Young, illus. 1998. (Carousel Mysteries Ser.: Vol. 1). 60p. (J). (gr. 4-8). pap. 6.95 (978-0-931209-81-9(1)) Mid-Prairie Bks.

—Stage Fright. Miller, Amy Young, illus. 1999. (Carousel Mystery Ser.: Vol. 3). 164p. (J). (gr. 3-8). pap. 7.50 (978-0-931209-89-5(7)) Mid-Prairie Bks.

Holland, Robert. The Black Queen. 2003. (Books Boys Want to Read). 220p. (J). pap. 12.00 (978-0-9720922-1-0(8)) Frost Hollow Pubs., LLC.

—Charlie Dollarhide. 2002. 185p. (J). per. 10.95 (978-0-9720922-0-3(X)) Frost Hollow Pubs., LLC.

Holm, Jennifer & Hamel. To Scratch a Thief. Weinman, Brad, illus. 2005. (Stink Files Ser.: Bk.2). 144p. pap. 4.99 (978-0-06-052984-0(9) , Harper Trophy) HarperCollins Pubs.

Holm, Jennifer L. The Creek. 2004. 304p. (YA). (gr. 7 up). pap. 6.99 (978-0-06-000135-3(6) , Harper Trophy) HarperCollins Pubs.

Holm, Jennifer L. & Hamel. To Scratch a Thief. Weinman, Brad, illus. 2004. (Stink Files, Dossier Ser.: No. 2). 144p. (J). 14.99 (978-0-06-052982-6(2)) HarperCollins Pubs.

Holm, Jennifer L. & Hamel, Jonathan. The Postman Always Brings Mice. Weinman, Brad, illus. 2004. (Stink Files, Dossier Ser.). 144p. (J). 14.99 (978-0-06-052979-6(2)); lib. bdg. 15.89 (978-0-06-052980-2(6)) HarperCollins Pubs.

—You Only Have Nine Lives. Weinman, Brad, illus. 2007. (Stink Files, Dossier Ser.: No. 3). 144p. (J). pap. 4.99 (978-0-06-052987-1(3)) HarperCollins Pubs.

Holmes, Barbara W. Following Fake Man. 2002. (Illus.). 240p. (J). (gr. 5 up). pap. 5.99 (978-0-440-41855-9(0) , Yearling) Random Hse. Children's Bks.

—Following Fake Man. 2002. (gr. 3-6). lib. bdg. 13.00 (978-0-613-61839-7(4)) Tandem Library Bks.

Holsather, Kent. Henry of York: The Secret of Juan de Vega. Holsather, Bill, illus. 2003. 176p. (YA). (gr. 5 up). 22.95 (978-0-9729101-0-1(7)); 2nd ed. per. 12.95 (978-0-9729101-1-8(5)) Lonejack Mountain Pr.

Hoobler, Dorothy. The Ghost in the Tokaido Inn. 2001. (J). 12.64 (978-0-606-21212-0(4)) Tandem Library Bks.

Hoobler, Dorothy & Hoobler, Thomas. The Demon in the Teahouse. 2005. 192p. (J). (gr. 7). pap. 5.99 (978-0-14-240540-6(X) , Puffin) Penguin Group (USA) Inc.

—The Ghost in the Tokaido Inn. (J). 2005. 240p. (gr. 4). pap. 5.99 (978-0-14-240541-3(8) , Puffin); 1999. 1p. (gr. 5-9). 17.99 (978-0-399-23330-2(X) , Philomel) Penguin Group (USA) Inc.

—A Samurai Never Fears Death. 2007. (Samurai Mystery Ser.). 224p. (YA). (gr. 5-9). 14.99 (978-0-399-24609-8(6) , Philomel) Penguin Group (USA) Inc.

—The Sword That Cut the Burning Grass. (J). (gr. 5). 2006. 224p. pap. 5.99 (978-0-14-240689-2(9) , Puffin); 2005. 212p. 10.99 (978-0-399-24272-4(4) , Philomel) Penguin Group (USA) Inc.

Hood, Karen Jean Matsko. Spokane Falls Falcon: Mysteries of the Brothers Hood-Children's Fiction. 2006. (J). 19.95 (978-1-59434-220-2(2)); 24.95 (978-1-59434-228-8(8)); per. 19.95 (978-1-59434-226-4(1)); ring bd. 24.95 (978-1-59434-223-3(7)); cd-rom 13.95 (978-1-59434-221-9(0)) Whispering Pine Pr., Inc.

Hood, Susan. Pup & Hound Catch a Thief. Hendry, Linda, illus. 2007. (Kids Can Read Ser.). 32p. (J). (gr. k-1). (*978-1-55337-972-0(1)); (*978-1-55337-973-7(X)) Kids Can Pr., Ltd.

Hope, Laura. Bobbsey Twins or Merry Days Indoors and. 2006. 18.99 (*978-1-4219-7001-1(5)) IndyPublish.com.

Hope, Laura Lee. The Bobbsey Twins & the Mystery at Snow Lodge, Vol. 5. 2004. (Bobbsey Twins Ser.: Vol. 5). (Illus.). 196p. (J). (gr. 3-8). 5.99 (978-0-448-43756-9(2) , Grosset & Dunlap) Penguin Group (USA) Inc.

—The Bobbsey Twins at Meadow Brook. 2004. 200p. pap. 12.95 (978-1-59540-103-8(2) , 1st World Library - Literary Society) 1st World Publishing, Inc.

—The Bobbsey Twins at School. 2004. per. 11.95 (978-1-59540-104-5(0)) 1st World Publishing, Inc.

—The Bobbsey Twins in the Country. 2004. 208p. pap. 12.95 (978-1-59540-105-2(9) , 1st World Library - Literary Society) 1st World Publishing, Inc.

—Bobbsey Twins in Washington. 2006. 62.99 (*978-1-4280-2468-7(9)) IndyPublish.com.

—The Bobbsey Twins' Mystery at Meadowbrook, Vol. 7. 2004. (Bobbsey Twins Ser.: Vol. 7). (Illus.). 196p. (J). (gr. 3-8). 5.99 (978-0-448-43758-3(9) , Grosset & Dunlap) Penguin Group (USA) Inc.

—The Bobbsey Twins' Mystery at School. 2004. (Bobbsey Twins Ser.: Vol. 4). (Illus.). 196p. (J). (gr. 3-8). 5.99 (978-0-448-43755-2(4) , Grosset & Dunlap) Penguin Group (USA) Inc.

—Bobbsey Twins on A Houseboat. 2006. 62.99 (*978-1-4280-2339-0(9)) IndyPublish.com.

—The Bobbsey Twins on a Houseboat, Vol. 6. 2004. (Bobbsey Twins Ser.: Vol. 6). (Illus.). 196p. (J). (gr. 3-8). 5.99 (978-0-448-43757-6(0) , Grosset & Dunlap) Penguin Group (USA) Inc.

—The Bobbsey Twins' Search in the Great City: The Bobbsey Twins, Vol. 9. 2004. (Bobbsey Twins Ser.: Vol. 9). (Illus.). 192p. (J). 5.99 (978-0-448-43760-6(0) , Grosset & Dunlap) Penguin Group (USA) Inc.

—The Mystery of the Ghost in the Attic. Ruppert, Larry, illus. 2005. (Bobbsey Twins Ser.). 24p. (J). pap. 3.99 (978-1-4169-0704-6(1) , Little Simon) Simon & Schuster Children's Publishing.

—Mystery on the Deep Blue Sea, Vol. 11. 2004. (Bobbsey Twins Ser.: Vol. 11). (Illus.). 196p. (J). (gr. 3-8). 5.99 (978-0-448-43762-0(7) , Grosset & Dunlap) Penguin Group (USA) Inc.

Horowitz, Anthony. The Falcon's Malteser. 2004. (Diamond Brothers Ser.). 192p. (J). (gr. 5). 16.99 (978-0-399-24153-6(1) , Philomel) Penguin Group (USA) Inc.

—Groosham Grange. 2008. 192p. (YA). (gr. 5-8). 15.99 (*978-0-399-25061-3(1) , Philomel) Penguin Group (USA) Inc.

—Public Enemy Number Two. 2004. (Diamond Brothers Ser.). 208p. (J). (gr. 5). 16.99 (978-0-399-24154-3(X) , Philomel); pap. 6.99 (978-0-14-240218-4(4) , Puffin) Penguin Group (USA) Inc.

—South by Southeast. 2005. (Diamond Brothers Ser.). 160p. (J). (gr. 3-9). pap. 5.99 (978-0-14-240374-7(1) , Puffin); (YA). (gr. 5-9). 16.99 (978-0-399-24155-0(8) , Philomel) Penguin Group (USA) Inc.

—Three of Diamonds. 2005. (Diamond Brothers Ser.). 240p. (J). (gr. 5). pap. 6.99 (978-0-14-240298-6(2) , Puffin); (YA). (gr. 4). 16.99 (978-0-399-24157-4(4) , Philomel) Penguin Group (USA) Inc.

Horrocks, Anita. Topher. 2000. 212p. (YA). (gr. 5-9). pap. 7.95 (978-0-7737-6092-9(X)) Stoddart Kids CAN. *Dist:* Fitzhenry & Whiteside, Ltd.

—What They Don't Know. 1999. (Illus.). 240p. (YA). (gr. 7-10). pap. 8.95 (978-0-7737-6001-1(6)) Stoddart Kids CAN. *Dist:* Fitzhenry & Whiteside, Ltd.

Horseshoe Canyon. 2005. (J). 30.00 (978-1-884270-38-3(7)) Hall, Nancy Inc.

Horton, Ed J. Buzzy Ghent Mysteries: The Attic's Hidden Secret. 2005. 124p. (J). pap. 12.99 (978-1-4141-0516-1(9)) Pleasant Word.

The Hound of Baskervilles Study Guide. 2000. (Illus.). 48p. (YA). per. 17.95 (978-1-56254-290-0(7) , SP2907) Saddleback Educational Publishing.

Howard, Milly. The Case of the Sassy Parrot. Day, Bruce, illus. 2002. (Crimebusters, Inc Ser.: Bk. 2). 168p. (J). pap. 6.49 (978-1-57924-721-8(0)) Jones, Bob Univ. Pr.

—Case of the Sassy Parrot. 2002. (gr. 3-6). lib. bdg. 14.70 (978-0-613-79328-5(5)) Tandem Library Bks.

Howe, Deborah & Howe, James. A Rabbit-Tale of Mystery. Daniel, Alan, illus. 2006. 128p. (J). pap. 4.99 (978-1-4169-2817-1(0) , Aladdin) Simon & Schuster Children's Publishing.

Howe, James. Bud Barkin, Private Eye. Helquist, Brett, illus. (Tales from the House of Bunnicula Ser.). (J). 2004. 112p. pap. 3.99 (978-0-689-86989-1(4) , Aladdin); 2003. 96p. 9.95 (978-0-689-85632-7(6) , Atheneum) Simon & Schuster Children's Publishing.

—Bunnicula Strikes Again! Daniel, Alan, illus. 1999. (Bunnicula Ser.). 128p. (J). (gr. 3-5). 16.00 (978-0-689-81463-1(1) , Atheneum) Simon & Schuster Children's Publishing.

—Dew Drop Dead. 2000. (Sebastian Barth Mysteries Ser.). 160p. (J). (gr. 3-7). pap. 5.99 (978-0-689-80760-2(0) , Aladdin) Simon & Schuster Children's Publishing.

—Dew Drop Dead. 2000. (gr. 5-8). lib. bdg. 13.00 (978-0-613-22818-1(3)) Tandem Library Bks.

—Dew Drop Dead: A Sebastian Barth Mystery. 2000. (J). 11.64 (978-0-606-17314-8(5)) Tandem Library Bks.

—Howliday Inn. unabr. ed. 2004. (Bunnicula Ser.). 195p. (J). (gr. 3-7). pap. 29.00 incl. audio (978-0-8072-8382-0(7) , YA179SP, Listening Library) Random Hse. Audio Publishing Group.

—Howliday Inn. Munsinger, Lynn, illus. 2nd ed. 2006. 224p. (J). pap. 5.99 (978-1-4169-2815-7(4) , Aladdin) Simon & Schuster Children's Publishing.

—Howliday Inn. 2001. (Bunnicula Ser.). 11.64 (978-0-606-22105-4(0)) Tandem Library Bks.

—Nighty-Nightmare. Morrill, Leslie, illus. 2007. 144p. (J). pap. 5.99 (*978-1-4169-3966-5(0) , Aladdin) Simon & Schuster Children's Publishing.

—Return to Howliday Inn. Daniel, Alan, illus. 2007. (Bunnicula Ser.). 192p. (J). pap. 5.99 (*978-1-4169-3967-2(9) , Aladdin) Simon & Schuster Children's Publishing.

Howell, Kathy. Skoob. Linton, Vera, illus. 2004. (J). per. 6.95 (978-1-59571-026-0(4)) Word Association Pubs.

Hrdlitschka, Shelley. Tangled Web. 2000. 240p. (J). (gr. 5-10). pap. 6.95 (978-1-55143-178-9(5)) Orca Bk. Pubs. USA.

—Tangled Web. 2000. (gr. 5-8). lib. bdg. 15.25 (978-0-613-34994-9(6)) Tandem Library Bks.

Hubbard, Coleen. Louisiana Blue. Rabinowitz, Sandy & Keiffer, Christa, illus. l.t. ed. 1999. (Treasured Horses Collection). 128p. (J). (gr. 4 up). lib. bdg. 23.33 (978-0-8368-2403-2(2)) Stevens, Gareth Inc.

Hubner, Carol Korb. The Devora Doresh Mysteries 2. 2007. (Illus.). 280p. (J). 16.95 (*978-1-932443-68-4(1)) Judaica Pr., Inc., The.

Hubner, Carol Korb. The Twisted Menora: And Other Devora Doresh Mysteries. Morganroth, G. A., illus. 3rd ed. 2000. (Judaica Youth Ser.). 123p. (J). (gr. 3-8). pap. 9.95 (978-1-880582-48-0(1)) Judaica Pr., Inc., The.

Hughes, Holly. Hoofbeats of Danger. 1999. 13.60 (978-0-606-17517-3(2)) Tandem Library Bks.

Hughes, Monica. Jan on the Trail. Freire, Carlos, illus. 2000. (New First Novels Ser.). 61p. (gr. 1-5). 4.95 (978-0-88780-502-8(7)); (J). (978-0-88780-503-5(5)) Formac Publishing Co., Ltd. CAN. *Dist:* Casemate Pubs. & Bk. Distributors, LLC.

Hull, Larry A. & Plummer, Sherry K. The Thump in the Attic. Nichols, Elizabeth L., illus. 1998. 14p. (J). (gr. k-6). pap. 5.95 (978-1-892225-13-9(1) , THMP-1) Winmark Communications.

Hunt, Elizabeth Singer. The Caper of the Crowned Jewels. 2008. (Secret Agent Jack Stalwart Ser.). 128p. (J). (gr. 1-4). pap. 4.99 (*978-1-60286-013-1(0)) Weinstein Bks.

—The Escape of the Deadly Dinosaur. 2007. (Secret Agent Jack Stalwart Ser.). 128p. (J). (gr. 1-4). pap. 4.99 (*978-1-60286-004-9(1)) Weinstein Bks.

—The Mystery of the Mona Lisa. 2007. (Secret Agent Jack Stalwart Ser.). 128p. (J). (gr. 1-4). pap. 4.99 (*978-1-60286-001-8(7)) Weinstein Bks.

—The Search for the Sunken Treasure. 2007. (Secret Agent Jack Stalwart Ser.). 128p. (J). (gr. 1-4). pap. 4.99 (*978-1-60286-002-5(5)) Weinstein Bks.

Hurd, Thacher. Mystery on the Docks. Hurd, Thacher, illus. 2001. (Illus.). pap. 39.95 incl. audio compact disk (978-1-59112-529-7(4)) Live Oak Media.

Hurley, Jo. Scooby-Doo Case Files 04. 2008. 80p. pap. 3.99 (*978-0-545-00668-2(6) , Scholastic) Scholastic, Inc.

Hurwitz, Johanna. Russell's Secret. 2001. (Illus.). 32p. (J). (ps-3). 15.89 (978-0-688-17575-7(9)) HarperCollins Pubs.

—Russell's Secret. Maione, Heather Harms, illus. 2001. 32p. (J). (ps-3). 15.95 (978-0-688-17574-0(0)) HarperCollins Pubs.

Hutchens, Paul. The Brown Box Mystery. rev. ed. 1998. (Sugar Creek Gang Ser.: No. 27). 128p. (J). (gr. 4-7). 4.99 (978-0-8024-7031-7(9)) Moody Pubs.

—The Brown Box Mystery. 1998. (gr. 3-6). lib. bdg. 13.00 (978-0-613-90328-8(5)) Tandem Library Bks.

—The Case of the Missing Calf. rev. ed. 1999. (Sugar Creek Gang Ser.: No. 36). 96p. (J). (gr. 4-7). 4.99 (978-0-8024-7040-9(8)) Moody Pubs.

—The Case of the Missing Calf. 1999. (gr. 3-6). lib. bdg. 13.00 (978-0-613-88825-7(1)) Tandem Library Bks.

—The Colorado Kidnapping. rev. ed. 1998. (Sugar Creek Gang Ser.: Vol. 24). 128p. (Orig.). (J). (gr. 4-7). 4.99 (978-0-8024-7028-7(9)) Moody Pubs.

—The Colorado Kidnapping. 1998. (Orig.). (gr. 3-6). lib. bdg. 13.00 (978-0-613-90554-1(7)) Tandem Library Bks.

—The Haunted House. 1998. (gr. 3-6). lib. bdg. 13.00 (978-0-613-88121-0(4)) Tandem Library Bks.

—The Trapline Thief. rev. ed. 1998. (Sugar Creek Gang Ser.: No. 29). 144p. (J). (gr. 4-7). 4.99 (978-0-8024-7033-1(5)) Moody Pubs.

—The Trapline Thief. 1998. (gr. 3-6). lib. bdg. 13.00 (978-0-613-88824-0(3)) Tandem Library Bks.

—Tree House Mystery. 1999. (gr. 3-6). lib. bdg. 13.00 (978-0-613-90329-5(3)) Tandem Library Bks.

—The Watermelon Mystery. rev. ed. 1998. (Sugar Creek Gang Ser.: No. 28). 160p. (J). (gr. 4-7). 4.99 (978-0-8024-7032-4(7)) Moody Pubs.

Ibbotson. Maia Se Va Al Amazonas. 2002. (SPA.). 256p. (978-84-7888-791-0(1) , 1952) Emece Editores.

Ibbotson, Eva. The Star of Kazan. 2006. (Illus.). 416p. (J). (gr. 3). reprint ed. 6.99 (978-0-14-240582-6(5) , Puffin) Penguin Group (USA) Inc.

Ibbotson, Eva & Minneapolis Institute of Arts Staff, Minneapolis Institute of Arts. The Star of Kazan. Hawkes, Kevin, illus. 2004. 416p. (J). (gr. 5). 16.99 (978-0-525-47347-3(5) , Dutton Juvenile) Penguin Group (USA) Inc.

Ikids & Hapka, Cathy. Innovative Kids Readers: Clue School - the Lost Lunch Mystery. Larranaga, Ana & Torrey, Richard, illus. 2007. 32p. (J). (gr. 2-17). pap. 6.99 (978-1-58476-541-7(0)) Innovative Kids.

Inspector Grub & the Fizzer-X Spy: Individual Title Six-Packs. (Bookweb Ser.). 32p. (gr. 5 up). 34.00 (978-0-7635-3786-9(1)) Rigby Education.

Inspector Grub & the Gourmet Mystery: Individual Title Six-Packs. (Bookweb Ser.). 32p. (gr. 4 up). 34.00 (978-0-7635-3726-5(8)) Rigby Education.

Inspector Grub & the Jelly Bean Robber: Individual Title Six-Packs. (Bookweb Ser.). 32p. (gr. 3 up). 34.00 (978-0-7635-3934-4(1)) Rigby Education.

Ip, Ivy S. Clues at the Carnival. 2001. (ps-2). lib. bdg. 11.80 (978-0-613-54137-4(5)) Tandem Library Bks.

Jackson, Melanie. The Mask on the Cruise Ship. 2004. 192p. (J). (gr. 3-7). pap. 6.95 (978-1-55143-305-9(2)) Orca Bk. Pubs. USA.

—Shadows on the Train: A Dinah Galloway Mystery. 2007. 208p. (J). (gr. 3-7). pap. (*978-1-55143-660-9(4)) Orca Bk. Pubs.

—The Spy in the Alley. 2002. (Dinah Galloway Mystery Ser.). 176p. (J). (gr. 3-7). pap. 6.95 (978-1-55143-207-6(2)) Orca Bk. Pubs. USA.

—The Summer of the Spotted Owl. 2005. (Orca Young Readers Ser.: Book 4). (Illus.). 176p. (J). (gr. 3-7). pap. 6.95 (978-1-55143-412-4(1)) Orca Bk. Pubs. USA.

Jacobs, Edgar P. Blake & Mortimer the Yellow M. 2007. (Illus.). 48p. pap. 14.45 (*978-1-905460-21-2(X)) Cine-Book GBR. *Dist:* Biblio Distribution.

Jacobson, Jack. No Ordinary Boy. 2003. 188p. (YA). pap. 13.95 (978-1-58736-165-4(5) , Starbound Bks.) Wheatmark.

Jaffe, Michele. Bad Kitty. 2006. (Illus.). 288p. (J). 16.99 (978-0-06-078108-8(4)); lib. bdg. 17.89 (978-0-06-078109-5(2)) HarperCollins Pubs.

James, David. Sherlock Holmes & the Midnight Bell. Wilkes, Ian, ed. unabr. ed. 2003. 164p. (YA). (gr. 4-12). 30.00 (978-0-86025-292-4(2)) Henry, Ian Pubns. GBR. *Dist:* Empire Publishing Service.

James, Richard E., III. Adventures of the Elements Vol. 3: Dangerous Games. Lyle, Maryann, ed. Welch, Chad, illus. 2004. 169p. (YA). (gr. 3-12). pap. 5.95 (978-0-9675901-2-7(4)) Three Rivers Council, BSA, Inc.

Jan Baer: And the Mystery of the Silent Circus. 2005. (J). per. 10.00 (978-1-930052-29-1(4)) Cherokee Bks.

Jardine, Quintin. Wearing Purple. 1999. (Oz Blackstone Mysteries Ser.). 344p. pap. 9.99 (978-0-7472-5666-3(7)) Headline Bk. Publishing GBR. *Dist:* Independent Pubs. Group.

Jasper: A Christmas Caper. 2004. (Illus.). 85p. (J). 24.95 (978-1-928624-20-2(0)) Lucky 3 Ranch, Inc.

Javaka, Steptoe. The Scream. 2002. (Illus.). 16p. (J). 15.99 (978-0-7868-0831-1(4)) Disney Pr.

Jenkins, Jerry B. & Fabry, Chris. Canyon Echoes. 2005. (Tyndale Kids Ser.). 240p. (J). pap. 5.99 (978-1-4143-0147-1(2)) Tyndale Hse. Pubs.

—Dead End. 2006. (Red Rock Mysteries Ser.). 256p. (J). pap. 5.99 (978-1-4143-0154-9(5) , Tyndale Kids) Tyndale Hse. Pubs.

—Double Fault. 2005. (Tyndale Kids Ser.). 272p. (J). pap. 5.99 (978-1-4143-0146-4(4)) Tyndale Hse. Pubs.

—Escaping Darkness. 2006. (Red Rock Mysteries Ser.). 240p. (J). pap. 5.99 (978-1-4143-0149-5(9)) Tyndale Hse. Pubs.

—Hidden Riches. 2006. (Tyndale Kids Ser.). 272p. (J). pap. 5.99 (978-1-4143-0152-5(9)) Tyndale Hse. Pubs.

—Hollywood Holdup. 2006. (Red Rock Mysteries Ser.). 224p. (J). pap. 5.99 (978-1-4143-0151-8(0)) Tyndale Hse. Pubs.

—Instant Menace. 2006. (Tyndale Kids Ser.). 256p. (J). pap. 5.99 (978-1-4143-0148-8(0)) Tyndale Hse. Pubs.

—Phantom Writer. 2005. (Red Rock Mysteries Ser.). 256p. (J). pap. 5.99 (978-1-4143-0145-7(6)) Tyndale Hse. Pubs.

—Wind Chill. 2006. (Tyndale Kids Ser.). 240p. (J). pap. 5.99 (978-1-4143-0153-2(7) , Tyndale Kids) Tyndale Hse. Pubs.

—Windy City Danger. 2006. (Red Rock Mysteries Ser.). 246p. (J). pap. 5.99 (978-1-4143-0150-1(2)) Tyndale Hse. Pubs.

Jennings, Paul. Uncovered! Weird, Weird, Stories. l.t. ed. 2005. (J). pap. (978-0-7540-7894-4(9) , CLP 465) BBC Audio.

Jennings, Richard W. Mystery in Mt. Mole. 2003. 160p. (J). (gr. 4-6). 15.00 (978-0-618-28478-8(8)) Houghton Mifflin Co. Trade & Reference Div.

Jennings, Sharon. Franklin the Detective. 2004. (Illus.). 32p. (J). (ps-ps). lib. bdg. 10.75 (978-0-606-32910-1(2)) Tandem Library Bks.

Jennings, Sharon, et al. Franklin the Detective. Gagnon, Celeste, illus. 2005. (Kids Can Read Ser.). 32p. (J). (gr. 1-2). (978-1-55337-498-5(3)); (978-1-55337-497-8(5)) Kids Can Pr., Ltd.

Jewel Cases: Five Classic Mysteries of Theft. 2002. (Fingerprint Classics Ser.). 112p. (J). (978-1-57924-841-3(1)) Jones, Bob Univ. Pr.

Jewel Cases: Five Classic Mysteries of Theft. 2002. (gr. 7-12). lib. bdg. 14.70 (978-0-613-79334-6(X)) Tandem Library Bks.

Jimenez, Angeles. Vecinos. Prestifilippo, Pablo, illus. 2002. (Libros para Soñar Ser.). (SPA.). 36p. 15.95 (978-84-8464-141-4(4)) Kalandraka Editora, S.L. ESP. *Dist:* Lectorum Pubns., Inc.

Johansen, K. V. The Cassandra Virus. 2006. 176p. (gr. 3-7). pap. 7.95 (978-1-55143-497-1(0)) Orca Bk. Pubs. USA.

Johansen, Zdenka. When You Give of Yourself. 2006. 28p. pap. 9.95 (*978-1-4327-0059-1(6)) Outskirts Press, Inc.

Johns, Linda. Hannah West in Deep Water. 2006. (Hannah West Ser.). (Illus.). 160p. (J). (gr. 5). pap. 5.99 (978-0-14-240700-4(3) , Puffin) Penguin Group (USA) Inc.

—Hannah West in the Center of the Universe. 2007. (Hannah West Ser.). 176p. (J). pap. 5.99 (978-0-14-240756-1(9) , Puffin) Penguin Group (USA) Inc.

Johns, Linda. Hannah West on Millionaire's Row. 2007. (Hannah West Ser.). 160p. (J). (gr. 5). 6.99 (***978-0-14-240824-7(7)*** , Puffin) Penguin Group (USA) Inc.

Johnson, Jan G. Orcas Island Mystery. 1999. 125p. (J). pap. 7.99 (978-0-8280-1314-7(4)) Review & Herald Publishing Assn.

Johnson, Pete. Mind Reader. 1999. 92p. (J). 16.95 (978-0-7540-6069-7(1) , Galaxy Children's Large Print) BBC Audiobooks America.

Johnson, Rodney. Curse of the Royal Ruby: A Rinnah Two Feathers Mystery. 2002. (gr. 7-12). lib. bdg. 19.90 (978-0-613-90288-5(2)) Tandem Library Bks.

—The Secret of Dead Man's Mine. Thompson, Jill, illus. 2001. 248p. (J). (gr. 4-7). pap. 12.00 (978-0-9663473-3-3(1)) Uglytown Productions.

Johnston, Mark & Spizman, Robyn Freedman. The Secret Agents Strike Back. 2008. 160p. (J). (gr. 4-7). 16.99 (978-1-4169-0086-3(1) , Atheneum) Simon & Schuster Children's Publishing.

Johse, Jill Taylor. Beyond the Third Floor. 2003. (gr. 7-12). lib. bdg. 22.20 (978-0-613-86202-8(3)) Tandem Library Bks.

—Beyond the Third Floor. 2003. 166p. (YA). pap. 12.95 (978-0-595-28006-3(4)) iUniverse, Inc.

Jones, Elizabeth McDavid. Mystery at Skull Island. 2001. (American Girl Collection). (Illus.). (J). (978-0-606-21343-1(0)) Tandem Library Bks.

—The Night Flyers. 1999. (978-0-606-17518-0(0)) Tandem Library Bks.

—Secrets on 26th Street. 1999. (American Girl Collection Ser.). (978-0-606-17519-7(9)) Tandem Library Bks.

—Watcher in the Piney Woods. 2000. (American Girl Collection). (Illus.). (J). (978-0-606-20981-6(6)) Tandem Library Bks.

Jones, Verda Boyd. Maureen the Detective: The Age of Immigration. 2005. (Sisters in Time Ser.). 144p. (J). pap. 4.97 (978-1-59310-661-4(0)) Barbour Publishing, Inc.

Joosse, Barbara M. Alien Brain Fryout. Truesdell, Sue, illus. 2000. (Wild Willie Mystery Ser.). 108p. (J). (gr. 4-6). tchr. ed. 15.00 (978-0-395-68964-6(3) , Clarion Bks.) Houghton Mifflin Co. Trade & Reference Div.

—Ghost Trap. Truesdell, Sue, illus. 1998. (Wild Willie Mystery Ser.). 80p. (J). (gr. 4-6). tchr. ed. 15.00 (978-0-395-66587-9(6) , Clarion Bks.) Houghton Mifflin Co. Trade & Reference Div.

Jorda, Jordi Suris. La Chica de los Zapatos Verdes. 1998. (SPA.). (gr. 7-12). lib. bdg. 14.10 (978-0-613-80705-0(7)) Tandem Library Bks.

Joubert, Dereck & Joubert, Beverly. Whispers: The Story of a Baby Elephant. 2000. (Illus.). 32p. (gr. k-3). 11.99 (978-0-7868-0454-2(8)) Disney Pr.

Julian, B. T. Mirror Me This. 2006. 172p. per. 12.95 (978-1-59886-056-6(9)) Tate Publishing & Enterprises, L.L.C.

Kabeto, Rita Traut. Weird Steffi. 2001. 164p. pap. 12.95 (978-0-595-19047-8(2)) iUniverse, Inc.

Kadono, Kouhei. Boogiepop & Others. 2006. (Illus.). 250p. pap. 9.99 (978-1-933164-16-8(6)) Seven Seas Entertainment, LLC.

—Boogiepop Doesn't Laugh, Vol. 1. 2006. 192p. pap. 10.99 (978-1-933164-18-2(2)) Seven Seas Entertainment, LLC.

Kallevig, Christine P. Please Pass Grandma's Leg: Aka, the Case of the Sacked Potatoes. 2003. (Illus.). 128p. (J). per. 9.95 (978-0-9628769-3-6(3)) Storytime Ink International.

Kanzaka, Hajime & Yoshinaka, Shoko. Slayers Super-Explosive Demon Story 5: City of Lost Souls, Vol. 5. 2004. (Slayers Ser.). (Illus.). 184p. pap. 9.99 (978-1-58664-915-9(9) , CMX 64605G, CPM Manga) Central Park Media Corp.

Karbo, Karen. Minerva Clark Gets a Clue. (J). 2006. 256p. pap. 6.95 (978-1-58234-747-9(6)); 2005. 224p. 16.95 (978-1-58234-677-9(1)) Bloomsbury Publishing. (Bloomsbury Children).

—Minerva Clark Gives up the Ghost. 2007. 244p. (J). (gr. 5 up). 16.95 (***978-1-58234-679-3(8)*** , Bloomsbury Children) Bloomsbury Publishing.

Karbo, Karen. Minerva Clark Goes to the Dogs. 2006. 244p. (YA). 16.95 (978-1-58234-678-6(X) , Bloomsbury Children) Bloomsbury Publishing.

Karkevandian, Parisa. No Way Out. 2004. 108p. (YA). 20.95 (978-0-595-66242-5(0)); pap. 10.95 (978-0-595-31011-1(7)) iUniverse, Inc.

Karr, Kathleen. The Seventh Knot. 2003. (Illus.). 192p. (J). 15.95 (978-0-7614-5135-8(8)) Cavendish, Marshall Corp.

Kastner, Erich. Emil & the Detectives, Level 3. 2001. (Illus.). 64p. (C). pap. 9.00 (978-0-582-42699-3(5)) Longman Publishing Group.

—Emil & the Detectives. Stahl, J. D., tr. Trier, Walter & Walter, Trier, illus. 2007. 220p. (J). (gr. 3 up). 17.95 (978-1-58567-586-9(5)) Overlook Pr., The.

—Emil und die Detektive. 2000. Tr. of Emil & the Detective. (GER.). (YA). pap. 12.95 (978-3-423-70500-4(0)) Deutscher Taschenbuch Verlag GmbH & Co KG DEU. *Dist:* Distribooks, Inc.

Katschke, Judy. Case of the Candy Cane Clue. 2002. (gr. 3-6). lib. bdg. 12.40 (978-0-613-64697-0(5)) Tandem Library Bks.

—The Case of the Weird Science Mystery. 2002. (New Adventures of Mary-Kate & Ashley Ser.: 29). (Illus.). 96p. (gr. 1-5). mass mkt. 4.50 (978-0-06-106651-1(6)) HarperCollins Pubs.

—The Case of the Wild Wolf River. 1998. (New Adventures of Mary-Kate & Ashley Ser.). 87p. (J). (gr. 2-7). pap. 3.99 (978-0-590-29401-0(6)) Scholastic, Inc.

Kaula, Radhika. The Mysterious Robbery. Kaula, Radhika, illus. 2000. (Illus.). 16p. (J). (gr. k-5). pap. 12.00 (978-0-9653862-3-4(6)) Transnational Computing Services.

Kchodl, Joseph 'PaleoJoe' & Caszatt-Allen, Wendy. The Disappearance of Dinosaur Sue. 2006. (PaleoJoe's Dinosaur Detective Club Ser.: 1). (Illus.). 150p. (J). pap. (978-1-934133-03-3(5)) Mackinac Island Pr., Inc.

—Raptor's Revenge. 2007. (Illus.). 160p. (J). pap. 6.95 (***978-1-934133-37-8(X)***) Mackinac Island Pr., Inc.

—Secret Sabertooth. 2007. (PaleoJoe's Dinosaur Detective Club Ser.: 3). (Illus.). 140p. (J). pap. 6.95 (***978-1-934133-10-1(8)***) Mackinac Island Pr., Inc.

Keane, Dave. The Art Teacher's Vanishing Masterpie. Keane, Dave, illus. 2007. (J). 128p. 15.99 (***978-0-06-085472-0(3));*** (Joe Sherlock Ser.: No. 5). 96p. pap. 3.99 (***978-0-06-085471-3(5)*** , Harper Trophy) HarperCollins Pubs.

—The Haunted Toolshed. Keane, Dave, illus. 2006. (Joe Sherlock Ser.). 128p. (J). pap. 3.99 (978-0-06-076188-2(1) , Harper Trophy) HarperCollins Pubs.

—The Headless Mummy. Keane, Dave, illus. 2007. (Joe Sherlock Ser.: No. 4). (Illus.). 128p. (J). pap. 3.99 (978-0-06-076192-9(X) , Harper Trophy) HarperCollins Pubs.

—The Missing Monkey-Eye Diamond. Keane, Dave, illus. 2006. (Joe Sherlock Ser.: No. 3). (Illus.). 128p. (J). 15.99 (978-0-06-076191-2(1)) HarperCollins Pubs.

—The Neighborhood Stink. Keane, Dave, illus. 2006. (Joe Sherlock Ser.). 112p. (J). pap. 3.99 (978-0-06-076186-8(5) , Harper Trophy) HarperCollins Pubs.

—The Neighborhood Stink: Case 000002. Keane, Dave, illus. 2006. (Joe Sherlock Ser.). (Illus.). 112p. (J). 15.99 (978-0-06-076187-5(3)) HarperCollins Pubs.

Keane, David & Keane, Dave. The Missing Monkey-Eye Diamond. Keane, Dave, illus. 2006. (Joe Sherlock Ser.). (Illus.). 128p. (J). pap. 3.99 (978-0-06-076190-5(3) , Harper Trophy) HarperCollins Pubs.

Keene, Carolyn. Action! ed. 2005. (Nancy Drew Ser.: 6). 138p. (J). lib. bdg. 15.00 (978-1-59054-809-7(4)) Fitzgerald Bks.

—Action!, No. 6. 2004. (Nancy Drew Ser.: No. 6). 144p. (J). pap. 4.99 (978-0-689-86571-8(6) , Aladdin) Simon & Schuster Children's Publishing.

—Alien in the Classroom. Acardo, Anthony, illus. 2004. 72p. (J). lib. bdg. 15.00 (***978-1-4242-0369-7(4)***) Fitzgerald Bks.

—Alien in the Classroom. 1998. (Nancy Drew Notebooks: No. 23). (Illus.). 80p. (J). (gr. k-3). pap. 3.99 (978-0-671-00818-5(8) , Aladdin) Simon & Schuster Children's Publishing.

—Alien in the Classroom. 1998. (Nancy Drew Notebooks: No. 23). (J). (gr. k-3). 10.79 (978-0-606-13653-2(3)) Tandem Library Bks.

—The Apple Bandit. Jones, Jan Naimo, illus. 2005. 74p. (J). lib. bdg. 15.00 (***978-1-4242-0917-0(X)***) Fitzgerald Bks.

—The Apple Bandit. Jones, Jan Naimo, illus. Frost, Michael, photos by. 2005. (Nancy Drew Notebooks: Vol. 68). 80p. (J). pap. 3.99 (978-1-4169-0829-6(3) , Aladdin) Simon & Schuster Children's Publishing.

—The Apple Bandit. Jones, Jan Naimo, illus. 2005. 74p. (J). (978-1-4156-2882-9(3) , Aladdin) Simon & Schuster Children's Publishing.

—Bad Times, Big Crimes. 2005. 139p. (J). lib. bdg. 15.00 (***978-1-4242-0242-3(6)***) Fitzgerald Bks.

—Bad Times, Big Crimes. 2005. (Nancy Drew Ser.: Vol. 14). 160p. (J). (gr. 3-7). pap. 4.99 (978-0-689-87883-1(4) , Aladdin) Simon & Schuster Children's Publishing.

—The Best of Nancy Drew Classic Collection: The Hidden Staircase; The Ghost of Blackwood Hall; The Thirteenth Pearl, Vol. 2. 2004. (Nancy Drew Mystery Stories: 2). (Illus.). 546p. (J). (gr. 3-8). 12.99 (978-0-448-44080-4(6) , Grosset & Dunlap) Penguin Group (USA) Inc.

—The Best of Nancy Drew Classic Collection Vol. 1: The Secret of the Old Clock; The Bungalow Mystery; The Mystery of the 99 Steps. 2004. (Nancy Drew Mystery Stories: 1). 546p. (J). (gr. 3-8). 12.99 (978-0-448-44079-8(2) , Grosset & Dunlap) Penguin Group (USA) Inc.

—The Black Velvet Mystery. 1999. (Nancy Drew Notebooks: No. 32). (J). (gr. k-3). (978-0-606-19059-6(7)) Tandem Library Bks.

—The Bungalow Mystery, No. 3. Tandy, Russell H., illus. fac. ed. 2004. (Nancy Drew Mystery Stories: No. 3). 204p. (J). (gr. 4-7). reprint ed. 17.95 (978-1-55709-157-4(9)) Applewood Bks.

—The Bunny-Hop Hoax. Jones, Jan Naimo, illus. 2005. 70p. (J). lib. bdg. 15.00 (***978-1-4242-0921-7(8)***) Fitzgerald Bks.

—The Bunny-Hop Hoax. Jones, Jan Naimo, illus. Frost, Michael, photos by. 2005. (Nancy Drew Notebooks). 80p. (J). pap. 3.99 (978-0-689-87754-4(4) , Aladdin) Simon & Schuster Children's Publishing.

—Candy Is Dandy. Jones, Jan Naimo, illus. 2000. (Nancy Drew Notebooks: No. 38). 80p. (gr. k-3). mass mkt. 3.99 (978-0-671-04269-1(6) , Aladdin) Simon & Schuster Children's Publishing.

—Candy Is Dandy. 2002. (gr. 3-6). lib. bdg. 11.80 (978-0-613-62549-4(8)) Tandem Library Bks.

—Captive Witness. 2005. (Nancy Drew Mystery Stories: No. 64). (Illus.). 192p. (J). (gr. 3-8). 6.99 (978-0-448-43695-1(7) , Grosset & Dunlap) Penguin Group (USA) Inc.

—The Case of Capital Intrigue. 1998. (Nancy Drew Mystery Stories: No. 142). (J). (gr. 3-6). 11.64 (978-0-606-13644-0(4)) Tandem Library Bks.

—The Case of the Creative Crime. 2002. (Nancy Drew Mystery Stories: Vol. 166). (Illus.). 160p. (J). (gr. 3-6). pap. 4.99 (978-0-7434-3748-6(9) , Aladdin) Simon & Schuster Children's Publishing.

—The Case of the Creative Crime. 2002. (gr. 5-8). lib. bdg. 13.00 (978-0-613-45020-1(5)) Tandem Library Bks.

—The Case of the Lost Song. 2001. (Nancy Drew Mystery Stories: Vol. 162). (Illus.). 160p. (J). (gr. 3-6). pap. 4.99 (978-0-7434-0688-8(5) , Aladdin) Simon & Schuster Children's Publishing.

—The Case of the Lost Song. 2001. (gr. 5-8). lib. bdg. 13.00 (978-0-613-63388-8(1)) Tandem Library Bks.

—Case of the Sneaky Snowman. Pamintuan, Macky, illus. 2006. (Nancy Drew & the Clue Crew Ser.: No. 5). 96p. (J). pap. 3.99 (978-1-4169-1254-5(1) , Aladdin) Simon & Schuster Children's Publishing.

—The Case of the Vanishing Veil. 2001. (Nancy Drew on Campus Ser.: Vol. 83). (Illus.). 160p. (J). (gr. 3-6). reprint ed. pap. 4.99 (978-0-7434-2344-1(5) , Aladdin) Simon & Schuster Children's Publishing.

—The Case of the Vanishing Veil. 2001. (gr. 5-8). lib. bdg. 13.00 (978-0-613-63390-1(3)) Tandem Library Bks.

—The Chinese New Year Mystery. 2001. (gr. 3-6). lib. bdg. 11.80 (978-0-613-58356-5(6)) Tandem Library Bks.

—The Chocolate-Covered Contest. 1999. (Nancy Drew Mystery Stories: No. 151). 160p. (J). (gr. 3-6). pap. 4.99 (978-0-671-03443-6(X) , Aladdin) Simon & Schuster Children's Publishing.

—The Chocolate-Covered Contest. 1999. (gr. 5-8). lib. bdg. 13.00 (978-0-613-21340-0(8)); (Nancy Drew Mystery Stories: No. 151). (J). (gr. 3-6). 11.64 (978-0-606-19058-9(9)) Tandem Library Bks.

—The Cinderella Ballet Mystery. Pamintuan, Macky, illus. 2006. (Nancy Drew & the Clue Crew Ser.: No. 4). 96p. (J). pap. 3.99 (978-1-4169-1256-9(8) , Aladdin) Simon & Schuster Children's Publishing.

—The Cinderella Ballet Mystery. 2007. (Nancy Drew & the Clue Crew Ser.). 96p. (J). (gr. 2-4). 24.21 (***978-1-59961-345-1(X)***) Spotlight.

—Close Encounters. 2006. (Nancy Drew Ser.: No. 21). 176p. (J). pap. 4.99 (978-1-4169-1245-3(2) , Aladdin) Simon & Schuster Children's Publishing.

—The Clue in the Diary. Tandy, Russell H., illus. fac. ed. 2004. (Nancy Drew Mystery Stories: No. 7). 228p. (J). (gr. 4-7). reprint ed. 17.95 (978-1-55709-161-1(7)) Applewood Bks.

—The Clue in the Jewel Box, Vol. 20. Tandy, Russell H., illus. 2005. (Nancy Drew Mystery Stories). 216p. (J). (gr. 5-9). 17.95 (978-1-55709-277-9(X)) Applewood Bks.

—The Clue of the Broken Locket. Tandy, Russell H., illus. fac. ed. 2004. (Nancy Drew Mystery Stories: No. 11). 228p. (J). (gr. 4-7). reprint ed. 14.95 (978-1-55709-165-9(X)) Applewood Bks.

—The Clue of the Tapping Heels. Tandy, Russell H., illus. 2001. (Nancy Drew Mystery Stories: Vol. 16). 214p. (J). (gr. 4-7). per. 14.95 (978-1-55709-262-5(1)) Applewood Bks.

—The Clues Challenge. 2001. (Nancy Drew Mystery Stories: Vol. 163). 160p. (J). pap. 4.99 (978-0-7434-0689-5(3) , Aladdin) Simon & Schuster Children's Publishing.

—The Clues Challenge. 2003. (gr. 5-8). lib. bdg. 13.00 (978-0-613-63395-6(4)) Tandem Library Bks.

—Clues to Good Sleuthing. 2007. (Nancy Drew Mystery Stories). 160p. (J). (gr. 3-8). 7.99 (978-0-448-44568-7(9) , Grosset & Dunlap) Penguin Group (USA) Inc.

—The Crime Lab Case. 2002. (gr. 5-8). lib. bdg. 13.00 (978-0-613-45025-6(6)) Tandem Library Bks.

—Danger on the Great Lakes. 2003. (gr. 5-8). lib. bdg. 13.00 (978-0-613-66491-2(4)) Tandem Library Bks.

—Dangerous Plays. 2006. (J). (Nancy Drew Ser.: No. 16). 160p. pap. 4.99 (978-1-4169-0605-6(3)); 146p. (978-1-4156-5040-0(3)) Simon & Schuster Children's Publishing. (Aladdin).

—Dare at the Fair. 1998. (Nancy Drew Notebooks: No. 25). (J). (gr. 2-4). (978-0-606-13655-6(X)) Tandem Library Bks.

—The Dashing Dog Mystery. Jones, Jan Naimo, illus. 2001. 73p. (gr. 3-6). lib. bdg. 11.80 (978-0-613-58360-2(4)) Tandem Library Bks.

—The Dollhouse Mystery. Jones, Jan Naimo, illus. 2004. 68p. (J). lib. bdg. 15.00 (***978-1-4242-0927-9(7)***) Fitzgerald Bks.

—The Dollhouse Mystery. Jones, Jan Naimo, illus. 2004. (Nancy Drew Notebooks). 80p. (J). pap. 4.99 (978-0-689-86534-3(1) , Aladdin) Simon & Schuster Children's Publishing.

—The Dollhouse Mystery. Jones, Jan Naimo, illus. 2004. 68p. (J). (gr. 1-4). lib. bdg. 12.10 (978-0-613-95311-5(8)) Tandem Library Bks.

—Double Horror of Fenley Place. 2001. (gr. 5-8). lib. bdg. 13.00 (978-0-613-63401-4(2)) Tandem Library Bks.

—The Double Horror of Fenley Place. 2001. (Nancy Drew on Campus Ser.: Vol. 79). (Illus.). 160p. (J). (gr. 3-6). reprint ed. pap. 4.99 (978-0-7434-2343-4(7) , Aladdin) Simon & Schuster Children's Publishing.

—Dressed to Steal. 2007. (Nancy Drew Ser.: No. 22). 160p. (J). pap. 4.99 (978-1-4169-3385-4(9) , Aladdin) Simon & Schuster Children's Publishing.

—The E-Mail Mystery, Vol. 144. 1998. (Nancy Drew Mystery Stories: No. 144). 160p. (gr. 3-6). pap. 4.99 (978-0-671-00121-6(3) , Aladdin) Simon & Schuster Children's Publishing.

—The E-Mail Mystery. 1998. (Nancy Drew Mystery Stories: No. 144). (J). (gr. 3-6). 11.64 (978-0-606-13646-4(0)) Tandem Library Bks.

—En Garde. 2006. (Nancy Drew Ser.: No. 17). 160p. (J). pap. 4.99 (978-1-4169-0603-2(7)) Simon & Schuster Children's Publishing.

—False Notes. 2004. (Nancy Drew Ser.: No. 3). 160p. (J). pap. 4.99 (978-0-689-86568-8(6) , Aladdin) Simon & Schuster Children's Publishing.

—The Fashion Disaster. Pamintuan, Macky, illus. 2007. (Nancy Drew & the Clue Crew Ser.: No. 6). 96p. (J). pap. 3.99 (978-1-4169-3485-1(5) , Aladdin) Simon & Schuster Children's Publishing.

—Fishing for Clues. 2007. (Nancy Drew Ser.: No. 26). 144p. (J). pap. 4.99 (***978-1-4169-3525-4(8)*** , Aladdin) Simon & Schuster Children's Publishing.

—The Flying Saucer Mystery, Vol. 58. 2005. (Nancy Drew Mystery Stories). (Illus.). 176p. (J). (gr. 3-9). 6.99 (978-0-448-43689-0(2) , Grosset & Dunlap) Penguin Group (USA) Inc.

—Framed. (J). 2006. 149p. (978-1-4156-4605-2(8)); 2005. 160p. pap. 4.99 (978-0-689-87863-3(X)) Simon & Schuster Children's Publishing. (Aladdin).

—Getting Burned. 2006. (Nancy Drew Ser.: No. 21). 160p. (J). pap. 4.99 (978-0-689-87703-2(X) , Aladdin) Simon & Schuster Children's Publishing.

—The Greek Symbol Mystery. 2005. (Nancy Drew Mystery Stories: No. 60). (Illus.). 182p. (J). (gr. 3-8). pap. 6.99 (978-0-448-43691-3(4) , Grosset & Dunlap) Penguin Group (USA) Inc.

—The Gumdrop Ghost. 1999. (Nancy Drew Notebooks: No. 33). (J). (gr. k-3). (978-0-606-19060-2(0)) Tandem Library Bks.

—The Hidden Staircase, No. 2. Tandy, Russell H., illus. fac. ed. 2004. (Nancy Drew Mystery Stories: No. 2). 206p. (J). (gr. 4-7). reprint ed. 17.95 (978-1-55709-156-7(0)) Applewood Bks.

—The Hidden Treasures. Accardo, Anthony, illus. 1998. (Nancy Drew Notebooks: No. 24). 80p. (J). (gr. k-3). pap. 3.99 (978-0-671-00819-2(6) , Aladdin) Simon & Schuster Children's Publishing.

—The Hidden Treasures. 1998. (Nancy Drew Notebooks: No. 24). (J). (gr. k-3). 10.79 (978-0-606-13654-9(1)) Tandem Library Bks.

—High Risk. 2004. (Nancy Drew Ser.). 160p. mass mkt. 4.99 (978-0-689-86569-5(4) , Aladdin) Simon & Schuster Children's Publishing.

—Intruder. 2007. (Nancy Drew Ser.: No. 27). 160p. (J). pap. 4.99 (***978-1-4169-3526-1(6)*** , Aladdin) Simon & Schuster Children's Publishing.

—The Kachina Doll Mystery, Vol. 62. 2005. (Nancy Drew Mystery Stories). (Illus.). 192p. (J). (gr. 3-8). 6.99 (978-0-448-43693-7(0) , Grosset & Dunlap) Penguin Group (USA) Inc.

—The Key in the Satin Pocket. 2000. (gr. 5-8). lib. bdg. 13.00 (978-0-613-21851-1(5)) Tandem Library Bks.

—The Kitten Caper. Jones, Jan Naimo, illus. 2005. 72p. (J). lib. bdg. 15.00 (***978-1-4242-0916-3(1)***) Fitzgerald Bks.

—The Kitten Caper. Jones, Jan Naimo, illus. Frost, Michael, photos by. 2005. (Nancy Drew Notebooks: No. 69). 80p. (J). (gr. 1-4). pap. 3.99 (978-1-4169-0830-2(7) , Aladdin) Simon & Schuster Children's Publishing.

—The Legend of the Emerald Lady. 2000. (Nancy Drew Mystery Stories: No. 154). 160p. (J). (gr. 3-6). pap. 4.99 (978-0-671-04262-2(9) , Aladdin) Simon & Schuster Children's Publishing.

—Legend of the Emerald Lady. 2000. (gr. 5-8). lib. bdg. 13.00 (978-0-613-27933-8(6)) Tandem Library Bks.

—The Lost Files of Nancy Drew. 2007. (Nancy Drew Mystery Stories). 32p. (J). (gr. 3-9). 19.99 (***978-0-448-44647-9(2)*** , Grosset & Dunlap) Penguin Group (USA) Inc.

—The Message in the Haunted Mansion. 2001. 154p. (J). (gr. 4-7). per. 13.00 (978-0-613-63431-1(4)) Tandem Library Bks.

—The Message in the Hollow Oak. Tandy, Russell H., illus. fac. ed. 2004. (Nancy Drew Mystery Stories Ser.: No. 12). 210p. (J). (gr. 4-7). 17.95 (978-1-55709-258-8(3)) Applewood Bks.

—Mistletoe Mystery. 2002. (Nancy Drew Mystery Stories). 160p. (J). pap. 4.99 (978-0-7434-3765-3(9) , Aladdin) Simon & Schuster Children's Publishing.

—Mistletoe Mystery. 2002. (gr. 5-8). lib. bdg. 13.00 (978-0-613-63432-8(2)) Tandem Library Bks.

—Murder on the Set. 2007. (Nancy Drew Ser.: No. 24). 176p. (J). pap. 4.99 (978-1-4169-3397-7(2) , Aladdin) Simon & Schuster Children's Publishing.

—Mystery at Moorsea Manor. 1999. (Nancy Drew Mystery Stories: No. 150). (J). (gr. 3-6). (978-0-606-19038-1(4)) Tandem Library Bks.

—Mystery by Moonlight. 2002. (Nancy Drew Mystery Stories: Vol. 167). 160p. (J). (gr. 3-7). pap. 4.99 (978-0-7434-3762-2(4) , Aladdin) Simon & Schuster Children's Publishing.

—Mystery by Moonlight. 2002. (gr. 5-8). lib. bdg. 13.00 (978-0-613-45083-6(3)) Tandem Library Bks.

—The Mystery of Mother Wolf. 2002. (Nancy Drew Mystery Stories: Vol. 164). 160p. (J). pap. 4.99 (978-0-7434-3743-1(8) , Aladdin) Simon & Schuster Children's Publishing.

—The Mystery of the Ivory Charm, No. 13. Tandy, Russell H., illus. fac. ed. 2004. (Nancy Drew Mystery Stories: No. 13). 228p. (J). (gr. 4-7). 14.95 (978-1-55709-259-5(1)) Applewood Bks.

—The Mystery of the Moss-Covered Mansion. Tandy, Russell H., illus. 2003. (Nancy Drew Mystery Stories). 215p. (J). (gr. 4-7). per. 14.95 (978-1-55709-264-9(8)) Applewood Bks.

—Mystery of the Mother Wolf. 2002. (gr. 5-8). lib. bdg. 13.00 (978-0-613-45084-3(1)) Tandem Library Bks.

—Mystery on Maui. 1998. (Nancy Drew Mystery Stories: No. 143). 160p. (gr. 3-6). mass mkt. 4.99 (978-0-671-00753-9(X) , Aladdin) Simon & Schuster Children's Publishing.

—Mystery on Maui. 1998. (Nancy Drew Mystery Stories: No. 143). (J). (gr. 3-6). (978-0-606-13645-7(2)) Tandem Library Bks.

—Nancy Drew, Vols. 1-6. 1998. (J). 22.98 (978-0-448-41673-1(5) , Grosset & Dunlap) Penguin Group (USA) Inc.

—Nancy Drew: The Scarlet Macaw Scandal. Frost, Michael, illus. 2004. (Nancy Drew Ser.). 160p. (J). pap. 4.99 (978-0-689-86844-3(8) , Aladdin) Simon & Schuster Children's Publishing.

—Nancy Drew Collection. 2004. 149p. (978-1-4169-0079-5(9)) Simon & Schuster Children's Publishing.

—Nancy Drew Girl Detective (Boxed Set) Sleuth Set: Without a Trace; A Race Against Time; False Notes; High Risk. 2004. (Nancy Drew Ser.). (Illus.). 640p. (J). pap. 19.99 (978-0-689-03691-0(4) , Aladdin) Simon & Schuster Children's Publishing.

—The Nancy Drew Pocketbook Mysteries. 2007. (Nancy Drew Mystery Stories). 192p. (J). (gr. 3-8). 19.99 (978-0-448-44544-1(1) , Grosset & Dunlap) Penguin Group (USA) Inc.

—Nancy Drew Starter Set. 2007. (Nancy Drew Ser.). (J). (gr. 3-8). lthr. 25.98 (*978-0-448-44801-5(7) , Grosset & Dunlap) Penguin Group (USA) Inc.

—Nancy's Mysterious Letter. Tandy, Russell H., illus. fac. ed. 2004. (Nancy Drew Mystery Stories Ser.: No. 8). 210p. (J). (gr. 4-7). reprint ed. 14.95 (978-1-55709-162-8(5)) Applewood Bks.

—Once upon a Crime. 2006. (J). (Nancy Drew Ser.: No. 2). 192p. pap. 5.99 (978-1-4169-1248-4(7)); 185p. (978-1-4156-7698-1(4)) Simon & Schuster Children's Publishing. (Aladdin).

—The Orchid Thief. 2006. (Nancy Drew Ser.: No. 19). 144p. (J). pap. 4.99 (978-1-4169-0980-4(X) , Aladdin) Simon & Schuster Children's Publishing.

—Pit of Vipers. 2006. (Nancy Drew Ser.: No. 18). 160p. (J). pap. 4.99 (978-1-4169-1180-7(4) , Aladdin) Simon & Schuster Children's Publishing.

—Pony Problems. Pamintuan, Macky, illus. 2006. (Nancy Drew & the Clue Crew Ser.: No. 3). 96p. (J). pap. 3.99 (978-1-4169-1815-8(9) , Aladdin) Simon & Schuster Children's Publishing.

—Pony Problems. 2007. (Nancy Drew & the Clue Crew Ser.). 96p. (J). (gr. 2-4). 24.21 (*978-1-59961-346-8(8)) Spotlight.

—The Quest of the Missing Map. 2004. (Nancy Drew Mystery Stories: No. 19). 228p. (J). (gr. 4-7). 17.95 (978-1-55709-265-6(6)) Applewood Bks.

—Real Fake. 2007. (Nancy Drew Ser.). 224p. (J). pap. 5.99 (978-1-4169-3881-1(8) , Aladdin) Simon & Schuster Children's Publishing.

—Riding Club Crime. 2003. (gr. 5-8). lib. bdg. 13.00 (978-0-613-65082-3(4)) Tandem Library Bks.

—Scream for Ice Cream. Pamintuan, Macky, illus. 2006. (Nancy Drew & the Clue Crew Ser.: No. 2). 96p. (J). pap. 3.99 (978-1-4169-1253-8(3) , Aladdin) Simon & Schuster Children's Publishing.

—Scream for Ice Cream. 2007. (Nancy Drew & the Clue Crew Ser.). 96p. (J). (gr. 2-4). 24.21 (*978-1-59961-347-5(6)) Spotlight.

—The Secret in the Old Attic. 2005. (Nancy Drew Mystery Stories). (Illus.). 210p. (J). (gr. 4-7). 17.95 (978-1-55709-278-6(8)) Applewood Bks.

—The Secret in the Old Lace. 2005. (Nancy Drew Mystery Stories: No. 59). (Illus.). 176p. (J). (gr. 3-9). 6.99 (978-0-448-43690-6(6) , Grosset & Dunlap) Penguin Group (USA) Inc.

—Secret in the Stars. 2000. lib. bdg. 13.00 (978-0-613-63459-5(4)) Tandem Library Bks.

—The Secret of Red Gate Farm, No. 6. Tandy, Russell H., illus. fac. ed. 2004. (Nancy Drew Mystery Stories: No. 6). 228p. (J). (gr. 4-7). reprint ed. 17.95 (978-1-55709-160-4(9)) Applewood Bks.

—The Secret of Shadow Ranch, No. 5. Tandy, Russell H., illus. fac. ed. 2004. (Nancy Drew Mystery Stories: No. 5). 224p. (J). (gr. 4-7). reprint ed. 17.95 (978-1-55709-159-8(5)) Applewood Bks.

—The Secret of Shady Glen. 2001. (Nancy Drew Mystery Stories: Vol. 85). 160p. (J). (gr. 3-6). reprint ed. pap. 4.99 (978-0-7434-1936-9(7) , Aladdin) Simon & Schuster Children's Publishing.

—The Secret of Shady Glen. 2001. (gr. 5-8). lib. bdg. 13.00 (978-0-613-63460-1(8)) Tandem Library Bks.

—The Secret of the Fiery Chamber. 2001. (Nancy Drew Mystery Stories: Vol. 159). (Illus.). 160p. (J). (gr. 3-6). pap. 4.99 (978-0-7434-0662-8(1) , Aladdin) Simon & Schuster Children's Publishing.

—Secret of the Fiery Chamber. 2002. (gr. 5-8). lib. bdg. 13.00 (978-0-613-63461-8(6)) Tandem Library Bks.

—The Secret of the Old Clock. Tandy, Russell H., illus. fac. ed. 2004. (Nancy Drew Mystery Stories: No. 1). 210p. (J). (gr. 4-7). reprint ed. 17.95 (978-1-55709-155-0(2)) Applewood Bks.

—Secret of the Spa, Vol. 9. 2005. (Nancy Drew Ser.). 160p. (J). pap. 4.99 (978-0-689-86858-0(8) , Aladdin) Simon & Schuster Children's Publishing.

—The Sign of the Twisted Candles, No. 9. Tandy, Russell H., illus. fac. ed. 2004. (Nancy Drew Mystery Stories: No. 9). 210p. (J). (gr. 4-7). reprint ed. 17.95 (978-1-55709-163-5(3)) Applewood Bks.

—The Singing Suspects. Jones, Jan, illus. 2005. 69p. (J). lib. bdg. 15.00 (*978-1-4242-0918-7(8)) Fitzgerald Bks.

—Ski School Sneak. Pamintuan, Macky, illus. 2007. (Nancy Drew & the Clue Crew Ser.: No. 11). 96p. (J). (gr. 1-4). pap. 3.99 (*978-1-4169-4936-7(4) , Aladdin) Simon & Schuster Children's Publishing.

—Sleepover Sleuths. Pamintuan, Macky, illus. 2006. (Nancy Drew & the Clue Crew Ser.: No. 1). 96p. (J). (gr. 1-4). pap. 3.99 (978-1-4169-1255-2(X) , Aladdin) Simon & Schuster Children's Publishing.

—Sleepover Sleuths. 2007. (Nancy Drew & the Clue Crew Ser.). 96p. (J). (gr. 2-4). 24.21 (*978-1-59961-348-2(4)) Spotlight.

—Snowman Surprise. Casale, Paul, illus. Frost, Michael, photos by. 2004. (Nancy Drew Notebooks: No. 63). 80p. (J). pap. 3.99 (978-0-689-87411-6(1) , Aladdin) Simon & Schuster Children's Publishing.

—Space Case. Jones, Jan, illus. 2004. 68p. (J). lib. bdg. 15.00 (*978-1-4242-0924-8(2)) Fitzgerald Bks.

—The Stolen Relic. 2004. (Nancy Drew Ser.: #7). 160p. mass mkt. 4.99 (978-0-689-86843-6(X) , Aladdin) Simon & Schuster Children's Publishing.

—Strike-Out Scare. Jones, Jan Naimo, illus. 2005. 70p. (J). (978-1-4155-7741-7(2) , Aladdin) Simon & Schuster Children's Publishing.

—The Swami's Ring. 2005. (Nancy Drew Mystery Stories Ser.: Vol. 61). (Illus.). 192p. (J). (gr. 3-8). 6.99 (978-0-448-43692-0(2) , Grosset & Dunlap) Penguin Group (USA) Inc.

—Ticket Trouble. Pamintuan, Macky, illus. 2007. (Nancy Drew & the Clue Crew Ser.: No. 10). 87p. (J). (gr. 1-4). per. 3.99 (*978-1-4169-4733-2(7) , Aladdin) Simon & Schuster Children's Publishing.

—Trade Wind Danger. 2005. 148p. (J). lib. bdg. 15.00 (*978-1-4242-0243-0(4)) Fitzgerald Bks.

—Trails of Treachery. 2007. (Nancy Drew Ser.). 144p. (J). pap. 4.99 (*978-1-4169-3524-7(X) , Aladdin) Simon & Schuster Children's Publishing.

—The Triple Hoax, Vol. 57. 2005. (Nancy Drew Mystery Stories: No. 57). (Illus.). 192p. (J). (gr. 3-9). 6.99 (978-0-448-43688-3(4) , Grosset & Dunlap) Penguin Group (USA) Inc.

—Troubled Waters. 2007. (Nancy Drew Ser.). 160p. (J). pap. 4.99 (978-1-4169-2513-2(9) , Aladdin) Simon & Schuster Children's Publishing.

—The Twin Dilemma. 2005. (Nancy Drew Mystery Stories: Vol. 63). (Illus.). 196p. (J). (gr. 3-8). pap. 6.99 (978-0-448-43694-4(9) , Grosset & Dunlap) Penguin Group (USA) Inc.

—Uncivil Acts. 2005. (Nancy Drew Ser.). 160p. (J). pap. 4.99 (978-0-689-86937-2(1) , Aladdin) Simon & Schuster Children's Publishing.

—Valentine's Day Secret. 2007. (Nancy Drew & the Clue Crew Ser.). 96p. (J). pap. 3.99 (*978-1-4169-4944-2(5) , Aladdin) Simon & Schuster Children's Publishing.

—The Walkie-Talkie Mystery. 2001. (Nancy Drew Notebooks: No. 43). (Illus.). 80p. (J). (gr. k-3). pap. 3.99 (978-0-7434-0691-8(5) , Aladdin) Simon & Schuster Children's Publishing.

—The Walkie-Talkie Mystery. 2002. (gr. 3-6). lib. bdg. 11.80 (978-0-613-58393-0(0)) Tandem Library Bks.

—Where's Nancy? 2005. (Nancy Drew Ser.). 176p. (J). pap. 4.99 (978-1-4169-0034-4(9) , Aladdin) Simon & Schuster Children's Publishing.

—The Whispering Statue, No. 14. 2000. (Nancy Drew Mystery Stories Ser.: No. 14). (Illus.). 228p. (J). (gr. 4-7). 17.95 (978-1-55709-260-1(5)) Applewood Bks.

—The Wild Cat Crime. 1998. (Nancy Drew Mystery Stories: No. 141). (J). (gr. 3-6). (978-0-606-13643-3(6)) Tandem Library Bks.

—Without a Trace. ed. 2005. (Nancy Drew Ser.: 1). (Illus.). 154p. (J). lib. bdg. 15.00 (978-1-59054-819-6(1)) Fitzgerald Bks.

—Without a Trace. 2004. (Nancy Drew Ser.: No. 1). 160p. (J). pap. 4.99 (978-0-689-86566-4(X) , Aladdin) Simon & Schuster Children's Publishing.

Keene, Carolyn. Zoo Clue. Jones, Jan, illus. 2005. 74p. (J). lib. bdg. 15.00 (*978-1-4242-0919-4(6)) Fitzgerald Bks.

Keene, Carolyn & Benson, Mildred Wirt. The Mystery at Lilac Inn. Tandy, Russell H., illus. fac. ed. 2004. (Nancy Drew Mystery Stories Ser.: No. 4). 224p. (J). (gr. 4-7). reprint ed. 17.95 (978-1-55709-158-1(7)) Applewood Bks.

Keene, Carolyn & Dixon, Franklin W. Terror on Tour. 2007. (Nancy Drew & the Hardy Boys Ser.: No. 1). 224p. (J). pap. 5.99 (*978-1-4169-2726-6(3) , Aladdin) Simon & Schuster Children's Publishing.

Keene, Carolyn & Drew, Nancy. Lights, Camera. 2004. (Nancy Drew Ser.). (Illus.). 160p. (J). pap. 4.99 (978-0-689-86570-1(8) , Aladdin) Simon & Schuster Children's Publishing.

Keene, Carolyn & Greene, James. The Missing Horse Mystery. 1998. (Nancy Drew Mystery Stories: No. 145). 160p. (J). (gr. 3-6). pap. 4.99 (978-0-671-00754-6(8) , Aladdin) Simon & Schuster Children's Publishing.

Keene, Carolyn & Jones, Jan Naimo. The Chinese New Year Mystery. Jones, Jan Naimo, illus. 2000. (Nancy Drew Notebooks: No. 39). (Illus.). 80p. (J). (gr. k-3). pap. 3.99 (978-0-671-78752-3(7) , Aladdin) Simon & Schuster Children's Publishing.

Keene, Carolyn & Whelan, Patrick. Danger on the Great Lakes. 2003. (Nancy Drew Mystery Stories). (Illus.). 160p. (J). pap. 4.99 (978-0-689-86146-8(X) , 53545777, Aladdin) Simon & Schuster Children's Publishing.

Kehm, Michelle. Suzi Clue: the Prom Queen Curse: The Prom Queen Curse. 2008. 192p. (YA). 15.99 (*978-0-525-47953-6(8) , Dutton Juvenile) Penguin Group (USA) Inc.

Kehret, Peg. Terror at the Zoo. 2001. (gr. 3-6). lib. bdg. 14.15 (978-0-613-44421-7(3)) Tandem Library Bks.

—Terror at the Zoo. l.t. ed. 2002. (Juvenile Ser.). 164p. (J). 23.95 (978-0-7862-4511-6(5)) Thorndike Pr.

Kelly, Erin. The Mystery at the Eiffel Tower: Paris, France. 2005. (Carole Marsh Mysteries Ser.). (Illus.). 144p. (J). (gr. 3-5). 14.95 (978-0-635-03471-7(9)); pap. 5.95 (978-0-635-03468-7(9)) Gallopade International.

Kelly, John & Tincknell, Cathy. Scoop! An Exclusive by Monty Molenski. Kelly, John & Tincknell, Cathy, illus. 2007. (Illus.). 32p. (J). (gr. k-3). 15.99 (978-0-7636-3059-1(4)) Candlewick Pr.

Kelly, Matt. Scooby-Doo! Camera Clues. Wanhala, Dwight, illus. 2004. 14p. (J). bds. (978-0-7853-9954-4(2) , 7209900) Publications International, Ltd.

Kemp, Gene. The Hairy Hands. l.t. ed. 1999. 187p. (J). pap. (978-0-7540-6072-7(1) , CLP 275) BBC Audio.

Kendal, Penny. Keeping Quiet. 2007. 192p. (YA). (gr. 7-9). pap. 9.99 (978-1-84270-455-4(9)) Andersen GBR. *Dist:* Independent Pubs. Group.

Kenny, Kathryn. The Black Jacket Mystery. 2004. (Trixie Belden Ser.: Vol. 8). (Illus.). 272p. (gr. 3-7). lib. bdg. 9.99 (978-0-375-92979-3(7) , Random Hse. Bks. for Young Readers) Random Hse. Children's Bks.

—The Black Jacket Mystery. Frame, Paul, illus. 2004. (Trixie Belden Ser.: Vol. 8). 272p. (J). (gr. 3-7). 6.99 (978-0-375-82979-6(2) , Random Hse. Bks. for Young Readers) Random Hse. Children's Bks.

—The Happy Valley Mystery. 2004. (Trixie Belden Ser.: Vol. 9). (Illus.). 272p. (J). (gr. 3). 6.99 (978-0-375-83022-8(7) , Random Hse. Bks. for Young Readers) Random Hse. Children's Bks.

—The Marshland Mystery. Frame, Paul, illus. 2005. (Trixie Belden Ser.: Vol. 10). 272p. (J). (gr. 3-7). lib. bdg. 9.99 (978-0-375-93050-8(7)); Vol. 10. 6.99 (978-0-375-83050-1(2)) Random Hse. Children's Bks. (Random Hse. Bks. for Young Readers).

—The Mysterious Code. 2004. (Trixie Belden Ser.: No. 7). (Illus.). 272p. (J). (gr. 3-7). lib. bdg. 9.99 (978-0-375-92978-6(9) , Random Hse. Bks. for Young Readers) Random Hse. Children's Bks.

—The Mysterious Code, Vol. 7. Frame, Paul, illus. 2004. (Trixie Belden Ser.: Vol. 7). 272p. (J). (gr. 3-7). 6.99 (978-0-375-82978-9(4) , Random Hse. Bks. for Young Readers) Random Hse. Children's Bks.

—The Mystery at Bob-White Cave. Frame, Paul, illus. 2005. (Trixie Belden Ser.: Vol. 11). 256p. (J). (gr. 3-7). lib. bdg. 9.99 (978-0-375-93051-5(5) , Random Hse. Bks. for Young Readers) Random Hse. Children's Bks.

—The Mystery of the Emeralds. 2006. (Trixie Belden Ser.). (Illus.). 272p. (J). (gr. 3-7). 6.99 (978-0-375-83054-9(5) , Random Hse. Bks. for Young Readers) Random Hse. Children's Bks.

—The Mystery on the Mississippi. 2006. (Illus.). 256p. (J). (gr. 3-7). lib. bdg. 9.99 (978-0-375-93055-3(8)); (Trixie Belden Ser.: No. 15). 6.99 (978-0-375-83055-6(3)) Random Hse. Children's Bks. (Random Hse. Bks. for Young Readers).

Kenny, Kathryn & Koelsch, Michael. The Mystery of the Blinking Eye. Frame, Paul, illus. 2005. (Trixie Belden Ser.: Vol. 12). 256p. (J). (gr. 3-7). 6.99 (978-0-375-83052-5(9)); lib. bdg. 9.99 (978-0-375-93052-2(3)) Random Hse. Children's Bks. (Random Hse. Bks. for Young Readers).

—The Mystery on Cobbett's Island. Frame, Paul, illus. 2005. (Trixie Belden Ser.: Vol. 13). 272p. (J). (gr. 3-7). 6.99 (978-0-375-83053-2(7)); lib. bdg. 9.99 (978-0-375-93053-9(1)) Random Hse. Children's Bks. (Random Hse. Bks. for Young Readers).

Kerl, Mary Ann. Janessa's Clues to the Cabin Mystery. 2001. (gr. 7-12). lib. bdg. 26.85 (978-0-613-82104-9(1)) Tandem Library Bks.

Kerr, Kathleen. 7th Knot. 2007. 192p. (J). pap. 5.99 (*978-0-7614-5368-0(7)) Cavendish, Marshall Corp.

Kerr, M. E. What Became of Her. 2002. 256p. (J). (gr. 7 up). pap. 5.95 (978-0-06-447210-4(8) , Harper Trophy) HarperCollins Pubs.

Kervanoglu, Seda. A Dark, Dark Tale. 2002. (TUR & ENG., Illus.). 29p. (J). 19.95 (978-1-85269-400-5(9)) Mantra Publishing, Ltd. GBR. *Dist:* AIMS International Bks., Inc.

Kidd, Ronald. Undercover Kid: Comic Book King. Sklar, Andy, illus. 2007. (All Aboard Mystery Reader Ser.). 48p. (J). pap. 3.99 (*978-0-448-44438-3(0) , Grosset & Dunlap) Penguin Group (USA) Inc.

Kidd, Ronald. Undercover Kid: Station Stop 3. Sklar, Andy, illus. 2006. (All Aboard Mystery Reader Ser.). 48p. (J). (gr. 2-4). pap. 3.99 (978-0-448-44128-3(4) , Grosset & Dunlap) Penguin Group (USA) Inc.

Kilman, Nancy. The Lockgate Mystery: Level O, 6 vols. 128p. (gr. 3-6). 36.95 (978-0-322-05895-8(3)) Wright Group, The.

Kilpatrick, Irene. The Movie Star Mystery. 2007. (Nancy Drew Movie Ser.). 24p. (J). pap. 3.99 (978-1-4169-3901-6(6) , Simon Spotlight) Simon & Schuster Children's Publishing.

Kimball, K. M. The Star-Spangled Secret. 2001. 234p. (J). (gr. 4-7). lib. bdg. 11.64 (978-0-606-22096-5(8)) Tandem Library Bks.

Kimpton, Diana. Princess Ellie Solves a Mystery. 8th rev. ed. 2007. (Pony Crazed Princess Ser.: No. 8). 96p. (gr. 1-4). pap. 3.99 (*978-1-4231-0901-3(5)) Disney Pr.

Kimpton, Diana. Princess Ellie's Camping Trip. Finlay, Lizzie, illus. 5th rev. ed. 2006. (Pony-Crazed Princess Ser.). 96p. (gr. 1-4). pap. 3.99 (978-0-7868-4874-4(X)) Hyperion Pr.

Kindl, Patrice. Lost in the Labyrinth. 2005. 208p. (YA). (gr. 5-9). pap. 7.99 (978-0-618-39402-9(8) , Graphia) Houghton Mifflin Co. Trade & Reference Div.

King, Daren. Mouse Noses on Toast. Roberts, David, illus. 2008. 128p. (J). (gr. 3). 15.99 (*978-0-399-25037-8(9) , Putnam Juvenile) Penguin Group (USA) Inc.

King, Laurie R. The Beekeeper's Apprentice. 2002. (Mary Russell Mystery Ser.: Vol. 1). (gr. 7-12). lib. bdg. 21.05 (978-0-613-57620-8(9)) Tandem Library Bks.

—The Moor. 1999. (Mary Russell Mystery Ser.: Vol. 4). (gr. 7-12). lib. bdg. 15.30 (978-0-613-15009-5(0)) Tandem Library Bks.

King-Smith, Dick. Mysterious Miss Slade. Kronheimer, Ann, illus. 2002. 128p. (gr. 3-5). 4.99 (978-0-440-41674-6(4) , Yearling) Random Hse. Children's Bks.

Kir-On, Calanitte. The Adventures of the Gimmel Gang I: The Fake Mezuza. 2002. 75p. (YA). pap. 8.95 (978-1-931681-21-6(X)) Israel Bk. Shop.

—The Adventures of the Gimmel Gang II: The Secret in the Basement. 2002. (Illus.). 110p. (J). pap. 8.95 (978-1-931681-36-0(8)) Israel Bk. Shop.

Kirk, Daniel. Rex Tabby: Cat Detective. (Illus.). 144p. (J). 2005. (gr. 2-5). pap. 3.99 (978-0-439-45287-8(2) , Scholastic Paperbacks); 2004. pap. 9.95 (978-0-439-45286-1(4) , Orchard Bks.) Scholastic, Inc.

Kleyla, Mary Pat. Identity Unknown. 2003. (gr. 7-12). lib. bdg. 22.20 (978-0-613-83502-2(6)) Tandem Library Bks.

—Identity Unknown. 2003. 154p. (YA). 22.95 (978-0-595-65812-1(1)); pap. 12.95 (978-0-595-28473-3(6)) iUniverse, Inc.

Klim, Christopher. Firecracker Jones Is on the Case. 2005. (Illus.). 111p. (J). per. 9.95 (978-0-9726906-7-6(0)) Hopewell Pubns., LLC.

Kline, Suzy. Horrible Harry & the Locked Closet. 2004. (Illus.). 80p. (J). (gr. 2). 13.99 (978-0-670-05944-7(7) , Viking Juvenile) Penguin Group (USA) Inc.

—Horrible Harry & the Locked Closet. Remkiewicz, Frank, illus. 2005. (Horrible Harry Ser.). 80p. (J). (gr. 2-5). pap. 3.99 (978-0-14-240451-5(9) , Puffin) Penguin Group (USA) Inc.

—Horrible Harry Cracks the Code. Remkiewicz, Frank, illus. 2007. 80p. (J). 13.99 (978-0-670-06200-3(6) , Viking Juvenile) Penguin Group (USA) Inc.

Klise, Kate. Letters from Camp. Klise, M. Sarah, illus. 2000. 192p. (J). (gr. 4-7). pap. 5.99 (978-0-380-79348-8(2) , Harper Trophy) HarperCollins Pubs.

—Letters from Camp. 2000. (gr. 3-6). lib. bdg. 14.15 (978-0-613-28552-0(2)) Tandem Library Bks.

—Regarding the Bathrooms: A Privy to the Past. Klise, M. Sarah, illus. 2006. (Regarding The ... Ser.). 160p. (YA). 15.00 (978-0-15-205164-8(3)) Harcourt Trade Pubs.

—Trial by Journal. Klise, M. Sarah, illus. 256p. (J). 2002. (gr. 3-6). pap. 6.99 (978-0-380-81672-9(5)); 2001. (gr. 4-6). 15.95 (978-0-380-97880-9(6)); 2001. (gr. 4-6). 16.89 (978-0-06-029541-7(4)) HarperCollins Pubs.

—Trial by Journal. 2002. (gr. 5-8). lib. bdg. 15.30 (978-0-613-60649-3(3)) Tandem Library Bks.

Knight. Dead Beckoning. (Thumbprint Mysteries Ser.). 32.86 (978-0-8092-0421-2(5)) McGraw-Hill/Contemporary.

—The Monster in the Loch. (Thumbprint Mysteries Ser.). 32.86 (978-0-8092-0411-3(8)) McGraw-Hill/Contemporary.

Knight, Melanie. Schoolgirl Shamuses, Incorporated. Carpentieri, Tony, ed. 1998. (Illus.). 580p. spiral bd. 39.90 (978-1-891388-01-9(0)) SynSine Pr.

Knoche, Keith & Wood, Jeff. Mystery of Moosehead Falls. 2000. 20p. (gr. k-7). 14.99 (978-5-550-03633-4(9)); pap. 11.99 incl. audio (978-5-550-03634-1(7)) Faith Factory.

Koenig, Sharolett. One on Nothing. 2002. (Tim MacCulfsky Mystery Ser.: 3). 250p. (YA). pap. 19.95 (978-0-9700458-7-4(5)) Koenisha Pubns.

Kohl, Susan. The Ghost of Gracie Mansion. Butterfield, Ned, illus. 1999. (Mysteries in Time Ser.: Vol. 8). 96p. (J). (gr. 3-7). lib. bdg. 14.95 (978-1-893110-04-5(4)) Silver Moon Pr.

Konigsburg, E. L. The Dragon in the Ghetto Caper. 1998. (Illus.). 128p. (J). (gr. 3-7). pap. 5.99 (978-0-689-82328-2(2) , Aladdin) Simon & Schuster Children's Publishing.

—Father's Arcane Daughter. 1999. (J). (978-0-606-19131-9(3)) Tandem Library Bks.

Koontz, Dean. Icebound. 2000. (gr. 7-12). lib. bdg. 16.45 (978-0-7857-7869-1(1)) Tandem Library Bks.

Korman, Gordon. Public Enemies, 2005. (On the Run Ser.: No. 5). 160p. (J). (gr. 3-7). pap. 4.99 (978-0-439-65140-0(9) , Scholastic Paperbacks) Scholastic, Inc.

—The Search. 2006. (Kidnapped Ser.: Bk. 2). 144p. (J). pap. 4.99 (978-0-439-84778-0(8) , Scholastic Paperbacks) Scholastic, Inc.

—The Stowaway Solution, 2005. (On the Run Ser.: No. 4). 160p. (J). (gr. 3-7). pap. 4.99 (978-0-439-65139-4(5) , Scholastic Paperbacks) Scholastic, Inc.

Kotzwinkle, William & Murray, Glenn. Walter the Farting Dog: Trouble at the Yard Sale. Coleman, Audrey, illus. 2006. 32p. (J). (gr. k). reprint ed. pap. 6.99 (978-0-14-240626-7(0) , Puffin) Penguin Group (USA) Inc.

Kraft, Amanda. Silver Wings. 2002. (YA). pap. 13.95 (978-1-59088-892-6(8)) Wings ePress, Inc.

Krailing, Tessa. La Mano Verde. (SPA.). 96p. (J). (gr. 3-5). 7.95 (978-84-88061-84-3(6)) Serres, Ediciones, S. L. ESP. *Dist:* Lectorum Pubns., Inc.

Krensky, Stephen. Arthur Accused! 1998. (Arthur Chapter Bks.: Bk. 5). (J). (gr. 3-6). pap. 3.95 (978-0-316-12150-7(9)) Little, Brown Bks. for Young Readers.

—Arthur's Mystery Envelope. 1998. (Arthur Chapter Bks. : Bk. 1). (Illus.). 64p. (J). (gr. 2-4). pap. 4.25 (978-0-316-11547-6(9)) Little, Brown Bks. for Young Readers.

—Arthur's Mystery Envelope. unabr. ed. 1998. (Arthur Chapter Bks.: Bk. 1). 58p. (J). (gr. 2-4). pap. 17.00 incl. audio (978-0-8072-0372-9(6) , FTR187SP, Listening Library) Random Hse. Audio Publishing Group.

—Arthur's Mystery Envelope. 1998. (Arthur Chapter Bks.: Bk. 1). (J). (gr. 3-6). 11.05 (978-0-606-13154-4(X)) Tandem Library Bks.

—Case of the Missing Mice: A Simon Mystery. 2003. (Illus.). 14.95 (978-1-59319-022-4(0)) LeapFrog Enterprises, Inc.

—Case of the Missing Pail. 2003. (Illus.). (J). 14.95 (978-1-59319-018-7(2)) LeapFrog Enterprises, Inc.

Kropp, Paul. The Countess & Me. 2003. 144p. (J). pap. (978-1-55041-689-3(8)); 2003. (Illus.). (YA). pap. (978-1-55041-692-3(8)); 2002. 140p. (YA). (gr. 7-10). (978-1-55041-680-0(4)) Fitzhenry & Whiteside, Ltd.

—Countess & Me. 2003. (gr. 7-12). lib. bdg. 16.40 (978-0-613-89114-1(7)) Tandem Library Bks.

Krulik, Nancy E. Anyone but Me, No. 1. John and Wendy Staff, illus. 2006. (Katie Kazoo, Switcheroo Ser.: No. 1). 80p. (J). 2.99 (978-0-448-44259-4(0) , Grosset & Dunlap) Penguin Group (USA) Inc.

—Oh, Baby!, No. 3. 2002. (Katie Kazoo, Switcheroo Ser.: No. 3). (gr. 3-6). lib. bdg. 11.80 (978-0-613-60311-9(7)) Tandem Library Bks.

Labatt, Mary. Aliens in Woodford. Hill-Jackson, Troy, illus. 2000. (Sam Ser.). 120p. (J). (gr. 4-6). (978-1-55074-607-5(3)); (978-1-55074-611-2(1)) Kids Can Pr., Ltd.

—Aliens in Woodford. 2000. (gr. 3-6). lib. bdg. 12.95 (978-0-613-30214-2(1)); (Illus.). (J). 11.60 (978-0-606-21020-1(2)) Tandem Library Bks.

—The Ghost of Captain Briggs. Hill-Jackson, Troy, illus. 1999. (Sam Ser.). 120p. (J). (gr. 4-6). (978-1-55074-636-5(7)) Kids Can Pr., Ltd.

—The Ghost of Captain Briggs. Jackson, Troy, illus. 1999. (Sam Ser.). 120p. (J). (gr. 4-6). (978-1-55074-638-9(3)) Kids Can Pr., Ltd.

—The Ghost of Captain Briggs. 1999. (J). 11.60 (978-0-606-19016-9(3)) Tandem Library Bks.

—Mummy Lives! 2002. (gr. 3-6). lib. bdg. 12.95 (978-0-613-62530-2(7)) Tandem Library Bks.

—The Mummy Lives! unabr. ed. 2002. (Sam Ser.). (Illus.). 120p. (J). (gr. 4-6). (978-1-55337-042-0(2)) Kids Can Pr., Ltd.

—The Mummy Lives! Hill-Jackson, Troy, illus. unabr. ed. 2002. (Sam Ser.). 120p. (J). (gr. 4-6). (978-1-55337-023-9(6)) Kids Can Pr., Ltd.

—Secret of Sagawa Lake. 2001. (gr. 3-6). lib. bdg. 12.95 (978-0-613-51586-3(2)) Tandem Library Bks.

—Spying on Dracula. Jackson, Troy, illus. 1999. (Sam Ser.). 120p. (J). (gr. 4-6). (978-1-55074-632-7(4)) Kids Can Pr., Ltd.

—Spying on Dracula. Hill-Jackson, Troy, illus. 1999. (Sam Ser.). 120p. (J). (gr. 4-6). (978-1-55074-634-1(0)) Kids Can Pr., Ltd.

—Spying on Dracula. 1999. (J). (978-0-606-19023-7(6)) Tandem Library Bks.

—Strange Neighbors. Hill-Jackson, Troy, illus. unabr. ed. 2000. (Sam Ser.). 120p. (J). (gr. 4-6). (978-1-55074-603-7(0)); (978-1-55074-605-1(7)) Kids Can Pr., Ltd.

—A Weekend at the Grand Hotel. Hill-Jackson, Troy, illus. unabr. ed. 2001. (Sam Ser.). 120p. (J). (gr. 4-6). (978-1-55074-885-7(8)); (978-1-55074-883-3(1)) Kids Can Pr., Ltd.

—A Weekend at the Grand Hotel. 2000. (Sam Dog Detective Ser.). (Illus.). (J). (978-0-606-21512-1(3)) Tandem Library Bks.

LaBrot, Matthew & Daniel, Hale. Green Streak. 2004. (Zeke Armstrong Mysteries Ser.: 2). 236p. (J). per. 8.95 (978-1-929976-28-7(3)) Top Pubns., Ltd.

Lachtman, Ofelia Dumas. The Summer of El Pintor. 2001. (Illus.). 240p. (J). (gr. 11 up). pap. 9.95 (978-1-55885-327-0(8) , Piñata Books) Arte Publico Pr.

—Summer of el Pintor. 2001. (gr. 5-8). lib. bdg. 18.75 (978-0-613-59023-5(6)) Tandem Library Bks.

Lachtman, Ofelia Dumas. The Truth about las Mariposas. 2007. 144p. (YA). (gr. 6 up). pap. 9.95 (***978-1-55885-494-9(0)*** , Piñata Books) Arte Publico Pr.

Ladd, Debbie. Ethan the Ending Eater. Nakasone, Shaun, illus. 2007. 64p. (J). 16.95 (978-0-9727615-2-9(7)) Deb on Air Bks.

Laden, Nina. Private I. Guana: The Case of the Missing Chameleon. 1999. (Illus.). 32p. (J). (ps-5). pap. 6.95 (978-0-8118-2463-7(2)) Chronicle Bks. LLC.

—Private I Guana: The Case of the Missing Chameleon. 1999. (gr. k-3). lib. bdg. 15.25 (978-0-613-89998-7(9)) Tandem Library Bks.

Lalicki, Tom. Shots at Sea. Cerniglia, Carlyn, illus. 2007. (Houdini & Nate Mysteries Ser.). 208p. (J). (gr. 3-7). 15.95 (***978-0-374-31679-2(1)***) Farrar, Straus & Giroux.

Lambert, Janet. One for the Money. 2001. (Candy Kane Ser.: Vol. 3). (YA). pap. 12.95 (978-1-930009-47-9(X)) Image Cascade Publishing.

Lamberti, B. J. Nelson Paige & the Treasure Trove. 2006. 174p. per. 12.95 (978-1-59886-193-8(X)) Tate Publishing & Enterprises, L.L.C.

Lamplighter Staff. What Is Her Name. 2004. 16.00 (978-1-58474-036-0(1)) Cornerstone Family Ministries/ Lamplighter Publishing.

Landon, Lucinda. Meg Mackintosh & the Mystery on Main Street: A Solve-It-Yourself Mystery. Murray, Wendy, ed. Landon, Lucinda, illus. 2000. (Meg Mackintosh Mystery Ser.). (Illus.). 48p. (J). pap. 5.95 (978-1-888695-06-9(4)) Secret Passage Pr.

—Meg Mackintosh & the Mystery on Main Street: A Solve It Yourself Mystery. 2000. (gr. 3-6). lib. bdg. 12.95 (978-0-613-53279-2(1)) Tandem Library Bks.

—Meg Mackintosh & the Stage Fright Secret: A Solve-It-Yourself Mystery. 2004. (Meg Mackintosh Mystery Ser.). (Illus.). 48p. (J). pap. 5.95 (978-1-888695-07-6(2)) Secret Passage Pr.

Lane, Jeanette. Magic School Bus & the Missing Tooth. 2007. (Magic School Bus Ser.). 32p. (J). pap. 3.99 (978-0-439-80107-2(9) , Cartwheel Bks.) Scholastic, Inc.

Langlais, Heather M. Mummy's Home Town: The Curse of the Amulet. Gillespie, P. J., illus. 1999. 144p. (J). (gr. 4-8). pap. 7.95 (978-1-930506-00-8(7)) March Forth Pubns.

Lanier, Virginia. Blind Bloodhound Justice. 1999. 337p. (gr. 7-12). per. 15.30 (978-0-613-23687-4(4)) Tandem Library Bks.

Lanthier, Jennifer. The Mystery of the Martello Tower. 2008. 272p. (J). 16.99 (***978-0-06-125712-4(5)***); lib. bdg. 17.89 (***978-0-06-125713-1(3)***) HarperCollins Pubs. (Geringer, Laura Book).

Lantz, Francess L. The Case of the Missing Mummy. 1998. (New Adventures of Mary-Kate & Ashley Ser.). (Illus.). 82p. (J). (gr. 2-7). pap. 3.99 (978-0-590-29404-1(0)) Scholastic, Inc.

LaRochelle, David. The Mighty Big BookTM of Travel Mysteries. 2002. (Illus.). 288p. (J). (gr. 3-7). mass mkt. 5.99 (978-0-8431-7734-3(9) , Price Stern Sloan) Penguin Group (USA) Inc.

Larry, H. I. Zac Power #1: Poison Island. Oswald, Ash, illus. 2008. (Zac Power Ser.). 96p. (J). pap. 3.99 (***978-0-312-34659-1(X)***) Feiwel & Friends.

—Zac Power #2: Deep Waters. Oswald, Ash, illus. 2008. (Zac Power Ser.). 96p. (J). pap. 3.99 (***978-0-312-34655-3(7)***) Feiwel & Friends.

Larsen, Sandy. Ice Festival. Taylor, Wanda, illus. 1999. (Jackpine Point Adventure Ser.: Vol. 2). 126p. (J). (gr. 4-6). pap. 5.99 (978-0-9666677-1-4(9)) Merritt Park Pr.

Lasky, Kathryn. Born to Rule. Walton, Tony, illus. 2006. (Camp Princess Ser.: No. 1). 160p. (J). pap. 4.99 (978-0-06-058763-5(6) , Harper Trophy); 15.99 (978-0-06-058761-1(X)) HarperCollins Pubs.

—The Rescue. 2003. (Guardians of Ga'Hoole Ser.: Bk. 3). (J). (gr. 3-6). lib. bdg. 13.00 (978-0-613-72136-3(5)) Tandem Library Bks.

Latorre, Jose Maria. La Incognita del Volcan. Ibarz, Miguel, illus. 2000. (Periscopio Ser.).Tr. of Mystery of the Volcano. (SPA.). 236p. (YA). (gr. 9 up). (978-84-236-5517-5(2)) Edebé ESP. *Dist:* Baker & Taylor Bks.

Latta, Ruth. The Revenant & Other Stories for Hallowe'en. 2004. 54p. (***978-0-9683382-8-5(3)***) Latta, Roger K.

Latta, Sara L. Stella Brite & the Dark Matter Mystery. Johnson, Meredith, illus. 2006. 32p. (J). 16.95 (978-1-57091-883-4(X)); pap. 6.95 (978-1-57091-884-1(8)) Charlesbridge Publishing, Inc.

Lattimore, Deborah Nourse. Mystery at Midnight Museum. Date not set. 32p. (J). 15.89 (978-0-06-026202-0(8)) HarperCollins Pubs.

Lauber, Patricia. The True-or-False Book of Cats. Lauber, Patricia, illus. 2001. (Illus.). 32p. (J). (gr. 3-7). pap. 6.95 (978-0-7922-6694-5(3) , National Geographic Children's Bks.) National Geographic Society.

Lawlor, Laurie. The Worst Kid Who Ever Lived on Eighth Avenue: A Holiday House Reader. Fisher, Cynthia, illus. 48p. (J). (gr. k-3). tchr. ed. 14.95 (978-0-8234-1350-8(0)) Holiday Hse., Inc.

Lawrence, Caroline. The Assassins of Rome, Vol. 4. 2005. (Illus.). 176p. (J). (gr. 3-7). pap. 5.99 (978-0-14-240214-6(1) , Puffin) Penguin Group (USA) Inc.

—The Charioteer of Delphi. 2007. (Roman Mysteries Ser.). (Illus.). 210p. (J). (gr. 6-9). 16.95 (***978-1-59643-085-3(0)***) Roaring Brook Pr.

—The Colossus of Rhodes. 2006. (Roman Mysteries Ser.). (Illus.). 208p. (J). 16.95 (978-1-59643-082-2(6)) Roaring Brook Pr.

—The Dolphins of Laurentium: Roman Mysteries. 2005. (Illus.). 176p. (J). (gr. 3). pap. 5.99 (978-0-14-240379-2(2) , Puffin) Penguin Group (USA) Inc.

—The Enemies of Jupiter. 2005. (Roman Mysteries Ser.). (Illus.). 192p. (J). 16.95 (978-1-59643-048-8(6)) Roaring Brook Pr.

—The Fugitive from Corinth. 2006. (Roman Mysteries Ser.). (Illus.). 208p. (J). 16.95 (978-1-59643-083-9(4)) Roaring Brook Pr.

—The Gladiators from Capua. 2005. (Roman Mysteries Ser.). (Illus.). 208p. (J). (gr. 6-9). 16.95 (978-1-59643-074-7(5)) Roaring Brook Pr.

—Los Piratas de Pompeyа. 2003. (SPA.). 192p. (978-84-7888-798-9(9) , 1952) Emece Editores.

—Pirates of Pompeii, Vol. 3. 2004. (Roman Mysteries Ser.: No. 3). (Illus.). 176p. (J). (gr. 3). pap. 5.99 (978-0-14-240227-6(3) , Puffin) Penguin Group (USA) Inc.

—Secrets of Vesuvius. 2004. (Roman Mysteries Ser.: No. 2). (Illus.). 192p. (J). (gr. 3 up). pap. 5.99 (978-0-14-240118-7(8) , Puffin) Penguin Group (USA) Inc.

—The Sirens of Surrentum. 2007. (Roman Mysteries Ser.). (Illus.). 224p. (J). 16.95 (***978-1-59643-084-6(2)***) Roaring Brook Pr.

—Thieves of Ostia. 2004. (Roman Mysteries Ser.: No. 1). (Illus.). 160p. (J). (gr. 3 up). pap. 5.99 (978-0-14-240147-7(1) , Puffin) Penguin Group (USA) Inc.

—The Twelve Tasks of Flavia Gemina. 2004. (Roman Mysteries Ser.: Bk. 4). 176p. (J). 15.95 (978-1-59643-012-9(5)) Roaring Brook Pr.

Lay, Eddie. Mystery of the Hats. 2006. 61p. pap. 12.95 (978-1-4241-2649-1(5)) PublishAmerica, Inc.

Layos, Alexandra. Timeless: Blue Ribbon Days #2, 2, 2. 2005. (Illus.). 128p. (YA). pap. 10.95 (978-0-9655501-4-7(1)) Saddle & Bridle, Inc.

Le Queux, William. The House of Whispers. 2006. 260p. pap. 13.99 (***978-1-4264-4356-5(0)***); 284p. pap. 17.99 (***978-1-4264-4394-7(3)***) BiblioBazaar.

LeapFrog Staff, compiled by. Scooby Doo & the Disappearing Donuts. 2001. (J). (ps-2). spiral bd. 14.99 (978-1-58605-107-5(5)) LeapFrog Enterprises, Inc.

—Scooby Doo & the Haunted Castle. 2001. (J). (ps-2). spiral bd. 14.99 (978-1-58605-108-2(3)) LeapFrog Enterprises, Inc.

—Scooby Doo & the Zombie's Treasure. 2001. (J). (ps-2). spiral bd. 14.99 (978-1-58605-218-8(7)) LeapFrog Enterprises, Inc.

Leather, Sue. Dead Cold Book/Audio CD Pack: Level 2 Elementary/Lower Intermediate. 2007. (Cambridge English Readers Ser.). (Illus.). 48p. pap. 11.00 incl. audio compact disk (978-0-521-69392-9(6)) Cambridge Univ. Pr.

—Just Like a Movie, Level 1. 2000. (Cambridge English Readers Ser.). (Illus.). 32p. pap. 6.00 (978-0-521-78813-7(7)) Cambridge Univ. Pr.

Leavey, Peggy Dymond. Sky Lake Summer. 1999. 184p. (YA). (gr. 4-7). pap. 6.95 (978-0-929141-64-0(4)) Napoleon Publishing/Rendezvous Pr. CAN. *Dist:* AtlasBooks Distribution.

Leavitt, Caroline. The Haunted Clubhouse. l.t. ed. 1999. (Wishbone Mysteries Ser.: No. 2). 144p. (J). (gr. 4 up). lib. bdg. 22.60 (978-0-8368-2383-7(4)) Stevens, Gareth Inc.

Leblanc, Louise. Le Tombeau Mysterieux. 2002. (Premier Roman Ser.). (FRE.). 64p. (J). (gr. 2-5). pap. (978-2-89021-222-0(X)) Diffusion du livre Mirabel.

Lee Hope, Laura. The Bobbsey Twins in the Great West. 2005. 200p. pap. 12.95 (978-1-4218-0465-1(4) , 1st World Library - Literary Society) 1st World Publishing, Inc.

—The Bobbsey Twins in the Great West. 2004. reprint ed. pap. 20.95 (978-1-4191-5444-7(3)); pap. 1.99 (978-1-4192-5444-4(8)) Kessinger Publishing, LLC.

Lee, Kathy. Phoebe Finds Her Feet. 2004. 128p. 6.49 (978-1-85999-701-7(5)) Scripture Union GBR. *Dist:* Gabriel Resources.

Lee, Marian. Solve a Mystery. Crombie, Stephen, illus. unabr. ed. 1999. (J). (gr. k-5). Bk. 1. pap. 12.95 incl. audio compact disk (978-1-928632-03-0(3)); Bk. 2. pap. 8.95 incl. audio (978-1-928632-10-8(6)); Bk. 2. pap. 12.95 incl. audio compact disk (978-1-928632-11-5(4)) Writers Marketplace:Consulting, Critiquing & Publishing.

Lee, Marie G. Night of the Chupacabras. 1999. 128p. (gr. 3-7). pap. 3.99 (978-0-380-79773-8(9)) HarperCollins Pubs.

—Night of the Chupacabras. 1999. (978-0-606-17336-0(6)) Tandem Library Bks.

Leeson, Robert. Liar. 128p. (J). 9.95 (978-0-14-130143-3(0)) Penguin Bks., Ltd. GBR. *Dist:* Trafalgar Square Publishing.

Lehr, Norma. Haunting at Black Water Cove. 2000. (Illus.). (J). (978-0-606-18311-6(6)) Tandem Library Bks.

Lemieux, Jean. Pas de S pour Copernic. Casson, Sophie, illus. 2001. (Premier Roman Ser.). (FRE.). 64p. (J). (gr. 1-4). pap. (978-2-89021-454-5(0)) Diffusion du livre Mirabel.

Lemieux, Michele. Stormy Night. 1999. (Illus.). 240p. (J). (gr. 4-6). (978-1-55074-692-1(8)) Kids Can Pr., Ltd.

Lenhard, Elizabeth. Spring Fever. 9th rev. ed. 2004. (Spykids Adventures Ser.: Bk. 9). (Illus.). 144p. (gr. 3-7). pap. 4.99 (978-0-7868-0989-9(2)) Hyperion Bks. for Children.

Lennon, Joan. There's a Kangaroo in My Soup! Rasmussen, Wendy, illus. 2000. 128p. (J). (gr. 1-4). 16.95 (978-0-8126-2898-2(5)) Cricket Bks.

Leonhardt, Alice. The Mystery of the Missing Leopard. 1999. (Illus.). (J). pap. 5.65 (978-0-7398-0884-9(2)) Steck-Vaughn.

Leppard, Lois Gladys. Mandie & the Buried Stranger. 1999. (gr. 3-6). lib. bdg. 13.00 (978-0-613-27967-3(0)); (Mandie Bks.: No. 31). (J). (gr. 4-7). (978-0-606-18918-7(1)) Tandem Library Bks.

—Mandie & the Cherokee Legend. 2007. (Mandie Bks.: No. 2). 144p. (J). (gr. 4-7). reprint ed. mass mkt. 5.99 (978-0-87123-321-9(5)) Bethany Hse. Pubs.

—Mandie & the Dark Alley. (Mandie Bks.: No. 33). (J). (gr. 4-7). 1999. mass mkt. 4.99 (978-0-7642-1674-9(0)); Vol. 33. 2000. (Illus.). 160p. mass mkt. 5.99 (978-1-55661-674-7(0)) Bethany Hse. Pubs.

—Mandie & the Dark Alley. 2000. (gr. 3-6). lib. bdg. 13.00 (978-0-613-27968-0(9)) Tandem Library Bks.

—Mandie & the Graduation Mystery. 2004. (Mandie Bks.). 160p. (J). reprint ed. mass mkt. 5.99 (978-0-7642-2643-4(6)) Bethany Hse. Pubs.

—Mandie & the Hidden Past. 2003. (Mandie Bks.). 160p. (J). mass mkt. 5.99 (978-0-7642-2641-0(X)) Bethany Hse. Pubs.

—Mandie & the Hidden Past. 2003. (gr. 5-8). lib. bdg. 13.00 (978-0-613-85057-5(2)) Tandem Library Bks.

—Mandie & the Long Goodbye, Vol. 30. 40th ed. 1998. (Mandie Bks.: No. 30). 160p. (J). (gr. 4-7). mass mkt. 5.99 (978-1-55661-557-3(4)) Bethany Hse. Pubs.

—Mandie & the New York Secret, Vol. 36. 2003. (Mandie Bks.). (Illus.). 160p. (J). (gr. 3-8). mass mkt. 5.99 (978-0-7642-2639-7(8)) Bethany Hse. Pubs.

—Mandie & the Night Thief, Vol. 37. 2003. (Mandie Bks.). (Illus.). 160p. (J). mass mkt. 5.99 (978-0-7642-2640-3(1)) Bethany Hse. Pubs.

—Mandie & the Night Thief. 2003. (gr. k-3). lib. bdg. 13.00 (978-0-613-84504-5(8)) Tandem Library Bks.

—Mandie & the Quilt Mystery, Vol. 35. 2002. (Mandie Bks.). 160p. (J). mass mkt. 5.99 (978-1-55661-676-1(7)) Bethany Hse. Pubs.

—Mandie & the Quilt Mystery. 2002. (gr. 3-6). lib. bdg. 13.00 (978-0-613-67464-5(2)) Tandem Library Bks.

—Mandie & the Seaside Rendezvous, Vol. 32. 2000. (Mandie Bks.: No. 32). 176p. (J). (gr. 4-7). mass mkt. 5.99 (978-1-55661-673-0(2)) Bethany Hse. Pubs.

—Mandie & the Seaside Rendezvous. 2000. (Mandie Bks.: No. 32). (J). (gr. 4-7). (978-0-606-18919-4(X)); 1999. (gr. 3-6). lib. bdg. 13.00 (978-0-613-27969-7(7)) Tandem Library Bks.

—Mandie & the Tornado!, Vol. 34. 2001. (Mandie Bks.: No. 34). 160p. (J). (gr. 4-7). mass mkt. 5.99 (978-1-55661-675-4(9)) Bethany Hse. Pubs.

—Mandie & the Tornado! 2001. (gr. 3-6). lib. bdg. 13.00 (978-0-613-53361-4(5)) Tandem Library Bks.

—The Missing Book. 2002. (Illus.). 112p. (J). (gr. 2-5). 4.50 (978-0-553-48718-3(3) , Skylark) Random Hse. Children's Bks.

—Mystery at Miss Abigail's. 1999. (J). (978-0-606-18962-0(9)) Tandem Library Bks.

—The Secret in the Woods. 2001. (Young Mandie Mystery Ser.). (Illus.). (J). (978-0-606-21424-7(0)) Tandem Library Bks.

—The Talking Snowman. 2001. (Young Mandie Mystery Ser.). (Illus.). (J). (978-0-606-20935-9(2)) Tandem Library Bks.

—Who's Mandie? 1999. (Young Mandie Mystery Ser.). (978-0-606-20315-9(X)) Tandem Library Bks.

Lerangis, Peter. The Junior Novel. 2005. (Batman Begins Ser.). (Illus.). 160p. (ps-k). 4.99 (978-0-439-72509-5(7)) Scholastic, Inc.

—Lab 6. 1999. (Watchers Ser.: No. 6). 156p. (J). (gr. 4-7). pap. 4.50 (978-0-590-11501-8(4) , Scholastic Paperbacks) Scholastic, Inc.

—Spy X: Hide & Seek. 2004. 142p. (J). (978-0-439-70282-9(8)) Scholastic, Inc.

—Spy X: The Code. 2004. (Spy X Ser.). 144p. (Orig.). (J). 4.99 (978-0-439-50725-7(1) , Scholastic Paperbacks) Scholastic, Inc.

—Watchers #3: I.D. 1999. (Watchers Ser.: No. 3). 165p. (J). (gr. 4-7). pap. 4.50 (978-0-590-10998-7(7)) Scholastic, Inc.

—Wow! Blast from the Past! Talbot, Jim, illus. 2003. (Abracadabra Ser.: No. 8). 112p. (J). pap. 3.99 (978-0-439-38939-6(9) , Scholastic Paperbacks) Scholastic, Inc.

Levitt, Shirley Young. The Skelton Key Mystery, 8 vols. Bowman, Leslie, illus. 2001. (Kids on the Case Ser.: Vol. 3). 68p. pap. 4.75 Beaver's Pond Pr., Inc.

Levy, Elizabeth. The Creepy Computer Mystery. Brunkus, Denise, illus. 2004. 48p. (J). lib. bdg. 15.00 (978-1-59054-534-8(6)) Fitzgerald Bks.

—A Hare-Raising Tale: A Fletcher Mystery. Gorstein, Mordicai, illus. unabr. ed. 2006. (First Chapter Bks.). (J). (gr. 2-4). pap. 17.95 incl. audio (***978-1-59519-704-7(4)***); pap. 20.95 incl. audio compact disk (***978-1-59519-705-4(2)***) Live Oak Media.

—The Mixed-Up Mask Mystery: A Fletcher Mystery. Gorstein, Mordicai, illus. unabr. ed. 2006. (First Chapter Bks.). (J). (gr. 2-4). pap. 20.95 incl. audio compact disk (***978-1-59519-711-5(7)***); pap. 17.95 incl. audio (***978-1-59519-710-8(9)***) Live Oak Media.

—Parents' Night Fright. Brunkus, Denise, illus. 1998. (Hello Reader! Ser.). (J). (gr. 2-4). pap. 3.99 (978-0-590-60324-9(8)) Scholastic, Inc.

—The Schoolyard Mystery. Brunkus, Denise, illus. 2004. 48p. (J). lib. bdg. 15.00 (978-1-59054-531-7(1)) Fitzgerald Bks.

—The Snack Attack Mystery. Brunkus, Denise, illus. 2004. 48p. (J). lib. bdg. 15.00 (978-1-59054-533-1(8)) Fitzgerald Bks.

Levy, Elizabeth & Brunkus, Denise. The Mystery of the Missing Dog. (Hello Reader! Ser.). (FRE., Illus.). (J). pap. 5.99 (978-0-590-16010-0(9)) Scholastic, Inc.

Levy, Elizabeth & Coville, Bruce. The Dragon of Doom. Gerstein, Mordicai & Coville, Katherine, illus. ed. 2005. 71p. (J). lib. bdg. 15.00 (978-1-59054-903-2(1)) Fitzgerald Bks.

Levy, Elizabeth & Gerstein, Mordicai. A Hare-Raising Tail. 2002. (Fletcher Mystery Ser.: No. 1). (Illus.). 80p. (J). (gr. 2-5). pap. 3.99 (978-0-689-84626-7(6) , Aladdin) Simon & Schuster Children's Publishing.

—The Principal's on the Roof. 2002. (Ready-for-Chapters Ser.). (Illus.). 80p. (J). pap. 3.99 (978-0-689-84627-4(4) , Aladdin) Simon & Schuster Children's Publishing.

Lewis, Beverly. The Midnight Mystery. 2007. (Cul-de-Sac Kids Ser.: Vol. 24). (Illus.). 80p. (J). (gr. 2-5). pap. 3.99 (978-0-7642-2129-3(9)) Bethany Hse. Pubs.

—The Mystery of Case D. Luc. Birch, Barbara, illus. 2007. (Cul-de-Sac Kids Ser.: Vol. 6). 80p. (J). (gr. 2-5). pap. 3.99 (978-1-55661-646-4(5)) Bethany Hse. Pubs.

—The Upside-Down Day. 2001. (Cul-de-Sac Kids Ser.: Vol. 23). (Illus.). 80p. (J). (gr. 2-5). reprint ed. pap. 3.99 (978-0-7642-2128-6(0)) Bethany Hse. Pubs.

—Windows on the Hill. 1999. (Summerhill Secrets Ser.: Vol. 9). 144p. (J). (gr. 6-9). pap. 6.99 (978-1-55661-875-8(1)) Bethany Hse. Pubs.

Lewis, Echo. A Long Way from Welcome. 2002. (Morning Gate Bks.). 192p. pap. 12.95 (978-1-883937-64-5(7)) Bethlehem Bks.

Lewis, J. Patrick, text. El Ultimo Refugio. 2003. (Illus.). 48p. (J). (ps-7). 14.99 (978-968-16-6860-0(X)) Fondo de Cultura Economica USA.

Lewis, Johnnie W. The Writing Police & the Case of the Missing Commas. Lewis, Johnnie W., illus. 2002. 32p. (J). pap. 7.95 (978-0-9719480-1-3(1)) Wright, Franklin Enterprises.

—The Writing Police & the Point of the Perplexing Periods. Lewis, Johnnie W., illus. 2002. 32p. (J). pap. 7.95 (978-0-9719480-2-0(X)) Wright, Franklin Enterprises.

Lewis, Wendy. Graveyard Girl & Other Stories. 2004. 176p. (YA). (gr. 9 up). pap. 7.95 (978-0-88995-202-7(7)) Red Deer Pr. CAN. *Dist:* Fitzhenry & Whiteside, Ltd.

Lewman, David. SpongeBob DetectivePants: The Case of the Missing Spatula. Moore, Harry, illus. 2006. (SpongeBob SquarePants Ser.). 16p. (J). pap. 5.99 (978-1-4169-1319-1(X) , Simon Spotlight/Nickelodeon) Simon & Schuster Children's Publishing.

L'Homme, Erik. The Mystery of Lord Sha. 2006. (Book of the Stars Ser.: Bk. 2). 288p. (J). pap. 5.99 (978-0-439-65073-1(9) , Scholastic Paperbacks) Scholastic, Inc.

Libby Solves the Mystery. 2002. per. 12.95 (978-0-9658468-2-0(2)) Adbeth Pr.

Lipe, Riki. The Mystery at Ricena's Pond. Spears-Stewart, Reta, ed. Lipe, Riki, illus. Payton, Leland, photos by. 2000. (Illus.). 36p. (J). (ps-6). 10.00 (978-0-9659381-2-9(3)) Hoot N' Cackle Pr.

Lisle, Janet Taylor. The Crying Rocks. 2005. (Illus.). 288p. (YA). (gr. 7-12). mass mkt. 6.99 (978-0-689-85320-3(3) , Simon Pulse) Simon & Schuster Children's Publishing.

—La Tarde de los Elfos. 2001. (SPA.). (YA). (gr. 5-8). 8.95 (978-958-04-2385-0(7) , NR2410) Norma S.A. COL. *Dist:* Distribuidora Norma, Inc., Lectorum Pubns., Inc.

Littke, Lael. Lake of Secrets. rev. ed. 2002. 208p. (YA). (gr. 7-9). 16.95 (978-0-8050-6730-9(2) , Holt, Henry & Co. Bks. For Young Readers) Holt, Henry & Co.

Littleton, Mark. Hoofbeats on the Trail. 2002. (Ally OConnor Adventures Ser.: Vol. 3). 128p. (J). (gr. 4-7). pap. 5.99 (978-0-8010-6427-2(9)) Baker Bks.

Lobdell, Scott. The Hardy Boys #8: Board to Death. Henrique, Paulo, illus. 8th rev. ed. 2007. (Hardy Boys: Undercover Brothers Ser.). 112p. (J). 12.95 (978-1-59707-054-6(8)); pap. 7.95 (978-1-59707-053-9(X)) Papercutz.

MNO

—Identity Theft. 2006. (J). (gr. 3-8). 24.21 (978-1-59961-062-7(0)) Spotlight.

—Mad House. 2006. (J). (gr. 3-8). 24.21 (978-1-59961-063-4(9)) Spotlight.

—Malled. Rendon, Daniel, illus. 4th rev. ed. 2006. (Hardy Boys Graphic Novel Ser.: No. 4). 96p. (J). 12.95 (978-1-59707-015-7(7)); pap. 7.95 (978-1-59707-014-0(9)) Papercutz.

—Ocean of Osyria. 2006. (J). (gr. 3-8). 24.21 (978-1-59961-061-0(2)) Spotlight.

—The Opposite Numbers. Rendon, Daniel, illus. 7th rev. ed. 2006. (Hardy Boys Ser.: No. 7). 96p. (J). pap. 7.95 (978-1-59707-034-8(3)) Papercutz.

—The Oppsite Numbers. Rendon, Daniel, illus. 7th rev. ed. 2006. (Hardy Boys Ser.: No. 7). 96p. (J). 12.95 (978-1-59707-035-5(1)) Papercutz.

Lobdell, Scott & Rendon, Daniel. Hyde & Shriek. 6th rev. ed. 2006. (Hardy Boys Ser.: No. 6). (Illus.). 96p. (J). pap. 7.95 (978-1-59707-028-7(9)) Papercutz.

—Identity Theft. 2nd rev. ed. 2005. (Hardy Boys Graphic Novel Ser.: No. 2). (Illus.). 96p. (J). (gr. 3-9). 12.95 (978-1-59707-007-2(6)); pap., pap. 7.95 (978-1-59707-003-4(3)) Papercutz.

—Mad House. 3rd rev. ed. 2005. (Hardy Boys Graphic Novel Ser.: No. 3). (Illus.). 96p. (J). (gr. 3-7). pap., pap. 7.95 (978-1-59707-010-2(6)) Papercutz.

Long, Donna Lee. A Guide for Using Boxcar Children: Surprise Island in the Classroom. 2000. (Literature Units Ser.). (Illus.). 48p. (J). pap., tchr. ed. 7.99 (978-1-57690-338-4(9) , TCM 2338) Teacher Created Materials, Inc.

The Long-Lost Friends, 6 vols., Vol. 3. (Woodland Mysteriestm Ser.). 133p. (gr. 3-7). 42.50 (978-0-322-02377-2(7)) Wright Group, The.

Lord, Kenniston. The Pirates of Peary Village. 2004. 182p. (J). pap. 9.18 (978-1-4116-7893-4(1)) Lulu.com.

Lorimer, Janet. Boneyard. 2003. (Illus.). 80p. (YA). per. 3.95 (978-1-56254-700-4(3) , SP7003) Saddleback Educational Publishing.

—Danger on Ice: Set 1. 2003. 32p. (YA). 2.95 (978-1-56254-406-5(3) , SP 4063) Saddleback Educational Publishing.

—Deadly Game. 2001. (gr. 7-12). lib. bdg. 11.80 (978-0-613-34174-5(0)) Tandem Library Bks.

—The Tiger Lily Code: Set 2. 2002. 32p. (YA). 2.95 (978-1-56254-422-5(5) , SP 4225) Saddleback Educational Publishing.

—Tuesday Raven. 2001. (PageTurner Spy Ser.). 80p. (YA). per. 3.95 (978-1-56254-140-8(4) , SP 1404) Saddleback Educational Publishing.

—Tuesday Raven. 2001. (gr. 7-12). lib. bdg. 11.80 (978-0-613-34513-2(4)) Tandem Library Bks.

Lost Medal. 2006. (YA). 19.95 (978-1-59808-618-8(9)); (YA). spiral bd. 19.95 (978-1-59808-617-1(0)); (YA). cd-rom 13.95 (978-1-59808-619-5(7)); (Illus.). 120p. (J). (gr. 4-8). 24.95 (978-1-930948-94-5(8)); (Illus.). (J). (gr. 4-8). per. 19.95 (978-1-930948-95-2(6)) Whispering Pine Pr., Inc.

Loughead, Deb. Time & Again. 2005. 192p. (J). pap. 9.95 (978-1-894549-39-4(2)) Sumach Pr. CAN. Dist: Orca Bk. Pubs. USA.

Lovelace, Tommy & Streett, Betty. Murder at Rainbow Falls. Califf, Mara D., illus. 1999. 144p. (gr. 5-7). pap. 8.00 (978-0-88028-208-6(8) , 1505) Forward Movement Pubns.

Lowenstein, Sallie. Sender Unknown. 2002. (Illus.). 258p. (YA). per. 16.00 (978-0-9658486-4-0(7)) Lion Stone Bks.

Lowery, Rae. Case of the Lost Kid. l.t. ed. 2002. (Adventures of Charlie Ser.: No. 2). 111p. (YA). pap. 9.95 (978-1-891429-26-2(4) , 26-4) Armadillo Publishing Corp.

—Case of the Pack-Rat Park. l.t. ed. 2002. (Adventures of Charlie Ser.: No. 1). 87p. (YA). pap. 9.95 (978-1-891429-25-5(6) , 25-6) Armadillo Publishing Corp.

—The Case of the Terrible Teacher. 2004. 71p. pap. 14.95 (978-1-4137-2803-3(0)) PublishAmerica, Inc.

Lu, Tina. The Mystery of the Starry Night. Liu, Jenny, ed. 2004. (ENG & CHI., Illus.). 64p. (J). pap. 12.00 net. (978-0-9759126-0-7(7)) Global Alliances.

Lubar, David. Dog Days. 80p. (J). (gr. 4-8). 2005. pap. 4.99 (978-1-58196-025-9(5)); 2004. 15.95 (978-1-58196-013-6(1)) Darby Creek Publishing.

Luna, Rachel Nickerson. The Haunting of Captain Snow. 2005. (Eel Grass Girls Mystery Ser.: No. 2). (Illus.). 332p. pap. 11.95 (978-1-886551-08-4(1)) Howard, Emma Bks.

—The Strange Disappearance of Agatha Buck. 2005. (Eel Grass Girls Mystery Ser.: Book 3). (Illus.). 284p. pap. 11.95 (978-1-886551-09-1(X)) Howard, Emma Bks.

Luxa, Sue. One Golden Summer. 2004. (Illus.). 80p. (J). pap. 8.95 (978-1-890437-99-2(9) , 1234248) Western Reflections Publishing Co.

Lynch, Chris. Freewill. 2006. 148p. (YA). (gr. 7-10). reprint ed. 16.00 (978-0-7567-9869-7(8)) DIANE Publishing Co.

MacDonald, Marion. Christmas Ice Mystery/San Juan Secret. 2002. (Twin Spins Ser.: 7). 200p. (YA). pap. 10.95 (978-0-7599-1006-5(5)) Hard Shell Word Factory.

—Twin Spins, No. 7. 2001. (gr. 7-12). lib. bdg. 19.90 (978-0-613-74642-7(2)) Tandem Library Bks.

MacDonald, Wendy. Castaway Convict. Wilson, Mark, illus. 2005. 136p. (J). pap. 15.25 (978-1-920694-35-7(8)) Univ. of Western Australia Pr. AUS. Dist: International Specialized Bk. Services.

MacGregor, Roy. Death down Under. 2001. (Screech Owls Ser.: No. 15). (Illus.). 128p. (J). (gr. 4-7). mass mkt. 4.95 (978-0-7710-5644-4(3) , Screech Owls) McClelland & Stewart CAN. Dist: Random Hse., Inc.

—The Ghost of the Stanley Cup. Banning, Gregory C., illus. 1999. (Screech Owls Ser.: No. 11). 128p. (J). (gr. 4-7). mass mkt. 4.95 (978-0-7710-5622-2(2) , Screech Owls) McClelland & Stewart CAN. Dist: Random Hse., Inc.

—Horror on River Road. 2000. (Screech Owls Ser.: No. 14). (Illus.). 128p. (J). (gr. 4-7). mass mkt. 4.95 (978-0-7710-5643-7(5) , Screech Owls) McClelland & Stewart CAN. Dist: Random Hse., Inc.

—Nightmare in Nagano. Banning, Gregory C., illus. 1998. (Screech Owls Ser.: No. 9). 120p. (J). (gr. 4-7). mass mkt. 3.95 (978-0-7710-5619-2(2) , Screech Owls) McClelland & Stewart CAN. Dist: Random Hse., Inc.

—The Quebec City Crisis. Banning, Gregory C., illus. 1998. (Screech Owls Ser.: No. 7). 120p. (J). (gr. 4-7). mass mkt. 4.95 (978-0-7710-5617-8(6) , Screech Owls) McClelland & Stewart CAN. Dist: Random Hse., Inc.

—The Screech Owls's Home Loss. Banning, Gregory C., illus. 1998. (Screech Owls Ser.: No. 8). 128p. (J). (gr. 4-7). mass mkt. 4.95 (978-0-7710-5618-5(4) , Screech Owls) McClelland & Stewart CAN. Dist: Random Hse., Inc.

—Sudden Death in New York City. 2000. (Screech Owls Ser.: No. 13). (Illus.). 128p. (J). (gr. 4-7). mass mkt. 3.95 (978-0-7710-5642-0(7) , Screech Owls) McClelland & Stewart CAN. Dist: Random Hse., Inc.

—The West Coast Murders. Banning, Gregory C., illus. 2000. (Screech Owls Ser.: No. 12). 128p. (J). (gr. 4-7). mass mkt. 4.95 (978-0-7710-5623-9(0) , Screech Owls) McClelland & Stewart CAN. Dist: Random Hse., Inc.

MacHado, Ana Maria. El Misterio de la Isla. 2004. Tr. of Mystery of the Island. (SPA., Illus.). 72p. (YA). 9.99 (978-84-241-8653-1(2)) Everest de Ediciones y Distribucion, S.L. ESP. Dist: Lectorum Pubns., Inc.

Mack, Tracy & Citrin, Michael. The Fall of the Amazing Zalindas. Ruth, Greg, illus. 2006. (Sherlock Holmes & the BSI Ser.). 272p. (J). (gr. 4-7). pap. 16.99 (978-0-439-82836-9(8) , Orchard Bks.) Scholastic, Inc.

—The Fall of the Amazing Zalindas. 2006. (Illus.). 259p. (J). (*978-1-4287-0951-5(7) , Orchard Bks.) Scholastic, Inc.

MacKall, Dandi Daley. Case of the Missing Memory. 1999. (Puzzle Club Ser.: Vol. 8). 80p. (J). (gr. 1-5). pap. 5.00 (978-0-570-05558-7(X)) Concordia Publishing Hse.

Mackall, Dandi Daley. Cinnamon Lake Mysteries Set, 6 vols. (Cinnamon Lake Mysteries Ser.). (J). 33.74 (978-0-7586-0006-6(2)) Concordia Publishing Hse.

MacKall, Dandi Daley. The Cinnamon Lake-Ness Monster. 1998. (Cinnamon Lake Mysteries Ser.: Vol. 7). 80p. (J). (gr. 1-4). 5.99 (978-0-570-05336-1(6) , 12-3384) Concordia Publishing Hse.

—Meets the Jigsaw Kids, Vol. 7. 1999. (Puzzle Club Ser.: Vol. 7). 80p. (J). (gr. 1-5). pap. 4.99 (978-0-570-05475-7(3)) Concordia Publishing Hse.

—Musical Mystery. 1998. (Puzzle Club Ser.: Vol. 5). (Illus.). 80p. (J). (gr. 1-5). pap. 4.99 (978-0-570-05059-9(6)) Concordia Publishing Hse.

—The Presidential Mystery. 1999. (Cinnamon Lake Mysteries Ser.: Vol. 8). 80p. (J). (ps-2). 5.99 (978-0-570-05354-5(4) , 12-3405GJ) Concordia Publishing Hse.

MacKall, Dandi Daley, adapted by. Pet-Napping Mystery. 2000. (Puzzle Club Ser.). (Illus.). 32p. (J). (ps-2). 6.99 (978-0-570-07124-2(0)) Concordia Publishing Hse.

Mackey, R. Scott. The Bugfish Experiment. 208p. 2003. 17.95 (978-1-930093-12-6(8)); 2002. pap. 7.95 (978-1-930093-14-0(4)) Brookfield Reader, Inc., The.

MacPhail, Catherine. Fighting Back. (Illus.). 128p. (J). 7.95 (978-0-14-038270-9(4)) Penguin Bks., Ltd. GBR. Dist: Trafalgar Square Publishing.

—Fugitive. 128p. (J). (gr. k-6). 7.95 (978-0-14-038271-6(2)) Penguin Bks., Ltd. GBR. Dist: Trafalgar Square Publishing.

Madison, Bennett. Lulu Dark & the Summer of the Fox. (YA). (gr. 7-12). 2007. 208p. 5.99 (978-1-59514-154-5(5)); 2006. 256p. 10.99 (978-1-59514-086-9(7)) Penguin Group (USA) Inc. (Razorbill).

—Lulu Dark Can See Through Walls. 256p. (YA). (gr. 7-12). 2006. pap. 5.99 (978-1-59514-104-0(9)); 2005. 9.99 (978-1-59514-010-4(7)) Penguin Group (USA) Inc. (Razorbill).

Madsen, Wayne. The Case of Stolen Time: The Misadventures of Inspector Moustachio. 2007. (Misadventures of Inspector Moustachio Ser.: Bk. 1). 156p. (J). per. 16.99 (*978-0-9790878-9-9(9)) Community Pr.

Mahy, Margaret. The Horrendous Hullabaloo. 1999. (Illus.). 32p. pap. (978-0-14-054533-3(6) , N A L Trade) Penguin Group (USA) Inc.

Malcolm, Jahnna N. Who Framed Mary Bubnik? Mary's Not a Thief or Is She? 2001. (Bad News Ballet Ser.: Vol. 4). Tr. of Quien veut a Mary Bubnik?. 160p. (J). (gr. 4-6). pap. 3.95 (978-0-9700164-3-0(3)) Starcatcher Pr.

The Mall Mystery, 6 vols., Vol. 3. (Woodland Mysteriestm Ser.). 133p. (gr. 3-7). 42.50 (978-0-322-02370-3(X)) Wright Group, The.

Malton, Mel. The Drowned Violin: An Alan Dearing Mystery. 2006. 152p. (J). pap. 8.95 (978-1-894917-23-0(5)) Napoleon Publishing/Rendezvous Pr. CAN. Dist: Atlas-Books Distribution.

Mancusi, Mari. Girls That Growl. 2007. 249p. (YA). (gr. 12-12). per. 9.99 (*978-0-425-21716-0(7) , Berkley Trade) Penguin Group (USA) Inc.

Mandelberg, Robert. The Case of the Curious Campaign: A Whodunit of Many Mini-Mysteries. 2003. (Illus.). 96p. (J). pap. 6.95 (978-1-4027-0382-9(1)) Sterling Publishing Co., Inc.

Mangano, J. M. Crossing Cadogan Bay. 2002. 222p. pap. 14.95 (978-0-595-22370-1(2) , Writer's Showcase Pr.) iUniverse, Inc.

Marathon Team. Spies in Space. 4th rev. ed. 2007. (Totally Spies Ser.: No. 4). (Illus.). 112p. (J). 12.95 (978-1-59707-056-0(4)); pap. 7.95 (978-1-59707-055-3(6)) Papercutz.

Mariconda, Barbara. Turn the Cup Around. 1998. (978-0-606-13878-9(1)) Tandem Library Bks.

Mariotti, Celine Rose. Olivia Macallister, Who Are You? A Ghost Mystery Set in Maine. Tango-Schurmann, Ann, illus. 2004. 85p. (YA). (gr. 3-6). pap. 12.95 (978-0-9721389-6-3(X)) Rock Village Publishing.

Markas, Jenny. Monster of Mexico. Mackenzie, Kevin, illus. movie tie-in ed. 2003. (Scooby-Doo Ser.). 80p. (J). pap. 4.99 (978-0-439-44919-9(7) , Scholastic Paperbacks) Scholastic, Inc.

—Scooby-Doo! & You: The Case of the Headless Henry. 2001. (Collect the Clues Mystery Ser.). (Illus.). 60p. (J). (978-0-439-23162-6(0)) Scholastic, Inc.

—Scooby-Doo! & You: The Case of the Leaping Lion. 2001. (Collect the Clues Mystery Ser.). (Illus.). 62p. (J). (978-0-439-23154-1(X)) Scholastic, Inc.

Marks, Burton. Tanya Tinker & the Gizmo Gang. Smath, Jerry, illus. 2003. 20p. (J). (ps-3). reprint ed. 22.00 (978-0-7567-6760-0(1)) DIANE Publishing Co.

Marlow, Herb. The Classroom Vandal. 2003. (J). 19.95 (978-1-893595-36-1(6)) Four Seasons Bks., Inc.

Marriotte, Jeff. Door to Alternity. 2001. (gr. 7-12). lib. bdg. 15.30 (978-0-613-63279-9(6)) Tandem Library Bks.

Marsh, Carole. The Awesome Aquarium Mystery. 2006. 128p. pap. 5.99 (978-0-635-06225-3(9) , Marsh, Carole Bks.) Gallopade International.

—The Baseball Bully. 2006. 64p. (gr. 2-4). 14.95 (*978-0-635-06221-5(6)); pap. (*978-0-635-06215-4(1)) Gallopade International.

—The Baskerville Basketball. 2006. 64p. (gr. 2-4). 14.95 (*978-0-635-06222-2(4)); pap. 3.99 (*978-0-635-06216-1(X)) Gallopade International.

—The Case of the Crybaby Cowboy. 2006. 64p. (gr. 1-3). pap. 3.99 (978-0-635-06166-9(X) , Marsh, Carole Bks.); 14.95 (*978-0-635-06199-7(6)) Gallopade International.

—The Case of the Hunchback Hairdresser. 2006. 64p. (gr. 1-3). pap. 3.99 (978-0-635-06169-0(4) , Marsh, Carole Bks.); 14.95 (*978-0-635-06202-4(X)) Gallopade International.

—The Castaway Cheerleaders. 2006. 64p. (gr. 2-4). 14.95 (*978-0-635-06224-6(0)); pap. 3.99 (*978-0-635-06218-5(6)) Gallopade International.

—The Cruise Ship Mystery. 2006. 128p. (gr. 3-5). pap. 5.99 (*978-0-635-06226-0(7)); (gr. 7-14). 14.95 (*978-0-635-06228-4(3)) Gallopade International.

—Dear Alien: The Little Green Man Mystery. 2007. (Postcard Mysteries Ser.). 128p. (J). (gr. 2-9). 14.95 (*978-0-635-06397-7(2)); pap. 5.99 (*978-0-635-06341-0(7)) Gallopade International. (Marsh, Carole Family CD-Rom).

—Dear Bats: The Creepy Cave Caper. 2007. (Postcard Mysteries Ser.). 128p. (J). (gr. 2-9). 14.95 (*978-0-635-06398-4(0) , Marsh, Carole Family CD-Rom); pap. 5.99 (*978-0-635-06342-7(5)) Gallopade International.

—Dear Granny: The Spooky State Fair Fiasco. 2007. (Postcard Mysteries Ser.). 128p. (J). (gr. 2-9). 14.95 (*978-0-635-06399-1(9)); pap. 5.99 (*978-0-635-06343-4(3)) Gallopade International. (Marsh, Carole Family CD-Rom).

—The Earthshaking Earthquake MYST. 2007. 128p. pap. 5.99 (*978-0-635-06339-7(5)) Gallopade International.

—The Football Phantom. 2006. 64p. (gr. 2-4). 14.95 (*978-0-635-06223-9(2)); pap. 3.99 (*978-0-635-06217-8(8)) Gallopade International.

—The Gargoyle Golf Course. 2006. 64p. (gr. 2-4). 14.95 (*978-0-635-06220-8(8)); pap. 3.99 (*978-0-635-06214-7(3)) Gallopade International.

—The Ghost of Pickpocket Plantation. 2006. 128p. (gr. 3-5). pap. 5.99 (*978-0-635-06233-8(X)); (gr. 7-14). 14.95 (*978-0-635-06237-6(2)) Gallopade International.

—The Goshawful Gold Rush MYST. 2007. 160p. pap. 5.95 (*978-0-635-06334-2(4)) Gallopade International.

—The Horrendous Hurricane MYST. 2007. 128p. pap. 5.99 (*978-0-635-06340-3(9)) Gallopade International.

—The MYST in Chocolate Town... Hershey,Pennsylvania. 2007. 160p. pap. 5.95 (*978-0-635-06333-5(6)) Gallopade International.

—The Mystery at Big Ben: London, England. 2005. (Carole Marsh Mysteries Ser.). (Illus.). 144p. (J). (gr. 3-5). 14.95 (978-0-635-03472-4(7)); pap. 5.95 (978-0-635-03469-4(7)) Gallopade International.

—The Mystery at the Ancient Pyramid. 2006. 144p. (gr. 3-5). 14.95 (*978-0-635-03473-1(5)) Gallopade International.

—The Mystery at the Boston Marathon. 2003. 160p. (gr. 2-8). 14.95 (978-0-635-01642-3(7) , Marsh, Carole Bks.); pap. 5.95 (978-0-635-01640-9(0)) Gallopade International.

—Mystery at the Boston Marathon. 2003. (gr. 3-6). lib. bdg. 14.10 (978-0-613-73036-5(4)) Tandem Library Bks.

—The Mystery at the Georgia Aquarium. 2006. 128p. (gr. 7-14). 14.95 (*978-0-635-06227-7(5)) Gallopade International.

—The Mystery at the Imperial Palace. 2007. 144p. (gr. 3-5). 14.95 (*978-0-635-06211-6(9)); pap. 5.95 (*978-0-635-06207-9(0)) Gallopade International.

—The Mystery at the Kentucky Derby. 2001. 160p. (J). (gr. 2-8). 14.95 (978-0-635-02394-0(6)); pap. 5.95 (978-0-635-02393-3(8)) Gallopade International.

—The Mystery at the Roman Coloseum. 2006. 144p. (gr. 3-5). 14.95 (*978-0-635-06157-7(0)) Gallopade International.

—Mystery at the Roman Colosseum. 2006. 144p. (gr. 3-5). pap. 5.95 (978-0-635-06156-0(2) , Marsh, Carole Bks.) Gallopade International.

—The Mystery in New York City. 2003. (Carole Marsh Mysteries Ser.). 160p. (J). (gr. 2-8). pap. 5.95 (978-0-635-02099-4(8)) Gallopade International.

—The Mystery in the Amazon Rainforest. 2007. 144p. (gr. 3-5). 14.95 (*978-0-635-06212-3(7)) Gallopade International.

—The Mystery in the Amazon Rainforest: South America. 2007. (Around the World in 80 Mysteries (Paperback) Ser.). (Illus.). 131p. (J). (gr. 3-5). per. 5.95 (*978-0-635-06208-6(9)) Gallopade International.

—The Mystery in the Rocky Mountains. 2001. 160p. (J). (gr. 2-8). pap. 5.95 (978-0-635-02389-6(X)) Gallopade International.

—The Mystery of Biltmore House. 2002. 160p. (gr. 2-8). 14.95 (978-0-635-01467-2(X) , 1467X) Gallopade International.

—The Mystery of Blackbeard the Pirate. 2003. (Carole Marsh Mysteries Ser.). 160p. (J). (gr. 2-8). 14.95 (978-0-635-01650-8(8)); pap. 5.95 (978-0-635-01648-5(6)) Gallopade International.

—Mystery of Blackbeard the Pirate. 2003. (gr. 5-8). lib. bdg. 14.10 (978-0-613-73037-2(2)) Tandem Library Bks.

—The Mystery of Kill Devil Hills. 2003. (Carole Marsh Mysteries Ser.). 160p. (J). (gr. 2-8). 14.95 (978-0-635-02095-6(5)); pap. 5.95 (978-0-635-02094-9(7)) Gallopade International.

—The Mystery of the Alamo Ghost. 2003. (Carole Marsh Mysteries Ser.). 160p. (J). (gr. 2-8). 14.95 (978-0-635-01654-6(0)); pap. 5.95 (978-0-635-01652-2(4)) Gallopade International.

—Mystery of the Alamo Ghost. 2003. (gr. 3-6). lib. bdg. 14.10 (978-0-613-73038-9(0)) Tandem Library Bks.

—Mystery of the Ancient Pyramid. 2006. 144p. (gr. 3-5). pap. 5.95 (978-0-635-03470-0(0) , Marsh, Carole Bks.) Gallopade International.

—Mystery of the Biltmore House. 2002. (gr. k-3). lib. bdg. 14.10 (978-0-613-72988-8(9)) Tandem Library Bks.

—The Mystery of the Chicago Dinosaurs. 2003. lib. bdg. 14.10 (978-0-613-73040-2(2)) Tandem Library Bks.

—The Mystery of the Ghost of the Grand Canyon. 2001. 160p. (J). (gr. 2-8). pap. 5.95 (978-0-635-02395-7(4)) Gallopade International.

—The Mystery of the Missing Angel. 2006. 96p. (gr. 2-4). 14.95 (*978-0-635-06232-1(1)); 14.95 (*978-0-635-06230-7(5)); pap. 4.99 (*978-0-635-06229-1(1)) Gallopade International.

—The Mystery of the Vanished Player. 2006. 96p. (gr. 2-4). pap. 4.99 (*978-0-635-06231-4(3)) Gallopade International.

—The Mystery on the California Mission Trail. 2003. (gr. 3-6). lib. bdg. 14.10 (978-0-613-73039-6(9)) Tandem Library Bks.

—The Mystery on the Great Barrier Reef. 2006. 144p. (gr. 3-5). 14.95 (*978-0-635-06210-9(0)); pap. 5.95 (*978-0-635-06206-2(2)) Gallopade International.

—The Mystery on the Great Wall of China. 2006. 144p. (gr. 3-5). 14.95 (*978-0-635-06209-3(7)); pap. 5.95 (*978-0-635-06205-5(4)) Gallopade International.

—The Mystery on the Mighty Mississippi. 2001. 160p. (J). (gr. 2-8). pap. 5.95 (978-0-635-02391-9(1)) Gallopade International.

—The Phantom of Thunderbolt Fort. 2007. 128p. (gr. 3-5). pap. 5.99 (*978-0-635-06235-2(6)); (gr. 7-14). 14.95 (*978-0-635-06239-0(9)) Gallopade International.

—The Puzzle of the Indian Arrowhead. 2006. 64p. (gr. 1-3). pap. 3.99 (978-0-635-06168-3(6) , Marsh, Carole Bks.); 14.95 (*978-0-635-06201-7(1)) Gallopade International.

—The Puzzle of the Shark Surfer Girl. 2006. 64p. (gr. 1-3). pap. 3.99 (978-0-635-06171-3(6) , Marsh, Carole Bks.); 14.95 (*978-0-635-06204-8(6)) Gallopade International.

—The Riddle of the Missing Puppies. 2006. 64p. (gr. 1-3). 14.95 (*978-0-635-06203-1(8)); pap. 3.99 (978-0-635-06170-6(8) , Marsh, Carole Bks.) Gallopade International.

—The Riddle of the Oogli Boogli. 2006. 64p. (gr. 1-3). 14.95 (*978-0-635-06200-0(3)) Gallopade International.

—The Secret of Eyesocket Island. 2007. 128p. (gr. 3-5). pap. 5.99 (*978-0-635-06236-9(4)); (gr. 7-14). 14.95 (*978-0-635-06240-6(2)) Gallopade International.

—The Secret of Skullcracker Swamp. 2006. 128p. (gr. 3-5). pap. 5.99 (*978-0-635-06234-5(8)); (gr. 7-14). 14.95 (*978-0-635-06238-3(0)) Gallopade International.

—The Secret Soccer Ball. 2006. 64p. (gr. 2-4). 14.95 (*978-0-635-06219-2(4)); pap. 3.99 (*978-0-635-06213-0(5)) Gallopade International.

—Three Amigos. 2006. 64p. (gr. 1-3). pap. 3.99 (978-0-635-06167-6(8) , Marsh, Carole Bks.) Gallopade International.

—The Treacherous Tornado Mystery! 2007. 128p. pap. 5.99 (*978-0-635-06338-0(7)) Gallopade International.

—The White House Christmas Mystery. 2003. (Carole Marsh Mysteries Ser.). 160p. (J). (gr. 2-8). 14.95 (978-0-635-01666-9(4)); pap. 5.95 (978-0-635-01664-5(8)) Gallopade International.

—The White House Christmas Mystery. 2003. (gr. 5-8). lib. bdg. 14.10 (978-0-613-73041-9(0)) Tandem Library Bks.

Marsh, Carole. The Zany Zoo MYST. 2007. 128p. pap. 5.99 (*978-0-635-06332-8(8)) Gallopade International.

Martin, Andreu & Ribero, J. No Pidas Sardinas Fuera de Temporada. 35th ed. 2003. (SPA., Illus.). 178p. (J). (gr. 8-12). pap. 11.95 (978-84-204-4796-4(X)) Santillana USA Publishing Co., Inc.

Martin, Ann M. Abby & the Notorious Neighbor. 1998. (Baby-Sitters Club Mystery Ser.: No. 35). (Illus.). (J). (gr. 3-7). pap. 3.99 (978-0-590-05975-6(0) , Scholastic Paperbacks) Scholastic, Inc.

—Claudia y las Llamadas Fant... 2000. (Baby-Sitters Club Ser.).Tr. of Claudia & the Phantom Phone.... (SPA., Illus.). 168p. (YA). 11.95 (978-84-272-3652-3(2)) Molino, Editorial ESP. Dist: AIMS International Bks., Inc.

MNO

—Karen's Spy Mystery. 1999. (Babysitters Little Sister Ser.: No. 111). (Illus.). 109p. (J). (gr. 3-7). pap. 3.99 (978-0-590-52356-1(2)) Scholastic, Inc.

—Kristy & the Cat Burglar. 1998. (Baby-Sitters Club Mystery Ser.: No. 36). (J). (gr. 3-7). pap. 3.99 (978-0-590-05976-3(9) , Scholastic Paperbacks) Scholastic, Inc.

—Mary Anne & the Haunted Bookstore. 1998. (Baby-Sitters Club Mystery Ser.: No. 34). (J). (gr. 3-7). pap. 3.99 (978-0-590-05974-9(2) , Scholastic Paperbacks) Scholastic, Inc.

—Stacey & the Stolen Hearts. 1998. (Baby-Sitters Club Mystery Ser.: No. 33). (J). (gr. 3-7). pap. 3.99 (978-0-590-05973-2(4)) Scholastic, Inc.

Martin, Faith Ellen. The Lost & Found Colony. 2008. 280p. (YA). pap. 14.99 (978-1-59092-396-2(0) , Blue Works) Windstorm Creative.

Martin, Terri L. A Family Trait. 1999. 160p. (J). (gr. 4-6). tchr. ed. 15.95 (978-0-8234-1467-3(1)) Holiday Hse., Inc.

Martini, Steve. Critical Mass. 1999. (gr. 7-12). lib. bdg. 16.45 (978-0-613-21386-6(8)) Tandem Library Bks.

Marzollo, Jean. I Spy: Four Picture Riddle Books. Wick, Walter, photos by. 2005. (Scholastic Reader Collection). (Illus.). 128p. (J). pap. 6.99 (978-0-439-76309-7(6) , Cartwheel Bks.) Scholastic, Inc.

Maselli, Christopher P. N. Hot Pursuit Bk. 6: Steer Clear of Golden Opportunities. 2003. 128p. (J). pap. 4.99 (978-0-310-70665-6(3)) Zonderkidz.

Maselli, Christopher P. N. The Runaway Mission. 2004. 104p. ***978-1-57562-805-9(8))** Copeland, Kenneth Pubns.

Mason, Adrienne. Lu & Clancy's Spy Stuff. Cupples, Pat, illus. unabr. ed. 2001. (Lu & Clancy Ser.). 40p. (J). (gr. k-3). (978-1-55074-693-8(6)) Kids Can Pr., Ltd.

—Secret Codes. Cupples, Pat, illus. 1999. 40p. (J). (ps-k). lib. bdg. 14.10 (978-0-613-21939-6(2)) Tandem Library Bks.

Mason, Adrienne & Cupples, Pat. The Carnival Caper. 2002. (Illus.). 39p. (J). (gr. 3-7). lib. bdg. 15.25 (978-0-613-57708-3(6)) Tandem Library Bks.

Mason, Jane B. & Stephens, Sarah Hines. Bella Baxter & the Lighthouse Mystery. Shelley, John, illus. 2006. (Bella Baxter Ser.). 80p. (J). pap. 3.99 (978-0-689-86282-3(2) , Aladdin) Simon & Schuster Children's Publishing.

Mason, Lynn. Disappeared. 2003. (Illus.). 208p. (YA). (gr. 7). mass mkt. 5.99 (978-0-553-49400-6(7) , Bantam Bks. for Young Readers) Random Hse. Children's Bks.

—Disappeared. 2003. (gr. 7-12). lib. bdg. 14.15 (978-0-613-72717-4(7)) Tandem Library Bks.

Matthews. Death in the Desert. (Thumbprint Mysteries Ser.). 32.86 (978-0-8092-0416-8(9)) McGraw-Hill/ Contemporary.

Matthies, Don-Oliver. Detective Mazes. 2004. (Maze Craze Book Ser.). (Illus.). 40p. pap. 3.95 (978-1-4027-1293-7(6)) Sterling Publishing Co., Inc.

Maupin Schmid, Susan. Lost Time. 2008. 224p. (J). (gr. 5-8). 16.99 (***978-0-399-24460-5(3)** , Philomel) Penguin Group (USA) Inc.

May, Kyla. Kyla May Miss. Behaves As an International Super Spy. 2006. (Illus.). 64p. (J). (gr. 3-6). pap. 4.99 (978-0-8431-1397-6(9) , Price Stern Sloan) Penguin Group (USA) Inc.

Mayer, Jeni. The Mystery of the Missing Will. 2004. 160p. mass mkt. (978-0-920633-90-8(0)) Thistledown Pr., Ltd.

—Suspicion Island, No. 3. 2004. 176p. pap. (978-1-895449-00-6(6)) Thistledown Pr., Ltd.

Mayoral, Juana Aurora. Enigma en el Curi-Cancha. 1998. (SPA.). 200p. (YA). (gr. 5-8). (978-84-216-1115-9(1) , BU3868) Bruño, Editorial ESP. *Dist:* Lectorum Pubns., Inc.

—Tres Monedas de un Penique. (SPA.). 160p. (YA). (gr. 5-8). (978-84-216-2066-3(5) , BU6190) Bruño, Editorial ESP. *Dist:* Lectorum Pubns., Inc.

Mazer, Anne. Now You See It, Now You Don't. 2005. (Amazing Days of Abby Hayes Ser.: No. 15). 126p. (J). lib. bdg. 16.92 (***978-1-4242-0751-0(7))** Fitzgerald Bks.

—Now You See It, Now You Don't. 2005. (Amazing Days of Abby Hayes Ser.: No. 15). (J). 128p. 4.99 (978-0-439-68066-0(2) , Scholastic Paperbacks); (Illus.). 126p. (978-1-4156-0511-0(4)) Scholastic, Inc.

—Reach for the Stars, No. 3. 2000. (Amazing Days of Abby Hayes Ser.: No. 3). (Illus.). 128p. (gr. 4-7). mass mkt. 4.99 (978-0-439-17877-8(0)) Scholastic, Inc.

—Reach for the Stars. 2000. (Amazing Days of Abby Hayes Ser.: No. 3). (gr. 3-6). lib. bdg. 12.40 (978-0-613-32988-0(0)); (J). (gr. 4-6). (978-0-606-19528-7(9)) Tandem Library Bks.

Mazzeo Zocchi, Judy. Lord Zip's Bubble Mystery. Vannozzi, Don, illus. 2000. (Lord Zip Ser.). 8p. (J). (ps). mass mkt. 4.99 (978-1-891997-11-2(4)) Dingles & Co.

McAllister, Angela. Digory & the Lost King. Beck, Ian, illus. 2007. 128p. (J). (gr. 3-5). 14.95 (***978-1-59990-088-9(2));** pap. 5.95 (***978-1-59990-089-6(0))** Bloomsbury Publishing.

McCaffrey, Tony. Emmanuel McClue & The Mystery of the Shroud. 2002. 155p. (J). (gr. 5-9). pap. 11.95 (978-1-929039-08-1(5)) Ambassador Bks., Inc.

McCann, Jesse Leon. And the Fishy Phantom. 2006. (Scooby-doo 8x8 Ser.). 24p. (J). pap. 3.99 (978-0-439-78807-6(2) , Scholastic Paperbacks) Scholastic, Inc.

—Case of the Disappeared Doggie. 2001. (gr. 3-6). lib. bdg. 11.80 (978-0-613-32375-8(0)) Tandem Library Bks.

—The Case of the Hollywood Hound. Fantascope Staff, illus. 2001. (Ace Ventura Chapter Book Ser.: Vol. 4). 64p. (J). (gr. 1-4). pap. 3.99 (978-0-439-20862-8(9)) Scholastic, Inc.

—The Case of the Hollywood Hound. 2001. (Ace Ventura Chapter Bks.: No. 4). (Illus.). (J). 10.79 (978-0-606-20532-0(2)) Tandem Library Bks.

—The Case of the Karate Kitty-Nappers. 2000. (Illus.). 57p. (J). (ps-3). pap. 3.99 (978-0-439-20654-9(5)) Scholastic, Inc.

—The Case of the Karate Kitty-Nappers. 2000. (Ace Ventura Chapter Bk.: Vol. 1). (J). 10.79 (978-0-606-19525-6(4)) Tandem Library Bks.

—The Case of the Lost Unicorn. Fantascope Staff, illus. 2001. (Ace Ventura Chapter Book Ser.: No. 3). 64p. (J). (gr. 1-4). pap. 3.99 (978-0-439-20861-1(0)) Scholastic, Inc.

—The Case of the Lost Unicorn. 2001. (Ace Ventura Chapter Bk.: Vol. 3). (J). (gr. 1-4). (978-0-606-19909-4(8)) Tandem Library Bks.

—The Case of the Stolen Stallion. Fantascope Staff, illus. 2001. (Ace Ventura Chapter Book Ser.: No. 2). 64p. (J). (gr. 6). pap. 3.99 (978-0-439-20655-6(3)) Scholastic, Inc.

—The Case of the Stolen Stallion. 2000. (Ace Ventura Chapter Bk.: Vol. 2). (J). 10.79 (978-0-606-19526-3(2)) Tandem Library Bks.

—Haunted Halloween Mask. 2003. (gr. k-3). lib. bdg. 14.15 (978-0-613-72207-0(8)) Tandem Library Bks.

—The Mystery Mall. 1998. (Scooby-Doo 3-D Storybooks: No. 2). (Illus.). 16p. (J). (ps-3). pap. 5.99 (978-0-590-38656-2(5)) Scholastic, Inc.

—Scooby-Doo & Santa's Bake Shop. del Sur, Duendes, illus. 2000. (Scooby-Doo Ser.). 24p. (J). (ps-3). pap. 5.99 (978-0-439-20999-1(4)) Scholastic, Inc.

—Scooby-Doo! & Santa's Bake Shop. 2000. (gr. 3-6). lib. bdg. 14.15 (978-0-613-54349-1(1)) Tandem Library Bks.

—Scooby-Doo & the Creepy Carnival. 1998. (Scooby-Doo 3-D Storybooks: No. 1). (Illus.). 16p. (J). (ps-3). pap. 5.99 (978-0-590-38654-8(9)) Scholastic, Inc.

—Scooby-Doo & the Cyber Chase. 2001. (gr. k-3). lib. bdg. 11.25 (978-0-613-50734-9(7)) Tandem Library Bks.

—Scooby-Doo! & the Eerie Ice Monster. 2000. (gr. k-3). lib. bdg. 14.15 (978-0-613-54351-4(3)) Tandem Library Bks.

—Scooby-Doo & the Fantastic Puppet Factory. 2000. (gr. k-3). lib. bdg. 11.25 (978-0-613-26852-3(0)) Tandem Library Bks.

—Scooby Doo & the Halloween Hotel Haunt. 1999. (gr. k-3). lib. bdg. 14.15 (978-0-613-29739-4(3)) Tandem Library Bks.

—Scooby-Doo & the Halloween Hotel Haunt: A Glow in the Dark Mystery! del Sur, Duendes, illus. 1999. (Scooby-Doo Ser.). 24p. (J). (ps-3). pap. 5.99 (978-0-439-11768-5(2)) Scholastic, Inc.

—Scooby-Doo & the Haunted Lab: Scooby-Doo Decoder Book. del Sur, Duendes, illus. 2002. (Scooby-Doo Ser.). 32p. (J). (ps-3). pap. 5.99 (978-0-439-40789-2(3)) Scholastic, Inc.

—Scooby Doo! & the Monster of Mexico. 2003. (Scooby-Doo Ser.). (Illus.). 32p. (J). 3.50 (978-0-439-44946-5(4) , Scholastic Paperbacks) Scholastic, Inc.

—Scooby-Doo & the Phantom Cowboy. McCann, Jesse Leon & del Sur, Duendes, illus. 2002. (Scooby-Doo Ser.). 32p. (J). (ps-3). pap. 3.50 (978-0-439-36586-4(4)) Scholastic, Inc.

—Scooby-Doo & the Phantom Cowboy. 2002. (gr. k-3). lib. bdg. 11.25 (978-0-613-50736-3(3)) Tandem Library Bks.

—Scooby-Doo & the Rock 'n' Roll Zombie. 2007. (Scooby-doo 8x8 Ser.). 24p. (J). pap. 3.99 (978-0-439-78808-3(0)) Scholastic, Inc.

—Scooby-Doo & the Tiki's Curse. 2004. (Scooby-Doo Ser.). (Illus.). 24p. (J). 3.50 (978-0-439-54604-1(4) , Scholastic Paperbacks) Scholastic, Inc.

—Scooby-Doo & the Weird Water Park. 2000. (Scooby-Doo Original Titles Ser.: No. 3). (Illus.). 32p. (J). (ps-3). 3.50 (978-0-439-17253-0(5)) Scholastic, Inc.

—Scooby-Doo & the Weird Water Park. 2000. (gr. k-3). lib. bdg. 11.25 (978-0-613-26855-4(5)) Tandem Library Bks.

—Scooby-Doo! & You. del Sur, Duendes, illus. 2001. (Collect the Clues Mystery Ser.). 60p. (J). (978-0-439-23156-5(6)) Scholastic, Inc.

—Scooby-Doo! & You: The Case of the Mad Mermaid. 2001. (Collect the Clues Mystery Ser.). (Illus.). 62p. (J). pap. (978-0-439-23164-0(7)) Scholastic, Inc.

—Scooby-Doo!TM & the Eerie Ice Monster. 2000. (Scooby-Doo Ser.). (Illus.). 24p. (J). (ps-3). 5.99 (978-0-439-20667-9(7)) Scholastic, Inc.

—Scooby-Doo!TM & the Fantastic Puppet Factory. 2000. (Scooby-Doo Original Titles Ser.: No. 4). (Illus.). 32p. (J). (ps-3). 3.50 (978-0-439-17254-7(3)) Scholastic, Inc.

McCann, Jesse Leon, adapted by. Scooby-Doo & the Alien Invaders. 2000. (Scooby-Doo Movie Storybooks). (Illus.). 32p. (J). (ps-3). 3.50 (978-0-439-17700-9(6)) Scholastic, Inc.

McCann, Jesse Leon, et al. Haunted Halloween Mask. del Sur, Duendes, illus. 2003. (Scooby-Doo Ser.). 24p. (J). pap. 5.99 (978-0-439-44937-3(5) , Scholastic Paperbacks) Scholastic, Inc.

McCann, M. L. The Search for Black January: Third Mystery in the Longjohners' Series. 2004. 100p. per. 15.95 (978-0-9754823-2-2(7)) Pumpkin Patch Publishing.

McCarthy, Rebecca. Midnight Mystery #1. 2008. 80p. (J). (gr. 2-5). 3.99 (***978-0-448-44672-1(3)** , Grosset & Dunlap) Penguin Group (USA) Inc.

McCaughren, Tom. Children of the Forge. (Illus.). 128p. 3.95 (978-0-900068-98-0(1)) Penguin Group (USA) Inc.

—Legend of the Corrib King. (Illus.). 96p. 2.25 (978-0-900068-86-7(8)) Penguin Group (USA) Inc.

McCay, Bill & Simmons, Alex. The Raven League. 2006. 192p. (J). (gr. 4-7). 10.99 (978-1-59514-072-2(7) , Razorbill) Penguin Group (USA) Inc.

McClements, George. Jake Gander, Storyville Detective: The Case of the Greedy Granny. 2002. (Illus.). 32p. (ps-2). 15.99 (978-0-7868-0662-1(1)) Hyperion Bks. for Children.

McClintock, Norah. Tell. 2006. 112p. (YA). (gr. 7 up). pap. 8.95 (978-1-55143-511-4(X)); lib. bdg. 14.95 (978-1-55143-672-2(8)) Orca Bk. Pubs. USA.

McCloskey, Larry. Tom Thomson's Last Paddle: A Dani & Caitlin Mystery. 2005. 160p. (Orig.). (YA). pap., tchr. ed. (978-0-88878-430-8(9) , Sandcastle Bks.) Dundurn Group, The.

McCoy, Lois, et al. The Byte Brothers Input an Investigation. Morrill, Leslie H., illus. 2000. (J). mass mkt. 2.25 (978-0-380-85571-1(2) , 85571) HarperCollins Pubs.

McCracken, Craig, creator. The Day is Saved. 2001. (Powerpuff Girls Ser.). (Illus.). 10p. (J). bds. 7.98 (978-0-7853-4754-5(2)) Publications International, Ltd.

McDonald, Megan. Shadows in the Glasshouse. 2000. (American Girl Collection). (Illus.). (J). (978-0-606-20906-9(9)) Tandem Library Bks.

McElhatten, Betty. Stringer: And the Blue Bat Mystery. 2003. 168p. (J). pap. 19.95 (978-1-59286-029-6(X)) PublishAmerica, Inc.

McFall, Jessica & McFall, Ernest. Unselfish Love. l.t. ed. 2006. (ENG., Illus.). 28p. per. 9.95 (***978-1-4327-0076-8(6))** Outskirts Press, Inc.

McGee, Warner, illus. The Mystery of the Jeweled Eggs. 2007. (Backyardigans Ser.). 24p. (J). pap. 3.99 (978-1-4169-4070-8(7) , Simon Spotlight/Nickelodeon) Simon & Schuster Children's Publishing.

McGrady, Kayla. Dead Ball Foul. 2000. 154p. (YA). pap. 12.50 (978-1-57072-133-5(5)) Overmountain Pr.

McLean, Allan Campbell. The Hill of the Red Fox. 2nd ed. 2006. (Kelpies Ser.). 272p. (J). pap. 11.95 (978-0-86315-556-7(1)) Floris Bks. GBR. *Dist:* SteinerBooks, Inc.

McMahon, P. J. The Case of the Psychic Hamster. 2005. (Freaky Joe Club Ser.: No. 4). (Illus.). 153p. (J). (978-1-4155-7725-7(0) , Aladdin) Simon & Schuster Children's Publishing.

—The Case of the Psychic Hamster. Manders, John, illus. 2005. (Freaky Joe Club Ser.: No. 4). 160p. (J). pap. 4.99 (978-0-689-86263-2(6) , Aladdin) Simon & Schuster Children's Publishing.

—Case of the Psychic Hamster. Manders, John, illus. 2005. 153p. (J). lib. bdg. 15.38 (***978-1-4242-0404-5(6))** Fitzgerald Bks.

—The Case of the Singing Sea Dragons. Manders, John, illus. 2005. (Freaky Joe Club Ser.: No. 6). 160p. (J). pap. 4.99 (978-1-4169-0050-4(0) , Aladdin) Simon & Schuster Children's Publishing.

—The Case of the Singing Sea Dragons. 2005. (Freaky Joe Club Ser.: No. 6). (Illus.). 153p. (J). (978-1-4156-4221-4(4) , Aladdin) Simon & Schuster Children's Publishing.

—Case of the Singing Sea Dragons. Manders, John, illus. 2005. 153p. (J). lib. bdg. 15.38 (***978-1-4242-0406-9(2))** Fitzgerald Bks.

—The Case of the Smiling Shark. Manders, John, illus. 2004. (Freaky Joe Club Ser.: No. 2). 128p. (J). pap. 4.99 (978-0-689-86261-8(X) , Aladdin) Simon & Schuster Children's Publishing.

—Case of the Smiling Shark. Manders, John, illus. 2004. 116p. (J). lib. bdg. 15.38 (***978-1-4242-0402-1(X))** Fitzgerald Bks.

—The Mystery of the Disappearing Dinosaurs. Manders, John, illus. 2005. (Freaky Joe Club Ser.: No. 5). 128p. (J). pap. 3.99 (978-1-4169-0049-8(7) , Aladdin) Simon & Schuster Children's Publishing.

—Mystery of the Disappearing Dinosaurs. Manders, John, illus. 2005. 120p. (J). lib. bdg. 15.38 (***978-1-4242-0405-2(4))** Fitzgerald Bks.

—The Mystery of the Morphing Hockey Stick. Manders, John, illus. 2004. (Ready-for-Chapters Ser.). 144p. (J). pap. 4.99 (978-0-689-86262-5(8) , Aladdin) Simon & Schuster Children's Publishing.

—The Mystery of the Swimming Gorilla. Manders, John, illus. 2004. (Freaky Joe Club Ser.: No. 1). 112p. (J). pap. 4.99 (978-0-689-86260-1(1) , Aladdin) Simon & Schuster Children's Publishing.

—The Mystery of the Swimming Gorilla. Manders, John, illus. 2004. (Freaky Joe Club Ser.: No. 1). 106p. (J). (gr. 2-5). lib. bdg. 11.19 (978-0-606-32533-2(6)) Tandem Library Bks.

McMahon, P. J. Mystery of the Swimming Gorilla. Manders, John, illus. 2004. 106p. (J). lib. bdg. 15.38 (***978-1-4242-0401-4(1))** Fitzgerald Bks.

McNab, Andy & Rigby, Robert. Avenger. 2007. 272p. (YA). (gr. 7). 16.99 (***978-0-399-24685-2(1)** , Putnam Juvenile) Penguin Group (USA) Inc.

McNamee, Graham. Acceleration. (YA). (gr. 7). 2003. 224p. lib. bdg. 17.99 (978-0-385-90144-4(5) , Lamb, Wendy); 2005. 240p. reprint ed. pap. 6.50 (978-0-440-23836-2(6) , Laurel Leaf) Random Hse. Children's Bks.

McNicoll, Sylvia. Grave Secrets. l.t. ed. 1999. (Illus.). 176p. (J). (gr. 7-9). pap. 8.95 (978-0-7737-6015-8(6)) Stoddart Kids CAN. *Dist:* Fitzhenry & Whiteside, Ltd.

—Grave Secrets. 1999. (J). 228p. (gr. 3-7). per. 17.60 (978-0-613-28858-3(0)); (978-0-606-19641-3(2)) Tandem Library Bks.

McOmber, Rachel B., ed. McOmber Phonics Storybooks: The Cove of Gloom. rev. ed. (Illus.). (J). (978-0-944991-83-1(1)) Swift Learning Resources.

McVeity, Jen. Frogs of Betts. 1999. (gr. 3-6). lib. bdg. 12.60 (978-0-613-19363-4(6)) Tandem Library Bks.

Medearis, Angela Shelf. The Case of the Missing Trophy. Papp, Robert, illus. 2004. (Little Apple Ser.). 135p. (J). pap. (978-0-439-52325-7(7)) Scholastic, Inc.

Meier, Leslie. Christmas Cookie Murder. 2000. (Lucy Stone Mystery Ser.). 256p. pap. 5.99 (978-1-57566-691-4(X)) Kensington Publishing Corp.

Meisels, Dovid. Bar Mitzvah & Tefillin Secrets: The Mysteries Revealed. 2004. 245p. 24.95 (978-1-931681-56-8(2)) Israel Bk. Shop.

Mercati, Cynthia. The Secret Room. Bovy, Deb, illus. 2000. (Cover-to-Cover Bks.). 72p. (J). (gr. 2-5). lib. bdg. 13.95 (978-0-7807-9059-9(6) , Covercraft); (gr. 4-7). mass mkt. 5.60 (978-0-7891-5108-7(1)) Perfection Learning Corp.

Metz, Melinda. The Case of the Creepy Castle. 2000. (New Adventures of Mary-Kate & Ashley Ser.). (Illus.). (J). 11.15 (978-0-606-21914-3(5)) Tandem Library Bks.

—The Case of the Flapper 'Napper. 2001. (New Adventures of Mary-Kate & Ashley Ser.). (Illus.). (J). 11.15 (978-0-606-21916-7(1)) Tandem Library Bks.

—The Case of the Flying Phantom. 2001. (New Adventures of Mary-Kate & Ashley Ser.). (Illus.). (J). 11.05 (978-0-606-21917-4(X)) Tandem Library Bks.

—The Case of the Golden Slipper. 2000. (New Adventures of Mary-Kate & Ashley Ser.). (Illus.). (J). 11.30 (978-0-606-21918-1(8)) Tandem Library Bks.

—The Case of the Surprise Call. 1999. (New Adventures of Mary-Kate & Ashley Ser.). 86p. (J). (gr. 2-7). pap. 3.99 (978-0-590-29403-4(2)) Scholastic, Inc.

Meyer, M. D. The Mystery of the Lost Friend. 2003. 65p. pap. 9.95 (978-0-7414-1378-9(7)) Infinity Publishing.

Mickey, Mouse Clubhouse. MYST of Missing Muffins. rev. ed. 2008. 24p. pap. 3.99 (***978-1-4231-0741-5(1))** Disney Pr.

Midnight at the August Tree House. 2004. (Illus.). 100p. (J). per. 15.95 (978-0-9754823-1-5(9)) Pumpkin Patch Publishing.

Miles, Ellen. The Hidden Fortune. 2002. (Seven Sisters Mysteries Ser.: No. 2). (J). 176p. pap. 4.50 (978-0-439-35968-9(6)); (gr. 3-7). pap. 4.50 (978-0-439-43646-5(X)) Scholastic, Inc.

—The Secret in the Attic. 2002. (Seven Sisters Mysteries Ser.: No. 1). 176p. (J). (gr. 3-7). pap. 4.50 (978-0-439-23813-7(7)) Scholastic, Inc.

—Stage Fright. 2002. (Seven Sisters Mysteries Ser.: No. 3). 158p. (J). (gr. 3-7). pap. 4.50 (978-0-439-36005-0(6)) Scholastic, Inc.

—Trouble in Paradise. 2002. 161p. (J). (978-0-439-36006-7(4)) Scholastic, Inc.

Miley, Berry. Christmas Village Chronicles & Other Short Stories. 2005. 63p. pap. 8.95 (978-1-4116-2617-1(6)) Lulu.com.

Miller, D. C. Hurricane Hunters: A Craig Hancock Adventure. 2005. (YA). pap. 9.95 (978-1-59088-646-5(1)) Wings ePress, Inc.

Miller, Michael. Hilde und Gunter - Level One German Reader. House, Josh, illus. 2002. 44p. (J). 6.00 (978-0-9723474-7-1(X)) Miller, Michael.

Millman, Calanitte. The Adventures of the Gimmel Gang III: The Cave. 2005. (J). pap. 8.95 (***978-1-931681-84-1(8))** Israel Bk. Shop.

Mills, Charles. The Bandit of Benson Park. 2003. (Honors Club Story Ser.: Vol. 1). 127p. (J). (978-0-8163-1977-0(4)) Pacific Pr. Pubns.

—The Secret of Scarlett Cove. 2004. (Honors Club Story Ser.: Bk. 3). 127p. (J). (978-0-8163-1999-2(5)) Pacific Pr. Publishing Assn.

Mills, Steven L. Rafi's Search for the Torah Munching Monster. 2001. (Illus.). 48p. (J). 9.95 (978-1-881283-31-7(3)) Alef Design Group.

Milne, A. A. The Red House Mystery. 2001. 202p. (J). per. 6.49 (978-1-57924-702-7(4)) Jones, Bob Univ. Pr.

Miner, Sharon. Octavia's Quest. 2005. 113p. pap. 11.95 (978-0-7414-2647-5(1)) Infinity Publishing.

Miss O, Harlie, Justine, and Isabella, with Devra Newberger Speregen, Juliette. Miss O & Friends: Picture Perfecto! 2006. (Miss O & Friends Ser.). (Illus.). 128p. (J). pap. 5.99 (978-0-8230-2949-5(2)) Watson-Guptill Pubns., Inc.

The Missing Will, 6 vols., Vol. 3. (Woodland Mysteriestm Ser.). 133p. (gr. 3-7). 42.50 (978-0-322-02369-7(6)) Wright Group, The.

El misterio de los trajes Desaparecidos 21: Leveled Books. 2001. (McGraw-Hill. Lectura Ser.). (ENG & SPA.). (gr. 2 up). (978-0-02-188046-1(8)) Macmillan/McGraw-Hill Schl. Div.

Mitchelhill, Barbara. The Case of the Disappearing Daughter. Ross, Tony, illus. 2007. 72p. (J). (***978-1-59889-269-7(X))** Stone Arch Bks.

Mitchelhill, Barbara & Ross, Tony. How to Be a Detective. 2004. (Illus.). 64p. (J). pap. 8.99 (978-1-84270-360-1(9)) Andersen GBR. *Dist:* Independent Pubs. Group.

Mitchell, Mark E. The Curious Courtship of King George, 5 vols. 1998. (Chronicles of the House of Chax Ser.: Bk. 4). 84p. (J). (ps-k). pap. 9.99 (978-0-88092-351-4(2) , 3512) Royal Fireworks Publishing Co.

Mitchell, Todd. The Traitor King. 2007. 368p. (J). (gr. 4-7). pap. 16.99 (978-0-439-82788-1(4) , Scholastic Pr.) Scholastic, Inc.

Mockford, Caroline. What's This? (Illus.). 32p. (J). pap. 6.99 (978-1-84148-166-1(1)) Barefoot Bks., Inc.

Mockford, Caroline, illus. What's This? 2000. 32p. (J). (ps-1). 15.95 (978-1-84148-018-3(5)) Barefoot Bks., Inc.

Moloney, James. Black Taxi. 2005. 272p. (J). (gr. 7 up). 15.99 (978-0-06-055937-3(3)); lib. bdg. 16.89 (978-0-06-055938-0(1)) HarperCollins Pubs.

Monfredo, Miriam G. The Stalking Horse. 1999. (978-0-606-16386-6(7)) Tandem Library Bks.

Monte, Emily C. The Lost Sword of the Confederate Ghost: A Mystery in Two Centuries. 1999. 116p. (J). (gr. 4-7). 5.99 (978-1-57249-132-8(9)) White Mane Publishing Co., Inc.

Montgomery, R. A. Lost on the Amazon. 2006. (Choose Your Own Adventure Ser.: No. 9). (Illus.). 144p. (J). mass mkt. 5.99 (978-1-933390-09-3(3) , CHCL09) Chooseco LLC.

—Lost on the Amazon. 1999. (Illus.). 114p. mass mkt. (978-0-553-23733-7(0)) Random Hse., Inc.

—Lost on the Amazon. 2005. (Illus.). 114p. (J). pap. (*978-0-7608-9697-6(6)) Sundance/Newbridge Educational Publishing.

The Monument Mystery. 2001. mass mkt. 5.99 (978-0-9708721-1-1(9)) Palmtree Publishing.

Moore, Eva. The Search for the Missing Bones. Enik, Ted, illus. 2000. (Magic School Bus Chapter Bks.: No. 2). 80p. (gr. 1-4). mass mkt. 4.99 (978-0-439-10799-0(7)) Scholastic, Inc.

Moore, Inga. The Truffle Hunter. Moore, Inga, illus. 1999. (Illus.). 32p. (J). (gr. k-3). pap. 7.95 (978-0-916291-92-1(8)) Kane/Miller Bk. Pubs., Inc.

Moore, James A. Newbies. 2004. (YA). mass mkt. 5.99 (978-0-8439-5474-6(4)) Dorchester Publishing Co., Inc.

Moore, Ulysses. The Long-Lost Map. Bruno, Iacopo, illus. 2006. (Ulysses Moore Ser.: No. 2). 272p. (J). pap. 12.99 (978-0-439-77439-0(X) , Scholastic) Scholastic, Inc.

Mooser, Stephen. Goofball Malone: Smell That Clue! Biggs, Brian, illus. 2006. (All Aboard Reading Ser.). 48p. (J). (gr. 2-4). pap. 3.99 (978-0-448-43912-9(3) , Grosset & Dunlap) Penguin Group (USA) Inc.

—Goofball Malone Ace Detective: All Aboard Mystery Reader Station Stop 3. Biggs, Brian, illus. 2005. (All Aboard Reading Ser.). 48p. (J). 13.99 (978-0-448-43894-8(1)); (gr. 2-4). pap. 3.99 (978-0-448-43893-1(3)) Penguin Group (USA) Inc. (Grosset & Dunlap).

Moreno, Elena. El Misterio de la Llave. 1998. (SPA.). (gr. 7-12). lib. bdg. 14.10 (978-0-613-80728-9(6)) Tandem Library Bks.

Morgan, Harry. The Monteverdi Mystery. 2006. per. (*978-1-84685-409-5(1) , Exposure Publishing) Meadow Bks.

Morris, Deborah. Bear Attack & Other True Stories. 2003. (J). 21.95 (978-0-7862-5173-5(5)) Thorndike Pr.

Morris, Gilbert. The Temptations of Pleasure Island, Vol. 5. 2000. (Seven Sleepers the Lost Chronicles Ser.: Vol. 5). (Illus.). 176p. (J). (gr. 3-7). pap. 5.99 (978-0-8024-3671-9(4)) Moody Pubs.

—The Terrible Beast of Zor. 2000. (Seven Sleepers the Lost Chronicles Ser.: Vol. 7). (Illus.). 144p. (J). (gr. 3-7). pap. 5.99 (978-0-8024-3673-3(0)) Moody Pubs.

—Too Smart Jones & the Cat's Secret: A Gilbert Morris Mystery. 2000. (Gilbert Morris Mysteries Ser.: Vol. 6). (Illus.). 124p. (J). (gr. 2-7). pap. 5.99 (978-0-8024-4030-3(4)) Moody Pubs.

—Too Smart Jones & the Disappearing Dogs: A Gilbert Morris Mystery. 2000. (Gilbert Morris Mysteries Ser.: Vol. 3). (Illus.). 128p. (J). (gr. 4-7). pap. 5.99 (978-0-8024-4027-3(4)) Moody Pubs.

—Too Smart Jones & the Pool Party Thief: A Gilbert Morris Mystery. 1999. (Gilbert Morris Mysteries Ser.: Vol. 1). (Illus.). 115p. (J). (gr. 2-7). pap. 5.99 (978-0-8024-4025-9(8)) Moody Pubs.

—Too Smart Jones & the Stolen Bicycle: A Gilbert Morris Mystery. 2000. (Gilbert Morris Mysteries Ser.: Vol. 9). (Illus.). 133p. (J). (gr. 4-7). pap. 5.99 (978-0-8024-4031-0(2)) Moody Pubs.

—The Victims of Nimbo. 2000. (Seven Sleepers the Lost Chronicles Ser.: Vol. 6). (Illus.). 160p. (J). (gr. 3-7). pap. 5.99 (978-0-8024-3672-6(2)) Moody Pubs.

Moss, Merrilee. Thriller & Me. 2000. 115p. pap. 8.95 (978-1-875843-05-3(1)) Spinifex Pr. AUS. *Dist:* Independent Pubs. Group.

Mosso, Tyfanny. The Mud Puddle Gang. 2006. 17.00 (978-0-8059-9067-6(4)) Dorrance Publishing Co., Inc.

Muldrow, Diane. Recipe for Trouble. Pollak, Barbara, illus. 2007. (Dish Ser.: No. 7). 160p. (J). pap. 4.99 (978-0-448-44532-8(8) , Grosset & Dunlap) Penguin Group (USA) Inc.

Muller, Rachel Dunstan. When the Curtain Rises. 2007. 144p. (J). (gr. 4-7). pap. (*978-1-55143-615-9(9)) Orca Bk. Pubs.

Mullin, Caryl Cude. A Riddle of Roses. 2000. (Illus.). 222p. (YA). (gr. 5-8). pap. 6.95 (978-1-896764-28-3(2)) Second Story Pr. CAN. *Dist:* Orca Bk. Pubs. USA, Univ. of Toronto Pr.

Munro, Ken. The Cross Keys Caper. 2006. (Sammy & Brian Mystery Ser.: 18). 154p. pap. 5.95 (*978-1-932864-94-6(6)) Masthof Pr.

—Fire, Smoke, & Secrets: Sammy & Brian Mystery #14. 2002. (Sammy & Brian Mystery Ser.: 14). (J). pap. 5.95 (978-1-930353-64-0(2)) Masthof Pr.

—Fireball. 2003. (Sammy & Brian Mystery Ser.: No. 15). (J). pap. 5.95 (978-1-930353-84-8(7)) Masthof Pr.

—Grandfather's Secret. 2004. (Sammy & Brian Mystery Ser.: 16). (J). pap. 5.95 (978-1-932864-04-5(0)) Masthof Pr.

—The Medallion's Secret: A Sammy & Brian Mystery #11. 2000. 128ppp. (J). pap. 5.95 (978-1-930353-20-6(0)) Masthof Pr.

—The Mysterious Baseball Scorecard. 2005. (Sammy & Brian Mystery Ser.: 17). pap. 5.95 (978-1-932864-31-1(8)) Masthof Pr.

—The Mysterious Guesthouse: Sammy & Brian Mystery #13. 2002. (Sammy & Brian Mystery Ser.: 13). (J). pap. 5.95 (978-1-930353-53-4(7)) Masthof Pr.

—Secret under the Floorboard: A Sammy & Brian Mystery #12. 2001. 149ppp. (J). pap. 5.95 (978-1-930353-31-2(6)) Masthof Pr.

—The Tin Box: A Sammy & Brian Mystery #9. 1999. 139ppp. (J). pap. 5.95 (978-1-883294-84-7(3)) Masthof Pr.

—The Toy Factory: A Sammy & Brian Mystery #10. 2000. 150ppp. (J). pap. 5.95 (978-1-930353-00-8(6)) Masthof Pr.

Murase, Sho & Petrucha, Stefan. The Haunted Dollhouse. 3rd rev. ed. 2005. (Nancy Drew Ser.: No. 3). (Illus.). 96p. (J). (gr. 3-7). 12.95 (978-1-59707-009-6(2)) Papercutz.

Murder in Cabin A-13. 1999. (SmartReader Ser.). (J). pap., tchr. ed. 19.95 incl. audio (978-0-7887-0116-0(9) , 79304T3) Recorded Bks., LLC.

Murhall, J. J. Smash 'n' Grab Squirrels. 2003. (Illus.). 96p. pap. (978-0-340-84346-8(2) , Hodder Children's Books) Hodder Children's Division.

—Stick 'em up, Bunny! 2003. (Illus.). 96p. pap. (978-0-340-84347-5(0) , Hodder Children's Books) Hodder Children's Division.

Murphy, Antoinette S. Does It Hurt When You Die? 2004. 30p. (J). pap. 14.95 (978-1-4137-3520-8(7)) PublishAmerica, Inc.

Murphy, Elspeth Campbell. The Mystery of the Butterfly Garden. 1999. (Three Cousins Detective Club Ser.). (J). (gr. 2-5). (978-0-606-19304-7(9)) Tandem Library Bks.

—The Mystery of the Golden Reindeer. 2000. (Three Cousins Detective Club Ser.: No. 30). (Illus.). 64p. (J). (gr. 2-5). pap. 3.99 (978-0-7642-2138-5(8)) Bethany Hse. Pubs.

—Mystery of the Sand Castle. 1998. (gr. 3-6). lib. bdg. 11.80 (978-0-613-86064-2(0)) Tandem Library Bks.

—Three Cousins Detective Club Boxed Set: The Mystery of the Coon Cat; the Mystery of the Runaway Scarecrow; the Mystery of the Attic Lion; the Mystery of the Backdoor Bundle; the Mystery of the Painted Snake; the Mystery of the Golden Reindeer, Vol. 25-30. 2000. (Three Cousins Detective Club Ser.: Nos. 25-30). (J). (gr. 4-7). pap. 23.99 (978-0-7642-8704-6(4)) Bethany Hse. Pubs.

—Three Cousins Detective Club Mix. 1999. (Three Cousins Detective Club Ser.). (J). (gr. 2-5). pap. 23.99 (978-0-7642-8463-2(0)) Bethany Hse. Pubs.

—Young Cousins, Vols. 1-6. 2002. (Young Cousins Ser.). (Illus.). (J). pap. 29.99 (978-0-7642-8893-7(8)) Bethany Hse. Pubs.

Murphy, T. M. The Secrets of Belltown. 2001. (Belltown Mystery Ser.: Vol. 1). 176p. (J). (gr. 4-7). pap. 9.95 (978-1-880158-34-0(5)) Townsend, J.N. Publishing.

—The Secrets of Cain's Castle. 2001. (Belltown Mystery Ser.). 144p. (J). (978-1-880158-38-8(8)) Townsend, J.N. Publishing.

—The Secrets of Cranberry Beach. 2001. (Belltown Mystery Ser.). (Illus.). 156p. (J). 9.95 (978-1-880158-36-4(1)) Townsend, J.N. Publishing.

—The Secrets of Pilgrim Pond. 2001. (Belltown Mystery Ser.). 144p. (J). (gr. 4-7). pap. 9.95 (978-1-880158-39-5(6)) Townsend, J.N. Publishing.

—The Secrets of the Twisted Cross. 2002. (Belltown Mystery Ser.). (Illus.). 176p. (J). (978-1-880158-43-2(4)) Townsend, J.N. Publishing.

Murray, Peter J. Mokee Joe Is Coming. 2006. (Mokee Joe Ser.: Bk. 1). 160p. (J). (gr. 4-6). pap. 8.99 (978-0-340-88470-6(3) , Hodder & Stoughton) Hodder General Publishing Division GBR. *Dist:* Trafalgar Square Publishing.

—Mokey Jo Recharged. 2006. (Mokee Joe Ser.: Bk. 2). 192p. (J). (gr. 4-6). pap. 8.99 (978-0-340-89296-1(X) , Hodder & Stoughton) Hodder General Publishing Division GBR. *Dist:* Trafalgar Square Publishing.

Murray, Susan & Davies, Robert. Outrage in Orlando. 2000. (KC Flanagan Girl Detective Ser.). 192p. (YA). (gr. 5-11). pap. (978-1-55207-023-9(9)) Studio 9 Bks.

Murray, William. Key Words Reading Scheme. Aitchison, M., illus. (Key Words Readers Ser.: A Series, No. 641-11a). 56p. (J). (ps-5). 3.50 (978-0-7214-0011-2(6) , Dutton Juvenile) Penguin Group (USA) Inc.

—Key Words Reading Scheme. Wingfield, J. H., illus. (Key Words Readers Ser.: A Series, No. 641-12a). 56p. (J). (ps-5). 3.50 (978-0-7214-0012-9(4) , Dutton Juvenile) Penguin Group (USA) Inc.

Musa, Boy Spy (Children's Reading Book - 2001-2002) 2001. (2001-2002 Children's Reading Book Ser.). 32p. (J). pap. 2.85 (978-0-8341-1849-2(1)) Beacon Hill Pr. of Kansas City.

Musick, David. Jeremy Daniels & the Bambles:The Mystery in the Forest. 2002. 132p. (YA). 21.95 (978-0-595-65150-4(X) , Writers Club Pr.) iUniverse, Inc.

Myers, Bill. The Case of the Hiccupping Ears, Vol. 5. 2004. (Secret Agent Dingledorf Ser.: Vol. 5). (Illus.). 96p. (J). pap. 4.99 (978-1-4003-0178-2(5)) Nelson, Thomas Inc.

—Phantom of the Haunted Church. 1998. (Bloodhounds, Inc. Ser.: Vol. 3). (Illus.). 128p. (J). (gr. 3-8). pap. 5.99 (978-1-55661-892-5(1)) Bethany Hse. Pubs.

Myers, Bill & Wimbish, Dave. I Want My Mummy. 2000. (Bloodhounds, Inc. Ser.: Vol. 8). (Illus.). 128p. (J). (gr. 3-8). pap. 5.99 (978-1-55661-492-7(6)) Bethany Hse. Pubs.

Myers, Bill & Wimbish, David. Mystery of the Melodies from Mars. 2002. (Bloodhounds, Inc. Ser.: No. 11). 128p. (J). pap. 5.99 (978-0-7642-2623-6(1)) Bethany Hse. Pubs.

—Room with a Boo. 2002. (Bloodhounds Inc Ser.). 128p. (J). pap. 5.99 (978-0-7642-2624-3(X)) Bethany Hse. Pubs.

Myers, Walter Dean. Smiffy Blue: Ace Crime Detective. 1999. (978-0-606-18607-0(7)) Tandem Library Bks.

—Somewhere in the Darkness. 2003. 176p. (J). 5.99 (978-0-439-52356-1(7) , Scholastic Paperbacks) Scholastic, Inc.

Mysteries. 2001. (Illus.). 48p. (J). (ps-3). 12.95 (978-0-439-23801-4(3)) Scholastic, Inc.

The Mysteries of Shapeville. l.t. ed. 2005. (Illus.). 48p. (J). 18.95 (978-0-9747509-1-0(3)) Del Gatto, Maria.

Mysterious Chills & Thrills: 10 creepy, strange, adventurous short stories for kids to tickle the Imagination. 2004. (J). per. 6.95 (978-0-9749013-0-5(X)) LH Pubns. & Productions.

The Mysterious IOU, 6 vols., Vol. 3. (Woodland Mysteriestm Ser.). 133p. (gr. 3-7). 42.50 (978-0-322-02375-8(0)) Wright Group, The.

The Mysterious Mansion. (Get a Clue Mystery Puzzles Ser.). 16p. (J). (gr. 5). 12.99 (978-0-7847-0734-0(0)) Standard Publishing.

Mystery Bay: Individual Title Six-Packs. (Action Packs Ser.). 128p. (gr. 3-5). 44.00 (978-0-7635-3310-6(6)) Rigby Education.

Mystery in the Arctic, 6 Packs. 32p. (gr. 5 up). 44.00 (978-0-7578-0991-0(X)) Rigby Education.

Mystery Mountain: Individual Title Six-Packs. (Bookweb Ser.). 32p. (gr. 6 up). 34.00 (978-0-7578-0897-5(2)) Rigby Education.

The Mystery of Moody Manor, 6 vols. (Ragged Island Mysteriestm Ser.). 161p. (gr. 5-7). 42.50 (978-0-322-01655-2(X)) Wright Group, The.

The Mystery of October Island. 2003. (Illus.). 50p. (J). per. 12.95 (978-0-9754823-0-8(0)) Pumpkin Patch Publishing.

The Mystery of the Dark Old House, 6 vols., Vol. 2. (Woodland Mysteriestm Ser.). 133p. (gr. 3-7). 42.50 (978-0-7802-7940-7(9)) Wright Group, The.

Mystery Of the Missing Ring (2001-2002 Children's Mission Ed Book) 2001. 32p. (J). pap. 3.50 (978-0-8341-1842-3(4)) Beacon Hill Pr. of Kansas City.

Mystery of the Secret Treasure. 2001. (Mickey Mysteries Ser.: No. 2). (Illus.). 96p. (gr. 2-5). reprint ed. pap. 4.99 (978-0-7868-4450-0(7)) Disney Pr.

The Mystery of the Smoking Chimney. 1999. 112p. (J). (gr. 3-7). pap. 6.95 (978-1-889062-04-4(9)) Artel Publishing.

The Mystery of the Three Keys, 6 vols., Vol. 3. (Woodland Mysteriestm Ser.). 133p. (gr. 3-7). 42.50 (978-0-322-02371-0(8)) Wright Group, The.

The Mystery of Veggie Island. 2003. (Big Idea Bks.). (978-0-310-70744-8(7)) Zondervan.

Mystery Valley: Individual Title Six-Packs. (Bookweb Ser.). 32p. (gr. 4 up). 34.00 (978-0-7635-3730-2(6)) Rigby Education.

Nagler, Michelle H. Haunted Pumpkins. 2001. (gr. k-3). lib. bdg. 11.80 (978-0-613-54532-7(X)) Tandem Library Bks.

—Meet Big Foot. 2002. (gr. k-3). lib. bdg. 11.80 (978-0-613-54285-2(1)) Tandem Library Bks.

Nalbantsky, Danail. Bludnia Sin (the Prodigal Son) Guetov, Dimitar, ed. 2nd unabr. ed. 2004. (BUL.). 228p. per. 9.99 (978-0-9753970-3-9(6)) Capricorn Publishing.

Nancy Drew. 2006. (J). (gr. 3-8). 72.63 (978-1-59961-056-6(6)) Spotlight.

Napoli, Donna Jo & Furrow, Robert. Sly the Sleuth & the Food Mysteries. Maione, Heather Harms, illus. 2007. 144p. (J). (gr. 2-4). 16.99 (978-0-8037-3119-6(1) , Dial) Penguin Group (USA) Inc.

—Sly the Sleuth & the Pet Mysteries. Maione, Heather Harms, illus. 2005. 96p. (J). (gr. 2). 15.99 (978-0-8037-2993-3(6) , Dial) Penguin Group (USA) Inc.

—Sly the Sleuth & the Sports Mysteries. Maione, Heather Harms, illus. 2006. 128p. (J). 15.99 (978-0-8037-2994-0(4) , Dial) Penguin Group (USA) Inc.

Nash, Scott. Tuff Fluff: The Case of Duckie's Missing Brain. Nash, Scott, illus. 2004. (Illus.). (J). 101.94 (978-0-7636-2503-0(5)) Candlewick Pr.

—Tuff Fluff: The Case of Duckie's Missing Brain. 2004. (Illus.). 40p. (J). (gr. 1-4). 16.99 (978-0-7636-1882-7(9)) Candlewick Pr.

Natti, Susanna, illus. Cam Jansen & the Snowy Day Mystery. 2004. (Cam Jansen Ser.: No. 24). 64p. (J). (gr. 3-7). 13.99 (978-0-670-05922-5(6) , Viking Juvenile) Penguin Group (USA) Inc.

Naylor, Phyllis Reynolds. Bernie Magruder & the Case of the Big Stink. 2001. 11.64 (978-0-606-22812-1(8)) Tandem Library Bks.

—Bernie Magruder & the Disappearing Bodies. 2001. (Bernie Magruder Ser.). (Illus.). 160p. (J). (gr. 4-7). pap. 4.99 (978-0-689-84127-9(2) , Aladdin) Simon & Schuster Children's Publishing.

—Bernie Magruder & the Disappearing Bodies. 2001. 11.64 (978-0-606-22813-8(6)); (gr. 3-6). lib. bdg. 13.00 (978-0-613-50182-8(9)) Tandem Library Bks.

—Bernie Magruder & the Disappearing Bodies. l.t. ed. 2001. (Juvenile Ser.). 153p. (J). 20.95 (978-0-7862-3467-7(9)) Thorndike Pr.

—Bernie Magruder & the Haunted Hotel. 2001. 11.64 (978-0-606-22814-5(4)) Tandem Library Bks.

—Bernie Magruder & the Haunted Hotel. l.t. ed. 2001. 127p. (J). 20.95 (978-0-7862-3600-8(0)) Thorndike Pr.

—Bernie Magruder & the Parachute Peril. DiTerlizzi, Tony, illus. 2001. (Bernie Magruder Ser.). 160p. (J). pap. 4.99 (978-0-689-83166-9(8) , Aladdin) Simon & Schuster Children's Publishing.

—Bernie Magruder & the Pirate's Treasure. 2001. (978-0-606-22788-9(1)); (gr. 3-6). lib. bdg. 13.00 (978-0-613-22950-0(9)) Tandem Library Bks.

Neebe, Charles A. How Back-Back Got His Name. 2007. (J). 15.95 (978-1-933872-20-9(9)) Lima Bear Pr LLC, The.

Neenan, Colin. Thick. 2006. 102p. (J). pap. 6.95 (978-0-9746481-9-4(1)) Brown Barn Bks.

Nelson, Betty. The Mystery of Vanishing Trees. 2004. 192p. (J). 12.95 (978-1-56315-319-8(X)) SterlingHouse Pubs., Inc.

Nelson, Kelly. Boreal, Dragon of the North. 2005. 68p. (YA). pap. 9.99 (978-1-4141-0292-4(5)) Pleasant Word.

Nelson, Patricia. Mystery of Apartment 2a. Rene, Noel, illus. 2004. 76p. pap. 14.95 (978-1-4137-4252-7(1)) PublishAmerica, Inc.

Neri, Kris. Dem Bones' Revenge: A Tracy Eaton Mystery. Wright, Betty, ed. 2000. 294p. 22.95 (978-1-56825-077-9(0) , 077-0); pap. 14.95 (978-1-56825-081-6(9)) Rainbow Bks., Inc.

Nettrour, Nelani. The Dragon Lands Bk. 1: The Ripple. Nettrour, Heather, illus. 2003. 100p. pap. 11.95 (978-1-929381-46-3(8) , Third Millennium Publishing) Sci Fi-Arizona, Inc.

Newbery, Linda. Lost Boy. 2008. (J). (*978-0-375-84574-1(7)); lib. bdg. (*978-0-375-93617-3(3)) Random Hse. Children's Bks. (Fickling, David Bks.).

Newcomb, Ambrose. Eagles of the Sky or with Jack Ralston along the Air Lanes. 2005. reprint ed. pap. 26.95 (978-1-4179-8865-5(7)) Kessinger Publishing, LLC.

Nicieza, Fabian. Bosom Buddies. 2006. (Illus.). 144p. (YA). pap. 14.99 (978-0-7851-1869-5(1)) Marvel Enterprises, Inc.

Nickerson, Sara. How to Disappear Completely & Never Be Found. Comport, Sally Wern, illus. 288p. (J). (gr. 5 up). 2003. pap. 5.99 (978-0-06-441027-4(7)); 2002. 16.99 (978-0-06-029771-8(9)); 2002. lib. bdg. 17.89 (978-0-06-029772-5(7)) HarperCollins Pubs.

—How to Disappear Completely & Never Be Found. 2003. (gr. 7-12). lib. bdg. 14.15 (978-0-613-62207-3(3)) Tandem Library Bks.

Nimmo, Jenny. Charlie Bone & the Beast. 2007. (Children of the Red King Ser.: Bk. 6). 464p. (J). 10.99 (*978-0-439-84665-3(X) , Orchard Bks.) Scholastic, Inc.

Nix, Garth. Grim Tuesday. 2005. (Keys to the Kingdom Ser.: No. 2). 336p. (J). (gr. 4-7). pap. 15.95 (978-0-439-70370-3(0) , Scholastic Pr.) Scholastic, Inc.

Nixon & Brush. Champagne with a Corpse. (Thumbprint Mysteries Ser.). 32.86 (978-0-8092-0420-5(7)) McGraw-Hill/Contemporary.

Nixon, Joan Lowery. A Deadly Game of Magic. 2004. (gr. 7-12). lib. bdg. 14.10 (978-0-613-71631-4(0)) Tandem Library Bks.

—Gus & Gertie & the Missing Pearl. deGroat, Diane, illus. 2000. 48p. (J). (ps-3). 15.50 (978-1-58717-023-2(X) , SeaStar Bks.) Chronicle Bks. LLC.

—The Haunting. 2005. 192p. (gr. 5). 5.99 (978-0-440-42002-6(4) , Yearling) Random Hse. Children's Bks.

—The Haunting. Horowitz, Beverly, ed. 2000. 192p. (YA). (gr. 7-12). mass mkt. 5.99 (978-0-440-22008-4(4) , Laurel Leaf) Random Hse. Children's Bks.

—The Haunting. 2000. (YA). 11.64 (978-0-606-19191-3(7)) Tandem Library Bks.

—The Kidnapping of Christina Lattimore. 2004. 320p. (YA). pap. 5.95 (978-0-15-205031-3(0) , Harcourt Paperbacks) Harcourt Children's Bks.

—Laugh till You Cry. 112p. 2006. (gr. 7). 5.50 (978-0-440-23774-7(2) , Yearling); 2004. (J). (gr. 5). lib. bdg. 17.99 (978-0-385-90186-4(0) , Delacorte Bks. for Young Readers) Random Hse. Children's Bks.

—Murdered, My Sweet. 2004. (Illus.). 208p. (J). (gr. 5). pap. 4.99 (978-0-440-41988-4(3) , Yearling) Random Hse. Children's Bks.

—Nightmare. 2003. 176p. (YA). (gr. 7). 15.95 (978-0-385-73026-6(8)); lib. bdg. 17.99 (978-0-385-90151-2(8)) Random Hse. Children's Bks. (Delacorte Bks. for Young Readers).

—Nightmare. l.t. ed. 2004. 200p. 22.95 (978-0-7862-6911-2(1) , Large Print Pr.) Thorndike Pr.

—Nobody's There. 2001. 208p. (YA). (gr. 7). mass mkt. 5.99 (978-0-440-22760-1(7) , Laurel Leaf) Random Hse. Children's Bks.

—Nobody's There. 2001. (gr. 7-12). lib. bdg. 13.55 (978-0-613-36851-3(7)) Tandem Library Bks.

—Playing for Keeps. 2003. 208p. (YA). (gr. 7). pap. 5.50 (978-0-440-22867-7(0) , Laurel Leaf) Random Hse. Children's Bks.

—Playing for Keeps. 2003. (gr. 7-12). lib. bdg. 13.55 (978-0-613-64782-3(3)) Tandem Library Bks.

—The Seance. 2004. (gr. 7-12). lib. bdg. 14.10 (978-0-613-71629-1(9)) Tandem Library Bks.

—Search for the Shadowman. 1998. 160p. (gr. 3-7). reprint ed. 5.50 (978-0-440-41128-4(9) , Yearling) Random Hse. Children's Bks.

—Search for the Shadowman. 1998. (J). (978-0-606-13083-7(7)) Tandem Library Bks.

—The Trap. 2004. 176p. (J). (gr. 5). pap. 5.50 (978-0-440-22870-7(0) , Yearling) Random Hse. Children's Bks.

—Two Mysteries. 2005. 384p. (YA). (gr. 7). lib. bdg. 11.99 (978-0-385-90939-6(X) , Laurel Leaf) Random Hse. Children's Bks.

—Two Mysteries: The Other Side of Dark & the Name of the Game Was Murder. 2005. 384p. (YA). (gr. 7). mass mkt. 6.99 (978-0-553-49453-2(8) , Laurel Leaf) Random Hse. Children's Bks.

Noble, Sarah. Hannah & Horatio Pea. 2006. (Illus.). 336p. pap. (*978-1-84401-673-0(0)) Athena Pr.

Nordin, Ruth Ann. Witness to a Murder. 2007. 140p. per. 11.95 (*978-0-595-45089-3(X)) iUniverse, Inc.

North, Bill. The Disappearing Airplane. 2001. 108p. pap. 9.95 (978-0-595-18789-8(7) , Writers Club Pr.) iUniverse, Inc.

Norton, Andre. Ralestone Luck. 2006. 96.99 (*978-1-4280-4411-1(6)); pap. 89.99 (*978-1-4280-4419-7(1)) Indy-Publish.com.

Norton, Andre Alice. Ralestone Luck. 2006. pap. (*978-1-4068-3557-1(9)) Echo Library.

Norville, Rod. Moonshine Express: Revised Edition with a History of Moonshine Today & Yesterday. 2003. 178p. (YA). per. 13.95 (978-1-891929-99-1(2)) Four Seasons Pubs.

Nowhere to Hide. 1999. (SmartReader Ser.). (J). Level 1. pap., tchr. ed. 19.95 incl. audio (978-0-7887-0770-4(1) , 79350T3); Level 2. pap., tchr. ed. 19.95 incl. audio (978-0-7887-0117-7(7) , 79305T3) Recorded Bks., LLC.

Nye, Julie & Nye, Julie. Scout: The Secret at les Cheneaux. 2007. (Illus.). 160p. (YA). per. (*978-0-9767762-1-5(9)) Fieldstone Hill Pr.

O'Brien, Bill. Unmasked. 2002. (Crime Waves Ser.). (Illus.). 160p. (YA). pap. (978-0-7344-0303-2(8) , Lothian Bks.) Hachette Livre Australia.

—Unmasked. 2001. (gr. 7-12). lib. bdg. 18.75 (978-0-613-86957-7(5)) Tandem Library Bks.

Obrist, Jurg. Case Closed?! 40 Mini-Mysteries for You to Solve. 2003. (Single Titles Ser.). 96p. (J). pap. 6.95 (978-0-7613-1999-3(9)); 22.90 (978-0-7613-2739-4(8)) Lerner Publishing Group. (Millbrook Pr.).

Obrist, Jurg. Complex Cases: Three Major Mysteries for You to Solve. 2006. (Mini-Mysteries Ser.). (Illus.). 93p. (J). 23.93 (978-0-7613-3419-4(X) , Millbrook Pr.) Lerner Publishing Group.

Obrist, Jurg. Complex Cases: Three Major Mysteries for You to Solve. 2006. (Illus.). (J). pap. 6.95 (978-0-8225-5975-7(7) , First Avenue Editions) Lerner Publishing Group.

—Open & Shut Case? 40 More Mini - Mysteries for You to Solve. 2004. 96p. (J). lib. bdg. (978-0-7613-2740-0(1) , Millbrook Pr.) Lerner Publishing Group.

—Open & Shut Cases: 40 More Mini-Mysteries for You to Solve. 2005. (Illus.). 96p. (J). (gr. 4-7). pap. 6.95 (978-0-7613-2344-0(9) , First Avenue Editions) Lerner Publishing Group.

Ocker, Christa Holder. A Crow Named Robin. 2006. (J). per. (*978-1-59872-712-8(5)) Instantpublisher.com.

Odgers, Darrel & Odgers, Sally. The Awful Pawful: Jack Russell: Dog Detective. Dawson, Janine, illus. 2007. (Jack Russell: Dog Detective Ser.: No. 5). 80p. (J). (gr. 2-6). pap. 4.95 (*978-1-933605-53-1(7)) Kane/Miller Bk. Pubs., Inc.

—The Sausage Situation: Jack Russell: Dog Detective. Dawson, Janine, illus. 2007. (Jack Russell: Dog Detective Ser.: No. 6). 80p. (J). (gr. 2-6). 4.95 (*978-1-933605-54-8(5)) Kane/Miller Bk. Pubs., Inc.

Odgers, Sally & Odgers, Darrel. The Buried Biscuits. Dawson, Janine, illus. 2008. (Jack Russell: Dog Detective Ser.: 7). 84p. (J). pap. 4.95 (*978-1-933605-77-7(4)) Kane/Miller Bk. Pubs., Inc.

Odgers, Sally & Odgers, Darrel. Jack Russell: Dog Detective Dog Den Mystery. 2006. (Jack Russell: Dog Detective Ser.: 1). (Illus.). 84p. (J). pap. 4.95 (978-1-933605-18-0(9)) Kane/Miller Bk. Pubs., Inc.

Ogilvie, Elizabeth. Masquerade at Sea House. (J). reprint ed. lib. bdg. 19.95 (978-0-88411-333-1(7)) Amereon LTD.

O'Hara, Diarmuid H. The Pool. 2004. 184p. pap. 19.95 (978-1-4137-2116-4(8)) PublishAmerica, Inc.

Olds, Barbara Anne. Haven House. Amatrula, Michele, illus. 2007. 141p. (J). pap. 8.95 (978-0-9744446-0-4(X)) All About Kids Publishing.

O'Leary, Edward J. Murder in the I. R. S. 2003. (YA). per. 18.95 (978-0-9708590-9-9(0)) First Word Publishing, The.

Oliver, Andrew. Haunted Hill. 2006. (Sam & Stephanie Mystery Ser.). 268p. (J). (gr. 5-9). per. 12.95 (978-0-9661009-7-6(2)) Adams-Pomeroy Pr.

—If Photos Could Talk. 2005. (Sam & Stephanie Mystery Ser.). 264p. (J). per. 12.95 (978-0-9661009-6-9(4)) Adams-Pomeroy Pr.

Oliver, Andrew. Scrambled. 2007. 288p. (J). per. 12.95 (*978-0-9661009-8-3(0)) Adams-Pomeroy Pr.

Oliver, M. Search for the Sunken City. 1999. (Puzzle Adventures Ser.). (Illus.). 48p. (J). (gr. 3-8). lib. bdg. 13.95 (978-0-88110-409-7(4)); pap. 5.95 (978-0-7460-0304-6(8)) EDC Publishing.

Olsen, Mary-Kate. Case of the Giggling Ghost. 2002. (gr. 3-6). lib. bdg. 12.40 (978-0-613-50424-9(0)) Tandem Library Bks.

Olsen, Mary-Kate & Olsen, Ashley. The Case of the Icy Igloo Inn. 2002. (Illus.). (J). pap. 18.00 (978-0-06-052114-1(7) , Harper Entertainment) HarperCollins Pubs.

Olsen, Mary-Kate, et al. The Case of the Giggling Ghost. 2002. (New Adventures of Mary-Kate & Ashley Ser.: No. 31). (Illus.). 96p. mass mkt. 4.50 (978-0-06-106653-5(2)) HarperCollins Pubs.

O'Malley, Kevin. Captain Raptor & the Moon Mystery. O'Brien, Patrick, illus. 2005. 32p. (J). 17.85 (978-0-8027-8936-5(6)); 16.95 (978-0-8027-8935-8(8)) Walker & Co.

Orme, David. Boffin Boy & the Temples of Mars. 2007. (Boffin Boy Ser.). (Illus.). 36p. pap. 7.95 (*978-1-84167-623-4(3)) Ransom Publishing Ltd. GBR. *Dist:* International Publishers Marketing.

Osborne, Mary Pope. Carnival at Candlelight. Murdocca, Sal, illus. 2005. (Magic Tree House Ser.: No. 33). 128p. (J). (gr. k-3). lib. bdg. 13.99 (978-0-375-93033-1(7) , Random Hse. Bks. for Young Readers) Random Hse. Children's Bks.

—Rocking Horse Christmas. Bittinger, Ned, illus. 2004. (Bookshelf Ser.). 32p. (J). (gr. k-ps). pap. 5.99 (978-0-439-66938-2(3) , Scholastic Paperbacks) Scholastic, Inc.

—Spider Kane & the Mystery at Jumbo Nightcrawler's. 1999. (J). (978-0-606-19083-1(X)) Tandem Library Bks.

—Spider Kane & the Mystery under the May-Apple. 1999. (J). (978-0-606-19084-8(8)) Tandem Library Bks.

Osorio, Rick. The Great Adventure of Sally Rock & el Lobo. 2007. (ENG.). 96p. per. 14.95 (*978-1-4241-5869-0(9)) PublishAmerica, Inc.

Osterlund, Anne. Aurelia. 2008. 288p. (YA). (gr. 7). pap. 8.99 (*978-0-14-240579-6(5) , Puffin) Penguin Group (USA) Inc.

Overton, Max & Overton, Ariana. Glass House. 2003. 208p. 22.00 (978-1-59426-010-0(9) , gh-hc) Mundania Pr.

Page, Katherine Hall. Bon Voyage, Christie & Company. (Christie & Company Ser.). (YA). (gr. 6-8). 1999. (Illus.). 10p. pap. 3.99 (978-0-380-78035-8(6)); 1998. 288p. 14.00 (978-0-380-97398-9(7)) HarperCollins Pubs.

—Down East. 1998. (Christie & Company Ser.). (YA). (gr. 6-8). reprint ed. pap. 3.99 (978-0-380-78033-4(X)) HarperCollins Pubs.

Pagliarulo, Antonio. The Celebutantes: In the Club. 2008. (YA). (*978-0-385-73473-8(5)); 12.99 (*978-0-385-90472-8(X)) Dell Publishing. (Delacorte Pr.).

Pagliarulo, Antonio. On the Avenue. 2007. (Celebutantes Ser.). 352p. (YA). (gr. 9 up). pap. 9.99 (978-0-385-73404-2(2)); lib. bdg. 12.99 (978-0-385-90415-5(0)) Random Hse. Children's Bks. (Delacorte Bks. for Young Readers).

Panagopoulos, Janie Lynn. The Runes of Isle Royale: A Great Lakes Adventure in History & Mystery. 2000. (Illus.). 158p. (J). (gr. 3-7). pap. 8.95 (978-0-938682-63-9(6) , 982-63-6) River Road Pubns., Inc.

Panec, D. J. We Both Read-the Mystery of Pirate's Point. Spangler, Brie, illus. 2008. (We Both Read Ser.). 44p. (J). 7.99 (*978-1-60115-009-7(1)); pap. 3.99 (*978-1-60115-010-3(5)) Treasure Bay, Inc.

Papp, Robert, illus. The Game Store Mystery, 104. 2005. (Boxcar Children Mysteries Ser.: No. 104). 131p. (J). (gr. 2-7). pap. 4.50 (978-0-8075-2739-9(4)); lib. bdg. 14.95 (978-0-8075-2738-2(6)) Whitman, Albert & Co.

—The Ghost of the Chattering Bones, Vol. 102. 2005. (Boxcar Children Mysteries Ser.: 102). 128p. (J). pap. 4.50 (978-0-8075-0874-9(8)) Whitman, Albert & Co.

—The Giant Yo-Yo Mystery. 2006. 124p. (J). (*978-1-4156-6756-9(X)) Whitman, Albert & Co.

—The Mystery of the Orphan Train, 105. 2005. (Boxcar Children Mysteries Ser.: No. 105). 120p. (J). (gr. 2-7). lib. bdg. 14.95 (978-0-8075-5558-3(4)) Whitman, Albert & Co.

—The Sword of the Silver Knight, Vol. 103. 2005. (Boxcar Children Mysteries Ser.: 103). 112p. (J). (ps-7). 14.95 (978-0-8075-0877-0(2)) Whitman, Albert & Co.

Paris, Nick. The Spread of Darkness. 2001. 57p. (YA). (gr. 10 up). pap. 8.99 (978-0-9714885-0-2(9)) Incite Insight, LLC.

Parker, Robert B. The Boxer & the Spy. 2008. 224p. (YA). (gr. 7). 17.99 (*978-0-399-24775-0(0) , Philomel) Penguin Group (USA) Inc.

Parker, Robert B. Edenville Owls. 2007. 208p. (YA). (gr. 4 up). 17.99 (978-0-399-24656-2(8) , Philomel) Penguin Group (USA) Inc.

Parkin, Lance & Jones, Mark. Dark Matters: An Unofficial & Unauthorised Guide to Philip Pullman's Dark Materials Trilogy. 2005. 272p. (YA). pap. 7.95 (978-0-7535-1025-4(1)) Virgin Bks. Ltd. GBR. *Dist:* Macmillan.

Parkinson, Curtis. Death in Kingsport. 2007. 224p. (J). (gr. 5-9). pap. 11.95 (*978-0-88776-827-9(X)) Tundra Bks., Inc./Livres Toundra, Inc. CAN. *Dist:* Random Hse., Inc.

Parrott, David L. Trouble at Trashy Lake: A Thomas Beaver Mystery. 2002. per. (978-0-9718006-1-8(8)) Parrott Pr., The.

Parsons, Carol. Mystery at Eagle Harbor Lighthouse. 2006. (J). pap. 9.95 (978-1-59705-985-5(4)) Wings ePress, Inc.

Parsons, Tom. Pinky the Rat at the Brussels Sprout Museum. 2007. 194p. 27.76 (*978-1-4303-1538-4(5)) Lulu.com.

Parus, M. V. The Adventures of Mamma Simone, Jodie & Zed: The Mystery of the Pirate's Lost Treasure. 2006. 115p. (YA). per. 12.95 (*978-1-58374-148-1(8)) Chicago Spectrum Pr.

Pascal, Francine. Alone. 2002. (gr. 7-12). lib. bdg. 14.15 (978-0-613-67047-0(7)) Tandem Library Bks.

—Flee. 2001. (Fearless Ser.: No. 17). (gr. 7-12). lib. bdg. 14.15 (978-0-613-67086-9(8)) Tandem Library Bks.

—Killer Party. 2000. (Sweet Valley University Ser.: No. 13). (gr. 7-12). lib. bdg. 13.00 (978-0-613-21857-3(4)) Tandem Library Bks.

—Love. 2001. (Fearless Ser.: No. 18). (gr. 7-12). lib. bdg. 14.15 (978-0-613-67101-9(5)) Tandem Library Bks.

—Naked Eye. 2006. (Fearless FBI Ser.: No. 4). 240p. (YA). pap. 7.99 (978-0-689-87824-4(9) , Simon Pulse) Simon & Schuster Children's Publishing.

—Run. 2000. 206p. pap. (978-0-671-03748-2(X) , Simon & Schuster Children's Publishing) Simon & Schuster Children's Publishing.

Pasha, Georgia. Jelly Bean & Key Mystery. 2005. 17.00 (978-0-8059-9909-9(4) , RoseDog Bks.) Dorrance Publishing Co., Inc.

Paterson, Katherine. La Busqueda de Park. 2003. (Katherine Patterson Ser.).Tr. of Park's Quest. (SPA., Illus.). 208p. (J). (gr. 4-7). 9.95 (978-84-239-2816-3(0) , EC3399) Espasa Calpe, S.A. ESP. *Dist:* Planeta Publishing Corp.

Patterson, James. When the Wind Blows. 1999. 432p. (gr. 7-12). per. 16.45 (978-0-613-22618-9(6)) Tandem Library Bks.

Pattison, Caroline. The Whole, Entire, Complete Truth: A Sarah Martin Mystery. 2006. 180p. (YA). pap. 12.99 (*978-1-55002-583-5(X) , Dundurn Pr.) Dundurn Group, The CAN. *Dist:* Univ. of Toronto Pr.

Paul, Catherine. Waterview Manor. West, Kelly, ed. 1999. 150p. (YA). (gr. 6-10). pap. 6.50 (978-0-9670006-0-2(2)) F.A.M.E. (Fiction & Mysteries Etc.).

Paulits, John. Philip & the Case of the Mistaken Identity & Philip & the Baby. 2007. (YA). pap. 7.50 (*978-1-59705-109-5(8)); pap. 13.95 (*978-1-59705-897-1(1)) Wings ePress, Inc.

Paulson, Michael W. The Baker Street Bunch & the Missing Pig Mystery. l.t. ed. 2004. (Illus.). 90p. (J). per. 3.95 (978-0-9754241-1-7(4)) MiMar Publishing.

Paulson, Michael William. The Baker Street Bunch & the Hidden Map Mystery. 2005. (Illus.). (J). per. (978-0-9754241-4-8(9)) MiMar Publishing.

—The Baker Street Bunch & the Missing Bracelet Mystery. 2005. (Illus.). (J). per. (978-0-9754241-2-4(2)) MiMar Publishing.

—The Baker Street Bunch & the Missing Pie Mystery. 2005. (J). per. (978-0-9754241-9-3(X)) MiMar Publishing.

Pausacker, Jenny. Looking for Blondie. 2002. (Crime Waves Ser.). (Illus.). 96p. (YA). pap. (978-0-7344-0167-0(1) , Lothian Bks.) Hachette Livre Australia.

—Scam. 2002. (Crime Waves Ser.). (Illus.). 96p. (YA). pap. (978-0-7344-0277-6(5) , Lothian Bks.) Hachette Livre Australia.

Peacock, Shane. Eye of the Crow: The Boy Sherlock Holmes, His First Case. 2007. (Boy Sherlock Holmes Ser.). 260p. (J). (gr. 5-9). 19.95 (*978-0-88776-850-7(4)) Tundra Bks., Inc./Livres Toundra, Inc. CAN. *Dist:* Random Hse., Inc.

Peck, Richard. Dreamland Lake. 2000. (Illus.). 160p. (YA). (gr. 7-12). pap. 4.99 (978-0-14-130812-8(5) , Puffin) Penguin Group (USA) Inc.

—Dreamland Lake. 2000. (gr. 7-12). lib. bdg. 13.00 (978-0-8335-4119-2(6)) Tandem Library Bks.

Peckham, Lori, ed. Guide's Greatest Mystery Stories. 2007. 160p. (J). pap. 11.99 (*978-0-8280-2038-1(8)) Review & Herald Publishing Assn.

Pelletier, Marthe & Sottolichio, Rafael. Le Secret de Max. 2002. (Roman Jeunesse Ser.). (FRE., Illus.). 96p. (J). (gr. 4-7). pap. (978-2-89021-574-0(1)) Diffusion du livre Mirabel.

Pellowski, Michael. Double Trouble Mansion Mystery. 1998. (Illus.). 160p. (J). (gr. 4-6). pap. 3.99 (978-0-87406-892-4(4) , Willowisp Pr.) Darby Creek Publishing.

Penn, Audrey. Blackbeard & the Gift of Silence. 2007. 355p. (gr. 3-7). 15.95 (*978-1-933718-11-8(0)) Tanglewood Pr.

—Mystery at Blackbeard's Cove. 2006. (Illus.). 200p. (J). 14.95 (978-0-9749303-1-2(8)) American Media Intl.

—Mystery at Blackbeard's Cove. 2007. 347p. pap. 7.95 (*978-1-933718-09-5(9)) Tanglewood Pr.

Pennell, Kathleen. Circus of Fear. Pennell, Lauren, illus. 2002. (Pony Investigators Ser.: Vol. III). 96p. (J). (gr. 3-6). pap. 5.95 (978-1-930353-47-3(2)) Masthof Pr.

—Missing Money. Pennell, Lauren, illus. 2000. (Pony Investigators Ser.: Vol. 1). 88p. (J). (gr. 3-6). pap. 5.95 (978-1-930353-21-3(9)) Masthof Pr.

—The Phantom Stallion. Pennell, Lauren, illus. 2003. (Pony Investigators Ser.: Vol. 4). 118p. (J). (gr. 3-7). pap. 5.95 (978-1-930353-73-2(1)) Masthof Pr.

—The Secret Passage: Pony Investigators. 2005. (Pony Investigators Ser.: 5). (Illus.). 108p. (J). pap. 5.95 (978-1-932864-42-7(3)) Masthof Pr.

Peralta, Joaquin. An Almost Private Eye: Mystery of the Starfighter. 2008. 260p. (YA). per. 17.00 (*978-1-934376-17-1(5)) Balona Bks.

Perdew, Suzanne, et al. The Mystery of the Abandoned Lighthouse. 2001. (Shoebox Kids Ser.: Bk. 12). (Illus.). 93p. (J). (978-0-8163-1819-3(0)) Pacific Pr. Publishing Assn.

Peretti, Frank. Hangman's Curse: The Veritas Project - Volume 1. 2008. 352p. (YA). mass mkt. 7.99 (*978-1-4003-1016-6(4)) Nelson, Thomas Inc.

—Nightmare Academy: The Veritas Project - Volume 2. 2008. 352p. (YA). mass mkt. 7.99 (*978-1-4003-1017-3(2)) Nelson, Thomas Inc.

Peretti, Frank E. Trapped at the Bottom of the Sea: Russian Language Edition. Life Publishers International Staff, tr. 1999. (Cooper Kids Adventure Ser.: Vol. 3). (RUS., Illus.). 206p. (J). (gr. 3-12). pap. (978-0-7361-0126-4(8)) Life Pubs. International.

Perkins, T J. Image in the Tapestry: A Kim & Kelly Mystery. 2005. (Illus.). 155p. (YA). 10.99 (978-0-9777538-3-3(2)) GumShoe Press.

—In the Grand Scheme of Things: A Kim & Kelly Mystery. 2007. (Illus.). 151p. (YA). 10.99 (*978-0-9777538-4-0(0)) GumShoe Press.

Perkins, T J. Mystery of the Attic. 2006. (Illus.). 113p. (YA). 10.99 (978-0-9777538-6-4(7)) GumShoe Press.

Perkins, T. J. The Secret in Phantom Forest: A Kim & Kelly Mystery. 2004. (Illus.). 130p. (YA). 10.99 (978-0-9777538-1-9(6)) GumShoe Press.

Perkins, T J. Wound Too Tight. 2006. (Illus.). 141p. (YA). 10.99 (978-0-9777538-5-7(9)) GumShoe Press.

Perkins, TJ. Fantasies Are Murder: A Kim & Kelly Mystery. novel ed. 2005. (Illus.). 148p. (YA). 10.99 (978-0-9777538-0-2(8)) GumShoe Press.

—Trade Secret: A Kim & Kelly Mystery. 2004. (Illus.). 175p. (YA). 10.99 (978-0-9777538-2-6(4)) GumShoe Press.

Perry, Phyllis J. Mr Crumb's Secret. 2003. (gr. k-3). lib. bdg. 26.85 (978-0-613-81770-7(2)) Tandem Library Bks.

—Mr. Crumb's Secret. 2002. per. 16.95 (978-1-57950-080-1(3) , Upstart Bks.) Highsmith Inc.

—The Secret of the Silver Key. Lipking, Ron, illus. 2003. (Fribble Mouse Library Mystery Ser.). 90p. (J). pap. 16.95 (978-1-932146-03-5(2)) Highsmith Inc.

—The Secrets of the Rock. Lipking, Ron, illus. 2004. (Fribble Mouse Library Mystery Ser.). 96p. (J). 16.95 (978-1-932146-22-6(9)) Highsmith Inc.

Perry, R. W. Kelly Mccabe in Slow Boat to Terror. 2003. 160p. (J). (gr. 3-6). pap. 11.95 (978-0-9745522-0-0(8)) Greenleaf Book Group Pr.

Peters, Elizabeth, pseud. The Falcon at the Portal. 2000. 450p. (gr. 7-12). per. 15.90 (978-0-613-25117-4(2)) Tandem Library Bks.

Peters, Julie Anne. Romance of The Snob Squad. 1999. 144p. (J). (gr. 3-7). 13.95 (978-0-316-70627-8(2)) Little Brown & Co.

Peterson, Doug. Dial M for Mercy. Big Idea Design Staff, illus. 2005. (Mess Detectives Ser.). 40p. (ps). pap. 6.99 (978-0-310-70740-0(4)) Zonderkidz.

—The Mess Detectives: The Big Sleepover. 2004. (Mess Detectives Ser.). (Illus.). 40p. 6.99 (978-0-310-70736-3(6)) Zonderkidz.

—The Mess Detectives: The Don't-Touchables. 2004. (Big Idea Bks.). (Illus.). 40p. 6.99 (978-0-310-70735-6(8)) Zonderkidz.

—The Mess Detectives: The Slobfather. 2003. 40p. 6.99 (978-0-310-70702-8(1)) Zonderkidz.

—The Trouble with Larry. Big Idea Design Staff, illus. 2006. (Mess Detectives Ser.). 40p. 6.99 (978-0-310-70741-7(2)) Zonderkidz.

Petit, Karen. The Mystery of the Screecher Creature: A Shandon's Ivy League Mystery. 2006. (J). per. 14.95 (*978-1-59872-666-4(8)) Instantpublisher.com.

Petrucha, Stefan. The Charmed Bracelet. Ross, Vaughn, illus. 2006. (Nancy Drew Ser.). 96p. (J). rev. ed. 12.95 (978-1-59707-037-9(8)); 7th rev. ed. pap. 7.95 (978-1-59707-036-2(X)) Papercutz.

—Demon of River Heights. 2006. (J). (gr. 3-8). 24.21 (978-1-59961-057-3(4)) Spotlight.

—Global Warning. Murase, Sho, illus. 8th rev. ed. 2007. (Nancy Drew Ser.: No. 8). 112p. (J). 12.95 (978-1-59707-052-2(1)); pap. 7.95 (978-1-59707-051-5(3)) Papercutz.

—Haunted Dollhouse. 2006. (J). (gr. 3-8). 24.21 (978-1-59961-059-7(0)) Spotlight.

—Writ in Stone. 2006. (J). (gr. 3-8). 24.21 (978-1-59961-058-0(2)) Spotlight.

Petrucha, Stefan & Murase, Sho. Mr. Cheeters Is Missing. 6th rev. ed. 2006. (Nancy Drew Ser.: No. 6). (Illus.). 96p. (J). pap. 7.95 (978-1-59707-030-0(0)) Papercutz.

—Writ in Stone. 2nd rev. ed. 2005. (Nancy Drew Ser.: No. 2). (Illus.). 96p. (J). (gr. 3-9). 12.95 (978-1-59707-006-5(8)); pap., pap. 7.95 (978-1-59707-002-7(5)) Papercutz.

Pevsner, Stella. Would My Fortune Cookie Lie? 1999. (978-0-606-14369-1(6)) Tandem Library Bks.

Pfeffer, Susan Beth. The Pizza Puzzle. 1999. 119p. (YA). (gr. 7-9). reprint ed. 16.00 (978-0-7881-6640-2(9)) DIANE Publishing Co.

—Revenge of the Aztecs. 2004. 118p. (J). lib. bdg. 16.92 (*978-1-4242-0763-3(0)) Fitzgerald Bks.

Pfeffer, Susan Beth. Revenge of the Aztecs: A Story of 1920s Hollywood. 2001. (American Portraits Ser.). (Illus.). 114p. (J). (gr. 5-8). 15.32 (978-0-8092-0586-8(6) , 9780809205868) Jamestown.

—Revenge of the Aztecs: A Story of 1920s Hollywood. 2004. (Jamestown's American Portraits Ser.). (Illus.). 120p. (J). (gr. 5-7). pap. 4.95 (978-0-7696-3431-9(1) , Waterbird Bks.) School Specialty Publishing.

—Revenge of the Aztecs: A Story of 1920s Hollywood. 2000. (978-0-606-21875-7(0)); (gr. 5-8). lib. bdg. 14.95 (978-0-613-36866-7(5)) Tandem Library Bks.

Pfeffer, Susan Beth & McGraw-Hill Staff. Revenge of the Aztecs: A Story of 1920s Hollywood. 2001. (Jamestown Classics Ser.). (Illus.). 114p. (J). (gr. 5-8). pap. 10.00 (978-0-8092-0627-8(7) , 9780809206278) Jamestown.

Pfitsch, Patricia Curtis. Riding the Flume. 2004. (Illus.). 240p. (J). pap. 4.99 (978-0-689-86692-0(5) , Aladdin) Simon & Schuster Children's Publishing.

Phalen, Dan. The Chumash Circle. 2001. (Rose Doolittle Mystery Ser.: Vol. 1). 150p. (J). pap. 10.95 (978-0-9712971-0-4(X)) Creston Hall Pubns.

Philip, Jimmy. Precious Moments: An Adventure in Wellmore. 2001. 132p. pap. 10.95 (978-0-595-19555-8(5) , Writers Club Pr.) iUniverse, Inc.

Phillips, Grant R. Jay Walker & the Case of the Missing Action Figure. 2004. (J). pap. 10.95 (978-0-9749608-4-5(5)) Quiet Storm Publishing Group.

Pierson, Jan. The Carson Kids & the Mystery of Five Finger Island. 2000. (Carson Kids Ser.: Vol. 1). (Illus.). 128p. (gr. 4-7). pap. 9.95 (978-0-595-09075-4(3) , Backinprint.com) iUniverse, Inc.

—The Carson Kids & the Mystery of Skull Rocks Mansion. 2000. (Carson Kids Ser.: Vol. 3). (Illus.). 120p. (gr. 4-7). pap. 9.95 (978-0-595-09074-7(5) , Backinprint.com) iUniverse, Inc.

—The Carson Kids & the Mystery of the Cove Point Stallion. 2000. 128p. (Orig.). pap. 9.95 (978-0-595-09073-0(7) , Backinprint.com) iUniverse, Inc.

—The Carson Kids & the Secret of Howling Cove. 2000. (Carson Kids Ser.: Vol. 2). (Illus.). 124p. (gr. 4-7). pap. 9.95 (978-0-595-09076-1(1) , Backinprint.com) iUniverse, Inc.

—Carson Kids & the Shipwreck on Grizzly Island. 2000. (Carson Kids Ser.: Vol. 5). (Illus.). 116p. pap. 9.95 (978-0-595-09072-3(9) , Backinprint.com) iUniverse, Inc.

—The Haunted Horse of Gold Hill (Gold Hill, Nevada) 2006. (Ghostowners Ser.: Vol. 4). (Illus.). 109p. pap. 9.95 (978-0-9721800-3-0(6)) WildWest Publishing.

—Shadow of Shaniko (Shaniko, Oregon) 2002. (Ghostowners Ser.: Vol. 3). (Illus.). 105p. (Orig.). pap. 10.00 (978-0-9721800-2-3(8)) WildWest Publishing.

Pike, Christopher, pseud. Die Softly. 2001. 256p. (YA). mass mkt. 5.99 (978-0-7434-2423-3(9) , Simon Pulse) Simon & Schuster Children's Publishing.

—Die Softly. 2002. (gr. 7-12). lib. bdg. 14.15 (978-0-613-74175-0(7)) Tandem Library Bks.

Pinkwater, Daniel M. The Werewolf Club Meets the Hound of the Basketballs. Pinkwater, Jill, illus. 4th ed. 2001. (Werewolf Club Ser.: Vol. 4). 64p. (J). pap. 7.95 (978-0-689-84473-7(5) , Aladdin) Simon & Schuster Children's Publishing.

—The Werewolf Club Meets the Hound of the Basketballs. 2001. (978-0-606-22089-7(5)) Tandem Library Bks.

Pirone, James & Sweeney, Paula. Mystery at Monster Lake. 2000. (Jake Montana Ser.: Bk. 3). (YA). (gr. 6 up). pap. 9.99 (978-0-88092-407-8(1) , 2958) Royal Fireworks Publishing Co.

Pitzorno, Blanca. Un Extrano Entre Nosotros. 1999. Tr. of Stranger among Us. (978-0-606-17758-0(2)) Tandem Library Bks.

Place, Marian T. Mystery of the Wild Horse Trap. 2004. (Classic Ser.). (Illus.). 212p. (gr. 4-7). pap. 15.95 (978-0-87004-411-3(7)) Caxton Pr.

Plante, Raymond & Delezenne, Christine. Les Rats du Yellow Star. 2001. (Roman Jeunesse Ser.). (FRE., Illus.). 96p. (J). pap. (978-2-89021-480-4(X)) Diffusion du livre Mirabel.

Platt, Kin. Big Max & the Mystery of the Missing Giraffe. Cravath, Lynne, illus. (I Can Read Bks.). 64p. (J). 2006. pap. 3.99 (978-0-06-009920-6(8) , Harper Trophy); 2005. 15.99 (978-0-06-009918-3(6)); 2005. lib. bdg. 17.89 (978-0-06-009919-0(4)) HarperCollins Pubs.

Platt, Richard. Spy. Dann, Geoff & Gorton, Steve, photos by. 2000. (Eyewitness Bks.). (Illus.). 64p. (J). (gr. 4-7). 15.99 (978-0-7894-5852-0(7)) Dorling Kindersley Publishing, Inc.

Pluckrose, Henry Arthur. Under the Ground. 1999. (Machines at Work Ser.). (Illus.). 32p. (J). (gr. k-2). pap. 6.95 (978-0-531-15356-7(8) , Watts, Franklin) Scholastic Library Publishing.

Plummer, Rachel. Mystery of the Wizard's Tomb. 2006. (Knights of the Silver Dragon Ser.: Bk. 11). (Illus.). 192p. (J). pap. 5.99 (978-0-7869-3990-9(7) , Mirrorstone) Wizards of the Coast.

Poe, Edgar Allan. Cuentos Policiacos. 2000. (SPA., Illus.). 215p. (YA). (gr. 7 up). 9.95 (978-84-207-1226-0(4)) Grupo Anaya, S.A. ESP. *Dist:* Libros Sin Fronteras.

—Tales of Mystery & Terror. Pablo Marcos Studio Staff, illus. 2002. (Great Illustrated Classics Ser.). 240p. (J). (gr. 3-8). 21.35 (978-1-57765-815-3(9) , ABDO & Daughters) ABDO Publishing Co.

Poe, Edgar Allan & Coleman, Wim. Retold Edgar Allan Poe. Aspengren, Michael A., illus. 2000. (Retold Classics Anthologies Ser.). 128p. (J). (978-0-7891-5123-0(5)) Perfection Learning Corp.

Pohl-Weary, Emily. Strange Times at Western High. Cowles, Rose, illus. 2006. (Natalie Fuentes Mystery Ser.). 219p. (YA). (gr. 7-12). 19.95 (978-1-55451-040-5(6)); pap. 9.95 (978-1-55451-039-9(2)) Annick Pr., Ltd. CAN. *Dist:* Firefly Bks., Ltd.

Polak, Monique. All In. 2006. (SideStreets Ser.). 168p. (YA). (gr. 7-12). (***978-1-55028-913-8(6)***); 7.95 (978-1-55028-912-1(8)) Lorimer, James & Co., Ltd., Pubs. CAN. *Dist:* Casemate Pubs. & Bk. Distributors, LLC.

Pollack, Pam. Web Sight. 2000. (So Weird Ser.: No. 5). (Illus.). 144p. (gr. 3-7). pap. 4.99 (978-0-7868-4441-8(8)) Disney Pr.

Pollack, Pamela. Curse of Beetenkaumun. 2000. (gr. 3-6). lib. bdg. 13.00 (978-0-613-31101-4(9)) Tandem Library Bks.

—The Curse of the Beetenkaumun. 2000. (Funnie Mysteries Ser.: No. 4). (Illus.). 80p. (gr. 2-7). pap. 4.99 (978-0-7868-4410-4(8)) Disney Pr.

Pommaux, Yvan. Detective John Chatterton. 2002. (SPA., Illus.). 36p. (J). (gr. 2-4). (978-980-257-236-6(5)) Ekare, Ediciones VEN. *Dist:* Lectorum Pubns., Inc.

—Lilia. 1999. (SPA.). 36p. (J). (gr. 2-4). 16.95 (978-980-257-237-3(3)) Ekare, Ediciones VEN. *Dist:* Lectorum Pubns., Inc.

Portman, Frank. Andromeda Klein. 2008. 256p. (YA). (gr. 9). 16.99 (***978-0-385-73525-4(1)***); lib. bdg. 19.99 (***978-0-385-90512-1(2)***) Random Hse. Children's Bks. (Delacorte Bks. for Young Readers).

Portman, Frank. King Dork. 352p. (YA). (gr. 9). 2007. pap. 8.99 (***978-0-385-73450-9(6)***); 2006. (Illus.). 16.95 (978-0-385-73291-8(0)); 2006. (Illus.). lib. bdg. 18.99 (978-0-385-90312-7(X)) Random Hse. Children's Bks. (Delacorte Bks. for Young Readers).

Potter, Ellen. Pish Posh. 2006. 224p. (J). (gr. 3-6). 15.99 (978-0-399-23995-3(2) , Philomel) Penguin Group (USA) Inc.

Poulsen, David A. The Book of Vampire. 4th rev. ed. 2007. (Salt & Pepper Chronicles). 160p. (gr. 3-7). pap. 6.95 (***978-1-55263-805-7(7)***) Key Porter Bks. CAN. *Dist:* Perseus Distribution.

—No Time Like the Past. 3rd rev. ed. 2007. (Salt & Pepper Chronicles). 160p. (gr. 3-7). pap. 6.95 (***978-1-55263-807-1(3)***) Key Porter Bks. CAN. *Dist:* Perseus Distribution.

Prachett, Terry. Men at Arms. 2000. (gr. 7-12). lib. bdg. 15.30 (978-0-613-34006-9(X)) Tandem Library Bks.

Preiss, Pauline. The Case of the Dog Camp Mystery. 2001. (New Adventures of Mary-Kate & Ashley Ser.). (Illus.). (J). 11.79 (978-0-606-21915-0(3)) Tandem Library Bks.

—The Case of the Logical I Ranch. 2001. (New Adventures of Mary-Kate & Ashley Ser.). (Illus.). (J). 11.30 (978-0-606-21920-4(X)) Tandem Library Bks.

Preller, James. The Case of the Best Pet Ever. 2003. (Jigsaw Jones Ser.). 80p. (J). pap. 3.99 (978-0-439-55995-9(2) , Scholastic Paperbacks) Scholastic, Inc.

—Case of the Best Pet Ever. 2003. (gr. k-3). lib. bdg. 11.80 (978-0-613-72227-8(2)) Tandem Library Bks.

—The Case of the Bicycle Bandit. 2001. (Jigsaw Jones Mystery Ser.: No. 14). (Illus.). 80p. (J). (gr. 1-4). pap. 3.99 (978-0-439-18477-9(0)) Scholastic, Inc.

—The Case of the Bicycle Bandit. 2001. (Jigsaw Jones Mystery Ser.). (Illus.). (J). 10.79 (978-0-606-21268-7(X)) Tandem Library Bks.

—Case of the Bicycle Bandit. 2001. (gr. 3-6). lib. bdg. 11.80 (978-0-613-35680-0(2)) Tandem Library Bks.

—The Case of the Buried Treasure. 2002. (Jigsaw Jones Mystery Ser.: No. 1). (Illus.). 112p. (J). (gr. 1-4). 3.99 (978-0-439-30931-8(X) , Scholastic Paperbacks) Scholastic, Inc.

—Case of the Buried Treasure. 2002. (gr. 3-6). lib. bdg. 11.80 (978-0-613-50419-5(4)) Tandem Library Bks.

—The Case of the Class Clown. 2001. (Jigsaw Jones Mystery Ser.: No. 12). (Illus.). 80p. (J). (gr. 1-4). pap. 3.99 (978-0-439-18474-8(6)) Scholastic, Inc.

—The Case of the Class Clown. 2001. (Jigsaw Jones Mystery Ser.). (Illus.). (J). 10.79 (978-0-606-20742-3(2)) Tandem Library Bks.

—Case of the Class Clown. 2000. (gr. 3-6). lib. bdg. 11.80 (978-0-613-32374-1(2)) Tandem Library Bks.

—The Case of the Detective in Disguise. 2001. (Jigsaw Jones Mystery Ser.: No. 13). (Illus.). 80p. (J). (gr. 1-4). pap. 3.99 (978-0-439-18476-2(2)) Scholastic, Inc.

—The Case of the Detective in Disguise. 2001. (Jigsaw Jones Mystery Ser.). (Illus.). (J). 10.79 (978-0-606-21267-0(1)) Tandem Library Bks.

—Case of the Detective in Disguise. 2001. (gr. 3-6). lib. bdg. 11.80 (978-0-613-35681-7(0)) Tandem Library Bks.

—The Case of the Disappearing Dinosaur. Smith, Jamie & Alley, R. W., illus. 2002. (Jigsaw Jones Mystery Ser.: No. 17). 96p. (J). pap. 3.99 (978-0-439-30639-3(6)) Scholastic, Inc.

—Case of the Disappearing Dinosaur. 2002. (gr. 3-6). lib. bdg. 11.80 (978-0-613-50420-1(8)) Tandem Library Bks.

—The Case of the Double Trouble Detectives. Smith, Jamie C., illus. 2005. 79p. (J). (***978-1-4155-7908-4(3)***) Scholastic, Inc.

—The Case of the Double Trouble Detectives, No.24. 2005. (Jigsaw Jones Ser.). (Illus.). 96p. (J). pap. 3.99 (978-0-439-67804-9(8) , Scholastic Paperbacks) Scholastic, Inc.

—The Case of the Double Trouble Detectives. 2005. (Illus.). 80p. (J). (ps-ps). lib. bdg. 10.79 (978-0-606-33280-4(4)) Tandem Library Bks.

—The Case of the Food Fight. Smith, Jamie C., illus. 2005. (Little Apple Ser.). 75p. (J). (978-1-4156-2391-6(0)) Scholastic, Inc.

—Case of the Ghostwriter. 2000. (gr. 3-6). lib. bdg. 11.80 (978-0-613-32376-5(9)) Tandem Library Bks.

—The Case of the Great Sled Race. 1999. (Jigsaw Jones Mystery Ser.: No. 8). (Illus.). (J). (gr. 1-4). 10.79 (978-0-606-18527-1(5)) Tandem Library Bks.

—Case of the Great Sled Race. 2000. (gr. 3-6). lib. bdg. 11.80 (978-0-613-21298-4(3)) Tandem Library Bks.

—The Case of the Haunted Scarecrow. Alley, R. W., illus. 2001. (Jigsaw Jones Mystery Ser.: No. 15). 80p. (J). (gr. 1-4). pap. 3.99 (978-0-439-30637-9(X) , Scholastic Paperbacks) Scholastic, Inc.

—The Case of the Haunted Scarecrow. 2001. (Jigsaw Jones Mystery Ser.). (Illus.). (J). 10.79 (978-0-606-21269-4(8)) Tandem Library Bks.

—Case of the Kidnapped Candy. 2007. (Jigsaw Jones Ser.: No. 30). (Illus.). 80p. (J). pap. 3.99 (978-0-439-89618-4(5) , Scholastic Paperbacks) Scholastic, Inc.

—The Case of the Marshmallow Monster. 2001. (Jigsaw Jones Mystery Ser.: No. 11). (Illus.). 80p. (J). (gr. 1-4). pap. 3.99 (978-0-439-18473-1(8)) Scholastic, Inc.

—The Case of the Marshmallow Monster. 2001. (Jigsaw Jones Mystery Ser.). (Illus.). (J). 10.79 (978-0-606-20741-6(4)) Tandem Library Bks.

—Case of the Marshmallow Monster. 2000. (gr. 3-6). lib. bdg. 11.80 (978-0-613-32379-6(3)) Tandem Library Bks.

—The Case of the Million Dollar Mystery. 2002. (Jigsaw Jones Mystery Super Special Ser.: No. 2). (Illus.). 112p. (J). (gr. 1-5). pap. 3.99 (978-0-439-42629-9(4) , Scholastic Paperbacks) Scholastic, Inc.

—Case of the Million Dollar Mystery. 2002. (gr. 3-6). lib. bdg. 11.80 (978-0-613-63267-6(2)) Tandem Library Bks.

—The Case of the Mummy Mystery. Alley, R. W., illus. 2001. (Jigsaw Jones Mystery Ser.: No. 6). 80p. (J). (gr. 1-4). pap. 3.99 (978-0-439-08094-1(0)) Scholastic, Inc.

—The Case of the Mummy Mystery. 2000. (Jigsaw Jones Mystery Ser.: No. 6). (Illus.). (J). (gr. 1-4). 10.79 (978-0-606-18528-8(3)) Tandem Library Bks.

—Case of the Mummy Mystery. 1999. (gr. 3-6). lib. bdg. 11.80 (978-0-613-17901-0(3)) Tandem Library Bks.

—The Case of the Perfect Prank. Smith, Jamie & Alley, R. W., illus. 2004. 66p. (J). (ps). 11.19 (978-0-606-33039-8(9)) Tandem Library Bks.

—Case of the Race Against Time. 2003. (gr. 3-6). lib. bdg. 11.80 (978-0-613-63389-5(X)) Tandem Library Bks.

—The Case of the Rainy Day Mystery. Smith, Jamie, illus. 2003. (Jigsaw Jones Mystery Ser.: No. 21). 80p. (J). mass mkt. 3.99 (978-0-439-42631-2(6) , Scholastic Paperbacks) Scholastic, Inc.

—Case of the Rainy Day Mystery. 2003. (gr. k-3). lib. bdg. 11.80 (978-0-613-72130-1(6)) Tandem Library Bks.

—The Case of the Runaway Dog. 1999. (Jigsaw Jones Mystery Ser.: No. 7). (Illus.). (J). (gr. 1-4). 10.79 (978-0-606-18529-5(1)) Tandem Library Bks.

—Case of the Runaway Dog. 1999. (gr. 3-6). lib. bdg. 11.80 (978-0-613-21301-1(7)) Tandem Library Bks.

—The Case of the Secret Valentine. 1999. (Jigsaw Jones Mystery Ser.: No. 3). (J). (gr. 1-4). 10.79 (978-0-606-15986-9(X)) Tandem Library Bks.

—Case of the Secret Valentine. 1999. (gr. 3-6). lib. bdg. 11.80 (978-0-613-16906-6(9)) Tandem Library Bks.

—The Case of the Secret Valentine, No. 3. Alley, R. W. & Speirs, John, illus. 1999. (Jigsaw Jones Mystery Ser.: No. 3). 80p. (J). (gr. 1-4). 3.99 (978-0-590-69127-7(9)) Scholastic, Inc.

—The Case of the Snowboarding Superstar. 2006. (Jigsaw Jones Ser.: No. 29). (Illus.). 80p. (J). pap. 3.99 (978-0-439-79395-7(5) , Scholastic Paperbacks) Scholastic, Inc.

—The Case of the Spoiled Rotten Spy. 2007. (Jigsaw Jones Ser.: No. 31). 80p. (J). pap. 3.99 (978-0-439-89623-8(1) , Scholastic Paperbacks) Scholastic, Inc.

—The Case of the Spooky Sleepover. Alley, R. W., illus. 2001. (Jigsaw Jones Mystery Ser.: No. 4). 80p. (J). (gr. 1-4). pap. 3.99 (978-0-590-69129-1(5)) Scholastic, Inc.

—The Case of the Spooky Sleepover. 1999. (Jigsaw Jones Mystery Ser.: No. 4). (Illus.). (J). (gr. 1-4). 10.79 (978-0-606-16586-0(X)) Tandem Library Bks.

—Case of the Spooky Sleepover. 1999. (gr. 3-6). lib. bdg. 11.80 (978-0-613-16907-3(7)) Tandem Library Bks.

—Case of the Stinky Science Project. 2000. (gr. 3-6). lib. bdg. 11.80 (978-0-613-24496-1(6)) Tandem Library Bks.

—The Case of the Stolen Baseball Card. 1999. (Jigsaw Jones Mystery Ser.: No. 5). (J). (gr. 1-4). 10.79 (978-0-606-16933-2(4)) Tandem Library Bks.

—Case of the Stolen Baseball Card. 1999. (gr. 3-6). lib. bdg. 11.80 (978-0-613-16622-5(1)) Tandem Library Bks.

—The Case of the Stolen Baseball Cards. Alley, R. W. & Speirs, John, illus. 2001. (Jigsaw Jones Mystery Ser.: No. 5). 80p. (J). (gr. 1-4). mass mkt. 3.99 (978-0-439-08083-5(5)) Scholastic, Inc.

—The Case of the Vanishing Painting. Smith, Jamie & Alley, R. W., illus. 2004. (Jigsaw Jones Ser.). 96p. (J). (gr. 2-4). pap. 3.99 (978-0-439-66165-2(X) , Scholastic Paperbacks) Scholastic, Inc.

—The Case of the Vanishing Painting. Smith, Jamie & Alley, Robert W., illus. 2004. 81p. (J). (ps-3). lib. bdg. 11.19 (978-0-606-32763-3(0)) Tandem Library Bks.

—Jigsaw Jones: Case of the Frog-Jumping Contest. 2005. (Jigsaw Jones Ser.: No. 27). (Illus.). 80p. (J). pap. 3.99 (978-0-439-67805-6(6) , Scholastic Paperbacks) Scholastic, Inc.

—A Jigsaw Jones Mystery, Vol. 30. Alley, R. W. & Smith, Jamie, illus. 2006. (Jigsaw Jones Super Special Ser.). 112p. (J). pap. 4.99 (978-0-439-79396-4(3)) Scholastic, Inc.

—The Race Against Time. 2003. (Jigsaw Jones Mystery Ser.: No. 20). (Illus.). 96p. (J). pap. 3.99 (978-0-439-42630-5(8) , Scholastic Paperbacks) Scholastic, Inc.

Preller, James & Preller, Jimmy. The Great Sled Race. Alley, R. W., illus. 2001. (Jigsaw Jones Mystery Ser.: No. 8). 80p. (J). (gr. 1-4). pap. 3.99 (978-0-439-11427-1(6) , Scholastic Paperbacks) Scholastic, Inc.

Preller, James, et al. The Case of the Runaway Dog. Alley, R. W., illus. 2001. (Jigsaw Jones Mystery Ser.: No. 7). 80p. (J). (gr. 1-4). pap. 3.99 (978-0-439-11426-4(8)) Scholastic, Inc.

Preller, Jimmy. The Case of the Stinky Science Project. Alley, R. W., illus. 2001. (Jigsaw Jones Mystery Ser.: No. 9). 80p. (J). (gr. 1-4). pap. 3.99 (978-0-439-11428-8(4)) Scholastic, Inc.

—The Case of the Stinky Science Project. 2000. (Jigsaw Jones Mystery Ser.: No. 9). (Illus.). (J). (gr. 1-4). 10.79 (978-0-606-18530-1(5)) Tandem Library Bks.

—The Ease of the Ghostwriter. 2001. (Jigsaw Jones Mystery Ser.: No. 10). 80p. (J). (gr. 1-4). pap. 3.99 (978-0-439-11429-5(2)) Scholastic, Inc.

Press, Julian. The Treasure of Blackbird Rock #1. 2008. 128p. (J). (gr. 3-6). pap. 4.99 (***978-0-448-44873-2(4)*** , Grosset & Dunlap) Penguin Group (USA) Inc.

Price, Roger & Stern, Leonard. Nancy Drew Mad Libs. 2005. (Mad Libs Ser.). 48p. (J). (gr. 3). pap. 3.99 (978-0-8431-1659-5(5) , Price Stern Sloan) Penguin Group (USA) Inc.

Priestley, Chris. Death & the Arrow. l.t. ed. 2005. (J). pap. (978-0-7540-7899-9(X) , CLP 467) BBC Audio.

—Death & the Arrow. 2005. 176p. (YA). (gr. 7). pap. 5.50 (978-0-440-23811-9(0) , Laurel Leaf) Random Hse. Children's Bks.

—Death & the Arrow. 2007. (Tom Marlowe Serie Ser.). (Illus.). 230p. (J). (gr. 4-6). 9.99 (***978-0-552-55475-6(8)*** , Corgi) Transworld Publishers Ltd. GBR. *Dist:* Independent Pubs. Group.

—The White Rider. 2006. (Tom Marlowe Ser.). (Illus.). 256p. (J). (gr. 4-6). 9.99 (***978-0-552-55474-9(X)*** , Corgi) Transworld Publishers Ltd. GBR. *Dist:* Independent Pubs. Group.

Prins, Piet. The Flying Phantom. 2006. (Illus.). 142p. (J). pap. (978-1-894666-45-9(3)) Inheritance Pubns.

—The Haunted Castle. 2006. (Illus.). 139p. (J). pap. (978-1-894666-44-2(5)) Inheritance Pubns.

—The Mystery of the Abandoned Mill. Kramer, Jaap, illus. 2006. 127p. (J). pap. (978-1-894666-48-0(8)) Inheritance Pubns.

—The Sailing Sleuths. Kramer, Jaap, illus. 2006. 137p. (J). pap. (978-1-894666-46-6(1)) Inheritance Pubns.

—Scout's Distant Journey. 2006. (Illus.). 141p. (J). pap. (978-1-894666-49-7(6)) Inheritance Pubns.

—The Treasure of Rodensteyn Castle. Kramer, Jaap, illus. 2006. 132p. (J). pap. (978-1-894666-47-3(X)) Inheritance Pubns.

Prisant, Guillermo Murray & Murray, Guillermo. Mas que Oscuro. Orozco, Benjamin, illus. rev. ed. 2003. (Castillo del Terror Ser.). (SPA.). 136p. (J). (gr. 2-6). pap. 6.95 (978-970-20-0217-8(6)) Castillo, Ediciones, S. A. de C. V. MEX. *Dist:* Macmillan.

Prophet, John. Mystery at the Salt Marsh Winery: A Casey Miller Mystery. 2003. 240p. (YA). pap. 16.95 (978-0-595-26598-5(7) , Mystery & Suspense Pr.) iUniverse, Inc.

Prophet, John M. Body in the Salt Marsh Boatyard: A Casey Miller Mystery. 2004. 162p. (YA). pap. 13.95 (978-0-595-30991-7(7) , Mystery & Suspense Pr.) iUniverse, Inc.

Prowse, Philip. Double Cross: Level 3. 1999. (Cambridge English Readers Ser.). (Illus.). 64p. pap. 6.00 (978-0-521-65617-7(6)) Cambridge Univ. Pr.

Pullman, Philip. El Reloj Mecanico. Netzel, Carmen, tr. 2005. (Escritura desatada Ser.). (SPA.). 112p. (J). 15.95 (978-84-406-8065-5(1)) Ediciones B ESP. *Dist:* Independent Pubs. Group.

—The Ruby in the Smoke. 2004. 230p. (J). (gr. 7 up). pap. 38.00 incl. audio (978-1-4000-9015-0(6) , Listening Library) Random Hse. Audio Publishing Group.

—The Ruby in the Smoke. 2003. (Sally Lockhart Trilogy: Bk. 1). (Illus.). (YA). pap. 9.95 (978-0-375-82545-3(2) , Knopf Bks. for Young Readers) Random Hse. Children's Bks.

—The Ruby in the Smoke. 2002. (Sally Lockhart Trilogy: Bk. 1). 22.00 (978-0-8446-7230-4(0)) Smith, Peter Pub., Inc.

—Shadow in the North. 2006. 21.75 (978-0-8446-7289-2(0)) Smith, Peter Pub., Inc.

—The Shadow in the North. 2003. (Illus.). (J). pap. 9.95 (978-0-375-82546-0(0) , Knopf Bks. for Young Readers) Random Hse. Children's Bks.

—The Tiger in the Well. 2003. (Illus.). (J). pap. 9.95 (978-0-375-82547-7(9)) Random Hse. Children's Bks.

Pyle, Jack R. The Gold Bug of Farrow Point. 2003. 130p. (J). (978-1-887905-78-7(2)) Parkway Pubs., Inc.

Quackenbush, Robert. Flamenco to Mischief: A Miss Mallard Mystery. 2000. (Miss Mallard Mystery Ser.: Vol. 16). (Illus.). 48p. (J). (gr. 2-4). pap. 5.95 (978-0-9612518-2-6(4)) Quackenbush, Robert Studios.

—Mishap in Kaiserslautern: A Miss Mallard Mystery. 2001. (Miss Mallard Mystery Ser.). (Illus.). 48p. (J). (gr. 2-4). pap. 5.95 (978-0-9612518-5-7(9)) Quackenbush, Robert Studios.

—Miss Mallard's Case Book. 2000. (Miss Mallard Mystery Ser.: Vol. 17). (Illus.). 48p. (J). (ps-4). pap. 5.95 (978-0-9612518-3-3(2)) Quackenbush, Robert Studios.

—Two Miss Mallard Mysteries: Surfboard to Peril & Stage Door to Terror, 2 vols. in 1. Quackenbush, Robert, illus. rev. ed. 1998. (Miss Mallard Mystery Ser.: Vol. 1). (Illus.). 64p. (J). (gr. 1-5). reprint ed. per. 4.95 (978-0-9612518-9-5(1)) Quackenbush, Robert Studios.

Qualey, Marsha. Close to a Killer. 2000. 11.64 (978-0-606-20499-6(7)) Tandem Library Bks.

—Thin Ice. 1999. (978-0-606-17348-3(X)) Tandem Library Bks.

The Queen & the Gardener. 2001. (Illus.). 32p. (J). lib. bdg. 19.95 (978-0-9712640-0-7(9)) Billinna Publishing Co.

Rabb, M. E. The Chocolate Lover, Vol. 2. 2004. 192p. (YA). pap. 5.99 (978-0-14-250042-2(9) , Puffin) Penguin Group (USA) Inc.

—Missing Persons Vol. 1: The Rose Queen. 2004. (Missing Persons Ser.). 192p. (YA). pap. 5.99 (978-0-14-250041-5(0) , Puffin) Penguin Group (USA) Inc.

Rabley, Stephen. Marcel & the Mona Lisa. 2002. (Illus.). 16p. pap. (978-0-582-40173-0(9) , Putnam Juvenile) Penguin Group (USA) Inc.

Rader, Josh. Detective Stephy Wephy Holmes: In the Missing Cake. Meyers, Sarah, illus. 2007. (J). per. 14.99 (***978-1-59879-399-4(3)***) Lifevest Publishing, Inc.

Ragged Island Mysteries: Classroom Library Set. (Ragged Island Mysteriestm Ser.). (gr. 5-7). 150.95 (978-0-322-02634-6(2)) Wright Group, The.

Raintree Steck-Vaughn Staff. The Mystery of the Missing Leopard. 1999. (J). pap. 35.60 (978-0-7398-0915-0(6)) Steck-Vaughn.

Ralph, Grampa. How Santa Knows. 2007. 56p. pap. 12.95 (***978-1-4241-2284-4(8)***) PublishAmerica, Inc.

Rameaka, T. Mystery of Wolf Den Cave. 2005. 74p. pap. 14.95 (978-1-4137-5551-0(8)) PublishAmerica, Inc.

Ramthun, Bonnie. The White Gates. 2008. (J). (***978-0-375-84554-3(2)***); pap. (***978-0-375-84555-0(0)***); lib. bdg. (***978-0-375-94554-0(7)***) Random Hse., Inc.

Random House Disney Staff. The Sky Is Falling! 2005. (Step into Reading Ser.). (Illus.). 32p. (J). (ps-2). pap. 3.99 (978-0-7364-2318-2(4) , RH/Disney) Random Hse. Children's Bks.

Rankin, Laura. Merl & Jasper's Supper Caper. 1998. (J). pap. 6.99 (978-0-679-89311-0(3) , Random Hse. Bks. for Young Readers) Random Hse. Children's Bks.

Ransome, Arthur. The Big Six. 1999. (Swallows & Amazons Ser.). (Illus.). 367p. (J). (gr. 5 up). reprint ed. pap. 14.95 (978-1-56792-119-9(1)) Godine, David R. Pub.

Raskin, Ellen. The Westing Game. 2002. (Illus.). (J). 13.19 (978-0-7587-0224-1(8)) Book Wholesalers, Inc.

—The Westing Game. 2004. (Puffin Modern Classics Ser.). (Illus.). 192p. (J). (gr. 8). pap. 6.99 (978-0-14-240120-0(X) , Puffin) Penguin Group (USA) Inc.

—Westing Game. 2003. 182p. (J). lib. bdg. 15.00 (***978-1-4242-2271-1(0)***) Fitzgerald Bks.

Raskin, Ellen. The Westing Game. 25th anniv. ed. 2003. 192p. (J). (gr. 7). 16.99 (978-0-525-47137-0(5) , Dutton Juvenile) Penguin Group (USA) Inc.

RavenWolf, Silver. Witches' Key to Terror. Zins, Rebecca, ed. 2001. (Witches Chillers Ser.: Vol. 3). (Illus.). 288p. (gr. 8-12). pap. 5.99 (978-0-7387-0049-6(5)) Llewellyn Pubns.

—Witches' Key to Terror. 2001. (gr. 7-12). lib. bdg. 14.15 (978-0-613-87046-7(8)) Tandem Library Bks.

—Witches' Night of Fear. Zins, Rebecca, ed. 2001. (Witches Chillers Ser.). 368p. (gr. 7-12). pap. 5.99 (978-1-56718-718-2(8)) Llewellyn Pubns.

Rayes, Michael. Bank Robbery! 2007. (J). per. 13.95 (***978-0-9779628-0-8(6)***) Rafka Pr. LLC.

Razzi, Jim. The Sherluck Bones Mystery-Detective Book 1. 2003. 62p. pap. 9.95 (978-0-595-29088-8(4) , Mystery Writers of America Presents) iUniverse, Inc.

—The Sherluck Bones Mystery-Detective Book 2. 2003. 62p. pap. 9.95 (978-0-595-29089-5(2) , Mystery Writers of America Presents) iUniverse, Inc.

Read, Miss. The Howards of Caxley. (J). 17.95 (978-0-8488-1454-0(1)) Amereon LTD.

RealBuzz Studios Staff. Come & Play: Goofyfoot Gurl Vol 3. 2007. 96p. (YA). pap. 4.97 (***978-1-59789-575-0(X)***) Barbour Publishing, Inc.

RealBuzz Studios Staff. When Dolphins Fly. 2007. (Goofyfoot Gurl Ser.: No. 2). 96p. (YA). pap. 4.97 (978-1-59789-574-3(1) , Barbour Bks.) Barbour Publishing, Inc.

Reasoner, Charles. Who's There? 1999. (Halloween Ser.). (Illus.). 14p. (J). bds. 4.99 (978-0-8431-7514-1(1) , Price Stern Sloan) Penguin Group (USA) Inc.

Rebecca. 2002. (HEB & ENG.). (J). per. 9.95 (978-0-939144-39-6(5)) EKS Publishing Co.

Reece, Colleen L. Mysterious Monday. l.t. ed. 2001. (Christian Mystery Ser.). 192p. (J). 23.95 (978-0-7862-3068-6(1)) Thorndike Pr.

—Saturday Scare. l.t. ed. 2002. (Juli Scott, Super Sleuth Ser.). (Illus.). 211p. (J). 24.95 (978-0-7862-3195-9(5)) Thomson Gale.

M N O

—Thursday Trials. 1998. (Juli Scott, Super Sleuth Ser.: Bk. 4). 176p. (J). (gr. 4-10). pap. 2.97 (978-1-57748-180-5(1)) Barbour Publishing, Inc.

—Thursday Trials. l.t. ed. 2001. (Juli Scott, Super Sleuth Ser.). (Illus.). 204p. (J). 23.95 (978-0-7862-3201-7(3)) Thorndike Pr.

—Trouble on Tuesday. l.t. ed. 2001. (Thorndike Christian Mystery Ser.). (Illus.). 192p. (J). 23.95 (978-0-7862-3178-2(5)) Thorndike Pr.

—Wednesday Witness. l.t. ed. 2001. (Juli Scott, Super Sleuth Ser.). (Illus.). 189p. (J). 23.95 (978-0-7862-3202-4(1)) Thorndike Pr.

Reed, W. F. Andy & Mark & the Time Machine: Pickett's Charge at Gettysburg. 2000. 144p. (YA). pap. 10.95 (978-0-595-12885-3(8)) iUniverse, Inc.

Reiche, Dietlof. Ghost Ship. 2006. 320p. (J). pap. 5.99 (978-0-439-59705-0(6)) Scholastic, Inc.

—Ghost Ship. Brownjohn, John, tr. from GER. 2005. 320p. (J). pap. 16.95 (978-0-439-59704-3(8)) Scholastic, Inc.

Reiss, Kathryn. Blackthorn Winter: A Murder Mystery. (YA). 2007. (Illus.). 348p. pap. 6.95 (***978-0-15-206109-8(6)***, Harcourt Paperbacks); 2006. 352p. 17.00 (978-0-15-205479-3(0)) Harcourt Children's Bks.

—PaperQuake: A Puzzle. 2002. 288p. (YA). pap. 6.00 (978-0-15-216782-0(X), Harcourt Paperbacks) Harcourt Children's Bks.

—Riddle of the Prairie Bride. 2001. (American Girl Collection). (Illus.). (J). (978-0-606-21400-1(3)) Tandem Library Bks.

Rennie Pattison, Caroline. The Law of Three: A Sarah Martin Mystery. 2007. 200p. (YA). pap. 10.99 (***978-1-55002-733-4(6)***, Boardwalk Bks.) Dundurn Group, The CAN. *Dist:* Univ. of Toronto Pr.

Repp, Gloria. The Mystery of the Indian Carvings. Pelicano, Christopher J., illus. 2002. 118p. (J). (gr. 4-7). pap. 7.49 (978-1-57924-726-3(1)) Jones, Bob Univ. Pr.

Return Payment. 2001. 32p. (YA). (gr. 6-12). pap. (978-0-8224-1458-2(9)) Globe Fearon Educational Publishing.

Reynolds, Adrian, illus. Mystery Stories. 2003. (Red Hot Reads Ser.). 224p. (gr. 4-8). pap. 6.95 (978-0-7534-5640-8(0), Kingfisher) Houghton Mifflin Co. Trade & Reference Div.

Rhodes, O. K. The Rock Holler Gang: Jr. Detectives Mystery of the Cornerstone. 2003. 11.99 (978-0-9740799-0-5(1)) Maple Bend Farms Pr.

Ricci, Christine. Dora's Mystery of the Missing Shoes. Savitsky, Steven, illus. 2007. (Dora the Explorer Ser.). 24p. (J). pap. 3.99 (***978-1-4169-3824-8(9)***, Simon Spotlight/Nickelodeon) Simon & Schuster Children's Publishing.

Richards, Justin. The Chaos Code. 2007. 416p. (YA). (gr. 7 up). 17.95 (***978-1-59990-124-4(2)***) Bloomsbury Publishing.

—The Death Collector. 336p. (YA). 2007. (gr. 7 up). pap. 7.95 (***978-1-59990-148-0(X)***); 2006. 16.95 (978-1-58234-721-9(2)) Bloomsbury Publishing. (Bloomsbury Children).

—The Invisible Detective: Double Life. 2005. 160p. (J). (gr. 4). 10.99 (978-0-399-24313-4(5), Putnam Juvenile) Penguin Group (USA) Inc.

—The Invisible Detective: Ghost Soldiers. 2006. 160p. (J). (gr. 4). 11.99 (978-0-399-24500-8(6), Putnam Juvenile) Penguin Group (USA) Inc.

—The Invisible Detective: Shadow Beast. 2005. 160p. (YA). (gr. 4). 10.99 (978-0-399-24314-1(3), Putnam Juvenile) Penguin Group (USA) Inc.

Ridden, Brian. Blind Fear. 2002. (Crime Waves Ser.). (Illus.). 96p. (YA). pap. (978-0-7344-0276-9(7), Lothian Bks.) Hachette Livre Australia.

Riddle of Penncroft Farm. 2000. (YA). 9.95 (978-1-56137-597-4(7)) Novel Units, Inc.

Riehecky, Janet. The Mystery of the Dragon in the Dungeon, Vol. 3. Halverson, Lydia, illus. 1999. (Red Door Detective Club Ser.: Bk. 3). 100p. (J). (gr. 3-6). lib. bdg. 12.95 (978-1-56674-089-0(4)) Forest Hse. Publishing Co., Inc.

—The Red Door Detective Club Mysteries, 4 bks., Set. Halverson, Lydia, illus. (J). (gr. 3-6). lib. bdg. 51.80 (978-1-56674-900-8(X)) Forest Hse. Publishing Co., Inc.

Rigby Education Staff. The Robbers. (Sails Literacy Ser.). (Illus.). 16p. (gr. 1-2). 27.00 (978-0-7635-9913-3(1), 699131C99) Rigby Education.

Riise, Torben. Emily & the Arabic Letter. 2001. 164p. (YA). pap. 11.95 (978-0-595-17399-0(3), Writers Club Pr.) iUniverse, Inc.

Riker, Richard K. Scary Days Daze. l.t. ed. 2005. (Illus.). 224p. (J). 15.95 (978-0-9760416-1-0(8), 3,000) Safe Harbor Pubns.

Rinaldi, Ann. The Blue Door. 1999. (Quilt Trilogy: Bk. 3). (J). 12.64 (978-0-606-16658-4(0)) Tandem Library Bks.

—The Staircase. 2002. (Great Episodes Ser.). 240p. (YA). pap. 6.00 (978-0-15-216788-2(9), Gulliver Bks.) Harcourt Children's Bks.

Rinehart, Mary Roberts. Bab: A Sub-Deb. 2005. (Illus.). 300p. per. 15.95 (978-0-9740636-8-3(1)) ARose Bks. Publishing.

Ripley, Virginia. The Little Troll's Big Adventure. Dintzer, Josh, illus. 1999. 32p. (J). (gr. k-2). pap. 12.00 (978-0-9674612-0-5(0)) Strike Publishing.

Ripslinger, Jon. Last Kiss. 2007. 288p. (J). (gr. 4-7). pap. 9.95 (***978-0-7387-1072-3(5)***) Llewellyn Pubns.

The Rise of Death Valley. 2006. (YA). (***978-0-9786681-0-5(3)***) Children's Heart Publishing Co.

Roberts, Kelly. The Haunting of Ellen. 2002. per. 8.95 (978-0-9727046-0-1(4)) Roberts Publishing.

Roberts, Laura Peyton. A Secret Life. 2003. 208p. (YA). (gr. 7). mass mkt. 5.99 (978-0-553-49399-3(X), Bantam Bks. for Young Readers) Random Hse. Children's Bks.

—Sister Spy. 2003. (gr. 7-12). lib. bdg. 14.15 (978-0-613-72718-1(5)) Tandem Library Bks.

Roberts, Willo Davis. Buddy Is a Stupid Name for a Girl. Cipolla, Karen, illus. 2002. 224p. (J). pap. 5.99 (978-0-689-85164-3(2), Aladdin) Simon & Schuster Children's Publishing.

—Buddy Is a Stupid Name for a Girl. 2001. (Illus.). 224p. (J). (gr. 3-7). 16.00 (978-0-689-81670-3(7), Atheneum) Simon & Schuster Children's Publishing.

—Pawns. 2000. (978-0-606-17934-8(3)) Tandem Library Bks.

—Rebel. 160p. (J). 2005. pap. 5.99 (978-0-689-85081-3(6), Aladdin); 2003. (Illus.). 16.95 (978-0-689-85073-8(5), Atheneum) Simon & Schuster Children's Publishing.

—Scared Stiff. 2001. (Illus.). 192p. (J). pap. 4.99 (978-0-689-84689-2(4), Aladdin) Simon & Schuster Children's Publishing.

—Scared Stiff. 2001. (gr. 3-6). lib. bdg. 13.00 (978-0-613-73314-4(2)); (978-0-606-22095-8(X)) Tandem Library Bks.

—Twisted Summer. 1998. 192p. (YA). (gr. 7-12). mass mkt. 4.99 (978-0-689-80600-1(0), Simon Pulse) Simon & Schuster Children's Publishing.

—Twisted Summer. 1998. (978-0-606-13089-9(6)) Tandem Library Bks.

—Undercurrents. 2003. (Illus.). 240p. (J). pap. 4.99 (978-0-689-85994-6(5), Aladdin) Simon & Schuster Children's Publishing.

—Undercurrents. Downey, Mark, illus. 2002. 240p. (J). (gr. 5-8). 16.95 (978-0-689-81671-0(5), Atheneum) Simon & Schuster Children's Publishing.

—Undercurrents. 2002. (gr. 3-6). lib. bdg. 13.00 (978-0-613-66553-7(8)) Tandem Library Bks.

Robins, Eleanor. The Last Time. 2004. (Illus.). 48p. (YA). per. 3.95 (978-1-56254-786-8(0), SP7860) Saddleback Educational Publishing.

Rocheleau, Nicole. Ryan, Me, & the Mysterious Book. 2006. (ENG.). 204p. per. 19.95 (***978-1-4241-3422-9(6)***) PublishAmerica, Inc.

Rochester, B. The Joey Jenkins Mysteries: Something Is Missing at Redding Lake. 2005. 67p. pap. 14.95 (978-1-4241-0065-1(8)) PublishAmerica, Inc.

—Joey Jenkins Mysteries: The Mystery at C. 2005. 48p. pap. 12.95 (978-1-4137-7528-0(4)) PublishAmerica, Inc.

Rocklin, Joanne. The Case of the Shrunken Allowance, Level 4. Van Wright, Cornelius & Hu, Ying-Hwa, illus. 1999. (Hello Reader! Math Ser.). 48p. (J). (gr. 2-4). pap. 3.99 (978-0-590-12006-7(9)) Scholastic, Inc.

Rodda, Emily. Beware the Gingerbread House. 2005. (Raven Hill Mysteries Ser.: No. 3). 128p. (J). (gr. 4-7). pap. 4.99 (978-0-439-78248-7(1), Scholastic Paperbacks) Scholastic, Inc.

—Deep Secrets. 2006. (Raven Hill Mysteries Ser.: No. 4). 128p. (J). pap. 4.99 (978-0-439-78249-4(X), Scholastic Paperbacks) Scholastic, Inc.

—Dirty Tricks. 2006. (Raven Hill Mysteries Ser.: No. 5). (Illus.). 128p. (J). pap. 4.99 (978-0-439-79571-5(0), Scholastic Paperbacks) Scholastic, Inc.

—The Ghost of Raven Hill ; the Sorcerer's Apprentice. 2005. (Raven Hill Mysteries Ser.: Vols. 1 & 2). 256p. (J). pap. 4.99 (978-0-439-77915-9(4), Scholastic Paperbacks) Scholastic, Inc.

Roeder, Mark A. Someone Is Watching. (YA). 2004. 286p. pap. 17.95 (978-0-595-29894-5(X), iUniverse, Inc.); 2002. 304p. pap. 16.95 (978-0-595-26073-7(X), Writers Club Pr.) iUniverse, Inc.

Rogers, Kirby. Operation Dewey. 2002. (Illus.). ix, 100p. (J). pap. (978-1-877633-65-2(8)) Luthers.

Rogers, Marion Diane. The Fruit of the Spirit. 2002. 218p. (YA). pap. 16.95 (978-1-58736-115-9(9), Starbound Bks.) Wheatmark.

—Fruit of the Spirit. 2002. (gr. 7-12). lib. bdg. 26.85 (978-0-613-86823-5(4)) Tandem Library Bks.

Rolfs, Judith. Tommy Smurlee & the Missing Statue. 2007. 216p. (J). per. 13.95 (***978-0-595-45250-7(7)***) iUniverse, Inc.

Romeu, Emma. Gregorio Vuelve a Mexico. 2003. (SPA., Illus.). 148p. (J). (gr. 5-8). pap. 12.95 (978-968-19-0367-1(6)) Santillana USA Publishing Co., Inc.

—Gregorio Vuelve a Mexico. 2000. (SPA.). (gr. 5-8). lib bdg. 18.75 (978-0-613-82709-6(0)) Tandem Library Bks.

Ronco, Dan. PeaceMaker. Pidlubny, Donna, illus. 2004. (YA). per. 15.49 (978-0-9752711-4-8(8)) Winterwolf Publishing.

Rooney, Anne. Wallace & Gromit's World of Mysteries. 2004. (Illus.). 30p. (gr. 5-9). reprint ed. 30.00 (978-0-7567-7410-3(1)) DIANE Publishing Co.

Roop, Meg. Summer Mystery. 2002. (Illus.). 172p. (YA). pap. 13.95 (978-1-58736-072-5(1), Starbound Bks.) Wheatmark.

Rose, Malcolm. Blood Brother. 2008. (Traces Ser.). 160p. (J). (gr. 4-9). pap. 5.95 (***978-0-7534-6170-9(6)***, Kingfisher) Houghton Mifflin Co. Trade & Reference Div.

—Double Check. 2007. (Traces Ser.). 224p. (J). (gr. 5). pap. 5.95 (978-0-7534-6004-7(1), Kingfisher) Houghton Mifflin Co. Trade & Reference Div.

—Final Lap. 2007. (Traces Ser.). 232p. (J). (gr. 7). pap. 5.95 (978-0-7534-6005-4(X), Kingfisher) Houghton Mifflin Co. Trade & Reference Div.

—Lost Bullet. (Traces Ser.). (J). 2007. 212p. (gr. 5-9). pap. 5.95 (978-0-7534-5980-5(9)); 2005. 232p. (gr. 4-6). pap. 5.95 (978-0-7534-5830-3(6)) Houghton Mifflin Co. Trade & Reference Div. (Kingfisher).

—Roll Call. 224p. (J). (gr. 5-9). 2007. (Traces Ser.). pap. 5.95 (978-0-7534-5981-2(7)); 2005. (Traces Ser. : Vol. 3). pap. 5.95 (978-0-7534-5923-2(X)) Houghton Mifflin Co. Trade & Reference Div. (Kingfisher).

Rose, Sherrie. A Girl, A Guy & A Ghost. 2003. (YA). mass mkt. 5.99 (978-0-8439-5276-6(8)) Dorchester Publishing Co., Inc.

Rosellini, Eleanor. Mystery of the Ancient Coins. 2003. (Illus.). 116p. 18.95 (978-1-57860-122-6(3)) Emmis Bks.

Rosellini, Eleanor F. The Puzzle in the Portrait. 2003. (Illus.). 112p. (J). pap. 9.95 (978-1-57860-127-1(4)) Emmis Bks.

—The Puzzle in the Portrait. Vogt, Elizabeth, illus. 1999. 112p. (J). (gr. 3-6). pap. 18.95 (978-1-57860-026-7(X)) Emmis Bks.

Rosellini, Eleanor Florence. The Mystery on Observatory Hill. 2005. (Illus.). 128p. (J). (ps-7). pap. 5.95 (978-1-57860-235-3(1)) Emmis Bks.

Rouse, Marisa K. Hildigarde of Willow Hollow. 2007. 64p. pap. 9.95 (***978-1-4327-0127-7(4)***) Outskirts Press, Inc.

Rowland, Della. The Case of the Soccer Camp Mystery. 1998. (Clue Jr. Ser.: No. 13). (Illus.). (J). (gr. 2-4). pap. 3.99 (978-0-590-13788-1(3), Scholastic Paperbacks) Scholastic, Inc.

Rowley, B. J. Missing Children. 2000. (Light Traveler Adventure Ser.: Vol. 3). 252p. (YA). (gr. 6-12). pap. 13.95 (978-0-9700103-3-9(8)) Golden Wings Enterprises.

—Silver Hawk's Revenge. 2000. (Light Traveler Adventure Ser.: Vol. 2). 256p. (YA). (gr. 6-12). pap. 12.95 (978-0-9700103-2-2(X)) Golden Wings Enterprises.

Roxbee-Cox, Phil. Find the Duck. 2007. (Find-its Board Bks). 12p. (J). bds. 6.99 (***978-0-7945-1804-2(4)***, Usborne) EDC Publishing.

—Find the Kitten. 2007. (Find-its Board Bks). 12p. (J). bds. 6.99 (***978-0-7945-1803-5(6)***, Usborne) EDC Publishing.

—Find the Puppy. 2007. (Find-its Board Bks). 12p. (J). bds. 6.99 (***978-0-7945-1802-8(8)***, Usborne) EDC Publishing.

—Find the Teddy. 2007. (Find-its Board Bks). 12p. (J). bds. 6.99 (***978-0-7945-1805-9(2)***, Usborne) EDC Publishing.

Roy, James. Ichabod Hart & the Lighthouse Mystery. 2003. (Steampunk Ser.). (Illus.). 392p. pap. 15.50 (978-0-7022-3364-7(1)) Univ. of Queensland Pr. AUS. *Dist:* International Specialized Bk. Services.

Roy, Ron. The Absent Author. Gurney, John Steven, illus. unabr. ed. 2004. (A to Z Mysteries Ser.: No. 1). 86p. (J). (gr. k-3). pap. 17.00 incl. audio (978-0-8072-1703-0(4), S FTR 269 SP, Listening Library) Random Hse. Audio Publishing Group.

—The Bald Bandit. Gurney, John Steven, illus. unabr. ed. 2004. (A to Z Mysteries Ser.: No. 2). 80p. (J). (gr. k-3). pap. 17.00 incl. audio (978-0-8072-1704-7(2), S FTR 270 SP, Listening Library) Random Hse. Audio Publishing Group.

—The Canary Caper. Gurney, John Steven, illus. unabr. ed. 2004. (A to Z Mysteries Ser.: No. 3). 80p. (J). (gr. k-3). pap. 17.00 incl. audio (978-0-8072-1705-4(0), S FTR 271 SP, Listening Library) Random Hse. Audio Publishing Group.

—The Canary Caper. Gurney, John Steven, illus. 1998. (A to Z Mysteries Ser.: No. 3). 96p. (gr. 1-4). (J). mass mkt. 3.99 (978-0-679-88593-1(5)); lib. bdg. 11.99 (978-0-679-98593-8(X)) Random Hse. Children's Bks. (Random Hse. Bks. for Young Readers).

—The Canary Caper. Gurney, John Steven, illus. 1998. (A to Z Mysteries Ser.: No. 3). (J). (gr. k-3). 10.79 (978-0-606-12864-3(6)) Tandem Library Bks.

—The Deadly Dungeon. Gurney, John Steven, illus. 1998. (A to Z Mysteries Ser.: No. 4). 96p. (gr. k-3). lib. bdg. 11.99 (978-0-679-98755-0(X)); (J). (gr. 1-4). mass mkt. 3.99 (978-0-679-88755-3(5)) Random Hse. Children's Bks. (Random Hse. Bks. for Young Readers).

—The Deadly Dungeon. Gurney, John Steven, illus. 1998. (A to Z Mysteries Ser.: No. 4). (J). (ps-k). 86p. lib. bdg. 11.80 (978-0-613-04817-0(2)); 4. 10.79 (978-0-606-12865-0(4)) Tandem Library Bks.

—Detective Camp. Gurney, John Steven, illus. 2006. (A to Z Mysteries Ser.: No. 27). 144p. (J). (gr. 1-4). pap. 4.99 (978-0-375-83534-6(2)); lib. bdg. 11.99 (978-0-375-93534-3(7)) Random Hse. Children's Bks. (Random Hse. Bks. for Young Readers).

—The Empty Envelope. Gurney, John Steven, illus. 1998. (A to Z Mysteries Ser.: No. 5). 96p. (J). (gr. 1-4). mass mkt. 3.99 (978-0-679-89054-6(8), Random Hse. Bks. for Young Readers) Random Hse. Children's Bks.

—The Empty Envelope. Gurney, John Steven, illus. 1998. (A to Z Mysteries Ser.: No. 5). (J). (gr. k-3). 10.79 (978-0-606-13949-6(4)) Tandem Library Bks.

—The Goose's Gold. Gurney, John Steven, illus. (A to Z Mysteries Ser.: No. 7). 96p. (gr. k-3). 1999. lib. bdg. 11.99 (978-0-679-99078-9(X)); 1998. (J). mass mkt. 3.99 (978-0-679-89078-2(5)) Random Hse. Children's Bks. (Random Hse. Bks. for Young Readers).

—The Goose's Gold. Gurney, John Steven, illus. 1999. (A to Z Mysteries Ser.: No. 7). (J). (gr. k-3). 10.79 (978-0-606-15977-7(0)); lib. bdg. 11.80 (978-0-613-11591-9(0)) Tandem Library Bks.

—The Haunted Hotel. Gurney, John Steven, illus. 1999. (A to Z Mysteries Ser.: No. 8). (J). (gr. k-3). lib. bdg. 11.80 (978-0-613-16122-0(X)) Tandem Library Bks.

—The Invisible Island. Gurney, John Steven, illus. 1999. (A to Z Mysteries Ser.: No. 9). 96p. (J). (gr. k-3). lib. bdg. 11.99 (978-0-679-99457-2(2)); pap. 3.99 (978-0-679-89457-5(8)) Random Hse. Children's Bks. (Random Hse. Bks. for Young Readers).

—The Invisible Island. Gurney, John Steven, illus. 1999. (A to Z Mysteries Ser.: No. 9). (gr. k-3). 90p. lib. bdg. 10.79 (978-0-606-17265-3(3)); (J). lib. bdg. 11.80 (978-0-613-21768-2(3)) Tandem Library Bks.

—The Jaguar's Jewel. Gurney, John Steven, illus. 2000. (A to Z Mysteries Ser.: No. 10). 96p. (J). (gr. k-3). lib. bdg. 11.99 (978-0-679-99458-9(0)); pap. 3.99 (978-0-679-89458-2(6)) Random Hse. Children's Bks. (Random Hse. Bks. for Young Readers).

—The Jaguar's Jewel. Gurney, John Steven, illus. 2000. (A to Z Mysteries Ser.: No. 10). (J). (ps-k). 86p. lib. bdg. 11.80 (978-0-613-21793-4(4)); 10.79 (978-0-606-18480-9(5)) Tandem Library Bks.

—The Kidnapped King. Gurney, John Steven, illus. 2000. (A to Z Mysteries Ser.: No. 11). 96p. (J). (gr. k-3). lib. bdg. 11.99 (978-0-679-99459-6(9)); pap. 3.99 (978-0-679-89459-9(4)) Random Hse. Children's Bks. (Random Hse. Bks. for Young Readers).

—The Kidnapped King. Gurney, John Steven, illus. 2000. (A to Z Mysteries Ser.: No. 11). (J). (gr. k-3). lib. bdg. 11.80 (978-0-613-25876-0(2)); (978-0-606-18481-6(3)) Tandem Library Bks.

—The Lucky Lottery. Thomas, Jim, ed. Gurney, John Steven, illus. 2000. (A to Z Mysteries Ser.: No. 12). 96p. (J). (gr. k-3). pap. 3.99 (978-0-679-89460-5(8)); lib. bdg. 11.99 (978-0-679-99460-2(2)) Random Hse. Children's Bks. (Random Hse. Bks. for Young Readers).

—The Lucky Lottery. Gurney, John Steven, illus. 2000. (A to Z Mysteries Ser.: No. 12). (J). (gr. k-3). (978-0-606-19886-8(5)); lib. bdg. 11.80 (978-0-613-28342-7(2)) Tandem Library Bks.

—Mayflower Treasure Hunt. Gurney, John Steven, illus. 2nd ed. 2007. (A to Z Mysteries Ser.: No. 28). 128p. (J). (gr. 1-4). pap. 4.99 (978-0-375-83937-5(2)); lib. bdg. 11.99 (978-0-375-93937-2(7)) Random Hse. Children's Bks. (Random Hse. Bks. for Young Readers).

—The Missing Mummy. Gurney, John Steven, illus. 2001. (A to Z Mysteries Ser.: No. 13). 96p. (J). (gr. k-3). 11.99 (978-0-375-90268-0(6)); pap. 3.99 (978-0-375-80268-3(1)) Random Hse. Children's Bks. (Random Hse. Bks. for Young Readers).

—The Missing Mummy. Gurney, John Steven, illus. 2001. (A to Z Mysteries Ser.: No. 13). (J). 83p. (ps). lib. bdg. 11.80 (978-0-613-35603-9(9)); (gr. 1-4). (978-0-606-21011-9(3)) Tandem Library Bks.

—Mystery at the Washington Monument. Bush, Timothy, illus. 2007. (J). (Capital Mysteries Ser.: No. 8). 96p. (gr. 2-6). 3.99 (978-0-375-83970-2(4), Random Hse. Bks. for Young Readers); (Capital Mysteries Ser.: No. 8). 96p. (gr. 2-6). lib. bdg. 11.99 (978-0-375-93970-9(9), Random Hse. Bks. for Young Readers); 87p. (***978-1-4287-4577-3(7)***) Random Hse. Children's Bks.

—The Ninth Nugget. Gurney, John Steven, illus. 2001. (A to Z Mysteries Ser.: No. 14). 96p. (J). (gr. k-3). 11.99 (978-0-375-90269-7(4)); (gr. 2-5). pap. 3.99 (978-0-375-80269-0(X)) Random Hse. Children's Bks. (Random Hse. Bks. for Young Readers).

—The Ninth Nugget. Gurney, John Steven, illus. 2001. (A to Z Mysteries Ser.: No. 14). (J). (gr. k-3). lib. bdg. 11.80 (978-0-613-33773-1(5)); (978-0-606-21012-6(1)) Tandem Library Bks.

—The Orange Outlaw. Gurney, John Steven, illus. 2001. (A to Z Mysteries Ser.: No. 15). 96p. (J). (gr. 2-5). lib. bdg. 11.99 (978-0-375-90270-3(8), Random Hse. Bks. for Young Readers) Random Hse. Children's Bks.

—The Orange Outlaw. Gurney, John Steven, illus. 2001. (A to Z Mysteries Ser.: No. 15). (J). (gr. k-3). lib. bdg. 11.80 (978-0-613-36856-8(8)) Tandem Library Bks.

—The Panda Puzzle. Gurney, John Steven, illus. 2002. (A to Z Mysteries Ser.: No. 16). 96p. (J). (gr. k-3). lib. bdg. 11.99 (978-0-375-90271-0(6)); (gr. 2-5). mass mkt. 3.99 (978-0-375-80271-3(1)) Random Hse. Children's Bks. (Random Hse. Bks. for Young Readers).

—The Panda Puzzle. Gurney, John Steven, illus. 2002. (A to Z Mysteries Ser.: No. 16). 84p. (J). (ps-k). lib. bdg. 11.80 (978-0-613-50485-0(2)) Tandem Library Bks.

—The Quicksand Question. Gurney, John Steven, illus. 2002. (A to Z Mysteries Ser.: No. 17). 96p. (J). (gr. 1-4). lib. bdg. 11.99 (978-0-375-90272-7(4)); pap. 3.99 (978-0-375-80272-0(X)) Random Hse. Children's Bks. (Random Hse. Bks. for Young Readers).

—The Quicksand Question. Gurney, John Steven, illus. 2002. (A to Z Mysteries Ser.: No. 17). (J). (gr. k-3). lib. bdg. 11.80 (978-0-613-50491-1(7)) Tandem Library Bks.

—The Runaway Racehorse. Gurney, John Steven, illus. 2002. (A to Z Mysteries Ser.: No. 18). 96p. (J). (gr. 2-5). 11.99 (978-0-375-91367-9(X)); pap. 3.99 (978-0-375-81367-2(5)) Random Hse. Children's Bks. (Random Hse. Bks. for Young Readers).

—The Runaway Racehorse. Gurney, John Steven, illus. 2002. (A to Z Mysteries Ser.: No. 18). (J). (gr. k-3). lib. bdg. 11.80 (978-0-613-50495-9(X)) Tandem Library Bks.

—The School Skeleton. Gurney, John Steven, illus. 2003. (A to Z Mysteries Ser.: No. 19). 96p. (J). (gr. 2-5). lib. bdg. 11.99 (978-0-375-91368-6(8)); pap. 3.99 (978-0-375-81368-9(3)) Random Hse. Children's Bks. (Random Hse. Bks. for Young Readers).

—The School Skeleton. Gurney, John Steven, illus. 2003. (A to Z Mysteries Ser.: No. 19). (J). (gr. k-3). lib. bdg. 11.80 (978-0-613-62405-3(X)) Tandem Library Bks.

—A Spy in the White House. Bush, Timothy, tr. Bush, Timothy, illus. 2004. (Capital Mysteries Ser.: Vol. 4). 96p. (J). (gr. 1-4). pap. 3.99 (978-0-375-82557-6(6)); lib. bdg. 11.99 (978-0-375-92557-3(0)) Random Hse. Children's Bks. (Random Hse. Bks. for Young Readers).

—The Talking T. Rex. Gurney, John Steven, illus. 2003. (A to Z Mysteries Ser.: No. 20). 96p. (J). (gr. 2-5). pap. 3.99 (978-0-375-81369-6(1)); lib. bdg. 11.99 (978-0-375-91369-3(6)) Random Hse. Children's Bks. (Random Hse. Bks. for Young Readers).

—A Thief at the National Zoo. 2007. 96p. (J). lib. bdg. (***978-0-375-94804-6(X)***); pap. 3.99 (***978-0-375-84804-9(5)***) Random Hse., Inc.

—Trouble at the Treasury. Bush, Timothy, illus. 2006. (Capital Mysteries Ser.: No. 7). 96p. (J). (gr. 2-4). pap. 3.99 (978-0-375-83969-6(0)); lib. bdg. 11.99 (978-0-375-93969-3(5)) Random Hse. Children's Bks. (Random Hse. Bks. for Young Readers).

—The Unwilling Umpire. Gurney, John Steven, illus. 2004. (A to Z Mysteries Ser.: No. 21). 112p. (J). (gr. 1-4). lib. bdg. 11.99 (978-0-375-91370-9(X), Random Hse. Bks. for Young Readers) Random Hse. Children's Bks.

—The Unwilling Umpire. Gurney, John Steven, illus. 2004. (A to Z Mysteries Ser.: No. 21). (J). (gr. k-3). lib. bdg. 11.80 (978-0-613-82496-5(2)) Tandem Library Bks.

—The Unwilling Umpire: A to Z Mysteries. Gurney, John Steven, illus. 2004. (A to Z Mysteries Ser.: No. 21). 112p. (J). (gr. 1-4). pap. 3.99 (978-0-375-81370-2(5) , Random Hse. Bks. for Young Readers) Random Hse. Children's Bks.

—The Vampire's Vacation. Gurney, John Steven, illus. 2004. (A to Z Mysteries Ser.: No. 22). 96p. (J). (gr. 1-4). pap. 3.99 (978-0-375-82479-1(0)); lib. bdg. 11.99 (978-0-375-92479-8(5)) Random Hse. Children's Bks. (Random Hse. Bks. for Young Readers).

—The White Wolf. Gurney, John Steven, tr. Gurney, John Steven, illus. 2004. (A to Z Mysteries Ser.: No. 23). 96p. (J). (gr. 1-4). pap. 3.99 (978-0-375-82480-7(4)); lib. bdg. 11.99 (978-0-375-92480-4(9)) Random Hse. Children's Bks. (Random Hse. Bks. for Young Readers).

—Who Broke Lincoln's Thumb? Bush, Timothy, illus. 2005. (Capital Mysteries Ser.: Vol. 5). 96p. (J). lib. bdg. 11.99 (978-0-375-92558-0(9) , Random Hse. Bks. for Young Readers) Random Hse. Children's Bks.

—Who Broke Lincoln's Thumb. Bush, Timothy, illus. 2005. (Capital Mysteries Ser.: Vol. 5). 96p. (J). (gr. 2-4). pap. 3.99 (978-0-375-82558-3(4) , Random Hse. Bks. for Young Readers) Random Hse. Children's Bks.

—The X'ed-Out X-Ray. Gurney, John Steven, illus. 2005. (A to Z Mysteries Ser.: No. 24). 96p. (J). (gr. k-3). pap. 3.99 (978-0-375-82481-4(2)); lib. bdg. 11.99 (978-0-375-92481-1(7)) Random Hse. Children's Bks. (Random Hse. Bks. for Young Readers).

—The X'ed-Out X-Ray. Gurney, John Steven, illus. 2005. (A to Z Mysteries Ser.: No. 25). 85p. (J). (gr. k-3). lib. bdg. 11.19 (978-0-606-33236-1(7)) Tandem Library Bks.

—The Yellow Yacht. Gurney, John Steven, illus. 2005. (A to Z Mysteries Ser.: No. 25). 96p. (J). (gr. k-3). pap. 3.99 (978-0-375-82482-1(0)); lib. bdg. 11.99 (978-0-375-92482-8(5)) Random Hse. Children's Bks. (Random Hse. Bks. for Young Readers).

—The Yellow Yacht. Gurney, John Steven, illus. 2005. (A to Z Mysteries Ser.: No. 25). 85p. (J). (gr. k-3). lib. bdg. 11.19 (978-0-606-33237-8(5)) Tandem Library Bks.

—The Zombie Zone. Gurney, John Steven, illus. 2005. (A to Z Mysteries Ser.: No. 26). 96p. (J). (gr. k-3). pap. 3.99 (978-0-375-82483-8(9)); (gr. 1-4). lib. bdg. 11.99 (978-0-375-92483-5(3)) Random Hse. Children's Bks. (Random Hse. Bks. for Young Readers).

—The Zombie Zone. Gurney, John Steven, illus. 2005. (A to Z Mysteries Ser.: No. 26). 85p. (J). (gr. k-3). lib. bdg. 11.19 (978-0-606-33238-5(3)) Tandem Library Bks.

Roy, Ron & Gurney, John Steven. The Orange Outlaw. 2001. (A to Z Mysteries Ser.: No.15). (Illus.). 96p. (J). (gr. 2-5). mass mkt. 3.99 (978-0-375-80270-6(3) , Random Hse. Bks. for Young Readers) Random Hse. Children's Bks.

Rozan, S. J. Bitter Feast. 1999. (gr. 7-12). lib. bdg. 14.15 (978-0-613-29200-9(6)) Tandem Library Bks.

Ruby, Laura. The Chaos King. 2007. 336p. (J). lib. bdg. 17.89 (***978-0-06-075259-0(9)***); (gr. 5 up). 16.99 (***978-0-06-075258-3(0)***) HarperCollins Pubs. (Eos).

Ruby, Lois. Soon to Be Free. 2002. (gr. 3-6). lib. bdg. 14.15 (978-0-613-45107-9(4)) Tandem Library Bks.

Rucker, Noah. Mystery of the Shadows. 2005. 27p. (J). 5.00 (978-1-882695-21-8(6)) Patagonia Pr.

Runholt, Susan. The Mystery of the Third Lucretia. 2008. (J). (gr. 6). 16.99 (***978-0-670-06252-2(9)*** , Viking Juvenile) Penguin Group (USA) Inc.

Rushford, Patricia H. Desperate Measures. l.t. ed. 2000. (Jennie McGrady Mysteries Ser.: No. 11). 333p. (J). (gr. 4-7). 23.95 (978-0-7862-2374-9(X)) Thorndike Pr.

Rushford, Patricia H. Secrets of Ghost Island. 2007. (J). (***978-88-02-46255-4(0)***) Moody Pubs.

Russell, Elaine. Martin Mcmillan & the Lost Inca City. Cornell du Houx, Emily M. D., illus. 2005. 128p. (gr. 5 up). pap. 10.00 (978-1-882190-86-7(6)) Polar Bear & Co.

Russo, Marisabina. The Big Brown Box. Russo, Marisabina, illus. 2000. (Illus.). 32p. (J). (ps up). 16.99 (978-0-688-17096-7(X)) HarperCollins Pubs.

Russo-Stark, Marisabina. The Big Brown Box. 2000. (Illus.). (J). lib. bdg. (978-0-688-17097-4(8)) HarperCollins Pubs.

Ryan, Bob & Hasbro Staff. The Case of the Missing Glasses: A Surprise Adventure. 2004. (Illus.). 32p. (J). 9.95 (978-0-7624-1842-8(7) , Running Pr. Kids) Running Pr. Bk. Pubs.

Ryan-Herndon, Lisa. Robin's Case Files: Slade's Apprentice. 2005. (Teen Titans Ser.: No. 2). 64p. (J). (gr. 3-6). pap. 5.99 (978-0-439-69637-1(2)) Scholastic, Inc.

Ryan, Margaret. Scratch & Sniff. Reed, Nathan, illus. 2006. 48p. (J). lib. bdg. (***978-1-4048-3130-8(4)***) Picture Window Bks.

Ryan, Mary C. The Secret in the West Woods. 2000. (ENG.). 115p. (J). (gr. 3-7). pap. 7.95 (978-0-9678115-0-5(3)) Dragonseed Pr.

Rylant, Cynthia. The Case of the Baffled Bear. Karas, G. Brian, illus. 2004. (High-Rise Private Eyes Ser.: No. 7). 48p. (J). (gr. 1 up). 14.99 (978-0-06-053448-6(6)); lib. bdg. 16.89 (978-0-06-053449-3(4)) HarperCollins Pubs.

—The Case of the Climbing Cat. Karas, G. Brian, illus. (High-Rise Private Eyes Ser.: No. 2). 48p. (J). 2001. (ps-3). pap. 3.99 (978-0-06-444307-4(8) , Harper Trophy); 2000. (gr. 1 up). 14.89 (978-0-688-16309-9(2)) HarperCollins Pubs.

—The Case of the Climbing Cat. Karas, G. Brian, illus. 2003. (High-Rise Private Eyes Ser.: No. 2). (J). (gr. k-3). 28.95 incl. audio compact disk (978-1-59112-611-9(8)); pap. 31.95 incl. audio compact disk (978-1-59112-612-6(6)) Live Oak Media.

—The Case of the Climbing Cat. 2001. (High-Rise Private Eyes Ser.: No. 2). (J). (ps-3). 10.79 (978-0-606-22320-1(7)) Tandem Library Bks.

—The Case of the Desperate Duck. Karas, G. Brian, illus. (High-Rise Private Eyes Ser.: No. 8). 48p. (J). (gr. k-3). 2006. pap. 3.99 (978-0-06-053453-0(2) , Harper Trophy); 2005. 14.99 (978-0-06-053451-6(6)); 2005. lib. bdg. 15.89 (978-0-06-053452-3(4)) HarperCollins Pubs.

—The Case of the Fidgety Fox. Karas, G. Brian, illus. (High-Rise Private Eyes Ser.: No. 6). (J). 2004. 64p. (gr. k-3). pap. 3.99 (978-0-06-009103-3(7) , Harper Trophy); 2003. 56p. (gr. 1 up). 15.99 (978-0-06-009101-9(0)) HarperCollins Pubs.

—The Case of the Fidgety Fox. Karas, G. Brian, illus. unabr. ed. 2005. (High-Rise Private Eyes Ser.: No. 6). (J). (gr. k-4). 25.95 incl. audio (978-1-59519-405-3(3)); 28.95 incl. audio compact disk (978-1-59519-409-1(6)); pap. 18.95 incl. audio compact disk (978-1-59519-408-4(8)); pap. 16.95 incl. audio (978-1-59519-404-6(5)); Set. pap. 29.95 incl. audio (978-1-59519-406-0(1)); Set. pap. 31.95 incl. audio compact disk (978-1-59519-410-7(X)) Live Oak Media.

—The Case of the Missing Monkey. Karas, G. Brian, illus. (High-Rise Private Eyes Ser.: No. 1). 48p. (J). 2001. (ps-3). pap. 3.99 (978-0-06-444306-7(X) , Harper Trophy); 2000. (gr. 1 up). 14.95 (978-0-688-16306-8(8)) HarperCollins Pubs.

—The Case of the Missing Monkey. Karas, G. Brian, illus. 2003. (High-Rise Private Eyes Ser.: No. 1). 28.95 incl. audio compact disk (978-1-59112-615-7(0)); pap. 31.95 incl. audio compact disk (978-1-59112-616-4(9)) Live Oak Media.

—The Case of the Missing Monkey. 2001. (High-Rise Private Eyes Ser.: No. 1). (J). 10.79 (978-0-606-22319-5(3)) Tandem Library Bks.

—The Case of the Puzzling Possum. Karas, G. Brian, illus. 2002. (High-Rise Private Eyes Ser.: No. 3). 48p. (J). pap. 3.99 (978-0-06-444316-6(7) , Harper Trophy) HarperCollins Pubs.

—The Case of the Puzzling Possum. Karas, G. Brian, illus. 2003. (High-Rise Private Eyes Ser.: No. 3). (J). (gr. k-3). 28.95 incl. audio compact disk (978-1-59112-619-5(3)); pap. 31.95 incl. audio compact disk (978-1-59112-620-1(7)) Live Oak Media.

—The Case of the Sleepy Sloth. Karas, G. Brian, illus. 2004. (High-Rise Private Eyes Ser.: No. 5). 48p. (J). (gr. k-3). pap. 3.99 (978-0-06-009100-2(2) , Harper Trophy) HarperCollins Pubs.

—The Case of the Sleepy Sloth. Karas, G. Brian, illus. unabr. ed. 2005. (High-Rise Private Eyes Ser.: No. 5). (J). (gr. k-4). 29.95 incl. audio (978-1-59519-413-8(4)); 28.95 incl. audio compact disk (978-1-59519-417-6(7)); pap. 18.95 incl. audio compact disk (978-1-59519-416-9(9)); pap. 16.95 incl. audio (978-1-59519-412-1(6)); Set. pap. 29.95 incl. audio (978-1-59519-414-5(2)); Set. pap. 31.95 incl. audio compact disk (978-1-59519-418-3(5)) Live Oak Media.

—The Case of the Sleepy Sloth. 2004. (High-Rise Private Eyes Ser.: No. 5). (J). (gr. k-3). lib. bdg. 11.80 (978-0-613-85152-7(8)) Tandem Library Bks.

—The Case of the Troublesome Turtle. Karas, G. Brian, illus. 2002. (High-Rise Private Eyes Ser.: No. 4). 48p. (J). pap. 3.99 (978-0-06-001323-3(0) , Harper Trophy) HarperCollins Pubs.

—The Case of the Troublesome Turtle. Karas, G. Brian, illus. 2003. (High-Rise Private Eyes Ser.: No. 4). (J). (gr. k-3). 25.95 incl. audio (978-1-59112-202-9(3)); 28.95 incl. audio compact disk (978-1-59112-623-2(1)); pap. 29.95 incl. audio (978-1-59112-203-6(1)); pap. 31.95 incl. audio compact disk (978-1-59112-624-9(X)); pap. 16.95 incl. audio (978-1-59112-201-2(5)) Live Oak Media.

—The Case of the Troublesome Turtle. 2002. (High-Rise Private Eyes Ser.: No. 4). (J). (gr. k-3). lib. bdg. 11.80 (978-0-613-46123-8(1)) Tandem Library Bks.

—El Caso del Mono Extraviado. (SPA.). (J). 7.95 (978-958-04-6866-0(4)) Norma S.A. COL. *Dist:* Distribuidora Norma, Inc.

—The High-Rise Private Eyes Series. Karas, G. Brian, illus. 2003. pap. 61.95 incl. audio (978-1-59112-430-6(1)); pap. 68.95 incl. audio compact disk (978-1-59112-858-8(7)) Live Oak Media.

Saha, Mark. Mystery Manor: A Three-Dimensional Playset with Sound! Wilson, Phil, illus. 2001. 16p. (J). (ps-k). 19.95 (978-1-58117-108-2(0) , Intervisual/Piggy Toes) Dalmatian Pr.

Salisbury, Linda G. The Mysterious Jamestown Suitcase: A Bailey Fish Adventure. Grotke, Christopher, illus. 2007. 192p. (J). per. 8.95 (978-1-881539-43-8(1)) Tabby Hse. Bks.

—The Thief at Keswick Inn: A Bailey Fish Adventure. 2005. (Illus.). 192p. (J). per. 8.95 (978-1-881539-41-4(5)) Tabby Hse. Bks.

Salmon, Charles Ray, afterword by. The Adventures of Pittypat & Tippytoe. 2004. 232p. (YA). per. (978-0-9760045-0-9(X) , Reluctant Reader Bks.) e-Pluribus Unum Publishing Co.

Sampson, Brent. Aidan's Shoes. Switzer, Bobbi, illus. 2006. (ENG.). 28p. per. 12.95 (***978-1-59800-684-1(3)***) Outskirts Press, Inc.

Sam's Last Summer. 2006. (J). per. 5.95 (***978-0-9790796-3-4(2)***) PJR Assocs., Ltd.

San Souci, Robert D. At the End of the Well. 1999. (J). (978-0-385-32147-1(3) , Dell Books for Young Readers) Random Hse. Children's Bks.

Sander, Sonia. Strawberry Shortcake's Seaberry Mystery. Yee, Josie & Durk, Jim, illus. 2005. (Strawberry Shortcake Ser.). 32p. (J). (ps-2). mass mkt. 3.99 (978-0-448-43639-5(6) , Grosset & Dunlap) Penguin Group (USA) Inc.

Santomenna, Joan E. & Santomenna, Marco D. Caribbean Capers. 2003. (Illus.). 144p. (YA). (gr. 3-9). pap. 9.95 (978-0-9643407-2-5(0)) WindSpirit Publishing.

Santomero, Angela C. Blue Skidoos to the Farm A Storybook with 63 Stickers. Speer-Lyon, Tammie, illus. 1998. (Blue's Clues Ser.). 24p. (J). (ps-k). pap. 3.99 (978-0-689-81698-7(7) , Simon Spotlight/Nickelodeon) Simon & Schuster Children's Publishing.

—Blue's Big Treasure Hunt. Johnson, Traci Paige & Kim, Soo Kyung, illus. 1999. (Blue's Clues Ser.). 24p. (J). (ps-k). 5.99 (978-0-689-82540-8(4) , Simon Spotlight/Nickelodeon) Simon & Schuster Children's Publishing.

—Blue's Big Treasure Hunt. 1999. (gr. k-3). lib. bdg. 14.15 (978-0-613-63255-3(9)) Tandem Library Bks.

—Welcome to Blue's Clues! Kim, Soo Kyung, illus. 1999. (Blue's Clues Ser.). 12p. (J). (ps-k). bds. 10.95 (978-0-689-82952-9(3) , Simon Spotlight/Nickelodeon) Simon & Schuster Children's Publishing.

Sarfati, Sonia. La Comédienne Disparue. 2003. (Roman Jeunesse Ser.). (FRE.). 96p. (YA). (gr. 4-7). pap. (978-2-89021-211-4(4)) Diffusion du livre Mirabel.

Sathre, Vivian. Stage Invader. l.t. ed. 2000. (Wishbone Mysteries Ser.: No. 15). (Illus.). 140p. (J). (gr. 4 up). lib. bdg. 23.33 (978-0-8368-2698-2(1)) Stevens, Gareth Inc.

—Stage Invader. 1999. (Wishbone Mysteries Ser.: No. 15). (J). (gr. 2-5). (978-0-606-15826-8(X)) Tandem Library Bks.

Saunders, Joanne D. Secret at the Winthrop House. 2007. 192p. per. 12.99 (***978-1-59886-622-3(2)***) Tate Publishing & Enterprises, L.L.C.

Savageau, Tony. The Mud House Mystery: A Wild Bunch Adventure. Raditz, JoAnne, illus. 2004. (J). pap. 9.95 (978-0-9759737-0-7(3)) Blue Mustang Pr.

Savary, Fabien. Caillou Peek-a-Boo! 2007. (Pull-tab Ser.). 12p. (J). bds. 4.95 (***978-2-89450-621-9(X)***) Chouette Publishing CAN. *Dist:* Independent Pubs. Group.

Sawyer, Flora. Jack Frost's Window. 2005. 54p. pap. 12.95 (978-1-4137-6958-6(6)) PublishAmerica, Inc.

Sayers, Susan. Aventures. 2000. (Living Word Living Water Ser.). 144p. (YA). pap. 24.95 (978-1-58595-105-5(6)) Twenty-Third Pubns./Bayard.

Scanes, Amy. The Chosen: Book Two of the Abon Trilogy. 2007. 304p. per. 18.95 (***978-0-595-45990-2(0)***) iUniverse, Inc.

Scarry, Richard. Richard Scarry's Great Pirate Mystery. 2005. (Random House Pictureback Book Ser.). (J). (978-0-375-83213-0(0)) Random Hse., Inc.

Schenker, Dona. Secret Circle. 2000. (978-0-606-18240-9(3)) Tandem Library Bks.

Scheunemann, Pam. Cat Tails. Chawla, Neena, illus. 2006. (Fact & Fiction Ser.). 24p. (J). pap. (978-1-59679-928-8(5)); (gr. 1-3). 21.35 (978-1-59679-927-1(7) , SandCastle) ABDO Publishing Co.

Scholastic Editorial Staff. Scooby Doo Reader 2 in 1 Bind-Up. 2007. 64p. (J). pap. 4.99 (***978-0-545-00115-1(3)***) Scholastic, Inc.

Scholastic, Inc. Staff. The Case of the Missing Mummy. 1998. (J). pap. 71.82 (978-0-590-63041-2(5)) Scholastic, Inc.

—The Christmas Cookie Case. del Sur, Duendes, illus. 2004. (Scooby Doo Ser.). 32p. (J). pap. 3.99 (978-0-439-55714-6(3)) Scholastic, Inc.

—Long-lost Map. 2007. (Ulysses Moore Ser.). 272p. (J). pap. 5.99 (***978-0-439-77673-8(2)***) Scholastic, Inc.

Scholastic, Inc. Staff. Scooby Doo Storybook Collection, 8 vols., Set. 2002. (Scooby-Doo Ser.). (Illus.). 256p. (J). (ps-1). 10.99 (978-0-439-51320-3(0) , Scholastic Paperbacks) Scholastic, Inc.

Scholastic, Inc. Staff, et al. Scooby-Doo & the Witch's Ghost. 1999. (Scooby-Doo Movie Storybooks). (Illus.). 32p. (J). (ps-3). pap. 3.50 (978-0-439-08786-5(4)) Scholastic, Inc.

Schraff, Anne. As the Eagle Goes. rev. ed. 1999. (Standing Tall Mysteries Ser.). 48p. (YA). (gr. 4 up). pap. 3.95 (978-1-58659-086-4(3)) Artesian Pr.

—As the Eagle Goes. 2000. (gr. 5-8). lib. bdg. 12.95 (978-0-613-51201-5(4)) Tandem Library Bks.

—Beyond Glory. rev. ed. 1999. (Standing Tall Mysteries Ser.). 49p. (YA). (gr. 4 up). pap. 3.95 (978-1-58659-087-1(1)) Artesian Pr.

—The Case of the Bad Seed: PageTurner Detective. 2002. 80p. (YA). per. 3.95 (978-1-56254-386-0(5) , SP 3865) Saddleback Educational Publishing.

—The Case of the Cursed Chalet: PageTurner Detective. 2002. 80p. (YA). per. 3.95 (978-1-56254-387-7(3) , SP 3873) Saddleback Educational Publishing.

—The Case of the Dead Duck. 2002. (PageTurner Detective Ser.). 80p. (YA). per. 3.95 (978-1-56254-388-4(1) , SP 3881) Saddleback Educational Publishing.

—The Case of the Wanted Man. 2002. (PageTurner Detective Ser.). 80p. (YA). per. 3.95 (978-1-56254-389-1(X) , SP 389X) Saddleback Educational Publishing.

—The Case of the Watery Grave. 2002. (PageTurner Detective Ser.). 80p. (YA). per. 3.95 (978-1-56254-390-7(3) , SP 3903) Saddleback Educational Publishing.

—The Cold, Cold Shoulder. 2003. (Illus.). 80p. (YA). per. 3.95 (978-1-56254-701-1(1)) Saddleback Educational Publishing.

—Don't Look Now or Ever. rev. ed. 1999. (Standing Tall Mysteries Ser.). 49p. (YA). (gr. 4-12). pap. 3.95 (978-1-58659-084-0(7)) Artesian Pr.

—Don't Look Now or Ever. 2000. (gr. 5-8). lib. bdg. 12.95 (978-0-613-51209-1(X)) Tandem Library Bks.

—Ghost Biker. rev. ed. 1999. (Standing Tall Mysteries Ser.). 50p. (YA). (gr. 4-12). pap. 3.95 (978-1-58659-082-6(0)) Artesian Pr.

—Ghost Biker. 2000. (gr. 5-8). lib. bdg. 12.95 (978-0-613-51211-4(1)) Tandem Library Bks.

—The Haunted Hound. rev. ed. 1999. (Standing Tall Mysteries Ser.). 49p. (YA). (gr. 4-12). pap. 3.95 (978-1-58659-085-7(5)) Artesian Pr.

—Howling House. 2000. (gr. 5-8). lib. bdg. 12.95 (978-0-613-51215-2(4)) Tandem Library Bks.

—The Howling House. rev. ed. 1999. (Standing Tall Mysteries Ser.). 51p. (YA). (gr. 4-12). pap. 3.95 (978-1-58659-083-3(9)) Artesian Pr.

—The Hunter. 2001. (PageTurner Mystery Ser.). 80p. (YA). per. 3.95 (978-1-56254-181-1(1) , SP 1811) Saddleback Educational Publishing.

—Nobody Lives in Apartment N-2. rev. ed. 1999. (Take Ten Ser.). (Illus.). 49p. (YA). (gr. 4-12). pap. 3.95 (978-1-58659-001-7(4)) Artesian Pr.

—Nobody Lives in Apartment N-2. 2000. (gr. 5-8). lib. bdg. 11.80 (978-0-613-51220-6(0)) Tandem Library Bks.

—Once upon a Crime. 2001. (PageTurner Mystery Ser.). 80p. (YA). per. 3.95 (978-1-56254-179-8(X) , SP 179X) Saddleback Educational Publishing.

—Once upon a Crime. 2001. (gr. 7-12). lib. bdg. 11.80 (978-0-613-32914-9(7)) Tandem Library Bks.

—Planet Doom. 2001. (PageTurner Adventure Ser.). 80p. (YA). per. 3.95 (978-1-56254-184-2(6) , SP 1846) Saddleback Educational Publishing.

—Planet Doom. 2001. (gr. 7-12). lib. bdg. 11.80 (978-0-613-32953-8(8)) Tandem Library Bks.

—Roses Red As Blood. 2003. (Illus.). 80p. (YA). per. 3.95 (978-1-56254-704-2(6) , SP7046) Saddleback Educational Publishing.

—Shadow on the Snow. rev. ed. 1999. (Standing Tall Mysteries Ser.). 49p. (YA). (gr. 4 up). pap. 3.95 (978-1-58659-088-8(X)) Artesian Pr.

—Shadow on the Snow. 2000. (gr. 5-8). lib. bdg. 12.95 (978-0-613-51224-4(3)) Tandem Library Bks.

—Something Dreadful down Below: Set 3. 2002. 32p. (YA). 2.95 (978-1-56254-432-4(2) , SP 4322) Saddleback Educational Publishing.

—Terror on Tulip Lane. rev. ed. 1999. 52p. (YA). (gr. 4 up). pap. 3.95 (978-1-58659-089-5(8)) Artesian Pr.

—Terror on Tulip Lane. 2000. (gr. 7-12). lib. bdg. 12.95 (978-0-613-51057-8(7)) Tandem Library Bks.

—Twin. 2000. (gr. 7-12). lib. bdg. 12.95 (978-0-613-51059-2(3)) Tandem Library Bks.

—The Twin. rev. ed. 1999. (Standing Tall Mysteries Ser.). 49p. (YA). (gr. 4-12). pap. 3.95 (978-1-58659-081-9(2)) Artesian Pr.

—Whatever Happened to Megan Marie? 2001. (PageTurner Mystery Ser.). 80p. (YA). per. 3.95 (978-1-56254-178-1(1) , SP 1781) Saddleback Educational Publishing.

—Whatever Happened to Megan Marie? 2001. (gr. 7-12). lib. bdg. 11.80 (978-0-613-33232-3(6)); (Illus.). 75p. (J). (gr. 4-7). lib. bdg. 12.15 (978-0-606-21579-4(4)) Tandem Library Bks.

—When Sleeping Dogs Awaken. 2001. (PageTurner Mystery Ser.). 80p. (YA). per. 3.95 (978-1-56254-180-4(3) , SP 1803) Saddleback Educational Publishing.

—When Sleeping Dogs Awaken. 2001. (gr. 7-12). lib. bdg. 11.80 (978-0-613-33238-5(5)) Tandem Library Bks.

—Where's Dudley? 2001. (PageTurner Mystery Ser.). 80p. (YA). per. 3.95 (978-1-56254-177-4(3) , SP 1773) Saddleback Educational Publishing.

—Where's Dudley? 2001. (gr. 7-12). lib. bdg. 11.80 (978-0-613-33240-8(7)) Tandem Library Bks.

—The White Room: Set 2. 2002. 32p. (YA). 2.95 (978-1-56254-424-9(1) , SP 4241) Saddleback Educational Publishing.

Schroder, Jack. Mystery of the Ancestral Rites. 2004. 160p. per. 9.95 (978-0-9745665-7-3(8)) Catalpa Pr.

Schurch, Maylan. The Case of the Stolen Red Mary. 2001. (Justin Case Adventures Ser.: Vol. 1). 112p. (YA). pap. 6.99 (978-0-8280-1611-7(9)) Review & Herald Publishing Assn.

Schurch, Maylan Henry. The Meatless Mayhem Mystery. 2003. (Justin Case Adventures Ser.: 5). 121p. (J). pap. 7.99 (978-0-8280-1615-5(1) , 133-650) Review & Herald Publishing Assn.

Schwarz, Larry. Ellen's 11-Star Spectacular Super Deluxe Hotel. Denato, Kelly, illus. 2006. 32p. (J). (ps-1). 15.99 (978-0-316-86902-7(3)) Little Brown & Co.

Schwarz, Laurence. Ellen's 11-Star Spectacular Super Deluxe Hotel. Denato, Kelly, illus. 2006. (J). (978-1-4156-8083-4(3)) Little Brown & Co.

Scooby Doo & the Pirate Ghost. 2001. (Illus.). (J). 15.98 (978-0-7853-4875-7(1)) Publications International, Ltd.

Scooby-Doo Mystery Mania Box Set with Coloring Books. 2000. (Scooby-Doo Ser.). (J). (ps-3). (978-1-58805-136-3(6)) DS-Max USA, Inc.

Scooby Doo Storybook Box Set. 2003. (Illus.). 14.00 (978-0-439-55194-6(3)) Scholastic, Inc.

Scoppettone, Sandra. Gonna Take a Homicidal Journey. 1999. (Lauren Laurano Mystery Ser.: Bk. 5). (gr. 7-12). lib. bdg. 15.30 (978-0-613-21616-6(4)) Tandem Library Bks.

Scott, Christina. All in A Night's Work. 2006. (J). lib. bdg. 19.95 (***978-1-933732-19-0(9)*** , Bear Hug Bks.) MidAmerica Publishing Co.

—The Chimney. 2006. (J). lib. bdg. 19.95 (***978-1-933732-18-3(0)*** , Bear Hug Bks.) MidAmerica Publishing Co.

Scott, James. Killing Mr. Griffin: Reproducible Teaching Unit. 1999. 39p. tchr. ed., ring bd. 29.50 (978-1-58049-097-9(2) , TU93) Prestwick Hse., Inc.

Scott, Terrence. Bryce Coris Blessing. 2006. 28p. pap. 9.95 (***978-1-4327-0000-3(6)***) Outskirts Press, Inc.

Scrimger, Richard. From Charlie's Point of View. 2007. 288p. (YA). (gr. 3). pap. 6.99 (978-0-14-240818-6(2) , Puffin) Penguin Group (USA) Inc.

The Search for the Lost Cave, 6 vols. (Woodland Mysteriestm Ser.). 133p. (gr. 3-7). 42.50 (978-0-7802-7943-8(3)) Wright Group, The.

Secret Agent Cat Purse: The Case of the Dog with Golden Wings. 2006. (J). (978-0-9743359-3-3(2)) Murdock Publishing Co.

The Secret of the Monster Book, 6 vols., Vol. 2. (Woodland Mysteriestm Ser.). 133p. (gr. 3-7). 42.50 (978-0-7802-7933-9(6)) Wright Group, The.

The Secret of the Old Oak Trunk, 6 vols. (Woodland Mysteriestm Ser.). 133p. (gr. 3-7). 42.50 (978-0-7802-7926-1(3)) Wright Group, The.

The Secret of the Song, 6 vols., Vol. 2. (Woodland Mysteriestm Ser.). 133p. (gr. 3-7). 42.50 (978-0-7802-7937-7(9)) Wright Group, The.

The Secret on the Wall. 2002. (Illus.). (J). pap. (978-0-7398-5135-7(7)) Steck-Vaughn.

A Secret Silver Lining, 6 vols. (Ragged Island Mysteriestm Ser.). 161p. (gr. 5-7). 42.50 (978-0-322-01647-7(9)) Wright Group, The.

Seher, H. R. Virtual Law. 2005. 154p. pap. 19.95 (978-1-4137-5249-6(7)) PublishAmerica, Inc.

Sensel, Joni. Reality Leak. Slade, Christian, illus. 2007. (J). 224p. 16.95 (978-0-8050-8125-1(9)); 218p. (***978-1-4287-3983-3(1)***) Holt, Henry & Co.

Shafer, Wanda Rutman. The Dark Little Candy Store. 2000. (Illus.). 83p. (J). 17.95 (978-0-7541-1156-6(3)) Minerva Pr. GBR. *Dist:* Unity Distribution.

Shannon, George. More Stories to Solve: Fifteen Folktales from Around the World. Sis, Peter, illus. 2001. 64p. (J). (gr. 2 up). pap. 4.99 (978-0-380-73261-6(0) , Harper Trophy) HarperCollins Pubs.

—True Lies: 10 Tales for You to Judge. O'Brien, John, illus. 1998. 64p. (J). (gr. 3 up). reprint ed. pap. 4.99 (978-0-688-16371-6(8) , Harper Trophy) HarperCollins Pubs.

Sharmat, Marjorie Weinman. Nate the Great. Simont, Marc, illus. (Nate the Great Ser.). 48p. (J). (gr. 1-4). pap. 4.50 (978-0-8072-1351-3(9) , Listening Library) Random Hse. Audio Publishing Group.

—Nate the Great. Simont, Marc, illus. anniv. ed. 2002. 64p. (gr. 1-4). 13.95 (978-0-385-73017-4(9) , Delacorte Bks. for Young Readers) Random Hse. Children's Bks.

—Nate the Great & Me: The Case of the Fleeing Fang. Simont, Marc, illus. 2000. (Nate the Great Ser.). 64p. (J). (gr. 1-4). pap. 4.50 (978-0-440-41381-3(8) , Yearling) Random Hse. Children's Bks.

—Nate the Great & Me: The Case of the Fleeing Fang. 2000. (gr. 3-6). lib. bdg. 12.40 (978-0-613-28583-4(2)) Tandem Library Bks.

—Nate the Great & the Big Sniff. Weston, Martha, illus. 2003. (Nate the Great Ser.). 48p. (gr. 1-4). pap. 4.50 (978-0-440-41502-2(0) , Yearling) Random Hse. Children's Bks.

—Nate the Great & the Big Sniff. 2003. (gr. k-3). lib. bdg. 12.40 (978-0-613-63966-8(9)) Tandem Library Bks.

—Nate the Great & the Halloween Hunt. Simont, Marc, illus. (Nate the Great Ser.). 48p. (J). (gr. 1-4). pap. 4.50 (978-0-8072-1283-7(0) , Listening Library) Random Hse. Audio Publishing Group.

—Nate the Great & the Missing Key. Simont, Marc, illus. (Nate the Great Ser.). 48p. (J). (gr. 1-4). pap. 4.50 (978-0-8072-1335-3(7) , Listening Library) Random Hse. Audio Publishing Group.

—Nate the Great & the Monster Mess. Weston, Martha, illus. 1999. (Nate the Great Ser.). 48p. (gr. 1-4). 14.95 (978-0-385-32114-3(7) , Delacorte Bks. for Young Readers) Random Hse. Children's Bks.

—Nate the Great & the Sticky Case. Simont, Marc, illus. 1999. (Nate the Great Ser.). (J). (gr. 1-4). 9.95 (978-1-56137-263-8(3)) Novel Units, Inc.

—Nate the Great Goes Undercover. Simont, Marc, illus. (Nate the Great Ser.). 48p. (J). (gr. 1-4). pap. 4.50 (978-0-8072-1284-4(9) , Listening Library) Random Hse. Audio Publishing Group.

—Nate the Great on the Owl Express. Sharmat, Mitchell & Weston, Martha, illus. 2004. 80p. (J). (gr. 1-4). 4.50 (978-0-440-41927-3(1) , Yearling) Random Hse. Children's Bks.

—Nate the Great Saves the King of Sweden. Simont, Marc, illus. 1999. (Nate the Great Ser.). 80p. (J). (gr. 1-4). 4.50 (978-0-440-41302-8(8) , Yearling) Random Hse. Children's Bks.

—Yo, el Gran Fercho y el Ladron. (Torre de Papel Ser.).Tr. of Nate the Great Goes Undercover. (SPA., Illus.). (J). 7.95 (978-958-04-2540-3(X)) Norma S.A. COL. *Dist:* Distribuidora Norma, Inc.

—Yo, el Gran Fercho y la Lista Perdida. (Torre de Papel Ser.).Tr. of Nate the Great & the Lost List. (SPA.). (J). 7.95 (978-958-04-2600-4(7)) Norma S.A. COL. *Dist:* Distribuidora Norma, Inc.

Sharmat, Marjorie Weinman & Sharmat, Marjorie Weinman. The Case of the Fleeing Fang. Simont, Marc, illus. 2000. 63p. (J). (ps-7). lib. bdg. 11.30 (978-0-606-17894-5(5)) Tandem Library Bks.

Sharmat, Marjorie Weinman & Sharmat, Mitchell. Nate the Great on the Owl Express. Weston, Martha, illus. 2003. (Nate the Great Ser.). 48p. (gr. 1-4). (J). 14.95 (978-0-385-73078-5(0)); lib. bdg. 16.99 (978-0-385-90102-4(X)) Random Hse. Children's Bks. (Delacorte Bks. for Young Readers).

—Nate the Great Talks Turkey. Wheeler, Jody, illus. 2007. (Nate the Great Ser.). 96p. (J). (gr. 1-4). pap. 4.50 (***978-0-440-42126-9(8)*** , Yearling) Random Hse. Children's Bks.

Sharmat, Marjorie Weinman & Sharmat, Mitchell. The Pizza Monster. Brunkus, Denise, illus. 2nd ed. 2005. 80p. (J). (gr. 1-4). reprint ed. pap. 4.50 (978-0-440-42059-0(8) , Yearling) Random Hse. Children's Bks.

Sharmat, Marjorie Weinman, et al. The Green Toenails Gang. Brunkus, Denise, illus. 2005. (Oliver Sharp Ser.: Vol. 4). 80p. (J). (gr. 1-4). pap. 4.50 (978-0-440-42063-7(6) , Yearling) Random Hse. Children's Bks.

—Nate the Great & the Big Sniff. Weston, Martha, illus. 2001. (Nate the Great Ser.). 48p. (J). (gr. 1-4). 13.95 (978-0-385-32604-9(1) , Delacorte Bks. for Young Readers) Random Hse. Children's Bks.

—Nate the Great, San Francisco Detective. Bui, Francoise, ed. Weston, Martha, illus. 2000. (Nate the Great Ser.). 48p. (gr. 1-4). lib. bdg. 15.99 (978-0-385-90000-3(7) , Delacorte Bks. for Young Readers) Random Hse. Children's Bks.

Sharmat, Mitchell & Sharmat, Marjorie Weinman. Nate the Great Talks Turkey. Wheeler, Jody, illus. 2006. 80p. (J). (gr. 1-4). 11.95 (978-0-385-73336-6(4)); lib. bdg. 13.99 (978-0-385-90353-0(7)) Random Hse. Children's Bks. (Delacorte Bks. for Young Readers).

Shaskan, Trisha. The Ticket. Demski, James, illus. 2006. (Read-It! Readers Ser.). (J). 19.93 (978-1-4048-2423-2(5)) Picture Window Bks.

Shaw, Janet. The Silent Stranger: A Kaya Mystery. 2005. (American Girls Collection). (Illus.). 132p. (J). (ps-7). pap. 6.95 (978-1-58485-990-1(3) , American Girl) American Girl Publishing, Inc.

Shearer, Alex. Canned. 2008. (J). 240p. 16.99 (***978-0-439-90309-7(2)); (978-0-439-90310-3(6))*** Scholastic, Inc. (Scholastic Pr.).

Shepard, Sara. Flawless. 2008. (Pretty Little Liars Ser.: Bk. 2). 352p. (J). pap. 8.99 (***978-0-06-088735-3(4)*** , HarperTeen) HarperCollins Pubs.

—Perfect. 2007. (Pretty Little Liars Ser.: Bk. 3). 320p. (YA). (gr. 9 up). 16.99 (***978-0-06-088736-0(2)*** , HarperTeen) HarperCollins Pubs.

—Pretty Little Liars. 2007. (Pretty Little Liars Ser.: Bk. 1). 304p. (J). pap. 8.99 (***978-0-06-088732-2(X)*** , HarperTeen) HarperCollins Pubs.

—Unbelievable. 2008. (Pretty Little Liars Ser.: Bk. 4). 352p. (J). 16.99 (***978-0-06-088739-1(7)*** , HarperTeen) HarperCollins Pubs.

Sheppard, Mary C. Seven for a Secret. 2003. 192p. (YA). (gr. 7-10). pap. 6.95 (978-0-88899-507-0(5)) Groundwood Bks. CAN. *Dist:* Perseus Distribution.

—Seven for a Secret. 2003. (gr. 7-12). lib. bdg. 15.25 (978-0-613-88589-8(9)) Tandem Library Bks.

Sherrard, Valerie. Chasing Shadows: A Shelby Belgarden Mystery. 2004. 200p. pap. 9.99 (978-1-55002-502-6(3)) Dundurn Group, The CAN. *Dist:* Univ. of Toronto Pr.

—Eyes of a Stalker. 2006. 180p. (YA). pap. 12.99 (***978-1-55002-643-6(7)*** , Boardwalk Bks.) Dundurn Group, The CAN. *Dist:* Univ. of Toronto Pr.

—In Too Deep: A Shelby Belgarden Mystery. 2004. 200p. pap. 8.99 (978-1-55002-443-2(4)) Dundurn Group, The CAN. *Dist:* Univ. of Toronto Pr.

—In Too Deep: A Shelby Belgarden Mystery. 2003. (gr. 7-12). lib. bdg. 17.60 (978-0-613-90075-1(8)) Tandem Library Bks.

—Out of the Ashes: A Shelby Belgarden Mystery. 2004. 220p. pap. 8.99 (978-1-55002-382-4(9)) Dundurn Group, The CAN. *Dist:* Univ. of Toronto Pr.

—Out of the Ashes: A Shelby Belgarden Mystery. 2002. (gr. 7-12). lib. bdg. 17.60 (978-0-613-90269-4(6)) Tandem Library Bks.

The Ship in a Bottle, 6 vols. (Ragged Island Mysteriestm Ser.). 161p. (gr. 5-7). 42.50 (978-0-322-01648-4(7)) Wright Group, The.

Shortall, Leonard, illus. Encyclopedia Brown Keeps the Peace. 2002. (Encyclopedia Brown Ser.: No. 6). (J). 12.87 (978-0-7587-0848-9(3)) Book Wholesalers, Inc.

—Encyclopedia Brown Saves the Day. 2002. (Encyclopedia Brown Ser.). (J). 12.87 (978-0-7587-0850-2(5)) Book Wholesalers, Inc.

—Encyclopedia Brown Solves Them All. 2002. (Encyclopedia Brown Ser.: No. 5). (J). 12.87 (978-0-7587-0862-5(9)) Book Wholesalers, Inc.

Shusterman, Neal. Shusterman Mystery. 1998. 160p. (J). (gr. 3-7). Bk. 1. 14.95 (978-0-06-025309-7(6)); No. 1. lib. bdg. 14.89 (978-0-06-025312-7(6)) HarperCollins Pubs.

Siamon, Sharon. Fire Horse. 2002. (gr. 3-6). lib. bdg. 15.25 (978-0-613-78589-1(4)) Tandem Library Bks.

—Fire Horse. 2002. (Mustang Mountain Ser.). 144p. (J). (gr. 3-7). pap. 6.95 (978-1-55285-457-0(4)) Whitecap Bks., Ltd. CAN. *Dist:* Firefly Bks., Ltd.

—Night Horse. 2002. (Mustang Mountain Ser.: No. 3). 144p. (J). (gr. 3-7). pap. 6.95 (978-1-55285-363-4(2)) Whitecap Bks., Ltd. CAN. *Dist:* Firefly Bks., Ltd.

Siamon, Sharon. Race to the Rescue. 2007. (Saddle Island Ser.). 172p. (J). (gr. 3-7). pap. 6.95 (***978-1-55285-855-4(3)*** , Walrus Bks.) Whitecap Bks., Ltd. CAN. *Dist:* Firefly Bks., Ltd.

Sieweke, Susan. Annie Nell & the Sock Gnomes. 2007. (J). per. 9.99 (***978-1-60247-017-0(0)***) Tate Publishing & Enterprises, L.L.C.

Simmons, Alex & McCay, Bill. Buffalo Bill Wanted! 2007. 208p. (J). (gr. 4-6). 10.99 (978-1-59514-073-9(5) , Razorbill) Penguin Group (USA) Inc.

Simmons, Alexander. Sherlock Holmes is Missing. 1998. (J). 5.99 (978-0-679-88204-6(9) , Random Hse. Bks. for Young Readers) Random Hse. Children's Bks.

Simmons, H. Two Tales from Our Corner Lot. 2004. 68p. pap. 14.95 (978-1-4137-5251-9(9)) PublishAmerica, Inc.

Simmons, Lynn Sheffield. Bo & the Missing Dogs. Hampton, Lin, illus. 2002. 117p. (J). (gr. 4-7). pap. 6.95 (978-0-9642573-3-7(5)) Argyle Bks.

—Bo & the Missing Dogs. 2004. (Illus.). 128p. (YA). 8.95 (978-1-58980-219-3(5)) Pelican Publishing Co., Inc.

Simner, Janni Lee. Secret of the Three Treasures. 2005. 160p. (J). 16.95 (978-0-8234-1914-2(2)) Holiday Hse., Inc.

Simon, Les. The Secret of the Red Silk Pouch. 1998. 157p. (YA). (gr. 8-12). pap. 9.99 (978-0-88092-362-0(8) , 3628) Royal Fireworks Publishing Co.

Simon, Seymour. The Gigantic Ants & Other Cases. 1998. (Einstein Anderson, Science Detective Ser.). (Illus.). (J). (gr. 3-6). pap. 3.99 (978-0-380-72657-8(2)) HarperCollins Pubs.

—The Halloween Horror & Other Cases, Bk. 2. Schindler, S. D., illus. 1998. (Einstein Anderson, Science Detective Ser.). (J). (gr. 3-6). pap. 3.99 (978-0-380-72656-1(4)) HarperCollins Pubs.

—The Howling Dog & Other Cases. 1998. (Einstein Anderson, Science Detective Ser.). (Illus.). (J). (gr. 3-6). pap. 3.99 (978-0-380-72655-4(6)) HarperCollins Pubs.

—The Howling Dog & Other Cases. 2000. (Einstein Anderson, Science Detective Ser.). (J). (gr. 3-6). pap. 32.00 incl. audio (978-0-7887-4457-0(7) , 41148) Recorded Bks., LLC.

—The Invisible Man & Other Cases. 1999. (Einstein Anderson, Science Detective Ser.: Vol. 7). 96p. (J). (gr. 3-7). pap. 3.99 (978-0-380-72661-5(0) , Harper Trophy) HarperCollins Pubs.

—The Invisible Man & Other Cases. 1999. (Einstein Anderson, Science Detective Ser.). (J). (gr. 3-6). (978-0-606-16358-3(1)) Tandem Library Bks.

—The On-Line Spaceman & Other Cases. 1998. (Einstein Anderson, Science Detective Ser.). (Illus.). 96p. (J). (gr. 3-6). reprint ed. pap. 3.99 (978-0-380-72662-2(9)) HarperCollins Pubs.

—The On-Line Spaceman & Other Cases. 1998. (Einstein Anderson, Science Detective Ser.). (J). (gr. 3-6). (978-0-606-13352-4(6)) Tandem Library Bks.

—The Time Machine & Other Cases. Schindler, S. D., illus. 1999. (Einstein Anderson, Science Detective Ser.). (J). (gr. 3-6). pap. 3.99 (978-0-380-72658-5(0)) HarperCollins Pubs.

—The Time Machine & Other Cases. 1999. (Einstein Anderson, Science Detective Ser.). (J). (gr. 3-6). (978-0-606-16005-6(1)) Tandem Library Bks.

—The Wings of Darkness & Other Cases, Bk. 5. Schindler, S. D., illus. 1999. (Einstein Anderson, Science Detective Ser.). 80p. (J). (gr. 3-6). pap. 3.99 (978-0-380-72659-2(9) , Harper Trophy) HarperCollins Pubs.

—The Wings of Darkness & Other Cases. 1999. (Einstein Anderson, Science Detective Ser.). (J). (gr. 3-6). (978-0-606-16341-5(7)) Tandem Library Bks.

Simont, Marc, illus. Nate the Great. 2002. (Nate the Great Ser.). (J). 12.87 (978-0-7587-0695-9(2)) Book Wholesalers, Inc.

—Nate the Great & the Crunchy Christmas. 2002. (Nate the Great Ser.). (J). 12.87 (978-0-7587-0704-8(5)) Book Wholesalers, Inc.

—Nate the Great & the Fishy Prize. 2002. (Nate the Great Ser.). (J). 12.87 (978-0-7587-0705-5(3)) Book Wholesalers, Inc.

—Nate the Great & the Halloween Hunt. 2002. (Nate the Great Ser.). (J). 12.87 (978-0-7587-0697-3(9)) Book Wholesalers, Inc.

—Nate the Great & the Lost List. 2002. (Nate the Great Ser.). (J). 12.87 (978-0-7587-0706-2(1)) Book Wholesalers, Inc.

—Nate the Great & the Missing Key. 2002. (Nate the Great Ser.). (J). 12.87 (978-0-7587-0699-7(5)) Book Wholesalers, Inc.

—Nate the Great & the Mushy Valentine. 2002. (Nate the Great Ser.). (J). 12.87 (978-0-7587-0707-9(X)) Book Wholesalers, Inc.

—Nate the Great & the Musical Note. 2002. (Nate the Great Ser.). (J). 12.87 (978-0-7587-0700-0(2)) Book Wholesalers, Inc.

—Nate the Great & the Phony Clue. 2002. (Nate the Great Ser.). (J). 12.87 (978-0-7587-0701-7(0)) Book Wholesalers, Inc.

—Nate the Great & the Pillowcase. 2002. (Nate the Great Ser.). (J). 12.87 (978-0-7587-0708-6(8)) Book Wholesalers, Inc.

—Nate the Great & the Snowy Trail. 2002. (Nate the Great Ser.). (J). 12.87 (978-0-7587-0709-3(6)) Book Wholesalers, Inc.

—Nate the Great & the Sticky Case. 2002. (Nate the Great Ser.). (J). 12.87 (978-0-7587-0702-4(9)) Book Wholesalers, Inc.

—Nate the Great & the Stolen Base. 2002. (Nate the Great Ser.). (J). 12.87 (978-0-7587-0703-1(7)) Book Wholesalers, Inc.

—Nate the Great & the Tardy Tortoise. 2002. (Nate the Great Ser.). (J). 12.87 (978-0-7587-0711-6(8)) Book Wholesalers, Inc.

—Nate the Great Goes down in the Dumps. 2002. (Nate the Great Ser.). (J). 12.87 (978-0-7587-0712-3(6)) Book Wholesalers, Inc.

—Nate the Great Goes Undercover. 2002. (Nate the Great Ser.). (J). 12.87 (978-0-7587-0713-0(4)) Book Wholesalers, Inc.

—Nate the Great Saves the King of Sweden. 2002. (Nate the Great Ser.). (J). 12.87 (978-0-7587-0714-7(2)) Book Wholesalers, Inc.

—Nate the Great Stalks Stupidweed. 2002. (Nate the Great Ser.). (J). 12.87 (978-0-7587-0715-4(0)) Book Wholesalers, Inc.

Singleton, Linda Joy. Melissa's Mission Impossible. 2003. pap. 4.99 (978-1-58608-609-1(X)) New Concepts Publishing.

—Witch Ball. 2006. (Seer Ser.: Bk. 3). 264p. pap. 6.99 (978-0-7387-0821-8(6)) Llewellyn Pubns.

Skead, Robert. Safe at Home: A Baseball Card Mystery. 1999. 80p. (J). pap. 5.95 (978-1-887002-91-2(X)) Cross Training Publishing.

Skelton, Vonda Skinner. Bitsy & the Mystery at Amelia Island. 2005. (Bitsy Burroughs Mysteries Ser.). 183p. (J). 15.95 (978-1-57072-306-3(0) , Silver Dagger Mysteries) Overmountain Pr.

—Bitsy & the Mystery at Tybee Island. 2003. (Bitsy Burroughs Mysteries Ser.). 120p. (J). 23.95 (978-1-57072-253-0(6)); pap. 13.95 (978-1-57072-254-7(4)) Overmountain Pr. (Silver Dagger Mysteries).

Skillchecks for Mystery. 2005. (Double Fastback Ser.). (J). (gr. 6-12). 64p. pap. 5.95 (978-0-13-024473-4(2)); 32p. pap. 5.95 (978-0-13-024455-0(4)) Globe Fearon Educational Publishing.

Skofield, James. Detective Dinosaur. Alley, R. W., illus. 1998. (I Can Read Bks.). 48p. (J). (gr. k-3). pap. 3.99 (978-0-06-444235-0(7) , Harper Trophy) HarperCollins Pubs.

—Detective Dinosaur. 1998. (I Can Read Bks.). (J). (gr. 1-3). 10.79 (978-0-606-12912-1(X)) Tandem Library Bks.

—Detective Dinosaur Lost & Found. Alley, R. W., illus. 1999. (I Can Read Bks.). 48p. (J). (ps-3). pap. 3.99 (978-0-06-444257-2(8) , Harper Trophy) HarperCollins Pubs.

—Detective Dinosaur Lost & Found. 1999. (I Can Read Bks.). (J). 10.79 (978-0-606-16693-5(9)); lib. bdg. 11.80 (978-0-613-16089-6(4)) Tandem Library Bks.

Skoob: The Kingdom Awaits. 2005. (J). per. 7.95 (978-1-59571-072-7(8)) Word Association Pubs.

Skurzynski, Gloria. Buried Alive. 2003. (gr. 3-6). lib. bdg. 14.10 (978-0-613-70935-4(7)) Tandem Library Bks.

—Cliff-Hanger. 2001. (gr. 3-6). lib. bdg. 14.10 (978-0-613-81326-6(X)); (Illus.). (J). 12.60 (978-0-606-21111-6(X)) Tandem Library Bks.

—Deadly Waters. 2001. (gr. 3-6). lib. bdg. 14.10 (978-0-613-81327-3(8)); (Illus.). (J). 12.60 (978-0-606-21142-0(X)) Tandem Library Bks.

—The Hunted. 2001. 12.60 (978-0-606-22147-4(6)); (gr. 3-6). lib. bdg. 14.10 (978-0-613-62422-0(X)) Tandem Library Bks.

—Out of the Deep. 2002. (gr. 3-6). lib. bdg. 14.10 (978-0-613-62818-1(7)) Tandem Library Bks.

—Over the Edge. 2002. (gr. 3-6). lib. bdg. 14.10 (978-0-613-62819-8(5)) Tandem Library Bks.

—Running Scared. 2002. (gr. 3-6). lib. bdg. 14.10 (978-0-613-62832-7(2)) Tandem Library Bks.

—Valley of Death. 2002. (gr. 3-6). lib. bdg. 14.10 (978-0-613-62873-0(X)) Tandem Library Bks.

—Wolf Stalker. 2001. (gr. 3-6). lib. bdg. 14.10 (978-0-613-84040-8(2)) Tandem Library Bks.

Skurzynski, Gloria & Ferguson. Wolf Stalker. 2001. (National Parks Mystery Ser.). (Illus.). (J). (978-0-606-21533-6(6)) Tandem Library Bks.

Skurzynski, Gloria & Ferguson, Alane. Buried Alive. 2003. (Mysteries in Our National Parks Ser.: No. 12). 160p. (J). (gr. 3-7). 15.95 (978-0-7922-6966-3(7)); pap. 5.95 (978-0-7922-6968-7(3)) National Geographic Society. (National Geographic Children's Bks.).

—Cliff-Hanger. (Illus.). 160p. (J). (gr. 3-7). 2007. (Mysteries in Our National Park Ser.). 4.99 (978-1-4263-0092-9(1)); 1998. (National Parks Mysteries Ser.: No. 3). 15.95 (978-0-7922-7036-2(3)) National Geographic Society. (National Geographic Children's Bks.).

—Deadly Waters. (Illus.). (J). (gr. 3-7). 2001. (Mysteries in Our National Parks Ser.: No. 3). 143p. pap. 5.95 (978-0-7922-7655-5(8)); 1999. (National Parks Mysteries Ser.: No. 4). 160p. 15.95 (978-0-7922-7037-9(1)) National Geographic Society. (National Geographic Children's Bks.).

—Ghost Horses. (Illus.). 160p. (J). (gr. 3-7). 2007. (Mysteries in Our National Park Ser.). 4.99 (978-1-4263-0108-7(1)); 2000. (National Parks Mysteries Ser.: Vol. 6). 15.95 (978-0-7922-7055-3(X)) National Geographic Society. (National Geographic Children's Bks.).

—The Hunted. (National Parks Mysteries Ser.: No. 5). 160p. (J). (gr. 3-7). 2000. (Illus.). 15.95 (978-0-7922-7053-9(3)); 5th ed. 2001. pap. 5.95 (978-0-7922-7665-4(5)) National Geographic Society. (National Geographic Children's Bks.).

—Night of the Black Bear: A Mystery in Great Smoky Mountains National Park. 2007. (Mysteries in Our National Park Ser.). (Illus.). 160p. (J). (gr. 3-7). 4.99 (978-1-4263-0094-3(8)); 18.90 (978-1-4263-0105-6(7)) National Geographic Society. (National Geographic Children's Bks.).

—Out of the Deep. 2002. (Mysteries in Our National Parks Ser.: Vol. 10). 160p. (J). (gr. 3-7). 15.95 (978-0-7922-8230-3(2)); pap. 5.95 (978-0-7922-8231-0(0)) National Geographic Society. (National Geographic Children's Bks.).

—Over the Edge. 2002. (Mysteries in Our National Parks Ser.: Vol. 7). 160p. (J). (gr. 3-7). pap. 5.95 (978-0-7922-6686-0(2)); Vol. 7. 15.95 (978-0-7922-6677-8(3)) National Geographic Society. (National Geographic Children's Bks.).

—Rage of Fire. (J). (gr. 3-7). 2001. (Mysteries in Our National Parks Ser.). 160p. pap. 5.95 (978-0-7922-7653-1(1)); 1999. (National Parks Mysteries Ser.: No. 2). (Illus.). 164p. 15.95 (978-0-7922-7035-5(5)) National Geographic Society. (National Geographic Children's Bks.).

—Running Scared. 2002. (Mysteries in Our National Parks Ser.: Vol. 11). 160p. (J). (gr. 3-7). 15.95 (978-0-7922-8232-7(9)); pap. 5.95 (978-0-7922-6948-9(9)) National Geographic Society. (National Geographic Children's Bks.).

—Valley of Death. 2002. (Mysteries in Our National Parks Ser.: Vol. 8). 160p. (J). (gr. 3-7). pap. 5.95 (978-0-7922-6699-0(4)); Vol. 8. 15.95 (978-0-7922-6698-3(6)) National Geographic Society. (National Geographic Children's Bks.).

—Wolf Stalker. (Illus.). 160p. (J). (gr. 3-7). 2007. (Mysteries in Our National Park Ser.). 4.99 (978-1-4263-0096-7(4)); 1998. (National Parks Mysteries Ser.: Vol. 1). 15.95 (978-0-7922-7034-8(7)) National Geographic Society. (National Geographic Children's Bks.).

Sleep, Betty. Purrlock Holmes, & the Case of the Vanishing Valuables. 2004. (J). mass mkt. 8.95 (978-1-58961-330-0(9)) PageFree Publishing, Inc.

Sleepers. 64p. (YA). (gr. 6-12). pap. (978-0-8224-2366-9(9)) Globe Fearon Educational Publishing.

Sloan, Glenna. Stealing Time. 1998. 126p. (YA). (gr. 7-17). pap. 9.99 (978-0-88092-266-1(4) , 2664) Royal Fireworks Publishing Co.

Small, David. The River in Winter. 2001. 324p. (YA). pap. 21.95 (978-0-595-19798-9(1)) iUniverse, Inc.

Smalley, Elisa. Zoe Sophia in New York: The Mystery of the Pink Phoenix Papers. Mauner, Claudia, illus. 2006. 36p. (J). 14.95 (978-0-8118-4877-0(9)) Chronicle Bks. LLC.

Smith, Alexander McCall. Harriet Bean & the League of Cheats. Rankin, Laura, illus. 80p. (J). 2007. pap. 4.95 (978-1-59990-054-4(8)); 2006. 9.95 (978-1-58234-976-3(2)) Bloomsbury Publishing. (Bloomsbury Children).

—Max & Maddy & the Bursting Balloons Mystery. Pamintuan, Macky, illus. 2007. 128p. (J). (gr. 2-4). 9.95 (978-1-59990-035-3(1) , Bloomsbury Children) Bloomsbury Publishing.

—Max & Maddy & the Chocolate Money Mystery. Pamintuan, Macky, illus. 2007. 128p. (J). (gr. 2-4). 9.95 (978-1-59990-036-0(X) , Bloomsbury Children) Bloomsbury Publishing.

Smith, Bernard. The Last Photo. 2002. (Illus.). 16p. pap. (978-0-582-40282-9(4) , Putnam Juvenile) Penguin Group (USA) Inc.

Smith, Jeff. Old Man's Cave. 2007. (Bone Ser.: No. 6). 128p. (J). pap. 19.99 (*978-0-439-70628-5(9)); pap. 9.99 (*978-0-439-70635-3(1)) Scholastic, Inc.

Smith, Roland. Cryptid Hunters. 2005. 352p. (J). (gr. 5-17). 15.99 (978-0-7868-5161-4(9)) Hyperion Bks. for Children.

—Cryptid Hunters. 2006. 352p. (gr. 5-17). pap. 5.99 (978-0-7868-5162-1(7)) Hyperion Pr.

Smith, Tara Bray. Betwixt. 2007. 488p. (YA). (gr. 10-17). 17.99 (*978-0-316-06033-2(X)) Little, Brown Bks. for Young Readers.

Smith, Tim. Who Stole the Animal Poop? 2006. (Buck Wilder's Adventure Ser.). 60p. (J). pap. (978-1-934133-05-7(1)) Mackinac Island Pr., Inc.

Smith, Timothy R. The Owls Don't Give a Hoot. 2007. (Buck Wilder's Adventure Ser.: 4). (Illus.). 96p. (J). pap. 5.95 (*978-1-934133-11-8(6)) Mackinac Island Pr., Inc.

—The Salmon Stop Running. 2007. (Illus.). 80p. (J). pap. 5.95 (*978-1-934133-34-7(5)) Mackinac Island Pr., Inc.

Snell, J. Roy. Curlie Carson Listens In. 2007. (ENG.). 136p. 41.99 (*978-1-4280-7269-5(1)); per. 34.99 (*978-1-4280-7273-2(X)) IndyPublish.com.

—Triple Spies. 2006. 32.99 (*978-1-4280-1776-4(3)) IndyPublish.com.

Snyder, Lavinia Branca. The Mystery of the Lost Bells: The Kyss Family Mysteries. 2002. 32p. (J). mass mkt. (978-1-932233-67-4(9)) Aurora Libris Corp.

—The Treasure of Lodian: The Kyss Family Mysteries. 2003. (Illus.). (J). mass mkt. (978-1-932233-68-1(7)) Aurora Libris Corp.

Snyder, Zilpha Keatley. The Treasures of Weatherby. 2006. 224p. (J). 15.95 (978-1-4169-1398-6(X) , Atheneum) Simon & Schuster Children's Publishing.

Sobol, Donald J. Encyclopedia Brown & the Case of the Dead Eagles. 2008. (Encyclopedia Brown Ser.). 96p. (J). (gr. 1-3). pap. 4.99 (*978-0-14-241135-3(3) , Puffin) Penguin Group (USA) Inc.

—Encyclopedia Brown & the Case of the Jumping Frogs. (Encyclopedia Brown Ser.: No. 23). 80p. (gr. 3-7). 2005. (J). pap. 5.50 (978-0-553-48758-9(2) , Yearling); 2003. (Illus.). 14.95 (978-0-385-72931-4(6) , Delacorte Bks. for Young Readers); 2003. (Illus.). lib. bdg. 16.99 (978-0-385-90148-2(8) , Delacorte Bks. for Young Readers) Random Hse. Children's Bks.

—Encyclopedia Brown & the Case of the Midnight Visitor. 2008. (Encyclopedia Brown Ser.). 96p. (J). (gr. 1-3). pap. 4.99 (*978-0-14-241106-3(X) , Puffin) Penguin Group (USA) Inc.

—Encyclopedia Brown & the Case of the Secret Pitch. 2007. (Encyclopedia Brown Ser.: No. 2). 96p. (J). (gr. 2-6). 4.99 (*978-0-14-240889-6(1) , Puffin) Penguin Group (USA) Inc.

—Encyclopedia Brown & the Case of the Secret Pitch. 2004. (Encyclopedia Brown Ser.: No. 2). 112p. (J). (gr. 3-7). pap. 17.00 incl. audio (978-0-8072-1985-0(1) , Listening Library) Random Hse. Audio Publishing Group.

—Encyclopedia Brown & the Case of the Sleeping Dog. Chang, Warren, illus. 1999. (Encyclopedia Brown Ser.: No. 21). 80p. (J). (gr. 3-7). pap. 5.50 (978-0-553-48517-2(2) , Yearling) Random Hse. Children's Bks.

—Encyclopedia Brown & the Case of the Sleeping Dog. 1999. (Encyclopedia Brown Ser.: No. 21). (gr. 3-6). lib. bdg. 12.40 (978-0-613-22846-6(4)); (Illus.). (J). 11.30 (978-0-606-18628-5(X)) Tandem Library Bks.

—Encyclopedia Brown & the Case of the Slippery Salamander. (Encyclopedia Brown Ser.: No. 22). 2000. (gr. 3-6). lib. bdg. 12.40 (978-0-613-28475-2(5)); 1999. (Illus.). (J). 11.30 (978-0-606-18629-2(8)) Tandem Library Bks.

—Encyclopedia Brown, Boy Detective. 2007. (Encyclopedia Brown Ser.: No. 1). 96p. (J). (gr. 2). 4.99 (*978-0-14-240888-9(3) , Puffin) Penguin Group (USA) Inc.

—Encyclopedia Brown, Boy Detective. 2004. (Encyclopedia Brown Ser.: No. 1). 128p. (J). (gr. 3-7). pap. 17.00 incl. audio (978-0-8072-1984-3(3) , Listening Library) Random Hse. Audio Publishing Group.

—Encyclopedia Brown Cracks the Case. 2007. 128p. (J). (gr. 3). 15.99 (*978-0-525-47924-6(4) , Dutton Juvenile) Penguin Group (USA) Inc.

—Encyclopedia Brown Finds the Clues. 2007. (Encyclopedia Brown Ser.: No. 3). 96p. (J). (gr. 2). 4.99 (*978-0-14-240890-2(5) , Puffin) Penguin Group (USA) Inc.

—Encyclopedia Brown Gets His Man. 2007. (Encyclopedia Brown Ser.: No. 4). 96p. (J). (gr. 2). pap. 4.99 (*978-0-14-240891-9(3) , Puffin) Penguin Group (USA) Inc.

—Encyclopedia Brown Lends a Hand. 2008. (Encyclopedia Brown Ser.). 96p. (J). (gr. 1-3). pap. 4.99 (*978-0-14-241105-6(1) , Puffin) Penguin Group (USA) Inc.

—Encyclopedia Brown Saves the Day. 2008. (Encyclopedia Brown Ser.: No. 7). 96p. (J). (gr. 2). 4.99 (*978-0-14-240921-3(9) , Puffin) Penguin Group (USA) Inc.

—Encyclopedia Brown Shows the Way. Shortall, Leonard, illus. 2008. (Encyclopedia Brown Ser.). 96p. (J). (gr. 2). 4.99 (*978-0-14-241086-8(1) , Puffin) Penguin Group (USA) Inc.

—Encyclopedia Brown Solves Them All. 2008. (Encyclopedia Brown Ser.: No. 5). 96p. (J). (gr. 2). 4.99 (*978-0-14-240920-6(0) , Puffin) Penguin Group (USA) Inc.

—Encyclopedia Brown Takes the Case. 2008. (Encyclopedia Brown Ser.: No. 10). 96p. (J). (gr. 2). 4.99 (*978-0-14-241085-1(3) , Puffin) Penguin Group (USA) Inc.

—Encyclopedia Brown Tracks Them Down. Shortall, Leonard, illus. 2008. (Encyclopedia Brown Ser.: No. 8). 96p. (J). (gr. 2). 4.99 (*978-0-14-240951-0(0) , Puffin) Penguin Group (USA) Inc.

—Keeps the Peace. 2008. (Encyclopedia Brown Ser.: No. 6). 96p. (J). (gr. 2). 4.99 (*978-0-14-240950-3(2) , Puffin) Penguin Group (USA) Inc.

Soderberg, Erin. Dinosaur Dig. 2000. (gr. k-3). lib. bdg. 11.80 (978-0-613-54167-1(7)) Tandem Library Bks.

—Spooky Sports Day. 2002. (gr. k-3). lib. bdg. 11.80 (978-0-613-63348-2(2)) Tandem Library Bks.

Soileau, Hodges, illus. The Great Shark Mystery, Vol. 20. 2004. (Boxcar Children Mysteries Ser.: Vol. 20). 128p. pap. 4.50 (978-0-8075-5532-3(0)) Whitman, Albert & Co.

—The Haunted Clock Tower Mystery, Vol. 84. 2004. (Boxcar Children Ser.: No. 84). 128p. (J). (gr. 2-7). pap. 3.95 (978-0-8075-5485-2(5)) Whitman, Albert & Co.

—The Mystery in the Fortune Cookie, Vol. 96. 2004. (Boxcar Children Ser.: Vol. 96). 136p. (J). pap. 3.95 (978-0-8075-5540-8(1)) Whitman, Albert & Co.

—The Radio Mystery, Vol. 97. 2004. (Boxcar Children Ser.: Vol. 97). 128p. (J). mass mkt. 3.95 (978-0-8075-5547-7(9)) Whitman, Albert & Co.

Somoskey, Rebecca. Summer of the Buckeye Whistle. 2004. (J). 5.00 (978-0-9768514-0-0(7)) Bearwallow Blessings Ministries.

Sonik, Madeline. Belinda & the Dustbunnys. Bridal, Grania, tr. 2004. (Illus.). 80p. (J). (gr. 4-7). 12.95 (978-0-9730831-4-9(X)) Hodgepog Bks. CAN. *Dist:* Coteau Bks., Fitzhenry & Whiteside, Ltd.

Sorrells, Walter. Club Dread. (Hunted Ser.). 272p. (YA). 2007. (gr. 7). 7.99 (*978-0-14-240904-6(9) , Puffin); 2006. (gr. 6-10). 10.99 (978-0-525-47618-4(0) , Dutton Juvenile) Penguin Group (USA) Inc.

Sorrells, Walter. Fake ID: A Mystery. 2007. (Hunted Ser.). 336p. (YA). (gr. 7 up). pap. 6.99 (978-0-14-240762-2(3) , Puffin) Penguin Group (USA) Inc.

Sorrentino, Scott. Inspector Gadget. 1999. (Disney's Junior Novel Ser.). (Illus.). 96p. (J). (gr. 3-7). pap. 4.99 (978-0-7868-4292-6(X)) Disney Pr.

Souhami, Jessica. In the Dark, Dark Wood. 2007. (Illus.). 24p. (J). 7.95 (*978-1-84507-755-6(5)) Lincoln, Frances Ltd. GBR. *Dist:* Perseus Distribution.

Spalding, Andrea. Heart of the Hill. 2005. (Dinah Galloway Mystery Ser.: Bk. 3Three). 192p. (J). (gr. 3-7). pap. 7.95 (978-1-55143-486-5(5)) Orca Bk. Pubs. USA.

Spalding, Andrea & Spalding, David. The Silver Boulder. (Adventure Net Ser.). 8p. tchr. ed. 3.95 (978-1-55285-160-9(5) , Walrus Bks.); 2000. (Illus.). 128p. (J). (gr. 3-2). pap. 6.95 (978-1-55285-105-0(2)) Whitecap Bks., Ltd. CAN. *Dist:* Graphic Arts Ctr. Publishing Co., Firefly Bks., Ltd.

Speck, Nancy. The Freedom Trail Mystery. Barstow, Susannah Driver, ed. Farnsworth, Bill, illus. 2001. (Going to Ser.). 173p. (gr. 4-8). pap. 6.95 (978-1-893577-07-7(4)) Four Corners Publishing Co., Inc.

—Secret of the Hidden Room. Thomas, Jerry D., ed. Ford, Mark, illus. 1999. (Shoebox Kids Ser.: Vol. 9). 93p. (J). pap. 6.99 (978-0-8163-1682-3(1)) Pacific Pr. Publishing Assn.

Spirn, Michele Sobel. The Bridges in Paris. 2000. (Going to Ser.). (Illus.). 121p. (J). (gr. 4-8). pap. 6.95 (978-1-893577-04-6(X)) Four Corners Publishing Co., Inc.

Springer, Nancy. Blood Trail. 164p. (YA). (gr. 7 up). pap. 6.95 (*978-0-8234-2063-6(9)) Holiday Hse., Inc.

—The Case of the Bizarre Bouquets: An Enola Holmes Mystery. 2008. 192p. (YA). (gr. 4). 14.99 (*978-0-399-24518-3(9) , Philomel) Penguin Group (USA) Inc.

—The Case of the Left-Handed Lady: An Enola Holmes Mystery. 2008. 256p. (J). (gr. 4-8). pap. 6.99 (*978-0-14-241190-2(6) , Puffin); 2007. 224p. (YA). (gr. 5-9). 12.99 (978-0-399-24517-6(0) , Philomel) Penguin Group (USA) Inc.

Springer, Nancy. The Case of the Missing Marquess: An Enola Holmes Mystery. (J). 2007. 224p. (gr. 3). 6.99 (*978-0-14-240933-6(2) , Puffin); 2006. 208p. (gr. 4). 10.99 (978-0-399-24304-2(6) , Philomel) Penguin Group (USA) Inc.

The Spy down the Street, 6 vols., Vol. 2. (Woodland Mysteriestm Ser.). 133p. (gr. 3-7). 42.50 (978-0-7802-7938-4(7)) Wright Group, The.

St. George, Judith. Mystery Isle. 2007. 192p. (YA). pap. 5.99 (978-0-14-240841-4(7) , Puffin) Penguin Group (USA) Inc.

Stamper, Judith Bauer. Boom! Zoom! 1998. (Hello Reader! Ser.). (J). (gr. 1-2). (978-0-606-13763-8(7)) Tandem Library Bks.

—Dinosaur Detectives: Reading Comprehension & Activities. Enik, Ted, illus. 2002. (Magic School Bus Chapter Bks.: No. 9). 96p. (J). pap. 4.99 (978-0-439-20423-1(2) , Scholastic Paperbacks) Scholastic, Inc.

Stanek, Mary Beth. The Fire Keepers: Mystery at Manitou Beach. Stanek, Mary Beth, illus. Stanek, Linda, photos by. 2003. (J). pap. 20.00 (978-0-9747556-0-1(5)) Stanek, Mary Beth.

Stangherlin, Tonia. T-Bird & the Island of Lost Cats. 2006. 116p. pap. 14.99 (978-1-4116-6697-9(6)) Lulu.com.

Stanley, Diane. The Mysterious Case of the Allbright Academy. 2008. 272p. (J). lib. bdg. 17.89 (*978-0-06-085818-6(4)); (gr. 3-7). 16.99 (*978-0-06-085817-9(6)) HarperCollins Pubs.

Stanley, Diane. The Mysterious Matter of I. M. Fine. 208p. (J). (gr. 4 up). 2002. pap. 5.99 (978-0-380-73327-9(7)); 2001. (Illus.). 15.99 (978-0-688-17546-7(5)); 2001. (Illus.). lib. bdg. 16.89 (978-0-06-029619-3(4)) HarperCollins Pubs.

—The Mysterious Matter of I. M. Fine. 2002. (gr. 3-6). lib. bdg. 14.15 (978-0-613-60392-8(3)) Tandem Library Bks.

Stanley, George. The Case of the Dirty Clue: Third-Grade Detectives. Murdocca, Salvatore, illus. 2005. (Ready-for-Chapters Ser.). (J). lib. bdg. 15.00 (978-1-59054-898-1(1)) Fitzgerald Bks.

Stanley, George E. The Case of the Sweaty Bank Robber. Murdocca, Salvatore, illus. 2004. (Third-Grade Detectives Ser.). 80p. (J). pap. 7.95 (978-0-689-86489-6(2) , Aladdin) Simon & Schuster Children's Publishing.

Stanley, George Edward. Adam Sharp No. 3: Swimming with Sharks. 2003. (gr. k-3). lib. bdg. 11.80 (978-0-613-82722-5(8)) Tandem Library Bks.

—The Case of the Dirty Clue. Murdocca, Salvatore, illus. 2003. (Third Grade Detectives Ser.: No. 7). 80p. (J). pap. 3.99 (978-0-689-86357-8(8) , Aladdin) Simon & Schuster Children's Publishing.

—Clue of the Left-Handed Envelope. 2000. (gr. 3-6). lib. bdg. 11.80 (978-0-613-31078-9(0)) Tandem Library Bks.

—The Clue of the Left-Handed Envelope/The Puzzle of the Pretty Pink Handkerchief. Murdocca, Sal, illus. 2004. (Third-Grade Detectives Ser.). 144p. (J). pap. 3.99 (978-0-689-87106-1(6) , Aladdin) Simon & Schuster Children's Publishing.

—Cobweb Confession. 2001. (gr. 3-6). lib. bdg. 11.80 (978-0-613-35666-4(7)) Tandem Library Bks.

—The Cobweb Confession, No. 4. 2001. (Third Grade Detectives Ser.). (Illus.). (J). 10.79 (978-0-606-20942-7(5)) Tandem Library Bks.

—The Mystery of the Hairy Tomatoes. Murdocca, Salvatore, illus. 2001. (Third Grade Detectives Ser.: No. 3). 80p. (J). (gr. 1-4). pap. 3.99 (978-0-689-82209-4(X) , Aladdin) Simon & Schuster Children's Publishing.

—The Mystery of the Hairy Tomatoes. 2001. (gr. 3-6). lib. bdg. 11.80 (978-0-613-31518-0(9)); No. 3. (Illus.). (J). (978-0-606-20941-0(7)) Tandem Library Bks.

—The Mystery of the Stolen Statue. Murdocca, Sal, illus. 2004. (Third-Grade Detectives Ser.). 80p. (J). pap. 3.99 (978-0-689-86491-9(4) , Aladdin) Simon & Schuster Children's Publishing.

—Riddle of the Stolen Sand. 2003. (gr. 3-6). lib. bdg. 11.80 (978-0-613-61825-0(4)) Tandem Library Bks.

—The Riddle of the Stolen Sand. Murdocca, Salvatore, illus. ed. 2005. 62p. (J). lib. bdg. 15.00 (978-1-59054-913-1(9)) Fitzgerald Bks.

—Secret of the Green Skin. 2003. (gr. 3-6). lib. bdg. 11.80 (978-0-613-66539-1(2)) Tandem Library Bks.

—The Secret of the Green Skin. Murducco, Salvatore, illus. ed. 2005. 62p. (J). lib. bdg. 15.00 (978-1-59054-916-2(3)) Fitzgerald Bks.

—The Secret of the Wooden Witness. Murdocca, Salvatore, illus. 2004. (Third Grade Detectives Ser.). 80p. (J). pap. 3.99 (978-0-689-86487-2(6) , Aladdin) Simon & Schuster Children's Publishing.

—Secret of the Wooden Witness. 2004. (gr. k-3). lib. bdg. 11.80 (978-0-613-88074-9(9)) Tandem Library Bks.

Stanley, Phillip Orin, 2nd. The Castle Rock Critter. Stanley, Christopher Heath & Parsons, Arielle, illus. l.t. ed. 2004. 16p. (J). 8.00 (978-0-9761355-0-0(7)) Floodgate Publishing.

Staples, Gwen E. The Lice Out Case. Marensk, Suzanne Lazenby, illus. 1999. 24p. (J). (gr. k-6). pap. 6.95 (978-0-9675824-0-5(7)) Wal-Med, Inc.

Star, Nancy. The Case of the April Fool's Frogs. 2006. 77p. (978-0-439-67266-5(X)) Scholastic, Inc.

—The Case of the Missing Pumpkins. Bernardin, James, illus. 2004. 79p. (J). (978-0-439-67260-3(0)) Scholastic, Inc.

—The Case of the Thanksgiving Thief. Bernardin, James, illus. 2004. 79p. (J). (978-0-439-67261-0(9)) Scholastic, Inc.

Star, Nancy. Mystery of the Snow Day Bigfoot. Bernardin, James, illus. 2005. (Calendar Club Mysteries Ser.: Vol. 3). 77p. (J). pap. (*978-0-439-67262-7(7)) Scholastic, Inc.

Starke, Ruth. Dead Red. 2002. (Illus.). 96p. (YA). pap. (978-0-7344-0250-9(3) , Lothian Bks.) Hachette Livre Australia.

Staub, Wendy Corsi. Lily Dale: Awakening. 2007. 240p. (YA). (gr. 7 up). 15.95 (*978-0-8027-9654-7(0)) Walker & Co.

Staunton, Ted. Morgan's Secret. Slavin, Bill, illus. 2000. (New First Novels Ser.). 58p. (gr. 1-5). 4.95 (978-0-88780-494-6(2)) Formac Publishing Co., Ltd. CAN. *Dist:* Casemate Pubs. & Bk. Distributors, LLC.

Steck-Vaughn Staff. Case of the Canival Cash. 2002. (Illus.). pap. 41.60 incl. audio compact disk (978-0-7398-6957-4(4)) Steck-Vaughn.

—Pet Day. 1999. (Illus.). (J). pap. (978-0-8172-8704-7(3)) Steck-Vaughn.

Steel, Richard. Touchdown. Taylor, Marjorie, illus. rev. ed. 1999. (Take Ten Ser.). 48p. (YA). (gr. 4 up). pap. 3.95 (978-1-58659-003-1(0)) Artesian Pr.

Steele, Alexander. Case of the Breaking Story. l.t. ed. 2000. (Wishbone Mysteries Ser.: No. 20). (Illus.). 144p. (J). (gr. 4 up). lib. bdg. 23.33 (978-0-8368-2703-3(1)) Stevens, Gareth Inc.

—Case of the On-Line Alien. l.t. ed. 1999. (Wishbone Mysteries Ser.: No. 9). 144p. (J). (gr. 4 up). lib. bdg. 23.33 (978-0-8368-2449-0(0)) Stevens, Gareth Inc.

—Case of the Unsolved Case. l.t. ed. 2000. (Wishbone Mysteries Ser.: No. 13). (Illus.). 139p. (J). (gr. 4 up). lib. bdg. 23.33 (978-0-8368-2696-8(5)) Stevens, Gareth Inc.

Steele, Michael Anthony. Case of the Impounded Hounds. l.t. ed. 2000. (Wishbone Mysteries Ser.: No. 17). 138p. (J). (gr. 4 up). lib. bdg. 23.33 (978-0-8368-2700-2(7)) Stevens, Gareth Inc.

—Case of the Impounded Hounds. 1999. (Wishbone Mysteries Ser.: No. 17). (978-0-606-17769-6(8)) Tandem Library Bks.

—Forgotten Heroes. l.t. ed. 2000. (Wishbone Mysteries Ser.: No. 12). (Illus.). 139p. (J). (gr. 4 up). lib. bdg. 23.33 (978-0-8368-2695-1(7)) Stevens, Gareth Inc.

Steiner. Murder Takes a Fast Track. (Thumbprint Mysteries Ser.). 32.86 (978-0-8092-0417-5(7)) McGraw-Hill/Contemporary.

Steiner, Barbara. 23 Shadow Street: Deadly Dreams. 2006. 304p. pap. 8.95 (978-1-59687-329-2(9)) ibooks, Inc.

Stem, Jacqueline. The Borrowed Grave. Laronde, Gary, illus. 2001. v, 153p. (J). pap. 11.95 (978-1-57168-556-8(1) , Eakin Pr.) Eakin Pr.

—The Borrowed Grave, Vol. 3. 2001. (Hollow Tree Mystery Ser.). (Illus.). 160p. 16.95 (978-1-57168-451-6(4)) Eakin Pr.

—The Cellar in the Woods. 1998. (Hollow Tree Mystery Ser.). (Illus.). 152p. (gr. 5-6). 14.95 (978-1-57168-115-7(9)) Eakin Pr.

—Dangerous Games, Vol. 4. Eckhardt, Jason C., illus. 2002. (Hollow Tree Mystery Ser.). 160p. 16.95 (978-1-57168-701-2(7)); 12.95 (978-1-57168-702-9(5)) Eakin Pr.

—The Ghosts of Goliad. 2003. iii, 165p. (J). 17.95 (978-1-57168-785-2(8) , Eakin Pr.) Eakin Pr.

—Mystery of the Whispering Walls. 2004. (J). 148p. pap. (978-1-57168-844-6(7)); (Hollow Tree Mystery Ser.: Bk. 6). (Illus.). v, 142p. (978-1-57168-850-7(1) , Eakin Pr.) Eakin Pr.

—The Secret of Little Creek Farm, Vol. 2. 1999. (Hollow Tree Mystery Ser.). (Illus.). 136p. 14.95 (978-1-57168-293-2(7)) Eakin Pr.

—The Secret of the Dragonfly Pin. 2006. (Hollow Tree Mystery Ser.: 7). 122p. (J). pap. 12.95 (978-1-57168-264-2(3) , Eakin Pr.) Eakin Pr.

Stemach. Nick Ford Mysteries, Set. 2001. (J). (gr. 1). pap., tchr. ed. 8.00 (978-1-58702-665-2(1)) Johnston, Don Inc.

Stengel, Joyce A. Mystery at Kittiwake Bay. 2001. 176p. (J). pap. 9.95 (978-0-689-84595-6(2) , Aladdin) Simon & Schuster Children's Publishing.

—Mystery of the Island Jewels. 2002. 208p. (J). (gr. 3-7). pap. 4.99 (978-0-689-85049-3(2) , Aladdin) Simon & Schuster Children's Publishing.

—Mystery of the Island Jewels. 2002. (gr. 3-6). lib. bdg. 13.00 (978-0-613-70940-8(3)) Tandem Library Bks.

Stenhouse, Ted. Murder on the ridge. 2006. 240p. 6.95 (978-1-55337-893-8(8)) Kids Can Pr., Ltd. CAN. *Dist:* Wybel Marketing Group.

Stephens, Tracy L. What could it Be? 2005. pap. 7.95 (978-0-533-15332-9(8)) Vantage Pr., Inc.

Sternberg, Libby. Finding the Forger. 2004. 192p. (YA). 19.95 (978-1-890862-32-9(0)); pap. 14.95 (978-1-890862-37-4(1)) Bancroft Pr.

—Finding the Forger. 2006. (YA). mass mkt. 5.99 (978-0-8439-5503-3(1) , SMOOCH) Dorchester Publishing Co., Inc.

—Uncovering Sadie's Secrets: A Bianca Balducci Mystery. 2003. 183p. (YA). pap. 19.95 (978-1-890862-28-2(2)); (gr. 5-9). 16.95 (978-1-890862-23-7(1)) Bancroft Pr.

Steuerwald, Shannon B. From Scrawny to Brawny. 2006. (J). per. 9.95 (978-1-931787-19-2(0)) Fundamental Christian Endeavors.

Stevenson, James. Mud Flat Mystery. Stevenson, James, illus. 2003. (Illus.). 64p. (J). pap. 4.99 (978-0-06-051181-4(8) , Harper Trophy) HarperCollins Pubs.

Stevenson, Robert Louis & Grant, John. DR JEKYLL & Mister HYDE. 2004. 144p. (J). pap. 4.95 (978-0-7945-0238-6(5) , Usborne) EDC Publishing.

Stewart, Jane. The Island Escapade. 2003. 102p. (YA). pap. 9.95 (978-0-595-27734-6(9)) iUniverse, Inc.

Stewart, Linda. The Maltese Kitten: A Sam the Cat Mystery. 2002. 135p. (J). (gr. 4-7). pap. 10.95 (978-0-9675073-8-5(3)) Cheshire House Bks.

Stewart, Whitney. Jammin' on the Avenue. Barstow, Susannah Driver, ed. Farnsworth, Bill, illus. 2001. (Going to Ser.). 151p. (gr. 4-8). pap. 6.95 (978-1-893577-06-0(6)) Four Corners Publishing Co., Inc.

Stilton, Geronimo. Geronimo & the Gold Medal Mystery. 2008. (Geronimo Stilton Ser.). 128p. (J). 6.99 (*978-0-545-02133-3(2) , Scholastic Paperbacks) Scholastic, Inc.

—The Mona Mousa Code. Wolf, Matt, illus. 2005. (Geronimo Stilton Ser.: No. 15). 113p. (J). lib. bdg. 10.00 (*978-1-4242-0284-3(1)) Fitzgerald Bks.

—The Mona Mousa Code. Wolf, Matt, illus. 2005. (Geronimo Stilton Ser.: No. 15). 113p. (J). (ps-k). lib. bdg. 13.54 (978-0-606-33278-1(2)) Tandem Library Bks.

—The Mysterious Cheese Thief. 2007. (Geronimo Stilton Ser.: No. 31). 128p. (J). pap. 6.99 (*978-0-439-02312-2(2)) Scholastic, Inc.

—Paws off, Cheddarface! Wolf, Matt & Keys, Larry, illus. 2004. (Geronimo Stilton Ser.: No. 6). 128p. (J). mass mkt. 6.99 (978-0-439-55968-3(5)) Scholastic, Inc.

—The Phantom of the Subway. Wolf, Matt, illus. 2004. (Geronimo Stilton Ser.: No. 13). 112p. (J). lib. bdg. 10.00 (*978-1-4242-0282-9(5)) Fitzgerald Bks.

—The Phantom of the Subway. 2004. (Geronimo Stilton Ser.: No. 13). (Illus.). 128p. (J). (gr. 2-5). pap. 5.99 (978-0-439-66162-1(5) , Scholastic Paperbacks) Scholastic, Inc.

—The Phantom of the Subway. 2004. (Geronimo Stilton Ser.: No. 13). (Illus.). 112p. (J). (gr. 2-5). lib. bdg. 13.94 (978-0-606-33276-7(6)) Tandem Library Bks.

Stine, R. L. The Nightmare Room Vol. 1-2-3: The Nightmare Begins! 2005. (Nightmare Room Ser.). 432p. (gr. 5 up). pap. 7.99 (978-0-06-076674-0(3)) HarperCollins Pubs.

—The Perfect Date. 2005. (Fear Street Ser.). 160p. (YA). pap. 5.99 (978-1-4169-0323-9(2) , Simon Pulse) Simon & Schuster Children's Publishing.

Stinson, Kathy. One More Clue. 2005. (Streetlights Ser.). 104p. (J). (gr. 2). 7.95 (978-1-55028-888-9(1)) Lorimer, James & Co., Ltd., Pubs. CAN. *Dist:* Casemate Pubs. & Bk. Distributors, LLC.

—Seven Clues. 2005. (Streetlights Ser.). 104p. (J). (gr. 2-5). 7.95 (978-1-55028-889-6(X)) Lorimer, James & Co., Ltd., Pubs. CAN. *Dist:* Casemate Pubs. & Bk. Distributors, LLC.

Stitely, Margaret. Renee Peterson: Case #1 the Secret Admirer. 2003. 59p. pap. 9.95 (978-1-59286-401-0(5)) PublishAmerica, Inc.

Stoffle, Eric D. Adventure on Wild Horse Mountain. 1999. (Shoebox Kids Ser.: Vol. 10). (J). (gr. 2-7). pap. 6.99 (978-0-8163-1683-0(X)) Pacific Pr. Publishing Assn.

Stokes, Eliot Roy. Andy at Yale or the Great Quadrangle Mys. 2006. 96.99 (*978-1-4280-4960-4(6)); pap. 90.99 (*978-1-4280-4951-2(7)) IndyPublish.com.

Stokes, N. L. Mystery of the Missing Teacup. l.t. ed. 2003. (Illus.). 48p. per. 19.95 (978-0-9729411-1-2(8)) Stylewriter Pubns.

Stone, Tom B. Aullidos Alrededor del Fogon. 2002. (Graveyard School Ser.). (SPA.). (J). 5.95 (978-950-24-0898-9(5) , AL30677) Albatros ARG. *Dist:* Lectorum Pubns., Inc.

—Colonia de Vacaciones Dracula. 2002. (Graveyard School Ser.). (SPA.). (J). 5.95 (978-950-24-0774-6(1) , AL30659) Albatros ARG. *Dist:* Lectorum Pubns., Inc.

—El Equipo del Terror. 2002. (Graveyard School Ser.). (SPA.). (J). pap. 5.95 (978-950-24-0790-6(3) , AL30665) Albatros ARG. *Dist:* Lectorum Pubns., Inc.

—El Esqueleto del Skate. 2002. (Graveyard School Ser.). (SPA.). (J). pap. 5.95 (978-950-24-0770-8(9) , AL30655) Albatros ARG. *Dist:* Lectorum Pubns., Inc.

—Un Fantasma en el Bano de Varones. 2002. (Graveyard School Ser.). (SPA.). (J). pap. 5.95 (978-950-24-0788-3(1) , AL30663) Albatros ARG. *Dist:* Lectorum Pubns., Inc.

—Jack y los Frijoles Magicos. 2002. (Graveyard School Ser.). (SPA.). (J). pap. 5.95 (978-950-24-0899-6(3) , AL30670) Albatros ARG. *Dist:* Lectorum Pubns., Inc.

—El Lago de Lodo. 2002. (Graveyard School Ser.). (SPA.). (J). pap. 5.95 (978-950-24-0775-3(X) , AL30660) Albatros ARG. *Dist:* Lectorum Pubns., Inc.

—La Maestra Horripilante. 2002. (Graveyard School Ser.). (SPA.). (J). pap. 5.95 (978-950-24-0894-1(2) , AL30673) Albatros ARG. *Dist:* Lectorum Pubns., Inc.

—No le Cuentes a la Momia. 2002. (Graveyard School Ser.). (SPA.). (J). pap. 5.95 (978-950-24-0875-0(6) , AL30669) Albatros ARG. *Dist:* Lectorum Pubns., Inc.

—Pequeno Hombre Lobo. 2002. (Graveyard School Ser.). (SPA.). (J). pap. 5.95 (978-950-24-0772-2(5) , AL30657) Albatros ARG. *Dist:* Lectorum Pubns., Inc.

—Un Susto Mortal! 2002. (Graveyard School Ser.). (SPA.). (J). pap. 5.95 (978-950-24-0776-0(8) , Al30661) Albatros ARG. *Dist:* Lectorum Pubns., Inc.

—Un Susto Navideno. 2002. (Graveyard School Ser.). (SPA.). (J). pap. 5.95 (978-950-24-0874-3(8) , AL30668) Albatros ARG. *Dist:* Lectorum Pubns., Inc.

—La Venganza de los Dinosaurios. 2002. (Graveyard School Ser.). (SPA.). (J). pap. 5.95 (978-950-24-0773-9(3) , AL30658) Albatros ARG. *Dist:* Lectorum Pubns., Inc.

—Le Venganza del Esqueleto. 2002. (Graveyard School Ser.). (SPA.). (J). pap. 5.95 (978-950-24-0895-8(0) , AL30674) Albatros ARG. *Dist:* Lectorum Pubns., Inc.

Storer, Megan. Cowbelle - Snow Day. 2005. (Illus.). 54p. (J). per. 6.99 (978-0-9769856-0-0(8) , 0-9769856-0-8) Little River Bookshelf.

Strange, Spencer. Operation Billion Gazillion. 2005. (Spy Five Ser.). 93p. (*978-0-439-70352-9(2)) Scholastic, Inc.

Straub, Peter. Mr X. 2000. (gr. 7-12). lib. bdg. 16.45 (978-0-613-27980-2(8)) Tandem Library Bks.

Strickland, Brad & Fuller, Thomas E. The Disappearing Dinosaurs. l.t. ed. 1999. (Wishbone Mysteries Ser.: No. 10). 144p. (J). (gr. 4 up). lib. bdg. 23.33 (978-0-8368-2450-6(4)) Stevens, Gareth Inc.

—The Riddle of the Wayward Books. l.t. ed. 1999. (Wishbone Mysteries Ser.: No. 3). 144p. (J). (gr. 4 up). lib. bdg. 23.33 (978-0-8368-2384-4(2)) Stevens, Gareth Inc.

Strickland, Brad, et al. Disoriented Express. l.t. ed. 2000. (Wishbone Mysteries Ser.: No. 14). 167p. (J). (gr. 4 up). lib. bdg. 23.33 (978-0-8368-2697-5(3)) Stevens, Gareth Inc.

—Drive-In of Doom. l.t. ed. 1999. (Wishbone Mysteries Ser.: No. 7). 144p. (J). (gr. 4 up). lib. bdg. 23.33 (978-0-8368-2388-2(5)) Stevens, Gareth Inc.

Strong, Jeremy. I'm Telling You, They're Aliens! Sharratt, Nick, illus. l.t. ed. 2005. 144p. (J). pap. (978-0-7540-6150-2(7) , CLP 343) BBC Audio.

Sturges, Philemon & Lass, Bonnie. Who Took the Cookies from the Cookie Jar? Wolff, Ashley, illus. 2000. 32p. (J). (ps-1). 16.99 (978-0-316-82016-5(4)) Little Brown & Co.

Stutley, Doris. Operation Foxtrot Five. 2002. 160p. (YA). pap. (978-0-7344-0180-9(9) , Lothian Bks.) Hachette Livre Australia.

Sukach, Jim. Baffling Whodunit Puzzles: Dr. Quicksolve Mini-Mysteries. Corvino, Lucy, illus. 2003. (Dr. Quicksolve Mini-Mysteries Ser.). 96p. (gr. 4-7). pap. 6.95 (978-0-8069-6119-4(8)) Sterling Publishing Co., Inc.

—Elliott Finds a Clue: And Other Quicksolve Mini-Mysteries. 2004. (Illus.). 96p. (J). pap. 6.95 (978-1-4027-1074-2(7)) Sterling Publishing Co., Inc.

Summer of the Secret Squadron. 2005. Orig. Title: Return of the Secret Squadron. (YA). kivar 14.95 (978-0-9765750-0-9(0)) Ball, Michael.

Summers, George J. The Great Book of Mind Teasers & Mind Puzzlers. 2003. (Illus.). 256p. (gr. 4-7). pap. 8.95 (978-0-8069-6320-4(4)) Sterling Publishing Co., Inc.

Suris, J. El Hombre del Bar: Nivel 2. 1998. (SPA.). (gr. 7-12). lib. bdg. 14.10 (978-0-613-80712-8(X)) Tandem Library Bks.

Suter, Joanne. Tomorrow's Child. (gr. 7-12). lib. bdg. 17.60 (978-0-613-09873-1(0)) Tandem Library Bks.

Sutton, Margaret. Secret of the Sand Castle. 2001. (Judy Bolton Mystery Ser.: Vol. 38). (Illus.). 174p. (J). (gr. 4-7). per. 24.95 (978-1-55709-252-6(4)) Applewood Bks.

Sutton, Margaret & Bolton, Judy. The Vanishing Shadow. 2004. (Judy Bolton Mystery Ser.). 224p. (J). (gr. 4-7). reprint ed. 24.95 (978-1-55709-250-2(8)) Applewood Bks.

Sutton, Scott E. The Secret of GorBee Grotto. Sutton, Scott E., illus. rev. ed. 2001. (Family of Ree Ser.). (Illus.). 56p. (gr. 1-5). 14.95 (978-1-888045-13-0(2)) Action Publishing, LLC.

Swados, Elizabeth. Dreamtective: The Dreamy & Daring Adventures of Cobra Kite. 1999. (Kid Genesis Ser.). (Illus.). 177p. (J). pap. 5.95 (978-1-885478-45-0(3)) Kensington Publishing Corp.

Swallow, Donald. Secret Game. 2000. (gr. 7-12). lib. bdg. 21.60 (978-0-613-74554-3(X)) Tandem Library Bks.

Swartz, Michael. Bikes & Bullies: A Neil Everheart Mystery. 2003. 163p. pap. 11.95 (978-0-595-26550-3(2) , Writers Club Pr.) iUniverse, Inc.

Swift, John. Tea with a Vampire. 2007. pap. 9.00 (*978-0-8059-8963-2(3)) Dorrance Publishing Co., Inc.

Swinford, Betty. Cry of the Wild. 2004. 192p. (YA). mass mkt. 5.99 (978-1-85792-853-2(9) , Christian Focus) Christian Focus Pubns. GBR. *Dist:* Riverside.

Swobud, I. K. The Case of the Blue-Ribbon-Horse. 1998. (New Adventures of Mary-Kate & Ashley Ser.). 86p. (J). (gr. 2-7). pap. 3.99 (978-0-590-29309-9(5)) Scholastic, Inc.

Tabb, Robert C. The Rules: Trust No One. 2007. 156p. per. 11.95 (*978-0-595-44797-8(X)) iUniverse, Inc.

A Tale of Three Amigos: Cat Detectives. 2002. (Cat Detectives Present Ser.: Vol. 2). (Illus.). 88p. (J). per. 6.99 (978-0-9706062-3-5(0)) Aloha Publications.

Tales for the House of Bunnicula. 2005. (J). (978-1-59564-678-1(7)) Steps To Literacy, LLC.

Talone, Augusto. The Adventures of Max & Sandy: Three Short Stories about a Yellow Labrador Retriever Named Max & a Simese House Cat Named Sandy, Who Solve Mysteries. 2006. 96p. (J). pap. 11.99 (978-1-59977-005-5(9)) Annotation Pr.

Tang, Charles, illus. The Basketball Mystery, Vol. 68. 1999. (Boxcar Children Ser.: No. 68). 128p. (J). (gr. 2-5). pap. 3.95 (978-0-8075-0576-2(5)) Whitman, Albert & Co.

—The Black Pearl Mystery, Vol. 64. 1998. (Boxcar Children Ser.: No. 64). 128p. (J). (gr. 2-7). pap. 4.50 (978-0-8075-0784-1(9)) Whitman, Albert & Co.

—The Cereal Box Mystery. 1998. (Boxcar Children Ser.: No. 65). (J). (gr. 2-5). 10.60 (978-0-606-13214-5(7)) Tandem Library Bks.

—The Cereal Box Mystery, Vol. 65. 1998. (Boxcar Children Ser.: No. 65). (J). (gr. 2-5). 128p. 14.95 (978-0-8075-1114-5(5)); 111p. pap. 4.50 (978-0-8075-1115-2(3)) Whitman, Albert & Co.

—The Gymnastics Mystery, Vol. 73. 2004. (Boxcar Children Ser.: No. 73). 128p. (gr. 2-5). mass mkt. 4.50 (978-0-8075-3101-3(4)) Whitman, Albert & Co.

—The Mystery in New York, Vol. 13. 2004. (Boxcar Children Special Ser.: No. 13). 121p. (J). (gr. 2-5). 14.95 (978-0-8075-5459-3(6)); pap. 4.50 (978-0-8075-5460-9(X)) Whitman, Albert & Co.

—The Mystery of the Empty Safe. 2000. (Boxcar Children Ser.: No. 75). (J). (gr. 2-5). (978-0-606-18768-8(5)) Tandem Library Bks.

—The Mystery of the Empty Safe, Vol. 75. 2004. (Boxcar Children Ser.: No. 75). 120p. (J). (gr. 2-5). pap. 4.50 (978-0-8075-5463-0(4)) Whitman, Albert & Co.

—The Mystery of the Pirate's Map. 1999. 121p. (J). (ps-7). per. 11.80 (978-0-613-16287-6(0)) Tandem Library Bks.

—The Mystery of the Stolen Sword. 1998. (Boxcar Children Ser.: No. 67). 121p. (J). (gr. 2-5). mass mkt. 4.50 (978-0-8075-7623-6(9)) Whitman, Albert & Co.

Tapp, Kathy Kennedy. Deadbolts & Dinkles. 2000. (gr. 3-6). lib. bdg. 11.80 (978-0-613-27788-4(0)) Tandem Library Bks.

Tashjian, Janet. Marty Frye, Private Eye. Keller, Laurie, illus. rev. ed. 1998. (Redfeather Bks.). 64p. (J). (gr. 1-3). 15.95 (978-0-8050-5888-8(5) , Holt, Henry & Co. Bks. For Young Readers) Holt, Henry & Co.

—Marty Frye, Private Eye. 2000. (978-0-606-18880-7(0)) Tandem Library Bks.

Tate, Eleanora E. The Minstrel's Melody. 2001. (American Girl Collection). (Illus.). (J). (978-0-606-21331-8(7)) Tandem Library Bks.

Taylor, Bonnie Highsmith. Indian Ghost Mystery. Marks, Dea, illus. 2000. (Cover-to-Cover Novel Ser.). 99p. (J). pap. (978-0-7891-5170-4(7)); (gr. 3-6). lib. bdg. 13.95 (978-0-7807-9317-0(X)) Perfection Learning Corp.

Taylor, Cora. Murder in Mexico. 2007. (Spy Who Wasn't There Ser.). (Illus.). 360p. (J). (gr. 4-7). pap. 7.95 (*978-1-55050-353-1(7)) Coteau Bks. CAN. *Dist:* Fitzhenry & Whiteside, Ltd.

Taylor, Mary Ann. Spies: A Gander's Cove Mystery. Casteel, Kay, illus. 2006. (J). mass mkt. 5.99 (*978-0-9753367-7-9(0)) Onstage Publishing, LLC.

—Traitors: A Gander's Cove Mystery. Casteel, Kay, illus. 2006. (J). mass mkt. 5.99 (*978-0-9753367-9-3(7)) Onstage Publishing, LLC.

Taylor, Theodore. Lord of the Kill. 2004. 256p. (J). pap. 5.99 (978-0-439-55956-0(1) , Scholastic Paperbacks) Scholastic, Inc.

—Teetoncey. 2004. (Illus.). 228p. (J). pap. 5.95 (978-0-15-205294-2(1) , Odyssey Classics) Harcourt Children's Bks.

Tell Me No Lies, 6 vols. (Ragged Island Mysteriestm Ser.). 161p. (gr. 5-7). 42.50 (978-0-322-01654-5(1)) Wright Group, The.

Thoene, Jake & Thoene, Luke. The Giant Rat of Sumatra. 1998. (Baker Street Mysteries Ser.: Vol. 2). 168p. (J). (gr. 4-7). pap. 5.99 (978-0-7852-7079-9(5)) Nelson, Thomas Inc.

—The Giant Rat of Sumatra. 2006. (Tyndale Kids Ser.). 144p. (J). 9.99 (978-1-4143-0367-3(X)) Tyndale Hse. Pubs.

—The Jeweled Peacock of Persia. 2006. (Baker Street Detectives Ser.). 144p. (J). 9.99 (978-1-4143-0368-0(8)) Tyndale Hse. Pubs.

—The Jewelled Peacock of Persia. 1998. (Baker Street Mysteries Ser.: Vol. 3). 168p. (J). (gr. 4-7). pap. 5.99 (978-0-7852-7080-5(9)) Nelson, Thomas Inc.

—The Mystery of the Yellow Hands. 2006. (Baker Street Detectives Ser.). 144p. (J). 9.99 (978-1-4143-0370-3(X)) Tyndale Hse. Pubs.

Thoene, Luke & Thoene, Jake. The Thundering Underground. 2006. (Baker Street Detectives Ser.). 128p. (J). 9.99 (978-1-4143-0369-7(6) , Tyndale Kids) Tyndale Hse. Pubs.

Thomas, Brent, ed. The Magic Camera, No. 1. Thomas, Natalie B., illus. 2000. 117p. (J). (gr. 4-7). pap. 11.95 (978-0-9666919-3-1(8)) Independent Spirit Publishing.

Thomas, Earl. Mystery of the Strange Creature. 1999. (gr. 7-12). lib. bdg. 11.60 (978-0-613-29175-0(1)) Tandem Library Bks.

Thomas, Earl W. Mystery of the Pirates' Treasure. 1999. (Illus.). 44p. (J). (ps-7). lib. bdg. 11.60 (978-0-613-29174-3(3)) Tandem Library Bks.

Thomas, Jerry D. Danger at Dinosaur Camp. 2002. (Detective Zack Ser.). (Illus.). 132p. (J). pap., pap. 6.99 (978-0-7814-3732-5(6) , 0781437326) Cook, David C. Publishing Co.

—Danger at Dinosaur Camp. 2002. (gr. 3-6). lib. bdg. 14.15 (978-0-613-74879-7(4)) Tandem Library Bks.

—Detective Zack Secret of Blackloch Castle. 1998. (Detective Zack Ser.: Vol. 10). (Illus.). 126p. (J). (gr. 3-6). pap. 6.99 (978-0-8163-1399-0(7)) Pacific Pr. Publishing Assn.

—The Missing Manger Mystery. Odell, Lad, illus. 2003. (Detective Zack Ser.). 132p. (J). pap., pap. 6.99 (978-0-7814-3789-9(X) , 078143789X) Cook, David C. Publishing Co.

—Mystery at Thunder Mountain. 2003. (Detective Zack Ser.). (Illus.). 132p. (J). pap., pap. 6.99 (978-0-7814-3731-8(8) , 0781437318) Cook, David C. Publishing Co.

—Mystery at Thunder Mountain. 2002. (gr. 3-6). lib. bdg. 14.15 (978-0-613-74878-0(6)) Tandem Library Bks.

—The Red Hat Mystery. Odell, Lad, illus. 2003. (Detective Zack Ser.). 132p. (J). pap., pap. 6.99 (978-0-7814-3802-5(0) , 0781438020) Cook, David C. Publishing Co.

—Secret of Noah's Flood. 2002. (gr. 3-6). lib. bdg. 14.15 (978-0-613-74877-3(8)) Tandem Library Bks.

—The Secrets in the Sand. Odell, Lad, illus. 2003. (Detective Zack Ser.). 132p. (J). pap., pap. 6.99 (978-0-7814-3803-2(9) , 0781438039) Cook, David C. Publishing Co.

Thomas, Jerry D. & Zaugg, Sandy. Rattlesnake River Adventure. 2000. (Shoebox Kids Ser.: Vol. 11). (Illus.). 94p. (J). (gr. 2-4). pap. 6.99 (978-0-8163-1757-8(7)) Pacific Pr. Publishing Assn.

Thompson, Colin. Unknown. Pignataro, Anna, illus. 2000. 32p. (J). (gr. k-3). lib. bdg. 16.85 (978-0-8027-8731-6(2)) Walker & Co.

Thompson, Colin, et al. Unknown. 2000. (Illus.). 31p. (J). (gr. k-3). 15.95 (978-0-8027-8730-9(4)) Walker & Co.

Thompson, Lisa. Amazing Africa. Harvey, Roger, illus. 2006. 80p. (J). (gr. 2-4). 19.95 (978-1-4048-1674-9(7)) Picture Window Bks.

Thompson, Richard. The Night Walker. Springett, Martin, illus. 2002. 32p. (J). (gr. k-3). (978-1-55041-672-5(3)) Fitzhenry & Whiteside, Ltd.

Thorpe, Kiki. The New Ron, Bk. 2. rev. ed. 2003. (Kim Possible Chapter Bks.). (Illus.). 80p. (J). (gr. 2-5). pap. 3.99 (978-0-7868-4488-3(4)) Disney Pr.

Tibo, Gilles. Naomi & the Secret Message. Ouriou, Susan, tr. from FRE. Laliberte, Louise-Andree, illus. 2004. 168p. (J). (gr. 1-4). pap. 7.95 (978-0-88776-668-8(4)) Tundra Bks., Inc./Livres Toundra, Inc. CAN. *Dist:* Random Hse., Inc.

Tidball, Lee. Hidden Talents: Ginah's Journals. 2000. 176p. (J). pap. 14.95 (978-0-7414-0557-9(1)) Infinity Publishing.

Tiernan, Cate. Calling. 2001. (gr. 7-12). lib. bdg. 13.00 (978-0-613-64029-9(2)) Tandem Library Bks.

Tindall, Steve. The Quest of the Black Knight. 2006. (ENG.). 168p. (J). per. (978-1-84685-303-6(6) , Exposure Publishing) Meadow Bks.

Tinkler, David. The Case of the Feeble Weeble. l.t. ed. 1998. (Illus.). 117p. (J). pap. 16.95 (978-0-7540-6025-3(X) , Galaxy Children's Large Print) BBC Audiobooks America.

Toda, Akihito. Pokemon Gold & Silver Tales Vol. 1: Detective Chikorita. Kizuki, Sumiyashi, illus. 2002. (Pokemon Gold & Silver Tales Ser.). 18p. (YA). 5.50 (978-1-56931-657-3(0)) Viz Media.

—Pokemon Gold & Silver Tales Vol. 2: Cyndaquil & the Mysterious Hole. Aoki, Toshinao & Kizuki, Sumiyashi, illus. 2002. (Pokemon Gold & Silver Tales Ser.). 18p. (YA). 5.50 (978-1-56931-658-0(9)) Viz Media.

Tolan, Stephanie S. Plague Year. 1999. (Illus.). 208p. (J). (gr. 7 up). pap. 5.95 (978-0-688-16125-5(1) , Harper Trophy) HarperCollins Pubs.

Tomblin, Marian Strong. The Mystery at Hotel Ormond, 2004. (Illus.). 142p. (J). per. 9.95 (978-0-9766620-0-6(0)) Avery Goode-Reid Pubs.

—Where's Capone's Cash? 2005. (Illus.). 232p. (J). per. 9.95 (978-0-9766620-1-3(9)) Avery Goode-Reid Pubs.

Tooley, S. D. The Skull. 2006. (YA). 178p. 23.00 (978-0-9785402-1-0(2)); per. 12.95 (978-0-9785402-0-3(4)) Full Moon Publishing LLC.

Torrey, Michele. The Case of the Gasping Garbage. Johansen Newman, Barbara & Newman, Barbara, illus. 2001. (Doyle & Fossey, Science Detectives Ser.). 112p. (J). (gr. 3-6). 14.99 (978-0-525-46657-4(6) , Dutton Juvenile) Penguin Group (USA) Inc.

—The Case of the Graveyard Ghost. Johansen Newman, Barbara, illus. 2002. (Doyle & Fossey, Science Detectives Ser.). 80p. (J). (gr. 2-4). 14.99 (978-0-525-46893-6(5) , Dutton Juvenile) Penguin Group (USA) Inc.

—Doyle & Fossey Science Detectives: Case of the Mossy Lake Monster. Newman, Barbara, illus. 2002. 112p. (J). (gr. 3-6). 14.99 (978-0-525-46815-8(3) , Dutton Juvenile) Penguin Group (USA) Inc.

Tosal, Oscar. Adios, Papa! 1998. (SPA.). (gr. 7-12). lib. bdg. 14.10 (978-0-613-80723-4(5)) Tandem Library Bks.

Totten, Kathryn. Daley Bread. 2003. 118p. (J). pap. 16.95 (978-1-59286-109-5(1)) PublishAmerica, Inc.

Townley, Roderick. The Red Thread: A Novel in Three Incarnations. 2007. 304p. (YA). (gr. 7 up). 17.99 (978-1-4169-0894-4(3) , Atheneum/Richard Jackson Bks.) Simon & Schuster Children's Publishing.

Townley, Roderick. The Red Thread: A Novel in Three Incarnations. 2007. 304p. (YA). 17.99 (*978-1-4169-2930-7(4) , Atheneum) Simon & Schuster Children's Publishing.

Townsend, John. The Messenger. 2004. (Shades Ser.). 64p. (J). pap. 7.99 (978-0-237-52809-6(6) , Evans Brothers, Limited) Evans Publishing Group GBR. *Dist:* Independent Pubs. Group.

Townsend, John Rowe. The Hound of the Baskervilles. 2007. (Oxford Children's Classics). (Illus.). 320p. (YA). 9.95 (*978-0-19-272004-7(X)) Oxford Univ. Pr., Inc.

Townson, Hazel. Deathwood Letters. 2003. (Illus.). 112p. (YA). 8.99 (978-1-84270-228-4(9)) Andersen GBR. *Dist:* Independent Pubs. Group.

—Diamond Hunt. 2003. 188p. (YA). pap. 9.99 (978-1-84270-302-1(1)) Andersen GBR. *Dist:* Independent Pubs. Group.

—The Vanishing Gran. Dupasquier, Philippe, illus. l.t. ed. 1998. 72p. (J). pap. (978-0-7540-6029-1(2) , CLP 232) BBC Audio.

Trebi-Ollennu, Flora. A Number, a Nerd & a Mystery. Darko, Anima A., illus. 2001. 118p. pap. (*978-1-894718-01-1(1)) Amerley Treb Bks.

Trembath, Don. Emville Confidential. 2007. 192p. (J). (gr. 4-8). pap. (*978-1-55143-671-5(X)) Orca Bk. Pubs.

Tromp, Janyre. That Sinking Feeling: Blue Water Mysteries. 2006. 128p. (J). pap. (978-0-8254-3887-5(X)) Kregel Pubns.

Truckey, Don. The Adventures of Caraway Kim— Southpaw. 2005. 192p. pap. 8.95 (978-1-894345-90-3(8)) Thistledown Pr., Ltd. CAN. *Dist:* Literary Pr. Group of Canada.

Trumbauer, Lisa. Mountain Manor Mystery. Hawkes, Kevin, illus. 2006. 96p. (J). pap. (978-1-59034-810-9(9)) Mondo Publishing.

Tryon, Leslie. Albert's Halloween: The Case of the Stolen Pumpkins. 2001. 13.79 (978-0-606-22101-6(8)) Tandem Library Bks.

Tuitel, Johnnie. Searching the Noonday Trail. 2000. (Gun Lake Adventure Ser.: Bk. 4). 112p. (J). (gr. 4-7). pap. 5.99 (978-0-9658075-3-1(3)) Cedar Tree Publishing.

Tuitel, Johnnie & Lamson, Sharon E. Mystery Explosion. Sharp, Dan, illus. 1998. (Gun Lake Adventure Ser.: No. 2). 121p. (J). (gr. 3-7). pap. 5.99 (978-0-9658075-1-7(7)) Cedar Tree Publishing.

Turner, Anthea. Westminster Mystery. Hunt, Andy, illus. 48p. (J). pap. 7.95 (978-0-14-056389-4(X)) Penguin Bks., Ltd. GBR. *Dist:* Trafalgar Square Publishing.

Twain, Mark. The Mysterious Stranger. 2004. 160p. pap. 11.95 (978-1-59540-326-1(4) , 1st World Library - Literary Society) 1st World Publishing, Inc.

—Tom Sawyer, Detective. (SPA., Illus.). 160p. (YA). 11.95 (978-84-7281-062-4(3) , AF0623) Auriga, Ediciones S.A. ESP. *Dist:* Continental Bk. Co., Inc.

—Tom Sawyer, Detective. unabr. ed. 2002. (Dover Juvenile Classics Ser.). 80p. (J). (gr. 4-7). pap. 2.00 (978-0-486-42109-4(0)) Dover Pubns., Inc.

—Tom Sawyer, Detective. 2002. (gr. 3-6). lib. bdg. 9.50 (978-0-613-90063-8(4)) Tandem Library Bks.

Tylander, Robert. Mystery at Manatee Creek. 2000. 182p. (J). pap. 11.95 (978-1-56315-204-7(5)) SterlingHouse Pubs., Inc.

Tyo, Courtney. Shamrock Scare. del Sur, Duendes, illus. 2004. (Scooby-Doo Ser.: No. 19). 32p. (J). pap. 3.99 (978-0-439-55715-3(1) , Scholastic Paperbacks) Scholastic, Inc.

Ulrich, Ann Carol. The Mystery at Hickory Hill: Annette Vetter Adventure #1. 2006. (Illus.). 196p. (YA). per. 9.95 (978-0-944851-25-8(8)) Earth Star Pubns.

Unexpected Treasure, 6 vols. (Ragged Island Mysteriestm Ser.). 161p. (gr. 5-7). 42.50 (978-0-322-01650-7(9)) Wright Group, The.

Unforgettable Stories for Young Hearts, No. 1. 2000. (Illus.). 45p. (J). (gr. 1-6). pap. 1.95 (978-0-929291-62-8(X)) Gospel Projects Pr.

Urrea, Lourdes, et al. La Computadora Maldita. rev. ed. 2006. (Ediciones Castillo Castillo Del Terror Ser.). (SPA.). 108p. (J). (gr. 2-6). pap. 6.95 (978-970-20-0315-1(6)) Castillo, Ediciones, S. A. de C. V. MEX. *Dist:* Macmillan.

—Escalofrio. rev. ed. 2006. (Ediciones Castillo Castillo Del Terror Ser.).Tr. of Spine-chill. (SPA.). 140p. (J). (gr. 2-6). pap. 6.95 (978-970-20-0293-2(1)) Castillo, Ediciones, S. A. de C. V. MEX. *Dist:* Macmillan.

—La Gente de Las Sombras. rev. ed. 2006. (Ediciones Castillo Castillo Del Terror Ser.).Tr. of People in the Shadows. (SPA.). 104p. (J). (gr. 2-6). pap. 6.95 (978-970-20-0336-6(9)) Castillo, Ediciones, S. A. de C. V. MEX. *Dist:* Macmillan.

—Tenebroso. 2005. (Ediciones Castillo Castillo Del Terror Ser.).Tr. of Sinister. (SPA.). (J). (gr. 2-6). pap. 7.95 (978-970-20-0332-8(6)) Castillo, Ediciones, S. A. de C. V. MEX. *Dist:* Iaconi, Mariuccia Bk. Imports.

Vail, Emily Blake. Carla & the Con Men. 2006. (J). per. 8.90 (978-0-935087-28-4(1)) Wright Publishing, Inc.

Van Draanen, Wendelin. Sammy Keyes & the Art of Deception. (Sammy Keyes Ser.: Bk. 8). (gr. 5). 2005. 304p. 5.99 (978-0-440-41992-1(1) , Yearling); 2003. 288p. 15.95 (978-0-375-81176-0(1) , Knopf Bks. for Young Readers); 2003. 288p. lib. bdg. 17.99 (978-0-375-91176-7(6) , Knopf Bks. for Young Readers) Random Hse. Children's Bks.

—Sammy Keyes & the Curse of Moustache Mary. Van-Draanen, Wendelin, illus. 2001. (Sammy Keyes Ser.: Bk. 5). pap. 36.95 incl. audio (978-0-87499-793-4(3)); pap. 49.95 incl. audio compact disk (978-0-87499-850-4(6)) Live Oak Media.

—Sammy Keyes & the Curse of Moustache Mary. 2001. (Sammy Keyes Ser.: Bk. 5). 272p. (J). (gr. 5-7). pap. 5.99 (978-0-440-41643-2(4) , Yearling) Random Hse. Children's Bks.

—Sammy Keyes & the Curse of Moustache Mary. 2001. (Sammy Keyes Ser.: Bk. 5). (Illus.). (J). (978-0-606-20897-0(6)) Tandem Library Bks.

—Sammy Keyes & the Dead Giveaway. unabr. ed. 2006. (Sammy Keyes Ser.: Bk. 10). (J). (gr. 5-7). pap. 36.95 incl. audio (***978-1-59519-770-2(2)***); pap. 54.95 incl. audio compact disk (***978-1-59519-771-9(0)***) Live Oak Media.

—Sammy Keyes & the Dead Giveaway. (Sammy Keyes Ser.: Bk. 10). (J). (gr. 5-8). 2007. 304p. 5.99 (978-0-440-41911-2(5) , Yearling); 2005. (Illus.). 288p. 15.95 (978-0-375-82350-3(6) , Knopf Bks. for Young Readers); 2005. (Illus.). 288p. lib. bdg. 17.99 (978-0-375-92350-0(0) , Knopf Bks. for Young Readers) Random Hse. Children's Bks.

—Sammy Keyes & the Hollywood Mummy. VanDraanen, Wendelin, illus. 2001. (Sammy Keyes Ser.: Bk. 6). pap. 36.95 incl. audio (978-0-87499-800-9(X)); pap. 54.95 incl. audio compact disk (978-0-87499-868-9(9)) Live Oak Media.

—Sammy Keyes & the Hollywood Mummy. 2002. (Sammy Keyes Ser.: Bk. 6). 288p. (J). (gr. 5). pap. 5.99 (978-0-440-41866-5(6) , Yearling) Random Hse. Children's Bks.

—Sammy Keyes & the Hollywood Mummy. 2002. (Sammy Keyes Ser.: Bk. 6). (gr. 5-8). lib. bdg. 13.00 (978-0-613-50639-7(1)) Tandem Library Bks.

—Sammy Keyes & the Hotel Thief. 2002. (Sammy Keyes Ser.: Bk. 1). (Illus.). (J). 13.40 (978-0-7587-6523-9(1)) Book Wholesalers, Inc.

—Sammy Keyes & the Hotel Thief. VanDraanen, Wendelin, illus. 2000. (Sammy Keyes Ser.: Bk. 1). pap. 39.95 incl. audio compact disk (978-0-87499-876-4(X)) Live Oak Media.

—Sammy Keyes & the Hotel Thief. unabr. ed. 2000. (Sammy Keyes Ser.: Bk. 1). (Illus.). (J). (gr. 4-7). 38.95 incl. audio (978-0-87499-694-4(5)); (gr. 4-7). pap. 30.95 incl. audio (978-0-87499-693-7(7)); pap., tchr. ed. 43.95 incl. audio (978-0-87499-695-1(3)) Live Oak Media.

—Sammy Keyes & the Hotel Thief. 1998. (Sammy Keyes Ser.: Bk. 1). (Illus.). 163p. (J). (gr. k-8). lib. bdg. 13.55 (978-0-613-12062-3(0)) Tandem Library Bks.

—Sammy Keyes & the Psycho Kitty Queen. 2006. (Sammy Keyes Ser.: Bk. 9). (Illus.). 320p. (J). (gr. 5-8). 5.99 (978-0-440-41910-5(7) , Yearling) Random Hse. Children's Bks.

—Sammy Keyes & the Psycho Kitty Queen. Yaccarino, Dan, illus. 2006. (Sammy Keyes Ser.: Bk. 9). 293p. (J). (***978-1-4156-6951-8(1)*** , Yearling) Random Hse. Children's Bks.

—Sammy Keyes & the Psycho Kitty Queen. 2004. (Sammy Keyes Ser.: Bk. 9). (Illus.). 304p. (J). (gr. 5-8). 15.95 (978-0-375-82349-7(2)); lib. bdg. 17.99 (978-0-375-92349-4(7)) Random Hse. Children's Bks. (Knopf Bks. for Young Readers).

—Sammy Keyes & the Runaway Elf. VanDraanen, Wendelin, illus. 2001. (Sammy Keyes Ser.: Bk. 4). pap. 39.95 incl. audio compact disk (978-0-87499-858-0(1)) Live Oak Media.

—Sammy Keyes & the Runaway Elf. 2000. (Sammy Keyes Ser.: Bk. 4). (Illus.). 208p. (J). (gr. 5-8). pap. 5.99 (978-0-375-80255-3(X) , Yearling) Random Hse. Children's Bks.

—Sammy Keyes & the Runaway Elf. 2000. (Sammy Keyes Ser.: Bk. 4). (gr. 5-8). lib. bdg. 13.00 (978-0-613-28240-6(X)) Tandem Library Bks.

—Sammy Keyes & the Search for Snake Eyes. VanDraanen, Wendelin, illus. 2003. (Sammy Keyes Ser.: Bk. 7). pap. 36.95 incl. audio (978-1-59112-273-9(2)); pap. 54.95 incl. audio compact disk (978-1-59112-281-4(3)) Live Oak Media.

—Sammy Keyes & the Search for Snake Eyes. (Sammy Keyes Ser.: Bk. 7). (gr. 5). 2003. 320p. (J). pap. 5.99 (978-0-440-41900-6(X) , Yearling); 2002. 272p. lib. bdg. 17.99 (978-0-375-91175-0(8) , Knopf Bks. for Young Readers) Random Hse. Children's Bks.

—Sammy Keyes & the Sisters of Mercy. VanDraanen, Wendelin, illus. 2001. (Sammy Keyes Ser.: Bk. 3). pap. 49.95 incl. audio compact disk (978-0-87499-838-2(7)) Live Oak Media.

—Sammy Keyes & the Sisters of Mercy. 1999. (Sammy Keyes Ser.: Bk. 3). (Illus.). 240p. (J). (gr. 5-8). pap. 5.99 (978-0-375-80183-9(9) , Yearling) Random Hse. Children's Bks.

—Sammy Keyes & the Sisters of Mercy. 1999. (Sammy Keyes Ser.: Bk. 3). (gr. 5-8). lib. bdg. 13.00 (978-0-613-22298-3(9)) Tandem Library Bks.

—Sammy Keyes & the Skeleton Man. VanDraanen, Wendelin, illus. 2000. (Sammy Keyes Ser.: Bk. 2). pap. 39.95 incl. audio compact disk (978-0-87499-884-9(0)) Live Oak Media.

—Sammy Keyes & the Skeleton Man. unabr. ed. 2000. (Sammy Keyes Ser.: Bk. 2). (Illus.). (J). pap., tchr. ed. 43.95 incl. audio (978-0-87499-702-6(X)); (gr. 4-7). 38.95 incl. audio (978-0-87499-701-9(1)); (gr. 4-7). pap. 30.95 incl. audio (978-0-87499-700-2(3)) Live Oak Media.

—Sammy Keyes & the Skeleton Man. 1999. (Sammy Keyes Ser.: Bk. 2). (Illus.). 172p. (J). (ps-7). lib. bdg. 11.64 (978-0-606-15566-2(5)); (gr. 5-8). lib. bdg. 13.00 (978-0-613-16187-9(4)) Tandem Library Bks.

—Sammy Keyes & the Wild Things. 2007. (Sammy Keyes Ser.: Bk. 11). 304p. (J). (gr. 5-8). 15.99 (978-0-375-83525-4(3) , Knopf Bks. for Young Readers) Random Hse. Children's Bks.

—Sammy Keyes & the Wild Things. Biggs, Brian, illus. 2007. (Sammy Keyes Ser.: Bk. 11). 304p. (J). (gr. 5-8). lib. bdg. 18.99 (978-0-375-93525-1(8) , Knopf Bks. for Young Readers) Random Hse. Children's Bks.

—Sammy Keyes Mystery Series. 2000. (Sammy Keyes Ser.). (Illus.). (J). (gr. 4-7). pap. 44.95 incl. audio (978-0-87499-710-1(0)) Live Oak Media.

Van Dyke, Edith. Mary Louise. l.t. ed. 2005. 280p. pap. (978-1-84637-096-0(5)) Echo Library.

Van Dyne, Edith. Aunt Jane's Nieces. l.t. ed. 2006. 170p. pap. 11.99 (***978-1-4264-3951-3(2)***); 186p. pap. 14.99 (***978-1-4264-4009-0(X)***) BiblioBazaar.

—Aunt Jane's Nieces & Uncle John. 2006. 95.99 (***978-1-4219-7416-3(9)***); pap. 88.99 (***978-1-4219-7434-7(7)***) IndyPublish.com.

—Aunt Jane's Nieces at Millville. l.t. ed. 2006. 158p. pap. 11.99 (***978-1-4264-4058-8(8)***); 172p. pap. 14.99 (***978-1-4264-4117-2(7)***) BiblioBazaar.

—Aunt Jane's Nieces at Millville. 2006. 95.99 (***978-1-4219-7454-5(1)***); pap. 89.99 (***978-1-4219-7453-8(3)***) IndyPublish.com.

—Aunt Jane's Nieces at Millville. 2004. reprint ed. pap. 21.95 (978-1-4191-0823-5(9)); pap. 1.99 (978-1-4192-0823-2(3)) Kessinger Publishing, LLC.

—Aunt Jane's Nieces at Work. 2006. 78.99 (***978-1-4142-5888-1(7)***); pap. 71.99 (***978-1-4142-5882-9(8)***) IndyPublish.com.

—Aunt Jane's Nieces in Society. 2006. 144p. pap. 10.99 (***978-1-4264-4161-5(4)***); 156p. pap. 14.99 (***978-1-4264-4202-5(5)***) BiblioBazaar.

—Aunt Jane's Nieces in Society. 2006. 41.99 (***978-1-4280-0211-1(1)***); pap. 35.99 (***978-1-4280-0196-1(4)***) IndyPublish.com.

—Aunt Jane's Nieces in Society. 2004. reprint ed. pap. 20.95 (978-1-4191-0824-2(7)); pap. 1.99 (978-1-4192-0824-9(1)) Kessinger Publishing, LLC.

—Aunt Jane's Nieces on Vacation. 2006. 95.99 (***978-1-4219-7507-8(6)***) IndyPublish.com.

—Aunt Jane's Nieces on Vacation. 2004. reprint ed. pap. 21.95 (978-1-4191-0825-9(5)); pap. 1.99 (978-1-4192-0825-6(X)) Kessinger Publishing, LLC.

—Aunt Jane's Nieces Out West. 2006. 42.99 (***978-1-4280-0248-7(0)***); pap. 35.99 (***978-1-4280-0254-8(5)***) IndyPublish.com.

—Aunt Jane's Nieces Out West. 2004. reprint ed. pap. 21.95 (978-1-4191-0826-6(3)); pap. 1.99 (978-1-4192-0826-3(8)) Kessinger Publishing, LLC.

—Mary Louise. 2006. 148p. pap. 10.99 (978-1-4264-1952-2(X)); 144p. pap. 13.99 (978-1-4264-2063-4(3)) BiblioBazaar.

Vande Velde, Vivian. Ghost of a Hanged Man. 1998. (Accelerated Reader Bks.). 96p. (J). (gr. 3-7). 14.95 (978-0-7614-5015-3(7) , Cavendish Children's Bks.) Cavendish, Marshall Corp.

Vandersteen, Willy. The Loch Ness Mystery. Geerts, Paul, illus. 1999. (Greatest Adventures of Spike & Suzy Ser.: Vol. 5). 36p. (J). (gr. 2-9). 11.95 (978-0-9533178-5-1(4)) Intes International (UK) Ltd. GBR. *Dist:* Diamond Comic Distributors, Inc.

VanDraanen, Wendelin. Sammy Keyes & the Art of Deception. VanDraanen, Wendelin, illus. 2004. (Sammy Keyes Ser.: Bk. 8). (Illus.). pap. 36.95 incl. audio (978-1-59519-001-7(5)); pap. 54.95 incl. audio compact disk (978-1-59519-003-1(1)) Live Oak Media.

Vanished. 64p. (YA). (gr. 6-12). pap. (978-0-8224-2367-6(7)) Globe Fearon Educational Publishing.

Vanneman, Alan. Sherlock Holmes & the Giant Rat of Sumatra. (Otto Penzler Bks.). 304p. 2002. pap. 14.00 (978-0-7867-1125-3(6)); 2001. (Illus.). 24.00 (978-0-7867-0956-4(1)) Avalon Publishing Group.

Velde, Vivian V. Magic Can Be Murder. 2002. 208p. (J). pap. 6.99 (978-0-14-230210-1(4) , Puffin) Penguin Group (USA) Inc.

Vicary, Tim & Hedge, Tricia. Death in the Freezer, Level 2. 2nd ed. 2000. (Bookworms Ser.). (Illus.). 64p. 6.50 (978-0-19-422969-2(6)) Oxford Univ. Pr., Inc.

Vile Villains. 1998. (Eyewitness Fun Fax Inserts Ser.). (Illus.). (J). (gr. 4-8). pap. 2.95 (978-0-7894-3016-8(9)) Dorling Kindersley Publishing, Inc.

Villar Liebana, Luisa. El Ladron de Salchichon. 2005. (Investigator Big Ears Ser.). (SPA., Illus.). 62p. (J). (gr. 2-3). 8.95 (978-84-348-9384-9(3)) SM Ediciones ESP. *Dist:* Iaconi, Mariuccia Bk. Imports.

Villeneuve, Mireille. Mysteries for Felicio. Villeneuve, Anne, illus. 2005. (Read-It! Readers Ser.). 32p. (J). (gr. k-3). 18.60 (978-1-4048-1033-4(1)) Picture Window Bks.

Villeneuve, Mireille, et al. Mysteries for Felicio. Villeneuve, Anne, illus. 2001. (Little Wolf Bks.: Level 2). 32p. (J). (gr. 1 up). pap. (978-1-894363-68-6(X)) Dominique & Friends.

Vincent, Cindy. Mystery of the Missing Ming: A Daisy Diamond Detective Novel. 2004. 172p. (YA). 9.97 (978-1-932169-37-9(7)) Mysteries by Vincent, LLC.

Vogelaar, Alie. No Place to Go. Bazen, Edith, tr. from DUT. Visser, Rino, illus. 2001. 114p. (YA). lib. bdg. 10.95 (978-0-9670728-7-6(5)) Early Foundations Pubs.

Voices in the Night. 64p. (YA). (gr. 6-12). pap. (978-0-8224-2368-3(5)) Globe Fearon Educational Publishing.

Voigt, Cynthia. The Callender Papers. Duranceau, Suzanne, illus. 2000. 272p. (J). (gr. 4-8). pap. 5.99 (978-0-689-83283-3(4) , Aladdin) Simon & Schuster Children's Publishing.

—The Callender Papers. 2001. (J). (gr. 4-8). 21.75 (978-0-8446-7192-5(4)) Smith, Peter Pub., Inc.

—The Callender Papers. 2000. (gr. 5-8). lib. bdg. 14.15 (978-0-8085-5948-1(6)) Tandem Library Bks.

—The Vandemark Mummy. 2001. (978-0-606-20968-7(9)) Tandem Library Bks.

Wade, Mary Dodson. Joan Lowery Nixon: Masterful Mystery Writer. 2004. (Authors Teens Love Ser.). (Illus.). 128p. (J). lib. bdg. 26.60 (978-0-7660-2194-5(7)) Enslow Pubs., Inc.

Waldron, Ann. The House on Pendleton Block. 2000. (Illus.). 156p. (YA). (gr. 4-7). pap. 10.95 (978-0-595-00068-5(1)) iUniverse, Inc.

Walker, Craig, ed. Mystery Stories for Girls. 2006. 432p. (J). pap. 5.99 (978-0-439-85858-8(5) , Scholastic) Scholastic, Inc.

—Tales of Suspense for Boys. 2006. 448p. (J). pap. 5.99 (978-0-439-85860-1(7) , Scholastic) Scholastic, Inc.

Walker, Jeff & Dixon, Franklin W. In Plane Sight. 2002. (Hardy Boys Ser.). (Illus.). 160p. (J). pap. 4.99 (978-0-7434-3760-8(8) , Aladdin) Simon & Schuster Children's Publishing.

Wallace, Barbara Brooks. Sparrows in the Scullery. 1999. (978-0-606-15943-2(6)) Tandem Library Bks.

Wallace, Bill. Trapped in Death Cave. 2002. 176p. (J). pap. 5.99 (978-0-689-85341-8(6) , Aladdin) Simon & Schuster Children's Publishing.

—Trapped in Death Cave. 2002. (gr. 3-6). lib. bdg. 13.00 (978-0-613-87051-1(4)) Tandem Library Bks.

Wallace, James. Tsunami: Ghost Eagle 1. 2003. 149p. (YA). pap. 11.95 (978-0-595-27372-0(6)) iUniverse, Inc.

Wallace, Karen. The Diamond Takers. 2007. (Lady Violet's Casebook Ser.). 224p. (J). (gr. 4-7). pap. 9.95 (***978-1-4169-0100-6(0)***) Simon & Schuster, Ltd. GBR. *Dist:* Independent Pubs. Group.

—The Man with Tiger Eyes. 2007. (Lady Violet's Casebook Ser.). 240p. (J). (gr. 4-7). pap. 9.95 (***978-1-4169-0099-3(3)***) Simon & Schuster, Ltd. GBR. *Dist:* Independent Pubs. Group.

—The Minestrone Mob. Brown, Judy, illus. 2007. (Read-It! Chapter Books). (J). (978-1-4048-2723-3(4)) Picture Window Bks.

—The Peanut Prankster. Brown, Judy, illus. 2007. (Read-It! Chapter Books). (J). 21.26 (978-1-4048-2724-0(2)) Picture Window Bks.

Wallace, Sheila Ryan. Diving for the Gold. 2004. 142p. (YA). pap. 15.95 (978-0-7414-2269-9(7)) Infinity Publishing.

Wallace, Sheila Ryan. Miss Abigail's Antique Treasures. 2007. 133p. pap. 15.95 (***978-0-7414-3942-0(5)***) Infinity Publishing.

Wallock, Donna Lea. Silver Skull. 2000. (Wallock Mysteries Ser.). 84p. (YA). pap. 0.95 (978-0-910653-41-1(0) , Red River Pr.) Red River Pr.

Walsh, Ellen Stoll. Dot & Jabber & the Big Bug Mystery. 2003. (Dot & Jabber Ser.). (Illus.). 40p. (J). 15.00 (978-0-15-216518-5(5)) Harcourt Trade Pubs.

Walsh, Laurence & Walsh, Suella. In the Middle of the Night. 2006. (J). pap. (***978-0-88092-473-3(X)***) Royal Fireworks Publishing Co.

Walsh, Lawrence & Walsh, Suella. Through a Dark Tunnel. 2001. 94p. (J). (ps-k). pap. 9.99 (978-0-88092-564-8(7) , 5647) Royal Fireworks Publishing Co.

Walsh, Suella & Walsh, Lawrence. Running Scared. 1998. 90p. (J). (ps-7). pap. 9.99 (978-0-88092-413-9(6) , 4136) Royal Fireworks Publishing Co.

Walters, Eric. Death by Exposure. Spreekmeester, Kevin, photos by. 2006. 88p. (J). pap. 9.99 (***978-1-55002-632-0(1)*** , Dundurn Pr.) Dundurn Group, The CAN. *Dist:* Univ. of Toronto Pr.

Walters, Eric. Hydrofoil Mystery. 2003. 224p. mass mkt. 4.99 (978-0-14-130220-1(8) , Penguin Global) Penguin Group (USA) Inc.

Walters, Eric & Spreekmeester, Kevin. Death by Exposure: An Interactive Mystery. 2005. (Illus.). 64p. (YA). pap. (978-0-88878-442-1(2) , Sandcastle Bks.) Dundurn Group, The.

Walton, Rick. Dog Day Detectives: Mini-Mysteries for a Summer Day. 2006. (Illus.). 80p. (J). pap. 6.95 (978-1-933317-49-6(3)) Leatherwood Pr.

—Mini Mysteries: 20 Tricky Tales to Untangle. American Girl Editorial Staff, ed. Scheuer, Lauren, illus. 2004. (Americangirl Library(R) Ser.). 80p. (J). (gr. 4 up). 7.95 (978-1-58485-871-3(0)) American Girl Publishing, Inc.

—Mini Mysteries: 20 Tricky Tales to Untangle. 2004. (gr. 3-6). lib. bdg. 16.40 (978-0-613-85506-8(X)) Tandem Library Bks.

Waltz, Dan. Kornstalkers: Corn Maze Massacre. Waltz, Dan, illus. l.t. ed. 2005. (Chilled to the Bone! Ser.: No. 1). (Illus.). 120p. (J). pap. 6.99 (978-0-9741774-3-4(1)) D. W. Publishing.

Ware, Fletcher K. The Empress Conspiracy. 2004. 285p. (YA). per. 14.95 (978-1-932496-17-8(3)) Penman Publishing, Inc.

Ware, Jim. Canyon Quest. 2004. (Last Chance Detectives Ser.). 272p. (YA). per. 7.99 (978-1-58997-239-1(2)) Focus on the Family Publishing.

Wargin, Kathy-Jo. Legend of the Lady's Slipper. 2003. (gr. k-3). lib. bdg. 16.40 (978-0-613-79712-2(4)) Tandem Library Bks.

Warner, Gertrude Chandler. Basketball Mystery. 1999. (gr. 3-6). lib. bdg. 11.80 (978-0-613-11312-0(8)) Tandem Library Bks.

—Benny Goes into Business. 1999. (gr. k-3). lib. bdg. 11.80 (978-0-613-11318-2(7)); (Adventures of Benny & Watch: No.5). (J). (gr. 1-3). 10.75 (978-0-606-16916-5(4)) Tandem Library Bks.

—The Black Widow Spider Mystery, Vol. 21. 2004. (Boxcar Children Special Ser.: Vol. 21). 128p. (J). 14.95 (978-0-8075-5543-9(6)); pap. 4.50 (978-0-8075-5544-6(4)) Whitman, Albert & Co.

—Blue Bay Mystery, Vol. 6. Gringhuis, Dirk, illus. 2004. (Boxcar Children Ser.: No. 6). 128p. (gr. 2-7). reprint ed. mass mkt. 4.50 (978-0-8075-0794-0(6)) Whitman, Albert & Co.

—The Box That Watch Found, Vol. 113. 2007. (Boxcar Children Mysteries Ser.). 128p. (J). (gr. 2-7). 14.95 (***978-0-8075-5568-2(1)***); pap. 4.50 (***978-0-8075-5569-9(X)***) Whitman, Albert & Co.

—The Boxcar Children. Date not set. (Boxcar Children Ser.: No. 1). (J). (gr. 2-5). lib. bdg. 18.95 (978-0-8488-1712-1(5)) Amereon LTD.

—The Boxcar Children. (Boxcar Children Ser.: No. 1). 154p. (J). (gr. 2-5). pap. 3.95 (978-0-8072-1447-3(7) , Listening Library) Random Hse. Audio Publishing Group.

—The Boxcar Children. 1998. (J). pap. 3.95 (978-0-439-04451-6(0)) Scholastic, Inc.

—The Boxcar Children. Deal, L. Kate, illus. (gr. 2-7). 2004. (Boxcar Children Ser.: No. 1). 128p. reprint ed. mass mkt. 4.50 (978-0-8075-0852-7(7)); 60th anniv. ed. 2002. 168p. (J). 18.95 (978-0-8075-0848-0(9)) Whitman, Albert & Co.

—Boxcar Children Winter Special. 2007. 376p. (J). pap. 7.95 (***978-0-8075-0886-2(1)***) Whitman, Albert & Co.

—The Caboose Mystery. Cunningham, David, illus. 1999. (Boxcar Children Ser.: No. 11). 128p. (J). (gr. 2-5). pap. (978-0-590-42681-7(8)) Scholastic, Inc.

—Candy Factory Mystery. 2002. (gr. 3-6). lib. bdg. 11.80 (978-0-613-58353-4(1)) Tandem Library Bks.

—The Candy Factory Mystery, Vol. 18. 2004. (Boxcar Children Special Ser.: Vol. 18). (Illus.). 128p. (J). pap. 4.50 (978-0-8075-5501-9(0)) Whitman, Albert & Co.

—Comic Book Mystery. 2003. (gr. 3-6). lib. bdg. 11.80 (978-0-613-65022-9(0)) Tandem Library Bks.

—The Comic Book Mystery, Vol. 93. 2004. (Boxcar Children Mysteries Ser.: Vol. 93). (Illus.). 128p. (J). pap. 4.50 (978-0-8075-5529-3(0)) Whitman, Albert & Co.

—The Copycat Mystery. Soileau, Hodges, illus. 2001. 137p. (J). (gr. 2-7). lib. bdg. 11.80 (978-0-613-35769-2(8)) Tandem Library Bks.

—The Copycat Mystery. 2001. (Boxcar Children Ser.). (Illus.). (J). 10.60 (978-0-606-21082-9(2)) Tandem Library Bks.

—The Copycat Mystery, Vol. 83. 2004. (Boxcar Children Ser.: No. 83). (Illus.). 128p. (J). (gr. 2-7). pap. 4.50 (978-0-8075-1297-5(4)) Whitman, Albert & Co.

—Disappearing Staircase Mystery. 2001. (gr. 3-6). lib. bdg. 11.80 (978-0-613-53176-4(0)) Tandem Library Bks.

—The Ghost in the First Row, Vol. 112. Papp, Robert, illus. 2007. (Boxcar Children Mysteries Ser.). 109p. (J). (gr. 2-7). pet. 4.50 (***978-0-8075-5567-5(3)***) Whitman, Albert & Co.

—The Ghost Town Mystery. 1999. (Boxcar Children Ser.: No. 71). (J). (gr. 2-5). 10.75 (978-0-606-18764-0(2)) Tandem Library Bks.

—Ghost Town Mystery. 1999. (gr. 3-6). lib. bdg. 11.80 (978-0-613-16266-1(8)) Tandem Library Bks.

—The Giant Yo-Yo Mystery. 2006. (Boxcar Children Mysteries Ser.: 107). (Illus.). 128p. (J). 14.95 (978-0-8075-0878-7(0)); pap. 4.50 (978-0-8075-0879-4(9)) Whitman, Albert & Co.

—The Great Bicycle Race Mystery. 2000. (Boxcar Children Ser.: No. 76). (Illus.). (J). (gr. 2-5). 10.60 (978-0-606-18907-1(6)) Tandem Library Bks.

—Great Bicycle Race Mystery. 2000. (gr. 3-6). lib. bdg. 11.80 (978-0-613-27863-8(1)) Tandem Library Bks.

—The Gymnastics Mystery. 1999. (Boxcar Children Ser.: No. 73). (J). (gr. 2-5). 10.60 (978-0-606-18766-4(9)) Tandem Library Bks.

—Haunted Clock Tower Mystery. 2001. (gr. 3-6). lib. bdg. 11.80 (978-0-613-49434-2(2)) Tandem Library Bks.

—The Hockey Mystery. 2001. (Boxcar Children Ser.: No. 80). 10.60 (978-0-606-20318-0(4)); (J). (978-0-606-20300-5(1)) Tandem Library Bks.

—Hockey Mystery. 2001. (gr. 3-6). lib. bdg. 11.80 (978-0-613-30474-0(8)) Tandem Library Bks.

—The Hockey Mystery, Vol. 80. 2004. (Boxcar Children Ser.: No. 80). (Illus.). 135p. (J). (gr. 2-5). pap. 4.50 (978-0-8075-3343-7(2)); 14.95 (978-0-8075-3342-0(4)) Whitman, Albert & Co.

—Home Run Mystery. 2000. (gr. 3-6). lib. bdg. 11.80 (978-0-613-27879-9(8)) Tandem Library Bks.

—The Homerun Mystery. 2000. (Boxcar Children Special Ser.: No. 14). (J). (gr. 2-5). 10.60 (978-0-606-18772-5(3)) Tandem Library Bks.

—The Honeybee Mystery. 2000. (Boxcar Children Special Ser.: No. 15). (J). (gr. 2-5). (978-0-606-20301-2(X)); 10.60 (978-0-606-20319-7(2)) Tandem Library Bks.

—Honeybee Mystery. 2000. (gr. 3-6). lib. bdg. 11.80 (978-0-613-30477-1(2)) Tandem Library Bks.

—The Honeybee Mystery, Vol. 15. 2004. (Boxcar Children Special Ser.: No. 15). (Illus.). 135p. (J). (gr. 2-5). 14.95 (978-0-8075-3373-4(4)); pap. 3.95 (978-0-8075-3374-1(2)) Whitman, Albert & Co.

—Ice Cream Mystery. 2003. (gr. 3-6). lib. bdg. 11.80 (978-0-613-75719-5(X)) Tandem Library Bks.

—The Ice Cream Mystery, Vol. 94. 2004. (Boxcar Children Mysteries Ser.). (Illus.). 128p. (J). pap. 3.95 (978-0-8075-5535-4(5)) Whitman, Albert & Co.

—The Lighthouse Mystery. (Boxcar Children Ser.: No. 8). 147p. (J). (gr. 2-5). pap. 3.95 (978-0-8072-1474-9(4) , Listening Library) Random Hse. Audio Publishing Group.

—The Lighthouse Mystery, Vol. 8. Cunningham, David, illus. 2004. (Boxcar Children Ser.: No. 8). 128p. (J). (gr. 2-7). reprint ed. pap. 4.50 (978-0-8075-4546-1(5)) Whitman, Albert & Co.

—Meet the Boxcar Children. Duffy, Daniel Mark, illus. 1998. (J). (ps-ps). lib. bdg. 11.80 (978-0-613-08335-5(0)) Tandem Library Bks.

—Midnight Mystery. 2003. (gr. 3-6). lib. bdg. 11.80 (978-0-613-75712-6(2)) Tandem Library Bks.

—The Midnight Mystery, Vol. 95. 2004. (Boxcar Children Mysteries Ser.). (Illus.). 128p. (J). 14.95 (978-0-8075-5537-8(1)); pap. 4.50 (978-0-8075-5538-5(X)) Whitman, Albert & Co.

—Mike's Mystery. (Boxcar Children Ser.: No. 5). 128p. (J). (gr. 2-5). pap. 3.95 (978-0-8072-1462-6(0) , Listening Library) Random Hse. Audio Publishing Group.

—Mike's Mystery, Vol. 5. Gringhuis, Dirk, illus. 2004. (Boxcar Children Ser.: No. 5). 128p. (J). (gr. 2-7). reprint ed. pap. 4.50 (978-0-8075-5141-7(4)) Whitman, Albert & Co.

—The Movie Star Mystery. 1999. (Boxcar Children Ser.: No. 69). (J). (gr. 2-5). (978-0-606-18762-6(6)) Tandem Library Bks.

—Movie Star Mystery. 1999. (gr. 3-6). lib. bdg. 11.80 (978-0-613-16285-2(4)) Tandem Library Bks.

—Mystery at Skeleton Point. 2002. (gr. 3-6). lib. bdg. 11.80 (978-0-613-65047-2(6)) Tandem Library Bks.

—The Mystery at Skeleton Point, Vol. 91. 2004. (Boxcar Children Mystery Ser.: No. 91). (Illus.). 128p. (J). (gr. 4-7). pap. 3.95 (978-0-8075-5520-0(7)) Whitman, Albert & Co.

—Mystery at the Crooked House. 2000. (gr. 3-6). lib. bdg. 11.80 (978-0-613-31517-3(0)) Tandem Library Bks.

—The Mystery in New York. Tang, Charles, illus. 1999. 121p. (J). (ps-7). per. 11.80 (978-0-613-22056-9(0)) Tandem Library Bks.

—The Mystery in the Computer Game. 2000. (Boxcar Children Ser.: No. 78). (J). (gr. 2-5). (978-0-606-20298-5(6)) Tandem Library Bks.

—Mystery in the Fortune Cookie. 2003. (gr. 3-6). lib. bdg. 11.80 (978-0-613-75713-3(0)) Tandem Library Bks.

—The Mystery in the Mall. Tang, Charles, illus. 1999. 115p. (J). (ps-7). per. 11.80 (978-0-613-22057-6(9)) Tandem Library Bks.

—Mystery of Alligator Swamp. 2002. (gr. 3-6). lib. bdg. 11.80 (978-0-613-65048-9(4)) Tandem Library Bks.

—The Mystery of Alligator Swamp, Vol. 19. 2004. (Boxcar Children Special Ser.: No. 19). (Illus.). 144p. (J). 14.95 (978-0-8075-5516-3(9)); (gr. 4-7). pap. 4.50 (978-0-8075-5517-0(7)) Whitman, Albert & Co.

—The Mystery of the Black Raven. 1999. (Boxcar Children Special Ser.: No. 12). (Illus.). (J). (gr. 2-5). (978-0-606-18770-1(7)) Tandem Library Bks.

—Mystery of the Black Raven. 1999. (gr. 3-6). lib. bdg. 11.80 (978-0-613-16286-9(2)) Tandem Library Bks.

—The Mystery of the Crooked House. 2000. (Boxcar Children Ser.: No. 79). (J). (gr. 2-5). (978-0-606-20299-2(4)) Tandem Library Bks.

—The Mystery of the Empty Safe. Tang, Charles, illus. 2000. 120p. (J). (gr. 2-7). lib. bdg. 11.80 (978-0-613-27992-5(1)) Tandem Library Bks.

—Mystery of the Midnight Dog. 2001. (gr. 3-6). lib. bdg. 11.80 (978-0-613-35789-0(2)) Tandem Library Bks.

—The Mystery of the Midnight Dog, Vol. 81. 2004. (Boxcar Children Ser.: No. 81). (Illus.). 122p. (J). (gr. 2-7). pap. 4.50 (978-0-8075-5476-0(6)) Whitman, Albert & Co.

—Mystery of the Mummy's Curse. 2002. (gr. 3-6). lib. bdg. 11.80 (978-0-613-58377-0(9)) Tandem Library Bks.

—The Mystery of the Mummy's Curse, Vol. 88. 2004. (Boxcar Children Ser.: Vol. 88). 128p. (J). pap. 4.50 (978-0-8075-5504-0(5)) Whitman, Albert & Co.

—The Mystery of the Orphan Train, 105. Papp, Robert, illus. 2005. (Boxcar Children Mysteries Ser.: No. 105). 120p. (J). (gr. 2-7). pap. 4.50 (978-0-8075-5559-0(2)) Whitman, Albert & Co.

—The Mystery of the Pirate's Map. 1999. (Boxcar Children Ser.: No. 70). (J). (gr. 2-5). (978-0-606-18763-3(4)) Tandem Library Bks.

—The Mystery of the Screech Owl. Soileau, Hodges, illus. 2001. 117p. (J). (gr. 2-7). per. 11.80 (978-0-613-35790-6(6)) Tandem Library Bks.

—The Mystery of the Screech Owl, Vol. 16. 2004. (Boxcar Children Special Ser.: No. 16). (Illus.). 144p. (J). (gr. 2-5). 14.95 (978-0-8075-5481-4(2)); pap. 3.95 (978-0-8075-5482-1(0)) Whitman, Albert & Co.

—Mystery of the Spider's Clue. 2002. (gr. 3-6). lib. bdg. 11.80 (978-0-613-58378-7(7)) Tandem Library Bks.

—The Mystery of the Spider's Clue, Vol. 87. 2004. (Boxcar Children Ser.: Vol. 87). (Illus.). 128p. (J). pap. 3.95 (978-0-8075-5497-5(9)) Whitman, Albert & Co.

—The Mystery of the Star Ruby. 2002. (Boxcar Children Ser.: Vol. 89). (Illus.). 128p. (J). lib. bdg. 13.95 (978-0-8075-5509-5(6)) Whitman, Albert & Co.

—Mystery of the Star Ruby. 2002. (gr. 3-6). lib. bdg. 11.80 (978-0-613-58379-4(5)) Tandem Library Bks.

—The Mystery of the Star Ruby, Vol. 89. 2004. (Boxcar Children Mystery Ser.: Vol. 89). (Illus.). 128p. (J). pap. 3.95 (978-0-8075-5510-1(X)) Whitman, Albert & Co.

—Mystery of the Tiger's Eye. 2001. (gr. 3-6). lib. bdg. 11.80 (978-0-613-49447-2(4)) Tandem Library Bks.

—The Mystery of the Wild Ponies. 2000. (Boxcar Children Ser.: Vol. 77). (Illus.). (J). (gr. 2-5). (978-0-606-18908-8(4)) Tandem Library Bks.

—Mystery of the Wild Ponies. 2000. (gr. 3-6). lib. bdg. 11.80 (978-0-613-27993-2(X)) Tandem Library Bks.

—Mystery on Blizzard Mountain. 2002. (gr. 3-6). lib. bdg. 11.80 (978-0-613-53287-7(2)) Tandem Library Bks.

—Mystery Ranch. (Boxcar Children Ser.: No. 4). 128p. (J). (gr. 2-5). pap. 3.95 (978-0-8072-1450-3(7) , Listening Library) Random Hse. Audio Publishing Group.

—Mystery Ranch, Vol. 4. Gringhuis, Dirk, illus. 2004. (Boxcar Children Ser.: No. 4). 128p. (J). (gr. 2-7). reprint ed. mass mkt. 4.50 (978-0-8075-5391-6(3)) Whitman, Albert & Co.

—The Poison Frog Mystery. 2000. (Boxcar Children Ser.: No. 74). (J). (gr. 2-5). (978-0-606-18767-1(7)) Tandem Library Bks.

—Poison Frog Mystery. 2000. (gr. 3-6). lib. bdg. 11.80 (978-0-613-22192-4(3)) Tandem Library Bks.

—The Radio Mystery, Vol. 97. 2004. (Boxcar Children Ser.: Vol. 97). 128p. (J). 14.95 (978-0-8075-5546-0(0)) Whitman, Albert & Co.

—The Seattle Puzzle. 2007. (Boxcar Children Mysteries Ser.: No. 111). 128p. (J). (gr. 2-7). pap. 4.50 (***978-0-8075-5561-3(4));*** lib. bdg. 14.95 (***978-0-8075-5560-6(6))*** Whitman, Albert & Co.

—The Secret of the Mask. 2007. (Boxcar Children Mysteries Ser.: No. 110). 128p. (J). (gr. 2-7). pap. 4.50 (***978-0-8075-5565-1(7));*** lib. bdg. 14.95 (***978-0-8075-5564-4(9))*** Whitman, Albert & Co.

—The Secret under the Tree. 2001. (Boxcar Children Early Reader Ser.). (Illus.). (J). (978-0-606-21083-6(0)) Tandem Library Bks.

—Special No.21, 2003. (gr. 3-6). lib. bdg. 11.80 (978-0-613-75714-0(9)) Tandem Library Bks.

—Stuffed Bear Mystery. 2002. (gr. 3-6). lib. bdg. 11.80 (978-0-613-62574-6(9)) Tandem Library Bks.

—The Stuffed Bear Mystery, Vol. 90. 2004. (Boxcar Children Mystery Ser.: No. 90). (Illus.). 128p. (J). (gr. 4-7). pap. 4.50 (978-0-8075-5513-2(4)) Whitman, Albert & Co.

—The Summer Camp Mystery. 2001. (Boxcar Children Ser.). (Illus.). (J). (978-0-606-21081-2(4)) Tandem Library Bks.

—The Summer Camp Mystery. 2001. (Boxcar Children Ser.: No. 82). 128p. (J). (gr. 2-7). lib. bdg. 13.95 (978-0-8075-5478-4(2)) Whitman, Albert & Co.

—Summer Camp Mystery. 2001. (gr. 3-6). lib. bdg. 11.80 (978-0-613-35798-2(1)) Tandem Library Bks.

—The Summer Camp Mystery, Vol. 82. 2004. (Boxcar Children Ser.: No.82). 128p. (J). (gr. 2-7). pap. 3.95 (978-0-8075-5479-1(0)) Whitman, Albert & Co.

—Surprise Island, Vol. 2. Gehr, Mary, illus. 2004. (Boxcar Children Ser.: No. 2). 128p. (YA). (gr. 2-7). reprint ed. mass mkt. 4.50 (978-0-8075-7674-8(3)) Whitman, Albert & Co.

—Tattletale Mystery. 2003. (gr. 3-6). lib. bdg. 11.80 (978-0-613-65061-8(1)) Tandem Library Bks.

—The Tattletale Mystery, Vol. 92. 2004. (Boxcar Children Ser.: No. 92). (Illus.). 128p. (J). pap. 3.95 (978-0-8075-5526-2(6)) Whitman, Albert & Co.

—The Vanishing Passenger. 2006. (Boxcar Children Mysteries Ser.: 106). (Illus.). 128p. (J). 14.95 (978-0-8075-1066-7(1)); pap. 4.50 (978-0-8075-1067-4(X)) Whitman, Albert & Co.

—Watch Runs Away. 1999. (Adventures of Benny & Watch: No. 6). (J). (gr. 1-3). (978-0-606-16915-8(6)) Tandem Library Bks.

—The Windy City Mystery. Tang, Charles, illus. 1998. 120p. (J). (ps-7). per. 11.80 (978-0-613-09091-9(8)) Tandem Library Bks.

—The Woodshed Mystery, Vol. 7. 2004. (Boxcar Children Ser.: No. 7). (Illus.). 128p. (J). (gr. 2-7). reprint ed. pap. 4.50 (978-0-8075-9207-6(2)) Whitman, Albert & Co.

—The Yellow House Mystery. (Boxcar Children Ser.: No. 3). 191p. (J). (gr. 2-5). pap. 3.95 (978-0-8072-1449-7(3) , Listening Library) Random Hse. Audio Publishing Group.

—The Yellow House Mystery, Vol. 3. Gehr, Mary, illus. 2004. (Boxcar Children Ser.: No. 3). 128p. (YA). (gr. 2-7). reprint ed. mass mkt. 4.50 (978-0-8075-9366-0(4)) Whitman, Albert & Co.

Warner, Gertrude Chandler, creator. The Basketball Mystery. 1999. (Boxcar Children Ser.: No. 68). (J). (gr. 2-5). 10.60 (978-0-606-17179-3(7)) Tandem Library Bks.

—The Basketball Mystery. 1999. (Boxcar Children Ser.: No. 68). (Illus.). 128p. (J). (gr. 2-5). lib. bdg. 13.95 (978-0-8075-0575-5(7)) Whitman, Albert & Co.

—Benny's New Friend. 1998. (Adventures of Benny & Watch: No. 3). (J). (gr. 1-3). 10.75 (978-0-606-13217-6(1)) Tandem Library Bks.

—The Black Pearl Mystery. 1998. (Boxcar Children Ser.: No. 64). (J). (gr. 2-5). 10.60 (978-0-606-13213-8(9)) Tandem Library Bks.

—The Black Pearl Mystery, Vol. 64. 1998. (Boxcar Children Ser.: No. 64). (Illus.). 128p. (J). (gr. 2-5). 14.95 (978-0-8075-0783-4(0)) Whitman, Albert & Co.

—The Boxcar Children Summer Special. 2007. (Boxcar Children Mysteries Ser.). 376p. (J). pap. 7.95 (***978-0-8075-0885-5(3))*** Whitman, Albert & Co.

—The Creature in Ogopogo Lake, Vol. 108. 2006. (Boxcar Children Mysteries Ser.: 108). (Illus.). 128p. (J). (gr. 2-7). 14.95 (978-0-8075-1336-1(9)); lib. bdg. 4.50 (978-0-8075-1337-8(7)) Whitman, Albert & Co.

—The Disappearing Staircase Mystery, Vol. 85. 2004. (Boxcar Children Ser.: No.85). (Illus.). 128p. (J). (gr. 2-7). 14.95 (978-0-8075-5490-6(1)) Whitman, Albert & Co.

—The Disappearing Staircase Mystery Vol. 85: The Boxcar Children Mysteries. 2004. (Boxcar Children Ser.: No.85). (Illus.). 128p. (J). (gr. 2-7). pap. 4.50 (978-0-8075-5491-3(X)) Whitman, Albert & Co.

—The Ghost Town Mystery, Vol. 71. 1999. (Boxcar Children Ser.: No. 71). (Illus.). 128p. (J). (gr. 2-5). 14.95 (978-0-8075-2858-7(7)); pap. 3.95 (978-0-8075-2859-4(5)) Whitman, Albert & Co.

—The Great Bicycle Race Mystery, Vol. 76. 2004. (Boxcar Children Ser.: No. 76). (Illus.). 115p. (J). (gr. 2-5). pap. 4.50 (978-0-8075-3049-8(2)) Whitman, Albert & Co.

—The Homerun Mystery. (Boxcar Children Special Ser.: No. 14). (Illus.). 120p. (J). (gr. 2-5). 2000. lib. bdg. 13.95 (978-0-8075-3368-0(8)); Vol. 14. 2004. pap. 4.50 (978-0-8075-3369-7(6)) Whitman, Albert & Co.

—Meet the Boxcar Children. 1998. (Adventures of Benny & Watch: No. 1). (J). (gr. 1-3). (978-0-606-13215-2(5)) Tandem Library Bks.

—The Movie Star Mystery, Vol. 69. 1999. (Boxcar Children Ser.: No. 69). (Illus.). 128p. (J). (gr. 2-5). 14.95 (978-0-8075-5303-9(4)); pap. 4.50 (978-0-8075-5304-6(2)) Whitman, Albert & Co.

—The Mystery at Peacock Hall. 1998. (Boxcar Children Ser.: No. 63). (J). (gr. 2-5). (978-0-606-13212-1(0)) Tandem Library Bks.

—The Mystery at Peacock Hall, Vol. 63. 1998. (Boxcar Children Ser.: No. 63). (Illus.). 128p. (J). (gr. 2-5). pap. 4.50 (978-0-8075-5445-6(6)) Whitman, Albert & Co.

—The Mystery in the Computer Game. (Boxcar Children Ser.: No. 78). (Illus.). 115p. (J). (gr. 2-5). 2000. lib. bdg. 13.95 (978-0-8075-5468-5(5)); Vol. 78. 2004. pap. 4.50 (978-0-8075-5469-2(3)) Whitman, Albert & Co.

—The Mystery in the Mall, Vol. 72. 2004. (Boxcar Children Ser.: No. 72). (Illus.). 128p. (J). (gr. 2-5). 14.95 (978-0-8075-5456-2(1)); pap. 4.50 (978-0-8075-5457-9(X)) Whitman, Albert & Co.

—The Mystery of the Black Raven, Vol. 12. 1999. (Boxcar Children Special Ser.: No. 12). (Illus.). 144p. (J). (gr. 2-5). 14.95 (978-0-8075-2988-1(5)); pap. 3.95 (978-0-8075-2989-8(3)) Whitman, Albert & Co.

—The Mystery of the Crooked House. (Boxcar Children Ser.: No. 79). (Illus.). 112p. (J). (gr. 2-5). 2000. lib. bdg. 13.95 (978-0-8075-5471-5(5)); Vol. 79. 2004. pap. 4.50 (978-0-8075-5472-2(3)) Whitman, Albert & Co.

—The Mystery of the Empty Safe, Vol. 75. 2004. (Boxcar Children Ser.: No. 75). (Illus.). 120p. (J). (gr. 2-5). 14.95 (978-0-8075-5462-3(6)) Whitman, Albert & Co.

—The Mystery of the Pirate's Map, Vol. 70. (Boxcar Children Ser.: No.70). (Illus.). (J). (gr. 2-5). 2004. 14.95 (978-0-8075-5453-1(7)); 1999. 128p. pap. 4.50 (978-0-8075-5454-8(5)) Whitman, Albert & Co.

—The Mystery of the Queen's Jewels, Vol. 11. 1998. (Boxcar Children Special Ser.: No. 11). (Illus.). 144p. (J). (gr. 2-5). 14.95 (978-0-8075-5450-0(2)); pap. 4.50 (978-0-8075-5451-7(0)) Whitman, Albert & Co.

—The Mystery of the Stolen Sword, Vol. 67. 1998. (Boxcar Children Ser.: No. 67). (Illus.). 128p. (J). (gr. 2-5). 14.95 (978-0-8075-7622-9(0)) Whitman, Albert & Co.

—The Mystery of the Tiger's Eye, Vol. 17. 2004. (Boxcar Children Special Ser.: No.17). (Illus.). 144p. (J). (gr. 2-5). pap. 4.50 (978-0-8075-5488-3(X)) Whitman, Albert & Co.

—The Mystery of the Wild Ponies, Vol. 77. 2004. (Boxcar Children Ser.: No. 77). (Illus.). 135p. (J). (gr. 2-5). pap. 3.95 (978-0-8075-5466-1(9)) Whitman, Albert & Co.

—The Mystery on Blizzard Mountain, Vol. 86. 2004. (Boxcar Children Ser.: No. 86). (Illus.). 122p. (J). (gr. 2-7). 14.95 (978-0-8075-5493-7(6)); pap. 4.50 (978-0-8075-5494-4(4)) Whitman, Albert & Co.

—The Panther Mystery, Vol. 66. 1998. (Boxcar Children Ser.: No. 66). (Illus.). 128p. (J). (gr. 2-5). pap. 4.50 (978-0-8075-6328-1(5)) Whitman, Albert & Co.

—The Poison Frog Mystery, Vol. 74. 2004. (Boxcar Children Ser.: No. 74). (Illus.). 128p. (J). (gr. 2-5). pap. 3.95 (978-0-8075-6587-2(3)) Whitman, Albert & Co.

—A Present for Grandfather. 1998. (Adventures of Benny & Watch: No. 2). (J). (gr. 1-3). (978-0-606-13216-9(3)) Tandem Library Bks.

—The Rock 'n' Roll Mystery, Vol. 109. 2006. (Boxcar Children Mysteries Ser.: 109). (Illus.). 128p. (J). (gr. 2-7). 14.95 (978-0-8075-7089-0(3)); lib. bdg. 4.50 (978-0-8075-7090-6(7)) Whitman, Albert & Co.

—The Sword of the Silver Knight, Vol. 103. 2005. (Boxcar Children Mysteries Ser.: 103). (Illus.). 128p. (J). pap. 4.50 (978-0-8075-0876-3(4)) Whitman, Albert & Co.

—The Windy City Mystery. 1998. (Boxcar Children Special Ser.: No. 10). (J). (gr. 2-5). (978-0-606-13219-0(8)) Tandem Library Bks.

—The Windy City Mystery, Vol. 10. 1998. (Boxcar Children Special Ser.: No. 10). (Illus.). 144p. (J). (gr. 2-5). 14.95 (978-0-8075-5447-0(2)); pap. 4.50 (978-0-8075-5448-7(0)) Whitman, Albert & Co.

Warnes, Tim. The Great Dinosaur Mystery. 2001. (Illus.). 24p. (J). 3.50 (978-1-58925-361-2(2) , tiger tales) ME Media LLC.

Warren George A. Staff. The Banner Boy Scouts. rev. ed. 2006. 248p. 27.95 (978-1-4218-1729-3(2)); pap. 12.95 (978-1-4218-1829-0(9)) 1st World Publishing, Inc. (1st World Library - Literary Society).

Warrington, Dean Grey. Perfiction. 2007. 188p. per. 13.95 (***978-0-595-43758-0(3))*** iUniverse, Inc.

Wasserman, Robin. Search for Scooby Snacks. del Sur, Duendes, illus. 2000. (Scooby-Doo! Picture Clue Book Ser.: No. 2). 32p. (J). (ps-3). pap. 3.99 (978-0-439-16166-4(5) , Scholastic Paperbacks) Scholastic, Inc.

Wassner, Gary. The Mystery of the Jubilee Emerald. 2006. (J). pap. (978-1-59336-712-1(0)) Mondo Publishing.

Watanabe, Taeko. Kaze Hikaru, Vol. 2. 2006. (Kaze Hikaru Ser.). 208p. (YA). pap. 8.99 (978-1-4215-0581-7(9)) Viz Media.

Watching Josh, 6 vols. (Ragged Island Mysteriestm Ser.). 161p. (gr. 5-7). 42.50 (978-0-322-01651-4(7)) Wright Group, The.

Waters, Gaby. Missing Clue. 1999. (Whodunnits Ser.). (Illus.). 48p. (J). (gr. 4 up). lib. bdg. 12.95 (978-0-88110-523-0(6)) EDC Publishing.

Waterton, Betty. Morris Rumpel & the Wings of Icarus. 2000. (Illus.). 112p. (J). (gr. 4-7). pap. 3.95 (978-0-88899-409-7(5)) Groundwood Bks. CAN. *Dist:* Perseus Distribution.

—Quincy Rumpel, P. I. 2000. (Illus.). 120p. (J). (gr. 4-7). pap. 3.95 (978-0-88899-408-0(7)) Groundwood Bks. CAN. *Dist:* Perseus Distribution.

Watkins, Tesha. Joey & the Ancient Horn / Mystery Revealed. 2006. (YA). pap. 12.95 (978-0-9762788-0-1(4)) Great I-AM Publishing Co., The.

Watson, Jude. The Deadly Hunter, No. 11. Nielsen, Cliff, illus. 2000. (Star Wars Ser.: Bk. 11). 128p. (J). (gr. 4-7). pap. 5.99 (978-0-439-13930-4(9)) Scholastic, Inc.

—The Deadly Hunter. 2000. (Star Wars Ser.: Bk. 11). (J). (gr. 4-7). 12.64 (978-0-606-19616-1(1)) Tandem Library Bks.

—Disappearance. 2005. (Premonitions Ser.: No. 2). 208p. (J). (gr. 7-17). pap. 6.99 (978-0-439-69688-3(7) , Scholastic Paperbacks) Scholastic, Inc.

—Premonitions. 2004. 256p. (J). pap. 6.99 (978-0-439-60995-1(X) , Scholastic Paperbacks) Scholastic, Inc.

Waysman, Dvora. Jewish Detective Stories for Kids. 2005. (Jewish Stories for Kids Ser.). 184p. (J). (gr. 5-9). 16.95 (978-1-930143-14-2(1)); pap. 12.95 (978-1-930143-15-9(X)) Pitspopany Pr. (Devora Publishing).

Webb, Janeen. Tales from Beyond. 2000. (gr. 7-12). lib. bdg. 12.10 (978-0-613-29091-3(7)) Tandem Library Bks.

Weber, Jen Funk. Hollywood Head Scratchers. 2007. (Nancy Drew Movie Ser.). 64p. (J). pap. 5.99 (978-1-4169-3380-9(8) , Simon Scribbles) Simon & Schuster Children's Publishing.

—Still Sleuthing! 2007. (Nancy Drew Movie Ser.: No. 2). 64p. (J). pap. 5.99 (978-1-4169-3381-6(6) , Simon Scribbles) Simon & Schuster Children's Publishing.

Weber, Ken. Cleverly Crafty Five-Minute Mysteries. 2007. 192p. (J). pap. 8.95 (***978-0-7624-3001-7(X)*** , Running Pr. Kids) Running Pr. Bk. Pubs.

—Five-Minute Halloween Mysteries. 2007. (Illus.). 128p. 4.95 (***978-0-7624-3076-5(1)*** , Running Pr. Minature Editions) Running Pr. Bk. Pubs.

Wegman, William. The Hardly Boys. Date not set. (J). (978-0-7868-0195-4(6)) Hyperion Pr.

Weil, Zoe. Claude & Medea: The Hellburn Dogs. 2007. 112p. (J). (gr. 4-7). pap. 30.00 (***978-1-59056-105-8(8))*** Lantern Bks.

Weir, Joan. Principal's Kid. 1999. (gr. 3-6). lib. bdg. 15.25 (978-0-613-29326-6(6)) Tandem Library Bks.

Weiss, Ellen. The Mystery of Microsneezia: A ClueFinders Mystery Adventure. 2004. (Illus.). 96p. (J). pap. 4.99 (978-0-7630-7619-1(8)) Learning Co. Bks.

Wells, Colin. Stick Like Glue. Taylor, Marjorie, illus. rev. ed. 1999. (Take Ten Ser.). 54p. (YA). (gr. 4-12). pap. 3.95 (978-1-58659-004-8(9)) Artesian Pr.

—Stick Like Glue. 2000. (gr. 7-12). lib. bdg. 11.80 (978-0-613-51056-1(9)) Tandem Library Bks.

Wells, Helen. Cherry Ames, Boarding School Nurse. 2007. (YA). (***978-0-8261-0413-7(4))*** Springer.

—Cherry Ames, Camp Nurse. 2007. (YA). (***978-0-8261-0417-5(7))*** Springer.

—Cherry Ames, Cruise Nurse. 2007. (YA). (***978-0-8261-0411-3(8))*** Springer.

—Cherry Ames, Department Store Nurse. 2007. (YA). (***978-0-8261-0415-1(0))*** Springer.

Wells, Rosemary. Leave Well Enough Alone. 2002. (gr. 5-8). lib. bdg. 14.15 (978-0-613-57909-4(7)) Tandem Library Bks.

—Max & Ruby in Pandora's Box. 1998. (Max & Ruby Ser.). (Illus.). 32p. (J). (gr. k-2). pap. 5.99 (978-0-14-056415-0(2) , Puffin) Penguin Group (USA) Inc.

—Through the Hidden Door. 2002. 272p. (J). pap. 5.99 (978-0-14-230150-0(7) , Puffin) Penguin Group (USA) Inc.

—When No One Was Looking. 2000. (gr. 7-12). lib. bdg. 14.15 (978-0-613-30190-9(0)) Tandem Library Bks.

Wenger, Shaunda. The Farm Stand Mystery. 2006. (Early Explorers Ser.). (J). 34.00 (***978-1-4108-6121-4(X))*** Benchmark Education Co.

Werlin, Nancy. Double Helix. 2004. 244p. (J). (gr. 6). 16.99 (978-0-8037-2606-2(6) , Dial) Penguin Group (USA) Inc.

—Locked Inside. 2001. (gr. 7-12). lib. bdg. 13.55 (978-0-613-62392-6(4)) Tandem Library Bks.

West, Tracey. Double Trouble Dwarfs. 2006. (Pixie Tricks Ser.: No. 7). (Illus.). 96p. (J). (gr. 1-4). 3.99 (978-0-439-17983-6(1) , Scholastic Paperbacks) Scholastic, Inc.

—Double Trouble Dwarfs. 2000. (gr. 3-6). lib. bdg. 11.80 (978-0-613-32485-4(4)) Tandem Library Bks.

West, Tracey & Noll, Katherine. Mayhem in Miami #2. 2008. 144p. (J). (gr. 4-6). 5.99 (***978-0-448-44843-5(2)*** , Grosset & Dunlap) Penguin Group (USA) Inc.

Westall, Robert. The Watch House. 1998. 224p. (YA). (gr. 7-12). mass mkt. 4.95 (978-0-688-16372-3(6)) HarperCollins Pubs.

Westerfeld, Scott. So Yesterday. 240p. (gr. 7-12). 2004. (J). 16.99 (978-1-59514-000-5(X)); 2005. (YA). reprint ed. pap. 7.99 (978-1-59514-032-6(8)) Penguin Group (USA) Inc. (Razorbill).

Weyn, Suzanne. Scooby-Doo! & You: The Case of the Batty Vampire. 2001. (Collect the Clues Mystery Ser.). (Illus.). 59p. (J). pap. (978-0-439-23168-8(X)) Scholastic, Inc.

—Scooby-Doo Movie Novelization. 2002. (gr. k-3). lib. bdg. 13.00 (978-0-613-50739-4(8)) Tandem Library Bks.

Weyn, Suzanne & Erwin, Vicky Berger. Scooby-Doo's Super Case Book. 2002. (Scooby-Doo Mysteries Ser.). (Illus.). 144p. (J). 4.50 (978-0-439-40788-5(5)) Scholastic, Inc.

Wheeler, Esther. The Loner. 2003. (J). pap. 4.99 (978-1-58608-614-5(6)) New Concepts Publishing.

Wheeler, Janet D. Billie Bradley & Her Inheritance or the Queer Homestead at Cherry Corners. 2004. reprint ed. pap. 20.95 (978-1-4191-0995-9(2)) Kessinger Publishing, LLC.

Whelan. Secret City. 2005. (978-0-06-029596-7(1)); (978-0-06-029597-4(X)) HarperCollins Canada, Ltd.

Whild, Katharine. Marlowe the Great Detective. Whild, Katharine, illus. l.t. ed. 2005. (Illus.). 36p. (J). 16.95 (978-0-9712488-4-7(2)) Deerbrook Editions.

White, Donal L. & Burrows, David. The Case of the Fortunate Fortune Cookie. 2000. 126p. (YA). (gr. 7 up). 9.99 (978-0-88092-372-9(5)) Royal Fireworks Publishing Co.

White, Ruth. Belle Prater's Boy. unabr. ed. 2004. 196p. (J). (gr. 5-9). pap. 38.00 incl. audio (978-0-8072-8682-1(6) , YA234SP, Listening Library) Random Hse. Audio Publishing Group.

—Belle Prater's Boy. 1998. (YA). 12.15 (978-0-606-12610-6(4)) Tandem Library Bks.

—Belle Prater's Boy. l.t. ed. 2000. (Illus.). 221p. (YA). (gr. 4-7). 21.95 (978-0-7862-2885-0(7)) Thorndike Pr.

White, T. H. Mistress Masham's Repose. Hargreaves, Martin, illus. 1998. 158p. (gr. 4-7). 19.95 (978-1-85149-700-3(5)) Antique Collectors' Club.

Whybrow, Ian. Little Wolf, Forest Detective. Ross, Tony, illus. 2005. (Middle Grade Fiction Ser.). 112p. (J). (gr. 3-6). 14.95 (978-1-57505-413-1(2)); pap. 6.95 (978-1-57505-829-0(4)) Lerner Publishing Group.

—Little Wolf, Pack Leader. Ross, Tony, illus. 2005. (Little Wolf Adventures Ser.). 126p. (gr. 3-6). 14.95 (978-1-57505-400-1(0)) Lerner Publishing Group.

Wickstrom, Lois June & Darling, Lucrecia. The Orange Forest Rabbit Mysteries: Book One. 2003. (J). per. 13.95 (978-0-916176-23-5(1)) Gripper Products.

Wiebe, Trina. Goats Don't Brush Their Teeth. Pavanel, Jane, ed. Sarrazin, Marisol, illus. 2004. (Abby & Tess Pet-Sitters Ser.). 96p. (J). (gr. 2-4). pap. 5.95 (978-1-894222-59-4(8)) Lobster Pr. CAN. *Dist:* Univ. of Toronto Pr.

—Goats Don't Brush Their Teeth. 2002. (gr. 3-6). lib. bdg. 14.10 (978-0-613-62554-8(4)) Tandem Library Bks.

—Max the Magnificent. Flook, Helen, illus. 2004. (Max-a-Million Ser.). 96p. (J). (gr. 2-4). pap. 5.95 (978-1-894222-55-6(5)) Lobster Pr. CAN. *Dist:* Univ. of Toronto Pr.

—Piglets Don't Watch Television. Pavanel, Jane, ed. Sarrazin, Marisol, illus. 2004. (Abby & Tess Pet-Sitters Ser.: Vol. 3). 96p. (J). (gr. 2-4). pap. 5.95 (978-1-894222-16-7(4)) Lobster Pr. CAN. *Dist:* Univ. of Toronto Pr.

Wilcox. The Hidden Men. (Thumbprint Mysteries Ser.). 32.86 (978-0-8092-0415-1(0)) McGraw-Hill/Contemporary.

Wilcox, Mary. The Hollywood Sisters: Star Quality. 2008. (J). (*978-0-385-90513-8(0)); pap. (*978-0-385-73527-8(8)) Dell Publishing. (Delacorte Pr.).

—The Hollywood Sisters: Backstage Pass. 2006. 256p. (J). (gr. 5). 7.95 (978-0-385-73354-0(2)); lib. bdg. 9.99 (978-0-385-90369-1(3)) Random Hse. Children's Bks. (Delacorte Bks. for Young Readers).

—On Location. 2007. (Hollywood Sisters Ser.). 240p. (J). (gr. 5). 7.99 (978-0-385-73355-7(0) , Delacorte Bks. for Young Readers) Random Hse. Children's Bks.

Wilcox, Mary. Truth or Dare. 2008. (J). (*978-0-385-90514-5(9)); pap. (*978-0-385-73528-5(6)) Dell Publishing. (Delacorte Pr.).

Wilder, Alice & Smith, Michael T. Blue's Lost Backpack. Johnson, Traci Paige & Pontillo, Jenine, illus. 1999. (Blue's Clues Ser.: Bk. 2). 16p. (J). (ps-k). 3.99 (978-0-689-82442-5(4) , Simon Spotlight/Nickelodeon) Simon & Schuster Children's Publishing.

Wildner, Martina & Skofield, James. Shooting Stars Everywhere. 2006. 192p. (J). (gr. 7). 15.95 (978-0-385-73250-5(3) , Delacorte Bks. for Young Readers) Random Hse. Children's Bks.

Wiles, Patricia. Early-Morning Cemetery: A Novel. 2006. 243p. (YA). pap. (978-1-59811-077-7(2)) Covenant Communications.

Wilgus, Alison. Kids Next Door 2x4 Technology Handbook. Roper, Bob, illus. 2005. (Codename Ser.). 64p. (J). (ps-k). pap. 4.99 (978-0-439-74662-5(0) , Scholastic Paperbacks) Scholastic, Inc.

Wilkey, David. Through the Black Hole: The Incredible Adventures of Justin Hart. 2003. 154p. pap. 12.95 (978-0-595-29497-8(9)) iUniverse, Inc.

Williams, Laura. Mystery of the Bad Luck Curse. 2001. (gr. 3-6). lib. bdg. 12.40 (978-0-613-54033-9(6)) Tandem Library Bks.

Williams, Laura E. The Mystery of Dead Man's Curve. 2002. (Mystic Lighthouse Mysteries Ser.). 128p. (J). (gr. 2-6). pap. 4.99 (978-0-439-21725-5(3)) Scholastic, Inc.

—Mystery of Dead Man's Curve. 2002. (gr. 3-6). lib. bdg. 12.40 (978-0-613-82236-7(6)) Tandem Library Bks.

—The Mystery of the Bad Luck Curse. 2002. (Mystic Lighthouse Mysteries Ser.). (Illus.). 128p. (J). (gr. 2-7). pap. 4.99 (978-0-439-21727-9(X)) Scholastic, Inc.

—The Mystery of the Missing Tiger. 2002. (Mystic Lighthouse Mysteries Ser.). 112p. (J). pap. 4.50 (978-0-439-21728-6(8)) Scholastic, Inc.

—Mystery of the Missing Tiger. 2002. (gr. 3-6). lib. bdg. 12.40 (978-0-613-83241-0(8)) Tandem Library Bks.

Williams, Quan. The Leopard Man. 2005. 183p. pap. 19.95 (978-1-4137-5214-4(4)) PublishAmerica, Inc.

Willis, Donald B. Mystery of the Waterloo Bagpipes. 2001. 196p. (YA). per. 9.95 (978-0-9707845-0-6(3)) Anubis Publishing.

Willis, Meredith Sue. The Secret Super Powers of Marco. 2nd ed. 2001. 104p. (J). pap. 7.95 (978-0-9674477-4-2(7)) Montemayor Pr.

Willson, Sarah. Secret-Agent Dad. 2002. (gr. k-3). lib. bdg. 11.25 (978-0-613-51325-8(8)) Tandem Library Bks.

Wilson, Eric. Case of the Golden Boy: A Tom Austen Mystery. 2001. (gr. 3-6). lib. bdg. 13.00 (978-0-613-54111-4(1)) Tandem Library Bks.

—Disneyland Hostage. 2000. (gr. 3-6). lib. bdg. 13.00 (978-0-613-29596-3(X)) Tandem Library Bks.

—Kootenay Kidnapper. 2001. (gr. 3-6). lib. bdg. 13.00 (978-0-613-54818-2(3)) Tandem Library Bks.

Wilson, Eric G. Code Red at the Supermall. 2000. (Illus.). 128p. (J). (gr. 3-7). pap. 4.99 (978-1-55143-172-7(6)) Orca Bk. Pubs. USA.

—Disneyland Hostage. 2000. (Illus.). 144p. (J). (gr. 6-8). pap. 4.99 (978-1-55143-174-1(2)) Orca Bk. Pubs. USA.

—The Kootenay Kidnapper. 2001. (Illus.). 112p. (J). (gr. 3-7). pap. 4.99 (978-1-55143-171-0(8)) Orca Bk. Pubs. USA.

—Murder on the Canadian: A Tom Austin Mystery. 2000. (Tom Austin Mysteries Ser.). (Illus.). 112p. (J). (gr. 4-8). pap. 4.99 (978-1-55143-151-2(3)) Orca Bk. Pubs. USA.

—Spirit in the Rainforest. 2001. (Tom & Liz Austen Mystery Ser.). (Illus.). 144p. (J). (gr. 3-7). pap. 4.99 (978-1-55143-224-3(2)) Orca Bk. Pubs. USA.

—Vancouver Nightmare: A Tom Austin Mystery. Row, Richard, illus. 2000. (Tom Austin Mysteries Ser.). 112p. (J). pap. 4.99 (978-1-55143-149-9(1)) Orca Bk. Pubs. USA.

Wilson, Pauline Hutchens & Dengler, Sandy. The Case of the Cold Turkey. 2001. (New Sugar Creek Gang Ser.: Vol. #3). (Illus.). 144p. (J). 5.99 (978-0-8024-8663-9(0)) Moody Pubs.

—The Case of the Dinosaur in the Desert, Vol. 4. 2001. (New Sugar Creek Gang Ser.: Vol. #4). (Illus.). 144p. (J). 5.99 (978-0-8024-8664-6(9)) Moody Pubs.

—The Case of the Monster in the Creek. 2001. (New Sugar Creek Gang Ser.: Vol. 6). 144p. (J). 5.99 (978-0-8024-8666-0(5)) Moody Pubs.

—The Case of the Red Hot Possum: The New Sugar Creek Gang. 2001. (New Sugar Creek Gang Ser.). 144p. (J). (gr. 2-8). 5.99 (978-0-8024-8661-5(4)) Moody Pubs.

Windle, Jeanette. Captured in Colombia, Vol. 3. 2002. (Parker Twins Ser.: No. 3). 160p. (gr. 3-8). pap. 5.99 (978-0-8254-4147-9(1)) Kregel Pubns.

—Cave of the Inca Re. 2001. (Parker Twins Ser.: No. 1). 160p. pap. 5.99 (978-0-8254-4145-5(5)) Kregel Pubns.

—Race for the Secret Code, Vol. 6. 2002. (Parker Twins Ser.: No. 6). 160p. pap. 5.99 (978-0-8254-4144-8(7)) Kregel Pubns.

Winfield, Arthur M. Putnam Hall Champions or Bound to Win Ou. 2006. pap. 28.95 (*978-1-4286-2346-0(9)) Kessinger Publishing, LLC.

Winfield, Arthur M. The Rover Boys on the Plains or the Mystery of Red Rock Ranch. 2004. reprint ed. pap. 27.95 (978-1-4179-2626-8(0)) Kessinger Publishing, LLC.

Winfield, M. Arthur. The Mystery at Putnam Hall or the School. 2006. 96.99 (*978-1-4280-0709-3(1)); pap. 90.99 (*978-1-4280-0711-6(3)) IndyPublish.com.

Wingo, W. There Grows a Crooked Tree. 2003. 188p. pap. 13.95 (978-0-595-28903-5(7)) iUniverse, Inc.

—There Grows a Crooked Tree. 2003. 188p. 23.95 (978-0-595-75271-3(3)) iUniverse, Inc.

Winterfeld, Henry. Detectives in Togas. Winston, Richard & Winston, Clara, trs. from GER. Kleinert, Charlotte, illus. 2002. 272p. (YA). (gr. 3 up). pap. 5.95 (978-0-15-216280-1(1) , Odyssey Classics) Harcourt Children's Bks.

—Detectives in Togas. 2002. (gr. 3-6). lib. bdg. 14.10 (978-0-613-56309-3(3)) Tandem Library Bks.

—Mystery of the Roman Ransom. McCormick, Edith Rockefeller, tr. from GER. Biermann, Fritz, illus. 2002. Tr. of Caius Geht ein Licht Auf. 240p. (YA). (gr. 3 up). pap. 6.95 (978-0-15-216268-9(2) , Odyssey Classics) Harcourt Children's Bks.

—Mystery of the Roman Ransom. 2002. Tr. of Caius Geht ein Licht Auf. (gr. 3-6). lib. bdg. 14.10 (978-0-613-56538-7(X)) Tandem Library Bks.

Wisemon, Tamar. Y. A. D. Investigators. 2002. (Illus.). 235p. 15.95 (978-0-9707572-6-5(3)) Jerusalem Pubns.

The Wishbone Mysteries, 20 bks. l.t. ed. Incl. Case of the Breaking Story. Steele, Alexander. (Illus.). 144p. 2000. lib. bdg. 23.33 (978-0-8368-2703-3(1)); Case of the Cyber-Hacker. Capeci, Anne. (Illus.). 141p. 2000. lib. bdg. 23.33 (978-0-8368-2702-6(3)); Case of the Impounded Hounds. Steele, Michael Anthony. 138p. 2000. lib. bdg. 23.33 (978-0-8368-2700-2(7)); Case of the On-Line Alien. Steele, Alexander. 144p. 1999. lib. bdg. 23.33 (978-0-8368-2449-0(0)); Case of the Unsolved Case. Steele, Alexander. (Illus.). 139p. 2000. lib. bdg. 23.33 (978-0-8368-2696-8(5)); Disappearing Dinosaurs. Strickland, Brad & Fuller, Thomas E. 144p. 1999. lib. bdg. 23.33 (978-0-8368-2450-6(4)); Disoriented Express. Strickland, Brad. 167p. 2000. lib. bdg. 23.33 (978-0-8368-2697-5(3)); Drive-In of Doom. Strickland, Brad & Fuller, Thomas E. 144p. 1999. lib. bdg. 23.33 (978-0-8368-2388-2(5)); Forgotten Heroes. Steele, Michael Anthony. (Illus.). 139p. 2000. lib. bdg. 23.33 (978-0-8368-2695-1(7)); Haunted Clubhouse. Leavitt, Caroline. 144p. 1999. lib. bdg. 22.60 (978-0-8368-2383-7(4)); Key to the Golden Dog. Capeci, Anne. 144p. 1999. lib. bdg. 23.33 (978-0-8368-2389-9(3)); Lights! Camera! Action Dog! Butcher, Nancy. (Illus.). 139p. 2000. lib. bdg. 23.33 (978-0-8368-2694-4(9)); Maltese Dog. Capeci, Anne. 144p. 1999. lib. bdg. 23.33 (978-0-8368-2387-5(7)); Phantom of the Video Store. Gantt, Leticia. (Illus.). 141p. 2000. lib. bdg. 23.33 (978-0-8368-2701-9(5)); Riddle of the Wayward Books. Strickland, Brad & Fuller, Thomas E. 144p. 1999. lib. bdg. 23.33 (978-0-8368-2384-4(2)); Sirian Conspiracy. Friedman, Michael Jan. (Illus.). 141p. 2000. lib. bdg. 23.33 (978-0-8368-2699-X(X)); Stage Invader. Sathre, Vivian. (Illus.). 140p. 2000. lib. bdg. 23.33 (978-0-8368-2698-2(1)); Stolen Trophy. Friedman, Michael Jan. 144p. 1999. lib. bdg. 23.33 (978-0-8368-2386-8(9)); Tale of the Missing Mascot. Steele, Alexander. 144p. 1999. lib. bdg. 23.33 (978-0-8368-2385-1(0)); Treasure of Skeleton Reef. Strickland, Brad & Fuller, Thomas E. 144p. 1999. lib. bdg. 23.33 (978-0-8368-2382-0(6)); (J). (gr. 4 up). Set lib. bdg. 443.27 (978-0-8368-2752-1(X)) Stevens, Gareth Inc.

Witkowski, Teri. Minute Mysteries: Brainteasers, Puzzlers, & Stories to Solve. Witkowski, Teri, ed. 2006. 64p. (J). pap. 5.95 (978-1-59369-030-4(4) , American Girl) American Girl Publishing, Inc.

Witkowski, Teri & Hirsch, Jennifer. Minute Mysteries 2: More Stories to Solve. Andreasen, Dan, illus. 2007. 64p. (J). pap. 5.95 (*978-1-59369-200-1(5)) American Girl Publishing, Inc.

Wolf-Tau, Kim. Secret of Fire & Ice. Tau, Bart, photos by. l.t. ed. 2000. (Cliffhanger Adventure Mystery Ser.: Vol. 2). (Illus.). 126p. (YA). (gr. 3-7). per. 24.95 incl. VHS (978-0-9668491-2-7(4)) Mental Interactive Systems.

Wolf-Tau, Kim & Wolf, Jeanne. Mystery at Lighthouse Point, 13 vols. Tau, Bart, photos by. 2nd ed. 2000. (Cliffhanger Adventure Mystery Ser.: Vol. 1). 122p. (YA). (gr. 4-7). reprint ed. per. 24.95 incl. VHS (978-0-9668491-1-0(6)) Mental Interactive Systems.

Wollman, Jessica. Bunches of Fun. MacNeil, Chris, illus. 2006. 149p. (J). (*978-1-4156-5003-5(9) , Aladdin) Simon & Schuster Children's Publishing.

Wood, Audrey. Alphabet Mystery. Wood, Bruce, illus. 2003. 40p. (J). pap. 15.95 (978-0-439-44337-1(7) , Blue Sky Pr., The) Scholastic, Inc.

Wood, Beverley & Wood, Chris. Golden Boy. 2007. (Sirius Mystery Ser.). 276p. (J). pap. 8.95 (978-1-55192-953-8(8) , Polestar Book Pubs.) Raincoast Bk. Distribution CAN. *Dist:* Perseus Distribution.

Woodbury, Mary. The Incredible Polly McDoodle. Schell, Wardol, illus. 2002. (Fourth in the Polly McDoodle Mystery Ser.). 182p. (J). (gr. 4-7). pap. 7.95 (978-1-55050-215-2(8)) Coteau Bks. CAN. *Dist:* Fitzhenry & Whiteside, Ltd.

—Incredible Polly Mcdoodle. 2003. (gr. 3-6). lib. bdg. 16.40 (978-0-613-78479-5(0)) Tandem Library Bks.

—The Innocent Polly McDoodle. 2005. (Polly McDoodle Mystery Ser.: Vol. 3). 192p. (J). (gr. 4-7). pap. 6.95 (978-1-55050-168-1(2)) Coteau Bks. CAN. *Dist:* Fitzhenry & Whiteside, Ltd.

—The Innocent Polly McDoodle. (J). 2001. (978-0-606-21827-6(0)); 2000. (Illus.). (gr. 3-6). lib. bdg. 15.25 (978-0-613-34782-2(X)) Tandem Library Bks.

—The International Polly McDoodle. 2004. (Polly Mcdoodle Mystery Ser.). 200p. (J). (gr. 4-7). pap. 7.95 (978-1-55050-293-0(X)) Coteau Bks. CAN. *Dist:* Fitzhenry & Whiteside, Ltd.

Woodland Mysteries. (gr. 3-7). Set 1. 424.95 (978-0-7802-7245-3(5)); Set 2. 424.95 (978-0-7802-8002-1(4)) Wright Group, The.

Woodland Mysteries: Classroom Library Set. (gr. 3-7). 313.95 (978-0-322-02628-5(8)) Wright Group, The.

Woodland Mysteries: Complete Boxed Set. (gr. 3-7). 1238.95 (978-0-322-02625-4(3)) Wright Group, The.

Woodruff, Elvira. The Ghost of Lizard Light. Clayton, Elaine, illus. 2001. 192p. (gr. 3-7). pap. 4.99 (978-0-440-41655-5(8) , Yearling) Random Hse. Children's Bks.

—The Ghost of Lizard Light. 2001. (gr. 3-6). lib. bdg. 13.00 (978-0-613-36814-8(2)) Tandem Library Bks.

Wortman, Barbara. Key in the Candle. (Young Hawk Mystery Ser.). 189p. (YA). (gr. 7 up). 9.99 (978-0-88092-379-8(2)) Royal Fireworks Publishing Co.

Wright, Betty Ren. Christina's Ghost. unabr. ed. 2002. (Illus.). (J). (ps-3). 39.95 incl. audio (978-0-87499-937-2(5)) Live Oak Media.

—Haunted Summer. 2001. 112p. (gr. 4-7). pap. 3.99 (978-0-439-24402-2(1)) Scholastic, Inc.

—Haunted Summer. 2001. (J). (978-0-606-21228-1(0)) Tandem Library Bks.

—Princess for a Week. Rogers, Jacqueline, illus. 160p. (J). (gr. 2-5). 16.95 (978-0-8234-1945-6(2)); 2007. pap. 6.95 (*978-0-8234-2111-4(2)) Holiday Hse., Inc.

—Too Many Secrets. 2002. 128p. (J). (gr. 3-7). pap. 4.99 (978-0-439-32665-0(6) , Scholastic Paperbacks) Scholastic, Inc.

Wright, Elsie. Patty & Jo, Detectives. 2005. reprint ed. pap. 24.95 (978-1-4179-9752-7(4)) Kessinger Publishing, LLC.

Wright Johnson, Shelli. Falcon in the Nest: A Story of Bes Adventure. 2004. 273p. pap. 21.95 (978-1-4137-5263-2(2)) PublishAmerica, Inc.

Wright, Nancy Means. The Pea Soup Poisonings. 2006. 128p. (J). 26.95 (978-1-59133-161-2(7)); pap. 14.95 (978-1-59133-162-9(5)) Hilliard & Harris.

Wulffson, Don L. The Golden Rat. 2007. 176p. (J). 16.95 (*978-1-59990-000-1(9)) Bloomsbury Publishing.

Wyatt, W. Joseph. The Millennium Man. 1999. 196p. (J). (gr. 8-12). 24.00 (978-0-9663622-4-4(1)) Third Millennium Pr.

Wynne-Jones, Tim. The Boy in the Burning House. braille ed. 2003. (J). (gr. 2). spiral bd. (978-0-616-15275-1(2)) Canadian National Institute for the Blind/Institut National Canadien pour les Aveugles.

—The Boy in the Burning House. 2000. (J). (978-0-7894-5621-2(4)) Dorling Kindersley Publishing, Inc.

—The Boy in the Burning House. 2003. 224p. (J). pap. 6.95 (978-0-374-40887-9(4) , Sunburst) Farrar, Straus & Giroux.

—The Boy in the Burning House. pap. 8.95 (978-0-88899-500-1(8)); 2000. (YA). (gr. 7-10). pap. 19.95 (978-0-88899-410-3(9)) Groundwood Bks. CAN. *Dist:* Transition Vendor.

—The Boy in the Burning House. 2001. (gr. 7-12). lib. bdg. 14.10 (978-0-613-69045-4(1)) Tandem Library Bks.

—The Boy in the Burning House. l.t. ed. 2002. 332p. (J). 23.95 (978-0-7862-4435-5(6)) Thorndike Pr.

The Yellow Yarn Mystery. 2005. (Emergent Library: Vol. 2). (YA). (ps-1). 23.94 (978-0-8215-8938-0(5)) Sadlier, William H. Inc.

The Yellow Yarn Mystery: Take-Home Book. 2005. (Emergent Library: Vol. 2). (YA). (ps-1). 12.60 (978-0-8215-7268-9(7)) Sadlier, William H. Inc.

Yep, Laurence. The Case of the Firecrackers. 1999. (Chinatown Mystery Ser.: No. 3). (Illus.). 192p. (J). (gr. 2-5). 15.89 (978-0-06-024452-1(6)) HarperCollins Pubs.

—The Case of the Goblin Pearls. Krenitsky, Nicholas, illus. 1998. (Chinatown Mystery Ser.: Vol. 1). 192p. (J). (gr. 3-7). pap. 5.99 (978-0-06-440552-2(4) , Harper Trophy) HarperCollins Pubs.

—The Case of the Lion Dance. 1998. (Chinatown Mystery Ser.: Vol. 2). 224p. (J). (gr. 3-7). 15.89 (978-0-06-024448-4(8)) HarperCollins Pubs.

Yep, Laurence & Yep, Laurence. The Case of the Goblin Pearls. 1998. 179p. (J). (ps-7). per. 14.15 (978-0-613-04692-3(7)) Tandem Library Bks.

Yolen, Jane & Stemple, Heidi Elisabet Yolen. The Salem Witch Trials: An Unsolved Mystery from History. Roth, Roger, illus. 2004. 32p. (J). 16.95 (978-0-689-84620-5(7)) Simon & Schuster Children's Publishing.

Yolen, Jane & Yolen-Stemple, Heidi Elizabet. The Mary Celeste: An Unsolved Mystery from History. Roth, Roger, illus. 2002. 32p. (J). (gr. 1 up). 6.99 (978-0-689-85122-3(7) , Aladdin) Simon & Schuster Children's Publishing.

Yorke, Malcolm. La Casa de los Sustez. (Raton de Biblioteca Coleccion). (SPA., Illus.). 128p. (J). (gr. 3). 7.95 (978-84-88061-71-3(4)) Serres, Ediciones, S. L. ESP. *Dist:* Lectorum Pubns., Inc.

Youree, Barbara. Senegal Sleuths. 2006. 56p. 7.75 (978-0-8341-2226-0(X)) Beacon Hill Pr. of Kansas City.

Yuricich, Jillian Grace, illus. What did Grandma See? 2006. (J). lib. bdg. 15.99 (978-0-9774696-0-4(3)) Gilboy Publishing.

Zalonis, C. B. Strangers in the Forest. 2006. (J). pap. 8.00 (978-0-8059-6820-0(2)) Dorrance Publishing Co., Inc.

Zindel, Paul. Camp Megadeth, No. 12. 2002. (P.C. Hawke Mysteries Ser.: Vol. 12). 144p. pap. 4.99 (978-0-7868-1624-8(4)) Disney Pr.

—Egyptian Mystery. 192p. (YA). (gr. 6 up). Date not set. lib. bdg. 16.89 (978-0-06-028509-8(5)); 2002. 15.95 (978-0-06-028508-1(7)) HarperCollins Pubs.

—The Houdini Whodunit. 2002. (P. C. Hawke Mysteries Ser.: Vol. 9). 160p. (J). pap. 4.99 (978-0-7868-1705-4(4)) Disney Pr.

—The Petrified Parrot. Date not set. (P. C. Hawke Mysteries Ser.: Bk. 11). 160p. (J). (gr. 3-7). pap. 4.99 (978-0-7868-1623-1(6)) Disney Pr.

—The Scream Museum. 2001. (gr. 3-6). lib. bdg. 13.00 (978-0-613-57441-9(9)) Tandem Library Bks.

—The Scream Museum. l.t. ed. 2002. (Illus.). 175p. (J). 22.95 (978-0-7862-4473-7(9)) Thorndike Pr.

—The Square Root of Murder. 2002. (P. C. Hawke Mysteries Ser.: Vol. 5). (Illus.). 144p. (gr. 3-7). pap. 4.99 (978-0-7868-1588-3(4) , Volo) Hyperion Bks. for Children.

—The Square Root of Murder. 2002. (gr. 3-6). lib. bdg. 13.00 (978-0-613-57445-7(1)) Tandem Library Bks.

—The Surfing Corpse. 2001. (P. C. Hawke Mystery Ser.: No. 2). 128p. pap. 4.99 (978-0-7868-1711-5(9)) Hyperion Bks. for Children.

—The Surfing Corpse. 2001. (gr. 3-6). lib. bdg. 13.00 (978-0-613-57447-1(8)) Tandem Library Bks.

—The Undertaker's Gone Bananas. 1999. mass mkt. (978-0-553-20172-7(7)) Random Hse., Inc.

Zinsser, Anne. Catch Him with Dragons. Moon, Ellen, illus. 2000. 115p. (J). pap. 6.95 (978-0-933951-90-7(6)) Locust Hill Pr.

MYTHICAL ANIMALS

see Animals, Mythical

MYTHOLOGY

see also Animals, Mythical; Art and Mythology; Folklore; Heroes; Indians of North America—Religion and Mythology; Totems and Totemism

Agbabian, Alidz. Fire & Water, Sister & Brother: An Armenian Myth. Sarkissian, Ananid, illus. 1998. 32p. (Orig.). (J). (ps-2). pap. 12.00 (978-0-9655507-2-7(9)) Dziludzar.

Alexander, David E. The Myths of the Lechuza. Smith, Duriel, illus. Date not set. 78p. (Orig.). (J). pap. 12.95 (978-0-9623078-5-0(8)) Alexander Pubns.

Altman, Linda Jacobs. African Mythology. Bock, William Sauts, illus. 2003. (Mythology Ser.). 112p. (J). lib. bdg. 26.60 (978-0-7660-2125-9(4)) Enslow Pubs., Inc.

Ambrus, Victor G., illus. The Iliad. 2000. 95p. (J). (ps-8). lib. bdg. 25.70 (978-0-613-90907-5(0)) Tandem Library Bks.

Ancient Myths, 6 bks. Incl. Adventures of Perseus. Hepplewhite, Peter. Bergin, Mark, illus. 32p. 23.93 (978-1-4048-0901-7(5)); Jason & the Argonauts. Malam, John. Antram, David, illus. 32p. 23.93 (978-1-4048-0902-4(3)); Theseus & the Minotaur. Ford, James Evelyn. Andrews, Gary, illus. 24p. 23.93 (978-1-4048-0903-1(1)); Twelve Labors of Hercules. Ford, James. Rutherford, Peter, illus. 32p. 23.93 (978-1-4048-0904-8(X)); Voyages of Odysseus. Reid, Sue. Bergin, Mark, illus. 32p. 23.93 (978-1-4048-0905-5(8)); Wooden Horse of Troy. Malam, John. Rutherford, Peter, illus. 32p. 23.93 (978-1-4048-0906-2(6)); (J). (gr. 3-5). 2004. 143.58 (978-1-4048-0907-9(4)) Picture Window Bks.

Anderson, Kirsten. From Zeus to Aliens. 2003. (Illus.). 60p. (978-0-7398-5177-7(2)) Steck-Vaughn.

Apel, Melanie Ann. Art & Religion in Ancient Greece. 2004. (Primary Sources of Ancient Civilizations Ser.). (Illus.). 24p. (J). lib. bdg. (978-0-8239-8938-6(0)); lib. bdg. 19.95 (978-0-8239-6770-4(0)) Rosen Publishing Group, Inc., The. (PowerKids Pr.).

Armitage, Kimo. Akua Hawaii: Hawaiian Gods & Their Stories. Enos, Solomon, illus. 2005. 72p. (J). 16.95 (978-1-58178-042-0(7)) Bishop Museum Pr.

Artzybasheff, Boris & Bock, Vera. Celtic Wonder Tales & Other Stories. 2001. (Illus.). 224p. (J). pap. 19.99 (978-0-86315-350-1(X)) Floris Bks. GBR. *Dist:* Steiner-Books, Inc.

Ashworth, Leon. Ancient Rome. 2002. (Illus.). 32p. (J). lib. bdg. 24.25 (978-1-58340-194-1(6)) Smart Apple Media.

Baldwin, James. Old Greek Stories. 2005. 192p. pap. 11.95 (978-1-4218-0155-1(8) , 1st World Library - Literary Society) 1st World Publishing, Inc.

—Old Greek Stories. 2004. reprint ed. pap. 19.95 (978-1-4191-3803-4(0)); pap. 1.99 (978-1-4192-3803-1(5)) Kessinger Publishing, LLC.

Baldwin, James. Old Greek Stories (Illustrated Edition) 2006. pap. (***978-1-4065-0511-5(0)***) Dodo Pr.

Bernard, Catherine. Celtic Mythology. Bock, William Sauts, illus. 2003. (Mythology Ser.). 104p. (J). lib. bdg. 26.60 (978-0-7660-2204-1(8)) Enslow Pubs., Inc.

Besant, Annie W. Legends & Tales Lotus Leaves for the Y. 2006. pap. 19.95 (***978-1-4286-2494-8(5)***) Kessinger Publishing, LLC.

Cann, Helen, illus. The Lady of Ten Thousand Names: Goddess Stories from Many Cultures. 2001. (J). 79p. (978-1-84148-143-2(2)); 80p. (gr. 3 up). 19.99 (978-1-84148-048-0(7)) Barefoot Bks., Inc.

Child's Book of Myths & Enchantments. (J). (gr. 4-7). 12.95 (978-1-56288-395-9(X)) Checkerboard Pr., Inc.

Climo, Shirley. Atalanta's Race: A Greek Myth. Koshkin, Alexander, illus. 2000. 40p. (J). (gr. 4-6). 6.95 (978-0-618-05154-0(6) , Clarion Bks.) Houghton Mifflin Co. Trade & Reference Div.

Colbert, David. Magical Worlds of Harry Potter: A Treasury of Myths, Legends, & Fascinating Facts. 2001. (Illus.). 223p. (YA). (gr. 5 up). 14.95 (978-0-9708442-0-0(4)) Lumina Pr. LLC.

Collier, Irene Dea. Chinese Mythology. Bock, William Sauts, illus. 2001. (Mythology Ser.). 128p. (YA). (gr. 6-12). lib. bdg. 26.60 (978-0-7660-1412-1(6)) Enslow Pubs., Inc.

Colum, Padraic. The Children of Odin: The Book of Northern Myths. Pogany, Willy, illus. 2004. 288p. (J). pap. 9.95 (978-0-689-86885-6(5) , Aladdin) Simon & Schuster Children's Publishing.

—The Golden Fleece & the Heroes Who Lived Before Achilles. Pogany, Willy, illus. 2004. 316p. (J). (gr. 4-8). reprint ed. pap. 10.00 (978-0-7567-7961-0(8)) DIANE Publishing Co.

—Myths of the World. Artzybasheff, Boris, illus. 2002. 328p. pap. 19.99 (978-0-86315-365-5(8)) Floris Bks. GBR. *Dist:* SteinerBooks, Inc.

Conley, Kate A. Greek Mythology. 2005. (Life in Ancient Days: Greece Ser.). (J). (978-1-59197-867-1(X)) ABDO Publishing Co.

Coolidge, Olivia E. Greek Myths. 2001. (gr. 5-8). lib. bdg. 14.10 (978-0-613-35521-6(0)) Tandem Library Bks.

Cooper, Gilly Cameron. How the World Began: Creation in Myths & Legends. 2006. (Illus.). 48p. pap., pap. 11.99 (978-1-84476-246-0(7) , Southwater) Anness Publishing GBR. *Dist:* National Bk. Network.

Dalal, Anita. Myths of Oceania. 2002. (Mythic World Ser.). (Illus.). 48p. (J). lib. bdg. 27.12 (978-0-7398-4978-1(6)) Raintree.

—Myths of Russia & the Slavs. 2002. (Mythic World Ser.). (Illus.). 48p. (YA). (gr. 7-10). lib. bdg. 27.12 (978-0-7398-4979-8(4)) Raintree.

Daning, Tom. The Four Dragons: A Chinese Myth. 2007. (Graphic Myths (New York, N.Y.) Ser.). (Illus.). 24p. (J). (978-1-4042-2343-1(6)); pap. (978-1-4042-2153-6(0)) Rosen Publishing Group, Inc., The. (PowerKids Pr.).

Dasi, Padmavati D., illus. Gopal the Infallible. 1999. (Gopal Trilogy Ser.: No. 1). 40p. (J). (gr. k-4). 9.75 (978-1-886069-17-6(4) , 1212) Mandala Publishing.

Davis, Kenneth C. Don't Know Much about World Myths. Ruzzier, Sergio, illus. 2005. (Don't Know Much About Ser.). 144p. (J). pap. 6.99 (978-0-06-440837-0(X) , Harper Trophy); 19.99 (978-0-06-028605-7(9)); lib. bdg. 20.89 (978-0-06-028606-4(7)) HarperCollins Pubs.

Denton, Kady MacDonald, illus. The Kingfisher Treasury of Myths & Legends. 2003. (Story Collections). 93p. (J). (gr. 3-5). pap. 12.95 (978-0-7534-5635-4(4) , Kingfisher) Houghton Mifflin Co. Trade & Reference Div.

Echlin, Kim A. Inanna: From the Myths of Ancient Sumer. Wolfsgruber, Linda, illus. 2003. 72p. (J). 19.95 (978-0-88899-496-7(6)) Groundwood Bks. CAN. *Dist:* Perseus Distribution.

The Encyclopedia of World Mythology. 2002. 320p. (YA). 29.95 (978-0-7525-8447-8(2)) Parragon, Inc.

Fisher, Micheal, illus. Chinese Myths & Legends. 2001. (World Book Myths & Legends Ser.). 64p. (J). (978-0-7166-2609-1(8)) World Bk., Inc.

Fleischman, Paul. Dateline: Troy. Frankfeldt, Gwen & Morrow, Glenn, illus. ed. 2006. 80p. (J). (gr. 7-11). 18.99 (978-0-7636-3083-6(7)) Candlewick Pr.

—Dateline: Troy. Frankfeldt, Gwen & Morrow, Glenn, illus. ed. 2006. 80p. (YA). (gr. 7-11). pap. 7.99 (978-0-7636-3084-3(5)) Candlewick Pr.

Gambino, Elena. Ancient Mesopotamians. 2001. (Myths & Civilization Ser.). (Illus.). 48p. (J). (gr. 3 up). 16.95 (978-0-87226-593-6(5) , 65935B, Bedrick, Peter Bks.) School Specialty Publishing.

Ganeri, Anita. Mesoamerican Myth: A Treasury of Central American Legends, Art, & History. 2007. (World of Mythology Ser.). (Illus.). 96p. (YA). (gr. 6 up). 35.95 (***978-0-7656-8106-5(4)***) Sharpe, M.E. Inc.

Garcia, Emmett Shkeme. Coyote & the Sky: How the Sun, Moon, & Stars Began. Pringle, Victoria, illus. 2006. 32p. (YA). (gr. 6 up). 17.95 (978-0-8263-3730-6(9)) Univ. of New Mexico Pr.

Gave, Marc. Hercules & Other Greek Myths. Harston, Jerry, illus. 1999. (Selected Classic Fairy Tales Ser.: Vol. 2). 20p. (J). (gr. k-6). lib. bdg. 13.95 (978-1-56674-221-4(8)) Forest Hse. Publishing Co., Inc.

Gershowitz, Paul. A Mythology for Children of the Twenty-First Century: Book One — In the Beginning. 2000. (Illus.). 32p. (J). pap. 9.00 (978-0-8059-4902-5(X)) Dorrance Publishing Co., Inc.

Gilbakian, Sita. The Gift of Gopal. Dasi, Padmavati D., illus. 1999. (Gopal Trilogy Ser.: No. 3). 44p. (J). (gr. k-4). 9.95 (978-1-886069-19-0(0) , 1213) Mandala Publishing.

—Miraculous Gopal. Dasi, Padmavati D., illus. 1999. (Gopal Trilogy Ser.: No. 2). 44p. (J). (gr. k-4). 9.95 (978-1-886069-18-3(2) , 1211) Mandala Publishing.

Giles, Bridget. Myths of West Africa. 2002. (Mythic World Ser.). (Illus.). 48p. (J). (gr. 7-10). lib. bdg. 27.12 (978-0-7398-4976-7(X)) Raintree.

Gill, Shelley. Up on Denali: Alaska's Wild Mountain. Cartwright, Shannon, illus. 2006. 32p. (J). 16.95 (978-1-57061-366-1(4)); pap. 10.95 (978-1-57061-365-4(6)) Sasquatch Bks.

Glaser, Jason & Bowman, Laurel. Mars. 2004. (World Mythology Ser.). (Illus.). 24p. (J). lib. bdg. 21.26 (978-0-7368-2661-7(0) , Bridgestone Bks.) Capstone Pr., Inc.

Green, Jen. Myths of China & Japan. 2002. (Mythic World Ser.). (Illus.). 48p. (J). lib. bdg. 27.12 (978-0-7398-4977-4(8)) Raintree.

Hamilton, John. Magic Rings & Other Magical Things. 2005. (Illus.). 32p. (J). (gr. 4-8). lib. bdg. 24.21 (978-1-59679-337-8(6) , ABDO & Daughters) ABDO Publishing Co.

Hamilton, Sue L. Lost Cities. 2007. (Unsolved Mysteries Ser.). (ENG., Illus.). 32p. (J). (gr. 4-8). lib. bdg. 25.65 (***978-1-59928-832-1(X)*** , ABDO & Daughters) ABDO Publishing Co.

Harcourt School Publishers Staff. A Fall from the Sky On Level. 3rd ed. 2002. (Trophies Reading Program Ser.). (Illus.). pap. 5.10 (978-0-15-323100-1(9)) Harcourt Schl. Pubs.

Hawthorne, Nathaniel. A Wonder Book: For Girls & Boys. Crane, Walter, illus. 1998. (Tor Classics Ser.). 192p. (gr. 4-7). 3.99 (978-0-8125-6523-2(1) , Tor Classics) Doherty, Tom Assocs., LLC.

—A Wonder Book for Girls & Boys. 1999. reprint ed. pap. 28.00 (978-1-4047-1351-2(4)) Classic Textbooks.

—A Wonder Book for Girls & Boys. 1998. (J). (978-0-606-13928-1(1)) Tandem Library Bks.

Hibberd, Claire & Dorling Kindersley Publishing Staff. Wonder Woman's Book of Myths. 2004. (Dk Readers Ser.). (Illus.). 48p. (J). 12.99 (978-0-7566-0241-3(6)); pap. 3.99 (978-0-7566-0242-0(4)) Dorling Kindersley Publishing, Inc.

Hicks, Peter, et al. In the Daily Life of the Ancient Romans. 2002. (Gods & Goddesses Ser.). (Illus.). 48p. (J). (gr. 4 up). 18.95 (978-0-87226-595-0(1) , Bedrick, Peter Bks.) School Specialty Publishing.

Horowitz, Anthony. Myths & Legends. 2003. (gr. 5-8). lib. bdg. 15.25 (978-0-613-90168-0(1)) Tandem Library Bks.

January, Brendan. New York Public Library Amazing Mythology: A Book of Answers for Kids. 2000. (gr. 5-8). lib. bdg. 22.20 (978-0-613-26380-1(4)) Tandem Library Bks.

January, Brendan, et al. The New York Public Library Amazing Mythology: A Book of Answers for Kids. 2000. (New York Public Library Books for Kids Ser.: Vol. 9). (Illus.). 176p. (gr. 5-9). pap. 13.95 (978-0-471-33205-3(4) , Capstone) Wiley, John & Sons, Inc.

Johari, Harish. Little Krishna. Weltevrede, Pieter, illus. 2002. 48p. (gr. 1-4). 16.95 (978-1-59143-001-8(1)) Bear & Co.

Jr. Graphic Mythologies, 6 bks., Set. Incl. Egyptian Mythology : Osiris & Isis. Daning, Tom. lib. bdg. 21.25 (978-1-4042-3399-7(7)); Four Dragons : A Chinese Myth. Daning, Tom. lib. bdg. 21.25 (978-1-4042-3400-0(4)); Greek Mythology : Jason & the Golden Fleece. Herdling, Glenn. lib. bdg. 21.25 (978-1-4042-3396-6(2)); Mesoamerican Mythology : Quetzalcoatl. Daning, Tom. lib. bdg. 21.25 (978-1-4042-3401-7(2)); Roman Mythology : Romulus & Remus. Daning, Tom. lib. bdg. 21.25 (978-1-4042-3397-3(0)); (Illus.). 24p. (J). (gr. 2-6). 2007. , PowerKids Pr. 2006. Set lib. bdg. 127.50 (978-1-4042-3551-9(5)) Rosen Publishing Group, Inc., The.

Keenan, Sheila. Gods, Goddesses, & Monsters: An Encyclopedia of World Mythology. Wedman, Belgin, illus. 2000. 128p. (J). (gr. 5-9). pap. 19.95 (978-0-439-04289-5(5) , Scholastic Reference) Scholastic, Inc.

Kerven, Rosalind. Fire! 1998. (Myths & Legends Ser.). (Illus.). 24p. (J). 14.60 (978-1-57572-018-0(3)) Heinemann Library.

Khanduri, Kamini, intro. & retold by. Tales of the Trojan War. Khanduri, Kamini, retold by. 2002. (Usborne Classics Ser.). (Illus.). 159p. (J). pap. (978-0-439-78708-6(4)) Scholastic, Inc.

Kingsley, Charles. The Heroes: Or Greek Fairy Tales for My Children. 2006. 308p. pap. 20.95 (978-1-59462-156-7(X) , 185, Book Jungle) Standard Pubns., Inc.

—Heroes of Greek Mythology. 2006. (Illus.). 240p. pap. 8.95 (978-0-486-44854-1(1)) Dover Pubns., Inc.

—The Heroes; or, Greek Fairy Tales: For My Children. 2000. 123p. reprint ed. pap. 9.95 (978-1-4021-9870-0(1) , Elibron Classics) Adamant Media.

Koralek, Jenny. Once upon Olympus. Holder, John, illus. 1998. (Cambridge Reading Ser.). 96p. pap. 12.00 (978-0-521-47630-0(5)) Cambridge Univ. Pr.

Lang, Andrew. Tales of Troy: Ulysses, the Sacker of Cities. 2004. reprint ed. pap. 1.99 (978-1-4192-5072-9(8)) Kessinger Publishing, LLC.

—Tales of Troy & Greece. Ford, H. J., illus. 2006. (Dover Value Editions Ser.). 336p. pap. 9.95 (978-0-486-44917-3(3)) Dover Pubns., Inc.

Levine, Gloria. Mythology. 1999. 44p. (YA). 11.95 (978-1-56137-817-3(8)) Novel Units, Inc.

Lindgren, Astrid. The Brothers Lionheart. Morgan, Jill, tr. from SWE. Wikland, Ilon, illus. 2004. 231p. (J). 17.95 (978-1-930900-24-0(4)) Purple Hse. Pr.

Lively, Penelope. In Search of a Homeland: The Story of the Aeneid. Andrew, Ian, illus. 2006. 128p. 19.95 (978-1-84507-685-6(0)) Lincoln, Frances Ltd. GBR. *Dist:* Perseus Distribution.

Loewen, Nancy. Greek & Roman Mythology, 4 bks. Incl. Athena. 1999. lib. bdg. 22.60 (978-0-7368-0048-8(4)); Hercules. 1999. lib. bdg. 22.60 (978-0-7368-0049-5(2)); Venus. 1998. lib. bdg. 22.60 (978-0-7368-0050-1(6)); Zeus. 1998. lib. bdg. 22.60 (978-0-7368-0051-8(4)); 48p. (J). (gr. 3-4). (Illus.). Set lib. bdg. 90.40 (978-0-7368-0464-6(1) , Bridgestone Bks.) Capstone Pr., Inc.

Masters, Anthony & Masters, Andrew. Greek Myths & Legends. Skilleter, Andrew, illus. 2000. (Myths & Legends Ser.). 48p. (J). (gr. 3 up). 18.95 (978-0-87226-609-4(5) , 66095B, Bedrick, Peter Bks.) School Specialty Publishing.

—Roman Myths & Legends. Skilleter, Andrew, illus. 2000. (Myths & Legends Ser.). 48p. (J). (gr. 3 up). 18.95 (978-0-87226-608-7(7) , 66087B, Bedrick, Peter Bks.) School Specialty Publishing.

Matthews, Caitlin. The Blessing Seed: A Creation Myth for the New Millennium. Dexter, Alison, illus. 1998. 32p. (J). (ps-7). 14.95 (978-1-901223-28-6(0)) Barefoot Bks., Inc.

May, Stephen, illus. Norse Myths & Legends. 2001. (World Book Myths & Legends Ser.). 64p. (J). (978-0-7166-2610-7(1)) World Bk., Inc.

Mayhew, James. Can You See a Little Bear? Morris, Jackie, illus. 2006. 32p. (J). pap. 7.95 (978-1-84507-364-0(9)) Lincoln, Frances Ltd. GBR. *Dist:* Perseus Distribution.

Mcbratney, Sam. Celtic Myths. 2005. (J). pap. 9.99 (978-0-340-88374-7(X) , Hodder & Stoughton) Hodder General Publishing Division GBR. *Dist:* Trafalgar Square Publishing.

McCaughrean, Geraldine. Golden Book of Myths & Legends. (Illus.). 240p. (J). pap. 12.00 (978-1-85881-675-3(0)) Dolphin Paperbacks GBR. *Dist:* Trafalgar Square Publishing.

McCaughrean, Geraldine & Ross. Jason y el Vellocino de Oro. 2005. (Mythology Series Collection Mitos Ser.). (SPA., Illus.). 50p. (J). (gr. 2-3). 9.95 (978-84-348-6425-2(8)) SM Ediciones ESP. *Dist:* Iaconi, Mariuccia Bk. Imports.

—Perseo y la Gorgona Medisa. 2005. (Mythology Series Collection Mitos Ser.). (SPA., Illus.). 50p. (J). (gr. 2-3). 9.95 (978-84-348-6430-6(4)) SM Ediciones ESP. *Dist:* Iaconi, Mariuccia Bk. Imports.

McGraw-Hill Staff. Mythology & You, Student Edition. 2005. 295p. (C). pap. 36.64 (978-0-07-872907-2(6) , 9780078729072) Glencoe/McGraw-Hill.

—World Mythology. 2005. 722p. (C). 62.00 (978-0-07-872909-6(2) , 9780078729096) Glencoe/McGraw-Hill.

McMullan, Kate. Get to Work, Hercules! 2003. (Myth-o-Mania Ser.: No. 7). (Illus.). (J). 9.99 (978-0-7868-0863-2(2)) Hyperion Bks. for Children.

The Minotaur: A Princess Book Collection by Princess Ena. 2000. 26p. (J). per. 19.00 (978-0-9705133-9-7(9)) World of Wonders, Inc.

Montpellier, Paul. Atlas. Montpellier, Paul, illus. unabr. ed. (Illus.). 28p. (J). (978-0-920080-10-8(3)) Harbour Publishing Co., Ltd.

Muten, Burleigh. Goddesses: A World of Myth & Magic. Guay, Rebecca, illus. 2003. 80p. (J). 19.99 (978-1-84148-075-6(4)) Barefoot Bks., Inc.

Mythic World, 8 bks., Set. 2002. (Illus.). (J). (gr. 5-6). lib. bdg. 216.96 (978-0-7398-4981-1(6)) Raintree.

Myths & Legends. pap. (978-1-84458-374-4(0)) Chrysalis Children's Bks.

Myths & Legends. (Illus.). 40p. (YA). (gr. 5 up). lib. bdg. (978-1-59084-480-9(7)) Mason Crest Pubs.

Noble, Marty. Invisible Mythological Creatures Magic Picture Book. 1998. 16p. (J). pap. 1.50 (978-0-486-40119-5(7)) Dover Pubns., Inc.

Nordenstrom, Michael, illus. & adapted by. Hina & the Sea of Stars. Nordenstrom, Michael, adapted by. 2003. 32p. 10.95 (978-1-57306-167-4(0)) Bess Pr., Inc.

Osborne, Mary Pope. Return to Ithaca. 5th rev. ed. 2004. (Odyssey Ser.: No. 5). (Illus.). 112p. (gr. 3-6). 9.99 (978-0-7868-0774-1(1)) Hyperion Bks. for Children.

Oxlade, Chris. Mystery of the Bermuda Triangle. 2001. (Can Science Solve? Ser.). (Illus.). (J). (978-0-606-21718-7(5)) Tandem Library Bks.

—The Mystery of the Bermuda Triangle, Set 1. 2002. (Can Science Solve? Ser.). (Illus.). 32p. (J). (gr. 4-7). pap. 7.50 (978-1-58810-313-0(7) , 91038) Heinemann Library.

Peters, Georgia, illus. African Myths & Legends. 2001. (World Book Myths & Legends Ser.). 64p. (J). (978-0-7166-2605-3(5)) World Bk., Inc.

Philip, Neil. Illustrated Book of Myths. Mistry, Nilesh, illus. 2007. 192p. (J). pap. 12.99 (978-0-7566-2223-7(9)) Dorling Kindersley Publishing, Inc.

—Mythology of the World. Palin, Nicki, illus. 2004. 160p. (J). (gr. 5-9). 24.95 (978-0-7534-5779-5(2) , Kingfisher) Houghton Mifflin Co. Trade & Reference Div.

Pickels, Dwayne E. Roman Mythological Gods & Goddesses. 1998. (Costume, Tradition & Culture). (Illus.). 64p. (J). 28.00 (978-0-7910-5164-1(1) , Chelsea Hse.) Facts On File, Inc.

Pilling, Ann. Kingfisher Treasury of Myths & Legends. 2003. (gr. 3-6). lib. bdg. 22.20 (978-0-613-67418-8(9)) Tandem Library Bks.

Posner, Pat. Fantastic Creatures from Greek Myths. Whelan, Olwyn, illus. 2003. (Greek Myths Ser.). 40p. (J). (gr. 1-4). 18.95 (978-1-57768-507-4(5) , Bedrick, Peter Bks.) School Specialty Publishing.

Ramen, Fred. Indian Mythology. 2006. (Mythology Around the World Ser.). (J). (978-1-4042-0735-6(X)) Rosen Publishing Group, Inc., The.

Randall, Ron. Amaterasu. 2007. (Graphic Myths & Legends Ser.). (Illus.). 48p. (J). (gr. 4-8). 26.60 (978-0-8225-5968-9(4)) Lerner Publishing Group.

Reed, Natasha. Mythical Creatures. Kincaid, Angela, illus. 2005. 24p. (J). (ps-7). pap. (978-1-84510-119-0(7)) Top That! Publishing PLC.

Remier. Mythology A to Z, 2 vols., Set. 2002. (YA). (gr. 5-9). 105.00 (978-0-8160-4760-4(X)) Facts On File, Inc.

Richardson, Adele D. Hades. 2003. (World Mythology Ser.). (Illus.). 24p. (J). (gr. 2-3). lib. bdg. 18.60 (978-0-7368-1610-6(0) , Bridgestone Bks.) Capstone Pr., Inc.

Riordan, James. Twelve Labours of Hercules. Balit, Christina, illus. 2000. 32p. (YA). (gr. 3 up). pap. (978-0-7112-1391-3(7)) Lincoln, Frances Ltd. GBR. *Dist:* Raincoast Bk. Distribution.

Robshaw, Brandon & Scholoar, Rochelle. Urban Myths. 2005. (Illus.). 32p. pap. 8.50 (978-0-340-87148-5(2)) Cambridge Univ. Pr.

Roman, Pedro Josél (Adaptacion). PANDORA -la portadora de todos los Dones- 2005. 32p. pap. (978-958-30-1924-1(0)) Panamericana Editorial.

Scott, James. Mythology - Timeless Tales of Gods & Heroes: Activity Pack. 2002. (YA). (gr. 7-12). pap., act. bk. ed. 34.95 (978-1-58049-608-7(3) , PA0116) Prestwick Hse., Inc.

Shahrukh Husain. Greece. 2004. (Stories from Ancient Civilizations Ser.). (J). lib. bdg. 27.10 (978-1-58340-619-9(0)) Smart Apple Media.

Shahrukh Husain & Willey, Bee. Indian Myths. 2007. (J). (***978-1-84234-438-5(2)***) Cherrytree Pubns., Inc.

Shone, Rob. Greek Myths. 2005. (Graphic Mythology Ser.). (Illus.). 48p. (J). pap. (978-1-4042-0813-1(5)); (gr. 5-8). lib. bdg. 29.95 (978-1-4042-0801-8(1)) Rosen Publishing Group, Inc., The.

Silva, Gabriel (Adaptacion). HERACLES -Doce años tras la Inmortalidad. 2006. 32p. pap. (978-958-30-2002-5(8)) Panamericana Editorial.

—POSIDON -el dios del Mar- 2005. 32p. pap. (978-958-30-2003-2(6)) Panamericana Editorial.

—ZEUS -el padre de los Dioses. 2006. 32p. pap. (978-958-30-2000-1(1)) Panamericana Editorial.

Sperling, Vatsala. Karna. 2007. 32pp. (J). 15.95 (***978-1-59143-073-5(9)***) Bear & Co.

Spies, Karen Bornemann. The Iliad & The Odyssey in Greek Mythology. 2002. (Mythology Ser.). (Illus.). 128p. (YA). (gr. 6-12). lib. bdg. 26.60 (978-0-7660-1561-6(0)) Enslow Pubs., Inc.

Spinner, Stephanie. Snake Hair: The Story of Medusa. Swan, Susan, illus. 1999. (All Aboard Reading Ser.). 48p. (J). (ps-1). pap. 3.99 (978-0-448-41981-7(5) , Grosset & Dunlap) Penguin Group (USA) Inc.

Steck-Vaughn Staff. From Zeus to Aliens. 2002. (Illus.). pap. 41.60 incl. audio compact disk (978-0-7398-6982-6(5)) Steck-Vaughn.

Steele, Phillip. Incredible Quests: Epic Journeys in Myth & Legend. 2006. (Illus.). 48p. pap., pap. 11.99 (978-1-84476-247-7(5) , Southwater) Anness Publishing GBR. *Dist:* National Bk. Network.

Sutcliff, Rosemary. Black Ships Before Troy. 2005. 160p. (YA). (gr. 7 up). mass mkt. 5.99 (978-0-553-49483-9(X) , Laurel Leaf) Random Hse. Children's Bks.

Taylor, C. J. How We Saw the World Vol. 4: Nine Native Stories of the Way Things Began. 1999. (gr. 3-6). lib. bdg. 17.60 (978-0-613-77276-1(8)) Tandem Library Bks.

Tom Streissguth. The Devil. 2005. (Mystery Library). (Illus.). 112p. (gr. 7-10). 29.95 (978-1-59018-446-2(7)) Thomson Gale.

Townsend. Mysterious Urban Myths, 6 Packs. 2004. (Out There Ser.). lib. bdg. 48.30 (978-1-4109-0977-0(8)) Raintree.

Tracy, Kathleen. The Life & Times of Homer. 2004. (Biography from Ancient Civilizations Ser.). (Illus.). 48p. (J). (gr. 4-8). lib. bdg. 29.95 (978-1-58415-260-6(5)) Mitchell Lane Pubs., Inc.

UXL Ency Myth, Vol. 7. 2007. 380.00 (***978-1-4144-3030-0(2)*** , UXL) Thomson Gale.

Verniero, Joan C., et al, eds. An Illustrated Treasury Read Aloud Myths & Legends: More Than 40 of the World's Best-Loved Myths & Legends Including Greek, Roman, Celtic, Scandinavian, Indian, Mexican, & Many More. 2004. (Illus.). 192p. (J). tchr. ed. 14.95 (978-1-57912-361-1(9) , 81361) Black Dog & Leventhal Pubs., Inc.

Wargin, Kathy-Jo. The Legend of the Petoskey Stone. van Frankenhuyzen, Gijsbert, illus. 2004. (Great Lakes Legend Ser.). 48p. (J). 17.95 (978-1-58536-217-2(4)) Sleeping Bear Pr.

Whitling, Matt. Greek Heroes. 2000. (Imitation in Writing Ser.: 4). 88p. (YA). (gr. 4 up). spiral bd. 20.00 (978-1-930443-20-4(X) , C086) Logos Schl.

—Greek Myths. 2000. (Imitation in Writing Ser.: 3). 105p. (YA). (gr. 4 up). spiral bd. 20.00 (978-1-930443-12-9(9) , C085) Logos Schl.

Wilkinson, Philip. Chinese Myth: A Treasury of Legends, Art, & History. 2007. (World of Mythology Ser.). (Illus.). 96p. (YA). (gr. 6 up). 35.95 (***978-0-7656-8103-4(X))** Sharpe, M.E. Inc.

Wolfson, Evelyn. Inuit Mythology. Bock, William Sauts, illus. 2001. (Mythology Ser.). 128p. (J). (gr. 6-12). lib. bdg. 26.60 (978-0-7660-1559-3(9)) Enslow Pubs., Inc.

Wolfson, Margaret Olivia. Marriage of the Rain Goddess: A South African Myth. Parms, Clifford Alexander, photos by. 1999. (Illus.). 32p. (J). (gr. 1-5). 15.95 (978-1-84148-100-5(9)) Barefoot Bks., Inc.

World Mythology. (Illus.). (J). (gr. 2-3). lib. bdg. 297.64 (978-0-7368-2758-4(7)) Capstone Pr., Inc.

World Mythology. 2003. 320p. 5.98 (978-1-4054-0326-9(8)) Parragon, Inc.

World Mythology, 6 bks. Incl. Athena. Hoena, Blake A. lib. bdg. 18.60 (978-0-7368-1608-3(9)); Diana. Richardson, Adele D. lib. bdg. 18.60 (978-0-7368-1609-0(7)); Hades. Richardson, Adele D. lib. bdg. 18.60 (978-0-7368-1610-6(0)); Hercules. Richardson, Adele D. lib. bdg. 18.60 (978-0-7368-1611-3(9)); Venus. Hoena, Blake A. lib. bdg. 18.60 (978-0-7368-1612-0(7)); Zeus. Hoena, Blake A. lib. bdg. 18.60 (978-0-7368-1613-7(5)); 24p. (J). (gr. 2-3). (Illus.). 2003. lib. bdg. (978-0-7368-1635-9(6) , Bridgestone Bks.) Capstone Pr., Inc.

Worth-Baker, Marcia. Greek Mythology Activities: Activities to Help Students Build Background Knowledge about Ancient Greece, Explore the Genre of Myths, & Learn Important Vocabulary. 2005. 80p. pap. 12.99 (978-0-439-51788-1(5) , Teaching Resources) Scholastic, Inc.

Yen, Clara. Why Rat Comes First: A Story of the Chinese Zodiac. Yoshida, Hideo, illus. 2002. 32p. (J). (gr. 1 up). pap. 7.95 (978-0-89239-174-5(X)) Bellerophon Bks.

Zeus. (World Mythology Ser.). (Illus.). 24p. (J). 6.95 (978-0-7368-3458-2(3)) Capstone Pr., Inc.

MYTHOLOGY, CLASSICAL

Activities Pro Liberis, Vol II: A Collection of Classical Studies Lessons & Activities for the Elementary School. 2000. spiral bd. (978-0-939507-57-3(9) , B35B) American Classical League, The.

Amery, Heather. Greek Myths. Edwards, Linda, illus. 2004. (Young Children Ser.). 128p. (J). (ps-3). 18.95 (978-0-7460-3725-6(2)); lib. bdg. 26.95 (978-1-58086-261-5(6)); 7.99 (978-0-7945-0141-9(8) , Usborne) EDC Publishing.

Athena. (World Mythology Ser.). (Illus.). 24p. (J). 6.95 (978-0-7368-3453-7(2)) Capstone Pr., Inc.

Bailey, Carolyn Sherwin. Wonder Stories the Best Myths for Boys & Girls. 2004. reprint ed. pap. 31.95 (978-1-4179-3481-2(6)) Kessinger Publishing, LLC.

Barkow, Henriette. Pandora's Box: English Only. Mayo, Diana, illus. 2004. (J). (978-1-84444-380-2(9)) Mantra Publishing, Ltd.

Barlow, Steve L. Surfer's Mad Myths: A Touch of Wind. (Illus.). 128p. (J). 7.95 (978-0-14-038346-1(8)) Penguin Bks., Ltd. GBR. *Dist:* Trafalgar Square Publishing.

Bingham, Jane. Classical Myth: A Treasury of Greek & Roman Legends, Art, & History. 2007. (World of Mythology Ser.). (Illus.). 96p. (YA). (gr. 6 up). 35.95 (***978-0-7656-8104-1(8))** Sharpe, M.E. Inc.

Blood, Danielle. Greek Myth Mini-Books: Reproducible Comic Book-Style Retellings That Introduce Kids to These Riveting Classic Stories-and Motivate All Readers, 15 bks., Set. 2001. (Illus.). 80p. pap. 11.95 (978-0-439-21561-9(7)) Scholastic, Inc.

Bloom, Harold. Oedipus Rex. 2007. (Bloom's Guides). 120p. (YA). (gr. 9 up). 30.00 (***978-0-7910-9360-3(3)** , Chelsea Hse.) Facts On File, Inc.

Burleigh, Robert. Pandora. Colon, Raul, illus. 2002. 32p. (J). (gr. 3-5). 17.00 (978-0-15-202178-8(7) , Silver Whistle) Harcourt Trade Pubs.

Cadnum, Michael. Nightsong: The Legend of Orpheus & Eurydice. 2006. (Nightsong Ser.). 144p. (J). (gr. 4-7). pap. 16.99 (978-0-439-54535-8(8) , Orchard Bks.) Scholastic, Inc.

Capstone Press Staff. Greek & Roman Mythology. 1998. (Illus.). (gr. 3-7). 76.00 (978-0-531-19245-0(8) , Children's Pr.) Scholastic Library Publishing.

Caselli, Giovanni. Greek Myths. 1998. (Myths of the World Ser.). (Illus.). 96p. (YA). (gr. 3 up). 22.50 (978-0-87226-560-8(9) , 65609B, Bedrick, Peter Bks.) School Specialty Publishing.

Catherine, Mary. Classic Myths. 2004. reprint ed. pap. 15.95 (978-1-4191-1334-5(8)); pap. 1.99 (978-1-4192-1334-2(2)) Kessinger Publishing, LLC.

Church, Alfred John. Stories of the Iliad & the Aeneid. 2006. pap. 24.95 (***978-1-4286-0468-1(5))** Kessinger Publishing, LLC.

Church, Alfred John. The Story of the Iliad. 2005. reprint ed. pap. 31.95 (978-1-4191-5466-9(4)) Kessinger Publishing, LLC.

Clement, David D. Trojan Horse. 1999. (J). (978-0-606-18992-7(0)) Tandem Library Bks.

Coolidge, Olivia E. Greek Myths. Sandoz, Edouard, illus. 2001. 272p. (YA). (gr. 7-9). tchr. ed. 16.00 (978-0-618-15425-8(6)); pap. 5.95 (978-0-618-15426-5(4)) Houghton Mifflin Co. Trade & Reference Div.

—Greek Myths. 2001. 12.60 (978-0-606-22594-6(3)) Tandem Library Bks.

Craft, Charlotte. King Midas & the Golden Touch. Craft, Kinuko Y., illus. 32p. (J). 2003. pap. 6.99 (978-0-06-054063-0(X)); 1999. (gr. 3 up). 16.99 (978-0-688-13165-4(4)) HarperCollins Pubs.

—King Midas & the Golden Touch. 2003. (gr. k-3). lib. bdg. 15.30 (978-0-613-68438-5(9)) Tandem Library Bks.

Craft, Kinuko Y., illus. King Midas & the Golden Touch. 1999. 32p. (J). (gr. 3 up). 15.89 (978-0-688-13166-1(2)) HarperCollins Pubs.

Curlee, Lynn. Classical Bestiary. Curlee, Lynn, illus. 2008. 40p. (J). 17.99 (978-1-4169-1453-2(6)) Simon & Schuster Children's Publishing.

Daly, Kathleen N. Greek & Roman Mythology A to Z: A Young Readers Companion. 2nd rev. ed. 2003. (Mythology A to Z Ser.). (Illus.). 160p. (J). (gr. 4-9). 40.00 (978-0-8160-5155-7(0)) Facts On File, Inc.

Davies, David. Trojan Horse. 1999. (gr. k-3). lib. bdg. 11.80 (978-0-613-17564-7(6)) Tandem Library Bks.

Davis, David C. Trojan Horse. 1999. (Eyewitness Bks.). (Illus.). 48p. (J). (ps-4). pap. 3.99 (978-0-7894-4474-5(7)) Dorling Kindersley Publishing, Inc.

Du Bouchet, Paule. Prince Orpheus. Negrin, Fabian, tr. from FRE. Negrin, Fabian, illus. 2004. (Books for Young Readers Ser.). 22p. 5.95 (978-0-89236-737-5(7)) Oxford Univ. Pr., Inc.

Evans, C & Millard, A. Greek Myths & Legends. 2004. (Myths & Legends Ser.). 64p. (J). pap. 10.95 (978-0-7945-0455-7(8)); lib. bdg. 18.95 (978-1-58086-553-1(4)) EDC Publishing.

Evans, Hestia & Evans, Lady. Mythology. Steer, Dugald, ed. 2007. (Ologies Ser.). (Illus.). 32p. (J). (gr. 3). 19.99 (***978-0-7636-3403-2(4))** Candlewick Pr.

Galloway, Priscilla. Aleta & the Queen: A Tale of Ancient Greece. Cousineau, Normand, illus. 2003. (Tales of Ancient Lands Ser.). 160p. (J). (gr. 5 up). pap. 14.95 (978-1-55037-462-9(1)) Annick Pr., Ltd. CAN. *Dist:* Firefly Bks., Ltd.

—Atalanta: The Fastest Runner in the World. Cousineau, Normand, illus. 2003. (Tales of Ancient Lands Ser.). 80p. (J). (gr. 4-7). pap. 12.95 (978-1-55037-463-6(X)) Annick Pr., Ltd. CAN. *Dist:* Firefly Bks., Ltd.

—Daedalus & the Minotaur. Cousineau, Normand, illus. 2003. (Tales of Ancient Lands Ser.). 112p. (J). (gr. 4-7). pap. 14.95 (978-1-55037-458-2(3)) Annick Pr., Ltd. CAN. *Dist:* Firefly Bks., Ltd.

Gave, Marc. Hercules & Other Greek Myths. Harston, Jerry, illus. 1999. (Selected Classic Fairy Tales Ser.: Vol. 2). 20p. (J). (gr. k-6). lib. bdg. 13.95 (978-1-56674-221-4(8)) Forest Hse. Publishing Co., Inc.

Geras, Adele. Troy. 2002. 376p. (YA). (gr. 9 up). pap. 6.95 (978-0-15-204570-8(8) , Harcourt Paperbacks) Harcourt Children's Bks.

—Troy. 2004. 368p. (J). (gr. 8 up). pap. 48.00 incl. audio (978-0-8072-2288-1(7) , Listening Library) Random Hse. Audio Publishing Group.

—Troy. 2002. (gr. 7-12). lib. bdg. 15.25 (978-0-613-55224-0(5)) Tandem Library Bks.

Goldish, Meish. Famous Fliers. Wallner, Alexandra, illus. 2002. 16p. (J). (978-0-439-35139-3(1)) Scholastic, Inc.

Green, Jen. Myths of Ancient Greece. 2001. (Mythic World Ser.). (Illus.). 48p. (J). lib. bdg. 27.12 (978-0-7398-3191-5(7)) Raintree.

Green, John. Greek Gods & Goddesses. 2001. (Pictorial Archive Ser.). (Illus.). 48p. (J). pap. 3.95 (978-0-486-41862-9(6)) Dover Pubns., Inc.

Guner, Kagan. The Children of Atlantis. 2002. (Illus.). 32p. 7.95 (978-1-84059-325-9(3)) Milet Publishing.

—Icarus. 2002. (Illus.). 32p. 7.95 (978-1-84059-326-6(1)) Milet Publishing.

Hamilton, Edith. Mythology. 1999. (J). (978-0-606-16245-6(3)) Tandem Library Bks.

Harris, John. Greece! Rome! Monsters! Brown, Calef, illus. 2002. (Books for Young Readers Ser.). 48p. 16.95 (978-0-89236-618-7(4)) Oxford Univ. Pr., Inc.

Hawthorne, Nathaniel. Tanglewood Tales. 1999. (978-0-606-18658-2(1)) Tandem Library Bks.

—Tanglewood Tales: A Wonder-Book for Girls & Boys. fac. ed. 2001. 384p. pap. 15.95 (978-1-4021-6651-8(6) , Elibron Classics) Adamant Media.

—Tanglewood Tales: For Girls & Boys. 1999. (Tor Classics Ser.). 192p. (gr. 4-7). 2.99 (978-0-8125-6515-7(0) , Tor Classics) Doherty, Tom Assocs., LLC.

—A Wonder Book: Heroes & Monsters of Greek Mythology. 2003. (Dover Evergreen Classics Ser.). 176p. (J). (gr. 4-7). pap. 3.00 (978-0-486-43209-0(2)) Dover Pubns., Inc.

—A Wonder Book & Tanglewood Tales. (Twelve-Point Ser.). 2002. 341p. lib. bdg. 25.00 (978-1-58287-190-5(6)); 2004. 563p. 26.00 (978-1-58287-673-3(8)) North Bks.

Herdling, Glenn. Greek Mythology: Jason & the Golden Fleece. 2007. (Jr. Graphic Mythologies Ser.). (Illus.). 24p. (J). (gr. 2-6). lib. bdg. 21.25 (978-1-4042-3396-6(2) , PowerKids Pr.) Rosen Publishing Group, Inc., The.

—Jason & the Golden Fleece: A Greek Myth. 2007. (Illus.). 24p. (J). (978-1-4042-2339-4(8)); pap. (978-1-4042-2149-9(2)) Rosen Publishing Group, Inc., The. (PowerKids Pr.).

Hoena, B. A. Aeneas. 2004. (Illus.). 24p. (J). 14.95 (978-0-7368-2496-5(0)) Capstone Pr., Inc.

—Cyclopes. 2004. (Illus.). 24p. (J). 14.95 (978-0-7368-2497-2(9)) Capstone Pr., Inc.

—Odysseus. 2004. (Illus.). 24p. (J). 14.95 (978-0-7368-2498-9(7)) Capstone Pr., Inc.

—Poseidon. 2004. (Illus.). 24p. (J). 14.95 (978-0-7368-2499-6(5)) Capstone Pr., Inc.

Hoena, Blake A. Athena. 2003. (World Mythology Ser.). (Illus.). 24p. (J). (gr. 2-3). lib. bdg. 18.60 (978-0-7368-1608-3(9) , Bridgestone Bks.) Capstone Pr., Inc.

—Venus. 2003. (World Mythology Ser.). (Illus.). 24p. (J). (gr. 2-3). lib. bdg. 18.60 (978-0-7368-1612-0(7) , Bridgestone Bks.) Capstone Pr., Inc.

—Zeus. 2003. (World Mythology Ser.). (Illus.). 24p. (J). (gr. 2-3). lib. bdg. 18.60 (978-0-7368-1613-7(5) , Bridgestone Bks.) Capstone Pr., Inc.

Homer. Iliad. 1999. (Illus.). lvi, 379p. (gr. 7-12). lib. bdg. 14.10 (978-0-613-37185-8(2)) Tandem Library Bks.

—The Odyssey. 2000. (Classics Ser.). (Illus.). 64p. (J). (gr. 2-5). 14.99 (978-0-7894-5455-3(6)) Dorling Kindersley Publishing, Inc.

—The Odyssey. adapted ed. (YA). (gr. 5-12). pap. 8.50 (978-0-8359-0232-8(3)) Globe Fearon Educational Publishing.

Houle, Michelle M. Gods & Goddesses in Greek Mythology. Bock, William Sauts, illus. 2001. (Mythology Ser.). 128p. (YA). (gr. 6-12). lib. bdg. 26.60 (978-0-7660-1408-4(8)) Enslow Pubs., Inc.

Innes, Brian. Myths of Ancient Rome. 2001. (Mythic World Ser.). (Illus.). 48p. (J). lib. bdg. 27.12 (978-0-7398-3192-2(5)) Raintree.

Israel, Fred L., intro. Egyptian Kings & Queens & Classical Deities. 1999. (Looking into the Past). (Illus.). 64p. (YA). (gr. 5 up). 28.00 (978-0-7910-4677-7(X) , Chelsea Hse.) Facts On File, Inc.

Johnson, Robert Bowie, Jr. The Parthenon Code. 2004. (Illus.). 288p. 29.95 (978-0-9705438-3-7(2)) Solving Light Bks.

Katz, Leon. The Greek Myths: Puppet Plays for Children from Ovid's Metamorphoses. 2004. 160p. pap. 12.95 (978-1-55783-502-4(0) , 1557835020, Applause Theatre & Cinema) Leonard, Hal Corp.

Kerisel, Francoise. Diogenes' Lantern. Mansot, Frederick, tr. from FRE. Mansot, Frederick, illus. 2004. (Books for Young Readers Ser.). 22p. 5.95 (978-0-89236-738-2(5)) Oxford Univ. Pr., Inc.

Kimmel, Eric A. The McElderry Book of Greek Myths. Montserrat, Pep, illus. 2008. 112p. (J). 21.99 (978-1-4169-1534-8(6) , McElderry, Margaret K.) Simon & Schuster Children's Publishing.

Korba, Joanna. Demeter & Persephone: A Myth from Ancient Greece. 2006. spiral bd. 42.00 (***978-1-4108-7166-4(5))** Benchmark Education Co.

Kovacs, Charles. Ancient Greece. 2004. 176p. (J). pap. 20.00 (978-0-86315-429-4(8)) Floris Bks. GBR. *Dist:* Steiner-Books, Inc.

Kurth, Steve, illus. Jason & the Golden Fleece. 2007. (Graphic Myths & Legends Ser.). 48p. (J). (gr. 4-8). 26.60 (978-0-8225-5967-2(6)) Lerner Publishing Group.

Lattimore, Deborah Nourse. Medusa. 2000. (Illus.). 32p. (J). (gr. 2-5). 15.95 (978-0-06-027904-2(4)); 15.89 (978-0-06-027905-9(2)) HarperCollins Pubs. (Cotler, Joanna Books).

Lee, Alan & Sutcliff, Rosemary. Black Ships Before Troy. 2005. (Illus.). 128p. (J). 19.95 (978-1-84507-359-6(2)) Lincoln, Frances Ltd. GBR. *Dist:* Perseus Distribution.

Lester, Julius. Cupid: A Tale of Love & Desire. 2007. 208p. (YA). (gr. 7 up). 17.00 (978-0-15-202056-9(X) , Silver Whistle) Harcourt Trade Pubs.

Lively, Penelope. In Search of a Homeland: The Story of the Aeneid. Andrews, Ian, illus. 2001. 119p. (J). (978-0-385-72930-7(8) , Delacorte Pr.) Dell Publishing.

Loewen, Nancy. Athena. 1999. (Greek & Roman Mythology Ser.). (Illus.). 48p. (J). (gr. 3-4). lib. bdg. 22.60 (978-0-7368-0048-8(4) , Bridgestone Bks.) Capstone Pr., Inc.

—Athena. 1998. (Greek & Roman Mythology Ser.). (J). pap. 19.00 (978-0-531-11612-8(3) , Watts, Franklin) Scholastic Library Publishing.

—Hercules. 1999. (Greek & Roman Mythology Ser.). (Illus.). 48p. (J). (gr. 3-4). lib. bdg. 22.60 (978-0-7368-0049-5(2) , Bridgestone Bks.) Capstone Pr., Inc.

—Venus. 1998. (Greek & Roman Mythology Ser.). (Illus.). 48p. (J). (gr. 3-4). lib. bdg. 22.60 (978-0-7368-0050-1(6) , Bridgestone Bks.) Capstone Pr., Inc.

—Zeus. 1998. (Greek & Roman Mythology Ser.). (Illus.). 48p. (J). (gr. 3-4). lib. bdg. 22.60 (978-0-7368-0051-8(4) , Bridgestone Bks.) Capstone Pr., Inc.

Lorenz, Albert & Schleh, Joy. The Trojan Horse. 2006. (Illus.). 34p. (J). (gr. k-4). 17.95 (978-0-8109-5986-6(0) , Abrams Bks. for Young Readers) Abrams, Harry N. , Inc.

MacDonald, Fiona. In the Daily Life of the Ancient Greeks. 2002. (Gods & Goddesses Ser.). (Illus.). 48p. (J). (gr. 4 up). 18.95 (978-0-87226-636-0(2) , Bedrick, Peter Bks.) School Specialty Publishing.

Malam, John. The Wooden Hoursе of Troy. Rutherford, Peter, illus. 2004. (Ancient Myths Ser.). (J). (978-0-7565-0664-3(6)) Compass Point Bks.

Martell, Hazel Mary. Myths & Civilization of the Ancient Greeks. Stalio, Ivan & D'Ottavi, Francesca, illus. 2000. (Myths & Civilization Ser.). 48p. (J). (gr. 3 up). 16.95 (978-0-87226-283-6(9) , 62839B, Bedrick, Peter Bks.) School Specialty Publishing.

Marzollo, Jean. Pandora's Box: A Greek Myth about the Constellations. 2006. (Illus.). 28p. (J). (ps-5). 12.99 (978-0-316-74133-0(7)) Little Brown & Co.

Mason, Jane. The Flying Horse: The Story of Pegasus. Swan, Susan, illus. 1999. (All Aboard Reading Ser.). 32p. (J). (ps-1). pap. 3.99 (978-0-448-41980-0(7) , Grosset & Dunlap) Penguin Group (USA) Inc.

Mayer, Marianna. Pegasus. Craft, Kinuko Y., illus. 1998. 40p. (J). (gr. k-3). 16.99 (978-0-688-13382-5(7)) HarperCollins Pubs.

—Pegasus. Craft, Kinuko, illus. 1998. 40p. (J). (gr. k-3). 16.89 (978-0-688-13383-2(5)) HarperCollins Pubs.

McCaughrean, Geraldine. Greek Gods & Goddesses. Clark, Emma Chichester, illus. 1998. 112p. (YA). (gr. 4-7). 22.95 (978-0-689-82084-7(4) , McElderry, Margaret K.) Simon & Schuster Children's Publishing.

McCaughrean, Geraldine, retold by. Odysseus. 2004. (Heroes Ser.). (Illus.). 128p. (J). 15.95 (978-0-8126-2721-3(0)) Cricket Bks.

McCaughrean, Geraldine & Ross. Los Doce Trabajos de Hercules. 2005. (Mythology Series Collection Mitos Ser.). (SPA., Illus.). 50p. (J). (gr. 2-3). 9.95 (978-84-348-6429-0(0)) SM Ediciones ESP. *Dist:* Iaconi, Mariuccia Bk. Imports.

Mitton, S. Kingdom of the Sun: A Book about the Planets. Mitton, Jacqueline & Balit, Christina, illus. 2001. 32p. (J). (ps-3). 16.95 (978-0-7922-7220-5(X) , National Geographic Children's Bks.) National Geographic Society.

Nardo, Don. Cyclops. 2004. (Illus.). 48p. (J). (gr. 4-7). 26.20 (978-0-7377-2615-2(6) , 1233932, Greenhaven Pr., Inc.) Thomson Gale.

Nardo, Don, ed. The Greenhaven Encyclopedia of Greek & Roman Mythology. 2002. (Greenhaven Encyclopedia of Ser.). (Illus.). 304p. (J). 77.45 (978-0-7377-0719-9(4) , GML12001-176976, Greenhaven Pr., Inc.) Thomson Gale.

Oberman, Sheldon. Island of the Minotaur: The Greek Myths of Ancient Crete. Drawson, Blair, illus. 2003. 96p. (J). 19.95 (978-1-56656-531-8(6) , Crocodile Bks.) Interlink Publishing Group, Inc.

Osborne, Mary Pope. Mitos Griegos. (Torre de Papel Ser.). (SPA.). (YA). (gr. 6 up). 8.95 (978-958-04-2863-3(8)) Norma S.A. COL. *Dist:* Distribuidora Norma, Inc.

Owens, L. L. Tales of Greek Mythology II: Retold Timeless Classics. Hargreaves, Greg, illus. (Retold Timeless Classics Ser.). 58p. (YA). 2000. (gr. 1-4). lib. bdg. 13.95 (978-0-7807-9035-3(9) , Covercraft); 1999. (gr. 5 up). pap. 5.60 (978-0-7891-5064-6(6)) Perfection Learning Corp.

Pandora's Box. 2004. (J). cd-rom (978-1-84444-465-6(1)) Mantra Publishing, Ltd.

Parker, Vic. Traditional Tales from Ancient Greece. 2000. (Traditional Tales from Around the World Ser.). (Illus.). 48p. (J). (gr. 2-6). lib. bdg. 16.95 (978-1-929298-72-3(2)) Chrysalis Education.

Perseus & the Gorgon's Head. 1999. (SmartReader Ser.). (J). Level 1. pap., tchr. ed. 19.95 incl. audio (978-0-7887-0784-1(1) , 79352T3); Level 2. pap., tchr. ed. 19.95 incl. audio (978-0-7887-0786-5(8) , 79353T3) Recorded Bks., LLC.

Profiles in Greek & Roman Mythology, 8 vols., Set. Incl. Artemis. O'Neal, Claire. lib. bdg. 29.95 (***978-1-58415-555-3(8));** Athena. Roberts, Russell. lib. bdg. 29.95 (***978-1-58415-556-0(6));** Dionysus. Roberts, Russell. lib. bdg. 29.95 (***978-1-58415-557-7(4));** Hercules. Whiting, Jim. lib. bdg. 29.95 (***978-1-58415-553-9(1));** Jason. Whiting, Jim. lib. bdg. 29.95 (***978-1-58415-552-2(3));** Perseus. Harkins, Susan and William. lib. bdg. 29.95 (***978-1-58415-558-4(2));** Theseus. Tracy, Kathleen. lib. bdg. 29.95 (***978-1-58415-554-6(X));** Zeus. Roberts, Russell. lib. bdg. 29.95 (***978-1-58415-559-1(0));** (Illus.). 48p. (J). (gr. 4-9). 2007. (Profiles in Greek & Roman Mythology Ser.). 2007. Set lib. bdg. 239.60 (***978-1-58415-560-7(4))** Mitchell Lane Pubs., Inc.

Richardson, Adele D. Diana. 2003. (World Mythology Ser.). (Illus.). 24p. (J). (gr. 2-3). lib. bdg. 18.60 (978-0-7368-1609-0(7) , Bridgestone Bks.) Capstone Pr., Inc.

—Hercules. 2003. (World Mythology Ser.). (Illus.). 24p. (J). (gr. 2-3). lib. bdg. 18.60 (978-0-7368-1611-3(9) , Bridgestone Bks.) Capstone Pr., Inc.

Riordan, James. Jason & the Golden Fleece. Cockcroft, Jason, illus. 64p. 2005. (J). pap. 12.95 (978-1-84507-061-8(5)); 2004. (YA). 19.95 (978-1-84507-271-1(5)) Lincoln, Frances Ltd. GBR. *Dist:* Perseus Distribution, Transition Vendor.

—Jason & the Golden Fleece. Cockcroft, Jason, tr. Cockcroft, Jason, illus. 2003. 64p. (J). 19.95 (978-0-7112-2081-2(6)) Lincoln, Frances Ltd. GBR. *Dist:* Transition Vendor.

Roberts, Russell. Athena. 2007. (Profiles in Greek & Roman Mythology Ser.). (Illus.). 48p. (J). (gr. 4-9). lib. bdg. 29.95 (***978-1-58415-556-0(6))** Mitchell Lane Pubs., Inc.

—Dionysus. 2007. (Profiles in Greek & Roman Mythology Ser.). (Illus.). 48p. (J). (gr. 4-9). lib. bdg. 29.95 (***978-1-58415-557-7(4))** Mitchell Lane Pubs., Inc.

—Zeus. 2007. (Profiles in Greek & Roman Mythology Ser.). (Illus.). 48p. (J). (gr. 4-9). lib. bdg. 29.95 (***978-1-58415-559-1(0))** Mitchell Lane Pubs., Inc.

Ross, Harriet, ed. Greek Myths: Tales of the Gods, Heroes & Heroines. 1999. (Illus.). 160p. (YA). (gr. 6-12). lib. bdg. 14.95 (978-0-87460-383-5(8)) Lion Bks.

Rumford, James. There's a Monster in the Alphabet. Rumford, James, illus. 2002. (Illus.). 40p. (J). (gr. k-4). tchr. ed. 16.00 (978-0-618-22140-0(9)) Houghton Mifflin Co. Trade & Reference Div.

Saunders, Nick. Pandora's Box. 2006. (Graphic Greek Myths & Legends Ser.). (Illus.). 48p. (J). (gr. 3-5). pap. 11.95 (***978-0-8368-8147-9(8));** lib. bdg. 22.60 (***978-0-8368-7747-2(0))** Stevens, Gareth Inc. (World Almanac Library).

Schomp, Virginia. The Ancient Greeks. 2007. (Myths of the World Ser.). 96p. (J). lib. bdg. 32.79 (***978-0-7614-2547-2(0)** , Benchmark Bks.) Cavendish, Marshall Corp.

Sophocles. Sophocles: The Complete Plays. 2001. (Signet Classics Ser.). (Illus.). (J). (978-0-606-21441-4(0)) Tandem Library Bks.

Spies, Karen Bornemann. Heroes in Greek Mythology. 2002. (Mythology Ser.). (Illus.). 128p. (YA). (gr. 6-12). lib. bdg. 26.60 (978-0-7660-1560-9(2)) Enslow Pubs., Inc.

Spinner, Stephanie. Atlanta, la Cazadora. Holguin, Magdalena, tr. 2003. (Zona Libre Ser.). (SPA.). 174p. 7.50 (978-958-04-7080-9(4)) Norma S.A. COL. *Dist:* Lectorum Pubns., Inc.

—Monster in the Maze: The Story of the Minotaur. 2000. (All Aboard Reading Ser.). (J). (978-0-606-20268-8(4)) Tandem Library Bks.

—Snake Hair: The Story of Medusa. Swan, Susan, illus. 1999. (All Aboard Reading Ser.). 48p. (J). (ps-1). pap. 3.99 (978-0-448-41981-7(5) , Grosset & Dunlap) Penguin Group (USA) Inc.

Steig, Jeanne. A Gift from Zeus: Sixteen Favorite Myths. Steig, William, illus. 2001. 176p. (gr. 9 up). 18.99 (978-0-06-028405-3(6) , Cotler, Joanna Books) HarperCollins Pubs.

Trujillo, Luis Francisco. Mitologia Maravillosa para Ninos: Relatos de Clasicos Griegos. (SPA.). (J). 8.98 (978-968-403-926-1(3)) Selector, S.A. de C.V. MEX. *Dist:* AIMS International Bks., Inc.

Usher, Kerry. Emperadores, Dioses y Heroes. 2002. Tr. of Roman Mythology. (SPA.). 136p. (J). 24.95 (978-84-207-3399-9(7)) Grupo Anaya, S.A. ESP. *Dist:* AIMS International Bks., Inc.

Whiting, Jim. Jason. 2007. (Profiles in Greek & Roman Mythology Ser.). (Illus.). 48p. (J). (gr. 4-9). lib. bdg. 29.95 (***978-1-58415-552-2(3)***) Mitchell Lane Pubs., Inc.

Wilbur, Helen L. Z is for Zeus. rev. ed. 2008. (General Alphabet Ser.). 40p. 17.95 (***978-1-58536-341-4(3)***) Sleeping Bear Pr.

Williams, Rose. The Labors of Aeneas: What a Pain It Was to Found the Roman Race. 2003. (Illus.). (YA). 14.00 (978-0-86516-556-4(4)) Bolchazy-Carducci Pubs.

Woff, Richard. A Pocket Dictionary of Ancient Greek Heroes & Heroines. 2005. (Getty Trust Publications: J. Paul Getty Museum Ser.). 48p. 9.95 (978-0-89236-795-5(4)) Getty Pubns.

—Pocket Dictionary of Greek & Roman Gods & Goddesses. 2003. (Books for Young Readers Ser.). (Illus.). 48p. (gr. 3-7). 9.95 (978-0-89236-706-1(7)) Oxford Univ. Pr., Inc.

Wolfson, Evelyn. Roman Mythology. 2002. (Mythology Ser.). (Illus.). 128p. (YA). (gr. 6-12). lib. bdg. 26.60 (978-0-7660-1558-6(0)) Enslow Pubs., Inc.

Yeates, Thomas. Atalanta: The Race Against Destiny: A Greek Myth. 2007. (Graphic Myths & Legends Ser.). (Illus.). 48p. (J). (gr. 4-8). 26.60 (978-0-8225-5965-8(X)) Lerner Publishing Group.

Zarabouka, Sofia & Perantakou-Cook, Mary. Jason & the Golden Fleece: The Most Adventurous & Exciting Expedition of All the Ages. 2004. (Books for Young Readers Ser.). (Illus.). 56p. 14.95 (978-0-89236-756-6(3)) Oxford Univ. Pr., Inc.

MYTHOLOGY, EGYPTIAN

Barker, Henry. Egyptian Gods & Goddesses. Crosby, Jeff, illus. 1999. (All Aboard Reading Ser.). 48p. (J). (gr. 1-3). pap. 3.99 (978-0-448-42029-5(5) , Grosset & Dunlap) Penguin Group (USA) Inc.

—Egyptian Gods & Goddesses. 1999. (gr. k-3). lib. bdg. 11.80 (978-0-613-21481-0(1)) Tandem Library Bks.

Broyles, Janell. Egyptian Mythology. 2005. (Mythology Around the World Ser.). (Illus.). 64p. (J). (978-1-4042-0770-7(8)) Rosen Publishing Group, Inc., The.

Daning, Tom. Egyptian Mythology: Osiris & Isis. 2007. (Jr. Graphic Mythologies Ser.). (Illus.). 24p. (J). (978-1-4042-2342-4(8)); pap. (978-1-4042-2152-9(2)); (gr. 2-6). lib. bdg. 21.25 (978-1-4042-3399-7(7)) Rosen Publishing Group, Inc., The. (PowerKids Pr.).

Gaytan, Leon Eduardo. Mitologia Egipcia para Ninos: Amenos Relatos de la Tierra de los Faraones. 1999. Tr. of Egyptian Mythology for Children. (SPA., Illus.). 118p. (J). mass mkt. 7.95 (978-970-643-174-5(8)) Selector, S.A. de C.V. MEX. *Dist:* Libros Sin Fronteras.

Isis & Osiris. 2004. (J). cd-rom (978-1-84444-461-8(9)) Mantra Publishing, Ltd.

Israel, Fred L., intro. Egyptian Kings & Queens & Classical Deities. 1999. (Looking into the Past). (Illus.). 64p. (YA). (gr. 5 up). 28.00 (978-0-7910-4677-7(X) , Chelsea Hse.) Facts On File, Inc.

Jacq, Christian. Cuentos y Leyendas de la Epoca de Las Piramides. Corral, Mercedes, tr. from FRE. 6th ed. 2003. (Fables & Legends Ser.). (SPA., Illus.). 144p. (J). 9.95 (978-84-239-8893-8(7)) Espasa Calpe, S.A. ESP. *Dist:* Planeta Publishing Corp.

Jeffrey, Gary. Egyptian Mythology. Felmang, Romano, illus. 2005. (Graphic Mythology Ser.). 48p. pap. (978-1-4042-0812-4(7)) Rosen Publishing Group, Inc., The.

—Egyptian Myths. Felmang, Romano, illus. 2005. (Graphic Mythology Ser.). 48p. (YA). (gr. 5-8). lib. bdg. 29.95 (978-1-4042-0800-1(3)) Rosen Publishing Group, Inc., The.

Kramer, Ann. Egyptian Myth: A Treasury of Legends, Art, & History. 2007. (World of Mythology Ser.). (Illus.). 96p. (YA). (gr. 6 up). 35.95 (***978-0-7656-8105-8(6)***) Sharpe, M.E. Inc.

Malam, John. Myths & Legends of the Desert. 2002. (Illus.). 32p. (J). (978-0-7534-0742-4(6) , Kingfisher) Houghton Mifflin Co. Trade & Reference Div.

Mayer, Danuta, illus. Ancient Egyptian Myths & Legends, 1 vols. 2001. (World Book Myths & Legends Ser.). 64p. (J). (978-0-7166-2606-0(3)); (978-0-7166-2607-7(1)) World Bk., Inc.

Mayo, Diana, illus. Isis & Osiris. 2004. (J). (ENG & ALB.). (978-1-84444-313-0(2)); (ENG & ARA.). (978-1-84444-314-7(0)); (ENG & BEN.). (978-1-84444-315-4(9)); (ENG & CHI.). (978-1-84444-316-1(7)); (ENG & PER.). (978-1-84444-318-5(3)); (ENG & FRE.). 30p. (978-1-84444-319-2(1)); (ENG & GER.). 30p. (978-1-84444-320-8(5)); (ENG & GUJ.). (978-1-84444-321-5(3)); (ENG & ITA.). (978-1-84444-322-2(1)); (ENG & PAN.). (978-1-84444-323-9(X)); (POR & ENG.). (978-1-84444-324-6(8)); (SER, ENG & CRO.). (978-1-84444-325-3(6)); (ENG & SOM.). (978-1-84444-326-0(4)); (ENG & SPA.). 30p. (978-1-84444-327-7(2)); (TAM & ENG.). (978-1-84444-328-4(0)); (ENG & TUR.). (978-1-84444-329-1(9)); (ENG & URD.). (978-1-84444-330-7(2)); (ENG & VIE.). (978-1-84444-331-4(0)); (ENG & HIN.). (978-1-84444-433-5(3)); (ENG & POL.). (978-1-84444-434-2(1)); (RUS & ENG.). (978-1-84444-435-9(X)) Mantra Publishing, Ltd.

McCall, Henrietta. In the Daily Life of the Ancient Egyptians. 2002. (Gods & Goddesses Ser.). (Illus.). 48p. (J). (gr. 4 up). 18.95 (978-0-87226-635-3(4) , Bedrick, Peter Bks.) School Specialty Publishing.

Nardo, Don. Egyptian Mythology. Bock, William Sauts, illus. 2001. (Mythology Ser.). 128p. (YA). (gr. 6-12). lib. bdg. 26.60 (978-0-7660-1407-7(X)) Enslow Pubs., Inc.

Remler, Pat. Egyptian Mythology A to Z. 2006. (Mythology A to Z Ser.). 256p. (J). (gr. 5-8). 40.00 (978-0-8160-6306-2(0)) Facts On File, Inc.

—Egyptian Mythology A to Z: A Young Reader's Companion. 2000. (Mythology A to Z Ser.). (Illus.). 192p. (YA). (gr. 4-9). 40.00 (978-0-8160-3984-5(4)) Facts On File, Inc.

Rowe, Anne. The Secret Name of Ra. 1998. (Myths & Legends Ser.). (Illus.). 24p. (J). 14.60 (978-1-57572-016-6(7)) Heinemann Library.

Shahrukh Husain & Willey, Bee. Egypt. 2004. (Stories from Ancient Civilizations Ser.). (J). lib. bdg. 27.10 (978-1-58340-618-2(2)) Smart Apple Media.

Viegas, Jennifer L., ed. Critical Perspectives on Natural Disasters. 2007. (Scientific American Critical Anthologies on Environment & Climate Ser.). (Illus.). 247p. (YA). (gr. 9-12). lib. bdg. 31.95 (978-1-4042-0824-7(0)) Rosen Publishing Group, Inc., The.

MYTHOLOGY, INDIAN

see Indians of North America—Religion and Mythology

MYTHOLOGY, NORSE

Branford, Henrietta. The Theft of Thor's Hammer. 1998. (Myths & Legends Ser.). (Illus.). 24p. (J). 14.95 (978-1-57572-014-2(0)) Heinemann Library.

Daly, Kathleen N. Norse Mythology A to Z: A Young Reader's Companion. 2nd rev. ed. 2003. (Mythology A to Z Ser.). (Illus.). 144p. (J). (gr. 4-9). 40.00 (978-0-8160-5156-4(9)) Facts On File, Inc.

Green, Jen, et al. In the Daily Life of the Vikings. 2002. (Gods & Goddesses Ser.). (Illus.). 48p. (J). (gr. 4 up). 18.95 (978-0-87226-594-3(3) , Bedrick, Peter Bks.) School Specialty Publishing.

Hall, Jennie. Viking Tales EasyRead Comfort Edition. 2006. pap. (***978-1-4250-0871-0(2)***) Assistedreadingbooks.com Inc.

—Viking Tales EasyRead Edition. 2006. pap. (***978-1-4250-0280-0(3)***) Assistedreadingbooks.com Inc.

—Viking Tales EasyRead Large Edition. 2006. pap. (***978-1-4250-1336-3(8)***) Assistedreadingbooks.com Inc.

Hopkins, Andrea. Viking Gods & Legends. 2002. (Viking Library). (Illus.). 24p. (J). (gr. 3). lib. bdg. 19.95 (978-0-8239-5814-6(0) , PowerKids Pr.) Rosen Publishing Group, Inc., The.

Husain, Shahrukh. The Vikings. 2005. (Stories from Ancient Civilizations Ser.). (Illus.). 32p. (J). (gr. 4 up). lib. bdg. 27.10 (978-1-58340-621-2(2) , 1236428) Smart Apple Media.

Limke, Jeff. Thor & Loki: In the Land of Giants: A Norse Myth. Randall, Ron, illus. 2007. (Graphic Myths & Legends Ser.). 48p. (J). 26.60 (978-0-8225-3087-9(2)) Lerner Publishing Group.

Mabie, Hamilton Wright. Norse Mythology: Great Stories from the Eddas. 2002. 96p. pap. 5.95 (978-0-486-42082-0(5)) Dover Pubns., Inc.

Mabie, Hamilton Wright. Norse Stories Retold from the Eddas. 2006. (Illus.). pap. 30.95 (***978-1-4254-9336-3(X)***) Kessinger Publishing, LLC.

Osborne, Mary Pope. Favorite Norse Myths. Howell, Troy, illus. 2001. 96p. (J). (gr. 8). pap. 7.99 (978-0-590-48047-5(2)) Scholastic, Inc.

—Favorite Norse Myths. 2000. (J). 14.79 (978-0-606-19561-4(0)) Tandem Library Bks.

Rayner, Olivia, illus. World Book Myths & Legends Series, 8 vols., Vol. 8. 2007. (World Book Myths & Legends Ser.). 64p. (gr. 4-8). 239.00 (978-0-7166-2613-8(6) , 31020) World Bk., Inc.

Rydberg, Viktor & Reaves, William P. Our Fathers' Godsaga: Retold for the Young. 2003. 223p. pap. 15.95 (978-0-595-29978-2(4)) iUniverse, Inc.

Rydberg, Viktor & Reeves, William P. Our Fathers' Godsaga: Retold for the Young. Rydberg, Viktor, tr. 2003. 223p. 25.95 (978-0-595-66097-1(5)) iUniverse, Inc.

Schomp, Virginia. The Norsemen. 2007. (Myths of the World Ser.). 96p. (J). lib. bdg. 32.79 (***978-0-7614-2548-9(9)*** , Benchmark Bks.) Cavendish, Marshall Corp.

Wilmot-Buxton, E. M. Viking Gods & Heroes. 2004. 160p. pap. 6.95 (978-0-486-43704-0(3)) Dover Pubns., Inc.

MYTHOLOGY IN ART

see Art and Mythology

MYTHS

see Mythology

N

NADER, RALPH, 1934-

Bowen, Nancy. Ralph Nader: Man with a Mission. 2002. (Single Titles Ser.). (Illus.). 144p. (gr. 7 up). lib. bdg. 24.90 (978-0-7613-2365-5(1) , Twenty-First Century Bks.) Lerner Publishing Group.

NAGASAKI (JAPAN)

The Atomic Bomb. 2004. (Historical Reader Ser.). (Illus.). 224p. (J). (gr. 6-12). 13.32 (978-0-395-98665-3(6) , 2-99909) McDougal Littell Inc.

Bodden, Valerie. The Bombing of Hiroshima & Nagasaki. 2007. (J). (978-1-58341-545-0(9) , Creative Education) Creative Co., The.

Langley, Andrew. Hiroshima & Nagasaki: Fire from the Sky. 2006. (Snapshots in History Ser.). (Illus.). 96p. (J). (gr. 5-7). 30.60 (978-0-7565-1621-5(8)) Compass Point Bks.

Orr, Tamra. The Atom Bomb: Creating & Exploding the First Nuclear Weapon. 2004. (Library of Weapons of Mass Destruction). (Illus.). 64p. (J). lib. bdg. 26.50 (978-1-4042-0292-4(7)) Rosen Publishing Group, Inc., The.

NAMES—FICTION

Blackstone, Stella. Who Are You, Baby Kangaroo? Beaton, Clare, illus. 2004. 32p. (J). 14.99 (978-1-84148-217-0(X)) Barefoot Bks., Inc.

Bourgeois, Paulette. Franklin's Nickname. Clark, Brenda, illus. 2004. (Franklin Ser.). 32p. (J). (ps-3). pap. 4.99 (978-0-439-62547-0(5)) Scholastic, Inc.

Choi, Yangsook. The Name Jar. 2003. (gr. k-3). lib. bdg. 15.30 (978-0-613-82979-3(4)) Tandem Library Bks.

Harcourt School Publishers Staff. Fire from Ice: Take-Home Book. 2001. (Collections Ser.). (Illus.). (J). pap. 1.90 (978-0-15-319514-3(2)) Harcourt Schl. Pubs.

—Fire from Ice Below Level. 3rd ed. 2002. (Trophies Reading Program Ser.). (Illus.). pap. 5.10 (978-0-15-323312-8(5)) Harcourt Schl. Pubs.

—This Is Who I Am. 3rd ed. 2002. (Trophies English Language Learners Ser.). (Illus.). (gr. 6). pap. 5.10 (978-0-15-327870-9(6)) Harcourt Schl. Pubs.

Kappler, Kathleen. Whitney's School Morning. 2004. 38p. pap. 17.95 (978-1-4137-3711-0(0)) PublishAmerica, Inc.

Katz, Karen. Princess Baby. 2008. (Illus.). 32p. (J). lib. bdg. 17.99 (***978-0-375-94119-1(3)*** , Schwartz & Wade Bks.) Random Hse. Children's Bks.

Korman, Gordon. The Sixth Grade Nickname Game. 2004. 160p. (gr. 3-7). pap. 5.99 (978-0-7868-5190-4(2)) Hyperion Paperbacks for Children.

Neelon, Caleb. Lilman Makes a Name for Himself. 2004. (J). lib. bdg. (978-0-9745150-7-0(0)) Cantab Publishing.

Raschka, Chris. New York Is English, Chattanooga Is Creek. 2005. (Illus.). 40p. (J). (gr. k-4). 16.95 (978-0-689-84600-7(2) , Atheneum) Simon & Schuster Children's Publishing.

Recorvits, Helen. Me Llama Yoon. Swiatkowska, Gabi, illus. 2004. Tr. of My Name is Yoon. (SPA.). (J). 19.95 (978-84-261-3335-9(5)) Juventud, Editorial ESP. *Dist:* Lectorum Pubns., Inc., Iaconi, Mariuccia Bk. Imports.

Sadu, Itah. Christopher Changes His Name. Condy, Roy, illus. 1998. 32p. (J). (gr. k-3). pap. 5.95 (978-1-55209-214-9(3)) Firefly Bks., Ltd.

Scillian, Devin. Fibblestax. K.L., Darnell, illus. 2003. 32p. (J). pap. 7.95 (978-1-58536-165-6(8)) Sleeping Bear Pr.

—Fibblestax. 2003. (gr. k-3). lib. bdg. 16.40 (978-0-613-79709-2(4)) Tandem Library Bks.

Siegel, Rv. A Bee Called Kangaroo. 2005. 81p. pap. 9.16 (978-1-4116-2890-8(X)) Lulu.com.

Trimble, Marcia. A Name for Kitty. Lapuyade, Gloria, illus. 2000. 32p. (J). (ps-2). 15.95 (978-1-891577-63-5(8)); pap. 7.95 (978-1-891577-64-2(6)) Images Pr.

Walters, Eric. Laggan Lard Butts. 2006. 112p. (gr. 5-10). pap. 7.95 (978-1-55143-518-3(7)); lib. bdg. 14.95 (978-1-55143-531-2(4)) Orca Bk. Pubs. USA.

NAMES, GEOGRAPHICAL

Hughes, Susan. Let's Call It Canada: Amazing Stories of Canadian Place Names. Dobson, Clive & Dobson, Jolie, illus. 2003. (Wow Canada! Ser.). 96p. (J). (gr. 3-7). pap. 16.95 (978-1-894379-50-2(0)); lib. bdg. 26.95 (978-1-894379-49-6(7)) Maple Tree Pr. CAN. *Dist:* Firefly Bks., Ltd.

Places in Time: A Kid's Historic Guide to the Changing Names & Places of the World, 6 vols., Set. Incl. Brief Political & Geographic History of Africa : Where Are the Belgian Congo, Rhodesia, & Kush? Davenport, John. lib. bdg. 37.10 (***978-1-58415-624-6(4));*** Brief Political & Geographic History of Asia : Where Are Saigon, Kampuchea, & Burma? Dillon, Doug. lib. bdg. 37.10 (***978-1-58415-623-9(6));*** Brief Political & Geographic History of Europe : Where Are Prussia, Gaul, & the Holy Roman Empire? Davey, Frances. lib. bdg. 37.10 (***978-1-58415-625-3(2));*** Brief Political & Geographic History of Latin America : Where Are Gran Colombia, la Plata, & Dutch Guiana? Rice, Earle, Jr. lib. bdg. 37.10 (***978-1-58415-626-0(0));*** Brief Political & Geographic History of North America : Where Are New France, New Netherland, & New Sweden? Johnston, Lissa. lib. bdg. 37.10 (***978-1-58415-627-7(9));*** Brief Political & Geographic History of the Middle East : Where Are Persia, Babylon, & the Ottoman Empire? Davenport, John. lib. bdg. 37.10 (***978-1-58415-622-2(8));*** (Illus.). 112p. (YA). (gr. 5-10). (Places in Time Ser.). 2007. Set lib. bdg. 222.60 (***978-1-58415-628-4(7)***) Mitchell Lane Pubs., Inc.

Scheunemann, Pam. Cities. l.t. ed. 2001. (Capital Letters Ser.). (Illus.). 24p. (J). (ps-3). lib. bdg. 19.93 (978-1-57765-610-4(5) , SandCastle) ABDO Publishing Co.

—Places. l.t. ed. 2001. (Capital Letters Ser.). (Illus.). 24p. (J). (ps-3). lib. bdg. 19.93 (978-1-57765-609-8(1) , SandCastle) ABDO Publishing Co.

—States. l.t. ed. 2001. (Capital Letters Ser.). (Illus.). 24p. (J). (ps-3). lib. bdg. 19.93 (978-1-57765-613-5(X) , SandCastle) ABDO Publishing Co.

NAMES, PERSONAL

Altman, Nathaniel. The Little Giant Encyclopedia of Names. 1999. 512p. (J). 9.95 (978-0-8069-9840-4(7)) Sterling Publishing Co., Inc.

EchoHawk, Terry. Call Me Little Echo Hawk. 2005. (Illus.). 22p. (J). 15.99 (978-1-55517-804-8(9) , Cedar Fort, Inc.) Cedar Fort, Inc./CFI Distribution.

Grambs, Alison. Nutty Names Knock-Knocks. Harpster, Steve, illus. 2006. (Giggle Fit Ser.). 48p. (J). 12.95 (978-1-4027-3025-2(X)) Sterling Publishing Co., Inc.

Hayes, Larry E. My Name Starts with J. Anderson, Airlie, illus. 2004. (My Name Starts With Ser.). 31p. (J). 12.95 (978-0-9725292-2-8(5)) Inspire Pubns.

—My Name Starts with M. Anderson, Airlie, illus. Hayes, Larry E., photos by. 2004. (My Name Starts With Ser.). 32p. (J). 12.95 (978-0-9725292-3-5(3) , 1) Inspire Pubns.

—My Name Starts with S. Anderson, Airlie, illus. Hayes, Larry E., photos by. 2003. (My Name Starts With Ser.). 32p. 10.95 (978-0-9725292-1-1(7)) Inspire Pubns.

Hayes, Larry E. & Anderson, Airlie. My Name Starts with A. 2002. (My Name Starts With Ser.). (Illus.). 32p. 10.95 (978-0-9725292-0-4(9)) Inspire Pubns.

Heurtelou, Maude. Mwen Rele Nadine. Corbett, Kecia & Corbett, Andrea, illus. 2001. (Big Book Ser.).Tr. of My Name is Nadine. (CRP.). 18p. (J). (gr. 3-5). 19.50 (978-1-58432-086-9(9)) Educa Vision.

My Other Name. 2007. (J). (978-0-9744935-7-2(0)) AllWrite Advertising & Publishing.

Onuoha-Ezemma, Glory. Don't Make Fun of My Name: My Name Is Special to My Parents & Me. unabr. ed. 2003. (Illus.). 47p. (J). (gr. k-6). pap. 9.95 (978-0-9661598-6-8(1)) Ekwike Bks. & Publishing.

Onyefulu, Ifeoma. Your Name Is Dede: An African Baby's Naming Ceremony. 2003. (Illus.). 32p. (J). 14.95 (978-0-7112-1938-0(9)) Lincoln, Frances Ltd. GBR. *Dist:* Transition Vendor.

Scheunemann, Pam. Names. l.t. ed. 2001. (Capital Letters Ser.). (Illus.). 24p. (J). (ps-3). lib. bdg. 19.93 (978-1-57765-608-1(3) , SandCastle) ABDO Publishing Co.

Schultz, Sam. Ivan to Make You Laugh: Jokes about Novel, Nifty, & Notorious Names. Gable, Brian, illus. 2005. (Make Me Laugh! Ser.). 32p. (J). (gr. k-3). lib. bdg. 19.93 (978-1-57505-659-3(3)) Lerner Publishing Group.

Taylor, Michael W. Tar Heels: How North Carolinians Got Their Nickname. 2004. (Popular Paperbacks Ser.). (Illus.). 27p. (gr. 8-12). pap. 6.00 (978-0-86526-288-1(8) , 03100) North Carolina Office of Archives & History.

Wood, Vanessa, ed. Antique Names: Tried & True & Truly Rare Historical Names. 2003. 92p. per. 11.00 (978-0-9744281-1-6(6)) Bisham Hill Bks.

NAMES, PERSONAL—FICTION

Alderton, Sylvia. A Real Name for Puppy. McCartney, Michael David, illus. 2006. (J). (978-1-930566-58-3(1) , WestWind Pr.) Scott, D.&F. Publishing, Inc.

Anderson, Robert Gordon, Seven O'Clock Stories. l.t. ed. 2006. 122p. pap. 13.99 (978-1-4264-2903-3(7)) BiblioBazaar.

Angelou, Maya. Cedric of Jamaica. Rockwell, Lizzy, illus. 2005. (Random House Pictureback Book Ser.). (J). (978-0-375-83269-7(6)); lib. bdg. (978-0-375-93269-4(0)) Random Hse., Inc.

Answer Why for Mee Mee: Work & Play Book. 2006. (J). (978-0-9748715-3-0(2)) Vision Harmony Publishing.

Benton, Jim. The Fran That Time Forgot. Benton, Jim, illus. 2005. (Franny K. Stein, Mad Scientist Ser.: Bk. 4). (Illus.). 112p. (J). mass mkt. 3.99 (978-0-689-86298-4(9) , Aladdin); 14.95 (978-0-689-86294-6(6) , Simon & Schuster Children's Publishing) Simon & Schuster Children's Publishing.

Blasi, Kathleen McAlpin. A Name of Honor. Bowman, Leslie W., illus. 2006. (J). (978-1-59336-692-6(2)) Mondo Publishing.

Brimmer, Debi & Coleson, Julie. How Six Little Ipu Got Their Names. 2005. (Illus.). 32p. (J). 16.95 incl. audio compact disk (978-1-57306-186-5(7)) Bess Pr., Inc.

Catalanotto, Peter. Matthew A. B. C. Catalanotto, Peter, illus. 2002. (Illus.). 32p. (J). (ps-2). 15.95 (978-0-689-84582-6(0) , Atheneum/Richard Jackson Bks.) Simon & Schuster Children's Publishing.

Choi, Yangsook. The Name Jar. Choi, Yangsook, illus. (Illus.). 40p. (J). (gr. k-3). 2003. pap. 6.99 (978-0-440-41799-6(6) , Dragonfly Bks.); 2001. 16.95 (978-0-375-80613-1(X) , Knopf Bks. for Young Readers) Random Hse. Children's Bks.

Colato Lainez, Rene. I Am Rene, the Boy. Graullera Ramirez, Fabiola, illus. Tr. of Yo Soy Rene, el Nino. (ENG & SPA.). 32p. (J). (ps-2). 15.95 (978-1-55885-378-2(2) , Piñata Books) Arte Publico Pr.

Cummings, Mary. Three Names of Me. Wang, Lin, illus. 2006. (J). 15.95 (978-0-8075-7903-9(3)) Whitman, Albert & Co.

Driscoll, Laura. Name That Ed. 2002. (gr. k-3). lib. bdg. 11.80 (978-0-613-45297-7(6)) Tandem Library Bks.

Flood, Pansie Hart. Tiger's Trouble with Donut Head. Wummer, Amy, illus. 2005. 71p. (J). lib. bdg. 19.93 (978-1-57505-814-6(6) , Carolrhoda Bks.) Lerner Publishing Group.

Foreman, George & Manushkin, Fran. Let George Do It! Martin, Whitney, illus. 2005. 32p. (J). 15.95 (978-0-689-87807-7(9) , Simon & Schuster Children's Publishing) Simon & Schuster Children's Publishing.

Gadot, A. S. The First Gift. Lafrance, Marie, illus. 2006. 24p. (J). 15.95 (978-1-58013-146-9(8)); pap. 6.95 (978-1-58013-149-0(2)) Kar-Ben Publishing.

Graves, Bonnie. No Copycats Allowed! 1998. (J). (978-0-606-13664-8(9)) Tandem Library Bks.

Greenspan, Shari Dash. Shemot Muzarim. Katz, Avi, illus. 2005. Tr. of Strange Names. (HEB.). 32p. 14.00 (978-965-7108-58-1(6)) Urim Pubns. ISR. *Dist:* Biblio Distribution.

Harcourt School Publishers Staff. Short for Estrallita Advanced Level. 3rd ed. 2002. (Trophies Reading Program Ser.). (Illus.). pap. 5.10 (978-0-15-323394-4(X)) Harcourt Schl. Pubs.

—This Is Who I Am. 3rd ed. 2002. (Trophies Ser.). pap. 25.60 (978-0-15-327900-3(1)) Harcourt Schl. Pubs.

Henkes, Kevin. Chrysanthemum. ed. 2004. (Illus.). (J). (gr. k-3). spiral bd. (978-0-616-14575-3(6)) Canadian National Institute for the Blind/Institut National Canadien pour les Aveugles.

Henkes, Kevin. Chrysanthemum Big Book. Henkes, Kevin, illus. 2007. 32p. (J). pap. 24.99 (***978-0-06-111974-3(1)*** , Harper Festival) HarperCollins Pubs.

Herman, Gail. Just Like Mike. 2001. (978-0-606-21277-9(9)) Tandem Library Bks.

Klass, Sheila S. The Uncivil War. 1999. (978-0-606-17477-0(X)) Tandem Library Bks.

Martin, Mary J. From Anne to Zach. Grejniec, Michael, illus. 2003. 32p. (J). (gr. k-2). 16.95 (978-1-56397-573-8(4)) Boyds Mills Pr.

Massicotte, Sylvie. Le Plus Beau Prenom du Monde. 2002. (Premier Roman Ser.). (Illus.). 64p. (J). (gr. 2-5). pap. (978-2-89021-348-7(X)) Diffusion du livre Mirabel.

Metcalf, Paula, illus. Norma No Friends. 1999. 40p. (J). (ps-3). 15.95 (978-1-902283-87-6(2)) Barefoot Bks., Inc.

Monk, Isabell. Hope. Porter, Janice Lee, illus. (Carolrhoda Picture Books Ser.). 32p. (J). (ps-3). 2004. pap. 6.95 (978-1-57505-792-7(1)); 1998. 15.95 (978-1-57505-230-4(X)) Lerner Publishing Group.

Myers, Tim & Arakaki, Daryl. Let's Call Him Lau-Wiliwili-Humuhumu-Nukunuku-Nukunuku-Apua'a-'Oi'Oi. 2005. (Illus.). 24p. (J). 16.95 incl. cd-rom (978-1-57306-252-7(9)) Bess Pr., Inc.

Nostlinger, Christine. Piruleta. Kaufman, Angelika, illus. (SPA.). 132p. (J). (gr. 3-5). pap. 9.95 (978-968-19-0983-3(6)) Santillana USA Publishing Co., Inc.

Pirotta, Saviour & Marks, Alan. Guess My Name. 2007. (J). ***978-1-59771-082-4(2))** Sea-To-Sea Pubns.

Pringle, Laurence P. Naming the Cat. Potter, Katherine, illus. 1999. 32p. (J). (gr. k-3). 15.95 (978-0-8027-8621-0(9)) Walker & Co.

Recorvits, Helen. My Name Is Yoon. Swiatkowska, Gabi, illus. 2003. 32p. (J). (gr. k-3). 16.00 (978-0-374-35114-4(7) , Farrar, Straus & Giroux (BYR)) Farrar, Straus & Giroux.

Rubin, Cathy. Eleanor, Ellatony, Ellencake, & Me. Fowler, Christopher, illus. 2003. (Eleanor Ser.). 32p. (J). (gr. k-3). 14.95 (978-1-57768-412-1(5) , Gingham Dog Pr.) School Specialty Publishing.

Sadu, Itah & Condy, Roy. Christopher Changes His Name. (Illus.). 32p. (J). pap. 4.99 (978-0-590-24624-8(0)) Scholastic, Inc.

Sharp, Rhonda Winchell. The Nine Most Famous Reindeer of All. Vandewater, Rena, illus. 2004. 40p. (J). pap. 15.99 (978-0-9748047-8-1(9)) Hickory Bark Productions.

Silverman, Manuel S. Rosie & the Mole: The Story of a Bris. 1999. (Illus.). 48p. (J). (gr. 1-4). 16.95 (978-0-943706-22-1(X) , Devora Publishing) Pitspopany Pr.

—Rosie & the Mole: The Story of a Bris. Kahn, Katherine Janus, illus. 1999. 48p. (J). (gr. 1-4). pap. 9.95 (978-0-943706-20-7(3) , Devora Publishing) Pitspopany Pr.

Waber, Bernard. A Lion Named Shirley Williamson. 2000. (Illus.). 40p. (J). (gr. k-3). pap. 6.95 (978-0-618-05580-7(0) , Walter Lorraine) Houghton Mifflin Co. Trade & Reference Div.

—A Lion Named Shirley Williamson. 2000. (Illus.). (J). (978-0-606-18212-6(8)) Tandem Library Bks.

Wishinsky, Frieda. Just Mabel. Heap, Sue, illus. (I Am Reading Ser.). (J). 2004. 48p. (gr. 1-3). pap. 3.95 (978-0-7534-5742-9(3)); 2001. 3.95 (978-0-7534-5353-7(3)) Houghton Mifflin Co. Trade & Reference Div. (Kingfisher).

Ziegler, Mark. Nutty Names: A Book of Name Jokes. Haugen, Ryan, illus. 2005. (Read-It! Readers Ser.). 24p. (J). (ps). lib. bdg. 18.60 (978-1-4048-1163-8(X)) Picture Window Bks.

NAMIBIA

Corwin, Jeff. Into Wild Namibia. Pascoe, Elaine, ed. 2003. (Jeff Corwin Experience Ser.). (Illus.). 48p. (J). 24.95 (978-1-56711-851-3(8)); 11.20 (978-1-4103-0172-7(9)) Thomson Gale. (Blackbirch Pr., Inc.).

NANTUCKET ISLAND (MASS.)

Herold, Vickey. Discover A Whaling Community: Nantucket. 2006. pap. 39.00 **(*978-1-4108-6429-1(4))** Benchmark Education Co.

Loeper, John J. Meet the Allens in Whaling Days. 1998. (Early American Family Ser.). (Illus.). 64p. (J). (gr. 3 up). lib. bdg. 25.64 (978-0-7614-0842-0(8) , Benchmark Bks.) Cavendish, Marshall Corp.

NANTUCKET ISLAND (MASS.)—FICTION

Arciero, Susan. Nantucket 1, 2, 3. Arciero, Susan, illus. l.t. ed. 2000. (Illus.). (J). (ps). 7.95 (978-0-9677548-2-6(8)) Pigtail Publishing.

Bagley, Conor. Ziggy McFinster's Nantucket Adventure. Westcott, Nadine Bernard, illus. 2008. 40p. **(*978-1-56625-315-4(2)** , Volt Pr.) Bonus Bks., Inc.

Barnes, Peter W. & Barnes, Cheryl Shaw. Nat, Nat, the Nantucket Cat Goes to the Beach. Arciero, Susan, illus. 2001. 32p. 15.95 (978-1-893622-05-0(3) , VSP Bks.) Vacation Spot Publishing.

Barnes, Peter W. & Barnes, Cheryl Shaw. Where's Nat? A Nat, Nat, the Nantucket Cat Adventure Book. Arciero, Susan, illus. 2007. 32p. (J). 17.95 **(*978-1-893622-19-7(3)** , VSP Bks.) Vacation Spot Publishing.

Bouton, Warren Hussey. The Captain's Return: A Spooky Tale from Nantucket. Locke, Barbara Kauffmann, illus. 2004. (J). per. 5.95 **(*978-0-9700555-4-5(4))** Hither Creek Pr.

Cunningham, Bradley S. Tucket Teddy's Day at Work. 7.95 (978-0-9653674-0-0(1)) Nantucket Cobblestones, Ltd.

Finley, Martha. Elsie at Nantucket. 2001. (Elsie Books: Vol. 10). 234p. (J). pap. 5.99 (978-1-931343-01-5(2)) Hibbard Pubns., Inc.

Finley, Martha. Elsie at Nantucket A Sequel to Elsies Ne. 2006. 34.99 **(*978-1-4280-2289-8(9))** IndyPublish.com.

Gamble, Adam. Good Night Nantucket. Rosen, Anne, illus. 2007. (Good Night Our World Ser.). 18p. (J). bds. 9.95 **(*978-1-60219-013-9(5))** Our World of Books.

Manley, Molly. A Nantucket Nanny. Marshall, Janet, illus. 2005. 24p. (J). 12.95 (978-1-889833-96-5(7)) Commonwealth Editions.

My Time on Nantucket. 2005. (J). cd-rom 11.95 (978-0-9755078-2-7(6)) Sweet Punkin Pr.

Rouillard, Wendy W. Barnaby-Seasons in the Park. Rouillard, Wendy W., ed. 2000. (Barnaby Ser.: Vol. 5). (Illus.). 32p. (J). 15.95 (978-0-9642836-9-5(7)) Barnaby & Co.

Snedeker, Caroline. Downright Dencey. Barney, Maginel Wright, illus. 2003. (Young Adult Library). 274p. (YA). pap. 11.95 (978-1-883937-79-9(5)) Bethlehem Bks.

Stowe, Cynthia. The Second Escape of Arthur Cooper. 2000. (Illus.). 112p. (YA). (gr. 5-9). 14.95 (978-0-7614-5069-6(6) , Cavendish Children's Bks.) Cavendish, Marshall Corp.

Trimble, Marcia. Malinda Martha & Her Skipping Stones. Grell, Susi, illus. 1999. 32p. (J). (ps-3). 15.95 (978-1-891577-72-7(7)) Images Pr.

—Serendipity Says to Know Me Is to Love Me. Grell, Susi, illus. 2000. 32p. (J). (ps-3). 15.95 (978-1-891577-77-2(8)) Images Pr.

—The Smiling Stone. Arciero, Susan, illus. 1998. 32p. (J). (ps-2). lib. bdg. 15.95 (978-1-891577-37-6(9)) Images Pr.

Turkle, Brinton. Obadiah the Bold. 2004. 36p. pap. 7.95 (978-1-893103-19-1(6)) Beautiful Feet Bks.

—Rachel & Obadiah. 2004. 30p. pap. 7.95 (978-1-893103-18-4(8)) Beautiful Feet Bks.

Watkins, Dawn L. Nantucket Cats. Bonge, Lynn E., illus. 1998. 32p. (J). (ps-1). pap. 5.49 (978-0-89084-975-0(7)) Jones, Bob Univ. Pr.

NAPOLEON I, EMPEROR OF THE FRENCH, 1769-1821

Boyd, David. Napoleon's Last Stand. Okum, David, illus. 2007. 48p. (J). lib. bdg. 23.08 **(*978-1-4242-1639-0(7))** Fitzgerald Bks.

Burleigh, Robert. Napoleon: The Story of the Little Corporal. 2007. (Illus.). 48p. (J). (gr. 4-7). 18.95 (978-0-8109-1378-3(X) , Abrams Bks. for Young Readers) Abrams, Harry N., Inc.

Crompton, Samuel Willard. Waterloo. 2002. (Battles That Changed the World Ser.). (Illus.). (J). 111p. pap. 13.25 (978-0-7910-7110-6(3)); 112p. (gr. 7-10). 30.00 (978-0-7910-6683-6(5)) Facts On File, Inc. (Chelsea Hse.).

Foa, Eugenie. The Boy Life of Napoleon: Afterwards Emperor of the French. l.t. ed. 2006. 154p. pap. 14.99 **(*978-1-4264-3615-4(7))** BiblioBazaar.

Foa, Eugenie. Boy Life of Napoleon Afterwards Emperor of the French. 2004. reprint ed. pap. 19.95 (978-1-4191-5499-7(0)); pap. 1.99 (978-1-4192-5499-4(5)) Kessinger Publishing, LLC.

Greenblatt, Miriam. Napoleon Bonaparte & Imperial France. 2005. (Rulers & Their Times Ser.). (Illus.). 96p. (J). (gr. 3-7). lib. bdg. (978-0-7614-1837-5(7) , Benchmark Bks.) Cavendish, Marshall Corp.

Henderson, Harry. The Age of Napoleon. 1998. (Illus.). 112p. (YA). (gr. 4-12). 27.45 (978-1-56006-319-3(X) , LML00902-177711, Lucent Bks.) Thomson Gale.

Landau, Elaine. The Louisiana Purchase: Would You Close the Deal? 2008. (What Would You Do? Ser.). (Illus.). 48p. (J). (gr. 3-4). lib. bdg. 23.93 **(*978-0-7660-2902-6(6)** , Enslow Elementary) Enslow Pubs., Inc.

Landau, Elaine. Napoleon Bonaparte. 2006. (Illus.). 112p. (J). 27.93 (978-0-8225-3420-4(7) , Twenty-First Century Bks.) Lerner Publishing Group.

Lethbridge, Lucy. Napoleon. 2005. (Illus.). 64p. (J). 8.95 (978-0-7945-1050-3(7) , Usborne) EDC Publishing.

Schaffer, David. The Louisiana Purchase—the Deal of the Century That Doubled the Nation. 2006. (Wild History of the American West Ser.). (Illus.). 128p. (J). lib. bdg. 33.27 (978-1-59845-018-7(2) , MyReportLinks.com Bks.) Enslow Pubs., Inc.

Schlaepfer, Gloria G. The Louisiana Purchase. 2005. (Watts Library). (Illus.). 63p. (J). (gr. 5-8). 25.50 (978-0-531-12300-3(6) , Watts, Franklin) Scholastic Library Publishing.

Streissguth, Thomas. The Napoleonic Wars: Defeat of the Grand Army. 2003. (History's Great Defeats Ser.). (Illus.). 112p. (J). 29.95 (978-1-59018-065-5(8) , Lucent Bks.) Thomson Gale.

Zurn, Jon. The Louisiana Purchase. 2007. (Essential Events Ser.). (ENG., Illus.). 112p. (YA). (gr. 8-12). lib. bdg. 32.79 **(*978-1-59928-853-6(2)** , Essential Library) ABDO Publishing Co.

NAPOLEON I, EMPEROR OF THE FRENCH, 1769-1821—FICTION

Brighton, Catherine. My Napoleon. Brighton, Catherine, illus. 2005. (Illus.). 26p. (J). (gr. k-4). reprint ed. 17.00 (978-0-7567-8931-2(1)) DIANE Publishing Co.

Marcellino, Fred. I, Crocodile. Marcellino, Fred, illus. (Illus.). (J). (ps-3). 2002. 32p. pap. 7.99 (978-0-06-008859-0(1) , Harper Trophy); 1999. 40p. 19.99 (978-0-06-205168-4(7)) HarperCollins Pubs.

Molloy, Michael. Peter Raven Under Fire. 2005. (Illus.). 512p. (J). (ps-7). pap. 17.95 (978-0-439-72454-8(6) , Chicken Hse., The) Scholastic, Inc.

Rabin, Staton. Betsy & the Emperor. 2006. (Illus.). 304p. (YA). reprint ed. mass mkt. 5.99 (978-1-4169-1336-8(X) , Simon Pulse) Simon & Schuster Children's Publishing.

NAPOLEONIC WARS, 1800-1815

Ashworth, Leon. Horatio Nelson. 2000. (British History Makers Ser.). (Illus.). 32p. (J). 22.95 (978-0-7451-5290-5(2) , Cherrytree Books) Evans Publishing Group GBR. *Dist:* Independent Pubs. Group.

Henderson, Harry. The Age of Napoleon. 1998. (Illus.). 112p. (YA). (gr. 4-12). 27.45 (978-1-56006-319-3(X) , LML00902-177711, Lucent Bks.) Thomson Gale.

Olszewski, Zbigniew. The Greatest Battle: Napoleon Against the Allies. 2001. 102p. (YA). per. 25.00 (978-0-9708198-0-2(3)) Olszewski, Zbigniew & Janis.

Streissguth, Thomas. The Napoleonic Wars: Defeat of the Grand Army. 2003. (History's Great Defeats Ser.). (Illus.). 112p. (J). 29.95 (978-1-59018-065-5(8) , Lucent Bks.) Thomson Gale.

Westwell, Ian. Revolutionary & Napoleonic Wars. 1999. (History of Warfare Ser.). (Illus.). 80p. (YA). (gr. 7-12). lib. bdg. 29.97 (978-0-8172-5446-9(3)) Raintree.

NARCOTIC HABIT

see Drug Addiction

NARCOTICS

Bankston, John. Ecstasy = Busted! 2005. (Busted! Ser.). (Illus.). 104p. (J). (gr. 6-13). lib. bdg. 31.93 (978-0-7660-2387-1(7)) Enslow Pubs., Inc.

Bingham, Jane. Heroin. 2005. (What's the Deal? Ser.). (Illus.). 56p. (J). (978-1-4034-7022-5(7)) Heinemann Library.

Charles, Robert B. Narcotics & Terrorism. 2003. (Securing the Nation Ser.). (Illus.). 112p. (J). (gr. 9-13). 30.00 (978-0-7910-7701-6(2) , Chelsea Hse.) Facts On File, Inc.

Glass, George. Narcotics: Dangerous Painkiller. rev. ed. 2005. (Drug Abuse Prevention Library). (Illus.). 64p. (YA). (gr. 7-12). lib. bdg. 25.25 (978-0-8239-3300-6(8)) Rosen Publishing Group, Inc., The.

Gleason, Carrie. The Biorgraphy of Tobacco. 2006. (How Did That Get Here? Ser.). (Illus.). 32p. (J). (gr. 5). pap. (978-0-7787-2525-1(1) , 1259497) Crabtree Publishing Co.

Greene, Meg. The Drug Enforcement Agency. 2001. (Your Government Ser.). (Illus.). 64p. (J). (gr. 4-7). 25.00 (978-0-7910-5992-0(8) , Chelsea Hse.) Facts On File, Inc.

Jaffe, Steven L., ed. Crack & Cocaine. 1999. (Junior Drug Awareness Ser.). (Illus.). 80p. (J). (gr. 4-8). 32.00 (978-0-7910-5177-1(3) , Chelsea Hse.) Facts On File, Inc.

Kerrigan, Michael. The War Against Drugs. 2002. (Crime & Detection Ser.). (Illus.). 96p. (J). (gr. 7 up). lib. bdg. (978-1-59084-368-0(1)) Mason Crest Pubs.

LeVert, Suzanne. The Facts about Cocaine. 2005. (Drugs Ser.). (Illus.). 96p. (J). (978-0-7614-1973-0(X) , Benchmark Bks.) Cavendish, Marshall Corp.

McGuigan, Jim. The Drug Trade. 2004. (Face the Facts Ser.). (Illus.). 56p. (J). 28.56 (978-1-4109-1072-1(5)) Harcourt Schl. Pubs.

Mirman, Heather Moehn. Issues in Drug Abuse. 2005. (Contemporary Issues Ser.). (Illus.). 112p. (YA). (gr. 7-10). 29.95 (978-1-59018-035-8(6) , Lucent Bks.) Thomson Gale.

Sanna, E. J. Heroin & Other Opiates: Poppies' Perilous Children. 2008. (J). **(*978-1-4222-0156-5(2))** Mason Crest Pubs.

Shepherd, Kenneth R. Drugs & Low Self-Esteem. 1999. (Drug Abuse Prevention Library). (Illus.). 64p. (YA). (gr. 7-12). lib. bdg. 25.25 (978-0-8239-2826-2(8) , DRSEES) Rosen Publishing Group, Inc., The.

Somerville, Clive. The Drug Enforcement Administration. 2002. (Rescue & Prevention Ser.). (Illus.). 96p. (J). (gr. 7 up). lib. bdg. (978-1-59084-413-7(0)) Mason Crest Pubs.

NARNIA (IMAGINARY PLACE)—FICTION

Beahm, George. Passport to Narnia: A Newcomer's Guide. 2005. (Illus.). 197p. pap. 12.95 (978-1-57174-465-4(7)) Hampton Roads Publishing Co., Inc.

—Passport to Narnia: The Unofficial Guide. Kirk, Tim, illus. 2005. (J). lib. bdg. 15.95 (978-1-57174-481-4(9)) Hampton Roads Publishing Co., Inc.

Bloom, Harold. The Chronicles of Narnia. 2006. (Bloom's Modern Critical Interpretations Ser.). 248p. (gr. 9). 45.00 (978-0-7910-9310-8(7) , Chelsea Hse.) Facts On File, Inc.

Clausen, Andrew. Prince Caspian. 2003. stu. ed., ring bd. 14.99 (978-1-58609-195-8(6)) Progeny Pr.

Flexer, Michael. Edmund's Struggle: Under the Spell of the White Witch. Baynes, Pauline, illus. 2006. (Narnia Ser.). 96p. (J). 14.99 (978-0-06-085232-0(1)) HarperCollins Pubs.

—Lucy's Adventure. 2005. 2005p. (J). lib. bdg. 15.00 **(*978-1-4242-0760-2(6))** Fitzgerald Bks.

Flexer, Michael. Lucy's Adventure: The Search for Aslan. Baynes, Pauline, illus. 2006. (Narnia Ser.). 96p. (J). 14.99 (978-0-06-085234-4(8)); pap. 3.99 (978-0-06-085233-7(X) , Harper Trophy) HarperCollins Pubs.

Frantz, Jennifer. Chronicles of Narnia: Prince Caspian. 2008. (I Can Read Bks.). 32p. (J). pap. 3.99 (978-0-06-123162-9(2) , Harper Trophy) HarperCollins Pubs.

Frantz, Jennifer, adapted by. Narnia: Tea with Mr Tumnus. 2005. (Illus.). 32p. (J). lib. bdg. 13.85 **(*978-1-4242-0616-2(2))** Fitzgerald Bks.

—Narnia: Welcome to Narnia. 2005. (Illus.). 32p. (J). lib. bdg. 13.85 **(*978-1-4242-0617-9(0))** Fitzgerald Bks.

Frantz, Jennifer & Zondervan. The Lion, the Witch & the Wardrobe: Welcome to Narnia. movie tie-in ed. 2005. (Chronicles of Narnia Ser.). (Illus.). 32p. (J). pap. 3.99 (978-0-06-076560-6(7) , Harper Trophy) HarperCollins Pubs.

Graham, Craig. Peter's Destiny. 2005. 71p. (J). lib. bdg. 15.00 **(*978-1-4242-0761-9(4))** Fitzgerald Bks.

Graham, Craig. Peter's Destiny: The Battle for Narnia. Baynes, Pauline, illus. 2006. (Narnia Ser.). 96p. (J). pap. 3.99 (978-0-06-085235-1(6) , Harper Trophy) HarperCollins Pubs.

Lewis, C. S. L' Armoire Magique. 6th ed. 1999. Orig. Title: The Lion, the Witch & the Wardrobe. (FRE.). (J). (gr. 4-7). pap. 12.95 (978-2-08-164414-4(2)) Distribooks, Inc.

—L' Armoire Magique. Orig. Title: The Lion, the Witch & the Wardrobe. (FRE.). pap. 12.95 (978-2-08-161994-4(6)) Flammarion et Cie FRA. *Dist:* Distribooks, Inc.

—Aslan's Triumph. 1999. (Illus.). (J). (978-0-606-18675-9(1)) Tandem Library Bks.

—The Chronicles of Narnia. Baynes, Pauline, illus. ed. (Narnia Ser.). (J). 2004. 784p. 32.99 (978-0-06-059824-2(7)); 2005. 768p. pap. 21.99 (978-0-06-076545-3(3)); Set. 2000. (gr. 3 up). pap., pap. 59.99 (978-0-06-440939-1(2)) HarperCollins Pubs.

—The Chronicles of Narnia, Set. movie tie-in ed. 2005. (Chronicles of Narnia Ser.). (Illus.). (J). pap., pap. 70.00 (978-0-06-082042-8(X)) HarperCollins Pubs.

—The Chronicles of Narnia. Baynes, Pauline, illus. (Narnia Ser.). (J). 2001. 768p. pap. 21.99 (978-0-06-623850-0(1)); Set. 2005. (gr. 3-7). pap., pap. 45.00 (978-0-06-076550-7(X)) Zonderkidz.

—The Chronicles of Narnia: Based on the Books by C. S. Lewis. Sabuda, Robert & Armstrong, Matthew, illus. 2007. (Narnia Ser.). 14p. (J). (ps-3). 29.99 **(*978-0-06-117612-8(5))** HarperCollins Pubs.

—Chronicles of Narnia: The Lion, the Witch & the Wardrobe Chapter Book. 2006. (Narnia Ser.). 384p. (J). pap. 14.99 (978-0-06-117453-7(X)) HarperCollins Pubs.

—The Chronicles of Narnia Book & Audio Box Set. Baynes, Pauline, illus. 2008. (Narnia Ser.). 768p. (J). pap. 99.99 **(*978-0-06-076552-1(6))** HarperCollins Pubs.

—The Chronicles of Narnia Box Set: The Magician's Nephew; The Lion, the Witch & the Wardrobe; The Hourse & His Boy; Prince Caspian; The Voyage of the Dawn Treader; The Silver Chair; The Last Battle, Books 1-7. Baynes, Pauline, illus. 2005. (Chronicles of Narnia Ser.: Bks. 1-7). (gr. 3 up). pap. 45.00 (978-0-06-447119-0(5)) Zonderkidz.

—The Complete Chronicles of Narnia. Baynes, Pauline, illus. deluxe ed. 1998. (Chronicles of Narnia Ser.). 528p. (J). (gr. 3 up). 50.00 (978-0-06-028137-3(5)) HarperCollins Pubs.

—Las Cronicas de Narnia. 2006. (SPA.). 816p. pap. 19.99 (978-0-06-119900-4(1) , Rayo) HarperCollins Pubs.

—The Horse & His Boy. Baynes, Pauline, illus. 240p. 2006. (Narnia Ser.). (J). 11.99 (978-0-06-112524-9(5)); 2000. (Chronicles of Narnia Ser.: Bk. 5). (YA). (gr. 3 up). pap. 8.99 (978-0-06-440940-7(6) , Harper Trophy) HarperCollins Pubs.

—The Horse & His Boy. 2000. (Chronicles of Narnia Ser.: Bk.5). (J). (gr. 4-8). (978-0-606-19976-6(4)) Tandem Library Bks.

—The Horse & His Boy. Baynes, Pauline, illus. l.t. ed. 2000. (Chronicles of Narnia Ser.: Bk. 5). 253p. (J). (gr. 4-8). 21.95 (978-0-7862-2233-9(6)) Thorndike Pr.

—The Last Battle. Baynes, Pauline, illus. 224p. 2006. (Narnia Ser.). (J). 11.99 (978-0-06-112529-4(6)); 2000. (Chronicles of Narnia Ser.: Bk. 7). (YA). (gr. 3 up). pap. 8.99 (978-0-06-440941-4(4) , Harper Trophy) HarperCollins Pubs.

—The Last Battle. 2000. (Chronicles of Narnia Ser.: Bk.7). (J). (gr. 4-8). (978-0-606-19980-3(2)) Tandem Library Bks.

—El Leon, la Bruja y el Ropera. 2002. (SPA.). (gr. 5-8). lib. bdg. 16.45 (978-0-613-62176-2(X)); 2000. (978-0-606-22688-2(5)) Tandem Library Bks.

—El Leon, la Bruja y el Ropero. 2005. (ESP & SPA.). 208p. pap. 9.95 (978-0-06-084253-6(9) , Rayo) HarperCollins Pubs.

—The Lion, the Witch & the Wardrobe. Humphries, Tudor, illus. 2004. (Narnia Ser.). 48p. (J). (ps-2). lib. bdg. 17.89 (978-0-06-055651-8(X)) HarperCollins Pubs.

—The Lion, the Witch & the Wardrobe. Baynes, Pauline, illus. 2003. (Narnia Ser.). 208p. (J). (gr. 3 up). 29.99 (978-0-06-055649-5(8)) HarperCollins Pubs.

—The Lion, the Witch & the Wardrobe. 2000. (Chronicles of Narnia Ser.: Bk.1). (J). (gr. 4-8). pap., tchr. ed. (978-0-06-447260-9(4) , Harper Trophy) HarperCollins Pubs.

—The Lion, the Witch & the Wardrobe. Baynes, Pauline, illus. 2000. (Chronicles of Narnia Ser.: Bk.1). 208p. (J). (gr. 3 up). pap. 8.99 (978-0-06-440942-1(2) , Harper Trophy) HarperCollins Pubs.

—The Lion, the Witch & the Wardrobe. 1999. (Chronicles of Narnia Ser.: Bk. 1). (J). (gr. 4-8). 11.95 (978-1-56137-704-6(X)); 40p. 9.95 (978-1-56137-243-0(9)) Novel Units, Inc.

—The Lion, the Witch & the Wardrobe. 2000. (Chronicles of Narnia Ser.: Bk.1). (J). (gr. 4-8). (978-0-606-19981-0(0)) Tandem Library Bks.

—The Lion, the Witch & the Wardrobe. 1999. (Chronicles of Narnia Ser.: Bk.1). (gr. 4-8). pap. 10.95 (978-1-84002-049-6(0)) Theatre Communications Group, Inc.

—The Lion, the Witch & the Wardrobe. Baynes, Pauline, illus. l.t. ed. 2000. (Chronicles of Narnia Ser.: Bk.1). 208p. (J). (gr. 4-8). 21.95 (978-0-7862-2232-2(8)) Thorndike Pr.

—The Lion, the Witch & the Wardrobe. Baynes, Pauline, illus. gif. ed. 2003. (Narnia Ser.). 112p. (J). (gr. 3 up). 19.99 (978-0-06-053083-9(9)) Zonderkidz.

—The Lion, the Witch & the Wardrobe: El leon, la bruja y el Ropero. Baynes, Pauline, illus. 2002. (Narnia Ser.). (SPA.). 208p. (J). (gr. 3 up). pap. 9.95 (978-0-06-008661-9(0)) Zonderkidz.

—The Magician's Nephew. Baynes, Pauline, illus. (J). 2006. (Narnia Ser.). 208p. 11.99 (978-0-06-112526-3(1)); 2000. (Chronicles of Narnia Ser.: Bk.6). 208p. (gr. 3 up). pap. 8.99 (978-0-06-440943-8(0) , Harper Trophy); 2004. (Narnia Ser.). 208p. (gr. 3 up). pap., pap. 29.99 incl. audio compact disk (978-0-06-059501-2(9)); 2003. (Narnia Ser.). 112p. (gr. 3 up). 19.99 (978-0-06-053084-6(7)) HarperCollins Pubs.

—The Magician's Nephew. l.t. ed. 2000. (Chronicles of Narnia Ser.: Bk.6). 224p. (J). (gr. 4-8). 21.95 (978-0-7862-2231-5(X)) Thorndike Pr.

—The Magician's Nephew Read-Aloud Edition. Baynes, Pauline, illus. 2006. (Narnia Ser.). 208p. (J). 15.99 (978-0-06-087588-6(7)) HarperCollins Pubs.

—Prince Caspian. Armstrong, Matthew S., illus. 2007. (Narnia Ser.). 32p. (J). lib. bdg. 17.89 **(*978-0-06-117328-8(2))** HarperCollins Pubs.

—Prince Caspian. Baynes, Pauline, illus. 2000. (Chronicles of Narnia Ser.: Bk.2). 240p. (YA). (gr. 3 up). pap. 8.99 (978-0-06-440944-5(9) , Harper Trophy) HarperCollins Pubs.

MNO

—Prince Caspian. 2000. (Chronicles of Narnia Ser.: Bk.2). (J). (gr. 4-8). (978-0-606-19995-7(0)) Tandem Library Bks.

—Prince Caspian. Baynes, Pauline, illus. l.t. ed. 2000. (Chronicles of Narnia Ser.: Bk. 2). 262p. (J). (gr. 4-8). 21.95 (978-0-7862-2234-6(4)) Thorndike Pr.

—Prince Caspian. 1998. (Chronicles of Narnia Ser.: Bk. 2). (J). (gr. 4-8). lib. bdg. 18.95 (978-1-56723-072-7(5)) Yestermorrow, Inc.

—Prince Caspian (paper-over-board) The Return to Narnia. Baynes, Pauline, illus. 2006. (Narnia Ser.). 240p. (J). 11.99 (978-0-06-112525-6(3)) HarperCollins Pubs.

—Prince Caspian Read-Aloud Edition: The Return to Narnia. Baynes, Pauline, illus. 2008. (Narnia Ser.). 240p. (J). 17.99 (***978-0-06-122764-6(1)***) HarperCollins Pubs.

—The Silver Chair. Baynes, Pauline, illus. 256p. 2006. (Narnia Ser.). (J). 11.99 (978-0-06-112528-7(8)); 2000. (Chronicles of Narnia Ser.: Bk.6). (YA). (gr. 3 up). pap. 8.99 (978-0-06-440945-2(7) , Harper Trophy) HarperCollins Pubs.

—The Silver Chair. 2000. (Chronicles of Narnia Ser.: Bk.4). (J). (gr. 4-8). (978-0-606-19997-1(7)) Tandem Library Bks.

—El Sobrino del Mago. 2003. (SPA.). pap. (978-956-13-1674-4(9) , AB4755) Bello, Andres CHL. *Dist:* Lectorum Pubns., Inc.

—El Sobrino del Mago. 2001. (978-0-606-22692-9(3)) Tandem Library Bks.

—La Ultima Batalla. 2003. (SPA.). pap. (978-956-13-1675-1(7) , AB3856) Bello, Andres CHL. *Dist:* Lectorum Pubns., Inc.

—La Ultima Batalla. 2001. (978-0-606-22702-5(4)) Tandem Library Bks.

—The Voyage of the Dawn Treader. Baynes, Pauline, illus. 256p. 2006. (Narnia Ser.). (J). 11.99 (978-0-06-112527-0(X)); 2000. (Chronicles of Narnia Ser.: Bk.3). (YA). (gr. 3 up). pap. 8.99 (978-0-06-440946-9(5) , Harper Trophy) HarperCollins Pubs.

—The Voyage of the Dawn Treader. 2000. (Chronicles of Narnia Ser.: Bk.3). (J). (gr. 4-8). (978-0-606-20005-9(3)) Tandem Library Bks.

—The Wood Between the Worlds. 2000. (978-0-606-18732-9(4)) Tandem Library Bks.

Lewis, C. S. & Orem, Hiawyn. The Lion, the Witch & the Wardrobe. Humphries, Tudor, illus. 2004. (Narnia Ser.). 48p. (J). (ps-2). 16.99 (978-0-06-055650-1(1)) HarperCollins Pubs.

Lewis, C. S., et al. The Lion, the Witch & the Wardrobe. 2000. (Chronicles of Narnia Ser.: Bk.1). (Illus.). (J). (gr. 4-8). lib. bdg. 14.89 (978-0-06-029013-9(7)) HarperCollins Pubs.

Papademetriou, Lisa & Jones, Jasmine. The Lion, the Witch & the Wardrobe: The Quest for Aslan. movie tie-in ed. 2005. (Chronicles of Narnia Ser.). (Illus.). 64p. (J). pap. 4.99 (978-0-06-076554-5(2)) HarperCollins Pubs.

Peacock, Ann & Lewis, C. S. The Chronicles of Narnia. Barbera, Tony et al, illus. Barbera, Tony et al, photos by. 2005. (Narnia Ser.). 64p. (J). (***978-1-4156-3678-7(8)***) HarperCollins Pubs.

—Welcome to Narnia. 2005. (Illus.). 32p. (J). (***978-1-4156-2261-2(2)***) HarperCollins Pubs.

Sage, Alison. Susan's Journey. 2005. 82p. (J). lib. bdg. 15.00 (***978-1-4242-0762-6(2)***) Fitzgerald Bks.

Sage, Alison. Susan's Journey: Step Through the Wardrobe. Baynes, Pauline, illus. 2006. (Narnia Ser.). 96p. (J). 14.99 (978-0-06-085238-2(0)); pap. 3.99 (978-0-06-085237-5(2) , Harper Trophy) HarperCollins Pubs.

Tbd. Prince Caspian: Chapter Book. 2006. (Narnia Ser.: No. 4). 96p. (J). pap. 3.99 (978-0-06-124065-2(6) , Harper Entertainment) HarperCollins Pubs.

—Prince Caspian Chapter Book #1. 2008. (Narnia Ser.). 96p. (J). pap. 3.99 (***978-0-06-147260-2(3)*** , Harper Trophy) HarperCollins Pubs.

—Prince Caspian Chapter Book #2. 2008. (Narnia Ser.). 96p. (J). pap. 3.99 (***978-0-06-147261-9(1)*** , Harper Trophy) HarperCollins Pubs.

—Prince Caspian Chapter Book #3. 2008. (Narnia Ser.). 96p. (J). pap. 3.99 (***978-0-06-147262-6(X)*** , Harper Trophy) HarperCollins Pubs.

—Prince Caspian Chapter Book #4. 2008. (Narnia Ser.). 96p. (J). pap. 3.99 (***978-0-06-147263-3(8)*** , Harper Trophy) HarperCollins Pubs.

La Travesia del "Explorador del Amanecer"Tr. of Voyage of the Dawn Treader. (SPA.). pap. (978-956-13-1671-3(4)) Bello, Andres CHL. *Dist:* Lectorum Pubns., Inc.

Wilson, Douglas, reader. What I Learned in Narnia. 2004. cd-rom 35.00 (***978-1-59128-438-3(4)***) Canon Pr.

NASCIMENTO, EDSON ARANTES DO, 1940-

see Pele, 1940-

NAST, THOMAS, 1840-1902

Pflueger, Lynda. Thomas Nast: Political Cartoonist. 2000. (Historical American Biographies Ser.). (Illus.). 128p. (J). (gr. 6-12). lib. bdg. 26.60 (978-0-7660-1251-6(4)) Enslow Pubs., Inc.

NATE THE GREAT (FICTITIOUS CHARACTER)—FICTION

Bolte, Mary. Nate the Great: A Classroom Guide. 1998. (Literature Unit Ser.). (Illus.). 48p. (gr. k-3). pap., tchr. ed. 7.99 (978-1-57690-346-9(X) , TCA2346) Teacher Created Materials, Inc.

Sharmat, Marjorie Weinman. Nate the Great. Simont, Marc, illus. (Nate the Great Ser.). 48p. (J). (gr. 1-4). pap. 4.50 (978-0-8072-1351-3(9) , Listening Library) Random Hse. Audio Publishing Group.

—Nate the Great. Simont, Marc, illus. anniv. ed. 2002. 64p. (gr. 1-4). 13.95 (978-0-385-73017-4(9) , Delacorte Bks. for Young Readers) Random Hse. Children's Bks.

—Nate the Great & Me: The Case of the Fleeing Fang. Simont, Marc, illus. 2000. (Nate the Great Ser.). 64p. (J). (gr. 1-4). pap. 4.50 (978-0-440-41381-3(8) , Yearling) Random Hse. Children's Bks.

—Nate the Great & Me: The Case of the Fleeing Fang. 2000. (gr. 3-6). lib. bdg. 12.40 (978-0-613-28583-4(2)) Tandem Library Bks.

—Nate the Great & the Big Sniff. Weston, Martha, illus. 2003. (Nate the Great Ser.). 48p. (gr. 1-4). pap. 4.50 (978-0-440-41502-2(0) , Yearling) Random Hse. Children's Bks.

—Nate the Great & the Big Sniff. 2003. (gr. k-3). lib. bdg. 12.40 (978-0-613-63966-8(9)) Tandem Library Bks.

—Nate the Great & the Halloween Hunt. Simont, Marc, illus. (Nate the Great Ser.). 48p. (J). (gr. 1-4). pap. 4.50 (978-0-8072-1283-7(0) , Listening Library) Random Hse. Audio Publishing Group.

—Nate the Great & the Missing Key. Simont, Marc, illus. (Nate the Great Ser.). 48p. (J). (gr. 1-4). pap. 4.50 (978-0-8072-1335-3(7) , Listening Library) Random Hse. Audio Publishing Group.

—Nate the Great & the Monster Mess. Weston, Martha, illus. (Nate the Great Ser.). (J). (gr. 1-4). 2001. 80p. (J). pap. 4.50 (978-0-440-41662-3(0) , Yearling); 1999. 48p. 14.95 (978-0-385-32114-3(7) , Delacorte Bks. for Young Readers) Random Hse. Children's Bks.

—Nate the Great & the Monster Mess. 2001. (978-0-606-22399-7(1)); (gr. 3-6). lib. bdg. 12.40 (978-0-613-36847-6(9)) Tandem Library Bks.

—Nate the Great & the Phony Clue. 1999. (Nate the Great Ser.). (Illus.). (J). (gr. 3-6). lib. bdg. 12.40 (978-0-8085-3753-3(9)) Tandem Library Bks.

—Nate the Great & the Sticky Case. Simont, Marc, illus. 1999. (Nate the Great Ser.). (J). (gr. 1-4). 9.95 (978-1-56137-263-8(3)) Novel Units, Inc.

—Nate the Great & the Sticky Case. 1999. (Nate the Great Ser.). (Illus.). (J). (gr. 3-6). lib. bdg. 12.40 (978-0-8085-3755-7(5)) Tandem Library Bks.

—Nate the Great Goes Undercover. Simont, Marc, illus. (Nate the Great Ser.). 48p. (J). (gr. 1-4). pap. 4.50 (978-0-8072-1284-4(9)); 2004. pap. 17.00 incl. audio (978-0-8072-0201-2(0) , FTR172SP) Random Hse. Audio Publishing Group. (Listening Library).

—Nate the Great, San Francisco Detective. 2000. (gr. 3-6). lib. bdg. 12.40 (978-0-613-50478-2(X)) Tandem Library Bks.

—Nate the Great Saves the King of Sweden. Simont, Marc, illus. 1999. (Nate the Great Ser.). 80p. (J). (gr. 1-4). 4.50 (978-0-440-41302-8(8) , Yearling) Random Hse. Children's Bks.

—Nate the Great Saves the King of Sweden. 1999. (Nate the Great Ser.). (J). (gr. 1-4). (978-0-606-16583-9(5)); (gr. 3-6). lib. bdg. 12.40 (978-0-613-18269-0(3)) Tandem Library Bks.

Sharmat, Marjorie Weinman & Sharmat, Marjorie Weinman. The Case of the Fleeing Fang. Simont, Marc, illus. 2000. 63p. (J). (ps-7). lib. bdg. 11.30 (978-0-606-17894-5(5)) Tandem Library Bks.

Sharmat, Marjorie Weinman & Sharmat, Mitchell. Nate the Great, San Francisco Detective. Weston, Martha, illus. 2002. (Nate the Great Ser.). 80p. (J). (gr. 1-4). pap. 4.50 (978-0-440-41821-4(6) , Yearling) Random Hse. Children's Bks.

Sharmat, Marjorie Weinman, et al. Nate the Great & the Big Sniff. Weston, Martha, illus. 2001. (Nate the Great Ser.). 48p. (J). (gr. 1-4). 13.95 (978-0-385-32604-9(1) , Delacorte Bks. for Young Readers) Random Hse. Children's Bks.

—Nate the Great, San Francisco Detective. Bui, Francoise, ed. Weston, Martha, illus. 2000. (Nate the Great Ser.). 48p. (gr. 1-4). lib. bdg. 15.99 (978-0-385-90000-3(7) , Delacorte Bks. for Young Readers) Random Hse. Children's Bks.

NATION OF ISLAM (MOVEMENT)

see Black Muslims

NATIONAL ANTHEMS

see National Songs

NATIONAL BASEBALL HALL OF FAME AND MUSEUM

Baseball Hall of Famers of the Negro Leagues, 6 bks. Incl. Buck Leonard. Payment, Simone. lib. bdg. 29.25 (978-0-8239-3473-7(X)); Cool Papa Bell. McCormack, Shaun. lib. bdg. 29.25 (978-0-8239-3474-4(8)); Josh Gibson. Twemlow, Nick. lib. bdg. 29.25 (978-0-8239-3475-1(6)); Judy Johnson. Billus, Kathleen. lib. bdg. 29.25 (978-0-8239-3476-8(4)); Monte Irvin. Haegele, Katie. lib. bdg. 29.25 (978-0-8239-3477-5(2)); Satchel Paige. Schmidt, Julie. lib. bdg. 29.25 (978-0-8239-3478-2(0)); 112p. (YA). (gr. 5-8). (Illus.). 2002. Set lib. bdg. 175.50 (978-0-8239-9686-5(7) , Rosen Central) Rosen Publishing Group, Inc., The.

Kellogg, David. True Stories of Baseball's Hall of Famers. 2000. (Illus.). 144p. (J). 8.95 (978-0-912517-41-4(7)) Bluewood Bks.

—True Stories of Baseball's Hall of Famers. 2000. (gr. 7-12). lib. bdg. 17.60 (978-0-613-90829-0(5)) Tandem Library Bks.

Nicholson, Lois. From Maryland to Cooperstown: Seven Maryland Natives in Baseball's Hall of Fame. 1998. (Illus.). 144p. (J). (gr. 4-8). 19.95 (978-0-87033-494-8(8) , Tidewater Pubs.) Cornell Maritime Pr., Inc.

NATIONAL BASKETBALL ASSOCIATION

Brock, Ted. The Pacific Division. 2006. (Above the Rim Ser.). (Illus.). 48p. (J). (gr. 1-5). 28.50 (978-1-59296-528-1(8)) Child's World, Inc.

Count to 100 with the NBA. 2001. (NBA Ser.). 32p. pap. 3.50 (978-0-439-34308-4(9)) Scholastic, Inc.

De Medeiros, Michael. NBA Finals. 2007. (J). (***978-1-59036-691-2(3)); (*978-1-59036-692-9(1)***) Weigl Pubs., Inc.

Gigliotti, Jim. The Atlantic Division. 2006. (Above the Rim Ser.). (Illus.). 48p. (J). (gr. 1-5). 28.50 (978-1-59296-525-0(3)) Child's World, Inc.

Gigliotti, Jim & Schnakenberg, Robert. The Southeast Division. 2006. (Above the Rim Ser.). (Illus.). 48p. (J). (gr. 1-5). 28.50 (978-1-59296-558-8(X)) Child's World, Inc.

Hareas, John. Lebron James. 2005. (NBA Reader Ser.). (Illus.). 32p. (J). pap. 3.99 (978-0-439-70397-0(2)) Scholastic, Inc.

—NBA Slam. 2000. (NBA Ser.). (Illus.). 32p. (J). (gr. 2-5). pap. 5.99 (978-0-439-14070-6(6)) Scholastic, Inc.

—NBA Slam. 2000. (978-0-606-18586-8(0)) Tandem Library Bks.

Hareas, John. NBA Slam Dunk 3-D. 2006. (J). pap. (***978-0-439-78814-4(5)***) Scholastic, Inc.

Ingram, Scott. A Basketball All-Star. (Making of a Champion Ser.). 48p. (J). 2005. pap. 8.50 (978-1-4034-5547-5(3)); 2004. lib. bdg. 29.93 (978-1-4034-5363-1(2)) Heinemann Library.

Layden, Joe. NBA Hot Shots. 1999. (Illus.). 24p. (ps-2). pap. 3.50 (978-0-590-06056-1(2)) Scholastic, Inc.

Schnakenberg, Robert E. The Central Division. 2006. (Above the Rim Ser.). 48p. (J). (gr. 1-5). 28.50 (978-1-59296-526-7(1)) Child's World, Inc.

Scholastic, Inc. Staff. NBA Play Book. 2000. (J). (978-0-606-19932-2(2)); (Illus.). (978-0-606-20391-3(5)) Tandem Library Bks.

Smallwood, John. Superstars. 2005. 32p. (J). pap. 5.99 (978-0-439-70400-7(6)) Scholastic, Inc.

Torres, John Albert. Top 10 NBA Finals Most Valuable Players. 2000. (Sports Top 10 Ser.). (Illus.). 48p. (YA). (gr. 4-10). lib. bdg. 23.93 (978-0-7660-1276-9(X)) Enslow Pubs., Inc.

Walters, John & Brock, Ted. The Northwest Division. 2006. (Above the Rim Ser.). (Illus.). 48p. (J). (gr. 1-5). 28.50 (978-1-59296-527-4(X)) Child's World, Inc.

Walters, John & Schnakenberg, Robert. The Southwest Division. 2006. (Above the Rim Ser.). (Illus.). 48p. (J). (gr. 1-5). 28.50 (978-1-59296-559-5(8)) Child's World, Inc.

Weber, Bruce. Greatest Moments of the NBA. 2000. (NBA Ser.). (Illus.). 32p. (J). (gr. 2-5). pap. 5.99 (978-0-439-14072-0(2)) Scholastic, Inc.

—Greatest Moments of the NBA. 2000. (Illus.). (J). (978-0-606-18553-0(4)) Tandem Library Bks.

—NBA Megastars 99. 1999. (Illus.). 32p. (J). (gr. 2-5). pap. 7.99 (978-0-590-05468-3(6)) Scholastic, Inc.

Xiao, Chunfei. Yao Ming: The Road to the NBA. 2004. 254p. 18.95 (978-1-59265-002-6(3) , YAMIRO) Long River Pr.

NATIONAL DANCES

see Folk Dancing

NATIONAL FOOTBALL LEAGUE

Buckley, James, Jr. NFL's Greatest Upsets. 2000. (Eyewitness Readers Ser.). (J). (978-0-606-20124-7(6)) Tandem Library Bks.

Buckley Jr., James. Aikman, Troy to Guard, Vol. 1. 2007. (Child's World' Encyclopedia of the NFL Ser.). 112p. (J). (gr. 2-6). 67.50 (***978-1-59296-922-7(4)***) Child's World, Inc.

—Hail Mary Pass to Numbers, Uniform, Vol. 2. 2007. (Child's World' Encyclopedia of the NFL Ser.). 112p. (J). (gr. 2-6). 67.50 (***978-1-59296-923-4(2)***) Child's World, Inc.

—Oakland Raiders to Super Bowl XII, Vol. 3. 2007. (Child's World' Encyclopedia of the NFL Ser.). 112p. (J). (gr. 2-6). 67.50 (***978-1-59296-924-1(0)***) Child's World, Inc.

—Super Bowl XIII to Zone Blitz, Vol. 4. 2007. (Child's World' Encyclopedia of the NFL Ser.). 112p. (J). (gr. 2-6). 67.50 (***978-1-59296-925-8(9)***) Child's World, Inc.

Knapp, Ron. Top 10 NFL Super Bowl Most Valuable Players. 2000. (Sports Top 10 Ser.). (Illus.). 48p. (YA). (gr. 4-10). lib. bdg. 23.93 (978-0-7660-1273-8(5)) Enslow Pubs., Inc.

Layden, Joseph. Rising Stars, NFL. 2005. (Illus.). 32p. (J). pap. (***978-0-439-80247-5(4)***) Scholastic, Inc.

Patrick, James. Football Madness: The Road to Super Bowl XXXVII. 2003. (Illus.). 24p. (J). (978-0-439-48650-7(5)) Scholastic, Inc.

Preller, James & Layden, Joe. Behind the Scenes. 2003. (NFL Ser.). (Illus.). 32p. (J). pap. 5.99 (978-0-439-53814-5(9)) Scholastic, Inc.

NATIONAL GUARD (UNITED STATES)

see United States—National Guard

NATIONAL HOLIDAYS

see Holidays

NATIONAL HYMNS

see National Songs

NATIONAL MONUMENTS

see Monuments; National Parks and Reserves; Natural Monuments

NATIONAL PARKS AND RESERVES

see also Natural Monuments

also names of national parks, e.g. Yellowstone National park

Adams, Colleen. Exploring the Grand Canyon. 2002. (Reading Room Collection). (Illus.). 24p. (J). pap. (978-0-8239-8163-2(0)); lib. bdg. 18.75 (978-0-8239-3726-4(7)) Rosen Publishing Group, Inc., The.

Ashabranner, Brent. Badge of Valor: The National Law Enforcement Officers Memorial. Ashabranner, Jennifer, illus. 2000. (Great American Memorials Ser.). 64p. (gr. 4-8). lib. bdg. (978-0-7613-1522-3(5) , Twenty-First Century Bks.) Lerner Publishing Group.

Baird, Biff & Rosen, Judy. B Is for Bryce Canyon. Purcell, Loren, illus. 2001. (Story Behind the Scenery Ser.). (J). (978-0-88714-218-5(4)) KC Pubns.

Burnham, Brad. Mammoth Cave: The World's Longest Cave System. 2003. (Famous Caves of the World Ser.). (Illus.). 24p. (J). lib. bdg. 18.75 (978-0-8239-6258-7(X) , PowerKids Pr.) Rosen Publishing Group, Inc., The.

Domeniconi, David. M Is for Majestic: A National Parks Alphabet. Carroll, Pam, illus. 2003. 40p. (J). 17.95 (978-1-58536-138-0(0)) Sleeping Bear Pr.

Domeniconi, David. A National Parks Alphabet. 2007. 40p. pap. 7.95 (***978-1-58536-333-9(2)***) Sleeping Bear Pr.

Dubois, Muriel L. The Vietnam Veterans Memorial. 2002. (National Landmarks Ser.). (Illus.). 24p. (J). (gr. 2-3). lib. bdg. 18.60 (978-0-7368-1116-3(8) , Bridgestone Bks.) Capstone Pr., Inc.

Establishment of Mount McKinley Park. (Shorey Historical Ser.). (Illus.). 32p. (J). reprint ed. pap. 10.00 (978-0-8466-0015-2(3) , S15) Shorey's Bookstore.

Fazio, Wende. Acadia National Park. (True Bks.). (Illus.). 48p. (J). (gr. 3-5). 1999. pap. 6.95 (978-0-516-26425-7(7)); 1998. 25.00 (978-0-516-20659-2(1)) Scholastic Library Publishing. (Children's Pr.).

—Everglades National Park. 1998. (True Bks.). (Illus.). 48p. (J). (gr. 3-5). 25.00 (978-0-516-20667-7(2) , Children's Pr.) Scholastic Library Publishing.

Graf, Mike. Grand Canyon National Park. 2002. (National Parks Ser.). (Illus.). 24p. (J). (gr. 2-3). lib. bdg. 18.60 (978-0-7368-1375-4(6) , Bridgestone Bks.) Capstone Pr., Inc.

—Great Smoky Mountains National Park. 2002. (National Parks Ser.). (Illus.). 24p. (J). (gr. 2-3). lib. bdg. 18.60 (978-0-7368-1376-1(4) , Bridgestone Bks.) Capstone Pr., Inc.

—Mammoth Cave National Park. 2003. (National Parks Ser.). (Illus.). 24p. (J). lib. bdg. 19.93 (978-0-7368-2221-3(6) , Bridgestone Bks.) Capstone Pr., Inc.

—National Parks, 6 bks. Incl. Grand Canyon National Park. lib. bdg. 18.60 (978-0-7368-1375-4(6)); Great Smoky Mountains National Park. lib. bdg. 18.60 (978-0-7368-1376-1(4)); Olympic National Park. lib. bdg. 18.60 (978-0-7368-1377-8(2)); Rocky Mountain National Park. lib. bdg. 18.60 (978-0-7368-1378-5(0)); Yellowstone National Park. lib. bdg. 18.60 (978-0-7368-1379-2(9)); Yosemite National Park. lib. bdg. 18.60 (978-0-7368-1380-8(2)); 24p. (J). (gr. 2-3). 2002. (Illus.). Set lib. bdg. 111.60 (978-0-7368-1381-5(0) , Bridgestone Bks.) Capstone Pr., Inc.

—Olympic National Park. 2002. (National Parks Ser.). (Illus.). 24p. (J). (gr. 2-3). lib. bdg. 18.60 (978-0-7368-1377-8(2) , Bridgestone Bks.) Capstone Pr., Inc.

—Rocky Mountain National Park. 2002. (National Parks Ser.). (Illus.). 24p. (J). (gr. 2-3). lib. bdg. 18.60 (978-0-7368-1378-5(0) , Bridgestone Bks.) Capstone Pr., Inc.

—Yellowstone National Park. 2002. (National Parks Ser.). (Illus.). 24p. (J). (gr. 2-3). lib. bdg. 18.60 (978-0-7368-1379-2(9) , Bridgestone Bks.) Capstone Pr., Inc.

—Zion National Park. 2003. (National Parks Ser.). (Illus.). 24p. (J). lib. bdg. 19.93 (978-0-7368-2222-0(4) , Bridgestone Bks.) Capstone Pr., Inc.

Harcourt School Publishers Staff. National Parks. 3rd ed. 2002. (Horizons Ser.). (Illus.). (J). pap. 3.70 (978-0-15-333162-6(3)) Harcourt Schl. Pubs.

Hargrove, Julia. Gettysburg National Military Park (1863) Mitchell, Judy, ed. Mohrman, Gary, illus. 2004. 48p. (J). pap. 6.95 (978-1-57310-430-2(2)) Teaching & Learning Co.

Herr, Jansen. Denali National Park Coloring Book for Kids. Brannon, Amanda, illus. 1999. 32p. (J). (ps-5). pap. (978-0-936425-62-7(8)) Greatland Graphics.

Howell, Theresa, ed. A-Maze-Ing Western National Parks & Monuments. 2002. (Illus.). 56p. (J). act. bk. ed. 7.95 (978-0-87358-810-2(X) , Rising Moon Bks. for Young Readers) Northland Publishing.

Hurtig, Jennifer. Uluru. 2007. (J). (978-1-59036-454-3(6)); lib. bdg. (978-1-59036-448-2(1)) Weigl Pubs., Inc.

January, Brendan. National Mall. 2000. (gr. 3-6). lib. bdg. 14.10 (978-0-613-52154-3(4)) Tandem Library Bks.

Lawrence, Jennie. Fort Laramie. 2004. (American Forts & Their Strategic Importance Ser.). (J). (978-1-59084-713-8(X)) Mason Crest Pubs.

Marcovitz, Hal. Fort Clatsop. 2004. (American Forts & Their Strategic Importance Ser.). (J). (978-1-59084-706-0(7)) Mason Crest Pubs.

Marsh, Robert. Kruger National Park: South African Edition. Meyer, Leo, illus. 1998. (Cambridge Reading Routes Ser.). 16p. pap. 5.00 (978-0-521-63666-7(3)) Cambridge Univ. Pr.

Maruca, Mary & Southwest Parks and Monuments Association Editors, contrib. by. A Kid's Guide to Saguaro National Park. 2000. (Illus.). 12p. (J). pap. 1.00 (978-1-58369-003-1(4)) Western National Parks Assn.

Miller, Debbie S. Disappearing Lake: Nature's Magic in Denali National Park. 1999. (J). (978-0-606-16875-5(3)) Tandem Library Bks.

National Parks. 2005. (J). (gr. 3-8). lib. bdg. 145.26 (978-1-59197-422-2(4)) ABDO Publishing Co.

Nelson, Sharlene P. & Nelson, Ted. Olympic National Park. 1998. (True Bks.). (Illus.). 48p. (J). (gr. 2). pap. 6.95 (978-0-516-26271-0(8) , Children's Pr.) Scholastic Library Publishing.

O'Hara-Kelly, Katie. What Are You Looking At? O'Hara-Kelly, Katie, illus. 2000. (Illus.). 32p. (J). (gr. k-3). 6.95 (978-1-878441-11-9(6)) Sequoia Natural History Assn.

O'Reilly, Wenda. Amazing places natl Parks. 2007. n/ap. pap. 119.40 (***978-1-59960-014-7(5)***) Birdcage Pr.

Parent, Laurence E. Capulin Volcano National Monument. Priehs, T. J. & Jorgen, Randolph, eds. Parent, Laurence E., photos by. 2006. (Illus.). 16p. (Orig.). pap. 4.95 (978-0-911408-94-2(0)) Western National Parks Assn.

Petersen, Christine. Land Preservation. 2004. (True Book Ser.). (Illus.). 48p. (J). 25.00 (978-0-516-22806-8(4) , Children's Pr.) Scholastic Library Publishing.

MNO

Petersen, David. Haleakala National Park. 2001. (National Parks Ser.). (Illus.). 48p. (J). (gr. 3-5). 25.00 (978-0-516-21666-9(X) , Children's Pr.) Scholastic Library Publishing.

—Haleakala National Park. 2001. (gr. 3-6). lib. bdg. 15.25 (978-0-613-54529-7(X)) Tandem Library Bks.

—National Parks. 2001. (gr. 3-6). lib. bdg. 15.25 (978-0-613-54040-7(9)) Tandem Library Bks.

—Saguaro National Park. 1999. (gr. 3-6). lib. bdg. 15.25 (978-0-613-54334-7(3)) Tandem Library Bks.

Peterson, David. Arches National Park. 2000. (True Bks.). (Illus.). 48p. (J). (gr. 3-5). pap. 6.95 (978-0-516-26572-8(5) , Children's Pr.) Scholastic Library Publishing.

—Great Sand Dunes National Monument. 1999. (gr. 3-6). lib. bdg. 15.25 (978-0-613-54526-6(5)) Tandem Library Bks.

—National Parks. 2001. (National Parks Ser.). (Illus.). 48p. (J). (gr. 3-5). 25.00 (978-0-516-21667-6(8) , Children's Pr.) Scholastic Library Publishing.

—Saguaro National Park. (True Bks.). (Illus.). 48p. (J). (gr. 3-5). 2000. pap. 6.95 (978-0-516-26771-5(X)); 1999. 25.00 (978-0-516-20944-9(2)) Scholastic Library Publishing. (Children's Pr.).

Steck-Vaughn Staff. National Parks. 2003. pap. 4.10 (978-0-7398-7651-0(1)) Steck-Vaughn.

Thompson, Gare. Science Chapters: Serengeti Journey: On Safari in Africa. 2006. (National Geographic Science Chapters Ser.). (Illus.). 48p. (gr. 1-4). 17.90 (978-0-7922-5952-7(1) , National Geographic Children's Bks.) National Geographic Society.

Trumbauer, Lisa. National Parks. 2005. (Yellow Umbrella Books for Early Readers). (Illus.). 16p. (J). (978-0-7368-5278-4(6)); (978-0-7368-5314-9(6)) Capstone Pr., Inc.

Vieira, Linda. Grand Canyon: A Trail Through Time. 2000. (Illus.). (J). (978-0-606-18743-5(X)) Tandem Library Bks.

Wade, Linda R. Acadia National Park. 2004. (J). (978-1-59197-423-9(2)) ABDO Publishing Co.

Williams, Colleen Madonna Flood. My Adventure at the Safari Park. 2007. 44p. (J). 8.99 (978-1-59092-577-5(7) , Orchard Academy Pr.) Windstorm Creative.

NATIONAL PARKS AND RESERVES—FICTION

Chandler, Mitzi. I See Something Grand. 2003. (Illus.). 32p. (J). (ps-1). pap. 8.95 (978-0-938216-50-6(3)) Grand Canyon Assn.

Dunbar, Paula J. Ruby's Rainbow: A Story of Acadia National Park. l.t. ed. 2005. (Illus.). 32p. (J). (978-1-931207-59-1(3)) Dilligaf Publishing.

Farnsworth, Frances. Cubby in Wonderland. 2005. pap. 20.95 (978-1-4179-8778-8(2)) Kessinger Publishing, LLC.

Farnsworth, Frances Joyce. Tike & Tiny in the Tetons. 2007. (Illus.). 172p. (J). pap. 14.95 (***978-0-943972-79-4(5)***) Homestead Publishing.

Ferguson, Alane & Skurzynski, Gloria. Deadly Waters. 2007. (Illus.). 160p. (J). (gr. 3-7). 4.99 (***978-1-4263-0093-6(X)*** , National Geographic Children's Bks.) National Geographic Society.

—The Hunted. 2007. (Mysteries in Our National Park Ser.). (Illus.). 160p. (J). (gr. 3-7). 4.99 (***978-1-4263-0095-0(6)*** , National Geographic Children's Bks.) National Geographic Society.

Fleck, Earl. Chasing Bears: A Canoe Country Adventure. 2004. (Illus.). 160p. (gr. 7-12). pap. 12.95 (978-0-930100-90-2(5)) Holy Cow! Pr.

Lauber, Patricia. The True-or-False Book of Cats. Lauber, Patricia, illus. 2001. (Illus.). 32p. (J). (gr. 3-7). pap. 6.95 (978-0-7922-6694-5(3) , National Geographic Children's Bks.) National Geographic Society.

Robinson, Sandra Chisholm. Expedition Yellowstone: A Mountain Adventure. Meloy, Ellen D., illus. 1999. 173p. (gr. 3-7). pap. 12.50 (978-0-911797-25-1(4)) Rinehart, Roberts Pubs.

Skurzynski, Gloria. Buried Alive. 2003. (gr. 3-6). lib. bdg. 14.10 (978-0-613-70935-4(7)) Tandem Library Bks.

—The Hunted. 2001. 12.60 (978-0-606-22147-4(6)); (gr. 3-6). lib. bdg. 14.10 (978-0-613-62422-0(X)) Tandem Library Bks.

—Out of the Deep. 2002. (gr. 3-6). lib. bdg. 14.10 (978-0-613-62818-1(7)) Tandem Library Bks.

—Over the Edge. 2002. (gr. 3-6). lib. bdg. 14.10 (978-0-613-62819-8(5)) Tandem Library Bks.

—Running Scared. 2002. (gr. 3-6). lib. bdg. 14.10 (978-0-613-62832-7(2)) Tandem Library Bks.

—Valley of Death. 2002. (gr. 3-6). lib. bdg. 14.10 (978-0-613-62873-0(X)) Tandem Library Bks.

—Wolf Stalker. 2001. (gr. 3-6). lib. bdg. 14.10 (978-0-613-84040-8(2)) Tandem Library Bks.

Skurzynski, Gloria & Ferguson. Wolf Stalker. 2001. (National Parks Mystery Ser.). (Illus.). (J). (978-0-606-21533-6(6)) Tandem Library Bks.

Skurzynski, Gloria & Ferguson, Alane. Buried Alive. 2003. (Mysteries in Our National Parks Ser.: No. 12). 160p. (J). (gr. 3-7). 15.95 (978-0-7922-6966-3(7)); pap. 5.95 (978-0-7922-6968-7(3)) National Geographic Society. (National Geographic Children's Bks.).

—Cliff-Hanger. (Illus.). 160p. (J). (gr. 3-7). 2007. (Mysteries in Our National Park Ser.). 4.99 (978-1-4263-0092-9(1)); 1998. (National Parks Mysteries Ser.: No. 3). 15.95 (978-0-7922-7036-2(3)) National Geographic Society. (National Geographic Children's Bks.).

—Ghost Horses. (Illus.). 160p. (J). (gr. 3-7). 2007. (Mysteries in Our National Park Ser.). 4.99 (978-1-4263-0108-7(1)); 2000. (National Parks Mysteries Ser.: Vol. 6). 15.95 (978-0-7922-7055-3(X)) National Geographic Society. (National Geographic Children's Bks.).

—The Hunted. (National Parks Mysteries Ser.: No. 5). 160p. (J). (gr. 3-7). 2000. (Illus.). 15.95 (978-0-7922-7053-9(3)); 5th ed. 2001. pap. 5.95 (978-0-7922-7665-4(5)) National Geographic Society. (National Geographic Children's Bks.).

—Night of the Black Bear: A Mystery in Great Smoky Mountains National Park. 2007. (Mysteries in Our National Park Ser.). (Illus.). 160p. (J). (gr. 3-7). 4.99 (978-1-4263-0094-3(8)); 18.90 (978-1-4263-0105-6(7)) National Geographic Society. (National Geographic Children's Bks.).

—Out of the Deep. 2002. (Mysteries in Our National Parks Ser.: Vol. 10). 160p. (J). (gr. 3-7). 15.95 (978-0-7922-8230-3(2)); pap. 5.95 (978-0-7922-8231-0(0)) National Geographic Society. (National Geographic Children's Bks.).

—Over the Edge. 2002. (Mysteries in Our National Parks Ser.: Vol. 7). 160p. (J). (gr. 3-7). pap. 5.95 (978-0-7922-6686-0(2)); Vol. 7. 15.95 (978-0-7922-6677-8(3)) National Geographic Society. (National Geographic Children's Bks.).

—Running Scared. 2002. (Mysteries in Our National Parks Ser.: Vol. 11). 160p. (J). (gr. 3-7). 15.95 (978-0-7922-8232-7(9)); pap. 5.95 (978-0-7922-6948-9(9)) National Geographic Society. (National Geographic Children's Bks.).

—Valley of Death. 2002. (Mysteries in Our National Parks Ser.: Vol. 8). 160p. (J). (gr. 3-7). pap. 5.95 (978-0-7922-6699-0(4)); Vol. 8. 15.95 (978-0-7922-6698-3(6)) National Geographic Society. (National Geographic Children's Bks.).

—Wolf Stalker. (Illus.). 160p. (J). (gr. 3-7). 2007. (Mysteries in Our National Park Ser.). 4.99 (978-1-4263-0096-7(4)); 1998. (National Parks Mysteries Ser.: Vol. 1). 15.95 (978-0-7922-7034-8(7)) National Geographic Society. (National Geographic Children's Bks.).

Uncle Markie. Piglette & Bobo in the National Parks. 2002. 66p. (YA). ring bd. 9.95 (978-1-933129-01-3(8)) Studio 403.

Wood, Audrey. The Bunyans. Wood, Audrey, illus. 2002. (Illus.). (J). 25.06 (978-0-7587-2160-0(9)) Book Wholesalers, Inc.

—The Bunyans. 2006. (Illus.). 32p. (J). pap. 5.99 (978-0-439-81214-6(3) , Scholastic Paperbacks) Scholastic, Inc.

NATIONAL PARKS AND RESERVES—UNITED STATES

AAA Staff. National Parks & Forests Journal Guide. 2003. 80p. (J). 14.99 (978-1-56251-803-5(8)) AAA.

Acadia National Park Park Pal Booklet: 7 Years or Younger. 2004. (Illus.). 16p. (J). 1.95 (978-1-59091-031-3(1)) Eastern National.

Ashabranner, Jennifer, illus. & photos by. On the Mall in Washington, D. C. A Visit to America's Front Yard. Ashabranner, Jennifer, photos by. Ashabranner, Brent K., photos by. 2002. (Single Titles Ser.). 64p. (gr. 5 up). lib. bdg. 23.90 (978-0-7613-2351-8(1) , Twenty-First Century Bks.) Lerner Publishing Group.

Beckman, Wendy Hart. National Parks in Crisis: Debating the Issues. 2004. (Issues in Focus Ser.). (Illus.). 128p. (J). lib. bdg. 26.60 (978-0-7660-1947-8(0)) Enslow Pubs., Inc.

Bottone, Ann. My National Parks & Monuments Photo Journal. 2007. (J). (ps-10). spiral bd. 9.95 (***978-1-58071-065-7(4)***) Sierra Pr.

Cooper, Jason. Gettysburg. 1999. (American Landmarks Ser.). (Illus.). (J). (gr. 1-4). lib. bdg. 20.64 (978-0-86593-545-7(9)) Rourke Publishing, LLC.

Corral, Kimberly. A Child's Glacier Bay. Corral, Roy, illus. 1998. 32p. (ps up). 15.95 (978-0-88240-503-2(9)) Graphic Arts Ctr. Publishing Co.

Cosson, M. J. Welcome to Death Valley National Park. 2006. (Visitor Guides Ser.). (Illus.). 32p. (J). (gr. 1-5). 27.07 (978-1-59296-694-3(2)) Child's World, Inc.

—Welcome to Redwood National & State Parks. 2006. (Visitor Guides Ser.). (Illus.). 32p. (J). (gr. 1-5). 27.07 (978-1-59296-701-8(9)) Child's World, Inc.

Curlee, Lynn. Rushmore: Monument for the Ages. 1998. 48p. (J). pap. 16.95 (978-0-590-22201-3(5)) Scholastic, Inc.

Dell, Pamela. Welcome to Mount Rainier National Park. 2006. (Visitor Guides Ser.). (Illus.). 32p. (J). (gr. 1-5). 27.07 (978-1-59296-700-1(0)) Child's World, Inc.

Denali State Park: an Alaskan Ecosystem: Creating Graphical Representation of Data. (Math Bog Bookstm Ser.). 32p. (YA). (gr. 6-7). 53.25 (978-1-4042-6368-0(3)) Rosen Publishing Group, Inc., The.

Dickmann, Nancy. Mesa Verde National Park. 2006. (Symbols of Freedom Ser.). (Illus.). 32p. (J). (978-1-4034-7797-2(3)) Heinemann Library.

—Sequoia & Kings Canyon National Parks. 2006. (Symbols of Freedom Ser.). (Illus.). 32p. (J). (978-1-4034-7798-9(1)) Heinemann Library.

Fazio, Wende. Acadia National Park. 1998. (True Bks.). (Illus.). 48p. (J). (gr. 3-5). 25.00 (978-0-516-20659-2(1) , Children's Pr.) Scholastic Library Publishing.

Gillis, Jennifer Blizin. Battlefields. 2008. (J). (***978-1-60044-559-0(4)***) Rourke Publishing, LLC.

Graham, Amy. Acadia National Park. 2008. (J). (***978-1-59845-090-3(5)*** , MyReportLinks.com Bks.) Enslow Pubs., Inc.

Hall, Margaret. Carlsbad Caverns National Park. 2006. (Symbols of Freedom Ser.). (Illus.). 32p. (J). (978-1-4034-7792-7(2)) Heinemann Library.

—Denali National Park. 2006. (Symbols of Freedom Ser.). (Illus.). 32p. (J). (978-1-4034-7794-1(9)) Heinemann Library.

—Welcome to Denali National Park. 2006. (Visitor Guides Ser.). (Illus.). 32p. (J). (gr. 1-5). 27.07 (978-1-59296-695-0(0)) Child's World, Inc.

—Yosemite National Park. 2006. (Symbols of Freedom Ser.). (Illus.). 32p. (J). (978-1-4034-7799-6(X)) Heinemann Library.

Hiker's Guide to Apostle Islands National Lakeshore. 2001. 64p. per. 4.95 (978-1-888213-73-7(6)) Eastern National.

Jankowski, Susan. Olympic National Park. 2008. (J). (***978-1-59845-092-7(1)*** , MyReportLinks.com Bks.) Enslow Pubs., Inc.

Lorbiecki, Marybeth. Welcome to Grand Teton National Park. 2006. (Visitor Guides Ser.). (Illus.). 32p. (J). (gr. 1-5). 27.07 (978-1-59296-698-1(5)) Child's World, Inc.

Meister, Cari. Grand Canyon. 2000. (Going Places Ser.). (Illus.). 24p. (J). (gr. k-6). lib. bdg. 21.35 (978-1-57765-024-9(7) , Checkerboard Library) ABDO Publishing Co.

—Yellowstone National Park. 2000. (Going Places Ser.). (Illus.). 24p. (J). (gr. k-6). lib. bdg. 21.35 (978-1-57765-026-3(3) , Checkerboard Library) ABDO Publishing Co.

National Parks. (Illus.). (J). (gr. 2-3). lib. bdg. 212.60 (978-0-7368-2345-6(X)) Capstone Pr., Inc.

Nelson, Sharlene P. & Nelson, Ted. Hawaii Volcanoes National Park. 1998. (True Bks.). (Illus.). 48p. (J). (gr. 3-5). pap. 6.95 (978-0-516-26378-6(1) , Children's Pr.) Scholastic Library Publishing.

Nelson, Sharlene P. & Nelson, Ted W. Hawaii Volcanoes National Park. 1998. (True Bks.). (Illus.). 48p. (J). (gr. 3-5). 25.00 (978-0-516-20623-3(0) , Children's Pr.) Scholastic Library Publishing.

—Mount Rainier National Park. De Capua, Sarah, ed. 1998. (True Bks.). (Illus.). 48p. (J). (gr. 3-5). 25.00 (978-0-516-20624-0(9) , Children's Pr.) Scholastic Library Publishing.

O'Donnell, Kerri. Denali National Park, an Alaskan Ecosystem: Creating Graphical Representations of Data. 2006. (Math for the Real World Ser.). (Illus.). 32p. (J). pap. (978-1-4042-6083-2(8)); lib. bdg. (978-1-4042-3365-2(2)) Rosen Publishing Group, Inc., The.

Pancella, Peggy. Death Valley National Park. 2006. (Symbols of Freedom Ser.). (Illus.). 32p. (J). (978-1-4034-7793-4(0)) Heinemann Library.

—Great Smoky Mountains National Park. 2006. (Symbols of Freedom Ser.). (Illus.). 32p. (J). (978-1-4034-7796-5(5)) Heinemann Library.

Petersen, David. Grand Canyon National Park. 2001. (True Bks.). (Illus.). 48p. (J). (gr. 3-5). pap. 6.95 (978-0-516-27316-7(7) , Children's Pr.) Scholastic Library Publishing.

—Grand Canyon National Park. 2001. (gr. 3-6). lib. bdg. 15.25 (978-0-613-54522-8(2)) Tandem Library Bks.

Peterson, David. Arches National Park. 1999. (True Bks.). (Illus.). 48p. (J). (gr. 3-5). 25.00 (978-0-516-20941-8(8) , Children's Pr.) Scholastic Library Publishing.

—Chaco Culture National Historical Park. 1999. (True Bks.). (Illus.). 48p. (J). (gr. 3-5). 25.00 (978-0-516-20942-5(6) , Children's Pr.) Scholastic Library Publishing.

—Great Sand Dunes National Monument. 1999. (True Bks.). (Illus.). 48p. (J). (gr. 3-5). 25.00 (978-0-516-20943-2(4) , Children's Pr.) Scholastic Library Publishing.

Purslow, Neil. Redwood National Park. 2006. (J). (978-1-59036-457-4(0)); lib. bdg. (978-1-59036-451-2(1)) Weigl Pubs., Inc.

Raatma, Lucia. Our National Parks. 2002. (Let's See Library). (Illus.). 24p. (J). (gr. 1 up). lib. bdg. 19.93 (978-0-7565-0195-2(4)) Compass Point Bks.

Robson, Gary D. Who Pooped in Park: Grand Teton. 2004. 48p. pap. 9.95 (978-1-56037-280-6(X)) Farcountry Pr.

—Who Pooped in the Park? Clark, Elijah Brady, illus. 2006. (J). 9.95 (978-1-56037-388-9(1)) Farcountry Pr.

Robson, Gary D. & Rath, Robert. Who Pooped in the Park? 2006. (Illus.). 48p. (J). 9.95 (978-1-56037-327-8(X)) Farcountry Pr.

Sanford, William R. The Natchez Trace Historic Trail in American History. 2001. (In American History Ser.). (Illus.). 112p. (YA). (gr. 5-12). lib. bdg. 26.60 (978-0-7660-1344-5(8)) Enslow Pubs., Inc.

Selda, Toby. Simply Father: Life with Theodore Roosevelt As Seen through the Eyes of His Children. Roosevelt, Theodore, illus. 2007. 28p. (J). 7.95 (978-1-59091-030-6(3)) Eastern National.

Stone, Lynn M. America's National Parks. 2003. (Land of Liberty Ser.). (Illus.). 24p. (gr. 2-5). 17.95 (978-1-58952-313-5(X)) Rourke Publishing, LLC.

Sullivan, Jenna M. & Sullivan, Laura C. Kid's Guide to the National Parks of California & Oregon: Written by Kids for Kids. Sullivan, Jenna M. & Sullivan, Laura C., photos by. Sullivan, P. Deborah, photos by. 2001. (Illus.). 116p. (J). (gr. 6-12). pap. 10.95 (978-1-880062-23-4(2)) E&S Geographic & Information Services.

Temple, Teri & Temple, Bob. Welcome to Badlands National Park. 2006. (Visitor Guides Ser.). (Illus.). 32p. (J). (gr. 1-5). 27.07 (978-1-59296-693-6(4)) Child's World, Inc.

—Welcome to Grand Canyon National Park. 2006. (Visitor Guides Ser.). (Illus.). 32p. (J). (gr. 1-5). 27.07 (978-1-59296-697-4(7)) Child's World, Inc.

—Welcome to Hawaii Volcanoes National Park. 2006. (Visitor Guides Ser.). (Illus.). 32p. (J). (gr. 1-5). 27.07 (978-1-59296-699-8(3)) Child's World, Inc.

Thames, Susan. MIS Parques Nacionales. 2007. (SPA & ENG.). (J). (***978-1-60044-303-9(6)***) Rourke Publishing, LLC.

Thames, Susan. My National Parks. 2007. (J). (978-1-59515-995-3(9)) Rourke Publishing, LLC.

Travelers Guide to National Parks 2005: Your Digital Gateway to 467 Vacation Destinations Across America. 2nd ed. 2004. cd-rom 15.00 (978-0-9747471-5-6(7)) Belknap Digital Archives.

Yanuchi, Lori & Yanuchi, Jeff. Ranger Trails: Jobs of Adventure in America's Parks. Morris, James R., illus. 2005. 64p. (J). per. 12.95 (978-0-9670177-2-3(6)) Ridge Rock Pr.

NATIONAL PLANNING

see Social Policy

see names of countries with the subdivision Economic Policy; Social Policy; e.g. United States—Economic Policy; United States—Social Policy

NATIONAL RESOURCES

see Natural Resources

see names of countries with the subdivision Economic Conditions, e.g. United States.—Economic Conditions

NATIONAL SECURITY

see also United States—Defenses

Baker, David. The Department of Homeland Security. 2006. (Fighting Terrorism Ser.). (Illus.). 48p. (gr. 4-8). 20.95 (978-1-59515-484-2(1)) Rourke Publishing, LLC.

Brownlie, Ali & Mason, Chris. Why Do People Fight Wars? 2002. (Exploring Tough Issues Ser.). (Illus.). 48p. (J). lib. bdg. 25.69 (978-0-7398-4961-3(1)) Raintree.

Campbell, Geoffrey A. A Vulnerable America: An Overview of National Security. 2003. (Lucent Library of Homeland Security). (Illus.). 112p. (J). 29.95 (978-1-59018-383-0(5) , Lucent Bks.) Thomson Gale.

Evans, Fred. Maritime & Port Security. 2003. (Securing the Nation Ser.). (Illus.). 112p. (J). (gr. 9-13). 30.00 (978-0-7910-7614-9(8) , Chelsea Hse.) Facts On File, Inc.

Freedman, Jeri. America Debates Privacy Versus Security. 2007. lib. bdg. (***978-1-4042-1929-8(3)***) Rosen Publishing Group, Inc., The.

Gaines, Ann Graham. Border Patrol Agent & Careers in Border Protection. 2006. (Homeland Security & Counterterrorism Careers Ser.). (Illus.). 128p. (J). lib. bdg. 31.93 (978-0-7660-2646-9(9)) Enslow Pubs., Inc.

Gottfried, Ted. Homeland Security vs. Constitutional Rights. 2003. (Single Titles Ser.). (Illus.). 128p. (gr. 7 up). lib. bdg. 24.90 (978-0-7613-2862-9(9) , Twenty-First Century Bks.) Lerner Publishing Group.

Hamilton, John. Operation Noble Eagle. 2002. (War on Terrorism Ser.). (Illus.). 64p. (J). (gr. 4-8). lib. bdg. 25.65 (978-1-57765-664-7(4) , ABDO & Daughters) ABDO Publishing Co.

Haulley, Fletcher. The Department of Homeland Security. 2005. (This Is Your Government Ser.). (Illus.). 64p. (J). (gr. k-3). pap. 13.25 (978-1-4042-0662-5(0)) Rosen Publishing Group, Inc., The.

—The Department of Homeland Security. 2005. (This Is Your Government Ser.). (Illus.). 64p. (J). lib. bdg. (978-1-4042-0209-2(9)) Rosen Publishing Group, Inc., The.

Jacobs, Dale W., ed. World Book Focus on Terrorism. 2002. (Illus.). 160p. (J). (978-0-7166-1295-7(X)) World Bk., Inc.

Katz, Samuel M. U. S. Counterstrike: American Counterterrorism. 2005. (Terrorist Dossiers Ser.). (Illus.). 72p. (J). (gr. 6-12). 26.60 (978-0-8225-1569-2(5)) Lerner Publishing Group.

Keeter, Hunter. The US Homeland Security Forces. 2004. (J). pap. 11.95 (978-0-8368-5689-7(9)); lib. bdg. 30.00 (978-0-8368-5682-8(1)) Stevens, Gareth Inc. (World Almanac Library).

Kerrigan, Michael. The Department of Homeland Security. 2002. (Rescue & Prevention Ser.). (Illus.). 96p. (J). (gr. 7 up). lib. bdg. (978-1-59084-409-0(2)) Mason Crest Pubs.

Koestler-Grack, Rachel A. The Department of Homeland Security. 2007. (U. S. Government Ser.). 104p. (YA). (gr. 5-8). 30.00 (***978-0-7910-9286-6(0)*** , Chelsea Hse.) Facts On File, Inc.

Kowalski, Kathiann M. A Pro/con Look at Homeland Security: Safety vs. Liberty After 9/11. 2008. (Issues in Focus Today Ser.). (Illus.). 104p. (J). (gr. 6 up). lib. bdg. 31.93 (***978-0-7660-2914-9(X)***) Enslow Pubs., Inc.

Labov, Steven L., ed. Rescue & Prevention: Defending Our Nation, 15 vols., Set. (Illus.). 96p. (YA). (gr. 7 up). lib. bdg. (978-1-59084-401-4(7)) Mason Crest Pubs.

Miller, Connie Colwell. The National Security Agency: Cracking Secret Codes. 2008. (J). (***978-1-4296-1274-6(6)***) Capstone Pr., Inc.

Miller, Debra. The Patriot Act. 2007. (Hot Topics Ser.). (Illus.). 128p. (J). (gr. 7-10). 32.45 (***978-1-59018-981-8(7)*** , Lucent Bks.) Thomson Gale.

Ruffin, David C. The Duties & Responsibilities of the Secretary of Homeland Security. 2005. (Your Government in Action Ser.). (Illus.). 32p. (J). 21.95 (978-1-4042-2693-7(1) , PowerKids Pr.) Rosen Publishing Group, Inc., The.

Ruschmann, Paul. Mandatory Military Service. 2003. (Point/Counterpoint Ser.). (Illus.). 112p. (gr. 9-13). 32.95 (978-0-7910-7919-5(8) , Chelsea Hse.) Facts On File, Inc.

Scott Ingram. The National Security Advisor. 2004. (Illus.). 32p. (J). 23.70 (978-1-56711-962-6(X) , Blackbirch Pr., Inc.) Thomson Gale.

Souter, Janet. Air Marshal & Careers in Transportation Security. 2006. (Homeland Security & Counterterrorism Careers Ser.). (Illus.). 128p. (J). lib. bdg. 31.93 (978-0-7660-2647-6(7)) Enslow Pubs., Inc.

Stefoff, Rebecca. Security vs. Privacy. 2007. (Open for Debate Ser.). (J). lib. bdg. (***978-0-7614-2578-6(0)*** , Benchmark Bks.) Cavendish, Marshall Corp.

Wade, Mary Dodson. Condoleezza Rice: Being the Best. 2003. (Gateway Biography Ser.: 4). 48p. lib. bdg. 23.90 (978-0-7613-2619-9(7)); (Illus.). (gr. 2-4). pap. (978-0-7613-1927-6(1)) Lerner Publishing Group. (Millbrook Pr.).

NATIONAL SOCIALISM

see also Socialism

Dolan, Sean. Adolf Eichmann: Engineer of Death. 2005. (Holocaust Biographies Ser.). (Illus.). 112p. (J). (gr. 7-12). lib. bdg. 26.50 (978-0-8239-3308-2(3) , HBE-ICH) Rosen Publishing Group, Inc., The.

Downing, David & Tames, Richard. Fascism. 2003. (Political & Economic Systems Ser.). (Illus.). 64p. (J). (gr. 6-8). lib. bdg. 28.50 (978-1-4034-0319-3(8)) Heinemann Library.

MNO

Dowswell, Paul. The Causes of World War II. 2003. (20th-Century Perspectives Ser.). (Illus.). 48p. (J). (gr. 5-7). lib. bdg. 27.07 (978-1-4034-0149-6(7)) Heinemann Library.

Dufner, Annette. The Rise of Adolf Hitler. 2003. (Illus.). 144p. (YA). pap. 23.70 (978-0-7377-1519-4(7)); lib. bdg. 33.70 (978-0-7377-1518-7(9)) Thomson Gale. (Greenhaven Pr., Inc.).

Freeman, Charles. The Rise of the Nazis. 1998. (New Perspectives Ser.). (Illus.). 80p. (J). (gr. 4-7). 28.54 (978-0-8172-5015-7(8)) Raintree.

—The Rise of the Nazis. 2005. (How Did It Happen? Ser.). (Illus.). 48p. (J). (gr. 7-10). lib. bdg. 29.95 (978-1-59018-608-4(7) , Lucent Bks.) Thomson Gale.

Gogerly, Liz. Adolf Hitler. 2003. (Twentieth Century History Makers Ser.). (Illus.). 112p. (J). lib. bdg. 32.85 (978-0-7398-5256-9(6)) Raintree.

Gottfried, Ted. Nazi Germany: The Face of Tyranny. Alcorn, Stephen, illus. (Holocaust History Ser.). 112p. (YA). (gr. 7-12). 22.95 (978-1-58013-203-9(0)) Kar-Ben Publishing.

—Nazi Germany: The Face of Tyranny. 2000. (Holocaust Ser.: up). (Illus.). 128p. (gr. 7 up). lib. bdg. (978-0-7613-1714-2(7) , Twenty-First Century Bks.) Lerner Publishing Group.

Harris, Nathaniel. The Rise of Hitler. 2004. (Illus.). 56p. (J). pap. 8.95 (978-1-4034-5526-0(0)); lib. bdg. 27.07 (978-1-4034-4866-8(3)) Heinemann Library.

Hay, Jeff. Personalities, 4 vols. 2003. (History of the Third Reich Ser.). (Illus.). 292p. (J). 78.70 (978-0-7377-1120-2(5) , Greenhaven Pr., Inc.) Thomson Gale.

Hitler's Treasure: Nazi Gold. 2004. (YA). cd-rom 1500.00 (978-0-934269-58-2(0)) UFO Photo Archives.

Knight, Patricia. Mussolini & Fascism. 2003. (Questions & Analysis in History Ser.). (Illus.). 144p. 90.00 (978-0-415-27921-5(6)); 20.95 (978-0-415-27922-2(4)) Routledge.

Lace, William W. Hitler & the Nazis. 1999. (American War Library). (Illus.). 112p. (YA). (gr. 4-12). 27.45 (978-1-56006-372-8(6) , LML00902-177757, Lucent Bks.) Thomson Gale.

Ramen, Fred. Albert Speer: Hitler's Architect. 2005. (Holocaust Biographies Ser.). (Illus.). 112p. (YA). (gr. 7-12). lib. bdg. 26.50 (978-0-8239-3372-3(5)) Rosen Publishing Group, Inc., The.

—Hermann Goering: Hitler's Second in Command. 2005. (Holocaust Biographies Ser.). (Illus.). 112p. (YA). (gr. 7-12). lib. bdg. 26.50 (978-0-8239-3307-5(5) , HB-GORI) Rosen Publishing Group, Inc., The.

Rice, Earle, Jr. Adolf Hitler & Nazi Germany. 2005. (World Leaders Ser.). (Illus.). 176p. (J). (gr. 3-7). lib. bdg. 26.95 (978-1-931798-78-5(8)) Reynolds, Morgan Inc.

Schmittroth, Linda. People of the Holocaust. 1998. (J). 49.00 (978-0-7876-1744-8(X)); pap. 49.00 (978-0-7876-1745-5(8)) Thomson Gale. (UXL).

Shuter, Jane. Life & Death in Hitler's Europe. 2003. (Holocaust Ser.). 56p. (Illus.). (J). lib. bdg. 28.50 (978-1-4034-0811-2(4)); pap. 8.95 (978-1-4034-3203-2(1)) Heinemann Library.

—Life & Death in Hitler's Europe. 2003. (gr. 5-8). lib. bdg. 17.60 (978-0-613-60969-2(7)) Tandem Library Bks.

Stalcup, Brenda. Adolf Hitler. (People Who Made History Ser.). (Illus.). 202p. (YA). (gr. 9-12). 2000. lib. bdg. 32.45 (978-0-7377-0223-1(0)); 1999. 21.20 (978-0-7377-0222-4(2)) Thomson Gale. (Greenhaven Pr., Inc.).

Tames, Richard. Fascism. 2001. (Ideas of the Modern World Ser.). (Illus.). 64p. (J). lib. bdg. 25.69 (978-0-7398-3159-5(3)) Raintree.

Taylor, David. Adolf Hitler. 2001. (Leading Lives Ser.). (Illus.). 64p. (J). (gr. 5-7). lib. bdg. 27.86 (978-1-58810-162-4(2)) Heinemann Library.

Ungerer, Tomi. Tomi: A Childhood under the Nazis. 1998. (Illus.). 175p. (YA). (gr. 6 up). 29.95 (978-1-57098-163-0(9) , Rinehart, Roberts International) Rinehart, Roberts Pubs.

Woolf, Alex. The Rise of Nazi Germany. 2004. (Questioning History Ser.). (J). lib. bdg. 28.50 (978-1-58340-442-3(2)) Smart Apple Media.

NATIONAL SOCIALISM—FICTION

Van Ryk, Laverne. A Garland of Emeralds. 2006. (Illus.). 305p. ***978-1-4122-0156-8(X))** Trafford Publishing.

NATIONAL SONGS

see also Folk Songs

Choral Songs in Honour of Queen Victoria. 2001. (YA). reprint ed. 150.00 (978-0-7222-6177-4(2)) Library Reprints, Inc.

Cohan, George M. & Kimble, Warren. You're a Grand Old Flag. Kimble, Warren, illus. 2007. (Illus.). 32p. (J). (ps-1). 17.85 (***978-0-8027-9576-2(5));** 16.95 (***978-0-8027-9575-5(7))** Walker & Co.

Cummings, William H. Dr. Arne & Rule, Britannia. 2001. 146p. (YA). reprint ed. 88.00 (978-0-7222-6190-3(X)) Library Reprints, Inc.

—God Save the King: The Origin, & History of the Music & Words of the National Anthem. 2001. 126p. (YA). reprint ed. 88.00 (978-0-7222-6189-7(6)) Library Reprints, Inc.

Dell, Pamela. The National Anthem. 2004. (Let's See Library). (Illus.). 24p. (J). (gr. 1 up). lib. bdg. 19.93 (978-0-7565-0619-3(0)) Compass Point Bks.

Douglas, Lloyd G. Pledge of Allegiance. 2003. (gr. k-3). lib. bdg. 12.95 (978-0-613-67758-5(7)) Tandem Library Bks.

Edens, Cooper, compiled by. The Glorious American Songbook. 2005. (Illus.). 80p. (J). (ps-ps). 19.95 (978-0-8118-4552-6(4)) Chronicle Bks. LLC.

Engel, Carl. The Literature of National Music. 2001. 108p. (YA). reprint ed. 88.00 (978-0-7222-5009-9(6)) Library Reprints, Inc.

Ferry, Joseph. The National Anthem. 2002. (American Symbols & Their Meanings Ser.). (Illus.). 48p. (YA). (gr. 4 up). lib. bdg. (978-1-59084-033-7(X)) Mason Crest Pubs.

Gershenson, Harold P. America the Musical 1776-1899: A Nation's History Through Music. Chesworth, Michael, illus. 2005. 21p. (J). (978-1-58987-116-8(2)) Kindermusik International.

Harrison, Ted. O Canada. ed. 2004. (J). (gr. k-3). spiral bd. (978-0-616-03038-7(X)) Canadian National Institute for the Blind/Institut National Canadien pour les Aveugles.

Healy, Nick. The Star-Spangled Banner. 2003. (J). (978-1-58417-055-6(7)); pap. (978-1-58417-118-8(9)) Lake Street Pubs.

Key, Francis Scott. The Star Spangled Banner. D'Aulaire, Edgar Parin & D'Aulaire, Ingri, illus. 2000. 40p. (J). (ps-3). 14.95 (978-1-55709-390-5(3)) Applewood Bks.

—The Star Spangled Banner. 2005. (Illus.). 32p. pap. 7.95 (978-1-894997-12-6(3)) Fox Music Bks. CAN. *Dist:* SCB Distributors.

—Star Spangled Banner. 2002. (gr. k-3). lib. bdg. 10.95 (978-0-613-89793-8(5)) Tandem Library Bks.

Kuitenbrouwer, Peter. Our Song: The Story of ¿O Canada¿:The Canadian National Anthem. Spires, Ashley, illus. 2004. 24p. (J). (gr. 3-5). 14.95 (978-1-894222-67-9(9)) Lobster Pr. CAN. *Dist:* Univ. of Toronto Pr.

Landau, Elaine. The National Anthem. 2008. (True Book-trade;: American History Ser.). 48p. (J). pap. 6.95 (***978-0-531-14783-2(5)** , Children's Pr.) Scholastic Library Publishing.

O Say Can You See. . . 2003. bds. 6.99 (978-0-9726762-0-5(1)) Star Spangled Baby, Ltd.

Ouren, Todd, illus. America: My Country 'Tis of Thee. 2004. (Patriotic Songs Ser.). 24p. (J). (ps-4). 22.60 (978-1-4048-0174-5(X)) Picture Window Bks.

—America the Beautiful. 2004. (Patriotic Songs Ser.). 24p. (J). (ps-4). 22.60 (978-1-4048-0172-1(3)) Picture Window Bks.

—Patriotic Songs, 6 bks. Incl. America : My Country 'Tis of Thee. 22.60 (978-1-4048-0174-5(X)); America the Beautiful. 22.60 (978-1-4048-0172-1(3)); Star Spangled Banner. 22.60 (978-1-4048-0175-2(8)); When Johnny Comes Marching Home. 22.60 (978-1-4048-0171-4(5)); Yankee Doodle. 22.60 (978-1-4048-0176-9(6)); You're a Grand Old Flag. 22.60 (978-1-4048-0173-8(1)); 24p. (J). (ps-4). 2004. (Illus.). 2003. 127.56 (978-1-4048-0170-7(7)) Picture Window Bks.

—The Star Spangled Banner. 2004. (Patriotic Songs Ser.). 24p. (J). (ps-4). 22.60 (978-1-4048-0175-2(8)) Picture Window Bks.

—When Johnny Comes Marching Home. 2004. (Patriotic Songs Ser.). 24p. (J). (ps-4). 22.60 (978-1-4048-0171-4(5)) Picture Window Bks.

—You're a Grand Old Flag. 2004. (Patriotic Songs Ser.). 24p. (J). (ps-4). 22.60 (978-1-4048-0173-8(1)) Picture Window Bks.

Pingry, Patricia. O Little Town of Bethlehem. 2005. (Illus.). 16p. (J). bds. 12.99 (978-0-8249-6566-2(3)) Ideals Pubns.

Scholastic, Inc. Staff. Star Spangled Banner. Rachel, E., ed. 2002. (Illus.). 24p. (J). pap. 3.99 (978-0-439-40767-0(2) , Scholastic Paperbacks) Scholastic, Inc.

Sonneborn, Liz. America the Beautiful: The Story Behind Our National Hymn. 2003. (America in Words & Song Ser.). (Illus.). 32p. (gr. 3-5). 23.00 (978-0-7910-7332-2(7) , Chelsea Hse.) Facts On File, Inc.

—The Star-Spangled Banner: The Story Behind Our National Anthem. 2003. (America in Words & Song Ser.). (Illus.). 32p. (gr. 3-5). 23.00 (978-0-7910-7337-7(8) , Chelsea Hse.) Facts On File, Inc.

Vilsaint, Fequiere. Children Songs from Haiti: Chante Timoun Ayiti. Date not set. 28p. (J). (gr. 1-5). wbk. ed. 25.00 (978-1-881839-55-2(9)) Educa Vision.

NATIONALITY (CITIZENSHIP)

see Citizenship

NATIONS, LAW OF

see International Law

NATIVE PEOPLES

see Indigenous Peoples

NATIVE RACES

see Indigenous Peoples

NATIVITY OF CHRIST

see Jesus Christ—Nativity

NATO

see North Atlantic Treaty Organization

NATURAL CALAMITIES

see Natural Disasters

NATURAL DISASTERS

see also Earthquakes; Floods; Forest Fires; Storms; Volcanoes

Adamson, Thomas K. Tsunamis. 2006. (Bridgestone Books). (Illus.). 24p. (J). (gr. 2-4). lib. bdg. 21.26 (978-0-7368-5248-7(4)) Capstone Pr., Inc.

Allaby, Michael. A Chronology of Weather. 2nd rev. ed. 2003. (Dangerous Weather Ser.). (Illus.). 208p. (YA). (gr. 6-12). 35.00 (978-0-8160-4792-5(8)) Facts On File, Inc.

Allen, John. Predicting Natural Disasters. 2005. (Science on the Edge Ser.). (Illus.). 48p. (J). (gr. 4-8). 24.95 (978-1-4103-0717-0(4) , Blackbirch Pr., Inc.) Thomson Gale.

Anaxos, Inc Staff, contrib. by. UXL Encyclopedia of Weather & Natural Disasters. 2007. (J). (***978-1-4144-1880-3(9)); (*978-1-4144-1881-0(7)); (*978-1-4144-1882-7(5)); (*978-1-4144-1883-4(3)); (*978-1-4144-1884-1(1))** Thomson Gale.

Armentrout, David & Armentrout, Patricia. Tsunamis. 2007. (Illus.). 32p. (J). (978-1-60044-234-6(X)) Rourke Publishing, LLC.

Barnard, Bryn. Dangerous Planet: Natural Disasters That Changed History. 2003. (Illus.). 48p. (J). (gr. 3-7). 17.95 (978-0-375-82249-0(6) , Crown Books For Young Readers) Random Hse. Children's Bks.

Bell, Trudy E. & McCollum, Sean. Volcanic Eruptions, Earthquakes, & Tsunamis. 2007. (Scientific American Ser.). 80p. (gr. 5-8). 30.00 (***978-0-7910-9047-3(7)** , Chelsea Hse.) Facts On File, Inc.

Bortz, Alfred B. Collision Course! Cosmic Impacts & Life on Earth. 2001. (Enthusiastic Astronomy Ser.). (Illus.). 72p. (gr. 5-8). lib. bdg. 25.90 (978-0-7613-1403-5(2) , Twenty-First Century Bks.) Lerner Publishing Group.

Boskey, Madeline. Natural Disasters. 2004. (True Tales Ser.). (J). (gr. 2-4). pap. 4.95 (978-0-516-24605-5(4) , Children's Pr.) Scholastic Library Publishing.

—Natural Disasters: A Chapter Book. 2003. (True Tales Ser.). (Illus.). 48p. (J). 22.50 (978-0-516-22918-8(4) , Children's Pr.) Scholastic Library Publishing.

Bradford, Marlene & Carmichael, Robert S., eds. Natural Disasters, 3 vols., 3 vols. 2000. (Illus.). 986p. (gr. 9 up). lib. bdg. 331.00 (978-0-89356-071-3(5) , 179) Salem Pr., Inc.

Bredeson, Carmen. Mount St. Helens Volcano: Violent Eruption. 2001. (American Disasters Ser.). (Illus.). 48p. (YA). (gr. 4-10). lib. bdg. 23.93 (978-0-7660-1552-4(1)) Enslow Pubs., Inc.

Bryan, Nichol. Environmental Disasters, 6 bks. Incl. Alamos : Wildfires. lib. bdg. 30.00 (978-0-8368-5507-4(8)); Bhopal : Chemical Plant Accident. lib. bdg. 30.00 (978-0-8368-5503-6(5)); Chernobyl : Nuclear Disaster. lib. bdg. 30.00 (978-0-8368-5504-3(3)); Danube : Cyanide Spill. lib. bdg. 30.00 (978-0-8368-5505-0(1)); Exxon Valdez : Oil Spill. lib. bdg. 30.00 (978-0-8368-5506-7(X)); Love Canal : Pollution Crisis. lib. bdg. 30.00 (978-0-8368-5508-1(6)); 48p. (YA). (gr. 5 up). (Illus.). 2003. Set lib. bdg. 180.00 (978-0-8368-5502-9(7) , World Almanac Library) Stevens, Gareth Inc.

Capaccio, George. Tsunamis. 2005. (Navigators Ser.). (J). pap. 42.00 (***978-1-4108-5081-2(1))** Benchmark Education Co.

Carruthers, Margaret W. Tsunamis. 2005. (Watts Library). (Illus.). 64p. (J). 25.50 (978-0-531-12286-0(7) , Watts, Franklin) Scholastic Library Publishing.

Ceban, Bonnie J. Hurricanes, Typhoons, & Cyclones: Disaster & Survival. 2005. (Deadly Disasters Ser.). (Illus.). 48p. (J). (gr. 4-10). lib. bdg. 23.93 (978-0-7660-2388-8(5)) Enslow Pubs., Inc.

Cefrey, Holly. What If an Asteroid Hit Earth? 2002. (What If Ser.). (Illus.). 48p. (YA). (gr. 7-12). 24.00 (978-0-516-23911-8(2) , Children's Pr.) Scholastic Library Publishing.

Challen, Paul C. Environmental Disaster Alert! 2004. (Disaster Alert! Ser.). (Illus.). 32p. (J). (978-0-7787-1581-8(7)); pap. (978-0-7787-1613-6(9)) Crabtree Publishing Co.

Challoner, Jack & Dorling Kindersley Publishing Staff. Hurricane & Tornado. 2004. (Eyewitness Books). (Illus.). 72p. (J). lib. bdg. 19.99 (978-0-7566-0689-3(6)) Dorling Kindersley Publishing, Inc.

Chambers, Catherine. Drought. 2007. (Illus.). 32p. (J). (***978-1-4034-9576-1(9))** Heinemann Library.

—Drought (2nd Edition) 2007. (Illus.). 32p. (J). (***978-1-4034-9585-3(8))** Heinemann Library.

Collins, Andrew. Science Chapters: Violent Weather: Thunderstorms, Tornadoes, & Hurricanes. 2006. (National Geographic Science Chapters Ser.). (Illus.). 48p. (gr. 1-4). 17.90 (978-0-7922-5947-3(5) , National Geographic Children's Bks.) National Geographic Society.

Connell, Kate. Dust Bowl Days: Hard Times for Farmers. 2004. (Illus.). 40p. (J). pap. (978-0-7922-4557-5(1)) National Geographic Society.

Creative Media Applications. Environmental Disasters Set. 2005. (Environmental Disasters Ser.). 112-112p. (gr. 6-12). 210.00 (978-0-8160-5753-5(2)) Facts On File, Inc.

Currie, Stephen. Escapes from Natural Disasters. 2003. (Great Escapes Ser.). (Illus.). 112p. (J). 29.95 (978-1-59018-278-9(2) , Lucent Bks.) Thomson Gale.

Dalton, Dave. Environmental Migrants. 2005. (People on the Move Ser.). (Illus.). 56p. (J). pap. (978-1-4034-6965-6(2)); (YA). (gr. 6-9). lib. bdg. 31.36 (978-1-4034-6960-1(1)) Heinemann Library.

Day, Trevor. Savage Earth. 2006. (DK Guides Ser.). 64p. (J). pap. 7.99 (978-0-7566-1791-2(X)) Dorling Kindersley Publishing, Inc.

Disaster Plan: Individual Title Six-Packs. (Bookweb Ser.). 32p. (gr. 5 up). 34.00 (978-0-7635-3794-4(2)) Rigby Education.

Dorling Kindersley Publishing Staff, ed. Hurricane & Tornado. 2004. (Dk Eyewitness Books Ser.). (Illus.). 72p. (J). 15.99 (978-0-7566-0690-9(X)) Dorling Kindersley Publishing, Inc.

Draper, Allison Stark. Coping with Natural Disasters. 2005. (Coping Ser.). (Illus.). 192p. (YA). (gr. 7-12). lib. bdg. 26.50 (978-0-8239-2071-6(2) , CONADI) Rosen Publishing Group, Inc., The.

Duey. Freaky Facts about Natural Disasters. 2000. (J). 11.64 (978-0-606-19709-0(5)) Tandem Library Bks.

Duey, Kathleen. More Freaky Facts about Natural Disasters. 2001. (gr. 3-6). lib. bdg. 13.00 (978-0-613-73281-9(2)); (Illus.). (J). (978-0-606-20810-9(0)) Tandem Library Bks.

Estigarribia, Diana. Learning about the Effects of Natural Events with Graphic Orgainizers. 2005. (Graphic Organizers in Science Ser.). (Illus.). 24p. (J). (ps). lib. bdg. 19.95 (978-1-4042-2804-7(7) , PowerKids Pr.) Rosen Publishing Group, Inc., The.

—Learning about the Effects of Natural Events with Graphic Organizers. 2005. (Graphic Organizers in Science Ser.). (Illus.). 24p. (J). pap. (978-1-4042-5038-3(7) , PowerKids Pr.) Rosen Publishing Group, Inc., The.

Fecher Sarah & Oliver Clare. Freaky Facts about Natural Disasters. 2006. (Illus.). 32p. (J). (978-1-58728-542-4(8) , Two Can Publishing) T&N Children's Publishing.

Fecher, Sarah & Oliver, Clare. Freaky Facts about Natural Disasters. Bines, Gary & Boller, Gary, illus. 2006. 32p. 13.95 (978-1-58728-539-4(8)) T&N Children's Publishing.

Feldman, Sarah. Twisters. ed. 2003. (Early Connections Ser.). (J). pap. 35.00 (978-1-4108-1544-6(7)) Benchmark Education Co.

Fine, Jil. Tsunamis. 2007. (Illus.). 48p. (J). pap. (978-0-531-18723-4(3)) Children's Pr., Ltd.

—Tsunamis. 2006. (Natural Disasters Ser.). (Illus.). 48p. (J). (978-0-531-12444-4(4) , Children's Pr.) Scholastic Library Publishing.

Flows & Quakes & Spinning Winds: Individual Title Six-Packs. (gr. k-1). 23.00 (978-0-7635-9043-7(6)) Rigby Education.

Ganeri, Anita. Volcano! 2007. (Illus.). 32p. (J). (978-1-84193-561-4(1)) Arcturus Pubs., Inc.

Gardiner, Lisa. Catastrophic Colorado! The History & Science of Our Natural Disasters. 2006. (J). (978-1-56579-549-5(0)) Westcliffe Pubs.

Gentle, Victor & Perry, Janet. Asteroid Strikes. 2001. (Natural Disasters Ser.). (Illus.). 24p. (J). (gr. 2 up). lib. bdg. 22.00 (978-0-8368-2831-3(3)) Stevens, Gareth Inc.

—Natural Disasters, 6 bks. Incl. Asteroid Strikes. lib. bdg. 22.00 (978-0-8368-2831-3(3)); Earthquakes. lib. bdg. 22.00 (978-0-8368-2832-0(1)); Fires. lib. bdg. 22.00 (978-0-8368-2833-7(X)); Hurricanes. lib. bdg. 22.00 (978-0-8368-2834-4(8)); Plagues. lib. bdg. 22.00 (978-0-8368-2835-1(6)); Volcanoes. lib. bdg. 22.00 (978-0-8368-2836-8(4)); 24p. (J). (gr. 2 up). (Illus.). 2001. Set lib. bdg. 132.00 (978-0-8368-2830-6(5)) Stevens, Gareth Inc.

Gibson, Karen Bush. Mudslide in la Conchita, CA 2005. 2005. (Natural Disasters Ser.). (Illus.). 32p. (J). (gr. 1-4). lib. bdg. (978-1-58415-418-1(7)) Mitchell Lane Pubs., Inc.

Goldstein, Natalie. Drought & Heat Waves. 2005. (Library of Emergency Preparedness). (Illus.). 64p. (J). (978-1-4042-0536-9(5)) Rosen Publishing Group, Inc., The.

Goyal, Anuj, ed. Higher Ground. Foreman, Michael, illus. 2006. 160p. (J). (gr. 7-9). pap. 8.99 (978-1-84458-516-6(6)) Chrysalis Children's Bks. GBR. *Dist:* Trafalgar Square Publishing.

Graphic Natural Disasters, 6 bks., Set. Incl. Avalanches & Landslides. Shone, Rob. (J). lib. bdg. 29.25 (***978-1-4042-1992-2(7));** Earthquakes. Shone, Rob. Spender, Nik, illus. (YA). lib. bdg. 29.25 (***978-1-4042-1989-2(7));** Hurricanes. Jeffrey, Gary. Lacey, Mike, illus. (YA). lib. bdg. 29.25 (***978-1-4042-1991-5(9));** Tornadoes & Superstorms. Jeffrey, Gary. Riley, Terry, illus. (J). lib. bdg. 29.25 (978-1-4042-1993-9(5)); Tsunamis & Floods. Jeffrey, Gary, illus. (YA). lib. bdg. 29.25 (***978-1-4042-1990-8(0));** Volcanoes. Shone, Rob. (J). lib. bdg. 29.25 (***978-1-4042-1988-5(9));** (Illus.). 48p. (gr. 5-8). 2007. 2007. Set lib. bdg. 175.50 (***978-1-4042-1064-6(4))** Rosen Publishing Group, Inc., The.

Green, Jen. In Nature. 2002. (Young Library). (Illus.). 32p. (J). lib. bdg. 25.69 (978-0-7398-6317-6(7)) Raintree.

Griffey, Harriet. Volcanoes & Other Natural Disasters. 1998. (Eyewitness Readers). (Illus.). 48p. (J). (gr. 2-4). pap. 3.99 (978-0-7894-2964-3(0)) Dorling Kindersley Publishing, Inc.

Griffey, Harriet & Dorling Kindersley Publishing Staff. Volcanoes & Other Natural Disasters. 1999. (Eyewitness Readers). (Illus.). 48p. (J). (gr. 2-4). 12.99 (978-0-7894-4257-4(4)) Dorling Kindersley Publishing, Inc.

Halley, Ned. Disasters. 1999. (Single Subject References Ser.). (Illus.). 64p. (J). (gr. 5-9). tchr. ed. 16.95 (978-0-7534-5221-9(9) , Kingfisher) Houghton Mifflin Co. Trade & Reference Div.

Hamilton, John. Droughts. 2006. (Illus.). 32p. (J). (gr. 3-8). lib. bdg. 24.21 (978-1-59679-329-3(5) , ABDO & Daughters) ABDO Publishing Co.

—Nature's Fury Set II. 2006. (J). (gr. 3-8). 145.26 (978-1-59679-327-9(9) , ABDO & Daughters) ABDO Publishing Co.

—Tsunamis. 2005. (Illus.). 32p. (J). (gr. 3-8). lib. bdg. 24.21 (978-1-59679-333-0(3) , ABDO & Daughters) ABDO Publishing Co.

Heat Hazard 6-Pack: Droughts. 2004. pap. 45.90 (978-1-4109-1215-2(9)) Harcourt Schl. Pubs.

Hoffman, Mary Ann. Hurricane Katrina. 2006. (Nature in the News Ser.). (Illus.). 32p. (J). lib. bdg. (978-1-4042-3537-3(X) , PowerKids Pr.) Rosen Publishing Group, Inc., The.

Hynes, Margaret. Rocks & Fossils. 2006. (Kingfisher Knowledge Ser.). (Illus.). 64p. (J). (gr. 5-9). 12.95 (978-0-7534-5974-4(4) , Kingfisher) Houghton Mifflin Co. Trade & Reference Div.

Isaacs, April. Tornadoes, Hurricanes, & Tsunamis: A Practical Survival Guide. 2005. (Library of Emergency Preparedness). (Illus.). 64p. (J). (978-1-4042-0533-8(0)) Rosen Publishing Group, Inc., The.

Jennings, Terry. Natural Disasters, 4 vols., Set. 1999. (Illus.). 32p. (J). lib. bdg. 67.80 (978-1-929298-48-8(X)) Chrysalis Education.

Karwoski, Gail Langer. Tsunami: The True Story of an April Fools' Day Disaster. MacDonald, John, illus. 2006. 64p. (J). 17.95 (978-1-58196-044-0(1)) Darby Creek Publishing.

Kenah, Katharine. Destruction Earth. 2004. (Extreme Readers Ser.). (Illus.). 32p. (J). (gr. k-1). pap. 3.95 (978-0-7696-3185-1(1)) School Specialty Publishing.

—Destruction Earth Destruccion. 2005. (English-Spanish Extreme Readers Ser.). 32p. (J). pap. 3.95 (978-0-7696-3810-2(4) , Waterbird Bks.) School Specialty Publishing.

Klutz, Inc Staff, contrib. by. Mother Nature Goes Nuts! Amazing Natural Disasters. 2006. (Illus.). 47p. (J). pap. (*978-1-59174-186-2(6)) Klutz.

Kummer, Patricia K. Nature's Power. 2000. (Pair-It Books). (Illus.). 40p. (J). pap. (978-0-7398-0875-7(3)) Steck-Vaughn.

Kusky, Timothy M. Landslides: Mass Wasting, Soil, & Mineral Hazards. 2008. (Hazardous Earth Ser.). 176p. (J). (gr. 6-12). 39.50 (*978-0-8160-6465-6(2)) Facts On File, Inc.

—Tsunami: Giant Waves from the Sea. 2008. (Hazardous Earth Ser.). 176p. (J). (gr. 6-12). 39.50 (*978-0-8160-6464-9(4)) Facts On File, Inc.

Langley, Andrew. Hurricanes, Tsunamis & Other Natural Disasters. 2006. (Kingfisher Knowledge Ser.). (Illus.). 64p. (J). (gr. 5-9). 12.95 (978-0-7534-5975-1(2) , Kingfisher) Houghton Mifflin Co. Trade & Reference Div.

Levey, Richard H. Dust Bowl! The 1930s Black Blizzard. 2005. (X-Treme Disasters That Changed America Ser.). (J). lib. bdg. 25.27 (978-1-59716-007-0(5)) Bearport Publishing Co., Inc.

Linde, Barbara M. Ecological Disasters. 2005. (Navigators Ser.). (J). pap. 44.00 (*978-1-4108-5091-1(9)) Benchmark Education Co.

Loeschnig, L. V. Experimentos Sencillos de Quimica. (Juego de la Ciencia Ser.). (SPA.). 124p. (gr. 5-8). 5.20 (978-84-95456-49-6(4) , 87802) Ediciones Oniro S.A. ESP. *Dist:* Bilingual Pubns. Co., The Lectorum Pubns., Inc., Libros Sin Fronteras.

—Experimentos Sencillos Sobre el Espacio y el Vuelo. (Juego de la Ciencia Ser.). (SPA.). 128p. (gr. 5-8). 5.20 (978-84-95456-56-4(7) , 87803) Ediciones Oniro S.A. ESP. *Dist:* Bilingual Pubns. Co., The Lectorum Pubns., Inc., Libros Sin Fronteras.

Malaspina, Ann. Tsunamis. 2006. (In the News Ser.). (Illus.). 64p. (J). (gr. 7-12). lib. bdg. 27.95 (*978-1-4042-0978-7(6)) Rosen Publishing Group, Inc., The.

Mason, Antony. Nature vs. Man: A Look at the Way the World Is Today. 2007. (Illus.). 48p. (J). (*978-1-59604-094-6(7)) Stargazer Bks.

Mason, Paul. The World's Most Dangerous Places. 2006. (Illus.). 32p. (J). (978-1-4109-2508-4(0)); pap. (978-1-4109-2513-8(7)) Steck-Vaughn.

McGuire, Bill. Natural Disasters. 2007. (Inside Access Ser.). 32p. (J). (gr. 1-5). 9.95 (*978-0-7534-6065-8(3) , Kingfisher) Houghton Mifflin Co. Trade & Reference Div.

Meister, Cari. Nature's Fury, Set. Incl. Blizzards. lib. bdg. 24.21 (978-1-57765-085-0(9)); Earthquakes. lib. bdg. 24.21 (978-1-57765-083-6(2)); Floods. lib. bdg. 24.21 (978-1-57765-082-9(4)); Hurricanes. lib. bdg. 24.21 (978-1-57765-080-5(8)); Tornadoes. lib. bdg. 24.21 (978-1-57765-081-2(6)); Volcanoes. lib. bdg. 24.21 (978-1-57765-084-3(0)); 32p. (J). (gr. 3-8). 1999. (Illus.). 1999. Set lib. bdg. 145.26 (978-1-57765-269-4(X) , ABDO & Daughters) ABDO Publishing Co.

Mitchell Lane Publishers. Natural Disasters. 2007. (Natural Disasters Ser.). (J). lib. bdg. 385.50 (*978-1-58415-572-0(8)) Mitchell Lane Pubs., Inc.

Moreno, Felix & Medina, Juan Ignacio. Cuidado con los Desastres Naturales! 2001. Tr. of Watch Out for Natural Disasters. (SPA.). 94p. 10.95 (978-84-348-7883-9(6)) SM Ediciones ESP. *Dist:* AIMS International Bks., Inc.

Morrison, Taylor. Tsunami Warning. 2007. (Illus.). 32p. (*978-1-4287-3955-0(6)) Houghton Mifflin Co.

—Tsunami Warning. 2007. (Illus.). 48p. (J). (gr. 4-6). 17.00 (*978-0-618-73463-4(5) , Walter Lorraine) Houghton Mifflin Co. Trade & Reference Div.

Nagel, Rob. Dangerous Planet: The Science of Natural Disasters, 3 vols. DesChenes, Betz, ed. 1999. (Illus.). (J). (978-0-7876-2850-5(6)) Thomson Gale.

Nagel, Rob & DesChenes, Betz, eds. Dangerous Planet: The Science of Natural Disasters, 3 vols. 1999. (Illus.). (J). (978-0-7876-2851-2(4) , UXL); (978-0-7876-2849-9(2)) Thomson Gale.

Nagel, Rob & Engelbert, Phillis. Dangerous Planet: The Science of Natural Disasters, 3 vols., Set. DesChenes, Betz, ed. 2001. (Illus.). 446p. (J). (gr. 4-7). lib. bdg. 99.00 net. (978-0-7876-2848-2(4) , GML00502-112408, UXL) Thomson Gale.

Natural Disasters. (Eyes on Adventure Ser.). 32p. (J). (gr. 1). pap. (978-1-882210-64-0(6)) Action Publishing, Inc.

Natural Disasters. 48p. (gr. 4-6). 8.99 (978-1-56417-962-3(1) , GA1605) Schaffer, Frank Pubns.

Natural Disasters. 2003. 128p. (gr. 5-8). 12.99 (978-1-56822-901-0(1) , IF87013) School Specialty Publishing.

Natural Disasters, 3 cass.; set. 2004. (NOVA Ser.). (gr. 7 up). 49.95 incl. VHS (978-1-57807-041-1(4) , WG165) WGBH Boston Video.

Natural Disasters, 8 bks. Incl. Avalanches. Ylvisaker, Anne. 2003. lib. bdg. 21.26 (978-0-7368-1504-8(X)); Blizzards. Allen, Jean. 2001. lib. bdg. 21.26 (978-0-7368-0899-6(X)); Droughts. Ylvisaker, Anne. 2003. lib. bdg. 21.26 (978-0-7368-1505-5(8)); Earthquakes. Lassieur, Allison. 2000. lib. bdg. 21.26 (978-0-7368-0586-5(9)); Floods. Allen, Jean. 2001. lib. bdg. 21.26 (978-0-7368-0900-9(7)); Forest Fires. Salas, Laura Purdie. 2001. lib. bdg. 21.26 (978-0-7368-0901-6(5)); Hurricanes. Allen, Jean. 2000. lib. bdg. 21.26 (978-0-7368-0587-2(7)); Ice Storms. Ylvisaker, Anne. 2003. lib. bdg. 21.26 (978-0-7368-1506-2(6)); Landslides. Ylvisaker, Anne. 2003. lib. bdg. 21.26 (978-0-7368-1507-9(4)); Tornadoes. Allen, Jean. 2000. lib. bdg. 21.26 (978-0-7368-0588-9(5)); Tsunamis. Bonar, Samantha. 2001. lib. bdg. 21.26 (978-0-7368-0902-3(3)); Volcanoes. Lassieur, Allison. 2000. lib. bdg. 21.26 (978-0-7368-0589-6(3)); 48p. (J). (gr. 3-4). (Illus.). 2000. Set lib. bdg. 255.12 (978-0-7368-1521-5(X) , Capstone High-Interest Bks.) Capstone Pr., Inc.

Natural Disasters, 11 bks., Set. Incl. Ancient Mystery of Easter Island. Jackson, Kay. 2006. lib. bdg. (978-1-58415-495-2(0)); Bermuda Triangle 1945. Jackson, Kay. 2006. lib. bdg. (978-1-58415-497-6(7)); Bubonic Plague. Jackson, Kay. 2006. lib. bdg. (978-1-58415-494-5(2)); Earthquake in Loma Prieta, CA 1989. Harkins, Susan Sales & Harkins, William. 2005. lib. bdg. (978-1-58415-417-4(9)); Fury of Hurricane Andrew 1992. Gibson, Karen Bush. 2005. lib. bdg. (978-1-58415-416-7(0)); Hurricane Katrina 2005. Torres, John. 2006. lib. bdg. (978-1-58415-498-3(5)); Lost Continent of Atlantis. Roberts, Russell. 2006. lib. bdg. 25.70 (978-1-58415-496-9(9)); Mt. Vesuvius & the Destruction of Pompei, A. D. 79. Roberts, Russell. 2005. lib. bdg. (978-1-58415-419-8(5)); Mudslide in la Conchita, CA 2005. Gibson, Karen Bush. 2005. lib. bdg. (978-1-58415-418-1(7)); Tsunami Disaster in Indonesia 2004. Torres, John Albert. 2005. lib. bdg. (978-1-58415-415-0(2)); Where Did All the Dinosaurs Go? Roberts, Russell. 2005. lib. bdg. (978-1-58415-420-4(9)); (Illus.). 32p. (J). (gr. 1-4). 2007. 186.45 (*978-1-58415-499-0(3)) Mitchell Lane Pubs., Inc.

Natural Disasters: Blizzards; Earthquakes; Floods; Forest Fires; Hurricanes; Tornadoes; Tsunamis; Volcanoes, 8 bks. (Illus.). (J). (gr. 3-4). lib. bdg. 170.08 (978-0-7368-1000-5(5) , Capstone High-Interest Bks.) Capstone Pr., Inc.

Newson, Joyce E. Natural Disasters. Chesi, Matteo, illus. 2002. (Nature's Record-Breakers Ser.). 32p. (J). (gr. 3 up). lib. bdg. 23.33 (978-0-8368-2906-8(9)) Stevens, Gareth Inc.

O'Connor, Rebecca K. How Should the World Respond to Natural Disasters? 2006. 80-244*p. (gr. 10-12). 29.95 (978-0-7377-3383-9(7)); pap. 21.20 (978-0-7377-3384-6(5)) Thomson Gale. (Greenhaven Pr., Inc.).

Oliver, Clare. Natural Disasters: Atlas in the Round. 2005. (Illus.). 32p. (J). (gr. k-4). 16.00 (978-0-7567-9190-2(1)) DIANE Publishing Co.

Olson, Nathan. Droughts. 2005. (Weather Update Ser.). (Illus.). 24p. (J). (ps-7). lib. bdg. 21.26 (978-0-7368-4331-7(0) , 1243958) Capstone Pr., Inc.

Orme, David, et al. Tsunamis. 2005. (What on Earth? Ser.). (Illus.). 32p. (J). 25.50 (978-0-516-25323-7(9) , Children's Pr.) Scholastic Library Publishing.

Osborne, Mary Pope & Boyce, Natalie Pope. Tsunamis & Other Natural Disasters. Murdocca, Sal, illus. 2007. (Magic Tree House Research Guide Ser.: No. 15). 128p. (J). (gr. 3-5). pap. 4.99 (978-0-375-83221-5(1) , Random Hse. Bks. for Young Readers) Random Hse. Children's Bks.

—Tsunamis & Other Natural Disasters: A Nonfiction Companion to Hide Tide in Hawaii. Murdocca, Sal, illus. 2007. (Magic Tree House Research Guide Ser.: No. 15). 128p. (J). (gr. 3-5). lib. bdg. 11.99 (978-0-375-93221-2(6) , Random Hse. Bks. for Young Readers) Random Hse. Children's Bks.

Otfinoski, Steven. Major Disasters in U.S. History. 2005. (Illus.). 48p. (J). (*978-0-669-51416-2(0)) Great Source Education Group, Inc.

Park, Louise. Droughts. 2007. (J). (*978-1-59920-113-9(5)) Smart Apple Media.

—Earthquakes. 2007. (J). (*978-1-59920-111-5(9)) Smart Apple Media.

—Hurricanes. 2007. (J). (*978-1-59920-112-2(7)) Smart Apple Media.

—Tornadoes. 2007. (J). (*978-1-59920-114-6(3)) Smart Apple Media.

—Tsunamis. 2007. (J). (*978-1-59920-115-3(1)) Smart Apple Media.

—Volcanoes. 2007. (J). (*978-1-59920-110-8(0)) Smart Apple Media.

Parks, Peggy J. Tsunamis. 2005. (Kidhaven Science Library). (Illus.). 48p. (J). (ps-8). lib. bdg. 26.20 (978-0-7377-3380-8(2) , Greenhaven Pr., Inc.) Thomson Gale.

Putnam, Jeff. Tsunami! Deadly Wall of Water. 2005. (High Five Reading Ser.). (Illus.). 64p. (J). (gr. 4-5). lib. bdg. incl. audio (978-0-7368-5753-6(2)) Capstone Pr., Inc.

Putnam, Jeff & Rasinski, Timothy V. Tsunami! Deadly Wall of Water. 2005. (High Five Reading Ser.). (Illus.). 48p. (J). (978-0-7368-5743-7(5)); (978-0-7368-5733-8(8)) Capstone Pr., Inc.

Raintree Steck-Vaughn Staff. Nature's Power. 1999. (Illus.). (J). pap. 35.60 (978-0-7398-0906-8(7)) Steck-Vaughn.

Reed, Hannah. Natural Disasters. 2001. (gr. k-3). lib. bdg. 11.65 (978-0-613-33403-7(5)) Tandem Library Bks.

The Remarkable World, 16 bks., Set. Incl. Birds of Prey. Penny, Malcolm. (Illus.). 1996. lib. bdg. 18.98 (978-1-56847-414-4(8)); Fossils & Bones. Pirotta, Saviour. (Illus.). 1997. lib. bdg. 18.98 (978-0-8172-4542-9(1)); Great Journeys. Chrisp, Peter. 1996. lib. bdg. 18.98 (978-0-8172-4537-5(5)); Hidden Past. Hicks, Peter. (Illus.). 1997. lib. bdg. 18.98 (978-0-8172-4541-2(3)); Land Predators. Stidworthy, John. (Illus.). 1996. lib. bdg. 18.98 (978-1-56847-416-8(4)); Mapping the Unknown. Chrisp, Peter. (Illus.). 1996. lib. bdg. 18.98 (978-0-8172-4535-1(9)); Monsters of the Deep. Pirotta, Saviour. (Illus.). 1995. lib. bdg. 18.98 (978-1-56847-367-3(2)); Night Creatures. Penny, Malcolm. (Illus.). 1996. lib. bdg. 18.98 (978-1-56847-371-0(0)); Pirates & Treasure. Pirotta, Saviour. (Illus.). 1997. lib. bdg. 18.98 (978-0-8172-4820-8(X)); Search for Riches. Langley, Andrew. (Illus.). 1997. lib. bdg. 18.98 (978-0-8172-4544-3(8)); Volcano, Earthquake & Hurricane. Arnold, Nick. (Illus.). 1997. lib. bdg. 18.98 (978-0-8172-4540-5(5)); Voyages of Exploration. Arnold, Nick. (Illus.). 1995. lib. bdg. 18.98 (978-1-56847-368-0(0)); Whalers. Chrisp, Peter. (Illus.). 1995. lib. bdg. 18.98 (978-1-56847-421-2(0)); When Dinosaurs Ruled the Earth. Theodorou, Rod. (Illus.). 1996. lib. bdg. 18.98 (978-1-56847-415-1(6)); Wild, Wild West. Pirotta, Saviour. (Illus.). 1997. lib. bdg. 18.98 (978-0-8172-4536-8(7)); World's Wild Places. Morgan, Sally. (Illus.). 1997. lib. bdg. 18.98 (978-0-8172-4538-2(3)); 48p. (J). (gr. 4-7). (Illus.). Set lib. bdg. 303.68 (978-0-8172-5397-4(1)) Raintree.

Remson, Billie. Mississippi Autumn on Bluebird Hill: A True Story about our Little Farm in the Hills of Southern Mississippi. 2006. (J). per. 14.95 (978-1-59571-121-2(X)) Word Association Pubs.

—A Mississippi Autumn on Bluebird Hill: A true story about our little farm in the hills of Southern Mississippi. 2006. (J). 21.95 (978-1-59571-158-8(9)) Word Association Pubs.

Richards, Julie. Natural Disasters Series, 6 bks. Incl. Ferocious Fires. 28.00 (978-0-7910-6583-9(9) , 010451); Furious Floods. 28.00 (978-0-7910-6580-8(4) , 010456); Howling Hurricanes. 28.00 (978-0-7910-6584-6(7) , 010452); Quivering Quakes. 28.00 (978-0-7910-6582-2(0) , 010453); Terrifying Tornadoes. 28.00 (978-0-7910-6579-2(0) , 010454); Vibrating Volcanoes. 28.00 (978-0-7910-6581-5(2) , 010455); (J). (gr. 5 up). 2001. (Illus.). 32p. 2005. Set pap. 168.00 (978-0-7910-6578-5(2) , 010450S, Chelsea Hse.) Facts On File, Inc.

Rooney, Anne. Earthquake! 2007. (Illus.). 32p. (J). (978-1-84193-565-2(4)) Arcturus Pubs., Inc.

—Tsunami! 2007. (Illus.). 32p. (J). (978-1-84193-562-1(X)) Arcturus Pubs., Inc.

Rosado, Maria. Blizzards & Ice Storms. 1999. (978-0-606-17527-2(X)) Tandem Library Bks.

Roza, Greg. The Indian Ocean Tsunami. 2006. (Nature in the News Ser.). (Illus.). 32p. (J). lib. bdg. (978-1-4042-3538-0(8) , PowerKids Pr.) Rosen Publishing Group, Inc., The.

Searl, Duncan. Trapped! 2005. (Illus.). 48p. (J). (*978-0-669-51413-1(6)) Great Source Education Group, Inc.

Simon, Seymour. Super Storms. 2002. (See More Readers Ser.). (Illus.). 32p. (J). 13.95 (978-1-58717-137-6(6)); Vol. 2. pap. 3.95 (978-1-58717-138-3(4)) Chronicle Bks. LLC. (SeaStar Bks.).

—Super Storms. 2002. (gr. 3-6). lib. bdg. 11.80 (978-0-613-58440-1(6)) Tandem Library Bks.

Spilsbury, Louise & Spilsbury, Richard. Awesome Forces of Nature, 5 bks., Set 2. 2004. (J). (gr. 3-5). lib. bdg. 135.36 (978-1-4034-4789-0(6)) Heinemann Library.

—Dreadful Droughts. 2003. (Illus.). 32p. (J). pap. (978-1-4034-4231-4(2)); lib. bdg. 24.22 (978-1-4034-3723-5(8)) Heinemann Library.

Steck-Vaughn Staff. Violent Earth: 10 Lab Classroom. 2000. pap. 727.90 (978-0-7398-3318-6(9)); pap. 727.90 (978-0-7398-3321-6(9)) Steck-Vaughn.

—Violent Earth: 3 Lab Classroom. 2000. pap. 311.90 (978-0-7398-3316-2(2)); pap. 311.90 (978-0-7398-3319-3(7)) Steck-Vaughn.

—Violent Earth: 5 Lab Classroom. 2000. pap. 447.10 (978-0-7398-3317-9(0)); pap. 447.10 (978-0-7398-3320-9(0)) Steck-Vaughn.

Stewart, Gail B. Catastrophe in Southern Asia: The Tsunami of 2004. 2005. (Overview Ser.). (Illus.). 112p. (YA). (gr. 5-8). lib. bdg. 29.95 (978-1-59018-831-6(4) , Lucent Bks.) Thomson Gale.

Thoron, Joe. Kaleidoscope Natural Disasters Group 1, 4 bks., Set. Incl. Earthquakes. lib. bdg. 28.50 (978-0-7614-2102-3(5)); Hurricanes. lib. bdg. 28.50 (978-0-7614-2103-0(3)); Tornadoes. lib. bdg. 28.50 (978-0-7614-2104-7(1)); Volcanoes. lib. bdg. 28.50 (978-0-7614-2105-4(X)); (Illus.). 48p. (J). 2006. 2007. lib. bdg. (*978-0-7614-2101-6(7) , Benchmark Bks.) Cavendish, Marshall Corp.

Torres, John Albert. Disaster in the Indian Ocean, Tsunami 2004. 2005. (Monumental Milestones Ser.). (Illus.). 48p. (J). (gr. 5-8). lib. bdg. 29.95 (978-1-58415-344-3(X)) Mitchell Lane Pubs., Inc.

—Tsunami Disaster in Indonesia 2004. 2005. (Natural Disasters Ser.). (Illus.). 32p. (J). (gr. 1-4). lib. bdg. (978-1-58415-415-0(2)) Mitchell Lane Pubs., Inc.

Townsend, John. The Asian Tsunami 2004. 2006. (When Disaster Struck Ser.). (Illus.). 56p. (J). lib. bdg. (978-1-4109-2277-9(4)) Heinemann Library.

Uhler, Karen. The 10 Worst Natural Disasters. 2008. (Tentrade; Ser.). 48p. (J). pap. 14.99 (*978-1-55448-469-0(3) , Watts, Franklin) Scholastic Library Publishing.

Vaughan, Jenny. Natural Disasters. 1999. (Fast Forward Ser.). (Illus.). 32p. (J). (gr. 4-8). pap. 29.00 (978-0-531-14583-8(2) , Watts, Franklin) Scholastic Library Publishing.

—Natural Disasters. Hewitson, Nick, illus. 1999. 32p. (J). (ps-8). lib. bdg. 18.75 (978-0-613-34869-0(9)) Tandem Library Bks.

Vogel, Carole Garbuny. Nature's Fury: Eyewitness Reports of Natural Disasters. 2000. (Illus.). 128p. (J). (gr. 4-7). pap. 16.95 (978-0-590-11502-5(2)) Scholastic, Inc.

Walker, Niki. Tsunami Alert! 2005. (Disaster Alert! Ser.). (Illus.). 32p. (J). (978-0-7787-1582-5(5)); pap. (978-0-7787-1614-3(7)) Crabtree Publishing Co.

Watts, Claire. Heat Hazard: Droughts. 2004. (Turbulent Planet Ser.). (Illus.). 48p. (J). 28.56 (978-1-4109-1098-1(9)) Harcourt Schl. Pubs.

—Heat Hazard Droughts. 2005. (Turbulent Planet Ser.). (J). pap. (978-1-4109-1753-9(3)); lib. bdg. (978-1-4109-1743-0(6)) Steck-Vaughn.

—Heat Hazards: Droughts. 2004. (Turbulent Planet Ser.). (Illus.). 48p. (J). pap. 8.50 (978-1-4109-1209-1(4)) Harcourt Schl. Pubs.

Watts, Claire & Day, Trevor. Natural Disasters. 2006. (Eyewitness Bks.). (Illus.). 72p. (J). 15.99 (978-0-7566-2072-1(4)); lib. bdg. 19.99 (978-0-7566-2073-8(2)) Dorling Kindersley Publishing, Inc.

Weil, Ann. Environmental Disasters. 2003. (Illus.). 64p. (YA). per. 3.95 (978-1-56254-654-0(6) , SP6546) Saddleback Educational Publishing.

—Mountain Disasters. 2003. (Illus.). 64p. (YA). per. 3.95 (978-1-56254-658-8(9) , SP6589) Saddleback Educational Publishing.

When Disaster Strikes! 2005. (Illus.). 48p. (gr. 5-8). lib. bdg. 143.70 (978-0-8239-3892-6(1)) Rosen Publishing Group, Inc., The.

Woods, Michael & Woods, Mary B. Droughts. 2007. (Disasters up Close Ser.). (J). 27.93 (978-0-8225-6576-5(5) , Lerner Pubns.) Lerner Publishing Group.

—Tsunamis. 2007. (Disasters up Close Ser.). (Illus.). 64p. (J). 27.93 (978-0-8225-6054-8(2) , Lerner Pubns.) Lerner Publishing Group.

World Book, Inc Staff, contrib. by. Droughts. 2007. (J). (*978-0-7166-9803-6(X)) World Bk., Inc.

—Heat Waves. 2007. (J). (*978-0-7166-9807-4(2)) World Bk., Inc.

—Ice Storms. 2007. (J). (*978-0-7166-9809-8(9)) World Bk., Inc.

—Tsunamis & Seiches. 2007. (J). (*978-0-7166-9814-2(5)) World Bk., Inc.

X-treme Disasters That Changed America, 6 vols., Set. 2005. (X-Treme Disasters That Changed America Ser.). (Illus.). (J). lib. bdg. 215.64 (978-1-59716-021-6(0)) Bearport Publishing Co., Inc.

NATURAL DISASTERS—FICTION

Barron, T. A. The Day the Stones Walked: A Tale of Easter Island. Low, William, illus. 2007. 32p. (J). (gr. 1-4). 16.99 (978-0-399-24263-2(5) , Philomel) Penguin Group (USA) Inc.

Bauer, Marion Dane. A Mama for Owen. Butler, John, illus. 2007. 32p. (J). 15.99 (978-0-689-85787-4(X) , Simon & Schuster Children's Publishing) Simon & Schuster Children's Publishing.

Bywaters, Mayer. Tempest. (J). 16.95 (978-1-58717-206-9(2) , SeaStar Bks.) Chronicle Bks. LLC.

Bywaters, Mayer & Mayer, Marianna. Tempest. Bywaters, Lynn, illus. 2005. 40p. (J). 16.95 (978-0-8118-5054-4(4) , SeaStar Bks.) Chronicle Bks. LLC.

Conway, David & Daly, Jude. Lila & the Secret of Rain. 2008. (Illus.). 32p. (J). 16.95 (*978-1-84507-407-4(6)) Lincoln, Frances Ltd. GBR. *Dist:* Perseus Distribution.

Craven, Tracy Leininger. Life of Faith/Kathleens Drought. 2007. (Life of Faith': Kathleen Mckenzie Ser.). 160p. (YA). pap. 6.99 (978-1-928749-27-1(5)) Mission City Pr., Inc.

Donald, Margaret. Eli the Elephant: A Tsunami Story. 2007. 25p. 7.95 (978-81-8386-024-6(9)) India Research Pr. IND. *Dist:* Independent Pubs. Group.

Fournier, Kevin Mark. Sandbag Shuffle. 2007. 240p. (YA). (gr. 9 up). pap. 10.95 (*978-1-897235-22-5(4)) Thistledown Pr., Ltd. CAN. *Dist:* Fitzhenry & Whiteside, Ltd.

Hall, Barbara. Dixie Storms. 2006. (Illus.). 224p. (J). pap. 6.95 (978-0-15-205756-5(0) , Harcourt Paperbacks) Harcourt Children's Bks.

Hanson, Ed. Mountain Blizzard. 2003. (Barclay Family Adventure Ser.: Bk. 7). 64p. (J). (gr. k-6). per. 3.95 (978-1-56254-556-7(6) , SP 5566) Saddleback Educational Publishing.

Kroll, Virginia L. Selvakumar Knew Better. Li, Xiaojun, illus. 2006. (J). 17.95 (978-1-885008-29-9(5)) Shen's Bks.

Laiz, Jana. Elephants of the Tsunami. Cafiero, Tara, illus. 2005. (J). 10.00 (978-0-9771818-3-4(9)) EarthBound Bks.

Leininger Craven, Tracy. Kathleen's Dreadful Drought. 2006. 12.99 (978-1-928749-90-5(9)) Mission City Pr., Inc.

Lewis, Richard. The Killing Sea: A Novel of the Tsunami. 2006. 192p. (YA). (gr. 6-10). 15.95 (978-1-4169-1165-4(0)) Simon & Schuster Children's Publishing.

Lutz, Norma Jean. Grace & the Bully: Drought on the Frontier. 2006. 144p. (J). pap. 4.97 (978-1-59789-102-8(9)) Barbour Publishing, Inc.

Meunier, Brian & Edgerton, Perky. Bravo, Tavo! 2007. (Illus.). 32p. (J). (gr. k-3). 16.99 (978-0-525-47478-4(1) , Dutton Juvenile) Penguin Group (USA) Inc.

Mitchell, Nancy. Global Warning. Christensen, Edie et al, illus. 1999. (Changing Earth Trilogy Ser.: Bk. 3). 178p. (Orig.). (J). (ps-12). mass mkt. 5.95 (978-1-892713-02-5(0)) Lightstream Pubns.

Pfeffer, Susan Beth. Life As We Knew It. 2006. (Illus.). 352p. (J). 17.00 (978-0-15-205826-5(5)) Harcourt Children's Bks.

Prentiss, Timothy. A Good Pick. 2006. (Early Explorers Ser.). (J). 34.00 (*978-1-4108-6111-5(2)) Benchmark Education Co.

Robbins, Sandra. The Earth & Me. 2004. (J). (978-1-882601-48-6(3)); 23.95 incl. audio compact disk (978-1-882601-49-3(1)); pap. 9.95 (978-1-882601-47-9(5)); pap. 16.95 incl. audio (978-1-882601-52-3(1)) See-More's Workshop.

—The Earth & Me (Hard Cover Book & Tape Set) 2004. (J). mass mkt. 21.95 incl. audio (978-1-882601-50-9(5)) See-More's Workshop.

Robbins, Sandra, told to. The Earth & Me (Soft Cover Book & CD Set) 2004. (J). pap. 18.95 incl. audio compact disk (978-1-882601-51-6(3)) See-More's Workshop.

Robison, Dan. Death Chant: Kimo's Battle with the Shamanic Forces. 2006. 194p. (J). pap. (978-0-922993-52-9(1)) Marquette Bks., LLC.

Robson, Walter. Ear2ear & the Gem1's. 2005. (ENG.). 192p. per. (*978-1-904988-05-2(9)) Donard Publishing.

NATURAL HISTORY

Here are entered popular works describing animals, plants, minerals and nature in general. Handbooks on the detailed study of birds, flowers, etc. are entered under Nature Study.

see also Aquariums; Biology; Botany; Fossils; Fresh-Water Biology; Geographical Distribution of Animals and Plants; Geology; Marine Biology; Mineralogy; Zoology

Andrews, Jane. The Stories Mother Nature Told Her Child. 2004. reprint ed. pap. 15.95 (978-1-4191-8357-7(5)) Kessinger Publishing, LLC.

—The Stories Mother Nature Told Her Children. 2004. reprint ed. pap. 1.99 (978-1-4192-8357-4(X)) Kessinger Publishing, LLC.

Anness Publishing Staff & Lorenz Editors. Nature. 2001. (Let's Look at Board Bks.). (Illus.). 12p. (gr. 1-5). bds. 5.00 (978-0-7548-0709-4(6)) Anness Publishing GBR. *Dist:* National Bk. Network.

Arnosky, Jim. Field Trips: Bug Hunting, Animal Tracking, Bird-Watching, Shore Walking. Arnosky, Jim, illus. 2002. (Illus.). 96p. (J). (gr. 3 up). 17.99 (978-0-688-15172-0(8)) HarperCollins Pubs.

Barlowe, Dot. Rocky Mountains Plants & Animals Coloring Book. 2004. (Illus.). 32p. (J). pap. 3.95 (978-0-486-43045-4(6)) Dover Pubns., Inc.

Barr, George. Outdoor Science Projects for Young People. 1998. Orig. Title: Young Scientist Takes a Walk: Guide to Outdoor Observations. (Illus.). 160p. (J). reprint ed. pap. 3.95 (978-0-486-26855-2(1) , 26855-1) Dover Pubns., Inc.

Beebe, Katherine & Kingsley, Nellie F. The First Year Nature Reader. 2004. reprint ed. pap. 21.95 (978-1-4191-3072-4(2)) Kessinger Publishing, LLC.

Bernhard, Durga. Earth, Sky, Wet, Dry: A Book of Opposites. Bernhard, Durga, illus. 2000. (Illus.). 40p. (J). (gr. k-4). pap. 16.95 (978-0-531-30213-2(X) , Orchard Bks.) Scholastic, Inc.

Boreman, Thomas, ed. A Description of Three Hundred Animals. (Illus.). (J). reprint ed. 18.00 (978-0-384-05125-6(1)) Johnson Reprint Corp.

Brown Bear Books (Firm) Staff, contrib. by. Backyard. 2007. (J). ***(978-1-933834-13-9(7))*** Brown Bear Books.

Brown, John. Journey into the Desert. 2002. (Illus.). 48p. (YA). 19.95 (978-0-19-515777-2(X)) Oxford Univ. Pr., Inc.

Brynie, Faith Hickman. Six-Minute Nature Experiments. Whittingham, Kim, illus. 2006. 80p. (J). (gr. 4-8). reprint ed. pap. 11.00 (978-1-4223-5105-5(X)) DIANE Publishing Co.

Bullock, Linda. Living in the Savannah. 2004. (Rookie Read-About Geography Ser.). (Illus.). 31p. (J). (gr. 1-2). pap. 5.95 (978-0-516-27327-3(2) , Children's Pr.) Scholastic Library Publishing.

Burton, Jane & Taylor, Kim. The Nature & Science of Patterns. Burton, Jane & Taylor, Kim, photos by. 1998. (Exploring the Science of Nature Ser.). (Illus.). 32p. (J). (gr. 3 up). lib. bdg. 23.93 (978-0-8368-2107-9(6)) Stevens, Gareth Inc.

Calhoun, Yael. Plant & Animal Science Fair Projects: Using Beetles, Weeds, Seeds, & More. 2005. (Biology! Best Science Projects Ser.). (Illus.). 128p. (J). (gr. 6-13). lib. bdg. 26.60 (978-0-7660-2368-0(0)) Enslow Pubs., Inc.

Castner, James L. River Life: Deep in the Amazon. 2002. (Deep in the Amazon Ser.). (Illus.). 32p. (J). (gr. 5 up). lib. bdg. 28.50 (978-0-7614-1127-7(5) , Benchmark Bks.) Cavendish, Marshall Corp.

Chapman, S. I. mon. In the Desert. 2006. (Illus.). 111p. (J). lib. bdg. 20.00 ***(978-1-4242-0628-5(6))*** Fitzgerald Bks.

Cherry, Lynne. A River Ran Wild: An Environmental History. 2002. (Illus.). 40p. (J). (gr. 1-4). pap. 7.00 (978-0-15-216372-3(7) , Voyager Bks./Libros Viajeros) Harcourt Children's Bks.

—A River Ran Wild: An Environmental History. 1998. (978-0-606-13093-6(4)) Tandem Library Bks.

Cherry, Lynne, as told by. A River Ran Wild: An Environmental History. 1998. (J). (gr. 4). pap. 3.95 (978-0-439-04468-4(5)) Scholastic, Inc.

Cornell, Joseph. Sharing Nature with Children II, Vol. 2. 1998. Orig. Title: Sharing the Joy of Nature. (Illus.). 168p. pap. 9.95 (978-1-883220-87-7(4)) Dawn Pubns.

Craats, Rennay. Natural Landmarks. 2004. (American Symbols Ser.). (J). pap. 6.95 (978-1-59036-177-1(6)); (Illus.). 24p. lib. bdg. 15.95 (978-1-59036-133-7(4)) Weigl Pubs., Inc.

Cunningham, Lawrence J. & Beatty, Janice J. Guam: A Natural History. 2001. (Illus.). 208p. (YA). (gr. 3 up). pap. 66.60 (978-1-57306-046-2(1)) Bess Pr., Inc.

DK Publishing. Nature Detectives. 2007. 48p. (J). (gr. 5-12). 3.99 ***(978-0-7566-3512-1(8))*** Dorling Kindersley Publishing, Inc.

Dorling Kindersley Publishing Staff. Pajaro. 2004. (Eyewitness Books).Tr. of Bird. 72p. (J). lib. bdg. 19.99 (978-0-7566-0798-2(1)) Dorling Kindersley Publishing, Inc.

Douglas, Vincent & School Specialty Publishing Staff. Tell Me about the World. 2004. (Tell Me Ser.). (Illus.). 224p. (J). pap. 14.95 (978-0-7696-3383-1(8) , Waterbird Bks.) School Specialty Publishing.

Fabre, J. Henri. Animal Life in Field & Garden. 2005. pap. 34.95 (978-1-4179-0762-5(2)) Kessinger Publishing, LLC.

Flatt, Lizann, et al. The Nature Treasury: A First Look at the Natural World. 2005. (Illus.). 48p. (J). 16.95 (978-1-897066-42-3(2)) Maple Tree Pr. CAN. *Dist:* Perseus Distribution.

Forte, Imogene. Nature Crafts. 2004. (Fun Things to Make & Do Ser.). (Illus.). 80p. (J). per. 9.95 (978-0-86530-617-2(6)) Incentive Pubns., Inc.

Fowler, Allan. The Wonder of a Waterfall. 1999. (Rookie Read-About Science Ser.). (Illus.). 32p. (gr. 1-2). pap. 4.95 (978-0-516-26483-7(4) , Children's Pr.) Scholastic Library Publishing.

Freeman, Stan, text. The Natural History of New York. 2002. (Illus.). 64p. (J). per. 9.95 (978-0-9636814-5-4(1)) Hampshire Hse. Publishing.

Ganeri, Anita. Protecting Polar Regions. 2005. (Protecting Habitats Ser.). (J). lib. bdg. 24.67 (978-0-8368-4993-6(0)) Stevens, Gareth Inc.

Gatty, Alfred. Parables from Nature. 2006. (ENG.). 272p. per. 19.95 (978-1-59462-139-0(X) , 168, Book Jungle) Standard Pubns., Inc.

Gilbert, Miquel Angel. The Land. 2002. (Living Planet Ser.). (Illus.). 32p. (J). 23.70 (978-1-56711-668-7(X) , Blackbirch Pr., Inc.) Thomson Gale.

Glover, David. Exploring Nature. 2001. (Experiments in Science Ser.). (Illus.). (J). (978-0-7894-7472-8(7)) Dorling Kindersley Publishing, Inc.

Green, Jen. A Dead Log. 1999. (Small Worlds Ser.). (Illus.). 32p. (J). (gr. 3-4). lib. bdg. (978-0-7787-0136-1(0)) Crabtree Publishing Co.

—Under a Stone. 1999. (Small Worlds Ser.). (Illus.). 32p. (J). (gr. 3-4). pap. (978-0-7787-0151-4(4)) Crabtree Publishing Co.

Grupper, Jonathan. Destination: Rocky Mountains. 2001. (Illus.). 32p. (J). (gr. 1-5). 16.95 (978-0-7922-7722-4(8) , National Geographic Children's Bks.) National Geographic Society.

Guin, Valerie. In the Country. 2005. (Illus.). 30p. (J). (gr. 3-7). lib. bdg. 27.10 (978-1-58340-695-3(6)) Smart Apple Media.

Harcourt School Publishers Staff. Horizon Walk in the Wilderness: Time for Kids Readers:State & Region 5 Pack. 3rd ed. 2002. (Harcourt Horizons Ser.). (gr. k-7). pap. 28.70 (978-0-15-333389-7(8)) Harcourt Schl. Pubs.

Helbrough, Emma. Great Planet Earth Search. Jackson, Ian, illus. 2006. 32p. (J). ***(978-0-439-83402-5(3))*** Scholastic, Inc.

Holland, Gini. I Live in the Country. 2004. (Weekly Reader Early Learning Library). (Illus.). 24p. (gr. k up). (J). pap. (978-0-8368-4086-5(0)); (YA). lib. bdg. 19.33 (978-0-8368-4079-7(8)) Stevens, Gareth Inc. (Weekly Reader Early Learning Library).

—I Live in the Country/Vivo en el Campo. Coffey, Colleen & Carrillo, Consuelo, trs. 2004. (Weekly Reader Early Learning Library). (Illus.). 24p. (J). (gr. k up). (ENG & SPA.). pap. 5.95 (978-0-8368-4134-3(4)); (SPA & ENG., lib. bdg. 19.33 (978-0-8368-4127-5(1)) Stevens, Gareth Inc. (Weekly Reader Early Learning Library).

Hunter, Anne. What's under the Log? 1999. (Illus.). 32p. (J). (gr. k-3). tchr. ed. 5.95 (978-0-395-75496-2(8)) Houghton Mifflin Co. Trade & Reference Div.

J. G. Ferguson Publishing Company Staff, contrib. by. Discovering Careers in Your Future/Nature. 2002. (Discovering Careers for Your Future Ser.). (Illus.). 96p. (J). (gr. 4-9). 21.95 (978-0-89434-396-4(3) , Ferguson Publishing Co.) Facts On File, Inc.

Jenkins, Steve. What Do You Do When Something Wants to Eat You? Jenkins, Steve, illus. 2001. (Illus.). 32p. (J). (gr. k-3). 5.95 (978-0-618-15243-8(1)) Houghton Mifflin Co. Trade & Reference Div.

—What Do You Do When Something Wants to Eat You? 2001. (gr. k-3). lib. bdg. 14.10 (978-0-613-35590-2(3)) Tandem Library Bks.

Kalman, Bobbie. What Is a Living Thing? 1999. (Science of Living Things Ser.). (Illus.). 32p. (J). (gr. 2-3). pap. (978-0-86505-891-0(1)) Crabtree Publishing Co.

Kerrod, Robin. 1000 Questions & Answers. 2002. (Illus.). 320p. (J). (978-0-7534-0763-9(9) , Kingfisher) Houghton Mifflin Co. Trade & Reference Div.

Klingel, Cynthia Fitterer. Europe. 2003. (Continents Ser.). (Illus.). 32p. (J). (gr. 2-6). 27.07 (978-1-59296-060-6(X)) Child's World, Inc.

Laskey, Elizabeth. Wild Nature, 4 bks. 2004. (J). (gr. 3-5). lib. bdg. 108.29 (978-1-4034-4961-0(9)) Heinemann Library.

Lawlor, Elizabeth P., et al. Discover Nature in Winter. 1998. (Discover Nature Ser.). (Illus.). 198p. pap. 14.95 (978-0-8117-2719-8(X)) Stackpole Bks.

Lindeen, Carol. Life in a Polar Region. 2003. (Pebble Plus: Living in a Biome Ser.). (Illus.). 24p. (J). lib. bdg. 17.26 (978-0-7368-2100-1(7) , Pebble Bks.) Capstone Pr., Inc.

Lucas, Diane. Walking with the Seasons in Kakadu. Searle, Ken, illus. 2005. 32p. (J). pap. 9.95 (978-1-74114-471-0(X)) Allen & Unwin AUS. *Dist:* Independent Pubs. Group.

Lynch, Wayne. Whose Baby Is This? Lynch, Wayne, photos by. 2003. (Name That Animal! Ser.). (Illus.). 32p. (J). (gr. 1 up). lib. bdg. 23.33 (978-0-8368 3638-7(3)) Stevens, Gareth Inc.

—Whose Baby Is This? 2000. (gr. k-3). lib. bdg. 15.25 (978-0-613-78598-3(3)) Tandem Library Bks.

—Whose Baby Is This? 2000. (Whose? Animal Ser.). (Illus.). 32p. (J). (ps-2). pap. 6.95 (978-1-55285-064-0(1)) Whitecap Bks., Ltd. CAN. *Dist:* Firefly Bks., Ltd.

Madgwick, Wendy. Living Things. 1999. (Science Starters Ser.). (Illus.). 32p. (J). (gr. k-4). lib. bdg. 25.70 (978-0-8172-5332-5(7)) Raintree.

—Living Things. 1999. (Science Starters Ser.). (Illus.). 32p. (gr. k-4). 7.95 (978-0-8172-5883-2(3)) Steck-Vaughn.

Mahaney, Ian F. Energy in Action, 6 bks., Set. Incl. Electricity. lib. bdg. 21.25 (978-1-4042-3478-9(0)); Heat. lib. bdg. 21.25 (978-1-4042-3477-2(2)); Light. lib. bdg. 21.25 (978-1-4042-3476-5(4)); Solar Energy. lib. bdg. 21.25 (978-1-4042-3479-6(9)); Sound Waves. lib. bdg. 21.25 (978-1-4042-3480-2(2)); Water Power. lib. bdg. 21.25 (978-1-4042-3481-9(0)); (Illus.). 24p. (J). (gr. 4-6). 2007. , PowerKids Pr. 2007. Set lib. bdg. 127.50 (978-1-4042-3504-5(3)) Rosen Publishing Group, Inc., The.

McLeod, Liz. Savage Planet: Real-life Stories Of Tragedy And Survival. 2000. (Illus.). 160p. (J). 35.00 (978-0-233-99731-5(8)) Andre Deutsch GBR. *Dist:* Independent Pubs. Group.

Morel, Gaud. Exploring Nature. Best, Clare et al, trs. 1998. (Creative Discoveries Ser.: Vol. 8). (Illus.). 75p. (J). (gr. 2-9). lib. bdg. 23.95 (978-0-88682-946-9(1) , Creative Education) Creative Co., The.

Morgan, Sally. Life In..., 4 vols., Set. Incl. Clearing in the Forest. lib. bdg. 16.95 (978-1-929298-84-6(6)); Giant Tree in the Rainforest. lib. bdg. 16.95 (978-1-929298-85-3(4)); Pond in the Meadow. lib. bdg. 16.95 (978-1-929298-86-0(2)); Tide on the Seashore. lib. bdg. 16.95 (978-1-929298-87-7(0)); 32p. (J). (gr. 2-6). (Illus.). 2000. Set lib. bdg. 67.80 (978-1-929298-88-4(9)) Chrysalis Education.

Morley, Margaret Warner. A Song of Life 1922. Forsyth, Robert, illus. 2004. reprint ed. pap. 21.95 (978-1-4179-7842-7(2)) Kessinger Publishing, LLC.

Morrison, Gordon. Nature in the Neighborhood. 2004. (Illus.). 32p. (J). (gr. 3-5). tchr. ed. 16.00 (978-0-618-35215-9(5) , Walter Lorraine) Houghton Mifflin Co. Trade & Reference Div.

National Geographic Society Staff, ed. Books for Young Explorers, 4 vols., Set 6. (J). lib. bdg. 16.95 (978-0-87044-250-6(3)) National Geographic Society.

Natural History. (Illus.). (J). (ps-6). pap., act. bk. ed. 2.95 (978-0-565-00857-4(9)) Natural History Museum Pubns. GBR. *Dist:* Parkwest Pubns., Inc.

The Natural World, 4 vols. (Illus.). 2003. (978-0-7398-6059-5(3)); 2003. 742.56 (978-0-7398-6060-1(7)); 1999. 216.96 (978-0-7398-1064-4(2)) Raintree.

Nature's Record-Breakers, 8 bks. Incl. Animals. Newson, Joyce E. Davico, Francesco et al, illus. 2000. lib. bdg. 23.33 (978-0-8368-2473-5(3)); Dinosaurs. Davies, Francis & Faleschini, Gian P. 2000. lib. bdg. 23.33 (978-0-8368-2474-2(1)); Earth. Davies, Francis. 2002. lib. bdg. 23.33 (978-0-8368-2907-5(7)); Human Body. Bruno, Stephen. 2002. lib. bdg. 23.33 (978-0-8368-2905-1(0)); Natural Disasters. Newson, Joyce E. Chesi, Matteo, illus. 2002. lib. bdg. 23.33 (978-0-8368-2906-8(9)); Plants. Meucci, Antonella. Holguin, Paola, illus. 2002. lib. bdg. 23.33 (978-0-8368-2908-2(5)); Seas & Oceans. Meucci, Antonella. Chesi, Matteo, illus. 2000. lib. bdg. 23.33 (978-0-8368-2475-9(X)); Universe. Davies, Francis. Davico, Francesco & Cecchi, Lorenzo, illus. 2000. lib. bdg. 23.33 (978-0-8368-2476-6(8)); 32p. (J). (gr. 3 up). 2000. Set lib. bdg. 186.64 (978-0-8368-3141-2(1)) Stevens, Gareth Inc.

O'Brien-Palmer, Michelle. How the Earth Works: 60 Fun Activities for Exploring Volcanoes, Fossils, Earthquakes, & More. 2002. (Illus.). 192p. (J). (gr. 1-4). pap. 14.95 (978-1-55652-442-4(0)) Chicago Review Pr., Inc.

O'Hare, Jeff. Searchin' Safari: Looking for Camouflaged Creatures. Hadel, Marc, illus. 2003. 32p. (YA). (gr. 2-7). pap. 7.95 (978-1-56397-817-3(2)) Boyds Mills Pr.

Olmstead, Adrienne. My Nature Journal: A Personal Nature Guide for Young People. Olmstead, Donald, ed. Olmstead, Adrienne, illus. unabr. ed. 2000. (ACE., Illus.). 176p. (gr. 3-8). 17.95 (978-0-9672459-1-1(5)) Pajaro.

Parker, Francis W. Uncle Robert's Geography (Uncle Robert's Visit, V. 3) 2006. 84p. pap. (978-1-84702-205-9(7)) Echo Library.

Pascoe, Elaine & Corwin, Jeff. Into Wild California. 2003. (Animal Planet Ser.). (Illus.). 48p. (J). 11.20 (978-1-4103-0178-9(8) , Blackbirch Pr., Inc.) Thomson Gale.

Pecorella, Jane. Yellowstone, Our First National Park. 2003. (Reading Room Collection). (Illus.). 24p. (J). lib. bdg. 18.75 (978-0-8239-3712-7(7)) Rosen Publishing Group, Inc., The.

Peel, John. Book of Earth, Vol. 5. 2005. 208p. pap. 4.99 (978-0-7387-0613-9(2)) Llewellyn Pubns.

—Book of Earth, 5. 1998. (Diadem Ser.). (J). (978-0-606-12913-8(8)) Tandem Library Bks.

Pratt-Serafini, Kristin Joy, illus. Saguaro Moon: A Desert Journal. 2004. (Sharing Nature with Children Book Ser.). 32p. (YA). 16.95 (978-1-58469-037-5(2)); pap. 7.95 (978-1-58469-036-8(4)) Dawn Pubns.

Press, Judy. The Kids' Natural History Book: Making Dinos, Fossils, Mammoths & More! Kline, Michael P., illus. 2000. (Kids Can Bks.). 132p. (J). (gr. 1-7). pap. 12.95 (978-1-885593-24-5(4) , Williamson Bks.) Ideals Pubns.

Questions & Answers of the Natural World. 2003. (Illus.). 256p. (J). 12.98 (978-1-4054-1682-5(3)) Parragon, Inc.

Rainis, Kenneth G. Nature Projects for Young Scientists. rev. ed. (Project for Young Scientists Ser.). (Illus.). 192p. (gr. 9-12). 2003. (YA). pap. 9.95 (978-0-531-16381-8(4)); 2002. (J). pap. 23.50 (978-0-531-11724-8(3)) Scholastic Library Publishing. (Watts, Franklin).

—Nature Projects for Young Scientists. 2002. (gr. 5-8). lib. bdg. 18.75 (978-0-613-59527-8(0)) Tandem Library Bks.

Richardson, Joy. Variety of Life, 8 Vols. 186.64 (978-0-8368-4501-3(3)) Stevens, Gareth Inc.

A Ride Around Presque Isle: Natural History along the Roadsides. 2004. (Illus.). spiral bd. 15.00 (978-0-9747001-1-3(8)) Edinboro Bk. Arts Collective.

Robertson, Kayo. Signs along the River: Learning to Read the Natural Landscape. 1999. 64p. (gr. 1-6). pap. 7.95 (978-0-911797-22-0(X)) Rinehart, Roberts Pubs.

Rossouw, Andre J. & Bitline S. A. 1010. Natural Sciences Matters Grade 8 Learner's Book Afrikaans Translation. 2006. 160p. pap. 14.00 (978-0-521-67894-0(3)) Cambridge Univ. Pr.

Rossouw, Andre J., et al. Natural Sciences Matters Grade 8 Learner's Book. 2006. 160p. pap. 14.00 (978-0-521-67892-6(7)) Cambridge Univ. Pr.

Ryan, Marla Felkins & Corwin, Jeff. Into Wild Tasmania. 2004. (Jeff Corwin Experience Ser.). (Illus.). 48p. (J). 11.20 (978-1-4103-0248-9(2)); (gr. 4-7). 24.95 (978-1-4103-0247-2(4)) Thomson Gale. (Blackbirch Pr., Inc.).

Sample, Geoff. Nature Safari. 2003. (Illus.). 192p. pap. 17.99 (978-0-00-713839-5(3)) HarperCollins Pubs. Ltd. GBR. *Dist:* Independent Pubs. Group.

Sayre, April Pulley. Greeting, Asia! The Ultimate Guide to America's 4 Regional Styles of 'Cue. 2003. (Illus.). 32p. lib. bdg. 21.90 (978-0-7613-2124-8(1) , Millbrook Pr.) Lerner Publishing Group.

Schonberg, Marcia. Michigan Plants & Animals. 2003. (Heinemann State Studies). (Illus.). 48p. (J). pap. 8.50 (978-1-4034-2679-6(1)) Heinemann Library.

Silva Lee, Alfonso. Mi Isla y Yo: La Naturaleza de Puerto Rico. Hayskar, Bonnie J., ed. Lago, Alexis, illus. 2007. (SPA.). 32p. (J). pap. 8.95 (978-1-929165-19-3(6)) PANGAEA.

—Mi Isla y Yo = My Island & I: La Naturaleza de Puerto Rico = the Nature of Puerto Rico. Hayskar, Bonnie J., ed. Lago, Alexis, illus. 2002. (SPA & ENG.). 32p. (J). (gr. 2-5). 15.95 (978-1-929165-06-3(4)) PANGAEA.

—Mi isla y yo = My Island & I: La naturaleza de Puerto Rico = the Nature of Puerto Rico. Hayskar, Bonnie J., ed. Lago, Alexis, illus. 2003. (SPA & ENG.). 32p. (J). pap. 9.95 (978-1-929165-12-4(9)) PANGAEA.

Smith, Lynn & Faust Kalscheur, Jann. ABC's Naturally: A Child's Guide to the Alphabet Through Nature. Faust Kalscheur, Jann, photos by. 2003. (Illus.). (J). 16.95 (978-1-931599-27-6(0) , Trails Bks.) Big Earth Publishing.

Smith, Susan Carlton. 3 Famous Artist-Naturalists of the Colonial Period: John Abbot, Insects; William Bartram, Flowers; Mark Catesby, Birds: A Coloring Book for All Ages. 2002. (Illus.). (J). pap. 7.00 (978-0-9718587-0-1(5)) Gazebo Pr., The.

Southwater Staff. Look & Learn about Nature. 2001. (Look & Learn Ser.). (Illus.). 32p. (ps). 7.95 (978-1-84215-282-9(3) , Southwater) Anness Publishing GBR. *Dist:* National Bk. Network.

St. Antoine, Sara, ed. The Great North American Prairie. Mirocha, Paul & Nicholson, Trudy, illus. 2004. (Stories from Where We Live Ser.). 208p. pap. 10.95 (978-1-57131-645-5(0)) Milkweed Editions.

—The Great North American Prairie. Nicholson, Trudy & Mirocha, Paul, illus. 2001. (Stories from Where We Live Ser.). 366p. (J). (gr. 4-7). 19.95 (978-1-57131-630-1(2)) Milkweed Editions.

—The North Atlantic Coast. 2004. (Stories from Where We Live Ser.). (Illus.). 288p. pap. 10.95 (978-1-57131-643-1(4)) Milkweed Editions.

Stewart, Robin. Darwin's Tortoise: The Amazing Story of Harriet, the World's Oldest Living Creature. Crichton, Anna, illus. 2006. 160p. (J). pap. (978-1-86395-373-3(6) , Black Inc. Agenda) Schwartz Publishing Pty, Ltd.

Swinburne, Stephen R. Lots & Lots of Zebra Stripes: Patterns in Nature. 2001. (ps-2). lib. bdg. 17.60 (978-0-613-51456-9(4)) Tandem Library Bks.

Tate, Suzanne & Maloney, Susan, eds. A Teaching Guide for Suzanne Tate's Nature Series, Bks. 19 & 20. 1998. (Illus.). 16p. pap. 2.95 (978-1-878405-24-1(1)) Nags Head Art, Inc.

Telford, Carole & Theodorou, Rod. Down a River. 2006. (Illus.). 32p. (J). ***(978-1-4034-8789-6(8))*** Heinemann Library.

—Down a River. 2nd ed. 2006. (Illus.). 32p. (J). pap. ***(978-1-4034-8796-4(0))*** Heinemann Library.

Theodorou, Rod. From the Arctic to the Antarctic. 2000. (Amazing Journeys Ser.). (Illus.). 32p. (J). (gr. 3-5). lib. bdg. 22.79 (978-1-57572-485-0(5)) Heinemann Library.

Trumbauer, Lisa. A Year in the Desert. 2005. (Yellow Umbrella Ser.). (Illus.). 16p. (J). (978-0-7368-5266-1(2)); (978-0-7368-5302-6(2)) Capstone Pr., Inc.

Tuxworth, Nicola & Lorenz Editors. Nature. 2004. (Let's Look at... Ser.). (Illus.). 20p. 5.99 (978-0-7548-1279-1(0)) Anness Publishing GBR. *Dist:* National Bk. Network.

Vierow, Wendy. Australia. 2004. (Atlas of the Seven Continents Ser.). (Illus.). 24p. (J). lib. bdg. 21.25 (978-0-8239-6690-5(9) , PowerKids Pr.) Rosen Publishing Group, Inc., The.

—Europe. 2004. (Atlas of the Seven Continents Ser.). (Illus.). 24p. (J). lib. bdg. 21.25 (978-0-8239-6691-2(7) , PowerKids Pr.) Rosen Publishing Group, Inc., The.

Wadsworth, Pamela. Gwahanol Blanhigion Ac Anifeiliaid. 2005. (WEL., Illus.). 24p. pap. (978-1-85596-223-1(3)) Dref Wen.

—Rhagor Am Wahanol Blanhigion Ac Anifeiliaid. 2005. (WEL., Illus.). 24p. pap. (978-1-85596-224-8(1)) Dref Wen.

Wendt, Jennifer. Park Naturalist. 1999. (Illus.). (YA). (gr. 5-12). pap. 19.93 (978-0-516-21891-5(3) , Children's Pr.) Scholastic Library Publishing.

Wild Life on the Rockies. 2001. 108p. pap. 11.95 (978-1-928878-21-6(0)) Temporal Mechanical Pr.

Williams, Zella. Experiments about the Natural World. 2007. (Do-It-Yourself Science Ser.). (Illus.). 24p. (J). (gr. 2-5). lib. bdg. 23.95 (978-1-4042-3661-5(9) , PowerKids Pr.) Rosen Publishing Group, Inc., The.

Woodward, John & Corwin, Jeff. Into Wild Tanzania. 2004. (Jeff Corwin Experience Ser.). (Illus.). 48p. (J). pap. 11.20 (978-1-4103-0250-2(4) , Blackbirch Pr., Inc.) Thomson Gale.

Wright, Julia McNair. Christian Liberty Nature Reader. Shewan, Edward J., ed. 2nd ed. 2000. (Nature Readers Ser.: Bk. 2). (Illus.). 156p. (J). (gr. 6-8). pap. 6.00 (978-1-930092-52-5(0) , CLP29960) Christian Liberty Pr.

—Christian Liberty Nature Reader. Shewan, Edward, ed. 2nd ed. 2000. (Nature Readers Ser.: Bk. 3). (Illus.). 160p. (J). (gr. 3-4). pap. 6.00 (978-1-930092-53-2(9) , CLP29955) Christian Liberty Pr.

X-treme Places. 2005. (X-treme Places Ser.). (J). lib. bdg. 143.76 (978-1-59716-095-7(4)) Bearport Publishing Co., Inc.

Young, Caroline & Needham, Kate. Great Wildlife Search: Big Bug Search, Great Animal Search & Great Undersea Search. Jackson, Ian, illus. 2004. (Great Searches Ser.). 112p. (J). pap. 15.99 (978-0-7945-0892-0(8) , Usborne) EDC Publishing.

NATURAL HISTORY—AFRICA

Corwin, Jeff. Into Wild Zanzibar. 2004. (Jeff Corwin Experience Ser.). (Illus.). 48p. (J). 11.20 (978-1-4103-0256-4(3)); (gr. 4-7). 24.95 (978-1-4103-0255-7(5)) Thomson Gale. (Blackbirch Pr., Inc.).

Dentro de Tanzania Salvaje. 2005. (Jeff Corwin Experience Ser.). (ENG & SPA., Illus.). 48p. (J). (ps-7). lib. bdg. 24.95 (978-1-4103-0686-9(0) , Blackbirch Pr., Inc.) Thomson Gale.

Inserra, Rose & Powell, Susan. The Kalahari. 1998. (Ends of the Earth Ser.). (Illus.). 48p. (J). lib. bdg. 25.45 (978-0-431-06932-6(8)) Heinemann.

Rebus, Anna. Victoria Falls: One of the World's Most Spectacular Waterfalls. 2007. (J). (978-1-59036-459-8(7)); lib. bdg. (978-1-59036-453-6(8)) Weigl Pubs., Inc.

Ryan, Marla Felkins. Into Wild Moracco. 2004. (Jeff Corwin Experience Ser.). (Illus.). 48p. (J). 11.20 (978-1-4103-0236-6(9)); (gr. 4-7). 24.95 (978-1-4103-0235-9(0)) Thomson Gale. (Blackbirch Pr., Inc.).

Woodward, John & Corwin, Jeff. Into Wild Tanzania. 2004. (Jeff Corwin Experience Ser.). (Illus.). 48p. (J). (gr. 4-7). 24.95 (978-1-4103-0249-6(0) , Blackbirch Pr., Inc.) Thomson Gale.

NATURAL HISTORY—AUSTRALIA

Collard, Sneed B., III. Lizard Island: Science & Scientists on Australia's Great Barrier Reef. (Single Title Science Pb Ser.). (Illus.). 144p. (YA). (gr. 9-12). 2001. pap. 12.95 (978-0-531-16519-5(1)); 2000. 26.00 (978-0-531-11719-4(7)) Scholastic Library Publishing. (Watts, Franklin).

Ehrich, Joanne. Koalas: Zen in Fur, Hardcover Edition. 2007. (Illus.). 96p. 44.99 (***978-0-9764698-6-5(3)***) Koala Jo Publishing.

Sayre, April Pulley. Australia. 1998. (Seven Continents Ser.: 8). (Illus.). 64p. (gr. 5-8). lib. bdg. 25.90 (978-0-7613-3007-3(0) , Millbrook Pr.) Lerner Publishing Group.

Vierow, Wendy. Australia. 2004. (Atlas of the Seven Continents Ser.). (Illus.). 24p. (J). lib. bdg. 21.25 (978-0-8239-6690-5(9) , PowerKids Pr.) Rosen Publishing Group, Inc., The.

NATURAL HISTORY, BIBLICAL

see Bible—Natural History

NATURAL HISTORY—CANADA

Tessier, Tess & Tess, Grandma. White Spirit Bear. 2000. (Illus.). 48p. pap. 12.95 (978-0-88839-475-0(6)) Hancock Hse. Pubs.

—White Spirit Bear. Miller, Nancy, ed. 2nd ed. 2000. (Illus.). 48p. (J). (gr. k-7). 17.95 (978-0-88839-462-0(4)) Hancock Hse. Pubs.

Todd, Tom, illus. Hooked on Nature: The Wanderings & Wondering of an Amateur Naturalist. 2001. 128p. per. (978-0-9689131-0-9(5)) Wales Village Pr.

NATURAL HISTORY—DICTIONARIES

Amos, Janine. Scholastic First Encyclopedia: Animals & Nature. 2000. (978-0-606-18598-1(4)) Tandem Library Bks.

Brooks, F. First Encyclopedia of Our World. 2004. (First Encyclopedia Ser.). (SPA., Illus.). 64p. (J). (gr. 3 up). 9.99 (978-0-7945-0216-4(4) , Usborne) EDC Publishing.

Burnie, David. The Concise Nature Encyclopedia. 2006. (Concise Ser.). (Illus.). 320p. (J). (gr. 5-9). 14.95 (978-0-7534-5949-2(3) , Kingfisher) Houghton Mifflin Co. Trade & Reference Div.

Dorling Kindersley Publishing Staff, contrib. by. Nature Encyclopedia. 1998. (Illus.). 304p. (J). (gr. 3-9). 29.99 (978-0-7894-3411-1(3)) Dorling Kindersley Publishing, Inc.

Natural World. 2002. 256p. (J). 25.95 (978-0-7525-4350-5(4)) Parragon, Inc.

Natural World, 14 bks., Set. Incl. Chimpanzee : Habitats, Life Cycles, Food Chains, Threats. Banks, Martin. (gr. 3-7). 2000. lib. bdg. 27.12 (978-0-7398-1062-0(6)); Crocodile : Habitats, Life Cycles, Food Chains, Threats. Pope, Joyce. (gr. 4-7). 2000. lib. bdg. 27.12 (978-0-7398-2764-2(2)); Dolphin : Habitats, Life Cycles, Food Chains, Threats. Davies, Nicola. (gr. 3-7). 2000. lib. bdg. 27.12 (978-0-7398-2766-6(9)); Elephant : Habitats, Life Cycles, Food Chains, Threats. Travers, Will. (gr. 3-7). 1999. lib. bdg. 27.12 (978-0-7398-1056-9(1)); Giant Panda : Habitats, Life Cycles, Food Chains, Threats. Penny, Malcolm. (gr. 4-7). 2000. lib. bdg. 27.12 (978-0-7398-1063-7(4)); Great White Shark : Habitats, Life Cycles, Food Chains, Threats. Westwood, Brett. (gr. 3-7). 2000. lib. bdg. 27.12 (978-0-7398-1061-3(8)); Grizzly Bear : Habitats, Life Cycles, Food Chains, Threats. Leach, Michael. (gr. 3-7). 2001. lib. bdg. 27.12 (978-0-7398-2768-0(5)); Hippopotamus : Habitats, Life Cycles, Food Chains, Threats. Leach, Michael. (gr. 3-7). 2001. lib. bdg. 27.12 (978-0-7398-2769-7(3)); Killer Whale : Habitats, Life Cycles, Food Chains, Threats. Carwardine, Mark. (gr. 3-7). 1999. lib. bdg. 27.12 (978-0-7398-1058-3(8)); Lion : Habitats, Life Cycles, Food Chains, Threats. Jordan, Bill. (gr. 3-7). 1999. lib. bdg. 27.12 (978-0-7398-1057-6(X)); Orangutan : Habitats, Life Cycles, Food Chains, Threats. Brend, Stephen. (gr. 4-7). 2000. lib. bdg. 27.12 (978-0-7398-2765-9(0)); Penguin : Habitats, Life Cycles, Food Chains, Threats. Reid, Keith. (gr. 4-7). 2000. lib. bdg. 27.12 (978-0-7398-2767-3(7)); Polar Bear : Habitats, Life Cycles, Food Chains, Threats. Penny, Malcolm. (gr. 4-7). 2000. lib. bdg. 27.12 (978-0-7398-1060-6(X)); Tiger : Habitats, Life Cycles, Food Chains, Threats. Thapar, Valmik. (gr. 3-7). 1999. lib. bdg. 27.12 (978-0-7398-1055-2(3)); 48p. (J). (Illus.). 1999. 265.72 (978-0-7398-2770-3(7)) Raintree.

Question & Answer Encyclopedia: The Natural World. 2002. 256p. (J). 15.98 (978-0-7525-3843-3(8)) Parragon, Inc.

NATURAL HISTORY—FICTION

Andrews, Jane. Stories Mother Nature Told Her Children. 2006. pap. (***978-1-4065-0875-8(6)***) Dodo Pr.

Ballantyne, Michael. Blown to Bits or the Lonely Man of Rakat. 2006. 36.99 (***978-1-4280-4221-6(0)***); pap. 30.99 (***978-1-4280-4226-1(1)***) IndyPublish.com.

Ballantyne, R. M. Blown to Bits; or, the Lonely Man of Rak. 2006. pap. (***978-1-4065-0515-3(3)***) Dodo Pr.

Barnum, P. T. Dick Broadhead: A Story of Perilous Adve. 2006. pap. 30.95 (***978-1-4286-1959-3(3)***) Kessinger Publishing, LLC.

Bloom, Stephanie. A Place to Grow. Murphy, Kelly, illus. 2002. 32p. (J). lib. bdg. 16.95 (978-1-931969-07-9(8)) Bloom & Grow Bks.

Bonners, Susan. Silver Balloon. 1999. (978-0-606-17355-1(2)); (gr. 3-6). lib. bdg. 12.95 (978-0-613-22775-9(1)) Tandem Library Bks.

Dawes, Claiborne. A Different Drummer: Thoreau & Will's Independence Day. Moyle, J. Stephen, illus. 1998. 32p. (J). (gr. 2-5). pap. 7.95 (978-1-57960-039-6(5)) History Compass, LLC.

Delacre, Lulu. Rafi & Rosi. Delacre, Lulu, illus. (I Can Read Bks.). 64p. (J). (gr. k-3). 2005. pap. 3.99 (978-0-06-009897-1(X) , Rayo); 2004. (Illus.). lib. bdg. 16.89 (978-0-06-009896-4(1)) HarperCollins Pubs.

—Rafi y Rosi. Delacre, Lulu, illus. 2006. (I Can Read Bks.). (SPA.). 64p. (J). 15.99 (978-0-06-087277-9(2)); pap. 3.99 (978-0-06-087278-6(0)) HarperCollins Pubs. (Rayo).

—Rafi y Rosi: Carnival! Delacre, Lulu, illus. 2006. (I Can Read Bks.). (SPA.). 64p. (J). 15.99 (978-0-06-113134-9(2)); pap. 3.99 (978-0-06-113135-6(0)) HarperCollins Pubs. (Rayo).

Elkins, Tilke. Jakes & Dustin Take Off. 2001. (Illus.). 96p. (978-0-9688648-0-7(5)) Parkhurst Publishing, Ltd. CAN. *Dist:* Words Distributing Co.

Grant, Robert. Jack in the Bush or A Summer on a Salmon River. 2005. pap. 33.95 (978-1-4179-5573-2(2)) Kessinger Publishing, LLC.

Hadley, Caroline. Woodside or Look Listen & Learn. 2007. pap. 87.99 (***978-1-4280-5242-0(9)***) IndyPublish.com.

—Woodside; or, Look, Listen & Learn. 2007. (ENG., Illus.). 80p. per. (***978-1-4065-1557-2(4)***) Dodo Pr.

Hardouin, Benny. Cumulus the Puffy Cloud: A Story about Dealing with Childhood Obesity. 1998. (Illus.). 20p. (J). (ps-3). pap. 4.50 (978-0-9664731-0-0(8)) Hardouin, Benny.

Johnson, Donald B. Henry Hikes to Fitchburg. 2002. (Illus.). (J). 24.04 (978-0-7587-4606-1(7)) Book Wholesalers, Inc.

—Henry Hikes to Fitchburg. 2000. (Illus.). 32p. (J). (gr. k-3). tchr. ed. 15.00 (978-0-395-96867-3(4)) Houghton Mifflin Co. Trade & Reference Div.

Karecki, Jason, illus. The Adventures of Drake Montana Vol. 4: The Pacific Ocean. 1998. 24p. (J). (gr. k-5). (978-1-890716-11-0(1)) K&M International.

Lappin, Jeff. Marcel Moves Mountains. Chili, Sabra, ed. Madl, Jeremy, illus. 2002. 44p. 16.95 (978-0-9708805-0-5(2)) Endurance Pubns., Inc.

—Simon Makes Waves! Chili, Jabra, ed. Madl, Jeremy, illus. 2002. 44p. (J). (gr. k-3). 16.95 (978-0-9708805-1-2(0)) Endurance Pubns., Inc.

Locker, Thomas. In Blue Mountains: An Artist's Return to America's First Wilderness. Locker, Thomas, illus. rev. ed. 2000. (Illus.). 36p. (J). (ps-3). 18.00 (978-0-88010-471-5(6)) SteinerBooks, Inc.

Loomis, Christine. Across America, I Love You. Kiesler, Kate A., illus. 2000. 32p. (ps-3). 16.49 (978-0-7868-2314-7(3)) Hyperion Bks. for Children.

Mccabe, Jr. Planting the Wilderness or, the Pioneer Boys: a Story of Frontier Life. 2007. pap. 27.95 (***978-1-4304-8187-4(0)***) Kessinger Publishing, LLC.

Meister, Cari. I Love Rocks. Sirrell, Terry, illus. 2001. (Rookie Reader Espanol Ser.). 32p. (J). (gr. k-2). pap. 4.95 (978-0-516-27293-1(4)); (gr. 1-2). 19.50 (978-0-516-22152-6(3)) Scholastic Library Publishing. (Children's Pr.).

—I Love Rocks. 2001. (gr. k-3). lib. bdg. 12.95 (978-0-613-89012-0(4)) Tandem Library Bks.

Rivers, Freya A. Becoming: A Kemetic Creation Story. Brooks, Julian A. & Rivers, Shariba W., eds. Moore, La Mailede, illus. 2001. 50p. (J). (gr. k-8). pap. 20.00 (978-0-9667215-5-3(1)) Sankofa Publishing Co.

Say, Allen. The Lost Lake. Say, Allen, illus. 2002. (Illus.). (J). 15.49 (978-0-7587-3034-3(9)) Book Wholesalers, Inc.

Stockton, Frank Richard. RoundAbout Rambles in Lands of Fact and. 2006. pap. (***978-1-4068-3083-5(6)***) Echo Library.

Waboose, Jan Bourdeau. Morning on the Lake. Reczuch, Karen, illus. 32p. (J). (gr. k-3). 2002. (978-1-55074-588-7(3)); 1998. (978-1-55074-373-9(2)) Kids Can Pr., Ltd.

—Morning on the Lake. 2002. (gr. k-3). lib. bdg. 14.10 (978-0-613-83962-4(5)) Tandem Library Bks.

Weaver, Anne H. The Voyage of the Beetle: A Journey Around the World with Charles Darwin & the Search for the Solution to the Mystery of Mysteries, as Narrated by Rosie, an Articulate Beetle. Lawrence, George, tr. Lawrence, George, illus. 2004. (Roman Mysteries Ser.). 80p. (J). (gr. 5-8). lib. bdg. 26.90 (978-0-7613-2923-7(4) , Millbrook Pr.) Lerner Publishing Group.

NATURAL HISTORY—NORTH AMERICA

Ashcroft, Minnie. North America. 2003. (National Geographic Reading Expeditions Ser.). (Illus.). 64p. (J). (978-0-7922-4381-6(1)) National Geographic Society.

Bauer, Marion Dane. The Rocky Mountains. Wallace, John, illus. 2006. (Wonders of America Ser.). 32p. (J). pap. 3.99 (978-0-689-86948-8(7)); lib. bdg. 11.89 (978-0-689-86949-5(5)) Simon & Schuster Children's Publishing. (Aladdin).

Kirkland, Jane. Take A Beach Walk. Burke, Dorothy & Palaisa, Melanie, eds. 2007. (Take a Walk Ser.). (ENG., Illus.). 32p. (J). pap. 9.95 (978-0-9709754-4-7(9) , Take a Walk Bks.) Stillwater Publishing.

Loughran, Donna. Living in the Tundra. 2004. (Rookie Read-About Geography Ser.). (Illus.). 31p. (J). (gr. 1-2). pap. 5.95 (978-0-516-27331-0(0) , Children's Pr.) Scholastic Library Publishing.

Sheinkin, Steve. North America. 2003. (National Geographic Reading Expeditions Ser.). (Illus.). 64p. (J). (978-0-7922-4380-9(3)) National Geographic Society.

NATURAL HISTORY—OUTDOOR BOOKS

see Nature Study

NATURAL HISTORY—SOUTH AMERICA

Banting, Erinn. Galapagos Islands. 2006. (J). (978-1-59036-455-0(4)); lib. bdg. (978-1-59036-449-9(X)) Weigl Pubs., Inc.

Dewey, Jennifer Owings. Poison Dart Frogs. Dewey, Jennifer Owings, illus. 2003. (Illus.). 32p. (J). (gr. k-2). pap. 10.95 (978-1-56397-945-3(4)) Boyds Mills Pr.

—Poison Dart Frogs. 1998. (Illus.). 32p. (J). (gr. k-5). 15.95 (978-1-56397-655-1(2)) Boyds Mills Pr.

NATURAL HISTORY—UNITED STATES

Burnham, Brad. Mammoth Cave: The World's Longest Cave System. 2003. (Famous Caves of the World Ser.). (Illus.). 24p. (J). lib. bdg. 18.75 (978-0-8239-6258-7(X) , PowerKids Pr.) Rosen Publishing Group, Inc., The.

Dentro de California Salvaje. 2005. (Jeff Corwin Experience Ser.). (ENG & SPA., Illus.). 48p. (J). (ps-7). lib. bdg. 24.95 (978-1-4103-0671-5(2) , Blackbirch Pr., Inc.) Thomson Gale.

Dentro de Madagascar Salvaje. 2005. (Jeff Corwin Experience Ser.). (ENG & SPA., Illus.). 48p. (J). (ps-7). lib. bdg. 24.95 (978-1-4103-0683-8(6) , Blackbirch Pr., Inc.) Thomson Gale.

Dunphy, Madeleine. Here Is the Southwestern Desert. Coe, Anne, illus. 2006. (Web of Life Ser.). 32p. (J). 16.95 (978-0-9773795-7-6(4)); pap. 9.95 (978-0-9773795-6-9(6)) Web of Life Children's Bks.

Feinstein, Stephen. California Plants & Animals. (Heinemann State Studies). (Illus.). 48p. (J). 2003. (gr. 3-5). lib. bdg. (978-1-4034-0343-8(0)); 2002. pap. 8.50 (978-1-4034-0560-9(3)) Heinemann Library.

—California Plants & Animals. 2003. (gr. 3-6). lib. bdg. 17.05 (978-0-613-60856-5(9)) Tandem Library Bks.

Fiorelli, Lalo. Wild Splendors of California. 2002. (Illus.). 140p. 45.95 (978-0-9717228-0-4(3)); pap. 29.95 (978-0-9717228-1-1(1)) Splendors Publishing.

Hall, Margaret. Denali National Park. 2006. (Symbols of Freedom Ser.). (Illus.). 32p. (J). (978-1-4034-7794-1(9)) Heinemann Library.

Helman, Andrea. O Is for Orca: An Alphabet Book. Wolfe, Art, illus. Wolfe, Art, photos by. 2003. 32p. (J). pap., pap. 10.95 (978-1-57061-392-0(3)) Sasquatch Bks.

—1, 2, 3 Moose: A Counting Book. Wolfe, Art, photos by. 2003. (Illus.). 32p. (J). pap., pap. 9.95 (978-1-57061-393-7(1)) Sasquatch Bks.

Hubbell, Sue. Country Year: Living the Questions. 1999. (gr. 7-12). lib. bdg. 22.25 (978-0-613-63700-8(3)) Tandem Library Bks.

Hubbs, Brian. Mountain Kings: A Collective Natural History of California, Sonoran, Durango & Queretaro Mountain Kingsnakes. 2004. (Illus.). 356p. per. 45.00 (978-0-9754641-0-6(8)) Tricolor Bks.

Knotts, Bob. Florida Plants & Animals. 2002. (State Studies). (Illus.). 48p. (J). pap. 8.50 (978-1-4034-0566-1(2)); lib. bdg. (978-1-4034-0350-6(3)) Heinemann Library.

Lantz, Peggy S. & Hale, Wendy. The Young Naturalist's Guide to Florida. 2nd ed. 2006. (Illus.). iv, 195p. (J). pap. (978-1-56164-377-6(7)) Pineapple Pr., Inc.

Leotti-Bachem, Janice. The Everglades. 2005. (Rookie Read-About Geography Ser.). (Illus.). 32p. (J). (gr. 1-2). 20.50 (978-0-516-22750-4(5) , Children's Pr.) Scholastic Library Publishing.

Levinson, Nancy Smiler. Death Valley Level 2: A Day in the Desert. Hearn, Diane Dawson, illus. (Reader Ser.). 32p. (J). (gr. k-3). tchr. ed. 14.95 (978-0-8234-1566-3(X)) Holiday Hse., Inc.

Obee, Ruth. A Sense of Place: Discovering the Stratton Open Space. 2002. (Illus.). 104p. per. 12.95 (978-1-884418-60-0(0)) Blue River Publishing, Inc.

Patent, Dorothy Hinshaw. Animals on the Trail with Lewis & Clark. Munoz, William, illus. 2002. 128p. (J). (gr. 4-6). 18.00 (978-0-395-91415-1(9) , Clarion Bks.) Houghton Mifflin Co. Trade & Reference Div.

—Plants on the Trail with Lewis & Clark. Munoz, William, photos by. 2003. (Illus.). 112p. (J). (gr. 4-6). tchr. ed. 18.00 (978-0-618-06776-3(0) , Clarion Bks.) Houghton Mifflin Co. Trade & Reference Div.

Pratt-Serafini, Kristin Joy. Saguaro Moon: A Desert Journal. 2002. (gr. 3-6). lib. bdg. 16.40 (978-0-613-52786-6(0)) Tandem Library Bks.

Schonberg, Marcia. Michigan Plants & Animals. 2003. (Heinemann State Studies). (Illus.). 48p. (J). 27.07 (978-1-4034-0662-0(6)) Heinemann Library.

Smith, Karla. Virginia Plants & Animals. 2003. (Heinemann State Studies). (Illus.). 48p. (J). pap. 8.50 (978-1-4034-0582-1(4)); (gr. 3-5). lib. bdg. (978-1-4034-0360-5(0)) Heinemann Library.

—Virginia Plants & Animals. 2003. (gr. 3-6). lib. bdg. 17.05 (978-0-613-60996-8(4)) Tandem Library Bks.

St. Antoine, Sara. The Great Lakes. 2005. (Stories from Where We Live Ser.). (Illus.). 264p. (J). pap. 10.95 (978-1-57131-654-7(X)) Milkweed Editions.

St. Antoine, Sara, ed. The California Coast. 2005. (Stories from Where We Live Ser.). (Illus.). 248p. (J). pap. 10.95 (978-1-57131-653-0(1)) Milkweed Editions.

—The South Atlantic Coast & Piedmont: A Literary Field Guide. Nicholson, Trudy, illus. 2006. (Stories from Where We Live Ser.). 256p. (J). pap. 10.95 (978-1-57131-664-6(7)) Milkweed Editions.

Steward, Mark. New York Plants & Animals. 2003. (Heinemann State Studies). (Illus.). 48p. (J). (gr. 3-5). lib. bdg. (978-1-4034-0356-8(2)) Heinemann Library.

Stewart, Mark. New York Plants & Animals. 2003. (Heinemann State Studies). (Illus.). 48p. (J). pap. 8.50 (978-1-4034-0578-4(6)) Heinemann Library.

—New York Plants & Animals. 2003. (gr. 3-6). lib. bdg. 17.05 (978-0-613-60976-0(X)) Tandem Library Bks.

Wade, Mary. Texas Plants & Animals. 2003. (Heinemann State Studies). (Illus.). 48p. (J). pap. 8.50 (978-1-4034-2698-7(8)) Heinemann Library.

Wade, Mary Dodson. Texas Plants & Animals. 2003. (Heinemann State Studies). (Illus.). 48p. (J). lib. bdg. 27.07 (978-1-4034-0690-3(1)) Heinemann Library.

—Texas Plants & Animals. 2003. (gr. 3-6). lib. bdg. 17.05 (978-0-613-88569-0(4)) Tandem Library Bks.

Webb, Sophie. Looking for Seabirds: Journal from an Alaskan Voyage. 2004. (Illus.). 48p. (J). (gr. 5 up). tchr. ed. 16.00 (978-0-618-21235-4(3)) Houghton Mifflin Co. Trade & Reference Div.

Weber, Sandra. Two in the Wilderness: Adventures of a Mother & Daughter in the Adirondack Mountains. Heilman, Carl, illus. 2005. 48p. (J). 19.95 (978-1-59078-182-1(1)) Boyds Mills Pr.

Weintraub, Aileen. The Grand Canyon: Widest Canyon. 2001. (Great Record Breakers in Nature Ser.). (Illus.). 24p. (J). (gr. 2-5). lib. bdg. 18.75 (978-0-8239-5641-8(5) , PowerKids Pr.) Rosen Publishing Group, Inc., The.

NATURAL HISTORY MUSEUMS

Leeper, Angela. The Nature Museum. 2004. (Field Trip! Ser.). (Illus.). 24p. (J). pap. (978-1-4034-5170-5(2)) Heinemann Library.

—To a Natural Science Museum. 2004. (Field Trip! Ser.). (Illus.). 24p. (J). lib. bdg. (978-1-4034-5164-4(8)) Heinemann Library.

NATURAL LAW

see Civil Rights; Ethics; International Law; Liberty

NATURAL MONUMENTS

Adams, Cynthia. Circling the World: World Famous Landmarks. 2003. (Circling the World Ser.). (Illus.). 176p. (gr. 4-6). 15.99 (978-1-56822-674-3(8) , IF20538) School Specialty Publishing.

Ashabranner, Brent. Badge of Valor: The National Law Enforcement Officers Memorial. Ashabranner, Jennifer, illus. 2000. (Great American Memorials Ser.). 64p. (gr. 4-8). lib. bdg. (978-0-7613-1522-3(5) , Twenty-First Century Bks.) Lerner Publishing Group.

Bateman, Teresa. Red, White, Blue & Uncle Who? The Story Behind Some of America's Patriotic Symbols. (Illus.). 64p. (J). (gr. 4-6). 6.95 (978-0-8234-1784-1(0)) Holiday Hse., Inc.

Binns, Tristan Boyer. Statue of Liberty. 2001. (978-0-606-22575-5(7)) Tandem Library Bks.

Britton, Tamara L. The Alamo. 2005. (Symbols, Landmarks, & Monuments Set Ii Ser.). (Illus.). 32p. (J). (gr. k-6). lib. bdg. 22.78 (978-1-59197-518-2(2)) ABDO Publishing Co.

—Symbols, Landmarks, & Monuments Set II. 2004. (Illus.). (J). (gr. k-6). lib. bdg. 136.68 (978-1-59197-517-5(4) , Checkerboard Library) ABDO Publishing Co.

—The Vietnam Veterans Memorial. 2005. (Symbols, Landmarks, & Monuments Set Ii Ser.). (Illus.). 32p. (J). (gr. k-6). lib. bdg. 22.78 (978-1-59197-523-6(9)) ABDO Publishing Co.

Cooper, Jason. Little Bighorn Battlefield. 2000. (Historic Landmarks Ser.). (Illus.). 24p. (J). (gr. 1-4). lib. bdg. 20.64 (978-1-55916-325-5(9)) Rourke Publishing, LLC.

Cox, Reg. The Seven Wonders of the Natural World. 2000. (Wonders of the World Ser.). (Illus.). 32p. (J). (gr. 4-7). 25.50 (978-0-7910-6049-0(7) , Chelsea Hse.) Facts On File, Inc.

Curlee, Lynn. Rushmore. (J). (gr. 3-5). (978-0-439-06013-4(3)) Scholastic, Inc.

DK Publishing Staff. Great Wonders of the Natural World. 2007. 64p. (J). (gr. 3-6). 19.99 (978-0-7566-2980-9(2)) Dorling Kindersley Publishing, Inc.

Keenan, Sheila. O, Say Can You See? America's Symbols, Landmarks, & Inspiring Words. Boyajian, Ann, illus. 2004. (Oh Say Can You See Ser.). 64p. (J). (ps-3). pap. 16.95 (978-0-439-42450-9(X) , Scholastic Reference) Scholastic, Inc.

Lewison, Wendy Cheyette. L Is for Liberty. Hines, Laura Freeman, illus. 2003. (Reading Railroad Bks.). 32p. (J). (ps-4). pap. 3.49 (978-0-448-43228-1(5) , Grosset & Dunlap) Penguin Group (USA) Inc.

Nathan, Emma. Lugares Conocidos. 2002. (Abre los Ojos y Aprende Serie).Tr. of Eyeopeners: Landmarks. (SPA.). 24p. (J). (-3). 24.94 (978-1-4103-0026-3(9) , Blackbirch Pr., Inc.) Thomson Gale.

Nobleman, Marc Tyler. The Lincoln Memorial. 2004. (Let's See Library). (Illus.). 24p. (J). (gr. 1 up). lib. bdg. 19.93 (978-0-7565-0618-6(2)) Compass Point Bks.

—The Washington Monument. 2004. (Let's See Library). (Illus.). 24p. (J). (gr. 1 up). lib. bdg. 19.93 (978-0-7565-0621-6(2)) Compass Point Bks.

O'Donnell, Kerri. Natural Wonders of the World: Converting Distance Measurements to Metric Units. 2005. (Illus.). 32p. (J). (978-1-4042-5120-5(0)) Rosen Publishing Group, Inc., The.

—Natural Wonders of the World: Converting Measurements to Metric Units. 2005. (PowerMath Ser.). (Illus.). 32p. (J). 22.50 (978-1-4042-2928-0(0) , PowerKids Pr.); pap. (978-1-4042-5119-9(7)) Rosen Publishing Group, Inc., The.

Raintree Steck-Vaughn Staff. Wonders of the World. 2000. (Read All about It Ser.). (Illus.). (J). pap. 4.95 (978-0-8114-3790-5(6)) Steck-Vaughn.

Stein, R. Conrad. The Korean War Veterans Memorial. 2002. (Cornerstones of Freedom: Vol. 2). (Illus.). 48p. (J). (gr. 4-6). 26.00 (978-0-516-22260-8(0) , Children's Pr.) Scholastic Library Publishing.

MNO

NATURAL MONUMENTS—UNITED STATES

Craats, Rennay. Natural Landmarks. 2004. (American Symbols Ser.). (J). pap. 6.95 (978-1-59036-177-1(6)); (Illus.). 24p. lib. bdg. 15.95 (978-1-59036-133-7(4)) Weigl Pubs., Inc.

DeFries, Cheryl L. Seven Natural Wonders of the United States & Canada: A MyReportLinks. com Book. 2005. (Seven Wonders of the World Ser.). (Illus.). 48p. (J). lib. bdg. 25.26 (978-0-7660-5291-8(5) , MyReportLinks.com Bks.) Enslow Pubs., Inc.

Parent, Laurence E. Capulin Volcano National Monument. Priehs, T. J. & Jorgen, Randolph, eds. Parent, Laurence E., photos by. 2006. (Illus.). 16p. (Orig.). pap. 4.95 (978-0-911408-94-2(0)) Western National Parks Assn.

NATURAL RESOURCES

see also Conservation of Natural Resources; Fisheries; Forests and Forestry; Marine Resources; Mines and Mineral Resources; Power Resources; Water Power; Water Resources Development; Water-Supply

Adil, Janeen R. Scarcity. 2006. (First Facts Ser.). (Illus.). 24p. (J). (978-0-7368-5399-6(5)) Capstone Pr., Inc.

Apel, Melanie Ann. Land & Resources in Ancient Greece. 2004. (Primary Sources of Ancient Civilizations Ser.). (Illus.). 24p. (J). lib. bdg. 19.95 (978-0-8239-6769-8(7) , PowerKids Pr.) Rosen Publishing Group, Inc., The.

—Land & Resources of Ancient Greece. 2004. (Primary Sources of Ancient Civilizations Ser.). (Illus.). 24p. (J). lib. bdg. (978-0-8239-8937-9(2) , PowerKids Pr.) Rosen Publishing Group, Inc., The.

Bachman, La. Recursos Naturales y Ambientes en un Mundo Global: Recursos Naturales y Ambiente. 2002. (SPA.). (gr. 3-6). lib. bdg. 12.35 (978-0-613-71083-1(5)) Tandem Library Bks.

Burton, Margie, et al. Riches from Nature. Adams, Alison, ed. 1999. (Early Connections Ser.). 16p. (J). (gr. k-2). pap. 4.50 (978-1-58344-080-3(1)) Benchmark Education Co.

Cambridge Educational, prod. Natural Resources Win Labpak. (YA). cd-rom 324.88 (978-0-7365-4369-9(4)) Films Media Group.

Downing, David. Geography & Resources of the Middle East. 2006. (World Almanac Library of the Middle East). (Illus.). 48p. (J). pap. (978-0-8368-7341-2(6)); lib. bdg. (978-0-8368-7334-4(3)) Stevens, Gareth Inc. (World Almanac Library).

Fredericks, Carrie. Natural Gas. 2006. (Fueling the Future Ser.). (Illus.). 244p. (YA). (gr. 10-12). 34.95 (978-0-7377-3598-7(8) , Greenhaven Pr., Inc.) Thomson Gale.

Gedacht, Daniel C. Land & Resources in Ancient Rome. 2004. (Primary Sources of Ancient Civilizations Ser.). (Illus.). 24p. (J). lib. bdg. 19.95 (978-0-8239-6775-9(1) , PowerKids Pr.) Rosen Publishing Group, Inc., The.

—Land & Resources of Ancient Rome. 2004. (Primary Sources of Ancient Civilizations Ser.). (Illus.). 24p. (J). lib. bdg. (978-0-8239-8943-0(7) , PowerKids Pr.) Rosen Publishing Group, Inc., The.

Harcourt School Publishers Staff. Kids Care. 3rd ed. 2002. (Trophies English Language Learners Ser.). (Illus.). pap. 5.10 (978-0-15-327823-5(4)) Harcourt Schl. Pubs.

—Working Together to Save Our Planet. 3rd ed. 2002. (Horizons Ser.). (Illus.). (J). pap. 3.70 (978-0-15-333202-9(6)) Harcourt Schl. Pubs.

Haugen, David M. Coal. 2006. (Fueling the Future Ser.). (Illus.). 244p. (YA). (gr. 10-12). 34.95 (978-0-7377-3591-8(0) , Greenhaven Pr., Inc.) Thomson Gale.

Holt, Rinehart and Winston Staff. Environmental Science Chptr. 18: Renewable Energy. 4th ed. Date not set. pap. 11.20 (978-0-03-068079-3(4)) Holt, Rinehart & Winston.

—Holt Science & Technology No. 6: Earth, Water & Air Resources: Texas Edition - Grade 8. 2nd ed. 2001. pap. 26.00 (978-0-03-064874-8(2)) Holt, Rinehart & Winston.

—Holt Science Spectrum Chptr. 23: Using Natural Resources. 4th ed. Date not set. pap. 11.20 (978-0-03-068062-5(X)) Holt, Rinehart & Winston.

Kaplan, Leslie C. Land & Resources in Ancient Egypt. 2004. (Primary Sources of Ancient Civilizations Ser.). (Illus.). 24p. (J). lib. bdg. 19.95 (978-0-8239-6781-0(6) , PowerKids Pr.) Rosen Publishing Group, Inc., The.

—Land & Resources of Ancient Egypt. 2004. (Primary Sources of Ancient Civilizations Ser.). (Illus.). 24p. (J). lib. bdg. (978-0-8239-8931-7(3) , PowerKids Pr.) Rosen Publishing Group, Inc., The.

Kerrod, Robin. New Materials. 2003. (21st Century Science Ser.). 48p. (J). lib. bdg. 27.10 (978-1-58340-353-2(1)) Smart Apple Media.

Llewellyn, Claire. Geysers. 2000. (Heinemann First Library). (Illus.). 32p. (J). (gr. k-2). lib. bdg. 21.36 (978-1-57572-204-7(6)) Heinemann Library.

—Geysers. 2000. (gr. k-3). lib. bdg. 14.75 (978-0-613-45763-7(3)) Tandem Library Bks.

Llewellyn, Claire, et al. Geysers. 2002. (Geography Starts Ser.). (Illus.). 32p. (J). (gr. k-2). pap. 6.95 (978-1-58810-972-9(0) , 91455) Heinemann Library.

Mason, Paul. Population. 2005. (Planet under Pressure Ser.). (Illus.). 48p. (J). lib. bdg. 31.43 (978-1-4034-7741-5(8)) Heinemann Library.

Orr, Tamra. Geothermal Energy. 2008. (J). pap. 7.95 (***978-1-60279-097-1(3)***) Cherry Lake Publishing.

Parks, Peggy J. Global Resources (Overview) 2004. (Overview Ser.). (Illus.). 112p. (J). (gr. 7-10). 29.95 (978-1-56006-979-9(1) , Lucent Bks.) Thomson Gale.

Resources: Nature's Riches. (Earthworks Ser.). (J). 29.93 (978-0-7614-1369-1(3) , Benchmark Bks.) Cavendish, Marshall Corp.

Richards, Julie. Geothermal Energy & Bio-Energy. 2003. 32p. (J). lib. bdg. 24.25 (978-1-58340-336-5(1)) Smart Apple Media.

Smuskiewicz, Alfred J. Earth's Resources. 2006. (J). pap. (***978-0-8368-7874-5(4)***) Stevens, Gareth Inc.

Spilsbury, Louise & Spilsbury, Richard. The Future—Bleak or Bright? Earth's Resources. 2005. (Illus.). 32p. lib. bdg. (978-1-4109-1928-1(5)) Steck-Vaughn.

Spilsbury, Richard & Spilsbury, Louise. The Future - Bleak or Bright? Earth's Resources. 2005. (Illus.). 32p. (J). (gr. 6-9). 7.85 (978-1-4109-1959-5(5)) Steck-Vaughn.

Stille, Darlene R. Earth Science, 4 titles, Set. 2005. (Exploring Science Ser.). (YA). (gr. 5-7). lib. bdg. 101.08 (978-0-7565-0883-8(5)) Compass Point Bks.

—Natural Resources: Using & Protecting Earth's Supplies. 2004. (Exploring Science Ser.). (Illus.). 48p. (J). 25.27 (978-0-7565-0856-2(8)) Compass Point Bks.

Windsor, Jo. Energy: Individual Title Six-Packs. (Sails Literacy Ser.). 20p. (gr. 4 up). 27.00 (978-0-7578-0786-2(0)) Rigby Education.

Winters, Adam. Sustainable Development. 2006. (Extreme Environmental Threats Ser.). (Illus.). 64p. (YA). lib. bdg. (978-1-4042-0746-2(5)) Rosen Publishing Group, Inc., The.

NATURAL RESOURCES—UNITED STATES

Camp, William G. & Daugherty, Thomas B. Managing Our Natural Resources. 4th rev. ed. 2000. (Illus.). 416p. (C). 108.95 (978-0-7668-1554-4(4)) Thomson Delmar Learning.

Davis, Wendy & Knight, Bertram T. Working at a Marine Institute. 1998. (Working Here Ser.). (Illus.). 32p. (J). (gr. 2-4). 23.50 (978-0-516-21223-4(0) , Children's Pr.) Scholastic Library Publishing.

NATURAL SELECTION

see also Evolution

Burton, Jane & Taylor, Kim. The Nature & Science of Survival. 2001. (Exploring the Science of Nature Ser.). (Illus.). 32p. (J). (gr. 3 up). lib. bdg. 24.67 (978-0-8368-2211-3(0)) Stevens, Gareth Inc.

Fullick, Ann. Inheritance & Selection. 2005. (Life Science In-Depth Ser.). (Illus.). 64p. (J). pap. (978-1-4034-7531-2(8)); lib. bdg. (978-1-4034-7523-7(7)) Heinemann Library.

Highet, Alistair. Lucas. 2001. 8.95 (978-1-56846-127-4(5)) Creative Co., The.

—Lucas. Delessert, Etienne, illus. 2000. 40p. (J). (gr. 3). pap. 8.95 (978-0-89812-014-1(4) , Creative Paperbacks) Creative Co., The.

NATURALISTS

Adamson, Heather. Charles Darwin & the Theory of Evolution. Purcell, Gordon & Milgrom, Al, illus. 2008. (J). (***978-1-4296-0145-0(0)***) Capstone Pr., Inc.

Anderson, Margaret J. Carl Linnaeus: Father of Classification. 2001. (Great Minds of Science Ser.). (Illus.). 128p. (YA). (gr. 4-10). pap. 13.26 (978-0-7660-1867-9(9)) Enslow Pubs., Inc.

Armentrout, David. John Muir. 2002. (SPA.). (gr. k-3). lib. bdg. 14.10 (978-0-613-79836-5(8)) Tandem Library Bks.

Armentrout, David & Armentrout, Patricia. John Muir. 2002. (Discover Someone Who Made a Difference Discovery Library Ser.). (Illus.). 24p. (J). (gr. 2-5). 14.95 (978-1-58952-055-4(6)) Rourke Publishing, LLC.

—John Muir. Sarfatti, Esther & de la Vega, Eida, trs. 2001. (Personas que Cambiaron la Historia Ser.). (SPA., Illus.). 24p. (J). (gr. 1-4). lib. bdg. 19.27 (978-1-58952-168-1(4) , RK7725) Rourke Publishing, LLC.

Bausum, Ann. Dragon Bones & Dinosaur Eggs: A Photo-Biography of Explorer Roy Chapman Andrews. 2000. (Illus.). 64p. (J). (gr. 3-7). 17.95 (978-0-7922-7123-9(8) , National Geographic Children's Bks.) National Geographic Society.

Chessen, Betsey & Chanko, Pamela. Jane Goodall & Her Chimpanzees. 1999. (Social Studies Emergent Readers). (J). 2.50 (978-0-439-04576-6(2)) Scholastic, Inc.

—Jane Goodall & Her Chimpanzees. 1999. (ps-2). lib. bdg. 10.10 (978-0-613-21797-2(7)) Tandem Library Bks.

Crum, Anna-Maria. Conductistas de animales & Animal Behaviorists. 2005. spiral bd. 77.00 (***978-1-4108-5679-1(8)***) Benchmark Education Co.

—Rastreadores de nuestra dinamica Tierra & Trackers of Dynamic Earth. 2005. spiral bd. 84.00 (***978-1-4108-5718-7(2)***) Benchmark Education Co.

Ferrara, Cos. Anna Comstock: A Love Affair with Nature. 2004. (Girls Explore, Reach for the Stars Ser.). (Illus.). 112p. (J). 20.00 (978-0-9749456-1-3(7) , Girls Explore) Girls Explore LLC.

Fullick, Ann. Charles Darwin. (Groundbreakers Ser.). (Illus.). 48p. (J). (gr. 5-7). 2002. pap. 8.50 (978-1-58810-990-3(9) , 91465); 2000. lib. bdg. 25.64 (978-1-57572-368-6(9)) Heinemann Library.

Gogerly, Liz. Dian Fossey. 2002. (Scientists Who Made History Ser.). (Illus.). 48p. (J). lib. bdg. 27.12 (978-0-7398-5225-5(6)) Raintree.

Goodall, Jane. The Chimpanzees I Love: Saving Their World & Ours. 2001. (Illus.). 80p. (J). (gr. 3 up). pap. 18.95 (978-0-439-21310-3(X) , Levine, Arthur A. Bks.) Scholastic, Inc.

Goodridge, Catherine. Jane Goodall (Spanish) & Jane Goodall. 2005. spiral bd. 70.00 (***978-1-4108-5658-6(5)***) Benchmark Education Co.

Hartzog, Brooke. The First Dinosaur Eggs & Roy Chapman Andrews. 1999. (Dinosaurs & Their Discoverers Ser.). (Illus.). 24p. (J). (gr. k-4). lib. bdg. 18.75 (978-0-8239-5329-5(7) , PowerKids Pr.) Rosen Publishing Group, Inc., The.

Haugen, Brenda. Jane Goodall: Legendary Zoologist. 2006. (Signature Lives Ser.). (Illus.). 112p. (J). (gr. 5-7). 30.60 (978-0-7565-1590-4(4)) Compass Point Bks.

Hopkinson, Deborah. Who Was Charles Darwin? Harrison, Nancy, illus. 2005. (Who Was— ? Ser.). 112p. (J). (gr. 2-5). pap. 4.99 (978-0-448-43764-4(3) , Grosset & Dunlap) Penguin Group (USA) Inc.

Jane Goodall. 2002. (Illus.). (J). pap. 5.43 (978-0-7398-5929-2(3)) Steck-Vaughn.

Kiely Miller, Barbara. John Muir. 2007. (J). pap. (***978-0-8368-8325-1(X)*** , Weekly Reader Early Learning Library) Stevens, Gareth Inc.

King, David C. Charles Darwin. 2007. (DK Biography Ser.). (Illus.). 128p. (J). (***978-1-4287-1710-7(2)***) Dorling Kindersley Publishing, Inc.

Krohn, Katherine E. Jane Goodall: Animal Scientist. 2006. (Graphic Library). (Illus.). 32p. (J). 25.26 (978-0-7368-5485-6(1)) Capstone Pr., Inc.

Lalley. Desert Scientists. 2001. (Scientists of the Biomes Ser.). (Illus.). (J). pap. (978-0-7398-4935-4(2)) Steck-Vaughn.

Lalley, Pat & Lalley, Janet. Desert Scientists. 2001. (Scientists of the Biomes Ser.). (Illus.). 48p. (J). (gr. 4-7). lib. bdg. 24.26 (978-0-7398-4754-1(6)) Raintree.

Lasky, Kathryn. Charles Darwin. Sorel, Edward, illus. 2004. (J). (978-0-7636-1436-2(X)) Candlewick Pr.

—John Muir: America's First Environmentalist. Fellows, Stan, illus. 2006. 48p. (J). (gr. 1-5). 16.99 (978-0-7636-1957-2(4)) Candlewick Pr.

—John Muir: America's First Environmentalist. Fellows, Stanley, illus. 2006. 41p. (J). (978-1-4156-7115-3(X)) Candlewick Pr.

Lawson, Kristan. Darwin & Evolution for Kids: His Life & Ideas with 21 Activities. 2003. (For Kids Ser.). (Illus.). 160p. (J). pap. 16.95 (978-1-55652-502-5(8)) Chicago Review Pr., Inc.

Locker, Thomas. John Muir: America's Naturalist. (Illus.). 32p. (gr. 4). 17.95 (978-1-55591-393-9(8)) Fulcrum Publishing.

Mara, Wil. John Muir. (Rookie Biographies Ser.). (Illus.). 32p. (J). (gr. 1-2). 2003. pap. 4.95 (978-0-516-27342-6(6)); 2002. 20.50 (978-0-516-22515-9(4)) Scholastic Library Publishing. (Children's Pr.).

—John Muir. 2002. (gr. k-3). lib. bdg. 12.95 (978-0-613-59504-9(1)) Tandem Library Bks.

Mathews, Tom L. Light Shining Through the Mist: A Photobiography of Dian Fossey. 1998. (Illus.). 64p. (J). (gr. 4-7). 17.95 (978-0-7922-7300-4(1) , T07300C, National Geographic Children's Bks.) National Geographic Society.

Matthewson, Sarah. On the Lookout: Lives of Naturalists. 2007. (Shockwave: Life Stories Ser.). (Illus.). 36p. (J). (gr. 4-6). lib. bdg. 25.00 (***978-0-531-17772-3(6)*** , Children's Pr.) Scholastic Library Publishing.

Maynard, Thane. Working with Wildlife: A Guide to Careers in the Animal World. 2000. (J). (978-0-606-19406-8(1)) Tandem Library Bks.

McCarthy, Pat. Henry David Thoreau: Writer, Thinker, Naturalist. 2003. (Historical American Biographies Ser.). (Illus.). 128p. (J). (gr. 6-12). lib. bdg. 26.60 (978-0-7660-1978-2(0)) Enslow Pubs., Inc.

McVey, James. Martha Maxwell: Natural History Pioneer. 2005. (Now You Know Bio Ser.: 4). (Illus.). 84p. (J). per. 8.95 (978-0-86541-075-6(5)) Filter Pr., LLC.

Meltzer, Milton. Henry David Thoreau: A Biography. 2007. (J). spiral bd. 31.93 (978-0-8225-5893-4(9) , Twenty-First Century Bks.) Lerner Publishing Group.

Miller. The Tundra Scientists. 2001. (Scientists of the Biomes Ser.). (Illus.). (J). pap. (978-0-7398-4940-8(9)) Steck-Vaughn.

Miller, Barbara Kiely. John Muir. 2007. (Great Americans Ser.). 24p. (J). (gr. 2-4). lib. bdg. 19.93 (***978-0-8368-8318-3(7)*** , Weekly Reader Early Learning Library) Stevens, Gareth Inc.

Miller, Chuck. Tundra Scientists. 2001. (Scientists of the Biomes Ser.). (Illus.). 48p. (J). (gr. 4-7). lib. bdg. 24.26 (978-0-7398-4752-7(X)) Raintree.

Muir, John. John Muir: My Life with Nature. 2000. lib. bdg. 17.60 (978-0-613-56465-6(0)) Tandem Library Bks.

—Stickeen: John Muir & the Brave Little Dog. Canyon, Christopher, illus. 1998. 32p. (YA). (ps-7). 16.95 (978-1-883220-79-2(3)); pap. 7.95 (978-1-883220-78-5(5)) Dawn Pubns.

Muir, John & Cornell, Joseph Bharat. John Muir: My Life with Nature. 2004. (Sharing Nature with Children Book Ser.). (Illus.). 80p. (YA). (gr. 4-7). pap. 8.95 (978-1-58469-009-2(7)) Dawn Pubns.

Naden, Corinne J. & Blue, Rose. Dian Fossey: At Home with the Giant Gorillas. 2002. (Gateway Greens Ser.). (Illus.). 48p. (gr. 2-4). lib. bdg. 23.90 (978-0-7613-2569-7(7) , Millbrook Pr.) Lerner Publishing Group.

Nardo, Don. Charles Darwin. 2004. (Importance of Ser.). (Illus.). 112p. (YA). (gr. 7-10). lib. bdg. 32.45 (978-1-59018-339-7(8) , Lucent Bks.) Thomson Gale.

Nicholson, Lois P. Dian Fossey. 2003. (Women in Science Ser.). pap. 30.00 (978-0-7910-7521-0(4) , Chelsea Hse.) Facts On File, Inc.

Senker, Cath. Charles Darwin. 2001. (Scientists Who Made History Ser.). (Illus.). 48p. (J). lib. bdg. 27.12 (978-0-7398-4843-2(7)) Raintree.

Sis, Peter. The Tree of Life: Charles Darwin. Sis, Peter, illus. 2003. (Illus.). 44p. (J). (gr. 3 up). 18.00 (978-0-374-45628-3(3) , Farrar, Straus & Giroux (BYR)) Farrar, Straus & Giroux.

—The Tree of Life: Charles Darwin. (Illus.). 22.95 (978-0-88899-564-3(4)) Groundwood Bks. CAN. *Dist:* Transition Vendor.

Smith, Susan Carlton. 3 Famous Artist-Naturalists of the Colonial Period: John Abbot, Insects; William Bartram, Flowers; Mark Catesby, Birds: A Coloring Book for All Ages. 2002. (Illus.). (J). pap. 7.00 (978-0-9718587-0-1(5)) Gazebo Pr., The.

Sproule, Anna. Charles Darwin: Visionary Behind the Theory of Evolution. 2002. (Scientists Who Have Changed the World Ser.). (Illus.). 64p. (J). 26.20 (978-1-56711-655-7(8) , Blackbirch Pr., Inc.) Thomson Gale.

Stanley, Phyllis M. Elizabeth Terwilliger - Someone Special: A Biography of the Celebrated Naturalist. 2003. (Illus.). 110p. (J). (gr. 4-10). pap. 17.95 (978-1-878044-54-9(0)) Mayhaven Publishing.

Stansfield, John. Enos Mills, Rocky Mountain Naturalist. 2005. (Now You Know Bio Ser.). (Illus.). 103p. (J). pap. (978-0-86541-072-5(0)) Filter Pr., LLC.

Topp, Patricia. Call Him Father Nature: The Story of John Muir. 2001. (Illus.). 97p. (J). (gr. 4-7). pap. 8.95 (978-1-57733-047-9(1)) Blue Dolphin Publishing, Inc.

Waxman, Laura Hamilton. Jane Goodall. Butler, Tad, illus. 2007. (History Maker Biographies Ser.). (J). 26.60 (***978-0-8225-7610-5(4)*** , Lerner Pubns.) Lerner Publishing Group.

Weaver, Anne H. The Voyage of the Beetle: A Journey Around the World with Charles Darwin & the Search for the Solution to the Mystery of Mysteries, As Narrated by Rosie, an Articulate Beetle. Lawrence, George, illus. 2007. 80p. (YA). (gr. 5 up). 16.95 (***978-0-8263-4304-8(X)***) Univ. of New Mexico Pr.

Whiting, Jim. Charles Darwin & the Origin of the Species. 2005. (Uncharted, Unexplored, & Unexplained Ser.). (Illus.). 48p. (J). (gr. 8). lib. bdg. 29.95 (978-1-58415-364-1(4)) Mitchell Lane Pubs., Inc.

Yannuzzi, Della A. Aldo Leopold: Protector/Wild. 2002. (Gateway Greens Ser.). (Illus.). 48p. (gr. 2-4). lib. bdg. 23.90 (978-0-7613-2465-2(8) , Millbrook Pr.) Lerner Publishing Group.

NATURE

Aigner-Clark, Julie. Nature Discovery CardsTM: Nature Photographs & Facts to Delight Your Baby. 2003. (Baby Einstein Ser.). (Illus.). 29p. (J). (ps-17). 9.99 (978-0-7868-1842-6(5)) Hyperion Bks. for Children.

Alexander, Cecil. All Things Bright & Beautiful. Vojtech, Anna, illus. 2004. 24p. (J). (ps-3). 15.95 (978-0-7358-1892-7(4)) North-South Bks., Inc.

Alexander, Cecil Frances. All Things Bright & Beautiful. McDaniels, Preston, illus. 2000. (Hymns for Children Ser.). 32p. (J). (ps-2). 17.95 (978-0-8192-1834-6(0) , 6257) Morehouse Publishing.

—All Things Bright & Beautiful. Vojtech, Anna, illus. ed. 2006. 24p. (J). (ps-2). pap. 6.95 (978-0-7358-2045-6(7)) North-South Bks., Inc.

—Todas las Cosas Radiantes y Bellas. Vojtech, Anna, illus. 2006. (SPA.). (J). (ps-1). 15.95 (978-0-7358-2046-3(5)) North-South Bks., Inc.

All Things Bright & Beautiful. 2006. 16p. (J). pap. 1.99 (978-0-7847-1588-8(2) , 22135) Standard Publishing.

Amato, Carol A. Chessie, the Meandering Manatee, Vol. 8. Wenzel, David, illus. 1998. (Young Reader Ser.). 48p. (J). (gr. 3-6). lib. bdg. 13.45 (978-1-56674-239-9(0)) Forest Hse. Publishing Co., Inc.

Amazing Magnets: Level E. 8p. 20.95 (978-0-322-00353-8(9)) Wright Group, The.

Anastasio, Dina & Herndon, Ryan. Guinness World Records Wild Lives. 2006. (Illus.). 103p. (J). pap. 4.99 (978-0-439-74585-7(3)) Scholastic, Inc.

Animals Hide & Seek: Level E. 8p. 20.95 (978-0-322-00354-5(7)) Wright Group, The.

Armentrout, David & Armentrout, Patricia. 50 Words About. 2003. (50 Words about Ser.). (gr. 2-4). 119.70 (978-1-58952-340-1(7)) Rourke Publishing, LLC.

Arnosky, Jim. Watching Desert Wildlife. Arnosky, Jim, illus. 2002. (Illus.). 32p. (J). (gr. 4-7). pap. 7.95 (978-0-7922-6737-9(0) , National Geographic Children's Bks.) National Geographic Society.

—Watching Desert Wildlife. 2003. (gr. 3-6). lib. bdg. 16.40 (978-0-613-84044-6(5)) Tandem Library Bks.

Ballard, Carol. The Search for Better Conservation. 2005. (Science Quest Ser.). (Illus.). 32p. (J). lib. bdg. 24.67 (978-0-8368-4553-2(6)) Stevens, Gareth Inc.

Bang, Molly Garrett. Common Ground: The Water, Earth & Air We Share. 2001. (J). 23.90 incl. audio Spoken Arts, Inc.

Barraclough, Sue. Protecting Species & Habitats. 2006. (What's Your View? Ser.). (Illus.). 48p. (J). (978-1-58340-976-3(9)) Smart Apple Media.

Barron's Educational Editorial Staff. Amazing Nature. 1998. (Megascope Ser.). (Illus.). 64p. (J). (gr. 5). 6.95 (978-0-7641-5090-6(1)) Barron's Educational Series, Inc.

Become a Junior Ranger. 2001. (Illus.). 12p. (J). (gr. 1-7). pap. 2.50 (978-1-888213-55-3(8)) Eastern National.

Benchmark Education Staff, compiled by. Cactus & Canyons & Ecosystems. 2005. spiral bd. 225.00 (***978-1-4108-5806-1(5)***) Benchmark Education Co.

—Cactus & Canyons & Regions. 2005. spiral bd. 225.00 (***978-1-4108-5805-4(7)***) Benchmark Education Co.

Bennett, Paul. En el Oceano. Nunez, Olga, tr. 2001. (Natural World Ser.). (SPA.). 32p. (J). (gr. 4-7). pap. (978-968-5308-26-7(8) , Silver Dolphin en Español) Advanced Marketing, S. de R. L. de C. V.

Berkowitz, Henry. Dangerous Creatures: An Educational Coloring Book. Berkowitz, Henry, illus. 2001. 32p. (J). (ps-3). pap. 4.95 (978-0-932855-68-8(7)) Winner Enterprises.

BHB International Staff. Nature. 1999. (Illus.). 131p. (J). (gr. 1-4). 9.95 (978-2-215-06283-7(5)) Editions Fleurus FRA. *Dist:* Continental Enterprises Group, Inc. (CEG).

Bradley, Catherine. Plains. 2004. (Life In... Ser.). (SPA., Illus.). (gr. 3-6). 32p. (J). pap. 6.95 (978-1-58728-571-4(1)); 31p. 12.95 (978-1-58728-556-1(8)) T&N Children's Publishing. (Two Can Publishing).

Brady, Irene. Illustrating Nature: Right-brain Art in a Left-Brain World. Brady, Irene, illus. 2004. spiral bd. 25.95 (978-0-915965-09-0(7)) Nature Works Press.

Brettle, Jane. Nature Is Busy. 1999. 10p. (J). pap. 3.95 (978-1-57717-103-4(9)) New Line Bks.

Brooks, Bruce, ed. The Red Wasteland: A Personal Selection of Writings about Nature for Young Readers. 2000. 143p. (YA). (gr. 6-8). 16.00 (978-0-7881-9058-2(X)) DIANE Publishing Co.

—The Red Wastland: A Personal Selection of Writings about Nature for Young Readers. 2002. 143p. (YA). reprint ed. pap. 12.00 (978-0-7567-5585-0(9)) DIANE Publishing Co.

M N O

Bruce. Colors in Nature, 24 Bks, 6 Packs. 2004. (Illus.). pap. 118.80 (978-1-4109-1248-0(5)) Raintree.

Bruce, Lisa. Blue. 2004. (Colors in Nature Ser.). (Illus.). 24p. pap. 5.50 (978-1-4109-0729-5(5)); (J). lib. bdg. 18.56 (978-1-4109-0724-0(4)) Raintree.

—Green. 2004. (Colors in Nature Ser.). (Illus.). 24p. (J). lib. bdg. 18.56 (978-1-4109-0722-6(8)); pap. 5.50 (978-1-4109-0727-1(9)) Raintree.

—Red. 2004. (Colors in Nature Ser.). (Illus.). 24p. (J). lib. bdg. 18.56 (978-1-4109-0723-3(6)); pap. 5.50 (978-1-4109-0728-8(7)) Raintree.

—Yellow. 2004. (Colors in Nature Ser.). (Illus.). 24p. (J). pap. 5.50 (978-1-4109-0730-1(9)); lib. bdg. 18.56 (978-1-4109-0725-7(2)) Raintree.

Brunelle, Lynn. Camp-Out! The Ultimate Kid's Guide. 2007. (Illus.). 384p. (J). (gr. 4-7). pap. 11.95 (978-0-7611-4122-8(7)) Workman Publishing Co., Inc.

Bulloch, Ivan & James, Diane. Sol, Nieve y Arco Iris! 2004. (Me Toca a Mi Ser.).Tr. of Sun, Snow, & Rainbow!. (SPA., Illus.). 12p. (J). (ps-k). bds. 6.95 (978-1-58728-495-3(2) , Two Can Publishing) T&N Children's Publishing.

Burnie, David. The Concise Nature Encyclopedia. 2006. (Concise Ser.). (Illus.). 320p. (J). (gr. 5-9). 14.95 (978-0-7534-5949-2(3) , Kingfisher) Houghton Mifflin Co. Trade & Reference Div.

Burnie, David & Walker, Richard. Nature Ranger. 2006. (Nature Activities Ser.). (Illus.). 72p. (J). pap. 9.99 (978-0-7566-2069-1(4)) Dorling Kindersley Publishing, Inc.

Burrill, Richard L. Somewhere Behind the Eyes: Surprise Images in Nature Aha! Date not set. (Somewhere Behind the Eyes Ser.). (Illus.). 96p. (J). (gr. 4-12). pap. 12.95 (978-1-878464-19-4(1)) Anthro Co., The.

—Somewhere Behind the Eyes Vol. 3: Surprise Images in Nature Aha! Date not set. (Illus.). 96p. (J). (gr. 4-12). 10.95 (978-1-878464-18-7(3)) Anthro Co., The.

Burton, Jane & Taylor, Kim. Exploring the Science of Nature, 22 bks. Incl. Nature & Science of Autumn. Burton, Jane & Taylor, Kim, photos by. 1999. lib. bdg. 24.67 (978-0-8368-2190-1(4)); Nature & Science of Bubbles. 1998. lib. bdg. 23.93 (978-0-8368-1939-7(X)); Nature & Science of Color. 1998. lib. bdg. 23.93 (978-0-8368-1940-3(3)); Nature & Science of Eggs. Burton, Jane & Taylor, Kim, photos by. 1998. lib. bdg. 23.93 (978-0-8368-2105-5(X)); Nature & Science of Energy. 1998. lib. bdg. 23.93 (978-0-8368-1941-0(1)); Nature & Science of Fire. 2001. lib. bdg. 24.67 (978-0-8368-2198-7(X)); Nature & Science of Fossils. Burton, Jane & Taylor, Kim, photos by. 1999. lib. bdg. 23.93 (978-0-8368-2183-3(1)); Nature & Science of Leaves. 1997. lib. bdg. 24.67 (978-0-8368-1942-7(X)); Nature & Science of Mud. 1997. lib. bdg. 24.67 (978-0-8368-1943-4(8)); Nature & Science of Numbers. 2001. lib. bdg. 24.67 (978-0-8368-2193-2(9)); Nature & Science of Patterns. Burton, Jane & Taylor, Kim, photos by. 1998. lib. bdg. 23.93 (978-0-8368-2107-9(6)); Nature & Science of Rain. 1997. lib. bdg. 24.67 (978-0-8368-1944-1(6)); Nature & Science of Reflections. 2001. lib. bdg. 24.67 (978-0-8368-2194-9(7)); Nature & Science of Seeds. Burton, Jane & Taylor, Kim, photos by. 1999. lib. bdg. 24.67 (978-0-8368-2184-0(X)); Nature & Science of Shells. Burton, Jane & Taylor, Kim, photos by. 1999. lib. bdg. 24.67 (978-0-8368-2185-7(8)); Nature & Science of Spring. Burton, Jane & Taylor, Kim, photos by. 1999. lib. bdg. 24.67 (978-0-8368-2188-8(2)); Nature & Science of Summer. Burton, Jane & Taylor, Kim, photos by. 1999. lib. bdg. 24.67 (978-0-8368-2189-5(0)); Nature & Science of Sunlight. 1997. lib. bdg. 24.67 (978-0-8368-1946-5(2)); Nature & Science of Survival. 2001. lib. bdg. 24.67 (978-0-8368-2211-3(0)); Nature & Science of Waste. Burton, Jane & Taylor, Kim, photos by. 1999. lib. bdg. 24.67 (978-0-8368-2186-4(6)); Nature & Science of Wings. Burton, Jane, photos by. 1998. lib. bdg. 23.93 (978-0-8368-2108-6(4)); Nature & Science of Winter. 1999. lib. bdg. 24.67 (978-0-8368-2191-8(2)); 32p. (J). (gr. 3 up). (Illus.). Set lib. bdg. 222.03 (978-0-8368-2865-8(8)) Stevens, Gareth Inc.

Burton, Margie, et al. The Power of Nature. Adams, Alison, ed. 1999. (Early Connections Ser.). 16p. (J). (gr. k-2). pap. 4.50 (978-1-58344-078-0(X)) Benchmark Education Co.

Butterfield, Moira. Where Am I?, 4 vols. 1999. 32p. (J). lib. bdg. 67.80 (978-1-929298-38-9(2)) Chrysalis Education.

Cambridge Educational, prod. Mysteries of Nature Hyb Lb. (YA). cd-rom 222.50 (978-0-7365-4360-6(0)) Films Media Group.

Canizares, Susan & Chessen, Betsey. Science Outside. 1999. (J). pap. (978-0-439-04604-6(1)) Scholastic, Inc.

Capogna, Vera Vullo. Did You Ever Wonder? Series: Accelerated Reader, 4 bks. Incl. Did You Ever Wonder about Things You Find at the Beach? 1998. lib. bdg. 22.79 (978-0-7614-0851-2(7)); Did You Ever Wonder about Things You Find in the Woods? 2000. lib. bdg. 22.79 (978-0-7614-0852-9(5)); Did You Ever Wonder about Things You Find in Your Backyard? 1999. lib. bdg. 22.79 (978-0-7614-0855-0(X)); Did You Ever Wonder about Things You See in the Sky? 1999. lib. bdg. 22.79 (978-0-7614-0853-6(3)); 32p. (J). (gr. k-3). (Illus.). 2000. Set lib. bdg. 91.14 (978-0-7614-0854-3(1) , Benchmark Bks.) Cavendish, Marshall Corp.

Carle, Eric. All Around Us. Carle, Eric, illus. 2007. 16p. (J). (ps-ps). bds. 16.99 (***978-0-399-25008-8(5)*** , Philomel) Penguin Group (USA) Inc.

Carroll, Michael W., et al. Rocks & Plants, Vol. 3. 2005. (God's Creation Ser.). 40p. (J). 7.99 (978-0-310-70580-2(0)) Zonderkidz.

—Sky & Sea, Vol. 2. 2005. (God's Creation Ser.). 40p. (J). 7.99 (978-0-310-70579-6(7)) Zonderkidz.

Chinery, Michael. Las Costas.Tr. of Seashores. (SPA.). 40p. (J). (gr. 3-5). 12.76 (978-84-241-2053-5(1)) Everest de Ediciones y Distribucion, S.L. ESP. *Dist:* Lectorum Pubns., Inc.

—Los Desiertos. (SPA.). 40p. (J). (gr. 3-5). 12.76 (978-84-241-2051-1(5)) Everest de Ediciones y Distribucion, S.L. ESP. *Dist:* Lectorum Pubns., Inc.

—Los Lagos y los Rios.Tr. of Lakes & Rivers. (SPA.). 40p. (J). (gr. 3-5). 12.76 (978-84-241-2058-0(2)) Everest de Ediciones y Distribucion, S.L. ESP. *Dist:* Lectorum Pubns., Inc.

—Los Oceanos.Tr. of Oceans. (SPA.). 40p. (J). (gr. 3-5). 12.76 (978-84-241-2055-9(8)) Everest de Ediciones y Distribucion, S.L. ESP. *Dist:* Lectorum Pubns., Inc.

—Los Polos.Tr. of Polar Lands. (SPA.). 40p. (J). (gr. 3-5). 12.76 (978-84-241-2056-6(6)) Everest de Ediciones y Distribucion, S.L. ESP. *Dist:* Lectorum Pubns., Inc.

—Las Sabanas y las Praderas. (SPA.). (J). (gr. 3-5). 12.76 (978-84-241-2054-2(X)) Everest de Ediciones y Distribucion, S.L. ESP. *Dist:* Lectorum Pubns., Inc.

Cicciarelli, Joellyn. October. 1998. (Illus.). 96p. (J). (gr. k-3). pap., tchr. ed. 10.99 (978-1-57471-351-0(5) , 2377) Creative Teaching Pr., Inc.

Colvin, L. & Speare, E. Living World Encyclopedia. 2004. (Encyclopedias Ser.). (Illus.). 128p. (J). 7.95 (978-0-7945-0005-4(6)) EDC Publishing.

Confluence 2004. 2004. (YA). per. (978-0-9745192-4-1(3)) Little Bay Pr.

Connolly, Randy, et al. Poison Ivy, Pets & People: Scratching the Poison Ivy, Oak & Sumac Itch. 2005. (10thingstoknow about ... Ser.). (Illus.). 104p. pap. 9.95 (978-0-9722400-1-7(2)) 2Lakes Publishing.

Cork, Barbara. Pocket Nature. 2004. (First Nature Ser.). (Illus.). 170p. (J). 8.95 (978-0-7945-0346-8(2) , Usborne) EDC Publishing.

Cowcher, Helen. Rainforest. (Illus.). 40p. (CHI, ENG, URD, TUR & VIE.). (J). 16.95 (978-1-84059-017-3(3)); (VIE, ENG, URD, TUR & CHI., (J). 16.95 (978-1-84059-022-7(X)); 2001. (GRE, ENG, URD, TUR & VIE., (YA). 16.95 (978-1-84059-018-0(1)); 2001. (GUJ, ENG, URD, TUR & VIE., (YA). 16.95 (978-1-84059-019-7(X)); 2001. (TUR, ENG, URD, VIE & CHI., (YA). 16.95 (978-1-84059-020-3(3)); 2001. (BEN, ENG, URD, TUR & VIE., (YA). 16.95 (978-1-84059-016-6(5)) Milet Publishing.

—Whistling Thorn. (Illus.). 40p. (CHI, ENG, URD, TUR & VIE.). (J). 16.95 (978-1-84059-033-3(5)); 2001. (GRE, ENG, URD, TUR & VIE., (YA). 16.95 (978-1-84059-034-0(3)); 2001. (GUJ, ENG, URD, TUR & VIE., (YA). 16.95 (978-1-84059-035-7(1)); 2001. (TUR, ENG, URD, VIE & CHI., (YA). 16.95 (978-1-84059-036-4(X)); 2001. (URD, ENG, TUR, VIE & CHI., (YA). 16.95 (978-1-84059-037-1(8)); 2001. (BEN, ENG, URD, TUR & VIE., (YA). 16.95 (978-1-84059-032-6(7)) Milet Publishing.

Dalby, L. Mysteries & Marvels of Nature. 2004. (First Stories Ser.). 128p. (J). 19.95 (978-0-7945-0597-4(X)); lib. bdg. 27.95 (978-1-58086-610-1(7) , Usborne) EDC Publishing.

Dann, Penny & Alter, Judy. Native Americans. 2002. (Spirit of America: Our Cultural Heritage Ser.). (Illus.). 32p. (J). (gr. 2-6). 27.07 (978-1-56766-152-1(1)) Child's World, Inc.

Day, Trevor. Taiga. 2006. (Biomes of the Earth Ser.). (Illus.). 240p. (J). (gr. 6-12). 39.50 (978-0-8160-5329-2(4)) Facts On File, Inc.

De Brandt. Nature Log Kids. 1998. (J). pap. 11.95 (978-1-885061-56-0(0)) Adventure Pubns., Inc.

de Panafieu, Jean Baptiste & Desplanche, Vincent. Charles Darwin. Gonzalez Batlle, Jorge, tr. 2007. (Tras los pasos de ... Ser.). (SPA., Illus.). 128p. (J). pap. 14.95 (978-84-89396-83-8(3)) Blume ESP. *Dist:* Independent Pubs. Group.

Discover Series: Science, Nature, Wildlife, 11 bks. (Illus.). (J). (gr. 3-6). lib. bdg. 175.45 (978-1-56674-935-0(2)) Forest Hse. Publishing Co., Inc.

DK Publishing Staff. Encyclopedia of Nature. 2007. 304p. (J). pap. 19.99 (***978-0-7566-3111-6(4)***) Dorling Kindersley Publishing, Inc.

Dorling Kindersley Publishing Staff. First Nature Activity Book. 2006. (Illus.). 48p. (J). 9.99 (978-0-7566-2581-8(5)) Dorling Kindersley Publishing, Inc.

—First Nature Encyclopedia. 2006. (Illus.). 160p. (J). 15.99 (978-0-7566-1415-7(5)) Dorling Kindersley Publishing, Inc.

Dorling Kindersley Publishing Staff, contrib. by. Nature Encyclopedia. 1998. (Illus.). 304p. (J). (gr. 3-9). 29.99 (978-0-7894-3411-1(3)) Dorling Kindersley Publishing, Inc.

Douglas, Vincent & School Specialty Publishing Staff. Experiments You Can Do in Your Backyard. 2003. (Science Experiments Ser.). (Illus.). 96p. (J). (gr. 5-8). 16.95 (978-1-57768-624-8(1) , Waterbird Bks.) School Specialty Publishing.

Drew, David. Natural World, 6 bks., Set. Batt, Deleece, tr. Falla, Dominique, illus. 1999. (Hello! Lote Ser.). (JPN.). (J). pap. 29.99 (978-0-7339-0896-5(9)) Pearson Education Australia AUS. *Dist:* Cheng & Tsui Co.

—Natural World, 6 bks., Set. Harradine, Dona, tr. Falla, Dominique, illus. Incl. All Sorts of Things. pap. 5.99 (978-0-7339-0875-0(6)); Find the Way Home. pap. 5.99 (978-0-7339-0876-7(4)); Fins & Feathers. pap. 5.99 (978-0-7339-0877-4(2)); Habitats. pap. 5.99 (978-0-7339-0878-1(0)); What Do They Eat? pap. 5.99 (978-0-7339-0879-8(9)); What If? pap. 5.99 (978-0-7339-0868-2(3)); 17p. (J). (Hello! Lote Ser.). (IND., Illus.). 1999. Set pap. 29.99 (978-0-7339-0880-4(2)) Pearson Education Australia AUS. *Dist:* Cheng & Tsui Co.

Earth's Treasures. (Eyes on Adventure Ser.). 32p. (J). (gr. 1). pap. (978-1-882210-63-3(8)) Action Publishing, Inc.

Earthworks Series, 6 bks., Set. 179.57 (978-0-7614-1364-6(2) , Benchmark Bks.) Cavendish, Marshall Corp.

Enciclopedia Ilustrada de Ciencia Naturaleza (Understanding Science & Nature), 16 bks. Incl. Comportamiento de los Animales (Animal Behavior) 17.95 (978-0-7835-3358-2(6)); Cuerpo Humano (Human Body) 17.95 (978-0-7835-3350-6(0)); Era de la Computadora. 17.95 (978-0-7835-3375-9(6)); Espacio y Planetas. 17.95 (978-0-7835-3370-4(5)); Estructura de la Materia (Structure of Matter) 17.95 (978-0-7835-3383-4(7)); Evolucion de la Vida. 17.95 (978-0-7835-3354-4(3)); Fuerzas Fisicas (Physical Forces) 17.95 (978-0-7835-3395-7(0)); Geografia. 17.95 (978-0-7835-3387-2(X)); Insectos y Aranas. 17.95 (978-0-7835-3398-8(5)); Maquinas e Inventos (Machines & Inventions) 17.95 (978-0-7835-3400-8(0)); Mundo Submarino (Underwater World) 17.95 (978-0-7835-3397-1(7)); Planeta Tierra (Planet Earth) 17.95 (978-0-7835-3396-4(9)); Plantas (Plant Life) 17.95 (978-0-7835-3399-5(3)); Tiempo y Clima (Weather & Climate) 17.95 (978-0-7835-3366-7(7)); Transporte y la Navegacion (Transportation) 17.95 (978-0-7835-3379-7(9)); 152p. (YA). (gr. 6 up). 1996. (Illus.). Set lib. bdg. 319.20 (978-0-7835-3391-9(8)) Time-Life, Inc.

Environmental Issues Package. 1999. (Illus.). (J). pap. 399.00 (978-0-7398-2799-4(5)) Raintree.

Explora la Naturaleza, Set. 2004. (SPA.). 170.50 (978-1-4042-7552-2(5)) Rosen Publishing Group, Inc., The.

Eyre, Jane. Creatures of the New Jersey Pine Barrens Coloring Book, 1 vol. Eyre, Jane, illus. 2004. (Illus.). 36p. spiral bd. 6.00 (978-0-9762483-0-9(1)) Pyxie Moss Pr.

Facts on File, Inc. Staff, ed. Nature Walk, 7 Vols., Set. 2006. (Nature Walk Ser.). 64p. 196.00 (978-0-7910-9445-7(6) , Chelsea Clubhouse) Facts On File, Inc.

Fishel, Randy, ed. The Factory: Cool & Crazy Facts about God's Created Wonders. 2001. 96p. (YA). pap. 5.99 (978-0-8280-1556-1(2)) Review & Herald Publishing Assn.

Fitch, Florence Mary. A Book about God. Sorensen, Henri, illus. 1999. 24p. (J). (ps-3). 15.89 (978-0-688-16129-3(4)) HarperCollins Pubs.

Flatt, Lizann, et al. The Nature Treasury: A First Look at the Natural World. 2005. (Illus.). 48p. (J). 16.95 (978-1-897066-42-3(2)) Maple Tree Pr. CAN. *Dist:* Perseus Distribution.

Fleming, Denise. Where Once There Was a Wood. Fleming, Denise, illus. 2002. (Illus.). (J). 15.49 (978-0-7587-3992-6(3)) Book Wholesalers, Inc.

—Where Once There Was a Wood. Fleming, Denise, illus. rev. ed. 2000. (Illus.). 32p. (J). (ps-5). pap. 7.95 (978-0-8050-6482-7(6) , Holt, Henry & Co. Bks. For Young Readers) Holt, Henry & Co.

—Where Once There Was a Wood. 2000. (ps-2). lib. bdg. 15.25 (978-0-613-28698-5(7)) Tandem Library Bks.

Foley, Cate. Hide & Seek, 6 bks., Set. 2004. (Illus.). 24p. (J). (ps-2). 87.00 (978-0-516-23228-7(2) , Children's Pr.) Scholastic Library Publishing.

Forbes. Our Wonderful World. 2000. (J). (978-0-606-20292-3(7)) Tandem Library Bks.

Fowler, Allan. The Wonder of a Waterfall. 1999. (gr. k-3). lib. bdg. 12.95 (978-0-613-54785-7(3)) Tandem Library Bks.

Fredericks, Anthony D. Nature Experiments. Gallagher, Jack, illus. 2005. 128p. pap. 5.95 (978-1-4027-2158-8(7)) Sterling Publishing Co., Inc.

Furgang, Kathy. Enfoque en la naturaleza & Nature in Focus. 2005. spiral bd. 84.00 (***978-1-4108-5690-6(9)***) Benchmark Education Co.

Furgang, Kathy. Nature in Focus. 2004. (Navigators Ser.). (J). pap. 42.00 (978-1-4108-0420-4(8)) Benchmark Education Co.

La Furia de la Naturaleza: El Poder del Clima. (Coleccion Ventana Transparente). (SPA., Illus.). (J). (gr. 3-5). (978-950-11-1361-7(2) , SG0561) Sigmar ARG. *Dist:* Lectorum Pubns., Inc.

Ganeri, Anita. Tell Me Where Is the Top of the World? And More about Planet Earth. 2004. (Illus.). 32p. (J). pap. (978-1-84458-060-6(1)) Chrysalis Children's Bks.

Gaspard, Karen. What's in the Swamp? Arrigo, Joseph A., illus. 1999. (J). (gr. 2-7). 3.50 (978-1-883100-05-6(4)) De Simonin Pubns.

Gatty, Alfred. Parables from Nature (Yesterday's Classics) 2006. (Illus.). 456p. (J). per. 14.95 (978-1-59915-005-5(0)) Yesterday's Classics.

God's Wonders. 3.50 (978-0-8054-5877-0(8)) B&H Publishing Grp.

Gondek, Heather J. Morning in the Garden. McDonald, Mercedes, illus. 2002. 20p. (J). (ps-1). 9.95 (978-0-7641-5460-7(5)) Barron's Educational Series, Inc.

Goodman, Susan E. Nature Did It First. 2003. 3. (Illus.). 24p. lib. bdg. 21.90 (978-0-7613-2413-3(5) , Millbrook Pr.) Lerner Publishing Group.

Green, Jen. Why Should I Protect Nature? Gordon, Mike, illus. 2005. 32p. (J). (ps-ps). lib. bdg. 13.15 (978-0-606-33631-4(1)) Tandem Library Bks.

Greenaway, Theresa. Cycles in Nature, 3 bks., Set. Incl. Food Chains. lib. bdg. 25.69 (978-0-7398-2730-7(8)); Plant Life. lib. bdg. 25.69 (978-0-7398-2729-1(4)); Water Cycle. lib. bdg. 25.69 (978-0-7398-2728-4(6)); (Illus.). 32p. (J). (gr. 2-4). 2000. Set lib. bdg. 77.07 (978-0-7398-2731-4(6)) Raintree.

Grolier Educational Staff, contrib. by. Albatross. 2001. (Nature's Children Ser.). (Illus.). 48p. (J). (978-0-7172-5532-0(8) , Grolier) Scholastic Library Publishing.

Gunzi, Christiane. Air. 2001. (Collectafact Ser.: Vol. 10). (Illus.). 48p. (J). (gr. 1-5). 4.95 (978-1-58728-762-6(5) , Two Can Publishing) T&N Children's Publishing.

Harcourt School Publishers Staff. Harcourt Science Unit B: Systems & Interactions in Nature. 2000. (Illus.). pap. 17.10 (978-0-15-315699-1(6)) Harcourt Schl. Pubs.

—Look Closer: Little Book. 2000. (Collections Ser.). (Illus.). (J). pap. 10.20 (978-0-15-314505-6(6)) Harcourt Schl. Pubs.

—Up in the Sky. 3rd ed. 2002. (Trophies English Language Learners Ser.). (Illus.). pap. 5.10 (978-0-15-327706-1(8)) Harcourt Schl. Pubs.

—Up the Hill: Independent Reader. 3rd ed. 2002. (Trophies Reading Program Ser.). (Illus.). (J). pap. 2.90 (978-0-15-325498-7(X)) Harcourt Schl. Pubs.

Harris, Nicholas. The World Around Us. 2006. 32p. (gr. 2-4). 23.70 (978-1-4103-0347-9(0) , Blackbirch Pr., Inc.) Thomson Gale.

Hays, Susan. Nature Friends Creativity Book. 2003. (Illus.). 52p. (J). 11.95 (978-0-9729192-0-3(1)) Art & Soul Expressions.

Helbrough, Emma. Great Planet Earth Search. Jackson, Ian, illus. 2005. 32p. (J). (ps-ps). pap. 7.95 (978-0-7945-1075-6(2) , Usborne) EDC Publishing.

Herd, Meg. Learn & Play in the Garden Vol. 7: Games, Crafts & Activities for Children. 1999. (Environmental Bks.). (Illus.). 128p. (J). (ps-6). lib. bdg. 18.95 (978-1-56674-242-9(0) , HTS Bks.) Forest Hse. Publishing Co., Inc.

Hewitt, Sally. Nature for Fun Projects. 2000. (978-0-606-20486-6(5)); 11.64 (978-0-606-30833-5(4)) Tandem Library Bks.

Hilton, Samantha. Nature's Neighborhoods. Holmes, Steve, illus. 2004. (Interfact Ladder Ser.). 48p. (J). (ps-2). 14.95 incl. cd-rom (978-1-58728-420-5(0) , Two Can Publishing) T&N Children's Publishing.

Hoffman, Mary. Cancion de la Tierra: Mitos, Leyendas y Tradiciones. Ray, Jane, illus. 2002. (SPA.). 80p. (gr. 1 up). 19.95 (978-84-89396-76-0(0)) Blume ESP. *Dist:* Independent Pubs. Group.

Holt, Rinehart and Winston Staff. Holt Science & Technology Chptr. 13: Cycles of Nature: Chapter Resources - Tennessee Edition. 3rd ed. 2003. (YA). pap. 11.40 (978-0-03-069144-7(3)) Holt, Rinehart & Winston.

—West Virginia Environmental Science Resources. 2nd ed. 2002. pap. 205.80 (978-0-03-064279-1(5)) Holt, Rinehart & Winston.

Hooker, Worthington. The Child's Book of Nature. 2005. reprint ed. pap. 37.95 (978-1-4179-3598-7(7)) Kessinger Publishing, LLC.

Hooper, Roseanne. Life in the Coastlines: Animals, People, Plants. 2000. (gr. 3-6). lib. bdg. 15.25 (978-0-613-43341-9(6)) Tandem Library Bks.

Horner, Susan. Why Do Birds Build Nests? 2004. (Miracle of Creation Ser.). (Illus.). 32p. (J). 9.99 (978-0-8024-0922-5(9)) Moody Pubs.

—Why Do Plants Grow? 2004. (Miracle of Creation Ser.). (Illus.). 32p. (J). 9.99 (978-0-8024-0921-8(0)) Moody Pubs.

Hughes, Monica. What Is the Sky? 2005. (J). pap. (978-1-4034-6284-8(4)) Heinemann Library.

—What Is the Sky? 2004. (Heinemann Read & Learn Ser.). (Illus.). 24p. (J). lib. bdg. (978-1-4034-6278-7(X)) Steck-Vaughn.

I See Patterns. 2006. (Yellow Umbrella Math Ser.). 8,16p. (J). 6.50 (978-0-7368-1694-6(1)) Red Brick Learning.

I See You: Level E. 8p. 20.95 (978-0-322-00342-2(3)) Wright Group, The.

In the Rain Forest: Level F. 16p. 31.50 (978-0-322-00376-7(8)) Wright Group, The.

Johannes, Avril. When the Wolf Calls. 2002. 266p. per. 12.95 (978-1-57833-202-1(8)) Todd Communications.

Johnson, Rebecca L. A Walk in the Tundra. Saroff, Phyllis V., illus. Braasch, Gary, photos by. 2005. (Biomes of North America Ser.). 48p. (gr. 3-6). lib. bdg. 23.93 (978-1-57505-157-4(5)) Lerner Publishing Group.

Johnston, Tony. The Whole Green World. Kleven, Elisa, illus. 2005. 32p. (J). 15.00 (978-0-374-38400-5(2) , Farrar, Straus & Giroux (BYR)) Farrar, Straus & Giroux.

Joyce, Susan. ABC Nature Riddles. DuBosque, Doug, illus. 2004. (ABC Riddles Ser.). 32p. (J). (ps-k). (978-0-939217-53-3(8)) Peel Productions, Inc.

Der Jugend Brockhaus: Natur und Technik. (GER., Illus.). 640p. (YA). (gr. 5-11). (978-3-7653-1851-1(5)) Brockhaus, F. A., GmbH DEU. *Dist:* International Bk. Import Service, Inc.

Kalman, Bobbie & Smithyman, Kathryn. El Ciclo de Vida del Arbol. Bedell, Barbara, illus. 2005. (Serie Ciclos de Vida Ser.). (SPA.). 32p. (J). (ps-ps). pap. (978-0-7787-8711-2(7)) Crabtree Publishing Co.

Kavanagh, James. In God's Kitchen. Belisle, John, illus. 2004. 32p. 15.95 (978-1-58355-241-4(3)) Waterford Pr., Ltd.

Keo, Ena. Theme Pack: Outdoors. 2002. (Pair-It Bks.). (J). pap. (978-0-7398-6372-5(X)) Steck-Vaughn.

Kids Can Press Staff, Press Can, ed. This Is Daniel Cook on A Hike. 2006. (Illus.). 28p. (J). (978-1-55453-080-9(6)); (978-1-55453-079-3(2)) Kids Can Pr., Ltd.

Kowalski, Kathiann M. The Everything Kids' Nature Book: Create Clouds, Make Waves, Defy Gravity & Much More! 2000. (Illus.). 132p. (J). (gr. 4-7). per. 13.35 (978-0-606-22490-1(4)) Tandem Library Bks.

Kranz, Linda. My Nature Book: A Journal & Activity Book for Kids. Garrow, Linda & McGee, John F., illus. 2004. 128p. (YA). (gr. 1-6). pap. 12.95 (978-1-55971-893-6(5) , NorthWord Bks. for Young Readers) T&N Children's Publishing.

Ladders Series, 6 vols., Set. 2000. 192p. (J). (gr. k-3). (978-0-7166-7722-2(9)) World Bk., Inc.

Lambert, David. Kingfisher Young People's Book of Oceans. 2001. (gr. 5-8). lib. bdg. 22.20 (978-0-613-90593-0(8)) Tandem Library Bks.

Land, Sea, Sky, 12 vols., Set. 2002. (Junior Adventure Ser.). (Illus.). 32p. (J). (gr. 3 up). lib. bdg. (978-1-59084-241-6(3)) Mason Crest Pubs.

Larousse Mexico Staff. Enciclopedia Mega: Naturaleza y Ecologia. 2003. (SPA.). (gr. 3-6). lib. bdg. 19.90 (978-0-613-89815-7(X)) Tandem Library Bks.

LeapFrog Staff, compiled by. Nature: (Blue Book) 2002. (J). (ps-2). 19.95 (978-1-58605-708-4(1)) LeapFrog Enterprises, Inc.

—Nature: (Green Book) 2002. (J). (ps-2). 19.95 (978-1-58605-706-0(5)) LeapFrog Enterprises, Inc.

—Nature: (Orange Book) 2002. (J). (ps-2). 19.95 (978-1-58605-707-7(3)) LeapFrog Enterprises, Inc.

—Nature: (Purple Book) 2002. (J). (ps-2). 19.95 (978-1-58605-705-3(7)) LeapFrog Enterprises, Inc.

Learning Horizons, creator. Treasury of Animals & Nature. 2005. (Illus.). 287p. (J). (ps-ps). 9.99 (978-1-58610-784-0(4)) Learning Horizons, Inc.

Levine, Shar & Johnstone, Leslie. First Science Experiments: Nifty Nature. 2006. (Illus.). 48p. (J). pap. 4.95 (978-1-4027-4052-7(2)) Sterling Publishing Co., Inc.

—First Science Experiments with Nature, Senses, Weather & Machines. Harpster, Steve, illus. 2005. 192p. (978-1-4027-2922-5(7)) Sterling Publishing Co., Inc.

Lewis, J. Earth & You, a Closer View: Nature's Features. 2000. (gr. 3-6). lib. bdg. 16.40 (978-0-613-49730-5(9)) Tandem Library Bks.

Lewis, J. Patrick. Earth & You - A Closer View: Nature's Features. Canyon, Christopher, illus. 2004. (Sharing Nature with Children Book Ser.). 36p. (J). (gr. 4-7). pap. 7.95 (978-1-58469-015-3(1)); (ps-3). 16.95 (978-1-58469-016-0(X)) Dawn Pubns.

Lindbergh, Reeve. The Circle of Days. 2002. (gr. 3-6). lib. bdg. 14.15 (978-0-613-74721-9(6)) Tandem Library Bks.

Litchfield, Jo. First Picture Nature. 2007. (First Picture Board Bks). 16p. (J). bds. 11.99 (***978-0-7945-1751-9(X)*** , Usborne) EDC Publishing.

The Little Buckeye. 2000. (Little Buckeye Ser.: 1,1).. (J). per. 6.95 (978-0-9703936-0-9(1) , 3000) Little Buckeye Publishing Co., The.

Londt, Claire, et al. English Matters for Zambia Basic Education Grade 3 Pupil's Book. 2nd ed. 2007. pap., stu. ed. 5.75 (978-0-521-68755-3(1)) Cambridge Univ. Pr.

Lorenz Editors. Nature: With over 50 Reusable Stickers. 2001. (Sticker Fun Ser.). (Illus.). 16p. pap. 2.95 (978-0-7548-0847-3(5) , Lorenz Bks.) Anness Publishing, Inc.

Lowcountry A to Z. 2004. (J). 24.95 (978-0-9744035-0-2(4)) Makai Concepts, LLC.

MacCoon, Nancy. Backyard Wonders. Watkins, Courtney, illus. l.t. ed. 2003. 38p. (J). pap. 14.95 (978-0-9742495-0-6(5)) Vibatorium LLC.

Martin, Eric B. Campfire Collection: Spine Tingling Tales to Tell. 2000. (J). 22.60 (978-0-606-22159-7(X)) Tandem Library Bks.

Marx, Nancy A. Sense. . . Abilities: A Children's Picture Book. 2002. (Illus.). 18p. (J). 21.95 (978-0-9727675-1-4(7)) Nature Sense Pr.

—Sense. . . Abilities: A Children's Picture Book. Boehmer, Kelly S., illus. 2002. 18p. (J). spiral bd. 17.95 (978-0-9727675-0-7(9)) Nature Sense Pr.

Mattern, Joanne & Herndon, Ryan, compiled by. Guinness World Records. 2005. (Illus.). 47p. pap. (***978-0-439-71568-3(7)***) Scholastic, Inc.

Mayer, Cassie. Valleys. 2006. (Illus.). 24p. (J). (978-1-4034-8436-9(8)); pap. (978-1-4034-8442-0(2)) Heinemann Library.

McBride, A. W. The Story of the Forest People: A Forever Fantasy for All of Us. Pioneer Heritage Staff, illus. 2001. 20p. (J). (ps-1). pap. 6.95 (978-0-9708289-0-3(X)) Pioneer Heritage.

McCarroll, Tolbert. A Winter Walk: Glimpses of the Sacred in Ordinary Life. 2006. (Illus.). 160p. 14.95 (978-0-8245-2416-6(0)) Crossroad Publishing Co.

McDaniel, Melissa. Busy Builders. 2001. (We Can Read about Nature Ser.). (Illus.). 32p. (J). (gr. 1-2). lib. bdg. 21.36 (978-0-7614-1255-7(7) , Benchmark Bks.) Cavendish, Marshall Corp.

McFarlane, Sheryl. What's That Sound by Sea. LaFave, Kim, illus. 2006. 20p. (J). bds. 7.95 (978-1-55041-957-3(9)) Fitzhenry & Whiteside, Ltd. CAN. *Dist:* F & W Pubns., Inc.

McHugh, Michael J. & Arwine, David K. Our Father's World. 1999. (God's Creation Ser.: Vol. 2). (Illus.). 112p. (J). (gr. 1-2). pap., wbk. ed. 8.95 (978-1-930092-05-1(9) , CLP69510) Christian Liberty Pr.

Merino, Azucena, ed. La Naturaleza. Terrer, Marta, tr. 2002. (Illustrated Juvenile Encyclopedia Ser.). (SPA., Illus.). 64p. (J). 12.95 (978-84-662-0301-2(X)) Libsa, Editorial S.A. ESP. *Dist:* Lectorum Pubns., Inc.

Miles Kelly Staff. Nature. 2003. (Ask Me a Question Ser.). (Illus.). 20p. spiral bd. 7.95 (978-1-84236-125-2(2)) Miles Kelly Publishing, Ltd. GBR. *Dist:* Independent Pubs. Group.

Molina, M. Isabel. Arco Iris (The Rainbow) (SPA.). (J). 7.95 (978-84-86563-03-5(8)) Nuevas Estructuras Gondomar ESP. *Dist:* AIMS International Bks., Inc.

Monroe, Colleen. The Wonders of Nature Sketchbook: Learn about Nature & How to Draw It. Monroe, Michael Glenn, illus. 2005. (J). 15.00 (978-0-9754942-1-9(X)) Storytime Pr., Inc.

Montgomery, Sy. Search for the Golden Moon Bear: Science & Adventure in the Asian Tropics. 2004. (Illus.). 80p. (J). (gr. 4-6). tchr. ed. 17.00 (978-0-618-35650-8(9)) Houghton Mifflin Co. Trade & Reference Div.

Morel, Gaud. Exploring Nature. Best, Clare et al, trs. 1998. (Creative Discoveries Ser.: Vol. 8). (Illus.). 75p. (J). (gr. 2-9). lib. bdg. 23.95 (978-0-88682-946-9(1) , Creative Education) Creative Co., The.

Morris, Neil. Our Wonderful World: Fun Finding Out. 2003. (Fun Finding Out Ser.). (Illus.). 48p. (J). pap. 7.95 (978-1-902947-36-5(3)) Miles Kelly Publishing, Ltd. GBR. *Dist:* Independent Pubs. Group.

—Wonders of Our World, 10 bks. Incl. Caves. 1995. pap. (978-0-86505-842-2(3)); Deserts. 1995. pap. (978-0-86505-839-2(3)); Earthquakes. 1998. pap. (978-0-86505-844-6(X)); Forests. 1998. pap. (978-0-86505-845-3(8)); Hurricanes & Tornadoes. 1998. pap. (978-0-86505-843-9(1)); Mountains. 1995. pap. (978-0-86505-841-5(5)); Oceans. 1995. pap. (978-0-86505-840-8(7)); Rivers & Lakes. 1998. pap. (978-0-86505-846-0(6)); Rocks & Minerals. 1998. pap. (978-0-86505-847-7(4)); Volcanoes. 1995. pap. (978-0-86505-838-5(5)); 32p. (J). (gr. 3-4). (Illus.). 2000. Set pap. (978-0-86505-849-1(0)) Crabtree Publishing Co.

Mullican, Judy. In the Meadow. Coates, Jennifer, illus. l.t. ed. 2000. (CB Ser.). 7p. (J). (ps-1). pap. 10.95 (978-1-57332-142-6(7)) HighReach Learning, Inc.

El Mundo de la Naturaleza. (Coleccion Lo Sabias?). (SPA., Illus.). 44p. (J). 12.95 (978-950-11-0938-2(0) , SGM9380) Sigmar ARG. *Dist:* Continental Bk. Co., Inc.

Murray, John A., ed. American Nature Writing 2003, Vol. 1. 2003. 224p. (gr. 4). pap. 17.95 (978-1-55591-353-3(9)) Fulcrum Publishing.

My First Nature Books, 11 bks., Set. Incl. Air. Benedict, Kitty & Soutter-Perrot, Andrienne. Delessert, Etienne, illus. lib. bdg. 14.60 (978-0-88682-547-8(4)); Ant. Benedict, Kitty. Felix, Monique, illus. lib. bdg. 14.60 (978-0-88682-564-5(4)); Cow. Benedict, Kitty. Wuest, Gerard, illus. lib. bdg. 14.60 (978-0-88682-567-6(9)); Earth. Soutter-Perrot, Andrienne. Delessert, Etienne, illus. lib. bdg. 14.60 (978-0-88682-548-5(2)); Earthworm. Soutter-Perrot, Andrienne. Delessert, Etienne, illus. lib. bdg. 14.60 (978-0-88682-566-9(0)); Fire. Soutter-Perrot, Andrienne. Gaudard, Patrick, illus. lib. bdg. 14.60 (978-0-88682-553-9(9)); Oak. Soutter-Perrot, Andrienne. Schmid, Eleonore, illus. lib. bdg. 14.60 (978-0-88682-550-8(4)); Toad. Felix, Monique, illus. lib. bdg. 14.60 (978-0-88682-568-3(7)); 32p. (J). (gr. 1-5). 1993. (978-0-88682-570-6(9) , Creative Education) Creative Co., The.

Nadeau, Isaac. Canyons. 2006. (Illus.). 24p. (J). (978-1-4042-3123-8(4) , PowerKids Pr.) Rosen Publishing Group, Inc., The.

National Wildlife Federation Staff. Wild & Crafty. 1999. (Ranger Rick's Naturescope Ser.). (Illus.). 96p. (gr. 4-7). lib. bdg. 21.95 (978-0-7910-4884-9(5) , Chelsea Hse.) Facts On File, Inc.

Naturaleza. 2005. (Coleccion Primeras Imagenes).Tr. of Wind & Weather. (SPA., Illus.). 86p. (J). (ps up). pap. 7.95 (978-950-11-0989-4(5) , SGM9895) Sigmar ARG. *Dist:* AIMS International Bks., Inc., Continental Bk. Co., Inc., Lectorum Pubns., Inc., Iaconi, Mariuccia Bk. Imports.

Nature Books II, 6 bks. Incl. Flowers. Dwyer, Jacqueline. lib. bdg. 16.00 (978-0-8239-5677-7(6) , PKFLOW); Fruits. Dwyer, Jacqueline. lib. bdg. 16.00 (978-0-8239-5678-4(4) , PKFRUI); Mountains. Dwyer, Jacqueline, contrib. by. lib. bdg. 16.00 (978-0-8239-5680-7(6) , PKMNTN); Rainbows. Dwyer, Jacqueline, contrib. by. lib. bdg. 16.00 (978-0-8239-5676-0(8)); Rivers. Dwyer, Jacqueline. lib. bdg. 16.00 (978-0-8239-5681-4(4) , PKRIVE); Vegetables. Dwyer, Jacqueline, contrib. by. lib. bdg. 16.00 (978-0-8239-5679-1(2) , PKVEGE); 24p. (J). (gr. 1). (Illus.). 2001. Set lib. bdg. 88.50 (978-0-8239-7074-2(4) , PKREN2, PowerKids Pr.) Rosen Publishing Group, Inc., The.

Nature (Gr. PreK-5) 2003. (J). (978-1-58232-023-6(3)) Bryan Hse. Pubs., Inc.

Nature Hike: Big Book: Level D. 8p. 20.95 (978-0-322-00366-8(0)) Wright Group, The.

Nature Kids, 8 vols., Set. 2002. (Illus.). 52p. (J). (gr. 3 up). lib. bdg. (978-1-59084-209-6(X)) Mason Crest Pubs.

Nature of the World Action Sticker Book. 2002. 12p. (J). pap. 3.98 (978-0-7525-8037-1(X)) Parragon, Inc.

Nature Series Books 23 & 24: Activities. 2002. (Suzanne Tate's Nature Ser.). (J). pap., instr.'s gde. ed. 2.95 (978-1-878405-36-4(5)) Nags Head Art, Inc.

Nature Unfolds, 4 bks. Incl. Nature Unfolds Mountains & Deserts. Cheshire, Gerard. Barrett, Peter, illus. 2002. lib. bdg. (978-0-7787-0311-2(8)); Nature Unfolds the Oceans. Williams, Andy. Camm, Martin, illus. 2002. lib. bdg. (978-0-7787-0310-5(X)); Nature Unfolds the Poles. Stonehouse, Bernard. 2001. lib. bdg. (978-0-7787-0309-9(6)); Nature Unfolds the Tropical Rainforest. Cheshire, Gerald & Cheshire, Gerald. 2001. lib. bdg. (978-0-7787-0308-2(8)); 40p. (J). (gr. 4). (Illus.). 2002. (978-0-7787-0306-8(1)); Set pap. (978-0-7787-0318-1(5)) Crabtree Publishing Co.

Nature Watch. 2004. (Illus.). lib. bdg. 7.95 (978-0-8225-4353-4(2)); 2004. (Illus.). lib. bdg. 7.95 (978-0-8225-4365-7(6)); Set. 2007. (J). (gr. 4-8). lib. bdg. 771.40 (***978-0-8225-8465-0(4)***) Lerner Publishing Group.

Nature's Greatest Hits, 6 bks. Incl. Angel Falls : World's Highest Waterfall. Mattern, Joanne. (gr. 2). lib. bdg. 17.25 (978-0-8239-6016-3(1)); Antarctica : World's Biggest Glacier. Mattern, Joanne. lib. bdg. 17.25 (978-0-8239-6017-0(X)); Asia : World's Largest Continent. Mattern, Joanne. (gr. 2). lib. bdg. 17.25 (978-0-8239-6015-6(3)); Greenland : World's Largest Island. Mattern, Joanne. (gr. 2). lib. bdg. 17.25 (978-0-8239-6018-7(8)); Mauna Loa : World's Largest Active Volcano. Mattern, Joanne. (gr. 2). lib. bdg. 17.25 (978-0-8239-6014-9(5)); Sahara : World's Largest Desert. Fine, Jill. (gr. 2). lib. bdg. 17.25 (978-0-8239-6013-2(7)); 24p. (J). 2002. (Illus.). 2001. Set lib. bdg. 96.00 (978-0-8239-7178-7(3) , PowerKids Pr.) Rosen Publishing Group, Inc., The.

Nature's Mysteries - Group 2, 3 bks., Set. Incl. How Insects Work Together. Bailey, Jill. lib. bdg. 22.79 (978-0-7614-0859-8(2)); How Monkeys "Talk" Banks, Martin. lib. bdg. 22.79 (978-0-7614-0858-1(4)); 32p. (J). (gr. 3-5). 1998. (Illus.). 1999. Set lib. bdg. 68.36 (978-0-7614-0856-7(8) , Benchmark Bks.) Cavendish, Marshall Corp.

Nichols, Catherine. If You Had a Tail. 2001. (We Can Read about Nature! Ser.). (Illus.). 32p. (J). (gr. 1-2). lib. bdg. 21.36 (978-0-7614-1251-9(4) , Benchmark Bks.) Cavendish, Marshall Corp.

Nuevo Investiguemos 8: Ciencias Naturales y de la Salud. (SPA.). (YA). (gr. 8). (978-958-02-1536-3(7)) Editorial Voluntad S.A. COL. *Dist:* Distribuidora Norma, Inc.

Nuevo Investiguemos 9: Ciencias Naturales y de la Salud. (SPA.). (YA). (gr. 9). (978-958-02-1537-0(5)) Editorial Voluntad S.A. COL. *Dist:* Distribuidora Norma, Inc.

Oberle, Mark William. Las Aves de Puerto Rico en Fotografias. Placer, José, tr. 2nd ed. 2006. (SPA., Illus.). 136p. per. 17.95 (978-0-9650104-2-9(2)) Editorial Humanitas.

Oehler, Janet. Nature's Call. Raviwongse, Rajata, illus. 2000. 32p. (J). (gr. 4-6). 18.00 (978-0-9671159-0-0(6)) Oehler, Janet.

Old John: A Voice for the Living Earth. 2000. (Illus.). (J). (gr. 1-5). 24.99 (978-0-9700611-0-2(2)) Foxglove Films, LLC.

Olmstead, Adrienne. My Nature Journal: A Personal Nature Guide for Young People. Olmstead, Donald, ed. Olmstead, Adrienne, illus. unabr. ed. 2000. (ACE., Illus.). 176p. (gr. 3-8). 17.95 (978-0-9672459-1-1(5)) Pajaro.

The Ooshes Make a Friend: The Little Stories of Manoosh & Baloosh, 31 vols. 2002. (Illus.). 24p. (J). mass mkt. (978-1-932233-00-1(8)) Aurora Libris Corp.

Our World: Our Future. 2005. 32p. pap. 140.00 (978-0-7910-9169-2(4) , Chelsea Hse.) Facts On File, Inc.

Papademetriou, Dorrie. Celebrate the Earth: Psalm 104. 2000. (Illus.). 32p. (J). 15.00 (978-0-88141-204-8(X)) St. Vladimir's Seminary Pr.

Parker, Gary. Exploring the World Around You: From the Ice of Abtarctuca to the Heat of the Sahara. 2002. (Illus.). 160p. (YA). pap. 13.99 (978-0-89051-377-4(5)) Master Bks.

Parker, Steve & Parker, Jane. Nature Works: Fun-to-Do Nature Projects for Younger Children. 2000. (Show Me How Ser.). (Illus.). 48p. (ps-2). pap. 7.95 (978-0-7548-0099-6(7)) Anness Publishing GBR. *Dist:* National Bk. Network.

Parramon, José María. Mi Calle. Borday, Irene, illus. (Coleccion Estoy En...).Tr. of My Street. (SPA.). 32p. (J). (gr. k-3). 6.36 (978-84-342-1003-5(7)) Parramon Ediciones S.A. ESP. *Dist:* Lectorum Pubns., Inc.

—Mi Casa. Borday, Irene, illus. (Coleccion Estoy En...).Tr. of My House. (SPA.). 32p. (J). (gr. k-3). 6.36 (978-84-342-1002-8(9)) Parramon Ediciones S.A. ESP. *Dist:* Lectorum Pubns., Inc.

—Mi Jardin. Borday, Irene, illus. (Coleccion Estoy En...).Tr. of My Garden. (SPA.). 32p. (J). (gr. k-3). 6.36 (978-84-342-1005-9(3)) Parramon Ediciones S.A. ESP. *Dist:* Lectorum Pubns., Inc.

Parramon, José María & Bordoy, Irene. Mi Calle.Tr. of My Street. (SPA., Illus.). (J). (ps-1). 6.95 (978-958-04-1277-9(4)) Norma S.A. COL. *Dist:* Distribuidora Norma, Inc.

Pellant, Chris, et al. Rock & Mineral. (Dk Eyewitness Books Ser.). (J). pap. 8.95 (978-0-7894-5805-6(5)) Dorling Kindersley Publishing, Inc.

Perols, Sylvaine. La Tierra y el Cielo. (Coleccion Mundo Maravilloso). (SPA., Illus.). 24p. (J). (gr. 2-4). (978-84-348-6322-4(7) , SM30014) SM Ediciones ESP. *Dist:* Lectorum Pubns., Inc.

Pichette, Marise & Rousseau, Serge. Show & Tell Nature. 2000. (Show & Tell Ser.). (Illus.). 12p. (J). (ps-1). bds. (978-2-922148-81-7(5)) Presses aventure/Adventure Pr.

Pipe, Jim. Seasons: Why Do Leaves Fall? 2007. (Science Starters Ser.). (Illus.). 32p. (J). (***978-1-59604-081-6(5)***) Stargazer Bks.

Podojil, Catherine. Saving Endangered Species. 2005. (Illus.). 24p. (J). (***978-0-328-13528-8(3)*** , Scott Foresman) Addison-Wesley Educational Pubs., Inc.

Polito, James A. My First Book of Critters. 2004. (Illus.). 24p. (J). spiral bd. 12.95 (978-0-9752842-0-9(7)) Kind Critter Junction.

Potter, Jean. La Naturaleza Explicada A Los Ninos En Pocas Palabras: Mas De 100 Actividades Realizables En 10 Minutos O Menos. 2003. (SPA.). 264p. (978-84-493-0278-7(1)) Ediciones Paidos Iberica, S.A.

Priest, Saira, photos by & des. If We Were... Priest, Saira, des. l.t. ed. 2003. 20p. 12.95 (978-0-9726628-7-1(1)) Native Nature.

Quadrillion Media Staff. Nature & Animals. 1999. (Start Me Up Ser.). (J). pap. 3.95 (978-1-58185-101-4(4)) Quadrillion Media LLC.

Raintree Steck-Vaughn Staff. In the Weedy Tide Pool. 2000. (Illus.). (J). pap. 4.95 (978-0-8114-3747-9(7)) Steck-Vaughn.

—It's Snowing. 2000. (Read All about It Ser.). (Illus.). (J). (gr. k-3). pap. 4.95 (978-0-8114-3767-7(1)) Steck-Vaughn.

—Natural World Book Set. 1999. (Illus.). (J). 102.76 (978-0-7398-1059-0(6)) Raintree.

—You & Me. 2000. (Read All about It Ser.). (Illus.). (J). pap. 4.95 (978-0-8114-3768-4(X)) Steck-Vaughn.

Raintree Steck-Vaughn Staff, ed. We Come From... 1999. (Illus.). (J). 63.92 (978-0-7398-2685-0(9)) Raintree.

Randolph, Joanne. All about a Day. 2008. (J). lib. bdg. (***978-1-4042-3767-4(4)*** , PowerKids Pr.) Rosen Publishing Group, Inc., The.

Ranger Rick's Naturescope. 2005. pap. 363.35 (978-0-7910-9168-5(6) , Chelsea Hse.) Facts On File, Inc.

Rappoport, Bernice. Outside My Window. Johnson, Pamela G., illus. 2004. (Treasure Tree Ser.). 32p. (J). (978-0-7166-1622-1(X)) World Bk., Inc.

Rau, Dana Meachen. El Arco Iris. 2007. (SPA.). 32p. (J). lib. bdg. 22.79 (***978-0-7614-2807-7(0)*** , Benchmark Bks.) Cavendish, Marshall Corp.

—Los Cataratas. 2007. (Maravillas de la Naturaleza Ser.). (SPA.). 32p. (J). lib. bdg. 22.79 (***978-0-7614-2810-7(0)*** , Benchmark Bks.) Cavendish, Marshall Corp.

—Cuando Voy a Chapalear en la Laguna. Marcuse, Aida E., tr. 2001. (Aventureros Ser.). (SPA., Illus.). 24p. (J). (gr. k-2). lib. bdg. 19.27 (978-1-57103-360-4(2) , RK31325) Rourke Publishing, LLC.

—Cuando Voy a Explorar Una Caverna. Marcuse, Aida E., tr. 2001. (Aventureros Ser.). (SPA., Illus.). 24p. (J). (gr. k-2). lib. bdg. 19.27 (978-1-57103-361-1(0) , RK31327) Rourke Publishing, LLC.

—Cuando Voy a Pasear al Bosque. Marcuse, Aida E., tr. 2001. (Aventureros Ser.). (SPA., Illus.). 24p. (J). (gr. k-2). lib. bdg. 19.27 (978-1-57103-359-8(9) , RK31328) Rourke Publishing, LLC.

—Rainbows. 2007. (Wonders of Nature Ser.). 32p. (J). lib. bdg. 22.79 (***978-0-7614-2669-1(8)*** , Benchmark Bks.) Cavendish, Marshall Corp.

—Rainbows/El Arco Iris. 2007. (Wonders of Nature/ Maravillas de la Naturaleza Ser.). (SPA & ENG.). 32p. (J). lib. bdg. 22.79 (***978-0-7614-2831-2(3)*** , Benchmark Bks.) Cavendish, Marshall Corp.

—Waterfalls. 2007. (Wonders of Nature Ser.). 32p. (J). lib. bdg. 22.79 (***978-0-7614-2671-4(X)*** , Benchmark Bks.) Cavendish, Marshall Corp.

—Waterfalls/Las Cataratas. 2007. (Wonders of Nature/ Maravillas de la Naturaleza Ser.). (SPA & ENG.). 32p. (J). lib. bdg. 22.79 (***978-0-7614-2833-6(X)*** , Benchmark Bks.) Cavendish, Marshall Corp.

Ready Set Learn Staff. Peeps Animals & Nature. 2005. (Illus.). 24p. (J). (ps-2). bds. 15.99 (978-1-59249-519-1(2) , 1C301) Soundprints.

Reda, Sheryl A. A Forest Tree House. Barrett, Peter, illus. 2004. (Treasure Tree Ser.). 32p. (J). (978-0-7166-1606-1(8)) World Bk., Inc.

Rhatigan, Joe, et al. Nature Smart: Awesome Projects to Make with Mother Nature's Help. 2004. (Illus.). 400p. (J). pap. 12.98 (978-1-4027-1435-1(1)) Sterling Publishing Co., Inc.

Riley, Barbara. Grow, Grow, Grow. Guggenheim, Jaenet, illus. l.t. ed. 2003. 40p. (J). 19.95 (978-1-929115-08-2(3)) Azro Pr., Inc.

Riley, Peter D. & Gerstein, Sherry. Nightwatch: Nightlife in the Tropical Rain Forest. Croucher, Barry & Edwards, Brin, illus. Coleman, Bruce & Natural History Photographs Agency Staff, photos by. 1999. (Windows on Science Ser.). 16p. (YA). (gr. 3-7). 12.99 (978-1-57584-251-6(3) , Reader's Digest Children's Bks.) Reader's Digest Children's Publishing, Inc.

Ring, Susan. I See Patterns. 2006. (Yellow Umbrella Books for Early Readers). (Illus.). (J). 16p. (978-0-7368-5978-3(0)); (ENG & SPA., 18p. (978-0-7368-6014-7(2)) Yellow Umbrella Pr.

—Nature Did It First. 2003. (Science Links Ser.). (Illus.). 32p. (gr. 3-5). 23.00 (978-0-7910-7427-5(7) , Chelsea Hse.) Facts On File, Inc.

Robb, Andy. Who Made The World?, 1. 1999. (Illus.). 26p. (J). (ps-2). 7.00 (978-0-570-05577-8(6)) Concordia Publishing Hse.

Roberts, Ley Honor, illus. Nature's Secret Codes. 2006. 16p. (J). pap. 5.95 (***978-1-903919-83-5(5)*** , Eden Project Books) Transworld Publishers Ltd. GBR. *Dist:* Independent Pubs. Group.

Ross, Michael Elsohn. Nature Art with Chiura Obata. Smith, Wendy, illus. 2005. (Naturalist's Apprentice Biographies Ser.). 48p. (gr. 3-6). lib. bdg. 19.93 (978-1-57505-378-3(0)) Lerner Publishing Group.

—Rolypolyology. 2003. (Backyard Buddies Ser.). 48p. (YA). (gr. 3-5). 6.95 (978-0-87614-901-0(8) , Carolrhoda Bks.) Lerner Publishing Group.

Salzmann, Mary Elizabeth. What Do You See?, Set. l.t. ed. Incl. In a Forest. lib. bdg. 19.93 (978-1-57765-565-7(6)); In a Valley. lib. bdg. 19.93 (978-1-57765-569-5(9)); In the Desert. lib. bdg. 19.93 (978-1-57765-564-0(8)); In the Ocean. lib. bdg. 19.93 (978-1-57765-567-1(2)); On a Mountain. lib. bdg. 19.93 (978-1-57765-566-4(4)); On a Prairie. lib. bdg. 19.93 (978-1-57765-568-8(0)); 24p. (J). (ps-3). 2001. (Illus.). 2001. Set lib. bdg. 119.58 (978-1-57765-506-0(0) , SandCastle) ABDO Publishing Co.

San Antonio 2004. 2003. (YA). 11.99 (978-0-9721368-0-8(0)) Apollo Pubs.

Sasman, Irene D. H. World of Nature: Caterpillars to Butterflies Children's Books, Media & Hands-On, Set. 1998. (Illus.). (J). (ps-4). pap. 199.95 (978-1-56831-350-4(0)) Learning Connection, The.

Schaefer, Lola M. What's up, What's Down? Bash, Barbara, illus. 2002. 32p. (J). 16.99 (978-0-06-029757-2(3)); lib. bdg. 17.89 (978-0-06-029758-9(1)) HarperCollins Pubs.

Schwartz, David M. Ciclos de Vida, 12 bks. Kuhn, Dwight, photos by. Incl. Arana Saltadora. lib. bdg. 20.67 (978-0-8368-2989-1(1) , GHS31408); Arce. lib. bdg. 20.67 (978-0-8368-2990-7(5)); Caballo. lib. bdg. 20.67 (978-0-8368-2991-4(3) , GHS31410); Catarina. lib. bdg. 20.67 (978-0-8368-2992-1(1) , GHS31411); Combatiente. lib. bdg. 20.67 (978-0-8368-2993-8(X) , GHS31412); Culebra Verde. lib. bdg. 20.67 (978-0-8368-2994-5(8)); Ejote. lib. bdg. 20.67 (978-0-8368-2995-2(6) , GHS31414); Gallina. lib. bdg. 20.67 (978-0-8368-2996-9(4) , GHS31415); Girasol. lib. bdg. 20.67 (978-0-8368-2997-6(2) , GHS31417); Mariposa Monarca. lib. bdg. 20.67 (978-0-8368-2998-3(0)); Picaflor. lib. bdg. 20.67 (978-0-8368-2999-0(9) , GHS31418); Rana de Bosque. lib. bdg. 20.67 (978-0-8368-3000-2(8)); 24p. (J). (gr. 1 up). 2001. (SPA., Illus.). Set lib. bdg. 248.04 (978-0-8368-2988-4(3)) Stevens, Gareth Inc.

—Exploring Habitats. Kuhn, Dwight, photos by. 2000. (Habitats Ser.). (Illus.). 80 p. (J). (gr. 1-3). pap., instr.'s gde. ed. 9.99 (978-1-57471-367-1(1) , 3096) Creative Teaching Pr., Inc.

—La Gallina. Kuhn, Dwight, photos by. 2001. (Springboards into Science Ser.). (SPA., Illus.). 24p. (J). (gr. 1 up). lib. bdg. 20.67 (978-0-8368-2996-9(4) , GHS31415) Stevens, Gareth Inc.

—El Girasol. Kuhn, Dwight, photos by. 2001. (Springboards into Science Ser.). (SPA., Illus.). 24p. (J). (gr. 1 up). lib. bdg. 20.67 (978-0-8368-2997-6(2) , GHS31417) Stevens, Gareth Inc.

—In the Meadow. Kuhn, Dwight, photos by. 1998. (Springboards into Science Ser.). (Illus.). 24p. (J). (gr. 1 up). lib. bdg. 20.67 (978-0-8368-2223-6(4)) Stevens, Gareth Inc.

—In the Park. Kuhn, Dwight, photos by. (Habitats Ser.). (Illus.). 16p. (J). (gr. 1-3). pap. 2.99 (978-1-57471-214-8(4) , 3006) Creative Teaching Pr., Inc.

—In the Park. Kuhn, Dwight, photos by. 1999. (Springboards into Science Ser.). (Illus.). 24p. (J). (gr. 1 up). lib. bdg. 20.67 (978-0-8368-2243-4(9)) Stevens, Gareth Inc.

—Underfoot. Kuhn, Dwight, photos by. 1999. (Springboards into Science Ser.). (Illus.). 24p. (J). (gr. 1 up). lib. bdg. 20.67 (978-0-8368-2246-5(3)) Stevens, Gareth Inc.

Science & Nature. (Britannica Learning Library). (Illus.). (gr. 2-5). 14.95 (978-1-59339-002-0(5) , 049903-EN-REF) Encyclopaedia Britannica, Inc.

Serra Deliz, Wenceslao, et al. En Las Cavernas de Camuy: Teron y Su Maravilloso Mundo Subterraneo. 1999. (Colleccion San Pedrito Ser.). 36p. 12.95 (978-0-8477-0221-3(9)) Univ. of Puerto Rico Pr.

Shaffer, Christy. Nature's Backyard Scenes Stained Glass Coloring Book. 2006. 16p. (J). pap. 5.95 (978-0-486-44708-7(1)) Dover Pubns., Inc.

Sharp, Katie John. Science & Nature. Barrett, Tom, illus. 2005. (Look, Find & Learn Ser.). 32p. (J). per. (978-1-4127-1046-6(4) , 7234600) Publications International, Ltd.

Silva Lee, Alfonso. Mi Isla y Yo: La Naturaleza de Republica Dominicana. Hayskar, Bonnie, ed. Lago, Alexis, illus. 2010. (SPA.). 32p. (J). pap. 9.95 (978-1-929165-25-4(0)) PANGAEA.

—Mon Ile et Moi: La Nature d'Haiti: Lanati an Ayti: Peym Avem. Hayskar, Bonnie, ed. Hilaire, Jean Vilmond, tr. Lago, Alexis, illus. 2010. (FRE & CRP.). 32p. (J). pap. 9.95 (978-1-929165-28-5(5)) PANGAEA.

Smith, Alastair. Nighttime. 2004. (Lift-the-Flap Learners Ser.). (Illus.). 16p. (J). (gr. 1 up). pap. 8.95 (978-0-7945-0366-6(7) , Usborne) EDC Publishing.

Smith, Alastair & Howell, Laura. On the Beach. 2004. (Lift-the-Flap Learners Ser.). (Illus.). 16p. (J). (gr. 1 up). pap. 8.95 (978-0-7945-0213-3(X) , Usborne) EDC Publishing.

Snyder, Margaret. All God's Things. deluxe ed. 1999. (Talking Pages Deluxe Ser.). (Illus.). 12p. (ps-3). 7.95 (978-1-58224-000-8(0)) Futech Interactive Products, Inc.

Steck-Vaughn Staff. Biomes Series. 2000. pap., tchr. ed. (978-0-7398-4163-1(7)) Steck-Vaughn.

Sterry, Paul. Nature Explorer: Discover Amazing Bugs & Plants in Your Yard & Beyond! 2005. (Illus.). 32p. (J). pap. 19.95 (978-0-7624-1846-6(X) , Running Pr. Kids) Running Pr. Bk. Pubs.

Stewart, Melissa. Extreme Nature! Q&A. 2006. (Illus.). 48p. (J). 16.99 (978-0-06-089937-0(9)); pap. 6.99 (978-0-06-089936-3(0)) HarperCollins Pubs.

Stille, Darlene R. Grasslands. 1998. (True Bks.). (Illus.). 48p. (J). (gr. 3-5). 25.00 (978-0-516-21509-9(4) , Children's Pr.) Scholastic Library Publishing.

Street, Sharon. Living Things Need Water. 2001. (Windows on Literacy Ser.). (Illus.). 16p. (J). (gr. k-2). (978-0-7922-9211-1(1)) National Geographic Society.

Sullivan, Lawrence Eugene. Nature & Rite in Shinto. 2002. (Religions of Mankind Ser.). (Illus.). 32p. (J). (gr. 5 up). 21.95 (978-0-7910-6631-7(2) , Chelsea Hse.) Facts On File, Inc.

Swanson-Natsues, Lyn. What Comes First. 2002. (gr. k-3). lib. bdg. 10.60 (978-0-613-85277-7(X)) Tandem Library Bks.

Swinburne, Stephen R. Lots & Lots of Zebra Stripes: Patterns in Nature. Swinburne, Stephen R., illus. 2003. (Illus.). 32p. (J). (gr. k-2). 15.95 (978-1-56397-707-7(9)) Boyds Mills Pr.

—What Color Is Nature? Swinburne, Stephen R., photos by. 2003. (Illus.). 32p. (J). (gr. k-2). pap. 9.95 (978-1-59078-008-4(6)) Boyds Mills Pr.

Swinburne, Stephen R. & Boyds Mills Press Staff. Lots & Lots of Zebra Stripes: Patterns in Nature. 2003. (Illus.). 32p. (J). (gr. k-2). pap. 9.95 (978-1-56397-980-4(2)) Boyds Mills Pr.

—What Color Is Nature? Swinburne, Stephen R., photos by. 2003. (Illus.). 32p. (J). (gr. k-2). 15.95 (978-1-56397-967-5(5)) Boyds Mills Pr.

Tallarico, Tony. Nature Trivia Mazes. 2007. 48p. (J). pap. 4.95 (978-0-486-45364-4(2)) Dover Pubns., Inc.

Taylor, Judith. Life & Journey of a Rainbow. 2000. 40p. pap. 8.00 (978-0-8059-4683-3(7)) Dorrance Publishing Co., Inc.

Tell Me Why, Tell Me How, 6 bks., Set. Incl. How Do Birds Fly? Stewart, Melissa. lib. bdg. 28.50 (978-0-7614-2110-8(6)); How Do Fish Breathe Underwater? Stewart, Melissa. lib. bdg. 28.50 (978-0-7614-2109-2(2)); How Do Plants Grow? Stewart, Melissa. lib. bdg. 28.50 (978-0-7614-2111-5(4)); How Does the Wind Blow? Murphy, Patricia J. lib. bdg. 28.50 (978-0-7614-2107-8(6)); Why Do the Seasons Change? Stewart, Melissa. lib. bdg. 28.50 (978-0-7614-2112-2(2)); Why Is the Sky Blue? Mara, Wil. lib. bdg. 28.50 (978-0-7614-2108-5(4)); (Illus.). 32p. (J). 2006. 2007. Set lib. bdg. 171.00 (***978-0-7614-2106-1(8)** , Benchmark Bks.) Cavendish, Marshall Corp.

Thornhill, Jan. Before & After: A Book of Nature Timescapes. Thornhill, Jan, illus. 2005. (Illus.). 32p. pap. 6.95 (978-1-897066-28-7(7)) Maple Tree Pr. CAN. *Dist:* Transition Vendor.

Tief im Meer. (GER.). 19.95 (978-3-411-09271-0(8)) Bibliographisches Institut & F. A. Brockhaus AG DEU. *Dist:* Distribooks, Inc., i.b.d., Ltd.

Tiere unter der Erde. (GER.). (978-3-411-09251-2(3)) Bibliographisches Institut & F. A. Brockhaus AG DEU. *Dist:* i.b.d., Ltd.

Timon & the Volcano, Level 2. 1999. (SmartReader Ser.). (J). pap., tchr. ed. 19.95 incl. audio (978-0-7887-0778-0(7) , 79341T3) Recorded Bks., LLC.

Treasury of Animals & Nature Volume II. 2006. (J). pap. 9.99 (***978-1-59545-014-2(9))** Learning Horizons, Inc.

Trumbauer, Lisa. Nature's Patterns: Student Book. Pliakas, Stephanie, ed. 1998. (Early Science Ser.). 16p. (Orig.). (J). (ps-2). pap., stu. ed. 3.33 (978-1-56784-376-7(X)) Sundance/Newbridge Educational Publishing.

Tuxworth, Nicola. Nature, 12 vols. 2006. (Learn-A-Word Picture Bks.). (Illus.). 12p. (ps-k). bds. 6.99 (978-0-7548-1454-2(8) , Lorenz Bks.) Anness Publishing GBR. *Dist:* National Bk. Network.

The Untamed World, 4 vols. 2003. (Illus.). (978-0-7398-6846-1(2)) Raintree.

Vess, Deborah, et al. AP World History (REA) - the Best Test Prep for the AP World History. Knight, Theodore, ed. 2006. (Test Preps Ser.). (Illus.). 768p. (gr. 5-12). pap. 17.95 (978-0-7386-0128-1(4)) Research & Education Assn.

Viseth, Heather. Wetlands. 1999. (Illus.). 64p. (YA). (gr. 5). 8.95 (978-1-58037-110-0(8)) Twain, Mark Media, Inc. Pubs.

Walker-Leslie, Clare. Nature All Year Long. 2002. (Illus.). 56p. 15.70 (978-0-7872-9399-4(7)) Kendall/Hunt Publishing Co.

Walton, Rick. The Sky's the Limit: Naturally Funny Jokes. Gable, Brian, illus. 2005. (Make Me Laugh! Ser.). 32p. (J). (gr. k-3). lib. bdg. 19.93 (978-1-57505-663-0(1)) Lerner Publishing Group.

Watson, Susan. Protecting Global Environments. 2003. 32p. (J). lib. bdg. 24.25 (978-1-58340-399-0(X)) Smart Apple Media.

We Can Read about Nature!, 2 groups. 2000. (Illus.). (J). (gr. 1-2). lib. bdg. 128.14 Cavendish, Marshall Corp.

We Can Read about Nature! - Group 2, 6 bks., Set. Incl. Animal Talk. Nichols, Catherine. lib. bdg. 21.36 (978-0-7614-1253-3(0)); Busy Builders. McDaniel, Melissa. lib. bdg. 21.36 (978-0-7614-1255-7(7)); Going Places. Nichols, Catherine. lib. bdg. 21.36 (978-0-7614-1252-6(2)); If You Had a Tail. Nichols, Catherine. lib. bdg. 21.36 (978-0-7614-1251-9(4)); It's the Wind! Nichols, Catherine. lib. bdg. 21.36 (978-0-7614-1254-0(9)); Water All Around. Nichols, Catherine. lib. bdg. 21.36 (978-0-7614-1256-4(5)); 32p. (J). (gr. 1-2). 2001. (Illus.). 2001. Set lib. bdg. 128.14 (978-0-7614-1250-2(6) , Benchmark Bks.) Cavendish, Marshall Corp.

We Can Read about Nature! - Group 3, 6 bks., Set. 128.14 (978-0-7614-1429-2(0) , Benchmark Bks.) Cavendish, Marshall Corp.

Webster, Christine. Canyons. 2005. (Illus.). 89p. (J). 21.26 (978-0-7368-3711-8(6)) Capstone Pr., Inc.

Wengerd, Marvin, ed. Nature Friend Index: 1983-2000. rev. ed. 2001. 56p. (J). (gr. 1-8). pap. 8.00 (978-1-890050-63-4(6)) Carlisle Pr.- Walnut Creek.

Whitehouse, Patricia. Verano. 2003. (Las Estaciones (Seasons) Ser.). (SPA.). 24p. (J). (ps-1). lib. bdg. 17.08 (978-1-4034-0334-6(1)) Heinemann Library.

Wilkinson, Doris J. Creatures of Nature. Wilkinson, Doris J., ed. Chipping, Oliver, illus. 2000. (Jacob's Magic Box Discovery Ser.). 20p. (J). (ps). pap. 4.95 (978-0-9700386-4-7(X)) Magic Box Pubns.

Willis, Shirley. Dime por Que Es Mojada la Lluvia. 1999. (Coleccion los Estupendos). (SPA., Illus.). 32p. (J). (gr. 2-4). 20.00 (978-0-531-11849-8(5) , OD30029, Watts, Franklin) Scholastic Library Publishing.

—Dime por Que Es Mojada la Lluvia. 2000. (Estupendos Ser.). (J). 12.75 (978-0-606-20150-6(5)) Tandem Library Bks.

Wright, Holly. Sky. 2004. (J). (978-0-9743690-9-9(8)) Britt Allcroft Productions.

Zimmerman, Eliot. Mother Nature Stories. Richlen, Michael, illus. 2001. 88p. (J). 24.95 (978-1-882987-06-1(3)) Eagle Bks.

Zoobooks, 56 bks., Set. Incl. Alligators & Crocodiles. Wexo, John Bonnett. 24p. (gr. 3-12). lib. bdg. 19.95 (978-0-88682-220-0(3)); Animal Champions. Wexo, John Bonnett. 32p. (gr. 1-4). lib. bdg. 19.95 (978-0-88682-409-9(5)); Animal Champions 2. Shaw, Marjorie B. & Elwood, Ann. 24p. (gr. 1-4). lib. bdg. 19.95 (978-0-88682-774-8(4)); Animal Wonders. Wexo, John Bonnett. 32p. (gr. 1-4). lib. bdg. 14.95 (978-0-88682-407-5(9)); Apes. Wexo, John Bonnett. 24p. (gr. 2-12). lib. bdg. 19.95 (978-0-88682-265-1(3)); Baby Animals. Wexo, John Bonnett. 24p. (gr. 1-4). lib. bdg. 19.95 (978-0-88682-270-5(X)); Baby Animals 2. Elwood, Ann. 32p. (gr. 1-4). lib. bdg. 19.95 (978-0-88682-418-1(4)); Bats. Wood, Linda C. & Rink, Deane. 24p. (gr. 2-12). lib. bdg. 19.95 (978-0-88682-337-5(4)); Bears. Wexo, John Bonnett. 24p. (gr. 3-12). lib. bdg. 19.95 (978-0-88682-221-7(1)); Big Cats. Wexo, John Bonnett. 24p. (gr. 2-12). lib. bdg. 19.95 (978-0-88682-264-4(5)); Birds of Prey. Wexo, John Bonnett. 24p. (gr. 2-12). lib. bdg. 19.95 (978-0-88682-332-0(3)); Butterflies. Brust, Beth Wagner. 32p. (gr. 3-12). lib. bdg. 19.95 (978-0-88682-421-1(4)); Camels. Wexo, John Bonnett. 32p. (gr. 2-12). lib. bdg. 19.95 (978-0-88682-222-4(X)); Cheetahs. Wood, Linda C. & Jenson, Cynthia L. 32p. (gr. 2-12). lib. bdg. 19.95 (978-0-88682-417-4(6)); Chimpanzees & Bonobos. Elwood, Ann. 24p. (gr. 2-12). lib. bdg. 19.95 (978-0-88682-340-5(4)); Deer Family. Biel, Timothy Levi. 24p. (gr. 2-12). lib. bdg. 19.95 (978-0-88682-775-5(2)); Dinosaurs. Wexo, John Bonnett. 24p. (gr. 2-12). lib. bdg. 19.95 (978-0-88682-223-1(8)); Dolphins & Porpoises. Brust, Beth Wagner. 24p. (gr. 2-12). lib. bdg. 19.95 (978-0-88682-339-9(0)); Ducks, Geese & Swans. Wexo, John Bonnett. 24p. (gr. 3-12). lib. bdg. 19.95 (978-0-88682-224-8(6)); Eagles. Richardson, Adele D. 24p. (gr. 2-12). lib. bdg. 19.95 (978-0-88682-225-5(4)); Elephants. Wexo, John Bonnett. 24p. (gr. 2-12). lib. bdg. 19.95 (978-0-88682-226-2(2)); Endangered Animals. Wexo, John Bonnett. 24p. (gr. 2-12). lib. bdg. 19.95 (978-0-88682-269-9(6)); Giant Pandas. Wexo, John Bonnett. 24p. (gr. 2-12). lib. bdg. 19.95 (978-0-88682-228-6(9)); Giraffes. Wexo, John Bonnett. 24p. (gr. 2-12). lib. bdg. 19.95 (978-0-88682-334-4(X)); Gorillas. Wexo, John Bonnett. 32p. (gr. 2-12). lib. bdg. 19.95 (978-0-88682-423-5(0)); Hippos. Brust, Beth Wagner. 32p. (gr. 2-12). lib. bdg. 19.95 (978-0-88682-424-2(9)); Hummingbirds. Biel, Timothy Levi. 24p. (gr. 2-12). lib. bdg. 19.95 (978-0-88682-336-8(6)); Insects. Wexo, John Bonnett. 24p. (gr. 2-12). lib. bdg. 19.95 (978-0-88682-335-1(8)); Insects 2. Wexo, John Bonnett. 24p. (gr. 2-12). lib. bdg. 19.95 (978-0-88682-776-2(0)); Kangaroos. Brust, Beth Wagner. 32p. (gr. 2-12). lib. bdg. 19.95 (978-0-88682-425-9(7)); Koalas. Wexo, John Bonnett. 24p. (gr. 2-12). lib. bdg. 19.95 (978-0-88682-227-9(0)); Lions. Elwood, Ann & Estrada, Jackie. 32p. (gr. 2-12). lib. bdg. 19.95 (978-0-88682-422-8(2)); Little Cats. Wexo, John Bonnett. 32p. (gr. 2-12). lib. bdg. 19.95 (978-0-88682-413-6(3)); Night Animals. Wexo, John Bonnett. 24p. (gr. 2-12). lib. bdg. 19.95 (978-0-88682-777-9(9)); Old World Monkeys. Elwood, Ann. 32p. (gr. 3-12). lib. bdg. 19.95 (978-0-88682-419-8(2)); Orangutans. Wexo, John Bonnett. 32p. (gr. 2-12). lib. bdg. 19.95 (978-0-88682-412-9(5)); Ostriches, Emus, Rheas, Kiwis & Cassowaries. Elwood, Ann. 24p. (gr. 2-12). lib. bdg. 19.95 (978-0-88682-338-2(2)); Owls. Biel, Timothy Levi. 24p. (gr. 3-12). lib. bdg. 19.95 (978-0-88682-268-2(8)); Parrots. Wexo, John Bonnett. 32p. (gr. 2-12). lib. bdg. 19.95 (978-0-88682-408-2(7)); Penguins. Wexo, John Bonnett. 24p. (gr. 2-12). lib. bdg. 19.95 (978-0-88682-263-7(7)); Polar Bears. Biel, Timothy Levi. 32p. (gr. 2-12). lib. bdg. 19.95 (978-0-88682-414-3(1)); Rattlesnakes. Brust, Beth Wagner & Dorn, Bob. 32p. (gr. 2-12). lib. bdg. 19.95 (978-0-88682-426-6(5)); Rhinos. Wexo, John Bonnett. 24p. (gr. 2-12). lib. bdg. 19.95 (978-0-88682-333-7(1)); Sea Birds. Brust, Beth Wagner. 32p. (gr. 2-12). lib. bdg. 19.95 (978-0-88682-416-7(8)); Sea Otters. Brust, Beth Wagner. 32p. (gr. 2-12). lib. bdg. 19.95 (978-0-88682-415-0(X)); Seals, Sea Lions & Walruses. Wexo, John Bonnett. 24p. (gr. 2-12). lib. bdg. 19.95 (978-0-88682-271-2(8)); Sharing the World with Animals. Shaw, Marjorie B. & Elwood, Ann. 24p. (gr. 1-4). lib. bdg. 19.95 (978-0-88682-778-6(7)); Sharks. Wexo, John Bonnett. 24p. (gr. 2-12). lib. bdg. 19.95 (978-0-88682-229-3(7)); Skunks & Their Relatives. Biel, Timothy Levi. 24p. (gr. 2-12). lib. bdg. 19.95 (978-0-88682-779-3(5)); Snakes. Wexo, John Bonnett. 24p. (gr. 2-12). lib. bdg. 19.95 (978-0-88682-331-3(5)); Spiders. Biel, Timothy Levi. 32p. (gr. 2-12). lib. bdg. 19.95 (978-0-88682-410-5(9)); Tigers. Biel, Timothy Levi. 24p. (gr. 2-12). lib. bdg. 19.95 (978-0-88682-266-8(1)); Turtles. Biel, Timothy Levi. 32p. (gr. 2-12). lib. bdg. 19.95 (978-0-88682-411-2(7)); Whales. Wexo, John Bonnett. 24p. (gr. 2-12). lib. bdg. 19.95 (978-0-88682-272-9(6)); Wild Dogs. Biel, Timothy Levi. 24p. (gr. 2-12). lib. bdg. 19.95 (978-0-88682-780-9(9)); Wild Horses. Wexo, John Bonnett. 24p. (gr. 2-12). lib. bdg. 19.95 (978-0-88682-781-6(7)); Wolves. Wexo, John Bonnett. 24p. (gr. 2-12). lib. bdg. 19.95 (978-0-88682-267-5(X)); Zebras. Wood, Linda C. 32p. (gr. 2-12). lib. bdg. 19.95 (978-0-88682-420-4(6)); (YA). 1995. (Illus.). 1157.10 (978-0-88682-238-5(6) , Creative Education) Creative Co., The.

NATURE (AESTHETICS)

Baumbusch, Brigitte. Nature in Art. 2005. (Illus.). 32p. (J). lib. bdg. 22.00 (978-0-8368-4448-1(3)) Stevens, Gareth Inc.

Luxbacher, Irene, illus. The Jumbo Book of Outdoor Art. Boudreau, Ray & Hall, Doug, photos by. 2006. 144p. (J). (gr. 3-6). (978-1-55337-680-4(3)) Kids Can Pr., Ltd.

NATURE CRAFT

Bledsoe, Karen E. & Norvell, Candyce. 365 Nature Crafts & Activities. Chicko, Terri & Chicko, Joe, illus. 1998. (Craft & Project Books for Children Ser.). 240p. (J). (gr. 3-6). lib. bdg. 24.95 (978-1-56674-227-6(7) , HTS Bks.) Forest Hse. Publishing Co., Inc.

Burckhardt, Ann L. Calabazas. 1998. (Coleccion Primeros Lectores). (SPA., Illus.). 24p. (J). (gr. k-3). lib. bdg. 18.60 (978-1-56065-786-6(3) , CAP1291, Bridgestone Bks.) Capstone Pr., Inc.

Caduto, Michael J. & Bruchac, Joseph. Keepers of the Earth: Native American Stories & Environmental Activities for Children. Fadden, John Kahionhes & Wood, Carol, illus. (Keepers Ser.). 240p. (gr. 1-3). reprint ed. pap. 21.95 (978-1-55591-385-4(7)) Fulcrum Publishing.

Carlson, Laurie M. Green Thumbs: A Kid's Activity Guide to Indoor & Outdoor Gardening. 2003. (Kid's Guide Ser.). (Illus.). 144p. (J). (gr. k-7). pap. 12.95 (978-1-55652-238-3(X)) Chicago Review Pr., Inc.

Chapman, Gillian & Robson, Pam. Art from Sand & Earth. 2007. (J). lib. bdg. (***978-1-4042-3723-0(2)** , PowerKids Pr.) Rosen Publishing Group, Inc., The.

—Art from Wood. 2007. (J). lib. bdg. (***978-1-4042-3726-1(7)** , PowerKids Pr.) Rosen Publishing Group, Inc., The.

Crexells, Cristina & Llimos Plomer, Anna. Plants & Seeds. 2003. (Let's Create! Ser.). (Illus.). 32p. (J). (gr. 2 up). lib. bdg. 23.33 (978-0-8368-3748-3(7)) Stevens, Gareth Inc.

Forte, Imogene. Nature Crafts. 2004. (Fun Things to Make & Do Ser.). (Illus.). 80p. (J). per. 9.95 (978-0-86530-617-2(6)) Incentive Pubns., Inc.

Juega con la Naturaleza. (Coleccion Manualidades Divertidas).Tr. of Playing with Nature. (SPA.). 32p. (J). (gr. k-3). 10.00 (978-84-342-2079-9(2)) Parramon Ediciones S.A. ESP. *Dist:* Distribuidora Norma, Inc., Lectorum Pubns., Inc.

Kohl, MaryAnn F. & Gainer, Cindy. Good Earth Art: Environmental Art for Kids. Gainer, Cindy, illus. 2003. (Bright Ideas for Learning Ser.: Vol. 3). (Illus.). 244p. (Orig.). (J). (ps-6). pap. 18.95 (978-0-935607-01-7(3)) Bright Ring Publishing, Inc.

Lovejoy, Sharon. Sunflower Houses: Inspiration from the Garden. 2001. (Illus.). 144p. (J). (gr. 4-7). pap. 13.95 (978-0-7611-2386-6(5) , 12386) Workman Publishing Co., Inc.

Martin, Laura C. & Cain, David. Nature's Art Box: From T-Shirts to Twig Baskets, 65 Cool Projects for Crafty Kids to Make with Natural Materials You Can Find Anywhere. 2003. (Illus.). (gr. 3-7). 224p. tchr. ed. 23.95 (978-1-58017-503-6(1) , 67503); 192p. (J). pap. 16.95 (978-1-58017-490-9(6) , 67490) Storey Publishing, LLC. (Storey Kids).

Parramon's Editorial Team Staff. Stones & "Stuff" Parramon's Editorial Team Staff, photos by. 2004. (Let's Create! Ser.). (Illus.). 32p. (J). (gr. 2 up). lib. bdg. 23.33 (978-0-8368-4019-3(4)) Stevens, Gareth Inc.

Seix, Victoria. Crafts from Nature. 2000. (Crafts for All Seasons Ser.). (Illus.). 32p. (J). (gr. 3-8). lib. bdg. 23.70 (978-1-56711-433-1(4) , Blackbirch Pr., Inc.) Thomson Gale.

Senisi, Ellen B. Berry Smudges & Leaf Prints: Finding & Making Colors from Nature. Senisi, Ellen B., photos by. 2005. (Illus.). 40p. (J). (gr. 4-8). reprint ed. 17.00 (978-0-7567-9707-2(1)) DIANE Publishing Co.

Williams, Joy. Creative Kids Nature Crafts. 2002. (Creative Kids Ser.). (Illus.). 64p. (J). pap. 12.99 (978-1-58180-292-4(7) , North Light Bks.) F & W Pubns., Inc.

NATURE—EFFECT OF HUMAN BEINGS ON

Barr, Gary E. Climate Change: Is the World in Danger? 2006. (Behind the News Ser.). (Illus.). 56p. (J). (gr. 5-8). lib. bdg. 32.86 (978-1-4034-8830-5(4)) Heinemann Library.

Cherry, Lynne. River Ran Wild: An Environmental History. 2002. (gr. 3-6). lib. bdg. 15.30 (978-0-613-53858-9(7)) Tandem Library Bks.

Chinery, Michael. Resources & Conservation. 2000. (Secrets of the Rainforest Ser.). (Illus.). 32p. (J). (gr. 3-4). pap. (978-0-7787-0231-3(6)); lib. bdg. (978-0-7787-0221-4(9)) Crabtree Publishing Co.

Connolly, Sean. Safeguarding the Environment. 2005. (Campaigns for Change Ser.). (Illus.). 48p. (J). (gr. 6-9). lib. bdg. 29.95 (978-1-58340-519-2(4)) Smart Apple Media.

Donnelly, Karen. Biomes of the Past & Future. 2003. (Earths Changing Weather & Climate Ser.). (Illus.). 24p. (J). lib. bdg. 18.75 (978-0-8239-6215-0(6) , PowerKids Pr.) Rosen Publishing Group, Inc., The.

—Rising Temperatures of the Past & the Future. 2003. (Earths Changing Weather & Climate Ser.). (Illus.). 24p. (J). lib. bdg. 18.75 (978-0-8239-6214-3(8) , PowerKids Pr.) Rosen Publishing Group, Inc., The.

Due, Andrea. People & the Earth: An Environmental Atlas, 6 vols. 1998. (Illus.). (J). lib. bdg. 235.00 (978-0-7172-9204-2(5) , Grolier) Scholastic Library Publishing.

Green, Jen. Feeding the People. 2004. (J). lib. bdg. (978-1-59389-138-1(5)) Chrysalis Education.

—Saving Oceans & Wetlands. 2004. (J). lib. bdg. 27.10 (978-1-59389-139-8(3)) Chrysalis Education.

Green, Mary. Rivers in Action. 2004. (Earth's Changing Landscape Ser.). (Illus.). 46p. (J). lib. bdg. 28.50 (978-1-58340-477-5(5)) Smart Apple Media.

Jerome, Kate Boehm. Protecting the Planet. 2003. (Life Science Ser.). (Illus.). 32p. (J). pap. (978-0-7922-8864-0(5)) National Geographic Society.

Kinsner, Kathy. Relaciones en la naturaleza & Relationships in Nature. 2005. spiral bd. 88.00 (***978-1-4108-5729-3(8))** Benchmark Education Co.

Leathers, Dan. The Snows of Kilimanjaro. 2007. (On the Verge of Extinction Ser.). (Illus.). 32p. (J). (gr. 1-4). lib. bdg. 25.70 (***978-1-58415-584-3(1))** Mitchell Lane Pubs., Inc.

Morgan, Sally. Changing Climate. 2007. (Illus.). 32p. (J). (***978-1-59771-067-1(9))** Sea-To-Sea Pubns.

Morris. Landscapes & People, Bks. 36, 6 Packs., Set. 2004. (Illus.). pap. 243.00 (978-1-4109-1259-6(0)) Raintree.

Morris, Neil. Earth's Changing Coasts. 2003. (Illus.). 32p. (J). pap. 7.50 (978-1-4109-0341-9(9)); lib. bdg. 25.70 (978-1-4109-0178-1(5)) Raintree.

—Earth's Changing Coasts. 2003. (gr. 3-6). lib. bdg. 15.90 (978-0-613-78235-7(6)) Tandem Library Bks.

—Earth's Changing Continents. 2003. (Illus.). (J). pap. 7.50 (978-1-4109-0342-6(7)); 32p. lib. bdg. 25.70 (978-1-4109-0179-8(3)) Raintree.

—Earth's Changing Continents. 2003. (gr. 3-6). lib. bdg. 15.90 (978-0-613-78236-4(4)) Tandem Library Bks.

—Earth's Changing Islands. 2003. (Illus.). 32p. (J). 7.50 (978-1-4109-0344-0(3)); lib. bdg. 25.70 (978-1-4109-0177-4(7)) Raintree.

—Earth's Changing Islands. 2003. (gr. 3-6). lib. bdg. 15.90 (978-0-613-78237-1(2)) Tandem Library Bks.

—Earth's Changing Mountains. 2003. (Illus.). (J). pap. 7.50 (978-1-4109-0345-7(1)); 32p. lib. bdg. 25.70 (978-1-4109-0174-3(2)) Raintree.

—Earth's Changing Mountains. 2003. (gr. 3-6). lib. bdg. 15.90 (978-0-613-78239-5(9)) Tandem Library Bks.

—Earth's Changing Rivers. 2003. (Illus.). (J). 7.50 (978-1-4109-0346-4(X)); 32p. lib. bdg. 25.70 (978-1-4109-0175-0(0)) Raintree.

—Earth's Changing Rivers. 2003. (gr. 3-6). lib. bdg. 15.90 (978-0-613-78240-1(2)) Tandem Library Bks.

Morrison, Yvonne. Earth Partners: Saving the Planet. 2007. (Shockwave: History & Politics Ser.). (Illus.). 36p. (J). (gr. 4-6). lib. bdg. 25.00 (***978-0-531-17753-2(X)** , Children's Pr.) Scholastic Library Publishing.

Our Future. 2003. (Our World Ser.). (Illus.). (gr. 4-8). lib. bdg. 113.70 (978-0-7910-7059-8(X) , Chelsea Hse.) Facts On File, Inc.

M N O

Raabe, Emily. Human Impact on the Environment. 2006. (Life Science Library). (J). 21.25 (978-1-4042-2822-1(5) , PowerKids Pr.) Rosen Publishing Group, Inc., The.

Reid, Greg. Human Impacts. 2005. (Illus.). 32p. (J). (gr. 4-7). lib. bdg. 27.10 (978-1-58340-763-9(4)) Smart Apple Media.

Riley, Joelle. Erosion. 2007. (Early Bird Earth Science Ser.). (J). 25.26 (978-0-8225-5949-8(8) , Lerner Pubns.) Lerner Publishing Group.

Sachidhanandam, Uma. Threatened Habitats. 2004. (Green Alert Ser.). (Illus.). 48p. (J). lib. bdg. 28.56 (978-0-7398-7015-0(7)) Raintree.

Scoones, Simon. Climate Change: Our Impact on the Planet. 2001. (Twenty-First Century Debates Ser.). (Illus.). 64p. (YA). (gr. 6-8). lib. bdg. 27.12 (978-0-7398-3177-9(1)) Raintree.

Shone, Rob. Avalanches & Landslides. 2007. (Graphic Natural Disasters Ser.). (Illus.). 48p. (J). (gr. 5-8). lib. bdg. 29.25 (***978-1-4042-1992-2(7)***) Rosen Publishing Group, Inc., The.

—Avalanches & Mudslides. 2007. (J). (***978-1-4042-1984-7(6)***); (Illus.). 48p. pap. (***978-1-4042-1983-0(8)***) Rosen Publishing Group, Inc., The.

Smith, Andrea Claire Harte. The Effects of Farming. 2004. (Earth's Changing Landscape Ser.). (Illus.). 45p. (J). lib. bdg. 28.50 (978-1-58340-475-1(9)) Smart Apple Media.

Snedden, Robert. The Growth of Cities. 2004. (Earth's Changing Landscape Ser.). (J). lib. bdg. 28.50 (978-1-58340-474-4(0)) Smart Apple Media.

Steele, Phillip W. Changing Coastlines. 2004. (Earth's Changing Landscape Ser.). (Illus.). 46p. (J). lib. bdg. 28.50 (978-1-58340-476-8(7)) Smart Apple Media.

Stein, Paul. Floods of the Future. 2001. (Library of Future Weather & Climate). (Illus.). 64p. (YA). (gr. 4-6). lib. bdg. 26.50 (978-0-8239-3412-6(8)) Rosen Publishing Group, Inc., The.

—Forecasting the Climate of the Future. 2001. (Library of Future Weather & Climate). (Illus.). 64p. (YA). (gr. 4-6). lib. bdg. 26.50 (978-0-8239-3413-3(6)) Rosen Publishing Group, Inc., The.

—Ice Ages in the Future. 2001. (Library of Future Weather & Climate). (Illus.). 64p. (YA). (gr. 4-6). lib. bdg. 26.50 (978-0-8239-3415-7(2)) Rosen Publishing Group, Inc., The.

Unwin, Mike. Climate Change. 2006. (Planet under Pressure Ser.). (Illus.). 48p. (YA). (gr. 6-8). lib. bdg. 31.43 (***978-1-4034-8216-7(0)***) Heinemann Library.

Vogel, Carole G. Human Impact. 2003. (Restless Sea Ser.). (Illus.). 96p. (J). (gr. 5-8). 30.50 (978-0-531-12323-2(5) , Watts, Franklin) Scholastic Library Publishing.

—Human Impact. 2003. (gr. 5-8). lib. bdg. 22.20 (978-0-613-67817-9(6)) Tandem Library Bks.

Walker, Jane. Famine, Drought, & Plagues. 2004. (Natural Disasters Ser.). (J). lib. bdg. 27.10 (978-1-932799-08-8(7)) Stargazer Bks.

Watson, Susan. Protecting Global Environments. 2003. 32p. (J). lib. bdg. 24.25 (978-1-58340-399-0(X)) Smart Apple Media.

NATURE—EFFECT OF HUMAN BEINGS ON—FICTION

Cooper, Susan. Green Boy. 2003. (Illus.). 208p. (J). pap. 5.99 (978-0-689-84760-8(2) , Aladdin) Simon & Schuster Children's Publishing.

Hale, Shannon. Enna Burning. (J). 2006. 336p. pap. 8.95 (978-1-58234-906-0(1)); 2004. (Illus.). 300p. 17.95 (978-1-58234-889-6(8)) Bloomsbury Publishing. (Bloomsbury Children).

—River Secrets. 2006. (Illus.). 304p. (J). 17.95 (978-1-58234-901-5(0)) Bloomsbury Publishing.

Liberto, Lorenzo. Save the Planet / Salva el Planeta. Gomez, Rocio, tr. Torres, Irving, illus. 2005. (Matt the Rat Ser. / La Serie de Raton Mateo). (ENG & SPA.). 32p. (J). lib. bdg. 20.00 (978-0-9743668-5-2(4)) Harvest Sun Pr., LLC.

Lorbiecki, Marybeth. Paul Bunyan's Sweetheart. Graef, Renee, illus. rev. ed. 2007. 32p. (J). (gr. 1-4). 16.95 (***978-1-58536-289-9(1)***) Sleeping Bear Pr.

Robson, Walter. Ear2ear & the Gem1's. 2005. (ENG.). 192p. per. (***978-1-904988-05 2(9)***) Donard Publishing.

Wood, Douglas. Old Turtle & the Broken Truth. Muth, Jon J., illus. 2003. 64p. (J). pap. 17.95 (978-0-439-32109-9(3)) Scholastic, Inc.

NATURE—FICTION

Addy, Sharon. In Grandpa's Woods. Akins, Tamlyn, illus. 2004. (J). (***978-1-931599-42-9(4)*** , Trails Bks.) Big Earth Publishing.

Adler, Eric. Is the Sky Always Blue? Nakahodo, Neil, illus. l.t. ed. 2002. 32p. (J). 14.95 (978-0-9717080-0-6(2)) Kansas City Star Bks.

Aigner-Clark, Julie. Baby Einstein: Baby Mozart Music Is Everywhere!, Spanish-Language Edition. Zaidi, Nadeem, illus. 2005. (Baby Einstein: Libros de Carton Ser.). (SPA.). 16p. (J). bds. 7.95 (978-970-718-309-4(8) , Silver Dolphin en Español) Advanced Marketing, S. de R. L. de C. V. MEX. *Dist:* Perseus Distribution.

Allamand, Maite. Alamito el Largo. (SPA.). (J). (gr. 2-3). pap. (978-956-13-1428-3(2) , AB3840) Bello, Andres CHL. *Dist:* Lectorum Pubns., Inc.

Allen, Page. Madison's Descent: A Child's Journey. (J). 2006. pap. 25.00 (***978-0-9752516-2-1(7)***); 2004. lib. bdg. 60.00 (***978-0-9752516-1-4(9)***) Otis & Randolph Pr.

—The Way to Davis: On the River of Stars. collector's ed. 2007. (J). 75.00 (***978-0-9752516-3-8(5)***) Otis & Randolph Pr.

Andrews, Julie & "BB". The Little Grey Men: A Story for the Young in Heart. Watkins-Pitchford, Denys, illus. ed. 2004. 304p. (J). 17.99 (978-0-06-055448-4(7) , Julie Andrews Collection) HarperCollins Pubs.

Arden, Carolyn. Goose Moon. 2004. (Illus.). 32p. (J). (gr. k-2). 15.95 (978-1-59078-040-4(X)) Boyds Mills Pr.

Auch, Mary Jane. Wing Nut. rev. ed. 2005. 256p. (J). 16.95 (978-0-8050-7531-1(3) , Holt, Henry & Co. Bks. For Young Readers) Holt, Henry & Co.

Avery, Alice. Mommy Someone Is Blowing Me Kisses. 2004. 24p. pap. 14.95 (978-1-4137-1352-7(1)) PublishAmerica, Inc.

Avignone, June. A Peek into the Secret Little Ones of Turtle Back Island. My Wolf Dog, illus. 2004. 40p. (J). pap. (978-0-9654628-2-2(X)) Mill Street Forward, The.

Baby Lauren & Theodore, Paperback. 2007. (J). pap. 9.95 (***978-0-9779643-0-7(2)***) Healing Tree Arts.

Base, Graeme. Uno's Garden. 2006. (Illus.). 44p. (J). (ps-3). 19.95 (978-0-8109-5473-1(7)) Abrams, Harry N. , Inc.

Bentley, Dawn. Saber-Tooth Trap. (Smithsonian's Prehistoric Pals Ser.). (Illus.). 36p. (J). (ps-2). 2.95 (978-1-59249-456-9(0) , S2456); 9.95 (978-1-59249-457-6(9) , PS2456); 14.95 incl. cd-rom (978-1-59249-453-8(6) , H2406) Soundprints.

—Saber-Tooth Trap. Reavely, Trevor, illus. 2005. (Smithsonian's Prehistoric Pals Ser.). 358p. (J). (ps-ps). pap. 6.95 (978-1-59249-454-5(4) , S2406) Soundprints.

Blanco, Julia. Agualinda Aguaclara. Mondeja, Omar, illus. 2000. (SPA.). 32p. (J). lib. bdg. (978-1-894628-00-6(4)) RosaBlanca.

Blume, Rebecca. When the World Was Green! Blume, Rebecca, illus. 2007. (Illus.). 32p. (J). per. 14.00 (***978-0-9785427-1-9(1)***) Liberty Artists Management.

Bogart, Jo Elllen. The Big Tree Gang. Griffiths, Dean, illus. 2005. 60p. (J). lib. bdg. 20.00 (***978-1-4242-1251-4(0)***) Fitzgerald Bks.

Bond, A. Russell. Scientific American Boy. 2006. (Illus.). 320p. (J). (gr. 4-7). per. 19.95 (978-1-55709-185-7(4)) Applewood Bks.

Bonnell, Kris. Look Up! 2007. (J). 3.95 (***978-1-933727-48-6(9)***) Reading Reading Bks., LLC.

Bougie, Victoria. Welcome Little One. Stanley, Ron, illus. 2002. 32p. per. 9.95 (978-0-9725022-0-7(3)) Alvin Bks., Inc.

Brodland, Rita, ed. All Dried Out. Freeman, Troy, illus. l.t. ed. 2006. (WeWrite Kids! Ser.: 50). 68p. (J). pap. 11.95 (***978-1-57635-063-8(0)***) WeWrite LLC.

Budbill, David. Snowshoe Trek to Otter River. 2005. (J). pap. (978-0-9657144-9-5(7)) Onion River Pr.

Bunting, Eve. Anna's Table. Morley, Taia, illus. 2003. 32p. (gr. k-3). 15.95 (978-1-55971-841-7(2) , NorthWord Bks. for Young Readers) T&N Children's Publishing.

Canyon, Christopher. John Denver's Sunshine on My Shoulders. 2003. (gr. k-3). lib. bdg. 17.60 (978-0-613-68518-4(0)) Tandem Library Bks.

Carle, Eric. Little Cloud: A Draw-with-Chalk Book. 2006. (World of Eric Carle Ser.). 10p. (J). (ps-1). bds. 6.99 (978-0-448-44418-5(6) , Grosset & Dunlap) Penguin Group (USA) Inc.

Channell, Jim. Quien Vive en el Campo? 2000. (SPA.). 10p. (J). (ps-k). 7.95 (978-84-392-8319-5(9)) Lectorum Pubns., Inc.

—Quien Vive en el Lago? 2000. (SPA.). 10p. (J). (ps-k). 7.95 (978-84-392-8317-1(2)) Lectorum Pubns., Inc.

—Quien Vive en el Mar? 2000. (SPA.). 10p. (J). (ps-k). 7.95 (978-84-392-8316-4(4)) Lectorum Pubns., Inc.

Cole, Gail. E. The Butterfly Kids. 2006. (ENG.). 32p. per. 19.99 (***978-1-4259-3003-5(4)***) AuthorHouse.

Cole, Henry. On Meadowview Street. Cole, Henry, illus. 2007. 32p. (J). lib. bdg. 17.89 (978-0-06-056482-7(2)); (Illus.). 16.99 (978-0-06-056481-0(4)) HarperCollins Pubs.

Cole, Joanna. The Magic School Bus Wet All Over: A Book about the Water Cycle. 2002. (Illus.). (J). 11.45 (978-0-7587-6705-9(6)) Book Wholesalers, Inc.

Coleman, David R. Old Troop, Rainbow Fairies, & the Forget-Me-Now Potion. 2007. (J). pap. 8.99 (***978-1-60247-054-5(5)***) Tate Publishing & Enterprises, L.L.C.

Collard, Sneed. Flash Point. 2006. 256p. (J). 15.95 (978-1-56145-385-6(4) , Peachtree Junior) Peachtree Pubs., Ltd.

Colman. Pearl Story Book A Collection of Tales O. 2006. pap. 87.99 (***978-1-4280-4925-3(8)***) IndyPublish.com.

Cook, Sherry & Johnson, Terri. Watery William, 26. Kuhn, Jesse, illus. l.t. ed. 2006. (Quirkles—Exploring Phonics through Science Ser.: 23). 32p. (J). 7.99 (978-1-933815-22-0(1) , Quirkles, The) Creative 3, LLC.

Cooke, Flora J. Nature Myths & Stories for Little Chil. 2006. pap. 19.95 (***978-1-4254-9629-6(6)***) Kessinger Publishing, LLC.

Costain, Meredith. Life in a Tree. 2000. (gr. k-3). lib. bdg. 11.80 (978-0-613-30553-2(1)) Tandem Library Bks.

Coste, Marion. Wild Beach. Gray, Cissy, illus. 2005. 32p. (J). pap. 8.25 (978-0-89317-062-2(3) , WW-623); lib. bdg. 17.95 (978-0-89317-061-5(5) , WW-0615) Finney Co., Inc. (Windward Publishing).

Crawford, Laura. In Arctic Waters. Hodson, Ben, illus. 2007. 32p. (J). (ps-2). 15.95 (978-0-9768823-4-3(5)) Sylvan Dell Pubng.

Crimi, Carolyn. Get Busy, Beaver! Bynum, Janie, illus. 2004. 32p. (J). (ps-3). pap. 15.95 (978-0-439-54866-3(7) , Orchard Bks.) Scholastic, Inc.

Dann, Colin. Lion Country. 2001. 114p. (J). pap. 8.99 (978-0-09-940777-5(9)) Random Hse. GBR. *Dist:* Independent Pubs. Group.

Decker, Betzie Mary Beth. Trashy Brew: Adventures in Recycling. Ashcraft, Wanda, illus. 2000. (J). mass mkt. 12.00 (978-1-889406-44-2(9)) Prell Bks. & Multimedia.

Denver, John. John Denver's Sunshine on My Shoulders. Canyon, Christopher, illus. 2004. 32p. pap. 8.95 incl. audio compact disk (978-1-58469-050-4(X)) Dawn Pubns.

Donnelly, Anthony James. When the Trees Held Their Breath. Whitler, Larry, illus. deluxe ed. 2000. 44p. (YA). pap. 12.95 (978-0-9702052-3-0(6)) Antix Pr., Inc.

Dower, Laura. Save the Date with Other. 2002. (gr. 3-6). lib. bdg. 13.00 (978-0-613-74966-4(9)) Tandem Library Bks.

Dubarle-Bossy, Philippe. Hello, Rainbow! Moon, Jo, illus. 2006. 8p. (J). 9.95 (978-1-4027-3235-5(X)) Sterling Publishing Co., Inc.

Duncan Sings-Alone. Grandpa Sings-Alone Favorite Tales. 2000. (J). audio 11.95 (978-1-929590-03-2(2)) Two Canoes Pr.

Durand, Delphine. Bob & Co. 2007. (Illus.). 64p. (J). (ps-3). pap. 9.95 (***978-1-85437-723-4(X)***) Tate Gallery Publishing, Ltd. GBR. *Dist:* Hachette Bk. Group.

Edwards, Pamela Duncan. Clara Caterpillar. Cole, Henry, illus. 2004. 40p. (J). (ps-1). reprint ed. pap. 6.99 (978-0-06-443691-5(8) , Harper Trophy) HarperCollins Pubs.

Ehlert, Lois. In My World. 2006. (Illus.). 40p. (J). (ps-ps). reprint ed. pap., pap. 7.00 (978-0-15-205429-8(4) , Voyager Bks./Libros Viajeros) Harcourt Children's Bks.

Eleanor, Coalson. Simon Says Run. 2006. (Illus.). (J). 8.95 (978-1-56167-944-7(5)) American Literary Pr.

Ellsworth, Barry. The Little Stream. Date not set. (Illus.). 48p. (J). 9.95 (978-1-56684-082-8(1)) Evans Bk. Distribution & Pubs., Inc.

Evers, Alf. Treasure of Watchdog Mountain: The Story of a Mountain in the Catskills. Yanow-Schwartz, Jo & Schwartz, Arthur, eds. 2006. 76p. (J). 16.95 (978-1-879504-19-6(7)) Woodstocker Books/Arthur Schwartz & Company.

Fletcher, Ralph J. Hello, Harvest Moon. Kiesler, Kate, illus. 2003. 32p. (J). (gr. k-3). 16.00 (978-0-618-16451-6(0) , Clarion Bks.) Houghton Mifflin Co. Trade & Reference Div.

Fontes, Justine. El Dia Que Jordan Se Enfermo: Jordan's Silly Sick Day. Lee Jared, illus. 2005. (Rookie Reader(R) Espanol Ser.). 32p. (gr. k-2). 19.50 (978-0-516-24445-7(0) , Children's Pr.) Scholastic Library Publishing.

Foster, F. Gordon. The Seasons of the Swans. 2006. (Illus.). 203p. (978-0-9760563-3-1(X)) Mechling Bookbindery.

Fox, Paula. Traces. Kuskin, Karla, illus. 2007. (J). (978-1-932425-43-7(8) , Front Street) Boyds Mills Pr.

Frasier, Debra. The Incredible Water Show. 2004. (Illus.). 40p. (J). 16.00 (978-0-15-216287-0(9) , Harcourt Children's Bks) Harcourt Children's Bks.

Gay, Marie-Louise. Stella, Princess of the Sky. 2007. (Stella Ser.). (Illus.). 32p. 7.95 (978-0-88899-749-4(3)) Groundwood Bks. CAN. *Dist:* Perseus Distribution.

Gentner, Norma L. & Young, Steve. Save a Tree for Me. (Song Box(R) Ser.). (Illus.). 16p. (J). (gr. 1-2). 31.50 (978-0-7802-2264-9(4)) Wright Group, The.

Gershator, Phillis. Listen, Listen. Jay, Alison, illus. 2008. 32p. (J). (ps-4). 16.99 (***978-1-84686-084-3(9)***) Barefoot Bks., Inc.

Gingold, Janet. Finch Goes Wild. 2007. 280p. (YA). pap. 14.99 (978-1-59092-385-6(5) , Blue Works) Windstorm Creative.

Gisbert, Joan Manuel. El Palacio de Los Tres Ojos. 2004. (SPA.). 127p. (J). 10.99 (978-84-263-4614-8(6)) Vives, Luis Editorial (Edelvives) ESP. *Dist:* Lectorum Pubns., Inc.

Glaser, Linda. It's Spring. 2002. (gr. k-3). lib. bdg. 16.40 (978-0-613-50625-0(1)) Tandem Library Bks.

Goddard, Mary Beth. How Would It Feel? Mycek-Wodecki, Anna, illus. 2005. 32p. (J). 15.95 (978-1-59143-050-6(X) , Bear Cub Bks.) Bear & Co.

Golden Books Staff. Eloise Wilkin Stories. Wilkin, Eloise, illus. 2005. (Little Golden Book Treasury Ser.). 224p. (J). (ps-3). 10.95 (978-0-375-82928-4(8) , Golden Bks.) Random Hse. Children's Bks.

Golden Eagle Productions Staff. Grandmother Moon & Sammy the Loon, 36 vols. l.t. ed. 2003. (Illus.). 24p. per. 9.95 (978-1-932338-24-9(1)) Lifevest Publishing, Inc.

Goodhart, Pippa. Slow Magic. Kelly, John, illus. 2003. (Flying Foxes Ser.). (J). (978-0-7787-1489-7(6)); pap. (978-0-7787-1535-1(3)); 48p. (978-0-7787-1528-3(0)); 48p. pap. (978-0-7787-1482-8(9)) Crabtree Publishing Co.

Greene, Rhonda Gowler. Sing Praise. Broxon, Janet, illus. 2005. 32p. (J). (ps-3). pap. 16.99 (978-0-8066-5120-0(2) , Augsburg Bks.) Augsburg Fortress, Pubs.

Grindley, Sally & Foreman, Michael. La Playa de Pedro. 2004. (SPA., Illus.). 32p. (J). 19.99 (978-84-261-3314-4(2)) Juventud, Editorial ESP. *Dist:* Lectorum Pubns., Inc.

Grooms, Molly. We Are Bears. 2002. (Illus.). 32p. (J). (ps-2). pap. 7.95 (978-1-55971-836-3(6) , NorthWord Bks. for Young Readers) T&N Children's Publishing.

—We Are Bears. 2000. (ps-2). lib. bdg. 16.40 (978-0-613-55921-8(5)) Tandem Library Bks.

Gruber, Michael. The Witch's Boy. 2006. 400p. (J). (gr. 6-9). pap. 7.99 (978-0-06-076167-7(9) , HarperTeen) HarperCollins Pubs.

—The Witch's Boy. l.t. ed. 2006. 448p. (YA). 22.95 (978-0-7862-8580-8(X)) Thorndike Pr.

Hallinan, P. K. Por Amor a Nuestra Tierra. Marcuse, Aida E., tr. 2000. (SPA., Illus.). (J). (gr. k-3). pap. 6.95 (978-1-880507-58-2(7) , LC4712) Lectorum Pubns., Inc.

Hamilton, L. Los Ninos y la Naturaleza. (SPA.). 198p. 12.00 (978-84-89920-62-0(1) , 87106) Ediciones Oniro S.A. ESP. *Dist:* Lectorum Pubns., Inc.

Hannigan, Katherine. Ida B: ... And Her Plans to Maximize Fun, Avoid Disaster, & (Possibly) Save the World. 256p. 2004. (J). (gr. 4 up). 16.99 (978-0-06-073024-6(2)); 2004. (gr. 4 up). lib. bdg. 16.89 (978-0-06-073025-3(0)); 2007. reprint ed. pap. 5.99 (978-0-06-073026-0(9) , Harper Trophy) HarperCollins Pubs.

Heck, Cathy. Little Pond. 2007. 10p. bds. 5.99 (***978-1-4037-3303-0(1)***) Dalmatian Pr.

Hemery, Kathleen Maresh. Sunflower Promise. Bordelois, Augusto, illus. 2005. (J). (978-1-56123-188-1(6)) Centering Corp.

Hensley, Sarah M. Water Fun. Crowell, Knox, illus. l.t. ed. 2005. (J). (ps-k). pap. 10.95 (978-1-57332-342-0(X)); pap. 10.95 (978-1-57332-343-7(8)) HighReach Learning, Inc.

Higashi/Glaser Design Inc. Staff. Hello Kitty Hello Nature! Explorer Kit. 2007. 16p. (J). (ps-3). 14.95 (***978-0-8109-9365-5(1)***) Abrams, Harry N. , Inc.

Hoffelt, Jane. We Share One World. Husted, Marty, illus. 2004. 32p. (J). per. 15.95 (978-0-9701907-8-9(6)) Illumination Arts Publishing Co., Inc.

Holbrook, Florence. Why the Crocodile Has a Wide Mouth: And Other Nature Myths. 2004. (Illus.). 128p. pap. 5.95 (978-0-486-43649-4(7)) Dover Pubns., Inc.

Hughes, Fox Carlton. Rainbow Rhino. Hughes, Fox Carlton, illus. 2007. (Illus.). 36p. 16.95 (***978-0-9790275-3-6(5)***) Ovation Bks.

Hyde, Dayton. Island of the Loons. 2002. (gr. 5-8). lib. bdg. 18.75 (978-0-613-57307-8(2)) Tandem Library Bks.

Jackson, Ellen. Earth Mother. Dillon, Leo & Dillon, Diane, illus. 2005. 32p. (J). (ps-2). 16.95 (978-0-8027-8992-1(7)) Walker & Co.

James, Ian. Why the Sky Is Far Away: A Take from Nigeria. 2006. 42.00 (***978-1-4108-6172-6(4)***) Benchmark Education Co.

Johnson, D. B. Henry Hikes to Fitchburg. 2006. (Illus.). 32p. (J). (gr. k-3). reprint ed. 6.95 (978-0-618-73749-9(9)) Houghton Mifflin Co. Trade & Reference Div.

—Henry Works. 2004. (Illus.). 32p. (J). (gr. k-3). tchr. ed. 15.00 (978-0-618-42003-2(7)) Houghton Mifflin Co. Trade & Reference Div.

Johnston, Julie. A Very Fine Line. 2006. 208p. (J). (gr. 6). 18.95 (978-0-88776-746-3(X)) Tundra Bks., Inc./Livres Toundra, Inc. CAN. *Dist:* Random Hse., Inc.

Jongbloed, Marijcke. Sophie the Sand Fox. 2000. (J). 5.95 (978-0-9534689-2-8(5) , TAX-SOPHIE) Serpent's Tale Natural History Bk. Distributors, Inc.

Kelly, Mary. Becky & Bear. 2006. (Illus.). 31p. (J). pap. 9.95 (***978-1-930596-64-1(2)***) Amherst Pr.

Kimmel, Elizabeth Cody. What Do You Dream? Kim, Joung Un, illus. 2003. 32p. (J). (ps-1). 14.99 (978-0-7636-1338-9(X)) Candlewick Pr.

Kitzmiller, Brenda. Muddy Mud — an Easy to Read Beginning Reader Book. 2005. 24p. 7.85 (978-1-4116-2937-0(X)) Lulu.com.

Knight, Hilary. A Firefly in a Fir Tree: A Carol for Mice. Knight, Hilary, illus. 2004. (Illus.). 32p. (J). (ps-3). lib. bdg. 15.89 (978-0-06-000992-2(6) , Tegen, Katherine Bks) HarperCollins Pubs.

Krohn, Kathryn T. Sarah's Most Perfect Day. 2007. 24p. (J). 13.99 (***978-1-59879-325-3(X)*** , Lifevest) Lifevest Publishing, Inc.

Larsen, Shannon. Marigold & the Stranger. 2005. pap. 10.95 (***978-1-59526-499-2(X)***) Media Creations, Inc.

Lassen, Christian Riese & Book Company Staff. Water World. 2002. (Pop-up Bks.). (Illus.). 14p. (J). 15.95 (978-1-74047-180-0(6)) Book Co. Publishing Pty, Ltd., The AUS. *Dist:* Penton Overseas, Inc.

Lavin, Christine. Amoeba Hop. Feeney, Betsy Franco, illus. 2003. 36p. (J). (gr. 2-3). 19.95 incl. audio compact disk (978-0-9726487-4-5(7)) Puddle Jump Pr., Ltd.

Lee, Jared D., illus. El Dia Que Jordan Se Enferms. 2005. (Rookie Reader Espanol Ser.). (SPA & ESP.). 31p. (J). (gr. k-2). pap. 4.95 (978-0-516-24694-9(1) , Children's Pr.) Scholastic Library Publishing.

Léger, Diane Carmel. Who's in Maxine's Tree. Gait, Darlene, illus. 2006. 32p. (ps-2). 17.95 (978-1-55143-346-2(X)) Orca Bk. Pubs. USA.

Lewis, J. Earth & Me, Our Family Tree: Nature's Creatures. 2002. (gr. k-3). lib. bdg. 16.40 (978-0-613-56752-7(8)) Tandem Library Bks.

Linke, Uwe. In the Meadow Moving Book. 2007. (J). bds. 8.95 (978-0-7358-2126-2(7)) North-South Bks., Inc.

Livingston, Timothy J. & Livingston, Mary A. Working with Nature Set, 2 bks. Livingston, Timothy J., illus. 2006th ed. 2006. (Illus.). (J). 32.95 (***978-0-9635757-3-9(2)***) Red Tail Publishing.

Lobel, Gillian. For Everyone to Share. Howarth, Daniel, illus. 2008. (J). (***978-1-56148-598-7(5)***) Good Bks.

Locker, Thomas. Cloud Dance. 2003. (Illus.). 32p. (J). pap. 7.00 (978-0-15-204596-8(1) , Voyager Bks./Libros Viajeros) Harcourt Children's Bks.

—Cloud Dance. Locker, Thomas, illus. 2000. (Illus.). 32p. (YA). (ps-3). 17.00 (978-0-15-202231-0(7) , Silver Whistle) Harcourt Trade Pubs.

—Cloud Dance. 2003. (gr. k-3). lib. bdg. 14.15 (978-0-613-59888-0(1)) Tandem Library Bks.

LoDestro, Christine. The Littlest Cloud. 2005. 15p. (J). 12.01 (978-1-4116-6377-0(7)) Lulu.com.

London, Jack. White Fang. 2005. 28.95 (978-1-4218-1472-8(2)); 276p. pap. 13.95 (978-1-4218-1572-5(9)) 1st World Publishing, Inc. (1st World Library - Literary Society).

—White Fang. 2005. (ENG.). 176p. (gr. 3-7). per. 14.95 (***978-1-59818-531-7(4)***) Aegypan.

—White Fang. 2005. 120p. per. 5.95 (978-1-4209-2246-2(7)) Digireads.com.

—White Fang. 2004. reprint ed. pap. 22.95 (978-1-4191-9386-6(4)); pap. 1.99 (978-1-4192-9386-3(9)) Kessinger Publishing, LLC.

—White Fang. 2006. (Scholastic Classics Ser.). v, 206p. (J). (gr. 9-12). 25.00 (978-0-531-16964-3(2) , Watts, Franklin) Scholastic Library Publishing.

—White Fang. 2006. (Aladdin Classics Ser.). (Illus.). 368p. (J). pap. 5.99 (978-1-4169-1414-3(5) , Aladdin) Simon & Schuster Children's Publishing.

London, Jonathan. Giving Thanks. Manchess, Gregory, illus. 2005. 32p. (J). (ps-2). pap. 6.99 (978-0-7636-2753-9(4)) Candlewick Pr.

M N O

MacCarthy, Patricia. Dewdrop Babies: Bluebell. 2008. (Illus.). 12p. (J). (gr. k). bds. 5.99 (*978-0-375-84357-0(4)) , Random Hse. Bks. for Young Readers) Random Hse. Children's Bks.

—Dewdrop Babies: Violet. 2008. (Illus.). 12p. (J). (gr. k-ps). bds. 5.99 (*978-0-375-84362-4(0)) , Random Hse. Bks. for Young Readers) Random Hse. Children's Bks.

Mackall, Dandi Daley. The Treetops Are Whispering. Nguyen, Vincent, illus. 2007. 16p. (J). 8.99 (978-1-4169-1496-9(X) , Little Simon Inspirations) Simon & Schuster Children's Publishing.

MacLachlan, Patricia & Charest, Emily MacLachlan. Fiona Loves the Night. Shepherd, Amanda, illus. 2007. (J). (ps-3). 40p. lib. bdg. 17.89 (*978-0-06-057032-3(6)); 32p. 16.99 (*978-0-06-057031-6(8)) HarperCollins Pubs. (Cotler, Joanna Books).

Madison's Descent: A Child's Journey. collector's ed. 2004. (J). 75.00 (*978-0-9752516-0-7(0)) Otis & Randolph Pr.

Maine, Margarita & Rojas. Un Mar Muy Mojado. 2004. (SPA.). 32p. 6.95 (978-1-4000-9290-1(6)) Editorial Sudamericana S.A. ARG. *Dist:* Random Hse., Inc.

Margulies, Paul. What Julianna Could See. Zonneveld, Famke, illus. 2004. 32p. (J). pap. 11.95 (978-0-88010-515-6(1)) SteinerBooks, Inc.

Mayer, Mercer. It's Earth Day, No. 5. 2008. (Little Critter Ser.). (Illus.). 24p. (J). pap. 3.99 (*978-0-06-053959-7(3)) , Harper Festival) HarperCollins Pubs.

Mayoral, Juana Aurora. La Cueva de la Luna. 1998. (SPA.). 192p. (J). (ps-3). (978-84-216-0975-0(0) , BU3871) Gmunder, Bruno Verlag GmbH.

Mboya, Deborah. Matunda Ya Kwanza: The First Fruits of Harvest. 2002. 8p. (J). pap. 9.00 (978-0-8059-5329-9(9)) Dorrance Publishing Co., Inc.

McCarthy, Mary. A Closer Look. McCarthy, Mary, illus. 2007. (Illus.). 40p. (J). (ps-k). 16.99 (*978-0-06-124073-7(7)); lib. bdg. 17.89 (*978-0-06-124074-4(5)) HarperCollins Pubs. (Greenwillow Bks.).

McGinty, Alice B. Thank You, World. Halperin, Wendy Anderson, illus. 2007. 32p. (J). (ps-k). 16.99 (978-0-8037-2705-2(4) , Dial) Penguin Group (USA) Inc.

Las Mil y una Noches. (Coleccion Estrella). (SPA., Illus.). 64p. (J). 14.95 (978-950-11-0001-3(4) , SGM001) Sigmar ARG. *Dist:* Continental Bk. Co., Inc.

Miles, Betty. Sky is Falling, Level 1. 1998. (Ready-to-Read Ser.). (978-0-606-13777-5(7)) Tandem Library Bks.

Monica, Carol. Fisher Price Let's Go on a Class Trip Lift the Flap. SI Artists, illus. 2007. 10p. (J). bds. 8.99 (*978-0-7944-1291-3(2)) Reader's Digest Assn., Inc., The.

Montijo, Rhode. Nino Nube. Mlawer, Teresa, tr. from ENG. 2006. (SPA & ENG., Illus.). 32p. (J). 12.99 (978-1-933032-06-1(5)) Lectorum Pubns., Inc.

Morel, Alicia. Cuentos Araucanos: La Gente de la Tierra. (SPA.). (J). (gr. 4-6). pap. (978-956-13-1152-7(6) , AB1252) Bello, Andres CHL. *Dist:* Lectorum Pubns., Inc.

Morningforest, Chris & Raymond, Rebecca. The Adventures of Nate & Naomi. 2006. 36p. (J). pap. 15.43 (978-1-4116-9244-2(6)) Lulu.com.

Mundy, Dawn. The Gift: A Woodsong Story. Tigue, Terry & Turner, Diane, illus. 2003. (J). lib. bdg. (978-1-932139-16-7(8)) DEMDACO.

Napoli, Donna Jo. North. 2006. (Illus.). 368p. (J). pap. 6.99 (978-0-06-057989-0(7) , Harper Trophy) HarperCollins Pubs.

Orr, Wendy. Spook's Shack. Millard, Kerry, illus. 2005. 120p. (J). (ps-ps). pap. 6.95 (978-1-86508-645-3(2)) Allen & Unwin AUS. *Dist:* Independent Pubs. Group.

Pages, Christina. Mountain Boy. 2007. (Illus.). 42p. (J). per. 12.95 (*978-0-9794863-9-5(4)) Summerland Publishing.

Pandell, Karen. I Love You, Sun I Love You, Moon: Te amo, sol Te amo, Luna. dePaola, Tomie, illus. 2007. 20p. (J). (gr. k-3). bds. 6.99 (*978-0-448-44800-8(9)) , Grosset & Dunlap) Penguin Group (USA) Inc.

Pandell, Karen. Te Amo Sol, Te Amo Luna/I Love You Sun, I Love You Moon. de Paola, Tomie, illus. 2003. (SPA & ENG.). 18p. (J). (ps-1). bds. 6.99 (978-0-399-24165-9(5) , Putnam Juvenile) Penguin Group (USA) Inc.

Patten, William. Animal & Nature Stories Vol. 8: The Junior Classics. 2004. reprint ed. pap. 1.99 (978-1-4192-6805-2(8)) Kessinger Publishing, LLC.

Patten, William. Junior Classics Volume 8 Animal & Natu. 2006. 67.99 (*978-1-4280-3505-8(2)); pap. 60.99 (*978-1-4280-3456-3(0)) IndyPublish.com.

Paulsen, Gary. The Island. 2006. 208p. (J). pap. 5.99 (978-0-439-78662-1(2) , Scholastic Paperbacks) Scholastic, Inc.

Penick Phillips-Cermak, Mosetta. The Wishing Flower. 2007. 24p. 16.50 (*978-0-615-15573-9(1)) PM Moon Pubs.

Perry, Rex, illus. All Things Bright & Beautiful. 2004. 24p. (J). lib. bdg. 8.00 (*978-1-4242-0638-4(3)) Fitzgerald Bks.

Pledger, Maurice, illus. In the Ocean: A Touch-and-Feel Adventure. 2002. (Nature Trails Ser.). 16p. (J). (ps-1). 12.95 (978-1-57145-453-9(5)) Advantage Pubs. Group.

Plourde, Lynn. The First Feud: Between the Mountain & the Sea. Sollers, Jim, illus. 2003. 30p. 15.95 (978-0-89272-611-0(3)) Down East Bks.

Raczka, Bob. Spring Things. Stead, Judy, illus. 2007. 32p. (J). 16.95 (978-0-8075-7596-3(8)) Whitman, Albert & Co.

Ramsey, Ann Louise. Me, the Tree. 2006. (Illus.). 56p. (J). per. 19.95 (978-0-9645663-4-7(6)) Crown Peak Publishing.

Rau, Dana Meachen. Floating. 2006. (On the Move Ser.). (Illus.). 24p. (J). lib. bdg. 22.79 (978-0-7614-2315-7(X) , Benchmark Bks.) Cavendish, Marshall Corp.

Reece, Colleen L. Secrets of the Sea. 2000. (Illus.). 112p. (J). pap. 6.99 (978-0-8280-1390-1(X)) Review & Herald Publishing Assn.

Reed-Jones, C. El Arbol Del Viejo Bosque. 2004. (SPA.). 32p. (978-84-7720-789-4(5)) Obelisco, Ediciones S.A.

Rehm, Carolyn. The Flower Pot Bunnies: Not A Good Place For A Nest. Schanck, Agnes, illus. 2004. 48p. (J). bds. 12.99 (978-0-9755390-1-9(9)) Fifth Ave Pr.

Rink, Cindy. Where Does the Wind Blow? 2002. (gr. k-3). lib. bdg. 16.40 (978-0-613-52797-2(6)) Tandem Library Bks.

Rivers, Dayna Kay. What a Mother Would Do. Mohr, J. Victoria, illus. 2002. (J). per. (978-0-9719806-0-0(8) , weespeak) Knife in the Toaster Publishing Co., LLC.

Ross, Thea. Molly Moe Takes a Nature Walk. 2004. (Lift-the-Flap Surprise on Every Spread! Ser.). 12p. (J). 5.99 (978-1-59384-045-7(4)) Parklane Publishing.

Rumble & Bolt. 2007. 14p. pap. 10.95 (*978-1-59125-913-8(4)) , Penton Kids) Penton Overseas, Inc.

Ryder, Joanne. The Waterfall's Gift. Watson, Richard Jesse, illus. 2004. 40p. pap. 7.95 (978-1-57805-113-7(4)) Gibbs Smith, Publisher.

Scelsa, Greg. Rainbow of Colors. Faulkner, Stacey, ed. Sexton, Brenda, illus. 2006. (J). pap. 2.99 (*978-1-59198-351-4(7)) Creative Teaching Pr., Inc.

—The World Is a Rainbow. Faulkner, Stacey, ed. Schneider, Christine, illus. 2006. (J). pap. 2.99 (*978-1-59198-319-4(3)) Creative Teaching Pr., Inc.

Schimmel, Schim. The Family of Earth. (Illus.). 22p. (ps up). 2002. (J). bds. 6.95 (978-1-55971-833-2(1)); 2001. 14.95 (978-1-55971-790-8(4)) T&N Children's Publishing. (NorthWord Bks. for Young Readers).

Schkolnik, Saul. Cuentos Ecologicos. Cardemil, Carmen, illus. 2nd ed. 2003. Tr. of Ecological Tales. (SPA.). 54p. (J). (ps-7). pap. 7.50 (978-968-16-4757-5(2) , FC6400) Fondo de Cultura Economica MEX. *Dist:* Lectorum Pubns., Inc.

Schmidt, Hans-Christian & Bieber, Hartmut. The Wondrous Day. 2004. (Illus.). 18p. (J). 10.99 (978-1-59384-047-1(0)) Parklane Publishing.

Schwartz, Tom. How Mother Nature Flowered the Fields. 2006. (Illus.). 120p. (J). per. 18.95 (978-1-57545-102-2(6) , Reagent Pr. Echo) Reagent Pr.

Segarra, Angelo M. Coca Finds a Shell. Segarra, Kirstie, ed. Segarra, Angelo M., illus. 2004. (Illus.). 24p. (J). 14.95 (978-0-9752664-0-3(3)) Segarra, Angelo.

Shadow, Nick & Graves, Damien. Midnight Library. 2006. (Apple Ser.: Vol. 2). (Illus.). 176p. (J). pap. 5.99 (978-0-439-87187-7(5) , Scholastic Paperbacks) Scholastic, Inc.

Shearer, Tony. The Praying Flute: Song of the Earth Mother. rev. ed. 2006. (Illus.). 96p. pap. 16.95 (978-0-87961-268-9(1)) Naturegraph Pubs., Inc.

Sherrell, Deborah. Baby Lauren & Theodore,hardcover. 2007. (J). bds. 17.95 (*978-0-9779643-5-2(3)) Healing Tree Arts.

Skipper, Cecil. The Deer Lick. 2004. 166p. (YA). pap. 12.95 (978-0-595-30949-8(6)) iUniverse, Inc.

Slawson, Michele Benoit. Apple Picking Time. Ray, Deborah Kogan, illus. 1998. (Dragonfly Bks.). 32p. (J). (gr. k-3). pap. 6.99 (978-0-517-88575-8(1) , Dragonfly Bks.) Random Hse. Children's Bks.

—Apple Picking Time. Ray, Deborah Kogan, illus. 1998. 32p. (J). (gr. 3-7). lib. bdg. 13.79 (978-0-606-15438-3(8)) Tandem Library Bks.

Steinberg, Laya. All Around Me, I See. Arbo, Cris, illus. 2005. (Sharing Nature with Children Book Ser.). 32p. (J). 16.95 (978-1-58469-068-9(2)); pap. 8.95 (978-1-58469-069-6(0)) Dawn Pubns.

Stuart, Tara. Trees: A Tara's Tale about Being Yourself. 2006. (Illus.). (J). bds. 15.00 (978-0-9765060-3-4(3)) TouchSmart Publishing, LLC.

Sweet, J.H. & Sierra, Holly. Periwinkle & the Cave of Courage: The Fairy Chronicles. 2007. (Fairy Chronicles Ser.). (Illus.). 128p. (J). (gr. 2 up). pap. 6.99 (*978-1-4022-1026-6(4)) , Sourcebooks Jabberwocky) Sourcebooks, Inc.

Tate, Suzanne. Skippy Scallop: A Tale of Bright Blue Eyes. Melvin, James, illus. 2003. (Suzanne Tate's Nature Ser.: 26). 28p. (J). pap. 4.95 (978-1-878405-43-2(8)) Nags Head Art, Inc.

Thompson & Hartmann. Then & Now. 1999. (First Flight Ser.). (Illus.). 32p. (J). (ps-k). lib. bdg. (978-1-55041-510-0(7)) Fitzhenry & Whiteside, Ltd.

Thompson, Lauren. Mouse's First Spring. Erdogan, Buket, illus. 2005. 32p. (J). 12.95 (978-0-689-85838-3(8) , Simon & Schuster Children's Publishing) Simon & Schuster Children's Publishing.

Thompson, Lauren & Erdogan, Buket. Mouse's First Fall. 2006. 32p. (J). (ps-1). 12.95 (978-0-689-85837-6(X) , Simon & Schuster Children's Publishing) Simon & Schuster Children's Publishing.

Thompson, Lisa. Artrageous! Thompson, Lisa & Stapleton, Matthew, illus. 2005. (Read-It! Chapter Bks.). 48p. (J). (ps-k). lib. bdg. 19.95 (978-1-4048-1348-9(9)) Picture Window Bks.

—Wild Ideas. Thompson, Lisa & Stapleton, Matthew, illus. 2005. (Read-It! Chapter Bks.). 48p. (J). (ps-k). lib. bdg. 19.95 (978-1-4048-1346-5(2)) Picture Window Bks.

Thompson, Richard. Then & Now. Hartmann, Barbara, illus. 1999. (First Flight Ser.). 32p. (J). (ps-k). pap. (978-1-55041-508-7(5)) Fitzhenry & Whiteside, Ltd.

Todd, Barbara. The Rainmaker. Roge, illus. 2003. 32p. (J). (ps-2). pap. 5.95 (978-1-55037-774-3(4)) Annick Pr., Ltd. CAN. *Dist:* Firefly Bks., Ltd.

—Rainmaker. 2003. (gr. k-3). lib. bdg. 14.10 (978-0-613-67925-1(3)) Tandem Library Bks.

Updike, John. A Child's Calendar. Updike, John & Hyman, Trina Schart, illus. 2004. (J). (gr. k-4). 28.95 incl. audio compact disk (978-1-59112-932-5(X)) Live Oak Media.

—A Child's Calendar. Hyman, Trina Schart, illus. unabr. ed. 2004. (J). (gr. k-4). 25.95 incl. audio (978-1-59112-472-6(7)) Live Oak Media.

Valverde, Mikel. Paula en Nueva York. Valverde, Mikel, illus. 2005. (SPA., Illus.). 32p. (J). 14.99 (978-1-933032-15-3(4)) Lectorum Pubns., Inc.

Weller, Duncan. The Boy from the Sun. 2007. (Illus.). 36p. 16.95 (978-1-894965-33-0(7)) Simply Read Bks. CAN. *Dist:* Perseus Distribution.

Welles, Lee. Gaia Girls Enter the Earth. Hameister, Ann, illus. 2007. (Gaia Girls Ser.). 336p. (YA). pap. 12.95 (*978-1-933609-01-0(X)) Daisyworld Pr.

—Gaia Girls Way of Water. 2007. (Gaia Girls Ser.). 336p. (J). pap. 12.95 (*978-1-933609-03-4(6)) Daisyworld Pr.

—Gaia Girls Way of Water. Hameister, Ann, illus. 2007. (Gaia Girls Ser.). 336p. (J). 18.95 (*978-1-933609-02-7(8)) Daisyworld Pr.

Welsh-Howard, Jim and Paula. Tell Me Tell Me If You Can. 2006. (J). per. 14.95 (*978-1-60002-291-3(X)) , Airleaf Publishing) Airleaf Publishing & Bookselling.

Weninger, Brigitte. Precious Water. 2003. (ps-2). lib. bdg. 14.10 (978-0-613-73546-9(3)) Tandem Library Bks.

When Clouds Cry. 2002. 32p. (J). 16.95 (978-1-930758-69-8(3) , Yeva Kids) Yeva Corp.

Wilshire, Florence. All from the Skies. 2005. 82p. pap. 18.08 (978-1-4116-3114-4(5)) Lulu.com.

Wolfson, Jill. Home, & Other Big, Fat Lies. 2006. (Illus.). 224p. (J). 16.95 (978-0-8050-7670-7(0) , Holt, Henry & Co. Bks. For Young Readers) Holt, Henry & Co.

Wynnejones, Pat & Ratcliffe, Sheila, illus. The Tale of Geronimo Grub: The Tale of Charlotte Caterpillar. 2001. 64p. (J). 6.99 (978-0-7459-4560-6(0) , Lion) Lion Hudson plc GBR. *Dist:* Independent Pubs. Group.

Yee, Wong Herbert. Abracadabra! Magic with Mouse & Mole. 2007. 48p. (J). (gr. k-3). 15.00 (*978-0-618-75926-2(3)) Houghton Mifflin Co.

Young, Sunshine. Mother Earth's ABC. 2007. (J). spiral bd. 14.95 (*978-0-9796180-2-4(9)) Williams, Benjamin Publishing.

NATURE IN LITERATURE

see also Nature in Poetry

Collins, Carolyn Strom & Eriksson, Christina Wyss. Inside the Secret Garden: A Treasury of Crafts, Recipes, & Activities. Tudor, Tasha, illus. 2004. 130p. (J). (gr. 2-8). reprint ed. 25.00 (978-0-7567-7630-5(9)) DIANE Publishing Co.

National Geographic Society Staff. Eyewitness to the 20th Century. 1998. (National Geographic Destinations Ser.). (Illus.). 400p. (J). (gr. 5-8). 40.00 (978-0-7922-7049-2(5) , National Geographic) National Geographic Society.

NATURE IN ORNAMENT

see Design, Decorative

NATURE IN POETRY

Alarcon, Francisco X. Angels Ride Bikes & Other Fall Poems. Gonzalez, Maya Christina, illus. 1999. 32p. (J). pap. 21.27 (978-0-516-21696-6(1) , Children's Pr.) Scholastic Library Publishing.

—Angels Ride Bikes & Other Fall Poems (Los Angeles Andan en Bicicleta y Otros Poemas de Otono) Gonzalez, Maya Christina, illus. 1999. (ENG & SPA.). 32p. (J). (gr. 1 up). 16.95 (978-0-89239-160-8(X)) Children's Bk. Pr.

Alexander, Cecil Frances. All Things Bright & Beautiful. Whatley, Bruce, illus. 2004. 32p. (J). pap. 6.99 (978-0-06-008339-7(5) , Harper Trophy) HarperCollins Pubs.

—All Things Bright & Beautiful. McDaniels, Preston, illus. 2nd ed. 2001. (Hymns for Children Ser.). 32p. (ps-2). pap. 4.95 (978-0-8192-1884-1(7)) Morehouse Publishing.

—All Things Bright & Beautiful. Heyer, Carol, illus. 2002. 26p. (ps-3). 9.95 (978-1-59093-019-9(3)) Warehousing & Fulfillment Specialists, LLC (WFS, LLC).

Brenner, Barbara. The Earth Is Painted Green: A Garden of Poems about Our Planet. 2000. (Illus.). 96p. (J). (ps-3). pap. 5.99 (978-0-590-45135-2(9)) Scholastic, Inc.

—The Earth Is Painted Green: A Garden of Poems about Our Planet. 2000. (Illus.). (J). (978-0-606-18538-7(0)) Tandem Library Bks.

Brown, Margaret Wise. Nibble Nibble. Minor, Wendell, illus. 2007. 32p. (J). (ps-3). 16.99 (978-0-06-059208-0(7)) HarperCollins Pubs.

Burton, Michael H. In the Light of a Child: A Journey Through the 52 Weeks of the Year in Both Hemispheres for Children & for the Child in Each Human Being. 1998. 64p. pap. 14.95 (978-0-88010-450-0(3)) SteinerBooks, Inc.

Cyrus, Kurt. Oddhopper Opera: A Bug's Garden of Verses. Cyrus, Kurt, illus. 2001. (Illus.). 32p. (J). (gr. k-5). 16.00 (978-0-15-202205-1(8)) Harcourt Children's Bks.

Dubois, Tevon. A Child on the Island: The Ageless Wisdom of a Ten-Year-Old. 2002. 64p. per. 9.95 (978-1-931105-05-7(7)) Opal Creek Pr., LLC.

Fisher, Aileen. The Story Goes On. Moriuchi, Mique, illus. rev. ed. 2005. 32p. (J). 16.95 (978-1-59643-037-2(0)) Roaring Brook Pr.

Galdone, Paul. Over in the Meadow. 1998. (J). pap. 5.95 (978-0-87628-986-0(3)) Ctr. for Applied Research in Education, The.

Marzollo, Jean. Home Sweet Home. 1998. (Illus.). 32p. (J). (ps-3). pap. 5.95 (978-0-06-443501-7(6)) HarperCollins Pubs.

—Home Sweet Home. 1998. (978-0-606-13483-5(2)) Tandem Library Bks.

Nash, Myrna Lee. Spinman, Katydid & Bump: A Spider Vane Collection. Johnson, Sharon, illus. 2003. 48p. (YA). (gr. 4-10). 11.95 (978-0-9724549-0-2(X)) Chapter & Verse Pr.

Paolilli, Paul. Silver Seeds: A Book of Nature Poems. 2003. (gr. k-3). lib. bdg. 15.30 (978-0-613-61657-7(X)) Tandem Library Bks.

Paolilli, Paul & Brewer, Dan. Silver Seeds: A Book of Nature Poems. Fancher, Lou & Johnson, Steve, illus. 2003. 32p. (J). (gr. k-4). pap. 6.99 (978-0-14-250010-1(0) , Puffin) Penguin Group (USA) Inc.

—Silver Seeds: A Book of Nature Poems. Johnson, Steve & Fancher, Lou, illus. 2001. 32p. (J). (gr. k-4). 15.99 (978-0-670-88941-9(5) , Viking Juvenile) Penguin Group (USA) Inc.

Rivers, Ruth, illus. This Amazing World: Poems & Prayers about Everything under the Sun. 2002. 48p. (J). (gr. 1-7). 16.00 (978-1-56148-363-1(X)) Good Bks.

Singer, Marilyn. Footprints on the Roof: Poems about the Earth. So, Meilo, illus. 2002. 48p. (gr. 3-7). 14.95 (978-0-375-81094-7(3)); lib. bdg. 16.99 (978-0-375-91094-4(8)) Random Hse. Children's Bks. (Knopf Bks. for Young Readers).

Yolen, Jane. Least Things: Poems about Small Natures. Stemple, Jason, photos by. 2003. (Illus.). 32p. (YA). (gr. 4-6). 17.95 (978-1-59078-098-5(1)) Boyds Mills Pr.

NATURE PHOTOGRAPHY

see also Photography of Animals

Fielder, John, photos by. Do You See What I See? 2006. (J). 14.99 (978-1-56579-554-9(7)) Westcliffe Pubs.

Martin, Jacqueline Briggs. Snowflake Bentley. ed. 2004. (Illus.). (J). (ps-3). spiral bd. (978-0-616-01714-2(6)) Canadian National Institute for the Blind/Institut National Canadien pour les Aveugles.

—Snowflake Bentley. Azarian, Mary, illus. 1998. 32p. (J). (gr. k-3). lib. bdg., tchr. ed. 16.00 (978-0-395-86162-2(4)) Houghton Mifflin Co. Trade & Reference Div.

McAdam, Claudia Cangilla & Reynolds, Richard. Do You See What I See? 2007. (J). 14.95 (*978-1-56579-589-1(X)) Westcliffe Pubs.

National Geographic Society Staff. Eyewitness to the 20th Century. 1998. (National Geographic Destinations Ser.). (Illus.). 400p. (J). (gr. 5-8). 40.00 (978-0-7922-7049-2(5) , National Geographic) National Geographic Society.

NATURE POETRY

see Nature in Poetry

NATURE STUDY

see also Animals—Habits and Behavior; Botany; Nature Photography; Zoology

Andryszewski, Tricia. Step by Step along the Appalachian Trail. 1998. (Step by Step Ser.). (Illus.). 80p. (gr. 4-7). lib. bdg. 24.90 (978-0-7613-0273-5(5) , Millbrook Pr.) Lerner Publishing Group.

—Step by Step along the Pacific Crest Trail. 1998. (Step by Step Ser.). (Illus.). 80p. (gr. 4-7). lib. bdg. 24.90 (978-0-7613-0274-2(3) , Twenty-First Century Bks.) Lerner Publishing Group.

Anthony, Joseph. The Dandelion Seed. 1999. (J). 14.75 (978-0-606-16436-8(7)) Tandem Library Bks.

Arnosky, Jim. Field Trips: Bug Hunting, Animal Tracking, Bird-Watching, Shore Walking. Arnosky, Jim, illus. 2002. (Illus.). 96p. (J). (gr. 3 up). 17.99 (978-0-688-15172-0(8)) HarperCollins Pubs.

Art, Henry W. & Robbins, Michael W. WoodsWalk: Peepers, Porcupines, & Exploding Puff Balls! 2003. (Illus.). 128p. (J). (gr. 3-7). pap. 14.95 (978-1-58017-452-7(3) , 67452, Storey Kids) Storey Publishing, LLC.

Barlowe, Dot. Backyard Nature Coloring Book. 1998. (Dover Coloring Bks.). (Illus.). 48p. (J). pap. 3.95 (978-0-486-40560-5(5)) Dover Pubns., Inc.

Barron's Educational Editorial Staff. Amazing Nature. 1998. (Megascope Ser.). (Illus.). 64p. (J). (gr. 5). 6.95 (978-0-7641-5090-6(1)) Barron's Educational Series, Inc.

Bauer, Cheryl. Our Visit to the Nature Center: Nuestra Visita Al Centro Ecologico. 2003. (SPA.). (J). lib. bdg. 22.00 (978-1-59298-013-0(9)) Beaver's Pond Pr., Inc.

Baumbusch, Brigitte. Looking at Nature: Art for Children Series. Paoli, Erika, tr. from ITA. 1999. (Art for Children Ser.). (Illus.). 32p. (J). (gr. 2-7). 9.95 (978-1-55670-971-5(4)) Stewart, Tabori & Chang.

Bellamy, David. The Rockpool. Dow, Jill, illus. 1999. (Our Changing World Ser.). 32p. (J). (gr. 1-5). pap. 7.99 (978-0-7112-1386-9(0)) Lincoln, Frances Ltd. GBR. *Dist:* Transition Vendor.

Birmingham, Maria, et al. 365 Outdoor Activities. Kennedy, Anne, illus. 2000. 240p. (978-0-7853-3898-7(5) , 3651500) Publications International, Ltd.

Bittinger, Gayle. Under the Sea. 1999. (Rhyme & Reason Workbook Ser.). (Illus.). 32p. (J). (ps-k). pap. 3.95 (978-1-57029-259-0(0) , WPH 01111, Totline Pubns.) Schaffer, Frank Pubns.

Bledsoe, Karen E. & Norvell, Candyce. 365 Nature Crafts & Activities. Chicko, Terri & Chicko, Joe, illus. 1998. (Craft & Project Books for Children Ser.). 240p. (J). (gr. 3-6). lib. bdg. 24.95 (978-1-56674-227-6(7) , HTS Bks.) Forest Hse. Publishing Co., Inc.

Boring, Mel, et al. Fun with Nature. Garrow, Linda, illus. 1998. (Take-Along Guide Ser.). (J). (gr. 1-5). pap. 22.95 (978-1-55971-684-0(3) , NorthWord Bks. for Young Readers) T&N Children's Publishing.

—Fun with Nature: Take-along Guide. Garrow, Linda, illus. 2004. (Take-Along Guide Ser.). 288p. (J). (gr. 2-5). 16.95 (978-1-55971-702-1(5) , NorthWord Bks. for Young Readers) T&N Children's Publishing.

Brettle, Jane. Nature Is Busy. 1999. 10p. (J). pap. 3.95 (978-1-57717-103-4(9)) New Line Bks.

Bright, Michael. Looking into Nature's Secrets. Abel, Simone, illus. 1999. (Looking Into... Ser.). 13p. (J). (ps-2). bds. 11.99 (978-1-57584-316-2(1) , Reader's Digest Children's Bks.) Reader's Digest Children's Publishing, Inc.

Brooks, Bruce. The Red Wasteland: Personal Selection of Writings about Nature. rev. ed. 1998. 160p. (J). (gr. 6-9). 15.95 (978-0-8050-4495-9(7) , Holt, Henry & Co. Bks. For Young Readers) Holt, Henry & Co.

Brown Bear Books (Firm) Staff, contrib. by. Backyard. 2007. (J). (*978-1-933834-13-9(7)) Brown Bear Books.

Burns, Diane L. Snakes, Salamanders & Lizards. Garrow, Linda, illus. 1998. 47p. (J). (gr. 2-5). lib. bdg. 16.40 (978-0-613-26969-8(1)) Tandem Library Bks.

Burton, Jane & Taylor, Kim. The Nature & Science of Numbers. 2001. (Exploring the Science of Nature Ser.). (Illus.). 32p. (J). (gr. 3 up). lib. bdg. 24.67 (978-0-8368-2193-2(9)) Stevens, Gareth Inc.

Burton, Margie, et al. Insects All Around. Adams, Alison, ed. 1999. (Early Connections Ser.). 16p. (J). (gr. k-2). pap. 4.50 (978-1-58344-067-4(4)) Benchmark Education Co.

—Trees. Adams, Alison, ed. 1999. (Early Connections Ser.). 16p. (J). (gr. k-2). pap. 4.50 (978-1-58344-084-1(4)) Benchmark Education Co.

—Water Goes Up! Water Comes Down! Adams, Alison, ed. 1999. (Early Connections Ser.). 16p. (J). (gr. k-2). pap. 4.50 (978-1-58344-085-8(2)) Benchmark Education Co.

Busch, Phyllis S. Autumn. Halsey, Megan, illus. 2000. (Nature Projects for Every Season Ser.). 48p. (J). (gr. 2 up). lib. bdg. 24.21 (978-0-7614-0988-5(2) , Benchmark Bks.) Cavendish, Marshall Corp.

—Nature Projects for Every Season. Incl. Autumn. Halsey, Megan, illus. lib. bdg. 24.21 (978-0-7614-0988-5(2)); Spring. Halsey, Megan, illus. lib. bdg. 24.21 (978-0-7614-0986-1(6)); Summer. Halsey, Megan. lib. bdg. 24.21 (978-0-7614-0987-8(4)); (J). (gr. 2 up). (Illus.). 48p. 2000. Set lib. bdg. 96.86 (978-0-7614-0985-4(8) , Benchmark Bks.) Cavendish, Marshall Corp.

Butram, Ray & Haidle, Helen. I'm Sorry You Can't Hatch an Egg. Chapman, Jim, illus. 1998. (God's Amazing World Ser.). 32p. (J). (ps-3). 7.99 (978-1-57673-312-7(2) , Multnomah) WaterBrook Pr.

—I've Never Seen a Worm Like You. Chapman, Jim, illus. 1998. (God's Amazing World Ser.). 32p. (J). (ps-3). 7.99 (978-1-57673-311-0(4) , Multnomah) WaterBrook Pr.

—A Raindrop Hit My Nose. Chapman, Jim, illus. 1998. (God's Amazing World Ser.). (J). (ps-3). 7.99 (978-1-57673-310-3(6) , Multnomah) WaterBrook Pr.

Castaldo, Nancy F. Sunny Days & Starry Nights: Nature Activities for Ages 2-6. 2005. (Illus.). 144p. (J). pap. 12.95 (978-1-55652-556-8(7)) Chicago Review Pr., Inc.

Cole, Henry. I Took a Walk. Cole, Henry, illus. 1998. (Illus.). 28p. (J). (ps-3). 16.99 (978-0-688-15115-7(9)) HarperCollins Pubs.

Cook, David Fuller, illus. Nature. 2000. (Find & Fit Ser.). 10p. (J). (ps-k). 14.95 (978-1-57145-433-1(0) , Silver Dolphin Bks.) Advantage Pubs. Group.

Day, Marlena & Nature Institute Staff. Cantos, Caminos y Juegos Para Ninos: Mas de 100 Actividades en la Naturaleza Para Ninos Pequenos. Moore, Rhonda & Campos, Patricia, trs. Day, Marlena, illus. 1998. (SPA., Illus.). 112p. (J). (gr. k-3). pap. 12.95 (978-0-9632753-6-3(4)) Children's Nature Institute, The.

Dewire, Bob. My Guide to America's Habitats. Sullivan, Beth, illus. 2000. 72p. (J). pap. 2.95 (978-1-56762-128-0(7)) Modern Learning Pr.

Dewire, Bob & Sullivan, Beth, contrib. by. Introducing America's Habitats: Natural Science Information & Interdisciplinary Activities. 2000. (Illus.). 180p. (J). pap., tchr. ed. 17.95 (978-1-56762-125-9(2)) Modern Learning Pr.

Ferrara, Cos. Anna Comstock: A Love Affair with Nature. 2004. (Girls Explore, Reach for the Stars Ser.). (Illus.). 112p. (J). 20.00 (978-0-9749456-1-3(7) , Girls Explore) Girls Explore LLC.

Fredericks, Anthony D. Simple Nature Experiments with Everyday Materials. Zweifel, Frances, illus. 2004. 128p. (J). (gr. 4-8). reprint ed. pap. 6.00 (978-0-7567-7727-2(5)) DIANE Publishing Co.

Ganeri, Anita. Bizarre Beast: And Other Oddities of Nature. 1999. (Weird & Wonderful! Ser.). (Illus.). 29p. (YA). (gr. 3 up). pap. 7.99 (978-0-7681-0191-1(3) , 57001, McClanahan Bk.) Learning Horizons, Inc.

—Hunt for Food. (Illus.). 32p. (YA). (gr. 4 up). lib. bdg. 27.10 (978-1-931983-88-4(7)) Chrysalis Education.

Gibson, Andrea. Become a Nature Detective. 2002. (Cool Kits Ser.). (Illus.). 64p. (J). (978-0-439-53076-7(8)) Scholastic, Inc.

Glover, David. Exploring Nature. 2001. (Experiments in Science Ser.). (Illus.). (J). (978-0-7894-7472-8(7)) Dorling Kindersley Publishing, Inc.

Gold-Dworkin, Heidi, et al. Fun with Water & Bubbles. 1999. (Little Scientists Ser.). (Illus.). 58p. (gr. k-3). pap. 12.95 (978-0-07-134823-2(9) , 9780071348232) McGraw-Hill Trade.

Greco, Jeff. North Woods Animal Tracks. l.t. ed. 2001. (North Woods Track Guide). 18p. 8.99 (978-0-9709294-0-2(4)) North Woods Enterprises.

Haidle, Helen & Butram, Ray. I Saw a Slimeball Wiggle. Chapman, Jim, illus. 1998. (Our Amazing World-Making Science Fun Ser.). 32p. (J). (ps-3). 7.99 (978-1-57673-309-7(2) , Multnomah) WaterBrook Pr.

Hands-On Nature. 2004. (Illus.). 96p. (J). (gr. 1-2). 11.95 (978-1-885358-66-0(0)); (gr. 3-4). 11.95 (978-1-885358-67-7(9)); (ps-k). 11.95 (978-1-885358-65-3(2)) Rainbow Pubs. & Legacy Pr.

Harris, Nicholas & Joanna, Turner. El Porque de las Cosas: Naturaleza y Ciencia. (Coleccion Enciclopedia Ilustrada del Conocimiento).Tr. of Why Things Occur: Nature & Science. (SPA., Illus.). 64p. (J). (gr. 3-5). 7.96 (978-84-7630-749-6(7)) Libsa, Editorial S.A. ESP. *Dist:* Lectorum Pubns., Inc.

Heinrichs, Ann. Nature's Friends, 4 vols. (Illus.). (J). (gr. k-2). 85.04 (978-0-7565-0213-3(6)); Set. 2003. lib. bdg. 170.80 (978-0-7565-0462-5(7)) Compass Point Bks.

Henderson, Douglas. Dinosaur Tree. 1999. (J). (978-0-606-17194-6(0)) Tandem Library Bks.

Hickman, Pamela. The Night Book: Exploring Nature after Dark with Activities, Experiments & Information. Mogensen, Suzanne, illus. unabr. ed. 1999. 48p. (J). (gr. 4-6). (978-1-55074-306-7(6)); (978-1-55074-318-0(X)) Kids Can Pr., Ltd.

—Starting with Nature Tree Book. Collins, Heather, illus. unabr. ed. 1999. (Starting with Nature Ser.). 32p. (J). (gr. 4-6). (978-1-55074-655-6(3)); (978-1-55074-485-9(2)) Kids Can Pr., Ltd.

Holmes, Anita. Can You Find Us? 2001. (We Can Read about Nature! Ser.). (Illus.). 32p. (J). (gr. 1-2). lib. bdg. 21.36 (978-0-7614-1108-6(9) , Benchmark Bks.) Cavendish, Marshall Corp.

—We Can Read about Nature! - Group 1, 6 bks., Set. Incl. Can You Find Us? 2001. lib. bdg. 21.36 (978-0-7614-1108-6(9)); Flowers & Friends. 2000. lib. bdg. 21.36 (978-0-7614-1113-0(5)); If Grass Could Talk. 2001. lib. bdg. 21.36 (978-0-7614-1111-6(9)); Insect Detector. 2000. lib. bdg. 21.36 (978-0-7614-1110-9(0)); Where Robins Fly. 2000. lib. bdg. 21.36 (978-0-7614-1109-3(7)); Who Dug This Hole? 2001. lib. bdg. 21.36 (978-0-7614-1112-3(7)); 32p. (J). (gr. 1-2). , Benchmark Bks. (Illus.). 2001. Set lib. bdg. 128.14 (978-0-7614-1107-9(0)) Cavendish, Marshall Corp.

—Who Dug This Hole? 2001. (We Can Read about Nature! Ser.). (Illus.). 32p. (J). (gr. 1-2). lib. bdg. 21.36 (978-0-7614-1112-3(7) , Benchmark Bks.) Cavendish, Marshall Corp.

Holt, Rinehart and Winston Staff. Holt Science & Technology Chapter 19: Life Science: Cycles in Nature. 5th ed. 2004. (Illus.). pap. 12.86 (978-0-03-030229-9(3)) Holt, Rinehart & Winston.

Koontz, Robin Michal. The Complete Backyard Nature Activity Book: Fun Projects for Kids to Learn about the Wonders of Wildlife & Nature. 1998. (Illus.). 64p. (gr. 3-7). pap. 12.95 (978-0-07-037134-7(2) , 9780070371347) McGraw-Hill Cos., The.

Kowalski, Kathiann. Everything Kids' Nature Book: Create Clouds, Make Waves, Defy Gravity & Much M. 2000. (gr. 3-6). lib. bdg. 15.25 (978-0-613-51248-0(0)) Tandem Library Bks.

Kowalski, Kathiann M. & Adams Media Corporation Staff. The Everything Kids' Nature Book: Create Clouds, Make Waves, Defy Gravity & Much More! 2000. (Everything Kids Ser.). 144p. (gr. 4-7). pap. 6.95 (978-1-58062-684-2(X)) Adams Media Corp.

Ladybird Books Staff. Smokey the Bear Nature Diary. 1999. (978-0-7214-5642-3(1) , Ladybird Books) Penguin Bks., Ltd.

Lawlor, Elizabeth P., et al. Discover Nature in Winter. 1998. (Discover Nature Ser.). (Illus.). 198p. pap. 14.95 (978-0-8117-2719-8(X)) Stackpole Bks.

Madgwick, Wendy. Living Things. 1999. (Science Starters Ser.). (Illus.). 32p. (J). (gr. k-4). lib. bdg. 25.70 (978-0-8172-5332-5(7)) Raintree.

—Living Things. 1999. (Science Starters Ser.). (Illus.). 32p. (J). (gr. k-4). 7.95 (978-0-8172-5883-2(3)) Steck-Vaughn.

Malone, Jeanette. Wild Adventures: A Guidebook of Activities for Building Connections. 1998. (Illus.). 188p. spiral bd. 27.60 (978-0-536-01782-6(4)) Pearson Custom Publishing.

Marie, Evelyn. Pick Your Own Strawberries. Stewart, Todd W., illus. 1998. 32p. (J). (gr. k-3). reprint ed. pap. 3.50 (978-0-9614746-3-8(7)) Berry Bks.

Marx, Nancy A. Sense. . . Abilities: A Children's Picture Book. 2002. (Illus.). 18p. (J). 21.95 (978-0-9727675-1-4(7)) Nature Sense Pr.

—Sense. . . Abilities: A Children's Picture Book. Boehmer, Kelly S., illus. 2002. 18p. (J). spiral bd. 17.95 (978-0-9727675-0-7(9)) Nature Sense Pr.

Maynard, Christopher. Why Do Sunflowers Face the Sun? Questions Children Ask about Nature. (Why Bks.). (Illus.). 24p. (J). pap. 10.99 (978-0-590-24954-6(1)) Scholastic, Inc.

Nadeau, Isaac. Learning about Earth's Cycles with Graphic Organizers. 2005. (Graphic Organizers in Science Ser.). (Illus.). 24p. (J). 19.95 (978-1-4042-2807-8(1)); pap. (978-1-4042-5044-4(1)) Rosen Publishing Group, Inc., The. (PowerKids Pr.).

National Wildlife Federation Staff. Wading into Wetlands. 1999. (Ranger Rick's Naturescope Ser.). (Illus.). 96p. (J). (gr. 1-7). lib. bdg. 19.95 (978-0-7910-4837-5(3) , Chelsea Hse.) Facts On File, Inc.

Nayer, Judy. Projects for Preschoolers-Nature. 1999. (Projects for Preschoolers Ser.). (Illus.). 48p. (J). (ps-1). mass mkt. 4.99 (978-0-7681-0079-2(8) , 67307, McClanahan Bk.) Learning Horizons, Inc.

O'Hara-Kelly, Katie. What Are You Looking At? O'Hara-Kelly, Katie, illus. 2000. (Illus.). 32p. (J). (gr. k-3). 6.95 (978-1-878441-11-9(6)) Sequoia Natural History Assn.

Orr, Richard. Richard Orr's Nature Cross-Sections. (Illus.). (J). pap. 22.99 (978-0-590-24633-0(X)) Scholastic, Inc.

Pastel, JoAnne & Fitzsimmons, Kakie. Anna Goes Hiking: Learn about Hiking & Nature. VanDeWeghe, Lindsay & Bohnet, Christopher, illus. l.t. ed. 2007. 40p. (J). lib. bdg. 14.95 ***(978-0-9777121-7-5(6))*** Interface Publishing.

Pelfrey, Wanda. Hands-On Nature. 1999. (Illus.). 96p. (J). (ps). pap. 11.95 (978-1-885358-64-6(4)) Rainbow Pubs. & Legacy Pr.

Perry, Phyllis J. Science Fair Success with Plants. 1999. (Science Fair Success Ser.). (Illus.). 104p. (YA). (gr. 6-12). lib. bdg. 26.60 (978-0-7660-1170-0(4)) Enslow Pubs., Inc.

Pipe, Jim. Minibeasts. 2007. (J). ***(978-1-59604-131-8(5))*** Stargazer Bks.

Powell, Consie. The First Day of Winter. Powell, Consie, illus. 2005. (Illus.). 32p. (J). (gr. k-4). lib. bdg. 15.95 (978-0-8075-2450-3(6)) Whitman, Albert & Co.

Prather, Eric & Prather, Joy. Color the Black Hills: A Nature Coloring & Activity Book. 1998. (Illus.). 32p. (J). (ps-3). pap. 3.95 (978-0-87108-300-5(0)) Pruett Publishing Co.

Quadrillion Media Staff. Nature & Animals. 1999. (Start Me Up Ser.). (J). pap. 3.95 (978-1-58185-101-4(4)) Quadrillion Media LLC.

Raintree Steck-Vaughn Staff, ed. Natural World. 1999. (Illus.). (J). 154.14 (978-0-7398-2776-5(6)); 102.76 (978-0-7398-2772-7(3)) Raintree.

Rau, Dana Meachen. Cuando Voy a Escalar Una Montana. Marcuse, Aida E., tr. 2001. (Aventureros Ser.). (SPA., Illus.). 24p. (J). (gr. k-2). lib. bdg. 19.27 (978-1-57103-363-5(7) , RK31326) Rourke Publishing, LLC.

—Cuando Voy a Pasear al Desierto. Marcuse, Aida E., tr. 2001. (Aventureros Ser.). (SPA., Illus.). 24p. (J). (gr. k-2). lib. bdg. 19.27 (978-1-57103-364-2(5) , RK31329) Rourke Publishing, LLC.

—Cuando Voy a Pasear al Mar. Marcuse, Aida E., tr. 2001. (SPA., Illus.). 24p. (J). (gr. k-2). lib. bdg. 19.27 (978-1-57103-362-8(9) , RK31330) Rourke Publishing, LLC.

Russo, Monica. Watching Nature: A Beginner's Field Guide. 2002. (gr. 3-6). lib. bdg. 18.75 (978-0-613-87486-1(2)) Tandem Library Bks.

Salzmann, Mary Elizabeth. In a Valley. l.t. ed. 2001. (What Do You See? Ser.). (Illus.). 24p. (J). (ps-3). lib. bdg. 19.93 (978-1-57765-569-5(9) , SandCastle) ABDO Publishing Co.

Schaffer, Donna. Pillbugs. 1999. (Life Cycles Ser.). (Illus.). 24p. (J). (gr. 2-3). lib. bdg. 18.60 (978-0-7368-0212-3(6) , Bridgestone Bks.) Capstone Pr., Inc.

Scholastic, Inc. Staff, ed. Hidden World: Under the Ground. 1999. (Hidden World Ser.). (Illus.). 26p. (J). (ps-2). 12.95 (978-0-590-43813-1(1)) Scholastic, Inc.

Schwartz, David M. Among the Flowers. Kuhn, Dwight, photos by. 1999. (Springboards into Science Ser.). (Illus.). 24p. (J). (gr. 1 up). lib. bdg. 19.93 (978-0-8368-2241-0(2)) Stevens, Gareth Inc.

—Animal Ears. Kuhn, Dwight, photos by. 1999. (Springboards into Science Ser.). (Illus.). 24p. (J). (gr. 1 up). lib. bdg. 20.67 (978-0-8368-2576-3(4)) Stevens, Gareth Inc.

—Animal Eyes. Kuhn, Dwight, photos by. 1999. (Springboards into Science Ser.). (Illus.). 24p. (J). (gr. 1 up). lib. bdg. 20.67 (978-0-8368-2423-0(7)) Stevens, Gareth Inc.

—Animal Feathers & Fur. Kuhn, Dwight, photos by. 1999. (Springboards into Science Ser.). (Illus.). 24p. (J). (gr. 1 up). lib. bdg. 20.67 (978-0-8368-2424-7(5)) Stevens, Gareth Inc.

—Animal Feet. Kuhn, Dwight, photos by. 1999. (Springboards into Science Ser.). (Illus.). 24p. (J). (gr. 1 up). lib. bdg. 20.67 (978-0-8368-2577-0(2)) Stevens, Gareth Inc.

—Animal Mouths. Kuhn, Dwight, photos by. 1999. (Springboards into Science Ser.). (Illus.). 24p. (J). (gr. 1 up). lib. bdg. 20.67 (978-0-8368-2425-4(3)) Stevens, Gareth Inc.

—Animal Noses. Kuhn, Dwight, photos by. 1999. (Springboards into Science Ser.). (Illus.). 24p. (J). (gr. 1 up). lib. bdg. 20.67 (978-0-8368-2578-7(0)) Stevens, Gareth Inc.

—Animal Skin & Scales. Kuhn, Dwight, photos by. 1999. (Springboards into Science Ser.). (Illus.). 24p. (J). (gr. 1 up). lib. bdg. 20.67 (978-0-8368-2579-4(9)) Stevens, Gareth Inc.

—Animal Tails. Kuhn, Dwight, photos by. 1999. (Springboards into Science Ser.). (Illus.). 24p. (J). (gr. 1 up). lib. bdg. 20.67 (978-0-8368-2426-1(1)) Stevens, Gareth Inc.

—At the Pond. Kuhn, Dwight, photos by. 1999. (Springboards into Science Ser.). (Illus.). 24p. (J). (gr. 1 up). lib. bdg. 19.93 (978-0-8368-2244-1(7)) Stevens, Gareth Inc.

—At the Seashore. Kuhn, Dwight, photos by. 1998. (Springboards into Science Ser.). (Illus.). 24p. (J). (gr. 1 up). lib. bdg. 19.93 (978-0-8368-2224-3(2)) Stevens, Gareth Inc.

—In a Tree. Kuhn, Dwight, photos by. 1999. (Springboards into Science Ser.). (Illus.). 24p. (J). (gr. 1 up). lib. bdg. 20.67 (978-0-8368-2245-8(5)) Stevens, Gareth Inc.

—In the Desert. Kuhn, Dwight, photos by. 1998. (Springboards into Science Ser.). (Illus.). 24p. (J). (gr. 1 up). lib. bdg. 20.67 (978-0-8368-2220-5(X)) Stevens, Gareth Inc.

—In the Forest. Kuhn, Dwight, photos by. 1998. (Springboards into Science Ser.). (Illus.). 24p. (J). (gr. 1 up). lib. bdg. 20.67 (978-0-8368-2222-9(6)) Stevens, Gareth Inc.

—In the Garden. Kuhn, Dwight, photos by. 1999. (Springboards into Science Ser.). (Illus.). 24p. (J). (gr. 1 up). lib. bdg. 19.93 (978-0-8368-2242-7(0)) Stevens, Gareth Inc.

—In the Meadow. Kuhn, Dwight, photos by. 1998. (Springboards into Science Ser.). (Illus.). 24p. (J). (gr. 1 up). lib. bdg. 20.67 (978-0-8368-2223-6(4)) Stevens, Gareth Inc.

—In the Park. Kuhn, Dwight, photos by. (Habitats Ser.). (Illus.). 16p. (J). (gr. 1-3). pap. 2.99 (978-1-57471-214-8(4) , 3006) Creative Teaching Pr., Inc.

—In the Park. Kuhn, Dwight, photos by. 1999. (Springboards into Science Ser.). (Illus.). 24p. (J). (gr. 1 up). lib. bdg. 20.67 (978-0-8368-2243-4(9)) Stevens, Gareth Inc.

—Look Once, Look Again, 24 bks. Kuhn, Dwight, photos by. Incl. Among the Flowers. 1999. lib. bdg. 19.93 (978-0-8368-2241-0(2)); Animal Ears. 1999. lib. bdg. 20.67 (978-0-8368-2576-3(4)); Animal Eyes. 1999. lib. bdg. 20.67 (978-0-8368-2423-0(7)); Animal Feathers & Fur. 1999. lib. bdg. 20.67 (978-0-8368-2424-7(5)); Animal Feet. 1999. lib. bdg. 20.67 (978-0-8368-2577-0(2)); Animal Mouths. 1999. lib. bdg. 20.67 (978-0-8368-2425-4(3)); Animal Noses. 1999. lib. bdg. 20.67 (978-0-8368-2578-7(0)); Animal Skin & Scales. 1999. lib. bdg. 20.67 (978-0-8368-2579-4(9)); Animal Tails. 1999. lib. bdg. 20.67 (978-0-8368-2426-1(1)); At the Farm. 1998. lib. bdg. 19.93 (978-0-8368-2221-2(8)); At the Pond. 1999. lib. bdg. 19.93 (978-0-8368-2244-1(7)); At the Seashore. 1998. lib. bdg. 19.93 (978-0-8368-2224-3(2)); At the Zoo. 1998. lib. bdg. 19.93 (978-0-8368-2225-0(0)); In a Tree. 1999. lib. bdg. 20.67 (978-0-8368-2245-8(5)); In the Desert. 1998. lib. bdg. 20.67 (978-0-8368-2220-5(X)); In the Forest. 1998. lib. bdg. 20.67 (978-0-8368-2222-9(6)); In the Garden. 1999. lib. bdg. 19.93 (978-0-8368-2242-7(0)); In the Meadow. 1998. lib. bdg. 20.67 (978-0-8368-2223-6(4)); In the Park. 1999. lib. bdg. 20.67 (978-0-8368-2243-4(9)); Plant Blossoms. 1999. lib. bdg. 20.67 (978-0-8368-2580-0(2)); Plant Fruits & Seeds. 1999. lib. bdg. 20.67 (978-0-8368-2427-8(X)); Plant Leaves. 1999. lib. bdg. 20.67 (978-0-8368-2428-5(8)); Plant Stems & Roots. 1999. lib. bdg. 20.67 (978-0-8368-2581-7(0)); Underfoot. 1999. lib. bdg. 20.67 (978-0-8368-2246-5(3)); (J). (gr. 1 up). (Springboards into Science Ser.). (Illus.). 24p. 1999. Set lib. bdg. 124.02 (978-0-8368-2657-9(4)) Stevens, Gareth Inc.

—Plant Blossoms. Kuhn, Dwight, photos by. 1999. (Springboards into Science Ser.). (Illus.). 24p. (J). (gr. 1 up). lib. bdg. 20.67 (978-0-8368-2580-0(2)) Stevens, Gareth Inc.

—Plant Fruits & Seeds. Kuhn, Dwight, photos by. 1999. (Springboards into Science Ser.). (Illus.). 24p. (J). (gr. 1 up). lib. bdg. 20.67 (978-0-8368-2427-8(X)) Stevens, Gareth Inc.

—Plant Leaves. Kuhn, Dwight, photos by. 1999. (Springboards into Science Ser.). (Illus.). 24p. (J). (gr. 1 up). lib. bdg. 20.67 (978-0-8368-2428-5(8)) Stevens, Gareth Inc.

—Plant Stems & Roots. Kuhn, Dwight, photos by. 1999. (Springboards into Science Ser.). (Illus.). 24p. (J). (gr. 1 up). lib. bdg. 20.67 (978-0-8368-2581-7(0)) Stevens, Gareth Inc.

—Underfoot. Kuhn, Dwight, photos by. 1999. (Springboards into Science Ser.). (Illus.). 24p. (J). (gr. 1 up). lib. bdg. 20.67 (978-0-8368-2246-5(3)) Stevens, Gareth Inc.

Scott, James. The Jungle: Reproducible Teaching Unit. 2002. 81p. (YA). (gr. 7-12). ring bd. 29.50 (978-1-58049-295-9(9) , TU180) Prestwick Hse., Inc.

Shedd, Warner. The Kids' Wildlife Book: Exploring Animal Worlds Through Indoor/Outdoor Experiences. 1999. (Kids Can Bks.: No. 11). (Illus.). 160p. (J). (ps-5). pap. 12.95 (978-0-913589-77-9(2) , Williamson Bks.) Ideals Pubns.

Southwater Staff. Fun with Nature. 2000. (Illus.). 96p. 12.95 (978-1-84215-140-2(1) , Southwater) Anness Publishing GBR. *Dist:* National Bk. Network.

Stevens, Ann Shepard. Strange Nests. Dewey, Jennifer Owings, illus. 1998. (All about Animals Ser.). 32p. (J). (gr. 2-5). lib. bdg. 21.90 (978-0-7613-0413-5(4) , Millbrook Pr.) Lerner Publishing Group.

Stewart, Melissa. Animals All Around. 2004. (Investigate Science Ser.). (Illus.). 32p. (J). (gr. 1 up). lib. bdg. 21.26 (978-0-7565-0594-3(1)) Compass Point Bks.

Tiffault, Benette W. Ghost Bat in a Gum Tree. Grosshauser, Peter, illus. 1998. 32p. (ps-3). pap. 9.95 (978-1-56044-618-7(8) , Falcon) Globe Pequot Pr., The.

Trumbauer, Lisa. What Is a Cycle? Pliakas, Stephanie, ed. 1998. (Early Science Big Bks.). (Illus.). 16p. (J). (ps-2). pap. 16.95 (978-1-56784-375-0(1)) Sundance/Newbridge Educational Publishing.

Ward, Kristin. Nature Books I, 6 bks. Incl. Apples. lib. bdg. 16.00 (978-0-8239-5528-2(1) , PKNAAP); Leaves. lib. bdg. 16.00 (978-0-8239-5533-6(8) , PKNALE); Oceans. lib. bdg. 16.00 (978-0-8239-5532-9(X) , PKNAOC); Rain. lib. bdg. 16.00 (978-0-8239-5531-2(1) , PKNARA); Sand. lib. bdg. 16.00 (978-0-8239-5530-5(3) , PKNASA); Snow. lib. bdg. 16.00 (978-0-8239-5529-9(X) , PKNASN); 24p. (J). (gr. 1). 2000. (Illus.). Set lib. bdg. 88.50 (978-0-8239-7003-2(5) , PKRENB, PowerKids Pr.) Rosen Publishing Group, Inc., The.

World Book, Inc. Staff, contrib. by. World Book's Science & Nature Guides, 12 vols. 2004. (World Book's Science & Nature Guides Ser.). (Illus.). 80p. (gr. 5-9). 319.00 (978-0-7166-4208-4(5) , SKU 30119) World Bk., Inc.

NATURE STUDY—DICTIONARIES

Dorling Kindersley Publishing Staff. The Concise Encyclopedia of Nature. 2000. (978-0-606-17804-4(X)) Tandem Library Bks.

Enciclopedia Juvenil de la Naturaleza. rev. ed. (SPA., Illus.). 256p. (J). 39.95 (978-84-272-5930-0(1) , MO500) Molino, Editorial ESP. *Dist:* Continental Bk. Co., Inc.

NATURE STUDY—FICTION

Baskwill, Jane. Touch the Earth. Fiore, Peter M., illus. 1999. 32p. (J). (gr. 1-5). pap. 4.95 (978-1-57255-428-3(2)) Mondo Publishing.

Below, Halina. Chestnut Dreams. 2002. (Illus.). 40p. pap. (978-1-55041-690-9(1)) Fitzhenry & Whiteside, Ltd.

—Chestnut Dreams. Below, Halina, illus. 2000. (Illus.). 40p. (J). (ps-1). (978-1-55041-545-2(X)) Fitzhenry & Whiteside, Ltd.

Bruna, Dick. Miffy Goes for a Walk. 1998. (Miffy Ser.). (Illus.). 8p. (J). (ps-k). 8.95 (978-1-56836-269-4(2)) Kodansha America, Inc.

Burgess, Thornton W. Old Mother West Wind. (J). 16.95 (978-0-8488-0385-8(X)) Amereon LTD.

Burnett, Frances Hodgson. The Land of the Blue Flower. 2002. (J). cd-rom (978-0-9724995-7-6(1)) Alcazar AudioWorks.

Crew, Linda. Nekomah Creek. Robinson, Charles, illus. 2001. 192p. (gr. 4-7). pap. 12.00 (978-0-375-89506-7(X) , Yearling) Random Hse. Children's Bks.

Cutler, Jane. Rose & Riley Come & Go. Yezerski, Thomas F., illus. 2005. (Rose & Riley Ser.). 48p. (J). 15.00 (978-0-374-36341-3(2) , Farrar, Straus & Giroux (BYR)) Farrar, Straus & Giroux.

Donaldson, Julia. The Wrong Kind of Bark. Parsons, Garry, illus. 2005. (Red Bananas Ser.). 48p. (J). (978-0-7787-1073-8(4)); pap. (978-0-7787-1089-9(0)) Crabtree Publishing Co.

Ehlert, Lois. In My World. 2002. (Illus.). 40p. (J). 15.00 (978-0-15-216269-6(0)) Harcourt Children's Bks.
Ehrlich, Gretel. A Blizzard Year. Kiesler, Kate A., illus. 2001. 128p. (gr. 4-8). pap. 5.99 (978-0-7868-1245-5(1)) Hyperion Bks. for Children.
—A Blizzard Year. 2001. (J). (gr. 4-8). 12.64 (978-0-606-22572-4(2)) Tandem Library Bks.
Frasier, Debra. Out of the Ocean. Frasier, Debra, illus. 1998. (Illus.). 40p. (J). (ps-3). 16.00 (978-0-15-258849-6(3), Red Wagon Bks.) Harcourt Children's Bks.
Garelick, May & Whitman, Candace. Sounds of a Summer Night. 2000. (Illus.). 32p. (J). (ps-3). 15.95 (978-1-57255-745-1(1)) Mondo Publishing.
Geis, Patricia. Pequena Masai. 2002. (Ninos y Ninas del Mundo Ser.). (SPA & ENG., Illus.). 10p. 5.95 (978-84-7864-350-9(8)) Combel Editorial, S.A. ESP. *Dist:* Independent Pubs. Group.
—Pequena Nenet. 2002. (Ninos y Ninas del Mundo Ser.). (SPA & ENG., Illus.). 10p. 5.95 (978-84-7864-351-6(6)) Combel Editorial, S.A. ESP. *Dist:* Independent Pubs. Group.
—Pequena Quiche. 2002. (Ninos y Ninas del Mundo Ser.). (SPA & ENG., Illus.). 10p. 5.95 (978-84-7864-348-6(6)) Combel Editorial, S.A. ESP. *Dist:* Independent Pubs. Group.
—Pequeno Inuit. 2002. (Ninos y Ninas del Mundo Ser.). (SPA & ENG., Illus.). 10p. 5.95 (978-84-7864-347-9(8)) Combel Editorial, S.A. ESP. *Dist:* Independent Pubs. Group.
—Pequeno Maori. 2002. (Ninos y Ninas del Mundo Ser.). (SPA & ENG., Illus.). 10p. 5.95 (978-84-7864-349-3(4)) Combel Editorial, S.A. ESP. *Dist:* Independent Pubs. Group.
—Pequeno Sioux. 2002. (Ninos y Ninas del Mundo Ser.). (ENG & SPA., Illus.). 10p. 5.95 (978-84-7864-346-2(X)) Combel Editorial, S.A. ESP. *Dist:* Independent Pubs. Group.
Glaser, Linda. It's Spring! Swan, Susan, illus. 2002. (Celebrate the Seasons! Ser.). 32p. (J). (gr. 1-3). pap. 7.95 (978-0-7613-1345-8(1), First Avenue Editions) Lerner Publishing Group.
Hilton, Nette. Collecting of Timothy Taylor. 2000. (Illus.). 32p. (ps-1). 16.00 (978-0-207-19698-0(2)) HarperCollins Pubs. AUS. *Dist:* Consortium Bk. Sales & Distribution.
Kefalos, Katina. Peace Pond. Schaefer, Rob, illus. 1999. 14p. (YA). (gr. 5-8). 0.95 (978-1-929172-09-2(5)) Emerald Productions.
Keller, Holly. I Am Angela. 1999. (Beech Tree Chapter Bks.). (Illus.). 64p. (J). (gr. 2-7). pap. 4.95 (978-0-688-16723-3(3)) HarperCollins Pubs.
—I Am Angela. 1999. (J). (978-0-606-16764-2(1)) Tandem Library Bks.
Lewis, J. Patrick. Earth & Me, Our Family Tree: Nature's Creatures. Canyon, Christopher, illus. 2004. (Sharing Nature with Children Book Ser.). 36p. (J). (ps-5). 16.95 (978-1-58469-031-3(3)); pap. 7.95 (978-1-58469-030-6(5)) Dawn Pubns.
Maddox, Tony. Spike's Best Nest. 1998. (978-0-606-13795-9(5)) Tandem Library Bks.
Morneau, Robert F. The Gift. 2000. (Illus.). 32p. (ps-3). 14.95 (978-0-8091-6673-2(9), 6673-9) Paulist Pr.
Peltzman, Adam. It's Spring, Blue! Pontillo, Jenine, illus. 2000. (Blue's Clues Ser.). 16p. (J). (ps-k). pap. 3.99 (978-0-689-83097-6(1), Simon Spotlight/Nickelodeon) Simon & Schuster Children's Publishing.
Plourde, Lynn. Thank You Grandpa. Cockroft, Jason, illus. 2003. 32p. (J). (gr. k). 15.99 (978-0-525-46992-6(3), Dutton Juvenile) Penguin Group (USA) Inc.
Poulsen, Allan. Freezy Breezy Fun. Raymond, Kim, illus. 2000. (Look-Look Bks.). 24p. (J). (ps-3). pap. 3.29 (978-0-307-12891-1(1), 12891, Golden Bks.) Random Hse. Children's Bks.
Ryan, Susan Jane. Esmeralda & the Enchanted Pond. Cook, Sandra, illus. 2001. 48p. (J). (gr. 2-5). 14.95 (978-1-56164-236-6(3)) Pineapple Pr., Inc.
Ryan, Susan Jane & Cook, Sandra G. Esmeralda & the Enchanted Pond. 2001. (Illus.). 48p. (gr. 4-7). pap., act. bk. ed. 5.00 (978-1-56164-247-2(9)) Pineapple Pr., Inc.
Stoutland, Allison. Put Your Best Foot Forward: More Little Lessons for a Happier World. Hofher, Cathy, illus. 2000. 32p. (J). 14.95 (978-0-9670941-1-3(9)) Inch By Inch Pubns., LLC.
Titherington, Jeanne. Citrouille, Ma Citrouille. l.t. ed. Tr. of Citrouille, Ma Citrouille. (FRE.). (J). bds. 29.99 (978-0-590-73546-9(2)) Scholastic, Inc.
—Pumpkin Pumpkin. l.t. ed. 1999. (J). pap. 19.95 (978-0-590-72452-4(5)) Scholastic, Inc.
Tozer, Al. Mr. Ant & His Friends: A Fun Insect Story. 2002. (J). 19.95 (978-0-9720493-0-6(4)) Junebug Pr.
Urdaneta, Josefina. El Sol y el Agua. 2000. 7.95 (978-980-6437-16-6(0)) Baker & Taylor Bks.
Veit, Wilbert, Jr. The Music of Sunlight: The First Molecular Adventure. Hamblin, Randy, illus. 2000. v, 169p. (YA). (gr. 6-13). pap. 19.95 (978-0-9678081-4-7(6)) Sunlight Bks.
Whelan, Gloria. That Wild Berries Should Grow. 2003. (gr. 3-6). lib. bdg. 16.45 (978-0-613-75569-6(3)) Tandem Library Bks.
Williams, Sue. I Went Walking. Vivas, Julie, illus. 2002. (J). 14.79 (978-0-7587-2823-4(9)) Book Wholesalers, Inc.
—I Went Walking, 2 bks., Set. Vivas, Julie, illus. unabr. ed. 2000. (ENG & SPA.). (J). (gr. k-3). pap. 33.95 incl. audio (978-0-87499-666-1(X)) Live Oak Media.
Yep, Laurence. Sweetwater. Noonan, Julia, illus. 2004. 191p. (J). pap. 5.99 (978-0-06-056029-4(0)) HarperCollins Pubs.

NAVAL ACADEMY, ANNAPOLIS
see United States Naval Academy, Annapolis

NAVAL ADMINISTRATION
see Naval Art and Science
see names of countries with the subhead Navy, e.g. United States—Navy

NAVAL AERONAUTICS
see Aeronautics, Military

NAVAL AIRPLANES
see Airplanes, Military

NAVAL ARCHITECTURE
see also Boatbuilding; Shipbuilding; Ships; Steamboats; Warships
Barron's Educational Editorial Staff. Submarines. 1998. (History Ser.). (Illus.). 32p. (J). (gr. 5). pap. 5.95 (978-0-7641-0536-4(1)) Barron's Educational Series, Inc.

NAVAL ART AND SCIENCE
see also Military Art and Science; Navigation; Sea Power; Shipbuilding; Signals and Signaling; Submarine Warfare; Submarines (Ships); Warships
Barron's Educational Editorial Staff. Submarines. 1998. (History Ser.). (Illus.). 32p. (J). (gr. 5). pap. 5.95 (978-0-7641-0536-4(1)) Barron's Educational Series, Inc.
Gilbert, Adrian. Going to War in Ancient Greece. 2001. (gr. 3-6). lib. bdg. 15.25 (978-0-613-54518-1(4)) Tandem Library Bks.
Green, Michael. Mine Hunting Ships. 2001. (Land & Sea Ser.). (Illus.). 48p. (J). (gr. 3-4). lib. bdg. 21.26 (978-0-7368-0758-6(6), Capstone High-Interest Bks.) Capstone Pr., Inc.
Hobbs, Richard R. Naval Science 2: Maritime History & Nautical Sciences for the NJROTC Student. 2nd ed. 2006. (Illus.). 344p. 29.95 (978-1-59114-366-6(7)) Naval Institute Pr.
—Naval Science 3: Naval Knowledge & Skills for the NJROTC Student. 2003. (Illus.). 360p. 27.95 (978-1-55750-319-0(2)) Naval Institute Pr.

NAVAL BATTLES
see Battles; Naval History
also names of countries with the subdivision History, Naval, e.g. U. S.—History, Naval, etc.; and names of battles
Barron's Educational Editorial Staff. Warships. 1998. (History Ser.). (Illus.). 32p. (J). (gr. 5). pap. 5.95 (978-0-7641-0535-7(3)) Barron's Educational Series, Inc.
Califf, David J. Battle of Actium. 2003. (Great Battles Through the Ages Ser.). (Illus.). 112p. (gr. 6-12). 30.00 (978-0-7910-7440-4(4), Chelsea Hse.) Facts On File, Inc.

NAVAL BIOGRAPHY
see also Admirals; Sailors
also names of navies with the subdivision Biography, e.g. United States—Navy—Biography
Cawthorne, Nigel. Military Commanders: The 100 Greatest Throughout History. 2004. (Illus.). 208p. 18.95 (978-1-59270-029-5(2)) Enchanted Lion Bks., LLC.

NAVAL HISTORY
see also Military History; Naval Biography; Pirates
also names of countries with the subhead Navy or the subdivision History, Naval, e.g. United States—Navy; United States—History, Naval
Barron's Educational Editorial Staff. Warships. 1998. (History Ser.). (Illus.). 32p. (J). (gr. 5). pap. 5.95 (978-0-7641-0535-7(3)) Barron's Educational Series, Inc.
Cawthorne, Nigel. Military Commanders: The 100 Greatest Throughout History. 2004. (Illus.). 208p. 18.95 (978-1-59270-029-5(2)) Enchanted Lion Bks., LLC.
Crompton, Samuel Willard. 100 Military Leaders Who Changed the World. 2003. (People Who Changed the World Ser.). (Illus.). 112p. (J). (gr. 5 up). lib. bdg. 30.00 (978-0-8368-5470-1(5), World Almanac Library) Stevens, Gareth Inc.
Hobbs, Richard R. Naval Science 2: Maritime History & Nautical Sciences for the NJROTC Student. 2nd ed. 2006. (Illus.). 344p. 29.95 (978-1-59114-366-6(7)) Naval Institute Pr.
Hull, Robert. Trade & Warfare. 2006. (World of Ancient Greece Ser.). (Illus.). 32p. (J). (978-1-59771-062-6(8)) Sea-To-Sea Pubns.
Hull, Robert E. Trade & Warfare. 2000. (World of Ancient Greece Ser.). (Illus.). 32p. (J). pap. 6.95 (978-0-531-15384-0(3), Watts, Franklin) Scholastic Library Publishing.
Thornton, Jeremy. The Birth of the American Navy. 2003. (Building Americas Democracy Ser.). (Illus.). 24p. (J). lib. bdg. 19.95 (978-0-8239-6274-7(1), PowerKids Pr.) Rosen Publishing Group, Inc., The.

NAVAL SCIENCE
see Naval Art and Science

NAVAL SIGNALING
see Signals and Signaling

NAVAL UNIFORMS
see Uniforms, Military

NAVAL WARFARE
see Naval Art and Science; Naval Battles; Submarine Warfare

NAVIGATION
see also Harbors; Inland Navigation; Knots and Splices; Lighthouses; Naval Art and Science; Pilots and Pilotage; Shipwrecks; Signals and Signaling; Tides; Winds
Bramwell, Martyn. Mapping the Seas & Airways. 1998. (Maps & Mapmakers Ser.). (Illus.). 48p. (J). (gr. 5-7). lib. bdg. 22.60 (978-0-8225-2921-7(1), Lerner Pubns.) Lerner Publishing Group.
Deboo, Ana. Mapping the Seas & Skies. 2006. (Illus.). 32p. (J). (978-1-4034-6793-5(5)); pap. (978-1-4034-6800-0(1)) Heinemann Library.
Dickinson, Rachel. Tools of Navigation: A Kid's Guide to the History & Science of Finding Your Way. 2005. (Tools of Discovery Ser.). (Illus.). 160p. (J). (ps-9). pap. 16.95 (978-0-9749344-0-2(2)) Nomad Pr.
Krebs, Laurie. A Day in the Life of a Colonial Lighthouse Keeper. 2004. (Library of Living & Working in Colonial Times). (Illus.). 24p. (J). lib. bdg. 18.75 (978-0-8239-6226-6(1), PowerKids Pr.) Rosen Publishing Group, Inc., The.
MacDonald, Fiona. You Wouldn't Want to Sail with Christopher Columbus! Uncharted Waters You'd Rather Not Cross. Antram, David, illus. 2004. (You Wouldn't Want to Ser.). 32p. (J). (gr. 2-5). pap. 9.95 (978-0-531-16060-2(2), Watts, Franklin) Scholastic Library Publishing.
MacDonald, Fiona, et al. You Wouldn't Want to Sail with Christopher Columbus! Uncharted Waters You'd Rather Not Cross. 2004. (You Wouldn't Want To Ser.). (J). 28.50 (978-0-531-12355-3(3), Watts, Franklin) Scholastic Library Publishing.
Nunan, David. Go for It!, Bk. 4. 1999. (Global ESL/ELT Ser.). (Illus.). 112p. (J). pap. 23.95 (978-0-8384-6785-5(7)) Thomson Heinle.
Pritchard, Herman S. The Nautical Road: A Straight Forward Approach to Learning the Navigation Rules. Helwig, Teresa L., ed. Sink, Cynthia, illus. 2nd rev. l.t. ed. 2004. 176p. (YA). 29.95 (978-0-9716479-3-0(3)) Selby Dean Ventures, Inc.
Rothstein, Ruth S., et al. ARIES Exploring Navigation: Location, Direction & Latitude: Science Journal. 2000. (Aries Ser.). (Illus.). (J). (gr. 3-8). pap. 3.80 (978-1-57091-255-9(6)) Charlesbridge Publishing, Inc.
Smith, A. G. Where Am I? The Story of Maps & Navigation. (Illus.). 89p. (YA). (gr. 4-9). pap. 15.95 (978-0-7737-6220-6(5)) Stoddart Kids CAN. *Dist:* Fitzhenry & Whiteside, Ltd.
—Where Am I? The Story of Maps & Navigation. 2001. (gr. 3-6). lib. bdg. 25.70 (978-0-613-81884-1(9)) Tandem Library Bks.
Storm, Rory. Sea Guide. 2002. (Survivors Ser.). 128p. (J). (gr. 3-7). pap. 4.99 (978-0-439-32857-9(8)) Scholastic, Inc.
Williams, Linda D. Navigational Aids. 2007. (Great Inventions Ser.). (Illus.). 144p. (YA). (gr. 9 up). lib. bdg. 39.93 (***978-0-7614-2599-1(3)***, Benchmark Bks.) Cavendish, Marshall Corp.
Young, Karen Romano. Across the Wide Ocean: The Why, How, & Where of Navigation for Humans & Animals at Sea. Young, Karen Romano, illus. 2007. 80p. (J). (gr. 5-7). lib. bdg. 19.89 (978-0-06-009087-6(1)); (Illus.). 18.99 (978-0-06-009086-9(3)) HarperCollins Pubs.

NAVIGATORS
see Explorers

NAVY
see Naval Art and Science; Sea Power
see names of countries with the subhead Navy, e.g. United States—Navy

NAZI MOVEMENT
see National Socialism

NEAR EAST
see Asia; Middle East

NEBRASKA
Bjorklund, Ruth. Nebraska. 2001. (Celebrate the States Ser.). (Illus.). 144p. (J). (gr. 4-8). lib. bdg. 37.07 (978-0-7614-1311-0(1), Benchmark Bks.) Cavendish, Marshall Corp.
Brown, Jonatha A. Nebraska. 2006. (Portraits of the States Ser.). (J). pap. (978-0-8368-4720-8(2)); lib. bdg. (978-0-8368-4703-1(2)) Stevens, Gareth Inc.
Capstone Press Staff, contrib. by. Nebraska. rev. ed. 2002. (One Nation Ser.). (Illus.). 48p. (J). (gr. 3-4). lib. bdg. 22.60 (978-0-7368-1251-1(2), Bridgestone Bks.) Capstone Pr., Inc.
Christian, Sandra J. Nebraska. 2003. (Land of Liberty Ser.). (Illus.). 64p. (J). lib. bdg. 25.26 (978-0-7368-2185-8(6)) Capstone Pr., Inc.
Flocker, Michael. Nebraska: The Cornhusker State. 2002. (World Almanac Library of the States). (Illus.). 48p. (J). (gr. 5 up). lib. bdg. 30.00 (978-0-8368-5140-3(4)); pap. 14.95 (978-0-8368-5310-0(5)) Stevens, Gareth Inc. (World Almanac Library).
Foran, Jill. A Guide to Nebraska. 2001. (For the Love of Sports Ser.). (Illus.). 32p. (J). lib. bdg. 16.95 (978-1-930954-97-7(2)); per. 7.95 (978-1-930954-88-5(3)) Weigl Pubs., Inc.
Galiano, Dean. Nebraska. 2006. (Bilingual Library of the United States of America: Set 2). (ENG & SPA., Illus.). 32p. (J). (gr. 3-6). lib. bdg. 22.50 (978-1-4042-3092-7(0), Buenas Letra) Rosen Publishing Group, Inc., The.
Haack, Kelly J. Nebraska: A MyReportLinks. Com Book. 2003. (States Ser.). (Illus.). 48p. (J). lib. bdg. 25.26 (978-0-7660-5145-4(5), MyReportLinks.com Bks.) Enslow Pubs., Inc.
Heinrichs, Ann. Nebraska. 2003. (This Land Is Your Land Ser.). (Illus.). 48p. (J). (gr. 3 up). lib. bdg. 22.60 (978-0-7565-0356-7(6)) Compass Point Bks.
—Nebraska. 2007. (America the Beautiful, Third Ser.). 144p. (J). spiral bd. 38.00 (***978-0-531-18577-3(X)***, Children's Pr.) Scholastic Library Publishing.
Kavanagh, James. Nebraska Birds. Leung, Raymond, illus. 1999. (Pocket Naturalist Ser.). (YA). 5.95 (978-1-58355-002-1(X)) Waterford Pr., Ltd.
Luebs Shepherd, Rajean. C Is for Cornhusker: A Nebraska Alphabet. Appleoff, Sandy, illus. 2004. (State Ser.). 40p. (J). 17.95 (978-1-58536-147-2(X)) Sleeping Bear Pr.
Marsh, Carole. The Big Nebraska Reproducible Activity Book. 2001. (Carole Marsh Nebraska Bks.). 96p. (J). (gr. 2-6). pap. 9.95 (978-0-7933-9948-2(3)) Gallopade International.
—My First Book about Nebraska. 2001. (Carole Marsh Nebraska Bks.). (Illus.). 32p. (J). (gr. k-4). pap. 7.95 (978-0-7933-9890-4(8)) Gallopade International.
—Nebraska Classic Christmas Trivia. 2002. (Carole Marsh Nebraska Bks.). (Illus.). 32p. pap. 6.95 (978-0-635-01421-4(1), 1421I, Marsh, Carole Bks.); lib. bdg. 21.95 (978-0-635-01422-1(X), 1422X) Gallopade International.
—Nebraska Current Events Projects: 30 Cool, Activities, Crafts, Experiments & More for Kids to Do to Learn about Your State! 2003. (Nebraska Experience Ser.). 32p. (gr. k-8). pap. 5.95 (978-0-635-02046-8(7), Marsh, Carole Bks.) Gallopade International.
—The Nebraska Experience Library State: Resource Set. 2001. (Illus.). (J). (gr. k-8). pap. 100.20 incl. cd-rom (978-0-635-00480-2(1)) Gallopade International.
—The Nebraska Experience Pocket Guide. 2001. (Carole Marsh Nebraska Bks.). (Illus.). 96p. (J). (gr. 3-8). pap. 6.95 (978-0-7933-9919-2(X)) Gallopade International.
—Nebraska Government Projects: 30 Cool, Activities, Crafts, Experiments & More for Kids to Do to Learn about Your State! 2003. (Nebraska Experience Ser.). 32p. (gr. k-5). pap. 5.95 (978-0-635-01946-2(9), Marsh, Carole Bks.) Gallopade International.
—Nebraska "Jography" A Fun Run Thru Our State! 2001. (Illus.). 32p. (J). (gr. 3-8). pap. 7.95 (978-0-7933-9832-4(0)) Gallopade International.
—Nebraska People Projects: 30 Cool, Activities, Crafts, Experiments & More for Kids to Do to Learn about Your State! 2003. (Nebraska Experience Ser.). 32p. (gr. k-5). pap. 5.95 (978-0-635-01996-7(5), Marsh, Carole Bks.) Gallopade International.
—Nebraska Symbols & Facts Projects: 30 Cool, Activities, Crafts, Experiments & More for Kids to Do to Learn about Your State! 2003. (Nebraska Experience Ser.). 32p. (gr. k-5). pap. 5.95 (978-0-635-01896-0(9), Marsh, Carole Bks.) Gallopade International.
McAuliffe, Emily. Nebraska Facts & Symbols. (States & Their Symbols Ser.). 24p. (J). 1998. (Illus.). (gr. 2-3). lib. bdg. 18.60 (978-0-7368-0084-6(0), Bridgestone Bks.); 2003. lib. bdg. 19.93 (978-0-7368-2257-2(7)) Capstone Pr., Inc.
McNamara, Connie. My First Nebraska Words. 2004. (J). bds. 11.95 (978-0-9759703-0-0(5)) Shamrock Publishing, Inc.
Murray, Julie. Nebraska. 2006. (Buddy Book Ser.). (Illus.). 32p. (J). (gr. k-4). lib. bdg. 22.78 (978-1-59197-686-8(3), Buddy Bks.) ABDO Publishing Co.
Nebraska. 2000. (Switched on Schoolhouse Ser.). (Illus.). (YA). (gr. 7-12). pap. 24.95 incl. cd-rom (978-0-7403-0279-4(5), SOSNE) Alpha Omega Pubns., Inc.
Porter, A. P. Nebraska. 2nd exp. rev. ed. 2003. (Hello U. S. A. Ser.). (Illus.). 84p. (J). (gr. 3-6). 25.26 (978-0-8225-4093-9(2), Lerner Pubns.) Lerner Publishing Group.
—Nebraska. rev. ed. 2003. (gr. 3-6). lib. bdg. 15.25 (978-0-613-52452-0(7)) Tandem Library Bks.
Sanders, Doug. Nebraska. 2005. (It's My State! Ser.). (Illus.). 80p. (J). (978-0-7614-1911-2(X), Benchmark Bks.) Cavendish, Marshall Corp.
Shepherd, Rajean Luebs. Nebraska Number. Appleoff, Sandy, illus. rev. ed. 2007. (State Counting Ser.). 40p. (J). 17.95 (***978-1-58536-190-8(9)***) Sleeping Bear Pr.
Stockman Opat, Jamie. Uniquely Nebraska. 2004. (Heinemann State Studies). (Illus.). 48p. (J). (ps-7). pap. 8.50 (978-1-4034-4718-0(7)); lib. bdg. 27.07 (978-1-4034-4649-7(0)) Heinemann Library.
Weatherly, Myra S. Nebraska. 2003. (From Sea to Shining Sea Ser.: 2). (Illus.). 80p. (J). 30.50 (978-0-516-22396-4(8), Children's Pr.) Scholastic Library Publishing.
Zollman, Pam. Nebraska. (Rookie Read-about' Geography: States Ser.). 32p. (J). 2007. pap. 5.95 (***978-0-531-16814-1(X)***); 2006. (gr. 1-2). 20.50 (978-0-516-25466-1(9)) Scholastic Library Publishing. (Children's Pr.).

NEBRASKA—FICTION
Bunting, Eve. Dandelions. 2001. 12.80 (978-0-606-21135-2(7)); lib. bdg. 14.15 (978-0-613-35502-5(4)) Tandem Library Bks.
Clements, Andrew. Room One: A Mystery or Two. Blair, Chris, illus. 2006. 176p. (J). (gr. 3-7). 15.95 (978-0-689-86686-9(0)) Simon & Schuster Children's Publishing.
Drake, Jane & Love, Ann. Farming. Cupples, Pat, illus. 2002. (America at Work Ser.). 32p. (J). (gr. k-3). (978-1-55074-451-4(8)) Kids Can Pr., Ltd.
Figley, Marty Rhodes. The Schoolchildren's Blizzard. Haas, Shelly O., illus. 2004. (On My Own History Ser.). 48p. (J). lib. bdg. 23.93 (978-1-57505-586-2(4), Carolrhoda Bks.) Lerner Publishing Group.
Gray, Dianne. Holding up the Earth. 2006. 224p. (J). (gr. 5-9). pap. 6.95 (978-0-618-73747-5(2)) Houghton Mifflin Co. Trade & Reference Div.
Gray, Dianne E. Holding up the Earth. 2000. 224p. (J). (gr. 5-9). tchr. ed. 15.00 (978-0-618-00703-5(2)) Houghton Mifflin Co. Trade & Reference Div.
Harcourt School Publishers Staff. Walking to Nebraska On Level. 3rd ed. 2002. (Trophies Reading Program Ser.). (Illus.). pap. 5.10 (978-0-15-323277-0(3)) Harcourt Schl. Pubs.
Hermes, Patricia. Calling Me Home. (J). 1999. 448p. pap. 3.99 (978-0-380-79100-2(5), Harper Trophy); 1998. 144p. (gr. 4-7). 15.00 (978-0-380-97451-1(7)) HarperCollins Pubs.
—Calling Me Home. 1999. (Illus.). (J). (978-0-606-17961-4(5)) Tandem Library Bks.
Korman, Gordon. Chasing the Falconers. 2005. (On the Run Ser.: No. 1). (Illus.). 160p. (J). pap. 4.99 (978-0-439-65136-3(0), Scholastic Paperbacks) Scholastic, Inc.
LaFaye, A. Worth. unabr. ed. 2006. (Live Oak Histories Ser.). (J). (gr. 3-6). pap. 24.95 incl. audio (***978-1-59519-766-5(4)***) Live Oak Media.

MNO

—Worth. 2006. 160p. (J). (gr. 4-7). reprint ed. pap. 5.99 (978-1-4169-1624-6(5) , Aladdin) Simon & Schuster Children's Publishing.

Loughrey, Eithne. Annie Moore, the Golden Dollar Girl. 2006. (J). lib. bdg. (***978-0-8368-7736-6(5)***) Stevens, Gareth Inc.

McNeal, Laura & McNeal, Tom. The Decoding of Lana Morris. 2007. 304p. (J). (gr. 7). lib. bdg. 18.99 (978-0-375-93106-2(6)); 15.99 (978-0-375-83106-5(1)) Random Hse. Children's Bks. (Knopf Bks. for Young Readers).

Sandburg, Carl. The Huckabuck Family & How They Raised: Popcorn in Nebraska & Quit & Came Back. Small, David, illus. 2006. 30p. (J). (gr. k-4). reprint ed. 16.00 (***978-1-4223-5854-2(2)***) DIANE Publishing Co.

Thomasma, Kenneth. Doe Sia: Bannock Girl & the Handcart Pioneer. 1999. (Amazing Indian Children: 8). (J). (gr. 3-8). pap. 7.99 (978-1-880114-20-9(8)); 12.99 (978-1-880114-21-6(6)) Grandview Publishing Co.

NEBRASKA—HISTORY

Heinrichs, Ann. Nebraska. 2005. (Welcome to the USA Ser.). 40p. (J). (gr. 1-5). 27.07 (978-1-59296-448-2(6)) Child's World, Inc.

Marsh, Carole. Jeopardy: Answers & Questions about Our State! 2001. (Nebraska Experience Ser.). 32p. (J). (gr. 3-8). pap. 7.95 (978-0-7933-9803-4(7)) Gallopade International.

—My First Pocket Guide Nebraska. 2000. (Nebraska Experience Ser.). (Illus.). 96p. (J). (gr. 3-8). 12.95 (978-0-635-01317-0(7) , 13177) Gallopade International.

—Nebraska History Projects: 30 Cool, Activities, Crafts, Experiments & More for Kids to Do to Learn about Your State! 2003. (Nebraska Experience Ser.). 32p. (gr. k-5). pap. 5.95 (978-0-635-01796-3(2) , Marsh, Carole Bks.) Gallopade International.

—Nebraska Millionaire. 2001. (GameBook Ser.). 32p. (J). (gr. 3-8). pap., act. bk. ed. 9.95 (978-0-635-00070-5(9)) Gallopade International.

—Nebraska Survivor. 2001. (GameBook Ser.). 32p. (J). (gr. 3-8). pap., act. bk. ed. 9.95 (978-0-635-00548-9(4)) Gallopade International.

—The Nebraska Survivor: A Class Challenge. 2001. (Carole Marsh Nebraska Bks.). (J). lib. bdg. 29.95 (978-0-635-00673-8(1)) Gallopade International.

—Wheel of Fortune. 2001. (Carole Marsh Nebraska Bks.). (J). lib. bdg. 29.95 (978-0-7933-9671-9(9)) Gallopade International.

—Who Wants to Be a Millionaire? 2001. (Carole Marsh Nebraska Bks.). (J). lib. bdg. 29.95 (978-0-635-00071-2(7)) Gallopade International.

Tully-Riccie, Cathleen. Nebraska. 2004. (Seeds of a Nation Ser.). (Illus.). 48p. (J). 26.20 (978-0-7377-2081-5(6) , Greenhaven Pr., Inc.) Thomson Gale.

Warren, Andrea. Pioneer Girl. 2000. (gr. 3-6). lib. bdg. 12.95 (978-0-613-28606-0(5)) Tandem Library Bks.

—Pioneer Girl: Growing up on the Prairie. 1998. (Illus.). 96p. (J). (gr. 3 up). 15.95 (978-0-688-15438-7(7)) HarperCollins Pubs.

Weintraub, A. How to Draw Nebraskas Sights & Symbols. 2002. (Kids Guide to Drawing America Ser.). 32p. (J). lib. bdg. 25.25 (978-0-8239-6083-5(8) , PowerKids Pr.) Rosen Publishing Group, Inc., The.

Weyers, Jack. Shadows of Time Forgotten. 2002. (Illus.). 48p. per. (978-0-9718677-0-3(4)) Infusionmedia Publishing.

NEBRASKA—HISTORY—FICTION

Blanc, Esther Silverstein & Eagle, Godeane. Long Johns for a Small Chicken. Dixon, Tennessee, illus. 2003. (J). 16.95 (978-1-884244-23-0(8)) Volcano Pr.

Gray, Dianne E. Together Apart. 2002. 208p. (J). (gr. 5-9). tchr. ed. 16.00 (978-0-618-18721-8(9)) Houghton Mifflin Co. Trade & Reference Div.

Hart, Alison. Anna's Blizzard. Bachem, Paul, photos by. 2005. (Illus.). 141p. (J). (gr. 3-5). 12.95 (978-1-56145-349-8(8)) Peachtree Pubs., Ltd.

Hoffman, Emily Allen. A Friend of the Enemy. 2003. 108p. (J). pap. 7.95 (978-1-57249-312-4(7) , White Mane Kids) White Mane Publishing Co., Inc.

LaFaye, A. Worth. unabr. ed. 2006. (Live Oak Histories Ser.). (J). (gr. 3-6). pap. 28.95 incl. audio compact disk (***978-1-59519-767-2(2)***) Live Oak Media.

—Worth. 2004. (Illus.). 160p. (J). (gr. 4-7). 16.99 (978-0-689-85730-0(6)) Simon & Schuster Children's Publishing.

Levinson, Nancy Smiler. Prairie Friends. Schuett, Stacey, illus. 2003. (I Can Read Bks.). 64p. (J). (gr. k-3). 15.99 (978-0-06-028001-7(8)) HarperCollins Pubs.

NECROMANCY

see Divination; Witchcraft

NEEDLEWORK

see also names of needlework; e.g. Dressmaking; Embroidery; Sewing; Tapestry

Klickmann, Flora. The Little Girl's Knitting & Crocheting Book. 2001. (Little Girl's Needlework Books Ser.: Vol. 1). 128p. (J). bds. 20.00 net. (978-1-891656-36-1(8)) Lacis Pubns.

NEFERTITI, QUEEN OF EGYPT, 14TH CENT. B.C.

Spirn, Michele Sobel. Mysterious People: A Chapter Book. 48p. (J). 2006. (gr. 2-4). pap. 4.95 (978-0-516-25454-8(5)); 2005. (Illus.). (ps-ps). 22.50 (978-0-516-25181-3(3)) Scholastic Library Publishing. (Children's Pr.).

NEGROES

see African Americans; Blacks

NEGRO RACE

see Blacks

NEIGHBORHOOD

see Community Life

NEIGHBORHOOD CENTERS

see Social Settlements

NEIGHBORHOOD SCHOOLS

see Schools

NEIGHBORS—FICTION

Accident Prone, 6 Nos., Pack. (Bookweb Ser.). 32p. (gr. 4 up). 34.00 (978-0-7635-3725-8(X)) Rigby Education.

Adler, David A. Andy Russell, Not Wanted by the Police. Franson, Leanne, illus. (Andy Russell Ser.). 128p. 2005. (J). pap. 4.95 (978-0-15-216719-6(6)); 2001. (YA). (gr. 2-5). 15.00 (978-0-15-216474-4(X) , Gulliver Bks.) Harcourt Children's Bks.

—Andy Russell, Not Wanted by the Police. Franson, Leanne, illus. 2005. (Andy Russell Ser.). 118p. (J). (ps-k). per. 11.60 (978-0-606-33408-2(4)) Tandem Library Bks.

Aigner-Clark, Julie. Neighborhood Numbers. Zaidi, Nadeem, illus. 2006. 16p. (J). (ps-17). 5.99 (978-1-4231-0001-0(8)) Baby Einstein Co., LLC, The.

America's Promise. 2002. (J). mass mkt. 191.76 (978-0-06-052165-3(1)) HarperCollins Pubs.

Atkinson, Beth. From Alice to Zen & Everyone in Between: A Novel. 2008. (Exceptional Reading & Language Arts Titles for Intermediate Grades Ser.). (J). 15.95 (***978-0-8225-7271-8(0)*** , Carolrhoda Bks.) Lerner Publishing Group.

Auerbach, Annie. Naughty Nautical Neighbors, Vol. 2. 2004. 64p. (J). (gr. 2-5). pap. 17.00 incl. audio (978-0-8072-1987-4(8) , Listening Library) Random Hse. Audio Publishing Group.

Babineaux, Jim. Cody Cottontail Makes a Wise Choice! Babineaux, Jim, illus. l.t. ed. 2005. (Illus.). 18p. (J). (978-0-9769769-0-5(0)) ALCAPS, LLC.

Baker, Jeannie. Home. Baker, Jeannie, illus. 2004. 32p. (J). 16.99 (978-0-06-623935-4(4)) HarperCollins Pubs.

Banks, Steven. The Song That Never Ends. DePorter, Vince, illus. 2004. (Ready-to-Read Ser.: Vol. 4). 32p. (J). pap. 3.99 (978-0-689-86528-2(7) , Simon Spotlight/ Nickelodeon) Simon & Schuster Children's Publishing.

—Song That Never Ends. 2004. (gr. k-3). lib. bdg. 11.80 (978-0-613-73449-3(1)) Tandem Library Bks.

Baraou, Anne & Sardon, Vincent. The Skeleton Family: The Neighbors from Elsewhere. 2005. (Illus.). 64p. (978-1-59687-825-9(8) , ipicturebooks) ibooks, Inc.

Barrows, Annie. Ivy & Bean, Bk. 1. Blackall, Sophie, illus. 2006. 120p. (J). (gr. 1-5). 14.95 (978-0-8118-4903-6(1)) Chronicle Bks. LLC.

—Ivy & Bean Break the Fossil Record, Bk. 3. Blackall, Sophie, illus. 2007. (Ivy & Bean Ser.). 132p. (J). (gr. 1-3). 14.95 (978-0-8118-5683-6(6)) Chronicle Bks. LLC.

Bedard, Michael. Emily. Cooney, Barbara, illus. 2008. 40p. (J). (gr. k-3). lib. bdg. 19.99 (***978-0-385-90539-8(4)*** , Doubleday Bks. for Young Readers) Random Hse. Children's Bks.

Benjamin, Cynthia. What's Going On? Handelman, Dorothy, photos by. 1999. (Real Kids Readers Ser.). (Illus.). 32p. (gr. k-2). lib. bdg. 18.90 (978-0-7613-2070-8(9) , Millbrook Pr.) Lerner Publishing Group.

—What's Going On? Handelman, Dorothy, illus. 1999. (Real Kids Readers Ser.). 32p. (J). (gr. k-2). pap. 4.99 (978-0-7613-2095-1(4) , Millbrook Pr.) Lerner Publishing Group.

—What's Going On? 1999. (J). (978-0-606-19180-7(1)); lib. bdg. 11.80 (978-0-613-18167-9(0)) Tandem Library Bks.

Best, Cari. When Catherine the Great & I Were Eight! Potter, Giselle, illus. 2003. 32p. (J). (gr. k-3). 16.00 (978-0-374-39954-2(9) , Farrar, Straus & Giroux (BYR)) Farrar, Straus & Giroux.

Birney, Betty G. The Seven Wonders of Sassafras Springs. Phelan, Matt, illus. 2005. 224p. (J). (ps-7). 16.95 (978-0-689-87136-8(8) , Atheneum) Simon & Schuster Children's Publishing.

—The Seven Wonders of Sassafras Springs. Phelan, Matt, illus. 2007. 224p. (J). pap. 5.99 (978-1-4169-3489-9(8) , Aladdin) Simon & Schuster Children's Publishing.

—The Seven Wonders of Sassafras Springs. l.t. ed. 2006. 206p. (J). 22.95 (978-0-7862-8287-6(8)) Thorndike Pr.

Blackaby, Susan. Lost on Owl Lane. Muehlenhardt, Amy Bailey, illus. 2007. (J). lib. bdg. (***978-1-4048-2333-4(6)***) Picture Window Bks.

Blackwood, Gary. The Just-So Woman. Manning, Jane, illus. 2007. (I Can Read Bks.). 48p. (J). pap. 3.99 (***978-0-06-057729-2(0)*** , Harper Trophy) HarperCollins Pubs.

Blackwood, Gary L. The Just-So Woman. Manning, Jane, illus. 2006. (I Can Read Bks.). 48p. (J). lib. bdg. 16.89 (978-0-06-057728-5(2)) HarperCollins Pubs.

—The Just So Woman. Manning, Jane, illus. 2006. (I Can Read Bks.). 48p. (J). 15.99 (978-0-06-057727-8(4)) HarperCollins Pubs.

Blume, Lesley. Cornelia & the Audacious Escapades of the Somerset Sisters. 2006. 272p. (J). (gr. 3-7). 15.95 (978-0-375-83523-0(7) , Knopf Bks. for Young Readers) Random Hse. Children's Bks.

Blume, Lesley M. M. Cornelia & the Audacious Escapades of the Somerset Sisters. 2006. 272p. (J). (gr. 3-7). lib. bdg. 17.99 (978-0-375-93523-7(1) , Knopf Bks. for Young Readers) Random Hse. Children's Bks.

Bourgeois, Paulette. Franklin's Neighborhood. ed. 2004. (Illus.). (J). (gr. k-3). spiral bd. (978-0-616-01588-9(7)); spiral bd. (978-0-616-01589-6(5)) Canadian National Institute for the Blind/Institut National Canadien pour les Aveugles.

—Franklin's Neighborhood. 1999. (Franklin Ser.). (J). (ps-3). 11.30 (978-0-606-17271-4(8)) Tandem Library Bks.

Bourgeois, Paulette & Clark, Brenda. Franklin's Neighborhood. 1999. (Franklin Ser.). (Illus.). 194p. (J). (ps-3). (978-1-55074-752-2(5)) Kids Can Pr., Ltd.

Brimner, Larry Dane. Country Bear's Good Neighbor. 2001. (ps-2). lib. bdg. 16.40 (978-0-613-58407-4(4)) Tandem Library Bks.

Broach, Elise. Shakespeare's Secret. 2007. 272p. (J). pap. 5.99 (***978-0-312-37132-6(2)***) Square Fish.

Brookins, Cara. Doris Free. Barrow, Ann, illus. 2006. 127p. (J). pap. (978-1-59336-333-8(8)) Mondo Publishing.

Buckman, Carole Duncan. Neighbors & Traitors. 2000. (StarMaker Bks.). 81p. (J). (gr. 6-9). pap. 5.50 (978-0-88489-548-0(3)) St. Mary's Pr.

Bullard, Lisa. My Neighborhood: Places & Faces. Wesley, Omarr, illus. 2004. (All about Me Ser.). 24p. (C). (gr. k-1). 21.26 (978-1-4048-0047-2(6)) Picture Window Bks.

Byrd, Lee. Treasure on Gold Street / el T. 2007. (SPA.). 40p. (J). pap. 8.95 (***978-1-933693-11-8(8)***) Cinco Puntos Pr.

Cain, Barbara S. I Don't Know Why... I Guess I'm Shy. Smith-Moore, J. J., illus. 1999. 32p. (J). (ps-3). (978-1-55798-596-5(0) , 441-5960, Magination Pr.) American Psychological Assn.

Canales, Viola. The Tequila Worm. 2005. 208p. (YA). (gr. 7 up). 15.95 (978-0-385-74674-8(1) , Lamb, Wendy) Random Hse. Children's Bks.

Carson, Drew. Summer Discovery. Thatch, Nancy R., ed. Carson, Drew, illus. 1998. (Books for Students by Students). (Illus.). 29p. (J). (gr. 2-4). lib. bdg. 15.95 (978-0-933849-68-6(0)) Landmark Editions, Inc.

Caseley, Judith. On the Town: A Community Adventure. Caseley, Judith, illus. 2002. (Illus.). 32p. (J). (gr. k-2). 16.99 (978-0-06-029584-4(8)); lib. bdg. 17.89 (978-0-06-029585-1(6)) HarperCollins Pubs.

Cepeda, Joe. The Swing. 2006. (Illus.). (J). 15.99 (978-0-439-14261-8(X)); 32p. pap. 15.99 (978-0-439-14260-1(1)); (***978-1-4287-0187-8(7)***) Scholastic, Inc. (Levine, Arthur A. Bks.).

Cheaney, J. B. My Friend the Enemy. 2007. 272p. (J). (gr. 5-9). 6.50 (***978-0-440-42102-3(0)*** , Yearling) Random Hse. Children's Bks.

Cheng, Andrea. The Lemon Sisters. Mai-Wyss, Tatjana, illus. 2006. 32p. (J). (ps). 16.99 (978-0-399-24023-2(3) , Putnam Juvenile) Penguin Group (USA) Inc.

—Tire Mountain. Condon, Ken, illus. 2007. 32p. (J). (ps-1). 15.95 (978-1-932425-60-4(8) , Front Street) Boyds Mills Pr.

Cormier, Robert. Frenchtown Summer. unabr. ed. 2004. 128p. (J). (gr. 7 up). pap. 29.00 incl. audio (978-0-8072-0663-8(6) , Listening Library) Random Hse. Audio Publishing Group.

—Frenchtown Summer. 2001. (YA). 12.64 (978-0-606-21200-7(0)) Tandem Library Bks.

Crebbin, June. The Dog Show. 2005. (Cambridge Storybooks Ser.). 32p. pap. 7.00 (978-0-521-67474-4(3)) Cambridge Univ. Pr.

Crimi, Carolyn. The Louds Move In! Dunnick, Regan, illus. 2006. 32p. (J). 14.95 (978-0-7614-5221-8(4)) Cavendish, Marshall Corp.

Cumpiano, Ina. Quinito's Neighborhood/el Vecindario de Quinito. Ramirez, Jose, illus. 2005. (ENG & SPA.). 24p. (J). (gr. k-2). 16.95 (978-0-89239-209-4(6)) Children's Bk. Pr.

Cusick, Richie Tankersley. The House Next Door. 2002. 272p. (YA). (gr. 6-10). mass mkt. 13.95 (978-0-7434-1838-6(7) , Simon Pulse) Simon & Schuster Children's Publishing.

Cutler, Jane. Common Sense & Fowls. Barasch, Lynne, illus. 2005. 144p. (J). 16.00 (978-0-374-32262-5(7) , Farrar, Straus & Giroux (BYR)) Farrar, Straus & Giroux.

Dadey, Debbie. The Slime Wars. Basso, Bill, illus. 2003. 80p. (J). 3.99 (978-0-439-42442-4(9)) Scholastic, Inc.

—The Slime Wars. 2003. (gr. k-3). lib. bdg. 11.80 (978-0-613-65059-5(X)) Tandem Library Bks.

David, Erica. There Goes the Neighborhood. 2006. (Over the Hedge Ser.). (Illus.). 32p. (J). pap. 3.99 (978-0-439-80143-0(5)) Scholastic, Inc.

Demas, Corinne. Two Christmas Mice. Roth, Stephanie, illus. 32p. (J). (ps). 16.95 (978-0-8234-1785-8(9)) Holiday Hse., Inc.

Deveze, Winky. Hewitch. Neate, Andy, illus. 2006. (J). (978-0-9787174-0-7(6)) Love Bug Bks.

DiCamillo, Kate. Mercy Watson to the Rescue. Van Dusen, Chris, illus. 2005. 80p. (J). (gr. 1-3). 12.99 (978-0-7636-2270-1(2)) Candlewick Pr.

Dooley, Norah. Everybody Brings Noodles. Thornton, Peter J., illus. (J). (gr. k-2). 2005. 32p. pap. 6.95 (978-1-57505-916-7(9)); 2003. 40p. 15.95 (978-0-87614-455-8(5) , Carolrhoda Bks.) Lerner Publishing Group.

Dr MacTavish's Creature: Individual Chapter Book Title Six-Packs. Vol. 25. 32p. (gr. 3-4). 44.00 (978-0-7635-4472-0(8)) Rigby Education.

Dupasquier, Philippe. Quack, Quack! 2001. (Illus.). 32p. (J). 17.99 (978-1-84270-015-0(4)) Andersen GBR. *Dist:* Independent Pubs. Group.

—Quack Quack! 2002. (Illus.). 32p. (J). (gr. k-3). pap. 8.99 (978-1-84270-112-6(6)) Andersen GBR. *Dist:* Trafalgar Square Publishing.

Edwards, Nancy. Glenna's Seeds. Hoctor, Sarah K., illus. 2000. 24p. (J). (ps-3). pap. 9.95 (978-0-87868-788-6(2) , 7882, Child & Family Pr.) Child Welfare League of America, Inc.

Elise Broach. Shakespeare's Secret. l.t. ed. 2006. 350p. (J). 22.95 (978-0-7862-8735-2(7)) Thorndike Pr.

Fearnley, Jan. Mr. Wolf's Pancakes. 2001. (Illus.). 32p. (J). (ps-k). 6.95 (978-1-58925-354-4(X) , tiger tales) ME Media LLC.

—Mr. Wolf's Pancakes. 2001. (Illus.). (J). (978-0-606-20483-5(0)) Tandem Library Bks.

Fisher, Valorie. When Ruby Tried to Grow Candy. 2008. (J). (***978-0-375-84015-9(X)***); 40p. lib. bdg. 19.99 (***978-0-375-94015-6(4)***) Random Hse. Children's Bks. (Schwartz & Wade Bks.).

Fogelin, Adrian. Crossing Jordan. Schultz, Suzy, illus. (J). 160p. pap. 6.95 (978-1-56145-281-1(5) , Q23381); 2000. 140p. (gr. 3-7). 14.95 (978-1-56145-215-6(7) , Q23381) Peachtree Pubs., Ltd.

—Crossing Jordan. 2002. (gr. 3-6). lib. bdg. 15.25 (978-0-613-54154-1(5)) Tandem Library Bks.

Fontaine, Catherine Silliman. Have a Not for Christmas ... & Always. 2006. (Illus.). 44p. (J). 11.95 (978-0-9776958-0-5(8)) CyPress Pubns.

Frabetti, Carlo. El Vampiro Vegetariano. Duran, Meritxell, illus. 2001. Tr. of Vegetarian Vampire. (SPA.). 110p. (J). 12.95 (978-84-348-7828-0(3)) SM Ediciones ESP. *Dist:* AIMS International Bks., Inc.

Frank, Lucy. Just Ask Iris. 2003. (Illus.). 224p. (J). pap. 4.99 (978-0-689-84454-6(9) , Aladdin) Simon & Schuster Children's Publishing.

—Just Ask Iris. 2003. (gr. 5-8). lib. bdg. 13.00 (978-0-613-66417-2(5)) Tandem Library Bks.

Freeman, Martha. The Trouble with Babies. Smith, Cat Bowman, illus. 2002. 80p. (J). (gr. 4-6). tchr. ed. 15.95 (978-0-8234-1698-1(4)) Holiday Hse., Inc.

Fries, Claudia. A Pig Is Moving In! Fries, Claudia, illus. 2000. (Illus.). 32p. (J). (ps-2). 16.99 (978-0-531-33307-5(8)); pap. 15.95 (978-0-531-30307-8(1)) Scholastic, Inc. (Orchard Bks.).

Gauthier, Gail. A Girl, A Boy, & Three Robbers. Cepeda, Joe, illus. 2008. 64p. (J). (gr. 1-3). 14.99 (***978-0-399-24690-6(8)*** , Putnam Juvenile) Penguin Group (USA) Inc.

Gilmore, Rachna. Roses for Gita. Priestley, Alice, illus. 2004. 24p. (J). (CHI, ENG, TUR, PAN & GUJ.). (978-1-85269-367-1(3)); (GUJ, CHI, ENG, PAN & TUR.). (978-1-85269-369-5(X)) Mantra Publishing, Ltd.

—Roses for Gita. 2001. (gr. k-3). lib. bdg. 16.40 (978-0-613-53301-0(1)) Tandem Library Bks.

—Roses for Gita. Priestley, Alice, illus. 2005. 24p. (J). (gr. 3-6). pap. 7.95 (978-0-88448-224-6(3)) Tilbury Hse. Pubs.

Gorbachev, Valeri. Heron & Turtle. Gorbachev, Valeri, illus. 2006. (Illus.). 40p. (J). (gr. k). 15.99 (978-0-399-24321-9(6) , Philomel) Penguin Group (USA) Inc.

Graef, Renee, illus. Laura & Mr. Edwards. 1999. (Little House Ser.: No. 13). 80p. (J). (gr. 3-6). 14.89 (978-0-06-027949-3(4)) HarperCollins Pubs.

Graham, Bob. Rose Meets Mr. Wintergarten. 2001. (Illus.). (J). (978-0-606-21404-9(6)) Tandem Library Bks.

Hamilton, Martha. The Stolen Smell. 2007. 32p. (J). pap. 3.95 (***978-0-87483-838-1(X)***) August Hse. Pubs., Inc.

Hamilton, Richard. Cal & the Amazing Anti-Gravity Machine. Hearn, Sam, illus. 2006. 128p. (J). 14.95 (978-1-58234-723-3(9) , Bloomsbury Children); pap. 5.95 (978-1-58234-714-1(X)) Bloomsbury Publishing.

Handelsman, Valerie. A Coral Reef Neighborhood. Handelsman, Valerie, illus. 2004. (J). 7.95 (978-0-9748884-1-5(9)) Little Thoughts For Little Ones Publishing, Inc.

Harcourt School Publishers Staff, Homegrown Advanced Level. 3rd ed. 2002. (Trophies Reading Program Ser.). (Illus.). pap. 5.10 (978-0-15-323289-3(7)) Harcourt Schl. Pubs.

—Honest Neighbors On Level. 3rd ed. 2002. (Trophies Reading Program Ser.). (Illus.). pap. 5.10 (978-0-15-323256-5(0)) Harcourt Schl. Pubs.

—Neighborhood Band Below Level. 3rd ed. 2002. (Trophies Reading Program Ser.). (Illus.). pap. 5.10 (978-0-15-323063-9(0)) Harcourt Schl. Pubs.

—Neighborhood Friends: Independent Reader. 3rd ed. 2002. (Trophies Reading Program Ser.). (Illus.). (J). pap. 2.90 (978-0-15-325497-0(1)) Harcourt Schl. Pubs.

—Neighborhood Help: Practice Book: Florida Edition. 3rd ed. 2002. (Trophies Reading Program Ser.). (Illus.). (J). pap. 2.00 (978-0-15-326605-8(8)) Harcourt Schl. Pubs.

—Neighborhood Helpers: Practice Book. 3rd ed. 2001. (Trophies Reading Program Ser.). (Illus.). (J). pap. 1.80 (978-0-15-325090-3(9)) Harcourt Schl. Pubs.

—Owen: Library Book. 1999. (Collections Ser.). (Illus.). pap. 14.90 (978-0-15-313401-2(1)) Harcourt Schl. Pubs.

—The Secrets of Mr. Mack: Take-Home Book. 1999. (Collections Ser.). (Illus.). (J). pap. 1.90 (978-0-15-317273-1(8)) Harcourt Schl. Pubs.

Harper, Charise Mericle. Just Grace. 2007. (Illus.). 144p. (J). (gr. 1-5). 15.00 (978-0-618-64642-5(6)) Houghton Mifflin Co. Trade & Reference Div.

HarperCollins Staff, ed. To Snoop or Not to Snoop. 1999. (gr. 3-6). lib. bdg. 13.00 (978-0-613-16225-8(0)) Tandem Library Bks.

Helmer, Marilyn. Mr. McGratt & the Ornery Cat. Gourbault, Martine, illus. unabr. ed. 2002. 32p. (J). (gr. k-3). (978-1-55337-162-5(3)) Kids Can Pr., Ltd.

Heo, Yumi. One Afternoon. 2000. (Metro Reading Program Ser.). (J). (gr. k). 7.98 (978-1-58120-971-6(1)); 45.95 (978-1-58830-029-4(3)) Metropolitan Teaching & Learning Co.

Herman, Gail. Clifford's Puppy Days: Halloween Howl. Goldberg, Barry, illus. 2004. (Clifford Ser.). 24p. (J). pap. 3.50 (978-0-439-58353-4(5) , Cartwheel Bks.) Scholastic, Inc.

—New Dog in Town. Nez, John A., illus. 2006. (Social Studies Connects). 32p. (J). pap. 4.99 (978-1-57565-165-1(3)) Kane Pr., The.

Hicks, Benjamin & Hicks, Rosetta. Byron's Tie. Hicks, Benjamin, ed. 2006. 35p. pap. 8.95 (978-1-929883-08-0(0)) Ingleside Pr.

Higgenson, Hadley. Keeker & the Sugar Shack. Andersen, Maja, illus. 2006. (Sneaky Pony Ser.: Bk. 3). 48p. (J). pap. 3.95 (978-0-8118-5456-6(6)) Chronicle Bks. LLC.

Higginson, Hadley. Keeker & the Crazy Upside-Down Day. Perrett, Lisa, illus. 2008. (J). (***978-0-8118-6255-4(0)***); pap. (***978-0-8118-6256-1(9)***) Chronicle Bks. LLC.

Higginson, Hadley. Keeker & the Sugar Shack, Bk. 3. Andersen, Maja, illus. 2006. 48p. (J). 15.50 (978-0-8118-5455-9(8)) Chronicle Bks. LLC.

M N O

Hodgson, Mona Gansberg. I Wonder Who Hung the Moon in the Sky. 1999. (I Wonder Ser.). (Illus.). 32p. (J). (ps-2). 6.99 (978-0-570-05067-4(7)) Concordia Publishing Hse.

Horvath, Polly. The Pepins & Their Problems. Hafner, Marylin, illus. 2004. 192p. (J). 16.00 (978-0-374-35817-4(6) , Farrar, Straus & Giroux (BYR)) Farrar, Straus & Giroux.

—The Pepins & Their Problems. Hafner, Marylin, illus. pap. 13.95 (978-0-88899-633-6(0)) Groundwood Bks. CAN. *Dist:* Transition Vendor.

—The Pepins & Their Problems. Hafner, Marylin, illus. 2008. 208p. (J). pap. 6.99 (***978-0-312-37751-9(7)***) Square Fish.

—The Pepins & Their Problems. Hafner, Marylin, illus. l.t. ed. 2004. 154p. (J). 22.95 (978-0-7862-7063-7(2)) Thorndike Pr.

Howard, Arthur. The Hubbub Above. 2005. (Illus.). 32p. (J). 16.00 (978-0-15-204592-0(9)) Harcourt Trade Pubs.

Howe, James. Pinky & Rex & the Mean Old Witch. 2006. (J). (gr. 1-4). 24.21 (978-1-59961-077-1(9)) Spotlight.

Hurwitz, Johanna. Nora & Mrs. Mind-Your-Own-Business. 2001. (gr. 3-6). lib. bdg. 12.10 (978-0-613-35646-6(2)) Tandem Library Bks.

Jahn-Clough, Lisa. Missing Molly. 2005. (Illus.). 32p. (J). (gr. k-3). reprint ed. pap. 5.95 (978-0-618-55562-8(5) , Walter Lorraine) Houghton Mifflin Co. Trade & Reference Div.

Jam, Teddy. The Stoneboat. Zhang, Ange, illus. 2nd ed. 1999. 32p. (J). (ps-2). 15.95 (978-0-88899-368-7(4) , Libros Tigrillo) Groundwood Bks. CAN. *Dist:* Perseus Distribution.

James, Betsy. My Chair. DePalma, Mary Newell, tr. DePalma, Mary Newell, illus. 2004. (J). 40p. pap. 16.95 (978-0-439-44421-7(7)); pap. (978-0-439-44422-4(5)) Scholastic, Inc. (Levine, Arthur A. Bks.).

Johnson, D. B. Eddie's Kingdom. 2005. (Illus.). 32p. (J). (gr. k-3). 16.00 (978-0-618-56299-2(0)) Houghton Mifflin Co. Trade & Reference Div.

Johnson, Paul Brett. Mr. Persnickety & Cat Lady. Johnson, Paul Brett, illus. 2000. (Illus.). 32p. (J). (ps-2). 16.99 (978-0-531-33283-2(7)); pap. 15.95 (978-0-531-30283-5(0)) Scholastic, Inc. (Orchard Bks.).

Johnson, Regan. Little Bunny Kung Fu. Johnson, Regan, illus. 2005. (Illus.). 32p. (J). 16.95 (978-0-9769417-8-1(3)) Blooming Tree Pr.

Johnson, Richard, illus. Don't Cry, Sly! 2004. 24p. (J). (TAM, CZE, VIE, SPA & GUJ.). pap. (978-1-85269-649-8(4)); (TAM, CZE, VIE, SPA & GUJ.). pap. (978-1-85269-650-4(8)); (TAM, CZE, VIE, SPA & GUJ.). pap. (978-1-85269-651-1(6)); (TAM, CZE, VIE, SPA & GUJ.). pap. (978-1-85269-652-8(4)); (TAM, CZE, VIE, SPA & GUJ.). pap. (978-1-85269-653-5(2)); (TAM, CZE, VIE, SPA & GUJ.). pap. (978-1-85269-655-9(9)); (TAM, CZE, VIE, SPA & GUJ.). pap. (978-1-85269-656-6(7)); (TAM, CZE, VIE, SPA & GUJ.). pap. (978-1-85269-657-3(5)); (TAM, CZE, VIE, SPA & GUJ.). pap. (978-1-85269-658-0(3)); (TAM, CZE, VIE, SPA & GUJ.). pap. (978-1-85269-659-7(1)); (TAM, CZE, VIE, SPA & GUJ.). pap. (978-1-85269-660-3(5)); (TAM, CZE, VIE, SPA & GUJ.). pap. (978-1-85269-661-0(3)); (TAM, CZE, VIE, SPA & GUJ.). pap. (978-1-85269-662-7(1)); (CZE, TAM, VIE, SPA & GUJ.). pap. (978-1-85269-663-4(X)); (TAM, CZE, VIE, SPA & GUJ.). pap. (978-1-85269-670-2(2)); (TAM, CZE, VIE, SPA & GUJ.). pap. (978-1-85269-671-9(0)); (TAM, CZE, VIE, SPA & GUJ.). pap. (978-1-85269-813-3(6)) Mantra Publishing, Ltd.

Jones, Shelley. My Street. 2000. (gr. k-3). lib. bdg. 11.80 (978-0-613-29706-6(7)) Tandem Library Bks.

Keane, Dave. The Haunted Toolshed. Keane, Dave, illus. 2006. (Joe Sherlock Ser.). 128p. (J). pap. 3.99 (978-0-06-076188-2(1) , Harper Trophy) HarperCollins Pubs.

—The Neighborhood Stink. Keane, Dave, illus. 2006. (Joe Sherlock Ser.). 112p. (J). pap. 3.99 (978-0-06-076186-8(5) , Harper Trophy) HarperCollins Pubs.

—The Neighborhood Stink: Case 000002. Keane, Dave, illus. 2006. (Joe Sherlock Ser.). (Illus.). 112p. (J). 15.99 (978-0-06-076187-5(3)) HarperCollins Pubs.

Keats, Ezra Jack. The Trip. 2007. 40p. (J). (gr. k up). 15.99 (978-0-670-06195-2(6) , Viking Juvenile) Penguin Group (USA) Inc.

Keller, Laurie. Do unto Otters: A Book about Manners. 2007. (Illus.). 40p. (J). (gr. k-3). 16.95 (***978-0-8050-7996-8(3)***) Holt, Henry & Co.

Kelly, Lisa. Love Your Neighbor. Wagner, Dennis, illus. 2006. (J). 16.00 (***978-0-8059-6985-6(3)***) Dorrance Publishing Co., Inc.

Kimmel, Haven. Kaline Klattermaster's Tree House. Brown, Peter, illus. 2008. 160p. (J). 15.99 (***978-0-689-87402-4(2)*** , Atheneum) Simon & Schuster Children's Publishing.

King-Smith, Dick. Mysterious Miss Slade. Kronheimer, Ann, illus. 2002. 128p. (gr. 3-5). 4.99 (978-0-440-41674-6(4) , Yearling) Random Hse. Children's Bks.

—Mysterious Miss Slade. 2002. (gr. 3-6). lib. bdg. 13.00 (978-0-613-88331-3(4)) Tandem Library Bks.

Kochka. The Boy Who Ate Stars. Adams, Sarah, tr. from FRE. 2006. 112p. (J). 12.95 (978-1-4169-0038-2(1)) Simon & Schuster Children's Publishing.

Kraus, Robert. Mouse in Love. Aruego, Jose & Dewey, Ariane, illus. 2000. 32p. (J). (ps-2). 16.99 (978-0-531-33297-9(7) , Orchard Bks.) Scholastic, Inc.

Kroll, Virginia L. Good Citizen Sarah. Cote, Nancy, illus. 2007. (Way I ACT Books). 24p. (J). (gr. 1-4). 15.95 (***978-0-8075-2992-8(3)***) Whitman, Albert & Co.

—Good Neighbor Nicholas. Cote, Nancy, illus. 2006. (Way I ACT Books: Vol. 5). 24p. (J). (gr. 1-3). 15.95 (978-0-8075-2998-0(2)) Whitman, Albert & Co.

—Makayla Cares about Others. Cote, Nancy, illus. 2007. (Way I ACT Books). 24p. (J). 15.95 (978-0-8075-4945-2(2)) Whitman, Albert & Co.

Krulik, Nancy E. Doggone It!, No. 8. John and Wendy Staff, illus. 2003. (Katie Kazoo, Switcheroo Ser.: No. 8). 80p. (J). (gr. 2-4). pap. 3.99 (978-0-448-43172-7(6) , Grosset & Dunlap) Penguin Group (USA) Inc.

—Doggone It!, No. 8. 2003. (Katie Kazoo, Switcheroo Ser.: No. 8). (gr. 3-6). lib. bdg. 11.80 (978-0-613-67541-3(X)) Tandem Library Bks.

Kvasnosky, Laura McGee. Zelda & Ivy: One Christmas. Kvasnosky, Laura McGee, illus. 2006. 40p. (J). (gr. 1-4). pap. 4.99 (978-0-7636-3047-8(0)) Candlewick Pr.

Lachtman, Ofelia Dumas. The Trouble with Tessa. 122p. (J). (ps-7). pap. 9.95 (978-1-55885-448-2(7) , Piñata Books) Arte Publico Pr.

Lakin, Patricia. Fat Chance Thanksgiving. Schuett, Stacey, illus. 2001. 32p. (J). (gr. 2-5). 15.95 (978-0-8075-2288-2(0)) Whitman, Albert & Co.

Langrish, Katherine. Troll Mill. 2006. (Illus.). 288p. (J). 15.99 (978-0-06-058307-1(X)); lib. bdg. 17.89 (978-0-06-058308-8(8)) HarperCollins Pubs.

Lansky, Bruce. Ninas al Rescate! I: Aventuras de Chicas Audaces de Todo el Mundo. Heredia, Ruben, tr. 2001. (Coleccion Literatura Infantil y Juvenil).Tr. of Girls to the Rescue. (SPA.). 146p. (J). (gr. 3-5). (978-970-643-319-0(8)) Selector, S.A. de C.V. MEX. *Dist:* Bilingual Pubns. Co., The.

LaReau, Kara. Rabbit & Squirrel. Magoon, Scott, illus. 2008. (J). (***978-0-15-206307-8(2)***) Harcourt Trade Pubs.

Lawlor, Laurie. The Worst Kid Who Ever Lived on Eighth Avenue: A Holiday House Reader. Fisher, Cynthia, illus. 48p. (J). (gr. k-3). tchr. ed. 14.95 (978-0-8234-1350-8(0)) Holiday Hse., Inc.

Levin, Betty. The Unmaking of Duncan Veerick. 2007. 204p. (YA). (gr. 5 up). 16.95 (***978-1-932425-96-3(9)*** , Front Street) Boyds Mills Pr.

Lloyd, Sam. Yummy Yummy! Food for My Tummy. Tickle, Jack, illus. 2004. 32p. (J). tchr. ed. 15.95 (978-1-58925-035-2(4) , tiger tales) ME Media LLC.

Lock, Deborah. A Trip to the Library. 2004. (Illus.). 32p. (J). (ps-ps). lib. bdg. 10.79 (978-0-606-30871-7(7)) Tandem Library Bks.

Look, Lenore. Ruby Lu, Brave & True. 2004. (Illus.). 104p. (J). lib. bdg. 15.00 (***978-1-4242-0914-9(5)***) Fitzgerald Bks.

—Ruby Lu, Brave & True. Wilsdorf, Anne, illus. 2006. (Ready-for-Chapters Ser.). 112p. (J). pap. 3.99 (978-1-4169-1389-4(0) , Aladdin) Simon & Schuster Children's Publishing.

Look, Lenore & Wilsdorf, Anne. Ruby Lu, Brave & True. 2004. (Illus.). 176p. (J). (gr. 1-2). 15.95 (978-0-689-84907-7(9) , Atheneum/Anne Schwartz Bks.) Simon & Schuster Children's Publishing.

Louie, Therese On. Raymond's Perfect Present. Wang, Suling, illus. 2002. (J). (gr. 2-4). 16.95 (978-1-58430-055-7(8)) Lee & Low Bks., Inc.

MacDonald, Alan. Trolls Go Home! Beech, Mark, illus. 2007. 128p. (J). 14.95 (***978-1-59990-077-3(7)***); pap. 5.95 (***978-1-59990-078-0(5)***) Bloomsbury Publishing.

Marsh, Carole. The Puzzle of the Shark Surfer Girl. 2006. 64p. (gr. 1-3). 14.95 (***978-0-635-06204-8(6)***) Gallopade International.

Martin, Ann M. Here Today. (J). 2005. 336p. (gr. 5-9). pap. 5.99 (978-0-439-57945-2(7) , Scholastic Paperbacks); 2004. 320p. (gr. 4-7). pap. 16.95 (978-0-439-57944-5(9) , Scholastic Pr.) Scholastic, Inc.

Mayer, Mercer. New Kid in Town, Vol. 3. 2002. (Little Critter First Readers Ser.). (Illus.). 24p. (J). (gr. 1-2). pap. 3.95 (978-1-57768-829-7(5)) School Specialty Publishing.

—New Kid in Town. 2001. (gr. k-3). lib. bdg. 11.80 (978-0-613-67654-0(8)) Tandem Library Bks.

Mayer, Mercer & Mayer, Gina. Just a New Neighbor. Mayer, Mercer, illus. 1999. (Little Critter Ser.). (J). (ps-3). 10.09 (978-0-606-19801-1(6)) Tandem Library Bks.

McElroy, Laurie. Drake & Josh: Chapter Book. 2007. (Teenick Ser.: No. 6). 112p. (J). pap. 4.99 (***978-0-439-91645-5(3)***) Scholastic, Inc.

Meltzer, Amy. A Mezuzah on the Door. Fried, Janice, illus. 2007. (Jewish Identity Ser.). 32p. (J). (ps-2). 17.95 (***978-1-58013-249-7(9)***); pap. 7.95 (***978-1-58013-251-0(0)***) Kar-Ben Publishing.

Michelin, Linda. Zuzu's Wishing Cake. Johnson, D. B., illus. 2006. 32p. (J). (gr. k-3). 16.00 (978-0-618-64640-1(X)) Houghton Mifflin Co. Trade & Reference Div.

Montes, Marisa. Who's That Girl. Cepeda, Joe, illus. 2003. (Get Ready for Gabi Ser.). 112p. (J). pap. 12.95 (978-0-439-51711-9(7) , Scholastic Pr.) Scholastic, Inc.

Moon, Nicola. Noisy Neighbors. Million, Liz, illus. 2004. (I Am Reading Ser.). 48p. (J). (gr. 1-3). pap. 3.95 (978-0-7534-5799-3(7) , Kingfisher) Houghton Mifflin Co. Trade & Reference Div.

Mullican, Judy. Someone New in the Neighborhood. Storch, Ellen N. & Gillen, Lisa P., illus. l.t. ed. 2005. 20p. (J). (ps-k). pap. 10.95 (978-1-57332-356-7(X)) HighReach Learning, Inc.

Munsch, Robert. Boo! Mart Chenko, Michael, illus. 2004. 32p. (J). pap. 3.99 (978-0-439-62331-5(6) , Cartwheel Bks.) Scholastic, Inc.

Muth, Jon J. Zen Ties. 2008. (J). pap. (***978-0-439-63425-0(3)*** , Scholastic Pr.) Scholastic, Inc.

My Neighborhood. (All about Me Ser.). 24p. (J). 6.95 (978-1-4048-0162-2(6)) Picture Window Bks.

Naylor, Phyllis Reynolds. Boys Rock! 144p. (gr. 4-7). 2007. 5.50 (***978-0-440-41990-7(5)*** , Yearling); 2005. (J). 15.95 (978-0-385-73140-9(X) , Delacorte Bks. for Young Readers); 2005. (J). lib. bdg. 17.99 (978-0-385-90171-0(2) , Delacorte Bks. for Young Readers) Random Hse. Children's Bks.

—The Boys Start the War. 2002. 144p. (gr. 4-7). pap. 5.99 (978-0-440-41841-2(0) , Yearling) Random Hse. Children's Bks.

—Cuckoo Feathers. Ramsey, Marcy Dunn, illus. 2006. 96p. (J). 14.95 (978-0-7614-5285-0(0)) Cavendish, Marshall Corp.

—The Girls Get Even. 2002. 144p. (gr. 4-7). mass mkt. 5.50 (978-0-440-41842-9(9) , Yearling) Random Hse. Children's Bks.

—The Girls Get Even. 2002. (Juvenile Ser.). (Illus.). (J). 23.95 (978-0-7862-4854-4(8)) Thorndike Pr.

—The Girls' Revenge. 1999. (gr. 3-6). lib. bdg. 13.00 (978-0-613-22858-9(8)) Tandem Library Bks.

—Girls Rule! 2004. 160p. (gr. 4-7). 15.95 (978-0-385-73139-3(6) , Delacorte Bks. for Young Readers) Random Hse. Children's Bks.

—The Girls Take Over. 2004. 160p. (gr. 4-7). pap. 5.99 (978-0-440-41678-4(7) , Yearling) Random Hse. Children's Bks.

—The Girls Take Over. 2004. (gr. 3-6). lib. bdg. 13.00 (978-0-613-81402-7(9)) Tandem Library Bks.

—The Girls Take Over. l.t. ed. 2004. (Boys Girl Battle Ser.). 170p. (J). 22.95 (978-0-7862-5823-9(3)) Thorndike Pr.

—Patches & Scratches. Ramsey, Marcy, illus. 2007. (Simply Sarah Ser.). 80p. (J). (gr. 2-4). 14.99 (***978-0-7614-5347-5(4)***) Cavendish, Marshall Corp.

—A Traitor among the Boys. 2001. (gr. 3-6). lib. bdg. 13.00 (978-0-613-33733-5(6)) Tandem Library Bks.

—Who Won the War? 2006. 160p. (J). (gr. 4-7). 15.95 (978-0-385-73141-6(8)); lib. bdg. 17.99 (978-0-385-90172-7(0)) Random Hse. Children's Bks. (Delacorte Bks. for Young Readers).

O'Connor, Barbara. Fame & Glory in Freedom, Georgia. l.t. ed. 2003. 126p. (J). 22.95 (978-0-7862-5994-6(9)) Thorndike Pr.

O'Connor, Ilett. A Born Leader - Our Francine. Kahn, Alisha, illus. Wells, Wadell, photos by. 2002. 32p. pap. 10.00 (978-0-9717003-1-4(1)) O'Connor, Ilett K.

O'Coyne, James. Gravelle's Land of Horror. Baer, Brian, illus. 2007. (J). per. 9.95 (***978-1-59649-604-0(5)***) Whispering Pine Pr., Inc.

Ortega, Cristina. The Key to Grandpa's House. Ortega, Luis Armando, illus. 2007. 24p. (J). (gr. 1 up). 14.95 (***978-0-8263-4205-8(1)***) Univ. of New Mexico Pr.

Peck, Robert Newton. Weeds in Bloom: Autobiography of an Ordinary Man. 2007. (Illus.). 224p. (YA). (gr. 7-11). mass mkt. 6.50 (978-0-375-82802-7(8) , Laurel Leaf) Random Hse. Children's Bks.

Polak, Monique. Home Invasion. 2005. (Orca Soundings Ser.). 112p. (J). (gr. 7-12). pap. 7.95 (978-1-55143-482-7(2)) Orca Bk. Pubs. USA.

Polk, James. Mr. & Mrs. Love & the Neighborhood Children. 2003. pap. 11.00 (978-0-8059-9232-8(4) , Rose-Dog Bks.) Dorrance Publishing Co., Inc.

Powell, Alma. America's Promise. Winborn, Marsha, illus. 2003. 32p. (J). (ps-2). 16.89 (978-0-06-052173-8(2)) HarperCollins Pubs.

—Promesa de America. Winborn, Marsha, illus. 2003. Tr. of America's Promise. (SPA.). 32p. (J). (ps-2). 15.99 (978-0-06-052175-2(9) , Rayo) HarperCollins Pubs.

Rabey, Katharine. Hare & the Big Green Lawn. MacDougall, Larry, illus. 2006. 32p. 15.95 (978-0-87358-889-8(4) , Rising Moon Bks. for Young Readers) Northland Publishing.

Ramos, Ian. Adventures of the G.C. Boys: The Cure for Death. 2001. 188p. (J). pap. 19.95 (978-1-58851-040-2(9)) PublishAmerica, Inc.

Reiner, Carl. Tell Me a Scary Story: ... But Not Too Scary. Bennett, James, illus. rev. ed. 2007. 32p. (J). (ps-1). pap. 7.99 (***978-0-316-00260-8(7)***) Little, Brown Bks. for Young Readers.

Reiner, Carl. Tell Me a Scary Story... but Not Too Scary! Bennett, James, illus. 2003. 32p. (J). (ps-17). 18.95 incl. audio (978-0-316-83329-5(0)) Little Brown & Co.

Rigby Education Staff. Jacko of Baker Street. (Sails Literacy Ser.). (Illus.). 16p. (gr. 1-2). 27.00 (978-0-7635-9931-7(X) , 699319C99) Rigby Education.

Rightious, Duke. The Wayward Neighbors. 2002. 180p. pap. 12.95 (978-0-595-23737-1(1) , Writers Club Pr.) iUniverse, Inc.

Roberts, Emma. Mrs. Murphy's Marvelous Mansion. Rogalski, Robert, illus. 2006. 32p. (J). 15.95 (978-0-9740190-4-8(6) , 888-210-8216) Illumination Arts Publishing Co., Inc.

Roberts, Willo Davis. Hostage. 2001. 144p. (J). pap. 5.99 (978-0-689-84446-1(8) , Aladdin) Simon & Schuster Children's Publishing.

—Hostage. 2001. (J). 11.64 (978-0-606-21237-3(X)) Tandem Library Bks.

Russo, Marisabina. Mama Talks Too Much. 1999. (Illus.). (J). lib. bdg. (978-0-688-16412-6(9)) HarperCollins Pubs.

—Mama Talks Too Much. Russo, Marisabina, illus. 1999. (Illus.). 288p. (J). (ps-3). 16.00 (978-0-688-16411-9(0)) HarperCollins Pubs.

Rylant, Cynthia. Mr. Putter & Tabby Make a Wish. 2005. (Illus.). 38p. (J). lib. bdg. 20.00 (***978-1-4242-1954-4(X)***) Fitzgerald Bks.

—Mr. Putter & Tabby Make a Wish. Howard, Arthur, illus. 2006. (Mr. Putter & Tabby Ser.). 44p. (J). pap. 5.95 (978-0-15-205443-4(X) , Harcourt Paperbacks) Harcourt Children's Bks.

—Mr. Putter & Tabby Make a Wish. Howard, Arthur, illus. 2005. (Mr. Putter & Tabby Ser.). 44p. (J). (ps-2). 14.00 (978-0-15-202426-0(3)) Harcourt Trade Pubs.

—Mr. Putter & Tabby Run the Race. Howard, Arthur, illus. 2008. (Mr. Putter & Tabby Ser.). 44p. (J). 15.00 (***978-0-15-206069-5(3)***) Harcourt Trade Pubs.

—Mr. Putter & Tabby See the Stars. Howard, Arthur, illus. 2008. (Mr. Putter & Tabby Ser.). 44p. (J). pap. 5.95 (***978-0-15-206366-5(8)*** , Harcourt Paperbacks) Harcourt Children's Bks.

—Mr. Putter & Tabby Spin the Yarn. Howard, Arthur, illus. 2007. (Mr. Putter & Tabby Ser.). 44p. (J). pap. 5.95 (***978-0-15-206095-4(2)*** , Harcourt Paperbacks) Harcourt Children's Bks.

—Mr. Putter & Tabby Spin the Yarn. Howard, Arthur, illus. 2006. (Mr. Putter & Tabby Ser.). 44p. (J). (gr. k-2). 14.00 (978-0-15-205067-2(1)) Harcourt Trade Pubs.

—Mr. Putter & Tabby Stir the Soup. Howard, Arthur, illus. (Mr. Putter & Tabby Ser.). 44p. (J). 2004. pap. 5.95 (978-0-15-205058-0(2) , Harcourt Paperbacks); 2003. 14.00 (978-0-15-202637-0(1)) Harcourt Children's Bks.

—Mr. Putter & Tabby Toot the Horn. Howard, Arthur, illus. (Mr. Putter & Tabby Ser.). 44p. (J). 1999. (ps-3). pap. 5.95 (978-0-15-200247-3(2) , Harcourt Paperbacks); 1998. (gr. 1-5). 14.00 (978-0-15-200244-2(8)) Harcourt Children's Bks.

—Mr. Putter & Tabby Toot the Horn. Howard, Arthur, illus. 1999. (Mr. Putter & Tabby Ser.). (J). (ps). lib. bdg. 14.10 (978-0-613-22895-4(2)) Tandem Library Bks.

—Mr. Putter & Tabby Toot the Horn. 1999. (Mr. Putter & Tabby Ser.). (J). 11.64 (978-0-606-17489-3(3)) Tandem Library Bks.

Sachs, Marilyn. The Four Ugly Cats in Apartment 3D. Litzinger, Rosanne, illus. 2003. (Ready-for-Chapters Ser.). 80p. (J). pap. 3.99 (978-0-689-86353-0(5) , Aladdin) Simon & Schuster Children's Publishing.

Sachs, Marilyn & Litzinger, Rosanne. The Four Ugly Cats in Apartment 3D. 2002. (Illus.). 80p. (J). (gr. 3-5). 15.00 (978-0-689-84581-9(2) , Atheneum/Richard Jackson Bks.) Simon & Schuster Children's Publishing.

Salas, Macarena. Peliaro en el Vecindario. 2006. (Over the Hedge Ser.). (SPA., Illus.). 32p. (J). pap. 3.99 (978-0-439-80906-1(1) , Scholastic en Espanol) Scholastic, Inc.

Scagliotti, Loti. They Say He Said She Said. 2006. (Silly Word & Number Stories Ser.). (Illus.). 28p. (J). 12.95 (978-9974-7925-0-0(9)) Hardenville SA URY. *Dist:* Independent Pubs. Group.

Schmauss, Judy Kentor. The People on My Street. 2006. (Reader's Clubhouse Set B Ser.). (Illus.). 24p. (J). pap. 3.99 (978-0-7641-3294-0(6)) Barron's Educational Series, Inc.

Schotter, Roni. The House of Joyful Living. Widener, Terry, illus. 2008. (J). (***978-0-374-33429-1(3)***) Farrar, Straus & Giroux.

Schubert, Ingrid & Schubert, Dieter. Hammer Soup. 2004. (Illus.). 40p. (J). 15.95 (978-1-932425-02-4(0) , Lemniscaat) Boyds Mills Pr.

Schubert, Leda. Here Comes Darrell. Azarian, Mary, illus. 2005. 32p. (J). (gr. k-3). 16.00 (978-0-618-41605-9(6)) Houghton Mifflin Co. Trade & Reference Div.

Schwartz, Amy. A Glorious Day. Schwartz, Amy, illus. 2004. (Illus.). 32p. (J). 16.95 (978-0-689-84802-5(1) , Atheneum/Richard Jackson Bks.) Simon & Schuster Children's Publishing.

Seher, H. R. Virtual Law. 2005. 154p. pap. 19.95 (978-1-4137-5249-6(7)) PublishAmerica, Inc.

Smith, Anne Warren. Tails of Spring Break. 2005. 136p. (J). (gr. 2-5). 15.95 (978-0-8075-6358-8(7)) Whitman, Albert & Co.

Spanyol, Jessica. Little Neighbors of Sunnyside Street. Spanyol, Jessica, illus. 2007. 64p. (J). (ps-1). 16.99 (978-0-7636-2986-1(3)) Candlewick Pr.

Stevens, April. Waking up Wendell. Hills, Tad, illus. 2007. 40p. (J). (ps-3). 15.99 (***978-0-375-83621-3(7)***); lib. bdg. 18.99 (***978-0-375-93893-1(1)***) Random Hse. Children's Bks. (Schwartz & Wade Bks.).

Stinson, Kathy. One More Clue. 2005. (Streetlights Ser.). 104p. (J). (gr. 2). 7.95 (978-1-55028-888-9(1)) Lorimer, James & Co., Ltd., Pubs. CAN. *Dist:* Casemate Pubs. & Bk. Distributors, LLC.

Stroud, Scott. Baby Kong. Hunt, Jim, illus. 2006. (J). 12.95 (978-1-60131-001-9(3)) Big Tent Bks.

Stroud, Scott. Grumpy Mr. Grady. 2007. (J). 12.95 (***978-1-60131-008-8(0)***) Big Tent Bks.

Thayer, Jane. Part-Time Dog. Barasch, Lynne & McCue, Lisa, illus. 2004. 32p. (J). (ps-3). 14.99 (978-0-06-029693-3(3)) HarperCollins Pubs.

Thiel, Annie. Danny Is Moving. 2006. (Playdate Kids Ser.). (Illus.). 32p. 14.95 (978-1-933721-02-6(2)) Playdate Kids Publishing.

Thompson, Colin. The Floods #1: Good Neighbors. Scrambly, Crab, illus. 2008. (Floods Ser.). 224p. (J). 15.99 (***978-0-06-113196-7(2)***); lib. bdg. 16.89 (***978-0-06-113199-8(7)***) HarperCollins Pubs.

Trowbridge, Terri. Tulowly the Possum. McConkey, Barbara, illus. l.t. ed. 2005. 24p. (J). 9.95 (978-0-9766418-0-3(1)) Sidewalk Publishing.

Trudel, Sylvain & Langlois, Suzane. Des Voisins Qui Inventent le Monde. 2000. (Premier Roman Ser.). (FRE.). 64p. (J). (gr. 2-5). pap. (978-2-89021-424-8(9)) Diffusion du livre Mirabel.

Tyler-Vaughn, Savanna. Flour Sack Wear. 2006. (ENG.). 48p. per. 12.95 (***978-1-4241-2501-2(4)***) PublishAmerica, Inc.

Vischer, Phil. Sidney & Norman: A Tale of Two Pigs. Gerard, Justin, illus. 2006. 48p. (J). 15.99 (978-1-4003-0834-7(8)) Nelson, Thomas Inc.

Wackwitz, Winnie. The Creature of Lost Bayou. 2004. (YA). pap. 12.95 (978-1-58752-107-2(5)) Timberwolf Pr., Inc.

Wahl, Jan. Candy Shop. Wong, Nicole, illus. 2005. 32p. (J). (ps-ps). pap. 6.95 (978-1-57091-668-7(3)) Charlesbridge Publishing, Inc.

Walsh, Ann. Flower Power. 2005. (Orca Currents Ser.). 112p. (J). (gr. 4-10). pap. 7.95 (978-1-55143-386-8(9)) Orca Bk. Pubs. USA.

Weiss, Ellen. Mickey's Neighborhood Discovery. 2000. (Lift the Flaps Bks.). 12p. (J). 6.99 (978-0-7364-1035-9(X)) Mouse Works.

M N O

Weller, Frances Ward. The Day the Animals Came: A Story of Saint Francis Day. Long, Loren, illus. 2006. 35p. (J). (gr. k-4). reprint ed. 17.00 (978-1-4223-5396-7(6)) DIANE Publishing Co.

—The Day the Animals Came: A Story of Saint Francis Day. Long, Loren, illus. 2003. 48p. (J). (ps-4). 16.99 (978-0-399-23630-3(9) , 53247533, Philomel) Penguin Group (USA) Inc.

Wells, Rosemary. McDuff Goes to School. Jeffers, Susan, illus. ed. 2005. 32p. (ps-k). 9.99 (978-0-7868-5676-3(9)) Hyperion Bks. for Children.

Wheeler, Kathryn. No Room for Neighbors: A Tale in Which Two Strangers Become Friends. Myers, Darcy, illus. 2000. (Stories to Grow By Ser.). 19p. (J). 3.95 (978-1-56822-594-4(6) , Instructional Fair) Schaffer, Frank Pubns.

Wilder, Laura Ingalls. Laura & Mr. Edwards. 1999. (Little House Chapter Bks.: No. 13). (J). (gr. 3-6). (978-0-606-16685-0(8)) Tandem Library Bks.

Wildsmith, Brian. The Owl & the Woodpecker. Wildsmith, Brian, illus. 2006. (Illus.). 32p. (J). 16.95 (978-1-59572-043-6(X)) Star Bright Bks., Inc.

Wood, Audrey. Sweet Dream Pie. 2002. (ps-2). lib. bdg. 14.15 (978-0-613-46233-4(5)) Tandem Library Bks.

Wood, Deanna Plummer. Whenever Monkeys Move Next Door, 1 volume. 2005. (Illus.). 24p. (J). pap. 8.50 (978-0-9762935-1-4(X)) Perkins Crawford.

Woodworth, Chris. When Ratboy Lived Next Door. 2005. (Illus.). 192p. (J). 16.00 (978-0-374-34677-5(1) , Farrar, Straus & Giroux (BYR)) Farrar, Straus & Giroux.

Wurtz, K. D. Digby Finds a Friend. Carrier, Tracey Dahle, illus. 2001. (Digby in Disguise Ser.: Vol. 2). (J). (978-0-9712840-2-9(4) , Bear & Co.) Bear & Co.

Yee, Wong Herbert. Upstairs Mouse, Downstairs Mole. 2005. (Illus.). 48p. (J). (gr. k-3). 15.00 (978-0-618-47313-7(0)) Houghton Mifflin Co. Trade & Reference Div.

Yee, Wong Herbert. Upstairs Mouse Downstairs Mole. 12th ed. 2007. (Illus.). 48p. (J). (gr. 1-5). 3.99 (***978-0-618-91586-6(9)***) Houghton Mifflin Co. Trade & Reference Div.

NELSON, HORATIO NELSON, VISCOUNT, 1758-1805

Ashworth, Leon. Horatio Nelson. 2000. (British History Makers Ser.). (Illus.). 32p. (J). 22.95 (978-0-7451-5290-5(2) , Cherrytree Books) Evans Publishing Group GBR. *Dist:* Independent Pubs. Group.

Lacey, Minna. Nelson - Internet Referenced. 2006. 64p. (J). 8.95 (978-0-7945-1121-0(X) , Usborne) EDC Publishing.

NEO-IMPRESSIONISM (ART)

see Impressionism (Art)

NEOLITHIC PERIOD

see Stone Age

NEPAL

Burbank, Jon. Nepal. 2nd ed. 2002. (Cultures of the World Ser.). (Illus.). 144p. (gr. 5 up). lib. bdg. 37.07 (978-0-7614-1476-6(2) , Cavendish, Marshall Reference Bks.) Cavendish, Marshall Corp.

Conley, Kate A. Nepal. 2004. (Countries Ser.). (Illus.). 40p. (J). (gr. k-6). lib. bdg. 22.78 (978-1-59197-293-8(0)) ABDO Publishing Co.

Into Wild Nepal. 2004. 11.20 (978-1-4103-0238-0(5) , Blackbirch Pr., Inc.) Thomson Gale.

Roberts-Davis, Tanya. We Need to Go to School: Voices of the Rugmark Children. 2003. (Illus.). 48p. (J). (gr. 5 up). pap. 7.95 (978-0-88899-426-4(5)) Groundwood Bks. CAN. *Dist:* Perseus Distribution.

Touba, Jacquiline, et al. Nepal: Chandra Bahadur Ale's Painting: Simple Living. 2001. (Young Artists of the World Ser.). (Illus.). 24p. (J). (ps-3). lib. bdg. 19.95 (978-0-8239-5103-1(0) , PowerKids Pr.) Rosen Publishing Group, Inc., The.

NEPAL—FICTION

Doyle, Bill. Iced! The 2007 Journal of Nick Fitzmorgan. Simpson, Philomena, illus. 2006. 133p. (J). lib. bdg. 18.46 (***978-1-4242-1734-2(2)***) Fitzgerald Bks.

Eric's Travel Diary 6 Pks: Individual Chapter Book Title. Vol. 29. 32p. (gr. 5 up). 44.00 (978-0-7578-0977-4(4)) Rigby Education.

Kerr, P. B. Cobra King of Kathmandu. 2007. (Children of the Lamp Ser.: No. 3). 400p. (J). pap. 6.99 (***978-0-439-67024-1(1)*** , Scholastic Paperbacks) Scholastic, Inc.

Kerr, P. B. The Cobra King of Kathmandu. 2007. (Children of the Lamp Ser.: No. 3). (Illus.). 384p. (J). (gr. 4-7). pap. 16.99 (978-0-439-67023-4(3) , Orchard Bks.) Scholastic, Inc.

Lama, Nurbu Tenzing. Himalaya. Tanaka, Shelley, tr. from FRE. Lama, Nurbu Tenzing, illus. 2002. (Illus.). 40p. (J). 16.95 (978-0-88899-480-6(X)) Groundwood Bks. CAN. *Dist:* Perseus Distribution.

Lumry, Amanda & Hurwitz, Laura. Tigers in Terai. McIntyre, Sarah, illus. 2003. (Adventures of Riley Ser.). 36p. 15.95 (978-0-9662257-7-8(5)) Eaglemont Pr.

McCormick, Patricia. Sold. 2006. 272p. (gr. 7 up). 15.99 (978-0-7868-5171-3(6)) Hyperion Pr.

Stewart, Jennifer J. Close Encounters of a Third World Kind. 2004. 128p. (J). (gr. 4-6). tchr. ed. 16.95 (978-0-8234-1850-3(2)) Holiday Hse., Inc.

Young, Ed. I, Doko: The Tale of a Basket. Young, Ed, illus. 2004. (Illus.). 32p. (J). (ps-3). 16.99 (978-0-399-23625-9(2) , Philomel) Penguin Group (USA) Inc.

NEPTUNE (PLANET)

Adamson, Thomas K. Neptune. 24p. (J). 2008. (***978-1-4296-0732-2(7)***); 2003. (Illus.). lib. bdg. 17.26 (978-0-7368-2115-5(5) , Pebble Bks.) Capstone Pr., Inc.

Adamson, Thomas K. Neptuno: Neptune. 2006. (ENG & SPA., Illus.). 24p. (J). (978-0-7368-5882-3(2)) Capstone Pr., Inc.

Asimov, Isaac & Hantula, Richard. Neptune. rev. ed. 2003. (Isaac Asimov's 21st Century Library of the Universe). (Illus.). 32p. (YA). (gr. 3 up). lib. bdg. 24.67 (978-0-8368-3239-6(6)) Stevens, Gareth Inc.

—Neptune: The Farthest Giant. 2003. (Isaac Asimov's 21st Century Library of the Universe). (Illus.). 32p. (J). (gr. 3 up). pap. (978-0-8368-3943-2(9) , Weekly Reader Early Learning Library) Stevens, Gareth Inc.

—Neptuno: El Gigante Mas Lejano. Porras, Carlos & D'Andrea, Patricia, trs. from ENG. 2003. (Isaac Asimov's Biblioteca del Universo del Siglo XXI). (SPA & ENG., Illus.). 32p. (J). (gr. 3 up). lib. bdg. 24.67 (978-0-8368-3858-9(0)); pap. 8.95 (978-0-8368-3871-8(8) , Weekly Reader Early Learning Library) Stevens, Gareth Inc.

Birch, Robin. Neptune. 2004. (Solar System Ser.). (Illus.). 32p. (gr. 3-5). 23.00 (978-0-7910-7930-0(9) , Chelsea Hse.) Facts On File, Inc.

Chrismer, Melanie. Neptune. (Scholastic News Nonfiction Readers: Space Science Ser.). 24p. (J). 2008. pap. 6.95 (***978-0-531-14765-8(7)***); 2007. (Illus.). (gr. 1-2). lib. bdg. 20.00 (***978-0-531-14750-4(9)***) Scholastic Library Publishing. (Children's Pr.).

Goss, Tim. Uranus, Neptune & Pluto. 2003. (Universe Ser.). (Illus.). 32p. (J). (gr. 3-5). lib. bdg. 22.79 (978-1-58810-918-7(6)); pap. 7.50 (978-1-4034-0619-4(7)) Heinemann Library.

Hayhurst, Chris. Neptune. 2006. (***978-1-4042-1966-3(8)***); 2004. (J). lib. bdg. 26.50 (978-1-4042-0171-2(8)) Rosen Publishing Group, Inc., The.

Howard, Fran. Neptune. 2007. (Planets Ser.). (ENG., Illus.). 32p. (J). (gr. k-4). lib. bdg. 24.21 (***978-1-59928-830-7(3)*** , Buddy Bks.) ABDO Publishing Co.

Landau, Elaine. Neptune. (True Booktrade;: Space Ser.). 48p. (J). 2008. pap. 6.95 (***978-0-531-14793-1(2)***); 2007. (Illus.). (gr. 3-5). lib. bdg. 26.00 (***978-0-531-12563-2(7)***) Scholastic Library Publishing. (Children's Pr.).

Neptune. (Galaxy Ser.). 24p. (J). 6.95 (978-0-7368-8889-9(6)) Capstone Pr., Inc.

Neptune, 6 vols. (gr. 2-5). 36.95 (978-0-7368-8971-1(X)) Red Brick Learning.

Orme, Helen & Orme, David. Let's Explore Neptune. 2006. (J). pap. (***978-0-8368-8129-5(X)***); lib. bdg. (***978-0-8368-7944-5(9)***) Stevens, Gareth Inc.

Potts, Steve. Neptune: Our Solar System. 2001. (Illus.). 23p. (J). lib. bdg. 21.35 (978-1-58340-100-2(8)) Smart Apple Media.

Rau, Dana Meachen. Neptune. 2002. (Illus.). 32p. (J). (gr. 3 up). lib. bdg. 21.26 (978-0-7565-0296-6(9)) Compass Point Bks.

Ring, Susan. Neptune. (Exploring Planets Ser.). (J). 2004. pap. (978-1-59036-229-7(2)); 2002. (Illus.). 24p. lib. bdg. 15.95 (978-1-59036-102-3(4)) Weigl Pubs., Inc.

Scherer, Glenn & Fletcher, Marty. Neptune: A MyReportLinks. com Book. 2005. (Solar System Ser.). (Illus.). 48p. (J). lib. bdg. 25.26 (978-0-7660-5211-6(7) , MyReportLinks.com Bks.) Enslow Pubs., Inc.

Sparrow, Giles. Uranus, Neptune & Pluto. (Exploring the Solar System Ser.). (Illus.). (J). (gr. 4-6). 2002. 40p. pap. 7.95 (978-1-58810-966-8(6) , 91449); 2001. 39p. lib. bdg. 24.22 (978-1-57572-397-6(2)) Heinemann Library.

Stille, Darlene R. Neptune. 2003. (Planets Ser.). (Illus.). 32p. (J). (gr. 2-6). 27.07 (978-1-59296-052-1(9)) Child's World, Inc.

Tabak, John. Look at Neptune. 2003. (gr. 7-12). lib. bdg. 24.55 (978-0-613-72676-4(6)) Tandem Library Bks.

Vogt, Gregory L. Jupiter, Saturn, Uranus & Neptune. 2000. (Our Universe Ser.). (Illus.). 48p. (YA). (gr. 5-12). lib. bdg. 22.83 (978-0-7398-3109-0(7)) Raintree.

Waxman, Laura Hamilton. Neptune. 2005. (Pull Ahead Bks.). (Illus.). 32p. (gr. 2-4). lib. bdg. 22.60 (978-0-8225-4655-9(8)) Lerner Publishing Group.

Wimmer, Teresa. Neptune. 2007. (J). (978-1-58341-520-7(3) , Creative Education) Creative Co., The.

Winrich, Ralph. Neptune. (J). 2008. (***978-1-4296-0726-1(2)***); 2005. (Illus.). 24p. 21.26 (978-0-7368-3692-0(6)) Capstone Pr., Inc.

World Book, contrib. by. Neptune & the Distant Dwarf Planets. 2nd ed. 2006. (World Book's Solar System & Space Exploration Library). (Illus.). 64p. (J). (***978-0-7166-9518-9(9)***) World Bk., Inc.

World Book, Inc Staff, contrib. by. Neptune & Pluto. 2006. (World Book's Solar System & Space Exploration Library). (Illus.). 63p. (J). (978-0-7166-9507-3(3)) World Bk., Inc.

NERO, EMPEROR OF ROME, 37-68

Morgan, Julian. Nero: Destroyer of Rome. 2003. (Leaders of Ancient Rome Ser.). (Illus.). 112p. (YA). (gr. 5-8). lib. bdg. 31.95 (978-0-8239-3596-3(5) , Rosen Central) Rosen Publishing Group, Inc., The.

Whiting, Jim. The Life & Times of Nero. 2005. (Biography from Ancient Civilizations Ser.). (Illus.). 48p. (J). (gr. 5-8). lib. bdg. 29.95 (978-1-58415-349-8(0)) Mitchell Lane Pubs., Inc.

NERO, EMPEROR OF ROME, 37-68—FICTION

Weerstand, R. Quintus: A Story about the Persecution of Christians at the Time of Emperor Nero. 2006. (Illus.). 135p. (J). (978-1-894666-70-1(4)) Inheritance Pubns.

NERVOUS SYSTEM

see also Brain; Psychology, Pathological

Andrews, Barbara. Discover the Nervous & Digestive Systems. 2006. pap. 39.00 (***978-1-4108-6515-1(0)***) Benchmark Education Co.

—The Nervous & Digestive Systems. 2006. pap. 42.00 (***978-1-4108-6512-0(6)***) Benchmark Education Co.

Angliss, Sarah. The Controls: Brain & Nervous System. 1999. (Human Machine Ser.). (Illus.). 32p. (J). lib. bdg. 16.95 (978-1-929298-22-8(6)) Chrysalis Education.

Ballard, Carol. The Brain & Nervous System. 2005. (Exploring the Human Body Ser.). (Illus.). 32p. (J). (gr. 4-7). lib. bdg. 24.95 (978-0-7377-3018-0(8) , Kidhaven) Thomson Gale.

Bayer, Linda N. Sleep Disorders. 2000. (Encyclopedia of Psychological Disorders Ser.). (Illus.). 88p. (J). (gr. 7 up). 35.00 (978-0-7910-5314-0(8) , Chelsea Hse.) Facts On File, Inc.

Creative Media Applications Staff. The Human Body & Environment: Nervous System & the Sense Organs, Vol. 5. 2003. (978-0-313-32563-2(4)) Greenwood Publishing Group, Inc.

Diagram Group. Brain & Nervous System. 2005. (Illus.). 112p. (J). (978-0-8160-5986-7(1)) Facts On File, Inc.

—Digestive System. 2005. (Illus.). 112p. (J). (978-0-8160-5984-3(5)) Facts On File, Inc.

Diagram Group, contrib. by. Heart & Circulatory System. 2005. (Illus.). 112p. (J). (978-0-8160-5982-9(9)) Facts On File, Inc.

French, Kathy. Your Nervous System. ed. 2003. (Early Connections Ser.). (J). pap. 35.00 (978-1-4108-1538-5(2)) Benchmark Education Co.

Frost, Helen. The Nervous System. Saunders-Smith, Gail, ed. 2000. (Human Body Systems Ser.). (Illus.). 24p. (J). (gr. k-1). lib. bdg. 15.93 (978-0-7368-0651-0(2) , Pebble Bks.) Capstone Pr., Inc.

Ganeri, Anita. Your Brain. Shott, Steve, photos by. 2003. (How Your Body Works). (Illus.). 32p. (J). (gr. 2 up). lib. bdg. 23.33 (978-0-8368-3632-5(4)) Stevens, Gareth Inc.

Gold, Martha V. The Nervous System. 2004. (Human Body Library Ser.). (Illus.). 48p. (J). lib. bdg. 23.93 (978-0-7660-2018-4(5)) Enslow Pubs., Inc.

Goldsmith, Connie. Meningitis. 2007. (J). lib. bdg. (***978-0-8225-7034-9(3)***) Twenty First Century Bks.

Gordon, Sharon. My Brain. 2004. (Bookworms Ser.). (ENG & SPA., Illus.). 31p. (J). 21.36 (978-0-7614-1781-1(8) , Benchmark Bks.) Cavendish, Marshall Corp.

Harrold, Kimberly. Sometimes, MS Is Yucky. Whitfield, Eric, illus. 2005. 32p. (J). 7.95 (978-1-59630-006-4(X) , 1-59630-006-X) Science & Humanities Pr.

Hayhurst, Chris. The Brain & Spinal Cord: Learning How We Think, Feel & Move. 2002. (3-D Library of the Human Body). (Illus.). 48p. (YA). (gr. 5-8). lib. bdg. 26.50 (978-0-8239-3528-4(0) , Rosen Central) Rosen Publishing Group, Inc., The.

Holt, Rinehart and Winston Staff. Holt Science & Technology Chapter 25: Life Science: Communication & Control. 5th ed. 2004. (Illus.). pap. 12.86 (978-0-03-030246-6(3)) Holt, Rinehart & Winston.

Houghton, Gillian. The Nervous System. 2007. (Body Works). (Illus.). 24p. (J). (978-1-4042-2373-8(8)); pap. (978-1-4042-2183-3(2)); lib. bdg. (978-1-4042-3474-1(8)) Rosen Publishing Group, Inc., The. (PowerKids Pr.).

Jakab, Cheryl. The Nervous System. 2006. (Our Body Ser.). (Illus.). 32p. (J). (gr. 3-5). lib. bdg. 27.10 (978-1-58340-735-6(9)) Smart Apple Media.

Jerome, Kate Boehm. Understanding the Brain. 2003. (Human Body Ser.). (Illus.). 32p. (J). pap. (978-0-7922-8859-6(9)) National Geographic Society.

Libra, Anna. Why Does My Head Hurt? An Inside Look at the Nervous System. 2003. (J). pap. (978-1-58417-065-5(4)); lib. bdg. (978-1-58417-002-0(6)) Lake Street Pubs.

Llamas, Andreu. The Nervous System. Rizo, Luis, illus. 1998. (Human Body Ser.). 32p. (J). (gr. 5 up). lib. bdg. 24.67 (978-0-8368-2113-0(0)) Stevens, Gareth Inc.

Nervensystem und Sinnesorgane: Fachliche Inhalte und Uebungsaufgaben. 2nd ed. (Duden Abiturhilfen Ser.). (GER.). 112p. (YA). (gr. 12-13). (978-3-411-04152-7(8)) Bibliographisches Institut & F. A. Brockhaus AG DEU. *Dist:* International Bk. Import Service, Inc.

The Nervous System. (Human Body Systems Ser.). 24p. (J). 5.95 (978-0-7368-8779-3(2)) Capstone Pr., Inc.

The Nervous System, 6 vols. (gr. k-2). 28.95 (978-0-7368-8803-5(9)) Red Brick Learning.

The Nervous System/The Senses/The Skin. 2006. (World Book's Human Body Works). (Illus.). 48p. (J). (978-0-7166-4430-9(4)) World Bk., Inc.

Oleksy, Walter. The Nervous System. 2001. (Insider's Guide to the Body Ser.). (Illus.). 48p. (YA). (gr. 5-8). lib. bdg. 23.95 (978-0-8239-3341-9(5) , Rosen Central) Rosen Publishing Group, Inc., The.

Olien, Rebecca. The Nervous System. 2006. (J). (978-0-7368-5412-2(6)) Capstone Pr., Inc.

Parker, Steve. The Brain & Nervous System. 2004. (Our Bodies Ser.). (Illus.). 48p. (J). lib. bdg. 28.56 (978-0-7398-6619-1(2)) Raintree.

—Brain, Nerves, & Senses. 2004. (Understanding the Human Body Ser.). (Illus.). 32p. (J). lib. bdg. 24.67 (978-0-8368-4204-3(9)) Stevens, Gareth Inc.

—Control Freak! 2006. (Illus.). 48p. (J). pap. (978-1-4109-1882-6(3)); lib. bdg. (978-1-4109-1875-8(0)) Steck-Vaughn.

—Nerves & Spinal Cord. 2003. (Body Focus Ser.). (Illus.). 48p. (J). pap. (978-1-4034-3301-5(1)) Heinemann Library.

—Nerves & Spinal Cord. 2003. (gr. 5-8). lib. bdg. 17.05 (978-0-613-84433-8(5)) Tandem Library Bks.

—Spinal Cord & Nerves. 2003. (Body Focus Ser.). 48p. pap. 8.50 (978-1-4034-3308-4(9)); (Illus.). (J). lib. bdg. 27.07 (978-1-4034-0753-5(3)) Heinemann Library.

Petrie, Kristin. The Nervous System. 2007. (Checkerboard Science Library). (Illus.). 32p. (J). 22.78 (978-1-59679-712-3(6)) ABDO Publishing Co.

Porterfield, Jason. Downers: Depressant Abuse. 2007. (J). lib. bdg. (***978-1-4042-1957-1(9)***) Rosen Publishing Group, Inc., The.

Rau, Dana Meachen. El Cerebro. 2006. (Bookworms Ser.). (SPA & ENG., Illus.). 32p. (J). lib. bdg. 22.79 (978-0-7614-2402-4(4)) Cavendish, Marshall Corp.

—My Brain (El Cerebro) 2006. (Bookworms Ser.). (SPA & ENG., Illus.). 32p. (J). lib. bdg. 22.79 (978-0-7614-2480-2(6)) Cavendish, Marshall Corp.

Riley, Joelle. The Nervous System. (Early Bird Body Systems Ser.). (Illus.). 48p. (J). 2005. (gr. 2-4). lib. bdg. 25.26 (978-0-8225-1249-3(1)); 2004. pap. (978-0-8225-2521-9(6)) Lerner Publishing Group.

—El Sistema Nervioso. 2006. (Libros Sobre el Cuerpo Humano para Madrugadores Ser.). (ENG & SPA.). 48p. (J). 25.26 (978-0-8225-6255-9(3)) Lerner Publishing Group.

Royston, Angela. Why Do I Get a Toothache? And Other Questions about Nerves. 2003. (Body Matters Ser.). (Illus.). 32p. (J). (gr. 3-5). lib. bdg. 24.22 (978-1-4034-0204-2(3)); pap. 7.50 (978-1-4034-0459-6(3)) Heinemann Library.

Silverman, Buffy. Who's in Control? 2006. (Illus.). 32p. (J). (978-1-4109-2583-1(8)); pap. (978-1-4109-2640-1(0)) Steck-Vaughn.

Simon, Seymour. The Brain: Our Nervous System. 2006. 32p. (J). 16.99 (978-0-06-087718-7(9)); (Illus.). pap. 6.99 (978-0-06-087719-4(7)) HarperCollins Pubs.

El Sistema Nervioso, Nuestro Proceso de Datos. (Coleccion Mundo Invisible).Tr. of Nervous System & the Brain. (SPA.). (YA). (gr. 5-8). pap. 8.00 (978-958-04-3226-5(0)) Norma S.A. COL. *Dist:* Distribuidora Norma, Inc., Lectorum Pubns., Inc.

El Sistema Nervioso Nuestro Proceso de Datos. (SPA.). (J). 10.00 (978-84-342-1907-6(7)) Parramon Ediciones S.A. ESP. *Dist:* Distribuidora Norma, Inc.

El sistema nervioso (the Nervous System) 2007. (J). pap. 7.95 (978-0-8225-6651-9(6) , Ediciones Lerner) Lerner Publishing Group.

Stille, Darlene R. The Nervous System. 1998. (True Bks.). (Illus.). 48p. (J). (gr. 3-5). pap. 6.95 (978-0-516-26270-3(X) , Children's Pr.) Scholastic Library Publishing.

Taylor-Butler, Christine. The Nervous System. 2007. (True Booktrade;: Health & the Human Body Ser.). 48p. (J). spiral bd. 26.00 (***978-0-531-16861-5(1)*** , Children's Pr.) Scholastic Library Publishing.

Viegas, Jennifer. The Revolution in Healing the Brain. 2005. (Library of Future Medicine). (Illus.). 64p. (YA). (gr. 7-12). lib. bdg. 26.50 (978-0-8239-3668-7(6)) Rosen Publishing Group, Inc., The.

Walker, Pam & Wood, Elaine. The Brain & Nervous System. 2002. (Understanding the Human Body Ser.). (Illus.). 112p. (J). 27.45 (978-1-59018-148-5(4) , Lucent Bks.) Thomson Gale.

West, Krista. Biofeedback. 2007. (Gray Matter Ser.). 104p. (J). (gr. 9). 32.95 (***978-0-7910-9436-5(7)*** , Chelsea Hse.) Facts On File, Inc.

NESS, LOCH (SCOTLAND)

Brassey, Richard. Nessie the Loch Ness Monster. 2003. (Illus.). 24p. (J). pap. 7.99 (978-1-85881-309-7(3)) Orion Bks. Ltd. GBR. *Dist:* Trafalgar Square Publishing.

Maddux, Marlaine. The Loch Pt. 2: The Knowledge Journey. Menchaca, Angelita, ed. Huddleston, Courtney, illus. 2001. (Mythics Ser.). 64p. (J). (gr. 3-6). 17.95 (978-0-9673683-4-4(0)) Penny-Farthing Pr., Inc.

Wallace, Holly. The Mystery of the Loch Ness Monster. 1999. (Can Science Solve? Ser.). 32p. (J). (gr. 4-7). lib. bdg. 22.79 (978-1-57572-805-6(2)) Heinemann Library.

NESTS

see Birds—Eggs and Nests

NETHERLANDS

Britton, Tamara L. The Netherlands. 2003. (Countries Ser.). (Illus.). 40p. (J). (gr. k-6). lib. bdg. 22.78 (978-1-57765-755-2(1)) ABDO Publishing Co.

Davis, Kevin A. & Harvey, Miles. Look What Came from The Netherlands. 2003. (Look What Came from Ser.). (Illus.). 32p. (J). (gr. 2-4). pap. 6.95 (978-0-531-16631-4(7) , Watts, Franklin) Scholastic Library Publishing.

Dunn, Joeming W. & Dunn, Ben. Anne Frank. Dunn, Joeming W. & Dunn, Ben, illus. 2007. (Bio-Graphics Ser.). (Illus.). 32p. (J). (gr. 3-6). lib. bdg. 27.07 (***978-1-60270-065-9(6)*** , Graphic Planet) Magic Wagon.

Heinrichs, Ann. The Netherlands. 2003. (True Bks.). (gr. 3-5). pap. 6.95 (978-0-516-27750-9(2)); (Illus.). 48p. (J). 25.00 (978-0-516-22675-0(4)) Scholastic Library Publishing. (Children's Pr.).

—Netherlands. 2003. (gr. 3-6). lib. bdg. 15.25 (978-0-613-67973-2(3)) Tandem Library Bks.

Hintz, Martin. The Netherlands. 1999. (Enchantment of the World, Second Ser.). (Illus.). 144p. (YA). (gr. 5-9). 36.00 (978-0-516-20962-3(0) , Children's Pr.) Scholastic Library Publishing.

Kaltenhauser, Bettina & van Swol-Ulbrich, Hilly. When Abroad - Do As the Local Children Do: Ori's Guide for Young Expats. 2004. (Illus.). 112p. (J). pap. 15.95 (978-90-5594-262-6(6)) Cyan Communications GBR. *Dist:* Independent Pubs. Group.

Maarsen, Jacqueline Van. A Friend Called Anne: One Girl's Story of War, Peace & a Unique Friendship with Anne Frank. 2005. (Illus.). 176p. (J). (gr. 3). 15.99 (978-0-670-05958-4(7) , Viking Juvenile) Penguin Group (USA) Inc.

Marran, James F. The Netherlands. 2003. (Modern World Nations Ser.). (Illus.). 150p. (gr. 6-12). 30.00 (978-0-7910-7476-3(5) , Chelsea Hse.) Facts On File, Inc.

NgCheong-Lum, Roseline. The Netherlands. 2001. (Countries of the World Ser.). (Illus.). 96p. (J). (gr. 6 up). lib. bdg. 30.00 (978-0-8368-2336-3(2)) Stevens, Gareth Inc.

Poole, Josephine. Anne Frank. Barrett, Angela, illus. 2005. 40p. (J). (gr. 5 up). 17.95 (978-0-375-83242-0(4) , Knopf Bks. for Young Readers) Random Hse. Children's Bks.

Reynolds, Simon & NgCheong-Lum, Roseline. Welcome to the Netherlands. 2002. (Welcome to My Country Ser.). (Illus.). 48p. (J). (gr. 2 up). lib. bdg. 26.00 (978-0-8368-2536-7(5)) Stevens, Gareth Inc.

Seth, Ronald. Netherlands. 1999. (Major World Nations Ser.). (Illus.). 144p. (gr. 4-7). 29.95 (978-0-7910-4745-3(8) , Chelsea Hse.) Facts On File, Inc.

Seward, Pat & Arora Lal, Sunandini. Netherlands. 2nd ed. 2006. (Cultures of the World Ser.). (Illus.). 144p. (J). (978-0-7614-2052-1(5) , Benchmark Bks.) Cavendish, Marshall Corp.

Simson, David. The Netherlands. Simson, David, photos by. 2004. (Changing Face Of... Ser.). (Illus.). 48p. (J). (gr. 4-7). lib. bdg. 28.56 (978-0-7398-6833-1(0)) Harcourt Schl. Pubs.

Van Fenema, Joyce. Netherlands. 1998. (Festivals of the World Ser.). (Illus.). 32p. (J). (gr. 3 up). lib. bdg. 24.67 (978-0-8368-2016-4(9)) Stevens, Gareth Inc.

Venable, Alan. The Story of Anne Frank. Ham, Jeff, illus. 2001. (J). (gr. 5-6). 65.00 incl. audio, cd-rom (978-1-58702-398-9(9)) Johnston, Don Inc.

NETHERLANDS—FICTION

Attema, Martha. Daughter of Light. McCallum, Stephen, illus. 2001. (Young Reader Ser.). 112p. (J). (gr. 3-6). pap. 4.99 (978-1-55143-179-6(3)) Orca Bk. Pubs. USA.

—Daughter of Light. 2001. (J). 11.64 (978-0-606-22770-4(9)) Tandem Library Bks.

Borden, Louise & Daly, Niki. The Greatest Skating Race: A World War II Story from the Netherlands. 2004. (Illus.). 48p. (J). 18.95 (978-0-689-84502-4(2) , McElderry, Margaret K.) Simon & Schuster Children's Publishing.

Brust, Beth Wagner. The Great Tulip Trade. Mattheson, Jenny, illus. 2005. (Step into Reading Ser.: Vol. 3). 48p. (J). (gr. 1-3). pap. 3.99 (978-0-375-82573-6(8) , Random Hse. Bks. for Young Readers) Random Hse. Children's Bks.

Chambers, Aidan. Postcards from No Man's Land. (gr. 9). 2007. 336p. (YA). pap. 10.00 (978-0-14-240788-2(7)); 2004. 320p. (J). reprint ed. pap. 7.99 (978-0-14-240145-3(5)) Penguin Group (USA) Inc. (Puffin).

Comora, Madeleine. Rembrandt & Titus: Father & Son. Locker, Thomas, illus. 2005. 32p. (J). (gr. 2-5). 17.95 (978-1-55591-490-5(X)) Fulcrum Publishing.

Coville, Bruce & Dodge, Mary Mapes. Hans Brinker. Long, Laurel, illus. 2007. 40p. (J). (ps up). 16.99 (***978-0-8037-2868-4(9)*** , Dial) Penguin Group (USA) Inc.

Cullen, Lynn. I Am Rembrandt's Daughter. 2007. 320p. (YA). (gr. 7 up). 16.95 (***978-1-59990-046-9(7)***) Bloomsbury Publishing.

Dodge, Mary. Hans Brinker, or the Silver Skates. 2005. (Illus.). 239p. (J). (***978-1-59605-666-4(5)***); pap. (***978-1-59605-415-8(8)***) Cosimo, Inc.

Dodge, Mary Mapes. Hans Brinker & the Silver Skates. Freshman, Floris, illus. 2002. (Great Illustrated Classics Ser.). 240p. (J). (gr. 3-8). 21.35 (978-1-57765-814-6(0) , ABDO & Daughters) ABDO Publishing Co.

—Hans Brinker or the Silver Skates. Lindskoog, Kathryn, ed. Wynne, Patrick, illus. 2001. (Classics for Young Readers Ser.). 224p. (J). (gr. 3-6). pap. 7.99 (978-0-87552-725-3(6)) P & R Publishing.

—Hans Brinker, or the Silver Skates. Kopito, Janet Baine, ed. 2003. (Dover Evergreen Classics Ser.). 288p. (J). (gr. 4-7). pap. 3.00 (978-0-486-42842-0(7)) Dover Pubns., Inc.

—Hans Brinker or the Silver Skates A Story of Life in Holland. Doggett, Allen B., illus. 2004. reprint ed. pap. 34.95 (978-1-4179-4127-8(8)) Kessinger Publishing, LLC.

Dodge, Mary Mapes. Hans Brinker; or, the Silver Skates (Dod. 2006. pap. (***978-1-4065-0961-8(2)***) Dodo Pr.

Duble, Kathleen Benner. Quest. 2008. 256p. (J). 15.99 (***978-1-4169-3386-1(7)*** , McElderry, Margaret K.) Simon & Schuster Children's Publishing.

Fleming, Candace. Boxes for Katje. Dressen-McQueen, Stacey, illus. 2003. 40p. (J). (gr. k-3). 16.00 (978-0-374-30922-0(1) , Farrar, Straus & Giroux (BYR)) Farrar, Straus & Giroux.

—Boxes for Katje. Dressen-McQueen, Stacey, illus. 2004. (J). 29.95 incl. audio compact disk (978-0-8045-4125-1(6) , SACD4125); (YA). 27.95 incl. audio (978-0-8045-6930-9(4) , SAC6930) Spoken Arts, Inc.

Gilson, Jamie. Stink Alley. 2002. 192p. (J). (gr. 3 up). 15.95 (978-0-688-17864-2(2)); lib. bdg. 15.89 (978-0-06-029217-1(2)) HarperCollins Pubs.

Griffis, William Elliot. Dutch Fairy Tales for Young Folks. 2004. reprint ed. pap. 1.99 (978-1-4192-1705-0(4)) Kessinger Publishing, LLC.

Jones, Douglas. Dutch Color. 224p. (J). 2000. (Illus.). per. 12.00 (978-1-885767-65-3(X)); 1999. (gr. 3-6). per. 12.00 (978-1-885767-52-3(8)) Canon Pr.

Jungman, Ann. Resistance. Marks, Alan, illus. 2006. 83p. (J). (gr. 2-3). lib. bdg. 15.95 (978-1-59889-001-3(8)) Stone Arch Bks.

Kuijer, Guus. The Book of Everything. Nieuwenhuizen, John, tr. from DUT. 2006. 112p. (J). (gr. 4-7). pap. 16.99 (978-0-439-74918-3(2) , Levine, Arthur A. Bks.) Scholastic, Inc.

Kuijer, Guus & Nieuwenhuizen, John. The Book of Everything. 2006. ix, 101p. (J). 16.99 (978-0-439-74919-0(0) , Levine, Arthur A. Bks.) Scholastic, Inc.

Miller, Jennifer. Run, Rasputin, Run! Trials & Friendships (Book 2) 2006. (ENG., Illus.). 172p. per. (***978-1-4120-8494-9(6)***) Trafford Publishing.

Noyes, Deborah. Hana in the Time of the Tulips. Ibatoulline, Bagram, illus. 2004. 40p. (J). (gr. 1-6). 16.99 (978-0-7636-1875-9(6)) Candlewick Pr.

Peet, Mal. Tamar: A Novel of Espionage, Passion, & Betrayal. 2007. (Illus.). 432p. (YA). (gr. 8 up). 17.99 (***978-0-7636-3488-9(3)***) Candlewick Pr.

Perkins, Lucy Fitch. Dutch Twins. 2006. pap. 25.99 (***978-1-4280-2261-4(9)***) IndyPublish.com.

Perkins, Lucy Fitch. The Dutch Twins. 2004. reprint ed. pap. 1.99 (978-1-4192-6040-7(5)) Kessinger Publishing, LLC.

Prins, Piet. The Flying Phantom. 2006. (Illus.). 142p. (J). pap. (978-1-894666-45-9(3)) Inheritance Pubns.

—The Grim Reaper. 2006. (Illus.). 130p. (J). pap. (978-1-894666-74-9(7)) Inheritance Pubns.

—The Haunted Castle. 2006. (Illus.). 139p. (J). pap. (978-1-894666-44-2(5)) Inheritance Pubns.

—Hideout in the Swamp. 2006. (Illus.). 136p. (J). pap. (978-1-894666-73-2(9)) Inheritance Pubns.

—The Lonely Sentinel. 2006. (Illus.). 140p. (J). pap. (978-1-894666-72-5(0)) Inheritance Pubns.

—The Mystery of the Abandoned Mill. Kramer, Jaap, illus. 2006. 127p. (J). pap. (978-1-894666-48-0(8)) Inheritance Pubns.

—The Sailing Sleuths. Kramer, Jaap, illus. 2006. 137p. (J). pap. (978-1-894666-46-6(1)) Inheritance Pubns.

—Scout's Distant Journey. 2006. (Illus.). 141p. (J). pap. (978-1-894666-49-7(6)) Inheritance Pubns.

—The Search for Sheltie. Kramer, Jaap, illus. 2006. 137p. (J). pap. (978-1-894666-43-5(7)) Inheritance Pubns.

—Stefan Derksen's Polar Adventure. 2004. (Illus.). 237p. (J). pap. (978-1-894666-67-1(4)) Inheritance Pubns.

—The Treasure of Rodensteyn Castle. Kramer, Jaap, illus. 2006. 132p. (J). pap. (978-1-894666-47-3(X)) Inheritance Pubns.

Prins, Piet & McAdam, Fraser. The Beggars Victory: The Sequel to Dispelling the Tyranny. 2006. (Illus.). 173p. (J). pap. (978-0-921100-53-9(1)) Inheritance Pubns.

Propp, Vera W. When the Soldiers Were Gone. 2001. (gr. 3-6). lib. bdg. 13.00 (978-0-613-36028-9(1)) Tandem Library Bks.

—When the Soldiers Were Gone: A Novel. 2006. 101p. (J). (gr. 4-8). reprint ed. 15.00 (978-1-4223-5310-3(9)) DIANE Publishing Co.

Rees, Elizabeth M. The Wedding: An Encounter with Jan Van Eyck. 2005. (Art Encounters Ser.). (Illus.). 176p. (ps-7). 15.95 (978-0-8230-0407-2(4)) Watson-Guptill Pubns., Inc.

Richardson, V. A. The House of Windjammer. (J). 2006. 352p. pap. 8.95 (978-1-58234-984-8(3)); 2003. (Illus.). 300p. 17.95 (978-1-58234-811-7(1)) Bloomsbury Publishing. (Bloomsbury Children).

—The Moneylender's Daughter. 2006. (Illus.). 300p. (YA). 17.95 (978-1-58234-885-8(5) , Bloomsbury Children) Bloomsbury Publishing.

Robb, Jackie & Stringle, Berny. The Story of Pea Brain. Duncan, Karen & Stringle, Sam, illus. 2004. (Bang on the Door Ser.). 32p. (YA). pap. (978-1-85602-383-2(4)) Chrysalis Children's Bks.

Shoup, Barbara. Vermeer's Daughter. 2006. 164p. (J). 16.95 (978-1-57860-131-8(2)) Emmis Bks.

Spring, Debbie. The Righteous Smuggler: A Holocaust Remembrance Book for Young Readers. 2005. (Illus.). 160p. (YA). pap. 6.95 (978-1-896764-97-9(5)) Second Story Pr. CAN. *Dist:* Univ. of Toronto Pr.

Suzuki, Etsuo. Anne Frank. 2006. (Illus.). 160p. pap. 9.95 (978-1-56970-974-0(2)) Digital Manga Publishing.

Van Ryk, Laverne. A Garland of Emeralds. 2006. (Illus.). 305p. (***978-1-4122-0156-8(X)***) Trafford Publishing.

Van Steenwyk, Elizabeth. A Traitor among Us. 2004. (Illus.). 143p. (J). (gr. 4-7). pap. 6.00 (978-0-8028-5157-4(6)) Eerdmans, William B. Publishing Co.

—A Traitor among Us. 1999. (978-0-606-17601-9(2)) Tandem Library Bks.

—Traitor among Us. 1999. (gr. 5-8). lib. bdg. 14.15 (978-0-613-59388-5(X)) Tandem Library Bks.

van Stockum, Hilda. A Day on Skates: 2007 Commemorative Edition. van Stockum, Hilda, illus. 2007. (Illus.). 44p. (J). 19.95 (***978-1-932350-18-0(7)***) Bethlehem Bks.

Vernon, Louise A. Peter & the Pilgrims. Eitzen, Allan, illus. 2nd ed. 2002. 128p. (YA). (gr. 4-9). 7.99 (978-0-8361-9226-1(5)) Herald Pr.

Weston, Carol. Melanie Martin Goes Dutch: The Private Diary of My Almost Bummer Summer with Cecily, Matt the Brat, & Vincent van Go Go Go. 2003. (Illus.). 240p. (J). (gr. 3-7). 5.99 (978-0-440-41899-3(2) , Yearling) Random Hse. Children's Bks.

—Melanie Martin Goes Dutch: The Private Diary of My Almost Bummer Summer with Cecily, Matt the Brat, & Vincent van Go Go Go. 2003. (gr. 3-6). lib. bdg. 25.70 (978-0-613-62527-2(7)) Tandem Library Bks.

Woelfle, Gretchen. Katje, the Windmill Cat. Bayley, Nicola, illus. 2006. 32p. (J). (ps). pap. 6.99 (978-0-7636-2089-9(0)) Candlewick Pr.

NETHERLANDS—HISTORY

Alagna, Magdalena. Anne Frank: Young Voice of the Holocaust. 2005. (Holocaust Biographies Ser.). (Illus.). 112p. (YA). (gr. 7-12). lib. bdg. 26.50 (978-0-8239-3373-0(3)) Rosen Publishing Group, Inc., The.

Brown, Jonatha A. Anne Frank. 2004. (Gente Que Hay Que Conocer Ser.). (Illus.). 24p. (J). pap. (978-0-8368-4358-3(4)) Stevens, Gareth Inc.

—Anne Frank. Acosta, Tatiana & Gutierrez, Guillermo, trs. 2004. (Gente Que Hay Que Conocer Ser.). (SPA., Illus.). 24p. (J). lib. bdg. 19.33 (978-0-8368-4351-4(7)) Stevens, Gareth Inc.

Davis, Kevin A. Look What Came from the Netherlands. 2002. (gr. 3-6). lib. bdg. 15.25 (978-0-613-59511-7(4)) Tandem Library Bks.

De Capua, Sarah. Netherlands. 2003. (First Reports). (Illus.). 48p. (J). (gr. 3 up). lib. bdg. 22.60 (978-0-7565-0426-7(0)) Compass Point Bks.

Docalavich, Heather. The Netherlands. 2006. (European Union Ser.). (Illus.). 88p. (YA). (gr. 5 up). lib. bdg. (978-1-4222-0057-5(4)) Mason Crest Pubs.

Dutch Colonies in the Americas, 6 Pks. (On Deck Ser.: Vol. 2). 24p. (gr. 4-5). 35.00 (978-0-7578-5800-0(7)) Rigby Education.

Gibson, Karen Bush. New Netherland: The Dutch Settle the Hudson Valley. 2006. (Building America Ser.). (Illus.). 48p. (J). (gr. 4-8). lib. bdg. 20.95 (978-1-58415-461-7(6)) Mitchell Lane Pubs., Inc.

Parker, Lewis K. Dutch Colonies in the Americas. 2003. (Reading Power Ser.). (Illus.). 24p. (J). lib. bdg. 17.25 (978-0-8239-6472-7(8) , PowerKids Pr.) Rosen Publishing Group, Inc., The.

Renaud, Anne. A Bloom of Friendship: The Story of the Canadian Tulip Festival. Spires, Ashley, illus. 2005. 24p. pap. (978-1-897073-35-3(6)) Lobster Pr.

Slier, Deborah & Shine, Ian, eds. Hidden Letters. Pritchard, Marion, tr. from DUT. 2007. Orig. Title: See You in Free Amsterdam: Letters of Flip Slier from the Molengoot Labor Camp. (Illus.). 160p. (YA). (gr. 7 up). 29.95 (978-1-887734-88-2(0)) Star Bright Bks., Inc.

Whitehurst, Susan. The Pilgrims Before the Mayflower. 2002. (Library of the Pilgrims). (Illus.). 24p. (J). (gr. 3). lib. bdg. 19.95 (978-0-8239-5811-5(6) , PowerKids Pr.) Rosen Publishing Group, Inc., The.

—A Plymouth Partnership: Pilgrims & Native Americans. 2002. (Library of the Pilgrims). (Illus.). 24p. (J). (gr. 3). lib. bdg. 19.95 (978-0-8239-5810-8(8) , PowerKids Pr.) Rosen Publishing Group, Inc., The.

Woog, Adam. Anne Frank. 2004. (Heroes & Villains Ser.). (Illus.). 112p. (J). 29.95 (978-1-59018-349-6(5) , Lucent Bks.) Thomson Gale.

NETHERLANDS—HISTORY—GERMAN OCCUPATION, 1940-1945

Wukovits, John F. Anne Frank. 1998. (Importance of Ser.). (Illus.). 96p. (YA). (gr. 7-10). 32.45 (978-1-56006-353-7(X) , Lucent Bks.) Thomson Gale.

NEUROLOGY

see Nervous System

NEUTRON, JIMMY (FICTITIOUS CHARACTER)—FICTION

Banks, Steve. Battle of the Band. 2003. (ps-2). lib. bdg. 11.25 (978-0-613-58144-8(X)) Tandem Library Bks.

Banks, Steven. Battle of the Band. Goldberg, Barry, illus. ed. 2005. (Adventures of Jimmy Neutron Ser.: 1). 24p. (J). lib. bdg. 15.00 (978-1-59054-779-3(9)) Fitzgerald Bks.

—Thanks a Lot, Robo-Turkey! LaPadula, Tom, illus. ed. 2005. (Adventures of Jimmy Neutron Ser.: 10). 24p. (J). lib. bdg. 15.00 (978-1-59054-787-8(X)) Fitzgerald Bks.

—When Pants Attack! Destefano, Stephen, illus. ed. 2005. (Adventures of Jimmy Neutron Ser.: 3). 24p. (J). lib. bdg. 15.00 (978-1-59054-789-2(6)) Fitzgerald Bks.

Beechen, Adam. Jimmy on Ice. Marderosian, Mark, illus. 2003. (Jimmy Neutron Ser.: Vol. 2). 32p. (J). pap. 3.99 (978-0-689-85294-7(0) , Simon Spotlight/Nickelodeon) Simon & Schuster Children's Publishing.

—Jimmy on Ice. 2003. (ps-2). lib. bdg. 11.80 (978-0-613-58154-7(7)) Tandem Library Bks.

Collins, Terry. Chew on This! 2003. (ps-2). lib. bdg. 11.25 (978-0-613-58145-5(8)) Tandem Library Bks.

DNA Productions Staff, ed. Jimmy Neutron, 2 vols., Vol. 1. 2003. (Illus.). 96p. pap. 7.99 (978-1-59182-401-5(X)) TOKYOPOP, Inc.

Koeppel, Ruth. Time Pincher. 2003. (ps-2). lib. bdg. 11.80 (978-0-613-58169-1(5)) Tandem Library Bks.

Mattern, Joanne. Dino Disaster! Spaziante, Patrick & Giles, Mike, illus. ed. 2005. (Adventures of Jimmy Neutron Ser.: 9). 24p. (J). lib. bdg. 15.00 (978-1-59054-782-3(9)) Fitzgerald Bks.

Miglis, Jenny. Return of the Pumpkin Head. Destefano, Stephen & Giles, Mike, illus. ed. 2005. (Adventures of Jimmy Neutron Ser.: 5). 24p. (J). lib. bdg. 15.00 (978-1-59054-785-4(3)) Fitzgerald Bks.

Redecker, Kent. Jimmy Neutron 101 Exploring My World. 2003. (ps-2). lib. bdg. 14.15 (978-0-613-58153-0(9)) Tandem Library Bks.

NEVADA

Bedunnah, Gary. Discovering Nevada. Baird, Madge, ed. 4th ed. 1998. (Illus.). 184p. (gr. 4-7). 27.95 (978-0-87905-570-7(7)) Gibbs Smith, Publisher.

Brown, Jonatha A. Nevada. 2006. (Portraits of the States Ser.). (Illus.). 32p. (J). pap. (978-0-8368-4690-4(7)); lib. bdg. 23.33 (978-0-8368-4671-3(0)) Stevens, Gareth Inc.

Coerr, Eleanor. S Is for Silver: A Nevada Alphabet. Park, Darcie, illus. 2004. (State Ser.). 40p. (J). 17.95 (978-1-58536-117-5(8)) Sleeping Bear Pr.

Deford, Debra. Nevada: The Silver State. 2003. (World Almanac Library of the States). (Illus.). 48p. (J). (gr. 5 up). pap. 14.95 (978-0-8368-5325-4(3)); lib. bdg. 30.00 (978-0-8368-5154-0(4)) Stevens, Gareth Inc. (World Almanac Library).

Feinstein, Stephen. Nevada: A MyReportLinks.com Book. 2002. (Illus.). 32p. (J). (gr. 4-10). lib. bdg. 25.26 (978-0-7660-5024-2(6) , MyReportLinks.com Bks.) Enslow Pubs., Inc.

Fradin, Dennis Brindell. Nevada. 1998. (From Sea to Shining Sea Ser.). (Illus.). 64p. (J). (gr. 3-5). pap. 7.95 (978-0-516-26280-2(7) , Children's Pr.) Scholastic Library Publishing.

Gibson, Karen Bush. Nevada Facts & Symbols. (States & Their Symbols Ser.). 24p. (J). 2000. (Illus.). (gr. 2-3). lib. bdg. 18.60 (978-0-7368-0641-1(5) , Bridgestone Bks.); 2003. lib. bdg. 19.93 (978-0-7368-2258-9(5)) Capstone Pr., Inc.

Glaser, Jason. Nevada. 2003. (Land of Liberty Ser.). (Illus.). 64p. (J). lib. bdg. 25.26 (978-0-7368-2186-5(4)) Capstone Pr., Inc.

Heinrichs, Ann. Nevada. Kania, Matt, illus. 2005. (Welcome to the USA Ser.). 40p. (J). (gr. 1-5). 27.07 (978-1-59296-476-5(1)) Child's World, Inc.

—Nevada. 2003. (This Land Is Your Land Ser.). (Illus.). 48p. (J). (gr. 3 up). lib. bdg. 22.60 (978-0-7565-0327-7(2)) Compass Point Bks.

—Nevada. 2007. (America the Beautiful, Third Ser.). (Illus.). 144p. (YA). (gr. 5-8). lib. bdg. 38.00 (***978-0-531-18586-5(9)*** , Children's Pr.) Scholastic Library Publishing.

Hicks, Terry Allan. Nevada. 2005. (It's My State! Ser.). (Illus.). 80p. (J). 27.07 (978-0-7614-1860-3(1) , Benchmark Bks.) Cavendish, Marshall Corp.

Kummer, Patricia K. Nevada. rev. ed. 2002. (One Nation Ser.). (Illus.). 48p. (J). (gr. 3-4). lib. bdg. 22.60 (978-0-7368-1252-8(0) , Bridgestone Bks.) Capstone Pr., Inc.

Labella, Susan. Nevada. (Rookie Read-about' Geography: States Ser.). 32p. (J). 2007. pap. 5.95 (***978-0-531-16815-8(8)***); 2006. (Illus.). (gr. 1-2). 20.50 (978-0-516-25467-8(7)) Scholastic Library Publishing. (Children's Pr.).

Lynch, Don & Thompson, David. Battle Born Nevada: People History Stories. Bean, James H., ed. Horton, Verne, illus. 2nd rev. ed. 1998. 356p. (YA). (gr. 7-8). 27.09 (978-0-913205-20-4(6)) Sage Hill Pubs., LLC.

Marsh, Carole. The Big Nevada Reproducible Activity Book. 2001. (Carole Marsh Nevada Bks.). (Illus.). 96p. (J). (gr. 2-6). pap. 9.95 (978-0-7933-9949-9(1)) Gallopade International.

—My First Book about Nevada. 2001. (Carole Marsh Nevada Bks.). (Illus.). 32p. (J). (gr. k-4). pap. 7.95 (978-0-7933-9891-1(6)) Gallopade International.

—Nevada Classic Christmas Trivia. 2002. (Carole Marsh Nevada Bks.). (Illus.). 32p. pap. 6.95 (978-0-635-01423-8(8) , 14238); lib. bdg. 21.95 (978-0-635-01424-5(6) , 14246) Gallopade International. (Marsh, Carole Bks.).

—Nevada Current Events Projects: 30 Cool, Activities, Crafts, Experiments & More for Kids to Do to Learn about Your State! 2003. (Nevada Experience Ser.). 32p. (gr. k-5). pap. 5.95 (978-0-635-02047-5(5) , Marsh, Carole Bks.) Gallopade International.

—The Nevada Experience Library State: Resource Set. 2001. (Illus.). (J). (gr. k-8). pap. 100.20 incl. cd-rom (978-0-635-00481-9(X)) Gallopade International.

—The Nevada Experience Pocket Guide. 2001. (Carole Marsh Nevada Bks.). (Illus.). 96p. (J). (gr. 3-8). pap. 6.95 (978-0-7933-9920-8(3)) Gallopade International.

—Nevada Geography Projects: 30 Cool, Activities, Crafts, Experiments & More for Kids to Do to Learn about Your State! 2003. (Nevada Experience Ser.). 32p. (gr. k-5). pap. 5.95 (978-0-635-01847-2(0) , Marsh, Carole Bks.) Gallopade International.

—Nevada Government Projects: 30 Cool, Activities, Crafts, Experiments & More for Kids to Do to Learn about Your State! 2003. (Nevada Experience Ser.). 32p. (gr. k-5). pap. 5.95 (978-0-635-01947-9(7) , Marsh, Carole Bks.) Gallopade International.

—Nevada Jeopardy! Answers & Questions about Our State! Line Art Staff, illus. 2001. 32p. (J). (gr. 3-8). pap. 7.95 (978-0-7933-9804-1(5)) Gallopade International.

—Nevada "Jography" A Fun Run Thru Our State! 2001. (Carole Marsh Nevada Bks.). (Illus.). 32p. (J). (gr. 3-8). pap. 7.95 (978-0-7933-9833-1(9)) Gallopade International.

—Nevada People Projects: 30 Cool, Activities, Crafts, Experiments & More for Kids to Do to Learn about Your State! 2003. (Nevada Experience Ser.). 32p. (gr. k-5). pap. 5.95 (978-0-635-01997-4(3) , Marsh, Carole Bks.) Gallopade International.

—Nevada Symbols & Facts Projects: 30 Cool, Activities, Crafts, Experiments & More for Kids to Do to Learn about Your State! 2003. (Nevada Experience Ser.). 32p. (gr. k-5). pap. 5.95 (978-0-635-01897-7(7) , Marsh, Carole Bks.) Gallopade International.

McLuskey, Krista. A Guide to Nevada. 2000. (American States Ser.). (Illus.). 32p. (J). (gr. 3-7). lib. bdg. 16.95 (978-1-930954-60-1(3)) Weigl Pubs., Inc.

Murray, Julie. Nevada. 2006. (Illus.). 32p. (J). (gr. 2-4). lib. bdg. 22.78 (978-1-59197-687-5(1) , Buddy Bks.) ABDO Publishing Co.

Nevada. 2000. (Switched on Schoolhouse Ser.). (Illus.). (YA). (gr. 7-12). pap. 24.95 incl. cd-rom (978-0-7403-0280-0(9) , SOSNV) Alpha Omega Pubns., Inc.

Obregon, José María & Brusca, María Cristina. Nevada. 2006. (Bilingual Library of the United States of America: Set 2). (ENG & SPA., Illus.). 32p. (J). (gr. 3-6). lib. bdg. 22.50 (978-1-4042-3093-4(9) , Buenas Letra) Rosen Publishing Group, Inc., The.

O'Connor, Rebecca & Myers, Dennis. Uniquely Nevada. 2004. (Illus.). 48p. (J). pap. (978-1-4034-4719-7(5)); lib. bdg. 27.07 (978-1-4034-4650-3(4)) Heinemann Library.

Sirvaitis, Karen. Nevada. 2nd exp. rev. ed. 2003. (Hello U. S. A. Ser.). (Illus.). 84p. (J). (gr. 3-6). 25.26 (978-0-8225-4095-3(9) , Lerner Pubns.) Lerner Publishing Group.

—Nevada. rev. ed. 2003. (gr. 3-6). lib. bdg. 15.25 (978-0-613-52454-4(3)) Tandem Library Bks.

Stefoff, Rebecca. Nevada. 2001. (Celebrate the States Ser.). (Illus.). 144p. (J). (gr. 4-8). lib. bdg. 37.07 (978-0-7614-1073-7(2) , Benchmark Bks.) Cavendish, Marshall Corp.

Williams, Suzanne Morgan. Nevada. 2003. (From Sea to Shining Sea Ser.: 2). (Illus.). 80p. (J). 30.50 (978-0-516-22488-6(3) , Children's Pr.) Scholastic Library Publishing.

NEVADA—FICTION

Asai, Carrie. Book of the Wind. 2003. lib. bdg. 15.30 (978-0-613-73443-1(2)) Tandem Library Bks.

Carabine, Sue. The Night Before Christmas in Nevada. Kawasaki, Shauna Mooney, illus. 2002. 60p. 5.95 (978-1-58685-168-2(3)) Gibbs Smith, Publisher.

Clark, Walter. Ox-Bow Incident. 2001. (gr. 7-12). lib. bdg. 18.75 (978-0-613-37164-3(X)) Tandem Library Bks.

Cox, Judy. Weird Stories from the Lonesome Cafe. Kidd, Diane, illus. 2000. 80p. (J). (gr. 2-4). 15.00 (978-0-15-202134-4(5)) Harcourt Children's Bks.

Farley, Terri. Heartbreak Bronco. 2004. 227p. (J). lib. bdg. 16.92 (***978-1-4242-0830-2(0)***) Fitzgerald Bks.

—Phantom Stallion. 2008. (Phantom Stallion: Wild Horse Island Ser.: No. 4). 240p. (J). pap. 4.99 (***978-0-06-088617-2(X)*** , Harper Trophy) HarperCollins Pubs.

—Rain Dance. 2004. 180p. (J). lib. bdg. 16.92 (***978-1-4242-0829-6(7)***) Fitzgerald Bks.

—Rain Forest Rose. 2007. (Phantom Stallion: Wild Horse Island Ser.). 224p. (J). (gr. 5 up). pap. 4.99 (***978-0-06-088616-5(1)*** , Harper Trophy) HarperCollins Pubs.

—Red Feather Filly. 2004. 201p. (J). lib. bdg. 16.92 (***978-1-4242-0828-9(9)***) Fitzgerald Bks.

Farley, Terri. Wild One. 2002. (gr. 5-8). lib. bdg. 13.00 (978-0-613-52735-4(6)) Tandem Library Bks.

Greenburg, Dan. Attack of the Evil Elvises. Pamintuan, Macky, illus. 2007. (Weird Planet Ser.: No. 4). 96p. (J). (gr. 2-4). lib. bdg. 11.99 (978-0-375-93347-9(6)); 3.99 (978-0-375-83347-2(1)) Random Hse. Children's Bks. (Random Hse. Bks. for Young Readers).

—Chilling with the Great Ones. Pamintuan, Macky, illus. 2006. 96p. (J). (gr. 2-5). lib. bdg. 11.99 (978-0-375-93346-2(8)); (Weird Planet Ser.: No. 3). (gr. 1-4). pap. 3.99 (978-0-375-83346-5(3)) Random Hse. Children's Bks. (Random Hse. Bks. for Young Readers).

—Lost in Las Vegas. Pamintuan, Macky, illus. 2006. 96p. (J). (gr. 2-5). pap. 3.99 (978-0-375-83345-8(5)); lib. bdg. 11.99 (978-0-375-93345-5(X)) Random Hse. Children's Bks. (Random Hse. Bks. for Young Readers).

Hancock, H. Irving. The Young Engineers in Nevada. rev. ed. 2006. 220p. 27.95 (978-1-4218-1754-5(3)); pap. 12.95 (978-1-4218-1854-2(X)) 1st World Publishing, Inc. (1st World Library - Literary Society).

Hancock, Irving H. The Young Engineers in Nevada or Seeking. 2006. pap. 72.99 (***978-1-4219-9874-9(2)***) IndyPublish.com.

—Young Engineers in Nevada or Seeking for. 2006. 78.99 (***978-1-4219-9871-8(8)***) IndyPublish.com.

Hautman, Pete. All-In. 2007. 192p. (YA). (gr. 7 up). 15.99 (***978-1-4169-1325-2(4)*** , Simon & Schuster Children's Publishing) Simon & Schuster Children's Publishing.

Hemphill, Helen. Long Gone Daddy. 2006. 176p. (J). 16.95 (978-1-932425-38-3(1) , Lemniscaat) Boyds Mills Pr.

Hoppe, Paul & Johnson, Henry. Travis & Freddy's Adventures in Vegas. 2006. 224p. (J). (gr. 5). 15.99 (978-0-525-47646-7(6) , Dutton Juvenile) Penguin Group (USA) Inc.

Horowitz, Anthony. Nightrise. 2007. (Gatekeepers Ser.: No. 3). 368p. (YA). pap. 17.99 (***978-0-439-68001-1(8)***) Scholastic, Inc.

Inagaki, Riichiro. Eyeshield 21, Volume 12. 2007. (Eyeshield 21 Ser.). 208p. (YA). pap. 7.99 (978-1-4215-1061-3(8)) Viz Media.

—Eyeshield 21, Volume 13. 2007. (Eyeshield 21 Ser.). 216p. (YA). pap. 7.99 (978-1-4215-1062-0(6)) Viz Media.

Jaffe, Michele. Bad Kitty. 2006. (Illus.). 288p. (J). 16.99 (978-0-06-078108-6(4)); lib. bdg. 17.89 (978-0-06-078109-5(2)) HarperCollins Pubs.

Lasky, Kathryn. Alice Rose & Sam. 1999. (J). (978-0-606-17380-3(3)) Tandem Library Bks.

Mason, Jane. Flintstones in Viva Rock Vegas: Flintstones Movie Storybook. 2000. (Illus.). 32p. (J). (ps-3). pap. 5.99 (978-0-439-17304-9(3)) Scholastic, Inc.

Otis, James. Dick in the Desert. 2005. reprint ed. pap. 15.95 (978-1-4179-0335-1(X)) Kessinger Publishing, LLC.

Penguin Books Staff. The Flintstones in Viva Rock Vegas, Level 2. 2001. (Illus.). 32p. (C). pap. 9.00 (978-0-582-45190-2(6)) Longman Publishing Group.

Pierson, Jan. The Haunted Horse of Gold Hill (Gold Hill, Nevada) 2006. (Ghostowners Ser.: Vol. 4). (Illus.). 109p. pap. 9.95 (978-0-9721800-3-0(6)) WildWest Publishing.

Platt, Chris. Moon Shadow. 2006. 192p. (J). 14.95 (978-1-56145-382-5(X) , Peachtree Junior) Peachtree Pubs., Ltd.

Reichart, George. A Bag of Lucky Rice. Mitchell, Mark, illus. 2004. 160p. pap. 10.95 (978-1-56792-278-3(3)) Godine, David R. Pub.

Sargent, Dave & Sargent, Pat. Gus: (Slate Grullo) Be Thankful, 30, 32. Lenoir, Jane, illus. 2003. (Saddle Up Ser.: Vol. 32). 42p. (J). lib. bdg. 22.60 (978-1-56763-693-2(4)); pap. 6.95 (978-1-56763-694-9(2)) Ozark Publishing.

Smith, Roland. Zach's Lie. 2003. 224p. (J). (gr. 5-17). pap. 5.99 (978-0-7868-1440-4(3)) Hyperion Bks. for Children.

—Zach's Lie. 2003. (gr. 5-8). lib. bdg. 14.15 (978-0-613-63491-5(8)) Tandem Library Bks.

Wilson, Karen Collett. Pogonip Magic. Zerga, Susan A., illus. 2002. 40p. (J). (ps-3). 14.95 (978-0-9722570-0-8(4)) Snowbound Bks.

Young, Jan. The Orange Slipknot. Lehmkuhl, Pat, illus. 2007. 178p. (J). per. 10.00 (***978-0-9772525-5-8(8)***) Raven Publishing Inc. of Montana.

NEVADA—HISTORY

Fein, E. How to Draw Nevadas Sights & Symbols. 2002. (Kids Guide to Drawing America Ser.). 32p. (J). lib. bdg. 25.25 (978-0-8239-6084-2(6) , PowerKids Pr.) Rosen Publishing Group, Inc., The.

Marsh, Carole. My First Pocket Guide Nevada. 2000. (Nevada Experience! Ser.). (Illus.). 96p. (J). (gr. 3-8). 12.95 (978-0-635-01318-7(5) , 13185) Gallopade International.

—Nevada History Projects: 30 Cool, Activities, Crafts, Experiments & More for Kids to Do to Learn about Your State! 2003. (Nevada Experience Ser.). 32p. (gr. k-5). pap. 5.95 (978-0-635-01797-0(0) , Marsh, Carole Bks.) Gallopade International.

—Nevada Millionaire. 2001. (GameBook Ser.). 32p. (J). (gr. 3-8). pap., act. bk. ed. 9.95 (978-0-635-00072-9(5)) Gallopade International.

—Nevada Survivor. 2001. (GameBook Ser.). 32p. (J). (gr. 3-8). pap., act. bk. ed. 9.95 (978-0-635-00549-6(2)) Gallopade International.

—Who Wants to Be a Millionaire? 2001. (Carole Marsh Nevada Bks.). (J). lib. bdg. 29.95 (978-0-635-00073-6(3)) Gallopade International.

NEVER-NEVER LAND (IMAGINARY PLACE)—FICTION

Barrie, J. M. Peter Pan. 2000. (Charming Classics). 240p. (J). (gr. 4-7). pap. 6.99 (978-0-694-01318-0(8) , Harper Festival) HarperCollins Pubs.

—Peter Pan: The Original Tale of Neverland. Jaramillo, Raquel, illus. Jaramillo, Raquel, photos by. unabr. ed. 2003. 135p. (YA). (gr. 5-8). reprint ed. 25.00 (978-0-7567-6883-6(7)) DIANE Publishing Co.

—Peter Pan & Other Plays: The Admirable Crichton; Peter Pan; When Wendy Grew Up; What Every Woman Knows; Mary Rose. Hollindale, Peter, ed. 1999. (Oxford World's Classics Ser.). (Illus.). 384p. 14.95 (978-0-19-283919-0(5)) Oxford Univ. Pr., Inc.

—Peter Pan & Other Plays Vol. 10: The Admirable Crichton; Peter Pan; When Wendy Grew Up; What Every Woman Knows; Mary Rose. (J). reprint ed. 57.50 (978-0-404-08790-6(6)) AMS Pr., Inc.

—Peter Pan & Wendy. Foreman, Michael, illus. 1999. (Abbeville Classics Ser.). 176p. (J). 12.95 (978-0-7892-0560-5(2)); pap. 7.95 (978-0-7892-0550-6(5)) Abbeville Pr., Inc. (Abbeville Kids).

—Peter Pan & Wendy. Foreman, Michael, illus. (J). 2007. 158p. pap. 13.95 (***978-1-84458-479-6(8));*** 2000. 176p. pap. 8.99 (978-1-85793-909-5(3) , Pavilion Bks., Ltd.) Anova Bks. GBR. *Dist:* Independent Pubs. Group, Trafalgar Square Publishing.

—Peter Pan & Wendy. Foreman, Michael, illus. 2003. (Chrysalis Children's Classics Ser.). 176p. (YA). pap. (978-1-84365-039-3(8)) Chrysalis Children's Bks.

—Peter Pan & Wendy. Carruth, Jane, ed. Johnstone, Anne G., illus. 2000. 92p. (J). (gr. 4-6). reprint ed. 25.00 (978-0-7881-9230-2(2)) DIANE Publishing Co.

—Peter Pan & Wendy. 2004. (Illus.). 96p. (J). 9.99 (978-0-517-22366-6(X) , Gramercy) Random Hse. Value Publishing.

—Peter Pan & Wendy: Centenary Edition. Ingpen, Robert R., illus. 2004. 216p. (J). (978-1-897035-12-2(8) , Blue Heron Bks.) Raincoast Bk. Distribution.

—Peter Pan in Kensington Gardens. (J). 18.95 (978-0-8488-0427-5(9)) Amereon LTD.

—Peter Pan in Kensington Gardens & Peter & Wendy. Hollingdale, Peter, ed. 1999. (Oxford World's Classics Ser.). (Illus.). 288p. 9.95 (978-0-19-283929-9(2)) Oxford Univ. Pr., Inc.

Levine, Gail Carson. Fairy Dust & the Quest for the Egg. 2008. 208p. (J). (gr. 1-5). pap. 9.99 (***978-1-4231-0819-1(1)***) Disney Pr.

NEW ENGLAND

Greene, Jacqueline Dembar. Powwow: A Good Day to Dance. Greene, Jacqueline Dembar, photos by. 1998. (First Bks.). (Illus.). 64p. (J). (gr. 5-7). 22.00 (978-0-531-20337-8(9) , Watts, Franklin) Scholastic Library Publishing.

Koestler-Grack, Rachel A. Northern Colonial Town: Plymouth. 2003. (J). pap. (978-1-58417-079-2(4)) Lake Street Pubs.

New England States Grades 4-6. 2002. 64p. (J). (gr. 4-6). pap. 8.94 (978-1-889369-42-6(X)) Teaching Ink, Inc.

Stewart, Mark. New England. 2006. (Regions of the USA Ser.). (Illus.). 56p. (J). (978-1-4109-2306-6(1)); pap. (978-1-4109-2314-1(2)) Steck-Vaughn.

NEW ENGLAND—FICTION

Alcott, Louisa May. Jack & Jill. Date not set. 352p. (YA). 25.95 (978-0-8488-2671-0(X)) Amereon LTD.

—Jo's Boys. 2000. 252p. (J). pap. 9.95 (978-0-594-05147-3(9)) 1873 Pr.

—Jo's Boys. (Dover Juvenile Classics Ser.). (J). 2002. 288p. (gr. 4-7). pap. 3.00 (978-0-486-42226-8(7)); 1999. (Illus.). 80p. pap. 1.00 (978-0-486-40789-0(6)) Dover Pubns., Inc.

—Jo's Boys. l.t. ed. 2005. 424p. pap. (978-1-84637-067-0(1)) Echo Library.

—Little Men: Life at Plumfield with Jo's Boys. (Early Best Sellers Ser.). reprint ed. (J). lib. bdg. 48.00 (978-0-7426-1004-0(7)); 2001. (Illus.). pap. 28.00 (978-0-7426-6004-5(4)) Classic Bks.

—Little Men: Life at Plumfield with Jo's Boys. 2001. (Dover Juvenile Classics Ser.). 304p. (J). (gr. 4-7). pap. 3.00 (978-0-486-41808-7(1)) Dover Pubns., Inc.

—Little Women. 2002. (Great Illustrated Classics Ser.). (Illus.). 240p. (J). (gr. 3-8). 21.35 (978-1-57765-693-7(8) , ABDO & Daughters) ABDO Publishing Co.

—Little Women. Dryhurst, Dinah, illus. 2000. 288p. (J). pap. 8.99 (978-1-86205-220-8(4) , Pavilion Bks., Ltd.) Anova Bks. GBR. *Dist:* Trafalgar Square Publishing.

—Little Women. 2002. (YA). 14.04 (978-0-7587-7589-4(X)) Book Wholesalers, Inc.

—Little Women. Alton, Anne Hiebert, ed. 2001. (Broadview Literary Texts Ser.). (Illus.). 619p. (J). pap. (978-1-55111-191-9(8)) Broadview Pr.

—Little Women. Lauter, Richard, illus. 192p. (J). 9.95 (978-1-56156-371-5(4)) Kidsbooks, Inc.

—Little Women. Lindskoog, Kathryn, ed. Chitouras, Barbara, illus. 2003. (Classics for Young Readers Ser.). 432p. (J). per. 12.99 (978-0-87552-734-5(5)) P & R Publishing.

—Little Women. 2001. (Classics Ser.). (Illus.). 528p. pap. 7.95 (978-0-375-75672-6(8) , Modern Library) Random House Publishing Group.

—Little Women. Smith, Jessie Willcox, illus. 2002. (Illustrated Library for Children). 400p. (J). 12.99 (978-0-517-22116-7(0) , Gramercy) Random Hse. Value Publishing.

—Little Women. 1998. (Children's Classics Ser.). (Illus.). 400p. (J). 6.99 (978-0-517-18954-2(2)) Random Hse. Value Publishing.

—Little Women. 2000. 576p. (J). (gr. 4-7). pap. 4.99 (978-0-439-10136-3(0)) Scholastic, Inc.

—Little Women. 2000. (Classics Ser.). 704p. (J). (gr. 4-7). pap. 5.99 (978-0-689-83531-5(0) , Aladdin) Simon & Schuster Children's Publishing.

—Little Women. 2001. (gr. k-3). lib. bdg. 14.15 (978-0-613-86261-5(9)); 2000. (gr. 3-6). lib. bdg. 10.65 (978-0-613-90409-4(5)); 2000. (gr. 3-6). lib. bdg. 14.15 (978-0-613-63211-9(7)); 2000. (gr. 5-8). lib. bdg. 13.00 (978-0-613-66717-3(4)) Tandem Library Bks.

—Little Women. 2001. (Signature Classics Ser.). (Illus.). 544p. (J). 12.95 (978-1-58279-069-5(8) , 64) Trident Pr. International.

—Little Women. Dryhurst, Dinah & Rust, Graham, illus. 2001. (Storytime Classics Ser.). 32p. (J). (ps-3). pap. 5.99 (978-0-14-131202-6(5) , Puffin) Penguin Group (USA) Inc.

—Little Women. Corvino, Lucy, illus. 2005. (Classic Starts Ser.). 160p. 4.95 (978-1-4027-1236-4(7)) Sterling Publishing Co., Inc.

—Little Women. unabr. ed. 2004. (Chrysalis Children's Classics Ser.). (Illus.). 190p. (YA). pap. (978-1-84365-049-2(5)) Chrysalis Children's Bks.

—Little Women. unabr. ed. 2000. (Dover Juvenile Classics Ser.). (Illus.). 608p. (J). (gr. 4-7). pap. 4.00 (978-0-486-41023-4(4)) Dover Pubns., Inc.

—Little Women. 1998. 559p. (J). reprint ed. lib. bdg. 25.00 (978-1-58287-046-5(2)) North Bks.

—Little Women, Bk. 1. 2003. (gr. 3-6). lib. bdg. 15.30 (978-0-613-70764-0(8)) Tandem Library Bks.

—Little Women. deluxe ed. 2000. (Signature Classics Ser.). (Illus.). 544p. (J). (978-1-58279-075-6(2)) Trident Pr. International.

—Little Women: Book & Charm. (Charming Classics). (Illus.). (J). 2003. 384p. 6.99 (978-0-06-051180-7(X)); 2000. 5.95 (978-0-694-01527-6(X)) HarperCollins Pubs. (Harper Festival).

—Little Women: Two Books in One. 2003. (gr. 3-6). lib. bdg. 22.25 (978-0-613-77101-6(X)) Tandem Library Bks.

—Little Women: With a Discussion of Family. Lauter, Richard, illus. 2003. (Values in Action Illustrated Classics Ser.). 191p. (J). (978-1-59203-032-3(7)) Learning Challenge, Inc.

—Little Women Bk. 2: Good Wives: Book with Charm. 2004. (Charming Classics). 416p. (J). pap. 6.99 (978-0-06-055991-5(8) , Harper Festival) HarperCollins Pubs.

—Little Women & Good Wives. 1998. (Children's Classics). (ENG.). 224p. (J). (gr. 4-7). pap. (978-1-85326-116-9(5) , 1165WW) Wordsworth Editions, Ltd.

—The Little Women Pop-Up Dollhouse. Krystanovich, Vesna, illus. 2000. 8p. (J). 21.95 (978-1-55263-290-1(3)) Key Porter Bks. CAN. *Dist:* Firefly Bks., Ltd.

—Mujercitas. (SPA., Illus.). 192p. (YA). 11.95 (978-84-7281-101-0(8) , AF1101) Auriga, Ediciones S.A. ESP. *Dist:* Continental Bk. Co., Inc.

—Mujercitas. 2002. (Classics for Young Readers Ser.). (SPA.). (YA). 14.95 (978-84-392-0901-0(0) , EV30608) Lectorum Pubns., Inc.

—Mujercitas. (YA). 7.95 (978-84-95311-16-0(X)) Mestas, Jorge A. Ediciones Escolares La Escuela Nueva y Alinorma, S.L. ESP. *Dist:* Continental Bk. Co., Inc.

—Mujercitas. 1998. (SPA., Illus.). 304p. (J). (978-84-01-46257-3(6)) Plaza & Janes Editories, S.A.

—Mujercitas. (Coleccion Estrella). (SPA., Illus.). 64p. (J). 14.95 (978-950-11-0010-5(3) , SGM010) Sigmar ARG. *Dist:* Continental Bk. Co., Inc.

—Mujercitas. 2000. (Coleccion "Clasicos Juveniles" Ser.). (SPA., Illus.). 292p. (gr. 4-7). pap. 12.95 (978-1-58348-784-6(0)) iUniverse, Inc.

—An Old-Fashioned Girl. 1999. (J). 25.01 (978-0-316-03809-6(1)) Little Brown & Co.

—An Old-Fashioned Thanksgiving. Bernardin, James, illus. 2005. 32p. (J). (ps-3). 15.99 (978-0-06-000450-7(9)); lib. bdg. 16.89 (978-0-06-000451-4(7)) HarperCollins Pubs.

Alcott, Louisa May. Rose in Bloom. 2002. (ENG.). 252p. pap. 20.99 (***978-1-4043-2865-5(3)***) IndyPublish.com.

—Rose in Bloom. l.t. ed. 2005. 456p. 29.95 (978-0-7862-7294-5(5) , Large Print Pr.) Thorndike Pr.

Alcott, Louisa May & Dorling Kindersley Publishing Staff. Little Women. Gerver, Jane E., ed. Molan, Chris, illus. 1999. (Eyewitness Classics Ser.). 64p. (J). (gr. 2 up). 14.99 (978-0-7894-4767-8(3)) Dorling Kindersley Publishing, Inc.

Alcott, Louisa May & Eiselein, Gregory. Little Women. 2003. (Illus.). 352p. (YA). pap. 13.00 (978-0-393-97614-4(9)) Norton, W. W. & Co., Inc.

Alcott, Louisa May, et al. Mujercitas. Prunier, James, tr. 2002. (SPA., Illus.). 268p. (J). 29.95 (978-84-348-5324-9(8)) SM Ediciones ESP. *Dist:* AIMS International Bks., Inc.

Aldrich, Thomas Bail. The Story of a Bad Boy. 2006. pap. (***978-1-4065-0613-6(3)***) Dodo Pr.

Alger, Horatio. Mark Manning's Mission: The Story of a Shoe Factory Boy. unabr. ed. 2002. (Polyglot Press Alger Ser.). (Illus.). (J). pap. 17.95 (978-1-4115-0022-8(9)) Polyglot Pr., Inc.

Alger, Horatio. Struggling Upward: Or, Luke Larkin's Luck. 2006. pap. (***978-1-4065-0723-2(7)***) Dodo Pr.

—Struggling Upward: Or, Luke Larkin's Luck. unabr. ed. 2002. (Polyglot Press Alger Ser.). (Illus.). (J). pap. 17.95 (978-1-4115-0053-2(9)) Polyglot Pr., Inc.

Barbour, Ralph Henry. The Adventure Club Afloat. 2006. 78.99 (***978-1-4280-1948-5(0)***) IndyPublish.com.

Bass, Ruth. Sarah's Daughter. 2007. pap. 14.95 (***978-0-9774053-4-3(6)***) North River Pr. Publishing Corp., The.

Bowen, Gary. The Mare's Nest. Kimble, Warren, illus. 2001. 48p. (J). (gr. 1-5). 17.95 (978-0-06-028408-4(0)); (gr. 3-6). 17.89 (978-0-06-028407-7(2)) HarperCollins Pubs.

Cathie & Jessie's Noisy New England Adventure. 2006. (Illus.). 32p. (J). cd-rom 12.99 (978-0-9773526-1-6(7)) Diversified A+ Pubns.

Clark, Catherine. Gilmore Girls No. 1: Like Mother, Like Daughter. 2002. 160p. (YA). mass mkt. 5.99 (978-0-06-009212-2(2)) HarperCollins Pubs.

Coatsworth, Elizabeth. Away Goes Sally. 2004. (Illus.). 118p. (J). pap. 10.95 (978-1-883937-83-6(3)) Bethlehem Bks.

Collier, James Lincoln. The Empty Mirror. 192p. 2006. (YA). pap. 6.95 (978-1-58234-904-6(5)); 2004. (J). 16.95 (978-1-58234-949-7(5)) Bloomsbury Publishing. (Bloomsbury Children).

Collins, Pat L. Schooner. Collins, Pat L., illus. 2002. (Illus.). 32p. (J). (gr. 2-5). 14.95 (978-1-889833-35-4(5)) Commonwealth Editions.

Croisetiere, Julie A. Private-Keep Out! 2004. 49p. pap. 12.95 (978-1-4137-3381-5(6)) PublishAmerica, Inc.

Dalgliesh, Alice. The Courage of Sarah Noble. Weisgard, Leonard, illus. 2002. (J). 13.40 (978-0-7587-0249-4(3)) Book Wholesalers, Inc.

DeMitchell, Terri. You Will Come Back. 2004. (Illus.). 176p. (J). pap. 14.95 (978-1-932278-02-6(8)) Mayhaven Publishing.

DiMare, Loren Spiotta. Rockwell: A Boy & His Dog. Miller, Cliff, illus. 2005. 32p. (J). 14.95 (978-0-7641-5790-5(6)) Barron's Educational Series, Inc.

Edwards, Nicholas. Our Hero. 2002. (gr. k-3). lib. bdg. 12.40 (978-0-613-72041-0(5)) Tandem Library Bks.

—Santa Paws, Our Hero. 2002. (Santa Paws Ser.: No. 5). 176p. (J). pap. 4.99 (978-0-439-37283-1(6)) Scholastic, Inc.

Emerson, Charlotte. Amy's True Prize. 1999. (Little Women Journals Ser.). (J). (978-0-606-16348-4(4)) Tandem Library Bks.

—Beth's Snow Dancer. 1999. (Little Women Journals Ser.). (J). (978-0-606-16347-7(6)) Tandem Library Bks.

—Meg's Dearest Wish. 1999. (Little Women Journals). (J). (978-0-606-16350-7(6)) Tandem Library Bks.

Emerson, Charlotte & Alcott, Louisa May. Amy's True Prize. Wasden, Kevin, illus. 1999. (Little Women Journals). 128p. (J). (gr. 3-7). mass mkt. 3.99 (978-0-380-79706-6(2)) HarperCollins Pubs.

—Beth's Snow Dancer. Wasden, Kevin, illus. 1999. (Little Women Journals). 128p. (J). (gr. 3-7). pap. 3.99 (978-0-380-79704-2(6)) HarperCollins Pubs.

—Jo's Troubled Heart. Wasden, Kevin, illus. 1999. (Little Women Journals). 128p. (J). (gr. 3-7). pap. 3.99 (978-0-380-79669-4(4)) HarperCollins Pubs.

—Meg's Dearest Wish. Wasden, Kevin, illus. 1999. (Little Women Journals). 128p. (J). (gr. 3-7). pap. 3.99 (978-0-380-79705-9(4)) HarperCollins Pubs.

Glencoe McGraw-Hill Staff & McGraw-Hill - Jamestown Education Staff. Topics from the Restless, Bk. 1. unabr. ed. 1999. (Wordsworth Classics Ser.). (gr. 10 up). pap. 24.64 (978-0-89061-116-6(5) , 9780890611166) Jamestown.

Hall, Donald. Ox-Cart Man. Cooney, Barbara, illus. 2002. (J). 14.04 (978-0-7587-0065-0(2)) Book Wholesalers, Inc.

—Ox-Cart Man. Cooney, Barbara, illus. 2000. (J). pap. 19.97 incl. audio (978-0-7366-9188-8(X)) Books on Tape, Inc.

—Ox-Cart Man. Cooney, Barbara, illus. 2004. 37p. (J). (gr. k-3). reprint ed. pap. 5.00 (978-0-7567-7110-2(2)) DIANE Publishing Co.

Harrar, George. Trouble with Jeremy Change. 2003. (gr. 5-8). lib. bdg. 15.25 (978-0-613 79199-1(1)) Tandem Library Bks.

Hawthorne, Nathaniel. The Scarlet Letter. Redondo, Virgilio, illus. 2nd ed. 1998. (Illustrated Classic Book Ser.). 61p. (J). (gr. 3 up). reprint ed. pap. 4.95 (978-1-56767-265-7(5)) Educational Insights, Inc.

Hawthorne, Nathaniel & Larkin, Rochelle. The House of the Seven Gables. Marcos, Pablo, illus. 2005. (Great Illustrated Classics Ser.). 240p. (J). (gr. 3-8). 21.35 (978-1-59679-242-5(6) , ABDO & Daughters) ABDO Publishing Co.

Heuston, Kimberley B. The Shakeress. 1998. 208p. (YA). (gr. 7 up). 16.95 (978-1-886910-56-0(1) , Lemniscaat) Boyds Mills Pr.

Heuston, Kimberley Burton. The Shakeress. 2008. (J). pap. (***978-1-59078-575-1(4)*** , Calkins Creek) Boyds Mills Pr.

Heuston, Kimberly. The Shakeress. 2004. 208p. (YA). pap. 6.99 (978-0-14-240054-8(8) , Puffin) Penguin Group (USA) Inc.

Howard, Ginger. William's House. Day, Larry, illus. 2001. 32p. (gr. k-3). lib. bdg. 22.90 (978-0-7613-1674-9(4) , Millbrook Pr.) Lerner Publishing Group.

James, Sara & Ruckdeschel, Liz. What If ... All the Boys Wanted You. 2006. 288p. (YA). (gr. 7). pap. 8.95 (978-0-385-73297-0(X) , Delacorte Bks. for Young Readers) Random Hse. Children's Bks.

Jenner, Caryn. Black Beauty. 2000. (gr. k-3). lib. bdg. 11.80 (978-0-613-24377-3(3)) Tandem Library Bks.

Jewett, Sarah Orne. A White Heron. Alvord, Douglas, illus. 2005. 32p. (J). pap. 10.95 (978-1-56792-287-5(2)) Godine, David R. Pub.

Kinkade, Thomas. Katherine's Story. 2004. (Girls of Lighthouse Lane Ser.). 176p. (J). (gr. 5 up). 13.89 (978-0-06-054342-6(6)) HarperCollins Pubs.

Kinkade, Thomas & Tamar, Erika. Rose's Story. 2004. (Girls of Lighthouse Lane Ser.: No. 2). (Illus.). 192p. (J). (gr. 5 up). 12.99 (978-0-06-054344-0(2)) HarperCollins Pubs.

Lendroth, Susan. Ocean Wide, Ocean Deep. Allen, Raul, illus. 2007. (J). ***(*978-1-58246-232-5(1)*** , Tricycle Pr.) Ten Speed Pr.

Levin, Betty. Shoddy Cove. 2003. 208p. (J). (gr. 5 up). 15.99 (978-0-06-052271-1(2)) HarperCollins Pubs.

Pfeffer, Susan Beth. Ghostly Tales: Four Stories. 2002. (Portraits of Little Women Ser.). (gr. 3-6). lib. bdg. 12.40 (978-0-613-85700-0(3)) Tandem Library Bks.

Rees, Celia. Sorceress. (Illus.). 352p. (YA). (gr. 9). 2003. pap. 8.99 (978-0-7636-2183-4(8)); 2002. 15.99 (978-0-7636-1847-6(0)) Candlewick Pr.

Seidler, Tor. The Dulcimer Boy. Selznick, Brian, illus. 160p. (J). reprint ed. 2004. pap. 6.99 (978-0-06-441048-9(X) , Harper Trophy); 2003. 15.99 (978-0-06-623609-4(6)) HarperCollins Pubs.

Sewell, Anna. Black Beauty. (Illus.). 226p. (YA). (978-0-681-99550-5(5) , Random House) Random House Publishing Group.

—Black Beauty: The Autobiography of a Horse. 2000. (gr. 5-8). lib. bdg. 12.40 (978-0-613-28253-6(1)) Tandem Library Bks.

Sewell, Anna & Marsh, Laura F. Black Beauty. 2006. (My First Classics Ser.). 112p. (J). pap. 4.99 (978-0-06-079148-3(9) , Harper Festival) HarperCollins Pubs.

Shaffer, Elizabeth N. Hannah & the Indian King, Vol. 2. Pratt, Fran, ed. 2002. (Historical Novel Ser.). pap. 9.95 (978-0-936369-35-8(3)) Son-Rise Pubns. & Distribution Co.

Sidney, Margaret. Five Little Peppers & How They Grew. 2006. (Dover Value Editions Ser.). (Illus.). 224p. (J). pap. 5.95 (978-0-486-45267-8(0)) Dover Pubns., Inc.

Stowe, Harriet Beecher. Betty's Bright Idea; Deacon Pitkin's Far. 2006. 77.99 ***(*978-1-4280-3123-4(5))*** IndyPublish.com.

—Bettys Bright Idea Deacon Pitkins Farm A. 2006. pap. ***(*978-1-4068-3093-4(3))*** Echo Library.

Swegles, Maryanne. Digging for Bottles. 2005. (Illus.). 28p. (J). 15.00 (978-0-9768418-0-7(0)) Hydrangea Pr.

Swicord, Robin. Little Women: The Children's Picture Book. 2004. (Illus.). 96p. (gr. 2 up). 15.95 (978-1-55704-216-3(0)) Newmarket Pr.

Tentas, Jane Grant. Alice & the Bird Lady. Tentas, Jane Grant, illus. l.t. ed. 2002. 36p. per. 13.95 (978-0-9658983-6-2(9)) Book Nook Pr.

Thorson, Robert & Thorson, Kristine. Stone Wall Secrets. Moore, Gustav, illus. 1998. 40p. (J). (gr. 3-7). 16.95 (978-0-88448-195-9(6)) Tilbury Hse. Pubs.

Tuthill, Louisa C. Hurrah for New England! or the Virginia Boy's Vacation. 2004. reprint ed. pap. 15.95 (978-1-4191-2504-1(4)); pap. 1.99 (978-1-4192-2504-8(9)) Kessinger Publishing, LLC.

Wall, Patricia Q. Child Out of Place: A Story for New England. Ronnquist, Debby, illus. 2003. 116p. (J). (gr. 6-9). pap. 12.00 (978-0-9742185-0-2(2)) Fall Rose Bks.

Wargin, Kathy-Jo. The Legend of Thanksgiving. Papp, Robert, illus. 2008. (J). (978-0-310-71179-7(7)) Zonderkidz.

Wiggin, Kate Douglas. Rebecca of Sunnybrook Farm. Tadiello, Ed, illus. 2002. (Great Illustrated Classics Ser.). 240p. (J). (gr. 3-8). 21.35 (978-1-57765-823-8(X) , ABDO & Daughters) ABDO Publishing Co.

—Rebecca of Sunnybrook Farm. (J). 23.95 (978-0-8488-0854-9(1)) Amereon LTD.

—Rebecca of Sunnybrook Farm. Warren, Eliza Gatewood, ed. Tadiello, Ed, illus. 2006. 240p. (YA). (gr. 4-8). reprint ed. 10.00 (978-0-7567-9830-7(2)) DIANE Publishing Co.

—Rebecca of Sunnybrook Farm. 1999. (Tor Classics Ser.). 288p. (J). (gr. 4-7). pap. 2.99 (978-0-8125-6590-4(8) , Tor Classics) Doherty, Tom Assocs., LLC.

—Rebecca of Sunnybrook Farm. 2003. (Dover Evergreen Classics Ser.). 208p. (J). (gr. 4-7). pap. 3.00 (978-0-486-42845-1(1)) Dover Pubns., Inc.

—Rebecca of Sunnybrook Farm. McClintock, Barbara, illus. 2003. 304p. (J). (gr. 5 up). tchr. ed. 20.00 (978-0-618-34694-3(5)) Houghton Mifflin Co. Trade & Reference Div.

—Rebecca of Sunnybrook Farm. 2006. 63.99 ***(*978-1-4280-3421-1(8))*** IndyPublish.com.

—Rebecca of Sunnybrook Farm. 2005. pap. 30.95 (978-1-4179-1457-9(2)); 2004. reprint ed. pap. 19.95 (978-1-4179-9996-5(9)); 2004. reprint ed. pap. 1.99 (978-1-4179-9946-0(2)) Kessinger Publishing, LLC.

—Rebecca of Sunnybrook Farm. l.t. ed. 1999. (Large Print Heritage Ser.). 340p. (YA). (gr. 7-12). lib. bdg. 33.95 (978-1-58118-045-9(4) , 22514) LRS.

—Rebecca of Sunnybrook Farm. 2003. (Aladdin Classics Ser.). 368p. (J). pap. 4.99 (978-0-689-86001-0(3) , Aladdin) Simon & Schuster Children's Publishing.

—Rebecca of Sunnybrook Farm. Akib, Jamel, illus. 2007. (Classic Starts Ser.). 160p. (J). 4.95 (978-1-4027-3693-3(2)) Sterling Publishing Co., Inc.

—Rebecca of Sunnybrook Farm. l.t. ed. 2002. (Perennial Bestsellers Ser.). 374p. 29.95 (978-0-7862-4625-0(1)) Thorndike Pr.

—Rebecca of Sunnybrook Farm Book & Charm. 2001. (Charming Classics). (Illus.). 336p. (J). (gr. 3-7). pap. 6.99 (978-0-694-01528-3(8) , Harper Festival) HarperCollins Pubs.

Winfield, Arthur M. The Rover Boys down East or the Struggle for the Stanhope Fortune. 2006. (ENG.). 316p. per. 30.95 ***(*978-1-4286-4113-6(0))*** Kessinger Publishing, LLC.

NEW ENGLAND—HISTORY

Arenstam, Peter, et al. MayFlower 1620: A New Look at a Pilgrim Voyage. 2004. (Illus.). 47p. (J). (gr. k-4). 18.00 (978-0-7567-7967-2(7)) DIANE Publishing Co.

Carole Marsh. New England Coloring. 2004. (City Bks.). 24p. (gr. k-5). pap., act. bk. ed. 3.95 (978-0-635-02233-2(8)) Gallopade International.

Cosson, M. J. Yankee Whalers. 2007. (Events in American History Ser.). (Illus.). 48p. (J). (gr. 4-6). lib. bdg. 29.93 (978-1-60044-140-0(8)) Rourke Publishing, LLC.

Cowan, Mary Morton. Timberrr! A History of Logging in New England. 2003. (Women at War Ser.). (Illus.). 128p. (gr. 5 up). lib. bdg. 25.90 (978-0-7613-1866-8(6) , Twenty-First Century Bks.) Lerner Publishing Group.

Drake, Samuel Adams. The Making of New England 1580-1643. 2001. 140p. (YA). reprint ed. (978-1-58218-399-2(6)); pap. (978-1-58218-398-5(8)) Digital Scanning, Inc.

—New England Legends & Folk Lore. 2001. 498p. (YA). reprint ed. pap. (978-1-58218-442-5(9)) Digital Scanning, Inc.

Isaacs, Sally Senzell. Life in a Whaling Town. (Picture the Past Ser.). (Illus.). 32p. (J). 2002. (gr. k-3). pap. 7.50 (978-1-58810-416-8(8) , 91189); 2001. (gr. 2-4). lib. bdg. 21.36 (978-1-58810-251-5(3)) Heinemann Library.

Jameson, W. C. Buried Treasures of New England. 1998. (gr. 3-6). lib. bdg. 21.05 (978-0-613-88810-3(3)) Tandem Library Bks.

Kent, Deborah. In Colonial New England. 1999. (How We Lived Ser.). (Illus.). 72p. (J). (gr. 4-8). lib. bdg. 28.50 (978-0-7614-0905-2(X) , Benchmark Bks.) Cavendish, Marshall Corp.

Koestler-Grack, Rachel A. Northern Colonial Town: Plymouth. 2003. (J). (978-1-58417-016-7(6)) Lake Street Pubs.

Nelson, Sheila. The Northern Colonies. 2005. (How America Became America Ser.). (Illus.). 96p. (J). lib. bdg. (978-1-59084-901-9(9)) Mason Crest Pubs.

NEW ENGLAND PATRIOTS (FOOTBALL TEAM)

Bell, Lonnie. The History of the New England Patriots. 2004. (NFL Today Ser.). (Illus.). 32p. 18.95 (978-1-58341-304-3(9) , Creative Education) Creative Co., The.

Leboutillier, Nate. New England Patriots. 2005. (Super Bowl Champions Ser.). (Illus.). 24p. (gr. 1-4). 16.95 (978-1-58341-386-9(3) , Creative Education) Creative Co., The.

Nelson, Julie. New England Patriots. 3rd rev. ed. 2000. (Pro Football Today Ser.). (Illus.). 32p. (J). (gr. 3). lib. bdg. 22.60 (978-1-58341-050-9(3) , Creative Education) Creative Co., The.

Stewart, Mark. The New England Patriots. 2006. (Team Spirit Ser.). (Illus.). 48p. (J). lib. bdg. 25.27 (978-1-59953-006-2(6)) Norwood Hse. Pr.

Wheeler, Jill C. Tom Brady. 2007. (Awesome Athletes Ser.). (Illus.). 32p. (J). 22.78 (978-1-59928-305-0(0)) ABDO Publishing Co.

NEW FRANCE—HISTORY

see Canada—History—To 1763 (New France); Mississippi Valley—History

NEW HAMPSHIRE

Appelbaum, Diana. Giants in the Land. McCurdy, Michael, illus. 2000. 32p. (J). (gr. 4-6). pap. 6.95 (978-0-618-03305-8(X)) Houghton Mifflin Co. Trade & Reference Div.

Brown, Dottie. New Hampshire. 2nd rev. exp. ed. 2002. (Hello U. S. A. Ser.). (Illus.). 84p. (J). (gr. 3-6). 25.26 (978-0-8225-4086-1(X) , Lerner Pubns.) Lerner Publishing Group.

—New Hampshire. rev. ed. 2002. (gr. 3-6). lib. bdg. 15.25 (978-0-613-46091-0(X)) Tandem Library Bks.

Craats, Rennay. A Guide to New Hampshire. 2001. (American States Ser.). (Illus.). 32p. (J). lib. bdg. 16.95 (978-1-59036-001-9(X)) Weigl Pubs., Inc.

Dubois, Muriel L. New Hampshire Facts & Symbols. (States & Their Symbols Ser.). 24p. (J). 2000. (Illus.). (gr. 2-3). lib. bdg. 13.95 (978-0-7368-0524-7(9) , Bridgestone Bks.); 2003. lib. bdg. 19.93 (978-0-7368-2259-6(3)) Capstone Pr., Inc.

Graham, Amy. New Hampshire: A MyReportLinks.com Book. 2003. (States Ser.). (Illus.). 48p. (J). (gr. 4-10). lib. bdg. 25.26 (978-0-7660-5108-9(0) , MyReportLinks.com Bks.) Enslow Pubs., Inc.

Harris, Marie. Primary Numbers: A New Hampshire Numbers Book. Holman, Karen, illus. 2004. 40p. (J). 16.95 (978-1-58536-192-5(5)) Sleeping Bear Pr.

Heinrichs, Ann. New Hampshire. Kania, Matt, illus. 2005. (Welcome to the USA Ser.). 40p. (J). (gr. 1-5). 27.07 (978-1-59296-477-2(X)) Child's World, Inc.

—New Hampshire. 2003. (This Land Is Your Land Ser.). (Illus.). 48p. (J). (gr. 3 up). lib. bdg. 22.60 (978-0-7565-0336-9(1)) Compass Point Bks.

Hicks, Terry Allan. New Hampshire. 2004. (It's My State! Ser.). (Illus.). 78p. (J). 27.07 (978-0-7614-1825-2(3) , Benchmark Bks.) Cavendish, Marshall Corp.

Kehoe, Stasia Ward. I Live in a Town. 2000. (Kids in Their Communities Ser.). (Illus.). 24p. (J). (gr. 3). lib. bdg. 18.75 (978-0-8239-5440-7(4) , PowerKids Pr.) Rosen Publishing Group, Inc., The.

Knox, Barbara. New Hampshire. 2003. (Land of Liberty Ser.). (Illus.). 64p. (J). lib. bdg. 25.26 (978-0-7368-2187-2(2)) Capstone Pr., Inc.

Kummer, Patricia K. New Hampshire. rev. ed. 2002. (One Nation Ser.). (Illus.). 48p. (J). (gr. 3-4). lib. bdg. 22.60 (978-0-7368-1253-5(9) , Bridgestone Bks.) Capstone Pr., Inc.

Marsh, Carole. The Big New Hampshire Reproducible Activity Book. 2001. (Carole Marsh New Hampshire Bks.). (Illus.). 96p. (J). (gr. 2-6). pap. 9.95 (978-0-7933-9950-5(5)) Gallopade International.

—My First Book about New Hampshire. 2001. (Carole Marsh New Hampshire Bks.). (Illus.). 32p. (J). (gr. k-4). pap. 7.95 (978-0-7933-9892-8(4)) Gallopade International.

—New Hampshire Classic Christmas Trivia. 2002. (Carole Marsh New Hampshire Bks.). (Illus.). 32p. pap. 6.95 (978-0-635-01425-2(4) , 14254); lib. bdg. 21.95 (978-0-635-01426-9(2) , 14262, Marsh, Carole Bks.) Gallopade International.

—New Hampshire Experience Library State: Resource Set. 2001. (Illus.). (J). (gr. k-8). 100.20 incl. cd-rom (978-0-635-00482-6(8)) Gallopade International.

—New Hampshire Geography Projects: 30 Cool, Activities, Crafts, Experiments & More for Kids to Do to Learn about Your State! 2003. (New Hampshire Experience Ser.). 32p. (gr. k-5). pap. 5.95 (978-0-635-01848-9(9) , Marsh, Carole Bks.) Gallopade International.

—New Hampshire Government Projects: 30 Cool, Activities, Crafts, Experiments & More for Kids to Do to Learn about Your State! 2003. (New Hampshire Experience Ser.). 32p. (gr. k-5). pap. 5.95 (978-0-635-01948-6(5) , Marsh, Carole Bks.) Gallopade International.

—New Hampshire Jeopardy! Answers & Questions about Our State! Line Art Staff, illus. 2001. 32p. (J). (gr. 3-8). pap. 7.95 (978-0-7933-9805-8(3)) Gallopade International.

—New Hampshire People Projects: 30 Cool, Activities, Crafts, Experiments & More for Kids to Do to Learn about Your State! 2003. (New Hampshire Experience Ser.). 32p. (gr. k-5). pap. 5.95 (978-0-635-01998-1(1) , Marsh, Carole Bks.) Gallopade International.

—New Hampshire Symbols & Facts Projects: 30 Cool, Activities, Crafts, Experiments & More for Kids to Do to Learn about Your State! 2003. (New Hampshire Experience Ser.). 32p. (gr. k-8). pap. 5.95 (978-0-635-01898-4(5) , Marsh, Carole Bks.) Gallopade International.

Mattern, Joanne. New Hampshire: The Granite State. 2003. (World Almanac Library of the States). (Illus.). 48p. (J). (gr. 5 up). pap. 14.95 (978-0-8368-5326-1(1)); lib. bdg. 30.00 (978-0-8368-5155-7(2)) Stevens, Gareth Inc. (World Almanac Library).

Melman, Peter Charles. Uniquely New Hampshire. 2004. (Heinemann State Studies). (Illus.). 48p. (J). 27.07 (978-1-4034-4651-0(2)); pap. 8.50 (978-1-4034-4720-3(9)) Heinemann Library.

Murray, Julie. New Hampshire. 2006. (Illus.). 32p. (J). (gr. k-4). lib. bdg. 22.78 (978-1-59197-688-2(X) , Buddy Bks.) ABDO Publishing Co.

New Hampshire. 2000. (Switched on Schoolhouse Ser.). (Illus.). (YA). (gr. 7-12). pap. 24.95 incl. cd-rom (978-0-7403-0281-7(7) , SOSNH) Alpha Omega Pubns., Inc.

Otfinoski, Steven. New Hampshire. (Celebrate the States Ser.). 1999. (Illus.). 144p. (gr. 4-8). lib. bdg. 37.07 (978-0-7614-0669-3(7)); 2nd ed. 2008. (J). lib. bdg. 39.93 ***(*978-0-7614-2718-6(X))*** Cavendish, Marshall Corp. (Benchmark Bks.).

Ribke, Simone T. New Hampshire. (Rookie Read-About Geography Ser.). (J). 2004. (gr. 1-2). pap. 5.95 (978-0-516-27898-8(3)); 2003. (Illus.). 32p. 20.50 (978-0-516-22742-9(4)) Scholastic Library Publishing. (Children's Pr.).

Shannon, Terry Miller. New Hampshire. 2002. (From Sea to Shining Sea Ser.: 2). (Illus.). 80p. (J). (gr. 3-5). 30.50 (978-0-516-22484-8(0) , Children's Pr.) Scholastic Library Publishing.

Teitelbaum, Michael. New Hampshire. 2004. (Life in the Thirteen Colonies Ser.). (Illus.). 124p. (J). 36.00 (978-0-516-24573-7(2) , Children's Pr.) Scholastic Library Publishing.

Thomas, William. New Hampshire. 2006. (Portraits of the States Ser.). (J). pap. (978-0-8368-4721-5(0)); lib. bdg. (978-0-8368-4704-8(0)) Stevens, Gareth Inc.

Way, Jennifer. New Hampshire (Nuevo Hampshire) 2006. (Bilingual Library of the United States of America: Set 2). (ENG & SPA., Illus.). 32p. (J). (gr. 3-6). lib. bdg. 22.50 (978-1-4042-3094-1(7) , Buenas Letra) Rosen Publishing Group, Inc., The.

NEW HAMPSHIRE—FICTION

Aldridge, Janet. The Meadow-Brook Girls in the Hills: Or the Missing Pilot of the White Mountains. 2006. pap. ***(*978-1-4065-0694-5(X))*** Dodo Pr.

Alger, Horatio. Risen from the Ranks: Or, Harry Walton's Success. 2007. 194p. pap. 11.99 ***(*978-1-4264-6391-4(X));*** 216p. pap. 15.99 ***(*978-1-4264-6465-2(7))*** BiblioBazaar.

—Risen from the Ranks: Or, Harry Walton's Success. 2006. pap. ***(*978-1-4065-0721-8(0))*** Dodo Pr.

—Risen from the Ranks: Or, Harry Walton's Success. 2006. 79.99 ***(*978-1-4219-9893-0(9));*** pap. 72.99 ***(*978-1-4219-9877-0(7))*** IndyPublish.com.

Banks, Kate. Dillon Dillon. 160p. (J). 2002. (gr. 3-6). 16.00 (978-0-374-31786-7(0) , Farrar, Straus & Giroux (BYR)); 2005. reprint ed. pap. 5.95 (978-0-374-41715-4(6) , Sunburst) Farrar, Straus & Giroux.

Bertrand, Lynne. Granite Baby. Hawkes, Kevin, illus. 2005. 40p. (J). 16.00 (978-0-374-32761-3(0) , Farrar, Straus & Giroux (BYR)) Farrar, Straus & Giroux.

Blos, Joan. A Gathering of Days: A New England Girl's Journal, 1830-1832. Blos, Joan, illus. 2002. (Illus.). 13.40 (978-0-7587-0184-8(5)) Book Wholesalers, Inc.

Boonstra, Jean. Adventist Girl Series, 4 vols. Lale, Tim, ed. 2002. pap. 29.99 (978-0-8163-1907-7(3)) Pacific Pr. Publishing Assn.

Buckey, Sarah Masters. Enemy in the Fort. 2001. (American Girl Collection). (Illus.). (J). 12.60 (978-0-606-21180-2(2)) Tandem Library Bks.

Clements, Louise. Old Man, Goodbye: A Farewell to the Old Man of the Mountain. Leach, Carol, illus. 2003. 36p. (J). per. 14.95 (978-0-9744803-0-5(4)) PublishingWorks.

Eaton, Walter Prichard. Boy Scouts in the White Mountains: the Story of a Long Hike. Merrill, Frank T., illus. 2006. (ENG.). 316p. per. 30.95 ***(*978-1-4286-4117-4(3))*** Kessinger Publishing, LLC.

Harrar, George. The Trouble with Jeremy Chance. 2007. (Historical Fiction for Young Readers Ser.). 168p. (J). pap. 6.95 (978-1-57131-669-1(8)) Milkweed Editions.

Jacobson, Jennifer Richard. Stained. 208p. (YA). (gr. 8 up). 2005. (Illus.). 16.95 (978-0-689-86745-3(X) , Atheneum); 2006. reprint ed. pap. 6.99 (978-1-4169-1337-5(8) , Simon Pulse) Simon & Schuster Children's Publishing.

Monninger, Joseph. Baby. 2007. 204p. (YA). (gr. 8 up). 16.95 ***(*978-1-59078-502-7(9)*** , Front Street) Boyds Mills Pr.

Schmidt, Gary. First Boy. 2007. 224p. (YA). pap. 6.99 ***(*978-0-312-37149-4(7))*** Square Fish.

Schmidt, Gary D. First Boy. rev. ed. 2005. 208p. (YA). (gr. 6). 17.95 (978-0-8050-7859-6(2)) Holt, Henry & Co.

Tomaszewski, Suzanne Lyon. Samuel's Exeter Walkabout. Dionne, Nina, illus. 2003. 37p. (J). (978-0-9744855-0-8(0)) Gold Charm Publishing, LLC.

Townley, Roderick. The Red Thread: A Novel in Three Incarnations. 2007. 304p. (YA). (gr. 7 up). 17.99 (978-1-4169-0894-4(3) , Atheneum/Richard Jackson Bks.) Simon & Schuster Children's Publishing.

Townley, Roderick. The Red Thread: A Novel in Three Incarnations. 2007. 304p. (YA). 17.99 ***(*978-1-4169-2930-7(4)*** , Atheneum) Simon & Schuster Children's Publishing.

Yates, Elizabeth. American Haven. 2002. (Illus.). 112p. (J). (gr. 4-7). 7.49 (978-1-57924-896-3(9)) Jones, Bob Univ. Pr.

NEW HAMPSHIRE—HISTORY

Auden, Scott. New Hampshire 1603-1776. 2007. (Voices from Colonial America Ser.). (Illus.). 112p. (J). (gr. 5-9). 21.95 (978-1-4263-0034-9(4)); lib. bdg. 32.90 (978-1-4263-0035-6(2)) National Geographic Society. (National Geographic Children's Bks.).

Blohm, Craig E. New Hampshire. 2001. (Thirteen Colonies Ser.). (Illus.). 104p. (YA). (gr. 4-12). lib. bdg. 29.95 (978-1-56006-991-1(0) , LML00902-179177, Lucent Bks.) Thomson Gale.

Davis, Kevin. The New Hampshire Colony. 2003. (Spirit of America). (Illus.). 40p. (J). (gr. 2-6). 28.50 (978-1-56766-617-5(5)) Child's World, Inc.

Deady, Kathleen W. The New Hampshire Colony. 2005. (Fact Finders Ser.). (Illus.). 32p. (J). (gr. 2-4). lib. bdg. 22.60 (978-0-7368-2677-8(7)) Capstone Pr., Inc.

Doherty, Craig A. & Doherty, Katherine M. New Hampshire. 2005. (Thirteen Colonies Ser.). (Illus.). 144p. (J). (gr. 4-9). 35.00 (978-0-8160-5411-4(8)) Facts On File, Inc.

Gagnon, Lauren. An Exeter Alphabet: Learning about Exeter from a to Z. 2005. (J). per. (978-1-933002-05-7(0)) PublishingWorks.

Harris, Marie. G Is for Granite: A New Hampshire Alphabet. Holman, Karen, illus. 2002. 40p. (J). 17.95 (978-1-58536-083-3(X)) Sleeping Bear Pr.

Haulley, Fletcher. A Primary Source History of the Colony of New Hampshire. 2005. (Primary Sources of the Thirteen Colonies & the Lost Colony Ser.). (Illus.). 64p. (J). (gr. 3-7). pap. 14.60 (978-1-4042-0676-2(0)); (YA). (gr. 5-8). lib. bdg. 29.25 (978-1-4042-0429-4(6)) Rosen Publishing Group, Inc., The.

Italia, Bob. The New Hampshire Colony. 2001. (Colonies Ser.). (Illus.). 32p. (J). (gr. k-6). lib. bdg. 22.78 (978-1-57765-585-5(0) , Checkerboard Library) ABDO Publishing Co.

Marsh, Carole. My First Pocket Guide New Hampshire. 2000. (New Hampshire Experience! Ser.). (Illus.). 96p. (J). (gr. 3-8). 12.95 (978-0-635-01319-4(3) , 13193) Gallopade International.

—New Hampshire History Projects: 30 Cool, Activities, Crafts, Experiments & More for Kids to Do to Learn about Your State! 2003. (New Hampshire Experience Ser.). 32p. (gr. k-5). pap. 5.95 (978-0-635-01798-7(9) , Marsh, Carole Bks.) Gallopade International.

—New Hampshire Millionaire. 2001. (GameBook Ser.). 32p. (J). (gr. 3-8). pap., act. bk. ed. 9.95 (978-0-635-00074-3(1)) Gallopade International.

—New Hampshire Survivor. 2001. (GameBook Ser.). 32p. (J). (gr. 3-8). pap., act. bk. ed. 9.95 (978-0-635-00550-2(6)) Gallopade International.

—The New Hampshire Survivor: A Class Challenge. 2001. (J). lib. bdg. 29.95 (978-0-635-00675-2(8)) Gallopade International.

—New Hampshire Wheel of Fortune. 2001. (GameBook Ser.). 32p. (J). (gr. 3-8). pap., act. bk. ed. 9.95 (978-0-7933-9674-0(3)) Gallopade International.

—Wheel of Fortune. 2001. (New Hampshire Experience! Ser.). (J). lib. bdg. 29.95 (978-0-7933-9675-7(1)) Gallopade International.

—Who Wants to Be a Millionaire? 2001. (Carole Marsh New Hampshire Bks.). (J). lib. bdg. 29.95 (978-0-635-00075-0(X)) Gallopade International.

Mis, Melody S. The Colony of New Hampshire: A Primary Source History. 2007. (Primary Source Library of the Thirteen Colonies & the Lost Colony). (Illus.). 24p. (J). lib. bdg. (978-1-4042-3435-2(7) , PowerKids Pr.) Rosen Publishing Group, Inc., The.

Peters, S. True. How to Draw New Hampshires Sights & Symbols. 2002. (Kids Guide to Drawing America Ser.). 32p. (J). lib. bdg. 25.25 (978-0-8239-6085-9(4) , PowerKids Pr.) Rosen Publishing Group, Inc., The.

Whitehurst, Susan. The Colony of New Hampshire. 2000. (Library of the Thirteen Colonies & the Lost Colony). (Illus.). 24p. (J). (gr. 3). lib. bdg. 19.95 (978-0-8239-5477-3(3) , PowerKids Pr.) Rosen Publishing Group, Inc., The.

Wiener, Roberta & Arnold, James R. New Hampshire. 2004. (J). 28.56 (978-0-7398-6882-9(9)) Harcourt Schl. Pubs.

—The 13 Colonies: New Hampshire. 2004. (Illus.). (J). 8.95 (978-1-4109-0306-8(0)) Harcourt Schl. Pubs.

Wyborny, Sheila. New Hampshire. 2003. (Seeds of a Nation Ser.). (Illus.). 48p. (J). (gr. 3-5). 23.70 (978-0-7377-1448-7(4) , Kidhaven) Thomson Gale.

NEW HAVEN (CONN.)—FICTION

Lawlor, Laurie. Horseback on the Boston Post Road, Seventeen Hundred & Four. 2002. (gr. 3-6). lib. bdg. 13.00 (978-0-613-50323-5(6)) Tandem Library Bks.

NEW JERSEY

Boraas, Tracey. New Jersey. 2003. (Land of Liberty Ser.). (Illus.). 64p. (J). lib. bdg. 25.26 (978-0-7368-2188-9(0)) Capstone Pr., Inc.

Brown, Vanessa. New Jersey (Nueva Jersey) 2006. (Bilingual Library of the United States of America: Set 2). (ENG & SPA., Illus.). 32p. (J). (gr. 3-6). lib. bdg. 22.50 (978-1-4042-3095-8(5) , Buenas Letra) Rosen Publishing Group, Inc., The.

Cameron, Eileen. G Is for Garden State: A New Jersey Alphabet. Ettlinger, Doris, illus. 2004. 40p. (J). 17.95 (978-1-58536-152-6(6)) Sleeping Bear Pr.

Cunningham, John T. Tu, New Jersey y el Mundo. Cunningham, Patricia, ed. Zanzo, Eliana, tr. 2000. Tr. of You, New Jersey & the World. (SPA., Illus.). 256p. (J). (gr. 4). 43.95 (978-0-89359-125-0(4)) Afton Publishing.

Evento, Susan. New Jersey. 2005. (Rookie Read-About Geography Ser.). (Illus.). 32p. (J). (gr. 1-2). pap. 5.95 (978-0-516-25928-4(8) , Children's Pr.) Scholastic Library Publishing.

—Nueva Jersey. (J). (gr. k-2). 2006. (SPA.). 32p. pap. 5.95 (978-0-516-25047-2(7)); 2005. (ENG & SPA., Illus.). 31p. 19.50 (978-0-516-25246-9(1)) Scholastic Library Publishing. (Children's Pr.).

Evento, Susan & Vargus, Nanci Reginelli. New Jersey. 2004. (Rookie Read-About Geography Ser.). (J). 20.50 (978-0-516-22754-2(8) , Children's Pr.) Scholastic Library Publishing.

Fredeen, Charles. New Jersey. 2nd exp. rev. ed. (Hello U. S. A. Ser.). (Illus.). 84p. (J). (gr. 3-6). 2003. pap. 6.95 (978-0-8225-4148-6(3)); 2002. 25.26 (978-0-8225-4060-1(6) , Lerner Pubns.) Lerner Publishing Group.

—New Jersey. 2001. (gr. 3-6). lib. bdg. 15.25 (978-0-613-84029-3(1)) Tandem Library Bks.

A Guide to New Jersey. 2001. (American States Ser.). 32p. (J). per. 7.95 (978-1-930954-91-5(3)) Weigl Pubs., Inc.

Harcourt School Publishers Staff. The Pine Barrens. 3rd ed. 2002. (Horizons Ser.). (Illus.). (J). pap. 5.50 (978-0-15-333397-2(9)) Harcourt Schl. Pubs.

Heinrichs, Ann. New Jersey. 2003. (This Land Is Your Land Ser.). (Illus.). 48p. (J). (gr. 3 up). lib. bdg. 22.60 (978-0-7565-0318-5(3)) Compass Point Bks.

Holden, Henry M. New Jersey: A MyReportLinks. Com Book. 2003. (States Ser.). (Illus.). 48p. (J). lib. bdg. 25.26 (978-0-7660-5124-9(2) , MyReportLinks.com Bks.) Enslow Pubs., Inc.

Holtz, Eric Siegfried. New Jersey: The Garden State. 2002. (World Almanac Library of the States). (Illus.). 48p. (J). (gr. 5 up). lib. bdg. 30.00 (978-0-8368-5141-0(2)); pap. 14.95 (978-0-8368-5311-7(3)) Stevens, Gareth Inc. (World Almanac Library).

—Nueva Jersey. Porras, Carlos & D'Andrea, Patricia, trs. 2003. (World Almanac Biblioteca de los Estados). (SPA., Illus.). 48p. (J). (gr. 5 up). lib. bdg. 30.00 (978-0-8368-5545-6(0) , World Almanac Library) Stevens, Gareth Inc.

Kent, Deborah. New Jersey. 2007. (America the Beautiful, Third Ser.). (Illus.). 144p. (YA). (gr. 5-8). lib. bdg. 38.00 (***978-0-531-18564-3(8)*** , Children's Pr.) Scholastic Library Publishing.

Kummer, Patricia K. New Jersey. rev. ed. 2002. (One Nation Ser.). (Illus.). 48p. (J). (gr. 3-4). lib. bdg. 22.60 (978-0-7368-1254-2(7) , Bridgestone Bks.) Capstone Pr., Inc.

Lohnes, Marilyn. F for Fiddlehead: Nb Alpha. Tooke, Susan, illus. rev. ed. 2007. (Provincial Alphabet Ser.). 40p. (J). 18.95 (***978-1-58536-318-6(9)***) Sleeping Bear Pr.

Malaspina, Ann. New Jersey. 2005. (Portraits of the States Ser.). (Illus.). 32p. (J). pap. (978-0-8368-4648-5(6)); lib. bdg. 23.33 (978-0-8368-4629-4(X)) Stevens, Gareth Inc.

Marsh, Carole. My First Book about New Jersey. 2004. (New Jersey Experience! Ser.). (Illus.). 32p. (J). (gr. k-4). pap. 7.95 (978-0-7933-9521-7(6)) Gallopade International.

—My First Pocket Guide New Jersey. 2004. (New Jersey Experience! Ser.). (Illus.). 96p. (J). (gr. 3-8). pap. 6.95 (978-0-7933-9453-1(8)) Gallopade International.

—New Jersey Classic Christmas Trivia. 2002. (Carole Marsh New Jersey Bks.). (Illus.). 32p. pap. 6.95 (978-0-635-01427-6(0) , 14270); lib. bdg. 21.95 (978-0-635-01428-3(9) , 14289) Gallopade International. (Marsh, Carole Bks.).

—New Jersey Current Events Projects: 30 Cool, Activities, Crafts, Experiments & More for Kids to Do to Learn about Your State! 2003. (New Jersey Experience Ser.). 32p. (gr. k-8). pap. 5.95 (978-0-635-02049-9(1) , Marsh, Carole Bks.) Gallopade International.

—The New Jersey Experience Liberay State: Resource Set. 2001. (Illus.). (J). (gr. k-8). pap. 100.20 incl. cd-rom (978-0-635-00483-3(6)) Gallopade International.

—New Jersey Geography Projects: 30 Cool, Activities, Crafts, Experiments & More for Kids to Do to Learn about Your State! 2003. (New Jersey Experience Ser.). 32p. (gr. k-5). pap. 5.95 (978-0-635-01849-6(7) , Marsh, Carole Bks.) Gallopade International.

—New Jersey Government Projects: 30 Cool, Activities, Crafts, Experiments & More for Kids to Do to Learn about Your State! 2003. (New Jersey Experience Ser.). 32p. (gr. k-5). pap. 5.95 (978-0-635-01949-3(3) , Marsh, Carole Bks.) Gallopade International.

—New Jersey Jeopardy! Answers & Questions about Our State! 2004. (New Jersey Experience! Ser.). (Illus.). 32p. (J). (gr. 3-8). pap. 7.95 (978-0-7933-9522-4(4)) Gallopade International.

—New Jersey "Jography" A Fun Run Thru Our State! 2004. (New Jersey Experience! Ser.). (Illus.). 32p. (J). (gr. 3-8). pap. 7.95 (978-0-7933-9523-1(2)) Gallopade International.

—New Jersey People Projects: 30 Cool, Activities, Crafts, Experiments & More for Kids to Do to Learn about Your State! 2003. (New Jersey Experience Ser.). 32p. (gr. k-5). pap. 5.95 (978-0-635-01999-8(X) , Marsh, Carole Bks.) Gallopade International.

—New Jersey Symbols & Facts Projects: 30 Cool, Activities, Crafts, Experiments & More for Kids to Do to Learn about Your State! 2003. (New Jersey Experience Ser.). 32p. (gr. k-5). pap. 5.95 (978-0-635-01899-1(3) , Marsh, Carole Bks.) Gallopade International.

—New Jersey's Big Activity Book. 2004. (New Jersey Experience! Ser.). (Illus.). 96p. (J). (gr. 2-6). pap. 9.95 (978-0-7933-9463-0(5)) Gallopade International.

—The Nifty New Jersey Coloring Book. 2004. (New Jersey Experience! Ser.). (Illus.). 32p. (J). (gr. k-2). pap. 3.95 (978-0-7933-9473-9(2)) Gallopade International.

Moragne, Wendy. New Jersey. 2000. (Celebrate the States Ser.). (Illus.). 144p. (gr. 4-8). lib. bdg. 37.07 (978-0-7614-0673-0(5) , Benchmark Bks.) Cavendish, Marshall Corp.

Murray, Julie. New Jersey. 2006. (Buddy Book Ser.). (Illus.). 32p. (J). (gr. k-4). lib. bdg. 22.78 (978-1-59197-689-9(8) , Buddy Bks.) ABDO Publishing Co.

Nault, Jennifer. A Guide to New Jersey. 2001. (American States Ser.). (Illus.). 32p. (J). lib. bdg. 16.95 (978-1-930954-48-9(4)) Weigl Pubs., Inc.

New Jersey. (Switched on Schoolhouse Ser.). 2003. cd-rom 24.95 (978-0-7403-0654-9(5)); 2000. (Illus.). (YA). (gr. 7-12). pap. 24.95 incl. cd-rom (978-0-7403-0282-4(5) , SOSNJ) Alpha Omega Pubns., Inc.

New Jersey. 2004. 79.00 (978-0-8416-5117-3(5)) American Map Corp.

Nueva Jersey. 2003. (World Almanac Biblioteca de los Estados). (SPA., Illus.). 48p. (J). (gr. 5 up). pap. 11.95 (978-0-8368-5552-4(3) , World Almanac Library) Stevens, Gareth Inc.

Sateren, Shelley Swanson. New Jersey: Facts & Symbols. 1999. (Illus.). 24p. (J). (gr. k-3). pap. 15.00 (978-0-531-12005-7(8) , Watts, Franklin) Scholastic Library Publishing.

Scholl, Elizabeth J. New Jersey. 80p. (J). 2008. (From Sea to Shining Sea, Second Ser.). pap. 7.95 (***978-0-531-18806-4(X)***); 2002. (From Sea to Shining Sea Ser.: 2). (Illus.). (gr. 3-5). pap. 30.50 (978-0-516-22321-6(0)) Scholastic Library Publishing. (Children's Pr.).

Sterngass, Jon & Kachur, Matthew. New Jersey. 2004. (Life in the Thirteen Colonies Ser.). (Illus.). 124p. (J). 36.00 (978-0-516-24574-4(0) , Children's Pr.) Scholastic Library Publishing.

Stewart, Mark. All Around New Jersey: Regions & Resources. 2003. (State Studies). (Illus.). 48p. (J). 27.07 (978-1-4034-0672-9(3)); pap. 8.50 (978-1-4034-2682-6(1)) Heinemann Library.

—New Jersey Plants & Animals. 2003. (State Studies). (Illus.). 48p. (J). pap. 8.50 (978-1-4034-2685-7(6)); lib. bdg. 27.07 (978-1-4034-0676-7(6)) Heinemann Library.

—Uniquely New Jersey. 2003. (State Studies). (Illus.). 48p. (J). 27.07 (978-1-4034-0677-4(4)); pap. 8.50 (978-1-4034-2687-1(2)) Heinemann Library.

You, New jersey & the World. 2004. lib. bdg. (978-0-89359-121-2(1)) Afton Publishing.

NEW JERSEY—FICTION

Bauer, A. C. E. No Castles Here. 2007. 288p. (J). (gr. 4-8). 15.99 (978-0-375-83921-4(6) , Random Hse. Bks. for Young Readers) Random Hse. Children's Bks.

Blume, Judy. Are You There God? It's Me, Margaret. 2002. (J). 13.94 (978-0-7587-9131-3(3)) Book Wholesalers, Inc.

—Are You There God? It's Me, Margaret. l.t. ed. 2002. (LRS Large Print Cornerstone Ser.). (J). lib. bdg. 28.95 (978-1-58118-088-6(8) , 24873) LRS.

—Then Again, Maybe I Won't. (J). 125p. pap. 3.99 (978-0-8072-1445-9(0)); 2004. 164p. (gr. 5-9). pap. 29.00 incl. audio (978 0 8072-0796-3(9) , LYA 354 SP) Random Hse. Audio Publishing Group. (Listening Library).

Brown, Michael. The Greatest Years. 2005. 153p. pap. 19.95 (978-1-4137-8393-3(7)) PublishAmerica, Inc.

Bryant, Jennifer. The Trial. (Illus.). 176p. (J). (gr. 3-7). 2005. pap. 5.99 (978-0-440-41986-0(7) , Yearling); 2004. lib. bdg. 16.99 (978-0-375-92752-2(2) , Knopf Bks. for Young Readers) Random Hse. Children's Bks.

Bryant, Jennifer. The Trial: A Novel. 2005. (Illus.). 169p. (J). (***978-1-4156-3151-5(4)*** , Yearling) Random Hse. Children's Bks.

Carlos the Sailor Visits Atlantic City. 2005. (J). pap. 12.95 (978-0-9766889-0-7(5)) ComteQ Publishing.

Dixon, Franklin W. Boardwalk Bust. 2005. 164p. (J). lib. bdg. 16.92 (***978-1-4242-0385-7(6)***) Fitzgerald Bks.

Fairbanks, Randy. The Weird Club: The Search for the Jersey Devil. 2007. (Weird Ser.). (Illus.). 144p. (J). (gr. 3-7). 12.95 (978-1-4027-4228-6(2)) Sterling Publishing Co., Inc.

Finale, Frank. A Gull's Story: A Tale of Learning about Life, the Shore & the ABCs. Valente, George C., ed. Moore, Margie, illus. 2007. 36p. (J). 22.00 (978-0-9632906-3-2(0)) Jersey Shore Pubns.

—A Gull's Story, Part 2: Counting at the Shore. Moore, Margie, illus. 2007. (J). 22.00 (978-0-9777077-0-6(9)) Jersey Shore Pubns.

Finale, Frank. A Gull's Story, Part 3: Colors at the Shore. Moore, Margie, illus. 2007. (J). 22.00 (***978-0-9777077-2-0(5)***) Jersey Shore Pubns.

Friedman, Robin. The Girlfriend Project. 2007. 192p. (YA). (gr. 7 up). 15.95 (978-0-8027-9624-0(9)) Walker & Co.

Funari Willever, Lisa. Nicky Fifth on 32 Dandelion Court. 2003. 160p. 5.95 (978-0-9679227-7-5(1) , 329-008) Franklin Mason Pr.

Golding, Theresa Martin. The Secret Within. 2003. (Illus.). 240p. (YA). (gr. 6-9). 16.95 (978-1-56397-995-8(0)) Boyds Mills Pr.

Griffiths, Sara. Thrown a Curve: A Novel. 2007. 151p. (YA). (gr. 6-10). pap. 12.95 (***978-1-890862-49-7(5)***) Bancroft Pr.

Gutman, Dan. The Edison Mystery: Back in Time. 2002. (Illus.). 201p. lib. bdg. 13.00 (978-0-613-62098-7(4)) Tandem Library Bks.

Helmer, Diana Star. We're Behind You, George Washington. Schneider, Rex, illus. 2000. (Cover-to-Cover Bks.). 56p. (J). pap. (978-0-7891-5081-3(6)); (gr. 1-4). lib. bdg. 16.95 (978-0-7807-9050-6(2)) Perfection Learning Corp.

Holm, Jennifer L. Penny from Heaven. (Illus.). (J). 2007. 272p. (gr. 5-7). 6.99 (978-0-375-83689-3(6) , Yearling); 2006. 288p. (gr. 3-7). 15.95 (978-0-375-83687-9(X) , Random Hse. Bks. for Young Readers); 2006. 288p. (gr. 3-7). lib. bdg. 17.99 (978-0-375-93687-6(4) , Random Hse. Bks. for Young Readers) Random Hse. Children's Bks.

Ismail, Suzy. The BFF Sisters: Jennah's New Friends. 2001. 64p. (J). (978-1-59008-005-4(X)) amana pubns.

Johnston, Norma. Feather in the Wind. 2001. (Illus.). 172p. (J). (gr. 5-9). 14.95 (978-0-7614-5063-4(7) , Cavendish Children's Bks.) Cavendish, Marshall Corp.

Lecesne, James. Absolute Brightness. 2008. 480p. (J). 17.99 (***978-0-06-125627-1(7)***); lib. bdg. 18.89 (***978-0-06-125628-8(5)***) HarperCollins Pubs. (HarperTeen).

Levchuk, Lisa. Everything Beautiful in the World. 2008. (YA). (***978-0-374-32238-0(4)***) Farrar, Straus & Giroux.

Lewis, Anne Margaret. What Am I? New Jersey. DeWildt, Jim, illus. 2007. 32p. (J). 9.95 (***978-1-934133-19-4(1)***) Mackinac Island Pr., Inc.

Litzenberg, Corinne. The Sand Lady: A Cape May Tale. 2006. 14.95 (978-0-7643-2479-6(9)) Schiffer Publishing, Ltd.

Lubar, David. Dunk. (YA). (gr. 7-10). 2002. 256p. tchr. ed. 15.00 (978-0-618-19455-1(X) , Clarion Bks.); 2004. 272p. reprint ed. pap. 6.99 (978-0-618-43909-6(9) , Graphia) Houghton Mifflin Co. Trade & Reference Div.

Martin, Ann M. Welcome to Camden Falls. 2007. (Main Street Ser.: No. 1). 192p. (J). (gr. 4-7). pap. 6.99 (***978-0-439-86879-2(3)*** , Scholastic Paperbacks) Scholastic, Inc.

Martino, Alfred C. Pinned. (YA). 2005. 320p. 17.00 (978-0-15-205355-0(7)); 2006. (Illus.). 324p. reprint ed. pap. 6.95 (978-0-15-205631-5(9) , Harcourt Paperbacks) Harcourt Children's Bks.

Maxwell, Ruth. Eighteen Roses Red: A Young Girl's Heroic Mission in the Revolutionary War. 2006. (YA). pap. 8.95 (978-1-57249-380-3(1) , White Mane Kids) White Mane Publishing Co., Inc.

Mayall, Beth. Mermaid Park. 2007. 256p. (YA). pap. 8.99 (978-1-59514-137-8(5) , Razorbill) Penguin Group (USA) Inc.

Mazzeo Zocchi, Judy. Paulie & Sasha: Circus or Not. Vannozzi, Don, illus. 2001. (Adventures of Paulie & Sasha Ser.). 32p. (J). (gr. k-4). 15.95 (978-1-891997-00-6(9) , Treehouse Court) Dingles & Co.

McDonald, Joyce. Shades of Simon Gray. (YA). (gr. 7). 2003. 272p. pap. 6.50 (978-0-440-22804-2(2) , Laurel Leaf); 2001. 256p. lib. bdg. 17.99 (978-0-385-90026-3(0) , Delacorte Bks. for Young Readers) Random Hse. Children's Bks.

—Shades of Simon Gray. 2003. (gr. 7-12). lib. bdg. 13.55 (978-0-613-60396-6(6)) Tandem Library Bks.

Myers, Robert J. When the Monarchs Fly. McGehee, Cricket, illus. 2005. 64p. 11.95 (978-0-945582-76-2(5)) Down The Shore Publishing.

Pinkwater, Daniel M. Looking for Bobowicz: A Hoboken Chicken Story. Pinkwater, Jill, illus. 2004. 208p. (J). lib. bdg. 16.89 (978-0-06-053555-1(5)) HarperCollins Pubs.

Prose, Francine. Bullyville. 2007. 272p. (J). (gr. 5-8). 16.99 (***978-0-06-057497-0(6)***); lib. bdg. 17.89 (***978-0-06-057498-7(4)***) HarperCollins Pubs. (HarperTeen).

Reiken, Frederick. Lost Legends of New Jersey. 2001. (gr. 7-12). lib. bdg. 22.25 (978-0-613-36486-7(4)) Tandem Library Bks.

Rinaldi, Ann. Keep Smiling Through. 2005. 208p. (J). pap. 6.95 (978-0-15-205399-4(9) , Gulliver Bks.) Harcourt Children's Bks.

—A Ride into Morning: The Story of Tempe Wick. 2003. (Great Episodes Ser.). 368p. (YA). pap. 6.95 (978-0-15-204683-5(6) , Gulliver Bks.) Harcourt Children's Bks.

—A Ride into Morning: The Story of Tempe Wick. l.t. ed. 2005. 383p. (YA). 21.95 (978-0-7862-7957-9(5) , Large Print Pr.) Thorndike Pr.

Robertson, Keith. Henry Reed, Inc. abr. ed. (J). (gr. 4-7). pap. 15.95 incl. audio (978-0-670-36801-3(6)) Live Oak Media.

—Henry Reed, Inc., Set. McCloskey, Robert, illus. abr. ed. (J). (gr. 4-7). 24.95 incl. audio (978-0-670-36800-6(8)) Live Oak Media.

Roth, Philip. The Human Stain. 2001. (gr. 7-12). lib. bdg. 23.45 (978-0-613-45775-0(7)) Tandem Library Bks.

Ruby, Laura. Lily's Ghosts. 2003. 272p. (J). (gr. 5 up). 16.99 (978-0-06-051829-5(4)) HarperCollins Pubs.

Schirripa, Steven R. & Fleming, Charles. Nicky Deuce: Home for the Holidays. 2006. 208p. (J). (gr. 4-7). 15.95 (978-0-385-73258-1(9)); lib. bdg. 17.99 (978-0-385-90276-2(X)) Random Hse. Children's Bks. (Delacorte Bks. for Young Readers).

Schumacher, Julie. The Book of One Hundred Truths. 192p. (gr. 4-7). 2008. 5.99 (***978-0-440-42085-9(7)*** , Yearling); 2006. (J). 15.95 (978-0-385-73290-1(2) , Delacorte Bks. for Young Readers); 2006. (J). lib. bdg. 17.99 (978-0-385-90311-0(1) , Delacorte Bks. for Young Readers) Random Hse. Children's Bks.

Seuling, Barbara. Robert Finds a Way. Brewer, Paul, illus. 2005. (Robert Bks.). 150p. (J). 15.95 (978-0-8126-2734-3(2)) Cricket Bks.

Smith, S. C. Mabell. Ethel Morton at Rose House. 2006. 77.99 (***978-1-4280-4780-8(8)***); pap. 70.99 (***978-1-4280-4784-6(0)***) IndyPublish.com.

Strasser, Todd. Shirt & Shoes Not Required. 2007. (Summer Share Ser.). 272p. (YA). (gr. 9 up). pap. 8.99 (978-1-4169-1153-1(7) , Simon Pulse) Simon & Schuster Children's Publishing.

Varela, Barry. Palmer's Gate. 2006. 112p. (J). 16.95 (978-1-59643-073-0(7)) Roaring Brook Pr.

Walker, Sally. 18 Penny Goose. 1999. (gr. k-3). lib. bdg. 11.80 (978-0-613-15776-6(1)) Tandem Library Bks.

Walker, Sally M. The 18 Penny Goose. Beier, Ellen, illus. 1998. (I Can Read Bks.). 64p. (J). (gr. k-3). 15.89 (978-0-06-027557-0(X)) HarperCollins Pubs.

Wallace, Rich. The Roar of the Crowd. 2005. (Winning Season Ser.: Bk. 1). 112p. (YA). (gr. 3-7). pap. 4.99 (978-0-14-240443-0(8) , Puffin) Penguin Group (USA) Inc.

—Roar of the Crowd. 2004. 101p. (J). lib. bdg. 15.38 (***978-1-4242-2165-3(X)***) Fitzgerald Bks.

—Takedown, No. 8. 2007. (Winning Season Ser.: No. 8). 128p. (YA). (gr. 2). pap. 4.99 (***978-0-14-240919-0(7)*** , Puffin) Penguin Group (USA) Inc.

—Takedown: Winning Season 8. 2006. (Winning Season Ser.). 128p. (J). (gr. 3). 14.99 (978-0-670-06096-2(8) , Viking Juvenile) Penguin Group (USA) Inc.

—Technical Foul: Winning Season. 2005. (Winning Season Ser.: Bk. 2). 128p. (YA). (gr. 3). pap. 4.99 (978-0-14-240444-7(6) , Puffin) Penguin Group (USA) Inc.

Zocchi, Judy. Paulie & Sasha: Circus or Not. Vannozzi, Don, illus. 2001. (Paulie & Sasha Ser.). 32p. (J). lib. bdg. 23.00 (978-1-891997-17-4(3)) Dingles & Co.

NEW JERSEY—HISTORY

ABC Atlantic City: An Alphabet Book, Travel Guide & Souvenir for Kids! 2006. (J). 8.95 (978-0-9760047-1-4(2)) Rosenberger, Matthew.

Capuzzo, Michael. Close to Shore: The Terrifying Shark Attacks of 1916. 2002. (gr. 7-12). lib. bdg. 24.55 (978-0-613-62735-1(0)) Tandem Library Bks.

The Colors of the Lighthouse: A Children's History of Absecon Lighthouse. ed. 2006. (J). 8.95 (***978-0-9779988-0-7(0)***) Absecon Lighthouse.

Corbett, Glenn. The Great Paterson Fire of 1902: The Story of New Jersey's Biggest Blaze. 2002. (Illus.). 145p. 20.00 (978-0-9722604-0-4(4)) Corbett, Glenn.

Doak, Robin S. New Jersey: New Jersey 1609 - 1776. 2005. (Voices from Colonial America Ser.). (Illus.). 112p. (J). (gr. 5-9). 32.90 (978-0-7922-6680-3(3) , National Geographic Children's Bks.) National Geographic Society.

Doak, Robin S. & McConville, Brendan. New Jersey: 1609 - 1776. 2005. (Voices from Colonial America Ser.). (Illus.). 112p. (J). (gr. 5-9). 21.95 (978-0-7922-6385-2(5) , National Geographic Children's Bks.) National Geographic Society.

Doherty, Craig A. & Doherty, Katherine M. New Jersey, 13 vols. 2005. (Thirteen Colonies Ser.). (Illus.). 128p. (J). (gr. 4-9). 35.00 (978-0-8160-5408-4(8)) Facts On File, Inc.

DuBois, Muriel L. The New Jersey Colony. 2005. (Fact Finders Ser.). (Illus.). 32p. (J). (gr. 2-4). lib. bdg. 22.60 (978-0-7368-2678-5(5)) Capstone Pr., Inc.

Heinrichs, Ann. New Jersey. Kania, Matt, illus. 2005. (Welcome to the USA Ser.). 40p. (J). (gr. 1-5). 27.07 (978-1-59296-378-2(1)) Child's World, Inc.

Hyman, Teresa L. New Jersey. 2003. (Seeds of a Nation Ser.). (Illus.). 48p. (J). 26.20 (978-0-7377-1022-9(5) , Greenhaven Pr., Inc.) Thomson Gale.

Italia, Bob. The New Jersey Colony. 2001. (Colonies Ser.). (Illus.). 32p. (J). (gr. k-6). lib. bdg. 22.78 (978-1-57765-590-9(7) , Checkerboard Library) ABDO Publishing Co.

Jordan, Joe. Cape May Point: The Illustrated History From 1875-Present. 2003. (Illus.). 144p. (gr. 10-13). 24.95 (978-0-7643-1830-6(6)) Schiffer Publishing, Ltd.

Marsh, Carole. My First Pocket Guide New Jersey. 2000. (New Jersey Experience! Ser.). (Illus.). 96p. (J). (gr. 3 8). 12.95 (978-0-635-01320-0(7) , 13207) Gallopade International.

—New Jersey History Projects: 30 Cool, Activities, Crafts, Experiments & More for Kids to Do to Learn about Your State! 2003. (New Jersey Experience Ser.). 32p. (gr. k-5). pap. 5.95 (978-0-635-01799-4(7) , Marsh, Carole Bks.) Gallopade International.

—New Jersey Millionaire. 2001. (GameBook Ser.). 32p. (J). (gr. 3-8). pap., act. bk. ed. 9.95 (978-0-635-00076-7(8)) Gallopade International.

—New Jersey Survivor. 2001. (GameBook Ser.). 32p. (J). (gr. 3-8). pap., act. bk. ed. 9.95 (978-0-635-00551-9(4)) Gallopade International.

—The New Jersey Survivor: A Classroom Challenge! 2001. (Carole Marsh New Jersey Bks.). lib. bdg. 29.95 (978-0-635-00676-9(6)) Gallopade International.

—New Jersey Wheel of Fortune. 2001. (GameBook Ser.). 32p. (J). (gr. 3-8). pap., act. bk. ed. 9.95 (978-0-7933-9676-4(X)) Gallopade International.

—Wheel of Fortune. 2001. (New Jersey Bks.). (J). lib. bdg. 29.95 (978-0-7933-9677-1(8)) Gallopade International.

—Who Wants to Be a Millionaire? 2001. (Carole Marsh New Jersey Bks.). (J). lib. bdg. 29.95 (978-0-635-00077-4(6)) Gallopade International.

McCloy, James F. & Miller, Ray, Jr. The Jersey Devil. 2005. (Illus.). 121p. pap. (978-0-912608-11-2(0)) Middle Atlantic Pr.

McMahon, William. Pine Barrens Legends, Lore. 2005. (Illus.). 149p. (J). pap. (978-0-912608-19-8(6)) Middle Atlantic Pr.

Miller, Jake. The Colony of New Jersey: A Primary Source History. 2006. (Primary Source Library of the Thirteen Colonies & the Lost Colony). (Illus.). 24p. (J). lib. bdg. (978-1-4042-3031-6(9) , PowerKids Pr.) Rosen Publishing Group, Inc., The.

Mis, Melody S. How to Draw New Jersey's Sights & Symbols. 2002. (Kids Guide to Drawing America Ser.). 32p. (J). lib. bdg. 25.25 (978-0-8239-6086-6(2) , PowerKids Pr.) Rosen Publishing Group, Inc., The.

Orr, Tamra. A Primary Source History of the Colony of New Jersey. 2005. (Primary Sources of the Thirteen Colonies & the Lost Colony Ser.). (Illus.). 64p. (YA). (gr. 5-8). lib. bdg. 29.25 (978-1-4042-0430-0(X)) Rosen Publishing Group, Inc., The.

Orr, Tamra B. A Primary Source History of the Colony of New Jersey. 2005. (Primary Sources of the Thirteen Colonies & the Lost Colony Ser.). (Illus.). 64p. (J). (gr. 3-7). pap. 14.60 (978-1-4042-0668-7(X)) Rosen Publishing Group, Inc., The.

Pfeffer, Wendy. Many Ways to Be a Soldier. 2008. (On My Own History Ser.). (J). lib. bdg. 25.26 ***(978-0-8225-7279-4(6)*** , Millbrook Pr.) Lerner Publishing Group.

Steward, Mark. New Jersey History. 2003. (Illus.). 48p. (J). 27.07 (978-1-4034-0673-6(1)); pap. 8.50 (978-1-4034-2683-3(X)) Heinemann Library.

Stewart, Mark. People of New Jersey. 2003. (State Studies). (Illus.). 48p. (J). 27.07 (978-1-4034-0675-0(8)); pap. 8.50 (978-1-4034-2686-4(4)) Heinemann Library.

Weatherly, Myra. The New Jersey Colony. 2003. (Spirit of America). (Illus.). 40p. (J). (gr. 2-6). 28.50 (978-1-56766-624-3(8)) Child's World, Inc.

Whitehurst, Susan. The Colony of New Jersey. 2000. (Library of the Thirteen Colonies & the Lost Colony). (Illus.). 24p. (J). (gr. 3). lib. bdg. 19.95 (978-0-8239-5480-3(3) , PowerKids Pr.) Rosen Publishing Group, Inc., The.

Wiener. The 13 Colonies Pack: New Jersey, 6. 2004. (Illus.). 48.30 (978-1-4109-0370-9(2)) Harcourt Schl. Pubs.

Wiener, Roberta & Arnold, James R. New Jersey. 2004. (Thirteen Colonies Ser.). (Illus.). 64p. (J). 28.56 (978-0-7398-6883-6(7)); 9.50 (978-1-4109-0307-5(9)) Harcourt Schl. Pubs.

NEW MARKET (VA.), BATTLE OF, 1864

Beller, Susan Provost. Cadets at War: The True Story of Teenage Heroism at the Battle of New Market. 2000. (gr. 3-6). lib. bdg. 18.75 (978-0-613-85694-2(5)) Tandem Library Bks.

—Cadets at War: The True Story of Teenage Heroism at the Battle of New Market. 2000. (Illus.). 108p. (gr. 4-7). pap. 9.95 (978-0-595-00787-5(2) , Backinprint.com) iUniverse, Inc.

NEW MEXICO

Alter, Judy. New Mexico: A MyReportLinks.com Book. 2002. (States Ser.). (Illus.). 48p. (J). (gr. 4-10). lib. bdg. 25.26 (978-0-7660-5098-3(X) , MyReportLinks.com Bks.) Enslow Pubs., Inc.

Barco, Kathy. READiscover New Mexico: A Tri-Lingual Adventure in Literacy. 2007. (ENG, SPA & NAV.). (J). pap. ***(978-0-86534-544-7(9))*** Sunstone Pr.

Bjorklund, Ruth. New Mexico. 2003. (It's My State! Ser.). (Illus.). 80p. (J). 27.07 (978-0-7614-1526-8(2) , Benchmark Bks.) Cavendish, Marshall Corp.

Burgan, Michael. New Mexico. 2008. (J). ***(978-0-531-18578-0(8))*** Children's Pr., Ltd.

Burgan, Michael. New Mexico: Land of Enchantment. 2003. (World Almanac Library of the States). (Illus.). 48p. (J). (gr. 5 up). pap. 14.95 (978-0-8368-5327-8(X)); lib. bdg. 30.00 (978-0-8368-5156-4(0)) Stevens, Gareth Inc. (World Almanac Library).

Craats, Rennay. A Guide to New Mexico. 2001. (American States Ser.). (Illus.). 32p. (J). lib. bdg. 16.95 (978-1-930954-74-8(3)) Weigl Pubs., Inc.

De Angelis, Therese. New Mexico. 2002. (From Sea to Shining Sea Ser.: 2). (Illus.). 80p. (J). (gr. 3-5). pap. 30.50 (978-0-516-22381-0(X) , Children's Pr.) Scholastic Library Publishing.

Early, Theresa S. New Mexico. 2nd exp. rev. ed. 2003. (Hello U. S. A. Ser.). (Illus.). 84p. (J). (gr. 3-6). 25.26 (978-0-8225-4096-0(7) , Lerner Pubns.) Lerner Publishing Group.

—New Mexico. rev. ed. 2003. (gr. 3-6). lib. bdg. 15.25 (978-0-613-52456-8(X)) Tandem Library Bks.

England, Tamara. Josefina's Cookbook: A Peek at Dining in the Past with Meals You Can Cook Today. 1998. (American Girls Collection). (YA). (gr. 2 up). (978-0-606-13542-9(1)) Tandem Library Bks.

Foster James, Helen. E Is for Enchantment: A New Mexico Alphabet. Twinem, Neecy, illus. 2004. (State Ser.). 40p. (J). 17.95 (978-1-58536-153-3(4) , 1235984) Sleeping Bear Pr.

Heinrichs, Ann. New Mexico. 2003. (This Land Is Your Land Ser.). (Illus.). 48p. (J). (gr. 3 up). lib. bdg. 22.60 (978-0-7565-0343-7(4)) Compass Point Bks.

Hubbard, Coleen. Uniquely New Mexico. 2003. (Heinemann State Studies). (Illus.). 48p. (J). pap. 8.50 (978-1-4034-4721-0(7)); lib. bdg. 27.07 (978-1-4034-4652-7(0)) Heinemann Library.

Kummer, Patricia K. New Mexico. rev. ed. 2002. (One Nation Ser.). (Illus.). 48p. (J). (gr. 3-4). lib. bdg. 22.60 (978-0-7368-1255-9(5) , Bridgestone Bks.) Capstone Pr., Inc.

Lavash, Donald R. A Journey Through New Mexico History: The Land of Enchantment. 3rd rev. ed. 2006. (Illus.). 208p. (YA). (gr. 8-12). pap. 26.95 (978-0-86534-194-4(X)) Sunstone Pr.

Marsh, Carole. The Big New Mexico Reproducible Activity Book. 2001. (Carole Marsh New Mexico Bks.). (Illus.). 96p. (J). (gr. 2-6). pap. 9.95 (978-0-7933-9951-2(3)) Gallopade International.

—My First Book about New Mexico. 2001. (Carole Marsh New Mexico Bks.). (Illus.). 32p. (J). (gr. k-4). pap. 7.95 (978-0-7933-9893-5(2)) Gallopade International.

—New Mexico Classic Christmas Trivia. 2002. (Carole Marsh New Mexico Bks.). (Illus.). 32p. pap. 6.95 (978-0-635-01429-0(7) , 14297); lib. bdg. 21.95 (978-0-635-01430-6(0) , 14300) Gallopade International. (Marsh, Carole Bks.).

—New Mexico Current Events Projects: 30 Cool, Activities, Crafts, Experiments & More for Kids to Do to Learn about Your State! 2003. (New Mexico Experience Ser.). 32p. (gr. k-8). pap. 5.95 (978-0-635-02050-5(5) , Marsh, Carole Bks.) Gallopade International.

—The New Mexico Experience Library State: Resource Set. 2001. (Illus.). (J). 100.20 incl. cd-rom (978-0-635-00484-0(4)) Gallopade International.

—New Mexico Geography Projects: 30 Cool, Activities, Crafts, Experiments & More for Kids to Do to Learn about Your State! 2003. (New Mexico Experience Ser.). 32p. (gr. k-5). pap. 5.95 (978-0-635-01850-2(0) , Marsh, Carole Bks.) Gallopade International.

—New Mexico Government Projects: 30 Cool, Activities, Crafts, Experiments & More for Kids to Do to Learn about Your State! 2003. (New Mexico Experience Ser.). 32p. (gr. k-5). pap. 5.95 (978-0-635-01950-9(7) , Marsh, Carole Bks.) Gallopade International.

—New Mexico Jeopardy! Answers & Questions about Our State! Line Art Staff, illus. 2001. 32p. (J). (gr. 3-8). pap. 7.95 (978-0-7933-9806-5(1)) Gallopade International.

—New Mexico People Projects: 30 Cool, Activities, Crafts, Experiments & More for Kids to Do to Learn about Your State! 2003. (New Mexico Experience Ser.). 32p. (gr. k-5). pap. 5.95 (978-0-635-02000-0(9) , Marsh, Carole Bks.) Gallopade International.

—New Mexico Symbols & Facts Projects: 30 Cool, Activities, Crafts, Experiments & More for Kids to Do to Learn about Your State! 2003. (New Mexico Experience Ser.). 32p. (gr. k-5). pap. 5.95 (978-0-635-01900-4(0) , Marsh, Carole Bks.) Gallopade International.

Maruca, Mary. A Kid's Guide to Exploring Chaco Culture National Historical Park. 2002. (Illus.). 12p. (J). pap. 1.00 (978-1-58369-022-0(0)) Western National Parks Assn.

McDaniel, Melissa. New Mexico. 1998. (Celebrate the States Ser.). (Illus.). 144p. (gr. 4-8). lib. bdg. 37.07 (978-0-7614-0659-4(X) , Benchmark Bks.) Cavendish, Marshall Corp.

McDaniel, Melissa, et al. New Mexico. 2nd ed. 2008. (Celebrate the States Ser.). (J). lib. bdg. 39.93 ***(978-0-7614-2719-3(8)*** , Benchmark Bks.) Cavendish, Marshall Corp.

Murray, Julie. New Mexico. 2006. (Buddy Book Ser.). (Illus.). 32p. (J). (gr. k-4). lib. bdg. 22.78 (978-1-59197-690-5(1) , Buddy Bks.) ABDO Publishing Co.

Nickell, Judy. A New Mexico Dictionary for Young People. 2001. (Illus.). 92p. spiral bd. 10.00 (978-0-9632261-4-3(2)) Canaima Pr.

Nuevo Mexico. (World Almanac Ser.).Tr. of New Mexico. (SPA.). (J). (gr. 3-5). 30.00 (978-0-8368-5725-2(9) , GHS32692) Stevens, Gareth Inc.

Obregon, José María. New Mexico (Nuevo México) 2006. (Bilingual Library of the United States of America: Set 2). (ENG & SPA., Illus.). 32p. (J). (gr. 3-6). lib. bdg. 22.50 (978-1-4042-3096-5(3) , Buenas Letra) Rosen Publishing Group, Inc., The.

Sateren, Shelley Swanson. New Mexico: Facts & Symbols. 1999. (States & Their Symbols Ser.). (Illus.). 24p. (J). (gr. k-3). pap. 15.00 (978-0-531-12006-4(6) , Watts, Franklin) Scholastic Library Publishing.

—New Mexico Facts & Symbols. (States & Their Symbols Ser.). 24p. (J). 2000. (Illus.). (gr. 2-3). lib. bdg. 18.60 (978-0-7368-0380-9(7) , Bridgestone Bks.); 2003. lib. bdg. 19.93 (978-0-7368-2261-9(5)) Capstone Pr., Inc.

Vivian, R. Gwinn & Anderson, Margaret J. Chaco Canyon. 2002. (Digging for the Past Ser.). (Illus.). 48p. (YA). (gr. 5 up). 22.95 (978-0-19-514280-8(2)) Oxford Univ. Pr., Inc.

Walker, Cynthia. New Mexico. 2005. (Rookie Read-About Geography Ser.). (Illus.). 32p. (J). (gr. 1-2). pap. 5.95 (978-0-516-25933-8(4) , Children's Pr.) Scholastic Library Publishing.

—Nuevo Mexico. (J). (gr. k-2). 2006. (SPA.). 32p. pap. 5.95 (978-0-516-25048-9(5)); 2005. (ENG & SPA., Illus.). 31p. 19.50 (978-0-516-25247-6(X)) Scholastic Library Publishing. (Children's Pr.).

Walker, Cynthia & Vargus, Nanci Reginelli. New Mexico. 2004. (Rookie Read-About Geography Ser.). (Illus.). 31p. (J). 20.50 (978-0-516-22755-9(6) , Children's Pr.) Scholastic Library Publishing.

Weiss-Malik, Linda S. New Mexico. 2006. (Portraits of the States Ser.). (J). pap. (978-0-8368-4722-2(9)); lib. bdg. (978-0-8368-4705-5(9)) Stevens, Gareth Inc.

NEW MEXICO—ANTIQUITIES

National Geographic Society Staff. Indian Tribes of the Americas. 1999. (Cultural & Geographical Exploration Ser.). (Illus.). 144p. (YA). (gr. 7-12). 21.95 (978-0-7910-5447-5(0) , Chelsea Hse.) Facts On File, Inc.

NEW MEXICO—FICTION

Abraham, Susan Gonzales & Abraham, Denise Gonzales. Cecilia's Year. 2007. (Latino Fiction for Young Adults Ser.). 210p. (J). pap. 11.95 (978-1-933693-02-6(9)) Cinco Puntos Pr.

—Surprising Cecilia. 2005. (Latino Fiction for Young Adults Ser.). 216p. (YA). 16.95 (978-0-938317-96-8(2)) Cinco Puntos Pr.

Abruzzo, Nancy. Pop Flop's Great Balloon Ride. Chilton, Noel, illus. 2005. 32p. (J). (gr. k-17). pap. 12.95 (978-0-89013-475-7(8)) Museum of New Mexico Pr.

Alarid, Carilyn & Markel, Marilyn. Talks All Day Has the Courage to Speak: Mimbres Children Learn Citizenship. Alarid, Carilyn & Markel, Marilyn, illus. 2006. (Illus.). 125p. (J). pap. 16.95 (978-0-86534-470-9(1)) Sunstone Pr.

Anaya, Rudolfo A. The Santero's Miracle: A Bilingual Story. Lamadrid, Enrique E., tr. Cordova, Amy, illus. 2004. (ENG & SPA.). 32p. (J). 16.95 (978-0-8263-2847-2(4)) Univ. of New Mexico Pr.

Beth, Hodder. The Ghost of Schafer Meadows. 2007. (J). per. 7.99 ***(978-0-9793963-0-4(1))*** Grizzly Ridge Publishing.

Bronson, Wilfrid S. Pinto's Journey. 2007. (J). pap. ***(978-0-86534-557-7(0))*** Sunstone Pr.

Buchanan, William J. Diablo: The Devil Steer. 2004. 151p. (J). (gr. 6-10). 9.95 (978-0-8263-3139-7(4)) Univ. of New Mexico Pr.

Burroughs, Jean M. Children of Destiny: True Adventures of Three Cultures. 2001. (Illus.). 108p. (J). pap. 12.95 (978-0-913270-75-2(X)) Sunstone Pr.

Cheek, Roland. Lincoln County Crucible, 6 vols. 2003. 288p. pap. 14.95 (978-0-918981-10-3(7) , 3) Skyline Publishing.

Creel, Ann Howard. Under a Stand Still Moon. 2005. 192p. (YA). pap. 8.95 (978-0-9746481-8-7(3)) Brown Barn Bks.

—Water at the Blue Earth. 1998. (Illus.). 148p. (gr. 5-9). pap. 8.95 (978-1-57098-224-8(4)) Rinehart, Roberts Pubs.

Darlington, Katherine. Gypsy Wind. 2003. 128p. (YA). pap. 12.95 (978-1-59113-417-6(X)) Booklocker.com, Inc.

de Paola, Tomie. The Night of las Posadas. de Paola, Tomie, illus. 2002. (Illus.). 14.04 (978-1-4046-0923-5(7)) Book Wholesalers, Inc.

—The Night of las Posadas. 2001. (gr. k-3). lib. bdg. 15.30 (978-0-613-44406-4(X)) Tandem Library Bks.

Deal, Paul. Lighting Candles. 2003. 122p. (YA). 20.95 (978-0-595-65804-6(0)); pap. 10.95 (978-0-595-28457-3(4)) iUniverse, Inc.

Foard, Sheila Wood. Harvey Girl. 2006. (Illus.). viii, 152p. (J). (978-0-89672-570-6(7)) Texas Tech Univ. Pr.

Hand, Jimmie. Long Way Around. 2003. (gr. 7-12). lib. bdg. 18.75 (978-0-613-77939-5(8)) Tandem Library Bks.

Hays, Anna Jane. The Secret of the Circle K Cave. Smath, Jerry, illus. 2006. (Science Solves It! Ser.). 32p. (J). (gr. k-3). pap. 4.99 (978-1-57565-189-7(0)) Kane Pr., The.

Hiscock, Bruce. Coyote & Badger: Desert Hunters of the Southwest. 2003. (Illus.). 32p. (J). (gr. 2-4). 15.95 (978-1-56397-848-7(2)) Boyds Mills Pr.

Hobbs, Will. Kokopelli's Flute. 2005. 160p. (J). (gr. k-9). pap. 4.99 (978-1-4169-0250-8(3) , Aladdin) Simon & Schuster Children's Publishing.

Hulme, Joy N. Climbing the Rainbow. 2004. 224p. (J). 15.99 (978-0-380-81572-2(9)); lib. bdg. 16.89 (978-0-06-054304-4(3)) HarperCollins Pubs.

—Through the Open Door. 2000. 176p. (J). (gr. 4-6). 14.95 (978-0-380-97870-0(9)) HarperCollins Pubs.

Kudlinski, Kathleen V. The Spirit Catchers: An Encounter with Georgia O'Keeffe. 2005. (Art Encounters Ser.). (Illus.). 176p. (YA). 15.95 (978-0-8230-0408-9(2)) Watson-Guptill Pubns., Inc.

Lasky, Kathryn. Blood Secret. 2006. 304p. (J). pap. 5.99 (978-0-06-000063-9(5) , Harper Trophy) HarperCollins Pubs.

Lehr, Norma. Dance of the Crystal Skull. rev. exp. ed. 2003. (Illus.). 238p. (J). (gr. 3-7). lib. bdg. 15.95 (978-0-87358-724-2(3) , Rising Moon Bks. for Young Readers) Northland Publishing.

—Dance of the Crystal Skull. 1999. (Illus.). (J). (978-0-606-18310-9(8)) Tandem Library Bks.

Little, Kimberley Griffiths. The Last Snake Runner. 2004. 208p. (YA). (gr. 7). pap. 5.99 (978-0-440-23782-2(3) , Laurel Leaf) Random Hse. Children's Bks.

Little, Kimberley Griffiths. The Last Snake Runner: A Novel. 2006. 201p. (YA). (gr. 7-10). reprint ed. 16.00 ***(978-1-4223-5838-2(0))*** DIANE Publishing Co.

McKann, Anna. Chavos: The Kids of Distrito Federal. 2006. (Illus.). 261p. (YA). per. ***(978-0-9554438-0-0(6))*** Sharon Hse. Publishing, Ltd.

Momaday, N. Scott. Circle of Wonder: A Native American Christmas Story. 1999. (Illus.). 44p. (gr. 4-7). 19.95 (978-0-8263-2149-7(6)) Univ. of New Mexico Pr.

Mora, Pat. Maria Paints the Hills. Hesch, Maria, illus. 2002. 32p. 19.95 (978-0-89013-401-6(4)); 1p. pap. 9.95 (978-0-89013-410-8(3)) Museum of New Mexico Pr.

Murphy, Barbara Beasley. Ace Flies Like an Eagle. 2003. (Can't Stop Ace Ser.: No. 3). 180p. (J). pap. 16.95 (978-0-86534-409-9(4)) Sunstone Pr.

New Mexico Night Before Christmas. 2006. (YA). per. 19.99 ***(978-0-9710675-5-4(4))*** 2020 Vision Pr.

Orona-Ramirez, Kristy. Kiki's Journey. Warm Day, Jonathan, illus. 2006. 32p. (J). 16.95 (978-0-89239-214-8(2)) Children's Bk. Pr.

Ortega, Cristina. The Eyes of the Weaver: Los Ojos Del Tejedor. Garcia, Patricio, illus. 2006. 64p. (J). 17.95 (978-0-8263-3990-4(5)) Univ. of New Mexico Pr.

Ortega, Cristina. The Key to Grandpa's House. Ortega, Luis Armando, illus. 2007. 24p. (J). (gr. 1 up). 14.95 ***(978-0-8263-4205-8(1))*** Univ. of New Mexico Pr.

Patchin, Gee Frank. Pony Rider Boys in New Mexico. 2006. pap. 19.99 ***(978-1-4280-3254-5(1))*** IndyPublish.com.

Pijoan, Teresa. Stories from a Dark & Evil World. Sharon, Franco, tr. Kosharek, Daniel, illus. 1999. (Bilingual Ser.).Tr. of Cuentos del Mundo Malevolo. (SPA.). 200p. (gr. 8-12). pap. 14.95 (978-1-878610-71-3(6)) Red Crane Bks., Inc.

Poulsen, David A. No Time Like the Past. 3rd rev. ed. 2007. (Salt & Pepper Chronicles). 160p. (gr. 3-7). pap. 6.95 ***(978-1-55263-807-1(3))*** Key Porter Bks. CAN. *Dist:* Perseus Distribution.

Reeder, Carolyn. The Secret Project Notebook. 2005. 247p. (J). (978-0-941232-33-3(6)) Los Alamos Historical Society.

Rinaldi, Ann. The Staircase. 2002. (gr. 7-12). lib. bdg. 14.15 (978-0-613-59929-0(2)) Tandem Library Bks.

Rue, Nancy N. The Choice. 2002. (Christian Heritage Ser.). 192p. (Orig.). (J). pap. (978-1-56179-896-4(7)) Focus on the Family Publishing.

—The Discovery. 2001. (Christian Heritage Ser.). (Illus.). 192p. (J). (gr. 3-7). pap. (978-1-56179-862-9(2)) Focus on the Family Publishing.

—The Struggle. 2002. (Christian Heritage Ser.). 192p. (J). pap. 5.99 (978-1-56179-895-7(9)) Bethany Hse. Pubs.

Ruiz, Joseph J. Angel on Daniel's Shoulder. 2004. (SPA & ENG., Illus.). 108p. (J). pap. 12.95 (978-0-86534-402-0(7)) Sunstone Pr.

—The Little Ghost Who Wouldn't Go Away: El Pequeno Fantasma Que No Queria Irse (Bilingual) Lucero, Juan S., tr. Hotvedt, Kris, illus. 2000. (SPA & ENG.). 96p. (J). (gr. 2-4). pap. 10.95 (978-0-86534-303-0(9)) Sunstone Pr.

—Manuel & the Magic Ring. 2003. (SPA & ENG., Illus.). 108p. (J). pap. 12.95 (978-0-86534-399-3(3)) Sunstone Pr.

Saenz, Benjamin Alire. Sammy & Juliana in Hollywood. 2004. 240p. (YA). 19.95 (978-0-938317-81-4(4)) Cinco Puntos Pr.

Sagel, Jim. Always the Heart. 1998. (Red Crane Literature Ser.).Tr. of Siempre el Corazon. (ENG & SPA., Illus.). 168p. (gr. 8-12). pap. 12.95 (978-1-878610-68-3(6)) Red Crane Bks., Inc.

—Always the Heart. 1998. Tr. of Siempre el Corazon. (gr. 7-12). lib. bdg. 22.20 (978-0-613-80111-9(3)) Tandem Library Bks.

Scruggs, Sandy. Ode to the Wart Hog. Scruggs, Sandy, illus. 1999. (Illus.). 56p. (YA). (gr. 3 up). pap. 11.95 (978-0-9660239-7-8(8)) Azro Pr., Inc.

Simmons, Marc. Jose's Buffalo Hunt: A Story from History. Kil, Ronald R., tr. Kil, Ronald R., illus. 2004. 64p. 17.95 (978-0-8263-3315-5(X)) Univ. of New Mexico Pr.

Skurzynski, Gloria. Running Scared. 2002. (gr. 3-6). lib. bdg. 14.10 (978-0-613-62832-7(2)) Tandem Library Bks.

Skurzynski, Gloria & Ferguson, Alane. Running Scared. 2002. (Mysteries in Our National Parks Ser.: Vol. 11). 160p. (J). (gr. 3-7). 15.95 (978-0-7922-8232-7(9)); pap. 5.95 (978-0-7922-6948-9(9)) National Geographic Society. (National Geographic Children's Bks.).

Slate, Joseph. The Secret Stars. Davalos, Felipe, illus. 32p. (J). 2005. pap. 5.95 (978-0-7614-5152-5(8)); 1998. 15.95 (978-0-7614-5027-6(0) , Cavendish Children's Bks.) Cavendish, Marshall Corp.

Stem, Jacqueline. Mystery of the Whispering Walls. 2004. (J). 148p. pap. (978-1-57168-844-6(7)); (Hollow Tree Mystery Ser.: Bk. 6). (Illus.). v, 142p. (978-1-57168-850-7(1) , Eakin Pr.) Eakin Pr.

Stevens, Jan Romero. Carlos y el Zorrillo. Arnold, Jeanne, illus. 2001. (SPA.). (J). (ps-ps). lib. bdg. 16.40 (978-0-613-36036-4(2)) Tandem Library Bks.

Stoddard, Michael Eugene. The Porthole to Time. 1999. 176p. (YA). pap. 9.95 (978-0-9675924-0-4(2)) Stoddard, Michael Eugene.

Strickland, Deborah. Mary Reeder, Prairie Girl. 2007. 68p. per. 8.95 ***(978-0-595-44514-1(4))*** iUniverse, Inc.

Sweet, J.H. & Sierra, Holly. Periwinkle & the Cave of Courage: The Fairy Chronicles. 2007. (Fairy Chronicles Ser.). (Illus.). 128p. (J). (gr. 2 up). pap. 6.99 ***(978-1-4022-1026-6(4)*** , Sourcebooks Jabberwocky) Sourcebooks, Inc.

Taschek, Karen. Horse of Seven Moons. 2005. (Illus.). 192p. (YA). pap. 14.95 (978-0-8263-3215-8(3)) Univ. of New Mexico Pr.

Tripp, Valerie. Changes for Josefina Bk. 6: A Winter Story. Tibbles, Jean-Paul & McAliley, Susan, illus. 1998. (American Girls Collection: Bk. 6). 80p. (J). (gr. 2 up). 12.95 (978-1-56247-592-5(4)); pap. 6.95 (978-1-56247-591-8(6)) American Girl Publishing, Inc.

—Changes for Josefina Bk. 6: A Winter Story. Tibbles, Jean-Paul, illus. 1998. (American Girls Collection: Bk. 6). (YA). (gr. 2 up). 12.75 (978-0-606-13264-0(3)) Tandem Library Bks.

—Happy Birthday, Josefina! A Springtime Story. Tibbles, Jean-Paul & McAliley, Susan, illus. 1998. (American Girls Collection: Bk. 4). 80p. (J). (gr. 2 up). 6.95 (978-1-56247-587-1(8)); Bk. 4. 12.95 (978-1-56247-588-8(6)) American Girl Publishing, Inc.

—Happy Birthday, Josefina! A Springtime Story. Tibbles, Jean-Paul, illus. 1998. (American Girls Collection: Bk. 4). (YA). (gr. 2 up). 12.75 (978-0-606-13456-9(5)) Tandem Library Bks.

—Josefina Entra en Accion: Un Cuento de Verano. Tibbles, Jean-Paul, illus. 1998. (American Girls Collection: Bk. 5). Tr. of Josefina Saves the Day. (SPA.). (YA). (gr. 2 up). 12.75 (978-0-606-13540-5(5)) Tandem Library Bks.

—Josefina Saves the Day Bk. 5: A Summer Story. Tibbles, Jean-Paul, illus. 1998. (American Girls Collection: Bk. 5). 80p. (J). (gr. 2 up). pap. 6.95 (978-1-56247-589-5(4)) American Girl Publishing, Inc.

—Josefina Saves the Day Bk. 5: A Summer Story, Bk. 5. Tibbles, Jean-Paul & McAliley, Susan, illus. 1998. (American Girls Collection: Bk. 5). 80p. (J). (gr. 2 up). 12.95 (978-1-56247-590-1(8)) American Girl Publishing, Inc.

—Josefina Saves the Day Bk. 5: A Summer Story. Tibbles, Jean-Paul, illus. 1998. (American Girls Collection: Bk. 5). (YA). (gr. 2 up). 12.75 (978-0-606-13541-2(3)) Tandem Library Bks.

Tripp, Valerie. Josefina's Short Story Collection. Tibbes, Jean-Paul & Graef, Renee, illus. 2006. 236p. (J). 12.95 ***(978-1-59369-124-0(6))*** American Girl Publishing, Inc.

Voorhees, Coert. Los Torres. 2008. 320p. 16.99 ***(978-1-4231-0304-2(1))*** Hyperion Pr.

Yeager, Graham. Diablo: The Third Millersburg Novel. 2006. 145p. (YA). per. 7.99 ***(978-0-9765478-4-6(8))*** Stone Acres Publishing Co.

Zindel, Paul. The Gadget. 2003. (Illus.). 192p. (YA). (gr. 7). pap. 6.50 (978-0-440-22951-3(0) , Laurel Leaf) Random Hse. Children's Bks.

—The Gadget. 2003. (gr. 5-8). lib. bdg. 13.55 (978-0-613-62203-5(0)) Tandem Library Bks.

NEW MEXICO—HISTORY

The Art Illustrations & Brief History of Padre Antonio Jose Martinez de Taos: New Mexico 1793-1867. 2003. pap. 10.00 (978-0-9748002-0-2(1)) Martinez, Leroy F.

Art Illustrations & Brief History of Padre Antonio Jose Martinez de Taos: New Mexico 1793-1867 Version: Color. 2003. pap. (978-0-9748002-1-9(X)) Martinez, Leroy F.

Brown, Rachel K. Santa Fe: Daily Life in a Western Trading Center. 2003. (J). pap. (978-1-58417-074-7(3)) Lake Street Pubs.

Bruchac, Joseph. Navajo Long Walk: The Tragic Story of a Proud People's Forced March from Their Homeland. Begay, Shonto W., illus. 2002. 64p. (J). (gr. 3-7). 18.95 (978-0-7922-7058-4(4) , National Geographic Children's Bks.) National Geographic Society.

Covert, Kim. New Mexico. 2003. (Land of Liberty Ser.). (Illus.). 64p. (J). lib. bdg. 25.26 (978-0-7368-2189-6(9)) Capstone Pr., Inc.

Embry-Litchman, Kristin. Secrets! Of a Los Alamos Kid 1946-1953. Ebinger, Virginia N., ed. 2001. (Illus.). 111p. (J). (gr. 4-9). pap. 12.95 (978-0-941232-27-2(1)) Los Alamos Historical Society.

Gonzales, Raymond Bences. A Boy on the Hill. Gursky, Judy, ed. Jandacek, Petr, illus. 2001. 70p. (J). pap. 10.95 (978-0-941232-29-6(8)) Los Alamos Historical Society.

Heinrichs, Ann. New Mexico. Kania, Matt, illus. 2005. (Welcome to the USA Ser.). 40p. (J). (gr. 1-5). 27.07 (978-1-59296-379-9(X)) Child's World, Inc.

Krull, Kathleen. What Really Happened in Roswell? Just the Facts. 2003. (gr. 3-6). lib. bdg. 12.10 (978-0-613-66747-0(6)) Tandem Library Bks.

—What Really Happened in Roswell? Just the Facts (Plus the Rumors) about UFOs & Aliens. Santoro, Christopher, illus. 2003. 64p. (J). (gr. 3 up). lib. bdg. 16.89 (978-0-688-17249-7(0)) HarperCollins Pubs.

La Pierre, Yvette. Welcome to Josefina's World, 1824: Growing up on America's Southwest Frontier. 1999. (American Girls Collection). (Illus.). 64p. (J). (gr. 2 up). 16.95 (978-1-56247-769-1(2)) American Girl Publishing, Inc.

Marsh, Carole. My First Pocket Guide New Mexico. 2000. (New Mexico Experience Ser.). (Illus.). 96p. (J). (gr. 3-8). 12.95 (978-0-635-01321-7(5) , 13215) Gallopade International.

—New Mexico History Projects: 30 Cool, Activities, Crafts, Experiments & More for Kids to Do to Learn about Your State! 2003. (New Mexico Experience Ser.). 32p. (gr. k-5). pap. 5.95 (978-0-635-01800-7(4) , Marsh, Carole Bks.) Gallopade International.

—New Mexico Survivor. 2001. (GameBook Ser.). 32p. (J). (gr. 3-8). pap., act. bk. ed. 9.95 (978-0-635-00552-6(2)) Gallopade International.

—The New Mexico Survivor: A Class Challenge. 2001. (Carole Marsh New Mexico Bks.). (J). lib. bdg. 29.95 (978-0-635-00677-6(4)) Gallopade International.

—New Mexico Wheel of Fortune. 2001. (GameBook Ser.). 32p. (J). (gr. 3-8). pap., act. bk. ed. 9.95 (978-0-7933-9678-8(6)) Gallopade International.

—Wheel of Fortune. 2001. (New Mexico Experience Ser.). (J). lib. bdg. 29.95 (978-0-7933-9679-5(4)) Gallopade International.

McNeese, Tim. Santa Fe. 2007. (Colonial Settlements in America Ser.). 120p. (J). (gr. 5-8). 30.00 (***978-0-7910-9332-0(8)*** , Chelsea Hse.) Facts On File, Inc.

Mondragon, Roberto & Roybal, Georgia. Pecos mi Pecos. 2002. (SPA.). per. 20.00 (978-0-9768474-7-2(7)) Aspectos Culturales.

Netzley, Patricia D. Apache Warrior. 2002. (Daily Life Ser.). (Illus.). 48p. (J). (gr. 3-5). 26.20 (978-0-7377-0989-6(8) , Greenhaven Pr., Inc.) Thomson Gale.

O'Neal, Bill. Long Before the Pilgrims: The First Thanksgiving, el Paso del Norte, 1598. Martinez, Lynn O'Neal, tr. Morgan, Polsky, illus. 2000. (ENG & SPA.). 48p. (J). 15.95 (978-1-57168-448-6(4)) Eakin Pr.

Torres, Elizar. Window on Historic New Mexico: Illustrated Historic Briefs for Young Readers. Trujillo, Patrick, illus. 2001. 64p. (J). (gr. 4-6). pap. 8.49 (978-0-9678599-3-4(X)) EP PUBS.

Weintraub, A. How to Draw New Mexicos Sights & Symbols. 2002. (Kids Guide to Drawing America Ser.). 32p. (J). lib. bdg. 25.25 (978-0-8239-6087-3(0) , PowerKids Pr.) Rosen Publishing Group, Inc., The.

NEW ORLEANS (LA.)

Bolding, Ebony. Before & after North Dorgenois. 2005. (Neighborhood Story Project Ser.). (Illus.). 76p. (J). pap. (978-1-933368-31-3(4)) Counterpoint.

Bridges, Ruby & Maccarone, Grace. Let's Read About—Ruby Bridges. Van Wright, Cornelius & Hu, Ying-Hwa, illus. 2003. (Scholastic First Biographies Ser.). (J). (978-0-439-51362-3(6)) Scholastic, Inc.

Bronston, Barri. The Lobster Kids' Guide to Exploring New Orleans. Fischer, Alison, ed. Battuz, Christine, illus. 2002. (Lobster Kids' City Explorers Ser.). 256p. (J). (ps-3). pap. 14.95 (978-1-894222-51-8(2)) Lobster Pr. CAN. *Dist:* Univ. of Toronto Pr.

Dennis, Jana. Palmyra Street. 2005. (Neighborhood Story Project Ser.). (Illus.). 88p. (J). pap. (978-1-933368-30-6(6)) Counterpoint.

Goodman, Steve. The Train They Call the City of New Orleans. 2005. (Live Oak Readalong Ser.). (Illus.). (J). pap. 25.95 incl. audio (978-1-59112-900-4(1)) Live Oak Media.

—The Train They Call the City of New Orleans. McCurdy, Michael, illus. 2003. 16.99 (978-3-00-100280-8(8) , Putnam Juvenile) Penguin Group (USA) Inc.

Hedlund, Stephanie F. New Orleans. 2007. (Cities Ser.). (Illus.). 32p. (J). 22.78 (978-1-59679-721-5(5)) ABDO Publishing Co.

Himelstein, Abram Shalom. What the Hell Am I Doing Here? The 100 T-Shirt Project. 2005. (Illus.). 128p. pap. 12.00 (978-1-881053-98-6(1)) Garrett County Pr.

Lundy, Kathleen Gould. In a Class of Her Own. Alward, Jeff, illus. 2007. 48p. (J). lib. bdg. 23.08 (***978-1-4242-1629-1(X)***) Fitzgerald Bks.

Prentzas, G. S. New Orleans. 1999. (Cities of the World Ser.). (Illus.). 64p. (YA). (gr. 4-9). pap. 9.95 (978-0-516-26397-7(8) , Children's Pr.) Scholastic Library Publishing.

NEW ORLEANS (LA.)—FICTION

Amoss, Berthe. The Chalk Cross. 2007. 160p. (J). (gr. 5). pap. 6.95 (***978-0-618-82997-2(0)*** , Clarion Bks.) Houghton Mifflin Co. Trade & Reference Div.

Blume, Lesley M. M. Tennyson. 2008. 240p. (J). (gr. 3-7). 15.99 (***978-0-375-84703-5(0)*** , Knopf Bks. for Young Readers) Random Hse. Children's Bks.

Buckey, Sarah Masters. The Smuggler's Treasure. 1999. (American Girl Collection Ser.). (978-0-606-17520-3(2)) Tandem Library Bks.

Davis, David. Jazz Cats. Galey, Chuck, illus. 2001. 32p. (J). (gr. 2-4). pap. 15.95 (978-1-56554-859-6(0)) Pelican Publishing Co., Inc.

Feinstein, John. Last Shot: A Final Four Mystery. 2005. 256p. (J). (gr. 6-10). 16.95 (978-0-375-83168-3(1) , Knopf Bks. for Young Readers) Random Hse. Children's Bks.

Gerowin, Sean. Catte au Lait & the Big Hurricane. 2005. 36p. (J). 8.99 (978-1-4116-5157-9(X)) Lulu.com.

Goodman, Steve. The Train They Call the City of New Orleans. McCurdy, Michael, illus. 2005. (J). pap. 28.95 incl. audio compact disk (978-1-59112-904-2(4)) Live Oak Media.

Gumbo Goes Downtown - Evaluation Guide: Evaluation Guide. 2006. (J). (978-1-55942-407-3(9)) Marsh Media.

Guzman, Lila & Guzman, Rick. Lorenzo & the Turncoat. 183p. (J). pap. 9.95 (978-1-55885-471-0(1) , Piñata Books) Arte Publico Pr.

MacBride, Roger Lea. On the Banks of the Bayou. Andreasen, Dan, illus. 1998. (Little House Ser.: Vol. 1). 240p. (J). (gr. 3-7). 15.95 (978-0-06-024973-1(0)) HarperCollins Pubs.

Miller, William. Rent Party Jazz. Riley-Webb, Charlotte, illus. 2001. 32p. (J). (gr. 1-5). 16.95 (978-1-58430-025-0(6)) Lee & Low Bks., Inc.

Muldrow, Diane. Recipe for Trouble. Pollak, Barbara, illus. 2007. (Dish Ser.: No. 7). 160p. (J). pap. 4.99 (978-0-448-44532-8(8) , Grosset & Dunlap) Penguin Group (USA) Inc.

—Recipe for Trouble. 2003. (gr. 3-6). lib. bdg. 13.00 (978-0-613-72489-0(5)) Tandem Library Bks.

Peck, Richard. The River Between Us. 2005. 164p. (J). (ps-7). lib. bdg. 12.64 (978-0-606-33120-3(4)) Tandem Library Bks.

Phillips, Betty Lou. Emily Goes Wild. Watts, Sharon, illus. 2nd ed. 2003. 32p. (J). (ps-3). reprint ed. 16.95 (978-1-58685-268-9(X)) Gibbs Smith, Publisher.

Pogo the Clown. A Taste of Shrimp: Harley's Great Adventures. Miller, Richard D., illus. 2005. (J). 12.95 (978-0-9755253-4-0(4)) Chiliric Pubns.

Preble, Laura. Lica's Angel. 2003. 142p. (YA). 21.95 (978-0-595-74914-0(3)); pap. 11.95 (978-0-595-28253-1(9)) iUniverse, Inc.

Rice, James. Gaston Goes to Mardi Gras. 2nd ed. 1999. (Illus.). 32p. (ps-3). 15.95 (978-1-56554-286-0(X)) Pelican Publishing Co., Inc.

Roy, Ron. The Zombie Zone. Gurney, John Steven, illus. 2005. (A to Z Mysteries Ser.: No. 26). 96p. (J). (gr. k-3). pap. 3.99 (978-0-375-82483-8(9)); (gr. 1-4). lib. bdg. 11.99 (978-0-375-92483-5(3)) Random Hse. Children's Bks. (Random Hse. Bks. for Young Readers).

—The Zombie Zone. Gurney, John Steven, illus. 2005. (A to Z Mysteries Ser.: No. 26). 85p. (J). (gr. k-3). lib. bdg. 11.19 (978-0-606-33238-5(3)) Tandem Library Bks.

Russell, Barbara Timberlake. Maggie's Amerikay. Burke, Jim, illus. 2006. 40p. (J). 17.00 (978-0-374-34722-2(0) , Farrar, Straus & Giroux (BYR)) Farrar, Straus & Giroux.

Sharenow, Robert. My Mother the Cheerleader. 2007. 304p. (gr. 7 up). (J). lib. bdg. 17.89 (978-0-06-114897-2(0)); (YA). 16.99 (978-0-06-114896-5(2)) HarperCollins Pubs. (Geringer, Laura Book).

Smith, Sherri L. Sparrow. 192p. (YA). (gr. 7). 2008. mass mkt. 6.50 (***978-0-440-23945-1(1)*** , Laurel Leaf); 2006. 15.95 (978-0-385-73324-3(0) , Delacorte Bks. for Young Readers); 2006. lib. bdg. 17.99 (978-0-385-90343-1(X) , Delacorte Bks. for Young Readers) Random Hse. Children's Bks.

Staub, Wendy Corsi. Voodoo Moon. 2000. (gr. 7-12). lib. bdg. 14.15 (978-0-613-73080-8(1)) Tandem Library Bks.

Stewart, Whitney. Jammin' on the Avenue. Barstow, Susannah Driver, ed. Farnsworth, Bill, illus. 2001. (Going to Ser.). 151p. (gr. 4-8). pap. 6.95 (978-1-893577-06-0(6)) Four Corners Publishing Co., Inc.

Tiernan, Cate. A Circle of Ashes, No. 2. 2005. (Balefire Ser.). 224p. (YA). (gr. 7-12). mass mkt. 6.99 (978-1-59514-046-3(8) , Razorbill) Penguin Group (USA) Inc.

—A Feather of Stone, No. 3. 2005. (Balefire Ser.). 240p. (YA). (gr. 7-12). mass mkt. 5.99 (978-1-59514-047-0(6) , Razorbill) Penguin Group (USA) Inc.

—A Necklace of Water, Vol. 4. 2006. (Balefire Ser.). 240p. (YA). (gr. 7-12). mass mkt. 5.99 (978-1-59514-048-7(4) , Razorbill) Penguin Group (USA) Inc.

NEW ORLEANS (LA.)—HISTORY

Allberti, Frances C. Finding Rover. Gremillion, Barry, illus. 2006. (J). per. (978-0-9785937-1-1(5)) Open Pages Publishing.

Foran, Jill. Mardi Gras. 2003. (Celebrating Cultures Ser.). (Illus.). 24p. (J). lib. bdg. 15.95 (978-1-59036-093-4(1)) Weigl Pubs., Inc.

Heinrichs, Ann. Mardi Gras. Bryan-Hunt, Jan, illus. 2006. (Holidays, Festivals, & Celebrations Ser.). 32p. (J). (gr. k-4). 22.79 (978-1-59296-578-6(4)) Child's World, Inc.

Strom, Laura Layton. Built below Sea Level: New Orleans. 2007. (Shockwave: People & Communities Ser.). 36p. (J). pap. 6.95 (***978-0-531-18774-6(8)***); (Illus.). (gr. 4-6). lib. bdg. 25.00 (***978-0-531-17746-4(7)***) Scholastic Library Publishing. (Children's Pr.).

Vierow, Wendy. The Capture of New Orleans: Union Fleet Takes Control of the Lower Mississippi River. 2004. (Headlines from History Ser.). (Illus.). 24p. (J). lib. bdg. 19.95 (978-0-8239-6222-8(9) , PowerKids Pr.) Rosen Publishing Group, Inc., The.

NEW ORLEANS, BATTLE OF, NEW ORLEANS, LA., 1815

King, David C. New Orleans. 1998. (Battlefields Across America Ser.: 8). (Illus.). 64p. (gr. 5-8). lib. bdg. 26.90 (978-0-7613-3010-3(0) , Twenty-First Century Bks.) Lerner Publishing Group.

Weintraub, Aileen. Jean Lafitte: Pirate Hero of the War of 1812. 2002. (Library of Pirates). (Illus.). 24p. (J). (gr. 3). lib. bdg. 18.75 (978-0-8239-5796-5(9) , PowerKids Pr.) Rosen Publishing Group, Inc., The.

NEW ORLEANS, BATTLE OF, NEW ORLEANS, LA., 1815—FICTION

Sargent, Dave & Sargent, Pat. Snow: (White) Be Truthful, 25, 53. Lenoir, Jane, illus. 2001. (Saddle Up Ser.: 53). 36p. (J). pap. 6.95 (978-1-56763-624-6(1)); lib. bdg. 22.60 (978-1-56763-623-9(3)) Ozark Publishing.

Williams Evans, Freddi & Evans, Freddi Williams. The Battle of New Orleans: The Drummer's Story. Henriquez, Emile, illus. 2005. 32p. (J). (gr. k-3). per. 15.95 (978-1-58980-300-8(0)) Pelican Publishing Co., Inc.

NEW SOUTH WALES—HISTORY

Mattern, Joanne. Sydney. 2006. (J). (978-1-59679-724-6(X)) ABDO Publishing Co.

NEW TESTAMENT

see Bible—New Testament

NEW WORDS

see Words, New

NEW YEAR

Bledsoe, Karen E. Chinese New Year Crafts. 2005. (Fun Holiday Crafts Kids Can Do Ser.). (Illus.). 32p. (J). lib. bdg. 22.60 (978-0-7660-2347-5(8) , Enslow Elementary) Enslow Pubs., Inc.

Chinese New Year, Vol. 2. 2005. (One World, Many Cultures Ser.). (YA). (gr. k-3). (978-0-7368-9426-5(8) , Pebble Bks.) Capstone Pr., Inc.

Chinese New Year's Dragon. (J). 48.95 (978-0-8136-2242-2(5)) Modern Curriculum Pr.

Compestine, Ying Chang. D Is for Dragon Dance. Xuan, Yong-Sheng, illus. 32p. (J). (ps-3). 17.95 (978-0-8234-1887-9(1)) Holiday Hse., Inc.

—D Is for Dragon Dance. Xuan, YongSheng, illus. 32p. (J). (ps-3). pap. 6.95 (***978-0-8234-2058-2(2)***) Holiday Hse., Inc.

Demi, Hitz. Happy New Year! Kung-hsi Fa-ts'ai! 1999. (J). (978-0-606-17343-8(9)) Tandem Library Bks.

DK Publishing. Chinese New Year. 2008. 16p. (J). pap. 2.49 (***978-0-7566-3317-2(6)***) Dorling Kindersley Publishing, Inc.

Drew, Rosa. Celebrating Chinese New Year: Nick's New Year. 1999. (ps-2). lib. bdg. 10.65 (978-0-613-34116-5(3)) Tandem Library Bks.

Eriback, Arlene. Happy New Year, Everywhere! 2001. (J). (978-0-606-22056-9(9)) Tandem Library Bks.

Erlbach, Arlene. Happy New Year, Everywhere. Holm, Sharon Lane, illus. 2000. (Holidays Everywhere! Ser.). 48p. (gr. k-3). lib. bdg. 23.90 (978-0-7613-1707-4(4) , Millbrook Pr.) Lerner Publishing Group.

Happy New Year: Kung-Hsi Fa-Ts'ai! 1999. (Illus.) (J). (ps-ps). lib. bdg. 15.30 (978-0-613-21676-0(8)) Tandem Library Bks.

Harcourt School Publishers Staff. Chuc Mung Nam Moi! Happy New Year! Advanced Level. 3rd ed. 2002. (Trophies Reading Program Ser.). (Illus.). pap. 5.10 (978-0-15-323482-8(2)) Harcourt Schl. Pubs.

—Happy New Year. 3rd ed. 2002. (Horizons Ser.). (Illus.). (J). pap. 3.70 (978-0-15-333123-7(2)) Harcourt Schl. Pubs.

Imler, Kathryn A. New Year's Day. 2003. (Holiday Histories Ser.). (Illus.). 32p. (J). pap. 6.95 (978-1-4034-3688-7(6)); lib. bdg. 22.79 (978-1-4034-3503-3(0)) Heinemann Library.

Jalali, Yassaman. Celebrating Norouz (Persian New Year) Zamanian, Marjan, illus. 2003. 28p. (J). (ps-6). pap. 12.99 (978-0-9728020-0-0(2)) Saman Publishing.

Jeffrey, Laura S. Celebrate Tet. 2007. (Celebrate Holidays Ser.). (Illus.). 104p. (J). (gr. 5). lib. bdg. 31.93 (***978-0-7660-2775-6(9)***) Enslow Pubs., Inc.

Kule, Elaine A. Celebrate Chinese New Year. 2006. (Celebrate Holidays Ser.). (Illus.). 104p. (J). lib. bdg. 31.93 (978-0-7660-2577-6(2)) Enslow Pubs., Inc.

MacMillan, Dianne M. Chinese New Year. 2008. (Best Holiday Books Ser.). 48p. (J). (gr. 3-4). lib. bdg. 23.93 (***978-0-7660-3038-1(5)***) Enslow Pubs., Inc.

Marx, David F. New Year's Day. 2000. (Rookie Read-About Holidays Ser.). (Illus.). 32p. (J). (gr. 1-2). 19.50 (978-0-516-22205-9(8)); pap. 5.95 (978-0-516-27156-9(3)) Scholastic Library Publishing. (Children's Pr.).

—New Year's Day. 2000. (gr. k-3). lib. bdg. 14.10 (978-0-613-54622-5(9)) Tandem Library Bks.

McNeil, Niki, et al. HOCPP1022 New Years. 2004. spiral bd. 17.50 (***978-1-60308-022-4(8)***) In the Hands of a Child.

Morrissey, Tricia. Hiss! Pop! Boom! Celebrating Chinese New Year. Lee, Kong, illus. 2006. 32p. 12.95 (978-0-9715940-7-4(4)) ThingsAsian Pr.

New Year's Day, Vol. 2. 2005. (One World, Many Cultures Ser.). (YA). (gr. k-3). (978-0-7368-9400-5(4) , Pebble Bks.) Capstone Pr., Inc.

New Year's Day, 6 vols. (gr. k-2). 28.95 (978-0-7368-9401-2(2)) Red Brick Learning.

Peter, Val J., creator. Reflections for a Happy New Year: From the Kids at Boys Town. 2004. 121p. pap. 5.95 (978-1-889322-40-7(7) , 19-016) Boys Town Pr.

Pirotta, Saviour. Chinese New Year. 2007. (J). lib. bdg. (978-1-4042-3709-4(7) , PowerKids Pr.) Rosen Publishing Group, Inc., The.

Rau, Dana. New Year's Day. 2000. (gr. 3-6). lib. bdg. 15.25 (978-0-613-53533-5(2)) Tandem Library Bks.

Schuh, Mari C. New Year's Day. 2002. (Holidays & Celebrations Ser.). (Illus.). 24p. (J). (gr. k-1). lib. bdg. 15.93 (978-0-7368-1446-1(9) , Pebble Bks.) Capstone Pr., Inc.

Sievert, Terri. Chinese New Year. 2006. (First Facts Ser.). (Illus.). 24p. (J). (978-0-7368-5386-6(3)) Capstone Pr., Inc.

Spirn, Michele Sobel. New Year. 1998. (World Celebrations & Ceremonies Ser.). (Illus.). 24p. (J). (gr. 3-5). 22.45 (978-1-56711-249-8(8) , Blackbirch Pr., Inc.) Thomson Gale.

Williams, Colleen Madonna Flood. My Adventure on New Year's Day. 2006. 44p. (J). 8.99 (978-1-59092-554-6(8) , Orchard Academy Pr.) Windstorm Creative.

World Book, Inc. Staff, contrib. by. New Year Celebrations. 2002. (World Book's Celebrations & Rituals Around the World Ser.). (Illus.). 44p. (J). (978-0-7166-5006-5(1)) World Bk., Inc.

Zocchi, Judy. Number 1 What Grows in the Sun? Wallis, Rebecca, illus. 2005. (Holiday Happenings Ser.). 32p. (J). per. 9.95 (978-1-59646-273-1(6)) Dingles & Co.

—On Chinese New Year. Wallis, Rebecca, illus. 2005. (Holiday Happenings Ser.). 32p. (J). per. 9.95 (978-1-59646-189-5(6)) Dingles & Co.

—On Chinese New Year/el Año Nuevo Chino. Wallis, Rebecca, illus. 2005. (Holiday Happenings Ser.).Tr. of Año Nuevo Chino. (ENG & SPA.). 32p. (J). per. 9.95 (978-1-59646-191-8(8)) Dingles & Co.

—On New Year's Eve. Wallis, Rebecca, illus. 2005. (Holiday Happenings Ser.). 32p. (J). pap. 9.95 (978-1-59646-216-8(7)); lib. bdg. 20.65 (978-1-891997-51-8(3)); per. 9.95 (978-1-59646-217-5(5)) Dingles & Co.

—On New Year's Eve/la Nochevieja. Wallis, Rebecca, illus. 2005. (Holiday Happenings Ser.).Tr. of Nochevieja. (ENG & SPA.). 32p. (J). pap. 9.95 (978-1-59646-218-2(3)); lib. bdg. 20.65 (978-1-891997-52-5(1)); per. 9.95 (978-1-59646-219-9(1)) Dingles & Co.

NEW YEAR—FICTION

Bae, Hyun-Joo. New Clothes for New Year's Day. Bae, Hyun-Joo, illus. 2007. (Illus.). 32p. (J). 15.95 (978-1-933605-29-6(4) , 05296) Kane/Miller Bk. Pubs., Inc.

Campoy, F. Isabel & Ada, Alma Flor. Celebrate Chinese New Year with the Fong Family. Castro, Mima, illus. 2006. (Stories to Celebrate Ser.). 31p. (J). (978-1-59820-126-0(3)) Santillana USA Publishing Co., Inc.

Campoy, F. Isabel, et al. Celebra el Ano Nuevo Chino con la Familia Fong. Castro, Mima, illus. 2006. (J). (978-1-59820-114-7(X) , Alfaguara) Santillana USA Publishing Co., Inc.

Crompton, Lee. 12 Months. 2006. 230p. pap. 9.14 (978-1-4116-2196-1(4)) Lulu.com.

Delacre, Lulu. Cuentos Con Sazon. 2001. Tr. of Stories with Season. (SPA.). (gr. 3-6). lib. bdg. 12.40 (978-0-613-82235-0(8)) Tandem Library Bks.

Edens, Cooper. Santa Cow Island. 1999. (J). (978-0-606-18952-1(1)) Tandem Library Bks.

Harcourt School Publishers Staff. Happy Chinese New Year! Below Level. 3rd ed. 2002. (Trophies Reading Program Ser.). (Illus.). pap. 5.10 (978-0-15-323065-3(7)) Harcourt Schl. Pubs.

Haugaard, Kay. The Day the Dragon Danced. Barritt, Carolyn Reed, illus. 2006. (J). (gr. 2-4). 16.95 (978-1-885008-30-5(9)) Shen's Bks.

Holabird, Katharine. Angelina Ice Skates. Craig, Helen, illus. 32p. (J). (ps). 2007. 13.99 (***978-0-670-06237-9(5)*** , Viking Juvenile); 2006. pap. 6.99 (978-0-14-240658-8(9) , Puffin) Penguin Group (USA) Inc.

Klein, Adria F. Max Celebrates Chinese New Year. 2007. (Read-It! Readers Ser.). (Illus.). 24p. (J). (***978-1-4048-3287-9(4)*** , 1265794) Picture Window Bks.

—Max Celebrates Chinese New Year. Gallagher-Cole, Mernie, illus. 2006. (Read-It! Readers Ser.). 24p. (J). (gr. k-2). lib. bdg. 19.93 (***978-1-4048-3147-6(9)*** , 1265794) Picture Window Bks.

Korman, Gordon. Invasion of the Nose Pickers. 2001. (gr. 3-6). lib. bdg. 13.00 (978-0-613-31362-9(3)) Tandem Library Bks.

Lewis, Paul Owen. P Bear's New Year's Party: A Counting Book. 1999. (ps-2). lib. bdg. 15.25 (978-0-613-86794-8(7)) Tandem Library Bks.

Lin, Grace. Bringing in the New Year. 2008. 32p. (J). (***978-0-375-83745-6(0)***); lib. bdg. (***978-0-375-93745-3(5)***) Knopf, Alfred A. Inc.

Lin, Grace. The Year of the Dog. 2007. (Illus.). 162p. (J). (gr. 3-7). pap. 5.99 (978-0-316-06002-8(X)) Little Brown & Co.

McDonald, Megan. Happy New Year, Julie, Bk. 3. McAliley, Susan, illus. 2007. 88p. (YA). (gr. 3 up). 12.95 (***978-1-59369-292-6(7)***) American Girl Publishing, Inc.

—Happy New Year, Julie, Bk. 3. McAliley, Susan & Hunt, Robert, illus. 2007. 88p. (YA). (gr. 3 up). pap. 6.95 (***978-1-59369-291-9(9)***) American Girl Publishing, Inc.

Mitsui Brown, Janet, illus. Oshogatsu with Obaachan. 2005. (J). (978-1-879965-24-9(0)) Polychrome Publishing Corp.

M N O

Muldrow, Diane. On the Back Burner with Other. 2003. (gr. 3-6). lib. bdg. 13.00 (978-0-613-72488-3(7)) Tandem Library Bks.

Piernas-Davenport, Gail. Shanté Keys & the New Year's Peas. Eldridge, Marion, illus. 2007. 32p. (J). (gr. k-4). 16.95 (*978-0-8075-7330-3(2)) Whitman, Albert & Co.

Ruelle, Karen Gray. Just in Time for New Year'S! A Harry & Emily Adventure. (Illus.). 32p. (J). tchr. ed. 14.95 (978-0-8234-1841-1(3)) Holiday Hse., Inc.

Thompson, Lisa. Sent to Sydney. Squire, Stan, illus. 2006. (Read-It! Chapter Books). 80p. (J). (gr. 2-4). 19.95 (978-1-4048-1671-8(2)) Picture Window Bks.

Thong, Roseanne. The Wishing Tree. McLennan, Connie, illus. 2004. 32p. (J). 16.95 (978-1-885008-26-8(0)) Shen's Bks.

Tran, Quoc. The Tet Pole/Su Tich Cay Neu Ngay Tet: The Story of Tet Festival. Smith, William, tr. from VIE. Nguyen, Bich, illus. 2006. (ENG & VIE.). 32p. (J). (gr. 1-4). 16.95 (978-0-9701654-5-9(5)) East West Discovery Pr.

Van Draanen, Wendelin. Sammy Keyes & the Curse of Moustache Mary. VanDraanen, Wendelin, illus. 2001. (Sammy Keyes Ser.: Bk. 5). pap. 36.95 incl. audio (978-0-87499-793-4(3)); pap. 49.95 incl. audio compact disk (978-0-87499-850-4(6)) Live Oak Media.

Zoehfeld, Kathleen Weidner. Happy New Year, Pooh! 2000. (My Very First Winnie the Pooh Ser.). (Illus.). 32p. (J). (ps-k). pap. 4.99 (978-0-7868-4418-0(3)) Disney Pr.

NEW YORK (N.Y.)

Ancona, George. Mi Barrio: My Neighborhood. 2005. (Somos Latinos (We Are Latinos) Ser.). (SPA., Illus.). 32p. (J). (gr. 1-3). pap. 8.95 (978-0-516-25064-9(7) , Children's Pr.) Scholastic Library Publishing.

—Mis Amigos: My Friends. 2005. (Somos Latinos (We Are Latinos) Ser.). (SPA., Illus.). 32p. (J). (gr. 1-3). pap. 8.95 (978-0-516-25068-7(X) , Children's Pr.) Scholastic Library Publishing.

But, Juanita, et al. The Place Where We Dwell: Reading & Writing about New York City. 2005. (Illus.). 354p. 48.25 (978-0-7575-2050-1(2) , 0757520502) Kendall/Hunt Publishing Co.

Cotter, Kristin. New York. 2008. (From Sea to Shining Sea, Second Ser.). 80p. (J). pap. 7.95 (*978-0-531-18807-1(8) , Children's Pr.) Scholastic Library Publishing.

De Capua, Sarah. Nueva York. 2004. (Rookie Readers - Spanish Ser.). 19.50 (978-0-516-25109-7(0) , Watts, Franklin) Scholastic Library Publishing.

—Nueva York: New York. 2005. (Rookie Espanol: Geografia Ser.). (SPA., Illus.). 32p. (J). (gr. k-2). pap. 5.95 (978-0-516-25515-6(0) , Children's Pr.) Scholastic Library Publishing.

Dugan, Joanne. 123 Nyc: A Counting Book of New York City. 2007. (Illus.). 48p. (J). (ps-1). 15.95 (*978-0-8109-1381-3(X) , Abrams Bks. for Young Readers) Abrams, Harry N. , Inc.

Fein, Eric. New York's Sights & Symbols. 2004. 48p. pap. 8.95 (978-1-4042-8505-7(9)) Rosen Publishing Group, Inc., The.

Garrington, Sally. New York. 2006. (Global Cities Ser.). 64p. (J). (gr. 5-8). 30.00 (978-0-7910-8853-1(7) , Chelsea Hse.) Facts On File, Inc.

Gutman, Anne. Lisa a New York. (FRE.). pap. 17.95 (978-2-01-224058-2(5)) Hachette Groupe Livre FRA. *Dist:* Distribooks, Inc.

Hall, Betty & Sullivan, Carter A. New York Survival en Espanol. 2002. (SPA.). 120p. (YA). per. 14.95 (978-1-931797-01-6(3)) Westwood Pr., Inc.

Hatt, Christine. New York. 2000. (World Cities Ser.). (Illus.). 48p. (J). (gr. 2-6). lib. bdg. 16.95 (978-1-929298-31-0(5)) Chrysalis Education.

Heinrichs, Ann. New York. Kania, Matt, illus. 2005. (Welcome to the USA Ser.). 40p. (J). (gr. 1-5). 27.07 (978-1-59296-380-5(3)) Child's World, Inc.

—New York. 2002. (This Land Is Your Land Ser.). (Illus.). 48p. (J). (gr. 3 up). lib. bdg. 22.60 (978-0-7565-0311-6(6)) Compass Point Bks.

Jakobsen, Kathy. My New York. Jakobsen, Kathy, illus. anniv. rev. ed. 2005. (Illus.). 54p. (J). (gr. k-4). 19.00 (978-0-7567-8588-8(X)) DIANE Publishing Co.

—My New York. Jakobsen, Kathy, illus. anniv. ed. 2003. (Illus.). (J). (ps-17). 48p. 18.95 (978-0-316-92711-6(2)); 54p. 18.95 (978-0-316-71350-4(3)) Little Brown & Co.

Johnson, Stephen T. City by Numbers. 2003. (gr. k-3). lib. bdg. 15.30 (978-0-613-67534-5(7)) Tandem Library Bks.

Kavanagh, James. New York City Birds. Leung, Raymond, illus. 2001. (Pocket Naturalist Ser.). 12p. pap. 5.95 (978-1-58355-012-0(7)) Waterford Pr., Ltd.

Ketchum, Ron, illus. Rochestrivia: 2,000 Amazing questions & answers all about Rochester NY, it's people & surrounding Towns. l.t. ed. 2005. 250p. per. 19.95 (978-0-930249-01-4(1)) Big Kids Productions (Publishing).

Kriegel, Otis & McDevitt, Michael. Suggestion. 2005. (Illus.). 416p. pap. 12.95 (978-0-8118-4749-0(7)) Chronicle Bks. LLC.

Leeb, Valorie. My Dad, the Guardian Angel. Tift, Jeanne, ed. Coomes, Sean, illus. 2002. 44p. (YA). (gr. 3 up). 15.95 (978-0-9721872-0-6(0)) Midnight Pr.

Levy, Debbie. The World Trade Center. 2005. (Great Structures in History Ser.). (Illus.). 48p. (J). (ps-8). lib. bdg. 26.20 (978-0-7377-2071-6(9) , Greenhaven Pr., Inc.) Thomson Gale.

Lusted, Marcia Amidon. The Empire State Building. 2004. (Building History Ser.). (Illus.). 112p. (YA). (gr. 7-10). lib. bdg. 32.45 (978-1-59018-546-9(3) , Lucent Bks.) Thomson Gale.

Mattern, Joanne. New York City. 2007. (Cities Ser.). (Illus.). 32p. (J). 22.78 (978-1-59679-719-2(3)) ABDO Publishing Co.

Melmed, Laura Krauss. New York, New York! The Big Apple from A to Z. Lessac, Frane, illus. 2005. 48p. (J). (ps-ps). lib. bdg. 17.89 (978-0-06-054876-6(2)) HarperCollins Pubs.

Munro, Roxie. The Inside-Outside Book of New York City. Munro, Roxie, illus. 2005. (Illus.). 44p. (J). (gr. 4-8). reprint ed. 16.00 (978-0-7567-9455-2(2)) DIANE Publishing Co.

—The Inside-Outside Book of New York City. 2001. (J). (978-0-606-20726-3(0)) Tandem Library Bks.

Neumann, Dietrich. Joe & the Skyscraper: The Empire State Building in New York City. Heritage, Anne, tr. 2005. (GER., Illus.). 28p. (J). (gr. 4-8). 17.00 (978-0-7567-9380-7(7)) DIANE Publishing Co.

Niz, Xavier. The Story of the Statue of Liberty. Martin, Cynthia & Schoonover, Brent, illus. 2006. (Graphic Library). 32p. (J). (978-0-7368-5494-8(0)) Capstone Pr., Inc.

Nueva York. 2003. (World Almanac Biblioteca de los Estados). (SPA., Illus.). 48p. (J). (gr. 5 up). pap. 11.95 (978-0-8368-5553-1(1) , World Almanac Library) Stevens, Gareth Inc.

Pericoli, Matteo. See the City: The Journey of Manhattan Unfurled. 2004. (Illus.). 64p. (J). (gr. 1-5). 15.95 (978-0-375-82469-2(3) , Knopf Bks. for Young Readers) Random Hse. Children's Bks.

Roma, Giancarlo T. & Roma, Thomas. Show & Tell. Roma, Thomas, illus. Roma, Giancarlo T., photos by. 2005. (Illus.). 80p. 19.95 (978-1-57687-133-1(9) , powerHouse Bks.) powerHouse Cultural Entertainment, Inc.

Rotner, Shelley & Kreisler, Ken. Citybook. 1998. (Illus.). 32p. (J). (ps-1). pap. 6.95 (978-0-531-07106-9(5) , Orchard Bks.) Scholastic, Inc.

Sasek, Miroslav. This Is New York. 2003. (This Is ... Ser.). (Illus.). 64p. (gr. k). 17.95 (978-0-7893-0884-9(3)) Universe Publishing.

Thompson, Gare. We Came Through Ellis Island: The Immigrant Adventures of Emma Markowitz. 2003. (I Am American Ser.). (Illus.). 40p. (J). (gr. 3-7). pap. 6.99 (978-0-7922-5682-3(4) , National Geographic Children's Bks.) National Geographic Society.

—We Came Through Ellis Island: The Immigrant Adventures of Emma Markowitz. 2003. (gr. 3-6). lib. bdg. 15.30 (978-0-613-67130-9(9)) Tandem Library Bks.

Valette, D. Von La. Cool Shops New York. 2005. (ENG, SPA, FRE, ITA & GER., Illus.). 135p. pap. 16.95 (978-3-8327-9021-9(7)) teNeues Publishing Co.

Wade, Angela. New York City. 2006. (Illus.). 8p. (J). pap. (*978-0-439-74035-7(5)) Scholastic, Inc.

Walsh, Frank. New York City. 2003. (Great Cities of the World Ser.). (Illus.). 48p. (J). (gr. 5 up). pap. 11.95 (978-0-8368-5185-4(4)); lib. bdg. 30.00 (978-0-8368-5025-3(4)) Stevens, Gareth Inc. (World Almanac Library).

Zschock, Martha Day & Zschock, Heather. Journey Around New York from A to Z. Zschock, Martha Day, illus. 2002. (Journey Around Ser.). (Illus.). 32p. (J). (gr. 4-7). 17.95 (978-1-889833-32-3(0)) Commonwealth Editions.

NEW YORK (N.Y.)—ANTIQUITIES

Goodman, Susan E. On This Spot: An Expedition Back Through Time. Christiansen, Lee, illus. 2004. 32p. (J). 16.99 (978-0-688-16913-8(9)) HarperCollins Pubs.

Standiford, Natalie. Stone Giant. 2001. (gr. 3-6). lib. bdg. 11.80 (978-0-613-33100-5(1)) Tandem Library Bks.

NEW YORK (N.Y.)—BRIDGES

Neuhaus, Beverly. The Bridges of Richmond County. Neuhaus, Beverly, photos by. 2002. 58p. 6.95 (978-0-9726805-0-9(0)) Trivia Tours Unlimited.

NEW YORK (N.Y.)—DESCRIPTION AND TRAVEL

Ashley, Susan. The Statue of Liberty. 2004. (Weekly Reader Early Learning Library). (Illus.). 24p. (J). (gr. 2 up). pap. 5.95 (978-0-8368-4150-3(6)); lib. bdg. 19.33 (978-0-8368-4143-5(3)) Stevens, Gareth Inc. (Weekly Reader Early Learning Library).

Banting, Erinn. Empire State Building. 2007. (J). (*978-1-59036-721-6(9)); (*978-1-59036-722-3(7)) Weigl Pubs., Inc.

Binns, Tristan Boyer. The Statue of Liberty. (Symbols of Freedom Ser.). (Illus.). 32p. (J). (gr. k-2). 2002. pap. 6.95 (978-1-58810-405-2(2) , 91147); 2001. lib. bdg. 21.36 (978-1-58810-121-1(5)) Heinemann Library.

Brown, Geoffrey, compiled by. Liberty, New York Memories. 2002. (Illus.). cd-rom 15.00 (978-0-9727403-0-2(9)) Between the Lakes Group, LLC.

—Old Neversink. 2002. (Illus.). cd-rom 15.00 net. (978-0-9727403-1-9(7)) Between the Lakes Group, LLC.

Bruna, Dick. Miffy Loves New York City! 2004. (Illus.). 32p. pap. 7.99 (978-1-59226-186-4(8)) Big Tent Entertainment, Inc.

Coring the Apple: The Best of New York. 2002. (YA). per. (978-1-932948-12-7(0)) Student Pr. Initiative.

Dugan, Joanne. ABC NYC: A Book about Seeing New York City. 2005. (Illus.). 56p. (J). (ps-1). 15.95 (978-0-8109-5854-8(6)) Abrams, Harry N. , Inc.

Fazio, Wende. Times Square. 1999. (gr. 3-6). lib. bdg. 14.10 (978-0-613-52200-7(1)) Tandem Library Bks.

Gamble, Adam. Good Night New York City. Veno, Joe, illus. 2006. (Good Night Our World Ser.). 24p. (J). bds. 9.95 (978-0-9777979-3-6(7)) Our World of Books.

Goode, Teresa. Wildcat Adventures: A Vacation in the Big Apple. Kotrous, Chad, illus. 2006. 31p. (J). pap. 5.95 (978-1-890622-13-8(3)) Leathers Publishing.

Harmon, Daniel E. The Hudson River. McNeese, Tim, ed. 2004. (Rivers in American Life & Times Ser.). (Illus.). 120p. (gr. 9-13). pap. 13.25 (978-0-7910-8005-4(6) , Chelsea Hse.) Facts On File, Inc.

Harris, Nancy. The Statue of Liberty. 2007. (J). (*978-1-4034-9382-8(0)); pap. (*978-1-4034-9389-7(8)) Heinemann Library.

High, Linda Oatman. Under New York. Rayevsky, Robert, illus. 2001. 32p. (J). (gr. k-3). tchr. ed. 16.95 (978-0-8234-1551-9(1)) Holiday Hse., Inc.

Jane, Pamela. Right on, Winky Blue! Tilley, Debbie, illus. 1999. 64p. (J). 3.95 (978-1-57255-623-2(4)) Mondo Publishing.

—Right on, Winky Blue! 1999. (gr. 3-6). lib. bdg. 11.80 (978-0-613-28044-0(X)) Tandem Library Bks.

Kallen, Stuart A. A Travel Guide to Harlem Renaissance. 2003. (J). 29.95 (978-1-59018-358-8(4) , Lucent Bks.) Thomson Gale.

Landau, Elaine. The Statue of Liberty. 2007. (True Bks.). (Illus.). 48p. (J). (gr. 3-5). lib. bdg. 26.00 (*978-0-531-12635-6(8) , Children's Pr.) Scholastic Library Publishing.

Marx, David F. New York City. 1999. (gr. k-3). lib. bdg. 14.10 (978-0-613-54623-2(7)) Tandem Library Bks.

Melmed, Laura & Melmed, Laura Krauss. New York, New York City: The Big Apple from A to Z. Lessac, Frané & Lessac, Frane, illus. 2005. 48p. (J). (ps-ps). 16.99 (978-0-06-054874-2(6)) HarperCollins Pubs.

New York Russian Language Restaurant Guide. 2005. (RUS.). per. (978-0-9764633-0-6(X)) Press Release Group Corp.

Plenty: The Ultimate Guide to Life & Leisure in Clinton Hill/Fort Greene. 2003. (Illus.). (YA). pap. 20.00 (978-0-9721708-0-2(4) , PCHFG01) RedMEDIA.

Sarg, Tony. Up & down New York. 2007. (Illus.). 30p. (J). 19.95 (978-0-7893-1548-9(3)) Universe Publishing.

Segal, Robin, ed. ABC in NYC. 2006. (Illus.). 32p. (J). 12.95 (978-0-9719697-6-6(0)) Murray Hill Bks., LLC.

Slovey, Christine. Harlem Renaissance. 2000. (Illus.). xxix, 293p. (J). (gr. 4-7). 67.00 (978-0-7876-4836-7(1) , GML00502-114880, UXL) Thomson Gale.

NEW YORK (N.Y.)—FICTION

Adler, David A. Don't Talk to Me about the War. 2008. (YA). (gr. 5). 15.99 (*978-0-670-06307-9(X) , Viking Adult) Penguin Group (USA) Inc.

Alda, Arlene. Morning Glory Monday. Kovalski, Maryann, illus. 2003. 32p. (J). (gr. k-3). 17.95 (978-0-88776-620-6(X)) Tundra Bks., Inc./Livres Toundra, Inc. CAN. *Dist:* Random Hse., Inc.

Alger Jr. Horatio Staff. Struggling Upward. rev. ed. 2006. 284p. 28.95 (978-1-4218-1760-6(8)); pap. 13.95 (978-1-4218-1860-3(4)) 1st World Publishing, Inc. (1st World Library - Literary Society).

Archibald, Laura. The Cats of Grand Central. Beckett, Garner, illus. 2004. 30p. 16.95 (978-0-9730951-0-4(5)) Solomon's Signature CAN. *Dist:* Hushion Hse. Publishing, Ltd.

Arrhenius, Peter. The Penguin Quartet. Peterson, Ingela, illus. 1998. (Picture Bks.). 28p. (J). (ps-3). 15.95 (978-1-57505-252-6(0) , Carolrhoda Bks.) Lerner Publishing Group.

Arruzza, Rick. El Paseo de Sparky. Newton, Pilar, illus. 2003. (SPA.). 24p. mass mkt. 7.95 (978-0-9744509-1-9(X)) Three Spots Productions.

—Sparky's Walk. Newton, Pilar, illus. 2003. 24p. (J). mass mkt. 7.95 (978-0-9744509-0-2(1)) Three Spots Productions.

Ashton, Victoria. Confessions of a Teen Nanny. 2005. (Confessions of a Teen Nanny Ser.). (J). (gr. 8 up). 15.99 (978-0-06-073173-1(7)) HarperCollins Pubs.

Auch, Mary Jane. Ashes of Roses. rev. ed. 2002. 256p. (YA). (gr. 7-10). 16.95 (978-0-8050-6686-9(1) , Holt, Henry & Co. Bks. For Young Readers) Holt, Henry & Co.

—Ashes of Roses. 2004. 256p. (YA). (gr. 7). reprint ed. pap. 5.99 (978-0-440-23851-5(X) , Laurel Leaf) Random Hse. Children's Bks.

—Ashes of Roses. 2004. (gr. 7-12). lib. bdg. 14.15 (978-0-613-72252-0(3)) Tandem Library Bks.

Averill, Esther Holden. Jenny's Birthday Book. Averill, Esther Holden, illus. 2005. (New York Review Children's Collection). (Illus.). 44p. (J). (ps-ps). reprint ed. pap. 15.95 (978-1-59017-154-7(3) , NYR Children's Collection) New York Review of Bks., Inc., The.

Avi. Abigail Takes the Wheel. Bolognese, Don, illus. 1999. (I Can Read Bks.). 64p. (J). (gr. 3 up). 14.95 (978-0-06-027662-1(2)); lib. bdg. 17.89 (978-0-06-027663-8(0)) HarperCollins Pubs.

—Abigail Takes the Wheel. 2000. (Illus.). (J). (978-0-606-18672-8(7)) Tandem Library Bks.

—Don't You Know There's a War On? 2003. 208p. (J). pap. 5.99 (978-0-380-81544-9(3) , Harper Trophy) HarperCollins Pubs.

—Never Mind! A Twin Novel. 2004. 208p. (J). (gr. 5 up). lib. bdg. 16.89 (978-0-06-054315-0(9)) HarperCollins Pubs.

—Silent Movie. Mordan, C. B., illus. 2003. 48p. (J). (gr. k-3). 16.95 (978-0-689-84145-3(0) , Atheneum/Anne Schwartz Bks.) Simon & Schuster Children's Publishing.

Avi & Vail, Rachel. Never Mind! A Twin Novel. 2004. 208p. (J). (gr. 5 up). 15.99 (978-0-06-054314-3(0)) HarperCollins Pubs.

Bailey's Birthday - Evaluation Guide: Evaluation Guide. 2006. (J). (978-1-55942-399-1(4)) Marsh Media.

Banks, Steven. King of the Creeps. 2006. 176p. (YA). (gr. 7). 15.95 (978-0-375-83291-8(2) , Knopf Bks. for Young Readers) Random Hse. Children's Bks.

Barracca, Debra. The Adventures of Taxi Dog. Buehner, Mark, illus. 2002. (J). 13.19 (978-0-7587-1907-2(8)) Book Wholesalers, Inc.

—Adventures of Taxi Dog. 2000. (ps-2). lib. bdg. 14.15 (978-0-613-28397-7(X)) Tandem Library Bks.

—Maxi, the Hero. Buehner, Mark, illus. 2002. (J). 14.04 (978-0-7587-3112-8(4)) Book Wholesalers, Inc.

Barracca, Debra & Barracca, Sal. The Adventures of Taxi Dog. Buehner, Mark, illus. 2000. 32p. (J). (ps-3). pap. 5.99 (978-0-14-056665-9(1) , Puffin) Penguin Group (USA) Inc.

—The Adventures of Taxi Dog. 2000. (Illus.). (J). 12.79 (978-0-606-18386-4(8)) Tandem Library Bks.

Bauer, Cat. Harley's Ninth. 2007. 208p. (YA). (gr. 9). 15.99 (978-0-375-83736-4(1)); lib. bdg. 18.99 (978-0-375-93736-1(6)) Random Hse. Children's Bks. (Knopf Bks. for Young Readers).

Becker, Suzy. Manny's Cows: The Niagara Falls Tale. Becker, Suzy, illus. 2006. (Illus.). 40p. (J). 15.99 (978-0-06-054152-1(0)); lib. bdg. 16.89 (978-0-06-054153-8(9)) HarperCollins Pubs.

Benedict, Helen. Opposite of Love. 2007. 256p. (J). (gr. 6 up). 16.99 (*978-0-670-06135-8(2) , Viking Juvenile) Penguin Group (USA) Inc.

Berry, Andrea. Goalie: The Dynamite Diaries. 2003. 144p. (YA). pap. 11.95 (978-0-595-27678-3(4)) iUniverse, Inc.

Betancourt, Jeanne. Exposed. 2003. (Three Girls in the City Ser.: No. 2). (Illus.). 160p. (J). pap. 4.99 (978-0-439-49840-1(6) , Scholastic Paperbacks) Scholastic, Inc.

Black, Holly. Valiant: A Modern Tale of Faerie. 2006. 320p. (YA). pap. 7.99 (978-0-689-86823-8(5) , Simon Pulse) Simon & Schuster Children's Publishing.

—Valiant: A Modern Tale of Faerie. rev. l.t. ed. 353p. 21.95 (978-0-7862-8226-5(6)) Thorndike Pr.

Blume, Judy. Otherwise Known As Sheila the Great. 2007. (Fudge Ser.). 144p. (J). 5.99 (978-0-14-240879-7(4) , Puffin) Penguin Group (USA) Inc.

Bode, N. E. The Somebodies. Ferguson, Peter, illus. 2006. 288p. (J). 16.99 (978-0-06-079111-7(X) , HarperCollins) HarperCollins Pubs.

Bracken, E E. No Place Like Loam: A Michael O'Brien Story. 2002. 143p. pap. 10.95 (978-0-595-25688-4(0)); (ENG.). 144p. (gr. 2-13). 20.95 (*978-0-595-65261-7(1)) iUniverse, Inc. (Writers Advantage Pr.).

Brown, Anne. The Dumari Chronicles: Year One: Year One. 2007. 376p. (YA). per. 20.95 (*978-0-595-45725-0(8)) iUniverse, Inc.

Brown, Don. Kid Blink Beats the World. Brown, Don, illus. rev. ed. 2004. (Illus.). 32p. (J). 16.95 (978-1-59643-003-7(6)) Roaring Brook Pr.

Brown, Marc. Arthur in New York. 2008. (J). (*978-0-375-82976-5(8)); (*978-0-375-92976-2(2)) Random Hse., Inc.

Bruna, Dick. Miffy Loves New York City! 2004. 32p. (ps-3). 9.99 (978-1-59226-179-6(5)) Big Tent Entertainment, Inc.

Bryant, Annie. Fashion Frenzy. (Beacon Street Girls Ser.: Bk. 9). 232p. (YA). pap. 7.99 (978-1-933566-02-3(7) , Beacon Street Girls) B*tween Productions, Inc.

Bryant, Bonnie. Horse Show. 2007. (Saddle Club Ser.: No. 8). 160p. (J). (gr. 4-6). lib. bdg. 11.99 (*978-0-385-90424-7(X) , Yearling) Random Hse. Children's Bks.

Buck, Nola & Godwin, Laura. Central Park Serenade. Root, Barry, illus. 2002. 32p. (J). (ps-k). 16.99 (978-0-06-025891-7(8) , Cotler, Joanna Books) HarperCollins Pubs.

Buckley, Michael. Once upon a Crime. Ferguson, Peter, illus. 2007. (Sisters Grimm Ser.: Bk. 4). 288p. (J). (gr. 2-8). 14.95 (*978-0-8109-1610-4(X) , Amulet Bks.) Abrams, Harry N. , Inc.

Budhos, Marina. Ask Me No Questions. 176p. (YA). 2007. pap. 8.99 (*978-1-4169-4920-6(8) , Simon Pulse); 2006. (Illus.). (gr. 5-9). 16.95 (978-1-4169-0351-2(8) , Atheneum) Simon & Schuster Children's Publishing.

Bunting, Eve. A Picnic in October. Carpenter, Nancy, illus. 2004. 32p. (J). (gr. 1-4). lib. bdg. 13.20 (978-0-606-30433-7(9)) Tandem Library Bks.

Burke, Morgan. Get It Started. 2005. (Party Room Ser.: No. 1). 272p. (YA). (gr. 11 up). pap. 5.99 (978-0-689-87225-9(9) , Simon Pulse) Simon & Schuster Children's Publishing.

Byalick, Marcia. Quit It. 2004. 176p. (J). (gr. 3-7). pap. 5.99 (978-0-440-41865-8(8) , Yearling) Random Hse. Children's Bks.

Byng, Georgia. Molly Moon's Incredible Book of Hypnotism. 2003. (Illus.). 384p. (J). (gr. 3-7). 16.99 (978-0-06-051406-8(X)); 2003. 135.92 (978-0-06-057217-4(5)); 2004. (Illus.). 400p. (J). reprint ed. pap. 7.99 (978-0-06-051409-9(4) , Harper Trophy) HarperCollins Pubs.

—Molly Moon's Incredible Book of Hypnotism. 2002. (Molly Moon Ser.: Bk. 1). 330p. (J). (gr. 3-7). (978-0-333-98489-5(7) , Macmillan Children's Bks.) Pan Macmillan.

Cabot, Meg. In Love. 2002. (Princess Diaries: Vol. 3). 240p. (YA). (gr. 7 up). 16.99 (978-0-06-029467-0(1)) HarperCollins Pubs.

—In Love, Vol. 3. 2004. (Princess Diaries: Vol. 3). 288p. (J). (gr. 7 up). pap. 38.00 incl. audio (978-0-8072-2284-3(4) , Listening Library) Random Hse. Audio Publishing Group.

—Jinx. 2007. 272p. (gr. 7 up). (J). 16.99 (*978-0-06-083764-8(0)); (YA). lib. bdg. 17.89 (*978-0-06-083765-5(9)) HarperCollins Pubs. (HarperTeen).

—The Princess Diaries. (Princess Diaries: Vol. 1). (gr. 7 up). 2000. 240p. (J). lib. bdg. 17.89 (978-0-06-029210-2(5)); 2001. 320p. (YA). pap. 6.99 (978-0-380-81402-2(1) , Harper Trophy); 2000. (Illus.). 240p. (J). 16.99 (978-0-380-97848-9(2)) HarperCollins Pubs.

—The Princess Diaries. unabr. ed. 2004. (Princess Diaries: Vol. I). 240p. (J). (gr. 7 up). pap. 38.00 incl. audio (978-0-8072-0669-0(5) , Listening Library) Random Hse. Audio Publishing Group.

—The Princess Diaries. 2001. (Princess Diaries: Vol. I). (gr. 7-12). lib. bdg. 15.30 (978-0-613-37165-0(8)); (Illus.). (J). (978-0-606-21844-3(0)) Tandem Library Bks.

—The Princess Diaries. l.t. ed. 2002. (Princess Diaries: Vol. I). 325p. (J). 24.95 (978-0-7862-4058-6(X)) Thomson Gale.

—The Princess Diaries, Volume IX: Princess Mia (international Edition) 2008. (Princess Diaries). 288p. (J). pap. 12.00 (*978-0-06-156819-0(8) , HarperTeen) HarperCollins Pubs.

—Princess in Pink. (Princess Diaries: Vol. 5). (J). (gr. 7 up). 2004. 272p. 15.99 (978-0-06-009610-6(1)); 2005. (Illus.). 304p. reprint ed. pap. 6.99 (978-0-06-009612-0(8)) , Harper Trophy) HarperCollins Pubs.

—Princess in Pink. l.t. ed. 2004. (Princess Diaries: Vol. 5). 304p. 23.95 (978-0-7862-6735-4(6) , Large Print Pr.) Thorndike Pr.

—Princess in the Spotlight. 2001. (Princess Diaries: Vol. II). 240p. (J). (gr. 7 up). 16.99 (978-0-06-029465-6(5)) HarperCollins Pubs.

—Princess in the Spotlight, unabr. ed. 2004. (Princess Diaries: Vol. II). 272p. (J). (gr. 7 up). pap. 38.00 incl. audio (978-0-8072-1197-7(4) , S YA 332 SP, Listening Library) Random Hse. Audio Publishing Group.

—Princess in Training. (Princess Diaries: Vol. 6). (Illus.). (J). 2006. 320p. pap. 6.99 (978-0-06-009615-1(2) , Harper Trophy); 2005. 288p. (gr. 7 up). 16.99 (978-0-06-009613-7(6)) HarperCollins Pubs.

—Princess in Training. l.t. ed. 2005. (Princess Diaries: Vol. 6). 355p. (YA). (gr. 7-12). per. 22.95 (978-0-7862-7753-7(X) , Large Print Pr.) Thorndike Pr.

—Princess Mia. 2008. (Princess Diaries: Vol. 9). 288p. (J). lib. bdg. 17.89 (*978-0-06-072462-7(5)*) HarperCollins Pubs.

Cabot, Meg. Princess on the Brink. (Princess Diaries: Vol. 8). (J). 2008. 288p. 16.99 (*978-0-06-072461-0(7)*); 2008. 272p. pap. 7.99 (*978-0-06-072460-3(9)* , Harper Trophy); 2007. 256p. 16.99 (978-0-06-072456-6(0)); 2007. 256p. lib. bdg. 17.89 (978-0-06-072457-3(9)) HarperCollins Pubs.

Cameron, Peter. Someday This Pain Will Be Useful to You. 2007. 240p. (YA). (gr. 9 up). 16.00 (978-0-374-30989-3(2)) Farrar, Straus & Giroux.

Cerasini, Marc. Meet Casey Jones. 2004. (gr. k-3). lib. bdg. 11.80 (978-0-613-83490-2(9)) Tandem Library Bks.

Christopher, Matt. Fairway Phenom. 2003. 144p. (J). (gr. 5-8). pap. 4.99 (978-0-316-07551-0(5)) Little, Brown Bks. for Young Readers.

Claire, Elizabeth. Where Is Taro? Rosenthal, Marilyn, ed. Lustig, Loretta, illus. 2000. (J). pap., act. bk. ed., instr.'s gde. ed. 15.00 (978-0-937630-10-5(1)) Eardley Pubns.

Clare, Cassandra. City of Ashes. 2008. (Mortal Instruments Ser.). 480p. (YA). 17.99 (*978-1-4169-1429-7(3)* , McElderry, Margaret K.) Simon & Schuster Children's Publishing.

Clark, Mary Higgins. Before I Say Good-Bye. 2001. (gr. 7-12). lib. bdg. 16.45 (978-0-613-33460-0(4)) Tandem Library Bks.

Clarke, Nicole. Copycat. 2007. (Flirt Ser.: No. 9). 224p. (J). (gr. 7). pap. 6.99 (978-0-448-44561-8(1) , Grosset & Dunlap) Penguin Group (USA) Inc.

—French Twist. 2007. (Flirt Ser.: Vol. 8). 224p. (YA). pap. 6.99 (978-0-448-44463-5(1) , Grosset & Dunlap) Penguin Group (USA) Inc.

—Issues. 2006. (Flirt Ser.: No. 5). 224p. (J). (gr. 7). pap. 6.99 (978-0-448-44394-2(5) , Grosset & Dunlap) Penguin Group (USA) Inc.

Clarke, Nicole & Henderson, Mel. Write Here, Right Now, No. 1. 2006. (Flirt Ser.: No. 1). 224p. (J). (gr. 7-10). pap. 6.99 (978-0-448-44263-1(9) , Grosset & Dunlap) Penguin Group (USA) Inc.

Clements, Andrew. Things Hoped For. 176p. (gr. 5). 2008. (J). 6.99 (*978-0-14-241073-8(X)* , Puffin); 2006. (YA). 16.99 (978-0-399-24350-9(X) , Philomel) Penguin Group (USA) Inc.

Coburn, Jake. Prep. 2005. 192p. (YA). (gr. 7). pap. 5.99 (978-0-14-240307-5(5) , Puffin) Penguin Group (USA) Inc.

Cofer, Judith Ortiz. Call Me Maria. 2006. 144p. (J). pap. 6.99 (978-0-439-38578-7(4) , Scholastic Paperbacks) Scholastic, Inc.

Cohen, Miriam. Down in the Subway. Greenberg, Melanie Hope, illus. 2003. 40p. (J). (gr. k-3). pap. 5.95 (978-1-932065-24-4(5)); 15.95 (978-1-932065-08-4(3)) Star Bright Bks., Inc.

Cohn, Rachel. Cupcake. 2007. 256p. (YA). 15.99 (978-1-4169-1217-0(7) , Simon & Schuster Children's Publishing) Simon & Schuster Children's Publishing.

Cohn, Rachel & Levithan, David. Nick & Norah's Infinite Playlist. (YA). (gr. 9 up). 2007. 200p. pap. 8.99 (*978-0-375-83533-9(4)*); 2006. 192p. 16.95 (978-0-375-83531-5(8)); 2006. 192p. lib. bdg. 18.99 (978-0-375-93531-2(2)) Random Hse. Children's Bks. (Knopf Bks. for Young Readers).

Collier, James Lincoln. The Rich & Famous. 2001. (Lost Treasures Ser.: No. 6). (Illus.). 240p. (gr. 3-7). pap. 1.99 (978-0-7868-1519-7(1) , Volo) Hyperion Bks. for Children.

Connor, Leslie. Waiting for Normal. 2008. 304p. (J). 16.99 (*978-0-06-089088-9(6)*); lib. bdg. 17.89 (*978-0-06-089089-6(4)*) HarperCollins Pubs.

Conrad, Pam. Our House. Selznick, Brian, illus. 10th anniv. ed. 2005. 160p. (J). (gr. 4-7). pap. 16.99 (978-0-439-74508-6(X) , Scholastic Pr.) Scholastic, Inc.

Cooney, Caroline B. Code Orange. 208p. (YA). (gr. 7). 2007. pap. 6.50 (978-0-385-73260-4(0) , Laurel Leaf); 2005. 15.95 (978-0-385-73259-8(7) , Delacorte Bks. for Young Readers) Random Hse. Children's Bks.

Corey, Shana. Milly & the Macy's Parade. Helquist, Brett, illus. 2006. 38p. (J). (gr. 4-8). reprint ed. 17.00 (978-1-4223-5174-1(2)) DIANE Publishing Co.

Crow, Kristyn. Cool Daddy Rat. Lester, Mike, illus. 2008. 32p. (J). (ps). 16.99 (*978-0-399-24375-2(5)* , Putnam Juvenile) Penguin Group (USA) Inc.

The Daisy Bug Kids Say Hello New York. 2004. (J). (978-0-9712349-2-5(2)) Univ. At Buffalo, Child Care Ctr.

La Dama de Cobre (the Copper Lady) 2006. (J). pap. 5.95 (978-0-8225-6616-8(8) , Ediciones Lerner) Lerner Publishing Group.

Danziger, Paula. Amber Brown Wants Extra Credit. Ross, Tony, illus. 2008. (Amber Brown Ser.: No. 4). 128p. (J). (gr. 2-6). 4.99 (*978-0-14-241049-3(7)* , Puffin) Penguin Group (USA) Inc.

Danziger, Paula. Remember Me to Harold Square. 1999. (Illus.). 160p. (J). (gr. 5-9). pap. 5.99 (978-0-698-11694-8(1) , Putnam Juvenile) Penguin Group (USA) Inc.

—Remember Me to Harold Square. 139p. (YA). (gr. 6 up). pap. 3.99 (978-0-8072-1472-5(8) , Listening Library) Random Hse. Audio Publishing Group.

—Remember Me to Harold Square. 1999. (gr. k-9). (Illus.). 139p. (J). per. 13.00 (978-0-8335-1660-2(4)); (978-0-606-16795-6(1)) Tandem Library Bks.

Davies, Valentine. Miracle on 34th Street. 2002. 80p. pap. 6.25 (978-0-573-62892-4(0)) French, Samuel Inc.

—Miracle on 34th Street. fac. ed. 2001. 136p. (YA). 13.95 (978-0-15-216377-8(8)) Harcourt Children's Bks.

Davis, Cynthia. Drink the Rain. 2007. 256p. (YA). per. 12.95 (*978-0-9712163-1-0(2)*) Greenroom Bks.

de la Cruz, Melissa. The Au Pairs. l.t. ed. 2006. (Au Pairs Ser.: No. 1). 417p. 21.95 (978-0-7862-8291-3(6)) Thorndike Pr.

—Blue Bloods. (gr. 7 up). 2007. 336p. (YA). pap. 8.99 (*978-1-4231-0126-0(X)*); 2006. 320p. 15.99 (978-0-7868-3892-9(2)) Hyperion Pr.

—Masquerade: A Blue Bloods Novel. 2007. 320p. (YA). (gr. 7 up). 15.99 (*978-0-7868-3893-6(0)*) Hyperion Pr.

—Skinny-dipping. 2006. (Au Pairs Ser.: No. 2). 304p. (YA). (gr. 9 up). reprint ed. pap. 8.99 (978-1-4169-0383-6(X) , Simon & Schuster Children's Publishing) Simon & Schuster Children's Publishing.

—Sun-Kissed. (Au Pairs Ser.: No. 3). 320p. (YA). 2007. pap. 8.99 (978-1-4169-1747-2(0) , Simon Pulse); 2006. (gr. 9 up). 15.95 (978-1-4169-1746-5(2)) Simon & Schuster Children's Publishing.

De Montano, Marty K. Coyote in Love with a Star. Coffin, Tom, illus. 1998. (Tales of the People Ser.). 30p. (ps up). 14.95 (978-0-7892-0162-1(3)) Abbeville Pr., Inc.

DeFelice, Cynthia C. Under the Same Sky. 2005. 224p. (J). pap. 5.95 (978-0-374-48065-3(6) , Sunburst) Farrar, Straus & Giroux.

DeKeyser, Stacy. Jump the Cracks. 2008. 216p. (J). pap. 9.95 (*978-0-7387-1274-1(4)* , Flux) Llewellyn Pubns.

Dell, Pamela. The Gold Coin: A Story about New York City's Lower East Side. 2002. (Scrapbooks of America Ser.). (Illus.). 48p. (J). (gr. 2-6). 28.50 (978-1-59187-017-3(8)) Child's World, Inc.

DiCerto, Joseph. The Wall People. 2006. 19.95 (978-1-58752-112-6(1)) Timberwolf Pr., Inc.

DK Publishing. Bee Movie: A Guide to the Sweet Life. 2007. (Bee Movie Ser.). (Illus.). 47p. (J). (gr. 1-6). 12.99 (*978-0-7566-3210-6(2)*) Dorling Kindersley Publishing, Inc.

Doherty, Amy. Rory's Random Walk down Wall Street. 2000. (Illus.). 32p. (J). 16.95 (978-0-9674572-0-8(3)) Playgroup Pr.

Dorfman, Ariel & Dorfman, Joaquin. The Burning City. 2005. 272p. (J). (gr. 5-9). lib. bdg. 17.95 (978-0-375-93203-8(8) , Random Hse. Bks. for Young Readers) Random Hse. Children's Bks.

—Burning City. (YA). mass mkt. (978-0-375-83205-5(X)); 2006. 288p. (J). (gr. 5-9). reprint ed. pap. 7.95 (978-0-375-83204-8(1) , Random Hse. Bks. for Young Readers) Random Hse. Children's Bks.

Dorros, Arthur. Abuela. Kleven, Elisa, illus. 2002. (J). 14.04 (978-0-7587-1901-0(9)) Book Wholesalers, Inc.

Dreyer, Ellen. Speechless in New York. 2000. (Going to Ser.). (Illus.). 96p. (J). pap. 7.95 (978-1-893577-01-5(5)) Four Corners Publishing Co., Inc.

—Speechless in New York. Huerta, Catherine, illus. 2nd rev. ed. 2003. (Going to Ser.). 136p. (gr. 4-8). pap. 6.95 (978-1-893577-09-1(0)) Four Corners Publishing Co., Inc.

Drummond, Allan. Liberty! Drummond, Allan, illus. 2006. (Illus.). 40p. (J). reprint ed. pap. 6.95 (978-0-374-44397-9(1)) Macmillan.

Duffield, W. J. The Radio Boys in the Thousand Islands O. 2006. pap. 71.99 (*978-1-4219-9966-1(8)*) IndyPublish.com.

—Radio Boys in the Thousand Islands or Th. 2006. 78.99 (*978-1-4219-9957-9(9)*) IndyPublish.com.

Dunn, Mary. Magical Message Machine: Book One. 2007. 120p. (YA). pap. 14.99 (978-1-59092-402-0(9) , Blue Works) Windstorm Creative.

Dyahnne. Sweetie's Place: A Moving Adventure. 2004. 26p. (J). per. 7.99 (978-1-4116-0760-6(0)) Lulu.com.

Edwards, Julie Andrews. The Great American Mousical. Walton, Tony, illus. 2007. 160p. (J). pap. 5.99 (*978-0-06-057920-3(X)* , Harper Trophy) HarperCollins Pubs.

Edwards, Julie Andrews & Hamilton, Emma Walton. The Great American Mousical. Walton, Tony, illus. 2006. (Julie Andrews Collection). 160p. (J). 15.99 (978-0-06-057918-0(8) , Julie Andrews Collection); lib. bdg. 16.89 (978-0-06-057919-7(6)) HarperCollins Pubs.

Egan, Tim. Dodsworth in New York. 2007. (Illus.). 48p. (J). (gr. 3-5). 15.00 (*978-0-618-77708-2(3)*) Houghton Mifflin Co.

Ehrenhaft, Daniel. 10 Things to Do Before I Die. 2006. 224p. (YA). (gr. 7). pap. 7.95 (978-0-385-73406-6(9) , Delacorte Bks. for Young Readers) Random Hse. Children's Bks.

Elish, Dan. Attack of the Frozen Woodchucks. 2008. 256p. (J). 17.89 (*978-0-06-113871-3(1)* , Geringer, Laura Book) HarperCollins Pubs.

—Attack of the Frozen Woodchucks. Call, Greg, illus. 2008. 256p. (J). 16.99 (*978-0-06-113870-6(3)* , Geringer, Laura Book) HarperCollins Pubs.

Enright, Elizabeth. The Saturdays. Enright, Elizabeth, illus. rev. ed. 2002. (Melendy Quartet Ser.: Bk. 1). (Illus.). 176p. (J). (gr. 3-6). 17.95 (978-0-8050-7060-6(5) , Holt, Henry & Co. Bks. For Young Readers) Holt, Henry & Co.

—The Saturdays. 2008. (Melendy Quartet Ser.). (Illus.). 208p. (J). pap. 6.99 (*978-0-312-37598-0(0)*) Square Fish.

Fast, Natalie. The Secret Apartment. 2007. 192p. (gr. 4-7). 5.99 (978-0-553-48794-7(9) , Yearling) Random Hse. Children's Bks.

Ferrari, Vincent. Blogosfear. 2005. 143p. (YA). pap. 15.00 (978-1-4116-6814-0(6)) Lulu.com.

Fitzhugh, Louise. Harriet the Spy. 298p. (J). (gr. 3-5). pap. 5.95 (978-0-8072-1535-7(X)); 1999. pap. 38.00 incl. audio (978-0-8072-8069-0(0) , YA993SP) Random Hse. Audio Publishing Group. (Listening Library).

—Harriet the Spy. (Illus.). (gr. 5-7). 2001. 320p. pap. 6.50 (978-0-440-41679-1(5) , Yearling); 2000. 304p. (J). 15.95 (978-0-385-32783-1(8) , Delacorte Bks. for Young Readers) Random Hse. Children's Bks.

Fitzhugh, Louise & Gold, Maya. Harriet the Spy, Double Agent. 2007. 160p. (J). (gr. 4-7). 6.50 (978-0-440-41691-3(4) , Yearling) Random Hse. Children's Bks.

Fitzhugh, Percy K. Pee-Wee Harris. 2004. reprint ed. pap. 1.99 (978-1-4192-4057-7(9)); pap. 15.95 (978-1-4191-4057-0(4)) Kessinger Publishing, LLC.

Fleming, Charles & Schirripa, Steven R. Nicky Deuce: Welcome to the Family. 2005. 176p. (J). (gr. 3-7). 15.95 (978-0-385-73257-4(0) , Delacorte Bks. for Young Readers) Random Hse. Children's Bks.

Fletcher, Ralph. The One O'Clock Chop. 2007. 192p. (J). (gr. 5-11). 16.95 (*978-0-8050-8143-5(7)* , Holt, Henry & Co. Bks. For Young Readers) Holt, Henry & Co.

Flinn, Alex. Beastly. 2007. 320p. (gr. 9 up). (J). 16.99 (*978-0-06-087416-2(3)*); (YA). lib. bdg. 17.89 (*978-0-06-087417-9(1)*) HarperCollins Pubs. (HarperTeen).

Frank, Lucy. Just Ask Iris. 2003. (Illus.). 224p. (J). pap. 4.99 (978-0-689-84454-6(9) , Aladdin) Simon & Schuster Children's Publishing.

—Just Ask Iris. 2003. (gr. 5-8). lib. bdg. 13.00 (978-0-613-66417-2(5)) Tandem Library Bks.

—Lucky Stars. (J). 2006. 240p. pap. 5.99 (978-0-689-85934-2(1) , Aladdin); 2005. (Illus.). 304p. 16.95 (978-0-689-85933-5(3) , Atheneum) Simon & Schuster Children's Publishing.

Frenette, Liza. Dead End. Gillis, Jane, illus. 2005. x, 65p. (J). (978-1-59531-001-9(0)) North Country Bks., Inc.

Freymann-Weyr, Garret. Stay with Me. 2006. 320p. (YA). (gr. 8). 16.00 (978-0-618-60571-2(1)) Houghton Mifflin Co.

—Stay with Me. 2007. 320p. (YA). (gr. 9 up). pap. 8.99 (*978-0-618-88404-9(1)*) Houghton Mifflin Co. Trade & Reference Div.

Freymann-Weyr, Garret. When I Was Older. 2000. (Illus.). 176p. (YA). (gr. 5-9). tchr. ed. 15.00 (978-0-618-05545-6(2)) Houghton Mifflin Co. Trade & Reference Div.

Giff, Patricia Reilly. A House of Tailors. 2004. 176p. (J). (gr. 4-7). 15.95 (978-0-385-73066-2(7) , Lamb, Wendy) Random Hse. Children's Bks.

Gilmour, H. B. & Reisfeld, Randi. Oh Baby! 2005. 336p. (J). (gr. 7). pap. 8.99 (978-0-439-67705-9(X) , Scholastic Paperbacks) Scholastic, Inc.

Glasthal, Jacqueline B. Liberty on 23rd Street. Reingold, Alan, illus. 2006. (Adventures in America Ser.). (J). (978-1-893110-45-8(1)) Silver Moon Pr.

Going, K. L. Fat Kid Rules the World. (YA). 2004. (gr. 8-12). 17.99 (978-0-8037-2948-3(0) , Dial); 2003. 224p. (gr. 4 up). 17.99 (978-0-399-23990-8(1) , Putnam Juvenile); 2004. 192p. (gr. 6). reprint ed. pap. 6.99 (978-0-14-240208-5(7) , Puffin) Penguin Group (USA) Inc.

Gold, Maya & Fitzhugh, Louise. Harriet the Spy, Double Agent. 2005. 160p. (J). (gr. 5 up). 15.95 (978-0-385-32787-9(0) , Delacorte Bks. for Young Readers) Random Hse. Children's Bks.

Gordon, Fran & Tischler, Faye. Dutch Double. 2007. (Illus.). 88p. pap. 15.95 (*978-1-59299-242-3(0)*) Inkwater Pr.

Gray, Lull. Falcon & the Carousel of Time. 2005. 128p. (J). (gr. 5-9). 15.00 (978-0-618-44895-1(0)) Houghton Mifflin Co. Trade & Reference Div.

—Falcon & the Charles Street Witch. 2002. 144p. (J). (gr. 5-9). 16.00 (978-0-618-16410-3(3)) Houghton Mifflin Co. Trade & Reference Div.

Greenberg, Melanie Hope. The Mermaid Parade. Greenberg, Melanie Hope, illus. 2008. 32p. (J). (ps-k). 16.99 (*978-0-399-24708-8(4)* , Putnam Juvenile) Penguin Group (USA) Inc.

Greenburg, Dan. The Day That Went from Bad to Verse. 2000. (Zack Files Ser.: No. 20). 11.79 (978-0-606-18851-7(7)) Tandem Library Bks.

Griffin, Adele. The Other Shepards. 1999. (978-0-606-17144-1(4)) Tandem Library Bks.

—The Other Shepards. l.t. ed. 2000. (Illus.). 209p. (J). (gr. 4-7). 20.95 (978-0-7862-2914-7(4)) Thorndike Pr.

Grimes, Nikki. Bronx Masquerade. 2003. 176p. (YA). (gr. 6-11). pap. 5.99 (978-0-14-250189-4(1) , Puffin) Penguin Group (USA) Inc.

—Bronx Masquerade. Myers, Chris, illus. 2001. 176p. (J). (gr. 7 up). 16.99 (978-0-8037-2569-0(8) , Dial) Penguin Group (USA) Inc.

—Bronx Masquerade. 2003. (gr. 7-12). lib. bdg. 14.15 (978-0-613-81701-1(X)) Tandem Library Bks.

—Dark Sons. 2005. 224p. (gr. 7-17). 15.99 (978-0-7868-1888-4(3)) Hyperion Bks. for Children.

Gunther, Joseph. The Bluff, 1. Sabiston, Susan, illus. l.t. ed. 2006. 28p. (J). 14.95 (*978-0-9789525-0-1(2)*) Young Readers Publications.

Gutman, Anne & Hallensleben, Georg. Lisa in New York. 2002. (Illus.). 32p. (J). (gr. k-3). 9.95 (978-0-375-81119-7(2) , Knopf Bks. for Young Readers) Random Hse. Children's Bks.

Hall, Bruce Edward. Henry & the Kite Dragon. Low, William, tr. Low, William, illus. 2004. 32p. (J). (gr. 1-5). 15.99 (978-0-399-23727-0(5) , Philomel) Penguin Group (USA) Inc.

Hall, Margaret. Sebastian in Central Park. Wenzel, David, illus. 2001. (Suitcase Bear Adventures Ser.: Vol. 1). (J). (978-0-9713174-0-6(2) , Bear & Co.) Bear & Co.

Hamilton, Virginia. Bluish. 2002. 128p. (J). (gr. 4-6). pap. 5.99 (978-0-439-36786-8(7) , Scholastic Paperbacks) Scholastic, Inc.

—Bluish. Dillon, Leo & Dillon, Diane, illus. 1999. 128p. (J). (gr. 4-9). pap. 16.95 (978-0-590-28879-8(2) , Blue Sky Pr., The) Scholastic, Inc.

—Bluish. 2002. (gr. 5-8). lib. bdg. 13.00 (978-0-613-53797-1(1)) Tandem Library Bks.

—The Planet of Junior Brown. 1998. (J). pap. 4.50 (978-0-87628-347-9(4)) Ctr. for Applied Research in Education, The.

Hansen, Joyce. One True Friend. 2005. 160p. (J). (gr. 5-9). pap. 6.95 (978-0-618-60991-8(1) , Clarion Bks.) Houghton Mifflin Co. Trade & Reference Div.

Harcourt School Publishers Staff. Cyber-Stuffing. 3rd ed. 2002. (Trophies English Language Learners Ser.). (Illus.). pap. 51.00 (978-0-15-327898-3(6)) Harcourt Schl. Pubs.

—Darci's Ballet Dream Advanced Level. 3rd ed. 2002. (Trophies Reading Program Ser.). (Illus.). pap. 5.10 (978-0-15-323194-0(7)) Harcourt Schl. Pubs.

Harper, Suzanne. The Secret Life of Sparrow Delaney. 2007. 368p. (gr. 7 up). (J). lib. bdg. 17.89 (978-0-06-113159-2(8)); (YA). 16.99 (978-0-06-113158-5(X)) HarperCollins Pubs.

Harrison, Lisi. Bratfest at Tiffany's. 2008. (Clique Ser.: No. 9). 300p. (gr. 7-12). pap. 9.99 (*978-0-316-00680-4(7)* , Poppy) Little, Brown Bks. for Young Readers.

—The Clique. 2004. (Clique Ser.: No. 1). 220p. (J). (ps-7). lib. bdg. 16.64 (978-0-606-33269-9(3)) Tandem Library Bks.

—The Clique: Second Collection. 2006. (Clique Ser.: Nos. 4-6). (J). (gr. 7-17). pap. 29.99 (978-0-316-06693-8(1) , Poppy) Little, Brown Bks. for Young Readers.

—The Clique Collection. 2006. (Clique Ser.: Nos. 1-3). (J). (gr. 7-17). pap. 29.99 (978-0-316-16705-5(3) , Poppy) Little, Brown Bks. for Young Readers.

—Dial L for Loser. 2006. (Clique Ser.). 272p. (J). (gr. 7-17). pap. 9.99 (978-0-316-11504-9(5) , Poppy) Little, Brown Bks. for Young Readers.

—It's Not Easy Being Mean. 7th rev. ed. 2007. (Clique Ser.: No. 7). 224p. (J). (gr. 7-17). pap. 9.99 (978-0-316-11505-6(3) , Poppy) Little, Brown Bks. for Young Readers.

—The Pretty Committee Strikes Back. 2006. (Clique Ser.: No. 5). 272p. (J). (gr. 7-12). pap. 9.99 (978-0-316-11500-1(2) , Poppy) Little, Brown Bks. for Young Readers.

Harrison, Lisi. Sealed with a Diss. 2007. (Clique Ser.: No. 8). 272p. (J). (gr. 7-17). pap. 9.99 (*978-0-316-11506-3(1)* , Poppy) Little, Brown Bks. for Young Readers.

Haseley, Dennis. The Invisible Moose. Kellogg, Steven, illus. 40p. (J). (ps). 2008. pap. 6.99 (*978-0-14-241066-0(7)* , Puffin); 2006. 16.99 (978-0-8037-2892-9(1) , Dial) Penguin Group (USA) Inc.

Herman, Gail. Everybody Hates Romeo & Juliet. 2007. (Everybody Hates Chris Ser.). 96p. (J). pap. 5.99 (*978-1-4169-3570-4(3)* , Simon Spotlight) Simon & Schuster Children's Publishing.

Herrera, Juan Felipe. Cinnamon Girl: Letters Found Inside a Cereal Box. 176p. (J). 2006. pap. 7.99 (978-0-06-057986-9(2) , HarperTeen); 2005. 15.99 (978-0-06-057984-5(6) , Cotler, Joanna Books) HarperCollins Pubs.

Hest, Amy. Love You, Soldier. Lamut, Sonja, illus. 2000. 80p. (J). (gr. 3-7). 16.99 (978-0-7636-0943-6(9)) Candlewick Pr.

—Remembering Mrs. Rossi. Maione, Heather, illus. 2007. 192p. (J). (gr. 3-7). 14.99 (978-0-7636-2163-6(3)) Candlewick Pr.

Heyes, Eileen. O'Dwyer & Grady Starring In: Acting Innocent. Carver, Steve, illus. 2002. 176p. (J). (gr. 4-7). pap. 4.99 (978-0-689-84911-4(7) , Aladdin) Simon & Schuster Children's Publishing.

—O'Dwyer & Grady Starring in Acting Innocents. 2002. (gr. 3-6). lib. bdg. 13.00 (978-0-613-57433-4(8)) Tandem Library Bks.

—O'Dwyer & Grady Starring in Tough Act to Follow. 2003. (gr. 3-6). lib. bdg. 13.00 (978-0-613-66465-3(5)) Tandem Library Bks.

Hinton, S. E. Rebeldes. (SPA., Illus.). 192p. (J). (gr. 5-8). pap. 9.95 (978-1-59437-807-2(X)) Santillana USA Publishing Co., Inc.

Hite, Sid. I'm Exploding Now. 2007. 192p. (YA). (gr. 5-9). 16.99 (*978-0-7868-3757-1(8)*) Hyperion Pr.

Hogan, Mary. Susanna Sees Stars. 2007. 256p. (YA). (gr. 7). pap. 7.99 (*978-0-385-73513-1(8)*); lib. bdg. 10.99 (*978-0-385-90502-2(5)*) Random Hse. Children's Bks. (Delacorte Bks. for Young Readers).

Holland, Isabelle. Paperboy. 1999. 144p. (J). (gr. 7 up). tchr. ed. 16.95 (978-0-8234-1422-2(1)) Holiday Hse., Inc.

Holt, Rinehart and Winston Staff. Wish You Well. 3rd ed. 2002. pap., stu. ed. 13.20 (978-0-03-068009-0(3)) Holt, Rinehart & Winston.

—Wish You Well: With Connections. 3rd ed. 2002. 14.64 (978-0-03-068008-3(5)) Holt, Rinehart & Winston.

Hopkinson, Deborah. Sky Boys: Building the Empire State Building. Ransome, James E., illus. 2006. 48p. (J). (ps-4). lib. bdg. 18.99 (978-0-375-93610-4(6) , Schwartz & Wade Bks.) Random Hse. Children's Bks.

—Sky Boys: How They Built the Empire State Building. Ransome, James E., illus. 2006. 48p. (J). (ps-4). 16.95 (978-0-375-83610-7(1) , Schwartz & Wade Bks.) Random Hse. Children's Bks.

Hurwitz, Johanna. Lexi's Tale. Brewster, Patience, illus. 2002. (Park Pals Adventure Ser.). 112p. (J). (gr. 2-5). pap. 4.95 (978-1-58717-160-4(0) , SeaStar Bks.) Chronicle Bks. LLC.

—Lexi's Tale. 2002. (gr. 3-6). lib. bdg. 11.80 (978-0-613-54420-7(X)) Tandem Library Bks.

—Pee-Wee's Tale. Brewster, Patience, illus. 2000. 104p. (J). pap. 14.95 (978-1-58717-028-7(0) , SeaStar Bks.) Chronicle Bks. LLC.

—Pee-Wee's Tale. Brewster, Patience, illus. 2001. 104p. (J). (ps-3). per. 11.80 (978-0-613-54426-9(8)) Tandem Library Bks.

Hurwitz, Johanna & Brewster, Patience. Pee-Wee's Tale. 2001. (Park Pals Adventure Ser.). (Illus.). 112p. (J). (gr. 2-5). pap. 4.95 (978-1-58717-111-6(2) , SeaStar Bks.) Chronicle Bks. LLC.

Hyde, Catherine Ryan. Becoming Chloe. 2006. 224p. (YA). (gr. 9). 15.95 (978-0-375-83258-1(0)); lib. bdg. 17.99 (978-0-375-93258-8(5)) Random Hse. Children's Bks. (Knopf Bks. for Young Readers).

Jablonski, Carla. Thicker Than Water. 2007. 272p. (YA). (gr. 9-12). pap. 8.99 (978-1-59514-123-1(5) , Razorbill) Penguin Group (USA) Inc.

Jacobs, Paul DuBois & Swender, Jennifer. My Subway Ride. Alko, Selina, illus. 2004. 32p. (J). 15.95 (978-1-58685-357-0(0)) Gibbs Smith, Publisher.

—My Taxi Ride. Alko, Selina, illus. 2006. 32p. (J). 15.95 (978-1-4236-0073-2(8)) Gibbs Smith, Publisher.

Jahn-Clough, Lisa. Country Girl, City Girl. 2004. 192p. (YA). (gr. 5). tchr. ed. 15.00 (978-0-618-44791-6(1) , Walter Lorraine) Houghton Mifflin Co. Trade & Reference Div.

James, Brian. Everybody Hates School Dances. 2007. (Everybody Hates Chris Ser.). 96p. (J). pap. 5.99 (***978-1-4169-3562-9(2)*** , Simon Spotlight) Simon & Schuster Children's Publishing.

James, Henry. Washington Square, Level 4. abr. ed. 2000. (Bookworms Ser.). (Illus.). 96p. 6.50 (978-0-19-423052-0(X)) Oxford Univ. Pr., Inc.

—Washington Square, Level 2. abr. ed. 1999. (Illus.). 48p. (C). pap. 9.00 (978-0-582-40162-4(3)) Pearson ESL.

—Washington Square. 2001. (Washington Square Press Enriched Classic Ser.). (Illus.). (J). (978-0-606-21510-7(7)) Tandem Library Bks.

Jane, Pamela. Winky Blue, Forever. 1999. (gr. 3-6). lib. bdg. 11.80 (978-0-613-28139-3(X)) Tandem Library Bks.

—Winky Blue Goes Wild! Tilley, Debbie, illus. 2003. 64p. (J). 13.95 (978-1-59034-588-7(6)); pap. (978-1-59034-589-4(4)) Mondo Publishing.

Jocelyn, Marthe. The Invisible Day. 1999. (Illus.). (J). (978-0-606-18413-7(9)) Tandem Library Bks.

—The Invisible Day. Carter, Abby, illus. 1999. 160p. (J). (gr. 3-7). reprint ed. pap. 6.99 (978-0-88776-477-6(0)) Tundra Bks., Inc./Livres Toundra, Inc. CAN. *Dist:* Random Hse., Inc.

Johnson, Angela. The First Part Last. l.t. ed. 2004. 241p. 22.95 (978-0-7862-6510-7(8)) Thorndike Pr.

Jones, Elizabeth McDavid. Secrets on 26th Street. 1999. (American Girl Collection Ser.). (978-0-606-17519-7(9)) Tandem Library Bks.

Jones, Jasmine. Enchanted: The Junior Novelization. rev. ed. 2007. 160p. (gr. 3-7). pap. 4.99 (***978-1-4231-0471-1(4))*** Disney Pr.

Kaldor, Connie. A Duck in New York City. 2005. (Illus.). 36p. (J). (ps-3). 16.95 incl. audio compact disk (978-2-923163-02-4(8)) La Montagne Secrete CAN. *Dist:* National Bk. Network.

Kantor, Melissa. Confessions of a Not It Girl. 2006. 256p. (gr. 7-17). pap. 8.99 (978-0-7868-1808-2(5)) Hyperion Pr.

Kantor, Melissa. If I Have a Wicked Stepmother, Where's My Prince? 2007. 320p. (gr. 7 up). pap. 8.99 (***978-0-7868-0961-5(2));*** 2005. 283p. (YA). (***978-1-4156-2763-1(0))*** Hyperion Pr.

Karasyov, Carrie & Kargman, Jill. Bittersweet Sixteen. 2007. 240p. (J). pap. 7.99 (***978-0-06-077846-0(6)*** , HarperTeen) HarperCollins Pubs.

—Summer Intern. 2007. 192p. (gr. 7 up). (J). lib. bdg. 17.89 (***978-0-06-115376-1(1));*** (YA). 16.99 (***978-0-06-115375-4(3))*** HarperCollins Pubs. (HarperTeen).

Kargman, Jill & Karasyov, Carrie. Bittersweet Sixteen. 2006. 240p. (J). 15.99 (978-0-06-077844-6(X)); lib. bdg. 16.89 (978-0-06-077845-3(8)) HarperCollins Pubs.

Karlins, Mark. Music over Manhattan. 1999. (J). (978-0-606-16712-3(9)) Tandem Library Bks.

Karr, Kathleen. The Boxer. 2000. (Illus.). 144p. (YA). (gr. 7 up). 17.00 (978-0-374-30921-3(3) , Farrar, Straus & Giroux (BYR)) Farrar, Straus & Giroux.

Keats, Ezra Jack. My Dog Is Lost. 1999. (gr. k-3). lib. bdg. 15.30 (978-0-613-15019-4(8)) Tandem Library Bks.

—My Dog Is Lost! Keats, Ezra Jack, illus. 2002. (Illus.). (J). 14.04 (978-0-7587-4531-6(1)) Book Wholesalers, Inc.

Kemp, Kristen. Breakfast at Bloomingdales. 2007. 304p. (J). pap. 16.99 (***978-0-439-80987-0(8)*** , Scholastic Pr.) Scholastic, Inc.

Kenny, Kathryn & Koelsch, Michael. The Mystery of the Blinking Eye. Frame, Paul, illus. 2005. (Trixie Belden Ser.: Vol. 12). 256p. (J). (gr. 3-7). 6.99 (978-0-375-83052-5(9)); lib. bdg. 9.99 (978-0-375-93052-2(3)) Random Hse. Children's Bks. (Random Hse. Bks. for Young Readers).

Kimmel, Elizabeth Cody. The Top Job. Neubecker, Robert, illus. 2007. 32p. (J). (gr. 1-4). 16.99 (978-0-525-47789-1(6) , Dutton Juvenile) Penguin Group (USA) Inc.

Knight, Joan. Charlotte in New York. Sweet, Melissa, illus. 2006. 52p. (J). 16.95 (978-0-8118-5005-6(6)) Chronicle Bks. LLC.

Konigsburg, E. L. Amy Elizabeth Explores Bloomingdale's. 1999. (J). 12.79 (978-0-606-17201-1(7)); lib. bdg. 14.15 (978-0-613-21097-3(2)) Tandem Library Bks.

—From the Mixed-Up Files of Mrs. Basil E. Frankweiler. 35th anniv. ed. 1998. (Illus.). 168p. (J). (gr. 3-7). pap. 6.99 (978-0-689-71181-7(6) , Aladdin) Simon & Schuster Children's Publishing.

—From the Mixed-Up Files of Mrs. Basil E. Frankweiler. 35th anniv. ed. 2002. (gr. 5-8). lib. bdg. 14.15 (978-0-613-73358-8(4)) Tandem Library Bks.

—From the Mixed-Up Files of Mrs. Basil E. Frankweiler. l.t. ed. 2005. 186p. pap. 10.95 (978-0-7862-7358-4(5) , Large Print Pr.) Thorndike Pr.

Korman, Gordon. Invasion of the Nose Pickers. Vaccaro, Victor, illus. 2000. (L.A.F. Bks.). 138p. (J). (gr. 2-6). lib. bdg. 14.49 (978-0-7868-2590-5(1)) Hyperion Paperbacks for Children.

Kraut, Julie & Lester, Shallon. Hot Mess: Summer in the City. 2008. 256p. (YA). (gr. 9). pap. 8.99 (***978-0-385-73506-3(5));*** lib. bdg. 12.99 (***978-0-385-90499-5(1))*** Random Hse. Children's Bks. (Delacorte Bks. for Young Readers).

Kroll-Smith, Steve. When I Dream of Heaven: Angelina's Story. 2000. (gr. 5-8). lib. bdg. 14.95 (978-0-613-36900-8(9)) Tandem Library Bks.

Kroll, Steven. Pooch on the Loose: A Christmas Adventure. Garland, Michael, illus. 2005. 32p. (J). (ps-3). per. 14.95 (978-0-7614-5239-3(7)) Cavendish, Marshall Corp.

—Sweet America: An Immigrant's Story. 2004. (Jamestown's American Portraits Ser.). (Illus.). 176p. (J). (gr. 5-7). pap. 4.95 (978-0-7696-3423-4(0) , Waterbird Bks.) School Specialty Publishing.

—When I Dream of Heaven. 2004. 156p. (J). lib. bdg. 16.92 (***978-1-4242-0770-1(3))*** Fitzgerald Bks.

Kroll, Steven. When I Dream of Heaven: Angelina's Story. 2004. (Jamestown's American Portraits Ser.). (Illus.). 160p. (J). (gr. 5-7). pap. 4.95 (978-0-7696-3424-1(9) , Waterbird Bks.) School Specialty Publishing.

—When I Dream of Heaven: Angelina's Story. 2000. (978-0-606-21879-5(3)) Tandem Library Bks.

Krovatin, Christopher. Heavy Metal & You. 2005. 192p. (J). (gr. 7-12). pap. 16.95 (978-0-439-73648-0(X)) Scholastic, Inc.

Krulik, Nancy E. Ripped at the Seams. 2004. (Romantic Comedies Ser.). 336p. (YA). mass mkt. 6.99 (978-0-689-86771-2(9) , Simon Pulse) Simon & Schuster Children's Publishing.

LaBate, Jim. Mickey Mantle Day in Amsterdam: Another Novella by Jim LaBate. Batemen, Brian, illus. 1999. 61p. (YA). (gr. 7-12). pap. 7.95 (978-0-9662100-7-1(7)) Mohawk River Pr.

LaBrot, Matthew & Daniel, Hale. Green Streak. 2004. (Zeke Armstrong Mysteries Ser.: 2). 236p. (J). per. 8.95 (978-1-929976-28-7(3)) Top Pubns., Ltd.

Lakin, Patricia. Fat Chance Thanksgiving. Schuett, Stacey, illus. 2001. 32p. (J). (gr. 2-5). 15.95 (978-0-8075-2288-2(0)) Whitman, Albert & Co.

—Subway Sonata. Maione, Heather Harms, illus. 2001. 32p. (J). (gr. k-4). lib. bdg. (978-0-7613-1464-6(4) , Millbrook Pr.) Lerner Publishing Group.

Lambert, Janet. A Bright Tomorrow. 2001. (Jordon Ser.: Vol. 9). (YA). pap. 12.95 (978-1-930009-40-0(2)) Image Cascade Publishing.

Larbalestier, Justine. Magic Lessons. 2007. 304p. (YA). pap. 7.99 (978-1-59514-124-8(3) , Razorbill) Penguin Group (USA) Inc.

—Magic or Madness. (gr. 7-12). 2006. 304p. (YA). pap. 7.99 (978-1-59514-070-8(0)); 2005. 288p. (J). 16.99 (978-1-59514-022-7(0)) Penguin Group (USA) Inc. (Razorbill).

Le Moult, Dolph. Running Horsemen. 2004. 272p. (YA). pap. (978-0-9746481-0-1(8)) Brown Barn Bks.

Leppard, Lois Gladys. Mandie & the New York Secret, Vol. 36. 2003. (Mandie Bks.). (Illus.). 160p. (J). (gr. 3-8). mass mkt. 5.99 (978-0-7642-2639-7(8)) Bethany Hse. Pubs.

Levine, Gail Carson. Dave at Night. 2001. 304p. (J). (gr. 3-7). reprint ed. pap. 6.99 (978-0-06-440747-2(0) , Harper Trophy) HarperCollins Pubs.

—Dave at Night. unabr. ed. 2004. 278p. (J). (gr. 4-7). pap. 38.00 incl. audio (978-0-8072-8379-0(7) , YA174SP, Listening Library) Random Hse. Audio Publishing Group.

—Dave at Night. 1999. (YA). pap., stu. ed. 69.95 incl. audio (978-0-7887-3794-7(5) , 41038) Recorded Bks., LLC.

Levithan, David & Cohn, Rachel. Naomi & Ely's No Kiss List. 2007. (YA). (gr. 9 up). 240p. 16.99 (***978-0-375-84440-9(6));*** 192p. lib. bdg. 19.99 (***978-0-375-94440-6(0))*** Random Hse. Children's Bks. (Knopf Bks. for Young Readers).

Levoy, Myron. Kelly 'n' Me. 2000. 212p. (YA). (gr. 7-12). pap. 13.95 (978-0-595-09356-4(6)) iUniverse, Inc.

Ling, Bettina. The Big City. Ong, Cristina, illus. 1999. (Scholastic At-Home Phonics Reading Program Ser.: Vol. 32). 24p. (J). (978-0-590-68780-5(8)) Scholastic, Inc.

Locker, Thomas. In Blue Mountains: An Artist's Return to America's First Wilderness. Locker, Thomas, illus. rev. ed. 2000. (Illus.). 36p. (J). (ps-3). 18.00 (978-0-88010-471-5(6)) SteinerBooks, Inc.

Lockhart, E. Fly on the Wall. 2007. 192p. (YA). (gr. 7). pap. 8.99 (***978-0-385-73282-6(1)*** , Delacorte Bks. for Young Readers) Random Hse. Children's Bks.

Lockhart, E. Fly on the Wall: How One Girl Saw Everything. 2006. 192p. (YA). (gr. 7). 15.95 (978-0-385-73281-9(3)); lib. bdg. 17.99 (978-0-385-90299-1(9)) Random Hse. Children's Bks. (Delacorte Bks. for Young Readers).

Lombard, Jenny. Drita, My Homegirl. (J). (gr. 4-6). 2008. 144p. pap. 5.99 (***978-0-14-240905-3(7)*** , Puffin); 2006. 176p. 15.99 (978-0-399-24380-6(1) , Putnam Juvenile) Penguin Group (USA) Inc.

Lovascio, Jane. Casey & Bella Go to New York City. 2007. (J). 15.95 (***978-1-60131-007-1(2))*** Big Tent Bks.

Luna, Rachel Nickerson. Darinka, the Little Artist Deer. Luna, Rachel Nickerson, illus. 1999. (Illus.). 36p. (J). (gr. 3-4). 12.95 (978-1-886551-06-0(5)) Howard, Emma Bks.

Lurie, April. The Latent Powers of Dylan Fontaine. 2008. 224p. (YA). (gr. 9). 15.99 (***978-0-385-73125-6(6)*** , Delacorte Bks. for Young Readers) Random Hse. Children's Bks.

Lyttleton, Kay. Jean Craig in New York. 2005. pap. 24.95 (978-1-4179-9293-5(X)) Kessinger Publishing, LLC.

Mack, Tracy. Birdland. 208p. (J). 2005. (gr. 7-17). pap. 5.99 (978-0-439-53591-5(3) , Scholastic Paperbacks); 2003. pap. 16.95 (978-0-439-53590-8(5)) Scholastic, Inc.

Mackler, Carolyn. The Earth, My Butt & Other Big Round Things. 2003. (Illus.). 256p. (YA). (gr. 9). 15.99 (978-0-7636-1958-9(2)) Candlewick Pr.

—The Earth, My Butt, & Other Big Round Things. 2005. 256p. (YA). (gr. 9 up). reprint ed. pap. 8.99 (978-0-7636-2091-2(2)) Candlewick Pr.

Mak, Kam. Chinatown. Date not set. 32p. (J). (gr. k-3). pap. 5.99 (978-0-06-443732-5(9)) HarperCollins Pubs.

—My Chinatown: One Year in Poems. Mak, Kam, illus. 2001. (Illus.). 32p. (J). (gr. k-3). 16.99 (978-0-06-029190-7(7)) HarperCollins Pubs.

Malkin, Nina. Orange Is the New Pink. 2007. 272p. (YA). (gr. 7 up). 8.99 (***978-0-439-89965-9(6))*** Scholastic, Inc.

Mancini, Kitty. Goatina Goes to New York. Piccolo, Rina, illus. 1999. 72p. (J). (gr. k-3). pap. 10.00 (978-0-9648010-7-3(8)) Hypertext Publishing Group.

Manzano, Sonia. No Dogs Allowed! Muth, Jon J., illus. 2005. (J). 27.95 incl. audio (978-0-8045-6927-9(4) , SAC6927); 29.95 incl. audio compact disk (978-0-8045-4101-5(9) , SACD4101) Spoken Arts, Inc.

Marciano, John Bemelmans. Harold's Tail. 2003. (Illus.). 144p. (J). (gr. 3-7). 15.99 (978-0-670-03660-8(9) , Viking Juvenile) Penguin Group (USA) Inc.

Margolis, Leslie Goldman. Night at the Museum: A Junior Novelization. 2006. (Illus.). 128p. (J). mass mkt. 4.99 (978-0-7641-3576-7(7)) Barron's Educational Series, Inc.

Marsh, Carole. The Mystery in New York City. 2003. (Carole Marsh Mysteries Ser.). 160p. (J). (gr. 2-8). pap. 5.95 (978-0-635-02099-4(8)) Gallopade International.

Marsh, Katherine. The Night Tourist. rev. ed. 2007. 240p. (YA). (gr. 7 up). 17.99 (***978-1-4231-0689-0(X))*** Hyperion Pr.

Martinez, Agnes. Poe Park. 2004. 128p. (J). (ps-7). tchr. ed. 16.95 (978-0-8234-1834-3(0)) Holiday Hse., Inc.

Marx, David F. See the City Level A. Revell, Cindy, illus. 2001. (Rookie Readers Ser.). 24p. (J). (gr. k-1). 19.50 (978-0-516-22254-7(6) , Children's Pr.) Scholastic Library Publishing.

Mason, Jeff. 9-11: Emergency Relief. 2002. (gr. 7-12). lib. bdg. 24.55 (978-0-613-51101-8(8)) Tandem Library Bks.

Matas, Carol. Rosie in New York City: Gotcha! 2003. (Aladdin Historical Fiction Ser.). (Illus.). 128p. (J). (gr. 3-6). pap. 9.95 (978-0-689-85714-0(4) , Aladdin) Simon & Schuster Children's Publishing.

—Rosie in New York City: Gotcha! 2003. (gr. 5-8). lib. bdg. 13.00 (978-0-613-66469-1(8)) Tandem Library Bks.

Mazer, Norma Fox. GoodNight, Maman. 1999. (C). 16.00 net. (978-0-15-202677-6(0)) Harcourt College Pubs.

McClatchy, Lisa & Thompson, Kay. Eloise & the Snowman. Lyon, Tammie, illus. 2006. (Eloise Ser.). 32p. (J). pap. 3.99 (978-0-689-87451-2(0) , Aladdin) Simon & Schuster Children's Publishing.

McDonald, Janet. Chill Wind. l.t. ed. 2003. 165p. (J). 24.95 (978-0-7862-5502-3(1)) Thorndike Pr.

—Harlem Hustle. 2006. 192p. (YA). 16.00 (978-0-374-37184-5(9) , Farrar, Straus & Giroux (BYR)) Farrar, Straus & Giroux.

McGarrahan, Margaret. Nessie's Manhattan Holiday. Wright, Kathleen, illus. 2000. 57p. (J). (gr. k-5). pap. 12.50 (978-0-9672639-1-5(3)) Smith Lane Pubs.

Mechling, Lauren & Moser, Laura. All Q, No A: More Tales of a 10th-Grade Social Climber. 2006. 288p. (YA). (gr. 7). pap. 7.99 (978-0-618-66378-1(9) , Graphia) Houghton Mifflin Co. Trade & Reference Div.

Metaxas, Eric. Mose the Fireman. Peck, Everett, illus. 2005. (Rabbit Ears-A Classic Tale Ser.). 40p. (J). (gr. k-5). 25.65 (978-1-59197-766-7(5)) Spotlight.

Mick Morris Myth Solver #3 Champ... A Wave of Terror! Five Ways to Finish. 2006. (J). mass mkt. 6.99 (***978-0-9774119-2-4(3)*** , Five Ways to Finish) Team B Creative LLC.

Miller, Kirsten. The Empress's Tomb. 2007. (Kiki Strike Ser.). 350p. (J). (gr. 5-9). 16.95 (***978-1-59990-047-6(5)*** , Bloomsbury Children) Bloomsbury Publishing.

Miller, Kirsten. Kiki Strike: Inside the Shadow City. (J). 2007. 400p. (gr. 5-9). pap. 7.95 (***978-1-59990-092-6(0));*** 2006. 250p. 16.95 (978-1-58234-960-2(6)) Bloomsbury Publishing. (Bloomsbury Children).

Minter, J. Hold on Tight. 2006. (Insiders Novel Ser.: Bk. 5). 256p. (YA). pap. 8.95 (978-1-58234-719-6(0) , Bloomsbury Children) Bloomsbury Publishing.

—Inside Girl: A Novel. 2007. (Insiders Novel Ser.). 240p. (YA). (gr. 7 up). pap. 8.95 (***978-1-59990-086-5(6))*** Bloomsbury Publishing.

—The Insiders. 2004. 200p. (gr. 9 up). pap. 8.95 (978-1-58234-895-7(2) , Bloomsbury Children) Bloomsbury Publishing.

—Pass It On. 2004. (Insiders Ser.). 200p. (YA). pap. 8.95 (978-1-58234-954-1(1) , Bloomsbury Children) Bloomsbury Publishing.

Mlynowski, Sarah. Bras & Broomsticks. 2005. 320p. (YA). (gr. 7). 15.95 (978-0-385-73181-2(7) , Delacorte Bks. for Young Readers) Random Hse. Children's Bks.

—Frogs & French Kisses. (gr. 7). 2007. 304p. (YA). pap. 8.99 (***978-0-385-73185-0(X));*** 2006. (Illus.). 288p. (J). 15.95 (978-0-385-73182-9(5)); 2006. (Illus.). 288p. (YA). lib. bdg. 17.99 (978-0-385-90219-9(0)) Random Hse. Children's Bks. (Delacorte Bks. for Young Readers).

Mohr, Nicholasa. Going Home. 1999. 192p. (J). (gr. 3-7). reprint ed. pap. 5.99 (978-0-14-130644-5(0) , Puffin) Penguin Group (USA) Inc.

—Going Home. 1999. (gr. 3-6). lib. bdg. 14.15 (978-0-8335-2939-8(0)) Tandem Library Bks.

Monfredo, Miriam G. The Stalking Horse. 1999. (978-0-606-16386-6(7)) Tandem Library Bks.

Morgan, Melissa J. Camp Confidential: TTYL. 2007. 22.78 (978-1-59961-154-9(6)) Spotlight.

—Camp Confidential No. 6: Rsvp. 2005. (Camp Confidential Ser.). (Illus.). 160p. (J). (gr. 4-7). pap. 4.99 (978-0-448-43962-4(X) , Grosset & Dunlap) Penguin Group (USA) Inc.

Mundis, Hester. My Chimp Friday: The Nana Banana Chronicles. 176p. (J). 2004. pap. 4.99 (978-0-689-87326-3(3) , Aladdin); 2002. (Illus.). (gr. 4-6). 16.00 (978-0-689-83837-8(9)) Simon & Schuster Children's Publishing.

Murphy, Barbara Beasley. Tripping the Runner. 2001. 192p. (gr. 4-7). pap. 12.95 (978-0-595-15398-5(4) , Backinprint.com) iUniverse, Inc.

Murphy, Barbara Beasley & Wolkoff, Judie. Ace Hits Rock Bottom. 2003. (Can't Stop Ace Ser.: No. 2). 204p. (J). pap. 16.95 (978-0-86534-408-2(6)) Sunstone Pr.

—Ace Hits the Big Time. 2003. (Can't Stop Ace Ser.: No. 1). 184p. (J). pap. 16.95 (978-0-86534-407-5(8)) Sunstone Pr.

Murphy, Steve. Look Out! It's Turtle Titan! Spaziante, Patrick, illus. 2004. (Teenage Mutant Ninja Turtles Ser.). 24p. (J). pap. 3.99 (978-0-689-86900-6(2) , Simon Spotlight) Simon & Schuster Children's Publishing.

—Look Out! It's Turtle Titan! 2004. (gr. k-3). lib. bdg. 11.80 (978-0-613-83491-9(7)) Tandem Library Bks.

—Mikey's Nightwatcher Scrapbook. Jourdan, Diego, illus. 2007. (Teenage Mutant Ninja Turtles Ser.). 16p. (J). pap. 4.99 (978-1-4169-3345-8(X) , Simon Spotlight) Simon & Schuster Children's Publishing.

My Day in New York City. 2004. (J). ring bd. 4.50 (978-0-9762740-1-8(9) , Flat Kids) Smart Smiles Co., The.

Nathan, Sarah. A Dream Come True. 2007. 32p. (gr. 1). pap. 3.99 (***978-1-4231-0909-9(0))*** Disney Pr.

—Enchanted Storybook. rev. ed. 2007. 48p. (J). (gr. 2-7). 8.99 (***978-1-4231-0911-2(2))*** Disney Pr.

Ned Visits New York. ed. 2006. (J). 15.95 (978-0-9789384-0-6(2)) Kip Kids of New York.

Neville, Emily Cheney. It's Like This, Cat. 2002. (Illus.). (J). 14.47 (978-0-7587-0195-4(0)) Book Wholesalers, Inc.

—It's Like This, Cat. 1999. (J). 9.95 (978-1-56137-101-3(7)) Novel Units, Inc.

Newman, Robert. Lost Treasures Bk. 3: The Teddy Bear Habit. 2001. 184p. (J). 13.49 (978-0-7868-2599-8(5)) Hyperion Pr.

Nishimura, Kae. I Am Dodo: Not a True Story. Nisfiimura, Kae, illus. 2005. (Illus.). 32p. (J). (ps-k). 15.00 (978-0-618-33614-2(1) , Clarion Bks.) Houghton Mifflin Co. Trade & Reference Div.

Nolan, Han. When We Were Saints. (YA). 2005. 312p. pap. 6.95 (978-0-15-205322-2(0) , Harcourt Paperbacks); 2003. (Illus.). 304p. 17.00 (978-0-15-216371-6(9) , 53586153) Harcourt Children's Bks.

O'Connor, Ilett. A Born Leader - Our Francine. Kahn, Alisha, illus. Wells, Wadell, photos by. 2002. 32p. pap. 10.00 (978-0-9717003-1-4(1)) O'Connor, Ilett K.

Olsen, Mary-Kate. Make-up, Shake-up. 2002. (gr. k-3). lib. bdg. 12.40 (978-0-613-64746-5(7)) Tandem Library Bks.

O'Neill, Elizabeth & McPherson, Missie. Alfred Visits New York City. 2003. (Illus.). 24p. (J). pap. 12.00 (978-1-4120-1338-3(0)) Trafford Publishing CAN. *Dist:* Atlas-Books Distribution.

Orr, Wendy. Nim at Sea. Millard, Kerry, illus. 2008. 192p. (J). (gr. 3-7). 12.99 (***978-0-440-42232-7(9)*** , Knopf Bks. for Young Readers) Random Hse. Children's Bks.

Ortiz Cofer, Judith. Call Me Maria. 2004. (First Person Fiction Ser.). 144p. (J). (gr. 4-7). pap. 16.95 (978-0-439-38577-0(6) , Orchard Bks.) Scholastic, Inc.

Osborne, Mary Pope. New York's Bravest. Johnson, Stephen T. et al, illus. 2002. 32p. (J). (gr. k-3). 15.95 (978-0-375-82196-7(1) , Knopf Bks. for Young Readers) Random Hse. Children's Bks.

—New York's Bravest. Johnson, Steve & Fancher, Lou, illus. 2006. 32p. (J). (gr. k-3). pap. 6.99 (978-0-375-83841-5(4) , Dragonfly Bks.) Random Hse. Children's Bks.

Pagliarulo, Antonio. The Celebutantes: In the Club. 2008. (YA). (***978-0-385-73473-8(5));*** 12.99 (***978-0-385-90472-8(X))*** Dell Publishing. (Delacorte Pr.).

Pagliarulo, Antonio. On the Avenue. 2007. (Celebutantes Ser.). 352p. (YA). (gr. 9 up). pap. 9.99 (978-0-385-73404-2(2)); lib. bdg. 12.99 (978-0-385-90415-5(0)) Random Hse. Children's Bks. (Delacorte Bks. for Young Readers).

Palatini, Margie. Three French Hens. Egielski, Richard, illus. 2005. 40p. (ps-3). 15.99 (978-0-7868-5167-6(8)) Hyperion Pr.

Pataki, Libby & Kimball, Wilson, texts. Madison in New York. l.t. ed. 2005. (Illus.). 32p. (J). 16.95 (978-1-893622-15-9(0) , VSP Bks.) Vacation Spot Publishing.

Patterson, James. Black Friday. 2000. (gr. 7-12). lib. bdg. 16.45 (978-0-613-27743-3(0)) Tandem Library Bks.

Pavlicin, Karen. Perch, Mrs. Sackets, & Crow's Nest. 2007. (J). 160p. 16.95 (***978-1-934617-00-7(8));*** pap. (***978-1-934617-01-4(6))*** Elva Resa Publishing, LLC. (Alma Little).

Perez, Loida Maritza. Geographies of Home. 2000. (gr. 7-12). lib. bdg. 22.20 (978-0-613-28168-3(3)) Tandem Library Bks.

Pfeffer, Susan Beth. Beth's Story. 2001. (Portraits of Little Women Ser.). (Illus.). (J). (978-0-606-21063-8(6)) Tandem Library Bks.

Pinkwater, Daniel M. The Artsy Smartsy Club. Pinkwater, Jill, illus. 2005. 176p. (J). 16.89 (978-0-06-053558-2(X)); 15.99 (978-0-06-053557-5(1)) HarperCollins Pubs.

Platt, Kin. The Blue Man. 3rd collector's ed. 2005. (YA). 125.00 (978-1-59885-000-0(8)); 192p. 24.95 (978-1-59885-001-7(6)) Two Lakes Pr., Inc.

Plourde, Josee & Lemelin, Linda. Une Voix d'Or a New York. 2000. (Premier Roman Ser.). (FRE.). 64p. (J). (gr. 2-5). pap. (978-2-89021-415-6(X)) Diffusion du livre Mirabel.

Pollack, Jenny. Klepto (Splashproof Edition) 2007. 1p. (J). (gr. 7). pap. 7.99 (978-0-14-240835-3(2), Puffin) Penguin Group (USA) Inc.

Pollet, Alison. Nobody Was Here: Seventh Grade in the Life of Me, Penelope. (Nobody Was Here Ser.). 2004. 224p. (J). pap. 15.95 (978-0-439-58394-7(2)); 2005. 240p. reprint ed. 5.99 (978-0-439-58395-4(0)) Scholastic, Inc. (Orchard Bks.).

—The Pity Party: 8th Grade in the Life of Me, Cass. (Pity Party Ser.). 160p. (J). 2006. pap. 5.99 (978-0-439-68195-7(2), Scholastic Paperbacks); 2005. (gr. 5-8). pap. 15.95 (978-0-439-68194-0(4), Orchard Bks.) Scholastic, Inc.

Porter, Connie Rose. All-Bright Court. 2000. (Illus.). 240p. pap. 12.00 (978-0-618-05679-8(3), Mariner Bks.) Houghton Mifflin Co. Trade & Reference Div.

—All-Bright Court. 2000. (gr. 7-12). lib. bdg. 21.10 (978-0-613-27703-7(1)) Tandem Library Bks.

Potter, Ellen. Olivia Kidney & the Exit Academy. Reynolds, Peter H., illus. 2005. 256p. (J). (gr. 4-6). 15.99 (978-0-399-24162-8(0), Philomel) Penguin Group (USA) Inc.

—Olivia Kidney & the Secret Beneath the City. 2007. 336p. (YA). (gr. 4 up). 16.99 (978-0-399-24701-9(7), Philomel) Penguin Group (USA) Inc.

—Pish Posh. 2006. 224p. (J). (gr. 3-6). 15.99 (978-0-399-23995-3(2), Philomel) Penguin Group (USA) Inc.

Practically Perfect: A Penny Parrish Story. 2001. (Penny Parrish Story). 192p. (YA). pap. 12.95 (978-1-930009-30-1(5)) Image Cascade Publishing.

Price, Dianne D. Enemy in the House: The Story of a Young Friendship Born of War in America. 2003. 123p. pap. 14.95 (978-1-59286-463-6(X)) PublishAmerica, Inc.

Priest, Robert. The Old Pirate of Central Park. Priest, Robert, illus. 1999. (Illus.). 32p. (J). (gr. k-3). tchr. ed. 16.00 (978-0-395-90505-0(2)) Houghton Mifflin Co. Trade & Reference Div.

Priest, Robert. The Old Pirate of Central Park PB. 2008. 32p. (J). (ps-3). pap. 6.95 (***978-0-618-99769-5(5)***) Houghton Mifflin Co. Trade & Reference Div.

Purtill, C. Leigh. Love, Meg. 2007. 304p. (YA). 16.99 (978-1-59514-116-3(2), Razorbill) Penguin Group (USA) Inc.

Quackenbush, Robert. Daughter of Liberty: A True Story of the American Revolution. 1999. (gr. 3-6). lib. bdg. 13.00 (978-0-613-16485-6(7)) Tandem Library Bks.

Rabb, Margo. Cures for Heartbreak. 2007. 256p. (YA). (gr. 9). 15.99 (978-0-385-73402-8(6)); lib. bdg. 18.99 (978-0-385-90414-8(2)) Random Hse. Children's Bks. (Delacorte Bks. for Young Readers).

Rael, Elsa Okon. What Zeesie Saw on Delancey Street. 2000. (978-0-606-17943-0(7)) Tandem Library Bks.

Raphael, Marie. Streets of Gold. rev. ed. 2001. (Illus.). 224p. (J). (gr. 5 up). pap. 9.95 (978-0-89255-256-6(5)) Persea Bks., Inc.

Rayban, Chloë. Hollywood Bliss: My Life So Far. 2007. 288p. (J). 16.95 (***978-1-59990-093-3(9)***) Bloomsbury Publishing.

Redbank, Tennant. Enchanted: A Storybook Life. 2nd rev. ed. 2007. 24p. (gr. 1). pap. 3.99 (***978-1-4231-1080-4(3)***) Disney Pr.

Reiss, Mike. Late for School. Austin, Michael, illus. 2003. 32p. (J). (gr. 1-5). 16.95 (978-1-56145-286-6(6), Q35957) Peachtree Pubs., Ltd.

Rennie, Gordon. Rain Dogs. 2002. 52p. 14.95 (978-1-56971-697-7(8)) Dark Horse Comics.

Ringgold, Faith. Cassie's Word Quilt. 2004. (Illus.). 32p. (J). (ps-1). pap. 6.99 (978-0-553-11233-7(3), Dragonfly Bks.) Random Hse. Children's Bks.

—Cassie's Word Quilt. Ringgold, Faith, illus. 2002. (Illus.). 32p. (J). (gr. k-ps). 13.95 (978-0-375-81200-2(8)); lib. bdg. 15.99 (978-0-375-91200-9(2)) Random Hse. Children's Bks. (Knopf Bks. for Young Readers).

Ritter, John H. Over the Wall. 2002. 320p. (J). pap. 6.99 (978-0-698-11931-4(2), Putnam Juvenile) Penguin Group (USA) Inc.

—Over the Wall. 2002. (gr. 5-8). lib. bdg. 15.30 (978-0-613-67112-5(0)) Tandem Library Bks.

Roberts, Willo Davis. The Kidnappers: A Mystery. 1999. (J). (978-0-606-16224-1(0)) Tandem Library Bks.

Robertson, Chris. Little Miss Liberty. 2005. (Illus.). 36p. (J). 15.95 (978-0-8118-4669-1(5)) Chronicle Bks. LLC.

Robinson, Gwen. The Renshaw Diversion. 2007. 204p. per. (***978-0-7552-0275-1(9)***) Authors OnLine, Ltd.

Robinson, Sharon. Safe at Home. 160p. (J). 2007. (gr. 4-7). pap. 4.99 (***978-0-439-67198-9(1)***, Scholastic Paperbacks); 2006. pap. 16.99 (978-0-439-67197-2(3), Scholastic) Scholastic, Inc.

Ronan, Anne M. Muffles in New York. 1999. (Illus.). 32p. (J). (ps-4). pap. 8.00 (978-1-930248-00-7(8)) Polka Dot Pr. Corp., The.

Ross, Alice & Ross, Kent. La Dama de Cobre (The Copper Lady) Bowman, Leslie, illus. 2006. (Yo Solo - Historia (on My Own - History) Ser.). (SPA.). 48p. (J). (gr. 2-4). lib. bdg. 25.26 (978-0-8225-6262-7(6), Ediciones Lerner) Lerner Publishing Group.

Roth, Susan L. It's a Dog's New York. 2001. (Illus.). 32p. (J). (gr. 5-3). 16.95 (978-0-7922-7054-6(1), National Geographic Children's Bks.) National Geographic Society.

—It's Still a Dogs New York: A Book of Healing. 2001. 32p. (J). (gr. k-7). 12.00 (978-0-7922-7050-8(9), National Geographic Children's Bks.) National Geographic Society.

Rouillard, Wendy W. Barnaby-Seasons in the Park. Rouillard, Wendy W., ed. 2000. (Barnaby Ser.: Vol. 5). (Illus.). 32p. (J). 15.95 (978-0-9642836-9-5(7)) Barnaby & Co.

Roy, Lillian Elizabeth. Polly in New York. Barbour, H. S., illus. 2004. reprint ed. pap. 28.95 (978-1-4179-0068-8(7)) Kessinger Publishing, LLC.

Roy, Ron. The Jaguar's Jewel. Gurney, John Steven, illus. 2000. (A to Z Mysteries Ser.: No. 10). 96p. (J). (gr. k-3). lib. bdg. 11.99 (978-0-679-99458-9(0)); pap. 3.99 (978-0-679-89458-2(6)) Random Hse. Children's Bks. (Random Hse. Bks. for Young Readers).

—The Jaguar's Jewel. Gurney, John Steven, illus. 2000. (A to Z Mysteries Ser.: No. 10). (J). (ps-k). 86p. lib. bdg. 11.80 (978-0-613-21793-4(4)); 10.79 (978-0-606-18840-9(5)) Tandem Library Bks.

—The Orange Outlaw. Gurney, John Steven, illus. 2001. (A to Z Mysteries Ser.: No. 15). (J). (gr. k-3). lib. bdg. 11.80 (978-0-613-36856-8(8)) Tandem Library Bks.

—The Runaway Racehorse. Gurney, John Steven, illus. 2002. (A to Z Mysteries Ser.: No. 18). (J). (gr. k-3). lib. bdg. 11.80 (978-0-613-50495-9(X)) Tandem Library Bks.

Rozan, S. J. Bitter Feast. 1999. (gr. 7-12). lib. bdg. 14.15 (978-0-613-29200-9(6)) Tandem Library Bks.

Ruby, Laura. The Wall & the Wing. (J). 2007. 352p. (gr. 5 up). pap. 6.99 (***978-0-06-075257-6(2)***, Eos); 2006. 336p. 16.99 (978-0-06-075255-2(6)) HarperCollins Pubs.

Salerni, Dianne K. High Spirits: A Tale of Ghostly Rapping & Romance. 2007. 368p. per. 20.95 (***978-0-595-42350-7(7)***) iUniverse, Inc.

Sargent, Dave & Sargent, Pat. Ring: (Silver Grullo) Grace & Pride, 25. Lenoir, Jane, illus. 2001. 36p. (J). (Animal Pride Ser.: 50). pap. 6.95 (978-1-56763-662-8(4)); 50. (Saddle Up Ser.). lib. bdg. 22.60 (978-1-56763-661-1(6)) Ozark Publishing.

Sattler, Jennifer Gordon. Bella's Saratoga Summer. 2002. (Illus.). (J). (978-0-9713069-4-3(X)); 32p. pap. 10.95 (978-0-9713069-3-6(1)) Burns, Nicholas K. Publishing.

Scholastic, Inc. Staff. Summer Boys. 2003. (gr. 7-12). lib. bdg. 17.60 (978-0-613-72220-9(5)) Tandem Library Bks.

Schotter, Roni. The House of Joyful Living. Widener, Terry, illus. 2008. (J). (***978-0-374-33429-1(3)***) Farrar, Straus & Giroux.

Schwartz, Virginia Frances. 4 Kids in 5E & 1 Crazy Year. 2006. 208p. (J). 16.95 (978-0-8234-1946-3(0)) Holiday Hse., Inc.

Scieszka, Jon. Hey Kid, Want to Buy a Bridge?, Vol. 11. McCauley, Adam, illus. 2004. (Time Warp Trio Ser.: No. 11). 96p. (J). (gr. 2 up). pap. 4.99 (978-0-14-240089-0(0), Puffin) Penguin Group (USA) Inc.

—Seen Art? Smith, Lane, illus. 2005. 48p. (J). (gr. 1). 16.99 (978-0-670-05986-7(2), Viking Juvenile) Penguin Group (USA) Inc.

—2095. (Time Warp Trio Ser.: No. 5). (SPA.). (J). (gr. 2). 7.95 (978-958-04-5638-4(0), NR31192) Norma S.A. COL. *Dist:* Distribuidora Norma, Inc., Lectorum Pubns., Inc.

—2095. Smith, Lane, illus. 2004. (Time Warp Trio Ser.: No. 5. 5). 80p. (J). (gr. 2-6). pap. 4.99 (978-0-14-240044-9(0), Puffin) Penguin Group (USA) Inc.

Scoppettone, Sandra. Gonna Take a Homicidal Journey. 1999. (Lauren Laurano Mystery Ser.: Bk. 5). (gr. 7-12). lib. bdg. 15.30 (978-0-613-21616-6(4)) Tandem Library Bks.

Scrimger, Richard. A Nose for Adventure. 2000. 184p. (J). (gr. 3-7). pap. 7.95 (978-0-88776-499-8(1)) Tundra Bks., Inc./Livres Toundra, Inc. CAN. *Dist:* Random Hse., Inc.

Seidler, Tor. A Rat's Tale. Marcellino, Fred, illus. 1999. 192p. (J). (gr. 5 up). pap. 5.99 (978-0-06-440779-3(9), Harper Trophy) HarperCollins Pubs.

—Rat's Tale. 1999. (978-0-606-16698-0(X)); (gr. 3-6). lib. bdg. 15.25 (978-0-613-12367-9(0)) Tandem Library Bks.

—The Revenge of Randal Reese-Rat. Helquist, Brett, illus. 2004. 240p. (J). reprint ed. pap. 5.99 (978-0-06-050867-8(1), Harper Trophy) HarperCollins Pubs.

Selden, George. Chester Cricket's Pigeon Ride. 2001. (gr. 3-6). lib. bdg. 14.10 (978-0-613-37140-7(2)) Tandem Library Bks.

—The Cricket in Times Square. Williams, Garth, illus. 1999. (Chester Cricket Ser.). 32p. (J). (gr. 3-6). 9.95 (978-1-56137-396-3(6)) Novel Units, Inc.

—The Cricket in Times Square. Williams, Garth, illus. (Chester Cricket Ser.). 151p. (J). (gr. 3-6). pap. 5.50 (978-0-8072-8311-0(8), Listening Library) Random Hse. Audio Publishing Group.

—The Cricket in Times Square. unabr. ed. 2004. (Chester Cricket Ser.). 151p. (J). (gr. 3-7). pap. 29.00 incl. audio (978-0-8072-8310-3(X), S YA 158 SP, Listening Library) Random Hse. Audio Publishing Group.

—The Cricket in Times Square. Williams, Garth, illus. 2008. 144p. (J). pap. 6.99 (***978-0-312-38003-8(8)***) Square Fish.

Selden, George. Harry Kitten & Tucker Mouse. Williams, Garth, illus. 2001. (Chester Cricket Ser.). 80p. (J). (gr. 3-6). reprint ed. pap. 5.95 (978-0-374-42895-2(6), Sunburst) Farrar, Straus & Giroux.

—Harry Kitten & Tucker Mouse. 2001. (gr. 3-6). lib. bdg. 14.10 (978-0-613-85136-7(6)) Tandem Library Bks.

Sherman, Delia. Changeling. 2008. 304p. (J). (gr. 4-6). pap. 8.99 (***978-0-14-241188-9(4)***, Puffin) Penguin Group (USA) Inc.

Shusterman, Neal. Downsiders. l.t. ed. 2000. 336p. (YA). (gr. 6-12). lib. bdg. 29.95 (978-1-58118-071-8(3)) LRS.

—Downsiders. 2001. 256p. (YA). (gr. 8-12). mass mkt. 5.99 (978-0-689-83969-6(3), Simon Pulse) Simon & Schuster Children's Publishing.

—Downsiders. 2001. (YA). 11.64 (978-0-606-20637-2(X)); (gr. 5-8). lib. bdg. 13.00 (978-0-613-33694-9(1)) Tandem Library Bks.

—The Schwa Was Here. 240p. (J). 2004. (gr. 6). 16.99 (978-0-525-47182-0(0), Dutton Juvenile); 2006. (gr. 3). reprint ed. pap. 5.99 (978-0-14-240577-2(9), Puffin) Penguin Group (USA) Inc.

Shyer, Marlene Fanta. Fleabiscuit Sings! 2005. 160p. (J). 15.95 (978-0-7614-5213-3(3)) Cavendish, Marshall Corp.

Sis, Peter. Madlenka. Sis, Peter, illus. 2000. (Illus.). 48p. (J). (ps-3). 17.00 (978-0-374-39969-6(7), Farrar, Straus & Giroux (BYR)) Farrar, Straus & Giroux.

—Madlenka. 2000. (Illus.). (J). (gr. k-3). 19.95 (978-0-88899-412-7(5)) Groundwood Bks. CAN. *Dist:* Transition Vendor.

Smalley, Elisa. Zoe Sophia in New York: The Mystery of the Pink Phoenix Papers. Mauner, Claudia, illus. 2006. 36p. (J). 14.95 (978-0-8118-4877-0(9)) Chronicle Bks. LLC.

Snyder, Lavinia Branca. The King of New York: Softi's Adventures, 2002. (Illus.). (J). mass mkt. (978-1-932233-34-6(2)) Aurora Libris Corp.

Southgate, Martha. Another Way to Dance. 1998. (978-0-606-12878-0(6)) Tandem Library Bks.

Spaziante, Patrick, illus. Meet Casey Jones. 2004. (Teenage Mutant Ninja Turtles Ser.). 24p. (J). pap. 3.99 (978-0-689-86899-3(5), Simon Spotlight) Simon & Schuster Children's Publishing.

Spizman, Robyn Freedman & Johnston, Mark. Secret Agent. 240p. (J). 2006. (gr. 4-7). pap. 5.99 (978-1-4169-1862-2(0), Aladdin); 2005. 16.95 (978-0-689-87044-6(2), Atheneum) Simon & Schuster Children's Publishing.

Springer, Nancy. Dusssie. 2007. 176p. (J). (gr. 5-9). 16.95 (***978-0-8027-9649-3(4)***) Walker & Co.

Stainton, Sue. Santa's Snow Cat. Mortimer, Anne, illus. 32p. (J). 2007. pap. 6.99 (***978-0-06-000540-5(8)***, Harper Trophy); 2001. 15.99 (978-0-06-623827-2(7)) HarperCollins Pubs.

Staub, Rusty. Hello, Mr. Met! Moore, Danny, illus. 2006. (J). 17.95 (***978-1-932888-82-9(9)***) Mascot Bks., Inc.

Stevenson, James. Runaway Horse! A Novel. Date not set. (J). 15.99 (978-0-06-051978-0(9)); 16.89 (978-0-06-051979-7(7)) HarperCollins Pubs.

Stewart, Linda. The Maltese Kitten: A Sam the Cat Mystery. 2002. 135p. (J). (gr. 4-7). pap. 10.95 (978-0-9675073-8-5(3)) Cheshire House Bks.

Stine, Catherine. Refugees. 288p. (gr. 7). 2006. (YA). pap. 5.99 (978-0-440-23876-8(5), Laurel Leaf); 2005. (J). 15.95 (978-0-385-73179-9(5), Delacorte Bks. for Young Readers); 2005. (YA). 17.99 (978-0-385-90216-8(6), Delacorte Bks. for Young Readers) Random Hse. Children's Bks.

Stock, Catherine. A Porc in New York. Stock, Catherine, illus. 2007. (Illus.). 32p. (J). (ps-3). 16.95 (978-0-8234-1994-4(0)) Holiday Hse., Inc.

Stoddard, William O. Dab Kinzer A Story of A Growing Boy. 2004. reprint ed. pap. 24.95 (978-1-4191-1488-5(3)); pap. 1.99 (978-1-4192-1488-2(8)) Kessinger Publishing, LLC.

Stone, Sadie. Jamal Martin & All That Jazz. Southivorarat, Sombat, illus. 2005. 71p. pap. 14.95 (978-1-4137-4768-3(X)) PublishAmerica, Inc.

Strasser, Todd. Can't Get There from Here. 208p. (YA). 2005. pap. 5.99 (978-0-689-84170-5(1), Simon Pulse); 2004. 16.95 (978-0-689-84169-9(8)) Simon & Schuster Children's Publishing.

Sutherland, Tui. Shadow Falling. 2007. (Avatars Ser.: Bk. 2). 368p. (YA). (gr. 7 up). 16.99 (***978-0-06-085146-0(5)***); (J). lib. bdg. 17.89 (***978-0-06-085147-7(3)***) HarperCollins Pubs. (Eos).

Takabayashi, Mari. I Live in Brooklyn. 2004. (Illus.). 32p. (J). (gr. k-3). tchr. ed. 16.00 (978-0-618-30899-6(7)) Houghton Mifflin Co. Trade & Reference Div.

Tang, Charles, illus. The Mystery in New York, Vol. 13. 2004. (Boxcar Children Special Ser.: No. 13). 121p. (J). (gr. 2-5). 14.95 (978-0-8075-5459-3(6)); pap. 4.50 (978-0-8075-5460-9(X)) Whitman, Albert & Co.

Taylor, S. G. Books of Merlin I. 2006. pap. 10.49 (***978-1-4259-6740-6(X)***) AuthorHouse.

Taylor, Sydney. All-of-a-Kind Family. John, Helen, illus. 2002. 13.94 (978-0-7587-9169-6(0)) Book Wholesalers, Inc.

—All-of-a-Kind Family. 2000. (All-of-a-Kind Family Ser.). (Illus.). 189p. (J). (gr. 4-7). reprint ed. pap. 13.95 (978-0-929093-08-6(9), Taylor Productions) GRM Assocs.

—All-of-a-Kind Family. John, Helen, illus. 2005. 192p. (J). (gr. 3-7). lib. bdg. 17.99 (978-0-385-90316-5(2), Delacorte Bks. for Young Readers) Random Hse. Children's Bks.

—All-of-a-Kind Family Downtown. Krush, Beth & Krush, Joe, illus. 2001. (All-of-a-Kind Family Ser.). 187p. (J). (gr. 5 up). reprint ed. pap. 13.95 (978-0-929093-07-9(0), Taylor Productions) GRM Assocs.

—All-of-a-Kind Family Uptown. Stevens, Mary, illus. 2001. (All-of-a-Kind Family Ser.). 160p. (J). (gr. 5 up). pap. 13.95 (978-0-929093-09-3(7), Taylor Productions) GRM Assocs.

—Ella of All-of-a-Kind Family. 2000. (All-of-a-Kind Family Ser.). 144p. (J). (gr. 4-7). reprint ed. pap. 12.95 (978-0-929093-05-5(4), Taylor Productions) GRM Assocs.

—More All-of-a-Kind Family. Stevens, Mary, illus. 2001. (All-of-a-Kind Family Ser.). 160p. (J). (gr. 5 up). pap. 13.95 (978-0-929093-10-9(0)); reprint ed. 16.95 (978-0-929093-02-4(X)) GRM Assocs. (Taylor Productions).

Testa, Maria. Becoming Joe Dimaggio. Hunt, Scott, illus. 2002. 64p. (J). (gr. 5-9). 14.99 (978-0-7636-1537-6(4)) Candlewick Pr.

—Becoming Joe DiMaggio. Hunt, Scott, illus. 2005. 64p. (J). (gr. 5-9). reprint ed. pap. 5.99 (978-0-7636-2444-6(6)) Candlewick Pr.

Thompson, Kay. Eloise. 2001. (Eloise Ser.). (Illus.). 64p. (J). (ps). 22.00 incl. audio compact disk (978-0-689-84311-2(9), Simon & Schuster Children's Publishing) Simon & Schuster Children's Publishing.

—Eloise: The Absolutely Essential. Knight, Hilary, illus. 50th anniv. ed. 2005. (Eloise Ser.). 80p. (J). (ps-3). 19.95 (978-1-4169-0823-4(4)) Simon & Schuster Children's Publishing.

—Eloise at the Wedding. Lyon, Tammie, illus. 2006. (Eloise Ser.). 32p. (J). (ps-1). pap. 3.99 (978-0-689-87449-9(9), Aladdin) Simon & Schuster Children's Publishing.

—Eloise the Ultimate Edition. Knight, Hilary, illus. 2000. 304p. (J). (ps-3). 39.99 (978-0-689-83990-0(1)) Simon & Schuster Children's Publishing.

Thompson, Kay & McClatchy, Lisa. Eloise & the Dinosaurs. Lyon, Tammie, illus. 2007. (Ready-to-Reads Ser.). 32p. (J). pap. 3.99 (978-0-689-87453-6(7), Aladdin) Simon & Schuster Children's Publishing.

—Eloise's New Bonnet. Lyon, Tammie, illus. 2007. (Eloise Ser.). 32p. (J). pap. 3.99 (978-0-689-87452-9(9), Aladdin) Simon & Schuster Children's Publishing.

Thompson, Lisa, illus. New York City. 2006. (Read-It! Chapter Books). 80p. (J). (gr. 2-4). 19.95 (978-1-4048-1670-1(4)) Picture Window Bks.

Thomson, Sarah L. The Manny. 2007. 192p. (YA). pap. 6.99 (978-0-14-240803-2(4), Puffin) Penguin Group (USA) Inc.

Tiernan, Cate. Calling, Bk. 7. 2008. (Sweep Ser.: Bk. 7). 192p. (YA). (gr. 7). 6.99 (***978-0-14-241022-6(5)***, Puffin) Penguin Group (USA) Inc.

Townley, Roderick. Sky. 2004. (Illus.). 272p. (J). 16.95 (978-0-689-85712-6(8), Atheneum/Richard Jackson Bks.) Simon & Schuster Children's Publishing.

Townsend, Wendy. Lizard Love. 2008. (J). (***978-1-932425-34-5(9)***, Front Street) Boyds Mills Pr.

Tripp, Valerie. Changes for Samantha: A Winter Story. Andreasen, Dan & Roberts, Luann, illus. 2004. (American Girls Collection: Bk. 6). 80p. (J). (gr. 2 up). pap. 6.95 (978-0-937295-47-2(7)) American Girl Publishing, Inc.

Trooboff & Bucher, Cecile. Ben, the Bells & the Peacocks. 2007. 36p. pap. 15.00 (***978-0-9773536-0-6(5)***) Tenley Circle Pr.

Vail, Rachel. Never Mind! A Twin Novel. 2005. 208p. (J). (gr. 5 up). reprint ed. pap. 5.99 (978-0-06-054316-7(7), Harper Trophy) HarperCollins Pubs.

Valentine, Sally. The Ghost of the Charlotte Lighthouse. 2006. (J). (***978-1-59531-013-2(4)***) North Country Bks., Inc.

Van Dyne, Edith. Aunt Jane's Nieces in Society. 2006. 144p. pap. 10.99 (***978-1-4264-4161-5(4)***); 156p. pap. 14.99 (***978-1-4264-4202-5(5)***) BiblioBazaar.

—Aunt Jane's Nieces in Society. 2004. reprint ed. pap. 20.95 (978-1-4191-0824-2(7)); pap. 1.99 (978-1-4192-0824-9(1)) Kessinger Publishing, LLC.

Varon, Sara. Chicken & Cat. 2006. (Illus.). 40p. (J). (ps-3). pap. 16.99 (978-0-439-63406-9(7), Scholastic Pr.) Scholastic, Inc.

Velasquez, Eric & de la Vega, Eida. Los Discos de Mi Abuela. 2002. (SPA., Illus.). (J). (gr. 1-3). 16.95 (978-1-930332-21-8(1), LC7246) Lectorum Pubns., Inc.

Vizzini, Ned. It's Kind of a Funny Story: A Novel. 448p. (gr. 8 up). 2007. pap. 8.99 (***978-0-7868-5197-3(X)***); 2006. 16.95 (978-0-7868-5196-6(1)) Miramax Bks.

Vogel, Amos. How Little Lori Visited Times Square. Sendak, Maurice, illus. 2001. (Sendak Reissues Ser.). 64p. (ps-3). 16.95 (978-0-06-028462-6(5)) HarperCollins Pubs.

von Ziegesar, Cecily. Don't You Forget about Me. 11th ed. 2007. 304p. (YA). (gr. 9 up). pap. 10.99 (***978-0-316-01184-6(3)***, Poppy) Little, Brown Bks. for Young Readers.

—Gossip Girl. 2003. (Gossip Girl Ser.: No. 1). 288p. (gr. 8 up). mass mkt. 5.99 (978-0-446-61315-6(0)) Grand Central Publishing.

—Gossip Girl. 208p. 2002. (Gossip Girl Ser.: No. 1). (YA). (gr. 9-17). pap. 10.99 (978-0-316-91033-0(3)); No. 1. 2007. pap. 10.99 (***978-0-316-02456-3(2)***) Little, Brown Bks. for Young Readers. (Poppy).

—Gossip Girl. 2002. (Gossip Girl Ser.: No. 1). (YA). (gr. 7-12). lib. bdg. 17.35 (978-0-613-60559-5(4)) Tandem Library Bks.

—Gossip Girl: The Second Collection. 2004. (Gossip Girl Ser.). (YA). (gr. 10-17). pap. 29.99 (978-0-316-01026-9(X), Poppy) Little, Brown Bks. for Young Readers.

—Gossip Girl: The Third Collection. 2006. (Gossip Girl Ser.). (YA). (gr. 10 up). pap. 29.99 (978-0-316-01653-7(5), Poppy) Little, Brown Bks. for Young Readers.

—Gossip Girl Collection, 3 bks., Set. 2003. (Gossip Girl Ser.). (YA). (gr. 10-17). pap., pap. 29.99 (978-0-316-72271-1(5), 53605112, Poppy) Little, Brown Bks. for Young Readers.

—I Like It Like That. 2004. (Gossip Girl Ser.: Bk. 5). 208p. (YA). (gr. 9-17). pap. 10.99 (978-0-316-73518-6(3), Poppy) Little, Brown Bks. for Young Readers.

von Ziegesar, Cecily. It Had to Be You: The Gossip Girl Prequel. 2007. 300p. 16.99 (***978-0-316-02065-7(6)***, Tingley, Megan Bks.) Little, Brown Bks. for Young Readers.

Von Ziegesar, Cecily. It Had to Be You: The Gossip Girl Prequel. 2007. 398p. (YA). (gr. 10-12). 17.99 (***978-0-316-01768-8(X)***, Poppy) Little, Brown Bks. for Young Readers.

M N O

von Ziegesar, Cecily. Lucky. 2007. (It Girl Ser.: No. 5). 256p. (YA). (gr. 10-17). pap. 9.99 (***978-0-316-11347-2(6)***, Poppy) Little, Brown Bks. for Young Readers.
—Nobody Does It Better. 2005. (Gossip Girl Ser.: 7). 240p. (YA). (gr. 9-17). pap. 10.99 (978-0-316-73512-4(4), Poppy) Little, Brown Bks. for Young Readers.
—Nothing Can Keep Us Together. 2005. (Gossip Girl Ser.: No. 8). 240p. (YA). (gr. 9-17). pap. 9.99 (978-0-316-73509-4(4), Poppy) Little, Brown Bks. for Young Readers.
—Only in Your Dreams. 9th ed. 2006. (Gossip Girl Ser.: No. 9). 240p. (YA). (gr. 9-17). pap. 9.99 (978-0-316-01182-2(7), Poppy) Little, Brown Bks. for Young Readers.
—Would I Lie to You. 10th ed. 2006. (Gossip Girl Ser.: No. 10). 208p. (YA). (gr. 9-17). pap. 10.99 (978-0-316-01183-9(5), Poppy) Little, Brown Bks. for Young Readers.
—You're the One That I Want. 2004. (Gossip Girl Ser.: No. 6). 224p. (YA). (gr. 9-17). pap. 10.99 (978-0-316-73516-2(7), Poppy) Little, Brown Bks. for Young Readers.
Wallace, Karen. The Man with Tiger Eyes. 2007. (Lady Violet's Casebook Ser.). 240p. (J). (gr. 4-7). pap. 9.95 (***978-1-4169-0099-3(3)***) Simon & Schuster, Ltd. GBR. *Dist:* Independent Pubs. Group.
Walters, Eric. I've Got an Idea. 2004. 166p. (J). pap. (***978-0-00-639196-8(6)***, HarperTrophy) HarperCollins Canada, Ltd.
Warner, Gertrude Chandler. The Mystery in New York. Tang, Charles, illus. 1999. 121p. (J). (ps-7). per. 11.80 (978-0-613-22056-9(0)) Tandem Library Bks.
—The Mystery in New York. 1999. (Boxcar Children Special Ser.: No.13). (Illus.). (J). (gr. 2-5). (978-0-606-18771-8(5)) Tandem Library Bks.
Warnes, Tim. Chalk & Cheese. 2008. (J). (***978-1-4169-1378-8(5)***, Simon & Schuster Children's Publishing) Simon & Schuster Children's Publishing.
Warwick, J. M. An Open Vein. 2007. (YA). per. 12.95 (978-1-933963-96-9(4)) Grove Creek Publishing, LLC.
Wax, Wendy. Empire Dreams. Doney, Todd, illus. 2000. (Adventures in America Ser.). 96p. (J). (gr. 4-7). lib. bdg. 14.95 (978-1-893110-19-9(2)) Silver Moon Pr.
Weil, Zoe. Claude & Medea: The Hellburn Dogs. 2007. 112p. (J). (gr. 4-7). pap. 30.00 (***978-1-59056-105-8(8)***) Lantern Bks.
Weiss, Ellen. Eloise & the Very Secret Room. Lyon, Tammie, illus. 2006. (Eloise Ser.). 32p. (J). pap. 3.99 (978-0-689-87450-5(2), Aladdin) Simon & Schuster Children's Publishing.
Weitzman, Jacqueline Preiss. You Can't Take a Balloon into the Metropolitan Museum. Glasser, Robin, illus. 1998. 40p. (J). (gr. k-3). 18.99 (978-0-8037-2301-6(6), Dial) Penguin Group (USA) Inc.
—You Can't Take a Balloon into the Metropolitan Museum. 2001. (Illus.). (J). (978-0-606-21004-1(0)); 2000. lib. bdg. 15.30 (978-0-613-33742-7(5)) Tandem Library Bks.
Weller, Frances Ward. The Day the Animals Came: A Story of Saint Francis Day. Long, Loren, illus. 2006. 35p. (J). (gr. k-4). reprint ed. 17.00 (978-1-4223-5396-7(6)) DIANE Publishing Co.
—The Day the Animals Came: A Story of Saint Francis Day. Long, Loren, illus. 2003. 48p. (J). (ps-4). 16.99 (978-0-399-23630-3(9), 53247533, Philomel) Penguin Group (USA) Inc.
Wells, Carolyn & E. C. CASWELL. Two Little Women on a Holiday. l.t. ed. 2006. 178p. pap. 14.99 (978-1-4264-2807-4(3)) BiblioBazaar.
Welsh, T. K. The Unresolved. 2006. 160p. (YA). (gr. 9). 16.99 (978-0-525-47731-0(4), Dutton Juvenile) Penguin Group (USA) Inc.
Westerfeld, Scott. Peeps. 2005. 320p. (YA). (gr. 9-12). 16.99 (978-1-59514-031-9(X), Razorbill) Penguin Group (USA) Inc.
—So Yesterday. 240p. (gr. 7-12). 2004. (J). 16.99 (978-1-59514-000-5(X)); 2005. (YA). reprint ed. pap. 7.99 (978-1-59514-032-6(8)) Penguin Group (USA) Inc. (Razorbill).
Weston, Carol. Melanie in Manhattan. 288p. (J). (gr. 3-7). 2006. 5.99 (978-0-440-42040-8(7), Yearling); 2005. (Illus.). 15.95 (978-0-375-83028-0(6), Knopf Bks. for Young Readers) Random Hse. Children's Bks.
Wiesner, David. Sector 7. Wiesner, David, illus. 2002. (Illus.). (J). 23.40 (978-0-7587-0142-8(X)) Book Wholesalers, Inc.
—Sector 7. Wiesner, David, illus. 1999. (Illus.). 48p. (J). (gr. k-3). tchr. ed. 16.00 (978-0-395-74656-1(6), Clarion Bks.) Houghton Mifflin Co. Trade & Reference Div.
Wilcox, Brian & David, Lawrence. Full Moon. Wilcox, Brian, illus. 2004. (Illus.). 30p. (J). (gr. k-4). reprint ed. 16.00 (978-0-7567-7762-3(3)) DIANE Publishing Co.
Willard, Eliza. New York Minute. movie tie-in ed. 2004. (New York Minute Ser.: Bk. 1). (Illus.). 192p. (gr. 3-6). mass mkt. 5.99 (978-0-06-059509-8(4), Harper Entertainment) HarperCollins Pubs.
Williams-Garcia, Rita. Every Time a Rainbow Dies. (Amistad Ser.). (Illus.). 176p. 2002. (J). pap. 6.99 (978-0-06-447303-3(1), HarperTeen); 2001. (YA). (gr. 9 up). 15.95 (978-0-688-16245-0(2)) HarperCollins Pubs.
—Every Time a Rainbow Dies. 2002. (gr. 7-12). lib. bdg. 15.25 (978-0-613-62381-0(9)) Tandem Library Bks.
—Fast Talk on a Slow Track. 1998. 192p. (J). (gr. 7-12). pap. 6.99 (978-0-14-130231-7(3), Puffin) Penguin Group (USA) Inc.
—No Laughter Here. 144p. (J). (gr. 7 up). 2007. pap. 6.99 (978-0-06-440992-6(9), Amistad); 2004. 15.99 (978-0-688-16247-4(9)); 2004. lib. bdg. 16.89 (978-0-688-16248-1(7)) HarperCollins Pubs.
Wilsdon, Christina. A New York Sailing Adventure. Hockerman, Dennis, illus. 2006. 26p. (J). 7.99 (978-1-59939-014-7(0), Reader's Digest Young Families, Inc.) Reader's Digest Children's Publishing, Inc.
Winfield, Arthur M. The Rover Boys in Business or the Search for the Missing Bonds. 2006. (ENG.). 316p. per. 30.95 (***978-1-4286-4098-6(3)***) Kessinger Publishing, LLC.
Winfield, Arthur M. The Rover Boys in New York or Saving the. 2004. reprint ed. pap. 22.95 (978-1-4191-8117-7(3)) Kessinger Publishing, LLC.
Winfield, Arthur M. The Rover Boys in New York or Saving Their Father's Honor. 2004. reprint ed. pap. 1.99 (978-1-4192-8117-4(8)) Kessinger Publishing, LLC.
Winfrey, Elizabeth. Let's Put on a Show. 2000. (gr. 3-6). lib. bdg. 11.80 (978-0-613-27935-2(2)) Tandem Library Bks.
Winter, Jeanette. Angelina's Island. 2007. (Illus.). 32p. (J). (ps-3). 16.00 (978-0-374-30349-5(5), Farrar, Straus & Giroux (BYR)) Farrar, Straus & Giroux.
—September Roses. 2004. (Illus.). 40p. (J). 14.00 (978-0-374-36736-7(1), Farrar, Straus & Giroux (BYR)) Farrar, Straus & Giroux.
Wood, Maryrose. My Life, the Musical. 2008. (YA). (***978-0-385-90297-7(2)***); 240p. (gr. 9). 15.99 (***978-0-385-73278-9(3)***) Dell Publishing. (Delacorte Pr.).
Wood, Maryrose. Sex Kittens & Horn Dawgs Fall in Love. 256p. (YA). (gr. 7). 2007. pap. 8.99 (***978-0-385-73277-2(5)***); 2006. 15.95 (978-0-385-73276-5(7)); 2006. lib. bdg. 17.99 (978-0-385-90296-0(4)) Random Hse. Children's Bks. (Delacorte Bks. for Young Readers).
Woodson, Jacqueline. After Tupac & D Foster. 2008. 160p. (YA). (gr. 5). 15.99 (***978-0-399-24654-8(1)***, Putnam Juvenile) Penguin Group (USA) Inc.
—Behind You. 128p. (YA). 2006. (gr. 7). pap. 5.99 (978-0-14-240390-7(3), Puffin); 2004. (gr. 5-12). 15.99 (978-0-399-23988-5(X), Putnam Juvenile) Penguin Group (USA) Inc.
—If You Come Softly. (gr. 5). 2006. 192p. (YA). pap. 5.99 (978-0-14-240601-4(5), Puffin); 1998. 1p. (J). 16.99 (978-0-399-23112-4(9), Putnam Juvenile) Penguin Group (USA) Inc.
—If You Come Softly. 2000. 12.64 (978-0-606-17863-1(5)) Tandem Library Bks.
—Miracle's Boys. 2000. 1p. (YA). (gr. 5 up). 15.99 (978-0-399-23113-1(7), Putnam Juvenile) Penguin Group (USA) Inc.
Woodward, J. Howland. A Moment in Time. 2006. 55p. pap. 12.95 (978-1-4241-1334-7(2)) PublishAmerica, Inc.
Wyeth, Sharon Dennis. Orphea Proud. 2006. 208p. (YA). (gr. 9). pap. 5.99 (978-0-440-22706-9(2), Laurel Leaf) Random Hse. Children's Bks.
Yoshida, Akimi. Banana Fish. 2007. (Banana Fish Ser.). 192p. (YA). Vol. 18. pap. 9.99 (978-1-4215-0876-4(1)); Vol. 19. pap. 9.99 (978-1-4215-0877-1(X)) Viz Media.
Zalben, Jane Breskin. Leap. 2007. 272p. (J). (gr. 5). 15.99 (978-0-375-83871-2(6)); lib. bdg. 18.99 (978-0-375-93871-9(0)) Random Hse. Children's Bks. (Knopf Bks. for Young Readers).
Zarin, Cynthia & Pratt, Pierre. Albert, the Dog Who Liked to Ride in Taxis. 2004. (Illus.). 32p. (J). 17.95 (978-0-689-84762-2(9), Atheneum/Richard Jackson Bks.) Simon & Schuster Children's Publishing.
Ziegesar, Cecily von. Gossip Girl #2: You Know You Love Me: A Gossip Girl Novel. 2008. 240p. pap. 10.99 (***978-0-316-02661-1(1)***, Poppy) Little, Brown Bks. for Young Readers.
Zindel, Lizabeth. Girl of the Moment. 288p. (YA). (gr. 7). 2008. pap. 8.99 (***978-0-14-241104-9(3)***, Puffin); 2007. 16.99 (978-0-670-06210-2(3), Viking Juvenile) Penguin Group (USA) Inc.
Zindel, Paul. The Scream Museum. l.t. ed. 2002. (Illus.). 175p. (J). 22.95 (978-0-7862-4473-7(9)) Thorndike Pr.

NEW YORK (N.Y.)—FIRES AND FIRE PREVENTION

Schaefer, A. R. The Triangle Shirtwaist Factory Fire. 2003. (Landmark Events in American History Ser.). (Illus.). 48p. (J). (gr. 5 up). lib. bdg. 30.00 (978-0-8368-5383-4(0), World Almanac Library) Stevens, Gareth Inc.

NEW YORK (N.Y.)—HISTORY

The All Five Boroughs NYC Activity Book. 2005. 24p. (gr. k-8). pap. 8.95 (***978-0-635-03080-1(2)***) Gallopade International.
Banks, Joan. Peter Stuyvesant: Dutch Military Leader. 2000. (gr. 5-8). lib. bdg. 17.60 (978-0-613-43365-5(3)) Tandem Library Bks.
Barter, James. Colonial New York. 2003. (Illus.). 112p. (J). 29.95 (978-1-59018-250-5(2), Lucent Bks.) Thomson Gale.
The Battle of Yorktown, 6 vols. (gr. 2-5). 39.95 (978-0-7368-4576-2(3)) Red Brick Learning.
Britton, Tamara L. The World Trade Center. 2005. (Symbols, Landmarks & Monuments Ser.). (Illus.). 40p. (J). (gr. k-6). lib. bdg. 22.78 (978-1-57765-850-4(7)) ABDO Publishing Co.
Burgan, Michael. New York 1609-1776. 2006. (Voices from Colonial America Ser.). 112p. (J). (gr. k-3). 21.95 (978-0-7922-6390-6(1), National Geographic Children's Bks.) National Geographic Society.
—Voices from Colonial America: New York 1609-1776. 2006. (Illus.). 112p. (J). (gr. k-3). 32.90 (978-0-7922-6860-4(1), National Geographic Children's Bks.) National Geographic Society.
Carole Marsh. New York City Coloring & Activity Book. 2004. (City Bks.). 24p. (gr. k-5). pap. 3.95 (978-0-635-02226-4(5)) Gallopade International.
Corona, Laurel. The World Trade Center. 2002. (Building History Ser.). (Illus.). 104p. (J). (gr. 6-9). 32.45 (978-1-59018-214-7(6), Lucent Bks.) Thomson Gale.
Crewe, Sabrina & Schaefer, Adam. The Triangle Shirtwaist Factory Fire. 2004. (Events That Shaped America Ser.). (Illus.). 32p. (J). (gr. 3 up). lib. bdg. 24.67 (978-0-8368-3402-4(X)) Stevens, Gareth Inc.
Curtiss, A. B. The Little Chapel That Stood, Golino, Mirto, illus. l.t. ed. 2005. 36p. 18.95 (978-0-932529-77-0(1)) Oldcastle Publishing.
De Hahn, Tracee. The Blizzard of 1888. 2000. (Great Disasters Ser.). (Illus.). 104p. (J). (gr. 5-9). 21.95 (978-0-7910-5787-2(9), Chelsea Hse.) Facts On File, Inc.
DeAngelis, Gina. Triangle Shirtwaist Company Fire of 1911. 2000. (Great Disasters, Reforms & Ramifications Ser.). (Illus.). 112p. (J). (gr. 5 up). 30.00 (978-0-7910-5267-9(2), Chelsea Hse.) Facts On File, Inc.
Fein, E. How to Draw New Yorks Sights & Symbols. 2002. (Kids Guide to Drawing America Ser.). 32p. (J). lib. bdg. 25.25 (978-0-8239-6088-0(9), PowerKids Pr.) Rosen Publishing Group, Inc., The.
Fischer, Laura. Life in New Amsterdam. 2003. (Picture the Past Ser.). (Illus.). 32p. (J). pap. 7.50 (978-1-4034-4285-7(1)) Heinemann Library.
—Life in New Amsterdam, New York. 2003. (Picture the Past Ser.). (Illus.). 32p. (J). lib. bdg. 24.22 (978-1-4034-3798-3(X)) Heinemann Library.
Gillis, Jennifer Blizin. Life on the Lower East Side. 2003. (Picture the Past Ser.). (Illus.). 32p. (J). pap. 7.50 (978-1-4034-4287-1(8)); lib. bdg. 22.79 (978-1-4034-3796-9(3)) Heinemann Library.
Goodman, Susan E. On This Spot: An Expedition Back Through Time. Christiansen, Lee, illus. 2004. 32p. (J). 16.99 (978-0-688-16913-8(9)) HarperCollins Pubs.
Granfield, Linda. 97 Orchard Street, New York: Stories of Immigrant Life. 2001. (gr. 3-6). lib. bdg. 24.60 (978-0-613-56823-4(0)) Tandem Library Bks.
—97 Orchard Street, New York: Stories of Immigrant Life. Alda, Arlene, photos by. 2001. (Illus.). 56p. (J). (gr. 3-6). pap. 15.00 (978-0-88776-580-3(7)) Tundra Bks., Inc./Livres Toundra, Inc. CAN. *Dist:* Random Hse., Inc.
Greene, Jacqueline Dembar. The Triangle Shirtwaist Factory Fire. 2007. (Code Red Ser.). (Illus.). 32p. (J). (gr. 3-7). lib. bdg. 25.27 (978-1-59716-359-0(7)) Bearport Publishing Co., Inc.
Gunderson, Jessica Sarah. The Triangle Shirtwaist Factory Fire. Miller, Phil & Barnett, Charles, illus. 2006. (Graphic Library). 32p. (J). (978-0-7368-5483-2(5)) Capstone Pr., Inc.
Hansen, Joyce, et al. Breaking Ground, Breaking Silence: The Story of New York's African Burial Ground. McGowan, Gary, illus. rev. ed. 1998. (Illus.). 144p. (J). (gr. 5-9). 19.95 (978-0-8050-5012-7(4), Holt, Henry & Co. Bks. For Young Readers) Holt, Henry & Co.
Harcourt School Publishers Staff. It Happened at Seneca Falls. 3rd ed. 2002. (Horizons Ser.). (Illus.). (J). pap. 5.50 (978-0-15-333399-6(5)) Harcourt Schl. Pubs.
—Old Amsterdam. 3rd ed. 2002. (Horizons Ser.). (Illus.). (J). pap. 7.30 (978-0-15-333563-1(7)) Harcourt Schl. Pubs.
Harmon, Daniel E. The Hudson River. McNeese, Tim, ed. 2004. (Rivers in American Life & Times Ser.). (Illus.). 120p. (gr. 9-13). pap. 13.25 (978-0-7910-8005-4(6), Chelsea Hse.) Facts On File, Inc.
Hopkinson, Deborah. Shutting Out the Sky: Life in the Tenements of New York, 1880-1924. 2003. (Illus.). 144p. (J). pap. 17.95 (978-0-439-37590-0(8), Orchard Bks.) Scholastic, Inc.
Houle, Michelle M. Triangle Shirtwaist Factory Fire: Flames of Labor Reform. 2002. (American Disasters Ser.). (Illus.). 48p. (J). (gr. 4-10). lib. bdg. 23.93 (978-0-7660-1785-6(0)) Enslow Pubs., Inc.
Kent, Deborah. The Great Civil War Draft Riots. 2005. (Cornerstones of Freedom Ser.). (Illus.). 48p. (J). 26.00 (978-0-516-23632-2(6), Children's Pr.) Scholastic Library Publishing.
King, David C. Victorian Days: Discover the Past with Fun Projects, Games, Activities, & Recipes. 2000. (Illus.). 96p. (J). (ps-7). lib. bdg. 22.20 (978-0-613-27413-5(X)) Tandem Library Bks.
Landau, Elaine. The Triangle Shirtwaist Factory Fire. 2005. (Cornerstones of Freedom Ser.). (Illus.). 48p. (J). (gr. 4-6). 26.00 (978-0-516-23626-1(1), Children's Pr.) Scholastic Library Publishing.
Lieurance, Suzanne. The Triangle Shirtwaist Fire & Sweatshop Reform in American History. 2003. (In American History Ser.). (Illus.). 128p. (J). (gr. 5-12). lib. bdg. 26.60 (978-0-7660-1839-6(3)) Enslow Pubs., Inc.
Louis, Nancy. Ground Zero. 2002. (War on Terrorism Ser.). (Illus.). 64p. (J). (gr. 4-8). lib. bdg. 25.65 (978-1-57765-657-9(1), ABDO & Daughters) ABDO Publishing Co.
Marsh, Carole. My First Pocket Guide New York. 2000. (New York Experience! Ser.). (Illus.). 96p. (J). (gr. 3-8). 12.95 (978-0-635-01322-4(3), 13223) Gallopade International.
—The New York Survivor: A Class Challenge. 2001. (Carole Marsh New York Bks.). (J). lib. bdg. 29.95 (978-0-635-00678-3(2)) Gallopade International.
McGovern, Ann. If You Lived 100 Years Ago. DiVito, Anna, illus. 1999. (If You Ser.). 80p. (J). (gr. 2-5). pap. 5.99 (978-0-590-96001-4(6)) Scholastic, Inc.
—If You Lived 100 Years Ago. 1999. 12.79 (978-0-606-17545-6(8)); (gr. 3-6). lib. bdg. 14.15 (978-0-613-17918-8(8)) Tandem Library Bks.
Murphy, Jim. Blizzard! The Storm That Changed America. Murphy, Jim, illus. 2000. (Illus.). 136p. (J). (gr. 5 up). pap. 18.95 (978-0-590-67309-9(2)) Scholastic, Inc.
Palermo, Blinky. Blinky Palermo: To the People of New York City. Cooke, Lynne & Kelly, Karen, eds. 2005. (Illus.). 112p. (YA). (gr. 13 up). 45.00 (978-0-944521-48-9(7)) Dia Ctr. for the Arts.
Peterson, Sheryl. Empire State Building. 2006. (Modern Wonders of the World Ser.). (Illus.). 32p. (J). 18.95 (978-1-58341-439-2(8), Creative Education) Creative Co., The.
Ringgold, Faith. My Grandmother's Story Quilt. (J). 1999. (978-0-517-70947-4(3)); 1998. lib. bdg. (978-0-517-70948-1(1)) Random Hse. Children's Bks. (Random Hse. Bks. for Young Readers).
Sanderson, Jeanette. A Visit to the New Amsterdam. 2005. 40.00 (***978-1-4108-4229-9(0)***) Benchmark Education Co.
Sherrow, Victoria. The World Trade Center Bombing: Terror in the Towers. 1998. (American Disasters Ser.). (Illus.). 48p. (YA). (gr. 4-10). lib. bdg. 23.93 (978-0-7660-1056-7(2)) Enslow Pubs., Inc.
Shields, Charles J. The World Trade Center Bombing. 2001. (Great Disasters, Reforms & Ramifications Ser.). (J). pap. 13.25 (978-0-7910-6915-8(X), Chelsea Hse.) Facts On File, Inc.
—The 1993 World Trade Center Bombing. 2001. (Great Disasters, Reforms & Ramifications Ser.). (Illus.). 112p. (YA). (gr. 6-9). 30.00 (978-0-7910-5789-6(5), Chelsea Hse.) Facts On File, Inc.
Stanley, Ed. Grand Central Terminal: Gateway to New York City. 2003. (Illus.). 48p. (J). 16.95 (978-1-59034-491-0(X)); pap. (978-1-59034-492-7(8)) Mondo Publishing.
Steward, Mark. New York, 6 bks., Set. 2003. (Heinemann State Studies). (J). (gr. 3-5). lib. bdg. 162.42 (978-1-58810-763-3(9)) Heinemann Library.
Thornton, Jeremy. The History of Early New York. 2003. (Building Americas Democracy Ser.). (Illus.). 24p. (J). lib. bdg. 19.95 (978-0-8239-6278-5(4), PowerKids Pr.) Rosen Publishing Group, Inc., The.
Vila, Laura. Building Manhattan. 2008. 40p. (J). (gr. 1-3). 15.99 (***978-0-670-06284-3(7)***, Viking Juvenile) Penguin Group (USA) Inc.
Weber, Paige. New York. 2003. (Great Cities Through the Ages Ser.). (Illus.). 44p. (J). 18.95 (978-1-59270-003-5(9)) Enchanted Lion Bks., LLC.
Wetterer, Charles M. & Wetterer, Margaret K. The Snow Walker. Young, Mary O'Keefe, illus. 1998. (On My Own History Ser.). 48p. (J). (gr. 1-3). pap. 5.95 (978-0-87614-959-1(X), Carolrhoda Bks.) Lerner Publishing Group.
Wetterer, Margaret K. & Wetterer, Charles M. Caminando Bajo la Nieve (The Snow Walker) Young, Mary O'Keefe, illus. 2007. (Yo Solo - Historia (on My Own - History) Ser.). (SPA.). 48p. (J). (gr. 2-4). lib. bdg. 25.26 (***978-0-8225-7786-7(0)***, Ediciones Lerner) Lerner Publishing Group.
Wiener. The 13 Colonies Pack: New York, 6. 2004. (Illus.). 48.30 (978-1-4109-0371-6(0)) Harcourt Schl. Pubs.

NEW YORK (N.Y.)—HISTORY—FICTION

Adler, David A. The Babe & I. Widener, Terry, illus. 2004. 32p. (J). reprint ed. pap. 6.00 (978-0-15-205026-9(4), Voyager Bks./Libros Viajeros) Harcourt Children's Bks.
Alger, Horatio. A Boy's Fortune: Or, The Strange Adventures of Ben Baker. unabr. ed. 2002. (Polyglot Press Alger Ser.). (Illus.). (J). pap. 17.95 (978-1-931927-79-6(0)) Polyglot Pr., Inc.
—Cast upon the Breakers. unabr. ed. 2002. (Polyglot Press Alger Ser.). (Illus.). (J). pap. 17.95 (978-1-931927-81-9(2)) Polyglot Pr., Inc.
—Helping Himself. 2006. 180p. pap. 13.99 (978-1-4264-0881-6(1)); 168p. pap. 16.99 (978-1-4264-0862-5(5)) BiblioBazaar.
—Helping Himself. 2006. pap. (***978-1-4065-0709-6(1)***) Dodo Pr.
—Helping Himself: Or, Grant Thornton's Ambition. unabr. ed. 2002. (Polyglot Press Alger Ser.). (Illus.). (J). pap. 17.95 (978-1-4115-0006-8(7)) Polyglot Pr., Inc.
—Jack's Ward. 2006. pap. (***978-1-4065-0711-9(3)***) Dodo Pr.
—Jack's Ward: Or, The Boy Guardian. 2006. 176p. pap. 13.99 (978-1-4264-0882-3(X)); 168p. pap. 16.99 (978-1-4264-0863-2(3)) BiblioBazaar.
—Paul Prescott's Charge: A Story for Boys. 2006. pap. (***978-1-4250-2995-1(7)***) Assistedreadingbooks.com Inc.
—Paul Prescott's Charge: A Story for Boys. unabr. ed. 2002. (Polyglot Press Alger Ser.). (Illus.). (J). pap. 17.95 (978-1-4115-0034-1(2)) Polyglot Pr., Inc.
—Phil the Fiddler. 2006. pap. (***978-1-4068-0667-0(6)***) Echo Library.
—The Store Boy. 2006. 170p. pap. 11.99 (***978-1-4264-4359-6(5)***); 182p. pap. 14.99 (***978-1-4264-4397-8(8)***) BiblioBazaar.
—The Store Boy. 2006. pap. (***978-1-4065-0722-5(9)***) Dodo Pr.
—Timothy Crump's Ward: A Story of American Life. 2006. pap. (***978-1-4250-3339-2(3)***) Assistedreadingbooks.com Inc.
Alger, Horatio. Tom Temple's Career. reprint ed. pap. 79.00 (978-1-4047-3611-5(5)) Classic Textbooks.
—Tom Temple's Career. l.t. ed. 2002. (Illus.). pap. 19.95 (978-1-4115-0422-6(4)); (J). pap. 17.95 (978-1-4115-0057-0(1)) Polyglot Pr., Inc.
Avi. The Mayor of Central Park. Floca, Brian, illus. 2003. 208p. (J). (gr. 3-6). 15.99 (978-0-06-000682-2(X)); lib. bdg. 16.89 (978-0-06-051556-0(2)) HarperCollins Pubs.
Baker, Sharon. A Nickel, a Trolley, a Treasure House. Peck, Beth, illus. 2007. 32p. (J). (gr. k-5). 16.99 (978-0-670-05982-9(X), Viking Juvenile) Penguin Group (USA) Inc.
Bildner, Phil. Twenty-One Elephants. Pham, LeUyen, illus. 2004. 40p. (J). 16.95 (978-0-689-87011-8(6)) Simon & Schuster Children's Publishing.
Brown, Don. The Notorious Izzy Fink. 2006. 160p. (J). 16.95 (978-1-59643-139-3(3)) Roaring Brook Pr.
Clark, Clara Gillow. Hattie on Her Way. Thompson, John, illus. 2005. 208p. (J). (gr. 5 up). 15.99 (978-0-7636-2286-2(9)) Candlewick Pr.
Collier, James Lincoln. Chipper. 2001. (Illus.). 144p. (J). (gr. 5-9). 14.95 (978-0-7614-5084-9(X), Cavendish Children's Bks.) Cavendish, Marshall Corp.
Haddix, Margaret Peterson. Uprising. 2007. 352p. (YA). (gr. 7 up). 16.99 (***978-1-4169-1171-5(5)***) Simon & Schuster Children's Publishing.
High, Linda Oatman. City of Snow: The Great Blizzard Of 1888. Filippucci, Laura Francesca, illus. 2004. 32p. (J). 17.85 (978-0-8027-8911-2(0)); 16.95 (978-0-8027-8910-5(2)) Walker & Co.
Hurwitz, Johanna. Dear Emma. 2002. (Illus.). 160p. (J). 15.99 (978-0-06-029840-1(5)) HarperCollins Pubs.

 For book reviews, descriptive annotations, tables of contents, cover images, author biographies & additional information, updated daily, subscribe to **www.booksinprint.com**

Killcoyne, Hope L. The Lost Village of Central Park. Majno, Mary L., illus. 1999. (Mysteries in Time Ser.: Vol. 9). 89p. (J). (gr. 3-7). lib. bdg. 14.95 (978-1-893110-02-1(8)) Silver Moon Pr.

Kirk, Connie Ann. Sky Dancers. Hale, Christy, illus. 2004. (J). (gr. 1-4). 16.95 (978-1-58430-162-2(7)) Lee & Low Bks., Inc.

Kirkpatrick, Katherine. Escape Across the Wide Sea. 2004. (Illus.). 224p. (J). (gr. 4-6). tchr. ed. 17.95 (978-0-8234-1854-1(5)) Holiday Hse., Inc.

Kohl, Susan. The Ghost of Gracie Mansion. Butterfield, Ned, illus. 1999. (Mysteries in Time Ser.: Vol. 8). 96p. (J). (gr. 3-7). lib. bdg. 14.95 (978-1-893110-04-5(4)) Silver Moon Pr.

Konigsburg, E. L. From the Mixed-Up Files of Mrs. Basil E. Frankweiler. l.t. ed. 2005. (Illus.). 205p. (J). 22.95 (978-0-7862-7297-6(X) , Large Print Pr.) Thorndike Pr.

Kroll, Steven. Sweet America. 2004. 172p. (J). lib. bdg. 16.92 (***978-1-4242-0773-2(8)***) Fitzgerald Bks.

Levine, Beth Seidel. When Christmas Comes Again: The World War I Diary of Simone Spencer. 2002. (Dear America Ser.). (Illus.). 176p. (J). (gr. 4-9). pap. 10.95 (978-0-439-43982-4(5)) Scholastic, Inc.

Lieurance, Suzanne. The Locket: Surviving the Triangle Shirtwaist Fire. 2008. (Historical Fiction Adventures (HFA) Ser.). (Illus.). 160p. (J). (gr. 3-6). lib. bdg. 27.93 (***978-0-7660-2928-6(X)***) Enslow Pubs., Inc.

Loughrey, Eithne. Annie Moore: New York City Girl. 2006. (YA). (***978-0-8368-7737-3(3)***) Stevens, Gareth Inc.

—Annie Moore: The Golden Dollar Girl. l.t. ed. 2006. (Dales Ser.). 208p. (J). 23.99 (978-1-84262-447-0(4)) Magna Large Print Bks. GBR. *Dist:* Ulverscroft Large Print Bks., Ltd.

—Annie Moore First in Line for America. l.t. ed. 2006. (Dales Ser.). 224p. (J). 23.99 (978-1-84262-446-3(6)) Magna Large Print Bks. GBR. *Dist:* Ulverscroft Large Print Bks., Ltd.

—Annie Moore, First in Line for Ellis Island. 2006. (J). lib. bdg. (***978-0-8368-7735-9(7)***) Stevens, Gareth Inc.

—Annie Moore New York City Girl. l.t. ed. 2006. (Dales Ser.). 208p. 23.99 (978-1-84262-448-7(2)) Dales Large Print Bks. GBR. *Dist:* Ulverscroft Large Print Bks., Ltd.

Loughrey, Eithne. Annie Moore, the Golden Dollar Girl. 2006. (J). lib. bdg. (***978-0-8368-7736-6(5)***) Stevens, Gareth Inc.

Martin, Ann M. Here Today. 2005. 336p. (J). (gr. 5-9). pap. 5.99 (978-0-439-57945-2(7) , Scholastic Paperbacks) Scholastic, Inc.

McGuigan, Mary Ann. Morning in a Different Place. 2008. (J). (***978-1-59078-551-5(7)*** , Front Street) Boyds Mills Pr.

Napoli, Donna Jo. The King of Mulberry Street. 256p. (gr. 3-7). 2007. 6.50 (***978-0-553-49416-7(3)*** , Yearling); 2005. (J). 15.95 (978-0-385-74653-3(9) , Lamb, Wendy); 2005. (J). lib. bdg. 17.99 (978-0-385-90890-0(3) , Lamb, Wendy) Random Hse. Children's Bks.

Nixon, Joan Lowery. Land of Hope. l.t. ed. 2001. (Ellis Island Stories Ser.). 171p. (J). (gr. 4 up). lib. bdg. 23.33 (978-0-8368-2811-5(9)) Stevens, Gareth Inc.

Nolan, Han. A Summer of Kings. 2006. (Illus.). 352p. (YA). 17.00 (978-0-15-205108-2(2)) Harcourt Children's Bks.

—A Summer of Kings. 2006. 334p. (J). (978-1-4156-7340-9(3)) Harcourt Trade Pubs.

Osborne, Mary Pope. Blizzard of the Blue Moon. Murdocca, Sal, illus. 2007. (Magic Tree House Ser.: No. 36). 144p. (J). (gr. 2-5). pap. 4.99 (978-0-375-83038-9(3) , Random Hse. Bks. for Young Readers) Random Hse. Children's Bks.

—Blizzard of the Blue Moon. 2006. (Magic Tree House Ser.: No. 36). (Illus.). 128p. (J). (gr. k-3). lib. bdg. 13.99 (978-0-375-93037-9(X)); (gr. 2-5). 11.95 (978-0-375-83037-2(5)) Random Hse. Children's Bks. (Random Hse. Bks. for Young Readers).

Osborne, Mary Pope, et al. A Time to Dance Bk. 3: Virginia's Civil War Diary. 2003. (My America Ser.). 112p. (J). pap. 12.95 (978-0-439-44341-8(5)) Scholastic, Inc.

Pollack, Jenny. Klepto. 288p. (gr. 7). 2008. (YA). pap. 7.99 (***978-0-14-241072-1(1)*** , Puffin); 2006. (J). 16.99 (978-0-670-06061-0(5) , Viking Juvenile) Penguin Group (USA) Inc.

Prince, April Jones. Twenty-One Elephants & Still Standing. Roca, Francois, illus. 2005. 32p. (J). (gr. k-3). 16.00 (978-0-618-44887-6(X)) Houghton Mifflin Co. Trade & Reference Div.

Rinaldi, Ann. The Color of Fire. 2006. 208p. (gr. 5-17). pap. 5.99 (978-0-7868-1825-9(5) , Jump at the Sun) Hyperion Bks. for Children.

Schwabach, Karen. A Pickpocket's Tale. 240p. (J). (gr. 3-7). 2008. 5.99 (***978-0-375-83380-9(3)*** , Yearling); 2006. (Illus.). 15.95 (978-0-375-83379-3(X) , Random Hse. Bks. for Young Readers); 2006. (Illus.). lib. bdg. 17.99 (978-0-375-93379-0(4) , Random Hse. Bks. for Young Readers) Random Hse. Children's Bks.

Stevens, Carla. Anna, Grandpa, & the Big Storm. Tomes, Margot, illus. 1998. (Puffin Chapters for Readers on the Move Ser.). 64p. (J). (gr. 2-5). pap. 5.99 (978-0-14-130083-2(3) , Puffin) Penguin Group (USA) Inc.

Torres, J. Days Like This. 2003. (Illus.). 80p. (YA). pap. 8.95 (978-1-929998-48-7(1)) Oni Pr., Inc.

Tripp, Valerie. Samantha's Short Story Collection. Buckey, Sarah & Andreasan, Dan, illus. 2006. 224p. (J). 12.95 (***978-1-59369-125-7(4)***) American Girl Publishing, Inc.

Waldman, Neil. Say-Hey & the Babe: Two Mostly-True Baseball Stories. Waldman, Neil, illus. 2005. (Illus.). 40p. (J). (gr. 1-5). 16.95 (978-0-8234-1857-2(X)) Holiday Hse., Inc.

Wells, Helen. Cherry Ames, Visiting Nurse. 2006. vii, 216p. (J). (978-0-8261-0399-4(5)) Springer.

Wemmlinger, Raymond. Booth's Daughter. 2007. 210p. (YA). (gr. 7 up). 17.95 (978-1-932425-86-4(1) , Front Street) Boyds Mills Pr.

NEW YORK (N.Y.)—POETRY

Myers, Walter Dean. Here in Harlem: Poems in Many Voices. 2004. (Illus.). 96p. (YA). (gr. 7 up). tchr. ed. 16.95 (978-0-8234-1853-4(7)) Holiday Hse., Inc.

NEW YORK (N.Y.)—POLITICS AND GOVERNMENT

Ashby, Ruth. Boss Tweed: And Tammany Hall. 2002. (Notorious Americans & Their Times Ser.). (Illus.). 112p. (YA). (gr. 5 up). 27.45 (978-1-56711-252-8(8) , Blackbirch Pr., Inc.) Thomson Gale.

Burby, Liza N. A Day in the Life of a Mayor: Featuring New York City Mayor Rudy Giuliani. 1999. (Kids' Career Library). (Illus.). 24p. (J). (gr. 3). lib. bdg. 18.75 (978-0-8239-5303-5(3) , PowerKids Pr.) Rosen Publishing Group, Inc., The.

Fremont, Eleanor. Rudolph W. Giuliani: America's Mayor. 2002. (Illus.). 96p. (J). (gr. 5-9). pap. 4.99 (978-0-689-85423-1(4) , Aladdin) Simon & Schuster Children's Publishing.

NEW YORK (N.Y.)—SOCIAL CONDITIONS

Bial, Raymond. Tenement: Immigrant Life on the Lower East Side. Bial, Raymond, illus. 2002. (Illus.). 48p. (J). (gr. 4-6). tchr. ed. 16.00 (978-0-618-13849-4(8)) Houghton Mifflin Co. Trade & Reference Div.

Bolden, Tonya. Maritcha: A Nineteenth-Century American Girl. 2005. (Illus.). 48p. (J). (gr. k-4). 17.95 (978-0-8109-5045-0(6)) Abrams, Harry N. , Inc.

Graves, Kerry, ed. Nineteenth-Century Schoolgirl: The Diary of Caroline Cowles Richards, 1852-1854. 1999. (Diaries, Letters & Memoirs Ser.). 32p. (J). (gr. 2-7). pap. 21.00 (978-0-516-21853-3(0) , Children's Pr.) Scholastic Library Publishing.

Halpern, Monica. Three Immigrant Communities: New York City In 1900. 2006. (Navigators Ser.). (J). pap. 38.00 (***978-1-4108-6249-5(6)***) Benchmark Education Co.

Hopkinson, Deborah. Shutting Out the Sky: Life in the Tenements of New York, 1880-1924. 2003. (Illus.). 144p. (J). pap. 17.95 (978-0-439-37590-0(8) , Orchard Bks.) Scholastic, Inc.

Pascal, Janet B. Jacob Riis: Reporter & Reformer. 2005. (Oxford Portraits Ser.). (Illus.). 176p. (YA). 28.00 (978-0-19-514527-4(5)) Oxford Univ. Pr., Inc.

Roosevelt, Theodore. The Boyhood Diary of Theodore Roosevelt, 1869-1870: Early Travels of the 26th U. S. President. Saterern, Shelley Swanson, ed. 2000. (Blue Earth Books). (Illus.). 32p. (J). (gr. 3-4). lib. bdg. 22.60 (978-0-7368-0601-5(6) , Bridgestone Bks.) Capstone Pr., Inc.

Stevens, B. C. Tales from Hinman Hollow. rev. ed. 2002. (Illus.). 112p. per. 7.95 (978-0-9677938-3-2(1)) Country Bumpkin Pubns.

Wolf, Bernard. Coming to America: A Muslim Family's Story. Wolf, Bernard, photos by. 2003. (Illus.). 48p. (J). (gr. k-8). 17.95 (978-1-58430-086-1(8)); pap. 7.95 (978-1-58430-177-6(5)) Lee & Low Bks., Inc.

—Coming to America: A Muslim Family's Story. 2003. (gr. 3-6). lib. bdg. 16.40 (978-0-613-67796-7(X)) Tandem Library Bks.

NEW YORK (STATE)

Ball, Jackie. New York: The Empire State. 2002. (gr. 5-8). lib. bdg. 24.15 (978-0-613-52458-2(6)) Tandem Library Bks.

Ball, Jacqueline A. New York: The Empire State. 2002. (World Almanac Library of the States). (Illus.). 48p. (J). (gr. 5 up). pap. 14.95 (978-0-8368-5288-2(5)); lib. bdg. 30.00 (978-0-8368-5118-2(8)) Stevens, Gareth Inc. (World Almanac Library).

Burg, Ann. E Is for Empire: A New York State Alphabet. Brookfield, Maureen, illus. 2003. 40p. (J). 17.95 (978-1-58536-113-7(5)) Sleeping Bear Pr.

Burg, Ann E. Times Square: A New York State Number Book. Brookfield, Maureen K., illus. 2005. (Count Your Way Across the USA Ser.). 40p. (J). (gr. k-5). 16.95 (978-1-58536-195-3(X)) Sleeping Bear Pr.

Capstone Press Staff, contrib. by. New York. rev. ed. 2002. (One Nation Ser.). (Illus.). 48p. (J). (gr. 3-4). lib. bdg. 22.60 (978-0-7368-1256-6(3) , Bridgestone Bks.) Capstone Pr., Inc.

Cotter, Kristin. New York. 2002. (From Sea to Shining Sea Ser.: 2). (Illus.). 80p. (J). (gr. 3-5). pap. 30.50 (978-0-516-22485-5(9) , Children's Pr.) Scholastic Library Publishing.

De Capua, Sarah. New York. 2003. (Rookie Read-About Geography Ser.). (Illus.). 32p. (J). (gr. 1-2). pap. 5.95 (978-0-516-27490-4(2) , Children's Pr.) Scholastic Library Publishing.

De Capua, Sarah & Bredeson, Carmen. New York. 2002. (Rookie Read-About Geography Ser.). (Illus.). 32p. (J). (gr. 1-2). 20.50 (978-0-516-22665-1(7) , Children's Pr.) Scholastic Library Publishing.

Decapua, Sarah. New York. 2002. (gr. k-3). lib. bdg. 14.10 (978-0-613-58721-1(9)) Tandem Library Bks.

Dunn, Mary. My Adventure in a Mohawk Village. 2006. 44p. (J). 8.99 (978-1-59092-419-8(3) , Orchard Academy Pr.) Windstorm Creative.

Elish, Dan. New York. 2002. (It's My State! Ser.). (Illus.). 80p. (J). 27.07 (978-0-7614-1419-3(3) , Benchmark Bks.) Cavendish, Marshall Corp.

Facklam, Margery & Thomas, Peggy. New York: The Empire State. Messer, Jon, illus. 2007. (J). (gr. 2-5). 44p. 16.95 (978-1-57091-660-1(8)); 40p. pap. 6.95 (***978-1-57091-661-8(6)***) Charlesbridge Publishing, Inc.

Gelman, Amy. New York. 2nd rev. exp. ed. (Hello U. S. A. Ser.). (Illus.). 84p. (J). (gr. 3-6). 2003. pap. 6.95 (978-0-8225-4151-6(3)); 2002. 25.26 (978-0-8225-4057-1(6) , Lerner Pubns.) Lerner Publishing Group.

Heinrichs, Ann, et al. New York. 2nd ed. 1999. (America the Beautiful, Second Ser.). (Illus.). 144p. (YA). (gr. 5-8). 36.00 (978-0-516-20691-2(5) , Children's Pr.) Scholastic Library Publishing.

Kehoe, Stasia Ward. I Live on a Farm. 2000. (Kids in Their Communities Ser.). (Illus.). 24p. (J). (gr. 3). lib. bdg. 18.75 (978-0-8239-5438-4(2) , PowerKids Pr.) Rosen Publishing Group, Inc., The.

Lawton, Val. A Guide to New York. 2001. (American States Ser.). 32p. (J). lib. bdg. 16.95 (978-1-930954-49-6(2)) Weigl Pubs., Inc.

Marsh, Carole. Jography. 2004. (New York Experience! Ser.). 32p. (J). (gr. 3-8). pap. 7.95 (978-0-635-00162-7(4)) Gallopade International.

—The New York Big Activity Book. 2004. (New York Experience! Ser.). 96p. (J). (gr. 2-6). pap. 9.95 (978-0-635-00165-8(9)) Gallopade International.

—New York Classic Christmas Trivia. 2002. (Carole Marsh New York Bks.). (Illus.). 32p. pap. 6.95 (978-0-635-01431-3(9) , 14319); lib. bdg. 21.95 (978-0-635-01432-0(7) , 14327) Gallopade International. (Marsh, Carole Bks.).

—New York Current Events Projects: 30 Cool, Activities, Crafts, Experiments & More for Kids to Do to Learn about Your State! 2003. (New York Experience Ser.). 32p. (gr. k-8). pap. 5.95 (978-0-635-02051-2(3) , Marsh, Carole Bks.) Gallopade International.

—New York Geography Projects: 30 Cool, Activities, Crafts, Experiments & More for Kids to Do to Learn about Your State! 2003. (New York Experience Ser.). 32p. (gr. k-5). pap. 5.95 (978-0-635-01851-9(9) , Marsh, Carole Bks.) Gallopade International.

—New York People Projects: 30 Cool, Activities, Crafts, Experiments & More for Kids to Do to Learn about Your State! 2003. (New York Experience Ser.). 32p. (gr. k-5). pap. 5.95 (978-0-635-02001-7(7) , Marsh, Carole Bks.) Gallopade International.

—New York Pocket Guide. 2004. (New York Experience! Ser.). 96p. (J). (gr. 3-8). pap. 6.95 (978-0-635-00163-4(2)) Gallopade International.

—New York Symbols & Facts Projects: 30 Cool, Activities, Crafts, Experiments & More for Kids to Do to Learn about Your State! 2003. (New York Experience Ser.). 32p. (gr. k-5). pap. 5.95 (978-0-635-01901-1(9) , Marsh, Carole Bks.) Gallopade International.

McAuliffe, Emily. New York: Facts & Symbols. 1998. (States & Their Symbols Ser.). 24p. (J). lib. bdg. 14.00 (978-0-531-11552-7(6) , Watts, Franklin) Scholastic Library Publishing.

—New York Facts & Symbols. rev. ed. 2003. (States & Their Symbols Ser.). 24p. (J). lib. bdg. 19.93 (978-0-7368-2262-6(3)) Capstone Pr., Inc.

Mezzanotte, Jim. New York. 2005. (Portraits of the States Ser.). (Illus.). 32p. (J). lib. bdg. 23.33 (978-0-8368-4630-0(3)) Stevens, Gareth Inc.

Murray, Julie. New York. 2006. (Buddy Book Ser.). (Illus.). 32p. (J). (gr. k-4). lib. bdg. 22.78 (978-1-59197-691-2(X) , Buddy Bks.) ABDO Publishing Co.

Naden, Corinne J. & Blue, Rose. New York: A MyReportLinks.com Book. 2002. (States Ser.). (Illus.). 48p. (J). (gr. 4-10). lib. bdg. 25.26 (978-0-7660-5016-7(5) , MyReportLinks.com Bks.) Enslow Pubs., Inc.

Obregon, José María. New York: Nueva York. 2006. (Bilingual Library of the United States of America). (SPA.). (J). lib. bdg. (978-1-4042-3138-2(2) , PowerKids Pr.) Rosen Publishing Group, Inc., The.

Obregon, Jose Maria. Nueva York. Brusca, Maria Cristina, tr. 2006. (Bilingual Library of the United States of America: Set 1). (ENG & SPA., Illus.). 32p. (J). (gr. 2-5). lib. bdg. 22.50 (978-1-4042-3097-2(1) , Buenas Letra) Rosen Publishing Group, Inc., The.

Paulson, Timothy J. New York. 2004. (Life in the Thirteen Colonies Ser.). (Illus.). 124p. (J). 36.00 (978-0-516-24575-1(9) , Children's Pr.) Scholastic Library Publishing.

Schomp, Virginia. New York. 2nd ed. 2005. (Celebrate the States Ser.). (Illus.). 144p. (J). (gr. 4-7). lib. bdg. 37.07 (978-0-7614-1738-5(9) , Benchmark Bks.) Cavendish, Marshall Corp.

Somervill, Barbara A. New York. 2007. (America the Beautiful, Third Ser.). (Illus.). 144p. (YA). (gr. 5-8). lib. bdg. 38.00 (***978-0-531-18565 0(6)*** , Children's Pr.) Scholastic Library Publishing.

Stewart, Mark. All Around New York. 2003. (gr. 3-6). lib. bdg. 17.05 (978-0-613-60950-0(6)) Tandem Library Bks.

—All Around New York: Regions & Resources. 2003. (Heinemann State Studies). (Illus.). 48p. (J). pap. 8.50 (978-1-4034-0574-6(3)) Heinemann Library.

—People of New York. 2003. (Heinemann State Studies). (Illus.). 48p. (J). pap. 8.50 (978-1-4034-0577-7(8)) Heinemann Library.

—People of New York. 2003. (gr. 3-6). lib. bdg. 17.05 (978-0-613-60979-1(4)) Tandem Library Bks.

—Uniquely New York. 2003. (Heinemann State Studies). (Illus.). 48p. (J). pap. 8.50 (978-1-4034-0579-1(4)) Heinemann Library.

—Uniquely New York. 2003. (gr. 3-6). lib. bdg. 17.05 (978-0-613-60991-3(3)) Tandem Library Bks.

Sturm, Ellen. New York. 2003. (Land of Liberty Ser.). (Illus.). 64p. (J). (gr. 3-4). lib. bdg. 23.93 (978-0-7368-1592-5(9) , Bridgestone Bks.) Capstone Pr., Inc.

Valette, D. Von La. Cool Shops New York. 2005. (ENG, SPA, FRE, ITA & GER., Illus.). 135p. pap. 16.95 (978-3-8327-9021-9(7)) teNeues Publishing Co.

Whitcraft, Melissa. Niagara River. 2001. (gr. 3-6). lib. bdg. 17.60 (978-0-613-37477-4(0)) Tandem Library Bks.

NEW YORK (STATE)—ANTIQUITIES

Standiford, Natalie. The Stone Giant. 2000. (J). (978-0-606-18928-6(9)) Tandem Library Bks.

NEW YORK (STATE)—FICTION

Alger, Horatio. Finding a Fortune. unabr. ed. 2002. (Polyglot Press Alger Ser.). (Illus.). (J). pap. 17.95 (978-1-4115-0089-1(X)) Polyglot Pr., Inc.

Auch, Mary Jane. Frozen Summer. 2000. (Illus.). (J). 11.15 (978-0-606-18783-1(9)) Tandem Library Bks.

Barham, Lisa. Accidentally Fabulous. 2008. (Fashion-Forward Adventures of Imogene Ser.). 256p. (YA). pap. 9.99 (***978-1-4169-1445-7(5)*** , Simon Pulse) Simon & Schuster Children's Publishing.

Bat-Ami, Miriam. Two Suns in the Sky. 1999. 208p. (YA). (gr. 7-12). 17.95 (978-0-8126-2900-2(0)) Cricket Bks.

—Two Suns in the Sky. 2001. 208p. (J). pap. 6.99 (978-0-14-230036-7(5) , Puffin) Penguin Group (USA) Inc.

—Two Suns in the Sky. 2001. (gr. 7-12). lib. bdg. 15.30 (978-0-613-44425-5(6)) Tandem Library Bks.

Bauer, Joan. Backwater. 2005. 185p. (YA). (gr. 7-12). pap. 7.99 (978-0-14-240434-8(9) , Puffin) Penguin Group (USA) Inc.

Benton, Amanda. Silent Stranger. 1998. pap. 3.99 (978-0-380-79222-1(2)) HarperCollins Pubs.

Blumenthal, Deborah. Ice Palace. Rand, Ted, illus. 2003. 32p. (J). (gr. k-3). 16.00 (978-0-618-15960-4(6) , Clarion Bks.) Houghton Mifflin Co. Trade & Reference Div.

Bruchac, Joseph. Hidden Roots. 2006. 160p. (J). pap. 5.99 (978-0-439-35359-5(9) , Scholastic Paperbacks) Scholastic, Inc.

—The Return of Skeleton Man. Comport, Sally Wern, illus. 2006. 144p. (J). lib. bdg. 16.89 (978-0-06-058091-9(7)) HarperCollins Pubs.

Crowe, Carole. Groover's Heart. 2003. (Illus.). 144p. (J). (gr. 4-6). 15.95 (978-1-56397-953-8(5)) Boyds Mills Pr.

Curtis, Alice Turner. A Little Maid of Old New York. Philsbry, Elizabeth, illus. 2004. (Little Maid Ser.). 192p. (J). (gr. 4-7). reprint ed. per. 9.95 (978-1-55709-326-4(1)) Applewood Bks.

DeFelice, Cynthia C. The Ghost of Poplar Point. 2007. (Ghost Mysteries Ser.). (Illus.). 192p. (J). (gr. 3-7). 16.00 (***978-0-374-32540-4(5)***) Farrar, Straus & Giroux.

Dreyer, Ellen. The Glow Stone. 2006. 186p. (J). 15.95 (978-1-56145-370-2(6) , Peachtree Junior) Peachtree Pubs., Ltd.

Drummond, Allan. Liberty! Drummond, Allan, illus. 2006. (Illus.). 40p. (J). reprint ed. pap. 6.95 (978-0-374-44397-9(1)) Macmillan.

Emery, Joanna. Brothers of the Falls. Erickson, David, illus. 2004. (Adventures in America Ser.). (J). 14.95 (978-1-893110-37-3(0)) Silver Moon Pr.

Feder, Harriet K. Death on Sacred Ground. 2003. (Young Adult Fiction Ser.). (Illus.). 192p. (J). (gr. 7 up). 14.95 (978-0-8225-0741-3(2) , Carolrhoda Bks.) Lerner Publishing Group.

Felin, M. Sindy. Touching Snow. 2007. 240p. (YA). (gr. 7 up). 16.99 (978-1-4169-1795-3(0) , Atheneum) Simon & Schuster Children's Publishing.

Fleming, Candace. Sunny Boy! The Life & Times of a Tortoise. Wilsdorf, Anne, illus. 2005. 40p. (J). 16.00 (978-0-374-37297-2(7) , Farrar, Straus & Giroux (BYR)) Farrar, Straus & Giroux.

Friedman, Aimee. Year My Sister Got Lucky. 2008. 384p. (J). pap. 16.99 (***978-0-439-92227-2(5)***) Scholastic, Inc.

George, Jean Craighead. Frightful's Mountain. 1999. (Illus.). 272p. (J). (gr. 4-7). 15.99 (978-0-525-46166-1(3) , Dutton Juvenile) Penguin Group (USA) Inc.

—My Side of the Mountain. l.t. ed. 2005. 198p. pap. 10.95 (978-0-7862-7359-1(3) , Large Print Pr.) Thorndike Pr.

Giff, Patricia Reilly. All the Way Home. 2003. (gr. 3-6). lib. bdg. 14.15 (978-0-613-57891-2(0)) Tandem Library Bks.

—Eleven. 2008. 144p. (J). (***978-0-385-73069-3(1)*** , Delacorte Pr.) Dell Publishing.

—Eleven. 2008. 176p. (J). (gr. 3-8). lib. bdg. 18.99 (***978-0-385-90098-0(8)*** , Lamb, Wendy) Random Hse. Children's Bks.

Giff, Patricia Reilly. Pictures of Hollis Woods. 176p. (gr. 3-8). 2004. (J). pap. 6.50 (978-0-440-41578-7(0) , Yearling); 2002. lib. bdg. 17.99 (978-0-385-90070-6(8) , Lamb, Wendy) Random Hse. Children's Bks.

—Pictures of Hollis Woods. Giff, Patricia Reilly, illus. 2002. (Illus.). 176p. (gr. 3-8). 15.95 (978-0-385-32655-1(6) , Lamb, Wendy) Random Hse. Children's Bks.

—Pictures of Hollis Woods. l.t. ed. 2003. 158p. (J). 23.95 (978-0-7862-5094-3(1)) Thorndike Pr.

Going, K. L. The Garden of Eve. 2007. (Illus.). 240p. (J). (gr. 3-7). 17.00 (***978-0-15-205986-6(5)***) Harcourt Children's Bks.

Grab, Daphne. Alive & Well in Prague, NY. 2008. 256p. (J). 16.99 (***978-0-06-125670-7(6)***); lib. bdg. 17.89 (***978-0-06-125671-4(4)***) HarperCollins Pubs. (Geringer, Laura Book).

Graver, Elizabeth. Honey Thief. 2000. (gr. 7-12). lib. bdg. 22.25 (978-0-613-36404-1(X)) Tandem Library Bks.

Greenwald, Sheila. Rosy Cole's Worst Ever, Best yet Tour of New York City. Greenwald, Sheila, illus. 2003. (Rosie Cole Ser.). (Illus.). 128p. (J). 16.00 (978-0-374-36349-9(8) , Farrar, Straus & Giroux (BYR)) Farrar, Straus & Giroux.

Harrison, Lisi. Best Friends for Never. 2004. (Clique Ser.: Bk. 2). 208p. (J). (gr. 5-8). pap. 9.99 (978-0-316-70131-0(9) , Poppy) Little, Brown Bks. for Young Readers.

—Revenge of the Wannabes. 2005. (Clique Ser.: No. 3). 304p. (YA). (gr. 5-8). pap. 9.99 (978-0-316-70133-4(5) , Poppy) Little, Brown Bks. for Young Readers.

Higginson, Hadley. Keeker & the Not-So-Sleepy Hollow. Perrett, Lisa, illus. 2008. (J). (***978-0-8118-6073-4(6)***); 56p. pap. 3.99 (***978-0-8118-6074-1(4)***) Chronicle Bks. LLC.

Irving, Washington. The Legend of Sleepy Hollow. Garland, Michael, illus. 2003. 64p. (J). (gr. 4-6). pap. 10.95 (978-1-56397-605-6(6)) Boyds Mills Pr.

—The Legend of Sleepy Hollow. Van Nutt, Robert, illus. 2005. (Rabbit Ears Ser.). 40p. (J). (gr. k-5). 25.65 (978-1-59679-225-8(6)) Spotlight.

M N O

—The Legend of Sleepy Hollow. Flint, Russ, illus. 2004. 64p. (J). (gr. 4-8). reprint ed. 17.00 (978-0-7567-8304-4(6)) DIANE Publishing Co.

—The Legend of Sleepy Hollow & Other Stories. 1999. (Penguin Classics Ser.). (Illus.). 368p. (gr. 12). pap. 8.95 (978-0-14-043769-0(X) , Penguin Classics) Penguin Group (USA) Inc.

—The Legend of Sleepy Hollow & Other Tales. Marshall, Michael J., ed. 1999. (Core Classics Ser.: Vol. 7). (Illus.). 132p. (J). (gr. 4-6). pap. 6.95 (978-1-890517-14-4(3)) Core Knowledge Foundation.

—The Legend of Sleepy Hollow & Rip Van Winkle. Marcos, Pablo, illus. 2002. (Great Illustrated Classics Ser.). 240p. (J). (gr. 3-8). 21.35 (978-1-57765-819-1(1) , ABDO & Daughters) ABDO Publishing Co.

—Rip Van Winkle. Meyerowitz, Rick, illus. 2005. (Rabbit Ears-A Classic Tale Ser.). 40p. (J). (gr. k-5). 25.65 (978-1-59197-770-4(3)) Spotlight.

Irving, Washington & Busch, Jeffrey. Rip Van Winkle. (Classics Illustrated Ser.). (Illus.). 52p. (YA). pap. 4.95 (978-1-57209-009-5(X)) Classics International Entertainment, Inc.

Irving, Washington & Moses, Will. Rip Van Winkle. 1999. (Illus.). 1p. (J). (ps-3). 17.99 (978-0-399-23152-0(8) , Philomel) Penguin Group (USA) Inc.

Jocelyn, Marthe. Earthly Astonishments. 2003. (gr. 3-6). lib. bdg. 16.40 (978-0-613-77300-3(4)) Tandem Library Bks.

Kerr, M. E. Your Eyes in Stars. 2006. 240p. (J). lib. bdg. 16.89 (978-0-06-075683-3(7)); (YA). 15.99 (978-0-06-075682-6(9)) HarperCollins Pubs.

Kimmel, Eric A. Rip Van Winkle's Return. Fisher, Leonard Everett, illus. 2007. 32p. (J). (gr. k-4). 17.00 (978-0-374-36308-6(0)) Farrar, Straus & Giroux.

Lakin, Patricia. Subway Sonata. Maione, Heather Harms, illus. 2001. 32p. (J). (gr. k-4). lib. bdg. (978-0-7613-1464-6(4) , Millbrook Pr.) Lerner Publishing Group.

Leppard, Lois Gladys. Mandie & the New York Secret. 2002. (gr. 3-6). lib. bdg. 13.00 (978-0-613-67463-8(4)) Tandem Library Bks.

Lesczynski, Jim. The Walton Street Tycoons. 2007. 269p. (YA). pap. 9.95 (*978-0-9791283-0-1(7)) East River Pr.

Lin, Grace. The Year of the Rat. rev. ed. 2008. 208p. (J). (gr. 3-7). 14.99 (*978-0-316-11426-4(X)) Little, Brown Bks. for Young Readers.

Littman, Sarah. Confessions of a Closet Catholic. McClelland, Charles E. & Scher, Steven P., eds. 2005. 176p. (J). (gr. 5-8). 15.99 (978-0-525-47365-7(3) , Dutton Juvenile) Penguin Group (USA) Inc.

Lourie, Peter. The Lost Treasure of Captain Kidd. 2003. (Illus.). 96p. (YA). (gr. 4-6). pap. 9.95 (978-1-56397-851-7(2)) Boyds Mills Pr.

Mapp, Edward. Wednesday at Weeksville. Potter, Nigel, illus. 2005. 27p. (J). per. 14.95 (978-1-59453-784-4(4) , Bookman Publishing) Airleaf Publishing & Bookselling.

Mason, Janet. The Legend of Sleepy Hollow. 2002. (Scholastic Junior Classics Ser.). 80p. (J). pap. 3.99 (978-0-439-22510-6(8)) Scholastic, Inc.

Mazer, Norma Fox. The Missing Girl. 2008. 288p. (J). 16.99 (*978-0-06-623776-3(9)); lib. bdg. 17.89 (*978-0-06-623777-0(7)) HarperCollins Pubs. (HarperTeen).

—Ten Ways to Make My Sister Disappear. 2007. (J). (*978-0-439-83984-6(X)); 160p. (gr. 4-7). pap. 16.99 (*978-0-439-83983-9(1)) Scholastic, Inc. (Levine, Arthur A. Bks.).

Mebus, Scott. Gods of Manhattan: the Hidden Light: The Hidden Light. 2008. 272p. (YA). (gr. 5). 17.99 (*978-0-525-47955-0(4) , Dutton Juvenile) Penguin Group (USA) Inc.

Michaels, Jamie. Kiss My Book. 2007. 288p. (YA). (gr. 7). pap. 7.99 (*978-0-385-73499-8(9)); lib. bdg. 10.99 (*978-0-385-90493-3(2)) Random Hse. Children's Bks. (Delacorte Bks. for Young Readers).

Minter, J. The Sweetest Thing: An Inside Girl Novel. 2007. (Insiders Novel Ser.). 224p. (J). (gr. 7 up). pap. 8.95 (*978-1-59990-087-2(4) , Bloomsbury Children) Bloomsbury Publishing.

Moses, Will. Legend of Sleepy Hollow. 1999. (gr. k-3). lib. bdg. 15.30 (978-0-613-19385-6(7)) Tandem Library Bks.

Moses, Will & Irving, Washington. The Legend of Sleepy Hollow. 1999. (Illus.). 48p. (J). (gr. 4-7). pap. 6.99 (978-0-698-11648-1(8) , Putnam Juvenile) Penguin Group (USA) Inc.

Paratore, Coleen. Mack McGinn's Big Win. 2007. 192p. (J). (gr. 4-7). 15.99 (*978-1-4169-1613-0(X) , Simon & Schuster Children's Publishing) Simon & Schuster Children's Publishing.

Petrie, Lettie A. Let Me Tell You About "Minnie the Mule & the Erie Canal" Petrie, Beth L., illus. 2001. (Erie Canal Ser.). (YA). (gr. 5-10). pap. 9.95 (978-0-9711638-0-5(4)) Petrie Pr.

Ray, Mary Lyn. The Basket Moon. Cooney, Barbara, illus. 1999. 32p. (J). (ps-3). 16.99 (978-0-316-73521-6(3)) Little Brown & Co.

Rizzo, Kay D. Old Friends & New. 2003. 96p. (J). (978-0-8163-1975-6(8)) Pacific Pr. Publishing Assn.

Rosenbloom, Fiona. You Are So Not Invited to My Bat Mitzvah! 2005. 208p. (gr. 7-17). 15.99 (978-0-7868-5616-9(5)) Hyperion Pr.

Roy, Ron. The Runaway Racehorse. Gurney, John Steven, illus. 2002. (A to Z Mysteries Ser.: No. 18). 96p. (J). (gr. 2-5). 11.99 (978-0-375-91367-9(X)); pap. 3.99 (978-0-375-81367-2(5)) Random Hse. Children's Bks. (Random Hse. Bks. for Young Readers).

Samantha's New York Adventure. 1998. (Illus.). 2p. (J). (ps-1). 15.00 (978-1-888074-88-8(4)) Pockets of Learning.

Savage, Derek. Cool Cat Goes to New York. Bustamante, Denny, illus. 2001. (Cool Cat Ser.: Vol. 4). 32p. (J). pap. 9.95 (978-0-9673000-6-1(1)) Savage Bks.

Shusterman, Neal. Downsiders. l.t. ed. 2000. 336p. (YA). (gr. 6-12). lib. bdg. 29.95 (978-1-58118-071-8(3)) LRS.

—Downsiders. 2001. 256p. (YA). (gr. 8-12). mass mkt. 5.99 (978-0-689-83969-6(3) , Simon Pulse) Simon & Schuster Children's Publishing.

Skolsky, Mindy Warshaw. You're the Best Hannah! 2000. (978-0-606-18733-6(2)) Tandem Library Bks.

Staub, Wendy Corsi. Lily Dale: Awakening. 2007. 240p. (YA). (gr. 7 up). 15.95 (*978-0-8027-9654-7(0)) Walker & Co.

Stilton, Geronimo. Field Trip to Niagara Falls. Keys, Larry et al, illus. 2005. (Geronimo Stilton Ser.: No. 24). 121p. (J). lib. bdg. 18.46 (*978-1-4242-0293-5(0)) Fitzgerald Bks.

—Field Trip to Niagara Falls. 2006. (Geronimo Stilton Ser.: No. 24). 128p. (J). pap. 6.99 (978-0-439-69146-8(X) , Scholastic Paperbacks) Scholastic, Inc.

Strobeck, Katherine M. The Fort in the Wilderness. Lamb, Emerson, illus. 1998. 86p. (J). (gr. 4-12). reprint ed. pap. 12.50 (978-0-925168-62-7(9)) North Country Bks., Inc.

Sweetzer, Anna Leah, et al. Treason Stops at Oyster Bay. 1999. (Mysteries in Time Ser.: Vol. 7). (Illus.). 90p. (J). (gr. 3-7). lib. bdg. 14.95 (978-1-893110-03-8(6)) Silver Moon Pr.

Taylor, Gaylia. George Crum & the Saratoga Chip. Morrison, Frank, illus. 2006. 32p. (J). (gr. 1-5). 16.95 (978-1-58430-255-1(0)) Lee & Low Bks., Inc.

Tocher, Timothy. Long Shot. 2001. (J). 137p. (978-0-88166-395-2(6)); 144p. pap. 4.95 (978-0-689-84331-0(3)) Meadowbrook Pr.

Urban, Betsy. Waiting for Deliverance. 2000. (Illus.). iv, 186p. (J). (gr. 7-12). pap. 17.95 (978-0-531-30310-8(1) , Orchard Bks.) Scholastic, Inc.

Vande Velde, Vivian. There's a Dead Person Following My Sister Around. 2001. 160p. (J). pap. 5.99 (978-0-14-131281-1(5) , Puffin) Penguin Group (USA) Inc.

—There's a Dead Person Following My Sister Around. 2001. (gr. 5-8). lib. bdg. 13.00 (978-0-613-43899-5(X)) Tandem Library Bks.

von Ziegesar, Cecily. The It Girl, No. 1. 2005. (It Girl Ser.: No. 1). 272p. (J). (gr. 7-17). pap. 9.99 (978-0-316-01185-3(1) , Poppy) Little, Brown Bks. for Young Readers.

—The It Girl Collection. 2006. (It Girl Ser.). (YA). (gr. 10-17). pap. 29.99 (978-0-316-02068-8(0) , Poppy) Little, Brown Bks. for Young Readers.

—Notorious. 2nd ed. 2006. (It Girl Ser.: No. 2). 288p. (J). (gr. 7-17). pap. 9.99 (978-0-316-01186-0(X) , Poppy) Little, Brown Bks. for Young Readers.

—Reckless. 2006. (It Girl Ser.: No. 3). 288p. (J). (gr. 7-17). pap. 9.99 (978-0-316-01187-7(8) , Poppy) Little, Brown Bks. for Young Readers.

Wax, Wendy. Empire Dreams. Doney, Todd, illus. 2000. (Adventures in America Ser.). 96p. (J). (gr. 4-7). lib. bdg. 14.95 (978-1-893110-19-9(2)) Silver Moon Pr.

Wilder, Laura Ingalls. Farmer Boy. Williams, Garth, illus. 2004. (Little House Ser.). 384p. (J). pap. 8.99 (978-0-06-058182-4(4) , Harper Trophy) HarperCollins Pubs.

—Farmer Boy. Williams, Garth, illus. l.t. ed. 2000. (Little House Ser.). 400p. (J). (gr. 3-6). lib. bdg. 33.95 (978-1-58118-079-4(9) , 24071) LRS.

Winfield, Arthur M. Putnam Hall Champions or Bound to Win Ou. 2006. pap. 28.95 (*978-1-4286-2346-0(9)) Kessinger Publishing, LLC.

NEW YORK (STATE)—HISTORY

Ashby, Ruth. Boss Tweed: And Tammany Hall. 2002. (Notorious Americans & Their Times Ser.). (Illus.). 112p. (YA). (gr. 5 up). 27.45 (978-1-56711-252-8(8) , Blackbirch Pr., Inc.) Thomson Gale.

Ball, Jackie & Behrens, Kristen. Nueva York. Porras, Carlos & D'Andrea, Patricia, trs. 2003. (World Almanac Biblioteca de los Estados). (SPA., Illus.). 48p. (J). (gr. 5 up). lib. bdg. 30.00 (978-0-8368-5546-3(9) , World Almanac Library) Stevens, Gareth Inc.

Banks, Joan. Peter Stuyvesant. (Colonial Leaders Ser.). (Illus.). 80p. (gr. 3 up). 2000. (YA). 27.50 (978-0-7910-5346-1(6)); 1999. (J). pap. (978-0-7910-5689-9(9)) Facts On File, Inc. (Chelsea Hse.).

—Peter Stuyvesant: Dutch Military Leader. 2000. (gr. 5-8). lib. bdg. 17.60 (978-0-613-43365-5(3)) Tandem Library Bks.

The Battle of Valcour Bay. 2003. (Triangle Histories of the American Revolution Ser.). (Illus.). 32p. (J). 22.45 (978-1-56711-778-3(3) , Blackbirch Pr., Inc.) Thomson Gale.

Bial, Raymond. Tenement: Immigrant Life on the Lower East Side. Bial, Raymond, illus. 2002. (Illus.). 48p. (J). (gr. 4-6). tchr. ed. 16.00 (978-0-618-13849-4(8)) Houghton Mifflin Co. Trade & Reference Div.

Bolden, Tonya. Maritcha: A Nineteenth-Century American Girl. 2005. (Illus.). 48p. (J). (gr. k-4). 17.95 (978-0-8109-5045-0(6)) Abrams, Harry N. , Inc.

Bowman-Kruhm, Mary. Fun Facts & Games: New York. Harris, Phyllis, illus. 2000. (Fun Facts & Games Activity Book Ser.). 64p. (J). (gr. 1-5). pap. 5.95 (978-1-892920-49-2(2)) GHB Publishers, LLC.

Bruun, Erik. New York. Peterson, Rick, illus. 2001. 48p. (J). (gr. 4-7). 9.95 (978-1-57912-169-3(1) , 81169) Black Dog & Leventhal Pubs., Inc.

Doherty, Craig A. & Doherty, Katherine M. New York, 13 vols. 2005. (Thirteen Colonies Ser.). (Illus.). 160p. (J). (gr. 4-9). 35.00 (978-0-8160-5410-7(X)) Facts On File, Inc.

Flanagan, Alice K. The Orphan Trains. 2006. (We the People Ser.). (Illus.). 48p. (J). (gr. 4-6). 23.93 (978-0-7565-1635-2(8)) Compass Point Bks.

Flynn, Andy. New York State's Mountain Heritage: Adirondack Attic 2. 2005. (Illus.). 240p. per. 18.00 (978-0-9754007-1-5(1)) Hungry Bear Publishing.

—New York State's Mountain Heritage Vol. 1: Adirondack Attic 1. 2004. (Illus.). 184p. per. 16.95 (978-0-9754007-0-8(3)) Hungry Bear Publishing.

Freeman, Stan, text. The Natural History of New York. 2002. (Illus.). 64p. (J). per. 9.95 (978-0-9636814-5-4(1)) Hampshire Hse. Publishing.

Hintz, Martin. The New York Colony. 2005. (Fact Finders Ser.). (Illus.). 32p. (J). (ps-7). lib. bdg. 22.60 (978-0-7368-2679-2(3)) Capstone Pr., Inc.

Italia, Bob. The New York Colony. 2001. (Colonies Ser.). (Illus.). 32p. (J). (gr. k-6). lib. bdg. 22.78 (978-1-57765-589-3(3) , Checkerboard Library) ABDO Publishing Co.

Kallen, Stuart A. & Boekhoff, P. M. New York. 2001. (Seeds of a Nation Ser.). (Illus.). 48p. (J). (gr. 3-5). (978-0-7377-0759-5(3) , LML00902-17870, Kidhaven) Thomson Gale.

Krizner, L. J. & Sita, Lisa. Peter Stuyvesant: New Amsterdam & the Origins of New York. 2005. (Library of American Lives & Times). (Illus.). 112p. (J). (gr. 4-8). lib. bdg. 31.95 (978-0-8239-5732-3(2)) Rosen Publishing Group, Inc., The.

Kupperberg, Paul. A Primary Source History of the Colony of New York. 2005. (Primary Sources of the Thirteen Colonies & the Lost Colony Ser.). (Illus.). 64p. (J). (gr. 3-7). pap. 14.60 (978-1-4042-0677-9(9)); (YA). (gr. 5-8). lib. bdg. 29.25 (978-1-4042-0431-7(8)) Rosen Publishing Group, Inc., The.

Marsh, Carole. My First Book. 2004. (New York Experience! Ser.). 32p. (J). (gr. k-4). pap. 7.95 (978-0-635-00160-3(8)) Gallopade International.

—New York History Projects: 30 Cool, Activities, Crafts, Experiments & More for Kids to Do to Learn about Your State! 2003. (New York Experience Ser.). 32p. (gr. k-5). pap. 5.95 (978-0-635-01801-4(2) , Marsh, Carole Bks.) Gallopade International.

—New York Millionaire. 2001. (GameBook Ser.). 32p. (J). (gr. 3-8). pap., act. bk. ed. 9.95 (978-0-635-00080-4(6)) Gallopade International.

—New York Survivor. 2001. (GameBook Ser.). 32p. (J). (gr. 3-8). pap., act. bk. ed. 9.95 (978-0-635-00553-3(0)) Gallopade International.

—New York Wheel of Fortune. 2001. (GameBook Ser.). 32p. (J). (gr. 3-8). pap., act. bk. ed. 9.95 (978-0-7933-9680-1(8)) Gallopade International.

—Wheel of Fortune. 2001. (New York Experience! Ser.). (J). lib. bdg. 29.95 (978-0-7933-9681-8(6)) Gallopade International.

—Who Wants to Be a Millionaire? 2001. (Carole Marsh New York Bks.). (J). lib. bdg. 29.95 (978-0-635-00081-1(4)) Gallopade International.

McAuliffe, Emily. New York: Facts & Symbols. 1998. (States & Their Symbols Ser.). 24p. (J). lib. bdg. 14.00 (978-0-531-11552-7(6) , Watts, Franklin) Scholastic Library Publishing.

McNeese, Tim. New Amsterdam. 2007. (Colonial Settlements in America Ser.). 112p. (J). (gr. 5-8). 30.00 (*978-0-7910-9334-4(4) , Chelsea Hse.) Facts On File, Inc.

Mezzanotte, Jim. New York. 2005. (Portraits of the States Ser.). (Illus.). 32p. (J). pap. (978-0-8368-4649-2(4)) Stevens, Gareth Inc.

Mis, Melody S. The Colony of New York: A Primary Source History. 2007. (Primary Source Library of the Thirteen Colonies & the Lost Colony). (Illus.). 24p. (J). lib. bdg. (978-1-4042-3432-1(2) , PowerKids Pr.) Rosen Publishing Group, Inc., The.

Morris, Ann. Grandma Esther Remembers: A Jewish-American Family Story. Linenthal, Peter, illus. 2002. (What Was It Like, Grandma? Ser.). 32p. (gr. k-3). lib. bdg. 22.90 (978-0-7613-2318-1(X) , Millbrook Pr.) Lerner Publishing Group.

Shaw, Maura D. Owl's Journey: Four Centuries of an American County. Tantillo, Joe, illus. 2000. 152p. (J). (gr. 4-7). reprint ed. pap. 9.95 (978-1-885482-07-5(8)) Shawangunk Pr., Inc.

Stevens, B. C. Hinman Hollow Road Dust. 2002. 130p. (J). (gr. 4 up). per. 8.95 (978-0-9677938-5-6(8)) Country Bumpkin Pubns.

Steward, Mark. All Around New York: Regions & Resources. 2003. (Heinemann State Studies). (Illus.). 48p. (J). (gr. 3-5). lib. bdg. (978-1-4034-0352-0(X)) Heinemann Library.

—New York History. 2003. (Heinemann State Studies). (Illus.). 48p. (J). (gr. 3-5). lib. bdg. (978-1-4034-0353-7(8)) Heinemann Library.

—People of New York. 2003. (Heinemann State Studies). (Illus.). 48p. (J). (gr. 3-5). lib. bdg. (978-1-4034-0355-1(4)) Heinemann Library.

—Uniquely New York. 2003. (Heinemann State Studies). (Illus.). 48p. (J). (gr. 3-5). lib. bdg. (978-1-4034-0357-5(0)) Heinemann Library.

Stewart, Mark. New York History. 2003. (Illus.). 48p. (J). 8.50 (978-1-4034-0575-3(1)) Heinemann Library.

—New York History. 2003. (gr. 3-6). lib. bdg. 17.05 (978-0-613-60974-6(3)) Tandem Library Bks.

Thompson, Gare. A Suburban Community of the 1950s. 2002. (Reading Expeditions Ser.). (Illus.). 24p. (J). pap. (978-0-7922-8691-2(X)) National Geographic Society.

Whitehurst, Susan. The Colony of New York. 2000. (Library of the Thirteen Colonies & the Lost Colony). (Illus.). 24p. (J). (gr. 3). lib. bdg. 19.95 (978-0-8239-5478-0(1) , PowerKids Pr.) Rosen Publishing Group, Inc., The.

Wiener, Roberta & Arnold, James R. New York. 2004. (Thirteen Colonies Ser.). (Illus.). 64p. (J). 28.56 (978-0-7398-6884-3(5)); 9.50 (978-1-4109-0308-2(7)) Harcourt Schl. Pubs.

Wood, Adam. New York. 2001. (Thirteen Colonies Ser.). (Illus.). 104p. (J). (gr. 4-12). lib. bdg. 29.95 (978-1-56006-992-8(9) , LML00902-179004, Lucent Bks.) Thomson Gale.

Worth, Richard. Harlem Renaissance: An Explosion of African-American Culture. 2008. (J). (*978-0-7660-2907-1(7)) Enslow Pubs., Inc.

NEW YORK (STATE)—HISTORY—FICTION

Alger, Horatio. Hector's Inheritance: Or, The Boys of Smith Institute. 2006. pap. (*978-1-4065-0708-9(3)) Dodo Pr.

—Hector's Inheritance: Or, The Boys of Smith Institute. unabr. ed. 2002. (Polyglot Press Alger Ser.). (Illus.). (J). pap. 17.95 (978-1-4115-0004-4(0)) Polyglot Pr., Inc.

Alger, Horatio. Herbert Carter's Legacy. 2006. pap. (*978-1-4065-0710-2(5)) Dodo Pr.

Alger Jr. Horatio Staff. Hector's Inheritance. rev. ed. 2006. 276p. 28.95 (978-1-4218-1758-3(6)); pap. 13.95 (978-1-4218-1858-0(2)) 1st World Publishing, Inc. (1st World Library - Literary Society).

Auch, M. J. One-Handed Catch. 2006. 256p. (J). 16.95 (978-0-8050-7900-5(9) , Holt, Henry & Co. Bks. For Young Readers) Holt, Henry & Co.

Cohen, Nancy Lipson. Exploring Orange: Adventures in Orange County, New York. 2000. (Illus.). 62p. (J). (gr. 3-6). 9.99 (978-0-88092-556-3(6)) Royal Fireworks Publishing Co.

Donnelly, Jennifer. A Northern Light. (YA). 2003. (Illus.). 400p. (gr. 9 up). 17.00 (978-0-15-216705-9(6)); 2004. 408p. reprint ed. pap. 8.95 (978-0-15-205310-9(7) , Harcourt Paperbacks) Harcourt Children's Bks.

Falk, Elizabeth Sullivan. Lettie's North Star. Wolf, Elizabeth, illus. 2006. (J). (978-1-59336-694-0(9)) Mondo Publishing.

Fletcher, Ralph. The One O'Clock Chop. 2007. 192p. (J). (gr. 5-11). 16.95 (*978-0-8050-8143-5(7) , Holt, Henry & Co. Bks. For Young Readers) Holt, Henry & Co.

Goodman, Joan Elizabeth. Hope's Crossing. 1998. (Illus.). 224p. (J). (gr. 4-6). tchr. ed. 16.00 (978-0-395-86195-0(0)) Houghton Mifflin Co. Trade & Reference Div.

—Hope's Crossing. 1999. (Illus.). 224p. (J). (gr. 3-7). pap. 6.99 (978-0-698-11807-2(3) , Putnam Juvenile) Penguin Group (USA) Inc.

—Hope's Crossing. 1999. (J). 12.64 (978-0-606-19068-8(6)); (gr. 3-6). lib. bdg. 14.15 (978-0-613-21719-4(5)) Tandem Library Bks.

Kerr, M. E. Your Eyes in Stars. 2007. 240p. (J). (gr. 7 up). pap. 6.99 (*978-0-06-075684-0(5) , HarperTeen) HarperCollins Pubs.

Kirkpatrick, Katherine. Redcoats & Petticoats. Himler, Ronald, illus. 1999. 32p. (J). (gr. 4-6). tchr. ed. 16.95 (978-0-8234-1416-1(7)) Holiday Hse., Inc.

Martin, Ann M. Here Today. 2004. 320p. (J). (gr. 4-7). pap. 16.95 (978-0-439-57944-5(9) , Scholastic Pr.) Scholastic, Inc.

Monfredo, Miriam G. The Stalking Horse. 1999. (978-0-606-16386-6(7)) Tandem Library Bks.

Myers, Anna. Hoggee. 2004. 160p. (J). 16.95 (978-0-8027-8926-6(9)) Walker & Co.

Namioka, Lensey. An Ocean Apart, a World Away. 2003. (gr. 7-12). lib. bdg. 13.55 (978-0-613-72264-3(7)) Tandem Library Bks.

Neale, Cynthia. Hope in New York City: The Continuing Story of the Irish Dresser. 2007. (ENG.). 176p. (J). pap. 7.95 (*978-1-57249-387-2(9) , White Mane Kids) White Mane Publishing Co., Inc.

Quackenbush, Robert. Daughter of Liberty. 1999. (J). 11.79 (978-0-606-16661-4(0)) Tandem Library Bks.

Rinaldi, Ann. The Color of Fire. 2005. 208p. (gr. 5-17). 15.99 (978-0-7868-0938-7(8) , Jump at the Sun) Hyperion Bks. for Children.

Rizzo, Kay D. & Ferree, Dennis. The Not-So-Secret Mission. 2003. 96p. (J). (978-0-8163-1966-4(9)) Pacific Pr. Publishing Assn.

Thomas, Peggy. Joshua & the Giant Frog. 2005. (Illus.). 32p. (J). 15.95 (978-1-58980-267-4(5)) Pelican Publishing Co., Inc.

Walvoord, Linda. Rosetta, Rosetts, Sit by Me! Velasquez, Eric, illus. 2004. 80p. (J). 14.95 (978-0-7614-5171-6(4)) Cavendish, Marshall Corp.

Watts, Leander. Stonecutter. 2006. 182p. (J). (gr. 5-9). reprint ed. pap. 7.99 (978-0-618-60577-4(0) , Graphia) Houghton Mifflin Co. Trade & Reference Div.

—Ten Thousand Charms. 2005. 240p. (YA). (gr. 5). 16.00 (978-0-618-44897-5(7)) Houghton Mifflin Co. Trade & Reference Div.

NEW YORK (STATE)—POLITICS AND GOVERNMENT

Powell, Phelan. John Jay: First Chief Justice of the Supreme Court. 2001. (gr. 5-8). lib. bdg. 17.60 (978-0-613-32726-8(8)) Tandem Library Bks.

White, Casey. John Jay. 2005. (Library of American Thinkers). (Illus.). 112p. (J). (978-1-4042-0507-9(1)) Rosen Publishing Group, Inc., The.

NEW YORK GIANTS (FOOTBALL TEAM)

Goodman, Michael E. The History of the New York Giants. 2004. (NFL Today Ser.). (Illus.). 32p. (J). 18.95 (978-1-58341-306-7(5) , Creative Education) Creative Co., The.

Leboutillier, Nate. New York Giants. 2005. (Super Bowl Champions Ser.). (Illus.). 24p. (gr. 1-4). 16.95 (978-1-58341-387-6(1) , Creative Education) Creative Co., The.

New York Giants. New York Giants. CWC Sports Inc., ed. 1998. (NFL Team Yearbooks Ser.). (J). (gr. 1-12). pap. 9.99 (978-1-891613-09-8(X)) Everett Sports Publishing & Marketing.

Stewart, Mark & Aikens, Jason. The New York Giants. 2008. (J). (*978-1-59953-133-5(X)) Norwood Hse. Pr.

NEW YORK JETS (FOOTBALL TEAM)

Goodman, Michael E. The History of the New York Jets. 2004. (NFL Today Ser.). (Illus.). 32p. 18.95 (978-1-58341-307-4(3) , Creative Education) Creative Co., The.

Nelson, Julie. New York Jets. 3rd rev. ed. 2000. (Pro Football Today Ser.). (Illus.). 32p. (J). lib. bdg. 22.60 (978-1-58341-053-0(8) , Creative Education) Creative Co., The.

New York Jets. New York Jets. CWC Sports Inc., ed. 1998. (NFL Team Yearbooks Ser.). (J). (gr. 1-12). pap. 9.99 (978-1-891613-17-3(0)) Everett Sports Publishing & Marketing.

NEW YORK METS (BASEBALL TEAM)

Epstein, Brad M. New York Mets 101: My first Team-board-book. l.t. ed. 2007. (101—My First Text-Board Books). (Illus.). 22p. (J). bds. 10.95 ***(978-1-932530-85-8(1)*** , 101 Bk.) Michaelson Entertainment.

Goodman, Michael E. The History of the New York Mets. 1998. (Baseball, the Great American Game Ser.). (Illus.). 32p. (YA). (gr. 3-12). pap. 21.30 (978-0-88682-917-9(8) , Creative Education) Creative Co., The.

—New York Mets. 2002. 32p. (J). pap. 5.95 (978-0-89812-350-0(X) , Creative Paperbacks); (Illus.). (978-1-58341-216-9(6)) Creative Co., The.

Goodman, Michael E. The Story of the New York Mets. 2007. ***(978-1-58341-494-1(0)*** , Creative Education) Creative Co., The.

Noble, Marty. Mike Piazza: Mike & the Mets. Rains, Rob, ed. 2003. (Superstar Ser.). (Illus.). 96p. (J). (gr. 4-7). pap. 4.95 (978-1-58261-051-1(7)) Sports Publishing, LLC.

Stewart, Mark. Los Mets de Nueva York. Kalmanovitz, Manuel, tr. from ENG. 2007. (Team Spirit Ser.). (SPA.). (J). lib. bdg. 25.27 ***(978-1-59953-103-8(8))*** Norwood Hse. Pr.

Stewart, Mark. New York Mets. 2006. (Team Spirit Ser.). (Illus.). 48p. (J). lib. bdg. 25.27 (978-1-59953-061-1(9)) Norwood Hse. Pr.

NEW YORK STOCK EXCHANGE

Blumenthal, Karen. Six Days in October: The Stock Market Crash of 1929; A Wall Street Journal Book for Children. 2002. (Wall Street Journal Book Ser.). (Illus.). 160p. (J). (gr. 6 up). 17.95 (978-0-689-84276-4(7) , Atheneum) Simon & Schuster Children's Publishing.

Ingram, Scott. The Stock Market Crash of 1929. 2004. (Landmark Events in American History Ser.). (J). pap. 11.95 (978-0-8368-5425-1(X)); lib. bdg. 30.00 (978-0-8368-5397-1(0)) Stevens, Gareth Inc. (World Almanac Library).

Woolf, Alex. The Wall Street Crash. 2002. (Days That Shook the World Ser.). (Illus.). 48p. (J). lib. bdg. (978-0-7398-5237-8(X)) Raintree.

NEW YORK TIMES

Gold, Susan Dudley. The Pentagon Papers: National Security or the Right to Know. 2004. (Supreme Court Milestones Ser.). (Illus.). 144p. (J). 37.07 (978-0-7614-1843-6(1) , Benchmark Bks.) Cavendish, Marshall Corp.

NEW YORK YANKEES (BASEBALL TEAM)

Aretha, David. Power in Pinstripes[97]the New York Yankees. 2007. (Sensational Sports Teams Ser.). (Illus.). 128p. (J). lib. bdg. 33.27 (978-1-59845-044-6(1) , MyReportLinks.com Bks.) Enslow Pubs., Inc.

Boothroyd, Jennifer. Lou Gehrig: A Life of Dedication. 2008. (Pull Ahead Books-Biographies Ser.). (J). lib. bdg. 22.60 ***(978-0-8225-8587-9(1)*** , Lerner Pubns.) Lerner Publishing Group.

Christopher, Matt. The New York Yankees. 2008. 128p. (J). (gr. 3-7). pap. 4.99 ***(978-0-316-01115-0(0))*** Little, Brown Bks. for Young Readers.

Epstein, Brad M. New York Yankees 101: My first Team-board-book. l.t. ed. 2007. (101—My First Text-Board Books). (Illus.). 22p. (J). bds. 10.95 ***(978-1-932530-99-5(1)*** , 101 Bk.) Michaelson Entertainment.

Fischer, David. The Story of the New York Yankees. 2003. (Major League Baseball Ser.). (Illus.). 48p. pap. 3.99 (978-0-7894-9251-7(2)) Dorling Kindersley Publishing, Inc.

—Story of the New York Yankees. 2003. (gr. k-3). lib. bdg. 11.80 (978-0-613-62437-4(8)) Tandem Library Bks.

Fischer, David & Dorling Kindersley Publishing Staff. The Story of the New York Yankees. 2003. (Major League Baseball Ser.). (Illus.). 48p. (J). 12.99 (978-0-7894-9545-7(7)) Dorling Kindersley Publishing, Inc.

Gilbert, Thomas W. Damn Yankees: Casey, Yogi, Whitey & the Mick. 1998. (J). pap. 9.95 (978-0-531-15879-1(9) , Watts, Franklin) Scholastic Library Publishing.

Goodman, Michael E. New York Yankees. 2002. 32p. (J). pap. 5.95 (978-0-89812-351-7(8)); (Illus.). (978-1-58341-217-6(4) , Creative Education) Creative Co., The.

Goodman, Michael E. The Story of the New York Yankees. 2007. (J). ***(978-1-58341-495-8(9)*** , Creative Education) Creative Co., The.

Grabowski, John F. The New York Yankees. 2001. (Great Sports Teams Ser.). (Illus.). 88p. (YA). (gr. 4-12). 29.95 (978-1-56006-946-1(5) , GML12001-178221, Lucent Bks.) Thomson Gale.

Greenberg, Keith Elliot. Derek Jeter. 2005. (Sports Heroes & Legends Ser.). (Illus.). 106p. (J). (gr. 3-7). 27.93 (978-0-8225-3068-8(6) , Lerner Pubns.) Lerner Publishing Group.

Kernan, Kevin. Bernie Williams: Quiet Superstar. Rains, Rob, ed. 1999. (Superstar Ser.). (Illus.). 112p. (J). (gr. 4-7). per. 4.95 (978-1-58261-044-3(4)) Sports Publishing, LLC.

Klein, Fredrick C. For the Love of the Yankees: An A-to-Z Primer for Yankees Fans of All Ages. Anderson, Mark, illus. 2003. 48p. (J). 19.95 (978-1-57243-579-7(8)) Triumph Bks.

Marlin, John. Mickey Mantle. 2005. (Sports Heroes & Legends Ser.). (Illus.). 112p. (J). (gr. 6-12). lib. bdg. 27.93 (978-0-8225-1796-2(5)) Lerner Publishing Group.

O'Connell, Jack. Derek Jeter: The Yankee Kid. Rains, Rob, ed. 2003. (Super Star Ser.). 96p. (J). pap. 4.95 (978-1-58261-043-6(6)) Sports Publishing, LLC.

Pietrusza, David. The New York Yankees Baseball Team. 1998. (Great Sports Teams Ser.). (Illus.). 48p. (YA). (gr. 4-10). lib. bdg. 23.93 (978-0-7660-1018-5(X)) Enslow Pubs., Inc.

Potts, Steve. New York Yankees. 2001. (Championship Teams Ser.). (Illus.). (J). (978-1-58340-085-2(0)) Smart Apple Media.

Rambeck, Richard. The History of the New York Yankees. 1998. (Baseball, the Great American Game Ser.). (Illus.). 32p. (YA). (gr. 3-12). pap. 21.30 (978-0-88682-918-6(6) , Creative Education) Creative Co., The.

Rappoport, Ken. Super Sports Star Derek Jeter. 2004. (Super Sports Star Ser.). (Illus.). 48p. (J). lib. bdg. 23.93 (978-0-7660-2139-6(4)) Enslow Pubs., Inc.

Reis, Ronald A. Lou Gehrig. 2007. (Baseball Superstars Ser.). 136p. (J). (gr. 6-12). 30.00 ***(978-0-7910-9423-5(5)*** , Chelsea Hse.) Facts On File, Inc.

Shaughnessy, Dan. The Legend of the Curse of the Bambino. Payne, C. F., illus. 2005. 32p. (J). 16.95 (978-0-689-87235-8(6) , Simon & Schuster Children's Publishing) Simon & Schuster Children's Publishing.

Stewart, Mark. Derek Jeter: Substance & Style. 1999. (New Wave Ser.). (Illus.). 48p. (gr. 4 up). lib. bdg. 22.90 (978-0-7613-1516-2(0) , Millbrook Pr.) Lerner Publishing Group.

—The New York Yankees. 2006. (Team Spirit Ser.). (J). lib. bdg. 25.27 (978-1-59953-003-1(1)) Norwood Hse. Pr.

Stewart, Mark. New York Yankees. 2007. 48p. pap. 9.95 ***(978-1-60357-005-3(5))*** Norwood Hse. Pr.

Viola, Kevin. Lou Gehrig. (Sports Heroes & Legends Ser.). (J). 2005. (Illus.). 112p. (gr. 6-12). lib. bdg. 27.93 (978-0-8225-1794-8(9)); 2004. pap. 8.95 (978-0-8225-5311-3(2) , LernerSports) Lerner Publishing Group.

NEW YORK ZOOLOGICAL PARK

Zoehfeld, Kathleen W. Wild Lives: A History of People & Animals of the Bronx Zoo. Wildlife Conservation Society, illus. 2006. 96p. (J). (gr. 3-7). 18.95 (978-0-375-80630-8(X) , Knopf Bks. for Young Readers) Random Hse. Children's Bks.

NEW ZEALAND

Belcher, Angie. To Our Shores. 2004. (Illus.). 84p. (J). pap. (978-1-86948-682-2(X)) Reed Publishing (NZ), Ltd.

Boyde, A. Postcards From the Century: A Lifetime of Memories from New Zealand Women. Harrison, Joyce, ed. 1999. (Illus.). 204p. (YA). pap. 29.95 (978-1-86950-329-1(5)) HarperCollins Pubs. New Zealand NZL. *Dist:* Antipodes Bks. & Beyond.

Britton, Tamara L. New Zealand. 2004. (Countries Ser.). (Illus.). 40p. (J). (gr. k-6). lib. bdg. 22.78 (978-1-59197-294-5(9)) ABDO Publishing Co.

Clarke, Liane. Liane at Large: Observations of a Big Chick. 1999. 168p. (YA). pap. 24.95 (978-1-86950-328-4(7)) HarperCollins Pubs. New Zealand NZL. *Dist:* Antipodes Bks. & Beyond.

Di Piazza, Francesca. New Zealand in Pictures. 2nd ed. 2006. (Visual Geography Series, Second Ser.). (Illus.). 80p. (J). (gr. 3-7). lib. bdg. 27.93 (978-0-8225-2550-9(X)) Lerner Publishing Group.

Ercelawn, Ayesha. New Zealand. 2001. (Countries of the World Ser.). (Illus.). 96p. (J). (gr. 6 up). lib. bdg. 30.00 (978-0-8368-2332-5(X)) Stevens, Gareth Inc.

Gillespie, Carol Ann. New Zealand. (Modern World Nations Ser.). (J). (Illus.). 144p. pap. 30.00 (978-0-7910-7107-6(3)); 2005. 150p. 30.00 (978-0-7910-8708-4(5)) Facts On File, Inc. (Chelsea Hse.).

Griffiths, Jonathan. New Zealand. 1999. (Festivals of the World Ser.). (Illus.). 32p. (J). (gr. 3 up). lib. bdg. 24.67 (978-0-8368-2033-1(9)) Stevens, Gareth Inc.

Guile, Melanie. New Zealand. 2003. 32p. (J). lib. bdg. 25.70 (978-1-4109-0471-3(7)) Raintree.

Harcourt School Publishers Staff. New Zealand Beginnings. 3rd ed. 2002. (Horizons Ser.). (Illus.). (J). pap. 7.30 (978-0-15-333646-1(3)) Harcourt Schl. Pubs.

Hill, Valerie. New Zealand. 2002. (Ask about Asia Ser.). (Illus.). 48p. (J). (gr. 4 up). lib. bdg. (978-1-59084-207-2(3)) Mason Crest Pubs.

Lamet, Rosalie. The Alpine Oasis. 2001. 294p. (YA). 19.95 (978-1-56871-292-5(8)) Targum Pr., Inc.

Landau, Elaine. Australia & New Zealand. 2000. (True Bks.). (Illus.). 48p. (J). (gr. 3-5). pap. 6.95 (978-0-516-26573-5(3) , Children's Pr.) Scholastic Library Publishing.

—Australia & New Zealand. 1999. (gr. 3-6). lib. bdg. 15.25 (978-0-613-50269-6(8)) Tandem Library Bks.

Moritz, Patricia M. New Zealand. 2000. (Dropping in on Ser.). (Illus.). 32p. (J). (gr. 2-5). lib. bdg. 28.50 (978-1-55916-283-8(X)) Rourke Publishing, LLC.

Ryan, Patrick. Welcome to New Zealand. 2008. (Welcome to the World Ser.). 32p. (J). (gr. 1-5). 27.07 ***(978-1-59296-973-9(9))*** Child's World, Inc.

Schroeder, Holly. New Zealand ABCs: A Book about the People & Places of New Zealand. Wolf, Claudia, illus. 2004. (Country ABCs Ser.). 32p. (J). (gr. k-5). 23.93 (978-1-4048-0178-3(2) , 1229507) Picture Window Bks.

Shepherd, Donna Walsh. New Zealand. 2002. (Enchantment of the World, Second Ser.). (Illus.). 144p. (J). (gr. 5-9). 36.00 (978-0-516-21099-5(8) , Children's Pr.) Scholastic Library Publishing.

Smelt, Roselynn. New Zealand. 1998. (Cultures of the World Ser.). (Illus.). 128p. (gr. 5-12). lib. bdg. 37.07 (978-0-7614-0808-6(8) , Benchmark Bks.) Cavendish, Marshall Corp.

Yip, Dora & Ercelawn, Ayesha. Welcome to New Zealand. 2002. (Welcome to My Country Ser.). (Illus.). 48p. (J). (gr. 2 up). lib. bdg. 26.00 (978-0-8368-2532-9(2)) Stevens, Gareth Inc.

NEW ZEALAND—FICTION

Beck, Katie. The Moas. Thatch, Nancy R., ed. 1999. (Books for Students by Students). (Illus.). 29p. (J). (gr. 4-7). lib. bdg. 15.95 (978-0-933849-73-0(7)) Landmark Editions, Inc.

Boock, Paula. Dare Truth or Promise. 1999. 176p. (YA). (gr. 7-12). tchr. ed. 15.00 (978-0-395-97117-8(9)) Houghton Mifflin Co. Trade & Reference Div.

Brammer, Deb. Two Sides to Everything. 2003. (Illus.). 151p. (J). (978-1-59166-166-5(8)) Jones, Bob Univ. Pr.

Bugmann, Marlies. Golden Wings. 2005. (Green Heart Ser.). 216p. (J). pap. 12.99 (978-1-55410-283-9(9) , PO 00132) Zumaya Pubns. LLC.

Catran, Ken. Dawn Hawk. 96p. pap. (978-0-7344-0468-8(9) , Lothian Bks.) Hachette Livre Australia.

Cowley, Joy. Hunter. 2004. 176p. (YA). (gr. 5). 17.99 (978-0-399-24227-4(9) , Philomel) Penguin Group (USA) Inc.

—The Video Shop Sparrow. Bishop, Gavin, illus. 2003. 32p. (YA). (gr. k-2). 15.95 (978-1-56397-826-5(1)) Boyds Mills Pr.

Duder, Tessa. Tiggie Thompson All at Sea. 2001. 232p. (YA). pap. (978-0-14-131323-8(4) , Puffin) Penguin Group (USA) Inc.

Gee, Maurice. The Fire Raiser. 2007. 172p. (J). (gr. 4-6). pap. 6.95 ***(978-0-618-75041-2(X))*** Houghton Mifflin Co. Trade & Reference Div.

Hamilton, Elizabeth L. Passport to Courage. 2002. (Character-in-Action Ser.: No. 1). (Illus.). 384p. (YA). per. 19.95 (978-0-9713749-3-5(7) , Character-in-Action) Quiet Impact, Inc.

Hantz, Sara. The Second Virginity of Suzy Green. 2007. 264p. (J). (gr. 4-7). pap. 9.95 ***(978-0-7387-1139-3(X)*** , Flux) Llewellyn Pubns.

Hill, David. Take It Easy. 2000. (Illus.). (J). pap. 5.99 (978-0-14-130349-9(2) , Puffin) Penguin Group (USA) Inc.

Ihimaera, Witi. The Whale Rider. 2003. Orig. Title: Te Kaieke Tohora. 168p. (YA). (gr. 3-6). pap. 8.00 (978-0-15-205016-0(7) , Harcourt Paperbacks) Harcourt Children's Bks.

—Whale Rider. 2003. (gr. 5-8). lib. bdg. 16.45 (978-0-613-70660-5(9)) Tandem Library Bks.

Ireland, Kenneth. Noises in the Night. 2004. 126p. (J). 5.00 (978-1-84161-031-3(3)) Ravette Publishing, Ltd. GBR. *Dist:* Parkwest Pubns., Inc.

Mahy, Margaret. The Catalogue of the Universe. Hopes, illus. 2002. 192p. (YA). pap. 7.99 (978-0-689-85353-1(X) , Simon Pulse) Simon & Schuster Children's Publishing.

—The Catalogue of the Universe. 2002. (gr. 7-12). lib. bdg. 16.45 (978-0-613-57621-5(7)) Tandem Library Bks.

—The Great Piratical Rumbustification & the Librarian & the Robbers. Blake, Quentin, illus. 2000. 32p. (J). pap. 6.95 (978-1-56792-169-4(8)) Godine, David R. Pub.

Morgan, Clay. The Boy Who Spoke Dog: Return to Dog Island. 2007. 176p. (J). (gr. 4). 16.99 ***(978-0-525-47401-2(3)*** , Dutton Juvenile) Penguin Group (USA) Inc.

Stokoe, Julian & Chambers, Brent. Tamatoa & the Big Wind. 2000. (Illus.). (J). pap. 12.95 (978-1-86950-345-1(7)) HarperCollins Pubs. New Zealand NZL. *Dist:* Antipodes Bks. & Beyond.

Taylor, William. The Blue Lawn. 1999. (J). 17.75 (978-0-606-19431-0(2)) Tandem Library Bks.

Temple, Philip & Gaskin, Chris. The Legend of the Kea. rev. ed. 2000. (Illus.). 32p. (J). (gr. 1-5). pap. 9.95 (978-1-877135-33-0(X)) Longacre Pr. NZL. *Dist:* Pacific Island Bks.

—The Story of the Kakapo. rev. ed. 2000. (Illus.). 32p. (J). (gr. 1-5). pap. 9.95 (978-1-877135-34-7(8)) Longacre Pr. NZL. *Dist:* Pacific Island Bks.

West, Joyce. The Drovers Road Collection: Three New Zealand Adventures, 3 books under one cover. 2003. (Bethlehem Budget Bks.). (Illus.). 448p. (YA). pap. 16.95 (978-1-883937-69-0(8)) Bethlehem Bks.

Wolfe, Richard. Hell-Hole of the Pacific. 2005. (Illus.). 240p. (gr. 12). pap. 21.00 (978-0-14-301987 9(2) , Penguin Global) Penguin Group (USA) Inc.

NEWBERY, JOHN, 1713-1767

Roberts, Russell. John Newbery & the Story of the Newbery Medal. 2003. (Great Achiever Awards Ser.). (Illus.). 48p. (J). (gr. 4-8). lib. bdg. 29.95 (978-1-58415-201-9(X)) Mitchell Lane Pubs., Inc.

NEWBERY MEDAL BOOKS

Roberts, Russell. John Newbery & the Story of the Newbery Medal. 2003. (Great Achiever Awards Ser.). (Illus.). 48p. (J). (gr. 4-8). lib. bdg. 29.95 (978-1-58415-201-9(X)) Mitchell Lane Pubs., Inc.

NEWFOUNDLAND

see Newfoundland and Labrador

NEWFOUNDLAND AND LABRADOR

Beckett, Harry. Newfoundland & Labrador. 2003. (Eye on Canada Ser.). (Illus.). 32p. (J). pap. 7.95 (978-1-894705-03-5(3)) Weigl Pubs., Inc.

LeVert, Suzanne. Newfoundland. Sheppard, George, ed. 2000. (Canada in the Twenty First Century Ser.). (Illus.). (J). (gr. 8-12). 18.95 (978-0-7910-6065-0(9) , Chelsea Hse.) Facts On File, Inc.

Skirving, Janet. P Is for Puffin: A Newfoundland & Labrador Alphabet. Archibald, Odell, illus. rev. ed. 2006. 40p. (J). 18.95 (978-1-58536-287-5(5)) Sleeping Bear Pr.

NEWFOUNDLAND AND LABRADOR—FICTION

Alberts, Nancy Markham. Just One More? Butler, John, illus. 2007. 24p. (J). (ps). 14.95 ***(978-1-59354-195-8(3))*** Handprint Bks.

Browne, Susan Chalker. The Land of a Thousand Whales. 2006. (Illus.). 32p. pap. ***(978-1-897174-08-1(X))*** Creative Bk. Publishing.

Butler, Geoff. The Hangashore. Butler, Geoff, illus. 1998. (Illus.). 32p. (J). (gr. 3-7). 15.95 (978-0-88776-444-8(4)) Tundra Bks., Inc./Livres Toundra, Inc. CAN. *Dist:* Random Hse., Inc.

—The Killick: A Newfoundland Story. Butler, Geoff, illus. 1998. (Illus.). 32p. (J). (gr. 5-9). reprint ed. pap. 8.95 (978-0-88776-449-3(5)) Tundra Bks., Inc./Livres Toundra, Inc. CAN. *Dist:* Random Hse., Inc.

Choyce, Lesley. Refuge Cove. 2002. (Orca Soundings Ser.). 96p. (J). (gr. 7-12). pap. 7.95 (978-1-55143-246-5(3)) Orca Bk. Pubs. USA.

—Refuge Cove. 2002. (gr. 7-12). lib. bdg. 16.40 (978-0-613-62990-4(6)) Tandem Library Bks.

Dorion, Betty F. Bay Girl. 1999. (Illus.). 136p. (J). (gr. 3-7). pap. 5.95 (978-1-55050-132-2(1)) Coteau Bks. CAN. *Dist:* Fitzhenry & Whiteside, Ltd.

Gostick, Adrian R. Jessica's Search: The Secret of Ballycater Cove. 1998. (J). 1.99 (978-1-57345-436-0(2)) Deseret Bk. Co.

Harlow, Joan Hiatt. Star in the Storm. 160p. 2005. pap. 2.99 (978-1-4169-0530-1(8)); 2001. (gr. 3-7). mass mkt. 5.99 (978-0-689-84621-2(5)) Simon & Schuster Children's Publishing. (Aladdin).

—Star in the Storm. 2001. (978-0-606-22107-8(7)); (gr. 3-6). lib. bdg. 13.00 (978-0-613-53446-8(8)) Tandem Library Bks.

—Thunder from the Sea. 2004. (Illus.). 256p. (J). 16.99 (978-0-689-86403-2(5) , McElderry, Margaret K.) Simon & Schuster Children's Publishing.

Harlow, Joan Hiatt & Minor, Wendell. Star in the Storm. 2000. (Illus.). 160p. (J). (gr. 3-7). 16.00 (978-0-689-82905-5(1) , McElderry, Margaret K.) Simon & Schuster Children's Publishing.

Hyland, Hilary. The Wreck of the Ethie. 1999. (978-0-606-22861-9(6)) Tandem Library Bks.

—Wreck of the Ethie. 1999. (gr. 3-6). lib. bdg. 16.40 (978-0-613-23823-6(0)) Tandem Library Bks.

Katz, Welwyn W. Out of the Dark. 2001. 185p. (J). (gr. 4). pap. 5.95 (978-0-88899-262-8(9)) Groundwood Bks. CAN. *Dist:* Perseus Distribution.

McNaughton, Janet. Make or Break Spring. 1999. 192p. (YA). (gr. 7 up). pap. (978-1-895387-93-3(0)) Creative Bk. Publishing.

Reed, Don C. The Kraken. Hunt, Judith, illus. 2003. 224p. (YA). (gr. 5-9). pap. 7.95 (978-1-56397-693-3(5)) Boyds Mills Pr.

Walsh, Alice. Heroes of Isle aux Morts. ed. 2004. (J). (gr. k-3). spiral bd. (978-0-616-11138-3(X)); spiral bd. (978-0-616-11139-0(8)) Canadian National Institute for the Blind/Institut National Canadien pour les Aveugles.

—Heroes of Isle aux Morts. Butler, Geoff, illus. 2001. 32p. (J). (gr. 3-7). 17.95 (978-0-88776-501-8(7)) Tundra Bks., Inc./Livres Toundra, Inc. CAN. *Dist:* Random Hse., Inc.

NEWS BROADCASTS

see Radio Broadcasting; Television Broadcasting

NEWS PHOTOGRAPHY

see Photojournalism

NEWSBOYS

Burgan, Michael. The American Newsboy. 2006. (Illus.). 48p. (J). lib. bdg. (978-0-7565-2458-6(X)) Compass Point Bks.

NEWSPAPER WORK

see Journalism; Reporters and Reporting

NEWSPAPERS

see also Periodicals; Reporters and Reporting

Anderson, Catherine. Newspaper. 2004. (Field Trip! Ser.). (Illus.). 24p. (J). pap. 5.50 (978-1-4034-6169-8(4)); lib. bdg. 20.64 (978-1-4034-6163-6(5)) Heinemann Library.

Chambers, Catherine. Newspapers. 2001. (Behind Media Ser.). (Illus.). 48p. (J). (gr. 5-8). lib. bdg. 24.22 (978-1-58810-033-7(2)) Heinemann Library.

Christian, Sandra J. Newspaper Carriers. 2002. (Community Helpers Ser.). (Illus.). 92p. (J). (gr. 1-2). 18.60 (978-0-7368-1131-6(1) , Bridgestone Bks.) Capstone Pr., Inc.

Emmer, Rae. Periodico Escolar. 2004. (Actividades Escolares Ser.). (SPA & ENG., Illus.). 24p. (J). lib. bdg. 17.25 (978-0-8239-6901-2(0) , Buenas Letra) Rosen Publishing Group, Inc., The.

—School Newspaper. 2002. (Reading Power Ser.). (Illus.). 24p. (J). (gr. 1). lib. bdg. 17.25 (978-0-8239-5966-2(X) , PowerKids Pr.) Rosen Publishing Group, Inc., The.

Gish, Melissa. A Newspaper Publisher. 2003. 24p. (J). lib. bdg. 21.35 (978-1-58340-324-2(8)) Smart Apple Media.

Hamilton, John. Newspapers. 2005. (Straight to the Source Ser.). (Illus.). 32p. (J). (gr. k-6). lib. bdg. 22.78 (978-1-59197-547-2(6)) ABDO Publishing Co.

Harcourt School Publishers Staff. Extra! Extra! Level D: Library Edition. 2001. (Collections Ser.). (Illus.). (J). (gr. 6). 6.90 (978-0-15-314439-4(4)) Harcourt Schl. Pubs.

—Read All about It. 3rd ed. 2002. (Horizons Ser.). (Illus.). (J). pap. 7.30 (978-0-15-333555-6(6)); pap. 5.10 (978-0-15-327767-2(X)) Harcourt Schl. Pubs.

Howe, Katherine & Edelstein, Judith. In the News: A Unit for Investigating Newspapers. 2000. (J). per. (978-1-883055-38-7(5)) Dandy Lion Pubns.

Levin, Mark. Kids in Print: Publishing A School Newspaper. 2nd ed. 2004. 80p. (J). (gr. 3-9). pap. 15.00 (978-0-9676409-2-1(X)) Mind - Stretch.

Mattern, Joanne. Katharine Graham & 20th Century American Journalism. 2003. (Reading Power Ser.). (Illus.). 24p. (J). lib. bdg. 17.25 (978-0-8239-6500-7(7) , PowerKids Pr.) Rosen Publishing Group, Inc., The.

Oxlade, Chris. Newspapers. 2001. (Illus.). 32p. (J). (gr. 1-3). lib. bdg. 22.79 (978-1-58810-065-8(0)) Heinemann Library.

Pascual Marquina, Cira. Newspapers: A Project by Siemon Allen. 2000th ed. 2004. (Illus.). 60p. per. 20.00 (978-0-9749296-1-3(1)) Drake Univ., Anderson Gallery.

Pelusey, Michael & Pelusey, Jane. Newspapers (Media) 2005. (Media Ser.). (Illus.). 32p. (J). (ps-8). lib. bdg. 21.95 (978-0-7910-8800-5(6) , Chelsea Hse.) Facts On File, Inc.

Periodico Escolar, 6 Packs. (On Deck en Espanol Ser.). (SPA.). 24p. (gr. 4-5). 35.00 (978-0-7578-6402-5(3)) Rigby Education.

Petley, Julian. Newspapers & Magazines. 2003. (Media Wise Ser.). (Illus.). 64p. (J). lib. bdg. 28.50 (978-1-58340-258-0(6)) Smart Apple Media.

Shea, Kitty. Out & about at the Newspaper. Trover, Zachary, illus. 2005. (Field Trips Ser.). 24p. (J). (ps). lib. bdg. 23.93 (978-1-4048-1149-2(4)) Picture Window Bks.

Whitelaw, Nancy. Joseph Pulitzer: And the New York World. 2004. (Makers of the Media Ser.). (Illus.). 112p. (YA). (gr. 6-12). 21.95 (978-1-883846-44-2(7) , First Biographies) Reynolds, Morgan Inc.

—William Randolph Hearst & the American Century. rev. exp. ed. 2004. (Makers of the Media Ser.). (Illus.). 128p. (YA). (gr. 6-12). 23.95 (978-1-931798-35-8(4)) Reynolds, Morgan Inc.

NEWSPAPERS—FICTION

Alger Jr. Horatio Staff. Herbert Carter's Legacy. rev. ed. 2006. 264p. 28.95 (978-1-4218-1756-9(X)); pap. 13.95 (978-1-4218-1856-6(6)) 1st World Publishing, Inc. (1st World Library - Literary Society).

Banks, Steven. Stop the Presses! DePorter, Vince, illus. 2005. 22p. (J). lib. bdg. 15.00 (***978-1-4242-0973-6(0)***) Fitzgerald Bks.

Breault, Christie Merriman. Logan West, Printer's Devil. Archembault, Matthew, illus. 2006. 142p. (J). pap. (978-1-59336-762-6(7)) Mondo Publishing.

Brooks, Walter R. Freddy & the Bean Home News. Wiese, Kurt, illus. 2000. (Freddy Ser.). 230p. (J). (gr. 3-7). 23.95 (978-1-58567-081-9(2)) Overlook Pr., The.

Clements, Andrew. Head of the Class: Frindle; the Landry News; the Janitor's Boy. Selznick, Brian, illus. 2007. 416p. (J). 17.99 (***978-1-4169-4974-9(7)*** , Aladdin) Simon & Schuster Children's Publishing.

—The Landry News. 2000. (gr. 3-6). lib. bdg. 13.00 (978-0-613-30001-8(7)) Tandem Library Bks.

—El Periodico Landry. Selznick, Brian, illus. 2004. Tr. of Landry News. (SPA.). (YA). pap. 9.99 (978-84-241-7886-4(6)) Everest de Ediciones y Distribucion, S.L. ESP. *Dist:* Lectorum Pubns., Inc.

De Amicis, Edmundo. Corazon. 2000. (Coleccion "Clasicos Juveniles" Ser.).Tr. of Heart. (SPA., Illus.). 308p. (gr. 4-7). pap. 14.95 (978-1-58348-827-0(8)) iUniverse, Inc.

El diario de mis Abejas: Individual Title, 6 packs. (Literatura 2000 Ser.). (SPA.). (gr. 2-3). 33.00 (978-0-7635-1647-5(3)) Rigby Education.

Ellerbee, Linda. Ghoul Reporter Digs up Zombies! 2000. (Get Real Ser.: No. 5). 208p. (J). (gr. 3-7). 14.89 (978-0-06-028249-3(5)); No. 5. pap. 4.99 (978-0-06-440759-5(4) , Avon) HarperCollins Pubs.

—Girl Reporter Blows Lid off Town! 2000. (Get Real Ser.: No. 1). (Illus.). 208p. (J). (gr. 3-7). 14.89 (978-0-06-028245-5(2)) HarperCollins Pubs.

—Girl Reporter Blows Lid off Town! 2000. (Get Real Ser.: No. 1). (Illus.). (J). (978-0-606-18691-9(3)) Tandem Library Bks.

—Girl Reporter Rocks Polls! 2000. (Get Real Ser.: No. 6). 224p. (J). (gr. 3-7). 14.89 (978-0-06-028250-9(9)) HarperCollins Pubs.

—Girl Reporter Sinks School! 2000. (Get Real Ser.: No. 2). (Illus.). 176p. (J). (gr. 3-7). 14.89 (978-0-06-028246-2(0)) HarperCollins Pubs.

—Girl Reporter Snags Crush! 2000. (Get Real Ser.: No. 4). (Illus.). 229p. (J). (gr. 3-7). 14.89 (978-0-06-028248-6(7)) HarperCollins Pubs.

—Girl Reporter Snags Crush! 2000. (Get Real Ser.: No. 4). (Illus.). (J). (978-0-606-18902-6(5)) Tandem Library Bks.

—Girl Reporter Stuck in Jam! 2000. (Get Real Ser.: No. 3). (Illus.). 224p. (J). (gr. 3-7). 14.89 (978-0-06-028247-9(9)) HarperCollins Pubs.

—Girl Reporter Stuck in Jam! 2000. (gr. 3-6). lib. bdg. 12.40 (978-0-613-25334-5(5)); (Get Real Ser.: No. 3). (Illus.). (J). (978-0-606-18901-9(7)) Tandem Library Bks.

Elmore, Barbara. Saviors of the Bugle. 2003. 208p. (YA). per. 6.99 (978-0-9714941-0-7(X)) Mud Pie Pr.

Frampton, David. Beastie ABC. Frampton, David, illus. Date not set. (Illus.). 32p. (J). (ps-1). pap. 5.99 (978-0-06-443653-3(5)) HarperCollins Pubs.

—My Beastie Book of ABC. Frampton, David, illus. 2002. (Illus.). 32p. (J). (ps-1). 15.89 (978-0-06-028824-2(8)) HarperCollins Pubs.

Harcourt School Publishers Staff. The Other Side of the Story Below Level. 3rd ed. 2002. (Trophies Reading Program Ser.). (Illus.). pap. 5.10 (978-0-15-323405-7(9)) Harcourt Schl. Pubs.

Hawkins, Colin & Hawkins, Jacqui. Fairytale News. Hawkins, Colin & Hawkins, Jacqui, illus. 2004. (Illus.). 40p. (J). (ps-3). 15.99 (978-0-7636-2166-7(8)) Candlewick Pr.

Holland, Isabelle. Paperboy. 1999. 144p. (J). (gr. 7 up). tchr. ed. 16.95 (978-0-8234-1422-2(1)) Holiday Hse., Inc.

Hudson, Iris. Ask Mia. Sims, Blanche, illus. 2006. (Math Matters Ser.). 32p. (J). (gr. k-3). pap. 4.95 (978-1-57565-188-0(2)) Kane Pr., The.

Kroeger, Mary Kay. Paperboy. 2001. (gr. k-3). lib. bdg. 15.25 (978-0-613-34023-6(X)) Tandem Library Bks.

Martin, Ann M. Karen's Paper Route. 1998. (Baby-Sitters Little Sister Ser.: No. 97). (J). (gr. 3-7). (978-0-606-13173-5(6)) Tandem Library Bks.

Mazer, Anne. The Pen Is Mightier Than the Sword. 2001. (Amazing Days of Abby Hayes Ser.: No. 6). (gr. 3-6). lib. bdg. 12.40 (978-0-613-43865-0(5)) Tandem Library Bks.

Mercer, Sienna. Fangtastic! 2007. (My Sister the Vampire Ser.: No. 2). 208p. (J). (gr. 3-7). pap. 5.99 (***978-0-06-087115-4(6)*** , Harper Trophy) HarperCollins Pubs.

Naylor, Phyllis Reynolds. Boys Rock! 144p. (gr. 4-7). 2007. 5.50 (***978-0-440-41990-7(5)*** , Yearling); 2005. (J). 15.95 (978-0-385-73140-9(X) , Delacorte Bks. for Young Readers); 2005. (J). lib. bdg. 17.99 (978-0-385-90171-0(2) , Delacorte Bks. for Young Readers) Random Hse. Children's Bks.

Nelson, Blake. The New Rules of High School. 2004. 240p. (YA). reprint ed. pap. 6.99 (978-0-14-240242-9(7) , Puffin) Penguin Group (USA) Inc.

Nixon, Joan Lowery. Maria's Story, 1773. 2004. (J). (978-0-87935-227-1(2)) Colonial Williamsburg Foundation.

Pilkey, Dav. The Paperboy. Pilkey, Dav, illus. 1999. (Illus.). (J). (ps-k). lib. bdg. 15.25 (978-0-613-28998-6(6)) Tandem Library Bks.

Pratchett, Terry. The Truth. 2001. (gr. 5-8). lib. bdg. 15.30 (978-0-613-57290-3(4)) Tandem Library Bks.

Rylant, Cynthia. Some Good News, Bk. 4. 2001. (Cobble Street Cousins Ser.: No. 3). (Illus.). (J). (978-0-606-21115-4(2)) Tandem Library Bks.

Sandin, Joan. Coyote School News. Sandin, Joan, illus. rev. ed. 2003. (Illus.). 48p. (J). 17.95 (978-0-8050-6558-9(X) , Holt, Henry & Co. Bks. For Young Readers) Holt, Henry & Co.

Steedman, Scott & Steele, Philip. Aztec News: Invaders Flee City. Steele, Philip, illus. 2000. (News Ser.). (Illus.). 32p. (J). (gr. 4-8). pap. 6.99 (978-0-7636-0427-1(5)) Candlewick Pr.

Steele, Philip & Steedman, Scott. Egyptian News: Boy King Murdered? 2000. (History News Ser.). (Illus.). 32p. (J). (gr. 4-8). pap. 6.99 (978-0-7636-0423-3(2)) Candlewick Pr.

Stilton, Geronimo. Watch Your Whiskers, Stilton! 2005. (Geronimo Stilton Ser.: No. 17). (Illus.). 111p. (J). (978-1-4155-8205-3(X)) Scholastic, Inc.

—Watch Your Whiskers, Stilton! 2005. (Geronimo Stilton Ser.: No. 17). (Illus.). 111p. (J). (gr. 2-5). lib. bdg. 13.94 (978-0-606-33292-7(8)) Tandem Library Bks.

Tripp, Valerie. Meet Kit, an American Girl. 2000. (gr. 3-6). lib. bdg. 14.10 (978-0-613-28952-8(8)) Tandem Library Bks.

Winerip, Michael. Adam Canfield of the Slash. (Adam Canfield of the Slash Ser.). 336p. (J). (gr. 3-7). 2007. pap. 5.99 (978-0-7636-2794-2(1)); 2005. 15.99 (978-0-7636-2340-1(7)) Candlewick Pr.

NEWSPAPERS—HISTORY

Asirvatham, Sandy. Katharine Graham. 2001. (Women of Achievement Ser.). (J). pap. (978-0-7910-6311-8(9)); 112p. (YA). (gr. 7 up). 30.00 (978-0-7910-6310-1(0)) Facts On File, Inc. (Chelsea Hse.).

NEWTON, ISAAC, SIR, 1642-1727

Anderson, Margaret J. Isaac Newton: The Greatest Scientist of All Time. 2001. (Great Minds of Science Ser.). (Illus.). 128p. (YA). (gr. 4-10). pap. 10.95 (978-0-7660-1872-3(5)) Enslow Pubs., Inc.

Atkinson, Mary. Genius or Madman? Sir Isaac Newton. 2008. (Shockwave: Life Stories Ser.). 32p. (J). pap. 6.95 (***978-0-531-18840-8(X)*** , Children's Pr.) Scholastic Library Publishing.

Benchmark Education Staff. Newton & His Laws. 2005. 2.00 (***978-1-4108-4670-9(9)***) Benchmark Education Co.

Boerst, William J. Isaac Newton: Organizing the Universe. 2004. (Great Scientists Ser.). (Illus.). 144p. (YA). (gr. 6-12). 26.95 (978-1-931798-01-3(X)) Reynolds, Morgan Inc.

Brannon, Barbara. Discover Sir Isaac Newton. 2005. 39.00 (***978-1-4108-5127-7(3)***) Benchmark Education Co.

Chiang, Mona. Isaac Newton & His Laws of Motion. 2005. (Navigators Ser.). (J). pap. 44.00 (***978-1-4108-5089-8(7)***) Benchmark Education Co.

Funk, Tara. Newton & His Laws. 2005. 39.00 (***978-1-4108-4622-8(9)***) Benchmark Education Co.

Gianopoulos, Andrea. Isaac Newton & the Laws of Motion. 2007. 32p. (J). (978-0-7368-6847-1(X)) Capstone Pr., Inc.

Hakim, Joy. The Story of Science: Newton at the Center. 2005. (Smithsonian's Story of Science Ser.). (Illus.). 463p. (YA). (gr. 7 up). 24.95 (978-1-58834-161-7(5)) Smithsonian Institution Pr.

Kramer, Alan & Kramer, Candice. Isaac Newton: The World in Motion. 2005. 40.00 (***978-1-4108-4222-0(3)***) Benchmark Education Co.

Krull, Kathleen. Isaac Newton. Kulikov, Boris, illus. 2006. (Giants of Science Ser.: No. 2). 128p. (J). (gr. 3-7). 15.99 (978-0-670-05921-8(8) , Viking Juvenile) Penguin Group (USA) Inc.

Mason, Paul. Isaac Newton. 2002. (Scientists Who Made History Ser.). (Illus.). 48p. (J). lib. bdg. 27.12 (978-0-7398-4845-6(3)) Raintree.

McNeil, Niki, et al. HOCPP 1059 Isaac Newton. 2006. spiral bd. 18.50 (***978-1-60308-059-0(7)***) In the Hands of a Child.

Michael White. Issac Newton. 2005. (Gigantes de Ciencia Ser.). (gr. 5-7). 28.70 (978-1-4103-0502-2(3) , Blackbirch Pr., Inc.) Thomson Gale.

O'Donnell, Kerri. Sir Isaac Newton: Using the Laws of Motion to Solve Problems. 2006. (Math for the Real World Ser.). (Illus.). 32p. (J). pap. (978-1-4042-6079-5(X)); lib. bdg. (978-1-4042-3363-8(6)) Rosen Publishing Group, Inc., The.

Phelan, Glen. Newton's Laws. 2004. (National Geographic Reading Expeditions Ser.). (Illus.). 32p. (J). pap. (978-0-7922-4584-1(9)) National Geographic Society.

Rosinsky, Natalie M. Sir Isaac Newton: Brilliant Mathematician & Scientist. 2007. (Signature Lives Ser.). (J). lib. bdg. 31.93 (***978-0-7565-2209-4(9)***) Compass Point Bks.

Salas, Laura Purdie. Discovering Nature's Laws: A Story about Isaac Newton. Reynolds, Emily C. S., tr. Reynolds, Emily C. S., illus. 2004. (Creative Minds Biography Ser.). 64p. (J). (gr. 4-8). lib. bdg. 22.60 (978-1-57505-183-3(4)) Lerner Publishing Group.

Sullivan, Anne Marie. Sir Isaac Newton: Famous English Scientist. 2002. (Great Names Ser.). (Illus.). 32p. (J). (gr. 3 up). lib. bdg. (978-1-59084-139-6(5)) Mason Crest Pubs.

NEWTS

Schaefer, Lola M. Newts. 2002. (Ooey-Gooey Animals Ser.). (Illus.). 24p. (J). (ps-1). pap. 5.25 (978-1-58810-716-9(7) , 91369); lib. bdg. 17.08 (978-1-58810-507-3(5)) Heinemann Library.

NIAGARA FALLS (N.Y. AND ONT.)

Bauer, Marion Dane. Niagara Falls. Wallace, John, illus. 2006. (Ready-To-Read Ser.). 32p. (J). lib. bdg. 11.89 (978-0-689-86945-7(2)); pap. 3.99 (978-0-689-86944-0(4)) Simon & Schuster Children's Publishing. (Aladdin).

Bryan, Nichol. Love Canal: Pollution Crisis. 2003. (Environmental Disasters Ser.). (Illus.). 48p. (YA). (gr. 5 up). lib. bdg. 30.00 (978-0-8368-5508-1(6) , World Almanac Library) Stevens, Gareth Inc.

Butcher, Timothy. ABACA Flows over Niagara Falls: An Illustrated History. 2006. (Illus.). 48p. (J). lib. bdg. 16.95 (978-0-9786473-0-8(0)) Amoeba Bks.

Charles, Veronika Martenova. Maiden of the Mist: A Legend of Niagara Falls. 2001. (Illus.). 32p. (J). (ps-3). 6.95 (978-0-7737-6207-7(8)); 13.95 (978-0-7737-3297-1(7)) Stoddart Kids CAN. *Dist:* Fitzhenry & Whiteside, Ltd.

De Capua, Sarah. Niagara Falls. 2002. (Rookie Read-About Geography Ser.). (Illus.). 32p. (J). (gr. 1-2). pap. 5.95 (978-0-516-27392-1(2)); 20.50 (978-0-516-22016-1(0)) Scholastic Library Publishing. (Children's Pr.).

—Niagara Falls. 2002. (gr. k-3). lib. bdg. 14.10 (978-0-613-54051-3(4)) Tandem Library Bks.

Tokunaga, Wendy. Niagara Falls. 2003. (Illus.). 48p. (J). 26.20 (978-0-7377-2056-3(5) , Greenhaven Pr., Inc.) Thomson Gale.

Whitcraft, Melissa. The Niagara River. 2001. (World of Water Ser.). (Illus.). 64p. (J). (gr. 5-7). 25.50 (978-0-531-11903-7(3) , Watts, Franklin) Scholastic Library Publishing.

—Niagara River. 2001. (gr. 3-6). lib. bdg. 17.60 (978-0-613-37477-4(0)) Tandem Library Bks.

White, Tekla N. The Flight of the Union. Ramstad, Ralph L., illus. 1998. (On My Own History Ser.). 48p. (J). (gr. 1-3). pap. 5.95 (978-1-57505-300-4(4)) Lerner Publishing Group.

NIBELUNGENLIED

Young, Filson. The Wagner Stories, Retold from the Music-Dramas. 2001. 304p. (YA). reprint ed. 98.00 (978-0-7222-5613-8(2)) Library Reprints, Inc.

NICARAGUA

Brimson, Samuel. Korea, North-Nicaragua, 8 vols. 2003. (Nations of the World Ser.: Vol. 5). (Illus.). 64p. (J). (gr. 5 up). lib. bdg. 30.00 (978-0-8368-5489-3(6) , World Almanac Library) Stevens, Gareth Inc.

Cooper, Sharon Katz. Venezuela ABCs: A Book about the People & Places of Venezuela. Previn, Stacey, illus. 2006. (Country ABCs Ser.). 32p. (J). (gr. k-5). lib. bdg. 25.26 (***978-1-4048-2250-4(X)***) Picture Window Bks.

Dominguez, Adriana. Nicaragua. 2003. (World Tour Ser.). (Illus.). 48p. (J). lib. bdg. 25.70 (978-0-7398-6814-0(4)) Raintree.

Griffiths, John. Nicaragua. 1999. (Major World Nations Ser.). (Illus.). 104p. (J). (gr. 4-7). lib. bdg. 21.95 (978-0-7910-4976-1(0) , Chelsea Hse.) Facts On File, Inc.

Grolier Educational Staff, contrib. by. Nicaragua. 2003. (Illus.). 32p. (J). (978-0-7172-5797-3(5) , Grolier) Scholastic Library Publishing.

Kott, Jennifer & Streiffert, Kristi. Nicaragua. 2nd ed. 2005. (Cultures of the World Ser.). (Illus.). 144p. (J). (gr. 6-10). lib. bdg. (978-0-7614-1969-3(1) , Benchmark Bks.) Cavendish, Marshall Corp.

Miller, Debra A. Nicaragua. 2005. (Modern Nations of the World Ser.). (Illus.). 112p. (YA). (gr. 7-10). lib. bdg. 29.95 (978-1-59018-731-9(8) , Lucent Bks.) Thomson Gale.

Morrison, Marion. Nicaragua. 2002. (Enchantment of the World, Second Ser.). (Illus.). 144p. (YA). (gr. 5-9). 36.00 (978-0-516-20963-0(9) , Children's Pr.) Scholastic Library Publishing.

Riehecky, Janet. Nicaragua. 2002. (Countries of the World Ser.). (Illus.). 24p. (J). (gr. 2-3). lib. bdg. 18.60 (978-0-7368-1107-1(9) , Bridgestone Bks.) Capstone Pr., Inc.

Shields, Charles J. Nicaragua. 2002. (Let's Discover Central America Ser.). (Illus.). 64p. (YA). (gr. 5 up). lib. bdg. (978-1-59084-097-9(6)) Mason Crest Pubs.

NICHOLAS, SAINT, BISHOP OF MYRA

Demi. The Legend of Saint Nicholas. Demi, illus. 2003. (Illus.). 40p. (J). (gr. k-5). 19.95 (978-0-689-84681-6(9) , McElderry, Margaret K.) Simon & Schuster Children's Publishing.

Mayer, Marianna. The Real Santa Claus: Legends of Saint Nicholas. 2001. (Illus.). 32p. (J). (gr. 3 up). 16.99 (978-0-8037-2624-6(4) , Dial) Penguin Group (USA) Inc.

Neuberger, Anne E. St Nicholas, the Wonder Worker. 2000. (Illus.). 120p. (J). pap. 8.95 (978-0-87973-481-7(7)) Our Sunday Visitor, Publishing Div.

Prokop, Paul. The True Story of Santa Claus. 2000. (Illus.). 32p. (J). pap. 5.95 (978-0-8198-7406-1(X) , 332-393) Pauline Bks. & Media.

Shepard, Aaron. The Baker's Dozen: A Saint Nicholas Tale. 1999. (J). (978-0-606-17192-2(4)) Tandem Library Bks.

Stiegemeyer, Julie. Saint Nicholas: The Real Story of the Christmas Legend. Ellison, Chris, illus. (ENG.). (J). (ps-17). 2005. 16p. 6.99 (978-0-7586-0688-4(5)); 2003. 32p. 12.99 (978-0-7586-0376-0(2)) Concordia Publishing Hse.

Tompert, Ann. Saint Nicholas. Garland, Michael, illus. 32p. (J). 2005. (ps-ps). pap. 8.95 (978-1-59078-336-8(0)); 2001. (gr. 1-4). 15.95 (978-1-56397-844-9(X)) Boyds Mills Pr.

NICHOLAS, SAINT, BISHOP OF MYRA—FICTION

Mackall, Dandi Daley. The Legend of Saint Nicholas: A Story of Christmas Giving. Porfirio, Guy, illus. 2007. 32p. (J). (978-0-310-71327-2(7)) Zonderkidz.

Stiegemeyer, Julie. Saint Nicholas. Ellison, Chris, illus. 2007. (ENG.). 32p. (J). pap. 6.99 (***978-0-7586-1341-7(5)***) Concordia Publishing Hse.

NICHOLAS II, EMPEROR OF RUSSIA, 1868-1918

Massie, Robert K. Nicholas & Alexandra. 2000. (gr. 7-12). lib. bdg. 28.05 (978-0-613-37162-9(3)) Tandem Library Bks.

NICKLAUS, JACK, 1940-

Wukovits, John F. Jack Nicklaus. 1999. (Golf Legends Ser.). (Illus.). 64p. (YA). (gr. 4-7). 18.65 (978-0-7910-4560-2(9) , Chelsea Hse.) Facts On File, Inc.

NIGER RIVER

Behnke, Alison. Niger in Pictures. 2008. (J). lib. bdg. (***978-0-8225-7147-6(1)***) Twenty First Century Bks.

NIGERIA

Berg, Elizabeth. Nigeria. 1998. (Festivals of the World Ser.). (Illus.). 32p. (J). (gr. 3 up). lib. bdg. 24.67 (978-0-8368-2017-1(7)) Stevens, Gareth Inc.

Bowden, Rob & Maconachie, Roy. Nigeria. 2003. (Changing Face Of... Ser.). (Illus.). 48p. (J). lib. bdg. 28.56 (978-0-7398-6829-4(2)) Raintree.

Brownlie, Alison. Nigeria. 2000. (We Come from Ser.). (Illus.). 32p. (J). (gr. 1-4). lib. bdg. 25.69 (978-0-8172-5513-8(3)) Raintree.

Brownlie Bojang, Ali. Nigeria. 2007. (J). (***978-1-84234-466-8(8)***) Cherrytree Pubns., Inc.

Brownlie Bojang, Ali & Bowden, Rob. Focus on Nigeria. 2006. (Illus.). 64p. (J). pap. (978-0-8368-6239-3(2)); lib. bdg. 32.67 (978-0-8368-6220-1(1)) Stevens, Gareth Inc. (World Almanac Library).

Dell, Pamela. Teens in Nigeria. 2007. (J). lib. bdg. (***978-0-7565-3306-9(6)***) Compass Point Bks.

Freville, Nicholas. Nigeria. 1999. (Major World Nations Ser.). (Illus.). 103p. (J). (gr. 4-7). 29.95 (978-0-7910-5390-4(3) , Chelsea Hse.) Facts On File, Inc.

Giles, Bridget. Nigeria. 2003. (Nations of the World Ser.). (Illus.). 128p. (J). pap. 34.28 (978-0-7398-6999-4(X)) Steck-Vaughn.

Graham, Ian. Nigeria. 2004. (Country File Ser.). (J). lib. bdg. 27.10 (978-1-58340-498-0(8)) Smart Apple Media.

Hamilton, Janice. Nigeria in Pictures. 2nd ed. 2003. (Visual Geography Ser.). (Illus.). 80p. (J). (gr. 5-12). 27.93 (978-0-8225-0373-6(5)) Lerner Publishing Group.

Ismail, Yinka. Nigeria. 2001. (Countries of the World Ser.). (Illus.). 96p. (J). (gr. 6 up). lib. bdg. 30.00 (978-0-8368-2337-0(0)) Stevens, Gareth Inc.

Kerr, Esther & Ismail, Yinka. Welcome to Nigeria. 2002. (Welcome to My Country Ser.). (Illus.). 48p. (J). (gr. 2 up). lib. bdg. 26.00 (978-0-8368-2537-4(3)) Stevens, Gareth Inc.

MacDonald, Fiona. An Ancient African Town. Wood, Gerald, illus. 1998. (Metropolis Ser.). 45p. (J). (gr. 3-7). 25.00 (978-0-531-14480-0(1) , Watts, Franklin) Scholastic Library Publishing.

Murphy, Patricia J. Nigeria. 2004. (Discovering Cultures Ser.). (J). 25.64 (978-0-7614-1795-8(8) , Benchmark Bks.) Cavendish, Marshall Corp.

Nnoromele, Salome C. Nigeria. 2001. (Modern Nations of the World Ser.). (Illus.). 112p. (J). (gr. 7-10). 29.95 (978-1-56006-762-7(4) , Lucent Bks.) Thomson Gale.

Oluonye, Mary N. Nigeria. (Country Explorers Ser.). 48p. (J). 2007. (gr. 4-8). lib. bdg. 27.93 (***978-0-8225-7131-5(5)*** , Lerner Pubns.); 1998. (Illus.). (gr. k-2). (978-1-57505-138-3(9) , Carolrhoda Bks.); 1998. (Illus.). (gr. 3-5). lib. bdg. 22.60 (978-1-57505-113-0(3) , Carolrhoda Bks.) Lerner Publishing Group.

Onyefulu, Ifeoma. Ikenna Goes to Nigeria. 2007. (Illus.). 40p. (J). (gr. 1-4). 16.95 (***978-1-84507-585-9(4)***) Lincoln, Frances Ltd. GBR. *Dist:* Perseus Distribution.

—One Big Family: Sharing Life in an African Village. Onyefulu, Ifeoma, illus. 2006. (Illus.). 32p. pap. 7.95 (978-1-84507-686-3(9)) Lincoln, Frances Ltd. GBR. *Dist:* Perseus Distribution.

—Saying Goodbye: A Special Farewell to Mama Nkwelle. 2001. (Around the World Ser.). (Illus.). 32p. (gr. 2-4). lib. bdg. 22.90 (978-0-7613-1965-8(4) , Millbrook Pr.) Lerner Publishing Group.

Orr, Tamra. Nigeria. 2006. (to Z Ser.). (Illus.). 40p. (J). (gr. 2-4). pap. 6.95 (978-0-516-24954-4(1) , Children's Pr.) Scholastic Library Publishing.

Phillips, Douglas A. Nigeria. 2003. (Modern World Nations Ser.). (Illus.). 150p. (gr. 6-12). 30.00 (978-0-7910-7475-6(7) , Chelsea Hse.) Facts On File, Inc.

Powell, Jillian. Looking at Nigeria. 2006. 32p. (J). pap. (***978-0-8368-7678-9(4)***); lib. bdg. (***978-0-8368-7671-0(7)***) Stevens, Gareth Inc.

Robson, Lorna. Nigeria. 2005. (Countries of the World Ser.). 64p. (J). (gr. 6-12). 30.00 (978-0-8160-6010-8(X)) Facts On File, Inc.

Rosenberg, Anne. Nigeria: The Culture. 2001. (gr. 3-6). lib. bdg. 16.40 (978-0-613-32889-0(2)) Tandem Library Bks.

—Nigeria: The Land. 2001. (gr. 3-6). lib. bdg. 16.40 (978-0-613-32890-6(6)) Tandem Library Bks.

MNO

—Nigeria: The People. 2001. (gr. 3-6). lib. bdg. 16.40 (978-0-613-32891-3(4)) Tandem Library Bks.

—Nigeria - The Culture. 2000. (Lands, Peoples & Cultures Ser.). (Illus.). 32p. (J). (gr. 4-5). (978-0-86505-249-9(2)); pap. (978-0-86505-329-8(4)) Crabtree Publishing Co.

—Nigeria - The Land. 2000. (Lands, Peoples & Cultures Ser.). (Illus.). 32p. (J). (gr. 4-5). (978-0-86505-247-5(6)); pap. (978-0-86505-327-4(8)) Crabtree Publishing Co.

—Nigeria - The People. 2000. (Lands, Peoples & Cultures Ser.). (Illus.). 32p. (J). (gr. 4-5). (978-0-86505-248-2(4)); pap. (978-0-86505-328-1(6)) Crabtree Publishing Co.

Thoennes, Kristin. Nigeria. 1999. (Countries of the World Ser.). (Illus.). 126p. (J). (gr. 2-3). 18.60 (978-0-7368-0154-6(5), Bridgestone Bks.) Capstone Pr., Inc.

Zocchi, Judy. In Nigeria. Brodie, Neale, illus. 2005. (Global Adventures II Ser.). 32p. (J). per. 9.95 (978-1-59646-144-4(6)) Dingles & Co.

—In Nigeria/en Nigeria. Brodie, Neale, illus. 2005. (Global Adventures II Ser.).Tr. of En Nigeria. (ENG & SPA.). 32p. (J). per. 9.95 (978-1-59646-146-8(2)) Dingles & Co.

NIGERIA—FICTION

Alexander, R. W. Born in an Eggshell. 2004. 135p. (YA). pap. 12.95 (978-0-7414-2241-5(7)) Infinity Publishing.

Bodden, Michelle, adapted by. Obara the Gatekeeper. 2007. (J). 14.95 (***978-0-9753089-1-2(2)***) Water Daughter Publishing.

Emecheta, Buchi & Border, Rosemary. The Bride Price. 2nd ed. 2000. (Oxford Bookworms Ser.). (Illus.). 106p. 6.50 (978-0-19-423059-9(7)) Oxford Univ. Pr., Inc.

Harcourt School Publishers Staff. The World Next Door: Take-Home Book. 1999. (Collections Ser.). (Illus.). (J). pap. 1.90 (978-0-15-317305-9(X)) Harcourt Schl. Pubs.

Obiadi, Boniface. The Good & the Bad Only in America: The Route from Nigeria to America. Strader, Jennifer, ed. Manser, Mark & Okoli, Gloria, illus. 1999. 154p. (YA). pap. 12.95 (978-0-9677864-0-7(1)) Bons Diversified Investment Co.

Onyefulu, Ifeoma. Grandfather's Work: A Traditional Healer in Nigeria. 1998. (Around the World Ser.). (Illus.). 32p. (gr. 2-4). lib. bdg. 22.90 (978-0-7613-0412-8(6), Millbrook Pr.) Lerner Publishing Group.

Unobagha, Uzo. Grandma, How Do You Say I Love You? Krassa, Victoria, illus. 2007. 28p. (J). 16.95 (978-0-9773180-0-1(1)) Adonoke Inc.

NIGERIA—HISTORY

National Geographic Society Staff & Giles, Bridget. Nigeria. 2007. (Countries of the World Ser.). (Illus.). 64p. (YA). (gr. 5 up). lib. bdg. 27.90 (***978-1-4263-0124-7(3)***, National Geographic Children's Bks.) National Geographic Society.

Orr, Tamra B. Nigeria. 2005. (to Z Ser.). (Illus.). 40p. (J). (ps-ps). 24.50 (978-0-516-23666-7(0), Children's Pr.) Scholastic Library Publishing.

Walker, Ida. Nigeria. 2004. (Africa Ser.). (Illus.). 79p. (J). lib. bdg. (978-1-59084-811-1(X)) Mason Crest Pubs.

Zocchi, Judy. In Nigeria. Brodie, Neale, illus. 2005. (Global Adventures I Ser.). 32p. (J). pap. 9.95 (978-1-59646-143-7(8)); lib. bdg. 20.65 (978-1-59646-010-2(5)) Dingles & Co.

—In Nigeria/en Nigeria. Brodie, Neale, illus. 2005. (Global Adventures I Ser.).Tr. of En Nigeria. (ENG & SPA.). 32p. (J). pap. 9.95 (978-1-59646-145-1(4)); lib. bdg. 20.65 (978-1-59646-011-9(3)) Dingles & Co.

NIGHT

Bailey, Jacqui. Sun Up, Sun Down: The Story of Day & Night. Lilly, Matthew, illus. 2004. (Science Works Ser.). 32p. (J). (gr. 3-6). 23.93 (978-1-4048-0567-5(2)) Picture Window Bks.

Burnham, Robert & Discovery Books Staff. Night Sky. 1999. (Explore Your World Ser.). (Illus.). 192p. (J). pap. 13.95 (978-1-56331-801-6(6)) Discovery Bks.

Dolan, Graham. The Greenwich Guide to Day & Night. 2001. (Illus.). 32p. (J). (gr. 2-4). lib. bdg. 22.79 (978-1-58810-042-9(1)) Heinemann Library.

Granowsky, Alvin. Night & Day. 2001. (978-0-606-22425-3(4)) Tandem Library Bks.

Hall, Margaret. Day & Night. 2007. (Pebble Plus Ser.). (Illus.). 24p. (J). 19.93 (978-0-7368-6338-4(9)) Capstone Pr., Inc.

Hall, Margaret. El Día y la Noche: Day & Night. 2008. (ENG & SPA.). (J). (***978-1-4296-0012-5(8)***) Capstone Pr., Inc.

Jestadt, Peter. City at Night. 1998. (Illus.). 48p. (J). (gr. 3 up). pap. 8.95 (978-1-55037-548-0(2)) Firefly Bks., Ltd.

Krautwurst, Terry. Night Science for Kids: Exploring the World after Dark. (Illus.). 144p. (J). 2005. pap. 12.95 (978-1-57990-670-2(2)); 2003. (gr. 3-9). 19.95 (978-1-57990-411-1(4)) Lark Bks.

Llewellyn, Claire. Day & Night. 2007. (Illus.). 24p. (J). (***978-1-59771-018-3(0)***) Sea-To-Sea Pubns.

Meithrin, Mudiad Ysgolion. Llyfr Lliwio Dydd a Nos. 2005. (WEL & ENG., Illus.). 26p. pap. (978-1-870222-48-8(2)) Mudiad Ysgolion Meithrin.

Murphy, Stuart J. It's about Time! Speirs, John, illus. 2005. (MathStart Ser.). 40p. (J). 15.99 (978-0-06-055768-3(0)); pap. 5.99 (978-0-06-055769-0(9)) HarperCollins Pubs.

Pluckrose, Henry. Day & Night. 2001. (Let's Explore Ser.). (Illus.). 32p. (J). (gr. 1 up). lib. bdg. 23.33 (978-0-8368-2958-7(1)) Stevens, Gareth Inc.

¿Por Que Es Oscura la Noche? (Coleccion Primeros Pasos en la Ciencia). (SPA., Illus.). (J). (gr. 1-3). pap. (978-950-724-112-3(4), LMA8218) Lumen ARG. *Dist:* Lectorum Pubns., Inc.

Sasso, Sandy Eisenberg. Adam & Eve's New Day. Rothenberg, Joani Keller, illus. 2006. 24p. (J). bds. 7.99 (978-1-59473-205-8(1)) SkyLight Paths Publishing.

Smith, Alastair. Nighttime. 2004. (Lift-the-Flap Learners Ser.). (Illus.). 16p. (J). (gr. 1 up). pap. 8.95 (978-0-7945-0366-6(7), Usborne) EDC Publishing.

Stone, Lynn M. Day & Night. 2007. (Illus.). 24p. (J). (978-1-60044-176-9(9)) Rourke Publishing, LLC.

Tagholm, Sally. The Complete Book of the Night. 2006. (Illus.). 96p. (J). (gr. 4-8). reprint ed. 19.00 (978-1-4223-5329-5(X)) DIANE Publishing Co.

Windsor, Jo. At Night: Emergent Level Satellite Individual Title Six-Packs. (Sails Literacy Ser.). (gr. k-1). 27.00 (978-0-7578-7944-9(6)) Rigby Education.

NIGHT—FICTION

Abrahams, Peter, et al. Up All Night: A Short Story Collection. 2008. 240p. (J). 16.99 (***978-0-06-137076-2(2);*** lib. bdg. 17.89 (***978-0-06-137077-9(0)***) HarperCollins Pubs. (Geringer, Laura Book).

Adele, Geras. Pictures of the Night. 1998. (Egerton Hall Trilogy). (978-0-606-13704-1(1)) Tandem Library Bks.

Albaut, Corrine. The Nights of the World. 2005. (Illus.). 16p. (J). (ps-7). 18.95 (978-1-929132-79-9(4)) Kane/Miller Bk. Pubs., Inc.

Alexander, Martha. You're a Genius, Blackboard Bear. Alexander, Martha, illus. 2002. (Blackboard Bear Ser.). (Illus.). (J). 11.91 (978-0-7587-4064-9(6)) Book Wholesalers, Inc.

Allgood, Jean. Come Follow Me Bk. 1: Understanding One's Worth: Color Orange. Smith, Sandra, illus. l.t. ed. 2004. 23p. (J). 14.95 (978-0-9741627-3-7(6)) Write Designs, Ltd.

Almond, David. Kate, the Cat & the Moon. Lambert, Steven, illus. 2005. 32p. (J). (ps-3). 15.95 (978-0-385-74691-5(1), Doubleday Bks. for Young Readers) Random Hse. Children's Bks.

Amstel, Marsha. Sybil Ludington's Midnight Ride. Beier, Ellen, illus. 2000. (On My Own History Ser.). 56p. (J). (gr. 1-3). lib. bdg. 23.93 (978-1-57505-211-3(3), Carolrhoda Bks.) Lerner Publishing Group.

Anderson, Sara. Noisy City Night. 2005. (Illus.). 6p. (J). bds. 7.95 (978-1-59354-055-5(8)) Handprint Bks.

Apperley, Dawn. Good Night, Sleep Tight, Little Bunnies. Apperley, Dawn, illus. 2002. (Illus.). 32p. (J). (ps-k). pap. 9.95 (978-0-439-22525-0(6), Cartwheel Bks.) Scholastic, Inc.

Arrigan, Mary. Maeve & the Goodnight Trail. 2002. (Illus.). 144p. (YA). (gr. 7 up). pap. 9.95 (978-1-901737-31-8(4)) Anvil Bks., Ltd. IRL. *Dist:* Dufour Editions, Inc.

Ashman, Linda. How to Make a Night. Tusa, Tricia, illus. (J). (ps-3). Date not set. 32p. pap. 5.99 (978-0-06-443699-1(3)); 2004. 40p. 15.99 (978-0-06-029032-0(3)) HarperCollins Pubs.

Awdry, Wilbert V. Blue Train, Green Train. Stubbs, Tommy, illus. 2006. 36p. (J). (gr. k-1). 8.99 (978-0-375-83463-9(X), Random Hse. Bks. for Young Readers) Random Hse. Children's Bks.

—Blue Train, Green Train. Stubbs, Tommy, illus. (J). (gr. k-ps). 2007. 24p. bds. 4.99 (***978-0-375-83984-9(4));*** 2006. 36p. lib. bdg. 12.99 (978-0-375-93463-6(4)) Random Hse. Children's Bks. (Random Hse. Bks. for Young Readers).

Babbitt, Natalie. The Something. 40p. (J). (gr. k-2). pap. 2.95 (978-0-8072-1333-9(0), Listening Library) Random Hse. Audio Publishing Group.

Baldwin, Christy. Nine Things Nathan Noticed at Night. Barnes, Sarah, illus. 2005. 24p. (J). per. 13.00 (978-0-9765072-1-5(8)) Tribute Bks.

Banks, Kate. And If the Moon Could Talk. Hallensleben, Georg, illus. 1998. 32p. (J). (ps-k). 15.00 (978-0-374-30299-3(5), Farrar, Straus & Giroux (BYR)) Farrar, Straus & Giroux.

—The Night Worker. Hallensleben, Georg, illus. 40p. (J). 2007. pap. 6.95 (978-0-374-40000-2(8)); 2000. 16.00 (978-0-374-35520-3(7)) Farrar, Straus & Giroux. (Farrar, Straus & Giroux (BYR)).

Beames, Margaret. Night Cat. Hitchcock, Sue, illus. 2003. 40p. (J). (gr. k-2). pap. 15.95 (978-0-439-38576-3(8), Orchard Bks.) Scholastic, Inc.

Bean, Jonathan. At Night. 2007. (Illus.). 32p. (J). (ps-3). 15.00 (***978-0-374-30446-1(7)***) Farrar, Straus & Giroux.

Beck, Andrea. Elliot's Noisy Night. Beck, Andrea, illus. 2004. (Elliot Moose Ser.). (Illus.). 32p. (J). (gr. k-3). (978-1-55337-654-5(4)); (978-1-55337-011-6(2)) Kids Can Pr., Ltd.

Bentley, Dawn. Goodnight Bear: A Book & Night Light. Couri, Kathryn A., illus. 2005. (Stories to Share Ser.). 12p. (J). 12.95 (978-1-58117-034-4(3), Intervisual/Piggy Toes) Dalmatian Pr.

Bond, Felicia. Poinsettia & the Firefighters. Bond, Felicia, illus. 2003. (Illus.). (J). (978-0-06-056871-9(2)); 32p. 14.99 (978-0-06-053509-4(1), Geringer, Laura Book); 32p. lib. bdg. 15.89 (978-0-06-053510-0(5), Geringer, Laura Book) HarperCollins Pubs.

Boynton, Sandra. The Going to Bed Book. Boynton, Sandra, illus. 2006. 14p. (J). 12.95 (978-1-4169-2794-5(8), Little Simon) Simon & Schuster Children's Publishing.

Bradbury, Ray. Switch on the Night. Dillon, Leo & Dillon, Diane, illus. 40p. (J). (gr. k-2). 2000. 14.95 (978-0-375-80608-7(3), Knopf Bks. for Young Readers); 2004. reprint ed. pap. 6.99 (978-0-553-11244-3(9), Dragonfly Bks.) Random Hse. Children's Bks.

Bradford, William. Jeremy Mcbright Was Afraid of the Night. 2006. (Illus.). 36p. (J). lib. bdg. 13.95 (978-0-9672585-2-2(9)) CyPress Pubns.

Brenner, Barbara. Moon Boy. Gabau, Jesus, illus. 1999. (Bank Street Reader Collection). 48p. (J). (gr. 1-3). lib. bdg. 18.60 (978-0-8368-1778-2(8)) Stevens, Gareth Inc.

Brown, Marc. Good Night, D. W. Brown, Marc, illus. 2004. (Arthur's 8 x 8 Bks.). (Illus.). 24p. (J). (ps-3). pap. 3.99 (978-0-316-73385-4(7)) Little, Brown Bks. for Young Readers.

Brown, Margaret Wise. A Child's Good Night Book. 2002. (Illus.). (J). 22.91 (978-0-7587-0101-5(2)) Book Wholesalers, Inc.

—A Child's Good Night Book. (J). 12.89 (978-0-201-09155-7(0)) HarperCollins Pubs.

Brown, Margaret Wise. Goodnight Moon 123 Board Book: A Counting Book. Hurd, Clement, illus. 2008. 30p. (J). 8.99 (***978-0-06-112597-3(0)***, Harper Festival) HarperCollins Pubs.

Brown, Richard. Rachel's Mysterious Drawings. 1998. (Cambridge Reading Ser.). (Illus.). 32p. (gr. 2-6). pap. 9.00 (978-0-521-63947-7(6)) Cambridge Univ. Pr.

Bunting, Eve. Noche de Humo. Andujar, Gloria de Aragon, tr. Diaz, David, illus. 1999. (SPA.). 36p. (J). (gr. 2-4). pap. 7.00 (978-0-15-201946-4(4), Voyager Bks./Libros Viajeros) Harcourt Children's Bks.

—Noche de Humo. 1999. (978-0-606-16516-7(9)); (SPA.). lib. bdg. 14.15 (978-0-613-16782-6(1)) Tandem Library Bks.

—Smoky Night. 2002. (Illus.). (J). 13.19 (978-0-7587-0073-5(3)) Book Wholesalers, Inc.

—Smoky Night. Diaz, David, illus. 1999. 36p. (J). (ps-3). pap. 7.00 (978-0-15-201884-9(0), Harcourt Paperbacks) Harcourt Children's Bks.

—Smoky Night. 1999. (978-0-606-16515-0(0)); lib. bdg. 14.15 (978-0-613-18279-9(0)) Tandem Library Bks.

Butterworth, Nick. One Snowy Night. Butterworth, Nick, illus. 2008. (Percy the Park Keeper Ser.). (Illus.). 32p. (J). 12.95 (***978-0-00-726024-9(5)***) HarperCollins Pubs. Ltd. GBR. *Dist:* Independent Pubs. Group.

—One Snowy Night: Hardback plus DVD. Butterworth, Nick, illus. 2007. (Illus.). 32p. (J). 24.00 (***978-0-00-725942-7(5)***) HarperCollins Pubs. Ltd. GBR. *Dist:* Independent Pubs. Group.

Cajun Night Before Christmas. (Illus.). (J). 29.95 (978-1-56554-883-1(3)) Pelican Publishing Co., Inc.

Capucilli, Alyssa Satin. Bizcocho. Mlawer, Teresa, tr. Schories, Pat, illus. 2nd ed. 2001. (Coleccion Ya Se Leer). (SPA.). 32p. (J). (ps up). pap. 4.99 (978-0-06-444310-4(8), HC30732) HarperCollins Pubs.

Catran, Ken. Tomorrow the Dark. 2005. 208p. pap. (978-0-7344-0417-6(4), Lothian Bks.) Hachette Livre Australia.

Christelow, Eileen. The Five-Dog Night. Christelow, Eileen, illus. 1998. (Illus.). 40p. (J). (gr. k-3). 6.95 (978-0-395-92862-2(1), Clarion Bks.) Houghton Mifflin Co. Trade & Reference Div.

Ciminera, Siobhan. Strawberry Shortcake Sleeps Over. 2004. (Strawberry Shortcake Ser.). (Illus.). 24p. (J). (ps-2). pap. 4.99 (978-0-448-43516-9(0), Grosset & Dunlap) Penguin Group (USA) Inc.

Cinderfella's Big Night: Individual Title Six-Packs. (Action Packs Ser.). 104p. (gr. 3-5). 44.00 (978-0-7635-2984-0(2)) Rigby Education.

Cohen, Caron Lee. Martin & the Giant Lions. Sayles, Elizabeth, illus. 2002. 32p. (J). (gr. k-3). 15.00 (978-0-618-04908-0(8), Clarion Bks.) Houghton Mifflin Co. Trade & Reference Div.

Condon, Tom. The Sandman: Stories to Read to Children. 2003. 136p. (J). pap. 11.95 (978-0-595-27291-4(6)) iUniverse, Inc.

Cosgrove, Stephen. Buttermilk. James, Robin, illus. ed. 2003. (Serendipity Ser.). 32p. (J). (gr. k-5). pap. 4.99 (978-0-8431-0487-5(2), Price Stern Sloan) Penguin Group (USA) Inc.

—Buttermilk. 2003. (gr. k-3). lib. bdg. 13.00 (978-0-613-89165-3(1)) Tandem Library Bks.

Costales, Amy. Hello Night: Hola Noche. McDonald, Mercedes, illus. 2007. (ENG & SPA.). 24p. 12.95 (***978-0-87358-927-7(0)***, Luna Rising) Northland Publishing.

Craft, Elizabeth. Prom Season: Three Novels. 2007. 560p. (YA). (gr. 7-11). lib. bdg. 11.99 (978-0-375-94074-3(X), Laurel Leaf) Random Hse. Children's Bks.

—Prom Season: Three Stories. 2007. 560p. (YA). (gr. 7-11). mass mkt. 7.99 (978-0-375-84074-6(5), Laurel Leaf) Random Hse. Children's Bks.

Crawford, Deborah. Tyler the Turtle Is Afraid of the Dark. Balzer, Jeremy, illus. 2006. 32p. (J). 14.95 (***978-0-9770516-1-8(7)***) Laffin Minor Pr.

Crelin, Bob. There Once Was Sky Full of Stars. 2006. 232p. pap. 17.95 (978-1-931559-37-9(6)) Sky Publishing.

Croteau-Fleury, Marie-Danielle. Fred's Midnight Prowler. Cummins, Sarah, tr. from FRE. St. Aubin, Bruno, illus. 2000. (First Novels Ser.). 64p. (gr. 1-5). 4.95 (978-0-88780-521-0(1)) Formac Publishing Co., Ltd. CAN. *Dist:* Casemate Pubs. & Bk. Distributors, LLC.

Croteau-Fleury, Marie-Danielle, et al. Fred's Midnight Prowler. Cummins, Sarah, tr. from FRE. Derome, Pierre-Andre & St. Aubin, Bruno, illus. 2000. (First Novels Ser.). 64p. (J). (gr. 1-5). (978-0-88780-523-3(X)) Formac Publishing Co., Ltd. CAN. *Dist:* Casemate Pubs. & Bk. Distributors, LLC.

Crum, Shutta. The Bravest of the Brave. Bowers, Tim, illus. 2005. 40p. (J). (ps-3). 15.95 (978-0-375-82637-5(8), Knopf Bks. for Young Readers) Random Hse. Children's Bks.

Crummel, Susan Stevens. All in One Hour. Donohue, Dorothy, illus. 2003. 32p. (J). 16.95 (978-0-7614-5129-7(3)) Cavendish, Marshall Corp.

Dalmatian Press Staff. Magic Night Paintbox BTC. 2004. 32p. pap. 2.99 (978-1-4037-0827-4(4)) Dalmatian Pr.

Davies, Jacqueline. The Night Is Singing Lullabies. Brooker, Kyrsten, illus. 2006. 40p. (J). (ps). 16.99 (978-0-8037-3004-5(7), Dial) Penguin Group (USA) Inc.

Deacon, Alexis. While You Are Sleeping. 2006. (Illus.). 36p. (J). 16.50 (978-0-374-38330-5(8), Farrar, Straus & Giroux (BYR)) Farrar, Straus & Giroux.

Disney Publishing Staff. Piglet's Night Lights, 15 vols. 2003. (It's Fun to Learn Ser.). (Illus.). 32p. (J). (ps-3). 3.99 (978-1-57973-127-4(9)) Advance Pubs. LLC.

Dorling Kindersley Publishing Staff. Night Sky. Parsons, Jayne, ed. 2002. (Ultimate Sticker Bks.). (Illus.). 16p. (J). (gr. k-3). pap. 6.99 (978-0-7894-8459-8(5)) Dorling Kindersley Publishing, Inc.

Edwards. Wake up Kisses. 2000. pap. 5.95 (978-0-06-443879-7(1)) HarperCollins Pubs.

Edwards, Pat. What's That? 1999. (gr. k-3). lib. bdg. 10.95 (978-0-613-30867-0(0)) Tandem Library Bks.

Engel, Diana. Circle Song. 1999. (Accelerated Reader Bks.). (Illus.). 32p. (J). (ps-k). 15.95 (978-0-7614-5040-5(8), Cavendish Children's Bks.) Cavendish, Marshall Corp.

Fast & Horr. Night Games. 2001. 32p. (YA). (gr. 6-12). pap. (978-0-8224-3768-0(6)) Globe Fearon Educational Publishing.

Ferraby, Sue. Run! Fiorin, Fabiano, illus. 2004. (Read-It! Readers Ser.). 32p. (C). (gr. k-3). 18.60 (978-1-4048-0552-1(4)) Picture Window Bks.

Findon, Joanne. When Night Eats the Moon. 2004. 176p. (J). (gr. 4-9). pap. 7.95 (978-0-88995-212-6(4)) Red Deer Pr. CAN. *Dist:* Fitzhenry & Whiteside, Ltd.

Ford, Bernette G. First Snow. Braun, Sebastien, illus. 2005. 32p. (J). (ps-ps). 16.95 (978-0-8234-1937-1(1)) Holiday Hse., Inc.

Fox, Sabrina. Who Can Help Me Sleep? Rothan, Ann, illus. 2004. 32p. (ps-3). 16.95 (978-1-885394-36-1(5)) Amber Lotus Publishing.

Franklin, Rosalind. Bodrick & the Magic Petals. 2006. (Illus.). (J). lib. bdg. (978-1-84685-020-2(7), Exposure Publishing) Meadow Bks.

Garelick, May & Whitman, Candace. Sounds of a Summer Night. 2000. (Illus.). 32p. (J). (ps-3). 15.95 (978-1-57255-745-1(1)) Mondo Publishing.

Gay, Marie-Louise. Stella, Princess of the Sky. 2007. (Stella Ser.). (Illus.). 32p. 7.95 (978-0-88899-749-4(3)) Groundwood Bks. CAN. *Dist:* Perseus Distribution.

Ginsburg, Mirra. The Sun's Asleep Behind the Hill. 2002. (Illus.). (J). 15.49 (978-0-7587-9822-0(9)) Book Wholesalers, Inc.

—The Sun's Asleep Behind the Hill. 2000. (J). (978-0-606-20412-5(1)); (978-0-606-20297-8(8)) Tandem Library Bks.

Glass, Beth Raisner & Lubner, Susan. Noises at Night. Whatley, Bruce, illus. 2005. 32p. (J). (ps-3). 15.95 (978-0-8109-5750-3(7), Abrams Bks. for Young Readers) Abrams, Harry N., Inc.

Grace, Will. Five Little Dinosaurs. Vere Hodgkinson, Ed, illus. 2004. 7p. (J). bds. 6.99 (978-0-439-58393-0(4), Cartwheel Bks.) Scholastic, Inc.

Greenaway, Elizabeth. Night Is the Time. 1999. (J). lib. bdg. 7.99 (978-0-679-99274-5(X), Random Hse. Bks. for Young Readers) Random Hse. Children's Bks.

Guilloppé, Antoine. One Scary Night. 2005. (Illus.). 32p. 15.95 (978-1-59687-185-4(7), Milk & Cookies) ibooks, Inc.

Half a Moon & One Whole Star. 1998. (J). pap. 5.99 (978-0-87628-391-2(1)) Ctr. for Applied Research in Education, The.

Half a Moon & One Whole Star. 1999. (J). (gr. k-3). 16.00 (978-0-689-82667-2(2), Atheneum) Simon & Schuster Children's Publishing.

Harshman, Marc. All the Way to Morning. Davalos, Felipe, illus. 1999. (Accelerated Reader Bks.). 32p. (J). (ps-k). 15.95 (978-0-7614-5042-9(4), Cavendish Children's Bks.) Cavendish, Marshall Corp.

—All the Way to Morning. Davalos, Felipe, illus. 2006. (J). per. 7.95 (978-1-891852-49-7(3)) Quarrier Pr.

Hartland, Jessie. Night Shift. Hartland, Jessie, illus. 2007. (Illus.). 32p. (J). 17.85 (***978-1-59990-138-1(2)***); 16.95 (***978-1-59990-025-4(4)***) Bloomsbury Publishing. (Bloomsbury Children).

Harwood, Beth. One Snowy Night. Ronchi, Susanna, illus. 2005. 12p. (J). (***978-1-84011-627-4(7)***) Templar Publishing, Dorking.

Hathon, Elizabeth, photos by. Good Night, Baby. 1998. (Photo Board Bks.). (Illus.). 20p. (J). (ps). bds. 2.99 (978-0-7681-0036-5(4), McClanahan Bk.) Learning Horizons, Inc.

Hawkins, Colin & Hawkins, Jacqui. Snap! Snap! 2005. (Illus.). 32p. (J). pap. 7.99 (978-1-4052-1099-7(0)) Egmont Bks., Ltd. GBR. *Dist:* Trafalgar Square Publishing.

Hébert, Marie-Francine & Gerard. Le Livre de la Nuit. 1998. (Roman Jeunesse Ser.). (Illus.). 96p. (YA). (gr. 4-7). pap. (978-2-89021-344-9(7)) Diffusion du livre Mirabel.

Heine, Helme. El Maravilloso Viaje a Traves de la Noche. 3rd ed. 2003. (SPA., Illus.). 250p. (978-84-85334-62-9(0)) Loguez Ediciones ESP. *Dist:* Lectorum Pubns., Inc.

—Wunderbare Reise Durch Die Na. 12.95 (978-3-7876-9528-7(1)) Middelhauve Verlags GmbH DEU. *Dist:* Distribooks, Inc.

Hendry, Diana. The Very Noisy Night. Chapman, Jane, illus. 2001. 32p. (J). pap. 6.99 (978-0-14-230012-1(8), Puffin) Penguin Group (USA) Inc.

—Very Noisy Night. 2001. (gr. k-3). lib. bdg. 14.15 (978-0-613-44427-9(2)) Tandem Library Bks.

Hertz, Grete Janus. Olie's Bedtime Walk. Rose, Tatin, tr. from DUT. Talsma, Nynke Mare, illus. 2002. 36p. (J). (ps-2). 12.95 (978-1-887734-90-5(2)) Star Bright Bks., Inc.

Hiebert, Elfrieda H. & Juel, Connie. The Night Sky. (Little Book Practice Reader Ser.). (J). (978-0-8136-0979-9(8)) Modern Curriculum Pr.

Hirschi, Ron. When Morning Comes. Mangelsen, Thomas D., tr. 2003. (Illus.). 32p. (J). (gr. k-2). 16.95 (978-1-56397-767-1(2)) Boyds Mills Pr.

—When Night Comes. Mangelsen, Thomas D., photos by. 2003. (Illus.). 32p. (J). (gr. k-2). 16.95 (978-1-56397-766-4(4)) Boyds Mills Pr.

Hood, Karen Jean Matsko. Goodnight, I Wish You Goodnight. 2005. (J). spiral bd. 15.95 (978-1-59649-920-1(6)) Whispering Pine Pr., Inc.

Hood, Karen Jean Matsko & Keyama. Goodnight, I Wish You Goodnight. 2005. (J). cd-rom 7.95 (978-1-59649-919-5(2)) Whispering Pine Pr., Inc.

Horacek, Petr. When the Moon Smiled. 2004. (Illus.). 32p. (J). (ps-k). 14.99 (978-0-7636-2209-1(5)) Candlewick Pr.

Hornsby, Ashley. Pretty Little Lilly & the Magical Night (Hard Bound) Couch, Greg, illus. 2007. 32p. 15.95 (978-0-9777241-0-9(7)) Cepia LLC.

Hornsby, Ashley Brooke. Pretty Little Lilly & the Magical Night (paperback) 2006. (J). (978-0-9777241-1-6(5)) Cepia LLC.

Hosta, Dar. I Love the Night. Hosta, Dar, illus. l.t. ed. 2003. (Illus.). 32p. (J). (gr. k-3). 16.95 (978-0-9721967-0-3(6)) Brown Dog Bks.

Impey, Rose. Scare Yourself to Sleep. Kemp, Moira, illus. 1998. (Creepies Ser.). 48p. (J). (gr. 1-3). pap. 6.95 (978-1-57505-316-5(0) , Carolrhoda Bks.) Lerner Publishing Group.

Isadora, Rachel. A South African Night. Isadora, Rachel, illus. 1998. (Illus.). (J). (ps-3). 32p. 16.99 (978-0-688-11389-6(3)); 24p. 14.89 (978-0-688-11390-2(7)) HarperCollins Pubs.

Jonas, Ann. The Quilt. Jonas, Ann, illus. 2002. (Illus.). (J). 13.19 (978-0-7587-3478-5(6)) Book Wholesalers, Inc.

Juan, Ana. The Night Eater. Juan, Ana, illus. 2004. (Illus.). 40p. (J). (ps-3). pap. 16.95 (978-0-439-48891-4(5) , Levine, Arthur A. Bks.) Scholastic, Inc.

—The Night Eater. 2004. (Illus.). (J). (978-0-439-48892-1(3) , Levine, Arthur A. Bks.) Scholastic, Inc.

Kalz, Jill. Mike's Nightlight. Spence, Tom, illus. 2006. (Read-It! Readers Ser.). 32p. (J). (ps-3). 18.60 (978-1-4048-1726-5(3)) Picture Window Bks.

Keats, Ezra Jack. Dreams. Keats, Ezra Jack, illus. 2000. (Illus.). 40p. (J). (ps-3). pap. 7.99 (978-0-14-056744-1(5) , Puffin) Penguin Group (USA) Inc.

—Dreams. 2000. 13.79 (978-0-606-20356-2(7)); (J). (978-0-606-20232-9(3)); lib. bdg. 15.30 (978-0-613-29937-4(X)) Tandem Library Bks.

Keats, Ezra Jack & Shaw, Tucker. Dreams. 2000. (Illus.). 40p. (J). (ps-2). 15.99 (978-0-670-89225-9(4) , Viking Juvenile) Penguin Group (USA) Inc.

Kemble, Mai. The Moon & the Night Sweeper. Kemble, Mai, illus. 2007. 32p. (J). (ps-2). 15.95 ***(978-1-60108-013-4(1))*** Red Cygnet Pr.

Klingel, Cynthia Fitterer & Noyed, Robert B. The Amazing Letter N. 2003. (Alphaphonics Ser.). (Illus.). 24p. (J). (ps-2). 21.36 (978-1-59296-104-7(5)) Child's World, Inc.

Krensky, Stephen. Fraidy Cats. Lewin, Betsy, illus. 2004. 32p. (J). lib. bdg. 15.00 (978-1-59054-383-2(1)) Fitzgerald Bks.

Lacoursiere, Patrick. Dream Songs Night Songs—China to Senegal. 2006. 16.95 (978-2-923163-24-6(9)) La Montagne Secrete CAN. *Dist:* National Bk. Network.

Landalf, Helen. The Secret Night World of Cats. Rimland, Mark, illus. 1998. 32p. (J). (gr. k-3). pap. 16.95 (978-1-57525-117-2(5)) Smith and Kraus Publishers, Incorporated.

Lemieux, Michele. Noche de Tormenta. Lopez, L. Rodriquez, tr. from GER. Lemieux, Michele, illus. 2nd ed. 2002. (SPA., Illus.). 186p. (J). (gr. 3-5). 23.95 (978-84-89804-27-2(3)) Loguez Ediciones ESP. *Dist:* Baker & Taylor Bks., Lectorum Pubns., Inc.

Lesynski, Loris. Night School. Lesynski, Loris, illus. 2001. (Illus.). 32p. (J). (ps-2). pap. 5.95 (978-1-55037-584-8(9)); lib. bdg. 18.95 (978-1-55037-585-5(7)) Annick Pr., Ltd. CAN. *Dist:* Firefly Bks., Ltd.

Levert, Mireille. Rose by Night. 1998. (Illus.). (J). (gr. 3-5). (978-0-88899-313-7(7)) Groundwood Bks. CAN. *Dist:* Transition Vendor.

L'Heureux, Christine. Caillou Time for Bed. Lambert, Carole, illus. 2004. (Carousel Ser.). 24p. (J). 5.95 (978-2-89450-412-3(8)) Chouette Publishing CAN. *Dist:* Perseus Distribution.

L'Heureux, Christine, et al. Good Night! Lapierre, Claude, illus. rev. ed. 2000. (J). pap. (978-2-89450-176-4(5)) Chouette Publishing.

Listening with Zachary. (J). pap. 13.75 (978-0-8136-4655-8(3)) Modern Curriculum Pr.

Loewer, Peter. The Moonflower. Loewer, Jean, illus. 2004. 32p. (J). (gr. 2-3). pap. 7.95 (978-1-56145-314-6(5)) Peachtree Pubs., Ltd.

Lou Weber Staff, ed. Boobah Say Good Night Night Light. 2004. 14p. 15.98 (978-1-4127-3297-0(2)) Publications International, Ltd.

MacLachlan. Before You Came. 2006. (978-0-06-051234-7(2)); lib. bdg. (978-0-06-051235-4(0)) HarperCollins Canada, Ltd.

MacLachlan, Patricia & Charest, Emily MacLachlan. Fiona Loves the Night. Shepherd, Amanda, illus. 2007. (J). (ps-3). 40p. lib. bdg. 17.89 ***(978-0-06-057032-3(6));*** 32p. 16.99 ***(978-0-06-057031-6(8))*** HarperCollins Pubs. (Cotler, Joanna Books).

McQueen, John Troy. A World Full of Monsters. Brown, Marc, illus. 2001. 32p. (J). (gr. 5 up). 15.89 (978-0-06-029770-1(0)); (ps up). 15.95 (978-0-06-029769-5(7)) HarperCollins Pubs.

Merski, P. K. Roaring, Boring Alice: A Story of the Aurora Borealis. Weber, Mark, illus. 2005. 32p. (ps). 16.95 (978-0-9747217-0-5(0)) Skeezel Pr.

Metzger, Steve. Five Little Bats Flying in the Night. Bryant, Laura, illus. 2006. 32p. (J). pap. 3.99 (978-0-439-77592-2(2) , Cartwheel Bks.) Scholastic, Inc.

Mills, Nancy Libbey. The Knight the Moon & the Stars Got Stuck. Thieves, Sam, illus. 2000. 32p. (J). (ps-4). 15.95 (978-1-893815-01-8(3)) Pie in the Sky Publishing, LLC.

Montardre, Helene. Night & Day. 2003. (Illus.). 8p. (J). bds. 7.95 (978-1-58728-481-6(2) , Two Can Publishing) T&N Children's Publishing.

Morales, Yuyi. Little Night. 2007. (Illus.). 32p. (J). (ps-3). 16.95 (978-1-59643-088-4(5)) Roaring Brook Pr.

Morales, Yuyi. Nochecita. 2007. (SPA., Illus.). 32p. (J). (ps-3). 16.95 ***(978-1-59643-232-1(2))*** Roaring Brook Pr.

Morgan, Allen. Matthew & the Midnight Pirates. Martchenko, Michael, illus. 2005. (First Flight Reader Ser.). 40p. (J). (gr. 1-3). pap. (978-1-55041-904-7(8)) Fitzhenry & Whiteside, Ltd.

Morpurgo, Michael. Red Eyes at Night. (Illus.). 64p. (J). pap. 7.99 (978-0-340-68753-6(3) , Hodder & Stoughton) Hodder General Publishing Division GBR. *Dist:* Trafalgar Square Publishing.

Moulton, Mark Kimball. The Visit. Winget, Susan, tr. Winget, Susan, illus. 2003. 56p. (J). 14.95 (978-0-8249-5859-6(4)) Ideals Pubns.

—The Visit. Winget, Susan, illus. 2001. 48p. (J). (gr. 3-6). 22.00 (978-0-7412-0866-8(0)) Lang Graphics, Ltd.

Murphy, Jill. Peace at Last. Murphy, Jill, illus. 2002. (Illus.). (J). 13.19 (978-0-7587-3382-5(8)) Book Wholesalers, Inc.

Murray, Marjorie Dennis. The Stars Are Waiting. Rogers, Jacqueline, illus. 1998. (Accelerated Reader Bks.). 32p. (J). (ps-k). lib. bdg. 15.95 (978-0-7614-5024-5(6) , Cavendish Children's Bks.) Cavendish, Marshall Corp.

Nortung, Sandra. Watching over You. Wimmer, Greg, illus. 2000. 32p. (J). (gr. k-5). 11.95 (978-1-892885-51-7(4)) Daring Child Pr.

Oxenbury, Helen. Say Goodnight. Oxenbury, Helen, illus. 1999. (Board Books Ser.). (Illus.). 10p. (J). (ps-k). pap 6.99 (978-0-689-81987-2(0) , Little Simon) Simon & Schuster Children's Publishing.

Parish, Peggy. Be Ready at Eight. Fisher, Cynthia, illus. 2000. (J). (gr. k-3). 24.95 incl. audio (978-0-87499-622-7(8)); pap. 16.95 incl. audio (978-0-87499-621-0(X)); pap., tchr. ed. 29.95 incl. audio (978-0-87499-623-4(6)) Live Oak Media.

Peck, Richard. Monster Night at Grandma's House. Freeman, Don, illus. 2003. 32p. (J). (gr. k-3). reprint ed. 12.99 (978-0-8037-2904-9(9) , Dial) Penguin Group (USA) Inc.

Peirce-Bale, Mary. Noah's Moon. 2006. (J). spiral bd. 10.90 (978-0-9773990-2-4(8)) Mother's Hse. Publishing.

—Twinkle, Twinkle Little Girl. 2005. (J). 6.95 (978-0-9743869-9-7(5)) Mother's Hse. Publishing.

Pendziwol, Jean. Dawn Watch. Debon, Nicolas, illus. 2004. 32p. (J). 15.95 (978-0-88899-512-4(1)) Groundwood Bks. CAN. *Dist:* Perseus Distribution.

Pfister, Marcus. The Rainbow Fish Coloring Storybook. 2001. (Rainbow Fish & Friends Ser.). (Illus.). 32p. (J). (ps-3). pap. 4.99 (978-1-59014-004-8(4)) North-South Bks., Inc.

Pierson, Judith. The Always Moon. Brooks, Karen S., illus. 1998. 24p. (J). (gr. k-2). 13.95 (978-1-890326-17-3(8)) First Story Pr.

Pla Valencia, Nancy. Under Bright Rays & Sparkling Stars. Pla Valencia, Nancy, illus. 1999. (J). (978-1-56492-283-0(9)) Laredo Publishing Co., Inc.

Plante, Raymond. Elisa de Noir et de Feu. 2002. (Roman + Ser.). 160p. (YA). (gr. 8 up). pap. (978-2-89021-315-9(3)) Diffusion du livre Mirabel.

—Les Lanternes de Shanghai. Delezenne, Christine, illus. 2002. (Roman Jeunesse Ser.). (FRE.). 96p. (J). (gr. 4-7). pap. (978-2-89021-570-2(9)) Diffusion du livre Mirabel.

Potter, Beatrix. Night, Night Peter Rabbit. 2006. (Illus.). 6p. (J). (ps). pap. 12.99 (978-0-7232-5742-4(6) , Warne) Penguin Group (USA) Inc.

Puddlepot, Bing. Jimmy Jonny Brownie Stays up All Night. Schwartzrock, Sherwin G., illus. 2000. 32p. (J). (ps-3). 14.95 (978-0-9676148-1-6(3)) Bing Puddlepot.

Rabe, Tish. Spooky Night! Sexton, Brenda, illus. 2006. (Nose Knows Ser.). 10p. (J). (ps-17). bds. 9.99 (978-1-58476-483-0(X) , IKIDS) Innovative Kids.

Reed, Neil, illus. The Midnight Unicorn. 2006. 36p. (J). (gr. k-2). 14.95 (978-1-4027-3218-8(X)) Sterling Publishing Co., Inc.

Ricci, Christine. Buenas Noches, Dora! Cuento Para Levantar la Tapita. Hall, Susan, illus. 2004. (Dora the Explorer Ser.).Tr. of Good Night, Dora!. (SPA.). 16p. (J). pap. 5.99 (978-0-689-86648-7(8) , Libros Para Ninos) Simon & Schuster Children's Publishing.

Richards, Lucy. The Magic Sky. 2004. (Illus.). 32p. (J). (ps). pap. 8.99 (978-1-4052-1335-6(3)) Egmont Bks., Ltd. GBR. *Dist:* Independent Pubs. Group.

Rockwell, Anne F. Here Comes the Night. 2006. (Illus.). 32p. (J). ***(978-0-7522-7663-2(8));*** 16.95 (978-0-8050-7663-9(8)) Holt, Henry & Co.

Rodgers, Frank. Ruidos en la Noche. (SPA.). 64p. (J). (gr. 3). 7.95 (978-84-88061-85-0(4)) Serres, Ediciones, S. L. ESP. *Dist:* Lectorum Pubns., Inc.

Rohmann, Eric. The Cinder-Eyed Cats. 2001. 40p. (J). (gr. k-3). pap. 6.99 (978-0-440-41743-9(0) , Dragonfly Bks.) Random Hse. Children's Bks.

—The Cinder-Eyed Cats. 2001. 13.79 (978-0-606-22187-0(5)) Tandem Library Bks.

Rosen, Michael. The Zoo at Night. Willey, Bee, illus. 2000. 12p. (J). (ps-k). (978-1-896580-00-5(9)) Tradewind Bks.

Rosen, Michael J. Night-Night, Knight & Other Poems: Level Three, Blue. Heap, Sue, illus. 1999. (Reading Together Ser.). 32p. (J). pap. (978-0-7636-0856-9(4)) Candlewick Pr.

Rosenberg, Liz. Eli's Night-Light. Yardley, Joanna, illus. 2001. 32p. (J). (ps-1). pap. 15.95 (978-0-531-30316-0(0) , Orchard Bks.) Scholastic, Inc.

Rosenberg, Liz & Yardley, Joanna. Eli's Night-Light. 2001. (Illus.). (J). lib. bdg. (978-0-531-33316-7(7) , Orchard Bks.) Scholastic, Inc.

Rydell, Katy. Wind Says Good Night. Jorgensen, David, illus. 2000. 32p. (J). (gr. k-3). pap. 5.95 (978-0-618-08585-9(8)) Houghton Mifflin Co. Trade & Reference Div.

—Wind Says Good Night. Jorgensen, David, illus. 2000. (ps-ps). lib. bdg. 14.10 (978-0-613-30193-0(5)) Tandem Library Bks.

—Wind Says Good Night. 2000. (Illus.). (J). (978-0-606-21735-4(5)) Tandem Library Bks.

Rylant, Cynthia. Mr. Putter & Tabby See the Stars. Howard, Arthur, illus. 2008. (Mr. Putter & Tabby Ser.). 44p. (J). pap. 5.95 ***(978-0-15-206366-5(8)*** , Harcourt Paperbacks) Harcourt Children's Bks.

—Mr. Putter & Tabby See the Stars. Howard, Arthur, illus. 2007. (Mr. Putter & Tabby Ser.). 44p. (J). (gr. 1-4). 14.00 ***(978-0-15-206075-6(8))*** Harcourt Trade Pubs.

Sanroman, Susana. Senora Reganona: A Mexican Bedtime Story. Domi, illus. 2006. 20p. (J). (gr. k-4). reprint ed. 15.00 (978-1-4223-5466-7(0)) DIANE Publishing Co.

Santomero, Angela C. Buenas Noches, Blue. Pontillo, Jenine, illus. 2003. (Blue's Clues Ser.). (SPA.). 22p. (J). bds. 4.99 (978-0-689-86309-7(8) , Libros Para Ninos) Simon & Schuster Children's Publishing.

Scarabosio, Holly. Happy Thoughts with Sandy D. Dandelion & Friends. 2002. 28p. (J). pap. 13.95 incl. audio compact disk (978-0-9721445-0-6(1)) Dandelion Productions.

Schwartz, Roslyn. The Mole Sisters & the Moonlit Night. Schwartz, Roslyn, illus. 2001. (Mole Sisters Ser.). (Illus.). 32p. (J). (ps-k). pap. 4.95 (978-1-55037-702-6(7)); lib. bdg. 14.95 (978-1-55037-703-3(5)) Annick Pr., Ltd. CAN. *Dist:* Firefly Bks., Ltd.

Scillian, Devin. Cosmo's Moon. Braught, Mark, illus. 2003. 40p. (J). (gr. k-5). 15.95 (978-1-58536-123-6(2)) Sleeping Bear Pr.

Selway, Martina, illus. What's That? 1999. (J). (978-0-7608-3195-3(5)) Sundance/Newbridge Educational Publishing.

Sendak, Maurice. La Cocina de Noche. Sendak, Maurice, illus. 2003. (Picture Books Collection). (SPA., Illus.). 40p. (J). (gr. k-3). 10.95 (978-84-204-4570-0(3)) Alfaguara, Ediciones, S.A.- Grupo Santillana ESP. *Dist:* Santillana USA Publishing Co., Inc.

—In the Night Kitchen. Sendak, Maurice, illus. 2004. (Illus.). 32p. (J). (gr. k-5). pap. 14.95 incl. audio (978-0-89719-778-6(X) , PRA302) Weston Woods Studios, Inc.

Sergeant, Kate. It's a Very Good Night. 2005. (J). (978-0-9770158-5-6(8)) BeachWalk Bks. Inc.

Shulevitz, Uri. So Sleepy Story. 2006. (Illus.). 32p. (J). (ps-1). 16.00 (978-0-374-37031-2(1)) Farrar, Straus & Giroux.

Singer, Marilyn. Good Day, Good Night. Goembel, Ponder, illus. 1998. (Accelerated Reader Bks.). 32p. (J). (ps-k). lib. bdg. 15.95 (978-0-7614-5018-4(1) , Cavendish Children's Bks.) Cavendish, Marshall Corp.

—Quiet Night. Manders, John, illus. 2002. 32p. (J). (gr. k-ps). 15.00 (978-0-618-12044-4(0) , Clarion Bks.) Houghton Mifflin Co. Trade & Reference Div.

Sites, Terry A. While You're Asleep. Huddleston, Christine, illus. 1998. 32p. (J). (ps-2). pap. 4.95 (978-0-8198-8292-9(5) , 332-403) Pauline Bks. & Media.

—While You're Asleep. 1998. (ps-2). lib. bdg. 12.95 (978-0-613-76562-6(1)) Tandem Library Bks.

Slegers, Liesbet. Kevin Spends the Night. 2002. (On My Way Ser.). (Illus.). 28p. (J). 7.95 (978-1-929132-32-4(8)) Kane/Miller Bk. Pubs., Inc.

Somary, Wolfgang. Night & the Candlemaker. Bartram, Simon, illus. 2000. 32p. (J). (ps-3). 16.99 (978-1-84148-137-1(8)) Barefoot Bks., Inc.

Spider Night! (Early Intervention Levels Ser.). 28.38 (978-0-7362-0411-8(3)) Hampton-Brown Bks.

Stadtler, Bea. Baked By Savta: A Collection of Childrens' Stories. 2002. 123p. (J). (gr. 4-7). pap. 10.95 (978-0-595-21389-4(8) , Writer's Showcase Pr.) iUniverse, Inc.

Stine, R. L. A Night in Terror Tower. 2004. (Goosebumps Ser.). 144p. (J). 4.99 (978-0-439-67111-8(6) , Scholastic Paperbacks) Scholastic, Inc.

Swanson, Susan Marie & Krommes, Beth. Light in the House. Swanson, Susan Marie & Krommes, Beth, illus. 2008. (J). ***(978-0-618-86244-3(7))*** Houghton Mifflin Co.

Thompson, Lauren. Little Quack's Bedtime. Anderson, Derek, illus. 2005. 32p. (J). 14.95 (978-0-689-86894-8(4)) Simon & Schuster Children's Publishing.

—Polar Bear Night. Savage, Stephen, illus. 2004. 32p. (J). pap. 15.95 (978-0-439-49524-0(5) , Scholastic Pr.) Scholastic, Inc.

Thomson, Sarah L. Imagine a Night. Gonsalves, Rob, illus. 2003. 40p. (J). 18.99 (978-0-689-85218-3(5) , Atheneum) Simon & Schuster Children's Publishing.

Thuswalder, Werner. Silent Night, Holy Night. Ingpen, Robert R., illus. 2005. 48p. (J). (ps). 16.99 (978-0-698-40032-0(1) , Minedition) Penguin Group (USA) Inc.

Tibo, Gilles. Le Voyage du Funambule. 2004. (Mon Roman Ser.). (FRE., Illus.). 64p. (J). (gr. 2). pap. (978-2-89021-701-0(9)) Diffusion du livre Mirabel.

Toten, Teresa. Bright Red Kisses. Betteridge, Deirdre, illus. 2005. 32p. (J). (ps-k). pap. 7.95 (978-1-55037-908-2(9)); lib. bdg. 19.95 (978-1-55037-909-9(7)) Annick Pr., Ltd. CAN. *Dist:* Firefly Bks., Ltd.

Trease, Geoffrey. No Horn at Midnight. 2000. 160p. (J). (gr. 4-7). pap. (978-0-330-34141-7(3) , Macmillan Children's Bks.) Pan Macmillan.

Tullet, Herve. El Dia y la Noche. (SPA.). 148p. (J). (978-84-233-3236-6(5)) Ediciones Destino ESP. *Dist:* Lectorum Pubns., Inc.

Uria, Fernando. Panico en la Discoteca. 1998. (SPA.). (gr. 7-12). lib. bdg. 14.10 (978-0-613-80702-9(2)) Tandem Library Bks.

Walker, Nan. The Midnight Kid. Gott, Barry, illus. 2007. (Science Solves It! Ser.). 32p. (J). ***(978-1-4287-1923-1(7))*** Kane Pr., The.

Wallen, Ila. The Moon in My Room. Sauber, Robert, illus. 2002. (Willowbe Woods Campfire Stories Ser.: Bk. 1). 32p. (J). (ps-3). 16.95 (978-0-9710627-0-2(6)) Bent Willow Publishing.

Walton, Rick & Bardhan-Quallen, Sudipta. A Very Hairy Scary Story. Clark, David, illus. 2004. 32p. (J). (ps-3). 15.99 (978-0-399-23858-1(1) , Putnam Juvenile) Penguin Group (USA) Inc.

Warner, Gertrude Chandler. The Midnight Mystery, Vol. 95. 2004. (Boxcar Children Mysteries Ser.). (Illus.). 128p. (J). 14.95 (978-0-8075-5537-8(1)); pap. 4.50 (978-0-8075-5538-5(X)) Whitman, Albert & Co.

Watson, Clyde. Midnight Moon. Natti, Susanna, illus. 2006. 24p. (J). 12.95 (978-1-59692-162-7(5)) MacAdam/Cage Publishing, Inc.

Wells, Rosemary. Felix & the Worrier. Wells, Rosemary, illus. 2003. (Illus.). 40p. (J). (ps up). 12.99 (978-0-7636-1405-8(X)) Candlewick Pr.

Weston, Carrie. If a Chicken Stayed for Supper. Fatus, Sophie, illus. 2007. 32p. (J). (ps-3). 16.95 (978-0-8234-2067-4(1)) Holiday Hse., Inc.

Willson, Sarah. Estrellita. Thompson Brothers Studio Staff, illus. 2003. (Dora the Explorer Ser.).Tr. of Little Star. (SPA.). 24p. (J). pap. 3.99 (978-0-689-86307-3(1) , Libros Para Ninos) Simon & Schuster Children's Publishing.

Wolf, Gita & Rao, Sirish. In the Dark. 2002. (Illus.). 36p. 9.99 (978-81-86211-54-0(3)) Penguin Group (USA) Inc.

Yaccarino, Dan. Good Night, Mr. Night. 2004. (Illus.). 26p. (J). bds. 6.95 (978-0-15-205351-2(4) , Red Wagon Bks.) Harcourt Children's Bks.

—Good Night, Mr. Night. Yaccarino, Dan, illus. 2001. (Illus.). 32p. (J). (ps-k). pap. 6.00 (978-0-15-216386-0(7) , Voyager Bks./Libros Viajeros) Harcourt Children's Bks.

—Good Night, Mr. Night. 2001. 12.80 (978-0-606-22601-1(X)) Tandem Library Bks.

Zagwyn, Deborah Turney. The Pumpkin Blanket. Zagwyn, Deborah Turney, illus. 2004. (Illus.). 32p. (J). (gr. k-3). 7.95 (978-1-883672-59-1(7) , Tricycle Pr.) Ten Speed Pr.

Ziefert, Harriet. Moon Ride. Chwast, Seymour, illus. 2000. 32p. (J). (gr. k-3). tchr. ed. 15.00 (978-0-618-00229-0(4) , Walter Lorraine) Houghton Mifflin Co. Trade & Reference Div.

—Nicky's Noisy Night. Brown, Richard, illus. 2003. 7p. (ps). bds. 6.95 (978-1-929766-79-6(3)) Blue Apple Bks.

Zolotow, Charlotte. Wake up & Goodnight. Paparone, Pamela, illus. 1998. 24p. (J). (ps up). 9.95 (978-0-694-01032-5(4)) HarperCollins Pubs.

Zschock, Heather. Whoo's There? A Bedtime Shadow Book. 2005. (Activity Book Ser.). (Illus.). 16p. 12.99 (978-1-59359-904-1(8)) Peter Pauper Pr. Inc.

NIGHT—POETRY

Dromgoole, Glenn. Good Night Cowboy. Clack, Barbra, illus. 2006. 32p. (J). 15.95 (978-1-931721-51-6(3)) Bright Sky Pr.

Gutmann, Bessie P., et al. My Goodnight Book. 2000. (Illus.). 48p. (J). (ps-3). 14.95 (978-1-884807-51-0(8) , EC 751) Blushing Rose Publishing.

O'Neill, Mary L. The Sound of Day: The Sound of Night. Jabar, Cynthia, illus. 1999. (J). (978-0-7894-2567-6(X)) Dorling Kindersley Publishing, Inc.

Tagel, Peggy, illus. Twinkle Twinkle Little Star: I Squeak! 2005. ***(978-1-4127-3573-5(4))*** Publications International, Ltd.

Turner, Steve. The Moon Has Got His Pants On: And Other Poems. Mostyn, David, illus. 2001. 96p. (J). pap. 16.99 (978-0-7459-4582-8(1) , Lion) Lion Hudson plc GBR. *Dist:* Independent Pubs. Group.

—The Moon Has Got His Pants on & Other Poems. Mostyn, David, illus. 2002. 96p. (J). pap. 8.99 (978-0-7459-4584-2(8) , Lion) Lion Hudson plc GBR. *Dist:* Independent Pubs. Group.

NIGHTINGALE, FLORENCE, 1820-1910

Alex, Ben. Florence Nightingale. Rava, Giuseppe, illus. 1998. (Heroes of Faith & Courage Ser.). 50p. (gr. 3-12). pap. 7.99 (978-1-884543-16-6(2)) Authentic Media.

Alexander, Carol. Florence Nightingale. 2005. (Rookie Biographies Ser.). (Illus.). 32p. (J). (gr. 1-2). pap. 4.95 (978-0-516-25828-7(1) , Children's Pr.) Scholastic Library Publishing.

Alexander, Carol & Vargus, Nanci Reginelli. Florence Nightingale. 2004. (Rookie Biography Ser.). (J). 20.50 (978-0-516-24406-8(X) , Children's Pr.) Scholastic Library Publishing.

Aller, Susan Bivin. Florence Nightingale. 2007. (History Maker Biographies Ser.). (J). 26.60 ***(978-0-8225-7609-9(0)*** , Lerner Pubns.) Lerner Publishing Group.

Armentrout, David & Armentrout, Patricia. Florence Nightingale. Sarfatti, Esther & de la Vega, Eida, trs. 2002. (Personas que Cambiaron la Historia (People Who Made a Difference) Ser.). (SPA., Illus.). 24p. mass mkt. 5.95 (978-1-58952-250-3(8) , RK31466) Rourke Publishing, LLC.

—Florence Nightingale. 2001. (Illus.). 24p. (J). (gr. 1-4). lib. bdg. 20.64 (978-1-58952-053-0(X)) Rourke Publishing, LLC.

—Florence Nightingale. Sarfatti, Esther & de la Vega, Eida, trs. 2001. (Personas que Cambiaron la Historia Ser.). (SPA., Illus.). 24p. (J). (gr. 1-3). lib. bdg. 19.27 (978-1-58952-169-8(2) , RK5887) Rourke Publishing, LLC.

Barnham, Kay. Florence Nightingale: The Lady of the Lamp. 2002. (Famous Lives Ser.). 48p. (J). lib. bdg. 27.12 (978-0-7398-5523-2(9)) Raintree.

Davis, Marc. Florence Nightingale: Founder of the Nightingale School of Nursing. 2003. (Spirit of America). (Illus.). 32p. (J). (gr. 2-6). 27.07 (978-1-59296-003-3(0)) Child's World, Inc.

Gorrell, Gena K. Heart & Soul: The Story of Florence Nightingale. 2005. (Illus.). 152p. (J). (gr. 5). pap. 11.95 (978-0-88776-703-6(6)) Tundra Bks., Inc./Livres Toundra, Inc. CAN. *Dist:* Random Hse., Inc.

Hinman, Bonnie. Florence Nightingale & the Advancement of Nursing. 2004. (Uncharted, Unexplored, & Unexplained Ser.). (Illus.). 48p. (J). (gr. 4-8). lib. bdg. 29.95 (978-1-58415-257-6(5)) Mitchell Lane Pubs., Inc.

Lethbridge, Lucy. Florence Nightingale. 2005. (Famous Lives Gift Books Ser.). 64p. (J). 8.95 (978-0-7945-0870-8(7) , Usborne) EDC Publishing.

Lynch, Emma. Florence Nightingale. 2005. (Illus.). 32p. (978-1-4034-6352-4(2)); pap. (978-1-4034-6366-1(2)) Heinemann Library.

Malam, John. Florence Nightingale. 2001. (Groundbreakers Ser.). (Illus.). 48p. (J). (gr. 5-7). lib. bdg. 25.64 (978-1-58810-051-1(0)) Heinemann Library.

Robbins, Trina. Florence Nightingale: Lady with the Lamp. Timmons, Anne, illus. 2007. 32p. (J). (978-0-7368-6850-1(X)) Capstone Pr., Inc.

Ross, Stewart. Don't Say No to Flo: The Story of Florence Nightingale. Shields, Susan, illus. 32p. (J). pap. (978-0-7502-3273-9(0) , Hodder Wayland) Hodder Children's Division.

Schaefer, Lola M. & Schaefer, Wyatt S. Florence Nightingale. 2004. (First Biographies Ser.). (Illus.). 24p. (J). lib. bdg. 15.93 (978-0-7368-2081-3(7) , Pebble Bks.) Capstone Pr., Inc.

Tieck, Sarah. Florence Nightingale. 2007. (First Biographies Ser.). (Illus.). 32p. (J). (gr. k-3). lib. bdg. 22.78 (978-1-59679-786-4(X) , Buddy Bks.) ABDO Publishing Co.

Vickers, Rebecca. Florence Nightingale. (Groundbreakers Ser.). 48p. pap. 8.50 (978-1-4034-4063-1(8)); 2002. (Illus.). 24p. (J). pap. 6.50 (978-1-4034-0028-4(8) , 91472); 2000. (Illus.). 24p. (J). lib. bdg. 19.92 (978-1-57572-402-7(2)) Heinemann Library.

—Florence Nightingale. 2002. (gr. k-3). lib. bdg. 12.95 (978-0-613-86990-4(7)) Tandem Library Bks.

Wood, Jill G. Florence Nightingale: Called to Serve with Buffalo Biff & Farley's Raiders. Cox, Brian T., illus. 2006. (Time Traveler's Adventure Ser.). 56p. (J). 13.50 incl. audio compact disk (978-1-932332-29-2(4)) Toy Box Productions.

Zemlicka, Shannon. Florence Nightingale. Debon, Nicolas, illus. (On My Own Biographies Ser.). 48p. 2005. (gr. 2-5). 23.93 (978-0-87614-917-1(4)); 2003. (J). (gr. 1-3). 5.95 (978-0-87614-102-1(5) , Carolrhoda Bks.) Lerner Publishing Group.

—Florence Nightingale. 2003. (gr. 3-6). lib. bdg. 14.10 (978-0-613-58902-4(5)) Tandem Library Bks.

NIGHTMARES

Apel, Melanie Ann. Let's Talk about Nightmares. 2002. (Let's Talk Library). (Illus.). 24p. (J). lib. bdg. 18.75 (978-0-8239-5860-3(4) , PowerKids Pr.) Rosen Publishing Group, Inc., The.

NIGHTMARES—FICTION

Andersen, Hans Christian. The Emperor & the Nightingale. Van Nutt, Robert, illus. 2007. (J). 25.65 (978-1-59961-307-9(7)) ABDO Publishing Co.

Balzola, Asun. Munia y el Cocolilo Naranja. (SPA.). 32p. (J). (978-84-233-1335-8(2)) Ediciones Destino ESP. *Dist:* Lectorum Pubns., Inc.

Berenstain, Stan & Berenstain, Jan. The Berenstain Bears & the Bad Dream. Berenstain, Stan & Berenstain, Jan, illus. 2002. (Berenstain Bears First Time Bks.). (Illus.). (J). 11.19 (978-0-7587-0957-8(9)) Book Wholesalers, Inc.

—The Berenstain Bears & the Bad Dream. ed. 2004. (Berenstain Bears First Time Bks.). (J). (ps-2). spiral bd. (978-0-616-01555-1(0)); spiral bd. (978-0-616-01556-8(9)) Canadian National Institute for the Blind/Institut National Canadien pour les Aveugles.

Bour, Daniele. Petit ours brun fait un Cauche. pap. 12.95 (978-2-227-70921-8(9)) Bayard Editions FRA. *Dist:* Distribooks, Inc.

Brown, Marc. Los Calzoncillos de Arturo. 2002. (SPA.). (gr. k-3). lib. bdg. 15.25 (978-0-613-64538-6(3)) Tandem Library Bks.

Butler, Darren J. The Secret of Crybaby Hollow. 2004. (YA). mass mkt. 6.99 (***978-0-9753367-5-5(4)***) Onstage Publishing, LLC.

Carnevale, Michael. The Hotel Coolidge. 2007. 91p. pap. 10.95 (***978-0-7414-3752-5(X)***) Infinity Publishing.

Constantin, Pascale, illus. Dan's Bad Dream. 2006. (I'm Going to Read Ser.). 32p. (J). pap. 3.95 (978-1-4027-3342-0(9)) Sterling Publishing Co., Inc.

Cordero, Silvia Jaeger. El Huevo Azul. Sunset Producciones Staff, illus. rev. ed. 2004. (Castillo de la Lectura Verde Ser.). (SPA.). 136p. (J). (gr. 4-6). pap. 7.95 (978-970-20-0127-0(7)) Castillo, Ediciones, S. A. de C. V. MEX. *Dist:* Macmillan.

Corentin, Philippe. Papa! (SPA.). 32p. (978-84-95150-38-7(7)) Corimbo, Editorial S.L.

Cox, Phil Roxbee. Mystery Mansion. 2005. (Young Reading Series 2 Ser.). 64p. (J). (gr. 2 up). pap. 5.99 (978-0-7945-0928-6(2) , Usborne) EDC Publishing.

de la Luz Uribe, Maria. El Cururia. 2002. (SPA., Illus.). 48p. (J). 6.50 (978-980-257-060-7(5) , EK3154) Ekare, Ediciones VEN. *Dist:* Lectorum Pubns., Inc.

De Lint, Charles. The Riddle of the Wren. 2002. (gr. 7-12). lib. bdg. 15.30 (978-0-613-56586-8(X)) Tandem Library Bks.

Dexter, Catherine. I Dream of Murder. 1999. 160p. (YA). (gr. 5-9). pap. 5.95 (978-0-688-16668-7(7)) HarperCollins Pubs.

—I Dream of Murder. 1999. (J). (978-0-606-16805-2(2)) Tandem Library Bks.

Dougherty, Brittany Luciani. God Is Laughing. 2004. 68p. pap. 14.95 (978-1-4137-4973-1(9)) PublishAmerica, Inc.

Drouin, Véronique. L' Ile D'Aurélie. 2004. (Mon Roman Ser.). (FRE.). 304p. (J). (gr. 2). pap. (978-2-89021-690-7(X)) Diffusion du livre Mirabel.

Gonzales, David. Spooky's Nightmare. Gonzales, Anthony, illus. 2005. (Mijos Digest Ser.: No. 3). 96p. (J). pap. 4.99 (978-0-439-56801-2(3) , Scholastic Paperbacks) Scholastic, Inc.

Good NighMare. 2007. (J). lib. bdg. 13.25 (***978-1-59616-001-9(2)***) Caballo Bks.

Gutierrez, Debbi Miller. Cactus Factory. 2007. (J). 6.00 (***978-0-9740173-4-1(5)***) Prints By Mail.

Hargreaves, Roger. Little Miss Lucky. 1999. (Little Miss Bks.). 32p. (J). pap. 3.99 (978-0-8431-7504-2(4) , Price Stern Sloan) Penguin Group (USA) Inc.

—Little Miss Lucky. 1999. (ps-2). lib. bdg. 10.65 (978-0-613-21914-3(7)) Tandem Library Bks.

Hartinger, Brent. Dreamquest: Tales of Slumberia. 2007. 160p. (J). (gr. 8 up). 16.95 (***978-0-7653-1397-3(9)*** , Starscape) Doherty, Tom Assocs., LLC.

Hill, Franklin. Wings of Change. Cheung, Aries, illus. l.t. ed. 2001. 32p. (J). (ps-3). 15.95 (978-0-935699-18-0(X) , 093569918x) Illumination Arts Publishing Co., Inc.

Janelle-Engle, Terry. Fraidy Cat's Nightmare. 1999. (Illus.). 28p. (J). mass mkt. (978-0-7541-0864-1(3)) Minerva Pr. GBR. *Dist:* Unity Distribution.

Johnson, Linda & Hodges, Quae. 21st Century Parables: A Child's Book. 2006. 48p. pap. 14.95 (***978-1-60145-071-5(0)***) Booklocker.com, Inc.

Johnson, Lindan Lee. The Dream Jar. Curmi, Serena, illus. 2005. 32p. (J). (gr. k-3). 16.00 (978-0-618-17698-4(5)) Houghton Mifflin Co. Trade & Reference Div.

Johnson, Pete. The Ghost Dog. l.t. ed. 2005. pap. 16.95 (978-1-4056-6028-0(7)) BBC Audio GBR. *Dist:* BBC Audiobooks America.

Jones, D. S. Doubletake. 2004. 183p. pap. 19.95 (978-1-4137-4268-8(8)) PublishAmerica, Inc.

Karas, G. Brian. Bebe's Bad Dream. 2000. (Illus.). 32p. (J). (gr. k up). 15.89 (978-0-688-16183-5(9)) HarperCollins Pubs.

Kitami, Yoko. Cactus. 2006. Tr. of Cactus. (SPA.). (J). (gr. 2-3). 8.80 (978-968-16-7386-4(7) , FC15223) Fondo de Cultura Economica MEX. *Dist:* Lectorum Pubns., Inc.

Klein, Abby. Help! A Vampire's Coming. McKinley, John, illus. 2005. (Ready, Freddy! Ser.). 96p. (J). pap. 3.99 (978-0-439-55606-4(6) , Blue Sky Pr., The) Scholastic, Inc.

—Worst Nightmare. McKinley, John, illus. 2005. (J). (978-0-439-55605-7(8) , Blue Sky Pr., The) Scholastic, Inc.

Klise, Kate & Klise, M. Sarah, illus. Little Rabbit & the Nightmare. 2008. (J). (***978-0-15-205717-6(X)***) Harcourt Trade Pubs.

Lowry, Lois. Gossamer. 2006. 144p. (J). (gr. 5). 16.00 (978-0-618-68550-9(2)) Houghton Mifflin Co.

—Gossamer. 2008. 160p. (J). (gr. 4-7). pap. 6.99 (***978-0-385-73416-5(6)*** , Delacorte Bks. for Young Readers) Random Hse. Children's Bks.

—Gossamer. l.t. ed. 2006. 151p. (YA). 23.95 (978-0-7862-8947-9(3)) Thorndike Pr.

Magoo, Biz. Pajama Sam Out to Lunch! DiCicco, Sue, illus. 2001. (Humongous Ser.). 14p. (J). (ps-k). bds. 5.99 incl. cd-rom (978-1-58668-065-7(X)) Lyrick Studios.

Martin, Jacqueline Briggs. Grandmother Bryant's Pocket. Mathers, Petra, illus. 2000. 48p. (J). (gr. k-3). pap. 5.95 (978-0-618-03309-6(2)) Houghton Mifflin Co. Trade & Reference Div.

—Grandmother Bryant's Pocket. 2000. (Illus.). (J). (978-0-606-18209-6(8)) Tandem Library Bks.

Mayer. Il y a Cauchemar dans Mon Placard.Tr. of There's a Nightmare in My Cupboard. (FRE.). (J). pap. 10.95 (978-2-07-050611-8(8)) Gallimard, Editions FRA. *Dist:* Distribooks, Inc.

Mayer, Mercer. There's a Nightmare in My Closet. Mayer, Mercer, illus. 2002. (Illus.). (J). 14.04 (978-0-7587-3783-0(1)) Book Wholesalers, Inc.

—What a Bad Dream. Mayer, Mercer, illus. 1999. (Little Critter Ser.). (Illus.). 24p. (J). (gr. k-k). pap. 3.99 (978-0-307-12685-6(4) , 12685, Random Hse. Bks. for Young Readers) Random Hse. Children's Bks.

Moffett, Rodney. The Eighth Crest. 2006. (ENG.). 228p. per. 19.95 (***978-1-4241-3907-1(4)***) PublishAmerica, Inc.

Nixon, Joan Lowery. Nightmare. 2003. 176p. (YA). (gr. 7). 15.95 (978-0-385-73026-6(8)); lib. bdg. 17.99 (978-0-385-90151-2(8)) Random Hse. Children's Bks. (Delacorte Bks. for Young Readers).

—Nightmare. l.t. ed. 2004. 200p. 22.95 (978-0-7862-6911-2(1) , Large Print Pr.) Thorndike Pr.

Piggy Toes Press Staff. All the Way's I Love You Mini. Downing, Julie, illus. 2005. 10p. (J). 4.95 (978-1-58117-437-3(3) , Intervisual/Piggy Toes) Dalmatian Pr.

Roman, Stacey. Some of Us Want Wrinkles. Wurster, Laurie, illus. 2005. (J). per. 16.95 (978-1-59858-033-4(7)) Dog Ear Publishing, LLC.

Sarfati, Sonia & Merola, Caroline. Le Crocrodile Qui Croquait les Cauchemars. 2000. (Itait une Fois Ser.). (FRE., Illus.). 24p. (YA). (ps up). pap. (978-2-89021-397-5(8)) Diffusion du livre Mirabel.

Schraff, Anne. The Very Bad Dream: Set 1. 2002. 32p. (YA). 2.95 (978-1-56254-414-0(4) , SP 4144) Saddleback Educational Publishing.

Senshu, Noriko. Sonny's Dream. Senshu, Noriko, illus. 2001. (Illus.). 40p. (J). (ps up). 16.95 (978-1-57174-215-5(8)) Hampton Roads Publishing Co., Inc.

Stine, R. L. Don't Go to Sleep! 2005. (Goosebumps Ser.). 144p. (J). (gr. 3-7). pap. 4.99 (978-0-439-77477-2(2)); pap. 1.99 (978-0-439-79626-2(1) , Scholastic Paperbacks) Scholastic, Inc.

Swindells, Robert. Nightmare Stairs. 2008. 176p. (YA). pap. 9.95 (***978-0-552-55590-6(8)***) Transworld Publishers Ltd. GBR. *Dist:* Independent Pubs. Group.

Tibo, Gilles. Le Gardien du Sommeil. Jorisch, Stephane, illus. 2004. (Mon Roman Ser.). (FRE.). 64p. (J). (gr. 2). pap. (978-2-89021-691-4(8)) Diffusion du livre Mirabel.

Van Zant, Dawn. No More Night Mares: A Dream of Freedom. McElroy, Kim, illus. 2005. (J). pap. 9.99 (978-0-9761768-1-7(5)) Wild Heart Ranch, Inc.

Villoro, Carmen & Perez, Federico. Amarina y el Viejo Pesadilla y Otros Cuentos. (Torre de Papel Ser.). (SPA.). (J). (gr. 2). 7.95 (978-958-04-3650-8(9)) Norma S.A. COL. *Dist:* Distribuidora Norma, Inc.

Waechter, Philip. Rosie & the Nightmares. 2005. (Illus.). 32p. (J). (ps-3). 15.95 (978-1-59354-115-6(5)) Handprint Bks.

Walsh, Ann. The Doctor's Apprentice. 2005. 160p. (YA). (gr. 3-8). pap., tchr. ed. 8.95 (978-0-88878-389-9(2)) Beach Holme Pubs., Ltd. CAN. *Dist:* Literary Pr. Group of Canada.

Walsh, Ann. The Doctors Apprentice. 2007. 160p. (J). pap. 9.99 (***978-1-55002-633-7(X)*** , Sandcastle Bks.) Dundurn Group, The CAN. *Dist:* Univ. of Toronto Pr.

Williams, Harland. The Kid with Too Many Nightmares. 2006. (Illus.). 32p. (J). (ps-2). pap. 3.99 (978-0-448-44365-2(1) , Grosset & Dunlap) Penguin Group (USA) Inc.

Williams, Harland, illus. The Kid with Too Many Nightmares. 2004. (J). (978-0-8431-1582-6(3) , Price Stern Sloan) Penguin Group (USA) Inc.

Winerip, Michael. Adam Canfield Watch Your Back! 2007. (Adam Canfield of the Slash Ser.). (Illus.). 256p. (J). (gr. 3-7). 15.99 (***978-0-7636-2341-8(5)***) Candlewick Pr.

Wynne-Jones, Tim. Stephen Fair. (J). pap. 6.95 (978-0-88899-360-1(9)); 1998. 192p. (YA). (gr. 7-10). pap. (978-0-88899-295-6(5)) Groundwood Bks. CAN. *Dist:* Transition Vendor.

—Stephen Fair. 2000. (978-0-606-18905-7(X)) Tandem Library Bks.

Zoehfeld, Kathleen Weidner. Pooh's Bad Dream. 2000. (My Very First Winnie the Pooh Ser.). (Illus.). 32p. (J). (ps-k). pap. 4.99 (978-0-7868-4377-0(2)) Disney Pr.

—Pooh's Bad Dream. Cuddy, Robbin, illus. 1998. (My Very First Winnie the Pooh Ser.). 32p. (J). (ps-k). 11.95 (978-0-7868-3137-1(5)) Disney Pr.

NILE RIVER AND VALLEY

Banting, Erinn. The Nile. 2004. (Illus.). 32p. (J). lib. bdg. 18.20 (978-1-59036-269-3(1)) Weigl Pubs., Inc.

Bowden, Rob. The Nile. 2003. (River Journey Ser.). (Illus.). 48p. (J). lib. bdg. 28.56 (978-0-7398-6072-4(0)) Raintree.

—Settlements of the Nile River. 2004. (Rivers Through Time Ser.). (Illus.). 48p. (J). pap. (978-1-4034-6251-0(8)); lib. bdg. 29.93 (978-1-4034-5720-2(4)) Heinemann Library.

—Settlements of the River Nile. 2005. (Rivers Through Time Ser.). 48p. (J). pap. 8.50 (978-1-4034-5725-7(5)) Heinemann Library.

Cumming, David. The Nile. 2003. (Great Rivers of the World Ser.). (Illus.). 48p. (YA). (gr. 5 up). lib. bdg. 30.00 (978-0-8368-5445-9(4) , World Almanac Library) Stevens, Gareth Inc.

Fowler, Allan. The Nile River. (Rookie Read-About Geography Ser.). (Illus.). 32p. (J). (gr. 1-2). 2000. pap. 5.95 (978-0-516-26559-9(8)); 1999. 20.50 (978-0-516-21559-4(0)) Scholastic Library Publishing. (Children's Pr.).

—The Nile River. 1999. (gr. k-3). lib. bdg. 14.10 (978-0-613-54052-0(2)) Tandem Library Bks.

Gilpin, Daniel. Burton & Speke's Source of the Nile Quest. 2007. (***978-1-4034-9752-9(4)***) Heinemann Library.

Graf, Mike. The Nile River. 2004. (Fact Finders Ser.). (Illus.). 32p. (J). 16.95 (978-0-7368-2484-2(7)) Capstone Pr., Inc.

Heinrichs, Ann. The Nile River. 2008. (***978-0-7614-2854-1(2)***) Cavendish, Marshall Bks., Ltd.

Johnson, Darv. The Longest River. 2002. (Extreme Places Ser.). (Illus.). 48p. (J). (gr. 3-5). 26.20 (978-0-7377-1417-3(4) , Kidhaven) Thomson Gale.

Meister, Cari. Nile River. 2002. (Rivers & Lakes Ser.). (Illus.). 24p. (J). (gr. k-6). lib. bdg. 21.35 (978-1-57765-098-0(0) , Checkerboard Library) ABDO Publishing Co.

Millard, Anne & Noon, Steve. Story of the Nile: A Journey Through Time along the World's Longest River. 2003. (Illus.). 36p. (J). 19.99 (978-0-7894-9871-7(5)) Dorling Kindersley Publishing, Inc.

Parks, Peggy J. Aswan High Dam. (Building World Landmarks Ser.). (J). 2004. 26.19 (978-1-4103-0204-5(0)); 2003. (Illus.). 48p. 24.95 (978-1-56711-329-7(X)) Thomson Gale. (Blackbirch Pr., Inc.).

Shuter, Jane. Life along the River Nile. 2004. (Picture the Past Ser.). (Illus.). 32p. (J). 24.22 (978-1-4034-5827-8(8)); pap. (978-1-4034-5835-3(9)) Heinemann Library.

Simon, Charnan. The Secrets of the Nile. 2004. (Geography of the World Ser.). (Illus.). 32p. (J). (gr. 2-6). 27.07 (978-1-59296-340-9(4)) Child's World, Inc.

Speke, John Hanning. Journal of the Discovery of the Source of the Nile. 2006. (Illus.). cd-rom (978-1-892824-52-3(3)) AFCHRON.

Weintraub, Aileen. The Nile: The Longest River. 2001. (Great Record Breakers in Nature Ser.). (Illus.). 24p. (J). lib. bdg. 18.75 (978-0-8239-5638-8(5) , PowerKids Pr.) Rosen Publishing Group, Inc., The.

NINO CURRENT

see El Nino Current

NIXON, RICHARD M. (RICHARD MILHOUS), 1913-1994

Anderson, Dale. Watergate: Scandal in the White House. 2006. (J). (978-0-7565-2010-6(X)) Compass Point Bks.

Aronson, Billy. Richard M. Nixon. 2007. (Presidents & Their Times Ser.). 96p. (J). lib. bdg. 32.79 (978-0-7614-2428-4(8) , Benchmark Bks.) Cavendish, Marshall Corp.

Barron, Rachel Stiffler. Richard Nixon: American Politician. rev. exp. ed. 2003. (Notable Americans Ser.). (Illus.). 128p. (J). (gr. 6-12). 23.95 (978-1-931798-30-3(3)) Reynolds, Morgan Inc.

Cohen, Daniel. Watergate: Deception in the White House. 1998. (Spotlight on American History Ser.). (Illus.). 64p. (gr. 4-6). lib. bdg. 24.90 (978-0-7613-0271-1(9) , Millbrook Pr.) Lerner Publishing Group.

Edelman, Rob. Watergate. 2005. (People at the Center of Ser.). (Illus.). 48p. (J). (ps-7). lib. bdg. 24.95 (978-1-56711-928-2(X) , Blackbirch Pr., Inc.) Thomson Gale.

Elish, Dan. The Watergate Scandal. (Cornerstones of Freedomtrade;, Second Ser.). 48p. (J). 2007. pap. 5.95 (***978-0-531-18771-5(3));*** 2004. (Illus.). 26.00 (978-0-516-24239-2(3)) Scholastic Library Publishing. (Children's Pr.).

Green, Robert. Richard M. Nixon. 2003. (Profiles of the Presidents Ser.). (Illus.). 64p. (J). (gr. 4 up). lib. bdg. 23.93 (978-0-7565-0281-2(0)) Compass Point Bks.

Hay, Jeff, ed. Richard M. Nixon. 2001. (Presidents & Their Decisions Ser.). (Illus.). 240p. (YA). (gr. 9 up). pap. 21.20 (978-0-7377-0404-4(7) , Greenhaven Pr., Inc.) Thomson Gale.

Joseph, Paul. Richard Nixon. 1999. (United States Presidents Ser.). (Illus.). 32p. (J). (gr. k-6). lib. bdg. 22.78 (978-1-56239-746-3(X) , Checkerboard Library) ABDO Publishing Co.

Lewis K., Parker. How to Draw the Life & Times of Richard M. Nixon. 2007. (Kid's Guide to Drawing the Presidents of the United States of America Ser.). (Illus.). 32p. (J). 25.25 (978-1-4042-3013-2(0) , PowerKids Pr.) Rosen Publishing Group, Inc., The.

Marquez, Heron. Richard Nixon. 2003. (Presidential Leaders Ser.). (Illus.). 112p. (J). 29.27 (978-0-8225-0098-8(1) , Lerner Pubns.) Lerner Publishing Group.

Nixon Resigns. 2002. (History in the Headlines Ser.). 32p. (gr. 6-8). 6.99 (978-0-7682-0470-4(4) , GA131695) School Specialty Publishing.

Ochester, Betsy. Richard M. Nixon. 2005. (Encyc of Presidents, 2ND Ser.). (Illus.). 112p. (J). (gr. 6-8). 34.00 (978-0-516-22978-2(8) , Watts, Franklin) Scholastic Library Publishing.

Schultz, Randy. Richard M. Nixon: A MyReportLinks. Com Book. 2003. (Presidents Ser.). (Illus.). 48p. (J). (gr. 4-10). lib. bdg. 25.26 (978-0-7660-5104-1(8) , MyReportLinks.com Bks.) Enslow Pubs., Inc.

Schuman, Michael A. Richard M. Nixon. rev. ed. 2003. (United States Presidents Ser.). (Illus.). 128p. (J). (gr. 5-12). lib. bdg. 26.60 (978-0-7660-2031-3(2)) Enslow Pubs., Inc.

Tracy, Kathleen. The Watergate Scandal. 2006. (Monumental Milestones Ser.). (Illus.). 48p. (J). lib. bdg. 20.95 (978-1-58415-470-9(5)) Mitchell Lane Pubs., Inc.

Van Meter, Larry A. & McNeese, Tim. United States V. Nixon: The Question of Executive Privilege. 2007. (Great Supreme Court Decisions Ser.). 112p. (J). (gr. 5-8). 30.00 (978-0-7910-9381-8(6) , Chelsea Hse.) Facts On File, Inc.

Venezia, Mike. Richard M. Nixon. Venezia, Mike, illus. 2007. (Getting to Know the U. S. Presidents Ser.). 32p. (J). 7.95 (***978-0-531-17949-9(4));*** (Illus.). (gr. 3-4). 27.00 (978-0-516-22641-5(X)) Scholastic Library Publishing. (Children's Pr.).

NOAH'S ARK

Adams, Georgie. Noah's Ark. Leplar, Anna C., illus. 1999. 24p. (J). (ps-2). 12.99 (978-0-8054-2037-1(1)) B&H Publishing Grp.

Adams, Pam. Noah's Ark: Giant Edition. 1999. (Illus.). 12p. (J). (ps-1). bds. 14.99 (978-0-85953-579-3(7)) Child's Play-International.

Amery, H. Noah's Ark. rev. ed. 2004. (Bible Tales Readers Ser.). (Illus.). 16p. (J). pap. 4.95 (978-0-7945-0416-8(7)); lib. bdg. 12.95 (978-1-58086-542-5(9)) EDC Publishing.

Arca de Noe Libro a Color. 2002. (Sabio y Prudente Ser.).Tr. of Noah's Ark Full-Color Story Book. (SPA., Illus.). 32p. (J). pap. 4.99 (978-0-8254-0964-6(0) , Editorial Portavoz) Kregel Pubns.

Arca de Noe Paquete. 2002. (Sabio y Prudente Ser.).Tr. of Package Noah's Ark. (SPA.). (J). (ps-2). 24.99 incl. audio (978-0-8254-0968-4(3) , Editorial Portavoz) Kregel Pubns.

The Ark. (J). bds. 9.95 (978-0-87162-415-4(X)) Warner Pr. Pubs.

Auld, Mary. Noah's Ark. 2000. (gr. 3-6). lib. bdg. 16.40 (978-0-613-62479-4(3)) Tandem Library Bks.

Ayliffe, Alex, illus. Who's on Noah's Ark? Tub Fun Book. 2000. (Baby Blessings Ser.). 6p. (J). (ps up). 11.99 (978-0-7847-1134-7(8) , 04314, Bean Sprouts) Standard Publishing.

Beaton, Clare. Make Your Own Noah's Ark. Beaton, Clare, illus. 2007. (Illus.). (J). (gr. k-3). 9.95 (***978-0-8198-4862-8(X)***) Pauline Bks. & Media.

Beck, Ian. Noah & the Ark. 2000. (Illus.). 25p. (J). 17.95 (978-0-385-40566-9(9)) Transworld Publishers Ltd. GBR. *Dist:* Trafalgar Square Publishing.

Berg, Michelle, illus. Noah's Ark: A Hand Puppet Board Book. 2007. 6p. (J). bds. 12.99 (***978-0-439-86396-4(1)***) Scholastic, Inc.

Beylon, Cathy. Noah's Ark Stained Glass Coloring Book. 2004. 8p. (J). pap. 1.50 (978-0-486-43843-6(0)) Dover Pubns., Inc.

Box, Su. The First Rainbow. Poole, Susie, illus. 2003. 32p. (J). (ps-2). 17.99 (978-0-7459-4100-4(1) , 0745941001) Cook, David C. Publishing Co.

Carlson, Melody. Noah & the Incredible Flood, 5 vols. Francisco, Wendy, illus. 2003. (Bible Adventure Club). 36p. wbk. ed. 19.99 incl. audio, cd-rom (978-1-58134-336-6(1)) Crossway Bks.

Cethial and Bossche Publishing Staff. Voyages of Noah's Ark. 1999. (Illus.). (J). (ps-3). (978-1-55274-004-0(8)) Cethial & Bossche Co.

Chancellor, Debra. Come Aboard Noah's Ark. Downing, Julie, illus. 2004. (ps). bds. 6.95 (978-0-8294-1379-3(0)) Loyola Pr.

Chariot Victor Publishing Staff. Noah. 2000. (Shadowbox Bks.). (J). (978-0-7814-3422-5(X)) Cook, David C. Publishing Co.

Coburn, Claudia. Did the Aardvarks Say "No Ark"? Hoard, Angela, illus. 2004. 32p. (J). (978-0-9759343-1-9(7)) Purfect Promises.

Cohen, Daphne M. In Search of the Seven Wonders of Noah. Jarcik, Katerina, illus. 1998. 64p. (J). (gr. 1-6). pap. 9.95 (978-0-9668892-0-8(7)) Treasure Garden Productions.

Concordia Publishing Staff. 2000 Years Since Then, 1. 1999. (J). 6.99 (978-0-570-05566-2(0)) Concordia Publishing Hse.

Courtney, Claudia. Saved by Faith: Noah & the Ark. Clark, Bill, illus. 1998. (Phonetic Bible Stories Ser.). 16p. (J). (ps-1). 2.99 (978-0-570-05461-0(3) , 56-1924GJ) Concordia Publishing Hse.

Cousins, Lucy. El Arca de Noe Noah's Ark. 1998. (SPA.). 20p. (ps-k). 11.95 (978-84-88061-66-9(8)) Lectorum Pubns., Inc.

—Noah's Ark. Cousins, Lucy, illus. 2002. (Illus.). (J). 13.83 (978-0-7587-5895-8(2)) Book Wholesalers, Inc.

—Noah's Ark. braille ed. 2000. (J). (gr. 1). bds. (978-0-616-01862-0(2)) Canadian National Institute for the Blind/ Institut National Canadien pour les Aveugles.

—Noah's Ark. Cousins, Lucy, illus. 2004. (Illus.). 22p. (J). (gr. k-k). bds. 6.99 (978-0-7636-2446-0(2)) Candlewick Pr.

Cousins, Lucy, retold by. Noah's Ark. 1999. (Illus.). 24p. (J). (ps). bds. 6.99 (978-0-8499-5972-1(1)) Nelson, Thomas Inc.

Dalmatian Press Staff. Noah's Ark. 2004. (Illus.). 24p. (J). 2.99 (978-1-4037-0968-4(8) , Spirit Pr.) Dalmatian Pr.

—Noah's Ark. 2002. (Illus.). 24p. (J). (gr. k-5). pap. 2.99 (978-1-57759-478-9(9)) Dalmatian Pr.

—Noah's Ark. 2000. (Illus.). (J). (ps-3). pap. 4.97 incl. audio (978-1-888567-37-3(6)) Dalmatian Pr.

Dalmatian Press Staff, creator. Noah's Ark. 2003. (Talking Book Ser.). (Illus.). 14p. (J). 16.99 (978-0-7948-1624-7(X)) Dalmatian Pr.

Daniels, Lucy. Animal Ark: Animals in the Ark. l.t. ed. 2001. 200p. (J). 16.95 (978-0-7540-6155-9(0) , Galaxy Children's Large Print) BBC Audiobooks America.

De Graaf, A. M. Noe y el Arca. (Divertidas Historias Biblicas para Ninos Ser.). (SPA.). (J). 3.49 (978-0-7899-0524-6(8) , 496641) Editorial Unilit.

De Graaf, Anne. Noah & the Ark. Perez-Montero, Jose, illus. 1998. (Little Children's Bible Bks.). 38p. (J). 5.99 (978-0-8054-1781-4(8)) B&H Publishing Grp.

Douglas, Vincent & School Specialty Publishing Staff. My Little Showcase of Noah's Ark. 2005. (My Little Showcase Ser.). (Illus.). 100p. (J). bds. 14.95 (978-1-58845-649-6(8) , Brighter Child) School Specialty Publishing.

Dowley, Tim. Follow Noah: Poster Sticker Book. Prole, Helen, illus. 2005. pap. 6.99 (978-0-8254-7303-6(9)) Kregel Pubns.

Ferri, Giuliano, illus. The Story of Noah & the Ark. 2001. 32p. (J). (ps-2). 16.99 (978-1-84148-361-0(3)) Barefoot Bks., Inc.

Forlini, Victoria, ed. Noah's Ark: Deluxe Sound Storybook. 2004. (ENG.). 22p. (J). 14.95 (978-0-696-22363-1(5)) Meredith Bks.

Forlini, Victoria & Sidey, Ken, eds. Noah's Ark. 2005. (I See, You See Ser.). (Illus.). 22p. (J). 6.99 (978-0-696-22820-9(3)) Meredith Bks.

Frank, Penny. Noah & the Great Flood. 1999. (Lion Story Bible Ser.). (Illus.). 24p. pap. 2.99 (978-0-7459-4103-5(6) , Lion) Lion Hudson plc GBR. *Dist:* Independent Pubs. Group.

Geisert, Arthur. The Ark. Geisert, Arthur, illus. 1999. (Illus.). 48p. (J). (gr. 4-6). pap. 8.95 (978-0-618-00608-3(7) , Walter Lorraine) Houghton Mifflin Co. Trade & Reference Div.

Golden Books Staff. Noah's Ark / Angels. Butcher, Samuel J., illus. 2000. (Precious Moments Ser.). 96p. (J). (ps-2). pap. 2.99 (978-0-307-25228-9(0) , Golden Bks.) Random Hse. Children's Bks.

Goldsack, Gaby & Dawson, Peter. Noah's Ark: My Little Bible Book. 2003. (Illus.). 12p. (J). bds. 10.99 (978-0-8254-7266-4(0)) Kregel Pubns.

Greene, Rhonda Gowler. Noah & the Mighty Ark. Cohen, Santiago, illus. 2007. 32p. (J). (ps-1). 9.99 (978-0-310-71097-4(9)) Zonderkidz.

Grob, John-Marc. Noah's Ark. 2000. (Bible Kingdom Ser.). (Illus.). (J). pap. 1.99 (978-0-8054-3324-1(4)) B&H Publishing Grp.

Hansen, Janis. Noah & the Incredible Flood. Francisco, Wendy, illus. 2001. (J). (978-1-58134-339-7(6)) Crossway Bks.

Hartman, Bob & Samuel, Janet. Noahs Big Boat. 2007. (Illus.). 32p. (J). pap. 9.95 (***978-0-7459-4995-6(9)***) Lion Hudson plc GBR. *Dist:* Independent Pubs. Group.

Hawksley, Gerald. Amazing Journey of Noah & His Incredible Ark. 2004. 20p. pap. 11.99 (978-0-8254-7275-6(X)) Kregel Pubns.

—Lift & Look Noah's Ark. Stanley, Mandy, illus. 2006. 8p. (J). bds. 7.99 (978-0-7847-1459-1(2) , 04086) Standard Publishing.

Hazen, Barbara Shook. Noah's Ark. Catusanu, Mircea, illus. 2003. 24p. (J). (gr. k-k). 2.99 (978-0-307-10440-3(0) , Golden Bks.) Random Hse. Children's Bks.

Heaps, Kelly S. & Dunn, Susan. Promise: The Story of Noah's Ark. Lindgren, Renae, illus. 1999. (Holy Bear's Travel Ser.). 32p. (J). (gr. k-5). pap. 7.95 (978-1-885628-30-5(7)) Buckaroo Bks.

Heck, Cathy. Noah'sArk. 2007. 10p. bds. 5.99 (***978-1-4037-3302-3(3)***) Dalmatian Pr.

Holder, Greg. Noah's Ark. McCallum, Jodie, illus. 1999. (Record Your Own Voice Ser.). 10p. (J). (ps-k). 14.99 (978-0-7847-1112-5(7) , 03538, Bean Sprouts) Standard Publishing.

—Noah's Ark. Shuttleworth, Cathie, illus. 1999. (Felt Board Bks.). 10p. (J). (ps-k). bds. 14.99 (978-0-7847-1117-0(8) , 03526) Standard Publishing.

Hood, Susan. Noah's Noisy Ark: A Peek-a-Boo Flap Book. Abel, Simone, illus. 2000. (Baby Blessings Ser.). 18p. (J). (ps-k). bds. 10.99 (978-0-7847-1140-8(2) , 04320, Bean Sprouts) Standard Publishing.

Hopkins, Mary Rice. Noah: A Faithful Man. Francisco, Wendy, illus. 1998. 32p. (ps-3). 10.99 (978-1-58134-002-0(8) , Crossway Bibles) Crossway Bks.

Hurry up, Noah. 2006. 16p. (J). pap. 1.99 (978-0-7847-1714-1(1) , 04175) Standard Publishing.

James, Annabelle. Noah's Ark: Story in a Box. 2003. (J). bds. 8.99 (978-1-883043-51-3(4)) Straight Edge Pr., The.

Janisch, Heinz. Noah's Ark. 2001. (gr. k-3). lib. bdg. 16.40 (978-0-613-33842-4(1)) Tandem Library Bks.

Jeffs, Stephanie. Come into the Ark with Noah. 2001. (Action Rhyme Bks.). (Illus.). (J). (ps-3). pap. 5.00 (978-0-687-04791-8(9)) Abingdon Pr.

Kirk, David. Nova's Ark, Set. 2005. (Nova the Robot Ser.). 40p. (J). 12.99 (978-0-448-43817-7(8) , Grosset & Dunlap) Penguin Group (USA) Inc.

Kuskin, Karla & Grejniec, Michael. Animals & the Ark. 2002. (Illus.). 44p. (J). (gr. k-3). 16.95 (978-0-689-83095-2(5) , Atheneum) Simon & Schuster Children's Publishing.

Ladybird Books Staff. Noah's Ark. (Bible Stories Ser.: No. S846-2). (Illus.). (J). (ps-2). pap. 3.95 (978-0-7214-5065-0(2) , Dutton Juvenile) Penguin Group (USA) Inc.

Lanning, Rosemary, tr. from GER. Noah's Ark. Zwerger, Lisbeth, illus. 2001. 36p. (J). (ps-2). pap. 7.95 (978-0-7358-1419-6(8)) North-South Bks., Inc.

Larcombe, Jennifer Rees. The Best Boat Ever Built. Bjorkman, Steve, illus. 2004. (Best Bible Stories Ser.). 24p. (ps-3). pap. 2.99 (978-1-58134-148-5(2)) Crossway Bks.

Lashbrook, Marilyn. Two by Two: The Story of Noah's Faith. 1998. (J). (ps-2). 5.95 (978-0-933657-66-3(8) , 3000850) Standard Publishing.

MacDonald, Mindy. Noah's Crew Came 2 By 2. 2004. (GodCounts Ser.). 24p. (J). bds. 10.99 (978-1-59052-409-1(8) , Multnomah Kidz) WaterBrook Pr.

MacKenzie, Carine. Noah Colouring Book. 16p. (J). pap., act. bk. ed. 1.50 (978-1-85792-823-5(7) , Christian Focus) Christian Focus Pubns. GBR. *Dist:* Riverside.

MacLean, Moira, illus. Noah & the Ark Pushalong. 2001. 10p. (J). (ps-k). 6.99 (978-0-8254-7215-2(6)) Kregel Pubns.

Make Believe Ideas. Noah. 2006. (Illus.). 32p. (J). (ps-3). 8.97 (978-1-59145-526-4(X)) Nelson, Thomas Inc.

Martin, Oscar, Jr., creator. Noah, l.t. ed. 2003. (Illus.). 25p. (J). E-Book 19.95 incl. cd-rom (978-0-9748416-1-8(7)) Build Your Story.

Miller, Susan Martins. Noah. 1999. (Young Reader's Christian Library). (Illus.). 224p. (J). (ps-3). pap. 1.39 (978-1-57748-654-1(4)) Barbour Publishing, Inc.

Morris, John. Noah's Ark, Noah's Flood: Lots of Water, Lots of Mud. Chong, Johanthan, illus. 1998. (DJ & Tracker John Ser.). 32p. (J). (gr. 1-5). 11.99 (978-0-89051-234-0(5)) Master Bks.

Morris, John D. Noah's Ark & the Ararat Adventure. rev. ed. 2001. (Illus.). 64p. (J). (gr. 3-5). 13.95 (978-0-89051-166-4(7)) Master Bks.

Nederveld, Patricia L. A Rainy, Rainy Day: The Story of Noah. 1998. (God Loves Me Ser.). (Illus.). 24p. (J). (ps-3). pap. 2.95 (978-1-56212-275-1(4) , 001206) CRC Pubns.

Neitzel, Shirley. This Is the Ark That Noah Built. Huang, Benrei, illus. 2004. 32p. (J). (ps-3). 9.99 (978-0-8066-4643-5(8) , Augsburg Bks.) Augsburg Fortress, Pubs.

Noah & the Animals. 2000. (Illus.). 10p. (J). 6.99 (978-0-570-07064-1(3)) Concordia Publishing Hse.

Noah & the Ark. (Bible Friends plus Book Ser.). (Illus.). 10p. (J). (ps-k). 6.99 (978-0-8254-7211-4(3)) Kregel Pubns.

Noah & the Ark. 2004. 5.95 (978-1-57264-240-9(8)) Parsons Technology.

Noah & the Ark. Date not set. (J). 8.95 (978-0-88271-533-9(X) , 10521) Regina Pr., Malhame & Co.

Noah's Ark. 2002. (Illus.). 24p. (J). 5.99 (978-1-57759-516-8(5)); pap. 2.29 (978-1-57759-052-1(X)); 1.49 (978-1-57759-272-3(7)) Dalmatian Pr.

Noah's Ark. Date not set. (Illus.). (J). bds. 9.98 (978-1-4054-2048-8(0)) Parragon, Inc.

Noah's Ark. 2000. (Illus.). (J). (ps-k). bds. 4.95 (978-0-88271-687-9(5)) Regina Pr., Malhame & Co.

Noah's Ark. 2002. (J). spiral bd. (978-0-9720158-9-9(2)) Story Reader, Inc.

Noah's Ark: A Bible Story to Color. (Illus.). 16p. (J). pap. 1.50 (978-0-87162-823-7(6) , E6017) Warner Pr. Pubs.

Noah's Ark: Sunday School Songs. 2001. (Illus.). (J). 7.98 (978-0-7853-4851-1(4) , 0785348514) Cook, David C. Publishing Co.

Noah's Ark Abc: My Wipe-off Book. 2003. spiral bd. (978-0-7853-8571-4(1)) Publications International, Ltd.

Noah's Ark Bible Sticker Book. 2003. (Illus.). 16p. (J). 2.98 (978-1-4054-1558-3(4)) Parragon, Inc.

Noah's Ark Fun Book. (Illus.). 16p. (J). pap. 1.50 (978-0-87162-977-7(1) , E4982) Warner Pr. Pubs.

Noahs Ark Penguin. 2004. bds. 6.99 (978-0-8254-7282-4(2)) Kregel Pubns.

Noble, Marty. Fun with Noah's Ark Stencils. 2006. (Dover Little Activity Bks.). 6p. (J). pap. 1.50 (978-0-486-44881-7(9)) Dover Pubns., Inc.

Nolan, Allia Zobel & Mitter, Matt. Noah's Wild Adventure: A Fun Goggly Eyes Book. McGee, Warner, illus. 2007. 12p. bds. 7.99 (978-1-59052-963-8(4) , Multnomah) WaterBrook Pr.

Page, Nick & Claire. Noah & the Ark. 2006. (Read with Me (Make Believe Ideas) Ser.). (Illus.). 32p. (J). (gr. k-2). 3.95 (978-1-84610-168-7(9)) Make Believe Ideas GBR. *Dist:* Ingram Pub. Services.

Pierce, David, et al. Tales from the Ark. LeBarre, Matt, illus. 2001. 128p. (J). 12.99 (978-0-310-23218-6(X)) Zonderkidz.

Pingry, Patricia A. Bible Story Cards: The Story of Noah. 2006. (Illus.). 10p. 7.95 (978-0-8249-1703-6(0)) Ideals Pubns.

—La Historia de Noe. Venturi-Pickett, Stacy, illus. 2000. (SPA.). 24p. (J). (ps-k). 6.95 (978-0-8249-4190-1(X)) Ideals Pubns.

—The Story of Noah. Venturi-Pickett, Stacy, illus. 2007. 32p. pap. 3.99 (***978-0-8249-5569-4(2)*** , Ideals Children's Bks.) Ideals Pubns.

Pingry, Patricia A. The Story of Noah & the Rainbow. Venturi-Pickett, Stacy, illus. 2001. (J). (ps-3). pap. 3.95 (978-0-8249-5414-7(9) , Ideals Children's Bks.) Ideals Pubns.

Pinkney, Jerry. Noah's Ark. 2002. (Illus.). 40p. (J). (gr. k-4). 16.95 (978-1-58717-201-4(1) , SeaStar Bks.) Chronicle Bks. LLC.

—Noah's Ark. 2004. (J). (gr. k-3). 24.95 incl. audio (978-1-55592-530-7(8)); 29.95 incl. cd-rom (978-1-55592-533-8(2)) Weston Woods Studios, Inc.

Pipe, Rhona. Where Is Noah? 1998. (Illus.). 24p. (J). (978-1-85608-171-9(0)) Hunt, John Publishing Ltd.

Prestofillopo, Mary Nazarene, tr. The Story of Noah's Ark. Flamini, Lorella, illus. 2003. 38p. (J). 9.95 (978-0-8198-7084-1(6) , 332-380) Pauline Bks. & Media.

Prole, Helen. Noah & his Big Boat. 2005. (J). 15.99 (978-0-8254-7294-7(6)) Kregel Pubns.

Publications International Staff, contrib. by. Noah's Ark ABC. 2001. (My Wipe-Off Book Ser.). (Illus.). (J). (978-0-7853-5101-6(9)) Publications International, Ltd.

Pulley, Kelly, illus. Noah & the Ark. 2007. (I Can Read!). 32p. (J). pap. 3.99 (***978-0-310-71458-3(3)***) Zonderkidz.

Reader's Digest Editors. Noah's Ark. Moroney, Tracey, illus. 1998. (Little Bible Playbks.: Vol. 1). 18p. (J). (ps-3). bds. 5.99 (978-1-57584-260-8(2) , Reader's Digest Children's Bks.) Reader's Digest Children's Publishing, Inc.

Reasoner, Charles. Inside Noah's Ark. Reasoner, Charles, illus. 2004. (Illus.). 12p. (J). (ps-2). reprint ed. (978-0-7567-7650-3(3)) DIANE Publishing Co.

—Inside Noah's Ark. Reasoner, Charles, illus. 2002. (Easy-to-Read! Easy-to-Draw! Ser.). (Illus.). 16p. (J). pap. 7.99 (978-0-8431-4885-5(3) , Price Stern Sloan) Penguin Group (USA) Inc.

Regina Press Staff. Noah's Ark. 1999. (ps-3). 4.95 (978-0-88271-671-8(9)); (J). 6.95 (978-0-88271-712-8(X)) Regina Pr., Malhame & Co.

Reinhart, Matthew. The Ark: A Pop-up Book. Reinhart, Matthew, illus. 2006. (Illus.). 12p. (J). (gr. k-4). reprint ed. 17.00 (978-1-4223-5673-9(6)) DIANE Publishing Co.

The Roach Approach. Noah's Journey of Faith. 2003. (J). per. 16.99 (978-0-9742997-0-9(7)) Wacky World Studios LLC.

Rowlands, Avril. All the Tales from the Ark. 2003. (Illus.). 416p. 13.99 (978-0-7459-4835-5(9) , Lion) Lion Hudson plc GBR. *Dist:* Trafalgar Square Publishing.

School Specialty Publishing. Story of Noah. 2004. 10p. (J). 1.99 (978-0-7647-1049-0(4) , In Celebration) Schaffer, Frank Pubns.

Seagrove, John K. Noah, Noah, Build an Ark. 1998. 300p. (Orig.). (YA). per. 15.00 (978-0-9647633-2-6(X)) Kendall Publishing.

Simon, Mary Mans. Noah's Ark: Read & Learn the Bible. 2005. (Illus.). 24p. (J). pap. 2.99 (978-1-4037-1157-1(7) , Spirit Pr.) Dalmatian Pr.

Smart Kids Publishing Staff. Noah & the Ark: All about Being Thankful. 2006. 12p. (ps). bds. 19.95 (978-0-8249-6658-4(9) , Candy Cane Pr.) Ideals Pubns.

Smart Kids Publishing Staff. Noah's Ark Story of Being Thankful. 2007. 16p. (J). 19.99 (***978-0-8249-6703-1(8)***) Ideals Pubns.

Smith, Dororthy. Noah's Ark Coloring Book. 2007. (Illus.). 16p. (J). pap. 1.89 (***978-1-59317-188-9(9)***) Warner Pr. Pubs.

Sokoloff, David. My Noah's Ark. Sokoloff, David, illus. 1998. (Illus.). 24p. (J). (ps-5). pap., act. bk. ed. 1.00 (978-1-889655-08-6(2)) Jewish Educational Toys.

Spirin, Gennady & King James Bible Staff. Story of Noah & the Ark: From the King James Bible. Spirin, Gennady, illus. rev. ed. 2004. (Illus.). 32p. (J). 18.95 (978-0-8050-6181-9(9) , Holt, Henry & Co. Bks. For Young Readers) Holt, Henry & Co.

Stewart, Jennifer, ed. Noah's Ark. Marlin, Kathy, illus. 1999. 28p. (J). (ps-2). pap. 3.49 (978-0-7847-1096-8(1) , 22080) Standard Publishing.

Stewig, John W. The Animals Watched: An Alphabet Book. Litzinger, Rosanne, illus. 2007. 32p. (J). (ps-3). 16.95 (978-0-8234-1906-7(1)) Holiday Hse., Inc.

The Story of Noah: La Historia de Noe. 2001. (ENG & SPA.). 28p. (J). pap. 3.95 (978-0-8249-4135-2(7)) Ideals Pubns.

Taylor, Damon. The Ark & the Park: The Story of Noah. 2002. (Child Sockology Ser.). 32p. 10.99 (978-0-8254-3857-8(8)) Kregel Pubns.

A to Z with Noah. ed. 2006. (J). bds. (978-0-9771117-3-2(3)) JMG Studio.

Tolan, Stephanie S. Welcome to the Ark. 2000. (Illus.). 256p. (J). pap. 7.99 (978-0-380-73319-4(6) , HarperTeen) HarperCollins Pubs.

—Welcome to the Ark. 1998. (J). (978-0-606-13893-2(5)) Tandem Library Bks.

Tucker, Jennifer Herrick. Two by Two: A Noah's Ark Adventure. Ward, Jordan, illus. 2002. 80p. (J). per. 11.95 (978-0-9715198-2-4(X)) PJN & Assocs.

Tulip, Jenny, illus. Noah's Ark. 2001. (Giant Zig-Zag Book Ser.). 10p. (J). (ps-k). 4.99 (978-0-8254-7214-5(8)) Kregel Pubns.

Two by Two a Puzzle Book. 2004. bds. 10.99 (978-0-8254-5510-0(3)) Kregel Pubns.

Umansky, Kaye. Noah's Ark, Vol. 7. 2nd ed. 2003. (Curtain up! Ser.: Vol. 7). (Illus.). 48p. (J). (gr. 1-4). pap. 16.95 (978-0-7136-4340-4(4)) A & C Black GBR. *Dist:* Lubrecht & Cramer, Ltd., Players Pr., Inc.

Wade, Connie. Noah's Ark. Overstreet, Laura, illus. 2006. (Sing A Story Ser.). 20p. (J). bds. 4.99 (978-0-7847-1812-4(1) , 04134) Standard Publishing.

Ward, Brenda. Noah & the Big Boat. Fuller, Dollar, photos by. 1998. (Bible Babies Ser.). (Illus.). 16p. (J). 7.95 (978-0-8054-1779-1(6)) B&H Publishing Grp.

Warnes, Tim, illus. Rise & Shine! 2007. 32p. (J). 12.99 (978-1-4169-1377-1(7) , Simon & Schuster Children's Publishing) Simon & Schuster Children's Publishing.

Winch, John. Two by Two. 2004. (Illus.). 32p. (J). (gr. k-3). tchr. ed. 16.95 (978-0-8234-1840-4(5)) Holiday Hse., Inc.

Wood, Tim & Wood, Jenny. Noah's Ark. Thatcher, Fran, illus. 1998. 10p. (J). (ps-2). 11.99 (978-0-8054-1797-5(4)) B&H Publishing Grp.

Zobel-Nolan, Allia. Noah & the Ark. MacLean, Moira, illus. 2000. (Baby's First Bible Stories Ser.). 10p. (J). (ps). 9.99 (978-0-7847-1210-8(7) , 04398) Standard Publishing.

Zobel Nolan, Allia & Davis, Caroline. Day the Rain Came. 2006. (Illus.). 8p. (J). bds. 12.99 (978-0-7847-1857-5(1)) Standard Publishing.

Zondervan. The Beginner's Bible' Noah's Ark Backpack. 2007. (J). 14.99 (***978-0-310-81170-1(8)***) Zondervan.

NOAH'S ARK—FICTION

Amoss, Berthe. Draw Yourself into the Ark with Noah & His Family. 2003. 32p. (J). spiral bd. 12.95 (978-1-59325-003-4(7)) Word Among Us Pr.

Apperley, Dawn. Noah's Ark: With Press-Out Ark & Animal Play Set. 1998. (Illus.). 20p. (J). pap. 6.95 (978-1-86233-021-4(2)) Sterling Publishing Co., Inc.

Auerbach, Annie. Traveling in Two's: The Journey to Noah's Ark. Dillard, Sarah, illus. 2005. 8p. (J). 10.95 (978-1-58117-236-2(2) , Intervisual/Piggy Toes) Dalmatian Pr.

Bell, Bill. Noah: The Incredible Voyager. Bell, Bill, illus. 2004. (Illus.). 48p. (J). (ps-3). pap. 14.99 (978-0-88092-801-4(8)) Royal Fireworks Publishing Co.

Brett, Jan. On Noah's Ark. 2003. (Illus.). 32p. (J). (ps-3). 16.99 (978-0-399-24028-7(4) , Putnam Juvenile) Penguin Group (USA) Inc.

Coplestone, Lis & Coplestone, Jim. Noah's Bed. 2005. (Illus.). 32p. (J). pap. 7.95 (978-1-84507-107-3(7)) Lincoln, Frances Ltd. GBR. *Dist:* Perseus Distribution.

Corman, Dick. Noah Knows. 2006. 183p. (YA). pap. 12.95 (***978-0-9655749-3-8(8)***) Corman Productions.

Cory, David. The Cruise of the Noah's Ark. 2006. pap. 33.99 (***978-1-4280-4090-8(0)***) IndyPublish.com.

Cullen, Lynn. Little Scraggly Hair: A Dog on Noah's Ark. Rogers, Jacqueline, illus. 2003. 32p. (J). (gr. k-3). tchr. ed. 16.95 (978-0-8234-1772-8(7)) Holiday Hse., Inc.

Curry, Kenneth. Mandu & Minka. 2007. (Illus.). 22p. (J). 10.95 (***978-0-9798364-7-3(6)***) Curry Brothers Publishing.

Dunn, Connie & Dunn, Erin J. Many Waters. 2002. (Illus.). 61p. pap. 50.00 (978-1-890641-08-5(1)) No Stress Pr.

Eitzen, Ruth & Eitzen, Allan, illus. Tara's Flight. 2008. (J). (***978-1-59078-563-8(0)***) Boyds Mills Pr.

Falewee, Samantha. The Stowaway aboard Noah's Ark. 2004. (YA). per. 8.95 (978-1-59712-001-2(4)) Catawba Publishing Co.

Farrer, Vashti & Curtis, Neil. Mr. Noah & the Cats. 2005. (Illus.). 62p. (J). (ps-ps). pap. (978-0-7344-0630-9(4) , Lothian Bks.) Hachette Livre Australia.

Forlini, Victoria, ed. Noah's Ark. Mada Design Staff, illus. 2005. 22p. (J). (ps-ps). 9.99 (978-0-696-22826-1(2)) Meredith Bks.

Jones, Liz. Noah's Bed. Copplestone, Jim, illus. 2004. 32p. (J). 14.95 (978-1-84507-002-1(X)) Lincoln, Frances Ltd. GBR. *Dist:* Transition Vendor.

King, Susan. Amy & the Birthday Story; Amy & the Labor Day Lamentations. King, Susan, illus. 2002. (Illus.). 79p. (J). (ps-5). 7.00 (978-0-9714446-6-9(8)) King RIT - ACKS Pubs.

Krensky, Stephen. Noah's Bark. Rogé, illus. 2008. (J). lib. bdg. (***978-0-8225-7645-7(7)*** , Carolrhoda Bks.) Lerner Publishing Group.

L'Engle, Madeleine. Many Waters. 2002. (Illus.). (J). 15.00 (978-0-7587-9605-9(6)) Book Wholesalers, Inc.

—Many Waters. Sis, Peter & Nelson, Cliff, illus. anniv. rev. ed. 1998. 336p. (J). (gr. 5-8). pap. 5.99 (978-0-440-22770-0(4) , Laurel Leaf) Random Hse. Children's Bks.

—Many Waters. 2007. 224p. (J). 6.99 (978-0-312-36861-6(5)); pap. 6.99 (978-0-312-36857-9(7)) Square Fish.

—Many Waters. 1998. (J). (978-0-606-13596-2(0)); (gr. 5-8). lib. bdg. 14.15 (978-0-613-72320-6(1)) Tandem Library Bks.

Lodge, Yvette. Baby's First Pop-up. Ali, Lodge, illus. gif. ed. 2006. 5p. (J). 19.95 (978-1-57791-217-0(9)) Brighter Minds Children's Publishing.

Lunge-Larsen, Lise. Noah's Mittens: How Noah Discovered Felt. Trueman, Matthew, illus. 2006. 32p. (J). (gr. k-3). 16.00 (978-0-618-32950-2(1)) Houghton Mifflin Co.

McCardell, Kenneth/W. Bible Rhymes' Noah's & the Ark. Chirco, Antonella, illus. 2007. 32p. (J). 17.95 (***978-0-9790605-1-9(6)*** , BibleRhymes) BibleRhymes Publishing, L.L.C.

M
N
O

McCaughrean, Geraldine. Not the End of the World. 256p. (J). 2005. 16.99 (978-0-06-076030-4(3)); 2005. lib. bdg. 17.89 (978-0-06-076031-1(1)); 2006. reprint ed. pap. 6.99 (978-0-06-076032-8(X)) HarperCollins Pubs. (HarperTeen).

—Not the End of the World. l.t. ed. 2006. 285p. 22.95 (978-0-7862-8642-3(3)) Thorndike Pr.

Mitton, Tony. All Afloat on Noah's Boat! Parker-Rees, Guy, illus. 2007. 32p. (J). (ps-3). pap. 16.99 (978-0-439-87397-0(5) , Orchard Bks.) Scholastic, Inc.

Monroe, Colleen. A Is for Ark: Noah's Journey. Monroe, Michael Glenn, illus. 2004. 38p. (ps-1). pap. 17.95 (978-0-9754942-0-2(1)) Storytime Pr., Inc.

My Very Own Noah's Ark Play Set. 2004. (J). (978-1-59292-007-5(1)) SoftPlay, Inc.

The Noah & the Ark, Beginner's Biblereg; 2007. (Biblia para Principiantes Ser.). 24p. (J). 5.99 (978-0-8297-4940-3(3)) Vida Pubs.

Noah's Ark Pillow Book. 2003. (J). (978-1-59292-025-9(X)) SoftPlay, Inc.

Okrant, Mark. Judson's Island. 2006. per. 10.95 (***978-0-9791757-2-5(0)***) Oak Manor Publishing, Inc.

Pigni, Guido & Hermsen, Ronald. The Story of Giraffe. Pigni, Guido, illus. 2007. (Illus.). 32p. (J). (ps-2). 16.95 (978-1-932425-87-1(X) , Front Street) Boyds Mills Pr.

Provoost, Anne. In the Shadow of the Ark. Nieuwenhuizen, John, tr. from DUT. 2004. 384p. (J). pap. 17.95 (978-0-439-44234-3(6) , Levine, Arthur A. Bks.) Scholastic, Inc.

—Voyagers on the Ark. Nieuwenhuizen, John, tr. from DUT. 2004. 368p. (J). 4.99 (978-0-439-44235-0(4) , Levine, Arthur A. Bks.) Scholastic, Inc.

Racklin-Siegel, Carol, illus. Noah's Ark. 2003. 32p. (J). per. 9.95 (978-0-939144-42-6(5)) EKS Publishing Co.

Ranson, Erin. The Story of Noah's Ark. Petrlik, Andrea, illus. 2007. 10p. (J). (ps). 8.99 (***978-1-84666-359-8(8)*** , Tide Mill Pr.) Top That! Publishing PLC GBR. *Dist:* Random Hse., Inc.

Rouss, Sylvia A. The Littlest Pair. Hannon, Holly, illus. 2005. 32p. (J). (ps-1). 14.95 (978-1-930143-17-3(6) , Devora Publishing) Pitspopany Pr.

Sasso, Sandy Eisenberg. Noah's Wife: The Story of Naamah. Andersen, Bethanne, illus. 2002. 32p. (J). 16.95 (978-1-58023-134-3(9)) Jewish Lights Publishing.

Saxon, Terrill. Baby's Noah's Ark. 2006. (Baby Blessings Ser.). (Illus.). 6p. 15.99 (978-0-7847-1430-0(4) , 04013) Standard Publishing.

Shook Hazen, Barbara & Muldrow, Diane. Noah's Ark. Catusanu, Mircea, illus. 2005. 26p. (J). (gr. k-ps). bds. 4.99 (978-0-375-83206-2(8) , Golden Inspirational) Random Hse. Children's Bks.

Sting. Rock Steady: A Story of Noah's Ark. Whyte, Hugh, illus. 2006. 28p. (J). (gr. k-4). reprint ed. 17.00 (978-1-4223-5556-5(X)) DIANE Publishing Co.

Weber, Lou, ed. Noah's Ark. 2005. 24p. (J). bds. 10.98 (978-1-4127-3442-4(8) , 3902502) Publications International, Ltd.

Westen, Betty. A Boat Ride for Two Raccoons. Thompson, Lisa Ann, illus. 2001. 93p. 14.95 (978-0-9718177-0-8(7) , W7770001) Westen Integrity Bk. Pubs.

Wiskur, Darrell. Really Big Barn on Noah's Farm. 2001. (Illus.). 40p. (J). 11.99 (978-0-89051-353-8(8)) Master Bks.

Zondervan. Elephant's Big Ride. Pulley, Kelly, illus. 2006. (Beginner's Bible' Ser.). 20p. (J). 6.99 (978-0-310-71340-1(4)) Zonderkidz.

—Noah#39;s Busy Ark GM. 2006. 14p. bds. 14.99 (978-0-310-60490-7(7)) Zondervan.

NOBEL, ALFRED BERNHARD, 1833-1896

Binns, Tristan Boyer. Alfred Nobel. 2004. (Great Life Stories Ser.). (Illus.). 111p. (J). 30.50 (978-0-531-12328-7(6) , Watts, Franklin) Scholastic Library Publishing.

NOBEL PRIZES

African-American Nobel Peace Prize Winners. 2000. (My Ancestors—My Heroes Ser.. Vol. 44). (J). (gr. 3-4). (978-1-893091-43-6(0)) Parker Publishing Co.

Alter, Judy & Rosenberg, Pam. Pocahontas: Native American Peacemaker. 2003. (Spirit of America). (Illus.). 32p. (J). (gr. 2-6). 27.07 (978-1-59296-010-1(3)) Child's World, Inc.

Armentrout, David & Armentrout, Patricia. Jane Addams. 2002. (People Who Made a Difference Ser.). (Illus.). 24p. (gr. 2-5). 14.95 (978-1-58952-054-7(8)) Rourke Publishing, LLC.

—Jane Addams. Sarfatti, Esther & de la Vega, Eida, trs. 2001. (Personas que Cambiaron la Historia Ser.). (SPA., Illus.). 24p. (J). (gr. 1-4). lib. bdg. 19.27 (978-1-58952-165-0(X) , RK7297) Rourke Publishing, LLC.

Bankston, John. Alexander Fleming & the Story of Penicillin. l.t. ed. 2002. (Unlocking the Secrets of Science Ser.). (Illus.). 56p. (gr. 4-10). lib. bdg. 25.70 (978-1-58415-106-7(4)) Mitchell Lane Pubs., Inc.

—Frederick Banting & the Discovery of Insulin. 2002. (Unlocking the Secrets of Science Ser.). (Illus.). 56p. (gr. 4-10). lib. bdg. 25.70 (978-1-58415-094-7(7)) Mitchell Lane Pubs., Inc.

Beecroft, Simon. The Release of Nelson Mandela. 2004. (Days That Changed the World Ser.). (Illus.). 48p. (J). (gr. 5 up). pap. 11.95 (978-0-8368-5577-4(7)); lib. bdg. 30.00 (978-0-8368-5571-5(X)) Stevens, Gareth Inc. (World Almanac Library).

Binns, Tristan Boyer. Alfred Nobel. 2004. (Great Life Stories Ser.). (Illus.). 111p. (J). 30.50 (978-0-531-12328-7(6) , Watts, Franklin) Scholastic Library Publishing.

Cullen, J. Heather. Barbara McClintock. 2003. (Women in the Science Ser.). (Illus.). 122p. pap. 30.00 (978-0-7910-7522-7(2)); 112p. (gr. 6-12). 30.00 (978-0-7910-7248-6(7)) Facts On File, Inc. (Chelsea Hse.).

Darraj, Susan Muaddi. Mairead Corrigan & Betty Williams: Partners for Peace in Northern Ireland. 2006. (Modern Peacemakers Ser.). (Illus.). 112p. (J). (gr. 9 up). 30.00 (978-0-7910-9001-5(9) , Chelsea Hse.) Facts On File, Inc.

DeWitt, Lisa F. Nobel Prize Winners Text/3 CD's Package: Biographical Sketches for Listening & Reading. 2005. pap. 27.00 incl. audio compact disk (978-0-86647-203-6(7)) Pro Lingua Assocs., Inc.

Fine, Edith Hope. Barbara McClintock: Nobel Prize Geneticist. 1998. (People to Know Ser.). (Illus.). 128p. (YA). (gr. 6-12). lib. bdg. 26.60 (978-0-89490-983-2(5)) Enslow Pubs., Inc.

Florence, Donne. John Steinbeck: America's Author. 2000. (People to Know Ser.). (Illus.). 128p. (YA). (gr. 6-12). lib. bdg. 26.60 (978-0-7660-1150-2(X)) Enslow Pubs., Inc.

Frisch, Aaron. Albert Einstein. 2005. (Illus.). 48p. (J). (gr. 5-9). 21.95 (978-1-58341-328-9(6) , Creative Education) Creative Co., The.

Gogerly, Liz. The Freeing of Nelson Mandela. 2004. (Days That Shook the World Ser.). (Illus.). 47p. (J). lib. bdg. 28.56 (978-0-7398-6648-1(6)) Raintree.

—Nelson Mandela. 2003. (Leading Lives Ser.). (Illus.). 64p. (J). lib. bdg. 28.50 (978-1-4034-0834-1(3)) Heinemann Library.

Hacker, Carlotta. Nobel Prize Winners. 1998. (Women in Profile Ser.). (Illus.). 48p. (J). (gr. 4). pap. (978-0-7787-0029-6(1)); lib. bdg. (978-0-7787-0007-4(0)) Crabtree Publishing Co.

Hager, Tom. Linus Pauling: And the Chemistry of Life. 1998. (Oxford Portraits in Science Ser.). (Illus.). 144p. (YA). (gr. 7 up). 30.00 (978-0-19-510853-8(1)) Oxford Univ. Pr., Inc.

Hantula, Richard. Alexander Fleming. 2003. (Trailblazers of the Modern World Ser.). (Illus.). 48p. (J). (gr. 5 up). pap. 14.95 (978-0-8368-5243-1(5)); lib. bdg. 30.00 (978-0-8368-5083-3(1)) Stevens, Gareth Inc. (World Almanac Library).

Hasday, Judy L. Albert Einstein: The Giant of 20th Century Science. 2004. (Nobel Prize-Winning Scientists Ser.). (Illus.). 128p. (J). lib. bdg. 26.60 (978-0-7660-2185-3(8)) Enslow Pubs., Inc.

Houghton, Sarah. Elie Wiesel: A Holocaust Survivor Cries Out for Peace. 2003. (High Five Reading Ser.). (Illus.). (J). 64p. lib. bdg. 22.60 (978-0-7368-2792-8(7)); 48p. pap. 8.75 (978-0-7368-2833-8(8)) Capstone Pr., Inc.

—Elie Wiesel: A Holocaust Survivor Cries Out for Peace, 6 vols. (gr. 4 up). 49.95 (978-0-7368-2843-7(5) , High Five) Red Brick Learning.

Kent, Deborah. Mario Molina: Chemist & Nobel Prize Winner. 2004. (Proud Heritage: the Hispanic Library Ser.). (Illus.). 40p. (J). (gr. 3-7). 28.50 (978-1-59296-170-2(3)) Child's World, Inc.

Kepnes, Caroline. Stephen Crane. 2004. (Classic Storytellers Ser.). (Illus.). 48p. (J). (gr. 4-8). lib. bdg. 20.95 (978-1-58415-272-9(9)) Mitchell Lane Pubs., Inc.

Oxlade, Chris. Albert Einstein. 2003. (20th Century History Makers Ser.). (Illus.). 112p. (J). lib. bdg. 32.85 (978-0-7398-5259-0(0)) Raintree.

Pasachoff, Naomi E. Linus Pauling: Advancing Science, Advocating Peace. 2004. (Nobel Prize-Winning Scientists Ser.). (Illus.). 128p. (J). lib. bdg. 26.60 (978-0-7660-2130-3(0)) Enslow Pubs., Inc.

—Niels Bohr: Physicist & Humanitarian. 2003. (Great Minds of Science Ser.). (Illus.). 128p. (J). (gr. 4-10). lib. bdg. 26.60 (978-0-7660-1997-3(7)) Enslow Pubs., Inc.

Raum, Elizabeth. Jane Addams. 2004. (American Lives (Heinemann Library (Firm))). (Illus.). 32p. (J). pap. 7.50 (978-1-4034-5707-3(7)); lib. bdg. (978-1-4034-4992-4(9)) Heinemann Library.

Sanna, Ellyn. John Steinbeck. 2003. (gr. 7-12). lib. bdg. 21.05 (978-0-613-57179-1(7)) Tandem Library Bks.

Slavicek, Louise Chipley. Jimmy Carter. (Great American Presidents Ser.). (Illus.). (gr. 4-8). 2004. 112p. pap. 30.00 (978-0-7910-7790-0(X)); 2003. 100p. 30.00 (978-0-7910-7646-0(6)) Facts On File, Inc. (Chelsea Hse.).

Stiekel, Bettina, et al. The Nobel Book of Answers: The Dalai Lama, Mikhail Gorbachev, Shimon Peres, & Other Nobel Prize Winners Answer Some of Life's Most Intriguing Questions for Young People. 2003. (Illus.). 272p. (J). 17.95 (978-0-689-86310-3(1) , Atheneum) Simon & Schuster Children's Publishing.

Stux, Erica. Enrico Fermi: Trailblazer in Nuclear Physics. 2004. (Nobel Prize-Winning Scientists Ser.). (Illus.). 128p. (J). lib. bdg. 26.60 (978-0-7660-2177-8(7)) Enslow Pubs., Inc.

Tracy, Kathleen. Barbara Mcclintock: Pioneering Geneticist. l.t. ed. 2002. (Unlocking the Secrets of Science Ser.). (Illus.). 56p. (gr. 4-10). lib. bdg. 25.70 (978-1-58415-111-1(0)) Mitchell Lane Pubs., Inc.

—John Steinbeck. 2004. (Classic Storytellers Ser.). (Illus.). 48p. (J). (gr. 4-8). lib. bdg. 20.95 (978-1-58415-271-2(0)) Mitchell Lane Pubs., Inc.

—Robert Koch & the Study of Anthrax. 2004. (Uncharted, Unexplored, & Unexplained Ser.). (Illus.). 48p. (J). (gr. 4-8). lib. bdg. 29.95 (978-1-58415-261-3(3)) Mitchell Lane Pubs., Inc.

Whiting, Jim. Otto Hahn & the Story of Nuclear Fission. 2003. (Unlocking the Secrets of Science Ser.). (Illus.). 56p. (gr. 4-10). lib. bdg. 25.70 (978-1-58415-204-0(4)) Mitchell Lane Pubs., Inc.

Williams, Colleen Madonna Flood. Yasir Arafat. (Major World Leaders Ser.). (Illus.). (gr. 6-12). 2003. 144p. pap. 30.00 (978-0-7910-7186-1(3)); 2002. 112p. 30.00 (978-0-7910-6941-7(9)) Facts On File, Inc. (Chelsea Hse.).

Zannos, Susan. Godfrey Hounsfield & the Invention of CAT Scans. 2002. (Unlocking the Secrets of Science Ser.). (Illus.). 56p. (gr. 4-10). lib. bdg. 17.95 (978-1-58415-119-7(6)) Mitchell Lane Pubs., Inc.

NOCTURNAL ANIMALS

Barlowe, Sy. Learning about Nocturnal Creatures. 2000. (Illus.). 16p. (J). (gr. 3-5). pap. 1.50 (978-0-486-41293-1(8)) Dover Pubns., Inc.

Barnett, Michelle Noble, et al. Theme Pockets - October: Halloween; Night Creatures; Healthy & Happy. Evans, Marilyn, ed. Larsen, Jo, illus. 1999. (Making Books with Pockets). 96p. (J). pap., tchr. ed. 12.99 (978-1-55799-707-4(1) , EMC 593) Evan-Moor Educational Pubs.

Bertolucci, Cristiano, et al. Night & Day. Cucchiariani, Fer, illus. 2003. (Contrasts Ser.). 32p. (J). (gr. 1-4). 14.95 (978-1-57768-523-4(7) , Waterbird Bks.) School Specialty Publishing.

Clarke, Ginjer L. Black Out!: Animals That Live in the Dark: Animals That Live in the Dark. Mueller, Pete, illus. 2008. (All Aboard Science Reader Ser.). 48p. (J). (gr. 1-3). pap. 3.99 (***978-0-448-44824-4(6)*** , Grosset & Dunlap) Penguin Group (USA) Inc.

Davies, Valerie. Animals at Night. 2004. (J). 23.70 (978-1-4103-0128-4(1) , Greenhaven Pr., Inc.) Thomson Gale.

DK Publishing. Night Creatures. 2007. 48p. (J). pap. 3.99 (***978-0-7566-3510-7(1)***) Dorling Kindersley Publishing, Inc.

Gallimard Jeunesse Publishing Staff. Night Creatures. Perols, Sylvaine, illus. 1998. (First Discovery Book Ser.). 24p. (J). (ps-2). 12.95 (978-0-590-11765-4(3)) Scholastic, Inc.

Hirschi, Ron. When Night Comes. 2006. 32p. pap. 9.95 (978-1-59078-417-4(0)) Boyds Mills Pr.

Hirschmann, Kris. Owls, Bats, Wolves & Other Nocturnal Animals. 2003. (World Discovery Science Readers Ser.). (Illus.). 32p. (J). (978-0-439-56628-5(2)) Scholastic, Inc.

Hoff, Mary. Life at Night. 2003. (Illus.). 32p. (J). lib. bdg. (978-1-58341-267-1(0) , Creative Education) Creative Co., The.

Kenah, Katharine. Animals Day & Night. 2004. (Extreme Readers Ser.). (Illus.). 32p. (J). (ps-2). pap. 3.95 (978-0-7696-3183-7(5)) School Specialty Publishing.

Krautwurst, Terry. Night Science for Kids: Exploring the World after Dark. 2005. (Illus.). 144p. (J). pap. 12.95 (978-1-57990-670-2(2)) Lark Bks.

Kudlinski, Kathleen V. The Sunset Switch. Burnett, Lindy, illus. 2005. (Picture Book Ser.). 32p. (978-1-55971-916-2(8) , Two Can Publishing) T&N Children's Publishing.

Lambilly-Bresson, Elisabeth de. Animals of the Night. 2006. (Illus.). 14p. (J). lib. bdg. (***978-0-8368-7833-2(7)***) Stevens, Gareth Inc.

Meredith, S. Night Animals. 2004. (Beginners Ser.). 32p. (J). (gr. 1 up). pap. 4.95 (978-0-7945-0383-3(7)) EDC Publishing.

Meredith, Sue. Night Animals - Interent Referenced (Level 1) 2007. 32p. (J). 4.99 (***978-0-7945-1656-7(4)*** , Usborne) EDC Publishing.

Riley, Terry, illus. Night Creatures. 2001. (Trackpack Ser.). 32p. (J). 4.99 (978-0-439-37477-4(4)) Scholastic, Inc.

Rose, Deborah Lee. One Nighttime Sea. Jenkins, Steve, illus. 2003. 40p. (J). pap. 16.95 (978-0-439-33906-3(5)) Scholastic, Inc.

Schaefer, Lola M. Que Esta Despierto?, 8 bks., Set. Cano, Patricia, tr. 2003. (SPA., Illus.). (J). pap. 37.80 (978-1-4034-2674-1(0)) Heinemann Library.

Smith, Alastair & Furnival, Keith. Night-Time. Butler, John, illus. 2002. (Usborne Lift-The-Flap Book Ser.). (J). (978-0-439-66484-4(5)) Scholastic, Inc.

Turner, Matt. Night Movers. 2003. (Amazing Nature Ser.). (Illus.). 32p. (J). pap. 7.50 (978-1-4034-5402-7(7)); lib. bdg. (978-1-4034-4706-7(3)) Heinemann Library.

Ward, Jennifer. Forest Bright, Forest Night. Henterly, Jamichael, illus. (J). (ps-ps). 2007. 26p. bds. 7.95 (***978-1-58469-089-4(5)***); 2005. 32p. 16.95 (978-1-58469-066-5(6)); 2005. 32p. pap. 8.95 (978-1-58469-067-2(4)) Dawn Pubns.

Weber, Belinda. Nighttime Animals. 2006. (Best Book of... Ser.). (Illus.). 32p. (J). (gr. k-3). 12.95 (978-0-7534-5985-0(X) , Kingfisher) Houghton Mifflin Co. Trade & Reference Div.

Whitehouse, Patricia. Que Esta Despierto? 1 2 3. 2002. (Que Esta Despierto? (What's Awake?) Ser.).Tr. of What's Awake? 1 2 3. (SPA.). 24p. (J). (ps-1). pap. 5.25 (978-1-4034-0640-8(5)) Heinemann Library.

NOISE

Costain, Meredith. Noise! 2000. (gr. k-3). lib. bdg. 11.80 (978-0-613-30635-5(X)) Tandem Library Bks.

Hewitt, Sally. Roar Like a Lion: (Sound) 2002. (Why Can't I Ser.). (Illus.). 32p. (J). lib. bdg. 24.25 (978-1-930643-69-7(1)) Chrysalis Education.

Johnson, Marion. Caillou, What's That Noise. CINAR Corporation Staff, illus. 2004. (Clubhouse Usa Ser.). 24p. (J). pap. 3.95 (978-2-89450-489-5(6)) Chouette Publishing CAN. *Dist:* Perseus Distribution.

Lemieux, Michele. What's That Noise. Lemieux, Michele, illus. unabr. ed. 1998. (Illus.). 32p. (J). (gr. k-3). (978-0-921103-69-1(7)) Kids Can Pr., Ltd.

MacDonald, Ross. Achoo! Bang! Crash! The Noisy Alphabet. MacDonald, Ross, illus. rev. ed. 2003. (Illus.). 32p. (J). (ps-3). 23.90 (978-0-7613-2900-8(5)) Roaring Brook Pr.

My Mini Box of Books: Noises, 4 bks. 2002. (J). bds. 3.98 (978-0-7525-7140-9(0)) Parragon, Inc.

Rau, Dana Meachen. So Many Sounds. Sorra, Kristin, illus. 2001. (Rookie Reader Skill Set Ser.). 24p. (J). (gr. k-2). pap. 4.95 (978-0-516-27290-0(X)); Level A. 19.50 (978-0-516-22209-7(0)) Scholastic Library Publishing. (Children's Pr.).

—So Many Sounds. 2001. (gr. k-3). lib. bdg. 12.95 (978-0-613-54672-0(5)) Tandem Library Bks.

The something Noise: Individual Title Six-Packs. (gr. 1-2). 25.00 (978-0-7635-9130-4(0)) Rigby Education.

Steck-Vaughn Staff. Cities: City Noises/Working Noises. 1998. pap. (978-0-8172-8628-6(4)) Steck-Vaughn.

Thomas, Joyce Carol. Shouting! Lee, Annie, illus. 2007. 32p. (gr. k-6). 16.99 (978-0-7868-0664-5(8)) Disney Pr.

Thomson, Ruth. Ruidos. (Coleccion Mi Primer Libro). (SPA.). 32p. (J). 13.95 (978-84-207-3779-9(8) , ANY872) Grupo Anaya, S.A. ESP. *Dist:* Continental Bk. Co., Inc.

Whitehouse, Patricia. Loud Sounds, Soft Sounds. 2007. (J). (978-1-60044-191-2(2)) Rourke Publishing, LLC.

NOISE—FICTION

Advantage Publishers Group & Rojany Buccieri, Lisa. Let's Make Noise Around the House. 2007. (Illus.). 10p. (J). 12.95 (978-1-59223-640-4(5) , Silver Dolphin Bks.) Advantage Pubs. Group.

Anderson, Sara. Noisy City Day. 2005. (Illus.). 6p. (J). bds. 7.95 (978-1-59354-054-8(X)) Handprint Bks.

—Noisy City Night. 2005. (Illus.). 6p. (J). bds. 7.95 (978-1-59354-055-5(8)) Handprint Bks.

Anthony, Mary. Noisy Workbench: My Electronic Sound & Lift-the-Flap Storybook. Giles, Mike, illus. 2004. (Little Tikes Ser.). 5p. (J). bds. 14.99 (978-0-7944-0364-5(6) , Reader's Digest Children's Bks.) Reader's Digest Children's Publishing, Inc.

Apperley, Dawn. Don't Wake the Baby. Apperley, Dawn, illus. 2001. (Illus.). 32p. (J). (ps-k). 17.99 (978-0-7475-5003-7(4)) Bloomsbury Publishing Plc GBR. *Dist:* Trafalgar Square Publishing.

Banks, Steven. The Song That Never Ends. DePorter, Vince, illus. 2004. (Ready-to-Read Ser.: Vol. 4). 32p. (J). pap. 3.99 (978-0-689-86528-2(7) , Simon Spotlight/ Nickelodeon) Simon & Schuster Children's Publishing.

—Song That Never Ends. 2004. (gr. k-3). lib. bdg. 11.80 (978-0-613-73449-3(1)) Tandem Library Bks.

Beckstrand, Karl. Sounds in the House. Jones, Channing, illus. 2004. 24p. (J). per. 5.95 (***978-0-9672012-5-2(X)***) Gozo Bks., LLC.

Berger, Samantha. Honk! Toot! Beep! 2001. (Hello Reader! Ser.). (Illus.). (J). (978-0-606-20709-6(0)) Tandem Library Bks.

Bernstein, Margery. Stop That Noise! Handelman, Dorothy, photos by. 1999. (Real Kids Readers Ser.). (Illus.). 48p. (gr. 1-3). lib. bdg. 18.90 (978-0-7613-2060-9(1)); 32p. (J). (gr. 2-4). pap. 4.99 (978-0-7613-2085-2(7)) Lerner Publishing Group. (Millbrook Pr.).

—Stop That Noise! 1999. (J). (978-0-606-19174-6(7)); (gr. 3-6). lib. bdg. 11.80 (978-0-613-16851-9(8)) Tandem Library Bks.

Bowdish, Lynea. Thunder Doesn't Scare Me! Wallace, John, illus. 2001. (Rookie Reader Espanol Ser.). 32p. (J). (gr. k-2). pap. 4.95 (978-0-516-27291-7(8) , Children's Pr.) Scholastic Library Publishing.

—Thunder Doesn't Scare Me! 2001. (gr. k-3). lib. bdg. 12.95 (978-0-613-54706-2(3)) Tandem Library Bks.

—Los Truenos No Me Asustan! Wallace, John, illus. 2001. (Rookie Espanol Ser.). (SPA.). 32p. (J). (gr. k-2). 19.50 (978-0-516-22354-4(2) , Children's Pr.) Scholastic Library Publishing.

Cleary, Beverly. The Hullabaloo ABC. 2000. pap. (978-0-688-17715-7(8)) HarperCollins Pubs.

Cowley, Rich. Bang! Bang! Toot Toot. Cowley, Rich, illus. 2001. (Snappy Sounds Ser.: No. 3). (Illus.). 24p. (J). (gr. k-ps). reprint ed. bds. 3.95 (978-1-55209-034-3(5)) Annick Pr., Ltd. CAN. *Dist:* Firefly Bks., Ltd.

Crimi, Carolyn. The Louds Move In! Dunnick, Regan, illus. 2006. 32p. (J). 14.95 (978-0-7614-5221-8(4)) Cavendish, Marshall Corp.

Davol, Marguerite W. Why Butterflies Go by on Silent Wings. Roth, Robert, illus. 2001. (J). lib. bdg. (978-0-531-33322-8(1) , Orchard Bks.) Scholastic, Inc.

Disney Staff. Pooh's Noisy Book. 1999. (Learn & Grow Busy Book Ser.). (Illus.). 12p. (J). (ps-3). 6.99 (978-0-7364-0136-4(9)) Mouse Works.

Dougherty, Terri. The Camping Scare. Thompson, Jeffrey, illus. 2006. (Read-It! Readers Ser.). (J). 19.93 (978-1-4048-2405-8(7)) Picture Window Bks.

Firth, Barbara, illus. Let's Go Home, Little Bear. 2002. (Little Bear Picture Bks.). (J). 13.83 (978-0-7587-2976-7(6)) Book Wholesalers, Inc.

Franco, Betsy. Summer's Beat. Middleton, Charlotte, illus. 2007. 40p. (J). 15.99 (978-1-4169-1237-8(1) , McElderry, Margaret K.) Simon & Schuster Children's Publishing.

Fuge, Charles. Yip! Snap! Yap! 2004. (Illus.). (J). 22p. bds. 6.95 (978-1-58246-097-0(3)); 24p. 14.95 (978-1-58246-046-8(9)) Ten Speed Pr. (Tricycle Pr.).

Gerstein, Mordecai. Carolinda Clatter! unabr. ed. 2007. (Illus.). (J). (ps-2). 28.95 incl. audio compact disk (***978-1-59519-958-4(6)***) Live Oak Media.

Gerstein, Mordicai. Carolinda Clatter! 2005. (Illus.). 40p. (J). 16.95 (978-1-59643-063-1(X)) Roaring Brook Pr.

Glass, Beth Raisner & Lubner, Susan. Noises at Night. Whatley, Bruce, illus. 2005. 32p. (J). (ps-3). 15.95 (978-0-8109-5750-3(7) , Abrams Bks. for Young Readers) Abrams, Harry N. , Inc.

Goss, Leon. By the Light of the Moon. Luo, Shiyin Sean, illus. 2005. (J). pap. (978-1-933156-12-5(0)); per. (978-1-933156-05-7(8)) GSVQ Publishing. (VisionQuest Kids).

Hill, Eric. Spot's Noisy Tractor. Hill, Eric, illus. 2008. 12p. (J). (ps-k). bds. 12.99 (***978-0-399-25166-5(9)*** , Putnam Juvenile) Penguin Group (USA) Inc.

Howard, Arthur. The Hubbub Above. 2005. (Illus.). 32p. (J). 16.00 (978-0-15-204592-0(9)) Harcourt Trade Pubs.

Hubbell, Patricia. Pots & Pans. deGroat, Diane, illus. 1998. (Growing Tree Ser.). 24p. (J). (ps up). 9.99 (978-0-694-01072-1(3)) HarperCollins Pubs.

Johansen, Hanna & Gleich, Jacky. Calla un Momento. 2002. (SPA., Illus.). 32p. (978-84-89804-53-1(2)) Loguez Ediciones ESP. *Dist:* Lectorum Pubns., Inc.

Keep, Richard. A Thump from Upstairs: Starring Mr. Boo & Max. Keep, Richard, illus. 2005. (Illus.). 36p. (J). (ps-ps). 15.95 (978-1-56145-348-1(X)) Peachtree Pubs., Ltd.

Kenyon, Tony. Oops! It's Olly Bear. 2003. (Illus.). 32p. (J). 18.00 (978-1-85881-899-3(0)) Orion Bks. Ltd. GBR. *Dist:* Trafalgar Square Publishing.

Kramer, Alan & Kramer, Candice. Brer Rabbit Hears a Big Noise in the Woods: An African /American Folktale. 2006. spiral bd. 42.00 (*978-1-4108-7163-3(0)) Benchmark Education Co.

Laguna, Sofie. Too Loud Lily. Argent, Kerry, illus. 2004. 32p. (J). pap. 14.95 (978-0-439-57913-1(9)) Scholastic, Inc.

Landry, Leo. Space Boy. 2007. 32p. (J). (gr. k-3). 16.00 (*978-0-618-60568-2(1)) Houghton Mifflin Co.

Maier, Inger M. When Fuzzy Was Afraid of Big & Loud Things. Candon, Jennifer, illus. 2005. 32p. (J). 14.95 (978-1-59147-322-0(5)); pap. 8.95 (978-1-59147-323-7(3)) American Psychological Assn. (Magination Pr.).

Mandy, et al. Hattie's House. (Illus.). (J). 2005. (URD, ENG, VIE, CHI & BEN.). 24p. 9.95 (978-1-84059-156-9(0)); 2000. (GUJ, ENG, VIE, URD & CHI., 16p. pap. 9.95 (978-1-84059-154-5(4)); 2000. (TUR, ENG, VIE, CHI & BEN., 16p. pap. 9.95 (978-1-84059-155-2(2)); 2000. (BEN, ENG, VIE, CHI & GUJ., 16p. pap. 9.95 (978-1-84059-152-1(8)) Milet Publishing.

—Hattie's House. Wood, Kim Marie, tr. from ENG. 2000. (Senses Ser.). (VIE, ENG, URD, TUR & CHI., Illus.). 16p. (J). pap. 9.95 (978-1-84059-157-6(9)) Milet Publishing.

Mayo, Margaret. Choo Choo Clickety-Clack! Ayliffe, Alex, illus. 2005. 32p. (J). (ps-2). 14.95 (978-1-57505-819-1(7)) Lerner Publishing Group.

McKee, David. Isabel's Noisy Tummy. 2007. (Illus.). 26p. (J). (ps-k). pap. 6.99 (978-1-84270-576-6(8)) Andersen GBR. *Dist:* Independent Pubs. Group.

Medearis, Angela Shelf. Lucy's Quiet Book. Ernst, Lisa Campbell, illus. 2004. (Green Light Readers Level 2 Ser.). 24p. (J). 12.95 (978-0-15-205144-0(9)); pap. 3.95 (978-0-15-205143-3(0)) Harcourt Children's Bks. (Green Light Readers).

Meyer, Eleanor Walsh. The Keeper of Ugly Sounds. Guzner, Vlad, illus. 1998. 32p. (J). (gr. k-3). 16.95 (978-1-890817-02-2(3)) Winslow Pr.

Milgrim, David. See Santa Nap. Milgrim, David, illus. 2004. (Adventures of Otto Ser.). (Illus.). 32p. (J). 14.95 (978-0-689-85928-1(7) , Atheneum) Simon & Schuster Children's Publishing.

Moody-Luther, Jacqueline. Stop that noise - word World. 2007. 12p. (J). 12.95 (*978-1-59764-296-5(7)) New Line Bks.

Morris, Eileen. And Next Came A Roar. 2005. 16p. pap. 3.99 (978-0-9768852-0-7(4)) Shnoozles, LLC.

Morton, Christine. No Te Preocupes, Guille. McMullen, Nigel, illus. (Buenas Noches Coleccion). (SPA.). 26p. (J). (gr. k-3). 8.95 (978-958-04-5088-7(9)) Norma S.A. COL. *Dist:* Distribuidora Norma, Inc., Lectorum Pubns., Inc.

Mozelle, Shirley. The Bear Upstairs. Cushman, Doug, illus. 2005. 32p. (J). 16.95 (978-0-8050-6820-7(1) , Holt, Henry & Co. Bks. For Young Readers) Holt, Henry & Co.

Murphy, Mary. Please Be Quiet! Murphy, Mary, illus. 1999. (Illus.). 32p. (J). (gr. k-ps). 9.95 (978-0-395-97113-0(6)) Houghton Mifflin Co. Trade & Reference Div.

Oneal, Katherine. Family Series Loud Family. 2008. (J). (978-0-310-70984-8(9)) Zonderkidz.

Packard, Mary. Don't Make a Sound. Yerkes, Lane, illus. 2004. 16p. (J). (gr. 1 up). lib. bdg. 19.33 (978-0-8368-4099-5(2)) Stevens, Gareth Inc.

Pearson, Debora. Big City Song! Reed, Lynn Rowe, illus. 2006. 32p. (J). 16.95 (978-0-8234-1988-3(6)) Holiday Hse., Inc.

Peters, Andrew Fusek & Peters, Polly. Roar Bull, Roar! Weckmann, Anke, illus. 2007. 155p. (J). pap. 8.95 (978-1-84507-520-0(X)) Lincoln, Frances Ltd. GBR. *Dist:* Perseus Distribution.

Rosen, Michael. Bear's Day Out. Reynolds, Adrian, illus. 2007. 32p. (J). (ps-3). 16.95 (*978-1-59990-007-0(6)) Bloomsbury Publishing.

Schotter, Roni. When the Wizzy Foot Goes Walking. Wohnoutka, Mike, illus. 2007. (J). (*978-0-525-47791-9(2)); 32p. 16.99 (978-0-525-47791-4(8)) Penguin Group (USA) Inc. (Dutton Juvenile).

Shore, Diane Z. A Rosa le Gusta Leer. Day, Larry, illus. 2005. (Rookie Reader Espanol Ser.). (SPA & ESP.). 31p. (J). (gr. k-2). pap. 4.95 (978-0-516-24698-7(4) , Children's Pr.) Scholastic Library Publishing.

Shore, Diane ZuHone. Rosa Loves to Read. Day, Larry, tr. Day, Larry, illus. 2004. (Rookie Reader Ser.). 31p. (J). 19.50 (978-0-516-21723-9(2) , Children's Pr.) Scholastic Library Publishing.

Singer, Marilyn. City Lullaby. Cneut, Carll, illus. 2007. 32p. (J). (ps-3). 16.00 (*978-0-618-60703-7(X) , Clarion Bks.) Houghton Mifflin Co. Trade & Reference Div.

Smith, Kathryn. Cheep! Cheep! Noisy Farmyard Fun. Bolton, Bill, illus. 2004. 10p. (J). bds. 5.95 (978-0-7641-5749-3(3)) Barron's Educational Series, Inc.

Spence, Rob & Spence, Amy. Clickety Clack. Spengler, Margaret, illus. 1999. 32p. (J). (ps-3). 15.99 (978-0-670-87946-5(0) , Viking Juvenile) Penguin Group (USA) Inc.

Stamper, Judith Bauer. A Squeak, a Squeal, & a Screech! Fisher, Cynthia, illus. 1999. (Scholastic At-Home Phonics Reading Program Ser.: Vol. 31). 24p. (J). (978-0-590-68779-9(4)) Scholastic, Inc.

Stevens, April. Waking up Wendell. Hills, Tad, illus. 2007. 40p. (J). (ps-3). 15.99 (*978-0-375-83621-3(7)); lib. bdg. 18.99 (*978-0-375-93893-1(1)) Random Hse. Children's Bks. (Schwartz & Wade Bks.).

Thiesing, Lisa. A Dark & Noisy Night: A Silly Thriller with Peggy the Pig. 2005. (Dutton Easy Reader Ser.). (Illus.). 32p. (J). (*978-1-4156-1784-7(8) , Dutton Juvenile) Penguin Group (USA) Inc.

Torrisi, Cathy. Not Now, Mr. N! Yeagle, Barbara, illus. 2002. (Read-to-Me Ser.). 24p. (J). (978-0-7665-1214-6(2)) Letter People, The.

Waber, Bernard. The Mouse That Snored. 2004. (Illus.). 32p. (J). (gr. k-3). 5.95 (978-0-618-43954-6(4) , Walter Lorraine) Houghton Mifflin Co. Trade & Reference Div.

Weiss, Ellen, et al. Babar & the Scary Day. Gibert, Jean Claude, illus. 2004. 24p. (J). (ps-3). 9.95 (978-0-8109-5019-1(7)) Abrams, Harry N. , Inc.

Wells, Rosemary. Noisy Nora. 32p. (J). (ps-2). 2000. (Pied Piper Bks.: Vol. 1). (Illus.). pap. 6.99 (978-0-14-056728-1(3) , Puffin); 1999. 15.99 (978-0-670-88722-4(6) , Viking Juvenile) Penguin Group (USA) Inc.

—Noisy Nora. 2000. (978-0-606-18437-3(6)) Tandem Library Bks.

Williams, Carol Ann. Loud Lily Ann. Mai-Wyss, Tatjana, illus. 2008. 32p. (J). (ps-3). 16.99 (978-0-399-24277-9(5) , Putnam Juvenile) Penguin Group (USA) Inc.

Willis, Jeanne. The Really Rude Rhino. Ross, Tony, illus. 2007. 32p. (J). pap. 9.95 (978-1-84270-571-1(7)) Andersen GBR. *Dist:* Independent Pubs. Group.

—Shhh! Ross, Tony, illus. 2007. 32p. (ps-2). pap. 7.99 (978-0-7868-5685-5(8)) Hyperion Pr.

Willson, Sarah. Do Not Wake Jake. Johnson, Meredith, illus. 2006. (Step-By-Step Readers Ser.). (J). (978-1-59939-059-8(0) , Reader's Digest Young Families, Inc.) Reader's Digest Children's Publishing, Inc.

Ziefert, Harriet. Noisy Barn! Taback, Simms, illus. 2003. 14p. 8.95 (978-1-59354-013-5(2)) Blue Apple Bks.

NOMADS

Gallagher, Debbie. Portable Homes. 2007. (J). (*978-1-59920-150-4(X)) Smart Apple Media.

NONCONFORMITY

see Dissent

NONOBJECTIVE ART

see Art, Abstract

NONSENSE VERSES

see also Limericks

Adams, Pam. There Was an Old Lady Who Swallowed a Fly. Adams, Pam, illus. 2002. (Illus.). (J). 22.72 (978-0-7587-0154-1(3)) Book Wholesalers, Inc.

—There Was an Old Lady Who Swallowed a Fly. Adams, Pam, illus. 2001. (Live Oak Readalong Ser.). (Illus.). (J). 28.95 incl. audio compact disk (978-1-59112-409-2(3)) Live Oak Media.

—There Was an Old Lady Who Swallowed a Fly. unabr. ed. 2001. (Live Oak Readalong Ser.). (Illus.). (J). (ps-2). 25.95 incl. audio (978-0-87499-779-8(8)) Live Oak Media.

Adams, Pam, illus. There Was an Old Lady Who Swallowed a Fly. 2000. 16p. (J). (ps-k). bds. 5.99 (978-0-85953-727-8(7)) Child's Play-International.

Adams, Pam, tr. & illus. There Was an Old Lady Who Swallowed a Fly. Adams, Pam, illus. 2003. (Classic Books with Holes). (J). 4.99 (978-0-85953-134-4(1)) Child's Play-International.

Agee, Jon. Sit on a Potato Pan, Otis! More Palindromes. Agee, Jon, illus. 1999. (Illus.). 80p. (J). (gr. 4-7). 14.41 (978-0-374-31808-6(5) , Farrar, Straus & Giroux (BYR)) Farrar, Straus & Giroux.

Barrett, Judi. I Knew Two Who Said Moo. Moreton, Daniel, illus. 2003. 32p. (J). pap. 7.99 (978-0-689-85935-9(X) , Aladdin) Simon & Schuster Children's Publishing.

Belloc, Hilaire. A Moral Alphabet: In Words of from One T. 2006. (Illus.). pap. 16.95 (*978-1-4286-1934-0(8)) Kessinger Publishing, LLC.

Carroll, Lewis, pseud. Jabberwocky. Myers, Christopher, illus. rev. ed. 2007. 32p. (YA). (gr. 4 up). 15.99 (*978-1-4231-0372-1(6) , Jump at the Sun) Hyperion Bks. for Children.

—Jabberwocky. Jorisch, Stephane, illus. 2004. (Beware the Jabberwock... Ser.). 40p. (YA). (gr. 3 up). (978-1-55337-079-6(1)) Kids Can Pr., Ltd.

Chaudet, Annette. The Nose Book. 2007. (Illus.). 56p. (J). pap. 16.95 (*978-1-932636-36-9(6)) Pronghorn Pr.

Child's Play Staff. There Was an Old Lady Who Swallowed a Fly. Adams, Pam, illus. 1999. (Books with Holes Ser.). 16p. (J). (ps-3). 19.99 (978-0-85953-635-6(1)) Child's Play-International.

Densmore, Don. The Tongue Twister Experiments Student Workbook. Evans, Andrew, illus. 2007. 60p. per. 20.00 (*978-0-9787113-5-1(1) , Ithaca Pr.) Authors & Artists Publishers of New York, Inc.

Dingles, Molly. Jinka, Jinka Jelly Bean. Bingler, Aimee, illus. 1998. 38p. (J). (ps-6). 23.00 (978-1-891997-03-7(3)) Dingles & Co.

Douglas, Vincent & School Specialty Publishing Staff. Rhymes, Songs, & Games. 2004. (Playful Learning Ser.). (Illus.). 128p. (J). (gr. k-k). pap. 10.95 (978-0-7696-3301-5(3) , American Education Publishing) School Specialty Publishing.

Dowell, Ruth I. Move over, Mother Goose! Finger Plays, Action Verses & Funny Rhymes. Charner, Kathleen, ed. Scott, Concetta C., illus. 2004. 126p. (Orig.). (ps-1). pap. 12.95 (978-0-87659-113-0(6) , 10006) Gryphon Hse., Inc.

Foster, John L. My First Oxford Book of Nonsense Poems. 2006. (Illus.). 96p. (YA). 14.95 (978-0-19-276275-7(3)) Oxford Univ. Pr., Inc.

Foster, John L., ed. Completely Crazy Poems. 2003. (Illus.). 96p. (J). pap. 7.99 (978-0-00-714802-8(X)) HarperCollins Pubs. Ltd. GBR. *Dist:* Independent Pubs. Group.

—Seriously Scary Poems. 2003. (Illus.). 96p. (J). pap. 7.95 (978-0-00-714801-1(1)) HarperCollins Pubs. Ltd. GBR. *Dist:* Independent Pubs. Group.

Fyleman, Rose. Mary Middling & Other Silly Folk: Nursery Rhymes & Nonsense Poems. Bandlow, Katja, illus. 2004. 32p. (J). (gr. k-3). tchr. ed. 16.00 (978-0-618-38141-8(4) , Clarion Bks.) Houghton Mifflin Co. Trade & Reference Div.

Grossman, Bill. Timothy Tunny Swallowed a Bunny. 2003. (gr. k-3). lib. bdg. 15.30 (978-0-613-60115-3(7)) Tandem Library Bks.

Guarino, Deborah. Is Your Mama a Llama? Kellogg, Steven, illus. 2002. (J). 13.83 (978-0-7587-2867-8(0)) Book Wholesalers, Inc.

Guarino, Deborah & Kellogg, Steven. Ta Maman Est-Elle un Lama? (FRE., Illus.). (J). pap. 7.99 (978-0-590-74555-0(7)) Scholastic, Inc.

Guinness, Louise, ed. The Everyman Book of Nonsense Verse. 2005. (Everyman Library Children's Classics). (Illus.). 256p. (J). (ps-17). 15.95 (978-1-4000-4425-2(1) , Everyman's Library) Knopf Publishing Group.

Hample, Stuart E. Silly Book. 2004. (Illus.). 32p. (J). 15.99 (978-0-7636-2256-5(7)) Candlewick Pr.

Lear, Edward. Bisky Bats & Pussy Cats: The Animal Nonsense of Edward Lear. Harrison, Matilda, illus. (J). 2001. 32p. pap. 11.00 (978-0-7475-4124-0(8)); 1998. 24p. 19.99 (978-0-7475-3556-0(6)) Bloomsbury Publishing Plc GBR. *Dist:* Trafalgar Square Publishing.

—Edward Lear. Mendelson, Edward, ed. Huliska-Beith, Laura, illus. 2001. (Poetry for Young People Ser.). 48p. 14.95 (978-0-8069-3077-0(2)) Sterling Publishing Co., Inc.

—Nonsense! Fisher, Valorie, illus. 2004. 40p. (J). 16.95 (978-0-689-86380-6(2) , Atheneum/Anne Schwartz Bks.) Simon & Schuster Children's Publishing.

—Nonsense Verse. 1999. (Illus.). 35p. 12.95 (978-1-85149-704-1(8)) Antique Collectors' Club.

—The Owl & the Pussycat. Marshall, James, illus. 1998. (Michael di Capua Bks.). 32p. (J). (gr. k up). 15.89 (978-0-06-205011-3(7)) HarperCollins Pubs.

—The Pelican Chorus: And Other Nonsense. Marcellino, Fred, illus. 2004. 40p. (J). pap. 6.99 (978-0-06-057571-7(9) , Harper Trophy) HarperCollins Pubs.

—The Quangle Wangle's Hat. Voce, Louise, illus. 2005. 40p. (J). (ps-2). 15.99 (978-0-7636-1289-4(8)) Candlewick Pr.

—There Was A Young Lady Whose Nose.... 2006. 132p. (J). 12.95 (978-1-59764-190-6(1)) New Line Bks.

—A Was Once an Apple Pie. MacDonald, Suse, illus. 2005. 32p. (J). (ps-ps). pap. 12.99 (978-0-439-66056-3(4) , Orchard Bks.) Scholastic, Inc.

Mimi. A Pot is Not... Webb, Thulula, illus. 1999. (Jake's World Ser.). 12p. (ps-k). 9.95 (978-1-892780-00-3(3)) Giggles Group, Inc., The.

Plourde, Lynn. Pigs in the Mud in the Middle of the Rud. Schoenherr, John, illus. ed. 2006. 32p. 15.95 (978-0-89272-719-3(5)) Down East Bks.

Radunsky, Eugenia. Yucka Drucka Droni. Radunsky, Vladimir, illus. 1998. 40p. (J). (ps-1). pap. 15.95 (978-0-590-09837-3(3)) Scholastic, Inc.

Ravishankar, Anushka & Ramanathan, Rathna, contrib. by. Anything but a Grabooberry. 2003. (Illus.). 48p. (J). 9.99 (978-81-86211-43-4(8)) Penguin Group (USA) Inc.

Rosen, Michael. Michael Rosen's Book of Nonsense. Mackie, Clare, illus. 2003. 48p. pap. (978-0-7500-2671-0(5) , Hodder Wayland) Hodder Children's Division.

—Walking the Bridge of Your Nose. 1999. (978-0-606-16560-0(6)) Tandem Library Bks.

Rosenbloom, Joseph. Giggle Fit: Tricky Tongue-Twisters. 2002. (ps-2). lib. bdg. 12.95 (978-0-613-87485-4(4)) Tandem Library Bks.

Ross, K. K. The Little Red Car. Alley, R. W., illus. (Jellybean Bks.). 24p. (J). (ps-k). 2000. 2.99 (978-0-375-80142-6(1)); 1999. lib. bdg. 7.99 (978-0-375-90142-3(6)) Random Hse. Children's Bks. (Random Hse. Bks. for Young Readers).

Rowinski, Kate. Cats in the Dark. Bishop, Bonnie, illus. 1998. 32p. (J). (ps-3). 14.95 (978-0-89272-427-7(7)) Down East Bks.

Sea Star Editors. Silly Stories to Tickle Your Funny Bone. 2000. (Reading Rainbow Readers Ser.). (YA). (978-0-606-19631-4(5)) Tandem Library Bks.

Seuss, Dr. Quomodo Invidiosulus Nomine Grinchus Christi Natalem Abrogaverit: How the Grinch Stole Christmas. Tunberg, Jennifer Morrish & Tunberg, Terence O., trs. from ENG. 1998. (LAT., Illus.). 64p. (ps-3). (J). 25.00 (978-0-86516-419-2(3)); (YA). 19.00 (978-0-86516-420-8(7)) Bolchazy-Carducci Pubs.

Shortsleeve, Kevin. 13 Monsters Who Should Be Avoided. Austin, Michael, illus. 1998. 32p. (J). (gr. 1-5). 16.95 (978-1-56145-146-3(0)) Peachtree Pubs., Ltd.

Sloat, Teri. There Was an Old Lady Who Swallowed a Trout. Ruffins, Reynold, illus. 2002. (J). 26.47 (978-0-7587-3781-6(5)) Book Wholesalers, Inc.

—There Was an Old Lady Who Swallowed a Trout. Ruffins, Reynold, illus. rev. ed. 32p. (J). (gr. k-2). 2002. pap. 7.95 (978-0-8050-6900-6(3)); 1998. 17.95 (978-0-8050-4294-8(6)) Holt, Henry & Co. (Holt, Henry & Co. Bks. For Young Readers).

—There Was an Old Lady Who Swallowed a Trout. 2002. (ps-2). lib. bdg. 15.25 (978-0-613-88115-9(X)) Tandem Library Bks.

Tripp, Wallace. Rose's Are Red, Violet's Are Blue: And Other Silly Poems. Tripp, Wallace, illus. 1999. (Illus.). 32p. (YA). (gr. 2-5). 15.95 (978-0-316-85440-5(9)) Little Brown & Co.

Walrus Books. Children's Treasure Chest: Fairy Tales, Nursery Rhymes, & Nonsense Verse. 2004. (Illus.). 386p. (J). (gr. k-12). 29.95 (978-1-55285-579-9(1)) Whitecap Bks., Ltd. CAN. *Dist:* Graphic Arts Ctr. Publishing Co.

Walsh, Maria Elena. El Reino del Reves. Hilb, Nora, illus. 2001. (SPA.). 96p. (J). (gr. 3-5). pap. 10.95 (978-950-511-636-2(5)) Santillana USA Publishing Co., Inc.

Westcott, Nadine Bernard. I Know an Old Lady Who Swallowed a Fly. Westcott, Nadine Bernard, illus. 2002. (Illus.). (J). 13.79 (978-0-7587-6681-6(5)) Book Wholesalers, Inc.

—I Know an Old Lady Who Swallowed a Fly, 3 vols. Westcott, Nadine Bernard, illus. 2003. (Sing-Along Stories Ser.). (Illus.). 11p. (J). (ps-ps). bds. 6.99 (978-0-316-93084-0(9) , Tingley, Megan Bks.) Little, Brown Bks. for Young Readers.

NONVIOLENCE

Semelin, Jacques. Nonviolence Explained to My Children. 2002. (Explained to My Child Ser.). 96p. 14.95 (978-1-56924-514-9(2)); pap. 7.95 (978-1-56924-515-6(0)) Da Capo Pr., Inc.

NORBY THE ROBOT (FICTITIOUS CHARACTER)—FICTION

Asimov, Isaac & Asimov, Janet. Norby & the Lost Princess. 129p. (J). lib. bdg. 20.90 (978-0-8027-6593-2(9)) Walker & Co.

Asimov, Janet & Asimov, Isaac. Norby & the Court Jester. l.t. ed. 1999. 168p. 24.95 (978-0-7838-8610-7(1)) Thorndike Pr.

NORMANDY, ATTACK ON, 1944

Rice, Earle. Normandy. 2002. (Battles That Changed the World Ser.). (Illus.). (J). 122p. pap. 13.25 (978-0-7910-7109-0(X)); 112p. 30.00 (978-0-7910-6687-4(8)) Facts On File, Inc. (Chelsea Hse.).

Sheehan, Sean. D-Day, June 6, 1944. 2002. (Days That Shook the World Ser.). (Illus.). 47p. (J). lib. bdg. 27.12 (978-0-7398-5232-3(9)) Raintree.

NORMANDY (FRANCE)—FICTION

Yonge, Charlotte M. The Little Duke. 2005. 26.95 (978-1-4218-0318-0(6)); 164p. pap. 11.95 (978-1-4218-0418-7(2)) 1st World Publishing, Inc. (1st World Library - Literary Society).

—The Little Duke. 2004. reprint ed. pap. 15.95 (978-1-4179-9958-3(6)); pap. 1.99 (978-1-4179-9908-8(X)) Kessinger Publishing, LLC.

—Little Duke EasyRead Comfort Edition. 2006. pap. (*978-1-4250-0856-7(9)) Assistedreadingbooks.com Inc.

—Little Duke EasyRead Edition. 2006. pap. (*978-1-4250-0269-5(2)) Assistedreadingbooks.com Inc.

—Little Duke EasyRead Large Edition. 2006. pap. (*978-1-4250-1299-1(X)) Assistedreadingbooks.com Inc.

NORMANS

see also Northmen

Abbott, Jacob. History of William the Conqueror. 2003. 291p. 89.00 (978-0-7950-4508-0(5)) New Library Press .Net.

Hamilton, Janice. The Norman Conquest of England. 2007. (Pivotal Moments in History Ser.). 160p. (YA). (gr. 9-12). lib. bdg. 38.60 (*978-0-8225-5902-3(1) , Twenty-First Century Bks.) Lerner Publishing Group.

HOCPP 1101 the Norman Conquest. 2006. spiral bd. 23.50 (*978-1-60308-101-6(1)) In the Hands of a Child.

Jarvie, Gordon & Jarvie, Frances. Scotland's Vikings. Galloway, Fhiona, illus. 1999. (Scottie Bks.). 40p. (J). (gr. 3-7). pap. 6.95 (978-0-11-495813-8(0)) Stationery Office, The GBR. *Dist:* Balogh International, Inc.

Shuter, Jane. Carisbrooke Castle. 1999. (Visiting the Past Ser.). 32p. (J). (gr. 5-7). lib. bdg. 24.22 (978-1-57572-857-5(5)) Heinemann Library.

NORMANS—FICTION

McCaughren, Tom. Ride a Pale Horse. 1999. (Illus.). 144p. (YA). (gr. 4 up). 14.95 (978-1-901737-08-0(X)) Anvil Bks., Ltd. IRL. *Dist:* Dufour Editions, Inc., Irish Bks. & Media, Inc.

—Ride a Pale Horse. 2001. (Illus.). 144p. pap. 11.95 (978-1-901737-09-7(8)) Dufour Editions, Inc.

NORSEMEN

see Northmen

NORTH AFRICA

see Africa, North

NORTH AMERICA

Adasiewicz, Sue. Your Papers, Please: Crossing Borders. 2007. (Shockwave: People & Communities Ser.). (Illus.). 36p. (J). (gr. 4-6). lib. bdg. 25.00 (*978-0-531-17572-9(3) , Children's Pr.) Scholastic Library Publishing.

Aloian, Molly & Kalman, Bobbie. Explore North America. 2007. (Explore the Continents Ser.). (Illus.). 32p. (J). (gr. 1-7). (*978-0-7787-3075-0(1)); pap. (*978-0-7787-3089-7(1)) Crabtree Publishing Co.

Alter, Judy. Discovering North America's Land, People, & Wildlife: A MyReportLinks.com Book. 2004. (Continents of the World Ser.). (Illus.). 48p. (J). lib. bdg. 25.26 (978-0-7660-5206-2(0) , MyReportLinks.com Bks.) Enslow Pubs., Inc.

Bagley, Katie. North America. 2002. (Continents Ser.). (Illus.). 79p. (J). (gr. 1-2). 18.60 (978-0-7368-1419-5(1) , Bridgestone Bks.) Capstone Pr., Inc.

Banting, Erinn. North America. 2005. (Illus.). 32p. (J). (ps-6). lib. bdg. 26.00 (978-1-59036-321-8(3)); pap. 7.95 (978-1-59036-328-7(0)) Weigl Pubs., Inc.

Bianchi, John-Paul, ed. North America. 2001. (World in Focus Ser.). (Illus.). (YA). (gr. 5 up). 64p. pap., suppl. ed. 16.20 (978-1-56711-348-6(6) , Blackbirch Pr., Inc.); 32p. pap., act. bk. ed. 11.20 (978-1-56711-350-1(8)) Thomson Gale.

Binns, Tristan Boyer. North America. 2007. (Illus.). 32p. (*978-1-4034-8246-4(2)) Heinemann Library.

Chin-Lee, Cynthia, et al. A Is for the Americas. 1999. (Illus.). 32p. (J). (gr. k-4). 16.99 (978-0-531-33194-1(6) , Orchard Bks.) Scholastic, Inc.

Donaldson, Madeline. North America. 2005. (Pull Ahead Bks.). (Illus.). 32p. (J). (gr. k-3). lib. bdg. 22.60 (978-0-8225-4722-8(8)) Lerner Publishing Group.

Encyclopaedia Britannica Publishers, Inc. Staff. Views of the Americas. 2004. (Britannica Learning Library). (Illus.). (J). lib. bdg. 14.95 (978-1-59339-012-9(2)) Encyclopaedia Britannica, Inc.

Fowler, Allan. North America. 2001. (Rookie Read-About Geography Ser.). (Illus.). 32p. (J). (gr. 1-2). pap. 5.95 (978-0-516-27299-3(3)); 20.50 (978-0-516-21671-3(6)) Scholastic Library Publishing. (Children's Pr.).

—North America. 2001. (gr. k-3). lib. bdg. 14.10 (978-0-613-54054-4(9)) Tandem Library Bks.

Fox, Mary Virginia. North America. (Continents Ser.). (Illus.). 32p. (J). (gr. k-2). 2001. lib. bdg. 21.36 (978-1-58810-001-6(4)); 2nd ed. 2006. lib. bdg. 25.36 ***978-1-4034-8544-1(5))** Heinemann Library.

Fox, Mary Virginia & Foster, Leila. North America. 2002. (Continents Ser.). (Illus.). 32p. (J). (gr. k-2). pap. 6.95 (978-1-58810-950-7(X) , 91440) Heinemann Library.

Gibson, Karen Bush. North America. 2006. (Illus.). 24p. (J). (978-0-7368-5430-6(4)) Capstone Pr., Inc.

Hovanec, Erin M. An Online Visit to North America. (Internet Field Trips Ser.). 24p. (J). 2002. lib. bdg. 18.75 (978-0-8239-6424-6(8)); 2001. (Illus.). (gr. 3). lib. bdg. 18.75 (978-0-8239-5654-8(7)) Rosen Publishing Group, Inc., The. (PowerKids Pr.).

Libal, Autumn. The Social, Monetary, & Moral Costs of Prisons. 2007. (Incarceration Issues Ser.). (Illus.). 111p. (J). (gr. 7 up). 22.95 (978-1-59084-992-7(2)) Mason Crest Pubs.

The Library of the Western Hemisphere Set 2. (J). (gr. 5 up). 119.70 (978-1-4042-2964-8(7)) Rosen Publishing Group, Inc., The.

The Libray of the Western Hemisphere Set 1. (J). (gr. 5 up). 119.70 (978-1-4042-2963-1(9)) Rosen Publishing Group, Inc., The.

Mary Virginia Fox. North America. 2nd ed. 2006. (Heinemann First Library). (Illus.). 32p. (J). pap. ***978-1-4034-8552-6(6))** Heinemann Library.

McClish, Bruce. Land Bridges & New World Continents. 2003. (Continents Ser.). (Illus.). 32p. pap. 7.50 (978-1-4034-4246-8(0)) Heinemann Library.

McNeil, Niki, et al. HOCPP 1076 North America. 2006. spiral bd. 24.00 ***978-1-60308-076-7(7))** In the Hands of a Child.

Nagle, Garrett. North America. 2006. (Illus.). 64p. (YA). (gr. 7-10). lib. bdg. 32.67 (978-0-8368-5914-0(6)); 2005. (J). pap. (978-0-8368-5921-8(9)) Stevens, Gareth Inc. (World Almanac Library).

North American Historical Atlases - Group 2, 5 bks., Set. 135.36 (978-0-7614-1344-8(8) , Benchmark Bks.) Cavendish, Marshall Corp.

Pearcey, Alice. Jigsaw Atlas of North America. King, Colin, illus. 2006. 14p. (J). bds. 14.99 (978-0-7945-1242-2(9) , Usborne) EDC Publishing.

Pelusey, Michael & Pelusey, Jane. North America. 2004. (Continents Ser.). (Illus.). 32p. (J). (gr. 2-4). 23.00 (978-0-7910-8276-8(8) , Chelsea Hse.) Facts On File, Inc.

Petersen, David. North America. 1999. (True Bks.). (Illus.). 48p. (J). (gr. 3-5). pap. 6.95 (978-0-516-26437-0(0) , Children's Pr.) Scholastic Library Publishing.

Rau, Dana Meachen. North America. 2003. (Continents Ser.). (Illus.). 32p. (J). (gr. 2-6). 27.07 (978-1-59296-061-3(8)) Child's World, Inc.

Ring, Susan. We Live in North America. (Yellow Umbrella Books for Early Readers). (J). 2006. (Illus.). 16p. 15.93 (978-0-7368-5845-8(8)); 2005. (978-0-7368-5311-8(1)); 2005. (Illus.). 16p. (978-0-7368-5275-3(1)) Capstone Pr., Inc.

Sammis, Fran. North America. 1998. (Mapping Our World Ser.). (Illus.). 64p. (J). (gr. 4-8). lib. bdg. 27.07 (978-0-7614-0368-5(X) , Benchmark Bks.) Cavendish, Marshall Corp.

Sayre, April Pulley. Welcome to North America! 2003. 32p. (J). (gr. 2-5). pap. 7.95 (978-0-7613-1988-7(3)); (Illus.). lib. bdg. 21.90 (978-0-7613-2150-7(0)) Lerner Publishing Group. (Millbrook Pr.).

—Welcome to North America! 2003. (gr. k-3). lib. bdg. 16.40 (978-0-613-88972-8(X)) Tandem Library Bks.

Striveildi, Cheryl. North America. 2003. (Continents Ser.). (Illus.). 32p. (J). (gr. k-4). lib. bdg. 22.78 (978-1-57765-963-1(5)) ABDO Publishing Co.

Tristan Boyer Binns. Exploring North America. 2007. (Illus.). 32p. pap. ***978-1-4034-8254-9(3))** Heinemann Library.

Vierow, Wendy. North America. 2004. (Atlas of the Seven Continents Ser.). (Illus.). 24p. (J). lib. bdg. 21.25 (978-0-8239-6692-9(5) , PowerKids Pr.) Rosen Publishing Group, Inc., The.

Whitecap Books Staff. North America. 2000. (Investigate Ser.). (Illus.). 64p. (J). (gr. 1-7). pap. 3.95 (978-1-55285-155-5(9)) Whitecap Bks., Ltd. CAN. *Dist:* Firefly Bks., Ltd.

NORTH AMERICA—ANTIQUITIES

Levy, Elizabeth & Havlan, J. R. Awesome Ancient Ancestors. McFeeley, Daniel, illus. 2001. (America's Horrible Histories Ser.: No. 2). 156p. (J). (gr. 4-6). pap. 12.95 (978-0-439-30349-1(4)) Scholastic, Inc.

NORTH AMERICA—DISCOVERY AND EXPLORATION

see America—Discovery and Exploration

NORTH AMERICA—HISTORY

Aloian, Molly & Kalman, Bobbie. Explora América del Norte. 2007. (SPA.). 32p. (gr. 6-10). pap. ***978-0-7787-8300-8(6))** Crabtree Publishing Co.

—Nations of the Northeast Coast. 2005. (Native Nations of North America Ser.). (Illus.). 32p. (J). (gr. 4-7). pap. (978-0-7787-0478-2(5)); (gr. 3-9). lib. bdg. (978-0-7787-0386-0(X)) Crabtree Publishing Co.

—Nations of the Southeast. 2005. (Native Nations of North America Ser.). (Illus.). 32p. (J). (gr. 3-9). lib. bdg. (978-0-7787-0385-3(1)); pap. (978-0-7787-0477-5(7)) Crabtree Publishing Co.

Bateman, Helen & Denshire, Jayne. North America. 2006. (Illus.). 32p. (J). 978-1-58340-802-5(9)) Smart Apple Media.

Benchmark Education Staff, compiled by. Historical Communities. 2006. spiral bd. 109.00 ***978-1-4108-7097-1(9))** Benchmark Education Co.

Bianchi, John-Paul. World Through Words North America. 2001. (gr. 5-8). lib. bdg. 24.50 (978-0-613-45455-1(3)) Tandem Library Bks.

Black Profiles: The North American Experience, Vol. 1. 2004. (YA). 12.99 (978-0-9762837-0-6(0)) Nubiano Project, Inc., The.

Chin-Lee, Cynthia. A Es para Decir Americas. 1999. (978-0-606-17568-5(7)) Tandem Library Bks.

Chin-Lee, Cynthia & De la Pena, Terri. A Es para Decir America's. Sanchez, Enrique O., illus. 1999. (SPA.). 32p. (J). (gr. k-4). pap. 6.95 (978-0-531-07134-2(0) , Orchard Bks.) Scholastic, Inc.

Chu, Godwin. After the Buffalo Jump Vol. 10: A Story of the Blackfoot Nation. Ham, Jeff, illus. 2001. (J). (gr. 5-6). 65.00 incl. audio, cd-rom (978-1-58702-684-3(8)) Johnston, Don Inc.

—After the Buffalo Jump Vol. 10: A Story of the Blackfoot Nation. Stemach, Jerry et al, eds. Ham, Jeff, illus. l.t. ed. 2001. (J). (gr. 5-6). 50.00 (978-1-58702-728-4(3)) Johnston, Don Inc.

Chu, Godwin, ed. After the Buffalo Jump Vol. 10: A Story of the Blackfoot Nation. Ham, Jeff, illus. l.t. ed. 2002. (J). (gr. 5-6). 150.00 (978-1-58702-046-9(7)) Johnston, Don Inc.

Coletti, Sharon. Everything You Need to Teach North America. 2005. (YA). ring bd. 149.95 (978-1-933558-05-9(9)) InspirEd Educators.

Cooke, Jacob E. & Klein, Milton M., eds. North America in Colonial Times: An Encyclopedia for Students, 4 vols., Set. 1998. (Illus.). 911p. (YA). 460.00 (978-0-684-80538-2(3) , GML00502-166554, Charles Scribner's Sons) Thomson Gale.

Fisher, James T. Catholics in America. 2000. (Religion in America Ser.). (Illus.). 176p. (YA). (gr. 8 up). reprint ed. 30.00 (978-0-19-511179-6(0)) Oxford Univ. Pr., Inc.

Gritzner, Charles & Desaulniers, Kristi. Northern America. 2006. (Modern World Cultures Ser.). (Illus.). 136p. (gr. 9-12). 30.00 (978-0-7910-8141-9(9) , Chelsea Hse.) Facts On File, Inc.

Harcourt School Publishers Staff. At Play on the Plains On Level. 3rd ed. 2002. (Trophies Reading Program Ser.). (Illus.). pap. 5.10 (978-0-15-323356-2(7)) Harcourt Schl. Pubs.

—Canada/Mexico/Central America. 2nd ed. (Horizons Ser.). (gr. k-7). 2003. (Illus.). act. bk. ed. 11.00 (978-0-15-335841-8(6)); 2002. pap., tchr. ed., act. bk. ed. 26.70 (978-0-15-335843-2(2)) Harcourt Schl. Pubs.

Harvey, Dan. The English Colonization of North America. 2002. (Exploration & Discovery Ser.). (Illus.). 64p. (J). (gr. 4-7). lib. bdg. (978-1-59084-051-1(8)) Mason Crest Pubs.

In North & South America. (J). (gr. 5). 3.80 (978-0-8374-1454-6(7) , 405) Weekly Reader Corp.

Isserman, Maurice. Exploring North America, 1800-1900. 2005. (Discovery & Exploration Ser.). (Illus.). 208p. (J). (gr. 6-12). 40.00 (978-0-8160-5263-9(8)) Facts On File, Inc.

Johnston, Lissa. A Brief Political & Geographic History of North America: Where Are New France, New Netherland, & New Sweden? 2007. (Places in Time Ser.). (Illus.). 112p. (YA). (gr. 5-10). lib. bdg. 37.10 ***978-1-58415-627-7(9))** Mitchell Lane Pubs., Inc.

Marsh, Carole. North Carolina History Projects: 30 Cool, Activities, Crafts, Experiments & More for Kids to Do to Learn about Your State! 2003. (North Carolina Experience Ser.). 32p. (gr. k-5). pap. 5.95 (978-0-635-01802-1(0) , Marsh, Carole Bks.) Gallopade International.

North America: Regions of the World. 2003. spiral bd. 16.95 (978-1-56004-160-3(9)) Social Studies Schl. Service.

North American Historical Atlases - Group 2, 5 bks., Set. 135.36 (978-0-7614-1344-8(8) , Benchmark Bks.) Cavendish, Marshall Corp.

Pascoe, Elaine. World in Focus: North America. 2000. (gr. 5-8). lib. bdg. 26.00 (978-0-613-45674-6(2)) Tandem Library Bks.

Pascoe, Elaine & Bianchi, John-Paul. North America. 2001. (World in Focus Ser.). (Illus.). 80p. (J). (gr. 5 up). pap. 17.45 (978-1-56711-345-7(1) , Blackbirch Pr., Inc.) Thomson Gale.

Peoples of North America, 10 vols. 2003. (Illus.). (J). 359.00 (978-0-7172-5777-5(0) , Grolier) Scholastic Library Publishing.

Religion & Modern Culture: Spiritual Beliefs That Influence North America Today, 13 vols., Set. Incl. Born-Again Believers : Evangelicals & Charismatics. McIntosh, Kenneth & McIntosh, Marsha. (YA). 2005. (978-1-59084-974-3(4)); Color, Culture, & Creed : How Ethnic Background Influences Belief. McIntosh, Kenneth & McIntosh, Marsha. (YA). 2006. lib. bdg. 22.95 (978-1-59084-976-7(0)); Controversial World of Biblical Archaeology : Tomb Raiders, Fakes, & Scholars. McIntosh, Kenneth. (YA). 2006. lib. bdg. 22.95 (978-1-59084-983-5(3)); Grail, the Shroud & Other Religious Relics : Secrets & Ancient Mysteries. McIntosh, Kenneth. (J). 2005. lib. bdg. (978-1-59084-978-1(7) , 1248067); Growth of North American Religious Beliefs : Spiritual Diversity. McIntosh, Kenneth & McIntosh, Jonathan S. (YA). 2006. lib. bdg. 22.95 (978-1-59084-975-0(2)); Issues of Church, State, & Religious Liberties : Whose Freedom, Whose Faith? McIntosh, Kenneth & McIntosh, Marsha. (YA). 2006. lib. bdg. 22.95 (978-1-59084-973-6(6)); Jesus, Fads, & the Media : The Passion & Popular Culture. Evans, Michael. (YA). 2005. lib. bdg. 22.95 (978-1-59084-972-9(8)); Lost Gospels & Hidden Codes : New Concepts of Scripture. McIntosh, Kenneth. (YA). 2006. lib. bdg. 22.95 (978-1-59084-982-8(5)); Popularity of Meditation & Spiritual Practices : Seeking Inner Peace. McIntosh, Kenneth & McIntosh, Marsha. (YA). 2005. (978-1-59084-980-4(9)); Prophecies & End-Time Speculations : The Shape of Things to Come. McIntosh, Kenneth. (J). 2005. (978-1-59084-979-8(5) , 1248068); Touching the Supernatural World : Angels, Miracles, & Demons. McIntosh, Kenneth & McIntosh, Marsha. (YA). 2005. (978-1-59084-981-1(7)); When Religion & Politics Mix : How Matters of Faith Influence Political Policies. McIntosh, Kenneth & McIntosh, Marsha. (J). 2006. lib. bdg. 22.95 (978-1-59084-971-2(X)); Women & Religion : Reinterpreting Scriptures to Find the Sacred Feminine. McIntosh, Kenneth. (J). 2005. (978-1-59084-977-4(9)); (gr. 7 up). (Illus.). 112p. 2006. Set lib. bdg. 298.35 (978-1-59084-970-5(1) , 1248067) Mason Crest Pubs.

Scribner Staff. North America in Colonial Times, 4 vols. 1998. (Junior North American Colonies Ser.: Vol. 1). (Illus.). (J). Vol. 1. 90.00 (978-0-684-80534-4(0)); Vol. 2. 90.00 (978-0-684-80535-1(9)); Vol. 3. 90.00 (978-0-684-80536-8(7)); Vol. 4. 90.00 (978-0-684-80537-5(5)) Thomson Gale. (Macmillan Reference USA).

Stanley, George Edward. The European Settlement of North America (1492-1754) 2005. (Illus.). 48p. (J). pap. (978-0-8368-5833-4(6)); lib. bdg. 30.00 (978-0-8368-5824-2(7)) Stevens, Gareth Inc. (World Almanac Library).

Stefoff, Rebecca. Cities & Towns. 2007. (Colonial Life Ser.). (Illus.). 96p. (gr. 6 up). 37.95 ***978-0-7656-8109-6(9))** Sharpe, M.E. Inc.

Tull, Mary & Franklin, Sharon. North America: Understanding Geography & History Through Art. 1999. (Artisans Around the World Ser.). (Illus.). 48p. (J). (gr. 4-7). lib. bdg. 27.12 (978-0-7398-0117-8(1)) Raintree.

Wingate, Philippa & Reid, Struan. Who Were the First North Americans? 2004. (Starting Point History Ser.). (Illus.). 32p. (J). pap. 4.99 (978-0-7945-0397-0(7) , Usborne); lib. bdg. 12.95 (978-1-58086-512-8(7)) EDC Publishing.

NORTH AMERICAN INDIANS

see Indians of North America

NORTH ATLANTIC TREATY ORGANIZATION

Grant, Reg. NATO. 2001. (World Organizations Ser.). (Illus.). 32p. (YA). (gr. 6-8). 24.00 (978-0-531-14622-4(7) , Watts, Franklin) Scholastic Library Publishing.

NORTH CAROLINA

Alex, Nan. North Carolina. 80p. (J). 2008. (From Sea to Shining Sea, Second Ser.). pap. 7.95 ***978-0-531-18808-8(6));** 2001. (From Sea to Shining Sea Ser.: 2). (Illus.). (gr. 3-5). 30.50 (978-0-516-22487-9(5)) Scholastic Library Publishing. (Children's Pr.).

Alter, Judy. North Carolina: A MyReportLinks. Com Book. 2003. (States Ser.). (Illus.). 48p. (J). (gr. 4-10). lib. bdg. 25.26 (978-0-7660-5135-5(8) , MyReportLinks.com Bks.) Enslow Pubs., Inc.

Bird, Janice W. Freddy in the City: Center City Sites. Bird, Richard E., photos by. Date not set. (Illus.). 32p. (J). (gr. 2-5). pap. 5.95 (978-0-9710071-1-6(X)) JFW, Ltd.

Boraas, Tracey. North Carolina. 2003. (Land of Liberty Ser.). (Illus.). 64p. (J). lib. bdg. 25.26 (978-0-7368-2190-2(2)) Capstone Pr., Inc.

Brennan, Linda Crotta. North Carolina. 2003. (Rookie Read-About Geography Ser.). (gr. 1-2). pap. 5.95 (978-0-516-27822-3(3) , Children's Pr.) Scholastic Library Publishing.

—North Carolina. 2003. (Illus.). 31p. (J). (ps-ps). lib. bdg. 14.10 (978-0-613-67918-3(0)) Tandem Library Bks.

Charlotte a Complete Photo Tour Book. 1998. (Illus.). 32p. (YA). (gr. 7-12). pap. 5.95 (978-1-880970-41-6(4)) Aerial Photography Services, Inc.

Crane, Carol. T Is for Tar Heel: A North Carolina Alphabet. Palmer, Gary, illus. 2003. 40p. (J). 17.95 (978-1-58536-082-6(1)) Sleeping Bear Pr.

—Wright Numbers: A North Carolina Number Book. Palmer, Gary, illus. 2005. (Count Your Way Across the USA Ser.). 40p. (J). (gr. k-5). 16.95 (978-1-58536-196-0(8)) Sleeping Bear Pr.

Edwards, Michael. The Last Battle for Independence: The Story of the Fort Fisher Hermit, 1. 2002. (Illus.). 97p. per. (978-0-9720952-2-8(5)) Edwards, Michael.

Foran, Jill. A Guide to North Carolina. 2001. (American States Ser.). (Illus.). 32p. (J). lib. bdg. 16.95 (978-1-59036-003-3(6)) Weigl Pubs., Inc.

Galiano, Dean. North Carolina (Carolina del Norte) 2006. (Bilingual Library of the United States of America: Set 2). (ENG & SPA., Illus.). 32p. (J). (gr. 3-6). lib. bdg. 22.50 (978-1-4042-3098-9(X) , Buenas Letra) Rosen Publishing Group, Inc., The.

George, Pamela & Brown, Walter M. The North Carolina Alphabet. 2005. 60p. (J). (978-0-932112-50-7(1)) Carolina Wren Pr.

Heinrichs, Ann. North Carolina. 2005. (Welcome to the USA Ser.). 40p. (J). (gr. 1-5). 27.07 (978-1-59296-287-7(4)) Child's World, Inc.

—North Carolina. 2003. (This Land Is Your Land Ser.). (Illus.). 48p. (J). (gr. 3 up). lib. bdg. 22.60 (978-0-7565-0324-6(8)) Compass Point Bks.

Hintz, Martin, et al. North Carolina. 2nd ed. 1998. (America the Beautiful, Second Ser.). (Illus.). 144p. (YA). (gr. 5-8). 36.00 (978-0-516-20638-7(9) , Children's Pr.) Scholastic Library Publishing.

Hyman, Teresa L. North Carolina. 2003. (Seeds of a Nation Ser.). (Illus.). 48p. (J). 23.70 (978-0-7377-1420-3(4)) Thomson Gale.

Kummer, Patricia K. North Carolina. rev. ed. 2002. (One Nation Ser.). (Illus.). 48p. (J). (gr. 3-4). lib. bdg. 22.60 (978-0-7368-1257-3(1) , Bridgestone Bks.) Capstone Pr., Inc.

Marsh, Carole. My First Book about North Carolina. 2004. (North Carolina Experience! Ser.). 32p. (J). (gr. k-4). pap. 7.95 (978-0-7933-9518-7(6)) Gallopade International.

—The Nifty North Carolina Coloring Book. 2004. (North Carolina Experience! Ser.). (Illus.). 32p. (J). (gr. k-2). pap. 3.95 (978-0-7933-9472-2(4)) Gallopade International.

—North Carolina Classic Christmas Trivia. 2002. (Carole Marsh North Carolina Bks.). (Illus.). 32p. pap. 6.95 (978-0-635-01433-7(5) , 14335); lib. bdg. 21.95 (978-0-635-01434-4(3) , 14343) Gallopade International. (Marsh, Carole Bks.).

—North Carolina Current Events Projects: 30 Cool, Activities, Crafts, Experiments & More for Kids to Do to Learn about Your State! 2003. (North Carolina Experience Ser.). 32p. (gr. k-8). pap. 5.95 (978-0-635-02052-9(1) , Marsh, Carole Bks.) Gallopade International.

—The North Carolina Experience Pocket Guide. 2004. (North Carolina Experience! Ser.). (Illus.). 96p. (J). (gr. 3-8). pap. 6.95 (978-0-7933-9452-4(X)) Gallopade International.

—North Carolina Geography Projects: 30 Cool, Activities, Crafts, Experiments & More for Kids to Do to Learn about Your State! 2003. (North Carolina Experience Ser.). 32p. (gr. k-5). pap. 5.95 (978-0-635-01852-6(7) , Marsh, Carole Bks.) Gallopade International.

—North Carolina Government Projects: 30 Cool, Activities, Crafts, Experiments & More for Kids to Do to Learn about Your State! 2003. (North Carolina Experience Ser.). 32p. (gr. k-5). pap. 5.95 (978-0-635-01952-3(3) , Marsh, Carole Bks.) Gallopade International.

—North Carolina Jeopardy! Answers & Questions about Our State! 2004. (North Carolina Experience! Ser.). (Illus.). 32p. (J). (gr. 3-8). pap. 7.95 (978-0-7933-9519-4(4)) Gallopade International.

—North Carolina "Jography" A Fun Run Through the Tarheel State! 2004. (North Carolina Experience! Ser.). (Illus.). 32p. (J). (gr. 3-8). pap. 7.95 (978-0-7933-9520-0(8)) Gallopade International.

—North Carolina People Projects: 30 Cool, Activities, Crafts, Experiments & More for Kids to Do to Learn about Your State! 2003. (North Carolina Experience Ser.). 32p. (gr. k-5). pap. 5.95 (978-0-635-02002-4(5) , Marsh, Carole Bks.) Gallopade International.

—North Carolina Symbols & Facts Projects: 30 Cool, Activities, Crafts, Experiments & More for Kids to Do to Learn about Your State! 2003. (North Carolina Experience Ser.). 32p. (gr. k-8). pap. 5.95 (978-0-635-01902-8(7) , Marsh, Carole Bks.) Gallopade International.

—North Carolina's Big Activity Book. 2004. (North Carolina Experience! Ser.). (Illus.). 96p. (J). (gr. 2-6). pap. 9.95 (978-0-7933-9462-3(7)) Gallopade International.

McClellan, Adam. Uniquely North Carolina. 2003. (Heinemann State Studies). (Illus.). 48p. (J). pap. 8.50 (978-1-4034-4722-7(5)); lib. bdg. 27.07 (978-1-4034-4653-4(9)) Heinemann Library.

McNeil, Niki, et al. HOCPP 1080 North Carolina. 2006. spiral bd. 24.00 ***978-1-60308-080-4(5))** In the Hands of a Child.

Meyer, John H. Wilmington Today: A Guide to Cape Fear Leisure. 2003. Orig. Title: A Guide to Cape Fear Leisure. (Illus.). 60p. 13.95 (978-0-9729573-0-4(8) , Wilmington Today Pubns.) Cape Fear Images, Inc.

Murray, Julie. North Carolina. 2006. (Buddy Book Ser.). (Illus.). 32p. (J). (gr. k-4). lib. bdg. 22.78 (978-1-59197-692-9(8) , Buddy Bks.) ABDO Publishing Co.

North Carolina. (One Nation Ser.). 48p. (YA). 6.95 (978-0-7368-8915-5(9)) Capstone Pr., Inc.

Peters, Stephanie True. North Carolina's Sights & Symbols. 2004. 48p. pap. 8.95 (978-1-4042-8504-0(0)) Rosen Publishing Group, Inc., The.

Rafle, Sarah. North Carolina: The Tar Heel State. 2002. (World Almanac Library of the States). (Illus.). 48p. (J). (gr. 5 up). pap. 14.95 (978-0-8368-5289-9(3)); lib. bdg. 30.00 (978-0-8368-5119-9(6)) Stevens, Gareth Inc. (World Almanac Library).

—North Carolina: The Tar Heel State. 2002. (gr. 5-8). lib. bdg. 24.15 (978-0-613-52460-5(8)) Tandem Library Bks.

Sateren, Shelley Swanson. North Carolina: Facts & Symbols. 1999. (States & Their Symbols Ser.). (Illus.). 24p. (J). (gr. k-3). pap. 15.00 (978-0-531-12007-1(4) , Watts, Franklin) Scholastic Library Publishing.

Schulz, Andrea. North Carolina. (Hello U. S. A. Ser.). (Illus.). (J). (gr. 3-6). 1998. 72p. pap. 5.95 (978-0-8225-9790-2(X)); 2nd exp. rev. ed. 2003. 84p. pap. 6.95 (978-0-8225-4137-0(8)); 2nd exp. rev. ed. 2002. 84p. 25.26 (978-0-8225-4072-4(X) , Lerner Pubns.) Lerner Publishing Group.

Shirley, David. North Carolina. 2001. (Celebrate the States Ser.). (Illus.). 144p. (J). (gr. 4-8). lib. bdg. 37.07 (978-0-7614-1072-0(4) , Benchmark Bks.) Cavendish, Marshall Corp.

Wiener, Roberta & Arnold, James R. North Carolina. 2004. (Illus.). 64p. (J). 28.56 (978-0-7398-6885-0(3)) Harcourt Schl. Pubs.

—The 13 Colonies: North Carolina. 2004. (Illus.). 64p. (J). 8.95 (978-1-4109-0309-9(5)) Harcourt Schl. Pubs.

NORTH CAROLINA—FICTION

Asim, Jabari. The Road to Freedom. 2004. 131p. (J). lib. bdg. 16.92 ***978-1-4242-0765-7(7))** Fitzgerald Bks.

Asim, Jabari. Road to Freedom: A Story of Reconstruction. 2000. (gr. 5-8). lib. bdg. 14.95 (978-0-613-36867-4(3)) Tandem Library Bks.

Ballard, Curt. A Child of the Veil. 2001. 126p. (J). pap. 7.99 (978-1-889893-64-8(1)) Emerald Hse. Group, Inc.

Barkley, Brad & Hepler, Heather. Scrambled Eggs at Midnight. 2007. 288p. (J). (gr. 7 up). pap. 7.99 (978-0-14-240867-4(0) , Puffin); 2006. 272p. (YA). (gr. 6). 16.99 (978-0-525-47760-0(8) , Dutton Juvenile) Penguin Group (USA) Inc.

Bird, Janie. Freddy in the City: Memorable Monday. Treffeisen, Brian, photos by. 2nd rev. ed. 2005. Tr. of Freddy en la Ciudad un Lunes Memorble. (SPA., Illus.). 32p. (J). 10.95 (978-1-59494-005-7(3)) CPCC Pr.

Bradfield, Carl. The Sullivans of Little Horsepen Creek: A Tale of Colonial North Carolina's Regulator Era, Circa: 1760s. (Illus.). 350p. (YA). (gr. 8-12). (978-0-9632319-2-5(8)) ASDA Publishing, Inc.

Brown, Sharon. Kit's Indian Summer. 2004. 68p. pap. 14.95 (978-1-4137-3956-5(3)) PublishAmerica, Inc.

Campbell, Donna. An Independent Spirit: The Tale of Betsy Dowdy & Black Bess. 2002. (Legends of the Carolinas Ser.). 200p. (J). 8.95 (978-1-928556-35-0(3)) Coastal Carolina Pr.

Carbone, Elisa. Storm Warriors. 2002. (gr. 5-8). lib. bdg. 13.55 (978-0-613-61730-7(4)) Tandem Library Bks.

Carris, Joan D. A Ghost of a Chance. 2003. (Legends of the Carolinas Ser.). 155p. (J). 8.95 (978-1-928556-40-4(X)) Coastal Carolina Pr.

Countess, Mary Alice. Cowpath Days. Fallis, Janet M., ed. Daggett, Susan, illus. 2001. 128p. (J). (gr. 4-8). pap. 6.95 (978-0-9662431-1-6(0)) Viewpoint Pr., Inc.

Dahl, Candy. Emma & the Civil Warrior. 2001. 158p. (J). 12.95 (978-0-9706358-3-9(4)); per. 6.95 (978-0-9706358-4-6(2)) Carolina Moon Publishing.

Davis, Donald. Listening for the Crack of Dawn: A Master Storyteller Recalls the Appalachia. 2000. (gr. 7-12). lib. bdg. 21.05 (978-0-7857-2705-7(1)) Tandem Library Bks.

Doherty, Patrick. Waves of Grace. 2008. (YA). pap. 5.99 (***978-0-9744446-6-6(9)**) All About Kids Publishing.

Dowell, Frances O'Roark. Dovey Coe. 192p. (J). 2001. (Illus.). pap. 5.99 (978-0-689-84667-0(3) , Aladdin); 2000. (gr. 4-7). 16.99 (978-0-689-83174-4(9) , Atheneum) Simon & Schuster Children's Publishing.

—Dovey Coe. 2001. 11.64 (978-0-606-22127-6(1)); (gr. 5-8). lib. bdg. 13.00 (978-0-613-55445-9(0)) Tandem Library Bks.

—Dovey Coe. l.t. ed. 2001. 171p. (J). 22.95 (978-0-7862-3590-2(X)) Thorndike Pr.

Doyle, Bill. Nabbed! The 1925 Journal of G. Codd Fitzmorgan. Lewis, Anthony, illus. 2006. 125p. (J). lib. bdg. 18.46 (***978-1-4242-1735-9(0)**) Fitzgerald Bks.

Dyahnne. Sweetie's Place: A Moving Adventure. 2004. 26p. (J). per. 7.99 (978-1-4116-0760-6(0)) Lulu.com.

Early, Tony. Jim the Boy. 2001. (gr. 7-12). lib. bdg. 21.95 (978-0-613-33827-1(8)) Tandem Library Bks.

Ernst, Kathleen. Highland Fling. 2006. 192p. (J). 15.95 (978-0-8126-2742-8(3)) Cricket Bks.

Fripp, Jon, et al. Kinnakeet & the Lighthouse. Moussa, Karen M., illus. 2000. 33p. (J). 5.50 (978-0-9638258-4-1(4)) Bicast, Inc.

Gantos, Jack. Jack Adrift: Fourth Grade Without a Clue. 2003. (Jack Henry Ser.). (Illus.). 208p. (J). 16.00 (978-0-374-39987-0(5) , Farrar, Straus & Giroux (BYR)) Farrar, Straus & Giroux.

—Jack Adrift: Fourth Grade Without a Clue. l.t. ed. 2004. 226p. (J). 22.95 (978-0-7862-6387-5(3)) Thorndike Pr.

Garza, Amy Ammons. Sterlen: And a Mosaic of Mountain Women. Ammons, David F. & Ammons, Sherilyn, eds. Cain, Doreyl Ammons, illus. 2005. 308p. (YA). per. 16.00 (978-0-9753023-2-3(9) , Catch the Spirit of Appalachia) Ammons Communications, Ltd.

Gutman, Dan. Race for the Sky. 2003. (Illus.). 192p. (J). (gr. 3-6). 16.99 (978-0-689-84554-3(5)) Simon & Schuster Children's Publishing.

—Race for the Sky: The Kitty Hawk Diaries of Johnny Moore. l.t. ed. 2004. 299p. 22.95 (978-0-7862-6466-7(7)) Thorndike Pr.

Harvell, Richard Brian. Adventures of the Book Battling Kids: The Carson Corners Chronicles. 2006. (J). per. 5.99 (978-0-9769044-7-2(0)) Waterwood Publishing Group.

Hicks, Betty. Get Real. 2006. 192p. (J). 16.95 (978-1-59643-089-1(3)) Roaring Brook Pr.

Holmes, Elizabeth. Pretty Is. 2007. 224p. (J). (gr. 4-6). 16.99 (978-0-525-47813-3(2) , Dutton Juvenile) Penguin Group (USA) Inc.

Hostetter, Joyce Moyer. Blue. 200p. (J). 16.95 (978-1-59078-389-4(1) , Calkins Creek) Boyds Mills Pr.

Johnson, Harriet McBryde. Accidents of Nature. rev. ed. 2006. 240p. (YA). 16.95 (978-0-8050-7634-9(4) , Holt, Henry & Co. Bks. For Young Readers) Holt, Henry & Co.

Jones, Elizabeth McDavid. The Night Flyers. 1999. (978-0-606-17518-0(0)) Tandem Library Bks.

Kimmel, Eric A. Blackbeard's Last Fight. Fisher, Leonard Everett, illus. 2006. 32p. (J). 17.00 (978-0-374-30780-6(6) , Farrar, Straus & Giroux (BYR)) Farrar, Straus & Giroux.

Krisher, Trudy. Fallout. 2006. 272p. (J). 17.95 (978-0-8234-2035-3(3)) Holiday Hse., Inc.

Lau, Barbara & Nesbitt, Kris. Sokita Celebrates the New Year: A Cambodian American Holiday. Chatterley, Cedric N., photos by. 2004. 32p. (J). per. 9.95 (978-0-9747456-0-2(X)) Greensboro Historical Museum, Inc.

Lawrenson, Judith. Petunia the Pirate of Port Royal Sound. 2007. (J). 14.95 (***978-0-9767278-0-4(3)**) Mrs. L's Reading Room.

Leppard, Lois Gladys. Mandie & the Buried Stranger. 1999. (gr. 3-6). lib. bdg. 13.00 (978-0-613-27967-3(0)); (Mandie Bks.: No. 31). (J). (gr. 4-7). (978-0-606-18918-7(1)) Tandem Library Bks.

Littleton, Mark. Tracks in the Sand. 2001. (Ally OConnor Adventures Ser.: Vol. 1). 128p. (J). (gr. 4-7). pap. 5.99 (978-0-8010-4490-8(1)) Baker Bks.

Looper, Grace W. Molasses Making Time. l.t. ed. 2004. 152p. (YA). pap. 8.95 (978-0-9747685-5-7(3)) Bella Rosa Bks.

Madden, Kerry. Gentle's Holler. (YA). 2007. 272p. (gr. 4 up). 6.99 (978-0-14-240751-6(8) , Puffin); 2005. 256p. (gr. 5). 16.99 (978-0-670-05998-0(6) , Viking Juvenile) Penguin Group (USA) Inc.

The Marsh Runners. 2004. (J). per. 14.95 (978-0-9761178-0-3(0)) Maritime Kids Quest Pr.

Martin, Timothy. Legend of Boomer Jack. 2007. 113p. 16.95 (***978-1-4241-0886-2(1)**) PublishAmerica, Inc.

Moses, Shelia P. The Baptism. 2007. 144p. (YA). (gr. 7 up). 15.99 (978-1-4169-0671-1(1) , McElderry, Margaret K.) Simon & Schuster Children's Publishing.

—The Legend of Buddy Bush. unabr. ed. 2005. (J). (gr. 3-7). 55.70 incl. audio (978-1-4193-3575-4(8) , 42043) Recorded Bks., LLC.

—The Legend of Buddy Bush. (Illus.). 224p. 2005. (YA). pap. 5.99 (978-1-4169-0716-9(5) , Simon Pulse); 2003. (J). 15.95 (978-0-689-85839-0(6) , McElderry, Margaret K.) Simon & Schuster Children's Publishing.

Moses, Shelia P. Sallie Gal & the Wall-a-Kee Man. Daly, Niki, illus. 2007. 160p. (J). (gr. 2-5). pap. 15.99 (***978-0-439-90890-0(6)**) Scholastic, Inc.

Mr. Bud's Country Store: A Story of Family & Community. 2003. (J). per. 18.95 (978-0-9711534-1-7(8)) Hidden Path Pubn., Inc.

O'Connor, Barbara. Greetings from Nowhere. 2008. 208p. (J). 16.00 (***978-0-374-39937-5(9)**) Farrar, Straus & Giroux.

—How to Steal a Dog. 2007. 176p. (J). (gr. 3-7). 16.00 (978-0-374-33497-0(8)) Farrar, Straus & Giroux.

—Me & Rupert Goody. 1999. 112p. (J). (gr. 4-7). 15.00 (978-0-374-34904-2(5) , Farrar, Straus & Giroux (BYR)) Farrar, Straus & Giroux.

—Me & Rupert Goody. l.t. ed. 2000. (Illus.). 126p. (J). (gr. 8-12). 21.95 (978-0-7862-2767-9(2)) Thorndike Pr.

Parker, Gary. Highland Hopes. 2001. (gr. 5-8). lib. bdg. 22.25 (978-0-613-55605-7(4)) Tandem Library Bks.

Penn, Audrey. Blackbeard & the Gift of Silence. 2007. 355p. (gr. 3-7). 15.95 (***978-1-933718-11-8(0)**) Tanglewood Pr.

Penn, Audrey. The Whistling Tree. Gibson, Barbara, illus. 2003. 32p. 16.95 (978-0-87868-852-4(8) , 8528, Child & Family Pr.) Child Welfare League of America, Inc.

—The Whistling Tree. Gibson, Barbara, illus. 2006. 32p. 16.95 (978-0-9749303-9-8(3)) Tanglewood Pr.

Pinkney, Gloria Jean. Back Home. 1999. (J). 13.79 (978-0-606-16773-4(0)); lib. bdg. 15.30 (978-0-613-18238-6(3)) Tandem Library Bks.

Ransom, Candice. Rescue on the Outer Banks. Ritz, Karen, illus. 2002. 48p. (J). (gr. 1-3). lib. bdg. 14.10 (978-0-613-46163-4(0)) Tandem Library Bks.

Ransom, Candice F. Rescue on the Outer Banks. Ritz, Karen, illus. (On My Own History Ser.). 48p. (J). (gr. 1-3). 2003. pap. 5.95 (978-0-87614-815-0(1)); 2002. lib. bdg. 23.93 (978-0-87614-460-2(1)) Lerner Publishing Group. (Carolrhoda Bks.).

Rathmell, Donna. Carolina's Story: Sea Turtles Get Sick Too! Bergwerf, Barbara J., illus. 2007. 1p. (J). 8.95 (***978-1-934359-00-6(9)**) Sylvan Dell Pubng.

—Carolina's Story: Sea Turtles Get Sick Too! Bergwerf, Barbara J., photos by. 2005. (Illus.). 32p. 15.95 (978-0-9764943-0-0(2)) Sylvan Dell Pubng.

Rodriguez, Elisabeth. Jumping Jack. 2006. pap. 14.99 (***978-1-4259-8197-6(6)**) AuthorHouse.

Russell, Anne. Seabiscuit: Wild Pony of the Outer Banks. Halpin, Diane Royder & Pearce, Brooks, illus. 2001. 32p. (J). (gr. k-8). 14.95 (978-1-928556-28-2(0)) Coastal Carolina Pr.

Smith, Donna Campbell. An Independent Spirit: The Tale of Betsy Dowdy & Black Bess. 2006. (Illus.). 182p. (J). per. 11.95 (978-0-9779889-0-7(2)) Faithful Publishing.

Starbuck, Veronica Anne. Heart of the Savannah. 2000. 267p. (YA). (gr. 9 up). pap. 12.95 (978-0-9658488-3-1(3)) Windigo Harbor Media.

Stauffacher, Sue. Bessie Smith & the Night Riders. Holyfield, John, illus. 2006. 32p. (J). (ps-3). 16.99 (978-0-399-24237-3(6) , Putnam Juvenile) Penguin Group (USA) Inc.

Strauss, Darin. Chang & Eng. 2001. (gr. 7-12). lib. bdg. 22.25 (978-0-613-34638-2(6)) Tandem Library Bks.

Tate, Suzanne. Holly from Hatteras: A Tale of Saving Lives. Melvin, James, illus. 1998. (Suzanne Tate's History Ser.: No. 1). 32p. (J). (ps-4). pap. 4.95 (978-1-878405-22-7(5)) Nags Head Art, Inc.

Taylor, Theodore. The Odyssey of Ben O'Neal. 2004. (Illus.). 264p. (J). pap. 5.95 (978-0-15-205295-9(X) , Odyssey Classics) Harcourt Children's Bks.

—Teetoncey. 2004. (Illus.). 228p. (J). 17.00 (978-0-15-205298-0(4) , Harcourt Young Classics); pap. 5.95 (978-0-15-205294-2(1) , Odyssey Classics) Harcourt Children's Bks.

—Teetoncey & Ben O'Neal. 2004. (Illus.). 240p. (J). 17.00 (978-0-15-205296-6(8) , Harcourt Young Classics); (Cape Hatteras Trilogy: Bk. 2). pap. 5.95 (978-0-15-205297-3(6) , Odyssey Classics) Harcourt Children's Bks.

—The Weirdo. 2006. (Illus.). 304p. (J). pap. 6.95 (978-0-15-205666-7(1) , Harcourt Paperbacks) Harcourt Children's Bks.

Teague, Bobbie T. Simon's Gold. Deppner, Charles, illus. 2001. 94p. (J). per. 13.00 (978-1-887774-09-3(2) , Wynden) Canmore Pr.

Thomas, Blair L. The Sabatini Prophecy. 2008. (ENG.). 496p. (YA). 8.99 (***978-0-9760237-4-6(1)**) Axiom Hse.

Tolan, Stephanie S. Listen! 2006. 208p. (J). 15.99 (978-0-06-057935-7(8)); lib. bdg. 16.89 (978-0-06-057936-4(6)) HarperCollins Pubs.

Warner, Gertrude Chandler. Mystery of the Wild Ponies. 2000. (gr. 3-6). lib. bdg. 11.80 (978-0-613-27993-2(X)) Tandem Library Bks.

Warner, Gertrude Chandler, creator. The Mystery of the Wild Ponies, Vol. 77. 2004. (Boxcar Children Ser.: No. 77). (Illus.). 135p. (J). (gr. 2-5). pap. 3.95 (978-0-8075-5466-1(9)) Whitman, Albert & Co.

Weatherford, Carole Boston. Freedom on the Menu: The Greensboro Sit-Ins. Lagarrigue, Jerome Lagarrigue, illus. 2007. 32p. (J). (ps). pap. 5.99 (***978-0-14-240894-0(8)** , Puffin) Penguin Group (USA) Inc.

—Freedom on the Menu: The Greensboro Sit-Ins. Lagarrigue, Jerome, illus. 2004. 32p. (J). (gr. 1). 16.99 (978-0-8037-2860-8(3) , Dial) Penguin Group (USA) Inc.

—Princeville: The 500 Year Flood. Alvord, Douglas, illus. 2001. 32p. 14.95 (978-1-928556-32-9(9)) Coastal Carolina Pr.

Weirdo. 2002. stu. ed. (978-1-56137-815-9(1)) Novel Units, Inc.

Whatley, Tom. James & Jessie (This Is Not A Mushy Romantic Novel) 2005. 70p. pap. 9.67 (978-1-4116-4370-3(4)) Lulu.com.

White, Ruth. Buttermilk Hill. 2004. 176p. (J). 16.00 (978-0-374-35112-0(0) , Farrar, Straus & Giroux (BYR)) Farrar, Straus & Giroux.

—Buttermilk Hill. 2006. 176p. (J). reprint ed. pap. 6.95 (978-0-374-41003-2(8)) Macmillan.

Wilson, Dawn. Saint Jude. 2000. (Illus.). 171p. (YA). (gr. 6-12). pap. 15.95 (978-0-936389-68-4(0)) Tudor Pubs., Inc.

Wood, Frances M. Becoming Rosemary. 2001. 256p. (gr. 5-9). pap. 12.00 (978-0-375-89504-3(3) , Delacorte Bks. for Young Readers) Random Hse. Children's Bks.

—Becoming Rosemary. 1998. (J). (978-0-606-13186-5(8)) Tandem Library Bks.

Wyche, Blonnie Bunn. The Anchor: P. Moore, Proprietor. 2003. 224p. 12.00 (978-1-889199-05-4(2)) Banks Channel Bks.

NORTH CAROLINA—HISTORY

Alter, Judy. The North Carolina Colony. 2003. (Spirit of America). (Illus.). 40p. (J). (gr. 2-6). 28.50 (978-1-56766-665-6(5)) Child's World, Inc.

Ashe County Historical Society Staff. Ashe County. 2000. (Images of America Ser.). 128p. (gr. 6 up). pap. 19.99 (978-0-7385-0615-9(X)) Arcadia Publishing.

Brickey, Peter, creator. Coastal Impressions... A photographic journey along the North Carolina Coast. 2004. (Illus.). 186p. cd-rom (978-0-9758964-1-9(5)) Brickey E-Publishing.

—From Currituck to Oak Island... A Photo Tour of North Carolina's Lighthouses. 2004. (Illus.). 88p. cd-rom 10.00 net. (978-0-9758964-0-2(7)) Brickey E-Publishing.

Britton, Tamara L. The North Carolina Colony. 2001. (Colonies Ser.). (Illus.). 32p. (J). (gr. k-6). lib. bdg. 22.78 (978-1-57765-582-4(6) , Checkerboard Library) ABDO Publishing Co.

Cannavale, Matthew C. North Carolina 1524-1776. 2007. (Voices from Colonial America Ser.). (Illus.). 112p. (J). (gr. 5-9). 21.95 (978-1-4263-0032-5(8)); lib. bdg. 32.90 (978-1-4263-0033-2(6)) National Geographic Society. (National Geographic Children's Bks.).

Davis, Lucile. R. J. Reynolds: He Saw the Future. 2000. (Community Builders Ser.). (J). (978-0-516-21600-3(7) , Children's Pr.) Scholastic Library Publishing.

Haberle, Susan E. The North Carolina Colony. 2005. (Fact Finders Ser.). (Illus.). 32p. (J). (ps-7). lib. bdg. 22.60 (978-0-7368-2680-8(7) , Fact Finders) Capstone Pr., Inc.

Harcourt School Publishers Staff. Horizons: North Carolina Edition. 3rd ed. 2003. (Illus.). (gr. 4). 73.50 (978-0-15-321347-2(7)) Harcourt Schl. Pubs.

Harkins, Susan. The Carolinas: Sir George Carteret & Sir Anthony Ashley Cooper. 2006. (J). lib. bdg. (978-1-58415-464-8(0)) Mitchell Lane Pubs., Inc.

Howell, Ray & Davidson County Historical Museum Staff. Davidson County. 2000. (Images of America Ser.). 128p. pap. 18.99 (978-0-7385-0637-1(0)) Arcadia Publishing.

Margulies, Phillip. The Colony of North Carolina. 2005. (Primary Sources of the Thirteen Colonies & the Lost Colony Ser.). (Illus.). 64p. (J). (gr. 3-7). pap. 14.60 (978-1-4042-0666-3(3)) Rosen Publishing Group, Inc., The.

—A Primary Source History of the Colony of North Carolina. 2005. (Primary Sources of the Thirteen Colonies & the Lost Colony Ser.). (Illus.). 64p. (YA). (gr. 5-8). lib. bdg. 29.25 (978-1-4042-0432-4(6)) Rosen Publishing Group, Inc., The.

Marsh, Carole. The Lost Colony Storybook. 2002. (Carole Marsh Bks.). (Illus.). (J). 32p. (gr. k-4). pap. 7.95 (978-0-635-01353-8(3) , 13533); 36p. (gr. 3-9). lib. bdg. 21.95 (978-0-635-01354-5(1) , 13541) Gallopade International. (Marsh, Carole Bks.).

—My First Pocket Guide North Carolina. 2000. (North Carolina Experience! Ser.). (Illus.). 96p. (J). (gr. 3-8). 12.95 (978-0-635-01323-1(1) , 13231) Gallopade International.

—North Carolina Millionaire. 2001. (GameBook Ser.). 32p. (J). (gr. 3-8). pap., act. bk. ed. 9.95 (978-0-635-00082-8(2)) Gallopade International.

—North Carolina Survivor. 2001. (GameBook Ser.). 32p. (J). (gr. 3-8). pap., act. bk. ed. 9.95 (978-0-635-00554-0(9)) Gallopade International.

—The North Carolina Survivor: A Class Challenge. 2001. (Carole Marsh North Carolina Bks.). lib. bdg. 29.95 (978-0-635-00679-0(0)); (J). lib. bdg. 29.95 (978-0-635-00680-6(4)) Gallopade International.

—North Carolina Wheel of Fortune. 2001. (GameBook Ser.). 32p. (J). (gr. 3-8). pap., act. bk. ed. 9.95 (978-0-7933-9682-5(4)) Gallopade International.

—Wheel of Fortune. 2001. (North Carolina Bks.). (J). lib. bdg. 29.95 (978-0-7933-9683-2(2)) Gallopade International.

—Who Wants to Be a Millionaire? 2001. (Carole Marsh North Carolina Bks.). (J). lib. bdg. 29.95 (978-0-635-00083-5(0)) Gallopade International.

Mayr, Diane. North Carolina. 2005. (Portraits of the States Ser.). (Illus.). 32p. (J). pap. (978-0-8368-4650-8(8)); lib. bdg. 23.33 (978-0-8368-4631-7(1)) Stevens, Gareth Inc.

Miller, Jake. The Lost Colony of Roanoke: A Primary Source History. 2006. (Primary Source Library of the Thirteen Colonies & the Lost Colony). (Illus.). 24p. (J). (gr. 3-5). lib. bdg. 21.25 (978-1-4042-3027-9(0) , PowerKids Pr.) Rosen Publishing Group, Inc., The.

Mis, Melody S. The Colony of North Carolina: A Primary Source History. 2007. (Primary Source Library of the Thirteen Colonies & the Lost Colony). (Illus.). 24p. (J). lib. bdg. (978-1-4042-3436-9(5) , PowerKids Pr.) Rosen Publishing Group, Inc., The.

Niz, Xavier. The Mystery of the Roanoke Colony. Denton, Shannon Eric, illus. 2007. (Graphic Library). 32p. (J). 25.26 (978-0-7368-6494-7(6)) Capstone Pr., Inc.

Norris, Sharon. Haywood County. 2000. (Black America Ser.). 128p. (gr. 5 up). pap. 18.99 (978-0-7385-0605-0(2)) Arcadia Publishing.

Passport to North Carolina Historic Sites. 1998. (Guides to State Historic Sites). (Illus.). 52p. (YA). (gr. 8-12). pap. 5.00 (978-0-86526-281-2(0)) North Carolina Office of Archives & History.

Patterson, Rusty & Hambright, Barry. Shelby & Cleveland County, North Carolina. 2000. (Images of America Ser.). (Illus.). 128p. (gr. 6 up). pap. 19.99 (978-0-7385-0610-4(9)) Arcadia Publishing.

Peters, S. True. How to Draw North Carolinas Sights & Symbols. 2002. (Kids Guide to Drawing America Ser.). 32p. (J). lib. bdg. 25.25 (978-0-8239-6089-7(7) , PowerKids Pr.) Rosen Publishing Group, Inc., The.

Stoesen, Alexander R. Guilford County: A Brief History. 2nd ed. 2000. (County History Ser.). (ENG., Illus.). 89p. (gr. 8-12). reprint ed. pap. 10.00 (978-0-86526-258-4(6)) North Carolina Office of Archives & History.

Surry County Genealogical Association Staff, et al. Surry County, North Carolina. 2000. (Images of America Ser.). 128p. pap. 19.99 (978-0-7385-0640-1(0)) Arcadia Publishing.

Taylor, Michael W. Tar Heels: How North Carolinians Got Their Nickname. 2004. (Popular Paperbacks Ser.). (Illus.). 27p. (gr. 8-12). pap. 6.00 (978-0-86526-288-1(8) , 03100) North Carolina Office of Archives & History.

Taylor, Michaelle. Singing Across the Old North State: Story-Songs of North Carolina. 2004. 44p. (J). pap. (978-1-880970-89-8(9)) Aerial Photography Services, Inc.

Tillage, Leon Walter. Leon's Story. Roth, Susan L., illus. 2000. 112p. (J). (gr. 3-7). pap. 5.95 (978-0-374-44330-6(0) , Sunburst) Farrar, Straus & Giroux.

—Leon's Story. 2000. (978-0-606-20397-5(4)); (J). (978-0-606-20134-6(3)) Tandem Library Bks.

Traylor, Waverley. Indian Legends of the Great Dismal Swamp. Traylor, Margaret, ed. Hancock, Stefanie, illus. 2004. 72p. (gr. 8 up). pap. 9.95 (978-0-9715068-3-1(3)) Traylor, Waverley Publishing.

Uschan, Michael V. North Carolina. 2001. (Thirteen Colonies Ser.). (Illus.). 112p. (YA). (gr. 4-12). lib. bdg. 29.95 (978-1-56006-885-3(X) , LML00902-178208, Lucent Bks.) Thomson Gale.

Whitehurst, Susan. The Colony of North Carolina. 2000. (Library of the Thirteen Colonies & the Lost Colony). (Illus.). 24p. (J). (gr. 3). lib. bdg. 19.95 (978-0-8239-5485-8(4) , PowerKids Pr.) Rosen Publishing Group, Inc., The.

Whitted, Fred. Fayetteville, North Carolina. 2000. (Black America Ser.). 128p. (gr. 6 up). pap. 18.99 (978-0-7385-0593-0(5)) Arcadia Publishing.

NORTH CENTRAL STATES

see Middle West

NORTH DAKOTA

Brown, Vanessa. North Dakota (Dakota del Norte) 2006. (Bilingual Library of the United States of America: Set 2). (ENG & SPA., Illus.). 32p. (J). (gr. 3-6). lib. bdg. 22.50 (978-1-4042-3099-6(8) , Buenas Letra) Rosen Publishing Group, Inc., The.

Fontes, Justine & Fontes, Ron. North Dakota: The Peace Garden State. 2003. (World Almanac Library of the States). (Illus.). 48p. (J). (gr. 5 up). pap. 14.95 (978-0-8368-5328-5(8)); lib. bdg. 30.00 (978-0-8368-5157-1(9)) Stevens, Gareth Inc. (World Almanac Library).

Gibson, Karen Bush. North Dakota Facts & Symbols. (States & Their Symbols Ser.). 24p. (J). 2000. (Illus.). (gr. 2-3). lib. bdg. 18.60 (978-0-7368-0642-8(3) , Bridgestone Bks.); 2003. lib. bdg. 19.93 (978-0-7368-2264-0(X)) Capstone Pr., Inc.

Glaser, Rebecca Stromstad. North Dakota. 2003. (Land of Liberty Ser.). (Illus.). 64p. (J). lib. bdg. 25.26 (978-0-7368-2191-9(0)) Capstone Pr., Inc.

Heinrichs, Ann. North Dakota. Kania, Matt, illus. 2005. (Welcome to the USA Ser.). 40p. (J). (gr. 1-5). 27.07 (978-1-59296-478-9(8)) Child's World, Inc.

—North Dakota. 2003. (This Land Is Your Land Ser.). (Illus.). 48p. (J). (gr. 3 up). lib. bdg. 22.60 (978-0-7565-0349-9(3)) Compass Point Bks.

Knapp, Ron. North Dakota: A MyReportLinks. Com Book. 2003. (States Ser.). (Illus.). 48p. (J). (gr. 4-10). lib. bdg. 25.26 (978-0-7660-5119-5(6) , MyReportLinks.com Bks.) Enslow Pubs., Inc.

Kummer, Patricia K. North Dakota. rev. ed. 2002. (One Nation Ser.). (Illus.). 48p. (J). (gr. 3-4). lib. bdg. 22.60 (978-0-7368-1258-0(X) , Bridgestone Bks.) Capstone Pr., Inc.

Marsh, Carole. The Big North Dakota Reproducible Activity Book. 2001. (Carole Marsh North Dakota Bks.). (Illus.). 96p. (J). (gr. 2-6). pap. 9.95 (978-0-7933-9952-9(1)) Gallopade International.

—My First Book about North Dakota. 2001. (Carole Marsh North Dakota Bks.). (Illus.). 32p. (J). (gr. k-4). pap. 7.95 (978-0-7933-9894-2(0)) Gallopade International.

—North Dakota Classic Christmas Trivia. 2002. (Carole Marsh North Dakota Bks.). (Illus.). 32p. pap. 6.95 (978-0-635-01435-1(1) , 14351, Marsh, Carole Bks.); lib. bdg. 21.95 (978-0-635-01436-8(X) , 01436X) Gallopade International.

—North Dakota Current Events Projects: 30 Cool, Activities, Crafts, Experiments & More for Kids to Do to Learn about Your State! 2003. (North Dakota Experience Ser.). 32p. (gr. k-8). pap. 5.95 (978-0-635-02053-6(X) , Marsh, Carole Bks.) Gallopade International.

—North Dakota Geography Projects: 30 Cool, Activities, Crafts, Experiments & More for Kids to Do to Learn about Your State! 2003. (North Dakota Experience Ser.). 32p. (gr. k-5). pap. 5.95 (978-0-635-01853-3(5) , Marsh, Carole Bks.) Gallopade International.

—North Dakota Government Projects: 30 Cool, Activities, Crafts, Experiments & More for Kids to Do to Learn about Your State! 2003. (North Dakota Experience Ser.). 32p. (gr. k-5). pap. 5.95 (978-0-635-01953-0(1) , Marsh, Carole Bks.) Gallopade International.

—North Dakota Jeopardy! Answers & Questions about Our State! Line Art Staff, illus. 2001. 32p. (J). (gr. 3-8). pap. 7.95 (978-0-7933-9807-2(X)) Gallopade International.

—North Dakota People Projects: 30 Cool, Activities, Crafts, Experiments & More for Kids to Do to Learn about Your State! 2003. (North Dakota Experience Ser.). 32p. (gr. k-5). pap. 5.95 (978-0-635-02003-1(3) , Marsh, Carole Bks.) Gallopade International.

—North Dakota Wheel of Fortune. 2001. (GameBook Ser.). 32p. (J). (gr. 3-8). pap., act. bk. ed. 9.95 (978-0-7933-9684-9(0)) Gallopade International.

McDaniel, Melissa. North Dakota. 2001. (Celebrate the States Ser.). (Illus.). 144p. (gr. 4-8). lib. bdg. 37.07 (978-0-7614-1314-1(6)); (J). lib. bdg. 35.64 (978-0-7614-1069-0(4)) Cavendish, Marshall Corp. (Benchmark Bks.).

Murray, Julie. North Dakota. 2006. (Buddy Book Ser.). (Illus.). 32p. (J). (gr. k-4). lib. bdg. 22.78 (978-1-59197-693-6(6) , Buddy Bks.) ABDO Publishing Co.

North Dakota. 2000. (Switched on Schoolhouse Ser.). (Illus.). (YA). (gr. 7-12). pap. 24.95 incl. cd-rom (978-0-7403-0286-2(8) , SOSND) Alpha Omega Pubns., Inc.

Redmond, Jim. Uniquely North Dakota. 2004. (Heinemann State Studies). (Illus.). 48p. (J). 27.07 (978-1-4034-4657-2(1)) Heinemann Library.

Redmond, Jim & Ross, D. J. Uniquely North Dakota. 2004. (Heinemann State Studies). (Illus.). 48p. (J). (ps-k). pap. 8.50 (978-1-4034-4726-5(8)) Heinemann Library.

Salonen, Roxane B. P Is for Peace Garden: A North Dakota Alphabet. Yardley, Joanna, illus. 2005. (Discover America State by State Ser.). 40p. (J). (ps-7). 17.95 (978-1-58536-142-7(9)) Sleeping Bear Pr.

Severin, E. Hoover. North Dakota. 2006. (Portraits of the States Ser.). (J). pap. (978-0-8368-4723-9(7)); lib. bdg. (978-0-8368-4706-2(7)) Stevens, Gareth Inc.

Silverman, Robin Landew. North Dakota. 2003. (From Sea to Shining Sea Ser.: 2). (Illus.). 80p. (J). 30.50 (978-0-516-22385-8(2) , Children's Pr.) Scholastic Library Publishing.

Verba, Joan Marie. North Dakota. 2nd exp. rev. ed. 2003. (Hello U. S. A. Ser.). (Illus.). 84p. (J). (gr. 3-6). 25.26 (978-0-8225-4097-7(5) , Lerner Pubns.) Lerner Publishing Group.

—North Dakota. rev. ed. 2003. (gr. 3-6). lib. bdg. 15.25 (978-0-613-52461-2(6)) Tandem Library Bks.

Watson, Galadriel Findlay. A Guide to North Dakota. 2001. (American States Ser.). (Illus.). 32p. (J). lib. bdg. 16.95 (978-1-930954-53-3(0)); per. 7.95 (978-1-930954-96-0(4)) Weigl Pubs., Inc.

Zollman, Pam. North Dakota. (J). 2006. 32p. (gr. 1-2). pap. 5.95 (978-0-516-25159-2(7)); 2005. (Illus.). 31p. (ps-ps). 20.50 (978-0-516-25259-9(3)) Scholastic Library Publishing. (Children's Pr.).

NORTH DAKOTA—FICTION

Brooke, Peggy. Jake's Orphan. 2001. 11.64 (978-0-606-22137-5(9)) Tandem Library Bks.

Fleischman, Paul. Mind's Eye. 2001. (gr. 7-12). lib. bdg. 13.55 (978-0-613-34013-7(2)) Tandem Library Bks.

Fournier, Kevin Mark. Sandbag Shuffle. 2007. 240p. (YA). (gr. 9 up). pap. 10.95 (*978-1-897235-22-5(4)) Thistledown Pr., Ltd. CAN. *Dist:* Fitzhenry & Whiteside, Ltd.

Johnson, Rodney. Curse of the Royal Ruby: A Rinnah Two Feathers Mystery. 2002. (gr. 7-12). lib. bdg. 19.90 (978-0-613-90288-5(2)) Tandem Library Bks.

—The Secret of Dead Man's Mine. Thompson, Jill, illus. 2001. 248p. (J). (gr. 4-7). pap. 12.00 (978-0-9663473-3-3(1)) Uglytown Productions.

Kurtz, Jane. River Friendly, River Wild. Brennan, Neil, illus. 2007. 40p. (J). 7.99 (978-1-4169-3487-5(1) , Aladdin) Simon & Schuster Children's Publishing.

Naylor, Phyllis Reynolds. Blizzard's Wake. (YA). 2004. (Illus.). 240p. pap. 5.99 (978-0-689-85221-3(5) , Simon Pulse); 2002. 224p. 16.95 (978-0-689-85220-6(7) , Atheneum) Simon & Schuster Children's Publishing.

—Blizzard's Wake. 2004. (gr. 7-12). lib. bdg. 14.15 (978-0-613-73409-7(2)) Tandem Library Bks.

—Blizzard's Wake. l.t. ed. 2003. 260p. (J). 22.95 (978-0-7862-5815-4(2)) Thorndike Pr.

Schuman, Burt E. Chanukah on the Prairie. Kaye, Rosalind Charney, illus. 2004. (gr. k-3). 13.95 (978-0-8074-0814-8(X) , 381780) URJ Pr.

Sorenson, Margo. Tori & the Sleigh of Midnight Blue. Austin, Brian, illus. 2002. 121p. (J). pap. 6.95 (978-0-911042-61-0(X)) North Dakota State Univ., Institute for Regional Studies.

Wilder, Laura Ingalls. By the Shores of Silver Lake. (Little House Ser.). (J). (gr. 3-6). lib. bdg. 23.95 (978-0-8488-2117-3(3)) Amereon LTD.

—By the Shores of Silver Lake. Williams, Garth, illus. 2004. (Little House Ser.). 304p. (J). pap. 8.99 (978-0-06-058184-8(0) , Harper Trophy) HarperCollins Pubs.

—By the Shores of Silver Lake. Williams, Garth, illus. l.t. ed. 2002. (LRS Large Print Cornerstone Ser.). (J). lib. bdg. 35.95 (978-1-58118-098-5(5)) LRS.

—By the Shores of Silver Lake. 2003. (gr. 3-6). lib. bdg. 14.15 (978-0-613-71429-7(6)) Tandem Library Bks.

NORTH DAKOTA—HISTORY

Cunningham, Robert G. Pearls of the Prairie: Life in Small Dakota Towns. 2002. (Illus.). 256p. lib. bdg. 17.95 (978-0-9717181-3-5(X)) Northern Lights, ND Pr.

Ehreth, Linda, et al. Where History Happens. Austin, Brian, illus. 1999. 35p. (Orig.). (J). (gr. k-7). pap. 2.95 (978-1-891419-17-1(X)) State Historical Society of North Dakota.

Marsh, Carole. My First Pocket Guide North Dakota. 2000. (North Dakota Experience! Ser.). (Illus.). 96p. (J). (gr. 3-8). 12.95 (978-0-635-01324-8(X)) Gallopade International.

—North Dakota History Projects: 30 Cool, Activities, Crafts, Experiments & More for Kids to Do to Learn about Your State! 2003. (North Dakota Experience Ser.). 32p. (gr. k-5). pap. 5.95 (978-0-635-01803-8(9) , Marsh, Carole Bks.) Gallopade International.

—North Dakota Millionaire. 2001. (GameBook Ser.). 32p. (J). (gr. 3-8). pap., act. bk. ed. 9.95 (978-0-635-00084-2(9)) Gallopade International.

—North Dakota Survivor. 2001. (GameBook Ser.). 32p. (J). (gr. 3-8). pap., act. bk. ed. 9.95 (978-0-635-00555-7(7)) Gallopade International.

Mis, Melody S. How to Draw North Dakota's Sights & Symbols. 2002. (Kids Guide to Drawing America Ser.). 32p. (J). lib. bdg. 25.25 (978-0-8239-6090-3(0) , PowerKids Pr.) Rosen Publishing Group, Inc., The.

NORTH POLE

see also Arctic Regions

Bedesky, Baron. Peary & Henson: The Race to the North Pole. 2006. (In the Footsteps of Explorers Ser.). (Illus.). 32p. (J). (gr. 3-9). pap. (978-0-7787-2462-9(X)); (978-0-7787-2426-1(3)) Crabtree Publishing Co.

Chapman, Simon. At the North Pole. 2005. (Illus.). 115p. (J). lib. bdg. 20.00 (*978-1-4242-0629-2(4)) Fitzgerald Bks.

Curlee, Lynn. Into the Ice: The Story of Arctic Exploration. 1998. (Illus.). 40p. (J). (gr. 4-6). tchr. ed. 16.00 (978-0-395-83013-0(3)) Houghton Mifflin Co. Trade & Reference Div.

Harcourt School Publishers Staff. To the Top of the World. 3rd ed. 2002. (Trophies English Language Learners Ser.). (Illus.). pap. 5.10 (978-0-15-327878-5(1)) Harcourt Schl. Pubs.

Hoena, B. A. Matthew Henson. 2005. (Illus.). 24p. (J). (ps-7). lib. bdg. 15.93 (978-0-7368-5249-4(2) , Pebble Bks.) Capstone Pr., Inc.

—Matthew Henson: Arctic Adventurer. Miller, Phil & Barnett, Charles, III, illus. 2005. (Graphic Library). 32p. (J). (gr. 3-7). lib. bdg. 25.26 (978-0-7368-4634-9(4)) Capstone Pr., Inc.

Johnson, Dolores. Onward: A Photobiography of African-American Polar Explorer Matthew Henson. 2005. (National Geographic Photographer Ser.). (Illus.). 64p. (J). (gr. k-3). 17.95 (978-0-7922-7914-3(X)); 27.90 (978-0-7922-7915-0(8)) National Geographic Society. (National Geographic Children's Bks.).

Patton, Geoff. Poles Apart. 2005. (X-Zone Ser.). (Illus.). 30p. (gr. 4-8). 23.00 (978-0-7910-8988-0(6)) Facts On File, Inc.

Petrie, Kristin. Robert Peary. 2007. (Rabbit Ears Ser.). (Illus.). 32p. (J). (gr. k-5). 22.78 (978-1-59679-746 8(0)) ABDO Publishing Co.

Revkin, Andrew. New York Times the North Pole Was Here: Puzzles & Perils at the Top of the World. 2006. (New York Times Ser.). (Illus.). 128p. (J). (gr. 5). 15.95 (978-0-7534-5993-5(0) , Kingfisher) Houghton Mifflin Co. Trade & Reference Div.

Revkin, Andrew. North Pole Was Here. 2007. 128p. (J). pap. 10.95 (*978-0-7534-6138-9(2) , Kingfisher) Houghton Mifflin Co. Trade & Reference Div.

Stamper, Judith Bauer. Magic School Bus Chapter Book: Polar Bear Patrol. Haefele, Steve, illus. 2003. (Magic School Bus Chapter Bks.: No. 13). 96p. (J). (gr. 2-4). pap. 4.99 (978-0-439-31433-6(X) , Scholastic Paperbacks) Scholastic, Inc.

—Polar Bear Patrol. 2002. (gr. 3-6). lib. bdg. 11.80 (978-0-613-63332-1(6)) Tandem Library Bks.

Weatherford, Carole Boston. I, Matthew Henson. Velasquez, Eric, illus. 2007. 32p. (J). 16.95 (*978-0-8027-9688-2(5)); 17.85 (*978-0-8027-9689-9(3)) Walker & Co.

Weidt, Maryann N. Matthew Henson. (History Maker Bios Ser.). (Illus.). 48p. (J). 2003. (gr. 2-4). 26.60 (978-0-8225-0397-2(2)); 2002. pap. 6.95 (978-0-8225-1565-4(2)) Lerner Publishing Group. (Lerner Pubns.).

NORTH POLE—FICTION

Christie, Michael G. Olive the Orphan Reindeer. Lucas, Margeaux, illus. 2000. 46p. (gr. 4-7). pap. 7.95 (978-1-889658-16-2(2)) New Canaan Publishing Co. LLC.

—The Story of Olive. 2000. (Illus.). 46p. (gr. 4-7). 14.95 (978-1-889658-18-6(9)) New Canaan Publishing Co. LLC.

Ehlenbeck, Stan. AllThumbs Mckringle by Stan Ehlenbeck & illustrated by Marilyn Martin. 2007. 29.00 (*978-0-8059-8957-1(9)) Dorrance Publishing Co., Inc.

Green, Rod. Santa's Reindeer. Wright, Carol et al, illus. 2007. 32p. (J). (ps-5). 16.99 (*978-1-4169-5070-7(2) , Atheneum) Simon & Schuster Children's Publishing.

Horse, Harry, illus. The Last Polar Bears. 2007. 76p. (J). (gr. 1-5). 12.95 (*978-1-56145-379-5(X) , Peachtree Junior) Peachtree Pubs., Ltd.

Johnson, Crockett. Harold at the North Pole. 2004. (Illus.). 48p. (J). (ps-3). pap. 5.99 (978-0-06-058628-7(1) , Harper Trophy) HarperCollins Pubs.

—Harold at the North Pole. Johnson, Crockett, illus. 1998. (Harold & the Purple Crayon Ser.). (Illus.). 48p. (J). (ps-3). 14.89 (978-0-06-028074-1(3)) HarperCollins Pubs.

Kramer, Candice. Matthew Henson en el Polo Norte & Matthew Henson at the North Pole. 2005. spiral bd. 76.00 (*978-1-4108-5790-3(5)) Benchmark Education Co.

Patterson, James. SantaKid. Garland, Michael, illus. 2004. 48p. (J). (gr. k-3). 14.99 (978-0-316-00061-1(2)) Little, Brown Bks. for Young Readers.

Primavera, Elise. Auntie Claus. 1999. (Illus.). 40p. (J). (ps-3). 16.00 (978-0-15-201909-9(X) , Silver Whistle) Harcourt Trade Pubs.

—Auntie Claus & the Key to Christmas. Primavera, Elise, illus. 2002. (Illus.). 40p. (J). (gr. k-3). 16.00 (978-0-15-202441-3(7) , Silver Whistle) Harcourt Trade Pubs.

Schomer Wendel, Gretchen & Schomer, Adam Anthony. Becka & the Big Bubble: Becka Goes to the North Pole. 2007. (Illus.). 28p. (J). 11.99 (*978-1-933754-11-6(7)) Waterside Publishing.

Tiller, Steve. Rudolf the Red Nose Rocket. Cremeans, Robert, illus. 2002. 28p. (J). (gr. k-3). 15.95 (978-0-9704597-9-4(3)) MichaelsMind LLC.

Van Allsburg, Chris. The Polar Express Sam's Edition. 2006. (J). (gr. k-3). 35.00 (978-0-618-83659-8(4)) Houghton Mifflin Co. Trade & Reference Div.

Weiss, Ellen, et al. Trip to the North Pole: A Junior Novel. movie tie-in ed. 2004. (Polar Express Ser.). (Illus.). 128p. (J). (gr. 5-6). pap. 4.99 (978-0-618-47790-6(X)) Houghton Mifflin Co. Trade & Reference Div.

West, Tracey, et al. The Magic Journey. 2004. (Polar Express Ser.). (Illus.). 32p. (J). (gr. k-3). 9.99 (978-0-618-47788-3(8)) Houghton Mifflin Co.

NORTHMEN

Here are entered works on the inhabitants of Scandinavia prior to the 10th century. Works on the Scandinavian sea-warriors who plundered the northern and western coasts of Europe from the 8th to the 10th centuries are entered under Vikings. Works on the inhabitants of Scandinavia since the 10th century are entered under Scandinavians.

see also Normans; Vikings

Ashman, Iain. Make This Viking Settlement. 1998. (Usborne Cut-Out Models Ser.). (Illus.). 32p. (J). (gr. 4-7). pap. 9.95 (978-0-7460-3692-1(2)) EDC Publishing.

Barron's Educational Editorial Staff. Viking Life. 1998. (Early Civilizations Ser.). (Illus.). 32p. (J). (gr. 5-9). pap. 5.95 (978-0-7641-0631-6(7)) Barron's Educational Series, Inc.

Binns, Tristan Boyer. The Vikings. 2005. (Ancient Civilizations Ser.). (Illus.). 32p. (J). (gr. 4-6). 26.60 (978-0-7565-1678-9(1)) Compass Point Bks.

British Museum Staff & Wilson. Vikings. 1999. (Illus.). 16p. (gr. 4-7). pap. 5.95 (978-0-7141-2174-1(6)) Brimfield Pubns.

Chrisp, Peter. Vikings. Englefield, John & McDonald, Brigitte, illus. 1998. (My World Ser.). 32p. (J). (gr. 2-7). 7.00 (978-0-7166-9412-0(3)) World Bk., Inc.

Hewitt, Sally. The Vikings. 2007. (J). (*978-1-59920-047-7(3)) Smart Apple Media.

Hindley, Judy, et al. Time Traveler: Visit Medieval Times, the Viking Age, the Roman World & Ancient Egypt. rev. ed. 2004. (Time Travelers Bks.). (Illus.). 130p. (J). (gr. 3-6). 22.95 (978-0-7460-3365-4(6)) EDC Publishing.

Hopkins, Andrea. Viking Families & Farms. 2002. (Viking Library). (Illus.). 24p. (J). (gr. 3). lib. bdg. 19.95 (978-0-8239-5815-3(9) , PowerKids Pr.) Rosen Publishing Group, Inc., The.

James, Louise. The Vikings. James, John, illus. 2001. (How We Know about Ser.). 32p. (J). (gr. 5 up). 17.95 (978-0-87226-535-6(8) , 65358B, Bedrick, Peter Bks.) School Specialty Publishing.

MacDonald, Fiona. Vikings. 2005. (First Look at History Ser.). (Illus.). 24p. (J). 22.00 (978-0-8368-4530-3(7)) Stevens, Gareth Inc.

MacDonald, Fiona. The Vikings. 2007. (J). lib. bdg. 19.95 (*978-1-59566-354-2(1)) QEB Publishing Inc.

Martell, Hazel Mary. Everyday Life in Viking Times. 2005. (Clues to the Past Ser.). (Illus.). 32p. (J). (gr. 4-7). lib. bdg. 27.10 (978-1-932889-80-2(9)) Sea-To-Sea Pubns.

Nardo, Don. The Vikings. 2005. (Life During the Great Civilizations Ser.). (Illus.). 48p. (J). (gr. k-7). lib. bdg. 24.95 (978-1-4103-0584-8(8) , Blackbirch Pr., Inc.) Thomson Gale.

Streissguth, Thomas. Life among the Vikings. 1998. (Way People Live Ser.). (Illus.). 96p. (YA). (gr. 7-10). 27.45 (978-1-56006-392-6(0) , LML00902-177774, Lucent Bks.) Thomson Gale.

Thompson, Ruth. The Vikings. 1998. (Footsteps in Time Ser.). (Illus.). 24p. (J). (gr. 2-3). pap. 3.95 (978-0-516-26234-5(3) , Children's Pr.) Scholastic Library Publishing.

The Vikings. 2002. (History Makers Ser.). 32p. (J). 9.95 (978-0-7525-7830-9(8)) Parragon, Inc.

Wright, Rachel. The Vikings. (Illus.). 32p. (YA). (gr. 3 up). lib. bdg. 27.10 (978-1-932889-03-1(5)) Sea-To-Sea Pubns.

NORTHMEN—FICTION

Katz, Welwyn W. Out of the Dark. 2001. 185p. (J). (gr. 4). pap. 5.95 (978-0-88899-262-8(9)) Groundwood Bks. CAN. *Dist:* Perseus Distribution.

NORTHWEST, OLD

see also Middle West

Connell, Kate. These Lands Are Ours: Tecumseh's Fight for the Old Northwest. 2001. (Nonfiction Bookbag Ser.). (J). (gr. 5-6). per. 8.45 (978-1-58830-206-9(7)) Metropolitan Teaching & Learning Co.

Stein, R. Conrad. On the Old Western Frontier. 1999. (How We Lived Ser.). (Illus.). 72p. (J). (gr. 4-8). lib. bdg. 28.50 (978-0-7614-0909-0(2) , Benchmark Bks.) Cavendish, Marshall Corp.

Thompson, Linda. The Great Lakes. 2006. (Expansion of America II Ser.). (Illus.). 48p. (gr. 4-8). 20.95 (978-1-59515-512-2(0)) Rourke Publishing, LLC.

NORTHWEST, PACIFIC

Ansary, Mir Tamim. Northwest Coast Indians. 2002. (Native Americans Ser.). (Illus.). 32p. (J). (gr. 1-4). pap. 7.50 (978-1-58810-350-5(1) , 91110) Heinemann Library.

—Northwest Coast Indians. 2001. (Native Americans Ser.). (Illus.). (J). (978-0-606-22012-5(7)) Tandem Library Bks.

Ansary, Mir Tamim, contrib. by. Northwest Coast Indians. 1999. (Native Americans Ser.). (Illus.). 32p. (J). (gr. 2-4). lib. bdg. 21.36 (978-1-57572-921-3(0)) Heinemann Library.

Benchmark Education Staff. The Pacific Northwest Region. 2005. 2.00 (*978-1-4108-4646-4(6)) Benchmark Education Co.

Blue, Rose. Exploring Pacific Northwest. 2003. (Exploring America Ser.). (Illus.). 64p. pap. 9.50 (978-1-4109-0044-9(4)) Raintree.

Blue, Rose & Naden, Corinne J. Exploring the Pacific Northwest. 2003. (Illus.). 64p. (J). lib. bdg. 28.56 (978-0-7398-4950-7(6)) Raintree.

Brannon, Barbara. Discover the Pacific Northwest Region. 2005. 39.00 (*978-1-4108-5150-5(8)) Benchmark Education Co.

Helman, Andrea. 1, 2, 3 Moose: A Counting Book. Wolfe, Art, photos by. 2003. (Illus.). 32p. (J). pap., pap. 9.95 (978-1-57061-393-7(1)) Sasquatch Bks.

Johnson, Michael & Clarke, Duncan. Native Tribes of the Great Basin & Plateau. 2004. (Native Tribes of North America Ser.). (Illus.). 64p. (J). (gr. 5 up). lib. bdg. 32.67 (978-0-8368-5610-1(4) , World Almanac Library) Stevens, Gareth Inc.

Leonardo, Victoria. The Pacific Northwest Region. 2005. 39.00 (*978-1-4108-4598-6(2)) Benchmark Education Co.

Shallop, Laura. The Pacific Northwest States. 2006. (Navigators Ser.). (J). pap. 42.00 (*978-1-4108-6255-6(0)) Benchmark Education Co.

Williams, Colleen Madonna Flood. My Adventure in the Pacific Northwest: Advanced My Adventure. 2007. 44p. (J). pap. 8.99 (978-1-59092-566-9(1) , Orchard Academy Pr.) Windstorm Creative.

NORTHWEST, PACIFIC—FICTION

Allen, Quinc. The Outdoor Chums after Big Game (Illust. 2006. pap. (*978-1-4065-0780-5(6)) Dodo Pr.

Allen, Quincy. Outdoor Chums after Big Game or Perilous. 2006. 77.99 (*978-1-4280-3810-3(8)); pap. 71.99 (*978-1-4280-3804-2(3)) IndyPublish.com.

Anderson, Margaret Jean. Olla-Piska: Tales of David Douglas. 2006. (Illus.). 144p. (J). pap. 19.95 (978-0-87595-297-0(6)) Oregon Historical Society Pr.

Banerjee, Anjali. Looking for Bapu. 2006. 176p. (J). (gr. 3-6). 15.95 (978-0-385-74657-1(1)); lib. bdg. 17.99 (978-0-385-90894-8(6)) Random Hse. Children's Bks. (Lamb, Wendy).

Capeci, Anne. Daredevils. Casale, Paul, illus. 2004. (Cascade Mountain Railroad Mysteries Ser.). 144p. (J). (gr. 2-3). 12.95 (978-1-56145-307-8(2)) Peachtree Pubs., Ltd.

—Ghost Train, Vol. 3. Casale, Paul, illus. 2004. (Cascade Moutain Railroad Mystery Ser.: 3). 144p. (J). (gr. 2-5). 12.95 (978-1-56145-324-5(2)) Peachtree Pubs., Ltd.

—Missing! Casale, Paul, illus. 2005. 144p. (J). 12.95 (978-1-56145-334-4(X)) Peachtree Pubs., Ltd.

Creedon, Catherine. Blue Wolf. Bentley, James, illus. 192p. (J). 2005. pap. 5.99 (978-0-06-050870-8(1)); 2003. lib. bdg. 16.89 (978-0-06-050869-2(8)) HarperCollins Pubs. (Julie Andrews Collection).

Hobbs, William. Ghost Canoe. 1998. (Avon Camelot Bks.). 208p. (J). (gr. 5-9). pap. 5.99 (978-0-380-72537-3(1)) HarperCollins Pubs.

—Ghost Canoe. 1998. (J). 12.64 (978-0-606-13420-0(4)) Tandem Library Bks.

LaMear, Arline. Lewis & Clark, the Astoria Cats. Goza, Benjamin, illus. 2002. 32p. (J). (gr. 3-7). pap. 9.95 (978-0-9720394-0-6(6)) Lucky Cat Publishing.

Nickerson, Sara. How to Disappear Completely & Never Be Found. Comport, Sally Wern, illus. 288p. (J). (gr. 5 up). 2003. pap. 5.99 (978-0-06-441027-4(7)); 2002. 16.99 (978-0-06-029771-8(9)); 2002. lib. bdg. 17.89 (978-0-06-029772-5(7)) HarperCollins Pubs.

—How to Disappear Completely & Never Be Found. 2003. (gr. 7-12). lib. bdg. 14.15 (978-0-613-62207-3(3)) Tandem Library Bks.

Salonen, Roxane Beauclair. First Salmon. 2005. (Illus.). 29p. (J). (gr. 3-7). 15.95 (978-1-59078-171-5(6)) Boyds Mills Pr.

Shaw, Janet. Kaya's Short Story Collection. Farnsworth, Bill & Graef, Renee, illus. 2006. 256p. (J). 12.95 (*978-1-59369-119-6(X)) American Girl Publishing, Inc.

Shaw, Janet. Kaya's Story Collection. Farnsworth, Bill, illus. 2005. (American Girls Collection). 407p. (J). (gr. 3-17). 29.95 (978-1-59369-046-5(0) , American Girl) American Girl Publishing, Inc.

Shaw, Janet Beeler. Changes for Kaya. 2002. (gr. 3-6). lib. bdg. 14.10 (978-0-613-46214-3(9)) Tandem Library Bks.

—Changes for Kaya Bk. 6: A Winter Story. Farnsworth, Bill & McAliley, Susan, illus. 2002. (American Girls Collection: Bk. 6). 80p. (gr. 2-7). (J). 12.95 (978-1-58485-434-0(0)); 6.95 (978-1-58485-433-3(2)) American Girl Publishing, Inc.

—Kaya: An American Girl. 2002. (American Girls Collection). (Illus.). (J). (gr. 2). pap. 39.95 (978-1-58485-511-8(8)) American Girl Publishing, Inc.

—Kaya & Lone Dog Bk. 4: A Friendship Story. Farnsworth, Bill & McAliley, Susan, illus. 2002. (American Girls Collection: Bk. 4). 96p. (J). (gr. 2-7). 12.95 (978-1-58485-430-2(8)); 6.95 (978-1-58485-429-6(4)) American Girl Publishing, Inc.

—Kaya Shows the Way Bk. 5: A Sister Story. Farnsworth, Bill & McAliley, Susan, illus. 2002. (American Girls Collection: Bk. 5). 88p. (gr. 2-7). (J). 12.95 (978-1-58485-432-6(4)); 6.95 (978-1-58485-431-9(6)) American Girl Publishing, Inc.

—Kaya's Escape. 2002. (gr. 3-6). lib. bdg. 14.10 (978-0-613-46223-5(8)) Tandem Library Bks.

—Kaya's Escape! A Survival Story, Bk. 2. Farnsworth, Bill & McAliley, Susan, illus. 2002. (American Girls Collection: Bk. 2). 88p. (gr. 2-7). (J). 12.95 (978-1-58485-426-5(X)); 6.95 (978-1-58485-425-8(1)) American Girl Publishing, Inc.

—Kaya's Hero. 2002. (gr. 3-6). lib. bdg. 14.10 (978-0-613-46224-2(6)) Tandem Library Bks.

—Kaya's Hero Bk. 3: A Story of Giving. Farnsworth, Bill & McAliley, Susan, illus. 2002. (American Girls Collection: Bk. 3). 88p. (gr. 2-7). (J). 12.95 (978-1-58485-428-9(6)); 6.95 (978-1-58485-427-2(8)) American Girl Publishing, Inc.

—Meet Kaya. 2002. (gr. 3-6). lib. bdg. 14.10 (978-0-613-46227-3(0)) Tandem Library Bks.

Sloat, Teri. There Was an Old Lady Who Swallowed a Trout. Ruffins, Reynold, illus. 2002. (J). 26.47 (978-0-7587-3781-6(5)) Book Wholesalers, Inc.

—There Was an Old Lady Who Swallowed a Trout. Ruffins, Reynold, illus. rev. ed. 32p. (J). (gr. k-2). 2002. pap. 7.95 (978-0-8050-6900-6(3)); 1998. 17.95 (978-0-8050-4294-8(6)) Holt, Henry & Co. (Holt, Henry & Co. Bks. For Young Readers).

—There Was an Old Lady Who Swallowed a Trout. 2002. (ps-2). lib. bdg. 15.25 (978-0-613-88115-9(X)) Tandem Library Bks.

Suzuki, David & Ellis, Sarah. The Salmon Forest. Lott, Sheena, illus. 2003. (David Suzuki Children's Titles Ser.). (gr. k-2). 15.95 (978-1-55054-937-9(5)) Douglas & McIntyre, Ltd. CAN. *Dist:* Transition Vendor.

—Salmon Forest. Lott, Sheena, illus. 2006. 32p. (J). pap. 8.95 (978-1-55365-163-5(4) , Greystone Bks.) Douglas & McIntyre, Ltd. CAN. *Dist:* Transition Vendor.

Vaughan, Richard Lee. Eagle Boy: A Pacific Northwest Native Tale. Christiansen, Lee, illus. 2002. 32p. (J). (gr. 1-5). 16.95 (978-1-57061-171-1(8)) Sasquatch Bks.

Vischer, Phil. 47 Beavers in the Big Blue Sea. 2007. (Illus.). 48p. (J). 15.99 (978-1-4003-0836-1(4)) Nelson, Thomas Inc.

NORTHWEST PASSAGE

Cookman, Scott. Ice Blink: The Tragic Fate of Sir John Franklin's Lost Polar Expedition. 2000. (gr. 7-12). lib. bdg. 25.70 (978-0-613-35414-1(1)) Tandem Library Bks.

Foran, Jill. Search for the Northwest Passage. 2004. (Great Journeys Ser.). (Illus.). 32p. (J). lib. bdg. 26.00 (978-1-59036-205-1(5)) Weigl Pubs., Inc.

—The Search for the Northwest Passage. 2005. (Great Journeys Ser.). 32p. pap. 7.95 (978-1-59036-259-4(4)) Weigl Pubs., Inc.

Knudsen, Anders. Sir John Franklin: The Search for the Northwest Passage. 2007. (Illus.). 32p. (J). (gr. 3-9). (***978-0-7787-2420-9(4)**); pap. (***978-0-7787-2456-8(5)**) Crabtree Publishing Co.

Warrick, Karen Clemens. The Perilous Search for the Fabled Northwest Passage in American History. 2004. (In American History Ser.). (Illus.). 128p. (J). lib. bdg. 26.60 (978-0-7660-2148-8(3)) Enslow Pubs., Inc.

NORTHWEST TERRITORIES

Daitch, Richard W. Northwest Territories. rev. ed. (Hello Canada Ser.). (Illus.). 72p. (J). pap. (978-1-55041-762-3(2)) Fitzhenry & Whiteside, Ltd.

Laws, Gordon D. & Laws, Lauren M. The Northwest Territories. 2003. (Exploring Canada Ser.). (Illus.). 112p. (J). 29.95 (978-1-59018-049-5(6) , Lucent Bks.) Thomson Gale.

LeVert, Suzanne. Northwest Territories. 2000. (Canada in the Twenty First Century Ser.). (Illus.). (J). (gr. 8-12). 29.50 (978-0-7910-6066-7(7) , Chelsea Hse.) Facts On File, Inc.

Stephenson, Wendy. Idaa Trail: In the Steps of Our Ancestors. Downey, Autumn, illus. 2005. 32p. (J). 18.95 (978-0-88899-576-6(8)) Groundwood Bks. CAN. *Dist:* Perseus Distribution.

NORTHWEST TERRITORIES—FICTION

Fletcher, Archibald Lee. Boy Scouts in Northern Wilds. 2007. 124p. pap. 10.99 (***978-1-4264-6161-3(5)**); 134p. pap. 13.99 (***978-1-4264-6216-0(6)**) BiblioBazaar.

Van Camp, Richard. What's the Most Beautiful Thing You Know about Horses? Littlechild, George, illus. 1998. 32p. (J). (gr. 1 up). 15.95 (978-0-89239-154-7(5)) Children's Bk. Pr.

Wilson, John. Across Frozen Seas. 2006. 128p. (YA). (gr. 3-8). pap., tchr. ed. 5.95 (978-0-88878-381-3(7) , Sandcastle Bks.) Dundurn Group, The CAN. *Dist:* Univ. of Toronto Pr.

NORWAY

Blashfield, Jean F. Norway. 2000. (Enchantment of the World, Second Ser.). (Illus.). 144p. (gr. 5-9). 36.00 (978-0-516-20651-6(6) , Children's Pr.) Scholastic Library Publishing.

Braun, Eric. Norway in Pictures. 2nd rev. ed. 2003. (Visual Geography Ser.). (Illus.). 80p. (J). (gr. 5-12). 27.93 (978-0-8225-0369-9(7)) Lerner Publishing Group.

Britton, Tamara L. Norway. 2003. (Countries Ser.). (Illus.). 40p. (J). (gr. k-6). lib. bdg. 22.78 (978-1-57765-839-9(6)) ABDO Publishing Co.

Corona, Laurel. Norway. 2000. (Modern Nations of the World Ser.). (Illus.). 128p. (J). (gr. 7-10). 29.95 (978-1-56006-647-7(4) , Lucent Bks.) Thomson Gale.

Deady, Kathleen W. Norway. 2001. (Countries of the World Ser.). (Illus.). 24p. (J). (gr. 2-3). lib. bdg. 18.60 (978-0-7368-0943-6(0) , Bridgestone Bks.) Capstone Pr., Inc.

Fouberg, Erin Hogan & Hogan, Edward Patrick, trs. Norway. 2003. (Modern World Nations Ser.). (Illus.). 150p. (gr. 6-12). 30.00 (978-0-7910-7479-4(X) , Chelsea Hse.) Facts On File, Inc.

Grolier Educational Staff, contrib. by. Norway. 2003. (Illus.). 32p. (J). (978-0-7172-5798-0(3) , Grolier) Scholastic Library Publishing.

Hepso, Mike. Norway. 2002. (Countries of the World Ser.). (Illus.). 96p. (J). (gr. 6 up). lib. bdg. 30.00 (978-0-8368-2362-2(1)) Stevens, Gareth Inc.

Kagda, Sakina & Alexander, Anne. Norway. 2nd ed. 2006. (Cultures of the World Ser.). 144p. (J). lib. bdg. 39.93 (978-0-7614-2067-5(3) , Benchmark Bks.) Cavendish, Marshall Corp.

Kopka, Deborah L. Norway. (Ticket to Ser.). (Illus.). 48p. 2005. (gr. 2-4). lib. bdg. 22.60 (978-1-57505-148-2(6)); 2000. (J). (gr. 3-5). lib. bdg. 22.60 (978-1-57505-123-9(0) , Carolrhoda Bks.) Lerner Publishing Group.

Landau, Elaine. Norway. (True Bks.). (Illus.). 48p. (J). (gr. 3-5). 2000. pap. 6.95 (978-0-516-26767-8(1)); 1999. 25.00 (978-0-516-20985-2(X)) Scholastic Library Publishing. (Children's Pr.).

—Norway. 1999. (gr. 3-6). lib. bdg. 15.25 (978-0-613-54060-5(3)) Tandem Library Bks.

Lunge-Larsen, Lise. Race of Birkebeiners. Azarian, Mary, illus. 2007. 32p. (J). (gr. k). 6.95 (***978-0-618-91599-6(0)**) Houghton Mifflin Co. Trade & Reference Div.

Munsen, Sylvia. Cooking the Norwegian Way. 2nd rev. expurg. ed. 2002. (Easy Menu Ethnic Cookbooks). (Illus.). 72p. (J). (gr. 5-12). 25.26 (978-0-8225-4118-9(1) , Lerner Pubns.) Lerner Publishing Group.

Murdico, Suzanne J. Norway: A Primary Source Cultural Guide. 2005. (Primary Sources of World Cultures Ser.). (J). (978-1-4042-0479-9(2)) Rosen Publishing Group, Inc., The.

Rose, Elizabeth. A Primary Source Guide to Norway. 2004. (Primary Sources of Countries of the World Ser.). (Illus.). 24p. (J). lib. bdg. 19.95 (978-0-8239-6732-2(8) , PowerKids Pr.) Rosen Publishing Group, Inc., The.

Thoennes, Kristin. Christmas in Norway. 1998. (Christmas Around the World Ser.). (Illus.). 24p. (J). (gr. 2-3). 18.60 (978-0-7368-0091-4(3) , Bridgestone Bks.) Capstone Pr., Inc.

Wan, Vanessa. Welcome to Norway. 2004. (Welcome to My Country Ser.). (Illus.). 48p. (J). (gr. 2 up). lib. bdg. 26.00 (978-0-8368-2562-6(4)) Stevens, Gareth Inc.

Zickgraf, Ralph. Norway. 1999. (Major World Nations Ser.). (Illus.). 144p. (YA). (gr. 4-7). 29.95 (978-0-7910-4747-7(4) , Chelsea Hse.) Facts On File, Inc.

NORWAY—FICTION

Asbjornsen, Peter Christen. East of the Sun & West of the Moon. 2001. (Children's Classics). 256p. (J). pap. 3.95 (978-1-85326-164-0(5)) Wordsworth Editions, Ltd. GBR. *Dist:* Advanced Global Distribution Services.

d'Aulaire, Edgar & d'Aulaire, Ingri. The Terrible Troll-Bird. 2007. (Illus.). 48p. (J). (ps-3). 15.95 (***978-1-59017-252-0(3)** , NYR Children's Collection) New York Review of Bks., Inc., The.

Egner, Thorbjorn. Karius & Baktus. Sevig, Mike, tr. from NOR. 2nd ed. 2002. (Illus.). 41p. (J). (gr. 1-3). 10.95 (978-0-9615394-1-2(0)) Skandisk, Inc.

A Foal Is Born. 2007. (J). (978-1-933343-46-4(X) , PONY) Stabenfeldt Inc.

Hagerup, Klaus. Markus & Diana. Chace, Tara, tr. from NOR. 2006. 192p. (J). 17.95 (978-1-932425-59-8(4) , Front Street) Boyds Mills Pr.

Haig, Matt. Samuel Blink & the Forbidden Forest. 2007. 352p. (J). 16.99 (978-0-399-24739-2(4) , Putnam Juvenile) Penguin Group (USA) Inc.

Inger's Promise: Evaluation Guide. 2006. (J). (978-1-55942-409-7(5)) Marsh Media.

Johnson, Lois Walfrid. Raider's Promise. 2006. (Raiders from the Sea Ser.). (Illus.). 304p. (J). pap. 8.99 (978-0-8024-3116-5(X)) Moody Pubs.

Lindy, Elaine L. The Ram & the Pig Who Set up House: A Folk Tale from Norway. 2002. (Whootie Owl's Test Prep Storytime Ser.). 32p. (J). 4.99 (978-0-9672831-5-9(9)) Whootie Owl International, LLC.

Lindy, Elaine L., creator. Boots & His Brothers: A Folk Tale from Norway. 2002. (Whootie Owl's Test Prep Storytime Ser.). (J). 4.99 (978-0-9672831-8-0(3)) Whootie Owl International, LLC.

Louise, Martha. Why Kings & Queens Don't Wear Crowns. Sevig-Fajardo, Mari Elise, tr. from NOR. Nyhus, Svein, illus. 2005. Orig. Title: Hvorfor de kongelige ikke har krone pa Hodet. 32p. (J). 17.95 (978-1-57534-037-1(2) , CSC 100) Skandisk, Inc.

MacHale, D. J. East of the Sun, West of the Moon. Flesher, Vivienne, illus. 2007. (J). 25.65 (978-1-59961-306-2(9)) ABDO Publishing Co.

Myers, Tim. Good Babies: A Tale of Trolls, Humans, a Witch & a Switch. Murphy, Kelly, illus. 2005. 32p. (J). (ps-3). 15.99 (978-0-7636-2227-5(3)) Candlewick Pr.

Newth, Mette. The Dark Light. Ingwersen, Faith, tr. 2004. 256p. (YA). reprint ed. pap. 6.95 (978-0-374-41688-1(5) , Sunburst) Farrar, Straus & Giroux.

NORWAY—HISTORY—FICTION

Casanova, Mary. Klipfish Code. 2007. 240p. (J). (gr. 5-7). 16.00 (***978-0-618-88393-6(2)**) Houghton Mifflin Co. Trade & Reference Div.

McSwigan, Marie. Snow Treasure. Mary, Reardon, illus. 2006. 208p. (J). (gr. 3). pap. 5.99 (978-0-14-240224-5(9) , Puffin) Penguin Group (USA) Inc.

NORWEGIAN LANGUAGE

Hippocrene Books, ed. Norwegian Children's Picture Dictionary: English-Norwegian/Norwegian-English. 2006. (Illus.). 114p. pap. 14.95 (978-0-7818-1164-4(3)) Hippocrene Bks., Inc.

Hippocrene Books Staff. Hippocrene Children's Illustrated Norwegian Dictionary: English-Norwegian. 2001. Tr. of Norweg. (ENG & NOR.). (gr. 3-6). lib. bdg. 21.05 (978-0-613-74949-7(9)) Tandem Library Bks.

Hippocrene Children's Illustrated Norwegian Dictionary: English-Norwegian/Norwegian-English. 2002. (Children's Illustrated Foreign Language Dictionaries Ser.). (ENG & NOR., Illus.). 94p. (gr. k-5). pap. 11.95 (978-0-7818-0887-3(1)) Hippocrene Bks., Inc.

NORWEGIANS—UNITED STATES

Heinrichs, Ann. Norwegian Americans. 2004. (Our Cultural Heritage Ser.). 32p. (J). (gr. 2-6). 27.07 (978-1-59296-182-5(7)) Child's World, Inc.

NORWEGIANS—UNITED STATES—FICTION

Lurie, April. Dancing in the Streets of Brooklyn. 208p. (gr. 3-7). 2004. pap. 5.99 (978-0-440-41825-2(9) , Yearling); 2002. lib. bdg. 17.99 (978-0-385-90066-9(X) , Delacorte Bks. for Young Readers) Random Hse. Children's Bks.

Peterson, Esther Allen. A Long Journey to a New Home. 2006. (J). pap. (978-0-88092-470-2(5)); lib. bdg. (978-0-88092-469-6(1)) Royal Fireworks Publishing Co.

Push to the West (Norwegians) 76p. (YA). (gr. 6-12). pap. 9.95 (978-0-8224-3678-2(7)) Globe Fearon Educational Publishing.

NOTATION, MUSICAL

see Musical Notation

NOVA SCOTIA

Beckett, Harry. Nova Scotia. 2003. (Eye on Canada Ser.). (Illus.). 32p. (J). pap. 7.95 (978-1-894705-05-9(X)) Weigl Pubs., Inc.

Grant, Vicki. The Halifax Citadel. Pilsworth, Graham, tr. Pilsworth, Graham, illus. 2003. (Dreadful Truth Ser.). 80p. (J). (gr. 3-8). (***978-0-88780-599-8(X)**) Formac Publishing Co., Ltd. CAN. *Dist:* Casemate Pubs. & Bk. Distributors, LLC.

Hozy, Penny & Thompson, Alexa. Nova Scotia. 2nd rev. ed. (Hello Canada Ser.). (Illus.). 72p. pap. (978-1-55041-440-0(2)) Fitzhenry & Whiteside, Ltd.

Kyi, Tanya Lloyd. Nova Scotia. 2003. (Canada Ser.). (Illus.). 96p. 17.95 (978-1-55285-418-1(3)) Whitecap Bks., Ltd. CAN. *Dist:* Firefly Bks., Ltd.

LeVert, Suzanne. Nova Scotia. 2000. (Canada in the Twenty First Century Ser.). (Illus.). 64p. (J). (gr. 8-12). 18.95 (978-0-7910-6067-4(5) , Chelsea Hse.) Facts On File, Inc.

Thompson, Alexa. Nova Scotia. 1998. (Hello Canada Ser.). (Illus.). (J). (gr. 3-6). pap. 6.95 (978-0-8225-9799-5(3)) Lerner Publishing Group.

NOVA SCOTIA—FICTION

Ashby, Freya Katrina. Summer at the Dunes: A Deirdre Carlisle Mystery. 2007. 108p. per. 9.95 (***978-0-595-43663-7(3)**) iUniverse, Inc.

Bastedo, Jamie. Free as the Wind: Saving the Horses of Sable Island. Tooke, Susan, illus. 2007. 32p. (J). (gr. k-3). 17.95 (***978-0-88995-350-5(3)**) Red Deer Pr. CAN. *Dist:* Fitzhenry & Whiteside, Ltd.

Bawtree, Michael. Joe Howe to the Rescue. Smith, David Preston, illus. 2004. 152p. pap. (978-1-55109-495-3(9)) Nimbus Publishing, Ltd.

Bennet, Amy. One Christmas in Lunenburg. Kilby, Don, illus. 2004. 24p. (J). 16.95 (978-1-55028-868-1(7)) Lorimer, James & Co., Ltd., Pubs. CAN. *Dist:* Casemate Pubs. & Bk. Distributors, LLC.

Bick, Janice. Belinda Lee. 2006. 17.00 (***978-0-8059-8850-5(5)**) Dorrance Publishing Co., Inc.

Carter, Anne. Elizabeth. 2002. (Our Canadian Girl Ser.). (Illus.). 104p. (J). pap. (978-0-14-100251-4(4)) Penguin Group (USA) Inc.

Cook, Lyn. Flight from the Fortress. 2004. 200p. (J). (gr. 4 up). (978-1-55041-790-6(8)) Fitzhenry & Whiteside, Ltd.

Couvillon, Alice W., et al. Evangeline for Children. Lyne, Alison Davis, illus. 2002. 32p. (J). (gr. k-3). 15.95 (978-1-56554-709-4(8)) Pelican Publishing Co., Inc.

Domm, Kristin. The Hatchling's Journey: A Blanding's Turtle Story. Domm, Jeff, illus. 2003. pap. 8.95 (978-1-55109-438-0(X)) Nimbus Publishing, Ltd. CAN. *Dist:* National Bk. Network.

Fox, Paula. The Moonlight Man. 2003. (Illus.). 176p. (J). pap. 5.99 (978-0-689-85886-4(8) , Aladdin) Simon & Schuster Children's Publishing.

—The Moonlight Man. 2003. (gr. 5-8). lib. bdg. 13.00 (978-0-613-66425-7(6)) Tandem Library Bks.

Frost, Helen. The Braid. 2006. (Illus.). 112p. (YA). (gr. 7 up). 16.00 (978-0-374-30962-6(0) , Frances Foster Bks.) Farrar, Straus & Giroux.

Gillard, Denise. Music from the Sky. Taylor, Stephen, illus. 2001. 32p. (J). (gr. k-2). 15.95 (978-0-88899-311-3(0)) Groundwood Bks. CAN. *Dist:* Perseus Distribution.

Gunnery, Sylvia. Personal Best. 2005. (Sports Stories Ser.). 112p. (J). (gr. 3-8). 7.95 (978-1-55028-896-4(2)); (***978-1-55028-897-1(0)**) Lorimer, James & Co., Ltd., Pubs. CAN. *Dist:* Casemate Pubs. & Bk. Distributors, LLC.

Hull, Maureen. The View from a Kite. 2007. (Illus.). 320p. (YA). (gr. 10 up). pap. (***978-1-55109-591-2(2)** , Vagrant Pr.) Nimbus Publishing, Ltd.

Montgomery, L. M. Anne of the Island. Date not set. mass mkt. (978-0-8125-6563-8(0) , Tor Bks.) Doherty, Tom Assocs., LLC.

—Anne of the Island. 2006. (ENG.). pap. (***978-1-4068-2171-0(3)**); pap. (***978-1-4068-3175-7(1)**) Echo Library.

—Anne of the Island. 2006. (ENG.). 102.99 (***978-1-4219-3295-8(4)**) IndyPublish.com.

—Anne of the Island. 2004. reprint ed. pap. 1.99 (978-1-4192-0718-1(0)); pap. 30.95 (978-1-4179-0885-1(8)) Kessinger Publishing, LLC.

—Anne of the Island. (Twelve-Point Ser.). 2001. 240p. lib. bdg. 25.00 (978-1-58287-157-8(4)); 2004. 396p. 26.00 (978-1-58287-640-5(1)) North Bks.

—Anne of the Island. abr. ed. 1998. (Avonlea Ser.: No. 4). 304p. (J). (gr. 5-8). pap. 4.99 (978-0-14-036777-5(2) , Puffin) Penguin Group (USA) Inc.

—Anne of the Island. 2000. (Anne of Green Gables Ser.: Vol. No. 3). (gr. 5-8). 182p. 24.95 (978-1-57646-309-3(5)); 182p. pap. 14.99 (978-1-57646-308-6(7)); 336p. pap. 19.99 (978-1-57646-310-9(9)) Quiet Vision Publishing.

—Anne of the Island. 2001. (gr. 7-12). lib. bdg. 30.40 (978-0-613-79774-0(4)) Tandem Library Bks.

—Anne of the Island Book & Charm. 2005. (Charming Classics). 304p. (J). pap. 6.99 (978-0-06-075859-2(7) , Harper Festival) HarperCollins Pubs.

Nervelle, Rosemarie. The Witch of Beaver Creek Mine. 2007. 160p. (gr. 5-9). 14.95 (***978-0-89272-741-4(1)**) Down East Bks.

Perkyns, Dorothy. Last Days in Africville. 2005. (Illus.). 144p. (YA). pap., tchr. ed. (978-0-88878-446-9(5) , Sandcastle Bks.) Dundurn Group, The.

—Last Days in Africville. 2006. 120p. (J). pap. 10.99 (***978-1-55002-630-6(5)** , Dundurn Pr.) Dundurn Group, The CAN. *Dist:* Univ. of Toronto Pr.

Siamon, Sharon. Race to the Rescue. 2007. (Saddle Island Ser.). 172p. (J). (gr. 3-7). pap. 6.95 (***978-1-55285-855-4(3)** , Walrus Bks.) Whitecap Bks., Ltd. CAN. *Dist:* Firefly Bks., Ltd.

Thompson, Lisa. Digging for Buried Treasure. Cantell, Brenda, illus. 2005. (Treasure Trackers Ser.). 80p. (gr. 5-9). 19.00 (978-0-7910-8872-2(3) , Chelsea Hse.) Facts On File, Inc.

Trottier, Maxine. There Have Always Been Foxes. Ricci, Regolo, illus. 2001. 20p. (ps-4). 15.95 (978-0-7737-3278-0(0)) Stoddart Kids CAN. *Dist:* Fitzhenry & Whiteside, Ltd.

Wilson, Budge. A Fiddle for Angus. Tooke, Susan, illus. 2006. 32p. (J). (gr. 1-4). pap. 9.95 (978-0-88776-785-2(0) , Random Hse. Puzzles & Games) Random Hse. Information Group.

—The Leaving. 176p. (J). mass mkt. 6.95 (978-0-7736-7363-2(6)) Stoddart Kids CAN. *Dist:* Fitzhenry & Whiteside, Ltd.

NOVELISTS

see Authors

NUCLEAR ENERGY

The Atomic Bomb. 2004. (Historical Reader Ser.). (Illus.). 224p. (J). (gr. 6-12). 13.32 (978-0-395-98665-3(6) , 2-99909) McDougal Littell Inc.

Capstone Press Editors. Nuclear Waste. 2002. (Our Planet in Peril Ser.). (Illus.). 48p. (J). (gr. 3-4). lib. bdg. 22.60 (978-0-7368-1362-4(4) , Bridgestone Bks.) Capstone Pr., Inc.

—Our Planet in Peril, 4 bks. Incl. Acid Rain. lib. bdg. 22.60 (978-0-7368-1360-0(8)); Global Warming. lib. bdg. 22.60 (978-0-7368-1361-7(6)); Nuclear Waste. lib. bdg. 22.60 (978-0-7368-1362-4(4)); Oil Spills. lib. bdg. 22.60 (978-0-7368-1363-1(2)); 48p. (J). (gr. 3-4). 2002. (Illus.). 2002. Set lib. bdg. 90.40 (978-0-7368-1364-8(0) , Bridgestone Bks.) Capstone Pr., Inc.

Fallout: Nuclear Disasters in Our World: Individual Title, 6 pack. (On Deck Ser.: Vol.*2). 24p. (gr. 4-5). 35.00 (978-0-7578-5831-4(7)) Rigby Education.

Gareth Stevens Publishing Staff, contrib. by. Nuclear Energy. 2003. (Discovery Channel School Science Ser.). (Illus.). 32p. (J). (gr. 5 up). lib. bdg. 24.67 (978-0-8368-3362-1(7)) Stevens, Gareth Inc.

Graham, Ian. Nuclear Power. 1999. (Energy Forever? Ser.). (Illus.). 48p. (J). (gr. 3-7). lib. bdg. 27.12 (978-0-8172-5763-7(2)) Raintree.

Greeley, August. Fallout: Nuclear Disasters in Our World. 2003. (Reading Power Ser.). (Illus.). 24p. (J). lib. bdg. 17.25 (978-0-8239-6484-0(1) , PowerKids Pr.) Rosen Publishing Group, Inc., The.

Holt, Rinehart and Winston Staff. Holt Science & Technology Chapter 16: Physical Science: Atomic Energy. 5th ed. 2004. (Illus.). pap. 12.86 (978-0-03-030413-2(X)) Holt, Rinehart & Winston.

—Holt Science & Technology Chptr. 22: Atomic Energy: Chapter Resources - Tennessee Edition. 3rd ed. 2003. (YA). pap. 11.40 (978-0-03-069184-3(2)) Holt, Rinehart & Winston.

Kidd, J. S. & Kidd, Renee A. Quarks & Sparks: The Story of Nuclear Power. 1999. (Science & Society Ser.). (Illus.). 160p. (YA). (gr. 7-12). 25.00 (978-0-8160-3587-8(3)) Facts On File, Inc.

Lace, William W. The Atom Bomb. 2001. (Building History Ser.). (Illus.). 112p. (J). (gr. 6-9). 32.45 (978-1-56006-724-5(1) , Lucent Bks.) Thomson Gale.

Manatt, Kathleen. Nuclear Energy. 2008. (J). pap. 7.95 (***978-1-60279-099-5(X)**) Cherry Lake Publishing.

McLeish, Ewan. Nuclear Power: The Pros & Cons. 2007. (J). lib. bdg. (***978-1-4042-3740-7(2)** , Rosen Central) Rosen Publishing Group, Inc., The.

Morris, Neil. Nuclear Power. 2006. (Illus.). 32p. (J). (978-1-58340-907-7(6)) Smart Apple Media.

M N O

Nardo, Don. Atoms. 2001. (Kidhaven Science Library). (Illus.). 48p. (J). (gr. 3-5). 23.70 (978-0-7377-0942-1(1) , LML00102-178579, Kidhaven) Thomson Gale.

Oxlade, Chris. Nuclear Energy. 2004. (Raintree Freestyle Ser.). (Illus.). 48p. (J). lib. bdg. 29.93 (978-1-4109-0496-6(2)) Raintree.

—Nuclear Energy 6-Pack. 2004. (Illus.). (J). lib. bdg. 42.90 (978-1-4109-0808-7(9)) Raintree.

Parker, Steve. Nuclear Energy. 2004. (Science Files Ser.). (Illus.). 32p. (J). (gr. 3 up). lib. bdg. 24.67 (978-0-8368-4030-8(5)) Stevens, Gareth Inc.

Richards, Julie. Nuclear Power. 2003. 30p. (J). lib. bdg. 24.25 (978-1-58340-337-2(X)) Smart Apple Media.

Richardson, Hazel. How to Split the Atom. Anderson, Scoular, illus. 2001. (How to Ser.). 96p. (J). (gr. 5-7). 16.00 (978-0-531-14646-0(4)); pap. 4.95 (978-0-531-16202-6(8)) Scholastic Library Publishing. (Watts, Franklin).

Saunders, Nigel & Chapman, Steven. Nuclear Energy. 2004. (Illus.). 48p. (J). (gr. 6-8). pap. 7.95 (978-1-4109-0502-4(0)) Raintree.

Sherman, Josepha. Nuclear Energy. 2004. (Fact Finders Ser.). (Illus.). 32p. (J). 16.95 (978-0-7368-2473-6(1)) Capstone Pr., Inc.

Snedden, Robert. Nuclear Energy. (Illus.). 48p. (J). 2006. (978-1-4034-8734-6(0)); 2001. (gr. 5-7). lib. bdg. 24.22 (978-1-57572-444-7(8)); 2nd ed. 2006. pap. (978-1-4034-8739-1(1)) Heinemann Library.

Stefan, V. Thermonuclear Fusion Energy. 2002. (Series on HIGH SCHOOL SCIENCE). (YA). per. (978-1-889545-52-3(X)) Stefan Univ. Pr., The.

Stoyles, Pennie, et al. Nuclear Energy. 2003. 32p. (J). lib. bdg. 24.25 (978-1-58340-331-0(0)) Smart Apple Media.

Tiner, John Hudson. Uranium & Plutonium Make Nuclear Power. 2003. (From Resource to Energy Source Ser.). (J). (978-1-58417-288-6(6)); pap. (978-1-58417-289-5(4)) Lake Street Pubs.

Wheeler, Jill C. Nuclear Power. 2007. (Eye on Energy Ser.). (Illus.). 32p. (J). (gr. k-6). lib. bdg. 24.21 (***978-1-59928-807-9(9)** , Checkerboard Library) ABDO Publishing Co.

NUCLEAR ENGINEERING

see also Nuclear Reactors

Chapman, Steven & Saunders, Nigel. Nuclear Energy. 2005. (Illus.). 48p. (J). (gr. 4-6). lib. bdg. 31.43 (978-1-4109-1694-5(4)) Steck-Vaughn.

Morris, Neil. Nuclear Power. 2006. (Illus.). 32p. (J). (978-1-58340-907-7(6)) Smart Apple Media.

Richards, Julie. Nuclear Power. 2003. 30p. (J). lib. bdg. 24.25 (978-1-58340-337-2(X)) Smart Apple Media.

Saunders, Nigel & Chapman, Steven. Nuclear Energy. 2005. (Illus.). 48p. (J). (978-1-4109-1699-0(5)) Steck-Vaughn.

Sherman, Josepha. Nuclear Energy. 2004. (Fact Finders Ser.). (Illus.). 32p. (J). 16.95 (978-0-7368-2473-6(1)) Capstone Pr., Inc.

NUCLEAR PHYSICS

see also Chemistry, Physical and Theoretical; Nuclear Engineering; Nuclear Reactors; Radioactivity

Barron, Rachel Stiffler. Lise Meitner: Discoverer of Nuclear Fission. 2004. (Profiles in Science Ser.). (Illus.). 112p. (YA). (gr. 6-12). lib. bdg. 23.95 (978-1-883846-52-7(8) , First Biographies) Reynolds, Morgan Inc.

Gallant, Roy A. The Ever Changing Atom. 2000. (Story of Science Ser.). (Illus.). 80p. (YA). (gr. 5 up). lib. bdg. 29.93 (978-0-7614-0961-8(0) , Benchmark Bks.) Cavendish, Marshall Corp.

Slade, Suzanne. The Structure of Atoms. 2007. (Illus.). 24p. (J). pap. (***978-1-4042-2161-1(1)** , PowerKids Pr.) Rosen Publishing Group, Inc., The.

NUCLEAR PHYSICS—HISTORY

Cooper, Dan. Enrico Fermi: And the Revolutions of Modern Physics. Gingerich, Owen, ed. 1998. (Oxford Portraits in Science Ser.). (Illus.). 120p. (YA). (gr. 7 up). 30.00 (978-0-19-511762-2(X)) Oxford Univ. Pr., Inc.

Pasachoff, Naomi E. Ernest Rutherford: Father of Nuclear Science. 2005. (Great Minds of Science Ser.). (Illus.). 128p. (J). lib. bdg. 26.60 (978-0-7660-2441-0(5)) Enslow Pubs., Inc.

NUCLEAR POWER

see also Atomic Bomb; Nuclear Engineering; Nuclear Reactors

Juettner, Bonnie. Nuclear Power. 2006. (Our Environment Ser.). (Illus.). 48p. (J). (gr. 4-8). 26.20 (978-0-7377-3618-2(6) , Kidhaven) Thomson Gale.

Kidd, J. S. & Kidd, Renee A. Nuclear Power: The Study of Quarks & Sparks. 2nd rev. ed. 2006. (Science & Society Ser.). 208-224p. (J). (gr. 6-12). 35.00 (978-0-8160-5606-4(4)) Facts On File, Inc.

Lopatka, Michael. Nuclear Power Facility Virtual Field Trip. 2003. (YA). cd-rom 15.95 (978-0-9723218-8-4(8)) Awesome Guides, Inc.

Metcalf, Gene & Tom. Nuclear Power. 2006. (Fueling the Future Ser.). (Illus.). 244p. (J). (gr. 10-12). 34.95 (978-0-7377-3587-1(2) , 1256645, Greenhaven Pr., Inc.) Thomson Gale.

Nuclear Power. (Energy at Work Ser.). 32p. (J). 7.95 (978-0-7368-5193-0(3)) Capstone Pr., Inc.

Parker, Steve. Nuclear Energy. 2004. (Science Files Ser.). (Illus.). 32p. (J). (gr. 3 up). lib. bdg. 24.67 (978-0-8368-4030-8(5)) Stevens, Gareth Inc.

Ward, Pat & Ward, Barb. Nuclear Energy. 1999. (Illus.). 64p. (YA). (gr. 5). pap. 8.95 (978-1-58037-087-5(X)) Twain, Mark Media, Inc. Pubs.

NUCLEAR POWER PLANTS

Bryan, Nichol. Chernobyl: Nuclear Disaster. 2003. (Environmental Disasters Ser.). (Illus.). 48p. (gr. 5 up). (YA). lib. bdg. 30.00 (978-0-8368-5504-3(3)); (J). pap. 11.95 (978-0-8368-5511-1(6)) Stevens, Gareth Inc. (World Almanac Library).

Cole, Michael D. Three Mile Island: Nuclear Disaster. 2002. (American Disasters Ser.). (Illus.). 48p. (J). (gr. 4-10). lib. bdg. 23.93 (978-0-7660-1556-2(4)) Enslow Pubs., Inc.

Condon, Judith. Chernobyl & Other Nuclear Accidents. 1999. (New Perspectives Ser.). (Illus.). 64p. (J). (gr. 4-7). lib. bdg. 28.54 (978-0-8172-5018-8(2)) Raintree.

Cruise, Robin. Nuclear Disaster at Chernobyl. 2000. (gr. 5-8). lib. bdg. 11.80 (978-0-613-51221-3(9)) Tandem Library Bks.

Derkins, Susie. The Meltdown of Three Mile Island. 2005. (When Disaster Strikes! Ser.). (Illus.). 48p. (YA). (gr. 5-8). lib. bdg. 23.95 (978-0-8239-3678-6(3)) Rosen Publishing Group, Inc., The.

Dowswell, Paul. The Chernobyl Disaster. 2003. (Days That Shook the World Ser.). (Illus.). 47p. (J). lib. bdg. 28.56 (978-0-7398-6049-6(6)) Raintree.

Feigenbaum, Aaron. Emergency at Three Mile Island. 2007. (Code Red Ser.). (Illus.). 32p. (J). (gr. 3-7). lib. bdg. 25.27 (978-1-59716-364-4(3)) Bearport Publishing Co., Inc.

Giacobello, John. Nuclear Power of the Future: New Ways of Turning Atoms into Energy. 2005. (Library of Energy of the Future). (Illus.). 64p. (YA). (gr. 7-12). lib. bdg. 26.50 (978-0-8239-3661-8(9)) Rosen Publishing Group, Inc., The.

Ingram, Scott. The Chernobyl Nuclear Disaster. 2005. (Environmental Disasters Ser.). (Illus.). 112p. (J). (gr. 6-12). 35.00 (978-0-8160-5755-9(9)) Facts On File, Inc.

Lusted, Marcia & Lusted, Greg. A Nuclear Power Plant. 2004. (Building History Ser.). (Illus.). 112p. (YA). (gr. 7-12). lib. bdg. 32.45 (978-1-59018-392-2(4)) Thomson Gale.

Parker, Victoria. Chernobyl 1986: An Explosion at a Nuclear Power Station. 2006. (When Disaster Struck Ser.). (Illus.). 56p. (J). (978-1-4109-2275-5(8)) Steck-Vaughn.

Sherman, Josepha. Nuclear Energy. 2004. (Fact Finders Ser.). (Illus.). 32p. (J). 16.95 (978-0-7368-2473-6(1)) Capstone Pr., Inc.

Smith, Jim & Beresford, Nicholas A. Chernobyl: Catastrophe, Consequences & Solutions. 2005. (Springer Praxis Books / Environmental Sciences Ser.). (Illus.). xxvi, 310p. 149.00 (978-3-540-23866-9(2) , 3540238662) Springer.

Snedden, Robert. Nuclear Energy. 2006. (Illus.). 48p. (J). (978-1-4034-8734-6(0)); 2nd ed. pap. (978-1-4034-8739-1(1)) Heinemann Library.

Woods, Michael & Woods, Mary B. Environmental Disasters. 2008. (Disasters up Close Ser.). (J). lib. bdg. 27.93 (***978-0-8225-6774-5(1)** , Lerner Pubns.) Lerner Publishing Group.

NUCLEAR REACTORS

Cruise, Robin. Nuclear Disaster at Chernobyl. 2000. (gr. 5-8). lib. bdg. 11.80 (978-0-613-51221-3(9)) Tandem Library Bks.

—The Nuclear Disaster at Chernobyl. Taylor, Marjorie, illus. rev. ed. 1999. (Take Ten Ser.). 46p. (YA). (gr. 4 up). pap. 3.95 (978-1-58659-022-2(7)) Artesian Pr.

De Angelis, Therese. Three Mile Island. 2001. (Great Disasters, Reforms & Ramifications Ser.). (Illus.). 126p. (J). (gr. 4-7). 30.00 (978-0-7910-5785-8(2) , Chelsea Hse.) Facts On File, Inc.

NUCLEAR SUBMARINES

Amato, William. Nuclear Submarines. 2002. (Reading Power Ser.). (Illus.). 24p. (J). (gr. 2). lib. bdg. 17.25 (978-0-8239-6011-8(0) , PowerKids Pr.) Rosen Publishing Group, Inc., The.

—Submarinos Nucleares. 2004. (Vehiculos de Alta Tecnologia Ser.). (SPA & ENG., Illus.). 24p. (J). (gr. 3-6). lib. bdg. 17.25 (978-0-8239-6882-4(0) , Buenas Letras) Rosen Publishing Group, Inc., The.

Clancy, Tom. Submarine: A Guided Tour Inside a Nuclear Warship. 2002. (gr. 7-12). lib. bdg. 16.45 (978-0-613-62851-8(9)) Tandem Library Bks.

Green, Michael. Nuclear Submarines. 2001. (Land & Sea Ser.). (Illus.). 48p. (J). (gr. 3-4). lib. bdg. 21.26 (978-0-7368-0759-3(4) , Capstone High-Interest Bks.) Capstone Pr., Inc.

Green, Michael & Green, Gladys. Attack Submarines: The Seawolf Class. 2004. (Edge Books, War Machines). (Illus.). 32p. (J). lib. bdg. 22.60 (978-0-7368-2721-8(8)) Capstone Pr., Inc.

Higgins, Chris. Nuclear Submarine Disasters. 2001. (Great Disasters, Reforms & Ramifications Ser.). (Illus.). 112p. (J). (gr. 6 up). 30.00 (978-0-7910-6329-3(1) , Chelsea Hse.) Facts On File, Inc.

Nuclear Submarines: Individual Title Six-Packs. (On Deck Ser.). 24p. (gr. 4-5). 35.00 (978-0-7578-1057-2(8)) Rigby Education.

NUCLEAR TEST BAN

see Disarmament

NUCLEAR WARFARE

Bjornlund, Britta. The Cold War. 2002. (World History Ser.). (Illus.). 112p. (J). (gr. 8-11). 27.45 (978-1-59018-003-7(8) , LML00902-178725, Lucent Bks.) Thomson Gale.

Blohm, Craig E. An Uneasy Peace: 1945 to 1980. 2002. (American War Library). (Illus.). 112p. (J). 29.95 (978-1-59018-201-7(4) , Lucent Bks.) Thomson Gale.

Deary, Terry. The Nuclear Winter Man. 2004. (Classified Ser.). 96p. (J). (gr. 5-8). pap. 4.95 (978-0-7534-5827-3(6) , Kingfisher) Houghton Mifflin Co. Trade & Reference Div.

Streissguth, Thomas. Nuclear Weapons: More Countries, More Threats. 2000. (Issues in Focus Ser.). (Illus.). 112p. (YA). (gr. 6-12). lib. bdg. 26.60 (978-0-7660-1248-6(4)) Enslow Pubs., Inc.

NUCLEAR WARFARE—FICTION

O'Brien, Robert C. Z for Zachariah. 2002. (Illus.). (J). 13.40 (978-0-7587-4827-0(2)) Book Wholesalers, Inc.

—Z for Zachariah. 2007. 240p. (YA). pap. 6.99 (***978-1-4169-3921-4(0)** , Simon Pulse) Simon & Schuster Children's Publishing.

NUCLEAR WEAPONS AND DISARMAMENT

see Disarmament

NUMBER CONCEPT

Advantage Publishers Group. Big Box of Early Learning, 4 bks., Set. 2002. (Big Box of Board Bks.). (Illus.). 10p. (J). (ps-k). (978-1-59069-180-9(6)) Studio Mouse LLC.

Advantage Publishers Group & Gordon, David Frederick. 3D Paint by Number under the Sea. 2006. (3-D Paint by Numbers Ser.). (Illus.). 40p. 17.95 (978-1-59223-460-8(7) , Silver Dolphin Bks.) Advantage Pubs. Group.

Advantage Publishers Group Staff, ed. Numbers. 1998. (Find & Fit Ser.). (Illus.). 10p. (J). (ps-k). bds. 14.95 (978-1-57145-356-3(3) , Silver Dolphin Bks.) Advantage Pubs. Group.

Aigner-Clark, Julie. My First Book of Numbers. 2007. (J). (ps-17). bds. 9.99 (***978-1-4231-0201-4(0))** Baby Einstein Co., LLC, The.

Aigner-Clark, Julie. Numbers & Shapes Discovery Cards. Zaidi, Nadeem, illus. 2004. 29p. (ps-17). pap. 9.99 (978-0-7868-0939-4(6)) Hyperion Bks. for Children.

Alvarez, Lourdes M. Numbers. Brooks, David, illus. 2005. (My First Book Ser.). 9p. (J). (ps-ps). bds. 3.95 (978-1-933050-06-5(3)) Sweetwater Pr.

—Numeros. Brooks, David, illus. 2005. (Mi primer libro Ser.). (SPA.). 9p. (J). (ps-ps). bds. 3.95 (978-1-933050-00-3(4)) Sweetwater Pr.

American Education Publishing Staff. Numbers. 2003. (Brighter Child Preschool Flash Cards Ser.). (Illus.). 36p. (J). (ps). 2.99 (978-1-56189-459-8(1) , 31042, American Education Publishing) School Specialty Publishing.

Anderson, Sara. Colors & Numbers. Anderson, Sara, illus. 2007. (J). bds. 19.95 (978-1-59354-183-5(X)) Chronicle Bks. LLC.

Anthony, Susan C. Casting Nines Quick Check For. 2004. pap. 8.00 (978-1-879478-09-1(9)) Instructional Resources Co.

Arnold, Clareen. Numbers Ages 3-6. 2003. (Skill Builders Ser.). 80p. 2.95 (978-1-887923-26-2(8)) Rainbow Bridge Publishing.

Aryai, Sia, photos by. 1 2 3s. (Baby Bright Board Bks.). (Illus.). 10p. (J). (ps). 5.95 (978-1-56565-824-0(8) , 08248W, Roxbury Park Juvenile) Lowell Hse. Juvenile.

Asimov, Isaac. How Did We Find Out about Numbers? Nevins, Daniel, illus. 63p. (J). lib. bdg. 19.90 (978-0-8027-6136-1(4)) Walker & Co.

Aufbau des Zahlensystems, Vollstaendige Induktion. (Duden-Schuelerhilfen Ser.). (GER.). 80p. (YA). (gr. 7-10). (978-3-411-02625-8(1)) Bibliographisches Institut & F. A. Brockhaus AG DEU. *Dist:* International Bk. Import Service, Inc.

Baker, Alan. Los Numeros. 2003. (SPA.). (gr. k-3). lib. bdg. 12.95 (978-0-613-88142-5(7)) Tandem Library Bks.

Balloon Books Staff. Dot to Dot Count to 75. 2006. (Illus.). 64p. (J). pap. 4.95 (978-1-4027-3770-1(X)) Sterling Publishing Co., Inc.

Balloon Books Staff, ed. Color by Numbers. 1999. (Balloon Ser.). (Illus.). 16p. (J). (ps-k). pap. 2.95 (978-0-8069-1939-3(6)) Sterling Publishing Co., Inc.

Barad, Alexis. World Around Me: Colors, Numbers & More. 2008. (Fisher-Price Ser.). 12p. (J). 7.99 (***978-0-06-145039-6(1)** , Harper Festival) HarperCollins Pubs.

Beaton, Clare, illus. Numbers/Los Numeros. l.t. ed. 1998. (English-Spanish Bilingual First Bks.). (ENG & SPA.). 24p. (J). (ps up). lib. bdg. 14.45 (978-1-56674-251-1(X)) Forest Hse. Publishing Co., Inc.

Berger, Samantha & Moreton, Daniel. Patterns. 1999. (Learning Center Emergent Readers Ser.). (J). 2.50 (978-0-439-04599-5(1)) Scholastic, Inc.

Blundell, Gillian. One to Ten. 2001. 32p. (J). (ps-5). pap. 10.00 (978-1-871098-37-2(8)) Claire Pubns. GBR. *Dist:* Parkwest Pubns., Inc.

Bokhari, Naila. Piece of Pi: Wit-Sharpening, Brain-Bruising, Number-Crunching Activities with Pi. 2nd ed. 2001. 48p. (J). per. 10.95 net. (978-1-883055-43-1(1)) Dandy Lion Pubns.

Book Company Staff. Lift & Learn Numbers. 2004. (Novelty Bks.). (Illus.). 10p. (J). (gr. 3-5). bds. 7.95 (978-1-74047-557-0(7)) Book Co. Publishing Pty, Ltd., The AUS. *Dist:* Penton Overseas, Inc.

Bottoni, Lois. Numbers 10 to 100 (Grades K - 1) 2000. (Step Ahead Workbooks Ser.). (Illus.). 32p. (J). (ps-3). pap. 2.99 (978-0-307-03586-8(7) , 03586, Golden Bks.) Random Hse. Children's Bks.

Boye, B. D. Easy As 1, 2, 3. Boye, B. D., illus. l.t. ed. 2005. (Illus.). 22p. (J). per. 4.99 (978-0-9768078-0-3(7)) Innerchild Publishing, Inc.

Brainy Baby Quad Book. 2005. (Brainy Baby Ser.). 40p. (J). bds. 10.39 (978-1-59394-240-3(0)) Bendon Publishing International.

Brighter Vision Publishing Staff. About Numbers. 2000. (My Discovery Bks.). (Illus.). 20p. (J). (ps). pap. 2.95 (978-1-55254-205-7(X)) Brighter Vision Pubns.

—Numbers - Pre-K. 2000. (Primary Skills Ser.). (Illus.). (J). (ps-3). pap. 2.25 (978-1-55254-173-9(8)) Brighter Vision Pubns.

—Numbers & Counting. 2000. (Illus.). 32p. (J). pap., act. bk. ed. 1.39 (978-1-55254-150-0(9)) Brighter Vision Pubns.

Brooks, F. & Litchfield, J. Primeros Numeros. 2004. Tr. of First Numbers. (SPA., Illus.). 48p. (J). (ps up). lib. bdg. 20.95 (978-1-58086-352-0(3)) EDC Publishing.

Brougher, Kevin J. Number Wonders: A Book of Amazing Number Facts! 2001. 144p. per. 9.95 (978-0-9703729-5-6(7)) Missing Piece Pr.

Bruna, Dick, et al. Elfis. 2006. (Illus.). 40p. (J). (ps-2). 12.99 (978-0-8431-1579-6(3) , Price Stern Sloan) Penguin Group (USA) Inc.

Burstein, John. Number Conservation: Planting Monster Melons. 2003. (Weekly Reader Early Learning Library). (Illus.). 24p. (J). (gr. 1 up). pap. 7.93 (978-0-8368-3829-9(7) , Weekly Reader Early Learning Library) Stevens, Gareth Inc.

—Number Lines: How Far to the Car? Destiny Images Staff, illus. 2003. (Math Monsters Ser.). 24p. (YA). (gr. 1 up). lib. bdg. 19.33 (978-0-8368-3815-2(7) , Weekly Reader Early Learning Library) Stevens, Gareth Inc.

Burton, Jane & Taylor, Kim. The Nature & Science of Numbers. 2001. (Exploring the Science of Nature Ser.). (Illus.). 32p. (J). (gr. 3 up). lib. bdg. 24.67 (978-0-8368-2193-2(9)) Stevens, Gareth Inc.

Caroll, Danielle. Place Value. 2006. 16p. (J). (gr. k-2). 15.93 (978-0-7368-5858-8(X) , Yellow Umbrella Bks.) Capstone Pr., Inc.

Carroll, Danielle. Place Value. 2005. (Yellow Umbrella Books for Early Readers). (Illus.). 17p. (J). (978-0-7368-5288-3(3)); (978-0-7368-5324-8(3)) Capstone Pr., Inc.

Carter, David, intro. The Glittery Crittery Counting Book. 2007. 16.95 (***978-1-58117-651-3(1)** , Intervisual/Piggy Toes) Dalmatian Pr.

Cassandra, Moore. Letter/Number Master. 2007. (Illus.). (J). spiral bd. 15.95 (***978-1-886297-29-6(0))** Omega Publishing Hse.

Cernek, Kim & Williams, Rozanne Lanczak. Build-a-Skill Instant Books Color, Shape & Number Words. Shiotsu, Vicky & Faulkner, Stacey, eds. Campbell, Jenny & Tom, Darcy, illus. 2007. (J). 4.99 (***978-1-59198-411-5(4))** Creative Teaching Pr., Inc.

Chang, Maria & Sevaly, Karen. Lace-up Cards Alphabet & Numbers. 2007. (In or Out Ser.). 256p. 9.99 (***978-0-439-91220-4(2)** , Teaching Resources) Scholastic, Inc.

Childs, Laura. Nimble with Numbers. 1999. 160p. (ps-3). pap. (978-1-57232-983-6(1)) Seymour, Dale Pubns.

Childs, Leigh. Nimble with Numbers. 1999. 160p. (ps-3). pap. 17.95 (978-1-57232-984-3(X)) Seymour, Dale Pubns.

Child's Play, ed. 5 Little Men Big Bk with Holes. 2006. (Illus.). 16p. 19.99 (978-1-84643-007-7(0)) Child's Play-International.

—10 Fat Sausages Big Bk with Holes. 2006. (Illus.). 16p. 19.99 (978-1-84643-008-4(9)) Child's Play-International.

Color, Cut, Paste, & Trace: Numbers 1-20. (ps-k). 2.99 (978-0-7424-0167-9(7) , IF0400) School Specialty Publishing.

Cooper, Terry, ed. Learning Numbers. 2006. (Kindergarten Ser.). 48p. pap. 5.99 (978-0-439-81940-4(7) , Teaching Resources) Scholastic, Inc.

Counting & Numbers with Mr Wiggle. 32p. (gr. 2 up). 4.99 (978-1-56451-992-4(9) , ID99008) School Specialty Publishing.

Counting, Numbers, & Shapes. 2004. (Beastieville Ser.). 198.80 (978-0-516-25145-5(7) , Children's Pr.) Scholastic Library Publishing.

Craig, Diane. No One Slumbers When We Use Numbers! 2006. (Illus.). 24p. (J). (978-1-59928-613-6(0)) ABDO Publishing Co.

Crane, Carol. Net Numbers: A South Carolina Number Book. Palmer, Gary, illus. 2006. 40p. (J). (gr. k-5). 17.95 (978-1-58536-202-8(6)) Sleeping Bear Pr.

Dalmatian Press Staff. Little Builder: Board Book Set, 4 bks., Set. 2003. (Illus.). 10p. (J). bds. 7.99 (978-1-57759-714-8(1)) Dalmatian Pr.

Dalmatian Press Staff. My Spanish Book of Numbers: Mi libro espanol de los Numeros. rev. ed. 2007. 12p. 7.99 (***978-1-4037-3053-4(9))** Dalmatian Pr.

Daniel, Becky. Using Standards Number & O Gr5. 2003. (100+ Seriestm Ser.). 128p. (J). (gr. 5-5). pap. 12.99 (978-0-7424-1815-8(4) , IFG99062) School Specialty Publishing.

Data & Graphing Activities for Every Month. 64p. (gr. 3-4). 7.99 (978-1-56451-164-5(2) , ID7286) School Specialty Publishing.

Daybell, Chad. Book of Mormon Numbers. Bonham, Bob, illus. 2004. (J). bds. 8.95 (978-1-55517-755-3(7) , 77557) Cedar Fort, Inc./CFI Distribution.

Del'Homme, Melissa. Number Recognition. McMahon, Kelly, illus. 1998. (Tutor Bks.). 80p. (YA). (gr. k up). pap., wbk. ed. 8.95 (978-1-56565-849-3(3) , 08493W) Lowell Hse. Juvenile.

Diaz, James & Gerth, Melanie, illus. Numbers: Learning Fun for Little Ones! 2007. 10p. (J). reprint ed. (***978-1-4223-6683-7(9))** DIANE Publishing Co.

Dingles, Molly. Number 1 What Grows in the Sun?/Numero 1 ¿Qué crece en el Sol? Wallis, Rebecca, illus. 2005. (Community of Counting Ser.).Tr. of Numero 1 ¿Qué crece en el Sol?. (ENG & SPA.). 32p. (J). per. 9.95 (978-1-59646-275-5(2)) Dingles & Co.

—Number 10 Where Is the Hen? Wallis, Rebecca, illus. 2005. (Community of Counting Ser.). 32p. (J). per. 9.95 (978-1-59646-309-7(0)) Dingles & Co.

—Number 10 Where Is the Hen?/Numero 10 ¿en donde esta la Gallina? Wallis, Rebecca, illus. 2005. (Community of Counting Ser.).Tr. of Numero 10 ¿en donde esta la Gallina?. (ENG & SPA.). 32p. (J). per. 9.95 (978-1-59646-311-0(2)) Dingles & Co.

—Number 2 Let's Go to the Zoo! Wallis, Rebecca, illus. 2005. (Community of Counting Ser.). 32p. (J). 9.95 (978-1-59646-277-9(9)) Dingles & Co.

—Number 2 Let's Go to the Zoo!/Numero 2 ¡Vamos al Zoologico! Wallis, Rebecca, illus. 2005. (Community of Counting Ser.).Tr. of Numero 2 ¡Vamos al Zoologico!. (ENG & SPA.). 32p. (J). per. 9.95 (978-1-59646-279-3(5)) Dingles & Co.

MNO

—Number 3 What's in the Sea? Wallis, Rebecca, illus. 2005. (Community of Counting Ser.). 32p. (J). per. 9.95 (978-1-59646-281-6(7)) Dingles & Co.

—Number 3 What's in the Sea?/Numero 3 ¿Qué hay en el Mar? Wallis, Rebecca, illus. 2005. (Community of Counting Ser.).Tr. of Numero 3 ¿Qué hay en el Mar?. (ENG & SPA.). 32p. (J). pap. 9.95 (978-1-59646-282-3(5)); per. 9.95 (978-1-59646-283-0(3)) Dingles & Co.

—Number 4 Shop at the Store! Wallis, Rebecca, illus. 2005. (Community of Counting Ser.). 32p. (J). per. 9.95 (978-1-59646-285-4(X)) Dingles & Co.

—Number 4 Shop at the Store!/Numero 4 ¡Vamos de compras a la Tienda! Wallis, Rebecca, illus. 2005. (Community of Counting Ser.).Tr. of Numero 4 ¡Vamos de compras a la Tienda!. (ENG & SPA.). 32p. (J). per. 9.95 (978-1-59646-287-8(6)) Dingles & Co.

—Number 5 Let's Go for a Drive! Wallis, Rebecca, illus. 2005. (Community of Counting Ser.). 32p. (J). per. 9.95 (978-1-59646-289-2(2)) Dingles & Co.

—Number 5 Let's Go for a Drive!/Numero 5 ¡Vamos a viajar en Coche! Wallis, Rebecca, illus. 2005. (Community of Counting Ser.).Tr. of Numero 5 ¡Vamos a viajar en Coche!. (ENG & SPA.). 32p. (J). per. 9.95 (978-1-59646-291-5(4)) Dingles & Co.

—Number 6 What Can We Mix? Wallis, Rebecca, illus. 2005. (Community of Counting Ser.). 32p. (J). per. 9.95 (978-1-59646-293-9(0)) Dingles & Co.

—Number 6 What Can We Mix?/Numero 6 ¿Qué podemos Mezclar? Wallis, Rebecca, illus. 2005. (Community of Counting Ser.).Tr. of Numero 6 ¿Que podemos Mezclar?. (ENG & SPA.). 32p. (J). per. 9.95 (978-1-59646-295-3(7)) Dingles & Co.

—Number 7 Stars in the Heaven. Wallis, Rebecca, illus. 2005. (Community of Counting Ser.). 32p. (J). per. 9.95 (978-1-59646-297-7(3)) Dingles & Co.

—Number 7 Stars in the Heaven/Numero 7 Estrellas en el Cielo. Wallis, Rebecca, illus. (Community of Counting Ser.).Tr. of Numero 7 Estrellas en el Cielo. (ENG & SPA.). 32p. (J). 2005. per. 9.95 (978-1-59646-299-1(X)); 2004. lib. bdg. 20.65 (978-1-891997-83-9(1)) Dingles & Co.

—Number 8 Let's Stay up Late! Wallis, Rebecca, illus. 2005. (Community of Counting Ser.). 32p. (J). per. 9.95 (978-1-59646-301-1(5)) Dingles & Co.

—Number 8 Let's Stay up Late!/Numero 8 ¡Vamos a quedarnos en vela hasta muy Noche! Wallis, Rebecca, illus. (Community of Counting Ser.).Tr. of Numero 8 ¡Vamos a quedarnos en vela hasta muy Noche!. (ENG & SPA.). 32p. (J). 2005. per. 9.95 (978-1-59646-303-5(1)); 2004. lib. bdg. 20.65 (978-1-891997-82-2(3)) Dingles & Co.

—Number 9 Dress up to Dine! Wallis, Rebecca, illus. 2005. (Community of Counting Ser.). 32p. (J). per. 9.95 (978-1-59646-305-9(8)) Dingles & Co.

—Number 9 Dress up to Dine!/Numero 9 ¡Vestirse con elegancia para Cenar! Wallis, Rebecca, illus. 2005. (Community of Counting Ser.).Tr. of Numero 9 ¡Vestirse con elegancia para Cenar!. (ENG & SPA.). 32p. (J). per. 9.95 (978-1-59646-307-3(4)) Dingles & Co.

DK Publishing. Numbers: Let's Get Counting. 2008. 28p. (J). (gr. 12). 9.99 (*978-0-7566-3604-3(3)) Dorling Kindersley Publishing, Inc.

DK Publishing Staff. First Numbers. 2007. 24p. (J). (ps-1). 4.99 (978-0-7566-2921-2(7)) Dorling Kindersley Publishing, Inc.

Donoghue, Stella. Magnet Matching: 123. 2006. (Illus.). 12p. (J). (gr. k-2). 14.95 (978-1-84610-122-9(0)) Make Believe Ideas GBR. *Dist:* Ingram Pub. Services.

Dora the Explorer Number Practice. 2004. (J). pap. 2.95 (*978-1-58610-887-8(5) , 74002) Learning Horizons, Inc.

Dorling Kindersley Publishing Staff. Barbie 123 Book. 2005. 32p. (J). 12.99 (978-0-7566-1113-2(X)) Dorling Kindersley Publishing, Inc.

—Barbie Me Primer Libro de Pegatinas de Numeros/Barbie My First Number Sticker Book. 2005. (Barbie sticker Bks.). 16p. (J). bds. 6.99 (978-0-7566-1112-5(1)) Dorling Kindersley Publishing, Inc.

—My First Number Book. rev. ed. 2003. (Illus.). 48p. (J). 16.99 (978-0-7894-9209-8(1)) Dorling Kindersley Publishing, Inc.

—My First Spanish Number Book. 2002. (Illus.). 36p. (J). (ps-1). bds. 6.99 (978-0-7894-8591-5(5)) Dorling Kindersley Publishing, Inc.

Dorling Kindersley Publishing Staff, contrib. by. My First Look At: Numbers. 2001. (My First Look At... Ser.). (Illus.). 24p. (J). (ps-k). pap. 3.95 (978-0-7894-7659-3(2) , D K Ink) Dorling Kindersley Publishing, Inc.

Dot-to-Dot Numbers 1-100 (Gr. 1-2) 2003. (J). (978-1-58232-069-4(1)) Bryan Hse. Pubs., Inc.

Dot-to-Dot Numbers 1-25 (Gr. K-1) 2003. (J). (978-1-58232-068-7(3)) Bryan Hse. Pubs., Inc.

Dot-to-Dot Numbers & Alphabet Booster. 2005. (J). per. 0.00 (978-1-59441-502-9(1) , C04034) Carson-Dellosa Publishing Co., Inc.

Doudna, Kelly. No One slumbers When We Use Numbers. 2007. (Illus.). 24p. (J). 19.93 (978-1-59928-612-9(2) , SandCastle) ABDO Publishing Co.

Douglas, Vincent & School Specialty Publishing Staff. Numbers. 2000. (Spectrum Flash Cards Ser.). (Illus.). 50p. (J). (gr. k-3). 2.99 (978-1-57768-127-4(4) , Learning Materials) School Specialty Publishing.

Edlund, Anita. From Zero to Hero. 2007. 72p. pap. 15.00 (*978-0-687-64294-6(9)) Abingdon Pr.

Edmonds, Tracy. Numbers: Cards, Games & Activities. 2006. 176p. pap. 21.99 (978-1-4206-8007-2(2)) Austin & Company, Inc.

Ekeland, Ivar. The Cat in Numberland. O'Brien, John, illus. 2006. 56p. (J). 19.95 (978-0-8126-2744-2(X)) Cricket Bks.

Encycbrita. Revisiting Numbers Mic 2006 G. 6th ed. 2005. pap. 10.60 (978-0-03-038568-1(7)) Harcourt Schl. Pubs.

Encyclopaedia Britannica Publishers, Inc. Staff. Math in Context: Picturing Numbers. 6th ed. 2005. (gr. 6). pap. 10.60 (978-0-03-042402-1(X)) Harcourt Schl. Pubs.

Equipo Staff. El Libro de la Oruga: Numeros. 2000. Tr. of Numbers. (SPA., Illus.). 32p. (J). (ps-k). 8.95 (978-84-488-0859-4(2)) Beascoa, Ediciones S.A. ESP. *Dist:* Distribooks, Inc.

ES ACSD Field Guide Stage Three W/CD: America's Choice School Design. 2004. spiral bd. 30.00 (978-1-932976-02-1(7)); spiral bd. 30.00 (978-1-932976-16-8(7) , America's Choice) National Ctr. on Education & The Economy.

Etringer, Kathy. Mrs. EOs Extraordinary Number Activities. Mitchell, Judy & Sussman, Ellen, eds. Rojas, Mary Galan, illus. 2006. 128p. (J). pap. 13.95 (*978-1-57310-506-4(6)) Teaching & Learning Co.

Farmer Fred's Sticker Book: 123. 2002. 16p. pap. 3.98 (978-0-7525-8345-7(X)) Parragon, Inc.

Filipowich, Bob. Splashtime Book of Numbers. 2000. (God's Creation Ser.). (Illus.). (J). pap. 4.99 (978-0-310-98096-4(8)) Zonderkidz.

First Number Skills (Gr. K-1) 2003. (J). (978-1-58232-081-6(0)) Bryan Hse. Pubs., Inc.

Fitashape. Numbers, Vol. 3. 2001. (Fit-a-Shape Ser.). (Illus.). 10p. (J). 6.95 (978-0-7624-1055-2(8) , Running Pr. Kids) Running Pr. Bk. Pubs.

Flora, Sherrill B. Number Fun. 1999. (Basic Skills Ser.). (Illus.). 48p. (J). (ps-2). pap. 6.99 (978-0-513-02255-3(4) , TSD22554, Instructional Fair) Schaffer, Frank Pubns.

Foil Book Colors & Numbers & Shapes, Oh My! (English) 2000. (J). (978-1-58805-033-5(5)) DS-Max USA, Inc.

Franco, Betsy. What's Zero? 2002. (Yellow Umbrella Books). (Illus.). 16p. (J). (gr. 1). lib. bdg. 14.60 (978-0-7368-1289-4(X) , Pebble Bks.) Capstone Pr., Inc.

Freeman, Marcia S. A Dozen Cousins: Exploring the Number 12. 2008. (J). (*978-1-60044-637-5(X)) Rourke Publishing, LLC.

—Multiply by Hand: The Nines Facts. 2008. (J). (*978-1-60044-643-6(4)) Rourke Publishing, LLC.

—My Sister Is in Third Grade: Putting Numbers in Order. 2008. (J). (*978-1-60044-638-2(8)) Rourke Publishing, LLC.

—What Makes Ten? Number Facts. 2008. (J). (*978-1-60044-642-9(6)) Rourke Publishing, LLC.

French, Vivian & Collins, Ross. From Zero to Ten: The Story of Numbers. 2002. (Illus.). 32p. (YA). 19.95 (978-0-19-521925-8(2)) Oxford Univ. Pr., Inc.

Furgang, Kathy. Number Games. 2003. (Early Connections Ser.). (J). pap. 33.00 (978-1-4108-1082-3(8)) Benchmark Education Co.

Gagliano, Eugene. Four Wheels West: A Wyoming Numbers Book. Guy, Susan, illus. 2006. 40p. (J). (gr. k-5). 17.95 (978-1-58536-210-3(7)) Sleeping Bear Pr.

Gibson, Leah. Conoce los Numeros. 2007. (Sesame Street Ser.). (SPA & ENG.). 24p. (J). pap., wbk. ed. 4.99 (*978-1-59545-067-8(X)) Learning Horizons, Inc.

Girard, Franck. Mi primer baul de Palabras. Jonniaux, Isabelle, illus. 2005. (Baul de Palabras Ser.). (SPA.). 120p. (J). 18.95 (978-84-7864-788-0(0)) Combel Editorial, S.A. ESP. *Dist:* Independent Pubs. Group.

Golden Books Staff. Number Skills (Kindergarten) 1999. (Step Ahead Workbooks Ser.). (Illus.). 64p. (J). (ps-3). pap., wbk. ed. 3.99 (978-0-307-03665-0(0) , 03665, Golden Bks.) Random Hse. Children's Bks.

Griffith, Nancy. One to Three. McKenna, Sharon, illus. 2000. 16p. (J). pap. 5.95 (978-1-891846-15-1(9)) Business Word, The.

Grundon, Holly & Novelli, Joan. Smartpads Numbers & Counting: 40 Fun Games to Help Kids Master Numbers & Counting. 2005. 48p. pap. 7.99 (978-0-439-72081-6(8) , Teaching Resources) Scholastic, Inc.

Gunzi, Christiane. Numbers. 2004. (My Very First Look at Ser.). (SPA., Illus.). (ps-k). 24p. (J). pap. 5.95 (978-1-58728-057-5(1)); 50p. 9.95 (978-1-58728-237-9(2)) T&N Children's Publishing. (Two Can Publishing).

Hammelef, Danielle S. Numbers Big & Small. 2006. (Early Explorers Ser.). (J). 36.00 (*978-1-4108-6130-6(9)) Benchmark Education Co.

Hammersmith, Craig. Numbers We Know. 2003. (Spyglass Books). (Illus.). 24p. (J). (gr. 1 up). lib. bdg. 18.60 (978-0-7565-0451-9(1)) Compass Point Bks.

Harcourt School Publishers Staff. Math Program Development, Grades K-2: Number Sense Binder Package. 3rd ed. 2003. ring bd. 355.40 (978-0-15-340574-7(0)) Harcourt Schl. Pubs.

—Numbers - Grade 4. 3rd ed. 2002. (Trophies English Language Learners Ser.). pap. 5.10 (978-0-15-327769-6(6)) Harcourt Schl. Pubs.

Harder Tangvald, Christine. God's 123s...for Me! 1999. (for Me! Bks.). (Illus.). 16p. (J). (ps). pap. 4.99 (978-0-7642-2281-8(3)) Bethany Hse. Pubs.

Harris, Nancy. Sticky Fingers: Exploring the Number 5. 2008. (J). (*978-1-60044-639-9(6)) Rourke Publishing, LLC.

Head, Debby & Pollett, Libby. BBY Practice Pages: Making Ten. 2004. (Illus.). 91p. spiral bd. 29.00 (978-1-885775-23-8(7)) BBY Pubns.

—BBY Practice Pages: Modeling Numbers 0-100. 2004. (Illus.). 92p. spiral bd. 29.00 (978-1-885775-19-1(9)) BBY Pubns.

—BBY Practice Pages: Numbers & Words 0-10. 2004. (Illus.). 90p. spiral bd. 29.00 (978-1-885775-22-1(9)) BBY Pubns.

—BBY Practice Pages: Numbers & Words 11-20. 2004. (Illus.). 90p. spiral bd. 29.00 (978-1-885775-25-2(3)) BBY Pubns.

Heinst, Marie. My First Number Book. (Illus.). (J). pap. 16.95 (978-0-590-74282-5(5)) Scholastic, Inc.

Hill, Eric. S. S. Happiness Crew: Book of Numbers. (Illus.). 11p. (J). (ps). (978-0-915696-65-9(7)) Determined Productions, Inc.

Hinkler Books. Slide & Learn 123. rev. ed. 2006. (Illus.). 12p. (J). (gr. 3-6). 7.95 (978-1-74157-603-0(2)) Hinkler Bks. Pty, Ltd. AUS. *Dist:* Penton Overseas, Inc.

Hoffman, Joan. Numbers. 2000. (Whimsy Workbooks Ser.). (Illus.). 32p. (J). (ps-1). pap., wbk. ed. 2.49 (978-0-88743-468-6(1)) School Zone Publishing Co.

—Readiness Basics: Grades K-1. 2001. (Super-Deluxe Wkbks.). (Illus.). 128p. (J). (gr. k-1). pap., wbk. ed. 7.99 (978-1-58947-005-7(2) , 02456) School Zone Publishing Co.

—1-25 Dot-to-Dot. rev. ed. 2001. (Get Ready! Wkbks.). (Illus.). 32p. (J). pap. 2.49 (978-0-88743-447-1(9) , 02068) School Zone Publishing Co.

Hop, L. L. C. Hooked on Kindergarten: Numbers 1-100. 2006. 64p. 3.79 (978-1-931020-65-7(5)) HOP, LLC.

HOP, LLC. Hooked on Numbers. 2006. 24.99 (978-1-60143-034-2(5)) HOP, LLC.

Horne, Jane. Busy Baby 123: First Concepts. 2007. (Busy Baby Ser.). (Illus.). 12p. (ps-k). per., bds. 6.95 (*978-1-84610-468-8(8)) Make Believe Ideas GBR. *Dist:* Ingram Pub. Services.

How Much Is a Million? 2004. 29.95 incl. cd-rom (978-1-55592-124-8(8)); 24.95 incl. audio (978-1-55592-059-3(4)); pap. 18.95 incl. audio compact disk (978-1-55592-106-4(X)); pap. 38.75 incl. audio compact disk (978-1-55592-633-5(9)); pap. 32.75 incl. audio (978-1-55592-242-9(2)); pap. 32.75 incl. audio (978-1-55592-243-6(0)); pap. 14.95 incl. audio (978-1-55592-060-9(8)) Weston Woods Studios, Inc.

How Much Is a Million. 2004. pap. 14.95 incl. audio (978-1-55592-659-5(2)) Weston Woods Studios, Inc.

HSP. Numbers to 100, Bk. A. 2nd ed. 2002. (First-Place Math Ser.). (gr. 1 up). pap. 12.60 (978-0-15-334609-5(4)) Harcourt Schl. Pubs.

—Numbers to 1,000, Bk. A. 2nd ed. 2002. (First-Place Math Ser.). (gr. 2 up). pap. 12.60 (978-0-15-334615-6(9)) Harcourt Schl. Pubs.

—Whole Number Operations, Bk. A. 2nd ed. 2002. (First-Place Math Ser.). (gr. 5 up). pap. 12.60 (978-0-15-334633-0(7)); (gr. 6 up). pap. 12.60 (978-0-15-334639-2(6)) Harcourt Schl. Pubs.

In Step with the Standards - Number Sense. 2005. (J). spiral bd. 15.95 (978-1-58123-375-9(2)) Larson Learning, Inc.

It's Counting Time. 2004. (J). per. 15.99 (978-0-9744205-2-3(2)) Golden Eagle Publishing Hse., Inc.

Jerome, Kate Boehm. Number Know-How. 2004. (Math Behind the Science Ser.). (Illus.). 24p. (J). pap. (978-0-7922-4591-9(1)) National Geographic Society.

Kenyon, Dolores. The History of Complex Numbers - A Genealogy. 2007. spiral bd. 8.95 net. (*978-1-60402-110-3(1)) Independent Pub.

King, Zelda. The Story of Our Numbers: The History of Arabic Numerals. 2004. (PowerMath Ser.). (Illus.). 24p. (J). lib. bdg. (978-0-8239-8870-9(8)); lib. bdg. 21.25 (978-0-8239-8965-2(8)) Rosen Publishing Group, Inc., The. (PowerKids Pr.).

Kirk, David. 123: A Miss Spider Concept Book. 2006. (Miss Spider Ser.). 16p. (J). (ps-ps). pap. 6.99 (978-0-448-44338-6(4) , Grosset & Dunlap) Penguin Group (USA) Inc.

Kleinberg, Naomi. 1, 2, 3 Count with Me. Moroney, Christopher, illus. 2005. 20p. (J). (gr. k-ps). bds. 7.99 (978-0-375-83227-7(0) , Random Hse. Bks. for Young Readers) Random Hse. Children's Bks.

La Jars, David. One, Two, Red & Blue. rev. ed. 2004. (Talk Together Ser.). (Illus.). 24p. (J). (ps-k). pap. 5.95 (978-1-58728-019-1(1) , Two Can Publishing) T&N Children's Publishing.

Lacome, Susie. The Big Shiny Sparkly Activity Book. 2003. (Illus.). 10p. (J). pap., act. bk. ed. 9.98 (978-0-7624-1647-9(5) , Courage Bks.) Running Pr. Bk. Pubs.

Lakeshore Learning Materials Staff, contrib. by. Number Sense Kit. 2000. (J). pap. 29.95 (978-1-929255-54-2(3)) Lakeshore Learning Materials.

Landoll Inc. Staff. Numbers Workbook. 2000. (Beginners Bible Ser.). (J). pap. 14.95 (978-1-56189-619-6(5) , American Education Publishing) School Specialty Publishing.

Larousse Color ABC y 123 (Amarillo), Vol. 1. 2003. (SPA., Illus.). 6p. (J). 2.98 (978-970-22-0163-2(2)) Larousse, Ediciones, S. A. de C. V. MEX. *Dist:* Giron Bks.

Law, Felicia. Patchwork First Poem Books - Number. Knight, Paula, illus. 24p. 8.95 (978-1-904668-82-4(8)) Mercury Bks. Ltd. GBR. *Dist:* International Publishers Marketing.

LeapFrog Staff. Thomas & the School Trip: Interactive Book & Cartridge. 2002. (J). pap. 12.99 (978-1-58605-805-0(3)) LeapFrog Enterprises, Inc.

Learn about Numbers. (My Wipe-off Book Ser.). 16p. (J). spiral bd., bds. (978-0-7853-4404-9(7) , 7109200) Publications International, Ltd.

Learning Horizons, creator. Numbers Play Date. 2005. (Illus.). 10p. (J). (ps-3). bds. 5.99 (978-1-59545-016-6(5)) Learning Horizons, Inc.

Learning Wrap-Ups Early Child. 2004. 29.99 (978-0-943343-18-1(6)) Learning Wrap-Ups.

Leber, Nancy Jolson. (Pre-K) Pre-K Practice. 2007. (Clear & Simple Ser.). 64p. (J). pap. 4.99 (978-0-448-44434-5(8) , Grosset & Dunlap) Penguin Group (USA) Inc.

El Libro de Contar de los Chocolates M & M's Brand. 2004. 32p. (J). pap. 6.95 (978-1-57091-370-9(6)) Charlesbridge Publishing, Inc.

Litchfield, Felicity. Primeros Numeros. 2004. Tr. of First Numbers. (SPA., Illus.). 48p. (J). (ps up). 12.95 (978-0-7460-4508-4(5)) EDC Publishing.

Litchfield, Jo, illus. First Picture 123. 2005. (First Picture Board Books Ser.). 16p. (J). 11.95 (978-0-7945-0939-2(8) , Usborne) EDC Publishing.

LoPresti, Angeline Sparagna. A Place for Zero: A Math Adventure. Hornung, Phyllis, illus. 2004. (Math Adventures Ser.). 32p. (J). pap. 6.95 (978-1-57091-196-5(7)); (YA). 16.95 (978-1-57091-602-1(0)) Charlesbridge Publishing, Inc.

Lucy Ladybug Learns Numbers. (Board Bks.). (Illus.). 6p. (J). (ps-k). 4.99 (978-0-7847-1119-4(4) , 03529, Bean Sprouts) Standard Publishing.

Maccarone, Grace, ed. Numbers & Counting. 2006. (Carry Wipe Clean Wheel Bks.). (Illus.). 26p. (J). 7.99 (978-0-439-85365-1(6) , Cartwheel Bks.) Scholastic, Inc.

Makeeff, Cyndi Sue. Inky Winky Spider 1,2,3,4. Riley, Kevin, illus. 2006. 32p. (J). pap. 7.99 (978-0-9778310-1-2(9)) New Vision Ent.

Marzollo, Jean. I Spy Little Learning Box: I Spy Little Book; I Spy Little Letters; I Spy Little Numbers, 3 bks. Wick, Walter, illus. Wick, Walter, photos by. 2003. (I Spy Ser.). 78p. (J). 19.95 (978-0-439-45537-4(5) , Cartwheel Bks.) Scholastic, Inc.

Matching & Counting, Set A. 2002. (J). (gr. k-2). act. bk. ed. 6.99 (978-1-56451-413-4(7)) School Specialty Publishing.

McDonald, Jill. Play with Me: Numbers. 2007. (Illus.). 10p. (J). pap. 6.95 (*978-1-58117-566-0(3)) Dalmatian Pr.

McGraw-Hill Staff. Everything for Letters & Numbers. 2003. (Early Learning Ser.). (Illus.). 320p. (J). (gr. 1-2). pap. 7.95 (978-0-7696-2189-0(9) , Learning Materials) School Specialty Publishing.

—Numbers: Hidden Pictures. 2001. (Homework Helpers Activity Bks.). (Illus.). 56p. (J). (gr. k-1). pap., act. bk. ed. 2.99 (978-0-7682-0677-7(4) , FS109006, Schaffer, Frank) Schaffer, Frank Pubns.

McGraw-Hill Staff & Schaffer, Frank. Numbers: Dot-to-Dot. 2001. (Homework Helpers Activity Bks.). (Illus.). 56p. (J). (gr. k-1). pap., act. bk. ed. 2.99 (978-0-7682-0676-0(6) , FS109005, Schaffer, Frank) Schaffer, Frank Pubns.

Mega Jumbo ABC And 123. 2006. (J). per. 9.95 (978-1-885920-13-3(X)) Pyramid Publishing, Inc.

Merry Monkeys' First Number Fun. 2002. (J). bds. 4.98 (978-0-7525-8865-0(6)) Parragon, Inc.

Merttens, Ruth. My World. 2005. (Heinemann Read & Learn Ser.). (Illus.). 24p. (J). pap. (978-1-4034-6468-2(5)) Heinemann Library.

—Numbers. 2005. (My World Ser.). (Illus.). 24p. (J). (gr. k-2). lib. bdg. 20.64 (978-1-4034-6461-3(8)) Heinemann Library.

—Sizes. 2005. (My World Ser.). (Illus.). 24p. (J). (gr. k-2). lib. bdg. 20.64 (978-1-4034-6463-7(4)) Heinemann Library.

Miles Kelly Staff & Nilsen, Anna. Numbers: Let's Learn. 2003. (Let's Learn Ser.). (Illus.). 20p. (J). 7.95 (978-1-84236-018-7(3)) Miles Kelly Publishing, Ltd. GBR. *Dist:* Independent Pubs. Group.

Mills, Liz, ed. My First Numbers. 2006. (Leapfrog Ser.). (Illus.). 12p. (J). pap. 9.99 (978-0-439-85096-4(7) , Cartwheel Bks.) Scholastic, Inc.

Miranda, Anne. Vroom, Chugga, Vroom-Vroom: A Number Identification Book. 2000. (978-0-606-18345-1(0)) Tandem Library Bks.

—Vroom, Chugga, Vroom-Vroom: A Number Identification Book. Murphy, David, illus. 2000. 40p. (J). (ps-k). pap. 7.95 (978-1-890515-19-5(1)) Turtle Bks.

Moncure, Jane Belk. My Eight Book. 2006. (My First Steps to Mathtrade; Ser.). (Illus.). 32p. (J). 21.36 (978-1-59296-663-9(2)) Child's World, Inc.

—My Five Book. 2006. (My First Steps to Mathtrade; Ser.). (Illus.). 32p. (J). 21.36 (978-1-59296-660-8(8)) Child's World, Inc.

—My Four Book. 2006. (My First Steps to Mathtrade; Ser.). (Illus.). 32p. (J). 21.36 (978-1-59296-659-2(4)) Child's World, Inc.

—My Nine Book. 2006. (My First Steps to Mathtrade; Ser.). (Illus.). 32p. (J). 21.36 (978-1-59296-664-6(0)) Child's World, Inc.

—My One Book. 2006. (My First Steps to Mathtrade; Ser.). (Illus.). 32p. (J). 21.36 (978-1-59296-656-1(X)) Child's World, Inc.

—My Seven Book. 2006. (My First Steps to Mathtrade; Ser.). (Illus.). 32p. (J). 21.36 (978-1-59296-662-2(4)) Child's World, Inc.

—My Six Book. 2006. (My First Steps to Mathtrade; Ser.). (Illus.). 32p. (J). 21.36 (978-1-59296-661-5(6)) Child's World, Inc.

—My Ten Book. 2006. (My First Steps to Mathtrade; Ser.). (Illus.). 32p. (J). 21.36 (978-1-59296-665-3(9)) Child's World, Inc.

—My Three Book. 2006. (My First Steps to Mathtrade; Ser.). (Illus.). 32p. (J). 21.36 (978-1-59296-658-5(6)) Child's World, Inc.

—My Two Book. 2006. (My First Steps to Mathtrade; Ser.). (Illus.). 32p. (J). 21.36 (978-1-59296-657-8(8)) Child's World, Inc.

Murphy, Stuart J. Dave's Down-to-Earth Rock Shop. 2000. (MathStart Ser.). (Illus.). 40p. (J). (gr. 2 up). 15.89 (978-0-06-028019-2(0)) HarperCollins Pubs.

—Dave's Down-to-Earth Rock Shop. 2000. (Mathstart Ser.). (Illus.). (J). 11.79 (978-0-606-18686-5(7)) Tandem Library Bks.

—Dave's down-to-Earth Rock Shop. Bowman Smith, Cat, illus. 2000. (Trophy Picture Bk.). 40p. (J). (gr. 2 up). pap. 5.99 (978-0-06-446729-2(5) , Harper Trophy) HarperCollins Pubs.

—Henry the Fourth. 1999. (ps-2). lib. bdg. 13.00 (978-0-613-11623-7(2)) Tandem Library Bks.

—Missing Mittens. Karas, G. Brian, illus. 2001. (MathStart Ser.). 40p. (J). (gr. 2-4). pap. 5.99 (978-0-06-446733-9(3) , Harper Trophy) HarperCollins Pubs.

My Big Book of Numbers. 2002. 4.00 (978-1-56021-399-4(X)) W.J. Fantasy, Inc.

My Numbers Book. 2006. (J). pap. (*978-1-57332-388-8(8))* HighReach Learning, Inc.

My TakeAlong Li, ed. Early Learning. 2007. (My Take-along Library). 120p. (J). (ps-k). bds. 14.95 (*978-0-7696-5549-9(1))* School Specialty Publishing.

Napier, Matt. Hat Tricks Count. rev. ed. 2007. (Board Ser.). 32p. bds. 7.99 (*978-1-58536-346-9(4))* Sleeping Bear Pr.

—Hat Tricks Count. Rose, Melanie, illus. rev. ed. 2005. (Sports Alphabet Ser.). 40p. (J). (gr. k-5). 16.95 (978-1-58536-163-2(1)) Sleeping Bear Pr.

Negative & Positive Numbers: CA Math Series II. 2004. 6.00 (978-1-932230-75-8(0)) National Ctr. on Education & The Economy.

Nimble with Numbers: Student Practice Book. 2003. (Nimble with Numbers Ser.). 11.95 (978-0-7690-2823-1(3)); 11.95 (978-0-7690-2824-8(1)); (J). (gr. 4). 11.95 (978-0-7690-2821-7(7)); (J). (gr. 5). 11.95 (978-0-7690-2820-0(9)); (J). (gr. 6). 11.95 (978-0-7690-2819-4(5)) Seymour, Dale Pubns.

Nolan, Helen. How Much, How Many, How Far, How Heavy, How Long, How Tall Is 1,000? Walker, Tracy, illus. unabr. ed. 2001. 32p. (J). (gr. k-3). (978-1-55074-816-1(5)) Kids Can Pr., Ltd.

Norton, Grace R. Count Us in Too. 2005. (Illus.). 32p. (J). (ps-4). 14.95 (978-1-889506-03-6(6)) Kendar Publishing, Inc.

Novick, Mary. Numbers. Harlin, Sybel, illus. 2002. (Double Delight Ser.). 24p. (J). (ps-k). 9.95 (978-1-57145-780-6(1) , Silver Dolphin Bks.) Advantage Pubs. Group.

Number 0-10. 2002. (Home Workbooks Ser.). 64p. pap. 2.49 (978-0-88724-714-9(8) , CD-4516) Carson-Dellosa Publishing Co., Inc.

Number Booster. 2005. (J). per. 0.00 (978-1-59441-505-0(6) , C04037) Carson-Dellosa Publishing Co., Inc.

Number Facts To 10 (Gr. 1-2) 2003. (J). (978-1-58232-083-0(7)) Bryan Hse. Pubs., Inc.

Number Facts to 10 Spanish Version. 2007. (J). per. (*978-1-58232-152-3(3))* Bryan Hse. Pubs., Inc.

Number Fun. 2002. (Home Workbooks Ser.). 64p. pap. 2.49 (978-0-88724-721-7(0) , CD-4523) Carson-Dellosa Publishing Co., Inc.

Number Fun. 2005. (Little Celebrations Thematic Packages Ser.). (J). (gr. k-3). 133.50 (978-0-673-75381-6(6)) Celebration Pr.

Number Patterns, Set C. 2002. (J). (gr. k-2). act. bk. ed. 6.99 (978-1-56451-415-8(3)) School Specialty Publishing.

The Number System Student: RUA the Number System Student. 2005. 110p. per. 7.50 (978-1-932976-70-0(1)) National Ctr. on Education & The Economy.

Numbers. 2003. (J). per. (978-1-884907-43-2(1)); per. (978-1-884907-47-0(4)) Paradise Pr., Inc.

Numbers. (Active Minds(R) Ser.). 22p. (J). spiral bd., bds. (978-0-7853-8611-7(4) , 7188100) Publications International, Ltd.

Numbers. 2004. (Practice Makes Perfect Ser.). 48p. 4.99 (978-0-7439-3309-4(5)); 4.99 (978-0-7439-3310-0(9)) Teacher Created Materials, Inc.

Numbers. 2004. (Early Days Ser.). (Illus.). 18p. (J). bds. (978-1-84229-973-9(5)) Top That! Publishing PLC.

Numbers - Book 2. 2005. (J). per. 8.95 (978-1-59566-158-6(1)) QEB Publishing Inc.

Numbers 0-20. 2002. (Home Workbooks Ser.). 64p. pap. 2.49 (978-0-88724-715-6(6) , CD-4517) Carson-Dellosa Publishing Co., Inc.

Numbers All Around. 2006. (Yellow Umbrella Math Ser.). 8,16p. (J). 6.50 (978-0-7368-1695-3(X)) Red Brick Learning.

Numbers & More. 2005. (J). bds. (978-1-4194-0051-3(7)) Paradise Pr., Inc.

Numbers & the Number Line Student: RUPA Numbers & the Number Line Student. 2005. 95p. per. 7.50 (978-1-932976-47-2(7)) National Ctr. on Education & The Economy.

Numbers Book 1. 2005. (J). per. 8.95 (978-1-59566-154-8(9)) QEB Publishing Inc.

Numbers Count. 2003. (J). per. (978-1-57657-951-0(4)) Paradise Pr., Inc.

Numbers in Everyday Life. 96p. (gr. 6-8). 9.99 (978-0-7424-0265-2(7) , IF19360) School Specialty Publishing.

Numbers, Shapes, & Colors. (Puppet & Flannelboard Stories Ser.). (Illus.). 2004. 96p. 11.99 (978-0-7439-3699-6(X)); 2003. 48p. (J). pap. 7.99 (978-0-7439-3230-1(7)) Teacher Created Materials, Inc.

Numberworks. 208p. (gr. 7 up). 18.99 (978-0-7682-0626-5(X) , GA13083) School Specialty Publishing.

Numeracy Through Spreadsheets. (Illus.). 48p. (J). (gr. 4-6). pap. (978-1-876367-63-3(6)) Wizard Bks.

Numeros del 1 al 20. 2007. (Sesame Street Ser.). (SPA & ENG.). 50p. (J). 2.95 (*978-1-59545-061-6(0))* Learning Horizons, Inc.

Numeros y Colores. 2007. (Dora The Explorer Ser.). (SPA & ENG., Illus.). 48p. (J). 2.95 (*978-1-59545-057-9(2))* Learning Horizons, Inc.

O'Donnell, Kerri. Numbers & Operations. 2004. 48p. pap. 6.95 (978-1-4042-8536-1(9)) Rosen Publishing Group, Inc., The.

Packard, Edward. Big Numbers: And Pictures That Show Just How Big They Are! Murdocca, Sal, illus. 2000. (Fun Early Math Concepts Ser.). 32p. (gr. k-3). lib. bdg. 22.90 (978-0-7613-1570-4(5) , Millbrook Pr.) Lerner Publishing Group.

Packard, Edward & Murdocca, Sal. Big Numbers: And Pictures That Show Just How Big They Are! 2000. (Illus.). 32p. (gr. k-3). (978-0-7613-1280-2(3) , Millbrook Pr.) Lerner Publishing Group.

Parker, Andrew & Stamford, Jane. Number Books. 1999. (Illus.). 31p. (J). Bk. 1. (ps-2). pap., wbk. ed. 15.00 (978-0-7217-2341-9(1)); Bk. 2. (gr. 1-3). pap., wbk. ed. 15.00 (978-0-7217-2342-6(X)); Bk. 3. (ps-2). pap., wbk. ed. 15.00 (978-0-7217-2343-3(8)); Bk. 4. (ps-2). pap., wbk. ed. 15.00 (978-0-7217-2344-0(6)); Bk. 5. (ps-2). pap., wbk. ed. 15.00 (978-0-7217-2345-7(4)) Schofield & Sims Ltd. GBR. *Dist:* State Mutual Bk. & Periodical Service, Ltd.

Patilla, Peter. Fun with Numbers. McDonald, Brigitte, illus. 1998. (Fun with... Ser.). 32p. (ps-2). lib. bdg. 23.90 (978-0-7613-0957-4(8) , Millbrook Pr.) Lerner Publishing Group.

Penton Overseas, Inc. Staff. Diego Numbers Slide & Learn: Interactive Flash Cards. rev. ed. 2007. (J). (gr. 3-6). 9.95 (*978-1-74181-172-8(4))* Hinkler Bks. Pty, Ltd. AUS. *Dist:* Penton Overseas, Inc.

Perrett, Lisa, illus. Princess 123. 2004. 12p. (J). bds. 4.95 (978-1-4027-1487-0(4)) Sterling Publishing Co., Inc.

Perry, Gayle. Numbers. Wolkoff, Stacey, ed. Yuh, Catherine, illus. 2000. (Primary Theme Ser.). 32p. (gr. k-2). pap., tchr. ed. 7.99 (978-1-57471-683-2(2) , CTP2431) Creative Teaching Pr., Inc.

Phillips, Sarah. Trace, Stick & Learn Wipe Clean 123 Activity Book. 2007. (Trace, Stick & Learn Ser.). (Illus.). 12p. (J). (ps-3). pap. 4.99 (*978-1-84610-431-2(9))* Make Believe Ideas GBR. *Dist:* Ingram Pub. Services.

Phillips, Sarah & Tattam, Mark. Numbers. 2005. (Baby-See-A Shape Ser.). (Illus.). 12p. (ps-k). per., bds. 4.95 (978-1-905051-91-5(3)) Make Believe Ideas GBR. *Dist:* Ingram Pub. Services.

Picture Window Books, contrib. by. From the Garden. (Know Your Numbers Ser.). 24p. (J). pap. 7.95 (978-1-4048-1116-4(8)) Picture Window Bks.

Practica de Numeros del 1 al 20. 2006. (Dora The Explorer Ser.). (SPA & ENG., Illus.). 24p. (J). pap. 2.95 (*978-1-59545-074-6(2))* Learning Horizons, Inc.

Priddy, ed. Wipe Clean Early Learning Activity Book Numbers. rev. ed. 2007. 20p. (J). bds. 4.75 (*978-0-312-49989-1(2)* , Priddy Bks.) St. Martin's Pr.

Priddy Books Staff. First Concepts: Numbers. 2003. (Illus.). (J). bds. (978-0-312-49232-8(4) , Priddy Bks.) St. Martin's Pr.

Priddy, Roger. Soft-to-Touch Slipcase 2: Colors,123,Abc. 2004. 84p. (J). bds. 22.95 (978-0-312-49423-0(8) , Priddy Bks.) St. Martin's Pr.

—Wipe Clean Early Learning Activity Book - Numbers. 2007. 12p. (J). bds. 3.47 (978-0-312-49906-8(X) , Priddy Bks.) St. Martin's Pr.

—Wipe Clean Flash Cards - 123. 2006. (Wipe Clean Ser.). 30p. (J). bds. 9.95 (978-0-312-49817-7(9) , Priddy Bks.) St. Martin's Pr.

Prince, Wallaker. Using Standards Number & O Gr3. 2003. (100+ Seriestm Ser.). 128p. (J). (gr. 3-3). pap. 12.99 (978-0-7424-1813-4(8) , IFG99060) School Specialty Publishing.

—Using Standards Number & O Gr4. 2003. (100+ Seriestm Ser.). 128p. (J). (gr. 4-4). pap. 12.99 (978-0-7424-1814-1(6) , IFG99061) School Specialty Publishing.

Professor Q's Chinese-English Language Books: Shu' Zi' - Numbers. 2006. (J). (978-0-9743359-6-4(7)) Murdock Publishing Co.

QEB Maths Club National Book Stores Edition: Using Numbers Book 1. 2006. (J). per. (978-1-59566-286-6(3)) QEB Publishing Inc.

QEB Maths Club National Book Stores Edition: Using Numbers Book 2. 2006. (J). per. (978-1-59566-290-3(1)) QEB Publishing Inc.

QEB Start Math Book National Book Stores Edition: Numbers - Book 1. 2006. (J). per. (978-1-59566-272-9(3)) QEB Publishing Inc.

QEB Start Math Book Stores Edition: Numbers - Book 2. 2006. (J). per. (978-1-59566-276-7(6)) QEB Publishing Inc.

Raintree Steck-Vaughn Staff. Number Concepts Preschool Skills. 1999. pap. (978-0-7398-2920-2(3)) Steck-Vaughn.

Rational Numbers Student's Edition: CA Math Series II. 2004. 6.00 (978-1-932230-73-4(4)) National Ctr. on Education & The Economy.

Rau, Dana Meachen. Five. 2008. (J). (*978-0-7614-2970-8(0))* Cavendish, Marshall Corp.

—Four. 2008. (J). (*978-0-7614-2969-2(7))* Cavendish, Marshall Corp.

—One. 2008. (J). (*978-0-7614-2966-1(2))* Cavendish, Marshall Corp.

—Ten. 2008. (J). (*978-0-7614-2971-5(9))* Cavendish, Marshall Corp.

—Three. 2008. (J). (*978-0-7614-2968-5(9))* Cavendish, Marshall Corp.

—Two. 2007. (J). (*978-0-7614-2967-8(0))* Cavendish, Marshall Corp.

Read-Think-Do Math: Numbers Book 1. 2006. pap. 4.49 (978-1-4206-8165-9(6)) Teacher Created Materials, Inc.

Read-Think-Do Math: Numbers Book 2. 2006. pap. 4.49 (978-1-4206-8169-7(9)) Teacher Created Materials, Inc.

Read-Think-Do Math: Using Numbers Book 1. 2006. pap. 4.49 (978-1-4206-8172-7(9)) Teacher Created Materials, Inc.

Read-Think-Do Math: Using Numbers Book 2. 2006. pap. 4.49 (978-1-4206-8173-4(7)) Teacher Created Materials, Inc.

Realtime Associates and Mazer Corporation Staff & LeapFrog Staff, compiled by. Identify Place Value in Numbers. 2002. (J). (gr. 3). 66.75 (978-1-58605-391-8(4) , LeapFrog Schl. Hse.) LeapFrog Enterprises, Inc.

—Locate Numbers on a Number Line. 2002. (J). (gr. 2). 66.75 (978-1-58605-349-9(3) , LeapFrog Schl. Hse.) LeapFrog Enterprises, Inc.

—Round Three-Digit Numbers to the Nearest Hundred. 2002. (J). (gr. 3). 66.75 (978-1-58605-408-3(2) , LeapFrog Schl. Hse.) LeapFrog Enterprises, Inc.

—Round Whole Numbers & Decimals Through Tenths. 2002. (J). (gr. 5). 66.75 (978-1-58605-526-4(7) , LeapFrog Schl. Hse.) LeapFrog Enterprises, Inc.

—Round Whole Numbers to Tens, Hundreds or Thousands. 2002. (J). (gr. 4). 66.75 (978-1-58605-467-0(8) , LeapFrog Schl. Hse.) LeapFrog Enterprises, Inc.

—Understand & Extend Number or Shape Patterns. 2002. (J). (gr. 3). 66.75 (978-1-58605-405-2(8) , LeapFrog Schl. Hse.) LeapFrog Enterprises, Inc.

—Write Numbers in Expanded Form. 2002. (J). (gr. 3). 66.75 (978-1-58605-392-5(2) , LeapFrog Schl. Hse.) LeapFrog Enterprises, Inc.

Repchuk, Caroline. Fairy Numbers. 2007. (J). bds. 5.99 (978-0-439-88705-2(4) , Cartwheel Bks.) Scholastic, Inc.

Reynolds, Cynthia Furlong. Fishing for Numbers: A Maine Number Book. Brett, Jeannie, illus. 2005. (Count Your Way Across the USA Ser.). 40p. (J). (gr. k-5). 16.95 (978-1-58536-035-2(X)) Sleeping Bear Pr.

Robinson, C. L. MATH1on1 Numbers & Operations. 2006. (YA). per. 9.99 (978-0-9786767-0-4(X)) Robinson, Consuelo.

Robleda, Margarita. Los Numeros Tragaldabas. Gurovich, Natalia, illus. 2004. (SPA.). 24p. (J). 12.95 (978-970-690-807-0(2)) Planeta Mexicana Editorial S. A. de C. V. MEX. *Dist:* Lectorum Pubns., Inc.

Rosa-Mendoza, Gladys. Numbers. Cifuentes, Carolina, ed. Noiset, Michele, illus. 2004. (English-Spanish Foundations Ser.).Tr. of Los Numeros. (ENG & SPA.). 20p. (J). bds. 6.95 (978-0-9679748-2-8(8)) Me+Mi Publishing.

Rosario, Sherwin, illus. Meet the Numbers Lift the Flap Book. 2005. 12p. (J). bds. 9.99 (978-0-9767008-1-4(6)) KRO Publishing.

—Meet the Numbers One to Ten. 2005. 10p. (J). bds. 7.99 (978-0-9767008-3-8(2)) KRO Publishing.

Rosenberg, Pam. Is It Still a Number? 2006. (Rookie Read-About Math Ser.). 31p. (J). (978-0-516-25443-2(X)) Children's Pr., Ltd.

Rosenberg, Pam. Is It Still a Number. 2007. (Rookie Read-About Math Ser.). (Illus.). 31p. (J). pap. (*978-0-516-25594-1(0))* Children's Pr., Ltd.

Roy, Jennifer Rozines & Roy, Gregory. Numbers on the Street. 2005. (Math All Around Ser.). (Illus.). 31p. (J). (978-0-7614-2002-6(9) , Benchmark Bks.) Cavendish, Marshall Corp.

Roza, Greg. The Hubble Space Telescope: Understanding & Representing Numbers in the Billions. 2005. (Illus.). 32p. (J). (978-1-4042-5130-4(8) , PowerKids Pr.) Rosen Publishing Group, Inc., The.

—The Hubble Space Telescope: Understanding & Representing Numbers up to 1 Billion. 2005. (PowerMath Ser.). (Illus.). 32p. (J). 22.50 (978-1-4042-2931-0(0) , PowerKids Pr.); pap. (978-1-4042-5129-8(4)) Rosen Publishing Group, Inc., The.

Sanders, Nancy I. Adventures with Numbers. 1998. (Archy's Activity Bks.). (Illus.). 16p. (J). (ps-2). pap. 3.99 (978-0-570-05078-0(2)) Concordia Publishing Hse.

Santillana & Dorling Kindersley Publishing Staff. Numeros. (Show Me Ser.). (SPA., Illus.). 16p. (J). (ps-k). bds. 6.95 (978-1-58986-326-2(7)) Santillana USA Publishing Co., Inc.

Sargent, Daina. Colors & the Number 1, 11 vols. Lenoir, Jane, illus. 2005. (Learn to Read Ser.: 11). 24p. (J). pap. 9.95 (978-1-59381-031-3(8)) Ozark Publishing.

—Colors & the Number 10/Los Colores y el Numero 10, 11 vols. Lenoir, Jane, illus. 2005. (Learn to Read Ser.: 11). (ENG & SPA.). 24p. (J). pap. 9.95 (978-1-59381-147-1(0)); lib. bdg. 19.95 (978-1-59381-146-4(2)) Ozark Publishing.

—Colors & the Number 2, 11. Lenoir, Jane, illus. l.t. ed. 2004. (Learn to Read Ser.). 24p. (J). lib. bdg. 19.95 (978-1-59381-032-0(6)) Ozark Publishing.

—Colors & the Number 3, 11. Lenoir, Jane, illus. l.t. ed. 2004. (Learn to Read Ser.). 24p. (J). lib. bdg. 19.95 (978-1-59381-034-4(2)) Ozark Publishing.

—Colors & the Number 4, 11 vols. Lenoir, Jane, illus. (Learn to Read Ser.). 24p. (J). 2005. pap. 9.95 (978-1-59381-037-5(7)); 2004. lib. bdg. 19.95 (978-1-59381-036-8(9)) Ozark Publishing.

—Colors & the Number 5, 11. Lenoir, Jane, illus. l.t. ed. 2004. (Learn to Read Ser.). 24p. (J). lib. bdg. 19.95 (978-1-59381-038-2(5)) Ozark Publishing.

—Colors & the Number 6, 11. Lenoir, Jane, illus. l.t. ed. 2004. (Learn to Read Ser.). 24p. (J). lib. bdg. 19.95 (978-1-59381-040-5(7)) Ozark Publishing.

—Colors & the Number 6/Los Colores y el Numero 6, 11 vols. Lenoir, Jane, illus. 2005. (Learn to Read Ser.: 11). (ENG & SPA.). 24p. (J). pap. 9.95 (978-1-59381-139-6(X)) Ozark Publishing.

—Colors & the Number 7, 11. Lenoir, Jane, illus. l.t. ed. 2004. (Learn to Read Ser.). 24p. (J). lib. bdg. 19.95 (978-1-59381-042-9(3)) Ozark Publishing.

—Colors & the Number 8, 11. Lenoir, Jane, illus. l.t. ed. 2004. (Learn to Read Ser.). 24p. (J). lib. bdg. 19.95 (978-1-59381-044-3(X)) Ozark Publishing.

—Colors & the Number 9, 11. Lenoir, Jane, illus. l.t. ed. 2004. (Learn to Read Ser.). 24p. (J). lib. bdg. 19.95 (978-1-59381-046-7(6)) Ozark Publishing.

—Introduction to Colors & Numbers, 11 vols. Lenoir, Jane, illus. l.t. ed. 2004. (Learn to Read Ser.: 11). 24p. (J). lib. bdg. 19.95 (978-1-59381-050-4(4)) Ozark Publishing.

—Introduction to Colors & Numbers/Introduccion a los Colores Numeros, 11 vols. Lenoir, Jane, illus. l.t. ed. 2005. (Learn to Read Ser.: 11). (SPA & ENG.). 24p. (J). pap. 9.95 (978-1-59381-149-5(7)) Ozark Publishing.

Sargent, Daina & Lenoir, Jane. Colors & the Number 6/Los colores y el Numero 6, 11 vols. 2005. (Learn to Read Ser.).Tr. of Los colores y el Numero 6. (ENG & SPA., Illus.). 24p. (J). lib. bdg. 19.95 (978-1-59381-138-9(1)) Ozark Publishing.

Schmandt-Besserat, Denise. The History of Counting. Hays, Michael, illus. 1999. 48p. (J). (gr. 3 up). 18.99 (978-0-688-14118-9(8)); (ps-7). lib. bdg. 18.89 (978-0-688-14119-6(6)) HarperCollins Pubs.

School Specialty Publishing. Counting & Numbers with Mr Wiggle. 2003. 32p. (J). (gr. k up). pap. 5.99 (978-1-56451-990-0(2) , ID99006); (gr. 1 up). pap. 5.99 (978-1-56451-991-7(0) , ID99007) School Specialty Publishing.

—Easy Alphabet, Colors, Numbers & Shapes. 2001. (Phonics Flash Cards Ser.). 104p. (C). 6.99 (978-0-86734-411-0(3) , Schaffer, Frank) Schaffer, Frank Pubns.

—Matching & Counting. 2000. (Funtastic Frogs Activity Cards Ser.). 18p. (J). (gr. k-2). 8.99 (978-1-56451-344-1(0)) School Specialty Publishing.

—Number Patterns. 2000. (Funtastic Frogs Activity Cards Ser.). 18p. (C). 8.99 (978-1-56451-346-5(7)) School Specialty Publishing.

—Numbers 1 to 100 / Numeros del 1 Al 100. 2006. (Brighter Child Flash Cards Ser.). 54p. (J). 2.99 (978-0-7696-4799-9(5) , Brighter Child) School Specialty Publishing.

—Starter Skills Numbers 0 To 20. 2007. (English-Espanol Starter Skills Ser.). 80p. (C). pap. 8.99 (*978-0-7682-3379-7(8)* , Schaffer, Frank) Schaffer, Frank Pubns.

—Total Numbers & Counting Learn. 2007. (Total Learning Kits Ser.). 1028p. (J). pap. 49.95 (*978-0-7696-5499-7(1))* School Specialty Publishing.

School Specialty Publishing. 101 Activities: Numbers. 2004. 80p. (J). pap. 10.99 (978-1-57029-488-4(7) , WPH99030, Totline Pubns.) Schaffer, Frank Pubns.

School Zone Publishing Company Staff. Whimsy Numbers. 2001. (Flash Cards Whimsy Ser.). 56p. (J). 2.79 (978-0-88743-490-7(8) , 04061) School Zone Publishing Co.

—1-25 Dot-to-Dot Bilingaul: Get Ready! rev. ed. 2004. 64p. (J). (gr. k-ps). pap. 3.79 (978-1-58947-971-5(8)) School Zone Publishing Co.

School Zone Staff. Numbers. (J). 2004. 2.79 (978-1-58947-983-8(1)); 2005. 2.79 (978-1-58947-478-9(3)) School Zone Publishing Co.

Schwartz, David M. How Much Is a Million? Kellogg, Steven, illus. 2000. (J). (gr. 1-4). pap. 12.95 incl. audio Weston Woods Studios, Inc.

Sesame Building Blocks: Cube Books. 2002. (J). (978-1-931312-81-3(8)) SoftPlay, Inc.

Sesame Street Numbers. 2005. (J). 2.95 (*978-1-58610-979-0(0))* Learning Horizons, Inc.

Sevaly, Karen, ed. Hands on Learning: Numbers & Counting Dominoes. 2006. 12.99 (978-0-439-82401-9(X) , Teaching Resources) Scholastic, Inc.

Shea. Working with Numbers. 2004. (Illus.). Level D. pap. 16.40 incl. cd-rom (978-0-7398-9159-9(6)); Level E. pap. 16.40 incl. cd-rom (978-0-7398-9160-5(X)); Level F. pap. 16.40 incl. cd-rom (978-0-7398-9161-2(8)) Steck-Vaughn.

Shepard, Daniel. Numbers All Around. 2006. (Illus.). (J). 16p. (978-0-7368-5982-0(9)); (ENG & SPA., 18p. (978-0-7368-6018-5(5)) Yellow Umbrella Pr.

Silver Dolphin en Español Editors. Disney Tesoro de libros de Calcomanias: Disney Sticker Book Treasury, Spanish-Language Edition. 2007. (Illus.). 48p. (J). 14.95 (*978-970-718-447-3(7)* , Silver Dolphin en Español) Advanced Marketing, S. de R. L. de C. V. MEX. *Dist:* Perseus Distribution.

Sing & Learn, ed. Numbers & Counting. 2007. (Sing & Learn Padded Board Bks.). 53p. (J). bds. 16.95 (*978-0-7696-5459-1(2))* School Specialty Publishing.

Slaughter, Tom. 1 2 3. 2005. (SPA.). (J). (gr. k up). pap. 7.95 (978-968-7381-54-1(X)) Tecolote, Ediciones, S.A. de C.V. MEX. *Dist:* Iaconi, Mariuccia Bk. Imports.

Spot Decouvre les Nombres. 2000. (FRE., Illus.). 16p. (J). bds. 11.95 (978-2-09-270193-5(2)) Nathan, Fernand FRA. *Dist:* Distribooks, Inc.

Stanley, Mandy, illus. Mi Primer Libro de Numeros. 2002. (Mi Primer Libro Ser.).Tr. of My First Book of Numeros. (SPA.). 48p. (J). (gr. k-ps). pap. 6.95 (978-0-7534-5543-2(9) , Kingfisher) Houghton Mifflin Co. Trade & Reference Div.

Steck-Vaughn Staff. At-Home Workbooks: Numbers. 2004. (Illus.). pap., wbk. ed. (978-0-7398-8529-1(4)) Steck-Vaughn.

—Early Math: Number Sense. 2005. pap. 2.99 (978-1-4190-0319-6(4)); pap. 29.95 (978-1-4190-0343-1(7)) Steck-Vaughn.

—How Much Is 100? 2003. pap. 4.10 (978-0-7398-7661-9(9)) Steck-Vaughn.

—Math Remediation: Number Concepts. 2005. pap. 5.49 (978-1-4190-0366-0(6)) Harcourt Schl. Pubs.

—Top Line Math 10-Pack: Number Concepts. 2005. pap. 54.95 (978-1-4190-0387-5(9)) Harcourt Schl. Pubs.

Sterling Publishing Company Staff. Color by Numbers. 1999. (Illus.). 16p. (J). (ps). pap. 2.95 (978-0-8069-1937-9(X)) Sterling Publishing Co., Inc.

Strazzabosco, John. Extreme Temperatures: Learning about Positive & Negative Numbers. 2004. (PowerMath Ser.). (Illus.). 32p. (J). lib. bdg. 22.50 (978-0-8239-8997-3(6) , PowerKids Pr.) Rosen Publishing Group, Inc., The.

Swinburne, Stephen R. What's a Pair? What's a Dozen? Swinburne, Stephen R., photos by. 2003. (Illus.). 32p. (YA). (gr. k-2). pap. 8.95 (978-1-56397-871-5(7)) Boyds Mills Pr.

—What's a Pair? What's a Dozen? 2000. (978-0-606-18017-7(6)); lib. bdg. 17.60 (978-0-613-29137-8(9)) Tandem Library Bks.

Tabletop Pocket Chart Counting & Numbers Card Set. 2004. (J). pap. 8.95 (978-1-56911-169-7(3)) Learning Resources, Inc.

Taylor, Damon. Bible Numbers 1 to 10. 2002. (Child Sockology Ser.). 24p. (J). (ps-k). 6.99 (978-0-8254-3853-0(5)) Kregel Pubns.

Teach-Me-Bears Learn Numbers. 2003. (J). per. (978-1-884907-62-3(8)) Paradise Pr., Inc.

TestSMART Plus Whole Numbers, Level B-1. 2004. (J). (978-1-57022-489-8(7)) ECS Learning Systems, Inc.

TestSMART Plus Whole Numbers, Level B-2. 2004. (J). (978-1-57022-490-4(0)) ECS Learning Systems, Inc.

TestSMART Plus Whole Numbers, Level C-1. 2004. (J). (978-1-57022-491-1(9)) ECS Learning Systems, Inc.

TestSMART Plus Whole Numbers, Level C-2. 2004. (J). (978-1-57022-492-8(7)) ECS Learning Systems, Inc.

TestSMART Plus Whole Numbers, Level D-1. 2004. (J). (978-1-57022-493-5(5)) ECS Learning Systems, Inc.

TestSMART Plus Whole Numbers, Level D-2. 2004. (J). (978-1-57022-494-2(3)) ECS Learning Systems, Inc.

TestSMART Plus Whole Numbers, Level E. 2004. (J). (978-1-57022-495-9(1)) ECS Learning Systems, Inc.

TestSMART Plus Whole Numbers, Level F. 2004. (J). (978-1-57022-496-6(X)) ECS Learning Systems, Inc.

TestSMART Plus Whole Numbers, Level G. 2004. (J). (978-1-57022-497-3(8)) ECS Learning Systems, Inc.

TestSMART Plus Whole Numbers, Level H. 2004. (J). (978-1-57022-498-0(6)) ECS Learning Systems, Inc.

TestSMART Plus Whole Numbers, Level I. 2004. (YA). (978-1-57022-499-7(4)) ECS Learning Systems, Inc.

Thomson, Ruth. 1, 2, 3. (Coleccion Mi Primer Libro). (SPA., Illus.). 32p. (J). 13.95 (978-84-207-3777-5(1) , ANY876) Grupo Anaya, S.A. ESP. *Dist:* Continental Bk. Co., Inc.

The TI Math Mate Calculator. 2004. suppl. ed. 265.50 (978-0-201-25341-2(0)); suppl. ed. 91.50 (978-0-201-25340-5(2)) Addison-Wesley Educational Pubs., Inc. (Scott Foresman).

Tipton, Stacey. The Complete Musical Spanish: With New Bonus Verbs Learning CD, 1. 2nd ed. 2005. (SPA., Illus.). 112p. 49.99 (978-0-9706829-7-0(2)) Musical Linguist, The.

Tonka Number Power Wife Off. 2002. (Illus.). 16p. (J). spiral bd., bds. (978-0-7853-6301-9(7) , 7158500) Publications International, Ltd.

Trimble, Richard M. Dice & Spinners. 2001. 32p. (J). (gr. k-7). pap. 12.00 (978-1-871098-34-1(3)) Claire Pubns. GBR. *Dist:* Parkwest Pubns., Inc.

Troiano, Joe. Spookley the Square Pumpkin: Colors & Numbers. Brooks, Nan, illus. 2006. 22p. (J). bds. 4.95 (978-1-4027-4109-8(X)) Sterling Publishing Co., Inc.

Tucker, Shirley & Rambo, Jane. Odd & Even Numbers. 2002. (Yellow Umbrella Books). (Illus.). 16p. (J). (gr. 1). lib. bdg. 14.60 (978-0-7368-1286-3(5) , Pebble Bks.) Capstone Pr., Inc.

Ward, Beck & Nicholson, Sue, eds. Numbers. Giraffe, Red, illus. 2002. (My First Write & Wipe Ser.). 26p. (J). (ps-k). 14.95 (978-1-57145-723-3(2) , Silver Dolphin Bks.) Advantage Pubs. Group.

Ward, Kristin, ed. My First Number Board Book. 2004. (Illus.). 36p. (J). (ps-3). bds. 5.99 (978-0-7894-9903-5(7)) Dorling Kindersley Publishing, Inc.

Watt, Fiona & Wells, Rachel. Adding II. 2004. (Usborne Sticker Math Ser.). (Illus.). 28p. (J). (gr. 1-2). pap., act. bk. ed. 6.95 (978-0-7460-4080-5(6)) EDC Publishing.

Weatherly. Working with Numbers. 2004. (Illus.). Level D. pap. 16.40 incl. cd-rom (978-0-7398-9158-2(8)); Level A. pap. 16.40 incl. cd-rom (978-0-7398-9156-8(1)); Level B. pap. 16.40 incl. cd-rom (978-0-7398-9157-5(X)) Steck-Vaughn.

Weber, Lou, ed. Fun with Numbers. 2004. 32p. wbk. ed. 12.98 incl. audio compact disk (978-0-7853-8957-6(1)) Publications International, Ltd.

Weekly Reader Early Learning Library (Firm) Staff, contrib. by. I Know Numbers. 2006. (I'm Ready for Math Ser.). (Illus.). 16p. (J). pap. (978-0-8368-6480-9(8)); lib. bdg. 16.67 (978-0-8368-6475-5(1)) Stevens, Gareth Inc.

—I Know Numbers: Los Numeros. 2006. (ENG & SPA., Illus.). 16p. (J). pap. 4.50 (978-0-8368-6490-8(5)); lib. bdg. 16.67 (978-0-8368-6485-4(9)) Stevens, Gareth Inc.

Whitehouse, Patricia. Zoo Pairs. 2002. 24p. (J). (ps-1). pap. (978-1-58810-757-2(4) , 91411); (Illus.). lib. bdg. 18.50 (978-1-58810-549-3(0)) Heinemann Library.

Wipe-Away Books: Numbers Dot-to-Dot. 2003. (Illus.). 16p. (J). (ps up). pap. 3.99 (978-0-7682-0068-3(7)) School Specialty Publishing.

Wipe-Away Books: Numbers to 100. 2003. (Illus.). 16p. (J). (ps up). pap. 3.99 (978-0-7682-0447-6(X)) School Specialty Publishing.

The World of Eric Carle My Numbers Activity Kit. 2007. (J). 16.99 (***978-0-9794445-1-7(9)**) Loew-Cornell, Inc.

Yolen, Jane. Animal Train: A Lift-the-Flap Concept Book. Cushman, Doug, illus. 2002. 14p. (J). (ps-1). bds. 8.99 (978-0-689-84838-4(2) , Little Simon) Simon & Schuster Children's Publishing.

Yoon, Salina, illus. Foil Fun Learning Books: Numbers, Colors, Opposites, Shapes, 4 bks. Incl. Foil Fun Colors. (J). bds. 4.95 (978-1-58117-061-0(0)); Foil Fun Numbers. bds. 4.95 (978-1-58117-062-7(9)); Foil Fun Opposites. (J). bds. 4.95 (978-1-58117-063-4(7)); Foil Fun Shapes. (J). bds. 4.95 (978-1-58117-064-1(5)); 10p. (ps). 2000. (Foil Fun Board Bks.). (Illus.). 2000. Set bds. 14.95 (978-1-58117-065-8(3) , Intervisual/Piggy Toes) Dalmatian Pr.

YoYo Books. Numbers: Mini Baby's First Library. 2005. 42p. bds. 4.95 (978-90-5843-804-1(X)) YoYo Bks. BEL. *Dist:* National Bk. Network.

Zakiyyah. ChatterWorld: My Numbers in Spanish/French. 2006. 40p. 14.99 (978-0-9777085-0-5(0)) Little Linguists Press.

Zaslavsky, Claudia. Number Sense & Nonsense: Building Math Creativity & Confidence Through Numbers. 2001. (gr. 3-6). lib. bdg. 24.55 (978-0-613-88773-1(5)) Tandem Library Bks.

1, 2, 3. (Coleccion Picaros Peluchines). (SPA.). (J). 5.50 (978-950-11-0399-1(4) , SGM399); (Illus.). 10p. pap. 5.50 (978-950-11-0791-3(4) , SGM914) Sigmar ARG. *Dist:* Continental Bk. Co., Inc.

1, 2, 3: Fun to Learn. 1999. (Illus.). 32p. (ps-3). 1.99 (978-1-58279-008-4(6) , 93) Trident Pr. International.

NUMBER THEORY

Douglas, Vincent & School Specialty Publishing Staff. Numbers. 2003. (Brighter Child Flash Cards Ser.). (Illus.). 54p. (J). (ps up). 2.99 (978-0-7696-2380-1(8) , Brighter Child) School Specialty Publishing.

—Numbers Early Learning Kit. 2004. (Early Learning Kits Ser.). (Illus.). 52p. (J). pap. 16.95 (978-1-58845-633-5(1) , Brighter Child) School Specialty Publishing.

Downey, Tika. The History of Zero: Exploring Our Place-Value Number System. 2004. (PowerMath Ser.). (Illus.). 32p. (J). lib. bdg. (978-0-8239-8869-3(4)); lib. bdg. 22.50 (978-0-8239-8982-9(8)) Rosen Publishing Group, Inc., The. (PowerKids Pr.).

Emerson Stonnel, Sharon. Number Systems. 2006. 372p. pap. 35.95 (***978-1-59800-658-2(4)**) Outskirts Press, Inc.

Flora, Sherrill B. Numbers. 1999. (My First Homework Booklets Ser.). 80p. (J). pap. 2.99 (978-1-56822-760-3(4) , IF0310) School Specialty Publishing.

Lappan, Glenda. Bits & Pieces II: Using Rational Numbers. Anderson, Cathy, ed. 1998. 157p. (Orig.). (J). (gr. 6). pap. 18.15 (978-1-57232-617-0(4) , 45812) Seymour, Dale Pubns.

Lundy, Miranda & McNaughton, Phoebe. Sacred Number: The Secret Quality of Quantities. Lundy, Miranda et al, illus. 2005. (Wooden Books). 64p. 10.00 (978-0-8027-1456-5(0)) Walker & Co.

Murphy, Stuart J. Safari Park. 2002. (gr. k-3). lib. bdg. 12.95 (978-0-613-59250-5(6)) Tandem Library Bks.

Number Theory: CA Math Series II. 2004. stu. ed. 6.00 (978-1-932230-71-0(8)) National Ctr. on Education & The Economy.

Numbers. 2004. (J). 12p. bds. 3.99 (978-1-85997-813-9(4)); 24p. 4.99 (978-1-85997-979-2(3)) Byeway Bks.

Numbers. (People's Bible Commentary Ser.). 264p. 14.99 (978-0-7586-0418-7(1)) Concordia Publishing Hse.

Numbers. 2003. (J). per. (978-1-57657-918-3(2)) Paradise Pr., Inc.

Numbers. 2002. 32p. (J). pap. 7.98 incl. audio compact disk (978-0-7525-8694-6(7)) Parragon, Inc.

Numbers. (Rainbow Ryhmes Ser.). (J). 12p. bds. (978-2-7643-0175-3(8)); 8p. bds. (978-2-7643-0184-5(7)) Phidal Publishing, Inc./Editions Phidal, Inc.

Numbers. (Skills for Every Child Ser.). 32p. 5.99 (978-1-57029-455-6(0) , WPH99011, Totline Pubns.); 4.29 (978-0-7647-0382-9(X) , FS30302) Schaffer, Frank Pubns.

Ostby, Kristen. Numbers. 2007. (Jelly Belly Ser.). 10p. (J). (ps-k). bds. 5.99 (978-0-448-44475-8(5) , Grosset & Dunlap) Penguin Group (USA) Inc.

Phidal Publishing Staff, ed. Numbers. (Turn & Learn Ser.). 12p. (J). (978-2-7643-0139-5(1)) Phidal Publishing, Inc./Editions Phidal, Inc.

Scholastic, Inc. Staff. Write-and-Learn Number Practice Pages. 2003. 72p. pap., tchr. ed. 11.95 (978-0-439-45865-8(X) , Teaching Resources) Scholastic, Inc.

School Specialty Publishing. Numbers. 2002. (Classroom Helpers Ser.). 24p. (J). (gr. k up). pap. 3.99 (978-0-7682-0804-7(1) , FS194103) Schaffer, Frank Pubns.

School Zone Publishing Co. Numbers Bingo Game. 2006. (J). (ps-k). 5.99 (***978-1-58947-495-6(3)**) School Zone Publishing Co.

Sterling, Kristin. Ordinal Numbers. 2008. (J). pap. (***978-0-8225-8846-7(3)**) Lerner Publishing Group.

TestSMART Plus Number Theory, Level A/B. 2004. (J). (978-1-57022-482-9(X)) ECS Learning Systems, Inc.

TestSMART Plus Number Theory, Level C/D. 2004. (J). (978-1-57022-483-6(8)) ECS Learning Systems, Inc.

TestSMART Plus Number Theory, Level E/F. 2004. (J). (978-1-57022-484-3(6)) ECS Learning Systems, Inc.

TestSMART Plus Number Theory, Level G. 2004. (J). (978-1-57022-485-0(4)) ECS Learning Systems, Inc.

TestSMART Plus Number Theory, Level H. 2004. (J). (978-1-57022-486-7(2)) ECS Learning Systems, Inc.

TestSMART Plus Number Theory, Level I. 2004. (YA). (978-1-57022-487-4(0)) ECS Learning Systems, Inc.

NUMISMATICS

see also Coins

Armentrout, David & Armentrout, Patricia. State Seals. 2001. (Guides to State Symbols). (Illus.). 48p. (J). (gr. 3-8). lib. bdg. 29.93 (978-1-58952-087-5(4)) Rourke Publishing, LLC.

Volpe, Ron, et al. The Kid's Guide to Collecting Statehood Quarters & Other Cool Coins. 2000. (Illus.). 96p. (J). per. 4.99 (978-1-58238-099-5(6)) Whitman Publishing LLC.

Yeoman, R. S. The Official Blue Book' Handbook of United States CoinsTM: With Premium List. Bressett, Ken, ed. 62nd ed. 2004. (Illus.). 224p. pap. 9.95 (978-0-7948-1787-9(4)) Whitman Publishing LLC.

NUNS

Demi. Mother Teresa. 2005. (Illus.). 40p. (J). (gr. 1-4). 19.95 (978-0-689-86407-0(8) , McElderry, Margaret K.) Simon & Schuster Children's Publishing.

Dils, Tracy. Mother Theresa. 2001. (Women of Achievement Ser.). (Illus.). 112p. (J). pap. 9.95 (978-0-7910-5888-6(3)); (gr. 4-7). 30.00 (978-0-7910-5887-9(5)) Facts On File, Inc. (Chelsea Hse.).

Fitzpatrick, Anne. Mother Teresa. 2005. (Genius Ser.). (Illus.). 48p. (gr. 5-9). 21.95 (978-1-58341-330-2(8) , Creative Education) Creative Co., The.

Glavich, Mary Kathleen. Blessed Teresa of Calcutta: Missionary of Charity. Kiwak, Barbara, tr. Kiwak, Barbara, illus. 2003. (Encounter the Saints Ser.: Vol. 17). 136p. (J). pap. 7.95 (978-0-8198-1160-8(2) , 332-024) Pauline Bks. & Media.

Johnson, Emma. Mother Teresa. 2003. (20th Century History Makers Ser.). (Illus.). 112p. (J). lib. bdg. 32.85 (978-0-7398-6143-1(3)) Raintree.

Middleton, Haydn. Mother Teresa. 2000. (Profiles Ser.). (Illus.). 56p. (J). (gr. 4-6). lib. bdg. 24.22 (978-1-57572-227-6(5)) Heinemann Library.

Mora, Pat. A Library for Juana: The World of Sor Juana Ines. Vidal, Beatriz, illus. 2002. 40p. (J). (gr. k-3). 15.95 (978-0-375-80643-8(1) , Knopf Bks. for Young Readers) Random Hse. Children's Bks.

Morgan, Nina. Mother Teresa: Saint of the Poor. 1998. (Illus.). 48p. (gr. 4-7). pap. 7.95 (978-0-8172-7848-9(6)) Steck-Vaughn.

Nelson, Robin. Mother Teresa: A Life of Caring. 2007. (Pull Ahead Books). (Illus.). 32p. (J). 22.60 (978-0-8225-6384-6(3) , Lerner Pubns.) Lerner Publishing Group.

Ransom, Candice F. Mother Teresa. Verstraete, Elaine, illus. 2000. (On My Own Biographies Ser.). 48p. (J). (gr. 1-3). 23.93 (978-1-57505-441-4(8) , Carolrhoda Bks.) Lerner Publishing Group.

Rice, Tanya. Mother Teresa. 1999. (Life & Times of Ser.). (Illus.). 48p. (YA). (gr. 5 up). 12.95 (978-0-7910-4637-1(0) , Chelsea Hse.) Facts On File, Inc.

Ross, Stewart. The Story of Mother Teresa. 2001. (Illus.). 48p. (J). lib. bdg. 24.25 (978-1-930643-21-5(7)) Chrysalis Education.

Ruth, Amy. Mother Teresa. 1999. (Biography Ser.). (Illus.). 112p. (YA). (gr. 6-12). lib. bdg. 27.93 (978-0-8225-4943-7(3) , Lerner Pubns.) Lerner Publishing Group.

Schaefer, Lola M. Mother Teresa, Vol. 2. 2005. (First Biographies Ser.). 24p. (YA). (gr. k-3). pap. (978-0-7368-3381-3(1) , Pebble Bks.) Capstone Pr., Inc.

Slavicek, Louise Chipley. Mother Teresa: Caring for the World's Poor. 2007. (Modern Peacemakers Ser.). (Illus.). 120p. (YA). (gr. 9 up). 30.00 (***978-0-7910-9433-4(2)** , Chelsea Hse.) Facts On File, Inc.

Stone, Elaine Murray. Mother Teresa: A Life of Love. 1999. (Illus.). 128p. (gr. 5-9). 7.95 (978-0-8091-6651-0(8) , 6651-8) Paulist Pr.

Sullivan, Anne Marie. Mother Theresa: Religious Humanitarian. 2002. (Great Names Ser.). (Illus.). 32p. (J). (gr. 3 up). lib. bdg. (978-1-59084-142-6(5)) Mason Crest Pubns.

Tilton, Rafael. Mother Teresa. 1999. (Importance of Ser.). (Illus.). 120p. (YA). (gr. 7-10). 27.45 (978-1-56006-565-4(6) , Lucent Bks.) Thomson Gale.

Valentine, Emily. Mother Teresa: With a Discussion of Compassion. 2004. (Values in Action Ser.). (J). (978-1-59203-070-5(X)) Learning Challenge, Inc.

Wellman, Sam. Mother Teresa: Missionary of Charity. 1999. (Heroes of the Faith Ser.). 208p. (YA). (gr. 4-7). 14.95 (978-0-7910-5033-0(5) , Chelsea Hse.) Facts On File, Inc.

—Mother Teresa: Missionary of Charity. l.t. ed. 2001. (Thorndike Christian Fiction Ser.). 274p. (J). 24.95 (978-0-7862-3250-5(1)) Thorndike Pr.

Wheeler, Jill C. Mother Teresa. 2002. (Breaking Barriers Ser.). (Illus.). 64p. (J). (gr. 3-8). lib. bdg. 25.65 (978-1-57765-315-8(7) , ABDO & Daughters) ABDO Publishing Co.

Woronoff, Kristen. Mother Teresa: Helper of the Poor. 2002. (Famous Women Juniors Ser.). (Illus.). 32p. (J). (gr. 3-5). 23.70 (978-1-56711-591-8(8) , Blackbirch Pr., Inc.) Thomson Gale.

NUNS—FICTION

Ahern, Dianne. Curse of the Coins: Adventures with Sister Philomena, Special Agent to the Pope. 2007. (J). pap. 11.95 (***978-0-9679437-7-0(9)**) Aunt Dee's Attic, Inc.

Carville, Declan. The Incredible Sister Brigid. Black, Kieron, illus. 29p. pap. 7.95 (978-0-9538222-2-5(2)) Discovery Pubns. GBR. *Dist:* Irish Bks. & Media, Inc.

Currier, Alvin Alexsi. Old Maria: A Grandfather's Tale of Spiritual Warfare Once upon a Time in Old Russia. Glazunova, Nadexda, illus. 2002. 28p. (J). (gr. 2-6). 14.95 (978-0-9723411-0-3(2)) Currier, Alvin Alexsi.

Keffer, Ann. The Seventh Chair. 2007. 76p. (J). per. 8.95 (***978-0-595-45917-9(X)**) iUniverse, Inc.

NUREMBERG TRIAL OF MAJOR GERMAN WAR CRIMINALS, NUREMBERG, GERMANY, 1945-1946

Bard, Mitchell G. Nuremberg Trials. 2001. (gr. 7-12). lib. bdg. 30.35 (978-0-613-73860-6(8)) Tandem Library Bks.

—Nuremburg Trials. 2002. (gr. 7-12). lib. bdg. 28.90 (978-0-613-57374-0(9)) Tandem Library Bks.

Fireside, Harvey. The Nuremberg Nazi War Crimes Trials: A Headline Court Case. 2000. (Headline Court Cases Ser.). (Illus.). 128p. (YA). (gr. 6-12). lib. bdg. 26.60 (978-0-7660-1384-1(7)) Enslow Pubs., Inc.

Just a Kid: A Guard at the Nuremberg Trials. 2004. (J). per. 9.95 (978-0-9744803-3-6(9)) PublishingWorks.

NUREYEV, RUDOLF, 1939-1993

Fandel, Jennifer. Rudolf Nureyev. 2005. (Extraordinary Artists Ser.). (Illus.). 48p. (J). (gr. 5-9). 21.95 (978-1-58341-380-7(4) , Creative Education) Creative Co., The.

NURSERY RHYMES

Ada, Alma Flor. Pio Peep! Escriva, Vivi, illus. 2003. (ENG & SPA.). 64p. (J). (ps-1). lib. bdg. 16.89 (978-0-688-16020-3(4)) HarperCollins Pubs.

—Pio Peep! Traditional Spanish Nursery Rhymes. Escriva, Vivi, illus. 2003. (ENG & SPA.). 64p. (J). (ps-1). 14.99 (978-0-688-16019-7(0)) HarperCollins Pubs.

Ada, Alma Flor, et al. Mama Goose: A Latino Nursery Treasury. Suarez, Maribel, illus. 2005. 128p. (ps-k). 19.99 (978-0-7868-1953-9(7)) Hyperion Bks. for Children.

Adams, Pam. House That Jack Built. 1999. (Books with Holes Ser.). (Illus.). 16p. (J). (ps-3). 19.99 (978-0-85953-638-7(6)) Child's Play-International.

—Old MacDonald. 1999. (Books with Holes Ser.). (Illus.). 16p. (J). (ps-3). 19.99 (978-0-85953-637-0(8)) Child's Play-International.

Adams, Pam, illus. The Farmer in the Dell. 2001. 16p. (J). 19.99 (978-0-85953-894-7(X)) Child's Play-International.

—Old Macdonald. 2005. (J). bds. 12.99 (978-0-85953-317-1(4)) Child's Play-International.

Anderson, Sara, illus. Hey Diddle Diddle: And Other Nursery Rhyme Favorites. 2003. (Felt Read-and-Play Ser.). 18p. (J). bds. 16.95 (978-1-929766-21-5(1)) Handprint Bks.

Arenson, Roberta. One, Two, Skip a Few! First Number Rhymes. Arenson, Roberta, illus. 2005. (Illus.). 32p. (J). pap. 6.99 (978-1-84148-130-2(0)) Barefoot Bks., Inc.

—One, Two, Skip a Few! First Number Rhymes. 1998. (Illus.). 32p. (J). (ps-2). 15.95 (978-1-901223-99-6(X)) Barefoot Bks., Inc.

—One, Two, Skip a Few! First Number Rhymes. Arenson, Roberta, illus. 2000. (Illus.). (ps-2). lib. bdg. 15.30 (978-0-613-31555-5(3)) Tandem Library Bks.

Atkins, Alison, illus. Humpty Dumpty & Friends. 2005. 10p. bds. (978-1-84510-767-3(5)) Top That! Publishing PLC.

—Incy Wincy Spider & Friends. 2005. 10p. bds. (978-1-84510-768-0(3)) Top That! Publishing PLC.

Atkinson, Ruth & Atkinson, Brett. Rhyme Templates. Atkinson, Ruth & Atkinson, Brett, illus. (Illus.). (J). (gr. k-2). pap. (978-1-875739-74-5(2)) Wizard Bks.

—Traditional Rhyme Templates. Atkinson, Ruth & Atkinson, Brett, illus. (Illus.). (J). (gr. k-2). pap. (978-1-875739-94-3(7)) Wizard Bks.

Audio & Kidzup Productions Staff. Animal Nursery Rhyme Songbook. 2001. (Kidzup Ser.). (J). pap. 12.99 incl. audio (978-1-894281-78-2(0)) Kidzup Entertainment CAN. *Dist:* Penton Overseas, Inc.

Aye, Nila. Little Yellow Book of Nursery Rhymes. 1998. (Illus.). 32p. (J). (ps-1). pap. 5.95 (978-0-531-30062-6(5) , Orchard Bks.) Scholastic, Inc.

—Orchard's Little Blue Book of Nursery Rhymes. 1998. (Illus.). 32p. (J). (ps-1). pap. 5.95 (978-0-531-30063-3(3) , Orchard Bks.) Scholastic, Inc.

—Orchard's Little Red Book of Nursery Rhymes. 1998. (Illus.). 32p. (J). (ps-1). pap. 5.95 (978-0-531-30061-9(7) , Orchard Bks.) Scholastic, Inc.

Baa Baa, Black Sheep! 2005. (Sign & Signalong Ser.). (Illus.). 8p. (J). (ps). per. 4.99 (978-1-904550-41-9(X)) Child's Play-International.

Baa Baa Black Sheep: Sing-Along Rhymes. 2002. (My First Mother Goose Ser.). (Illus.). 48p. (J). (ps-k). 11.95 incl. audio compact disk (978-1-56899-928-9(3) , MD1158) Soundprints.

Baa Baa Black Sheep: Sing-Along Rhymes, Including Toy. 2002. (My First Mother Goose Ser.). (Illus.). 48p. (J). (ps-k). 15.95 incl. audio compact disk (978-1-56899-930-2(5) , MPD1158) Soundprints.

Baker, Keith. Big Fat Hen. 2002. (Illus.). (J). 13.19 (978-0-7587-2095-5(5)) Book Wholesalers, Inc.

—Big Fat Hen. 1999. (Illus.). 32p. (J). pap. 6.00 (978-0-15-201951-8(0) , Voyager Bks./Libros Viajeros) Harcourt Children's Bks.

—Big Fat Hen. 1999. (gr. k-3). lib. bdg. 14.15 (978-0-613-15736-0(2)) Tandem Library Bks.

—Mama Clo-clo! Ada, Alma Flor & Campoy, F. Isabel, trs. 2007. (Illus.). 30p. (J). bds. 6.95 (978-0-15-205890-6(7) , Voyager Bks./Libros Viajeros) Harcourt Children's Bks.

Baker, Keith. Potato Joe. 2008. (J). (***978-0-15-206230-9(0)**) Harcourt Trade Pubs.

Barritt, Margaret. Hickory Dickory Dock. 2006. (Illus.). 7p. (J). bds. 7.95 (978-1-59354-153-8(8)) Handprint Bks.

Baum, F. E. & Baum, L. Frank. Mother Goose in Prose. Parrish, Maxfield, illus. unabr. ed. 2002. 288p. (J). (gr. 4-7). reprint ed. pap. 9.95 (978-0-486-42086-8(8)) Dover Pubns., Inc.

Beall, Pamela Conn & Nipp, Susan Hagen. Wee Sing Nursery Rhymes & Lullabies. 2005. (Wee Sing Ser.). 64p. (J). (ps-1). 9.99 (978-0-8431-1360-0(X) , Price Stern Sloan) Penguin Group (USA) Inc.

Beall, Pamela Conn & Nipp, Susan Hagen. Wee Sing Nursery Rhymes & Lullabies Gift Set. 2007. (Wee Sing Ser.). 64p. (J). (ps). 17.99 (***978-0-8431-2703-4(1)** , Price Stern Sloan) Penguin Group (USA) Inc.

Beer, Barbara Vagnozzi, illus. Sleepytime: Bedtime Nursery Rhymes. 2006. (Mother Goose Rhymes Ser.). 32p. (J). (ps-2). 25.26 (***978-1-4048-2345-7(X)** , 1265750) Picture Window Bks.

Berger, Ellie. Barney's I Love Nursery Rhymes! Amaral, Gayla, ed. McKee, Darren, illus. 2001. (Barney Ser.). 64p. (J). (ps-3). 1.99 (978-1-58668-132-6(X)) Scholastic, Inc.

Big Box of Board Books: Humpty Dumpty; Hey Diddle Diddle; Itsy Bitsy Spider & This Little Piggy, 4 bks., Set. 2002. (Nursery Rhymes Ser.). (Illus.). (J). bds. (978-1-59069-259-2(4) , MZ1001) Studio Mouse LLC.

Bittinger, Gayle. Under the Sea. 1999. (Rhyme & Reason Workbook Ser.). (Illus.). 32p. (J). (ps-k). pap. 3.95 (978-1-57029-259-0(0) , WPH 01111, Totline Pubns.) Schaffer, Frank Pubns.

Bolton, Bill & Smith, Jane, illus. Pat-a-Cake. 2002. (Nursery Rhymes Ser.). 10p. (J). bds. (978-1-59069-279-0(9) , MB1002) Studio Mouse LLC.

Borreguita Negra: Poems, Rhymes, & Songs Listening Packs. 2003. 34.50 (978-0-673-58629-2(4)) Celebration Pr.

Boynton, Sandra. Belly Button Book! 2005. (Illus.). 24p. (J). bds. 6.95 (978-0-7611-3799-3(8) , 13799) Workman Publishing Co., Inc.

Bradley, G. A. Hansel & Gretel. 2nd rev. ed. 1998. (Illus.). 36p. (J). (gr. 2-4). 29.95 (978-1-886123-09-0(8)) Geyer's Garten Cards & Bks.

Brighter Vision Publishing Staff. About Nursery Rhymes. 1999. (Illus.). 20p. (J). (ps). pap. 3.99 (978-1-55254-054-1(5)) Brighter Vision Pubns.

—About Nursery Rhymes Activity Book. 2000. (My Discovery Bks.). (Illus.). 20p. (J). (ps). pap. 2.95 (978-1-55254-206-4(8)) Brighter Vision Pubns.

Brilla, Brilla Estrellita: Poems, Rhymes & Songs Listening Packs. 2003. 34.50 (978-0-673-58608-7(1)) Celebration Pr.

Brilliant Beginnings, LLC Staff. Friendly Faces: Baby's Rhyming Photo Book. 1999. (Illus.). (J). (978-0-9665815-4-6(7)) Brilliant Beginnings, LLC.

Brown, Richard & Ruttle, Kate. Hickory, Dickory, Dock ELT Edition. Beardshaw, Rosalind, illus. 2001. (Cambridge Storybooks Ser.). 8p. pap. 3.00 (978-0-521-00707-8(0)) Cambridge Univ. Pr.

—Incy Wincy Spider ELT Edition. Chatterton, Martin, illus. 2001. (Cambridge Storybooks Ser.). 8p. pap. 3.00 (978-0-521-00702-3(X)) Cambridge Univ. Pr.

Browne, Anthony, illus. Anthony Browne Presents the Animal Fair: A Spectacular Pop-up. 2004. 12p. (J). (gr. k-4). reprint ed. 15.00 (978-0-7567-8005-0(5)) DIANE Publishing Co.

Brunelle, Lynn. Nursery Rhymes: Music & Dance. Herbert, Jennifer, illus. 1999. 20p. (J). 5.95 (978-1-892374-25-7(0)) Weldon Owen, Inc.

Bruriah, D. Around the Yamim Tovim. 14p. 13.99 (978-1-58330-620-8(X)) Feldheim Pubs.

—Let's Welcome Shabbos. 24p. 12.99 (978-1-58330-591-1(2)) Feldheim Pubs.

Burke, Dianne O'Quinn, illus. Itsy-Bitsy Spider. 1999. (Rhyme-Along Board Bks.). 12p. (J). (gr. k-1). reprint ed. 4.95 (978-1-56565-092-3(1) , 00921W, Roxbury Park) Lowell Hse.

Busby, Ailie, illus. Time for a Rhyme. 1999. 256p. (J). (gr. k-6). (978-1-85881-695-1(5)) Orion Children's Bks.

Bush, Timothy, illus. Teddy Bear, Teddy Bear: A Traditional Rhyme. 2005. 32p. (J). 14.99 (978-0-06-057835-0(1)); lib. bdg. 15.89 (978-0-06-057836-7(X)) HarperCollins Pubs.

Cabrera, Jane. Old Mother Hubbard. 2008. (J). (*978-0-8234-2132-9(5)) Holiday Hse., Inc.

Cabrera, Jane & Martin, Sarah Catherine. Old Mother Hubbard. Cabrera, Jane, illus. 2001. (Illus.). 32p. (J). (gr. k-3). 15.95 (978-0-8234-1659-2(3)) Holiday Hse., Inc.

Caldecott, Randolph. The Farmer's Boy. 2006. (Illus.). pap. (*978-1-4065-1223-6(0)) Dodo Pr.

Calmenson, Stephanie. Kindergarten Kids: Riddles, Rebuses, Wiggles, Giggles, & More! Sweet, Melissa, illus. 2005. 32p. (J). (ps-1). 16.99 (978-0-06-000713-3(3)); lib. bdg. 16.89 (978-0-06-000714-0(1)) HarperCollins Pubs.

Campoy, F. Isabel & Ada, Alma Flor. Mami Goose - A Latino Nursery Treasury. Suarez, Maribel, illus. 2006. 128p. (ps-k). pap. 9.99 (978-0-7868-5240-6(2)) Hyperion Pr.

Carlstrom, Nancy White. It's about Time, Jesse Bear: And Other Rhymes. 1998. (J). (978-0-606-13529-0(4)) Tandem Library Bks.

Carpenter, Stephen, illus. Mary Had a Little Jam, & Other Silly Rhymes. 2004. 32p. (J). (978-0-88166-470-6(7)) Meadowbrook Pr.

Carteles de Rimas y Canciones de Fonética (Phonics Songs & Rhymes Flip Chart) 2000. (SPA.). (gr. 1 up). suppl. ed. 116.50 (978-0-673-60598-6(1)) Addison-Wesley Educational Pubs., Inc.

Carter, David A., illus. Old MacDonald Had a Farm. 2001. 14p. (J). (ps-1). pap. 14.95 (978-0-439-26468-6(5) , Cartwheel Bks.) Scholastic, Inc.

Cat Rhymes. 1999. (Star Reading Program Ser.). (J). (ps-2). (978-0-8136-3379-4(6)) Modern Curriculum Pr.

Chamberlain, Margaret, illus. Playtime Rhymes. (Happytime Ser.: No. S871-8). 24p. (J). (ps). pap. 1.25 (978-0-7214-9552-1(4) , Dutton Juvenile) Penguin Group (USA) Inc.

Chapman, Jane. Sing a Song of Sixpence: A Pocketful of Nursery Rhymes & Tales. Chapman, Jane, illus. 2004. (Illus.). 64p. (J). (ps-1). 15.99 (978-0-7636-2545-0(0)) Candlewick Pr.

Charlip, Remy. Sleepytime Rhyme. Charlip, Remy, illus. 1999. (Illus.). 32p. (J). (ps). 17.99 (978-0-688-16271-9(1)); 15.89 (978-0-688-16272-6(X)) HarperCollins Pubs.

Child's Treasury of Nursery Rhymes. 2001. 256p. (J). 25.95 (978-0-7525-4180-8(3)) Parragon, Inc.

Chorao, Kay. The Baby's Bedtime Book. Chorao, Kay, illus. ed. 2004. (Illus.). 64p. (J). (ps). 16.99 (978-0-525-47327-5(0) , Dutton Juvenile) Penguin Group (USA) Inc.

—The Baby's Lap Book. Chorao, Kay, illus. ed. 2004. (Illus.). 64p. (J). (ps). 16.99 (978-0-525-47330-5(0) , Dutton Juvenile) Penguin Group (USA) Inc.

—Baby's Lap Book: A Collection of Classic Nursery Rhymes. 1998. (J). (978-0-606-13158-2(2)) Tandem Library Bks.

Christelow, Eileen. Five Little Monkeys Jumping on the Bed. 2006. 15p. (J). (gr. k-ps). bds. 12.99 (978-0-618-65109-2(8) , Clarion Bks.) Houghton Mifflin Co. Trade & Reference Div.

Christensen, James C. Rhymes & Reasons: An Annotated Collection of Mother Goose Rhymes. Christensen, James C., illus. 2003. (Illus.). 56p. (J). (ps-3). tchr. ed. 19.95 (978-0-86713-040-9(7) , 88082) Greenwich Workshop Pr.

Chronicle Books LLC Staff. Nick Jr. Nursery Rhyme Time: A Touch-and-See Activity Book. (J). 15.95 (978-0-8118-4726-1(8)) Chronicle Bks. LLC.

Church, Caroline Jayne. Humpty Dumpty's Favorite Nursery Rhymes. 1999. (Lamaze Ser.). (Illus.). 18p. (J). (ps). 10.99 (978-1-56799-897-9(6) , Friedman-Fairfax) Friedman, Michael Publishing Group, Inc.

Church, Ellen B. Great Big Book of Classroom Songs, Rhymes & Cheers: 200 Easy, Playful Language Experiences That Build Literacy & Community in Your Classroom. 2000. (Illus.). 248p. pap. 21.95 (978-0-590-37607-5(1)) Scholastic, Inc.

Cisneros, Jose, illus. El Ratoncito Pequno. 2003. Tr. of Little Mouse. (ENG & SPA.). 32p. (J). (gr. 1-5). 15.95 (978-0-938317-56-2(3)) Cinco Puntos Pr.

Cole, Joanna & Calmenson, Stephanie, eds. Tons of Fun: Over 300 Action Rhymes, Old & New Riddles, Tongue Twisters, & Play Rhymes. Tiegren, Alan, illus. 2004. 229p. (J). (gr. k-4). reprint ed. pap. 15.00 (978-0-7567-8222-1(8)) DIANE Publishing Co.

Collins, Heather, illus. Hey Diddle, Diddle. 2004. (Traditional Nursery Rhyme Board Bks.). 12p. (J). (ps-k). (978-1-55337-078-9(3)) Kids Can Pr., Ltd.

—Jack & Jill. 2004. (Traditional Nursery Rhyme Board Bks.). 12p. (J). (ps-k). (978-1-55337-075-8(9)) Kids Can Pr., Ltd.

—Little Miss Muffet. 2004. (Traditional Nursery Rhyme Board Bks.). 12p. (J). (ps-k). (978-1-55337-076-5(7)) Kids Can Pr., Ltd.

—Pat-a-Cake. 2004. (Traditional Nursery Rhyme Board Bks.). 12p. (J). (ps-k). (978-1-55337-077-2(5)) Kids Can Pr., Ltd.

—Rock-a-Bye Baby. 2004. (Traditional Nursery Rhyme Board Bks.). 12p. (J). (ps-k). (978-1-55074-572-6(7)) Kids Can Pr., Ltd.

—Row, Row, Row Your Boat. 2004. (Traditional Nursery Rhyme Board Bks.). 12p. (J). (ps-k). (978-1-55074-570-2(0)) Kids Can Pr., Ltd.

—Wee Willie Winkie. 2004. (Traditional Nursery Rhyme Board Bks.). 12p. (J). (ps-k). (978-1-55074-568-9(9)) Kids Can Pr., Ltd.

Combe, Charlotte & Smith, Jane, illus. Here We Go Round the Mulberry Bush. 2002. (Nursery Rhymes Ser.). 10p. (J). bds. (978-1-59069-283-7(7) , MB1006) Studio Mouse LLC.

—Jack Be Nimble. 2002. (Nursery Rhymes Ser.). 10p. (J). bds. (978-1-59069-278-3(0) , MB1001) Studio Mouse LLC.

Country Tot Song Book. 2001. (Kidzup Ser.). (J). pap. 12.99 incl. audio (978-1-894281-81-2(0)) Kidzup Entertainment CAN. *Dist:* Penton Overseas, Inc.

Courage Books Staff. Mother Goose: The Children's Classic Edition. 2002. (Courage Children's Ser.). (Illus.). 56p. (J). 9.98 (978-0-7624-0015-7(3) , Courage Bks.) Running Pr. Bk. Pubs.

Crane, Walter, et al, illus. Mother Goose Nursery Rhymes. 2007. 324p. (ps-k). pap. 19.95 (*978-1-4290-9005-6(7)) Applewood Bks.

Crews, Nina. The Neighborhood Mother Goose. Crews, Nina, illus. 2004. (Illus.). 64p. (J). 16.99 (978-0-06-051573-7(2)); lib. bdg. 16.89 (978-0-06-051574-4(0)) HarperCollins Pubs.

Cricket Magazine Group. Favorite Mother Goose. 2007. (Illus.). 20p. (J). bds. 7.95 (978-0-8126-7935-9(0)) Cricket Bks.

Currey, Anna, illus. Hush-a-Bye, Baby: And Other Nursery Rhymes. 2003. 16p. (J). bds. 8.99 (978-0-333-78086-2(8)) Macmillan Publishers Ltd. GBR. *Dist:* Trafalgar Square Publishing.

—Pat-a-Cake: And Other Nursery Rhymes. 2003. 16p. (J). bds. 6.95 (978-0-333-78083-1(3)) Macmillan Publishers Ltd. GBR. *Dist:* Trafalgar Square Publishing.

—Ring-a-Ring O' Roses: And Other Nursery Rhymes. 2003. 14p. (J). bds. 6.95 (978-0-333-78084-8(1)) Macmillan Publishers Ltd. GBR. *Dist:* Trafalgar Square Publishing.

Cushman, Doug & Banta, Susan, illus. Rhyme Time Learning, 4 bks. Incl. ABC : Alphabet Rhyme. Mitter, Matt. lib. bdg. 20.67 (978-0-8368-4095-7(X)); Once upon a Rhyme : Story Rhymes. Packard, Mary & Mitter, Matt. lib. bdg. 20.67 (978-0-8368-4096-4(8)); Same & Different : Comparison Rhymes. Packard, Mary & Mitier, Matt. lib. bdg. 20.67 (978-0-8368-4097-1(6)); 1, 2, 3 : Counting Rymes. Packard, Mary & Mitter, Matt. lib. bdg. 20.67 (978-0-8368-4094-0(1)); 16p. (J). (gr. 1 up). (Illus.). 2004. Set lib. bdg. 82.68 (978-0-8368-4093-3(3)) Stevens, Gareth Inc.

Dalamatian Press Staff. Nursery Rhymes for Little Ones. 2005. (Illus.). 10p. (J). bds. 8.99 (978-1-4037-1380-3(4)) Dalmatian Pr.

Dale, Penny, illus. Ten in the Bed. 2001. 12p. (J). (gr. k-ps). bds. 6.99 (978-0-7636-1575-8(7)) Candlewick Pr.

Dalmatian Press Staff. Mother Goose. 2002. (Illus.). 24p. (J). (gr. k-5). pap. 2.99 (978-1-57759-476-5(2)) Dalmatian Pr.

Dalmatian Press Staff, creator. Mother Goose. 2003. (Talking Book Ser.). (Illus.). 12p. (J). 16.99 (978-0-7948-1337-6(2)) Dalmatian Pr.

Dalmatian Press Staff, ed. Mother Goose: Board Book with Plush Toy. 2007. 11p. bds. 12.99 (*978-1-4037-2550-9(0)) Dalmatian Pr.

Dana, Katharine Floyd, et al. Alla en la Pradera: Un Poema para Contar. Vojtech, Anna, illus. 2003. (SPA.). 32p. (J). pap. 6.95 (978-0-7358-1866-8(5)) North-South Bks., Inc.

David C. Cook. Nursery Rhymes. 2003. (My Jesus Pocket Bks.). (Illus.). 32p. (J). (gr. 5-3). pap., pap. 8.90 (978-1-55513-102-9(6) , 1555131026) Cook, David C. Publishing Co.

Davidson, Susanna. Baby & Toddler Treasury. Ahmed, Hannah, illus. 2007. 96p. (J). 19.99 (978-0-7945-1150-0(3) , Usborne) EDC Publishing.

—Nursery Rhyme Treasury. Kolanovic, Dubravka, illus. 2006. 96p. (J). 19.99 (978-0-7945-1281-1(X) , Usborne) EDC Publishing.

Davies, Caroline, tr. & illus. Hey, Diddle Diddle. Davies, Caroline, illus. 2004. (Baby's First Nursery Rhymes Ser.). 12p. (J). bds. 3.99 (978-1-85854-622-3(2)) Brimax Books Ltd. GBR. *Dist:* Byeway Bks.

—Humpty Dumpty. Davies, Caroline, illus. 2004. (Baby's First Nursery Rhymes Ser.). 12p. (J). bds. 3.99 (978-1-85854-610-0(9)) Brimax Books Ltd. GBR. *Dist:* Byeway Bks.

—Little Miss Muffet. Davies, Caroline, illus. 2004. (Baby's First Nursery Rhymes Ser.). 12p. (J). bds. 3.99 (978-1-85854-623-0(0)) Brimax Books Ltd. GBR. *Dist:* Byeway Bks.

—Pat-A-Cake. Davies, Caroline, illus. 2004. (Baby's First Nursery Rhymes Ser.). 12p. (J). bds. 3.99 (978-1-85854-611-7(7)) Brimax Books Ltd. GBR. *Dist:* Byeway Bks.

Davies, Gill. My Nursery Rhyme Pop-up Book. Guile, Gill, illus. 2005. 20p. (J). (gr. k-4). reprint ed. 20.00 (978-0-7567-8704-2(1)) DIANE Publishing Co.

Davis, David. Texas Mother Goose. Ward, Sue Marshall, illus. 2006. 32p. (J). 16.95 (978-1-58980-369-5(8)) Pelican Publishing Co., Inc.

De La Cour, Gary, illus. Twinkle Twinkle & Other Sleepy-Time Rhymes. 2005. 36p. (J). 12.95 incl. cd-rom (978-1-59249-464-4(1) , 1D016) Soundprints.

de Paola, Tomie. Hey Diddle Diddle & Other Mother Goose Rhymes. de Paola, Tomie, illus. 1998. (Illus.). 32p. (J). (ps-k). pap. 6.99 (978-0-698-11640-5(2) , Putnam Juvenile) Penguin Group (USA) Inc.

—Hey Diddle Diddle & Other Mother Goose Rhymes. 1998. (ps-2). lib. bdg. 15.30 (978-0-613-86958-4(3)) Tandem Library Bks.

—Tomie de Paola's Mother Goose Favorites. 2000. (Reading Railroad Bks.). (Illus.). 32p. (J). (ps-3). pap. 3.99 (978-0-448-42155-1(0) , Grosset & Dunlap) Penguin Group (USA) Inc.

—Tomie de Paola's Mother Goose Favorites. 2000. (ps-2). lib. bdg. 11.25 (978-0-613-27281-0(1)) Tandem Library Bks.

—Tomie's Baa, Baa, Black Sheep & Other Rhymes. 2004. (Illus.). 32p. (J). (ps-1). bds. 7.99 (978-0-399-24326-4(7) , Putnam Juvenile) Penguin Group (USA) Inc.

Delacre, Lulu, illus. & compiled by. Arrorro Mi Nino: Latino Lullabies & Gentle Games. Delacre, Lulu, compiled by. 2004. (ENG & SPA.). 32p. (J). 16.95 (978-1-58430-159-2(7)) Lee & Low Bks., Inc.

Denton, Kady MacDonald. A Child's Treasury of Nursery Rhymes. ed. 2004. (J). (ps-2). spiral bd. (978-0-616-01640-4(9)) Canadian National Institute for the Blind/Institut National Canadien pour les Aveugles.

—A Child's Treasury of Nursery Rhymes. 2004. (Illus.). 96p. (J). (gr. k-ps). 12.95 (978-0-7534-5710-8(5) , Kingfisher) Houghton Mifflin Co. Trade & Reference Div.

Denton, Kady MacDonald, illus. A Child's Treasury of Nursery Rhymes. 2004. (J). (gr. k-ps). audio compact disk 12.95 (978-0-618-49306-7(9) , Kingfisher) Houghton Mifflin Co. Trade & Reference Div.

DeSantis, Susan & Holm, Sharon, illus. Nursery Rhymes, 2 Packs. 2006. (Read & Sing along Board Books with CDs Ser.). 36p. (J). bds. 14.98 (978-0-7696-4964-1(5)) School Specialty Publishing.

Dillon, Leo & Dillon, Diane. Mother Goose Numbers on the Loose. 2007. (Illus.). 56p. (J). (ps-2). 17.00 (978-0-15-205676-6(9)) Harcourt Trade Pubs.

Disney Staff. Winnie the Pooh's Play-Along Rhymes. 1999. (Learn & Grow Ser.). (Illus.). 16p. (J). (ps). bds. 7.99 (978-0-7364-0187-6(3) , RH/Disney) Random Hse. Children's Bks.

DK Publishing. Old MacDonald Had A Farm: Sound Book. 2007. 10p. (J). (ps-5). bds. 14.99 (*978-0-7566-3446-9(6)) Dorling Kindersley Publishing, Inc.

—Twinkle Little Star. 2008. 16p. (J). (ps-k). 4.99 (*978-0-7566-3868-9(2)) Dorling Kindersley Publishing, Inc.

DK Publishing Staff. Talking Baby. 2007. (Illus.). 16p. (J). 9.99 (978-0-7566-2598-6(X)) Dorling Kindersley Publishing, Inc.

Dodd, Lynley. Hairy Maclary's Bone. 2001. (ps-2). lib. bdg. 14.10 (978-0-613-57835-6(X)) Tandem Library Bks.

Dorling Kindersley Publishing Staff. Humpty Dumpty. 2004. (Baby Games Ser.). 16p. (J). bds. 5.99 (978-0-7566-0258-1(0)) Dorling Kindersley Publishing, Inc.

—Things That Go. 2007. (Touch & Feel Ser.). 16p. (J). 9.99 (978-0-7566-1970-1(X)) Dorling Kindersley Publishing, Inc.

Dorling Kindersley Publishing Staff, ed. Hush Little Baby, Don't Say a Word. 2004. (Baby Fun Ser.). 12p. (J). pap. 5.99 (978-0-7566-0763-0(9)) Dorling Kindersley Publishing, Inc.

Dot-to-Dots, Mazes & More: Nursery Rhymes. (Homework Booklets Ser.). 80p. (gr. k-1). 2.99 (978-0-7424-0256-0(8) , IF0412) School Specialty Publishing.

Douglas, Vincent & McCafferty, Catherine. Mother Goose Rhymes. Hullinger, C. D., illus. 2002. (Brighter Child Keepsake Stories Ser.). 32p. (J). (ps-3). pap. 3.99 (978-1-57768-369-8(2) , Brighter Child) School Specialty Publishing.

Douglas, Vincent & School Specialty Publishing Staff. My Block Book Schoolhouse of Nursery Rhymes, 4 bks. 2003. (My Block Book Schoolhouse Collection). (Illus.). 88p. (J). (ps up). bds. 12.95 (978-1-58845-504-8(1)) School Specialty Publishing.

Dowell, Ruth I. Move over, Mother Goose! Finger Plays, Action Verses & Funny Rhymes. Charner, Kathleen, ed. Scott, Concetta C., illus. 2004. 126p. (Orig.). (ps-1). pap. 12.95 (978-0-87659-113-0(6) , 10006) Gryphon Hse., Inc.

Downes, Belinda. Baby Days: A Quilt of Rhymes & Pictures. Downes, Belinda, illus. 2006. (Illus.). 32p. (J). (gr. k-ps). 14.99 (978-0-7636-2786-7(0)) Candlewick Pr.

Dunn, Opal. Un, Deux, Trois. Aggs, Patrice, illus. 2006. (FRE.). 24p. (J). pap. 9.95 (978-1-84507-623-8(0)) Lincoln, Frances Ltd. GBR. *Dist:* Perseus Distribution.

Dyer, Jane. A Box of Animal Crackers, 3 bks., Set. Dyer, Jane, illus. 2002. (Illus.). 8p. (J). (ps-k). bds. 12.95 (978-0-316-19687-1(8)) Little, Brown Bks. for Young Readers.

Eagle, Kin. Hey, Diddle Diddle. 1998. (Nursery Rhyme Ser.). (Illus.). 32p. (J). (ps-2). pap. 6.95 (978-1-58089-007-6(5)) Charlesbridge Publishing, Inc.

—Hey, Diddle Diddle. 1999. (Extended Nursery Rhymes Ser.). (Illus.). 32p. (J). (ps up). lib. bdg. 23.33 (978-0-8368-2485-8(7)) Stevens, Gareth Inc.

—Humpty Dumpty. ed. 2004. (Illus.). (J). (gr. 1 up). spiral bd., bds. (978-0-616-14612-5(4)) Canadian National Institute for the Blind/Institut National Canadien pour les Aveugles.

—Rub a Dub Dub. Gilbert, Rob, illus. 2004. 32p. (J). (ps-2). pap. 6.95 (978-1-58089-075-5(X)) Charlesbridge Publishing, Inc.

Eagle, Kin & Gilbert, Rob. Humpty Dumpty. 2004. (Illus.). 26p. (J). bds. 6.95 (978-1-58089-079-3(2)) Charlesbridge Publishing, Inc.

East, Jacqueline, illus. Hickory Dickory Dock & Other Silly-Time Rhymes. 2005. 36p. (J). 12.95 incl. cd-rom (978-1-59249-463-7(3) , 1D019) Soundprints.

Edwards. Neat Line. 2000. mass mkt. 5.95 (978-0-06-443876-6(7)) HarperCollins Pubs.

Eggleton, Jill. Should This Have Happened? Individual Title Six-Packs. Hoit, Richard, illus. (Sails Literacy Ser.). 20p. (gr. 4 up). 27.00 (978-0-7578-0794-7(1)) Rigby Education.

Elkins, Stephen. Nursery Rhymes for Babies. Colton, Ellie, illus. 2006. (Jesus Loves Me Ser.). 32p. (J). 6.99 (978-1-4169-1161-6(8) , Little Simon Inspirations) Simon & Schuster Children's Publishing.

Elliott, James W. Mother Goose's Nursery Rhymes & Nursery Songs. 2001. 110p. (YA). reprint ed. 88.00 (978-0-7222-6146-0(2)) Library Reprints, Inc.

Ember, Kathi, illus. Old MacDonald Had a Farm. 2001. (Little Golden Bks.). 24p. (J). (gr. k-k). 2.99 (978-0-307-98806-5(6) , 98806, Golden Bks.) Random Hse. Children's Bks.

Emoe, Nicola, illus. A Child's Treasury of Irish Rhymes. 2000. 48p. (J). (ps-3). 15.95 (978-1-902283-18-0(X)) Barefoot Bks., Inc.

—A Treasury of Irish Rhymes. 2000. 48p. (J). 6.99 (978-1-84148-399-3(0)) Barefoot Bks., Inc.

Engelbreit, Mary. Mary Engelbreit's Funny Mother Goose. Engelbreit, Mary, illus. 2008. 16p. (J). 6.99 (*978-0-06-008129-4(5) , Harper Festival) HarperCollins Pubs.

—Mary Engelbreit's Merry Mother Goose. Engelbreit, Mary, illus. 2008. 16p. (J). 6.99 (*978-0-06-008128-7(7) , Harper Festival) HarperCollins Pubs.

—Mary Engelbreit's Mother Goose Book & CD. Engelbreit, Mary, illus. 2008. 128p. (J). 24.99 (*978-0-06-143153-1(2)) HarperCollins Pubs.

Esparz, Esther LaMadrid. Rocking Horse Rhymes. 3rd ed. 2003. Tr. of Rimas Del Caballo Mecedor, Edicion 3. (SPA & ENG.). (J). lib. bdg. 24.95 (978-1-879817-32-6(2)) Star Light Pr.

Esparza, Thomas, Jr., prod. Esther's Playhouse, Disk G. 2004. (Illus.). (J). cd-rom (978-1-879817-48-7(9) , Children) Star Light Pr.

Evans, Mari. Singing Black: Alternative Nursery Rhymes for Children. 2nd ed. 1998. (Illus.). 32p. (J). (ps-2). pap. 4.95 (978-0-940975-80-4(7) , Sankofa Bks.) Just Us Bks., Inc.

Evans, Michael. Over in the Meadow. 2002. (Illus.). 16p. (J). 19.99 (978-0-85953-126-9(0)) Child's Play-International.

Evans, Michael, illus. Over in the Meadow. 2002. 16p. (J). 6.99 (978-0-85953-949-4(0)); bds. 5.99 (978-0-85953-143-6(0)) Child's Play-International.

Ewing, Susan. Ten Rowdy Ravens. Zerbetz, Evon, illus. 2005. 32p. (J). (ps-1). 15.95 (978-0-88240-606-0(X) , Alaska Northwest Bks.) Graphic Arts Ctr. Publishing Co.

Extended Nursery Rhymes, 12 bks. Incl. Hey, Diddle Diddle. Eagle, Kin. 1999. lib. bdg. 23.33 (978-0-8368-2485-8(7)); How Much Is That Doggie in the Window? Merrill, Bob. 1999. lib. bdg. 23.33 (978-0-8368-2486-5(5)); Humpty Dumpty. Eagle, Kin. Gilbert, Rob, illus. 2000. lib. bdg. 23.33 (978-0-8368-2667-8(1)); I'm a Little Teapot. Trapani, Iza. 1999. lib. bdg. 22.60 (978-0-8368-2487-2(3)); It's Raining, It's Pouring. Eagle, Kin. Gilbert, Rob, illus. 1996. lib. bdg. 23.33 (978 0 8368-1551-1(3)); Itsy Bitsy Spider. Trapani, Iza. Trapani, Iza, illus. 1996. lib. bdg. 23.33 (978-0-8368-1550-4(5)); Mary Had a Little Lamb. Trapani, Iza. 1999. lib. bdg. 23.33 (978-0-8368-2488-9(1)); Oh Where, Oh Where Has My Little Dog Gone? Trapani, Iza. Trapani, Iza, illus. 1996. lib. bdg. 23.33 (978-0-8368-1553-5(X)); Row Row Row Your Boat. Trapani, Iza. Trapani, Iza, illus. 2000. lib. bdg. 23.33 (978-0-8368-2668-5(X)); Rub a Dub Dub. Eagle, Kin. Gilbert, Rob, illus. 2000. lib. bdg. 23.33 (978-0-8368-2669-2(8)); Shoo Fly! Trapani, Iza. Trapani, Iza, illus. 2000. lib. bdg. 23.33 (978-0-8368-2670-8(1)); Twinkle, Twinkle, Little Star. Trapani, Iza. Trapani, Iza, illus. 1996. lib. bdg. 23.33 (978-0-8368-1552-8(1)); 32p. (J). (ps up). (Illus.). Set lib. bdg. 256.63 (978-0-8368-2740-8(6)) Stevens, Gareth Inc.

Ezozo, Wanda. According to the Book of Genesis Nursery Rhyme. 2005. (Illus.). 24p. (J). (978-1-4120-4425-7(1)) Trafford Publishing.

Farmer in Dell. 2005. (Mother Goose Ser.). (Illus.). 36p. (J). bds. 15.95 incl. audio compact disk (978-1-59249-387-6(4) , 1D006) Soundprints.

Fatchen, Max. Songs for My Dog & Other Wry Rhymes. 2000. (Illus.). 142p. (J). (gr. 3-7). pap. 12.95 (978-1-86254-472-7(7)) Wakefield Pr. Pty, Ltd. AUS. *Dist:* Continental Enterprises Group, Inc. (CEG).

Faundez, Anne. One, Two, Buckle My Shoe. 2004. (QEB Start Talking Ser.). (Illus.). 24p. (J). lib. bdg. 15.95 (978-1-59566-007-7(0)) QEB Publishing Inc.

Feierabend, John M. The Book of Bounces. 2000. (First Steps in Music Ser.). (Illus.). 112p. (J). (ps). pap. 12.95 (978-1-57999-055-8(X)) GIA Pubns., Inc.

Feniger, Susan. The Classic Treasury of Mother Goose. 2005. 56p. 9.98 (978-0-7624-1400-0(6)) Running Pr. Bk. Pubs.

M N O

Figuerola & Alonso. Que Llueva, Que Llueva. 2002. (SPA.). 8p. 5.99 (978-84-263-4740-4(1)) Vives, Luis Editorial (Edelvives) ESP. *Dist:* Lectorum Pubns., Inc.

—Sal, Caracol. 2005. (SPA.). 8p. 5.99 (978-84-263-4739-8(8)) Juventud, Editorial ESP. *Dist:* Lectorum Pubns., Inc.

—Tengo Tres Ovejas. 2005. (SPA.). 8p. 5.99 (978-84-263-4735-0(5)) Vives, Luis Editorial (Edelvives) ESP. *Dist:* Lectorum Pubns., Inc.

First Nursery Rhymes. 2004. (Baby's First Nursery Rhymes Gift Set Ser.). 12p. (J). bds. 12.99 (978-1-85854-693-3(1)) Brimax Books Ltd. GBR. *Dist:* Byeway Bks.

First Picture Nursery Rhymes. 2005. (Illus.). 16p. (J). (ps-ps). per. 11.99 (978-0-7945-1014-5(0) , Usborne) EDC Publishing.

Fisher Wright, Blanche, illus. The Real Mother Goose' Board Book. 1998. (Real Mother Goose Library). 32p. (J). (ps). bds. 6.99 (978-0-590-00368-1(2) , Cartwheel Bks.) Scholastic, Inc.

Foote, Samuel. Great Panjandrum Himself Illustrated Edi. 2006. (Illus.). pap. (***978-1-4065-1225-0(7)**) Dodo Pr.

Franck, Charlotte. Little Rhymes for Quiet Times. 2006. (Illus.). 32p. per. 15.95 (***978-1-60002-116-9(6)** , 4029, Airleaf Publishing) Airleaf Publishing & Bookselling.

Freed, Herb. Sing & Learn Spanish. 2004. 271p. (J). pap. 18.99 (978-0-9760472-0-9(9)) Global Village Kids, LLC.

Freeman, Tina, et al, illus. Ten Little Monkeys Jumping on the Bed. 2001. (Classic Books with Holes). 16p. (J). (gr. 3). bds. 5.99 (978-0-85953-798-8(6)) Child's Play-International.

Freeman, Tina, tr. & illus. Ten Little Monkeys Jumping on the Bed. Freeman, Tina, illus. 2003. (Classic Books with Holes). (J). 6.99 (978-0-85953-137-5(6)) Child's Play-International.

French, Vivian & McDonald, Ronald L. Once upon a Time. Prater, John, illus. 1999. (Read & Share Ser.). 32p. (J). (ps). pap. 3.99 (978-0-7636-0858-3(0)) Candlewick Pr.

Fuentes, Iliana, illus. Naranja Dulce, Limon Partido: Antologia de la Lirica Infantil Mexicana. (SPA.). (J). (gr. 2-4). pap. incl. audio compact disk (978-968-12-0049-7(7) , FC7387) El Colegio de México, A.C., Biblioteca Miguel Cosio Villegas MEX. *Dist:* Lectorum Pubns., Inc.

Fujikawa, Gyo, illus. Mother Goose. 2007. 130p. (J). (ps-2). 9.95 (***978-1-4027-5064-9(1)**) Sterling Publishing Co., Inc.

Fun-to-Learn: Ready for Rhyming. (Homework Booklets Ser.). 80p. (gr. k-1). 2.99 (978-0-7424-0259-1(2) , IF0415) School Specialty Publishing.

Funari Willever, Lisa. Where Do Snowmen Go? 2002. (Illus.). 32p. 9.95 (978-0-9679227-2-0(0) , 329-012) Franklin Mason Pr.

Fyleman, Rose. Mary Middling & Other Silly Folk: Nursery Rhymes & Nonsense Poems. Bandlow, Katja, illus. 2004. 32p. (J). (gr. k-3). tchr. ed. 16.00 (978-0-618-38141-8(4) , Clarion Bks.) Houghton Mifflin Co. Trade & Reference Div.

Galdone, Paul. Cat Goes Fiddle-I-Fee. Galdone, Paul, illus. 2002. (Illus.). (J). 14.74 (978-0-7587-2201-0(X)) Book Wholesalers, Inc.

Gallagher, Belinda, ed. 100 Best Loved Nursery Rhymes. 2007. (Illus.). 128p. 14.95 (***978-1-84236-123-8(6)**) Miles Kelly Publishing, Ltd. GBR. *Dist:* National Bk. Network.

Gentry, J. Richard & Craddock, Richard S. Nursery Rhyme Time. 2005. 6.95 (***978-1-931181-98-3(5)**) Universal Publishing.

George, Katie. Incy-Wincy Spider. 1999. (Mini Finger Puppet Bks.). (Illus.). 16p. (J). (ps). 6.95 (978-1-86233-034-4(4)) Sterling Publishing Co., Inc.

Gilbert, Rob, illus. Humpty Dumpty. 2004. 32p. (J). pap. 6.95 (978-1-58089-091-5(1)) Charlesbridge Publishing, Inc.

Gliori, Debi. Nursery Rhymes. 2005. (Illus.). 64p. (J). (ps-3). 19.99 incl. audio compact disk (978-0-7566-1467-6(8)) Dorling Kindersley Publishing, Inc.

Golden Books Staff. Dan Yaccarino's Mother Goose. Yaccarino, Dan, illus. 2004. 48p. (J). (gr. k-k). 14.95 (978-0-375-82849-2(4) , Golden Bks.) Random Hse. Children's Bks.

—Let's Play: A Story Rhyme. 1999. (Disney Ser.). (Illus.). 40p. (J). (ps-4). pap. 1.09 (978-0-307-08711-9(5) , 08711, Golden Bks.) Random Hse. Children's Bks.

Goose, Mother. Lets Listen. 2005. (Illus.). 36p. (J). bds. 7.95 (978-1-59249-533-7(8) , 1D203) Soundprints.

Graves, Sue. Miss Muffet & the Spider. Warburton, Sarah, illus. 2005. (Reading Corner Ser.). 24p. (J). (gr. k-3). lib. bdg. 22.80 (978-1-932889-99-4(X)) Sea-To-Sea Pubns.

Greenaway, Kate. Kate Greenaway's Mother Goose. 2006. (Illus.). 52p. 14.95 (978-0-87328-216-1(7)) Univ. of California Pr.

Greenaway, Kate, illus. A Apple Pie & Traditional Nursery Rhymes. 2002. 96p. 14.95 (978-0-375-41511-1(4) , Everyman's Library) Knopf Publishing Group.

Grimly, Gris. Gris Grimly's Wicked Nursery Rhymes. Grimly, Gris, illus. 2003. (Illus.). 32p. 16.95 (978-0-9729388-7-7(7)) Baby Tattoo Bks.

Gruenewald, Susanne, tr. Hansel und Gretel. Bradley, G. A., photos by. 1998. Tr. of Hansel & Gretel. (GER., Illus.). 36p. (J). (gr. 2-4). 29.95 (978-1-886123-08-3(X)) Geyer's Garten Cards & Bks.

Gruetzke, Mary, ed. Five Little Ducks. Bates, Ivan, illus. 2006. 32p. (J). (ps-k). pap. 12.99 (978-0-439-74693-9(0) , Orchard Bks.) Scholastic, Inc.

—Real Mother Goose. 2006. (Scholastic Hands-on Learning Ser.). (J). 9.99 (978-0-439-78532-7(4) , Cartwheel Bks.) Scholastic, Inc.

Guile, Gill, illus. In My Garden. 20p. (J). (978-1-932209-38-9(7)) Bendon Publishing International.

—My Nursery Rhyme Pop-up Book. 20p. (J). (978-1-59394-119-2(6)) Bendon Publishing International.

Gustafson, Scott. Favorite Nursery Rhymes from Mother Goose. 2007. (Illus.). 100p. (J). 19.95 (***978-0-86713-097-3(0)**) Greenwich Workshop Pr.

Gutmann, Bessie P. Nursery Poems & Prayers. 2007. 32p. (J). (ps-3). 6.99 (978-0-448-44500-7(X) , Grosset & Dunlap) Penguin Group (USA) Inc.

Hal Leonard Corp., creator. Nursery Rhymes. 1999. 24p. pap. 7.95 (978-0-634-00081-2(0) , 0634000810) Leonard, Hal Corp.

Hal Leonard Corporation Staff, creator. First Nursery Rhymes: Early Elementary Level. 2005. 32p. pap. 4.95 (978-0-87718-022-7(9) , 0877180229) Willis Music Co.

Hale, Sarah Josephbuell. Mary Had a Little Lamb. Mavor, Salley, illus. 2000. 32p. (J). (ps-1). pap. 5.95 (978-0-531-07165-6(0) , Orchard Bks.) Scholastic, Inc.

Hall, Dorothy & Cunningham, Patricia. Reading/Writing Complex Rhymes: Rhymes with More Than One Spelling Pattern. 2003. (Four-Blocks Ser.). 88p. (J). per. 29.99 (978-0-88724-920-4(5)) Carson-Dellosa Publishing Co., Inc.

—Reading/Writing Simple Rhymes: Rhymes with One Spelling Pattern. 2003. (Four-Blocks Ser.). 88p. (J). per. 29.99 (978-0-88724-919-8(1)) Carson-Dellosa Publishing Co., Inc.

Harbour, Elizabeth. First Picture Book of Nursery Rhymes. (Illus.). 32p. (J). pap. 9.95 (978-0-14-054973-7(0)) Penguin Bks., Ltd. GBR. *Dist:* Trafalgar Square Publishing.

Harcourt School Publishers Staff. Big Book of Rhymes. 3rd ed. 2003. (Trophies Reading Program Ser.). (ps). pap. 70.10 (978-0-15-340344-6(6)) Harcourt Schl. Pubs.

—Collections: Big Book of Rhymes. 1999. (Illus.). (gr. 1). pap. 70.90 (978-0-15-313490-6(9)); (gr. 2). pap. 70.90 (978-0-15-313491-3(7)) Harcourt Schl. Pubs.

—Collections: Big Book of Rhymes & Songs. 1999. (Illus.). pap. 59.80 (978-0-15-313419-7(4)) Harcourt Schl. Pubs.

—Rhymes & Songs Big Book. 3rd ed. 2002. (Trophies Reading Program Ser.). (Illus.). (gr. k-6). pap. 58.20 (978-0-15-325401-7(7)) Harcourt Schl. Pubs.

—Trophies Reading Program: Nursery Rhymes Anthology. 3rd ed. 2003. (Illus.). (gr. k). pap. 47.70 (978-0-15-340345-3(4)) Harcourt Schl. Pubs.

HarperCollins Children's Books. Rhymes & Riddles. 2007. (Word Play Ser.). 208p. (J). pap. 5.95 (***978-0-00-724334-1(0)**) HarperCollins Pubs. Ltd. GBR. *Dist:* Independent Pubs. Group.

Harrison, David L. The Animals' Song. Demarest, Chris L., illus. 2003. 32p. (J). (ps up). pap. 8.95 (978-1-59078-076-3(0)) Boyds Mills Pr.

Harvey, Barbara. Inner City Nursery Rhymes. 2004. 48p. (J). per. 11.95 (978-1-56167-863-1(5)) American Literary Pr.

Harwood, Beth. Nursery Rhymes: Well-Loved Verses to Share. Lancome, Susie, illus. 2003. (Nursery Collection Bks.). 24p. (J). (ps). 12.95 (978-1-57145-930-5(8) , Silver Dolphin Bks.) Advantage Pubs. Group.

—Twinkle, Twinkle! Dodd, Emily, illus. 2006. (Amazing Baby Ser.). 16p. (J). bds. 5.95 (978-1-59223-586-5(7) , Silver Dolphin Bks.) Advantage Pubs. Group.

Hawkins, Colin & Hawkins, Jacqui. I Know an Old Lady Who Swallowed a Fly. 2004. (Illus.). 24p. (J). pap. 9.99 (978-1-4052-0679-2(9)) Egmont Bks., Ltd. GBR. *Dist:* Trafalgar Square Publishing.

—Noah Built an Ark One Day. 2004. (Illus.). 24p. (J). pap. 9.99 (978-1-4052-0680-8(2)) Egmont Bks., Ltd. GBR. *Dist:* Trafalgar Square Publishing.

—Old Mother Hubbard. 2004. (Illus.). 24p. pap. 9.99 (978-1-4052-0682-2(9)) Egmont Bks., Ltd. GBR. *Dist:* Trafalgar Square Publishing.

Hayes, Eve. Rounding up the Rhymes. 2005. (Four-Blocks Ser.). 192p. (J). per. 19.99 (978-1-59441-197-7(2) , CD-104101) Carson-Dellosa Publishing Co., Inc.

Head Shoulders Knees & Toes. 2005. (Mother Goose Ser.). (Illus.). 36p. (J). bds. 12.95 incl. audio compact disk (978-1-59249-381-4(5) , 1D007) Soundprints.

Hefferan, Rob, illus. My Pop-up Nursery Rhymes. 2005. 10p. (J). (ps-ps). per. 4.95 (978-1-58117-439-7(X) , Intervisual/Piggy Toes) Dalmatian Pr.

—My Sparkling Nursery Rhymes. 2005. (Sparkling Foil Ser.). 10p. (J). 8.95 (978-1-58117-295-9(8) , Intervisual/Piggy Toes) Dalmatian Pr.

Hellen, Nancy. Jigsaw Books, 6 vols. Hellen, Nancy, illus. 2000. 6p. (J). 8.95 (978-1-902413-40-2(7)) Van der Meer, a Div. of PHPC GBR. *Dist:* Abbeville Pr., Inc.

Henley, Ralph. Action Rhymes & Active Games: Over 200 Bible Story Activities for Ages 2 To 5. 2004. (J). tchr. ed., per. 19.99 (978-1-933803-02-9(9)) Child Sensitive Communication, LLC.

Heras, Theo. What Will We Do with the Baby-O? Herbert, Jennifer, illus. 2004. 32p. (J). (gr. k-k). 12.95 (978-0-88776-689-3(7)) Tundra Bks., Inc./Livres Toundra, Inc. CAN. *Dist:* Random Hse., Inc.

Herman, R. A. Peas Porridge Hot! 2006. (Illus.). 7p. (J). bds. 7.95 (978-1-59354-152-1(X)) Handprint Bks.

Hey Diddle Diddle. 2004. (J). per. (978-1-57657-428-7(8)) Paradise Pr., Inc.

Hey Diddle Diddle. 2002. (Illus.). (J). bds. (978-1-59069-262-2(4) , MS1003) Studio Mouse LLC.

Hey! Diddle Diddle. 2002. (Nursery Rhymes Ser.). (Illus.). (J). (978-1-59069-064-2(8) , 1-2005) Studio Mouse LLC.

Hoberman, Mary Ann. Miss Mary Mack. Westcott, Nadine Bernard, illus. 2003. 32p. (J). (ps-1). pap. 6.99 (978-0-316-07614-2(7) , Tingley, Megan Bks.) Little, Brown Bks. for Young Readers.

—Miss Mary Mack. 2003. (ps-2). lib. bdg. 15.30 (978-0-613-71606-2(X)) Tandem Library Bks.

—Miss Mary Mack. Westcott, Nadine Bernard, illus. rev. ed. 1998. 32p. (J). (ps-3). 15.99 (978-0-316-93118-2(7) , Tingley, Megan Bks.) Little, Brown Bks. for Young Readers.

—Miss Mary Mack: A Hand-Clapping Rhyme. Bernard, Nadine, illus. 2002. (J). 21.45 (978-0-7587-8934-1(3)) Book Wholesalers, Inc.

—You Read to Me, I'll Read to You: Very Short Mother Goose Tales to Read Together. Emberley, Michael, illus. 3rd ed. 2005. 32p. (J). (ps-3). 16.99 (978-0-316-14431-5(2)) Little Brown & Co.

Hoberman, Mary Ann & Westcott, Nadine Bernard. Miss Mary Mack. Westcott, Nadine Bernard, illus. rev. ed. 2001. (Illus.). 24p. (J). (ps-k). bds. 6.99 (978-0-316-36642-7(0) , Tingley, Megan Bks.) Little, Brown Bks. for Young Readers.

Hodges, Susan. Up in Space. Barr, Marilynn G., illus. 1999. (Rhyme & Reason Workbook Ser.). 32p. (J). (ps-k). pap. 3.95 (978-1-57029-254-5(X) , WPH 01106, Totline Pubns.) Schaffer, Frank Pubns.

Hooper, C. Nursery Rhyme. 2005. (Illus.). 20p. (J). pap. 6.95 (978-0-7945-0355-0(1) , Usborne) EDC Publishing.

Hooper, Caroline & Danes, Emma. Little Book of Nursery Rhymes. 2005. 64p. (J). 6.99 (978-0-7945-0954-5(1) , Usborne) EDC Publishing.

Hope. Nursery Rhymes for Cats. 1998. (Illus.). 32p. (J). pap. 11.99 (978-0-553-50720-1(6)) Transworld Publishers Ltd. GBR. *Dist:* Independent Pubs. Group.

Hopkins, Lee Bennett. Mother Goose Through the Seasons. Fehlau, Dagmar et al, illus. 2005. (Lee Bennett Hopkins Mother Goose Ser.). (YA). (ps-1). 76.50 (978-0-8215-0480-2(0)); suppl. ed. 57.00 (978-0-8215-0484-0(3)) Sadlier, William H. Inc.

—Mother Goose Through the Seasons: Theme 3. Fehlau, Dagmar et al, illus. l.t. ed. 1999. (Sadlier Phonics Reading Program). 16p. (YA). (ps-1). 29.85 (978-0-8215-0482-6(7)) Sadlier, William H. Inc.

Howorth, Donald & Smith, Jane, illus. This Little Piggy. 2002. (Nursery Rhymes Ser.). 10p. (J). bds. (978-1-59069-280-6(2) , MB1003) Studio Mouse LLC.

Hughes, Shirley. Rhymes for Annie Rose. Hughes, Shirley, illus. 2006. (Illus.). 48p. (J). (ps-2). reprint ed. 16.99 (978-0-7636-2940-3(5)) Candlewick Pr.

Hullinger, C. D., illus. Mother Goose Rhymes. 2007. 22p. (J). bds. 12.95 (***978-0-7696-5267-2(0)** , Gingham Dog Pr.) School Specialty Publishing.

Humpty Dumpty. 2003. (J). per. (978-1-57657-800-1(3)) Paradise Pr., Inc.

Humpty Dumpty. 1999. (J). 6.99 (978-0-590-51124-7(6)) Scholastic, Inc.

Humpty Dumpty. 2002. (Nursery Rhymes Ser.). (Illus.). (J). (978-1-59069-061-1(3) , 1-2002); bds. (978-1-59069-263-9(2) , MS1004) Studio Mouse LLC.

Humpty Dumpty: 6 Small Books. (gr. k-2). 23.00 (978-0-7635-8498-6(3)) Rigby Education.

Humpty Dumpty: Story Rhymes. 2002. (My First Mother Goose Ser.). (Illus.). 48p. (J). (ps-k). 11.95 incl. audio compact disk (978-1-56899-932-6(1) , MD1151); 15.95 incl. audio compact disk (978-1-56899-934-0(8) , MPD1151) Soundprints.

Hurwitz, Andy Bl. Nursery Rhyme Jazz. 2007. 16p. (J). bds. 7.99 (***978-0-8431-2195-7(5)** , Price Stern Sloan) Penguin Group (USA) Inc.

Huseinovic, Andrea Petrlik, illus. Counting Your Way: Number Nursery Rhymes. 2007. (Mother Goose Rhymes Ser.). 32p. (J). (gr. k-2). 7.95 (***978-1-4048-2352-5(2)** , 1265751) Picture Window Bks.

—Cuddly Critters: Animal Nursery Rhymes. 2006. (Mother Goose Rhymes Ser.). 32p. (J). (ps-2). lib. bdg. 25.26 (***978-1-4048-2344-0(1)** , 1265749) Picture Window Bks.

I'm a Little Teapot. 2000. 10p. (J). (ps up). 6.95 (978-0-694-01311-1(0) , Harper Festival) HarperCollins Pubs.

Itchyka-Dana. Asian Nursery Rhymes. 2004. (J). (978-1-85269-701-3(6)) Mantra Publishing, Ltd.

It's Rhyne Time: Over 100 Rhymes, Songs, & Finger Plays That Teach. 2003. 80p. (J). per. 9.99 (978-0-88724-916-7(7)) Carson-Dellosa Publishing Co., Inc.

Itsy, Bitsy Spider. 2005. (Sign & Signalong Ser.). (Illus.). 10p. (J). (ps). per. 4.99 (978-1-904550-43-3(6)) Child's Play-International.

Ivanov, Aleksey, illus. Tall Book of Mother Goose. 2006. 80p. (J). 6.99 (978-0-06-054373-0(6) , Harper Festival) HarperCollins Pubs.

Jack & Jill. 2003. (J). per. (978-1-57657-801-8(1)) Paradise Pr., Inc.

Jack & Jill: 6 Small Books. (gr. k-2). 23.00 (978-0-7635-8492-4(4)) Rigby Education.

James, Diane. Baa, Baa, Black Sheep. 2004. (Jigsaw Nursery Rhymes Ser.). (Illus.). 12p. (J). (ps-k). bds. 9.95 (978-1-58728-625-4(4) , Two Can Publishing) T&N Children's Publishing.

—Pat-a-Cake. 2004. (Jigsaw Nursery Rhymes Ser.). (Illus.). 12p. (J). (ps-k). bds. 9.95 (978-1-58728-623-0(8) , Two Can Publishing) T&N Children's Publishing.

—Three Blind Mice. 2004. (Jigsaw Nursery Rhymes Ser.). (Illus.). 12p. (J). (ps-k). bds. 9.95 (978-1-58728-626-1(2) , Two Can Publishing) T&N Children's Publishing.

Jigsaw Nursery Rhymes. Blow, Wind, Blow. 2003. (Jigsaw Nursery Rhymes Ser.). 12p. (J). (ps). bds. 9.95 (978-1-58728-640-7(8) , Two Can Publishing) T&N Children's Publishing.

—Jack & Jill. 2003. (Jigsaw Nursery Rhymes Ser.). 12p. (J). (ps). bds. 9.95 (978-1-58728-641-4(6) , Two Can Publishing) T&N Children's Publishing.

—Old King Cole. 2003. (Jigsaw Nursery Rhymes Ser.). 12p. (J). (ps). bds. 9.95 (978-1-58728-642-1(4) , Two Can Publishing) T&N Children's Publishing.

—Rub-a-Dub-Dub. 2003. (Jigsaw Nursery Rhymes Ser.). 12p. (J). bds. 9.95 (978-1-58728-643-8(2) , Two Can Publishing) T&N Children's Publishing.

Johnson, Sharon. Recess Rhymes. Washington, Wayne, illus. 2000. viii, 52p. (J). (gr. 2-6). pap. 13.98 (978-0-9700523-0-8(8)) Kalona Publishing.

Jones, Carol. What's the Time, Mr. Wolf? 1999. (Illus.). 32p. (J). (gr. k-3). 15.00 (978-0-395-95800-1(8) , Walter Lorraine) Houghton Mifflin Co. Trade & Reference Div.

Jones, Carol, illus. Old MacDonald Had a Farm. 1998. 32p. (J). (gr. k-3). pap. 6.95 (978-0-395-90125-0(1) , Walter Lorraine) Houghton Mifflin Co. Trade & Reference Div.

Jones, Harold, illus. Lavender's Blue: A Book of Nursery Rhymes. 50th anniv. collector's fac. ed. 2005. 180p. (YA). 27.95 (978-0-19-278227-4(4)) Oxford Univ. Pr., Inc.

Keep Books Organization Staff. Mini-Sets Caption Books & Nursery Rhymes. (Illus.). (ps-5). pap. (978-1-893986-04-6(7)) Keep Bks.

—Mini-Sets Spanish Caption Books & Spanish Nursery Rhymes. (SPA., Illus.). 8p. (ps-5). pap. (978-1-893986-16-9(0)) Keep Bks.

Keith, Barbara Benson, illus. & compiled by. The Girls & Boys of Mother Goose. Keith, Barbara Benson, compiled by. 2006. 32p. (J). per. 7.99 (978-0-9789688-0-9(8)) Brownian Bee Pr.

Kelley, Marty. Fall Is Not Easy. 1998. (Illus.). 30p. (J). (ps-3). 12.95 (978-1-55933-234-7(4)) Zino Pr. Children's Bks.

Kemp, Moira. I'm a Little Teapot. 2003. (My Carry along Board Bks.). (Illus.). 10p. (J). 4.99 (978-0-7696-2989-6(X) , Gingham Dog Pr.) School Specialty Publishing.

—Knock at the Door. 2003. (My Carry along Board Bks.). (Illus.). 10p. (J). 4.99 (978-0-7696-3002-1(2) , Gingham Dog Pr.) School Specialty Publishing.

—Pat-a-Cake, Pat-a-Cake. 2003. (My Carry along Board Bks.). (Illus.). 10p. (J). 4.99 (978-0-7696-3000-7(6) , Gingham Dog Pr.) School Specialty Publishing.

Kenyon, Tony. Pat-a-Cake. Kenyon, Tony, illus. 1998. (Illus.). 16p. (J). (gr. k). bds. 4.99 (978-0-7636-0431-8(3)) Candlewick Pr.

Kienzle, Patricia Taylor. I Saw a Chicken on My Street. 2002. (Illus.). 24p. (J). (gr. k-2). pap. 4.00 (978-1-890798-14-7(2)) Kienzle, Patricia Taylor.

Knight, Paula, illus. Forecasting Fun: Weather Nursery Rhymes. 2007. (Mother Goose Rhymes Ser.). 32p. (J). (gr. k-2). 7.95 (***978-1-4048-2353-2(0)** , 1265752) Picture Window Bks.

Knight, Paula & Smith, Jane, illus. Hey Diddle Diddle. 2002. (Nursery Rhymes Ser.). 10p. (J). bds. (978-1-59069-285-1(3) , MB1008) Studio Mouse LLC.

Kole, Ted & Genet, John, eds. Katoufs in Nursery Rhymes Chapbook: Mother Goose. (Illus.). 48p. (Orig.). (J). (gr. 1-4). pap. 3.95 (978-0-9641381-0-0(7)) Kreative Character Kreations, Inc.

Konstadt, T. & Smith, Jane, illus. Rub-a-Dub-Dub. 2002. (Nursery Rhymes Ser.). 10p. (J). bds. (978-1-59069-284-4(5) , MB1007) Studio Mouse LLC.

Kubler, Annie. The Farmer in the Dell. Adams, Pam & Freeman, Tina, illus. 2001. (Classic Books with Holes). 16p. (J). (ps-3). bds. 5.99 (978-0-85953-796-4(X)) Child's Play-International.

—Head, Shoulders, Knees & Toes. 2004. (Illus.). (J). (ALB & ENG.). (978-1-84444-144-0(X)); (ARA & ENG., (978-1-84444-145-7(8)); (BEN & ENG., 20p. (978-1-84444-146-4(6)); (CHI & ENG., (978-1-84444-147-1(4)); (978-1-84444-148-8(2)); (ENG & FRE., (978-1-84444-149-5(0)); (ENG & GUJ., (978-1-84444-150-1(4)); (ENG & PAN., (978-1-84444-151-8(2)); (ENG & POR., (978-1-84444-152-5(0)); (ENG & SOM., (978-1-84444-153-2(9)); (ENG & SPA., (978-1-84444-154-9(7)); (ENG & TAM., (978-1-84444-155-6(5)); (ENG & TUR., (978-1-84444-156-3(3)) Mantra Publishing, Ltd.

—Ring Around a Rosie. 12p. (J). bds. 4.99 (978-0-85953-578-6(9)) Child's Play-International.

—Row, Row, Row Your Boat. 2002. (Illus.). 12p. (J). bds. 4.99 (978-0-85953-658-5(0)) Child's Play-International.

—Ten Little Fingers. 2002. (Baby Board Books). (Illus.). 12p. (J). (ps-7). bds. 4.99 (978-0-85953-610-3(6)) Child's Play-International.

Kubler, Annie, illus. Baa, Baa, Black Sheep! 2005. 12p. (J). bds. 4.99 (978-1-904550-01-3(0)) Child's Play-International.

Kubler, Annie, et al, illus. Here We Go Round the Mulberry Bush. 2001. (Classic Books with Holes). 16p. (J). (ps-3). bds. 5.99 (978-0-85953-795-7(1)) Child's Play-International.

Kubler, Annie, illus. Pat-a-Cake! Nursery Rhymes. 2006. 12p. bds. 6.99 (978-1-904550-82-2(7)) Child's Play-International.

—Peek-a-Boo! Nursery Games. 2006. 12p. (J). bds. 6.99 (978-1-904550-83-9(5)) Child's Play-International.

—See-Saw! Nursery Songs. 2006. 12p. bds. 6.99 (978-1-904550-81-5(9)) Child's Play-International.

—Teddy Bear, Teddy Bear. 2004. (Sign & Signalong Ser.). 12p. (J). (ps). bds. 4.99 (978-1-904550-40-2(1)) Child's Play-International.

—Twinkle, Twinkle, Little Star. (J). 2005. 12p. bds. 4.99 (978-1-904550-02-0(9)); 2002. 16p. bds. 5.99 (978-0-85953-142-9(2)); 2002. 12p. bds. 4.99 (978-1-904550-42-6(8)) Child's Play-International.

Kubler, Annie, et al, illus. The Wheels on the Bus Go Round & Round. 2001. (Classic Books with Holes). 16p. (J). (ps-3). bds. 5.99 (978-0-85953-797-1(8)) Child's Play-International.

Kubler, Annie, tr. & illus. The Wheels on the Bus Go Round & Round. Kubler, Annie, illus. 2003. (Classic Books with Holes). (J). 4.99 (978-0-85953-136-8(8)) Child's Play-International.

Kyle, Kathryn. Patience. 2002. (Wonder Books Level 3: Values Ser.). (Illus.). 32p. (J). (ps-3). 22.79 (978-1-56766-090-6(8)) Child's World, Inc.

Lacome, Julie. Walking Through the Jungle. Lacome, Julie, illus. (Big Books! Ser.). (Illus.). (J). (gr. k-1). 2004. 32p. pap. 19.99 (978-0-7636-2471-2(3)); 1999. 24p. pap. 3.99 (978-0-7636-0876-7(9)) Candlewick Pr.

Ladybird Books Staff. Humpty Dumpty. 1999. (Nursery Rhymes Ser.). (Illus.). 32p. (978-0-7214-2018-9(4) , Ladybird Books) Penguin Bks., Ltd.

—Incy Wincy. 1999. (Illus.). 32p. (978-0-7214-2019-6(2) , Ladybird Books) Penguin Bks., Ltd.

—Nursery Rhymes. (First Bks.: No. S808-5). (Illus.). (J). (ps). pap. 3.95 (978-0-7214-5056-8(3) , Dutton Juvenile) Penguin Group (USA) Inc.

—100 Favourite Nursery Rhymes. 1999. (Illus.). 32p. (J). pap. 4.99 (978-0-7214-2020-2(6) , Dutton Juvenile) Penguin Group (USA) Inc.

Ladybug, Ladybug. 2002. (Nursery Rhymes Ser.). (Illus.). (J). (978-1-59069-060-4(5) , 1-2001) Studio Mouse LLC.

Lamont, Priscilla. Ring O'Roses: Nursery Rhymes, Action Rhymes & Lullabies. 1999. (Illus.). 72p. (J). (ps-1). pap. 10.99 (978-0-7112-1245-9(7)) Lincoln, Frances Ltd. GBR. *Dist:* Transition Vendor.

L'Amour, Jenny. Mama Duck Rhymes: Variations on the Themes. Henderson-Farmer, Dawn, illus. 2001. 20p. (YA). (gr. 4-8). 5.95 (978-0-9707831-1-0(6)) Olive Media Services.

Langley, Jonathan. The Best Ever Nursery Rhymes & Tales. 2006. (Illus.). 256p. 29.95 (***978-0-00-198292-5(3)***) HarperCollins Pubs. Ltd. GBR. *Dist:* Independent Pubs. Group.

Language Works Rhyme Time. 8p. (J). (978-0-8136-3519-4(5)) Modern Curriculum Pr.

Lansky, Bruce. Peter Peter Pizza Eater. 2006. (Illus.). 32p. (J). 15.95 (978-0-684-03166-8(3)) Meadowbrook Pr.

Laurence, Jo. How to Be a Wizard at Nursery Rhymes. Ford, Kate, illus. 48p. (J). (gr. 1-3). pap. (978-1-876367-28-2(8)) Wizard Bks.

Laurila, P. K. Gus & Annie: Glacier Ice Worms. Miller, Dan, illus. 2001. 12p. (J). bds. 6.95 (978-0-930931-34-6(3)) Alaska Natural History Assn.

Lawton, Toni-Mckay. In Bloom. 2007. (Just in Rhyme Ser.). (Illus.). 12p. 6.95 (***978-1-84167-030-0(8)***) Ransom Publishing Ltd. GBR. *Dist:* International Publishers Marketing.

LeapFrog Staff, compiled by. Once upon a Rhyme. 2002. (J). (ps-k). spiral bd. 9.99 (978-1-58605-804-3(5)) LeapFrog Enterprises, Inc.

Lear, Edward. An Edward Lear Alphabet. Radunsky, Vladimir, illus. 1999. 32p. (J). (ps-2). 14.89 (978-0-06-028114-4(6)) HarperCollins Pubs.

The Lee Bennett Hopkins Mother Goose. 2005. (YA). (ps-1). 270.00 (978-0-8215-0459-8(2)) Sadlier, William H. Inc.

Leland, Debbie. Aggie Goose Rhymes. Hollis Rife, Ann, illus. 1998. 24p. (J). (ps-3). 17.95 (978-0-9667086-0-8(1)) Wildflower Run.

Leonard, Barry, ed. Humpty Dumpty & Other Rhymes. 2003. (Illus.). 12p. (J). (gr. k-5). reprint ed. 17.00 (978-0-7567-6855-3(1)) DIANE Publishing Co.

—Mary Had a Little Lamb & Other Rhymes. 2003. (Illus.). 12p. (J). (gr. k-4). reprint ed. 17.00 (978-0-7567-6861-4(6)) DIANE Publishing Co.

—Mary, Mary, Quite Contrary & Other Rhymes. 2003. (Illus.). 12p. (J). (gr. k-5). reprint ed. 17.00 (978-0-7567-6857-7(8)) DIANE Publishing Co.

—Rock-a-Bye, Baby & Other Rhymes. 2003. (Illus.). 12p. (J). (gr. k-4). reprint ed. 17.00 (978-0-7567-6863-8(2)) DIANE Publishing Co.

—See-Saw Margery Daw & Other Rhymes. 2003. (Illus.). 12p. (J). (gr. k-5). reprint ed. 17.00 (978-0-7567-6866-9(7)) DIANE Publishing Co.

—Wee Willie Winkie & Other Rhymes. 2003. (Illus.). 12p. (J). (gr. k-4). reprint ed. 17.00 (978-0-7567-6859-1(4)) DIANE Publishing Co.

Lewis, Jan. Jan Lewis' Nursery Rhymes. Lewis, Jan, illus. 2000. (Illus.). 90p. (J). (ps-1). 12.95 (978-1-57145-405-8(5) , Silver Dolphin Bks.) Advantage Pubs. Group.

Lewis, Jan, illus. Mother Goose Action Rhymes: Old MacDonald Had a Farm; One, Two, Buckle My Shoe; Round & Round the Garden; This Little Pig. 2004. 90p. (J). vinyl bd. (978-1-902272-32-0(3)) Tucker Slingsby, Ltd.

Lewis, Stephen. Action Rhymes for You & Your Friends. 2000. ([DK Read & Listen] Ser.). (Illus.). 29p. (J). pap. (978-0-7894-4873-6(4)) Dorling Kindersley Publishing, Inc.

Lilley, Diane, illus. Piggy Poems. 1998. 32p. (J). pap. 14.95 (978-0-7894-2485-3(1)) Dorling Kindersley Publishing, Inc.

Linch, Tanya. The Three Little Kittens. Linch, Tanya, illus. 2001. (Illus.). 32p. (J). (ps-k). (978-1-86233-204-1(5) , Gullane Children's Bks.) Pinwheel.

Linder, Dorothy Perillo. A Vegetable Collection: Recipes & Rhymes to Conquer Kids of All Ages. 2007. 35.00 (***978-0-9753334-2-6(9)***) Sanctuary Bks.

Listen! Listen! Letter Sounds in Rhyme: Blends & Digraphs Set. (gr. k-1). 89.95 (978-0-322-02639-1(3)) Wright Group, The.

Listen! Listen! Letter Sounds in Rhyme: Consonants Set. (gr. k-1). 84.95 (978-0-322-02637-7(7)) Wright Group, The.

Listen! Listen! Letter Sounds in Rhyme: Vowels Set. (gr. k-1). 52.95 (978-0-322-02638-4(5)) Wright Group, The.

Litchfield, Jo & Allen, Francesca, illus. First Picture Nursery Rhymes With. 2006. 18p. (J). bds. 18.99 (978-0-7945-1489-1(8) , Usborne) EDC Publishing.

Literature Pockets: Nursery Rhymes. 2001. (Illus.). 96p. (J). (gr. k-1). suppl. ed. 12.99 (978-1-55799-819-4(1) , EMC 2700) Evan-Moor Educational Pubs.

Little Jack Horner: 6 Small Books. (gr. k-2). 23.00 (978-0-7635-8500-6(9)) Rigby Education.

Lobel, Arnold. Arnold Lobel's Mother Goose for Babies. 2004. (Illus.). 20p. (J). (gr. k-ps). bds. 5.99 (978-0-375-82904-8(0) , Knopf Bks. for Young Readers) Random Hse. Children's Bks.

Lobel, Arnold, illus. The Arnold Lobel Book of Mother Goose: A Treasury of More Than 300 Classic Nursery Rhymes. unabr. ed. 2003. Orig. Title: The Random House Book of Mother Goose. 176p. (J). (gr. k-k). reprint ed. 19.95 (978-0-679-88736-2(9) , Knopf Bks. for Young Readers) Random Hse. Children's Bks.

Lodge, Bernard. There Was an Old Woman Who Lived in a Glove: A Picture Book. 1999. 32p. (J). (ps-3). pap. 6.95 (978-1-58089-018-2(0)) Charlesbridge Publishing, Inc.

Long, Sylvia. Mother Goose Block Books, 16 vols. Long, Sylvia, illus. 2002. (Illus.). 12p. (J). bds. 24.95 (978-0-8118-3574-9(X)) Chronicle Bks. LLC.

—Twinkle Twinkle Little Star. Long, Sylvia, illus. 2006. (Illus.). 26p. (J). bds. 6.95 (978-0-8118-5230-2(X)) Chronicle Bks. LLC.

Loper, Kathleen. Angelina Katrina: Builds Troy Snowman. Waltz, Dan, illus. l.t. ed. 2004. 36p. (J). 17.95 (978-0-9741774-5-8(8)) D. W. Publishing.

Losordo, Stephen. Cow Moo Me. Conteh-Morgan, Jane, illus. 1998. (Growing Tree Ser.). 16p. (J). (ps up). 5.95 (978-0-694-01108-7(8) , Harper Festival) HarperCollins Pubs.

Luiz, Fernando, illus. Friendly Faces: People Nursery Rhymes. (Mother Goose Rhymes Ser.). 32p. (J). (gr. k-2). 2007. 7.95 (***978-1-4048-2355-6(7)*** , 1265754); 2006. lib. bdg. 25.26 (***978-1-4048-2349-5(2)*** , 1265754) Picture Window Bks.

Lyon, Tammie Speer, illus. Three Little Kittens. 1999. (J). (978-0-7853-3362-3(2)) Publications International, Ltd.

Maccarone, Grace, ed. The Real Mother Goose Treasury. 2006. 144p. (J). pap. 12.99 (978-0-439-85875-5(5) , Cartwheel Bks.) Scholastic, Inc.

MacDonald, Suse. Here a Chick, Where a Chick? 2004. 12p. (J). pap. 10.95 (978-0-439-45594-7(4)) Scholastic, Inc.

MansBach, Sara. Round & Round the Garden, Finger Games in English & Spanish. Arroyave, Heidy, tr. Landau, Donna, illus. 2007. 42p. spiral bd. (***978-0-9785477-2-1(1)***) BladeRunner Publishing.

Marshall, James. Hey Diddle Diddle. Marshall, James, illus. rev. ed. 2003. (Illus.). 18p. (J). bds. 5.95 (978-0-374-33067-5(0) , Farrar, Straus & Giroux (BYR)) Farrar, Straus & Giroux.

Mary Had a Little Lamb. 2002. (Nursery Rhymes Ser.). (Illus.). (J). (978-1-59069-063-5(X) , 1-2004) Studio Mouse LLC.

Masterson, Linda & Butcher, Samuel J. Nursery Rhymes. 2003. (Padded Board Book Ser.). (Illus.). 24p. (J). (gr. k-k). bds. 7.99 (978-0-307-10428-1(1) , Golden Bks.) Random Hse. Children's Bks.

Mavor, Salley, illus. Hey Diddle Diddle. 2005. 8p. (J). (gr. k-ps). bds. 5.95 (978-0-618-49638-9(6)) Houghton Mifflin Co. Trade & Reference Div.

—Mary Had a Little Lamb. 2005. 9p. (J). (gr. k-ps). bds. 5.95 (978-0-618-49637-2(8)) Houghton Mifflin Co. Trade & Reference Div.

—Wee Willie Winkie. 2006. 14p. (J). (gr. k-ps). bds. 5.95 (978-0-618-49640-2(8)) Houghton Mifflin Co.

May, Scott. Outer Space Earl: Rhyme & Slime. 2000. mass mkt. 4.50 (978-1-931179-30-0(1)); mass mkt. 8.95 (978-1-931179-43-0(3)) Long Hill Productions, Inc.

Mayer, Marianna. The Mother Goose Cookbook: Rhymes & Recipes for the Very Young. Schwartz, Carol, illus. 1998. 37p. (J). (ps-3). 11.95 (978-0-688-15242-0(2)) HarperCollins Pubs.

McCord, Kathleen Garry, illus. The Ants Go Marching One by One. 16p. (J). (gr. k-3). pap. 4.95 (978-0-88272-446-1(0)) Santillana USA Publishing Co., Inc.

—She'll be Coming Around the Mountain. 16p. (J). (gr. k-3). pap. 4.95 (978-0-88272-447-8(9)) Santillana USA Publishing Co., Inc.

—There's a Hole in My Bucket. 16p. (J). (gr. k-3). pap. 4.95 (978-0-88272-445-4(2)) Santillana USA Publishing Co., Inc.

McDonald, Jill. Pat-a-Cake. 2006. (My First Taggies Book Ser.). (Illus.). 10p. (J). bds. 6.99 (978-0-439-68115-5(4) , Cartwheel Bks.) Scholastic, Inc.

McDonald, Jill, illus. Finger Puppet Storybook: Mother Goose Rhymes. rev. ed. 2007. (Alex Toys Ser.). 10p. (J). (ps-1). 11.99 (***978-0-316-06524-5(2)***) Little, Brown Bks. for Young Readers.

McDonald, Jill & Sexton, Brenda, illus. The Itsy-Bitsy Spider. 2007. (My First Taggies Book Ser.). 10p. (J). bds. 6.99 (978-0-439-85366-8(4) , Cartwheel Bks.) Scholastic, Inc.

McDonald, Ronald L. Over in the Meadow: A Counting Rhyme. Voce, Louise, ed. Voce, Louise, illus. 1999. (Reading Together Ser.). 32p. (J). (ps). pap. 3.99 (978-0-7636-0852-1(1)) Candlewick Pr.

McGraw-Hill Staff. Mother Goose. 2001. (gr. k-3). lib. bdg. 11.80 (978-0-613-83139-0(X)) Tandem Library Bks.

Meredith Seymour, Brenda, illus. First Nursery Rhymes. 2004. (First Books Ser.). 40p. (J). 8.00 (978-0-7188-1527-1(0)) Lutherworth Pr., The GBR. *Dist:* Parkwest Pubns., Inc.

Miranda, Anne. To Market, to Market. Stevens, Janet, illus. 2002. (J). 23.40 (978-0-7587-3820-2(X)) Book Wholesalers, Inc.

—To Market, to Market. Stevens, Janet, illus. 2001. 36p. (J). (ps-ps). pap. 7.00 (978-0-15-216398-3(0) , Voyager Bks./Libros Viajeros) Harcourt Children's Bks.

—To Market, to Market. 2001. (978-0-606-22597-7(8)); lib. bdg. 14.15 (978-0-613-60755-1(4)) Tandem Library Bks.

Mitter, Matt. ABC: Alphabet Rhyme. Cushman, Doug & Banta, Susan, illus. 2004. (Rhyme Time Learning Ser.). 16p. (J). (gr. 1 up). lib. bdg. 20.67 (978-0-8368-4095-7(X)) Stevens, Gareth Inc.

—Once upon a Rhyme. 2000. (Talking Pages Deluxe Ser.). (Illus.). (J). (ps-3). 12.95 (978-1-58224-131-9(7)) Futech Interactive Products, Inc.

Mitton, Tony. Riddledy Piggledy. Mounter, Paddy, illus. 2004. 48p. (J). (gr. k-1). 16.95 (978-0-385-75024-0(2) , Fickling, David Bks.) Random Hse. Children's Bks.

Mitzo Thompson, Kim & Mitzo Hilderbrand, Karen. ABC Nursery Rhymes. Holm, Sharon, illus. 2008. (Sing-A-Story Ser.). 16p. (J). bds. 10.95 (978-0-7696-4905-4(X)) School Specialty Publishing.

Mitzo Thompson, Kim & Mitzo Hilderbrand, Karen, adapted by. Hickory Dickory Dock & More! 2006. (Read & Sing along Board Books with CDs Ser.). 18p. (J). bds. 7.49 (978-0-7696-4587-2(9)) School Specialty Publishing.

—Humpty Dumpty & More! 2006. (Read & Sing along Board Books with CDs Ser.). 18p. (J). bds. 7.49 (978-0-7696-4586-5(0)) School Specialty Publishing.

Moerbeek, Kees. Nursery Rhymes. 2001. (Illus.). 24p. (J). (ps-1). 10.99 (978-0-85953-845-9(1)) Child's Play-International.

Moloney Cowgill, Ruth. Ruth's Rhymes. 2001. pap., act. bk. ed. 9.95 (978-0-9708761-1-9(4)) Cowgill, Ruth Moloney.

Montgomery, Michael G., illus. & compiled by. Over the Candlestick: Classic Nursery Rhymes & the Real Stories Behind Them. Montgomery, Michael G., compiled by. 2002. 32p. (J). (ps-2). 16.95 (978-1-56145-259-0(9) , Q33560) Peachtree Pubs., Ltd.

Moran, Erin. Colorful Spring. Pickett, Danny, illus. 2005. 32p. (J). mass mkt. 15.95 (978-0-9763778-0-1(2)) Seal Rock Publishing, LLC.

Moreillon, Judi. Vamos a Leer. Teis, Kyra, illus. 2005. (SPA.). 40p. (J). bds. 6.95 (978-1-59572-015-3(4)) Star Bright Bks., Inc.

—Vamos a Leer (Read to Me) Teis, Kyra, illus. 2003. (SPA.). 24p. (J). 6.95 (978-1-932065-50-3(4)) Star Bright Bks., Inc.

Morgan, Mary. Bunny's Nursery Rhymes. Morgan, Mary, illus. 2007. (Preschool Pop-Ups Ser.). 14p. (J). bds. 7.99 (978-1-4169-0978-1(8) , Little Simon) Simon & Schuster Children's Publishing.

Moses, Will. Mother Goose. Moses, Will, illus. 2006. 64p. (J). pap. 7.99 (978-0-14-240587-1(6) , Puffin) Penguin Group (USA) Inc.

Mother Goose, ed. Nursery Rhyme Songs. 2006. (Illus.). 12p. 17.95 incl. audio compact disk (978-1-59069-473-2(2)) Soundprints.

Mother Goose. 2002. (Puppy Tales Ser.). (Illus.). (J). (gr. k-3). 24p. 1.49 (978-1-57759-217-4(4)); 128p. 9.99 (978-1-57759-174-0(7)) Dalmatian Pr.

Mother Goose. 2001. (Keepsake Collection). (Illus.). 96p. (J). 12.98 (978-0-7853-5240-2(6) , 7136700) Publications International, Ltd.

Mother Goose & Nursery Rhymes. 1998. (J). pap. 9.95 incl. audio (978-1-887120-08-1(4)) Production Assocs., Inc.

The Mother Goose Book. (Everything Ser.). (J). 9.97 (978-1-58062-637-8(8)) Adams Media Corp.

Mother Goose Nursery Rhymes. 2002. (Illus.). 128p. (J). (gr. k-7). 9.99 (978-1-57759-419-2(3)) Dalmatian Pr.

Moxley, Sheila, illus. Skip Across the Ocean: Nursery Rhymes from Around the World. 2007. 48p. (J). pap. 7.95 (***978-1-84507-788-4(1)***) Lincoln, Frances Ltd. GBR. *Dist:* Perseus Distribution.

La Muneca Azul: Poems, Rhymes, & Songs Listening Packs. 2003. 34.50 (978-0-673-58631-5(6)) Celebration Pr.

The Music Four Fun Pack. 1998. (J). pap. 24.95 incl. audio (978-1-887120-09-8(2)) Production Assocs., Inc.

My Book of Rhyming Words. 2004. (Illus.). 80p. (J). per. 6.95 (978-4-7743-0761-9(0)) Kumon Publishing North America, Inc.

My Book of Rhyming Words & Phrases. 2004. (Illus.). 80p. (J). per. 6.95 (978-4-7743-0762-6(9)) Kumon Publishing North America, Inc.

My TakeAlong Li, ed. Nursery Rhymes. 2007. (My Take-along Library). 120p. (J). (ps-k). bds. 14.95 (***978-0-7696-5569-7(6)***) School Specialty Publishing.

Nelson, Esther & Hirsch, Davida. Riggeldy Jiggeldy Juggeldy I Am Can You Guess What I Am. Behr, Joyce, illus. 2000. 26p. (J). (gr. k-1). pap. 7.95 (978-0-945110-16-3(2)) Granny Pr.

The New York Rhymes: All That Rhymes about New York Times. 2002. (YA). bds. 15.00 (978-0-9721150-0-1(5)) Quint, Steven.

Newcome, Zita. Head, Shoulders, Knees, & Toes: And Other Action Counting Rhymes. Newcome, Zita, illus. 2002. (Illus.). 64p. (J). (ps). 15.99 (978-0-7636-1899-5(3)) Candlewick Pr.

Nicholls, Sue. Michael Finnigan, Tap Your Chinigan: Developing Music Skills with New Songs from Old Favorites. Breeze, Lynn, illus. unabr. ed. 1998. 64p. (gr. 1-2). spiral bd. 11.95 (978-0-7136-4716-7(7)) A & C Black GBR. *Dist:* Lubrecht & Cramer, Ltd.

Niño, Jairo Aníbal. El Jardin de las Ilusiones. 2003. (SPA.). 84p. (978-958-30-0701-9(3) , PV12806) Panamericana Editorial COL. *Dist:* Lectorum Pubns., Inc.

Nippert, Brenda & Nippert, George. An Alphabet of Catholic Saints. Nippert, Brenda & Nippert, George, illus. 2006. (Illus.). 60p. (J). pap. 11.95 (978-0-9787035-1-6(0)); (ACE., 19.95 (978-0-9787035-0-9(2)) Joseph's Heart-print.

Noe, David C. Tres Mures Caeci. Thoburn, Michelle, illus. 2005. (LAT.). 48p. (J). (gr. k-12). 11.99 (978-0-9714458-1-9(8)) Patrick Henry College Pr.

Novich, Mary. Nursery Rhymes Sticker Activity Book. Hale, Jenny, illus. 2005. 64p. (J). pap. (978-1-877003-75-2(1)) Little Hare Bks.

The Nursery Collection. 2002. (Little Treasuries Ser.). 256p. (J). 11.95 (978-0-7525-7688-6(7)) Parragon, Inc.

The Nursery Collection: Stories & Rhymes for the Vey Young. 2001. 384p. (J). (978-0-7525-4105-1(6)) Parragon, Inc.

Nursery Rhyme Puppet Set Series 2. 2006. (J). per. (978-1-57332-429-8(9)) HighReach Learning, Inc.

Nursery Rhyme Soundtracks. 2003. (Illus.). pap. 15.99 (978-0-7424-1529-4(5)) School Specialty Publishing.

Nursery Rhymes. 2000. (Learning Fun for Little Ones Ser.). (Illus.). 64p. (ps-1). pap. 8.99 (978-0-88724-572-5(2) , CD-6403) Carson-Dellosa Publishing Co., Inc.

Nursery Rhymes. 2001. (Early Learning Ser.). (J). (gr. k-12). vinyl bd. 4.95 (978-1-58845-053-1(8)) School Specialty Publishing.

Nursery Rhymes. (My First Sing-Alongs Ser.). (J). 7.99 incl. audio (978-1-55723-603-6(8)) Walt Disney Records.

Nursery Rhymes - Jack & Jill. 2005. (J). bds. (978-1-4194-0077-3(0)) Paradise Pr., Inc.

Nursery Rhymes - Old Mcdonald. 2005. (J). bds. (978-1-4194-0076-6(2)) Paradise Pr., Inc.

Nursery Rhymes - One, Two, Buckle my Shoe. 2005. (J). bds. (978-1-4194-0078-0(9)) Paradise Pr., Inc.

NUrsery rhymes- Bah,Bah black Sheep. 2005. (J). bds. (978-1-4194-0079-7(7)) Paradise Pr., Inc.

Nursery Rhymes: Hey Diddle Diddle; If You're Happy & You Know It; Itsy Bitsy Spider, Including Plush Finger Puppet, 3 bks., Set. 2002. (Illus.). (J). bds. (978-1-59069-295-0(0) , MB3004) Studio Mouse LLC.

Nursery Rhymes: Old MacDonald; I'm a Little Teapot; Here We Go Round the Mulberry Bush, Including Plush Finger Puppet, 3 bks., Set 2002. (Illus.). (J). bds. (978-1-59069-292-9(6) , MB3001) Studio Mouse LLC.

Nursery Rhymes: Pat-a-Cake; Jack Be Nimble; This Little Piggy, Including Plush Finger Puppet, 3 bks., Set 2002. (Illus.). (J). bds. (978-1-59069-294-3(2) , MB3003) Studio Mouse LLC.

Nursery Rhymes-Flip Chart. 2003. 10p. (J). (gr. k-12). spiral bd. 14.95 (978-1-58845-182-8(8)) School Specialty Publishing.

Nursery Rhymes of Winnie the Pooh. 2000. (Books Are Fun Ser.). 96p. (J). 14.95 (978-0-7868-3263-7(0)) Disney Pr.

Nursery Rhymes Set 800783, 5. 2005. (J). bds. (978-1-59794-018-4(6)) Environments, Inc.

Nursery Rymes Book. 2005. (J). bds. (978-1-4194-0070-4(3)) Paradise Pr., Inc.

Nursery Songs & Rhymes. 2005. (J). 26.95 (978-1-930873-74-2(3)) Neumann Pr., The.

Nursery Songs & Rhyms Gift Book. 2006. (J). 9.99 (978-1-934004-03-6(0)) Byeway Bks.

Nursey Rhymes, 6 No., Pack. 2002. (Illus.). bds. (978-1-59069-290-5(X) , MB2001); (J). bds. (978-1-59069-291-2(8) , MB2002) Studio Mouse LLC.

Nursey Rhymes: Humpty Dumpty; Rub-a-Dub-Dub; Little Miss Muffet, Including Plush Finger Puppet, 3 bks., Set. 2002. (Illus.). (J). bds. (978-1-59069-293-6(4) , MB3002) Studio Mouse LLC.

O'Brien, Eileen. Mary Had a Little Lamb. Tyler, Jenny, ed. Edward, Linda, illus. 2004. (Carry-Me Bks.). 16p. (J). 5.95 (978-0-7945-0124-2(9) , Usborne) EDC Publishing.

—Sing a Song of Sixpence. Tyler, Jenny, ed. Edward, Linda, illus. 2004. (Carry-Me Bks.). 16p. (J). (ps). 5.95 (978-0-7945-0122-8(2) , Usborne) EDC Publishing.

—This Little Piggy. Tyler, Jenny, ed. Edward, Linda, illus. 2004. (Carry-Me Bks.). 16p. (J). 5.95 (978-0-7945-0125-9(7) , Usborne) EDC Publishing.

Old Mother Hubbard. 2002. (Nursery Rhymes Ser.). (Illus.). (J). (978-1-59069-065-9(6) , 1-2006) Studio Mouse LLC.

Olsen, Madeline. Baby's Nursery Rhymes. Rutten, Nicole, illus. 2001. (Starring Me! Ser.). 10p. (J). (ps-k). bds. 7.95 (978-1-57145-464-5(0) , Silver Dolphin Bks.) Advantage Pubs. Group.

Olson, Carole. Rock-A-Bye-Baby Reader: A first book about Reading. Schneider, Cheryl, illus. 2nd ed. 2002. 20p. (J). 3.25 (978-0-9712816-1-5(0)) Third Week Bks.

Opie, Ian, ed. My Very First Mother Goose. Wells, Rosemary, illus. 2004. 107p. (J). reprint ed. 17.00 (978-0-7567-8384-6(4)) DIANE Publishing Co.

Opie, Iona. Mother Goose's Little Treasures. Wells, Rosemary, illus. 2007. (My Very First Mother Goose Ser.). 56p. (J). (ps). 17.99 (***978-0-7636-3655-5(X)***) Candlewick Pr.

Opie, Iona, ed. Humpty Dumpty & Other Rhymes. Wells, Rosemary, illus. 2001. (My Very First Mother Goose Ser.). 16p. (J). (gr. k-ps). bds. 4.99 (978-0-7636-1628-1(1)) Candlewick Pr.

Ormerod, Jan & Gardiner, Lindsey. Whoosh Around the Mulberry Bush. 2007. 32p. (J). (gr. k-k). 8.99 (978-0-7641-9313-2(9)) Barron's Educational Series, Inc.

Orozco, Jose-Luis. Diez Deditos & Other Play Rhymes & Action Songs from Latin America. 2002. (SPA.). (gr. k-3). lib. bdg. 16.45 (978-0-613-64434-1(4)) Tandem Library Bks.

Osborne, Nancy. Rhyming Words: Cut & Paste. l.t. ed. 2007. (Illus.). 52p. ring bd. 9.95 (***978-1-928856-07-8(1)***) Osborne Pr.

Oscar: Poems, Rhymes, & Songs Listening Packs. 2003. 34.50 (978-0-673-58622-3(7)) Celebration Pr.

Pace, David. Shouting Sharon: A Riotous Counting Rhyme. 1999. (Illus.). 36p. (J). (ps-k). pap. 6.99 (978-0-7112-0896-4(4)) Lincoln, Frances Ltd. GBR. *Dist:* Transition Vendor.

Page, Josephine & Ham, George E. Hey Diddle Diddle. McDonald, Jill, illus. 2006. (My First Taggies Book Ser.). 10p. (J). bds. 6.99 (978-0-439-68116-2(2) , Cartwheel Bks.) Scholastic, Inc.

Palatini, Margie. The Web Files. Egielski, Richard, illus. 2001. 32p. 15.99 (978-0-7868-0419-1(X) , Volo) Hyperion Bks. for Children.

Paparone, Pam. Cinco Patitos(Five Little Duck. 2006. (SPA., Illus.). 26p. (J). bds. 5.95 (978-0-7358-2083-8(X)) North-South Bks., Inc.

Paparone, Pamela. Five Little Ducks. Paparone, Pamela, illus. 2004. (Illus.). 26p. (J). bds. 5.95 (978-0-7358-1857-6(6)) North-South Bks., Inc.

Parekh, R. Nursery Rhymes. 2004. (Flashcards Ser.). (Illus.). 48p. (J). pap. 8.95 (978-0-7945-0530-1(9)) EDC Publishing.

Parmenter, Wayne, illus. Mother Goose Bedtime Rhymes. 2002. 40p. (J). bds. 12.98 (978-0-7853-7818-1(9) , 7176200) Publications International, Ltd.

Pat-a-Cake. 2003. (J). per. (978-1-57657-802-5(X)) Paradise Pr., Inc.

Pearson, Tracey Campbell. Diddle, Diddle, Dumpling. 2005. (Board Books). (Illus.). 14p. (J). (ps). bds. 5.95 (978-0-374-30861-2(6) , Farrar, Straus & Giroux (BYR)) Farrar, Straus & Giroux.

—Little Miss Muffet. 2005. (Mother Goose Board Bks.). (Illus.). 14p. (J). (ps). bds. 5.95 (978-0-374-30862-9(4) , Farrar, Straus & Giroux (BYR)) Farrar, Straus & Giroux.

Pedro, Pedrito: Poems, Rhymes, & Songs Listening Packs. 2003. 34.50 (978-0-673-58632-2(4)) Celebration Pr.

Penton Kids & Book Studio Staff. Twinkle, Twinkle Little Star. Macnaughton, Tina, illus. 2006. 10p. (J). (gr. 3-9). 12.95 (978-1-59125-637-3(2) , Penton Kids) Penton Overseas, Inc.

Penton Overseas, Inc. Staff. My Big Sticker Book of Nursery Rhymes. rev. ed. 2007. 150p. (J). (gr. 3-7). pap. 10.95 (***978-1-74181-251-0(8)***) Hinkler Bks. Pty, Ltd. AUS. *Dist:* Penton Overseas, Inc.

Petites Comptines Pour... 2000. Tr. of Nusery Rymes. (FRE.). (J). 29.95 (978-2-09-210618-1(X)) Nathan, Fernand FRA. *Dist:* AIMS International Bks., Inc.

Philip, Neil. World Mother Goose. 2007. 19.95 (978-0-7624-1892-3(3)) Westview Pr.

Phonics Songs & Rhymes. 2000. (SPA.). (gr. k up). suppl. ed. 116.50 (978-0-673-60597-9(3)) Addison-Wesley Educational Pubs., Inc.

Phonics Songs & Rhymes Flip Chart. 2004. (gr. k up). suppl. ed. 109.15 (978-0-328-02213-7(6)); 2004. (gr. 1 up). suppl. ed. 109.15 (978-0-673-59716-8(4)); 2004. (gr. 2 up). suppl. ed. 109.15 (978-0-673-59717-5(2)); 2004. (gr. 3 up). suppl. ed. 109.50 (978-0-673-59718-2(0)); 2000. (SPA.). (gr. 2 up). 116.50 (978-0-673-60599-3(X)); 2000. (SPA.). (gr. 3 up). suppl. ed. 19.49 (978-0-673-60600-6(7)) Addison-Wesley Educational Pubs., Inc.

Picture Window Books Staff. Counting Your Way: Number Nursery Rhymes. Huseinovic, Andrea Petrlik, illus. 2006. (Mother Goose Rhymes Ser.). 32p. (J). (ps-2). lib. bdg. 25.26 (***978-1-4048-2346-4(8)*** , 1265751) Picture Window Bks.

—Forecasting Fun: Weather Nursery Rhymes. Knight, Paula, illus. 2006. (Mother Goose Rhymes Ser.). 32p. (J). (ps-2). lib. bdg. 25.26 (***978-1-4048-2347-1(6)*** , 1265752) Picture Window Bks.

—Ticktock: Time Nursery Rhymes. Doerrfeld, Cori, illus. 2006. (Mother Goose Rhymes Ser.). 32p. (J). (ps-2). lib. bdg. 25.26 (***978-1-4048-2348-8(4)*** , 1265753) Picture Window Bks.

Pierce, Terry. Cuddly Critters. 2007. (Mother Goose Rhymes Ser.). (Illus.). 32p. (J). (***978-1-4048-2350-1(6)*** , 1265749) Picture Window Bks.

—Sleepytime. 2007. (Mother Goose Rhymes Ser.). (Illus.). 32p. (J). (***978-1-4048-2351-8(4)*** , 1265750) Picture Window Bks.

—Ticktock. 2007. (Mother Goose Rhymes Ser.). (Illus.). 32p. (J). (***978-1-4048-2354-9(9)*** , 1265753) Picture Window Bks.

Pierce, Terry, compiled by. Mother Goose Rhymes, 6 bks., Set. Incl. Counting Your Way : Number Nursery Rhymes. Picture Window Books Staff. Huseinovic, Andrea Petrlik, illus. lib. bdg. 25.26 (***978-1-4048-2346-4(8)*** , 1265751); Cuddly Critters : Animal Nursery Rhymes. Huseinovic, Andrea Petrlik, illus. lib. bdg. 25.26 (***978-1-4048-2344-0(1)*** , 1265749); Forecasting Fun : Weather Nursery Rhymes. Picture Window Books Staff. Knight, Paula, illus. lib. bdg. 25.26 (***978-1-4048-2347-1(6)*** , 1265752); Friendly Faces : People Nursery Rhymes. Luiz, Fernando, illus. lib. bdg. 25.26 (***978-1-4048-2349-5(2)*** , 1265754); Sleepytime : Bedtime Nursery Rhymes. Beer, Barbara Vagnozzi, illus. 25.26 (***978-1-4048-2345-7(X)*** , 1265750); Ticktock : Time Nursery Rhymes. Picture Window Books Staff. Doerrfeld, Cori, illus. lib. bdg. 25.26 (***978-1-4048-2348-8(4)*** , 1265753); 32p. (J). (ps-2). 2006. 2007. Set lib. bdg. 113.70 (***978-1-4048-3512-2(1)***) Picture Window Bks.

Polacco, Patricia. Babushka's Mother Goose. Polacco, Patricia, illus. 2000. (Mother Goose Ser.). (Illus.). 64p. (J). (ps-3). pap. 7.99 (978-0-698-11860-7(X) , Putnam Juvenile) Penguin Group (USA) Inc.

—Babushka's Mother Goose. 2000. (gr. k-3). lib. bdg. 15.30 (978-0-613-28408-0(9)); (Illus.). (J). 13.79 (978-0-606-18389-5(2)) Tandem Library Bks.

Potter, Beatrix. Appley Dapply's Nursery Rhymes, Vol. 22. 2002. (Illus.). 40p. (J). 6.99 (978-0-7232-4791-3(9) , Warne) Penguin Group (USA) Inc.

—Beatrix Potter's Nursery Rhyme Book. (Potter Ser.). (Illus.). (J). (ps). 2007. 80p. 12.99 (***978-0-7232-5771-4(X)***); 2000. 84p. 12.99 (978-0-7232-4650-3(5)) Penguin Group (USA) Inc. (Warne).

—Beatrix Potter's Nursery Rhymes. 2003. (Illus.). 48p. (J). (ps-ps). pap. 14.99 (978-0-7232-4803-3(6) , Warne) Penguin Group (USA) Inc.

—Cecily Parsley's Nursery Rhyme Book. Potter, Beatrix, illus. 2002. (Illus.). 15.23 (978-0-7587-4493-7(5)) Book Wholesalers, Inc.

—Cecily Parsley's Nursery Rhymes, Vol. 23. 2002. (Illus.). 40p. (J). 6.99 (978-0-7232-4792-0(7) , Warne) Penguin Group (USA) Inc.

—Peter Rabbit's Songs & Rhymes. 2002. (Illus.). 10p. (J). (ps-ps). bds. 5.99 (978-0-7232-4846-0(X) , Warne) Penguin Group (USA) Inc.

Potter, Debra, illus. I am the Music Man. 2005. (Classic Books with Holes). 16p. (J). bds. 5.99 (978-1-904550-60-0(6)) Child's Play-International.

—The Music Man. 2005. 16p. pap. 6.99 (978-1-904550-34-1(7)) Child's Play-International.

Price, Mathew. Carry & Rhyme Collection. 2004. (Illus.). 40p. (J). bds. 19.95 (978-0-7696-3457-9(5) , Gingham Dog Pr.) School Specialty Publishing.

Priddy Books Staff. My Bedtime Book of Favorite Nursery Rhymes: Including Ladybug, Baa Baa Black Sheep, I Had a Nut Tree, Plus Many More... 2003. (Illus.). (J). bds. (978-0-312-49174-1(3) , Priddy Bks.) St. Martin's Pr.

La Primavera: Poems, Rhymes, & Songs Listening Packs. 2003. 34.50 (978-0-673-58633-9(2)) Celebration Pr.

Publications International Staff, ed. Old MacDonald & Friends. 2002. (My First Treasury Ser.). (Illus.). 40p. (J). bds. 7.98 (978-0-7853-6331-6(9) , 7162000) Publications International, Ltd.

Pussy-Cat, Pussy-Cat. 2002. (Nursery Rhymes Ser.). (Illus.). (J). (978-1-59069-062-8(1) , 1-2003) Studio Mouse LLC.

Rasmussen, Wendy, illus. Picture Me As Yankee Doodle Dandy & Other Nursery Rhymes. 1999. (Picture Me Ser.). 10p. (J). (ps-3). bds. 4.99 (978-1-57151-544-5(5)) Playhouse Publishing.

Read along Nursery Rhymes - Student Books. 2005. (J). pap. 19.95 (978-1-58970-701-6(X)) Lakeshore Learning Materials.

Read along Nursery Rhymes Big Book. 2005. (J). pap. 16.95 (978-1-58970-700-9(1)) Lakeshore Learning Materials.

Rhyme, 77 vols., Set. 2004. (Beastieville Ser.). 1000.30 (978-0-516-25139-4(2) , Children's Pr.) Scholastic Library Publishing.

Rhyme Time. 2006. (J). bds. (978-1-4194-0144-2(0)) Paradise Pr., Inc.

Rhyme Time. 2002. (978-0-9720825-1-8(4)) Toy Box Pr., The.

Rhyme Time. 2000. (Wipe-Off Activity Bks.). (Illus.). 16p. (J). (ps-1). wbk. ed. 3.79 (978-1-889319-82-7(1)) Trend Enterprises, Inc.

Rhymes 'N Rhythms: For the ESL Classroom. 2001. 80p. pap. 18.00 (978-0-86647-133-6(2)) Pro Lingua Assocs., Inc.

Rigby Education Staff. Humpty Dumpty Bigbook: Rhyme 2. (gr. k-2). 21.00 (978-0-7635-2410-4(7)) Rigby Education.

—Jack & Jill Big Book: Rhyme 1. (gr. k-2). 21.00 (978-0-7635-2404-3(2)) Rigby Education.

—Little Jack. (gr. k-2). 21.00 (978-0-7635-2412-8(3)) Rigby Education.

—Mary Big Book: Rhyme 2. (gr. k-2). 21.00 (978-0-7635-2411-1(5)) Rigby Education.

—Old King: Rhyme 1. (gr. k-2). 21.00 (978-0-7635-2405-0(0)) Rigby Education.

Robleda, Margarita. Rebeca. Suarez, Maribel, illus. (Rana, Rema, Rimas Ser.). (SPA.). 16p. (J). (gr. k-3). 7.95 (978-1-59437-819-5(3)) Santillana USA Publishing Co., Inc.

—Suenos. Suarez, Maribel, illus. (Rana, Rema, Rimas Ser.). (SPA.). 16p. (J). (gr. k-3). 7.95 (978-1-59437-821-8(5)) Santillana USA Publishing Co., Inc.

Roig, Mercedes Diaz & Miaja, Maria Teresa, compiled by. Naranja Dulce, Limon Partido: Antologia de la Lirica Infantil Mexicana. (SPA.). (J). (gr. 1-5). pap. incl. audio compact disk (978-968-12-0712-0(2) , FC7387) El Colegio de México, A.C., Biblioteca Miguel Cosio Villegas MEX. *Dist:* Lectorum Pubns., Inc.

Ruiz, John. Humpty Dumpty Was Pushed. 2001. (Illus.). 24p. (J). (gr. k-6). pap. 3.99 (978-0-9715245-6-9(4)) Teamwork Foundation, Inc.

Sabuda, Robert. The Movable Mother Goose. Sabuda, Robert, illus. 1999. (Illus.). 12p. (J). (ps-3). 21.99 (978-0-689-81192-0(6) , Little Simon) Simon & Schuster Children's Publishing.

Salgado, Tono. Versos y Rimas para Ninos.Tr. of Verses & Ryhmes for Children. (SPA.). (J). 7.98 (978-968-403-880-6(1)) Selector, S.A. de C.V. MEX. *Dist:* AIMS International Bks., Inc.

Sanderson, Ruth. Mother Goose. 2008. 64p. (J). (ps-1). 16.99 (978-0-316-77718-6(8)) Little Brown & Co.

Scheffler, Axel & Green, Alison. Mother Goose's Storytime Nursery Rhymes. 2007. (J). (978-0-439-90307-3(6)); 128p. 19.99 (978-0-439-90306-6(8)) Scholastic, Inc. (Levine, Arthur A. Bks.).

Schietinger-Cachina, Daryl A. Hey New Baby in There. Schietinger-Cachina, Daryl A., illus. 1999. (Illus.). 8p. (J). (ps-5). pap. 5.00 (978-1-928641-02-5(4)) Daryl Ann Pubns.

—How about Some Manners. Schietinger-Cachina, Daryl A., illus. 1999. (Illus.). 10p. (J). (ps-8). pap. 5.00 (978-1-928641-05-6(9)) Daryl Ann Pubns.

Scholastic, Inc. Staff. Classic Counting Rhymes. Wright, Blanche Fisher & Yee, Josie, illus. 2002. (Real Mother Goose Library Ser.). 8p. (J). bds. 5.99 (978-0-439-39535-9(6)) Scholastic, Inc.

—Five Little Ducks. 2007. (Little Scholastic Ser.). (Illus.). 12p. (J). bds. 7.99 (***978-0-439-02147-0(2)***) Scholastic, Inc.

—Humpty Dumpty Loop Rattle, 12 Pack. 2003. (Sidekicks Ser.). (J). 83.88 (978-0-439-55402-2(0) , Sidekicks TM) Scholastic, Inc.

—Old Macdonald Puppet Book. Berg, Michelle, illus. 2004. (Hand Puppet Board Bks.). 6p. (J). 12.95 (978-0-439-69392-9(6) , Cartwheel Bks.) Scholastic, Inc.

—Real Mother Goose. 2005. (Mary Had A Little Lamb Stacking Ring Toy Ser.). (J). 19.99 (978-0-439-72170-7(9) , SideKicks TM Baby) Scholastic, Inc.

—The Real Mother Goose. 2005. (Mary Had A Little Lamb Plush W/ Rattle Ser.). (J). 9.99 (978-0-439-73709-8(5) , SideKicks TM Baby) Scholastic, Inc.

—The Real Mother Goose: Classic Color Rhymes. Wright, Blanche Fisher & Yee, Josie, illus. 2002. (Real Mother Goose Library Ser.). 8p. (J). bds. 5.99 (978-0-439-39536-6(4)) Scholastic, Inc.

—Spiders, Bats, & Pumpkin Eaters. Maccarone, Grace, ed. Smath, Jerry, illus. 2004. 5p. (J). bds. 5.95 (978-0-439-62333-9(2) , Cartwheel Bks.) Scholastic, Inc.

—Twinkle, Twinkle, Little Star. Berg, Michelle, illus. 2004. 8p. (J). 12.95 (978-0-439-61667-6(0) , Cartwheel Bks.) Scholastic, Inc.

Scholastic, Inc. Staff, ed. Georgie/Mother Ghost. 2000. (J). pap. 3.95 (978-0-590-04409-7(5)) Scholastic, Inc.

Scieszka, Jon. The Book That Jack Wrote. 2002. (Illus.). (J). 14.04 (978-0-7587-2132-7(3)) Book Wholesalers, Inc.

Sechi-Johnson, Patricia. Hickory Dickory Dock. Hurt-Newton, Tania, illus. 2000. (Mini Finger Puppet Bks.). 16p. (J). (ps-k). 6.95 (978-1-86233-127-3(8)) Sterling Publishing Co., Inc.

Sechi-Johnson, Patricia & Hurt-Newton, Tania. Hickory Dickory Dock. 1999. (Finger Puppet Bks.). (Illus.). 16p. (J). (ps-k). 10.95 (978-1-86233-058-0(1)) Sterling Publishing Co., Inc.

Sefton, Catherine. Watch Out Fred's About. (Illus.). 64p. (J). 7.95 (978-0-14-037891-7(X)) Penguin Bks., Ltd. GBR. *Dist:* Trafalgar Square Publishing.

Sellers, Amy. Miss Amy's: Hurray for Rhyme It's Story Time: Contemporary Rhyming Stories for Children of All Ages. 2007. 32p. (J). pap. 19.95 (***978-0-9787632-0-6(3)***) Sellers, Amy.

Sendak, Maurice. Hector Protector & As I Went over the Water: Two Nursery Rhymes. Sendak, Maurice, illus. 2001. (Sendak Reissues Ser.). (Illus.). 64p. (ps-3). 17.95 (978-0-06-028642-2(3)) HarperCollins Pubs.

Šenor Cascaron: Poems, Rhymes, & Songs Listening Packs. 2003. (SPA.). 34.50 (978-0-673-58623-0(5)) Celebration Pr.

Sing & Learn, ed. Nursery Rhymes. 2007. (Sing & Learn Padded Board Bks.). 53p. (J). bds. 16.95 (***978-0-7696-5469-0(X)***) School Specialty Publishing.

Siomades, Lorianne. Three Little Kittens. Siomades, Lorianne, illus. 2003. (Illus.). 24p. (J). (ps up). 12.95 (978-1-56397-845-6(8)) Boyds Mills Pr.

Smee, Nicola. Sleepyhead. 2002. (Baby Action Rhymes Ser.). (Illus.). 10p. (J). bds. 4.95 (978-0-7641-5453-9(2)) Barron's Educational Series, Inc.

—Sleepyhead. 2004. (URD, BEN, ENG & PAN., Illus.). 12p. (J). (978-1-85269-095-3(X)); (978-1-85269-096-0(8)); (978-1-85269-097-7(6)) Mantra Publishing, Ltd.

Smith, Eric, illus. This Little Piggy & Other Favorite Rhymes. 2005. 36p. (J). 12.95 incl. cd-rom (978-1-59249-466-8(8) , 1D013) Soundprints.

Smith, Jane, illus. Old MacDonald. 2002. (Nursery Rhymes Ser.). 10p. (J). bds. (978-1-59069-282-0(9) , MB1005) Studio Mouse LLC.

Smith, Jane & Atkins, Aileen, illus. Humpty Dumpty. 2002. (Nursery Rhymes Ser.). 10p. (J). bds. (978-1-59069-289-9(6) , MB1012) Studio Mouse LLC.

Souhami, Jessica. Mother Caught a Flea: Silly Rhymes about a Family. 1999. (Silly Rhymes Ser.). (Illus.). 24p. (J). (ps-1). 7.99 (978-0-7112-1243-5(0)) Lincoln, Frances Ltd. GBR. *Dist:* Antique Collectors' Club.

—One Potato, Two Potato. 1999. (Silly Rhymes Ser.). (Illus.). 24p. (J). (ps-1). 7.99 (978-0-7112-1244-2(9)) Lincoln, Frances Ltd. GBR. *Dist:* Antique Collectors' Club.

Soundprints. Farmer in Dell. 2005. (Mother Goose Ser.). (Illus.). 36p. (J). 12.95 incl. cd-rom (978-1-59249-380-7(7) , 1D005) Soundprints.

—Hey Diddle Diddle: Playtime Rhymes. 2002. (My First Mother Goose Ser.). (Illus.). 48p. (J). (ps-k). 9.95 (978-1-56899-919-7(4) , M1156) Soundprints.

—Hey Diddle Diddle & Other Favorites. (Mother Goose Nursery Rhymes Ser.). (Illus.). 36p. (J). bds. 10.95 incl. audio compact disk (978-1-59069-219-6(5) , MD1110); 2003. bds. 8.95 (978-1-59069-218-9(7)) Studio Mouse LLC.

—Hey Diddle Diddle & Other Favorites. (Mother Goose Nursery Rhymes Ser.). (Illus.). 36p. (J). bds. 14.95 incl. audio compact disk (978-1-59069-221-9(7) , MPD1110) Studio Mouse LLC.

—Humpty Dumpty: Story Rhymes. 2002. (My First Mother Goose Ser.). (Illus.). 48p. (J). (ps-k). 9.95 (978-1-56899-931-9(3) , M1151) Soundprints.

—I'm a Little Teapot & Other Favorites. 2003. (Nursery Sing-a-Longs Ser.). (Illus.). 36p. (J). 8.95 (978-1-59069-202-8(0)) Studio Mouse LLC.

—I've Been Workin on Railroad. 2005. (Mother Goose Ser.). (Illus.). 36p. (J). 12.95 incl. audio (978-1-59249-379-1(3) , 1D003) Soundprints.

—Mother Goose Bitsy Board Book Travel Pack. 2005. (Studio Mouse Ser.). (Illus.). 10p. (J). 9.95 incl. cd-rom (978-1-59069-359-9(0)); Vol. 2. 9.95 incl. cd-rom (978-1-59069-360-5(4)) Studio Mouse LLC.

—Mother Goose's HIDE n SEEK Book. 2005. (Studio Mouse Ser.). (Illus.). 24p. (J). 12.95 incl. cd-rom (978-1-59069-376-6(0)) Studio Mouse LLC.

—Nursery Rhymes: Story Time Treasury. 2005. (Studio Mouse Ser.). (Illus.). 256p. (J). (ps-2). 14.95 (978-1-59069-228-8(4) , MT1001) Studio Mouse LLC.

—Twinkle Twinkle: Sleepytime Rhymes. 2002. (My First Mother Goose Ser.). (Illus.). 48p. (J). (ps-k). 9.95 (978-1-56899-923-4(2) , M1157) Soundprints.

Soundprints Staff. Baa Baa Black Sheep: Sing-Along Rhymes. 2002. (My First Mother Goose Ser.). (Illus.). 36p. (J). (ps-k). 9.95 (978-1-56899-927-2(5) , M1158) Soundprints.

—Hey Diddle Diddle Playtime Rhymes: My First Mother Goose. 2002. (My First Mother Goose Ser.). (Illus.). 36p. (J). (ps-k). 11.95 incl. cd-rom (978-1-56899-920-3(8) , MD1156) Soundprints.

Southwater Staff. Old MacDonald's Farm. 2000. (Superstickers Ser.). (Illus.). 64p. (ps-2). pap. 7.95 (978-1-84215-261-4(0) , Southwater) Anness Publishing GBR. *Dist:* National Bk. Network.

Soy La Cafetera: Poems, Rhymes, & Songs Listening Packs. 2003. 34.50 (978-0-673-58634-6(0)) Celebration Pr.

Spengler, Margaret, illus. One, Two, Buckle My Shoe. 2004. (J). bds. 6.99 (978-1-890647-12-4(8)) RC2 Corp.

Spirin, Gennady. A Apple Pie. Spirin, Gennady, illus. 2005. (Illus.). 32p. (J). (ps-1). 16.99 (978-0-399-23981-6(2) , Philomel) Penguin Group (USA) Inc.

Squillace, Elisa, illus. Down in the Jungle. 2004. 16p. pap. 6.99 (978-1-904550-32-7(0)) Child's Play-International.

Steck-Vaughn Staff. Counting Rhymes: One Potato. 1998. (Illus.). (J). pap. (978-0-8172-8631-6(4)) Steck-Vaughn.

—Rhymes: Kinds of Rocks/Quiet Afternoon. 1998. (Illus.). (J). pap. (978-0-8172-8648-4(9)) Steck-Vaughn.

—Traditional Rhymes: Hickory/Jack. 1998. (Illus.). (J). pap. (978-0-8172-8629-3(2)) Steck-Vaughn.

Stetson, Emily & Congdon, Vicky. Little Hands Fingerplays & Action Songs: Seasonal Rhymes & Creative Play for 2 to 6 Year-Olds. Day, Betsy, illus. 2001. (Little Hands Bks.). 128p. (J). (ps-3). pap. 12.95 (978-1-885593-53-5(8) , Williamson Bks.) Ideals Pubns.

Stevens, Janet & Crummel, Susan Stevens. And the Dish Ran Away with the Spoon. Stevens, Janet, illus. 2001. (Illus.). 56p. (J). (gr. k-3). 17.00 (978-0-15-202298-3(8)) Harcourt Children's Bks.

Stevens, Janet & Crummel, Susan Stevens, as told by. And the Dish Ran Away with the Spoon. 2001. (J). (gr. k-3). incl. audio Spoken Arts, Inc.

Still, James. An Appalachian Mother Goose. Johnson, Paul Brett, illus. 1998. 64p. (ps-3). 16.95 (978-0-8131-2092-8(6)) Univ. Pr. of Kentucky.

Stockham, Jess. Down by the Station. 2002. (Illus.). 16p. (J). 19.99 (978-0-85953-123-8(6)) Child's Play-International.

Stockham, Jessica, illus. Down by the Station. 2002. 16p. (J). 6.99 (978-0-85953-942-5(3)) Child's Play-International.

Stockham, Jessica, tr. & illus. Ten Little Speckled Frogs. Stockham, Jessica, illus. 2003. 24p. (J). 9.99 (978-0-85953-959-3(8)) Child's Play-International.

Story Time Staff. Alfreda's Reader's Theatre: I No Comprehende They Habla Espanol. 1999. 12p. (YA). (gr. 5-12). lab manual ed. 8.95 (978-1-56820-368-3(3)) Story Time Stories That Rhyme.

Strevens-Marzo, Bridget. Bridget's Book of Nursery Rhymes. 2007. (Illus.). 24p. (J). (ps-k). 12.95 (***978-1-921049-52-1(9)***) Little Hare Bks. AUS. *Dist:* Independent Pubs. Group.

Studio Mouse. Head Shoulders Knees & Toes. 2005. (Mother Goose Ser.). (Illus.). 34p. (J). bds. 15.95 incl. audio compact disk (978-1-59249-386-9(6) , 1D008) Soundprints.

—Princess Rhyme Time. 2007. (Illus.). 36p. 12.99 incl. audio compact disk (978-1-59069-495-4(3) , 1A802) Studio Mouse LLC.

Style Guide Staff, illus. Blue's Bedtime Nursery Rhymes. 2004. (Blue's Clues Ser.). 36p. (J). bds. 8.99 (978-0-689-86831-3(6) , Simon Spotlight/Nickelodeon) Simon & Schuster Children's Publishing.

t, Randolph (Il. Come Lasses & Lads Illustrated Edition. 2006. pap. (***978-1-4065-1220-5(6)***) Dodo Pr.

—Hey Diddle Diddle & Baby Bunting Illus. 2006. pap. (***978-1-4065-1226-7(5)***) Dodo Pr.

—House That Jack Built Illustrated Editio. 2006. pap. (***978-1-4065-1227-4(3)***) Dodo Pr.

—Queen of Hearts & Sing A Song for Sixp. 2006. pap. (***978-1-4065-1228-1(1)***) Dodo Pr.

—Ride A CockHorse to Banbury Cross & A. 2006. pap. (***978-1-4065-1229-8(X)***) Dodo Pr.

—Three Jovial Huntsmen Illustrated Editio. 2007. pap. (***978-1-4065-1230-4(3)***) Dodo Pr.

Taback, Simms. This Is the House That Jack Built. Taback, Simms, illus. 32p. (J). (gr. k-3). 2002. (Illus.). 15.99 (978-0-399-23488-0(8) , Putnam Juvenile); 2004. reprint ed. pap. 6.99 (978-0-14-240200-9(1) , Puffin) Penguin Group (USA) Inc.

Tabori, Lena & Fried, Natasha Tabori. A Little Box of Books: Fairy Tales, Nursery Rhymes, Songs. 3 vols. (Illus.). 48p. 16.95 (978-0-941807-64-7(9) , Welcome Bks.) Welcome Enterprises, Inc.

Taggart, Katy, et al, illus. Workin' on the Railroad: And Other Favorite Rhymes. 2004. (Mother Goose Ser.). 36p. (J). bds. 15.95 incl. audio compact disk (978-1-59249-385-2(8) , 1D004) Soundprints.

Taylor, Geraldine & Harker, Jillian. Twinkle, Twinkle, Little Star. Sharratt, Nick, illus. 1999. (Baby Touch & Count Ser.). 12p. (J). 7.99 (978-0-7214-2737-9(5) , Dutton Juvenile) Penguin Group (USA) Inc.

Taylor, Jane, et al. Twinkle Twinkle. King, Dave, illus. King, Dave, photos by. 2004. (Baby Games Ser.). 16p. (J). bds. 5.99 (978-0-7566-0257-4(2)) Dorling Kindersley Publishing, Inc.

Tenuta, Lisa. Rhymes & Rhythms Package: For the ESL Classroom. 2001. pap. 27.00 incl. audio (978-0-86647-163-3(4)) Pro Lingua Assocs., Inc.

Thienes-Schunemann, Mary. Lavender's Blue Dilly Dilly. 1 bk, 1 CD. 2004. (J). spiral bd. 21.95 incl. audio compact disk (978-0-9708397-7-0(4)) Naturally You Can Sing.

Thompson, Richard & Spicer, Maggee. When They Are Up. Wakelin, Kirsti Anne, illus. 2004. 36p. (J). (978-1-55041-707-4(X)) Fitzhenry & Whiteside, Ltd.

Thompson, Richard & Spicer, Maggie. When They Are Up. Wakelin, Kirsti Anne, illus. 2007. 32p. pap. ***(978-1-55041-709-8(6))*** Fitzhenry & Whiteside, Ltd.

Tiger Tales Staff, ed. Hickory, Dickory, Dock: And Other Favorite Nursury Rhymes. Rescek, Sanja, illus. 2006. 22p. (J). bds. 7.95 (978-1-58925-786-3(3) , tiger tales) ME Media LLC.

—Twinkle, Twinkle Little Star: And Other Favorite Bedtime Rhymes. Rescek, Sanja, illus. 2006. 22p. (J). bds. 7.95 (978-1-58925-787-0(1) , tiger tales) ME Media LLC.

Tipoti, Alick. Mura Migi Kazika: Torres Strait Islander Nursery Rhymes. 2000. (Uupababa Ser.). (Illus.). 24p. (J). pap. 4.95 (978-1-875641-55-0(6)) Magabala Bks. AUS. *Dist:* International Specialized Bk. Services.

Trapani, Iza. Baa Baa Black Sheep. Trapani, Iza, illus. 2004. (Illus.). 32p. (J). (gr. k-3). 16.95 (978-1-58089-070-0(9)); pap. 6.95 (978-1-58089-071-7(7)) Charlesbridge Publishing, Inc.

—Baa Baa Black Sheep. 2001. 13.75 (978-0-606-22635-6(4)); lib. bdg. 15.25 (978-0-613-51235-0(9)) Tandem Library Bks.

—Brilla, Brilla, Linda Estrella. Lazaro, Georgina, tr. Trapani, Iza, illus. 2004. 32p. (J). pap. 7.95 (978-1-58089-092-2(X)) Charlesbridge Publishing, Inc.

—Jingle Bells. Trapani, Iza, illus. 2007. (Illus.). 32p. (J). (ps-k). pap. 6.95 (978-1-58089-096-0(2)) Charlesbridge Publishing, Inc.

—Mary Had a Little Lamb. Trapani, Iza, illus. 2004. (Illus.). 24p. (J). (ps-2). bds. 6.95 (978-1-58089-032-8(6)) Charlesbridge Publishing, Inc.

—Mary Had a Little Lamb. 1999. (Extended Nursery Rhymes Ser.). (Illus.). 32p. (J). (ps up). lib. bdg. 23.33 (978-0-8368-2488-9(1)) Stevens, Gareth Inc.

—Row, Row, Row Your Boat. 2004. (Illus.). 32p. (J). (ps-2). pap. 6.95 (978-1-58089-077-9(6)) Charlesbridge Publishing, Inc.

Trapani, Iza, illus. & as told by. Here We Go 'Round the Mulberry Bush. Trapani, Iza, as told by. 2006. 32p. (J). pap. 6.95 (978-1-57091-699-1(3)) Charlesbridge Publishing, Inc.

Tucker, Bob. Grandpa Tucker's Rhymes & Tales. Newlund, Christine & Smith, Larry, illus. 1999. 192p. (J). (gr. 1-6). pap. 13.95 (978-1-929146-00-0(0)) Keep Smiling.

Turner, Dona, illus. The Itsy Bitsy Spider. 1999. 20p. (J). reprint ed. 16.95 (978-1-892374-29-5(3)) Weldon Owen, Inc.

Twinkle, Twinkle, Little Star. 2002. (DK Ladybird Ser.). 12p. (J). bds. 6.95 (978-0-7894-8473-4(0)) Dorling Kindersley Publishing, Inc.

Van Fleet, Mara. Up the Water Spout & Other Nursery Rhymes. 2005. (Illus.). 10p. (J). (ps-k). bds. 12.99 (978-0-7944-0766-7(8)) Reader's Digest Assn., Inc., The.

Wadsworth, Olive A. Over in the Meadow. 2003. (ps-2). lib. bdg. 15.25 (978-0-613-73548-3(X)) Tandem Library Bks.

—Over in the Meadow: A Counting Rhyme. Vojtech, Anna, illus. 32p. (J). 2003. pap. 6.95 (978-0-7358-1871-2(1)); 2002. 15.95 (978-0-7358-1596-4(8)) North-South Bks., Inc.

Walrus Books. Children's Treasure Chest: Fairy Tales, Nursery Rhymes, & Nonsense Verse. 2004. (Illus.). 386p. (J). (gr. k-12). 29.95 (978-1-55285-579-9(1)) Whitecap Bks., Ltd. CAN. *Dist:* Graphic Arts Ctr. Publishing Co.

Warren, Jean. Alphabet Rhymes. 1998. (Reproducible Rhyme Book Ser.). (Illus.). 80p. (ps). 9.99 (978-1-57029-277-4(9) , WPH48001, Totline Pubns.) Schaffer, Frank Pubns.

Watson, Clyde. Father Fox's Pennyrhymes. 2001. (Illus.). 64p. (J). 15.89 (978-0-06-029502-8(3)) HarperCollins Pubs.

—Father Fox's Pennyrhymes. Watson, Wendy, illus. 2001. 64p. (J). 15.95 (978-0-06-029501-1(5)) HarperCollins Pubs.

Weeks, Sarah. Splish, Splash! Wolff, Ashley, illus. 1999. (My First I Can Read Bks.). 32p. (J). (ps up). 12.89 (978-0-06-027893-9(5)) HarperCollins Pubs.

Westcott, Nadine Bernard. The Lady with the Alligator Purse. Westcott, Nadine Bernard, illus. 2002. (Illus.). (J). 13.15 (978-0-7587-2950-7(2)) Book Wholesalers, Inc.

Whatley, Bruce, illus. My First Nursery Rhymes. 1999. (Growing Tree Ser.). 24p. (J). (ps-k). 9.99 (978-0-694-01205-3(X) , Harper Festival) HarperCollins Pubs.

The Wheels on the Bus: A Touch & Sing Book. 2002. (DK Ladybird Ser.). 12p. (J). bds. 6.95 (978-0-7894-8472-7(2)) Dorling Kindersley Publishing, Inc.

Winter. Twinkle Twinkle Little Star. 2000. (Illus.). (J). (978-0-15-204721-4(2)) Elsevier Australia.

Winter, Jeanette. Hey Diddle Diddle. 1999. (Illus.). 24p. (J). (ps). bds. 4.95 (978-0-15-202133-7(7) , Red Wagon Bks.) Harcourt Children's Bks.

—The House That Jack Built. Winter, Jeanette, illus. 2000. (Illus.). 32p. (J). (ps-1). 14.99 (978-0-8037-2524-9(8) , Dial) Penguin Group (USA) Inc.

—House That Jack Built. 2003. (gr. k-3). lib. bdg. 14.15 (978-0-613-61630-0(8)) Tandem Library Bks.

—The House that Jack Built. Winter, Jeanette, illus. 2003. (Illus.). 32p. (J). pap. 6.99 (978-0-14-230126-5(4) , Puffin) Penguin Group (USA) Inc.

—The Itsy-Bitsy Spider. 2000. (Illus.). 24p. (J). (ps). bds. 4.95 (978-0-15-202130-6(2) , Red Wagon Bks.) Harcourt Children's Bks.

—Rock-a-Bye Baby. 1999. (Illus.). 32p. (J). (ps). bds. 4.95 (978-0-15-202132-0(9) , Red Wagon Bks.) Harcourt Children's Bks.

—Twinkle Twinkle Little Star. 2000. (Illus.). 24p. (J). (ps). bds. 4.95 (978-0-15-202131-3(0) , Red Wagon Bks.) Harcourt Children's Bks.

Wohnoutka, Mike, illus. This Little Piggy. 2005. (J). (978-1-58987-106-9(5)) Kindermusik International.

Wordshop Editorial Staff. Twink 'n' Twinkle: The Beginning. 1999. (Illus.). 28p. (J). (ps-4). 19.95 (978-0-9668469-0-4(7)) WordSHOP, Inc.

Wright, Blanche Fisher. My First Real Mother Goose. Wright, Blanche Fisher, illus. 2000. (Mother Goose Ser.). (Illus.). 15p. (J). (ps-k). bds. 6.99 (978-0-439-14671-5(2)) Scholastic, Inc.

Wright, Blanche Fisher, illus. Real Mother Goose Clock Book. 22p. (J). (ps-2). 6.95 (978-1-56288-095-8(0)) Checkerboard Pr., Inc.

—Touch & Feel Book, 50 vols. 2001. (Real Mother Goose Ser.). 14p. (J). (ps up). bds. 6.99 (978-0-439-25481-6(7) , Cartwheel Bks.) Scholastic, Inc.

Wright, Fisher Blanc. The Real Mother Goose. 2006. (Illus.). pap. 88.99 ***(978-1-4280-2848-7(X))*** IndyPublish.com.

Wyndham, Robert & Young, Ed. Chinese Mother Goose Rhymes. 1998. (Illus.). 48p. (J). (ps-3). pap. 7.99 (978-0-698-11622-1(4) , Putnam Juvenile) Penguin Group (USA) Inc.

Yaccarino, Dan. Dan Yaccarino's Mother Goose. Yaccarino, Dan, illus. 2003. (Little Golden Book Ser.). (Illus.). 24p. (J). (gr. k-k). 2.99 (978-0-375-82571-2(1) , Golden Bks.) Random Hse. Children's Bks.

Yolen, Jane, ed. This Little Piggy & Other Rhymes to Sing & Play: Lap Songs, Finger Plays, Clapping Games & Pantomime Rhymes. Hillenbrand, Will, illus. 2006. 80p. (J). (gr. k-ps). 19.99 (978-0-7636-1348-8(7)) Candlewick Pr.

Yoon, Salina. Twinkle, Twinkle, Little Star. 2007. (Salina Yoon Bks.). 10p. (J). (ps-k). bds. 5.99 (978-0-8431-2177-3(7) , Price Stern Sloan) Penguin Group (USA) Inc.

Zemach, Margot. Mother Goose Picture Book. 2000. (Michael di Capua Bks.). (Illus.). (J). 14.95 (978-0-06-205046-5(X)); lib. bdg. 14.89 (978-0-06-205047-2(8)) HarperCollins Pubs.

—Some from the Moon, Some from the Sun: Poems & Songs for Everyone. Zemach, Margot, illus. 2001. (Illus.). 48p. (J). (ps-2). 17.00 (978-0-374-39960-3(3) , Farrar, Straus & Giroux (BYR)) Farrar, Straus & Giroux.

Ziefert, Harriet. What Happened to Jack & Jill? A Flip-and-Read Book. Rader, Laura, illus. 2004. 24p. (J). bds. 8.95 (978-1-4027-1784-0(9)) Sterling Publishing Co., Inc.

—Where Is Humpty Dumpty? A Flip-and-Read Book. Rader, Laura, illus. 2004. 24p. (J). bds. 8.95 (978-1-4027-1785-7(7)) Sterling Publishing Co., Inc.

Zinsmeister, Elke, illus. Ten Fat Sausages. 2004. 16p. pap. 6.99 (978-1-904550-31-0(2)) Child's Play-International.

NURSERY SCHOOLS

see also Kindergarten

Anderson, Pamela. My New School: Blonde Girl. Lee, Han & Wu, Stacie, illus. 2004. (J). 12.95 (978-1-932555-04-2(8)) Watch Me Grow Kids.

Beylon, Cathy. Fun at Nursery School. 2006. 32p. (J). (ps-3). pap. 3.95 (978-0-486-44536-6(4)) Dover Pubns., Inc.

Bunnett, Rochelle. Amigos en la Escuela. Brown, Matt, photos by. 2006. Tr. of Friends at School. (SPA., Illus.). 32p. (J). pap. (978-1-59572-041-2(3)) Star Bright Bks., Inc.

Burton, Marilee Robin. Kindergarten Scholar. 2004. 32p. (J). pap. 2.49 (978-1-58947-455-0(4)) School Zone Publishing Co.

Carder, Ken & Laroy, Sue. Songs That Teach Preschool Skills. 2006. (Songs That Teach Ser.). 72p. (J). pap. 14.95 (978-0-7696-6439-2(3) , American Education Publishing) School Specialty Publishing.

Carole, Jane. Get Ready for Pre-K. 2006. (Illus.). 320p. (J). spiral bd. 17.95 (978-1-57912-549-3(2)) Black Dog & Leventhal Pubs., Inc.

Cleveland, Alexandra, et al. Camino al Primer Grado. Franco, Sharon, tr. from ENG. Koeller, Carol, illus. 2004. (SPA.). 128p. (Orig.). (J). pap. 14.95 (978-0-943452-35-7(X)) Building Blocks, LLC.

Contando. 2005. (SPA.). (J). (ps up). pap. 6.95 (978-950-11-0903-0(8)) Sigmar ARG. *Dist:* AIMS International Bks., Inc., Lectorum Pubns., Inc., Iaconi, Mariuccia Bk. Imports.

de Fatima Campos, Maria. Victoria's Day. 2007. (Illus.). 32p. (J). (ps-k). 16.95 ***(978-1-84507-571-2(4))*** Lincoln, Frances Ltd. GBR. *Dist:* Perseus Distribution.

Douglas, Vincent. Everything for Early Learning Vol. 1: Preschool. 2004. (Everything for Early Learning Ser.: Vol. 1). (Illus.). 320p. (J). (gr. k-k). pap. 7.95 (978-0-7696-3347-3(1) , American Education Publishing) School Specialty Publishing.

Equipo Staff. La Escuela Infantil. (Coleccion Mundo Maravilloso). (SPA., Illus.). 36p. (J). (gr. 2-4). (978-84-348-7228-8(5) , SM31363) SM Ediciones ESP. *Dist:* Lectorum Pubns., Inc.

Gnojewski, Carol. Playtime Props for Toddlers. Burris, Priscilla, illus. 2001. (Time for Toddlers Ser.). 160p. (J). (ps). pap. 16.99 (978-1-57029-204-0(3) , WPH4701, Totline Pubns.) Schaffer, Frank Pubns.

Hanson, Marci J. It's Time for Preschool. 2001. (Me, Too! Ser.). (Illus.). 28p. pap. 19.95 (978-1-55766-510-2(9) , 5109) Brookes, Paul H. Publishing Co.

Heinemann Educational Ltd. Publishing Staff. Minbeasts Up Close Package. 2004. pap. 243.00 (978-1-4109-1386-9(4)) Harcourt Schl. Pubs.

Hoffman, Joan. Kindergarten Basics. 2004. 32p. (J). pap. 2.49 (978-1-58947-436-9(8)) School Zone Publishing Co.

Kannenberg, Stacey. Let's Get Ready for Kindergarten! rev. ed. 2006. (Illus.). 30p. (J). (ps-1). per. 19.00 (978-1-933476-00-1(1)) Cedar Valley Publishing.

Key Porter Books Staff. Gymboree in a Princess Castle. rev. ed. 2007. (Illus.). 1p. (J). 16.95 ***(978-1-55263-923-8(1))*** Key Porter Bks. CAN. *Dist:* Perseus Distribution.

—Gymboree on a Pirate Ship. rev. ed. 2007. (Illus.). 1p. (J). 16.95 ***(978-1-55263-921-4(5))*** Key Porter Bks. CAN. *Dist:* Perseus Distribution.

Mason, Jane B. & Hines Stephens, Sarah. Gymboree Dance Play. rev. ed. 2007. (Illus.). 36p. (J). (ps-2). bds. 16.95 ***(978-1-55263-960-3(6))*** Key Porter Bks. CAN. *Dist:* Perseus Distribution.

—Gymboree Face Painting: Imaginative Designs Plus Fun-Filled Activities! rev. ed. 2007. (Illus.). 36p. (J). (ps-2). bds. 16.95 ***(978-1-55263-962-7(2))*** Key Porter Bks. CAN. *Dist:* Perseus Distribution.

—Gymboree Music Play. rev. ed. 2007. (Illus.). 36p. (J). bds. 16.95 ***(978-1-55263-964-1(9))*** Key Porter Bks. CAN. *Dist:* Perseus Distribution.

Mitzo Thompson, Kim & Mitzo Hilderbrand, Karen. Songs That Teach Kindergarten Skills. 2006. (Songs That Teach Ser.). 72p. (J). pap. 14.95 (978-0-7696-6440-8(7) , American Education Publishing) School Specialty Publishing.

Neelly, Linda Page, et al, eds. Start the Music Strategies. 2000. (Illus.). 32p. pap. 6.00 (978-1-56545-144-5(9)) MENC - The National Assn. for Music Education.

Plum, Joan E. & Plum, Paul S. I Am Special Preschool 1 (3-Year-Olds) Activity Book, Vol. 1. 4th ed. 1999. (Illus.). 112p. (J). (ps). 9.32 (978-0-87973-116-8(8)) Our Sunday Visitor, Publishing Div.

Preschool Children. (Illus.). 8.00 (978-0-687-04974-5(1)) Abingdon Pr.

Preschool Excelerator, 2 CDs. 2002. cd-rom 9.99 (978-1-59150-011-7(7)) TOPICS Entertainment.

School Zone Interactive Staff. Kindergarten. (J). 2005. cd-rom 24.99 (978-1-58947-682-0(4)); 2002. 320p. 19.99 (978-1-58947-852-7(5)) School Zone Publishing Co.

Weber, Lou, ed. Get Dressed Lace & Learn. 2004. 16p. (J). spiral bd., bds. 9.98 (978-1-4127-3151-5(8) , 7232300) Publications International, Ltd.

NURSERY SCHOOLS—FICTION

Brown, Marc. D. W.'s Guide to Preschool. 2006. (D. W. Ser.). 32p. (J). (ps-1). reprint ed. pap. 5.99 (978-0-316-01315-4(3)) Little Brown & Co.

—D. W.'s Guide to Preschool. Brown, Marc, illus. 2003. (D. W. Ser.). (Illus.). 32p. (J). (ps-1). 15.95 (978-0-316-12069-2(3)) Little, Brown Bks. for Young Readers.

Caseley, Judith. Mr. Green Peas. 1998. (Illus.). 32p. (J). (ps-3). pap. 4.95 (978-0-688-16092-0(1)) HarperCollins Pubs.

Chodos-Irvine, Margaret. Best Best Friends. 2006. (Illus.). 40p. (J). 16.00 (978-0-15-205694-0(7)) Harcourt Trade Pubs.

Cork, Barbara. Sam Starts School. Smee, Nicola, illus. 2002. (First Experiences Ser.). 32p. (J). (gr. k-2). 15.00 (978-1-57768-989-8(5) , Waterbird Bks.) School Specialty Publishing.

Crabberg, Edna Dookie. Time to Go Home. 2000. (Illus.). 6p. (J). pap. 8.00 (978-0-9667830-5-6(0)) Early Learning Assessment 2000.

Edwards, Becky. My First Day at Nursery School. 2004. (Illus.). 32p. (J). (ps-1). pap. 6.95 (978-1-58234-909-1(6) , Bloomsbury Children) Bloomsbury Publishing.

—My First Day at Nursery School. Flintoft, Anthony, illus. 2002. 32p. (J). 15.95 (978-1-58234-761-5(1) , Bloomsbury Children) Bloomsbury Publishing.

Henkes, Kevin. Wemberly Worried. Henkes, Kevin, illus. 2000. (Illus.). 32p. (J). (ps-3). 16.99 (978-0-688-17027-1(7)); lib. bdg. 17.89 (978-0-688-17028-8(5)) HarperCollins Pubs.

—Wemberly Worried. Henkes, Kevin, illus. (Illus.). pap. 16.95 incl. audio (978-0-87499-806-1(9)); pap. incl. audio (978-0-87499-808-5(5)); pap. 18.95 incl. audio compact disk (978-1-59112-359-0(3)); pap. incl. audio compact disk (978-1-59112-561-7(8)) Live Oak Media.

—Wemberly Worried. unabr. ed. 2001. (Illus.). (J). (ps-2). 25.95 incl. audio (978-0-87499-807-8(7)) Live Oak Media.

Hurwitz, Johanna. Rip-Roaring Russell. Tilley, Debbie, illus. 2001. (Riverside Kids Ser.). 112p. (J). (gr. 1-4). pap. 4.99 (978-0-06-442155-3(4) , Harper Trophy) HarperCollins Pubs.

—Rip-Roaring Russell. 1999. (Beech Tree Chapter Bks.). (Illus.). 96p. (gr. k-4). mass mkt. 4.95 (978-0-688-16664-9(4)) HarperCollins Pubs.

—Rip-Roaring Russell. Tilley, Debbie, illus. 2001. 110p. (J). (ps-ps). per. 12.10 (978-0-613-34915-4(6)) Tandem Library Bks.

Jeffs, Stephanie. A Bad Day for Christopher Bear. Thomas, Jacqui, illus. 2004. (Christopher Bear Ser.). 30p. 5.99 (978-0-8066-4367-0(6) , Augsburg Bks.) Augsburg Fortress, Pubs.

—Christopher Bear Makes Friends. Thomas, Jacqui, illus. 2004. (Christopher Bear Ser.). 32p. 5.99 (978-0-8066-4401-1(X) , Augsburg Bks.) Augsburg Fortress, Pubs.

Metzger, Steve. I'm Having a Bad Day! Wilhelm, Hans, illus. 1998. (Dinofours Ser.: No. 2). 32p. (J). (ps-1). pap. 3.25 (978-0-590-03551-4(7)) Scholastic, Inc.

—I'm the Boss! Wilhelm, Hans, illus. 1998. (Dinofours Ser.: No. 6). 32p. (J). (ps-1). pap. 3.25 (978-0-590-37458-3(3)) Scholastic, Inc.

—It's Apple Picking Day! Wilhelm, Hans, illus. 1998. (Dinofours Ser.: No. 8). (J). (ps-1). 3.25 (978-0-590-03549-1(5)) Scholastic, Inc.

—It's Snowing. Wilhelm, Hans, illus. 1998. (Dinofours Ser.: No. 14). (J). (ps-1). pap. 3.25 (978-0-590-03550-7(9)) Scholastic, Inc.

—Rain! Rain! Go Away! Wilhelm, Hans, illus. 2002. (J). pap. 3.25 (978-0-439-29572-7(6)) Scholastic, Inc.

Ovenell-Carter, Julie. Adam's Daycare. Ohi, Ruth, illus. 2003. 32p. (J). (gr. k-2). pap. 5.95 (978-1-55037-444-5(3)) Annick Pr., Ltd. CAN. *Dist:* Firefly Bks., Ltd.

Rockwell, Anne F. Let's Go to Preschool. 2008. 32p. (J). ***(978-0-8050-7955-5(6))*** Holt, Henry & Co.

Schaefer, Carole Lexa. Someone Says. Morgan, Pierr, illus. 2003. 32p. (J). (gr. k-2). 15.99 (978-0-670-03664-6(1) , Viking Juvenile) Penguin Group (USA) Inc.

Senisi, Ellen B. Hurray for Pre-K! Senisi, Ellen B., illus. (Illus.). 32p. (J). (ps-k). 2000. 12.95 (978-0-06-028896-9(5)); 1999. 5.95 (978-0-06-443665-6(9)) HarperCollins Pubs.

Simpson, Lesley. The Shabbat Box. Bosch, Nicole in den, illus. 2001. 32p. (J). (ps-1). pap. 6.95 (978-1-58013-027-1(5)) Kar-Ben Publishing.

Zalben, Jane Breskin. Don't Go! Zalben, Jane Breskin, illus. 2001. (Illus.). 32p. (J). (gr. k-ps). tchr. ed. 15.00 (978-0-618-07250-7(0) , Clarion Bks.) Houghton Mifflin Co. Trade & Reference Div.

NURSES AND NURSING

see also Children—Health and Hygiene; Cookery for the Sick; First Aid; Hospitals; School Nursing

Alexander, Carol. Florence Nightingale. 2005. (Rookie Biographies Ser.). (Illus.). 32p. (J). (gr. 1-2). pap. 4.95 (978-0-516-25828-7(1) , Children's Pr.) Scholastic Library Publishing.

Alexander, Carol & Vargus, Nanci Reginelli. Florence Nightingale. 2004. (Rookie Biography Ser.). (J). 20.50 (978-0-516-24406-8(X) , Children's Pr.) Scholastic Library Publishing.

Aller, Susan Bivin. Florence Nightingale. 2007. (History Maker Biographies Ser.). (J). 26.60 ***(978-0-8225-7609-9(0)*** , Lerner Pubns.) Lerner Publishing Group.

Armentrout, David & Armentrout, Patricia. Florence Nightingale. Sarfatti, Esther & de la Vega, Eida, trs. 2002. (Personas que Cambiaron la Historia (People Who Made a Difference) Ser.). (SPA., Illus.). 24p. mass mkt. 5.95 (978-1-58952-250-3(8) , RK31466) Rourke Publishing, LLC.

—Florence Nightingale. 2001. (Illus.). 24p. (J). (gr. 1-4). lib. bdg. 20.64 (978-1-58952-053-0(X)) Rourke Publishing, LLC.

—Florence Nightingale. Sarfatti, Esther & de la Vega, Eida, trs. 2001. (Personas que Cambiaron la Historia Ser.). (SPA., Illus.). 24p. (J). (gr. 1-3). lib. bdg. 19.27 (978-1-58952-169-8(2) , RK5887) Rourke Publishing, LLC.

Barnham, Kay. Florence Nightingale: The Lady of the Lamp. 2002. (Famous Lives Ser.). 48p. (J). lib. bdg. 27.12 (978-0-7398-5523-2(9)) Raintree.

Batten, Jack. Silent in an Evil Time: The Brave War of Edith Cavell. 2007. 144p. (YA). (gr. 5 up). pap. 16.95 ***(978-0-88776-737-1(0))*** Tundra Bks., Inc./Livres Toundra, Inc. CAN. *Dist:* Random Hse., Inc.

Brill, Marlene Targ. Nurses. 2005. (Pull Ahead Bks.). 32p. (J). pap. 5.95 (978-0-8225-5476-9(3) , Lerner Pubns.); (Illus.). (gr. 3-7). 22.60 (978-0-8225-1692-7(6)) Lerner Publishing Group.

Burby, Liza N. A Day in the Life of a Nurse. Zindler, Ethan, illus. 1999. (Kids' Career Library). 24p. (J). (gr. 3). lib. bdg. 18.75 (978-0-8239-5302-8(5) , PowerKids Pr.) Rosen Publishing Group, Inc., The.

Caring, 6 vols. (gr. 2-5). 36.95 (978-0-7368-9258-2(3)) Red Brick Learning.

Clara Barton. 2005. (First Biographies Ser.). (YA). (gr. k-3). (978-0-7368-9410-4(1) , Pebble Bks.) Capstone Pr., Inc.

Collins, David R. Clara Barton. Landgraf, Ken, illus. 1999. (Young Reader's Christian Library). 224p. (J). (gr. 4-7). pap. 1.39 (978-1-57748-601-5(3)) Barbour Publishing, Inc.

Compass Point Books, contrib. by. Nurses. (Community Workers Ser.). 24p. (J). pap. 7.95 (978-0-7565-1194-4(1)) Compass Point Bks.

Davis, Marc. Florence Nightingale: Founder of the Nightingale School of Nursing. 2003. (Spirit of America). (Illus.). 32p. (J). (gr. 2-6). 27.07 (978-1-59296-003-3(0)) Child's World, Inc.

Deady, Kathleen W. Clara Barton. 2003. (Photo-Illustrated Biographies Ser.). (Illus.). 24p. (J). (gr. 2-3). lib. bdg. 18.60 (978-0-7368-1604-5(6) , Bridgestone Bks.) Capstone Pr., Inc.

Devillier, Christy. Clara Barton. 2004. (First Biographies Set Iv Ser.). (Illus.). 32p. (J). (gr. k-4). lib. bdg. 22.78 (978-1-59197-511-3(5)) ABDO Publishing Co.

Ditchfield, Christin. Clara Barton: Founder of the American Red Cross. 2004. (Great Life Stories Ser.). (Illus.). 111p. (J). 30.50 (978-0-531-12276-1(X) , Watts, Franklin) Scholastic Library Publishing.

Ferguson. What Can I Do Now: Nursing. 2nd rev. ed. 2007. (What Can I Do Now Ser.). 208p. (gr. 6-12). 29.95 ***(978-0-8160-6028-3(2)*** , Ferguson Publishing Co.) Facts On File, Inc.

Fluet, Connie. A Day in the Life of a Nurse. 2004. (First Facts Ser.). (Illus.). 24p. (J). (gr. k-3). lib. bdg. 21.26 (978-0-7368-2631-0(9) , First Facts) Capstone Pr., Inc.

Francis, Dorothy Brenner. Clara Barton: Founder of the American Red Cross. 2002. (Gateway Biography Ser.). (Illus.). 48p. (gr. 2-4). lib. bdg. 23.90 (978-0-7613-2621-2(9) , Millbrook Pr.) Lerner Publishing Group.

Hinman, Bonnie. Florence Nightingale & the Advancement of Nursing. 2004. (Uncharted, Unexplored, & Unexplained Ser.). (Illus.). 48p. (J). (gr. 4-8). lib. bdg. 29.95 (978-1-58415-257-6(5)) Mitchell Lane Pubs., Inc.

Howard, Pam. Natalie Nurse. Linke, Don, Jr., illus. 2000. 8p. (J). pap. 10.95 (978-1-57332-155-6(9)); pap. 10.95 (978-1-57332-154-9(0)) HighReach Learning, Inc.

Kishel, Ann-Marie. Nurse. 2007. (First Step Nonfiction Ser.). (J). pap. (978-0-8225-6846-9(2)) Lerner Publishing Group.

Klingel, Cynthia Fitterer & Noyed, Robert B. Clara Barton: Founder of the American Red Cross. 2002. (Spirit of America: Our People Ser.). (Illus.). 32p. (J). (gr. 2-6). 27.07 (978-1-56766-172-9(6)) Child's World, Inc.

—Nurses. 2002. (Community Workers Ser.). (Illus.). 32p. (J). (gr. 1 up). lib. bdg. 21.26 (978-0-7565-0306-2(X)) Compass Point Bks.

M
N
O

Koestler-Grack, Rachel A. The Story of Clara Barton. 2003. (Breakthrough Biographies Ser.). (Illus.). 32p. (gr. 3-5). 23.00 (978-0-7910-7312-4(2) , Chelsea Hse.) Facts On File, Inc.

Kuhn, Betsy. Angels of Mercy: The Army Nurses of World War II. Kuhn, Betsy, photos by. 1999. (Illus.). 128p. (J). (gr. 5-9). 26.00 (978-0-689-82044-1(5) , Atheneum) Simon & Schuster Children's Publishing.

Lakin, Patricia. Clara Barton: Spirit of the American Red Cross. Sullivan, Simon, illus. 2004. (Ready-to-Read Stories of Famous Americans Ser.). 48p. (J). pap. 3.99 (978-0-689-86513-8(9) , Aladdin) Simon & Schuster Children's Publishing.

Lassieur, Allison. Clara Barton: Angel of the Battlefield. Bascle, Brian, illus. 2005. (Graphic Library). 32p. (J). (gr. 3-7). lib. bdg. 25.27 (978-0-7368-4632-5(8)) Capstone Pr., Inc.

Liebman, Dan. Je veux etre Infirmiere. Lior, Tsipora, tr. from ENG. 2006. (Je veux Etre Ser.).Tr. of I Want to Be A Nurse. (FRE., Illus.). 24p. (J). (ps-2). pap. 5.95 (978-1-55407-107-4(0)) Firefly Bks., Ltd.

Liebman, Daniel. I Want to Be a Nurse. 2001. (I Want to Be Ser.). (Illus.). 24p. (J). (ps-2). pap. 3.99 (978-1-55209-566-9(5)); lib. bdg. 14.95 (978-1-55209-568-3(1)) Firefly Bks., Ltd.

—I Want to Be a Nurse. 2001. (I Want to Be Ser.). (Illus.). (J). 10.79 (978-0-606-21507-7(7)) Tandem Library Bks.

—Quiero Ser Enfermero. 2001. (Coleccion Quierno Ser.). (SPA., Illus.). 24p. (J). (ps-2). pap. 5.99 (978-1-55209-592-8(4) , AP30396) Firefly Bks., Ltd.

Lynch, Emma. Florence Nightingale. 2005. (Illus.). 32p. (978-1-4034-6352-4(2)); pap. (978-1-4034-6366-1(2)) Heinemann Library.

Macken, JoAnn Early. El Enfermero. 2003. Tr. of Nurse. (SPA.). (gr. k-3). lib. bdg. 14.10 (978-0-613-90107-9(X)) Tandem Library Bks.

—Nurse. 2003. (People in My Community Ser.). (Illus.). 24p. (J). (ps up). lib. bdg. 19.33 (978-0-8368-3591-5(3) , Weekly Reader Early Learning Library) Stevens, Gareth Inc.

—Nurse/El Enfermero. Coffey, Colleen & Carrillo, Consuelo, trs. 2003. (Weekly Reader Early Learning Library). (ENG & SPA., Illus.). 24p. (J). (ps up). lib. bdg. 19.33 (978-0-8368-3673-8(1) , Weekly Reader Early Learning Library) Stevens, Gareth Inc.

—People in My Community: Crossing Guard; Mail Carrier; Nurse; Sanitation Worker; Teacher; Veterinarian, 6 bks. (Weekly Reader Early Learning Library). (Illus.). (J). (ps up). lib. bdg. 111.60 (978-0-8368-3588-5(3) , Weekly Reader Early Learning Library) Stevens, Gareth Inc.

Macken, JoAnn Early & Gorman, Jacqueline Laks. Nurse. Andersen, Gregg, photos by. 2003. (Weekly Reader Early Learning Library). (Illus.). 24p. (J). (ps up). pap. 7.93 (978-0-8368-3598-4(0) , Weekly Reader Early Learning Library) Stevens, Gareth Inc.

—Nurse/El Enfermero. Coffey, Colleen & Carrillo, Consuelo, trs. Andersen, Gregg, photos by. 2003. (Weekly Reader Early Learning Library). (ENG & SPA., Illus.). 24p. (J). (ps up). pap. (978-0-8368-3687-5(1) , Weekly Reader Early Learning Library) Stevens, Gareth Inc.

Malam, John. Florence Nightingale. 2001. (Groundbreakers Ser.). (Illus.). 48p. (J). (gr. 5-7). lib. bdg. 25.64 (978-1-58810-051-1(0)) Heinemann Library.

—Mary Seacole. 2000. (Tell Me about Ser.). (Illus.). 22p. (J). 15.99 (978-0-237-51974-2(7) , Evans Brothers, Limited) Evans Publishing Group GBR. *Dist:* Independent Pubs. Group.

Mara, Wil. Clara Barton. (Rookie Biographies Ser.). (Illus.). 32p. (J). (gr. 1-2). 2003. pap. 4.95 (978-0-516-27339-6(6)); 2002. 20.50 (978-0-516-22523-4(5)) Scholastic Library Publishing. (Children's Pr.).

—Clara Barton. 2002. (gr. k-3). lib. bdg. 12.95 (978-0-613-59459-2(2)) Tandem Library Bks.

Marko, Eve. Clara Barton & the American Red Cross. Marcos, Pablo, illus. 2005. (Heroes of America Ser.). 240p. (J). (gr. 3-8). lib. bdg. 21.35 (978-1-59679-255-5(8)) ABDO Publishing Co.

McDoniel, Estelle. Registered Nurse to Rear Admiral: A First for Navy Women. 2003. (Illus.). viii, 81p. (J). 16.95 (978-1-57168-766-1(1) , Eakin Pr.) Eakin Pr.

Miller, Heather. Enfermero. 2003. (Esto es lo Que Quiero Ser (This Is What I Want to Be) Ser.). (SPA., Illus.). 24p. (J). (ps-1). lib. bdg. 18.50 (978-1-4034-0380-3(5)) Heinemann Library.

—Nurse. 2003. (This Is What I Want to Be Ser.). (Illus.). 24p. (ps-1). (J). lib. bdg. 18.50 (978-1-4034-0370-4(8)); pap. 5.25 (978-1-4034-0592-0(1)) Heinemann Library.

—Nurse. 2003. (ps-2). lib. bdg. 13.30 (978-0-613-86438-1(7)) Tandem Library Bks.

Minden, Cecilia & Armantrout, Linda M. Nurses. 2006. (Neighborhood Helpers Ser.). (Illus.). 32p. (J). (gr. k-4). 22.79 (978-1-59296-566-3(0)) Child's World, Inc.

Morris, Ann. That's Our Nurse! Linenthal, Peter, illus. 2003. (That's Our School Ser.). 32p. lib. bdg. 22.90 (978-0-7613-2402-7(X) , Millbrook Pr.) Lerner Publishing Group.

Nardo, Don. Clara Barton: "Face Danger, but Never Fear It" 2008. (Americans-the Spirit of a Nation Ser.). 128p. (J). (gr. 5 up). lib. bdg. 31.93 (*978-0-7660-3024-4(5)) Enslow Pubs., Inc.

Norman, Elizabeth. We Band of Angels: The Untold Story of American Nurses Trapped on Bataan by The. 2000. (gr. 7-12). lib. bdg. 24.55 (978-0-613-29136-1(0)) Tandem Library Bks.

Nurses. (Community Helpers Ser.). 24p. (J). 6.95 (978-0-7368-8458-7(0)) Capstone Pr., Inc.

Nurses, 6 vols. (gr. 2-5). 36.95 (978-0-7368-8473-0(4)) Red Brick Learning.

Picture Window Books, contrib. by. Helping You Heal. (Community Workers Ser.). 24p. (J). pap. 7.95 (978-1-4048-0480-7(3)) Picture Window Bks.

Quinlan, Kathryn A. Nurse Assistant. 1998. (Careers Without College Ser.). (Illus.). 48p. (J). (gr. 3-4). lib. bdg. 21.26 (978-0-7368-0036-5(0) , LifeMatters Bks.) Capstone Pr., Inc.

Ransom, Candice F. Clara Barton. 2003. (History Maker Bios Ser.). (Illus.). 48p. (J). (gr. 3-5). lib. bdg. 26.60 (978-0-8225-4677-1(9)) Lerner Publishing Group.

Raum, Elizabeth. Clara Barton. 2004. (Illus.). 32p. (J). pap. 6.95 (978-1-4034-5704-2(2)); lib. bdg. (978-1-4034-4993-1(7)) Heinemann Library.

Ready, Dee. Enfermeras y Enfermeros. Schon, Isabel, ed. Ferrer, Martín Luis Guzman, tr. from ENG. 1998. (Servidores Comunitarios Ser.). (SPA., Illus.). 24p. (J). (gr. 1-2). lib. bdg. 18.60 (978-1-56065-801-6(0) , Bridgestone Bks.) Capstone Pr., Inc.

Robbins, Trina. Florence Nightingale: Lady with the Lamp. Timmons, Anne, illus. 2007. 32p. (J). (978-0-7368-6850-1(X)) Capstone Pr., Inc.

Ross, Stewart. Don't Say No to Flo: The Story of Florence Nightingale. Shields, Susan, illus. 32p. (J). pap. (978-0-7502-3273-9(0) , Hodder Wayland) Hodder Children's Division.

Schaefer, Lola M. Clara Barton. Saunders-Smith, Gail, ed. 2002. (First Biographies Ser.). (Illus.). 24p. (J). (gr. k-1). lib. bdg. 15.93 (978-0-7368-1434-8(5) , Pebble Bks.) Capstone Pr., Inc.

—We Need Nurses. Saunders-Smith, Gail, ed. 2000. (Helpers in Our Community Ser.). (Illus.). 24p. (J). (gr. k-1). lib. bdg. 15.93 (978-0-7368-0393-9(9) , Pebble Bks.) Capstone Pr., Inc.

—We Need Nurses. 1999. pap. 13.25 (978-0-516-21906-6(5) , Children's Pr.) Scholastic Library Publishing.

Schaefer, Lola M. & Schaefer, Wyatt S. Florence Nightingale. 2004. (First Biographies Ser.). (Illus.). 24p. (J). lib. bdg. 15.93 (978-0-7368-2081-3(7) , Pebble Bks.) Capstone Pr., Inc.

Simons, Rae & Gommer, Viola Ruelke. Nurse. 2002. (Careers with Character Ser.). (Illus.). 96p. (YA). (gr. 7 up). (978-1-59084-319-2(3)) Mason Crest Pubs.

Somervill, Barbara A. Clara Barton: Founder of the American Red Cross. (Illus.). 112p. (J). 2007. pap. (*978-0-7565-2199-8(8)); 2006. (978-0-7565-1888-2(1)) Compass Point Bks.

Tieck, Sarah. Florence Nightingale. 2007. (First Biographies Ser.). (Illus.). 32p. (J). (gr. k-3). lib. bdg. 22.78 (978-1-59679-786-4(X) , Buddy Bks.) ABDO Publishing Co.

Time for Kids Editors. Clara Barton: Angel of the Battlefield. 2008. (Time for Kids Ser.). (Illus.). 48p. (J). 15.99 (*978-0-06-057623-3(5)); pap. 3.99 (*978-0-06-057622-6(7)) HarperCollins Pubs.

Trumbauer, Lisa. What Does a Nurse Do? 2006. (What Does a Community Helper Do? Ser.). (Illus.). 24p. (J). lib. bdg. 21.26 (978-0-7660-2325-3(7) , Enslow Elementary) Enslow Pubs., Inc.

Vickers, Rebecca. Florence Nightingale. (Groundbreakers Ser.). 48p. pap. 8.50 (978-1-4034-4063-1(8)); 2002. (Illus.). 24p. (J). pap. 6.50 (978-1-4034-0028-4(8) , 91472); 2000. (Illus.). 24p. (J). lib. bdg. 19.92 (978-1-57572-402-7(2)) Heinemann Library.

—Florence Nightingale. 2002. (gr. k-3). lib. bdg. 12.95 (978-0-613-86990-4(7)) Tandem Library Bks.

Vogel, Elizabeth. Meet the School Nurse. 2002. (PowerKids Readers Ser.). (Illus.). 24p. (J). (gr. 1). lib. bdg. 16.00 (978-0-8239-6034-7(X) , PowerKids Pr.) Rosen Publishing Group, Inc., The.

Wallner, Rosemary. Licensed Practical Nurse. 1999. (Career Exploration Ser.). (Illus.). 48p. lib. bdg. 21.26 (978-0-7368-0329-8(7) , LifeMatters Bks.) Capstone Pr., Inc.

—Licensed Practical Nurse. 1999. (Illus.). (YA). (gr. 5-12). pap. 19.93 (978-0-516-21888-5(3) , Children's Pr.) Scholastic Library Publishing.

We Need Nurses, 6 vols. (gr. k-2). 28.95 (978-0-7368-8603-1(6)) Red Brick Learning.

Wells, Rosemary. Mary on Horseback: Three Mountain Stories. McCarty, Peter, illus. (J). 2000. 64p. (gr. 3-7). pap. 4.99 (978-0-14-130815-9(X) , Puffin); 1999. 56p. (gr. 4-7). 16.99 (978-0-670-88923-5(7) , Viking Juvenile) Penguin Group (USA) Inc.

—Mary on Horseback: Three Mountain Stories. 2000. (J). (978-0-606-20243-5(9)); (gr. 3-6). lib. bdg. 13.00 (978-0-613-33711-3(5)) Tandem Library Bks.

Wheeler, Jill C. Clara Barton. 2002. (Breaking Barriers Ser.). (Illus.). 64p. (J). (gr. 3-8). lib. bdg. 25.65 (978-1-57765-317-2(3) , ABDO & Daughters) ABDO Publishing Co.

Wohlrabe, Sarah. Helping You Heal: A Book about Nurses. Thomas, Eric, illus. 2004. (Community Workers Ser.). 24p. (C). (gr. k-3). 22.60 (978-1-4048-0086-1(7)) Picture Window Bks.

Zakon, Miriam S. Sister in White: The Story of Schuester Selma. 1999. (Illus.). 118p. (YA). (gr. 3-10). 10.95 (978-1-56871-186-7(7)) Targum Pr., Inc.

Zemlicka, Shannon. Florence Nightingale. Debon, Nicolas, illus. 2003. (On My Own Biography Ser.). 48p. (J). (gr. 1-3). 5.95 (978-0-87614-102-1(5) , Carolrhoda Bks.) Lerner Publishing Group.

—Florence Nightingale. 2003. (gr. 3-6). lib. bdg. 14.10 (978-0-613-58902-4(5)) Tandem Library Bks.

NURSES AND NURSING—FICTION

Ahearn, Geri. The Nurse in the Purse, 2 vols. Staples, Deb, ed. Szramski, Raine, illus. 2002. 36p. per. 14.99 (978-0-7443-0373-5(7)) SynergEbks.

Carney, Karen L. Everything Changes, but Love Endures: Explaining Hospice to Children. Carney, Karen L., illus. 2000. (Barklay & Eve Ser.: Bk. 6). (Illus.). (J). pap. 6.95 (978-0-9667820-5-9(4)) Dragonfly Publishing.

Davidson, Michele R. Stowaways to Smith Island: Hayden & Chloe's Enchanted Journey with the Nurses to Maryland's Mysterious Smith Island. Watjen, Laureen, illus. 2004. 128p. (J). pap. 8.95 (978-0-9754170-1-0(0)) Smith Island Foundation.

Farenhorst, Christine. A Cup of Cold Water: The Compassion of Nurse Edith Cavell. 2007. (J). pap. (*978-1-59638-026-4(8)) P & R Publishing.

Gutman, Dan. Mrs. Cooney Is Loony! Paillot, Jim, illus. 2005. (My Weird School Ser.). 112p. (J). pap. 3.99 (978-0-06-074522-6(3)); lib. bdg. 15.89 (978-0-06-074523-3(1)) HarperCollins Pubs. (Harper Trophy).

Hartnett, Sonya. Stripes of Sidestep Wolf. 2007. (Illus.). 208p. (YA). (gr. 7). pap. 7.99 (*978-0-7636-3416-2(6)) Candlewick Pr.

Hathaway, Barbara. Missy Violet & Me. 2004. 112p. (J). (gr. 3-5). tchr. ed. 15.00 (978-0-618-37163-1(X)) Houghton Mifflin Co. Trade & Reference Div.

Hendry, Frances. Quest for a Queen: The Falcon. 2006. pap. (*978-1-905665-06-8(7)) Pollinger In Print.

Jackson, Kathryn. Nurse Nancy. Malvern, Corinne, illus. 2005. (Little Golden Book Classic Ser.). 24p. (J). (gr. k-k). 2.99 (978-0-375-83262-8(9) , Golden Bks.) Random Hse. Children's Bks.

Ladd, Debbie. Nurse Robin's Hats. Nakasone, Shaun, illus. 2006. 52p. (J). 16.95 (978-0-9727615-3-6(5)) Deb on Air Bks.

LoGuidice, Mike. Open up & Say Aggh! 2005. (J). pap. 16.00 (978-0-8059-7037-1(1)) Dorrance Publishing Co., Inc.

Norman, Thelma G. A Wife Called Tommie. 2005. 226p. (J). per. 12.95 (978-1-57258-295-8(2)) TEACH Services, Inc.

Nurse, B. A. Outrageously Cool Nurses. 2007. 84p. per. 8.95 (*978-0-595-43530-2(0)) iUniverse, Inc.

Nurse Pig: New Heroes Backpack Story. 2002. (J). (978-1-931312-60-8(5)) SoftPlay, Inc.

Paul, Bette. Nurses: Katie Goes to College (Large Pri. 2006. pap. (*978-1-905665-09-9(1)) Pollinger In Print.

Rothstein, Evelyn. My Great Grandpa Dave. 2007. (J). per. 12.95 (*978-0-9786745-1-9(0)) Marble House Editions.

Stockham, Leslie C. What's the Matter with the Baby? 1999. Tr. of Que le Pasa Al Bebito?. (Illus.). 18p. (J). (ps). 19.98 (978-1-893447-00-4(6)) Bilingual Language Materials.

Van Dyne, Edith. Aunt Jane's Nieces in the Red Cross. rev. ed. 2006. 180p. 26.95 (978-1-4218-1724-8(1)); pap. 11.95 (978-1-4218-1824-5(8)) 1st World Publishing, Inc. (1st World Library - Literary Society).

Wells, Helen. Cherry Ames, Army Nurse. 2005. (YA). pap. (978-0-9771597-2-7(8)) Springer.

—Cherry Ames, Boarding School Nurse. 2007. (YA). (*978-0-8261-0413-7(4)) Springer.

—Cherry Ames, Camp Nurse. 2007. (YA). (*978-0-8261-0417-5(7)) Springer.

—Cherry Ames, Chief Nurse. 2005. (YA). pap. (978-0-9771597-3-4(6)) Springer.

—Cherry Ames, Cruise Nurse. 2007. (YA). (*978-0-8261-0411-3(8)) Springer.

—Cherry Ames, Department Store Nurse. 2007. (YA). (*978-0-8261-0415-1(0)) Springer.

—Cherry Ames, Flight Nurse. 2006. ix, 211p. (J). (978-0-8261-0397-0(9)) Springer.

—Cherry Ames, Private Duty Nurse. 2006. vi, 218p. (J). (978-0-8261-0398-7(7)) Springer.

—Cherry Ames, Senior Nurse. 2005. (YA). pap. (978-0-9771597-1-0(X)) Springer.

—Cherry Ames, Student Nurse. 2005. (YA). pap. (978-0-9771597-0-3(1)) Springer.

—Cherry Ames, Veterans' Nurse. 2006. ix, 213p. (J). (978-0-8261-0400-7(2)) Springer.

—Cherry Ames, Visiting Nurse. 2006. vii, 216p. (J). (978-0-8261-0399-4(5)) Springer.

Wick, Elaine. It's MY Future: Should I Be a Nurse Practitioner? Tremaine, Michele, illus. 2004. 64p. (J). lib. bdg. 12.95 (978-0-9749769-0-7(3)) NAPNAP.

Woolf, Virginia. Nurse Lugton's Curtain. Vivas, Julie, illus. ed. 2004. 32p. (J). 16.00 (978-0-15-205048-1(5) , Gulliver Bks.) Harcourt Children's Bks.

Yonge, Charlotte M. Little Lucy's Wonderful Globe. 2004. reprint ed. pap. 15.95 (978-1-4191-3079-3(X)) Kessinger Publishing, LLC.

NURSING

see Nurses and Nursing

NUTRITION

see also Diet; Digestion; Food; Metabolism; Vitamins

Alexander's Enrichment Activties. 2006. (J). pap. 5.95 (*978-0-9742806-6-0(6)) Heart to Heart Publishing.

Allsop, Marcus. We Like to Help Cook. Iverson, Diane, illus. 2007. 32p. (J). pap. 9.95 (*978-1-890772-70-3(4)) Hohm Pr.

Anthony, Mark, et al. Gut Instinct: Diet's Missing Link. 2003. (Illus.). 216p. per. 19.95 (978-0-9743664-0-1(4)) Leap Forward Pubns.

April, Elyse. We Like to Eat Well. Agrell, Lewis, illus. 2007. 32p. (J). pap. 9.95 (*978-1-890772-69-7(0)) Hohm Pr.

Bagley, Katie. Eat Right: Tips for Good Nutrition. 2001. (Your Health Ser.). (Illus.). 32p. (J). (gr. 1-2). 18.60 (978-0-7368-0971-9(6) , Bridgestone Bks.) Capstone Pr., Inc.

Ballard, Carol. Food for Feeling Healthy. 2006. (Making Healthy Food Choices Ser.). (Illus.). 56p. (J). pap. (978-1-4034-8577-9(1)); (YA). (gr. 6-9). lib. bdg. 32.86 (978-1-4034-8571-7(2)) Heinemann Library.

—Special Diets & Food Allergies. 2006. (Making Healthy Food Choices Ser.). (Illus.). 56p. (J). (978-1-4034-8572-4(0)) Heinemann Library.

Beck, Leslie. Nutrition Guide for Teens. 2007. 304p. pap. 21.00 (978-0-14-301720-2(9) , Penguin Global) Penguin Group (USA) Inc.

Bellenir, Karen, ed. Diet Information for Teens: Health Tips about Diet & Nutrition. 2001. (Teen Health Ser.). (Illus.). 399p. (gr. 7 up). (978-0-7808-0441-8(4)) Omnigraphics, Inc.

Benchmark Education Staff, compiled by. Nutrition & Exercise. 2006. spiral bd. 85.00 (*978-1-4108-7036-0(7)) Benchmark Education Co.

Benduhn, Tea. Fruit: Fruta. 2007. (SPA & ENG.). (J). pap. (*978-0-8368-8462-3(0) , Weekly Reader Early Learning Library) Stevens, Gareth Inc.

—Fruit/Fruta. 2007. (Find Out about Food/Conoce la Comida Ser.). (SPA & ENG.). 24p. (J). (gr. k-2). lib. bdg. 19.93 (*978-0-8368-8455-5(8) , Weekly Reader Early Learning Library) Stevens, Gareth Inc.

Berry, Joy Wilt. Teach Me about Mealtime: A Special Times Book. Fitzpatrick, Roey, illus. rev. ed. 1999. (Teach Me about Ser. : Vol. 1). 32p. (J). (ps). bds. 5.95 (978-1-58634-000-1(X) , 01-0101-01) Goldstar Publishing, Inc.

Brown, Judith E. Nutrition: Through the Life Cycle. 2001. 512p. (YA). pap. 73.95 (978-0-534-58987-5(1)) Thomson Wadsworth.

Brynie, Faith Hickman. 101 Questions about Food & Digestion That Have Been Eating at You until Now. Holm, Sharon Lane, illus. 2002. (One Hundred One Questions... Ser.). 176p. (gr. 7 up). lib. bdg. 27.90 (978-0-7613-2309-9(0) , Twenty-First Century Bks.) Lerner Publishing Group.

Burke, Tracy W. Just the Fats Part II: Nutrition for Every Body. 2002. 108p. pap. 10.95 (978-0-595-22102-8(5) , Writers Club Pr.) iUniverse, Inc.

Burstein, John. Eating Right. McGinnis, Ben, illus. Pinchbeck, Chris, photos by. 2006. (Slim Goodbody's Good Health Guides Ser.). 32p. (J). (gr. 2-4). lib. bdg. 25.27 (*978-0-8368-7740-3(3)) Stevens, Gareth Inc.

Caole, Francis & Michael, Veronica. Cameg Nertussia? Sparck, Amy, illus. l.t. ed. 1999. Tr. of What Do I Eat?. (ESK.). 8p. (J). (gr. k-3). pap. 6.00 (978-1-58084-149-8(X)) Lower Kuskokwim Schl. District.

—Canek Nerlarcia? Sparck, Amy, illus. l.t. ed. 1999. Tr. of What Do I Eat?. (ESK.). 8p. (J). (gr. k-3). pap. 6.00 (978-1-58084-094-1(9)) Lower Kuskokwim Schl. District.

—What Do I Eat? Sparck, Amy, illus. l.t. ed. 1999. 8p. (J). (gr. k-3). pap. 6.00 (978-1-58084-093-4(0)) Lower Kuskokwim Schl. District.

Carol Ballard. Special Diets & Food Allergies. 2006. (Making Healthy Food Choices Ser.). (Illus.). 56p. (J). pap. (*978-1-4034-8578-6(X)) Heinemann Library.

CATTCH Kids Club Nutrition. 2005. per. (978-1-932032-19-2(3)) Flaghouse, Inc.

Coder, Kelly, ed. Investigating Science - Taking Care of Me. 2003. 48p. 9.95 (978-1-56234-570-9(2) , Mailbox Bks., The) Education Ctr., Inc.

Colored Nuts about Nutrition: Ages 7-11, 12 activity books. 2005. (J). 9.95 (978-1-57175-176-8(9) , 6508-C) Learning ZoneXpress.

Colored Nuts about Nutrition Activity Books: Ages 2-6, 12 activity books. 2005. (J). 9.95 (978-1-57175-174-4(2) , 6507-C) Learning ZoneXpress.

Colored Snack Attack Activity Books: Ages 2-6, 12 activity books. 2005. (J). 9.95 (978-1-57175-169-0(6) , 6503-C) Learning ZoneXpress.

Colored Snack Attack Activity Books: Ages 7-11, 12 activity books. 2005. (J). 9.95 (978-1-57175-171-3(8) , 6504-C) Learning ZoneXpress.

Creighton, Judith Matlock, et al. Health Education Primer. 2nd ed. 2006. (Illus.). 76p. (J). spiral bd. 29.95 (978-0-9773228-0-0(7)) WHA Publishing.

Creighton, Judith Matlock, et al. Nutrition Lessons for Kids: (and Their Parents) 2006. (J). spiral bd. 19.95 (*978-0-9773228-3-1(1)) WHA Publishing.

Dalgleish, Sharon. Fast Food. 2006. (Illus.). 32p. (J). (978-1-58340-747-9(2)) Smart Apple Media.

—Lunch Box Food/By Sharon Dalgleish. 2006. (Illus.). 32p. (J). (978-1-58340-749-3(9)) Smart Apple Media.

—Party Food. 2006. (Illus.). 32p. (J). (978-1-58340-746-2(4)) Smart Apple Media.

—Snack Food. 2006. (Illus.). 32p. (J). (978-1-58340-748-6(0)) Smart Apple Media.

Dalton, Cindy Devine. Avoid Fatty Foods. 2000. (Why Should I... Ser.). (Illus.). 24p. (J). (gr. 1-4). lib. bdg. 19.27 (978-1-55916-301-9(1)) Rourke Publishing, LLC.

—Eat Carbohydrates That Grow. 2000. (Why Should I... Ser.). (Illus.). 24p. (J). (gr. 1-4). lib. bdg. 19.27 (978-1-55916-303-3(8)) Rourke Publishing, LLC.

—Eat Power Proteins. 2000. (Why Should I... Ser.). (Illus.). 24p. (J). (gr. 1-4). lib. bdg. 19.27 (978-1-55916-304-0(6)) Rourke Publishing, LLC.

—Keep Cholesterol Low. 2000. (Why Should I... Ser.). (Illus.). 24p. (J). (gr. 1-4). lib. bdg. 19.27 (978-1-55916-305-7(4)) Rourke Publishing, LLC.

—Love My Vitamins. 2000. (Why Should I... Ser.). (Illus.). 24p. (J). lib. bdg. 19.27 (978-1-55916-306-4(2)) Rourke Publishing, LLC.

D'Amico, Joan & Drummond, Karen Eich. The Healthy Body Cookbook: Over 50 Fun Activities & Delicious Recipes for Kids. Cash-Walsh, Tina, illus. 1998. 192p. (gr. 4-7). pap. 12.95 (978-0-471-18888-9(3) , Wiley) Wiley, John & Sons, Inc.

Danger Zone: Dieting & Eating Disorders, 6 bks., Set. Incl. Anorexia. Watson, Stephanie. lib. bdg. 27.95 (*978-1-4042-1996-0(X)); Binge Eating. Watson, Stephanie. lib. bdg. 27.95 (*978-1-4042-1998-4(6)); Bulimia. Watson, Stephanie. lib. bdg. 27.95 (*978-1-4042-1997-7(8)); Diet Drugs. Williams, Kara. lib. bdg. 27.95 (*978-1-4042-1994-6(3)); Diet Fads. Zahensky, Barbara A. lib. bdg. 27.95 (*978-1-4042-1999-1(4)); Negative Body Image. Willett, Edward. lib. bdg. 27.95 (*978-1-4042-1995-3(1)); (Illus.). 64p. (J). (gr. 7-12). 2006. 2007. Set lib. bdg. 167.70 (*978-1-4042-1061-5(X)) Rosen Publishing Group, Inc., The.

Dawson, Susan H. & Norton, Susan R. Pyramid Pal - Fruits: Eating Should Always Be Fun for Kid. O'Hare, Mark, illus. 2000. (Adventures in Eating with the Nutrition Champion of Kids Ser.). 16p. (J). pap. 3.00 (978-1-58000-066-6(5)) Griffin Publishing Group.

M N O

—Pyramid Pal - Grains: Eating Should Always Be Fun for a Kid. O'Hare, Mark, illus. 2000. (Adventures in Eating with the Nutrition Champion of Kids Ser.). 24p. (J). pap. 3.50 (978-1-58000-064-2(9)) Griffin Publishing Group.

—Pyramid Pal - Meat, Poultry, Fish: Eating Should Always Be Fun for a Kid. O'Hare, Mark, illus. 2000. (Adventures in Eating with the Nutrition Champion of Kids Ser.). 32p. (J). pap. 4.00 (978-1-58000-068-0(1)) Griffin Publishing Group.

—Pyramid Pal - Milk: Eating Should Always Be Fun for a Kid. O'Hare, Mark, illus. 2000. (Adventures in Eating with the Nutrition Champion of Kids Ser.). 16p. (J). pap. 3.00 (978-1-58000-067-3(3)) Griffin Publishing Group.

—Pyramid Pal - Sweets: Eating Should Always Be Fun for a Kid. O'Hare, Mark, illus. 2000. (Adventures in Eating with the Nutrition Champion of Kids Ser.). 16p. (J). pap. 3.00 (978-1-58000-069-7(X)) Griffin Publishing Group.

—Pyramid Pal - The Begining: Eating Should Always Be Fun for a Kid. O'Hare, Mark, illus. 2000. (Adventures in Eating with the Nutrition Champion of Kids Ser.). 16p. (J). pap. 3.00 (978-1-58000-063-5(0)) Griffin Publishing Group.

—Pyramid Pal - Vegetables: Eating Should Always Be Fun for a Kid. O'Hare, Mark, illus. 2000. (Adventures in Eating with the Nutrition Champion of Kids Ser.). 16p. (J). pap. 3.00 (978-1-58000-065-9(7)) Griffin Publishing Group.

—Pyramid Pal's Adventures in Eating: Eating Should Always Be Fun for a Kid, 7 vols., Set. O'Hare, Mark, illus. 2000. (Adventures in Eating with the Nutrition Champion of Kids Ser.). 140p. (J). pap. 22.50 (978-1-58000-070-3(3)) Griffin Publishing Group.

Deal, Darlene. Play with Your Food & Learn How to Eat Right: Nutritional Book about Fruits & Vegetables. 2004. (ENG & SPA., Illus.). 22p. (J). (gr. 1-4). pap. 9.95 (978-0-9747299-0-9(6)) Deal, Darlene.

Deen, Darwin & Hark, Lisa. Nutrition for Life: A No Fad, No Nonsense Approach to Eating Well & Reaching Your Healthy Weight. 2005. (Illus.). 352p. 30.00 (978-0-7566-0522-3(9)) Dorling Kindersley Publishing, Inc.

Dell, Helen Sue. The Thinker's Pizza Cookbook. 2003. (Illus.). 64p. (J). pap. 5.99 (978-0-9747247-0-6(X)) Food Enhancement Enterprises.

DK Publishing Staff & Graimes, Nichola. Kids' Fun & Healthy Cookbook. 2007. 128p. (J). (gr. 2-5). 17.99 (978-0-7566-2916-8(0)) Dorling Kindersley Publishing, Inc.

Eat Right. (Your Health Ser.). 24p. (J). 6.95 (978-0-7368-4451-2(1)) Capstone Pr., Inc.

Eat Well. 2002. (YA). 21.95 (978-1-58810-135-8(5)) Heinemann Library.

Ely, Leanne. Healthy Foods: A Unit Study on Practical Nutrition & Wellness for Grades 6-9. 2002. 32p. (gr. 6-9). pap. 12.00 (978-1-891400-09-4(6)) Champion Pr., Ltd.

—Healthy Foods: A Unit Study on Practical Nutrtion & Wellness for Grades K-5. 2001. 32p. (J). (gr. k-5). pap. 12.00 (978-1-891400-15-5(0)) Champion Pr., Ltd.

Evers, Connie L. Good for You! Nutrition Game Board. Disney Storybook Artists Staff, illus. 2006. 48p. (gr. 1-4). 12.99 (978-0-7868-4748-8(4)) Disney Pr.

Faiella, Graham. The Food Pyramid & Basic Nutrition: Assembling the Building Blocks of a Healthy Diet. 2004. (Library of Nutrition). (Illus.). 48p. (J). lib. bdg. 25.25 (978-1-4042-0304-4(4)) Rosen Publishing Group, Inc., The.

Feeding the Baby: Individual Title Six-Packs. (ps-2). 23.00 (978-0-7635-8790-1(7)) Rigby Education.

Feldman, Heather. My Breakfast: A Book about a Great Morning Meal. 2000. (PowerKids Readers Ser.). (Illus.). 24p. (J). (gr. 1). lib. bdg. 16.00 (978-0-8239-5527-5(3), PKMYBR, PowerKids Pr.) Rosen Publishing Group, Inc., The.

Feldman, Julie, creator. The No Diet Diet: Healthy Meals in 5 Minutes. 2003. (YA). spiral bd. 19.95 (978-0-615-12437-7(2)) Creative Nutrition & Wellness.

Figtree, Dale. Eat Smarter: The Smarter Choice for Healthier Kids. 2006. (Illus.). 144p. (J). 19.95 (978-0-8329-7001-6(8), Z Health Bks.) New Win Publishing.

Fisher, Beverly. Mental Toughness for Weight Management: Workbook for Life. 2004. (Illus.). 60p. pap. 10.99 (978-0-9745066-1-6(3)) Sports In Mind.

Fletcher, Anne M. Weight Loss Confidential Journal: Week-By-Week Success Strategies for Teens from Teens. 2008. 240p. spiral bd. 15.00 (***978-0-618-43372-8(4)***) Houghton Mifflin Co.

Fontes, Justine & Fontes, Ron. Proteins. 2006. 32p. (J). (gr. k-2). pap. 5.95 (978-0-516-24650-5(X), Children's Pr.) Scholastic Library Publishing.

Friddle-Ponder, Alma. Chile Pepper Unit Study Comprehensive Edition. 2007. (Illus.). 93p. spiral bd. 19.95 (***978-1-934627-00-6(3)***) Fish Head Pubns., LLC.

—Chile Pepper Unit Study Graphic Edition. 2007. (Illus.). 63p. spiral bd. 14.95 (***978-1-934627-01-3(1)***) Fish Head Pubns., LLC.

—Chile Pepper Unit Study Reading Enhanced Edition. 2007. (Illus.). 68p. spiral bd. 14.95 (***978-1-934627-02-0(X)***) Fish Head Pubns., LLC.

Fromm, Jim, prod. Nutrition Mac Labpak. (YA). cd-rom 324.88 (978-0-7365-4370-5(8)) Films Media Group.

—Nutrition Win Labpak. (YA). cd-rom 324.88 (978-0-7365-4371-2(6)) Films Media Group.

Frost, Helen. The Dairy Group. Saunders-Smith, Gail, ed. 2000. (Food Guide Pyramid Ser.). (Illus.). 24p. (J). (gr. k-1). lib. bdg. 15.93 (978-0-7368-0540-7(0), Pebble Bks.) Capstone Pr., Inc.

—Eating Right. Saunders-Smith, Gail, ed. 2000. (Food Guide Pyramid Ser.). (Illus.). 24p. (J). (gr. k-1). lib. bdg. 15.93 (978-0-7368-0535-3(4), Pebble Bks.) Capstone Pr., Inc.

—Fats, Oils & Sweets. Saunders-Smith, Gail, ed. 2000. (Food Guide Pyramid Ser.). (Illus.). 24p. (J). (gr. k-1). lib. bdg. 15.93 (978-0-7368-0536-0(2), Pebble Bks.) Capstone Pr., Inc.

—Food for Healthy Teeth. Saunders-Smith, Gail, ed. 1998. (Dental Health Ser.). (Illus.). 24p. (J). (gr. k-1). lib. bdg. 15.93 (978-0-7368-0113-3(8), Pebble Bks.) Capstone Pr., Inc.

—Food for Healthy Teeth. 1998. (Dental Health Ser.). (J). lib. bdg. 13.25 (978-0-516-21493-1(4), Children's Pr.) Scholastic Library Publishing.

—The Food Guide Pyramid, 8 bks. Saunders-Smith, Gail, ed. Incl. Dairy Group. lib. bdg. 15.93 (978-0-7368-0540-7(0)); Drinking Water. lib. bdg. 15.93 (978-0-7368-0534-6(6)); Eating Right. lib. bdg. 15.93 (978-0-7368-0535-3(4)); Fats, Oils & Sweets. lib. bdg. 15.93 (978-0-7368-0536-0(2)); Fruit Group. lib. bdg. 15.93 (978-0-7368-0537-7(0)); Grain Group. lib. bdg. 15.93 (978-0-7368-0538-4(9)); Meat & Protein Group. lib. bdg. 15.93 (978-0-7368-0539-1(7)); Vegetable Group. lib. bdg. 15.93 (978-0-7368-0541-4(9)); 24p. (J). (gr. k-1). (Illus.). 2000. Set lib. bdg. 127.44 (978-0-7368-0561-2(3), Pebble Bks.) Capstone Pr., Inc.

—The Fruit Group. Saunders-Smith, Gail, ed. 2000. (Food Guide Pyramid Ser.). (Illus.). 24p. (J). (gr. k-1). lib. bdg. 15.93 (978-0-7368-0537-7(0), Pebble Bks.) Capstone Pr., Inc.

—The Grain Group. Saunders-Smith, Gail, ed. 2000. (Food Guide Pyramid Ser.). (Illus.). 24p. (J). (gr. k-1). lib. bdg. 15.93 (978-0-7368-0538-4(9), Pebble Bks.) Capstone Pr., Inc.

—The Vegetable Group. Saunders-Smith, Gail, ed. 2000. (Food Guide Pyramid Ser.). (Illus.). 24p. (J). (gr. k-1). lib. bdg. 15.93 (978-0-7368-0541-4(9), Pebble Bks.) Capstone Pr., Inc.

Fundamental Human Nutrition. 2000. (YA). cd-rom 125.00 (978-1-57078-761-4(1), CEV90761) C E V Multimedia, Ltd.

Furgang, Kathy. Tener habitos sanos & Having Healthful Habits. 2005. spiral bd. 84.00 (***978-1-4108-5710-1(7)***) Benchmark Education Co.

Gaff, Jackie. Why Must I... Eat Healthy Food? Fairclough, Chris, photos by. 2005. (Illus.). 32p. (J). (gr. 2-5). lib. bdg. (978-1-84234-349-4(1), Cherrytree Books) Evans Publishing Group.

Gardner, Robert. Health Science Projects about Nutrition. 2002. (Science Projects Ser.). (Illus.). 112p. (YA). (gr. 6-11). lib. bdg. 26.60 (978-0-7660-1442-8(8)) Enslow Pubs., Inc.

Gedatus, Gus. Weight Training. 2000. (Nutrition & Fitness Ser.). (Illus.). 64p. (J). (gr. 4-6). lib. bdg. 23.95 (978-0-7368-0708-1(X), LifeMatters Bks.) Capstone Pr., Inc.

Geil, Patricia Bazel & Ross, Tami A. Cooking up Fun for Kids with Diabetes. 2003. (Illus.). 128p. pap. 14.95 (978-1-58040-134-0(1), 9781580401340) McGraw-Hill/Contemporary.

Gillies, Judi. Jumbo Vegetarian Cookbook. 2002. (gr. 3-6). lib. bdg. 24.55 (978-0-613-56468-7(5)) Tandem Library Bks.

Gillies, Judi & Glossop, Jennifer. The Jumbo Vegetarian Cookbook. Phillips, Louise, illus. unabr. ed. 2002. (Jumbo Bks.). 256p. (J). (gr. 4-6). (978-1-55074-977-9(3)) Kids Can Pr., Ltd.

Good Times with Good Foods Activity Books: Ages 2-6, 12 vols. 2005. (J). 9.95 (978-1-57175-172-0(6), 6505-C) Learning ZoneXpress.

Good Times with Good Foods Activity Books: Ages 7-11, 12 vols. 2005. (J). 9.95 (978-1-57175-173-7(4), 6506-C) Learning ZoneXpress.

Gordon, Sharon. You Are What You Eat. (Rookie Read-About Health Ser.). (Illus.). 32p. (J). (gr. k-2). 2003. pap. 5.95 (978-0-516-26952-8(6)); 2002. pap. 20.50 (978-0-516-22573-9(1)) Scholastic Library Publishing. (Children's Pr.).

—You Are What You Eat. 2002. (gr. k-3). lib. bdg. 14.10 (978-0-613-59558-2(0)) Tandem Library Bks.

Gottlieb, Jeff & Gottlieb, Martha. Spriggles - Motivational Books for Children: Spriggles: Health & Nutrition. Gottlieb, Alexander, illus. 2002. 32p. (J). (ps-5). per. 8.95 (978-1-930439-01-6(6)) Mountain Watch Pr.

Goulding, Sylvia. Healthy Eating. 2005. (Healthy Kids Ser.). (Illus.). 32p. (gr. 3-6). 19.95 (978-1-59515-204-6(0)) Rourke Publishing, LLC.

Graham, Ian. Diet. 2006. (Illus.). 36p. (J). lib. bdg. 16.95 (978-1-59566-191-3(3)) QEB Publishing Inc.

Gray, Shirley W. Eating for Good Health. 2003. (Living Well). (Illus.). 32p. (J). (gr. 2-6). 27.07 (978-1-59296-079-8(0)) Child's World, Inc.

—Exercising for Good Health. 2003. (Living Well). (Illus.). 32p. (J). (gr. 2-6). 27.07 (978-1-59296-081-1(2)) Child's World, Inc.

Green, Emily K. Fruits. 2006. (Blastoff! Readers Ser.). (Illus.). 24p. (J). lib. bdg. 16.95 (978-1-60014-005-1(X)) Bellwether Media.

—Grains. 2006. (Blastoff! Readers Ser.). (Illus.). 24p. (J). lib. bdg. 16.95 (978-1-60014-003-7(3)) Bellwether Media.

—Healthy Eating. 2006. (Blastoff! Readers Ser.). (Illus.). 24p. (J). lib. bdg. 16.95 (978-1-60014-007-5(6)) Bellwether Media.

—Meat & Beans. 2006. (Blastoff! Readers Ser.). (Illus.). 24p. (J). lib. bdg. 16.95 (978-1-60014-004-4(1)) Bellwether Media.

—Milk, Yogurt, & Cheese. 2006. (Blastoff! Readers Ser.). (Illus.). 24p. (J). lib. bdg. 16.95 (978-1-60014-000-6(9)) Bellwether Media.

—Oils. 2006. (Blastoff! Readers Ser.). (Illus.). 24p. (J). lib. bdg. 16.95 (978-1-60014-001-3(7)) Bellwether Media.

—Vegetables. 2006. (Blastoff! Readers Ser.). (Illus.). 24p. (J). lib. bdg. 16.95 (978-1-60014-002-0(5)) Bellwether Media.

Gregson, Susan R. Healthy Eating. 2000. (Perspectives on Physical Health Ser.). (Illus.). 64p. (J). (gr. 4-6). lib. bdg. 23.93 (978-0-7368-0420-2(X), LifeMatters Bks.) Capstone Pr., Inc.

Hau, Stephanie. I Can Live To 100! Secrets Just for Kids. Hau, Joseph, illus. 2005. 60p. (J). per. 9.95 (978-0-9767324-0-2(8), Kids Can) Proactive Publishing.

Having a Healthy Baby - Diet & Nutrition. 2004. (YA). pap. 4.00 net. (978-1-930996-57-1(8)) Planned Parenthood Federation of America, Inc.

Healthy Eating New Food Guide Pyramid. 2006. (Illus.). 24p. (J). (gr. k-2). 18.50 (***978-0-531-17852-2(8)***) Scholastic Library Publishing.

Hewitt, Sally. Health & Diet: Looking after Myself. 2005. (Science Starters Ser.). (Illus.). 32p. (J). (gr. 3-7). lib. bdg. 27.10 (978-1-59604-011-3(4)) Stargazer Bks.

Hovius, Christopher. The Best You Can Be: A Teen's Guide to Fitness & Nutrition. 2004. (Science of Health Ser.). (Illus.). 128p. (J). (978-1-59084-848-7(9)) Mason Crest Pubs.

Hulme, Janet A. Bladder & Bowel Issues for Kids: A Handy Guide for Kids Ages 4-12. 2003. (Illus.). 92p. pap. 14.95 (978-1-928812-05-0(8), 4000-07) Phoenix Publishing.

Hurwitz, Sue. Choosing a Career in Nutrition. rev. ed. 1999. (World of Work Ser.). (Illus.). 64p. (YA). (gr. 7-12). lib. bdg. 25.25 (978-0-8239-3001-2(7), WWNUTR) Rosen Publishing Group, Inc., The.

Jones, Susan Smith & Warren, Dianne. Vegetable Soup - The Fruit Bowl. Lindman, Amy Sorvaag, illus. rev. ed. 2006. 64p. (J). (ps-3). per. 14.95 (978-0-9652736-0-2(1)) Oasis Pubns.

Jukes, Mavis. It's a Girl Thing: Food, Fitness, & Feeling Great. Ziss, Debra, illus. 2003. 128p. (J). (gr. 4-8). lib. bdg. 18.99 (978-0-679-99029-1(1), Crown Books For Young Readers) Random Hse. Children's Bks.

Jukes, Mavis, et al. Be Healthy! It's a Girl Thing: Food, Fitness, & Feeling Great. Ziss, Debra, illus. 2003. 128p. (J). (gr. 5). pap. 12.95 (978-0-679-89029-4(7), Crown Books For Young Readers) Random Hse. Children's Bks.

Kalz, Jill. Fruits. 2003. 24p. (J). lib. bdg. 21.35 (978-1-58340-299-3(3)) Smart Apple Media.

—Grains. 2003. 24p. (J). lib. bdg. 21.35 (978-1-58340-301-3(9)) Smart Apple Media.

—Meats & Protein. 2003. 24p. (J). lib. bdg. 21.35 (978-1-58340-298-6(5)) Smart Apple Media.

—Vegetables. 2003. 24p. (J). lib. bdg. 21.35 (978-1-58340-300-6(0)) Smart Apple Media.

Kids Mypyramid Tablet. 2005. (J). pap. 9.95 (978-1-57175-091-4(6), 4275-T) Learning ZoneXpress.

King, Hazel. Carbohydrates for a Healthy Body. 2003. (Body Needs Ser.). (Illus.). 48p. pap. 7.99 (978-1-4034-3310-7(0)); (J). lib. bdg. 27.07 (978-1-4034-0756-6(8)) Heinemann Library.

Kleinberg, Naomi. Grover's Guide to Good Eating. Leigh, Tom & Yee, Josie, illus. 2007. (Happy Healthy Monsters Ser.). 32p. (J). (ps-ps). 6.99 (***978-0-375-84063-0(X)***, Random Hse. Bks. for Young Readers) Random Hse. Children's Bks.

Klingel, Cynthia Fitterer & Noyed, Robert B. Bread & Cereal. Andersen, Gregg, photos by. 2002. (Weekly Reader Early Learning Library). (Illus.). 24p. (J). (ps up). pap. 5.95 (978-0-8368-3144-3(6), Weekly Reader Early Learning Library) Stevens, Gareth Inc.

—Fats & Sweets. Andersen, Gregg, photos by. 2002. (Weekly Reader Early Learning Library). (Illus.). 24p. (J). (ps up). pap. 7.93 (978-0-8368-3145-0(4)); lib. bdg. 19.33 (978-0-8368-3056-9(3)) Stevens, Gareth Inc. (Weekly Reader Early Learning Library).

—Fruit. Andersen, Gregg, photos by. 2002. (Weekly Reader Early Learning Library). (Illus.). 24p. (J). (ps up). pap. 5.95 (978-0-8368-3146-7(2)); lib. bdg. 19.33 (978-0-8368-3057-6(1)) Stevens, Gareth Inc. (Weekly Reader Early Learning Library).

—Meat. Andersen, Gregg, photos by. 2002. (Weekly Reader Early Learning Library). (Illus.). 24p. (J). (ps up). pap. 5.95 (978-0-8368-3147-4(0)); lib. bdg. 19.33 (978-0-8368-3058-3(X)) Stevens, Gareth Inc. (Weekly Reader Early Learning Library).

—Milk & Cheese. Andersen, Gregg, photos by. 2002. (Weekly Reader Early Learning Library). (Illus.). 24p. (J). (ps up). pap. 5.95 (978-0-8368-3148-1(9)); lib. bdg. 19.33 (978-0-8368-3059-0(8)) Stevens, Gareth Inc. (Weekly Reader Early Learning Library).

—Vegetables. Andersen, Gregg, photos by. 2002. (Weekly Reader Early Learning Library). (Illus.). 24p. (J). (ps up). pap. 7.93 (978-0-8368-3149-8(7)); lib. bdg. 19.33 (978-0-8368-3060-6(1)) Stevens, Gareth Inc. (Weekly Reader Early Learning Library).

Kudlinski, Kathleen V. Food for Life. 2003. (Science Links Ser.). (Illus.). 32p. (gr. 3-5). 23.00 (978-0-7910-7421-3(8), Chelsea Hse.) Facts On File, Inc.

Lair, Cynthia & Murdoch, Scott. Feeding the Young Athlete: Sports Nutrition Made Easy for Players & Parents. 2002. (Illus.). 112p. pap. 12.00 (978-0-9660346-9-1(4)) Moon Smile Pr.

Landau, Elaine. A Healthy Diet. 2003. (Watts Library). (Illus.). 64p. (J). 25.50 (978-0-531-12027-9(9), Watts, Franklin) Scholastic Library Publishing.

—Healthy Diet. 2003. (gr. 5-8). lib. bdg. 17.60 (978-0-613-67628-1(9)) Tandem Library Bks.

Lee, Brenda G. Lunch at the Zoo. 2002. 14.95 (978-0-9728732-0-8(1)) Little Cottage Bks.

Leedy, Loreen. The Edible Pyramid: Good Eating Every Day. Leedy, Loreen, illus. rev. ed. (Illus.). 32p. (J). (gr. k-3). 17.95 (***978-0-8234-2074-2(4)***); 6.95 (***978-0-8234-2075-9(2)***) Holiday Hse., Inc.

Levchuck, Leslie. Fuel Up! A Girl's Guide to Eating Well. 1999. (Girls' Guides). (Illus.). 48p. (YA). (gr. 5-8). lib. bdg. 23.95 (978-0-8239-2981-8(7), GGFUUP, Rosen Central) Rosen Publishing Group, Inc., The.

Levete, Sarah. Eating & Health. 2005. (Illus.). 32p. (J). (gr. 3-7). lib. bdg. 27.10 (978-1-59604-049-6(1)) Stargazer Bks.

The Library of Nutrition, 6 bk. set. 2005. (YA). (gr. 5-8). lib. bdg. 151.50 (978-1-4042-0369-3(9)) Rosen Publishing Group, Inc., The.

Llewellyn, Claire. Eating. 2004. (J). pap. 27.10 (978-1-58340-436-2(8)) Smart Apple Media.

—Health & Growth. 2005. (Illus.). 24p. (J). (gr. 1-4). lib. bdg. (978-1-84234-336-4(X), Cherrytree Books) Evans Publishing Group.

Llewellyn, Claire. Your Food. 2007. (J). (***978-1-59771-098-5(9)***) Sea-To-Sea Pubns.

Lobb, Janice. Munch! Crunch! What's for Lunch? Experiments in the Kitchen. Savage, Ann & Utton, Peter, illus. 2002. (At Home with Science Ser.). 32p. (J). pap. 5.95 (978-0-7534-5460-2(2), Kingfisher) Houghton Mifflin Co. Trade & Reference Div.

Lombardo, Michelle. The OrganWise Guys - Basic Training for Better Health Vol. 2, 2 vols. Herron, Mark, illus. 1998. 35p. (J). (gr. 2-5). (978-0-9648438-3-7(8)) Wellness, Inc.

Lori A. Smolin, ed. Eating Right: An Introduction to Human Nutrition. 2005. (Illus.). 160+p. (gr. 9-13). pap. 140.00 (978-0-7910-7849-5(3), Chelsea Hse.) Facts On File, Inc.

Marcom Group Ltd, prod. Contemporary Nutrition Win Lab. (YA). cd-rom 222.50 (978-0-7365-4343-9(0)) Films Media Group.

Mason, Paul. Training for the Top: Nutrition & Exercise. 2005. (Illus.). 32p. (J). (978-1-4109-1964-9(1)); lib. bdg. (978-1-4109-1933-5(1)) Steck-Vaughn.

Mayo Clinic Staff, contrib. by. Eating Out: Your Pocket Guide to Healthy Dining. 2002. (Mayo Clinic on Health Ser.). (Illus.). 36,52p. (YA). (gr. 8 up). lib. bdg. (978-1-59084-249-2(9)) Mason Crest Pubs.

—Healthy Meals for Hurried Lives. 2002. (Mayo Clinic on Health Ser.). (Illus.). 36,52p. (YA). (gr. 8 up). lib. bdg. (978-1-59084-252-2(9)) Mason Crest Pubs.

McCarthy, Rose. Food Labels: Using Nutritional Information to Create a Healthy Diet. 2004. (Library of Nutrition). (Illus.). 48p. (J). lib. bdg. 25.25 (978-1-4042-0300-6(1)) Rosen Publishing Group, Inc., The.

McGinty, Alice B. Eating Right. 1999. (Staying Healthy Ser.). (978-0-606-18161-7(X)) Tandem Library Bks.

McGraw-Hill Staff. Creative Instructional Methods For: Family & Consumer Sciences, Nutrition & Wellness Student Text. 2002. (gr. 6-12). pap. 55.96 (978-0-07-822616-8(3), 9780078226168) Glencoe/McGraw-Hill.

McGraw-Hill Staff, et al. Nutrition & Wellness, 2 vols. 7th l.t. ed. 2003. 596p. (gr. 9-12). stu. ed. 57.32 (978-0-07-846332-7(7), 9780078463327) Glencoe/McGraw-Hill.

McGraw, Jay. Ultimate Weight Solution for Teens: The 7 Keys to Weight Freedom. 2003. (gr. 7-12). lib. bdg. 24.55 (978-0-613-90788-0(4)) Tandem Library Bks.

Meat & Beans New Food Guide Pyramid. 2006. (Illus.). 24p. (J). (gr. k-2). 18.50 (***978-0-531-17854-6(4)***) Scholastic Library Publishing.

The Meat & Protein Group, 6 vols. (gr. k-2). 28.95 (978-0-7368-8747-2(4)) Red Brick Learning.

Mehas, Kay Yockey, et al. Food Science: The Biochemistry of Food & Nutrition, 2 vols. 4th ed. 2002. 496p. (gr. 9-12). stu. ed. 58.00 (978-0-07-822603-8(1), 9780078226038) Glencoe/McGraw-Hill.

Milk Yogurt & Cheese New Food Guide Pyramid. 2006. (Illus.). 24p. (J). (gr. k-2). 18.50 (***978-0-531-17855-3(2)***) Scholastic Library Publishing.

Miller, Edward. The Monster Health Book: A Guide to Eating Healthy, Being Active, & Feeling Great for Monsters & Kids! Miller, Edward, illus. 2006. (Illus.). 40p. (J). (gr. k-5). 16.95 (978-0-8234-1956-2(8)) Holiday Hse., Inc.

Minden, Cecilia. Cooking by the Numbers. 2008. (J). lib. bdg. 25.26 (***978-1-60279-007-0(8)***) Cherry Lake Publishing.

Monroe, Judy. Understanding Weight Loss Programs. 1999. (Teen Eating Disorder Prevention Library). 144p. (gr. 7-12). pap. 6.95 (978-1-56838-263-0(4)) Hazelden Publishing & Educational Services.

Montgomery, Paul J. Nutritional Cereal Counter. 1998. (Illus.). 102p. (Orig.). (YA). (gr. 9 up). pap. 3.50 (978-0-9621865-1-6(1)) Product Information & Analysis.

Moores, Jeff. The Body Book: An Owner's Guide to Fueling, Fixing, & Running the Most Important Machine You Own. 2002. (Read 180 Ser.). (Illus.). 69p. (YA). (978-0-439-12349-5(6)) Scholastic, Inc.

Morris, Neil. Do You Know What's in Your Food? 2006. (Making Healthy Food Choices Ser.). (Illus.). 56p. (J). pap. (978-1-4034-8580-9(1)); (YA). (gr. 6-10). lib. bdg. 32.86 (978-1-4034-8574-8(7)) Heinemann Library.

—Do You Know Where Your Food Comes From? 2006. (Making Healthy Food Choices Ser.). (Illus.). 56p. (J). pap. (978-1-4034-8581-6(X)); (YA). (gr. 6-9). lib. bdg. 32.86 (978-1-4034-8575-5(5)) Heinemann Library.

—Food for Sports. 2006. (Making Healthy Food Choices Ser.). (Illus.), 56p. (J). pap. (978-1-4034-8579-3(8)); (YA). (gr. 6-10). lib. bdg. 32.86 (978-1-4034-8573-1(9)) Heinemann Library.

MyPyramid for Kids Tablet. 2005. (J). pap. 9.95 (978-1-57175-179-9(3), 4281-T) Learning ZoneXpress.

Mysteries of the Food Pyramid. 2000. (Health & Human Development Resource Library). (J). (gr. 4-6). tchr. ed. 69.95 (978-1-55942-160-7(6), 9227V9) Marsh Media.

Naik, Anita. Wise Guide Health & Fitness. 2005. (Illus.). 128p. (J). pap. (978-0-340-90260-8(4), Hodder Children's Books) Hodder Children's Division.

Nelson, Robin. Dairy. 2003. (First Step Nonfiction Ser.). (Illus.). 24p. (J). (gr. k-2). lib. bdg. 18.60 (978-0-8225-4632-0(9)) Lerner Publishing Group.

—Fats, Oils, & Sweets. 2003. (First Step Nonfiction Ser.). (Illus.). 24p. (J). (gr. k-2). lib. bdg. 18.60 (978-0-8225-4634-4(5)) Lerner Publishing Group.

—Fruits. 2003. (First Step Nonfiction Ser.). (Illus.). 24p. (J). (gr. k-2). lib. bdg. 18.60 (978-0-8225-4624-5(8)) Lerner Publishing Group.

—Grains. 2003. (First Step Nonfiction Ser.). (Illus.). 24p. (J). (gr. k-2). lib. bdg. 18.60 (978-0-8225-4628-3(0)) Lerner Publishing Group.

—Vegetables. 2003. (First Step Nonfiction Ser.). (Illus.). 24p. (J). (gr. k-2). lib. bdg. 18.60 (978-0-8225-4626-9(4)) Lerner Publishing Group.

The New Food Guide Pyramid, 8 vols., Set. 2006. (Blastoff! Readers Ser.). (Illus.). (J). (gr. k-2). 148.00 ***978-0-531-16875-2(1))** Scholastic Library Publishing.

The Nutraceutical Reference Guide. 2005. (YA). per. 14.95 (978-1-59872-184-3(4)) Instantpublisher.com.

Nutrition & Fitness, 8 bks. Incl. Bicycling for Fitness. Gedatus, Gus. lib. bdg. 23.93 (978-0-7368-0705-0(5)); Exercise for Weight Management. Gedatus, Gus. lib. bdg. 23.93 (978-0-7368-0706-7(3)); Food & Emotions. Turck, Mary. lib. bdg. 23.93 (978-0-7368-0711-1(X)); Healthy Eating for Weight Management. Turck, Mary. lib. bdg. 23.95 (978-0-7368-0709-8(8)); Healthy Snack & Fast-Food Choices. Turck, Mary. lib. bdg. 23.93 (978-0-7368-0710-4(1)); In-Line Skating for Fitness. Gedatus, Gus. lib. bdg. 23.93 (978-0-7368-0707-4(1)); Vegetarianism for Teens. Duden, Jane. lib. bdg. 23.93 (978-0-7368-0712-8(8)); Weight Training. Gedatus, Gus. lib. bdg. 23.95 (978-0-7368-0708-1(X)); 64p. (J). (gr. 4-6). 2000. (Illus.). Set lib. bdg. 191.44 (978-0-7368-0719-7(5) , LifeMatters Bks.) Capstone Pr., Inc.

O'Brien, Eileen. Starving to Win: Athletes & Eating Disorders. 1998. (Teen Health Library of Eating Disorder Prevention). (Illus.). 64p. (J). (gr. 4-6). lib. bdg. 26.50 (978-0-8239-2764-7(4) , EDATEA) Rosen Publishing Group, Inc., The.

Oils New Food Guide Pyramid. 2006. (Illus.). 24p. (J). (gr. k-2). 18.50 ***978-0-531-17856-0(0))** Scholastic Library Publishing.

Oramasionwu, Angela. Sammy the Cell & the Healthy 1s: Let's Learn about Nutrition. 2004. 33p. pap. 17.95 (978-1-4137-3449-2(9)) PublishAmerica, Inc.

Parsons, William B., Jr. Tough Talk about Fat! How to Reach & Maintain Your Ideal Weight. 2003. 134p. per. 12.95 (978-0-9662568-9-5(1)) Lilac Pr.

Peters, Celeste A., contrib. by. Peppers, Popcorn & Pizza: The Science of Food. 1998. (Science @ Work Ser.). (Illus.). 48p. (J). (gr. 4-6). lib. bdg. 27.12 (978-0-7398-0136-9(8)) Raintree.

Petrie, Kristin. Conquering Carbs. 2004. (Nutrition Ser.). (Illus.). 32p. (J). (gr. k-6). lib. bdg. 22.78 (978-1-59197-401-7(1) , Checkerboard Library) ABDO Publishing Co.

—Fit & Fats. 2004. (Nutrition Ser.). (Illus.). 32p. (J). (gr. k-6). lib. bdg. 22.78 (978-1-59197-402-4(X) , Checkerboard Library) ABDO Publishing Co.

—The Food Pyramid. (Illus.). (J). 2007. (ENG.). lib. bdg. 22.78 (978-1-59928-692-1(0) , Checkerboard Library); 2004. 32p. lib. bdg. 22.78 (978-1-59197-403-1(8)) ABDO Publishing Co.

—Nutrition. 2004. (J). (gr. k-6). lib. bdg. 136.68 (978-1-59197-400-0(3) , Checkerboard Library) ABDO Publishing Co.

—Nutrition Anyone? 2004. (Nutrition Ser.). (Illus.). 32p. (J). (gr. k-6). lib. bdg. 22.78 (978-1-59197-404-8(6) , Checkerboard Library) ABDO Publishing Co.

—A Passion for Proteins. 2004. (Nutrition Ser.). (Illus.). 32p. (J). (gr. k-6). lib. bdg. 22.78 (978-1-59197-405-5(4) , Checkerboard Library) ABDO Publishing Co.

—Vitamins Are Vital. 2004. (Nutrition Ser.). (Illus.). 32p. (J). (gr. k-6). lib. bdg. 22.78 (978-1-59197-406-2(2) , Checkerboard Library) ABDO Publishing Co.

Pocket Chart Science: Nutrition. 2000. (J). pap. 9.95 (978-1-56911-701-9(2)) Learning Resources, Inc.

Powell, Jillian. Fats for a Healthy Body. 2003. (Body Needs Ser.). (Illus.). 48p. pap. 7.99 (978-1-4034-3311-4(9)); (J). lib. bdg. 27.07 (978-1-4034-0757-3(6)) Heinemann Library.

—Food Matters. (Life Files Ser.). (Illus.). 1999. 62p. pap. 15.99 (978-0-237-51812-7(0)); 1998. 64p. 24.99 (978-0-237-51811-0(2)) Evans Publishing Group GBR. (Evans Brothers, Limited). *Dist:* Independent Pubs. Group.

Que Debo Comer Hoy? 2005. (SPA.). (J). 10.99 (978-0-9770756-1-4(3)) Family Nutrition Ctr. P.C.

Randall, Ronne. What's So Good about Vegetables? 2003. (What? Where? Why? Ser.). (Illus.). 24p. (J). (gr. 1 up). lib. bdg. 20.67 (978-0-8368-3789-6(4)) Stevens, Gareth Inc.

Rees, Jonathan. Eating Properly. 2005. (It's Your Health Ser.). (Illus.). 44p. (J). (gr. 6-9). lib. bdg. 29.95 (978-1-58340-591-8(7)) Smart Apple Media.

Rizzo, Nicholas. Championship Nutrition & Performance: The Wrestler's Guide to Lifestyle, Diet & Healthy Weight Control. rev. ed. 2004. (Illus.). 114p. 15.95 (978-0-9748220-1-3(9) , Executive Performances Publishing) Executive Performances, Inc.

Rondeau, Amanda. Food Pyramid. 2003. (What Should I Eat? Ser.). (Illus.). 23p. (J). (ps-3). lib. bdg. 19.93 (978-1-57765-832-0(9)) ABDO Publishing Co.

—Grains Are Good. 2003. (What Should I Eat? Ser.). (Illus.). 23p. (J). (ps-3). lib. bdg. 19.93 (978-1-57765-833-7(7) , SandCastle) ABDO Publishing Co.

—Milk Is Magnificent. 2003. (What Should I Eat? Ser.). (Illus.). 23p. (J). (ps-3). lib. bdg. 19.93 (978-1-57765-837-5(X) , SandCastle) ABDO Publishing Co.

—Proteins Are Powerful. 2003. (What Should I Eat? Ser.). (Illus.). 23p. (J). (ps-3). lib. bdg. 19.93 (978-1-57765-836-8(1) , SandCastle) ABDO Publishing Co.

—Vegetables Are Vital. 2003. (What Should I Eat? Ser.). (Illus.). 23p. (J). (ps-3). lib. bdg. 19.93 (978-1-57765-835-1(3) , SandCastle) ABDO Publishing Co.

Rose, Elizabeth. Food & Nutrition. 2006. (Life Science Library). (Illus.). 24p. (J). 21.25 (978-1-4042-2821-4(7) , PowerKids Pr.) Rosen Publishing Group, Inc., The.

Ross, Veronica. Eating. 2002. (My Healthy Body Ser.). (Illus.). 32p. (J). lib. bdg. 24.25 (978-1-930643-83-3(7)) Chrysalis Education.

Royston. Eating. 2004. (My Amazing Body Ser.). (Illus.). pap. 7.50 (978-1-4109-0949-7(2)) Raintree.

Royston, Angela. Eat Well. 1999. (Illus.). 32p. (J). (gr. k-2). lib. bdg. 21.36 (978-1-57572-982-4(2)) Heinemann Library.

—Healthy Food. 2003. (Illus.). 32p. (J). pap. 6.95 (978-1-4034-4448-6(X)); lib. bdg. 22.79 (978-1-4034-4439-4(0)) Heinemann Library.

—Protein for a Healthy Body. 2003. (Body Needs Ser.). (Illus.). 48p. pap. 7.99 (978-1-4034-3312-1(7)); (J). (gr. 4-6). lib. bdg. 27.07 (978-1-4034-0759-7(2)) Heinemann Library.

—Protein for a Healthy Body. 2003. (gr. 3-6). lib. bdg. 16.40 (978-0-613-60982-1(4)) Tandem Library Bks.

—Vitamins & Minerals for a Healthy Body. 2003. (Illus.). 48p. (J). pap. 7.99 (978-1-4034-3313-8(5)); lib. bdg. 27.07 (978-1-4034-0758-0(4)) Heinemann Library.

—Water & Fiber for a Healthy Body. 2003. (Body Needs Ser.). (Illus.). 48p. pap. 7.99 (978-1-4034-3314-5(3)); (J). (gr. 4-6). lib. bdg. 27.07 (978-1-4034-0760-3(6)) Heinemann Library.

—Water & Fiber for a Healthy Body. 2003. (gr. 3-6). lib. bdg. 16.40 (978-0-613-60999-9(9)) Tandem Library Bks.

—What Should We Eat? 2005. (J). pap. (978-1-4034-7617-3(9)); pap. (978-1-4034-7612-8(8)); (Illus.). 24p. lib. bdg. 21.36 (978-1-4034-7607-4(1)) Heinemann Library.

—Why Do We Need to Eat? 2005. (Heinemann Read & Learn Ser.). (Illus.). 24p. (J). (978-1-4034-7606-7(3)); pap. (978-1-4034-7611-1(X)) Heinemann Library.

Salzmann, Mary Elizabeth. Eating Right. 2004. (Healthy Habits Ser.). (Illus.). 23p. (J). (ps-3). lib. bdg. 19.93 (978-1-59197-551-9(4)) ABDO Publishing Co.

Sanna, Ellyn. America's Unhealthy Lifestyle: Supersize It! 2004. (Obesity Ser.). (Illus.). 104p. (J). (ps-7). (978-1-59084-942-2(6)) Mason Crest Pubs.

Schaefer, A. R. Food Around the World. 2007. (ENG & SPA.). (J). (978-1-59515-959-5(2)) Rourke Publishing, LLC.

Schaefer, Lola M. Meat & Protein. 2007. (J). ***978-1-4329-0146-2(X));** pap. ***978-1-4329-0153-0(2))** Heinemann Library.

—Oils. 2007. (J). ***978-1-4329-0144-8(3));** pap. ***978-1-4329-0151-6(6))** Heinemann Library.

Schrank, Jeffrey. Protein: How Cows & Carrots Become People. 2000. (YA). pap., tchr. ed. 89.00 incl. VHS (978-0-917159-14-5(4)) Learning Seed Co.

Schuh, Mari C. The Fruit Group. 2006. (Illus.). 24p. (J). (978-0-7368-5370-5(7) , Pebble Bks.) Capstone Pr., Inc.

—The Grain Group. 2006. (Illus.). 24p. (J). (978-0-7368-5371-2(5) , Pebble Bks.) Capstone Pr., Inc.

—Healthy Snacks. 2006. (Illus.). 24p. (J). 19.93 (978-0-7368-5369-9(3) , Pebble Bks.) Capstone Pr., Inc.

—The Meat & Beans Group. 2006. (Illus.). 24p. (J). (978-0-7368-5372-9(3) , Pebble Bks.) Capstone Pr., Inc.

—The Milk Group. 2006. (Illus.). 24p. (J). (978-0-7368-5373-6(1) , Pebble Bks.) Capstone Pr., Inc.

—The Vegetable Group. 2006. (Illus.). 24p. (J). (978-0-7368-5374-3(X) , Pebble Bks.) Capstone Pr., Inc.

Science stories foss spanish food & nutrition ea Cr05. 2005. (J). (978-1-59242-596-9(8)) Delta Education, LLC.

Scott, Janine. The Food Pyramid. 2003. (Spyglass Books). (Illus.). 24p. (J). (gr. 1 up). lib. bdg. 18.60 (978-0-7565-0447-2(3)) Compass Point Bks.

Seaborn, Ron. The Children's Health Food Book. rev. ed. 2006. 40p. 16.95 ***978-0-9647089-2-1(2))** Life Line, Inc.

Secrets of the Food Pyramid. 2000. (Health & Human Development Resource Library). (J). (gr. k-3). tchr. ed. 69.95 (978-1-55942-159-1(2) , 9226V9) Marsh Media.

Sesame Street Healthy Foods. 2005. (J). spiral bd. 4.99 ***978-1-58610-938-7(3))** Learning Horizons, Inc.

Sesame's: A Giant Coloring Book that teaches Healthy Eating Habits. 2006. (J). 6.99 (978-1-59949-499-9(X)) Food Marketing Consultants, Inc.

Sheen, Barbara. Eating Right. 2007. (J). ***978-1-4034-9694-2(3));** pap. ***978-1-4034-9701-7(X))** Heinemann Library.

Shryer, Donna. Body Fuel: A Guide to Good Nutrition. 2007. (Food & Fitness Ser.). 144p. (J). lib. bdg. 37.07 ***978-0-7614-2552-6(7)** , Benchmark Bks.) Cavendish, Marshall Corp.

Silate, Jennifer. Planning & Preparing Healthy Meals & Snacks: A Day-to-Day Guide to a Healthier Diet. 2004. (Library of Nutrition). (Illus.). 48p. (J). lib. bdg. 25.25 (978-1-4042-0302-0(8)) Rosen Publishing Group, Inc., The.

Silverstein, Alvin. Eat Your Vegetables! Drink Your Milk! 2000. (gr. 3-6). lib. bdg. 15.25 (978-0-613-34190-5(2)); (Illus.). (J). 13.75 (978-0-606-20645-7(0)) Tandem Library Bks.

Silverstein, Alvin, et al. Eat Your Vegetables! Drink Your Milk! 2001. (My Health Ser.). (Illus.). 48p. (J). (gr. 3-5). pap. 6.95 (978-0-531-16507-2(8) , Watts, Franklin) Scholastic Library Publishing.

Smalley, Carol Parenzan. Fats, Oils, & Sweets. 2005. (Rookie Read-About Health Ser.). (Illus.). 31p. (J). (ps-ps). 20.50 (978-0-516-25289-6(5) , Children's Pr.) Scholastic Library Publishing.

—Fats, Oils & Sweets. 2006. 32p. (J). (gr. k-2). pap. 5.95 (978-0-516-24759-5(X) , Children's Pr.) Scholastic Library Publishing.

Smith, Alastair. What Happens to Your Food. Wheatley, Maria, illus. 2003. 16p. (J). (gr. 2 up). pap. 7.95 (978-0-7945-0643-8(7) , Usborne) EDC Publishing.

Smolin, Lori A. & Grosvenor, Mary B. Nutrition & Eating Disorders. 2004. (Eating Right Ser.). (J). pap. (978-0-7910-8016-0(1)); (Illus.). 160p. (gr. 9-13). 35.00 (978-0-7910-7851-8(5)) Facts On File, Inc. (Chelsea Hse.).

Sohn, Emily. Food & Nutrition. 2006. (Science News for Kids Ser.). (Illus.). 64p. (J). 30.00 (978-0-7910-9121-0(X) , Chelsea Clubhouse) Facts On File, Inc.

Spilsbury, Louise. Why Should I Eat This Carrot? And Other Questions about Healthy Eating. 2003. (Body Matters Ser.). (Illus.). 32p. (J). lib. bdg. (978-1-4034-4680-0(6)) Heinemann Library.

Sullivan, Robert J. Digestion & Nutrition. 2004. (Your Body, How It Works). (Illus.). 112p. (gr. 9-13). 31.95 (978-0-7910-7739-9(X) , Chelsea Hse.) Facts On File, Inc.

Swanson, Diane. Burp! The Most Interesting Book You'll Ever Read about Eating. 2001. (gr. 3-6). lib. bdg. 15.25 (978-0-613-36243-6(8)) Tandem Library Bks.

Tabletop Pocket Chart Nutrition Card Set. 2004. (J). 8.95 (978-1-56911-171-0(5)) Learning Resources, Inc.

Taylor-Butler, Christine. The Food Pyramid. 2007. (True Booktrade;: Health & the Human Body Ser.). 48p. (J). spiral bd. 26.00 ***978-0-531-16859-2(X)** , Children's Pr.) Scholastic Library Publishing.

Tecco, Betsy Dru. Food for Fuel: The Connection Between Food & Physical Activity. 2004. (Library of Nutrition). (Illus.). 48p. (J). lib. bdg. 25.25 (978-1-4042-0303-7(6)) Rosen Publishing Group, Inc., The.

Thomas, Ann. Dairy Products. 2002. (Food Ser.). (Illus.). 32p. (gr. k-2). 23.00 (978-0-7910-6980-6(X) , Chelsea Hse.) Facts On File, Inc.

—Fats, Oils, & Sweets. 2002. (Food Ser.). (Illus.). 32p. (gr. k-2). 23.00 (978-0-7910-6979-0(6) , Chelsea Hse.) Facts On File, Inc.

—Food: Grains. 2002. (Food Ser.). (Illus.). 32p. (gr. k-2). 23.00 (978-0-7910-6975-2(3) , Chelsea Hse.) Facts On File, Inc.

—Fruits. 2002. (Food Ser.). (Illus.). 32p. (gr. k-2). 23.00 (978-0-7910-6976-9(1) , Chelsea Hse.) Facts On File, Inc.

—Vegetables. 2002. (Food Ser.). (Illus.). 32p. (gr. k-2). 23.00 (978-0-7910-6977-6(X) , Chelsea Hse.) Facts On File, Inc.

Trumbauer, Lisa. Comiendo Bien. Ramos, Gloria, tr. 2005. (SPA., Illus.). 20p. (J). 15.93 (978-0-7368-4159-7(8) , Yellow Umbrella Bks.) Capstone Pr., Inc.

—Eating Well. (Science Ser.). (Illus.). (J). 2004. 16p. lib. bdg. 15.93 (978-0-7368-2937-3(7) , Yellow Umbrella Bks.); 2003. 17p. pap. (978-0-7368-2896-3(6)) Capstone Pr., Inc.

—Food for Thought. 2000. (Yellow Umbrella Books). (Illus.). 16p. (J). (gr. 1). lib. bdg. 14.60 (978-0-7368-0729-6(2) , Pebble Bks.) Capstone Pr., Inc.

Turck, Mary. Food & Emotions. 2000. (Nutrition & Fitness Ser.). (Illus.). 64p. (J). (gr. 4-6). lib. bdg. 23.93 (978-0-7368-0711-1(X) , LifeMatters Bks.) Capstone Pr., Inc.

—Healthy Eating for Weight Management. 2000. (Nutrition & Fitness Ser.). (Illus.). 64p. (J). (gr. 4-6). lib. bdg. 23.95 (978-0-7368-0709-8(8) , LifeMatters Bks.) Capstone Pr., Inc.

—Healthy Snack & Fast-Food Choices. 2000. (Nutrition & Fitness Ser.). (Illus.). 64p. (J). (gr. 4-6). lib. bdg. 23.93 (978-0-7368-0710-4(1) , LifeMatters Bks.) Capstone Pr., Inc.

Ureel, Jessica Mary. Allergy Express: Food Allergy Coloring & Activity Book. 2007. (J). per. 6.95 (978-0-9745033-1-8(2)) Main Street Pubns.

VanCleave, Janice Pratt. Janice VanCleave's Food & Nutrition for Every Kid. 1999. (gr. 3-6). lib. bdg. 22.20 (978-0-613-16517-4(9)) Tandem Library Bks.

—Janice VanCleave's Food & Nutrition for Every Kid: Easy Activities That Make Learning Science Fun. 1999. (Science for Every Kid Ser.: Vol. 117). (Illus.). 240p. (gr. 3-7). pap. 12.95 (978-0-471-17665-7(6) , Wiley) Wiley, John & Sons, Inc.

Vegetables New Food Guide Pyramid. 2006. (Illus.). 24p. (J). (gr. k-2). 18.50 ***978-0-531-17857-7(9))** Scholastic Library Publishing.

Vogel, Elizabeth. A Comer Sanamente! 2004. (Limpieza y Salud Todo el Dia Ser.). (SPA & ENG., Illus.). 24p. (J). lib. bdg. 16.00 (978-0-8239-6613-4(5)); (gr. 1-2). lib. bdg. 16.00 (978-0-8239-6612-7(7)) Rosen Publishing Group, Inc., The. (Buenas Letra).

—Eating Right. 2001. (PowerKids Readers Ser.). (Illus.). 24p. (J). (gr. 1). lib. bdg. 16.00 (978-0-8239-5686-9(5) , PKEATI, PowerKids Pr.) Rosen Publishing Group, Inc., The.

Wallach, Joel Dennis & Ma, Ian. Hell's Kitchen. 2005. 386p. (YA). pap. 19.95 (978-0-9748581-1-1(0)) Wellness Pubn.

Weintraub, Aileen. Everything You Need to Know about Eating Smart. 2005. (Need to Know Library). (Illus.). 64p. (YA). (gr. 7-12). lib. bdg. 25.25 (978-0-8239-3082-1(3) , NTEASM) Rosen Publishing Group, Inc., The.

West, Dorothy F. Nutrition & Fitness: Lifestyle Choices for Wellness. 2000. (Illus.). 496p. (YA). (gr. 9-12). 50.00 (978-1-56637-510-8(X)) Goodheart-Willcox Pub.

—Nutrition, Food, & Fitness: The Science of Wellness. 2006. (Illus.). 510p. (gr. 9-12). 42.75 (978-1-59070-527-8(0)) Goodheart-Willcox Pub.

Westcott, Patsy. Diet & Nutrition. 2000. (Health & Fitness Ser.). (Illus.). 48p. (J). (gr. 4-6). lib. bdg. 27.12 (978-0-7398-1344-7(7)) Raintree.

What Is a Vegetarian? 1999. (Illus.). 20p. (J). (ps-k). pap. 10.00 (978-0-9679561-2-1(9)) Debbie-Lou Productions.

What Should I Eat?, 6 vols. 2002. (Illus.). (J). (ps-3). lib. bdg. 119.58 (978-1-57765-831-3(0) , SandCastle) ABDO Publishing Co.

Where Does My Food Go. 2005. (J). 6.95 (978-0-9776850-0-4(4)) Sundback, Ruth.

Why Should I? Discovery Library, Set. 2001. (J). (gr. 1-4). lib. bdg. 115.62 (978-1-55916-300-2(3)) Rourke Publishing, LLC.

Williams, Kara. Frequently Asked Questions about My Pyramid: Eating Right. 2006. (FAQ Ser.). (Illus.). 64p. (J). (gr. 7-12). lib. bdg. 27.95 ***978-1-4042-1974-8(9))** Rosen Publishing Group, Inc., The.

Wilson, Scott & Wilkinson, Jody. Eating Healthy, Eating Right. 2004. 200p. 18.99 (978-0-8307-3022-3(2) , Gospel Light) Gospel Light Pubns.

Winchester, Bob. Excercise & Eating Right Are Okay, I Guess, 8 vols., Vol. 2. 2002. (Illus.). (J). per. (978-1-932062-09-0(2)) Hability Solution Services, Inc.

Wiseman, Wende & Dajani, Sari. Body Adventure. 2000. (Interactive Learning Kits Ser.). (Illus.). 24p. (J). (gr. k-2). pap. 14.99 incl. audio, cd-rom (978-1-894281-02-7(0)) Kidzup Entertainment CAN. *Dist:* Penton Overseas, Inc.

Zannos, Susan. Female Stars of Nutrition & Weight Control. 2000. (Legends of Health & Fitness Ser.). (Illus.). 96p. (gr. 6-10). lib. bdg. 25.70 (978-1-58415-015-2(7)) Mitchell Lane Pubs., Inc.

NUTS

Benduhn, Tea. Meat & Beans: Carne y Legumbres. 2007. (SPA & ENG.). (J). pap. ***978-0-8368-8463-0(9)** , Weekly Reader Early Learning Library) Stevens, Gareth Inc.

—Meat & Beans/Carne y Legumbres. 2007. (Find Out about Food/Conoce la Comida Ser.). (SPA & ENG.). 24p. (J). (gr. k-2). lib. bdg. 19.93 ***978-0-8368-8456-2(6)** , Weekly Reader Early Learning Library) Stevens, Gareth Inc.

Burns, Diane L. Berries, Nuts & Seeds. Garrow, Linda, illus. 2000. (Young Naturalist Field Guides Ser.). 40p. (J). (gr. 3 up). lib. bdg. 24.67 (978-0-8368-2144-4(0)) Stevens, Gareth Inc.

Hughes, Meredith Sayles. Hard to Crack: Nut Trees. 2005. (Plants We Eat Ser.). (Illus.). 104p. (gr. 6-9). 26.60 (978-0-8225-2838-8(X)) Lerner Publishing Group.

Llewellyn, Claire. Peanuts. Cohen, Helaine, ed. 1998. (What's for Lunch? Ser.). (Illus.). 32p. (J). (gr. k-2). pap. 6.95 (978-0-516-26222-2(X) , Children's Pr.) Scholastic Library Publishing.

Ocean, Suellen. The Acorn Mouse Vol. 1: A Children's Intro to Eating Acorns. Todd, Larry, illus. l.t. ed. 1999. 15p. (J). (gr. k-5). pap. 3.95 (978-0-9651140-4-2(X)) Ocean-Hose.

NYERERE, JULIUS K. (JULIUS KAMBARAGE), 1922-1999

Maillu, David G. Julius Nyerere: Father of Ujamaa. 2005. (Lion Book Ser.). (Illus.). ix, 81p. (J). (978-9966-951-32-8(6)) Sasa Sema Publications Ltd.

O

OAK

Cooper, Jason. Oak Tree. 2003. (Life Cycles Ser.). (Illus.). 24p. (gr. 1-4). 17.95 (978-1-58952-350-0(4)) Rourke Publishing, LLC.

Freeman, Marcia S. Oak Trees. Saunders-Smith, Gail, ed. 1998. (Trees Ser.). (Illus.). 24p. (J). (gr. k-1). lib. bdg. 15.93 (978-0-7368-0093-8(X) , Pebble Bks.) Capstone Pr., Inc.

—Oak Trees. (Trees Ser.). 24p. (J). pap. 5.95 (978-0-7368-8094-7(1)) Capstone Pr., Inc.

Hipp, Andrew. Oak. 2004. (Getting into Nature Ser.). (Illus.). 32p. (J). lib. bdg. 21.25 (978-0-8239-4206-0(6)) Rosen Publishing Group, Inc., The.

Mitchell, Melanie S. Oak Trees. (First Step Nonfiction Ser.). (Illus.). (gr. k-2). 2005. 24p. lib. bdg. 17.27 (978-0-8225-4610-8(8)); 2003. 23p. (J). pap. 5.95 (978-0-8225-4611-5(6) , Lerner Pubns.) Lerner Publishing Group.

Morrison, Gordon. Oak Tree. 2005. (Illus.). 32p. (J). (gr. k-3). 6.95 (978-0-618-60918-5(0) , Walter Lorraine) Houghton Mifflin Co. Trade & Reference Div.

Oak Trees, 6 vols. (gr. k-2). 28.95 (978-0-7368-8118-0(2)) Red Brick Learning.

Pfeffer, Wendy. A Log's Life. Brickman, Robin, illus. 2007. 32p. (J). 6.99 (978-1-4169-3483-7(9) , Aladdin) Simon & Schuster Children's Publishing.

Pugliano-Martin, Carol. Discover the Life Cycle of Oak Trees. 2006. (English Explorers Ser.). (J). pap. 39.00 ***978-1-4108-6472-7(3))** Benchmark Education Co.

—The Life Cycle of Oak Trees. 2006. (English Explorers Ser.). (J). pap. 39.00 ***978-1-4108-6469-7(3))** Benchmark Education Co.

Reid, Barbara. Acorn to Oak Tree. braille ed. 2004. (J). (gr. 1). spiral bd., bds. (978-0-616-03085-1(1)) Canadian National Institute for the Blind/Institut National Canadien pour les Aveugles.

—Acorn to Oak Tree. 2000. (Illus.). 14p. (J). (ps-3). 6.95 (978-0-00-224006-2(8)) HarperCollins Pubs.

Tagliaferro, Linda. The Life Cycle of an Oak Tree. 2007. (Pebble Plus Ser.). (Illus.). 24p. (J). (978-0-7368-6711-5(2) , 1264878) Capstone Pr., Inc.

OAK—FICTION

Danzig, Marsha. The Tiniest Acorn: A Story to Grow By. 1999. (Illus.). 32p. 12.95 (978-0-88391-001-6(2)) Fell, Frederick Pubs., Inc.

Emerson, Carl. Old Oak & the Autumn Leaf. Doerrfeld, Cori, illus. 2007. (J). (978-1-4048-2624-3(6)) Picture Window Bks.

—Old Oak & the Cold Winter Day. Doerrfeld, Cori, illus. 2007. (J). (978-1-4048-2627-4(0)) Picture Window Bks.

M N O

—Old Oak & the Summer Playground. Doerrfeld, Cori, illus. 2007. (J). (978-1-4048-2626-7(2)) Picture Window Bks.

Hilgendorf, L. B. Orville Oak & Friends. Dow, S. B., illus. 2005. 24p. bds. 11.95 (***978-1-58275-149-8(8)***) Black Forest Pr.

Hubery, Julia. A Friend for All Seasons. Matsuoka, Mei, illus. 2007. 32p. (J). (ps-2). 15.99 (***978-1-4169-2685-6(2)***) Simon & Schuster Children's Publishing.

Lucado, Max. The Oak Inside the Acorn. Angelini, George, illus. 2006. 48p. (J). 16.99 (978-1-4003-0601-5(9)) Nelson, Thomas Inc.

Penson, Mary. Billy Bardin & the Witness Tree. 2003. 140p. (J). 11.95 (978-0-87565-283-2(2)) Texas Christian Univ. Pr.

Taylor, Alice. Secrets of the Oak. Barnett, Russell, illus. 32p. 4.99 (978-0-86322-138-5(6)) Penguin Group (USA) Inc.

OAKLAND ATHLETICS (BASEBALL TEAM)

Frisch, Aaron. Oakland Athletics. 2002. 32p. (J). pap. 5.95 (978-0-89812-352-4(6) , Creative Paperbacks); (Illus.). (978-1-58341-218-3(2) , Creative Education) Creative Co., The.

Pueschner, Gordon. The Story of the Oakland Athletics. 2007. (J). (***978-1-58341-496-5(7)*** , Creative Education) Creative Co., The.

Rambeck, Richard. The History of the Oakland Athletics. 1998. (Baseball, the Great American Game Ser.). (Illus.). 32p. (YA). (gr. 3-12). pap. 21.30 (978-0-88682-919-3(4) , Creative Education) Creative Co., The.

OAKLAND RAIDERS (FOOTBALL TEAM)

Frisch, Aaron. The History of the Oakland Raiders. 2003. (NFL Today Ser.). (Illus.). 32p. 18.95 (978-1-58341-308-1(1) , Creative Education) Creative Co., The.

—Oakland Raiders. 2005. (Super Bowl Champions Ser.). (Illus.). 24p. (gr. 1-4). 16.95 (978-1-58341-388-3(X) , Creative Education) Creative Co., The.

Nelson, Julie. Oakland Raiders. 3rd rev. ed. 2000. (Pro Football Today Ser.). (Illus.). 32p. (J). (gr. 3 up). lib. bdg. 22.60 (978-1-58341-054-7(6) , Creative Education) Creative Co., The.

Oakland Raiders Staff. Oakland Raiders. CWC Sports Inc., ed. 1998. (NFL Team Yearbooks Ser.). (J). (gr. 1-12). pap. 9.99 (978-1-891613-18-0(9)) Everett Sports Publishing & Marketing.

OAKLEY, ANNIE, 1860-1926

Blair, Eric. Annie Oakley, Sharp Shooter: A Retelling of the Classic Traditional Tale. Chambers-Goldbert, Micah, illus. 2005. (Read-It! Readers Ser.). 32p. (C). (gr. k-3). 18.60 (978-1-4048-0970-3(8)) Picture Window Bks.

—La Pistolera Annie Oakley. Chambers-Goldberg, Micah, illus. 2006. (Read-It! Readers en Espanol Ser.).Tr. of Annie Oakley, Sharp Shooter. (SPA.). 32p. (J). (ps-3). 19.95 (978-1-4048-1653-4(4)) Picture Window Bks.

Dadey, Debbie. Shooting Star: Annie Oakley, the Legend. 1999. (978-0-606-16874-8(5)) Tandem Library Bks.

DiVito, Anna. Annie Oakley Saves the Day! DiVito, Anna, illus. 2004. (Ready-to-Read Cofa Ser.). 32p. (J). pap. 3.99 (978-0-689-86520-6(1) , Aladdin) Simon & Schuster Children's Publishing.

—Annie Oakley Saves the Day. DiVito, Anna, illus. 2004. (Illus.). 29p. (J). (ps-7). lib. bdg. 10.79 (978-0-606-32656-8(1)) Tandem Library Bks.

Feinstein, Stephen. Read about Annie Oakley. 2006. (I Like Biographies! Ser.). (Illus.). 24p. (J). lib. bdg. 21.26 (978-0-7660-2583-7(7) , Enslow Elementary) Enslow Pubs., Inc.

Flynn, Jean. Annie Oakley: Legendary Sharpshooter. 1998. (Historical American Biographies Ser.). (Illus.). 128p. (YA). (gr. 6-12). lib. bdg. 26.60 (978-0-7660-1012-3(0)) Enslow Pubs., Inc.

Foran, Jill. Annie Oakley. 2002. (Folk Heroes Ser.). (Illus.). 24p. (J). lib. bdg. 15.95 (978-1-59036-072-9(9)) Weigl Pubs., Inc.

Gilbert, Sara. Annie Oakley. 2005. (Illus.). 48p. (gr. 5-9). 21.95 (978-1-58341-334-0(0) , Creative Education) Creative Co., The.

Harcourt School Publishers Staff. Little Sure Shot Advanced Level. 3rd ed. 2002. (Trophies Reading Program Ser.). (Illus.). pap. 5.10 (978-0-15-323212-1(9)) Harcourt Schl. Pubs.

—Trofeos Advanced Level: Tiro Pequeno. 3rd ed. 2002. (SPA., Illus.). pap. 6.80 (978-0-15-324123-9(3)) Harcourt Schl. Pubs.

Haugen, Brenda. Annie Oakley: American Sharpshooter. (Illus.). 112p. (J). 2007. pap. (***978-0-7565-1974-2(8));*** 2006. lib. bdg. (***978-0-7565-1869-1(5)***) Compass Point Bks.

Krensky, Stephen. Shooting for the Moon: The Amazing Life & Times of Annie Oakley. Fuchs, Bernie, illus. 2001. 32p. (J). (gr. k-2). 17.00 (978-0-374-36843-2(0) , Farrar, Straus & Giroux (BYR)) Farrar, Straus & Giroux.

Kunstler, James Howard. Annie Oakley. Warter, Fred, illus. 2005. (Rabbit Ears-A Classic Tale Ser.). 40p. (J). (gr. k-5). 25.65 (978-1-59197-759-9(2)) Spotlight.

Landau, Elaine. Annie Oakley: Wild West Sharpshooter. 2004. (Best of the West Biographies Ser.). (Illus.). 48p. (J). lib. bdg. 23.93 (978-0-7660-2205-8(6)) Enslow Pubs., Inc.

Link, Theodore. Annie Oakley: Wild West Sharpshooter. 2003. (Primary Sources of Famous People in American History Ser.). (Illus.). 32p. (J). pap. (978-0-8239-4174-2(4)) Rosen Publishing Group, Inc., The.

Macy, Sue. Bulls - Eye: A Photobiography of Annie Oakley. 2001. (Illus.). 64p. (J). (gr. 3-7). 17.95 (978-0-7922-7008-9(8) , National Geographic Children's Bks.) National Geographic Society.

—Bull's Eye: A Photobiography of Annie Oakley. 2006. 64p. (gr. 5). pap. 7.95 (978-0-7922-5933-6(5) , National Geographic Children's Bks.) National Geographic Society.

Ruffin, Frances E. Annie Oakley. 2002. (American Legends Ser.). (Illus.). 24p. (J). (gr. 3). lib. bdg. 18.75 (978-0-8239-5824-5(8) , PowerKids Pr.) Rosen Publishing Group, Inc., The.

Shields, Charles J. Annie Oakley. 2001. (Famous Figures of the American Frontier Ser.). (Illus.). 64p. (J). (gr. 5 up). pap. 25.00 (978-0-7910-6490-0(5)); 25.00 (978-0-7910-6489-4(1)) Facts On File, Inc. (Chelsea Hse.).

Wadsworth, Ginger. Annie Oakley. 2006. (History Maker Bios Ser.). (Illus.). 48p. (J). (gr. 3-7). 26.60 (978-0-8225-2940-8(8) , Lerner Pubns.) Lerner Publishing Group.

Whiting, Jim. Annie Oakley. 2006. (What's So Great About... ? Ser.). (Illus.). 32p. (J). (gr. 1-4). lib. bdg. (978-1-58415-477-8(2)) Mitchell Lane Pubs., Inc.

Wills, Charles M. Annie Oakley. 2007. (DK Biography Ser.). 128p. (J). (gr. 3-8). 14.99 (978-0-7566-2986-1(1)); pap. 4.99 (978-0-7566-2997-7(0)) Dorling Kindersley Publishing, Inc.

OAKLEY, ANNIE, 1860-1926—FICTION

Dell, Pamela. Tag-along Tay: A Story about Annie Oakley & Buffalo Bill's Wild West Show. 2003. (Scrapbooks of America Ser.). (Illus.). 48p. (J). (gr. 2-6). 28.50 (978-1-59187-039-5(9)) Child's World, Inc.

Sargent, Dave & Sargent, Pat. Cactus: (Smoky Black) Competition Is Good, 25, 10. Lenoir, Jane, illus. 2001. (Saddle Up Ser.: 10). 36p. (J). pap. 6.95 (978-1-56763-672-7(1)); lib. bdg. 22.60 (978-1-56763-671-0(3)) Ozark Publishing.

OBAMA, BARACK, 1961-

Brill, Marlene Targ. Barack Obama. 2006. (J). pap. 6.95 (978-0-8225-6056-2(9) , First Avenue Editions) Lerner Publishing Group.

—Barack Obama: Working to Make a Difference. 2006. (Gateway Biographies Ser.). (Illus.). 48p. (J). 23.93 (978-0-8225-3417-4(7)) Lerner Publishing Group.

Davis, William Michael. Barack Obama: The Politics of Hope. 2007. (Illus.). 168p. (YA). (gr. 10 up). lib. bdg. 25.95 (***978-1-59556-024-7(6)***) OTTN Publishing.

Devaney, Sherri. Barack Obama. 2006. (Illus.). 112p. (J). (gr. 7-10). 32.45 (978-1-59018-937-5(X) , Lucent Bks.) Thomson Gale.

Edwards, Roberta. Barack Obama: An American Story. Call, Ken, illus. 2007. (All Aboard Reading Ser.). 48p. (J). (gr. 1-3). pap. 3.99 (***978-0-448-44799-5(1)*** , Grosset & Dunlap) Penguin Group (USA) Inc.

Sapet, Kerrily. Barack Obama. 2007. (Political Profiles Ser.). (Illus.). 128p. (YA). (gr. 5 up). lib. bdg. 27.95 (***978-1-59935-045-5(9)***) Reynolds, Morgan Inc.

Schuman, Michael. Barack Obama: We Are One People. 2008. (African-American Biography Library). (Illus.). 128p. (J). (gr. 6 up). lib. bdg. 31.93 (***978-0-7660-2891-3(7)***) Enslow Pubs., Inc.

OBEDIENCE

Aimwell, Walter. Oscar or the Boy Who Had His Own Way. 2006. pap. 89.99 (***978-1-4280-2158-7(2)***) IndyPublish.com.

Gordon, Sharon. Respetamos las Reglas. 2006. (Bookworms Ser.). (SPA & ENG., Illus.). 24p. (J). lib. bdg. 22.79 (978-0-7614-2358-4(3) , Benchmark Bks.) Cavendish, Marshall Corp.

—We Follow the Rules. 2005. (Bookworms Ser.). (ENG & SPA., Illus.). 24p. (J). (gr. 3-7). lib. bdg. (978-0-7614-1995-2(0) , Benchmark Bks.) Cavendish, Marshall Corp.

—We Follow the Rules (Respetamos las Reglas) 2006. (Bookworms Ser.). (ENG & SPA., Illus.). 24p. (J). lib. bdg. 22.79 (978-0-7614-2438-3(5)) Cavendish, Marshall Corp.

Mayer, Cassie. Following Rules. 2007. (J). (***978-1-4034-9487-0(8)***); pap. (***978-1-4034-9495-5(9)***) Heinemann Library.

Meiners, Cheri J. Know & Follow Rules. Johnson, Meredith, illus. 2005. (Learning to Get Along Ser.). 40p. (J). (ps-3). pap. 10.95 (978-1-57542-130-8(5)) Free Spirit Publishing, Inc.

Nelson, Robin. Following Rules. 2003. (First Step Nonfiction Ser.). (Illus.). (J). 23p. pap. 5.95 (978-0-8225-1321-6(8)); 24p. lib. bdg. 18.60 (978-0-8225-1284-4(X)) Lerner Publishing Group.

Robak, Raelinda. Herbie the Hippo. 2007. (J). (***978-0-8127-0465-5(7)***) Autumn Hse. Publishing Co.

Simon, Mary Manz. What Did Jesus Do? Kennedy, Anne, illus. 1998. (What Did Jesus Do? Ser.: Vol. 1). 40p. (J). (ps-3). 7.99 (978-0-8499-5856-4(3)) Nelson, Thomas Inc.

Warner Press Staff. Obedience. 2000. (Lion Cub Upside-Down Books Ser.). (Illus.). (J). (ps-3). pap. 5.95 (978-0-87162-820-6(1)) Warner Pr. Pubs.

Williams, Carla. Big Puzzles for Little Hands: People Who Obeyed God. 2004. (Illus.). 96p. (J). (ps-2). pap. 11.95 (978-1-885358-48-6(2)) Rainbow Pubs. & Legacy Pr.

OBEDIENCE—FICTION

Don't Do That, Dexter! 2006. 16p. (J). pap. 1.99 (978-0-7847-1690-8(0) , 02992) Standard Publishing.

Feiffer, Jules. I'm Not Bobby! Feiffer, Jules, illus. 2006. (Illus.). 28p. (J). (gr. k-4). reprint ed. 16.00 (978-0-7567-9853-6(1)) DIANE Publishing Co.

Finley, Martha. Elsie at Nantucket A Sequel to Elsies Ne. 2006. 34.99 (***978-1-4280-2289-8(9)***) IndyPublish.com.

Hamilton, Elizabeth L. Little Zoh's Submissive Trunk. 2003. (Character Critters Ser.: No. 3). (Illus.). 32p. (J). (ps-3). per. 5.95 (978-0-9713749-9-7(6) , Character-in-Action) Quiet Impact, Inc.

Knudsen, Michelle. Library Lion. Hawkes, Kevin, illus. 2006. 48p. (J). (ps-2). 16.99 (978-0-7636-2262-6(1)) Candlewick Pr.

Oke, Janette. Ducktails. Munger, Nancy, illus. 2001. (Animal Friends Ser.: Vol. 6). 80p. (J). (ps-3). pap. 6.99 (978-0-7642-2450-8(6)) Bethany Hse. Pubs.

—Ducktails. 2001. (gr. k-3). lib. bdg. 14.15 (978-0-613-82430-9(X)) Tandem Library Bks.

Sargent, Dave & Sargent, Pat. Kiowa: (Paint) Be Trustworthy, 25, 37. Lenoir, Jane, illus. 2001. (Saddle Up Ser.: 37). 36p. (J). pap. 6.95 (978-1-56763-618-5(7)); lib. bdg. 22.60 (978-1-56763-617-8(9)) Ozark Publishing.

Tamburri, Pasqualino. Alex & the Trampoline. 2007. 32p. (J). 14.95 (***978-1-60227-473-0(8)***) Above the Clouds Publishing.

Wax, Wendy. Watch Out, Otto! Pilar-Newton, Michelle, illus. 2002. (Rocket Power Ready-to-Read Ser.: Vol. 1). 32p. (J). pap. 3.99 (978-0-689-85008-0(5) , Simon Spotlight/ Nickelodeon) Simon & Schuster Children's Publishing.

—Watch Out, Otto! 2002. lib. bdg. 11.80 (978-0-613-57588-1(1)) Tandem Library Bks.

OBESITY

see Weight Control

OBI-WAN KENOBI (FICTITIOUS CHARACTER)—FICTION

see Kenobi, Obi-Wan (Fictitious Character)—Fiction

OBSCENITY (LAW)

Axelrod-Contrada, Joan. Reno v. ACLU: Internet Censorship. 2006. (Supreme Court Milestones Ser.). (Illus.). 144p. (J). lib. bdg. 39.93 (978-0-7614-2144-3(0) , Benchmark Bks.) Cavendish, Marshall Corp.

OBSERVATORIES, ASTRONOMICAL

see Astronomical Observatories

OBSTETRICS

see Childbirth

OCCULT SCIENCES

see Occultism

OCCULTISM

see also Astrology; Divination; Fortune-Telling; Magic; Superstition; Witchcraft

Baddiel, Ivor & Blezard, Tracey. The Supernatural. 1999. (Mysterious World Bks.). (Illus.). 32p. (YA). (gr. 5 up). pap. 6.95 (978-0-7641-0906-5(5)) Barron's Educational Series, Inc.

Blackwood, Gary L. Fateful Forebodings. 1998. (Secrets of the Unexplained Ser.). (Illus.). 64p. (J). (gr. 5-9). lib. bdg. 28.50 (978-0-7614-0467-5(8) , Benchmark Bks.) Cavendish, Marshall Corp.

Blohm, Craig E. The Possessed. 2007. (Mysterious Encounters Ser.). (Illus.). 48p. (J). (gr. 4-8). 23.70 (***978-0-7377-3781-3(6)*** , Kidhaven) Thomson Gale.

Fulbeck, Kip, et al. Part Asian, 100% Hapa. 2006. (Illus.). 264p. pap. 19.95 (978-0-8118-4959-3(7)) Chronicle Bks. LLC.

Innes, Brian. Amazing Predictions. 1999. (Unsolved Mysteries Ser.). (Illus.). 48p. (YA). (gr. 3-7). 25.69 (978-0-8172-5480-3(3)) Raintree.

—Millennium Prophecies. 1999. (Unsolved Mysteries Ser.). (Illus.). 48p. (YA). (gr. 3 up). lib. bdg. (978-0-8172-5486-5(2)) Raintree.

Jenson-Elliott, Cynthia. Zombies. 2006. 48p. (J). (gr. 4-8). 26.20 (978-0-7377-3557-4(0) , Kidhaven) Thomson Gale.

Lassiter, Rhiannon. The Supernatural. 2006. (Illus.). 36p. (J). lib. bdg. 24.67 (978-0-8368-6267-6(8)) Stevens, Gareth Inc.

McIntosh, Kenneth. Prophecies & End-Time Speculations: The Shape of Things to Come. 2005. (Religion & Modern Culture Ser.). (Illus.). 112p. (J). (gr. 7 up). (978-1-59084-979-8(5) , 1248068) Mason Crest Pubs.

Miller, Connie Colwell. Psychics. 2007. (Illus.). 32p. (J). (***978-0-7368-6761-0(9)***) Capstone Pr., Inc.

Tarot. 2002. 64p. (J). 3.98 (978-0-7525-7639-8(9)) Parragon, Inc.

Watkins, James N. Are There Really Ghosts? 2000. (Why Files Ser.). (Illus.). 160p. (YA). (gr. 7-11). 9.99 (978-0-570-05248-7(3)) Concordia Publishing Hse.

OCCULTISM—FICTION

Alexander, Brandon. Kiss of Darkness. 2000. (gr. 7-12). lib. bdg. 14.15 (978-0-613-73078-5(X)) Tandem Library Bks.

Alexander, Lloyd. The Fortune-Tellers. Hyman, Trina Schart, illus. 2002. (J). 14.04 (978-0-7587-2530-1(2)) Book Wholesalers, Inc.

Bird, Isobel. Circle of Three No.13: And It Harm None. 2002. (gr. 7-12). lib. bdg. 13.00 (978-0-613-71369-6(9)) Tandem Library Bks.

Carlson, Melody. Moon White. 2007. 224p. (YA). pap. 12.99 (978-1-57683-951-5(6) , Th1nk Bks.) NavPress Publishing Group.

Cote, Nancy. It Feels Like Snow. Cote, Nancy, illus. 2003. (Illus.). 32p. (YA). (gr. k-2). 15.95 (978-1-59078-054-1(X)) Boyds Mills Pr.

Fleischman, Paul. Graven Images. Ibatoulline, Bagram, illus. 128p. (J). (gr. 6-9). 2005. 5.99 (978-0-7636-2984-7(7)); 2006. reprint ed. 16.99 (978-0-7636-2775-1(5)) Candlewick Pr.

Gallagher, Diana G. Mist & Stone. 2003. (gr. 7-12). lib. bdg. 14.15 (978-0-613-66520-9(1)) Tandem Library Bks.

Harrison, Emma. A Tale of Two Pipers. 2004. (Charmed Ser.). 208p. (YA). mass mkt. 6.99 (978-0-689-86850-4(2) , Simon Spotlight Entertainment) Simon & Schuster.

Horowitz, Anthony. Evil Star. 2007. (Gatekeepers Ser.: No. 2). 320p. (J). pap. 7.99 (***978-0-439-68008-0(5));*** 2006. 318p. (YA). (***978-1-4156-7833-6(2)*** , Scholastic Pr.) Scholastic, Inc.

Lancaster, Susan. The Diamond Talisman. 2004. 168p. pap. 12.95 (978-0-9730350-0-1(5)) Snosrap Publishing CAN. *Dist:* Hushion Hse. Publishing, Ltd.

Loewer, Peter. The Moonflower. Loewer, Jean, illus. 2004. 32p. (J). (gr. 2-3). pap. 7.95 (978-1-56145-314-6(5)) Peachtree Pubs., Ltd.

Mead, Alice. Adem's Cross. 1998. (978-0-606-13110-0(8)) Tandem Library Bks.

Myers, Bill. The Curse. 2002. (Forbidden Doors Ser.: Vol. 7). 176p. (J). mass mkt. 4.99 (978-0-8423-5739-5(4)) Tyndale Hse. Pubs.

—Guardian. 2001. (gr. 5-8). lib. bdg. 13.00 (978-0-613-76842-9(6)) Tandem Library Bks.

—Haunting. 2001. (gr. 5-8). lib. bdg. 13.00 (978-0-613-76840-5(X)) Tandem Library Bks.

—My Life As a Haunted Hamburger, Hold the Pickles. 2006. (Incredible Worlds of Wally McDoogle Ser.: No. 27). 128p. (J). pap. 6.99 (978-1-4003-0636-7(1)) Nelson, Thomas Inc.

—Scream. 2002. (gr. 3-6). lib. bdg. 13.00 (978-0-613-76885-6(X)) Tandem Library Bks.

—Society: Who Can Overcome the Powers of Darkness? 2001. (gr. 5-8). lib. bdg. 10.65 (978-0-613-76838-2(8)) Tandem Library Bks.

—Spell. 2001. (gr. 5-8). lib. bdg. 13.00 (978-0-613-76839-9(6)) Tandem Library Bks.

Plante, Raymond. Marilou Forecasts the Future. Favreau, Marie-Claude & Cummins, Sarah, trs. Favreau, Marie-Claude, illus. 2003. (First Novel Ser.). 64p. (J). (gr. 2-5). 4.95 (978-0-88780-614-8(7)); (***978-0-88780-615-5(5)***) Formac Publishing Co., Ltd. CAN. *Dist:* Casemate Pubs. & Bk. Distributors, LLC.

Rees, Celia. Trap in Time. 2002. (Celia Rees Supernatural Trilogy: Bk. 2). 229p. (J). (gr. 3-6). pap. 7.99 (978-0-340-81801-5(8) , Hodder & Stoughton) Hodder General Publishing Division GBR. *Dist:* Trafalgar Square Publishing.

Roberts, Rachel. Circles in the Stream. 2007. (Avalon Ser.: Bk. 1). 175p. (J). 9.99 (***978-1-933164-64-9(6)***) Seven Seas Entertainment, LLC.

Showalter, Gena. Black Listed. 2007. 256p. pap. 9.95 (***978-1-4165-3225-5(0)*** , MTV) Simon & Schuster.

—Red Handed. 2007. 288p. pap. 9.95 (***978-1-4165-3224-8(2)*** , MTV) Simon & Schuster.

Somtow, S. P. Temple of Night. 1999. (Crow Ser.). 240p. pap. 13.00 (978-0-06-107348-9(2) , Harper Entertainment) HarperCollins Pubs.

Tarot Says Beware. 160p. (J). (gr. 4-6). pap. 3.99 (978-0-8072-1498-5(1) , Listening Library) Random Hse. Audio Publishing Group.

Taylor, G. P. Tersias the Oracle. (YA). 2007. 288p. (gr. 7). pap. 8.99 (978-0-14-240846-9(8) , Puffin); 2006. 262p. (gr. 5). 17.99 (978-0-399-24258-8(9) , Putnam Juvenile) Penguin Group (USA) Inc.

Teitelbaum, Michael. The Scary States of America. 2007. 416p. (J). (gr. 4-7). pap. 7.99 (978-0-385-73331-1(3)); lib. bdg. 12.99 (***978-0-385-90348-6(0)***) Random Hse. Children's Bks. (Delacorte Bks. for Young Readers).

Tiernan, Cate. Awakening, Bk. 5. 2007. (Sweep Ser.). 192p. (YA). pap. 6.99 (***978-0-14-241020-2(9)*** , Puffin) Penguin Group (USA) Inc.

—Book of Shadows, Bk. 1. 2007. (Sweep Ser.). 192p. (YA). pap. 6.99 (***978-0-14-240986-2(3)*** , Puffin) Penguin Group (USA) Inc.

—Calling, Bk. 7. 2008. (Sweep Ser.: Bk. 7). 192p. (YA). (gr. 7). 6.99 (***978-0-14-241022-6(5)*** , Puffin) Penguin Group (USA) Inc.

—The Coven, Bk. 2. 2007. (Sweep Ser.). 192p. (YA). pap. 6.99 (***978-0-14-240987-9(1)*** , Puffin) Penguin Group (USA) Inc.

—Dark Magick, Bk. 4. 2007. (Sweep Ser.). 192p. (YA). pap. 6.99 (***978-0-14-240989-3(8)*** , Puffin) Penguin Group (USA) Inc.

Tiernan, Cate. Moira's Story. 2003. (gr. 7-12). lib. bdg. 15.30 (978-0-613-66595-7(3)) Tandem Library Bks.

Ward, John. Le Secret de l'Alchimiste. Guitard, Agnes & Pineau, Severine, trs. from ENG. 2004. (FRE., Illus.). 336p. (J). pap. (978-2-89021-672-3(1)) Diffusion du livre Mirabel.

OCCUPATION, CHOICE OF

see Vocational Guidance

OCCUPATIONAL THERAPY—VOCATIONAL GUIDANCE

Quinlan, Kathryn A. Occupational Therapy Aide. 1998. (Careers Without College Ser.). (Illus.). 48p. (J). (gr. 3-4). lib. bdg. 21.26 (978-0-7368-0037-2(9) , LifeMatters Bks.) Capstone Pr., Inc.

OCCUPATIONS

see also Professions; Vocational Guidance

also names of countries, cities, etc. with the subdivision Occupations (e.g. U. S.—Occupations); also such headings as Law—Vocational Guidance

Adamson, Heather. A Day in the Life of a Child Care Worker. 2003. (First Facts Ser.). (Illus.). 24p. (J). 15.95 (978-0-7368-2504-7(5)) Capstone Pr., Inc.

—A Day in the Life of a Construction Worker. 2003. (First Facts Ser.). (Illus.). 24p. (J). 15.95 (978-0-7368-2505-4(3)) Capstone Pr., Inc.

—A Day in the Life of a Dentist. 2003. (First Facts Ser.). (Illus.). 24p. (J). lib. bdg. 21.26 (978-0-7368-2282-4(8)) Capstone Pr., Inc.

—A Day in the Life of a Police Officer. 2003. (First Facts Ser.). (Illus.). 24p. (J). lib. bdg. 21.26 (978-0-7368-2285-5(2)) Capstone Pr., Inc.

—A Day in the Life of a Teacher. 2003. (First Facts Ser.). (Illus.). 24p. (J). lib. bdg. 21.26 (978-0-7368-2286-2(0)) Capstone Pr., Inc.

—A Day in the Life of an EMT. 2004. (First Facts Ser.). (Illus.). 24p. (J). 15.95 (978-0-7368-2507-8(X)) Capstone Pr., Inc.

African-American Owners of International Companies. 2000. (My Ancestors—My Heroes Ser.: Vol. 45). (J). (gr. 3-4). (978-1-893091-44-3(9)) Parker Publishing Co.

Alagna, Magdalena. Life Inside the Air Force Academy. 2002. (Insider's Look Ser.). (Illus.). 48p. (J). (gr. 7-12). pap. 23.00 (978-0-516-23924-8(4) , Children's Pr.) Scholastic Library Publishing.

—Life Inside the Merchant Marine Academy. 2002. (Insider's Look Ser.). (Illus.). 48p. (J). (gr. 7-12). pap. 23.00 (978-0-516-23923-1(6) , Children's Pr.) Scholastic Library Publishing.

—Life Inside the Merchant Marine Academy. 2002. (gr. 7-12). lib. bdg. 15.25 (978-0-613-58711-2(1)) Tandem Library Bks.

Artsrunik, Valentina. How to Join the Club of the Rich & Famous - the Shortcut! 2nd ed. 2001. 100p. (YA). pap. 11.99 (978-1-903906-01-9(6)) Artnik Media GBR. *Dist:* De Breff, Vanko.

Baker, Yaba. Just Like Me: A Coloring Book of Careers. Oldham, Anne Marie, illus. 1999. 36p. (J). (gr. 4-7). pap. (978-1-928889-02-1(6)) Just Like Me, Inc.

—Just Like Me: Coloring Book of Careers. Oldham, Anne Marie, illus. 1998. 28p. (gr. k-6). pap. 4.95 (978-1-928889-03-8(4)) Just Like Me, Inc.

Bank Tellers. (Community Workers Ser.). 32p. (J). 7.95 (978-0-7565-1185-2(2)) Compass Point Bks.

Barbey, Dorine. People at Work. 2000. (Creative Discoveries Ser.). (Illus.). 75p. (J). (gr. 4 up). lib. bdg. 25.30 (978-0-88682-954-4(2) , Creative Education) Creative Co., The.

Bauld, Jane Scoggins. We Need Librarians. Saunders-Smith, Gail, ed. 2000. (Helpers in Our School Ser.). (Illus.). 24p. (J). (gr. k-1). lib. bdg. 15.93 (978-0-7368-0531-5(1) , Pebble Bks.) Capstone Pr., Inc.

Benchmark Education Staff, compiled by. Jobs. 2006. spiral bd. 109.00 (***978-1-4108-7041-4(3)***) Benchmark Education Co.

Beyer, Mark. The Secret Service. 2003. (High-Top Secret Ser.). (Illus.). 48p. (J). 23.00 (978-0-516-24313-9(6)); (YA). (gr. 7-12). pap. 6.95 (978-0-516-24376-4(4)) Scholastic Library Publishing. (Children's Pr.).

Blevins, Wiley. Who Am I? 2003. (Compass Point Phonics Readers Ser.). (Illus.). 16p. (J). (gr. 1 up). 13.26 (978-0-7565-0534-9(8)) Compass Point Bks.

Bolles, Richard Nelson & Christen, Carol. What Color Is Your Parachute? For Teens. 2006. (Parachute Library Ser.). (Illus.). 176p. (YA). pap. 14.95 (978-1-58008-713-1(2)) Ten Speed Pr.

Boraas, Tracey. Auto Mechanics. 1999. (Community Helpers Ser.). (Illus.). 24p. (J). lib. bdg. 18.60 (978-0-7368-0072-3(7) , Bridgestone Bks.) Capstone Pr., Inc.

—Plumbers. 1999. (Community Helpers Ser.). (Illus.). 24p. (J). (gr. 1-2). lib. bdg. 18.60 (978-0-7368-0073-0(5) , Bridgestone Bks.) Capstone Pr., Inc.

—School Principals. 1999. (Community Helpers Ser.). (Illus.). 92p. (J). (gr. 1-2). 18.60 (978-0-7368-0074-7(3) , Bridgestone Bks.) Capstone Pr., Inc.

—TV Reporters. 1999. (Community Helpers Ser.). (Illus.). 92p. (J). (gr. 1-2). 18.60 (978-0-7368-0075-4(1) , Bridgestone Bks.) Capstone Pr., Inc.

Bowman-Kruhm, Mary & Wirths, Claudine G. A Day in the Life of a Newspaper Reporter. 1999. (Kids' Career Library). (Illus.). 24p. (J). (gr. 3). lib. bdg. 18.75 (978-0-8239-5306-6(8) , PowerKids Pr.) Rosen Publishing Group, Inc., The.

Boyd, Nicole. A Doctor's Busy Day. 2002. (Reading Room Collection). (Illus.). 24p. (J). lib. bdg. 18.75 (978-0-8239-3734-9(8)) Rosen Publishing Group, Inc., The.

Bozak, Kristin & Cohen, Judith Love. You Can Be a Woman Botanist. Katz, David Arthur, illus. Date not set. 40p. (J). (gr. 3-6). 13.95 (978-1-880599-41-9(4)) Cascade Pass, Inc.

Bredeson, Carmen. Astronauts. 2003. (Rookie Read-About Science Ser.). (Illus.). 32p. (J). (gr. 1-2). 20.50 (978-0-516-22529-6(4) , Children's Pr.) Scholastic Library Publishing.

Brent, Lynnette R. At Work. 2003. (Times Change Ser.). (Illus.). 32p. (J). (978-1-4034-4542-1(7)) Heinemann Library.

—At Work: Long Ago & Today. 2003. (Times Change Ser.). (Illus.). 32p. (J). lib. bdg. 24.22 (978-1-4034-4536-0(2)) Heinemann Library.

Brill, Marlene Targ. Doctors. (Pull Ahead Bks.). (Illus.). 32p. (J). 2005. lib. bdg. 22.60 (978-0-8225-1689-7(6)); 2004. pap. 5.95 (978-0-8225-2531-8(3) , Lerner Pubns.) Lerner Publishing Group.

Brooks, Felicity. Daisy Doctor. Litchfield, Jo, illus. 2005. 24p. (J). pap. 6.95 (978-0-7945-0724-4(7) , Usborne) EDC Publishing.

—Frank the Farmer. Litchfield, Jo, illus. 2005. (Jobs People Do Ser.). 23p. (J). (ps-7). pap. 6.95 (978-0-7945-0723-7(9) , Usborne) EDC Publishing.

—Vicky the Vet. Litchfield, Jo, illus. 2004. (Jobs People Do Ser.). 24p. (J). pap. 6.95 (978-0-7945-0726-8(3) , Usborne) EDC Publishing.

Brown, Janet Allison. My First Book of Jobs. 2004. (Early Learning Ser.). (Illus.). 18p. (J). bds. 5.99 (978-1-85854-429-8(7)) Brimax Books Ltd. GBR. *Dist:* Byeway Bks.

Brown, Marcy. When I Grow Up. 2005. (Illus.). 40p. (J). (***978-1-4156-0673-5(0)***) Book Wholesalers, Inc.

Bryan, Nichol. The National Guard. 2003. (Everyday Heroes (cb) Ser.). (Illus.). 32p. (J). (gr. k-6). lib. bdg. 22.78 (978-1-57765-858-0(2)) ABDO Publishing Co.

—Paramedics. 2003. (Everyday Heroes (cb) Ser.). (Illus.). 32p. (J). (gr. k-6). lib. bdg. 22.78 (978-1-57765-856-6(6)) ABDO Publishing Co.

—Police Officers. 2003. (Everyday Heroes (cb) Ser.). (Illus.). 32p. (J). (gr. k-6). lib. bdg. 22.78 (978-1-57765-860-3(4)) ABDO Publishing Co.

Burby, Liza N. A Day in the Life of a Carpenter. 1999. (Kids' Career Library). (Illus.). 24p. (J). (gr. 3). lib. bdg. 18.75 (978-0-8239-5301-1(7) , PowerKids Pr.) Rosen Publishing Group, Inc., The.

—A Day in the Life of a Mayor: Featuring New York City Mayor Rudy Giuliani. 1999. (Kids' Career Library). (Illus.). 24p. (J). (gr. 3). lib. bdg. 18.75 (978-0-8239-5303-5(3) , PowerKids Pr.) Rosen Publishing Group, Inc., The.

—A Day in the Life of a Nurse. Zindler, Ethan, illus. 1999. (Kids' Career Library). 24p. (J). (gr. 3). lib. bdg. 18.75 (978-0-8239-5302-8(5) , PowerKids Pr.) Rosen Publishing Group, Inc., The.

—A Day in the Life of a Professional Golfer. 1999. (Kids' Career Library). (Illus.). 24p. (J). (gr. 3). lib. bdg. 18.75 (978-0-8239-5299-1(1) , PowerKids Pr.) Rosen Publishing Group, Inc., The.

—A Day in the Life of a Sculptor. 1999. (Kids' Career Library). (Illus.). 24p. (J). (gr. 3). lib. bdg. 18.75 (978-0-8239-5305-9(X) , PowerKids Pr.) Rosen Publishing Group, Inc., The.

Burchett. When I Grow Up: Level A. 2004. (Illus.). (J). pap. 6.00 (978-0-7398-8154-5(X)) Steck-Vaughn.

Burton, Margie, et al. Community Jobs. Adams, Alison, ed. 1999. (Early Connections Ser.). 16p. (J). (gr. k-2). pap. 4.50 (978-1-58344-058-2(5)) Benchmark Education Co.

—What People Do. Evento, Susan, ed. 1998. (Early Connections Ser.). 16p. (J). (gr. k-2). pap. 4.25 (978-1-892393-71-5(9)) Benchmark Education Co.

Burton, Marilee Robin. Artists at Work. 2003. (On the Job Ser.). (Illus.). 32p. (gr. 3-5). 23.00 (978-0-7910-7410-7(2) , Chelsea Hse.) Facts On File, Inc.

Butz, Christopher. I Go to Work as a Letter Carrier. 2003. (I Go to Work As Ser.). (Illus.). (J). pap. (978-1-58417-104-1(9)); lib. bdg. (978-1-58417-041-9(7)) Lake Street Pubs.

Canizares, Susan. Jobs. 1999. (J). pap. 2.50 (978-0-439-04551-3(7)) Scholastic, Inc.

Canizares, Susan & Betsey, Chessen. Jobs. 1999. (ps-2). lib. bdg. 10.10 (978-0-613-21811-5(6)) Tandem Library Bks.

Career Guide to America's Top Industries. 2002. (gr. 7-12). lib. bdg. 22.20 (978-0-613-51108-7(5)) Tandem Library Bks.

Careers Without College: Fast-Growing Jobs That Do Not Require a Four-Year Degree, 28 bks. Incl. Actor. Quinlan, Kathryn A. 1998. lib. bdg. 21.26 (978-1-56065-699-9(9)); Child Care Worker. Quinlan, Kathryn A. 1998. lib. bdg. 21.26 (978-0-7368-0032-7(8)); Correction Officer. Clinton, Susan & Primm, E. Russell. 1998. lib. bdg. 21.26 (978-1-56065-700-2(6)); Crime Lab Technician. Heath, David. 1999. lib. bdg. 21.26 (978-0-7368-0170-6(7)); Customer Service Representative. Quinlan, Kathryn A. 1999. lib. bdg. 21.26 (978-0-7368-0174-4(X)); Dental Hygienist. Simon, Charnan & Primm, E. Russell. 1998. lib. bdg. 21.26 (978-1-56065-701-9(4)); Emergency Medical Technician. Primm, E. Russell. 1998. lib. bdg. 21.26 (978-1-56065-702-6(2)); Fire Fighter. Goldberg, Jan. 1998. lib. bdg. 21.26 (978-0-7368-0033-4(6)); Food Service Manager. Quinlan, Kathryn A. 1998. lib. bdg. 21.26 (978-0-7368-0034-1(4)); Hazardous Waste Technician. Heath, David. 1999. lib. bdg. 21.26 (978-0-7368-0171-3(5)); Heating-and-Air Conditioning Servicer. Clinton, Susan. 1998. lib. bdg. 21.26 (978-1-56065-703-3(0)); Home Health Aide. Simon, Charnan. 1998. lib. bdg. 21.26 (978-1-56065-704-0(9)); Makeup Artist. Quinlan, Kathryn A. 1999. lib. bdg. 21.26 (978-0-7368-0175-1(8)); Medical Assistant. Primm, E. Russell. 1998. lib. bdg. 21.26 (978-1-56065-705-7(7)); Medical Record Technician. Goldberg, Jan. 1998. lib. bdg. 21.26 (978-0-7368-0035-8(2)); Nurse Assistant. Quinlan, Kathryn A. 1998. lib. bdg. 21.26 (978-0-7368-0036-5(0)); Occupational Therapy Aide. Quinlan, Kathryn A. 1998. lib. bdg. 21.26 (978-0-7368-0037-2(9)); Paralegal. Quinlan, Kathryn A. 1998. lib. bdg. 21.26 (978-1-56065-706-4(5)); Photographer. Quinian, Kathryn A. 1999. lib. bdg. 21.26 (978-0-7368-0176-8(6)); Physical Therapy Assistant. Quinlan, Kathryn A. 1998. lib. bdg. 21.26 (978-1-56065-707-1(3)); Private Investigator. Goldberg, Jan. 1998. lib. bdg. 21.26 (978-0-7368-0038-9(7)); Radio Announcer. Heath, David. 1999. lib. bdg. 21.26 (978-0-7368-0172-0(3)); Real Estate Sales Agent. Quinian, Kathryn A. 1999. lib. bdg. 21.26 (978-0-7368-0177-5(4)); Retail Salesperson. Simon, Charnan. 1998. lib. bdg. 21.26 (978-1-56065-708-8(1)); Security Guard. Goldberg, Jan. 1998. lib. bdg. 21.26 (978-0-7368-0039-6(5)); Surgical Technician. Primm, E. Russell. 1998. lib. bdg. 21.26 (978-1-56065-709-5(X)); Television Production Assistant. Heath, David. 1999. lib. bdg. 21.26 (978-0-7368-0173-7(1)); Tractor-Trailer-Truck Driver. Clinton, Susan. 1998. lib. bdg. 21.26 (978-1-56065-710-1(3)); 48p. (J). (gr. 3-4). (Illus.). Set lib. bdg. 595.28 (978-0-7368-0299-4(1) , LifeMatters Bks.) Capstone Pr., Inc.

Carson, Janet. You Can Do It! Learning the Y Sound. (PowerPhonics Ser.). (Illus.). (J). 2002. 24p. (gr. 1). lib. bdg. 18.50 (978-0-8239-5933-4(3)); 2001. 23p. pap. 26.40 (978-0-8239-8278-3(5)) Rosen Publishing Group, Inc., The. (PowerKids Pr.).

Cefrey, Holly. Your Governor: State Government in Action. 2003. (Primary Source Library of American Citizenship). (Illus.). 32p. (J). pap. (978-1-4042-5094-9(8)) Rosen Publishing Group, Inc., The.

CFKR Career Materials Staff. High School Career Course Planner. 2nd rev. ed. 2002. 6p. (YA). (gr. 6-10). pap. (978-0-934783-16-3(0)) CFKR Career Materials, Inc.

Children's Dictionary Of. 2005. (YA). cd-rom 79.95 (978-0-7365-9951-1(7)) Films Media Group.

Choosing Exciting Opportunities. 2005. (Careers & Opportunitiestm Ser.). (Illus.). (gr. 7-12). lib. bdg. 79.50 (978-0-8239-9308-6(6)) Rosen Publishing Group, Inc., The.

Christian, Sandra J. Lifeguards. 2002. (Community Helpers Ser.). (Illus.). 92p. (J). (gr. 1-2). 18.60 (978-0-7368-1129-3(X) , Bridgestone Bks.) Capstone Pr., Inc.

—Meteorologists. 2002. (Community Helpers Ser.). (Illus.). 24p. (J). (gr. 1-2). lib. bdg. 18.60 (978-0-7368-1130-9(3) , Bridgestone Bks.) Capstone Pr., Inc.

—Newspaper Carriers. 2002. (Community Helpers Ser.). (Illus.). 92p. (J). (gr. 1-2). 18.60 (978-0-7368-1131-6(1) , Bridgestone Bks.) Capstone Pr., Inc.

Christy, Lee Louis. I Go to Work as a Firefighter. 2003. (I Go to Work As Ser.). (Illus.). (J). (978-1-58417-039-6(5)) Lake Street Pubs.

—I Go to Work as a Police Officer. 2003. (I Go to Work As Ser.). (Illus.). (J). (978-1-58417-040-2(9)); pap. (978-1-58417-103-4(0)) Lake Street Pubs.

Cicciarelli, Joellyn. When I Grow Up. 2000. (gr. k-3). lib. bdg. 11.80 (978-0-613-29787-5(3)) Tandem Library Bks.

Claycomb, Patty. People at Work: Ages 3-5. 2002. (Early Learner Photo Fun Activities Ser.). 8p. (978-1-56472-385-7(2)) Edupress, Inc.

Collard, Sneed B., III. A Whale Biologist at Work. (Wildlife Conservation Society Bks.). (Illus.). 48p. (J). (gr. 4-6). 2001. pap. 6.95 (978-0-531-16526-3(4)); 2000. 24.50 (978-0-531-11786-6(3)) Scholastic Library Publishing. (Watts, Franklin).

—A Whale Biologist at Work. 2000. (Illus.). (J). (978-0-606-20984-7(0)) Tandem Library Bks.

Community Helpers - PowerPhonics Set II, 6 bks. Incl. At the Zoo : Learning the Z Sound. Battistoni, Ilse. lib. bdg. 18.50 (978-0-8239-5926-6(0)); I Fight Fires : Learning the Long I Sound. Battistoni, Ilse. lib. bdg. 18.50 (978-0-8239-5928-0(7)); Visiting the Vet : Learning the V Sound. Carson, Janet. lib. bdg. 18.50 (978-0-8239-5934-1(1)); What a Baker Makes : Learning the Long A Sound. McConnell, Sharon. lib. bdg. 18.50 (978-0-8239-5917-4(1)); What I Think : Learning the TH Sound. Vastola, Pam. lib. bdg. 18.50 (978-0-8239-5930-3(9)); You Can Do It! Learning the Y Sound. Carson, Janet. lib. bdg. 18.50 (978-0-8239-5933-4(3)); 24p. (J). (gr. 1). 2002. (Illus.). 2001. Set lib. bdg. 108.00 (978-0-8239-7206-7(2) , PowerKids Pr.) Rosen Publishing Group, Inc., The.

Community Helpers Puppet Set, Series 2. 2006. (J). per. (978-1-57332-430-4(2)) HighReach Learning, Inc.

Community Workers, 14 bks. Incl. Bank Tellers. Klingel, Cynthia Fitterer & Noyed, Robert B. 2002. lib. bdg. 21.26 (978-0-7565-0307-9(8)); Carpenters. Franchino, Vicky. 2000. lib. bdg. 21.26 (978-0-7565-0006-1(0)); Chefs. Quiri, Patricia Ryon. 2000. lib. bdg. 21.26 (978-0-7565-0007-8(9)); Doctors. Dornhoffer, Mary K. 2000. lib. bdg. 21.26 (978-0-7565-0008-5(7)); Farmers. Flanagan, Alice K. 2002. lib. bdg. 21.26 (978-0-7565-0305-5(1)); Fire Fighters. Raatma, Lucia. 2000. lib. bdg. 21.26 (978-0-7565-0009-2(5)); Letter Carriers. Flanagan, Alice K. 2000. lib. bdg. 21.26 (978-0-7565-0010-8(9)); Librarians. Flanagan, Alice K. 2001. lib. bdg. 21.26 (978-0-7565-0063-4(X)); Mayors. Flanagan, Alice K. 2001. lib. bdg. 21.26 (978-0-7565-0064-1(8)); Nurses. Klingel, Cynthia Fitterer & Noyed, Robert B. 2002. lib. bdg. 21.26 (978-0-7565-0306-2(X)); Pilots. Jaffe, Elizabeth Dana. 2001. lib. bdg. 21.26 (978-0-7565-0065-8(6)); Police Officers. Flanagan, Alice K. 2000. lib. bdg. 21.26 (978-0-7565-0011-5(7)); Teachers. Flanagan, Alice K. 2001. lib. bdg. 21.26 (978-0-7565-0066-5(4)); Veterinarians. Raatma, Lucia. 2002. lib. bdg. 21.26 (978-0-7565-0304-8(3)); (Illus.). 32p. (J). (gr. 1 up). 2003. Set lib. bdg. 297.64 (978-0-7565-0397-0(3)) Compass Point Bks.

Compass Point Books, contrib. by. Carpenters. (Community Workers Ser.). 24p. (J). pap. 7.95 (978-0-7565-1186-9(0)) Compass Point Bks.

—Chefs. (Community Workers Ser.). 24p. (J). pap. 7.95 (978-0-7565-1187-6(9)) Compass Point Bks.

—Farmers. (Community Workers Ser.). 24p. (J). pap. 7.95 (978-0-7565-1189-0(5)) Compass Point Bks.

—Letter Carriers. (Community Workers Ser.). 24p. (J). pap. 7.95 (978-0-7565-1191-3(7)) Compass Point Bks.

—Police Officers. (Community Workers Ser.). 24p. (J). pap. 7.95 (978-0-7565-1196-8(8)) Compass Point Bks.

Conrad, David. The Work We Do. 2002. (Spyglass Books). (Illus.). 24p. (J). (gr. 1 up). lib. bdg. 18.60 (978-0-7565-0382-6(5)) Compass Point Bks.

Construction Workers. (Community Helpers Ser.). 24p. (J). 6.95 (978-0-7368-8030-5(5)) Capstone Pr., Inc.

Coulter, Laurie. Cowboys & Coffin-Makers: One Hundred 19th-Century Jobs You Might Have Feared or Fancied. Newbigging, Martha, illus. 2007. 96p. (J). (gr. 4-7). 25.95 (***978-1-55451-068-9(6)***); pap. 16.95 (***978-1-55451-067-2(8)***) Annick Pr., Ltd. CAN. *Dist:* Firefly Bks., Ltd.

Crane, Natalie. I Go to Work as a Teacher. 2003. (I Go to Work As Ser.). (Illus.). (J). pap. (978-1-58417-106-5(5)); lib. bdg. (978-1-58417-043-3(3)); lib. bdg. (978-1-58417-044-0(1)) Lake Street Pubs.

Crowson, Andrew. Flip Flap People. 2003. (Illus.). 12p. bds. (978-1-85602-443-3(1)) Chrysalis Children's Bks.

Cummings, Pat & Cummings, Linda. Talking with Adventurers. 1998. (Illus.). 96p. (J). (gr. 3-5). 19.95 (978-0-7922-7068-3(1) , National Geographic Children's Bks.) National Geographic Society.

Cutler, Art, et al. Job-O 2000. 1999. (Illus.). 16p. (YA). (gr. 7 up). pap. 4.20 (978-1-887481-08-3(7)) CFKR Career Materials, Inc.

Dahlman, Tricia, ed. MnCareers 2005. 2004. (Illus.). 112p. (YA). per. 12.95 (978-0-9670505-7-7(X) , ES-90508-09) Minnesota Dept. Employment & Economic Development.

Daley, Patrick. You Call That a Job? Patrick Daley. 2006. 16p. (J). pap. (***978-0-439-74037-1(1)***) Scholastic, Inc.

Davis, Gary W. Working at a TV Station. 1998. (Working Here Ser.). (Illus.). 32p. (J). (gr. 2-4). 23.50 (978-0-516-20750-6(4) , Children's Pr.) Scholastic Library Publishing.

Davis, Wendy & Knight, Bertram T. Working at a Marine Institute. 1998. (Working Here Ser.). (Illus.). 32p. (J). (gr. 2-4). 23.50 (978-0-516-21223-4(0) , Children's Pr.) Scholastic Library Publishing.

Dawson, Jim. Marine Biologist. 1999. (Illus.). (YA). (gr. 5-12). pap. 19.93 (978-0-516-21889-2(1) , Children's Pr.) Scholastic Library Publishing.

Deedrick, Tami. Construction Workers. l.t. ed. 1998. (Community Helpers Ser.). (Illus.). 24p. (J). (gr. k-3). pap. 14.00 (978-0-516-21258-6(3) , Children's Pr.) Scholastic Library Publishing.

—Garbage Collectors. 1998. (Community Helpers Ser.). (Illus.). 24p. (J). (gr. k-3). pap. 14.00 (978-0-516-21259-3(1) , Children's Pr.) Scholastic Library Publishing.

—Zoo Keepers. l.t. ed. 1998. (Community Helpers Ser.). (Illus.). 24p. (J). (gr. k-3). lib. bdg. 14.00 Scholastic Library Publishing.

DeGezelle, Terri. Couriers. 2001. (Community Helpers Ser.). (Illus.). 24p. (J). (gr. 1-2). lib. bdg. 18.60 (978-0-7368-0957-3(0) , Bridgestone Bks.) Capstone Pr., Inc.

Diethelm, Laurie, ed. Occupational Guidance, Unit 4H, 8 vols. 2002. (YA). spiral bd. 115.00 (978-0-912486-91-8(0) , F-OG 4H) Finney Co., Inc.

—Occupational Guidance, Unit 5H, 5 vols. 2003. (YA). spiral bd. 115.00 (978-0-912486-92-5(9) , F-OG 5H) Finney Co., Inc.

Dixon, Tamecka & Cohen, Judith Love. You Can Be a Woman Basketball Player. 1999. (Illus.). (J). (gr. 4-8). 13.95 (978-1-880599-40-2(6)) Cascade Pass, Inc.

Domnauer, Teresa & Lithgow, John. Sing, Strum, & Beat the Drum!, Level 4: A Musical Adventure. 2005. (Lithgow Palooza Readers Ser.). (Illus.). 32p. (J). (gr. 2-3). pap. 3.95 (978-0-7696-4224-6(1)) School Specialty Publishing.

Dubois, Muriel L. I Like Computers: What Can I Be? 2000. (What Can I Be? Ser.). (Illus.). 24p. (J). (gr. 1-2). lib. bdg. 18.60 (978-0-7368-0631-2(8) , Bridgestone Bks.) Capstone Pr., Inc.

—I Like Sports: What Can I Be? 2000. (What Can I Be? Ser.). (Illus.). 24p. (J). (gr. 1-2). lib. bdg. 18.60 (978-0-7368-0633-6(4) , Bridgestone Bks.) Capstone Pr., Inc.

—What Can I Be?, 4 bks. Incl. I Like Animals : What Can I Be? lib. bdg. 18.60 (978-0-7368-0630-5(X)); I Like Computers : What Can I Be? lib. bdg. 18.60 (978-0-7368-0631-2(8)); I Like Music : What Can I Be? lib. bdg. 18.60 (978-0-7368-0632-9(6)); I Like Sports : What Can I Be? lib. bdg. 18.60 (978-0-7368-0633-6(4)); 24p. (J). (gr. 1-2). 2000. (Illus.). Set lib. bdg. 74.40 (978-0-7368-0686-2(5) , Bridgestone Bks.) Capstone Pr., Inc.

Ecker, Debbie. People Work. 2000. (Yellow Umbrella Books). (Illus.). 16p. (J). (gr. 1). lib. bdg. 14.60 (978-0-7368-0740-1(3) , Pebble Bks.) Capstone Pr., Inc.

English, June. The Most Dangerous Jobs in the U. S. A. 1998. (Illus.). 40p. (J). (gr. 1-5). pap. 4.99 (978-0-590-89751-8(9)) Scholastic, Inc.

—The Most Dangerous Jobs in the U. S. A. 1998. (978-0-606-13623-5(1)) Tandem Library Bks.

English, Melissa. Caution: Why You Need to Think about Careers NOW! 2004. (YA). per. 12.95 (978-0-9754148-0-4(1)) Caution Bks.

Everyday Heroes, Set. 2002. (J). (gr. k-6). lib. bdg. 136.68 (978-1-57765-854-2(X)) ABDO Publishing Co.

Exploring Careers: A Young Person's Guide to 1,000 Jobs. 2003. (gr. 7-12). lib. bdg. 41.95 (978-0-613-65224-7(X)) Tandem Library Bks.

Extreme Careers, 8 bks. Incl. Astronauts : Life Exploring Outer Space. Hayhurst, Chris. (YA). 2005. 26.50 (978-0-8239-3364-8(4)); Demolition Experts : Life Blowing Things Up. Beyer, Mark. (YA). 2005. 26.50 (978-0-8239-3365-5(2)); Fighter Pilots : Life at Mach Speed. Draper, Allison Stark. (YA). 2001. lib. bdg. 26.50 (978-0-8239-3366-2(0) , Rosen Central); Race Car Drivers : Life on the Fast Track. Cefrey, Holly. (YA). 2005. 26.50 (978-0-8239-3367-9(9)); Scuba Divers : Life under Water. Giacobello, John. (J). 2005. 26.50 (978-0-8239-3368-6(7)); Secret Agents : Life as a Professional Spy. Manley, Claudia B. (YA). 2005. 26.50 (978-0-8239-3369-3(5)); Smokejumpers : Life Fighting Fires. Beyer, Mark. (YA). 2005. 26.50 (978-0-8239-3370-9(9)); Stunt Performers : Life Before the Camera. Turner, Cherie. (YA). 2005. 26.50 (978-0-8239-3371-6(7)); 64p. (gr. 5-8). (Illus.). 2005. 212.00 (978-0-8239-9422-9(8)) Rosen Publishing Group, Inc., The.

Extreme Careers, 8 bks., Set 5. Incl. Disaster Relief Workers. Roza, Greg. (J). lib. bdg. 26.50 (978-1-4042-0943-5(3)); First Responders. Cobb, Allan B. (J). lib. bdg. 26.50 (978-1-4042-0944-2(1)); Frontline Marines : Fighting in the Marine Combat Arms Unit. Payment, Simone. (J). lib. bdg. 26.50 (978-1-4042-0946-6(8)); Homeland Security Officers. Meyer, Jared. (J). lib. bdg. 26.50 (978-1-4042-0945-9(X)); Hostage Rescuers. Poolos, Jamie. (YA). lib. bdg. 26.50 (978-1-4042-0941-1(7)); Refugee Workers. Levy, Janey. (J). lib. bdg. 26.50 (978-1-4042-0960-2(3)); U.S. Air Marshals. Broyles, Matthew. (J). lib. bdg. 26.50 (978-1-4042-0942-8(5)); Working in a War Zone : Military Contractors. Meyer, Jared. (J). lib. bdg. 26.50 (978-1-4042-0959-6(X)); (Illus.). 64p. (gr. 5-8). 2006. 2007. Set lib. bdg. 212.00 (***978-1-4042-1042-4(3)***) Rosen Publishing Group, Inc., The.

Facts on File, Inc. Staff. Politics. 2005. (Careers in Focus Ser.). (Illus.). 172p. (J). (gr. 6-12). 22.95 (978-0-8160-5844-0(X) , Ferguson Publishing Co.) Facts On File, Inc.

Families & Careers Activity Center with Puppet Theater. 2001. (Illus.). (J). (ps-2). 219.00 (978-0-9673268-3-2(4)) Learning Fasten-Ations, Inc.

Families & Careers Activity Center with Velcro Penguin Board. 2001. (Illus.). (J). (ps-2). pap. 199.00 (978-0-9673268-4-9(2)) Learning Fasten-Ations, Inc.

Farmers. (Community Helpers Ser.). 24p. (J). 6.95 (978-0-7368-8454-9(8)) Capstone Pr., Inc.

Ferry, Francis. Job-O E: Elementary. Ellis, Amy, illus. 3rd ed. 2003. (Job-O Ser.). (J). (978-1-887481-43-4(5)) CFKR Career Materials, Inc.

Ferry, Francis R. Career Steps. 1999. (Illus.). 20p. (J). (gr. 4-7). pap. 6.36 (978-1-887481-11-3(7)) CFKR Career Materials, Inc.

—Reflections of Your Future. Sabich, Marty, ed. 1999. (Illus.). 146p. (J). (gr. 1-9). pap. 14.95 (978-1-887481-10-6(9)) CFKR Career Materials, Inc.

Fine, Jil. Life Inside the Naval Academy. 2002. (Insider's Look Ser.). (Illus.). 48p. (YA). (gr. 7-12). pap. 23.00 (978-0-516-23922-4(8) , Children's Pr.) Scholastic Library Publishing.

Firefly Books Staff. I Want to Be a Cowboy. 1999. (J). 10.79 (978-0-606-20307-4(9)) Tandem Library Bks.

Firestone, Mary. Security Guards. 2003. (Community Helpers Ser.). (Illus.). 92p. (J). (gr. 1-2). 19.93 (978-0-7368-1616-8(X) , Bridgestone Bks.) Capstone Pr., Inc.

—Supermarket Managers. 2003. (Community Helpers Ser.). (Illus.). 24p. (J). (gr. 1-2). lib. bdg. (978-0-7368-1614-4(3) , Bridgestone Bks.) Capstone Pr., Inc.

Flanagan, Alice K. Buying a Pet from Ms. Chavez. Rau, Dana, ed. 1998. (Our Neighborhood Ser.). (Illus.). 32p. (J). (gr. 1-2). pap. 6.95 (978-0-516-26293-2(9) , Children's Pr.) Scholastic Library Publishing.

—Farmers. 2002. (Community Workers Ser.). (Illus.). 32p. (J). (gr. 1 up). lib. bdg. 21.26 (978-0-7565-0305-5(1)) Compass Point Bks.

—Flying an Agricultural Plane with Mr. Miller. Flanagan, Romie, illus. 1999. (Our Neighborhood Ser.). 32p. (J). (gr. 1-2). 20.00 (978-0-516-21132-9(3) , Children's Pr.) Scholastic Library Publishing.

—Flying an Agricultural Plane with Mr. Miller. 1999. (gr. k-3). lib. bdg. 15.25 (978-0-613-54488-7(9)) Tandem Library Bks.

—Mr. Paul & Mr. Luecke Build Communities. 1999. (gr. k-3). lib. bdg. 15.25 (978-0-613-54032-2(8)) Tandem Library Bks.

—Mrs. Scott's Beautiful Art. Flanagan, Romie, illus. 1999. (Our Neighborhood Ser.). 32p. (J). (gr. 1-2). 20.00 (978-0-516-21135-0(8) , Children's Pr.) Scholastic Library Publishing.

—Officer Brown Keeps Neighborhoods Safe. Osinski, Christine, ed. Osinski, Christine, illus. 1998. (Our Neighborhood Ser.). 32p. (J). (gr. 1-2). 20.00 (978-0-516-20780-3(6) , Children's Pr.) Scholastic Library Publishing.

—The Zieglers & Their Apple Orchard. Flanagan, Romie, illus. 1999. (Our Neighborhood Ser.). 32p. (J). (gr. 1-2). 20.00 (978-0-516-21134-3(X) , Children's Pr.) Scholastic Library Publishing.

Flanagan, Alice K. & Cornwell, Linda. Learning Is Fun with Mrs. Perez. Flanagan, Romie, illus. 1998. (Our Neighborhood Ser.). 32p. (J). (gr. 1-2). 20.00 (978-0-516-20774-2(1) , Children's Pr.) Scholastic Library Publishing.

Flanagan, Alice K. & Osinski, Christine. Learning about Bees from Mr. Krebs. 2000. (Our Neighborhood Ser.). (Illus.). 32p. (J). (gr. 1-2). pap. 6.95 (978-0-516-26539-1(3) , Children's Pr.) Scholastic Library Publishing.

Fluet, Connie. A Day in the Life of a Nurse. 2004. (First Facts Ser.). (Illus.). 24p. (J). (gr. k-3). lib. bdg. 21.26 (978-0-7368-2631-0(9) , First Facts) Capstone Pr., Inc.

Franks, Katie. Dream Jobs, 6 bks., Set. Incl. I Want to Be a Baseball Star. lib. bdg. 21.25 (978-1-4042-3622-6(8) , PowerKids Pr.); I Want to Be a Basketball Player. lib. bdg. 21.25 (978-1-4042-3621-9(X)); I Want to Be a Movie Star. lib. bdg. 21.25 (978-1-4042-3619-6(8)); I Want to Be a Race Car Driver. lib. bdg. 21.25 (978-1-4042-3623-3(6)); I Want to Be a Rock Star. lib. bdg. 21.25 (978-1-4042-3618-9(X) , PowerKids Pr.); I Want to Be a Supermodel. lib. bdg. 21.25 (978-1-4042-3620-2(1) , PowerKids Pr.); (Illus.). 24p. (J). (gr. 3-5). 2007. Set lib. bdg. 127.50 (978-1-4042-3598-4(1)) Rosen Publishing Group, Inc., The.

Frost, Helen. We Need Auto Mechanics. 2004. (Helpers in Our Community Ser.). (Illus.). 24p. (J). lib. bdg. 15.93 (978-0-7368-2574-0(6) , Pebble Bks.) Capstone Pr., Inc.

—We Need Pharmacists. 2004. (Helpers in Our Community Ser.). (Illus.). 24p. (J). lib. bdg. 15.93 (978-0-7368-2575-7(4) , Pebble Bks.) Capstone Pr., Inc.

—We Need Plumbers. 2004. (Helpers in Our Community Ser.). (Illus.). 24p. (J). lib. bdg. 15.93 (978-0-7368-2576-4(2) , Pebble Bks.) Capstone Pr., Inc.

—We Need School Bus Drivers. 2004. (Helpers in Our Community Ser.). (Illus.). 24p. (J). lib. bdg. 15.93 (978-0-7368-2577-1(0) , Pebble Bks.) Capstone Pr., Inc.

Galloway, Priscilla. Archers, Alchemists, & 98 Other Medieval Jobs You Might Have Loved or Loathed. Newbigging, Martha, illus. 2003. 96p. (J). (gr. 4-7). 24.95 (978-1-55037-811-5(2)); pap. 14.95 (978-1-55037-810-8(4)) Annick Pr., Ltd. CAN. *Dist:* Firefly Bks., Ltd.

—Archers, Alchemists, & 98 Other Medieval Jobs You Might Have Loved or Loathed. 2003. (gr. 3-6). lib. bdg. 24.55 (978-0-613-78469-6(3)) Tandem Library Bks.

Garbage Collectors. (Community Helpers Ser.). 24p. (J). 6.95 (978-0-7368-8031-2(3)) Capstone Pr., Inc.

La Gente de Mi Comunidad/People in My Community, 12 bks. Incl. Bus Driver/El Conductor del Autobus. Gorman, Jacqueline Laks. Acosta, Tatiana & Gutiérrez, Guillermo, trs. Andersen, Gregg, photos by. 2002. lib. bdg. 19.33 (978-0-8368-3306-5(6)); Crossing Guard/El Guardia de Cruce. Macken, JoAnn Early. Coffey, Colleen & Carrillo, Consuelo, trs. 2003. lib. bdg. 19.33 (978-0-8368-3671-4(5)); Dentist/El Dentista. Gorman, Jacqueline Laks. Acosta, Tatiana & Gutiérrez, Guillermo, trs. 2002. lib. bdg. 19.33 (978-0-8368-3307-2(4)); Doctor/El Medico. Gorman, Jacqueline Laks. Acosta, Tatiana & Gutiérrez, Guillermo, trs. 2002. lib. bdg. 19.33 (978-0-8368-3308-9(2)); Firefighter/El Bombero. Gorman, Jacqueline Laks. Acosta, Tatiana & Gutiérrez, Guillermo, trs. 2002. lib. bdg. 19.33 (978-0-8368-3309-6(0)); Librarian/El Bibliotecario. Gorman, Jacqueline Laks. Acosta, Tatiana & Gutiérrez, Guillermo, trs. 2002. lib. bdg. 19.33 (978-0-8368-3310-2(4)); Mail Carrier/El Cartero. Macken, JoAnn Early. Coffey, Colleen & Carrillo, Consuelo, trs. 2003. lib. bdg. 19.33 (978-0-8368-3672-1(3)); Nurse/El Enfermero. Macken, JoAnn Early. Coffey, Colleen & Carrillo, Consuelo, trs. 2003. lib. bdg. 19.33 (978-0-8368-3673-8(1)); Police Officer/El Policia. Gorman, Jacqueline Laks. Acosta, Tatiana & Gutiérrez, Guillermo, trs. 2002. lib. bdg. 19.33 (978-0-8368-3311-9(2)); Sanitation Worker/El Recogedor de Basura. Macken, JoAnn Early. Coffey, Colleen & Carrillo, Consuelo, trs. 2003. lib. bdg. 19.33 (978-0-8368-3674-5(X)); Teacher/El Maestro. Macken, JoAnn Early. Coffey, Colleen & Carrillo, Consuelo, trs. 2003. lib. bdg. 19.33 (978-0-8368-3675-2(8)); Veterinarian/El Veterinario. Macken, JoAnn Early. Coffey, Colleen & Carrillo, Consuelo, trs. 2003. lib. bdg. 19.33 (978-0-8368-3676-9(6)); 24p. (J). (ps up). (Weekly Reader Early Learning Library). (SPA & ENG., Illus.). Set lib. bdg. 231.96 (978-0-8368-3647-9(2) , Weekly Reader Early Learning Library) Stevens, Gareth Inc.

Gibson, Karen Bush. Child Care Workers. 2000. (Community Helpers Ser.). (Illus.). 92p. (J). (gr. 1-2). 18.60 (978-0-7368-0622-0(9) , Bridgestone Bks.) Capstone Pr., Inc.

—Emergency Medical Technicians. 2000. (Community Helpers Ser.). (Illus.). 92p. (J). (gr. 1-2). 18.60 (978-0-7368-0623-7(7) , Bridgestone Bks.) Capstone Pr., Inc.

—Pharmacists. 2000. (Community Helpers Ser.). (Illus.). 92p. (J). (gr. 1-2). 18.60 (978-0-7368-0624-4(5) , Bridgestone Bks.) Capstone Pr., Inc.

—Truck Drivers. 2000. (Community Helpers Ser.). (Illus.). 92p. (J). (gr. 1-2). 18.60 (978-0-7368-0625-1(3) , Bridgestone Bks.) Capstone Pr., Inc.

Gillis, Jennifer Blizin. Ayudantes Del Vecindario/Jennifer B. Gillis. 2007. (SPA & ENG., Illus.). 24p. (J). ***978-1-60044-292-6(7)*** Rourke Publishing, LLC.

—Jobs on Wheels. 2007. (978-1-60044-202-5(1)) Rourke Publishing, LLC.

—Neighborhood Helpers. 2007. (Illus.). 24p. (J). (978-1-60044-203-2(X)) Rourke Publishing, LLC.

Gillis, Jennifer Blizin. Trabajos Rodantes. 2007. (SPA & ENG., Illus.). 24p. (J). (***978-1-60044-291-9(9)***) Rourke Publishing, LLC.

Goldberg, Jan. Medical Record Technician. 1998. (Careers Without College Ser.). (Illus.). 48p. (J). (gr. 3-4). lib. bdg. 21.26 (978-0-7368-0035-8(2) , LifeMatters Bks.) Capstone Pr., Inc.

Gorman, Jacqueline Laks. Bus Driver. Andersen, Gregg, photos by. 2002. (People in My Community Ser.). (Illus.). 24p. (J). (ps up). lib. bdg. 19.33 (978-0-8368-3292-1(2) , Weekly Reader Early Learning Library) Stevens, Gareth Inc.

—Bus Driver/El Conductor del Autobus. Acosta, Tatiana & Gutiérrez, Guillermo, trs. Andersen, Gregg, photos by. 2002. (Weekly Reader Early Learning Library). (SPA & ENG., Illus.). 24p. (J). (ps up). lib. bdg. 19.33 (978-0-8368-3306-5(6) , Weekly Reader Early Learning Library) Stevens, Gareth Inc.

—Dentist/El Dentista. Acosta, Tatiana & Gutiérrez, Guillermo, trs. 2002. (Weekly Reader Early Learning Library). (SPA & ENG., Illus.). 24p. (J). (ps up). lib. bdg. 19.33 (978-0-8368-3307-2(4) , Weekly Reader Early Learning Library) Stevens, Gareth Inc.

—Doctor. Andersen, Gregg, photos by. 2002. (People in My Community Ser.). (Illus.). 24p. (J). (ps up). lib. bdg. 19.33 (978-0-8368-3294-5(9) , Weekly Reader Early Learning Library) Stevens, Gareth Inc.

—Doctor/El Medico. Acosta, Tatiana & Gutiérrez, Guillermo, trs. 2002. (Weekly Reader Early Learning Library). (ENG & SPA., Illus.). 24p. (J). (ps up). lib. bdg. 19.33 (978-0-8368-3308-9(2) , Weekly Reader Early Learning Library) Stevens, Gareth Inc.

—Firefighter. Andersen, Gregg, photos by. 2002. (People in My Community Ser.). (Illus.). 24p. (J). (ps up). lib. bdg. 19.33 (978-0-8368-3295-2(7) , Weekly Reader Early Learning Library) Stevens, Gareth Inc.

—Firefighter/El Bombero. Acosta, Tatiana & Gutiérrez, Guillermo, trs. 2002. (Weekly Reader Early Learning Library). (SPA & ENG., Illus.). 24p. (J). (ps up). lib. bdg. 19.33 (978-0-8368-3309-6(0) , Weekly Reader Early Learning Library) Stevens, Gareth Inc.

—Librarian. Andersen, Gregg, photos by. 2002. (People in My Community Ser.). (Illus.). 24p. (J). (ps up). lib. bdg. 19.33 (978-0-8368-3296-9(5) , Weekly Reader Early Learning Library) Stevens, Gareth Inc.

—Librarian/El Bibliotecario. Acosta, Tatiana & Gutiérrez, Guillermo, trs. 2002. (Weekly Reader Early Learning Library). (ENG & SPA., Illus.). 24p. (J). (ps up). lib. bdg. 19.33 (978-0-8368-3310-2(4) , Weekly Reader Early Learning Library) Stevens, Gareth Inc.

—People in My Community, 6 bks., Set I. Andersen, Gregg, photos by. Incl. Bus Driver. Macken, JoAnn Early. pap. 7.93 (978-0-8368-3299-0(X)); Dentist. Macken, JoAnn Early. pap. 7.93 (978-0-8368-3300-3(7)); Doctor. Macken, JoAnn Early. pap. 7.93 (978-0-8368-3301-0(5)); Firefighter. Macken, JoAnn Early. pap. 7.93 (978-0-8368-3302-7(3)); Librarian. Macken, JoAnn Early. pap. 7.93 (978-0-8368-3303-4(1)); Police Officer. pap. 7.93 (978-0-8368-3304-1(X)); 24p. (J). (ps up). 2002. (Weekly Reader Early Learning Library). (Illus.). 2002. pap. (978-0-8368-3298-3(1) , Weekly Reader Early Learning Library) Stevens, Gareth Inc.

—Police Officer. Andersen, Gregg, photos by. 2002. (People in My Community Ser.). (Illus.). 24p. (J). (ps up). lib. bdg. 19.33 (978-0-8368-3297-6(3)); pap. 7.93 (978-0-8368-3304-1(X)) Stevens, Gareth Inc. (Weekly Reader Early Learning Library).

Gorman, Jacqueline Laks & Gutiérrez, Guillermo. La Gente de Mi Comunidad/People in My Community: Bus Driver/El Conductor del Autobus; Dentist/El Dentista; Doctor/El Medico; Firefighter/El Bombero; Librarian/El Bibliotecario; Police Officer/El Policia, 6 bks. Acosta, Tatiana, tr. Andersen, Gregg, photos by. (Weekly Reader Early Learning Library). (SPA & ENG., Illus.). (J). (ps up). lib. bdg. 111.60 (978-0-8368-3305-8(8) , Weekly Reader Early Learning Library) Stevens, Gareth Inc.

Gorman, Jacqueline Laks & Macken, JoAnn Early. Bus Driver. Andersen, Gregg, photos by. 2002. (Weekly Reader Early Learning Library). (Illus.). 24p. (J). (ps up). pap. 7.93 (978-0-8368-3299-0(X) , Weekly Reader Early Learning Library) Stevens, Gareth Inc.

—Bus Driver/El Conductor del Autobus. Coffey, Colleen & Carrillo, Consuelo, trs. Andersen, Gregg, photos by. 2002. (Weekly Reader Early Learning Library). (ENG & SPA., Illus.). 24p. (J). (ps up). pap. 7.93 (978-0-8368-3340-9(6) , Weekly Reader Early Learning Library) Stevens, Gareth Inc.

—Dentist/El Dentista. Coffey, Colleen & Carrillo, Consuelo, trs. Andersen, Gregg, photos by. 2002. (Weekly Reader Early Learning Library). (ENG & SPA., Illus.). 24p. (J). (ps up). pap. 5.95 (978-0-8368-3341-6(4) , Weekly Reader Early Learning Library) Stevens, Gareth Inc.

—Doctor. Andersen, Gregg, photos by. 2002. (Weekly Reader Early Learning Library). (Illus.). 24p. (J). (ps up). pap. 7.93 (978-0-8368-3301-0(5) , Weekly Reader Early Learning Library) Stevens, Gareth Inc.

—Doctor/El Medico. Coffey, Colleen & Carrillo, Consuelo, trs. Andersen, Gregg, photos by. 2002. (Weekly Reader Early Learning Library). (ENG & SPA., Illus.). 24p. (J). (ps up). pap. 5.95 (978-0-8368-3342-3(2) , Weekly Reader Early Learning Library) Stevens, Gareth Inc.

—Firefighter. Andersen, Gregg, photos by. 2002. (Weekly Reader Early Learning Library). (Illus.). 24p. (J). (ps up). pap. 7.93 (978-0-8368-3302-7(3) , Weekly Reader Early Learning Library) Stevens, Gareth Inc.

—Firefighter/El Bombero. Coffey, Colleen & Carrillo, Consuelo, trs. from ENG. Andersen, Gregg, photos by. 2002. (Weekly Reader Early Learning Library). (ENG & SPA., Illus.). 24p. (J). (ps up). pap. 7.93 (978-0-8368-3343-0(0) , Weekly Reader Early Learning Library) Stevens, Gareth Inc.

—Librarian. Andersen, Gregg, photos by. 2002. (Weekly Reader Early Learning Library). (Illus.). 24p. (J). (ps up). pap. 7.93 (978-0-8368-3303-4(1) , Weekly Reader Early Learning Library) Stevens, Gareth Inc.

—Librarian/El Bibliotecario. Coffey, Colleen & Carrillo, Consuelo, trs. from ENG. Andersen, Gregg, photos by. 2002. (Weekly Reader Early Learning Library). (ENG & SPA., Illus.). 24p. (J). (ps up). pap. 7.93 (978-0-8368-3344-7(9) , Weekly Reader Early Learning Library) Stevens, Gareth Inc.

—People in My Community/La Gente de Mi Comunidad: Set I, 6 bks. Coffey, Colleen & Carrillo, Consuelo, trs. Andersen, Gregg, photos by. Incl. Bus Driver/El Conductor del Autobus. pap. 7.93 (978-0-8368-3340-9(6)); Dentist/El Dentista. pap. 5.95 (978-0-8368-3341-6(4)); Doctor/El Medico. pap. 5.95 (978-0-8368-3342-3(2)); Firefighter/El Bombero. pap. 7.93 (978-0-8368-3343-0(0)); Librarian/El Bibliotecario. pap. 7.93 (978-0-8368-3344-7(9)); Police Officer/El Policia. pap. 7.93 (978-0-8368-3345-4(7)); 24p. (J). (ps up). pap. , Weekly Reader Early Learning Library (SPA & ENG., Illus.). 2002. pap. (978-0-8368-3339-3(2)) Stevens, Gareth Inc.

Guerrero, Pablo. Mi Laberinto. Urberuaga, Emilio, illus. 2004. Tr. of My Labyrinth. (SPA.). (J). 21.99 (978-84-88342-42-3(X)) S.A. Kokinos ESP. *Dist:* Lectorum Pubns., Inc.

Hair Stylists. 2000. (My Ancestors—My Heroes Ser.: Vol. 46). (J). (gr. 3-4). (978-1-893091-45-0(7)) Parker Publishing Co.

Hanna, Jack. Jungle Jack Hanna's What Zookeepers Do. Prebeg, Rick A., illus. 1998. (Hello Reader! Ser.). 48p. (J). (gr. 2-4). pap. 3.99 (978-0-590-67324-2(6)) Scholastic, Inc.

—Jungle Jack Hanna's What Zookeepers Do. 1998. (Hello Reader! Ser.). (J). 10.79 (978-0-606-13548-1(0)) Tandem Library Bks.

Harcourt School Publishers Staff. Jobs of the Past. 3rd ed. 2002. (Horizons Ser.). (Illus.). (J). pap. 3.70 (978-0-15-333178-7(X)) Harcourt Schl. Pubs.

—Jobs People Do, No. 6. 2nd ed. 2003. (Illus.). pap. 139.70 (978-0-15-337561-3(2)) Harcourt Schl. Pubs.

—My Place. 3rd ed. 2002. (Trophies English Language Learners Ser.). (Illus.). pap. 5.10 (978-0-15-327655-2(X)) Harcourt Schl. Pubs.

—People Working: Little Book. 2000. (Collections Ser.). (Illus.). (J). pap. 10.20 (978-0-15-314503-2(X)) Harcourt Schl. Pubs.

—What Is My Job? 3rd ed. 2002. (Trophies English Language Learners Ser.). (Illus.). (J). pap. 4.10 (978-0-15-327585-2(5)) Harcourt Schl. Pubs.

—What Is My Job? Grade 1, 5 Packs. 3rd ed. 2002. (Trophies English Language Learners Ser.). 20.10 (978-0-15-327619-4(3)) Harcourt Schl. Pubs.

Hayhurst, Chris. Volcanologists: Life under a Volcano. 2005. (Extreme Careers Ser.). (Illus.). 64p. (YA). (gr. 5-8). 26.50 (978-0-8239-3637-3(6)) Rosen Publishing Group, Inc., The.

Hayward, Linda. Jobs People Do: A Day in the Life of a Teacher. 2001. (Jobs People Do Ser.). (Illus.). (J). 10.79 (978-0-606-21141-3(1)) Tandem Library Bks.

Hayward, Linda & Dorling Kindersley Publishing Staff. Jobs People Do: A Day in the Life of a Teacher. 2001. (Readers Ser.). (Illus.). 32p. (J). (ps-3). 14.99 (978-0-7894-7368-4(2)); pap. 3.99 (978-0-7894-7367-7(4)) Dorling Kindersley Publishing, Inc.

Head, Honor. Direction. Stower, Adam, illus. 1998. (Ed Mouse Finds Out about Ser.). 32p. (J). (ps-2). pap. 5.95 (978-0-8172-8100-7(2)) Steck-Vaughn.

Heyworth. Careers. 1999. (Illus.). (J). (gr. 2-3). pap. (978-0-7398-1219-8(X)); (gr. 4-5). pap. (978-0-7398-1220-4(3)) Steck-Vaughn.

Higashi/Glaser Design Inc. Staff. What Will I Be A to Z? 2005. (Hello Kitty Ser.). (Illus.). 28p. (J). (ps-k). bds. 6.95 (978-0-8109-5850-0(3)) Abrams, Harry N. , Inc.

Hodgkins, Fran. Pilots. 2001. (Community Helpers Ser.). (Illus.). 24p. (J). (gr. 1-2). lib. bdg. 18.60 (978-0-7368-0810-1(8) , Bridgestone Bks.) Capstone Pr., Inc.

Hughes, Sarah. My Dad Works on a Farm. (Welcome Bks.). (Illus.). 24p. (J). (ps-2). 2001. 17.00 (978-0-516-23178-5(2)); 2001. pap. 4.95 (978-0-516-29574-9(8)); 2000. lib. bdg. (978-0-516-23281-2(9)) Scholastic Library Publishing. (Children's Pr.).

—My Dad Works on a Farm. 2001. (gr. k-3). lib. bdg. 12.95 (978-0-613-58860-7(6)) Tandem Library Bks.

—My Family at Work, 6 bks., Set. 2004. (Illus.). 24p. (J). (ps-2). 87.00 (978-0-516-22996-6(6) , Children's Pr.) Scholastic Library Publishing.

—My Grandfather Works in a Bakery. 2001. (Welcome Bks.). (Illus.). 24p. (J). (ps-2). pap. 4.95 (978-0-516-29575-6(6)); lib. bdg. 13.50 (978-0-516-23282-9(7)) Scholastic Library Publishing. (Children's Pr.).

—My Grandfather Works in a Bakery. 2001. (Illus.). 24p. (J). (ps-3). lib. bdg. 12.95 (978-0-613-58864-5(9)) Tandem Library Bks.

—My Grandmother Works in a Dress Shop. 2000. (My Family at Work Ser.). (Illus.). 24p. (J). lib. bdg. (978-0-516-23283-6(5) , Children's Pr.) Scholastic Library Publishing.

—My Grandmother Works in a Dress Shop. 2001. (gr. k-3). lib. bdg. 12.95 (978-0-613-58865-2(7)) Tandem Library Bks.

—My Mom Is a Beekeeper. (Welcome Bks.). (Illus.). 24p. (J). (ps-2). 2001. pap. 4.95 (978-0-516-29577-0(2)); 2000. lib. bdg. (978-0-516-23284-3(3)) Scholastic Library Publishing. (Children's Pr.).

—My Mom Is a Beekeeper. 2001. (gr. k-3). lib. bdg. 12.95 (978-0-613-58868-3(1)) Tandem Library Bks.

Inseth, Zachary. Teachers. 2003. (Wonder Books Level 3: Careers Ser.). (Illus.). 32p. (J). (ps-2). 22.79 (978-1-56766-488-1(1)) Child's World, Inc.

J. G. Ferguson Publishing Company Staff. Careers in Focus: Business Managers. 2003. (Careers in Focus Ser.). 192p. (YA). (gr. 6-12). 22.95 (978-0-89434-414-5(5) , Ferguson Publishing Co.) Facts On File, Inc.

J. G. Ferguson Publishing Company Staff, contrib. by. Discovering Careers for Your Future. 2nd ed. 2005. (Discovering Careers for Your Future Ser.). (Illus.). 96p. (J). (gr. 4-9). 21.95 (978-0-8160-5870-9(9) , Ferguson Publishing Co.) Facts On File, Inc.

J. G. Ferguson Publishing Company Staff, ed. Career Discovery Encyclopedia, Set. 4th ed. 2000. 5308p. (YA). (gr. 5 up). 175.00 (978-0-89434-275-2(4) , F654, Ferguson Publishing Co.) Facts On File, Inc.

Jacobs, Nancy R., et al, eds. Careers & Occupations: Looking to the Future. 1998. (Information Plus Reference Ser.). (Illus.). 172p. (YA). pap. 32.00 (978-1-57302-079-4(6)) Thomson Gale.

Jango-Cohen, Judith. Librarians. (Pull Ahead Bks.). (J). 2005. (Illus.). 32p. lib. bdg. 22.60 (978-0-8225-1691-0(8)); 2004. pap. (978-0-8225-2533-2(X) , Lerner Pubns.) Lerner Publishing Group.

Jarrell, Jane & Saathoff, Deborah. Off to Work We Go. 2004. 50p. (ps up). pap., act. bk. ed. 6.99 (978-0-8054-0823-2(1)) B&H Publishing Grp.

JIST Editors. Young Person's Career Skills Handbook. 2006. (JIST's Young Person's Handbook Ser.). (Illus.). 256p. (J). pap. 19.95 (978-1-59357-243-3(3) , J2433, JIST Works) JIST Publishing.

JIST Works, Inc. Staff. People at Work! A Student's A-Z Guide to 350 Jobs. 2nd ed. 2005. (Early Start Career Ser.). (Illus.). 432p. (J). 27.95 (978-1-59357-078-1(3) , 1237657, JIST Works) JIST Publishing.

—Young Person's Occupational Outlook Handbook. 5th ed. 2004. (Illus.). 336p. pap. 19.95 (978-1-59357-125-2(9) , J1259, JIST Works) JIST Publishing.

JIST Works, Inc. Staff, ed. Occupational Outlook Handbook 2002-2003. 2002. (gr. 7-12). lib. bdg. 26.85 (978-0-613-44408-8(6)) Tandem Library Bks.

Jodway, Laurie. Me & My Job, 8 vols., Vol. 6. 2002. (Illus.). (J). per. (978-1-932062-32-8(7)) Hability Solution Services, Inc.

Jordan, Anna Louise. Lo Que Hacen Los EMT: What EMTs Do. 2007. (What Does a Community Helper Do? Bilingual Ser.). (ENG & SPA., Illus.). 32p. (J). lib. bdg. 22.60 (978-0-7660-2825-8(9) , Enslow Elementary) Enslow Pubs., Inc.

Kalman, Bobbie. Blacksmith. 2002. (gr. k-3). lib. bdg. 16.40 (978-0-613-85050-6(5)) Tandem Library Bks.

Kauk, Robert. Looking at Myself, Form II. 1999. (Illus.). 16p. (YA). (gr. 7). pap. 4.20 (978-0-934783-56-9(X)) CFKR Career Materials, Inc.

Kelley, Michelle. The Places I Go. 2007. (ENG & SPA.). (J). (978-1-59515-956-4(8)) Rourke Publishing, LLC.

Klingel, Cynthia Fitterer & Noyed, Robert B. Bank Tellers. 2002. (Community Workers Ser.). (Illus.). 32p. (J). (gr. 1 up). lib. bdg. 21.26 (978-0-7565-0307-9(8)) Compass Point Bks.

—Nurses. 2002. (Community Workers Ser.). (Illus.). 32p. (J). (gr. 1 up). lib. bdg. 21.26 (978-0-7565-0306-2(X)) Compass Point Bks.

—Postal Workers. 2001. (Wonder Books Level 1: Careers Ser.). (Illus.). 24p. (J). (ps-3). 22.79 (978-1-56766-941-1(7)) Child's World, Inc.

—School Bus Drivers. 2001. (My School Helpers). (Illus.). 24p. (J). (gr. 1-4). lib. bdg. 19.27 (978-1-57103-329-1(2)) Rourke Publishing, LLC.

—School Librarians. 2001. (School Helpers Ser.). (Illus.). 24p. (J). (gr. 1-4). lib. bdg. 19.27 (978-1-57103-331-4(9)) Rourke Publishing, LLC.

—School Principals. 2001. (School Helpers Ser.). (Illus.). 24p. (J). (gr. 1-4). lib. bdg. 19.27 (978-1-57103-330-7(0)) Rourke Publishing, LLC.

—School Secretaries. 2001. (School Helpers Ser.). (Illus.). 24p. (J). (gr. 1-4). lib. bdg. 19.27 (978-1-57103-328-4(9)) Rourke Publishing, LLC.

Knight, Bertram T. Working at a Zoo. 1998. (Working Here Ser.). (Illus.). 32p. (J). (gr. 2-4). 23.50 (978-0-516-20751-3(2) , Children's Pr.) Scholastic Library Publishing.

Kottke, Jan. Day with a Doctor. 2000. (gr. k-3). lib. bdg. 12.95 (978-0-613-58759-4(6)) Tandem Library Bks.

—Day with a Librarian. 2000. (gr. k-3). lib. bdg. 12.95 (978-0-613-58760-0(X)) Tandem Library Bks.

—Day with a Mail Carrier. 2000. (gr. k-3). lib. bdg. 12.95 (978-0-613-58761-7(8)) Tandem Library Bks.

—Day with Firefighters. 2000. (gr. k-3). lib. bdg. 12.95 (978-0-613-58766-2(9)) Tandem Library Bks.

—Day with Paramedics. 2000. (gr. k-3). lib. bdg. 12.95 (978-0-613-58767-9(7)) Tandem Library Bks.

—Day with Police Officers. 2000. (gr. k-3). lib. bdg. 12.95 (978-0-613-58768-6(5)) Tandem Library Bks.

Krebs, Laurie. A Day in the Life of a Colonial Miller. 2004. (Library of Living & Working in Colonial Times). (Illus.). 24p. (J). lib. bdg. 18.75 (978-0-8239-6230-3(X) , PowerKids Pr.) Rosen Publishing Group, Inc., The.

Lakeshore Learning Materials Staff, contrib. by. Skills for Living No. 3: On the Job. 2000. (J). pap. 29.95 (978-1-929255-96-2(9)) Lakeshore Learning Materials.

Lambert, Angela, illus. Jobs. 2006. (All Change! Ser.). 10p. (J). (ps). 6.99 (978-1-904550-17-4(7)) Child's Play-International.

Lansky, Bruce. When I Grow Up: Cool Jobs I Might Want to Have. Blough, Tim, illus. 2002. 12p. 9.95 (978-0-7432-2855-8(3)) Meadowbrook Pr.

Latinos at Work: Career Role Models for Young Adults, 10 vols., Set. 2002. (Illus.). (YA). (gr. 5-12). lib. bdg. 229.50 (978-1-58415-090-9(4)) Mitchell Lane Pubs., Inc.

Lawrence, Colton. Big Fat Paycheck. 2004. (Illus.). 288p. (gr. 5). lib. bdg. 11.99 (978-0-553-13122-2(2) , Bantam Bks. for Young Readers) Random Hse. Children's Bks.

LeBoutillier, Nate. A Day in the Life of a Garbage Collector. 2004. (First Facts Ser.). (Illus.). 24p. (J). lib. bdg. 21.26 (978-0-7368-2629-7(7)) Capstone Pr., Inc.

—A Day in the Life of a Zookeeper. 2004. (First Facts Ser.). (Illus.). 24p. (J). (gr. k-3). lib. bdg. 21.26 (978-0-7368-2632-7(7) , First Facts) Capstone Pr., Inc.

Lehn, Barbara. What Is a Teacher? Krauss, Carol, photos by. 2000. (What Is...? Ser.). (Illus.). 32p. (gr. k-3). lib. bdg. 21.90 (978-0-7613-1713-5(9) , Millbrook Pr.) Lerner Publishing Group.

Lerner Publishing Group Staff. Work People Do: Classroom Set. 2005. (Illus.). (J). (ps-1). 24.95 (978-0-8225-5356-4(2)) Lerner Publishing Group.

The Letter Uu: Jobs, 6 vols. (gr. k-2). 17.50 (978-0-7368-4120-7(2)) Red Brick Learning.

Levin, Amy. Hard Workers. 2003. (Compass Point Phonics Readers Ser.). (Illus.). 16p. (J). (gr. 1 up). 13.26 (978-0-7565-0508-0(9)) Compass Point Bks.

Lewison, Wendy Cheyette. What Will I Be? 2001. (Illus.). (J). (978-0-606-20986-1(7)) Tandem Library Bks.

Liebman, Dan. Quiero Ser Camionero. 2001. Tr. of I Want to Be a Truck Driver. (SPA.). (gr. k-3). lib. bdg. 14.15 (978-0-613-78562-4(2)) Tandem Library Bks.

—Quiero Ser Constructor. 2003. Tr. of I Want to Be a Builder. (SPA.). (gr. k-3). lib. bdg. 14.15 (978-0-613-78632-4(7)) Tandem Library Bks.

—Quiero Ser Enfermero. 2001. Tr. of I Want to Be a Nurse. (SPA.). (gr. k-3). lib. bdg. 14.15 (978-0-613-78558-7(4)) Tandem Library Bks.

—Quiero Ser Guardian de Zoologico. 2003. Tr. of I Want to Be a Zookeeper. (SPA.). (gr. k-3). lib. bdg. 14.15 (978-0-613-78623-2(8)) Tandem Library Bks.

—Quiero Ser Maestro. 2001. (SPA.). (gr. k-3). lib. bdg. 14.15 (978-0-613-78560-0(6)) Tandem Library Bks.

Liebman, Daniel. I Want to Be a Nurse. 2001. (I Want to Be Ser.). (Illus.). 24p. (J). (ps-2). pap. 3.99 (978-1-55209-566-9(5)); lib. bdg. 14.95 (978-1-55209-568-3(1)) Firefly Bks., Ltd.

—I Want to Be a Nurse. 2001. (I Want to Be Ser.). (Illus.). (J). 10.79 (978-0-606-21507-7(7)) Tandem Library Bks.

—I Want to Be a Teacher. 2001. (I Want to Be Ser.). (Illus.). 24p. (J). (ps-2). pap. 3.99 (978-1-55209-570-6(3)); lib. bdg. 14.95 (978-1-55209-572-0(X)) Firefly Bks., Ltd.

—I Want to Be a Teacher. 2001. (I Want to Be Ser.). (Illus.). (J). 10.79 (978-0-606-21508-4(5)) Tandem Library Bks.

Litchfield, Jo. Jobs. Litchfield, Jo, illus. 2006. (Illus.). 10p. (J). bds. 7.99 (978-0-7945-1353-5(0) , Usborne) EDC Publishing.

Lost Jobs: Individual Title Six-Packs. (Bookweb Ser.). 32p. (gr. 6 up). 34.00 (978-0-7578-0909-5(X)) Rigby Education.

Lucas, Debra. To the Rescue. 2003. (On the Job Ser.). (Illus.). 32p. (gr. 3-5). 23.00 (978-0-7910-7414-5(5) , Chelsea Hse.) Facts On File, Inc.

Luebke, Gayle M. When I Grow Up. 2005. 19p. 9.88 (978-1-4116-2790-1(3)) Lulu.com.

Maass, Robert. Fire Fighters. rev. ed. 2002. (Illus.). 32p. (J). pap. 5.99 (978-0-439-41781-5(3)) Scholastic, Inc.

Macken, JoAnn Early. Crossing Guard. 2003. (People in My Community Ser.). (Illus.). 24p. (J). (ps up). lib. bdg. 19.33 (978-0-8368-3589-2(1) , Weekly Reader Early Learning Library) Stevens, Gareth Inc.

—La Gente de Mi Comunidad/People in My Community: Crossing Guard/El Guardia de Cruce; Mail Carrier/El Artero; Nurse/El Enfermero; Sanitation Worker/El Recogedor de Basura; Teacher/El Maestro; Veterinarian/El Veterinario, 6 bks. Coffey, Colleen & Carrillo, Consuelo, trs. (Weekly Reader Early Learning Library). (SPA & ENG., Illus.). (J). (ps up). lib. bdg. 111.60 (978-0-8368-3670-7(7) , Weekly Reader Early Learning Library) Stevens, Gareth Inc.

—Mail Carrier. 2003. (People in My Community Ser.). (Illus.). 24p. (YA). (ps up). lib. bdg. 19.33 (978-0-8368-3590-8(5) , Weekly Reader Early Learning Library) Stevens, Gareth Inc.

—Mail Carrier/El Cartero. Coffey, Colleen & Carrillo, Consuelo, trs. 2003. (Weekly Reader Early Learning Library). (ENG & SPA., Illus.). 24p. (J). (ps up). lib. bdg. 19.33 (978-0-8368-3672-1(3) , Weekly Reader Early Learning Library) Stevens, Gareth Inc.

—Nurse. 2003. (People in My Community Ser.). (Illus.). 24p. (J). (ps up). lib. bdg. 19.33 (978-0-8368-3591-5(3) , Weekly Reader Early Learning Library) Stevens, Gareth Inc.

—Sanitation Worker. 2003. (People in My Community Ser.). (Illus.). 24p. (J). (ps up). lib. bdg. 19.33 (978-0-8368-3592-2(1) , Weekly Reader Early Learning Library) Stevens, Gareth Inc.

—Teacher. 2003. (People in My Community Ser.). (Illus.). 24p. (J). (ps up). lib. bdg. 19.33 (978-0-8368-3593-9(X) , Weekly Reader Early Learning Library) Stevens, Gareth Inc.

—Veterinarian. 2003. (People in My Community Ser.). (Illus.). 24p. (J). (ps up). lib. bdg. 19.33 (978-0-8368-3594-6(8) , Weekly Reader Early Learning Library) Stevens, Gareth Inc.

Macken, JoAnn Early & Gorman, Jacqueline Laks. Crossing Guard. Andersen, Gregg, photos by. 2003. (Weekly Reader Early Learning Library). (Illus.). 24p. (J). (ps up). pap. 7.93 (978-0-8368-3596-0(4) , Weekly Reader Early Learning Library) Stevens, Gareth Inc.

—Mail Carrier. Andersen, Gregg, photos by. 2003. (Weekly Reader Early Learning Library). (Illus.). 24p. (J). (ps up). pap. 7.93 (978-0-8368-3597-7(2) , Weekly Reader Early Learning Library) Stevens, Gareth Inc.

—Mail Carrier/El Cartero. Coffey, Colleen & Carrillo, Consuelo, trs. Andersen, Gregg, photos by. 2003. (Weekly Reader Early Learning Library). (ENG & SPA., Illus.). 24p. (J). (ps up). pap. 5.95 (978-0-8368-3686-8(3) , Weekly Reader Early Learning Library) Stevens, Gareth Inc.

—Nurse. Andersen, Gregg, photos by. 2003. (Weekly Reader Early Learning Library). (Illus.). 24p. (J). (ps up). pap. 7.93 (978-0-8368-3598-4(0) , Weekly Reader Early Learning Library) Stevens, Gareth Inc.

—Sanitation Worker. 2003. (Weekly Reader Early Learning Library). (Illus.). 24p. (J). (ps up). pap. 7.93 (978-0-8368-3599-1(9) , Weekly Reader Early Learning Library) Stevens, Gareth Inc.

—Teacher. Andersen, Gregg, photos by. 2003. (Weekly Reader Early Learning Library). (Illus.). 24p. (J). (ps up). pap. 7.93 (978-0-8368-3600-4(6) , Weekly Reader Early Learning Library) Stevens, Gareth Inc.

—Veterinarian. Andersen, Gregg, photos by. 2003. (Weekly Reader Early Learning Library). (Illus.). 24p. (J). (ps up). pap. 7.93 (978-0-8368-3601-1(4) , Weekly Reader Early Learning Library) Stevens, Gareth Inc.

Mail Carriers. (Community Helpers Ser.). 24p. (J). 6.95 (978-0-7368-8457-0(2)) Capstone Pr., Inc.

Malam, John. Ancient Egyptian Jobs. (People in the Past Ser.). (Illus.). 48p. (J). 2003. (gr. 4-6). lib. bdg. 27.07 (978-1-4034-0311-7(2)); 2002. pap. 8.50 (978-1-4034-0515-9(8)) Heinemann Library.

—Ancient Egyptian Jobs. 2002. (gr. 3-6). lib. bdg. 17.05 (978-0-613-86431-2(X)) Tandem Library Bks.

Mann, Holly & Running Press Staff. People: Pull the Tabs! Change the Pictures! 2004. (Illus.). 8p. pap. (978-0-7624-1906-7(7)) Running Pr. Bk. Pubs.

Marsh, Carole. Heroes & Helpers: The People We Count on Everyday! 2002. 48p. (J). (gr. 2-8). pap. 12.95 (978-0-635-01078-0(X)) Gallopade International.

Mattern, Joanne. Chefs. 2002. (Reading Power Ser.). (Illus.). 24p. (J). (gr. 1). lib. bdg. 17.25 (978-0-8239-5982-2(1) , PowerKids Pr.) Rosen Publishing Group, Inc., The.

—Working Together, 6 bks. Incl. Astronauts. (gr. 1). lib. bdg. 17.25 (978-0-8239-5977-8(5)); Chefs. (gr. 1). lib. bdg. 17.25 (978-0-8239-5982-2(1)); Emergency Medical Technicians. lib. bdg. 17.25 (978-0-8239-5980-8(5)); Mounted Police. (gr. 1). lib. bdg. 17.25 (978-0-8239-5981-5(3)); Pilots. lib. bdg. 17.25 (978-0-8239-5979-2(1)); Smoke Jumpers. (gr. 1). lib. bdg. 17.25 (978-0-8239-5978-5(3)); 24p. (J). 2002. (Illus.). 2001. Set lib. bdg. 96.00 (978-0-8239-7121-3(X) , PowerKids Pr.) Rosen Publishing Group, Inc., The.

Maynard, Thane. Working with Wildlife: A Guide to Careers in the Animal World. 2000. (Single Title Science Pb Ser.). (Illus.). 144p. (YA). (gr. 8-12). pap. 12.95 (978-0-531-16415-0(2) , Watts, Franklin) Scholastic Library Publishing.

Maze, Stephanie. I Want to Be... 1999. (gr. 4-9). 71.92 (978-0-7398-0997-6(0)) Raintree.

—I Want to Be..., 8 bks., Set. Incl. I Want to Be a Chef. 1999. pap. 18.98 (978-0-8172-6373-7(X)); I Want to Be a Dancer. 2000. lib. bdg. 27.12 (978-0-7398-1104-7(5)); I Want to Be a Fashion Designer. 2000. lib. bdg. 27.12 (978-0-7398-1970-8(4)); I Want to Be a Firefighter. 2000. lib. bdg. 18.98 (978-0-7398-1365-2(X)); I Want to Be a Veterinarian. 1999. pap. 18.98 (978-0-8172-6374-4(8)); I Want to Be an Astronaut. 1999. lib. bdg. 18.98 (978-0-8172-4159-9(0)); I Want to Be an Engineer. 1999. lib. bdg. 18.98 (978-0-8172-4160-5(4)); I Want to Be an Environmentalist. 2000. lib. bdg. 27.12 (978-0-7398-3071-0(6)); (Illus.). 48p. (YA). (gr. 4-9). 2000. Set lib. bdg. 216.96 (978-0-7398-3118-2(6)) Raintree.

—I Want to Be a Chef. 1999. (I Want to Be Ser.). (Illus.). 48p. (YA). (gr. 2-7). pap. 10.00 (978-0-15-201936-5(7)) Harcourt Children's Bks.

McGraw-Hill Staff. Entering the World of Work. 4th ed. 2006. stu. ed. 61.28 (978-0-07-861458-3(9) , 9780078614583) Glencoe/McGraw-Hill.

Meridian Education Corp, prod. Childrens Dictionary of Occupations. 2004. (Childrens Dictionary Career Ct Ser.). (YA). pap. 15.95 (978-0-7365-9386-1(1)) Films Media Group.

Metz, Lynn. On the Job: Learning the Short O Sound. (PowerPhonics Ser.). (Illus.). (J). 2002. 24p. (gr. 1). lib. bdg. 18.50 (978-0-8239-5905-1(8)); 2001. 23p. lib. bdg. 26.40 (978-0-8239-8250-9(5)) Rosen Publishing Group, Inc., The. (PowerKids Pr.).

Meyer, Jone. Vocational Biographies - The Good Life, 7. 2000. (Vocational Biographies: 7). (Illus.). 104p. (YA). (gr. 11-13). spiral bd. 265.00 (978-0-87063-788-9(6) , D-00) Vocational Biographies.

—Vocational Biographies Comprehensive Career Library, 35. 2000. (J). 1568.75 (978-0-87063-823-7(8) , c.l.2-a-b-c-d) Vocational Biographies.

Meyer, Jone, ed. Vocational Biographies - Series D-00: 175 Titles, 7 vols., Set. 2000. (Illus.). lib. bdg. 331.25 (978-0-87063-781-0(9) , D-00); (YA). spiral bd. 265.00 (978-0-87063-780-3(0) , D-00) Vocational Biographies.

—Vocational Biographies - The Good Life, 7. 2000. (Vocational Biographies: 7). (Illus.). 104p. (YA). (gr. 11-13). lib. bdg. 331.25 (978-0-87063-795-7(9)) Vocational Biographies.

—Vocational Biographies Budget Career Library. 2000. (YA). lib. bdg. 931.25 (978-0-87063-827-5(0)); spiral bd. 745.00 (978-0-87063-826-8(2) , B.L. - b-c-d) Vocational Biographies.

—Vocational Biographies Comprehensive Career Library. 2000. (YA). lib. bdg. 1255.00 (978-0-87063-822-0(X) , C.L.-2-a-b-c-d) Vocational Biographies.

—Vocational Biographies Economy Career Library. 2000. (YA). lib. bdg. 1243.75 (978-0-87063-825-1(4) , E.L. - a -b-c-d-); spiral bd. 995.00 (978-0-87063-824-4(6) , E.L.- a-b-c-d) Vocational Biographies.

—Vocational Biographies Starter Career Library. 2000. (YA). spiral bd. 498.00 (978-0-87063-829-9(7) , S.L. - C & D) Vocational Biographies.

Middleton, Haydn. Ancient Greek Jobs. 2002. (People in the Past Ser.). (Illus.). 48p. (J). (gr. 4-6). lib. bdg. 27.07 (978-1-58810-638-4(1)) Heinemann Library.

—Ancient Greek Jobs. 2002. (gr. 3-6). lib. bdg. 17.05 (978-0-613-84765-0(2)) Tandem Library Bks.

Middleton, Haydn & Tames, Richard. Ancient Greek Jobs. 2002. (People in the Past Ser.). 64p. (J). (gr. 4-7). pap. 8.50 (978-1-4034-0133-5(0) , 91638) Heinemann Library.

Miller, Connie Colwell. Disgusting Jobs. 2007. (Blazers Ser.). (Illus.). 32p. (J). ***978-0-7368-7878-4(5)** , 1264924) Capstone Pr., Inc.

—Disgusting Jobs. 2007. (Blazers Ser.). (Illus.). 32p. (J). (978-0-7368-6800-6(3) , 1264924) Capstone Publishing.

Miller, Heather. Artist. 2003. (This Is What I Want to Be Ser.). (Illus.). 24p. (J). lib. bdg. 18.50 (978-1-4034-0913-3(7)); pap. 5.25 (978-1-4034-3606-1(1)) Heinemann Library.

—Artist. 2003. (ps-2). lib. bdg. 13.30 (978-0-613-60953-1(0)) Tandem Library Bks.

—Artista. 2003. Tr. of Artist. (SPA.). 24p. (J). pap. 5.25 (978-1-4034-3393-0(3)) Heinemann Library.

—Chef. 2003. (This Is What I Want to Be Ser.). (Illus.). 24p. (J). lib. bdg. 18.50 (978-1-4034-0912-6(9)); pap. 5.25 (978-1-4034-3607-8(X)) Heinemann Library.

—Chef. 2003. (ps-2). lib. bdg. 13.30 (978-0-613-60958-6(1)) Tandem Library Bks.

—Cocinero. 2003. (Esto es lo Que Quiero Ser (This Is What I Want to Be) Ser.). (SPA.). 24p. (J). pap. 5.25 (978-1-4034-3395-4(X)) Heinemann Library.

—Cuidador del Zoologico. 2003. (Esto es lo Que Quiero Ser (This Is What I Want to Be) Ser.). (SPA.). 24p. (J). (ps-1). lib. bdg. 18.50 (978-1-4034-0383-4(X)) Heinemann Library.

—Doctor. 2003. (This Is What I Want to Be Ser.). (Illus.). 24p. (J). (ps-1). lib. bdg. 18.50 (978-1-4034-0367-4(8)); pap. 5.25 (978-1-4034-0589-0(1)) Heinemann Library.

—Esto es lo Que Quiero Ser (This Is What I Want to Be) Series, 4 bks., Set 2. 2003. (SPA & ENG., Illus.). (J). lib. bdg. 74.00 (978-1-4034-0949-2(8)) Heinemann Library.

—Nurse. 2003. (This Is What I Want to Be Ser.). (Illus.). 24p. (ps-1). (J). lib. bdg. 18.50 (978-1-4034-0370-4(8)); pap. 5.25 (978-1-4034-0592-0(1)) Heinemann Library.

—Nurse. 2003. (ps-2). lib. bdg. 13.30 (978-0-613-86438-1(7)) Tandem Library Bks.

—Obrero de Construccion. 2003. (Esto es lo Que Quiero Ser (This Is What I Want to Be) Ser.). (SPA., Illus.). 24p. (J). (ps-1). lib. bdg. 18.50 (978-1-4034-0375-9(9)) Heinemann Library.

—Police Officer. 2003. (This Is What I Want to Be Ser.). (Illus.). 24p. (J). (ps-1). lib. bdg. 18.50 (978-1-4034-0371-1(6)); pap. 5.25 (978-1-4034-0593-7(X)) Heinemann Library.

—Police Officer. 2003. (ps-2). lib. bdg. 13.30 (978-0-613-86439-8(5)) Tandem Library Bks.

—Teacher. 2003. (This Is What I Want to Be Ser.). (Illus.). 24p. (J). (ps-1). lib. bdg. (978-1-4034-0372-8(4)); pap. 5.25 (978-1-4034-0594-4(8)) Heinemann Library.

—Truck Driver. 2003. (This Is What I Want to Be Ser.). (Illus.). 24p. (J). lib. bdg. 18.50 (978-1-4034-0911-9(0)); pap. 5.25 (978-1-4034-3608-5(8)) Heinemann Library.

—Vaquero. Prieto, Carlos, tr. 2003. (Esto es lo Que Quiero Ser (This Is What I Want to Be) Ser.).Tr. of Cowboy. (SPA., 24p. (J). (ps-1). Illus.). lib. bdg. 18.50 (978-1-4034-0376-6(7)); pap. 5.25 (978-1-4034-0598-2(0)) Heinemann Library.

—Veterinarian. 2003. (This Is What I Want to Be Ser.). (Illus.). 24p. (J). lib. bdg. 18.50 (978-1-4034-0905-8(6)); pap. 5.25 (978-1-4034-3609-2(6)) Heinemann Library.

—Veterinarian. 2003. (ps-2). lib. bdg. 13.30 (978-0-613-60993-7(X)) Tandem Library Bks.

—Zookeeper. 2003. (This Is What I Want to Be Ser.). (Illus.). 24p. (ps-1). (J). lib. bdg. 18.50 (978-1-4034-0373-5(2)); pap. 5.25 (978-1-4034-0595-1(6)) Heinemann Library.

Minden, Cecilia. Letter Carriers. 2006. (Neighborhood Helpers Ser.). (Illus.). 32p. (J). (gr. k-4). 22.79 (978-1-59296-568-7(7)) Child's World, Inc.

Mitchell, Melanie. Principals. (Pull Ahead Bks.). (J). 2005. (Illus.). 32p. lib. bdg. 22.60 (978-0-8225-1694-1(2)); 2004. pap. (978-0-8225-2535-6(6) , Lerner Pubns.) Lerner Publishing Group.

—Teachers. (Pull Ahead Bks.). (Illus.). 32p. (J). 2005. lib. bdg. 22.60 (978-0-8225-1696-5(9)); 2004. pap. (978-0-8225-2536-3(4) , Lerner Pubns.) Lerner Publishing Group.

Mitzo Thompson, Kim. When I Grow up / Cuando Crezca. 2006. (Dual Language Readers Ser.). 32p. (J). pap. 4.99 (978-0-7696-4625-1(5)) School Specialty Publishing.

Monroe, Judy. A Day in the Life of a Librarian. 2004. (First Facts Ser.). (Illus.). 24p. (J). (gr. k-3). lib. bdg. 21.26 (978-0-7368-2630-3(0)) Capstone Pr., Inc.

Morris, Ann. That's Our Custodian! Linenthal, Peter, illus. 2003. (That's Our School Ser.). 32p. lib. bdg. 22.90 (978-0-7613-2401-0(1) , Millbrook Pr.) Lerner Publishing Group.

—That's Our Gym Teacher! Linenthal, Peter, illus. 2003. (That's Our School Ser.). 32p. lib. bdg. 22.90 (978-0-7613-2403-4(8) , Millbrook Pr.) Lerner Publishing Group.

—That's Our Nurse! Linenthal, Peter, illus. 2003. (That's Our School Ser.). 32p. lib. bdg. 22.90 (978-0-7613-2402-7(X) , Millbrook Pr.) Lerner Publishing Group.

—That's Our Principal! 2003. (That's Our School Ser.). 32p. lib. bdg. 22.90 (978-0-7613-2374-7(0) , Millbrook Pr.) Lerner Publishing Group.

—That's Our Teacher! 2003. (That's Our School Ser.). 32p. lib. bdg. 22.90 (978-0-7613-2373-0(2) , Millbrook Pr.) Lerner Publishing Group.

Murphy, Patricia J. Investigating Insects with a Scientist. 2004. (I Like Science! Ser.). (Illus.). 24p. (J). (gr. 1-3). lib. bdg. 21.26 (978-0-7660-2270-6(6)) Enslow Pubs., Inc.

Murray, Amy. The Character & Career Connection. 2005. (Illus.). 76p. (J). per. 19.95 (978-1-931636-45-2(1)) National Center For Youth Issues.

Nelson, Robin. Coaches. 2005. (Pull Ahead Bks.). (Illus.). 32p. (J). 22.60 (978-0-8225-1686-6(1)) Lerner Publishing Group.

—Custodians. 2005. (Pull Ahead Bks.). (Illus.). 32p. (J). 22.60 (978-0-8225-1687-3(X)) Lerner Publishing Group.

—Jobs. 2003. (First Step Nonfiction Ser.). (Illus.). 8p. (J). pap. 3.95 (978-0-8225-3929-2(2) , Lerner Pubns.) Lerner Publishing Group.

Nelson, Robin. Working Then & Now. 2008. (First Step Nonfiction - Then & Now Ser.). (J). lib. bdg. 18.60 ***978-0-8225-8604-3(5))** Lerner Publishing Group.

O'Brien, John & Bilkins, Maxi. The Beach Patrol, rev. ed. 2004. (Illus.). 32p. (J). 15.95 (978-0-8050-6911-2(9) , Holt, Henry & Co. Bks. For Young Readers) Holt, Henry & Co.

O'Keefe, Susan Heyboer. What Does a Priest Do? What Does a Nun Do? 2002. (Illus.). 32p. 7.95 (978-0-8091-6698-5(4) , 6698-4) Paulist Pr.

On the Edge: Individual Title Six-Packs. (Action Packs Ser.). 104p. (gr. 3-5). 44.00 (978-0-7635-2995-6(8)) Rigby Education.

O'Shei, Tim. The World's Most Dangerous Jobs. 2007. (Edge Books, the World's Top Tens). (Illus.). 32p. (J). 23.93 (978-0-7368-6438-1(5)) Capstone Pr., Inc.

Owen, Ann. Caring for Your Pets: A Book about Veterinarians. Thomas, Eric, illus. 2004. (Community Workers Ser.). 24p. (C). (gr. k-3). 22.60 (978-1-4048-0087-8(5)) Picture Window Bks.

—Delivering Your Mail: A Book about Mail Carriers. Thomas, Eric, illus. 2004. (Community Workers Ser.). 24p. (C). (gr. k-3). 22.60 (978-1-4048-0091-5(3)) Picture Window Bks.

—Keeping You Safe: A Book about Police Officers. Thomas, Eric, illus. 2004. (Community Workers Ser.). 24p. (C). (gr. k-3). 22.60 (978-1-4048-0089-2(1)) Picture Window Bks.

—Taking You Places: A Book about Bus Drivers. Thomas, Eric, illus. 2004. (Community Workers Ser.). 24p. (C). (gr. k-3). 22.60 (978-1-4048-0090-8(5)) Picture Window Bks.

Parks, Peggy J. Doctor. 2003. (Exploring Careers Ser.). (Illus.). 48p. (J). (gr. 3-5). 26.20 (978-0-7377-1484-5(0) , Kidhaven) Thomson Gale.

—Firefighter. 2004. (Illus.). 48p. (J). 26.20 (978-0-7377-2066-2(2) , Greenhaven Pr., Inc.) Thomson Gale.

—Lawyer. 2003. (Exploring Careers Ser.). (Illus.). 48p. (J). (gr. 3-5). 26.20 (978-0-7377-1485-2(9) , Kidhaven) Thomson Gale.

—Police Officer. 2003. (Exploring Careers Ser.). (Illus.). 48p. (J). (gr. 3-5). 26.20 (978-0-7377-1486-9(7) , Kidhaven) Thomson Gale.

—Teacher. 2003. (Exploring Careers Ser.). (Illus.). 48p. (J). (gr. 3-5). 26.20 (978-0-7377-1487-6(5) , Kidhaven) Thomson Gale.

Parramore, Barbara M. & Butler, Jane M. Children's Dictionary of Occupations Activities Grades 3-4. Sears, Twila et al, eds. Jones, R. Scott, illus. rev. ed. 1998. 29p. (J). (gr. 2-6). pap. 15.95 (978-1-56191-587-3(4) , 3055) Meridian Education Corp.

—Children's Dictionary of Occupations Activities Grades 5-6. Sears, Twila et al, eds. Jones, R. Scott, illus. rev. ed. 1998. (Childrens Dictionary Career Ct Ser.). 29p. (J). (gr. 2-6). pap. 15.95 (978-1-56191-588-0(2) , 3056) Meridian Education Corp.

Parramore, Barbara M., et al. Children's Dictionary of Occupations: Corporation. Sears, Twila et al, eds. Jones, R. Scott, illus. 3rd rev. ed. 1998. 126p. (J). (gr. 2-6). wbk. ed. 15.95 (978-1-56191-586-6(6) , 3054) Meridian Education Corp.

Pasternak, Ceel & Thornburg, Linda. Cool Careers for Girls in Air & Space. (Illus.). (gr. 7 up). 2001. 144p. pap. 12.95 (978-1-57023-146-9(X)); 2000. viii, 117p. (J). 12.95 (978-1-57023-147-6(8)) Impact Pubns.

—Cool Careers for Girls in Law. 2001. (YA). lib. bdg. 22.20 (978-0-613-79030-7(8)) Tandem Library Bks.

Patton, Geoff. On the Job. 2005. (X-Zone Ser.). (Illus.). 30p. (gr. 4-8). 23.00 (978-0-7910-8990-3(8)) Facts On File, Inc.

People in My Community, 12 bks. Incl. Bus Driver. Gorman, Jacqueline Laks. Andersen, Gregg, photos by. (J). 2002. lib. bdg. 19.33 (978-0-8368-3292-1(2)); Crossing Guard. Macken, JoAnn Early. (J). 2003. lib. bdg. 19.33 (978-0-8368-3589-2(1)); Dentist. Gorman, Jacqueline Laks. Andersen, Gregg, illus. (J). 2002. lib. bdg. 19.33 (978-0-8368-3293-8(0)); Doctor. Gorman, Jacqueline Laks. Andersen, Gregg, photos by. (J). 2002. lib. bdg. 19.33 (978-0-8368-3294-5(9)); Firefighter. Gorman, Jacqueline Laks. Andersen, Gregg, photos by. (J). 2002. lib. bdg. 19.33 (978-0-8368-3295-2(7)); Librarian. Gorman, Jacqueline Laks. Andersen, Gregg, photos by. (J). 2002. lib. bdg. 19.33 (978-0-8368-3296-9(5)); Mail Carrier. Macken, JoAnn Early. (YA). 2003. lib. bdg. 19.33 (978-0-8368-3590-8(5)); Nurse. Macken, JoAnn Early. (J). 2003. lib. bdg. 19.33 (978-0-8368-3591-5(3)); Police Officer. Gorman, Jacqueline Laks. Andersen, Gregg, photos by. (J). 2002. lib. bdg. 19.33 (978-0-8368-3297-6(3)); Sanitation Worker. Macken, JoAnn Early. (J). 2003. lib. bdg. 19.33 (978-0-8368-3592-2(1)); Teacher. Macken, JoAnn Early. (J). 2003. lib. bdg. 19.33 (978-0-8368-3593-9(X)); Veterinarian. Macken, JoAnn Early. (J). 2003. lib. bdg. 19.33 (978-0-8368-3594-6(8)); 24p. (ps up). (Weekly Reader Early Learning Library). (Illus.). Set lib. bdg. 231.96 (978-0-8368-3646-2(4) , Weekly Reader Early Learning Library) Stevens, Gareth Inc.

Picture Window Books, contrib. by. Delivering Your Mail. (Community Workers Ser.). 24p. (J). pap. 7.95 (978-1-4048-0485-2(4)) Picture Window Bks.

Plumbers. (Community Helpers Ser.). 24p. (J). 6.95 (978-0-7368-8459-4(9)) Capstone Pr., Inc.

Priddy Books Staff. I Want to Be a Builder & Firefighter, 2 bks. (Illus.). (J). bds. (978-0-312-49163-5(8) , Priddy Bks.) St. Martin's Pr.

Profile of the Perfect Employee (AVA) 2001. (YA). pap. 8.00 (978-1-57078-021-9(8) , CEV00021) C E V Multimedia, Ltd.

Quinlan, Kathryn A. Child Care Worker. 1998. (Careers Without College Ser.). (Illus.). 48p. (J). (gr. 3-4). lib. bdg. 21.26 (978-0-7368-0032-7(8) , LifeMatters Bks.) Capstone Pr., Inc.

—Food Service Manager. 1998. (Careers Without College Ser.). (Illus.). 48p. (J). (gr. 3-4). lib. bdg. 21.26 (978-0-7368-0034-1(4) , LifeMatters Bks.) Capstone Pr., Inc.

Raatma, Lucia. Veterinarians. 2002. (Community Workers Ser.). (Illus.). 32p. (J). (gr. 1 up). lib. bdg. 21.26 (978-0-7565-0304-8(3)) Compass Point Bks.

Raintree Steck-Vaughn Staff. People at Work. 2000. (Read All about It Ser.). (Illus.). (J). pap. 4.95 (978-0-8114-3801-8(5)) Steck-Vaughn.

—Podré Ser lo Que Quiera. 1999. (SPA.). (J). pap., stu. ed. 31.05 (978-0-7398-0771-2(4)) Steck-Vaughn.

—What People Do: Level A. 2000. (Read All about It Ser.). (Illus.). (J). pap. 4.95 (978-0-8114-3720-2(5)) Steck-Vaughn.

Rawley, Phyllis Caves. Career Tips for Teens: What You Need to Know Before You Leave High School. l.t. ed. 2002. 200p. (YA). per. 6.93 (978-0-9719057-0-2(3)) Brown Skin Girl Publishing.

Ready, Dee. Choferes de Autobuses Escolares. Schon, Isabel, ed. Ferrer, Martín Luis Guzman, tr. 1998. (Servidores Comunitarios Ser.). (SPA., Illus.). 24p. (J). (gr. 1-2). lib. bdg. 18.60 (978-1-56065-803-0(7) , Bridgestone Bks.) Capstone Pr., Inc.

—Enfermeras y Enfermeros. Schon, Isabel, ed. Ferrer, Martín Luis Guzman, tr. from ENG. 1998. (Servidores Comunitarios Ser.). (SPA., Illus.). 24p. (J). (gr. 1-2). lib. bdg. 18.60 (978-1-56065-801-6(0) , Bridgestone Bks.) Capstone Pr., Inc.

—Policías. Schon, Isabel, ed. Ferrer, Martín Luis Guzman, tr. from ENG. 1998. (Servidores Comunitarios Ser.). (SPA., Illus.). 24p. (J). (gr. 1-2). lib. bdg. 18.60 (978-1-56065-802-3(9) , Bridgestone Bks.) Capstone Pr., Inc.

—Servidores Comunitarios (Community Helpers), 10 bks. Ferrer, Martín Luis Guzman, tr. Incl. Bibliotecarios y Bibliotecarias. Schon, Isabel, ed. (gr. 1-2). lib. bdg. 18.60 (978-1-56065-799-6(5)); Bomberos y Bomberas. Schon, Isabel, ed. (gr. 2-4). lib. bdg. 18.60 (978-1-56065-797-2(9)); Carteros y Carteras. Schon, Isabel, ed. (gr. 1-2). lib. bdg. 18.60 (978-1-56065-800-9(2)); Choferes de Autobuses Escolares. Schon, Isabel, ed. (gr. 1-2). lib. bdg. 18.60 (978-1-56065-803-0(7)); Dentistas. (gr. 1-2). lib. bdg. 18.60 (978-1-56065-795-8(2)); Doctores y Doctoras. Schon, Isabel, ed. (gr. 1-2). lib. bdg. 18.60 (978-1-56065-796-5(0)); Enfermeras y Enfermeros. Schon, Isabel, ed. (gr. 1-2). lib. bdg. 18.60 (978-1-56065-801-6(0)); Granjeros y Granjeras. Schon, Isabel, ed. (gr. 1-2). lib. bdg. 18.60 (978-1-56065-798-9(7)); Policías. Schon, Isabel, ed. (gr. 1-2). lib. bdg. 18.60 (978-1-56065-802-3(9)); Veterinarios y Veterinarias. Schon, Isabel, ed. (gr. 1-2). lib. bdg. 18.60 (978-1-56065-804-7(5)); 24p. (J). 1998. (SPA., Illus.). Set lib. bdg. 186.00 (978-0-7368-0147-8(2) , Bridgestone Bks.) Capstone Pr., Inc.

—Veterinarios y Veterinarias. Schon, Isabel, ed. Ferrer, Martín Luis Guzman, tr. from ENG. 1998. (Servidores Comunitarios Ser.). (SPA., Illus.). 24p. (J). (gr. 1-2). lib. bdg. 18.60 (978-1-56065-804-7(5) , Bridgestone Bks.) Capstone Pr., Inc.

Reeves, Diane Lindsey. Career Ideas for Kids Who Like Talking. (Career Ideas for Kids Ser.). 1998. (Illus.). 176p. (YA). (gr. 5-9). pap. 12.95 (978-0-8160-3689-9(6)); 2nd rev. ed. 2008. 304p. (J). (gr. 4-9). pap. 18.95 (***978-0-8160-6554-7(3)** , Checkmark Bks.); 2nd rev. ed. 2007. 192p. (J). (gr. 4-9). 32.95 (***978-0-8160-6553-0(5)** , Checkmark Bks.) Facts On File, Inc.

—Career Ideas for Kids Who Like Talking. 1998. (gr. 5-8). lib. bdg. 22.20 (978-0-613-76190-1(1)) Tandem Library Bks.

—Career Ideas for Teens Set. 2005. (Career Ideas for Teens Ser.). 192-192p. (gr. 6-12). 320.00 (978-0-8160-5287-5(5) , Ferguson Publishing Co.) Facts On File, Inc.

Reeves, Diane Lindsey & Clasen, Lindsey. Career Ideas for Kids Who Like Art. Bond, Nancy, illus. 2nd rev. ed. (Career Ideas for Kids Ser.). 208p. (J). (gr. 4-9). pap. 16.95 (978-0-8160-6542-4(X)); 2007. 32.95 (978-0-8160-6541-7(1)) Facts On File, Inc. (Ferguson Publishing Co.).

Richer, William. What Do You Wanna-Bee? An Encyclopedia Activity Coloring Book of Professional Busy Bee's. 2nd ed. 2000. Orig. Title: To Be or not to Be, What Do You Wanna-Be?. (Illus.). 68p. (J). (gr. 1). pap. 6.95 (978-0-9703609-0-8(8)) I Wanna Bee.

Rigby Education Staff. Chug Chug, Choo Choo. (Illus.). 8p. (J). bds. 3.95 (978-0-7635-6451-3(6) , 764516C99) Rigby Education.

Ring, Susan. Animal Watch. 2003. (On the Job Ser.). (Illus.). 32p. (gr. 3-5). 23.00 (978-0-7910-7409-1(9) , Chelsea Hse.) Facts On File, Inc.

Rosa-Mendoza, Gladys, creator. Jobs Around My Neighborhood. 2004. (English-Spanish Foundations Ser.: Vol. 9). Tr. of Officios en Mi Vecindario. (SPA & ENG., Illus.). 20p. (J). bds. 6.95 (978-1-931398-09-1(7)) Me+Mi Publishing.

Ross, Kathy, illus. Community Workers. 2006. (Crafts for Kids Who Are Learning about Ser.). 48p. (J). (gr. k-2). lib. bdg. 25.26 (978-0-7613-2743-1(6)) Lerner Publishing Group.

Sanna, Ellyn. Career Assessments & Their Meanings. 2002. (Careers with Character Ser.). (Illus.). 96p. (YA). (gr. 7 up). lib. bdg. 22.95 (978-1-59084-309-3(6)) Mason Crest Pubs.

Saunders-Smith, Gail. Communities. 1998. (J). pap. 13.25 (978-0-516-21241-8(9) , Children's Pr.) Scholastic Library Publishing.

Saunders-Smith, Gail, ed. Helpers in Our Community. (Pebble Ser.). (Illus.). (J). (gr. k-1). lib. bdg. 254.88 (978-0-7368-2742-3(0)) Capstone Pr., Inc.

—Helpers in Our Community, 8 bks. Incl. We Need Child Care Workers. Trumbauer, Lisa. 2003. lib. bdg. 15.93 (978-0-7368-1648-9(8)); We Need Construction Workers. Trumbauer, Lisa. 2003. lib. bdg. 15.93 (978-0-7368-1649-6(6)); We Need Dentists. Schaefer, Lola M. 1999. lib. bdg. 15.93 (978-0-7368-0388-5(2)); We Need Doctors. Schaefer, Lola M. 1999. lib. bdg. 15.93 (978-0-7368-0389-2(0)); We Need Farmers. Schaefer, Lola M. 1999. lib. bdg. 15.93 (978-0-7368-0390-8(4)); We Need Fire Fighters. Schaefer, Lola M. 2000. lib. bdg. 15.93 (978-0-7368-0391-5(2)); We Need Garbage Collectors. Trumbauer, Lisa. 2003. lib. bdg. 15.93 (978-0-7368-1650-2(X)); We Need Mail Carriers. Schaefer, Lola M. 2000. lib. bdg. 15.93 (978-0-7368-0392-2(0)); We Need Nurses. Schaefer, Lola M. 2000. lib. bdg. 15.93 (978-0-7368-0393-9(9)); We Need Police Officers. Schaefer, Lola M. 2000. lib. bdg. 15.93 (978-0-7368-0394-6(7)); We Need Veterinarians. Schaefer, Lola M. 2000. lib. bdg. 15.93 (978-0-7368-0395-3(5)); We Need Zoo Keepers. Trumbauer, Lisa. 2003. lib. bdg. 15.93 (978-0-7368-1651-9(8)); 24p. (J). (gr. k-1). (Illus.). 2000. Set lib. bdg. 191.16 (978-0-7368-1670-0(4) , Pebble Bks.) Capstone Pr., Inc.

Schaefer, Lola M. Airport. 2000. (Who Works Here? Ser.). (Illus.). 32p. (J). (gr. 1-3). lib. bdg. 21.36 (978-1-57572-515-4(0)) Heinemann Library.

—Car Dealership. 2001. (Who Works Here? Ser.). (Illus.). 32p. (J). lib. bdg. 21.36 (978-1-58810-123-5(1)) Heinemann Library.

—Construction Site. 2000. (Who Works Here? Ser.). (Illus.). 32p. (J). (gr. 1-3). lib. bdg. 21.36 (978-1-57572-516-1(9)) Heinemann Library.

—Helpers in Our Community: We Need Dentists; We Need Doctors; We Need Farmers; We Need Fire Fighters; We Need Mail Carriers; We Need Nurses; We Need Police Officers; We Need Veterinarians, 8 bks. Saunders-Smith, Gail, ed. 2000. (Illus.). (J). (gr. k-1). lib. bdg. 116.80 (978-0-7368-0451-6(X) , Pebble Bks.) Capstone Pr., Inc.

—Hospital. 2000. (Who Works Here? Ser.). (Illus.). 32p. (J). (gr. 1-3). lib. bdg. 21.36 (978-1-57572-519-2(3)) Heinemann Library.

—Police Station. 2000. (Who Works Here? Ser.). (Illus.). 32p. (J). (gr. 1-3). lib. bdg. 21.36 (978-1-57572-520-8(7)) Heinemann Library.

—We Need Farmers. Saunders-Smith, Gail, ed. 1999. (Helpers in Our Community Ser.). (Illus.). 24p. (J). (gr. k-1). lib. bdg. 15.93 (978-0-7368-0390-8(4) , Pebble Bks.) Capstone Pr., Inc.

—We Need Nurses. Saunders-Smith, Gail, ed. 2000. (Helpers in Our Community Ser.). (Illus.). 24p. (J). (gr. k-1). lib. bdg. 15.93 (978-0-7368-0393-9(9) , Pebble Bks.) Capstone Pr., Inc.

—Who Works Here? Series, 6 bks., Set 1. Incl. Airport. lib. bdg. 21.36 (978-1-57572-515-4(0)); Construction Site. lib. bdg. 21.36 (978-1-57572-516-1(9)); Dental Office. lib. bdg. 21.36 (978-1-57572-517-8(7)); Hospital. lib. bdg. 21.36 (978-1-57572-519-2(3)); Police Station. lib. bdg. 21.36 (978-1-57572-520-8(7)); Supermarket. lib. bdg. 21.36 (978-1-57572-518-5(5)); 32p. (J). (gr. 1-3). 2000. (Illus.). 2000. Set lib. bdg. 128.16 (978-1-57572-514-7(2)) Heinemann Library.

—Who Works Here? Series: Learn about Jobs & Teamwork, 12 bks. 2001. (Illus.). (J). (gr. 1-3). Set. lib. bdg. 256.32 (978-1-58810-188-4(6)); Set 2. lib. bdg. 128.16 (978-1-58810-024-5(3)) Heinemann Library.

Schamp, Virginia. If You Were a Doctor. 2000. (If You Were A... Ser.). (Illus.). 32p. (J). (gr. 2-4). lib. bdg. 22.79 (978-0-7614-1000-3(7) , Benchmark Bks.) Cavendish, Marshall Corp.

Schomp, Virginia. If You Were a Ballplayer. 2000. (If You Were A... Ser.). (Illus.). 32p. (J). (gr. 2-4). lib. bdg. 22.79 (978-0-7614-0917-5(3) , Benchmark Bks.) Cavendish, Marshall Corp.

—If You Were a Farmer. 2000. (If You Were A... Ser.). (Illus.). 32p. (J). (gr. 2-4). lib. bdg. 22.79 (978-0-7614-1001-0(5) , Benchmark Bks.) Cavendish, Marshall Corp.

—If You Were a Zookeeper. 1999. (If You Were A... Ser.). (Illus.). 32p. (J). (gr. 2-4). lib. bdg. 22.79 (978-0-7614-0918-2(1) , Benchmark Bks.) Cavendish, Marshall Corp.

School Principals. (Community Helpers Ser.). 24p. (J). 6.95 (978-0-7368-8462-4(9)) Capstone Pr., Inc.

Schwartz, Linda & Wolfgang, Toni. Children's Occupational Outlook Handbook. Barrows, Laurie, photos by. 2nd ed. 1998. (Illus.). 240p. (J). pap. 18.95 (978-1-887481-09-0(5)) CFKR Career Materials, Inc.

Schwartz, Stuart B. Looking at Work, 4 vols. 1998. (J). (gr. 5-12). (978-0-516-29736-1(8) , Children's Pr.) Scholastic Library Publishing.

—Setting Career Goals. 1998. (J). lib. bdg. (978-0-516-21297-5(4) , Children's Pr.) Scholastic Library Publishing.

Schwartz, Stuart B. & Conley, Craig. Job Skills, 4 bks. Incl. Being a Leader. lib. bdg. 21.26 (978-1-56065-715-6(4)); Communicating with Others. lib. bdg. 21.26 (978-1-56065-716-3(2)); Taking Responsibility. lib. bdg. 21.26 (978-1-56065-717-0(0)); Working As a Team. lib. bdg. 21.26 (978-1-56065-718-7(9)); 32p. (J). (gr. 3-4). 1998. (Illus.). Set lib. bdg. 85.04 (978-1-56065-819-1(3) , LifeMatters Bks.) Capstone Pr., Inc.

—Looking at Work, 8 bks. Incl. Considering a Job Offer. (gr. 3-4). 1999. lib. bdg. 21.26 (978-0-7368-0178-2(2)); Earning Money. (gr. 3-4). 1998. lib. bdg. 21.26 (978-1-56065-711-8(1)); Exploring Job Skills. (gr. 3-4). 1998. lib. bdg. 21.26 (978-1-56065-712-5(X)); Finding Work. (gr. 3-4). 1998. lib. bdg. 21.26 (978-1-56065-713-2(8)); Interviewing for a Job. (gr. 3-4). 1998. lib. bdg. 21.26 (978-1-56065-714-9(6)); Interviewing for Information. (gr. 3-4). 1999. lib. bdg. 21.26 (978-0-7368-0179-9(0)); Networking to Find a Job. (gr. 2-3). 1999. lib. bdg. 21.26 (978-0-7368-0180-5(4)); Writing a Resume. (gr. 3-4). 1999. lib. bdg. 21.26 (978-0-7368-0181-2(2)); 32p. (J). (Illus.). Set lib. bdg. 170.08 (978-0-7368-0305-2(X) , LifeMatters Bks.) Capstone Pr., Inc.

—Networking to Find a Job. 1999. (Looking at Work Ser.). (Illus.). 32p. (J). (gr. 2-3). lib. bdg. 21.26 (978-0-7368-0180-5(4) , LifeMatters Bks.) Capstone Pr., Inc.

Scraper, Katherine. Kids Can Have Jobs. 2006. (Early Explorers Ser.). (J). 30.00 (***978-1-4108-6034-7(5)**) Benchmark Education Co.

Shepard, Daniel. Trabajando. 2005. Tr. of Working. (SPA., Illus.). 16p. (J). (gr. 1 up). lib. bdg. 15.93 (978-0-7368-4181-8(4)) Capstone Pr., Inc.

Silate, Jennifer. Your Mayor: Local Government in Action. 2003. (Primary Source Library of American Citizenship). (Illus.). 32p. (J). pap. (978-1-4042-5095-6(6)) Rosen Publishing Group, Inc., The.

Simon, Charnan. Dentist. 2003. (Wonder Books Level 3: Careers Ser.). (Illus.). 32p. (J). (ps-2). 22.79 (978-1-56766-463-8(6)) Child's World, Inc.

—Plumbers. 2003. (Wonder Books Level 3: Careers Ser.). (Illus.). 32p. (J). (ps-2). 22.79 (978-1-56766-471-3(7)) Child's World, Inc.

—Police Officers. 2003. (Wonder Books Level 3: Careers Ser.). (Illus.). 32p. (J). (ps-2). 22.79 (978-1-56766-476-8(8)) Child's World, Inc.

—Veterinarians. 2003. (Wonder Books Level 3: Careers Ser.). (Illus.). 32p. (J). (ps-2). 22.79 (978-1-56766-492-8(X)) Child's World, Inc.

Smith, Carrie. Jobs at School. 2006. (Early Explorers Ser.). (J). 30.00 (***978-1-4108-6032-3(9)**) Benchmark Education Co.

Snow, Panky. Radio Announcers. 2001. (Community Helpers Ser.). (Illus.). 24p. (J). (gr. 1-2). lib. bdg. 18.60 (978-0-7368-0958-0(9) , Bridgestone Bks.) Capstone Pr., Inc.

Sotnak, Lewann. Director. 1999. (Career Exploration Ser.). (Illus.). 48p. (J). (gr. 3-4). lib. bdg. 21.26 (978-0-7368-0327-4(0) , LifeMatters Bks.) Capstone Pr., Inc.

—Director. 1999. (Illus.). (YA). (gr. 5-12). pap. 19.93 (978-0-516-21886-1(7) , Children's Pr.) Scholastic Library Publishing.

Stickland, Paul. People. Stickland, Paul, illus. 1998. (Working Ser.). (Illus.). 16p. (J). (ps up). lib. bdg. 19.93 (978-0-8368-2157-4(2)) Stevens, Gareth Inc.

—Places. Stickland, Paul, illus. 1998. (Working Ser.). (Illus.). 16p. (J). (ps up). lib. bdg. 19.93 (978-0-8368-2158-1(0)) Stevens, Gareth Inc.

Students' Occupational Outlook Handbook: SOOH. 3rd rev. ed. 2000. (YA). pap. (978-1-887481-26-7(5) , SK00) CFKR Career Materials, Inc.

Sweeney, Alyse. Community Helpers, 6 bks., Set. Incl. Let's Visit a Dairy Farm. 2007. 19.00 (978-0-531-16843-1(3) , Watts, Franklin); Pets at the Vet. 2007. 19.00 (978-0-531-16811-0(5) , Watts, Franklin); Police Officers on the Go! 2006. 19.00 (978-0-531-16810-3(7)); 24p. (J). (gr. k-2). (Scholastic News Nonfiction Readers Ser.). (Illus.). 2006. 114.00 (***978-0-531-12474-1(6)** , Children's Pr.) Scholastic Library Publishing.

Sweeney, Alyse. Who Works at the Zoo? 2007. (Scholastic News Nonfiction Readers Ser.). (Illus.). 24p. (J). (gr. k-2). 19.00 (978-0-531-16842-4(5) , Watts, Franklin) Scholastic Library Publishing.

That's Working Together. 2002. (J). pap. (978-0-7398-5933-9(1)) Steck-Vaughn.

Thomas, Mark. Day with a Bricklayer. 2001. (gr. k-3). lib. bdg. 12.95 (978-0-613-58757-0(X)) Tandem Library Bks.

—Day with a Plumber. 2001. (gr. k-3). lib. bdg. 12.95 (978-0-613-58763-1(4)) Tandem Library Bks.

—A Day with an Electrician. 2001. (Welcome Bks.). (Illus.). 24p. (J). (ps-2). pap. 4.95 (978-0-516-23065-8(4) , Children's Pr.) Scholastic Library Publishing.

—Day with an Electrician. 2001. (gr. k-3). lib. bdg. 12.95 (978-0-613-58765-5(0)) Tandem Library Bks.

Thompson, Cheri Brown. I Can Be. Sharperson, Donald, illus. 2002. 32p. (YA). (gr. k-12). 9.95 (978-0-9716164-0-0(X)) Healing Species, The.

Thomson Gale Staff. Information Plus: Careers & Occupations November 2006. 2006. 45.00 (978-1-4144-0408-0(5)) Thomson Gale.

True Success in a Career: The High School Student's Guide To Discovering Career Satisfaction. 2000. (True Success Book). 110p. (J). pap. 22.95 (978-1-893320-24-6(3)) True Colors, Inc. Publishing.

Trumbauer, Lisa. Everyone Is a Scientist. 2000. (Yellow Umbrella Books). (Illus.). 16p. (J). (gr. 1). lib. bdg. 14.60 (978-0-7368-0722-7(5) , Pebble Bks.) Capstone Pr., Inc.

—Lo Que Hacen Los Carteros: What Mail Carriers Do. 2007. (What Does a Community Helper Do? Bilingual Ser.). (ENG & SPA., Illus.). 32p. (J). lib. bdg. 22.60 (978-0-7660-2827-2(5) , Enslow Elementary) Enslow Pubs., Inc.

—We Need Child Care Workers. Saunders-Smith, Gail, ed. 2003. (Helpers in Our Community Ser.). (Illus.). 24p. (J). (gr. k-1). lib. bdg. 15.93 (978-0-7368-1648-9(8) , Pebble Bks.) Capstone Pr., Inc.

—We Need Zoo Keepers. Saunders-Smith, Gail, ed. 2003. (Helpers in Our Community Ser.). (Illus.). 24p. (J). (gr. k-1). lib. bdg. 15.93 (978-0-7368-1651-9(8) , Pebble Bks.) Capstone Pr., Inc.

VanVoorst, Jennifer. Working. 2003. (Yellow Umbrella Books for Early Readers). (Illus.). 17p. (J). 15.93 (978-0-7368-2910-6(5)); pap. (978-0-7368-2869-7(9)) Yellow Umbrella Pr.

Vastola, Pam. What I Think: Learning the TH Sound. (PowerPhonics Ser.). (Illus.). (J). 2002. 24p. (gr. 1). lib. bdg. 18.50 (978-0-8239-5930-3(9)); 2001. 23p. pap. 26.40 (978-0-8239-8275-2(0)) Rosen Publishing Group, Inc., The. (PowerKids Pr.).

Vogel, Elizabeth. Meet My Teacher. 2002. (PowerKids Readers Ser.). (Illus.). 24p. (J). (gr. 1). lib. bdg. 16.00 (978-0-8239-6032-3(3) , PowerKids Pr.) Rosen Publishing Group, Inc., The.

—Meet the Cafeteria Workers. 2002. (PowerKids Readers Ser.). (Illus.). 24p. (J). (gr. 1). lib. bdg. 16.00 (978-0-8239-6035-4(8) , PowerKids Pr.) Rosen Publishing Group, Inc., The.

—Meet the Librarian. 2002. (PowerKids Readers Ser.). (Illus.). 24p. (J). (gr. 1). lib. bdg. 16.00 (978-0-8239-6031-6(5) , PowerKids Pr.) Rosen Publishing Group, Inc., The.

—Meet the Principal. 2002. (PowerKids Readers Ser.). (Illus.). 24p. (J). (gr. 1). lib. bdg. 16.00 (978-0-8239-6033-0(1) , PowerKids Pr.) Rosen Publishing Group, Inc., The.

—Meet the School Nurse. 2002. (PowerKids Readers Ser.). (Illus.). 24p. (J). (gr. 1). lib. bdg. 16.00 (978-0-8239-6034-7(X) , PowerKids Pr.) Rosen Publishing Group, Inc., The.

—Meet the School Secretary. 2002. (PowerKids Readers Ser.). (Illus.). 24p. (J). (gr. 1). lib. bdg. 16.00 (978-0-8239-6036-1(6) , PowerKids Pr.) Rosen Publishing Group, Inc., The.

Weedn, Flavia M. & Weedn, Lisa. When I Grow Up. Weedn, Flavia M., illus. 2000. (Illus.). 26p. (J). (ps-k). pap. 7.95 (978-0-7683-2156-2(5)) CEDCO Publishing.

Weintraub, Aileen. Life Inside the Coast Guard Academy. 2002. (Insider's Look Ser.). (Illus.). 48p. (J). (gr. 7-12). pap. 23.00 (978-0-516-23925-5(2) , Children's Pr.) Scholastic Library Publishing.

—Life Inside the Military Academy. 2002. (gr. 7-12). lib. bdg. 15.25 (978-0-613-55863-1(4)) Tandem Library Bks.

—Stunt Double. 2003. (High Interest Bks.). (Illus.). 48p. (J). 24.00 (978-0-516-24338-2(1)); (YA). (gr. 7-12). pap. 6.95 (978-0-516-27867-4(3)) Scholastic Library Publishing. (Children's Pr.).

—Stunt Double. 2003. (gr. 7-12). lib. bdg. 15.25 (978-0-613-67936-7(9)) Tandem Library Bks.

Weiss, Ellen. Odd Jobs: The Wackiest Jobs You've Never Heard Of. 2000. (978-0-606-17931-7(3)) Tandem Library Bks.

Wheeler, Jill C. Firefighters. 2003. (Everyday Heroes (cb) Ser.). (Illus.). 32p. (J). (gr. k-6). lib. bdg. 22.78 (978-1-57765-855-9(8)) ABDO Publishing Co.

When I Grow Up. 2001. (Learning Adventures Grade 1 Ser.). (Illus.). (J). (ps-3). pap. 2.25 (978-1-55254-238-5(6)) Brighter Vision Pubns.

When I Grow Up. 2003. (J). per. (978-1-884907-75-3(X)); per. (978-1-884907-56-2(3)) Paradise Pr., Inc.

Whitehouse, Patricia. Working in Space. 2004. (J). 24.21 (978-1-4034-5158-3(3)); pap. 6.95 (978-1-4034-5662-5(3)) Heinemann Library.

Wilcox, Charlotte. Work & Occupations in Colonial America. 2004. (Everyday Life Long Ago Ser.). (J). (978-0-7368-2165-0(1) , Blue Earth Bks.) Capstone Pr., Inc.

Willett, Edward. Careers in Outer Space: New Business Opportunities. 2005. (Career Resource Library). (Illus.). 192p. (YA). (gr. 7-12). lib. bdg. 26.50 (978-0-8239-3358-7(X)) Rosen Publishing Group, Inc., The.

Williams, Jack S. & Davis, Thomas L. Sailors, Merchants, & Muleteers. 2004. (People of the California Missions Ser.). (Illus.). 64p. (J). lib. bdg. 25.50 (978-0-8239-6282-2(2)) Rosen Publishing Group, Inc., The.

Williams, Judith. Exploring the Rain Forest Treetops with a Scientist. 2004. (I Like Science! Ser.). (Illus.). 24p. (J). lib. bdg. 21.26 (978-0-7660-2294-2(3)) Enslow Pubs., Inc.

—Saving Endangered Animals with a Scientist. 2004. (I Like Science! Ser.). (Illus.). 24p. (J). (gr. 2-4). lib. bdg. 21.26 (978-0-7660-2276-8(5)) Enslow Pubs., Inc.

Willis, Tammy A., ed. Community Helpers Puppet Set, Series 1. 2006. (J). per. (978-1-57332-400-7(0)) High-Reach Learning, Inc.

Winne, Joanne. Hard Work, 12 bks., Set. 2004. (Illus.). 24p. (J). (ps-2). 174.00 (978-0-516-23227-0(4) , Children's Pr.) Scholastic Library Publishing.

Wohlrabe, Sarah. Helping You Heal: A Book about Nurses. Thomas, Eric, illus. 2004. (Community Workers Ser.). 24p. (C). (gr. k-3). 22.60 (978-1-4048-0086-1(7)) Picture Window Bks.

—Helping You Learn: A Book about Teachers. Thomas, Eric, illus. 2004. (Community Workers Ser.). 24p. (C). (gr. k-3). 22.60 (978-1-4048-0084-7(0)) Picture Window Bks.

World of Work: A Path to an Exciting Career, 8 bks. Incl. Choosing a Career as a Model. Tobey, Cheryl. (YA). lib. bdg. 25.25 (978-0-8239-3243-6(5)); Choosing a Career as a Nurse-Midwife. Fields, Jennifer. (YA). lib. bdg. 25.25 (978-0-8239-3293-1(1)); Choosing a Career as an Entrepreneur. MacGregor, Lucy. (J). lib. bdg. 25.25 (978-0-8239-3329-7(6)); Choosing a Career in Agriculture. Olesky, Walter. (YA). lib. bdg. 25.25 (978-0-8239-3332-7(6)); Choosing a Career in Real Estate. Clark, Betty. (YA). lib. bdg. 25.25 (978-0-8239-3246-7(X) , WWREES); Choosing a Career in Teaching. Calhoun, Florence. (YA). lib. bdg. 25.25 (978-0-8239-3247-4(8)); Choosing a Career in the Fishing Industry. Winters, Adam. (YA). lib. bdg. 25.25 (978-0-8239-3330-3(X)); Choosing a Career in the Post Office. Chui, David. (YA). lib. bdg. 25.25 (978-0-8239-3242-9(7)); 64p. (gr. 7-12). 2005. (Illus.). 2001. Set lib. bdg. 191.60 (978-0-8239-9207-2(1)) Rosen Publishing Group, Inc., The.

Yanuchi, Lori & Yanuchi, Jeff. Ranger Trails: Jobs of Adventure in America's Parks. Morris, James R., illus. 2005. 64p. (J). per. 12.95 (978-0-9670177-2-3(6)) Ridge Rock Pr.

Yanuck, Debbie L. Carpenters. 2002. (Community Helpers Ser.). (Illus.). 24p. (J). (gr. 1-2). lib. bdg. 18.60 (978-0-7368-1126-2(5) , Bridgestone Bks.) Capstone Pr., Inc.

—Custodians. 2002. (Community Helpers Ser.). (Illus.). 24p. (J). (gr. 1-2). lib. bdg. 18.60 (978-0-7368-1127-9(3) , Bridgestone Bks.) Capstone Pr., Inc.

Yates, Vicki. Life at Work. 2007. (J). ***978-1-4034-9834-2(2));** pap. ***978-1-4034-9842-7(3))** Heinemann Library.

You Wouldn't Want To..., 4 bks. 2004. (YA). 104.00 (978-0-531-12426-0(6)) Scholastic Library Publishing.

Zoo Keepers. (Community Helpers Ser.). 24p. (J). 6.95 (978-0-7368-8033-6(X)) Capstone Pr., Inc.

Zoo Keepers, 6 vols. (gr. 2-5). 36.95 (978-0-7368-8052-7(6)) Red Brick Learning.

8-deck Careers for Kids Box Set. (Careers for Kids(R) Ser.). 7.00 (978-1-57281-409-7(8) , CFKS8) U. S. Games Systems, Inc.

OCCUPATIONS—FICTION

Blance, Ellen & Cook. Monster Gets a Job. Date not set. (Illus.). 40p. pap. 129.15 (978-0-582-19307-9(9)) Addison-Wesley Longman, Ltd. GBR. *Dist:* Trans-Atlantic Pubns., Inc.

Brooks, Walter R. Freddy & Mr. Camphor. Wiese, Kurt, illus. 2000. 234p. (J). (gr. 3-7). 23.95 (978-1-58567-027-7(8)) Overlook Pr., The.

Burton, Yvette M. A Twinkle in His Eye. Burton, Yvette M., illus. l.t. ed. 2000. (Illus.). 28p. (J). 10.00 (978-0-615-11477-4(6)) Shooting Star Publishing.

Calmenson, Stephanie, et al, illus. What's My Job? 2000. (Hello Reader! Ser.). (J). pap. (978-0-439-20473-6(9)) Scholastic, Inc.

Catalanotto, Peter. Kitten Red, Yellow, Blue. Catalanotto, Peter, illus. 2005. (Illus.). 32p. (J). 15.95 (978-0-689-86562-6(7) , Atheneum/Richard Jackson Bks.) Simon & Schuster Children's Publishing.

Cocca-Leffler, Maryann. Mr. Tanen's Ties Rule! Cocca-Leffler, Maryann, illus. 2005. (Illus.). 32p. (J). (gr. k-3). 15.95 (978-0-8075-5308-4(5)) Whitman, Albert & Co.

Cohn, Diana & Delgado, Francisco. Si, Se Puede! . 2005. Tr. of Yes, We Can!. (SPA.). 32p. pap. 7.95 (978-0-938317-89-0(X)) Cinco Puntos Pr.

Cordsen, Carol Foskett. The Milkman. Jones, Douglas B., illus. 2005. 32p. (J). (ps). 15.99 (978-0-525-47208-7(8) , Dutton Juvenile) Penguin Group (USA) Inc.

Cunliffe, John. Postman Pat & the Beast of Greendale, Bk. 12. (Illus.). 32p. (J). (978-0-340-67816-9(X) , Hodder & Stoughton) Hodder General Publishing Division.

—Postman Pat Has Too Many Parcels. (Illus.). 32p. (J). (978-0-340-67812-1(7) , Hodder & Stoughton) Hodder General Publishing Division.

Ferguson, Sally. What Will I Be When I Grow Up? 2005. (J). pap. 1.69 (978-1-59317-118-6(8)) Warner Pr. Pubs.

Fox, Diane, et al. Goodnight PiggyWiggy: A Pull-the-Page Book. Fox, Christyan, illus. 2000. 24p. (J). (ps-k). 12.95 (978-1-929766-06-2(8)) Handprint Bks.

Freeman, Don. Corduroy's Busy Street. 2005. 14p. (J). (ps-ps). pap. 5.99 (978-0-670-05994-2(3) , Viking Juvenile) Penguin Group (USA) Inc.

Friedman, Laurie B. Honestly, Mallory! Pollak, Barbara, illus. 2007. (Mallory Ser.). 160p. (J). (gr. 2-6). 15.95 **(*978-0-8225-6193-4(X)** , Carolrhoda Bks.) Lerner Publishing Group.

Guggenheim, Jaenet. Next Week When I'm Big. Verelst, Suana, illus. l.t. ed. 2005. 32p. (J). 19.95i (978-1-929115-13-6(X)) Azro Pr., Inc.

Hallinan, P. K. When I Grow Up. 24p. (J). 7.95 (978-0-8249-5392-8(4) , Ideals); 2001. (Illus.). 5.95 (978-0-8249-5393-5(2)) Ideals Pubns.

—When I Grow Up. Hallinan, P. K., illus. 2006. (Illus.). 26p. (J). (ps). bds. 7.95 (978-0-8249-6677-5(5) , Candy Cane Pr.) Ideals Pubns.

Handy, Libby & Newnham, Jack. Boss for a Week.Tr. of C'Est Moi Qui Mene. (FRE., Illus.). (J). 13.99 incl. audio (978-0-590-73908-5(5)) Scholastic, Inc.

Harcourt School Publishers Staff. Eight More Years Below Level. 3rd ed. 2002. (Trophies Reading Program Ser.). (Illus.). pap. 5.10 (978-0-15-323062-2(2)) Harcourt Schl. Pubs.

—In Eight More Years: Take-Home Book. 1999. (Collections Ser.). (Illus.). (J). pap. 1.90 (978-0-15-317242-7(8)) Harcourt Schl. Pubs.

—Trofeos Below Level: En el Parque. 3rd ed. 2002. (SPA., Illus.). (J). pap. 3.50 (978-0-15-323863-5(1)) Harcourt Schl. Pubs.

Hargreaves, Roger. Little Miss Chatterbox. 1999. (Mr. Men & Little Miss Ser.). (Illus.). 32p. (J). (gr. k up). pap. 3.99 (978-0-8431-7479-3(X) , Price Stern Sloan) Penguin Group (USA) Inc.

Hartland, Jessie. Night Shift. Hartland, Jessie, illus. 2007. (Illus.). 32p. (J). 17.95 ***978-1-59990-138-1(2));** 16.95 **(*978-1-59990-025-4(4))** Bloomsbury Publishing. (Bloomsbury Children).

Hendry, Diana. Que Ocupado Estoy! Chapman, Jane, illus. 2002. Tr. of Very Busy Day. (SPA.). 124p. (J). 14.95 (978-84-488-1154-9(2)) Lectorum Pubns., Inc.

Hilbrecht, Kirk. My Daddy Is an Airman. 2005. 32p. pap. 6.95 (978-1-889658-38-4(3)) New Canaan Publishing Co. LLC.

—My Mommy Is an Airman. 2005. 32p. pap. 6.95 (978-1-889658-39-1(1)) New Canaan Publishing Co. LLC.

Horn, Peter. When I Grow Up... 1999. (Illus.). (J). (978-0-606-20987-8(5)) Tandem Library Bks.

—When I Grow Up. 2001. (gr. k-3). lib. bdg. 15.25 (978-0-613-33860-8(X)) Tandem Library Bks.

Huneck, Stephen. Sally Gets a Job. 2008. 32p. (J). 16.95 **(*978-0-8109-9493-5(3)** , Abrams Bks. for Young Readers) Abrams, Harry N. , Inc.

Johnson, Angela. Those Building Men. Moser, Barry, illus. 2001. 32p. (J). (ps-3). pap. 16.95 (978-0-590-66521-6(9) , Blue Sky Pr., The) Scholastic, Inc.

Johnson, Michael. The Most Special Person. Latta, Doug, illus. 1999. 24p. (J). (gr. k-6). 12.95 (978-1-893672-00-0(X)) Johnson, Michael Presentations.

Jolin, Dominique. Washington & the Shampoo Job. Jolin, Dominique, illus. 2000. (Tickle Ser.). (Illus.). 16p. (YA). (ps up). bds. (978-1-894363-37-2(X)) Dominique & Friends.

Kimmel, Elizabeth Cody. The Top Job. Neubecker, Robert, illus. 2007. 32p. (J). (gr. 1-4). 16.99 (978-0-525-47789-1(6) , Dutton Juvenile) Penguin Group (USA) Inc.

Kittinger, Jo S. Cuando Sea Grande. Lucas, Margeaux, illus. 2005. (Rookie Reader Espanol Ser.). (SPA & ESP.). 23p. (J). (gr. k-2). pap. 4.95 (978-0-516-24692-5(5) , Children's Pr.) Scholastic Library Publishing.

Kleinhenz, Sydnie Meltzer. Work & Play. Reasor, Mick, illus. 2005. (Rookie Readers Skill Set Ser.). 23p. (J). (gr. k-2). pap. 4.95 (978-0-516-25282-7(8) , Children's Pr.) Scholastic Library Publishing.

Krensky, Stephen. How Santa Got His Job. Schindler, S. D., illus. 2002. (J). 24.04 (978-0-7587-2770-1(4)) Book Wholesalers, Inc.

—How Santa Got His Job. Schindler, S. D., illus. 2002. 32p. (J). pap. 6.99 (978-0-689-84668-7(1) , Aladdin) Simon & Schuster Children's Publishing.

—How Santa Got His Job. 2002. (gr. k-3). lib. bdg. 15.30 (978-0-613-90196-3(7)) Tandem Library Bks.

Kupchella, Rick. Girls Can! Make it Happen. Brown, Marilyn, illus. 2004. 40p. (J). 16.95 (978-0-9726504-3-4(1)) Tristan Publishing, Inc.

Lee, Jeanie. When I Grow Up! Valerio, Geraldo, illus. 2007. (Flips & Flaps Book Ser.). 12p. (J). 9.99 (978-1-4169-0933-0(8) , Little Simon) Simon & Schuster Children's Publishing.

Leonard, Marcia. Guess Who? 2000. (Hanna Bks.). (Illus.). 18p. (J). (ps up). 7.95 (978-0-694-01374-6(9) , Harper Festival) HarperCollins Pubs.

Liberto, Lorenzo. Matt the Rat & His Sister Maggie (Raton Mateo y Su Hermana Maggie) When I Grow Up (Cuando Yo Crezca) Gomez, Rocio, ed. Torres, Irving, illus. 2003. (Matt the Rat Ser. / La Serie de Raton Mateo). (SPA & ENG.). 40p. (J). lib. bdg. 20.00 (978-0-9743668-1-4(1)) Harvest Sun Pr., LLC.

Louise, Tina. When I Grow Up. Corwin, Oliver J., illus. 2007. 32p. (J). (ps-3). 15.95 (978-0-8109-3948-6(7) , Abrams Bks. for Young Readers) Abrams, Harry N. , Inc.

MacKinnon, Debbie. What Am I? Sieveking, Anthea, photos by. 1999. (Right Start Ser.). (Illus.). 24p. (J). (ps). pap. 7.99 (978-0-7112-1276-3(7)) Lincoln, Frances Ltd. GBR. *Dist:* Transition Vendor.

MacLean, Christine Kole. Even Firefighters Hug Their Moms. Reed, Mike, illus. 2002. 32p. (J). 16.99 (978-0-525-46996-4(6) , Dutton Juvenile) Penguin Group (USA) Inc.

Marsh, Carole. The Adventure Diaries of Brad, the U. S. Air Force Pilot!, 9 vols. 48p. (J). 2003. (gr. 1-4). pap. 5.95 (978-0-635-01149-7(2)); 2002. (Illus.). lib. bdg. 9.95 (978-0-635-01278-4(2)) Gallopade International.

—The Adventure Diaries of Dharma, the Dedicated Doctor! l.t. ed. 2002. (Illus.). 48p. (J). lib. bdg. 9.95 (978-0-635-01272-2(3)) Gallopade International.

—The Adventure Diaries of Felipe, the Fearless Firefighter!, 12 vols. 48p. 2003. (J). (gr. 1-4). pap. 5.95 (978-0-635-01096-4(8)); 2002. (Illus.). lib. bdg. 9.95 (978-0-635-01270-8(7)) Gallopade International.

—The Adventure Diaries of Hannah, the Humanitarian Aid Worker!, 6 vols. 48p. (J). 2003. (gr. 1-4). pap. 5.95 (978-0-635-01153-4(0)); 2002. (Illus.). lib. bdg. (978-0-635-01275-3(8)) Gallopade International.

—The Adventure Diaries of Haz Matt, the Hazardous Materials Worker!, 11 vols. 48p. (J). 2003. (gr. 1-4). pap. 5.95 (978-0-635-01152-7(2)); 2002. (Illus.). lib. bdg. 9.95 (978-0-635-01280-7(4)) Gallopade International.

—The Adventure Diaries of Jack, the U. S. Army Special Forces Solider!, 4 vols. 2003. 48p. (J). (gr. 1-4). pap. 5.95 (978-0-635-01147-3(6)) Gallopade International.

—The Adventure Diaries of Li, the Excellent EMT!, 7 vols. 48p. (J). 2004. (gr. 1-4). pap. 5.95 (978-0-635-01145-9(X)); 2002. (Illus.). lib. bdg. 9.95 (978-0-635-01276-0(6)) Gallopade International.

—The Adventure Diaries of Mike, the U. S. Marine!, 5 vols. 48p. (J). 2003. (gr. 1-4). pap. 5.95 (978-0-635-01150-3(6)); 2002. (Illus.). lib. bdg. 9.95 (978-0-635-01274-6(X)) Gallopade International.

—The Adventure Diaries of P. J., the Photo-Journalist!, 10 vols. 48p. (J). 2003. (gr. 1-4). pap. 5.95 (978-0-635-01154-1(9)); 2002. (Illus.). lib. bdg. 9.95 (978-0-635-01279-1(0)) Gallopade International.

—The Adventure Diaries of the Perils of Pauline, the Police Officer! l.t. ed. 2002. (Illus.). 48p. (J). lib. bdg. 9.95 (978-0-635-01271-5(5)) Gallopade International.

—The Adventure Diaries of Vicki, the Volunteer!, 12 vols. 48p. (J). 2003. (gr. 1-4). pap. 5.95 (978-0-635-01158-9(1)); 2002. (Illus.). lib. bdg. 9.95 (978-0-635-01281-4(2)) Gallopade International.

Martin, Ann M. Karen's Paper Route. 1998. (Baby-Sitters Little Sister Ser.: No. 97). (J). (gr. 3-7). (978-0-606-13173-5(6)) Tandem Library Bks.

Marzollo, Jean. Shanna's Doctor Show. 2003. (Illus.). 24p. (ps-2). pap. 3.50 (978-0-7868-1760-3(7)) Hyperion Bks. for Children.

Mayer, Mercer. When I Grow Up. 2003. (Illus.). 24p. (J). (ps-2). pap. 3.25 (978-0-375-82632-0(7) , Random Hse. Bks. for Young Readers) Random Hse. Children's Bks.

—When I Grow Up. 2003. (ps-2). lib. bdg. 10.95 (978-0-613-82737-9(6)) Tandem Library Bks.

McMullan, Kate. I'm Dirty! McMullan, Jim, illus. 2006. 40p. (J). 16.99 (978-0-06-009293-1(9) , Cotler, Joanna Books) HarperCollins Pubs.

McNamara, Margaret. Dad Goes to School. Gordon, Mike, illus. 2007. (Robin Hill School Ser.). 32p. (J). lib. bdg. 13.89 (978-1-4169-1542-3(7) , Aladdin Library) Simon & Schuster Children's Publishing.

McNamara, Margaret & Gordon, Mike. Dad Goes to School. 2007. (Robin Hill School Ser.). 32p. (J). pap. 3.99 (978-1-4169-1541-6(9) , Aladdin) Simon & Schuster Children's Publishing.

McNaughton, Colin. When I Grow Up. McNaughton, Colin, illus. 2005. (Illus.). 40p. (J). (ps-1). 12.99 (978-0-7636-2675-4(9)) Candlewick Pr.

Meltzer Kleinhenz, Sydnie. Work & Play. Reasor, Mick, illus. 2005. (Rookie Reader Ser.). 24p. (J). (gr. k-1). 17.00 (978-0-516-24433-4(7) , Children's Pr.) Scholastic Library Publishing.

Moncure, Jane Belk. Word Bird's Hats. 2002. (New Word Bird Library). (Illus.). 32p. (J). (ps-3). 22.79 (978-1-56766-997-8(2)) Child's World, Inc.

Morris, Bridgette. I Wish I Was All Grown-up. 2004. 20p. pap. 8.99 (978-1-4116-1719-3(3)) Lulu.com.

Nikola-Lisa, W. My Teacher Can Teach—Anyone! Galindo, Felipe, illus. 2004. 32p. (J). (ps-2). 16.95 (978-1-58430-163-9(5)) Lee & Low Bks., Inc.

No Pay, No Way. 2002. (Illus.). (J). pap. (978-0-7398-5065-7(2)) Steck-Vaughn.

Nuttle, Jim, illus. If I Were... A Book of Make-Believe. Shorten, Chris, photos by. 1999. (J). reprint ed. 5.95 (978-1-892374-24-0(2)) Weldon Owen, Inc.

O'Book, Irene. Maybe My Baby. Hible, Paula, illus. 1998. (Growing Tree Ser.). 14p. (J). (ps up). 6.99 (978-0-694-00872-8(9) , Harper Festival) HarperCollins Pubs.

O'Neill, Cynthia, ed. Mujer Profesional. 2004. (SPA.). 48p. (J). pap. 6.99 (978-0-7566-0448-6(6)) Dorling Kindersley Publishing, Inc.

Park, Barbara. Junie B. Jones Is a Beauty Shop Guy. Brunkus, Denise & Silverpin Studio Staff, illus. 1998. (Junie B. Jones Ser.: No. 11). 80p. (J). (gr. k-3). lib. bdg. 11.99 (978-0-679-98931-8(5) , Random Hse. Bks. for Young Readers) Random Hse. Children's Bks.

—Junie B. Jones Is a Beauty Shop Guy. Brunkus, Denise, illus. 1998. (Junie B. Jones Ser.: No. 11). 80p. (J). (gr. 1-4). pap. 3.99 (978-0-679-88931-1(0) , Random Hse. Bks. for Young Readers) Random Hse. Children's Bks.

—Junie B. Jones Is a Beauty Shop Guy. Brunkus, Denise, illus. 1998. (Junie B. Jones Ser.: No. 11). (J). (gr. k-3). 10.79 (978-0-606-13963-2(X)) Tandem Library Bks.

—Junie B. Jones y su Gran Bocota. Brunkus, Denise, illus. 2005. (Junie B. Jones Ser.).Tr. of Junie B. Jones Big Fat Mouth. (SPA.). 80p. (J). pap. 3.99 (978-0-439-42516-2(6) , Scholastic en Espanol) Scholastic, Inc.

Parker, Marjorie. Your Kind of Mommy. Moore, Cyd, illus. 2007. 32p. (J). (ps). 12.99 (978-0-525-46989-6(3) , Dutton Juvenile) Penguin Group (USA) Inc.

Paulsen, Gary. Worksong. Paulsen, Ruth Wright, illus. 2000. 32p. (J). (ps-3). pap. 7.00 (978-0-15-202371-3(2) , Harcourt Paperbacks) Harcourt Children's Bks.

—Worksong. 2000. (978-0-606-18199-0(7)); lib. bdg. 15.30 (978-0-613-28707-4(X)) Tandem Library Bks.

Pearson, Mary E. I Can Do It All. Shelly, Jeff, illus. 2002. (Rookie Reader Espanol Ser.). 32p. (J). (gr. k-2). pap. 4.95 (978-0-516-27383-9(3) , Children's Pr.) Scholastic Library Publishing.

—I Can Do It All. 2002. (gr. k-3). lib. bdg. 12.95 (978-0-613-53821-3(8)) Tandem Library Bks.

Pedersen, Marika. Mommy Works, Daddy Works. 2000. (J). (978-0-606-20140-7(8)) Tandem Library Bks.

Pinkston, Ronald. A Police Officer That's What I'll Be! Rivera, Israel, illus. 1999. 26p. (J). (gr. k-2). 12.99 (978-0-9671708-0-0(X)) Pinkston Publishing.

Poirier, Mark Jude. Unsung Heroes of American Industry. 2002. (Illus.). 144p. 22.00 (978-0-7868-6827-8(9)) Talk Miramax Bks.

Rey, H. A. Curious George Takes a Job. Rey, Margret, illus. 2007. 48p. (J). (ps-k). pap. 9.95 incl. audio compact disk **(*978-0-618-72406-2(0))** Houghton Mifflin Co. Trade & Reference Div.

Richburg, Shirley. Benny & the Grocer. Richburg, Shirley, illus. 1998. (Illus.). (Orig.). (J). (gr. 2-5). pap. 4.95 (978-0-9658432-2-5(X)) People's Pr., The.

Rockwell, Anne F. Career Day. Rockwell, Lizzy, illus. 2000. 40p. (J). (ps-k). lib. bdg. 17.89 (978-0-06-027566-2(9)); 15.99 (978-0-06-027565-5(0)) HarperCollins Pubs.

Sassy Wants to Be a Star Bk. 5: "The Audition" l.t. ed. 1999. (Illus.). 30p. (J). (ps-5). 6.00 (978-1-893727-02-1(5)) Mustafa, Malik.

Schmauss, Judy Kentor. The People on My Street. 2006. (Reader's Clubhouse Set B Ser.). (Illus.). 24p. (J). pap. 3.99 (978-0-7641-3294-0(6)) Barron's Educational Series, Inc.

Shulman, Mark. Jazzy Jobs. Harris, Jenny, illus. 2003. (Funny Fingers Ser.). 14p. (J). bds. 3.95 (978-1-4027-0705-6(3)) Sterling Publishing Co., Inc.

Sommer, Carl. Your Job Is Easy. 2003. (Another Sommer-Time Story Ser.). (Illus.). 48p. (J). (gr. 1-4). 16.95 incl. audio compact disk (978-1-57537-517-5(6)); 16.95 incl. audio (978-1-57537-566-3(4)) Advance Publishing, Inc.

—Your Job Is Easy. James, Kennon, illus. 2000. (Another Sommer-Time Story Ser.). 48p. (J). (gr. 2-4). lib. bdg. 16.95 (978-1-57537-067-5(0)); (ps-4). 9.95 (978-1-57537-018-7(2)) Advance Publishing, Inc.

Standish, Burt L. Frank Merriwell's First Job. Rudman, Jack, ed. 2003. (Frank Merriwell Ser.). 29.95 (978-0-8373-9330-8(2)); (YA). (gr. 9 up). pap. 9.95 (978-0-8373-9030-7(3)) Merriwell, Frank Inc.

Tong, Kevin. The Earth Machine. Tong, Kevin, illus. 2007. (Illus.). 32p. (J). 15.95 (978-1-60108-001-1(8)) Red Cygnet Pr.

Wang, Margaret C. When I Grow Up: A Touch & Feel Book. Gevry, Claudine, illus. 2005. 12p. (J). bds. 10.95 (978-1-58117-423-6(3) , Intervisual/Piggy Toes) Dalmatian Pr.

Wegman, William. My Town. Wegman, William, photos by. 1998. (Illus.). 40p. (ps-1). 16.95 (978-0-7868-0410-8(6)) Hyperion Bks. for Children.

Wells, Rosemary. When I Grow Up. Wheeler, Jody, illus. 2003. (Yoko & Friends School Days Ser.: Bk. 12). 32p. (gr. k-2). 9.99 (978-0-7868-0731-4(8) , Volo) Hyperion Bks. for Children.

What Do You Want to Be? 2002. lib. bdg. (978-1-58970-175-5(5)) Lakeshore Learning Materials.

Willis, Jeanne & Rees, Mary. What Do You Want to Be, Brian? 1998. (Illus.). 32p. (J). pap. 9.99 (978-0-86264-809-1(2)) Andersen GBR. *Dist:* Trafalgar Square Publishing.

Wilson-Max, Ken. Firefighter. 2005. (Illus.). 10p. (J). (ps-3). 8.95 (978-0-8109-5776-3(0) , Abrams Bks. for Young Readers) Abrams, Harry N. , Inc.

Zierfert, Harriet. The Biggest Job of All. Brown, Lauren, illus. 2005. 40p. (J). 15.95 (978-1-59354-100-2(7)) Blue Apple Bks.

OCEAN

see also Icebergs; Oceanography; Seashore; Storms; Tides

The Antarctic Ocean. (Oceans Ser.). 24p. (J). 6.95 (978-0-7368-3417-9(6)) Capstone Pr., Inc.

The Arctic Ocean. (Oceans Ser.). 24p. (J). 6.95 (978-0-7368-3418-6(4)) Capstone Pr., Inc.

The Atlantic Ocean. (Oceans Ser.). 24p. (J). 6.95 (978-0-7368-3419-3(2)) Capstone Pr., Inc.

Aubinais, Marie. Sea Animals. Martin, Jean-Francois, illus. 1998. (Big, Bigger, Biggest Ser.). 32p. (J). 16.95 (978-0-7892-0386-1(3) , Abbeville Kids) Abbeville Pr., Inc.

Baines, Francesca. El Mundo Marino. Sanz, Maria Teresa, tr. 2004. (Discovery Guides Ser.). (SPA., Illus.). 32p. (gr. 2-5). (J). pap. 11.95 (978-1-58728-701-5(3)); 6.95 (978-1-58728-644-5(0)) T&N Children's Publishing. (Two Can Publishing).

—Ocean Worlds. 2004. (Discovery Guides Ser.). (SPA., Illus.). 32p. (J). (gr. 2-5). pap. 6.95 (978-1-58728-215-7(1) , Two Can Publishing) T&N Children's Publishing.

—Ocean Worlds. 2001. (gr. 3-6). lib. bdg. 15.25 (978-0-613-43482-9(X)) Tandem Library Bks.

Baker, Lucy. Los Oceanos. 2004. (Ecologia Ser.). (SPA., Illus.). 32p. (gr. 3-6). 12.95 (978-1-58728-978-1(4) , Two Can Publishing) T&N Children's Publishing.

—Oceans. (Interfact Ser.). (J). 2004. (SPA., Illus.). 48p. (gr. 3-6). pap. 14.95 incl. cd-rom (978-1-58728-459-5(6)); 2002. 14.95 (978-1-58728-694-0(7)); 2002. pap. 7.95 (978-1-58728-770-1(6)); 2000. (Illus.). 48p. (gr. 1-5). 4.95 (978-1-58728-756-5(0)) T&N Children's Publishing. (Two Can Publishing).

Barnes, Julia. 101 Facts about Oceans. 2003. (One Hundred One Facts about Our World Ser.). (Illus.). 32p. (J). (gr. 3 up). lib. bdg. 23.33 (978-0-8368-3709-4(6)) Stevens, Gareth Inc.

Batten, Mary. The Winking, Blinking Sea: All about Bioluminescence. 2000. (Our World Ser.). (Illus.). 32p. (gr. 2-4). lib. bdg. (978-0-7613-1550-6(0) , Millbrook Pr.) Lerner Publishing Group.

Bayrock, Fiona. The Ocean Explorer's Handbook. 2005. (Undersea University Ser.). (Illus.). 48p. (J). pap. (978-0-439-71184-5(3)) Scholastic, Inc.

BBC Discovery Channel Staff. Seas of Life: Ocean World. 2001. (J). (978-0-606-22275-4(8)) Tandem Library Bks.

Bell, Mary. Oceans. 2001. (Water Worlds Ser.). (Illus.). 32p. (J). (gr. 4 up). 28.00 (978-0-7910-6570-9(7) , 010355, Chelsea Hse.) Facts On File, Inc.

Benchmark Education Staff. Ocean Pollution. 2005. 2.00 (*978-1-4108-4678-5(4))* Benchmark Education Co.

Bennett, Paul. Ocean Habitats. 2006. (Exploring Habitats Ser.). (Illus.). 36p. (J). lib. bdg. (978-0-8368-7255-2(X)) Stevens, Gareth Inc.

—Under the Ocean. 1999. (Natural World Ser.). (Illus.). 31p. (J). (gr. 5-9). pap. 5.95 (978-0-7641-0641-5(4)) Barron's Educational Series, Inc.

Berger, Melvin & Berger, Gilda. What Makes an Ocean Wave? Questions & Answers about Oceans. Rice, John, illus. 2001. (Question & Answer Ser.). 48p. (J). (gr. 2-4). pap. 14.95 (978-0-439-09588-4(3)) Scholastic, Inc.

Bevan, Finn. Waters of Life. 1998. (Landscapes of Legend Ser.). (Illus.). 32p. (J). (gr. 4-8). pap. 6.95 (978-0-516-26301-4(3) , Children's Pr.) Scholastic Library Publishing.

Bodden, Valerie. Oceans. 2006. (Illus.). 24p. (J). 16.95 (978-1-58341-464-4(9) , Creative Education) Creative Co., The.

Bozanksy, Mary K., et al. The Ocean: A Science Workbook. Lowe, Dave C. & Manwaring, Kerry, illus. 1998. (Gifted & Talented Ser.). 64p. (J). (ps-1). pap., wbk. ed. 5.95 (978-1-56565-672-7(5) , 06725W) Lowell Hse. Juvenile.

Brannon, Barbara. Discover Ocean Pollution. 2005. 39.00 (*978-1-4108-5140-6(0))* Benchmark Education Co.

Britton, Tamara L. Red Sea. 2003. (Oceans & Seas Ser.). (Illus.). 24p. (J). (gr. k-6). lib. bdg. 21.35 (978-1-57765-990-7(2)) ABDO Publishing Co.

Bruton, Mike. Oceans: South African Edition. 1998. (Cambridge Reading Routes Ser.). (Illus.). 16p. pap. 5.00 (978-0-521-63661-2(2)) Cambridge Univ. Pr.

Bulletpoints Oceans & Rivers. 2005. (Illus.). (J). per. 4.99 (978-1-933581-01-9(8)) Byeway Bks.

Butterfield, Moira. Ocean. 1999. (Where Am I? Ser.). (Illus.). 32p. (J). (gr. 2-6). lib. bdg. 16.95 (978-1-929298-36-5(6)) Chrysalis Education.

Casado, Dami. El Mar. 2005. (SPA., Illus.). 14p. (J). per. 8.99 (978-84-272-7298-9(7)) Molino, Editorial ESP. *Dist:* Santillana USA Publishing Co., Inc.

Caudle, Brad & Caudle, Melissa. Oceans: Includes Cassette. Guerra, Anthony, illus. unabr. ed. 1998. (Rock 'N Learn Ser.). 32p. (J). (gr. 2 up). pap. 12.99 incl. audio compact disk (978-1-878489-75-3(5) , RL975) Rock 'N Learn, Inc.

Cecchini, Marie E. Under the Sea: A Cross-Curricular Unit for Grades 1-3. Mitchell, Judy & Lindeen, Mary, eds. Armbrust, Janet & Skiles, Janet, illus. 2007. 32p. (J). pap. 6.95 (*978-1-57310-529-3(5))* Teaching & Learning Co.

Cefrey, Holly. Oceans. 2003. (Reading Power Ser.). (Illus.). 24p. (J). lib. bdg. 17.25 (978-0-8239-6453-6(1) , PowerKids Pr.) Rosen Publishing Group, Inc., The.

Cerullo, Mary M. Ocean Detectives: Solving the Mysteries of the Sea. 1999. (Turnstone Ocean Explorer Ser.). (Illus.). 64p. (YA). (gr. 5-9). pap. 8.95 (978-0-7398-1237-2(8)) Steck-Vaughn.

Chambers, Catherine & Lapthorn, Nicholas. Oceans & Seas. 2nd ed. 2007. (J). (*978-1-4034-9603-4(X));* pap. (*978-1-4034-9613-3(7))* Heinemann.

Champion, Neil. Seas & Oceans. 2005. (Caring for the Planet Ser.). (Illus.). 48p. (J). (978-1-58340-511-6(9)) Smart Apple Media.

Clarke, Phil. Seas & Oceans Sticker Atlas. 2006. 24p. (J). pap. 8.95 (978-0-7945-1218-7(6) , Usborne) EDC Publishing.

Claybourne, Anna. Deep Oceans. 2007. (J). (*978-1-4329-0108-0(7));* pap. (*978-1-4329-0114-1(1))* Heinemann Library.

Cobb, Allan B. Super Science Projects about Oceans. 2005. (Psyched for Science Ser.). (Illus.). 48p. (YA). (gr. 5-8). lib. bdg. 23.95 (978-0-8239-3174-3(9) , SCOCEA) Rosen Publishing Group, Inc., The.

Dalgleish, Sharon & Turner, Garda. People & the Sea. 2003. (Ocean Facts Ser.). (Illus.). 24p. (J). (gr. 2-4). 23.00 (978-0-7910-7287-5(8) , Chelsea Hse.) Facts On File, Inc.

Daniels, Patricia. Oceans. 1999. (Nature Library). (Illus.). (J). (978-0-7922-7545-9(4)) National Geographic Society.

Davies, Nicola. Oceans & Seas. (Science Kids Ser.). (Illus.). 48p. (J). 2007. pap. 6.95 (*978-0-7534-6165-5(X));* 2004. 9.95 (978-0-7534-5758-0(X)) Houghton Mifflin Co. Trade & Reference Div. (Kingfisher).

Davis, Wendy & Knight, Bertram T. Working at a Marine Institute. 1998. (Working Here Ser.). (Illus.). 32p. (J). (gr. 2-4). 23.50 (978-0-516-21223-4(0) , Children's Pr.) Scholastic Library Publishing.

Day. Oceans & Beaches. 2003. (Biomes Atlas Ser.). (Illus.). 64p. pap. 9.50 (978-1-4109-0013-5(4)) ; (J). pap. 48.30 (978-1-4109-0248-1(X)) Raintree.

Day, Trevor. Exploring the Oceans, 4 vols. 2003. (Illus.). (J). (978-0-19-521967-8(8)) ; (978-0-19-521968-5(6)) ; (978-0-19-521969-2(4)) ; (978-0-19-521970-8(8)) Oxford Univ. Pr., Inc.

—Oceans & Beaches. 2003. (Biomes Atlases Ser.). (Illus.). 64p. (J). lib. bdg. 31.42 (978-0-7398-5512-6(3)) Raintree.

Daynes, Katie. 1001 Cosas Que Buscar en el Mar. 2005. (Titles in Spanish Ser.). 32p. (J). pap. 6.99 (978-0-7460-6391-0(1) , Usborne) EDC Publishing.

Denne, B. First Encyclopedia of Seas & Oceans. 2004. (First Encyclopedias Ser.). (Illus.). 64p. (J). (gr. 3 up). pap. 9.99 (978-0-7945-0111-2(7) , Usborne); lib. bdg. 17.95 (978-1-58086-380-3(9)) EDC Publishing.

Denne, Ben. First Encyclopedia of Seas & Oceans. 2002. (gr. k-3). lib. bdg. 18.75 (978-0-613-75317-3(8)) Tandem Library Bks.

—Little Encyclopedia of Seas & Oceans - Internet Linked. 2005. 64p. (J). 6.95 (978-0-7945-1090-9(6) , Usborne) EDC Publishing.

Desonie, Dana. Oceans. 2007. (Our Fragile Planet Ser.). 232p. (J). (gr. 6-12). 35.00 (*978-0-8160-6216-4(1)* , Chelsea Hse.) Facts On File, Inc.

Dipper, F. D. Misterios de los Oceanos. (Coleccion Misterios De). (SPA., Illus.). 48p. (YA). (gr. 5-8). 19.95 (978-84-348-5691-2(3) , SM6117) SM Ediciones ESP. *Dist:* AIMS International Bks., Inc., Lectorum Pubns., Inc.

Dipper, Frances, contrib. by. Ocean. 2006. (Illus.). 64p. (J). (gr. 8). pap. 7.99 (978-0-7566-2231-2(X)) Dorling Kindersley Publishing, Inc.

DK Publishing. Ocean. 2008. 512p. pap. 24.95 (*978-0-7566-3692-0(2))* Dorling Kindersley Publishing, Inc.

—Water Magic Ocean. 2008. 16p. (J). bds. 7.99 (*978-0-7566-3450-6(4))* Dorling Kindersley Publishing, Inc.

Dodge, Sheila H. Ocean Adventure. Chadbourne, Glenn, illus. 2002. 9p. (J). (ps-3). pap. 7.95 (978-0-9718808-0-1(8)) Patsher Pr.

Dorling Kindersley Publishing Staff. Ocean. 2003. (Dk Picture Stickers Ser.). (Illus.). 16p. (J). pap. 3.99 (978-0-7894-9829-8(4)) Dorling Kindersley Publishing, Inc.

Dorling Kindersley Publishing Staff, ed. Ocean. 2004. (Dk Eyewitness Books Ser.). (Illus.). 72p. (J). 15.99 (978-0-7566-0711-1(6)) Dorling Kindersley Publishing, Inc.

Dorling Kindersley Publishing Staff & Millard, Anne. In the Sea. 2002. (Little Windows Ser.). (Illus.). 16p. (J). 6.99 (978-0-7894-8571-7(0)) Dorling Kindersley Publishing, Inc.

Dudley, William. Endangered Oceans. 1999. (Opposing Viewpoints Ser.). (Illus.). 312p. (J). lib. bdg. 32.45 (978-0-7377-0063-3(7) , Greenhaven Pr., Inc.) Thomson Gale.

Edgecombe, Jane. Secrets of the Sea. Lassen, Christian Riese, illus. 2002. 6p. (J). (gr. 2-6). (978-1-55285-224-8(5)) Whitecap Bks., Ltd.

Edmunds, Tracy. In the Ocean (Full-Color) (Prek-K) 2006. pap. 16.99 (978-1-4206-8145-1(1)) Teacher Created Resources, Inc.

Equipo Staff. Quimica. 1999. (SPA.). 88p. (978-84-494-1283-7(8) , 1380) Oceano Grupo Editoria, S.A.

Fine, John Christopher. Big Stuff in the Ocean. 1998. (Illus.). 32p. (J). (gr. 4-7). 16.95 (978-1-55591-357-1(1)) Fulcrum Publishing.

First Encyclopedia of Seas & Oceans Kid Kit. (Illus.). 64p. (YA). (gr. k up). 16.95 (978-1-58086-438-1(4)); 16.96 (978-1-58086-447-3(3)) EDC Publishing.

Fleurus. Sea. 1999. (ps-3). (978-2-215-06241-7(X)) Editions Fleurus.

Foxxe, Ellen. The Rising Seas: Shorelines under Threat. 2006. (Extreme Environmental Threats Ser.). (Illus.). 64p. (J). lib. bdg. (978-1-4042-0742-4(2)) Rosen Publishing Group, Inc., The.

Frahm, Randy. Oceans: Lifeblood of the Earth. 2001. (Life on Earth Ser.). (Illus.). 32p. (J). lib. bdg. (978-1-58341-021-9(X) , Creative Education) Creative Co., The.

Fredericks, Anthony D. Exploring the Oceans: Science Activities for Kids. Shea, Shawn, illus. 1998. 128p. (gr. 4-7). pap. 16.95 (978-1-55591-379-3(2)) Fulcrum Publishing.

Furlong, Kate A. Southern Ocean. 2003. (Oceans & Seas Ser.). (Illus.). 24p. (J). (gr. k-6). lib. bdg. 21.35 (978-1-57765-991-4(0)) ABDO Publishing Co.

Gabbi & Somaschini. Los Oceanos. (SPA.). 242p. (YA). (gr. 5-8). (978-84-7131-935-7(7)) Editex, Editorial S A ESP. *Dist:* Lectorum Pubns., Inc.

Gaff, Jackie & Dorling Kindersley Publishing Staff. Aquaman's Guide to the Ocean. 2004. (Dk Readers Ser.). (Illus.). 48p. (J). 12.99 (978-0-7566-0229-1(7)); pap. 3.99 (978-0-7566-0230-7(0)) Dorling Kindersley Publishing, Inc.

Galko, Francine. Sea Animals. 2003. (Animals in Their Habitats Ser.). 32p. (gr. k-2). (Illus.). (J). lib. bdg. 21.36 (978-1-4034-0184-7(5)); pap. 6.95 (978-1-4034-0441-1(0)) Heinemann Library.

—Sea Animals. 2003. (gr. k-3). lib. bdg. 14.75 (978-0-613-45826-9(5)) Tandem Library Bks.

Ganeri, Anita. Esos Inmensos Oceanos. (Coleccion Esa Horrible Geografia).Tr. of Odious Oceans. (SPA., Illus.). 160p. (YA). (gr. 5-8). (978-84-272-2152-9(5) , ML3927) Molino, Editorial ESP. *Dist:* Lectorum Pubns., Inc.

—I Wonder Why the Sea Is Salty: And Other Questions about the Oceans. 2003. (I Wonder Why Ser.). 32p. (J). (gr. k-3). pap. 6.95 (978-0-7534-5611-8(7) , Kingfisher) Houghton Mifflin Co. Trade & Reference Div.

—I Wonder Why the Sea Is Salty: And Other Questions about the Oceans. 2003. (gr. k-3). lib. bdg. 14.10 (978-0-613-63165-5(X)) Tandem Library Bks.

—Oceans. 2003. (Science Files Ser.). (Illus.). 32p. (J). (gr. 3 up). lib. bdg. 24.67 (978-0-8368-3570-0(0)) Stevens, Gareth Inc.

—Protecting Ocean Habitats. 2005. (Protecting Habitats Ser.). (Illus.). 32p. (J). lib. bdg. 24.67 (978-0-8368-4992-9(2)) Stevens, Gareth Inc.

—The Sea. (Information Ser.). (Illus.). 32p. (J). 3.50 (978-0-7214-1750-9(7) , Dutton Juvenile) Penguin Group (USA) Inc.

Goldsack, Gaby. Ocean Animals. Bampton, Bob, illus. (J). (978-1-57755-508-7(2)) Allied Publishing.

Goldstein, Natalie. How Do We Know the Nature of the Ocean? 2005. (Great Scientific Questions & the Scientists Who Answered Them Ser.). (Illus.). 112p. (J). (gr. 7-12). lib. bdg. 26.50 (978-1-4042-0079-1(7)) Rosen Publishing Group, Inc., The.

Gonzales, Doreen. The Southern Ocean: A MyReportLinks.com Book. 2004. (Oceans of the World Ser.). (Illus.). 48p. (J). lib. bdg. 25.26 (978-0-7660-5196-6(X) , MyReportLinks.com Bks.) Enslow Pubs., Inc.

Gordon, Sharon. At Home by the Ocean. 2005. (Bookworms Ser.). (ENG & SPA., Illus.). 32p. (J). (gr. 3-7). lib. bdg. (978-0-7614-1959-4(4) , Benchmark Bks.) Cavendish, Marshall Corp.

Gray, Susan Heinrichs. Oceans. 2000. (First Reports). (Illus.). 48p. (J). (gr. 3 up). lib. bdg. 21.26 (978-0-7565-0022-1(2)) Compass Point Bks.

Green, Emily K. Oceans. 2006. (Blastoff! Readers Ser.). (Illus.). 24p. (J). lib. bdg. 16.95 (978-1-60014-039-6(4)) Bellwether Media.

Green, Jen. Arctic Ocean. 2006. (Illus.). 48p. (J). pap. (978-0-8368-6278-2(3)); lib. bdg. 30.00 (978-0-8368-6270-6(8)) Stevens, Gareth Inc. (World Almanac Library).

—Atlantic Ocean. 2006. (Illus.). 48p. (J). pap. (978-0-8368-6279-9(1)); lib. bdg. 30.00 (978-0-8368-6271-3(6)) Stevens, Gareth Inc. (World Almanac Library).

—Indian Ocean. 2006. (Illus.). 48p. (J). pap. (978-0-8368-6281-2(3)); lib. bdg. 30.00 (978-0-8368-6273-7(2)) Stevens, Gareth Inc. (World Almanac Library).

—Mediterranean Sea. 2006. (Illus.). 48p. (J). pap. (978-0-8368-6282-9(1)); lib. bdg. 30.00 (978-0-8368-6274-4(0)) Stevens, Gareth Inc. (World Almanac Library).

—Saving Oceans & Wetlands. 2004. (J). lib. bdg. 27.10 (978-1-59389-139-8(3)) Chrysalis Education.

Group/McGraw-Hill, Wright. Our World's Oceans, 6 vols. (Book2WebTM Ser.). (gr. 4-8). 36.50 (978-0-322-04447-0(2)) Wright Group, The.

Gunzi, Christiane & Greenaway, Theresa. Ocean Foldout Book. 2002. (Foldout Bks.). (Illus.). 6p. (J). (gr. 3-7). 9.95 (978-1-57145-757-8(7) , Silver Dolphin Bks.) Advantage Pubs. Group.

Hall, Kirsten. Deep Sea Adventures. 2004. (True Tales Ser.). (J). (gr. 2-4). pap. 4.95 (978-0-516-24604-8(6) , Children's Pr.) Scholastic Library Publishing.

Hall, Stephen. Exploring the Oceans. 2000. (Inside Look Ser.). (Illus.). 48p. (J). (gr. 4 up). lib. bdg. 26.00 (978-0-8368-2726-2(0)) Stevens, Gareth Inc.

Hamaguchi, Carla, ed. Ocean Stickety-Splits, 12 vols., 0649. Schamber, Kimberly, illus. 2001. 10p. (Orig.). (J). pap. 6.99 (978-1-57471-897-3(5)) Creative Teaching Pr., Inc.

Hamilton, Kersten R. & Siomades, Lorianne. This Is the Ocean. 2003. (Illus.). 32p. (J). (gr. k-2). 14.95 (978-1-56397-890-6(3)) Boyds Mills Pr.

Harcourt School Publishers Staff. Sea Gifts. 3rd ed. 2002. (Trophies English Language Learners Ser.). (Illus.). pap. 5.10 (978-0-15-327822-8(6)) Harcourt Schl. Pubs.

—Secrets under the Sands & the Seas On Level. 3rd ed. 2002. (Trophies Reading Program Ser.). (Illus.). pap. 5.10 (978-0-15-323354-8(0)) Harcourt Schl. Pubs.

—Under the Ocean: Theme Book. 1999. (Collections Ser.). (Illus.). (J). pap. 3.00 (978-0-15-314028-0(3)) Harcourt Schl. Pubs.

Harker, Katie. Oceans. 2007. (Illus.). 32p. (J). (*978-1-59604-102-8(1))* Stargazer Bks.

Harrison, David L. Oceans: The Vast, Mysterious Deep. Nathan, Cheryl, illus. 2003. 32p. (J). (gr. k-2). 15.95 (978-1-59078-018-3(3)) Boyds Mills Pr.

Harvey, Bob. Get Inside the Sea. (Get Inside Ser.). (Illus.). 48p. (J). pap. 18.95 (978-1-904668-93-0(3)) Mercury Bks. Ltd. GBR. *Dist:* International Publishers Marketing.

Haslam, Andrew. Fleuves et Rivieres. 2000. (Make It Work! Geography Ser.). (FRE., Illus.). 48p. (J). (gr. 3-6). pap. 6.95 (978-1-58728-187-7(2) , Two Can Publishing) T&N Children's Publishing.

—Mers et Oceans. 2000. (Make It Work! Geography Ser.). (FRE.). 48p. (J). (gr. 3-6). pap. 6.95 (978-1-58728-190-7(7) , Two Can Publishing) T&N Children's Publishing.

Heller, Ruth. How to Hide an Octopus: And Other Sea Creatures. unabr. ed. 2001. (How to Hide Ser.). (Illus.). (J). (gr. k-3). pap. 14.45 incl. audio (978-0-8045-6571-4(6) , 6571) Spoken Arts, Inc.

Hill-Ward, Robin. Global Healing: A Children's Book for All Ages. Hill-Ward, Robin, illus. l.t. ed. 2000. (Illus.). vii, 50p. (J). (gr. k-8). pap. 8.95 (978-0-9677955-6-0(7)) Hill-Ward, Robin.

Holland, Gini. I Live near the Ocean. 2004. (Weekly Reader Early Learning Library). (Illus.). 24p. (gr. k up). (J). pap. 5.95 (978-0-8368-4089-6(5)); (YA). lib. bdg. 19.33 (978-0-8368-4082-7(8)) Stevens, Gareth Inc. (Weekly Reader Early Learning Library).

—I Live near the Ocean/Vivo cerca del Mar. Coffey, Colleen & Carrillo, Consuelo, trs. 2004. (Weekly Reader Early Learning Library). (SPA & ENG., Illus.). 24p. (J). (gr. k up). pap. 5.95 (978-0-8368-4137-4(9)); lib. bdg. 19.33 (978-0-8368-4130-5(1)) Stevens, Gareth Inc. (Weekly Reader Early Learning Library).

Holt, Rinehart and Winston Staff. Holt Science & Technology Chptr. 14: Exploring the Oceans: Chapter Resources - Tennessee Edition. 3rd ed. 2003. (YA). pap. 11.40 (978-0-03-069174-4(5)) Holt, Rinehart & Winston.

Hughes, Monica. Have You Seen the Ocean? 2004. (Heinemann Read & Learn Ser.). (Illus.). 24p. (J). pap. (978-1-4034-6283-1(6)) Steck-Vaughn.

—What Is the Ocean? 2004. (Heinemann Read & Learn Ser.). (Illus.). 24p. (J). lib. bdg. (978-1-4034-6277-0(1)) Steck-Vaughn.

The Indian Ocean. (Oceans Ser.). 24p. (J). 6.95 (978-0-7368-3420-9(6)) Capstone Pr., Inc.

Investigating Earth Systems Oceans. 2002. stu. ed., bds. (978-1-58591-110-3(0)); 2001. stu. ed. (978-1-58591-074-8(0)) It's About Time, Herff Jones Education Diiv.

Jackson, Kay. Oceans. 2006. (Illus.). 24p. (J). (978-0-7368-5406-1(1) , 1252619) Capstone Pr., Inc.

James, Ian, ed. Oceans. (Illus.). 32p. (J). (978-0-7540-9031-1(0) , Cherrytree Books) Evans Publishing Group.

Jedicke, Peter. Exploring the Ocean Depths. 2003. (Hot Science Ser.). (J). lib. bdg. 28.50 (978-1-58340-367-9(1)) Smart Apple Media.

Johnson, Rebecca L. A Journey into the Ocean. Saroff, Phyllis V., illus. 2004. (J). pap. 6.95 (978-0-8225-2046-7(X) , l); 48p. (gr. 3-6). lib. bdg. 23.93 (978-1-57505-591-6(0)) Lerner Publishing Group.

Jordano, Kimberly & Corcoran, Tebra. Oceans of Fun. Fisch, Teri L., ed. Campbell, Jenny, illus. 2003. (Stepping into Standards Theme Ser.). 64p. (J). (gr. k-2). pap. 10.99 (978-1-57471-946-8(7) , 2474) Creative Teaching Pr., Inc.

Kalman, Bobbie. The ABCs of Oceans. 2007. (ABCs of the Natural World Ser.). (Illus.). 32p. (J). (gr. 1-5). pap. (*978-0-7787-3432-1(3))* Crabtree Publishing Co.

Kalman, Bobbie. Ocean Biome. 2003. (gr. 3-6). lib. bdg. 15.25 (978-0-613-59134-8(8)) Tandem Library Bks.

Karas, G. Brian. Atlantic. Karas, G. Brian, illus. 2004. (Illus.). 32p. (J). (ps-2). reprint ed. pap. 6.99 (978-0-14-240027-2(0) , Puffin) Penguin Group (USA) Inc.

Kerrod, Robin. The Sea. 2000. (Fantastic Facts Ser.). (Illus.). 64p. (gr. 2-7). pap. 6.95 (978-1-84215-321-5(8) , Southwater) Anness Publishing GBR. *Dist:* National Bk. Network.

—The Sea. Sweet, Stephen & Whetton, John, illus. 1998. (Young Scientist Concepts & Projects Ser.). 68p. (J). (gr. 4 up). lib. bdg. 26.60 (978-0-8368-2164-2(5)) Stevens, Gareth Inc.

Kids: Explore Oceans & Activity Booklet. 2003. (J). 1.00 (978-1-888631-26-5(0)) Watercourse, The.

Klingel, Cynthia Fitterer & Noyed, Robert B. Oceans. 2001. (Wonder Books Level 2: Habitats Ser.). (Illus.). 24p. (J). (ps-3). 22.79 (978-1-56766-974-9(3)) Child's World, Inc.

Kovacs. Off to Sea. 1999. (Illus.). (J). pap. (978-0-7398-0001-0(9)) Steck-Vaughn.

Kovacs, Deborah. Dive to the Deep Ocean: Voyages of Exploration & Discovery. 1999. (Turnstone Ocean Explorer Ser.). (Illus.). 64p. (YA). (gr. 5-9). pap. 8.95 (978-0-7398-1235-8(1)) Steck-Vaughn.

—Dive to the Deep Ocean: Voyages of Exploration & Discovery. 2001. (gr. 5-8). lib. bdg. 17.60 (978-0-613-73989-4(2)) Tandem Library Bks.

Lalley. Ocean Scientists. 2001. (Scientists of the Biomes Ser.). (Illus.). (J). pap. (978-0-7398-4938-5(7)) Steck-Vaughn.

Lalley, Pat & Kittmans-Lalley, Janet. Ocean Scientists. 2001. (Scientists of the Biomes Ser.). (Illus.). 48p. (J). lib. bdg. 24.26 (978-0-7398-4750-3(3)) Raintree.

Lambert, David. The Kingfisher Young People's Book of Oceans. 2001. (Kingfisher Book of Ser.). (Illus.). 96p. (J). (gr. 4-8). pap. 13.95 (978-0-7534-5394-0(0) , Kingfisher) Houghton Mifflin Co. Trade & Reference Div.

—Kingfisher Young People's Book of Oceans. 2001. (gr. 5-8). lib. bdg. 22.20 (978-0-613-90593-0(8)) Tandem Library Bks.

LaPenta, Marilyn. 1 2 3 in the Sea: Including Abacus. Canals, Sonia, illus. 1999. 12p. (J). (ps-1). 9.95 (978-0-7641-7256-4(5)) Barron's Educational Series, Inc.

Leardi, Jeanette. Protecting Our Oceans. 2005. (Navigators Ser.). (J). pap. 44.00 (*978-1-4108-5092-8(7))* Benchmark Education Co.

Leonhardt, Alice. Why the Ocean Is Salty. 1999. pap. (978-0-7398-0868-9(0)) Steck-Vaughn.

The Letter Ww: The Ocean, 6 vols. (gr. k-2). 17.50 (978-0-7368-4122-1(9)) Red Brick Learning.

Llewellyn, Claire. The Sea. 2003. (Starters Ser.). 24p. (J). lib. bdg. 21.35 (978-1-58340-262-7(4)) Smart Apple Media.

Locke, Ian. Deadly Deep. Rowe, Alan, illus. 17th ed. 2003. 60p. (J). pap. 3.99 (978-0-330-37500-9(8) , Pan) Pan Macmillan GBR. *Dist:* Trafalgar Square Publishing.

Look Who's Popping Up: Under the Sea. 2003. (J). (ps-k). 4.98 (978-0-7525-8904-6(0)) Parragon, Inc.

Lynch, Emma. Ocean. 2004. (Raintree Sprouts Ser.). (Illus.). 24p. (J). pap. 5.50 (978-1-4109-0874-2(7)) Raintree.

—Under the Sea. 2004. (Raintree Sprouts Ser.). (Illus.). 24p. (J). lib. bdg. 18.56 (978-1-4109-0869-8(0)) Raintree.

MacAulay, Kelley. Tropical Oceans. Kalman, Bobbie, illus. 2005. (Living Ocean Ser.). 32p. (J). pap. (978-0-7787-1322-7(9)) Crabtree Publishing Co.

MacAulay, Kelley & Kalman, Bobbie. Tropical Oceans. 2005. (Living Ocean Ser.). (Illus.). 32p. (J). (978-0-7787-1300-5(8)) Crabtree Publishing Co.

MacDonald, Suse. Sea Shapes. MacDonald, Suse, illus. 2002. (Illus.). (J). 19.96 (978-0-7587-3585-0(5)) Book Wholesalers, Inc.

—Sea Shapes. 1998. (978-0-606-13765-2(3)) Tandem Library Bks.

Macken, JoAnn Early. Seas. 2006. (Illus.). 24p. (J). pap. (978-0-8368-6405-2(0)); lib. bdg. 19.33 (978-0-8368-6398-7(4)) Stevens, Gareth Inc.

MacQuitty, Miranda. El Mar. Greenaway, Frank, photos by. 2005. (Dk eyewitness Bks.). (Illus.). 72p. (J). (gr. 4-7). 15.99 (978-0-7566-1486-7(4)); lib. bdg. 19.99 (978-0-7566-1492-8(9)) Dorling Kindersley Publishing, Inc.

MacQuitty, Miranda. Ocean. 2008. (DK Eyewitness Bks.). 72p. (J). (gr. 3-8). 15.99 (*978-0-7566-3776-7(7))* Dorling Kindersley Publishing, Inc.

MacQuitty, Miranda & Dorling Kindersley Publishing Staff. Ocean. Greenaway, Frank, photos by. 2004. (Eyewitness Books). (Illus.). 72p. (J). lib. bdg. 19.99 (978-0-7566-0710-4(8)) Dorling Kindersley Publishing, Inc.

Madin, Kate. Down to a Sunless Sea: The Strange World of Hydrothermal Vents. 1999. (Illus.). 64p. (J). (gr. 5-9). pap. 8.95 (978-0-7398-1239-6(4)) Steck-Vaughn.

Mayer, Cassie. Ocean. 2007. (J). (***978-1-4034-9430-6(4));*** pap. (***978-1-4034-9436-8(3))*** Heinemann Library.

—Océanos y Mares. 2007. (SPA & ENG.). (J). pap. (***978-1-4329-0386-2(1));*** lib. bdg. (***978-1-4329-0381-7(0))*** Heinemann Library.

—Oceans & Seas. 2007. (J). (***978-1-4034-9363-7(4));*** pap. (***978-1-4034-9367-5(7))*** Heinemann Library.

McFarlane, Sheryl. What's That Sound by Sea. LaFave, Kim, illus. 2006. 20p. (J). bds. 7.95 (978-1-55041-957-3(9)) Fitzhenry & Whiteside, Ltd. CAN. *Dist:* F & W Pubns., Inc.

McGraw-Hill Staff & Schaffer, Frank. Ocean: Dot-to-Dot. 2001. (Homework Helpers Activity Bks.). (Illus.). 56p. (J). (gr. k-k). pap., act. bk. ed. 2.99 (978-0-7682-0688-3(X) , FS109017, Schaffer, Frank) Schaffer, Frank Pubns.

McGuinness, Rik. Cloze Encounters Vol. 2: The Sea, 3 vols. 2000. 48p. pap. 6.95 (978-1-58324-045-8(4) , World Teachers Pr.) Didax Educational Resources, Inc.

McKay, Sindy. We Both Read-about the Ocean. 2001. (We Both Read Ser.). (Illus.). 44p. (J). (gr. 1-2). 7.99 (978-1-891327-31-5(3)); pap. 3.99 (978-1-891327-32-2(1)) Treasure Bay, Inc.

McKissack, Fredrick, Jr. & McKissack, Lisa Beringer. Counting in the Oceans. 2008. (J). (***978-0-7660-2994-1(8))*** Enslow Pubs., Inc.

McMillan, Beverly & Musick, John A. Oceans. 2007. (Insiders Ser.). 64p. (J). 16.99 (***978-1-4169-3859-0(1))*** Simon & Schuster Children's Publishing.

Meister, Cari. The Ocean. 2000. (Going Places Ser.). (Illus.). 24p. (J). (gr. k-6). lib. bdg. 21.35 (978-1-57765-027-0(1) , Checkerboard Library) ABDO Publishing Co.

Mitton, Tony & Hammond, Andrew. I-Read Year 1 Anthology: Splish Splash Splosh. 2007. (I-read Ser.). (Illus.). 48p. pap. (***978-0-521-70481-6(2))*** Cambridge Univ. Pr.

Moor, Jo Ellen. Life in the Ocean. Evans, Marilyn, ed. Larsen, Jo, illus. 1998. (Science Picture Cards Ser.: Vol. 3). 24p. (J). (gr. 1-3). pap., tchr. ed. 12.95 (978-1-55799-694-7(6) , EMC 865) Evan-Moor Educational Pubs.

Morey, Allan. Ocean Food Chains. 2003. (What Eats What? Ser.). (J). pap. (978-1-58417-219-2(3)); lib. bdg. (978-1-58417-218-5(5)) Lake Street Pubs.

Morgan, Sally. Oceans. (Extreme Survival Ser.). (Illus.). 32p. (J). 2004. pap. 7.95 (978-1-4109-0361-7(3)); 2003. lib. bdg. 25.70 (978-1-4109-0002-9(9)) Raintree.

—Oceans. 2003. (gr. 3-6). lib. bdg. 16.40 (978-0-613-78254-8(2)) Tandem Library Bks.

Morris, Neil. Living at the Coast. 2004. (J). lib. bdg. 27.10 (978-1-58340-486-7(4)) Smart Apple Media.

Mykowski, Michelle. Explore God's Ocean. Ring, Laura, ed. Mykowski, Michelle, illus. 1999. (Shaped Paperback Bks.). (Illus.). 24p. (J). (ps-1). pap. 3.99 (978-0-7847-0897-2(5) , 03787, Bean Sprouts) Standard Publishing.

Nadeau, Isaac. Water in Oceans. 2003. (Water Cycle Ser.). (Illus.). 24p. (J). lib. bdg. 18.75 (978-0-8239-6267-9(9) , PowerKids Pr.) Rosen Publishing Group, Inc., The.

Nelson, Robin. From Sea to Salt. 2004. (Start to Finish Ser.). (Illus.). 24p. (J). 18.60 (978-0-8225-0946-2(6) , Lerner Pubns.) Lerner Publishing Group.

Ocean. 1999. (Pop into Nature Ser.). 12p. (J). 6.99 (978-0-7681-0099-0(2) , McClanahan Bk.) Learning Horizons, Inc.

Ocean. 2003. (J). per. (978-1-57657-886-5(0)) Paradise Pr., Inc.

Ocean. 2002. (Fuzzy Felts Ser.). (J). 4.98 (978-0-7525-5234-7(1)) Parragon, Inc.

The Ocean. 2004. (Illus.). lib. bdg. 7.95 (978-0-8225-4535-4(7)) Lerner Publishing Group.

Ocean 6-Pack. 2004. (Illus.). (J). pap. 29.70 (978-1-4109-0879-7(8)) Raintree.

Ocean Facts, 4 vols., Set. 2005. (Illus.). 24p. (gr. 2-4). pap. 92.00 (978-0-7910-7284-4(3) , Chelsea Hse.) Facts On File, Inc.

Ocean (Gr. PreK-5) 2003. (J). (978-1-58232-024-3(1)) Bryan Hse. Pubs., Inc.

The Ocean Science, 6 vols. (gr. k-2). 28.95 (978-0-7368-2997-7(0) , Yellow Umbrella Bks.) Capstone Pr., Inc.

Oceans. 2004. (Discovery Channel School Science Ser.). (Illus.). 32p. (J). (gr. 5 up). lib. bdg. 24.67 (978-0-8368-3383-6(X)) Stevens, Gareth Inc.

Oceans & Seas. 2003. (J). (gr. k-6). lib. bdg. 170.80 (978-1-57765-992-1(9) , Checkerboard Library) ABDO Publishing Co.

Oceans & Underwater Life. 2001. (J). (978-0-307-10539-4(3) , 10539, Golden Bks.) Random Hse. Children's Bks.

Oceans Learning about the Earth. 2006. (Illus.). 24p. (J). (gr. k-2). 18.50 (***978-0-531-17891-1(9))*** Scholastic Library Publishing.

The Oceans with Book & Puzzle. 2000. (Illus.). 16p. (J). (ps-3). 9.95 (978-1-878427-80-9(6)) Cimino Publishing Group.

Olesky, Walter. Mapping the Seas. 2002. (gr. 3-6). lib. bdg. 17.60 (978-0-613-59513-1(0)) Tandem Library Bks.

Oliver, Clare. 100 Things You Should Know about Oceans. 2003. (Illus.). 48p. (J). (gr. 3 up). lib. bdg. (978-1-59084-452-6(1)) Mason Crest Pubs.

Ostopowich, Melanie. Oceans, Rivers, & Lakes. 2005. (Science Matters Ser.). (Illus.). 24p. (J). (ps-7). pap. 6.95 (978-1-59036-310-2(8)); lib. bdg. 24.45 (978-1-59036-304-1(3)) Weigl Pubs., Inc.

Owen, Andy, et al. Seas & Oceans. 2002. (Geography Starts Ser.). (Illus.). 32p. (J). (gr. k-2). pap. 6.95 (978-1-58810-978-1(X) , 91461) Heinemann Library.

Parker, Jane & Parker, Steve. Seas & Oceans. 1998. (Take 5 Geography Ser.). (Illus.). 32p. (J). (gr. 3-5). 21.00 (978-0-531-14459-6(3) , Watts, Franklin) Scholastic Library Publishing.

Parsons, Michelle Hyde. Ocean Pollution. 2005. 42.00 (***978-1-4108-4630-3(X))*** Benchmark Education Co.

Patchett, F. Under the Sea "Velvet Art" Kid Kit. 2007. (Kid Kits Ser.). 32p. (J). 11.99 (***978-1-60130-049-2(2)*** , Usborne) EDC Publishing.

—Under the Sea "Velvet Art" Kid Kit (Bag) 2007. (Kid Kits Ser.). 32p. (J). 11.99 (***978-1-60130-048-5(4)*** , Usborne) EDC Publishing.

Patchett, Fiona. Under the Sea. Kushii, Tetsuo & Wray, Zoë, illus. 2006. (Usborne Beginners Ser.). 32p. (J). (***978-0-439-02673-4(3))*** Scholastic, Inc.

Patchett, Fiona. Under the Sea (Level 1) - Internet Referenced. 2006. (Illus.). 32p. (J). 4.99 (978-0-7945-1336-8(0) , Usborne) EDC Publishing.

Penguin Books Staff, ed. The Sea. (Information Activity Ser.). 24p. (J). 3.50 (978-0-7214-3442-1(8) , Dutton Juvenile) Penguin Group (USA) Inc.

Petersen, Christine. Atlantic Ocean. 2001. (gr. 3-6). lib. bdg. 15.25 (978-0-613-53938-8(9)) Tandem Library Bks.

Pienkowski, Jan. Jan Pienkowski's Sea. 1998. (Animal Action Pops Ser.). (Illus.). 10p. (J). (gr. 2 up). 4.95 (978-1-58117-019-1(X) , Intervisual/Piggy Toes) Dalmatian Pr.

Pike, Katy & O'Keefe, Maureen. Oceans. 2003. (Ocean Facts Ser.). (Illus.). 24p. (gr. 2-4). 23.00 (978-0-7910-7286-8(X) , Chelsea Hse.) Facts On File, Inc.

Plisson, Phillip. Mar Explicado a los ninos. 2005. 80p. (978-970-651-911-5(4)) Editorial Oceano De Mexico, S.A. DE C.V.

Prevost, John F. Indian Ocean. 2003. (Oceans & Seas Ser.). (Illus.). 24p. (J). (gr. k-6). lib. bdg. 21.35 (978-1-57765-094-2(8)) ABDO Publishing Co.

—Mediterranean Sea. 2003. (Oceans & Seas Ser.). (Illus.). 24p. (J). (gr. k-6). lib. bdg. 21.35 (978-1-57765-097-3(2)) ABDO Publishing Co.

Priddy, Roger. Pop-up Ocean IQ. 2007. 12p. (J). bds. 5.95 (978-0-312-49916-7(7) , Priddy Bks.) St. Martin's Pr.

Pringle, Laurence P. Come to the Ocean's Edge: A Nature Cycle Book. Chesworth, Michael, illus. 2003. 32p. (YA). (gr. k-2). 15.95 (978-1-56397-779-4(6)) Boyds Mills Pr.

Pyers. Ocean Explorer. 2004. (Illus.). (J). pap. 7.50 (978-1-4109-0839-1(9)) Raintree.

—Ocean Explorer 6-Pack. 2004. (Illus.). (J). lib. bdg. 40.50 (978-1-4109-0845-2(3)) Raintree.

Pyers, Greg. Ocean Explorer. 2004. (Habitat Explorer Ser.). (Illus.). 32p. (J). (ps-ps). lib. bdg. 25.70 (978-1-4109-0510-9(1)) Raintree.

¿Que Hay Debajo del Mar? (Coleccion Primeros Pasos en la Ciencia). (SPA., Illus.). (J). (gr. 1-3). pap. (978-950-724-419-3(0) , LMA8226) Lumen ARG. *Dist:* Lectorum Pubns., Inc.

Rabe, Tish. The Cat in the Hat's Learning Library: All about the Beach. Ruiz, Aristides & Mathieu, Joe, illus. 2005. (Cat in the Hat's Learning Library). 48p. (J). (gr. k-3). lib. bdg. 12.99 (978-0-375-92280-0(6) , Random Hse. Bks. for Young Readers) Random Hse. Children's Bks.

—Clam-I-Am! All about the Beach. Ruiz, Aristides & Mathieu, Joe, illus. 2005. (Cat in the Hat's Learning Library). 48p. (J). (gr. k-3). 8.99 (978-0-375-82280-3(1) , Random Hse. Bks. for Young Readers) Random Hse. Children's Bks.

Raintree Steck-Vaughn Staff. True Tales from the Seas. 1999. (J). pap. 13.00 (978-0-7398-0852-8(4)) Steck-Vaughn.

Ramsden, Julie & Ramsden, Michael. Discover the Deep. 2005. (X-Zone Ser.). (Illus.). 30p. (gr. 4-8). 23.00 (978-0-7910-8974-3(6)) Facts On File, Inc.

Reid, Greg. Oceans. 2004. (Ecosystems Ser.). (Illus.). 32p. (J). (gr. 3-5). 23.00 (978-0-7910-7940-9(6) , Chelsea Hse.) Facts On File, Inc.

Richardson, Adele D. Oceans. 2001. (Bridgestone Science Library). (Illus.). 24p. (J). (gr. 2-3). lib. bdg. 18.60 (978-0-7368-0838-5(8) , Bridgestone Bks.) Capstone Pr., Inc.

—Oceans, 6 vols. (gr. 2-5). 36.95 (978-0-7368-9265-0(6)) Red Brick Learning.

Riley, Peter D. Our Mysterious Ocean. Hargreaves, Toni, illus. 1998. (Windows on Science Ser.). 14p. (J). (gr. 3-7). 14.00 (978-1-57584-058-1(8)) Reader's Digest Children's Publishing, Inc.

Ring, Susan. The Ocean. 2003. (Yellow Umbrella Books for Early Readers). (Illus.). 17p. (J). 15.93 (978-0-7368-2920-5(2)); pap. (978-0-7368-2879-6(6)) Yellow Umbrella Pr.

Rivera, Sheila. Ocean. 2005. (First Step Nonfiction Ser.). (Illus.). 23p. (J). (ps-7). 18.60 (978-0-8225-2795-4(2) , Lerner Pubns.) Lerner Publishing Group.

Rod Theodorou. To the Depths of the Ocean. 2nd ed. 2006. (Illus.). 32p. (J). pap. (***978-1-4034-8799-5(5))*** Heinemann Library.

Royston, Angela. Oceans. 2004. (My World of Geography Ser.). (J). 22.79 (978-1-4034-5593-2(7)) Heinemann Library.

Ryan, William T. World of Water. 2003. (Science Links Ser.). (Illus.). 32p. (gr. 3-5). 23.00 (978-0-7910-7429-9(3) , Chelsea Hse.) Facts On File, Inc.

Sacks, Janet. Oceans & Art Activities. 2002. (gr. 3-6). lib. bdg. 17.60 (978-0-613-52889-4(1)) Tandem Library Bks.

Sacks, Janet & Goodman, Polly, texts. Oceans & Art Activities. 2002. (Arty Facts Ser.). (Illus.). 48p. (J). (gr. 3-4). pap. (978-0-7787-1143-8(9)); lib. bdg. (978-0-7787-1115-5(3)) Crabtree Publishing Co.

Saffer, Barbara. Science Questions & Answers: The Ocean. 1999. (Science Questions & Answers Ser.). (Illus.). 63p. (J). (gr. 1-3). pap. 5.95 (978-0-7373-0210-3(0)) Lowell Hse.

Salas, Laura Purdie. Oceans. 2007. (Amazing Science Ser.). (Illus.). 24p. (J). (***978-1-4048-3471-2(0)*** , 1265693) Picture Window Bks.

Salas, Laura Purdie. Oceans: Underwater Worlds. Yesh, Jeff, illus. 2006. (Amazing Science Ser.). 24p. (J). (978-1-4048-3097-4(9) , 1265693) Picture Window Bks.

Salzmann, Mary Elizabeth. In the Ocean. l.t. ed. 2001. (What Do You See? Ser.). (Illus.). 24p. (J). (ps-3). lib. bdg. 19.93 (978-1-57765-567-1(2) , SandCastle) ABDO Publishing Co.

Sammis, Fran. Oceans & Skies. 1999. (Mapping Our World Ser.). (Illus.). 64p. (J). (gr. 4-8). lib. bdg. 27.07 (978-0-7614-0374-6(4) , Benchmark Bks.) Cavendish, Marshall Corp.

Saunders-Smith, Gail, ed. Earth Features, 8 bks. Incl. What Are Caves? Schuh, Mari C. 2002. lib. bdg. 15.93 (978-0-7368-1169-9(9)); What Are Deserts? Trumbauer, Lisa. 2001. lib. bdg. 15.93 (978-0-7368-0987-0(2)); What Are Forests? Trumbauer, Lisa. 2001. lib. bdg. 15.93 (978-0-7368-0988-7(0)); What Are Lakes? Schuh, Mari C. 2002. lib. bdg. 15.93 (978-0-7368-1170-5(2)); What Are Mountains? Trumbauer, Lisa. 2001. lib. bdg. 15.93 (978-0-7368-0989-4(9)); What Are Oceans? Trumbauer, Lisa. 2001. lib. bdg. 15.93 (978-0-7368-0990-0(2)); What Are Rivers? Schuh, Mari C. 2002. lib. bdg. 15.93 (978-0-7368-1171-2(0)); What Are Volcanoes? Schuh, Mari C. 2002. lib. bdg. 15.93 (978-0-7368-1172-9(9)); 24p. (J). (gr. k-1). (Illus.). 2001. Set lib. bdg. 127.44 (978-0-7368-1198-9(2) , Pebble Bks.) Capstone Pr., Inc.

Savage, Stephen, et al. Oceans. 2006. (Kingfisher Voyages Ser.). (Illus.). 60p. (J). (gr. 4-6). 15.95 (978-0-7534-5903-4(5) , Kingfisher) Houghton Mifflin Co. Trade & Reference Div.

Schaffer, Frank. Ocean. 2001. 32p. (J). pap. 1.99 (978-0-7682-0241-0(8) , FS144003) Schaffer, Frank Pubns.

Schatz, Dennis. Totally Sea Creatures. 2004. (Totally Ser.). (Illus.). 32p. (J). 16.95 (978-1-59223-087-7(3)) Advantage Pubs. Group.

School Specialty Publishing. Learn about the Ocean. 2005. (Learn about Coloring Bks.). 32p. (J). (ps-3). pap. 1.99 (978-0-7696-4162-1(8) , Brighter Child) School Specialty Publishing.

The Sea. (Eyes on Adventure Ser.). 32p. (J). (gr. 1). pap. (978-1-882210-81-7(6)) Action Publishing, Inc.

The Sea & its Marvels. (Action Bks.). 64p. (J). (gr. 3-7). pap. (978-1-882210-66-4(2)) Action Publishing, Inc.

Seas & Oceans, 8 vol., set. 1999. (Illus.). (gr. 5-9). 151.84 (978-0-8172-4516-0(2)) Raintree.

Sepheri, Sandy. The Seven Oceans. 2008. (J). (***978-1-60044-549-1(7))*** Rourke Publishing, LLC.

Serrano, Marta. Oceans. 2002. (Living Planet Ser.). (Illus.). 32p. (J). 23.70 (978-1-56711-669-4(8) , Blackbirch Pr., Inc.) Thomson Gale.

Simon, Seymour. Oceans. 2006. 40p. (J). 16.99 (978-0-06-088998-2(5)); (Illus.). pap. 6.99 (978-0-06-088999-9(3)) HarperCollins Pubs.

Smithyman, Kathryn. The Ocean Biome. 2003. (Living Ocean Ser.). (Illus.). 32p. (J). (gr. 2-9). (978-0-7787-1296-1(6)) Crabtree Publishing Co.

Smithyman, Kathryn & Kalman, Bobbie. El bioma Marino. 2006. (SPA., Illus.). 32p. (gr. 3-4). pap. (978-0-7787-8414-2(2)) Crabtree Publishing Co.

Somervill, Barbara A. Our Living World: Earth's Biomes, 7 vols., Set. 2005. (Illus.). (J). (gr. 4-8). 350.00 (978-1-59187-052-4(6)) Tradition Publishing Co.

Spencer, Carolyn. Alphabet Sea. Harris, David, photos by. 1999. (Illus.). 31p. (J). (ps-3). 14.95 (978-1-893561-00-7(3)) Tortuga Bks.

Steck-Vaughn Staff. Follow That Fin & Secrets of the Sea. 1999. (Illus.). 48p. (J). (gr. 3-7). 34.60 incl. VHS (978-0-7398-2830-4(4)) Steck-Vaughn.

—The Living Ocean. 2002. (J). pap. (978-0-7398-6162-2(X)) Steck-Vaughn.

—Wonders of the Ocean. 2002. (Illus.). pap. (978-0-7398-5980-3(3)) Steck-Vaughn.

Steele. Oceans. 2000. (Biomes Ser.). (Illus.). (J). pap. (978-0-7398-4161-7(0)) Steck-Vaughn.

Steele, Christy. Oceans. Sloan, Frank, ed. 2001. (Biomes Ser.). (Illus.). 32p. (J). (gr. 4-7). lib. bdg. 22.83 (978-0-7398-3564-7(5)) Raintree.

Stille, Darlene R. Oceans. 2000. (True Bks.). (Illus.). 48p. (J). (gr. 3-5). pap. 6.95 (978-0-516-26768-5(X) , Children's Pr.) Scholastic Library Publishing.

—Oceans. 1999. (gr. 3-6). lib. bdg. 15.25 (978-0-613-37482-8(7)) Tandem Library Bks.

Stone, Lynn M. Oceans. 2003. (Illus.). 24p. (J). 20.64 (978-1-58952-686-0(4)) Rourke Publishing, LLC.

—Science under the Sea. 2003. (Science under the Sea Discovery Library Ser.). (gr. 2-5). 59.80 (978-1-58952-316-6(4)) Rourke Publishing, LLC.

Tagliaferro, Linda. How Many Fish in the Sea? A Book about Oceans. 2007. (First Facts Ser.). (Illus.). 24p. (J). (978-0-7368-6786-3(4) , 1264904) Capstone Pr., Inc.

Tahta, Sophie. What's under the Sea. rev. ed. 2006. 24p. (J). pap. 4.99 (978-0-7945-1409-9(X) , Usborne) EDC Publishing.

Tallarico, Tony. Ultimate Hidden Pictures under the Sea. 2003. (Illus.). 48p. (J). (ps-4). mass mkt. 3.99 (978-0-8431-0266-6(7) , Price Stern Sloan) Penguin Group (USA) Inc.

Taylor, Barbara. Oceans. 2004. (Make It Work! Geography Ser.). (Illus.). 48p. (J). (gr. 3-6). 12.95 (978-1-58728-255-3(0)); pap. 6.95 (978-1-58728-251-5(8)) T&N Children's Publishing. (Two Can Publishing).

—Oceans: The Hands-on Approach to Geography. 2001. (gr. 3-6). lib. bdg. 15.25 (978-0-613-43483-6(8)) Tandem Library Bks.

—Oceans & Rivers. 2002. (Questions & Answers about... Ser.). (Illus.). 40p. (J). (gr. 4-8). pap. 7.95 (978-0-7534-5491-6(2) , Kingfisher) Houghton Mifflin Co. Trade & Reference Div.

—Rivers & Oceans. 2002. (Young Discoverers Ser.). (Illus.). 32p. (J). (gr. k-3). pap. 7.95 (978-0-7534-5508-1(0) , Kingfisher) Houghton Mifflin Co. Trade & Reference Div.

—Rivers & Oceans: Geography Facts & Experiments. 2002. (gr. k-3). lib. bdg. 16.40 (978-0-613-90579-4(2)) Tandem Library Bks.

Telford & Theodorou, Rod. To the Depths of the Ocean. 2002. (Illus.). 32p. (J). (gr. 2-6). pap. 7.50 (978-1-58810-306-2(4) , 91073) Heinemann Library.

Theodorou, Rod. To the Depths of the Ocean. 32p. (J). 2006. (Illus.). (***978-1-4034-8792-6(8));*** 2000. (gr. 3-5). lib. bdg. 22.79 (978-1-57572-484-3(7)) Heinemann Library.

—To the Depths of the Ocean. 2001. (gr. k-3). lib. bdg. 15.90 (978-0-613-89895-9(8)) Tandem Library Bks.

TNT Stone and Associates Staff. Continents & Oceans. Petertil Design Partners Staff, illus. 1998. (Powertools for Kids Ser.: No. 17). 4p. (J). (gr. 2-5). pap., wbk. ed. 4.95 (978-1-58220-016-3(5) , 32507, PowerTools for Kids) Navigator Systems, Inc.

Tocci, Salvatore. Marine Habitats: Life in the Ocean. 2004. (Watts Library Ser.). (J). 25.50 (978-0-531-12306-5(5) , Watts, Franklin) Scholastic Library Publishing.

Trumbauer, Lisa. What Are Oceans? Saunders-Smith, Gail, ed. 2001. (Earth Features Ser.). (Illus.). 24p. (J). (gr. k-1). lib. bdg. 15.93 (978-0-7368-0990-0(2) , Pebble Bks.) Capstone Pr., Inc.

The Usborne Book of the Seas. (Illus.). 32p. (J). (gr. 3-6). lib. bdg. 14.95 (978-0-88110-564-3(3)) EDC Publishing.

VanVoorst, Jennifer. Oceano. 2005. Tr. of Ocean. (SPA., Illus.). 16p. (J). (gr. k-1). lib. bdg. 15.93 (978-0-7368-4167-2(9)) Capstone Pr., Inc.

Wade, Laura. Sea & Sealife. 2003. (Knowledge Masters Ser.). (Illus.). 32p. (YA). pap. incl. cd-rom (978-1-903954-10-2(X)) Chrysalis Children's Bks.

Ward, Beck. Under the Sea. Embleton, Chris, illus. 2004. (Magic Windows Ser.). 10p. (J). (ps-ps). pap. 7.95 (978-0-7624-1848-0(6) , Running Pr. Kids) Running Pr. Bk. Pubs.

Waters, Jennifer. The Great Ocean. 2002. (Spyglass Books). (Illus.). 24p. (J). (gr. 1 up). lib. bdg. 18.60 (978-0-7565-0379-6(5)) Compass Point Bks.

West, Krista, ed. Critical Perspectives on the Oceans. 2006. (Scientific American Critical Anthologies on Environment & Climate Ser.). (Illus.). 200p. (J). (978-1-4042-0692-2(2)) Rosen Publishing Group, Inc., The.

What Are Oceans?, 6 vols., Vol. 2. 2005. (Earth & Outer Space Ser.). (gr. k-2). 28.95 (978-0-7368-3278-6(5)) Red Brick Learning.

Whitehouse, Patricia. Living in an Ocean. 2007. (Illus.). 24p. (J). (978-1-60044-187-5(4)) Rourke Publishing, LLC.

Williams, Andy. Nature Unfolds the Oceans. Camm, Martin, illus. 2002. (Nature Unfolds Ser.). 40p. (J). (gr. 4). pap. (978-0-7787-0322-8(3)); lib. bdg. (978-0-7787-0310-5(X)) Crabtree Publishing Co.

Wolfe, Frances. One Wish. 2004. (Illus.). 32p. (J). (ps-1). 15.95 (978-0-88776-662-6(5)) Tundra Bks., Inc./Livres Toundra, Inc. CAN. *Dist:* Random Hse., Inc.

Woodward, John. Exporing the Oceans, 5 bks. 2004. (J). (gr. 4-6). lib. bdg. 149.64 (978-1-4034-5130-9(3)) Heinemann Library.

—Oceans. (Illus.). 64p. (YA). (gr. 4 up). lib. bdg. 29.95 (978-1-59389-125-1(3)) Chrysalis Education.

—Oceans. 2008. (Dk Online Ser.). 96p. (J). 17.99 (***978-0-7566-3463-6(6));*** pap. 9.99 (***978-0-7566-3462-9(8))*** Dorling Kindersley Publishing, Inc.

—Oceans. 2004. (Geography Fact Files Ser.). (J). lib. bdg. 28.50 (978-1-58340-427-0(9)) Smart Apple Media.

—Oceans Atlas: An Incredible Voyage of Discovery & Exploration. 2007. (Illus.). 96p. (J). (gr. 4-8). 19.99 (978-0-7566-2557-3(2)) Dorling Kindersley Publishing, Inc.

Ylvisaker, Anne. Oceans, 5 bks. Incl. Antarctic Ocean. lib. bdg. 18.60 (978-0-7368-1420-1(5)); Arctic Ocean. lib. bdg. 18.60 (978-0-7368-1423-2(X)); Atlantic Ocean. lib. bdg. 18.60 (978-0-7368-1424-9(8)); Indian Ocean. lib. bdg. 18.60 (978-0-7368-1425-6(6)); Pacific Ocean. lib. bdg. 18.60 (978-0-7368-1426-3(4)); 24p. (J). (gr. 1-2). 2002. (Illus.). 2002. Set lib. bdg. 93.00 (978-0-7368-1427-0(2) , Bridgestone Bks.) Capstone Pr., Inc.

Young, Karen Romano. Across the Wide Ocean: The Why, How, & Where of Navigation for Humans & Animals at Sea. Young, Karen Romano, illus. 2007. 80p. (J). (gr. 5-7). lib. bdg. 19.89 (978-0-06-009087-6(1)); (Illus.). 18.99 (978-0-06-009086-9(3)) HarperCollins Pubs.

OCEAN—ECONOMIC ASPECTS

see Marine Resources

OCEAN—FICTION

Aigner-Clark, Julie. World Around Me: Oceans. 2003. (Baby Einstein Ser.). 12p. (ps-17). 15.99 (978-0-7868-1913-3(8)) Disney Pr.

Ardizzone, Edward. Tim in Danger. 2006. (Little Tim Ser.). (Illus.). 48p. 15.95 (978-1-84507-544-6(7)) Lincoln, Frances Ltd. GBR. *Dist:* Perseus Distribution.

At the Ocean. 2000. (J). (978-1-58453-091-6(X)) Pioneer Valley Educational Pr., Inc.

Averill, Esther Holden. Jenny Goes to Sea. Averill, Esther Holden, illus. 2005. (New York Review Children's Collection). (Illus.). 140p. (J). (ps-17). reprint ed. pap. 17.95 (978-1-59017-155-4(1) , NYR Children's Collection) New York Review of Bks., Inc., The.

Banks, Kate. A Gift from the Sea. Hallensleben, Georg, illus. 2001. 40p. (J). (gr. 3-6). 16.00 (978-0-374-32566-4(9) , Farrar, Straus & Giroux (BYR)) Farrar, Straus & Giroux.

Batten, Mary. The Winking, Blinking Sea. 2001. 4. (Illus.). 32p. (J). (gr. 2-4). pap. 7.95 (978-0-7613-1484-4(9) , Millbrook Pr.) Lerner Publishing Group.

Berkes, Marianne. Over in the Ocean: In a Coral Reef. Canyon, Jeanette, illus. 2006. 26p. (J). bds. 7.95 (978-1-58469-082-5(8)) Dawn Pubns.

Bishop, Gavin. Conejito y el Mar. 2000. (SPA., Illus.). (J). (978-0-606-18317-8(5)) Tandem Library Bks.

—Little Rabbit & the Sea. 2000. (Illus.). 32p. (J). (ps-1). pap. 6.95 (978-0-7358-1312-0(4)) North-South Bks., Inc.

—Little Rabbit & the Sea. 2000. (gr. k-3). lib. bdg. 15.25 (978-0-613-28558-2(1)); (Illus.). (J). (978-0-606-18322-2(1)) Tandem Library Bks.

Boey, Stephanie. Undersea Treasure Hunt: Find the Treasure with Little Fish & Friends. Boey, Stephanie, illus. 2005. (Illus.). 20p. (J). 15.95 (978-0-8118-4622-6(9)) Chronicle Bks. LLC.

Buckingham, Matt. Bright Stanley. Buckingham, Matt, illus. 2006. (Illus.). 32p. (J). (ps-2). 15.95 (978-1-58925-059-8(1) , tiger tales) ME Media LLC.

Cain, Sheridan. Little Turtle & the Song of the Sea. Burgin, Norma, illus. 2000. 32p. (J). (ps-3). 15.95 (978-1-56656-355-0(0) , Crocodile Bks.) Interlink Publishing Group, Inc.

Capsize! Individual Title Six-Packs. (Bookweb Ser.). 32p. (gr. 4 up). 34.00 (978-0-7635-3727-2(6)) Rigby Education.

Chapman, Jason. Ted, Bo, & Diz: The First Adventure. 2007. 28p. (J). (ps-2). 16.00 (***978-1-56148-592-5(6)***) Good Bks.

Clownfish Reef. 2002. (Oceanic Mini Bks.). (Illus.). 32p. (J). (978-1-59069-011-6(7) , H1012) Studio Mouse LLC.

Cowan, Catherine. My Life with the Wave. ed. 2004. (Illus.). (J). (gr. k-3). spiral bd. (978-0-616-01621-3(2)) Canadian National Institute for the Blind/Institut National Canadien pour les Aveugles.

—My Life with the Wave. Buehner, Mark, illus. 2004. 32p. (J). (ps-3). reprint ed. pap. 6.99 (978-0-06-056200-7(5) , Harper Trophy) HarperCollins Pubs.

—My Life with the Wave. 2004. (gr. k-3). lib. bdg. 15.30 (978-0-613-83570-1(0)) Tandem Library Bks.

Croteau, Marie-Danielle. Gabby's School by the Sea. Casson, Sophie, illus. 2005. (Read-It! Readers Ser.). 32p. (J). (gr. k-3). 18.60 (978-1-4048-1072-3(2)) Picture Window Bks.

Croteau, Marie-Danielle & St. Aubin, Bruno. Des Fantomes Sous la Mer. 2003. (Roman Jeunesse Ser.). (FRE., Illus.). 96p. (J). (gr. 4-7). pap. (978-2-89021-610-5(1)) Diffusion du livre Mirabel.

Cuentos de Siempre Oceano. l.t. ed. 2000. Tr. of Stories for All Time from Oceano. (SPA., Illus.). 96p. 28.00 (978-84-494-1307-0(9) , GML06502-176440) Oceano Grupo Editoria, S.A. ESP. *Dist:* Thomson Gale.

Diaz, Enrique Perez. El Nino Que Conversaba Con la Mar. 2000. Tr. of Boy Who Talked to the Sea. (SPA., Illus.). 128p. (J). (gr. 5 up). (978-84-236-5075-0(8) , ED4246) Edebé ESP. *Dist:* Lectorum Pubns., Inc.

—El Nino Que Conversaba Con la Mar. 2000. Tr. of Boy Who Talked to the Sea. (SPA.). (gr. 5-8). lib. bdg. 18.75 (978-0-613-85811-3(5)) Tandem Library Bks.

Farmer Bob Oceans Series. 2001. (978-1-883772-86-4(9)); (J). (978-1-883772-78-9(8)) Flying Rhinoceros, Inc.

Finding Nemo. 2003. 128p. (J). 19.95 (978-0-7868-5400-4(6)) Disney Pr.

Fisher, Leonard Everett. Sky, Sea, the Jetty, & Me. 2001. (Illus.). 32p. (J). (gr. k-3). 15.95 (978-0-7614-5082-5(3) , Cavendish Children's Bks.) Cavendish, Marshall Corp.

Flynn, Pat. To the Light. Stewart, Chantal, illus. 2005. 120p. (Orig.). (YA). pap. 16.95 (978-0-7022-3492-7(3)) Univ. of Queensland Pr. AUS. *Dist:* International Specialized Bk. Services.

Follow the Fish: A Touch & Say ABC Book. 2002. (DK Ladybird Ser.). 12p. (J). bds. 6.95 (978-0-7894-8470-3(6)) Dorling Kindersley Publishing, Inc.

Frasier, Debra. Out of the Ocean. Frasier, Debra, illus. 1998. (Illus.). 40p. (J). (ps-3). 16.00 (978-0-15-258849-6(3) , Red Wagon Bks.) Harcourt Children's Bks.

Gall, Chris. Dear Fish. 2006. (Illus.). 36p. (J). (ps-1). 16.99 (978-0-316-05847-6(5)) Little Brown & Co.

Groves. Bee & the Sea, Bk. 9. Date not set. (Illus.). 32p. (J). pap. 129.15 (978-0-582-18770-2(2)) Addison-Wesley Longman, Ltd. GBR. *Dist:* Trans-Atlantic Pubns., Inc.

Hamilton, Harriet E. The Sunbeam & the Wave. Bowen, Connie, illus. 2000. 33p. (J). (gr. 4-7). 17.95 (978-0-87159-250-7(9)) Unity Schl. of Christianity.

Harcourt School Publishers Staff. At the Beach. 3rd ed. 2002. (Trophies English Language Learners Ser.). (Illus.). pap. 5.10 (978-0-15-327888-4(9)) Harcourt Schl. Pubs.

—At the Beach: Independent Reader. 3rd ed. 2002. (Trophies Reading Program Ser.). (Illus.). (J). pap. 2.90 (978-0-15-325501-4(3)) Harcourt Schl. Pubs.

—En la Playa. 2000. (SPA., Illus.). pap. 82.60 (978-0-15-315094-4(7)) Harcourt Schl. Pubs.

—Wave Rider. 3rd ed. 2002. (Trophies English Language Learners Ser.). (Illus.). (gr. 5). pap. 5.10 (978-0-15-327819-8(6)) Harcourt Schl. Pubs.

—What Do You See at the Sea. 3rd ed. 2002. (Trophies English Language Learners Ser.). (Illus.). (J). pap. 3.20 (978-0-15-327573-9(1)) Harcourt Schl. Pubs.

Hoffman, Basia. The Ocean & Pebbles. Solcyk, Phyllis, illus. l.t. ed. 1999. 32p. (J). (ps-2). pap. (978-1-890582-02-9(6)) Creations by Basia.

Kalan, Robert. Blue Sea. 2002. (Illus.). (J). 14.43 (978-0-7587-2127-3(7)) Book Wholesalers, Inc.

Karas, G. Brian. Atlantic. Karas, G. Brian, illus. 2002. (Illus.). 32p. (J). (ps-3). 15.99 (978-0-399-23632-7(5) , Putnam Juvenile) Penguin Group (USA) Inc.

—Atlantic. 2004. (gr. k-3). lib. bdg. 15.30 (978-0-613-82996-0(4)) Tandem Library Bks.

Karwoski, Gail Langer. Water Beds: Sleeping in the Ocean. McLennan, Connie, illus. (J). 2007. 1p. 8.95 (***978-1-934359-01-3(7)); *** 2005. 32p. 15.95 (978-0-9764943-1-7(0)) Sylvan Dell Pubng.

Kessler, Liz. The Tail of Emily Windsnap. Gibb, Sarah, illus. 2004. (Emily Windsnap Ser.). 224p. (J). (gr. 3-7). 15.99 (978-0-7636-2483-5(7)) Candlewick Pr.

Korman, Gordon. The Discovery. 2003. (Dive Ser.: No. 1). (gr. 3-6). lib. bdg. 12.40 (978-0-613-67481-2(2)) Tandem Library Bks.

Kranking, Kathy & Kranking, Kathleen W. The Ocean Is. . . Wu, Norbert, photos by. 2003. (Illus.). 32p. (J). (ps-2). 17.95 (978-0-8050-7097-2(4) , Holt, Henry & Co. Bks. For Young Readers) Holt, Henry & Co.

Learning Colors. 1999. (Illus.). (J). (978-1-56156-835-2(X)) Kidsbooks, Inc.

Lewis, Anthony, illus. Little Ocean Explorers. 2007. 14p. bds. 7.99 (***978-1-84643-039-8(9)***) Child's Play International Ltd. GBR. *Dist:* Child's Play-International.

Maine, Margarita. Un Mar Muy Mojado. (SPA.). pap. 8.95 (978-950-07-1985-8(1)) Editorial Sudamericana S.A. ARG. *Dist:* Distribooks, Inc.

Marsh, T. F. Quest for Courage. Marsh, T. F., illus. 2006. (Amazing Travels of Wannabeb Ser.). (Illus.). 32p. (J). 8.99 (978-0-7847-1801-8(6) , 04127) Standard Publishing.

Marshall, Edward & Marshall, James. Three by the Sea. 48p. (J). (gr. k-3). pap. 3.99 (978-0-8072-1342-1(X) , Listening Library) Random Hse. Audio Publishing Group.

McClear, Preston. The Sailor & the Sea Witch. Dollak, Nicholas, illus. 1999. 31p. (J). (gr. k-5). 16.95 (978-1-929084-00-5(5)); pap. 12.95 (978-1-929084-01-2(3)) Malibu Bks. for Children.

McKillip, Patricia A. Changeling Sea. 2003. (gr. 7-12). lib. bdg. 14.15 (978-0-613-61615-7(4)) Tandem Library Bks.

Morris, John D. A Trip to the Ocean. Chong, Jonathan, illus. 2000. (DJ & Tracker John Ser.). 40p. (J). (ps-3). 11.99 (978-0-89051-285-2(X) , 303-058) Master Bks.

Morrison, P. R. Wave Traveller. 2007. 300p. (J). (gr. 3-7). 16.95 (***978-1-59990-123-7(4)***) Bloomsbury Publishing.

Mullican, Judy. Under the Sea. Carroll, Ken, Jr., illus. 1998. (Big Bks.). 8p. (J). (ps-k). pap. 10.95 (978-1-57332-093-1(5)) HighReach Learning, Inc.

Navarro, Dawn E., et al. Chelonia: El Retorno de la Tortuga Marina. 2002. (SPA., Illus.). (J). (gr. 3-5). 16.95 (978-0-930118-35-8(9) , SCH31403) Sea Challengers, Inc.

Nye, Bill & Saunders, Ian G. Bill Nye the Science Guy's Great Big Book of Science: Featuring Oceans & Dinosaurs. Dykes, John & Koelsch, Michael, illus. 2005. 96p. (gr. 2-5). pap., pap. 12.99 (978-0-7868-5591-9(6)) Hyperion Pr.

Ocean Explorers: Individual Title Six-Packs. (Rigby Infoquest Ser.). 24p. (gr. 3 up). 34.00 (978-0-7578-5773-7(6)) Rigby Education.

O'Neill, Michael Patrick. Fishy Friends: A Journey Through the Coral Kingdom. O'Neill, Michael Patrick, photos by. 2003. (Illus.). 64p. (J). 19.95 (978-0-9728653-0-2(6)) Batfish Bks.

O'Rourke, Carol J. Sea Critters Vol. 2: The Splangywangba Adventure. 1998. (Illus.). 14p. (J). (gr. k-4). pap. 2.95 (978-0-9665692-1-6(0)) Sea Critters.

Pallotta, Jerry. Dory Story. Biedrzycki, David, illus. 32p. (J). (gr. k-2). 2004. pap. 7.95 (978-0-88106-076-8(3)); 2000. 15.95 (978-0-88106-075-1(5)) Charlesbridge Publishing, Inc.

—Dory Story. Biedrzycki, David, illus. 2004. (J). (ps-ps). lib. bdg. 14.50 (978-0-606-30230-2(1)) Tandem Library Bks.

Papineau, Lucie. Gilda the Giraffe & Leonardo the Lion Cub. Sarrazin, Marisol, illus. 2005. (Gilda the Giraffe Ser.). 32p. (J). (ps-3). lib. bdg. 22.60 (978-1-4048-1294-9(6)) Picture Window Bks.

Peck, Jan. Way down Deep in the Deep Blue Sea. Petrone, Valeria, illus. 2004. 32p. (J). 16.99 (978-0-689-85110-0(3)) Simon & Schuster Children's Publishing.

Piano, Maureen & Sykes, Christine. When Flamingos Fly. 2006. 44p. (J). 12.99 (978-1-59092-362-7(6) , Orchard Academy Pr.) Windstorm Creative.

Pierre, Stephanie. What the Sea Saw. Doyle, Beverly, illus. 2006. 48p. (J). 16.95 (978-1-56145-359-7(5)) Peachtree Pubs., Ltd.

Plourde, Lynn. The First Feud: Between the Mountain & the Sea. Sollers, Jim, illus. 2003. 30p. 15.95 (978-0-89272-611-0(3)) Down East Bks.

Raintree Steck-Vaughn Staff. Why the Ocean is Salty. 1999. (Illus.). (J). pap. 35.60 (978-0-7398-0899-3(0)) Steck-Vaughn.

Rockhill, Dennis. Ocean Whisper/Susurro del Océano. de la Vega, Eida, tr. Rockhill, Dennis, illus. 2005. Tr. of Susurro del Océano. (SPA & ENG., Illus.). 32p. (J). 16.95 (978-0-9741992-4-5(9) , 626999) Raven Tree Pr.

Rundstrom, T. S. Sherman the Sheep: A Sheep Adventure Story about Dreams, Doing Stuff & Happiness. Miller, Bryan & Marshall, H. Keene, illus. l.t. ed. 2002. per. (978-1-932062-00-7(9) , 02-0232SH) Hability Solution Services, Inc.

Russon, Penni. Undine. 2006. (Illus.). 336p. (J). 16.99 (978-0-06-079389-0(9)); lib. bdg. 17.89 (978-0-06-079390-6(2)) HarperCollins Pubs.

Ryan, Pam Muñoz. Hello, Ocean. Astrella, Mark, illus. 2001. Tr. of Hola Mar. 32p. (J). (ps-3). 16.95 (978-0-88106-987-7(6)); pap. 6.95 (978-0-88106-988-4(4)) Charlesbridge Publishing, Inc.

—Hello, Ocean. 2001. Tr. of Hola Mar. (gr. 3-6). lib. bdg. 15.25 (978-0-613-46076-7(6)); (Illus.). (J). 13.75 (978-0-606-20698-3(1)) Tandem Library Bks.

—Hello, Ocean: Hola Mar. Canetti, Yanitzia, tr. Astrella, Mark, illus. 2004. (ENG & SPA.). 32p. (J). (gr. k-3). pap. 7.95 (978-1-57091-372-3(2)) Charlesbridge Publishing, Inc.

Sackin, Jacob. Islands. 2008. 280p. (YA). pap. 14.99 (978-1-59092-392-4(8) , Blue Works) Windstorm Creative.

Santillo, LuAnn. Flap. Santillo, LuAnn, ed. 2003. (Half-Pint Kids Readers Ser.). (Illus.). 7p. (J). (ps-1). pap. (978-1-59256-096-7(2)) Half-Pint Kids, Inc.

Shepard, Aaron. The Sea King's Daughter: A Russian Legend. 1999. (Illus.). 28p. (J). (gr. k-3). per. 17.00 (978-0-689-82743-3(1) , Simon & Schuster Children's Publishing) Simon & Schuster Children's Publishing.

Shih, Bernadette L. Follow the Sea. Turner, Francia, tr. Turner, Francia, illus. 1998. 32p. (J). (ps-3). (ENG & SPA.). 16.95 (978-1-889736-07-5(4)); pap. (978-1-889736-06-8(6)) Ridyl Publishing.

Simmons, Derek. Flash of Life. 2006. 85p. pap. 14.95 (***978-1-4241-3890-6(6)***) PublishAmerica, Inc.

Simpson, Dorothy. Visitors from the Sea. Date not set. 188p. (J). 20.95 (978-0-8488-2632-1(9)) Amereon LTD.

Smith, Geof & Hands, Cynthia. A Christmas Coral. 2001. (Little Golden Bks.). 32p. (J). (ps-3). pap. 3.99 (978-0-307-29055-7(7) , Golden Bks.) Random Hse. Children's Bks.

Stratemeyer, Edward. The Rover Boys on the Ocean: Or, a Chase for a Fortune. 2006. 158p. pap. 11.99 (978-1-4264-2766-4(2)); 170p. pap. 14.99 (978-1-4264-2804-3(9)) BiblioBazaar.

Thompson, D. R. The Big Ocean: An Underwater Naptime Adventure. Thompson, D. R. & Thompson, Dave, illus. 2004. (Naptime Adventure Ser.: Vol. 2). 32p. (J). (ps-3). 14.95 (978-0-9723252-2-6(0)) This New World Publishing, LLC.

ToyBox Innovations, creator. Disney's Princess Little Mermaid. abr. ed. 2006. (Disney's Read along Collection). (J). (ps-3). pap. 14.99 incl. audio compact disk (978-0-7634-2184-7(7)) Walt Disney Records.

Whalen, Erin T. Charlie Goes to Sea! Grant, Stacey, ed. Conde, Donna, photos by. l.t. ed. 2001. (Charlie's Head Ser.). (Illus.). 32p. (J). (gr. 1-3). 16.95 (978-1-929265-02-2(6)); pap. 8.95 (978-1-929265-03-9(4)) Lily & Co. Publishing.

What's under the Sea? (J). 12.99 (978-1-58086-936-2(X)) EDC Publishing.

What's under the Sea? 2003. (J). per. (978-1-57657-934-3(4)) Paradise Pr., Inc.

Winfield (Edward Str Staff. The Rover Boys on the Ocean or a Chase F. 2006. 63.99 (***978-1-4280-1827-3(1)***) Indy-Publish.com.

Yee, Paul. The Jade Necklace. Lin, Grace, illus. 2006. 29p. (J). (gr. 4-8). reprint ed. 16.00 (978-1-4223-5135-2(1)) DIANE Publishing Co.

OCEAN BOTTOM

Aleshire & Peter. Ocean Ridges & Trenches. 2007. (Extreme Earth Ser.). 168p. (J). (gr. 6-12). 35.00 (978-0-8160-5919-5(5)) Facts On File, Inc.

Cole, Joanna. The Magic School Bus on the Ocean Floor. Degen, Bruce, illus. (Magic School Bus Ser.). (FRE.). (J). (gr. 1-4). pap. 6.99 (978-0-590-24318-6(7)) Scholastic, Inc.

Kavocs. Dive into the Deep Ocean. 1998. (J). pap. 10.80 (978-0-7398-0021-8(3)) Steck-Vaughn.

Macken, JoAnn Early. Ocean Floors. 2005. (Illus.). 24p. (J). (978-0-8368-4892-2(6)); lib. bdg. 19.33 (978-0-8368-4885-4(3)) Stevens, Gareth Inc.

—Ocean Floors: Fondos Oceanicos. 2005. (SPA., Illus.). 24p. (J). (978-0-8368-6037-5(3)) Stevens, Gareth Inc.

—Ocean Floors/Fondos Oceanicos. 2005. (SPA., Illus.). 24p. (J). (ps-17). lib. bdg. 19.33 (978-0-8368-6030-6(6)) Stevens, Gareth Inc.

Woodward, John. The Seafloor. 2004. (Illus.). 48p. (J). pap. 8.50 (978-1-4034-5132-3(X)); lib. bdg. 27.07 (978-1-4034-5126-2(5)) Heinemann Library.

OCEAN LIFE

see Marine Biology

OCEAN ROUTES

see Trade Routes

OCEAN TRAVEL

Amato, William. Cruceros. 2004. (Vehiculos de Alta Tecnologia Ser.). (SPA & ENG., Illus.). 24p. (J). (gr. 3-6). lib. bdg. 17.25 (978-0-8239-6884-8(7) , Buenas Letra) Rosen Publishing Group, Inc., The.

Birnbaum Travel Guides Staff. Birnbaum's Disney Cruise Line 2007. 2006. (Illus.). 224p. (ps-17). pap. 13.95 (978-1-4231-0052-2(2) , Disney Editions) Disney Pr.

Cooper, Jason. Cruise Ships. 1999. (Boats & Ships Discovery Library). (Illus.). 24p. (J). (gr. 1-4). lib. bdg. 19.27 (978-0-86593-563-1(7)) Rourke Publishing, LLC.

Cruise Ships: Individual Title Six-Packs. (On Deck Ser.). 24p. (gr. 4-5). 35.00 (978-0-7578-1056-5(X)) Rigby Education.

MacDonald, Fiona, et al. You Wouldn't Want to Sail with Christopher Columbus! Uncharted Waters You'd Rather Not Cross. 2004. (You Wouldn't Want To Ser.). (J). 28.50 (978-0-531-12355-3(3) , Watts, Franklin) Scholastic Library Publishing.

O'Brien, Patrick. The Mutiny on the Bounty. O'Brien, Patrick, illus. 2007. (Illus.). 40p. (J). (gr. 3-6). 17.95 (978-0-8027-9587-8(0)); 18.85 (978-0-8027-9588-5(9)) Walker & Co.

Patterson, Kevin. Water in Between: A Journey at Sea. 2001. (gr. 7-12). lib. bdg. 22.25 (978-0-613-36892-6(4)) Tandem Library Bks.

Paulsen, Gary. Caught by the Sea. l.t. ed. 2002. 104p. (J). 22.95 (978-0-7862-4160-6(8)) Thomson Gale.

—Caught by the Sea: My Life on Boats. (Illus.). 112p. (YA). 2003. (gr. 7). mass mkt. 5.50 (978-0-440-40716-4(8) , Laurel Leaf); 2001. (gr. 5 up). 15.95 (978-0-385-32645-2(9) , Delacorte Bks. for Young Readers) Random Hse. Children's Bks.

—Caught by the Sea: My Life on Boats. 2003. (gr. 7-12). lib. bdg. 13.55 (978-0-613-72185-1(3)) Tandem Library Bks.

Shuter, Jane. Making Waves: Travel by Sea. 2004. (Technology Through Time Ser.). (Illus.). 32p. (J). lib. bdg. 25.70 (978-1-4109-0581-9(0)) Raintree.

OCEAN TRAVEL—FICTION

Bunting, Eve. Dreaming of America: An Ellis Island Story. 2001. (J). (978-0-606-21164-2(0)) Tandem Library Bks.

Chambers, Veronica. Amistad Rising: A Story of Freedom. 1998. (Illus.). 40p. (J). (gr. 4-7). lib. bdg. (978-0-8172-5510-7(9)) Raintree.

Coatsworth, Elizabeth Jane. The Fair American. Sewell, Helen, illus. 2005. 137p. (J). (***978-1-883937-85-0(X)***) Bethlehem Bks.

Creech, Sharon. The Wanderer. Diaz, David, illus. 2000. 320p. (J). (ps-3). 16.99 (978-0-06-027730-7(0) , Cotler, Joanna Books) HarperCollins Pubs.

—The Wanderer. l.t. ed. 2003. 263p. pap. 10.95 (978-0-7862-6186-4(2)) Thorndike Pr.

Glaser, Linda. Bridge to America: Based on a True Story. 2005. (Illus.). 208p. (J). (gr. 4-6). 16.00 (978-0-618-56301-2(6)) Houghton Mifflin Co. Trade & Reference Div.

Holabird, Katharine. All Dancers on Deck. Craig, Helen, illus. 2006. (Angelina Ballerina Ser.). 32p. (J). (ps-1). 3.99 (978-0-448-44388-1(0) , Grosset & Dunlap) Penguin Group (USA) Inc.

Hunt, Angela Elwell. The Deadly Chase. 2000. (Colonial Captives Ser.: Vol. 2). 192p. (gr. 4-7). pap. 12.95 (978-0-595-08997-0(6) , Backinprint.com) iUniverse, Inc.

Jantti, Mariana. Christopher Has a Dream. 2006. (Illus.). 28p. (J). 12.95 (978-9974-7960-0-3(8)) Hardenville SA URY. *Dist:* Independent Pubs. Group.

Lalicki, Tom. Shots at Sea. Cerniglia, Carlyn, illus. 2007. (Houdini & Nate Mysteries Ser.). 208p. (J). (gr. 3-7). 15.95 (***978-0-374-31679-2(1)***) Farrar, Straus & Giroux.

Lawlor, Laurie. Voyage to a Free Land, 1630. 2001. (American Sisters Ser.). (Illus.). (J). (978-0-606-20975-5(1)) Tandem Library Bks.

Lawrence, Caroline. The Colossus of Rhodes. 2006. (Roman Mysteries Ser.). (Illus.). 208p. (J). 16.95 (978-1-59643-082-2(6)) Roaring Brook Pr.

Lawrence, Iain. The Cannibals. 2005. 240p. (J). (gr. 7-9). lib. bdg. 17.99 (978-0-385-90110-9(0) , Delacorte Bks. for Young Readers) Random Hse. Children's Bks.

—The Cannibals: The Curse of the Jolly Stone Trilogy. 2007. (Curse of the Jolly Stone Trilogy Ser.: Bk. II). 240p. (YA). (gr. 7 up). mass mkt. 6.50 (978-0-440-41933-4(6) , Laurel Leaf) Random Hse. Children's Bks.

—The Convicts. 2005. 208p. (gr. 7-9). (J). lib. bdg. 17.99 (978-0-385-90109-3(7)); (YA). 15.95 (978-0-385-73087-7(X)) Random Hse. Children's Bks. (Delacorte Bks. for Young Readers).

Manus, Willard. A Dog Called Leka. 2007. (ENG.). 122p. pap. 7.99 (***978-0-9740551-3-8(1)***) Smith, Viveca Publishing.

Martel, Yann. Life of Pi: A Novel. 2003. (gr. 7-12). lib. bdg. 23.45 (978-0-613-59907-8(1)) Tandem Library Bks.

Neale, Cynthia G. The Irish Dresser: A Story of Hope During the Great Hunger (an Gorta Mor, 1845-1850) 2003. 148p. (J). pap. 7.95 (978-1-57249-344-5(5) , White Mane Kids) White Mane Publishing Co., Inc.

Penn, Audrey. Blackbeard & the Gift of Silence. 2007. 355p. (gr. 3-7). 15.95 (***978-1-933718-11-8(0)***) Tanglewood Pr.

Riddell, Chris & Stewart, Paul. Far-Flung Adventures: Corby Flood. 2006. (Illus.). 256p. (J). (gr. 3-7). 14.95 (978-0-385-75090-5(0)); lib. bdg. 17.99 (978-0-385-75091-2(9)) Random Hse. Children's Bks. (Fickling, David Bks.).

Sandoval, Lynda. Chicks Ahoy. 2006. 224p. (YA). pap. 7.99 (978-0-689-86441-4(8) , Simon Pulse) Simon & Schuster Children's Publishing.

Shearer, Alex. Sea Legs. 2005. 320p. (J). 16.95 (978-0-689-87143-6(0)) Simon & Schuster Children's Publishing.

Tanaka, Shelley. On Board the Titanic: What It Was Like When the Great Liner Sank. 1999. (Illus.). (J). (978-0-606-15659-2(3)) Tandem Library Bks.

Trottier, Maxine. Dreamstones. 2000. (gr. 3-6). lib. bdg. 16.40 (978-0-613-49487-8(3)) Tandem Library Bks.

Wall, Bill. That Black Day: A Lusitania Story. 2001. 128p. (J). pap. 7.95 (978-1-85635-325-0(7)) Mercier Pr., Ltd., The IRL. *Dist:* Irish Bks. & Media, Inc.

Winfield, Arthur M. The Rover Boys on Land & Sea or the Crusoes of Seven Islands. 2006. (ENG.). 284p. per. 28.95 (***978-1-4286-4097-9(5)***) Kessinger Publishing, LLC.

Woolf, Virginia. The Voyage Out. 2001. (gr. 7-12). lib. bdg. 21.05 (978-0-613-50140-8(3)) Tandem Library Bks.

Yin. Coolies. Soentpiet, Chris, illus. 2003. 40p. (J). (gr. k-3). pap. 7.99 (978-0-14-250055-2(0) , Puffin) Penguin Group (USA) Inc.

—Coolies. Soentpiet, Chris K., illus. 2001. 1p. (J). (ps-3). 16.99 (978-0-399-23227-5(3) , Philomel) Penguin Group (USA) Inc.

—Coolies. 2003. (gr. 3-6). lib. bdg. 16.45 (978-0-613-62936-2(1)) Tandem Library Bks.

Zaugg, Sandra L. Hidden Notes & High Seas. 2005. (Illus.). 95p. (J). (978-0-8163-2052-3(7)) Pacific Pr. Pubns.

OCEAN WAVES

Drohan, Michele Ingber. Tsunamis. 1999. (Natural Disasters Ser.). (Illus.). 24p. (J). (gr. k-4). lib. bdg. 19.95 (978-0-8239-5286-1(X) , PowerKids Pr.) Rosen Publishing Group, Inc., The.

Gleason, Carrie. Ocean Storm Alert! 2004. (Disaster Alert! Ser.). (Illus.). 32p. (J). (978-0-7787-1579-5(5)) Crabtree Publishing Co.

Ingram, Scott. Tsunami! The 1946 Hilo Wave of Terror. 2005. (X-Treme Disasters That Changed America Ser.). (Illus.). 32p. (J). lib. bdg. 25.27 (978-1-59716-010-0(5)) Bearport Publishing Co., Inc.

Kampion, Drew. Waves: From Surfing to Tsunami. Drew, Jeff & Peterson, Jeff, illus. 2005. 80p. (YA). 19.95 (978-1-58685-212-2(4)) Gibbs Smith, Publisher.

Meister, Cari. Earthquakes. 1999. (Nature's Fury Ser.). (Illus.). 32p. (J). (gr. 3-8). lib. bdg. 24.21 (978-1-57765-083-6(2) , ABDO & Daughters) ABDO Publishing Co.

Spilsbury, Louise & Spilsbury, Richard. Sweeping Tsunamis. 32p. (J). 2005. lib. bdg. 27.07 (978-1-4034-7275-5(0)); 2005. pap. 7.50 (978-1-4034-7276-2(9)); 2003. (Illus.). pap. (978-1-4034-4233-8(9)); 2003. (Illus.). lib. bdg. 24.22 (978-1-4034-3725-9(4)) Heinemann Library.

Thompson, Luke. Tsunamis. 2000. (High Interest Bks.). (Illus.). 48p. (YA). (gr. 7-12). pap. 6.95 (978-0-516-23568-4(0) , Children's Pr.) Scholastic Library Publishing.

Vogel, Carole G. Shifting Shores. 2003. (Restless Sea Ser.). (Illus.). 80p. (J). (gr. 5-8). 30.50 (978-0-531-12322-5(7) , Watts, Franklin) Scholastic Library Publishing.

—Shifting Shores. 2003. (gr. 5-8). lib. bdg. 22.20 (978-0-613-67855-1(9)) Tandem Library Bks.

Walker, Jane & Saunders, Mike. Tidal Waves & Flooding. 2004. (Natural Disasters Ser.). (J). lib. bdg. 27.10 (978-1-932799-62-0(1)) Stargazer Bks.

OCEANIA

see Islands of the Pacific

OCEANOGRAPHIC RESEARCH

see Oceanography—Research

OCEANOGRAPHY

see also Marine Biology; Marine Resources; Navigation; Ocean Waves; Submarine Geology

Baker, Lucy. Life in the Oceans. 2001. (World Book Ecology Ser.). (Illus.). 32p. (J). (978-0-7166-5222-9(6)) World Bk., Inc.

Barnes, Julia. 101 Facts about Oceans. 2003. (One Hundred One Facts about Our World Ser.). (Illus.). 32p. (J). (gr. 3 up). lib. bdg. 23.33 (978-0-8368-3709-4(6)) Stevens, Gareth Inc.

Bayrock, Fiona. The Ocean Explorer's Handbook. 2005. (Undersea University Ser.). (Illus.). 48p. (J). pap. (978-0-439-71184-5(3)) Scholastic, Inc.

BBC Staff, contrib. by. Ocean World. 2002. (Blue Planet Ser.). (Illus.). 64p. (J). (gr. 3-7). pap. 4.95 (978-0-439-33412-9(8)) Scholastic, Inc.

Berger, Melvin & Berger, Gilda. What Makes an Ocean Wave? Questions & Answers about Oceans. 2001. (Scholastic Question & Answer Ser.). (J). pap. 4.99 (978-0-439-09589-1(1)) Scholastic, Inc.

—What Makes an Ocean Wave? Questions & Answers about Oceans. Rice, John, illus. 2001. (Question & Answer Ser.). 48p. (J). (gr. 2-4). pap. 14.95 (978-0-439-09588-4(3)) Scholastic, Inc.

Bramwell, Martyn. Alerta, Oceanos: Una Guia para Proteger el Mundo en que Vivimos. Misol, Fernando Bort, tr. 2001. Tr. of Ocean Watch: A Guide to Protecting the World in Which we Live. 60p. (J). (978-84-348-7427-5(X)) SM Ediciones ESP. *Dist:* AIMS International Bks., Inc.

Burns, Loree Griffin. Tracking Trash: Flotsam, Jetsam, & the Science of Ocean Motion. 2007. (Scientists in the Field Ser.). (Illus.). 64p. (J). (gr. 5-8). 18.00 (978-0-618-58131-3(6)) Houghton Mifflin Co.

Claybourne, Anna. Deep Oceans. 2007. (J). ***(978-1-4329-0108-0(7));*** pap. ***(978-1-4329-0114-1(1))*** Heinemann Library.

Collard, Sneed B., III. The Deep-Sea Floor. Wenzell, Gregory, illus. 2003. 32p. (J). (gr. 2-6). 16.95 (978-1-57091-402-7(8)); pap. 6.95 (978-1-57091-403-4(6)) Charlesbridge Publishing, Inc.

La Conservacion del Mar. (Coleccion Biblioteca Juvenil de Ecología). (SPA., Illus.). (YA). (gr. 5-8). pap. (978-958-04-2405-5(5) , 80424055) Norma S.A. COL. *Dist:* Lectorum Pubns., Inc.

Dalgleish, Sharon & Turner, Garda. People & the Sea. 2003. (Ocean Facts Ser.). (Illus.). 24p. (gr. 2-4). 23.00 (978-0-7910-7287-5(8) , Chelsea Hse.) Facts On File, Inc.

Day, Trevor. Exploring the Oceans, 4 vols. 2003. (Illus.). (J). (978-0-19-521967-8(8)); (978-0-19-521968-5(6)); (978-0-19-521969-2(4)); (978-0-19-521970-8(8)) Oxford Univ. Pr., Inc.

Deboo, Ana. Mapping the Seas & Skies. 2006. (Illus.). 32p. (J). (978-1-4034-6793-5(5)); pap. (978-1-4034-6800-0(1)) Heinemann Library.

Desonie, Dana. Oceans. 2007. (Our Fragile Planet Ser.). 232p. (J). (gr. 6-12). 35.00 ***(978-0-8160-6216-4(1)*** , Chelsea Hse.) Facts On File, Inc.

Diamond, Claudia C. What's under the Sea? 2002. (Reading Room Collection). (Illus.). 24p. (J). lib. bdg. 18.75 (978-0-8239-3743-1(7)) Rosen Publishing Group, Inc., The.

Franks, Sharon E. & Cohen, Judith Love. You Can Be A Woman Oceanographer. Katz, David Arthur, illus. 2004. (J). pap. 13.95 incl. DVD (978-1-880599-66-2(X)); 40p. 19.95 incl. DVD (978-1-880599-67-9(8)) Cascade Pass, Inc.

Furgang, Kathy. Let's Take a Field Trip to a Deep Sea Community. 2000. (Neighborhoods in Nature Ser.). (Illus.). 24p. (J). (gr. k-4). lib. bdg. 18.75 (978-0-8239-5448-3(X) , PowerKids Pr.) Rosen Publishing Group, Inc., The.

Goldstein, Natalie. How Do We Know the Nature of the Ocean? 2005. (Great Scientific Questions & the Scientists Who Answered Them Ser.). (Illus.). 112p. (J). (gr. 7-12). lib. bdg. 26.50 (978-1-4042-0079-1(7)) Rosen Publishing Group, Inc., The.

Gonzales, Doreen. The Arctic Ocean: A MyReportLinks. com Book. 2004. (Oceans of the World Ser.). (Illus.). 48p. (J). lib. bdg. 25.26 (978-0-7660-5193-5(5) , MyReportLinks.com Bks.) Enslow Pubs., Inc.

—The Atlantic Ocean: A MyReportLinks. com Book. 2004. (Oceans of the World Ser.). (Illus.). 48p. (J). lib. bdg. 25.26 (978-0-7660-5194-2(3) , MyReportLinks.com Bks.) Enslow Pubs., Inc.

—The Pacific Ocean: A MyReportLinks. com Book. 2004. (Oceans of the World Ser.). (Illus.). 48p. (J). lib. bdg. 25.26 (978-0-7660-5192-8(7) , MyReportLinks.com Bks.) Enslow Pubs., Inc.

Gonzalez, Doreen. The Indian Ocean: A MyReportLinks. com Book. 2004. (Oceans of the World Ser.). (Illus.). 48p. (J). lib. bdg. 25.26 (978-0-7660-5195-9(1) , MyReportLinks.com Bks.) Enslow Pubs., Inc.

Gordon, Sharon. At Home by the Ocean. 2005. (Bookworms Ser.). (ENG & SPA., Illus.). 32p. (J). (gr. 3-7). lib. bdg. (978-0-7614-1959-4(4) , Benchmark Bks.) Cavendish, Marshall Corp.

—At Home by the Ocean (Mi Casa Junto Al Mar) 2006. (Bookworms Ser.). (ENG & SPA., Illus.). 32p. (J). lib. bdg. 22.79 (978-0-7614-2456-7(3)) Cavendish, Marshall Corp.

—Mi Casa Junto Al Mar. 2006. (Bookworms Ser.). (SPA & ENG., Illus.). 32p. (J). lib. bdg. 22.79 (978-0-7614-2377-5(X)) Cavendish, Marshall Corp.

Hall, Stephen. Exploring the Oceans. 2000. (Inside Look Ser.). (Illus.). 48p. (J). (gr. 4 up). lib. bdg. 26.00 (978-0-8368-2726-2(0)) Stevens, Gareth Inc.

Harcourt School Publishers Staff. Planet H2O Below Level. 3rd ed. 2002. (Illus.). pap. 5.10 (978-0-15-323430-9(X)) Harcourt Schl. Pubs.

Hill, Christine M. Robert Ballard: Oceanographer Who Discovered the Titanic. 1999. (People to Know Ser.). (Illus.). 128p. (YA). (gr. 6-12). lib. bdg. 26.60 (978-0-7660-1147-2(X)) Enslow Pubs., Inc.

Holt, Rinehart and Winston Staff. Holt Science & Technology Chapter 13: Earth Science: Exploring the Oceans. 5th ed. 2004. (Illus.). pap. 12.86 (978-0-03-030319-7(2)) Holt, Rinehart & Winston.

—Holt Science & Technology Chapter 14: Earth Science: Movement of the Ocean. 5th ed. 2004. (Illus.). pap. 12.86 (978-0-03-030321-0(4)) Holt, Rinehart & Winston.

—Holt Science & Technology Chptr. 6: Movement of the Oceans: Chapter Resources - Tennessee Edition. 3rd ed. 2003. (J). pap. 11.40 (978-0-03-069112-6(5)) Holt, Rinehart & Winston.

Jedicke, Peter. Exploring the Ocean Depths. 2003. (Hot Science Ser.). (J). lib. bdg. 28.50 (978-1-58340-367-9(1)) Smart Apple Media.

Kerrod, Robin. The Sea. 2000. (Fantastic Facts Ser.). (Illus.). 64p. (gr. 2-7). pap. 6.95 (978-1-84215-321-5(8) , Southwater) Anness Publishing GBR. *Dist:* National Bk. Network.

—The Sea. Sweet, Stephen & Whetton, John, illus. 1998. (Young Scientist Concepts & Projects Ser.). 68p. (J). (gr. 4 up). lib. bdg. 26.60 (978-0-8368-2164-2(5)) Stevens, Gareth Inc.

Kling, Andrew A. Tsunamis. 2002. (Natural Disasters Ser.). (Illus.). 112p. (J). (gr. 6-10). 27.45 (978-1-59018-222-2(7) , Lucent Bks.) Thomson Gale.

Life on an Ocean Planet Laboratory & Activity Manual. 2005. (YA). spiral bd. (978-1-878663-35-1(6)) Current Publishing Corp.

Littlefield, Cindy A. Awesome Ocean Science. 2006. (Illus.). 120p. (J). 16.95 (978-0-8249-6797-0(6) , Williamson Bks.) Ideals Pubns.

Llewellyn, Claire. The Sea. 2003. (Starters Ser.). 24p. (J). lib. bdg. 21.35 (978-1-58340-262-7(4)) Smart Apple Media.

Madin, Kate. Down to a Sunless Sea: The Strange World of Hydrothermal Vents. 1999. (Illus.). 64p. (J). (gr. 5-9). pap. 8.95 (978-0-7398-1239-6(4)) Steck-Vaughn.

Mara, Wil. The Four Oceans. 2005. (Rookie Read-about Geography Ser.). (Illus.). (J). (gr. 1-2). 31p. pap. 5.95 (978-0-516-25817-1(6)); 32p. 20.50 (978-0-516-22749-8(1)) Scholastic Library Publishing. (Children's Pr.).

Myers, Janet Nuzum. Water Wonders of the World: From Killer Waves to Monsters of the Deep. 2006. (Illus.). 96p. (J). pap. (978-1-59336-729-9(5)) Mondo Publishing.

Nye, Bill. Bill Nye the Science Guy's Big Blue Ocean. 2003. (J). lib. bdg. 15.00 (978-0-613-61365-1(1)) Tandem Library Bks.

Oceans. 2004. (Discovery Channel School Science Ser.). (Illus.). 32p. (J). (gr. 5 up). lib. bdg. 24.67 (978-0-8368-3383-6(X)) Stevens, Gareth Inc.

Olesky, Walter. Mapping the Seas. 2002. (gr. 3-6). lib. bdg. 17.60 (978-0-613-59513-1(0)) Tandem Library Bks.

Packard, Mary. Mysteries of the Sea. Zalme, Ron, illus. 2005. (Ripley's Believe It of Not! Ser.). 85p. (J). pap. (978-0-439-72563-7(1)) Scholastic, Inc.

Palmer, Joy A. Oceans. 2000. (What About...? Ser.). 32p. (J). (gr. 1-4). pap. 5.72 (978-0-8114-4915-1(7)) Steck-Vaughn.

Petersen, Christine. Atlantic Ocean. 2001. (gr. 3-6). lib. bdg. 15.25 (978-0-613-53938-8(9)) Tandem Library Bks.

Petersen, David & Petersen, Christine. The Atlantic Ocean. 2001. (True Bks.). (Illus.). 48p. (J). (gr. 3-5). pap. 6.95 (978-0-516-27312-9(4) , Children's Pr.) Scholastic Library Publishing.

Petersen, David & Petersen, Christine A. The Atlantic Ocean. 2001. (Geography Ser.). (Illus.). 48p. (J). (gr. 3-5). 25.00 (978-0-516-22042-0(X) , Children's Pr.) Scholastic Library Publishing.

—The Pacific Ocean. 2001. (Geography Ser.). (Illus.). 48p. (J). (gr. 3-5). 25.00 (978-0-516-22043-7(8) , Children's Pr.) Scholastic Library Publishing.

Peterson, David. The Gulf of Mexico. 2001. (Geography Ser.). (Illus.). 48p. (J). (gr. 3-5). 25.00 (978-0-516-21665-2(1) , Children's Pr.) Scholastic Library Publishing.

Pike, Katy & O'Keefe, Maureen. Oceans. 2003. (Ocean Facts Ser.). (Illus.). 24p. (gr. 2-4). 23.00 (978-0-7910-7286-8(X) , Chelsea Hse.) Facts On File, Inc.

Riley, Peter D. The Ocean. 2004. (Survivor's Science Ser.). 28.56 (978-1-4109-0229-0(3)) Harcourt Schl. Pubs.

Rod Theodorou. To the Depths of the Ocean. 2nd ed. 2006. (Illus.). 32p. (J). pap. ***(978-1-4034-8799-5(5))*** Heinemann Library.

Royston, Angela. Oceans. 2004. (My World of Geography Ser.). (J). 22.79 (978-1-4034-5593-2(7)) Heinemann Library.

Saffer, Barbara. Science Questions & Answers: The Ocean. 1999. (Science Questions & Answers Ser.). (Illus.). 63p. (J). (gr. 1-3). pap. 5.95 (978-0-7373-0210-3(0)) Lowell Hse.

Savage, Stephen, et al. Oceans. 2006. (Kingfisher Voyages Ser.). (Illus.). 60p. (J). (gr. 4-6). 15.95 (978-0-7534-5903-4(5) , Kingfisher) Houghton Mifflin Co. Trade & Reference Div.

Serrano, Marta. Oceans. 2002. (Living Planet Ser.). (Illus.). 32p. (J). 23.70 (978-1-56711-669-4(8) , Blackbirch Pr., Inc.) Thomson Gale.

Sherwin, Frank. The Ocean Book. 2004. (Wonders of Creation Ser.). (Illus.). 80p. (J). 15.99 (978-0-89051-401-6(1)) Master Bks.

—The Ocean Book- Study Guide. 2005. pap. 3.99 (978-1-893345-62-1(9)) Answers in Genesis Ministries.

Steck-Vaughn Staff. Ocean Pilot, 4 bks., Set. 1999. (C). pap. (978-0-7398-1815-2(5)) Steck-Vaughn.

—Ocean Pilot Video. 1999. pap. 34.60 (978-0-7398-1263-1(7)) Steck-Vaughn.

Stille, Darlene R. Oceans. 2000. (True Bks.). (Illus.). 48p. (J). (gr. 3-5). pap. 6.95 (978-0-516-26768-5(X) , Children's Pr.) Scholastic Library Publishing.

—Oceans. 1999. (gr. 3-6). lib. bdg. 15.25 (978-0-613-37482-8(7)) Tandem Library Bks.

—Submarines. 2004. (Illus.). 32p. (J). (gr. 1 up). lib. bdg. 21.26 (978-0-7565-0610-0(7)) Compass Point Bks.

Theodorou, Rod. To the Depths of the Ocean. 32p. (J). 2006. (Illus.). ***(978-1-4034-8792-6(8));*** 2000. (gr. 3-5). lib. bdg. 22.79 (978-1-57572-484-3(7)) Heinemann Library.

—To the Depths of the Ocean. 2001. (gr. k-3). lib. bdg. 15.90 (978-0-613-89895-9(8)) Tandem Library Bks.

Vogel, Carole G. Savage Waters. 2003. (Restless Sea Ser.). (Illus.). 80p. (J). 30.50 (978-0-531-12321-8(9) , Watts, Franklin) Scholastic Library Publishing.

—Savage Waters. 2003. (gr. 5-8). lib. bdg. 22.20 (978-0-613-67852-0(4)) Tandem Library Bks.

Walker, Pam & Wood, Elaine. The Open Ocean. 2005. (Life in the Sea Ser.). (Illus.). 132p. (J). (gr. 4-9). 35.00 (978-0-8160-5705-4(2)) Facts On File, Inc.

—People & the Sea. 2005. (Life in the Sea Ser.). (Illus.). 132p. (J). (gr. 4-9). 35.00 (978-0-8160-5706-1(0)) Facts On File, Inc.

West, Krista. Hands-On Projects about Oceans. 2002. (Great Earth Science Projects Ser.). (Illus.). 24p. (J). lib. bdg. 19.95 (978-0-8239-5846-7(9) , PowerKids Pr.) Rosen Publishing Group, Inc., The.

Wohlers, Bob. Life on an Ocean Planet Student Text Book. 2005. (Illus.). lib. bdg. (978-1-878663-34-4(8)) Current Publishing Corp.

Wood, Lisa. Marine Science. 2005. Bk. 1. 72p. 12.95 (978-1-59363-096-6(4)); Vol. 2. 88p. 12.95 (978-1-59363-097-3(2)); Vol. 3. 80p. 12.95 (978-1-59363-098-0(0)) Prufrock Pr.

Woodward, John. Midnight Zone. 2004. (Illus.). 48p. (J). lib. bdg. (978-1-4034-5125-5(7)) Heinemann Library.

—The Midnight Zone. 2004. (Illus.). 48p. (J). pap. 8.50 (978-1-4034-5131-6(1)) Heinemann Library.

—Oceans. (Illus.). 64p. (YA). (gr. 4 up). lib. bdg. 29.95 (978-1-59389-125-1(3)) Chrysalis Education.

—Oceans. 2004. (Geography Fact Files Ser.). (J). lib. bdg. 28.50 (978-1-58340-427-0(9)) Smart Apple Media.

—The Seafloor. 2004. (Illus.). 48p. (J). pap. 8.50 (978-1-4034-5132-3(X)); lib. bdg. 27.07 (978-1-4034-5126-2(5)) Heinemann Library.

—The Sunlit Zone. 2004. (Illus.). 48p. (J). pap. 8.50 (978-1-4034-5133-0(8)); lib. bdg. (978-1-4034-5127-9(3)) Heinemann Library.

—The Tidal Zone. 2004. (Illus.). 48p. (J). pap. 8.50 (978-1-4034-5134-7(6)); lib. bdg. (978-1-4034-5128-6(1)) Heinemann Library.

—The Twilight Zone. 2004. (Illus.). 48p. (J). pap. 8.50 (978-1-4034-5135-4(4)); lib. bdg. (978-1-4034-5129-3(X)) Heinemann Library.

Ylvisaker, Anne. The Antarctic Ocean. 2002. (Oceans Ser.). (Illus.). 24p. (J). (gr. 1-2). lib. bdg. 18.60 (978-0-7368-1420-1(5) , Bridgestone Bks.) Capstone Pr., Inc.

—The Arctic Ocean. 2002. (Oceans Ser.). (Illus.). 24p. (J). (gr. 1-2). lib. bdg. 18.60 (978-0-7368-1423-2(X) , Bridgestone Bks.) Capstone Pr., Inc.

—The Atlantic Ocean. 2002. (Oceans Ser.). (Illus.). 24p. (J). (gr. 1-2). lib. bdg. 18.60 (978-0-7368-1424-9(8) , Bridgestone Bks.) Capstone Pr., Inc.

—The Indian Ocean. 2002. (Oceans Ser.). (Illus.). 24p. (J). (gr. 1-2). lib. bdg. 18.60 (978-0-7368-1425-6(6) , Bridgestone Bks.) Capstone Pr., Inc.

—The Pacific Ocean. 2002. (Oceans Ser.). (Illus.). 24p. (J). (gr. 1-2). lib. bdg. 18.60 (978-0-7368-1426-3(4) , Bridgestone Bks.) Capstone Pr., Inc.

OCEANOGRAPHY—BIOGRAPHY

Bankston, John. Jacques-Yves Cousteau: His Story under the Sea. 1.t. ed. 2002. (Unlocking the Secrets of Science Ser.). (Illus.). 56p. (gr. 4-10). lib. bdg. 17.95 (978-1-58415-112-8(9)) Mitchell Lane Pubs., Inc.

Polking, Kirk. Oceanographers & Explorers of the Sea. 1999. (Collective Biographies Ser.). (Illus.). 128p. (YA). (gr. 6-12). lib. bdg. 20.95 (978-0-7660-1113-7(5)) Enslow Pubs., Inc.

Zronik, John. Jacques Cousteau: Conserving Underwater Worlds. 2007. (Illus.). 32p. (J). (gr. 3-9). ***(978-0-7787-2419-3(0));*** pap. ***(978-0-7787-2455-1(7))*** Crabtree Publishing Co.

OCEANOGRAPHY—FICTION

Cook, Robin. Abduction. 2000. (gr. 7-12). lib. bdg. 16.45 (978-0-613-33574-4(0)) Tandem Library Bks.

Osborne, Mary Pope. Dark Day in the Deep Sea. Murdocca, Sal, illus. 2008. (Stepping Stone Bks.). 128p. (J). (gr. 3-7). lib. bdg. 14.99 ***(978-0-375-93731-6(5)*** , Random Hse. Bks. for Young Readers) Random Hse. Children's Bks.

Ricci, Christine. Dora in the Deep Sea. Roper, Robert, illus. 2003. (Dora the Explorer Ser.: Vol. 3). 24p. (J). pap. 3.99 (978-0-689-85845-1(0) , Simon Spotlight/ Nickelodeon) Simon & Schuster Children's Publishing.

—Dora in the Deep Sea. 2003. (ps-2). lib. bdg. 11.80 (978-0-613-73392-2(4)) Tandem Library Bks.

OCEANOGRAPHY—RESEARCH

see also Bathyscaphe; Skin Diving; Underwater Exploration

Diagram Group & Facts on File, Inc. Staff. Marine Science: An Illustrated Guide to Science. 2006. (Science Visual Resources Ser.). 208p. (J). (gr. 6-12). 49.50 (978-0-8160-6166-2(1)) Facts On File, Inc.

Kovacs, Deborah. Off to Sea: An Inside Look at a Research Cruise. 1999. (Turnstone Ocean Pilot Bks.). (Illus.). 48p. (J). (gr. 3-7). pap. 7.95 (978-0-7398-1229-7(7)) Steck-Vaughn.

Yount, Lisa. Modern Marine Science: Exploring the Deep. 2006. (Milestones in Discovery & Invention Ser.). 224p. (J). (gr. 6-12). 35.00 (978-0-8160-5747-4(8)) Facts On File, Inc.

OCEANOGRAPHY—VOCATIONAL GUIDANCE

Rauf, Don & Vescia, Monique. Oceanographer. 2008. (Virtual Apprentice Ser.). 64p. (J). (gr. 6-12). 29.95 ***(978-0-8160-6762-6(7)*** , Ferguson Publishing Co.) Facts On File, Inc.

OCEANOLOGY

see Oceanography

OCELOTS

Dollar, Sam. Ocelots. Sloan, Frank, ed. 2001. (Animals of the Rain Forest Ser.). (Illus.). 32p. (J). (gr. 4-7). lib. bdg. 22.83 (978-0-7398-3554-8(8)) Raintree.

Eckart, Edana. Ocelot. 2003. (Welcome Book Ser.). (Illus.). 24p. (J). 17.00 (978-0-516-24297-2(0) , Children's Pr.); pap. 4.95 (978-0-516-27894-0(0)) Scholastic Library Publishing.

OCTOPUSES

Baby's Bathtime Kid Kit. (Illus.). 10p. (YA). (ps up). 14.95 (978-1-58086-406-0(6)) EDC Publishing.

Berger, Melvin & Berger, Gilda. Octopus. 2003. (Scholastic Readers Ser.). (Illus.). (J). pap. (978-0-439-47391-0(8)) Scholastic, Inc.

Claybourne, Anna. Octopuses. 2003. (Secret World Of... Ser.). (Illus.). 48p. (J). lib. bdg. 27.14 (978-0-7398-7024-2(6)) Raintree.

Coldiron, Deborah. Octopuses. 2007. (Underwater World Ser.). (ENG., Illus.). 32p. (J). (gr. k-4). lib. bdg. 24.21 ***(978-1-59928-815-4(X)*** , Buddy Bks.) ABDO Publishing Co.

Gordon, Sharon. Adivina Quién Atrapa. 2006. (Bookworms Ser.). (SPA & ENG.). 32p. (J). lib. bdg. 22.79 (978-0-7614-2383-6(4)) Cavendish, Marshall Corp.

—Guess Who Grabs (Adivina Quién Atrapa) 2006. (Bookworms Ser.). (ENG & SPA.). 32p. (J). lib. bdg. 22.79 (978-0-7614-2464-2(4)) Cavendish, Marshall Corp.

The Greedy Gray Octopus: 6 Small Books. (gr. k-3). 24.00 (978-0-7635-6235-9(1)) Rigby Education.

Greenburg, Nicki. It's True! an Octopus Has Deadly Spit. Greenburg, Nicki, illus. 2007. (It's True! Ser.). (Illus.). 88p. (J). (gr. 5-8). 19.95 ***(978-1-55451-078-8(3));*** pap. 5.95 ***(978-1-55451-077-1(5))*** Annick Pr., Ltd. CAN. *Dist:* Firefly Bks., Ltd.

Gross, Miriam J. The Octopus. 2006. (Weird Sea Creatures Ser.). (Illus.). 23p. (J). lib. bdg. (978-1-4042-3188-7(9) , PowerKids Pr.) Rosen Publishing Group, Inc., The.

Herriges, Ann. Octopuses. 2006. (Blastoff! Readers Ser.). (Illus.). 24p. (J). (gr. k-3). lib. bdg. 16.95 (978-1-60014-019-8(X)) Bellwether Media.

Hirschi, Ron. Octopuses. 2000. (Nature Watch Ser.). (Illus.). 48p. (J). (gr. 3-6). lib. bdg. 25.26 (978-1-57505-386-8(1) , Carolrhoda Bks.) Lerner Publishing Group.

Hirschmann, Kris. The Octopus. 2002. (Creatures of the Sea Ser.). (Illus.). 48p. (J). (gr. 3-5). 23.70 (978-0-7377-0986-5(3) , Kidhaven) Thomson Gale.

Kalman, Bobbie. Amazing Octopus. 2003. (gr. 3-6). lib. bdg. 15.25 (978-0-613-59122-5(4)) Tandem Library Bks.

Kalman, Bobbie & Sjonger, Rebecca. The Amazing Octopus. 2003. (Living Ocean Ser.). (Illus.). 32p. (J). (gr. 2-9). (978-0-7787-1299-2(0)); pap. (978-0-7787-1321-0(0)) Crabtree Publishing Co.

Labella, Susan. Octopuses & Other Animals with Amazing Senses. 2005. (Scholastic News Nonfiction Readers Ser.). (Illus.). 24p. (J). (gr. 1-2). 19.00 (978-0-516-24928-5(2) , Children's Pr.) Scholastic Library Publishing.

Legg, Gerald. Octopuses & Squid. Francis, John, illus. 2004. (Scary Creatures Ser.). (J). 22.50 (978-0-531-12377-5(4)); 32p. (gr. 2-4). pap. 6.95 (978-0-531-16748-9(8)) Scholastic Library Publishing. (Watts, Franklin).

Lindeen, Carol K. Octopuses. 2005. (Under the Sea Ser.). (Illus.). 24p. (J). 19.93 (978-0-7368-3661-6(6)) Capstone Pr., Inc.

Markert, Jenny. Octopuses. 2007. (New Naturebooks Ser.). 32p. (J). (gr. 1-5). 27.07 ***(978-1-59296-849-7(X))*** Child's World, Inc.

Markle, Sandra. Octopuses. 2007. (Animal Prey Ser.). (Illus.). 40p. (J). (gr. 4-6). 25.26 (978-0-8225-6063-0(1) , Lerner Pubns.) Lerner Publishing Group.

Ocopuses. (Under the Sea Ser.). 24p. (J). 6.95 (978-0-7368-5117-6(8)) Capstone Pr., Inc.

Octopus. 2004. (J). 5.99 (978-0-7566-0251-2(3)) Dorling Kindersley Publishing, Inc.

MNO

Octopuses, 6 vols. (gr. k-2). 28.95 (978-0-7368-8257-6(X)) Red Brick Learning.

Octopuses Oceans Alive. 2006. (Illus.). 24p. (J). (gr. k-2). 18.50 (***978-0-531-17871-3(4)***) Scholastic Library Publishing.

Rhodes, Mary Jo & Hall, David. Octopuses & Squids. 2006. (Illus.). 48p. (J). (gr. 3-5). pap. 6.95 (978-0-516-25350-3(6) , Children's Pr.) Scholastic Library Publishing.

—Octopuses & Squids. Hall, David, photos by. 2005. (Undersea Encounters Ser.). (Illus.). 48p. (J). (ps-7). 27.00 (978-0-516-24394-8(2) , Children's Pr.) Scholastic Library Publishing.

Roop, Connie & Roop, Peter. Un Pulpo en el Mar. Schwartz, Carol, illus. 2002. (Coleccion "Hola, Lector" Ser.).Tr. of Octopus under the Sea. (SPA.). 32p. (J). pap. 3.99 (978-0-439-25041-2(2) , SO30880, Scholastic en Espanol) Scholastic, Inc.

Roop, Connie, et al. Octopus under the Sea. 2001. (Hello Reader! Science Ser.). (Illus.). 32p. (J). (ps-1). pap. 3.99 (978-0-439-20635-8(9)) Scholastic, Inc.

Schaefer, Lola M. Octopuses. 2005. (Ocean Life Ser.). 24p. (YA). (gr. k-3). pap. (978-0-7368-8217-0(0) , Pebble Bks.) Capstone Pr., Inc.

Souza, Dorothy M. Sea Creatures with Many Arms. 1998. (Creatures All Around Us Ser.). (Illus.). 40p. (J). (gr. 2-4). lib. bdg. (978-1-57505-262-5(8) , Carolrhoda Bks.) Lerner Publishing Group.

Spirn, Michele. Octopuses. 2006. (Smart Animals! Ser.). (Illus.). 32p. (J). (gr. 3-7). lib. bdg. 25.27 (978-1-59716-250-0(7)) Bearport Publishing Co., Inc.

Stille, Darlene R. Octopuses. 2003. (Sea Creatures Ser.). (Illus.). 32p. (J). lib. bdg. 22.79 (978-1-4034-0959-1(5)) Heinemann Library.

Stone, Lynn M. Octopus. 2006. (Rourke Discovery Library). (Illus.). 24p. (gr. 1-4). 14.95 (978-1-59515-440-8(X)) Rourke Publishing, LLC.

Stone, Tanya Lee. Octopuses. 2003. (Wild Wild World Ser.). 24p. (YA). 24.94 (978-1-56711-817-9(8) , Blackbirch Pr., Inc.) Thomson Gale.

Swanson, Diane. Octopuses. 2002. (Welcome to the World of Animals Ser.). (Illus.). 32p. (J). (gr. 3 up). lib. bdg. 23.33 (978-0-8368-3314-0(7)) Stevens, Gareth Inc.

—Welcome to the World of Octopuses. 2000. (Welcome to the World Ser.). (Illus.). 32p. (J). (ps-2). pap. 5.95 (978-1-55285-023-7(4)) Whitecap Bks., Ltd. CAN. *Dist:* Firefly Bks., Ltd.

Taylor, L. R. Octopuses. Wu, Norbert, illus. Wu, Norbert, photos by. 2002. (Early Bird Nature Bks.). 48p. (J). (gr. 2-4). lib. bdg. 25.26 (978-0-8225-0068-1(X) , Lerner Pubns.) Lerner Publishing Group.

Thompson, Paul. Octopuses. 2004. (Nature's Children Ser.). (J). (978-0-7172-5970-0(6) , Grolier) Scholastic Library Publishing.

Trueit, Trudi Strain. Octopuses, Squids, & Cuttlefish. (Animals in Order Ser.). (Illus.). 48p. (J). 2003. (gr. 4-6). pap. 6.95 (978-0-531-16377-1(6)); 2002. (gr. 5-7). pap. 26.50 (978-0-531-11930-3(0)) Scholastic Library Publishing. (Watts, Franklin).

—Octopuses, Squids, & Cuttlefish. 2002. (gr. 3-6). lib. bdg. 15.25 (978-0-613-59531-5(9)) Tandem Library Bks.

Wallace, Karen. Gentle Giant Octopus. Bostock, Mike, illus. 2002. (Read & Wonder Ser.). 32p. (J). (ps-3). pap. 6.99 (978-0-7636-1730-1(X)) Candlewick Pr.

—Gentle Giant Octopus. 2002. (gr. k-3). lib. bdg. 14.15 (978-0-613-74766-0(6)) Tandem Library Bks.

Windsor, Jo. Rubbery Arms & Baggy Bodies: Individual Title Six-Packs. (Sails Literacy Ser.). 20p. (gr. 2-3). 27.00 (978-0-7578-0717-6(8)) Rigby Education.

Yin, Robert, illus. & photos by. Octopuses, Squid & Cuttlefish. Yin, Robert, photos by. 1999. 24p. (J). 6.50 (978-0-7685-0351-7(5)) Dominie Pr., Inc.

Zuchora-Walske, Christine. Giant Octopuses. Bavendam, Fred, illus. 1999. (Pull Ahead Bks.). 32p. (J). (gr. k-2). lib. bdg. 22.60 (978-0-8225-3633-8(1) , Lerner Pubns.) Lerner Publishing Group.

—Giant Octopuses. 2000. (gr. k-3). lib. bdg. 14.10 (978-0-613-43828-5(0)) Tandem Library Bks.

OCTOPUSES—FICTION

Baron, Andrew, illus. The Adventures of Octopus Rex. 2003. (J). per. 17.95 (978-0-9760348-0-3(8)) BaHart Pubns. / Eight Legs Publishing.

Beinstein, Phoebe. Counting with Oswald. Kahata, Etsu, illus. 2003. (Oswald Ser.). 22p. (J). bds. 4.99 (978-0-689-85434-7(X) , Simon Spotlight/Nickelodeon) Simon & Schuster Children's Publishing.

Cazet, Denys. Grandpa Spanielson's Chicken Pox Stories No. 1: The Octopus. Cazet, Denys, illus. 2005. (I Can Read Bks.). (Illus.). 48p. (J). (ps-3). lib. bdg. 16.89 (978-0-06-051089-3(7)) HarperCollins Pubs.

—Octopus. Cazet, Denys, illus. 2005. (I Can Read Bks.). (Illus.). 48p. (J). (ps-3). 15.99 (978-0-06-051088-6(9)) HarperCollins Pubs.

—Octopus No. 1: Grandpa Spanielson's Chicken Pox Stories. Cazet, Denys, illus. 2006. (I Can Read Bks.). 48p. (J). pap. 3.99 (978-0-06-051092-3(7) , Harper Trophy) HarperCollins Pubs.

Chanda, J-P. I Love Big City! Kahata, Etsu, illus. 2003. (Oswald Ser.). 12p. (J). bds. 7.99 (978-0-689-85851-2(5) , Simon Spotlight/Nickelodeon) Simon & Schuster Children's Publishing.

Daniels, Lucy. Oscar's Best Friends. 2005. 57p. (***978-0-439-68199-5(5)***) Scholastic, Inc.

DeLorge, Jaqueline. Gilfinton under the Sea. 2005. (Illus.). 28p. (J). per. 7.99 (978-1-932338-97-3(7)) Lifevest Publishing, Inc.

Douglas, Babette. Oscarpus. 2004. (J). 9.99 (978-1-890343-30-9(7)) Kiss A Me Productions, Inc.

Douglas, Vincent & School Specialty Publishing Staff. Olivia Octopus. 2006. (Bath Buddies Ser.). 7p. (J). 12.95 (978-0-7696-4599-5(2) , Brighter Child) School Specialty Publishing.

Friendly Octopus. 2004. (J). per. (978-1-57657-373-0(7)) Paradise Pr., Inc.

Galloway, Ruth. Clumsy Crab. Galloway, Ruth, illus. 2005. (Illus.). 28p. (J). (ps-ps). 15.95 (978-1-58925-050-5(8) , tiger tales) ME Media LLC.

—Tickly Octopus. Galloway, Ruth, illus. 2007. (Illus.). (J). 15.95 (978-1-58925-064-2(8) , tiger tales) ME Media LLC.

Greenfield Educational Center Staff. Little Octopus. 2000. (I Can Read Ser.: Bk. 3). (CHI & ENG., Illus.). 8p. (J). pap. 2.99 (978-962-563-096-0(1)) Greenfield Enterprises, Ltd. HKG. *Dist:* Cheng & Tsui Co.

Holmes, Steve, illus. Animales Marinos: Mezcla y Diviertete. 2005. (Mezcla y Diviertete Ser.). (SPA.). 5p. (J). (ps-7). 7.95 (978-970-718-291-2(1) , Silver Dolphin en Español) Advanced Marketing, S. de R. L. de C. V. MEX. *Dist:* Perseus Distribution.

Kompelien, Tracy. Octopus's Garden. Nobens, C. A., illus. 2007. (Fact & Fiction Ser.). 24p. (J). 21.35 (978-1-59928-456-9(1) , SandCastle) ABDO Publishing Co.

Making Waves. 2004. (J). per. (978-1-57657-460-7(1)) Paradise Pr., Inc.

Martenz, Arden. Ocho: A Character-Education Story. 2002. 32p. (J). 6.95 (978-1-57543-112-3(2)) MAR*CO Products, Inc.

Morano, John. Makoona. 2nd rev. ed. 2005. (Morano Eco-Adventure Ser.: 2). 280p. (YA). (gr. 8-12). pap. 14.99 (978-1-59092-111-1(9) , Blue Works) Windstorm Creative.

Octopus Finds a Home. 2002. (Oceanic Mini Bks.). (Illus.). 32p. (J). (978-1-59069-003-1(6) , H1004) Studio Mouse LLC.

Pitcher, Caroline. Nico's Octopus. Mistry, Nilesh, illus. 2003. 32p. (J). (gr. k-3). 15.95 (978-1-56656-483-0(2) , Crocodile Bks.) Interlink Publishing Group, Inc.

Puckett, A. J., creator. If I Had a Pet Octopus. 2005. (Illus.). 24p. (J). (978-0-9764938-0-8(2)) Puckett Publishing, Inc.

Rathmell, Donna & Rathmell, Doreen. Octavia Octopus & Her Purple Ink Cloud. McLennan, Connie, illus. 2006. 32p. (J). 15.95 (978-0-9764943-5-5(3)) Sylvan Dell Pubng.

Rice, R. Hugh. Mother Octopus. Bosson, Jo-Ellen, illus. 1999. (Books for Young Learners). 12p. (J). (gr. k-2). pap. 5.00 (978-1-57274-272-7(0) , A2472) Owen, Richard C. Pubs., Inc.

Roop, Connie. Octopus under the Sea. 2001. (gr. k-3). lib. bdg. 11.80 (978-0-613-35544-5(X)); (Illus.). (J). (978-0-606-21363-9(5)) Tandem Library Bks.

Rylant, Cynthia. The Octopus. McDaniels, Preston, illus. 2005. (Lighthouse Family Ser.). 64p. (J). 15.99 (978-0-689-86246-5(6)) Simon & Schuster Children's Publishing.

Scieszka, Jon. Cowboy & Octopus. Smith, Lane, illus. 2007. 40p. (J). (ps-5). 16.99 (***978-0-670-91058-8(9)*** , Viking Juvenile) Penguin Group (USA) Inc.

Stile, Darlene. Octupuses. 2003. (Sea Creatures Ser.). (Illus.). 32p. (J). pap. 6.95 (978-1-4034-3563-7(4)) Heinemann Library.

Strub, Scott Richard. Otto the Outerspace Octopus. 2007. (J). per. 10.00 (***978-1-59872-782-1(6)***) Instantpublisher.com.

Sula, Sondra & Sula, Robert. Briny Town: Shark Showdown. Sula, Robert, illus. 2000. (Illus.). 32p. (J). (gr. 1-3). pap. (978-0-9701450-6-2(3)) Long Hill Productions, Inc.

Tomkins, Jasper. My Cousin Has Eight Legs. Tomkins, Jasper, illus. 2002. (Illus.). 40p. (Orig.). (YA). (gr. 7 up). pap. 9.95 (978-0-912365-68-8(4)) Bay Soma Publishing.

Trimble, Marcia. The Adventure of Pushy Octopus & His Friends. Sprague, Dean, illus. 2005. 18p. (J). (gr. k-2). 4.95 (978-1-891577-61-1(1) , SAN2994844) Images Pr.

Weidner Zoehfeld, Kathleen & Langeland, Deirdre. Smithsonian Oceanic Dolphin & Octopus Box. Petruccio, Steven James, illus. 2002. (Smithsonian Soundprints Ser.). 64p. (J). 19.95 (978-1-931465-58-8(4) , Silver Dolphin Bks.) Advantage Pubs. Group.

Yaccarino, Dan. An Octopus Followed Me Home. 2000. (978-0-606-18438-0(4)) Tandem Library Bks.

—Oswald. Yaccarino, Dan, illus. 2004. (Oswald Ser.: Vol. 5). (Illus.). 24p. (J). pap. 3.99 (978-0-689-87331-7(X) , Simon Spotlight/Nickelodeon) Simon & Schuster Children's Publishing.

—Oswald's Camping Trip. Oxley, Jennifer, illus. 2003. (Oswald Ser.). 24p. (J). pap. 3.50 (978-0-689-85432-3(3) , Simon Spotlight/Nickelodeon) Simon & Schuster Children's Publishing.

—Oswald's Sleepover. Schigiel, Gregg, illus. 2003. (Oswald Ser.). 24p. (J). pap. 3.50 (978-0-689-85433-0(1) , Simon Spotlight/Nickelodeon) Simon & Schuster Children's Publishing.

ODYSSEUS (GREEK MYTHOLOGY)

Church, Alfred John. Story of the Odyssey. 2006. 62.99 (***978-1-4219-9763-6(0)***) IndyPublish.com.

Church, Alfred John. The Story of the Odyssey. 2004. reprint ed. pap. 19.95 (978-1-4191-8412-3(1)); pap. 1.99 (978-1-4192-8412-0(6)) Kessinger Publishing, LLC.

Claybourne, A. & Khanduri, K. Greek Myths: Ulysses & the Trojan War: Mini-Edition. 2004. (Spotter's Guides). 160p. (J). 8.95 (978-0-7945-0535-6(X)) EDC Publishing.

Colum, Padraic. Adventures of Odysseus & the Tale of T. 2006. pap. 35.99 (***978-1-4219-6450-8(3)***) IndyPublish.com.

Colum, Padraic. The Adventures of Odysseus & the Tale of Troy. Pogany, Willy, illus. 2004. 176p. (J). (gr. 4-7). pap. 4.95 (978-0-486-43455-1(9)) Dover Pubns., Inc.

Hoena, B. A. Odysseus. 2004. (Illus.). 24p. (J). 14.95 (978-0-7368-2498-9(7)) Capstone Pr., Inc.

Homer. The Odyssey. 2000. (Classics Ser.). (Illus.). 64p. (J). (gr. 2-5). 14.99 (978-0-7894-5455-3(6)) Dorling Kindersley Publishing, Inc.

—Odyssey. (gr. 7-12). 2003. lib. bdg. 18.80 (978-0-613-64563-8(4)); 1999. lib. bdg. 14.10 (978-0-613-37192-6(5)) Tandem Library Bks.

—The Odyssey. adapted ed. (YA). (gr. 5-12). pap. 8.50 (978-0-8359-0232-8(3)) Globe Fearon Educational Publishing.

Jonas, Anne. Ulises y Casimiro. (SPA.). 32p. (J). (gr. 2-4). (978-84-8418-043-2(3)) Zendrera Zariquiey, Editorial ESP. *Dist:* Lectorum Pubns., Inc.

LaFontaine, Bruce. The Adventures of Ulysses. 2004. (Dover Coloring Bks.). (Illus.). 32p. (J). pap. 3.95 (978-0-486-43328-8(5)) Dover Pubns., Inc.

Lupton, Hugh, et al. The Adventures of Odysseus. 2006. (Illus.). (J). (gr. 3-7). 19.99 (978-1-84148-800-4(3)) Barefoot Bks., Inc.

Osborne, Mary Pope. The Land of the Dead. 2002. (Tales from the Odyssey Ser.). (gr. 3-6). lib. bdg. 13.00 (978-0-613-68248-0(3)) Tandem Library Bks.

—The One-Eyed Giant. 2002. (Tales from the Odyssey Ser.: Bk. 1). (gr. 3-6). lib. bdg. 13.00 (978-0-613-68273-2(4)) Tandem Library Bks.

—Return to Ithaca. 5th rev. ed. 2004. (Odyssey Ser.: No. 5). (Illus.). 112p. (gr. 3-6). 9.99 (978-0-7868-0774-1(1)) Hyperion Bks. for Children.

Smith, Patrick. Land Remembered. 2001. (gr. 5-8). lib. bdg. 16.40 (978-0-613-55623-1(2)) Tandem Library Bks.

Sutcliff, Rosemary. The Wanderings of Odysseus. 2005. 144p. (YA). (gr. 7 up). mass mkt. 5.99 (978-0-553-49482-2(1) , Laurel Leaf) Random Hse. Children's Bks.

—The Wanderings of Odysseus: The Story of the Odyssey. Lee, Alan, illus. 2005. 120p. (J). (ps-k). 19.95 (978-1-84507-360-2(6)) Lincoln, Frances Ltd. GBR. *Dist:* Perseus Distribution.

Yeates, Thomas. Odysseus: Escaping Poseidon's Curse: A Greek Myth. 2007. (Graphic Myths & Legends Ser.). 48p. (J). (gr. 4-8). 26.60 (***978-0-8225-6208-5(1)*** , Graphic Universe) Lerner Publishing Group.

OFFICE WORK—TRAINING

see Business Education

OFFICIALS

see Civil Service

see names of countries, cities, etc. and organizations with subdivision Officials and Employees, e.g. United States—Officials and Employees

OGLETHORPE, JAMES EDWARD, 1696-1785

Lommel, Cookie. James Oglethorpe. 2001. (gr. 5-8). lib. bdg. 17.60 (978-0-613-32706-0(3)) Tandem Library Bks.

—James Oglethorpe: Humanitarian & Soldier. 2000. (Colonial Leaders Ser.). (Illus.). 80p. (J). (gr. 4-7). pap. 27.50 (978-0-7910-6120-6(5)); 27.50 (978-0-7910-5963-0(4)) Facts On File, Inc. (Chelsea Hse.).

Walsh, Kieran. James Oglethorpe. (Discover the Life of a Colonial American Ser.). 24p. 2005. (Illus.). (gr. 2-5). 14.95 (978-1-59515-138-4(9)); 2004. pap. 4.95 (978-1-59515-339-5(X)) Rourke Publishing, LLC.

Whiting, Jim. The Life & Times of Samuel de Champlain. 2007. (Profiles in American History Ser.). (J). lib. bdg. (978-1-58415-432-7(2)) Mitchell Lane Pubs., Inc.

OHIO

Barker, Charles Ferguson. Under Ohio: The Story of Ohio's Rocks & Fossils. 2007. (Illus.). 56p. (J). 17.95 (***978-0-8214-1755-3(X)***) Ohio Univ. Pr.

Brown, Dottie. Ohio. 2nd ed. (Hello U. S. A. Ser.). (J). 2001. pap. (978-0-8225-4246-9(3) , Lerner Pubns.); 2003. (Illus.). 84p. (gr. 3-6). pap. 6.95 (978-0-8225-4134-9(3)); 2002. (Illus.). 84p. (gr. 3-6). 25.26 (978-0-8225-4075-5(4) , Lerner Pubns.) Lerner Publishing Group.

—Ohio. 2001. (Illus.). 84p. (J). (ps-7). lib. bdg. 15.25 (978-0-613-81320-4(0)) Tandem Library Bks.

Capstone Press Staff, contrib. by. Ohio. rev. ed. 2002. (One Nation Ser.). (Illus.). 48p. (J). (gr. 3-4). lib. bdg. 22.60 (978-0-7368-1259-7(8) , Bridgestone Bks.) Capstone Pr., Inc.

Dagton Gold C 2005. 2004. 404p. (YA). pap. 15.00 (978-1-58553-952-9(X) , 05GC0004) Entertainment Publications, Inc.

Drake, Samuel Adams. the Making of the Ohio Valley States 1660-1837. 2001. 282p. (YA). reprint ed. (978-1-58218-423-4(2)); pap. (978-1-58218-422-7(4)) Digital Scanning, Inc.

Hart, Joyce. Ohio. 2005. (It's My State! Ser.). (Illus.). 80p. (J). (978-0-7614-1907-5(1) , Benchmark Bks.) Cavendish, Marshall Corp.

Heinrichs, Ann. Ohio. Kania, Matt, illus. 2005. (Welcome to the USA Ser.). 40p. (J). (gr. 1-5). 27.07 (978-1-59296-449-9(4)) Child's World, Inc.

—Ohio. 2003. (This Land Is Your Land Ser.). (Illus.). 48p. (J). (gr. 3 up). lib. bdg. 22.60 (978-0-7565-0316-1(7)) Compass Point Bks.

Houghton, Gillian. Mildred Taylor. 2004. (Library of Author Biographies). (Illus.). 112p. (YA). 26.50 (978-1-4042-0330-3(3)) Rosen Publishing, Inc.

Kline, Nancy. Ohio. 2002. (From Sea to Shining Sea Ser.: 2). (Illus.). 80p. (J). (gr. 3-5). pap. 30.50 (978-0-516-22483-1(2) , Children's Pr.) Scholastic Library Publishing.

Knapp, Ron. Ohio: A MyReportLinks.com Book. 2002. (States Ser.). (Illus.). 48p. (J). (gr. 4-10). lib. bdg. 25.26 (978-0-7660-5022-8(X) , MyReportLinks.com Bks.) Enslow Pubs., Inc.

Lawton, Val. A Guide to Ohio. 2001. (American States Ser.). (Illus.). 32p. (J). lib. bdg. 16.95 (978-1-930954-03-8(4)); per. 7.95 (978-1-930954-93-9(X)) Weigl Pubs., Inc.

Marsh, Carole. My First Book about Ohio. 2000. (Ohio Experience! Ser.). (Illus.). 32p. (J). (gr. k-4). pap. 7.95 (978-0-7933-9524-8(0)) Gallopade International.

—Ohio Current Events Projects: 30 Cool, Activities, Crafts, Experiments & More for Kids to Do to Learn about Your State! 2003. (Ohio Experience Ser.). 32p. (gr. k-5). pap. 5.95 (978-0-635-02054-3(8) , Marsh, Carole Bks.) Gallopade International.

—The Ohio Experience Pocket Guide. 2001. (Ohio Experience! Ser.). (Illus.). 96p. (J). (gr. 3-8). pap. 6.95 (978-0-7933-9454-8(6)) Gallopade International.

—Ohio Geography Projects: 30 Cool, Activities, Crafts, Experiments & More for Kids to Do to Learn about Your State! 2003. (Ohio Experience Ser.). 32p. (gr. k-5). pap. 5.95 (978-0-635-01854-0(3) , Marsh, Carole Bks.) Gallopade International.

—Ohio Government Projects: 30 Cool, Activities, Crafts, Experiments & More for Kids to Do to Learn about Your State! 2003. (Ohio Experience Ser.). 32p. (gr. k-5). pap. 5.95 (978-0-635-01954-7(X) , Marsh, Carole Bks.) Gallopade International.

—Ohio History Projects: 30 Cool, Activities, Crafts, Experiments & More for Kids to Do to Learn about Your State! 2003. (Ohio Experience Ser.). 32p. (gr. k-5). pap. 5.95 (978-0-635-01804-5(7) , Marsh, Carole Bks.) Gallopade International.

—Ohio Jeopardy. 2000. (Ohio Experience! Ser.). 32p. (J). (gr. 3-8). pap. 7.95 (978-0-7933-9525-5(9)) Gallopade International.

—Ohio "Jography" A Fun Run Thru Our State! 2000. (Ohio Experience! Ser.). (Illus.). 32p. (J). (gr. 3-8). pap. 7.95 (978-0-7933-9526-2(7)) Gallopade International.

—Ohio People Projects: 30 Cool, Activities, Crafts, Experiments & More for Kids to Do to Learn about Your State! 2003. (Ohio Experience Ser.). 32p. (gr. k-5). pap. 5.95 (978-0-635-02004-8(1) , Marsh, Carole Bks.) Gallopade International.

—Ohio Symbols & Facts Projects: 30 Cool, Activities, Crafts, Experiments & More for Kids to Do to Learn about Your State! 2003. (Ohio Experience Ser.). 32p. (gr. k-5). pap. 5.95 (978-0-635-01904-2(3) , Marsh, Carole Bks.) Gallopade International.

—Ohio's Big Activity Book. 2004. (Ohio Experience! Ser.). (Illus.). 96p. (J). (gr. 2-6). pap. 9.95 (978-0-7933-9464-7(3)) Gallopade International.

—The Out of This World Ohio Coloring Book. 2000. (Ohio Experience! Ser.). (Illus.). 32p. (J). (gr. k-2). pap. 3.95 (978-0-7933-9474-6(0)) Gallopade International.

Martin, Michael A. Ohio: The Buckeye State. 2002. (World Almanac Library of the States). (Illus.). 48p. (J). (gr. 5 up). pap. 14.95 (978-0-8368-5290-5(7)); lib. bdg. 30.00 (978-0-8368-5124-3(2)) Stevens, Gareth Inc. (World Almanac Library).

McAuliffe, Emily. Ohio. 1998. (States & Their Symbols Ser.). (J). (ps-3). pap. 14.00 (978-0-531-11609-8(3) , Orchard Bks.) Scholastic, Inc.

—Ohio Facts & Symbols. (States & Their Symbols Ser.). 24p. (J). 1998. (Illus.). (gr. 2-3). lib. bdg. 18.60 (978-0-7368-0085-3(9) , Bridgestone Bks.); 2003. lib. bdg. 19.93 (978-0-7368-2265-7(8)) Capstone Pr., Inc.

McHugh, Erin & Schrier, Alfred. State Shapes: Ohio. 2007. (Illus.). 48p. (J). 9.95 (978-1-57912-702-2(9)) Black Dog & Leventhal Pubs., Inc.

McNamara, Connie. My First Ohio State Words. 2004. (J). bds. 11.95 (978-0-9743244-5-6(0)) Shamrock Publishing, Inc.

Murray, Julie. Ohio. 2006. (Buddy Book Ser.). (Illus.). 32p. (J). (gr. k-4). lib. bdg. 22.78 (978-1-59197-694-3(4) , Buddy Bks.) ABDO Publishing Co.

Oehler, David A. The Cincinnati Zoo & Botanical Garden. 2003. (Great Zoos of the United States Ser.). (Illus.). 24p. (J). lib. bdg. 18.75 (978-0-8239-6320-1(9) , PowerKids Pr.) Rosen Publishing Group, Inc., The.

Ohio. 2000. (Switched on Schoolhouse Ser.). (Illus.). (YA). (gr. 7-12). pap. 24.95 incl. cd-rom (978-0-7403-0287-9(6) , SOSOH) Alpha Omega Pubns., Inc.

Ohio - Northern Fishing Map Guide: Lake Maps & Fishing Information for over 130 Inland Lakes in Northern Ohio Plus Lake Erie. 2001. (Illus.). 192p. (YA). spiral bd. 21.95 (978-1-885010-46-9(X)) Sportsman's Connection.

Ohio - Southern Fishing Map Guide: Lake Maps & Fishing Information for over 80 Inland Lakes in Southern Ohio Plus the Ohio River. 2001. (Illus.). 192p. (YA). spiral bd. 21.95 (978-1-885010-47-6(8)) Sportsman's Connection.

Ohio from the Sky. 2006. (J). 9.95 (***978-1-57166-420-4(3)***) Quixote Pr.

Schonberg, Marcia. All Around Ohio: Regions & Resources. 2003. (Heinemann State Studies). (Illus.). 48p. (J). pap. 8.50 (978-1-4034-2688-8(0)); lib. bdg. 27.07 (978-1-4034-0665-1(0)) Heinemann Library.

—All Around Ohio: Regions & Resources. 2003. (gr. 3-6). lib. bdg. 17.05 (978-0-613-60846-6(1)) Tandem Library Bks.

—Cardinal Numbers: An Ohio Counting Book. Langton, Bruce, illus. 2002. 40p. (J). 16.95 (978-1-58536-084-0(8)) Sleeping Bear Pr.

—Ohio, 6 bks., Set. 2003. (Heinemann State Studies). (Illus.). (J). (gr. 3-5). lib. bdg. 162.42 (978-1-4034-0671-2(5)) Heinemann Library.

—Ohio Plants & Animals. 2003. (Heinemann State Studies). (Illus.). 48p. (J). pap. 8.50 (978-1-4034-2691-8(0)); lib. bdg. 27.07 (978-1-4034-0669-9(3)) Heinemann Library.

—Ohio Reader. Darnell, Kathryn, illus. rev. ed. 2007. (State Readers Ser.). 96p. (J). 12.95 (***978-1-58536-321-6(9)***) Sleeping Bear Pr.

Schonberg, Marcia. Uniquely Ohio. 2003. (Heinemann State Studies). (Illus.). 48p. (J). pap. 8.50 (978-1-4034-2693-2(7)); lib. bdg. 27.07 (978-1-4034-0670-5(7)) Heinemann Library.

M N O

Sherrow, Victoria. Ohio. (Celebrate the States Ser.). 1998. (Illus.). 144p. (gr. 4-8). lib. bdg. 37.07 (978-0-7614-0656-3(5)); 2nd ed. 2007. (J). lib. bdg. 39.93 (*978-0-7614-2558-8(6)) Cavendish, Marshall Corp. (Benchmark Bks.).

Shonberg, Marcia. B Is for Buckeye: An Ohio Alphabet. Langton, Bruce, illus. 2000. 40p. (J). (ps-3). 16.95 (978-1-58536-004-8(X)) Sleeping Bear Pr.

Sturm, Ellen. Ohio. 2003. (Land of Liberty Ser.). (Illus.). 64p. (J). (gr. 3-4). lib. bdg. 23.93 (978-0-7368-1593-2(7) , Bridgestone Bks.) Capstone Pr., Inc.

Swainston, Jeani. Grandma Stuff: ... it's what love Is made Of. 2006. (J). (*978-0-9791384-0-9(X)) Rock Cliff Media.

Taylor-Butler, Christine. Ohio. 2007. (Rookie Read-about' Geography: States Ser.). 32p. (J). pap. 5.95 (*978-0-531-16816-5(6)); (Illus.). (gr. 1-2). 20.50 (978-0-531-12573-1(4)) Scholastic Library Publishing. (Children's Pr.).

Way, Jennifer. Ohio. 2006. (Bilingual Library of the United States of America: Set 2). (ENG & SPA., Illus.). 32p. (J). (gr. 3-6). lib. bdg. 22.50 (978-1-4042-3100-9(5) , Buenas Letra) Rosen Publishing Group, Inc., The.

Woodyard, Chris. Haunted Ohio V: 200 Years of Ghosts. 2003. (Illus.). 240p. pap. (978-0-9628472-8-8(3)) Kestrel Pubns.

Ziarkowski, Steven & Ziarkowski, Carmen. Around Ohio in 80 Days. Jarbo, Marrin, illus. 1999. 104p. (J). (gr. 4-8). spiral bd. 24.95 (978-1-881153-04-7(5)) Color the Classics.

OHIO—BIOGRAPHY

Andreasen, Dan. The Giant of Seville: A "Tall" Tale Based on a True Story. 2007. (Illus.). 32p. (J). (ps-3). 15.95 (978-0-8109-0988-5(X) , Abrams Bks. for Young Readers) Abrams, Harry N. , Inc.

Georgiady, Nicholas P., et al. Ohio Men, Vol. 2. Collins, Julia B., illus. 2nd rev. ed. Date not set. 44p. (J). (gr. 4-8). pap. 4.50 (978-0-917961-04-5(8)) Argee Pubs.

Mangal, Melina. Mildred Taylor. 2004. (Classic Storytellers Ser.). (Illus.). 48p. (J). (gr. 4-8). lib. bdg. 20.95 (978-1-58415-311-5(3)) Mitchell Lane Pubs., Inc.

Marsh, Carole. Father Hidalgo: An Ohio Experience Reader. 2001. (J). (gr. k-5). pap. 1.95 (978-0-635-00436-9(4)) Gallopade International.

—The Ohio Experience Library State Resource Set. 2001. (Ohio Experience! Ser.). (Illus.). (J). lib. bdg. 100.20 incl. cd-rom (978-0-635-00488-8(7)) Gallopade International.

—The Ohio Experience Sol Biographies. 2001. (Illus.). (J). (gr. 2-9). pap. 12.95 (978-0-635-00391-1(0)) Gallopade International.

Rappaport, Doreen. Freedom River. Collier, Bryan, illus. rev. ed. 2007. 32p. pap. 6.99 (*978-1-4231-0634-0(2) , Jump at the Sun) Hyperion Bks. for Children.

Schonberg, Marcia. People of Ohio. 2003. (Heinemann State Studies). (Illus.). 48p. (J). pap. 8.50 (978-1-4034-2692-5(9)); lib. bdg. 27.07 (978-1-4034-0668-2(5)) Heinemann Library.

Seaver, Derrick. Kid in the House. 2002. 108p. (YA). pap. 9.95 (978-0-595-25053-0(X) , Writers Club Pr.) iUniverse, Inc.

Sowash, Rick. Heroes of Ohio: 23 True Tales of Courage & Character. 2003. (J). 19.95 (978-0-9762412-5-6(0)); pap. 11.95 (978-0-9762412-4-9(2)) Sowash, Rick Publishing Co.

—Heroes of Ohio Coloring Book. 2003. (J). 5.95 (978-0-9762412-6-3(9)) Sowash, Rick Publishing Co.

Williams, Dave. Windgalore Farm. 2005. (Illus.). 182p. pap. 21.95 (978-0-937921-56-2(4)) Acorn Publishing.

OHIO—FICTION

Aryal, Aimee. Hello, Brutus! 2006. (J). 14.95 (*978-1-932888-51-5(9)) Mascot Bks., Inc.

Berten, Jinny Powers & Holt, Norah. Littsie of Cincinnati. 2003. (Illus.). 125p. (J). per. 9.95 (978-0-9724421-0-7(3)) Fountain Square Publishing.

Borntrager, Mary Christner. Andy. l.t. ed. 2002. 161p. 25.95 (978-0-7862-4029-6(0)) Thomson Gale.

—Ellie. l.t. ed. 2001. (Christian Fiction Ser.). 208p. 23.95 (978-0-7862-3383-0(4)) Thorndike Pr.

—Mandy Bk. 9: Ellie's People. l.t. ed. 2002. (Christian Fiction Ser.). 25.95 (978-0-7862-4539-0(5)) Thorndike Pr.

—Rebecca. l.t. ed. 2001. (Thorndike Christian Fiction Ser.). 245p. 24.95 (978-0-7862-3252-9(8)) Thorndike Pr.

—Sarah. l.t. ed. 2002. (Christian Fiction Ser.). 177p. 25.95 (978-0-7862-4526-0(3)) Thorndike Pr.

Brown, Ruth. Homey's Tales of Love & Adventure. 2005. 74p. pap. 14.95 (978-1-4137-7144-2(0)) PublishAmerica, Inc.

Cheng, Andrea. Honeysuckle House. 2004. 136p. (YA). 16.95 (978-1-886910-99-7(5) , Lemniscaat) Boyds Mills Pr.

Cockley, David H. Over the Falls: A Child's Storybook Guide to Chagrin Falls. Ascherman, Herbert, Jr., tr. 2000. (Illus.). 24p. (J). (ps-10). pap. 5.95 (978-0-9700846-1-3(7)) Fireside Book Shop, Inc.

Drake, Jane & Love, Ann. Farming. Cupples, Pat, illus. 2002. (America at Work Ser.). 32p. (J). (gr. k-3). (978-1-55074-451-4(8)) Kids Can Pr., Ltd.

Draper, Sharon M. Double Dutch. 2003. 192p. (J). pap. 5.99 (978-0-689-84231-3(7) , Aladdin) Simon & Schuster Children's Publishing.

—Double Dutch. Gabbidon, O'Lanso, illus. 2002. 192p. (J). (gr. 7 up). 16.99 (978-0-689-84230-6(9) , Atheneum) Simon & Schuster Children's Publishing.

Ferrer, Caridad. It's Not about the Accent. 2007. 288p. (YA). (gr. 7 up). pap. 9.95 (*978-1-4165-2491-5(6) , MTV) Simon & Schuster.

FitzGerald, Dawn. Getting in the Game. 2007. 160p. (J). pap. 6.99 (*978-0-312-37753-3(3)) Square Fish.

Fitzgerald, Dawn. Getting in the Game. rev. ed. 2005. 144p. (J). 15.95 (978-1-59643-044-0(3)) Roaring Brook Pr.

—Soccer Chick Rules. 2006. 160p. (J). 16.95 (978-1-59643-137-9(7)) Roaring Brook Pr.

FitzGerald, Dawn. Soccer Chick Rules. 2007. 160p. (J). pap. 6.99 (*978-0-312-37662-8(6)) Square Fish.

Giblin, James Cross. The Boy Who Saved Cleveland: Based on a True Story. Dooling, Michael, illus. rev. ed. 2006. 80p. (J). 15.95 (978-0-8050-7355-3(8) , Holt, Henry & Co. Bks. For Young Readers) Holt, Henry & Co.

Greenburg, Dan. Attack of the Giant Octopus. Fischer, Scott M., illus. 2007. (Secrets of Dripping Fang Ser.: Bk. 6). 160p. (J). 9.95 (978-0-15-206041-1(3)) Harcourt Children's Bks.

—Fall of the House of Mandible. Fischer, Scott M., illus. 2006. (Outrageously Funny Ser.: Bk. 4). 160p. (J). 9.95 (978-0-15-205475-5(8)) Harcourt Children's Bks.

—The Onts. Fischer, Scott M., illus. 2006. (Secrets of Dripping Fang Ser.: Bk. 1). 144p. (J). 2.99 (978-0-15-205995-8(4) , Harcourt Paperbacks) Harcourt Children's Bks.

—Please Don't Eat the Children. Fischer, Scott M., illus. 2007. (Secrets of Dripping Fang Ser.: Bk. 7). 160p. (J). 9.95 (978-0-15-206047-3(2)) Harcourt Children's Bks.

—Treachery & Betrayal at Jolly Days. Fischer, Scott M., illus. 2006. (Secrets of Dripping Fang Ser.: Bk. 2). 144p. (J). 9.95 (978-0-15-205463-2(4)) Harcourt Children's Bks.

Greenburg, Dan & Diterlizzi, Angela. The Vampire's Curse. Fischer, Scott M., illus. 2006. (Secrets of Dripping Fang Ser.: Bk. 3). 144p. (J). 9.95 (978-0-15-205469-4(3)) Harcourt Children's Bks.

Greene, Stephanie. Queen Sophie Hartley. 2005. 144p. (J). (gr. 3-5). 15.00 (978-0-618-49461-3(8) , Clarion Bks.) Houghton Mifflin Co. Trade & Reference Div.

Gundisch, Karin. How I Became an American. Skofield, James, tr. from GER. 2001. (Illus.). 144p. (J). (gr. 3-7). 15.95 (978-0-8126-4875-1(7)) Cricket Bks.

Hamilton, Virginia. The House of Dies Drear. 1998. 32p. (J). 9.95 (978-1-56137-516-5(0) , NU5168) Novel Units, Inc.

—The House of Dies Drear. 2001. (Assessment Packs Ser.). 15p. pap. 15.95 (978-1-58303-122-3(7)) Pathways Publishing.

—The House of Dies Drear. 8.97 (978-0-13-437491-8(6)) Prentice Hall PTR.

—M. C. Higgins, the Great. 1998. (J). pap. 4.50 (978-0-87628-568-8(X)) Ctr. for Applied Research in Education, The.

—M. C. Higgins, the Great. (J). pap., stu. ed. (978-0-13-620246-2(2)); 3rd ed. pap. 23.70 (978-0-13-620220-2(9)); 3rd ed. pap. 3.95 (978-0-13-800137-7(5)) Prentice Hall (Schl. Div.).

—M. C. Higgins, the Great. 2006. (Illus.). 288p. (J). pap. 5.99 (978-1-4169-1407-5(2) , Aladdin) Simon & Schuster Children's Publishing.

—M. C. Higgins, the Great. Palencar, John J., illus. 25th anniv. ed. 1999. 240p. (J). (gr. 7). 19.99 (978-0-689-83074-7(2)) Simon & Schuster Children's Publishing.

Hickman, Janet. Susannah. 2000. (Illus.). 192p. (J). (gr. 5 up). mass mkt. 4.95 (978-0-380-73224-1(6) , Harper Trophy) HarperCollins Pubs.

—Susannah. 2001. (J). (978-0-606-20934-2(4)) Tandem Library Bks.

Huff, Barb. Perfect Girl. 2003. (gr. 3-6). lib. bdg. 11.80 (978-0-613-79653-8(5)) Tandem Library Bks.

Levine, Phyllis. At the Skylight with Matlida. 2007. 156p. pap. 12.95 (*978-1-60047-089-9(0)) Wasteland Pr.

Literature Connections English: The House of Dies Drear. 2004. (gr. 6-12). (978-0-395-77523-3(X) , 2-80092) McDougal Littell Inc.

Logsdon, Gene. The Man Who Created Paradise: A Fable. 2001. (Illus.). 68p. 20.00 (978-0-8214-1407-1(0)) Ohio Univ. Pr.

Lutz, Norma Jean. Escape from Slavery: A Family's Fight for Freedom. 1999. (American Adventure Ser.: No. 16). 144p. (J). (gr. 3-7). 11.95 (978-0-7910-5590-8(6) , Chelsea Hse.) Facts On File, Inc.

Mackall, Dandi Daley. Grace Notes. 2006. (Faithgirlz Ser.). (Illus.). 128p. (J). pap. 6.99 (978-0-310-71093-6(6)) Zonderkidz.

—Upsetting Annie. 2007. (Faithgirlz!#8482; / Blog On! Ser.). 128p. (J). pap. 6.99 (978-0-310-71264-0(5)) Zonderkidz.

Martin, Rebella. Joanna's Journey. Yoder, Laura, illus. 2006. 168p. (YA). pap. 10.99 (978-1-933753-01-0(3)) Carlisle Pr.- Walnut Creek.

Morehead, Don & Morehead, Ann. A Short Season: Story of a Montana Childhood. 1998. (Illus.). 190p. pap. 13.00 (978-0-8032-8244-5(3) , MORSHX, A Bison Original) Univ. of Nebraska Pr.

Mortensen, Denise Dowling. Ohio Thunder. Kiesler, Kate, illus. 2006. 32p. (J). (gr. k-3). 16.00 (978-0-618-59542-6(2) , Clarion Bks.) Houghton Mifflin Co. Trade & Reference Div.

Mullen, Paul Michael. The Day I Hit a Home Run at Great American Ball Park. 2007. (J). (*978-1-933197-29-6(3)) Orange Frazer Pr.

Murphy, Buelina. Boke. 2003. 32p. pap. 8.00 (978-0-8059-5524-8(0)) Dorrance Publishing Co., Inc.

O'Neill, Elizabeth. Alfred Visits Ohio. 2005. 26p. per. 12.50 (978-1-59453-408-9(X) , 2442) Airleaf Publishing & Bookselling.

Oneill, Elizabeth. Alfred Visits Ohio. 2006. 24p. pap. 12.00 (978-0-9771836-4-7(5)) Funny Bone Bks.

Osorio, Rick. The Great Adventure of Sally Rock & the Cretaceous Chicken. 2006. 65p. pap. 12.95 (978-1-4241-0971-5(X)) PublishAmerica, Inc.

Ottman, Frank. Not Wanted: The Memories of Cain Mann. 2005. 194p. pap. 19.95 (978-1-4241-0163-4(8)) PublishAmerica, Inc.

Pearsall, Shelley. Crooked River. 2007. 272p. (J). (gr. 5-9). pap. 6.50 (978-0-440-42101-6(2) , Yearling) Random Hse. Children's Bks.

Per, Sharon Mills. Double Dutch. 2004. (gr. 5-8). lib. bdg. 13.00 (978-0-613-88160-9(5)) Tandem Library Bks.

Pilkey, Dav. Captain Underpants & the Preposterous Plight of the Purple Potty People. 2006. (Captain Underpants Ser.: Bk. 8). 176p. (J). (gr. 2-5). pap. 16.99 (978-0-439-37613-6(0) , Blue Sky Pr., The) Scholastic, Inc.

Reed, Stephanie. Across the Wide River: A Novel. 2004. 176p. (J). pap. 9.99 (978-0-8254-3576-8(5)) Kregel Pubns.

Rexroth, Sharon. Ohio. 2006. (J). per. 19.95 (*978-1-57166-421-1(1)) Quixote Pr.

Rinaldi, Ann. The Second Bend in the River. 1999. 288p. (J). (gr. 5-9). pap. 4.99 (978-0-590-74259-7(0)) Scholastic, Inc.

Roos, Stephen. Recycling George. 2003. (Illus.). 144p. (J). pap. 4.99 (978-0-689-86351-6(9) , Aladdin) Simon & Schuster Children's Publishing.

—Recycling George. 2003. (gr. 3-6). lib. bdg. 13.00 (978-0-613-90717-0(5)) Tandem Library Bks.

—Recycling George. 2003. 22.95 (978-0-7862-5015-8(1)) Thorndike Pr.

Rosen, Michael J. Don't Shoot! Chase R's Top Ten Reasons NOT to Move to the Country. 2007. (Illus.). 160p. (YA). (gr. 7). pap. 6.99 (*978-0-7636-2088-2(2)) Candlewick Pr.

Sanders, Scott R. Aurora Means Dawn. 1998. (978-0-606-13155-1(8)) Tandem Library Bks.

Sanders, Scott Russell. Warm as Wool. Cogancherry, Helen, illus. 2007. (J). lib. bdg. 18.00 (*978-1-59098-421-5(8)) Wooster Bk. Co., The.

Saturen, Myra. Journey to a New World: Mystic River of the West. 2006. (J). pap. (*978-0-88092-495-5(0)) Royal Fireworks Publishing Co.

Schraff, Anne. Darkness. 2000. 119p. (J). pap. (978-0-7891-5183-4(9)); (gr. 5-12). lib. bdg. 13.95 (978-0-7807-9367-5(6)) Perfection Learning Corp.

—Wait until Spring. 2000. 125p. (J). pap. (978-0-7891-5139-1(1)); (gr. 5-12). lib. bdg. 13.95 (978-0-7807-9282-1(3)) Perfection Learning Corp.

Schumacher, Julie. Grass Angel. 2004. 208p. (gr. 5-9). lib. bdg. 17.99 (978-0-385-90163-5(1) , Delacorte Bks. for Young Readers) Random Hse. Children's Bks.

—Grass Angel. 2005. 196p. (J). (gr. k-9). per. 12.55 (978-0-606-33725-0(3)) Tandem Library Bks.

Shoup, Andrew J. Andy & Elmer's Apple Dumpling Adventure. 2nd ed. 2007. (J). 16.95 (*978-0-9720436-3-2(2)) TokoBooks.

—Andy & Elmer's Apple Dumpling Adventure Coloring & Activity Book. Shoup, Andrew J., illus. 2007. (Illus.). 36p. (J). 3.95 (*978-0-9720436-2-5(4)) TokoBooks.

Sowach, Rick. Critters, Flitters & Spitters: 24 Amazing Ohio Animal Tales. 2003. (J). 19.95 (978-0-9762412-3-2(4)) Sowash, Rick Publishing Co.

Sowash, Rick. Critters, Flitters & Spitters: 24 Amazing Ohio Animal Tales. 2003. (J). pap. 11.95 (978-0-9762412-2-5(6)) Sowash, Rick Publishing Co.

—Ripsnorting Whoppers! A Book of Ohio Tall Tales. 2003. (J). 19.95 (978-0-9762412-1-8(8)); pap. 11.95 (978-0-9762412-0-1(X)) Sowash, Rick Publishing Co.

Stratemeyer, Edward. On the Trail of Pontiac or the Pioneer B. 2006. 63.99 (*978-1-4219-9636-3(7)); pap. 57.99 (*978-1-4219-9640-0(5)) IndyPublish.com.

Tripp, Valerie. Changes for Kit: A Winter Story. Rane, Walter & McAliley, Susan, illus. 2001. (American Girls Collection: Bk. 6). 86p. (J). (gr. 2 up). 12.95 (978-1-58485-027-4(2)); 6.95 (978-1-58485-026-7(4)) American Girl Publishing, Inc.

—Changes for Kit: A Winter Story. 2001. (American Girls Collection). (Illus.). (J). 12.75 (978-0-606-21107-9(1)) Tandem Library Bks.

—Changes for Kit: A Winter Story 1934. Rane, Walter & McAliley, Susan, illus. 2001. 64p. (J). (gr. 3-6). lib. bdg. 14.10 (978-0-613-44636-5(4)) Tandem Library Bks.

Vivian, Siobhan. A Little Friendly Advice. 2008. 256p. (J). pap. 16.99 (*978-0-545-00404-6(7) , PUSH) Scholastic, Inc.

Willis, Donald B. Mystery of the Waterloo Bagpipes. 2001. 196p. (YA). per. 9.95 (978-0-9707845-0-6(3)) Anubis Publishing.

Wilsdon, Christina. An Amusement Park Mystery in Ohio. Ebert, Len, illus. 2006. 26p. (J). 7.99 (978-1-59939-013-0(2) , Reader's Digest Young Families, Inc.) Reader's Digest Children's Publishing, Inc.

Zinnen, Linda. The Dragons of Spratt, Ohio. 2004. 240p. (J). 15.99 (978-0-06-000021-9(X)); lib. bdg. 17.89 (978-0-06-000022-6(8)) HarperCollins Pubs.

—The Truth about Rats, Rules, & Seventh Grade. 2001. 160p. (J). (gr. 3-7). 14.95 (978-0-06-028799-3(3)); (gr. 4-7). lib. bdg. 15.89 (978-0-06-028800-6(0)) HarperCollins Pubs.

OHIO—HISTORY

Boekhoff, P. M. & Kallen, Stuart A. Ohio. 2001. (Seeds of a Nation Ser.). (Illus.). 48p. (J). (gr. 3-5). 23.70 (978-0-7377-0948-3(0) , LML00902-178582, Kidhaven) Thomson Gale.

Cafmeyer, Judy. Ready, Set, Show What You Know' on the Ohio Acheivement Test for Gr. 3: Student Edition. 2004. (J). per. 10.95 (978-1-59230-062-4(6)) Englefield & Assocs., Inc.

Dalton, Curt. Dayton Inventions: Fact & Fiction. 2003. (Illus.). 74p. per. 12.95 (978-0-9720965-1-5(5)) Montgomery County Historical Society.

Deady, Kathleen W. Ohio. 2005. (Portraits of the States Ser.). (Illus.). 32p. (J). pap. (978-0-8368-4651-5(6)); lib. bdg. 23.33 (978-0-8368-4632-4(X)) Stevens, Gareth Inc.

Gray, Susan. All Across Ohio: A Bird's Eye View with Worthington Cardinal, 7 bks. Messer, Celia, illus. 2003. 24p. (J). 7.95 (978-0-9742862-0-4(6)) Two's Company.

—Colorful Ohio! A Bird's Eye View with Worthington Cardinal, 7 bks. Gray, Susan & Messer, Celia, illus. 2003. 28p. (J). 4.95 (978-0-9742862-5-9(7)) Two's Company.

—Plain & Simple: A Bird's Eye View with Worthington Cardinal, 7 bks. Messer, Celia, illus. 2003. 24p. (J). 7.95 (978-0-9742862-4-2(9)) Two's Company.

—A River Ride: A Bird's Eye View with Worthington Cardinal, 7 bks. Messer, Celia, illus. 2003. 24p. (J). 7.95 (978-0-9742862-3-5(0)) Two's Company.

—Wagon-O! A Bird's Eye View with Worthington Cardinal, 7 bks. Messer, Celia, illus. 2003. 24p. (J). 7.95 (978-0-9742862-2-8(2)) Two's Company.

—We Can Fly! A Bird's Eye View with Worthington Cardinal, 7 bks. Messer, Celia, illus. 2003. 24p. (J). 7.95 (978-0-9742862-1-1(4)) Two's Company.

Kandel, Megan. Let's Celebrate Ohio. 2003. pap. 10.95 (978-1-931334-20-4(X) , CLC0287) Pieces of Learning.

Marsh, Carole. My First Pocket Guide Ohio. 2000. (Ohio Experience! Ser.). (Illus.). 96p. (J). (gr. 3-8). 12.95 (978-0-635-01325-5(8) , 13258) Gallopade International.

—Ohio Survivor. 2001. (GameBook Ser.). 32p. (J). (gr. 3-8). pap., act. bk. ed. 9.95 (978-0-635-00556-4(5)) Gallopade International.

—The Ohio Survivor: A Class Challenge. 2001. (Carole Marsh Ohio Bks.). (J). lib. bdg. 29.95 (978-0-635-00681-3(2)) Gallopade International.

—Ohio Wheel of Fortune. 2001. (GameBook Ser.). 32p. (J). (gr. 3-8). pap., act. bk. ed. 9.95 (978-0-7933-9686-3(7)) Gallopade International.

—Wheel of Fortune. 2001. (Ohio Experience! Ser.). (J). lib. bdg. 29.95 (978-0-7933-9687-0(5)) Gallopade International.

—Who Wants to Be a Millionaire? 2001. (Carole Marsh Ohio Bks.). (J). lib. bdg. 29.95 (978-0-635-00087-3(3)) Gallopade International.

Martin, Michael. Ohio: The Buckeye State. 2002. (gr. 5-8). lib. bdg. 24.15 (978-0-613-52463-6(2)) Tandem Library Bks.

McNeese, Tim. Ohio River. 2004. (Rivers in American Life & Times Ser.). (Illus.). 120p. (gr. 9-13). 30.00 (978-0-7910-7725-2(X)); pap. 13.25 (978-0-7910-8008-5(0)) Facts On File, Inc. (Chelsea Hse.).

Ohio Historical Society. Ohio, A Sentimental Journey Study Guide, 1 CD. 2004. (Illus.). 102p. (YA). cd-rom (978-0-9747666-1-4(5)) American Retrospects, LLC.

Raizk, Mary Ann. Happy Birthday, Ohio: Celebrating Ohio's Bicentennial 1803-2003, 1. Raizk, Leyla Marie, illus. 2003. 32p. (J). pap. 14.95 (978-1-882203-97-0(6)) Orange Frazer Pr.

Regina, Karen. Cincinnati, an Urban History. x, 270p. (978-0-911497-13-7(7)) Cincinnati Museum Ctr., The.

Schonberg, Marcia. Ohio History. 2003. (Heinemann State Studies). (Illus.). 48p. (J). pap. 8.50 (978-1-4034-2689-5(9)); lib. bdg. 27.07 (978-1-4034-0666-8(9)) Heinemann Library.

—People of Ohio. 2003. (Heinemann State Studies). (Illus.). 48p. (J). pap. 8.50 (978-1-4034-2692-5(9)); lib. bdg. 27.07 (978-1-4034-0668-2(5)) Heinemann Library.

Simpson, Floyd. True Stories of the Drovers Trail: True Stories of the Eastern Ohio Drovers Trail. Simpson, Floyd, illus. 2001. (Illus.). 29p. (YA). pap. 7.75 (978-0-9710919-1-7(9)) F. S. Portrait Art.

Weymouth Seguin, Marilyn. The Freedom Stairs: The Story of Adam Lowry Rankin, Underground Railroad Conductor. 2004. (Illus.). 93p. (J). (ps-7). per. 12.95 net. (978-0-8283-2084-9(5)) Branden Bks.

OHIO—HISTORY—FICTION

Bildner, Phil & Long, Loren. Game 1. Long, Loren, illus. 2007. (Barnstormers Ser.). (Illus.). 144p. (J). (gr. 2-5). 9.99 (978-1-4169-1863-9(9)) Simon & Schuster Children's Publishing.

Cheng, Andrea. Eclipse. 2006. 320p. (J). 16.95 (978-1-932425-21-5(7) , Front Street) Boyds Mills Pr.

Craven, Tracy Leininger. Life of Faith/Kathleens Drought. 2007. (Life of Faith': Kathleen Mckenzie Ser.). 160p. (YA). pap. 6.99 (978-1-928749-27-1(5)) Mission City Pr., Inc.

Hulme, Lucy V. Passages, 1 bk. Redpath, Dale, illus. 2005. 40p. (J). 7.95 (978-0-9769854-0-2(3) , 001) Combs-Hulme Publishing.

Jones, Veda Boyd. Emma's Secret: The Cincinnati Epidemic. 2005. (Sisters in Time Ser.). 141p. (J). (*978-1-4156-0074-0(0)) Barbour Publishing, Inc.

Leininger Craven, Tracy. Kathleen's Dreadful Drought. 2006. 12.99 (978-1-928749-90-5(9)) Mission City Pr., Inc.

Pearsall, Shelley. Crooked River. 2005. 256p. (J). (gr. 5-9). 15.95 (978-0-375-82389-3(1)); lib. bdg. 17.99 (978-0-375-92389-0(6)) Random Hse. Children's Bks. (Knopf Bks. for Young Readers).

Saturen, Myra. Journey to a New World: Mystic River of the West. 2006. (J). pap. (*978-0-88092-495-5(0)) Royal Fireworks Publishing Co.

Tripp, Valerie. Kit's Short Story Collection. Rane, Walter & Graef, Renee, illus. 2006. 256p. (J). 12.95 (*978-1-59369-126-4(2)) American Girl Publishing, Inc.

Van Leeuwen, Jean. Cabin on Trouble Creek. 2004. 224p. (J). (gr. 4). 16.99 (978-0-8037-2548-5(5) , Dial) Penguin Group (USA) Inc.

OHIO RIVER AND VALLEY—FICTION

Hemphill, Kris. Ambush in the Wilderness. 2003. (Adventures in America Ser.). (Illus.). 90p. (J). 14.95 (978-1-893110-34-2(6)) Silver Moon Pr.

Sanders, Scott Russell. Bad Man Ballad. 2004. (Library of Indiana Classics). (J). reprint ed. 256p. 32.95 (978-0-253-34414-4(X)); 192p. 14.95 (978-0-253-34408-3(5)) Indiana Univ. Pr.

Willis, Patricia. Danger along the Ohio. 1999. 192p. (J). (gr. 3-7). pap. 6.99 (978-0-380-73151-0(7) , Harper Trophy) HarperCollins Pubs.

—Danger along the Ohio. 1999. (J). 12.64 (978-0-606-16343-9(3)); (gr. 3-6). lib. bdg. 14.15 (978-0-7857-0159-0(1)) Tandem Library Bks.

Winfield, Arthur M. The Rover Boys on the River or the Search for the Missing. 2006. (ENG.). 272p. per. 27.95 ***(*978-1-4286-4115-0(7))*** Kessinger Publishing, LLC.

OIL

see Petroleum

OIL FUEL

see Petroleum As Fuel

OIL SPILLS

Alcraft, Rob. Oil Disasters. 1999. (World's Worst Ser.). 32p. (J). (gr. 4-6). lib. bdg. 22.79 (978-1-57572-990-9(3)) Heinemann Library.

Beech, Linda Ward. The Exxon Valdez's Deadly Oil Spill. 2007. (Code Red Ser.). (Illus.). 32p. (J). (gr. 3-7). lib. bdg. 25.27 (978-1-59716-366-8(X)) Bearport Publishing Co., Inc.

Benchmark Education Staff. Oil Spills. 2005. 2.00 ***(*978-1-4108-4671-6(7))*** Benchmark Education Co.

Brannon, Barbara. Discover Oil Spills. 2005. 39.00 ***(*978-1-4108-5139-0(7))*** Benchmark Education Co.

Bryan, Nichol. Exxon Valdez: Oil Spill. 2003. (Environmental Disasters Ser.). (Illus.). 48p. (gr. 5 up). (J). pap. 11.95 (978-0-8368-5513-5(2)); (YA). lib. bdg. 30.00 (978-0-8368-5506-7(X)) Stevens, Gareth Inc. (World Almanac Library).

Capstone Press Editors. Oil Spills. 2002. (Our Planet in Peril Ser.). (Illus.). 48p. (J). (gr. 3-4). lib. bdg. 22.60 (978-0-7368-1363-1(2) , Bridgestone Bks.) Capstone Pr., Inc.

—Our Planet in Peril, 4 bks. Incl. Acid Rain. lib. bdg. 22.60 (978-0-7368-1360-0(8)); Global Warming. lib. bdg. 22.60 (978-0-7368-1361-7(6)); Nuclear Waste. lib. bdg. 22.60 (978-0-7368-1362-4(4)); Oil Spills. lib. bdg. 22.60 (978-0-7368-1363-1(2)); 48p. (J). (gr. 3-4). 2002. (Illus.). 2002. Set lib. bdg. 90.40 (978-0-7368-1364-8(0) , Bridgestone Bks.) Capstone Pr., Inc.

Chandler, Gil. The Exxon Valdez: The Oil Spill off the Alaskan Coast. 2002. (Disaster! Ser.). (Illus.). 32p. (J). (gr. 3-4). lib. bdg. 21.26 (978-0-7368-1320-4(9) , Capstone High-Interest Bks.) Capstone Pr., Inc.

Dils, Tracey E. The Exxon Valdez. 2001. (Great Disasters, Reforms & Ramifications Ser.). (Illus.). 112p. (J). (gr. 4-7). 30.00 (978-0-7910-5784-1(4) , Chelsea Hse.) Facts On File, Inc.

Greeley, August. Sludge & Slime: Oil Spills in Our World. 2003. (Man-Made Disasters Ser.). (Illus.). 24p. (J). lib. bdg. 17.25 (978-0-8239-6485-7(X) , PowerKids Pr.) Rosen Publishing Group, Inc., The.

Leacock, Elspeth. Exxon Valdez Oil Spill. 2005. (Environmental Disasters Ser.). (Illus.). 112p. (J). (gr. 6-12). 35.00 (978-0-8160-5754-2(0)) Facts On File, Inc.

Margulies, Phillip. The Exxon Valdez Oil Spill: When Disaster Strikes! 2005. (When Disaster Strikes! Ser.). (Illus.). 48p. (YA). (gr. 5-8). lib. bdg. 23.95 (978-0-8239-3675-5(9)) Rosen Publishing Group, Inc., The.

Parks, Peggy J. Oil Spills. 2005. (Our Environment Ser.). (Illus.). 48p. (J). (ps-7). lib. bdg. 26.20 (978-0-7377-2629-9(6) , Greenhaven Pr., Inc.) Thomson Gale.

Parsons, Michelle Hyde. Oil Spills. 2005. 39.00 ***(*978-1-4108-4623-5(7))*** Benchmark Education Co.

Sherrow, Victoria. The Exxon Valdez: Tragic Oil Spill. 1998. (American Disasters Ser.). (Illus.). 48p. (YA). (gr. 4-10). lib. bdg. 23.93 (978-0-7660-1058-1(9)) Enslow Pubs., Inc.

Sludge & Slime: Oil Spills in Our World: Individual Title Six-Packs. (On Deck Ser.: Vol. 2). 24p. (gr. 4-5). 35.00 (978-0-7578-5833-8(3)) Rigby Education.

Smith, Roland. Sea Otter Rescue: The Aftermath of an Oil Spill. 1999. (978-0-606-17426-8(5)) Tandem Library Bks.

Townsend, John. When Disaster Struck: The Exxon Valdez 1989. 2006. (Illus.). 56p. (978-1-4109-2280-9(4)) Steck-Vaughn.

Walker, Jane. Oil Spills. 2004. (J). lib. bdg. 27.10 (978-1-932799-10-1(9)) Stargazer Bks.

OIL WELLS

see Petroleum

OKEFENOKEE SWAMP (GA. AND FLA.)

Bateman, Donna M. Deep in the Swamp. Lies, Brian, illus. 2007. 32p. (J). (gr. k-3). pap. 6.95 ***(*978-1-57091-597-0(0))*** Charlesbridge Publishing, Inc.

OKEFENOKEE SWAMP (GA. AND FLA.)—FICTION

Jackson's Plan: Evaluation Guide. 2006. (J). (978-1-55942-410-3(9)) Marsh Media.

Talley, Linda. Jackson's Plan. Chase, Andra, illus. 1998. (Key Concepts in Personal Development Ser.). 32p. (J). (gr. k-4). 17.95 (978-1-55942-104-1(5) , 7665) Marsh Media.

OKLAHOMA

Anderson, J. Christopher. Uniquely Oklahoma. 2004. (Heinemann State Studies). (Illus.). 48p. (J). pap. (978-1-4034-4727-2(6)); lib. bdg. 27.07 (978-1-4034-4658-9(X)) Heinemann Library.

Baldwin, Guy. Oklahoma. 2000. (Celebrate the States Ser.). (Illus.). 144p. (J). (gr. 4-8). lib. bdg. 37.07 (978-0-7614-1067-6(8) , Benchmark Bks.) Cavendish, Marshall Corp.

Banks, James A. Oklahoma. 2001. (Adventures in Time & Place Ser.). (Illus.). (J). (978-0-02-149174-2(7)); tchr. ed. (978-0-02-149175-9(5)) National Geographic Society.

Boraas, Tracey. Oklahoma. 2003. (Land of Liberty Ser.). (Illus.). 64p. (J). lib. bdg. 25.26 (978-0-7368-2192-6(9)) Capstone Pr., Inc.

Brown, Jonatha A. Oklahoma. 2006. (Portraits of the States Ser.). (Illus.). 32p. (J). pap. 8.95 (978-0-8368-4691-1(5)); lib. bdg. 23.33 (978-0-8368-4672-0(9)) Stevens, Gareth Inc.

Brown, Vanessa. Oklahoma. 2006. (Bilingual Library of the United States of America: Set 2). (ENG & SPA.). 32p. (J). (gr. 3-6). lib. bdg. 22.50 (978-1-4042-3101-6(3) , Buenas Letra) Rosen Publishing Group, Inc., The.

Brownell, Richard. The Oklahoma City Bombing. 2007. (Crime Scene Investigations Ser.). 128p. (J). (gr. 7-10). 32.45 ***(*978-1-59018-843-9(8)*** , Lucent Bks.) Thomson Gale.

Gibson, Karen Bush. Oklahoma Facts & Symbols. (States & Their Symbols Ser.). 24p. (J). 2000. (Illus.). (gr. 2-3). lib. bdg. 18.60 (978-0-7368-0643-5(1) , Bridgestone Bks.); 2003. lib. bdg. 19.93 (978-0-7368-2266-4(6)) Capstone Pr., Inc.

A Guide to Oklahoma. 2001. (American States Ser.). 32p. (J). per. 7.95 (978-1-930954-98-4(0)) Weigl Pubs., Inc.

Heinrichs, Ann. Oklahoma. Hamilton, Ann, ed. Kania, Matt, illus. 2005. (Welcome to the USA Ser.). 40p. (J). (gr. 1-5). 27.07 (978-1-59296-381-2(1)) Child's World, Inc.

—Oklahoma. 2003. (This Land Is Your Land Ser.). (Illus.). 48p. (J). (gr. 3 up). lib. bdg. 22.60 (978-0-7565-0330-7(2)) Compass Point Bks.

Hinkle, Donald Henry. Oklahoma: A MyReportLinks. Com Book. 2003. (States Ser.). (Illus.). 48p. (J). lib. bdg. 25.26 (978-0-7660-5138-6(2) , MyReportLinks.com Bks.) Enslow Pubs., Inc.

Kavanagh, James. Oklahoma Birds. Leung, Raymond, illus. 2001. (Pocket Naturalist Ser.). 12p. (gr. 9). pap. 5.95 (978-1-58355-008-3(9)) Waterford Pr., Ltd.

Kummer, Patricia K. Oklahoma. rev. ed. 2002. (One Nation Ser.). (Illus.). 48p. (J). (gr. 3-4). lib. bdg. 22.60 (978-0-7368-1260-3(1) , Bridgestone Bks.) Capstone Pr., Inc.

LaBella, Susan. Oklahoma. 2006. (Rookie Read-About Geography Ser.). (Illus.). 32p. (J). (gr. 1-2). 20.50 (978-0-516-25468-5(5) , Children's Pr.) Scholastic Library Publishing.

Labella, Susan. Oklahoma. 2007. (Rookie Read-about' Geography: States Ser.). 32p. (J). pap. 5.95 ***(*978-0-531-16817-2(4)*** , Children's Pr.) Scholastic Library Publishing.

LaDoux, Rita C. Oklahoma. 2nd exp. rev. ed. 2003. (Hello U. S. A. Ser.). (Illus.). 84p. (J). (gr. 3-6). 25.26 (978-0-8225-4098-4(3) , Lerner Pubns.) Lerner Publishing Group.

—Oklahoma. rev. ed. 2003. (gr. 3-6). lib. bdg. 15.25 (978-0-613-52464-3(0)) Tandem Library Bks.

Marsh, Carole. My First Book about Oklahoma. 2004. (Oklahoma Experience! Ser.). (Illus.). 32p. (J). (gr. k-4). pap. 7.95 (978-0-7933-9595-8(X)) Gallopade International.

—My First Pocket Guide: Oklahoma. 2004. (Oklahoma Experience! Ser.). (Illus.). 96p. (J). (gr. 3-8). per. 6.95 (978-0-7933-9594-1(1)) Gallopade International.

—Oklahoma Classic Christmas Trivia. 2002. (Carole Marsh Oklahoma Bks.). (Illus.). 32p. (J). pap. 6.95 (978-0-635-01437-5(8) , 14378); lib. bdg. 21.95 (978-0-635-01438-2(6) , 14386) Gallopade International. (Marsh, Carole Bks.).

—Oklahoma Current Events Projects: 30 Cool, Activities, Crafts, Experiments & More for Kids to Do to Learn about Your State! 2003. (Oklahoma Experience Ser.). 32p. (gr. k-8). pap. 5.95 (978-0-635-02055-0(6) , Marsh, Carole Bks.) Gallopade International.

—Oklahoma Geography Projects: 30 Cool, Activities, Crafts, Experiments & More for Kids to Do to Learn about Your State! 2003. (Oklahoma Experience Ser.). 32p. (gr. k-5). pap. 5.95 (978-0-635-01855-7(1) , Marsh, Carole Bks.) Gallopade International.

—Oklahoma Government Projects: 30 Cool, Activities, Crafts, Experiments & More for Kids to Do to Learn about Your State! 2003. (Oklahoma Experience Ser.). 32p. (gr. k-5). pap. 5.95 (978-0-635-01955-4(8) , Marsh, Carole Bks.) Gallopade International.

—Oklahoma History Projects: 30 Cool, Activities, Crafts, Experiments & More for Kids to Do to Learn about Your State! 2003. (Oklahoma Experience Ser.). 32p. (gr. k-5). pap. 5.95 (978-0-635-01805-2(5) , Marsh, Carole Bks.) Gallopade International.

—Oklahoma Jeopardy! Answers & Questions about Our State! 2004. (Oklahoma Experience! Ser.). (Illus.). 32p. (J). (gr. 3-8). pap. 7.95 (978-0-7933-9596-5(8)) Gallopade International.

—Oklahoma "Jography" A Fun Run Thru Our State! 2004. (Oklahoma Experience! Ser.). (Illus.). 32p. (J). (gr. 3-8). pap. 7.95 (978-0-7933-9597-2(6)) Gallopade International.

—Oklahoma People Projects: 30 Cool, Activities, Crafts, Experiments & More for Kids to Do to Learn about Your State! 2003. (Oklahoma Experience Ser.). 32p. (gr. k-5). pap. 5.95 (978-0-635-02005-5(X) , Marsh, Carole Bks.) Gallopade International.

—Oklahoma Symbols & Facts Projects: 30 Cool, Activities, Crafts, Experiments & More for Kids to Do to Learn about Your State! 2003. (Oklahoma Experience Ser.). 32p. (gr. k-5). pap. 5.95 (978-0-635-01905-9(1) , Marsh, Carole Bks.) Gallopade International.

—The Out of This World Oklahoma Coloring Book. 2004. (Oklahoma Experience! Ser.). (Illus.). 32p. (J). (gr. k-2). pap. 3.95 (978-0-7933-9599-6(2)) Gallopade International.

Martin, Michael A. Oklahoma: The Sooner State. 2002. (World Almanac Library of the States). (Illus.). 48p. (J). (gr. 5 up). lib. bdg. 30.00 (978-0-8368-5142-7(0)); pap. 14.95 (978-0-8368-5312-4(1)) Stevens, Gareth Inc. (World Almanac Library).

Murray, Julie. Oklahoma. 2006. (Buddy Book Ser.). (Illus.). 32p. (J). (gr. k-4). lib. bdg. 22.78 (978-1-59197-695-0(2) , Buddy Bks.) ABDO Publishing Co.

Orr, Tamra. Oklahoma. 2007. (America the Beautiful, Third Ser.). (Illus.). 144p. (YA). (gr. 5-8). lib. bdg. 38.00 ***(*978-0-531-18567-4(2)*** , Children's Pr.) Scholastic Library Publishing.

Sanders, Doug. Oklahoma. 2005. (It's My State! Ser.). (Illus.). 80p. (J). (978-0-7614-1906-8(3) , Benchmark Bks.) Cavendish, Marshall Corp.

Saylor-Marchant, Linda. Oklahoma. 2003. (From Sea to Shining Sea Ser.: 2). (Illus.). 80p. (J). 30.50 (978-0-516-22393-3(3) , Children's Pr.) Scholastic Library Publishing.

Scillian, Devin. S Is for Sooner: An Oklahoma Alphabet. Doner, Kim, illus. 2003. 40p. (J). 17.95 (978-1-58536-062-8(7)) Sleeping Bear Pr.

Strudwick, Leslie. A Guide to Oklahoma. 2001. (American States Ser.). (Illus.). 32p. (J). lib. bdg. 16.95 (978-1-930954-08-3(5)) Weigl Pubs., Inc.

Webb, Dave. Color Oklahoma Characters: Poster-Coloring Book. Buntin, Phillip R., illus. 1999. 64p. (YA). (gr. 1 up). pap. 7.95 (978-1-882404-12-4(2)) Kansas Heritage Ctr.

OKLAHOMA—FICTION

Aryal, Aimee. Let's Go Sooners! Shrestha, Anuj, illus. 2004. (J). 19.95 (978-1-932888-29-4(2)) Mascot Bks., Inc.

Beard, Darleen Bailey. The Babbs Switch Story. 2002. 176p. (J). 16.00 (978-0-374-30475-1(0) , Farrar, Straus & Giroux (BYR)) Farrar, Straus & Giroux.

—The Flimflam Man. Christelow, Eileen, illus. 96p. (J). 2003. pap. 5.95 (978-0-374-42345-2(8) , Sunburst); 1998. (gr. 2-6). 15.00 (978-0-374-32346-2(1) , Farrar, Straus & Giroux (BYR)) Farrar, Straus & Giroux.

Gassett, John D. Little John - The Webb City Kid. Skrzeczkoski, Jeanne & Andrews, Erica, illus. 1999. 125p. (J). (gr. 1-8). pap. (978-0-9671895-0-5(0)) Gassett, John D.

Gilbert, Barbara Snow. Paper Trail. 2005. 161p. (YA). (gr. 7-12). pap. 8.95 (978-1-932425-54-3(3) , Lemniscaat) Boyds Mills Pr.

Griffis, Molly Levite. The Feester Filibuster. 2002. (Illus.). vi, 236p. (J). pap. 8.95 (978-1-57168-694-7(0) , Eakin Pr.) Eakin Pr.

—The Feester Filibuster. 2002. (gr. 3-6). lib. bdg. 17.60 (978-0-613-79188-5(6)) Tandem Library Bks.

—The Rachel Resistance. 224p. 8.95 (978-1-57168-553-7(7)); 2001. 17.95 (978-1-57168-541-4(3)) Eakin Pr.

Grove, Vicki. The Starplace. 2000. (Illus.). 224p. (J). (gr. 5-9). pap. 6.99 (978-0-698-11868-3(5) , Putnam Juvenile) Penguin Group (USA) Inc.

—The Starplace. 2000. (978-0-606-20373-9(7)); (J). (978-0-606-20257-2(9)) Tandem Library Bks.

—Starplace. 2000. (gr. 5-8). lib. bdg. 14.15 (978-0-613-30759-8(3)) Tandem Library Bks.

Hartgraves, Richard. Little Cedar. 2006. 130p. pap. 19.95 ***(*978-1-4241-4603-1(8))*** PublishAmerica, Inc.

Hesse, Karen. Out of the Dust. 2002. (Illus.). (J). 13.19 (978-0-7587-0207-4(8)) Book Wholesalers, Inc.

—Out of the Dust. 240p. (gr. 5 up). (YA). pap. 4.99 (978-0-8072-1526-5(0)); 1998. (J). pap. 29.00 incl. audio (978-0-8072-8013-3(5) , YA967SP) Random Hse. Audio Publishing Group. (Listening Library).

—Out of the Dust. 1999. (Apple Signature Edition Ser.). 240p. (gr. 4-7). mass mkt. 5.99 (978-0-590-37125-4(8)) Scholastic, Inc.

—Out of the Dust. 1999. (978-0-606-15665-3(8)); (gr. 5-8). lib. bdg. 13.00 (978-0-613-11953-5(3)) Tandem Library Bks.

Hudson, Marilyn A. Annie Oklahoma: An Original Oklahoma Tall Tale. 2007. (J). per. ***(*978-0-9778850-3-9(8))*** Hudson House Publishing & Productions.

—Elephant Hips Are Expensive! A Tale of the Sooner State. Fulco, Haley, illus. 2007. 50p. (J). per. ***(*978-0-9778850-2-2(X))*** Hudson House Publishing & Productions.

I'm Not Afraid of Needles. 2004. (J). 4.99 (978-0-9776144-0-0(9)) Kidstalk, LLC.

Krueger, Kathryn L. Road to Grandma's House. 2005. 128p. pap. 13.95 (978-1-59800-366-6(6)) Outskirts Press, Inc.

Letts, Billie. The Honk & Holler Opening Soon. 1999. (gr. 7-12). lib. bdg. 23.40 (978-0-613-17283-7(3)) Tandem Library Bks.

Morrow, John. Happy Birthday Oklahoma! collector's ed. 2007. (Illus.). (J). lib. bdg. 17.95 ***(*978-0-9790832-2-8(2))*** Three Ring Circus Publishing Company.

—Ostrich Egg Omelets. 2006. (Illus.). (J). per. 14.95 ***(*978-0-9790832-1-1(4))*** Three Ring Circus Publishing Company.

Myers, Anna. Confessions from the Principal's Chair. 2006. 192p. 16.95 (978-0-8027-9560-1(9)) Walker & Co.

—Ethan Between Us. 2000. (Illus.). (J). (978-0-606-18742-8(1)) Tandem Library Bks.

Myers, Anna. Wart. 2007. 224p. (J). (gr. 5-9). 16.95 ***(*978-0-8027-8977-8(3))*** Walker & Co.

Paulsen, Gary. The Legend of Bass Reeves. 2006. 160p. (YA). (gr. 7). 15.95 (978-0-385-74661-8(X)); lib. bdg. 17.99 (978-0-385-90898-6(9)) Random Hse. Children's Bks. (Lamb, Wendy).

Porter, Tracey. Treasures in the Dust. 1999. (978-0-606-16702-4(1)); (gr. 3-6). lib. bdg. 14.15 (978-0-613-18284-3(7)) Tandem Library Bks.

Schuck, Philip. A Ricochet from Circumstance. 2005. (YA). 19.95 (978-0-9764670-0-7(3)) Smithfield Capital Corp.

Skye, Obert. Leven Thumps & the Eyes of the Want. 2007. (Leven Thumps Ser.: Bk. 3). (Illus.). 406p. (J). (gr. 5 up). 18.95 ***(*978-1-59038-800-6(3)*** , Shadow Mountain) Deseret Bk. Co.

Tharp, Tim. Knights of the Hill Country. 2006. 240p. (YA). (gr. 7). 16.95 (978-0-375-83653-4(5)); lib. bdg. 18.99 (978-0-375-93653-1(X)) Random Hse. Children's Bks. (Knopf Bks. for Young Readers).

Thomas, Joyce Carol. Marked by Fire. rev. ed. 2007. 192p. (YA). (gr. 8-17). 15.99 ***(*978-1-4231-0143-7(X));*** pap. 7.99 ***(*978-1-4231-0144-4(8))*** Hyperion Bks. for Children. (Jump at the Sun).

Tomlinson, Sylvia. Maddie. Cartmell, Ginny, illus. 2002. 124p. (J). (gr. 3-7). 12.95 (978-0-9720293-0-8(3)) Redbud Publishing Co.

Townsend, Una Belle. Grady's in the Silo. Artley, Bob, illus. 2003. 32p. (J). 15.95 (978-1-58980-098-4(2)) Pelican Publishing Co., Inc.

(Trantham) Rogers Staff. Barefoot in the Cotton Fields of Oklahom. 2005. (Illus.). 123p. pap. 17.95 (978-1-4137-7205-0(6)) PublishAmerica, Inc.

Wallace, Bill. Coyote Autumn. 2002. 208p. (J). pap. 5.99 (978-0-7434-2836-1(6) , Aladdin) Simon & Schuster Children's Publishing.

—Coyote Autumn. 2002. (gr. 3-6). lib. bdg. 13.00 (978-0-613-68225-1(4)) Tandem Library Bks.

Wallace, Bill. The Dog Who Thought He Was Santa. 2007. 224p. (J). (gr. 3-7). 16.95 ***(*978-0-8234-2114-5(7))*** Holiday Hse., Inc.

Westerfeld, Scott. The Secret Hour. 2004. (Midnighters Ser.: No. 1). 304p. (YA). (gr. 7 up). 16.99 (978-0-06-051951-3(7)) HarperCollins Pubs.

Wheelus, Doris. The Plum Jelly Kids. 2005. 223p. pap. 19.95 (978-1-4137-5649-4(2)) PublishAmerica, Inc.

OKLAHOMA—HISTORY

Brean, Alta. Dear Grandchildren: Growing up on the Frontier. 2003. (Illus.). 144p. 18.95 (978-0-9726360-0-1(5) , (408) 718-5654) Alta Omnimedia.

Douglas, Bettye. Portrait of a People: The Bettye Douglas Forum, Inc. Multicultural Resource Book. Douglas, Bettye, ed. Douglas, Ana & Douglas, Garbrielle, illus. 222p. (YA). (gr. 5-13). 100.00 (978-0-9703183-1-2(6)) Douglas, Bettye Forum, Inc., The.

—Safari Oklahoma Presents: God Bless America Historical. Douglas, Garbrielle, illus. 2003. 22p. (J). (gr. 2-7). wbk. ed. 19.95 (978-0-9703183-6-7(7)) Douglas, Bettye Forum, Inc., The.

Durrett, Deanne. Oklahoma. 2003. (Seeds of a Nation Ser.). (Illus.). 48p. (J). (gr. 3-5). 23.70 (978-0-7377-1479-1(4) , Kidhaven) Thomson Gale.

Faulk, Odie B. & Welge, William D. Oklahoma: A Rich Heritage. 2004. (Illus.). 384p. 34.95 (978-1-892724-46-5(4)) American Historical Pr.

Fein, E. How to Draw Oklahomas Sights & Symbols. 2002. (Kids Guide to Drawing America Ser.). 32p. (J). lib. bdg. 25.25 (978-0-8239-6092-7(7) , PowerKids Pr.) Rosen Publishing Group, Inc., The.

Isaacs, Sally Senzell. The Great Land Rush. 2003. (Illus.). 32p. (J). pap. 7.50 (978-1-4034-4771-5(3)); lib. bdg. 25.64 (978-1-4034-2505-8(1)) Heinemann Library.

Kent, Deborah. The Trail of Tears. 2007. (Cornerstones of Freedomtrade;, Second Ser.). 48p. (J). 5.95 ***(*978-0-531-18693-0(8)*** , Children's Pr.) Scholastic Library Publishing.

Marcovitz, Hal. The Oklahoma City Bombing. 2002. (Great Disasters, Reforms & Ramifications Ser.). (Illus.). (J). 114p. pap. 13.25 (978-0-7910-6912-7(5)); 112p. 30.00 (978-0-7910-6738-3(6)) Facts On File, Inc. (Chelsea Hse.).

—Oklahoma City Bombing. 2002. (gr. 5-8). lib. bdg. 18.75 (978-0-613-50979-4(X)) Tandem Library Bks.

Marsh, Carole. My First Pocket Guide Oklahoma. 2000. (Oklahoma Experience! Ser.). (Illus.). 96p. (J). (gr. 3-8). 12.95 (978-0-635-01326-2(6) , 13266) Gallopade International.

—Oklahoma Millionaire. 2001. (GameBook Ser.). 32p. (J). (gr. 3-8). pap., act. bk. ed. 9.95 (978-0-635-00088-0(1)) Gallopade International.

—Oklahoma Survivor. 2001. (GameBook Ser.). 32p. (J). (gr. 3-8). pap., act. bk. ed. 9.95 (978-0-635-00557-1(3)) Gallopade International.

—The Oklahoma Survivor: A Class Challenge. 2001. (Carole Marsh Oklahoma Bks.). (J). lib. bdg. 29.95 (978-0-635-00682-0(0)) Gallopade International.

—Oklahoma Wheel of Fortune. 2001. (GameBook Ser.). 32p. (J). (gr. 3-8). pap., act. bk. ed. 9.95 (978-0-7933-9688-7(3)) Gallopade International.

—Wheel of Fortune. 2001. (Oklahoma Bks.). (J). lib. bdg. 29.95 (978-0-7933-9689-4(1)) Gallopade International.

—Who Wants to Be a Millionaire? 2001. (Carole Marsh Oklahoma Bks.). (J). lib. bdg. 29.95 (978-0-635-00089-7(X)) Gallopade International.

Sherrow, Victoria. The Oklahoma City Bombing: Terror in the Heartland. 1998. (American Disasters Ser.). (Illus.). 48p. (YA). (gr. 4-10). lib. bdg. 23.93 (978-0-7660-1061-1(9)) Enslow Pubs., Inc.

Smallwood, James. Oklahoma & Its Heroes. 2001. (Illus.). 104p. 15.95 (978-1-57168-581-0(2)) Eakin Pr.

OKLAHOMA—HISTORY—FICTION

Ashabranner, Brent K. & Davis, Russell G. The Choctaw Code. 2006. 121p. (J). (978-1-59166-621-9(X)) Jones, Bob Univ. Pr.

Griffis, Molly Levite. The Feester Filibuster. 2002. (Illus.). 224p. 18.95 (978-1-57168-693-0(2)) Eakin Pr.

—Simon Says. 2004. vi, 263p. (J). 22.95 (978-1-57168-836-1(6)); pap. (978-1-57168-847-7(1)) Eakin Pr. (Eakin Pr.).

Hesse, Karen. Out of the Dust. l.t. ed. 2004. 180p. 22.95 (978-0-7862-7006-4(3) , Large Print Pr.) Thorndike Pr.

Love, D. Anne. Semiprecious. 2006. 304p. (J). (gr. 5-9). 16.95 (978-0-689-85638-9(5) , McElderry, Margaret K.) Simon & Schuster Children's Publishing.

McCaughrean, Geraldine. Stop the Train! (J). (gr. 5 up). 2003. 304p. 16.99 (978-0-06-050749-7(7)); 2005. 384p. reprint ed. pap. 6.99 (978-0-06-050751-0(9) , Harper Trophy) HarperCollins Pubs.

M N O

Myers, Anna. Tulsa Burning. 2004. 184p. (J). pap. 7.95 (978-0-8027-7696-9(5)); (Illus.). (gr. 3-7). 16.95 (978-0-8027-8829-0(7)) Walker & Co.

Scillian, Devin. Pappy's Handkerchief. Ellison, Chris, illus. rev. ed. 2007. (Tales of Young Americans Ser.). 40p. (J). (gr. 3-7). 17.95 (*978-1-58536-316-2(2)) Sleeping Bear Pr.

Thomas, Joyce Carol. I Have Heard of a Land. Cooper, Floyd, illus. 2000. (Trophy Picture Bk.). 32p. (J). (gr. k-3). pap. 6.99 (978-0-06-443617-5(9) , Harper Trophy) HarperCollins Pubs.

—I Have Heard of a Land. 1998. (Illus.). 32p. (J). (gr. 2-6). 15.95 (978-0-06-023477-5(6) , Cotler, Joanna Books) HarperCollins Pubs.

—I Have Heard of a Land. Cooper, Floyd, illus. 1998. 32p. (J). (gr. 3 up). lib. bdg. 14.89 (978-0-06-023478-2(4) , Cotler, Joanna Books) HarperCollins Pubs.

OLD AGE

see also Older People

Ali, Rasheda. I'll Hold Your Hand So You Won't Fall: A Child's Guide to Parkinson's Disease. 2005. (Illus.). 40p. (J). pap. 19.95 (978-1-873413-13-5(0)) Merit Publishing International, Inc.

Arnold, Nick. How to Live Forever. Benton, Tim, illus. 2001. (How to Ser.). 96p. (J). (gr. 5-7). 16.00 (978-0-531-14641-5(3)); pap. 4.95 (978-0-531-14818-1(1)) Scholastic Library Publishing. (Watts, Franklin).

—How to Live Forever. 2001. (gr. 5-8). lib. bdg. 12.95 (978-0-613-54548-8(6)) Tandem Library Bks.

Bregoli, Jane. The Goat Lady. 2005. 32p. (J). (gr. 3-6). 16.95 (978-0-88448-260-4(X)) Tilbury Hse. Pubs.

Helmer, Diana Star. Let's Talk about When Someone You Love Is in a Nursing Home. 1999. (Let's Talk Library). (Illus.). 24p. (J). (gr. 3). lib. bdg. 18.75 (978-0-8239-5190-1(1) , PowerKids Pr.) Rosen Publishing Group, Inc., The.

Lakin, Patricia. Grandparents: Around the World. 1999. (We All Share Ser.). (Illus.). 32p. (J). (gr. 3-6). 22.45 (978-1-56711-146-0(7) , Blackbirch Pr., Inc.) Thomson Gale.

Panno, Joseph. The Science of Aging. (New Biology Ser.). (Illus.). 176p. (gr. 6-12). pap. 18.95 (978-0-8160-6930-9(1) , Checkmark Bks.) Facts On File, Inc.

OLD AGE—FICTION

Almond, David. Kit's Wilderness. l.t. ed. 2000. 263p. (J). pap. 16.95 (978-0-7540-6115-1(9) , Galaxy Children's Large Print) BBC Audiobooks America.

—Kit's Wilderness. unabr. ed. 2004. 240p. (J). (gr. 7 up). pap. 36.00 incl. audio (978-0-8072-8216-8(2) , Listening Library) Random Hse. Audio Publishing Group.

—Kit's Wilderness. (YA). (gr. 7). 2001. (Illus.). 256p. mass mkt. 5.99 (978-0-440-41605-0(1) , Laurel Leaf); 2000. 240p. 15.95 (978-0-385-32665-0(3) , Delacorte Bks. for Young Readers) Random Hse. Children's Bks.

—Kit's Wilderness. 2001. 229p. (YA). (gr. 8-12). lib. bdg. 13.00 (978-0-613-36836-0(3)); (978-0-606-22406-2(8)) Tandem Library Bks.

—Kit's Wilderness. l.t. ed. 2001. (Illus.). 272p. (J). (gr. 4-7). 22.95 (978-0-7862-2772-3(9)) Thorndike Pr.

Arnosky, Jim. Grandfather Buffalo. Arnosky, Jim, illus. 2006. (Illus.). 32p. (J). (ps). 16.99 (978-0-399-24169-7(8) , Putnam Juvenile) Penguin Group (USA) Inc.

Babbitt, Natalie. Tuck Everlasting. Babbitt, Natalie, illus. 2002. (Illus.). (J). 14.43 (978-0-7587-6382-2(4)) Book Wholesalers, Inc.

—Tuck Everlasting. 1999. 195p. (J). 17.90 (978-0-03-054783-6(0)) Holt, Rinehart & Winston.

—Tuck Everlasting. 2003. 152p. (J). 25.95 (978-0-7862-5181-0(6)) Thorndike Pr.

Bauer, Joan. Best Foot Forward. 2006. 192p. (YA). (gr. 7). reprint ed. pap. 7.99 (978-0-14-240690-8(2) , Puffin) Penguin Group (USA) Inc.

—Rules of the Road. 208p. (gr. 7). 2005. (YA). pap. 7.99 (978-0-14-240425-6(X) , Puffin); 1998. (J). 16.99 (978-0-399-23140-7(4) , Putnam Juvenile) Penguin Group (USA) Inc.

—Rules of the Road. 2000. (YA). (978-0-606-20252-7(8)); 201p. (gr. 7-12). lib. bdg. 13.64 (978-0-606-20370-8(2)) Tandem Library Bks.

Bogart, Jo Ellen. Jeremiah Learns to Read. Fernandez, Laura & Jacobson, Rick, illus. 1999. 32p. (J). (gr. k-4). 15.95 (978-0-531-30190-6(7) , Orchard Bks.) Scholastic, Inc.

Bogart, JoEllen. Jeremiah Learns to Read. Jacobson, Rick & Fernandez, Laura, illus. 1999. 32p. (J). (gr. k-4). lib. bdg. 16.99 (978-0-531-33190-3(3) , Orchard Bks.) Scholastic, Inc.

Brooks, Mel & Reiner, Carl. The 2000 Year Old Man Goes to School. Bennett, James, illus. 2005. 40p. (J). (ps-3). 17.99 (978-0-06-076676-4(X)); lib. bdg. 18.89 (978-0-06-076677-1(8)) HarperCollins Pubs.

Bunting, Eve. Can You Do This, Old Badger? Pham, LeUyen, illus. 2000. (Little Badger Bks.). 32p. (J). (ps). 15.00 (978-0-15-201654-8(6)) Harcourt Children's Bks.

—Can You Do This, Old Badger? Pham, LeUyen, illus. 2004. 26p. (J). (ps-ps). lib. bdg. 12.80 (978-0-606-30397-2(9)) Tandem Library Bks.

—Sunshine Home. De Groat, Diane, illus. 2005. 32p. (J). (gr. k-3). pap. 5.95 (978-0-618-55157-6(3) , Clarion Bks.) Houghton Mifflin Co. Trade & Reference Div.

Butcher, Kristin. Gramma War. 2001. (gr. 3-6). lib. bdg. 15.25 (978-0-613-45662-3(9)) Tandem Library Bks.

Caletti, Deb. Honey, Baby, Sweetheart. 320p. (YA). 2005. pap. 7.99 (978-0-689-86474-2(4) , Simon Pulse); 2004. 15.95 (978-0-689-86765-1(4)) Simon & Schuster Children's Publishing.

—Honey, Baby, Sweetheart. l.t. ed. 2005. 367p. 22.95 (978-0-7862-7308-9(9) , Large Print Pr.) Thorndike Pr.

Cannon, Janell. Verdi. Cannon, Janell, illus. 2002. (Illus.). (J). 23.40 (978-0-7587-3898-1(6)) Book Wholesalers, Inc.

—Verdi. (SPA., Illus.). 48p. (J). 2003. (gr. 1-3). (978-84-261-3042-6(9) , JV7591); 2000. 22.50 (978-84-261-2949-9(8) , JV9498) Juventud, Editorial ESP. *Dist:* Lectorum Pubns., Inc., AIMS International Bks., Inc., Continental Bk. Co., Inc., Distribooks, Inc.

—Verdi. pap. 24.95 (978-85-325-1343-4(3)) Rocco, Editora, Ltda BRA. *Dist:* Distribooks, Inc.

Cheng, Andrea. The Key Collection. Choi, Yangsook, illus. rev. ed. 2003. 128p. (J). (gr. 3-6). 16.95 (978-0-8050-7153-5(9) , Holt, Henry & Co. Bks. For Young Readers) Holt, Henry & Co.

—The Lemon Sisters. Mai-Wyss, Tatjana, illus. 2006. 32p. (J). (ps). 16.99 (978-0-399-24023-2(3) , Putnam Juvenile) Penguin Group (USA) Inc.

Cooney, Caroline B. Hit the Road. 2006. 192p. (gr. 7). (J). lib. bdg. 17.99 (978-0-385-90174-1(7)); (YA). 15.95 (978-0-385-72944-4(8)) Random Hse. Children's Bks. (Delacorte Bks. for Young Readers).

de Paola, Tomie. Nana Upstairs & Nana Downstairs. 2000. (Illus.). 32p. (J). (ps-3). pap. 6.99 (978-0-698-11836-2(7) , Putnam Juvenile) Penguin Group (USA) Inc.

—Nana Upstairs & Nana Downstairs. unabr. ed. 2006. (J). (gr. k-3). pap. 17.95 incl. audio (978-0-8045-6943-9(6)); pap. 19.95 incl. audio compact disk (978-0-8045-4157-2(4)) Spoken Arts, Inc.

—Nana Upstairs & Nana Downstairs. 2000. (gr. k-3). lib. bdg. 15.30 (978-0-8085-2686-5(3)) Tandem Library Bks.

Dion. Fishing with Balloons. 2004. (Illus.). 68p. (J). (978-1-881929-34-5(5)) Oxton Hse., Pubs.

Fleischman, Paul. Mind's Eye. 2001. 112p. (YA). (gr. 7 up). pap. 5.50 (978-0-440-22901-8(4) , Laurel Leaf) Random Hse. Children's Bks.

Flood, Pansie Hart. Sometimey Friend. Marshall, Felicia, illus. 2005. 128p. (J). (gr. 4-6). 15.95 (978-1-57505-866-5(9)) Lerner Publishing Group.

—Sylvia & Miz Lula Maye. Marshall, Felicia, illus. 2003. (Middle Grade Fiction Ser.). 120p. (J). (gr. 3-6). 15.95 (978-0-87614-204-2(8) , Carolrhoda Bks.) Lerner Publishing Group.

Forrestal, Elaine. Graffiti on the Fence. 1999. 144p. (J). pap. (978-0-14-130519-6(3) , Puffin) Penguin Group (USA) Inc.

Fox, Mem. Wilfrid Gordon McDonald Partridge. 2004. pap. 14.95 incl. audio (978-0-7882-0665-8(6)); (J). 24.95 incl. audio (978-0-89719-799-1(2)) Weston Woods Studios, Inc.

Franklin, Kristine L. The Gift. Lavallee, Barbara, illus. 1999. 40p. (J). (ps-3). 14.95 (978-0-8118-0447-9(X)) Chronicle Bks. LLC.

Gardiner, John Reynolds. General Butterfingers. Smith, Catharine Bowman, illus. 2007. 40p. (J). (gr. 5). 4.95 (*978-0-618-75922-4(0)) Houghton Mifflin Co. Trade & Reference Div.

Giff, Patricia Reilly. Pictures of Hollis Woods. 176p. (gr. 3-8). 2004. (J). pap. 6.50 (978-0-440-41578-7(0) , Yearling); 2002. lib. bdg. 17.99 (978-0-385-90070-6(8) , Lamb, Wendy) Random Hse. Children's Bks.

—Pictures of Hollis Woods. Giff, Patricia Reilly, illus. 2002. (Illus.). 176p. (gr. 3-8). 15.95 (978-0-385-32655-1(6) , Lamb, Wendy) Random Hse. Children's Bks.

—Pictures of Hollis Woods. l.t. ed. 2003. 158p. (J). 23.95 (978-0-7862-5094-3(1)) Thorndike Pr.

Givens, Steven J. Stony Point: A Triangle Club Adventure. 2001. 106p. pap. 5.95 (978-1-889658-21-6(9)) New Canaan Publishing Co. LLC.

Greene, Stephanie. Queen Sophie Hartley. 2005. 144p. (J). (gr. 3-5). 15.00 (978-0-618-49461-3(8) , Clarion Bks.) Houghton Mifflin Co. Trade & Reference Div.

Gunn, Robin Jones. In Your Dreams. 1998. (Sierra Jensen Ser.: Bk. 2). 144p. (Orig.). (YA). (gr. 7-11). pap. (978-1-56179-444-7(9)) Focus on the Family Publishing.

—In Your Dreams. 1998. (Sierra Jensen Ser.: Bk. 2). (Orig.). (gr. 7-12). lib. bdg. 15.30 (978-0-613-86409-1(3)) Tandem Library Bks.

Hazen, Barbara Shook. Digby. Phillips-Duke, Barbara J., illus. 1998. (I Can Read Bks.). 32p. (J). (ps-2). pap. 4.99 (978-0-06-444239-8(X) , Harper Trophy) HarperCollins Pubs.

—Digby. Phillips-Duke, Barbara J., illus. 1998. 32p. (J). (ps-ps). lib. bdg. 13.00 (978-0-613-07618-0(4)) Tandem Library Bks.

Hest, Amy. Mr. George Baker. Muth, Jon J., illus. 2004. 32p. (J). (gr. k-3). 16.99 (978-0-7636-1233-7(2)) Candlewick Pr.

—Mr. George Baker. Muth, Jon J., illus. 2007. 32p. (J). (gr. k-3). pap. 6.99 (978-0-7636-3308-0(9)) Candlewick Pr.

Hilton, Nette. Web. 1998. (Illus.). 88p. (ps-3). 5.95 (978-0-207-17245-8(5)) HarperCollins Pubs.

Holt, Kimberly Willis. Dancing in Cadillac Light. 2002. 176p. (J). (gr. 5 up). pap. 5.99 (978-0-698-11970-3(3) , Putnam Juvenile) Penguin Group (USA) Inc.

—Dancing in Cadillac Light. 2004. 176p. (J). (gr. 4-7). pap. 36.00 incl. audio (978-0-8072-2095-5(7) , Listening Library) Random Hse. Audio Publishing Group.

—Dancing in Cadillac Light. 2002. (gr. 5-8). lib. bdg. 14.15 (978-0-613-66873-6(1)) Tandem Library Bks.

Howe, James. Pinky & Rex & the Mean Old Witch. 2006. (J). (gr. 1-4). 24.21 (978-1-59961-077-1(9)) Spotlight.

Jeffers, Dawn. Vegetable Dreams/Huerto Soñado. Schneider, Claude, illus. 2006. Tr. of Huerto Soñado. (SPA & ENG.). (J). pap. 14.99 (978-0-9770906-0-0(4) , 626999); 32p. lib. bdg. 16.95 (978-0-9741992-9-0(X) , 626999) Raven Tree Pr.

Joyce, William. Leaf Men & the Brave Good Bugs. 2001. (gr. k-3). lib. bdg. 15.25 (978-0-613-35969-6(0)) Tandem Library Bks.

Karon, Jan. Miss Fannie's Hat. Goffe, Toni, illus. 2001. (Picture Puffin Ser.). 32p. (J). (ps-3). pap. 6.99 (978-0-14-056812-7(3) , Puffin) Penguin Group (USA) Inc.

Kimmel, Elizabeth Cody. Visiting Miss Caples. 2001. (978-0-606-22533-5(1)) Tandem Library Bks.

Knowlton, Laurie Lazzaro. A Young Man's Dance. Johnson, Layne, illus. 2006. 32p. (J). 15.95 (978-1-59078-259-0(3)) Boyds Mills Pr.

Laminack, Lester L. The Sunsets of Miss Olivia Wiggins. Bergum, Constance Rummel, illus. 1998. 32p. (J). (gr. 1-5). 15.95 (978-1-56145-139-5(8)) Peachtree Pubs., Ltd.

Levin, Betty. The Unmaking of Duncan Veerick. 2007. 204p. (YA). (gr. 5 up). 16.95 (*978-1-932425-96-3(9) , Front Street) Boyds Mills Pr.

Lindbergh, Reeve. My Little Grandmother Often Forgets. Brown, Kathryn, illus. 2007. (J). (ps-1). 32p. 16.99 (978-0-7636-1989-3(2)); (*978-1-4287-3962-8(9)) Candlewick Pr.

Matott, Justin. Ol' Lady Grizelda. Woods, John, Jr., illus. 1998. 36p. (J). (ps-3). 16.95 (978-1-889191-09-6(4)) Clove Pubns.

Mazer, Norma Fox. Ten Ways to Make My Sister Disappear. 2007. (J). (*978-0-439-83984-6(X)); 160p. (gr. 4-7). pap. 16.99 (*978-0-439-83983-9(1)) Scholastic, Inc. (Levine, Arthur A. Bks.).

Mead, Alice. Junebug & the Reverend. 2002. (Illus.). (J). 13.40 (978-0-7587-6518-5(5)) Book Wholesalers, Inc.

—Junebug & the Reverend. 2000. (J). (ps-7). 186p. per. 13.00 (978-0-613-21831-3(0)); (Illus.). 11.64 (978-0-606-18785-5(5)) Tandem Library Bks.

Mikaelsen, Ben. Petey. 1998. 256p. (gr. 5-17). 15.95 (978-0-7868-0426-9(2)) Disney Pr.

Miller, William. The Piano. Keeter, Susan, illus. 2000. 32p. (J). (ps up). 15.95 (978-1-880000-98-4(9)) Lee & Low Bks., Inc.

Mills, Claudia. Makeovers by Marcia. 2005. 160p. (J). 16.00 (978-0-374-34654-6(2) , Farrar, Straus & Giroux (BYR)) Farrar, Straus & Giroux.

Murphy, Barbara Beasley & Wolkoff, Judie. Ace Hits Rock Bottom. 2003. (Can't Stop Ace Ser.: No. 2). 204p. (J). pap. 16.95 (978-0-86534-408-2(6)) Sunstone Pr.

Myers, Walter Dean. Won't Know Till I Get There. 2000. (J). (gr. 4-8). 20.25 (978-0-8446-7149-9(5)) Smith, Peter Pub., Inc.

Oboh, Rolic. Treasure Hunt. 2006. pap. (*978-1-84426-318-9(5)) Upfront Publishing Ltd.

Pearsall, Shelley. Trouble Don't Last. 256p. (gr. 4-8). 2002. (Illus.). 14.95 (978-0-375-81490-7(6) , Knopf Bks. for Young Readers); 2002. (Illus.). lib. bdg. 16.99 (978-0-375-91490-4(0) , Knopf Bks. for Young Readers); 2003. (J). reprint ed. pap. 5.99 (978-0-440-41811-5(9) , Yearling) Random Hse. Children's Bks.

—Trouble Don't Last. 2003. (gr. 3-6). lib. bdg. 13.55 (978-0-613-85706-2(2)) Tandem Library Bks.

Pham, LeUyen. Can You Do This, Old Badger? 2004. (ps-2). lib. bdg. 14.15 (978-0-613-83873-3(4)) Tandem Library Bks.

Reynolds, Cynthia Furlong. Across the Reach. 2007. 144p. (J). 16.95 (*978-1-58726-518-1(4) , Mitten Pr.) Ann Arbor Media Group, LLC.

Ruby, Lois. The Moxie Kid. 2002. 218p. 17.95 (978-1-57168-677-0(0)); 2001. iv, 214p. (J). pap. 15.95 (978-1-57168-608-4(8) , Eakin Pr.) Eakin Pr.

Rylant, Cynthia. Henry & Mudge & the Great Grandpas. Stevenson, Sucie, illus. (Henry & Mudge Ser.). 40p. (J). (gr. k-2). 2006. pap. 3.99 (978-0-689-83447-9(0) , Aladdin); 2005. 14.95 (978-0-689-81170-8(5) , Simon & Schuster Children's Publishing) Simon & Schuster Children's Publishing.

—Mr. Putter & Tabby Fly the Plane. Howard, Arthur, illus. 2002. (Mr. Putter & Tabby Ser.). (J). 13.15 (978-0-7587-0681-2(2)) Book Wholesalers, Inc.

—Mr. Putter & Tabby Make a Wish. 2005. (Illus.). 38p. (J). lib. bdg. 20.00 (*978-1-4242-1954-4(X)) Fitzgerald Bks.

—Mr. Putter & Tabby Make a Wish. Howard, Arthur, illus. 2006. (Mr. Putter & Tabby Ser.). 44p. (J). pap. 5.95 (978-0-15-205443-4(X) , Harcourt Paperbacks) Harcourt Children's Bks.

—Mr. Putter & Tabby Make a Wish. Howard, Arthur, illus. 2005. (Mr. Putter & Tabby Ser.). 44p. (J). (ps-2). 14.00 (978-0-15-202426-0(3)) Harcourt Trade Pubs.

—Mr. Putter & Tabby Run the Race. Howard, Arthur, illus. 2008. (Mr. Putter & Tabby Ser.). 44p. (J). 15.00 (*978-0-15-206069-5(3)) Harcourt Trade Pubs.

—Mr. Putter & Tabby Take the Train. Howard, Arthur, illus. 1998. (Mr. Putter & Tabby Ser.). 44p. (J). (gr. 1-5). 14.00 (978-0-15-201786-6(0)) Harcourt Children's Bks.

—Mr. Putter & Tabby Toot the Horn. Howard, Arthur, illus. (Mr. Putter & Tabby Ser.). 44p. (J). 1999. (ps-3). pap. 5.95 (978-0-15-200247-3(2) , Harcourt Paperbacks); 1998. (gr. 1-5). 14.00 (978-0-15-200244-2(8)) Harcourt Children's Bks.

—Mr. Putter & Tabby Toot the Horn. Howard, Arthur, illus. 1999. (Mr. Putter & Tabby Ser.). (J). (ps). lib. bdg. 14.10 (978-0-613-22895-4(2)) Tandem Library Bks.

—Mr. Putter & Tabby Toot the Horn. 1999. (Mr. Putter & Tabby Ser.). (978-0-606-17489-3(3)) Tandem Library Bks.

Schachner, Judith B. The Grannyman. 1999. (gr. k-3). lib. bdg. 15.30 (978-0-613-68241-1(6)) Tandem Library Bks.

Siebold, Jan. Doing Time Online. 2002. 96p. (J). (gr. 4-7). pap. 5.95 (978-0-8075-1665-2(1)) Whitman, Albert & Co.

—Doing Time Online. McClure, Wendy, ed. 2002. 96p. (J). (gr. 4-7). 14.95 (978-0-8075-5959-8(8)) Whitman, Albert & Co.

Smelcer, John. The Trap. 2006. 176p. (YA). (gr. 4-7). 15.95 (978-0-8050-7939-5(4)) Holt, Henry & Co.

—The Trap. 2007. 192p. (YA). pap. 7.99 (*978-0-312-37755-7(X)) Square Fish.

Soto, Gary. The Old Man & His Door. Cepeda, Joe, illus. 1998. 32p. (J). (ps-3). pap. 6.99 (978-0-698-11654-2(2) , Putnam Juvenile) Penguin Group (USA) Inc.

—El Viejo y Su Puerta. Cepeda, Joe, illus. 1998. (SPA.). 32p. (J). (ps-3). pap. 6.99 (978-0-698-11655-9(0) , PU8557, Putnam Juvenile) Penguin Group (USA) Inc.

Stengel, Joyce A. Mystery at Kittiwake Bay. 2001. 176p. (J). pap. 9.95 (978-0-689-84595-6(2) , Aladdin) Simon & Schuster Children's Publishing.

Stevens, Carla. Who's Knocking at the Door? Chapman, Lee, illus. 2004. 40p. (J). 16.95 (978-0-7614-5168-6(4)) Cavendish, Marshall Corp.

Tremblay, Carole. The Old Man & the C. 2006. (Illus.). 27p. (J). 15.95 (978-1-56164-354-7(8)) Pineapple Pr., Inc.

Waboose, Jan Bourdeau. Firedancers. Taylor, C. J., illus. 2000. 26p. (J). (ps-3). 14.95 (978-0-7737-3138-7(5)) Stoddart Kids CAN. *Dist:* Fitzhenry & Whiteside, Ltd.

Watkins, Dawn L. Jenny Wren. 2000. (J). (gr. 3-7). pap. 14.98 incl. audio (978-0-89084-909-5(9) , 100065) Jones, Bob Univ. Pr.

Whinnem, Reade Scott. Utten & Plumley. 2003. (gr. 3-6). lib. bdg. 21.05 (978-0-613-79189-2(4)) Tandem Library Bks.

Yep, Laurence. The Magic Paintbrush. Wang, Suling, illus. 2003. 96p. (J). (gr. 3-7). pap. 4.99 (978-0-06-440852-3(3)) HarperCollins Pubs.

—The Magic Paintbrush. 2003. (gr. 3-6). lib. bdg. 13.00 (978-0-613-65808-9(6)) Tandem Library Bks.

Yumoto, Kazumi. The Letters. 2003. 176p. (YA). (gr. 7). pap. 5.50 (978-0-440-23822-5(6) , Laurel Leaf) Random Hse. Children's Bks.

OLD STURBRIDGE VILLAGE

Kauffman, Dorothy. Two Villages: Two Hundred Years Apart. 2005. (Content Area Readers Ser.). 4.95 (978-0-19-430952-3(5)) Oxford Univ. Pr., Inc.

OLD TESTAMENT

see Bible—Old Testament

OLDER PEOPLE

Martz, Sandra, ed. When I Am an Old Woman I Shall Wear Purple: Petite Version. 2nd gif. rev. ed. 2006. (Illus.). 64p. (C). pap. 47.70 (978-1-57601-093-8(7) , Papier-Mache Pr.) Moyer Bell.

Richmond, Marianne R. The DIY Guide to Age Defiance. 2004. (Illus.). 40p. (J). 7.95 (978-0-9753528-5-4(7)) Marianne Richmond Studios, Inc.

OLDER PEOPLE—FICTION

Adams, Pam, illus. There Was an Old Lady Who Swallowed a Fly. 2005. (J). bds. 12.99 (978-0-85953-314-0(X)) Child's Play-International.

Alsenas, Linas. Peanut. 2007. 32p. (J). (ps-k). pap. 16.99 (*978-0-439-77980-7(4)) Scholastic, Inc.

Amon, Ras Ran. Gerald Fish of the Spirit! Activity Book. 2006. (J). act. bk. ed. 3.99 (*978-0-9776603-2-2(X)) One Love Assn. Books.

Anderson, Launi K. Jillian's Discovery. 1999. (Choose the Right Ser.: Bk. 3). 60p. (J). pap. (978-1-57008-673-1(7)) Scribbulations LLC.

Atkinson, Ruth & Atkinson, Brett. Story Templates. Atkinson, Ruth & Atkinson, Brett, illus. (Illus.). (J). (gr. k-2). pap. (978-1-875739-73-8(4)) Wizard Bks.

Babbitt, Natalie. Tuck Everlasting. 2007. 144p. (J). pap. 6.99 (*978-0-312-36981-1(6)) Square Fish.

Brodt, Burton P. Four Little Old Men: A (Mostly) True Tale from a Small Cajun Town. Melanson, Luc, illus. 2005. 32p. (J). 14.95 (978-1-4027-2006-2(8)) Sterling Publishing Co., Inc.

Burton, Margie, et al. Growing Older. Adams, Alison, ed. 1999. (Early Connections Ser.). 16p. (J). (gr. k-2). pap. 4.50 (978-1-58344-064-3(X)) Benchmark Education Co.

Butterworth, W. E., pseud. Leroy & the Old Man. 1999. 176p. (J). (gr. 7-9). pap. 5.99 (978-0-590-42711-1(3)) Scholastic, Inc.

Byars, Betsy. The Black Tower. 2007. (Herculeah Jones Ser.). 144p. (J). (gr. 3). 6.99 (*978-0-14-240937-4(5) , Puffin) Penguin Group (USA) Inc.

Cruise, Robin. Little Mama Forgets. Dressen-McQueen, Stacey, illus. 2006. 40p. (J). 16.00 (978-0-374-34613-3(5) , Farrar, Straus & Giroux (BYR)) Farrar, Straus & Giroux.

Fusco, Kimberly Newton. Tending to Grace. 2004. 176p. (gr. 7). (J). lib. bdg. 16.99 (978-0-375-92862-8(6)); (YA). 14.95 (978-0-375-82862-1(1)) Random Hse. Children's Bks. (Knopf Bks. for Young Readers).

Haddix, Margaret Peterson. Turnabout. 2007. 240p. (YA). mass mkt. 5.99 (978-1-4169-3653-4(X) , Simon Pulse) Simon & Schuster Children's Publishing.

Hemingway, Ernest. Le Vieil Homme et la Mer. 2000. (FRE.). (J). pap. 16.95 (978-2-07-051388-8(2)) Gallimard, Editions FRA. *Dist:* Distribooks, Inc.

Leedahl, Shelley A. The Bone Talker. Slavin, Bill, illus. 2004. (Northern Lights Books for Children Ser.). 32p. (ps-3). 15.95 (978-0-88995-214-0(0)) Red Deer Pr. CAN. *Dist:* Fitzhenry & Whiteside, Ltd.

McMurtry, Larry. Duane's Depressed: A Novel. 1999. (Last Picture Show Trilogy: No. 3). (gr. 7-12). lib. bdg. 16.45 (978-0-613-24945-4(3)) Tandem Library Bks.

The Old Woman in a Shoe: 6 Small Books. (gr. k-2). 23.00 (978-0-7635-8501-3(7)) Rigby Education.

Penton Overseas, Inc. Staff, contrib. by. There Was an Old Lady Who Swallowed a Fly. rev. ed. 2007. 14p. 10.95 (*978-1-74181-191-9(0)) Hinkler Bks. Pty, Ltd. AUS. *Dist:* Penton Overseas, Inc.

Pitcher, Caroline. Mariana & the Merchild: A Folk Tale from Chile. Morris, Jackie, illus. 2006. 24p. (J). (gr. k-4). reprint ed. 17.00 (978-1-4223-5136-9(X)) DIANE Publishing Co.

Porter-Gaylord, Laurel. I Love My Mommy Because. Wolff, Ashley, illus. 2004. (SPA.). 24p. (J). bds. 6.99 (978-0-525-47248-3(7) , Dutton Juvenile) Penguin Group (USA) Inc.

Rigby Education Staff. Jumble Tumble Old Woman. (gr. k-2). 21.00 (978-0-7635-2413-5(1)) Rigby Education.

Scott, Cynthia A. Old Jake's Skirts. Slonim, David, illus. 2003. 36p. (J). 7.95 (978-0-87358-839-3(8) , Rising Moon Bks. for Young Readers) Northland Publishing.

Shawver, Margaret. What's Wrong with Grandma? A Family's Experience with Alzheimer's. Bagby, Jeffrey K., illus. 2004. 62p. pap. 16.00 (978-1-59102-174-2(X)) Prometheus Bks., Pubs.

Sorela, Pedro. Aire de Mar en Gador. 1998. (SPA.). (gr. 7-12). lib. bdg. 15.25 (978-0-613-80719-7(7)) Tandem Library Bks.

Stark, Ulf. Can You Whistle, Johanna? A Boy's Search for a Grandfather. Segerberg, Ebba, tr. from SWE. Hoglund, Anna, illus. 2004. 48p. (gr. 2-5). 16.95 (978-1-57143-057-1(1)) RDR Bks.

Thurston, Dorie. Thank-You for the Thistle. Hawkins, Mecca, illus. 2001. 36p. (J). (ps-3). pap. 9.95 (978-0-9703326-0-8(2)) Dorie Bks.

Tibo, Gilles. Naomi & Mrs Lumbago. 2001. (gr. 3-6). lib. bdg. 15.25 (978-0-613-58380-0(9)) Tandem Library Bks.

Vanoosting, James. Walking Mary. 2005. 144p. (J). (gr. 7 up). lib. bdg. 16.89 (978-0-06-028472-5(2)) HarperCollins Pubs.

Walters, Celeste. The Glass Mountain. 2003. 280p. (YA). pap. 17.00 (978-0-7022-3297-8(1)) Univ. of Queensland Pr. AUS. *Dist:* International Specialized Bk. Services.

Ward, Helen. Moon Dog. 2005. (Illus.). 40p. (J). ***978-1-84011-864-3(4))** Templar Publishing, Dorking.

White, Linda. Too Many Pumpkins. Lloyd, Megan, illus. 32p. (J). (gr. k-3). reprint ed. 6.95 (978-0-8234-1320-1(9)) Holiday Hse., Inc.

Wiggin, Kate Douglas. Rebecca of Sunnybrook Farm. McClintock, Barbara, illus. anniv. ed. 2006. 290p. (J). (gr. 4-8). reprint ed. 22.00 (978-1-4223-5332-5(X)) DIANE Publishing Co.

Williams, Carol. Dickey. 2005. 16.00 (978-0-8059-9830-6(6)) Dorrance Publishing Co., Inc.

Winch, John. Old Man Who Loved to Sing. 1998. pap. 4.99 (978-0-590-22641-7(X)) Scholastic, Inc.

OLIVIA (FICTITIOUS CHARACTER)—FICTION

Falconer, Ian. Olivia. Falconer, Ian, illus. 2002. (Olivia Ser.). (YA). 26.13 (978-1-4046-0034-8(5)) Book Wholesalers, Inc.

—Olivia. ed. 2004. (Olivia Ser.). (J). (gr. k-3). (FRE., Illus.). spiral bd. (978-0-616-14599-9(3)); spiral bd. (978-0-616-07232-5(5)); spiral bd. (978-0-616-07233-2(3)) Canadian National Institute for the Blind/Institut National Canadien pour les Aveugles.

—Olivia. (Olivia Ser.). (FRE.). pap. 29.95 (978-2-02-041087-8(7)) Editions du Seuil FRA. *Dist:* Distribooks, Inc.

—Olivia. (Olivia Ser.). pap. 27.95 (978-85-250-3380-2(4)) Globo, Editora SA BRA. *Dist:* Distribooks, Inc.

—Olivia. Mlawer, Teresa, tr. (Olivia Ser.). (SPA., Illus.). (J). (gr. k-2). 16.00 (978-1-930332-20-1(3) , LC5675); 2002. 30p. 16.00 (978-1-930332-08-9(4) , LC30181) Lectorum Pubns., Inc.

—Olivia. (Olivia Ser.). (978-3-7891-6504-7(2)) Oetinger, Friedrich GmbH Verlag.

—Olivia. 2001. (Olivia Ser.). (Illus.). (J). (SPA.). 146p. (978-84-8488-016-5(8)); (CAT., 40p. (978-84-8488-017-2(6)) Serres, Ediciones, S. L. ESP. *Dist:* Lectorum Pubns., Inc.

—Olivia. Falconer, Ian, illus. 2000. (Olivia Ser.). (Illus.). (J). (gr. k-3). 33p. per. 17.00 (978-0-689-83495-0(0) , Simon & Schuster Children's Publishing); 40p. 16.95 (978-0-689-82953-6(1) , Atheneum/Anne Schwartz Bks.) Simon & Schuster Children's Publishing.

—Olivia: The Essential Latin Edition. High, Amy, tr. Falconer, Ian, illus. 2007. (Illus.). 40p. (J). (ps-2). 17.99 ***978-1-4169-4218-4(1)** , Atheneum) Simon & Schuster Children's Publishing.

—Olivia & the Missing Toy. Falconer, Ian, illus. 2003. (Olivia Ser.). (Illus.). 42p. (J). (ps up). 16.95 (978-0-689-85291-6(6) , Atheneum) Simon & Schuster Children's Publishing.

—Olivia Counts. 2002. (Olivia Ser.). bds. 6.99 (978-0-689-85447-7(1) , Atheneum) Simon & Schuster Children's Publishing.

—Olivia Counts. Falconer, Ian, illus. 2002. (Olivia Ser.). (Illus.). 12p. (J). (ps-1). bds. 6.99 (978-0-689-85087-5(5) , Atheneum) Simon & Schuster Children's Publishing.

—Olivia Helps with Christmas. Falconer, Ian, illus. 2007. (Olivia Ser.). (Illus.). 58p. (J). (ps-2). 18.99 (978-1-4169-0786-2(6) , Atheneum/Anne Schwartz Bks.) Simon & Schuster Children's Publishing.

—Olivia Saves the Circus. ed. 2004. (Olivia Ser.). (J). (gr. k-2). spiral bd. (978-0-616-11110-9(X)); spiral bd. (978-0-616-11111-6(8)) Canadian National Institute for the Blind/Institut National Canadien pour les Aveugles.

—Olivia Saves the Circus. Falconer, Ian, illus. (Olivia Ser.). (Illus.). 44p. (J). (ps-2). 2001. 17.95 (978-0-689-82954-3(X) , Atheneum/Anne Schwartz Bks.); 2002. 150.00 (978-0-689-85039-4(5) , Atheneum) Simon & Schuster Children's Publishing.

—Olivia's Carry-along Coloring Kit. 2007. 64p. (J). 6.99 ***978-1-4169-5427-9(9)** , Simon Scribbles) Simon & Schuster Children's Publishing.

Falconer, Ian. Olivia's Opposites. Falconer, Ian, illus. 2002. (Olivia Ser.). (J). bds. 6.99 (978-0-689-85448-4(X)); (Illus.). 12p. bds. 6.99 (978-0-689-85088-2(3)) Simon & Schuster Children's Publishing. (Atheneum).

OLMSTED, FREDERICK LAW, 1822-1903

Wishinsky, Frieda. The Man Who Made Parks: The Story of Parkbuilder Frederick Law Olmsted. Zhang, Song Nan, illus. 1999. 32p. (J). (gr. k-12). 15.95 (978-0-88776-435-6(5)) Tundra Bks., Inc./Livres Toundra, Inc. CAN. *Dist:* Random Hse., Inc.

OLSEN TWINS (FICTITIOUS CHARACTERS)—FICTION

Alexander, Heather. The Case of the Easter Egg Race. 2004. 84p. (J). (ps-17). 11.79 (978-0-606-32976-7(5)) Tandem Library Bks.

Alexander, Nina. The Case of the 202 Clues. 1998. (New Adventures of Mary-Kate & Ashley Ser.). (Illus.). 87p. (J). (gr. 2-7). pap. 3.99 (978-0-590-29307-5(9)) Scholastic, Inc.

—The Case of the Haunted Camp. 1998. (New Adventures of Mary-Kate & Ashley Ser.). (Illus.). 85p. (J). (gr. 2-7). pap. 3.99 (978-0-590-29397-6(4)) Scholastic, Inc.

Banim, Lisa, et al. Winner Take All. 2000. (Two of a Kind Ser.: No. 10). (Illus.). 112p. (gr. 3-7). mass mkt. 4.99 (978-0-06-106580-4(3) , Harper Entertainment) HarperCollins Pubs.

Butcher, Nancy. It's Snow Problem. 2001. (gr. 3-6). lib. bdg. 13.00 (978-0-613-43934-3(1)) Tandem Library Bks.

Carr, Jan. Ballet Party! 1998. (You're Invited to Mary-Kate & Ashley's Ser.). (Illus.). 48p. (J). (gr. 2-4). pap. 3.99 (978-0-590-29399-0(0)) Scholastic, Inc.

Carroll, Jacqueline. The Case of the Cheerleading Tattletale. 2004. 81p. (J). (gr. 1-5). lib. bdg. 12.19 (978-0-606-32973-6(0)) Tandem Library Bks.

Eisenberg, Lisa. The Case of the Rock & Roll Mystery. 1998. (New Adventures of Mary-Kate & Ashley Ser.). 87p. (J). (gr. 2-7). pap. 3.99 (978-0-590-29402-7(4)) Scholastic, Inc.

HarperCollins Staff, ed. Calling All Boys. 2000. (gr. 3-6). lib. bdg. 13.00 (978-0-613-21280-9(0)) Tandem Library Bks.

—It's a Twin Thing. 1999. (gr. 3-6). lib. bdg. 13.00 (978-0-613-16134-3(3)) Tandem Library Bks.

—To Snoop or Not to Snoop. 1999. (gr. 3-6). lib. bdg. 13.00 (978-0-613-16225-8(0)) Tandem Library Bks.

Katschke, Judy. The Case of the Weird Science Mystery. 2002. (New Adventures of Mary-Kate & Ashley Ser.: 29). (Illus.). 96p. (gr. 1-5). mass mkt. 4.50 (978-0-06-106651-1(6)) HarperCollins Pubs.

—The Case of the Wild Wolf River. 1998. (New Adventures of Mary-Kate & Ashley Ser.). 87p. (J). (gr. 2-7). pap. 3.99 (978-0-590-29401-0(6)) Scholastic, Inc.

—Facts about Flirting. 2003. (gr. 3-6). lib. bdg. 13.00 (978-0-613-66355-7(1)) Tandem Library Bks.

—Shore Thing. 2001. (gr. 3-6). lib. bdg. 13.00 (978-0-613-43957-2(0)) Tandem Library Bks.

Katschke, Judy, et al. To Snoop or Not to Snoop? 1999. (Two of a Kind Ser.: No. 5). 112p. (gr. 3-7). mass mkt. 4.99 (978-0-06-106575-0(7) , Harper Entertainment) HarperCollins Pubs.

Lantz, Francess L. The Case of the Missing Mummy. 1998. (New Adventures of Mary-Kate & Ashley Ser.). (Illus.). 82p. (J). (gr. 2-7). pap. 3.99 (978-0-590-29404-1(0)) Scholastic, Inc.

Metz, Melinda. The Case of the Creepy Castle. 2000. (New Adventures of Mary-Kate & Ashley Ser.). (Illus.). (J). 11.15 (978-0-606-21914-3(5)) Tandem Library Bks.

—The Case of the Golden Slipper. 2000. (New Adventures of Mary-Kate & Ashley Ser.). (Illus.). (J). 11.30 (978-0-606-21918-1(8)) Tandem Library Bks.

—The Case of the Surprise Call. 1999. (New Adventures of Mary-Kate & Ashley Ser.). 86p. (J). (gr. 2-7). pap. 3.99 (978-0-590-29403-4(2)) Scholastic, Inc.

Older, Effin. Birthday Party. 1998. (You're Invited to Mary-Kate & Ashley's Ser.). (Illus.). 48p. (J). (gr. 2-4). pap. 12.95 (978-0-590-22593-9(6)) Scholastic, Inc.

Olsen, Mary-Kate. My Best Friend's Boyfriend. 2002. (gr. 5-8). lib. bdg. 13.00 (978-0-613-64749-6(1)) Tandem Library Bks.

—Switching Goals. 2000. (gr. 3-6). lib. bdg. 13.00 (978-0-613-27146-2(7)) Tandem Library Bks.

—Two for the Road. 2001. (gr. 3-6). lib. bdg. 13.00 (978-0-613-43966-4(X)) Tandem Library Bks.

Olsen, Mary-Kate & Olsen, Ashley. The Case of the Icy Igloo Inn. 2002. (Illus.). (J). pap. 18.00 (978-0-06-052114-1(7) , Harper Entertainment) HarperCollins Pubs.

—Forget Me Not, Set. 2002. (J). pap. 19.96 (978-0-06-052112-7(0) , Harper Entertainment) HarperCollins Pubs.

—Mary-Kate & Ashley: Our Story: Mary-Kate & Ashley Olsen's Official Biography. 2000. (Illus.). 96p. (J). (gr. 3-7). mass mkt. 4.99 (978-0-06-107569-8(8)) HarperCollins Pubs.

—Mary-Kate & Ashley Starring in... 2002. (Illus.). (J). pap. 19.96 (978-0-06-052110-3(4) , Harper Entertainment) HarperCollins Pubs.

—Mary-Kate & Ashley Switching Goals. 2000. (Mary-Kate & Ashley Ser.). 128p. (gr. 2-4). mass mkt. 4.99 (978-0-06-107603-9(1) , Harper Entertainment) HarperCollins Pubs.

—Starring You & Me. 2002. (Mary-Kate & Ashley Sweet 16 Ser.: No. 5). (Illus.). 128p. 4.99 (978-0-06-052811-9(7) , Harper Entertainment) HarperCollins Pubs.

—We Can't Wait. 2004. (Mary-Kate & Ashley Graduation Summer Ser.: No. 1). 144p. mass mkt. 4.99 (978-0-06-072282-1(7) , Harper Entertainment) HarperCollins Pubs.

Preiss, Pauline. The Case of the Logical I Ranch. 2001. (New Adventures of Mary-Kate & Ashley Ser.). (Illus.). (J). 11.30 (978-0-606-21920-4(X)) Tandem Library Bks.

Scholastic, Inc. Staff. The Case of the Missing Mummy. 1998. (J). pap. 71.82 (978-0-590-63041-2(5)) Scholastic, Inc.

Stine, Megan. Surprise, Surprise. 2001. (gr. 3-6). lib. bdg. 13.00 (978-0-613-43960-2(0)) Tandem Library Bks.

Stine, Megan, et al. Surprise, Surprise! 2001. (Two of a Kind Ser.: No. 19). (Illus.). 112p. (gr. 3-7). mass mkt. 4.99 (978-0-06-106659-7(1) , Harper Entertainment) HarperCollins Pubs.

Swobud, I. K. The Case of the Blue-Ribbon-Horse. 1998. (New Adventures of Mary-Kate & Ashley Ser.). 86p. (J). (gr. 2-7). pap. 3.99 (978-0-590-29309-9(5)) Scholastic, Inc.

Willard, Eliza. New York Minute. movie tie-in ed. 2004. (New York Minute Ser.: Bk. 1). (Illus.). 192p. (gr. 3-6). mass mkt. 5.99 (978-0-06-059509-8(4) , Harper Entertainment) HarperCollins Pubs.

OLYMPICS

Anderson, Dave. The Story of the Olympics. rev. ed. 2000. (Illus.). 168p. (YA). (gr. 4-7). 15.95 (978-0-688-16734-9(9)); (gr. 5 up). pap. 9.95 (978-0-688-17640-2(2) , Harper Trophy) HarperCollins Pubs.

Bachrach, Susan D. The Nazi Olympics. 2000. (YA). (978-0-606-19450-1(9)) Tandem Library Bks.

Bailey, Linda. Adventures in Ancient Greece. Slavin, Bill, illus. 2004. (Good Times Travel Agency Ser.). 48p. (J). (gr. 4-6). (978-1-55074-536-8(0)); (978-1-55074-534-4(4)) Kids Can Pr., Ltd.

—Adventures in Ancient Greece. Slavin, Bill, illus. 2002. 48p. (J). (gr. 4-7). lib. bdg. 16.40 (978-0-613-70945-3(4)) Tandem Library Bks.

Bailey, Tom. Jennifer Chandler: Olympic Champion Diver. 2005. (Alabama Roots Biography Ser.). (Illus.). 112p. (J). (978-1-59421-014-3(4)) Seacoast Publishing, Inc.

Belval, Brian. Olympic Track & Field. 2007. (Great Moments in Olympic History Ser.). (Illus.). 48p. (J). (gr. 5-8). lib. bdg. 26.50 ***978-1-4042-0971-8(9))** Rosen Publishing Group, Inc., The.

Bingham, Jane. Welcome to the Ancient Olympics! Ancient Greek Olympics. 2007. (J). ***978-1-4109-2889-4(6));** pap. ***978-1-4109-2896-2(9))** Steck-Vaughn.

Boast, Clare. The Ancient Olympics. 1998. (Olympic Library). (Illus.). 32p. (J). (978-1-57572-034-0(5)) Heinemann Library.

—Field. 1998. (Olympic Library). (J). pap. (978-1-57572-038-8(8)) Heinemann Library.

Burgan, Michael. Great Moments in the Olympics. 2002. (Great Moments in Sports Ser.). (Illus.). 48p. (J). (gr. 5 up). pap. 14.60 (978-0-8368-5362-9(8) , World Almanac Library) Stevens, Gareth Inc.

Conway, Hollis. Grasshopper: The Hollis Conway Story. 2004. 30p. (J). per. (978-1-59196-584-8(5)) Instantpublisher.com.

Dillon, Christine J. Olympics. rev. ed. 1999. (My First Report Ser.). (Illus.). 50p. (J). (gr. 1-3). ring bd. 5.95 (978-1-57896-049-1(5) , Hewitt Homeschooling Resources) Hewitt Research Foundation, Inc.

Ditchfield, Christin. Swimming & Diving. 2000. (True Bks.). (Illus.). 48p. (J). (gr. 3-5). 25.00 (978-0-516-21065-0(3) , Children's Pr.) Scholastic Library Publishing.

Donkin, Andrew. Going for Gold! 1999. (Eyewitness Readers Ser.). (Illus.). 48p. (J). (gr. 2-4). lib. bdg. 10.79 (978-0-606-19382-5(0)); (gr. k-3). lib. bdg. 11.80 (978-0-613-21609-8(1)) Tandem Library Bks.

Donkin, Andrew & Dorling Kindersley Publishing Staff. Going for Gold! 1999. (Eyewitness Readers). (Illus.). 48p. (J). (gr. 2-4). 14.99 (978-0-7894-4765-4(7)); pap. 3.99 (978-0-7894-4764-7(9) , 0-7894-4756-8) Dorling Kindersley Publishing, Inc.

Dublin, Anne. Bobbie Rosenfeld: The Olympian Who Could Do Everything. 2005. (Illus.). 148p. (YA). pap. 11.95 (978-1-896764-82-5(7)) Second Story Pr. CAN. *Dist:* Orca Bk. Pubs. USA, Univ. of Toronto Pr.

Dunn, Joeming W. Miracle on Ice. Dunn, Ben, illus. 2007. (Graphic History Ser.). 32p. (J). (gr. 3-6). lib. bdg. 27.07 ***978-1-60270-077-2(X)** , Graphic Planet) Magic Wagon.

Faster, Higher, Stronger: The Olympics, 6 vols. (Book2WebTM Ser.). (gr. 4-8). 36.50 (978-0-322-02984-2(8)) Wright Group, The.

Fieffe, Kathleen & Herzog, Brad. Olympic Facts & Fun. Holder, Sherie, ed. 2000. 16p. (J). (gr. 2-8). pap. (978-1-886749-92-4(2)) Sports Illustrated For Kids.

Fischer, David. The Encyclopedia of the Summer Olympics. 2003. (Watts Reference Ser.). (Illus.). 160p. (J). 37.00 (978-0-531-11886-3(X) , Watts, Franklin) Scholastic Library Publishing.

Flinders, Steve. The Olympic Games. 2001. (Oxford Bookworms Factfiles Ser.). (Illus.). 32p. 7.50 (978-0-19-422872-5(X)) Oxford Univ. Pr., Inc.

Forbes, Evan D., ed. The Olympic Dream. 2000. (Illus.). 80p. (J). (gr. k-3). pap. 9.95 (978-1-58000-014-7(2)) Griffin Publishing Group.

Ford, Michael & Salariya, David. You Wouldn't Want to Be a Greek Athlete! Races You'd Rather Not Run. Antram, David, illus. 2004. (You Wouldn't Want To Ser.). 32p. (J). 28.50 (978-0-531-12352-2(9) , Watts, Franklin) Scholastic Library Publishing.

Gaff, Jackie. The Ancient Olympics. 2004. (Illus.). 32p. (J). lib. bdg. 24.22 (978-1-4034-4676-3(8)) Heinemann Library.

Gifford, Clive. Summer Olympics: The Definitive Guide to the World's Greatest Sports Celebration. 2004. (Illus.). 80p. (J). (gr. 5-9). 12.95 (978-0-7534-5693-4(1) , Kingfisher) Houghton Mifflin Co. Trade & Reference Div.

Girginov, Vassill, et al. The Olympic Games Explained. 2005. (Student Sport Studies). (Illus.). 288p. 41.95 (978-0-415-34604-7(5)); 125.00 (978-0-415-34603-0(7)) Routledge.

Gonsalves, Kelly A. & La Mondia, Susan A. First to the Wall: 100 Years of Olympic Swimming. Gonsalves, Kelly A., illus. Morse, Tim, photos by. 1999. (Illus.). 374p. (J). pap. 24.95 (978-0-9674171-0-3(4)) FreeStyle Pubns., Inc.

Great Moments in Olympic History, 6 bks., Set. Incl. Olympic Basketball. Hofstetter, Adam B. lib. bdg. 26.50 ***978-1-4042-0967-1(0));** Olympic Gymnastics. Hofstetter, Adam B. lib. bdg. 26.50 (978-1-4042-0968-8(9) , Rosen Central); Olympic Ice Skating. Farbs, C. lib. bdg. 26.50 ***978-1-4042-0969-5(7));** Olympic Swimming & Diving. Kehm, Greg. lib. bdg. 26.50 (978-1-4042-0970-1(0) , Rosen Central); Olympic Track & Field. Belval, Brian. lib. bdg. 26.50 ***978-1-4042-0971-8(9));** Olympic Wrestling. Linde, Barbara M. lib. bdg. 26.50 ***978-1-4042-0972-5(7));** (Illus.). 48p. (J). (gr. 5-8). 2007. 2007. Set lib. bdg. 159.00 ***978-1-4042-0933-6(6))** Rosen Publishing Group, Inc., The.

Harcourt School Publishers Staff. Olympic Sports. 3rd ed. 2002. (Horizons Ser.). (Illus.). (J). pap. 3.70 (978-0-15-333166-4(6)) Harcourt Schl. Pubs.

Hennessy, B. G. Olympics. 2000. (978-0-606-18440-3(6)) Tandem Library Bks.

Hofstetter, Adam B. Olympic Gymnastics. 2007. (Great Moments in Olympic History Ser.). (Illus.). 48p. (J). (gr. 5-8). lib. bdg. 26.50 (978-1-4042-0968-8(9) , Rosen Central) Rosen Publishing Group, Inc., The.

Hotchkiss, Ron. The Matchless Six: The Story of Canada's First Women's Olympic Team. 2006. (Illus.). 200p. (J). (gr. 6). pap. 16.95 (978-0-88776-738-8(9)) Tundra Bks., Inc./Livres Toundra, Inc. CAN. *Dist:* Random Hse., Inc.

Kehm, Greg. Olympic Swimming & Diving. 2007. (Great Moments in Olympic History Ser.). (Illus.). 48p. (J). (gr. 5-8). lib. bdg. 26.50 (978-1-4042-0970-1(0) , Rosen Central) Rosen Publishing Group, Inc., The.

Knapp, Ron. Top 10 American Men's Olympic Gold Medalists. 2000. (Sports Top 10 Ser.). (Illus.). 48p. (YA). (gr. 4-10). lib. bdg. 23.93 (978-0-7660-1274-5(3)) Enslow Pubs., Inc.

Knotts, Bob. The Summer Olympics. 2000. (True Bks.). (Illus.). 48p. (J). (gr. 3-5). pap. 6.95 (978-0-516-27029-6(X) ; Children's Pr.) Scholastic Library Publishing.

Larsen, Kathy. Celebrate the Fire Within. Decker, Cynthia, illus. 2001. 23p. (J). 15.95 (978-1-930458-01-7(0)) North Star Pubns.

Levin, Ina. Journey to Athens: Grades 4-6. 2004. (U. S. Olympic Committee's Activity Book Ser.). 64p. (J). pap. 9.99 (978-1-58000-121-2(1)) Griffin Publishing Group.

Levin, Ina & Siskind, Ellyn. Journey to Athens: Grades 1-3. 2004. (U. S. Olympic Committee's Activity Book Ser.). (Illus.). 32p. (J). pap. 7.99 (978-1-58000-120-5(3)) Griffin Publishing Group.

Linde, Barbara M. Olympic Wrestling. 2007. (Great Moments in Olympic History Ser.). (Illus.). 48p. (J). (gr. 5-8). lib. bdg. 26.50 ***978-1-4042-0972-5(7))** Rosen Publishing Group, Inc., The.

Lobosco, Teresa. Hitting the Mark Vol. 4561: The Olympic Sport of Taekwondo. Samoiloff, Sheri, ed. Allsport Staff, photos by. 2002. (Illus.). 16p. (J). (gr. 3-6). pap. 3.49 (978-1-57471-932-1(7)) Creative Teaching Pr., Inc.

Lyons, Michele. Going for the Gold. 2003. (On the Job Ser.). (Illus.). 32p. (J). (gr. 3-5). 23.00 (978-0-7910-7412-1(9) , Chelsea Hse.) Facts On File, Inc.

Macy, Sue. Freeze Frame: A Photographic History of the Winter Olympics. 2006. (Illus.). 96p. (J). (gr. 5). 28.90 (978-0-7922-7888-7(7) , National Geographic Children's Bks.) National Geographic Society.

—Swifter, Higher, Stronger: A Photographic History of the Summer Olympics. 2004. (Illus.). 96p. (J). (gr. 5-8). 18.95 (978-0-7922-6667-9(6)); 28.90 (978-0-7922-6980-9(2)) National Geographic Society. (National Geographic Children's Bks.).

Marcovitz, Hal. The Munich Olympics. 2002. (Great Disasters, Reforms & Ramifications Ser.). (Illus.). 112p. (J). 30.00 (978-0-7910-6737-6(8)); pap. 13.25 (978-0-7910-6911-0(7)) Facts On File, Inc. (Chelsea Hse.).

Middleton, Haydn. Ancient Olympic Games. 1999. (Olympics Ser.). (Illus.). 32p. (J). (gr. 4-6). lib. bdg. 22.79 (978 1 57572-450-8(2)) Heinemann Library.

—Crises at the Olympics. 1999. (Olympics Ser.). (Illus.). 32p. (J). (gr. 4-6). lib. bdg. 22.79 (978-1-57572-452-2(9)) Heinemann Library.

—Great Olympic Moments. 1999. (Olympics Ser.). 32p. (J). (gr. 4-6). lib. bdg. 22.79 (978-1-57572-451-5(0)) Heinemann Library.

—Modern Olympic Games. 1999. (Olympics Ser.). (Illus.). 32p. (J). (gr. 4-6). lib. bdg. 22.79 (978-1-57572-453-9(7)) Heinemann Library.

—The Modern Olympics. 2003. (Illus.). 32p. (J). lib. bdg. 16.95 (978-1-4034-4677-0(6)) Heinemann Library.

Migliaccio, Eric. Baseball & Softball Easy Olympic Sports Reader. 2004. (U. S. Olympic Committee Easy Olympic Sports Readers Ser.). (Illus.). 16p. (J). pap. 2.99 (978-1-58000-110-6(6)) Griffin Publishing Group.

Olympic Winter Games: With Tattoos. 2001. pap. (978-0-9702195-4-1(7)); (YA). pap. (978-0-9702195-3-4(9)) Tattoo Manufacturing.

Osborne, Mary Pope & Boyce, Natalie Pope. Ancient Greece & the Olympics: A Nonfiction Companion to Hour of the Olympics. Murdocca, Sal, tr. Murdocca, Sal, illus. 2004. (Magic Tree House Research Guide Ser.: No. 10). 128p. (J). (gr. k-3). pap. 4.99 (978-0-375-82378-7(6)); lib. bdg. 11.99 (978-0-375-92378-4(0)) Random Hse. Children's Bks. (Random Hse. Bks. for Young Readers).

Oxlade, Chris, et al. Olympics. 2005. (Eyewitness Books). (Illus.). 72p. (J). (gr. k-8). 15.99 (978-0-7566-1083-8(4)); lib. bdg. 19.99 (978-0-7566-1084-5(2)) Dorling Kindersley Publishing, Inc.

Page, Jason. Athletics, Track: 100 Meters, 200 Meters, Relays, Hurdles & Lots, Lots More. 2000. (Zeke's Olympic Pocket Guide Ser.). (Illus.). 32p. (J). (gr. 3 up). pap. 3.95 (978-0-8225-5054-9(7) , LernerSports) Lerner Publishing Group.

M
N
O

—Ball Games: Soccer, Table Tennis, Handball, Hockey, Badminton & Lots, Lots More. Alston, John, illus. 2000. (Zeke's Olympic Pocket Guide Ser.). 32p. (J). pap. 3.95 (978-0-8225-5057-0(1) , LernerSports) Lerner Publishing Group.

—Combat: Fencing, Judo, Wrestling, Boxing, Taekwondo & Lots, Lots More. 2000. (Zeke's Olympic Pocket Guide Ser.). (Illus.). 32p. (J). pap. 3.95 (978-0-8225-5055-6(5) , LernerSports) Lerner Publishing Group.

—Power & Precision: Cycling, Equestrian, Shooting & Lots, Lots More. Alston, John, illus. 2000. (Zeke's Olympic Pocket Guide Ser.). 32p. (J). (gr. 3-7). 3.95 (978-0-8225-5050-1(4) , LernerSports) Lerner Publishing Group.

Readhead, Lloyd. Gymnastics. 1998. (Olympic Library). (Illus.). (J). pap. (978-1-57572-036-4(1)) Heinemann Library.

Roza, Greg. Olympic Math: Working with Percents & Decimals. 2006. (Math for the Real World Ser.). (Illus.). 32p. (J). pap. (978-1-4042-6057-3(9)); lib. bdg. (978-1-4042-3352-2(0)) Rosen Publishing Group, Inc., The.

Sherrow, Victoria. Wilma Rudolph. Johnson, Larry, illus. 2006. (Yo Solo Biografías Ser.). (ENG & SPA.). (J). 23.93 (978-0-8225-6260-3(X) , Ediciones Lerner) Lerner Publishing Group.

Sullivan, Erin Ash. Matematicas en las olimpiadas & Math at the Olympics. 2005. spiral bd. 84.00 (***978-1-4108-5707-1(7)**) Benchmark Education Co.

Sylvester, Kevin. Gold Medal for Weird. 2007. 112p. (YA). (gr. 2 up). pap. (***978-1-55453-021-2(0)**) Kids Can Pr., Ltd.

Tames, Richard. The Modern Olympics. 1998. (Olympic Library). 32p. (J). 15.95 (978-1-57572-035-7(3)) Heinemann Library.

U. S. Olympic Committee. A Basic Guide to Decathlon. 2001. (Olympic Guides). (Illus.). 160p. (J). (gr. 6 up). lib. bdg. 23.33 (978-0-8368-2796-5(1)) Stevens, Gareth Inc.

—A Basic Guide to Equestrian. 2001. (Olympic Guides). (Illus.). 160p. (J). (gr. 6 up). lib. bdg. 23.33 (978-0-8368-2797-2(X)) Stevens, Gareth Inc.

—A Basic Guide to Wrestling. 2001. (Olympic Guides). (Illus.). 160p. (J). (gr. 6 up). lib. bdg. 23.33 (978-0-8368-2799-6(6)) Stevens, Gareth Inc.

—Olympic Guides, 11 bks. Incl. Basic Guide to Bobsledding. Kummer, Hans, contrib. by. 2002. lib. bdg. 23.33 (978-0-8368-3101-6(2)); Basic Guide to Cycling. 2001. lib. bdg. 23.33 (978-0-8368-2795-8(3)); Basic Guide to Decathlon. 2001. lib. bdg. 23.33 (978-0-8368-2796-5(1)); Basic Guide to Equestrian. 2001. lib. bdg. 23.33 (978-0-8368-2797-2(X)); Basic Guide to Figure Skating. 2002. lib. bdg. 23.33 (978-0-8368-3102-3(0)); Basic Guide to Ice Hockey. 2002. lib. bdg. 23.33 (978-0-8368-3103-0(9)); Basic Guide to Skiing & Snowboarding. 2002. lib. bdg. 23.33 (978-0-8368-3104-7(7)); Basic Guide to Softball. 2001. lib. bdg. 23.33 (978-0-8368-2798-9(8)); Basic Guide to Speed Skating. 2002. lib. bdg. 23.33 (978-0-8368-3105-4(5)); Basic Guide to Wrestling. 2001. lib. bdg. 23.33 (978-0-8368-2799-6(6)); Olympism : A Basic Guide to the History, Ideals & Sports of the Olympic Movement. 2001. lib. bdg. 23.33 (978-0-8368-2800-9(3)); 160p. (J). (gr. 6 up). (Illus.). 2002. Set lib. bdg. 209.97 (978-0-8368-3142-9(X)) Stevens, Gareth Inc.

—Olympism: A Basic Guide to the History, Ideals & Sports of the Olympic Movement. 2001. (Olympic Guides). (Illus.). 160p. (J). (gr. 6 up). lib. bdg. 23.33 (978-0-8368-2800-9(3)) Stevens, Gareth Inc.

Verrier, John. Swimming & Diving. 1998. (Olympic Library). (J). pap. (978-1-57572-039-5(6)) Heinemann Library.

Ward, Tony. Track. 1998. (Olympic Library). (J). pap. (978-1-57572-037-1(X)) Heinemann Library.

Watts, Claire & Nicholson, Robert. Olympic Gold. 2000. (Info Adventure Ser.). (J). (gr. 2-7). pap. 3.95 (978-1-58728-108-2(2) , Two Can Publishing) T&N Children's Publishing.

Wukovits, John F. Encyclopedia of the Winter Olympics. 2001. (gr. 5-8). lib. bdg. 30.35 (978-0-613-51639-6(7)) Tandem Library Bks.

Zuehlke, Jeffrey. Michael Phelps. 2005. (Amazing Athletes Ser.). (Illus.). 32p. (J). 23.93 (978-0-8225-2431-1(7) , LernerSports) Lerner Publishing Group.

OLYMPICS—FICTION

Arena, Felice & Kettle, Phil. Olympics. Cox, David, illus. 2004. (J). pap. (978-1-59336-374-1(5)) Mondo Publishing.

Case, Cassandra. Run with Me, Nike! The Olympics in 420, B.C. Brown, Dan, illus. 1999. (Smithsonian Odyssey Ser.: No. 12). 32p. (J). (gr. 2-5). 14.95 (978-1-56899-604-2(7) , B6012); pap. 5.95 (978-1-56899-605-9(5)) Soundprints.

—Run with Me, Nike! The Olympics in Four Hundred Twenty. 1999. (gr. 3-6). lib. bdg. 14.10 (978-0-613-51585-6(4)) Tandem Library Bks.

Denham, Larry Allen. Pioneers. 2007. 392p. per. 21.95 (***978-0-595-41965-4(8)**) iUniverse, Inc.

Goscinny, René. Asterix aux jeux Olympiques. 21.95 (978-2-01-210012-1(0)) Hachette Groupe Livre FRA. *Dist:* Distribooks, Inc.

Goscinny, René & Uderzo, Albert. Asterix at the Olympic Games. Uderzo, Albert, illus. 2004. (Illus.). 48p. pap. 9.95 (978-0-7528-6627-7(3)) Orion Bks. Ltd. GBR. *Dist:* Sterling Publishing Co., Inc.

Goscinny, René & Uderzo, Albert. Asterix Omnibus 2. 2008. (Illus.). 144p. 27.95 (***978-0-7528-9156-9(1)**) Orion Bks. Ltd. GBR. *Dist:* Sterling Publishing Co., Inc.

Hoobler, Dorothy & Hoobler, Thomas. The 1930s: Directions. Hoffman, Robin, illus. 2000. (Century Kids Ser.). 160p. (J). (gr. 5-8). lib. bdg. 22.90 (978-0-7613-1603-9(5) , Twenty-First Century Bks.) Lerner Publishing Group.

MacGregor, Roy. Murder at the Winter Games. 2004. (Screech Owls Ser.: No. 18). (Illus.). 128p. (YA). mass mkt. 4.95 (978-0-7710-5647-5(8) , Screech Owls) McClelland & Stewart CAN. *Dist:* Random Hse., Inc.

Massey, Barbara & DeLoach, Sylvia. Darby down Under. Robinson, Amy Giles, illus. 2000. (Child Like Me Ser.: Vol. 4). (J). (gr. 2-5). 6.99 (978-1-56309-766-9(4)) New Hope Pubs.

Mosher, Eunice D. Olympics, 2004? Ask Yia Yia & Pa Pou. Caso, Adolph, ed. Mosher, Eunice D. & Wenzel, Lauren M., illus. l.t. ed. 1998. 32p. (J). (ps-3). pap. 9.95 (978-0-8283-2033-7(0)) Branden Bks.

Osborne, Mary Pope. Hour of the Olympics. unabr. ed. 2004. (Magic Tree House Ser. : No. 16). 70p. (J). (gr. k-3). pap. 17.00 incl. audio (978-0-8072-0785-7(3) , LFTR 244 SP, Listening Library) Random Hse. Audio Publishing Group.

—Hour of the Olympics. Murdocca, Sal, illus. 1998. (Magic Tree House Ser.: No. 16). 96p. (J). (gr. k-3). lib. bdg. 11.99 (978-0-679-99062-8(3)); mass mkt. 3.99 (978-0-679-89062-1(9)) Random Hse. Children's Bks. (Random Hse. Bks. for Young Readers).

Richards, Jean. The First Olympic Games: A Gruesome Greek Myth with a Happy Ending. Thacker, Kat, illus. 2004. 32p. pap. 10.95 (978-0-7613-2443-0(7) , Millbrook Pr.) Lerner Publishing Group.

Roberts, Katherine. The Olympic Conspiracy. 2004. (Seven Fabulous Wonders Ser.). (Illus.). 300p. (J). pap. 11.99 (978-0-00-711282-1(3)) HarperCollins Pubs. Ltd. GBR. *Dist:* Independent Pubs. Group.

Stilton, Geronimo. Geronimo & the Gold Medal Mystery. 2008. (Geronimo Stilton Ser.). 128p. (J). 6.99 (***978-0-545-02133-3(2)** , Scholastic Paperbacks) Scholastic, Inc.

Tobey, Carole A. The Frog Olympics. 2005. (Illus.). 70p. (J). per. 12.00 (978-0-9773648-3-1(6)) Legend eXpress Publishing.

Walters, Celeste. The Last Race. 2000. (UQP Young Adult Fiction Ser.). 224p. (J). pap. 16.95 (978-0-7022-3172-8(X)) Univ. of Queensland Pr. AUS. *Dist:* International Specialized Bk. Services.

Watson, Katy. Juice. 2000. 200p. (J). pap. 13.95 (978-1-86368-304-3(6)) Fremantle Pr. AUS. *Dist:* International Specialized Bk. Services.

—Juice. 2000. (gr. 7-12). lib. bdg. 23.40 (978-0-613-58398-5(1)) Tandem Library Bks.

Zucker, Jonny. Speed Star. Troiano, Enzo, illus. 2007. 33p. (J). pap. (***978-1-59889-431-8(5)** , 1264997); 40p. (YA). (gr. 5-9). lib. bdg. 21.26 (***978-1-59889-335-9(1)** , 1264997) Stone Arch Bks.

O'MALLEY, GRACE, 1530?-1600?—FICTION

Faulkner, Matt. The Pirate Meets the Queen: Two Women of Consequence. Faulkner, Matt, illus. 2005. (Illus.). 32p. (J). (gr. 1-5). 15.99 (978-0-399-24038-6(1) , Philomel) Penguin Group (USA) Inc.

OMAN

Allen, Calvin H., Jr. Oman. 2002. (Creation of the Modern Middle East Ser.). (Illus.). 125p. (gr. 6-12). 35.00 (978-0-7910-6508-2(1) , Chelsea Hse.) Facts On File, Inc.

Barnett, Tracy. Oman. 2003. (Modern Middle East Nations & Their Strategic Place in the World Ser.). (Illus.). 112,128p. (YA). (gr. 7 up). lib. bdg. (978-1-59084-517-2(X)) Mason Crest Pubs.

Foster, Leila Merrell. Oman. 1999. (Enchantment of the World, Second Ser.). (Illus.). 144p. (YA). (gr. 5-9). 36.00 (978-0-516-20964-7(7) , Children's Pr.) Scholastic Library Publishing.

ONASSIS, JACQUELINE KENNEDY, 1929-1994

Agins, Donna Brown. Jacqueline Kennedy Onassis: Legendary First Lady. 2004. (People to Know Ser.). (Illus.). 128p. (J). lib. bdg. 26.60 (978-0-7660-2186-0(6)) Enslow Pubs., Inc.

Ashby, Ruth. John & Jacqueline Kennedy. 2004. (Illus.). 48p. (J). pap. (978-0-8368-5700-9(3)); lib. bdg. 30.00 (978-0-8368-5694-1(5)) Stevens, Gareth Inc. (World Almanac Library).

Gormley, Beatrice. Jacqueline Kennedy Onassis: Friend of the Arts. 2002. (gr. 3-6). lib. bdg. 13.00 (978-0-613-57576-8(8)) Tandem Library Bks.

Hawes, Esme. Jackie Onassis. 1999. (Life & Times of Ser.). (Illus.). 48p. (YA). (gr. 5 up). lib. bdg. 18.65 (978-0-7910-4640-1(0) , Chelsea Hse.) Facts On File, Inc.

Mattern, Joanne. Jacqueline Kennedy. 2007. (First Ladies Ser.). (Illus.). 32p. (J). (gr. k-6). lib. bdg. 24.21 (***978-1-59928-796-6(X)** , Checkerboard Library) ABDO Publishing Co.

Tierney, Tom. Jacqueline Kennedy Onassis Paper Dolls. 1999. 32p. (J). (gr. 3). pap. 6.95 (978-0-486-40815-6(9)) Dover Pubns., Inc.

ONE-ACT PLAYS

Brown, Kent R., ed. 25 in 10. 2002. 287p. (YA). 16.95 (978-1-58342-099-7(1) , TD5) Dramatic Publishing Co.

Burack, Sylvia K., ed. The Big Book of Large-Cast Plays: Twenty-Seven One-Act Plays for Young Actors. 2001. 350p. (J). 12.95 (978-0-8238-0302-6(3)) Kalmbach Publishing Co., Bks. Div.

Friesen, Lauren. Best Student One Acts. 2002. 316p. (YA). pap. 16.95 (978-1-58342-126-0(2) , BA6) Dramatic Publishing Co.

Sacco, Christopher & Haehnel, Alan. The Education of Janet O'Malley: One-Act Comedy Play. 2003. (YA). pap. 4.25 (978-1-932404-10-4(4) , 728) Brooklyn Pubs.

ONTARIO

Barnes, Michael. Ontario. 1999. (Hello Canada Ser.). (Illus.). 72p. (J). pap. (978-1-55041-270-3(1)) Fitzhenry & Whiteside, Ltd.

Cooper, John. Season of Rage: Hugh Burnett & the Struggle for Civil Rights. 2005. (Illus.). 80p. (J). (gr. 5-12). pap. 9.95 (978-0-88776-700-5(1)) Tundra Bks., Inc./Livres Toundra, Inc. CAN. *Dist:* Random Hse., Inc.

Ferry, Steven. Ontario. 2002. (Exploring Canada Ser.). (Illus.). (J). 29.95 (978-1-59018-050-1(X) , Lucent Bks.) Thomson Gale.

Gorman, Lovenia. A Is for Algonquin: An Ontario Alphabet. Rose, Melanie, illus. rev. ed. 2005. (World/Country Alphabet Ser.). 40p. (J). (gr. k-5). 17.95 (978-1-58536-263-9(8)) Sleeping Bear Pr.

A Is for Algonquin: Ont Alpha. 2005. 8.95 (***978-1-58536-297-4(2)**) Sleeping Bear Pr.

LeVert, Suzanne. Ontario. 2000. (Canada in the Twenty First Century Ser.). (Illus.). 64p. (J). (gr. 8-12). 18.95 (978-0-7910-6068-1(3) , Chelsea Hse.) Facts On File, Inc.

Whitcraft, Melissa. Niagara River. 2001. (gr. 3-6). lib. bdg. 17.60 (978-0-613-37477-4(0)) Tandem Library Bks.

ONTARIO—FICTION

Bow, Patricia. The Ruby Kingdom. 2007. 256p. (J). pap. 12.99 (***978-1-55002-667-2(4)** , Boardwalk Bks.) Dundurn Group, The CAN. *Dist:* Univ. of Toronto Pr.

Brouwer, Sigmund. Timberwolf Chase. 2006. (Illus.). 64p. (J). pap. 4.99 (978-1-55143-548-0(9)) Orca Bk. Pubs. USA.

Buja, John E. Race to Freedom. Morrison, Melody, illus. 2002. 132p. pap. 7.95 (978-1-894303-24-8(5)) RRP Pubs.

Chan, Gillian. A Foreign Field. 2004. (Illus.). 192p. (YA). (gr. 13 up). (978-1-55337-350-6(2)) Kids Can Pr., Ltd.

Cliffe, Susan. Thread of Deceit: A Young Adult Novel. 2005. (Illus.). 200p. (YA). pap. 9.95 (978-1-894549-38-7(4)) Sumach Pr. CAN. *Dist:* Orca Bk. Pubs. USA.

Coburn, Judi. The Shacklands. 1999. (Illus.). 287p. pap. (978-1-896764-13-9(4)) Second Story Pr.

Curtis, Christopher Paul. Elijah of Buxton. 2007. (J). (***978-0-439-02345-0(9)**); 352p. (gr. 4-7). 16.99 (***978-0-439-02344-3(0)** , Scholastic Pr.) Scholastic, Inc.

Doyle, Brian. Pure Spring. 2007. 174p. (J). (gr. 6-9). 16.95 (***978-0-88899-774-6(4)**) Groundwood Bks. CAN. *Dist:* Perseus Distribution.

Duffield, W. J. The Radio Boys in the Thousand Islands O. 2006. pap. 71.99 (***978-1-4219-9966-1(8)**) IndyPublish.com.

—Radio Boys in the Thousand Islands or Th. 2006. 78.99 (***978-1-4219-9957-9(9)**) IndyPublish.com.

Fleck, Earl. Chasing Fire: Danger in Canoe Country. 2002. (Illus.). 160p. pap. 12.95 (978-0-930100-53-7(0)) Holy Cow! Pr.

Freedman, Zelda. Rosie's Dream Cape. 2005. (Illus.). 90p. (J). pap. 6.95 (978-1-55380-025-5(7)) Ronsdale Pr. CAN. *Dist:* Literary Pr. Group of Canada.

Gamble, Adam. Good Night Toronto. Kelly, Cooper, illus. 2008. (Good Night Our World Ser.). 20p. (J). bds. 9.95 (***978-1-60219-016-0(X)**) Our World of Books.

Ghent, Natale. No Small Thing. 2005. 256p. (J). (gr. 5-9). 15.99 (978-0-7636-2422-4(5)) Candlewick Pr.

Hill, James. Larry the Lunker. 2004. 35p. pap. 17.95 (978-1-4137-2972-6(X)) PublishAmerica, Inc.

Jocelyn, Marthe. Mable Riley: A Reliable Record of Humdrum, Peril, & Romance. 2007. 288p. (J). (gr. 5). 6.99 (978-0-7636-3287-8(2)) Candlewick Pr.

Johnston, Julie. The Only Outcast. 1999. (J). (978-0-606-19122-7(4)) Tandem Library Bks.

—Only Outcast. 1999. (gr. 7-12). lib. bdg. 15.25 (978-0-613-28008-2(3)) Tandem Library Bks.

—The Only Outcast. 1999. 248p. (J). (gr. 6-9). reprint ed. pap. 6.95 (978-0-88776-488-2(6)) Tundra Bks., Inc./Livres Toundra, Inc. CAN. *Dist:* Random Hse., Inc.

—A Very Fine Line. 2006. 208p. (J). (gr. 6). 18.95 (978-0-88776-746-3(X)) Tundra Bks., Inc./Livres Toundra, Inc. CAN. *Dist:* Random Hse., Inc.

Lemire, Jeff. Essex County Vol. 1: Tales from the Farm. 2007. (Illus.). 112p. (YA). pap. 9.95 (***978-1-891830-88-4(0)**) Top Shelf Productions.

—Essex County Vol. 2: Ghost Stories. 2007. (Illus.). 112p. (YA). pap. 14.95 (***978-1-891830-94-5(5)**) Top Shelf Productions.

McCurdy, J. Fitzgerald. The Serpent's Egg. 2001. (Illus.). 280p. (J). (gr. 9-13). (978-0-9688713-0-0(5)) Saratime, Inc.

McFarlane, Leslie. McGonigle Scores! 2006. 256p. (J). pap. 9.95 (***978-1-55263-834-7(0)**) Key Porter Bks. CAN. *Dist:* Perseus Distribution.

McNamee, Graham. Acceleration. 2003. 224p. (YA). (gr. 7). lib. bdg. 17.99 (978-0-385-90144-4(5) , Lamb, Wendy) Random Hse. Children's Bks.

McRae, David. Blood of the Donnellys. 2008. 152p. (YA). pap. 9.99 (***978-1-55002-754-9(9)** , Sandcastle Bks.) Dundurn Group, The CAN. *Dist:* Univ. of Toronto Pr.

Milord, Susan. The Ghost on the Hearth. Dabcovich, Lydia, illus. 2003. (Family Heritage Ser.). 36p. (J). (gr. 1-5). 15.95 (978-0-916718-18-3(2)) Vermont Folklife Ctr.

Nugent, Matthew A. The Legend of Timber Island. Nugent, Louise M., illus. 2001. (YA). (gr. 4-9). pap. 14.95 (978-0-9705812-1-1(1)) CBI Pr.

Posesorski, Sherie. Escape Plans. Pearcey, Dawn, illus. 2005. 272p. (J). (gr. 5). 8.95 (978-1-55050-177-3(1)) Coteau Bks. CAN. *Dist:* Fitzhenry & Whiteside, Ltd.

Skrypuch, Marsha Forchuk. Aram's Choice. Wood, Muriel, illus. 2006. 72p. (J). (gr. 2-4). (***978-1-55041-352-6(X)**) Fitzhenry & Whiteside, Ltd.

—Aram's Choice. Wood, Muriel, illus. 2006. 72p. (J). (gr. 2-4). pap. 8.95 (978-1-55041-354-0(6)) Fitzhenry & Whiteside, Ltd. CAN. *Dist:* F & W Pubns., Inc.

Stinson, Kathy. One Year Commencing. 2004. 152p. pap. (978-1-895449-65-5(0)) Thistledown Pr., Ltd.

Taylor, Drew Hayden. The Night Wanderer: A Native Gothic Novel. 2007. 224p. (YA). (gr. 7-12). 21.95 (***978-1-55451-100-6(3)**); pap. 10.95 (***978-1-55451-099-3(6)**) Annick Pr., Ltd. CAN. *Dist:* Firefly Bks., Ltd.

Vandervelde, Beatrice. Home Ice. 2004. (Sports Stories Ser.). 104p. (J). (gr. 4-8). (***978-1-55028-863-6(6)**); 7.95 (978-1-55028-862-9(8)) Lorimer, James & Co., Ltd., Pubs. CAN. *Dist:* Casemate Pubs. & Bk. Distributors, LLC.

Walmsley, Tom. Kid Stuff: A Novel. 2003. 288p. pap. 17.95 (978-1-55152-153-4(9)) Arsenal Pulp Pr. CAN. *Dist:* Consortium Bk. Sales & Distribution.

Wilson, Eric G. The Lost Treasure of Casa Loma. 6th ed. 2001. (Tom & Liz Austen Mysteries Ser.). (Illus.). 103p. (J). (gr. 3-6). mass mkt. 5.95 (978-0-7736-7492-9(6)) Stoddart Kids CAN. *Dist:* Fitzhenry & Whiteside, Ltd.

Woods, Shirley. Black Nell: The Adventures of a Coyote. 2000. (Illus.). (J). 13.75 (978-0-606-21882-5(3)) Tandem Library Bks.

Wynne-Jones, Tim. Rex Zero & the End of the World. 2007. (Illus.). 192p. (J). (gr. 3-7). 16.00 (978-0-374-33467-3(6)) Farrar, Straus & Giroux.

Wynne-Jones, Tim. Rex Zero, the King of Nothing. 2008. 224p. (J). 16.95 (***978-0-374-36259-1(9)**) Farrar, Straus & Giroux.

ONTARIO, LAKE (N.Y. AND ONT.)

Ylvisaker, Anne. Lake Ontario. 2003. (Fact Finders Ser.). (Illus.). 32p. (J). lib. bdg. 22.60 (978-0-7368-2211-4(9) , Bridgestone Bks.) Capstone Pr., Inc.

OPERA

see also Ballet; Operetta

Annesley, Charles. The Standard Operaglass. 2001. 423p. (YA). reprint ed. 98.00 (978-0-7222-6251-1(5)) Library Reprints, Inc.

Brasch, Nicolas. Classical Music & Opera. 2004. (J). lib. bdg. 27.10 (978-1-58340-547-5(X)) Smart Apple Media.

Chamberlain, Houston S. The Wagnerian Drama: An Attempt to Inspire a Better Appreciation of Wagner As a Dramatic Poet. 2001. 240p. (YA). reprint ed. 98.00 (978-0-7222-5565-0(9)) Library Reprints, Inc.

Cleather, Alice L. Wagner's Dramas: Interpretations, 4 vols., set. 2001. (YA). reprint ed. 500.00 (978-0-7222-5566-7(7)) Library Reprints, Inc.

Crowest, Frederick J. Cherubini. 2001. 115p. (YA). reprint ed. 88.00 (978-0-7222-5190-4(4)) Library Reprints, Inc.

Dent, Edward J. Mozart's Operas: A Critical Study. 2001. 432p. (YA). reprint ed. 98.00 (978-0-7222-5476-9(8)) Library Reprints, Inc.

Dry, Wakeling. Nights at the Opera, 11 vols., set. 2001. (YA). reprint ed. 1375.00 (978-0-7222-6253-5(1)) Library Reprints, Inc.

Edwards, Henry Sutherland. The Lyrical Drama: Essays on Subjects, Composers, & Executants of Modern Opera, 2 Vols., Set. 2001. (YA). reprint ed. 250.00 (978-0-7222-6238-2(8)) Library Reprints, Inc.

—Rossini & His School. 3rd ed. 2001. 114p. (YA). reprint ed. 88.00 (978-0-7222-5192-8(0)) Library Reprints, Inc.

Elson, Arthur. A Critical History of Opera. 2001. 391p. (YA). reprint ed. 98.00 (978-0-7222-6240-5(X)) Library Reprints, Inc.

Evans, Edwin. Wagner's Teachings by Analogy: His Views on Absolute Music & of the Relations of Articulate & Tonal Speech. 2001. 79p. (YA). reprint ed. 88.00 (978-0-7222-5569-8(1)) Library Reprints, Inc.

Fitzgerald, J. A. The Story of the Savoy Opera. 2001. (YA). reprint ed. 150.00 (978-0-7222-5540-7(3)) Library Reprints, Inc.

Fitzgerald, Percy Hetherington. The Savoy Opera & the Savoyards. 2001. 248p. (YA). reprint ed. 98.00 (978-0-7222-5539-1(X)) Library Reprints, Inc.

Ganeri, Anita, et al. The Young Person's Guide to the Opera: With Music from the Great Operas. 2001. (Illus.). 64p. (J). (gr. 3 up). 25.00 (978-0-15-216498-0(7)) Harcourt Children's Bks.

Gish, D. L. Opera. 2001. (World of Music Ser.). (Illus.). 32p. (J). (gr. 2-7). lib. bdg. 22.60 (978-1-58340-045-6(1)) Smart Apple Media.

Gribble, George D. The Master Works of Richard Wagner. 2001. (YA). reprint ed. 150.00 (978-0-7222-5574-2(8)) Library Reprints, Inc.

Hadden, James C. The Operas of Wagner: Their Plots, Music & History. 2001. 245p. (YA). reprint ed. 98.00 (978-0-7222-5576-6(4)) Library Reprints, Inc.

Irvine, David. Parsifal & Wagner's Christianity. 2001. (YA). reprint ed. 150.00 (978-0-7222-5583-4(7)) Library Reprints, Inc.

—A Wagnerian Midsummer Madness. 2001. 348p. (YA). reprint ed. 98.00 (978-0-7222-5584-1(5)) Library Reprints, Inc.

Krehbiel, Henry E. More Chapters of Opera. 2001. 474p. (YA). reprint ed. 98.00 (978-0-7222-6259-7(0)) Library Reprints, Inc.

—Studies in the Wagnerian Drama. 2001. 197p. (YA). reprint ed. 88.00 (978-0-7222-5585-8(3)) Library Reprints, Inc.

Kushner, Tony. Brundibar. Sendak, Maurice, illus. 2003. 56p. (J). (ps-17). (978-0-7868-0904-2(3)) Hyperion Bks. for Children.

Newmarch, Rosa H. The Russian Opera. 2001. 403p. (YA). reprint ed. 98.00 (978-0-7222-5144-7(0)) Library Reprints, Inc.

Ordway, Edith B. The Opera Book. 2001. 603p. (YA). reprint ed. 128.00 (978-0-7222-6264-1(7)) Library Reprints, Inc.

Riggs, Kate. Opera Music. 2008. (J). (***978-1-58341-568-9(8)** , Creative Education) Creative Co., The.

Roosevelt, Blanche. Verdi: Milan & Othello. 2001. 249p. (YA). reprint ed. 98.00 (978-0-7222-5554-4(3)) Library Reprints, Inc.

Streatfield, Richard A. The Opera: A Sketch of the Development of Opera. 2001. 351p. (YA). reprint ed. 98.00 (978-0-7222-5601-5(9)) Library Reprints, Inc.

OPTIONS (FINANCE)

see Stock Exchanges

OPTOMETRY—FICTION

Dooley, Virginia. I Need Glasses: My Visit to the Optometrist. Roth, Stephanie, illus. 2002. 32p. (J). (ps-2). pap. 6.00 (978-1-59034-040-0(X)) Mondo Publishing.

ORANGES

Keller, Kristin Thoennes. Oranges to Orange Juice. 2004. (First Facts Ser.). (Illus.). 24p. (J). lib. bdg. 21.26 (978-0-7368-2636-5(X)) Capstone Pr., Inc.

Lilly, Melinda. Oranges. 2001. (Around the World with Food & Spices Ser.). (Illus.). 32p. (J). (gr. 3-5). lib. bdg. 26.60 (978-1-58952-045-5(9)) Rourke Publishing, LLC.

Mayo, Gretchen Will. Orange Juice. 2004. (Weekly Reader Early Learning Library). (Illus.). 24p. (gr. 2 up). (J). pap. 5.95 (978-0-8368-4075-9(5)); (YA). lib. bdg. 19.33 (978-0-8368-4068-1(2)) Stevens, Gareth Inc. (Weekly Reader Early Learning Library).

Pickering, Robin. I Like Oranges. 2000. (Welcome Bks.). (Illus.). 24p. (J). (ps-2). 17.00 (978-0-516-23086-3(7) , Children's Pr.) Scholastic Library Publishing.

Snyder, Inez. Oranges. 2004. (Harvesttime Ser.). (J). 18.00 (978-0-516-27593-2(3)); pap. 4.95 (978-0-516-25913-0(X)) Scholastic Library Publishing. (Children's Pr.).

—Oranges to Orange Juice. 2003. (How Things Are Made Ser.). (Illus.). 24p. (J). 18.00 (978-0-516-24265-1(2) , Children's Pr.); pap. 4.95 (978-0-516-24357-3(8) , Watts, Franklin) Scholastic Library Publishing.

—Oranges to Orange Juice. 2003. (gr. k-3). lib. bdg. 12.95 (978-0-613-59701-2(X)) Tandem Library Bks.

Spilsbury, Louise. La Naranja. 2003. (Alimentos Ser.).Tr. of Oranges. (ENG & SPA.). 32p. (J). pap. 6.50 (978-1-4034-3742-6(4)) Heinemann Library.

—Oranges. (Food Ser.). 32p. pap. 6.95 (978-1-4034-4048-8(4)); 2003. (Illus.). (J). lib. bdg. 22.79 (978-1-58810-618-6(7)) Heinemann Library.

Spilsbury, Louise & Hall, Margaret. La Naranja. 2003. (Alimentos Ser.).Tr. of Oranges. (SPA & ENG., Illus.). 32p. (J). lib. bdg. 22.79 (978-1-4034-3736-5(X)) Heinemann Library.

ORANGUTAN

Armentrout, David & Armentrout, Patricia. Orangutans. 2008. (J). (***978-1-60044-568-2(3)***) Rourke Publishing, LLC.

Brend, Stephen. Orangutan. 2000. (Natural World Ser.). (Illus.). 48p. (J). (gr. 4-7). 9.95 (978-0-7398-3126-7(7)) Steck-Vaughn.

—Orangutan: Habitats, Life Cycles, Food Chains, Threats. 2000. (Natural World Ser.). (Illus.). 48p. (J). (gr. 4-7). lib. bdg. 27.12 (978-0-7398-2765-9(0)) Raintree.

Costain, Meredith. Orangutans. 2000. (gr. k-3). lib. bdg. 11.80 (978-0-613-30652-2(5)) Tandem Library Bks.

Dennard, Deborah. Apes & Monkeys. McGee, John F., illus. 2004. (Our Wild World Ser.). 192p. (J). (gr. 2-5). ring bd. 16.95 (978-1-55971-863-9(3) , NorthWord Bks. for Young Readers) T&N Children's Publishing.

—Orangutans. McGee, John F., illus. 2004. (Our Wild World Ser.). 48p. (J). (gr. 2-5). ring bd. 10.95 (978-1-55971-848-6(X)); pap. 7.95 (978-1-55971-847-9(1)) T&N Children's Publishing. (NorthWord Bks. for Young Readers).

—Orangutans. 2003. (gr. 3-6). lib. bdg. 16.40 (978-0-613-67977-0(6)) Tandem Library Bks.

Eckart, Edana. Orangutan. 2003. (Welcome Book Ser.). (Illus.). 24p. (J). 17.00 (978-0-516-24299-6(7)); pap. 4.95 (978-0-516-27895-7(9)) Scholastic Library Publishing. (Children's Pr.).

Harkrader, Lisa. The Orangutan: A Myreportlinks. com Book. 2005. (Endangered & Threatened Animals Ser.). (Illus.). 48p. (J). (ps-10). lib. bdg. 25.26 (978-0-7660-5068-6(8) , MyReportLinks.com Bks.) Enslow Pubs., Inc.

Hibbert, Adam & Dixon, Dougal. Orangutan Rescue. 2005. (Animal Story Ser.). (Illus.). 32p. (J). 9.95 (978-1-57768-898-3(8) , Bedrick, Peter Bks.) School Specialty Publishing.

Hughes, Monica. Orangutan Baby. 2006. (I Love Reading Ser.). (Illus.). 24p. (J). lib. bdg. 19.96 (978-1-59716-153-4(5)) Bearport Publishing Co., Inc.

Kendell, Patricia. Orangutans. 2003. (In the Wild Ser.). (Illus.). 32p. (J). lib. bdg. 25.70 (978-0-7398-6636-8(2)) Raintree.

Knudsen Shannon. Climbing Orangutans. 2007. (Pull Ahead Books-Animals Ser.). (J). 22.60 (***978-0-8225-6704-2(0)*** , Lerner Pubns.); pap. 6.95 (***978-0-8225-6708-0(3)*** , First Avenue Editions) Lerner Publishing Group.

Kueffner, Sue. Orangutans. 2006. (J). (***978-1-59939-113-7(9)*** , Reader's Digest Young Families, Inc.) Reader's Digest Children's Publishing, Inc.

Levine, Stuart P. The Orangutan. 1999. (Endangered Animals & Habitats Ser.). (Illus.). 112p. (YA). (gr. 4-12). 27.45 (978-1-56006-560-9(5) , Lucent Bks.) Thomson Gale.

Martin, Patricia A. Fink. Orangutans. 2000. (True Bks.). (Illus.). 48p. (J). (gr. 3-5). pap. 6.95 (978-0-516-27020-3(6)); 25.00 (978-0-516-21571-6(X)) Scholastic Library Publishing. (Children's Pr.).

Morgan, Sally. Orang-utans. 2006. (QEB Animal Lives Ser.). (Illus.). 32p. (J). lib. bdg. 19.95 (978-1-59566-204-0(9)) QEB Publishing Inc.

Murray, Julie. Orangutans. 2005. (Animal Kingdom Set Ii Ser.). (Illus.). 24p. (J). (gr. k-4). lib. bdg. 21.35 (978-1-59197-327-0(9)) ABDO Publishing Co.

Orme, David. Orangutan. 2004. (Animals under Threat Ser.). (Illus.). 48p. (J). 29.93 (978-1-4034-5586-4(4)) Heinemann Library.

—The Orangutan. 2004. (Animals under Threat Ser.). (Illus.). 48p. (J). pap. 8.50 (978-1-4034-5693-9(3)) Heinemann Library.

Orme, Helen. Orangutans in Danger. 2007. (Wildlife Survival Ser.). (Illus.). 32p. (J). lib. bdg. 25.27 (978-1-59716-263-0(9)) Bearport Publishing Co., Inc.

Ring, Susan. Project Orangutan. 2003. (gr. 3-6). lib. bdg. 15.25 (978-0-613-79812-9(0)) Tandem Library Bks.

—Project Orangutan. Marshall, Diana & Nault, Jennifer, eds. 2003. (Zoo Life Ser.). (Illus.). 24p. (J). pap. 6.95 (978-1-59036-058-3(3)) Weigl Pubs., Inc.

—Project Orangutan. 2002. (Zoo Babies Ser.). (Illus.). 24p. (J). lib. bdg. 15.15 (978-1-59036-017-0(6)) Weigl Pubs., Inc.

Shively, Julie. Baby Orangutan. Johnson, Meredith, illus. 2005. (San Diego Zoo Animal Library: Vol. 9). 24p. (J). bds. 6.95 (978-0-8249-6578-5(7)) Ideals Pubns.

Sourd, Christine. The Orangutan: Forest Acrobat. Visage, Albert & Ferrero, Jean Paul, photos by. 2001. (Animal Close-Ups Ser.). (Illus.). 28p. (J). (gr. 2-5). pap. 6.95 (978-1-57091-429-4(X)) Charlesbridge Publishing, Inc.

—Orangutan: Forest Acrobat. 2001. (gr. 3-6). lib. bdg. 15.25 (978-0-613-51262-6(6)) Tandem Library Bks.

Steele, Christy. Orangutans. Sloan, Frank, ed. 2001. (Animals of the Rain Forest Ser.). (Illus.). 32p. (J). (gr. 4-7). lib. bdg. 22.83 (978-0-7398-3555-5(6)) Raintree.

Swanson, Diane. Orangutans. 2003. (Welcome to the Whole World Ser.). (Illus.). 32p. (J). (gr. k-2). pap. 5.95 (978-1-55285-472-3(8)) Whitecap Bks., Ltd. CAN. *Dist:* Firefly Bks., Ltd.

—Welcome to the Whole World of Orangutans. 2004. (gr. k-3). lib. bdg. 14.10 (978-0-613-78593-8(2)) Tandem Library Bks.

Underwood, Deborah. Watching Orangutans in Asia. 2006. (Heinemann First Library). (Illus.). 32p. (J). (978-1-4034-7231-1(9)); pap. (978-1-4034-7244-1(0)) Heinemann Library.

Wildlife Education, Ltd. Staff. Orangutans. Meltzer, Davis, illus. 2000. (Zoobooks Ser.). 18p. (YA). (gr. 5 up). pap. 2.95 (978-0-937934-02-9(X)) Wildlife Education, Ltd.

Wildlife Education, Ltd. Staff & Wexo, John Bonnett. Orangutans. 2001. (Zoobooks Ser.). (Illus.). 24p. (J). (gr. 5 up). 15.95 (978-0-937934-83-8(6)) Wildlife Education, Ltd.

ORANGUTAN—FICTION

Daddo, Andrew. Goodnight, Me. Quay, Emma, illus. 2007. 32p. (J). (ps). 11.95 (***978-1-59990-153-4(6)***) Bloomsbury Publishing.

de Beer, Hans. El Pequeno Coco. 1999. Tr. of Little Coconut. (978-0-606-17554-8(7)) Tandem Library Bks.

Lumry, Amanda & Hurwitz, Laura. Operation Orangutan. 2007. 36p. 15.95 (978-0-9748411-4-4(5)) Eaglemont Pr.

Romanelli, Serena. El Pequeno Coco. Lamas, Blanca Rosa, tr. from GER. de Beer, Hans, illus. 2004. (SPA.). 24p. (J). (gr. k-4). reprint ed. 16.00 (978-0-7567-7707-4(0)) DIANE Publishing Co.

ORATORY

see Public Speaking

ORBITING VEHICLES

see Artificial Satellites

ORCHARDS

see Fruit Culture

ORCHESTRA

see also Bands (Music); Orchestral Music

Abbado, Claudio. Yo Sere Director de Orquesta. 2007. 48p. (J). (gr. 2-5). 19.95 (***978-84-8470-052-4(6)***) Corimbo, Editorial S.L. ESP. *Dist:* Lectorum Pubns., Inc.

Almeida, Artie. The Ultimate Game & Activity Pack for Orchestra: Grades 3-6. 2004. act. bk. ed. 39.95 (978-0-89328-006-2(2) , 30/1966H) Heritage Music Pr.

Berlioz, Hector. A Treatise on Modern Instrumentation & Orchestration. 2001. 257p. (YA). reprint ed. 98.00 (978-0-7222-5775-3(9)) Library Reprints, Inc.

Gordon, L. M. Modern School Orchestra & Its Development. 2001. (YA). reprint ed. 150.00 (978-0-7222-5787-6(2)) Library Reprints, Inc.

Guy, Suzanne & Lacy, Donna. The Orchestra, the Orchestra! Lacy, Donna, illus. 2002. (Illus.). (J). (978-0-9672885-6-7(8)) Live Wire Pr.

Henderson, William J. The Orchestra & Orchestral Music. 2001. 238p. (YA). reprint ed. 98.00 (978-0-7222-5781-4(3)) Library Reprints, Inc.

Koscielniak, Bruce. Story of the Incredible Orchestra: An Introduction to Musical Instruments & Th. 2000. (gr. k-3). lib. bdg. 15.25 (978-0-613-60837-4(2)) Tandem Library Bks.

—The Story of the Incredible Orchestra: An Introduction to Musical Instruments & the Symphony Orchestra. 2000. (Illus.). 32p. (J). (gr. 4-6). reprint ed. 17.00 (978-0-7567-5682-6(0)) DIANE Publishing Co.

—The Story of the Incredible Orchestra: An Introduction to Musical Instruments & the Symphony Orchestra. 2003. (Illus.). 40p. (J). (gr. k-3). pap. 6.95 (978-0-618-31112-5(2)) Houghton Mifflin Co. Trade & Reference Div.

LeFrak, Karen. Jake the Philharmonic Dog. Baranski, Marcin, illus. 2006. 32p. (J). 17.85 (978-0-8027-9553-3(6)) Walker & Co.

Levine, Robert T. & Hamilton, Meredith. The Story of the Orchestra: Listen While You Learn about the Instruments, the Music & the Composers Who Wrote the Music! 2000. (Illus.). 96p. (J). (gr. 4-7). tchr. ed. 19.95 (978-1-57912-148-8(9) , 81148) Black Dog & Leventhal Pubs., Inc.

Lyon, James. A Practical Guide to the Modern Orchestra. 2001. 93p. (YA). reprint ed. 88.00 (978-0-7222-5783-8(X)) Library Reprints, Inc.

Out & about at the Orchestra. (Field Trips Ser.). 24p. (J). 8.95 (978-1-4048-0168-4(5)) Picture Window Bks.

Rubin, Daniel. Orchestra. (J). pap. 9.95 (978-0-88899-051-8(0)) Groundwood Bks. CAN. *Dist:* Transition Vendor.

Rubin, Mark & Daniel, Alan. The Orchestra. 2003. (Illus.). 48p. (J). (ps-2). pap. 8.95 (978-0-920668-99-3(2)) Firefly Bks., Ltd.

Swalin, Benjamin. Hard Circus Road: The Odyssey of the North Carolina Symphony. McVaugh, Julia A., ed. (Illus.). 158p. (YA). 24.95 (978-0-9618952-0-4(9)) North Carolina Symphony Society, Inc., The.

Turner, Barbara. Out & About at the Orchestra. McMullen, Anne, illus. 2004. (Field Trips Ser.). 24p. (C). (gr. k-3). 23.93 (978-1-4048-0040-3(9)) Picture Window Bks.

Ustinov, Peter. The Orchestra. (J). (ps up). 19.98 incl. audio Music for Little People, Inc.

ORCHESTRA—FICTION

Barnes, Peter W. Maestro Mouse: And the Mystery of the Missing Baton. Barnes, Cheryl Shaw, illus. 2005. 32p. (J). 16.95 (978-1-893622-17-3(7) , VSP Bks.) Vacation Spot Publishing.

Gustafson, Scott. Animal Orchestra: A Counting Book. Gustafson, Scott, illus. 2003. (Illus.). 32p. (J). (ps-k). 14.95 (978-0-86713-030-0(X) , 88070) Greenwich Workshop Pr.

Hambrick, Sharon. The Year of Abi Crim. 2000. (Illus.). 118p. (J). (gr. 4-7). pap. 7.49 (978-1-57924-374-6(6) , 124255) Jones, Bob Univ. Pr.

Hoff, Syd. Arturo's Baton. 2002. (gr. k-3). lib. bdg. 14.10 (978-0-613-65159-2(6)) Tandem Library Bks.

Keillor, Garrison & Nilsson. The Sandy Bottom Orchestra. 1998. (978-0-606-13757-7(2)) Tandem Library Bks.

Keillor, Garrison & Nilsson, Jenny Lind. The Sandy Bottom Orchestra. l.t. ed. 2002. (LRS Large Print Cornerstone Ser.). (J). lib. bdg. 32.95 (978-1-58118-091-6(8)) LRS.

Law, Felicia. Rumble Meets Vikki Viper. Pak, Yoon Mi, illus. 2006. (Read-It! Readers Ser.). 32p. (J). (gr. 2-4). 18.60 (978-1-4048-1342-7(X)) Picture Window Bks.

LeFrak, Karen. Jake the Philharmonic Dog. Baranski, Marcin, illus. 2006. 32p. (J). 16.95 (978-0-8027-9552-6(8)) Walker & Co.

Orleans, Ilo. Animal Orchestra. Gergely, Tibor, illus. (Little Golden Treasures Ser.). (J). (gr. k-k). 2004. 26p. bds. 4.99 (978-0-375-82775-4(7)); 2001. 24p. 2.99 (978-0-307-98287-2(4)) Random Hse. Children's Bks. (Golden Bks.).

Shackman, Julie. Olivia's Orchestra. 2000. (Illus.). 24p. (J). (ps-1). pap. (978-1-84210-008-0(4)) Mentor Bks.

Snicket, Lemony, pseud & Stookey, Nathaniel. The Composer Is Dead. Ellis, Carson, illus. 2008. (J). (***978-0-06-123627-3(6)***); lib. bdg. (***978-0-06-123628-0(4)***) HarperCollins Pubs.

Tashiro, Chisato. Five Nice Mice. Uchida, Sayako, tr. from JPN. Tashiro, Chisato, illus. 2007. 36p. (J). (ps-2). 16.99 (***978-0-698-40058-0(5)*** , Minedition) Penguin Group (USA) Inc.

Tripp, Paul. Tubby the Tuba. Cole, Henry, illus. 2006. 32p. (J). (ps). pap. 16.99 (978-0-525-47717-4(9) , Dutton Juvenile) Penguin Group (USA) Inc.

Wilson, Budge. A Fiddle for Angus. ed. 2004. (Illus.). (J). (gr. k-3). spiral bd. (978-0-616-11140-6(1)) Canadian National Institute for the Blind/Institut National Canadien pour les Aveugles.

ORCHESTRAL MUSIC

Henderson, William J. The Orchestra & Orchestral Music. 2001. 238p. (YA). reprint ed. 98.00 (978-0-7222-5781-4(3)) Library Reprints, Inc.

Heyens, Gudrun & Engel, Gerhard. Fun & Games with the Alto Recorder Bk. 1: Tune. 2004. 46p. pap. 9.95 (978-1-902455-14-3(2) , 1902455142) Schott Musik International GmbH & Co. KG DEU. *Dist:* Leonard, Hal Corp.

—Fun & Games with the Alto Recorder Bk. 1: Tuto. 2004. 80p. pap. 14.95 (978-1-902455-13-6(4) , 1902455134) Schott Musik International GmbH & Co. KG DEU. *Dist:* Leonard, Hal Corp.

—Fun & Games with the Alto Recorder Bk. 2: Tune. 2005. 92p. pap. 10.95 (978-1-902455-16-7(9) , 1902455169) Schott Musik International GmbH & Co. KG DEU. *Dist:* Leonard, Hal Corp.

Little Drummer Boy. 1999. (Illus.). 20p. (J). bds. 4.95 (978-0-88271-678-7(6)) Regina Pr., Malhame & Co.

Masters of Music, 12 bks., Set. 2004. (Masters of Music Ser.). (Illus.). 7p. (gr. 4-8). lib. bdg. 239.40 (978-1-58415-253-8(2)) Mitchell Lane Pubs., Inc.

Stravinsky, Igor. The Firebird: Original 1910 Version. unabr. ed. 2000. (Illus.). 176p. pap. 7.95 (978-0-486-41403-4(5)) Dover Pubns., Inc.

—Fireworks & Song of the Nightingale in Full Score. 2000. 128p. pap. 12.95 (978-0-486-41392-1(6)) Dover Pubns., Inc.

ORCHIDS

Brown, Deni. Orchids: The Green World. 2000. (Illus.). 47p. (J). (gr. 5-7). reprint ed. 15.00 (978-0-7881-9435-1(6)) DIANE Publishing Co.

Curtis, Bruce. Orchids. 2005. (Illus.). 96p. 9.98 (978-0-7624-2456-6(7) , Courage Bks.) Running Pr. Bk. Pubs.

Fell, Derek. Orchids. 1999. (Let's Investigate Ser.). (Illus.). 32p. (J). (gr. 1-4). pap. (978-1-58341-003-5(1) , Creative Education) Creative Co., The.

Hansen, Eric. Orchid Fever: A Horticultural Tale of Love, Lust, & Lunacy. 2001. (Vintage Departures Ser.). (Illus.). 288p. (YA). (gr. 8). 13.00 (978-0-679-77183-8(2) , Vintage) Knopf Publishing Group.

ORDNANCE

see also names of general and specific military ordnance, e.g. Atomic Weapons; also names of armies with the subdivision Ordnance and Ordnance Stores, e.g. U. S. Army—Ordnance and Ordnance Stores

Culver, Bruce & Feist, Uwe. Tiger I & Stormtiger in Detail. (Illus.). 168p. (YA). 40.00 (978-0-9633824-0-5(3)) Ryton Pubns.

OREGON

Boone, Mary. Uniquely Oregon. 2004. (Heinemann State Studies). (J). pap. 8.50 (978-1-4034-4728-9(4)) Heinemann Library.

Bratvold, Gretchen. Oregon. 2nd exp. rev. ed. 2003. (Hello U. S. A. Ser.). (Illus.). 84p. (J). (gr. 3-6). 25.26 (978-0-8225-4099-1(1) , Lerner Pubns.) Lerner Publishing Group.

—Oregon. rev. ed. 2003. (gr. 3-6). lib. bdg. 15.25 (978-0-613-52467-4(5)) Tandem Library Bks.

Capstone Press Staff, contrib. by. Oregon. rev. ed. 2002. (One Nation Ser.). (Illus.). 48p. (J). (gr. 3-4). lib. bdg. 22.60 (978-0-7368-1261-0(X) , Bridgestone Bks.) Capstone Pr., Inc.

Graf, Mike. Oregon. 2003. (Land of Liberty Ser.). (Illus.). 64p. (J). lib. bdg. 25.26 (978-0-7368-2193-3(7)) Capstone Pr., Inc.

Hart, Joyce. Oregon. 2005. (It's My State! Ser.). (Illus.). 80p. (J). 978-0-7614-1908-2(X) , Benchmark Bks.) Cavendish, Marshall Corp.

Heinrichs, Ann. Oregon. Kania, Matt, illus. 2005. (Welcome to the USA Ser.). 40p. (J). (gr. 1-5). 27.07 (978-1-59296-479-6(6)) Child's World, Inc.

—Oregon. 2003. (This Land Is Your Land Ser.). (Illus.). 48p. (J). (gr. 3 up). lib. bdg. 22.60 (978-0-7565-0317-8(5)) Compass Point Bks.

Hood, Karen Jean Matsko. Oregon State: Adventures in Learning Book. 2007. (Educational Activity & Coloring Book Ser.). (J). 22.95 (***978-1-59434-684-2(4)***); 24.95 (***978-1-59434-683-5(6)***); ring bd. 24.95 (***978-1-59434-685-9(2)***) Whispering Pine Pr., Inc.

—Oregon State: Adventures in Learning Book, State Educational Book Series. braille ed. 2006. (Educational Activity & Coloring Book Ser.). (J). spiral bd. 22.95 (978-1-59434-814-3(6)) Whispering Pine Pr., Inc.

Hood, Karen Jean Matsko. Oregon State Activity & Coloring Book. 2007. (Educational Activity & Coloring Book Ser.). (J). 22.95 (***978-1-59210-015-6(5)***); ring bd. 24.95 (***978-1-59210-014-9(7)***) Whispering Pine Pr., Inc.

Ingram, Scott. Oregon: The Beaver State. 2002. (World Almanac Library of the States). (Illus.). 48p. (J). (gr. 5 up). lib. bdg. 30.00 (978-0-8368-5143-4(9)); pap. 14.95 (978-0-8368-5313-1(X)) Stevens, Gareth Inc. (World Almanac Library).

Knapp, Ron. Oregon: A MyReportLinks.com Book. 2002. (States Ser.). (Illus.). 48p. (J). (gr. 4-10). lib. bdg. 25.26 (978-0-7660-5021-1(1) , MyReportLinks.com Bks.) Enslow Pubs., Inc.

Labella, Susan. Oregon. 2006. (Rookie Read-About Geography Ser.). (Illus.). 32p. (J). (gr. 1-2). 20.50 (***978-0-516-25386-2(7)***) Scholastic Library Publishing.

MacMillan, Daniel Emerson. Golfing in Oregon. 12th ed. 2003. 270p. per. 12.95 (978-1-878591-59-3(2)) MAC Productions.

Marsh, Carole. The Big Oregon Reproducible Activity Book. 2001. (Carole Marsh Oregon Bks.). (Illus.). 96p. (J). (gr. 2-6). pap. 9.95 (978-0-7933-9953-6(X)) Gallopade International.

—My First Book about Oregon. 2001. (Illus.). 32p. (J). (gr. k-4). pap. 7.95 (978-0-7933-9895-9(9)) Gallopade International.

—Oregon Classic Christmas Trivia. 2002. (Carole Marsh Oregon Bks.). (Illus.). 32p. (J). pap. 14.95 (978-0-635-01439-9(4) , 14394); lib. bdg. 21.95 (978-0-635-01440-5(8) , 14408, Marsh, Carole Bks.) Gallopade International.

—Oregon Current Events Projects: 30 Cool, Activities, Crafts, Experiments & More for Kids to Do to Learn about Your State! 2003. (Oregon Experience Ser.). 32p. (gr. k-5). pap. 5.95 (978-0-635-02056-7(4) , Marsh, Carole Bks.) Gallopade International.

—The Oregon Experience Pocket Guide. 2001. (Carole Marsh Oregon Bks.). (Illus.). 96p. (J). (gr. 3-8). pap. 6.95 (978-0-7933-9924-6(6)) Gallopade International.

—Oregon Geography Projects: 30 Cool, Activities, Crafts, Experiments & More for Kids to Do to Learn about Your State! 2003. (Oregon Experience Ser.). 32p. (gr. k-5). pap. 5.95 (978-0-635-01856-4(X) , Marsh, Carole Bks.) Gallopade International.

—Oregon Government Projects: 30 Cool, Activities, Crafts, Experiments & More for Kids to Do to Learn about Your State! 2003. (Oregon Experience Ser.). 32p. (gr. k-5). pap. 5.95 (978-0-635-01956-1(6) , Marsh, Carole Bks.) Gallopade International.

—Oregon Jeopardy! Answers & Questions about Our State! 2001. (Carole Marsh Oregon Bks.). (Illus.). 32p. (J). (gr. 3-8). pap. 7.95 (978-0-7933-9808-9(8)) Gallopade International.

—Oregon "Jography" A Fun Run Thru Our State! 2001. (Carole Marsh Oregon Bks.). (Illus.). 32p. (J). (gr. 3-8). pap. 7.95 (978-0-7933-9837-9(1)) Gallopade International.

—Oregon People Projects: 30 Cool, Activities, Crafts, Experiments & More for Kids to Do to Learn about Your State! 2003. (Oregon Experience Ser.). 32p. (gr. k-5). pap. 5.95 (978-0-635-02006-2(8) , Marsh, Carole Bks.) Gallopade International.

—Oregon Symbols & Facts Projects: 30 Cool, Activities, Crafts, Experiments & More for Kids to Do to Learn about Your State! 2003. (Oregon Experience Ser.). 32p. (gr. k-5). pap. 5.95 (978-0-635-01906-6(X) , Marsh, Carole Bks.) Gallopade International.

McAuliffe, Emily. Oregon Facts & Symbols. (J). 1999. lib. bdg. 14.00 (978-0-531-11804-7(5)); 1999. (Illus.). 24p. (gr. 2-3). lib. bdg. 18.60 (978-0-7368-0216-1(9) , Bridgestone Bks.); 2003. 24p. lib. bdg. 19.93 (978-0-7368-2267-1(4)) Capstone Pr., Inc.

Murray, Julie. Oregon. 2006. (Illus.). 32p. (J). (gr. k-4). lib. bdg. 22.78 (978-1-59197-696-7(0) , Buddy Bks.) ABDO Publishing Co.

Nix, Nelleke. Out & about Portland with Kids: The Ultimate Guide for Fun & Learning. 2nd ed. 2002. 240p. (J). pap. 14.95 (978-0-9715644-0-4(X)) Northwest Parent Publishing.

Oregon. 2000. (Switched on Schoolhouse Ser.). (Illus.). (YA). (gr. 7-12). pap. 24.95 incl. cd-rom (978-0-7403-0289-3(2) , SOSOR) Alpha Omega Pubns., Inc.

The Oregon Trail, 6 vols. (gr. 2-5). 39.95 (978-0-7368-4591-5(7)) Red Brick Learning.

Peterson del Mar, David. Oregon's Promise: An Interpretive History. 2003. (Illus.). 320p. 19.95 (978-0-87071-558-7(5)) Oregon State Univ. Pr.

Portland Sold C 2005. 2004. 308p. (YA). pap. 15.00 (978-1-58553-962-8(7) , 05GC0013) Entertainment Publications, Inc.

Shannon, Terry Miller. Oregon. 2003. (From Sea to Shining Sea Ser.: 2). (Illus.). 80p. (J). 30.50 (978-0-516-22397-1(6) , Children's Pr.) Scholastic Library Publishing.

Smith, Marie & Smith, Roland. B Is for Beaver: An Oregon Alphabet. Roydon, Michael, illus. 2003. 40p. (J). 17.95 (978-1-58536-071-0(6)) Sleeping Bear Pr.

Sonneborn, Liz. Oregon. 2006. (Portraits of the States Ser.). (Illus.). 32p. (J). pap. (978-0-8368-4692-8(3)); lib. bdg. 23.33 (978-0-8368-4673-7(7)) Stevens, Gareth Inc.

Stefoff, Rebecca. Oregon. 2nd ed. 2006. (Celebrate the States Ser.). (Illus.). 143p. (J). (978-0-7614-2031-6(2)); (978-0-7614-2022-4(3)) Cavendish, Marshall Corp. (Benchmark Bks.).

Sullivan, Jenna M. & Sullivan, Laura C. Kid's Guide to the National Parks of California & Oregon: Written by Kids for Kids. Sullivan, Jenna M. & Sullivan, Laura C., photos by. Sullivan, P. Deborah, photos by. 2001. (Illus.). 116p. (J). (gr. 6-12). pap. 10.95 (978-1-880062-23-4(2)) E&S Geographic & Information Services.

Way, Jennifer. Oregon (Oregon) 2006. (Bilingual Library of the United States of America: Set 2). (ENG & SPA., Illus.). 32p. (J). (gr. 2-6). lib. bdg. 22.50 (978-1-4042-3102-3(1) , Buenas Letra) Rosen Publishing Group, Inc., The.

Winans, Jay D. A Guide to Oregon. 2001. (American States Ser.). (Illus.). 32p. (J). lib. bdg. 16.95 (978-1-59036-002-6(8)) Weigl Pubs., Inc.

OREGON—FICTION

Beard, Darleen Bailey. Operation Clean Sweep. 2004. (Illus.). 160p. (J). 16.00 (978-0-374-38034-2(1) , Farrar, Straus & Giroux (BYR)) Farrar, Straus & Giroux.

Bunting, Eve. The Summer of Riley. 2002. (gr. 3-6). lib. bdg. 14.10 (978-0-613-44482-8(5)) Tandem Library Bks.

Carabine, Sue. The Night Before Christmas in Oregon. Kawasaki, Shauna Mooney, illus. 2002. 60p. 5.95 (978-1-58685-170-5(5)) Gibbs Smith, Publisher.

Carlson, Melody. Project, Girl Power. 2007. (Faithgirlz!#8482; / Girls of 622 Harbor View Ser.). 144p. (J). pap. 6.99 (978-0-310-71186-5(X)) Zonderkidz.

—Project, Mystery Bus. 2007. (Faithgirlz!#8482; / Girls of 622 Harbor View Ser.). 144p. (J). pap. 6.99 (978-0-310-71187-2(8)) Zonderkidz.

—Project, Rescue Chelsea. 2007. (Faithgirlz!#8482; / Girls of 622 Harbor View Ser.). 144p. (J). pap. 6.99 (978-0-310-71188-9(6)) Zonderkidz.

—Project, Take Charge. 2007. (Faithgirlz!#8482; / Girls of 622 Harbor View Ser.). 144p. (J). pap. 6.99 (978-0-310-71189-6(4)) Zonderkidz.

Carson, Drew. Summer Discovery. Thatch, Nancy R., ed. Carson, Drew, illus. 1998. (Books for Students by Students). (Illus.). 29p. (J). (gr. 2-4). lib. bdg. 15.95 (978-0-933849-68-6(0)) Landmark Editions, Inc.

Cereghino, Sandy. Oscar: The Short Legged Reindeer. 2006. (Illus.). 48p. (J). 24.95 ***(978-1-59299-248-5(X))*** Inkwater Pr.

Cleary, Beverly. Emily's Runaway Imagination. 2002. (J). 13.83 (978-0-7587-9141-2(0)) Book Wholesalers, Inc.

—Emily's Runaway Imagination. 221p. (J). (gr. 2-4). pap. 4.95 (978-0-8072-1416-9(7) , Listening Library) Random Hse. Audio Publishing Group.

Crew, Linda. Brides of Eden: A True Story Imagined. (gr. 5 up). 2003. 256p. (J). pap. 6.99 (978-0-06-447217-3(5)); 2001. (Illus.). 240p. (YA). 15.89 (978-0-06-028751-1(9)) HarperCollins Pubs.

Davis, Susan Page. Sarah's Long Ride. 2007. 173p. (J). ***(978-1-59166-737-7(2))*** Jones, Bob Univ. Pr.

Foster, Kinsley. Wild Abandon Vol. 2: Slam. 1999. (YA). pap. 10.95 (978-0-9667634-8-5(3)) What's Inside Pr.

—Wild Abandon Vol. 5: Mirror, Mirror. 2000. (YA). (gr. 6-12). pap. 10.95 (978-0-9667634-4-7(0)) What's Inside Pr.

Grandpa & Little Guy. 2004. (J). 15.95 (978-0-9764012-0-9(7)) Rockmill Publishing Co.

Hermes, Patricia. A Perfect Place Bk. 2: Joshua's Oregon Trail Diary. 2002. (My America Ser.: Bk. 2). 112p. (J). (gr. 2-5). pap. 10.95 (978-0-439-19999-5(9) , Scholastic Pr.) Scholastic, Inc.

—A Perfect Place Bk. 2: Joshua's Oregon Trail Diary. 2002. (gr. 3-6). lib. bdg. 13.00 (978-0-613-57261-3(0)) Tandem Library Bks.

—The Wild Year Bk. 3: Joshua's Oregon Trail Diary. 2003. (My America Ser.). (Illus.). 112p. (J). 4.99 (978-0-439-37056-1(6)) Scholastic, Inc.

—The Wild Year Bk. 3: Joshua's Oregon Trail Diary. 2003. (gr. 3-6). lib. bdg. 13.00 (978-0-613-72033-5(4)) Tandem Library Bks.

Herrick, Ann. Walk Softly & Watch Out for Bigfoot. 2006. (YA). pap. 9.95 (978-0-7599-4489-3(X)) Hard Shell Word Factory.

Holcomb, Jerry K. The Chinquapin Tree. 1998. (Accelerated Reader Bks.). 192p. (J). (gr. 3-7). 14.95 (978-0-7614-5028-3(9) , Cavendish Children's Bks.) Cavendish, Marshall Corp.

Humphrey, Matthew J. Coastal Magic. 2007. lib. bdg. 21.95 ***(978-1-59872-997-9(7))*** Instantpublisher.com.

James, Brian. Dirty Liar. 2006. 304p. (J). (gr. 10 up). pap. 16.99 (978-0-439-79623-1(7) , PUSH) Scholastic, Inc.

Karbo, Karen. Minerva Clark Gives up the Ghost. 2007. 244p. (J). (gr. 5 up). 16.95 ***(978-1-58234-679-3(8)*** , Bloomsbury Children) Bloomsbury Publishing.

Kehret, Peg. Escaping the Giant Wave. (Illus.). 160p. (J). 2004. pap. 5.99 (978-0-689-85273-2(8) , Aladdin); 2003. 16.99 (978-0-689-85272-5(X)) Simon & Schuster Children's Publishing.

—Escaping the Giant Wave. Lt. ed. 2003. 152p. (J). 21.95 (978-0-7862-5985-4(X)) Thorndike Pr.

Moss, Marissa. Rachel's Journal: The Story of A Pioneer Girl. 2001. (gr. 3-6). lib. bdg. 15.30 (978-0-613-35560-5(1)) Tandem Library Bks.

Mullin, Penn. Off to Oregon. 1999. (gr. 7-12). lib. bdg. 11.60 (978-0-613-28988-7(9)) Tandem Library Bks.

Nelson, Blake. The New Rules of High School. 2004. 240p. (YA). reprint ed. pap. 6.99 (978-0-14-240242-9(7) , Puffin) Penguin Group (USA) Inc.

Olson, Gretchen. Call Me Hope. 2007. 288p. (J). (gr. 3-7). 15.99 ***(978-0-316-01236-2(X))*** Little Brown & Co.

—Call Me Hope: A Novel. 2007. 272p. (J). ***(978-1-4287-4131-7(3))*** Little Brown & Co.

Patneaude, David. A Piece of the Sky. 2007. 194p. (J). 15.95 (978-0-8075-6536-0(9)) Whitman, Albert & Co.

Prescott, Duncan. The Wave. 2004. 226p. pap. 19.95 (978-1-4137-1006-9(9)) PublishAmerica, Inc.

Prowense, Mary J. Amy Goes Country. 2007. (ENG.). 136p. per. 19.95 ***(978-1-4241-5519-4(3))*** PublishAmerica, Inc.

Rescue Flight! 2003. 150p. (J). (gr. 4-6). per. 12.95 (978-0-9740202-0-4(6)) Skyword Pr.

Roberts, Kristi. My Thirteenth Season. rev. ed. 2005. (Illus.). 160p. (J). 15.95 (978-0-8050-7495-6(3) , Holt, Henry & Co. Bks. For Young Readers) Holt, Henry & Co.

Ryan, Sarah. The Rules for Hearts: A Family Drama. 2007. 224p. (YA). (gr. 9 up). 16.99 (978-0-670-05906-5(4) , Viking Juvenile) Penguin Group (USA) Inc.

Shands, Linda I. White Water. 2001. (Wakara of Eagle Lodge Ser.).Tr. of Juv033010. (Illus.). 176p. (YA). (gr. 7-9). pap. 5.99 (978-0-8007-5772-4(6) , Spire) Revell.

—Wild Fire. 2001. (Wakara of Eagle Lodge Ser.: Vol. 1). (Illus.). 176p. (J). (gr. 7-9). pap. 5.99 (978-0-8007-5746-5(7)) Revell.

Singleton, Linda Joy. Sea Switch. 2005. (Illus.). 264p. (ps-7). pap. 5.99 (978-0-7387-0712-9(0)) Llewellyn Pubns.

Snelling, Lauraine. The Long Way Home. 2001. (gr. 5-8). lib. bdg. 21.10 (978-0-613-55627-9(5)) Tandem Library Bks.

Spiotta-DiMare, Loren. Norman. 1998. (J). 12.95 (978-1-58021-058-4(9)); pap. 5.95 (978-1-58021-053-9(8)) Benefactory, Inc., The.

Stanley, Diane. Roughing It on the Oregon Trail. 2001. (gr. 3-6). lib. bdg. 14.10 (978-0-613-44250-3(4)) Tandem Library Bks.

Stelljes, Susan. Wonder Dog: The Story of Silverton Bobbie. 2005. (Illus.). 167p. (YA). pap. 14.95 (978-0-9761124-7-1(7)) For The Love of Dog Bks.

Van Sickle, Lisa. Secret Little City. 2000. 230p. (YA). (gr. 5-8). 15.95 (978-1-930167-11-7(3)) Palmae Publishing.

Wolff, Virginia Euwer. Bat 6. 256p. (J). (gr. 4-6). pap. 4.99 (978-0-8072-8223-6(5)); 2004. (gr. 5-9). pap. 36.00 incl. audio (978-0-8072-8222-9(7) , YYA144SP) Random Hse. Audio Publishing Group. (Listening Library).

—Bat 6. 240p. (gr. 5-9). 2000. (Illus.). (J). pap. 4.99 (978-0-590-89800-3(0) , Scholastic Reference); 1998. (YA). pap. 16.95 (978-0-590-89799-0(3)) Scholastic, Inc.

—Bat 6. 2000. (Illus.). (J). 11.64 (978-0-606-18516-5(X)) Tandem Library Bks.

OREGON—HISTORY

Ancona, George. Mi Casa: My House. 2004. (Somos Latino (We Are Latinos) Ser.). (ENG & SPA., Illus.). 32p. (J). 20.00 (978-0-516-23688-9(1) , Children's Pr.) Scholastic Library Publishing.

Boekhoff, P. M. & Kallen, Stuart A. Oregon. 2003. (Seeds of a Nation Ser.). (Illus.). 48p. (J). (gr. 3-5). 23.70 (978-0-7377-1482-1(4) , Kidhaven) Thomson Gale.

Crewe, Sabrina & Uschan, Michael V. The Oregon Trail. 2004. (Events That Shaped America Ser.). (Illus.). 32p. (J). lib. bdg. 24.67 (978-0-8368-3405-5(4)) Stevens, Gareth Inc.

The Famous Oregon Events Guide ~ 2006. 2005. (YA). per. 15.95 (978-1-881005-50-6(X)) Gail's Guides.

Frazier, Neta Lohnes. Stout-Hearted Seven: Orphaned on the Oregon Trail. 2006. (Sterling Point Bks.). (Illus.). 208p. (J). 12.95 (978-1-4027-3188-4(4)) Sterling Publishing Co., Inc.

Harness, Cheryl. The Tragic Tale of Narcissa Whitman & a Faithful History of the Oregon Trail. Harness, Cheryl, illus. 2006. (Illus.). 144p. (J). (gr. 5-9). 16.95 (978-0-7922-5920-6(3)); lib. bdg. 25.90 (978-0-7922-5921-3(1)) National Geographic Society. (National Geographic Children's Bks.).

Hood, Karen Jean Matsko. Oregan State Activity & Coloring Book: Geographical Educational Book Series. 2006. (J). per. 19.95 (978-1-59434-988-1(6)) Whispering Pine Pr., Inc.

—Oregon Coast: Facts & Stories about the Oregon Coast - Blue Level. 2006. (J). 19.95 (978-1-59434-260-8(1)); spiral bd. 19.95 (978-1-59434-259-2(8)); per. 19.95 (978-1-59434-256-1(3)); cd-rom 13.95 (978-1-59434-262-2(8)) Whispering Pine Pr., Inc.

—Oregon Coast: Facts & Stories about the Oregon Coast-Green Level. 2006. (J). 19.95 (978-1-59434-436-7(1)); spiral bd. 19.95 (978-1-59434-435-0(3)); per. 19.95 (978-1-59434-434-3(5)); cd-rom 13.95 (978-1-59434-439-8(6)) Whispering Pine Pr., Inc.

—Oregon Coast Activity & Coloring Book: Geographical Educational Book Series. 2006. (J). 19.95 (978-1-59434-963-8(0)); spiral bd. 19.95 (978-1-59434-962-1(2)); per. 19.95 (978-1-59434-961-4(4)); cd-rom 13.95 (978-1-59434-965-2(7)); spiral bd. 22.95 (978-1-59434-964-5(9)) Whispering Pine Pr., Inc.

—Oregon State: Activity & Coloring Book, State Educational Book Series. 2006. (J). 19.95 (978-1-59434-990-4(8)); spiral bd. 19.95 (978-1-59434-989-8(4)); per. 24.95 (978-1-59434-991-1(6)); cd-rom 13.95 (978-1-59434-992-8(4)) Whispering Pine Pr., Inc.

Marcovitz, Hal. Fort Clatsop. 2004. (American Forts & Their Strategic Importance Ser.). (J). (978-1-59084-706-0(7)) Mason Crest Pubs.

Marsh, Carole. My First Pocket Guide Oregon. 2000. (Oregon Experience! Ser.). (Illus.). 96p. (J). (gr. 3-8). 12.95 (978-0-635-01327-9(4) , 13274) Gallopade International.

—Oregon History Projects: 30 Cool, Activities, Crafts, Experiments & More for Kids to Do to Learn about Your State! 2003. (Oregon Experience Ser.). 32p. (gr. k-5). pap. 5.95 (978-0-635-01806-9(3) , Marsh, Carole Bks.) Gallopade International.

—Oregon Millionaire. 2001. (GameBook Ser.). 32p. (J). (gr. 3-8). pap., act. bk. ed. 9.95 (978-0-635-00090-3(3)) Gallopade International.

—Oregon Survivor. 2001. (GameBook Ser.). 32p. (J). (gr. 3-8). pap., act. bk. ed. 9.95 (978-0-635-00558-8(1)) Gallopade International.

—Oregon Wheel of Fortune. 2001. (GameBook Ser.). 32p. (J). (gr. 3-8). pap., act. bk. ed. 9.95 (978-0-7933-9690-0(5)) Gallopade International.

—Wheel of Fortune. 2001. (Oregon Experience! Ser.). (J). lib. bdg. 29.95 (978-0-7933-9691-7(3)) Gallopade International.

—Who Wants to Be a Millionaire? 2001. (Carole Marsh Oregon Bks.). (J). lib. bdg. 29.95 (978-0-635-00091-0(1)) Gallopade International.

Matchette, Katharine E. Discovering Oregon. Comfort, Mike & Baisley, Stephen, illus. Matchette, Dennis, photos by. (YA). (gr. 5-9). spiral bd. 13.00 (978-0-9645045-4-7(5)) Deka Pr.

Peters, S. True. How to Draw Oregons Sights & Symbols. 2002. (Kids Guide to Drawing America Ser.). 32p. (J). lib. bdg. 25.25 (978-0-8239-6093-4(5) , PowerKids Pr.) Rosen Publishing Group, Inc., The.

OREGON NATIONAL HISTORIC TRAIL

Blackwood, Gary L. Life on the Oregon Trail. 1999. (Way People Live Ser.). (Illus.). 112p. (YA). (gr. 7-10). 28.70 (978-1-56006-540-1(0) , LML00902-177897, Lucent Bks.) Thomson Gale.

Blashfield, Jean F. The Oregon Trail. 2000. (We the People Ser.). (Illus.). 48p. (J). (gr. 4 up). lib. bdg. 22.60 (978-0-7565-0045-0(1)) Compass Point Bks.

Cooper, Terry, ed. Oregon Trail: Scholastic Technology Activity Folder. 2001. (Instant Internet Activities Folder Ser.). 6p. 3.95 (978-0-439-30955-4(7)) Scholastic, Inc.

Crewe, Sabrina & Uschan, Michael V. The Oregon Trail. 2004. (Events That Shaped America Ser.). (Illus.). 32p. (J). lib. bdg. 24.67 (978-0-8368-3405-5(4)) Stevens, Gareth Inc.

Dean, Arlan. The Oregon Trail: From Independence, Missouri to Oregon City, Oregon. 2003. (Reading Power Ser.). (Illus.). 24p. (J). lib. bdg. 17.25 (978-0-8239-6478-9(7) , PowerKids Pr.) Rosen Publishing Group, Inc., The.

Frazier, Neta Lohnes. Stout-Hearted Seven: Orphaned on the Oregon Trail. 2006. (Sterling Point Bks.). (Illus.). 208p. (J). pap. 6.95 (978-1-4027-3617-9(7)) Sterling Publishing Co., Inc.

Graham, Amy. The Oregon Trail & the Daring Journey West by Wagon. 2006. (Wild History of the American West Ser.). (Illus.). 128p. (J). lib. bdg. 33.27 (978-1-59845-021-7(2) , MyReportLinks.com Bks.) Enslow Pubs., Inc.

Group/McGraw-Hill, Wright. History: The Oregon Trail, 6 vols. (Book2WebTM Ser.). (gr. 4-8). 36.50 (978-0-322-04452-4(9)) Wright Group, The.

Gunderson, Mary. Oregon Trail Cooking. 2000. (Blue Earth Books). (Illus.). 32p. (J). (gr. 3-4). lib. bdg. 22.60 (978-0-7368-0355-7(6) , Bridgestone Bks.) Capstone Pr., Inc.

—Oregon Trail Cooking. 1999. (Exploring History Through Simple Recipes Ser.). (Illus.). 32p. (J). (gr. 2-7). pap. 14.60 (978-0-516-21866-3(2) , Children's Pr.) Scholastic Library Publishing.

Harness, Cheryl. The Tragic Tale of Narcissa Whitman & a Faithful History of the Oregon Trail. Harness, Cheryl, illus. 2006. (Illus.). 144p. (J). (gr. 5-9). 16.95 (978-0-7922-5920-6(3)); lib. bdg. 25.90 (978-0-7922-5921-3(1)) National Geographic Society. (National Geographic Children's Bks.).

Hunsaker, Joyce Badgley. Seeing the Elephant: Voices from the Oregon Trail. 2003. (Illus.). 272p. (J). 24.95 (978-0-89672-504-1(9)) Texas Tech Univ. Pr.

Jaffe, Elizabeth Dana. The Oregon Trail. 2002. (Let Freedom Ring Ser.). (Illus.). 48p. (J). (gr. 3-4). lib. bdg. 22.60 (978-0-7368-1101-9(X) , Bridgestone Bks.) Capstone Pr., Inc.

Landau, Elaine. The Oregon Trail. 2006. 48p. (gr. 3-5). (YA). pap. 6.95 (978-0-516-27903-9(3)); (Illus.). (J). 25.00 (978-0-516-25871-3(0)) Scholastic Library Publishing. (Children's Pr.).

Loeper, John J. Meet the Wards on the Oregon Trail. 1998. (Early American Family Ser.). (Illus.). 64p. (J). (gr. 2-4). lib. bdg. 25.64 (978-0-7614-0844-4(4) , Benchmark Bks.) Cavendish, Marshall Corp.

Oregon Trail. (Exploring the West Ser.). 48p. (YA). 7.95 (978-0-7368-4508-3(9)) Capstone Pr., Inc.

The Oregon Trail, 6 Packs. (On Deck Ser.: Vol. 2). 24p. (gr. 4-5). 35.00 (978-0-7578-5813-0(9)) Rigby Education.

The Oregon Trail. 2003. (Crossing America Ser.). 48p. (gr. 5-8). 5.99 (978-1-56822-654-5(3) , IF6022) School Specialty Publishing.

Thompson, Gare. Our Journey West: The Oregon Trail Adventures of Sarah Marshall. 2003. (gr. 3-6). lib. bdg. 15.30 (978-0-613-67111-8(2)) Tandem Library Bks.

Thompson, Linda. The Oregon Trail. (Expansion of America Ser.). 48p. 2005. (Illus.). (gr. 4-8). 20.95 (978-1-59515-225-1(3)); 2004. pap. 7.95 (978-1-59515-324-1(1)) Rourke Publishing, LLC.

Uschan, Michael V. The Oregon Trail. 2004. (Great Cities of the World Ser.). (Illus.). 48p. (J). (gr. 5 up). pap. 11.95 (978-0-8368-5414-5(4)); lib. bdg. 30.00 (978-0-8368-5386-5(5)) Stevens, Gareth Inc. (World Almanac Library).

OREGON NATIONAL HISTORIC TRAIL—FICTION

Bly, Stephen A. The Buffalo's Last Stand. 2002. (Retta Barre's Oregon Trail Ser.: 2). 111p. pap. 5.99 (978-1-58134-392-2(2)) Crossway Bks.

—The Lost Wagon Train. 2005. (Retta Barre's Oregon Trail Ser.: Vol. 1). 110p. pap. 5.99 (978-1-58134-391-5(4) , Crossway Bibles) Crossway Bks.

Kurtz, Jane. I'm Sorry, Almira Ann. 2001. (978-0-606-22234-1(0)) Tandem Library Bks.

Levine, Ellen. The Journal of Jedediah Barstow: An Emigrant on the Oregon Trail. 2002. (My Name Is America Ser.). (Illus.). 176p. (J). (gr. 4-9). pap. 10.95 (978-0-439-06310-4(8) , Scholastic Pr.) Scholastic, Inc.

Mercati, Cynthia. Wagons Ho! A Diary of the Oregon Trail. Kabel, Larassa, illus. 2000. (Cover-to-Cover Bks.). 56p. (J). pap. (978-0-7891-5039-4(5)); (gr. 1-4). lib. bdg. 16.95 (978-0-7807-9011-7(1)) Perfection Learning Corp.

Plowhead, Ruth Gipson. Lucretia Ann on the Sagebrush Plains. Moore, Agnes Randall, illus. 2004. (Classic Ser.). 358p. (gr. 4-7). pap. 18.95 (978-0-87004-408-3(7)) Caxton Pr.

Schulte, Elaine L. Daniel Colton under Fire. 2001. (Illus.). 137p. (J). (gr. 4-7). pap. 7.49 (978-1-57924-564-1(1)) Jones, Bob Univ. Pr.

Spooner, Michael. Daniel's Walk. rev. ed. 176p. 2004. (J). pap. 7.95 (978-0-8050-7543-4(7)); 2001. (Illus.). (YA). (gr. 7 up). 16.95 (978-0-8050-6750-7(7)) Holt, Henry & Co. (Holt, Henry & Co. Bks. For Young Readers).

Stanley, Diane. Roughing It on the Oregon Trail. Berry, Holly, illus. 2001. (Time-Traveling Twins Ser.: No. 1). 48p. (J). (gr. k-5). pap. 6.99 (978-0-06-449006-1(8) , Harper Trophy) HarperCollins Pubs.

Van Leeuwen, Jean. Papa & the Pioneer Quilt. Bond, Rebecca, illus. 2007. (J). ***(978-1-4287-3972-7(6)*** , Dial) Penguin Group (USA) Inc.

Wilson, Laura. How I Survived the Oregon Trail: The Journal of Jesse Adams. 2006. (Illus.). 37p. (J). (gr. 4-8). reprint ed. pap. 10.00 (978-0-7567-9925-0(2)) DIANE Publishing Co.

—How I Survived the Oregon Trail: The Journal of Jesse Adams. 1999. (Time Travellers Ser.). (Illus.). 38p. (J). (gr. 4-7). pap. 9.95 (978-0-688-17276-3(8)) HarperCollins Pubs.

OREGON TRAIL

see Oregon National Historic Trail

ORGANIC CHEMISTRY

see Chemistry, Organic

ORGANIC FARMING

see Organiculture

ORGANIC GARDENING

see Organiculture

ORGANICULTURE

Dunn-Georgiou, Elisha. Everything You Need to Know about Organic Foods. 2005. (Need to Know Library). (Illus.). 64p. (YA). (gr. 4-6). lib. bdg. 25.25 (978-0-8239-3551-2(5)) Rosen Publishing Group, Inc., The.

Hamilton, Geoff. Organic Gardening. 2004. (Illus.). 288p. (Orig.). pap. 20.00 (978-0-7566-0531-5(8)) Dorling Kindersley Publishing, Inc.

Pupeza, Lori K. Organic Gardens. 2002. (Gardening Ser.). (Illus.). 32p. (J). (gr. k-6). lib. bdg. 22.78 (978-1-57765-748-4(9) , Checkerboard Library) ABDO Publishing Co.

Winckler, Suzanne. Planting the Seed: A Guide to Gardening. 2005. (Illus.). 64p. (gr. 5-12). 25.76 (978-0-8225-0081-0(7)) Lerner Publishing Group.

ORGANIZATION, INTERNATIONAL

see International Organization

ORGANIZATION AND MANAGEMENT

see Management

ORGANIZED CRIME

see Racketeering

ORGANIZED LABOR

see Labor Unions

ORIENTATION

De Capua, Sarah. We Need Directions! (Rookie Read-About Geography Ser.). (Illus.). 32p. (J). (gr. 1-2). 2002. pap. 5.95 (978-0-516-27380-8(9)); 2001. 20.50 (978-0-516-22574-6(X)) Scholastic Library Publishing. (Children's Pr.).

De Capua, Sarah E. Como Nos Orientamos? 2005. (Rookie Reader Espanol Ser.). (SPA., Illus.). 32p. (J). (gr. k-2). 19.50 (978-0-516-24442-6(6) , Children's Pr.) Scholastic Library Publishing.

Decapua, Sarah. We Need Directions. 2002. (gr. k-3). lib. bdg. 14.10 (978-0-613-54387-3(4)) Tandem Library Bks.

Johnson, Tami. Above & Below. 2007. 32p. (J). (978-0-7368-6735-1(X)) Capstone Pr., Inc.

Johnson, Tami. Up & Down. 2007. 32p. (J). ***(978-0-7368-6734-4(1))*** Capstone Pr., Inc.

Murphy. Bug Dance Big Book. 2002. (Illus.). (J). pap. (978-0-7398-6786-0(5)) Steck-Vaughn.

M N O

Murphy, Stuart J. Bug Dance. 2001. (MathStart Ser.). (Illus.). 40p. (J). 15.95 (978-0-06-028910-2(4)); 15.89 (978-0-06-028911-9(2)) HarperCollins Pubs.

—Bug Dance. Santoro, Christopher, illus. 2001. (MathStart Ser.). 40p. (J). pap. 5.99 (978-0-06-446252-5(8) , Harper Trophy) HarperCollins Pubs.

—Bug Dance. 2002. (gr. k-3). lib. bdg. 13.00 (978-0-613-59229-1(8)) Tandem Library Bks.

Nelson, Robin. Staying Clean. 2006. (Pull Ahead Bks.). (Illus.). 32p. (J). (gr. 3-7). 22.60 (978-0-8225-2638-4(7) , Lerner Pubns.) Lerner Publishing Group.

Rivera, Sheila. Above & Below. 2004. (First Step Nonfiction Ser.). (J). pap. (978-0-8225-5355-7(4) , Lerner Pubns.) Lerner Publishing Group.

—Behind & in Front. (First Step Nonfiction Ser.). 2005. (Illus.). 32p. (J). 23.93 (978-0-8225-2639-1(5)); 2004. pap. (978-0-8225-5352-6(X)) Lerner Publishing Group. (Lerner Pubns.).

—Left & Right. 2004. (First Step Nonfiction Ser.). (J). pap. (978-0-8225-5351-9(1) , Lerner Pubns.) Lerner Publishing Group.

Woods, Michael & Woods, Mary B. The History of Medicine. 2006. (Major Inventions Through History Ser.). (Illus.). 56p. (J). (gr. 3-7). 26.60 (978-0-8225-2636-0(0) , Twenty-First Century Bks.) Lerner Publishing Group.

ORIGAMI

see also Paper Work

Araki, Chiyo. Origami Activities for Children. 2002. (Illus.). 64p. pap. 8.95 (978-0-8048-3311-0(7)) Tuttle Publishing.

Arnstein, Bennett Roy. The Saturday Afternoon Public Library Origami Club Manual: Not Just Another Origami Book. 2004. (Illus.). 69p. 11.95 (978-0-9620058-2-4(7)) Arnstein, Bennett.

Biddle, Steve & Biddle, Megumi. Underwater Origami: Underwater Paper Folding for Kids. 2000. (Illus.). 32p. (J). (gr. 4 up). pap. 12.99 (978-0-7641-1446-5(8)) Barron's Educational Series, Inc.

Boonyadhistarn, Thiranut. The Fun & Funky Art of Paper Folding. 2007. (Snap Books). (Illus.). 32p. (J). 25.26 (978-0-7368-6476-3(8)) Capstone Pr., Inc.

Boursin, Didier. Easy Origami: 24 Simple, Easy-to-follow Projects for Beginners to the Art of Origami. 2005. (Illus.). 64p. (J). (gr. 2-7). pap. 9.95 (978-1-55297-939-6(3)) Firefly Bks., Ltd.

—Origami Paper Airplanes. 2001. (Illus.). 64p. (J). (gr. 2-7). 19.95 (978-1-55209-626-0(2)); pap. 9.95 (978-1-55209-616-1(5)) Firefly Bks., Ltd.

—Origami Paper Airplanes. 2001. (gr. 3-6). lib. bdg. 18.75 (978-0-613-78566-2(5)) Tandem Library Bks.

Dare, Sterling. Money Menagerie: A Collection of Wild or Strange Animals. 2004. 15.00 (978-0-9727938-3-4(6)) H&R Magic Bks.

Dover Staff. Metallic Foil Origami Paper. 2001. (Illus.). (gr. 3). pap. 5.95 (978-0-486-41770-7(0)) Dover Pubns., Inc.

Froebel Kan Editorial Group Staff. Origami Fairy Tales Gift Pack, 4 bks. 2004. (Illus.). pap. 19.95 (978-0-89346-941-2(6)) Heian International Publishing, Inc.

Guide to Hawaiian Style Origami for Keiki. 2001. (J). 7.99 (978-0-89610-331-3(5)) Island Heritage Publishing.

Idea Network LA Inc. Origami: 15 Easy & Fun Origami Designs. ed. 2006. (CHI & SPA.). (J). DVD 24.95 (978-0-9773301-0-2(9)) Idea Network LA Inc.

Jackson, Paul. Incredible Action Origami: That Really Works. 2000. (Illus.). 32p. (J). (gr. 3-7). pap. 7.95 (978-0-7373-0516-6(9)) Lowell Hse. Juvenile.

Jackson, Paul & A'Court, Angela. Best Ever Book of Paper Fun & Origami. 2000. (Illus.). 256p. (gr. 4-7). pap. 24.95 (978-0-7548-0244-0(2) , Lorenz Bks.) Anness Publishing GBR. *Dist:* National Bk. Network.

Johnson, Anne Akers. Origami. 88p. (J). 2005. (SPA., Illus.). spiral bd. 19.95 (978-987-1078-26-4(9)); 2004. spiral bd. 19.95 (978-987-1078-15-8(3)) Klutz Latino MEX. *Dist:* Independent Pubs. Group.

Kasahara, Kunihiko. Amazing Origami. 2002. (Illus.). 64p. pap. 9.95 (978-0-8069-7420-0(6)) Sterling Publishing Co., Inc.

Kneissler, Irmgard. Super Simple Origami. 2001. (Illus.). 64p. (gr. 4-7). pap. 6.95 (978-0-8069-6525-3(8)) Sterling Publishing Co., Inc.

—Super Simple Origami. 2001. (Illus.). (J). (978-0-606-21474-2(7)) Tandem Library Bks.

Krier, Ann Kristen. Totally Cool Origami Animals. 2007. (Illus.). 96p. (J). (gr. 5-7). 19.95 (978-1-4027-2448-0(9)) Sterling Publishing Co., Inc.

LaFosse, Michael. Making Basic Origami Shapes Step by Step. Reiman, Cindy, photos by. 2002. (Kid's Guide to Origami Ser.). (Illus.). 24p. (J). (gr. 1-4). lib. bdg. 21.25 (978-0-8239-5872-6(8) , PowerKids Pr.) Rosen Publishing Group, Inc., The.

—Making Origami Animals Step by Step. 2002. (Kid's Guide to Origami Ser.). (Illus.). 24p. (J). lib. bdg. 21.25 (978-0-8239-5877-1(9) , PowerKids Pr.) Rosen Publishing Group, Inc., The.

—Making Origami Birds Step by Step. 2004. (Kid's Guide to Origami Ser.). (Illus.). 24p. (J). lib. bdg. 21.25 (978-0-8239-6702-5(6) , PowerKids Pr.) Rosen Publishing Group, Inc., The.

—Making Origami Cards Step by Step. 2004. (Kid's Guide to Origami Ser.). (Illus.). 24p. (J). lib. bdg. 21.25 (978-0-8239-6701-8(8) , PowerKids Pr.) Rosen Publishing Group, Inc., The.

—Making Origami Christmas Decorations Step by Step. LaFosse, Michael, illus. 2002. (Kid's Guide to Origami Ser.). (Illus.). 24p. (J). (gr. 2-4). lib. bdg. 21.25 (978-0-8239-5874-0(4) , PowerKids Pr.) Rosen Publishing Group, Inc., The.

—Making Origami Fish Step by Step. Reiman, Cindy, photos by. 2002. (Kid's Guide to Origami Ser.). (Illus.). 24p. (J). (gr. 1-4). lib. bdg. 21.25 (978-0-8239-5873-3(6) , PowerKids Pr.) Rosen Publishing Group, Inc., The.

—Making Origami Masks Step by Step. 2004. (Kid's Guide to Origami Ser.). (Illus.). 24p. (J). lib. bdg. 21.25 (978-0-8239-6703-2(4) , PowerKids Pr.) Rosen Publishing Group, Inc., The.

—Making Origami Paper Airplanes Step by Step. 2004. (Kid's Guide to Origami Ser.). (Illus.). 24p. (J). lib. bdg. 21.25 (978-0-8239-6700-1(X) , PowerKids Pr.) Rosen Publishing Group, Inc., The.

—Making Origami Puzzles Step by Step. 2004. (Kid's Guide to Origami Ser.). (Illus.). 24p. (J). lib. bdg. 21.25 (978-0-8239-6704-9(2) , PowerKids Pr.) Rosen Publishing Group, Inc., The.

—Making Origami Science Experiments Step by Step. 2004. (Kid's Guide to Origami Ser.). (Illus.). 24p. (J). lib. bdg. 21.25 (978-0-8239-6705-6(0) , PowerKids Pr.) Rosen Publishing Group, Inc., The.

—Making Origami Toys Step by Step. 2002. (Kid's Guide to Origami Ser.). (Illus.). 24p. (J). lib. bdg. 21.25 (978-0-8239-5876-4(0) , PowerKids Pr.) Rosen Publishing Group, Inc., The.

—Making Origami Vehicles Step by Step. 2002. (Kid's Guide to Origami Ser.). (Illus.). 24p. (J). lib. bdg. 21.25 (978-0-8239-5875-7(2) , PowerKids Pr.) Rosen Publishing Group, Inc., The.

—Origami Activities: Asian Arts & Crafts for Creatve Kids. 2003. (Asian Arts & Crafts for Creative Kids Ser.). (Illus.). 64p. (gr. 2-6). 12.95 (978-0-8048-3497-1(0)) Tuttle Publishing.

Linde, Barbara M. Origami: Identifying Right Angles in Geometric Figures. 2004. (PowerMath Ser.). (Illus.). 24p. (J). lib. bdg. (978-0-8239-8882-2(1)); lib. bdg. 21.25 (978-0-8239-8968-3(2)) Rosen Publishing Group, Inc., The. (PowerKids Pr.).

Montroll, John. Dollar Bill Origami. 2003. (Illus.). 120p. (YA). per. 14.94 net. (978-1-877656-17-0(8)) Antroll Publishing Co.

Nguyen, Duy. Jungle Animal Origami. 2004. (Illus.). 96p. (J). pap. 9.95 (978-1-4027-1764-2(4)) Sterling Publishing Co., Inc.

—Origami Birds. 2006. (Illus.). 96p. 19.95 (978-1-4027-1932-5(9)) Sterling Publishing Co., Inc.

—Super-Easy Origami. 2005. (Illus.). 72p. 14.95 (978-1-4027-2288-2(5)) Sterling Publishing Co., Inc.

Nishida, Ryoko. Pokemon Origami. Aoyama, Minami, illus. (Pokemon Ser.). 80p. (YA). Vol. 1. 1999. (gr. 4-7). pap. 8.95 (978-1-56931-391-6(1)); Vol. 2. 2000. (ps-3). pap. 8.95 (978-1-56931-415-9(2)) Viz Media.

O'Brien, Eileen & Needham, Kate. Origami Pack. 2004. (Activity Kits Ser.). 24p. (J). act. bk. ed. 14.95 (978-0-7945-0460-1(4)) EDC Publishing.

Olexiewicz, Charlene. Super More Origami Crafts. 2000. (Fifty Nifty Ser.). (Illus.). 80p. (J). (gr. 3-7). pap. 6.95 (978-0-7373-0481-7(2) , 04812W, Roxbury Park Juvenile) Lowell Hse. Juvenile.

Petty, David. Origami A-B-C. Forrester, Paul, photos by. 2006. (Illus.). 128p. (gr. 5-9). 24.95 (978-1-4027-3563-9(4)) Sterling Publishing Co., Inc.

Planet Origami. 1999. (Illus.). 32p. (J). (gr. 3 up). lib. bdg. 17.95 (978-1-56674-268-9(4)) Forest Hse. Publishing Co., Inc.

Robinson, Nick. Origami Adventures. 2006. (Origami Adventures Ser.). (Illus.). 48p. (J). 12.99 (978-0-7641-5969-5(0)) Barron's Educational Series, Inc.

—Origami Adventures: Dinosaurs. 2006. (Origami Adventures Ser.). (Illus.). 48p. (J). 12.99 (978-0-7641-5970-1(4)) Barron's Educational Series, Inc.

—Super Quick Origami Animals. 2002. (Illus.). 80p. pap. 12.95 (978-0-8069-7729-4(9)) Sterling Publishing Co., Inc.

Rosado, Raul. Hands-On Origami. 1998. (Illus.). 120p. (YA). (gr. 3 up). 10.95 (978-0-9664101-0-5(6)) Rosado Arts, Inc.

Sarasas, Claude. ABCs of Origami: Paper Folding for Children. 2002. (gr. k-3). lib. bdg. 12.95 (978-0-613-75502-3(2)) Tandem Library Bks.

—ABCs of Origami: Paper Folding for Children. 2nd ed. 2002. (JPN & ENG., Illus.). 32p. pap. 4.95 (978-0-8048-3307-3(9)) Tuttle Publishing.

Saunders, Mary Chloe Schoolcraft. Spread Your Wings & Fly: An Origami Fold & Tell. Mihelich, Carla McGregor, illus. 2001. 48p. 16.95 (978-1-879181-75-5(4)) Bear & Co.

Smith, Soonboke. Origami. 2004. (For the First Time Ser.). (Illus.). 112p. (J). pap. 9.95 (978-1-4027-1767-3(9)) Sterling Publishing Co., Inc.

Smolinski, Jill. The First Timers Guide to Origami. Yamamoto, Neal, illus. 2000. (First-Timers Guides). 80p. (J). (gr. 1-4). pap. 8.95 (978-0-7373-0370-4(0) , 03700W, Roxbury Park Juvenile) Lowell Hse. Juvenile.

—Girls Wanna Have Fun: Friendship Origami. 1999. (Girls Wanna Have Fun! Ser.). (Illus.). 64p. (J). (gr. 3-7). pap. 9.95 (978-0-7373-0071-0(X) , 0071XW) McGraw-Hill/Contemporary.

—Holiday Origami. Fraser, Mary Ann, illus. 2nd rev. ed. 1999. (Origami Ser.). 48p. (gr. 3-7). pap. 8.95 (978-0-7373-0094-9(9) , 9780737300949) McGraw-Hill Cos., The.

—Holiday Origami. 1999. (gr. 3-6). lib. bdg. 17.60 (978-0-613-73742-5(3)) Tandem Library Bks.

—50 Nifty Super Animal Origami Crafts. Olexiewicz, Charlene, illus. 1998. (Fifty Nifty Super Ser.). 80p. (J). (gr. 3-7). pap. 6.95 (978-1-56565-928-5(7) , 09287W) Lowell Hse. Juvenile.

Stevens, Clive. Origami. (Step-by-Step Ser.). (Illus.). 32p. 2003. pap. 7.95 (978-1-4034-0718-4(5)); 2002. (J). (gr. 3-5). lib. bdg. 25.64 (978-1-4034-0699-6(5)) Heinemann Library.

—Origami. 2002. (Step-by-Step Children's Crafts Ser.). (Illus.). 32p. pap. 7.95 (978-1-903975-35-0(2) , 5352) Search Pr., Ltd. GBR. *Dist:* Independent Pubs. Group.

Takagi, Satoshi. Origami for Playtime. 2004. (Illus.). 158p. pap. 12.95 (978-4-88996-131-7(3)) Japan Pubn. Trading Co. JPN. *Dist:* Oxford Univ. Pr., Inc.

Walker, Mar. Inverse Origami: The Art of Unfolding. 1998. (Illus.). 52p. (YA). 6.00 (978-0-9664864-0-7(4) , IO-01) Out-of-the-Mist Pr.

ORIGIN OF HUMAN BEINGS

see Human Beings—Origin

ORIGIN OF SPECIES

see Evolution

ORNAMENT

see Decoration and Ornament

ORNAMENTAL ALPHABETS

see Lettering

ORNAMENTAL DESIGN

see Design, Decorative

ORNITHOLOGY

see Birds

ORPHANAGES

Benge, Janet & Benge, Geoff. Lillian Trasher: The Greatest Wonder in Egypt. 2003. (Christian Heroes, Then & Now Ser.). 190p. (J). pap. 8.99 (978-1-57658-305-0(8)) YWAM Publishing.

Jocelyn, Marthe. A Home for Foundlings. 2005. (Lord Museum Book Ser.). (Illus.). 120p. (J). pap. 16.95 (978-0-88776-709-8(5)) Tundra Bks., Inc./Livres Toundra, Inc. CAN. *Dist:* Random Hse., Inc.

Reef, Catherine. Alone in the World: Orphans & Orphanages in America. 2005. (Illus.). 144p. (J). (gr. 5-9). 18.00 (978-0-618-35670-6(3) , Clarion Bks.) Houghton Mifflin Co. Trade & Reference Div.

ORPHANAGES—FICTION

Bundschuh, Rick & Hamilton, Bethany. Soul Surfer Crunch. 2007. (Soul Surfer#8482; Ser.). 144p. (J). pap. 6.99 (978-0-310-71225-1(4)) Zonderkidz.

Byng, Georgia. Molly Moon y el Increible Libro. 2003. (SPA.). 349p. (J). 18.99 (978-84-348-9076-3(3)) SM Ediciones ESP. *Dist:* Lectorum Pubns., Inc.

Daringer, Helen Fern. Adopted Jane. Seredy, Kate, illus. 2002. 224p. (gr. 3-6). reprint ed. 12.95 (978-0-9714612-4-6(4)) Green Mansion Pr. LLC.

Doty, Kathryn Adams. Wild Orphan. 2006. 144p. pap. 14.95 (978-1-889020-20-4(6)) Edinborough Pr.

Levine, Gail Carson. Dave at Night. 2001. 304p. (J). (gr. 3-7). reprint ed. pap. 6.99 (978-0-06-440747-2(0) , Harper Trophy) HarperCollins Pubs.

—Dave at Night. unabr. ed. 2004. 278p. (J). (gr. 4-7). pap. 38.00 incl. audio (978-0-8072-8379-0(7) , YA174SP, Listening Library) Random Hse. Audio Publishing Group.

—Dave at Night. 1999. (YA). pap., stu. ed. 69.95 incl. audio (978-0-7887-3794-7(5) , 41038) Recorded Bks., LLC.

Mandeville, Terry M. Just Waiting for My Family. l.t. ed. 2005. (Illus.). 52p. (J). 14.95 (978-0-9762475-0-0(X)) Mandeville, Terry M.

Marino, Jan. The Mona Lisa of Salem Street. 1999. 155p. (J). (gr. 3-6). reprint ed. 15.00 (978-0-7881-6635-8(2)) DIANE Publishing Co.

Noyes, Deborah. When I Met the Wolf Girls. Hall, August, illus. 2007. (J). (***978-1-4287-4686-2(2)***) Houghton Mifflin Co.

Pitcher, Caroline. Sky Shifter. 2005. 160p. (J). pap. 8.99 (***978-1-4052-0850-5(3)***) Egmont Bks., Ltd. GBR. *Dist:* Independent Pubs. Group.

Pollack, P., et al. Bloo Done It. 2007. (Foster's Home for Imaginary Friends Ser.: No. 3). 48p. (J). pap. 3.99 (978-0-439-89948-2(6)) Scholastic, Inc.

Roesti, Delores. Mareena Maree Mulligan & the Flying Wheel Chair: Book 1: School Days. 2007. 81p. pap. 9.95 (***978-0-7414-4048-8(2)***) Infinity Publishing.

Ruby, Laura. The Wall & the Wing. 2007. 352p. (J). (gr. 5 up). pap. 6.99 (***978-0-06-075257-6(2)*** , Eos) HarperCollins Pubs.

Ryan, Pam Muñoz. Riding Freedom. Selznick, Brian, illus. 2007. 144p. (J). (gr. 3-7). mass mkt. 4.99 (978-0-439-08796-4(1) , Scholastic Paperbacks) Scholastic, Inc.

—Riding Freedom. Selznick, Brian, illus. 1999. 138p. per. 11.64 (978-0-606-17445-9(1)) Tandem Library Bks.

Tripp, Valerie. Nellie's Promise. 2004. (American Girl Ser.). (Illus.). 96p. (J). 12.95 (978-1-58485-893-5(1)) American Girl Publishing, Inc.

—Nellie's Promise. Andreasen, Dan, illus. 2004. (American Girl Ser.). 96p. (gr. 2 up). pap. 6.95 (978-1-58485-890-4(7)) American Girl Publishing, Inc.

Urasawa, Naoki. Naoki Urasawa's Monster, Vol. 7. 2007. (Naoki Urasawa's Monster Ser.). 216p. (YA). pap. 9.99 (978-1-4215-0500-8(2)) Viz Media.

ORPHANS

Flanagan, Alice K. The Orphan Trains. 2006. (We the People Ser.). (Illus.). 48p. (J). (gr. 4-6). 23.93 (978-0-7565-1635-2(8)) Compass Point Bks.

Littlefield, Holly. Children of the Orphan Trains. 2005. (Picture the American Past Ser.). (Illus.). 48p. (gr. 2-5). lib. bdg. 22.60 (978-1-57505-466-7(3)) Lerner Publishing Group.

Lynette, Rachel. Ana Dodson: Advocate for Peruvian Orphanages. 2007. (Young Heroes Ser.). (Illus.). 64p. (J). (gr. 4-8). 24.95 (***978-0-7377-3865-0(0)*** , Kidhaven) Thomson Gale.

My Life Changed: A Journal for Coping with Loss & Grief. 2004. 96p. pap. 4.95 (978-1-57542-139-1(9)) Free Spirit Publishing, Inc.

Naidoo, Beverly, intro. Making It Home: Real-Life Stories from Children Forced to Flee. 2005. (Illus.). 128p. (J). (gr. 5-7). pap. 6.99 (978-0-14-240455-3(1) , Puffin) Penguin Group (USA) Inc.

Pedlar, Paige. Who Will Cuddle Them When They Sleep? 2004. 24p. (J). (978-1-55306-790-0(8)) Essence Publishing.

Reef, Catherine. Alone in the World: Orphans & Orphanages in America. 2005. (Illus.). 144p. (J). (gr. 5-9). 18.00 (978-0-618-35670-6(3) , Clarion Bks.) Houghton Mifflin Co. Trade & Reference Div.

Ruckel, Izidor. Abandoned for Life: The Incredible Story of One Romanian Orphan, Hidden from the World. His Life. His Words. Bramsch, Joan, ed. 2003. (YA). mass mkt. 19.97 (978-0-934334-13-6(7)) JB Information Station.

Stevens, Dylan. Wooded Sanctuary. 2004. 136p. (YA). pap. 13.95 (978-0-595-31093-7(1)) iUniverse, Inc.

Uschan, Michael V. Matt Dalio: China Care Founder. 2007. (Young Heroes Ser.). (Illus.). 64p. (J). (gr. 4-8). 27.45 (***978-0-7377-3670-0(4)*** , Kidhaven) Thomson Gale.

Warren, Andrea. Escape from Saigon: How a Vietnam War Orphan Became an American Boy. 2004. (Illus.). 128p. (J). 17.00 (978-0-374-32224-3(4) , Nelanie Kroupa Bks.) Farrar, Straus & Giroux.

—The Orphan Train Rider: One Boy's True Story. 1998. (Illus.). 80p. (J). (gr. 4-6). pap. 8.95 (978-0-395-91362-8(4)) Houghton Mifflin Co. Trade & Reference Div.

—We Rode the Orphan Trains. (Illus.). 144p. (J). (gr. 4-6). 2001. tchr. ed. 18.00 (978-0-618-11712-3(1)); 2004. reprint ed. pap. 9.95 (978-0-618-43235-6(3)) Houghton Mifflin Co. Trade & Reference Div.

ORPHANS—FICTION

A. B. Publishing Staff. Adopting an Orphan. 1998. (J). (gr. 4-7). pap. 6.95 (978-1-881545-87-3(3)) A B Publishing.

Abbott, Tony. Kringle. Call, Greg, illus. 2005. 304p. (J). (gr. 4-7). pap. 14.99 (978-0-439-74942-8(5) , Scholastic Pr.) Scholastic, Inc.

Accola, Juli. The Adventures of Amanda Humperdink. 2002. (Illus.). 148p. (J). per. (978-1-888223-39-2(1)) McMillen Publishing.

Adams, W. Royce. Jay. 2005. viii, 115p. (YA). pap. (***978-1-58832-120-6(7)***) Unlimited Publishing LLC.

Aguila, Priscilla. As Different As Can Be. 2006. 48p. pap. 17.96 (978-1-4116-5609-3(1)) Lulu.com.

Ahlberg, Allan. My Brother's Ghost. l.t. ed. 2005. (Illus.). 64p. (J). pap. (978-0-7540-6181-6(7) , CLP 372) BBC Audio.

Aiken, Joan. Go Saddle the Sea. 2007. (Illus.). 384p. (YA). pap. 6.95 (978-0-15-206064-0(2)) Harcourt Trade Pubs.

Alcott, Louisa May. Eight Cousins. 2000. 252p. (J). pap. 9.95 (978-0-594-06118-2(0)) 1873 Pr.

—Eight Cousins. 2005. 29.95 (978-1-4218-0976-2(1) , 1st World Library - Literary Society) 1st World Publishing, Inc.

—Juventud. 2002. Tr. of Eight Cousins. (SPA.). (J). 6.95 (978-84-243-0117-0(X)) Publicaciones Fher, S.A. ESP. *Dist:* AIMS International Bks., Inc.

Alexander, Lloyd. The Book of Three. 2006. (Chronicles of Prydain Ser.: Bk. 1). 224p. (J). (gr. 3-7). pap. 5.99 (978-0-8050-8048-3(1) , Holt, Henry & Co. Bks. For Young Readers) Holt, Henry & Co.

Alger, Horatio. Cast upon the Breakers. unabr. ed. 2002. (Polyglot Press Alger Ser.). (Illus.). (J). pap. 17.95 (978-1-931927-81-9(2)) Polyglot Pr., Inc.

—Facing the World. 2006. pap. (***978-1-4250-2212-9(X)***) Assistedreadingbooks.com Inc.

—Facing the World. 2006. pap. (***978-1-4065-0704-1(0)***) Dodo Pr.

—Frank Fowler, the Cash Boy. reprint ed. pap. 79.00 (978-1-4047-3558-3(5)) Classic Textbooks.

—Joe's Luck: Or, Always Wide Awake. 2007. 172p. pap. 11.99 (***978-1-4264-6426-3(6)***); 2006. 176p. pap. 13.99 (978-1-4264-0883-0(8)); 2007. 186p. pap. 14.99 (***978-1-4264-6500-0(9)***); 2006. 170p. pap. 16.99 (978-1-4264-0864-9(1)) BiblioBazaar.

—Joe's Luck: Or, Always Wide Awake. 2006. pap. (***978-1-4065-0713-3(X)***) Dodo Pr.

—Paul Prescott's Charge: A Story for Boys. 2006. pap. (***978-1-4250-2995-1(7)***) Assistedreadingbooks.com Inc.

—Paul Prescott's Charge: A Story for Boys. unabr. ed. 2002. (Polyglot Press Alger Ser.). (Illus.). (J). pap. 17.95 (978-1-4115-0034-1(2)) Polyglot Pr., Inc.

Almond, David. Heaven Eyes. 2002. 256p. (YA). (gr. 5). mass mkt. 5.99 (978-0-440-22910-0(3) , Laurel Leaf) Random Hse. Children's Bks.

—Heaven Eyes. 2002. 233p. (J). (gr. k-17). lib. bdg. 13.55 (978-0-613-72281-0(7)) Tandem Library Bks.

—Heaven Eyes. l.t. ed. 2001. 263p. (J). 24.95 (978-0-7862-3696-1(5)) Thorndike Pr.

Andrews, V. C. Orphans. 2000. (gr. 7-12). lib. bdg. 16.45 (978-0-613-33602-4(X)) Tandem Library Bks.

Askounis, Christina. The Dream of the Stone. 2007. 304p. (YA). 17.99 (978-1-4169-3568-1(1) , Atheneum) Simon & Schuster Children's Publishing.

Avi. Crispin: La Cruz de Plomo. 2004. Tr. of Crispin: The Cross of Lead. (SPA., Illus.). (YA). pap. 7.99 (978-84-348-9601-7(X)) SM Ediciones ESP. *Dist:* Lectorum Pubns., Inc.

—Crispin: The Cross of Lead. 2002. 256p. (gr. 5-9). 16.49 (978-0-7868-2647-6(9)) Disney Pr.

—Crispin: The Cross of Lead. 2002. (Illus.). 272p. (gr. 5-9). 15.99 (978-0-7868-0828-1(4)) Hyperion Bks. for Children.

—Crispin: The Cross of Lead. 2004. 320p. (J). (gr. 3-7). reprint ed. pap. 6.99 (978-0-7868-1658-3(9)) Hyperion Paperbacks for Children.

—Crispin: The Cross of Lead. 2004. (gr. 3-6). lib. bdg. 15.30 (978-0-613-74965-7(0)) Tandem Library Bks.

—Crispin: The Cross of Lead. 2003. 303p. (J). 25.95 (978-0-7862-5501-6(3)) Thorndike Pr.

—Night Journeys. 2000. (Illus.). 160p. (J). (gr. 3-7). pap. 5.99 (978-0-380-73242-5(4) , Harper Trophy) HarperCollins Pubs.

—Night Journeys. 2000. (978-0-606-17978-2(X)); (gr. 5-8). lib. bdg. 14.15 (978-0-613-22094-1(3)) Tandem Library Bks.

Aviles, Donna Nordmark. Fly Little Bird, Fly! 2004. 80p. per. 10.00 (978-1-932852-07-3(7)) Wasteland Pr.

Ayres, Katherine. Under Copp's Hill. 2000. (American Girl Collection). (Illus.). (J). (978-0-606-20963-2(8)) Tandem Library Bks.

Bajoria, Paul. The Printer's Devil. 2007. 400p. (J). (gr. 4-8). pap. 6.99 (978-0-316-10678-8(X)) Little Brown & Co.

Balmes, Kathy. Thunder on the Sierra. Catapano, Vicki, illus. 2001. (Adventures in America Ser.). 96p. (J). (gr. 3-7). lib. bdg. 14.95 (978-1-893110-10-6(9)) Silver Moon Pr.

Banks, Kimberly E. Mask Man. Wroe, Dameon K., ed. 2003. 57p. (YA). pap. 9.99 (978-0-9740685-0-3(0)) Another Ep Publishing.

Barnard, Victoria. Joe on Holiday. Barnard, Victoria & Stephens, Andrew, illus. 2005. 18p. (J). (gr. k-4). reprint ed. 19.00 (978-0-7567-8531-4(6)) DIANE Publishing Co.

Barry, Dave & Pearson, Ridley. Peter & the Starcatchers. Call, Greg, illus. 2006. 480p. (gr. 5-17). reprint ed. pap. 7.99 (978-0-7868-4907-9(X) , Disney Editions) Disney Pr.

—Peter & the Starcatchers. 2004. 464p. (gr. 5-17). 17.99 (978-0-7868-5445-5(6)) Hyperion Bks. for Children.

Bateman, Colin. Bring Me the Head of Oliver Plunkett. 2005. 272p. (gr. 4-7). (J). 15.95 (978-0-385-73245-1(7)); lib. bdg. 17.99 (978-0-385-90269-4(7)) Random Hse. Children's Bks. (Delacorte Bks. for Young Readers).

Bath, K. P. The Secret of Castle Cant. 2006. 304p. (J). (gr. 3-7). reprint ed. pap. 6.99 (978-0-316-05991-6(9)) Little Brown & Co.

Beake, Lesley. Home Now. Littlewood, Karin, illus. 2007. 32p. (J). (gr. k-3). 16.95 (978-1-58089-162-2(4)); pap. 6.95 (*978-1-58089-163-9(2)*) Charlesbridge Publishing, Inc.

Begamudre, Ven. Phantom Queen. 2003. (gr. 7-12). lib. bdg. 19.90 (978-0-613-78476-4(6)) Tandem Library Bks.

Beliveau, Beverly Hicks. Noelle's Wish. 2003. (Illus.). 27p. pap. 7.95 (978-0-533-14205-7(9)) Vantage Pr., Inc.

Bemelmans, Ludwig. Madeline. 2007. (Puffin Storytime Ser.). 48p. (J). (ps). pap. 9.99 (978-0-14-240871-1(9) , Puffin) Penguin Group (USA) Inc.

—Madeline & the Bad Hat. Bemelmans, Ludwig, illus. 2000. (Madeline Ser.). (Illus.). 64p. (J). (ps-3). pap. 7.99 (978-0-14-056648-2(1) , Viking Juvenile) Penguin Group (USA) Inc.

—Madeline & the Bad Hat. Bemelmans, Ludwig, illus. 2000. (Madeline Ser.). (Illus.). (J). (ps-3). (978-0-606-18427-4(9)) Tandem Library Bks.

—Madeline & the Gypsies. Bemelmans, Ludwig, illus. 2000. (Madeline Ser.). (Illus.). 64p. (J). (ps-3). pap. 7.99 (978-0-14-056647-5(3) , Viking Juvenile) Penguin Group (USA) Inc.

—Madeline & the Gypsies. 2000. (gr. k-3). lib. bdg. 15.30 (978-0-8085-2352-9(X)) Tandem Library Bks.

—Madeline & the Gypsies. Bemelmans, Ludwig, illus. 2000. (Madeline Ser.). (Illus.). (J). (ps-3). (978-0-606-18428-1(7)) Tandem Library Bks.

—Madeline in America & Other Holiday Tales. Bemelmans, Ludwig, illus. 2002. (Madeline Ser.). (Illus.). (J). 18.68 (978-0-7587-4186-8(3)) Book Wholesalers, Inc.

—Madeline in America & Other Holiday Tales. Marciano, John Bemelmans, illus. 1999. (Madeline Ser.). (J). (ps-3). 112p. pap. 19.95 (978-0-590-03910-9(5) , Levine, Arthur A. Bks.); pap. 125.00 (978-0-439-09633-1(2)) Scholastic, Inc.

—Madeline in London. Bemelmans, Ludwig, illus. 2002. (Madeline Ser.). (Illus.). (J). 14.04 (978-0-7587-5002-0(1)) Book Wholesalers, Inc.

—Madeline in London. Bemelmans, Ludwig, illus. deluxe ed. 2000. (Madeline Ser.). (Illus.). 64p. (J). (ps-3). pap. 7.99 (978-0-14-056649-9(X) , Viking Juvenile) Penguin Group (USA) Inc.

—Madeline in London. 2000. (gr. k-3). lib. bdg. 15.30 (978-0-8085-2353-6(8)) Tandem Library Bks.

—Madeline in London. Bemelmans, Ludwig, illus. 2000. (Madeline Ser.). (Illus.). (J). (ps-3). (978-0-606-18429-8(5)) Tandem Library Bks.

—Madeline's Christmas. Bemelmans, Ludwig, illus. 2002. (Madeline Ser.). (Illus.). (J). 14.04 (978-0-7587-5650-3(X)) Book Wholesalers, Inc.

—Madeline's Christmas. Bemelmans, Ludwig, illus. deluxe ed. 2000. (Madeline Ser.). (Illus.). 32p. (J). (ps-3). pap. 7.99 (978-0-14-056650-5(3) , Viking Juvenile) Penguin Group (USA) Inc.

—Madeline's Christmas. 1999. (ps-2). lib. bdg. 15.30 (978-0-613-30014-8(9)) Tandem Library Bks.

—Madeline's Rescue. Bemelmans, Ludwig, illus. 2000. (Madeline Ser.). (Illus.). 64p. (J). (ps-3). pap. 7.99 (978-0-14-056651-2(1) , Viking Juvenile) Penguin Group (USA) Inc.

Bemelmans, Ludwig & Wheeler, Jody. Madeline's Birthday. 1999. (Madeline Ser.). (Illus.). 16p. (J). (ps-3). act. bk. ed. 7.99 (978-0-670-88767-5(6) , Viking Juvenile) Penguin Group (USA) Inc.

Bemelsman, Ludwig. Madeleine. 2000. (Adventures of Madeleine Ser.). (FRE.). (J). pap. 14.95 (978-2-211-02156-2(5)) Archimede Editions FRA. *Dist:* Distribooks, Inc.

Berkeley, Jon. The Palace of Laughter: The Wednesday Tales No. 1. Dorman, Brandon, illus. (J). 2007. 464p. (gr. 3-7). pap. 7.99 (*978-0-06-075509-6(1)* , Harper Trophy); 2006. 448p. 16.99 (978-0-06-075507-2(5) , Julie Andrews Collection); 2006. 448p. lib. bdg. 17.89 (978-0-06-075508-9(3) , Julie Andrews Collection) HarperCollins Pubs.

—The Tiger's Egg. Dorman, Brandon, illus. 2007. 416p. (J). (gr. 3-7). lib. bdg. 17.89 (*978-0-06-075511-9(3)*); (Wednesday Tales Ser.: No. 2). 16.99 (*978-0-06-075510-2(5)*) HarperCollins Pubs. (Julie Andrews Collection).

Besser, Kenneth/R. Arnie Carver & the Plague of Demeverde. 2007. (Illus.). x, 338p. (J). (*978-1-934316-02-3(4)*) RTMC Organization, LLC.

Bethers, Linda, retold by. Christmas Oranges. 2004. 13p. pap. 3.95 (978-1-57734-546-6(0) , 01114387) Covenant Communications, Inc.

Billingsley, Franny. The Folk Keeper. unabr. ed. 2004. 176p. (J). (gr. 5-9). pap. 36.00 incl. audio (978-0-8072-0662-1(8) , Listening Library) Random Hse. Audio Publishing Group.

—The Folk Keeper. Gore, Leonid, illus. 2001. 176p. (J). pap. 4.99 (978-0-689-84461-4(1) , Aladdin) Simon & Schuster Children's Publishing.

—The Folk Keeper. 2001. 11.64 (978-0-606-22111-5(5)) Tandem Library Bks.

—The Folk Keeper. l.t. ed. 2000. 224p. (YA). (gr. 5-9). 20.95 (978-0-7862-2461-6(4)) Thorndike Pr.

Billingsley, Franny & Gore, Leonid. The Folk Keeper. 1999. (Illus.). 176p. (YA). (gr. 5-9). 16.95 (978-0-689-82876-8(4) , Atheneum) Simon & Schuster Children's Publishing.

Blake, Heather Lynn. Anne's Quest: The Wishing Stone. 2005. 153p. pap. 19.95 (978-1-4137-5749-1(9)) PublishAmerica, Inc.

Bodett, Tom, reader. Saving Sweetness. 2005. (Live Oak Readalong Ser.). (Illus.). (J). pap. 16.95 incl. audio (978-0-87499-898-6(0)) BBC Audiobooks America.

—Saving Sweetness. 2002. (Illus.). (J). pap., tchr.'s planning gde. ed. 37.95 incl. audio (978-0-87499-900-6(6)); 25.95 incl. audio (978-0-87499-899-3(9)) Live Oak Media.

Bouani, Jennifer. Future Business Leaders' Series: Tyler & His Solve-a-matic Machine. Shelley, Jennifer, ed. Smalley, Guy, illus. 2006. 128p. (J). per. 6.99 (978-0-9779265-0-3(8)) Bouje Publishing, LLC.

Bradley, Kimberly Brubaker. Ruthie's Gift. 1999. (978-0-606-17476-3(1)); (gr. 3-6). lib. bdg. 12.40 (978-0-613-22805-3(7)) Tandem Library Bks.

Brandis, Marianne. The Quarter-Pie Window. 2003. (gr. 5-8). lib. bdg. 18.75 (978-0-613-77299-0(7)) Tandem Library Bks.

Bredsdorff, Bodil. The Crow-Girl: The Children of Crow Cove. Ingwersen, Faith, tr. from DAN. 160p. (J). 2004. (Illus.). 16.00 (978-0-374-31247-3(8)); 2006. reprint ed. pap. 5.95 (978-0-374-40003-3(2)) Farrar, Straus & Giroux. (Farrar, Straus & Giroux (BYR)).

Brewer, Heather. The Chronicles of Vladimir Tod: Eighth Grade Bites. 2008. 288p. (J). (gr. 4-6). pap. 7.99 (*978-0-14-241187-2(6)* , Puffin) Penguin Group (USA) Inc.

Brontë, Charlotte & Larkin, Rochelle. Jane Eyre. Marcos, Pablo, illus. 2005. (Great Illustrated Classics Ser.). 240p. (J). (gr. 3-8). 21.35 (978-1-59679-243-2(4) , ABDO & Daughters) ABDO Publishing Co.

Brooke, Peggy. Jake's Orphan. 2001. 11.64 (978-0-606-22137-5(9)) Tandem Library Bks.

Brouwer, Sigmund. Cobra Threat: Football. 2007. (Orca Sports Ser.). 176p. (YA). (gr. 5 up). pap. (*978-1-55143-725-5(2)*) Orca Bk. Pubs.

Brown, Brian & Melrose, Andrew. The Storykeepers. 2000. (Storykeepers' Ser.). 128p. pap., tchr. ed. 26.99 (978-0-310-23674-0(6)) Zonderkidz.

Bruchac, Joseph. Whisper in the Dark. Comport, Sally Wern, illus. 2005. 192p. (J). (gr. 5 up). 15.99 (978-0-06-058087-2(9)); lib. bdg. 16.89 (978-0-06-058088-9(7)) HarperCollins Pubs.

Buckley, Michael. The Fairy Tale Detectives. Ferguson, Peter, illus. 2007. (Sisters Grimm Ser.: Bk. 1). 312p. (J). (gr. 2-8). pap. 5.95 (*978-0-8109-9322-8(8)* , Amulet Bks.) Abrams, Harry N. , Inc.

Buckley, Michael. The Problem Child. Ferguson, Peter, illus. 2006. (Sisters Grimm Ser.: Bk. 3). 320p. (J). (gr. 3-7). 14.95 (978-0-8109-4914-0(8) , Amulet Bks.) Abrams, Harry N. , Inc.

Bunce, Elizabeth. A Curse Dark As Gold. 2008. 400p. (J). pap. 17.99 (*978-0-439-89576-7(6)* , Levine, Arthur A. Bks.) Scholastic, Inc.

Bunney, Ronald. No One Owns Me. 2004. (Illus.). 256p. (YA). pap. 13.50 (978-1-920731-86-1(5)) Fremantle Pr. AUS. *Dist:* International Specialized Bk. Services.

Bunting, Eve. Train to Somewhere. 2002. (Illus.). (J). 14.43 (978-0-7587-3856-1(0)) Book Wholesalers, Inc.

—Train to Somewhere. Himler, Ronald, illus. 2000. 32p. (J). (gr. k-3). 6.95 (978-0-618-04031-5(5) , Clarion Bks.) Houghton Mifflin Co. Trade & Reference Div.

Burnett, Frances Hodgson. El Jardin Secreto. 2001. (Illus.). (J). 16.60 (978-0-606-20735-5(X)) Tandem Library Bks.

—A Little Princess. Corvino, Lucy, illus. 2005. (Classic Starts Ser.). 160p. 4.95 (978-1-4027-1275-3(8)) Sterling Publishing Co., Inc.

—A Little Princess. Marcos, Pablo, illus. 2005. (Great Illustrated Classics Ser.). 239p. (J). (gr. 3-8). 21.35 (978-1-59679-246-3(9) , ABDO & Daughters) ABDO Publishing Co.

—A Little Princess: The Story of Sara Crewe. (J). 16.95 (978-0-8488-1253-9(0)) Amereon LTD.

—A Little Princess: The Story of Sara Crewe. Warren, Eliza, ed. Marcos, Pablo, illus. 2006. 239p. (YA). reprint ed. 10.00 (978-0-7567-9835-2(3)) DIANE Publishing Co.

—A Little Princess: The Story of Sara Crewe. unabr. ed. 2000. (Dover Juvenile Classics Ser.). (Illus.). 240p. (J). (gr. 4-7). pap. 2.00 (978-0-486-41446-1(9)) Dover Pubns., Inc.

—A Little Princess: The Story of Sara Crewe. Rust, Graham, illus. 2000. 192p. (YA). (gr. 4-7). reprint ed. 18.95 (978-0-87923-784-4(8)) Godine, David R. Pub.

—A Little Princess: The Story of Sara Crewe. Collier, Mary & McClintock, Barbara, illus. 2000. 32p. (J). (ps-3). 18.99 (978-0-06-027891-5(9)) HarperCollins Pubs.

—A Little Princess: The Story of Sara Crewe. 2000. (Illus.). 32p. (J). (ps-3). 16.89 (978-0-06-029010-8(2)) HarperCollins Pubs.

—A Little Princess: The Story of Sara Crewe. Tudor, Tasha, illus. 1999. 336p. (J). (gr. 4 up). 17.99 (978-0-397-30693-0(8)) HarperCollins Pubs.

—A Little Princess: The Story of Sara Crewe. Lindskoog, Kathryn, ed. Chitouras, Barbara, illus. 2002. (Classics for Young Readers Ser.). 208p. (J). pap. 7.99 (978-0-87552-727-7(2)) P & R Publishing.

—A Little Princess: The Story of Sara Crewe. 2002. (Classics Ser.). (Illus.). 272p. pap. 10.00 (978-0-14-243701-8(8) , Penguin Classics) Penguin Group (USA) Inc.

—A Little Princess: The Story of Sara Crewe. 2006. (Scholastic Classics Ser.). v, 178p. (J). (gr. 9-12). 25.00 (978-0-531-16991-9(X) , Watts, Franklin) Scholastic Library Publishing.

—A Little Princess: The Story of Sara Crewe. Rust, Graham, illus. (J). pap. 22.95 (978-0-590-24079-6(X)) Scholastic, Inc.

—A Little Princess: The Story of Sara Crewe. 2001. (gr. 3-6). lib. bdg. 11.80 (978-0-613-63210-2(9)) Tandem Library Bks.

—A Little Princess: The Story of Sara Crewe. l.t. ed. 2003. 342p. (J). 29.95 (978-0-7862-5842-0(X)) Thorndike Pr.

—A Little Princess: With a Discussion of Generosity. Gribbon, Sean & Jael, trs. Gribbon, Sean & Jael, illus. 2003. (Values in Action Illustrated Classics Ser.). (J). (978-1-59203-050-7(5)) Learning Challenge, Inc.

—A Little Princess Book & Charm. Tudor, Tasha, illus. 1999. (Charming Classics). 336p. (J). (gr. 4 up). pap. 6.99 (978-0-694-01236-7(X) , Harper Festival) HarperCollins Pubs.

—Sara Crewe. l.t. ed. 2006. 92p. pap. (978-1-84637-263-6(1)) Echo Library.

—Sara Crewe or What Happened at Miss Minc. 2005. pap. 20.95 (978-0-7661-9708-4(5)) Kessinger Publishing, LLC.

—Sara Crewe or What Happened at Miss Minchin's. 2006. (ENG.). 88p. per. 9.45 (978-1-59462-359-2(7) , 395, Book Jungle) Standard Pubns., Inc.

—Sara Crewe or What Happened at Miss Minchin's - 1903. 2006. (ENG.). 88p. per. 9.45 (978-1-59462-360-8(0) , 396, Book Jungle) Standard Pubns., Inc.

—The Secret Garden. 2008. (Puffin Classics Ser.). 368p. (J). (gr. 3). pap. 4.99 (*978-0-14-132106-6(7)* , Puffin) Penguin Group (USA) Inc.

—The Secret Garden. 2002. (Illustrated Children's Library Ser.). (Illus.). 288p. (J). 12.99 (978-0-517-22115-0(2) , Gramercy) Random Hse. Value Publishing.

—The Secret Garden. Corvino, Lucy, illus. 2005. (Classic Starts Ser.). 160p. 4.95 (978-1-4027-1319-4(3)) Sterling Publishing Co., Inc.

—The Secret Garden. Engelbreit, Mary, illus. 2007. (Mary Engelbreit's Classic Library). 368p. (J). (gr. 3-7). 9.99 (*978-0-06-008136-2(8)* , Harper Festival) HarperCollins Pubs.

—The Secret Garden: A Young Reader's Edition of the Classic Story. Kaster, Shelley Austin, illus. 2002. (Great Illustrated Classics Ser.). 240p. (J). (gr. 3-8). 21.35 (978-1-57765-809-2(4) , ABDO & Daughters) ABDO Publishing Co.

—The Secret Garden: A Young Reader's Edition of the Classic Story. (J). 22.95 (978-0-8488-0692-7(1)) Amereon LTD.

—The Secret Garden: A Young Reader's Edition of the Classic Story. ed. 2004. (Illus.). (J). (gr. 1-4). spiral bd. (978-0-616-14566-1(7)); spiral bd. (978-0-616-14565-4(9)) Canadian National Institute for the Blind/Institut National Canadien pour les Aveugles.

—The Secret Garden: A Young Reader's Edition of the Classic Story. Moore, Inga, illus. 2008. 272p. (J). (gr. 1). 21.99 (*978-0-7636-3161-1(2)*) Candlewick Pr.

—The Secret Garden: A Young Reader's Edition of the Classic Story. 1999. (Illus.). 256p. (J). (gr. 4-7). pap. 3.00 (978-0-486-40784-5(5)) Dover Pubns., Inc.

—The Secret Garden: A Young Reader's Edition of the Classic Story. Tudor, Tasha, illus. 1998. 368p. (gr. 4 up). (YA). 17.99 (978-0-397-32165-0(1)); (J). reprint ed. pap. 6.99 (978-0-06-440188-3(X) , Harper Trophy) HarperCollins Pubs.

—The Secret Garden: A Young Reader's Edition of the Classic Story. Cockcroft, Jason, illus. 2002. (Kingfisher Classics Ser.). 384p. (J). (gr. k-3). tchr. ed. 15.95 (978-0-7534-5479-4(3) , Kingfisher) Houghton Mifflin Co. Trade & Reference Div.

—The Secret Garden: A Young Reader's Edition of the Classic Story. (English As a Second Language Bk.). (Illus.). 92p. pap. 4.46 net. (978-0-582-53417-9(8)) Longman Publishing Group.

—The Secret Garden: A Young Reader's Edition of the Classic Story. 1998. 248p. (J). reprint ed. lib. bdg. 25.00 (978-1-58287-069-4(1)) North Bks.

—The Secret Garden: A Young Reader's Edition of the Classic Story. 2002. (Oxford World's Classics Ser.). (Illus.). 368p. 8.95 (978-0-19-283596-3(3)) Oxford Univ. Pr., Inc.

—The Secret Garden: A Young Reader's Edition of the Classic Story. 288p. 2003. (gr. 12). mass mkt. 3.95 (978-0-451-52883-4(2) , Signet Classics); 2002. pap. 8.00 (978-0-14-243705-6(0) , Penguin Classics) Penguin Group (USA) Inc.

—The Secret Garden: A Young Reader's Edition of the Classic Story. 2003. (Modern Library Classics Ser.). 288p. pap. 7.95 (978-0-8129-6998-6(7) , Modern Library) Random House Publishing Group.

—The Secret Garden: A Young Reader's Edition of the Classic Story. Sauber, Robert G., illus. 2001. 56p. (J). (ps up). 9.98 (978-0-7624-0572-5(4) , Courage Bks.) Running Pr. Bk. Pubs.

—The Secret Garden: A Young Reader's Edition of the Classic Story. 2006. (Scholastic Classics Ser.). vi, 222p. (J). (gr. 9-12). 25.00 (978-0-531-16960-5(X) , Watts, Franklin) Scholastic Library Publishing.

—The Secret Garden: A Young Reader's Edition of the Classic Story. 1999. (Illus.). 320p. (J). (gr. 4-7). pap. 4.99 (978-0-439-09939-4(0)) Scholastic, Inc.

—The Secret Garden: A Young Reader's Edition of the Classic Story. Rust, Graham, illus. 1999. (J). pap. 22.95 (978-0-590-24077-2(3)) Scholastic, Inc.

—The Secret Garden: A Young Reader's Edition of the Classic Story. (gr. 3-6). 2003. lib. bdg. 11.80 (978-0-613-83894-8(7)); 1999. lib. bdg. 11.80 (978-0-613-63230-0(3)) Tandem Library Bks.

—The Secret Garden: A Young Reader's Edition of the Classic Story. 1998. (Children's Classics). (ENG.). 224p. (YA). (gr. 8-12). pap. (978-1-85326-104-6(1) , 1041WW) Wordsworth Editions, Ltd.

—The Secret Garden: With a Discussion of Compassion. Lauter, Richard, illus. 2003. (Values in Action Illustrated Classics Ser.). 191p. (J). (978-1-59203-037-8(8)) Learning Challenge, Inc.

—The Secret Garden Includes Charm. Tudor, Tasha, illus. adapted ed. 1998. (Charming Classics). 368p. (YA). (gr. 5 up). pap. 6.99 (978-0-694-01110-0(X)) HarperCollins Pubs.

—The Secret Garden Book & Charm. Tudor, Tasha, illus. deluxe ed. 2005. (Charming Classics). 368p. (J). 9.99 (978-0-06-075771-7(X) , Harper Festival) HarperCollins Pubs.

Burnett, Frances Hodgson & Cockcroft, Jason. The Secret Garden: A Young Reader's Edition of the Classic Story. 2002. (Kingfisher Classics Ser.). (Illus.). 384p. (J). (978-0-7534-0602-1(0) , Kingfisher) Houghton Mifflin Co. Trade & Reference Div.

Burnett, Frances Hodgson & Rust, Graham. The Secret Garden: A Young Reader's Edition of the Classic Story. 2000. (Illus.). 224p. (YA). (gr. 5 up). reprint ed. 18.95 (978-0-87923-649-6(3)) Godine, David R. Pub.

Bush, Suzanne & Takes, Deb. Time Will Tell. 2004. 279p. (YA). lib. bdg. 15.95 (978-0-9747426-0-1(0)) Imagining Possibilities.

Butler, Amy. Virginia Bound. 2003. 192p. (J). (gr. 5-9). tchr. ed. 15.00 (978-0-618-24752-3(1) , Clarion Bks.) Houghton Mifflin Co. Trade & Reference Div.

Byng, Georgia. Molly Moon Stops the World. 2004. (Illus.). 384p. (J). 16.99 (978-0-06-051410-5(8)); lib. bdg. 17.89 (978-0-06-051413-6(2)) HarperCollins Pubs.

—Molly Moon y el Increible Libro. 2003. (SPA.). 349p. (J). 18.99 (978-84-348-9076-3(3)) SM Ediciones ESP. *Dist:* Lectorum Pubns., Inc.

—Molly Moon's Incredible Book of Hypnotism. 2003. (Illus.). 384p. (J). (gr. 3-7). 16.99 (978-0-06-051406-8(X)); 2003. 135.92 (978-0-06-057217-4(5)); 2004. (Illus.). 400p. (J). reprint ed. pap. 7.99 (978-0-06-051409-9(4) , Harper Trophy) HarperCollins Pubs.

—Molly Moon's Incredible Book of Hypnotism. 2002. (Molly Moon Ser.: Bk. 1). 330p. (J). (gr. 3-7). (978-0-333-98489-5(7) , Macmillan Children's Bks.) Pan Macmillan.

Calaci, Iris. Matthew Mouse. Karper, Deborah, ed. Gonzalez, David, Jr., illus. 2002. 40p. (J). pap. (978-1-928681-07-6(7) , MM077) Gladstone Publishing.

Carman, Patrick. Atherton: The House of Power. 2007. (Illus.). (J). 352p. (gr. 3-7). 16.99 (*978-0-316-16670-6(7)*); 330p. (*978-1-4287-4140-9(2)*) Little Brown & Co.

—Into the Mist. 2007. 304p. (J). (gr. 4-7). pap. 11.99 (*978-0-439-89952-9(4)* , Orchard Bks.) Scholastic, Inc.

Carney, Jeffrey K. The Adventures of Michael MacInnes. 2006. 256p. (YA). 17.00 (978-0-374-30146-0(8)) Farrar, Straus & Giroux.

Carr, Pat. Border Ransom. 2006. (Illus.). 146p. (J). pap. 11.95 (978-0-87565-332-7(4)) Texas Christian Univ. Pr.

Cassedy, Sylvia. Behind the Attic Wall. 1998. (gr. 4-7). 22.50 (978-0-8446-6965-6(2)) Smith, Peter Pub., Inc.

Center for Learning Network Staff. Oliver Twist: Curriculum Unit —Novel Series. 2001. (Novel Ser.). 65p. (YA). tchr. ed., spiral bd. 19.95 (978-1-56077-684-0(6)) Ctr. for Learning, The.

Chan, Gillian. The Carved Box. Fernandez, Laura, illus. 232p. (YA). (gr. 13 up). 2004. (978-1-55337-016-1(3)); 2001. (978-1-55074-895-6(5)) Kids Can Pr., Ltd.

Chimombo, S. Bird Boy's Song. 2004. 91p. 13.95 (978-99908-48-07-6(6)) Wasi Pubns. ZWE. *Dist:* Michigan State Univ. Pr.

Chronicles of Avonlea. 2004. 142p. (YA). pap. 7.95 (978-1-57646-893-7(3)) Quiet Vision Publishing.

Church, Lisa R. & Spyri, Johanna. Heidi. Akib, Jamel, illus. 2007. (Classic Starts Ser.). 152p. (J). (*978-1-4287-4211-6(5)*) Sterling Publishing Co., Inc.

Coats, Lucy. Heidi. 2000. (gr. k-3). lib. bdg. 11.80 (978-0-613-25481-6(3)) Tandem Library Bks.

Coats, Lucy, et al. Heidi, Vol. 3. 2000. (Classic Readers Ser.). (Illus.). 48p. (J). (gr. 2-3). pap. 3.99 (978-0-7894-5390-7(8)) Dorling Kindersley Publishing, Inc.

Coatsworth, Elizabeth Jane. The Fair American. Sewell, Helen, illus. 2005. 137p. (J). (*978-1-883937-85-0(X)*) Bethlehem Bks.

Cole, Brock. Good Enough to Eat. 2007. (Illus.). 32p. (J). (gr. k). 16.00 (*978-0-374-32737-8(8)* , Farrar, Straus & Giroux (BYR)) Farrar, Straus & Giroux.

Colfer, Eoin. The Supernaturalist. 2004. (Illus.). 272p. (gr. 5-17). 16.95 (978-0-7868-5148-5(1)) Hyperion Bks. for Children.

—The Supernaturalist. l.t. ed. 2004. 312p. 23.95 (978-0-7862-6766-8(6) , Large Print Pr.) Thorndike Pr.

Collier, James Lincoln. Chipper. 2001. (Illus.). 144p. (J). (gr. 5-9). 14.95 (978-0-7614-5084-9(X) , Cavendish Children's Bks.) Cavendish, Marshall Corp.

—The Empty Mirror. 192p. 2006. (YA). pap. 6.95 (978-1-58234-904-6(5)); 2004. (J). 16.95 (978-1-58234-949-7(5)) Bloomsbury Publishing. (Bloomsbury Children).

—Me & Billy. 2004. 192p. (J). 15.95 (978-0-7614-5174-7(9)) Cavendish, Marshall Corp.

Collins, Alan. Boys from Bondi. 160p. pap. 11.95 (978-0-7022-2084-5(1)) Univ. of Queensland Pr. AUS. *Dist:* International Specialized Bk. Services.

Collins, Sonny. Mouse Tails. 2006. (ENG.). 52p. per. 12.95 (***978-1-4241-4589-8(9)***) PublishAmerica, Inc.

Collison, Linda. Star-Crossed. 2006. (Illus.). 416p. (YA). (gr. 9). 16.95 (978-0-375-83363-2(3)); lib. bdg. 18.99 (978-0-375-93363-9(8)) Random Hse. Children's Bks. (Knopf Bks. for Young Readers).

Cormier, Robert. Heroes. 2006. (York Notes Ser.). 112p. pap. (978-1-4058-3559-6(1)) Pearson Education, Ltd.

—Heroes. 2000. 144p. (YA). (gr. 7-12). pap. 5.99 (978-0-440-22769-4(0) , Laurel Leaf) Random Hse. Children's Bks.

—Heroes. 2000. 135p. (YA). (gr. 7-12). lib. bdg. 13.55 (978-0-613-23622-5(X)); per. 12.15 (978-0-606-17836-5(8)) Tandem Library Bks.

—Heroes. l.t. ed. 2000. 147p. (YA). (gr. 8-12). 21.95 (978-0-7862-2909-3(8)) Thorndike Pr.

Cornish, D. M. Foundling, Bk. 1. 2007. (Monster Blood Tattoo Ser.). 448p. (YA). (gr. 7 up). 8.99 (***978-0-14-240913-8(8)*** , Puffin) Penguin Group (USA) Inc.

Couloumbis, Audrey. Maude March on the Run! 2007. (Illus.). 320p. (J). (gr. 3-7). 15.99 (978-0-375-83246-8(7) , Random Hse. Bks. for Young Readers) Random Hse. Children's Bks.

—Maude March on the Run!, or, Trouble Is Her Middle Name. 2007. (Illus.). 309p. (J). pap. (978-0-375-83248-2(3)) Random Hse., Inc.

—Maude March on the Run!, Or, Trouble Is Her Middle Name. 2007. (Illus.). 320p. (J). (gr. 3-7). lib. bdg. 17.99 (978-0-375-93246-5(1) , Random Hse. Bks. for Young Readers) Random Hse. Children's Bks.

—The Misadventures of Maude March: Or Trouble Rides a Fast Horse. 2005. (Illus.). 304p. (J). (gr. 5-9). 15.95 (978-0-375-83245-1(9)); lib. bdg. 17.99 (978-0-375-93245-8(3)) Random Hse. Children's Bks. (Random Hse. Bks. for Young Readers).

—The Misadventures of Maude Marche. 2007. (Illus.). 320p. (J). (gr. 3-7). 6.50 (978-0-375-83247-5(5) , Yearling) Random Hse. Children's Bks.

Cowling, Douglas. Vivaldi's Ring of Mystery. Fernandez, Laura & Jacobson, Rick, illus. 2004. 44p. (J). pap. (***978-0-439-96904-8(2)*** , North Winds Pr) Scholastic Canada, Ltd.

Creech, Sharon. The Castle Corona. Diaz, David, illus. 2007. 336p. (J). (gr. 3-7). lib. bdg. 19.89 (***978-0-06-084622-0(4)***); 18.99 (***978-0-06-084621-3(6)***) HarperCollins Pubs. (Cotler, Joanna Books).

Creech, Sharon. Ruby Holler. (J). 2004. 336p. pap. 6.99 (978-0-06-056015-7(0) , Harper Trophy); 2002. 320p. (gr. 3-7). lib. bdg. 17.89 (978-0-06-027733-8(5) , Cotler, Joanna Books); 2002. 320p. (gr. 4-7). 16.99 (978-0-06-027732-1(7) , Cotler, Joanna Books) HarperCollins Pubs.

—Ruby Holler. 2004. (gr. 3-6). lib. bdg. 14.15 (978-0-613-86272-1(4)) Tandem Library Bks.

—Ruby Holler. l.t. ed. 2003. (Juvenile Ser.). 250p. (J). 22.95 (978-0-7862-5429-3(7)) Thorndike Pr.

Crew, Gary. Gothic Hospital. 2002. (Illus.). 160p. (YA). pap. (978-0-7344-0232-5(5) , Lothian Bks.) Hachette Livre Australia.

Croggon, Alison. The Crow. 2007. (Pellinor Ser.: Bk. 3). (Illus.). 528p. (YA). (gr. 7 up). 18.99 (***978-0-7636-3409-4(3)***) Candlewick Pr.

Croggon, Alison. The Naming. 2006. (Pellinor Ser.: Bk. 1). 528p. (YA). (gr. 7). pap. 8.99 (978-0-7636-3162-8(0)) Candlewick Pr.

Croggon, Allison. Naming: The First Book of Pellinor, No. 1. 2005. 528p. (YA). (gr. 7 up). 17.99 (978-0-7636-2639-6(2)) Candlewick Pr.

Crowe, Carole. Groover's Heart. 2003. (Illus.). 144p. (J). (gr. 4-6). 15.95 (978-1-56397-953-8(5)) Boyds Mills Pr.

Curtis, Christopher Paul. Bud, Not Buddy. 1999. (Illus.). 256p. (J). (gr. 4-7). 16.95 (978-0-385-32306-2(9) , Delacorte Bks. for Young Readers) Random Hse. Children's Bks.

—Bud, Not Buddy. l.t. ed. 2000. (Illus.). 279p. (J). (gr. 8-12). 22.95 (978-0-7862-2574-3(2)) Thorndike Pr.

Cushman, Karen. Rodzina. 2003. Tr. of Rodzina. 224p. (J). (gr. 5-9). tchr. ed. 16.00 (978-0-618-13351-2(8) , Clarion Bks.) Houghton Mifflin Co. Trade & Reference Div.

—Rodzina. 2005. Tr. of Rodzina. 224p. (gr. 5). 6.50 (978-0-440-41993-8(X) , Yearling) Random Hse. Children's Bks.

Cusick, Richie Tankersley. The Unseen 1 It Begins. 2005. 304p. (YA). (gr. 7). pap. 6.99 (978-0-14-240463-8(2) , Puffin) Penguin Group (USA) Inc.

Dadey, Debbie. Whistler's Hollow. 2002. 130p. (J). 14.95 (978-1-58234-789-9(1) , Bloomsbury Children) Bloomsbury Publishing.

Dahl, Roald. The BFG. Blake, Quentin, illus. 2007. 208p. (J). (gr. 2). 6.99 (***978-0-14-241038-7(1)*** , Puffin) Penguin Group (USA) Inc.

Dalmatian Press Staff. Anne of Green Gables. (Great Classics for Children Ser.). (Illus.). 192p. (J). 5.99 (978-1-4037-0591-4(7)) Dalmatian Pr.

Dalmatian Press Staff, adapted by. Anne of Green Gables. 2002. (Spot the Classics Ser.). (Illus.). 176p. (J). (gr. k-5). 4.99 (978-1-57759-543-4(2)) Dalmatian Pr.

—Heidi. (SPA., Illus.). (YA). 11.95 (978-84-7281-082-2(8) , AF1082) Auriga, Ediciones S.A. ESP. *Dist:* Continental Bk. Co., Inc.

—Heidi. (Young Collector's Illustrated Classics Ser.). (Illus.). 192p. (J). (gr. 3-7). 9.95 (978-1-56156-455-2(9)) Kidsbooks, Inc.

—The Secret Garden. 2002. (Spot the Classics Ser.). (Illus.). 180p. (J). (gr. k-5). 4.99 (978-1-57759-555-7(6)) Dalmatian Pr.

—The Secret Garden. 1999. (978-0-14-771399-5(4) , Penguin Classics) Penguin Group (USA) Inc.

La Dama de Cobre (the Copper Lady) 2006. (J). pap. 5.95 (978-0-8225-6616-8(8) , Ediciones Lerner) Lerner Publishing Group.

Daringer, Helen Fern. Adopted Jane. Seredy, Kate, illus. 2002. 224p. (gr. 3-6). reprint ed. 12.95 (978-0-9714612-4-6(4)) Green Mansion Pr. LLC.

Davidson, Susanna. Heidi (Picture Book) 2007. (Picture Book Classics Ser.). 24p. (J). 9.99 (***978-0-7945-1716-8(1)*** , Usborne) EDC Publishing.

Davis, Susan Page. Sarah's Long Ride. 2007. 173p. (J). (***978-1-59166-737-7(2)***) Jones, Bob Univ. Pr.

Davis, Terry. Mysterious Ways. 2002. 284p. (YA). pap. 15.95 (978-0-910055-81-9(5)) Eastern Washington Univ. Pr.

De Haven, Tom. The Orphan's Tent. 2005. (Illus.). 192p. mass mkt. 5.99 (978-0-7434-9772-5(4)) ibooks, Inc.

De Lint, Charles. The Harp of the Grey Rose: The Legend of Cerin Songweaver. 2004. (gr. 7-12). lib. bdg. 15.30 (978-0-613-71570-6(5)) Tandem Library Bks.

DeFelice, Cynthia. The Apprenticeship of Lucas Whitaker. 2007. 160p. (J). pap. 6.95 (978-0-374-40014-9(8) , Farrar, Straus & Giroux (BYR)) Farrar, Straus & Giroux.

DeFelice, Cynthia C. Nowhere to Call Home. 2000. (YA). pap., stu. ed. 60.00 incl. audio (978-0-7887-4179-1(9) , 41113) Recorded Bks., LLC.

—Nowhere to Call Home. 2001. (gr. 5-8). lib. bdg. 14.10 (978-0-613-35992-4(5)) Tandem Library Bks.

D'Elia, Amy & Clerman, Lisa. Dreams Come True: A story about the blessing of Adoption. 2007. (***978-0-9777744-1-8(4)***) Finneran, Lisa.

Dell, Pamela. A Song for Sung Li: A Story of the 1906 San Francisco Earthquake. 2002. (Scrapbooks of America Ser.). (Illus.). 48p. (J). (gr. 2-6). 28.50 (978-1-59187-015-9(1)) Child's World, Inc.

Dennis, Jeanne Gowen & Seifert, Sheila. Escape! Hohn, David, tr. Hohn, David, illus. 2003. (Strive to Thrive Ser.). 96p. (J). pap., pap. 5.99 (978-0-7814-3895-7(0) , 0781438950) Cook, David C. Publishing Co.

deVries, Maggie. Chance & the Butterfly. Ghent, Cindy, illus. 2002. (Orca Young Readers Ser.). 160p. (J). (gr. 3-6). pap. 4.99 (978-1-55143-208-3(0)) Orca Bk. Pubs. USA.

Dickens, Charles. David Copperfield. Marcos, Pablo, illus. 2002. (Great Illustrated Classics Ser.). 240p. (J). (gr. 3-8). 21.35 (978-1-57765-685-2(7) , ABDO & Daughters) ABDO Publishing Co.

—David Copperfield: Level 5. 2nd ed. 2000. (Bookworms Ser.). (Illus.). 112p. 6.50 (978-0-19-423060-5(0)) Oxford Univ. Pr., Inc.

—Great Expectations. Lynch, Brendan, illus. 2002. (Great Illustrated Classics Ser.). 240p. (J). (gr. 3-8). 21.35 (978-1-57765-687-6(3) , ABDO & Daughters) ABDO Publishing Co.

—Great Expectations. 1998. (YA). (978-0-14-771272-1(6)) Penguin Group (USA) Inc.

—Great Expectations. 1999. (Saddleback Classics). (Illus.). (J). 13.75 (978-0-606-21552-7(2)) Tandem Library Bks.

—Great Expectations. Hegarty, Carol, ed. 1998. (Classics Ser.: Set II). (Illus.). 77p. (YA). (gr. 5-12). pap. 6.95 (978-1-56254-266-5(4) , SP2664) Saddleback Educational Publishing.

—Great Expectations, Level 6. 2000. 128p. (C). pap. 9.00 (978-0-582-41947-6(6)) Longman Publishing Group.

—Oliver Twist. 2002. (Classics for Young Readers Ser.). (SPA.). (YA). 14.95 (978-84-392-0919-5(3) , EV30603) Gaviota Ediciones ESP. *Dist:* Lectorum Pubns., Inc.

—Oliver Twist. 2000. (SPA.). 288p. (YA). (gr. 4-7). pap. 14.95 (978-0-595-13258-4(8)) iUniverse, Inc.

—Oliver Twist. Andreasen, Dan, illus. 2006. (Classic Starts Ser.). 160p. 4.95 (978-1-4027-2665-1(1)) Sterling Publishing Co., Inc.

—Oliver Twist. Gelev, Penko, illus. 2006. (Graphic Classics Ser.). 48p. (J). (gr. 4-8). 15.99 (978-0-7641-5975-6(5)); pap. 8.99 (978-0-7641-3490-6(6)) Barron's Educational Series, Inc.

—Oliver Twist. abr. ed. Date not set. (Nelson Readers Ser.). (J). pap. (978-0-17-557020-1(5)) Addison-Wesley Longman, Inc.

—Oliver Twist. abr. ed. (J). 9.95 (978-1-56156-372-2(2)) Kidsbooks, Inc.

—Oliver Twist. 2nd abr. ed. 2000. (Green Apple). 96p. (YA). pap. (978-1-57159-008-4(0)) Los Andes Publishing Co.

—Oliver Twist: With a Discussion of Honesty. 2003. (Values in Action Illustrated Classics Ser.). (J). (978-1-59203-051-4(3)) Learning Challenge, Inc.

Dike, Tina. His Greatest Challenge. Schulman, Cory & Johnstone, Sandy, eds. 2000. 125p. (YA). (gr. 7-9). pap. 9.95 (978-0-9642997-1-9(2)) Best Seller Pubns., Inc.

Domínguez, José A. Mamerto: A Children's Story. 2006. (J). mass mkt. 12.50 (978-1-59835-022-7(6)) Cambridge BrickHouse, Inc.

Dowell, Frances O'Roark. Where I'd Like to Be. 240p. (J). 2003. (Illus.). (gr. 5-9). 15.95 (978-0-689-84420-1(4) , Atheneum); 2004. reprint ed. pap. 5.99 (978-0-689-87067-5(1) , Aladdin) Simon & Schuster Children's Publishing.

—Where I'd Like to Be. 2004. 232p. (J). (gr. k-9). lib. bdg. 11.64 (978-0-606-32673-5(1)) Tandem Library Bks.

—Where I'd Like to Be. l.t. ed. 2003. 162p. (J). 22.95 (978-0-7862-5741-6(5)) Thorndike Pr.

Downing, Wick. Leonardo's Hand. 2001. (Illus.). 208p. (J). (gr. 5-9). tchr. ed. 15.00 (978-0-618-07893-6(2)) Houghton Mifflin Co. Trade & Reference Div.

Doyle, Brian. Easy Avenue. 2004. 122p. (YA). pap. 6.95 (978-0-88899-605-3(5)) Groundwood Bks. CAN. *Dist:* Perseus Distribution.

Du Jardin, Rosamond. Young & Fair. 2003. (YA). pap. 12.95 (978-1-930009-79-0(8) , 800-691-7779) Image Cascade Publishing.

Duey, Kathleen. Amelina Carrett: Thibodeau, Louisiana 1870. 1999. (American Diaries Ser.: No. 12). (J). (gr. 3-7). 10.64 (978-0-606-16281-4(X)) Tandem Library Bks.

—Margret & Flynn 1875. 2008. 160p. (J). (gr. 3). 5.99 (***978-0-14-241019-6(5)*** , Puffin) Penguin Group (USA) Inc.

—Silver Thread. 2001. (gr. 3-6). lib. bdg. 11.80 (978-0-613-58389-3(2)) Tandem Library Bks.

—Sunset Gates. 2002. (gr. 3-6). lib. bdg. 11.80 (978-0-613-57584-3(9)) Tandem Library Bks.

Duffy, Daniel M., illus. Benny Goes into Business, Vol. 5. 1999. (Adventures of Benny & Watch: Vol. 5). 32p. (J). (ps-2). pap. 3.95 (978-0-8075-0637-0(0)) Whitman, Albert & Co.

—Benny's New Friend, Vol. 3. 1998. (Adventures of Benny & Watch: Vol. No. 3). 32p. (J). (ps-2). pap. 3.95 (978-0-8075-0649-3(4)) Whitman, Albert & Co.

—Meet the Boxcar Children. 1998. (Adventures of Benny & Watch: Vol. No. 1). 48p. (J). (ps-2). pap. 3.95 (978-0-8075-5034-2(5)) Whitman, Albert & Co.

—A Present for Grandfather, Vol. 2. 1998. (Adventures of Benny & Watch: Vol. No. 2). 32p. (J). (ps-2). pap. 3.95 (978-0-8075-6625-1(X)) Whitman, Albert & Co.

—Watch Runs Away, Vol. 6. 1999. (Adventures of Benny & Watch: Vol. No. 6). 32p. (J). (ps-2). pap. 3.95 (978-0-8075-8681-5(1)) Whitman, Albert & Co.

Duffy, Daniel Mark, illus. Benny's New Friend. 1998. (J). (ps-ps). lib. bdg. 11.80 (978-0-613-07332-5(0)) Tandem Library Bks.

Dunkle, Clare B. The Hollow Kingdom. 2003. (Hollow Kingdom Trilogy Ser.). (Illus.). 240p. (YA). (gr. 7). 16.95 (978-0-8050-7390-4(6) , Holt, Henry & Co. Bks. For Young Readers) Holt, Henry & Co.

—Hollow Kingdom. 2006. (Hollow Kingdom Trilogy Ser.). 240p. (YA). reprint ed. pap. 6.95 (978-0-8050-8108-4(9) , Holt, Henry & Co. Bks. For Young Readers) Holt, Henry & Co.

—The Hollow Kingdom, Vol. 5. l.t. ed. 2004. 360p. 21.95 (978-0-7862-6769-9(0) , Large Print Pr.) Thorndike Pr.

Dussling, Jennifer. L. M. Montgomery's Anne of Green Gables. 2001. (gr. k-3). lib. bdg. 11.80 (978-0-613-35608-4(X)) Tandem Library Bks.

Dussling, Jennifer & Montgomery, L. M. Anne of Green Gables. Halverson, Lydia, illus. 2001. (All Aboard Reading Ser.). 48p. (J). (gr. 4-7). pap. 3.99 (978-0-448-42459-0(2) , Grosset & Dunlap) Penguin Group (USA) Inc.

Edwards, Julie Andrews. Mandy. Westerman, Johanna, illus. 2nd ed. 2006. (Julie Andrews Collection). 320p. (J). 16.99 (978-0-06-113162-2(8)); pap. 6.99 (978-0-06-120707-5(1)) HarperCollins Pubs. (Julie Andrews Collection).

Edwards, S. Neil. My Dog, Digger. 2006. 122p. pap. 17.95 (978-1-4241-0514-4(5)) PublishAmerica, Inc.

Ekwensi, Cyprian. Motherless Baby. 1999. pap. (978-978-129-256-9(3)) Heinemann Educational Bks. (Nigeria), Ltd.

Elliot, Patricia. Murkmere. 2006. 344p. (J). 16.99 (978-0-316-01365-9(X)) Little Brown & Co.

Elliott, David. Jeremy Cabbage & the Museum of Human Oddballs & Quadruped Delights. 2008. 320p. (J). (gr. 3-7). 15.99 (***978-0-375-84333-4(7)*** , Knopf Bks. for Young Readers) Random Hse. Children's Bks.

Elliott, Patricia. Ambergate. 2007. 400p. (J). (gr. 7-17). 16.99 (978-0-316-01060-3(X)) Little Brown & Co.

Ellis, Deborah. The Heaven Shop. 2004. 186p. (978-1-55041-908-5(0)); 192p. (J). (gr. 6-9). pap. (978-1-55041-907-8(2)) Fitzhenry & Whiteside, Ltd.

Ellis, Mary. Elephant Child. 2003. (Illus.). 128p. (J). pap. 7.99 (978-0-00-712820-4(7)) HarperCollins Pubs. Ltd. GBR. *Dist:* Independent Pubs. Group.

Ellis, Sarah. The Several Lives of Orphan Jack. St. Aubin, Bruno, illus. (J). 2005. 88p. pap. 6.95 (978-0-88899-618-3(7)); 2003. (gr. 2-5). 14.95 (978-0-88899-529-2(6)) Groundwood Bks. CAN. *Dist:* Perseus Distribution, Transition Vendor.

Emerson, Alice B. Ruth Fielding at Snow Camp or Lost in the Backwoods. 2005. reprint ed. pap. 24.95 (978-1-4179-3132-3(9)) Kessinger Publishing, LLC.

—Ruth Fielding in the Red Cross or Doing. 2005. pap. 24.95 (978-1-4179-1799-0(7)) Kessinger Publishing, LLC.

—Ruth Fielding on the St. Lawrence or the. 2005. pap. 24.95 (978-0-7661-9911-8(8)) Kessinger Publishing, LLC.

Emerson, B. Alice. Ruth Fielding in Moving Pictures or Help. 2006. 32.99 (***978-1-4280-2942-2(7)***) IndyPublish.com.

—Ruth Fielding on Cliff Island or the Old. 2006. 32.99 (***978-1-4280-2823-4(4)***) IndyPublish.com.

Emery, Joanna. Brothers of the Falls. Erickson, David, illus. 2004. (Adventures in America Ser.). (J). 14.95 (978-1-893110-37-3(0)) Silver Moon Pr.

Enright, Elizabeth. Then There Were Five. Enright, Elizabeth, illus. rev. ed. 2002. (Melendy Quartet Ser.: Bk. 3). (Illus.). 176p. (J). (gr. 3-7). 16.95 (978-0-8050-7062-0(1) , Holt, Henry & Co. Bks. For Young Readers) Holt, Henry & Co.

Ernst, Kathleen. Hearts of Stone. 2006. 240p. (J). (gr. 7). 16.99 (978-0-525-47686-3(5) , Dutton Juvenile) Penguin Group (USA) Inc.

Estrada, Ric, illus. Oliver Twist. 2002. (Great Illustrated Classics Ser.). 240p. (J). (gr. 3-8). 21.35 (978-1-57765-697-5(0) , ABDO & Daughters) ABDO Publishing Co.

Fann, Lisa. Uprooted. 2002. (YA). 128p. 18.50 (978-0-9719167-3-9(X)); per. 10.00 (978-0-9719167-0-8(5)) Open Bk. Publishing.

Feeney, R. K. Little Orphan Boy. 2002. (gr. 7-12). lib. bdg. 24.00 (978-0-613-78098-8(1)) Tandem Library Bks.

Ferris, Jean. Much Ado about Grubstake. 2006. (Illus.). 272p. (YA). 17.00 (978-0-15-205706-0(4)) Harcourt Children's Bks.

Ficklin, Jonene H. The Garden Gate. 2005. (YA). 14.95 (978-0-9761188-2-4(3)) Victor's Crown Publishing.

Findlay, Jamieson. The Blue Roan Girl. 2004. (Illus.). 272p. (J). 16.95 (978-0-439-62752-8(4)) Scholastic, Inc.

Finley, Martha. Mildred's New Daughter, 7 Vols., Vol. 7. (Mildred Classics: Vol. 7). 288p. pap. 6.95 (978-1-58182-233-5(2)) Cumberland Hse. Publishing.

Fisher, Dorothy Canfield. Understood Betsy. Root, Kimberly B., illus. rev. ed. 1999. 240p. (J). (gr. 4-6). 17.95 (978-0-8050-6073-7(1) , Holt, Henry & Co. Bks. For Young Readers) Holt, Henry & Co.

—Understood Betsy. 2004. reprint ed. pap. 1.99 (978-1-4192-9201-9(3)); pap. 24.95 (978-1-4179-0955-1(2)) Kessinger Publishing, LLC.

—Understood Betsy. 1999. (Hardscrabble Bks.). 182p. (J). reprint ed. pap. 9.95 (978-0-87451-920-4(9)) Univ. Pr. of New England.

Fleischman, Sid. Bo & Mzzz Mad. 112p. (J). (gr. 3 up). 2002. pap. 6.99 (978-0-06-440972-8(4)); 2001. lib. bdg. 15.89 (978-0-06-029398-7(5)) HarperCollins Pubs.

—Bo & Mzzz Mad. Hunt, Jonathan, illus. 2001. 112p. (J). (gr. 3 up). 14.99 (978-0-06-029397-0(7)) HarperCollins Pubs.

—Bo & Mzzz Mad. 2002. 103p. (J). (ps-7). lib. bdg. 13.00 (978-0-613-61838-0(6)) Tandem Library Bks.

—Disappearing Act. 2003. (Illus.). 144p. (J). (gr. 3 up). 15.99 (978-0-06-051962-9(2)); lib. bdg. 16.89 (978-0-06-051963-6(0)) HarperCollins Pubs.

Floyer, Edith S. The Young Huguenots. 1998. (Huguenots Inheritance Ser.). (J). (978-0-921100-65-2(5)) Inheritance Pubns.

Forrester, Sandra. Wheel of the Moon. 2000. (Illus.). 176p. (J). (gr. 5-9). 15.95 (978-0-688-17149-0(4)) HarperCollins Pubs.

Francis, Pauline & Dickens, Charles. Oliver Twist. 2000. (Fast Track Classics Ser.). (Illus.). 48p. (YA). pap. 9.99 (978-0-237-52537-8(2) , Evans Brothers, Limited) Evans Publishing Group GBR. *Dist:* Independent Pubs. Group.

Fuchs, Bernie. Ride Like the Wind: A Tale of the Pony Express. Fuchs, Bernie, illus. 2004. (Illus.). 32p. (J). pap. 16.95 (978-0-439-26645-1(9) , Blue Sky Pr., The) Scholastic, Inc.

Funke, Cornelia. The Thief Lord. l.t. ed. 2005. 483p. (J). (gr. 4-7). pap. 10.95 (978-0-7862-8092-6(1)) Thorndike Pr.

Funke, Cornelia. Thief Lord ('el Senor de Los Ladrones) 2007. 352p. (J). pap. 7.99 (***978-0-545-00517-3(5)*** , Scholastic en Espanol) Scholastic, Inc.

Funke, Cornelia & Latsch, Oliver. The Thief Lord. l.t. ed. 2004. 422p. (J). 23.95 (978-0-7862-7084-2(5)) Thorndike Pr.

Gaberman, Judith. Dear Lola: Or How to Build Your Own Family. 2000. 180p. (gr. 4-7). pap. 11.95 (978-0-595-15795-2(5) , Backinprint.com) iUniverse, Inc.

Garland, Sherry. Valley of the Moon: The Diary of Maria Rosalia de Milagros, Sonoma Valley, Alta California, 1846. 2001. (Dear America Ser.). (Illus.). 208p. (J). (gr. 4-9). pap. 10.95 (978-0-439-08820-6(8)) Scholastic, Inc.

George, Jessica Day. Dragon Slippers. 2007. 336p. (J). 16.95 (***978-1-59990-057-5(2)*** , Bloomsbury Children) Bloomsbury Publishing.

Giff, Patricia Reilly. Eleven. 2008. 144p. (J). (***978-0-385-73069-3(1)*** , Delacorte Pr.) Dell Publishing.

—Eleven. 2008. 176p. (J). (gr. 3-8). lib. bdg. 18.99 (***978-0-385-90098-0(8)*** , Lamb, Wendy) Random Hse. Children's Bks.

Giff, Patricia Reilly. Pictures of Hollis Woods. 176p. (gr. 3-8). 2004. (J). pap. 6.50 (978-0-440-41578-7(0) , Yearling); 2002. lib. bdg. 17.99 (978-0-385-90070-6(8) , Lamb, Wendy) Random Hse. Children's Bks.

—Pictures of Hollis Woods. Giff, Patricia Reilly, illus. 2002. (Illus.). 176p. (gr. 3-8). 15.95 (978-0-385-32655-1(6) , Lamb, Wendy) Random Hse. Children's Bks.

—Pictures of Hollis Woods. l.t. ed. 2003. 158p. (J). 23.95 (978-0-7862-5094-3(1)) Thorndike Pr.

Gildea, Kathy. The Adventures of Baylee Beagle—Annabelle Beagle. Larson, Amanda, illus. 2005. 28p. (J). 7.95 (978-0-9767096-1-9(9)) Maxim Pr.

—The Adventures of Baylee Beagle—Greenville. 2005. (Illus.). 20p. (J). 7.95 (978-0-9767096-0-2(0)) Maxim Pr.

—The Adventures of Baylee Beagle—Hurricane Hound. Larson, Amanda, illus. 2005. 28p. (J). 7.95 (978-0-9767096-2-6(7)) Maxim Pr.

Gingerich, Neeltje & Peterson, Joyce. The Secret Garden. 1999. 38p. (gr. 1-12). pap. 10.00 (978-0-88734-045-1(8)) Players Pr., Inc.

Godden, Rumer. Gypsy Girl. 2002. Orig. Title: The Diddakoi. (Illus.). 176p. (J). 15.89 (978-0-06-029192-1(3)) HarperCollins Pubs.

—Story of Holly & Ivy, the R/I. Cooney, Barbara, illus. 2006. 32p. (J). (gr. k). 17.99 (978-0-670-06219-5(7) , Viking Juvenile) Penguin Group (USA) Inc.

Gonick, Larry. Attack of the Smart Pies. 2005. (Illus.). 192p. (J). 15.95 (978-0-8126-2740-4(7)) Cricket Bks.

Goudge, Elizabeth. The Little White Horse. 2001. 240p. (YA). (gr. 3-6). pap. 5.99 (978-0-14-230027-5(6) , Puffin) Penguin Group (USA) Inc.

—Little White Horse. 2001. (gr. 5-8). lib. bdg. 14.15 (978-0-613-44399-9(3)) Tandem Library Bks.

Gray, Nigel. Oliver Twist Finds a Home. McLean, Andrew, illus. 2002. 32p. (YA). pap. 11.95 (978-1-876268-88-6(3)) Univ. of Western Australia Pr. AUS. *Dist:* International Specialized Bk. Services.

—Pip & the Convict. McLean, Andrew, illus. 2005. 32p. (J). 24.25 (978-1-920694-23-4(4)) ; pap. 15.25 (978-1-920694-66-1(8)) Univ. of Western Australia Pr. AUS. (Cygnet Bks.). *Dist:* International Specialized Bk. Services.

Greenburg, Dan. The Onts. Fischer, Scott M., illus. 2005. (Secrets of Dripping Fang Ser.: Bk. 1). 144p. (J). (gr. 3-7). 9.95 (978-0-15-205457-1(X)) Harcourt Children's Bks.

—Treachery & Betrayal at Jolly Days. Fischer, Scott M., illus. 2006. (Secrets of Dripping Fang Ser.: Bk. 2). 144p. (J). 9.95 (978-0-15-205463-2(4)) Harcourt Children's Bks.

Greenland, Shannon. Down to the Wire. 2007. (Specialists Ser.). 224p. (J). (gr. 5). 6.99 ***(978-0-14-240917-6(0)***, Puffin) Penguin Group (USA) Inc.

—Model Spy. 2007. (Specialists Ser.). 224p. (YA). pap. 6.99 (978-0-14-240849-0(2) , Puffin) Penguin Group (USA) Inc.

Greenland, Shannon. The Winning Element. 2008. (Specialists Ser.). 224p. (J). (gr. 5). 6.99 ***(*978-0-14-241052-3(7)***, Puffin) Penguin Group (USA) Inc.

Gregory, Kristiana. Journey of Faith. 2003. (gr. 3-6). lib. bdg. 13.00 (978-0-613-72119-6(5)) Tandem Library Bks.

—Orphan Runaways. (J). 2004. 160p. (gr. 4-7). pap. 4.99 (978-0-590-60367-6(1) , Scholastic Paperbacks); 1998. 144p. (gr. 3-7). pap. 15.95 (978-0-590-60366-9(3)) Scholastic, Inc.

Griffin, A. C. America's Child. (YA). pap. 9.99 (978-0-88092-492-4(6)) Royal Fireworks Publishing Co.

Grogan, Joy. Into the Fold. 2003. 156p. per. 15.00 (978-0-9740321-6-0(6)) Open Bk. Publishing.

Guzman, Lila. Lorenzo's Revolutionary Quest. 2003. (gr. 7-12). lib. bdg. 18.75 (978-0-613-84279-2(0)) Tandem Library Bks.

—Lorenzo's Secret Mission. 2001. (gr. 3-6). lib. bdg. 18.75 (978-0-613-84747-6(4)) Tandem Library Bks.

Guzman, Lila & Guzman, Rick. Lorenzo's Revolutionary Quest. 176p. (YA). pap. 9.95 (978-1-55885-392-8(8) , Piñata Books) Arte Publico Pr.

—Lorenzo's Secret Mission. 160p. (YA). pap. 9.95 (978-1-55885-341-6(3) , Piñata Books) Arte Publico Pr.

Haarsma, P. J. The Softwire: Virus on Orbis 1. 2008. (Illus.). 288p. (J). (gr. 5). 6.99 ***(*978-0-7636-3638-8(X))*** Candlewick Pr.

Haas, Jessie. Unbroken. 2001. 208p. (J). (gr. 5 up). pap. 6.99 (978-0-380-73313-2(7) , Harper Trophy) HarperCollins Pubs.

—Unbroken. l.t. ed. 2000. (Juvenile Ser.). 248p. (J). (gr. 4-7). 21.95 (978-0-7862-2769-3(9)) Thorndike Pr.

Hagman, Harvey Dixon. Majesty from Assateague. Aiken, David, illus. 2003. 76p. (J). pap. 8.95 (978-0-87033-552-5(9) , Tidewater Pubs.) Cornell Maritime Pr., Inc.

Hahn, Mary Downing. Anna on the Farm. 2001. lib. bdg. 14.15 (978-0-613-68401-9(X)) Tandem Library Bks.

—Promises to the Dead. 2000. 208p. (J). (gr. 5-9). tchr. ed. 15.00 (978-0-395-96394-4(X) , Clarion Bks.) Houghton Mifflin Co. Trade & Reference Div.

Haig, Matt. Samuel Blink & the Forbidden Forest. 2007. 352p. (J). 16.99 (978-0-399-24739-2(4) , Putnam Juvenile) Penguin Group (USA) Inc.

Hamilton, K. R. Caleb, Son of None. 2007. (J). pap. (978-0-7847-1859-9(8)) Standard Publishing.

Hamilton, K. R. A Freaky Kind of Courage. 2007. (J). ***(*978-0-7847-1909-1(8))*** Standard Publishing.

Hamilton, Kersten. The Battle of Trickum County. 2007. (Caleb Pascal & the Peculiar People Ser.). 141p. (J). per. 6.99 ***(*978-0-7847-1910-7(1))*** Standard Publishing.

—A Gathering of Brothers. 2007. (Caleb Pascal & the Peculiar People Ser.). 143p. (J). per. 6.99 ***(*978-0-7847-1911-4(X))*** Standard Publishing.

Hansen, Joyce. One True Friend. 2005. 160p. (J). (gr. 5-9). pap. 6.95 (978-0-618-60991-8(1) , Clarion Bks.) Houghton Mifflin Co. Trade & Reference Div.

Harley, Bill. The Amazing Flight of Darius Frobisher. 2006. (Illus.). 160p. (J). 14.95 (978-1-56145-381-8(1) , Peachtree Junior) Peachtree Pubs., Ltd.

Harlow, Joan Hiatt. Midnight Rider. 2006. 384p. (J). pap. 5.99 (978-0-689-87010-1(8) , Aladdin) Simon & Schuster Children's Publishing.

—Thunder from the Sea. 2004. (Illus.). 256p. (J). 16.99 (978-0-689-86403-2(5) , McElderry, Margaret K.) Simon & Schuster Children's Publishing.

Harlow, Joan Hiatt & Minor, Wendell. Midnight Rider. 2005. (Illus.). 416p. (J). 15.95 (978-0-689-87009-5(4) , McElderry, Margaret K.) Simon & Schuster Children's Publishing.

Harris, Christine. Undercover Girl #5: Twisted. 2007. 136p. (J). per. 10.95 ***(*978-1-59594-151-0(7)***, Wingspan Pr.) WingSpan Publishing.

Harris, Ruth Elwin. Julia's Story. 2002. (gr. 7-12). lib. bdg. 14.15 (978-0-613-74777-6(1)) Tandem Library Bks.

—Sarah's Story. 2002. (Quantock's Quartet Ser.). (Illus.). 288p. (YA). (gr. 7 up). pap. 5.99 (978-0-7636-1707-3(5)) Candlewick Pr.

—Sarah's Story. 2002. (gr. 7-12). lib. bdg. 14.15 (978-0-613-74779-0(8)) Tandem Library Bks.

Harrison, Barbara Grizzuti. Theo. 1999. 176p. (J). (gr. 5-9). tchr. ed. 15.00 (978-0-89919-959-7(3) , Clarion Bks.) Houghton Mifflin Co. Trade & Reference Div.

Harrison, Troon. A Bushel of Light. 2001. 244p. (gr. 7-9). pap. 7.95 (978-0-7737-6140-7(3)) Stoddart Kids CAN. *Dist:* Fitzhenry & Whiteside, Ltd.

—Bushel of Light. 2001. (gr. 5-8). lib. bdg. 16.40 (978-0-613-44633-4(X)) Tandem Library Bks.

Hartinger, Brent. The Last Chance Texaco. 2004. 240p. (J). 15.99 (978-0-06-050912-5(0) , HarperTeen) HarperCollins Pubs.

Harvey, Gill. Orphan of the Sun. 2006. (Illus.). 320p. (J). (gr. 5-8). 16.95 (978-1-58234-685-4(2) , Bloomsbury Children) Bloomsbury Publishing.

Hawes, Charles Boardman. The Dark Frigate. 2005. pap. 27.95 (978-1-4179-3209-2(0)) Kessinger Publishing, LLC.

Hawse, Alberta. Encounter Christ Through the Dramatic Story of Vinegar Boy. 2002. (Wholesome Adventure & Positive Influence for Today's Youth Ser.). 224p. (YA). pap. 9.99 (978-0-8024-6588-7(9)) Moody Pubs.

Helldorfer, Mary-Claire. Anne of Green Gables. Beier, Ellen, illus. 2003. 40p. (J). (gr. k-3). pap. 6.99 (978-0-440-41614-2(0) , Dragonfly Bks.) Random Hse. Children's Bks.

Hemphill, Kris. Ambush in the Wilderness. 2003. (Adventures in America Ser.). (Illus.). 90p. (J). 14.95 (978-1-893110-34-2(6)) Silver Moon Pr.

Hendry, Diana. Harvey Angell & the Ghost Child. 2002. (gr. 3-6). lib. bdg. 13.00 (978-0-613-57904-9(6)) Tandem Library Bks.

Hershenhorn, Esther. Fancy That. Lloyd, Megan, illus. 2003. 32p. (J). (gr. k-3). tchr. ed. 16.95 (978-0-8234-1605-9(4)) Holiday Hse., Inc.

Heuston, Kimberley B. The Shakeress. 1998. 208p. (YA). (gr. 7 up). 16.95 (978-1-886910-56-0(1) , Lemniscaat) Boyds Mills Pr.

Heuston, Kimberley Burton. The Shakeress. 2008. (J). pap. ***(*978-1-59078-575-1(4)***, Calkins Creek) Boyds Mills Pr.

Heuston, Kimberly. The Shakeress. 2004. 208p. (YA). pap. 6.99 (978-0-14-240054-8(8) , Puffin) Penguin Group (USA) Inc.

Hill, Elizabeth Starr. Wildfire! Shepperson, Rob, illus. 2004. 80p. (J). 16.00 (978-0-374-31712-6(7) , Farrar, Straus & Giroux (BYR)) Farrar, Straus & Giroux.

Hobbs, Will. Jason's Gold. 2000. (gr. 5-8). lib. bdg. 14.15 (978-0-613-29995-4(7)) Tandem Library Bks.

Hobbs, William. Jason's Gold. (Illus.). 240p. (J). (gr. 6 up). 2000. pap. 5.99 (978-0-380-72914-2(8)); 1999. 16.99 (978-0-688-15093-8(4)) HarperCollins Pubs.

—Jason's Gold. unabr. ed. 2004. 240p. (J). (gr. 5-9). pap. 38.00 incl. audio (978-0-8072-8229-8(4) , Listening Library) Random Hse. Audio Publishing Group.

—Jason's Gold. 2000. (J). (978-0-606-19979-7(9)) Tandem Library Bks.

Holm, Jennifer L. Boston Jane. 2002. (gr. 3-6). lib. bdg. 15.30 (978-0-613-56251-5(8)) Tandem Library Bks.

—Boston Jane: The Claim. l.t. ed. 2005. (Boston Jane Ser.). 288p. 22.95 (978-0-7862-7392-8(5) , Large Print Pr.) Thorndike Pr.

—Wilderness Days. (Boston Jane Ser.). 256p. (J). (gr. 5 up). 2004. pap. 5.99 (978-0-06-440881-3(7) , Harper Trophy); 2002. 16.99 (978-0-06-029043-6(9)); 2002. lib. bdg. 18.89 (978-0-06-029044-3(7)) HarperCollins Pubs.

Holtwijk, Inele. Asphalt Angels. Boeke, Wanda, tr. 2004. 184p. (YA). pap. 7.95 (978-1-886910-43-0(X) , Lemniscaat) Boyds Mills Pr.

Holub, Joan. Charlotte's Choice. 2003. (gr. 3-6). lib. bdg. 11.80 (978-0-613-72096-0(2)) Tandem Library Bks.

Holub, Josef. The Robber & Me. 1999. (J). (gr. 4-7). 19.25 (978-0-8446-7007-2(3)) Smith, Peter Pub., Inc.

—The Robber & Me. 1999. (978-0-606-15909-8(6)) Tandem Library Bks.

Hopkinson, Deborah. Into the Firestorm: A Novel of San Francisco, 1906. 2006. 208p. (J). (gr. 3-7). 15.95 (978-0-375-83652-7(7)); lib. bdg. 17.99 (978-0-375-93652-4(1)) Random Hse. Children's Bks. (Knopf Bks. for Young Readers).

—Into the Firestorm: A Novel of San Francisco 1906. 2008. 208p. (J). (gr. 4-7). 5.99 ***(*978-0-440-42129-0(2)***, Yearling) Random Hse. Children's Bks.

Hopkinson, Deborah. Sailing for Gold. Farnsworth, Bill, illus. 2004. (Ready-for-Chapters Ser.). 64p. (J). pap. 3.99 (978-0-689-86031-7(5) , Aladdin); lib. bdg. 11.89 (978-0-689-86032-4(3) , Aladdin Library) Simon & Schuster Children's Publishing.

—Sailing for Gold. 2004. (gr. k-3). lib. bdg. 11.80 (978-0-613-88994-0(0)) Tandem Library Bks.

Hoppenstedt, Elbert M. President Harrison's Horse Race. 2006. (ENG.). 48p. per. 12.95 (978-1-4241-5017-5(5)) PublishAmerica, Inc.

Horne, Constance. The Accidental Orphan. 2005. 144p. (YA). (gr. 3-8). pap., tchr. ed. (978-0-88878-385-1(X) , Sandcastle Bks.) Dundurn Group, The.

Horowitz, Anthony. Ark Angel. (Alex Rider Ser.: Bk. 6). 2007. 336p. (J). 7.99 (978-0-14-240738-7(0) , Puffin); 2006. 326p. (YA). (gr. 5). 17.99 (978-0-399-24152-9(3) , Philomel) Penguin Group (USA) Inc.

—Eagle Strike. (Alex Rider Ser.: Bk. 4). 2006. 352p. (J). (gr. 7). pap. 7.99 (978-0-14-240613-7(9) , Puffin); 2004. (Illus.). 272p. (YA). (gr. 4). 17.99 (978-0-399-23979-3(0) , Philomel) Penguin Group (USA) Inc.

—Eagle Strike. 2003. 352p. (YA). pap. (978-0-7445-9057-9(4)) Walker & Co.

—The Falcon's Malteser. 2004. (Diamond Brothers Ser.: No. 1). 208p. (J). (gr. 3-6). pap. 6.99 (978-0-14-240219-1(2) , Puffin) Penguin Group (USA) Inc.

—Point Blank. (Alex Rider Ser.: Bk. 2). 2006. 304p. (J). (gr. 7). pap. 7.99 (978-0-14-240612-0(0) , Puffin); 2002. 208p. (YA). (gr. 5 up). 17.99 (978-0-399-23621-1(X) , Philomel) Penguin Group (USA) Inc.

—Scorpia. (Alex Rider Ser.: Bk. 5). (YA). (gr. 5). 2006. 400p. pap. 7.99 (978-0-14-240578-9(7) , Puffin); 2005. 320p. 17.99 (978-0-399-24151-2(5) , Philomel) Penguin Group (USA) Inc.

—Skeleton Key. (Alex Rider Ser.: Bk. 3). 2006. 352p. (J). (gr. 7). pap. 7.99 (978-0-14-240614-4(7) , Puffin); 2003. 240p. (YA). (gr. 5). 17.99 (978-0-399-23777-5(1) , Philomel) Penguin Group (USA) Inc.

—Snakehead. 2007. 400p. (J). (gr. 5). 17.99 ***(*978-0-399-24161-1(2)***, Philomel) Penguin Group (USA) Inc.

—Stormbreaker. (Alex Rider Ser.: Bk. 1). 2006. 256p. (J). (gr. 7). pap. 7.99 (978-0-14-240611-3(2) , Puffin); 2002. (Illus.). (J). (gr. 4-7). 5.99 (978-0-698-11932-1(0) , Puffin); 2001. (Illus.). 1p. (YA). (gr. 5 up). 17.99 (978-0-399-23620-4(1) , Philomel); 2006. 264p. (J). (gr. 5). 7.99 (978-0-14-240656-4(2) , Puffin) Penguin Group (USA) Inc.

—Stormbreaker. 2004. (Alex Rider Ser.: Bk. 1). 208p. (J). (gr. 4-7). pap. 38.00 incl. audio (978-0-8072-2277-5(1) , Listening Library) Random Hse. Audio Publishing Group.

—Stormbreaker: The Graphic Novel. Kanako & Yuzuru, illus. 2006. (Alex Rider Ser.). 144p. (J). (gr. 4). pap. 14.99 (978-0-399-24633-3(9) , Philomel) Penguin Group (USA) Inc.

Howell, Robert. Third Times the Charm. 2007. 224p. (J). (gr. 1-7). pap. 10.95 ***(*978-1-897235-20-1(8))*** Thistledown Pr., Ltd. CAN. *Dist:* Fitzhenry & Whiteside, Ltd.

Humphrey, Robert. The Christmas Poodle. 2004. 112p. 9.95 (978-1-58961-029-3(6)); 19.95 (978-1-58961-040-8(7)) PageFree Publishing, Inc.

—The Christmas Poodle Christmas Wish. 2004. 9.95 (978-1-58961-201-3(9)) PageFree Publishing, Inc.

Hurst, Carol Otis. Through the Lock. 2001. 176p. (J). (gr. 5-9). tchr. ed. 15.00 (978-0-618-03036-1(0) , Walter Lorraine) Houghton Mifflin Co. Trade & Reference Div.

Hurwitz, Johanna. Dear Emma. 2002. (Illus.). 160p. (J). 15.99 (978-0-06-029840-1(5)) HarperCollins Pubs.

Hussey, Charmian. The Valley of Secrets. Crump, Christopher, illus. 400p. 2006. (J). pap. 9.99 (978-1-4169-0015-3(2) , Simon Pulse); 2005. (YA). 17.95 (978-0-689-87862-6(1)) Simon & Schuster Children's Publishing.

Hutchinson, Emily. Oliver Twist. abr. ed. 2001. (gr. 7-12). lib. bdg. 15.25 (978-0-613-36566-6(6)) Tandem Library Bks.

Ibbotson, Eva. Dial-a-Ghost. Hawkes, Kevin, illus. 2003. 224p. (J). (gr. 3-6). pap. 5.99 (978-0-14-250018-7(6) , Puffin) Penguin Group (USA) Inc.

—Dial-a-Ghost. 2003. (gr. 3-6). lib. bdg. 14.15 (978-0-613-61618-8(9)) Tandem Library Bks.

—Dial-a-Ghost. Hawkes, Kevin, illus. l.t. ed. 2002. 212p. (J). 22.95 (978-0-7862-3927-6(1)) Thomson Gale.

—Journey to the River Sea. Hawkes, Kevin, illus. 2002. 336p. (J). (gr. 4-8). 17.99 (978-0-525-46739-7(4) , Dutton Juvenile) Penguin Group (USA) Inc.

—Journey to the River Sea. 2003. (gr. 3-6). lib. bdg. 14.15 (978-0-613-86704-7(1)) Tandem Library Bks.

—Journey to the River Sea. Hawkes, Kevin, illus. 2003. 304p. (J). (gr. 3-7). pap. 5.99 (978-0-14-250184-9(0) , Puffin) Penguin Group (USA) Inc.

Imbernon, Maite & Dickens, Charles. Oliver Twist. 2003. (Timeless Classics Ser.). (SPA., Illus.). 92p. (J). pap. 10.95 (978-84-204-5750-5(7)) Santillana USA Publishing Co., Inc.

Inman, Robert. Christmas Bus. Baskin, Lyle, illus. 2006. 84p. (J). 19.95 (978-0-9760963-6-8(6)) Novello Festival Pr.

Irvine, Patricia McCune. Pedro & Mac. 2000. 128p. (J). (gr. 4-7). pap. 9.95 (978-0-595-14507-2(8)) iUniverse, Inc.

Jackson, Dave. Roundup of the Street Rovers. 2001. (gr. 3-6). lib. bdg. 14.15 (978-0-613-82920-5(4)) Tandem Library Bks.

—Sinking the Dayspring: John G. Paton. 2001. (gr. 3-6). lib. bdg. 14.15 (978-0-613-82919-9(0)) Tandem Library Bks.

Jackson, Dave & Jackson, Neta. The Mayflower Secret: Governor William Bradford. Jackson, Julian & McLaughlin, Catherine R., illus. 1998. (Trailblazer Bks.: Vol. 26). 160p. (J). (gr. 3-7). pap. 6.99 (978-0-7642-2010-4(1)) Bethany Hse. Pubs.

—Roundup of the Street Rovers: Charles Loring Brace. Gavitt, Anne, illus. 2001. (Trailblazer Bks.: Vol. 36). 160p. (J). (gr. 3-7). reprint ed. pap. 6.99 (978-0-7642-2269-6(4)) Bethany Hse. Pubs.

Jacques, Brian. Voyage of Slaves. (Castaways of the Flying Dutchman Ser.: No. 3). 2007. 320p. (gr. 12). mass mkt. 7.99 ***(*978-0-441-01528-3(X)***, Ace Bks.); 2006. (Illus.). 368p. (YA). (gr. 5). 23.99 (978-0-399-24549-7(9) , Philomel) Penguin Group (USA) Inc.

James, Will. Cowboy in the Making. rev. ed. (Illus.). 104p. (gr. 4-6). pap. 15.00 (978-0-87842-439-9(3) , 811) Mountain Pr. Publishing Co., Inc.

Jarvis, Robin. The Whitby Witches. Petersen, Jeff, illus. 2006. 296p. (J). 17.95 (978-0-8118-5413-9(2)) Chronicle Bks. LLC.

Jarvis, Robin & Jarvis, Robert M. The Alchemist's Cat. 2004. 320p. (YA). 17.95 (978-1-58717-257-1(7) , Sea-Star Bks.) Chronicle Bks. LLC.

Jeram, Anita. All Together Now. Jeram, Anita, illus. 2005. (Illus.). 40p. (J). (gr. k-k). reprint ed. pap. 5.99 (978-0-7636-2690-7(2)) Candlewick Pr.

Jinks, Catherine. Pagan's Crusade. 2003. (Pagan Chronicles Ser.: Bk. 1). (Illus.). 256p. (YA). 15.99 (978-0-7636-2019-6(X)) Candlewick Pr.

—Pagan's Daughter. 2008. (YA). ***(*978-0-7636-3650-0(9))*** Candlewick Pr.

Jinks, Catherine. Pagan's Scribe. 2006. (Pagan Chronicles Ser.: Bk. 4). 368p. (YA). (gr. 7). pap. 6.99 (978-0-7636-2973-1(1)) Candlewick Pr.

Johnson, Nancy. A Sweet-Sounding Place: A Civil War Story. 2007. 160p. (gr. 5-9). 14.95 ***(*978-0-89272-757-5(8))*** Down East Bks.

Johnston, Adam & Eve & Pinch-Me. 2003. (gr. 7-12). lib. bdg. 18.75 (978-0-613-77312-6(8)) Tandem Library Bks.

Joosse, Barbara M. Nikolai, the Only Bear. Liwska, Renata, illus. 2005. 32p. (J). (ps-3). 16.99 (978-0-399-23884-0(0) , Philomel) Penguin Group (USA) Inc.

Katschke, Judy & Hogan, Mary. Dinosaurs: Two of a Kind. 2000. (Dinosaur Ser.). (Illus.). 32p. (J). (gr. k-2). pap. 3.99 (978-0-7868-4388-6(8)) Disney Pr.

Kehret, Peg. The Hideout. 2002. (gr. 3-6). lib. bdg. 13.00 (978-0-613-63944-6(8)) Tandem Library Bks.

Kelton, Elmer. Cloudy in the West. 1999. (gr. 7-12). lib. bdg. 18.75 (978-0-613-28796-8(7)) Tandem Library Bks.

Kennedy, X. J. Owlstone Crown. 2005. 176p. (J). pap. (978-1-932425-35-2(7) , Lemniscaat) Boyds Mills Pr.

Ketchum, Liza. Orphan Journey Home. 2002. 144p. (J). pap. 5.99 (978-0-380-80988-2(5)) HarperCollins Pubs.

Ketchum, Liza & Mordan, C. B. Orphan Journey Home. 2000. (Illus.). 176p. (J). (gr. 3-7). 15.99 (978-0-380-97811-3(3)) HarperCollins Pubs.

Key, Watt. Alabama Moon. 2006. 304p. (J). 16.00 (978-0-374-30184-2(0)) Farrar, Straus & Giroux.

Kindl, Patrice. Goose Chase. 2001. 224p. (J). (gr. 5-9). tchr. ed. 16.00 (978-0-618-03377-5(7)) Houghton Mifflin Co. Trade & Reference Div.

—Goose Chase. 2002. 224p. (YA). pap. 5.99 (978-0-14-230208-8(2) , Puffin) Penguin Group (USA) Inc.

—Goose Chase. 2002. (gr. 5-8). lib. bdg. 14.15 (978-0-613-60805-3(4)) Tandem Library Bks.

Kirkpatrick, Katherine. The Voyage of the Continental. 2002. (Illus.). 256p. (J). (gr. 7 up). tchr. ed. 16.95 (978-0-8234-1580-9(5)) Holiday Hse., Inc.

Klearman-Cooper, Mel. The Dirty Little Orphan Girl. 2005. 50p. pap. 12.95 (978-1-4137-5891-7(6)) PublishAmerica, Inc.

Kluger, Jeffrey. Nacky Patcher & the Curse of the Dry-Land Boats. Elliot, David, illus. 2007. 384p. (YA). (gr. 4 up). 18.99 (978-0-399-24604-3(5) , Philomel) Penguin Group (USA) Inc.

Koertge, Ron. Strays. 2006. 176p. (YA). (gr. 9 up). 16.99 (978-0-7636-2705-8(4)) Candlewick Pr.

Koge-Donbo. Kamichama Karin, Vol. 5. 5th rev. ed. 2006. pap. 9.99 (978-1-59816-186-1(5) , Tokyopop Kids) TOKYOPOP, Inc.

Koja, Kathe. Buddha Boy. 2003. 128p. (YA). (gr. 7 up). 16.00 (978-0-374-30998-5(1) , Farrar, Straus & Giroux (BYR)) Farrar, Straus & Giroux.

—Buddha Boy. 2004. 128p. (YA). (gr. 6-11). reprint ed. pap. 5.99 (978-0-14-240209-2(5) , Puffin) Penguin Group (USA) Inc.

—Buddha Boy. l.t. ed. 2003. 113p. (J). 24.95 (978-0-7862-6012-6(2)) Thomson Gale.

LaFaye, A. Worth. unabr. ed. 2006. (Live Oak Histories Ser.). (J). (gr. 3-6). pap. 28.95 incl. audio compact disk ***(*978-1-59519-767-2(2))*** Live Oak Media.

—Worth. 2004. (Illus.). 160p. (J). (gr. 4-7). 16.99 (978-0-689-85730-0(6)) Simon & Schuster Children's Publishing.

Laird, Marnie. Water Rat. 2001. (J). (978-0-606-21511-4(5)) Tandem Library Bks.

—Water Rat. 2001. 192p. (J). (gr. 4-7). pap. 5.95 (978-1-58837-002-0(X)) Winslow Pr.

Landowne, Youme. Selavi, That Is Life: A Haitian Story of Hope. 2005. (Illus.). 40p. (ps-7). pap. 8.95 (978-0-938317-95-1(4)) Cinco Puntos Pr.

Langrish, Katherine. Troll Fell. (J). 2005. 368p. (gr. 7 up). pap. 6.99 (978-0-06-058306-4(1)); 2004. (Illus.). 272p. (gr. 5 up). 16.99 (978-0-06-058304-0(5)); 2004. (Illus.). 272p. (gr. 5 up). lib. bdg. 16.89 (978-0-06-058305-7(3)) HarperCollins Pubs.

Langrish, Katherine. Troll Mill. (J). 2008. 384p. 7.99 ***(*978-0-06-058309-5(6)***, Eos); 2006. (Illus.). 288p. 15.99 (978-0-06-058307-1(X)); 2006. (Illus.). 288p. lib. bdg. 17.89 (978-0-06-058308-8(8)) HarperCollins Pubs.

Larson, Kirby. Hattie Big Sky. 2006. 304p. (J). (gr. 7). 15.95 (978-0-385-73313-7(5)); lib. bdg. 17.99 (978-0-385-90332-5(4)) Random Hse. Children's Bks. (Delacorte Bks. for Young Readers).

—Hattie Big Sky. l.t. ed. 2007. 400p. (YA). 23.95 ***(*978-0-7862-9697-2(6))*** Thorndike Pr.

Lavender, William. Just Jane: A Daughter of England Caught in the Struggle of the American Revolution. (Great Episodes Ser.). (YA). 2005. 336p. pap. 6.95 (978-0-15-205472-4(3)); 2002. 288p. 17.00 (978-0-15-202587-8(1)) Harcourt Children's Bks. (Gulliver Bks.).

Lawlor, Laurie. Dead Reckoning: A Pirate Voyage with Captain Drake. 2007. 336p. (J). pap. 5.99 (978-0-689-86578-7(3) , Aladdin) Simon & Schuster Children's Publishing.

Lawlor, Laurie & Barkat, Jonathan. Dead Reckoning: A Pirate Voyage with Captain Drake. 2005. (Illus.). 272p. (J). 15.95 (978-0-689-86577-0(5) , Simon & Schuster Children's Publishing) Simon & Schuster Children's Publishing.

Le Feuvre, Amy. Harebell's Friend. 2004. (Golden Inheritance Ser.: Vol. 8). (Illus.). 140p. (J). pap. (978-0-921100-84-3(1)) Inheritance Pubns.

LeapFrog Staff, compiled by. The Secret Garden. 2001. (J). spiral bd. 14.99 (978-1-58605-043-6(5)) LeapFrog Enterprises, Inc.

Lee, Tanith. Wolf Tower. 2001. (Claidi Journals: Bk. 1). (gr. 7-12). lib. bdg. 15.30 (978-0-613-44433-0(7)) Tandem Library Bks.

Lemire, Jeff. Essex County Vol. 1: Tales from the Farm. 2007. (Illus.). 112p. (YA). pap. 9.95 ***(*978-1-891830-88-4(0))*** Top Shelf Productions.

—Essex County Vol. 2: Ghost Stories. 2007. (Illus.). 112p. (YA). pap. 14.95 ***(*978-1-891830-94-5(5))*** Top Shelf Productions.

L'Engle, Madeleine. The Joys of Love. 2008. 272p. (YA). 16.95 ***(*978-0-374-33870-1(1))*** Farrar, Straus & Giroux.

M
N
O

L'Engle, Madeleine. Meet the Austins. 2002. (Austin Family Ser.: No. 1). (Illus.). (J). 13.94 (978-0-7587-8955-6(6)) Book Wholesalers, Inc.

Leppard, Lois Gladys. Mandie & Joe's Christmas Surprise. 2000. (Mandie Bks.). (Illus.). 128p. (J). (gr. 3-9). pap. 4.99 (978-0-7642-2414-0(X)) Bethany Hse. Pubs.

Lethcoe, Jason. You Wish, No. 1. Lethcoe, Jason, illus. 2007. (Misadventures of Benjamin Bartholomew Piff Ser.: No. 1). (Illus.). 224p. (J). (gr. 4-7). 9.99 (978-0-448-44496-3(8) , Grosset & Dunlap) Penguin Group (USA) Inc.

Levine, Ellen. The Journal of Jedediah Barstow: An Emigrant on the Oregon Trail. 2002. (My Name Is America Ser.). (Illus.). 176p. (J). (gr. 4-9). pap. 10.95 (978-0-439-06310-4(8) , Scholastic Pr.) Scholastic, Inc.

Levine, Gail Carson. Dave at Night. 1999. (YA). pap., stu. ed. 69.95 incl. audio (978-0-7887-3794-7(5) , 41038) Recorded Bks., LLC.

—Dave at Night. 2001. (ps-7). 281p. (J). lib. bdg. 14.15 (978-0-613-34669-6(6)); 12.64 (978-0-606-21137-6(3)) Tandem Library Bks.

Lightle, Lugenia L. Ruguma: New to America. 2005. 135p. pap. 19.95 (978-1-4137-6723-0(0)) PublishAmerica, Inc.

Like Mike. novel ed. 2002. 112p. (J). pap. 4.99 (978-0-439-44527-6(2)) Scholastic, Inc.

Lincoln, Christopher. Billy Bones. 2007. 208p. (J). (978-0-316-01473-1(7)) Little Brown & Co.

Lincoln Collier, James. The Corn Raid. 2004. 142p. (J). lib. bdg. 16.92 (***978-1-4242-0768-8(1)***) Fitzgerald Bks.

Lindgren, Astrid. The Red Bird. Crampton, Patricia, tr. from SWE. Tornqvist, Marit, illus. 2005. 48p. (J). reprint ed. pap. 16.95 (978-0-439-62796-2(6) , Levine, Arthur A. Bks.) Scholastic, Inc.

Lindgren, Astrid & Crampton, Patricia. The Red Bird. Tornqvist, Marit, illus. 2005. (J). 5.99 (978-0-439-62797-9(4) , Levine, Arthur A. Bks.) Scholastic, Inc.

Lisle, Janet Taylor. The Crying Rocks. (Illus.). (YA). 2005. 288p. (gr. 7-12). mass mkt. 6.99 (978-0-689-85320-3(3) , Simon Pulse); 2003. 208p. 16.95 (978-0-689-85319-7(X) , Atheneum/Richard Jackson Bks.) Simon & Schuster Children's Publishing.

—The Crying Rocks. l.t. ed. 2004. (Thorndike Press Large Print Literacy Bridge Ser.). 273p. (J). 22.95 (978-0-7862-6140-6(4)) Thorndike Pr.

Literature Connections English: Jane Eyre. 2004. (gr. 6-12). (978-0-395-77557-8(4) , 2-80126) McDougal Littell Inc.

Literature Connections Spanish: Jane Eyre. 2004. (gr. 6-12). (978-0-395-81741-4(2) , 2-70491) McDougal Littell Inc.

Llorente, Pilar Molina. Aura Gris. (SPA.). 192p. (YA). (gr. 5-8). (978-84-216-0993-4(9) , BU3870) Bruño, Editorial ESP. *Dist:* Lectorum Pubns., Inc.

Lloyd-Jones, Robin. Moonfleet. 2007. (Young Reading Series 3 Gift Bks). 64p. (J). 8.99 (***978-0-7945-1906-3(7)*** , Usborne) EDC Publishing.

London, Victoria. Emily Cobbs & the Naked School Bk. 1: A Gifted Girls Series. 2005. (Gifted Girls Ser.). (J). per. 7.99 (978-1-59748-857-0(7)) Sparklesoup Studios, Inc.

—Emily Cobbs Collection, Bks. 1 & 2. 2nd ed. 2005. (Gifted Girls Ser.). 164p. (J). pap. 10.95 (978-1-59748-358-2(3)) Sparklesoup Studios, Inc.

—Emily Cobbs Collection Bk. 1 & Bk. 2: A Gifted Girls Series. 2005. (Gifted Girls Ser.). (J). per. 12.95 (978-1-59748-859-4(3)) Sparklesoup Studios, Inc.

Long, Donna Lee. A Guide for Using Boxcar Children: Surprise Island in the Classroom. 2000. (Literature Units Ser.). (Illus.). 48p. (J). pap., tchr. ed. 7.99 (978-1-57690-338-4(9) , TCM 2338) Teacher Created Materials, Inc.

Love, D. Anne. The Puppeteer's Apprentice. 192p. (J). 2003. 16.95 (978-0-689-84424-9(7) , McElderry, Margaret K.); 2004. (Illus.). reprint ed. pap. 4.99 (978-0-689-84425-6(5) , Aladdin) Simon & Schuster Children's Publishing.

Lowry, Lois. Gathering Blue. 2000. (Illus.). 224p. (YA). (gr. 7 up). 16.00 (978-0-618-05581-4(9) , Mariner Bks.) Houghton Mifflin Co. Trade & Reference Div.

—Gathering Blue. unabr. ed. 2004. (Middle Grade Cassette Librariestm Ser.). 224p. (J). (gr. 5-9). pap. 38.00 incl. audio (978-0-8072-0989-9(9) , S YA 250 SP, Listening Library) Random Hse. Audio Publishing Group.

—Gathering Blue. (YA). (gr. 7). 2006. 240p. pap. 8.95 (978-0-385-73256-7(2) , Delacorte Bks. for Young Readers); 2005. 224p. mass mkt. 6.99 (978-0-553-49478-5(3) , Bantam Bks. for Young Readers); 2002. 224p. mass mkt. 6.50 (978-0-440-22949-0(9) , Laurel Leaf) Random Hse. Children's Bks.

—Gathering Blue. 2002. (gr. 5-8). lib. bdg. 14.75 (978-0-613-57593-5(8)) Tandem Library Bks.

—Gathering Blue. l.t. ed. 2000. 256p. (J). (gr. 8-12). 22.95 (978-0-7862-3048-8(7)) Thorndike Pr.

Lowry, Lois. The Willoughbys. 2008. (J). (***978-0-618-97974-5(3)***) Houghton Mifflin Co.

Lucado, Max. Just the Way You Are. Martinez, Sergio, illus. 1999. Orig. Title: Children of the King. 31p. (ps-5). reprint ed. 15.99 (978-1-58134-114-0(8) , Crossway Bibles) Crossway Bks.

Lupica, Mike. Heat. 2007. 240p. (J). pap. 6.99 (978-0-14-240757-8(7) , Puffin); 2006. 220p. (YA). (gr. 5). 16.99 (978-0-399-24301-1(1) , Philomel) Penguin Group (USA) Inc.

Lutz, Norma Jean. Trouble on the Ohio River: Drought Shuts Down a City, 1999. (American Adventure Ser.: No. 15). 144p. (J). (gr. 3-7). lib. bdg. 15.95 (978-0-7910-5588-5(4) , Chelsea Hse.) Facts On File, Inc.

Luxa, Sue. Denver Days. 2004. (Illus.). 82p. (J). pap. 8.95 (978-1-890437-98-5(0) , 1234247) Western Reflections Publishing Co.

MacDonald, George. A Rough Shaking. 2006. 66.99 (***978-1-4280-3048-0(4)***) IndyPublish.com.

MacDonald, George. Sir Gibbie. Lindskoog, Kathryn, ed. Wynne, Patrick, illus. 2001. (Classics for Young Readers Ser.). 224p. (J). (gr. 3-6). pap. 7.99 (978-0-87552-726-0(4)) P & R Publishing.

Macguire, Gregory. Missing Sisters. 1998. (J). (978-0-606-13612-9(6)) Tandem Library Bks.

MacKall, Dandi Daley. All the King's Horses, Vol. 8. 2001. (Horsefeathers Ser.: Vol. 8). (Illus.). 192p. (J). (gr. 7-11). 5.99 (978-0-570-07129-7(1)) Concordia Publishing Hse.

—Horsefeathers. 2000. (gr. 7-12). lib. bdg. 14.15 (978-0-613-72829-4(7)) Tandem Library Bks.

—Horsefeathers' Mystery. 2001. (gr. 7-12). lib. bdg. 14.15 (978-0-613-72845-4(9)) Tandem Library Bks.

—Horsefeathers Mystery, Vol. 7. 2001. (Horsefeathers Ser.: Vol. 7). (Illus.). 192p. (J). (gr. 7-12). 5.99 (978-0-570-07128-0(3)) Concordia Publishing Hse.

Malcolm, Jahnna N. The Stallion of Box Canyon. Rabinowitz, Sandy & Keiffer, Christa, illus. l.t. ed. 1999. (Treasured Horses Collection). 122p. (J). (gr. 4 up). lib. bdg. 23.33 (978-0-8368-2283-0(8)) Stevens, Gareth Inc.

Malot, Hector & Crewe-Jones, Florence. Nobody's Boy: Companion Story to Nobody's Girl. Gooch, Thelma & Gruelle, Johnny, illus. 2006. 237p. (J). pap. (978-1-894666-75-6(5)) Inheritance Pubns.

—Nobody's Girl: Companion Story to Nobody's Boy. Gooch, Thelma, illus. 2006. 220p. (J). pap. (978-1-894666-76-3(3)) Inheritance Pubns.

Markowicz, Elaine C. Bride of the Blood Moon. 2004. 190p. pap. 19.95 (978-1-4137-3927-5(X)) PublishAmerica, Inc.

Marryat, Frederick. The Children of the New Forest. fac. ed. 2000. 341p. pap. 15.95 (978-1-4021-9975-2(9) , Elibron Classics) Adamant Media.

—The Children of the New Forest. 2004. reprint ed. pap. 28.95 (978-1-4191-5655-7(1)); pap. 1.99 (978-1-4192-5655-4(6)) Kessinger Publishing, LLC.

Marshall, Felicity. Sage's Ark. 2000. 32p. (J). (Illus.). pap. 12.95 (978-1-86368-253-4(8)); 21.95 (978-1-86368-290-9(2)) Fremantle Pr. AUS. *Dist:* International Specialized Bk. Services.

Martel, Yann. Life of Pi: A Novel. 2003. (gr. 7-12). lib. bdg. 23.45 (978-0-613-59907-8(1)) Tandem Library Bks.

Martin, Jacqueline Briggs. The Water Gift & the Pig of the Pig. Wingerter, Linda S., illus. 2003. 32p. (J). (gr. k-3). tchr. ed. 15.00 (978-0-618-07436-5(8)) Houghton Mifflin Co. Trade & Reference Div.

Maselli, Christopher P. N. The Quest for the Second Half. 1998. (Commander Kellie & the Superkids' Early Adventures Ser.). (J). pap. (978-1-57562-216-3(5)) Copeland, Kenneth Pubns.

Matcheck, Diane. The Sacrifice. 1999. (978-0-606-17598-2(9)) Tandem Library Bks.

Matute, Ana M. El Polizon del Ulises. (SPA.). 96p. (J). (978-84-264-3401-2(0) , LM4015) Editorial Lumen ESP. *Dist:* Lectorum Pubns., Inc.

Mazer, Norma Fox. Girlhearts. 2001. 224p. (J). (gr. 5 up). 15.99 (978-0-688-13350-4(9)) HarperCollins Pubs.

—Girlhearts. 2002. (gr. 7-12). lib. bdg. 15.30 (978-0-613-58571-2(2)) Tandem Library Bks.

McAdoo, Grami. Adventures of Sergeant Socks: The Journey Home. 2003. (gr. 5-8). lib. bdg. 18.75 (978-0-613-85568-6(X)) Tandem Library Bks.

McAllister, M. I. Urchin of the Riding Stars. Rayyan, Omar, illus. 2006. (Mistmantle Chronicles Ser.: Bk. 1). 288p. (gr. 3-7). pap. 7.99 (978-0-7868-5487-5(1)) Hyperion Bks. for Children.

McDaniel, Lurlene. The Girl Death Left Behind. 1999. 192p. (YA). (gr. 7-12). pap. 5.50 (978-0-553-57091-5(9) , Laurel Leaf) Random Hse. Children's Bks.

—The Girl Death Left Behind. 1999. (J). 11.64 (978-0-606-16371-2(9)); (gr. 7-12). lib. bdg. 13.00 (978-0-613-16116-9(5)) Tandem Library Bks.

McDonald, Megan. Shadows in the Glasshouse. 2000. (American Girl Collection). (Illus.). (J). (978-0-606-20906-9(9)) Tandem Library Bks.

McGraw-Hill - Jamestown Education Staff. Aliens & UFOs. 1999. (Wordsworth Classics Ser.). (gr. 6-12). pap. 16.64 (978-0-89061-104-3(1) , 9780890611043) Jamestown.

McHugh, Fiona, adapted by. Anne of Green Gables Storybook. 2007. (Illus.). 80p. (J). (gr. 2-7). pap. 9.95 (978-0-920668-42-9(9)) Firefly Bks., Ltd.

McKinstry, J. A. The Adventures of the 31st Street Saints: Book 1: the Eno. 2007. pap. 10.99 (***978-1-59886-892-0(6)***) Tate Publishing & Enterprises, L.L.C.

McNab, Andy & Rigby, Robert. Meltdown. 2008. 276p. (YA). (gr. 7). 16.99 (***978-0-399-24686-9(X)*** , Putnam Juvenile) Penguin Group (USA) Inc.

—Payback. 2006. 272p. (YA). (ps-k). 16.99 (978-0-399-24465-0(4) , Putnam Juvenile) Penguin Group (USA) Inc.

—Traitor. 2006. 288p. (YA). (gr. 7). pap. 6.99 (978-0-14-240727-1(5) , Puffin) Penguin Group (USA) Inc.

McNaughton, Janet. The Secret under My Skin. (J). 2006. 368p. pap. 6.99 (978-0-06-008991-7(1)); 2005. 272p. (gr. 7 up). 15.99 (978-0-06-008989-4(X)); 2005. 272p. (gr. 7 up). lib. bdg. 16.89 (978-0-06-008990-0(3)) HarperCollins Pubs.

Meeker, Clare Hodgson. Lootas, the Little Wave-Eater: An Orphaned Sea Otter's Story. Casson, C. J., photos by. 2002. (Illus.). 48p. (J). (gr. 1-5). pap. 12.95 (978-1-57061-164-3(5)) Sasquatch Bks.

Meyer, Carolyn. Duchessina: A Novel of Catherine de' Medici. 2007. (Young Royals Ser.). (Illus.). 272p. (YA). 17.00 (978-0-15-205588-2(6)) Harcourt Children's Bks.

Meyer, Kai. The Glass Word. Crawford, Elizabeth D., tr. from GER. 2008. (Dark Reflections Trilogy Ser.). 288p. (YA). (gr. 7 up). 16.99 (***978-0-689-87791-9(9)*** , McElderry, Margaret K.) Simon & Schuster Children's Publishing.

—Pirate Curse. Crawford, Elizabeth D., tr. from GER. 2006. (Wave Walkers Ser.). 336p. (J). (gr. 5-9). 15.95 (978-1-4169-2421-0(3) , McElderry, Margaret K.) Simon & Schuster Children's Publishing.

—The Stone Light. Crawford, Elizabeth D., tr. (Dark Reflections Trilogy Ser.). (YA). 2007. 384p. pap. 8.99 (***978-0-689-87790-2(0)*** , Simon Pulse); 2006. 368p. (gr. 7 up). 16.95 (978-0-689-87789-6(7) , McElderry, Margaret K.) Simon & Schuster Children's Publishing.

Meyer, Kai. The Water Mirror. Crawford, Elizabeth D., tr. 2006. (Dark Reflections Trilogy Ser.). 272p. (YA). pap. 7.99 (978-0-689-87788-9(9) , Simon Pulse); 2005. (Dark Reflections Ser.: Bk. 1). 256p. (J). (gr. 7 up). 15.95 (978-0-689-87787-2(0) , McElderry, Margaret K.) Simon & Schuster Children's Publishing.

—The Water Mirror. l.t. ed. 2006. 260p. (YA). 22.95 (978-0-7862-8288-3(6)) Thorndike Pr.

Meyer, Kai & Crawford, Elizabeth D. The Water Mirror. 2005. (J). (978-978-068-987-2(7) , McElderry, Margaret K.) Simon & Schuster Children's Publishing.

Meyer, L. A. Mississippi Jack: Being an Account of the Further Waterborne Adventures of Jacky Faber, Midshipman, Fine Lady, & Lily of the West. 2007. (Bloody Jack Adventures Ser.). (Illus.). 624p. (YA). (gr. 7 up). 17.00 (***978-0-15-206003-9(0)***) Harcourt Trade Pubs.

Meyer, L. A. Under the Jolly Roger: Being an Account of the Further Nautical Adventures of Jacky Faber. 2007. (Bloody Jack Adventures Ser.). (Illus.). 544p. (YA). pap. 6.95 (978-0-15-205873-9(7) , Harcourt Paperbacks) Harcourt Children's Bks.

—Under the Jolly Roger: Being an Account of the Further Nautical Adventures of Jacky Faber. 2005. (Bloody Jack Adventures Ser.). (Illus.). 528p. (YA). (gr. 7-17). 17.00 (978-0-15-205345-1(X)) Harcourt Trade Pubs.

Meyer, Louis A. Bloody Jack: Being an Account of the Curious Adventures of Mary Jacky Faber, Ship's Boy. 2002. (Bloody Jack Adventures Ser.). (Illus.). 336p. (YA). (gr. 6-9). 17.00 (978-0-15-216731-8(5)) Harcourt Children's Bks.

—Curse of the Blue Tattoo: Being an Account of the Misadventures of Jacky Faber, Midshipman & Fine Lady. 2004. (Bloody Jack Adventures Ser.). (Illus.). 496p. (YA). 17.00 (978-0-15-205115-0(5)) Harcourt Children's Bks.

Meyer, Louis A. & Nielsen, Cliff. In the Belly of the Bloodhound: Being an Account of a Particularly Peculiar Adventure in the Life of Jacky Faber. 2006. (Bloody Jack Adventures Ser.). (Illus.). 528p. (J). (gr. 8 up). 17.00 (978-0-15-205557-8(6)) Harcourt Children's Bks.

Michael, Livi. The Whispering Road. 2006. 336p. (J). (gr. 5). pap. 6.99 (978-0-14-240724-0(0) , Puffin); 2005. 272p. (YA). (gr. 4). 17.99 (978-0-399-24357-8(7) , Putnam Juvenile) Penguin Group (USA) Inc.

Miklowitz, Gloria. Secrets in the House of Delgado. 2001. (gr. 5-8). lib. bdg. 15.30 (978-0-613-55662-0(3)) Tandem Library Bks.

Miklowitz, Gloria D. Secrets in the House of Delgado. 2004. 192p. (J). (gr. 4 up). pap. 8.00 (978-0-8028-5210-6(6)) Eerdmans, William B. Publishing Co.

Mills, Wilmer. Light for the Orphans. 2002. (First Book Ser.). 64p. pap. 12.95 (978-1-58654-015-9(7)) Story Line Pr.

Molesworth, Mary Louisa. The Cuckoo Clock. 2004. reprint ed. pap. 19.95 (978-1-4191-5839-1(2)); pap. 1.99 (978-1-4192-5839-8(7)) Kessinger Publishing, LLC.

Montgomery, L. M. Akin to Anne: Tales of Other Orphans. (YA). 22.95 (978-0-8488-2656-7(6)) Amereon LTD.

—Ana la de Avonlea. 5th ed. (Coleccion "Ana, la de Tejas Verdes"). (SPA., Illus.). 254p. (YA). (gr. 5-8). (978-84-7888-632-6(X) , SAL3943) Emece Editores ESP. *Dist:* Lectorum Pubns., Inc.

—Ana la de Avonlea. 2001. (SPA.). 254p. (J). (gr. 4-7). 10.95 (978-84-7888-160-4(3)) Scholastic, Inc.

—Ana la de Ingleside. 2nd ed. (Coleccion "Ana, la de Tejas Verdes"). (SPA., Illus.). 288p. (YA). (gr. 5-8). (978-84-7888-634-0(6) , SAL3088) Emece Editores ESP. *Dist:* Lectorum Pubns., Inc.

—Ana la de Ingleside. 2001. (SPA.). 284p. (J). (gr. 4-7). 10.95 (978-84-7888-218-2(9)) Scholastic, Inc.

—Ana la de Isla. 4th ed. (Coleccion "Ana, la de Tejas Verdes"). (SPA., Illus.). 240p. (YA). (gr. 5-8). (978-84-7888-635-7(4) , SAL5036) Emece Editores ESP. *Dist:* Lectorum Pubns., Inc.

—Ana la de Isla. 2001. (SPA.). 240p. (J). (gr. 4-7). 10.95 (978-84-7888-161-1(1)) Scholastic, Inc.

—Ana la de Isla. 2001. (J). (978-0-606-22674-5(5)) Tandem Library Bks.

—Ana la de Tejas Verdes. 7th ed. (Coleccion "Ana, la de Tejas Verdes"). (SPA., Illus.). 288p. (YA). (gr. 5-8). (978-84-7888-633-3(8)) Emece Editores ESP. *Dist:* Lectorum Pubns., Inc.

—Ana la de Tejas Verdes. 2001. (SPA.). (J). (gr. 4-7). pap. 10.95 (978-84-7888-159-8(X)) Scholastic, Inc.

—Anne of Avonlea. 2004. 352p. per. 15.95 (978-1-59540-109-0(1)) 1st World Publishing, Inc.

—Anne of Avonlea. 2006. (Scholastic Classics Ser.). (Illus.). viii, 239p. (J). 25.00 (978-0-531-16979-7(0) , Watts, Franklin) Scholastic Library Publishing.

—Anne of Avonlea. 2005. (Aladdin Classics Ser.). (Illus.). 398p. (J). (gr. 4-7). pap. 4.99 (978-1-4169-0328-4(3) , Aladdin) Simon & Schuster Children's Publishing.

—Anne of Avonlea. unabr. ed. 2002. (Dover Juvenile Classics Ser.). 272p. (J). (gr. 4-7). pap. 3.00 (978-0-486-42239-8(9)) Dover Pubns., Inc.

—Anne of Avonlea. l.t. ed. 2006. (ENG.). pap. (***978-1-4068-3173-3(5)***) Echo Library.

—Anne of Avonlea. l.t. ed. 1998. (Avonlea Ser.: No. 2). 401p. (YA). (gr. 5-8). lib. bdg. 35.95 (978-1-58118-039-8(X) , 22507) LRS.

—Anne of Avonlea. 1998. 270p. (YA). (gr. 5-8). reprint ed. lib. bdg. 25.00 (978-1-58287-013-7(6)) North Bks.

—Anne of Avonlea. l.t. ed. 2000. (Anne of Green Gables Ser.: Vol. 2). 366p. (gr. 5-8). pap. 21.99 (978-1-57646-306-2(0)) Quiet Vision Publishing.

—Anne of Green Gables. 2004. 400p. per. 16.95 (978-1-59540-110-6(5)) 1st World Publishing, Inc.

—Anne of Green Gables. Miralles, Joseph, illus. 2002. (Great Illustrated Classics Ser.). 240p. (J). (gr. 3-8). 21.35 (978-1-57765-816-0(7) , ABDO & Daughters) ABDO Publishing Co.

—Anne of Green Gables. 349p. (978-1-58726-053-7(0)) Ann Arbor Media Group, LLC.

—Anne of Green Gables. 2000. (Avonlea Ser.: No. 1). 280p. (YA). (gr. 5-8). pap. 15.00 (978-0-7881-9155-8(1)) DIANE Publishing Co.

—Anne of Green Gables. (J). 2005. (Illus.). 192p. 5.99 (978-1-4037-1388-9(X)); 2004. 288p. 5.99 (978-1-4037-0980-6(7)) Dalmatian Pr.

—Anne of Green Gables. 2007. per. 6.99 (***978-1-4209-2922-5(4)***) Digireads.com.

—Anne of Green Gables. 2000. (Avonlea Ser.: No. 1). 320p. (J). (gr. 4-7). pap. 3.50 (978-0-486-41025-8(0)) Dover Pubns., Inc.

—Anne of Green Gables. 2005. (My First Classics Ser.). 112p. (J). (gr. k-3). pap. 4.99 (978-0-06-079147-6(0) , Harper Festival); 2000. (Avonlea Ser.: No. 1). (YA). (gr. 5-8). (978-0-06-028227-1(4)); 1999. (Charming Classics). 400p. (J). (ps up). pap. 6.99 (978-0-694-01251-0(3) , Harper Festival) HarperCollins Pubs.

—Anne of Green Gables. (Avonlea Ser.: No. 1). (YA). (gr. 5-8). pap. (978-0-340-71500-0(6) , Hodder & Stoughton) Hodder General Publishing Division.

—Anne of Green Gables. 2003. 276p. pap. 15.99 (***978-1-4043-6066-2(2)***) IndyPublish.com.

—Anne of Green Gables. Stemach, Jerry, ed. Ham, Jeff, illus. 2000. 65.00 incl. audio, cd-rom (978-1-58702-311-8(3)) Johnston, Don Inc.

—Anne of Green Gables. 1998. 352p. (J). pap. (978-1-55109-249-2(2)) Nimbus Publishing, Ltd.

—Anne of Green Gables. Rubio, Mary & Waterson, Elizabeth, eds. 2006. (Norton Critical Edition Ser.). (Illus.). 400p. (C). pap. 9.00 (978-0-393-92695-8(8)) Norton, W. W. & Co., Inc.

—Anne of Green Gables. (Oxford Children's Classics). 2007. 400p. (YA). 9.95 (***978-0-19-272000-9(7)***); 2004. 8.50 (978-0-19-423273-9(5)) Oxford Univ. Pr., Inc.

—Anne of Green Gables. 2003. 320p. (gr. 12). 4.95 (978-0-451-52882-7(4) , Signet Classics); 2002. (Illus.). (J). pap. 9.99 (978-0-14-250102-3(6) , Puffin) Penguin Group (USA) Inc.

—Anne of Green Gables. Howell, Troy, illus. 2002. 256p. (J). 12.99 (978-0-517-22111-2(X) , Gramercy) Random Hse. Value Publishing.

—Anne of Green Gables. 1998. (Children's Classics Ser.: No. 1). (Illus.). 256p. (J). (gr. 4-7). 6.99 (978-0-517-18968-9(2) , Children's Classics) Random Hse. Value Publishing.

—Anne of Green Gables. 2006. (Scholastic Classics Ser.). (Illus.). viii, 272p. (J). (gr. 9-12). 25.00 (978-0-531-16980-3(4) , Watts, Franklin) Scholastic Library Publishing.

—Anne of Green Gables. 2001. (Aladdin Classics Ser.). (Illus.). 480p. (J). pap. 5.99 (978-0-689-84622-9(3) , Aladdin) Simon & Schuster Children's Publishing.

—Anne of Green Gables. McKowen, Scott, illus. 2004. (Unabridged Classics Ser.). 304p. 9.95 (978-1-4027-1451-1(3)) Sterling Publishing Co., Inc.

—Anne of Green Gables. 1999. (Avonlea Ser.: No. 1). (YA). (gr. 5-8). 23.95 (978-0-8057-8090-1(4) , Macmillan Reference USA) Thomson Gale.

—Anne of Green Gables. Fernandez, Laura & Jacobson, Rick, illus. 2000. (Avonlea Ser.: No. 1). 328p. (J). (gr. 5-8). 24.95 (978-0-88776-515-5(7)) Tundra Bks., Inc./ Livres Toundra, Inc. CAN. *Dist:* Random Hse., Inc.

—Anne of Green Gables. MQ Publications Staff, ed. 1998. (Little Brown Notebooks Ser.). (Illus.). 256p. (978-1-84072-063-1(8)) Watson-Guptill Pubns., Inc.

—Anne of Green Gables. 2001. (Children's Classics). (ENG.). 288p. (J). pap. (978-1-85326-139-8(4)) Wordsworth Editions, Ltd.

—Anne of Green Gables. Corvino, Lucy, illus. 2005. (Classic Starts Ser.). 160p. 4.95 (978-1-4027-1130-5(1)) Sterling Publishing Co., Inc.

—Anne of Green Gables. l.t. ed. 2006. (ENG.). pap. (***978-1-4068-3174-0(3)***) Echo Library.

—Anne of Green Gables. Stemach, Jerry, ed. Ham, Jeff, illus. l.t. ed. 2000. 50.00 (978-1-58702-502-0(7)) Johnston, Don Inc.

—Anne of Green Gables. 1998. (Avonlea Ser.). 252p. (YA). (gr. 5-8). reprint ed. (978-1-55109-013-9(9)) Nimbus Publishing, Ltd.

—Anne of Green Gables. 1998. 310p. (YA). (gr. 5-8). reprint ed. lib. bdg. 25.00 (978-1-58287-014-4(4)) North Bks.

—Anne of Green Gables. l.t. ed. 2000. (Anne of Green Gables Ser.: Vol. 1). 294p. (gr. 5-8). pap. 17.95 (978-1-57646-302-4(8)) Quiet Vision Publishing.

—Anne of Green Gables. rev. ed. 2002. (Scholastic Classic Ser.). 400p. (J). pap. 4.99 (978-0-439-29577-2(7)) Scholastic, Inc.

—Anne of Green Gables, 100th Anniversary Edition. 2008. 19.95 (***978-0-399-15478-2(7)*** , Putnam Adult) Penguin Group (USA) Inc.

—Anne of the Island. Date not set. mass mkt. (978-0-8125-6563-8(0) , Tor Bks.) Doherty, Tom Assocs., LLC.

—Anne of the Island. 2006. (ENG.). pap. (***978-1-4068-2171-0(3)***); pap. (***978-1-4068-3175-7(1)***) Echo Library.

—Anne of the Island. 2006. (ENG.). 102.99 (***978-1-4219-3295-8(4)***) IndyPublish.com.

—Anne of the Island. 2004. reprint ed. pap. 1.99 (978-1-4192-0718-1(0)); pap. 30.95 (978-1-4179-0885-1(8)) Kessinger Publishing, LLC.

M
N
O

—Anne of the Island. (Twelve-Point Ser.). 2001. 240p. lib. bdg. 25.00 (978-1-58287-157-8(4)); 2004. 396p. 26.00 (978-1-58287-640-5(1)) North Bks.

—Anne of the Island. abr. ed. 1998. (Avonlea Ser.: No. 4). 304p. (J). (gr. 5-8). pap. 4.99 (978-0-14-036777-5(2), Puffin) Penguin Group (USA) Inc.

—Anne of the Island. 2000. (Anne of Green Gables Ser.: Vol. No. 3). (gr. 5-8). 182p. 24.95 (978-1-57646-309-3(5)); 182p. pap. 14.99 (978-1-57646-308-6(7)); 336p. pap. 19.99 (978-1-57646-310-9(9)) Quiet Vision Publishing.

—Anne of the Island. 2001. (gr. 7-12). lib. bdg. 30.40 (978-0-613-79774-0(4)) Tandem Library Bks.

—Anne of the Island Book & Charm. 2005. (Charming Classics). 304p. (J). pap. 6.99 (978-0-06-075859-2(7), Harper Festival) HarperCollins Pubs.

—Anne's House of Dreams. l.t. ed. 1999. (Avonlea Ser.: No. 5). 364p. (YA). (gr. 5-8). lib. bdg. 34.95 (978-1-58118-048-0(9), 22517) LRS.

—Anne's House of Dreams, Vol. 5. 1999. 320p. (J). 3.99 (978-0-14-036799-7(3), Putnam Juvenile) Penguin Group (USA) Inc.

—Anne's House of Dreams. 2000. (Anne of Green Gables Ser.: Vol. No. 5). (gr. 5-8). 182p. 24.95 (978-1-57646-313-0(3)); 182p. pap. 14.99 (978-1-57646-312-3(5)); 336p. pap. 19.99 (978-1-57646-314-7(1)) Quiet Vision Publishing.

—The Complete Anne of Green Gables: Anne of Green Gables; Anne of the Island; Anne of Avonlea; Anne of Windy Poplars; Anne's House of Dreams; Anne of Ingleside; Rainbow Valley; Rilla of Ingleside, 8 vols. gif. ed. 1998. (J). (gr. 4-7). mass mkt. 40.43 (978-0-553-60941-7(6), Starfire) Random Hse. Children's Bks.

Montgomery, L. M. Mary Engelbreit's Classic Library: Anne of Green Gables. Engelbreit, Mary, illus. 2008. (Mary Engelbreit's Classic Library). 464p. (J). 9.99 (*978-0-06-008138-6(4), Harper Festival) HarperCollins Pubs.

Montgomery, L. M. & Greenwood, Barbara. Anne of Green Gables. Wood, Muriel, illus. rev. ed. 2001. (Avonlea Ser.: No. 1). 94p. (J). (gr. 5-8). pap. 9.95 (978-1-55013-431-5(0)) Key Porter Bks. CAN. *Dist:* Firefly Bks., Ltd.

Moore, Robin. The Man with the Silver Oar. 2002. 192p. (J). (gr. 5 up). 15.89 (978-0-06-000048-6(1)) HarperCollins Pubs.

Morgan, Clay. The Boy Who Spoke Dog. (J). (gr. 4-7). 2005. 176p. pap. 5.99 (978-0-14-240343-3(1), Puffin); 2003. 192p. 15.99 (978-0-525-47159-2(6), Dutton Juvenile) Penguin Group (USA) Inc.

Morgan, Clay. The Boy Who Spoke Dog: Return to Dog Island. 2007. 176p. (J). (gr. 4). 16.99 (*978-0-525-47401-2(3), Dutton Juvenile) Penguin Group (USA) Inc.

Mosher, Richard. Zazoo. (YA). (gr. 7 up). 2001. 256p. tchr. ed. 16.00 (978-0-618-13534-9(0), Clarion Bks.); 2004. 272p. reprint ed. pap. 6.99 (978-0-618-43904-1(8), Graphia) Houghton Mifflin Co. Trade & Reference Div.

Moulton, Mark Kimball. A Cricket's Carol. Blowers, Lisa, illus. 2004. 32p. (J). 14.95 (978-0-8249-5488-8(2)) Ideals Pubns.

—A Cricket's Carol. Blowers, Lisa, illus. 2000. 32p. (J). (gr. k-3). 18.00 (978-0-7412-0735-7(4)) Lang Graphics, Ltd.

Muschla, Gary Robert. Crusader. 2006. (YA). pap. (978-0-88092-491-7(8)) Royal Fireworks Publishing Co.

Myers, Anna. Flying Blind. 2003. 192p. (YA). 16.95 (978-0-8027-8879-5(3)) Walker & Co.

—Stolen by the Sea. 2006. 144p. (J). pap. 6.95 (978-0-8027-8976-1(5)) Walker & Co.

Naidoo, Beverley. No Turning Back: A Novel of South Africa. 1999. 208p. (J). (gr. 3-7). pap. 5.99 (978-0-06-440749-6(7), Harper Trophy) HarperCollins Pubs.

—No Turning Back: A Novel of South Africa. 1999. 189p. lib. bdg. 12.64 (978-0-606-15856-5(1)) Tandem Library Bks.

Naylor, Phyllis Reynolds. Jade Green: A Ghost Story. 2001. 176p. (YA). (gr. 4-7). mass mkt. 5.99 (978-0-689-82002-1(X), Simon Pulse) Simon & Schuster Children's Publishing.

—Jade Green: A Ghost Story. Elliott, Mark, illus. 2000. 176p. (YA). (gr. 5-9). 16.95 (978-0-689-82005-2(4), Atheneum) Simon & Schuster Children's Publishing.

—Jade Green: A Ghost Story. l.t. ed. 2000. 174p. (J). (gr. 4-7). 21.95 (978-0-7862-2886-7(5)) Thorndike Pr.

—Sang Spell. 224p. (YA). (gr. 5 up). pap. 4.99 (978-0-8072-8294-6(4), Listening Library) Random Hse. Audio Publishing Group.

Naylor, Phyllis Reynolds & Duda, Jana. Sang Spell. 2000. (Illus.). 224p. (YA). (gr. 6-12). pap. 5.99 (978-0-689-82006-9(2), Simon Pulse) Simon & Schuster Children's Publishing.

Nikola-Lisa, W. Magic in the Margins: A Medieval Tale of Bookmaking. Christensen, Bonnie, illus. 2007. 32p. (J). (gr. 3-5). 17.00 (978-0-618-49642-6(4)) Houghton Mifflin Co. Trade & Reference Div.

Nixon, Joan Lowery. Aggie's Home. 2000. (978-0-606-17888-4(0)) Tandem Library Bks.

—Caught in the Act. l.t. ed. 1999. (Orphan Train Adventures Ser.: No. 2). 150p. (J). (gr. 4 up). lib. bdg. 23.33 (978-0-8368-2639-5(6)) Stevens, Gareth Inc.

—Circle of Love. 1998. (Orphan Train Ser.). (978-0-606-13276-3(7)) Tandem Library Bks.

—A Dangerous Promise. l.t. ed. 1999. (Orphan Train Adventures Ser.: No. 5). 148p. (J). (gr. 4 up). lib. bdg. 23.33 (978-0-8368-2642-5(6)) Stevens, Gareth Inc.

—David's Search. 2000. 11.15 (978-0-606-17831-0(7)) Tandem Library Bks.

—A Family Apart. 2000. (Orphan Train Adventures Ser.: Bk. 1). (YA). (gr. 5 up). pap. 49.75 incl. audio (978-0-7887-4331-3(7), 41126) Recorded Bks., LLC.

—A Family Apart. l.t. ed. 1999. (Orphan Train Adventures Ser.: No. 1). 162p. (J). (gr. 4 up). lib. bdg. 23.33 (978-0-8368-2638-8(8)) Stevens, Gareth Inc.

—In the Face of Danger. l.t. ed. 1999. (Orphan Train Adventures Ser.: No. 3). (J). (gr. 4 up). lib. bdg. 23.33 (978-0-8368-2640-1(X)) Stevens, Gareth Inc.

—Keeping Secrets. l.t. ed. 1999. (Orphan Train Adventures Ser.: No. 6). 163p. (J). (gr. 4 up). lib. bdg. 23.33 (978-0-8368-2643-2(4)) Stevens, Gareth Inc.

—The Orphan Train Adventures, 6 bks. l.t. ed. Incl. Caught in the Act. 150p. lib. bdg. 23.33 (978-0-8368-2639-5(6)); Dangerous Promise. 148p. lib. bdg. 23.33 (978-0-8368-2642-5(6)); Family Apart. 162p. lib. bdg. 23.33 (978-0-8368-2638-8(8)); In the Face of Danger. lib. bdg. 23.33 (978-0-8368-2640-1(X)); Keeping Secrets. 163p. lib. bdg. 23.33 (978-0-8368-2643-2(4)); Place to Belong. lib. bdg. 23.33 (978-0-8368-2641-8(8)); (J). (gr. 4 up). 1999. Set lib. bdg. 139.98 (978-0-8368-2637-1(X)) Stevens, Gareth Inc.

—A Place to Belong. l.t. ed. 1999. (Orphan Train Adventures Ser.: No. 4). (J). (gr. 4 up). lib. bdg. 23.33 (978-0-8368-2641-8(8)) Stevens, Gareth Inc.

—Will's Choice. 1999. (978-0-606-17478-7(8)) Tandem Library Bks.

Ogilvy, Ian. Measle & the Wrathmonk. 2004. 224p. (J). (gr. 4-6). 15.99 (978-0-06-058685-0(0)); lib. bdg. 16.89 (978-0-06-058686-7(9)) HarperCollins Pubs.

Olds, Barbara Anne. Haven House. Amatrula, Michele, illus. 2007. 141p. (J). pap. 8.95 (978-0-9744446-0-4(X)) All About Kids Publishing.

Olmstead, Kathleen & Porter, Eleanor H. Pollyanna. Akib, Jamel, illus. 2007. (Classic Starts Ser.). 154p. (J). (*978-1-4287-4209-3(3)) Sterling Publishing Co., Inc.

Orenstein, Denise Gosliner. The Secret Twin. McCarthy, Dan, illus. 2007. 400p. (J). lib. bdg. 17.89 (978-0-06-078565-9(9)); (gr. 7 up). 16.99 (978-0-06-078564-2(0)) HarperCollins Pubs.

—Unseen Companion. 368p. (J). 2003. 15.99 (978-0-06-052056-4(6)); 2003. lib. bdg. 16.89 (978-0-06-052057-1(4)); 2005. reprint ed. pap. 7.99 (978-0-06-052058-8(2), HarperTeen) HarperCollins Pubs.

Otten, Charlotte. Home in a Wilderness Fort: Copper Harbor 1844. 2006. (J). pap. 14.95 (978-0-9766104-5-8(0)) Arbutus Pr.

Owens, Tom. Flames of Freedom. Muchmore, Pat, illus. 2001. (Cover-to-Cover Bks.). 56p. (J). (gr. 1-4). lib. bdg. 16.95 (978-0-7807-9040-7(5)) Perfection Learning Corp.

Palmer, Pamela. Horse of the Dawn. 2005. 89p. pap. 14.95 (978-1-4137-9545-5(5)) PublishAmerica, Inc.

Papineau, Lucie. Gilda the Giraffe & Lucky the Leopard. Sarrazin, Marisol, illus. 2005. (Gilda the Giraffe Ser.). 32p. (J). 22.60 (978-1-4048-1295-6(4)) Picture Window Bks.

Papp, Robert, illus. The Ghost of the Chattering Bones, Vol. 102. 2005. (Boxcar Children Mysteries Ser.: 102). 128p. (J). pap. 4.50 (978-0-8075-0874-9(8)) Whitman, Albert & Co.

—The Giant Yo-Yo Mystery. 2006. 124p. (J). (*978-1-4156-6756-9(X)) Whitman, Albert & Co.

Papp, Robert, illus. The Sword of the Silver Knight, Vol. 103. 2005. (Boxcar Children Mysteries Ser.: 103). 112p. (J). (ps-7). 14.95 (978-0-8075-0877-0(2)) Whitman, Albert & Co.

Pausacker, Jenny. Freedom Fighters: Mindfire, Starfight, Endgame. 2005. (Triple Play Ser.). (Illus.). 48p. (gr. 4-8). 41.85 (978-0-7910-9073-2(6)) Facts On File, Inc.

Peart, Hendry. Red Falcons of Tremoine. Brevannes, Maurice, illus. 2007. 239p. (J). pap. 12.95 (*978-1-932350-15-9(2)) Bethlehem Bks.

Peart, Jane. Orphan Train West Trilogy. 2004. (Orphan Train West Ser.). pap. 11.98 (978-0-8007-5843-1(9)) Baker Publishing Group.

Peck, Robert Newton. Horse Thief: A Novel. 2003. (gr. 7-12). lib. bdg. 14.15 (978-0-613-65695-5(4)) Tandem Library Bks.

Petersen, Alicia. A Sparrow Alone. 2004. 154p. (YA). (978-1-59166-204-4(4)) Jones, Bob Univ. Pr.

Peterson. Anne of Green Gables. 1999. (Avonlea Ser.: No. 1). 32p. (YA). (gr. 5-8). pap. 4.95 (978-0-06-443535-2(0)) HarperCollins Pubs.

Petrucha, Stefan. Teen, Inc. 2007. 224p. (YA). (gr. 7 up). 16.95 (*978-0-8027-9650-9(8)) Walker & Co.

Pfeffer, Susan Beth. Nobody's Daughter. 1999. 154p. (J). (gr. 5-7). reprint ed. 15.00 (978-0-7881-6627-3(1)) DIANE Publishing Co.

—Revenge of the Aztecs. 2004. 118p. (J). lib. bdg. 16.92 (*978-1-4242-0763-3(0)) Fitzgerald Bks.

Pfeffer, Susan Beth. Revenge of the Aztecs: A Story of 1920s Hollywood. 2001. (American Portraits Ser.). (Illus.). 114p. (J). (gr. 5-8). 15.32 (978-0-8092-0586-8(6), 9780809205868) Jamestown.

—Revenge of the Aztecs: A Story of 1920s Hollywood. 2004. (Jamestown's American Portraits Ser.). (Illus.). 120p. (J). (gr. 5-7). pap. 4.95 (978-0-7696-3431-9(1), Waterbird Bks.) School Specialty Publishing.

—Revenge of the Aztecs: A Story of 1920s Hollywood. 2000. (978-0-606-21875-7(0)); (gr. 5-8). lib. bdg. 14.95 (978-0-613-36866-7(5)) Tandem Library Bks.

Pfeffer, Susan B & McGraw-Hill Staff. Revenge of the Aztecs: A Story of 1920s Hollywood. 2001. (Jamestown Classics Ser.). (Illus.). 114p. (J). (gr. 5-8). pap. 10.00 (978-0-8092-0627-8(7), 9780809206278) Jamestown.

Philbrick, Rodman. The Journal of Douglas Allen Deeds: The Donner Party Expedition, 1846. 2001. (My Name Is America Ser.). (Illus.). 160p. (J). (gr. 4-9). pap. 10.95 (978-0-439-21600-5(1)) Scholastic, Inc.

Pierce, Tamora. Wild Magic. 2003. (Immortals Ser.: No. 1). (Illus.). 320p. (YA). 11.99 (978-0-689-85611-2(3), Atheneum) Simon & Schuster Children's Publishing.

The Pinballs. 1999. (J). 11.95 (978-1-56137-827-2(5)); 9.95 (978-1-56137-082-5(7)) Novel Units, Inc.

Pinson, Mary E. You're an Orphan, Molly Brown. 1998. 128p. (gr. 5-7). 8.95 (978-1-57168-263-5(5)) Eakin Pr.

Pollet, Alison. The Pity Party: 8th Grade in the Life of Me, Cass. (Pity Party Ser.). 160p. (J). 2006. pap. 5.99 (978-0-439-68195-7(2), Scholastic Paperbacks); 2005. (gr. 5-8). pap. 15.95 (978-0-439-68194-0(4), Orchard Bks.) Scholastic, Inc.

Porter, Eleanor. Pollyanna. 2005. 104p. per. 4.95 (978-1-4209-2555-5(5)) Digireads.com.

Porter, Eleanor, ed. Pollyanna: Juvenile Classic. 2004. (Great Classics for Children Ser.). (Illus.). 182p. (J). 5.99 (978-1-4037-0796-3(0)) Dalmatian Pr.

Porter, Eleanor H. Classic Starts: Pollyanna. Akib, Jamel, illus. 2007. (Classic Starts Ser.). 160p. (J). 4.95 (978-1-4027-3692-6(4)) Sterling Publishing Co., Inc.

—Pollyanna. Gual, illus. 2002. (Great Illustrated Classics Ser.). 240p. (J). (gr. 3-8). 21.35 (978-1-57765-822-1(1), ABDO & Daughters) ABDO Publishing Co.

—Pollyanna. 2000. (Historias de Siempre Ser.). (SPA., Illus.). 198p. (YA). (gr. 4-7). 15.95 (978-84-204-5730-7(2)) Alfaguara, Ediciones, S.A.- Grupo Santillana ESP. *Dist:* Santillana USA Publishing Co., Inc.

—Pollyanna. (J). 21.95 (978-0-8488-1445-8(2)) Amereon LTD.

—Pollyanna. 2002. 256p. (J). pap. 7.99 (978-1-84222-615-5(0)) Carlton Bks., Ltd. GBR. *Dist:* Independent Pubs. Group.

—Pollyanna. 2003. (Dover Evergreen Classics Ser.). 208p. (J). (gr. 4-7). pap. 3.00 (978-0-486-43206-9(8)) Dover Pubns., Inc.

—Pollyanna. Date not set. (J). 14.99 (978-0-06-028226-4(6)); 32p. pap. 4.99 (978-0-06-443536-9(9)) HarperCollins Pubs.

—Pollyanna. l.t. ed. 2000. (Large Print Heritage Ser.). 310p. (J). (gr. 7-12). lib. bdg. 29.95 (978-1-58118-069-5(1), 23663) LRS.

—Pollyanna. 2002. (Classics Ser.). (Illus.). 304p. (J). pap. 4.99 (978-0-689-84910-7(9), Aladdin) Simon & Schuster Children's Publishing.

—Pollyanna. 2002. (gr. 3-6). lib. bdg. 11.80 (978-0-613-63223-2(0)) Tandem Library Bks.

—Pollyanna. l.t. ed. 2001. 267p. (J). 27.95 (978-0-7838-9602-1(6), Hall, G. K. & Co.) Thomson Gale.

Porter, Gene. Freckles. 2006. pap. (*978-1-4250-2281-5(2)) Assistedreadingbooks.com Inc.

Porter, H. Eleanor. Pollyanna. 2006. 52.99 (*978-1-4219-7974-8(8)); pap. 46.99 (*978-1-4219-7968-7(3)) IndyPublish.com.

—Pollyanna Grows up. 2006. pap. 58.99 (*978-1-4280-1137-3(4)) IndyPublish.com.

Price, Olive. Three Golden Rivers. l.t. ed. 1999. (Golden Triangle Bks.). 272p. (YA). (gr. 4-7). pap. 9.95 (978-0-8229-5707-2(8)) Univ. of Pittsburgh Pr.

Prigger, Mary Skillings. Aunt Minnie McGranahan. Lewin, Betsy, illus. 1999. 40p. (J). (gr. k-3). tchr. ed. 15.00 (978-0-395-82270-8(X), Clarion Bks.) Houghton Mifflin Co. Trade & Reference Div.

—Aunt Minnie McGranahan. Lewin, Betsy, illus. 2005. 40p. (J). (gr. k-3). reprint ed. 5.95 (978-0-618-60488-3(X), Clarion Bks.) Houghton Mifflin Co. Trade & Reference Div.

Puckett, Kelley. Batman's Dark Secret. Muth, Jon J., illus. 2000. (Hello Reader! Ser.). 32p. (J). (gr. 1-3). pap. 3.99 (978-0-439-09551-8(4)) Scholastic, Inc.

—Batman's Dark Secret. 2000. (Hello Reader! Ser.). (Illus.). (J). 10.79 (978-0-606-18517-2(8)) Tandem Library Bks.

Pullman, Philip. The Ruby in the Smoke. 2004. 230p. (J). (gr. 7 up). pap. 38.00 incl. audio (978-1-4000-9015-0(6), Listening Library) Random Hse. Audio Publishing Group.

Qualey, Marsha. Thin Ice. 2007. (YA). (*978-0-9793444-0-4(9)) Quercus Pr.

—Thin Ice. 1999. (978-0-606-17348-3(X)) Tandem Library Bks.

Rand, Edward A. The Knights of the White Shield: Up-the-Ladder Club Series Round One Play. 2007. 166p. pap. 11.99 (*978-1-4264-8273-1(6)); 184p. pap. 14.99 (*978-1-4264-8310-3(4)) BiblioBazaar.

Random House Value Publishing Staff & Burnett, Frances Hodgson. Secret Garden. 1998. (Children's Classics Ser.). 288p. (J). (gr. 5-9). 5.99 (978-0-517-18960-3(7), Children's Classics) Random Hse. Value Publishing.

Reeder, Carolyn. Shade of Gray. 1999. (978-0-606-16311-8(5)) Tandem Library Bks.

—Shades of Gray. O'Brien, Tim, illus. 1999. 160p. (J). (gr. 3-7). pap. 4.99 (978-0-689-82696-2(6), 076714004993, Aladdin) Simon & Schuster Children's Publishing.

Rees, Celia. Herencia de Bruja. Abos, Elena, tr. 2002. (Gran Angular Ser.). (SPA.). 222p. (978-84-348-9121-0(2)) SM Ediciones ESP. *Dist:* Lectorum Pubns., Inc.

Reisberg, Joanne A. Save the Colors: A Civil War Battle Cry. 2001. (Young Americans Ser.: Vol. 5). (Illus.). 92p. (J). 5.95 (978-1-57249-247-9(3), White Mane Kids) White Mane Publishing Co., Inc.

Rewa. Molly May on the High Seas. Westmoreland, Christy Hulden & Westmoreland, Lori, illus. 2000. 96p. (J). (gr. 2-7). pap. 9.95 (978-1-56474-340-4(3)) Fithian Pr.

—Molly May on the High Seas. (Illus.). 9.95 (978-0-9726375-1-0(6)) Little Red Cat Publishing.

Richards, E. Laura. Captain January. 2006. pap. 87.99 (*978-1-4280-3642-0(3)) IndyPublish.com.

Richards, Laura E. Captain January. 2004. reprint ed. pap. 15.95 (978-1-4191-1199-0(X)); pap. 1.99 (978-1-4192-1199-7(4)) Kessinger Publishing, LLC.

Richardson, Arleta. Looking for Home. 2001. (gr. 3-6). lib. bdg. 14.15 (978-0-613-74903-9(0)) Tandem Library Bks.

Rigsby, Annelle & Raffa, Edwina. Race to Kitty Hawk. 2003. (Adventures in America Ser.). (Illus.). 84p. (J). 14.95 (978-1-893110-33-5(8)) Silver Moon Pr.

Rizzo, Kay D. Bells & Whistles. 2003. 96p. (J). (978-0-8163-1984-8(7)) Pacific Pr. Publishing Assn.

Rodowsky, Colby. The Turnabout Shop. 2000. (978-0-606-17885-3(6)) Tandem Library Bks.

Roesti, Delores. Mareena Maree Mulligan & the Flying Wheel Chair: Book 1: School Days. 2007. 81p. pap. 9.95 (*978-0-7414-4048-8(2)) Infinity Publishing.

Roll, Renee. The Wolf Pups. 2006. (YA). pap. (*978-0-9727995-2-2(4)) Roll, Renee.

Roman, Annette. 1 World Manga, Vol. 5. Ng, Leandro, illus. 2007. (1 World Manga Ser.). 240p. (YA). pap. 3.99 (978-1-4215-1169-6(X)) Viz Media.

Ross, Alice & Ross, Kent. La Dama de Cobre (The Copper Lady) Bowman, Leslie, illus. 2006. (Yo Solo - Historia (on My Own - History) Ser.). (SPA.). 48p. (J). (gr. 2-4). lib. bdg. 25.26 (978-0-8225-6262-7(6), Ediciones Lerner) Lerner Publishing Group.

Rottman, S. L. Rough Waters. 1998. (Illus.). 144p. (YA). (gr. 7-11). 14.95 (978-1-56145-172-2(X), Q17398) Peachtree Pubs., Ltd.

—Rough Waters. 2000. (Illus.). 224p. (J). (gr. 7-12). pap. 6.99 (978-0-14-130703-9(X), Puffin) Penguin Group (USA) Inc.

—Rough Waters. 2000. (978-0-606-17869-3(4)); (gr. 7-12). lib. bdg. 15.30 (978-0-613-28627-5(8)) Tandem Library Bks.

Rowling, J. K. Harry Potter y la Piedra Filosofal. 2001. (SPA.). (gr. 3-6). lib. bdg. 18.80 (978-0-613-35960-3(7)) Tandem Library Bks.

Rubright, Lynn. Mama's Window. 2005. (Illus.). 144p. (J). (gr. 4-8). 16.95 (978-1-58430-160-8(0)) Lee & Low Bks., Inc.

—Mama's Window. Smith, Duane, illus. 2005. 89p. (J). 16.95 (978-1-57480-160-6(0)) Lee & Low Bks., Inc.

Ruby, Laura. The Wall & the Wing. (J). 2007. 352p. (gr. 5 up). pap. 6.99 (*978-0-06-075257-6(2), Eos); 2006. 336p. 16.99 (978-0-06-075255-2(6)) HarperCollins Pubs.

Ruiz, Celia & Spyri, Johanna. Heidi. 2001. (SPA., Illus.). 184p. (J). 15.95 (978-84-372-2237-0(0)) Altea, Ediciones, S.A. - Grupo Santillana ESP. *Dist:* Santillana USA Publishing Co., Inc.

Russell, Christopher. Dogboy. 2006. 272p. (J). 15.99 (978-0-06-084116-4(8)); lib. bdg. 16.89 (978-0-06-084117-1(6)) HarperCollins Pubs.

Rust, Ann O'Connell. Torry Island. Rust, Allen F., ed. 2002. (Nonie of the Everglades Ser.: Vol. II). 94p. (J). (gr. 4-7). pap. 7.95 (978-1-883203-06-1(6)) Amaro Bks.

Ryan, Pam Muñoz. Paint the Wind. 2007. 336p. (J). (gr. 4-7). pap. 16.99 (*978-0-439-87362-8(2), Scholastic Pr.) Scholastic, Inc.

Rylant, Cynthia. The Bird House. Moser, Barry, illus. 1998. 32p. (J). (gr. 1-4). pap. 16.95 (978-0-590-47345-3(X), Blue Sky Pr., The) Scholastic, Inc.

—The Islander. 1999. (Illus.). 112p. (J). (gr. 5-17). reprint ed. pap. 5.50 (978-0-440-41542-8(X), Yearling) Random Hse. Children's Bks.

—The Islander. 1999. (gr. 5-8). lib. bdg. 13.00 (978-0-613-23002-5(7)) Tandem Library Bks.

Sadi, Hendrik E. Ernholder. 2002. 165p. (J). pap. 12.95 (978-0-595-21870-7(9), Writers Club Pr.) iUniverse, Inc.

Sandwall-Bergstrom, Martha. Goldie at the Orphanage. Stalsjo, Eva, illus. 2004. 24p. (J). 16.95 (978-0-86315-443-0(3)) Floris Bks. GBR. *Dist:* SteinerBooks, Inc.

Sautereau, Francois. Les Orpheline de Mars. 2000. Tr. of Orphans of March. (FRE.). (J). pap. 15.95 (978-2-09-282210-4(1)) Nathan, Fernand FRA. *Dist:* Distribooks, Inc.

Sawada, Hijime & Akita, Yoshinobu. Orphen, Vol. 4. 2006. (Illus.). 168p. (YA). pap. (978-1-4139-0269-3(3)) ADV Manga.

Schlabach, Janet. Riverboat Runaways. 1999. (Illus.). 138p. (J). (gr. 4-8). pap. 15.95 (978-0-936389-75-2(3)) Tudor Pubs., Inc.

Schwabach, Karen. A Pickpocket's Tale. 240p. (J). (gr. 3-7). 2008. 5.99 (*978-0-375-83380-9(3), Yearling); 2006. (Illus.). 15.95 (978-0-375-83379-3(X), Random Hse. Bks for Young Readers); 2006. (Illus.). lib. bdg. 17.99 (978-0-375-93379-0(4), Random Hse. Bks. for Young Readers) Random Hse. Children's Bks.

Scott, Elaine. Secrets of the Cirque Medrano. 2008. (J). (*978-1-57091-712-7(4)) Charlesbridge Publishing, Inc.

Scott, Elaine. The Spanish Web: An Encounter with Picasso. 2004. (Art Encounters Ser.). (J). 15.95 (978-0-8230-0410-2(4)); pap. 6.99 (978-0-8230-0413-3(9)) Watson-Guptill Pubns., Inc.

Seabrooke, Brenda. Stonewolf. 2004. 240p. (J). (gr. 7 up). tchr. ed. 16.95 (978-0-8234-1848-0(0)) Holiday Hse., Inc.

Sedgwick, Marcus. The Book of Dead Days. 2006. pap. 5.50 (978-0-440-41909-9(3)); 288p. (J). (gr. 5). reprint ed. pap. 7.95 (978-0-385-74704-2(7), Lamb, Wendy) Random Hse. Children's Bks.

Seidler, Tor. Brainboy & the DeathMaster. 320p. (J). 2005. pap. 6.99 (978-0-06-440935-3(X), Harper Trophy); 2003. (gr. 3 up). 16.99 (978-0-06-029181-5(8)); 2003. (gr. 3 up). lib. bdg. 17.89 (978-0-06-029182-2(6)) HarperCollins Pubs.

—The Dulcimer Boy. Selznick, Brian, illus. 160p. (J). reprint ed. 2004. pap. 6.99 (978-0-06-441048-9(X), Harper Trophy); 2003. 15.99 (978-0-06-623609-4(6)) HarperCollins Pubs.

Selznick, Brian. The Invention of Hugo Cabret. Selznick, Brian, illus. 2007. (Illus.). 544p. (J). (gr. 4-7). pap. 22.99 (978-0-439-81378-5(6), Scholastic Pr.) Scholastic, Inc.

Sfar, Joann. Little Vampire Does Kung Fu! Sfar, Joann, illus. 2003. (Illus.). 40p. (J). 12.95 (978-0-689-85769-0(1)) Simon & Schuster Children's Publishing.

Shapiro, David L. Sara's Journey. 2005. 293p. (YA). (gr. 7-12). pap. 12.95 (978-0-8276-0776-7(8)) Jewish Pubn. Society.

Shea, Pegi Deitz. Tangled Threads: A Hmong Girl's Story. 2003. 240p. (J). (gr. 5-9). tchr. ed. 15.00 (978-0-618-24748-6(3) , Clarion Bks.) Houghton Mifflin Co. Trade & Reference Div.

Shimko, Bonnie. Kat's Promise. 2006. 288p. (J). 17.00 (978-0-15-205473-1(1)) Harcourt Children's Bks.

Skot, Joelle. The Legend of the Blue Squid. 2007. (J). per. 17.99 (***978-1-933156-16-3(3)*** , Visikid Bks.) GSVQ Publishing.

Skrypuch, Marsha Forchuk. Nobody's Child. 2004. 200p. (J). pap. 8.99 (978-1-55002-442-5(6)) Dundurn Group, The CAN. *Dist:* Univ. of Toronto Pr.

—Nobody's Child. 2003. (gr. 7-12). lib. bdg. 17.60 (978-0-613-84757-5(1)) Tandem Library Bks.

Smith, Cynthia Leitich. Tantalize. 2007. (Illus.). 336p. (YA). (gr. 9). 16.99 (978-0-7636-2791-1(7)) Candlewick Pr.

Snedeker, Caroline. Downright Dencey. Barney, Maginel Wright, illus. 2003. (Young Adult Library). 274p. (YA). pap. 11.95 (978-1-883937-79-9(5)) Bethlehem Bks.

Snicket, Lemony, pseud. El Ascensor Artificioso. 2004. (Coleccion Una Serie de Catastroficas Desdichas A Series of Unfortunate Events Ser.). (SPA., Illus.). 232p. (YA). 12.95 (978-84-8441-215-1(6)) Grijalbo Mondadori, S.A.-Montena ESP. *Dist:* Lectorum Pubns., Inc.

—El Ascensor Artificioso. Canales, Veronica, tr. Helquist, Brett, illus. 2004. (Catastroficas Desdichas Ser.). (SPA.). 224p. (J). pap. 7.95 (978-0-307-20939-9(3) , Montena) Random House Mondadori ESP. *Dist:* Random Hse., Inc.

—El Aserradero Lugubre. Busquets, Néstor, tr. Helquist, Brett, illus. 2004. (SPA.). 208p. (J). pap. 7.95 (978-0-307-20938-2(5) , Montena) Random House Mondadori ESP. *Dist:* Random Hse., Inc.

—The Austere Academy. Helquist, Brett, illus. 2008. (Series of Unfortunate Events Ser.: Bk. 5). 240p. (J). (gr. 5 up). pap. 6.99 (***978-0-06-114634-3(X)*** , Harper Trophy) HarperCollins Pubs.

—The Austere Academy. 2000. (Series of Unfortunate Events Ser.: Bk. 5). (J). (gr. 4-7). pupil's gde. ed. (978-0-06-029312-3(8)) HarperCollins Pubs.

—The Austere Academy. Helquist, Brett, illus. 2000. (Series of Unfortunate Events Ser.: Bk. 5). 240p. (J). (gr. 5 up). 12.99 (978-0-06-440863-9(9)); lib. bdg. 15.89 (978-0-06-028888-4(4)) HarperCollins Pubs.

—The Bad Beginning. Helquist, Brett, illus. l.t. ed. 2002. (Series of Unfortunate Events Ser.: Bk. 1). 168p. (J). 16.95 (978-0-7540-7812-8(4) , Galaxy Children's Large Print) BBC Audiobooks America.

—The Bad Beginning. Helquist, Brett, illus. 1999. (Series of Unfortunate Events Ser.: Bk. 1). 176p. (J). (gr. 5 up). 12.99 (978-0-06-440766-3(7)); lib. bdg. 15.89 (978-0-06-028312-4(2)) HarperCollins Pubs.

—The Carnivorous Carnival. Helquist, Brett, illus. 2002. (Series of Unfortunate Events Ser.: Bk. 9). 304p. (J). (gr. 4-7). 12.99 (978-0-06-441012-0(9) , Harper Trophy); (ps-3). lib. bdg. 15.89 (978-0-06-029640-7(2)) HarperCollins Pubs.

—The Ersatz Elevator. Helquist, Brett, illus. 2001. (Series of Unfortunate Events Ser.: Bk. 6). 272p. (J). (gr. 5 up). 12.99 (978-0-06-440864-6(7)); 6th ed. lib. bdg. 15.89 (978-0-06-028889-1(2)) HarperCollins Pubs.

—Una Funesta Finestra. pap. 21.95 (978-88-7782-953-5(2)) Salani ITA. *Dist:* Distribooks, Inc.

—The Gloom Looms, Bks. 10-12. Helquist, Brett, illus. 2005. (Series of Unfortunate Events Ser.). (J). 38.99 (978-0-06-083909-3(0)) HarperCollins Pubs.

—The Grim Grotto. Helquist, Brett, illus. 2004. (Series of Unfortunate Events Ser.: Bk. 11). 352p. (YA). (gr. 3-6). 12.99 (978-0-06-441014-4(5) , HarperCollins) HarperCollins Pubs.

—La Habitacion de los Reptiles. Helquist, Brett, illus. 2002. (Series of Unfortunate Events Ser.). (SPA.). 208p. (J). (gr. 4-6). 10.95 (978-84-264-3741-9(9) , LM31164) Editorial Lumen ESP. *Dist:* Lectorum Pubns., Inc.

—La Habitacion de los Reptiles. Busquets, Nestor, tr. Helquist, Brett, illus. 2004. (Catastroficas Desdichas Ser.). (SPA.). 208p. (J). pap. 7.95 (978-0-307-20935-1(0) , Montena) Random House Mondadori ESP. *Dist:* Random Hse., Inc.

—The Hostile Hospital. Helquist, Brett, illus. 2001. (Series of Unfortunate Events Ser.: Bk. 8). (J). 272p. (gr. 5 up). 12.99 (978-0-06-440866-0(3)); 255p. (gr. 4-7). lib. bdg. (978-0-06-623919-4(2)); 8th ed. 272p. (gr. 5 up). lib. bdg. 15.89 (978-0-06-028891-4(4)) HarperCollins Pubs.

—Un Infausto Inizio. pap. 23.95 (978-88-7782-951-1(6)) Salani ITA. *Dist:* Distribooks, Inc.

—The Loathsome Library, Bks. 1-6. Helquist, Brett, illus. 2005. (Series of Unfortunate Events Ser.: Vol. 1). (J). 65.00 (978-0-06-083353-4(X)) HarperCollins Pubs.

—Un Mal Principio. Helquist, Brett, illus. 2002. (Series of Unfortunate Events Ser.). (SPA.). 224p. (J). (gr. 4-6). 10.95 (978-84-264-3740-2(0) , LM31162) Editorial Lumen ESP. *Dist:* Lectorum Pubns., Inc.

—Un Mal Principio. Busquets, Nestor, tr. Helquist, Brett, illus. 2004. (Catastroficas Desdichas Ser.). (SPA.). 176p. (J). pap. 7.95 (978-0-307-20934-4(2) , Montena) Random House Mondadori ESP. *Dist:* Random Hse., Inc.

—The Miserable Mill. Helquist, Brett, illus. 2000. (Series of Unfortunate Events Ser.: Bk. 4). 208p. (J). (gr. 3-6). 12.99 (978-0-06-440769-4(1)); (ps-2). lib. bdg. 15.89 (978-0-06-028315-5(7)) HarperCollins Pubs.

—The Notorious Notations. Helquist, Brett, illus. 2006. (Series of Unfortunate Events Ser.). 176p. (J). pap. 9.99 (978-0-06-087235-9(7) , Harper Festival) HarperCollins Pubs.

—Omnibus. Helquist, Brett, illus. movie tie-in ed. 2004. (Series of Unfortunate Events Ser.). (J). 35.99 (978-0-06-075773-1(6)) HarperCollins Pubs.

—Piege au College. pap. 24.95 (978-2-09-282599-0(2)) Nathan, Fernand FRA. *Dist:* Distribooks, Inc.

—The Reptile Room. Helquist, Brett, illus. l.t. ed. 2002. (Series of Unfortunate Events Ser.: Bk. 2). 184p. (J). pap. 16.95 (978-0-7540-7823-4(X) , Galaxy Children's Large Print) BBC Audiobooks America.

—The Reptile Room. Helquist, Brett, illus. 1999. (Series of Unfortunate Events Ser.: Bk. 2). 208p. (J). (gr. 5 up). 12.99 (978-0-06-440767-0(5)); lib. bdg. 15.89 (978-0-06-028313-1(0)) HarperCollins Pubs.

—The Slippery Slope. Helquist, Brett, illus. 2003. (Series of Unfortunate Events Ser.: Bk. 10). (YA). (gr. 5 up). 197.82 (978-0-06-057743-8(6)); 352p. (J). (gr. 3-6). 12.99 (978-0-06-441013-7(7)); 352p. (J). (gr. 3-6). lib. bdg. 15.89 (978-0-06-029641-4(0)) HarperCollins Pubs.

—El Ventanal. Busquets, Nestor, tr. Helquist, Brett, illus. 2004. (Catastroficas Desdichas Ser.). (SPA.). 224p. (J). pap. 7.95 (978-0-307-20937-5(7) , Montena) Random House Mondadori ESP. *Dist:* Random Hse., Inc.

—The Vile Village. Helquist, Brett, illus. 2001. (Series of Unfortunate Events Ser.: Bk. 7). 272p. (J). (gr. 5 up). 12.99 (978-0-06-440865-3(5)); 7th ed. lib. bdg. 15.89 (978-0-06-028890-7(6)) HarperCollins Pubs.

—The Wide Window. l.t. ed. 2003. (Series of Unfortunate Events Ser.: Bk. 3). (Illus.). 216p. (J). 16.95 (978-0-7540-7850-0(7) , Galaxy Children's Large Print) BBC Audiobooks America.

—The Wide Window. Helquist, Brett, illus. 2000. (Series of Unfortunate Events Ser.: Bk. 3). 224p. (J). (gr. 5 up). 12.99 (978-0-06-440768-7(3)) HarperCollins Pubs.

—The Wide Window. Helquist, Brett & Kupperman, Michael, illus. 2000. (Series of Unfortunate Events Ser.: Bk. 3). 224p. (J). (ps-2). lib. bdg. 15.89 (978-0-06-028314-8(9)) HarperCollins Pubs.

Snyder, Zilpha Keatley. Gib & the Gray Ghost. 2001. 230p. (gr. 3-6). lib. bdg. 13.55 (978-0-613-36816-2(9)) Tandem Library Bks.

—Gib Rides Home. 1999. (YA). (gr. 5 up). pap. 59.75 incl. audio (978-0-7887-2993-5(4) , 40875) Recorded Bks., LLC.

—Gib Rides Home. 1999. (J). 11.64 (978-0-606-16723-9(4)) Tandem Library Bks.

—Gib Rides Home. 2002. (Juvenile Ser.). (Illus.). (J). 21.95 (978-0-7862-4856-8(4)) Thorndike Pr.

Soileau, Hodges, illus. The Haunted Clock Tower Mystery, Vol. 84. 2004. (Boxcar Children Ser.: No. 84). 128p. (J). (gr. 2-7). pap. 3.95 (978-0-8075-5485-2(5)) Whitman, Albert & Co.

Sowards, Ben, illus. Christmas Oranges. 2004. 32p. 17.95 (978-1-59156-098-2(5)) Covenant Communications, Inc.

Spence, Eleanor. Jamberoo Road. 2007. 198p. (YA). pap. 12.95 (***978-1-932350-17-3(9)***) Bethlehem Bks.

Spyri, Johanna. Classic Starts: Heidi. Akib, Jamel, illus. 2007. (Classic Starts Ser.). 160p. (J). 4.95 (978-1-4027-3691-9(6)) Sterling Publishing Co., Inc.

—Heidi. 2002. (Great Illustrated Classics Ser.). (Illus.). 240p. (J). (gr. 3-8). 21.35 (978-1-57765-688-3(1) , ABDO & Daughters) ABDO Publishing Co.

—Heidi. 1999. (Andre Deutsch Classics). 316p. (J). 9.95 (978-0-233-99227-3(8)) Andre Deutsch GBR. *Dist:* Trafalgar Square Publishing.

—Heidi. Rinaldi, Angelo, illus. 2002. (Kingfisher Classics Ser.). 352p. (J). (gr. k-3). tchr. ed. 15.95 (978-0-7534-5494-7(7) , Kingfisher) Houghton Mifflin Co. Trade & Reference Div.

—Heidi. 2002. (Twelve-Point Ser.). lib. bdg. 25.00 (978-1-58287-183-7(3)) North Bks.

—Heidi. 2000. (Aladdin Classics Ser.). (Illus.). 304p. (J). (gr. 4-7). pap. 5.99 (978-0-689-83962-7(6) , Aladdin) Simon & Schuster Children's Publishing.

—Heidi. 1998. (Children's Classics). (ENG., Illus.). 240p. (J). pap. (978-1-85326-125-1(4) , 1254WW) Wordsworth Editions, Ltd.

—Heidi. 2002. (Spot the Classics Ser.). (Illus.). 180p. (J). (gr. k-5). 4.99 (978-1-57759-546-5(7)) Dalmatian Pr.

—Heidi. unabr. ed. 2000. (Dover Juvenile Classics Ser.). (Illus.). 304p. (J). (gr. 4-7). pap. 3.00 (978-0-486-41235-1(0)) Dover Pubns., Inc.

—Heidi. 2nd ed. (Coleccion Clasicos en Accion). (SPA., Illus.). 80p. (YA). (gr. 5-8). 15.95 (978-84-241-5784-5(2) , EV0790) Everest de Ediciones y Distribucion, S.L. ESP. *Dist:* Lectorum Pubns., Inc.

—Heidi: With a Discussion of Optimism. Clift, Eva, illus. 2003. (Values in Action Illustrated Classics Ser.). 190p. (J). (978-1-59203-030-9(0)) Learning Challenge, Inc.

Spyri, Johanna. Heidi EasyRead Large Edition. 2006. pap. (***978-1-4250-4150-2(7)***) Assistedreadingbooks.com Inc.

St. Jean, Alan. Aidan of Oren: The Journey Begins. Friedman, Judith, illus. 2004. 208p. 19.95 (978-0-9724853-5-7(X)) Keene Publishing.

Stanley, Diane. Raising Sweetness. Karas, G. Brian, illus. 2002. 14.04 (978-1-4046-1758-2(2)) Book Wholesalers, Inc.

—Raising Sweetness. Karas, G. Brian, illus. 2004. (Live Oak Readalong Ser.). (J). (ps-3). audio compact disk 18.95 (978-1-59112-494-8(8)) Live Oak Media.

—Raising Sweetness. 2003. (Illus.). (J). 25.95 incl. audio (978-1-59112-266-1(4)); 28.95 incl. audio compact disk (978-1-59112-516-7(2)); pap. 16.95 incl. audio (978-1-59112-265-4(1)) Live Oak Media.

—Raising Sweetness, 4 bks. Stanley, Diane, illus. 2003. (Illus.). (J). pap. 37.95 incl. audio (978-1-59112-267-8(8)) Live Oak Media.

—Raising Sweetness, 4 bks. 2003. (Illus.). (J). pap. 39.95 incl. audio compact disk (978-1-59112-524-2(3)) Live Oak Media.

—Raising Sweetness. Karas, G. Brian, illus. (J). 2002. 32p. pap. 6.99 (978-0-698-11962-8(2)); 1999. 1p. 16.99 (978-0-399-23225-1(7)) Penguin Group (USA) Inc. (Putnam Juvenile).

—Raising Sweetness. 2002. lib. bdg. 15.30 (978-0-613-60831-2(3)) Tandem Library Bks.

—Saving Sweetness. Karas, G. Brian, illus. 2002. 13.19 (978-1-4046-0940-2(7)) Book Wholesalers, Inc.

—Saving Sweetness. Karas, G. Brian, illus. 2005. (J). pap. 18.95 incl. audio compact disk (978-1-59112-330-9(5)); 2002. 28.95 incl. audio compact disk (978-1-59112-548-8(0)); 2002. pap. 39.95 incl. audio compact disk (978-1-59112-547-1(2)) Live Oak Media.

—Saving Sweetness. Karas, G. Brian, illus. 2001. 32p. (J). (ps-ps). pap. 5.99 (978-0-698-11767-9(0) , Putnam Juvenile) Penguin Group (USA) Inc.

—Saving Sweetness. Karas, G. Brian, illus. 2001. (J). (ps-ps). lib. bdg. 14.15 (978-0-613-44412-5(4)) Tandem Library Bks.

—Sweetness Series. Karas, G. Brian, illus. 2003. pap. 30.95 incl. audio (978-1-59112-847-2(1)); pap. 34.95 incl. audio compact disk (978-1-59112-860-1(9)) Live Oak Media.

Stevenson, James. Runaway Horse! A Novel. Date not set. (J). 15.99 (978-0-06-051978-0(9)); 16.89 (978-0-06-051979-7(7)) HarperCollins Pubs.

Stevenson, Robert Louis. Kidnapped Promotion: Being Memoirs of the Adventures of David Balfour in the Year 1751. 2000. (Cageworld Ser.). 336p. (J). pap. 2.99 (978-0-14-130936-1(9) , Puffin) Penguin Group (USA) Inc.

Stewart, Jennifer J. The Bean King's Daughter. 2002. 144p. (J). (gr. 4-6). tchr. ed. 15.95 (978-0-8234-1644-8(5)) Holiday Hse., Inc.

Stewart, Paul & Riddell, Chris. Hugo Pepper. 2007. (Far-Flung Adventures Ser.). (Illus.). 272p. (J). (gr. 3-7). 14.99 (978-0-385-75092-9(7)); lib. bdg. 16.99 (978-0-385-75093-6(5)) Random Hse. Children's Bks. (Fickling, David Bks.).

—The Last of the Sky Pirates. 2005. (Edge Chronicles Ser.: Bk. 5). (Illus.). 384p. (gr. 5-7). 12.95 (978-0-385-75078-3(1) , Fickling, David Bks.) Random Hse. Children's Bks.

Stone, Marie. On Their Own: A Journey to Jamestown. 2006. (J). (978-1-57249-385-8(2) , White Mane Kids) White Mane Publishing Co., Inc.

Stratton, Allan. Chanda's Wars. 2008. 400p. (J). 17.99 (***978-0-06-087262-5(4)***); lib. bdg. 18.89 (***978-0-06-087264-9(0)***) HarperCollins Pubs.

Stratton Porter, Gene. Freckles. 2006. 236p. (YA). 19.95 (***978-1-934169-32-2(3)***); pap. 8.95 (***978-1-934169-33-9(1)***) Norilana Bks.

Stratton-Porter, Gene. Freckles. (J). reprint ed. lib. bdg. 24.95 (978-0-89190-949-1(4) , Rivercity Pr.) Amereon LTD.

—Freckles EasyRead Comfort Edition. 2006. pap. (***978-1-4250-1125-3(X)***) Assistedreadingbooks.com Inc.

—Freckles EasyRead Edition. 2006. pap. (***978-1-4250-0577-1(2)***) Assistedreadingbooks.com Inc.

—Freckles EasyRead Large Edition. 2006. pap. (***978-1-4250-1603-6(0)***) Assistedreadingbooks.com Inc.

Stratton-Porter, Gene & Matthews, Andrew. Freckles. 2000. (Illus.). 32p. (C). pap. 9.00 (978-0-582-42655-9(3)) Pearson ESL.

Swan, Bill. Corner Kick. 2004. (Sports Stories Ser.). 120p. (J). (gr. 3-8). 7.95 (978-1-55028-816-2(4)); (***978-1-55028-817-9(2)***) Lorimer, James & Co., Ltd., Pubs. CAN. *Dist:* Casemate Pubs. & Bk. Distributors, LLC.

Swan, S. Annie. Thankful Rest (a Tale) 2006. 77.99 (***978-1-4219-9988-3(9)***); pap. 70.99 (***978-1-4142-5872-0(0)***) IndyPublish.com.

Tang, Charles, illus. The Basketball Mystery, Vol. 68. 1999. (Boxcar Children Ser.: No. 68). 128p. (J). (gr. 2-5). pap. 3.95 (978-0-8075-0576-2(5)) Whitman, Albert & Co.

—The Black Pearl Mystery, Vol. 64. 1998. (Boxcar Children Ser.: No. 64). 128p. (J). (gr. 2-7). pap. 4.50 (978-0-8075-0784-1(9)) Whitman, Albert & Co.

—The Cereal Box Mystery. 1998. (Boxcar Children Ser.: No. 65). (J). (gr. 2-5). 10.60 (978-0-606-13214-5(7)) Tandem Library Bks.

—The Cereal Box Mystery, Vol. 65. 1998. (Boxcar Children Ser.: No. 65). (J). (gr. 2-5). 128p. 14.95 (978-0-8075-1114-5(5)); 111p. pap. 4.50 (978-0-8075-1115-2(3)) Whitman, Albert & Co.

—The Gymnastics Mystery, Vol. 73. 2004. (Boxcar Children Ser.: No. 73). 128p. (gr. 2-5). mass mkt. 4.50 (978-0-8075-3101-3(4)) Whitman, Albert & Co.

—The Mystery in New York, Vol. 13. 2004. (Boxcar Children Special Ser.: No. 13). 121p. (J). (gr. 2-5). 14.95 (978-0-8075-5459-3(6)); pap. 4.50 (978-0-8075-5460-9(X)) Whitman, Albert & Co.

—The Mystery of the Empty Safe. 2000. (Boxcar Children Ser.: No. 75). (J). (gr. 2-5). (978-0-606-18768-8(5)) Tandem Library Bks.

—The Mystery of the Empty Safe, Vol. 75. 2004. (Boxcar Children Ser.: No. 75). 120p. (J). (gr. 2-5). pap. 4.50 (978-0-8075-5463-0(4)) Whitman, Albert & Co.

—The Mystery of the Pirate's Map. 1999. 121p. (J). (ps-7). per. 11.80 (978-0-613-16287-6(0)) Tandem Library Bks.

—The Mystery of the Stolen Sword. 1998. (Boxcar Children Ser.: No. 67). 121p. (J). (gr. 2-5). mass mkt. 4.50 (978-0-8075-7623-6(9)) Whitman, Albert & Co.

Taylor, Bonnie Highsmith. Kodi's Mare. Marks, Dea, illus. 2000. (Cover-to-Cover Novel Ser.). 82p. (J). pap. (978-0-7891-2929-1(9)); (gr. 2-5). lib. bdg. 13.95 (978-0-7807-8962-3(8)) Perfection Learning Corp.

Taylor, Richard A. Ships of Children. 2nd rev. ed. 2006. (Illus.). 191p. (YA). lib. bdg. 37.95 (978-0-9764403-7-6(7)) Klare Taylor Pubs.

Taylor, S. G. Books of Merlin I. 2006. pap. 10.49 (***978-1-4259-6740-6(X)***) AuthorHouse.

Torrey, Michele. Voyage of Midnight. 2006. 240p. (gr. 5). (J). 17.99 (978-0-375-92382-1(9)); (YA). 15.95 (978-0-375-82382-4(4)) Random Hse. Children's Bks. (Knopf Bks. for Young Readers).

Trent, Tiffany. In the Serpent's Coils. 2007. (Hallowmere Ser.). 312p. (YA). (gr. 7-11). 8.95 (***978-0-7869-4229-9(0)*** , Mirrorstone) Wizards of the Coast.

Tripp, Valerie. Changes for Samantha: A Winter Story. Andreasen, Dan & Roberts, Luann, illus. 2004. (American Girls Collection: Bk. 6). 80p. (J). (gr. 2 up). pap. 6.95 (978-0-937295-47-2(7)) American Girl Publishing, Inc.

—Samantha's Short Story Collection. Buckey, Sarah & Andreasen, Dan, illus. 2006. 224p. (J). 12.95 (***978-1-59369-125-7(4)***) American Girl Publishing, Inc.

Tripp, Valerie. Samantha's Story Collection. 2005. (American Girls Collection). (Illus.). 398p. (J). 29.95 (978-1-59369-051-9(7) , American Girl) American Girl Publishing, Inc.

Twomey, Cathleen. Charlotte's Choice. 2003. 192p. (YA). (gr. 6-9). pap. 9.95 (978-1-59078-036-7(1)); (Illus.). 15.95 (978-1-56397-938-5(1)) Boyds Mills Pr.

—Charlotte's Choice. 2002. (gr. 7-12). lib. bdg. 18.75 (978-0-613-51537-5(4)) Tandem Library Bks.

Ungerer, Tomi. Three Robbers. 1998. (Illus.). 40p. (J). (ps-1). pap. 6.95 (978-1-57098-206-4(6)) Rinehart, Roberts Pubs.

Urban, Betsy. Waiting for Deliverance. 2000. (Illus.). iv, 186p. (J). (gr. 7-12). pap. 17.95 (978-0-531-30310-8(1) , Orchard Bks.) Scholastic, Inc.

Ure, Jean. Little Daisy. 2002. (Illus.). 96p. pap. 7.99 (978-0-00-713369-7(3)) HarperCollins Pubs. Ltd. GBR. *Dist:* Independent Pubs. Group.

Van Draanen, Wendelin. Runaway. 256p. 2008. (YA). (gr. 3-7). mass mkt. 6.50 (***978-0-440-42109-2(8)*** , Laurel Leaf); 2006. (J). (gr. 5). 15.95 (978-0-375-83522-3(9) , Knopf Bks. for Young Readers) Random Hse. Children's Bks.

Vander Zee, Ruth. Always with You. Himler, Ronald, illus. 2008. (J). (***978-0-8028-5295-3(5)*** , Eerdmans Bks For Young Readers) Eerdmans, William B. Publishing Co.

Vanni, Gian Berto & Siff, Lowell A., illus. Love. 2000. 78p. (ps up). 20.00 (978-0-8076-1426-6(2)) Braziller, George Inc.

Veldkamp, Tjibbe & Hopsman, Philip. 22 Huerfanos. (SPA.). 36p. 12.99 (978-968-16-6291-2(1)) Fondo de Cultura Economica USA.

Vernon, Louise A. Peter & the Pilgrims. Eitzen, Allan, illus. 2nd ed. 2002. 128p. (YA). (gr. 4-9). 7.99 (978-0-8361-9226-1(5)) Herald Pr.

Vickers, Maydie. My Name Is Judy Ophelia Horton, I Think. 2005. 234p. pap. 19.95 (978-1-4137-8503-6(4)) PublishAmerica, Inc.

Vincent, Victoria. The City of Kind Words: A Story by Tory. l.t. ed. 2006. (Illus.). 56p. (J). per. 19.95 (***978-0-9788950-0-6(2)***) All Over Creation.

Voigt, Cynthia. The Callender Papers. Duranceau, Suzanne, illus. 2000. 272p. (J). (gr. 4-8). pap. 5.99 (978-0-689-83283-3(4) , Aladdin) Simon & Schuster Children's Publishing.

—The Callender Papers. 2001. (J). (gr. 4-8). 21.75 (978-0-8446-7192-5(4)) Smith, Peter Pub., Inc.

—The Callender Papers. 2000. (gr. 5-8). lib. bdg. 14.15 (978-0-8085-5948-1(6)) Tandem Library Bks.

Vyner, Sue. Things Had to Work This Time - They Had To... Lawrie, Robin, illus. 2001. (Go for It! Ser.). 127p. pap. 12.00 (978-0-237-52329-9(9) , Evans Brothers, Limited) Evans Publishing Group GBR. *Dist:* Independent Pubs. Group.

Wacker, Mary Langley. Landmarks. 2002. 211p. (gr. 8-12). pap. 19.95 (978-1-59129-374-3(X)) PublishAmerica, Inc.

Wait, Lea. Stopping to Home. 2003. (gr. 3-6). lib. bdg. 13.00 (978-0-613-61659-1(6)) Tandem Library Bks.

Wallace, Barbara Brooks. The Perils of Peppermints. (Illus.). 272p. (J). 2005. pap. 4.99 (978-0-689-85045-5(X) , Aladdin); 2003. 16.95 (978-0-689-85043-1(3) , Atheneum) Simon & Schuster Children's Publishing.

—Sparrows in the Scullery. 1999. (978-0-606-15943-2(6)) Tandem Library Bks.

Walters, Eric. Diamonds in the Rough. 1998. (Gemini Bks.). 252p. (YA). (gr. 7-10). mass mkt. 6.95 (978-0-7736-7470-7(5)) Stoddart Kids CAN. *Dist:* Fitzhenry & Whiteside, Ltd., Stoddart Publishing.

—Diamonds in the Rough. 1998. (gr. 7-12). lib. bdg. 14.10 (978-0-613-85640-9(6)) Tandem Library Bks.

Warner, Gertrude Chandler. Benny Goes into Business. 1999. (gr. k-3). lib. bdg. 11.80 (978-0-613-11318-2(7)); (Adventures of Benny & Watch: No.5). (J). (gr. 1-3). 10.75 (978-0-606-16916-5(4)) Tandem Library Bks.

—Blue Bay Mystery, Vol. 6. Gringhuis, Dirk, illus. 2004. (Boxcar Children Ser.: No. 6). 128p. (gr. 2-7). reprint ed. mass mkt. 4.50 (978-0-8075-0794-0(6)) Whitman, Albert & Co.

—The Boxcar Children. Date not set. (Boxcar Children Ser.: No. 1). (J). (gr. 2-5). lib. bdg. 18.95 (978-0-8488-1712-1(5)) Amereon LTD.

—The Boxcar Children. (Boxcar Children Ser.: No. 1). 154p. (J). (gr. 2-5). pap. 3.95 (978-0-8072-1447-3(7) , Listening Library) Random Hse. Audio Publishing Group.

—The Boxcar Children. 1998. (J). pap. 3.95 (978-0-439-04451-6(0)) Scholastic, Inc.

—The Boxcar Children. Deal, L. Kate, illus. (gr. 2-7). 2004. (Boxcar Children Ser.: No. 1). 128p. reprint ed. mass mkt. 4.50 (978-0-8075-0852-7(7)); 60th anniv. ed. 2002. 168p. (J). 18.95 (978-0-8075-0848-0(9)) Whitman, Albert & Co.

—The Caboose Mystery. Cunningham, David, illus. 1999. (Boxcar Children Ser.: No. 11). 128p. (J). (gr. 2-5). pap. (978-0-590-42681-7(8)) Scholastic, Inc.

—Candy Factory Mystery. 2002. (gr. 3-6). lib. bdg. 11.80 (978-0-613-58353-4(1)) Tandem Library Bks.

—The Candy Factory Mystery, Vol. 18. 2004. (Boxcar Children Special Ser.: Vol. 18). (Illus.). 128p. (J). pap. 4.50 (978-0-8075-5501-9(0)) Whitman, Albert & Co.

—The Copycat Mystery. Soileau, Hodges, illus. 2001. 137p. (J). (gr. 2-7). lib. bdg. 11.80 (978-0-613-35769-2(8)) Tandem Library Bks.
—The Copycat Mystery. 2001. (Boxcar Children Ser.). (Illus.). (J). 10.60 (978-0-606-21082-9(2)) Tandem Library Bks.
—The Copycat Mystery, Vol. 83. 2004. (Boxcar Children Ser.: No. 83). (Illus.). 128p. (J). (gr. 2-7). pap. 4.50 (978-0-8075-1297-5(4)) Whitman, Albert & Co.
—Disappearing Staircase Mystery. 2001. (gr. 3-6). lib. bdg. 11.80 (978-0-613-53176-4(0)) Tandem Library Bks.
—The Ghost Town Mystery. 1999. (Boxcar Children Ser.: No. 71). (J). (gr. 2-5). 10.75 (978-0-606-18764-0(2)) Tandem Library Bks.
—Ghost Town Mystery. 1999. (gr. 3-6). lib. bdg. 11.80 (978-0-613-16266-1(8)) Tandem Library Bks.
—The Giant Yo-Yo Mystery. 2006. (Boxcar Children Mysteries Ser.: 107). (Illus.). 128p. (J). 14.95 (978-0-8075-0878-7(0)); pap. 4.50 (978-0-8075-0879-4(9)) Whitman, Albert & Co.
—The Great Bicycle Race Mystery. 2000. (Boxcar Children Ser.: No. 76). (Illus.). (J). (gr. 2-5). 10.60 (978-0-606-18907-1(6)) Tandem Library Bks.
—Great Bicycle Race Mystery. 2000. (gr. 3-6). lib. bdg. 11.80 (978-0-613-27863-8(1)) Tandem Library Bks.
—The Gymnastics Mystery. 1999. (Boxcar Children Ser.: No. 73). (J). (gr. 2-5). 10.60 (978-0-606-18766-4(9)) Tandem Library Bks.
—Haunted Clock Tower Mystery. 2001. (gr. 3-6). lib. bdg. 11.80 (978-0-613-49434-2(2)) Tandem Library Bks.
—Hockey Mystery. 2001. (gr. 3-6). lib. bdg. 11.80 (978-0-613-30474-0(8)) Tandem Library Bks.
—The Hockey Mystery, Vol. 80. 2004. (Boxcar Children Ser.: No. 80). (Illus.). 135p. (J). (gr. 2-5). pap. 4.50 (978-0-8075-3343-7(2)); 14.95 (978-0-8075-3342-0(4)) Whitman, Albert & Co.
—The Honeybee Mystery. 2000. (Boxcar Children Special Ser.: No. 15). (J). (gr. 2-5). (978-0-606-20301-2(X)); 10.60 (978-0-606-20319-7(2)) Tandem Library Bks.
—Honeybee Mystery. 2000. (gr. 3-6). lib. bdg. 11.80 (978-0-613-30477-1(2)) Tandem Library Bks.
—The Honeybee Mystery, Vol. 15. 2004. (Boxcar Children Special Ser.: No. 15). (Illus.). 135p. (J). (gr. 2-5). 14.95 (978-0-8075-3373-4(4)); pap. 3.95 (978-0-8075-3374-1(2)) Whitman, Albert & Co.
—The Lighthouse Mystery. (Boxcar Children Ser.: No. 8). 147p. (J). (gr. 2-5). pap. 3.95 (978-0-8072-1474-9(4) , Listening Library) Random Hse. Audio Publishing Group.
—The Lighthouse Mystery, Vol. 8. Cunningham, David, illus. 2004. (Boxcar Children Ser.: No. 8). 128p. (J). (gr. 2-7). reprint ed. pap. 4.50 (978-0-8075-4546-1(5)) Whitman, Albert & Co.
—Meet the Boxcar Children. Duffy, Daniel Mark, illus. 1998. (J). (ps-ps). lib. bdg. 11.80 (978-0-613-08335-5(0)) Tandem Library Bks.
—Mike's Mystery. (Boxcar Children Ser.: No. 5). 128p. (J). (gr. 2-5). pap. 3.95 (978-0-8072-1462-6(0) , Listening Library) Random Hse. Audio Publishing Group.
—Mike's Mystery, Vol. 5. Gringhuis, Dirk, illus. 2004. (Boxcar Children Ser.: No. 5). 128p. (J). (gr. 2-7). reprint ed. pap. 4.50 (978-0-8075-5141-7(4)) Whitman, Albert & Co.
—The Movie Star Mystery. 1999. (Boxcar Children Ser.: No. 69). (J). (gr. 2-5). (978-0-606-18762-6(6)) Tandem Library Bks.
—Movie Star Mystery. 1999. (gr. 3-6). lib. bdg. 11.80 (978-0-613-16285-2(4)) Tandem Library Bks.
—Mystery at the Crooked House. 2000. (gr. 3-6). lib. bdg. 11.80 (978-0-613-31517-3(0)) Tandem Library Bks.
—The Mystery in New York. Tang, Charles, illus. 1999. 121p. (J). (ps-7). per. 11.80 (978-0-613-22056-9(0)) Tandem Library Bks.
—The Mystery in New York. 1999. (Boxcar Children Special Ser.: No.13). (Illus.). (J). (gr. 2-5). (978-0-606-18771-8(5)) Tandem Library Bks.
—The Mystery in the Computer Game. 2000. (Boxcar Children Ser.: No. 78). (J). (gr. 2-5). (978-0-606-20298-5(6)) Tandem Library Bks.
—The Mystery in the Mall. Tang, Charles, illus. 1999. 115p. (J). (ps-7). per. 11.80 (978-0-613-22057-6(9)) Tandem Library Bks.
—The Mystery in the Mall. 1999. (Boxcar Children Ser.: No. 72). (J). (gr. 2-5). (978-0-606-18765-7(0)) Tandem Library Bks.
—Mystery of Alligator Swamp. 2002. (gr. 3-6). lib. bdg. 11.80 (978-0-613-65048-9(4)) Tandem Library Bks.
—The Mystery of the Black Raven. 1999. (Boxcar Children Special Ser.: No. 12). (Illus.). (J). (gr. 2-5). (978-0-606-18770-1(7)) Tandem Library Bks.
—Mystery of the Black Raven. 1999. (gr. 3-6). lib. bdg. 11.80 (978-0-613-16286-9(2)) Tandem Library Bks.
—The Mystery of the Crooked House. 2000. (Boxcar Children Ser.: No. 79). (J). (gr. 2-5). (978-0-606-20299-2(4)) Tandem Library Bks.
—The Mystery of the Empty Safe. Tang, Charles, illus. 2000. 120p. (J). (gr. 2-7). lib. bdg. 11.80 (978-0-613-27992-5(1)) Tandem Library Bks.
—The Mystery of the Midnight Dog. 2001. (Boxcar Children Ser.). (Illus.). (J). (978-0-606-21080-5(6)) Tandem Library Bks.
—Mystery of the Midnight Dog. 2001. (gr. 3-6). lib. bdg. 11.80 (978-0-613-35789-0(2)) Tandem Library Bks.
—The Mystery of the Midnight Dog, Vol. 81. 2004. (Boxcar Children Ser.: No. 81). (Illus.). 122p. (J). (gr. 2-7). pap. 4.50 (978-0-8075-5476-0(6)) Whitman, Albert & Co.
—The Mystery of the Pirate's Map. 1999. (Boxcar Children Ser.: No. 70). (J). (gr. 2-5). (978-0-606-18763-3(4)) Tandem Library Bks.
—The Mystery of the Screech Owl. Soileau, Hodges, illus. 2001. 117p. (J). (gr. 2-7). per. 11.80 (978-0-613-35790-6(6)) Tandem Library Bks.
—The Mystery of the Screech Owl. 2001. (Boxcar Children Special Ser.). (Illus.). (J). (978-0-606-21085-0(7)) Tandem Library Bks.
—The Mystery of the Screech Owl, Vol. 16. 2004. (Boxcar Children Special Ser.: No. 16). (Illus.). 144p. (J). (gr. 2-5). 14.95 (978-0-8075-5481-4(2)); pap. 3.95 (978-0-8075-5482-1(0)) Whitman, Albert & Co.
—Mystery of the Spider's Clue. 2002. (gr. 3-6). lib. bdg. 11.80 (978-0-613-58378-7(7)) Tandem Library Bks.
—The Mystery of the Spider's Clue, Vol. 87. 2004. (Boxcar Children Ser.: Vol. 87). (Illus.). 128p. (J). pap. 3.95 (978-0-8075-5497-5(9)) Whitman, Albert & Co.
—Mystery of the Star Ruby. 2002. (gr. 3-6). lib. bdg. 11.80 (978-0-613-58379-4(5)) Tandem Library Bks.
—Mystery of the Tiger's Eye. 2001. (gr. 3-6). lib. bdg. 11.80 (978-0-613-49447-2(4)) Tandem Library Bks.
—The Mystery of the Wild Ponies. 2000. (Boxcar Children Ser.: Vol. 77). (Illus.). (J). (gr. 2-5). (978-0-606-18908-8(4)) Tandem Library Bks.
—Mystery of the Wild Ponies. 2000. (gr. 3-6). lib. bdg. 11.80 (978-0-613-27993-2(X)) Tandem Library Bks.
—Mystery on Blizzard Mountain. 2002. (gr. 3-6). lib. bdg. 11.80 (978-0-613-53287-7(2)) Tandem Library Bks.
—Mystery Ranch. (Boxcar Children Ser.: No. 4). 128p. (J). (gr. 2-5). pap. 3.95 (978-0-8072-1450-3(7) , Listening Library) Random Hse. Audio Publishing Group.
—Mystery Ranch, Vol. 4. Gringhuis, Dirk, illus. 2004. (Boxcar Children Ser.: No. 4). 128p. (gr. 2-7). reprint ed. mass mkt. 4.50 (978-0-8075-5391-6(3)) Whitman, Albert & Co.
—The Poison Frog Mystery. 2000. (Boxcar Children Ser.: No. 74). (J). (gr. 2-5). (978-0-606-18767-1(7)) Tandem Library Bks.
—Poison Frog Mystery. 2000. (gr. 3-6). lib. bdg. 11.80 (978-0-613-22192-4(3)) Tandem Library Bks.
—The Seattle Puzzle. 2007. (Boxcar Children Mysteries Ser.: No. 111). 128p. (J). (gr. 2-7). pap. 4.50 (***978-0-8075-5561-3(4)*** **);** lib. bdg. 14.95 (***978-0-8075-5560-6(6)***) Whitman, Albert & Co.
—The Summer Camp Mystery. 2001. (Boxcar Children Ser.). (Illus.). (J). (978-0-606-21081-2(4)) Tandem Library Bks.
—Surprise Island, Vol. 2. Gehr, Mary, illus. 2004. (Boxcar Children Ser.: No. 2). 128p. (YA). (gr. 2-7). reprint ed. mass mkt. 4.50 (978-0-8075-7674-8(3)) Whitman, Albert & Co.
—The Vanishing Passenger. 2006. (Boxcar Children Mysteries Ser.: 106). (Illus.). 128p. (J). 14.95 (978-0-8075-1066-7(1)); pap. 4.50 (978-0-8075-1067-4(X)) Whitman, Albert & Co.
—Watch Runs Away. 1999. (Adventures of Benny & Watch: No. 6). (J). (gr. 1-3). (978-0-606-16915-8(6)) Tandem Library Bks.
—The Woodshed Mystery, Vol. 7. 2004. (Boxcar Children Ser.: No. 7). (Illus.). 128p. (J). (gr. 2-7). reprint ed. pap. 4.50 (978-0-8075-9207-6(2)) Whitman, Albert & Co.
—The Yellow House Mystery. (Boxcar Children Ser.: No. 3). 191p. (J). (gr. 2-5). pap. 3.95 (978-0-8072-1449-7(3) , Listening Library) Random Hse. Audio Publishing Group.
—The Yellow House Mystery, Vol. 3. Gehr, Mary, illus. 2004. (Boxcar Children Ser.: No. 3). 128p. (YA). (gr. 2-7). reprint ed. mass mkt. 4.50 (978-0-8075-9366-0(4)) Whitman, Albert & Co.
Warner, Gertrude Chandler, creator. The Basketball Mystery. 1999. (Boxcar Children Ser.: No. 68). (J). (gr. 2-5). 10.60 (978-0-606-17179-3(7)) Tandem Library Bks.
—The Basketball Mystery. 1999. (Boxcar Children Ser.: No. 68). (Illus.). 128p. (J). (gr. 2-5). lib. bdg. 13.95 (978-0-8075-0575-5(7)) Whitman, Albert & Co.
—Benny's New Friend. 1998. (Adventures of Benny & Watch: No. 3). (J). (gr. 1-3). 10.75 (978-0-606-13217-6(1)) Tandem Library Bks.
—The Black Pearl Mystery. 1998. (Boxcar Children Ser.: No. 64). (J). (gr. 2-5). 10.60 (978-0-606-13213-8(9)) Tandem Library Bks.
—The Black Pearl Mystery, Vol. 64. 1998. (Boxcar Children Ser.: No. 64). (Illus.). 128p. (J). (gr. 2-5). 14.95 (978-0-8075-0783-4(0)) Whitman, Albert & Co.
—The Boxcar Children Summer Special. 2007. (Boxcar Children Mysteries Ser.). 376p. (J). pap. 7.95 (***978-0-8075-0885-5(3)***) Whitman, Albert & Co.
—The Creature in Ogopogo Lake, Vol. 108. 2006. (Boxcar Children Mysteries Ser.: 108). (Illus.). 128p. (J). (gr. 2-7). 14.95 (978-0-8075-1336-1(9)); lib. bdg. 4.50 (978-0-8075-1337-8(7)) Whitman, Albert & Co.
—The Ghost Town Mystery, Vol. 71. 1999. (Boxcar Children Ser.: No. 71). (Illus.). 128p. (J). (gr. 2-5). 14.95 (978-0-8075-2858-7(7)); pap. 3.95 (978-0-8075-2859-4(5)) Whitman, Albert & Co.
—The Great Bicycle Race Mystery, Vol. 76. 2004. (Boxcar Children Ser.: No. 76). (Illus.). 115p. (J). (gr. 2-5). pap. 4.50 (978-0-8075-3049-8(2)) Whitman, Albert & Co.
—The Homerun Mystery. (Boxcar Children Special Ser.: No. 14). (Illus.). 120p. (J). (gr. 2-5). 2000. lib. bdg. 13.95 (978-0-8075-3368-0(8)); Vol. 14. 2004. pap. 4.50 (978-0-8075-3369-7(6)) Whitman, Albert & Co.
—Meet the Boxcar Children. 1998. (Adventures of Benny & Watch: No. 1). (J). (gr. 1-3). (978-0-606-13215-2(5)) Tandem Library Bks.
—The Movie Star Mystery, Vol. 69. 1999. (Boxcar Children Ser.: No. 69). (Illus.). 128p. (J). (gr. 2-5). 14.95 (978-0-8075-5303-9(4)); pap. 4.50 (978-0-8075-5304-6(2)) Whitman, Albert & Co.
—The Mystery at Peacock Hall. 1998. (Boxcar Children Ser.: No. 63). (J). (gr. 2-5). (978-0-606-13212-1(0)) Tandem Library Bks.
—The Mystery at Peacock Hall, Vol. 63. 1998. (Boxcar Children Ser.: No. 63). (Illus.). 128p. (J). (gr. 2-5). pap. 4.50 (978-0-8075-5445-6(6)) Whitman, Albert & Co.
—The Mystery in the Computer Game. (Boxcar Children Ser.: No. 78). (Illus.). 115p. (J). (gr. 2-5). 2000. lib. bdg. 13.95 (978-0-8075-5468-5(5)); Vol. 78. 2004. pap. 4.50 (978-0-8075-5469-2(3)) Whitman, Albert & Co.
—The Mystery in the Mall, Vol. 72. 2004. (Boxcar Children Ser.: No. 72). (Illus.). 128p. (J). (gr. 2-5). 14.95 (978-0-8075-5456-2(1)); pap. 4.50 (978-0-8075-5457-9(X)) Whitman, Albert & Co.
—The Mystery of the Black Raven, Vol. 12. 1999. (Boxcar Children Special Ser.: No. 12). (Illus.). 144p. (J). (gr. 2-5). 14.95 (978-0-8075-2988-1(5)); pap. 3.95 (978-0-8075-2989-8(3)) Whitman, Albert & Co.
—The Mystery of the Crooked House. (Boxcar Children Ser.: No. 79). (Illus.). 112p. (J). (gr. 2-5). 2000. lib. bdg. 13.95 (978-0-8075-5471-5(5)); Vol. 79. 2004. pap. 4.50 (978-0-8075-5472-2(3)) Whitman, Albert & Co.
—The Mystery of the Empty Safe, Vol. 75. 2004. (Boxcar Children Ser.: No. 75). (Illus.). 120p. (J). (gr. 2-5). 14.95 (978-0-8075-5462-3(6)) Whitman, Albert & Co.
—The Mystery of the Pirate's Map, Vol. 70. (Boxcar Children Ser.: No.70). (Illus.). (J). (gr. 2-5). 2004. 14.95 (978-0-8075-5453-1(7)); 1999. 128p. pap. 4.50 (978-0-8075-5454-8(5)) Whitman, Albert & Co.
—The Mystery of the Queen's Jewels, Vol. 11. 1998. (Boxcar Children Special Ser.: No. 11). (Illus.). 144p. (J). (gr. 2-5). 14.95 (978-0-8075-5450-0(2)); pap. 4.50 (978-0-8075-5451-7(0)) Whitman, Albert & Co.
—The Mystery of the Stolen Sword, Vol. 67. 1998. (Boxcar Children Ser.: No. 67). (Illus.). 128p. (J). (gr. 2-5). 14.95 (978-0-8075-7622-9(0)) Whitman, Albert & Co.
—The Mystery of the Tiger's Eye, Vol. 17. 2004. (Boxcar Children Special Ser.: No.17). (Illus.). 144p. (J). (gr. 2-5). pap. 4.50 (978-0-8075-5488-3(X)) Whitman, Albert & Co.
—The Mystery of the Wild Ponies, Vol. 77. 2004. (Boxcar Children Ser.: No. 77). (Illus.). 135p. (J). (gr. 2-5). pap. 3.95 (978-0-8075-5466-1(9)) Whitman, Albert & Co.
—The Mystery on Blizzard Mountain, Vol. 86. 2004. (Boxcar Children Ser.: No. 86). (Illus.). 122p. (J). (gr. 2-7). 14.95 (978-0-8075-5493-7(6)); pap. 4.50 (978-0-8075-5494-4(4)) Whitman, Albert & Co.
—The Panther Mystery, Vol. 66. 1998. (Boxcar Children Ser.: No. 66). (Illus.). 128p. (J). (gr. 2-5). pap. 4.50 (978-0-8075-6328-1(5)) Whitman, Albert & Co.
—The Poison Frog Mystery, Vol. 74. 2004. (Boxcar Children Ser.: No. 74). (Illus.). 128p. (J). (gr. 2-5). pap. 3.95 (978-0-8075-6587-2(3)) Whitman, Albert & Co.
—A Present for Grandfather. 1998. (Adventures of Benny & Watch: No. 2). (J). (gr. 1-3). (978-0-606-13216-9(3)) Tandem Library Bks.
—The Rock 'n' Roll Mystery, Vol. 109. 2006. (Boxcar Children Mysteries Ser.: 109). (Illus.). 128p. (J). (gr. 2-7). 14.95 (978-0-8075-7089-0(3)); lib. bdg. 4.50 (978-0-8075-7090-6(7)) Whitman, Albert & Co.
—The Sword of the Silver Knight, Vol. 103. 2005. (Boxcar Children Mysteries Ser.: 103). (Illus.). 128p. (J). pap. 4.50 (978-0-8075-0876-3(4)) Whitman, Albert & Co.
—The Windy City Mystery. 1998. (Boxcar Children Special Ser.: No. 10). (J). (gr. 2-5). (978-0-606-13219-0(8)) Tandem Library Bks.
—The Windy City Mystery, Vol. 10. 1998. (Boxcar Children Special Ser.: No. 10). (Illus.). 144p. (J). (gr. 2-5). 14.95 (978-0-8075-5447-0(2)); pap. 4.50 (978-0-8075-5448-7(0)) Whitman, Albert & Co.
Warner, Sally. This Isn't about the Money. 2002. 224p. (J). (gr. 3-6). 15.99 (978-0-670-03574-8(2) , Viking Juvenile) Penguin Group (USA) Inc.
Waters, Zack C. Blood Moon Rider. 2006. 126p. (J). 13.95 (978-1-56164-350-9(5)) Pineapple Pr., Inc.
Watkins, Dawn L., et al. Pollyanna. 2006. (J). (978-1-59166-669-1(4)) Jones, Bob Univ. Pr.
Watkins, Tracey. Paperstation. 2000. 224p. (YA). pap. 12.95 (978-0-595-14328-3(8)) iUniverse, Inc.
Watts, Irene N. When the Bough Breaks. 2007. 152p. (J). (gr. 4-7). pap. 9.95 (***978-0-88776-821-7(0)***) Tundra Bks., Inc./Livres Toundra, Inc. CAN. *Dist:* Random Hse., Inc.
Webster, Jean. Daddy-Long-Legs. (J). 19.95 (978-0-8488-0323-0(X)) Amereon LTD.
—Daddy-Long-Legs. 2003. (gr. 3-6). lib. bdg. 47.80 (978-0-613-83363-9(5)) Tandem Library Bks.
—Daddy Long Legs. 2004. reprint ed. pap. 19.95 (978-1-4191-1490-8(5)); pap. 1.99 (978-1-4192-1490-5(X)) Kessinger Publishing, LLC.
—Daddy-Long-Legs. unabr. ed. 2002. (Dover Evergreen Classics Ser.). (Illus.). 144p. (J). (gr. 4-7). pap. 2.00 (978-0-486-42367-8(0)) Dover Pubns., Inc.
—Dear Enemy. (J). 21.95 (978-0-8488-0324-7(8)) Amereon LTD.
—Dear Enemy. (Best Sellers of 1916 Ser.). (J). reprint ed. lib. bdg. 48.00 (978-0-7426-1275-4(9)); 2001. (Illus.). pap. 28.00 (978-0-7426-6275-9(6)) Classic Bks.
—Dear Enemy. 2006. (ENG.). 63.99 (***978-1-4280-4576-7(7)*** **);** pap. 57.99 (***978-1-4280-4596-5(1)***) IndyPublish.com.
—Dear Enemy. 2004. reprint ed. pap. 31.95 (978-1-4179-1744-0(X)) Kessinger Publishing, LLC.
Weir, Joan. The Brideship. 1999. (Illus.). 218p. (YA). (gr. 7 up). mass mkt. 5.95 (978-0-7736-7474-5(8)) Stoddart Kids CAN. *Dist:* Fitzhenry & Whiteside, Ltd.
Welsh, Charles. Goody Two Shoes. 2005. reprint ed. pap. 22.95 (978-1-4179-6775-9(7)) Kessinger Publishing, LLC.
Weninger, Brigitte. A Child Is a Child. Tharlet, Eve, illus. 2004. 32p. (J). (ps-3). 14.99 (978-0-698-40006-1(2) , Minedition) Penguin Group (USA) Inc.
Whelan, Gloria. Listening for Lions. 208p. (J). 2006. pap. 5.99 (978-0-06-058176-3(X) , Harper Trophy); 2005. (gr. 5 up). 15.99 (978-0-06-058174-9(3)); 2005. (Illus.). (gr. 5 up). lib. bdg. 16.89 (978-0-06-058175-6(1)) HarperCollins Pubs.
White, Ruth. Tadpole. 2003. 208p. (J). (gr. 4-8). 16.00 (978-0-374-31002-8(5) , Farrar, Straus & Giroux (BYR)) Farrar, Straus & Giroux.
—Tadpole. 2004. 208p. (gr. 5). 5.99 (978-0-440-41979-2(4) , Yearling) Random Hse. Children's Bks.
—Tadpole. l.t. ed. 2003. 201p. (J). 24.95 (978-0-7862-5813-0(6)) Thorndike Pr.
—Way down Deep. 2007. (Illus.). 208p. (J). (gr. 5 up). 16.00 (978-0-374-38251-3(4) , Farrar, Straus & Giroux (BYR)) Farrar, Straus & Giroux.
Wild, Margaret. Woolvs in the Sitee. Spudvilas, Anne, illus. 2007. 40p. (YA). (gr. 7 up). 17.95 (***978-1-59078-500-3(2)*** , Front Street) Boyds Mills Pr.
Williams, Mary. Brothers in Hope: The Story of the Lost Boys of Sudan. Christie, R. Gregory, illus. 2005. (J). 17.95 (978-1-58430-232-2(1)) Lee & Low Bks., Inc.
Wilson, Jacqueline. The Story of Tracy Beaker. Sharratt, Nick, illus. 2002. 144p. (gr. 3-7). 5.50 (978-0-440-41807-8(0) , Yearling) Random Hse. Children's Bks.
Winter, Kathryn. Katarina. 1999. (J). (978-0-606-17441-1(9)) Tandem Library Bks.
Wood, June Rae. Turtle on a Fence Post. 2001. 264p. (J). (gr. k-9). per. 15.30 (978-0-613-44424-8(8)) Tandem Library Bks.
Woodruff, Elvira. The Christmas Doll. McClintock, Barbara, illus. 2002. 160p. (J). pap. 4.99 (978-0-590-31879-2(9) , Scholastic Paperbacks) Scholastic, Inc.
—Fearless. 2008. 240p. (J). 16.99 (978-0-439-67703-5(3) , Scholastic Pr.) Scholastic, Inc.
Woodson, Jacqueline. Miracle's Boys. (gr. 5). 2006. 144p. (J). pap. 5.99 (978-0-14-240602-1(3) , Puffin); 2000. 1p. (YA). 15.99 (978-0-399-23113-1(7) , Putnam Juvenile) Penguin Group (USA) Inc.
Worley, Roger. The Wishbone Journal II. 2005. 76p. pap. 14.95 (978-1-4137-6314-0(6)) PublishAmerica, Inc.
Wright, Betty Ren. Crandall's Castle. 2005. 184p. (YA). (gr. 4-6). tchr. ed. 16.95 (978-0-8234-1726-1(3)) Holiday Hse., Inc.
Wright, Randall. Hunchback. rev. ed. 2004. (Illus.). 256p. (J). 16.95 (978-0-8050-7232-7(2) , Holt, Henry & Co. Bks. For Young Readers) Holt, Henry & Co.
Wulf, Linda Press. The Night of the Burning: Devorah's Story. 2006. (Illus.). 224p. (J). (gr. 5-8). 16.00 (978-0-374-36419-9(2) , Farrar, Straus & Giroux (BYR)) Farrar, Straus & Giroux.
Wyss, Thelma Hatch. A Tale of Gold. 2007. 160p. (J). (gr. 3-7). 16.99 (***978-1-4169-4212-2(2)*** , McElderry, Margaret K.) Simon & Schuster Children's Publishing.
Yancey, Rick. Alfred Kropp No. 2: The Seal of Solomon. 2007. 336p. (J). (gr. 7 up). 16.95 (***978-1-59990-045-2(9)***) Bloomsbury Publishing.
Yancey, Rick. The Extraordinary Adventures of Alfred Kropp. 2006. (Illus.). 352p. (YA). reprint ed. pap. 7.95 (978-1-59990-044-5(0) , Bloomsbury Children) Bloomsbury Publishing.
Yep, Laurence. The Amah. 2001. 192p. (J). (gr. 4-7). pap. 6.99 (978-0-698-11878-2(2) , Putnam Juvenile) Penguin Group (USA) Inc.
—The Amah. 2001. (J). 12.64 (978-0-606-20542-9(X)) Tandem Library Bks.
—The Magic Paintbrush. Wang, Suling, illus. 2003. 96p. (J). (gr. 3-7). pap. 4.99 (978-0-06-440852-3(3)) HarperCollins Pubs.
—The Magic Paintbrush. 2003. (gr. 3-6). lib. bdg. 13.00 (978-0-613-65808-9(6)) Tandem Library Bks.
—Tiger's Apprentice. 2005. 184p. (J). lib. bdg. 24.62 (***978-1-4242-0449-6(6)***) Fitzgerald Bks.
—Tiger's Apprentice. 2005. 184p. (J). (gr. k-9). per. 12.64 (978-0-606-33327-6(4)) Tandem Library Bks.
—The Tiger's Apprentice. 2005. (Tiger's Apprentice Ser.: Bk. 1). 208p. (J). (gr. 5 up). reprint ed. pap. 5.99 (978-0-06-001015-7(0) , Harper Trophy) HarperCollins Pubs.
Yolen, Jane. Sister Light, Sister Dark: Book One in the Great Alta Saga. 2003. (gr. 7-12). lib. bdg. 15.30 (978-0-613-74858-2(1)) Tandem Library Bks.
Zahn, Timothy. Dragon & Herdsman. 2007. (Dragonback Ser.). 304p. (J). mass mkt. 5.99 (***978-0-7653-5276-7(1)*** , Starscape) Doherty, Tom Assocs., LLC.
Zoehfeld, Kathleen Weidner. Dinosaur: Aladar's Story. Clarke, Judith et al, illus. 2000. (Dinosaur Ser.). 32p. (J). (ps-3). 12.99 (978-0-7868-3259-0(2)) Disney Pr.

ORWELL, GEORGE, 1903-1950

Bloom, Harold. George Orwell's 1984. 2004. (gr. 7-12). lib. bdg. 18.75 (978-0-613-70824-1(5)) Tandem Library Bks.
Bloom, Harold, ed. 1984 - George Orwell. 2nd rev. ed. 2006. (Bloom's Modern Critical Interpretations Ser.). 216p. (YA). (gr. 9 up). 45.00 (978-0-7910-9300-9(X) , Chelsea Hse.) Facts On File, Inc.
Boerst, William J. Generous Anger: The Story of George Orwell. 2004. (World Writers Ser.). (Illus.). 112p. (YA). (gr. 6-12). 23.95 (978-1-883846-74-9(9) , First Biographies) Reynolds, Morgan Inc.
Brown, Alan. The Story Behind George Orwell's Animal Farm. 2006. (History in Literature Ser.). (Illus.). 56p. (YA). (gr. 6-9). lib. bdg. 32.86 (978-1-4034-8203-7(9)) Heinemann Library.

OSCEOLA, SEMINOLE CHIEF, 1800?-1838

Koestler-Grack, Rachel A. Osceola 1804-1838. 2002. (American Indian Biographies Ser.). (Illus.). 32p. (J). (gr. 3-4). lib. bdg. 23.93 (978-0-7368-1211-5(3) , Blue Earth Bks.) Capstone Pr., Inc.
Todd, Anne M. Osceola. 2004. (Illus.). 32p. (J). pap. 7.50 (978-1-4034-5010-4(2)); lib. bdg. 24.22 (978-1-4034-5003-6(X)) Heinemann Library.

OSTEOLOGY

see Bones

OSTRICHES

Arnold, Caroline. Ostriches. Hewett, Richard, photos by. 2000. (Early Bird Nature Bks.). (Illus.). 48p. (J). (gr. 2-4). lib. bdg. 25.26 (978-0-8225-3044-2(9) , Lerner Pubns.) Lerner Publishing Group.

Jacobs, Liza. Ostriches. 2003. (Wild Wild World Ser.). (Illus.). 24p. (J). 21.20 (978-1-4103-0040-9(4) , Blackbirch Pr., Inc.) Thomson Gale.

Lunis, Natalie. Ostrich: The World's Biggest Bird. 2007. (SuperSized! Ser.). (Illus.). 24p. (J). lib. bdg. 21.28 (978-1-59716-394-1(5) , 1265939) Bearport Publishing Co., Inc.

Maynard, Thane. Ostriches. 2006. (New Naturebooks). (Illus.). 32p. (J). (gr. 1-5). 27.07 (978-1-59296-645-5(4)) Child's World, Inc.

Rigby Education Staff. Ostriches. (Sails Literacy Ser.). (Illus.). 16p. (gr. 2-3). 27.00 (978-0-7635-9956-0(5)) Rigby Education.

Ripple, William John. Ostriches. 2005. (Desert Animals Ser.). (Illus.). 24p. (J). 15.93 (978-0-7368-3636-4(5)) Capstone Pr., Inc.

Seddon, Tony. Ostrich: South African Edition. 1998. (Cambridge Reading Routes Ser.). (Illus.). 16p. pap. 5.00 (978-0-521-63667-4(1)) Cambridge Univ. Pr.

Whitehouse, Patricia. El Avestruz. 2003. (Animales del Zoologico (Zoo Animals) Ser.). (SPA., Illus.). 24p. (ps-1). (J). lib. bdg. 17.08 (978-1-4034-0335-3(X)); pap. 5.25 (978-1-4034-0553-1(0)) Heinemann Library.

—Ostrich. 2003. (Zoo Animals Ser.). (Illus.). 24p. (ps-1). (J). lib. bdg. 17.08 (978-1-58810-887-6(2)); pap. 5.25 (978-1-4034-0543-2(3)) Heinemann Library.

—Ostrich. 2002. (ps-2). lib. bdg. 13.30 (978-0-613-81251-1(4)) Tandem Library Bks.

Wildlife Education, Ltd. Staff. Ostriches & other Ratites. 1999. (Zoobooks Ser.). (Illus.). 18p. (J). pap. 2.95 (978-0-937934-60-9(7)) Wildlife Education, Ltd.

OSTRICHES—FICTION

Aardema, Verna. The Lonely Lioness & the Ostrich Chicks. Heo, Yumi, illus. 2001. 30p. (J). (gr. 4-6). 17.00 (978-0-7567-5004-6(0)) DIANE Publishing Co.

Brown, Ken. Why Can't I Fly? (Illus.). 28p. (J). pap. 9.99 (978-1-84270-017-4(0)) Andersen GBR. *Dist:* Trafalgar Square Publishing.

McManis, Margaret Olivia. Ima & the Great Texas Ostrich Race. Dupree, Bruce, illus. 2002. (J). pap. (978-1-57168-671-8(1) , Eakin Pr.) Eakin Pr.

—Ima & the Great Texas Ostrich Race. 2002. (Illus.). 32p. 15.95 (978-1-57168-605-3(3)) Eakin Pr.

Morrow, John. Ostrich Egg Omelets. 2006. (Illus.). (J). per. 14.95 ***(978-0-9790832-1-1(4))*** Three Ring Circus Publishing Company.

Simon, Francesca & Layton, Neal. Three Cheers for Ostrich! 2001. (Illus.). 32p. (J). (ps-1). (978-1-86233-179-2(0) , Gullane Children's Bks.) Pinwheel.

Stockton, Lucille. Hallo, Mallo & Pallo: The Ostracized Ostrich Family. Sampson, April, illus. ed. 2005. 31p. (J). 19.95 (978-1-59408-511-6(0)) Cork Hill Pr.

Walker, Wayne. Henrietta. Powers, Daniel, illus. 1998. (J). (gr. 1-6). pap. 12.95 (978-0-944576-18-2(4)) Rocky River Pubs., LLC.

Wallace. Flash Harriet & Ostrich Eggs Mys. (Illus.). 64p. (J). pap. (978-0-340-61961-2(9) , Hodder & Stoughton) Hodder General Publishing Division.

Wilson, D. Arthur. Little Red Rhupert. 2006. 15.95 (978-0-9785144-0-2(8)) Ostrageous Publishing.

OTTERS

Arnosky, Jim. Otters under Water. 1999. (Illus.). 32p. (J). (ps-1). pap. 6.99 (978-0-698-11556-9(2) , Putnam Juvenile) Penguin Group (USA) Inc.

—Otters under Water. 1999. (gr. k-3). lib. bdg. 14.15 (978-0-613-15060-6(0)) Tandem Library Bks.

Feeding the Otters: Third Grade Guided Reading Level J. (On Our Way to English Ser.). (gr. 3 up). 34.50 (978-0-7578-7106-1(2)) Rigby Education.

Godkin, Celia. Sea Otter Inlet. Godkin, Celia, illus. 2001. (Illus.). 42p. (978-1-55041-663-3(4)) Fitzhenry & Whiteside, Ltd.

Grolier Educational Staff. Sea Otters. 2001. (Nature's Children Ser.). (Illus.). 48p. (J). (978-0-7172-5548-1(4) , Grolier) Scholastic Library Publishing.

Hirschmann, Kris. Sea Otters. 2005. (Creatures of the Sea Ser.). (Illus.). 48p. (J). (ps-8). lib. bdg. 26.20 (978-0-7377-3010-4(2) , Greenhaven Pr., Inc.) Thomson Gale.

Kendell, Patricia. Sea Otters. 2003. (In the Wild Ser.). (Illus.). 32p. (J). lib. bdg. 25.70 (978-0-7398-6639-9(7)) Raintree.

Mara, Wil. Otters. 2007. (Animals Animals Ser.). 48p. (J). (gr. 4-7). lib. bdg. 28.50 (978-0-7614-2527-4(6) , Benchmark Bks.) Cavendish, Marshall Corp.

Mason, Adrienne. Otters. Ogle, Nancy Gray, illus. 2004. (Kids Can Press Wildlife Ser.). 32p. (J). (gr. k-3). (978-1-55337-407-7(X)); (978-1-55337-406-0(1)) Kids Can Pr., Ltd.

Meeker, Clare Hodgson. Lootas, the Little Wave Eater: An Orphaned Sea Otter's Story. 2003. (gr. 3-6). lib. bdg. 22.20 (978-0-613-79110-6(X)) Tandem Library Bks.

Miller, Sara Swan. Otters. 2008. (J). lib. bdg. ***(978-1-4042-4162-6(0)*** , PowerKids Pr.) Rosen Publishing Group, Inc., The.

Morris, Ting. Otter. Rosewarne, Graham, illus. 2005. 32p. (J). (gr. 3-7). lib. bdg. 27.10 (978-1-58340-522-2(4)) Smart Apple Media.

Otters: Individual Title Six-Packs. (Sails Literacy Ser.). (gr. 1-2). 36.00 (978-0-7578-6772-9(3)) Rigby Education.

Rake, Jody Sullivan. Sea Otters. 2007. (J). ***(978-1-4296-0034-7(9)*** , Pebble Bks.) Capstone Pr., Inc.

Ransford, Sandy. The Otter. Kitchen, Bert, illus. 2003. (Animal Lives Ser.). 32p. (J). (gr. k-3). pap. 4.95 (978-0-7534-5602-6(8) , Kingfisher) Houghton Mifflin Co. Trade & Reference Div.

—Otter. 2003. (gr. k-3). lib. bdg. 12.95 (978-0-613-87036-8(0)) Tandem Library Bks.

Ransford, Sandy & Tagholm, Sally. The Otter. Kitchen, Bert, illus. 1999. (Animal Lives Ser.). 32p. (J). (gr. k-3). tchr. ed. 9.95 (978-0-7534-5176-2(X) , Kingfisher) Houghton Mifflin Co. Trade & Reference Div.

Ring, Susan. Project Otter. 2003. (gr. 3-6). lib. bdg. 15.25 (978-0-613-79818-1(X)) Tandem Library Bks.

—Project Otter. Kissock, Heather & Marshall, Diana, eds. 2003. (Zoo Life Ser.). (Illus.). 24p. (J). pap. 6.95 (978-1-59036-059-0(1)) Weigl Pubs., Inc.

—Project Otter. 2002. (Zoo Life Ser.). (Illus.). 24p. (J). lib. bdg. 22.80 (978-1-59036-018-7(4)) Weigl Pubs., Inc.

Seaworld Photographers, photos by. Baby Sea Otter. 2006. (SeaWorld Library: Vol. 7). (Illus.). 26p. (J). bds. 6.95 (978-0-8249-6646-1(5) , Candy Cane Pr.) Ideals Pubns.

Stone, Lynn M. Sea Otter. 2003. (Animals in U.S. History Ser.). (Illus.). 24p. (J). 25.64 (978-1-58952-701-0(1)) Rourke Publishing, LLC.

Swanson, Diane. Otters. 1998. (Illus.). 32p. (J). (gr. 3 up). lib. bdg. 22.60 (978-0-8368-2214-4(5)) Stevens, Gareth Inc.

Taylor, Bonnie Highsmith. Tilly: A River Otter. 2001. (Cover-to-Cover Chapter Bks.). (Illus.). (J). 54p. pap. (978-0-7891-5264-0(9)); 56p. (gr. 1-4). lib. bdg. 16.95 (978-0-7807-9686-7(1)) Perfection Learning Corp.

VanBlaricom, Glenn. Sea Otters. 2003. (gr. 5-8). lib. bdg. 26.85 (978-0-613-88688-8(7)) Tandem Library Bks.

VanBlaricom, Glenn, text. Sea Otters. 2001. (WorldLife Library Ser.). (Illus.). 72p. (gr. 5 up). pap. 17.95 (978-0-89658-562-1(X)) Voyageur Pr., Inc.

Wildlife Education, Ltd. Staff. Sea Otters. Hayward, Tim & Stuart, Walter, illus. 2000. (Zoobooks Ser.). 24p. (J). 15.95 (978-0-937934-87-6(9)) Wildlife Education, Ltd.

Wildlife Education, Ltd. Staff & Wagner, Beth. Seabirds. Hayward, Tim & Stuart, Walter, illus. 2000. (Zoobooks Ser.). 18p. (J). pap. 2.95 (978-0-937934-70-8(4)) Wildlife Education, Ltd.

Wilsdon, Christina. Otters. 2007. (J). ***(978-1-59939-138-0(4)*** , Reader's Digest Young Families, Inc.) Reader's Digest Children's Publishing, Inc.

OTTERS—FICTION

Anderson, Dee, retold by. Otter Gets Tricked! A Cherokee Trickster Story. l.t. ed. 2004. (Illus.). 32p. (J). pap. 6.00 (978-0-9755934-1-7(2)) Colonel Davenport Historical Foundation.

Bedford, David. Little Otter's Big Journey. Winter, Susan, illus. 2006. 28p. (J). 16.00 (978-1-56148-548-2(9)) Good Bks.

Berger, Barbara Helen. A Lot of Otters. Berger, Barbara Helen, illus. 32p. (J). (ps). 2008. bds. 7.99 ***(978-0-399-25015-6(8)*** , Philomel); 2000. (Illus.). pap. 6.99 (978-0-698-11863-8(4) , Putnam Juvenile) Penguin Group (USA) Inc.

Boyle, Doe. Otter on His Own: The Story of A Sea Otter. 2002. (gr. k-3). lib. bdg. 15.25 (978-0-613-50226-9(4)) Tandem Library Bks.

—Otter on His Own: The Story of a Sea Otter. Lawson, Robert, illus. 2nd ed. 2005. (Smithsonian Oceanic Collection). 32p. (J). (ps-2). pap. 6.95 (978-1-931465-53-3(3) , S4022) Soundprints.

Boyle, Doe & Hollenbeck, Kathleen M. Smithsonian Oceanic & Harp Seal Box. Bonforte, Lisa & Genzo, John Paul, illus. 2002. (Smithsonian Soundprints Ser.). 64p. (J). 19.95 (978-1-931465-57-1(6) , Thunder Bay Pr.) Advantage Pubs. Group.

Burgess, Thornton W. Little Joe Otter. (J). 18.95 (978-0-8488-0398-8(1)) Amereon LTD.

Butler, M. Christina. Snow Friends. Macnaughton, Tina, illus. 2005. 28p. (J). (ps-2). 16.00 (978-1-56148-485-0(7)) Good Bks.

Collins, Yvonne & Rideout, Sandy. The Black Sheep. 2007. 352p. (gr. 5 up). 15.99 ***(978-1-4231-0156-7(1))*** Hyperion Pr.

Crerand, John J. & Crerand, Teresa. The Adventures of Christopher Otter: Stories for Storytellers. Dannerfelter, Bea, illus. 2002. 42p. (J). (gr. k-6). pap. 9.95 (978-0-9719724-0-7(0) , CO-1) TACCO.

Cross, Gillian. Pictures in the Dark. 1998. (978-0-606-13703-4(3)) Tandem Library Bks.

deRubertis, Barbara. Perky Otter. Cockrille, Eva V., illus. 1998. (Let's Read Together Ser.). 32p. (J). (ps-3). pap. 4.95 (978-1-57565-045-6(2)); pap. 8.95 incl. audio (978-1-57565-050-0(9)) Kane Pr., The.

Dorfman, Louis. Otters on the Loose: An Otter's Adventure Story. 1998. 147p. (J). (gr. 5-9). pap. 8.95 (978-1-881636-35-9(6)) Windsor Hse. Publishing Group, The.

Eagle, Golden. You Can Play All Day If You Know the Way: Otter Medicine. 2005. (Illus.). 18p. (J). per. 9.95 (978-1-932338-64-5(0)) Lifevest Publishing, Inc.

The Exciting Adventures of Hydra & Muste Otter: Life in the Big Sea. 2001. 108p. (J). per. 16.95 (978-0-9669852-1-4(4)) G Sharp Productions.

Freschet, Gina. Up & at 'Em with Winnie & Ernst. 2005. (Winnie & Ernst Ser.). (Illus.). 48p. (J). 15.00 (978-0-374-38446-3(0) , Farrar, Straus & Giroux (BYR)) Farrar, Straus & Giroux.

—Winnie & Ernst. Freschet, Gina, illus. 2003. (Winnie & Ernst Ser.). (Illus.). 48p. (J). 15.00 (978-0-374-38452-4(5) , Farrar, Straus & Giroux (BYR)) Farrar, Straus & Giroux.

Galvin, Laura Gates. River Otter at Autumn Lane. Leeper, Christopher, illus. 2005. (Smithsonian's Backyard Ser.). 32p. (J). (ps-2). 4.95 (978-1-931465-62-5(2) , B5073); 15.95 (978-1-931465-61-8(4) , B5023); 19.95 incl. reel tape (978-1-931465-63-2(0) , BC5023); pap. 6.95 (978-1-931465-70-0(3) , S5023) Soundprints.

—River Otter at Autumn Lane. 2002. (gr. k-3). lib. bdg. 15.25 (978-0-613-70919-4(5)) Tandem Library Bks.

—River Otter at Autumn Lane: Including 12" Toy. Leeper, Christopher, illus. 2002. (Smithsonian's Backyard Ser.). 32p. (J). (ps-2). 32.95 (978-1-931465-65-6(7) , PB5023) Soundprints.

—River Otter at Autumn Lane: Including 6" Toy. Leeper, Christopher, illus. 2005. (Smithsonian's Backyard Ser.). 32p. (J). (ps-2). 9.95 (978-1-931465-66-3(5) , PB5073) Soundprints.

Grandpa & Little Guy. 2004. (J). 15.95 (978-0-9764012-0-9(7)) Rockmill Publishing Co.

Greeley, Michael. An Otter Day in Paradise. 2006. 86p. (J). pap. 12.95 (978-0-9777290-2-9(8) , 349-023) High-Pitched Hum Inc.

Hanks, Jacqueline. Splash! A Little Otter in Big Trouble. 1998. (Illus.). 24p. (J). (gr. k-3). pap. 3.99 (978-0-87406-904-4(1) , Willowisp Pr.) Darby Creek Publishing.

Hedderwick, Mairie. Utterly Otterleys. 2006. (Illus.). 32p. (J). (ps). 19.99 (978-0-340-87368-7(X) , Hodder & Stoughton) Hodder General Publishing Division GBR. *Dist:* Trafalgar Square Publishing.

Henri, Linda. The Way It Otter Bee. 2002. 72p. (J). pap. 12.00 (978-0-8059-5426-5(0)) Dorrance Publishing Co., Inc.

Jacques, Brian. The Taggerung. Standley, Peter, illus. (Redwall Ser.). 448p. 2003. pap. 8.99 (978-0-14-250154-2(9) , Puffin); 2001. (J). (gr. 3-6). 23.99 (978-0-399-23720-1(8) , Philomel) Penguin Group (USA) Inc.

—The Taggerung. 2002. (Redwall Ser.). (Illus.). 416p. reprint ed. mass mkt. 7.99 (978-0-441-00968-8(9) , Ace Bks.) Penguin Group (USA) Inc.

—The Taggerung. 2001. (Redwall Ser.). (Illus.). 384p. (J). (978-0-09-176928-4(0) , Hutchinson) Random Hse.

—The Taggerung. Standley, Peter, illus. l.t. ed. 2002. (Redwall Ser.). 683p. (J). 25.95 (978-0-7862-4014-2(8)) Thomson Gale.

Jennings, Sharon. Franklin & Otter's Visit. Koren, Mark et al, illus. 2003. (Franklin TV StoryBks.). 32p. (J). (gr. k-3). (978-1-55337-021-5(X)) Kids Can Pr., Ltd.

Jinkins, Jim. Hide & Seek Hunny Pot. 1999. (P B & J Otter Noodle Stories Ser.). (Illus.). 10p. (J). (ps). 4.99 (978-0-7364-0067-1(2)) Mouse Works.

Keiser, Frances R. Annie the River Otter: The Adventures of Pelican Pete. Keiser, Hugh M., illus. l.t. ed. 2006. 32p. (J). 17.00 (978-0-9668845-4-8(X)) Sagaponack Bks.

Keller, Laurie. Do unto Otters: A Book about Manners. 2007. (Illus.). 40p. (J). (gr. k-3). 16.95 ***(*978-0-8050-7996-8(3))*** Holt, Henry & Co.

Leavy, Diana C. Backstroke the Sea Otter & the Perfect Day. 2003. 32p. (J). per. (978-1-59196-258-8(7)) Instantpublisher.com.

Meeker, Clare Hodgson. Lootas, the Little Wave-Eater: An Orphaned Sea Otter's Story. Casson, C. J., photos by. 2002. (Illus.). 48p. (J). (gr. 1-5). pap. 12.95 (978-1-57061-164-3(5)) Sasquatch Bks.

Miles, Victoria. Pup's Supper. Tachiera, Andrea Z., illus. 1998. (J). bds. 5.95 (978-1-878244-22-2(1)) Monterey Bay Aquarium.

Mouse Works Staff. Peanut's Shapes. 1999. (P B & J Otter Noodle Stories Ser.). (Illus.). 16p. (J). (ps-k). 3.50 (978-0-7364-0183-8(0)) Mouse Works.

Napp, Daniel. Professor Bumble & the Monster of the Deep. 2008. 32p. (J). 15.95 ***(*978-0-8109-9484-3(4)*** , Abrams Bks. for Young Readers) Abrams, Harry N. , Inc.

Otter, Otter. (J). 26.20 (978-0-8136-8416-1(1)); 59.50 (978-0-8136-7954-9(0)) Modern Curriculum Pr.

Purkapile, Sue. Otto the Blind Otter. Ducommun, Barbara, illus. 2004. (J). 13.95 (978-1-930596-27-6(8)) Amherst Pr.

Sargent, Dave & Sargent, Pat. Odi Otter: Cheater! Cheater!, 38 vols., 32. Huff, Jeane, illus. 2001. (Animal Pride Ser.: Vol. 32). 36p. (J). pap. 6.95 (978-1-56763-381-8(1)) Ozark Publishing.

Sea Otter Cove. 2002. (Oceanic Mini Bks.). (Illus.). 32p. (978-1-59069-000-0(1) , H1001) Studio Mouse LLC.

Smith, Roland. Sea Otter Rescue: The Aftermath of an Oil Spill. Smith, Roland, illus. 1999. (Illus.). 64p. (J). (gr. 2-5). pap. 6.99 (978-0-14-056621-5(X) , Puffin) Penguin Group (USA) Inc.

Springer, Susan Woodward. Seldovia Sam & the Sea Otter Rescue. Meissner, Amy, illus. 2005. (Seldovia Sam Ser.: Vol. 2). 64p. pap. 6.95 (978-0-88240-571-1(3)) Graphic Arts Ctr. Publishing Co.

—Seldovia Sam & the Sea Otter Rescue. 2003. (gr. 3-6). lib. bdg. 15.25 (978-0-613-77295-2(4)) Tandem Library Bks.

Webster, Christine. Otter Everywhere. Nihoff, Tim, illus. 2007. (Brand New Readers Ser.). 48p. (J). (ps-2). 15.99 (978-0-7636-2921-2(9)); pap. 5.99 (978-0-7636-2922-9(7)) Candlewick Pr.

Williamson, Kelly Alan. Ollie the Otter. Bucich, Richard & Studley, Alan, photos by. collector's deluxe ed. 2001. (Talking Critter Ser.: No. 1). (Illus.). 178p. (J). (gr. 3-7). pap. 14.99 (978-0-9706467-0-5(4)) Cherubs Play.

OUTBOARD MOTORS

see Motorboats

OUTDOOR COOKERY

White, Katherine L. Cooking in a Can: More Campfire Recipes for Kids. Dixon, Debra Spina, illus. 2006. 64p. (J). (gr. 3-6). pap. 9.95 (978-1-58685-814-8(9) , 1255566) Gibbs Smith, Publisher.

White, Linda. Cooking on a Stick: Campfire Recipes for Kids. Lee, Fran, illus. 2000. 48p. (YA). (gr. 2-6). reprint ed. pap. 9.95 (978-0-87905-727-5(0)) Gibbs Smith, Publisher.

OUTDOOR LIFE

see also Camping; Country Life; Hiking; Mountaineering; Nature Study; Sports; Wilderness Survival

Beard, Lina & Beard, Adelia B. The American Girl's Handy Book: Making the Most of Outdoor Fun. 2002. 480p. pap. 11.95 (978-1-58667-089-4(1)) Derrydale Pr., The.

Birmingham, Maria, et al. 365 Outdoor Activities. Kennedy, Anne, illus. 2000. 240p. (978-0-7853-3898-7(5) , 3651500) Publications International, Ltd.

Bull, Jane. The Sunny Day Book. 2004. (Illus.). 48p. (J). 12.99 (978-0-7566-0308-3(0)) Dorling Kindersley Publishing, Inc.

Carlson, Laurie M. & Dammel, Judith. Kids Camp! Activities for the Backyard or Wilderness. 2003. (Kid's Guide Ser.). (Illus.). 174p. (J). (gr. k-7). pap. 14.95 (978-1-55652-237-6(1)) Chicago Review Pr., Inc.

Dann, Geoff. Outdoors. 1999. (Baby's World Ser.). (Illus.). 10p. (J). (ps). (978-0-7112-1124-7(8)) Lincoln, Frances Ltd.

Dillon, Christine J. Outdoor Activities. rev. ed. 1999. (My First Report Ser.). (Illus.). 56p. (J). ring bd. 5.95 (978-1-57896-050-7(9) , 2573, Hewitt Homeschooling Resources) Hewitt Research Foundation, Inc.

Douglas, Vincent & School Specialty Publishing Staff. Backyard Discoveries. 2004. (Playful Learning Ser.). (Illus.). 128p. (J). (gr. k-k). pap. 10.95 (978-0-7696-3300-8(5) , American Education Publishing) School Specialty Publishing.

Drake, Jane & Love, Ann. The Kids Campfire Book. Collins, Heather, illus. unabr. ed. 1998. (Fun for All Seasons Ser.). 128p. (J). (gr. 4-6). (978-1-55074-454-5(2)); (978-1-55074-539-9(5)) Kids Can Pr., Ltd.

Golden Books Staff. Outdoor Adventure. 2000. (Illus.). 128p. (J). (ps-2). pap. 0.99 (978-0-307-44331-1(0) , Golden Bks.) Random Hse. Children's Bks.

The Great Outdoors, 10 bks. Incl. Camping. Keller, Kristin Thoennes. 2001. lib. bdg. 21.26 (978-0-7368-0911-5(2)); Canoeing. Salas, Laura Purdie. 2002. lib. bdg. 21.26 (978-0-7368-1055-5(2)); Deer Hunting. Frahm, Randy. 2001. lib. bdg. 21.26 (978-0-7368-0912-2(0)); Duck Hunting. Frahm, Randy. 2001. lib. bdg. 21.26 (978-0-7368-0913-9(9)); Fly Fishing. Hopkins, Ellen. 2001. lib. bdg. 21.26 (978-0-7368-0914-6(7)); Freshwater Fishing. Hopkins, Ellen. 2001. lib. bdg. 21.26 (978-0-7368-0915-3(5)); Hiking. Keller, Kristin Thoennes. 2001. lib. bdg. 21.26 (978-0-7368-0916-0(3)); Ice Fishing. Salas, Laura Purdie. 2002. lib. bdg. 21.26 (978-0-7368-1056-2(0)); Pheasant Hunting. Martin, Michael J. 2002. lib. bdg. 21.26 (978-0-7368-1057-9(9)); Snowmobiling. Salas, Laura Purdie. 2002. lib. bdg. 21.26 (978-0-7368-1058-6(7)); 48p. (J). (gr. 3-4). (Illus.). Set lib. bdg. 212.60 (978-0-7368-1080-7(3) , Capstone High-Interest Bks.) Capstone Pr., Inc.

Martin, Eric B. Campfire Collection: Spine Tingling Tales to Tell. 2000. (J). 22.60 (978-0-606-22159-7(X)) Tandem Library Bks.

Mattern, Joanne. Orienteering. 2004. (Great Outdoors Ser.). (Illus.). 48p. (J). 16.95 (978-0-7368-2411-8(1)) Capstone Pr., Inc.

Paulsen, Gary. Puppies, Dogs, & Blue Northers: Reflections on Being Raised by a Pack of Sled Dogs. 2007. (Illus.). 80p. (J). pap. 5.95 ***(*978-0-15-206103-6(7)*** , Harcourt Paperbacks) Harcourt Children's Bks.

—Woodsong. 2007. 144p. (J). pap. 5.99 ***(*978-1-4169-3939-9(3)*** , Aladdin) Simon & Schuster Children's Publishing.

—Woodsong. 2000. (J). (gr. 6 up). 20.25 (978-0-8446-7152-9(5)) Smith, Peter Pub., Inc.

Reeves, Diane Lindsey. Career Ideas for Kids Who Like Animals & Nature. 2nd rev. ed. (Career Ideas for Kids Ser.). 208p. (J). (gr. 4-9). pap. 16.95 ***(*978-0-8160-6540-0(3)*** , Checkmark Bks.); 2007. 32.95 ***(*978-0-8160-6539-4(X)*** , Ferguson Publishing Co.) Facts On File, Inc.

Slade, Suzanne. Adventures Outdoors, 6 bks., Set. Incl. Let's Go Camping. lib. bdg. 23.95 (978-1-4042-3650-9(3)); Let's Go Canoeing & Kayaking. lib. bdg. 23.95 (978-1-4042-3649-3(X)); Let's Go Fishing. lib. bdg. 23.95 (978-1-4042-3647-9(3)); Let's Go Hiking. lib. bdg. 23.95 (978-1-4042-3651-6(1)); Let's Go Hunting. lib. bdg. 23.95 (978-1-4042-3646-2(5)); Let's Go Snowboarding. lib. bdg. 23.95 (978-1-4042-3648-6(1)); (Illus.). 32p. (J). (gr. 4-6). 2007. 2007. Set lib. bdg. 143.70 ***(*978-1-4042-3603-5(1)*** , PowerKids Pr.) Rosen Publishing Group, Inc., The.

Smith, Roger. Teens & Rural Sports: Rodeos, Horses, Hunting, & Fishing. 2008. (J). ***(*978-1-4222-0022-3(1))*** Mason Crest Pubs.

Thomas, Maryann. Summer at the Beach: Learning the EA Sound. 2001. (PowerPhonics Ser.). (Illus.). 23p. (J). pap. 26.40 (978-0-8239-8295-0(5) , PowerKids Pr.) Rosen Publishing Group, Inc., The.

Watts, Claire. On Safari. 2004. (My First Look at Animals Ser.). (SPA., Illus.). 24p. (ps-2). 9.95 (978-1-58728-856-2(7)); (J). pap. 5.95 (978-1-58728-863-0(X)) T&N Children's Publishing. (Two Can Publishing).

—On Safari. 2001. (ps-2). lib. bdg. 14.10 (978-0-613-43485-0(4)) Tandem Library Bks.

Winner, Cherie. Kids Gone Campin' The Young Camper's Guide to Having More Fun Outdoors. 2006. (Illus.). 96p. pap. 12.95 (978-1-58923-225-9(9) , Creative Publishing International) Quayside.

OUTDOOR LIFE—FICTION

Aimard, Gustave. The Indian Scout: a Story of the Aster City. 2006. (ENG.). 464p. per. 37.95 ***(*978-1-4286-1776-6(0))*** Kessinger Publishing, LLC.

Allen, Quinc. The Outdoor Chums. 2006. pap. ***(*978-1-4065-0782-9(2))*** Dodo Pr.

—The Outdoor Chums after Big Game (Illust. 2006. pap. ***(*978-1-4065-0780-5(6))*** Dodo Pr.

—The Outdoor Chums on the Gulf. 2006. pap. ***(*978-1-4065-0781-2(4))*** Dodo Pr.

Allen, Quincy. Outdoor Chums after Big Game or Perilous. 2006. 77.99 ***(*978-1-4280-3810-3(8))*** ; pap. 71.99 ***(*978-1-4280-3804-2(3))*** IndyPublish.com.

M N O

Bruna, Dick. Let's Learn: The Great Outdoors. 2004. (Illus.). 24p. pap. 4.99 (978-1-59226-169-7(8)) Big Tent Entertainment, Inc.

Canady, Pat. Boots the World's Best Kid-Sitter: Springtime Adventures. Bartley, Michael, illus. 2000. 6p. (J). (ps-4). pap. 10.00 (978-1-929889-02-0(X)) Canady SW Publishing.

Clark, Henry Scott. The Legionaires: A Story of the Great Raid. 2005. reprint ed. pap. 34.95 (978-1-4191-3923-9(1)) Kessinger Publishing, LLC.

Cole, Henry. On the Way to the Beach. Cole, Henry, illus. 2003. (Illus.). 32p. (J). 16.99 (978-0-688-17515-3(5)) HarperCollins Pubs.

Cunningham, Bill. Lighting Grandma's Fire: Mountain Skills & Valley Pastimes. 1999. (Illus.). 153p. (J). pap. 12.95 (978-1-890437-33-6(6)) Western Reflections Publishing Co.

Daley, Patrick. Run, Gus, Run!, Level 1. 1998. (Disney's First Readers Ser.: No. 10). (Illus.). 24p. (J). (gr. k-1). pap. 2.95 (978-0-7868-4169-1(9)) Disney Pr.

Fleischman, Sid. Humbug Mountain. 1998. (978-0-606-13498-9(0)) Tandem Library Bks.

Grant, Robert. Jack in the Bush or A Summer on a Salmon River. 2005. pap. 33.95 (978-1-4179-5573-2(2)) Kessinger Publishing, LLC.

Greene, Stephanie. Owen Foote, Frontiersman. Weston, Martha, illus. 96p. (J). (gr. k-3). 2002. pap. 4.95 (978-0-618-24620-5(7)); 1999. tchr. ed. 14.00 (978-0-395-61578-2(X)) Houghton Mifflin Co. Trade & Reference Div. (Clarion Bks.).

—Owen Foote, Frontiersman. 2002. (gr. k-3). lib. bdg. 12.95 (978-0-613-72910-9(2)) Tandem Library Bks.

Henry, Patrick. The Spectacular Adventures of John Cross. 2005. (J). per. 8.99 (978-0-9773990-1-7(X)) Mother's Hse. Publishing.

Keller, Jeff, Jr. Ricky Climbs Pikes Peak. 2006. (J). 8.95 (978-0-9773990-9-3(5)) Mother's Hse. Publishing.

Marcum, Lance. The Cottonmouth Club. 2005. 336p. (J). 18.00 (978-0-374-31562-7(0) , Farrar, Straus & Giroux (BYR)) Farrar, Straus & Giroux.

Montgomery, Rutherford G. Pekan the Shadow. Nenninger, J. D., illus. 2004. (Classic Ser.). 164p. (gr. 4-7). pap. 13.95 (978-0-87004-406-9(0)) Caxton Pr.

Peep for Keeps. 2005. 43p. (J). 3.99 (978-0-9763213-4-7(3)) OHC Group LLC.

Peirce-Bale, Mary. Wilma Wombat's Trek to Back of Beyond. 2006. (J). 9.90 (978-0-9773990-4-8(4)) Mother's Hse. Publishing.

Santillo, LuAnn. Mike. Santillo, LuAnn, ed. 2003. (Half-Pint Kids Readers Ser.). (Illus.). 7p. (J). (ps-1). pap. (978-1-59256-100-1(4)) Half-Pint Kids, Inc.

Sculthorp, Jeffrey A. Heidi's Hike. Wingate, Lynae & Kober, John R., eds. Walter, Lorin, illus. 2000. (Wickleville Woods Ser.). 28p. (J). (ps-2). pap. 4.99 (978-1-889319-72-8(4) , Wickleville Woods) Trend Enterprises, Inc.

Seton, Ernest Thompson. Two Little Savages. 2006. pap. 30.99 (***978-1-4280-0828-1(4)***) IndyPublish.com.

Truax, Doug. A Good Day for Ducks. Smith, Jack K., illus. 2003. 32p. (gr. k-4). 16.95 (978-1-932052-12-1(7)) Ducks Unlimited, Inc.

Waboose, Jan Bourdeau. Morning on the Lake. Reczuch, Karen, illus. 32p. (J). (gr. k-3). 2002. (978-1-55074-588-7(3)); 1998. (978-1-55074-373-9(2)) Kids Can Pr., Ltd.

—Morning on the Lake. 2002. (gr. k-3). lib. bdg. 14.10 (978-0-613-83962-4(5)) Tandem Library Bks.

Wang, Adria. My World: My Outdoors. Nicholls, Paul, illus. 2005. (My World Bks.). 10p. (J). 4.95 (978-1-58117-249-2(4) , Intervisual/Piggy Toes) Dalmatian Pr.

Wright, Caleb E. Marcus Blair A Story of Provincial Times. 2006. pap. 22.95 (***978-1-4286-6303-9(7)***) Kessinger Publishing, LLC.

OUTDOOR SURVIVAL

see Wilderness Survival

OUTER SPACE

Adair, Amy. Space Adventure: Ligt-A-Flap Fun. Birmingham, Lloyd, tr. Birmingham, Lloyd, illus. 2002. (Leap Frog Ser.). 12p. (J). bds. 7.98 (978-0-7853-6347-7(5) , 7159300) Publications International, Ltd.

Aguilar, David. Our Universe: A Visual Encyclopedia of Our Universe. 2007. 192p. (YA). (gr. 5 up). lib. bdg. 38.90 (***978-1-4263-0171-1(5)*** , National Geographic Children's Bks.) National Geographic Society.

—Planets, Stars, & Galaxies: A Visual Encyclopedia of Our Universe. 2007. (Illus.). 192p. (YA). (gr. 5 up). 24.95 (***978-1-4263-0170-4(7)*** , National Geographic Children's Bks.) National Geographic Society.

Ames, Lee J. & Estrada, Ric. Draw 50 Aliens: UFOS, Galaxy Ghouls, Milky Way Marauders, & Other Extraterrestrial Creatures. 1998. (Illus.). 64p. pap. 8.95 (978-0-385-49145-7(X) , Broadway) Broadway Bks.

Asimov, Isaac & Hantula, Richard. Asteroides. Porras, Carlos & D'Andrea, Patricia, trs. 2003. (Isaac Asimov's Biblioteca del Universo del Siglo XXI). (SPA., Illus.). 32p. (J). (gr. 3 up). lib. bdg. 24.67 (978-0-8368-3853-4(X)); pap. 8.95 (978-0-8368-3866-4(1) , Weekly Reader Early Learning Library) Stevens, Gareth Inc.

Aylmore, Angela. I Like Outer Space. 2007. (Illus.). 24p. (J). (978-1-4034-9274-6(3)); lib. bdg. 21.36 (978-1-4034-9265-4(4)) Heinemann Library.

Barnett, Alex & Dorling Kindersley Publishing Staff. Space. 2004. (Dk Revealed Ser.). (Illus.). 48p. (J). 12.99 (978-0-7566-0305-2(6)) Dorling Kindersley Publishing, Inc.

Barnett, Michelle Noble, et al. Theme Pockets - July: America the Beautiful; Space; Transportation. Evans, Marilyn, ed. Larsen, Jo, illus. 1999. (Making Books with Pockets). 96p. (J). pap., tchr. ed. 12.99 (978-1-55799-704-3(7) , EMC 590) Evan-Moor Educational Pubs.

Becklake, Sue. Space. 2003. (Illus.). 48p. (J). (gr. 3 up). lib. bdg. (978-1-59084-457-1(2)) Mason Crest Pubs.

—Space. 2004. (Picture Reference Ser.). (SPA., Illus.). 48p. (gr. 3-6). (J). pap. 7.95 (978-1-58728-660-5(2)); 13.95 (978-1-58728-653-7(X)) T&N Children's Publishing. (Two Can Publishing).

—Space: The Book & Disk That Work Together. 2000. (Interfact Reference Ser.). (Illus.). 48p. (J). (gr. 3-6). 19.95 incl. cd-rom (978-1-58728-473-1(1) , Two Can Publishing) T&N Children's Publishing.

Becklake, Sue, et al. All about Space. 1998. (Scholastic First Encyclopedia Ser.). (Illus.). 80p. (J). (gr. k-3). pap. 14.95 (978-0-590-10471-5(3)) Scholastic, Inc.

Berger, Melvin & Berger, Gilda. Can You Hear a Shout in Space? Questions & Answers about Space Exploration. Di Fate, Vincent, illus. 2001. (Question & Answer Ser.). 48p. (J). (gr. 2-4). pap. 5.95 (978-0-439-14879-5(0) , Scholastic Reference) Scholastic, Inc.

Bond, Peter. Space. 2006. 64p. (J). (gr. 8). pap. 7.99 (978-0-7566-2230-5(1)) Dorling Kindersley Publishing, Inc.

Bown, Deni & Becklake, Sue. Space, Stars, Planets, & Spacecraft: See & Explore Library. 1998. (See & Explore Library Ser.). (Illus.). 64p. (J). (gr. 4-7). pap. 7.99 (978-0-7894-2966-7(7)) Dorling Kindersley Publishing, Inc.

Bramwell, Martyn. Mapping the Planets & Space. 1998. (Maps & Mapmakers Ser.). (Illus.). 48p. (J). (gr. 5-7). lib. bdg. 22.60 (978-0-8225-2922-4(X) , Lerner Pubns.) Lerner Publishing Group.

Branley, Franklyn M. Is There Life in Outer Space? Miller, Edward, illus. 1999. (Let's-Read-and-Find-Out Science Ser.). 40p. (J). (ps-1). 15.89 (978-0-06-028145-8(6)); pap. 5.99 (978-0-06-445192-5(5) , Harper Trophy) HarperCollins Pubs.

Branley, Franklyn Mansfield. Is There Life in Outer Space? Miller, Edward, illus. 1999. 31p. (J). (ps-ps). lib. bdg. 13.00 (978-0-613-22877-0(4)) Tandem Library Bks.

Brighter Vision Publishing Staff. Space & the Planets. 2000. (Learning Adventures Kindergarten Ser.). (Illus.). (J). (gr. k-1). pap. 2.25 (978-1-55254-146-3(0)) Brighter Vision Pubns.

Burton, Margie, et al. Looking into Space. Adams, Alison, ed. 1999. (Early Connections Ser.). 16p. (J). (gr. k-2). pap. 4.50 (978-1-58344-072-8(0)) Benchmark Education Co.

Carson, Mary Kay. Exploring the Solar System: A History with 22 Activities. rev. ed. 2008. 176p. (J). (gr. 4 up). pap. 17.95 (***978-1-55652-715-9(2)***) Chicago Review Pr., Inc.

Carson, Mary Kay. Space: Easy Internet Explorations. 2001. (Illus.). 48p. (J). (gr. 3-6). pap. 9.95 (978-0-439-24441-1(2)) Scholastic, Inc.

Chicko, Joe & Chicko, Terri, illus. Space. 1998. (At Your Fingertips Ser.). 10p. (J). (ps-3). 6.95 (978-0-7681-0075-4(5) , McClanahan Bk.) Learning Horizons, Inc.

Clifford, Tim. Space. 2008. (J). (***978-1-60044-624-5(8)***) Rourke Publishing, LLC.

Cohen, Dennis. The Big Book of Space Discovery: A Fun-Filled Adventure into the Planets, Stars & Space Exploration. Fry, Sharon, ed. Estrine, Ron, illus. l.t. ed. 1999. 12p. (J). (gr. k-7), mass mkt. 12.00 (978-0-9674289-0-1(4)) Schmidt-Cannon International.

Couper, Heather & Henbest, Nigel. Space Encyclopedia. 1999. (Illus.). 304p. (J). (gr. 3-7). 29.99 (978-0-7894-4708-1(8)) Dorling Kindersley Publishing, Inc.

Coupper, Heather. Atlas Visual del Espacio. (Coleccion Atlas Visual). (SPA., Illus.). 64p. (YA). (gr. 5-8). (978-84-216-1816-5(4) , BU5067) Bruño, Editorial ESP. *Dist:* Lectorum Pubns., Inc.

Dillon, Christine J., ed. The Solar System & Space. 1998. (My First Report Ser.). (Illus.). 58p. (J). (gr. 1-4). ring bd. 5.95 (978-1-57896-019-4(3) , 2472) Hewitt Research Foundation, Inc.

Discovery Channel & Staff. Builders. 2004. (Planet's Most Extreme Ser.). (Illus.). 48p. (J). (gr. 4-7). 24.95 (978-1-4103-0384-4(5) , Blackbirch Pr., Inc.) Thomson Gale.

DiSpezio, Michael Anthony. Space Mania. Discovering Distant Worlds Without Leaving Your Own. 2004. (Illus.). 80p. (J). pap. 6.95 (978-1-4027-1772-7(5)) Sterling Publishing Co., Inc.

DK Publishing. First Space Encyclopedia. 2007. 128p. (J). 15.99 (***978-0-7566-3366-0(4)***) Dorling Kindersley Publishing, Inc.

Dorling Kindersley Publishing Staff, et al. Space Facts. 2nd rev. ed. 2003. (Pockets Ser.). (Illus.). 160p. (J). pap. 6.99 (978-0-7894-9593-8(7)) Dorling Kindersley Publishing, Inc.

Dowswell, Paul. Mi Primera Enciclopedia del Espacio. 2004. (Titles in Spanish Ser.).Tr. of First Encyclopedia of Space. (SPA.). (J). pap. 9.95 (978-0-7460-5075-0(5)) EDC Publishing.

—The Usborne Little Encyclopedia of Space. Bines, Gary & Hancock, David, illus. 2005. 64p. (J). 6.95 (978-0-7945-1091-6(4) , Usborne) EDC Publishing.

Doyle, Bill. The Space Explorer's Guide to the Universe. Labat, Yancey C., illus. 2003. (Space University Ser.). 48p. (J). (978-0-439-55739-9(9)) Scholastic, Inc.

Draw 50 Aliens: Ufos, Galaxy Ghouls, Milky Way Marauders, & Other Extraterrestrial Creatures. 2002. (Draw 50 Ser.). (Illus.). (J). 17.60 (978-0-7587-4132-5(4)) Book Wholesalers, Inc.

Dyer, Alan. Space. 2007. (Insiders Ser.). 64p. (J). 16.99 (***978-1-4169-3860-6(5)***) Simon & Schuster Children's Publishing.

Earth & Space. Date not set. (Illus.). 48p. (J). 5.98 (978-1-4054-0206-4(7)); 2003. (Illus.). 256p. (J). 12.98 (978-1-4054-1543-9(6)); 2000. 40p. (YA). 8.33 (978-0-7525-4530-1(2)) Parragon, Inc.

Fleurus. Space. 1999. (ps-3). (978-2-215-06243-1(6)) Editions Fleurus.

Ford, Harry & Barnham, Kay. Outer Space. 2003. (Knowledge Masters Ser.). (Illus.). 32p. (YA). pap. incl. cd-rom (978-1-903954-09-6(6)) Chrysalis Children's Bks.

Gibson, Diane. Geothermal Power. 2001. (Sources of Energy Ser.). (Illus.). 24p. (J). (gr. 2-7). lib. bdg. 21.30 (978-1-887068-76-5(7)) Smart Apple Media.

Glover, David. Transportation. 2004. (Picture Reference Ser.). (SPA., Illus.). 48p. (gr. 3-6). (J). pap. 7.95 (978-1-58728-657-5(2)); 13.95 (978-1-58728-654-4(8)) T&N Children's Publishing. (Two Can Publishing).

God Made Outer Space. 2006. 16p. (J). pap. 1.99 (978-0-7847-1702-8(8) , 04163) Standard Publishing.

Goldsmith, Mike. Space: Travel to Space & Back with Astronaut Sally Ride. 2005. (Kingfisher Voyages Ser.). (Illus.). 60p. (J). (gr. 4-6). 14.95 (978-0-7534-5910-2(8) , Kingfisher) Houghton Mifflin Co. Trade & Reference Div.

—Space Mysteries. 2001. (Spinning Through Space Ser.). (Illus.). 32p. (J). (gr. 2-4). lib. bdg. 25.69 (978-0-7398-2745-1(6)) Raintree.

Graham, Ian. My Book of Space. 2001. (My Book of... Ser.). (Illus.). 48p. (J). (ps-k). tchr. ed. 14.95 (978-0-7534-5399-5(1) , Kingfisher) Houghton Mifflin Co. Trade & Reference Div.

—Space. 1999. (Tomorrow's Technology Ser.). (Illus.). 32p. (J). lib. bdg. 16.95 (978-1-929298-41-9(2)) Chrysalis Education.

—Los Volcanes: El Libro y EL CD-ROM Que Interactuan. 2000. (Interfact Ser.). (SPA.). (J). (gr. 2-7). spiral bd. 14.95 (978-1-58728-477-9(4) , Two Can Publishing) T&N Children's Publishing.

Grenier, Christian. Infinite Space. 1999. (Megascope Ser.). (Illus.). 63p. (J). (gr. 5-9). 6.95 (978-0-7641-5180-4(0)) Barron's Educational Series, Inc.

Gribbin, John R. Time & Space. 2000. (Eyewitness Bks.). (Illus.). 64p. (J). (gr. 3-7). 15.99 (978-0-7894-5578-9(1)) Dorling Kindersley Publishing, Inc.

Halls, Kelly Milner. Astronomy & Space. 2006. (Science Fair Projects Ser.). (Illus.). 48p. (J). (gr. 6-9). lib. bdg. 30.00 (978-1-4034-7908-2(9)) Heinemann Library.

Hansen, Rosanna. Space. 2004. (True Tales Ser.). (J). (gr. 2-4). pap. 4.95 (978-0-516-24608-6(9) , Children's Pr.) Scholastic Library Publishing.

Harris, Nicholas, ed. Space. 2002. (Zoom Ser.). (Illus.). 32p. (J). 23.70 (978-1-56711-696-0(5) , Blackbirch Pr., Inc.) Thomson Gale.

Haslam, Andrew. Space. 2004. (Make It Work! Science Ser.). (Illus.). 48p. (gr. 3-6). 12.95 (978-1-58728-366-6(2) , Two Can Publishing) T&N Children's Publishing.

Haslam, Andrew, et al. Space. (Make It Work! Ser.). (Illus.). 48p. (J). pap. 7.99 (978-0-590-24690-3(9)) Scholastic, Inc.

Hirschmann, Kris. Space & the Planets. Bollinger, Peter, illus. 2003. (Magic School Bus Fact Finder Ser.). 96p. (J). pap. 4.99 (978-0-439-38175-8(4)) Scholastic, Inc.

Hodges, Susan. Up in Space. Barr, Marilynn G., illus. 1999. (Rhyme & Reason Workbook Ser.). 32p. (J). (ps-k). pap. 3.95 (978-1-57029-254-5(X) , WPH 01106, Totline Pubns.) Schaffer, Frank Pubns.

Holland, Simon & Dorling Kindersley Publishing Staff. Space. 2001. (Eye Wonder Ser.). (Illus.). 48p. (J). (gr. k-3). lib. bdg. 17.95 (978-0-7894-8182-5(0)) Dorling Kindersley Publishing, Inc.

Holland, Simon & Stott, Carole. Space. Holland, Simon & Ling, Mary, eds. 2001. (Eye Wonder Ser.). (Illus.). 48p. (J). (gr. k-3). 9.99 (978-0-7894-7854-2(4)) Dorling Kindersley Publishing, Inc.

Holt, Rinehart and Winston Staff. Holt Science & Technology Chptr. 11: Exploring Space: Chapter Resources - Tennessee Edition. 3rd ed. 2003. (J). pap. 11.40 (978-0-03-069118-8(4)) Holt, Rinehart & Winston.

Howell, Laura & Rogers, Kirsteen. Earth & Space. 2004. (Library of Science Ser.). 64p. (J). lib. bdg. 17.95 (978-1-58086-373-5(6)) EDC Publishing.

Jensen, Connie. Spaced Out. 2000. (Illus.). 64p. (J). pap. 6.95 (978-1-880505-77-9(0) , CLC0237) Pieces of Learning.

Jerome, Kate Boehm. Exploring Space. 2002. (Earth Science Ser.). (Illus.). 32p. (J). (978-0-7922-8870-1(X)) National Geographic Society.

Kelleher, Pat & Twist, Clint. Puzzle Quest Through Space. Pastor, Terry, illus. 2006. (Puzzle Quest Ser.). 22p. (J). bds., bds. 22.95 (978-0-7696-4877-4(0) , Brighter Child) School Specialty Publishing.

Kermani, Faiz. My Alien Penfriend. 2005. (ENG., Illus.). 89p. pap. 11.49 (***978-1-4208-5860-0(2)***) AuthorHouse.

Kespert, Deborah. Exploring Space. Holmes, Stephen, illus. 2004. (Interfact Play & Discover Ser.). 48p. (J). (ps-2). 14.95 incl. cd-rom (978-1-58728-630-8(0) , Two Can Publishing) T&N Children's Publishing.

Kolaczek, Marie. Exploring Space. Latyk, Olivier & Mignon, Philippe, illus. 2006. (Explore Your World Ser.). 28p. (J). (ps-1). 15.95 (978-1-55407-006-0(6)) Firefly Bks., Ltd.

Kortenkamp, Steve. Space Junk. 2008. (J). (***978-1-4296-1258-6(4)***) Capstone Pr., Inc.

—Space Tourism. 2008. (J). (***978-1-4296-1260-9(6)***) Capstone Pr., Inc.

Little & Large Sticker Activity - Space. 2006. (J). 3.99 (978-1-933581-36-1(0)) Byeway Bks.

Looking at Space. (Jump Ser.). 36p. (J). (gr. 2-7). pap. (978-1-882210-20-6(4)) Action Publishing, Inc.

MacDonald, Fiona. Space. 2000. (Topic Bks.). (Illus.). 32p. (J). (gr. 2-5). 23.50 (978-0-531-14542-5(5)); pap. 6.95 (978-0-531-15426-7(2)) Scholastic Library Publishing. (Watts, Franklin).

—Space. 2000. (J). (978-0-606-19794-6(X)); (gr. 3-6). lib. bdg. 15.25 (978-0-613-54680-5(6)) Tandem Library Bks.

MacDonald, Olive. What If We Lived on Another Planet? 2002. (What If Ser.). (Illus.). 48p. (YA). (gr. 7-12). 24.00 (978-0-516-23912-5(0) , Children's Pr.) Scholastic Library Publishing.

McCourt, Lisa, et al. Mysterious Science. 2000. (Brain Builders Ser.). (Illus.). 48p. (J). (gr. k-3). pap. 7.95 (978-0-7373-0465-7(0) , 04650W, Roxbury Park Juvenile) Lowell Hse. Juvenile.

McDonald, Kim. Life in Outer Space: The Search for Extra-terrestrials. 1999. (Space Explorer Ser.). (Illus.). 64p. (J). (gr. 6-8). lib. bdg. 28.54 (978-0-7398-2213-5(6)) Raintree.

Miller, Ron. Space Exploration. 2007. (Space Innovations Ser.). 112p. (YA). (gr. 6-8). lib. bdg. 31.93 (***978-0-8225-7155-1(2)*** , Twenty-First Century Bks.) Lerner Publishing Group.

Moore, Jo Ellen. Exploring Space. Evans, Marilyn, ed. Robison, Don, illus. 1998. (ScienceWorks for Kids Ser.: Vol. 1). 80p. (J). (gr. 1-3). pap., tchr. ed. 9.95 (978-1-55799-682-4(2) , EMC 853) Evan-Moor Educational Pubs.

Morris, Neil. Amazing Space. 2006. (Amazing World). 28p. (J). (gr. 3-8). 17.95 (978-0-7696-4833-0(9)) School Specialty Publishing.

Nelson, Nigel. Looking into Space. Harper, Piers, illus. 1998. (Looking Into... Ser.: Vol. 3). 13p. (J). (ps-2). 12.99 (978-1-57584-243-1(2) , Reader's Digest Children's Bks.) Reader's Digest Children's Publishing, Inc.

Outer Space. Date not set. (Illus.). 12p. (J). 3.98 (978-1-4054-0498-3(1)) Parragon, Inc.

Outer Space, 12 vols., Set. 1998. (Illus.). (YA). lib. bdg. 285.00 (978-0-7172-9179-3(0) , Grolier) Scholastic Library Publishing.

Parker. Space Mysteries - Space Busters. 2004. (YA). pap. 48.30 (978-1-4109-0293-1(5)) Harcourt Schl. Pubs.

Parker, Steve. Space Mysteries. 2002. (Young Library - Space Busters Ser.). (Illus.). 32p. (J). (gr. 3-5). lib. bdg. 25.69 (978-0-7398-4853-1(4)) Raintree.

Pearce, Querida L. Strange Science: Outer Space. 1999. (978-0-606-18656-8(5)) Tandem Library Bks.

Penguin Books Staff, ed. Space. (Learners Ser.). (Illus.). 48p. (J). 3.50 (978-0-7214-1702-8(7) , Dutton Juvenile) Penguin Group (USA) Inc.

Quadrillion Media Staff. International Space Station (Die Internationale Raumstation) A Journey into Space. 1998. (Start Me Up Ser.). 64p. (J). (gr. 4-7). mass mkt. 15.95 (978-1-58185-004-8(2) , Tessloff Publishing) Quadrillion Media LLC.

—Space. 1999. (Start Me Up Ser.). (J). pap. 3.95 (978-1-58185-102-1(2)) Quadrillion Media LLC.

¿Que Hay en el Espacio? (Coleccion Primeros Pasos en la Ciencia). (SPA., Illus.). (J). (gr. 1-3). pap. (978-950-724-099-7(3) , LMA8217) Lumen ARG. *Dist:* Lectorum Pubns., Inc.

Quigley, Sebastian & Pickering, Mel, illus. All about Space. 1998. (Scholastic First Encyclopedia Ser.). (J). pap. (978-0-590-10472-2(1)) Scholastic, Inc.

Randinelli, Tracy & Prokos, Anna. Secrets of Space. Snow, Alan, illus. 2002. (Crash Course Ser.). 68p. (J). (gr. 2-17). spiral bd. 16.99 (978-1-58476-137-2(7)) Innovative Kids.

Red Bird Press Staff. Space. 2004. (Mission Xtreme 3D Ser.). 18p. (J). pap. 5.95 (978-1-902626-62-8(1)) Red Bird Publishing GBR. *Dist:* Weatherhill, Inc.

Redfern, Martin. The Kingfisher Young Peoples Book of Space. 1998. (Kingfisher Book of Ser.). (Illus.). 96p. (J). (gr. 4-8). 22.95 (978-0-7534-5136-6(0) , Kingfisher) Houghton Mifflin Co. Trade & Reference Div.

Redpath, Barrett. The Outer Space Book. 2006. 12p. (J). 7.58 (978-1-4116-8498-0(2)) Lulu.com.

Reynolds, David West. Star Wars Episode I: Episode 1 Incredible Cross-Sections. Chasemore, Richard & Jenssen, Hans, illus. 1999. (Star Wars Ser.). 32p. (J). (gr. 3-7). 19.95 (978-0-7894-3962-8(X)) Dorling Kindersley Publishing, Inc.

Riley, Peter D. The Earth & Space. 2005. (Illus.). 32p. (J). (gr. 4-7). lib. bdg. 27.10 (978-1-58340-713-4(8)) Smart Apple Media.

—Earth in Space. 1999. (gr. 3-6). lib. bdg. 15.25 (978-0-613-31148-9(5)) Tandem Library Bks.

Rockwell, Anne F. Our Stars. 2002. (gr. k-3). lib. bdg. 14.15 (978-0-613-53848-0(X)) Tandem Library Bks.

Roza, Greg. Space Math. 2003. (Reading Room Collection). (Illus.). 24p. (J). lib. bdg. 18.75 (978-0-8239-3705-9(4)) Rosen Publishing Group, Inc., The.

Rustad, Martha E. H. Out in Space, 4 bks. Saunders-Smith, Gail, ed. Incl. Moon. lib. bdg. 15.93 (978-0-7368-1177-4(X)); Planets. lib. bdg. 15.93 (978-0-7368-1178-1(8)); Stars. lib. bdg. 15.93 (978-0-7368-1179-8(6)); Sun. lib. bdg. 15.93 (978-0-7368-1180-4(X)); 24p. (J). (gr. k-1). 2002. (Illus.). 2001. Set lib. bdg. 63.72 (978-0-7368-1200-9(8) , Pebble Bks.) Capstone Pr., Inc.

Secrets of Space. (Science & Technology Ser.). (Illus.). 64p. (978-0-7613-3096-7(8) , Twenty-First Century Bks.) Lerner Publishing Group.

Sibila, Tom. Space Ship One: Making History in Outerspace. 2005. (High Five Reading Ser.). (Illus.). 64p. (J). (gr. 4-5). lib. bdg. incl. audio (978-0-7368-5754-3(0)) Capstone Pr., Inc.

Smith, A. Book of Astronomy & Space. 2004. (Complete Bks.). (SPA., Illus.), 96p. (J). lib. bdg. 22.95 (978-1-58086-385-8(X)) EDC Publishing.

Smith, Alastair & Miles, Lisa. Book of Astronomy & Space. 2004. (Complete Bks.). (SPA., Illus.). 96p. (J). pap. 14.95 (978-0-7945-0116-7(8) , Usborne) EDC Publishing.

Space. (Eyes on Adventure Ser.). (J). 32p. (gr. 1). pap. (978-1-882210-62-6(X)); 42p. (gr. 4-8). pap. (978-1-882210-49-7(2)) Action Publishing, Inc.

Space. 1998. (Illus.). 5p. (J). (ps-3). 10.99 (978-1-929174-12-6(8)) Oshkosh B'Gosh, Inc.

M N O

Spahr, Candy Cain. Mission S. T. A. R. (Space Travel & Recreation) 2000. 50p. (J). (gr. k-6). pap. 4.00 (978-1-58193-189-1(1)) Brown Bag Productions.

Stott, Carole. I Wonder Why Stars Twinkle: And Other Questions about Space. 2003. (I Wonder Why Ser.). 32p. (J). (gr. k-3). pap. 6.95 (978-0-7534-5614-9(1), Kingfisher) Houghton Mifflin Co. Trade & Reference Div.

—I Wonder Why Stars Twinkle: And Other Questions about Space. 2003. (J). lib. bdg. 14.10 (978-0-613-63164-8(1)) Tandem Library Bks.

Stott, Carole & Twist, Clint. 1,001 Facts about Space. Grabham, Sue, ed. 2002. (Backpack Book Ser.). (Illus.). 192p. (J). (gr. k-3). pap. 8.99 (978-0-7894-8450-5(1)) Dorling Kindersley Publishing, Inc.

Sumners, Carolyn. Earthling Guide to Deep Space. 1998. (gr. 3-6). lib. bdg. 22.20 (978-0-613-71539-3(X)) Tandem Library Bks.

Sumners, Carolyn T. & Handron, Kerry. Earthling Guide to Deep Space: Explore the Galaxy Through the Eye of the Hubble Space Telescope. 1998. (Illus.). 160p. (C). (gr. 4-7). pap. 12.95 (978-0-07-021988-5(5), 9780070219885) McGraw-Hill Cos., The.

Time-Life Books Editors. Space. 1999. (How Things Work Ser.). (J). (gr. 3). 19.95 (978-0-8094-7862-0(5)) Time-Life, Inc.

Vogt, Gregory L. Asteroids. 2002. (Galaxy Ser.). (Illus.). 24p. (J). (gr. 2-3). lib. bdg. 18.60 (978-0-7368-1118-7(4), Bridgestone Bks.) Capstone Pr., Inc.

Wadsworth, Pamela. Amser a Gofod. 2005. (WEL., Illus.). 24p. pap. (978-1-85596-241-5(1)) Dref Wen.

—Rhagor Am Amser a Gofod. 2005. (WEL., Illus.). 24p. pap. (978-1-85596-242-2(X)) Dref Wen.

Walsh, Kieran. Space Math. 2005. (Math & My World Ser.). (Illus.). 48p. (gr. 4-6). 20.95 (978-1-59515-494-1(9)) Rourke Publishing, LLC.

Whitecap Books Staff. Space. 2000. (Investigate Ser.). (Illus.). 64p. (J). (gr. 1-7). pap. 3.95 (978-1-55285-128-9(1)) Whitecap Bks., Ltd. CAN. *Dist:* Firefly Bks., Ltd.

Whitehouse, Patricia. Space Travel. 2004. (Heinemann First Library). (Illus.). 32p. (J). 24.21 (978-1-4034-5155-2(9)); pap. 7.25 (978-1-4034-5659-5(3)) Heinemann Library.

—Working in Space. 2004. (J). 24.21 (978-1-4034-5158-3(3)); pap. 6.95 (978-1-4034-5662-5(3)) Heinemann Library.

Wyatt, Valerie. Space. Fernandes, Matthew, illus. 2004. (FAQ Ser.). 40p. (J). (gr. 4-6). (978-1-55074-975-5(7)); (978-1-55074-973-1(0)) Kids Can Pr., Ltd.

1000 Things You Should Know about Space. (Illus.). 64p. (YA). (gr. 5 up). lib. bdg. (978-1-59084-472-4(6)) Mason Crest Pubs.

OUTER SPACE—COMMUNICATION

see Interstellar Communication

OUTER SPACE—EXPLORATION

Ackroyd, Peter. Escape from Earth. 2005. (Voyages Through Time Ser.). 144p. (J). pap. 9.99 (978-0-7566-0831-6(7)) Dorling Kindersley Publishing, Inc.

Adamson, Thomas K. Astronauts. 2007. (J). (978-0-7368-6758-0(9)) Capstone Pr., Inc.

Agle, D. C. Heroes of Space: A Three-Dimensional Tribute to 40 Years of Space Exploration. 1999. (Illus.). 8p. 19.95 (978-1-58117-054-2(8), Intervisual/Piggy Toes) Dalmatian Pr.

Alexander, Florence & Alexander, Stanley. Space Exploration. l.t. ed. 2003. (Come with Me & See Ser.). (ENG & SPA., Illus.). 32p. (J). 7.99 (978-0-915960-75-0(3)) Ebon Research Systems Publishing, LLC.

Angelo, Joseph A., Jr. Encyclopedia of Space Exploration. 2000. (Facts on File Science Library). (Illus.). 328p. (YA). (gr. 9 up). 55.00 (978-0-8160-3942-5(9)) Facts On File, Inc.

—Human Spaceflight. 2007. (Frontiers in Space Ser.). 384p. (J). (gr. 9). 39.50 (978-0-8160-5775-7(3)) Facts On File, Inc.

Armentrout, David & Armentrout, Patricia. Space. 2003. (50 Words about Ser.). (Illus.). 32p. (gr. 2-4). 19.95 (978-1-58952-343-2(1)) Rourke Publishing, LLC.

Arnold, Eric. Race into Space. Torrisi, Gary, illus. 2004. 48p. (J). (gr. 1-3). lib. bdg. 11.19 (978-0-606-32797-8(5)) Tandem Library Bks.

Asimov, Isaac & Hantula, Richard. Global Space Programs. 2005. (Isaac Asimov's 21st Century Library of the Universe). (Illus.). 32p. (J). lib. bdg. 24.67 (978-0-8368-3982-1(X)) Stevens, Gareth Inc.

Atkinson. Space Travel. 2003. (Space Busters Ser.). (Illus.). 32p. (J). pap. 7.95 (978-1-4109-0076-0(2)) Raintree.

Banquieri, Eduardo. Space. 2005. (Our Planet Ser.). (Illus.). 32p. (J). (gr. 4-8). lib. bdg. 28.00 (978-0-7910-9009-1(4), Chelsea Clubhouse) Facts On File, Inc.

Barnes-Svarney, Patricia L. Secrets of the Sun: A Closer Look at Our Star. 2000. (Space Explorer Ser.). (Illus.). 64p. (YA). (gr. 6-8). pap. 8.95 (978-0-7398-2224-1(1)) Steck-Vaughn.

Bednarz, Robert, et al. TIME for Kids Readers: Welcome to the Space Age. 3rd ed. 2002. (Harcourt Horizons Ser.). (gr. k-7). pap. 38.10 (978-0-15-335313-0(9)) Harcourt Schl. Pubs.

Berger, Gilda & Berger, Melvin. Se Puede Escuchar un Grito en el Espacio. 2007. Tr. of Can You Hear a Shout in Space?. (SPA., Illus.). 48p. (J). (gr. 3-5). pap. 5.99 (978-0-439-76538-1(2), SO3881, Scholastic en Espanol) Scholastic, Inc.

Berger, Melvin. Can You Hear a Shout in Space? 2000. (gr. 3-6). lib. bdg. 14.10 (978-0-613-32367-3(X)) Tandem Library Bks.

—Can You Hear a Shout in Space? Questions & Answers about Space Exploration. 2001. (Question & Answer Ser.). (Illus.). (J). 12.75 (978-0-606-20589-4(6)) Tandem Library Bks.

Berger, Melvin & Berger, Gilda. Can You Hear a Shout in Space? Questions & Answers about Space Exploration. Di Fate, Vincent, illus. 2001. (Question & Answer Ser.). 48p. (J). (gr. 2-4). pap. 14.95 (978-0-439-09582-2(4)) Scholastic, Inc.

Berger, Melvin, et al. Can You Hear a Shout in Space? Questions & Answers about Space Exploration. 2000. (Question & Answer Ser.). (Illus.). 48p. (J). pap. (978-0-439-09583-9(2)) Scholastic, Inc.

Bergin, Mark. Space Shuttle. 1999. (Fast Forward Ser.). (Illus.). 32p. (J). (gr. 4-8). pap. 9.95 (978-0-531-15423-6(8)); 29.00 (978-0-531-14573-9(5)) Scholastic Library Publishing. (Watts, Franklin).

—Space Shuttle. 1999. (gr. 3-6). lib. bdg. 18.75 (978-0-613-34966-6(0)) Tandem Library Bks.

Bernards, Neal. Mir Space Station. 2000. (Above & Beyond Ser.). (Illus.). 32p. (J). (gr. 4-7). lib. bdg. 16.95 (978-1-58340-049-4(4)) Smart Apple Media.

Beyer, Mark. Space Exploration. 2002. (Life in the Future Ser.). (Illus.). 48p. (YA). (gr. 7-12). pap. 23.00 (978-0-516-23917-0(1)); pap. 6.95 (978-0-516-24008-4(0)) Scholastic Library Publishing. (Children's Pr.).

—Space Exploration. 2002. (gr. 7-12). lib. bdg. 15.25 (978-0-613-58734-1(0)) Tandem Library Bks.

Birch, Robin. Exploring Space. 2002. (Space Ser.). (Illus.). 32p. (gr. k-2). 23.00 (978-0-7910-6974-5(5), Chelsea Hse.) Facts On File, Inc.

Bitetto, Marco A. V., ed. Space Enterprise. braille ed. 2000. (YA). (978-1-58578-076-1(6)) Institute of Cybernetics Research, Inc.

Branley, Franklyn M. Floating in Space, Stage 2. 1998. (J). 11.79 (978-0-606-12934-3(0)) Tandem Library Bks.

Branley, Franklyn Mansfield. Floating in Space. Kelley, True, illus. 1998. 32p. (J). (ps-ps). lib. bdg. 13.00 (978-0-613-07789-7(X)) Tandem Library Bks.

Bredeson, Carmen. NASA Planetary Spacecraft: Galileo, Magellan, Pathfinder & Voyager. 2000. (Countdown to Space Ser.). (Illus.). 48p. (YA). (gr. 4-10). lib. bdg. 23.93 (978-0-7660-1303-2(0)) Enslow Pubs., Inc.

—Our Space Program. (I Know America Ser.: 4). (Illus.). 48p. (gr. 2-4). 2000. pap. (978-0-7613-1349-6(4)); 1999. lib. bdg. 24.90 (978-0-7613-0952-9(7)) Lerner Publishing Group. (Millbrook Pr.).

—Our Space Program. 2000. (I Know America Ser.). (Illus.). (J). (978-0-606-18292-8(6)) Tandem Library Bks.

Cannarella, Deborah & Fournier, Jane. Exploration. 1999. (Into the Next Millennium Ser.). (Illus.). 32p. (J). (gr. 4-8). lib. bdg. 27.93 (978-1-57103-273-7(8)) Rourke Publishing, LLC.

Capstone Press, contrib. by. Space Walks. (Explore Space! Ser.). 24p. (J). pap. 6.95 (978-0-7368-4534-2(8)) Capstone Pr., Inc.

Carlisle, Rodney P. Exploring Space. 2004. (Discovery & Exploration Ser.). (Illus.). 160p. (J). (gr. 6-12). 40.00 (978-0-8160-5265-3(4)) Facts On File, Inc.

Carroll, Jillian. Hot Spot. 2003. (J). pap. (978-1-58417-235-2(5)); lib. bdg. (978-1-58417-234-5(7)) Lake Street Pubs.

—Zoom Around a Moon. 2003. (J). pap. (978-1-58417-241-3(X)); lib. bdg. (978-1-58417-240-6(1)) Lake Street Pubs.

Casanellas, Antonio. Great Discoveries & Inventions That Helped Explore Earth & Space. Garousi, Ali, illus. 2000. (Great Discoveries & Inventions Ser.). 32p. (J). (gr. 4 up). lib. bdg. 24.67 (978-0-8368-2584-8(5)) Stevens, Gareth Inc.

Chrismer, Melanie. Highlights from the Hubble Telescope: Postcards from Space. 2003. (Countdown to Space Ser.). (Illus.). 48p. (J). lib. bdg. 23.93 (978-0-7660-2135-8(1)) Enslow Pubs., Inc.

Cole, Joanna & Moore, Eva. The Space Explorers. 2000. (Magic School Bus Chapter Bks.: No. 4). (Illus.). 80p. (J). (gr. 1-4). pap. 4.99 (978-0-439-11493-6(4)) Scholastic, Inc.

Cole, Michael D. Galileo Spacecraft: Mission to Jupiter. 1999. (Countdown to Space Ser.). (Illus.). 48p. (YA). (gr. 4-10). lib. bdg. 23.93 (978-0-7660-1119-9(4)) Enslow Pubs., Inc.

—Hubble Space Telescope: Exploring the Universe. 1999. (Countdown to Space Ser.). (Illus.). 48p. (YA). (gr. 4-10). lib. bdg. 23.93 (978-0-7660-1120-5(8)) Enslow Pubs., Inc.

—NASA Space Vehicles: Capsules, Shuttles & Space Stations. 2000. (Countdown to Space Ser.). (Illus.). 48p. (YA). (gr. 4-10). lib. bdg. 23.93 (978-0-7660-1308-7(1)) Enslow Pubs., Inc.

—Space Emergency: Astronauts in Danger. 2000. (Countdown to Space Ser.). (Illus.). 48p. (YA). (gr. 4-10). lib. bdg. 23.93 (978-0-7660-1307-0(3)) Enslow Pubs., Inc.

—Space Launch Disaster: When Liftoff Goes Wrong. 2000. (Countdown to Space Ser.). (Illus.). 48p. (YA). (gr. 4-10). lib. bdg. 23.93 (978-0-7660-1309-4(X)) Enslow Pubs., Inc.

Countdown to Space, 40 bks., Set. (Illus.). (YA). (gr. 4-10). lib. bdg. 758.00 (978-0-89490-562-9(7)) Enslow Pubs., Inc.

Cullen, David. The First Man in Space. 2004. (Days That Changed the World Ser.). (Illus.). 48p. (J). (gr. 5 up). pap. 11.95 (978-0-8368-5577-7(9)); lib. bdg. 30.00 (978-0-8368-5570-8(1)) Stevens, Gareth Inc. (World Almanac Library).

Currie, Stephen. Missions in Space: 1955-Present. 2004. (National Geographic Reading Expeditions Ser.). (Illus.). 32p. (J). (978-0-7922-4546-9(6)) National Geographic Society.

Davis, Kenneth C. Don't Know Much about Space. 2001. (gr. 3-6). lib. bdg. 15.25 (978-0-613-36149-1(0)) Tandem Library Bks.

—Don't Know Much about the Universe. 2002. (gr. 7-12). lib. bdg. 23.40 (978-0-613-59238-3(7)) Tandem Library Bks.

De Goursac, Olivier. Space: Exploring the Moon, the Planets, & Beyond. Laye, Pascal, illus. 2006. 76p. (J). (gr. 3-7). 18.95 (978-0-8109-5719-0(1)) Abrams, Harry N., Inc.

Dorling Kindersley Publishing Staff. El Espacio. 2004. (Dk Eyewitness Books Ser.). 72p. (J). 15.99 (978-0-7566-0635-0(7)) Dorling Kindersley Publishing, Inc.

Einspruch, Andrew. Mysteries of the Universe: How Astronomers Explore the Depths of Space. 2006. (National Geographic Science Chapters Ser.). (Illus.). 48p. (gr. 1-4). 17.90 (978-0-7922-5956-5(4), National Geographic Children's Bks.) National Geographic Society.

Elish, Dan. Nasa. 2006. (Kaleidoscope Space Ser.). (Illus.). 48p. (J). lib. bdg. 28.50 (***978-0-7614-2046-0(0)***, Benchmark Bks.) Cavendish, Marshall Corp.

Eugene, Toni. Exploring Space. 1999. (978-0-7922-9433-7(5)); (978-0-7922-9426-9(2)) National Geographic Society.

Explore Space. (Color & Learn Ser.). 36p. (J). (gr. 1-5). pap. (978-1-882210-13-8(1)) Action Publishing, Inc.

Exploring Space. 2004. (J). cd-rom (978-0-9764218-3-2(6)) Dawasoft.

Exploring Space. (Britannica Learning Library). (gr. 2-5). 14.95 (978-1-59339-000-6(9), 049001-EN-REF) Encyclopaedia Britannica, Inc.

Exploring Space. (Eyes on Adventure Ser.). (Illus.). 32p. (J). (gr. 1 up). 7.95 (978-1-56156-488-0(5)) Kidsbooks, Inc.

Exploring Space, 6 vols. (Sunshinetm Science Ser.). 24p. (gr. 1-2). 31.50 (978-0-7802-0294-8(5)); 36.95 (978-0-7802-0545-1(6)) Wright Group, The.

Farbman, Melinda & Gaillard, Frye. Spacechimp: NASA's Ape in Space. 2000. (Countdown to Space Ser.). (Illus.). 48p. (YA). (gr. 4-10). lib. bdg. 23.93 (978-0-7660-1478-7(9)) Enslow Pubs., Inc.

Finke, Stephanie. Exploring Outer Space: 30 Amazing Projects That Explore the Wonders of God's Creation. 2000. (And God Created Science Ser.). (Illus.). 100p. (J). (gr. 1-6). pap. 9.99 (978-1-57748-884-2(9)) Barbour Publishing, Inc.

Flowers, Sarah. Space Exploration: A Pro/Con Issue. 2000. (Hot Pro/Con Issues Ser.). (Illus.). 64p. (YA). (gr. 6-12). lib. bdg. 27.93 (978-0-7660-1199-1(2)) Enslow Pubs., Inc.

Furniss, Tim. The Earth. 2000. (Spinning Through Space Ser.). (Illus.). 32p. (J). (gr. 2-4). lib. bdg. (978-0-7398-2737-6(5)) Raintree.

—The Earth. 2000. (Spinning Through Space Ser.). (Illus.). 32p. (J). (gr. 2-4). pap. 10.34 (978-0-7398-3089-5(9)) Steck-Vaughn.

—The Moon. 2000. (Spinning Through Space Ser.). (Illus.). 32p. (J). (gr. 2-4). lib. bdg. 25.69 (978-0-7398-2738-3(3)) Raintree.

—The Moon. 2000. (Spinning Through Space Ser.). (Illus.). 32p. (J). (gr. 2-4). pap. 10.34 (978-0-7398-3090-1(2)) Steck-Vaughn.

—The Solar System. 2000. (Spinning Through Space Ser.). (Illus.). 32p. (J). (gr. 2-4). pap. 10.34 (978-0-7398-3092-5(9)) Steck-Vaughn.

—The Sun. 2000. (Spinning Through Space Ser.). (Illus.). 32p. (J). (gr. 2-4). lib. bdg. 25.69 (978-0-7398-2739-0(1)) Raintree.

—The Sun. 2000. (Spinning Through Space Ser.). (Illus.). 32p. (J). (gr. 2-4). pap. 10.34 (978-0-7398-3091-8(0)) Steck-Vaughn.

Furniss, Tim, et al. The Solar System. 2000. (Spinning Through Space Ser.). (Illus.). 32p. (J). (gr. 2-4). lib. bdg. 25.69 (978-0-7398-2740-6(5)) Raintree.

Gaffney, Timothy R. Secret Spy Satellites: America's Eyes in Space. 2000. (Countdown to Space Ser.). (Illus.). 48p. (YA). (gr. 4-10). lib. bdg. 23.93 (978-0-7660-1402-2(9)) Enslow Pubs., Inc.

Gaines, Ann Graham & Richardson, Adele D. Journey to Mars. 1999. (Above & Beyond Ser.). (Illus.). 32p. (J). (gr. 4-7). lib. bdg. 16.95 (978-1-58340-048-7(6)) Smart Apple Media.

Gareth Stevens Publishing Staff, contrib. by. Space Exploration. 2003. (Discovery Channel School Science Ser.). (Illus.). 32p. (J). (gr. 5 up). lib. bdg. 24.67 (978-0-8368-3373-7(2)) Stevens, Gareth Inc.

Garton, Anne. Livewire Our World & Beyond the Space Race. 2002. (Livewires Ser.). (Illus.). 32p. pap. 5.00 (978-0-521-52676-0(0)) Cambridge Univ. Pr.

Gibson, Diane. Geothermal Power. 2001. (Sources of Energy Ser.). (Illus.). 24p. (J). (gr. 2-7). lib. bdg. 21.30 (978-1-887068-76-5(7)) Smart Apple Media.

Gifford, Clive. Space Exploration. 2005. (Technology All Around Us Ser.). (Illus.). 32p. (J). (gr. 4-7). lib. bdg. 27.10 (978-1-58340-753-0(7)) Smart Apple Media.

Gillingham, Sarah. A Is for Astronaut: Space Exploration from A to Z. 2006. (Illus.). 40p. (J). 14.95 (978-0-8118-5462-7(0)) Chronicle Bks. LLC.

Goldsmith, Mike. Space Travel. 2001. (Spinning Through Space Ser.). (Illus.). 32p. (J). (gr. 2-4). lib. bdg. 25.69 (978-0-7398-2744-4(8)) Raintree.

Graham, Ian. The Best Book of Spaceships. 1998. (Best Book of... Ser.). (Illus.). 32p. (J). (gr. k-3). tchr. ed. 12.95 (978-0-7534-5133-5(6), Kingfisher) Houghton Mifflin Co. Trade & Reference Div.

—My Book of Space. 2001. (My Book of... Ser.). (Illus.). 48p. (J). (ps-k). tchr. ed. 14.95 (978-0-7534-5399-5(1), Kingfisher) Houghton Mifflin Co. Trade & Reference Div.

—The Spaceships. 2008. (Best Book of... Ser.). (Illus.). 32p. (J). pap. 6.95 (***978-0-7534-6167-9(6)***, Kingfisher) Houghton Mifflin Co. Trade & Reference Div.

—Voyage Through Space: An Interactive Journey Through the Solar System & Beyond. 2007. (Discoverology Ser.). 32p. (J). (gr. 3 up). 18.99 (***978-0-7641-6062-2(1)***) Barron's Educational Series, Inc.

Green, J. Space Explorer Stained Glass Coloring Book. 2005. (Illus.). (J). 1.00 (978-0-486-28533-7(2)) Dover Pubns., Inc.

Group/McGraw-Hill, Wright. History: Space Exploration, 6 vols. (Book2WebTM Ser.). (gr. 4-8). 36.50 (978-0-322-04456-2(1)) Wright Group, The.

Haines, Tim & Riley, Christopher. Voyage to the Planets & Beyond: A Space Exploration. 2005. (Illus.). 192p. (J). 30.00 (978-0-7566-1265-8(9), 1241329) Dorling Kindersley Publishing, Inc.

Hakkila, Jon Eric & Richardson, Adele D. Hubble Space Telescope. 1999. (Above & Beyond Ser.). (Illus.). 32p. (J). (gr. 4-7). lib. bdg. 16.95 (978-1-58340-047-0(8)) Smart Apple Media.

—Voyager. 1999. (Above & Beyond Ser.). (Illus.). 32p. (J). (gr. 4 up). lib. bdg. 16.95 (978-1-58340-053-1(2)) Smart Apple Media.

Han, E. M. Comets & Asteroids. 2001. (Spinning Through Space Ser.). (Illus.). 32p. (J). (gr. 3-4). lib. bdg. 25.69 (978-0-7398-2742-0(1)) Raintree.

Hansen, Rosanna. Space: A Chapter Book. 2003. (True Tales Ser.). (Illus.). 48p. (J). 22.50 (978-0-516-22919-5(2), Children's Pr.) Scholastic Library Publishing.

Hermsen, Sarah. Space Exploration Library Cumulative Index. 2004. 42p. (J). lib. bdg. 5.00 (978-0-7876-9214-8(X), UXL) Thomson Gale.

Hewitt, Sally. Space. 2007. (J). (***978-1-59604-141-7(2)***) Stargazer Bks.

The History of Space Exporation, 8 Vols. 180.00 (978-0-8368-5704-7(6)) Stevens, Gareth Inc.

Hopping, Lorraine Jean. Space Rocks: The Story of Planetary Geologist Adriana Ocampo. 2006. (Women's Adventures in Science Ser.). (Illus.). 128p. pap. 9.95 (978-0-309-09555-6(7), Joseph Henry Pr.) National Academies Pr.

Hwang, William Liang & Mian, Matthew K., eds. InnoWorks: Explorations, Student Edition. 2006. (YA). spiral bd. (***978-0-9771380-4-3(6)***) United InnoWorks Academy.

Ingebretsen, Karen, et al. Human Space Exploration. 2006. (World Book's Solar System & Space Exploration Library). (Illus.). 63p. (J). (978-0-7166-9509-7(X)) World Bk., Inc.

Jayawardhana, Ray. Star Factories: The Birth of Stars & Planets. 2000. (Space Explorer Ser.). (Illus.). 64p. (YA). (gr. 6-8). pap. 8.95 (978-0-7398-2222-7(5)) Steck-Vaughn.

Jedicke, Peter. Scientific American. 2007. (Scientific American Ser.). 72p. (J). (gr. 5-8). 30.00 (978-0-7910-9046-6(9), Chelsea Hse.) Facts On File, Inc.

Jefferis, David. Into Infinity: From Earth to the Stars. 2001. (Megatech Ser.). (Illus.). 32p. (J). (gr. 4-5). pap. (978-0-7787-0060-9(7)); lib. bdg. (978-0-7787-0050-0(X)) Crabtree Publishing Co.

—Into Infinity: From Earth to the Stars. 2002. (gr. 3-6). lib. bdg. 17.60 (978-0-613-52963-1(4)) Tandem Library Bks.

Jiménez, Vita. What Is in Space. 2006. (Yellow Umbrella Books for Early Readers). (Illus.). 16p. (J). (978-0-7368-5972-1(1)) Yellow Umbrella Pr.

—What Is in Space? 2006. (J). (SPA.). (978-0-7368-5990-5(X)); (ENG & SPA., Illus.). 18p. (978-0-7368-6008-6(8)) Yellow Umbrella Pr.

Johnstone, Michael. History News in Space. 1999. (History News Ser.). (Illus.). 32p. (J). (gr. 5-9). 16.99 (978-0-7636-0490-5(9)) Candlewick Pr.

—In Space. 2001. (History News Ser.). (Illus.). 32p. (J). (gr. 3 up). lib. bdg. 24.67 (978-0-8368-2876-4(3)) Stevens, Gareth Inc.

Kemnitz, Tom, Jr. Winning the Race to the Moon: Space. 2001. (Adventures on the American Frontiers Ser.). (Illus.). 80p. (J). (gr. 3-6). pap. 9.99 (978-0-89824-319-2(X), 319x) Royal Fireworks Publishing Co.

Kenah, Katharine. Space Mysteries Misterios Del. 2005. (English-Spanish Extreme Readers Ser.). 32p. (J). pap. 3.95 (978-0-7696-3812-6(0), Waterbird Bks.) School Specialty Publishing.

Kerrod, Robin. Space. 2003. 48p. (J). lib. bdg. 27.10 (978-1-58340-351-8(5)) Smart Apple Media.

Khan, Hena. The Space Explorer's Guide to Earth's Neighborhood. 2003. (Space University Ser.). (Illus.). 48p. (J). (978-0-439-55741-2(0)) Scholastic, Inc.

Khan, Hena & Dyson, Marianne J. The Space Explorer's Guide to Out-Of-This-World Science. 2004. (Space University Ser.). (Illus.). 48p. (J). (***978-0-439-55747-4(X)***) Scholastic, Inc.

Kortenkamp, Steve. Space Probes. 2008. (J). (***978-1-4296-0063-7(2)***) Capstone Pr., Inc.

Kranz, Rachel. La exploracion del Espacio. ed. 2004. (SPA.). 32p. (J). pap. 6.00 (978-1-4108-2344-1(X), A2344X) Benchmark Education Co.

—Our Solar System/el sistema Solar: English/Spanish Pair, 12 texts, 2 titles, Vol. 2. ed. 2004. (Navigators Ser.). (J). pap., instr.'s gde. ed. 84.00 (978-1-4108-1766-2(0), 17660) Benchmark Education Co.

Landau, Elaine. Space Disasters. 1999. (gr. 3-6). lib. bdg. 17.60 (978-0-613-29512-3(9)) Tandem Library Bks.

Marcom, Robert, compiled by. Cosmic Photo Book: Photos & Facts from the Archives of Nasa. 2001. cd-rom 10.00 (978-1-931457-11-8(5)) Stargate Electronic Library, Inc.

Mason. Space Race. 2003. (Space Busters Ser.). (Illus.). 32p. (J). pap. 7.95 (978-1-4109-0075-3(4)) Raintree.

McDonald, Kim. Life in Outer Space: The Search for Extraterrestrials. 2000. (Space Explorer Ser.). (Illus.). 64p. (YA). (gr. 6-8). pap. 8.95 (978-0-7398-2223-4(3)) Steck-Vaughn.

Mitton, Tony. Roaring Rockets. 2000. (J). (978-0-606-19827-1(X)) Tandem Library Bks.

Moore, Eva. The Space Explorers. 2000. (Magic School Bus Chapter Bks.: No. 4). (J). (gr. 1-4). (978-0-606-19577-5(7)) Tandem Library Bks.

Moore, Jo Ellen. Exploring Space. Evans, Marilyn, ed. Robison, Don, illus. 1998. (ScienceWorks for Kids Ser.: Vol. 1). 80p. (J). (gr. 1-3). pap., tchr. ed. 9.95 (978-1-55799-682-4(2) , EMC 853) Evan-Moor Educational Pubs.

Moskal, Greg. The History of Space Exploration: Sequencing Events Chronologically on a Timeline. 2004. (PowerMath Ser.). (Illus.). 24p. (J). lib. bdg. (978-0-8239-8850-1(3)); lib. bdg. 21.25 (978-0-8239-8962-1(3)) Rosen Publishing Group, Inc., The. (PowerKids Pr.).

Murphy, Patricia J., tr. Exploring Space with an Astronaut. 2004. (I Like Science! Ser.). (Illus.). 24p. (J). lib. bdg. 21.26 (978-0-7660-2268-3(4)) Enslow Pubs., Inc.

Naaeye, Robert. Signals from Outer Space: The Chandra X-Ray Observatory. 2000. (Space Explorer Ser.). (Illus.). 64p. (YA). (gr. 6-8). pap. 8.95 (978-0-7398-2225-8(X)) Steck-Vaughn.

Nagel, Rob. Space Exploration - Almanac, 2 vols. 2004. (Space Exploration Reference Library). (Illus.). lib. bdg. 120.00 (978-0-7876-9209-4(3) , UXL) Thomson Gale.

Nicolson. Starting with Space: Exploring Space. 2000. (J). (978-0-606-20185-8(8)) Tandem Library Bks.

Nicolson, Cynthia. Discover Space. Slavin, Bill, illus. 2005. 32p. (J). lib. bdg. 15.38 (***978-1-4242-1193-7(X)***) Fitzgerald Bks.

Nicolson, Cynthia Pratt. Discover Space. Slavin, Bill, illus. 2005. (Kids Can Read Alone Ser.). 32p. (J). (ps-ps). (978-1-55337-824-2(5)) Kids Can Pr., Ltd.

—Exploring Space. Slavin, Bill, illus. 2000. (Starting with Space Ser.). 40p. (J). (gr. 4-6). (978-1-55074-713-3(4)); (978-1-55074-711-9(8)) Kids Can Pr., Ltd.

—Exploring Space. 2000. (gr. 3-6). lib. bdg. 15.25 (978-0-613-30391-0(1)) Tandem Library Bks.

O'Brien, Eileen & Denne, Ben. Space. 2004. (Discovery Program Ser.). (SPA., Illus.). 48p. (J). pap. 8.95 (978-0-7945-0126-6(5) , Usborne); lib. bdg. 16.95 (978-1-58086-388-9(4)) EDC Publishing.

Owen, David. Final Frontier: Voyages into Outer Space. 2004. (Illus.). 128p. (J). (gr. 6-9). 19.95 (978-1-55297-776-7(5)); pap. 9.95 (978-1-55297-775-0(7)) Firefly Bks., Ltd.

Oxlade, Chris. The Mystery of Life on Other Planets. 2002. (Can Science Solve? Ser.). 32p. (Illus.). (J). (gr. 4-7). lib. bdg. 22.79 (978-1-58810-666-7(7)); pap. 7.50 (978-1-58810-929-3(1) , 91564) Heinemann Library.

—The Mystery of Life on Other Planets. 2002. (Illus.). 32p. (J). (gr. 4-7). lib. bdg. 15.90 (978-0-613-45802-3(8)) Tandem Library Bks.

Parker. Space Mysteries. 2003. (Space Busters Ser.). (Illus.). 32p. (J). pap. 7.95 (978-1-4109-0074-6(6)) Raintree.

Price, Sean. Eye on the Universe. 2003. (Science Links Ser.). (Illus.). 32p. (gr. 3-5). 23.00 (978-0-7910-7423-7(4) , Chelsea Hse.) Facts On File, Inc.

Rau, Dana Meachen. Space Exploration. 2003. (Our Solar System Ser.). (Illus.). 32p. (J). (gr. 3 up). lib. bdg. 21.26 (978-0-7565-0439-7(2)) Compass Point Bks.

Richardson, Adele D. Space Shuttle. 1999. (Above & Beyond Ser.). (Illus.). 32p. (J). (gr. 4-7). lib. bdg. 16.95 (978-1-58340-052-4(4)) Smart Apple Media.

Rooney, Anne. Outer Space. 2007. (J). (***978-1-4329-0112-7(5)***); pap. (***978-1-4329-0118-9(4)***) Heinemann Library.

Royston, Angela. Alien Neighbors? 2005. (Illus.). 32p. (J). lib. bdg. (978-1-4109-1931-1(5)) Steck-Vaughn.

—Alien Neighbors? The Solar System. 2005. (Illus.). 32p. (J). (gr. 3-5). 7.85 (978-1-4109-1962-5(5)) Steck-Vaughn.

Roza, Greg. The Hubble Space Telescope: Understanding & Representing Numbers in the Billions. 2005. (Illus.). 32p. (J). (978-1-4042-5130-4(8) , PowerKids Pr.) Rosen Publishing Group, Inc., The.

—The Hubble Space Telescope: Understanding & Representing Numbers up to 1 Billion. 2005. (PowerMath Ser.). (Illus.). 32p. (J). 22.50 (978-1-4042-2931-0(0) , PowerKids Pr.); pap. (978-1-4042-5129-8(4)) Rosen Publishing Group, Inc., The.

Scott, Elaine. Adventures in Space: The Flight to Fix the Hubble. 1998. (J). (978-0-606-13111-7(6)) Tandem Library Bks.

—Close Encounters: Exploring the Universe with the Hubble Space Telescope. 1998. (Illus.). 64p. (J). (gr. 3-7). 16.95 (978-0-7868-0147-3(6)) Hyperion Bks. for Children.

Shearer, Deborah A. Space Missions. 2002. (Explore Space! Ser.). (Illus.). 24p. (J). (gr. 1-2). lib. bdg. 18.60 (978-0-7368-1401-0(9) , Bridgestone Bks.) Capstone Pr., Inc.

Sherman, Josepha. Deep Space Observation Satellites. 2003. (Library of Satellites). (Illus.). 64p. (YA). (gr. 5-8). lib. bdg. 26.50 (978-0-8239-3852-0(2) , Rosen Central) Rosen Publishing Group, Inc., The.

Sigmar. Planeta Tierra - 101 Preguntas. 2001. (SPA.). (gr. 3-6). lib. bdg. 18.55 (978-0-613-82563-4(2)) Tandem Library Bks.

Solway, Andrew. Can We Travel to the Stars? Space Flight & Space Exploration. 2006. (Stargazers Guides Ser.). (Illus.). 48p. (J). (978-1-4034-7711-8(6)); pap. (978-1-4034-7718-7(3)) Heinemann Library.

Space Busters, 5 bks., Set. 2003. (Illus.). (J). pap. (978-1-4109-0150-7(5)) Raintree.

Space Exploration. 2001. 63p. (YA). 8.65 (978-0-7525-5605-5(3)) Parragon, Inc.

Space Explorer, 4 bks. Incl. Life in Outer Space : The Search for Extraterrestrials. McDonald, Kim. 1999. lib. bdg. 28.54 (978-0-7398-2213-5(6)); Secrets of the Sun : A Closer Look at Our Star. Barnes-Svarney, Patricia L. 2000. lib. bdg. 28.54 (978-0-7398-2214-2(4)); Signals from Outer Space : The Chandra X-Ray Observatory. Naaeye, Robert. 2000. lib. bdg. 28.54 (978-0-7398-2215-9(2)); Star Factories : The Birth of Stars & Planets. Jayawardhana, Ray. 1999. lib. bdg. 28.54 (978-0-7398-2212-8(8)); 64p. (J). (gr. 6-8). (Illus.). 1999. Set lib. bdg. 114.16 (978-0-7398-2216-6(0)) Raintree.

Space Missions. (Explore Space! Ser.). 24p. (J). 6.95 (978-0-7368-4533-5(X)) Capstone Pr., Inc.

Spangenburg, Ray. The History of NASA. 2000. (978-0-606-20706-5(6)) Tandem Library Bks.

—Project Mercury. 2001. (gr. 5-8). lib. bdg. 24.55 (978-0-613-54305-7(X)) Tandem Library Bks.

Spangenburg, Ray & Moser, Kit. Project Mercury. 2001. (Out of This World Ser.). (Illus.). 112p. (YA). (gr. 7-9). pap. 14.95 (978-0-531-13974-5(3) , Watts, Franklin) Scholastic Library Publishing.

Sparrow, Giles. Exploring the Universe. 2006. (Illus.). 48p. (J). pap. (978-0-8368-7283-5(5)); lib. bdg. (978-0-8368-7276-7(2)) Stevens, Gareth Inc. (World Almanac Library).

—Probing Deep Space. 2006. (Illus.). 48p. (J). pap. (978-0-8368-7286-6(X)); lib. bdg. (978-0-8368-7279-8(7)) Stevens, Gareth Inc. (World Almanac Library).

Steck-Vaughn Staff. The Moon & Beyond. 2002. (Illus.). pap. 41.60 incl. audio compact disk (978-0-7398-6978-9(7)) Steck-Vaughn.

Stone, Tanya Lee. Mercury. 2002. (Blastoff! Ser.). (Illus.). 64p. (J). 28.50 (978-0-7614-1403-2(7) , Benchmark Bks.) Cavendish, Marshall Corp.

—Venus. 2002. (Blastoff! Ser.). (Illus.). 64p. (J). 28.50 (978-0-7614-1405-6(3) , Benchmark Bks.) Cavendish, Marshall Corp.

Stott, Carole & Dorling Kindersley Publishing Staff. Space Exploration. 2004. (Eyewitness Books). 72p. (J). lib. bdg. 19.99 (978-0-7566-0730-2(2)) Dorling Kindersley Publishing, Inc.

Taylor, Robert. Life Aboard the Space Shuttle. 2002. (Way People Live Ser.). (Illus.). 112p. (J). (gr. 7-10). 29.95 (978-1-59018-154-6(9) , LML00902-181109, Lucent Bks.) Thomson Gale.

Teitelbaum, Michael. Mars & Venus Space Exploration. 2006. (Navigators Ser.). (J). pap. 44.00 (***978-1-4108-6243-3(7)***) Benchmark Education Co.

Telescopes & Space Probes. 2006. (World Book's Solar System & Space Exploration Library). (Illus.). (J). 63p. (978-0-7166-9510-3(3)); 2nd ed. 64p. (***978-0-7166-9520-2(0)***) World Bk., Inc.

Tesar, Jenny. Space Travel. 1998. (Space Observer Ser.). (Illus.). 24p. (ps-3). pap. (978-1-57572-581-9(9)) Heinemann Library.

Tocci, Salvatore. Nasa. 2004. (Watts Library). (J). (gr. 5-7). pap. 8.95 (978-0-531-15598-1(6) , Watts, Franklin) Scholastic Library Publishing.

Trautmann Wunsch, Susi. The Adventures of Sojourner: The Mission to Mars That Thrilled the World. JPL Staff, illus. 1998. 64p. (J). (gr. 4-7). pap. 9.95 (978-0-9650493-6-8(1)); lib. bdg. 22.95 (978-0-9650493-5-1(3)) Mikaya Pr.

Vogt, Gregory L. Apollo Moonwalks: The Amazing Lunar Missions. 2000. (Countdown to Space Ser.). (Illus.). 48p. (YA). (gr. 4-10). lib. bdg. 23.93 (978-0-7660-1306-3(5)) Enslow Pubs., Inc.

—Exploring Space. 2000. (Our Universe Ser.). (Illus.). 48p. (J). (gr. 5-12). lib. bdg. 22.83 (978-0-7398-3113-7(5)) Raintree.

—Exploring Space. 2000. (Our Universe Ser.). (Illus.). (J). pap. (978-0-7398-3352-0(9)) Steck-Vaughn.

—Spacewalks: The Ultimate Adventure in Orbit. 2000. (Countdown to Space Ser.). (Illus.). 48p. (YA). (gr. 4-10). lib. bdg. 23.93 (978-0-7660-1305-6(7)) Enslow Pubs., Inc.

Wallace, Karen. Rockets & Spaceships. 2001. (gr. k-3). lib. bdg. 11.80 (978-0-613-35217-8(3)); (Illus.). (J). (978-0-606-21403-2(8)) Tandem Library Bks.

Weil, Ann. The Moon & Beyond. 2003. (Illus.). 60p. (J). (978-0-7398-5173-9(X)) Steck-Vaughn.

What Is in Space? 2006. (Yellow Umbrella Science Ser.). 8,16p. (J). 6.50 (978-0-7368-1705-9(0)) Red Brick Learning.

Wilkinson, Philip & Dorling Kindersley Publishing Staff. Space Busters: The Race to the Moon. 1999. (Eyewitness Readers). (Illus.). 48p. (J). (gr. 2-4). 14.99 (978-0-7894-4250-5(7)) Dorling Kindersley Publishing, Inc.

Williams, Brian. Space. 2001. (Great Inventions Ser.). (Illus.). 48p. (YA). (gr. 6-8). lib. bdg. 25.64 (978-1-58810-215-7(7)) Heinemann Library.

World Book, contrib. by. Human Space Exploration. 2nd ed. 2006. (World Book's Solar System & Space Exploration Library). (Illus.). 64p. (J). (***978-0-7166-9514-1(6)***) World Bk., Inc.

Wunsch, Susi Trautmann. The Adventures of Sojourner: The Mission to Mars That Thrilled the World. 1998. (Illus.). 60p. (J). (ps-7). lib. bdg. 18.75 incl. 5.25 hd (978-0-613-23064-3(7)) Tandem Library Bks.

York, Pat. Exploring Space. 2002. (Science Matters Ser.). (Illus.). 24p. (J). lib. bdg. 15.95 (978-1-59036-085-9(0)) Weigl Pubs., Inc.

OUTER SPACE—FICTION

Act-Two Staff. Space Mission. 2004. (Illus.). (J). pap. 8.99 incl. cd-rom (978-0-7868-3418-1(8)) Hyperion Bks. for Children.

Adams, Renee. Cosmic Kate: The First Mission. Hartman, David, illus. 1999. 23p. (J). (ps-2). pap. (978-0-9675994-0-3(7)) Make Believe Publishing.

Adventures Beyond the Solar System: Planetron & Me. 2005. (J). audio, cd-rom 24.95 (978-0-9771381-5-9(1)) Williams, Geoffrey T.

Adventures in the Solar System: Planetron & Me. 2005. (J). audio, cd-rom 24.95 (978-0-9771381-4-2(3)) Williams, Geoffrey T.

Alexander, Alec. My Fantastic Dream of the Marshmallow Martians. 2000. (Marshmallow Martian Ser.: Vol. 1). (Illus.). 32p. (J). (ps-5). 5.95 (978-0-9670091-0-0(3)) Smart Alec Toys Publishing.

—My Magical Christmas Dream of the Marshmallow Martians. 2000. (Marshmallow Martian Ser.: Vol. 2). (Illus.). 32p. (J). (ps-5). 5.95 (978-0-9670091-1-7(1)) Smart Alec Toys Publishing.

Amodeo, John, et al. The Crystal Planet. 2004. (Zenda Ser.: 3). 144p. (J). (gr. 5 up). pap. 4.99 (978-0-448-43255-7(2) , Grosset & Dunlap) Penguin Group (USA) Inc.

Auerbach, Annie. My Race into Space! A Water Wonder Book. Garofoli, Viviana, illus. 2005. 18p. (J). 9.95 (978-1-58117-351-2(2) , Intervisual/Piggy Toes) Dalmatian Pr.

Baldry, Cherith. Surfers Mutiny in Space. (Illus.). 128p. (J). 7.95 (978-0-14-038489-5(8)) Penguin Bks., Ltd. GBR. *Dist:* Trafalgar Square Publishing.

Banks, Steven. Space Oddity. 2000. (gr. 3-6). lib. bdg. 11.80 (978-0-613-27021-2(5)) Tandem Library Bks.

Barlow, Steve & Skidmore, Steve. The Hunt. 2003. (Outernet Ser.: No. 5). 192p. (J). pap. 4.99 (978-0-439-43018-0(6) , Chicken Hse., The) Scholastic, Inc.

Barlow, Steve L. & Skidmore, Steve. Friend or Foe? 2002. (Outernet Ser.: No. 1). (Illus.). 176p. (J). (gr. 3-7). pap. 4.99 (978-0-439-34351-0(8)) Scholastic, Inc.

—Odyssey. 2002. (Outernet Ser.: No. 3). 192p. (J). (gr. 3-7). pap. 4.99 (978-0-439-34353-4(4) , Chicken Hse., The) Scholastic, Inc.

Barton, Byron. I Want to Be an Astronaut. Barton, Byron, illus. 2002. (Illus.). (J). 15.49 (978-0-7587-4224-7(X)) Book Wholesalers, Inc.

Bisson, Terry. Crossfire. 2003. (Star Wars Ser.). 144p. mass mkt. 5.99 (978-0-439-39002-6(8)) Scholastic, Inc.

Branley, Franklyn M. Floating in Space, Stage 2. 1998. (J). 11.79 (978-0-606-12934-3(0)) Tandem Library Bks.

Branley, Franklyn Mansfield. Floating in Space. Kelley, True, illus. 1998. 32p. (J). (ps-ps). lib. bdg. 13.00 (978-0-613-07789-7(X)) Tandem Library Bks.

Brookes, Diane. The Man in the Moon. Timmins, Ann, illus. 1998. 32p. (J). (ps-3). pap. (978-0-9683234-0-3(5)) Raven Rock Publishing.

Brooks, Walter R. Freddy & the Flying Saucer Plans. Wiese, Kurt, illus. 1998. (Freddy Ser.). 243p. (J). (gr. 3-7). 23.95 (978-0-87951-883-7(9)) Overlook Pr., The.

Chiaramonti, Gregory. Probie: the Space Probe, Mission One: the Ocean of Europa. 2007. 32p. (J). 16.72 (***978-0-615-13848-0(9)***) Chiaramonti, Gregory.

Coffelt, Nancy. The Great Space Doghouse. Eagle, Lynnea & Siegel, Joseph, eds. Coffelt, Nancy, illus. 2000. (Illus.). 36p. (J). pap. 9.95 (978-1-883772-53-6(2)) Flying Rhinoceros, Inc.

Connely, Chris L. & Vaughan, Mark. An Alien from Earth. 2003. 175p. per. 9.95 (978-0-9745544-0-2(5)) Lewis Lynn Bks.

Cosmo & the Robot Solar System Belt. 2000. (J). (978-0-688-18010-2(8)) HarperCollins Pubs.

Counsel, June. But Martin! Layton, Neal, illus. 2005. 32p. (J). (ps). pap. 9.99 (978-0-552-55138-0(4) , Corgi) Transworld Publishers Ltd. GBR. *Dist:* Independent Pubs. Group.

Dadey, Debbie & Jones, Marcia Thornton. Mrs. Jeepers in Outer Space. 1999. (Adventures of the Bailey School Kids Super Special Ser.: No. 4). (J). (gr. 2-4). (978-0-606-19912-4(8)) Tandem Library Bks.

Dahl, Roald. Charlie & the Great Glass Elevator. Blake, Quentin, illus. 2007. 176p. (J). (gr. 2). 6.99 (***978-0-14-241032-5(2)*** , Puffin) Penguin Group (USA) Inc.

—Charlie & the Great Glass Elevator. Blake, Quentin, illus. 2001. 176p. (J). (gr. 3-7). 15.95 (978-0-375-81525-6(2) , Knopf Bks. for Young Readers) Random Hse. Children's Bks.

—Charlie & the Great Glass Elevator. Blake, Quentin, illus. 2005. (Puffin Modern Classics Ser.). 176p. (J). (gr. 3-6). pap. 6.99 (978-0-14-240412-6(8) , Puffin) Penguin Group (USA) Inc.

Davies, Tristan, et al. Crackers in Space. 2000. (Illus.). 48p. (J). pap. (978-0-340-71290-0(2) , Hodder & Stoughton) Hodder General Publishing Division.

—Crackers in Space. 2000. (Illus.). 48p. (J). 16.99 (978-0-340-71289-4(9) , Hodder & Stoughton) Hodder General Publishing Division GBR. *Dist:* Trafalgar Square Publishing.

Delton, Judy. Planet Pee Wee. Tiegreen, Alan, illus. 1998. (Pee Wee Scouts Ser.: No. 34). (J). (gr. 2-5). (978-0-606-13699-0(1)) Tandem Library Bks.

Disney Staff. The Smartest Guy in the Galaxy. 2002. (Illus.). 24p. (J). pap. 3.25 (978-0-7364-2007-5(X) , RH/Disney) Random Hse. Children's Bks.

Dodd, Quentin. Beatnik Rutabagas from Beyond the Stars. 2001. (Illus.). 224p. (J). (gr. 4-6). 17.00 (978-0-374-30515-4(3) , Farrar, Straus & Giroux (BYR)) Farrar, Straus & Giroux.

—The Princess of Neptune. 2004. 224p. (J). 17.00 (978-0-374-36119-8(3) , Farrar, Straus & Giroux (BYR)) Farrar, Straus & Giroux.

Dong, Claxton. Save Our Star. 2002. 144p. (YA). (gr. 5-9). pap. 5.99 (978-0-9717993-0-1(X)) Brown Swan Pubs.

Edick, Grant. Space Station. 2004. (Two Boys Adventure Story Ser.). 98p. (J). (gr. 3-6). 15.95 (978-0-9677839-9-4(2)) Wysteria Publishing.

Etra, Jonathan. Aliens for Breakfast. Bjorkman, Steve, illus. 2002. (J). 11.91 (978-0-7587-5970-2(3)) Book Wholesalers, Inc.

Farber, Erica. The Alien from Outer Space. Mayer, Mercer, illus. 2006. (Critter Kids Adventure Ser.). 32p. (J). (gr. 2-3). pap. 4.95 (978-0-7696-4763-0(4) , Gingham Dog Pr.) School Specialty Publishing.

Fontenay, Charles L. Kipton on Phobos, 18 vols. 1999. (Kipton Chronicles Ser.: Bk. 13). 188p. (J). (gr. 5 up). pap. 9.99 (978-0-88092-416-0(0) , 4160) Royal Fireworks Publishing Co.

Fowler Companies, Inc. Staff & Rabbit, Daddy. Marty the Little Lost Martian. 1998. (Illus.). iii, 29p. (J). (ps-6). 14.95 (978-0-9661365-0-0(0)) Fowler Cos., Inc., The.

Fraknoi, Andrew. Disney's Wonderful World of Space. 2007. 128p. (gr. 1-4). 12.99 (***978-0-7868-4969-7(X)***) Disney Pr.

Gardner, J. J. Robotworld. 1998. (Lost in Space the New Journeys Ser.). (J). (gr. 4-7). pap. 3.99 (978-0-590-18938-5(7)) Scholastic, Inc.

—Warriors. 1999. (Lost in Space the New Journeys Ser.). 128p. (gr. 3-7). pap. 3.99 (978-0-590-18942-2(5)) Scholastic, Inc.

Gioseffi, Anthony P. Mainframe. 2007. 144p. per. 11.95 (***978-0-595-44953-8(0)***) iUniverse, Inc.

Girard, Philippe. Gustave et le Capitaine Planète. Girard, Philippe, illus. 2004. (Mon Roman Ser.). (FRE., Illus.). 96p. (J). (gr. 2). pap. (978-2-89021-649-5(7)) Diffusion du livre Mirabel.

Guest, Ann Hutchinson. The Adventures of Klig & Gop: In Balance-Land. Dulieu, Jane, ed. Guest, Ann Hutchinson & Dulieu, Jane, illus. 2000. (Starbies Ser.: Bk. 2). 60p. (J). (ps-6). pap. 15.00 (978-1-930798-02-1(4) , 00-3) National Dance Education Organization.

—The Adventures of Klig & Gop: In Flextend-Land. Dulieu, Jane, ed. Guest, Ann Hutchinson & Dulieu, Jane, illus. 2000. (Starbies Ser.: Bk. 3). 64p. (J). (ps-6). pap. 15.00 (978-1-930798-03-8(2) , 00-4) National Dance Education Organization.

—The Adventures of Klig & Gop: In Travel Land. Dulieu, Jane, ed. Guest, Ann Hutchinson & Dulieu, Jane, illus. 2000. (Starbies Ser.: Bk. 1). 84p. (J). (ps-6). pap. 15.00 (978-1-930798-01-4(6) , 00-2) National Dance Education Organization.

—Parent & Teacher Guide for In Travel-Land, In Balance-Land, In Flextend-Land, Grades Preschool-6. Dulieu, Jane, ed. Guest, Ann Hutchinson & Dulieu, Jane, illus. 2000. (Starbies Ser.). 60p. (J). pap., tchr. ed. 15.00 (978-1-930798-00-7(8) , 00-1) National Dance Education Organization.

Guibert, Emmanuel. Sardine in Outer Space. Watson, Sasha, tr. from FRE. Sfar, Joann, illus. deluxe ed. 2006. (Sardine in Outer Space Ser.). 128p. (J). pap. 12.95 (978-1-59643-126-3(1) , First Second Bks.) Roaring Brook Pr.

—Sardine in Outer Space 3. Brizzi, Elisabeth & Siegel, Alexis, trs. from FRE. Sfar, Joann, illus. 3rd rev. ed. 2007. (Sardine in Outer Space Ser.). 112p. (J). (gr. 1-5). pap. 12.95 (***978-1-59643-128-7(8)*** , First Second Bks.) Roaring Brook Pr.

—Space Pirate Sardine in Outer Space. Sfar, Joann, illus. 2008. 64p. (J). pap. 6.99 (***978-0-312-38056-4(9)***) Square Fish.

Henderson, Lyndsey. Buzz (Space Facts) 2001. (Teacher's Pet Ser.). 48p. (J). 4.95 (978-0-439-17346-9(9)) Scholastic, Inc.

Hoena, Blake A. Ooze Slingers from Outer Space. Harpster, Steve, illus. 2007. (J). 33p. pap. (***978-1-59889-410-3(2)***); 40p. (gr. 2-4). lib. bdg. 21.26 (***978-1-59889-315-1(7)***) Stone Arch Bks.

Into the Black Hole. 1999. (SmartReader Ser.). (J). pap., tchr. ed. 19.95 incl. audio (978-0-7887-0279-2(3) , 79319T3) Recorded Bks., LLC.

Johnson, Crockett. Harold's Trip to the Sky. Johnson, Crockett, illus. 2002. (Illus.). (J). 15.53 (978-0-7587-2698-8(8)) Book Wholesalers, Inc.

Johnson, David. Trapped in Space. Liew, Sonny, illus. 2007. (J). 80p. (***978-1-59889-354-0(8)***); 74p. pap. (***978-1-59889-449-3(8)***) Stone Arch Bks.

Kettner, Christine. Oliver Cat on Planet B. Kettner, Christine, illus. 2003. (Illus.). 48p. (J). (gr. 1-3). 15.99 (978-0-525-47094-6(8) , Dutton Juvenile) Penguin Group (USA) Inc.

Krulik, Nancy E. Journey to the Planet of the Blawps. 1998. (Lost in Space Ser.: Vol. 4). (Illus.). 128p. (gr. 3-7). pap. 3.99 (978-0-590-18941-5(7)) Scholastic, Inc.

—Passengers. 1998. (Lost in Space the New Journeys Ser.). (J). (gr. 4-7). pap. 3.99 (978-0-590-18939-2(5)) Scholastic, Inc.

Krupp, Edwin C. Big Dipper & You. 1999. (Illus.). 48p. (J). (gr. k-3). pap. 4.95 (978-0-688-16702-8(0)) HarperCollins Pubs.

Lanse, Hal W. Penelope Quagmire & the Lizard Men from Outer Space. (J). 2004. 15.00 (978-1-893896-40-6(4)); 2001. 172p. (gr. 4 7). pap. 10.50 (978-1-893896-46-8(3)) ImaJinn Bks.

Lehman, Seth. The Color Pets. 2006. (Illus.). 52p. (J). 7.00 net. (***978-0-9787986-0-4(0)***) 4All Ages LLC.

L'Engle, Madeleine. A Swiftly Tilting Planet. 1998. (978-0-606-13831-4(5)) Tandem Library Bks.

Lewis, Anthony, illus. Little Space Explorers. 2007. 14p. bds. 7.99 (***978-1-84643-038-1(0)***) Child's Play International Ltd. GBR. *Dist:* Child's Play-International.

Loomis, Christine. Astro Bunnies. Loomis, Christine & Eitan, Ora, illus. 2001. 1p. (J). (ps-3). 15.99 (978-0-399-23175-9(7) , Putnam Juvenile) Penguin Group (USA) Inc.

Mangano, Tom, illus. Dora's Outer Space Adventure. 2004. (Dora the Explorer Ser.). 12p. (J). bds. 6.99 (978-0-689-86794-1(8) , Simon Spotlight/Nickelodeon) Simon & Schuster Children's Publishing.

Martyr, Andrew & Martyr, Paula, illus. Space Dog Shock. 32p. (J). pap. 7.95 (978-0-14-038839-8(7)) Penguin Bks., Ltd. GBR. *Dist:* Trafalgar Square Publishing.

May, Scott. Outer Space Earl: The Trees Have the Blues. 2000. mass mkt. 8.95 incl. audio compact disk (978-1-931179-06-5(9)) Long Hill Productions, Inc.

—Outer Space Earl: The Trees Have the Blues. Fisher, Brian Patrick, illus. 2000. 32p. (J). (gr. 1-3). pap. (978-0-9701450-1-7(2)) Long Hill Productions, Inc.

McBride, Earvin, Jr. Space - M. D. 3001. McBride, Earvin, Jr., illus. 2nd unabr. ed. 2003. (Earvin MacBride's Amazing Sci-Fi & Adventure Heroes Ser.). (Illus.). 329p. (J). (gr. 7-12). pap. 4.95 (978-1-892511-09-6(6)) MacBride, E. J. Pubn., Inc.

Molina, Alicia. El Agujero Negro. Martinez, Enrique, illus. 2nd ed. 2000. Tr. of Black Hole. (SPA.). 48p. (J). (ps-7). pap. 5.95 (978-968-16-4711-7(4)) Fondo de Cultura Economica USA.

MNO

Montgomery, R. A. Trouble on Planet Earth. 2006. (Choose Your Own Adventure Ser.: No. 11). (Illus.). 144p. (J). mass mkt. 5.99 (978-1-933390-11-6(5) , CHCL11) Chooseco LLC.

O'Neil, Amy. There's No Space Like Home. Van Patter, Bruce, tr. Van Patter, Bruce, illus. 2002. (Read-to-Me Ser.). 24p. (J). (978-0-7665-1221-4(5)) Letter People, The.

O'Neil, Sarah. Space Travel. 2000. (gr. k-3). lib. bdg. 11.80 (978-0-613-29752-3(0)) Tandem Library Bks.

Orme, David. Space Wreck. Savage, Paul, illus. 2006. 33p. (J). (978-1-59889-015-0(8)) Stone Arch Bks.

Ostrow, Vivian. My Brother Is from Outer Space: The Book of Proof. Brace, Eric, illus. 1999. 32p. (J). (gr. k-4). pap. 6.95 (978-0-8075-5326-8(3)) Whitman, Albert & Co.

Peel, John. Fight for Justice: By Luke Skywalker. 1998. (Star Wars Journals). 115p. (J). (gr. 4-7). pap. 3.99 (978-0-590-18902-6(6)) Scholastic, Inc.

—Fight for Justice: By Luke Skywalker. 1998. (Star Wars Journals). (J). (gr. 4-7). (978-0-606-13810-9(2)) Tandem Library Bks.

Pilkey, Dav. Ricky Ricotta's Mighty Robot vs. the Stupid Stinkbugs from Saturn. Ontiveros, Martin, illus. 2003. (Ricky Ricotta Ser.: No. 6). 128p. (J). mass mkt. 3.99 (978-0-439-37645-7(9) , Blue Sky Pr., The) Scholastic, Inc.

Rabe, Tish. Is a Camel a Mammal. Durk, Jim, illus. 1998. (Cat in the Hat's Learning Library). 48p. (J). (gr. k-3). 8.99 (978-0-679-87302-0(3) , Random Hse. Bks. for Young Readers) Random Hse. Children's Bks.

Random House Disney Staff. Wall-E. 2008. (Read-Aloud Storybook Ser.). 72p. (J). (ps-3). 8.99 (*978-0-7364-2528-5(4) , RH/Disney) Random Hse. Children's Bks.

Reeve, Philip. Larklight: A Rousing Tale of Dauntless Pluck in the Farthest Reaches of Space. Wyatt, David, illus. 2007. 416p. (J). (gr. 5 up). pap. 7.95 (*978-1-59990-145-9(5) , Bloomsbury Children) Bloomsbury Publishing.

—Starcross: An Intergalactic Adventure of Spies & Time Travel. Wyatt, David, illus. 2007. 320p. (J). (gr. 5 up). 16.95 (*978-1-59990-121-3(8) , Bloomsbury Children) Bloomsbury Publishing.

Rockwell, Carey. Stand by for Mars! 2007. (ENG.). 208p. per. 89.99 (*978-1-4280-7416-3(3)) IndyPublish.com.

—Treachery in Outer Space. 2006. 95.99 (*978-1-4280-4384-8(5)); pap. 89.99 (*978-1-4280-4383-1(7)) IndyPublish.com.

Rodriguez, Lisa M. Bopo Gets Lost in Space (Bopo Se Pierde en el Espacio) Rodriguez, David A., ed. Rodriguez, David A., tr. Rodriguez, Lisa M., illus. 2000. (ENG & SPA., Illus.). 32p. (J). (ps-3). 14.95 (978-0-9665575-2-7(2)) BOPO Biligual Bks.

Rouss, Sylvia A. Reach for the Stars. 2005. (Illus.). 40p. (J). (gr. 3-7). 16.95 (978-1-930143-82-1(6)); pap. 9.95 (978-1-930143-83-8(4)) Pitspopany Pr. (Devora Publishing).

Santillo, LuAnn. The Big Job. Santillo, LuAnn, ed. 2003. (Half-Pint Kids Readers Ser.). (Illus.). 7p. (J). (ps-1). pap. (978-1-59256-044-8(X)) Half-Pint Kids, Inc.

—Outerspace, 6 vols. Santillo, LuAnn, ed. 2003. (Half-Pint Kids Readers Ser.). (Illus.). 42p. (J). (ps-1). pap. 6.99 (978-1-59256-042-4(3)) Half-Pint Kids, Inc.

Schade, Susan & Buller, Jon. Space Dog Jack. 2001. (Hello Reader! Ser.). (Illus.). 32p. (J). (ps-1). pap. (978-0-439-20541-2(7)) Scholastic, Inc.

Scholastic, Inc. Staff. Lost in Space Deluxe Storybook. 1998. (Illus.). 48p. (J). (ps-3). pap. 5.98 (978-0-590-18935-4(2) , Cartwheel Bks.) Scholastic, Inc.

—Lost in Space Hello Reader. 1998. (Hello Reader! Ser.). (Illus.). 48p. (J). (gr. 1-3). pap. 3.99 (978-0-590-18937-8(9) , Cartwheel Bks.) Scholastic, Inc.

Schooley, Bob & McCorkle, Mark. Liar of Kudzu. 2007. 192p. (J). 15.99 (978-1-4169-1488-4(9)) Simon & Schuster Children's Publishing.

Scroggs, Kirk Brandon. Hair Ball from Outer Space. 6th ed. 2007. (Wiley & Grampa Ser.: No. 6). 112p. (J). (gr. 3-7). pap. 3.99 (*978-0-316-05951-0(X)); 12.99 (*978-0-316-05950-3(1)) Little, Brown Bks. for Young Readers.

Seuss, Dr. & Rabe, Tish. There's No Place Like Space: All about Our Solar System. Ruiz, Aristides, illus. 1999. (Cat in the Hat's Learning Library). 48p. (J). (gr. k-3). 8.99 (978-0-679-89115-4(3)); lib. bdg. 11.99 (978-0-679-99115-1(8)) Random Hse. Children's Bks. (Random Hse. Bks. for Young Readers).

Shannon, Ronnie Jay. Samurai Force: the Final Hope: The Junior Novel. 2007. (ENG.). 76p. per. 14.95 (*978-1-4241-6528-5(8)) PublishAmerica, Inc.

Simmons, Monica. Aster City: 2Kul4Skul - The Hyperspace Hero. Ward, Jon, illus. 1998. (Aster Planet Chronicles Ser.: Vol. 5). 32p. (J). (gr. k-4). 15.95 (978-0-9658128-6-3(3)) Long Wind Publishing.

Smiley, Mark. A Journey Far Away. 2005. pap. 13.95 (*978-1-59526-494-7(9)) Media Creations, Inc.

Smith, Dona. My Favorite Martian. 1999. (Disney's Junior Novel Ser.). (Illus.). 92p. (J). (gr. 3-7). pap. 4.99 (978-0-7868-4239-1(3)) Hyperion Pr.

Steele, Alexander. Unleashed in Space. 1999. (Super Adventures of Wishbone Ser.: No. 3). (J). (gr. 4-7). (978-0-606-19032-9(5)) Tandem Library Bks.

Strasser, Dirk. Lost in Space. 2005. (Thrillogy Ser.). (Illus.). 48p. (gr. 4-8). 17.50 (978-0-7910-8868-5(5)) Facts On File, Inc.

Strub, Scott Richard. Otto the Outerspace Octopus. 2007. (J). per. 10.00 (*978-1-59872-782-1(6)) Instantpublisher.com.

Tauscher, Donna. Hero for Hire: By Han Solo. 1998. (Star Wars Journals). 104p. (J). (gr. 4-7). pap. 3.99 (978-0-590-18901-9(8)) Scholastic, Inc.

Watson, Jude. Captive to Evil: By Princess Leia Organa. 1998. (Star Wars Journals). 91p. (J). (gr. 4-7). pap. 3.99 (978-0-590-18900-2(X)) Scholastic, Inc.

—Captive to Evil: By Princess Leia Organa. 1998. (Star Wars Journals). (J). (gr. 4-7). (978-0-606-13808-6(0)) Tandem Library Bks.

—The False Peace. Buelow, Alicia, illus. 2004. (Star Wars Ser.: No. 9). 160p. (J). 5.99 (978-0-439-33925-4(1) , Scholastic Paperbacks) Scholastic, Inc.

—Journey Across Planet X. 1999. (Star Wars Science Adventures Ser.). (978-0-606-16616-4(5)) Tandem Library Bks.

—Queen Amidala. 1999. (gr. 3-6). lib. bdg. 14.15 (978-0-613-87068-9(9)) Tandem Library Bks.

—The Shadow Trap. Buelow, Alice & Mattingly, David, illus. 2003. (Star Wars Ser.: No. 6). 144p. (J). pap. 4.99 (978-0-439-33922-3(7)) Scholastic, Inc.

Watson, Jude & Burkett, K. D. Journey Across Planet X. 1999. (Star Wars Science Adventures Ser.). (Illus.). 96p. (J). (gr. 3-7). pap. 3.99 (978-0-590-20228-2(6)) Scholastic, Inc.

Wells, H. G. & Card, Orson Scott. War of the Worlds: With an Introduction by Orson Scott Card. 2004. (Scholastic Classics Ser.). 304p. (J). pap. 3.99 (978-0-439-51849-9(0) , Scholastic Paperbacks) Scholastic, Inc.

Whitman, John. Army of Terror. l.t. ed. 1998. (Star Wars Ser.: No. 6). 144p. (J). (gr. 4 up). lib. bdg. 22.60 (978-0-8368-2240-3(4)) Stevens, Gareth Inc.

—City of the Dead. l.t. ed. 1998. (Star Wars Ser.: No. 2). 144p. (J). (gr. 4 up). lib. bdg. 22.60 (978-0-8368-2236-6(6)) Stevens, Gareth Inc.

—Eaten Alive. l.t. ed. 1998. (Star Wars Ser.: No. 1). 144p. (J). (gr. 4 up). lib. bdg. 22.60 (978-0-8368-2235-9(8)) Stevens, Gareth Inc.

—Ghost of the Jedi. l.t. ed. 1998. (Star Wars Ser.: No. 5). 144p. (J). (gr. 4 up). lib. bdg. 22.60 (978-0-8368-2239-7(0)) Stevens, Gareth Inc.

—The Nightmare Machine. l.t. ed. 1998. (Star Wars Ser.: No. 4). 144p. (J). (gr. 4 up). lib. bdg. 22.60 (978-0-8368-2238-0(2)) Stevens, Gareth Inc.

—Planet Plague. l.t. ed. 1998. (Star Wars Ser.: No. 3). 144p. (J). (gr. 4 up). lib. bdg. 22.60 (978-0-8368-2237-3(4)) Stevens, Gareth Inc.

—Spore. 1998. (Star Wars Ser.: No. 9). (J). (gr. 4-7). (978-0-606-13807-9(2)) Tandem Library Bks.

—The Swarm. 1998. (Star Wars Ser.: No. 8). (J). (gr. 4-7). (978-0-606-13806-2(4)) Tandem Library Bks.

Winn, L. B. Butterpod Jerome & the Planet of Gabool. Winn, L. B., illus. 2007. (J). pap. 18.95 (*978-0-9791884-0-4(7)) Winn, Lynnette.

OUTLAWS

see Robbers and Outlaws

OVERLAND JOURNEYS TO THE PACIFIC

Blackwood, Gary L. Life on the Oregon Trail. 1999. (Way People Live Ser.). (Illus.). 112p. (YA). (gr. 7-10). 28.70 (978-1-56006-540-1(0) , LML00902-177897, Lucent Bks.) Thomson Gale.

Braidich, Victoria. Making History: A Covered Wagon. 2006. (Tony Stead Nonfiction Independent Reading Collection). (J). pap. (978-1-4042-5589-0(3)) Rosen Publishing Group, Inc., The.

Bryant, Jill. Wagon Train. 2003. (Real Life Stories Ser.). (Illus.). 24p. (J). lib. bdg. 15.95 (978-1-59036-082-8(6)) Weigl Pubs., Inc.

Burger, James P. The Oregon Trail. 2002. (Library of the Westward Expansion). (Illus.). 24p. (J). (gr. 3). lib. bdg. 19.95 (978-0-8239-5850-4(7) , PowerKids Pr.) Rosen Publishing Group, Inc., The.

Calabro, Marian. The Perilous Journey of the Donner Party. 1999. (Illus.). 192p. (J). (gr. 5-9). tchr. ed. 20.00 (978-0-395-86610-8(3) , Clarion Bks.) Houghton Mifflin Co. Trade & Reference Div.

Crewe, Sabrina & Uschan, Michael V. The Oregon Trail. 2004. (Events That Shaped America Ser.). (Illus.). 32p. (J). lib. bdg. 24.67 (978-0-8368-3405-5(4)) Stevens, Gareth Inc.

Dean, Arlan. The Oregon Trail: From Independence, Missouri to Oregon City, Oregon. 2003. (Reading Power Ser.). (Illus.). 24p. (J). lib. bdg. 17.25 (978-0-8239-6478-9(7) , PowerKids Pr.) Rosen Publishing Group, Inc., The.

—The Overland Trail: From Atchison, Kansas, to Fort Bridger, Wyoming. 2003. (Reading Power Ser.). (Illus.). 24p. (J). lib. bdg. 17.25 (978-0-8239-6479-6(5) , PowerKids Pr.) Rosen Publishing Group, Inc., The.

Goldsmith, Connie. Lost in Death Valley: The True Story of Four Families in California's Gold Rush. 2001. (Single Titles Ser.: up). (Illus.). 144p. (J). (gr. 7-12). lib. bdg. 24.90 (978-0-7613-1915-3(8) , Millbrook Pr.) Lerner Publishing Group.

Graham, Amy. The Oregon Trail & the Daring Journey West by Wagon. 2006. (Wild History of the American West Ser.). (Illus.). 128p. (J). lib. bdg. 33.27 (978-1-59845-021-7(2) , MyReportLinks.com Bks.) Enslow Pubs., Inc.

Hamilton, John. To the Pacific. 2003. (Lewis & Clark Expedition Ser.). (Illus.). 32p. (J). (gr. 3-8). lib. bdg. 24.21 (978-1-57765-765-1(9)) ABDO Publishing Co.

Harberts, Bernie. Woody & Maggie Walk Across America. ed. 2006. (Illus.). 40p. (J). per. 16.96 (978-0-9787722-9-1(6)) RiverEarth.

Harness, Cheryl. The Tragic Tale of Narcissa Whitman & a Faithful History of the Oregon Trail. Harness, Cheryl, illus. 2006. (Illus.). 144p. (J). (gr. 5-9). 16.95 (978-0-7922-5920-6(3)); lib. bdg. 25.90 (978-0-7922-5921-3(1)) National Geographic Society. (National Geographic Children's Bks.).

Hunsaker, Joyce Badgley. Seeing the Elephant: Voices from the Oregon Trail. 2003. (Illus.). 272p. (J). 24.95 (978-0-89672-504-1(9)) Texas Tech Univ. Pr.

Isaacs, Sally Senzell. The Oregon Trail. 2003. 32p. (J). pap. 7.50 (978-1-4034-4775-3(6)); lib. bdg. 25.65 (978-1-4034-2504-1(3)) Heinemann Library.

Jaffe, Elizabeth Dana. The Oregon Trail. 2002. (Let Freedom Ring Ser.). (Illus.). 48p. (J). (gr. 3-4). lib. bdg. 22.60 (978-0-7368-1101-9(X) , Bridgestone Bks.) Capstone Pr., Inc.

Johmann, Carol A. Going West! Journey on a Wagon Train to Settle a Frontier Town. 2000. (J). 17.60 (978-0-606-22459-8(9)) Tandem Library Bks.

Johmann, Carol A. & Rieth, Elizabeth J. Going West! Journey on a Wagon Train to Settle a Frontier Town. 2000. (Illus.). 96p. (J). (gr. 2-7). per. 19.90 (978-0-613-27857-7(7)) Tandem Library Bks.

Landau, Elaine. The Oregon Trail. 2006. 48p. (gr. 3-5). (YA). pap. 6.95 (978-0-516-27903-9(3)); (Illus.). (J). 25.00 (978-0-516-25871-3(0)) Scholastic Library Publishing. (Children's Pr.).

Lawlor, Laurie. Pacific Odyssey to California 1905. 2002. (gr. 3-6). lib. bdg. 13.00 (978-0-613-45089-8(2)) Tandem Library Bks.

Life on a Wagon Train. (Rosen Real Readers Big Bookstm Ser.). 16p. (J). (gr. 2-3). 38.75 (978-1-4042-6224-9(5)) Rosen Publishing Group, Inc., The.

Littlefield, Holly. Children of the Trail West. 1999. (Picture the American Past Ser.). (Illus.). 48p. (gr. 2-5). lib. bdg. 22.60 (978-1-57505-304-2(7)) Lerner Publishing Group.

Morley, Jacqueline. You Wouldn't Want to Be an American Pioneer! Antram, David, illus. 2002. (You Wouldn't Want to Ser.). 32p. (J). (gr. 2-5). 28.50 (978-0-531-14608-8(1)); pap. 9.95 (978-0-531-16369-6(5)) Scholastic Library Publishing. (Watts, Franklin).

—You Wouldn't Want to Be an American Pioneer! 2002. (gr. 3-6). lib. bdg. 18.75 (978-0-613-53886-2(2)) Tandem Library Bks.

The Old Spanish Trail, 6 Packs. (On Deck Ser.: Vol. 2). 24p. (gr. 4-5). 35.00 (978-0-7578-5812-3(0)) Rigby Education.

Oregon Trail. (Exploring the West Ser.). 48p. (YA). 7.95 (978-0-7368-4508-3(9)) Capstone Pr., Inc.

The Oregon Trail, 6 Packs. (On Deck Ser.: Vol. 2). 24p. (gr. 4-5). 35.00 (978-0-7578-5813-0(9)) Rigby Education.

The Overland Trail: Individual Title Six-Packs. (On Deck Ser.: Vol. 2). 24p. (gr. 4-5). 35.00 (978-0-7578-5814-7(7)) Rigby Education.

Quasha, Jennifer. Covered Wagons: Hands-On Projects about America's Westward Expansion. 2001. (Great Social Studies Projects Ser.). (Illus.). 24p. (J). (gr. 3). lib. bdg. 19.95 (978-0-8239-5704-0(7) , PowerKids Pr.) Rosen Publishing Group, Inc., The.

Roop, Connie & Roop, Peter, eds. The Diary of David R. Leeper: Rushing for Gold. 2000. (In My Own Words Ser.). (Illus.). 78p. (J). (gr. 5 up). lib. bdg. 27.07 (978-0-7614-1011-9(2) , Benchmark Bks.) Cavendish, Marshall Corp.

Steele, Christy. Famous Wagon Trails. 2005. (Illus.). 48p. (J). pap. (978-0-8368-5795-5(X)); lib. bdg. 30.00 (978-0-8368-5788-7(7)) Stevens, Gareth Inc. (World Almanac Library).

Thompson, Gare. Our Journey West: The Oregon Trail Adventures of Sarah Marshall. 2003. (gr. 3-6). lib. bdg. 15.30 (978-0-613-67111-8(2)) Tandem Library Bks.

Wadsworth, Ginger. Words West: The Voices of Young Pioneers. 2003. (Illus.). 208p. (J). (gr. 5-9). tchr. ed. 18.00 (978-0-618-23475-2(6) , Clarion Bks.) Houghton Mifflin Co. Trade & Reference Div.

Welveart, Scott R. The Donner Party. Frenz, Ron & Barnett, Charles, illus. 2006. (Graphic Library). 32p. (J). (978-0-7368-5479-5(7)) Capstone Pr., Inc.

Werther, Scott P. The Donner Party. 2002. (Survivors Ser.). (Illus.). 48p. (YA). (gr. 7-12). 24.00 (978-0-516-23901-9(5) , Children's Pr.) Scholastic Library Publishing.

OVERLAND JOURNEYS TO THE PACIFIC—FICTION

Ackerman, Karen. Araminta's Paint Box. Lewin, Betsy, illus. 1998. 32p. (J). (gr. 1-3). 6.99 (978-0-689-82091-5(7) , Aladdin) Simon & Schuster Children's Publishing.

Applegate, Katherine. The Buffalo Storm. Ormerod, Jan, illus. 2007. 32p. (J). (ps-3). 16.00 (978-0-618-53597-2(7) , Clarion Bks.) Houghton Mifflin Co. Trade & Reference Div.

Baird, Janet H. Journey to the Edge of Nowhere. 132p. (gr. 3-7). 2000. (Illus.). pap. 6.95 (978-1-889658-15-5(4)); 1999. (J). 11.95 (978-1-889658-19-3(7)) New Canaan Publishing Co. LLC.

Bly, Stephen A. The Lost Wagon Train. 2005. (Retta Barre's Oregon Trail Ser.: Vol. 1). 110p. pap. 5.99 (978-1-58134-391-5(4) , Crossway Bibles) Crossway Bks.

Coerr, Eleanor. The Josefina Story Quilt: Josefina y la colcha de Retazos. Degen, Bruce, illus. 2006. (I Can Read Bks.). (SPA.). 64p. (J). pap. 3.99 (978-0-06-088713-1(3)) HarperCollins Pubs.

Crawford, Neil. The Journeyers. 2006. (J). pap. (*978-0-9778205-4-2(8)) Helm Publishing.

Fitzgerald, John D. Brave Buffalo Fighter. 2003. (Young Adult Historical Library). 192p. (YA). pap. 11.95 (978-1-883937-59-1(0)) Bethlehem Bks.

Gerrard, Roy. Wagons West! Gerrard, Roy, illus. 2000. (Illus.). 32p. (J). (ps-3). pap. 5.95 (978-0-374-48210-7(1) , Sunburst) Farrar, Straus & Giroux.

—Wagons West! 2000. (J). (ps-ps). (Illus.). lib. bdg. 14.10 (978-0-613-30179-4(X)); (978-0-606-20138-4(6)); (Illus.). (978-0-606-20401-9(6)) Tandem Library Bks.

Graham, Christine. When Pioneer Wagons Rumbled West. Meidell, Sherry, illus. 1998. 32p. (J). (ps-3). 14.95 (978-1-57345-272-4(6) , Shadow Mountain) Deseret Bk. Co.

Hermes, Patricia. Westward to Home Bk. 1: Joshua's Oregon Trail Diary. 2002. (gr. 3-6). lib. bdg. 13.00 (978-0-613-60738-4(4)) Tandem Library Bks.

Hopkinson, Deborah & Carpenter, Nancy. Apples to Oregon: Being the (Slightly) True Narrative of How a Brave Pioneer Father Brought Apples, Peaches, Pears, Plums, Grapes, & Cherries (And Children) Across the Plains. 2004. (Illus.). 40p. (J). 16.95 (978-0-689-84769-1(6) , Atheneum) Simon & Schuster Children's Publishing.

Kay, Verla. Covered Wagons, Bumpy Trails. Schindler, S. D., illus. 2000. 1p. (J). (ps-3). 15.99 (978-0-399-22928-2(0) , Putnam Juvenile) Penguin Group (USA) Inc.

Lawlor, Laurie. He Will Go Fearless. 2006. 224p. (J). 15.95 (978-0-689-86579-4(1)) Simon & Schuster Children's Publishing.

Levine, Ellen. The Journal of Jedediah Barstow: An Emigrant on the Oregon Trail. 2002. (My Name Is America Ser.). (Illus.). 176p. (J). (gr. 4-9). pap. 10.95 (978-0-439-06310-4(8) , Scholastic Pr.) Scholastic, Inc.

Levitin, Sonia. Clem's Chances. 2001. (Illus.). 208p. (J). (gr. 2-7). pap. 17.95 (978-0-439-29314-3(6) , Orchard Bks.) Scholastic, Inc.

Mercati, Cynthia. Wagons Ho! A Diary of the Oregon Trail. Kabel, Larassa, illus. 2000. (Cover-to-Cover Bks.). 56p. (J). pap. (978-0-7891-5039-4(5)); (gr. 1-4). lib. bdg. 16.95 (978-0-7807-9011-7(1)) Perfection Learning Corp.

Philbrick, Rodman. The Journal of Douglas Allen Deeds: The Donner Party Expedition, 1846. 2001. (My Name Is America Ser.). (Illus.). 160p. (J). (gr. 4-9). pap. 10.95 (978-0-439-21600-5(1)) Scholastic, Inc.

Rizzo, Kay D. Wagon Train West. 2003. 96p. (J). (978-0-8163-1986-2(3)) Pacific Pr. Publishing Assn.

Sargent, Dave & Sargent, Pat. Dizzy: (Claybank) Have Courage, 25 vols., Vol. 22. Lenoir, Jane, illus. 2001. (Saddle Up Ser.: 22). 36p. (J). pap. 6.95 (978-1-56763-680-2(2)); lib. bdg. 22.60 (978-1-56763-679-6(9)) Ozark Publishing.

Schulte, Elaine L. Daniel Colton under Fire. 2001. (Illus.). 137p. (J). (gr. 4-7). pap. 7.49 (978-1-57924-564-1(1)) Jones, Bob Univ. Pr.

—Suzannah Strikes Gold. 2001. (Illus.). 144p. (J). (gr. 4-7). pap. 7.49 (978-1-57924-565-8(X)) Jones, Bob Univ. Pr.

Spooner, Michael. Daniel's Walk. rev. ed. 176p. 2004. (J). pap. 7.95 (978-0-8050-7543-4(7)); 2001. (Illus.). (YA). (gr. 7 up). 16.95 (978-0-8050-6750-7(7)) Holt, Henry & Co. (Holt, Henry & Co. Bks. For Young Readers).

Stanley, Diane. Roughing It on the Oregon Trail. Berry, Holly, illus. 2001. (Time-Traveling Twins Ser.: No. 1). 48p. (J). (gr. k-5). pap. 6.99 (978-0-06-449006-1(8) , Harper Trophy) HarperCollins Pubs.

—Roughing It on the Oregon Trail. 2001. (gr. 3-6). lib. bdg. 14.10 (978-0-613-44250-3(4)) Tandem Library Bks.

Thompson, Gare. Our Journey West: An Adventure on the Oregon Trail. 2003. 40p. (J). pap. 6.99 (978-0-7922-5199-6(7)) National Geographic Society.

—Our Journey West: The Oregon Trail Adventures of Sarah Marshall. 2003. (I Am American Ser.). (Illus.). 40p. (J). (gr. 3-7). pap. 6.99 (978-0-7922-5178-1(4) , National Geographic Children's Bks.) National Geographic Society.

Van Leeuwen, Jean. Papa & the Pioneer Quilt. Bond, Rebecca, illus. 2007. (J). (gr. k-3). 32p. 16.99 (978-0-8037-3028-1(4)); (*978-1-4287-3972-7(6)) Penguin Group (USA) Inc. (Dial).

Wilson, Laura. How I Survived the Oregon Trail: The Journal of Jesse Adams. 2006. (Illus.). 37p. (J). (gr. 4-8). reprint ed. pap. 10.00 (978-0-7567-9925-0(2)) DIANE Publishing Co.

—How I Survived the Oregon Trail: The Journal of Jesse Adams. 1999. (Time Travellers Ser.). (Illus.). 38p. (J). (gr. 4-7). pap. 9.95 (978-0-688-17276-3(8)) HarperCollins Pubs.

Wolf, Allan. New Found Land: Lewis & Clark's Voyage of Discovery. 2007. (Illus.). 512p. (YA). (gr. 7). pap. 8.99 (*978-0-7636-3288-5(0)) Candlewick Pr.

OVERWEIGHT

see Weight Control

OWENS, JESSE, 1913-1980

Eboch, Chris. Jesse Owens: Young Record Breaker. Henderson, Meryl, illus. 2008. (Childhood of Famous Americans Ser.). 208p. (J). pap. 5.99 (*978-1-4169-3922-1(9) , Aladdin) Simon & Schuster Children's Publishing.

Gentry, Tony. Jesse Owens: Champion Athlete. 2005. (Black Americans of Achievement Ser.). (Illus.). 112p. (J). (gr. 6-12). 30.00 (978-0-7910-8252-2(0)); pap. 13.25 (978-0-7910-8372-7(1)) Facts On File, Inc. (Chelsea Hse.).

Hind, Devon & Bergstresser, Kate, trs. Jesse Owens: World's Fastest Human. 2003. (Alabama Roots Biography Ser.). (Illus.). 120p. (J). (978-1-878561-38-1(3)) Seacoast Publishing, Inc.

McKissack, Patricia C. & McKissack, Fredrick L. Jesse Owens: Olympic Star. rev. ed. 2001. (Great African Americans Ser.). (Illus.). 32p. (J). (gr. 1-4). lib. bdg. 18.60 (978-0-7660-1681-1(1)) Enslow Pubs., Inc.

Monroe, Judy. Jesse Owens: Track-and-Field Champion. 2005. (Fact Finders Ser.). (Illus.). 32p. (J). (ps-7). lib. bdg. 22.60 (978-0-7368-3744-6(2)) Capstone Pr., Inc.

Raatma, Lucia. Jesse Owens: Track-and-Field Olympian. 2003. (Journey to Freedom Ser.). (Illus.). 40p. (J). (gr. 3-7). 28.50 (978-1-56766-532-1(2)) Child's World, Inc.

Shafer, Susan. Jesse Owens: Fastest Human. 2005. 22.00 (*978-1-4108-4207-7(X)) Benchmark Education Co.

Steele, Philip. Jesse Owens. 2001. (Profiles Ser.). (Illus.). 56p. (J). (gr. 4-6). lib. bdg. (978-1-58810-059-7(6)) Heinemann Library.

Streissguth, Thomas. Jesse Owens. (Sports Heroes & Legends Ser.). (Illus.). 2006. 106p. (J). (gr. 3-7). 27.93 (978-0-8225-3070-1(8) , Lerner Pubns.); 1999. 112p. (gr. 6-12). lib. bdg. 27.93 (978-0-8225-4940-6(9)) Lerner Publishing Group.

Streissguth, Tom. Jesse Owens. 2005. (Bios for Challenged Readers Ser.). (Illus.). 112p. (J). (gr. 6-12). lib. bdg. 27.93 (978-0-8225-2256-0(X)) Lerner Publishing Group.

Sutcliffe, Jane. Jesse Owens. Porter, Janice Lee, illus. (On My Own Biographies Ser.). 48p. (J). (gr. 1-3). 2003. 5.95 (978-1-57505-487-2(6)); 2000. lib. bdg. 23.93 (978-1-57505-451-3(5) , Carolrhoda Bks.) Lerner Publishing Group.

—Jesse Owens. 2000. (gr. 3-6). lib. bdg. 15.25 (978-0-613-79243-1(2)) Tandem Library Bks.

Time for Kids Editors. Jesse Owens: Running into History. 2008. (Time for Kids Ser.). (Illus.). 48p. (J). 15.99 (*978-0-06-057621-9(9)); pap. 3.99 (*978-0-06-057620-2(0) , Collins) HarperCollins Pubs.

Weatherford, Carole Boston. Jesse Owens: Fastest Man Alive. Velasquez, Eric, illus. 2006. 32p. (J). (gr. 1-6). 16.95 (978-0-8027-9550-2(1)) Walker & Co.

OWLS

Adams, Pam. Owl. 1999. (Pocket Pals Ser.). (Illus.). 12p. (J). (ps-1). bds. 1.99 (978-0-85953-862-6(1)) Child's Play-International.

Arjas, Pirkko & Butcher, Sally K., illus. Friend Owl: A Children's Book. 1000th ed. 2005. 48p. (J). 18.00 (978-0-9762132-0-8(6)) Old Bess Publishing Co.

Arnosky, Jim. All about Owls. 1999. (J). 12.79 (978-0-606-17437-4(0)) Tandem Library Bks.

Bauman, Amy & Niemuth, Neal D. The Wonder of Owls. 2000. (Animal Wonders Ser.). (Illus.). 48p. (J). (gr. 1 up). lib. bdg. 26.00 (978-0-8368-2664-7(7)) Stevens, Gareth Inc.

Berger, Melvin & Berger, Gilda. Owls Live in Trees. 2003. (Illus.). (J). (978-0-439-47178-7(8)) Scholastic, Inc.

Biel, Timothy Levi & Quality Productions Staff. Owls. 2001. (Zoobooks Ser.). (Illus.). 24p. (J). (gr. 1-6). 15.95 (978-1-888153-44-6(X)) Wildlife Education, Ltd.

Buhos: Por Dentro y Por Fuera. 2004. (SPA., Illus.). 32p. lib. bdg. 21.25 (978-1-4042-2866-5(7)) Rosen Publishing Group, Inc., The.

Davies, Nicola. White Owl, Barn Owl. Foreman, Michael, illus. 2007. 32p. (J). (gr. k-3). 16.99 (978-0-7636-3364-6(X)) Candlewick Pr.

DK Publishing. Owl. 2007. (See How They Grow Ser.). 24p. (J). pap. 3.99 (*978-0-7566-3372-1(9)) Dorling Kindersley Publishing, Inc.

Ellwood, Nancy. Owls. 2000. (Smart Start Reader Ser.). (Illus.). 31p. (J). (978-0-439-23780-2(7)) Scholastic, Inc.

Franks, Katie. Owls up Close. 2008. (J). lib. bdg. (*978-1-4042-4140-4(X) , PowerKids Pr.) Rosen Publishing Group, Inc., The.

Frost, Helen. Snowy Owls. 2006. (Polar Animals Ser.). (Illus.). 24p. (J). (978-0-7368-4246-4(2)) Capstone Pr., Inc.

Gallimard Jeunesse Publishing Staff. Night Creatures. Perols, Sylvaine, illus. 1998. (First Discovery Book Ser.). 24p. (J). (ps-2). 12.95 (978-0-590-11765-4(3)) Scholastic, Inc.

George, Jean Craighead. Winter Moon. 2003. (J). (gr. 3-7). 20.75 (978-0-8446-7244-1(0)) Smith, Peter Pub., Inc.

Gibbons, Gail. Owls. Gibbons, Gail, illus. 2006. (Illus.). 32p. (J). (ps-3). 6.95 (978-0-8234-2014-8(0)) Holiday Hse., Inc.

—Owls. 2005. (Illus.). 32p. (J). (ps-3). 16.95 (978-0-8234-1880-0(4)) Holiday Hse., Inc.

Gibson, Deborah C. Owls & Their Homes. 1999. (Animal Habitats Ser.). (Illus.). 24p. (J). (gr. k-4). lib. bdg. 18.75 (978-0-8239-5308-0(4) , PowerKids Pr.) Rosen Publishing Group, Inc., The.

Gilkerson, Patricia. My Adventure with Owls. 2007. 44p. (J). 8.99 (978-1-59092-460-0(6) , Orchard Academy Pr.) Windstorm Creative.

Gordon, Sharon. Adivina Quién Baja en Picada. 2006. (Bookworms Ser.). (SPA & ENG., Illus.). 32p. (J). lib. bdg. 22.79 (978-0-7614-2387-4(7)) Cavendish, Marshall Corp.

—Guess Who Swoops (Adivina Quién Baja en Picada) 2006. (Bookworms Ser.). (SPA & ENG., Illus.). 32p. (J). lib. bdg. 22.79 (978-0-7614-2468-0(7)) Cavendish, Marshall Corp.

Hammerslough, Jane. Owl Puke: Book & Owl Pellet. 2003. (Illus.). 92p. (J). (gr. 3-6). pap. 13.95 (978-0-7611-3186-1(8) , 13186) Workman Publishing Co., Inc.

Hiscock, Bruce, illus. Ookpik: The Travels of a Snowy Owl. 2008. (J). (*978-1-59078-461-7(8)) Boyds Mills Pr.

Houghton, Gillian. Owl. 2004. (Getting into Nature Ser.). (Illus.). 32p. (J). lib. bdg. 21.25 (978-0-8239-4208-4(2)) Rosen Publishing Group, Inc., The.

Jacobs, Liza. Owls. 2003. (Wild Wild World Ser.). (Illus.). 24p. (J). 23.70 (978-1-4103-0050-8(1) , Blackbirch Pr., Inc.) Thomson Gale.

Labella, Susan. Owls & Other Animals with Amazing Eyes. 2005. (Scholastic News Nonfiction Readers Ser.). (Illus.). 24p. (J). (gr. 1-2). 19.00 (978-0-516-24927-8(4) , Children's Pr.) Scholastic Library Publishing.

Landau, Elaine. Owls: Hunters of the Night. 2007. (Animals after Dark Ser.). (Illus.). 32p. (J). (gr. 2-4). lib. bdg. 22.60 (978-0-7660-2768-8(6) , Enslow Elementary) Enslow Pubs., Inc.

Lynch, Wayne. Owls. Neidigh, Sherry, illus. 2005. (Our Wild World Ser.). 48p. (J). pap. 7.95 (978-1-55971-915-5(X) , NorthWord Bks. for Young Readers) T&N Children's Publishing.

—Owls. Neidigh, Sherry, illus. 2005. 47p. (J). (gr. 2-5). lib. bdg. 15.15 (978-0-606-33698-7(2)) Tandem Library Bks.

Lynch, Wayne, contrib. by. Owls. 2005. (Our Wild World Ser.). (Illus.). 48p. 10.95 (978-1-55971-914-8(1) , NorthWord Bks. for Young Readers) T&N Children's Publishing.

Lynch, Wayne, photos by. Baby Owl. (Nature Babies Ser.). (Illus.). 36p. (J). (gr. k-3). pap. (978-1-55041-798-2(3)); 2003. (978-1-55041-796-8(7)) Fitzhenry & Whiteside, Ltd.

Macken, JoAnn Early. Owls. 2005. (Illus.). 24p. (J). pap. (978-0-8368-4491-7(2)); (YA). lib. bdg. 19.33 (978-0-8368-4484-9(X)) Stevens, Gareth Inc.

Markle, Sandra. Owls. 40p. (J). 2005. (gr. 4-6). pap. 7.95 (978-1-57505-745-3(X)); 2004. (Illus.). (gr. 3-6). lib. bdg. 25.26 (978-1-57505-729-3(8)) Lerner Publishing Group.

Mason, Adrienne. Owls. Ogle, Nancy Gray, illus. 2005. (Kids Can Press Wildlife Ser.). 32p. (J). (gr. k-5). (978-1-55337-624-8(2)); (978-1-55337-623-1(4)) Kids Can Pr., Ltd.

Mattern, Joanne. Owls Are Night Animals. 2006. (Illus.). 24p. (J). pap. (*978-0-8368-7855-4(8)); lib. bdg. (*978-0-8368-7848-6(5)) Stevens, Gareth Inc. (Weekly Reader Early Learning Library).

—Owls Are Night Animals: Los Buhos Son Animales Nocturnos. 2006. (SPA & ENG., Illus.). 24p. (J). pap. (*978-0-8368-8052-6(8)); lib. bdg. (*978-0-8368-8045-8(5)) Stevens, Gareth Inc. (Weekly Reader Early Learning Library).

Miller, Sara Swan. Owls: The Silent Hunters. 2008. (J). lib. bdg. (*978-1-4042-4165-7(5) , PowerKids Pr.) Rosen Publishing Group, Inc., The.

—Owls: The Silent Hunters. 2000. (gr. 3-6). lib. bdg. 15.25 (978-0-613-34397-8(2)) Tandem Library Bks.

Miller, Sara Swan & Savage, Stephen. Owls: The Silent Hunters. 2001. (Animals in Order Ser.). (Illus.). 48p. (gr. 4-6). pap. 6.95 (978-0-531-16496-9(9) , Watts, Franklin) Scholastic Library Publishing.

Mudd-Ruth, Maria. Owls. 2004. (Animals, Animals Ser.). (Illus.). 46p. (J). 25.64 (978-0-7614-1752-1(4) , Benchmark Bks.) Cavendish, Marshall Corp.

Murray, Julie. Owls. 2005. (Animal Kingdom Set Ii Ser.). (Illus.). 24p. (J). (gr. k-4). lib. bdg. 21.35 (978-1-59197-328-7(7)) ABDO Publishing Co.

Oddey the Owl. 2005. (J). 9.95 (978-0-9765502-0-4(2)) ON-TRAK.

Owls: Individual Title Six-Packs. (Story Steps Ser.). (gr. k-2). 32.00 (978-0-7635-9800-6(3)); 16p. (gr. 2 up). 36.00 (978-0-7635-9392-6(3)) Rigby Education.

Owls in the Snow: Individual Title Six-Packs. (Sails Literacy Ser.). (gr. 1-2). 36.00 (978-0-7578-4020-3(5)) Rigby Education.

Povey, Karen D. Owls. 2005. (Nature's Predators Ser.). (Illus.). 48p. (J). (gr. 4-8). 26.20 (978-0-7377-2349-6(1) , Greenhaven Pr., Inc.) Thomson Gale.

Quality Productions Staff. Lechuzas. Rountree, Monica, tr. 2003. (Zoobooks). Orig. Title: Owls. (SPA., Illus.). 24p. (J). (gr. 1-7). lib. bdg. 15.95 (978-1-888153-81-1(4)) Wildlife Education, Ltd.

—Owls. rev. ed. 2003. (Illus.). 24p. (J). (gr. 1-7). 10.95 (978-1-888153-93-4(8) , Zoo Bks.) Wildlife Education, Ltd.

Reid, Mary Ebeltoft. Owls & Other Birds of Prey, Vol. 8. World Book, Inc. Staff, ed. 2002. (World Book's Animals of the World Ser.: Set 1). 64p. (J). (978-0-7166-1245-2(3)) World Bk., Inc.

Richardson, Adele D. Owls: Flat-Faced Flyers. 2002. (Wild World of Animals Ser.). (Illus.). 24p. (J). (gr. 1). lib. bdg. 18.60 (978-0-7368-1396-9(9) , Bridgestone Bks.) Capstone Pr., Inc.

Riley, Joelle. Quiet Owls. 2004. (Pull Ahead Books). (Illus.). 32p. (J). 22.60 (978-0-8225-3771-7(0) , Carolrhoda Bks.) Lerner Publishing Group.

Sattler, Helen Roney. Book of North American Owls. 1998. (978-0-606-13210-7(4)) Tandem Library Bks.

—The Book of North American Owls. Zallinger, Helen R. & Zallinger, Jean Day, illus. 1998. 64p. (J). (gr. 4-6). pap. 7.95 (978-0-395-90017-8(4) , Clarion Bks.) Houghton Mifflin Co. Trade & Reference Div.

—The Book of North American Owls. Zallinger, Helen R., illus. 1998. 64p. (J). (ps-7). lib. bdg. 17.55 (978-0-613-06898-7(X)) Tandem Library Bks.

Smith, Dwight G. Great Horned Owl. 2004. (Wild Bird Guides Ser.). (Illus.). 106p. pap. 19.95 (978-0-8117-2689-4(4)) Stackpole Bks.

Swanson, Diane. Owls. 1998. (Welcome to the World of Animals Ser.). (Illus.). 32p. (J). (gr. 3 up). lib. bdg. 23.33 (978-0-8368-2215-1(3)) Stevens, Gareth Inc.

Tagholm, Sally. The Barn Owl. Kitchen, Bert, illus. 2003. (Animal Lives Ser.). 32p. (J). (gr. k-3). pap. 4.95 (978-0-7534-5606-4(0) , Kingfisher) Houghton Mifflin Co. Trade & Reference Div.

—Barn Owl. 2003. (gr. k-3). lib. bdg. 12.95 (978-0-613-87037-5(9)) Tandem Library Bks.

Taylor, Bonnie Highsmith. Callie: A Great Gray Owl. 2000. (Cover-to-Cover Chapter Bks.). (Illus.). (J). 55p. pap. (978-0-7891-5272-5(X)); 56p. (gr. 1-4). lib. bdg. 16.95 (978-0-7807-9652-2(7)) Perfection Learning Corp.

Townsend, Emily Rose. Owls. Saunders-Smith, Gail, ed. 2004. (Woodland Animals Ser.). (Illus.). 24p. (J). (gr. k-1). lib. bdg. 15.93 (978-0-7368-2068-4(X) , Pebble Bks.) Capstone Pr., Inc.

Van Vorst, Fran. Owls. Hale, Janet, ed. Hedges, Bruce, illus. 1999. (Thematic Units Ser.). 80p. (J). (gr. k-3). pap., tchr. ed. 9.99 (978-1-57690-375-9(3) , TCM2375) Teacher Created Materials, Inc.

Warhol, Tom. Owls. 2007. (Animalways Ser.). 112p. (J). lib. bdg. 34.21 (978-0-7614-2537-3(3) , Benchmark Bks.) Cavendish, Marshall Corp.

Wechsler, Doug. Great Horned Owls. 2001. (Really Wild Life of Birds of Prey Ser.). (Illus.). 24p. (J). lib. bdg. 18.75 (978-0-8239-5599-2(0) , PowerKids Pr.) Rosen Publishing Group, Inc., The.

Whitehouse, Patricia. Barn Owls. 2003. (What's Awake? Ser.). (Illus.). 24p. (J). (ps-1). lib. bdg. 17.08 (978-1-58810-877-7(5)); (978-1-4034-0624-8(3)) Heinemann Library.

—La Lechuza. 2003. (Que Esta Despierto? (What's Awake?) Ser.).Tr. of Barn Owls. 24p. (ps-1). (SPA.). (J). lib. bdg. 17.08 (978-1-4034-0392-6(9)); (Illus.). pap. 5.25 (978-1-4034-0633-0(2)) Heinemann Library.

—La Lechuza. 2002. Tr. of Barn Owls. (SPA.). (ps-2). lib. bdg. 13.30 (978-0-613-89121-9(X)) Tandem Library Bks.

Wildlife Education, Ltd. Staff & Quality Productions Staff. Owls. Boyer, Trevor et al, illus. 2002. (Zoobooks Ser.). 18p. (Orig.). (YA). (gr. 5 up). pap. 2.95 (978-0-937934-32-6(1)) Wildlife Education, Ltd.

Wyatt, Laura. Those Outrageous Owls. Weaver, Steve, illus. Moore III, H. G., photos by. 2006. 55p. (J). 14.95 (978-1-56164-365-3(3)); 8.95 (978-1-56164-366-0(1)) Pineapple Pr., Inc.

OWLS—FICTION

Addabbo, Carole. Dina the Deaf Dinosaur. Valentine, illus. 1998. 32p. (J). (ps-5). 19.95 (978-1-889262-04-8(8)) Hannacroix Creek Bks., Inc.

Adshead, Paul S. The Farmer in the Dell. 2001. (Illus.). 16p. (J). 7.99 (978-0-85953-886-2(9)) Child's Play-International.

Allen, Jonathan. I'm Not Cute. 2006. (Illus.). 32p. (ps-k). 14.99 (978-0-7868-3720-5(9)) Hyperion Pr.

Anastasio, Dina. How Raven Became Black & Owl Got Its Spots. 2003. (Early Connections Ser.). (J). pap. 33.00 (978-1-4108-1093-9(3)) Benchmark Education Co.

Anastasio, Dina. Por qué el cuervo es negro y el buho tiene manchitas & How Raven Became Black & Owl Got Its Spots. 2005. spiral bd. 66.00 (*978-1-4108-5626-5(7)) Benchmark Education Co.

Avi. Poppy. Floca, Brian, illus. 1999. (Poppy Stories Ser.). 192p. (J). (gr. 3-7). pap. 5.99 (978-0-380-72769-8(2) , Harper Trophy) HarperCollins Pubs.

Baby Owl Goes Away: Early Level Satellite, 6 packs. (Sails Literacy Ser.). 16p. (gr. 1-2). 27.00 (978-0-7578-2919-2(8)) Rigby Education.

Bailey, Arthur Scott. Tuck-Me-in Tales: The Tale of Solomon Ow. 2006. (Illus.). pap. (*978-1-4065-0452-1(1)) Dodo Pr.

Bailey, Scott Arthur. Tale of Solomon Owl. 2006. pap. 33.99 (*978-1-4280-4924-6(X)) IndyPublish.com.

Barnwell, Dan. The Fire in Thunder Hollow. 2006. pap. 10.99 (*978-1-4259-6741-3(8)) AuthorHouse.

—Tree in Thunder Hollow. 2006. pap. 10.99 (*978-1-4259-6742-0(6)) AuthorHouse.

Bornstein, Ruth. Brave Bunny. Bornstein, Ruth, illus. 2003. (Illus.). 32p. (J). 9.95 (978-1-58685-282-5(5)) Gibbs Smith, Publisher.

Bruchac, Joseph. Wabi: A Hero's Tale. 208p. (gr. 7). 2007. (YA). 6.99 (*978-0-14-240947-3(2) , Puffin); 2006. (J). 16.99 (978-0-8037-3098-4(5) , Dial) Penguin Group (USA) Inc.

Brunelle, Nicholas. Snow Moon. 2005. (Illus.). 36p. (J). 15.99 (978-0-670-06024-5(0) , Viking Juvenile) Penguin Group (USA) Inc.

Chambers, Melinda. We Are Whoooo We Are. Spiker, Sue Ann, illus. 2006. 32p. (J). 16.95 (978-0-929915-46-3(1)) Headline Bks., Inc.

Charlotte Latin School Staff. Ann & the Owl. Sher, illus. 2001. 32p. (J). per. 4.95 (978-0-9707920-5-1(0)) Charlotte's Storybooks.

Christmas Surprise for Owl. 2002. (J). bds. 3.98 (978-1-84250-586-1(6) , Bright Sparks) Parragon, Inc.

Cockcroft, Jason & Nicholls, Judith. Billywise. Cockcroft, Jason, illus. 2004. (Illus.). 32p. (J). (ps-2). pap. 6.95 (978-1-58234-893-3(6) , Bloomsbury Children) Bloomsbury Publishing.

Debowski, Sharon. The Snowman, the Owl, & the Groundhog. 2007. (J). lib. bdg. 15.95 (*978-1-60227-468-6(1)); (Illus.). 32p. 14.95 (*978-1-60227-470-9(3)) Above the Clouds Publishing.

Duffie, Charles. The Mole & the Owl: A Romantic Fable about Braving the Wide World for Love. 1998. (Illus.). 120p. 18.95 (978-1-57174-082-3(1)) Hampton Roads Publishing Co., Inc.

Eagle, Golden. The Owl Who Lives in My House. l.t. ed. 2003. (Illus.). 24p. (J). per. 9.95 (978-1-932338-34-8(9)) Lifevest Publishing, Inc.

Eggleton, Jill. Baby Owl Is Scared: Early Level Satellite, 6 packs. (Sails Literacy Ser.) 16p. (gr. 1 2). 27.00 (978-0-7578-2931-4(7)) Rigby Education.

Entz, Susan & Galarza, Sheri. The Guardian Owl. Hale, Bruce, illus. 1999. (Hawaiian Values Ser.: Vol. 4). 24p. (J). (ps-2). 5.95 (978-1-57306-090-5(9)) Bess Pr., Inc.

Frank, Rochelle. So What, Saw-Whet? Gast, Linda, photos by. 2004. (J). per. 9.95 (978-0-9746792-0-4(8)) Hummingbird Mountain Pr.

French, Jennifer Pratt. Hoot Owl Shares the Dawn. 2004. 128p. (YA). per. 9.95 (978-0-9709104-4-8(4)) Hickory Tales Publishing.

Gibbons, Joyce. The Little Brown Owl & Me. Lenoir, Jane, illus. 2001. (J). (gr. k-5). lib. bdg. 14.95 (978-0-9705727-6-9(X)) Coastal Publishing Carolina, Inc.

Good-Night Owl. 2004. (J). 24.95 incl. audio (978-1-56008-206-4(2)) Weston Woods Studios, Inc.

Gray, Kes. Twoo Twit. McQuillan, Mary, illus. 2006. 32p. (J). 14.99 (978-0-7641-6008-0(7)) Barron's Educational Series, Inc.

Groce, Michelle. Jasper. Duis, Laura, illus. 2003. 174p. (J). 17.95 (978-0-9708972-6-8(X)) Novello Festival Pr.

Guardians of Ga'hoole Staff & Lasky, Kathryn. The Coming of Hoole. 2006. (Guardians of Ga'Hoole Ser.: Bk. 10). (Illus.). 224p. (J). (gr. 4-7). pap. 5.99 (978-0-439-79569-2(9) , Scholastic Paperbacks) Scholastic, Inc.

Hanson, Anders. Night Owl. Haberstroh, Anne, illus. 2006. (Fact & Fiction Ser.). 24p. (J). 21.35 (978-1-59679-953-0(6) , SandCastle); pap. (978-1-59679-954-7(4)) ABDO Publishing Co.

Harper, Piers. Little Owl. Harper, Piers, illus. 2004. (Illus.). 32p. (J). 15.95 (978-0-439-59703-6(X) , Cartwheel Bks.) Scholastic, Inc.

Hayden, Torey L. The Very Worst Thing. 2003. 176p. (J). (gr. 5 up). 15.99 (978-0-06-029792-3(1)) HarperCollins Pubs.

Hiaasen, Carl. Hoot. 304p. (gr. 5 up). 2002. (Illus.). (J). 15.95 (978-0-375-82181-3(3)); 2002. (Illus.). (J). lib. bdg. 17.99 (978-0-375-92181-0(8)); 2004. (YA). reprint ed. pap. 8.95 (978-0-375-82916-1(4)) Random Hse. Children's Bks. (Knopf Bks. for Young Readers).

—Hoot. 2003. 25.95 (978-0-7862-5014-1(3)) Thorndike Pr.

Hillenbrand, Will. Asleep in the Stable. (Illus.). 32p. (J). (gr. k-3). tchr. ed. 16.95 (978-0-8234-1824-4(3)) Holiday Hse., Inc.

Hodgson, Mona Gansberg. Clubhouse Surprises. Sharp, Chris, illus. 1999. (Desert Critter Friends Ser.: Vol. 6). 48p. (J). (ps-2). 4.99 (978-0-570-05082-7(0) , 56-1906GJ) Concordia Publishing Hse.

—Clubhouse Surprises. 1998. (ps-2). lib. bdg. 13.00 (978-0-613-72809-6(2)) Tandem Library Bks.

Holman, Doris Anne. Ollie the Little Burrowing Owl. unabr. ed. 2001. (Illus.). 22p. (J). (gr. k-5). pap. 11.00 (978-0-9667192-5-3(5)) Holman, Doris Anne.

Huggins, Peter. Trosclair & the Alligator. Gardiner, Lindsey, illus. 2006. 32p. (J). 15.95 (978-1-932065-98-5(9)) Star Bright Bks., Inc.

Hutchins, Pat. Good Night, Owl! Hutchins, Pat, illus. 2002. (Illus.). (J). 15.53 (978-0-7587-2620-9(1)) Book Wholesalers, Inc.

I Heard the Owl Call My Name. 1999. (YA). 9.95 (978-1-56137-142-6(4)) Novel Units, Inc.

Irvin-Marston, Hope. My Little Book of Burrowing Owls. Magdalena-Brown, Maria, illus. 2nd ed. 2004. 32p. (J). pap. 7.95 (978-0-89317-054-7(2) , WW-0542, Windward Publishing) Finney Co., Inc.

Jacquemain, Patti. Journey of the Great Bear: Through California's Golden Past. Jacquemain, Patti, illus. 2006. (J). (978-0-929702-10-0(7)) Mission Creek Studios.

Johansen, Hanna & Barrett, John S. The Duck & the Owl. Bhend, Kathi, illus. 2005. 80p. (J). 17.95 (978-1-56792-285-1(6)) Godine, David R. Pub.

Johnston, Tony. The Barn Owls. Ray, Deborah Kogan, illus. 2000. 32p. (J). (ps-4). 15.95 (978-0-88106-981-5(7)); 6.95 (978-0-88106-982-2(5)) Charlesbridge Publishing, Inc.

—Barn Owls. 2000. lib. bdg. 15.25 (978-0-613-51236-7(7)) Tandem Library Bks.

Kindl, Patrice. Owl in Love. 2004. 224p. (YA). (gr. 7 up). pap. 6.99 (978-0-618-43910-2(2) , Graphia) Houghton Mifflin Co. Trade & Reference Div.

—Owl in Love. unabr. ed. 1998. (J). Class Set. 102.80 incl. audio (978-0-7887-2562-3(9) , 46732); Homework Set. 49.75 incl. audio (978-0-7887-2106-9(2) , 40701) Recorded Bks., LLC.

Krauel, Janann. Flying Lessons. 2005. 73p. pap. 14.95 (978-1-4137-2732-6(8)) PublishAmerica, Inc.

Landry, Leo. Fat Bat & Swoop. rev. ed. 2005. (Illus.). 64p. (J). (gr. 1-3). 15.95 (978-0-8050-7003-6(3) , Holt, Henry & Co. Bks. For Young Readers) Holt, Henry & Co.

Lasky, Kathryn. The Capture. 2003. (Guardians of Ga'Hoole Ser.: Bk. 1). 240p. (gr. 3-7). mass mkt. 5.99 (978-0-439-40557-7(2) , Scholastic Paperbacks) Scholastic, Inc.

—The Capture. 2003. (Guardians of Ga'Hoole Ser.: Bk. 1). (J). (gr. 3-6). lib. bdg. 13.00 (978-0-613-67484-3(7)) Tandem Library Bks.

—Guardians of Ga'Hoole #14 Exile. 2008. 224p. pap. 5.99 (*978-0-439-88808-0(5) , Scholastic Paperbacks) Scholastic, Inc.

—The Rescue. 2004. (Guardians of Ga'Hoole Ser.: Bk. 3). (Illus.). 208p. (J). (gr. 3-7). pap. 4.99 (978-0-439-40559-1(9) , Scholastic Paperbacks) Scholastic, Inc.

—River of Wind. 2007. (Guardians of Ga'Hoole Ser.: No. 13). 224p. (J). pap. 5.99 (*978-0-439-88807-3(7)) Scholastic, Inc.

Lasky, Kathryn. The Siege. 2004. (Guardians of Ga'Hoole Ser.: Bk. 4). (Illus.). 224p. (J). (gr. 3-7). mass mkt. 4.99 (978-0-439-40560-7(2) , Scholastic Paperbacks) Scholastic, Inc.

Laurie, Peter. Mauby & the Hurricane. 2007. 56p. pap. 16.00 (*978-1-4050-7718-7(2)) Macmillan Caribbean GBR. *Dist:* Interlink Publishing Group, Inc.

Lear, Edward. Buho y la Gatita.Tr. of Owl & the Cat. (SPA., Illus.). 32p. (J). 14.95 (978-84-261-3023-5(2)) Juventud, Editorial ESP. *Dist:* AIMS International Bks., Inc.

Las Lechucitas: Individual Title Six-Packs. (Coleccion Pm Ser.).Tr. of Baby Owls. (SPA.). 16p. (gr. 1 up). 26.00 (978-0-7578-2975-8(9)) Rigby Education.

Lesynski, Loris. Night School. 2001. lib. bdg. 14.10 (978-0-613-50352-5(X)) Tandem Library Bks.

Llewellyn, Claire. An Owl at School. 2000. (Cambridge Reading Ser.). (Illus.). 14p. pap. 5.00 (978-0-521-77451-2(9)) Cambridge Univ. Pr.

Lobel, Arnold. Buho en Casa. 2000. (First Readers Ser.). (SPA., Illus.). 64p. (J). (gr. k-2). pap. 7.99 (978-980-257-253-5(5) , EK7847) Ekare, Ediciones VEN. *Dist:* Lectorum Pubns., Inc.

Loyie, Larry. As Long as the Rivers Flow. Holmlund, Heather D., illus. 2005. 40p. (J). pap. 8.95 (978-0-88899-696-1(9)) Groundwood Bks. CAN. *Dist:* Perseus Distribution.

MacGregor, Roy. The Complete Screech Owls. (J). Vol. 2. 2006. 592p. pap. 15.95 (978-0-7710-5486-0(6)); Vol. 5. 2007. 488p. (gr. 3-7). pap. 15.95 (978-0-7710-5497-6(1)) McClelland & Stewart CAN. (Screech Owls). *Dist:* Random Hse., Inc.

Manning, Mick. Cock-a-Doodle-Hooooooo! Granstrom, Brita, illus. 2007. 28p. (J). (ps-2). 16.95 (*978-1-56148-568-0(3)) Good Bks.

Marchus, Linda. Hoot'N Annie. 2002. (J). lib. bdg. 15.95 (978-0-9723122-0-2(X)) Wee Read Publishing.

Markowitz, Susan Meredith. The el gran bosque verde & Great Green Forest. 2005. spiral bd. 66.00 (*978-1-4108-5653-1(4)) Benchmark Education Co.

Melmed Corace. Little Hoot. 2008. 36p. (J). 12.99 (978-0-8118-6023-9(X)) Chronicle Bks. LLC.

Murphy, Mary. Little Owl & the Star: A Christmas Story. Murphy, Mary, illus. 2003. (Illus.). 32p. (J). (gr. k-k). 12.99 (978-0-7636-2268-8(0)) Candlewick Pr.

Owl & Mouse in the House: Individual Title Six-Packs. (Sails Literacy Ser.). (gr. 1-2). 36.00 (978-0-7578-4016-6(7)) Rigby Education.

Owls in the Family. 1999. (J). 9.95 (978-1-56137-199-0(8)) Novel Units, Inc.

Owls in the Garden: Individual Title Six-Packs. 16p. (gr. 2 up). 35.00 (978-0-7635-9374-2(5)) Rigby Education.

Pfister, Marcus. The Sleepy Owl. 1998. (Illus.). 32p. (J). (ps-2). pap. 6.95 (978-1-55858-905-6(8)) North-South Bks., Inc.

Pinkney, Andrea Davis. Sleeping Cutie. Pinkney, Brian, illus. 2004. 32p. (J). 16.00 (978-0-15-202544-1(8) , Harcourt Children's Bks) Harcourt Children's Bks.

Potter, Alan Mitchell & Williams, Virginia. Hoo-Hoo Hooty-Hoo-Who. 2005. 9.00 (978-0-8059-9807-8(1)) Dorrance Publishing Co., Inc.

Powell, Richard. Hoot! Hoot! Martín Larrañaga, Ana, illus. 2003. (Lift-the-Flap Bks.). 24p. (J). (gr. k-k). 8.99 (978-0-7636-2107-0(2)) Candlewick Pr.

Powers, Paul. Tales of the Swamp Creatures. 2003. 71p. pap. 11.95 (978-1-4137-0160-9(4)) PublishAmerica, Inc.

Ramage, Jan. Eyes in the Night. Peterson, Laura, illus. 2006. 32p. pap. 15.25 (978-1-920694-67-8(6)) Univ. of Western Australia Pr. AUS. *Dist:* International Specialized Bk. Services.

Rigby Education Staff. Baby Owl. (Sails Literacy Ser.). (Illus.). 16p. (gr. k-1). 27.00 (978-0-7635-9878-5(X) , 698789C99) Rigby Education.

Runton, Andy. Owly Volume 4. 2007. (Illus.). 120p. pap. 10.00 (*978-1-891830-89-1(9)) Top Shelf Productions.

Russell, D. Z. The Amazing Adventures of Andy Owl: A Children's Guide to Understanding Music. Stone, John, illus. 2003. 34p. (J). per. 7.95 (978-0-9725398-0-7(8)) World Famous Children's Bks.

Sargent, Dave & Sargent, David, Jr. Hoot Owl: Mind Your Mamma, 19, 9. Lenoir, Jane, illus. 2003. (Feather Tales Ser.: 9). 42p. (J). pap. 6.95 (978-1-56763-736-6(1)) Ozark Publishing.

Sargent, Dave & Sargent, David M., Jr. Hoot Owl: Mind Your Mamma, 20, 9. Lenoir, Jane, illus. 2nd ed. 2003. (Feather Tales Ser.: 9). 42p. (J). lib. bdg. (978-1-56763-735-9(3)) Ozark Publishing.

The Secret Song & Other Stories: Individual Title Six-Pack. (Story Steps Ser.). (gr. k-2). 48.00 (978-0-7635-9808-2(9)) Rigby Education.

See, Linda. Cindy & Sean Centipede's: It Was Magical, Granny Wise Owl. 1998. (Illus.). 32p. (J). (gr. k-3). pap. 8.00 (978-0-8059-4458-7(3)) Dorrance Publishing Co., Inc.

Serfozo, Mary. Whooo's There? Scherer, Jeffrey, illus. 2007. 40p. (J). (gr. k-1). 9.99 (978-0-375-84050-0(8)); lib. bdg. 12.99 (978-0-375-94050-7(2)) Random Hse. Children's Bks. (Random Hse. Bks. for Young Readers).

Shannon, Star Erian. Erian's Friend Jeremiah the Owl. 2003. (J). pap. 9.00 (978-0-8059-6068-6(6)) Dorrance Publishing Co., Inc.

Sharmat, Marjorie Weinman. Nate the Great on the Owl Express. Sharmat, Mitchell & Weston, Martha, illus. 2004. 80p. (J). (gr. 1-4). 4.50 (978-0-440-41927-3(1) , Yearling) Random Hse. Children's Bks.

Sharmat, Marjorie Weinman & Sharmat, Mitchell. Nate the Great on the Owl Express. Weston, Martha, illus. 2003. (Nate the Great Ser.). 48p. (gr. 1-4). (J). 14.95 (978-0-385-73078-5(0)); lib. bdg. 16.99 (978-0-385-90102-4(X)) Random Hse. Children's Bks. (Delacorte Bks. for Young Readers).

Smith, Jeffrey B. Stubby. 2006. 15p. 8.28 (978-1-4116-8215-3(7)) Lulu.com.

Smith van Frankenhuyzen, Robbyn. Adopted by an Owl: The True Story of Jackson the Owl. van Frankenhuyzen, Gijsbert, illus. 2001. 48p. (J). 17.95 (978-1-58536-070-3(8)) Sleeping Bear Pr.

Spurling, Margaret. Bilby Moon. Snell, Danny, illus. 2001. 32p. (J). (ps-4). 14.95 (978-1-929132-06-5(9)) Kane/Miller Bk. Pubs., Inc.

Staheli, Bee, ed. The Owl Who Couldn't Say Whoo. Clish, Lori, illus. l.t. ed. (J). (gr. k-5). pap. 7.95 (978-1-928632-50-4(5)) Writers Marketplace:Consulting, Critiquing & Publishing.

Tomlinson, Jill. Owl Who Was Afraid of the Dark. (Illus.). 95p. (J). pap. 6.99 (978-0-7497-0795-8(X)) Egmont Bks., Ltd. GBR. *Dist:* Trafalgar Square Publishing.

—Owl Who Was Afraid of the Dark. Howard, Paul, illus. 2005. 96p. (J). reprint ed. pap. 6.99 (978-1-4052-1093-5(1)) Egmont Bks., Ltd. GBR. *Dist:* Trafalgar Square Publishing.

Waddell, Martin. Las Lechucitas. Benson, Patrick, illus. (SPA.). 28p. (J). (gr. k-3). 14.95 (978-0-88272-137-8(2)) Santillana USA Publishing Co., Inc.

—Owl Babies. 2002. (Illus.). (J). 13.83 (978-1-4046-3008-6(2)) Book Wholesalers, Inc.

—Owl Babies. 2003. (Illus.). 22p. (J). 12.99 (978-0-7636-2157-5(9)) Candlewick Pr.

—Owl Babies. Benson, Patrick, illus. 32p. (J). (ps-2). 2002. pap. 5.99 (978-0-7636-1710-3(5)); 2000. pap. 19.99 (978-0-7636-1283-2(9)) Candlewick Pr.

—Owl Babies. (Illus.). 25p. (J). (CHI, ENG, URD, TUR & VIE.). (978-1-85430-343-1(0) , 93441); (ENG, VIE, URD, TUR & CHI., (978-1-85430-348-6(1) , 93442) Magi Pubns.

—Owl Babies. 2002. (ps-2). lib. bdg. 14.15 (978-0-613-74780-6(1)) Tandem Library Bks.

West, Judy & Westerink, Gerda. The Christmas Owls. 2004. (Illus.). 32p. (J). 16.95 (978-0-86315-421-8(2)) Floris Bks. GBR. *Dist:* SteinerBooks, Inc.

Wildsmith, Brian. The Owl & the Woodpecker. Wildsmith, Brian, illus. 2006. (Illus.). 32p. (J). 16.95 (978-1-59572-043-6(X)); pap. 6.95 (978-1-59572-050-4(2)) Star Bright Bks., Inc.

Wilson, Karma. Bear's New Friend. Chapman, Jane, illus. 2006. 40p. (J). (ps-2). 16.95 (978-0-689-85984-7(8) , McElderry, Margaret K.) Simon & Schuster Children's Publishing.

Yolen, Jane. Owl Moon. 2002. (Illus.). (J). 23.64 (978-0-7587-0064-3(4)) Book Wholesalers, Inc.

Yolen, Jane. Owl Moon: 20th Anniversary Edition. Schoenherr, John, illus. 2007. 40p. (J). (ps). 16.99 (*978-0-399-24799-6(8) , Philomel) Penguin Group (USA) Inc.

OXYACETYLENE WELDING

see Welding

OZ (IMAGINARY PLACE)—FICTION

Baum, L. Frank. Collected Short Stories of L. Frank Baum. 2006. (J). 29.95 (978-1-930764-14-9(6)) International Wizard of Oz Club, The.

—Dorothy & the Wizard in Oz. 2006. pap. 26.99 (*978-1-4219-7695-2(1)) IndyPublish.com.

—Dorothy & the Wizard in Oz. 2004. reprint ed. pap. 20.95 (978-1-4191-1655-1(X)); pap. 1.99 (978-1-4192-1655-8(4)) Kessinger Publishing, LLC.

—Dorothy & the Wizard of Oz. 2003. (Illus.). 264p. pap. 14.95 (978-1-58726-036-0(0) , For Your Knowledge) Ann Arbor Media Group, LLC.

—Dorothy & the Wizard of Oz. l.t. ed. 2004. (Large Print Ser.). lib. bdg. 25.00 (978-1-58287-769-3(6)) North Bks.

—The Emerald City of Oz. (Oz Ser.). (YA). (gr. 5-8). 21.95 (978-0-8488-0733-7(2)) Amereon LTD.

—The Emerald City of Oz. 2002. (Illus.). 294p. (J). per. (978-1-58726-023-0(9) , Mundus) Ann Arbor Media Group, LLC.

—The Emerald City of Oz. Neill, John R., illus. 2002. 296p. (YA). pap. 17.00 (978-0-7567-6271-1(5)) DIANE Publishing Co.

—The Emerald City of Oz. 2003. (Twelve-Point Ser.). lib. bdg. 24.00 (978-1-58287-254-4(6)) North Bks.

—Glinda of Oz. rev. ed. 2006. 184p. 26.95 (978-1-4218-1786-6(1)); pap. 11.95 (978-1-4218-1886-3(8)) 1st World Publishing, Inc. (1st World Library - Literary Society).

—Glinda of Oz. (Oz Ser.). (YA). (gr. 5-8). 21.95 (978-0-8488-0784-9(7)) Amereon LTD.

—Glinda of Oz. 2002. (Illus.). 276p. (J). per. (978-1-58726-024-7(7) , Mundus) Ann Arbor Media Group, LLC.

—Glinda of Oz. Neill, John R., illus. 2000. (Oz Ser.). 288p. (J). (gr. 4-7). pap. 7.95 (978-0-486-41018-0(8)) Dover Pubns., Inc.

—Glinda of Oz. (Twelve-Point Ser.). 2003. lib. bdg. 24.00 (978-1-58287-256-8(2)); 2004. 210p. 25.00 (978-1-58287-740-2(8)) North Bks.

—The Land of Oz. 1999. (Oz Ser.). (Illus.). 320p. (YA). (gr. 5-8). reprint ed. 12.95 (978-1-56852-226-5(6) , Konecky & Konecky) Konecky, William S. Assocs., Inc.

—The Lost Princess of Oz. (Oz Ser.). (YA). (gr. 5-8). 22.95 (978-0-8488-0786-3(3)) Amereon LTD.

—The Lost Princess of Oz. 2002. (Illus.). 302p. (J). per. (978-1-58726-022-3(0) , Mundus) Ann Arbor Media Group, LLC.

—The Lost Princess of Oz. Neill, John R., illus. 2002. 312p. (J). (gr. 3-6). pap. 17.00 (978-0-7567-6273-5(1)) DIANE Publishing Co.

—The Lost Princess of Oz. Neill, John R., illus. unabr. ed. 1998. (Oz Ser.). 332p. (J). (gr. 4-7). pap. 9.95 (978-0-486-40344-1(0)) Dover Pubns., Inc.

—The Lost Princess of Oz. (Twelve-Point Ser.). 2003. lib. bdg. 24.00 (978-1-58287-255-1(4)); 2004. 241p. 25.00 (978-1-58287-739-6(4)) North Bks.

—The Magic of Oz. 2004. (Twelve-Point Ser.). lib. bdg. 24.00 (978-1-58287-279-7(1)) North Bks.

—Magic of Oz. 2006. pap. 12.99 (*978-1-4280-2747-3(5)) IndyPublish.com.

—The Magic of Oz. l.t. ed. 2004. (Large Print Ser.). lib. bdg. 25.00 (978-1-58287-775-4(0)) North Bks.

—El Maravilloso Mago de Oz. (Oz Ser.). (SPA., Illus.). 160p. (YA). (gr. 5-8). 14.95 (978-84-7281-184-3(0) , AF1184) Auriga, Ediciones S.A. ESP. *Dist:* Continental Bk. Co., Inc.

—El Maravilloso Mago de Oz. 3rd ed. 2002. (Clover Ser.). (SPA., Illus.). 264p. (YA). 11.50 (978-84-392-8002-6(5) , EV3454) Lectorum Pubns., Inc.

—El Maravilloso Mago de Oz. (SPA.). pap. 11.95 (978-84-95311-19-1(4)) Mestas, Jorge A. Ediciones Escolares La Escuela Nueva y Alinorma, S.L. ESP. *Dist:* Distribooks, Inc.

—The Marvelous Land of Oz. 2004. (Twelve-Point Ser.). lib. bdg. 24.00 (978-1-58287-272-8(4)); lib. bdg. 25.00 (978-1-58287-768-6(8)) North Bks.

—Ozma of Oz. 2003. pap. 14.95 (978-1-58726-035-3(2) , For Your Knowledge) Ann Arbor Media Group, LLC.

—Ozma of Oz. Neill, John R., illus. 2001. (Books of Wonder). 272p. (J). (gr. 3 up). pap. 7.99 (978-0-06-440962-9(7) , Harper Trophy) HarperCollins Pubs.

—Ozma of Oz. 2006. pap. 44.99 (*978-1-4219-7955-7(1)) IndyPublish.com.

—Ozma of Oz. (Twelve-Point Ser.). 2003. lib. bdg. 24.00 (978-1-58287-252-0(X)); 2004. 210p. 25.00 (978-1-58287-736-5(X)) North Bks.

—Ozma of Oz. l.t. ed. 2003. (Perennial Bestsellers Ser.). 288p. (J). 29.95 (978-0-7862-5888-8(8)) Thorndike Pr.

—The Patchwork Girl of Oz. (Oz Ser.).Tr. of 220. (YA). (gr. 5-8). 25.95 (978-0-8488-0705-4(7)) Amereon LTD.

—The Patchwork Girl of Oz. 2003. Tr. of 220. (Illus.). 342p. pap. 14.95 (978-1-58726-038-4(7) , For Your Knowledge) Ann Arbor Media Group, LLC.

—The Patchwork Girl of OZ. l.t. ed. 2004. (Large Print Ser.). lib. bdg. 25.00 (978-1-58287-771-6(8)) North Bks.

—Rinkitink in Oz. rev. ed. 2006. 216p. 27.95 (978-1-4218-1791-0(8)); pap. 12.95 (978-1-4218-1891-7(4)) 1st World Publishing, Inc. (1st World Library - Literary Society).

—Rinkitink in Oz. (Oz Ser.). (YA). (gr. 5-8). 22.95 (978-0-8488-0735-1(9)) Amereon LTD.

—Rinkitink in Oz. 2003. (Illus.). 318p. pap. 14.95 (978-1-58726-041-4(7) , Mundus) Ann Arbor Media Group, LLC.

—Rinkitink in Oz. Neill, John R., illus. 1998. (Oz Ser.). 352p. (gr. 5-8). 24.99 (978-0-688-14720-4(8)) HarperCollins Pubs.

—Rinkitink in Oz. 2004. reprint ed. pap. 20.95 (978-1-4191-6718-8(9)); pap. 1.99 (978-1-4192-6718-5(3)) Kessinger Publishing, LLC.

—Rinkitink in Oz. 2004. (Twelve-Point Ser.). lib. bdg. 24.00 (978-1-58287-278-0(3)); lib. bdg. 25.00 (978-1-58287-774-7(2)) North Bks.

—The Road to Oz. (Oz Ser.). (YA). (gr. 5-8). 20.95 (978-0-8488-0788-7(X)) Amereon LTD.

—The Road to Oz. 2003. (Illus.). 262p. pap. 14.95 (978-1-58726-037-7(9) , For Your Knowledge) Ann Arbor Media Group, LLC.

—The Road to Oz. 2004. (Twelve-Point Ser.). lib. bdg. 24.00 (978-1-58287-274-2(0)); lib. bdg. 25.00 (978-1-58287-770-9(X)) North Bks.

—The Royal Book of Oz. 2000. (YA). 26.95 (978-0-8488-2914-8(X)) Amereon LTD.

—The Royal Book of Oz. Thompson, Ruth Plumly, ed. enl. ed. 2001. (Oz Ser.). (Illus.). 320p. (J). (gr. 4-7). pap. 9.95 (978-0-486-41766-0(2)) Dover Pubns., Inc.

—The Scarecrow of Oz. (Oz Ser.). (YA). (gr. 5-8). 20.95 (978-0-8488-0707-8(3)) Amereon LTD.

—The Scarecrow of Oz. 2003. pap. (978-1-58726-040-7(9) , Mundus) Ann Arbor Media Group, LLC.

—The Scarecrow of Oz. Neill, John R., illus. 1998. (Oz Ser.). 304p. (J). (gr. 4-7). pap. 9.95 (978-0-486-40548-3(6)) Dover Pubns., Inc.

—The Scarecrow of Oz. 2004. (Twelve-Point Ser.). lib. bdg. 24.00 (978-1-58287-277-3(5)); lib. bdg. 25.00 (978-1-58287-773-0(4)) North Bks.

—Tik-Tok of Oz. 2003. (Illus.). 285p. pap. 14.95 (978-1-58726-039-1(5) , For Your Knowledge) Ann Arbor Media Group, LLC.

—Tik-Tok of Oz. 2004. (Twelve-Point Ser.). lib. bdg. 24.00 (978-1-58287-276-6(7)); lib. bdg. 25.00 (978-1-58287-772-3(6)) North Bks.

—The Tin Woodman of Oz. (J). 20.95 (978-0-8488-0709-2(X)) Amereon LTD.

—The Tin Woodman of Oz. 2000. (Oz Ser.). (Illus.). 288p. (J). (gr. 4-7). pap. 8.95 (978-0-486-41302-0(0)) Dover Pubns., Inc.

—The Tin Woodman of Oz. Neill, John R., illus. 1999. (Books of Wonder). 336p. (gr. 5). 25.99 (978-0-688-14976-5(6)) HarperCollins Pubs.

—The Tin Woodman of Oz. (Twelve-Point Ser.). 2003. lib. bdg. 24.00 (978-1-58287-257-5(0)); 2004. 230p. 25.00 (978-1-58287-741-9(6)) North Bks.

—The Wizard of Oz. 2002. (Great Illustrated Classics Ser.). (Illus.). 240p. (J). (gr. 3-8). 21.35 (978-1-57765-807-8(8) , ABDO & Daughters) ABDO Publishing Co.

—The Wizard of Oz. Denslow, W. W., illus. 2002. 208p. (J). (gr. 5-7). 25.00 (978-0-7567-5917-9(X)) DIANE Publishing Co.

—The Wizard of Oz. Zwerger, Lisbeth, illus. 2004. 103p. (J). (gr. 4-8). reprint ed. 20.00 (978-0-7567-7708-1(9)) DIANE Publishing Co.

—The Wizard of Oz. 2004. (Great Classics for Children Ser.). (Illus.). 192p. (J). 5.99 (978-1-4037-0601-0(8)) Dalmatian Pr.

—The Wizard of Oz. 2004. reprint ed. pap. 19.95 (978-1-4191-8832-9(1)) Kessinger Publishing, LLC.

—The Wizard of Oz. 1999. (Illus.). 272p. (YA). (gr. 3 up). reprint ed. 12.95 (978-1-56852-225-8(8) , Konecky & Konecky) Konecky, William S. Assocs., Inc.

—The Wizard of Oz. Kilgras, Heidi, ed. Santore, Charles, illus. 100th anniv. ed. 2000. 96p. (J). (ps-3). 21.95 (978-0-375-81137-1(0) , Random Hse. Bks. for Young Readers) Random Hse. Children's Bks.

—The Wizard of Oz. (SPA.). 256p. (J). 9.95 (978-84-204-3509-1(0)) Santillana USA Publishing Co., Inc.

—The Wizard of Oz. Granger, Paul, illus. 2001. 160p. (J). pap. 3.99 (978-0-439-23641-6(X)) Scholastic, Inc.

—The Wizard of Oz. 1999. (Aladdin Classics Ser.). 224p. (gr. 4-7). mass mkt. 4.99 (978-0-689-83142-3(0) , Aladdin) Simon & Schuster Children's Publishing.

—The Wizard of Oz. 2006. (J). (gr. 4-8). 24.21 (978-1-59961-120-4(1)) Spotlight.

—The Wizard of Oz. 1999. (978-0-606-17516-6(4)); (gr. 3-6). lib. bdg. 11.80 (978-0-613-63243-0(5)) Tandem Library Bks.

—The Wizard of Oz. 1998. (Children's Classics). (ENG., Illus.). 144p. (J). (gr. 4-7). pap. (978-1-85326-112-1(2) , 1122WW) Wordsworth Editions, Ltd.

—The Wizard of Oz Book & Charm. deluxe ed. 2005. (Charming Classics). 208p. (J). 9.99 (978-0-06-075772-4(8) , Harper Festival) HarperCollins Pubs.

—A Wonderful Welcome to Oz: The Marvelous Land of Oz, Ozma of Oz, & the Emerald City of Oz. Maguire, Gregory, ed. Neill, John R., illus. 2006. (Modern Library Classics). 624p. 15.95 (978-0-8129-7494-2(8) , Modern Library) Random House Publishing Group.

—The Wonderful Wizard of Oz. 2004. 180p. pap. 11.95 (978-1-59540-102-1(4) , 1st World Library - Literary Society) 1st World Publishing, Inc.

—The Wonderful Wizard of Oz. (Oz Ser.). (YA). (gr. 5-8). 20.95 (978-0-88411-772-8(3)) Amereon LTD.

—The Wonderful Wizard of Oz. 2003. (Illus.). 268p. pap. 14.95 (978-1-58726-034-6(4) , For Your Knowledge) Ann Arbor Media Group, LLC.

—The Wonderful Wizard of Oz. Foreman, Michael, illus. 1999. 160p. (J). pap. 18.00 (978-1-84365-007-2(X) , Pavilion Bks., Ltd.) Anova Bks. GBR. *Dist:* Independent Pubs. Group.

—The Wonderful Wizard of Oz. 2002. (Spot the Classics Ser.). (Illus.). 181p. (J). (gr. k-5). 4.99 (978-1-57759-551-9(3)) Dalmatian Pr.

—The Wonderful Wizard of Oz. Denslow, W. W., illus. 2001. (Books of Wonder). 320p. (J). pap. 7.99 (978-0-688-16677-9(6) , Harper Trophy) HarperCollins Pubs.

—The Wonderful Wizard of Oz. 2003. (ENG.). 136p. 23.99 (*978-1-4043-4042-8(4)) IndyPublish.com.

—The Wonderful Wizard of Oz. Wolstenholme, Susan, ed. 2000. (Oz Ser.). (Illus.). 336p. (gr. 5-8). 13.95 (978-0-19-283930-5(6)) Oxford Univ. Pr., Inc.

—The Wonderful Wizard of Oz. 2003. (Modern Library Classics Ser.). (Illus.). 224p. pap. 11.95 (978-0-8129-7011-1(X) , Modern Library) Random House Publishing Group.

—The Wonderful Wizard of Oz. Hildebrandt, Greg, illus. 2003. 64p. (J). 9.98 (978-0-7624-1628-8(9) , Courage Bks.) Running Pr. Bk. Pubs.

—The Wonderful Wizard of Oz. Sabuda, Robert, illus. 2000. (Classic Collectible Pop-Up Ser.). 16p. (J). (ps-3). pap. 26.99 (978-0-689-81751-9(7) , Little Simon) Simon & Schuster Children's Publishing.

—The Wonderful Wizard of Oz. Foreman, Michael, illus. 2005. 176p. (J). (gr. 2-7). 12.95 (978-1-4027-2535-7(3)) Sterling Publishing Co., Inc.

—The Wonderful Wizard of Oz. McKowen, Scott, illus. 2005. (Unabridged Classics Ser.). 176p. (J). (gr. 5). 9.95 (978-1-4027-2504-3(3)) Sterling Publishing Co., Inc.

—The Wonderful Wizard of Oz. 2000. 129p. reprint ed. pap. 9.95 (978-1-4021-9983-7(X) , Elibron Classics) Adamant Media.

—The Wonderful Wizard of Oz. l.t. unabr. ed. 2002. (Dover Large Print Classics Ser.). (Illus.). 256p. pap. 9.95 (978-0-486-42248-0(8)) Dover Pubns., Inc.

—The Wonderful Wizard of Oz. Denslow, W. W., illus. 100th anniv. ed. 2000. (Books of Wonder). 272p. (gr. 5-8). 24.99 (978-0-06-029323-9(3)) HarperCollins Pubs.

—Wonderful Wizard of Oz: A Classic Story about Cooperation. 2003. (Illus.). 32p. per. 3.95 (978-0-9747133-5-9(X) , Values to Live By Classic Stories) Thomas, Frederic Inc.

—The Wonderful Wizard of Oz: The Centennial Edition. Foreman, Michael, illus. 2002. (Oz Ser.). 160p. (J). (gr. 5-8). 29.99 (978-1-86205-343-4(X) , Pavilion Bks., Ltd.) Anova Bks. GBR. *Dist:* Independent Pubs. Group.

Baum, L. Frank, told to. The Emerald City of Oz. l.t. ed. 2004. (Large Print Ser.). 285p. 25.00 (978-1-58287-738-9(6)) North Bks.

Baum, L. Frank & Denslow, W. W. Oz-Story 5. Maxine, David, ed. Shanower, Eric & Denslow, W. W., illus. 1999. (Oz Ser.:). 128p. (Orig.). (YA). (gr. 5-8). pap. 14.95 (978-1-929527-00-7(4)) Hungry Tiger Pr.

Baum, L. Frank & Dickins, Rosie. Wizard of Oz. 2007. 64p. (J). 8.99 (978-0-7945-1457-0(X) , Usborne) EDC Publishing.

Baum, L. Frank & Glassman, Peter. Glinda of Oz. Neill, John R., illus. 2000. (Books of Wonder). 304p. (gr. 5-8). 25.99 (978-0-688-14978-9(2)) HarperCollins Pubs.

—The Lost Princess of Oz. Neill, John R., illus. 1998. (Books of Wonder). 352p. (gr. 5-8). 24.99 (978-0-688-14975-8(8)) HarperCollins Pubs.

—The Magic of Oz. Neill, John R., illus. 1999. (Books of Wonder). 292p. (gr. 5-8). 25.99 (978-0-688-14977-2(4)) HarperCollins Pubs.

Baum, L. Frank, et al. Oz-Story 4. Maxine, David, ed. Shanower, Eric, illus. 1998. (Oz Ser.). 128p. (Orig.). (YA). (gr. 5-8). pap. 14.95 (978-0-9644988-7-7(1)) Hungry Tiger Pr.

Baum, Roger S. The Lion of Oz & the Badge of Courage. Coons, Dean, illus. 2nd ed. 2003. 247p. (J). 24.95 (978-1-57072-255-4(2)) Overmountain Pr.

—The Oz Odyssey. Seitzinger, Victoria, illus. 2006. 176p. (J). 19.95 (978-1-57072-299-8(4)) Overmountain Pr.

—Toto in Candy Land of Oz. Berkovitz, Ronit, illus. 2002. 32p. (J). 14.95 (978-1-57072-224-0(2)) Overmountain Pr.

—The Wizard of Oz & The Magic Merry-Go-Round. Seitzinger, Victoria, illus. 2002. 32p. (J). 14.95 (978-1-57072-245-5(5)) Overmountain Pr.

Baum, Roger S. & Seitzinger, Victoria. Toto of Oz & the Surprise Party. 2004. 32p. (J). 13.95 (978-1-57072-284-4(6)) Overmountain Pr.

Baun, Frank L. The Wonderful Wizard of Oz: Juvenile Classic. 2005. (Illus.). 192p. (J). 5.99 (978-1-4037-1385-8(6)) Dalmatian Pr.

Conlon, Mara, adapted by. Scratch & Sketch Wizard of Oz: An Art Activity Story Book for Artists on Both Sides of the Rainbow. 2005. (Activity Book Ser.). (Illus.). 64p. (J). 14.99 (978-1-59359-906-5(4)) Peter Pauper Pr. Inc.

Einhorn, Edward. The Living House of Oz. Shanower, Eric, illus. 2005. 239p. (J). 27.95 (978-1-929527-08-3(X)) Hungry Tiger Pr.

Einhorn, Edward A. Paradox in Oz. Shanower, Eric, illus. 2000. 238p. (J). (gr. 3 up). 24.95 (978-1-929527-01-4(2)) Hungry Tiger Pr.

Evans, Robert J. Dorothy's Mystical Adventures in Oz. 2004. reprint ed. pap. 1.99 (978-1-4192-1658-9(9)) Kessinger Publishing, LLC.

Glassman, Peter, ed. Oz: The Hundredth Anniversary Celebration. 2000. (Illus.). 55p. (YA). reprint ed. 25.00 (978-0-7567-5499-0(2)) DIANE Publishing Co.

Hildebrandt, Greg. Magical Storybook Treasury. 2006. (Illus.). 184p. 14.98 (978-0-7624-2837-3(6) , Running Pr.) Running Pr. Bk. Pubs.

iBooks Staff. The Wonderful Wizard of Oz: Centennial Edition. 100th ed. 2001. (Illus.). 320p. pap. 14.95 (978-0-7434-1298-8(2)) ibooks, Inc.

Kirshenblatt, Shane. Dorothy Gale - Journey to Oz. 2005. 64p. Vol. 2. 7.99 (978-1-894998-89-5(8)); Vol. 3. 7.99 (978-1-894998-90-1(1)) Lake, Jack Productions, Inc. CAN. *Dist:* Hushion Hse. Publishing, Ltd.

Landes, William-Alan & Standish, Marilyn. The Wizard of Oz. rev. ed. 2003. (Wondrawhopper Ser.). 40p. (J). (gr. 3-12). pap. 6.00 (978-0-88734-105-2(5)) Players Pr., Inc.

Martin, Dick. The Ozmapolitan of Oz. 2006. (J). 24.95 (978-1-930764-11-8(1)) International Wizard of Oz Club, The.

McGraw, Eloise Jarvis & McGraw, Lauren Lynn. The Forbidden Fountain of Oz. 2006. (J). 24.95 (978-1-930764-12-5(X)) International Wizard of Oz Club, The.

Shanower, Eric. Adventures in Oz. Shanower, Eric, illus. 2007. (Illus.). 256p. (J). (gr. 5-7). 75.00 (***978-1-60010-071-0(6)***) Idea & Design Works, LLC.

—Adventures in Oz. 2006. (Illus.). 272p. (gr. 5-7). pap. 39.99 (978-1-933239-61-3(1)) Idea & Design Works, LLC.

—The Salt Sorcerer of Oz & Other Stories. Shanower, Eric, illus. 2003. (Oz Ser.). (Illus.). 288p. (J). 24.95 (978-1-929527-06-9(3)) Hungry Tiger Pr.

Smith, Sherwood. Emerald Wand of Oz. Stout, William, illus. 2005. 272p. (J). (gr. 3 up). lib. bdg. 17.89 (978-0-06-029608-7(9)) HarperCollins Pubs.

—The Emerald Wand of Oz. Stout, William, illus. 2007. 262p. (J). 17.00 (***978-1-4223-6710-0(X)***) DIANE Publishing Co.

—The Emerald Wand of Oz. Stout, William, illus. 2005. 262p. (J). (ps-17). 16.99 (978-0-06-029607-0(0)) HarperCollins Pubs.

—Trouble under Oz: Dreams of the Tin Man. Stout, William, illus. 2006. 256p. (J). 16.99 (978-0-06-029609-4(7)); lib. bdg. 17.89 (978-0-06-029610-0(0)) HarperCollins Pubs.

Stillman, William & Scarfone, Jay. The Wizard of Oz: The Film Classic Comes to Life with Music & Stunning 3-Dimension! 2000. (Illus.). 10p. (J). (gr. 4-7). 24.95 (978-1-58117-058-0(0), Intervisual/Piggy Toes) Dalmatian Pr.

Thompson, Ruth Plumly. The Enchanted Island of Oz. 2006. (J). 24.95 (978-1-930764-10-1(3)) International Wizard of Oz Club, The.

—The Royal Book of Oz. 2004. reprint ed. pap. 20.95 (978-1-4191-8123-8(8)); pap. 1.99 (978-1-4192-8123-5(2)) Kessinger Publishing, LLC.

—The Wonder Book. 2006. (J). 24.95 (978-1-930764-15-6(4)) International Wizard of Oz Club, The.

—Yankee in Oz. 2006. (J). 24.95 (978-1-930764-13-2(8)) International Wizard of Oz Club, The.

OZARK MOUNTAINS REGION—FICTION

Blackwood, Gary L. Moonshine. 1999. (Accelerated Reader Bks.). 160p. (J). (gr. 3-7). 14.95 (978-0-7614-5056-6(4), Cavendish Children's Bks.) Cavendish, Marshall Corp.

Byers, Stephen P. Lost River Bridge. Mack, Greg, illus. 2001. 165p. (J). pap. 12.95 (978-1-929663-02-6(1)) Books By Byers.

Lipe, Riki. Sooty. Spears-Stewart, Reta, ed. 1998. (Illus.). 34p. (J). (ps-6). 10.00 (978-0-9659381-3-6(1)) Hoot N' Cackle Pr.

Literature Connections English: Where the Red Fern Grows. 2004. (gr. 6-12). (978-0-395-77528-8(0), 2-80097) McDougal Littell Inc.

Rawls, Wilson. Where the Red Fern Grows. 1999. (Masterpiece Series Access Editions). (Illus.). xvii, 235p. (J). 10.95 (978-0-8219-1987-3(3), 35337) Paradigm Publishing, Inc.

—Where the Red Fern Grows. 249p. (YA). (gr. 5 up). pap. 5.99 (978-0-8072-1467-1(1)); pap. 5.99 (978-0-8072-1358-2(6)) Random Hse. Audio Publishing Group. (Listening Library).

—Where the Red Fern Grows. l.t. ed. 2005. 376p. pap. 10.95 (978-0-7862-7312-6(7), Large Print Pr.) Thorndike Pr.

P

PACIFIC ISLANDS

see Islands of the Pacific

PACIFIC NORTHWEST

see Northwest, Pacific

PACIFIC OCEAN

Gonzales, Doreen. The Pacific Ocean: A MyReportLinks.com Book. 2004. (Oceans of the World Ser.). (Illus.). 48p. (J). lib. bdg. 25.26 (978-0-7660-5192-8(7), MyReportLinks.com Bks.) Enslow Pubs., Inc.

Green, Jen. Pacific Ocean/Jen Green. 2006. (Illus.). 48p. (J). pap. (978-0-8368-6283-6(X)); lib. bdg. 30.00 (978-0-8368-6275-1(9)) Stevens, Gareth Inc. (World Almanac Library).

Mara, Wil. The Four Oceans. 2005. (Rookie Read-about Geography Ser.). (Illus.). (J). (gr. 1-2). 31p. pap. 5.95 (978-0-516-25817-1(6)); 32p. 20.50 (978-0-516-22749-8(1)) Scholastic Library Publishing. (Children's Pr.).

Marcovitz, Hal. Vasco Nuanez de Balboa & the Discovery of the South Sea. 2001. (Explorers of New Worlds Ser.). (Illus.). (J). 63p. pap. 25.00 (978-0-7910-6429-0(8)); 64p. 25.00 (978-0-7910-6428-3(X)) Facts On File, Inc. (Chelsea Hse.).

Otfinoski, Steven. Vasco Nunez de Balboa: Explorer of the Pacific. 2004. (Great Explorations Ser.). (Illus.). 79p. (J). 29.93 (978-0-7614-1609-8(9), Benchmark Bks.) Cavendish, Marshall Corp.

The Pacific Ocean. (Oceans Ser.). 24p. (J). 6.95 (978-0-7368-3421-6(4)) Capstone Pr., Inc.

Petersen, Christine. Pacific Ocean. 2001. (gr. 3-6). lib. bdg. 15.25 (978-0-613-54068-1(9)) Tandem Library Bks.

Petersen, David & Petersen, Christine A. The Pacific Ocean. 2001. (Geography Ser.). (Illus.). 48p. (J). (gr. 3-5). 25.00 (978-0-516-22043-7(8), Children's Pr.) Scholastic Library Publishing.

Petrie, Kristin. Vasco Nuñez de Balboa. 2007. (Illus.). 32p. (J). 22.78 (978-1-59679-740-6(1)) ABDO Publishing Co.

Prevost, John F. Pacific Ocean. 2003. (Oceans & Seas Ser.). (Illus.). 24p. (J). (gr. k-6). lib. bdg. 21.35 (978-1-57765-093-5(X)) ABDO Publishing Co.

Sandler, Michael. Oceans: Surviving in the Deep Sea. 2005. (X-treme Places Ser.). (Illus.). 32p. (J). (gr. 3-7). lib. bdg. 25.27 (978-1-59716-087-2(3)) Bearport Publishing Co., Inc.

Vail, Martha. Exploring the Pacific. Bowman, John S. & Isserman, Maurice, eds. 2005. (Discovery & Exploration Ser.). (Illus.). 176p. (J). (gr. 6-12). 40.00 (978-0-8160-5256-5(1)) Facts On File, Inc.

Weintraub, Aileen. The Pacific Ocean: The Deepest Ocean. 2001. (Great Record Breakers in Nature Ser.). (Illus.). 24p. (J). lib. bdg. 18.75 (978-0-8239-5639-5(3), PowerKids Pr.) Rosen Publishing Group, Inc., The.

Ylvisaker, Anne. The Pacific Ocean. 2002. (Oceans Ser.). (Illus.). 24p. (J). (gr. 1-2). lib. bdg. 18.60 (978-0-7368-1426-3(4), Bridgestone Bks.) Capstone Pr., Inc.

PACIFIC RAILROADS

Blashfield, Jean F. The Transcontinental Railroad. 2001. (We the People Ser.). (Illus.). 48p. (J). (gr. 4 up). lib. bdg. 22.60 (978-0-7565-0153-2(9)) Compass Point Bks.

Burger, James P. The Transcontinental Railroad. 2002. (Library of the Westward Expansion). (Illus.). 24p. (J). (gr. 3). lib. bdg. 19.95 (978-0-8239-5852-8(3), PowerKids Pr.) Rosen Publishing Group, Inc., The.

Coleman, Wim & Perrin, Pat. The Transcontinental Railroad & the Great Race to Connect the Nation. 2006. (Wild History of the American West Ser.). (Illus.). 128p. (J). lib. bdg. 33.27 (978-1-59845-014-9(X), MyReportLinks.com Bks.) Enslow Pubs., Inc.

Dolan, Edward F., Jr. The Transcontinental Railroad. 2002. (Kaleidoscope - American History Ser.). (Illus.). 48p. (J). 25.64 (978-0-7614-1455-1(X), Benchmark Bks.) Cavendish, Marshall Corp.

Fine, Jil. The Transcontinental Railroad: Tracks Across America. 2005. (Trailblazers of the West Ser.). (Illus.). 48p. (J). (ps-7). 24.00 (978-0-516-25128-8(7)); (YA). (gr. 7-12). pap. 6.95 (978-0-516-25098-4(1)) Scholastic Library Publishing. (Children's Pr.).

Halpern, Monica. Building the Transcontinental Railroad. 2002. (Reading Expeditions Ser.). (Illus.). 40p. (J). (978-0-7922-8690-5(1)) National Geographic Society.

—Railroad Fever: Building the Transcontinental Railroad 1830-1870. 2004. (Crossroads America Ser.). (Illus.). 40p. (J). (gr. 5-9). 21.90 (978-0-7922-6993-9(4)); 12.95 (978-0-7922-6767-6(2)) National Geographic Society. (National Geographic Children's Bks.).

Hanson-Harding, Alexandra. Transcontinental Railroad. 2002. (Instant Social Studies Activities Folders Ser.). (Illus.). 6p. (gr. 4-8). 3.95 (978-0-439-37087-5(6)) Scholastic, Inc.

Kraft, Eric. The el ferrocarril Transcontinental & Transcontinental Railroad. 2005. spiral bd. 84.00 (***978-1-4108-5709-5(3)***) Benchmark Education Co.

Landau, Elaine. The Transcontinental Railroad. 2005. (Watts Library). (Illus.). 63p. (J). (gr. 5-8). 25.50 (978-0-531-12326-3(X), Watts, Franklin) Scholastic Library Publishing.

McNeese, Tim. The Transcontinental Railroad & Westward Expansion: Chasing the American Frontier. 2006. (American Saga Ser.). (Illus.). 128p. (J). lib. bdg. 31.93 (978-0-7660-2572-1(1)) Enslow Pubs., Inc.

Olson, Nathan. The Building of the Transcontinental Railroad. 2007. (Graphic Library). (Illus.). 32p. 25.26 (978-0-7368-6490-9(3)) Capstone Pr., Inc.

Rach, Julie. The Transcontinental Railroad. 2002. (History of the Old West Ser.). (Illus.). 64p. (J). (gr. 5 up). lib. bdg. (978-1-59084-063-4(1)) Mason Crest Pubs.

Striessguth, Thomas. The Transcontinental Railroad. 2001. (Building History Ser.). (Illus.). 96p. (YA). (gr. 6-9). 28.70 (978-1-56006-564-7(8), Lucent Bks.) Thomson Gale.

Thompson, Linda. The Transcontinental Railroad. (Expansion of America Ser.). 48p. 2005. (Illus.). (gr. 4-8). 20.95 (978-1-59515-227-5(X)); 2004. pap. 7.95 (978-1-59515-326-5(8)) Rourke Publishing, LLC.

The Transcontinental Railroad: Using Algebra to Represent Situations & Solve Problems. (Math Big Bookstm Ser.). 32p. (YA). (gr. 6-7). 53.25 (978-1-4042-6365-9(9)) Rosen Publishing Group, Inc., The.

Uschan, Michael V. The Transcontinental Railroad. 2003. (Landmark Events in American History Ser.). (Illus.). 48p. (J). (gr. 5 up). pap. 14.95 (978-0-8368-5410-7(1)); lib. bdg. 30.00 (978-0-8368-5382-7(2)) Stevens, Gareth Inc. (World Almanac Library).

PACIFIC STATES

Here are entered works discussing collectively the states of California, Oregon, and Washington.

Feinstein, Stephen. The Pacific States. 2006. (Regions of the USA Ser.). (Illus.). 56p. (J). (978-1-4109-2310-3(X)); pap. (978-1-4109-2318-9(5)) Steck-Vaughn.

Mudd-Ruth, Maria. The Pacific Coast. 2001. (Ecosystems of North America Ser.). (Illus.). 64p. (J). (gr. 6 up). lib. bdg. 28.50 (978-0-7614-0935-9(1), Benchmark Bks.) Cavendish, Marshall Corp.

PACKAGING

Chapman, Gillian & Robson, Pam. Art from Packaging. 2007. (J). lib. bdg. (***978-1-4042-3724-7(0)***, PowerKids Pr.) Rosen Publishing Group, Inc., The.

PACKAGING—FICTION

Santillo, LuAnn. Packing. Santillo, LuAnn, ed. 2003. (Half-Pint Kids Readers Ser.). (Illus.). 7p. (J). (ps-1). pap. (978-1-59256-072-1(5)) Half-Pint Kids, Inc.

PACKING INDUSTRY

see Meat Industry and Trade

PADDINGTON BEAR (FICTITIOUS CHARACTER)—FICTION

Bond, Michael. A Bear Called Paddington. Fortnum, Peggy, illus. rev. ed. 1998. (Paddington Ser.). (SPA.). 144p. (J). (gr. 4-6). 15.00 (978-0-395-92951-3(2)) Houghton Mifflin Co. Trade & Reference Div.

—My Scrapbook. Alley, R. W., illus. 1999. (Paddington Ser.). 20p. (J). (ps-3). 12.95 (978-0-694-00886-5(9), Harper Festival) HarperCollins Pubs.

—Paddington. Alley, R. W., illus. 2007. 40p. (J). 16.99 (***978-0-06-117074-4(7)***) HarperCollins Pubs.

—Paddington Bear. Alley, R. W., illus. rev. ed. 1998. (Paddington Ser.). 40p. (J). (ps-3). 15.99 (978-0-06-027854-0(4)) HarperCollins Pubs.

—Paddington Bear All Day. braille ed. 2004. (Illus.). (J). (gr. 1). spiral bd., bds. (978-0-616-01860-6(6)) Canadian National Institute for the Blind/Institut National Canadien pour les Aveugles.

—Paddington Bear All Day. Alley, R. W., illus. 1998. (Paddington Ser.). 7p. (J). (ps up). 5.95 (978-0-694-00893-3(1), Harper Festival) HarperCollins Pubs.

—Paddington Bear All Day. Alley, R. W., illus. 2004. (VIE, GUJ, SOM, CHI & ARA.). 12p. (J). (978-1-85269-443-2(2)); (978-1-85269-444-9(0)); (978-1-85269-445-6(9)); (978-1-85269-456-2(4)); (978-1-85269-442-5(4)) Mantra Publishing, Ltd.

—Paddington Bear & the Busy Bee Carnival. Alley, R. W., illus. 1998. (Paddington Ser.). 40p. (J). (ps-3). 13.95 (978-0-06-027765-9(3)) HarperCollins Pubs.

—Paddington Bear & the Christmas Surprise. 1999. (ps-2). lib. bdg. 14.10 (978-0-613-22917-3(7)); (J). (978-0-606-17305-6(6)) Tandem Library Bks.

—Paddington Bear at the Circus. Alley, R. W., illus. 2000. (Paddington Ser.). 40p. (J). (ps-3). 15.99 (978-0-06-028213-4(4)) HarperCollins Pubs.

—Paddington Bear Board Book & Rattle Paddington Bear All Day. Alley, R. W., illus. 1999. (Paddington Bear Ser.). 14p. (J). (ps up). 15.95 (978-0-694-00887-2(7), Harper Festival) HarperCollins Pubs.

—Paddington Bear Goes to Market. Alley, R. W., illus. 1998. (Paddington Ser.). 7p. (J). (ps up). 5.95 (978-0-694-00891-9(5), Harper Festival) HarperCollins Pubs.

—Paddington Bear Goes to Market. Alley, R. W., illus. 2004. (VIE, GUJ, SOM, CHI & ARA.). 12p. (J). (978-1-85269-455-5(6)); (978-1-85269-451-7(3)) Mantra Publishing, Ltd.

—Paddington Bear in the Garden. Alley, R. W., illus. 2002. (Paddington Bear Ser.). 40p. (J). (ps-3). 15.99 (978-0-06-029696-4(8)) HarperCollins Pubs.

—Paddington Takes the Air. Fortnum, Peggy, illus. 2003. 144p. (J). (gr. 4-6). 15.00 (978-0-618-33141-3(7)) Houghton Mifflin Co. Trade & Reference Div.

—Paddington Takes the Test. Fortnum, Peggy, illus. 2002. (Paddington Bear Ser.). 144p. (J). (gr. 4-6). 15.00 (978-0-618-18384-5(1)) Houghton Mifflin Co. Trade & Reference Div.

Bond, Michael & Jankel, Karen. Paddington Bear Goes to the Hospital. Alley, R. W., illus. 2001. (Paddington Ser.). 40p. (J). (ps-3). 12.95 (978-0-694-01563-4(6)) HarperCollins Pubs.

PAGEANTS

see also Mysteries and Miracle Plays

Bordenkercher, S. A. How to Win Your Crown: A Teen's Guide to Pageant Competition. 2nd rev. ed. 1998. (ENG., Illus.). 88p. (YA). pap. 12.95 (978-0-9661771-0-7(X), 07508) Abby Publishing.

Pritchard, Gretchen Wolff. Go, Tell It on the Mountain: Three Christmas Pageants for Church Schools. 2001. (Illus.). xv, 110p. (J). pap. 25.00 (978-0-89869-365-2(9)) Church Publishing, Inc.

PAIGE, SATCHEL, 1906-1982

Adler, David A. Satchel Paige: Don't Look Back. Widener, Terry, illus. 2007. 32p. (J). 16.00 (978-0-15-205585-1(1)) Harcourt Trade Pubs.

Cline-Ransome, Lesa. Satchel Paige. Ransome, James E., illus. 2004. 31p. (J). (gr. k-4). reprint ed. pap. 7.00 (978-0-7567-7799-9(2)) DIANE Publishing Co.

—Satchel Paige. Ransome, James E., illus. 40p. (J). (gr. 1-5). 2003. 6.99 (978-0-689-85681-5(4), Aladdin); 2000. 17.99 (978-0-689-81151-7(9)) Simon & Schuster Children's Publishing.

—Satchel Paige. 2003. (gr. 3-6). lib. bdg. 15.30 (978-0-613-55361-2(6)) Tandem Library Bks.

Frystak, Timothy D. Jackie Robinson: With Profiles of Satchel Paige & & Branch Rickey. 2006. (Biographical Connections Ser.). (Illus.). 112p. (J). (978-0-7166-1828-7(1)) World Bk., Inc.

McKissack, Patricia C. & McKissack, Fredrick L. Satchel Paige: The Best Arm in Baseball. rev. ed. 2002. (Great African Americans Ser.). (Illus.). 32p. (J). (gr. 1-4). lib. bdg. 18.60 (978-0-7660-1699-6(4)) Enslow Pubs., Inc.

Schmidt, Julie. Satchel Paige. 2002. (Baseball Hall of Famers of the Negro League Ser.). (Illus.). 112p. (YA). (gr. 5-8). lib. bdg. 29.25 (978-0-8239-3478-2(0), Rosen Central) Rosen Publishing Group, Inc., The.

Sturm, James. Satchel Paige: Striking Out Jim Crow. Tomasso, Rich, illus. rev. ed. 2007. 96p. (gr. 5 up). 16.99 (***978-0-7868-3900-1(7)***); pap. 9.99 (***978-0-7868-3901-8(5)***) Hyperion Bks. for Children.

PAINE, THOMAS, 1737-1809

Burgan, Michael. Thomas Paine: Great Writer of the Revolution. 2004. (Signature Lives Ser.). (Illus.). 112p. (J). 30.60 (978-0-7565-0830-2(4)) Compass Point Bks.

Crompton, Samuel Willard. Thomas Paine & the Fight for Liberty. 2005. (Leaders of the American Revolution Ser.). (Illus.). 132p. (J). (gr. 4-8). lib. bdg. 30.00 (978-0-7910-8625-4(9), Chelsea Hse.) Facts On File, Inc.

Fish, Bruce. Thomas Paine. 1999. (Revolutionary War Leaders Ser.). (Illus.). 80p. (YA). (gr. 3 up). pap. 27.50 (978-0-7910-5699-8(6), Chelsea Hse.) Facts On File, Inc.

Fisher, Bruce. Thomas Paine. 1999. (Revolutionary War Leaders Ser.). 80p. (J). (gr. 3 up). 31.00 (978-0-7910-5356-0(3), Chelsea Hse.) Facts On File, Inc.

McCarthy, Pat. Thomas Paine: Revolutionary Patriot & Writer. 2001. (Historical American Biographies Ser.). (Illus.). 128p. (J). (gr. 6-12). lib. bdg. 26.60 (978-0-7660-1446-6(0)) Enslow Pubs., Inc.

McCartin, Brain. Thomas Paine: "Common Sense" & Revolutionary Pamphleteering. 2005. (Library of American Lives & Times). (Illus.). 112p. (J). (gr. 4-8). lib. bdg. 31.95 (978-0-8239-5729-3(2)) Rosen Publishing Group, Inc., The.

McLeese, Don. Thomas Paine. (Heroes of the American Revolution Ser.). 32p. 2005. (Illus.). (gr. 2-5). 19.95 (978-1-59515-215-2(6)); 2004. pap. 5.95 (978-1-59515-319-7(5)) Rourke Publishing, LLC.

Waxman, Laura Hamilton. An Uncommon Revolutionary: A Story about Thomas Paine. Orback, Craig, illus. (Creative Minds Biography Ser.). (J). 2004. 64p. 22.60 (978-1-57505-180-2(X)); 2003. pap. 5.95 (978-1-57505-608-1(9)) Lerner Publishing Group. (Carolrhoda Bks.).

PAINTED GLASS

see Glass Painting and Staining

PAINTERS

see also Artists

also names of individual painters

Ada, Alma Flor & Campoy, F. Isabel, contrib. by. Pasos. (Literature Collection of Puertas Al Sol Ser.). (SPA.). 32p. (J). (gr. k-6). pap. 13.95 (978-1-59437-704-4(9)) Santillana USA Publishing Co., Inc.

—Paths. (Literature Collection of Gateways to the Sun Ser.). 48p. (J). (gr. k-6). pap. 16.95 (978-1-59437-722-8(7)) Santillana USA Publishing Co., Inc.

—Voces. (Literature Collection of Puertas Al Sol Ser.). (SPA.). 32p. (J). (gr. k-6). pap. 13.95 (978-1-59437-707-5(3)) Santillana USA Publishing Co., Inc.

Anderson, Robert. Salvador Dali. Giralt Jorda, Ana, tr. 2006. (Los artistas en su mundo Ser.). (SPA., Illus.). 46p. (J). 19.95 (978-84-932442-0-0(1)) Blume ESP. *Dist:* Independent Pubs. Group.

Bacon, Dolores. Pictures Every Child Should Know (a Sele. 2006. 27.99 (***978-1-4219-7621-1(8)***); pap. 21.99 (***978-1-4219-7620-4(X)***) IndyPublish.com.

—Pictures Every Child Should Know (Illust. 2006. pap. (***978-1-4065-0424-8(6)***) Dodo Pr.

Bankston, John. Diego Rivera. 2003. (Latinos in American History Ser.). (Illus.). 56p. (gr. 4-8). lib. bdg. 29.95 (978-1-58415-208-8(7)) Mitchell Lane Pubs., Inc.

Bassil, Andrea & Van Gogh, Vincent. Vincent Van Gogh. 2004. (Lives of the Artists Ser.). (Illus.). 48p. (J). (gr. 5 up). pap. 29.26 (978-0-8368-5607-1(4)); lib. bdg. 30.00 (978-0-8368-5602-6(3)) Stevens, Gareth Inc. (World Almanac Library).

Bevan, Clare. The Story of Vincent Van Gogh. 2002. (Lifetimes Ser.). (Illus.). 48p. (J). lib. bdg. 28.50 (978-1-931983-16-7(X)) Chrysalis Education.

Bogart, Jo Ellen. Capturing Joy: The Story of Maud Lewis. Lang, Mark, illus. 2002. 32p. (J). (gr. 3-7). 16.95 (978-0-88776-568-1(8)) Tundra Bks., Inc./Livres Toundra, Inc. CAN. *Dist:* Random Hse., Inc.

Bogart, JoEllen. Emily Carr: At the Edge of the World. Newhouse, Maxwell, illus. 2003. 40p. (J). (gr. 5 up). 18.95 (978-0-88776-640-4(4)) Tundra Bks., Inc./Livres Toundra, Inc. CAN. *Dist:* Random Hse., Inc.

Bolton, Linda. Post Impressionists. 2002. (Artists in Profile Ser.). (Illus.). 64p. (J). lib. bdg. 28.50 (978-1-58810-643-8(8)) Heinemann Library.

Burleigh, Robert. Paul Cezanne: A Painter's Journey. 2006. (Illus.). 32p. (J). (gr. k-4). 17.95 (978-0-8109-5784-8(1)) Abrams, Harry N., Inc.

Connolly, Sean. Botticelli. 2004. (Lives of the Artists Ser.). (Illus.). 48p. (J). pap. 11.95 (978-0-8368-5653-8(8)); lib. bdg. 30.00 (978-0-8368-5648-4(1)) Stevens, Gareth Inc. (World Almanac Library).

—Paul Cézanne. 2006. (Heinemann First Library). (Illus.). 32p. (J). lib. bdg. (***978-1-4034-8495-6(3)***) Heinemann Library.

—Paul Klee. 2006. (Heinemann First Library). (Illus.). 32p. (J). lib. bdg. (***978-1-4034-8496-3(1)***) Heinemann Library.

—Vincent Van Gogh. 2006. (Heinemann First Library). (Illus.). 32p. (J). lib. bdg. (***978-1-4034-8497-0(X)***) Heinemann Library.

Crispino, Enrica. Van Gogh. 2008. (YA). lib. bdg. 24.95 net. (***978-1-934545-05-8(8)***) Oliver Pr., Inc.

Cruz, Barbara C. Jose Clemente Orozco: Mexican Artist. 1998. (Hispanic Biographies Ser.). (Illus.). 128p. (YA). (gr. 6-12). lib. bdg. 26.60 (978-0-7660-1041-3(4)) Enslow Pubs., Inc.

Cutler, May Ebbitt. Breaking Free: The Story of William Kurelek. Kurelek, William, illus. 2002. 32p. (J). (gr. 5 up). 17.95 (978-0-88776-617-6(X)) Tundra Bks., Inc./Livres Toundra, Inc. CAN. *Dist:* Random Hse., Inc.

de Bie, Ceciel. My Brother Vincent Van Gogh. Williams, Kate, tr. 2003. (Books for Young Readers Ser.). (Illus.). 64p. 19.95 (978-0-89236-711-5(3)) Oxford Univ. Pr., Inc.

Debon, Nicolas. Four Pictures by Emily Carr. 2007. (Illus.). 32p. (J). pap. 6.95 (*978-0-88899-814-9(7)*) Groundwood Bks. CAN. *Dist:* Perseus Distribution.

Duggleby, John. Artist in Overalls: The Life of Grant Wood. 2005. (Illus.). 64p. (J). (ps-7). pap. 7.95 (978-0-8118-4908-1(2)) Chronicle Bks. LLC.

Fisher, Leonard Everett. The Limners: America's Earliest Portrait Painters. 1999. (Colonial Craftsmen Ser.). (Illus.). 48p. (J). (gr. 4-8). lib. bdg. 24.21 (978-0-7614-0932-8(7) , Benchmark Bks.) Cavendish, Marshall Corp.

Flux, Paul. The Life & Work of Georges Seurat, Set 2. 2002. (Illus.). 32p. (J). (gr. k-2). pap. 6.50 (978-1-4034-0001-7(6) , 91619) Heinemann Library.

—Wassily Kandinsky. 2002. (Life & Work of. . . Ser.). (Illus.). 32p. (J). (gr. k-2). lib. bdg. 22.79 (978-1-58810-607-0(1)) Heinemann Library.

Green, Jen. Vincent Van Gogh. 2002. (Artists in Their Time Ser.). (J). (gr. 5-7). pap. 6.95 (978-0-531-16648-2(1)); (Illus.). 48p. pap. 23.50 (978-0-531-12238-9(7)) Scholastic Library Publishing. (Watts, Franklin).

—Vincent Van Gogh. 2002. (gr. 5-8). lib. bdg. 15.25 (978-0-613-54378-1(5)) Tandem Library Bks.

Greenberg, Jan & Jordan, Sandra. Action Jackson. Parker, Robert Andrew, illus. rev. ed. 2002. 32p. (J). (gr. 1-5). 23.90 (978-0-7613-2770-7(3)); 16.95 (978-0-7613-1682-4(5)) Roaring Brook Pr.

Guzman, Lila & Guzman, Rick. Diego Rivera: Artist of Mexico. 2006. (Famous Latinos Ser.). (Illus.). 32p. (J). lib. bdg. 22.60 (978-0-7660-2641-4(8) , Enslow Elementary) Enslow Pubs., Inc.

—Frida Kahlo: Painting Her Life. 2006. (Famous Latinos Ser.). (Illus.). 32p. (J). lib. bdg. 22.60 (978-0-7660-2643-8(4) , Enslow Elementary) Enslow Pubs., Inc.

Gwilliam, Heather. Livewire Real Lives Tom Roberts. 1999. (Livewire Real Lives Ser.). 32p. (gr. 6-9). pap. 6.00 (978-0-521-77620-2(1)) Cambridge Univ. Pr.

Hawes, Louise. Willem de Kooning: The Life of an Artist. 2002. (Artist Biographies Ser.). (Illus.). 48p. (J). (gr. 1-4). lib. bdg. 23.93 (978-0-7660-1884-6(9)) Enslow Pubs., Inc.

Hersey, Bob, illus. Norman Rockwell: A Pop-Up Art Experience. 2004. 6p. (J). (gr. k-4). reprint ed. 19.00 (978-0-7567-7642-8(2)) DIANE Publishing Co.

Hillstrom, Laurie. Frida Kahlo. 2007. (Twentieth Century Most Influential Hispanics Ser.). (Illus.). 128p. (gr. 7-10). 31.20 (*978-1-4205-0019-6(8)* , Lucent Bks.) Thomson Gale.

Holub, Joan. Vincent Van Gogh: Sunflowers & Swirly Stars. Holub, Joan, illus. 2001. (Smart about Art Ser.). (Illus.). 32p. (J). (gr. k-4). pap. 5.99 (978-0-448-42521-4(1) , Grosset & Dunlap) Penguin Group (USA) Inc.

Johnston, Lissa Jones & Kahlo, Frida. Frida Kahlo: Painter of Strength. 2006. (Fact Finders Ser.). (Illus.). 32p. (J). 22.60 (978-0-7368-6417-6(2)) Capstone Pr., Inc.

Kent, Deborah. Frida Kahlo: An Artist Celebrates Life. 2004. (Proud Heritage: the Hispanic Library Ser.). 40p. (J). (gr. 3-7). 28.50 (978-1-59296-167-2(3)) Child's World, Inc.

Klein, Adam G. & Bruegel, Pieter. Pieter Bruegel. 2007. (Illus.). 32p. (J). 22.78 (978-1-59679-727-7(4)) ABDO Publishing Co.

Klein, Adam G. & Kahlo, Frida. Frida Kahlo. 2007. (Illus.). 32p. (J). 22.78 (978-1-59679-731-4(2)) ABDO Publishing Co.

Klein, Adam G. & Raphael. Raphael. 2007. (Illus.). 32p. (J). 22.78 (978-1-59679-734-5(7)) ABDO Publishing Co.

Koja, Stephan. Gustav Klimt: A Painted Fairy Tale. Wynne, Christopher, tr. from GER. 2007. (Adventures in Art Ser.). 32p. (YA). (gr. 6-8). 14.95 (*978-3-7913-3704-3(1)*) Prestel Publishing.

Larsen, Wayne. A. Y. Jackson: A Love for the Land. 2003. (Quest Library : Vol. 21). (Illus.). 192p. pap. (978-1-894852-06-7(0)) X Y Z Publishing.

Litwin, Laura Baskes. Diego Rivera: Legendary Mexican Painter. 2005. (Latino Biography Library). (Illus.). 128p. (J). (gr. 6-13). lib. bdg. 31.93 (978-0-7660-2486-1(5)) Enslow Pubs., Inc.

Mattern, Joanne. Diego Rivera. 2005. (Checkerboard Biography Library). (Illus.). 32p. (J). (gr. k-6). lib. bdg. 22.78 (978-1-59197-849-7(1)) ABDO Publishing Co.

—Jacob Lawrence. 2005. (Great Artists Ser.). (Illus.). 32p. (J). (gr. k-6). lib. bdg. 22.78 (978-1-59197-844-2(0)) ABDO Publishing Co.

—Sandro Botticelli. 2005. (Checkerboard Biography Library). (Illus.). 32p. (J). (gr. k-6). lib. bdg. 22.78 (978-1-59197-839-8(4)) ABDO Publishing Co.

Nelson, Andy. The Renaissance Painters Coloring Book: Donatello, Raphael, Leonardo & Michelangelo. 2nd ed. 2004. (Illus.). 96p. (J). (gr. 1-6). pap. 8.95 (978-0-929636-27-6(9)) Syren Bk. Co.

Nichols, Catherine. Vincent Van Gogh. 2006. (Primary Source Library of Famous Artists). (Illus.). 32p. (J). 21.95 (978-1-4042-2766-8(0) , PowerKids Pr.) Rosen Publishing Group, Inc., The.

Restrepo, Felipe. Francis Bacon -Retrato de una Pesadilla. 2006. 136p. pap. (978-958-30-1693-6(4)) Panamericana Editorial.

Richard Tames. Michelangelo Buonarroti. 2nd ed. 2006. (Heinemann First Library). (Illus.). 32p. (J). pap. (*978-1-4034-8505-2(4)*) Heinemann Library.

Romeo, Francesca. Leonardo Da Vinci. 2008. (YA). lib. bdg. 24.95 net. (*978-1-934545-00-3(7)*) Oliver Pr., Inc.

Roy, Jennifer Rozines & Roy, Gregory. Jacob Lawrence: Painter of African-American Life. 2003. (J). 18.95 (978-0-7660-1878-5(4)) Enslow Pubs., Inc.

—Norman Rockwell: The Life of an Artist. 2002. (Artist Biographies Ser.). (Illus.). 48p. (J). (gr. 1-4). lib. bdg. 23.93 (978-0-7660-1883-9(0)) Enslow Pubs., Inc.

Rubin, Susan Goldman. Degas & the Dance: The Painter & the Petits Rats, Perfecting Their Art. 2005. (Illus.). 31p. (J). (gr. 4-8). reprint ed. 18.00 (978-0-7567-9291-6(6)) DIANE Publishing Co.

—The Yellow House: Vincent Van Gogh & Paul Gauguin Side by Side. Smith, Joseph A., illus. 2001. 40p. (J). (gr. k-4). 17.95 (978-0-8109-4588-3(6)) Abrams, Harry N. , Inc.

La Salle. (Exploring the World Ser.). 48p. (YA). 8.95 (978-0-7565-1145-6(3)) Compass Point Bks.

Salvi, Francesco. The Impressionists. 2008. (YA). lib. bdg. 24.95 net. (*978-1-934545-03-4(1)*) Oliver Pr., Inc.

Schoeneberger, Megan & Rivera, Diego. Diego Rivera: Artist & Muralist. 2006. (Fact Finders Ser.). (Illus.). 32p. (J). (978-0-7368-5437-5(1)) Capstone Pr., Inc.

Schwartzman, Myron. Romare Bearden: Celebrating the Victory. 2000. (Illus.). 143p. (YA). (gr. 8-12). lib. bdg. 22.20 (978-0-613-29504-8(8)) Tandem Library Bks.

Sean Connolly. Paul Klee. 2nd ed. 2006. (Heinemann First Library). (Illus.). 32p. (J). pap. (*978-1-4034-8507-6(0)*) Heinemann Library.

Shull, Jodie A. Georgia O'Keeffe: Legendary American Painter. 2003. (People to Know Ser.). (Illus.). 128p. (J). lib. bdg. 26.60 (978-0-7660-2104-4(1)) Enslow Pubs., Inc.

Soni, Jaymee & Schubert, Charles. A Kid at Art - Wassily Kandinsky. 2003. (J). pap. 14.99 (978-0-9743760-2-8(7)) Little Noggin LLC.

Tames, Richard. Michelangelo Buonarroti. 2006. (Heinemann First Library). (Illus.). 32p. (J). lib. bdg. (*978-1-4034-8494-9(5)*) Heinemann Library.

Van Gogh, Vincent. Vincent's Colors: Words & Pictures by Vincent van Gogh. Metropolitan Museum of Art Staff, ed. 2005. (Illus.). 48p. (J). (ps-3). 14.95 (978-0-8118-5099-5(4)) Chronicle Bks. LLC.

Van Gogh, Vincent & Lach, William. Vincent's Colors: Words & Pictures by Van Gogh. 2005. (Illus.). 48p. (J). 14.95 (978-1-58839-155-1(8)) Metropolitan Museum of Art, The.

Vaughan, Carolyn. The Painters. 2001. (Illus.). 50p. (J). (gr. 4-7). 9.95 (978-0-7611-2359-0(8) , 12359) Workman Publishing Co., Inc.

Venezia, Mike. Diego Velazquez. Venezia, Mike, illus. 2004. (Getting to Know the World's Greatest Artists Ser.). (Illus.). 32p. (J). (gr. 3-4). pap. 6.95 (978-0-516-26980-1(1) , Children's Pr.) Scholastic Library Publishing.

—Frida Kahlo. 1999. (Getting to Know the World's Greatest Artists Ser.). (Illus.). 32p. (J). (gr. 3-4). pap. 6.95 (978-0-516-26466-0(4)); (J). 27.00 (978-0-516-20975-3(2)) Scholastic Library Publishing. (Children's Pr.).

—Frida Kahlo. 1999. (gr. 3-6). lib. bdg. 15.25 (978-0-613-37352-4(9)) Tandem Library Bks.

—Horace Pippin. Venezia, Mike, illus. 2007. (Getting to Know the World's Greatest Artists Ser.). 32p. (J). 28.00 (*978-0-531-18527-8(3)* , Children's Pr.) Scholastic Library Publishing.

Venezia, Mike. Rene Magritte. Venezia, Mike, illus. 2002. (Getting to Know World Artists Ser.). (Illus.). 32p. (J). (gr. 3-4). pap. 27.00 (978-0-516-22029-1(2) , Children's Pr.) Scholastic Library Publishing.

—Rene Magritte. 2002. (gr. 3-6). lib. bdg. 15.25 (978-0-613-59544-5(0)) Tandem Library Bks.

Venezia, Mike & Magritte, Rene. Rene Magritte. 2003. (Getting to Know the World's Greatest Artists Ser.). (Illus.). 32p. (J). (gr. 3-4). pap. 6.95 (978-0-516-27814-8(2) , Children's Pr.) Scholastic Library Publishing.

Wallis, Jeremy. Impressionists. 2002. (Artists in Profile Ser.). (Illus.). 64p. (J). lib. bdg. 28.50 (978-1-58810-642-1(X)) Heinemann Library.

Whiting, Jim. Claude Monet. 2007. (Art Profiles for Kids Ser.). (Illus.). 48p. (J). lib. bdg. 29.95 (*978-1-58415-563-8(9)*) Mitchell Lane Pubs., Inc.

—Vincent Van Gogh. 2007. (Art Profiles for Kids Ser.). (Illus.). 48p. (J). lib. bdg. 29.95 (*978-1-58415-564-5(7)*) Mitchell Lane Pubs., Inc.

Winter, Jonah. Frida. Juan, Ana, illus. 2002. 32p. (J). (ps-4). (SPA.). 16.95 (978-0-439-37308-1(5)); pap. 16.95 (978-0-590-20320-3(7)); (SPA.). pap. 5.99 (978-0-439-33118-0(8)) Scholastic, Inc. (Levine, Arthur A. Bks.).

—Frida. 2002. (SPA.). (ps-2). lib. bdg. 14.15 (978-0-613-49429-8(6)) Tandem Library Bks.

Winter, Jonah, et al. Frida. 2002. (Illus.). (J). (978-0-590-20321-0(5)) Scholastic, Inc.

Woodhouse, Jane. Michelangelo Buonarroti, Set 1. 2002. (Illus.). 32p. (J). (gr. k-2). pap. 6.50 (978-1-58810-289-8(0) , 91057) Heinemann Library.

Woodhouse, Jayne. Peter Bruegel. 2000. (Heinemann First Library). (Illus.). 32p. (J). (gr. k-2). lib. bdg. 21.36 (978-1-57572-344-0(1)) Heinemann Library.

Wooten, Sara McIntosh. Frida Kahlo: Her Life in Paintings. 2005. (Latino Biography Library). (Illus.). 128p. (J). (gr. 6-13). lib. bdg. 31.93 (978-0-7660-2487-8(3)) Enslow Pubs., Inc.

Woronoff, Kristen. Frida Kahlo: Mexican Painter. 2002. (Famous Women Juniors Ser.). (Illus.). 32p. (J). (gr. 3-5). 23.70 (978-1-56711-594-9(2) , Blackbirch Pr., Inc.) Thomson Gale.

PAINTERS—FICTION

Bailie, James. The Steam Genie. 2005. 53p. (YA). 11.84 (978-1-4116-3998-0(7)) Lulu.com.

Blain, Christophe. Los Hielos, Vol. 2. 2005. (SPA., Illus.). 48p. (gr. 8-17). 19.95 (978-1-59497-114-3(5)) Public Square Bks.

Chinto & Paloma, David. Aquilino Pinta una Nube y un Camaleon. 'Pinto, illus. 2003. (Caballo Alado Ser.). (SPA & ENG.). 24p. pap. 4.95 (978-84-7864-672-2(8)) Combel Editorial, S.A. ESP. *Dist:* Independent Pubs. Group.

Clancy, Kaycee. Sky Painters. 2007. (J). per. 11.95 (*978-0-9776777-8-8(8)*) Legacy Publishing Services, Inc.

Cullen, Lynn. I Am Rembrandt's Daughter. 2007. 320p. (YA). (gr. 7 up). 16.95 (*978-1-59990-046-9(7)*) Bloomsbury Publishing.

De Noble, Augustine. Brother Joseph, The Painter of Icons. Brown, Judith, illus. 2000. (Golden Key Bks.). 32p. (J). (ps-3). 14.95 (978-1-883937-40-9(X)) Bethlehem Bks.

Dunrea, Olivier. Painter Who Loved Chickens. 1998. (978-0-606-13693-8(2)) Tandem Library Bks.

Greene, Sefton. Space Painters. 2003. 18p. bds. (978-1-904502-30-2(X)) MediaWorld/BestBooks.

Hawes, Louise. Vanishing Point. 2007. 240p. (YA). (gr. 5). pap. 7.99 (*978-0-618-74788-7(5)*) Houghton Mifflin Co. Trade & Reference Div.

Humphrey, Melanie Friedersdorf. The Tiny Town. Biddix, Cheryl L., illus. 1999. 48p. (J). (ps-3). 16.00 (978-0-9658061-7-6(0)) Peaceful Village Publishing.

Isom, Joan Shaddox. The First Starry Night. Isom, Joan Shaddox, illus. 2001. (Illus.). 32p. (J). (gr. k-7). pap. 6.95 (978-1-58089-027-4(X)) Charlesbridge Publishing, Inc.

—The First Starry Night. 2001. (978-0-606-20660-0(4)) Tandem Library Bks.

Juliette, the Modern Art Monkey: Individual Title Six-Packs. (Bookweb Ser.). 32p. (gr. 5 up). 34.00 (978-0-7635-3776-0(4)) Rigby Education.

Klinting, Lars. Harvey the Painter. 2006. (Handy Harvey Ser.). (Illus.). 40p. (J). (ps-k). pap. 4.95 (978-0-7534-5955-3(8) , Kingfisher) Houghton Mifflin Co. Trade & Reference Div.

Literature Connections Spanish: Yo, Juan de Pareja (I, Juan de Pareja) 2004. (gr. 6-12). (978-0-395-84375-8(8) , 2-70788) McDougal Littell Inc.

Llorente, Pilar Molina. El Terrible Florentino. 8th ed. (SPA., Illus.). 109p. (YA). (gr. 5-8). (978-84-279-3147-3(6) , NG5362) Noguer y Caralt Editores, S. A. ESP. *Dist:* Lectorum Pubns., Inc.

—El Terrible Florentino. 2001. (SPA.). (gr. 7-12). lib. bdg. 17.60 (978-0-613-80649-7(2)) Tandem Library Bks.

The Magnificent Mural, 6 vols., Pack. (Bookweb Ser.). 32p. (gr. 6 up). 34.00 (978-0-7578-0889-0(1)) Rigby Education.

Raj, Amita. The Shattering Flame. 2003. 320p. (YA). per. 19.95 (978-0-9744910-0-4(4)) Snake Goddess Bks.

Resnick, Mike. Club in Montmartre. 2006. (Art Encounters Ser.). (Illus.). 176p. (YA). 16.95 (978-0-8230-0420-1(1)) Watson-Guptill Pubns., Inc.

Shoup, Barbara. Vermeer's Daughter. 2006. 164p. (J). 16.95 (978-1-57860-131-8(2)) Emmis Bks.

Wallace, Karen. The Man with Tiger Eyes. 2007. (Lady Violet's Casebook Ser.). 240p. (J). (gr. 4-7). pap. 9.95 (*978-1-4169-0099-3(3)*) Simon & Schuster, Ltd. GBR. *Dist:* Independent Pubs. Group.

Wynne-Jones, Tim. On Tumbledown Hill. Petricic, Dusan, illus. 1998. (Northern Lights Books for Children Ser.). 32p. (ps-3). 15.95 (978-0-88995-186-0(1)) Red Deer Pr. CAN. *Dist:* Fitzhenry & Whiteside, Ltd.

PAINTERS—FRANCE

Anderson, Poul. Paul Gauguin. 2003. (gr. 5-8). lib. bdg. 15.25 (978-0-613-59536-0(X)) Tandem Library Bks.

Becker, Christoph. Paul Gauguin: A Journey to Tahiti. Jackson, Rosie, tr. from GER. 2001. (Adventures in Art Ser.). (Illus.). 30p. (gr. 5-8). 14.95 (978-3-7913-2572-9(8)) Prestel Publishing.

Burleigh, Robert. Seurat & la Grande Jatte: Connecting the Dots. 2004. (Illus.). 32p. (J). (gr. k-4). 17.95 (978-0-8109-4811-2(7)) Abrams, Harry N. , Inc.

Connolly, Sean. Claude Monet. 2006. (Heinemann First Library). (Illus.). 32p. (J). lib. bdg. (*978-1-4034-8489-5(9)*) Heinemann Library.

Connolly, Sean, contrib. by. Claude Monet. 1999. (Life & Work of. . . Ser.). (Illus.). 32p. (J). (gr. k-2). lib. bdg. 21.36 (978-1-57572-956-5(3)) Heinemann Library.

Connolly, Sean & Monet, Claude. Claude Monet. 2004. (Lives of the Artists Ser.). (Illus.). 48p. (J). pap. (978-0-8368-5655-2(4)); lib. bdg. 30.00 (978-0-8368-5650-7(3)) Stevens, Gareth Inc. (World Almanac Library).

Consuelo, Sanchez. Claudet Monet. 2005. 132p. pap. (978-958-30-1869-5(4)) Panamericana Editorial.

Dickins, Rosie & Ball, Karen. Leonardo Da Vinci - Internet Referenced. 2007. (Famous Lives Gift Bks). 64p. (J). 8.99 (*978-0-7945-1594-2(0)* , Usborne) EDC Publishing.

Flux, Paul. Georges Seurat. 2002. (Life & Work of. . . Ser.). (Illus.). 32p. (J). (gr. k-2). lib. bdg. 22.79 (978-1-58810-603-2(9)) Heinemann Library.

—Georges Seurat. 2002. (gr. k-3). lib. bdg. 14.75 (978-0-613-45762-0(5)) Tandem Library Bks.

—Henri Matisse. 2002. (Life & Work of. . . Ser.). (Illus.). 32p. (J). (gr. k-2). lib. bdg. 22.79 (978-1-58810-604-9(7)) Heinemann Library.

—Paul Gauguin. 2002. (Life & Work of. . . Ser.). (Illus.). 32p. (J). (gr. k-2). lib. bdg. 22.79 (978-1-58810-605-6(5)) Heinemann Library.

Gauguin, Paul & Noble, Marty. Color Your Own Gaugin Paintings. 2001. (Illus.). 32p. (J). pap. 3.95 (978-0-486-41325-9(X)) Dover Pubns., Inc.

Harris, Nathaniel. Paul Cezanne. 2003. (Artists in Their Time Ser.). (Illus.). 48p. (J). 23.50 (978-0-531-12242-6(5)); (gr. 5-7). pap. 6.95 (978-0-531-16646-8(5)) Scholastic Library Publishing. (Watts, Franklin).

—Paul Cezanne. 2003. (Illus.). 46p. (gr. 5-8). lib. bdg. 15.25 (978-0-613-59535-3(1)) Tandem Library Bks.

Hodge, Susie. Claude Monet. 2002. (Artists in Their Time Ser.). (J). (gr. 5-7). pap. 6.95 (978-0-531-16619-2(8)); (Illus.). 48p. pap. 23.50 (978-0-531-12226-6(3)) Scholastic Library Publishing. (Watts, Franklin).

—Claude Monet. 2002. (gr. 5-8). lib. bdg. 15.25 (978-0-613-54133-6(2)) Tandem Library Bks.

Kelley, True. Claude Monet: Sunshine & Waterlilies. Kelley, True, illus. 2001. (Smart about Art Ser.). (Illus.). 32p. (J). (gr. k-4). pap. 5.99 (978-0-448-42522-1(X) , Grosset & Dunlap) Penguin Group (USA) Inc.

—Claude Monet: Sunshine & Waterlilies. 2001. (gr. k-3). lib. bdg. 14.15 (978-0-613-45253-3(4)) Tandem Library Bks.

—Pierre-Auguste Renoir: Paintings That Smile. 2005. (Smart about Art Ser.). (Illus.). 32p. (J). (gr. k-5). pap. 5.99 (978-0-448-43371-4(0) , Grosset & Dunlap) Penguin Group (USA) Inc.

Klein, Adam G. & Gauguin, Paul. Paul Gauguin. 2007. (Great Artists Ser.). (Illus.). 32p. (J). (gr. 2-5). lib. bdg. 22.78 (978-1-59679-729-1(0)) ABDO Publishing Co.

Klein, Adam G. & Monet, Claude. Claude Monet. 2007. (Illus.). 32p. (J). 22.78 (978-1-59679-732-1(0)) ABDO Publishing Co.

Klein, Adam G. & Renoir, Auguste. Pierre-Auguste Renoir. 2007. (Illus.). 32p. (J). 22.78 (978-1-59679-736-9(3)) ABDO Publishing Co.

Manet, Edouard. Color Your Own Manet Paintings. 2008. 32p. pap. 3.95 (*978-0-486-46202-8(1)*) Dover Pubns., Inc.

Mattern, Joanne. Edgar Degas. 2005. (Checkerboard Biography Library). (Illus.). 32p. (J). (gr. k-6). lib. bdg. 22.78 (978-1-59197-843-5(2)) ABDO Publishing Co.

Merberg, Julie & Bober, Suzanne. A Picnic with Monet. 2003. (Illus.). 22p. (J). bds. 6.95 (978-0-8118-4046-0(8)) Chronicle Bks. LLC.

Mis, Melody S. Edgar Degas. 2008. (J). lib. bdg. (*978-1-4042-3839-8(5)* , PowerKids Pr.) Rosen Publishing Group, Inc., The.

—Edouard Manet. 2008. (J). lib. bdg. (*978-1-4042-3841-1(7)* , PowerKids Pr.) Rosen Publishing Group, Inc., The.

—Paul Cezanne. 2008. (J). lib. bdg. (*978-1-4042-3842-8(5)* , PowerKids Pr.) Rosen Publishing Group, Inc., The.

Nichols, Catherine. Claude Monet. 2006. (Primary Source Library of Famous Artists). (Illus.). 32p. (J). 21.95 (978-1-4042-2761-3(X) , PowerKids Pr.) Rosen Publishing Group, Inc., The.

Nichols, Catherine & Renoir, Auguste. Pierre-Auguste Renoir. 2006. (Primary Source Library of Famous Artists). (Illus.). 32p. (J). 21.95 (978-1-4042-2765-1(2) , PowerKids Pr.) Rosen Publishing Group, Inc., The.

Northeast, Brenda V. Claude con Amor. 2001. Tr. of For the Love of Claude. (CAT., Illus.). 32p. (J). (gr. 1-4). 14.95 (978-84-95040-93-0(X)) Serres, Ediciones, S. L. ESP. *Dist:* Lectorum Pubns., Inc.

—Claude con Amor. Mendo, Miguel Angel, tr. 2001. Tr. of For the Love of Claude. (SPA., Illus.). 32p. (J). (gr. 1-4). 14.95 (978-84-95040-92-3(1)) Serres, Ediciones, S. L. ESP. *Dist:* Lectorum Pubns., Inc.

Sateren, Shelley Swanson. Monet. 2001. (Masterpieces). (Illus.). 24p. (J). (gr. 2-3). lib. bdg. 18.60 (978-0-7368-1123-1(0) , Bridgestone Bks.) Capstone Pr., Inc.

Sateren, Shelley Swanson & Picasso, Pablo. Picasso. 2002. (Masterpieces). (Illus.). 24p. (J). (gr. 2-3). lib. bdg. 18.60 (978-0-7368-1122-4(2) , Bridgestone Bks.) Capstone Pr., Inc.

Somervill, Barbara. Pierre-Auguste Renoir. 2007. (Art Profiles for Kids Ser.). (Illus.). 48p. (J). lib. bdg. 29.95 (*978-1-58415-566-9(3)*) Mitchell Lane Pubs., Inc.

Spence, David. Gauguin: Huida al Eden. (Coleccion Grandes Artistas).Tr. of Gauguin: Escape to Eden. (SPA.). 266p. (YA). (gr. 5-8). 12.76 (978-84-8211-138-4(8)) Celeste Ediciones, S.A. ESP. *Dist:* Lectorum Pubns., Inc.

—Monet: Impresionismo. (Coleccion Grandes Artistas). (SPA.). 220p. (YA). (gr. 5-8). 12.76 (978-84-8211-133-9(7)) Celeste Ediciones, S.A. ESP. *Dist:* Lectorum Pubns., Inc.

Tracy, Kathleen. Paul Cézanne. 2007. (Art Profiles for Kids Ser.). (Illus.). 48p. (J). lib. bdg. 29.95 (*978-1-58415-565-2(5)*) Mitchell Lane Pubs., Inc.

Ungerer, Tomi. Tomi: A Childhood under the Nazis. 1998. (Illus.). 175p. (YA). (gr. 6 up). 29.95 (978-1-57098-163-0(9) , Rinehart, Roberts International) Rinehart, Roberts Pubs.

Venezia, Mike. Camille Pissarro. (Getting. . Know Artists Ser.). (J). 2004. (gr. 3-4). pap. 6.95 (978-0-516-26977-1(1)); 2003. (Illus.). 32p. 27.00 (978-0-516-22577-7(4)) Scholastic Library Publishing. (Children's Pr.).

—Edgar Degas. Venezia, Mike, illus. 2001. (Getting to Know the World's Greatest Artists Ser.). (Illus.). 32p. (J). (gr. 3-4). pap. 6.95 (978-0-516-27172-9(5) , Children's Pr.) Scholastic Library Publishing.

—Edgar Degas. 2000. (Getting to Know the World's Greatest Artists Ser.). (Illus.). 32p. (J). (gr. 3-4). 27.00 (978-0-516-21593-8(0) , Children's Pr.) Scholastic Library Publishing.

—Edgar Degas. Venezia, Mike, illus. 2001. (Illus.). 31p. (J). (ps-ps). lib. bdg. 15.25 (978-0-613-50683-0(9)) Tandem Library Bks.

—Eugene Delacroix. 2003. (Getting to Know World Artists Ser.). (Illus.). 32p. (J). 27.00 (978-0-516-22576-0(6) , Children's Pr.) Scholastic Library Publishing.

Welton, Jude & Dorling Kindersley Publishing Staff. Monet. 2000. (Eyewitness Bks.). (Illus.). 64p. (J). (gr. 4-7). lib. bdg. 19.99 (978-0-7894-6815-4(8)) Dorling Kindersley Publishing, Inc.

PAINTERS—SPAIN

Anderson, Robert. Salvador Dali. 2002. (Artists in Their Time Ser.). (Illus.). 48p. (J). (gr. 5-7). pap. 23.50 (978-0-531-12231-0(X) , Watts, Franklin) Scholastic Library Publishing.

Venezia, Mike. El Greco. 1998. (Getting to Know the World's Greatest Artists Ser.). (Illus.). 32p. (J). (gr. 3-4). pap. 6.95 (978-0-516-26243-7(2) , Children's Pr.) Scholastic Library Publishing.

Venezia, Mike, tr. & illus. Diego Velazquez. Venezia, Mike, illus. 2004. (Getting to Know World Artists Ser.). 32p. (J). 27.00 (978-0-516-22580-7(4) , Children's Pr.) Scholastic Library Publishing.

PAINTERS—UNITED STATES

Barnes, Rachel. Abstract Expressionists. 2002. (Artists in Profile Ser.). (Illus.). 64p. (J). lib. bdg. 28.50 (978-1-58810-644-5(6)) Heinemann Library.

Benke. Georgia O'Keeffe: The Artists in the Desert. (Illus.). 30p. 14.95 (978-3-7913-3558-2(8)) Prestel Publishing.

Bennett, Leonie. Jackson Pollack. 2004. (Life & Work Of-Ser.). (Illus.). 32p. (J). lib. bdg. 22.79 (978-1-4034-5073-9(0)) Heinemann Library.

—Jackson Pollock. 2004. (Life & Work Of- Ser.). (Illus.). 32p. (J). pap. 7.25 (978-1-4034-5562-8(7)) Heinemann Library.

Davies, Jacqueline. The Boy Who Drew Birds: A Story of John James Audubon. Sweet, Melissa, illus. 2004. 32p. (J). (gr. k-3). tchr. ed. 16.00 (978-0-618-24343-3(7)) Houghton Mifflin Co. Trade & Reference Div.

Gherman, Beverly & Rockwell, Family Trust. Norman Rockwell: Storyteller with a Brush. 2000. (Illus.). 64p. (J). (gr. 3-7). 20.99 (978-0-689-82001-4(1) , Atheneum) Simon & Schuster Children's Publishing.

Giesecke, Ernestine. Frederic Remington. 2006. (Heinemann First Library). (Illus.). 32p. (J). ***(978-1-4034-8490-1(2))*** Heinemann Library.

Greenberg, Jan & Jordan, Sandra. Action Jackson. Parker, Robert Andrew, illus. 2007. 32p. (J). pap. 6.95 ***(978-0-312-36751-0(1))*** Square Fish.

Greenberg, Jan & Jordan, Sandra. Action Jackson. Parker, Robert Andrew, illus. 2005. 32p. (J). (gr. 4-8). reprint ed. 17.00 (978-0-7567-8934-3(6)) DIANE Publishing Co.

Igus, Toyomi, ed. Going Back Home: An Artist Returns to the South. Wood, Michele, illus. 2004. 32p. (J). (gr. 1 up). pap. 7.95 (978-0-89239-197-4(9)) Children's Bk. Pr.

Jordan, Sandra & Greenberg, Jan. Action Jackson. Parker, Robert Andrew, illus. pap. 16.95 incl. audio (978-1-59112-959-2(1)); pap. incl. audio (978-1-59112-961-5(3)); pap. 18.95 incl. audio compact disk (978-1-59112-963-9(X)); pap. incl. audio compact disk (978-1-59112-965-3(6)); 2005. (J). 25.95 incl. audio (978-1-59112-960-8(5)); 2005. (J). 28.95 incl. audio compact disk (978-1-59112-964-6(8)) Live Oak Media.

Klein, Adam G. & Moses. Grandma Moses. 2007. (Illus.). 32p. (J). 22.78 (978-1-59679-737-6(1)) ABDO Publishing Co.

Klein, Adam G. & Rockwell, Norman. Norman Rockwell. 2007. (Illus.). 32p. (J). 22.78 (978-1-59679-738-3(X)) ABDO Publishing Co.

Koerner, Henry. The Early Works of Henry Koerner 1945-1957. 2004. (Illus.). 96p. (YA). (gr. 13 up). pap. 35.00 (978-0-9703425-5-3(1)) Frick Art & Historical Ctr.,The.

Kreiter, Eshel & Zabludoff, Marc. John Singer Sargent: The Life of an Artist. 2002. (Artist Ser.). (Illus.). 48p. (J). (gr. 1-4). lib. bdg. 23.93 (978-0-7660-1879-2(2)) Enslow Pubs., Inc.

Kucharczyk, Emily Rose. Georgia O'Keeffe: Desert Painter. 2002. (Famous Women Juniors Ser.). (Illus.). 32p. (J). 23.70 (978-1-56711-592-5(6) , Blackbirch Pr., Inc.) Thomson Gale.

Mattern, Joanne. Georgia O'Keeffe. 2005. (Checkerboard Biography Library). (Illus.). 32p. (J). (gr. k-6). lib. bdg. 22.78 (978-1-59197-846-6(7)) ABDO Publishing Co.

—Jackson Pollock. 2005. (Great Artists Ser.). (Illus.). 32p. (J). (gr. k-6). lib. bdg. 22.78 (978-1-59197-847-3(5)) ABDO Publishing Co.

McLellan, Richard A. The Land of Truth & Phantasy: Life & Painting at Ring Farm USA. Wyeth, Andrew N. & Kuerner, Karl J., illus. gif. ed. 2005. (ENG.). 187p. 24.00 (978-0-9747536-0-7(2)) McLellan Bks.

Nikola-Lisa, W. & Moses, Grandma. The Year with Grandma Moses. rev. ed. 2000. (Illus.). 32p. (J). (ps-5). 20.00 (978-0-8050-6243-4(2) , Holt, Henry & Co. Bks. For Young Readers) Holt, Henry & Co.

O'Connor, Jane. Mary Cassatt: Family Pictures. Kalis, Jennifer, illus. 2003. (Smart about Art Ser.). 32p. (J). (gr. k-3). 14.89 (978-0-448-43153-6(X)); pap. 5.99 (978-0-448-43152-9(1)) Penguin Group (USA) Inc. (Grosset & Dunlap).

—Mary Cassatt: Family Pictures. 2003. (gr. k-3). lib. bdg. 14.15 (978-0-613-61641-6(3)) Tandem Library Bks.

Oliver, Clare. Jackson Pollock. 2003. (Artists in Their Time Ser.). (Illus.). 48p. (J). 23.50 (978-0-531-12237-2(9)); (gr. 5-7). pap. 6.95 (978-0-531-16644-4(9)) Scholastic Library Publishing. (Watts, Franklin).

—Jackson Pollock. 2003. (gr. 5-8). lib. bdg. 15.25 (978-0-613-59502-5(5)) Tandem Library Bks.

Olmstead, Mary. Judy Baca. 2004. (Hispanic-American Biographies Ser.). (Illus.). 64p. (J). pap. 9.50 (978-1-4109-0915-2(8)) Harcourt Schl. Pubs.

—Judy Baca. 2004. (Hispanic-American Biographies Ser.). (Illus.). 64p. (J). (gr. 4-6). 32.86 (978-1-4109-0709-7(0)) Raintree.

Rodriguez, Rachel. Through Georgia's Eyes. Paschkis, Julie, illus. rev. ed. 2006. 32p. (J). 16.95 (978-0-8050-7740-7(5)) Holt, Henry & Co.

Stephens, Pamela Geiger. Dropping in on Romare Bearden. McNeill, Jim, illus. 2007. (J). ***(978-1-56290-539-2(2))*** Crystal Productions.

Streissguth, Thomas. Mary Cassatt: Portrait of an American Impressionist. 1998. (Trailblazers Biographies Ser.). (Illus.). 112p. (J). (gr. 4-7). lib. bdg. 22.60 (978-1-57505-291-5(1) , Carolrhoda Bks.) Lerner Publishing Group.

Venezia, Mike. Grandma Moses. 2003. (Getting to Know World Artists Ser.). (Illus.). 32p. (J). 27.00 (978-0-516-22027-7(6) , Children's Pr.) Scholastic Library Publishing.

—Horace Pippin. 2008. (Getting to Know the World's Greatest Artists Ser.). 32p. (J). pap. 6.95 ***(978-0-531-14758-0(4)*** , Children's Pr.) Scholastic Library Publishing.

—James McNeill Whistler. 2004. (Getting to Know the World's Greatest Artists Ser.). (J). (gr. 3-4). pap. 6.95 (978-0-516-26978-8(X) , Children's Pr.) Scholastic Library Publishing.

—Winslow Homer. Venezia, Mike, illus. 2004. (Getting. . Know Artists Pb Ser.). (Illus.). 32p. (J). (gr. 3-4). pap. 6.95 (978-0-516-26979-5(8) , Children's Pr.) Scholastic Library Publishing.

Webb, Spider. Butterfly Flash. 2001. (Schiffer Design Book Ser.). (Illus.). 96p. (gr. 10-13). pap. 19.95 (978-0-7643-1505-3(6)) Schiffer Publishing, Ltd.

PAINTING

see also Animal Painting and Illustration; Color; Finger Painting; Flower Painting and Illustration; Impressionism (Art); Landscape Painting; Marine Painting; Perspective; Post-Impressionism (Art); Stencil Work; Textile Painting; Watercolor Painting

Abramson, Jordan. Paint Your Own Dreidel. 2006. (Illus.). 32p. pap. 6.95 (978-0-7624-2818-2(X) , Running Pr.) Running Pr. Bk. Pubs.

Ada, Alma Flor & Campoy, F. Isabel, contrib. by. Blue & Green. (Literature Collection of Gateways to the Sun Ser.). 32p. (J). (gr. k-6). pap. 13.95 (978-1-59437-714-3(6)) Santillana USA Publishing Co., Inc.

—Brush & Paint. (Literature Collection of Gateways to the Sun Ser.). 32p. (J). (gr. k-6). pap. 13.95 (978-1-59437-717-4(0)) Santillana USA Publishing Co., Inc.

—Canvas & Paper. (Literature Collection of Gateways to the Sun Ser.). 32p. (J). (gr. k-6). pap. 13.95 (978-1-59437-723-5(5)) Santillana USA Publishing Co., Inc.

Adolphe, Bruce. Red Dogs & Pink Skies: Paul Gauguin on Painting & Music. 2002. (Illus.). 24p. (J). 18.95 (978-0-9701249-1-3(0)) PollyRhythm Productions.

Aigner-Clark, Julie. Master Pieces. Zaidi, Nadeem, illus. 2004. (SPA.). 10p. (J). 9.95 (978-970-718-211-0(3) , Silver Dolphin Bks.) Advantage Pubs. Group.

Ancona, George. Murals: Walls That Sing. 2003. (Illus.). 48p. (YA). 17.95 (978-0-7614-5131-0(5)) Cavendish, Marshall Corp.

Anderson, Robert. Paul Gauguin. 2003. (Artists in Their Time Ser.). (Illus.). 48p. (J). 23.50 (978-0-531-12239-6(5)); (gr. 5-7). pap. 6.95 (978-0-531-16647-5(3)) Scholastic Library Publishing. (Watts, Franklin).

Anness Publishing Staff & Tuxworth, Nicola. Messy. 2000. (Very First Picture Board Bks.). (Illus.). 12p. (gr. 1-5). bds. 5.00 (978-0-7548-0708-7(8)) Anness Publishing GBR. *Dist:* National Bk. Network.

Armstrong, Carole. My Sticker Art Gallery: Monet. (Illus.). 16p. (J). (gr. 2 up). pap. 9.99 (978-0-7112-0962-6(6)) Lincoln, Frances Ltd. GBR. *Dist:* Transition Vendor.

The Art of Glass Painting. 2004. (Classic Craft Cases Ser.). (Illus.). 64p. (978-1-84229-801-5(1)) Top That! Publishing PLC.

Bacon, Dolores. Pictures Every Child Should Know (a Sele. 2006. 27.99 ***(978-1-4219-7621-1(8));*** pap. 21.99 ***(978-1-4219-7620-4(X))*** IndyPublish.com.

—Pictures Every Child Should Know (Illust. 2006. pap. ***(978-1-4065-0424-8(6))*** Dodo Pr.

Barlowe, Dot. Flower Gardens to Paint or Color. 2007. 48p. pap., pap. 4.95 ***(978-0-486-46204-2(8))*** Dover Pubns., Inc.

Barter, James E. A Renaissance Painter's Studio. 2002. (Working Life Ser.). (Illus.). 112p. (J). 29.95 (978-1-59018-178-2(6)) Thomson Gale.

Becker, Christoph. Paul Gauguin: A Journey to Tahiti. Jackson, Rosie, tr. from GER. 2001. (Adventures in Art Ser.). (Illus.). 30p. (gr. 5-8). 14.95 (978-3-7913-2572-9(8)) Prestel Publishing.

Binam, Sharyn. The Sidload: Garden. 2004. 64p. pap. 11.95 (978-1-57377-186-3(4) , 0-1988-4-02500-9) Eas'l Pubns.

Blizzard, Gladys S. Come Look with Me: Animals in Art. 2006. (Come Look with Me Ser.). 32p. (YA). (gr. k-12). 15.95 (978-1-56566-013-7(7)) Charlesbridge Publishing, Inc.

Bower, Jane. Painting. Cohen, Helaine, ed. 1998. (Arts & Crafts Skills Ser.). (Illus.). 32p. (J). (gr. 3-6). pap., stu. ed. 6.95 (978-0-516-26214-7(9) , Children's Pr.) Scholastic Library Publishing.

Bramich, Melvin, illus. Create Your Own Masterpiece: On a Journey Through Art. 2005. 48p. (J). (ps). pap. 7.95 (978-1-84507-450-0(5)) Lincoln, Frances Ltd. GBR. *Dist:* Perseus Distribution.

Buckingham, Linda. Projection Art for Kids: Murals & Painting Projects for Kids of All Ages. 2002. (Illus.). 128p. pap. 14.95 (978-0-88179-197-6(0)) Hartley & Marks Publishers, Inc. CAN. *Dist:* Perseus Distribution.

Bulloch, Ivan. Paint. James, Diane, illus. rev. ed. 2000. (Let's Ser.). 24p. (J). (ps-1). 9.95 (978-1-58728-026-9(4) , Two Can Publishing) T&N Children's Publishing.

Bulloch, Ivan & James, Diane. Paint. 2000. (Let's Ser.). (Illus.). 24p. (J). (ps-1). pap. 5.95 (978-1-58728-030-6(2) , Two Can Publishing) T&N Children's Publishing.

—La Peinture. 2000. (Let's Ser.). (FRE., Illus.). 24p. (J). (ps-1). pap. 5.95 (978-1-58728-209-6(7) , Two Can Publishing) T&N Children's Publishing.

Caillou Paint with Water Books. 2004. (J). (978-0-7666-1144-3(2) , 15300); (978-0-7666-1145-0(0) , 15300) Modern Publishing.

Canizares, Susan & Moreton, Daniel. In a Painting. 1999. (J). 2.50 (978-0-439-04593-3(2)) Scholastic, Inc.

Care Bears Paint with Water Books. 2004. (J). (978-0-7666-1291-4(0) , 15340); (978-0-7666-1292-1(9) , 15340) Modern Publishing.

Carroll, Colleen. How Artists See America: East, West, South, Midwest. 2002. (How Artists See Ser.). (Illus.). 48p. (gr. 2-5). 12.95 (978-0-7892-0772-2(9)) Abbeville Pr., Inc.

Catalanotto, Peter. Painter. 1999. (978-0-606-16920-2(2)) Tandem Library Bks.

Chaudron, Chris & Childs, Caro. Face Painting. 1998. (How to Make Ser.). (Illus.). 32p. (J). (gr. 3-7). lib. bdg. 15.95 (978-0-88110-649-7(6)) EDC Publishing.

Chaudron, Chris, et al. Face Painting. 1998. (How to Make Ser.). (Illus.). 32p. (J). (gr. 3-7). pap. 7.95 (978-0-7460-1445-5(7)) EDC Publishing.

Conroy, Don. Colouring & Activity Book. 1999. (J). (gr. 1-4). per. (978-1-902586-53-3(0)) Mentor Bks.

Constable, John. Colour Your Own John Constable Paintings. 2007. 32p. pap. 3.95 ***(978-0-486-46201-1(3))*** Dover Pubns., Inc.

Conway, Agnes Ethel & Conway, Martin. The Book of Art for Young People. 2007. (ENG., Illus.). 136p. per. ***(978-1-4065-1514-5(0))*** Dodo Pr.

Conway, Ethel Agnes. The Book of Art for Young People. 2006. 94.99 ***(978-1-4280-0411-5(4));*** pap. 88.99 ***(978-1-4280-0410-8(6))*** IndyPublish.com.

Cressy, Judith. Can You Find It? Search & Discover More Than 150 Details in 19 Works of Art. 2002. (Illus.). 48p. (J). (gr. k-4). 15.95 (978-0-8109-3279-1(2)) Abrams, Harry N., Inc.

Crismon, Joy. Chinese Brush Painting. 84p. (J). (gr. 1-7). pap. (978-1-56861-049-8(1)) Swift Learning Resources.

Crowe, Ellie. Little Princess Ka'Iulani in Her Garden by the Sea. Koski, Mary B., illus. 2nd rev. ed. 1998. 32p. (J). 12.99 (978-0-9712885-1-5(8)) Regent Music & Bk. Publishing.

Dalamatian Press Staff. Easy Wipe-Off Printing. 1999. (Easy Wipe-Off Ser.). (Illus.). 16p. (J). (gr. k-1). pap., wbk. ed. 2.99 (978-1-57759-136-8(4)) Dalmatian Pr.

Dali, Salvador. Dali: 16 Art Stickers. 2000. (Illus.). 4p. pap. 1.50 (978-0-486-41074-6(9)) Dover Pubns., Inc.

Davies, Carolyn. Josef Herman in Wales. 2004. (Illus.). 31p. pap. 15.95 (978-1-85902-999-2(X)) Beekman Bks., Inc.

Degas, Edgar. Color Your Own Degas Paintings. 2002. (Illus.). 32p. (J). pap. 3.95 (978-0-486-42376-0(X)) Dover Pubns., Inc.

Desnoettes, Caroline. Look Closer: Art Masterpeices Through the Ages. 2006. (Illus.). 64p. (J). 18.95 (978-0-8027-9614-1(1)) Walker & Co.

Disney Princess Paint n' Play with Sticker Rolls. 2005. (J). spiral bd. (978-1-59487-148-1(5)) Artist Studios, Ltd.

Dorling Kindersley Publishing Staff. Watercolor. 2000. (Eyewitness Bks.). (Illus.). 64p. (J). (gr. 3 up). lib. bdg. 19.99 (978-0-7894-6817-8(4)) Dorling Kindersley Publishing, Inc.

Etape Par Etape L'aquarelle. 2002. (How to Draw & Paint Ser.). Orig. Title: Step-by-Step Watercolor. (FRE.). pap. 7.95 (978-1-56010-677-7(8)) Foster, Walter Publishing, Inc.

Ewing, Patrick & Lewis, Linda. In the Paint. 1999. (Illus.). 64p. (gr. 2-5). 15.95 (978-0-7892-0542-1(4)) Abbeville Pr., Inc.

Finley, Carol. Aboriginal Art of Australia: Exploring Cultural Traditions. 1998. (Art Around the World Ser.). (Illus.). 56-64p. (gr. 4-8). 23.93 (978-0-8225-2076-4(1)) Lerner Publishing Group.

—Art of Japan: Wood-Block Color Prints. 1998. (Art Around the World Ser.). (Illus.). 56-64p. (gr. 4-8). 23.93 (978-0-8225-2077-1(X)) Lerner Publishing Group.

Fisher, Leonard Everett. The Limners: America's Earliest Portrait Painters. 1999. (Colonial Craftsmen Ser.). (Illus.). 48p. (J). (gr. 4-8). lib. bdg. 24.21 (978-0-7614-0932-8(7) , Benchmark Bks.) Cavendish, Marshall Corp.

Fisher-Price Little People Paint with Water Books. 2004. (J). (978-0-7666-0896-2(4) , 15200); (978-0-7666-0897-9(2) , 15200); (978-0-7666-0898-6(0) , 15200); (978-0-7666-0899-3(9) , 15200) Modern Publishing.

Fitzrandolph, Joyce. Learn to Paint with the Alexander Brush Club. (Illus.). 24p. (J). (gr. 4-6). pap. (978-1-883576-32-5(6) , KT-220B) Alexander Art L.P.

Les Fleurs a L'aquarelle. 2002. (How to Draw & Paint Ser.). Orig. Title: Watercolor - Flowers - Special Effects. (FRE.). pap. 7.95 (978-1-56010 673-9(5)) Foster, Walter Publishing, Inc.

Foa, Emma. Edward Hopper. 2003. (Artists in Their Time Ser.). (Illus.). 48p. (J). 23.50 (978-0-531-12240-2(9)); (gr. 5-7). pap. 6.95 (978-0-531-16641-3(4)) Scholastic Library Publishing. (Watts, Franklin).

—Edward Hopper. 2003. (Illus.). 46p. (J). (gr. 4-7). lib. bdg. 15.25 (978-0-613-59466-0(5)) Tandem Library Bks.

Foster, Patience. Painting. 1999. (Hobby Guides Ser.). (Illus.). 32p. (J). (gr. 5 up). lib. bdg. 14.95 (978-0-88110-026-6(9)) EDC Publishing.

Foster, Walter, ed. Painting Techniques. Fisher, Diana, illus. 2004. (WF /Color & Co. Art for Kids Ser.). 40p. (J). pap. 4.95 (978-1-56010-852-8(5)) Foster, Walter Publishing, Inc.

Galford, Ellen. Transportation by Land, Sea & Air: Exploring History Through Art. 2007. 64p. ***(978-1-58728-590-5(8)*** , Two Can Publishing) T&N Children's Publishing.

Gauguin, Paul. Gauguin Paintings: 24 Cards. 2000. (Illus.). 6p. pap. 5.95 (978-0-486-41340-2(3)) Dover Pubns., Inc.

Gibson, R. What Shall I Paint? 2004. (What Shall I Do Today? Ser.). 32p. (J). pap. 7.95 (978-0-7945-0377-2(2)); lib. bdg. 15.95 (978-1-58086-549-4(6)) EDC Publishing.

Giesecke, Ernestine. Mary Cassatt. 2006. (Heinemann First Library). (Illus.). 32p. (J). lib. bdg. ***(978-1-4034-8493-2(7))*** Heinemann Library.

Gluck, Larry. The Basic Painting Course. 2004. (YA). spiral bd. (978-1-929473-05-2(2)) Renaissance Pubns.

Golden Books Staff. Working Buddies. 2007. (Paint Box Book Ser.). (Illus.). 48p. (J). (ps-2). pap. 3.99 (978-0-7364-2448-6(2) , Golden/Disney) Random Hse. Children's Bks.

Harcourt School Publishers Staff. WPA Art Advanced Level. 3rd ed. 2002. (Trophies Reading Program Ser.). (Illus.). pap. 5.10 (978-0-15-323211-4(0)) Harcourt Schl. Pubs.

Harron, Nancy. Harron's Nest Floor Decor & More. 2004. 68p. pap. 16.95 (978-1-57377-202-0(X) , 0-1988-4-2524) Eas'l Pubns.

Henry, Sandi. Using Color in Your Art! Choosing Colors for Impact & Pizzazz. Rakitin, Sarah, illus. 2005. (Kids Can Ser.). 128p. (J). (ps-7). pap. 12.95 (978-0-8249-6754-3(2) , Williamson Bks.) Ideals Pubns.

Hodge, Anthony. Painting. 2004. (J). lib. bdg. 27.10 (978-1-932799-00-2(1)) Stargazer Bks.

Hoena, Blake A. Mary Cassatt. 2003. (Masterpieces, Artists & Their Works). (Illus.). 24p. (J). lib. bdg. 19.93 (978-0-7368-2229-9(1) , Bridgestone Bks.) Capstone Pr., Inc.

Hunter Museum of American Art Staff. 20th-Century American Paintings in the Collections of the Hunter Museum of American Art: 24 Full-Color Cards. 2000. (Illus.). 6p. pap. 6.95 (978-0-486-41062-3(5)) Dover Pubns., Inc.

Hyde, Margaret, ed. Van Gogh for Kids. 2004. (Illus.). 14p. (J). bds. 8.95 (978-1-58980-279-7(9)) Pelican Publishing Co., Inc.

Hyde, Margaret E., ed. Cassatt for Kids. 2004. (Great Art for Kids Ser.). (Illus.). 10p. (J). pap. 8.95 (978-1-58980-202-5(0)) Pelican Publishing Co., Inc.

—Matisse for Kids. 2004. (Great Art for Kids Ser.). (Illus.). 10p. (J). pap. 8.95 (978-1-58980-204-9(7)) Pelican Publishing Co., Inc.

—Picasso for Kids. 2004. (Great Art for Kids Ser.). (Illus.). 12p. (J). pap. 8.95 (978-1-58980-205-6(5)) Pelican Publishing Co., Inc.

—Renoir for Kids. 2004. (Great Art for Kids Ser.). (Illus.). 10p. (J). pap. 8.95 (978-1-58980-206-3(3)) Pelican Publishing Co., Inc.

Jakopovich, Kathy. Paint on a Happy Face, Vol. 2. 2004. 68p. pap. 11.95 (978-1-57377-198-6(8) , 0-1988-4-02516-0) Eas'l Pubns.

Jo Tuttle, Mary. Tuttles Touches. 2004. 60p. pap. 11.95 (978-1-57377-203-7(8) , 0-1988-4-2526-9) Eas'l Pubns.

Kranz, Linda. Let's Rock! 2003. (Craft Ser.). (Illus.). 64p. (YA). (gr. 1-6). pap. 11.95 (978-1-55971-870-7(6) , NorthWord Bks. for Young Readers) T&N Children's Publishing.

Lang, Annie J. Pleased to Greet You. 2002. 52p. (J). pap. 10.95 (978-1-57377-160-3(0)) Eas'l Pubns.

—Who Let the Kids Out. 2003. 48p. pap. 10.95 (978-1-57377-168-9(6)) Eas'l Pubns.

Las pinturas de Pepe: Individual Title-Six Packs. (Chiquilibros Ser.). (SPA.). (gr. k-1). 23.00 (978-0-7635-8608-9(0)) Rigby Education.

Let's Paint! (Early Intervention Levels Ser.). 23.10 (978-0-7362-0012-7(6)) Hampton-Brown Bks.

Levy, Janey. Renaissance Paintings: Using Perspective to Represent Three-Dimensional Objects. 2005. (PowerMath Ser.). (Illus.). 32p. (J). 22.50 (978-1-4042-2926-6(4) , PowerKids Pr.); (978-1-4042-5116-8(2) , PowerKids Pr.); pap. (978-1-4042-5115-1(4)) Rosen Publishing Group, Inc., The.

Lipsey, Jennifer. I Love to Paint! 2005. (My Very Favorite Art Bks.). (Illus.). 48p. (J). (gr. k-3). 9.95 (978-1-57990-630-6(3)) Lark Bks.

Louchard, Antonin & Couprie, Katy. A Whole World. 2002. (Illus.). 256p. (J). 15.95 (978-1-84059-342-6(3)) Milet Publishing.

Manet, Edouard. Color Your Own Manet Paintings. 2008. 32p. pap. 3.95 ***(978-0-486-46202-8(1))*** Dover Pubns., Inc.

Manet, Edouard. Manet Paintings: 24 Art Cards. 2001. (Illus.). 6p. pap. 5.95 (978-0-486-41339-6(X)) Dover Pubns., Inc.

McLean, Sandra. Monkey Business. 2004. (Illus.). 68p. pap. 10.95 (978-1-57377-187-0(2) , 0-1988-4-02502-3) Eas'l Pubns.

McLewn, Sandra. Cuisine D'art. 2004. 60p. pap. 11.95 (978-1-57377-199-3(6) , 0-1988-4-02518-4) Eas'l Pubns.

Medina, Sarah. Having Fun with Paint. 2007. (J). ***(978-1-4042-3718-6(6)*** , PowerKids Pr.) Rosen Publishing Group, Inc., The.

Meet the Artists, 6 vols., Pack. (Bookweb Ser.). 32p. (gr. 6 up). 34.00 (978-0-7578-0905-7(7)) Rigby Education.

Micklethwait, Lucy. I Spy Colors in Art. 2007. 40p. (J). (ps-3). 19.99 ***(978-0-06-134837-2(6)*** , Greenwillow Bks.) HarperCollins Pubs.

Monet, Claude. Monet Paintings. 2000. (Illus.). 6p. pap. 6.95 (978-0-486-41341-9(1)) Dover Pubns., Inc.

Muhlberger, Richard. What Makes a Degas a Degas? 2002. (Illus.). 48p. (YA). 16.99 (978-0-670-03571-7(8) , Viking Juvenile) Penguin Group (USA) Inc.

—What Makes a Rembrandt a Rembrandt? 2002. (Illus.). 48p. (J). 16.99 (978-0-670-03572-4(6) , Viking Juvenile) Penguin Group (USA) Inc.

—What Makes a Van Gogh a Van Gogh? 2002. (Illus.). 48p. (YA). 16.99 (978-0-670-03573-1(4) , Viking Juvenile) Penguin Group (USA) Inc.

My Little Pony Paint n' Play. 2005. (J). spiral bd. (978-1-59487-072-9(1)) Artist Studios, Ltd.

My Little Pony Paint n' Play with Sticker Rolls. 2005. (J). spiral bd. (978-1-59487-143-6(4)) Artist Studios, Ltd.

Nilsen, Anna. Art Auction Mystery: Find the Fakes, Save the Sale! 2005. (Illus.). 48p. (J). (gr. 5-9). 17.95 (978-0-7534-5842-6(X) , Kingfisher) Houghton Mifflin Co. Trade & Reference Div.

—The Great Art Scandal: Solve the Crime, Save the Show! 2003. (Illus.). 48p. (J). (gr. 5-9). tchr. ed. 16.95 (978-0-7534-5587-6(0) , Kingfisher) Houghton Mifflin Co. Trade & Reference Div.

Niz, Xavier. Rembrandt. 2003. (Masterpieces, Artists & Their Works). (Illus.). 24p. (J). lib. bdg. 19.93 (978-0-7368-2230-5(5) , Bridgestone Bks.) Capstone Pr., Inc.

P Q R

Noble, Marty. Color Your Own Great Paintings by Women Artists. 2006. (Illus.). 32p. (J). pap. 3.95 (978-0-486-45108-4(9)) Dover Pubns., Inc.

—Color Your Own Impressionist Paintings. 2004. (Illus.). 32p. (J). pap. 3.95 (978-0-486-43592-3(X)) Dover Pubns., Inc.

Noble, Marty & Van Gogh, Vincent. Color Your Own Van Gogh Paintings. 1998. (Illus.). 32p. (J). pap. 4.95 (978-0-486-40570-4(2)) Dover Pubns., Inc.

Nudelman, Edwar, ed. A Halloween Reader. 2004. (Illus.). 12p. 8.95 (978-1-58980-260-5(8)) Pelican Publishing Co., Inc.

Paint. (Jump Ser.). (Illus.). 36p. (J). (gr. 2-6). pap. (978-1-882210-32-9(8)) Action Publishing, Inc.

Painting History: Third Grade Guided Reading Level H. (On Our Way to English Ser.). (gr. 3 up). 34.50 (978-0-7578-7111-5(9)) Rigby Education.

Painting the Car: KinderConcepts Individual Title Six-Packs. (Kinderstarters Ser.). 8p. (ps-1). 21.00 (978-0-7635-8732-1(X)) Rigby Education.

Palomaki, Kurt. Floating Men & Pale Faces: The Paintings of Kurt Palomaki. 2003. (Illus.). 48p. (YA). per. 19.99 (978-0-9645655-5-5(2)) BurnhillWolf.

Papel, Dibujos y Pinturas. (One Hundred One Things to Do Ser.).Tr. of Paper, Drawing & Painting. (SPA.). (J). (gr. 3-5). pap. 4.76 (978-950-724-204-5(X)) Lumen ARG. *Dist:* Lectorum Pubns., Inc.

Pete Paints a Picture, 6 Packs. (Story Steps Ser.). (gr. k-2). 20.00 (978-0-7635-9602-6(7)) Rigby Education.

Powell, William. Color Mixing Recipes for Portraits: More Than 500 Color Combinations for Skin, Eyes, Lips & Hair. 2006. (Color Mixing Recipes Ser.). (Illus.). 48p. 9.95 (978-1-56010-990-7(4)) Foster, Walter Publishing, Inc.

Price, Jamie Mills. Christmastime: Between the Vines, Vol. 3. 2004. 84p. pap. 12.95 (978-1-57377-195-5(3) , 0-1988-4-02510-8) Eas'l Pubns.

QEB Learn Art National Book Stores Edition: Painting. 2006. (J). per. (978-1-59566-281-1(2)) QEB Publishing Inc.

QEB Let's Start! Art National Book Stores Edition: Painting. 2006. (J). per. (978-1-59566-303-0(7)) QEB Publishing Inc.

Raczka, Bob. Artful Reading. 2007. (Bob Raczka's Art Adventures Ser.). 32p. (J). (ps-3). 25.26 (*978-0-8225-6754-7(7) , Millbrook Pr.) Lerner Publishing Group.

—More Than Meets the Eye: Seeing Art with All Five Senses. 2003. (Illus.). 32p. (J). pap. 9.95 (978-0-7613-1994-8(8) , First Avenue Editions) Lerner Publishing Group.

—More Than Meets the Eye: Seeing Art with All Five Senses. 2003. (gr. k-3). lib. bdg. 18.75 (978-0-613-90443-8(5)) Tandem Library Bks.

—No One Saw. 2001. (gr. k-3). lib. bdg. 18.75 (978-0-613-90694-4(2)) Tandem Library Bks.

Random House Disney Staff. Finding Nemo: Tales from down Under. 2003. (Illus.). 32p. (J). (ps-2). pap. 3.99 (978-0-7364-2153-9(X) , Golden/Disney) Random Hse. Children's Bks.

—Welcome to Radiator Springs. Disney Storybook Artists Staff, illus. 2006. (Paint Box Book Ser.). 32p. (J). (ps-2). pap. 3.99 (978-0-375-83378-6(1) , Golden/Disney) Random Hse. Children's Bks.

Rendall, Richard & Abrams, Elise. Hand Painted Porcelain Plates: Nineteenth Century to the Present. 2003. (Schiffer Book for Collectors Ser.). (Illus.). 240p. (gr. 10-13). 59.95 (978-0-7643-1692-0(3)) Schiffer Publishing, Ltd.

Richardson, Joy. Using Color in Art. 1999. (How to Look at Art Ser.). (Illus.). 32p. (J). (gr. 1 up). lib. bdg. 23.33 (978-0-8368-2629-6(9)) Stevens, Gareth Inc.

Roca, Nuria. Que Es el Arte? Pintura y Escultura. 2004. (Libros Que Es el Arte? Ser.). (SPA.). 36p. (J). pap. 6.95 (978-0-7641-2704-5(7)) Barron's Educational Series, Inc.

Schmitz, Diane Ridley, et al, eds. Paint Magic. 2001. (Art Magic Ser.). (Illus.). 64p. (J). (gr. 1-7). pap. 12.99 (978-1-58180-231-3(5) , 32004, North Light Bks.) F & W Pubns., Inc.

Scholastic, Inc. Staff. Shrek: Classic Shrek Paintbox Book. Simpson, Fiona, ed. 2005. (Shrek Ser.). 32p. (J). pap. 3.99 (978-0-439-80587-2(2)) Scholastic, Inc.

Schulte, Jessica. Can You Find It Inside? Search & Discover for Young Art Lovers. 2005. (Illus.). 32p. (J). (gr. k-4). 10.95 (978-0-8109-5794-7(9) , Abrams Bks. for Young Readers) Abrams, Harry N. , Inc.

—Can You Find It Outside? Search & Discover for Young Art Lovers. 2005. (Illus.). 32p. (J). (gr. k-4). 10.95 (978-0-8109-5795-4(7) , Abrams Bks. for Young Readers) Abrams, Harry N. , Inc.

Seligman, Patricia. The Watercolor Artist's Flower Handbook: Leading Floral Artists Show How to Capture the Beauty of Flowers. 2005. (Illus.). 144p. 19.95 (978-0-8230-5616-3(3)) Watson-Guptill Pubns., Inc.

Souter, Gillian. Paints Plus. Watson, Clare, illus. Martin, Andre, photos by. 2001. (Handy Crafts Ser.). 48p. (J). (gr. 2 up). lib. bdg. 24.67 (978-0-8368-2821-4(6)) Stevens, Gareth Inc.

Strawberry Shortcake Paint n' Play with Sticker Rolls. 2005. (J). spiral bd. (978-1-59487-146-7(9)) Artist Studios, Ltd.

Sturm, Ellen. Matisse. 2003. (Masterpieces, Artists & Their Works). (Illus.). 24p. (J). lib. bdg. 19.93 (978-0-7368-2227-5(5) , Bridgestone Bks.) Capstone Pr., Inc.

Teenage Mutant Ninja Turtles Paint Master Activity Books. 2004. (J). act. bk. ed. 2.99 (978-0-7666-1301-0(1) , 15330); act. bk. ed. 2.99 (978-0-7666-1302-7(X) , 15330) Modern Publishing.

Tesche-Mentzen, A. Children's Art. (Illus.). 144p. 29.95 (978-3-89405-446-5(8)) Frederking & Thaler Verlag GmbH DEU. *Dist:* Prestel Publishing.

Thomas, John. The Ultimate Book of Kid Concoctions 2. 2006. (Illus.). 80p. (J). pap. 14.99 (978-0-8054-4444-5(0)) B&H Publishing Grp.

Thomas, John & Thomas, Danita. The Ultimate Book of All Occasion Kid Concoctions: More Than 50 Wacky, Wild & Crazy Concoctions for All Occasions. 2006. (Illus.). 80p. (J). pap. 14.99 (978-0-8054-4445-2(9)) B&H Publishing Grp.

—The Ultimate Book of Kid Concoctions. 2006. (Illus.). 80p. (J). pap. 14.99 (978-0-8054-4443-8(2)) B&H Publishing Grp.

Thomson, Ruth. Portraits. 2003. (First Look at Art Ser.). (Illus.). 32p. (gr. 3-5). 23.00 (978-0-7910-7948-5(1) , Chelsea Hse.) Facts On File, Inc.

Tolliver, Gabrielle. Paint Your Own Easter Bunny. 2007. 32p. (J). pap. 6.95 (978-0-7624-2982-0(8) , Running Pr. Minature Editions) Running Pr. Bk. Pubs.

Top That Publishing Staff, ed. Drawing with Pastels. 2006. 64p. (978-1-84510-615-7(6)) Top That! Publishing PLC.

—Glass Painting. 2004. (Creative Studios Ser.). (Illus.). 48p. (J). (978-1-84510-248-7(7)) Top That! Publishing PLC.

—Puffy Paints. 2004. (Creative Studios Ser.). (Illus.). 48p. (J). (978-1-84510-251-7(7)) Top That! Publishing PLC.

Torres, Laura. Rocas Pintadas. 2005. (SPA.). 64p. (J). spiral bd. 17.95 (978-968-5528-07-8(1)) Klutz Latino MEX. *Dist:* Independent Pubs. Group.

Trago Publishing Staff. The Alphabet 1 Painting Pad. 1999. (My Art Ser.: Vol. 1). 26p. (J). (ps-3). pap. 7.95 (978-0-9683883-0-3(2)) Sterling Publishing Co., Inc.

Venezia, Mike. Paul Cezanne. 1998. (Getting to Know the World's Greatest Artists Ser.). (Illus.). 32p. (J). (gr. 3-4). 27.00 (978-0-516-20762-9(8) , Children's Pr.) Scholastic Library Publishing.

Wagner, Lisa. Cool Painted Stuff. 2005. (Cool Crafts Ser.). (Illus.). 32p. (J). (gr. k-6). lib. bdg. 22.78 (978-1-59197-742-1(8) , Checkerboard Library) ABDO Publishing Co.

Watt, Fiona. 50 Things to Draw & Paint. 2006. 50p. (J). 9.99 (978-0-7945-1215-6(1) , Usborne) EDC Publishing.

Wilmes, Liz & Wilmes, Dick. Easel Art. Koeller, Carol, illus. 2004. 128p. (J). pap. 12.95 (978-0-943452-25-8(2)) Building Blocks, LLC.

Wisner, Karen. Country Seasons, Vol. 3. 2004. 60p. pap. 11.95 (978-1-57377-201-3(1) , 0-1988-4-2522-1) Eas'l Pubns.

Witteman, Barbara. Leonardo Da Vinci. 2003. (Masterpieces, Artists & Their Works). (Illus.). 24p. (J). lib. bdg. 19.93 (978-0-7368-2228-2(3) , Bridgestone Bks.) Capstone Pr., Inc.

Wolfe, Gillian. Look: Seeing the Light in Art. 2006. (Look! Ser.). (Illus.). 40p. (J). (gr. 1-5). 16.95 (*978-1-84507-467-8(X)) Lincoln, Frances Ltd. GBR. *Dist:* Perseus Distribution.

—Look! Zoom in on Art. 2007. (Illus.). 40p. (J). 16.95 (*978-1-84507-796-9(2)) Lincoln, Frances Ltd. GBR. *Dist:* Perseus Distribution.

PAINTING, ABSTRACT

see Art, Abstract

PAINTING—COLOR REPRODUCTION

see Prints

PAINTING, DUTCH

Bassil, Andrea & Van Gogh, Vincent. Vincent Van Gogh. 2004. (Lives of the Artists Ser.). (Illus.). 48p. (J). (gr. 5 up). pap. 29.26 (978-0-8368-5607-1(4)); lib. bdg. 30.00 (978-0-8368-5602-6(3)) Stevens, Gareth Inc. (World Almanac Library).

Claybourne, Anna & Van Gogh, Vincent. Vincent Van Gogh. 2004. (Illus.). 48p. (J). lib. bdg. 28.56 (978-0-7398-6631-3(1)) Raintree.

Connolly, Sean. Vincent Van Gogh. 2006. (Heinemann First Library). (Illus.). 32p. (J). lib. bdg. (*978-1-4034-8497-0(X)) Heinemann Library.

Hyde, Margaret E., ed. Van Gogh for Kids. 2005. (Great Art for Kids Ser.). (Illus.). 10p. (J). pap. 8.95 (978-1-58980-207-0(1)) Pelican Publishing Co., Inc.

Nichols, Catherine. Vincent Van Gogh. 2006. (Primary Source Library of Famous Artists). (Illus.). 32p. (J). 21.95 (978-1-4042-2766-8(0) , PowerKids Pr.) Rosen Publishing Group, Inc., The.

Sateren, Shelley Swanson. Van Gogh. 2002. (Masterpieces). (Illus.). 24p. (J). (gr. 2-3). lib. bdg. 18.60 (978-0-7368-1124-8(9) , Bridgestone Bks.) Capstone Pr., Inc.

Woodhouse, Jayne. Rembrandt Van Rijn. 2002. (Life & Work of. . . Ser.). (Illus.). 32p. (J). (gr. k-2). lib. bdg. 22.79 (978-1-58810-606-3(3)) Heinemann Library.

—Rembrandt Van Rijn. 2002. (gr. k-3). lib. bdg. 14.75 (978-0-613-45817-7(6)) Tandem Library Bks.

PAINTING—FICTION

Adams, Adrienne. The Easter Egg Artists. Adams, Adrienne, illus. 2002. (Illus.). (J). 14.47 (978-0-7587-2429-8(2)) Book Wholesalers, Inc.

Alphin, Elaine Marie. Simon Says. (YA). (gr. 9-12). 2005. 264p. pap. 6.95 (978-0-15-204678-1(X) , Harcourt Paperbacks); 2002. (Illus.). 272p. 17.00 (978-0-15-216355-6(7)) Harcourt Children's Bks.

Anderson, Dawn. I Am the Artist! Cunningham, Kelley, illus. 2006. (Rookie Reader Skill Set Ser.). 32p. (J). (gr. k-2). 19.50 (978-0-516-24976-6(2) , Children's Pr.) Scholastic Library Publishing.

Anderson, Dawn & Cunningham, Kelley. I Am the Artist! 2006. (Rookie Reader Ser.). (Illus.). 32p. (J). pap. 4.95 (978-0-516-24912-4(6) , Children's Pr.) Scholastic Library Publishing.

Arnosky, Jim. Mouse Colors: A Very First Book. Arnosky, Jim, illus. 2001. (Illus.). 48p. (J). (gr. k-ps). tchr. ed. 5.95 (978-0-618-01521-4(3) , Clarion Bks.) Houghton Mifflin Co. Trade & Reference Div.

Arrigan, Mary & Mclure, Gillian. Mario's Angels: A Story about the Artist Giotto. 2006. (Illus.). 32p. (J). 15.95 (978-1-84507-404-3(1)) Lincoln, Frances Ltd. GBR. *Dist:* Perseus Distribution.

Arvella, Wendy. Pray for a Rainbow. Takazono, Wayne, illus. 2002. pap. 5.99 (978-0-89610-201-9(7)) Island Heritage Publishing.

Baker, Alan. Black & White Rabbit's ABC. Baker, Alan, illus. 2002. (Illus.). (J). 11.87 (978-0-7587-4101-1(4)) Book Wholesalers, Inc.

—Black & White Rabbit's ABC. 1999. (Little Rabbit Bks.). (Illus.). 24p. (J). (gr. k-ps). 4.95 (978-0-7534-5253-0(7) , Kingfisher) Houghton Mifflin Co. Trade & Reference Div.

Baker, Keith. More Mr. & Mrs. Green. (Mr. & Mrs. Green Ser.). (Illus.). 68p. (J). 2005. pap. 5.95 (978-0-15-205246-1(1) , Harcourt Paperbacks); 2004. 16.00 (978-0-15-216494-2(4)) Harcourt Children's Bks.

—More Mr. & Mrs. Green. 2007. (Mr. & Mrs. Green Ser.). 72p. (J). (gr. 2-4). 27.07 (*978-1-59961-302-4(6)) Spotlight.

Beaumont, Karen. I Ain't Gonna Paint No More! Catrow, David, illus. 2005. 32p. (J). 16.00 (978-0-15-202488-8(3)) Harcourt Trade Pubs.

Blackaby, Susan. El Cuadro de Mary. Haugen, Ryan, illus. 2006. (Read-It! Readers en Espanol Ser.).Tr. of Mary's Art. (SPA.). 32p. (J). (ps-3). 19.95 (978-1-4048-1649-7(6)) Picture Window Bks.

—Mary's Art. Haugen, Ryan, illus. 2005. (Read-It! Readers Ser.). 32p. (J). (gr. k-3). 18.60 (978-1-4048-1056-3(0)) Picture Window Bks.

Bowen, Gary. The Mare's Nest. Kimble, Warren, illus. 2001. 48p. (J). (gr. 1-5). 17.95 (978-0-06-028408-4(0)); (gr. 3-6). 17.89 (978-0-06-028407-7(2)) HarperCollins Pubs.

Bridges, Shirin Yim. The Umbrella Queen. Yoo, Tae-Eun, illus. 2008. 32p. (J). 16.99 (978-0-06-075040-4(5)); lib. bdg. 17.89 (978-0-06-075041-1(3)) HarperCollins Pubs.

Buchholz, Quint. El Coleccionista de Momentos. 2nd ed. 2003. (Rosa y Manzana Ser.). (SPA., Illus.). 48p. (J). (978-84-89804-16-6(8)) Loguez Ediciones ESP. *Dist:* Lectorum Pubns., Inc.

Bulla, Clyde Robert. The Paint Brush Kid. 1999. (gr. 3-6). lib. bdg. 11.80 (978-0-613-11956-6(8)) Tandem Library Bks.

Buono, Gloria M. The Painting Ballerina. 1999. (Illus.). 80p. (J). (gr. 3 up). pap. 12.95 (978-0-9669818-0-3(4)) Aaba-Glo Media.

Capatti, Bérénice. Klimt & His Cat. Monaco, Octavia, illus. 2005. 40p. (J). 18.00 (978-0-8028-5282-3(3)) Eerdmans, William B. Publishing Co.

Caple, Kathy. Worm Gets a Job. Caple, Kathy, illus. 2004. (Illus.). 40p. (J). (gr. k-3). 15.99 (978-0-7636-1694-6(X)) Candlewick Pr.

Carr, Roger. Paint My Room! 2000. (gr. k-3). lib. bdg. 11.80 (978-0-613-29712-7(1)) Tandem Library Bks.

Cheng, Terrence. Deep in the Mountains: An Encounter with Zhu Qizhan. 2007. (Illus.). 192p. (YA). 16.95 (*978-0-8230-0423-2(6)) Watson-Guptill Pubns., Inc.

Chinto & Paloma, David. Aquilino Pinta una Nube y un Camaleon. 'Pinto, illus. 2003. (Caballo Alado Ser.). (SPA & ENG.). 24p. pap. 4.95 (978-84-7864-672-2(8)) Combel Editorial, S.A. ESP. *Dist:* Independent Pubs. Group.

Cohn, Diana. Mr. Goethe's Garden. Mirocha, Paul, illus. 2003. 32p. 17.95 (978-0-88010-521-7(6)) SteinerBooks, Inc.

Coulton, Mia. Danny Paints a Picture. Coulton, Mia, photos by. 2004. (J). 4.95 (978-0-9746475-5-5(1)) Maryruth Bks., Inc.

Deuker, Carl. Painting the Black. 1999. 256p. (J). (gr. 7 up). pap. 5.99 (978-0-380-73104-6(5) , Harper Trophy) HarperCollins Pubs.

—Painting the Black. 1999. 248p. (YA). (gr. 7-12). lib. bdg. 14.15 (978-0-613-17059-8(8)); (978-0-606-16242-5(9)) Tandem Library Bks.

Dickins, Rosie. Dragon Painter. Nez, John, illus. 2006. 48p. (J). 8.99 (978-0-7945-1275-0(5) , Usborne) EDC Publishing.

Edwards, Pamela Duncan. Warthogs Paint: A Messy Color Book. Cole, Henry, illus. 2001. 32p. (ps-4). 15.49 (978-0-7868-2412-0(3)) Hyperion Bks. for Children.

Falwell, Cathryn. Butterflies for Kiri. Falwell, Cathryn, illus. 2003. (Illus.). 32p. (J). (978-1-58430-100-4(7)) Lee & Low Bks., Inc.

Fox, Paula. Portrait of Ivan. 2004. 160p. (J). reprint ed. pap. 7.95 (978-1-886910-60-7(X) , Lemniscaat) Boyds Mills Pr.

Franklin, Emily. The Other Half of Me. 2007. 256p. (YA). (gr. 9). 15.99 (*978-0-385-73445-5(X)); lib. bdg. 18.99 (*978-0-385-90449-0(5)) Random Hse. Children's Bks. (Delacorte Bks. for Young Readers).

Frueh, Stacy. Jonah's Weird, but Totally Cool Field Tr. 2005. 50p. pap. 12.95 (978-1-4137-9818-0(7)) PublishAmerica, Inc.

Geeslin, Campbell. Clara & Senor Frog. Sanchez, Ryan, illus. 2007. 40p. (J). (ps-3). 16.99 (978-0-375-83613-8(6)); lib. bdg. 19.99 (978-0-375-93613-5(0)) Random Hse. Children's Bks. (Schwartz & Wade Bks.).

Gisbert, Montse. Salvador Dalí, Píntame un Sueño. 2004. (SPA., Illus.). (J). 19.99 (978-84-8488-127-8(X)) Serres, Ediciones, S. L. ESP. *Dist:* Lectorum Pubns., Inc.

Golden Books Staff. Colorful Dino World! 2008. (Illus.). 48p. (J). (ps-2). pap. 3.99 (978-0-375-83715-9(9) , Golden Bks.) Random Hse. Children's Bks.

Graves, Sue. Oh, George! Collins, Ross, illus. 2005. (Reading Corner Ser.). 24p. (J). (gr. k-3). lib. bdg. 22.80 (978-1-59771-000-8(8)) Sea-To-Sea Pubns.

The Great Paint Problem. 2001. (Illus.). 32p. (ps-3). pap. 3.99 (978-0-439-20321-0(X)) Scholastic, Inc.

Grey, Christopher Peter. Leonardo's Shadow: Or, My Astonishing Life as Leonardo da Vinci's Servant. 2006. 400p. (YA). 16.95 (978-1-4169-0543-1(X) , Atheneum) Simon & Schuster Children's Publishing.

Harcourt School Publishers Staff. Dale Lightfoot & the Moon: Take-Home Book. 1999. (Collections Ser.). (Illus.). (J). pap. 1.90 (978-0-15-317231-1(2)) Harcourt Schl. Pubs.

—Paint. 3rd ed. 2002. (Trophies Ser.). pap. 51.00 (978-0-15-327899-0(4)) Harcourt Schl. Pubs.

—Parent's Night. 3rd ed. 2002. (Trophies English Language Learners Ser.). (Illus.). (J). pap. 3.20 (978-0-15-327574-6(X)) Harcourt Schl. Pubs.

—Rainy Day Pictures Below Level. 3rd ed. 2002. (Trophies Reading Program Ser.). (Illus.). pap. 5.10 (978-0-15-323059-2(2)) Harcourt Schl. Pubs.

—Sunshine Place. 3rd ed. 2002. (Trophies English Language Learners Ser.). (Illus.). pap. 5.10 (978-0-15-327756-6(4)) Harcourt Schl. Pubs.

—Trofeos Advanced Level: Donde Estamos? 3rd ed. 2002. (SPA., Illus.). pap. 6.80 (978-0-15-323934-2(4)) Harcourt Schl. Pubs.

—Where Is This Place? Advanced Level. 3rd ed. 2002. (Trophies Reading Program Ser.). (Illus.). pap. 5.10 (978-0-15-323023-3(1)) Harcourt Schl. Pubs.

Hasley, Dennis. Painting A Horse. 2008. (Illus.). 32p. (J). 16.95 (*978-1-59643-238-3(1)) Roaring Brook Pr.

Hest, Amy. Jamaica Louise James. (gr. k-3). lib. bdg. 14.15 (978-0-613-70961-3(6)) Tandem Library Bks.

Hill, Laban Carrick. A Brush with Napoleon: An Encounter with Jacques-Louis David. 2007. (Art Encounters Ser.). (Illus.). 176p. (YA). (gr. 7 up). 16.95 (978-0-8230-0417-1(1)) Watson-Guptill Pubns., Inc.

Hill, Susan. Ruby Paints a Picture. Moore, Margie, illus. 2005. (I Can Read Bks.). 32p. (J). (ps-ps). 15.99 (978-0-06-008978-8(4)) HarperCollins Pubs.

Hoffman, Mary. The Color of Home. Littlewood, Karin, illus. 2002. 32p. (J). (gr. k). 17.99 (978-0-8037-2841-7(7) , Dial) Penguin Group (USA) Inc.

Hooper, Meredith. La Gran Noche de los Perros. Curless, Allan, illus. 2000. Tr. of Dogs' Night. (CAT.). 32p. (J). (gr. 1-3). 14.95 (978-84-95040-31-2(X)) Serres, Ediciones, S. L. ESP. *Dist:* Lectorum Pubns., Inc.

—La Gran Noche de los Perros. Curless, Allan & Burgess, Mark, illus. 2000. Tr. of Dogs' Night. (SPA.). 32p. (J). (gr. 1-3). 14.95 (978-84-95040-30-5(1)) Serres, Ediciones, S. L. ESP. *Dist:* Lectorum Pubns., Inc.

Hughes, Shirley. Alfie Wins a Prize. 2007. (Illus.). 32p. (J). pap. 8.95 (*978-0-09-945638-4(9) , Red Fox) Random Hse. Children's Bks. GBR. *Dist:* Independent Pubs. Group.

—Alfie Wins a Prize. 2006. (Illus.). 32p. (J). 19.95 (*978-0-370-32824-9(8)) Transworld Publishers Ltd. GBR. *Dist:* Independent Pubs. Group.

I Love to Paint. 2003. (Illus.). (J). per. (978-1-57657-961-9(0)) Paradise Pr., Inc.

Jarrell, Pamela R. & Gray, Stacy A. Carol Paints Everything. l.t. ed. 2001. (Big Bks.). (J). (ps-1). 10.95 (978-1-57332-212-6(1)) HighReach Learning, Inc.

Johnson, Angela. Daddy Calls Me Man. Mitchell, Rhonda, illus. 2000. (Richard Jackson Bks.). 32p. (J). (ps-k). pap. 6.95 (978-0-531-07175-5(8) , Orchard Bks.) Scholastic, Inc.

—Daddy Calls Me Man. 2000. (J). 13.75 (978-0-606-19856-1(3)); lib. bdg. 15.25 (978-0-613-44555-9(4)) Tandem Library Bks.

—Lily Brown's Paintings. Lewis, E. B., illus. 2007. 32p. (J). (ps-3). pap. 16.99 (978-0-439-78225-8(2) , Orchard Bks.) Scholastic, Inc.

Jones, Douglas. Dutch Color. 224p. (J). 2000. (Illus.). per. 12.00 (978-1-885767-65-3(X)); 1999. (gr. 3-6). per. 12.00 (978-1-885767-52-3(8)) Canon Pr.

Kalar, Bonnie. Ann Paints & Plays. Spreen, Kathe, illus. Date not set. 12p. (J). (ps-2). pap. (978-1-891619-40-3(3)) Corona Pr.

King, Kirsty. My New Friends. 2005. 52p. pap. (*978-1-84401-576-4(9)) Athena Pr.

Knight, Jean MacPhail. Charlotte en Giverny. Sweet, Melissa, illus. 2002. Tr. of Charlotte in Giverny. 64p. (J). (SPA.). 14.95 (978-84-8488-006-6(0)); (CAT.). 14.95 (978-84-8488-015-8(X)) Serres, Ediciones, S. L. ESP. *Dist:* Lectorum Pubns., Inc.

Knight, Joan. Charlotte in Paris. Sweet, Melissa, illus. 2003. 52p. (J). 16.95 (978-0-8118-3766-8(1)) Chronicle Bks. LLC.

Knight, Joan MacPhail. Charlotte in Giverny. Rock, Victoria, ed. Sweet, Melissa, illus. 2000. 64p. (J). (gr. 4-7). 16.95 (978-0-8118-2383-8(0)) Chronicle Bks. LLC.

Lagonegro, Melissa. Lots of Pots. 2005. (Pooh's Readables Ser.). (J). (978-0-7364-8035-2(8)) Random Hse., Inc.

Lagonegro, Melissa & Random House Disney Staff. Lots of Pots. 2005. (Pooh's Readables Ser.). (Illus.). 32p. (J). (ps-1). 4.99 (978-0-7364-2278-9(1) , RH/Disney) Random Hse. Children's Bks.

Lee, Quinlan B. Oh, Where Is My Paintbrush? 2006. (VeggieTales Ser.). 32p. (J). 4.99 (978-1-4169-1785-4(3) , Simon Scribbles) Simon & Schuster Children's Publishing.

Locker, Thomas. In Blue Mountains: An Artist's Return to America's First Wilderness. Locker, Thomas, illus. rev. ed. 2000. (Illus.). 36p. (J). (ps-3). 18.00 (978-0-88010-471-5(6)) SteinerBooks, Inc.

London, Victoria. Emily Cobbs & the Naked Painting. 2002. (Gifted Girls Ser.: Bk. 1). (Illus.). 64p. (J). (gr. 2-7). pap. 6.95 (978-0-9714776-2-9(0) , 083-003) Sparklesoup Studios, Inc.

MacLachlan, Patricia & MacLachlan, Emily. Painting the Wind. Schneider, Katy, illus. 40p. (J). (ps-3). 2003. 15.99 (978-0-06-029798-5(0) , Cotler, Joanna Books); 2003. lib. bdg. 16.89 (978-0-06-029799-2(9) , Cotler, Joanna Books); 2006. reprint ed. pap. 6.99 (978-0-06-443825-4(2) , Harper Trophy) HarperCollins Pubs.

Mayer, Mercer & Capozzi, Suzy. Bob Paints the Town. Mayer, Mercer, illus. 2003. (Little Critter Ser.). (Illus.). 10p. (J). (gr. k-1). 7.99 (978-0-307-10603-2(9) , 10603, Golden Bks.) Random Hse. Children's Bks.

Mazer, Anne. The More, the Merrier. 2002. (Amazing Days of Abby Hayes Ser.: No. 8). (Illus.). 128p. mass mkt. 4.99 (978-0-439-35367-0(X)) Scholastic, Inc.

McPhail, David. Big Brown Bear/El gran oso Pardo. Campoy, F. Isabel & Ada, Alma Flor, trs. from ENG. 2007. (Green Light Readers Level 1 Ser.). (ENG & SPA., Illus.). 28p. (J). 12.95 (978-0-15-205965-1(2)); pap. 3.95 (978-0-15-205970-5(9)) Harcourt Trade Pubs.

Merberg, Julie & Bober, Suzanne. Dreaming with Rousseau. 2007. (Illus.). 22p. (J). (ps). bds. 6.95 (978-0-8118-5712-3(3)) Chronicle Bks. LLC.

Merberg, Julie, et al. Painting with Picasso. 2006. (Illus.). 22p. (J). bds. 6.95 (978-0-8118-5505-1(8)) Chronicle Bks. LLC.

Munsch, Robert. Boo! Mart Chenko, Michael, illus. 2004. 32p. (J). pap. 3.99 (978-0-439-62331-5(6) , Cartwheel Bks.) Scholastic, Inc.

Perkins, Mitali. Rickshaw Girl. Hogan, Jamie, illus. 2007. 91p. (J). (gr. 2-5). 13.95 (978-1-58089-308-4(2)) Charlesbridge Publishing, Inc.

Pinkwater, Daniel M. Bear's Picture. Johnson, D. B., illus. 2008. 32p. (J). (gr. 3-5). 16.00 ***978-0-618-75923-1(9))*** Houghton Mifflin Co.

Pirotta, Saviour. Patrick Paints a Picture. West, Linzi, illus. 2007. 32p. (J). (ps-1). 16.95 ***(*978-1-84507-296-4(0))*** Lincoln, Frances Ltd. GBR. *Dist:* Perseus Distribution.

Plant, Timothy. Beyond the Wall. 2005. (Illus.). 192p. pap. 8.95 (978-1-56315-368-6(8)) SterlingHouse Pubs., Inc.

Preller, James. The Case of the Vanishing Painting. Smith, Jamie & Alley, Robert W., illus. 2007. 81p. (J). (ps-3). lib. bdg. 11.19 (978-0-606-32763-3(0)) Tandem Library Bks.

Rau, Dana Meachen. Purple Is Best. Cressy, Mike, illus. (Rookie Reader Skill Set Ser.). 32p. (J). 2000. (gr. k-2). pap. 4.95 (978-0-516-27001-2(X)); 1999. (gr. 1-2). 19.50 (978-0-516-21638-6(4)) Scholastic Library Publishing. (Children's Pr.).

—Purple Is Best. 1999. (gr. k-3). lib. bdg. 12.95 (978-0-613-54849-6(3)) Tandem Library Bks.

Rex, Michael. Where Can Bunny Paint? Rex, Michael, illus. 2003. (Word-by-Word First Reader Ser.). (Illus.). 32p. (J). (ps-k). pap. 3.99 (978-0-439-36605-2(4) , Cartwheel Bks.) Scholastic, Inc.

Rich, Beatrice. Vanessa & the Enchanted Painting. Rich, Beatrice, illus. 2002. (Illus.). 32p. (J). per. 14.95 (978-0-9672215-1-9(X)) Bridge Hse. Publishing, Inc.

Rigby Education Staff. Tom Sawyer: Jumbled Tumble. (gr. k-2). 26.00 (978-0-7635-2424-1(7)) Rigby Education.

Rudolph, Tammy. Lucy's Mysterious Paint Brush. 2005. 17.00 (978-0-8059-9765-1(2)) Dorrance Publishing Co., Inc.

Schwartz, Amy. Begin at the Beginning: A Little Artist Learns about Life. Schwartz, Amy, illus. 2005. 40p. (J). (ps-2). lib. bdg. 16.89 (978-0-06-000112-4(7)) HarperCollins Pubs.

Segal, Lore. Morris the Artist. Kulikov, Boris, illus. 2003. 32p. (J). (gr. k-4). 16.00 (978-0-374-35063-5(9) , Farrar, Straus & Giroux (BYR)) Farrar, Straus & Giroux.

Sweet, Melissa. Carmine: A Little More Red. 2005. (Illus.). 40p. (J). (gr. k-3). 16.00 (978-0-618-38794-6(3)) Houghton Mifflin Co. Trade & Reference Div.

Tim's Paintings: Individual Title-Six Packs. (Chiquilibros Ser.). (gr. k-1). 23.00 (978-0-7635-0430-4(0)) Rigby Education.

Tom Sawyer: 6 Small Books. (gr. k-2). 23.00 (978-0-7635-8507-5(6)) Rigby Education.

Umansky, Kaye. Sophie & the Wonderful Picture. Currey, Anna, illus. 2004. 30p. (J). 3.95 (978-1-56148-445-4(8)); 9.95 (978-1-56148-437-9(7)) Good Bks.

Velásquez, Crystal. Paint the Town. 2006. (Maya & Miguel Ser.). 32p. (J). pap. 3.99 (978-0-439-83008-9(7)) Scholastic, Inc.

Ward, John. Secret of the Alchemist. 2003. (gr. 3-6). lib. bdg. 17.60 (978-0-613-78582-2(7)) Tandem Library Bks.

Wells, Rosemary. Doris's Dinosaur. Wheeler, Jody & Nez, John, illus. 2001. (Yoko & Friends School Days Ser.: No. 4). 32p. (gr. k-2). 9.99 (978-0-7868-0726-0(1) , Volo) Hyperion Bks. for Children.

—Doris's Dinosaur. 2001. (J). 10.79 (978-0-606-22550-2(1)) Tandem Library Bks.

Wells, Rosemary. Max's Work of Art: A Coloring & Activity Book. 2008. (Max & Ruby Ser.). 16p. (J). (ps-k). 4.99 ***(*978-0-448-44785-8(1)*** , Grosset & Dunlap) Penguin Group (USA) Inc.

Williams, Deborah. Artist in the Woods. Dellard, Kristine, illus. 2000. 12p. (J). (gr. k-2). pap. 3.75 (978-1-58323-032-9(7) , Seedling Pubns.) Continental Pr., Inc.

Williams, Karen L. Painted Dreams. Stock, Catherine, illus. 1998. 40p. (J). (gr. k-3). 17.99 (978-0-688-13901-8(9)); 15.89 (978-0-688-13902-5(7)) HarperCollins Pubs.

Willson, Sarah. Picture Perfect Tommy. 2001. (gr. k-3). lib. bdg. 11.80 (978-0-613-43949-7(X)) Tandem Library Bks.

Wolf, Gita & Rao, Sirish. That's How I See Things. Shyam, Bhajju, illus. 2007. 32p. (J). (ps-2). 16.95 ***(*978-81-86211-10-6(1))*** Tara Publishing IND. *Dist:* Consortium Bk. Sales & Distribution.

Wolkstein, Diane. Little Mouse's Painting. 2002. (gr. k-3). lib. bdg. 14.10 (978-0-613-63049-8(1)) Tandem Library Bks.

YKids Staff. Leonardo da Vinci. 2008. (Great Figures in History Ser.). 144p. (J). pap. 14.95 ***(*978-981-05-7555-7(6))*** Youngjin (Singapore) Pte Ltd. SGP. *Dist:* Independent Pubs. Group.

PAINTING, FINGER

see Finger Painting

PAINTING, FLEMISH

Malam, John. Pieter Bruegel. 1999. (Tell Me about Ser.). (Illus.). 24p. (gr. 2-5). lib. bdg. 19.93 (978-1-57505-366-0(7)) Lerner Publishing Group.

Woodhouse, Jayne. Peter Bruegel. 2000. (Heinemann First Library). (Illus.). 32p. (J). (gr. k-2). lib. bdg. 21.36 (978-1-57572-344-0(1)) Heinemann Library.

—Pieter Bruegel. 2001. (gr. k-3). lib. bdg. 14.75 (978-0-613-45811-5(7)) Tandem Library Bks.

PAINTING—HISTORY

Anderson, Robert. Salvador Dali. 2002. (Artists in Their Time Ser.). (Illus.). 48p. (J). (gr. 5-7). pap. 23.50 (978-0-531-12231-0(X) , Watts, Franklin) Scholastic Library Publishing.

Burleigh, Robert. Seurat & la Grande Jatte: Connecting the Dots. 2004. (Illus.). 32p. (J). (gr. k-4). 17.95 (978-0-8109-4811-2(7)) Abrams, Harry N. , Inc.

Cocca-Leffler, Maryann. Edgar Degas: Paintings That Dance. Cocca-Leffler, Maryann, illus. 2001. (Smart about Art Ser.). (Illus.). 32p. (J). (gr. k-4). pap. 5.99 (978-0-448-42520-7(3) , Grosset & Dunlap) Penguin Group (USA) Inc.

—Edgar Degas: Paintings That Dance. 2001. (gr. k-3). lib. bdg. 14.15 (978-0-613-45259-5(3)) Tandem Library Bks.

Connolly, Sean, contrib. by. Claude Monet. 1999. (Life & Work of. . . Ser.). (Illus.). 32p. (J). (gr. k-2). lib. bdg. 21.36 (978-1-57572-956-5(3)) Heinemann Library.

De Magalhaes, Roberto Carvalho. Claude Monet. 2003. (Great Artists Ser.). (Illus.). 40p. (J). 15.95 (978-1-59270-009-7(8)) Enchanted Lion Bks., LLC.

d'Harcourt, Claire. Masterpieces up Close: Western Painting from the 14th to 20th Centuries. Kirk, Shoshanna, tr. from FRE. 2006. (Illus.). 64p. (J). (gr. 6-8). 22.95 (978-0-8118-5403-0(5)) Chronicle Bks. LLC.

Fandel, Jennifer. Pablo Picasso. 2005. (Xtraordinary Artists Ser.). (Illus.). 48p. (gr. 5-9). 21.95 (978-1-58341-331-9(6) , Creative Education) Creative Co., The.

Gaff, Jackie. Alberto Giacometti. 2002. (Artists in Their Time Ser.). (Illus.). (J). (gr. 5-7). 46p. pap. 6.95 (978-0-531-16617-8(1)); 48p. pap. 23.50 (978-0-531-12224-2(7)) Scholastic Library Publishing. (Watts, Franklin).

—Alberto Giacometti. 2002. (Illus.). 46p. (J). (gr. 3-7). lib. bdg. 15.25 (978-0-613-53900-5(1)) Tandem Library Bks.

Gogerly, Liz. Pablo Picasso: Master of Modern Art. Picasso, Pablo, illus. 2004. (Famous Lives Ser.). 48p. (J). (gr. 3-5). lib. bdg. 29.93 (978-0-7398-6628-3(1)) Raintree.

—The Story of Pablo Picasso. 2002. (Lifetimes Ser.). (Illus.). 48p. (J). lib. bdg. 28.50 (978-1-931983-17-4(8)) Chrysalis Education.

Harcourt School Publishers Staff. The First Artists: Take-Home Book. 2001. (Collections Ser.). (Illus.). (J). pap. 1.90 (978-0-15-319553-2(3)) Harcourt Schl. Pubs.

—Secrets from a Cave Advanced Level. 3rd ed. 2002. (Trophies Reading Program Ser.). (Illus.). pap. 5.10 (978-0-15-323119-3(X)) Harcourt Schl. Pubs.

Harris, Nathaniel. Paul Cezanne. 2003. (Artists in Their Time Ser.). (Illus.). 48p. (J). 23.50 (978-0-531-12242-6(5)); (gr. 5-7). pap. 6.95 (978-0-531-16646-8(5)) Scholastic Library Publishing. (Watts, Franklin).

—Paul Cezanne. 2003. (Illus.). 46p. (gr. 5-8). lib. bdg. 15.25 (978-0-613-59535-3(1)) Tandem Library Bks.

Hodge, Susie. Claude Monet. 2002. (Artists in Their Time Ser.). (J). (gr. 5-7). pap. 6.95 (978-0-531-16619-2(8)); (Illus.). 48p. pap. 23.50 (978-0-531-12226-6(3)) Scholastic Library Publishing. (Watts, Franklin).

—Claude Monet. 2002. (gr. 5-8). lib. bdg. 15.25 (978-0-613-54133-6(2)) Tandem Library Bks.

Hodge, Susie & Picasso, Pablo. Pablo Picasso. 2004. (Lives of the Artists Ser.). (Illus.). 48p. (J). (gr. 5 up). pap. 29.26 (978-0-8368-5606-4(6)); lib. bdg. 30.00 (978-0-8368-5601-9(5)) Stevens, Gareth Inc. (World Almanac Library).

Holland, Gini. Pablo Picasso. 2003. (Trailblazers of the Modern World Ser.). (Illus.). 48p. (J). (gr. 5 up). pap. 14.95 (978-0-8368-5244-8(3)); lib. bdg. 30.00 (978-0-8368-5084-0(X)) Stevens, Gareth Inc. (World Almanac Library).

Holub, Joan. Vincent Van Gogh: Sunflowers & Swirly Stars. Holub, Joan, illus. 2001. (Smart about Art Ser.). (Illus.). 32p. (J). (gr. k-4). pap. 5.99 (978-0-448-42521-4(1) , Grosset & Dunlap) Penguin Group (USA) Inc.

Kelley, True. Pablo Picasso: Breaking All the Rules. Kelley, True, illus. 2002. (Smart about Art Ser.). (Illus.). 32p. (J). pap. 5.99 (978-0-448-42862-8(8) , Grosset & Dunlap) Penguin Group (USA) Inc.

—Pablo Picasso: Breaking All the Rules. 2002. (gr. 3-6). lib. bdg. 14.15 (978-0-613-62151-9(4)) Tandem Library Bks.

Lyons, Deborah. Edward Hopper: Summer at the Seaside. 2003. (Adventures in Art Ser.). (Illus.). 30p. (gr. 5 up). 14.95 (978-3-7913-2737-2(2)) Prestel Publishing.

Nichols, Catherine. Claude Monet. 2006. (Primary Source Library of Famous Artists). (Illus.). 32p. (J). 21.95 (978-1-4042-2761-3(X) , PowerKids Pr.) Rosen Publishing Group, Inc., The.

Nichols, Catherine & Renoir, Auguste. Pierre-Auguste Renoir. 2006. (Primary Source Library of Famous Artists). (Illus.). 32p. (J). 21.95 (978-1-4042-2765-1(2) , PowerKids Pr.) Rosen Publishing Group, Inc., The.

Pfleger, Susanne. A Day with Picasso. Wynne, Christopher, tr. from GER. 1999. (Adventures in Art Ser.). (Illus.). 30p. (gr. 3-10). 14.95 (978-3-7913-2165-3(X)) Prestel Publishing.

Raczka, Bob. No One Saw... Ordinary Things Through the Eyes of an Artist. 2001. (Illus.). 32p. (J). (gr. k-2). pap. 9.95 (978-0-7613-1648-0(5) , First Avenue Editions) Lerner Publishing Group.

Sateren, Shelley Swanson & Picasso, Pablo. Picasso. 2002. (Masterpieces). (Illus.). 24p. (J). (gr. 2-3). lib. bdg. 18.60 (978-0-7368-1122-4(2) , Bridgestone Bks.) Capstone Pr., Inc.

Scarborough, Kate. Pablo Picasso. 2002. (Artists in Their Time Ser.). (Illus.). (J). (gr. 5-7). 46p. pap. 6.95 (978-0-531-16622-2(8)); 48p. pap. 23.50 (978-0-531-12229-7(8)) Scholastic Library Publishing. (Watts, Franklin).

—Pablo Picasso. 2002. (Illus.). 46p. (J). (gr. 3-7). lib. bdg. 15.25 (978-0-613-54067-4(0)) Tandem Library Bks.

Tucker, Mary. Washington Crossing the Delaware. Mitchell, Judy, ed. Hierstein, Judith, illus. 2002. (History - Hands On! Ser.). 32p. (J). (gr. 1-4). pap. 6.95 (978-1-57310-352-7(7)) Teaching & Learning Co.

Venezia, Mike. Raphael. Venezia, Mike, illus. 2001. (Getting to Know the World's Greatest Artists Ser.). (Illus.). 32p. (J). (gr. 3-4). pap. 6.95 (978-0-516-27285-6(3)); 27.00 (978-0-516-22028-4(4)) Scholastic Library Publishing. (Children's Pr.).

—Raphael. 2001. (gr. 3-6). lib. bdg. 15.25 (978-0-613-49592-9(6)) Tandem Library Bks.

Welton, Jude & Dorling Kindersley Publishing Staff. Monet. 2000. (Eyewitness Bks.). (Illus.). 64p. (J). (gr. 4-7). lib. bdg. 19.99 (978-0-7894-6815-4(8)) Dorling Kindersley Publishing, Inc.

Wheatley, Abigail. Story of Painting. 2007. (Story of Painting Ser.). 96p. (J). 10.99 ***(*978-0-7945-1678-9(5)*** , Usborne) EDC Publishing.

PAINTING, ITALIAN

Connolly, Sean. Leonardo Da Vinci. 2006. (Heinemann First Library). (Illus.). 32p. (J). lib. bdg. ***(*978-1-4034-8492-5(9))*** Heinemann Library.

Radziewsky, Elke von. Paolo Ucello: La Batalla de la Caballeria. 2002. (Coleccion Joven Arte).Tr. of Paolo Ucello: The Battle at San Romano. (SPA., Illus.). 124p. (YA). 11.96 (978-84-89804-24-1(9)) Loguez Ediciones ESP. *Dist:* Lectorum Pubns., Inc.

Venezia, Mike. Giotto. 2000. (Getting to Know the World's Greatest Artists Ser.). (Illus.). 32p. (J). (gr. 3-4). pap. 6.95 (978-0-516-27040-1(0)); 27.00 (978-0-516-21592-1(2)) Scholastic Library Publishing. (Children's Pr.).

—Giotto. 2000. (gr. 3-6). lib. bdg. 15.25 (978-0-613-37362-3(6)) Tandem Library Bks.

—Raphael. Venezia, Mike, illus. 2001. (Getting to Know the World's Greatest Artists Ser.). (Illus.). 32p. (J). (gr. 3-4). pap. 6.95 (978-0-516-27285-6(3)); 27.00 (978-0-516-22028-4(4)) Scholastic Library Publishing. (Children's Pr.).

—Raphael. 2001. (gr. 3-6). lib. bdg. 15.25 (978-0-613-49592-9(6)) Tandem Library Bks.

—Titian. Venezia, Mike, illus. 2003. (Getting to Know the World's Greatest Artists Ser.). (Illus.). (gr. 3-4). pap. 6.95 (978-0-516-26975-7(5) , Children's Pr.) Scholastic Library Publishing.

—Titian. 2003. (Getting to Know World Artists Ser.). (Illus.). 32p. (J). 27.00 (978-0-516-22575-3(8) , Children's Pr.) Scholastic Library Publishing.

—Titian. 2003. (gr. 3-6). lib. bdg. 15.25 (978-0-613-67938-1(5)) Tandem Library Bks.

PAINTING—POETRY

Bernier-Grand, Carmen T. Frida: ¡Viva la Vida! Long Live Life! 2007. 64p. (YA). (gr. 6 up). 18.99 (978-0-7614-5336-9(9) , Cavendish Children's Bks.) Cavendish, Marshall Corp.

PAINTING, RELIGIOUS

see Christian Art and Symbolism

PAINTING—TECHNIQUE

Appel, Julie & Guglielmo, Amy. Brush Mona Lisa's Hair. 2006. (Touch the Art Ser.). (Illus.). 20p. (J). bds. 9.95 (978-1-4027-3566-0(9)) Sterling Publishing Co., Inc.

—Feed Matisse's Fish. 2006. (Touch the Art Ser.). (Illus.). 24p. (J). bds. 9.95 (978-1-4027-3568-4(5)) Sterling Publishing Co., Inc.

Balchin, Judy. Decorative Painting. (Step-by-Step Ser.). (Illus.). 32p. 2003. pap. 7.95 (978-1-4034-0708-5(8)); 2001. (J). (gr. 3-5). lib. bdg. 24.22 (978-1-57572-330-3(1)) Heinemann Library.

—Decorative Painting. 2002. (gr. 3-6). lib. bdg. 16.40 (978-0-613-86422-0(0)) Tandem Library Bks.

Cruz, Barbara C. Jose Clemente Orozco: Mexican Artist. 1998. (Hispanic Biographies Ser.). (Illus.). 128p. (YA). (gr. 6-12). lib. bdg. 26.60 (978-0-7660-1041-3(4)) Enslow Pubs., Inc.

De la cera a la crayon (from Wax to Crayon) 2007. (J). pap. 4.95 (978-0-8225-6635-9(4) , Ediciones Lerner) Lerner Publishing Group.

De la Cera a la Crayon (From Wax to Crayon) 2006. (De Principio a Fin Ser.). (SPA.). 24p. (J). 18.60 (978-0-8225-6493-5(9) , Ediciones Lerner) Lerner Publishing Group.

Dorling Kindersley Publishing Staff. First Paint Activity Book. 2006. (Illus.). 48p. (J). 9.99 (978-0-7566-2580-1(7)) Dorling Kindersley Publishing, Inc.

Douglas, Vincent & School Specialty Publishing Staff. Paper & Paint. 2003. (Crafty Kids Ser.). (Illus.). 48p. (J). (gr. k-3). 12.95 (978-1-57768-527-2(X) , Waterbird Bks.) School Specialty Publishing.

Flux, Paul. Color. 2007. (Illus.). 32p. (J). ***(*978-1-4034-9629-4(3))*** Heinemann Library.

—Color (2nd Edition) 2007. (Illus.). 32p. (J). ***(*978-1-4034-9635-5(8))*** Heinemann Library.

—Line & Tone. (Illus.). 32p. (J). 2007. ***(*978-1-4034-9630-0(7));*** 2002. (gr. 1-4). pap. 6.95 (978-1-58810-437-3(0) , 91165); 2001. (gr. 1-3). lib. bdg. 22.79 (978-1-58810-079-5(0)) Heinemann Library.

—Line & Tone (2nd Edition) 2007. (Illus.). 32p. (J). ***(*978-1-4034-9636-2(6))*** Heinemann Library.

—Perspective. (Illus.). 32p. (J). 2007. ***(*978-1-4034-9632-4(3));*** 2001. (gr. 1-3). lib. bdg. 22.79 (978-1-58810-080-1(4)) Heinemann Library.

—Perspective (2nd Edition) 2007. (Illus.). 32p. (J). ***(*978-1-4034-9638-6(2))*** Heinemann Library.

Foster, Walter & Wyland. Step by Step Painting with Wyland: Favorite Animals of the Sea. 2006. (Wyland Art Ser.). (Illus.). 32p. (J). pap. 5.95 (978-1-56010-970-9(X)) Foster, Walter Publishing, Inc.

Goldman, Ken. Beginner's Guide - Acrylic, Bk. 1. Foster, Walter T., ed. 2003. (How to Draw & Paint Ser.). Orig. Title: Starting Out in Acrylic. (Illus.). 32p. pap. 7.95 (978-1-56010-491-9(0)) Foster, Walter Publishing, Inc.

Henson, Paige. Drawing with Charcoal & Pastels. 1999. (How to Paint & Draw Ser.). (Illus.). 32p. (J). (gr. 3-6). lib. bdg. 26.60 (978-1-57103-313-0(0)) Rourke Publishing, LLC.

—Painting with Tempera. 1999. (How to Paint & Draw Ser.). (Illus.). 32p. (J). (gr. 3-6). lib. bdg. 26.60 (978-1-57103-311-6(4)) Rourke Publishing, LLC.

—Painting with Watercolors. 1999. (How to Paint & Draw Ser.). (Illus.). 32p. (J). (gr. 3-6). lib. bdg. 26.60 (978-1-57103-312-3(2)) Rourke Publishing, LLC.

Jacobs, Lana. Open Season: Paint Book. Jones, Cathy, illus. 2006. (Open Season Ser.). 32p. (J). pap. 4.99 (978-0-06-084613-8(5)) HarperCollins Pubs.

Kane, Barbara. Sun Paint: Use Sunshine to Make Colorful Fabric Prints. 2002. (Illus.). 60p. (J). (ps-3). spiral bd. 19.95 (978-1-57054-763-8(7)) Klutz.

Klutz Editors. Magic Painting. 2006. (Illus.). 12p. (YA). 12.95 (978-1-59174-197-8(1)) Klutz.

Luxbacher, Irene. 123 I Can Paint! 2007. (Starting Art Ser.). 24p. (J). (ps-2). ***(*978-1-55453-037-3(7))*** Kids Can Pr., Ltd.

—123 I Can Paint! Luxbacher, Irene, illus. 2007. (Starting Art Ser.). (Illus.). 23p. (J). (ps-2). pap. ***(*978-1-55453-150-9(0))*** Kids Can Pr., Ltd.

McQueen, Donna. Painting. 2005. (Illus.). 32p. (J). (gr. 3-7). lib. bdg. 27.10 (978-1-932889-84-0(1)) Sea-To-Sea Pubns.

Muller, Brunhild. Painting with Children. 2nd rev. ed. 2002. (Illus.). 48p. pap. 12.95 (978-0-86315-366-2(6)) Floris Bks. GBR. *Dist:* SteinerBooks, Inc.

Olson, Pat & Johnson, Kristin. The Ultimate Kids Painting Book. 2001. 72p. 10.99 (978-1-59612-031-0(2)) Grace Pubns., LLC.

Otten, Jack. Watch Me Paint a Picture. 2002. (Wel-Making Things Ser.). (Illus.). 24p. (J). (ps-2). 18.00 (978-0-516-23947-7(3)); pap. 4.95 (978-0-516-23592-9(3)) Scholastic Library Publishing. (Children's Pr.).

Parramon's Editorial Team Staff. Light & Color. 2004. (Painter's Corner Ser.). (Illus.). 96p. 12.95 (978-0-7641-5704-2(3)) Barron's Educational Series, Inc.

Powell, Michelle. Mosaics. 2003. (Step-by-Step Ser.). (Illus.). 32p. (YA). pap. 7.95 (978-1-4034-0710-8(X)) Heinemann Library.

Reader's Clubhouse Staff. Mixing Colors Is Fun. 2007. (Reader's Clubhouse Ser.). 24p. (J). (gr. k-2). pap. 3.99 (978-0-7641-3729-7(8)) Barron's Educational Series, Inc.

Renoir, Pierre Auguste. Color Your Own Renoir Paintings. Noble, Marty, illus. 2001. 32p. (J). pap. 3.95 (978-0-486-41546-8(5)) Dover Pubns., Inc.

Robins Deri. Painting. 2006. (Art Smart Ser.). (Illus.). 32p. (J). 9.95 (978-1-58728-534-9(7) , 1253682, Two Can Publishing) T&N Children's Publishing.

Rohlander, Nathan. Acrylic - Still Lifes. 2005. (How to Draw & Paint/Art Instruction Program Ser.). (Illus.). 32p. pap. 7.95 (978-1-56010-884-9(3)) Foster, Walter Publishing, Inc.

Schecter, Deborah. Wonderful Watercolor Art. 2002. (I Am an Artist Club Ser.). (Illus.). 32p. (J). (978-0-439-33627-7(9)) Scholastic, Inc.

Swimm, Tom. Acrylic - Scenes Around the World. Foster, Walter, ed. 2005. (How to Draw & Paint/Art Instruction Program Ser.). (Illus.). 32p. pap. 7.95 (978-1-56010-885-6(1)) Foster, Walter Publishing, Inc.

Thomas, Isabel. Action Art: Painting. 2005. (Heinemann Read & Learn Ser.). (Illus.). 24p. (J). (978-1-4034-6919-9(9)); pap. (978-1-4034-6925-0(3)) Heinemann Library.

Trout, Kerry. Painting Made Easy. Corbett, Allyson, ed. 2006. (J). 9.99 (978-0-439-77774-2(7) , Tangerine Pr.) Scholastic, Inc.

Waltz, Dan. Airbrushing Woodcrafts. Easler, Michael, ed. 2001. (Illus.). 24p. 14.95 (978-0-9743767-0-7(1)) Winfield Collection, The.

Yarnell, Jerry. Landscapes with TV Artist Jerry Yarnell. Foster, Walter T., ed. 2003. (How to Draw & Paint Ser.). Orig. Title: TV Artist Jerry Yarnell Paints Landscapes in Acrylic. (Illus.). 32p. (J). (gr. k-6). pap. 8.95 (978-1-56010-363-9(9)) Foster, Walter Publishing, Inc.

PAINTINGS

see Painting

PAIR SYSTEM

see Binary System (Mathematics)

PAKISTAN

Black, Carolyn. Pakistan: The Culture. 2003. (gr. 3-6). lib. bdg. 16.40 (978-0-613-52892-4(1)) Tandem Library Bks.

—Pakistan: The Land. 2003. (gr. 3-6). lib. bdg. 16.40 (978-0-613-52893-1(X)) Tandem Library Bks.

—Pakistan: The People. 2003. (gr. 3-6). lib. bdg. 16.40 (978-0-613-52894-8(8)) Tandem Library Bks.

—Pakistan - The Culture. 2002. (Lands, Peoples & Cultures Ser.). (Illus.). 32p. (J). (gr. 4-5). (978-0-7787-9348-9(6)); pap. (978-0-7787-9716-6(3)) Crabtree Publishing Co.

—Pakistan - The Land. 2002. (Lands, Peoples & Cultures Ser.). (Illus.). 32p. (J). (gr. 4-5). (978-0-7787-9346-5(X)); pap. (978-0-7787-9714-2(7)) Crabtree Publishing Co.

—Pakistan - The People. 2002. (Lands, Peoples & Cultures Ser.). (Illus.). 32p. (J). (gr. 4-5). (978-0-7787-9347-2(8)); pap. (978-0-7787-9715-9(5)) Crabtree Publishing Co.

Britton, Tamara L. Pakistan. 2002. (Countries Ser.). (Illus.). 40p. (J). (gr. k-6). lib. bdg. 22.78 (978-1-57765-654-8(7) , Checkerboard Library) ABDO Publishing Co.

Caldwell, John C. Pakistan. 1999. (Major World Nations Ser.). (Illus.). 104p. (J). (gr. 4-7). 19.95 (978-0-7910-5392-8(X) , Chelsea Hse.) Facts On File, Inc.

Clayton, Elspeth. Pakistan. 1998. (Worldfocus Ser.). (Illus.). 32p. (J). pap. (978-1-57572-077-7(9)) Heinemann Library.

Crompton, Samuel Willard. Pakistan. 2003. (Modern World Nations Ser.). (Illus.). 150p. (gr. 6-12). 30.00 (978-0-7910-7098-7(0) , Chelsea Hse.) Facts On File, Inc.

Crompton, Samuel Willard & Gritzner, Charles F. Pakistan. 2nd rev. ed. 2006. (Modern World Nations Ser.). (Illus.). 112p. (J). (gr. 6-12). 30.00 (978-0-7910-9208-8(9) , Chelsea Hse.) Facts On File, Inc.

DeAngelis, Gina. Pakistan. 2003. (Many Cultures, One World Ser.). (Illus.). 32p. (J). (gr. 2-3). lib. bdg. 23.93 (978-0-7368-2169-8(4) , Bridgestone Bks.) Capstone Pr., Inc.

Downing, David. India & Pakistan Conflict. 2004. (Troubled World Ser.). (Illus.). 64p. (J). 28.56 (978-1-4109-0181-1(5)) Raintree.

Dubois, Muriel L. Pakistan. 2001. (Countries of the World Ser.). (Illus.). 126p. (J). (gr. 2-3). 18.60 (978-0-7368-0815-6(9) , Bridgestone Bks.) Capstone Pr., Inc.

Fazzi, Cindy. How to Draw Pakistan's Sights & Symbols. 2005. (Kid's Guide to Drawing the Countries of the World Ser.). (J). 26.50 (978-1-4042-2739-2(3) , PowerKids Pr.) Rosen Publishing Group, Inc., The.

Goodwin, William. Pakistan. 2002. (Modern Nations of the World Ser.). (Illus.). 120p. (J). (gr. 7-10). 29.95 (978-1-59018-218-5(9) , Lucent Bks.) Thomson Gale.

Graham, Ian. Pakistan. 2003. (Country Files Ser.). 32p. (J). lib. bdg. 24.25 (978-1-58340-239-9(X)) Smart Apple Media.

Haque, Jameel. Pakistan. 2002. (Countries of the World Ser.). (Illus.). 96p. (J). (gr. 6 up). lib. bdg. 30.00 (978-0-8368-2352-3(4)) Stevens, Gareth Inc.

Harmon, Daniel E. Pervez Musharraf: President of Pakistan. 2007. (J). ***(978-1-4042-1905-2(6))*** Rosen Publishing Group, Inc., The.

Heinrichs, Ann. Pakistan. 2004. (True Book Ser.). (J). 25.00 (978-0-516-22813-6(7)); (Illus.). 144p. (YA). (gr. 5-9). 36.00 (978-0-516-24248-4(2)) Scholastic Library Publishing. (Children's Pr.).

Kras, Sara Louise. Pervez Musharraf. 2003. (Major World Leaders Ser.). (Illus.). 112p. (gr. 6-12). 30.00 (978-0-7910-7650-7(4) , Chelsea Hse.) Facts On File, Inc.

Kwek, Karen & Haque, Jameel. Welcome to Pakistan. 2003. (Welcome to My Country Ser.). (Illus.). 48p. (J). (gr. 2 up). lib. bdg. 26.00 (978-0-8368-2552-7(7)) Stevens, Gareth Inc.

Lynch, Emma. We're from Pakistan. 2005. 32p. (J). pap. 7.60 (978-1-4034-5816-2(2)) Heinemann Library.

Morgan, Sally. Focus on Pakistan. 2007. pap. ***(978-0-8368-6759-6(9));*** 64p. (J). (gr. 5-8). lib. bdg. 33.27 ***(978-0-8368-6752-7(1))*** Stevens, Gareth Inc. (World Almanac Library).

Nobleman, Marc Tyler. Pakistan. 2003. (Countries & Cultures Ser.). (Illus.). 64p. (J). (gr. 3-4). lib. bdg. 18.60 (978-0-7368-1550-5(3) , Bridgestone Bks.) Capstone Pr., Inc.

O'Donnell, Kerri. A Primary Source Guide to Pakistan. 2003. (Countries of the World : A Primary Source Journey Ser.). (Illus.). 24p. (J). pap. (978-0-8239-8079-6(0)); lib. bdg. 19.95 (978-0-8239-6595-3(3)) Rosen Publishing Group, Inc., The.

Olson, Gillia M. Pakistan. 2005. (Fact Finders Ser.). (Illus.). 32p. (J). 22.60 (978-0-7368-3757-6(4)) Capstone Pr., Inc.

Razzak, Shazia. P Is for Pakistan. Das, Prodeepta, photos by. 2007. (World Alphabets Ser.). (Illus.). 32p. (J). (ps-2). 16.95 ***(978-1-84507-483-8(1))*** Lincoln, Frances Ltd. GBR. *Dist:* Perseus Distribution.

Roraback, Amanda. Pakistan in a Nutshell. 2nd ed. 2004. (Nutshell Notes Ser.). (Illus.). 64p. pap. 7.95 (978-0-9702908-9-2(6)) Enisen Publishing.

Sharth, Sharon. Pakistan. 2003. (Countries: Faces & Places Ser.). (Illus.). 32p. (J). (gr. 1-5). 25.64 (978-1-56766-637-3(X)) Child's World, Inc.

Sheehan, Sean. Pakistan. 2nd ed. 2004. (Cultures of the World Ser.). (Illus.). 144p. (J). 37.07 (978-0-7614-1787-3(7) , Benchmark Bks.) Cavendish, Marshall Corp.

Taus-Bolstad, Stacy. Pakistan in Pictures. 2003. (Visual Geography Ser.). (Illus.). 80p. (J). (gr. 5-12). 27.93 (978-0-8225-4682-5(5)) Lerner Publishing Group.

Walsh, Kieran. Pakistan. 2003. (Countries in the News Ser.). (Illus.). 24p. (J). 25.64 (978-1-58952-680-8(5)) Rourke Publishing, LLC.

Worth, Richard & Jr. Pervez Musharraf. 2nd rev. ed. 2007. (Modern World Leaders Ser.). 104p. (gr. 6-12). 30.00 ***(978-0-7910-9264-4(X)*** , Chelsea Hse.) Facts On File, Inc.

PAKISTAN—FICTION

Antieau, Kim. Broken Moon. 2007. 192p. (YA). (gr. 9 up). 15.99 (978-1-4169-1767-0(5) , McElderry, Margaret K.) Simon & Schuster Children's Publishing.

Clifford, Mary Louise. The Shalamar Code. 2006. 192p. (J). (gr. 7 up). pap. 8.95 (978-0-7387-0934-5(4) , Flux) Llewellyn Pubns.

Deitz Shea, Pegi. The Carpet Boy's Gift. Morin, Leane, illus. 2006. 32p. (J). pap. 7.95 (978-0-88448-249-9(9)) Tilbury Hse. Pubs.

DeLoach, Sylvia & Massey, Barbara. A Is for Aleeya. Robinson, Amy Giles, illus. 1999. (Child Like Me Ser.). 30p. (J). (gr. 1-5). 10.99 (978-1-56309-366-1(9)) New Hope Pubs.

Ellis, Deborah. Mud City. (Illus.). 176p. 2004. (J). pap. 5.95 (978-0-88899-542-1(3)); 2003. (gr. 5-9). 15.95 (978-0-88899-518-6(0)) Groundwood Bks. CAN. *Dist:* Perseus Distribution.

Khan, Rukhsana. The Roses in My Carpets. Himler, Ronald, illus. 1998. 32p. (J). (ps-3). 15.95 (978-0-8234-1399-7(3)) Holiday Hse., Inc.

—The Roses in My Carpets. Himler, Ronald, illus. 26p. 16.95 (978-0-7737-3092-2(3)) Stoddart Kids CAN. *Dist:* Fitzhenry & Whiteside, Ltd.

Khan, Rukshana. Silly Chicken. Kyong, Yunmee, illus. 2005. 32p. (J). (ps-3). 15.99 (978-0-670-05912-6(9) , Viking Juvenile) Penguin Group (USA) Inc.

Qamar, Amjed. Beneath My Mother's Feet. 2008. 208p. (J). ***(978-1-4169-4728-8(0))*** Simon & Schuster Children's Publishing.

Shea, Pegi Deitz. The Carpet Boy's Gift. Morin, Leane, illus. 2005. 40p. (J). (gr. 3-6). 16.95 (978-0-88448-248-2(0)) Tilbury Hse. Pubs.

Staples, Suzanne Fisher. Haveli. 2006. 21.50 (978-0-8446-7291-5(2)) Smith, Peter Pub., Inc.

—Jameel & the House of Djinn. 2008. 224p. (YA). 16.95 ***(978-0-374-39936-8(0))*** Farrar, Straus & Giroux.

—Shabanu: Daughter of the Wind. 3rd ed. (J). pap. 3.99 (978-0-13-800053-0(0)) Prentice Hall (Schl. Div.).

—Shabanu: Daughter of the Wind. 2003. 288p. (YA). (gr. 7). pap. 6.99 (978-0-440-23856-0(0) , Laurel Leaf) Random Hse. Children's Bks.

—Shabanu: Daughter of the Wind. 2003. (gr. 7-12). lib. bdg. 14.75 (978-0-613-72260-5(4)) Tandem Library Bks.

Staples, Suzanne Fisher. Under the Persimmon Tree. 2005. (Illus.). 288p. (YA). 17.00 (978-0-374-38025-0(2)) Farrar, Straus & Giroux.

—Under the Persimmon Tree. 2008. 304p. (YA). pap. 7.99 ***(978-0-312-37776-2(2))*** Square Fish.

PAKISTAN—HISTORY

Englar, Mary. Benazir Bhutto: Pakistani Prime Minister & Activist. 2006. (Signature Lives Ser.). (Illus.). 112p. (J). (gr. 5-7). 30.60 (978-0-7565-1578-2(5)) Compass Point Bks.

Hughes, Christopher. India & Pakistan. 2003. (Nations in Conflict Ser.). (Illus.). 48p. (J). 24.95 (978-1-56711-539-0(X) , Blackbirch Pr., Inc.) Thomson Gale.

Lynch, Emma. Brazil. 2005. (We're from Ser.). (Illus.). 32p. (J). (ps-ps). pap. 7.60 (978-1-4034-5811-7(1)) Heinemann.

—We're from Pakistan. 2005. (We're from Ser.). (J). lib. bdg. 24.21 (978-1-4034-5807-0(3)) Heinemann.

Martin, Michael. India & Pakistan: Conflict over Kashmir. 2006. (J). (978-1-59018-643-5(5) , Lucent Bks.) Thomson Gale.

Mohiuddin, Yasmeen Niaz. Pakistan: A Global Studies Handbook. Ellington, Lucien, ed. 2006. (Global Studies - Asia Ser.). (Illus.). xxi, 382p. lib. bdg. 55.00 (978-1-85109-801-9(1)) ABC-CLIO, Inc.

Sinkler, Adrian. Pakistan. 2004. (Illus.). 126p. (YA). (gr. 10-13). lib. bdg. 32.45 (978-0-7377-1208-7(2) , Greenhaven Pr., Inc.) Thomson Gale.

PAKISTANIS—UNITED STATES

Koenig, Angela T. Pakistani Americans. 2003. (Spirit of America). (Illus.). 32p. (J). (gr. 2-6). 27.07 (978-1-59296-017-0(0)) Child's World, Inc.

Price Hossell, Karen. Pakistani Americans. 2004. (We Are America Ser.). (Illus.). 32p. (J). lib. bdg. 24.22 (978-1-4034-5023-4(4)) Heinemann Library.

PALACES

Alderton, David. Castles & Palaces. (Information Ser.). (Illus.). 32p. (J). 3.25 (978-0-7214-1741-7(8) , Dutton Juvenile) Penguin Group (USA) Inc.

Ball, Jacqueline A. Windsor Castle: England's Royal Fortress. 2005. (Castles, Palaces, & Tombs Ser.). (Illus.). 32p. (J). lib. bdg. 25.27 (978-1-59716-005-6(9)) Bearport Publishing Co., Inc.

Barter, James E. The Palace of Versailles. 1998. (Building History Ser.). (Illus.). 112p. (YA). (gr. 6-9). 27.45 (978-1-56006-433-6(1) , Lucent Bks.) Thomson Gale.

Gallagher, Debbie. Palaces, Mansions, & Castles. 2007. (J). ***(978-1-59920-151-1(8))*** Smart Apple Media.

Hodge, Susie. The Forbidden City. 2005. (Places in History Ser.). (Illus.). 48p. (J). pap. (978-0-8368-5817-4(4)); lib. bdg. 30.00 (978-0-8368-5810-5(7)) Stevens, Gareth Inc. (World Almanac Library).

Mason, Anthony. Versailles. 2005. (Places in History Ser.). (Illus.). 48p. (J). pap. (978-0-8368-5822-8(0)); lib. bdg. 30.00 (978-0-8368-5815-0(8)) Stevens, Gareth Inc. (World Almanac Library).

PALACES—FICTION

Fowles, Shelley. Climbing Rosa. 2006. (Illus.). 32p. (J). 15.95 (978-1-84507-079-3(8)) Lincoln, Frances Ltd. GBR. *Dist:* Perseus Distribution.

Marsh, Carole. The Mystery at the Imperial Palace. 2007. 144p. (gr. 3-5). 14.95 ***(978-0-635-06211-6(9));*** pap. 5.95 ***(978-0-635-06207-9(0))*** Gallopade International.

Piggy Toes Press Staff. Princess Palace. 2006. 22.95 (978-1-58117-492-2(6) , Intervisual/Piggy Toes) Dalmatian Pr.

Prasadam, Smriti & Finn, Rebecca. My Princess Palace. 2008. (Illus.). 12p. (J). bds. 6.95 ***(978-0-7475-8808-5(2))*** Bloomsbury Publishing Plc GBR. *Dist:* Independent Pubs. Group.

PALEOBOTANY

see Plants, Fossil

PALEOLITHIC PERIOD

see Stone Age

PALEONTOLOGISTS

Anholt, Laurence. Stone Girl, Bone Girl: The Story of Mary Anning. Moxley, Sheila, illus. 1999. 32p. (J). (gr. k-4). pap. 15.95 (978-0-531-30148-7(6) , Orchard Bks.) Scholastic, Inc.

Atkins, Jeannine. Mary Anning & the Sea Dragon. Dooling, Michael, illus. 1999. 32p. (J). (gr. k-3). 16.00 (978-0-374-34840-3(5) , Farrar, Straus & Giroux (BYR)) Farrar, Straus & Giroux.

Bausum, Ann. Dragon Bones & Dinosaur Eggs: A Photo-Biography of Explorer Roy Chapman Andrews. 2000. (Illus.). 64p. (J). (gr. 3-7). 17.95 (978-0-7922-7123-9(8) , National Geographic Children's Bks.) National Geographic Society.

Bennett, Leonie. Dinosaur Fossils. 2008. (J). lib. bdg. ***(978-1-59716-555-6(7))*** Bearport Publishing Co., Inc.

—Dinosaur Hunting. 2008. (I Love Reading Ser.). (J). lib. bdg. 19.96 ***(978-1-59716-554-9(9))*** Bearport Publishing Co., Inc.

Brighton, Catherine. The Fossil Girl: Mary Anning's Dinosaur Discovery. 1999. (Illus.). 32p. (gr. k-3). lib. bdg. 22.90 (978-0-7613-1468-4(7) , Millbrook Pr.) Lerner Publishing Group.

Butz, Steve. The Bone Race: A Quest for Dinosaur Fossils. 2007. 248p. (YA). pap. 16.95 ***(978-1-933255-30-9(7))*** DNA Pr.

Chrisp, Peter. Dinosaur Detectives. Martin, Linda, ed. 2001. (Readers Ser.). (Illus.). 32p. (J). (ps-3). pap. 3.99 (978-0-7894-7383-7(6)) Dorling Kindersley Publishing, Inc.

Chrisp, Peter & Dorling Kindersley Publishing Staff. Dinosaur Detectives. 2001. (Readers Ser.). (Illus.). 48p. (J). (ps-3). 14.99 (978-0-7894-7384-4(4)) Dorling Kindersley Publishing, Inc.

Gabriel, Diane L. & Cohen, Judith Love. You Can Be a Woman Paleontologist. Martin, Janice, ed. Katz, David Arthur, illus. rev. ed. 1999. 40p. (J). (gr. 3-6). reprint ed. 13.95 (978-1-880599-43-3(0)) Cascade Pass, Inc.

Goldish, Meish. The Fossil Feud: Marsh & Cope's Bone Wars. 2007. (Fossil Hunters Ser.). 32p. (J). (gr. 3-7). lib. bdg. 25.27 (978-1-59716-256-2(6)) Bearport Publishing Co., Inc.

—Fossil Tales. 2003. (On the Job Ser.). (Illus.). 32p. (gr. 3-5). 23.00 (978-0-7910-7411-4(0) , Chelsea Hse.) Facts On File, Inc.

Hartzog, Brooke. Tyrannosaurus Rex & Barnum Brown. 1999. (Dinosaurs & Their Discoverers Ser.). (Illus.). 24p. (J). (gr. k-4). lib. bdg. 18.75 (978-0-8239-5328-8(9) , PowerKids Pr.) Rosen Publishing Group, Inc., The.

Hendrickson, Sue. Hunt for the Past: My Life as an Explorer. 2001. (J). 10.79 (978-0-606-21243-4(4)) Tandem Library Bks.

Hendrickson, Sue & Weinberger, Kimberly. Hunt for the Past: My Life as an Explorer. 2001. (Illus.). 48p. (J). (gr. 1-4). pap. 3.99 (978-0-439-27191-2(6)) Scholastic, Inc.

Holmes, Thom & Holmes, Laurie. Great Dinosaur Expeditions & Discoveries: Adventures with the Fossil Hunters. Skrepnick, Michael William, illus. 2003. (Dinosaur Library). 112p. (J). lib. bdg. 26.60 (978-0-7660-2078-8(9)) Enslow Pubs., Inc.

Kurtz, Jane. Mister Bones: Dinosaur Hunter. Haverfield, Mary, illus. 2004. (Ready-to-Read Ser.). 32p. (J). pap. 3.99 (978-0-689-85960-1(0) , Aladdin) Simon & Schuster Children's Publishing.

Larson, Peter L. & Donnan, Kristin. Bones Rock! Everything You Need to Know to Be a Paleontologist. 2004. (Illus.). 160p. (J). pap. 19.95 (978-1-931229-35-7(X)) Invisible Cities Pr.

Marrin, Albert. Secrets from the Rocks: Dinosaur Hunting with Roy Chapman Andrews. Marrin, Albert, illus. 2002. (Illus.). 64p. (J). (gr. 4-8). 18.99 (978-0-525-46743-4(2) , Dutton Juvenile) Penguin Group (USA) Inc.

Mary Anning: Fossil Hunter. 2007. (J). pap. 5.95 ***(978-1-57505-457-5(4)*** , First Avenue Editions) Lerner Publishing Group.

Morrison, Taylor. The Great Unknown. 2001. (Illus.). 32p. (J). (gr. k-3). tchr. ed. 16.00 (978-0-395-97494-0(1) , Walter Lorraine) Houghton Mifflin Co. Trade & Reference Div.

Patent, Dorothy Hinshaw. Secrets of the Ice Man. 1999. (Frozen in Time Ser.). (Illus.). 72p. (J). (gr. 5-9). lib. bdg. 28.50 (978-0-7614-0782-9(0) , Benchmark Bks.) Cavendish, Marshall Corp.

Sheldon, David. Barnum Brown: Dinosaur Hunter. Sheldon, David, illus. 2006. (Illus.). 32p. (J). (gr. 1-3). 16.95 (978-0-8027-9602-8(8)); 17.85 (978-0-8027-9603-5(6)) Walker & Co.

Spilsbury, Louise & Spilsbury, Richard. Journal of a Fossil Hunter: Fossils. 2005. (Illus.). 32p. (J). (978-1-4109-1954-0(4)); lib. bdg. (978-1-4109-1923-6(4)) Steck-Vaughn.

Spilsbury, Richard & Spilsbury, Louise. Dinosaur Hunters: Palaeontologists. 2007. (J). ***(978-1-4034-9947-9(0));*** pap. ***(978-1-4034-9954-7(3))*** Heinemann Library.

Walker, Sally M. Mary Anning: Fossil Hunter. Saroff, Phyllis V., illus. 2000. (On My Own Biographies Ser.). 64p. (J). (gr. 1-3). lib. bdg. 23.93 (978-1-57505-425-4(6) , Carolrhoda Bks.) Lerner Publishing Group.

PALEONTOLOGY

see Fossils

PALESTINE

Carew-Miller, Anna. The Palestinians. 2003. (Modern Middle East Nations & Their Strategic Place in the World Ser.). (Illus.). 112,128p. (YA). (gr. 7 up). lib. bdg. (978-1-59084-513-4(7)) Mason Crest Pubs.

Dowing, David. Yasser Arafat. 2002. (Leading Lives Ser.). 64p. (J). (gr. 5-7). pap. 8.95 (978-1-4034-0125-0(X) , 91617) Heinemann Library.

Downing, David. Yasser Arafat. 2002. (Leading Lives Ser.). (Illus.). 64p. (J). (gr. 5-7). lib. bdg. 28.50 (978-1-58810-583-7(0)) Heinemann Library.

Gonzales, Todd. Palestine in the News: Past, Present, & Future. 2006. (Middle East Nations in the News Ser.). (Illus.). 128p. (J). lib. bdg. 33.27 (978-1-59845-029-3(8) , MyReportLinks.com Bks.) Enslow Pubs., Inc.

Holy Land Caravan: The Holy Land in the Old Testament & the New Testament Funspirational Kit: Older Elementary. 2004. (BibleZone Ser.: No. 12). (gr. 4-6). 44.99 (978-0-687-08990-1(5)) Abingdon Pr.

Holy Land Caravan: The Holy Land in the Old Testament & the New Testament Funspirational Kit: Preschool. 2004. (BibleZone Ser.: No. 12). (ps-k). 44.99 (978-0-687-08984-0(0)) Abingdon Pr.

Holy Land Caravan: The Holy Land in the Old Testament & the New Testament Funspirational Kit: Younger Elementary. 2004. (BibleZone Ser.: No. 12). (gr. 1-3). 44.99 (978-0-687-08987-1(5)) Abingdon Pr.

Katz, Samuel M. Jerusalem or Death: Palestinian Terrorism. 72p. (YA). (gr. 9 up). 19.95 (978-1-58013-208-4(1)) Kar-Ben Publishing.

—Jerusalem or Death: Palestinian Terrorism. 2003. (Terrorist Dossiers Ser.). (Illus.). 72p. (J). (gr. 6-12). 26.60 (978-0-8225-4033-5(9)) Lerner Publishing Group.

Sacco, Joe. Palestine. 2001. (gr. 7-12). lib. bdg. 36.15 (978-0-613-50981-7(1)) Tandem Library Bks.

Sha'Ban, Mervet A., et al. If You Could Be My Friend: Letters of Mervet Akram Sha'Ban & Galit Fink. Ellbaz, Ariane & Khadige, Beatrice, trs. from FRE. 1998. (Illus.). 118p. (YA). (gr. 5-9). 16.99 (978-0-531-33113-2(X) , Orchard Bks.) Scholastic, Inc.

—If You Could Be My Friend: Letters of Mervet Akram Sha'Ban & Galit Fink. Elbaz, Ariane & Khadige, Beatrice, trs. from FRE. 1998. (Illus.). 118p. (YA). (gr. 5-9). pap. 15.95 (978-0-531-30113-5(3) , Orchard Bks.) Scholastic, Inc.

Sharp, Anne Wallace. The Palestinians. 2004. (Lucent Library of Conflict in the Middle East). (Illus.). 112p. (J). (gr. 7-10). 29.95 (978-1-59018-493-6(9) , Lucent Bks.) Thomson Gale.

PALESTINE—FICTION

Carmi, Daniella. Samir & Yonatan. Lotan, Yael, tr. from HEB. 2002. 192p. (J). (gr. 3-7). pap. 4.99 (978-0-439-13523-8(0) , Scholastic Paperbacks) Scholastic, Inc.

—Samir & Yonatan. 2000. (gr. 3-6). lib. bdg. 13.00 (978-0-613-45824-5(9)) Tandem Library Bks.

—Samir & Yonatan. 2000. (Illus.). 192p. (J). (gr. 3-7). pap. 15.95 (978-0-439-13504-7(4) , Levine, Arthur A. Bks.) Scholastic, Inc.

Elmer, Robert. Brother Enemy. 2001. (Promise of Zion Ser.). 176p. (J). (gr. 3-8). pap. 5.99 (978-0-7642-2298-6(8)) Bethany Hse. Pubs.

—Freedom Trap. 2002. (Promise of Zion Ser.: Vol. 5). (Illus.). 160p. (J). pap. 5.99 (978-0-7642-2313-6(5)) Bethany Hse. Pubs.

—Promise of Zion, Vols. 1-6. 2002. (Promise of Zion Ser.). (Illus.). (J). pap. 35.99 (978-0-7642-8057-3(0)) Bethany Hse. Pubs.

Evans, Lauralee. The King's Heir. 2006. (YA). ***(978-1-55517-865-9(0)*** , Bonneville Bks.) Cedar Fort, Inc./CFI Distribution.

Heimerdinger, Chris. Kingdoms & Conquerors: A Novel. 2005. 434p. (YA). ***(978-1-59156-740-0(8))*** Covenant Communications.

Muhawi, Ibrahim & Kananah, Sharif. Tunjur! Tunjur! Tunjur! A Palestinian Folktale. Arzoumanian, Alik, illus. 2006. 32p. (J). (ps-3). 16.95 (978-0-7614-5225-6(7)) Cavendish, Marshall Corp.

Orlev, Uri. Lidia, Reina de Palestina. 2001. (SPA.). (gr. 3-6). lib. bdg. 17.60 (978-0-613-80732-6(4)) Tandem Library Bks.

Ray, Mary. Beyond the Desert Gate. 2nd ed. 2001. (Young Adult Historical Library). (Illus.). 190p. (YA). (gr. 3-9). 11.95 (978-1-883937-54-6(X) , 54-X) Bethlehem Bks.

Speare, Elizabeth George. The Bronze Bow. 2002. (J). 14.74 (978-0-7587-0173-2(X)) Book Wholesalers, Inc.

—The Bronze Bow. 1999. (J). 9.95 (978-1-56137-726-8(0)) Novel Units, Inc.

PALESTINE—HISTORY

Gottfried, Ted. Displaced Persons: Growing up American after the Holocaust. 2001. (Holocaust Ser.). (Illus.). 112p. (gr. 7 up). lib. bdg. 29.90 (978-0-7613-1924-5(7) , Twenty-First Century Bks.) Lerner Publishing Group.

Hall, John G. The Palestinian Authority. 2002. (Creation of the Modern Middle East Ser.). (Illus.). 125p. (gr. 6-12). 35.00 (978-0-7910-6515-0(4) , Chelsea Hse.) Facts On File, Inc.

Hans, Julia. Lamps, Scrolls, & Goatskin Bottles: A Handbook of Bible Customs for Kids. 2000. (Illus.). 144p. (YA). 16.99 (978-0-7847-1165-1(8) , 02271) Standard Publishing.

Jones, Graham. How They Lived in Bible Times. Deverell, Richard, illus. 2003. 48p. 6.49 (978-1-85999-435-1(0)) Scripture Union GBR. *Dist:* Gabriel Resources.

Lion of Ain Jaloot. 2000. (ARA.). (J). 9.99 incl. audio (978-1-932008-01-2(2)) Fine Media Group.

McNeese, Tim. Masada. 2003. (Sieges That Changed the World Ser.). (Illus.). 112p. (gr. 6-12). 30.00 (978-0-7910-7103-8(0) , Chelsea Hse.) Facts On File, Inc.

Wagner, Heather Lehr. Israel & the Arab World. 2002. (People at Odds Ser.). (Illus.). 112p. (J). (gr. 5 up). 30.00 (978-0-7910-6705-5(X) , Chelsea Hse.) Facts On File, Inc.

PALMER, ARNOLD, 1929-

Durbin, William. Arnold Palmer. 1999. (Golf Legends Ser.). (Illus.). 64p. (YA). (gr. 4-7). 18.65 (978-0-7910-4562-6(5) , Chelsea Hse.) Facts On File, Inc.

PALMER, BERTHA HONORE, 1849-1919

Alter, Judy. Cissie Palmer: Putting Wealth to Work. 1999. (Community Builders Ser.). (Illus.). 48p. (J). (gr. 3-5). pap. 6.95 (978-0-516-26345-8(5) , Children's Pr.) Scholastic Library Publishing.

PALMER, NATHANIEL BROWN, 1799-1877

Sanford, Candace. Captain Nathaniel Brown Palmer. Scala, Susan, illus. 2007. 96p. (YA). pap. 14.95 (*978-0-9773725-9-1(6)) Flat Hammock Pr.

PALSY, CEREBRAL

see Cerebral Palsy

PANAMA

Armstrong, David M. Panama. 2004. (Modern Nations of the World Ser.). (Illus.). 112p. (J). (gr. 7-10). 29.95 (978-1-59018-119-5(0) , Lucent Bks.) Thomson Gale.

Augustin, Byron. Panama. 2005. (Enchantment of the World, Second Ser.). (Illus.). 144p. (gr. 5-9). 36.00 (978-0-516-23676-6(8) , Children's Pr.) Scholastic Library Publishing.

Corwin, Jeff. Into Wild Panama. Pascoe, Elaine, ed. 2003. (Jeff Corwin Experience Ser.). (Illus.). 48p. (J). 24.95 (978-1-56711-856-8(9)); 11.20 (978-1-4103-0176-5(1)) Thomson Gale. (Blackbirch Pr., Inc.).

Freire, Carolina. Panama. 2004. lib. bdg. 30.00 (978-0-8368-3117-7(9)) Stevens, Gareth Inc.

Haynes, Tricia. Panama. 1999. (Major World Nations Ser.). (Illus.). 144p. (YA). (gr. 4-7). 29.95 (978-0-7910-4977-8(9) , Chelsea Hse.) Facts On File, Inc.

Markun, Patricia Maloney. It's Panama's Canal! 1999. (Illus.). xii, 128p. (J). (gr. 5-9). 22.50 (978-0-208-02499-2(9)) Shoe String Pr., Inc.

Nobleman, Marc Tyler. Panama. 2002. (Countries of the World Ser.). (Illus.). 126p. (J). (gr. 2-3). 18.60 (978-0-7368-1372-3(1) , Bridgestone Bks.) Capstone Pr., Inc.

Park, Ted. Panama. 2000. (Taking Your Camera to Ser.). (Illus.). 32p. (J). (gr. 4-7). lib. bdg. 22.83 (978-0-7398-1808-4(2)) Raintree.

—Taking Your Camera to Panama. 2001. (Illus.). (YA). pap. (978-0-7398-3329-2(4)) Steck-Vaughn.

Rau, Dana Meachen. Panama. 1999. (True Bks.). (Illus.). 48p. (J). (gr. 3-5). pap. 6.95 (978-0-516-26497-4(4) , Children's Pr.) Scholastic Library Publishing.

Steck-Vaughn Staff. Noises in the Night: Teacher's Resource Binder. 1999. (J). pap., tchr. ed. (978-0-7398-2475-7(9)) Steck-Vaughn.

Streissguth, Thomas. Panama in Pictures. 2nd ed. 2005. (Visual Geography Series, Second Ser.). (Illus.). 80p. (J). (gr. 5-12). 27.93 (978-0-8225-2395-6(7)) Lerner Publishing Group.

Tan, Ronald. Welcome to Panama. 2005. (Welcome to My Country Ser.). (Illus.). 48p. (J). lib. bdg. 26.00 (978-0-8368-3135-1(7)) Stevens, Gareth Inc.

PANAMA—FICTION

Andrews, Carol. The Giggle Wind. 2003. (Illus.). 40p. 17.95 (978-0-9725609-2-4(0)) Diakonia Publishing.

Appleton, Victor. The Moving Picture Boys at Panama. 2005. 27.95 (978-1-4218-1499-5(4)); 208p. pap. 12.95 (978-1-4218-1599-2(0)) 1st World Publishing, Inc. (1st World Library - Literary Society).

—The Moving Picture Boys at Panama. 2004. reprint ed. pap. 20.95 (978-1-4191-7472-8(X)); pap. 1.99 (978-1-4192-7472-5(4)) Kessinger Publishing, LLC.

Appleton, Victor. Moving Picture Boys at Panama or Stirrin. 2006. pap. 26.99 (*978-1-4280-3337-5(8)) IndyPublish-.com.

Chambers, Veronica. Marisol & Magdalena. 2001. 176p. (gr. 3-7). pap. 5.99 (978-0-7868-1304-9(0)) Hyperion Bks. for Children.

—Marisol & Magdalena: The Sound of Our Sisterhood. 2001. (gr. 5-8). lib. bdg. 14.15 (978-0-613-60642-4(6)) Tandem Library Bks.

MacDonald, Margaret Read. Conejito: A Folktale from Panama. Valerio, Geraldo, illus. 2006. 32p. 16.95 (978-0-87483-779-7(0)) August Hse. Pubs., Inc.

Payson, Lieutenent H. The Boy Scouts at the Panama Canal. 2005. reprint ed. pap. 30.95 (978-1-4179-2457-8(8)) Kessinger Publishing, LLC.

Welcome Home, Mrs. Jordon. 2000. (Tippy Parrish Story Ser.). (YA). (gr. 6-10). per. 12.95 (978-1-930009-23-3(2)) Image Cascade Publishing.

Wells, Helen. Cherry Ames, Army Nurse. 2005. (YA). pap. (978-0-9771597-2-7(8)) Springer.

PANAMA CANAL

Anderson, Dale. Building the Panama Canal. 2004. (Landmark Events in American History Ser.). (Illus.). 48p. (J). 11.95 (978-0-8368-5422-0(5)); lib. bdg. 30.00 (978-0-8368-5394-0(6)) Stevens, Gareth Inc. (World Almanac Library).

Crewe, Sabrina & Anderson, Dale. Building the Panama Canal. 2005. (Events That Shaped America Ser.). (Illus.). 32p. (J). 24.67 (978-0-8368-3413-0(5)) Stevens, Gareth Inc.

Dudley Gold, Susan. The Panama Canal Transfer: Controversy at the Crossroads. 1999. 128p. (J). (gr. 4-7). 19.98 (978-0-8172-5762-0(4)) Raintree.

DuTemple, Lesley A. The Panama Canal: Great Building Feats Ser. 2003. (Great Building Feats Ser.). (Illus.). 96p. (J). (gr. 5-9). 27.93 (978-0-8225-0079-7(5)) Lerner Publishing Group.

Gaines, Ann Graham. The Panama Canal in American History. 1999. (In American History Ser.). (Illus.). 128p. (YA). (gr. 5-12). lib. bdg. 26.60 (978-0-7660-1216-5(6)) Enslow Pubs., Inc.

Ingram, Scott. Panama Canal. 2003. (Building World Landmarks Ser.). (Illus.). 48p. (J). 24.95 (978-1-56711-332-7(X) , Blackbirch Pr., Inc.) Thomson Gale.

Mann, Elizabeth. The Panama Canal: The Story of how a jungle was conquered & the world made Smaller. Rangel, Fernando, illus. (Wonders of the World Book Ser.). 48p. (J). (gr. 4-8). 2006. pap. 9.95 (978-1-931414-14-2(9)); 1998. 19.95 (978-0-9650493-4-4(5)) Mikaya Pr.

Markun, Patricia Maloney. It's Panama's Canal! 1999. (Illus.). xii, 128p. (J). (gr. 5-9). 22.50 (978-0-208-02499-2(9)) Shoe String Pr., Inc.

Schlesinger, Arthur M., Jr. & Israel, Fred L., eds. Building the Panama Canal. 1999. (Cultural & Geographical Exploration Ser.). (Illus.). 144p. (YA). (gr. 5 up). lib. bdg. 21.95 (978-0-7910-5102-3(1) , Chelsea Hse.) Facts On File, Inc.

Winkelman, Barbara Gaines. Panama Canal. 1999. (gr. 3-6). lib. bdg. 14.10 (978-0-613-52161-1(7)) Tandem Library Bks.

PANAMANIANS IN NEW YORK (CITY)—FICTION

Chambers, Veronica. Marisol & Magdalena. 2001. 176p. (gr. 3-7). pap. 5.99 (978-0-7868-1304-9(0)) Hyperion Bks. for Children.

—Marisol & Magdalena: The Sound of Our Sisterhood. 2001. (gr. 5-8). lib. bdg. 14.15 (978-0-613-60642-4(6)) Tandem Library Bks.

PANDAS

Anderson, Jill. Giant Pandas. 2006. (Illus.). 24p. (J). 6.95 (978-1-55971-938-4(9)); 12.95 (978-1-55971-937-7(0)) T&N Children's Publishing. (NorthWord Bks. for Young Readers).

Angel, Heather. Pandas. Angel, Heather, photos by. rev. ed. 1998. (WorldLife Library). (Illus.). 72p. pap. 17.95 (978-0-89658-364-1(3)) Voyageur Pr., Inc.

Arnold, Caroline, illus. A Panda's World. 2006. 24p. (J). (gr. k-2). 23.93 (978-1-4048-1322-9(5) , 1253184) Picture Window Bks.

Bodkin, Odds. Belly Button. 2003. (Illus.). 12p. (J). bds. (978-0-9657170-5-2(4)) Perkins Schl. for the Blind.

Bortolotti, Dan. Panda Rescue: Changing the Future for Endangered Wildlife. 2003. (Firefly Animal Rescue Ser.). (Illus.). 64p. (J). (gr. 5). pap. 9.95 (978-1-55297-557-2(6)); lib. bdg. 19.95 (978-1-55297-598-5(3)) Firefly Bks., Ltd.

—Panda Rescue: Changing the Future for Endangered Wildlife. 2003. (gr. 5-8). lib. bdg. 18.75 (978-0-613-78595-2(9)) Tandem Library Bks.

Bredeson, Carmen. Giant Pandas up Close. 2006. (Zoom in on Animals! Ser.). (Illus.). 24p. (J). lib. bdg. 21.26 (978-0-7660-2496-0(2) , Enslow Elementary) Enslow Pubs., Inc.

Bright, Michael. Bears & Pandas, 3 vols. Anness Publishing Staff, ed. 1999. (Nature Watch Ser.). (Illus.). 64p. (gr. 3-7). 12.95 (978-1-85967-642-4(1) , Lorenz Bks.) Anness Publishing GBR. *Dist:* National Bk. Network.

Butterfield, Moira. Panda. (Who Am I? Ser.). (Illus.). 32p. lib. bdg. 24.25 (978-1-930643-91-8(8)) Chrysalis Education.

Claybourne, Anna. Giant Panda. 2004. (Animals under Threat Ser.). (Illus.). 48p. (J). 29.93 (978-1-4034-5582-6(1)) Heinemann Library.

—The Giant Panda. 2004. (Animals under Threat Ser.). (Illus.). 48p. (J). pap. 8.50 (978-1-4034-5689-2(5)) Heinemann Library.

Cole & Leeson. El Oso Panda. 2002. (Osos Salvajes Serie).Tr. of Wild Bears: The Panda Bear. (SPA.). 24p. (J). (gr. 3-5). 24.94 (978-1-4103-0001-0(3) , Blackbirch Pr., Inc.) Thomson Gale.

Cooper, Jason. Cub to Panda. 2003. (Illus.). 24p. (J). 20.64 (978-1-58952-692-1(9)) Rourke Publishing, LLC.

Crossingham, John & Kalman, Bobbie. Endangered Pandas. 2005. (Earth's Endangered Animals Ser.). (Illus.). 32p. (J). (978-0-7787-1858-1(1)); (gr. 3-5). pap. (978-0-7787-1904-5(9)) Crabtree Publishing Co.

Cruickshank, Don. Giant Pandas. 2006. (Amazing Animals Ser.). (J). (978-1-59036-389-8(2)); (978-1-59036-395-9(7)) Weigl Pubs., Inc.

DK Publishing. Panda. 2008. (Watch Me Grow Ser.). 24p. (J). 7.99 (*978-0-7566-3432-2(6)) Dorling Kindersley Publishing, Inc.

Dolbear, Emily J. & Primm, E. Russell. Pandas Have Cubs. 2001. (Animals & Their Young Ser.). (Illus.). 24p. (J). (gr. 1 up). lib. bdg. 18.60 (978-0-7565-0062-7(1)) Compass Point Bks.

Eckart, Edana. Giant Panda. 2003. (Welcome Book Ser.). (Illus.). 24p. (J). 17.00 (978-0-516-24298-9(9)); pap. 4.95 (978-0-516-27884-1(3)) Scholastic Library Publishing. (Children's Pr.).

—Giant Panda. 2003. (gr. k-3). lib. bdg. 12.95 (978-0-613-67715-8(3)) Tandem Library Bks.

Faundez, Anne. Animals in Danger. 2004. (QEB Start Reading Ser.). (Illus.). 24p. (J). lib. bdg. 15.95 (978-1-59566-009-1(7)) QEB Publishing Inc.

Feeny, Kathy. Panda Magic for Kids. McGee, John F., illus. 1999. (Animal Magic for Kids Ser.). 48p. (J). (gr. 3 up). lib. bdg. 26.00 (978-0-8368-2636-4(1)) Stevens, Gareth Inc.

Freeman, Marcia S. Giant Pandas. Saunders-Smith, Gail, ed. 1998. (Bears Ser.). (Illus.). 24p. (J). (gr. k-1). lib. bdg. 14.60 (978-0-7368-0098-3(0) , Pebble Bks.) Capstone Pr., Inc.

—Giant Pandas. 1998. (J). lib. bdg. 13.25 (978-0-516-21486-3(1) , Children's Pr.) Scholastic Library Publishing.

Gareth Stevens Publishing Staff, contrib. by. Pandas. 2004. (All about Wild Animals Ser.). (Illus.). 32p. (J). (gr. 2 up). lib. bdg. 23.33 (978-0-8368-4121-3(2)) Stevens, Gareth Inc.

Giant Pandas, Vol. 4. 2005. (Animals, Animals, Animals Ser.). (YA). (gr. k-3). (978-0-7368-8099-2(2) , Pebble Bks.) Capstone Pr., Inc.

Giant Pandas, 6 vols. (gr. k-2). 28.95 (978-0-7368-8123-4(9)) Red Brick Learning.

Gibbons, Gail. Giant Pandas. 2002. (Illus.). 32p. (J). (gr. k-3). pap. 6.95 (978-0-8234-1828-2(6)) Holiday Hse., Inc.

Green, Carl R. The Giant Panda: A MyReportLinks. com Book. 2004. (Endangered & Threatened Animals Ser.). (Illus.). 48p. (J). lib. bdg. 25.26 (978-0-7660-5061-7(0) , MyReportLinks.com Bks.) Enslow Pubs., Inc.

Harcourt School Publishers Staff. Trofeos Advanced Level: El Oso Panda. 3rd ed. 2002. (SPA., Illus.). pap. 6.80 (978-0-15-323946-5(8)) Harcourt Schl. Pubs.

—The Wild Giant Panda Advanced Level. 3rd ed. 2002. (Trophies Reading Program Ser.). (Illus.). pap. 5.10 (978-0-15-323035-6(5)) Harcourt Schl. Pubs.

Imbriaco, Alison. The Giant Panda: Help Save This Endangered Species! 2006. (Saving Endangered Species Ser.). (Illus.). 128p. (J). lib. bdg. 33.27 (978-1-59845-037-8(9) , MyReportLinks.com Bks.) Enslow Pubs., Inc.

Johnson, Jinny. Giant Panda. Rosewarne, Graham, illus. 2005. 32p. (J). (gr. 2-5). lib. bdg. 27.10 (978-1-58340-645-8(X)) Smart Apple Media.

Kueffner, Sue. Pandas. 2007. (J). (*978-1-59939-126-7(0) , Reader's Digest Young Families, Inc.) Reader's Digest Children's Publishing, Inc.

Lantier-Sampon, Patricia & Feeney, Kathy. The Wonder of Pandas. McGee, John F., illus. 2001. (Animal Wonders Ser.). 48p. (J). (gr. 1 up). lib. bdg. 26.00 (978-0-8368-2768-2(6)) Stevens, Gareth Inc.

Levine, Michelle. Giant Pandas. 2006. (Pull Ahead Books). (Illus.). 32p. (J). 22.60 (978-0-8225-3482-2(7) , Lerner Pubns.) Lerner Publishing Group.

Levine, Stuart P. My Panda Book. 2007. 16p. (J). 5.99 (*978-0-06-089962-2(X)) HarperCollins Pubs.

Miller, Sara Swan. Red Pandas. 2008. (J). lib. bdg. (*978-1-4042-4164-0(7) , PowerKids Pr.) Rosen Publishing Group, Inc., The.

Murray, Julie. Pandas. 2005. (Animal Kingdom Set Ii Ser.). (Illus.). 24p. (J). (gr. k-4). lib. bdg. 21.35 (978-1-59197-329-4(5)) ABDO Publishing Co.

Panda. 1999. (Pocket Pals Ser.). (FRE.). (J). (ps-1). pap. 1.99 (978-0-85953-737-7(4)) Child's Play-International.

Pandas & other Animals. 2007. 24p. pap. 2.99 (*978-1-4037-3438-9(0)) Dalmatian Pr.

Panda's Bamboo Forest. 2002. (Animal's Around the World Mini Bks.). (Illus.). 32p. (J). (978-1-59069-167-0(9) , H4003) Studio Mouse LLC.

Pandas Have Cubs. (Animals & Their Young Ser.). 24p. (J). 7.95 (978-0-7565-1244-6(1)) Compass Point Bks.

Penny, Malcolm. Giant Panda. 2000. (Natural World Ser.). (Illus.). 48p. (J). (gr. 4-7). pap. 9.95 (978-0-7398-2028-5(1)) Steck-Vaughn.

—Giant Panda: Habitats, Life Cycles, Food Chains, Threats. 2000. (Natural World Ser.). (Illus.). 48p. (J). (gr. 4-7). lib. bdg. 27.12 (978-0-7398-1063-7(4)) Raintree.

Pingry, Patricia A. Baby Panda. Sharp, Chris, illus. 2004. (San Diego Zoo Animal Library: Vol. 7). 26p. (J). bds. 6.95 (978-0-8249-6555-6(8)) Ideals Pubns.

Pohl, Kathleen. Pandas. 2007. (J). pap. (*978-0-8368-8227-8(X)); 24p. lib. bdg. 19.93 (*978-0-8368-8220-9(2)) Stevens, Gareth Inc. (Weekly Reader Early Learning Library).

—Pandas: Pandas. 2007. (SPA & ENG.). (J). (*978-0-8368-8241-4(5) , Weekly Reader Early Learning Library) Stevens, Gareth Inc.

—Pandas/Pandas. 2007. (Animals I See at the Zoo/Animales que Veo en el Zoologico Ser.). (SPA & ENG.). 24p. (J). (gr. k-2). 19.93 (*978-0-8368-8234-6(2) , Weekly Reader Early Learning Library) Stevens, Gareth Inc.

Ryder, Joanne. Little Panda: The World Welcomes Hua Mei at the San Diego Zoo. World-Famous San Diego Zoo Staff, photos by. 2004. (Illus.). 32p. (J). 6.99 (978-0-689-86616-6(X) , Aladdin) Simon & Schuster Children's Publishing.

—Little Panda: The World Welcomes Hua Mei at the San Diego Zoo. 2001. (Illus.). 32p. (J). (gr. 1-3). 16.95 (978-0-689-84310-5(0)) Simon & Schuster Children's Publishing.

Scheff, Duncan. Giant Pandas. 2002. (Animals of the Rain Forest Ser.). (Illus.). 32p. (YA). lib. bdg. 22.83 (978-0-7398-5529-4(8)) Raintree.

Shively, Julie. Baby Panda Book & Stuffed Panda, Set. 2006. (Illus.). 26p. (J). bds. 16.95 (978-0-8249-6675-1(9)) Ideals Pubns.

Simon, Mary Manz. Panda Is Polite. 2006. (First Virtuestm for Toddlers Ser.). (Illus.). 20p. (J). 5.99 (978-0-7847-1577-2(7) , 04071) Standard Publishing.

Spilsbury, Louise & Spilsbury, Richard. Save the Giant Panda. 2006. (Illus.). 32p. (J). 25.36 (978-1-4034-7807-8(4)); pap. (978-1-4034-7815-3(5)) Heinemann Library.

Stone, Lynn M. Giant Pandas. 2004. (Nature Watch Ser.). (Illus.). 48p. (J). 25.26 (978-1-57505-343-1(8) , Carolrhoda Bks.) Lerner Publishing Group.

—Giant Pandas. Su, Keren, illus. Su, Keren, photos by. 2001. (Early Bird Nature Bks.). 48p. (J). (gr. 2-4). lib. bdg. 25.26 (978-0-8225-3042-8(2) , Lerner Pubns.) Lerner Publishing Group.

—Panda. 2001. (Wildlife in Danger Ser.). (Illus.). 24p. (gr. 1-4). 14.95 (978-1-58952-020-2(3)) Rourke Publishing, LLC.

Theodorou, Rod. Giant Panda. 2000. (Animals in Danger Ser.). (Illus.). 32p. (J). (gr. k-2). lib. bdg. 21.36 (978-1-57572-264-1(X)) Heinemann Library.

Tracqui, Valerie. Panda: Wild about Bamboo. 1999. (Animal Close-Ups Ser.). (978-0-606-18028-3(1)) Tandem Library Bks.

Volke, Gordon, et al, illus. Panda Patrol Sticker, Story & Activity Book, Vol. 2. 2004. 16p. pap., act. bk. ed. 6.00 (978-1-84161-112-9(3)) Ravette Publishing, Ltd. GBR. *Dist:* Parkwest Pubns., Inc.

—Panda Patrol Sticker, Story & Activity Book. 2004. 16p. pap., act. bk. ed. 6.00 (978-1-84161-072-6(0)) Ravette Publishing, Ltd. GBR. *Dist:* Parkwest Pubns., Inc.

—Panda Patrol Travel Games with Stickers. 2004. 16p. pap., act. bk. ed. 6.00 (978-1-84161-110-5(7)) Ravette Publishing, Ltd. GBR. *Dist:* Parkwest Pubns., Inc.

Ward, Rebecca. Panda. 1999. (J). (978-1-84100-213-2(5)) Quadrillion Publishing.

Wexo, John Bonnett. Giant Pandas. 2001. (Zoobooks). (Illus.). 24p. (J). (gr. 1-7). 15.95 (978-1-888153-32-3(6) , 228-9) Wildlife Education, Ltd.

PANDAS—FICTION

Adams, Pam. Proud Parents Panda. 2004. (Illus.). 12p. (J). bds. 5.99 (978-0-85953-681-3(5)) Child's Play-International.

Allen, Margaret. Click, Click. 1999. (ps-2). lib. bdg. 10.65 (978-0-613-34145-5(7)) Tandem Library Bks.

Amato, Carol A. The Giant Panda. Werizel, David, illus. 2001. (Young Reader Ser.). (J). lib. bdg. 14.95 (978-1-56674-303-7(6)) Forest Hse. Publishing Co., Inc.

Bamboo Zoo Set: Meet Lester Panda & his Friends. 2006. (J). 17.95 (978-0-9774493-1-6(9)) Bamboo Zoo, LLC.

Barber, Antonia & So, Meilo. The Monkey & the Panda. 1999. (Illus.). 32p. (J). (ps-4). pap. 7.99 (978-0-7112-1085-1(3)) Lincoln, Frances Ltd. GBR. *Dist:* Transition Vendor.

Bell, Frank. Feng Suey's Special Garden. Seaman, Paul, illus. 2004. 24p. pap. 7.00 (978-1-84161-071-9(2)) Ravette Publishing, Ltd. GBR. *Dist:* Parkwest Pubns., Inc.

—How Slip Slap Slop Got His Name. Seaman, Paul, illus. 2004. 24p. pap. 7.00 (978-1-84161-069-6(0)) Ravette Publishing, Ltd. GBR. *Dist:* Parkwest Pubns., Inc.

—Ma Jong & the Magic Carpet. Seaman, Paul, illus. 2004. 24p. pap. 7.00 (978-1-84161-070-2(4)) Ravette Publishing, Ltd. GBR. *Dist:* Parkwest Pubns., Inc.

Book Buddy: Panda with Story Book. Orig. Title: Child's Play. (Illus.). 10p. (J). (ps-3). reprint ed. (978-1-881469-44-5(1)) Safari, Ltd.

Bowen, Sherry. Little Panda. Wallace, Chad, illus. 2003. (Books for Young Learners). 12p. (J). pap. 5.00 net. (978-1-57274-673-2(4) , 2459) Owen, Richard C. Pubs., Inc.

Briant, Ed. A Day at the Beach. Briant, Ed, illus. 2006. (Illus.). 32p. (J). 16.99 (978-0-06-079981-6(1)); No. 1. lib. bdg. 17.89 (978-0-06-079982-3(X)) HarperCollins Pubs.

Brown, Beverly Swerdlow. Panda's Birthday Surprise. Christian, Sara, illus. 1998. 8p. (J). (gr. k-2). pap. 3.75 (978-1-880612-80-4(1) , Seedling Pubns.) Continental Pr., Inc.

Cook, Sherry & Johnson, Terri. Pressure Pete, 26 vols. Kuhn, Jesse, illus. l.t. ed. 2006. (Quirkles—Exploring Phonics through Science Ser.: 16). 32p. (J). 7.99 (978-1-933815-15-2(9) , Quirkles, The) Creative 3, LLC.

Cornish, Linda Sowa Young. Pong's Birthday Journey. 2006. (J). pap. 15.00 (978-0-8059-6993-1(4)) Dorrance Publishing Co., Inc.

Cousins, Lucy. Where Is Maisy's Panda? A Lift-the-Flap Book. Cousins, Lucy, illus. 1999. (Maisy Bks.). (Illus.). 14p. (J). (gr. k-k). bds. 4.99 (978-0-7636-0753-1(3)) Candlewick Pr.

Delval, Marie-Helene. Como estas, pequeno Panda? Courtin, Thierry, illus. 2004. (Palabras menudas Ser.). (SPA.). 14p. 5.95 (978-84-7864-707-1(4)) Combel Editorial, S.A. ESP. *Dist:* Independent Pubs. Group.

DK Publishing. Kung Fu Panda: the Warrior's Guide: The Warrior's Guide. 2008. 48p. (J). (gr. 2-6). 12.99 (*978-0-7566-3825-2(9)) Dorling Kindersley Publishing, Inc.

—Kung Fu Panda Ultimate Sticker Book. 2008. (Ultimate Sticker Bks.). 16p. (J). (gr. 2-6). pap. 6.99 (*978-0-7566-3824-5(0)) Dorling Kindersley Publishing, Inc.

Dowson, Nick. Tracks of a Panda. Rong, Yu, illus. 2007. 32p. (J). (gr. k-3). 16.99 (*978-0-7636-3146-8(9)) Candlewick Pr.

Dunbar, Joyce. Gander's Pond. Craig, Helen, illus. 1998. (Panda & Gander Stories Ser.). (J). pap. (978-0-7636-0721-0(5)) Candlewick Pr.

—Pomegranate Seeds. Craig, Helen, illus. 1998. (Panda & Gander Stories Ser.). (J). pap. (978-0-7636-0707-4(X)) Candlewick Pr.

—The Secret Friend. Craig, Helen, illus. 1998. (Panda & Gander Stories Ser.). (J). pap. (978-0-7636-0719-7(3)) Candlewick Pr.

Effler, Jim, illus. A Home for Panda. 2005. (Soundprints' Amazing Animal Adventures! Ser.), 36p. (J). (ps-2). 9.95 (978-1-59249-058-5(1) , PS7152) Soundprints.

Ehrlich, Fred. Does a Panda Go to School? 2006. (Illus.). 28p. pap. 5.95 (978-1-59354-159-0(7)) Blue Apple Bks.

Foreman, Michael. Surprise! Surprise! 2004. (Illus.). 32p. (J). pap. (978-1-84270-379-3(X)) Andersen.

Gates-Galvin, Laura. Panda's Busy Day. Cohen, Jessie, photos by. 1999. (Let's Go to the Zoo! Ser.: Vol. 1). (Illus.). 16p. (J). (ps-k). bds. 5.95 (978-1-56899-794-0(9) , B9001) Soundprints.

Gibbs, Lynne. Ping Won't Share. Mitchell, Melanie, illus. 2003. (Growing Pains Ser.). 32p. (J). pap. 4.95 (978-1-57768-927-0(5)); 12.95 (978-1-57768-480-0(X)) School Specialty Publishing. (Gingham Dog Pr.).

Halsey, Megan. Three Pandas Planting. 2000. (978-0-606-17900-3(3)) Tandem Library Bks.

Hay DeSimone, Corkey. Panda Promise Activity & Coloring Book. Hay DeSimone, Corkey, illus. 2006. (J). 4.95 (978-0-9747921-9-4(5)) Gentle Giraffe Pr.

—Panda Promise Hard Bound: Hard Bound Book. Hay DeSimone, Corkey, illus. 2006. (J). 9.95 (978-0-9747921-7-0(9)) Gentle Giraffe Pr.

A Home for Panda. 2005. (Soundprints' Amazing Animal Adventures! Ser.). (Illus.). 36p. (J). (ps-2). 19.95 incl. reel tape (978-1-59249-392-0(0) , BC7102) Soundprints.

Kennaway, Adrienne. A Tale of Two Pandas. 2000. (Illus.). 16p. (J). (ps). 5.95 (978-1-899248-79-7(X)); 14.95 (978-1-899248-74-2(9)) Happy Cat Bks. GBR. *Dist:* Star Bright Bks., Inc.

Kraus, Robert. Milton the Early Riser. Aruego, Jose & Dewey, Ariane, illus. 2006. (Stories to Go! Ser.). 32p. (J). pap. 4.99 (978-1-4169-1856-1(6) , Aladdin) Simon & Schuster Children's Publishing.

Law, Felicia. The Bookseller Bird. Evans, Nicola, illus. 2005. (Bamboo & Friends Ser.). 24p. (J). (ps-7). lib. bdg. 22.60 (978-1-4048-1283-3(0)) Picture Window Bks.

—The Creeping Vine. Evans, Nicola, illus. 2005. (Bamboo & Friends Ser.). 24p. (J). (ps-3). lib. bdg. 22.60 (978-1-4048-1284-0(9)) Picture Window Bks.

—The Dragonfly. Philpott, Claire, illus. 2005. (Bamboo & Friends Ser.). 24p. (J). (ps-3). lib. bdg. 22.60 (978-1-4048-1302-1(0)) Picture Window Bks.

—The Flower's Busy Day. Evans, Nicola, illus. 2005. (Bamboo & Friends Ser.). 24p. (J). (ps-3). lib. bdg. 22.60 (978-1-4048-1281-9(4)) Picture Window Bks.

—Marvelous Meals. Evans, Nicola, illus. 2005. (Bamboo & Friends Ser.). 24p. (J). (ps-3). lib. bdg. 22.60 (978-1-4048-1285-7(7)) Picture Window Bks.

—The Snowflakes. Philpott, Claire & Radford, Karen, illus. 2007. (J). (978-1-4048-2597-0(5)) Picture Window Bks.

—The Tree. Philpott, Claire, illus. 2005. (Bamboo & Friends Ser.). 24p. (J). (ps-3). lib. bdg. 22.60 (978-1-4048-1301-4(2)) Picture Window Bks.

Luther, Jacqueline. Panda Bear Cub. Nelson, Will, illus. 2006. (Soundprints' Read-And-Discover Ser.). 32p. (J). pap. 3.95 (978-1-59249-585-6(0)) Soundprints.

Lynn, Jeffrey. The Adventures of Pablo, . the Ecuadorian Panda. 2004. (YA). per. (978-0-9763025-0-6(0)) Penner/Lynn Publishing.

Martin, Bill, Jr. Panda Bear, Panda Bear, What Do You See? Carle, Eric, illus. rev. ed. 2003. 32p. (J). 16.95 (978-0-8050-1758-8(5) , Holt, Henry & Co. Bks. For Young Readers) Holt, Henry & Co.

Mathur-Kamat, Ambika. Miss Panda in England & Scotland. Crawford, K. Michael, illus. 2001. (Miss Panda Ser.). 40p. (J). (ps-5). pap. 11.99 (978-1-883573-01-0(7) , Little Blue Works) Windstorm Creative.

Meredith Books Staff, ed. I Can Find It Kung Fu Panda. 2008. 22p. 7.99 (*978-0-696-23484-2(X)) Meredith Bks.

—Kung Fu Panda 3-D Puzzle BK. 2008. 10p. 9.99 (*978-0-696-23485-9(8)) Meredith Bks.

—Kung Fu Panda BK w/Activity Kit. 2008. 32p. 14.99 (*978-0-696-23483-5(1)) Meredith Bks.

—Kung Fu Panda Soundbook. 2008. 22p. 15.95 (*978-0-696-23482-8(3)) Meredith Bks.

Milbourne, A. & Wells, R. Panda in the Park. 2004. (Look-Through Board Bks.). (Illus.). 10p. (J). (ps up). 4.95 (978-0-7945-0158-7(3) , Usborne) EDC Publishing.

Murphy, Mary. Panda Foo & the New Friend. Murphy, Mary, illus. 2007. (Illus.). 32p. (J). (ps-k). 15.99 (*978-0-7636-3405-6(0)) Candlewick Pr.

Muth, Jon J. Zen Shorts (Collector's Edition) 2008. 40p. (J). 25.00 (*978-0-545-04087-7(6) , Scholastic) Scholastic, Inc.

—Zen Ties. 2008. (J). pap. (*978-0-439-63425-0(3) , Scholastic Pr.) Scholastic, Inc.

Nagda, Ann Whitehead. A Home for Panda. 2005. (Soundprints' Amazing Animal Adventures! Ser.). (Illus.). (J). (ps-2). 32p. 2.95 (978-1-59249-047-9(6) , S7152); 36p. 8.95 incl. audio (978-1-59249-393-7(9) , SC7102) Soundprints.

—A Home for Panda. Effler, Jim, illus. 2005. (Amazing Animal Adventures Ser.). 36p. (J). (ps-2). 15.95 (978-1-59249-045-5(X) , B7102); pap. 6.95 (978-1-59249-046-2(8) , S7102) Soundprints.

Nagda, Ann Whitehead, text. Time to Eat, Panda! 2005. (Soundprints' Read-and-Discover Ser.). (Illus.). 32p. (J). (ps-1). pap. 3.95 (978-1-59249-147-6(2) , S2011) Soundprints.

Pandas Are Coming! Fourth Grade Guided Comprehension Level O. (On Our Way to English Ser.). (gr. 4 up). 34.50 (978-0-7578-7167-2(4)) Rigby Education.

Pandas in the Mountains: Individual Title, 6 packs. 16p. (gr. 2 up). 35.00 (978-0-7635-9385-8(0)) Rigby Education.

Papineau, Lucie. Gilda the Giraffe & Papaya the Panda. Sarrazin, Marisol, illus. 2005. (Gilda the Giraffe Ser.). 32p. (J). (ps-3). lib. bdg. 22.60 (978-1-4048-1293-2(8)) Picture Window Bks.

—Papaya the Panda. Phillips, Charles, tr. Sarrazin, Marisol, illus. 1999. (Adventures of Gilda Ser.). 32p. (J). (ps up). pap. (978-1-894363-18-1(3)) Dominique & Friends.

Piquemal, Michel. The Panda. Nomdedeu, Clara & Merlin, C., illus. 2000. (My Animal Library). 32p. (J). (ps-1). pap. 6.95 (978-0-7892-0664-0(1)) Abbeville Pr., Inc.

Powell, Richard. Peter Panda. Rhodes, Katie, illus. 2004. (Fuzzy Friends Ser.). 10p. (J). 7.95 (978-1-58925-721-4(9) , tiger tales) ME Media LLC.

Roy, Ron. The Panda Puzzle. Gurney, John Steven, illus. 2002. (A to Z Mysteries Ser.: No. 16). 96p. (J). (gr. k-3). lib. bdg. 11.99 (978-0-375-90271-0(6)); (gr. 2-5). mass mkt. 3.99 (978-0-375-80271-3(1)) Random Hse. Children's Bks. (Random Hse. Bks. for Young Readers).

—The Panda Puzzle. Gurney, John Steven, illus. 2002. (A to Z Mysteries Ser.: No. 16). 84p. (J). (ps-k). lib. bdg. 11.80 (978-0-613-50485-0(2)) Tandem Library Bks.

Sang, Franchesca Ho, compiled by. Wisdom of Pandas. 2006. (Illus.). 128p. (J). (978-1-59258-253-2(2)) Hylas Publishing.

Sargent, Dave & Sargent, Pat. Patty Panda: Disposition, 56 vols., 54. Lenoir, Jane, illus. 2000. (Cherokee Indian Legend Ser.: Vol. 54). 36p. (J). lib. bdg. 19.95 (978-1-56763-549-2(0)) Ozark Publishing.

Shealeya, Mildred. Pookie Lookie: The Pink Spotted Panda Bear. Gang, Jobie, illus. 2007. 32p. (J). per. 12.95 (*978-0-9669595-7-4(4)) SMS Cos., Inc.

Wahl, Jan. Three Pandas. Naava, Jan, photos by. 2003. (Illus.). 32p. (J). (ps up). 15.95 (978-1-56397-749-7(4)) Boyds Mills Pr.

PANTHERS

Big Cats. 2004. (Explorasaws Ser.). (Illus.). 48p. (J). pap. (978-1-84229-758-2(9)) Top That! Publishing PLC.

Caper, William. Florida Panthers: Struggle for Survival. 2008. (J). lib. bdg. 25.27 (*978-1-59716-532-7(8)) Bearport Publishing Co., Inc.

Fletcher, Marty & Scherer, Glenn. The Florida Panther: Help Save This Endangered Species! 2006. (Saving Endangered Species Ser.). (Illus.). 128p. (J). lib. bdg. 33.27 (978-1-59845-034-7(4) , MyReportLinks.com Bks.) Enslow Pubs., Inc.

Group/McGraw-Hill, Wright. Panther Level: Adventure Journal Set. (Wildcatstm Ser.). (gr. 2-8). 31.95 (978-0-322-05793-7(0)) Wright Group, The.

—Panther Level: Wildcats Panther Complete Kit. (Wildcatstm Ser.). (gr. 2-8). 599.95 (978-0-322-06490-4(2)) Wright Group, The.

Wexo, John Bonnett. Panteras. Rountree, Monica, tr. 2003. (Zoobooks). Orig. Title: Bit Cats. (SPA., Illus.). 24p. (J). (gr. k-6). lib. bdg. 15.95 (978-1-888153-80-4(6)) Wildlife Education, Ltd.

PANTHERS—FICTION

Costello, Emily. Realm of the Panther: A Story of South Florida's Forest. 2005. (Soundprints' Wild Habitats Ser.). (Illus.). 32p. (J). (gr. 1-4). 8.95 incl. audio (978-1-59249-104-9(9)) Soundprints.

Farley, Steven. The Yearling. Schwartz, Joanie, illus. 1999. (Young Black Stallion Ser.: No. 5). 144p. (J). (gr. 4-6). lib. bdg. 11.99 (978-0-375-90091-4(8) , Random Hse. Bks. for Young Readers) Random Hse. Children's Bks.

—The Yearling. 1999. (Young Black Stallion Ser.: No. 5). (J). (gr. 4-6). (978-0-606-16964-6(4)) Tandem Library Bks.

Harrison, Emma. The Pink Panther Movie Storybook. 2006. (Illus.). 48p. (gr. 2-5). pap. 6.99 (978-0-7868-3714-4(4)) Hyperion Bks. for Children.

Law, Felicia. Rumble Meets Penny Panther. 2005. (Read-It! Readers Ser.). (Illus.). 32p. (J). (ps-k). lib. bdg. 18.60 (978-1-4048-1331-1(4)) Picture Window Bks.

Puerto, Carlos. Las Alas de la Pantera. (Barco de Vapor). (SPA.). 128p. (YA). (gr. 5-8). (978-84-348-4667-8(5)) SM Ediciones.

Sarfati, Sonia. Panthere, Civiere et Vive Colere. 2000. (Premier Roman Ser.). (FRE.). 64p. (J). (gr. 2-5). pap. (978-2-89021-406-4(0)) Diffusion du livre Mirabel.

Sargent, Dave & Sargent, Pat. Bingo the Black Panther: Practice Makes Perfect, 56 vols., Vol. 24. Huff, Jeane, illus. 2001. (Animal Pride Ser.: Vol. 24). 36p. (J). lib. bdg. 19.95 (978-1-56763-364-1(1)) Ozark Publishing.

—Leo Lion: Responsibility, 56 vols., 51. Lenoir, Jane, illus. 2001. (Animal Pride Ser.: Vol. 51). 36p. (J). lib. bdg. 19.95 (978-1-56763-541-6(5)) Ozark Publishing.

Sargent, Dave, et al. Leo Lion: Responsibility, 17, 51. 2000. (Animal Pride Ser.: 51). (Illus.). 42p. (J). pap. 6.95 (978-1-56763-542-3(3)) Ozark Publishing.

Sargent, Pat. The Black Panther, 8, Vol. 2. Lenoir, Jane, illus. 2003. (Barney the Bear Killer Ser.: Vol. 2). 137p. (J). lib. bdg. 25.25 (978-1-56763-965-0(8)) Ozark Publishing.

Thomas, Lowell P. The Panther & the Windigo. 2002. (Illus.). 264p. (YA). (gr. 5-9). per. 10.99 (978-0-9668559-3-7(0)) East of the Sun Publishing.

Townsend, John. Hunter's Moon. Dietrich, Sean, illus. 2007. (J). 80p. (*978-1-59889-352-6(1)); 71p. pap. (*978-1-59889-447-9(1)) Stone Arch Bks.

Wallace, Bill. Danger on Panther Peak. 2008. 176p. (J). pap. 5.99 (*978-1-4169-4110-1(X) , Aladdin) Simon & Schuster Children's Publishing.

Wallin, Luke. Ceremony of the Panther. 2001. 136p. (YA). (gr. 4-7). pap. 11.95 (978-0-595-19275-5(0)) iUniverse, Inc.

Warner, Gertrude Chandler, creator. The Panther Mystery, Vol. 66. 1998. (Boxcar Children Ser.: No. 66). (Illus.). 128p. (J). (gr. 2-5). pap. 4.50 (978-0-8075-6328-1(5)) Whitman, Albert & Co.

PAPACY—HISTORY

Marchione, Margherita. Pope Pius XII: Bilingual Coloring Book. Elliott, John, illus. 2004. (SPA & ENG.). 32p. 1.00 (978-0-8091-6721-0(2) , 6721-2) Paulist Pr.

PAPER

Costain, Meredith. Making Paper. 2000. (gr. k-3). lib. bdg. 11.80 (978-0-613-30593-8(0)) Tandem Library Bks.

Doney, Meryl. Paper Crafts. 2004. (Crafts from Many Cultures Ser.). (Illus.). 32p. (J). (gr. 3 up). lib. bdg. 23.33 (978-0-8368-4046-9(1)) Stevens, Gareth Inc.

Fix, Alexandra. Paper. 2007. (J). (*978-1-4034-9712-3(5)); pap. (*978-1-4034-9720-8(6)) Heinemann Library.

Kras, Sara Louise. Paper. 2004. (First Facts Ser.). (Illus.). 24p. (J). 15.95 (978-0-7368-2513-9(4)) Capstone Pr., Inc.

Levete, Sarah. Paper. 2006. (Material Matters Ser.). (978-1-59389-271-5(3)) Chrysalis Education.

Oxlade, Chris. How We Use Paper. (Using Materials Ser.). (Illus.). (J). 2005. 32p. (gr. 6-9). lib. bdg. 25.70 (978-1-4109-0603-8(5)); Pack. 2004. pap. 40.50 (978-1-4109-0901-5(8)) Harcourt Schl. Pubs.

—Paper. (Materials, Materials, Materials Ser.). 32p. pap. 6.95 (978-1-4034-4099-0(9)); 2001. (Illus.). (J). lib. bdg. 21.36 (978-1-58810-156-3(8)) Heinemann Library.

Paper. (Jump Ser.). (Illus.). 36p. (J). (gr. 2-6). pap. (978-1-882210-33-6(6)) Action Publishing, Inc.

Richards, Roy. En Papel. (Coleccion 101 Trucos Cientificos). (SPA., Illus.). (J). (gr. 3-5). pap. (978-950-724-178-9(7) , LMA8752) Lumen ARG. *Dist:* Lectorum Pubns., Inc.

Royston, Angela. Paper: Let's Look at a Comic Book. 2005. (Heinemann Read & Learn Ser.). (Illus.). 24p. (J). (978-1-4034-7671-5(3)); pap. (978-1-4034-7680-7(2)) Heinemann Library.

Smith, A. G. Cut & Make GI Paper Soldiers. 1999. (Illus.). (J). pap. 5.95 (978-0-486-40581-0(8)) Dover Pubns., Inc.

Smith, Terri Peterson. Paper. 2003. (Matter & Materials Ser.). (J). pap. (978-1-58417-165-2(0)); lib. bdg. (978-1-58417-159-1(6)) Lake Street Pubs.

Thomson, Ruth. Paper. 2006. (Illus.). 29p. (978-1-58340-940-4(8) , 1262423) Smart Apple Media.

Walker, Kate. Paper. 2004. (Recycle, Reduce, Reuse, Rethink Ser.). lib. bdg. 27.10 (978-1-58340-558-1(5)) Smart Apple Media.

PAPER CRAFT

see Paper Work

PAPER FOLDING (HANDICRAFT)

see Paper Work

PAPER MAKING AND TRADE

see also Book Industries and Trade

Barraclough, Sue. A Paper Bag. 2006. (How It's Made Ser.). (Illus.). 32p. (J). lib. bdg. (978-0-8368-6703-9(3)) Stevens, Gareth Inc.

Brocker, Susan. Paper Trail: History of an Everyday Material. 2007. (Shockwave: Technology & Manufacturing Ser.). (Illus.). 36p. (J). (gr. 4-6). lib. bdg. 25.00 (*978-0-531-17589-7(8) , Children's Pr.) Scholastic Library Publishing.

Draper, Allison Stark. Choosing a Career in the Pulp & Paper Industry. 2005. (World of Work Ser.). (Illus.). 64p. (YA). (gr. 7-12). lib. bdg. 25.25 (978-0-8239-3333-4(4)) Rosen Publishing Group, Inc., The.

Fisher, Leonard Everett. The Papermakers. 2000. (Colonial Craftsmen Ser.). (Illus.). 48p. (J). (gr. 4-8). lib. bdg. 21.36 (978-0-7614-1147-5(X) , Benchmark Bks.) Cavendish, Marshall Corp.

Harcourt School Publishers Staff. Where Paper Comes From. 3rd ed. 2002. (Horizons Ser.). (Illus.). (J). pap. 3.70 (978-0-15-333148-0(8)) Harcourt Schl. Pubs.

How to Make Paper: Third Grade Guided Reading Level K. (On Our Way to English Ser.). (gr. 3 up). 34.50 (978-0-7578-7122-1(4)) Rigby Education.

Hufford, Deborah. Book Making & Paper Making: Be Your Own Publisher. 2005. (Snap Books Craft Ser.). (Illus.). 32p. (J). (gr. 3-5). lib. bdg. 22.60 (978-0-7368-4382-9(5)) Capstone Pr., Inc.

Kras, Sara Louise. Paper. 2004. (First Facts Ser.). (Illus.). 24p. (J). 15.95 (978-0-7368-2513-9(4)) Capstone Pr., Inc.

Llewellyn, Claire. Paper. 2002. (Material World Ser.). (J). (gr. 2-4). pap. 6.95 (978-0-531-14831-0(9) , Watts, Franklin) Scholastic Library Publishing.

—Paper. 2005. (Illus.). 24p. (J). (gr. 1-4). lib. bdg. 22.80 (978-1-932889-54-3(X)) Sea-To-Sea Pubns.

Making Paper: Individual Title Six-Packs. (Rigby Focus Ser.). 16p. (gr. 1 up). 28.00 (978-0-7578-5309-8(9)); 30.00 (978-0-7578-5541-2(5)) Rigby Education.

Marshall, Pam. From Tree to Paper. (From Start to Finish Ser.). (J). 2003. (Illus.). 24p. 18.60 (978-0-8225-0720-8(X) , Lerner Pubns.); 2002. pap. 4.95 (978-0-8225-0672-0(6)) Lerner Publishing Group.

Snyder, Inez. Trees to Paper. 2003. (How Things Are Made Ser.). (Illus.). 24p. (J). 18.00 (978-0-516-24264-4(4) , Children's Pr.); pap. 4.95 (978-0-516-24356-6(X) , Watts, Franklin) Scholastic Library Publishing.

—Trees to Paper. 2003. (gr. k-3). lib. bdg. 12.95 (978-0-613-59745-6(1)) Tandem Library Bks.

Walker, Kate. Paper. 2004. (Recycle, Reduce, Reuse, Rethink Ser.). lib. bdg. 27.10 (978-1-58340-558-1(5)) Smart Apple Media.

PAPER MONEY

Dahl, Michael. Pass the Buck! A Fun Song about the Famous Faces & Places on American Money. D'Antonio, Sandra, illus. 2004. (Fun Songs Ser.). 24p. (gr. k-3). 22.60 (978-1-4048-0132-5(4)) Picture Window Bks.

Giesecke, Ernestine. From Seashells to Smart Cards: Money & Currency. 2003. (Everyday Economics Ser.). (Illus.). 48p. (J). (gr. 3-5). lib. bdg. 27.07 (978-1-58810-491-5(5)) Heinemann Library.

Kompelien, Tracy. We Have the Skills to Know U. S. Bills. 2007. (Illus.). 24p. (J). 19.93 (978-1-59928-549-8(5) , SandCastle) ABDO Publishing Co.

—We Have the Skills to Know U.S. Bills! 2006. (Illus.). 24p. (J). (978-1-59928-550-4(9)) ABDO Publishing Co.

Rau, Dana Meachen. Paper Money. 2005. (Money & Banks Ser.). (Illus.). 24p. (J). pap. (978-0-8368-4877-9(2)); lib. bdg. 19.33 (978-0-8368-4870-0(5)) Stevens, Gareth Inc.

PAPER SCULPTURE

see Paper Work

PAPER WORK

see also names of paper crafts, e.g. Origami.

Akaishi, Shinobu & Eno, Sarris, eds. Animals: Lion & Mouse (Kumon 3-D Paper Crafts), 2 vols. 2005. (Illus.). 24p. (J). per. 5.95 (978-1-933241-17-3(9)) Kumon Publishing North America, Inc.

Akaishi, Shinobu & Sarris, Eno, eds. Dinosaurs: Tyrannosaurus & Apatosaurus (Kumon 3-D Paper Crafts), 2 vols. 2005. (Illus.). 24p. (J). per. 5.95 (978-1-933241-16-6(0)) Kumon Publishing North America, Inc.

—My Book of Amazing Crafts. 2006. (Illus.). 80p. (J). per. 6.95 (978-1-933241-30-2(6)) Kumon Publishing North America, Inc.

Allert, Kathy. Helen Scot Sticker Paper Doll. 2001. (Illus.). 4p. (J). pap. 1.50 (978-0-486-41631-1(3)) Dover Pubns., Inc.

—Little Northwest Indian Girl Paper Doll. 2000. (Illus.). 8p. (J). pap. 1.50 (978-0-486-40998-6(8)) Dover Pubns., Inc.

—Nurse Paper Doll. 2000. (J). pap. 1.00 (978-0-486-41307-5(1)) Dover Pubns., Inc.

—Teacher Paper Doll. 2000. (J). pap. 1.00 (978-0-486-41311-2(X)) Dover Pubns., Inc.

Amerikaner, Phyllis. The Jewish Paper Doll Book: Celebrating Special Days Throughout the Jewish Year. Clark Editorial and Design Staff, ed. Aronoff, Rae, illus. 1998. 56p. (J). (gr. k-7). pap. 9.95 (978-0-88160-306-4(6) , LW375) Creative Teaching Pr., Inc.

—Paper Doll Christmas: Holiday Fun for Creative Kids. Clark Editorial and Design Staff, ed. Aronoff, Rae, illus. 1998. 56p. (J). (gr. k-7). pap. 9.95 (978-0-88160-304-0(X) , LW373) Creative Teaching Pr., Inc.

Axe, John. Effanbee's Wee Patsy Paper Dolls & Playhouse: Wee Edition. 2000. (Illus.). (J). (gr. 4-7). pap. (978-0-87588-461-5(X)) Hobby Hse. Pr., Inc.

Balchin, Judy. Paper Mache. 2000. (Step-by-Step Ser.). (Illus.). 32p. (J). (gr. 3-5). lib. bdg. 24.22 (978-1-57572-328-0(X)) Heinemann Library.

—Papier Mache. 2003. (Step-by-Step Ser.). (Illus.). 32p. pap. 7.95 (978-1-4034-0706-1(1)) Heinemann Library.

—Papier Mache. 2001. (Step-by-Step Children's Crafts Ser.). (Illus.). 32p. pap. 7.95 (978-0-85532-912-9(2) , 9122) Search Pr., Ltd. GBR. *Dist:* Independent Pubs. Group.

—Papier Mache. 2002. (gr. 3-6). lib. bdg. 16.40 (978-0-613-88909-4(6)) Tandem Library Bks.

Barker, Cicely Mary. Flower Fairies Paper Dolls. 2005. 13p. (J). 6.99 (978-0-7232-5432-4(X) , Warne) Penguin Group (USA) Inc.

Bawden, Juliet & Moxley, Susan. Papier Mache. 2004. (Crafty Ideas Ser.). (SPA., Illus.). 32p. (gr. 2-5). (J). pap. 5.95 (978-1-58728-127-3(9)); 9.95 (978-1-58728-259-1(3)) T&N Children's Publishing. (Two Can Publishing).

Beylon, Cathy. Amanda Dresses up Sticker Paper Doll. 1999. (Illus.). 4p. (J). 1.50 (978-0-486-40753-1(5)) Dover Pubns., Inc.

Biddle, Steve. Underwater Origami. Biddle, Megumi, illus. 2001. (Drawing, Paper Folding & Craft Books for Children). 32p. (J). lib. bdg. 18.95 (978-1-56674-304-4(4)) Forest Hse. Publishing Co., Inc.

Blanchette, Peg & Thibault, Terri. Make Your Own Cool Cards: 40 Awesome Notes & Invitations! 2004. (Quick Starts for Kids! Ser.). (Illus.). 64p. (J). 8.95 (978-1-885593-96-2(1) , Williamson Bks.) Ideals Pubns.

Bliss, Helen. Paper. 1998. (Craft Workshop Ser.). (Illus.). 32p. (J). (gr. 3). pap. (978-0-86505-791-3(5)); lib. bdg. (978-0-86505-781-4(8)) Crabtree Publishing Co.

Boase, Petra & Beak, Nick Huckleberry. Crafty Badges. Freeman, John, photos by. 2000. (Crafty Kids Ser.). (Illus.). 64p. (J). (gr. 3 up). lib. bdg. 26.00 (978-0-8368-2500-8(4)) Stevens, Gareth Inc.

Bounford, Trevor. Paper Gliders: To Cut Out, Make & Fly. 2004. (Illus.). 32p. 10.00 (978-1-899618-54-5(6)) Tarquin Pubns. GBR. *Dist:* Parkwest Pubns., Inc.

Boursin, Didier. Folding for Fun: 16 Easy Origami Projects - For Ages 4 & Up. 2007. (Illus.). 64p. (J). (ps-12). 19.95 (*978-1-55407-253-8(0)) Firefly Bks., Ltd.

—Folding for Fun: For Ages 4 & Up. 2007. (Illus.). 64p. (J). (ps-12). pap. 9.95 (*978-1-55407-252-1(2)) Firefly Bks., Ltd.

—Origami Paper Airplanes. 2001. (Illus.). 64p. (J). (gr. 2-7). 19.95 (978-1-55209-626-0(2)); pap. 9.95 (978-1-55209-616-1(5)) Firefly Bks., Ltd.

—Origami Paper Airplanes. 2001. (gr. 3-6). lib. bdg. 18.75 (978-0-613-78566-2(5)) Tandem Library Bks.

—Paper Folding Fun. 2005. (I Made It Myself! Ser.). (Illus.). 24p. (J). lib. bdg. 22.00 (978-0-8368-5965-2(0)) Stevens, Gareth Inc.

Boyds Mills, ed. Paper Planes That Soar. 2006. 256p. pap. 16.98 (978-1-59078-388-7(3)) Boyds Mills Pr.

Broutzas, Sharon, et al. Paper Crafts. 1998. (Drawing, Paper Folding & Craft Books for Children). (Illus.). 48p. (J). (gr. k-5). lib. bdg. 17.95 (978-1-56674-229-0(3)) Forest Hse. Publishing Co., Inc.

Brust, Beth Wagner. The Amazing Paper Cuttings of Hans Christian Andersen. Seng, Terry & Andersen, Hans Christian, illus. 2003. 80p. (J). (gr. 5-6). pap. 9.95 (978-0-618-31109-5(2)) Houghton Mifflin Co. Trade & Reference Div.

—Amazing Paper Cuttings of Hans Christian Andersen. 2003. (gr. 5-8). lib. bdg. 18.75 (978-0-613-60760-5(0)) Tandem Library Bks.

Bull, Jane. Create-A-Card. 2006. 16p. (J). 15.99 (978-0-7566-1832-2(0)) Dorling Kindersley Publishing, Inc.

Bulloch, Ivan. Play with Paper. James, Diane, illus. rev. ed. 2000. (Let's Ser.). 24p. (J). (ps-1). 9.95 (978-1-58728-027-6(2)); pap. 5.95 (978-1-58728-031-3(0)) T&N Children's Publishing. (Two Can Publishing).

Bulloch, Ivan & James, Diane. Le Papier. 2000. (Let's Ser.). (FRE., Illus.). 24p. (J). (ps-1). pap. 4.95 (978-1-58728-210-2(0) , Two Can Publishing) T&N Children's Publishing.

Burke, Judy. Look What You Can Make with Paper Bags. Schneider, Hank, photos by. 2003. (Illus.). 48p. (YA). (ps-7). pap. 5.95 (978-1-56397-717-6(6)) Boyds Mills Pr.

—Look What You Can Make with Paper Bags. 1999. (gr. k-3). lib. bdg. 14.10 (978-0-613-16747-5(3)) Tandem Library Bks.

Burnett, Frances Hodgson. The Secret Garden Paper Dolls. adapted ed. 1998. (Illus.). 24p. (J). (ps-3). 7.95 (978-0-694-00969-5(5)) HarperCollins Pubs.

Cannon, Joanne Mary. Girlfriends Party Time Sticker Paper Dolls. 2006. 4p. (J). pap. 5.95 (978-0-486-44821-3(5)) Dover Pubns., Inc.

—Girlfriends Sticker Paper Dolls. 2004. 4p. (J). pap. 5.95 (978-0-486-43349-3(8)) Dover Pubns., Inc.

Carola, Leslie Conron & Grossman, Andrea. Mrs. Grossman's Sticker Magic. 2006. 128p. (978-0-88363-707-4(3)) Levin, Hugh Lauter Assocs.

Chapman, Gillian & Robson, Pam. Art from Packaging. 2007. (J). lib. bdg. (***978-1-4042-3724-7(0)*** , PowerKids Pr.) Rosen Publishing Group, Inc., The.

—Art from Paper. 2007. (J). lib. bdg. (***978-1-4042-3725-4(9)*** , PowerKids Pr.) Rosen Publishing Group, Inc., The.

Check, Laura. The Kids' Guide to Making Scrapbooks & Photo Albums! How to Collect, Design, Assemble, Decorate. Day, Betsy, illus. 2001. (Kids Can Bks.). 128p. (J). (gr. 3 up). pap. 12.95 (978-1-885593-59-7(7) , Williamson Bks.) Ideals Pubns.

Chicken Socks Editors. Make Your Own Paper Flowers. 2007. 18p. (J). (ps up). spiral bd. 12.95 (***978-1-59174-443-6(1)***) Klutz.

Collins, Francis. The Second Boys' Book of Model Aeroplanes. 2004. (Illus.). 262p. per. 16.95 (978-0-9758914-4-5(8)) Gustav's Library.

Cressy, Judith. What Can You Do with a Paper Bag? Hats, Wigs, Masks, Crowns, Helmets, & Headdresses Inspired by Works of Art from the Metropolitan Museum of Art. 2001. (gr. 3-6). lib. bdg. 24.55 (978-0-613-51097-4(6)) Tandem Library Bks.

Cressy, Judith, et al. What Can You Do with a Paper Bag? Hats, Wigs, Masks, Crowns, Helmets, & Headdresses Inspired by Works of Art from the Metropolitan Museum of Art. Heins, Edward et al, illus. Butler, Christine, photos by. 2001. 64p. (J). (gr. 3-7). pap. 15.95 (978-0-8118-3220-5(1)) Chronicle Bks. LLC.

Currier, Mary. Easy Paper Crafts. (Illus.). (J). Bk. 1. 1998. 119p. pap. 6.95 (978-0-87813-570-7(7)); Bk. 2. 1999. pap. 6.95 (978-0-87813-586-8(3)) Christian Light Pubns., Inc.

Curti, Anna, illus. Fun to Make Paper Craft. 1999. 40p. (J). (gr. k-3). 13.95 (978-1-85479-381-2(0)) O'Mara, Michael Bks., Ltd. GBR. *Dist:* Trans-Atlantic Pubns., Inc.

Curtis, Annabelle. Paper People: A Collection of Delightful Paper Characters to Make Yourself. 2004. (Illus.). 32p. (J). (ps-3). 12.00 (978-0-906212-61-5(8)) Tarquin Pubns. GBR. *Dist:* Parkwest Pubns., Inc.

Disney Staff. Make Your Own Valentines. 1999. (Illus.). 40p. (J). (gr. k-3). 7.99 (978-0-7364-0100-5(8)) Mouse Works.

Doherty, Patrick A. & Magruder, Trula. Paper Fun! Projects to Fold, Bend, Cut, & Curl! 2006. (Illus.). 48p. (YA). 17.95 (978-1-59369-104-2(1) , American Girl) American Girl Publishing, Inc.

Doney, Meryl. Paper Crafts. 2004. (Crafts from Many Cultures Ser.). (Illus.). 32p. (J). (gr. 3 up). lib. bdg. 23.33 (978-0-8368-4046-9(1)) Stevens, Gareth Inc.

—Papercrafts. 1998. (World Crafts Ser.). (Illus.). 32p. (J). (gr. 3-5). pap. 6.95 (978-0-531-15330-7(4) , Watts, Franklin) Scholastic Library Publishing.

Douglas, Vincent & School Specialty Publishing Staff. Paper & Paint. 2003. (Crafty Kids Ser.). (Illus.). 48p. (J). (gr. k-3). 12.95 (978-1-57768-527-2(X) , Waterbird Bks.) School Specialty Publishing.

Dover Staff. Girls from Around the World Sticker Paper Dolls: With over 300 Reusable Sticker Costumes. 2006. (Illus.). 18p. (J). (ps-3). pap. 9.95 (978-0-486-42895-6(8)) Dover Pubns., Inc.

—Metallic Foil Origami Paper. 2001. (Illus.). (gr. 3). pap. 5.95 (978-0-486-41770-7(0)) Dover Pubns., Inc.

Elliot, Adam, illus. Night Fighter: The Ultimate Book of Paper Airplanes. 2005. 80p. (J). pap. 14.95 (978-0-7641-3153-0(2)) Barron's Educational Series, Inc.

Fisher, Phyllis Mae Richardson, illus. Chrissy (#1 in the 1989 Family Friends Paper Doll Set) l.t. ed. 2004. 24p. (J). 10.00 (978-0-9745615-5-4(X)) PJs Corner.

—Janae, #3 in the 1989 Family Friends Paper Doll Set, Vol. 3. l.t. ed. 2003. 24p. (J). 10.00 (978-0-9745615-7-8(6)) PJs Corner.

—Melly, #2 in the 1989 Family Friends Paper Doll Set, Vols. 3, Vol. 2. l.t. ed. 2004. 24p. (J). 10.00 (978-0-9745615-6-1(8)) PJs Corner.

—Natasha, an International Friends Paper Doll from Russia. 2004. 15p. (J). 10.00 (978-0-9745615-8-5(4)) PJs Corner.

—Tess, an International Friends Paper Doll from Africa. 2004. (J). 10.00 (978-0-9745615-9-2(2)) PJs Corner.

Folder, Alan. Paper Tricks. Galvani, Maureen, illus. 2001. (Paper Magic Ser.). 48p. (J). (gr. 3-7). 7.95 (978-0-439-26034-3(5)) Scholastic, Inc.

Forte, Imogene. Holidays & Special Days. 2004. (Fun Things to Make & Do Ser.). (Illus.). 80p. (J). per. 9.95 (978-0-86530-616-5(8)) Incentive Pubns., Inc.

—Paper Capers. 2004. (Fun Things to Make & Do Ser.). (Illus.). 80p. (J). per. 9.95 (978-0-86530-615-8(X)) Incentive Pubns., Inc.

French, Cathy. Haz un avion de papel & Make a Paper Airplane. 2005. spiral bd. 66.00 (***978-1-4108-5631-9(3)***) Benchmark Education Co.

Gaylord, Susan Kapuscinski & Jabbour, Joyce. Make, Draw, & Design Your Own Book. Labat, Yancey C., illus. 2006. 48p. (J). (***978-0-439-81339-6(5)***) Scholastic, Inc.

Gilpin, Rebecca. Fairy Things to Make & Do. 2004. (Usborne Activities Ser.). (Illus.). 31p. (J). (978-0-439-67250-4(3)) Scholastic, Inc.

Green, Yuko. Korean Girl & Boy Paper Dolls. 2003. (Paper Dolls Ser.). (Illus.). 16p. (J). pap. 3.95 (978-0-486-43056-0(1)) Dover Pubns., Inc.

—Maya from India Sticker Paper Doll. 2002. (Illus.). 4p. (J). (gr. k-5). pap. 1.50 (978-0-486-41815-5(4)) Dover Pubns., Inc.

—Northwest Indian Girl & Boy Paper Dolls. 2003. (Paper Dolls Ser.). (Illus.). 16p. (J). 3.95 (978-0-486-43051-5(0)) Dover Pubns., Inc.

Gulliver, Amanda & Turnbull, Stephanie. Things to Make & Do with Paper. Sage, Molly, illus. 2004. (Activity Books). 32p. (J). pap. 6.95 (978-0-7945-0674-2(7) , Usborne) EDC Publishing.

Hankin, Rosie. Cut & Paste Farm Animals. 2006. (Illus.). 32p. (J). lib. bdg. (***978-0-8368-7719-9(5)***) Stevens, Gareth Inc.

—Cut & Paste Sea Creatures. 2006. (Illus.). 32p. (J). lib. bdg. (***978-0-8368-7720-5(9)***) Stevens, Gareth Inc.

Harcourt School Publishers Staff. How to Make a Paper Airplane Advanced Level. 3rd ed. 2002. (Trophies Reading Program Ser.). (Illus.). pap. 5.10 (978-0-15-323108-7(4)) Harcourt Schl. Pubs.

Hartelius, Margaret A. Zoom! The Complete Paper Airplane Kit. Hartelius, Margaret A. & Eagle, Cameron, illus. ed. 2003. (Trend Friends Ser.). 64p. (J). (ps-4). pap. 8.99 (978-0-448-43174-1(2) , Grosset & Dunlap) Penguin Group (USA) Inc.

—Zoom! The Complete Paper Airplane Kit with Sticker & Other. 2003. (gr. 3-6). lib. bdg. 16.45 (978-0-613-72476-0(3)) Tandem Library Bks.

Higham, Cindy. Snowflakes for All Seasons. 2nd rev. ed. 1998. Orig. Title: Snowflakes Made Easy & Fun. (Illus.). 72p. (Orig.). (J). pap. 8.95 (978-0-9664524-0-2(2)) All Season Snowflakes.

—Snowflakes for All Seasons. 2004. Orig. Title: Snowflakes Made Easy & Fun. (Illus.). 80p. (Orig.). pap. 9.95 (978-1-58685-528-4(X)) Gibbs Smith, Publisher.

Highlights for Children Editorial Staff. Look What You Can Make with Paper Plates. 2003. (Illus.). 48p. (YA). (ps). pap., stu. ed. 5.95 (978-1-56397-643-8(9)) Boyds Mills Pr.

Hilton, Nanette. Teddy Twins Sticker Paper Doll. 2001. 4p. (J). pap. 1.50 (978-0-486-41844-5(8)) Dover Pubns., Inc.

Hirschmann, Kris. Hello Kitty Stationery. 2001. (Hello Kitty & Her Friends Crafts Club Ser.). (Illus.). 44p. (J). act. bk. ed. (978-0-439-32837-1(3)) Scholastic, Inc.

Hollein, Max & Hollein, Nina. Matisse: Cut-Out Fun with Matisse. 2003. (Adventures in Art Ser.). (Illus.). 38p. (gr. 5 up). 14.95 (978-3-7913-2858-4(1)) Prestel Publishing.

How to Make & Fly Paper Planes. 2002. 64p. (J). pap. 9.98 (978-0-7525-4211-9(7)) Parragon, Inc.

Howell, Will C. Zooflakes ABC. 2002. (Illus.). 32p. (J). 16.85 (978-0-8027-8827-6(0)) Walker & Co.

Humphrey, Paul. How to Make a Mask. 2007. (J). (***978-1-59771-101-2(2)***) Sea-To-Sea Pubns.

Im, Angela, ed. Glitter Art. 2005. (Fun Pack Ser.). (Illus.). 48p. (J). lthr. 7.99 (978-0-439-67617-5(7) , Tangerine Pr.) Scholastic, Inc.

Indian Princess Paper Dolls. Date not set. (J). pap. 2.95 (978-1-57122-080-6(1)) Nickel Pr.

Irvin, Christine M. Cardboard Tube Mania. 2002. (gr. 3-6). lib. bdg. 15.25 (978-0-613-59456-1(8)) Tandem Library Bks.

—Paper Cup Mania. 2002. (gr. 3-6). lib. bdg. 15.25 (978-0-613-59533-9(5)) Tandem Library Bks.

—Paper Plate Mania. 2002. (Craft Mania Ser.). (Illus.). 32p. (J). (gr. 2-4). pap. 23.50 (978-0-516-21675-1(9) , Children's Pr.) Scholastic Library Publishing.

—Paper Plate Mania. 2003. (Illus.). 31p. (J). (ps-3). lib. bdg. 15.25 (978-0-613-59534-6(3)) Tandem Library Bks.

Jackson, Paul. Best Ever Paper Planes That Really Fly! (Illus.). 36p. pap. 8.95 (978-1-85479-334-8(9)) O'Mara, Michael Bks., Ltd. GBR. *Dist:* Andrews McMeel Publishing.

—Folding Paper Fun. 2007. 64p. (J). (gr. k-5). 17.95 (978-1-904613-93-0(4) , Buster Bks.) O'Mara, Michael Bks., Ltd. GBR. *Dist:* Independent Pubs. Group.

James, Diane. Paper. 2004. (Crafty Ideas Ser.). (SPA., Illus.). 32p. (J). (gr. 2-5). pap. 5.95 (978-1-58728-126-6(0) , Two Can Publishing) T&N Children's Publishing.

—Paper. Barnes, Jon, photos by. 2004. (Crafty Ideas Ser.). (SPA., Illus.). 30p. (gr. 2-5). 9.95 (978-1-58728-261-4(5) , Two Can Publishing) T&N Children's Publishing.

Johnson, Anne Akers. Handmade Cards: Simple Designs for Beautiful Cards. 2002. (Illus.). 60p. (J). (gr. 9 up). pap. 24.95 (978-1-57054-950-2(8)) Klutz.

Johnson, Ginger. Paper-Folding Fun! 50 Awesome Crafts to Weave, Twist, & Curl. Day, Betsy, illus. 2002. (Williamson Kids Can!(R) Ser.). 128p. (J). (gr. 3 up). pap. 12.95 (978-1-885593-67-2(8) , Williamson Bks.) Ideals Pubns.

Joly, Kimberly. Unfold Your Future. Middlewick, Paul, illus. 2004. 28p. (J). pap. 4.95 (978-0-7641-2778-6(0)) Barron's Educational Series, Inc.

Jones, Robert. Paper Folding: Student Workbooik. 1999. (Student Workbook Ser.). (Illus.). 80p. (J). (gr. 5-12). pap., stu. ed., wbk. ed. 5.00 (978-0-9648724-1-7(2)) LWCD, Inc.

Kelly, Emery J. Paper Airplanes: Models to Build & Fly. 2003. (Activities & Crafts Ser.). (Illus.). 64p. (J). (gr. 4-7). pap. 8.95 (978-0-8225-9903-6(1)) Lerner Publishing Group.

—Paper Airplanes: Models to Build & Fly. 2000. (gr. 5-8). lib. bdg. 17.60 (978-0-613-64571-3(5)) Tandem Library Bks.

Klutz Editors. Paper Purses. 2007. 28p. (J). pap. 14.95 (***978-1-59174-344-6(3)*** , Chicken Socks) Klutz.

Krcmar, Karol. Kirigami Greeting Cards: The Art of Paper Cutting & Folding. Simekova, Jela, ed. Chorvathova, Michaela, tr. Holoska, Jiri, photos by. 2005. (Kirigami Craft Books Ser.). (Illus.). 80p. (J). pap. 14.95 (978-0-9715411-7-7(5)) Kotzig Publishing, Inc.

—Kirigami Paper Kingdom: The Art of Paper Cutting & Folding. Simekova, Jela, ed. Kovac, Stefan Patrik, tr. Holoska, Jiri, photos by. 2005. (Kirigami Craft Books Ser.). (Illus.). 112p. (J). pap. 14.95 (978-0-9715411-6-0(7)) Kotzig Publishing, Inc.

Kumon Publishing North America, creator. Let's Cut Paper! A Kumon First Steps Workbook, 4 vols. 2005. (Illus.). 40p. (J). (ps). per. 5.95 (978-1-933241-14-2(4)) Kumon Publishing North America, Inc.

Kumon Publishing Staff. More Let's Cut Paper. 2006. (Illus.). 40p. 5.95 (978-1-933241-33-3(0)) Kumon U.S.A., Inc.

—More Let's Fold. 2006. (Illus.). 40p. 5.95 (978-1-933241-35-7(7)) Kumon U.S.A., Inc.

LaFosse, Michael. Making Origami Cards Step by Step. 2004. (Kid's Guide to Origami Ser.). (Illus.). 24p. (J). lib. bdg. 21.25 (978-0-8239-6701-8(8) , PowerKids Pr.) Rosen Publishing Group, Inc., The.

—Making Origami Masks Step by Step. 2004. (Kid's Guide to Origami Ser.). (Illus.). 24p. (J). lib. bdg. 21.25 (978-0-8239-6703-2(4) , PowerKids Pr.) Rosen Publishing Group, Inc., The.

—Making Origami Paper Airplanes Step by Step. 2004. (Kid's Guide to Origami Ser.). (Illus.). 24p. (J). lib. bdg. 21.25 (978-0-8239-6700-1(X) , PowerKids Pr.) Rosen Publishing Group, Inc., The.

—Making Origami Puzzles Step by Step. 2004. (Kid's Guide to Origami Ser.). (Illus.). 24p. (J). lib. bdg. 21.25 (978-0-8239-6704-9(2) , PowerKids Pr.) Rosen Publishing Group, Inc., The.

—Making Origami Science Experiments Step by Step. 2004. (Kid's Guide to Origami Ser.). (Illus.). 24p. (J). lib. bdg. 21.25 (978-0-8239-6705-6(0) , PowerKids Pr.) Rosen Publishing Group, Inc., The.

Lamerand, Violaine. Crafts from Papier-Mache. 2002. (Step by Step Ser.). (Illus.). 32p. (J). (gr. 2-3). lib. bdg. 22.60 (978-0-7368-1478-2(7) , Bridgestone Bks.) Capstone Pr., Inc.

Lawson, Rose Mary. Shaker Paper Dolls. McGraw, Marjorie, illus. 1998. 16p. (Orig.). (J). (gr. 2-5). pap. 5.00 (978-0-9655018-2-8(5)) Knot Garden Pr.

Lee, Jacqueline. Twirled Paper: Make Almost Anything with Simple Paper Strips. 2004. (Illus.). 60p. (YA). spiral bd. 16.95 (978-1-57054-808-6(0)) Klutz.

Lehri, R. M. Girl & Boy from India Paper Dolls. 2002. (Illus.). 16p. (J). pap. 3.95 (978-0-486-42189-6(9)) Dover Pubns., Inc.

Lewis, Amanda. The Jumbo Book of Paper Crafts. Kurisu, Jane, illus. 2004. (Jumbo Bks.). 160p. (J). (gr. 4-6). (978-1-55074-940-3(4)) Kids Can Pr., Ltd.

Llimos Plomer, Anna. Easy Crafts in 5 Steps: Easy Cardboard Crafts in 5 Steps. 2008. (Easy Crafts in 5 Steps Ser.). 32p. (J). (gr. 3-4). lib. bdg. 22.60 (***978-0-7660-3083-1(0)***) Enslow Pubs., Inc.

—Easy Paper Crafts in 5 Steps. 2008. (Easy Crafts in 5 Steps Ser.). 32p. (J). (gr. 3-4). lib. bdg. 22.60 (***978-0-7660-3087-9(3)***) Enslow Pubs., Inc.

Llimos Plomer, Anna. Papel. Casanova, Jose Maria, illus. 2001. (Let's Create Ser.). (SPA.). 32p. (J). 12.00 (978-84-342-2343-1(0)) Parramon Ediciones S.A. ESP. *Dist:* Lectorum Pubns., Inc.

—Papel Mache. Casanova, Jose Maria, illus. 2002. (Let's Create Ser.). (SPA.). 32p. (J). 12.00 (978-84-342-2468-1(2)) Parramon Ediciones S.A. ESP. *Dist:* Lectorum Pubns., Inc.

—Paper. 2003. (Let's Create! Ser.). (Illus.). 32p. (J). (gr. 2 up). lib. bdg. 23.33 (978-0-8368-3747-6(9)) Stevens, Gareth Inc.

Lomas Garza, Carmen. Making Magic Windows (Creating Papel Picado) Cut Paper Art with Carmen Lomas Garza. Lomas Garza, Carmen, illus. 1999. (ENG & SPA., Illus.). 64p. (J). (gr. 4-7). pap. 9.95 (978-0-89239-159-2(6)) Children's Bk. Pr.

Lonergan, Lei-Seu. The Great Paper Toy Book. 2004. (YA). spiral bd. (978-0-9759014-0-3(0)) Stonechester, Inc.

Lou, Weber. Crafty Paper Projects. 2005. (Illus.). 240p. (J). 12.98 (978-1-4127-1036-7(7) , 7233900) Publications International, Ltd.

Massey, Cal. Whitney the TV Star Paper Doll. 2001. 8p. (J). pap. 1.50 (978-0-486-41666-3(6)) Dover Pubns., Inc.

Mattox, Brenda Sneathen. Three Antique Paper Dolls. 2000. (J). pap. 5.95 (978-0-486-41045-6(5)) Dover Pubns., Inc.

McGee, Randel. Paper Crafts for Chinese New Year. 2008. (Paper Craft Fun for Holidays Ser.). (Illus.). 48p. (J). (gr. 3-4). lib. bdg. 23.93 (***978-0-7660-2950-7(6)*** , Enslow Elementary) Enslow Pubs., Inc.

—Paper Crafts for Day of the Dead. 2008. (Paper Craft Fun for Holidays Ser.). (Illus.). 48p. (J). (gr. 3-4). lib. bdg. 23.93 (***978-0-7660-2951-4(4)*** , Enslow Elementary) Enslow Pubs., Inc.

—Paper Crafts for Kwanzaa. 2008. (Paper Craft Fun for Holidays Ser.). (Illus.). 48p. (J). (gr. 3-4). lib. bdg. 23.93 (***978-0-7660-2949-1(2)*** , Enslow Elementary) Enslow Pubs., Inc.

—Paper Crafts for Valentine's Day. 2008. (J). (***978-0-7660-2948-4(4)***) Enslow Pubs., Inc.

McMillan, Michael M. Paper Airplane: The Flight of Change. 2nd ed. 2001. (Illus.). 72p. (J). pap. 16.95 (978-0-9708885-0-1(3)) McMillan Assocs.

Medina, Sarah. Having Fun with Paper. 2007. (J). lib. bdg. (978-1-4042-3716-2(X) , Berkley) Penguin Group (USA) Inc.

Memory Makers Staff. All kids scrapbook Pages. 2005. (Illus.). 112p. pap. 19.99 (978-1-892127-63-1(6) , Memory Makers Bks.) F & W Pubns., Inc.

Moffatt, Judith. Snow Shapes: A Read & Do Book. Moffatt, Judith, illus. 2000. (Hello Reader! Ser.). (Illus.). 32p. (J). (gr. k-2). pap. 3.99 (978-0-439-09858-8(0)) Scholastic, Inc.

—Snow Shapes: A Read-and-Do Book. 2000. (Hello Reader! Ser.). (Illus.). (J). (978-0-606-19614-7(5)) Tandem Library Bks.

Morris, Ting & Morris, Neil. Dinosaurs. Levy, Ruth & Cowne, Joanne, illus. 2007. 32p. (J). (***978-1-59771-029-9(6)***) Sea-To-Sea Pubns.

Munson, Don & Rosse, Allianora. Big Book of Papercraft Projects. 2001. (Illus.). 192p. pap. 10.95 (978-0-486-41749-3(2)) Dover Pubns., Inc.

Newell, Keith. Models. 2005. (Illus.). 32p. (J). (gr. 3-7). lib. bdg. 27.10 (978-1-932889-85-7(X) , 1247657) Sea-To-Sea Pubns.

Oxlade, Chris. How We Use Paper. 2005. (Using Materials Ser.). (Illus.). 32p. (J). (gr. 6-9). lib. bdg. 25.70 (978-1-4109-0603-8(5)) Harcourt Schl. Pubs.

Paper Animals. 2004. (Art Rom Create Your Own... Ser.). (Illus.). 24p. (J). pap. incl. audio compact disk (978-1-84229-771-1(6)) Top That! Publishing PLC.

Paper Dinosaurs. 2004. (Art Rom Create Your Own... Ser.). (Illus.). 24p. (J). pap. incl. audio compact disk (978-1-84229-770-4(8)) Top That! Publishing PLC.

Paper Fliers. 2004. (Art Rom Create Your Own... Ser.). (Illus.). 24p. (J). pap. incl. audio compact disk (978-1-84229-772-8(4)) Top That! Publishing PLC.

Paper Flower Kid Kit. 2004. (Illus.). 32p. (J). 16.99 (978-1-58086-452-7(X)) EDC Publishing.

Paper Planes Boxed Kit. (J). 7.90 (978-1-57755-401-1(9)) Allied Publishing.

Papier Mache. (Jump Ser.). (Illus.). 36p. (J). (gr. 2-6). pap. (978-1-882210-35-0(2)) Action Publishing, Inc.

Parramon's Editorial Team Staff. Papier Mache. Parramon's Editorial Team Staff, photos by. 2004. (Let's Create! Ser.). (Illus.). 32p. (J). (gr. 2 up). lib. bdg. 23.33 (978-0-8368-4017-9(8)) Stevens, Gareth Inc.

Pavarin, Franco. Fold-and-Fly Paper Airplanes. 1998. (Illus.). 80p. (J). (gr. 4-7). 19.95 (978-0-8069-4257-5(6)) Sterling Publishing Co., Inc.

Pinol, Roser. Creating with Paper. 2000. (Crafts for All Seasons Ser.). (Illus.). 32p. (J). (gr. 3-8). lib. bdg. 23.70 (978-1-56711-434-8(2) , Blackbirch Pr., Inc.) Thomson Gale.

Pomaska, Anna. Ballerina Paper Doll. 2000. (J). pap. 2.00 (978-0-486-41313-6(6)) Dover Pubns., Inc.

—Decorative Sun, Moon & Stars. 2000. (Illus.). 4p. pap. 4.95 (978-0-486-41070-8(6)) Dover Pubns., Inc.

—Maria the Scientist Paper Doll. 2001. 8p. (J). pap. 1.50 (978-0-486-41665-6(8)) Dover Pubns., Inc.

Prins, M. D. Paper Galaxy: Out-of-This-World Projects to Cut, Fold & Paste. 2007. (Illus.). 128p. pap. 12.95 (978-1-4027-4716-8(0)) Sterling Publishing Co., Inc.

Rhatigan, Joe & Newcomb, Rain. Kids' Crafts: Paper Fantastic: 50 Creative Projects to Fold, Cut, Glue, Paint & Weave. 2006. (Illus.). 112p. (J). pap. 9.95 (978-1-57990-959-8(0)) Lark Bks.

Robinson, Nick. Super Simple Paper Airplanes: Step-by-Step Instructions to Make Planes That Really Fly from a Tri-Plane to a Jet Fighter. 2005. (Illus.). 128p. pap. 9.95 (978-1-4027-1900-4(0)) Sterling Publishing Co., Inc.

Rocky Mountain Snowflakes: New Edition. 2006. 8.95 (978-0-9661572-3-9(0)) Dream Bee Pubns.

Ross, Kathy. Look What You Can Make with Newspapers, Magazines, & Greeting Cards. 2001. (gr. 3-6). lib. bdg. 14.10 (978-0-613-59327-4(8)) Tandem Library Bks.

Rueben & Rachel's Paper Doll Book. 2003. (J). 10.00 (978-0-9745615-3-0(3)) PJs Corner.

Samuel, Anna, ed. Decorative Leaves Stickers. 2004. (Illus.). 8p. 1.50 (978-0-486-43352-3(8)) Dover Pubns., Inc.

Sarasas, Claude. ABCs of Origami: Paper Folding for Children. 2002. (gr. k-3). lib. bdg. 12.95 (978-0-613-75502-3(2)) Tandem Library Bks.

—ABCs of Origami: Paper Folding for Children. 2nd ed. 2002. (JPN & ENG., Illus.). 32p. pap. 4.95 (978-0-8048-3307-3(9)) Tuttle Publishing.

Sarris, Eno & Akaishi, Shinobu, eds. Animals: Cat & Dog (Kumon 3-D Paper Crafts), 4 vols. 2006. (Illus.). 40p. (J). per. 5.95 (978-1-933241-18-0(7)) Kumon Publishing North America, Inc.

—Dinosaurs: Triceratops & Pteranodon (Kumon 3-D Paper Crafts), 4 vols. 2006. (Illus.). 40p. (J). per. 5.95 (978-1-933241-19-7(5)) Kumon Publishing North America, Inc.

Schecter, Deborah. Hello Kitty Glitter. 2002. (Hello Kitty & Her Friends Crafts Club Ser.). (Illus.). 44p. (J). act. bk. ed. (978-0-439-32848-7(9)) Scholastic, Inc.

Schmidt, Norman. Best Ever Paper Airplanes. 2007. (Illus.). 96p. (J). pap. 7.95 (978-1-895569-83-4(4)) Tamos Bks., Inc. CAN. *Dist:* Sterling Publishing Co., Inc.

—Best Ever Paper Kites. 2003. (Illus.). 96p. pap. 7.95 (978-1-895569-53-7(2)) Tamos Bks., Inc. CAN. *Dist:* Sterling Publishing Co., Inc.

Scholastic, Inc. Staff. Mr. Magorium's Paper Airplane Designs. 2007. (Mr. Magorium's Wonder Emporium Ser.). 48p. (J). pap. 4.99 (***978-0-439-91251-8(2)***) Scholastic, Inc.

Schuh, Debby & Stephani, Julie. Kids Scrapbooking: Easy As 1-2-3. 2002. (gr. 3-6). lib. bdg. 18.75 (978-0-613-77108-5(7)) Tandem Library Bks.

Schwarz, Renee. Papier-Mache. 2000. (gr. 3-6). lib. bdg. 14.10 (978-0-613-26522-5(X)) Tandem Library Bks.

Schwarz, Renee F. Making Masks. 2004. (Kids Can Do It Ser.). (Illus.). 40p. (J). (gr. 4-6). (978-1-55074-931-1(5)) Kids Can Pr., Ltd.

—Making Masks. Schwarz, Renee F., illus. unabr. ed. 2004. (Kids Can Do It Ser.). (Illus.). 40p. (J). (gr. 4-6). (978-1-55074-929-8(3)) Kids Can Pr., Ltd.

—Papier-Mache. Schwarz, Renee F., illus. unabr. ed. 2004. (Kids Can Do It Ser.). (Illus.). (J). (gr. 4-6). 134p. (978-1-55074-727-0(4)); 332p. (978-1-55074-833-8(5)) Kids Can Pr., Ltd.

The Scrapbooker's Idea Book. 2006. (Illus.). (J). pap. 7.95 (978-0-8225-6511-6(0) , First Avenue Editions) Lerner Publishing Group.

Shanahan, Sue. Cut & Color Paper Dolls: Maria & Megan. 2005. (Illus.). 32p. (J). (ps-ps). pap. 3.95 (978-0-486-44122-1(9)) Dover Pubns., Inc.
—Southern Belle Sisters: Sticker Paper Dolls. 2005. (Illus.). 4p. (J). (ps-3). pap. 1.50 (978-0-486-44197-9(0)) Dover Pubns., Inc.
Smith, A. Cut & Assemble Main Street. (Illus.). 48p. (J). pap. 6.95 (978-0-486-24473-0(3)) Dover Pubns., Inc.
—Papercraft. 2004. 96p. (J). pap. 14.95 (978-0-7945-0140-2(0)) EDC Publishing.
Smith, A. G. South Pacific Seafarers. 2002. (Illus.). 32p. (J). pap. 3.95 (978-0-486-42380-7(8)) Dover Pubns., Inc.
Smolinski, Jill. Holiday Origami. Fraser, Mary Ann, illus. 2nd rev. ed. 1999. (Origami Ser.). 48p. (gr. 3-7). pap. 8.95 (978-0-7373-0094-9(9) , 9780737300949) McGraw-Hill Cos., The.
—Holiday Origami. 1999. (gr. 3-6). lib. bdg. 17.60 (978-0-613-73742-5(3)) Tandem Library Bks.
Southwater Staff. Fun with Paper. 2000. (Illus.). 96p. 12.95 (978-1-84215-139-6(8) , Southwater) Anness Publishing GBR. *Dist:* National Bk. Network.
—Paper Perfect. 2000. (Illus.). 256p. pap. 19.95 (978-1-84215-296-6(3)) Anness Publishing, Inc.
Steadman, Barbara. Bride & Bridesmaid Paper Dolls. 2002. (Sticker Paper Dolls Ser.). (Illus.). 8p. (J). pap. 4.95 (978-0-486-42394-4(8)) Dover Pubns., Inc.
—Caitlin the Irish Dancer Sticker Paper Doll. 2000. 4p. (J). pap. 1.50 (978-0-486-40994-8(5)) Dover Pubns., Inc.
—Christmas Princess Sticker Paper Doll. 2005. (Illus.). 4p. (J). (ps-3). 1.50 (978-0-486-44105-4(9)) Dover Pubns., Inc.
—Glitter Ballerina Sticker Paper Doll. 2005. 2p. (J). (ps-5). 1.50 (978-0-486-44479-6(1)) Dover Pubns., Inc.
—Little Scandinavian Girls Sticker Paper Dolls. 2005. (Illus.). 4p. (J). (ps-5). pap. 1.50 (978-0-486-44450-5(3)) Dover Pubns., Inc.
—Storybook Princess Sticker Paper Doll. 2004. (Illus.). 4p. (J). pap. 1.50 (978-0-486-43726-2(4)) Dover Pubns., Inc.
—Sweet Valentine Sticker Paper Doll. 2004. 4p. (J). pap. 1.50 (978-0-486-43751-4(5)) Dover Pubns., Inc.
Stevens, Clive. Paperfolding. (Step-by-Step Ser.). (Illus.). 32p. (J). 2003. pap. 7.95 (978-1-4034-0711-5(8)); 2001. (gr. 3-5). lib. bdg. 24.22 (978-1-57572-333-4(6)) Heinemann Library.
—Paperfolding. 2001. (Step-by-Step Children's Crafts Ser.). (Illus.). 32p. pap. 7.95 (978-0-85532-908-2(4) , 9084) Search Pr., Ltd. GBR. *Dist:* Independent Pubs. Group.
Stewart, Pat. Jennifer the Career Girl Paper Doll. 2001. 8p. (J). pap. 1.50 (978-0-486-41664-9(X)) Dover Pubns., Inc.
Stillerman, Robbie. Candie the Circus Girl Sticker Paper Doll. 2000. (Illus.). 4p. (J). pap. 1.00 (978-0-486-40991-7(0)) Dover Pubns., Inc.
—Cut & Color Paper Dolls: Kati & Kayla. 2005. (Illus.). 32p. (J). (ps-ps). pap. 3.95 (978-0-486-44146-7(6)) Dover Pubns., Inc.
—Glitter Pretty in Pink Sticker Paper Doll. 2005. (Illus.). 2p. (J). (ps-5). 1.50 (978-0-486-44475-8(9)) Dover Pubns., Inc.
—Princess Paper Doll. 2000. (J). pap. 1.00 (978-0-486-41314-3(4)) Dover Pubns., Inc.
Stillinger, Doug. The Klutz Book of Paper Airplanes. 2004. (Illus.). 56p. (YA). spiral bd. 16.95 (978-1-57054-830-7(7)) Klutz.
—Klutz Building Cards How to Build Spaceships. 2006. 32p. (J). spiral bd. 12.95 (978-1-57054-231-2(7)) Klutz.
Stohs, Anita Reith. Praise God with Paper Bags. 2004. (ENG., Illus.). 64p. (J). (gr. 2-5). 9.99 (978-0-7586-0643-3(5)) Concordia Publishing Hse.
Stunt Planes. 2004. (Fantastic Fliers Ser.). (Illus.). 48p. (J). pap. (978-1-84229-726-1(0)) Top That! Publishing PLC.
Sun, Ming-Ju. Cut & Color Paper Dolls: Alice & Anna. 2005. (Illus.). 32p. (J). (ps-ps). pap. 3.95 (978-0-486-44166-5(0)) Dover Pubns., Inc.
—Godey's Early Victorian Fashions Paper Dolls. 2004. (Illus.). 32p. (J). pap. 5.95 (978-0-486-43687-6(X)) Dover Pubns., Inc.
—Godey's Fashions Paper Dolls 1860-1879. 2004. 32p. (J). pap. 5.95 (978-0-486-43424-7(9)) Dover Pubns., Inc.
—Japanese Kimono Paper Dolls in Full Color. 1998. (Dover Coloring Bks.). 32p. (J). reprint ed. pap. 5.95 (978-0-486-25094-6(6)) Dover Pubns., Inc.
—Japanese Warrior Costumes Paper Dolls. 2000. (J). pap. 6.95 (978-0-486-41046-3(3)) Dover Pubns., Inc.
—Russian Folk Costumes Paper Dolls. 2003. 32p. (J). pap. 5.95 (978-0-486-42390-6(5)) Dover Pubns., Inc.
Supercool Fliers. 2004. (Fantastic Fliers Ser.). (Illus.). 48p. (J). pap. (978-1-84229-729-2(5)) Top That! Publishing PLC.
Tierney, Tom. American Family of the 1970s Paper Dolls. 2001. 32p. (J). (gr. 3). pap. 5.95 (978-0-486-41872-8(3)) Dover Pubns., Inc.
—American Family of the 1980s Paper Dolls. 2003. (Paper Dolls Ser.). (Illus.). 32p. (J). (gr. 3). pap. 5.95 (978-0-486-43052-2(9)) Dover Pubns., Inc.
—American Family Paper Dolls. 2002. (Illus.). 68p. (J). pap. 12.95 (978-0-486-42740-9(4)) Dover Pubns., Inc.
—Art Deco Fashions Paper Dolls. 2005. (Illus.). 32p. (J). (ps-3). pap. 6.95 (978-0-486-44158-0(X)) Dover Pubns., Inc.
—Balenciaga Fashion Review. 2000. (Illus.). (J). pap. 6.95 (978-0-486-41047-0(1)) Dover Pubns., Inc.
—Ballet Princesses Paper Doll. 2005. 16p. (J). (gr. 3-6). pap. 4.95 (978-0-486-44468-0(6)) Dover Pubns., Inc.
—Best Actresses of the 1990s Paper Dolls. 2006. 32p. (J). pap. 6.95 (978-0-486-44897-8(5)) Dover Pubns., Inc.
—Brides from Around the World Paper Dolls. 2005. (Illus.). 32p. (gr. 3). pap. 6.95 (978-0-486-44439-0(2)) Dover Pubns., Inc.
—Broadway Musical Stars Paper Dolls. 2004. (Illus.). 32p. (J). pap. 5.95 (978-0-486-43348-6(X)) Dover Pubns., Inc.
—Byzantine Costume Paper Dolls. 2002. (Illus.). 16p. (J). pap. 4.95 (978-0-486-42077-6(9)) Dover Pubns., Inc.
—Camelot Paper Dolls. 2002. (Illus.). 32p. (J). pap. 5.95 (978-0-486-42393-7(X)) Dover Pubns., Inc.
—Campus Fashions Paper Dolls: 1900s-1980s. 2001. 32p. (J). pap. 5.95 (978-0-486-41674-8(7)) Dover Pubns., Inc.
—The Dalai Lama Paper Doll. 2006. 32p. pap. 6.95 (978-0-486-45181-7(X)) Dover Pubns., Inc.
—Edwardian Costumes Paper Dolls. 2001. (Illus.). 16p. (J). pap. 3.95 (978-0-486-41556-7(2)) Dover Pubns., Inc.
—Elizabeth the Queen Mother Paper Dolls. 2001. (Illus.). 32p. (J). pap. 5.95 (978-0-486-41771-4(9)) Dover Pubns., Inc.
—Famous Child Stars Paper Dolls. 2003. (Paper Dolls Ser.). (Illus.). 32p. (J). pap. 5.95 (978-0-486-43057-7(X)) Dover Pubns., Inc.
—Famous Country Singers Paper Dolls. 2006. 32p. (J). pap. 6.95 (978-0-486-44741-4(3)) Dover Pubns., Inc.
—Fashion Parade Paper Dolls: 4 Decades of Great Designs, from 1960 To 2000. 2002. (Illus.). 136p. (J). pap. 12.95 (978-0-486-42738-6(2)) Dover Pubns., Inc.
—Fashions of the First Ladies Paper Dolls. 2006. 32p. (J). pap. 6.95 (978-0-486-44879-4(7)) Dover Pubns., Inc.
—French Baroque & Rococo Fashions. 2002. (Dover Coloring Bks.). (Illus.). 48p. (J). pap. 3.95 (978-0-486-42383-8(2)) Dover Pubns., Inc.
—French Film Stars Paper Dolls. 2005. (FRE.). 32p. (J). pap. 6.95 (978-0-486-44132-0(6)) Dover Pubns., Inc.
—Glamorous Latin Film Stars Paper Dolls. 2003. (Paper Dolls Ser.). (Illus.). 32p. (J). pap. 5.95 (978-0-486-43055-3(3)) Dover Pubns., Inc.
—Glamorous Movie Stars of the Nineties Paper Dolls. 2004. (Paper Dolls Ser.). (Illus.). 32p. (J). pap. 5.95 (978-0-486-43053-9(7)) Dover Pubns., Inc.
—Glamorous Movie Stars of the Seventies Paper Dolls. 2001. 32p. (J). pap. 5.95 (978-0-486-41557-4(0)) Dover Pubns., Inc.
—Glamorous Television Stars Paper Dolls. 2005. (Illus.). 32p. (J). (gr. 3). pap. 6.95 (978-0-486-44462-8(7)) Dover Pubns., Inc.
—Gothic Costumes Paper Dolls. 2001. (J). pap. 5.95 (978-0-486-41329-7(2)) Dover Pubns., Inc.
—Great Characters from Shakespeare Paper Dolls. 2000. (Illus.). 32p. (J). pap. 6.95 (978-0-486-41330-3(6)) Dover Pubns., Inc.
—Great Fashion Designs of the Nineties Paper Dolls. 2000. (Illus.). 16p. (J). pap. 6.95 (978-0-486-41331-0(4)) Dover Pubns., Inc.
—Great Movie Dance Couples Paper Dolls. 2004. (Paper Dolls Ser.). (Illus.). 16p. (J). pap. 6.95 (978-0-486-43054-6(5)) Dover Pubns., Inc.
—Hollywood Movie Star Paper Dolls. 2002. (Illus.). 120p. (J). pap. 12.95 (978-0-486-42739-3(0)) Dover Pubns., Inc.
—Hoop Skirts & Crinoline Paper Dolls. 2006. (Illus.). 32p. (J). (gr. 3). pap. 6.95 (978-0-486-44492-5(9)) Dover Pubns., Inc.
—Louis XIV & His Court Paper Dolls. 2005. (Illus.). 32p. (J). pap. 5.95 (978-0-486-43837-5(6)) Dover Pubns., Inc.
—Mae West Paper Doll. 2005. (Illus.). 32p. (J). pap. 5.95 (978-0-486-44099-6(0)) Dover Pubns., Inc.
—Marie Antoinette Paper Dolls. 2001. (Illus.). 32p. (J). (gr. 3). pap. 6.95 (978-0-486-41874-2(X)) Dover Pubns., Inc.
—A Midsummer Night's Dream Fairies Paper Dolls. 2005. (Illus.). 32p. (gr. 3). pap. 6.95 (978-0-486-44442-0(2)) Dover Pubns., Inc.
—Mumtaz of the Taj Mahal Paper Dolls. 2002. 16p. (J). pap. 5.95 (978-0-486-41984-8(3)) Dover Pubns., Inc.
—Newport Fashions of the Gilded Age Paper Dolls. 2005. 32p. (J). (gr. 3). pap. 6.95 (978-0-486-44449-9(X)) Dover Pubns., Inc.
—Queen Elizabeth I Paper Doll. 2002. (Illus.). 16p. (J). (gr. 3). pap. 4.95 (978-0-486-42192-6(9)) Dover Pubns., Inc.
—Rock 'n' Pop Stars of the Sixties Paper Dolls. 2001. (Illus.). 32p. (J). pap. 5.95 (978-0-486-41558-1(9)) Dover Pubns., Inc.
—Royal Weddings: Paper Dolls. 2005. (Illus.). 32p. (ps-ps). pap. 6.95 (978-0-486-44178-8(4)) Dover Pubns., Inc.
—Sarah Bernhardt Paper Dolls. 2002. 16p. (J). pap. 4.95 (978-0-486-42391-3(3)) Dover Pubns., Inc.
—Tudor & Elizabethan Fashions. 2000. (Illus.). 48p. (J). pap. 3.95 (978-0-486-41320-4(9)) Dover Pubns., Inc.
—Ziegfeld Girls Paper Dolls. 2004. (Illus.). 32p. (J). pap. 5.95 (978-0-486-43679-1(9)) Dover Pubns., Inc.
—16 Great Stars of the Broadway Musical Paper Dolls. 2004. (Illus.). 32p. (J). pap. 5.95 (978-0-486-43684-5(5)) Dover Pubns., Inc.
Top That! Team Staff, contrib. by. Design & Fly Paper Airplanes. 2003. (Illus.). 48p. (J). (978-0-439-57192-0(8)) Scholastic, Inc.
Trionfante, Jeffrey V. Sunclocks: Sundials to Make & Use. Trionfante, Jeffrey V., illus. 1999. (Illus.). 56p. (J). (gr. 3-9). pap. 12.95 (978-1-893812-51-2(0)) JVT Pubns. & Creations.
Tucker, Mary. Cut & Create! Ocean Life. Mitchell, Judy & Lindeen, Mary, eds. Rankin, Kim, illus. 2007. 80p. (J). pap. 9.95 (***978-1-57310-526-2(0)***) Teaching & Learning Co.
—Cut & Create! Spring & Summer. Mitchell, Judy & Lindeen, Mary, eds. Rankin, Kim, illus. 2007. 80p. (J). pap. 9.95 (***978-1-57310-535-4(X)***) Teaching & Learning Co.
Victorian Paper Dolls. Date not set. (J). pap. 2.95 (978-1-57122-079-0(8)) Nickel Pr.
Voituriez, Marie-Anne & Lassus, Irene. Papier Mache Fun. 2005. (I Made It Myself! Ser.). (Illus.). 24p. (J). (ps-17). lib. bdg. 22.00 (978-0-8368-5966-9(9)) Stevens, Gareth Inc.
Wallace, Holly. Paper. 2007. (***978-1-59920-004-0(X)***) Smart Apple Media.
Watson, David. Papermaking. 2003. (Step-by-Step Ser.). 32p. pap. 7.95 (978-1-4034-0705-4(3)) Heinemann Library.
Williams, Joy. Paper Creations. 2002. (gr. 3-6). lib. bdg. 22.25 (978-0-613-57375-7(7)) Tandem Library Bks.
With Paper. 2004. (Illus.). (J). lib. bdg. 27.10 (978-1-932889-24-6(8)) Sea-To-Sea Pubns.

PAPERCRAFT

see Paper Work

PAPIER-MACHE

see Paper Work

PAPUA NEW GUINEA

Gascoigne, Ingrid. Papua New Guinea. 1998. (Cultures of the World Ser.). (Illus.). 128p. (gr. 5-12). lib. bdg. 37.07 (978-0-7614-0813-0(4) , Benchmark Bks.) Cavendish, Marshall Corp.
Guile, Melanie. Papua New Guinea. 2003. (Illus.). 32p. (J). lib. bdg. 25.70 (978-1-4109-0473-7(3)) Raintree.

PAPUA NEW GUINEA—FICTION

Carlson, Melody. Notes from a Spinning Planet—Papua, New Guinea. 2007. (Notes from a Spinning Planet Ser.). 240p. (YA). pap. 12.99 (978-1-4000-7145-6(3) , WaterBrook Pr.) WaterBrook Pr.
Hathorn, Libby. Volcano Boy. 2002. 208p. (YA). pap. (978-0-7344-0249-3(X) , Lothian Bks.) Hachette Livre Australia.
Kelly, David. Canoes of the Dead. 144p. pap. 11.95 (978-0-7022-2509-3(6)) Univ. of Queensland Pr. AUS. *Dist:* International Specialized Bk. Services.

PARABLES

see also Allegories; Fables; Jesus Christ—Parables

Adeyemi, Sam. The Parable of Dollars: Proven Strategies for Your Financial Success. 2nd ed. 2004. Orig. Title: Parable of Dollars. 208p. per. 14.95 (978-0-9746735-1-6(X)) Summit House Pubs.
Amery, Heather. El Buen Samaritano. 2001. (Coleccion Cuentos de la Biblia).Tr. of Good Samaritan. (SPA., Illus.). 16p. (J). (gr. k-3). 6.95 (978-0-7460-3875-8(5)) EDC Publishing.
Ball, Liz, illus. Miracles & Parables of Jesus: Find-the-Picture Puzzles. 2004. (Find-the-Picture Puzzle Ser.: 2). 24p. (J). pap. 2.95 (978-0-8198-4830-7(1) , 332-221) Pauline Bks. & Media.
Bauld, Jane S. Parables for Children. 1998. (J). (ps-2). 8.95 (978-1-880384-16-9(7)) Coldwater Pr.
Butcher, Sam. Precious Moments Bible Stories. 2000. (Illus.). (J). (978-0-8010-4447-2(2)) Baker Bks.
Bynum, Juanita, ed. A Parable about the King. 2004. Tr. of Una Parabola Sobre el Rey. (SPA.). 32p. 8.99 (978-0-88419-998-4(3) , Casa Creacion) Strang Communications Co.
Carlson, Melody. Farmer Brown's Field Trip. Bjorkman, Steve, illus. 2004. 40p. (ps-3). 9.99 (978-1-58134-142-3(3)) Crossway Bks.
—A Treasure Beyond Measure. Bjorkman, Steve, illus. 2005. 32p. 9.99 (978-1-58134-343-4(4) , Crossway Bibles) Crossway Bks.
Eder, Enelle. Create & Take Bible Crafts: Parables & Miracles. 2004. (Create & Take Bible Crafts). (Illus.). 96p. (J). pap. 11.95 (978-1-58411-007-1(4)) Rainbow Pubs. & Legacy Pr.
Fitzpatrick, Marie-Louise. I Am I. Fitzpatrick, Marie-Louise, illus. 2006. (Illus.). 32p. (J). 16.95 (978-1-59643-054-9(0)) Roaring Brook Pr.
Gatty, Alfred. Parables from Nature (Yesterday's Classics) 2006. (Illus.). 456p. (J). per. 14.95 (978-1-59915-005-5(0)) Yesterday's Classics.
Groenboom, Roger, et al. Sharable Parables. (Walk with Me Ser.). (gr. k-8). 24.95 (978-1-59255-176-7(9) , 017210, Faith Alive Christian Resources) CRC Pubns.
Haines, Geri Berger. The Little Lost Lamb. rev. ed. 2001. (Illus.). 40p. (J). pap. 5.50 (978-0-8198-4489-7(6) , 332-170) Pauline Bks. & Media.
Higgs, Liz Curtis. The Pumpkin Patch Parable. (J). 2006. 32p. 7.99 (978-1-4003-0846-0(1)); 2002. (Illus.). 20p. bds. 6.99 (978-1-4003-0011-2(8)) Nelson, Thomas Inc.
Holmes, Wayne & Pelletier, Christine. Lost & Found Teaching Unit. Kalvoda, LeAnn, illus. rev. ed. 2003. 96p. (J). ring bd. 35.00 (978-1-58302-232-0(5)) One Way St., Inc.
King, Robert A. The Song of the Temple Stones. Vandervoort, Gene, illus. 1999. 16p. (J). (gr. 1-4). pap. 4.95 (978-0-8198-7017-9(X)) Pauline Bks. & Media.
—The Three Lumps of Clay. Vandervoort, Gene, illus. 1999. 16p. (J). (gr. 1-4). pap. 4.95 (978-0-8198-7399-6(3)) Pauline Bks. & Media.
Larcombe, Jennifer Rees. Danger on the Lonely Road. Bjorkman, Steve, illus. 2004. (Best Bible Stories Ser.). 24p. (ps-3). pap. 2.99 (978-1-58134-149-2(0)) Crossway Bks.
Littleton, Mark. Stories Jesus Told: Lift-the-Flap. Moroney, Trace, illus. 2004. 20p. (J). bds. 10.99 (978-0-8254-5519-3(7)) Kregel Pubns.
Lucado, Max. You Are Special. Martinez, Sergio, illus. rev. ed. 2007. 32p. 19.99 (***978-1-58134-894-1(0)***) Crossway Bks.
Osborne, Susan Titus. Dog Paws & Sandy Claws. Durrell, Julie, illus. 2001. (Parables in Action Ser.: Vol. 8). 48p. (J). (ps-2). 4.99 (978-0-570-07140-2(2)) Concordia Publishing Hse.
—Flip-Flop Fishing. Durrell, Julie, illus. 2001. (Parables in Action Ser.: Vol. 7). 48p. (J). (ps-2). 4.99 (978-0-570-07139-6(9)) Concordia Publishing Hse.
Pfeiffer, Chaviva Krohn & Shvadron, Shalom Mordekhai. More Maggid Stories for Children. Nodel, Norman & Katz, Tova, illus. 2000. (ArtScroll Youth Ser.). 48p. (J). 14.99 (978-1-57819-497-1(0) , YMAG2) Mesorah Pubns., Ltd.
Sanders, Nancy I. Comet Campout. 2000. (Parables in Action Ser.: Vol. 3). (Illus.). 48p. (J). (ps-2). 4.99 (978-0-570-07014-6(7)) Concordia Publishing Hse.
—Comet Campout. 2000. (ps-2). lib. bdg. 13.00 (978-0-613-72837-9(8)) Tandem Library Bks.
—Hidden Treasure. 2000. (Parables in Action Ser.: Vol. 2). (Illus.). 48p. (J). (ps-2). 4.99 (978-0-570-07013-9(9)) Concordia Publishing Hse.
—Hidden Treasure. 2000. (ps-2). lib. bdg. 13.00 (978-0-613-72836-2(X)) Tandem Library Bks.
—Lost & Found. 2000. (Parables in Action Ser.: Vol. 1). (Illus.). 48p. (J). (ps-2). 4.99 (978-0-570-07012-2(0)) Concordia Publishing Hse.
—Lost & Found. 2000. (ps-2). lib. bdg. 13.00 (978-0-613-72835-5(1)) Tandem Library Bks.
—Moon Rocks & Dinosaur Bones. 2000. (Parables in Action Ser.: Vol. 4). (Illus.). 48p. (J). (ps-2). 4.99 (978-0-570-07015-3(5)) Concordia Publishing Hse.
—Moon Rocks & Dinosaur Bones. 2000. (ps-2). lib. bdg. 13.00 (978-0-613-72838-6(6)) Tandem Library Bks.
Smith, Cyncie. The Joyful Shepherd. 2004. (Illus.). 32p. (J). 9.99 (978-1-56309-484-2(3)) New Hope Pubs.
Walker, John. Pioneer Parables. 2005. (Illus.). (YA). per. 6.50 (978-0-9677379-1-1(5)) North Gap Publishing.
Ward, Elaine M. Answering Children's Faith Questions: Through Parables, Poetry & Prayer. 1999. 100p. (J). (gr. 1-6). pap. 10.95 (978-1-57438-031-6(1) , 5302) Educational Ministries, Inc.
Wooding, Marnie. The Guy Who Lost His Beach House: One-Minute Bible Parables for Kids. Kielesinski, Chris, illus. 2000. 432p. (J). 12.99 (978-0-8054-9398-6(0)) B&H Publishing Grp.

PARACHUTE TROOPS

Hopkins, Ellen H. The Golden Knights: The U. S. Army Parachute Team. 2001. (Serving Your Country Ser.). (Illus.). 48p. (J). (gr. 3-4). lib. bdg. 21.26 (978-0-7368-0775-3(6) , Capstone High-Interest Bks.) Capstone Pr., Inc.
Kennedy, Robert C. Life As a Paratrooper. 2000. (gr. 7-12). lib. bdg. 15.25 (978-0-613-52119-2(6)) Tandem Library Bks.
McGowen, Tom. Assault from the Sky: Airborne Infantry of World War II. 2002. (Military Might Ser.). (Illus.). 64p. (J). (gr. 5-8). lib. bdg. 26.90 (978-0-7613-1809-5(7) , Twenty-First Century Bks.) Lerner Publishing Group.

PARACHUTES

see also Parachute Troops

Ballooning Adventures, 6 vols. (gr. 4 up). 39.95 (978-0-7368-9028-1(9)) Red Brick Learning.

PARACHUTING

see Skydiving

PARADES

Campbell, Mel. Parades of Arrays. 2007. (Illus.). 24p. (J). (978-1-59515-980-9(0)) Rourke Publishing, LLC.
Catala, Ellen. I Love a Parade. 2006. (Illus.). (J). 16p. (978-0-7368-5981-3(0)); (SPA & ENG., 18p. (978-0-7368-6017-8(7)) Yellow Umbrella Pr.
I Love a Parade. 2006. (Yellow Umbrella Math Ser.). 8,16p. (J). 6.50 (978-0-7368-1693-9(3)) Red Brick Learning.
McGahey, Suzanne. Winter Guard. 2006. (Illus.). 64p. (J). lib. bdg. (978-1-4042-0732-5(5)) Rosen Publishing Group, Inc., The.
Mullican, Judy. Let's Have a Parade! Lent, Marion W., illus. l.t. ed. 1999. (Cuddle Bks.). 7p. (J). (ps-k). pap. 10.95 (978-1-57332-139-6(7)) HighReach Learning, Inc.

PARADES—FICTION

Arterburn, Stephen & Hunt, Angela Elwell. Paige. 2004. (Young Believer on Tour Ser.). (J). pap. 3.99 (978-0-8423-8338-7(7)) Tyndale Hse. Pubs.
Awdry, Wilbert V. Thomas & Percy & the Dragon. 2003. (ps-2). lib. bdg. 11.80 (978-0-613-89791-4(9)) Tandem Library Bks.
Banks, Steven. SpongeBob's Easter Parade. Goldberg, Barry, illus. 2005. (Spongebob Squarepants Ser.). 24p. (J). pap. 3.99 (978-0-689-87314-0(X) , Simon Spotlight/ Nickelodeon) Simon & Schuster Children's Publishing.
Barner, Bob. Parade Day: Marching Through the Calendar Year. 2003. (Illus.). 32p. (J). (gr. k-3). tchr. ed. 16.95 (978-0-8234-1690-5(9)) Holiday Hse., Inc.
Bennerson, Denise. Daniel & the Christmas Festival. Vega, Edwin, illus. 2001. 12p. (J). 4.00 (978-0-9646279-6-3(5)) Bennerson, Denise.
Bond, Rebecca. The Great Doughnut Parade. 2007. (Illus.). 40p. (J). (ps-k). 17.00 (***978-0-618-77705-1(9)***) Houghton Mifflin Co.
Boswell, Addie K. The Rain Stomper. Velasquez, Eric, illus. 2008. (J). (***978-0-7614-5393-2(8)***) Cavendish, Marshall Corp.
Bridwell, Norman. Clifford & the Big Parade. Bridwell, Norman, illus. 2002. (Clifford, the Big Red Dog Ser.). (Illus.). (J). 11.45 (978-0-7587-6372-3(7)) Book Wholesalers, Inc.
—Clifford & the Big Parade. Bridwell, Norman, illus. 1998. (Clifford, the Big Red Dog Ser.). (Illus.). 32p. (J). (gr. k-2). pap. 3.50 (978-0-590-10811-5(9)) Scholastic, Inc.
—Clifford & the Big Parade. 1998. (Clifford, the Big Red Dog Ser.). (J). (gr. k-2). 10.30 (978-0-606-13284-8(8)) Tandem Library Bks.
—Clifford y el Gran Desfile. 1998. (Clifford, the Big Red Dog Ser.). (SPA.). (J). (gr. k-2). 10.30 (978-0-606-13285-5(6)) Tandem Library Bks.

Brown, Rick, illus. I'm Going to Read (Level 2): Hooray for the 4th of July. 2007. (I'm Going to Read Ser.). 28p. (J). pap. 3.95 (978-1-4027-4241-5(X)) Sterling Publishing Co., Inc.

Buchanan, Paul. Don't Rock the Float. 2000. (gr. 3-6). lib. bdg. 14.15 (978-0-613-72843-0(2)) Tandem Library Bks.

Buchanan, Paul & Randall, Rod. Don't Rock the Float, Vol. 17. 2001. (Misadventures of Willie Plummett Ser.: Vol. 17). (Illus.). 128p. (J). (gr. 3-7). 5.99 (978-0-570-07125-9(9)) Concordia Publishing Hse.

Clark, Katie. Grandma Drove the Garbage Truck. Huntington, Amy, illus. 2006. 32p. 15.95 (978-0-89272-698-1(9)) Down East Bks.

Corey, Shana. Milly & the Macy's Parade. Helquist, Brett, illus. 2006. 38p. (J). (gr. 4-8). reprint ed. 17.00 (978-1-4223-5174-1(2)) DIANE Publishing Co.

—Milly & the Macy's Parade. 2006. 40p. (J). pap. 5.99 (978-0-439-29755-4(9)) Scholastic, Inc.

Cotton, Jolie Jean. Pua's Paniolo Parade. Pratt, Christine Joy, illus. 2002. (J). pap. 10.99 (978-0-89610-428-0(1)) Island Heritage Publishing.

Engelbreit, Mary. Queen of Easter. Engelbreit, Mary, illus. 2006. (Ann Estelle Stories Ser.). (Illus.). 32p. (J). 15.99 (978-0-06-008184-3(8)); lib. bdg. 16.89 (978-0-06-008185-0(6)) HarperCollins Pubs.

Estes, Don. Willy: The Little Jeep Who Wanted to Be a Fire Truck. Garrison, Sue, illus. 2003. (J). lib. bdg. 14.95 (978-1-883551-47-6(1) , ASP-471, Attic Studio Pr.) Attic Studio Publishing Hse.

—Willy & Friends traveling through the Seasons: The continuing story of Willy the little fire Jeep. Glass, Eric, illus. 2006. (J). (978-1-883551-75-9(7) , Maple Corners Press) Attic Studio Publishing Hse.

Eurpsville U. S. A. Inc. Staff. Alphabet Eurps on Parade. 1999. (Concept Bks.). (J). 7.95 (978-1-892522-01-6(2)) Eurpsville USA, Inc.

Eurpsville U. S. A. Inc. Staff, ed. The Alphabet Eurps on Parade. 1999. (Illus.). (J). 19.95 (978-1-892522-12-2(8)) Eurpsville USA, Inc.

Garvin, Sharon. Alexandra's Rag-Time Band. 2006. 28p. (J). per. 12.95 (978-1-56167-926-3(7)) American Literary Pr.

Ghigna, Charles. The Alphabet Parade. Woods, Patti, illus. 2002. 32p. (J). 17.95 (978-1-880216-74-3(4)) River City Publishing.

Greenberg, Melanie Hope. The Mermaid Parade. Greenberg, Melanie Hope, illus. 2008. 32p. (J). (ps-k). 16.99 (***978-0-399-24708-8(4)*** , Putnam Juvenile) Penguin Group (USA) Inc.

Hirsch, Odo. Hazel Green. (J). 2005. 190p. (gr. 3-6). pap. 5.95 (978-1-58234-940-4(1)); 2003. (Illus.). 188p. (gr. 2-6). 15.95 (978-1-58234-820-9(0)) Bloomsbury Publishing. (Bloomsbury Children).

—Hazel Green. 2004. 190p. (J). (gr. 3-7). lib. bdg. 13.60 (978-0-606-30296-8(4)) Tandem Library Bks.

Hoffman, Mary. Princess Grace. Van Wright, Cornelius & Hu, Ying-Hwa, illus. 2008. 32p. (J). (ps). 16.99 (***978-0-8037-3260-5(0)*** , Dial) Penguin Group (USA) Inc.

Holub, Joan. Good Luck! A St. Patrick's Day Story. Terry, Will, illus. 2007. (Ant Hill Ser.). 24p. (J). pap. 3.99 (978-1-4169-0955-2(9) , Aladdin); lib. bdg. 11.89 (978-1-4169-2560-6(0) , Aladdin Library) Simon & Schuster Children's Publishing.

Jane, Pamela. Milo & the Fire Engine Parade. Johnson, Meredith, ed. Johnson, Meredith, illus. 2002. 32p. (J). pap. 13.95 (978-1-59034-036-3(1)); (gr. 1-4). 13.95 (978-1-59034-192-6(9)) Mondo Publishing.

Kerrin, Jessica Scott. Out of Orbit! Kelly, Joseph, illus. 2007. (Martin Bridge Ser.). 112p. (J). (gr. 2-5). pap. (***978-1-55453-149-3(7)***) Kids Can Pr., Ltd.

Labatt, Mary. A Parade for Sam. Sarrazin, Marisol, illus. 2005. 32p. (J). lib. bdg. 15.38 (***978-1-4242-1154-8(9)***) Fitzgerald Bks.

Leonard, Marcia. The Tin Can Man. Handelman, Dorothy, photos by. 1998. (Real Kids Readers Ser.). (Illus.). 32p. (ps-1). lib. bdg. 18.90 (978-0-7613-2012-8(1)), (J). pap. 4.99 (978-0-7613-2037-1(7)) Lerner Publishing Group. (Millbrook Pr.).

London, Jonathan. Froggy Plays in the Band. Remkiewicz, Frank, illus. (Froggy Ser.). 32p. (J). 2004. pap. 5.99 (978-0-14-240051-7(3) , Puffin); 2002. 15.99 (978-0-670-03532-8(7) , Viking Juvenile) Penguin Group (USA) Inc.

Masurel, Claire. Happy Thanksgiving, Emily! Calitri, Susan, illus. 2004. (Emily Ser.). 16p. (J). pap. 6.99 (978-0-14-240201-6(X) , Puffin) Penguin Group (USA) Inc.

McGrath, Barbara Barbieri. The M & M's' Brand All-American Parade Book. Tagel, Peggy, illus. 2004. 12p. (J). (ps-k). bds. 6.95 (978-1-57091-430-0(3)) Charlesbridge Publishing, Inc.

McKnight, Susan & Thornton, Suzi. The Mardi Gras Swamp Parade. Schexnayder, Paul, illus. 2000. 38p. (J). (gr. k-6). pap. 14.00 (978-1-882913-12-1(4)) Thornton Publishing.

Mishica, Clare. Here Comes the Parade. Richard, Ilene, illus. 24p. (J). (gr. k-2). 2006. pap. 4.95 (978-0-516-25016-8(7)); 2005. 19.50 (978-0-516-24857-8(X)) Scholastic Library Publishing. (Children's Pr.).

Mishica, Clare & Richard, Ilene. Vamos Al Desfile. Richard, Ilene, illus. 2006. (Rookie Reader Español Ser.). (ENG & SPA., Illus.). 22p. (J). (978-0-516-25309-1(3)) Children's Pr., Ltd.

Moncure, Jane Belk. My Sound Parade. King, Colin, illus. 2000. (New Sound Box Library). 32p. (J). (ps-3). 22.79 (978-1-56766-766-0(X)) Child's World, Inc.

Murphy. Best Bug Parade: Comparing Sizes Big Book. 2002. (Illus.). (J). pap. (978-0-7398-6775-4(X)) Steck-Vaughn.

Murphy, Stuart J. Spunky Monkeys on Parade. Cravath, Lynne W., illus. 1999. (MathStart Ser.). 40p. (J). (gr. 1 up). pap. 5.99 (978-0-06-446727-8(9) , Harper Trophy) HarperCollins Pubs.

—Spunky Monkeys on Parade. 1999. (MathStart Ser.). (Illus.). 40p. (YA). (gr. 1 up). 15.95 (978-0-06-028014-7(X)) HarperCollins Pubs.

—Spunky Monkeys on Parade. 1999. (Math Start Ser.). (978-0-606-17496-1(6)); lib. bdg. 13.00 (978-0-613-22430-7(2)) Tandem Library Bks.

Pease, Pamela. Macy's on Parade: A Pop-Up Celebration of the Macy's Thanksgiving Day Parade. Pease, Pamela, illus. 2002. (Illus.). 16p. (J). 36.00 (978-0-9669433-2-0(5)) Paintbox Pr.

Pinczes, Elinor J. Remainder of One. 2002. (gr. k-3). lib. bdg. 14.10 (978-0-613-90724-8(8)) Tandem Library Bks.

Piper, Watty. The Little Engine That Could Saves the Thanksgiving Day Parade. Ong, Cristina, illus. 2002. (Reading Railroad Bks.). 32p. (J). pap. 3.49 (978-0-448-42861-1(X) , Grosset & Dunlap) Penguin Group (USA) Inc.

Raintree Steck-Vaughn Staff. Aquí Viene el Desfile! 1999. (Coleccion en Parejas). (SPA.). (J). pap., stu. ed. 21.50 (978-0-7398-0814-6(1)) Steck-Vaughn.

—Desfiles! 1999. (Coleccion en Parejas). (SPA.). (J). pap., stu. ed. 21.50 (978-0-7398-0815-3(X)) Steck-Vaughn.

Rey, Margret. Curious George at the Parade. 1999. (gr. k-3). lib. bdg. 11.80 (978-0-613-21390-5(4)) Tandem Library Bks.

Rodgers, Frank. Little T & the Crown Jewels. 2007. (Read-It! Chapter Books). (J). 21.26 (978-1-4048-2726-4(9)) Picture Window Bks.

Schmauss, Judy Kentor. Parade Day. 2006. (Reader's Clubhouse Set B Ser.). (Illus.). 24p. (J). pap. 3.99 (978-0-7641-3293-3(8)) Barron's Educational Series, Inc.

Scholastic, Inc. Staff. The Greatest Parade. Hult, Gene, ed. 2004. (Clifford Ser.). 144p. (J). pap. 3.99 (978-0-439-60701-8(9)) Scholastic, Inc.

Thacker, Becky. The Chorus Kids' Memorial Day Parade. Thacker, Becky, illus. 2006. (J). 10.95 (978-0-9786276-1-4(X)) Mentzer Printing Ink.

Vincent, Mary. Tommy's Ticker Tape Parades. Vincent, Mary, ed. 2nd ed. 2001. 50p. (J). per. 14.95 (978-0-9670911-3-6(6)) Eastbank Publishing.

Warner, Gertrude Chandler. Watch, the Superdog! 2002. (gr. k-3). lib. bdg. 11.80 (978-0-613-70864-7(4)) Tandem Library Bks.

—Watch, the Superdog!, Vol. 10. Life, Kay, illus. 2004. (Adventures of Benny & Watch: Vol. 10). 32p. (J). (ps-2). pap. 3.95 (978-0-8075-0647-9(8)) Whitman, Albert & Co.

Wax, Wendy. Runaway Turkey. 2003. (ps-2). lib. bdg. 11.80 (978-0-613-73407-3(6)) Tandem Library Bks.

Weber, Lou, ed. Little People the Big Parade. 24p. 15.98 (978-1-4127-0637-7(8)) Publications International, Ltd.

Wells, Rosemary. The Halloween Parade. Wheeler, Jody, illus. 2001. (Yoko & Friends School Days Ser.: No. 3). 32p. (gr. k-2). 9.99 (978-0-7868-0723-9(7) , Volo) Hyperion Bks. for Children.

—The Halloween Parade. 2001. (J). 10.79 (978-0-606-22548-9(X)); lib. bdg. 11.80 (978-0-613-53195-5(7)) Tandem Library Bks.

Whitehead, Kathy. Looking for Uncle Louie on the Fourth of July. Torrecilla, Pablo, illus. 2004. 32p. (J). 15.95 (978-1-59078-061-9(2)) Boyds Mills Pr.

Winter, Jeanette. Angelina's Island. 2007. (Illus.). 32p. (J). (ps-3). 16.00 (978-0-374-30349-5(5) , Farrar, Straus & Giroux (BYR)) Farrar, Straus & Giroux.

Winthrop, Elizabeth. The Biggest Parade. Ulriksen, Mark, illus. rev. ed. 2006. 32p. (J). 16.95 (978-0-8050-7685-1(9)) Holt, Henry & Co.

Ziefert, Harriet. Hats off for the Fourth of July! Miller, Gustaf, illus. 2002. 32p. (J). (ps-ps). pap. 6.99 (978-0-14-056709-0(7) , Puffin) Penguin Group (USA) Inc.

PARAGUAY

Augustin, Byron. Paraguay. 2005. (Enchantment of the World, Second Ser.). (Illus.). 144p. (YA). (gr. 5-9). 36.00 (978-0-516-23675-9(X) , Children's Pr.) Scholastic Library Publishing.

Harcourt School Publishers Staff. Social Studies: Argentina, Chile, Paraguay & Uruguay. 2000. (Harcourt Brace Social Studies). (Illus.). (gr. k-7). pap. 33.90 (978-0-15-317433-9(1)) Harcourt Schl. Pubs.

Hernandez, Roger E. Paraguay. 2003. (Discovering Latin America Ser.). (Illus.). 64p. (J). (gr. 5 up). lib. bdg. (978-1-59084-297-3(9)) Mason Crest Pubs.

Jermyn, Leslie. Paraguay. 2000. (Cultures of the World Ser.). (Illus.). 128p. (gr. 5-12). lib. bdg. 37.07 (978-0-7614-0979-3(3) , Benchmark Bks.) Cavendish, Marshall Corp.

Selby, Anna. Argentina, Chile, Paraguay, Uruguay. 1999. (Country Fact Files Ser.). (Illus.). 48p. (J). (gr. 4-8). lib. bdg. 27.12 (978-0-8172-5408-7(0)) Raintree.

PARAPSYCHOLOGY

see also Apparitions; Extrasensory Perception; Ghosts; Mind and Body; Thought Transference

Allen, Charlotte Vale. The Young Person's Dreambook: An Abuse Workbook. 2002. 32p. (YA). 3.00 (978-1-892738-35-6(X)) Island Nation Pr., LLC.

Allen, Judy. Unexplained: An Encyclopedia of Curious Phenomena, Strange Superstitions, & Ancient Mysteries. Hook, Richard & Ludlow, Patricia, illus. 2006. 144p. (J). (gr. 5-9). 19.95 (978-0-7534-5950-8(7) , Kingfisher) Houghton Mifflin Co. Trade & Reference Div.

Andrews, Ted. Psychic Power. Alexander-Harding, Pagyn & Haugen, Diane, eds. 2000. (Young Person's School of Magic & Mystery Ser.: Vol. 3). (Illus.). xiii, 304p. (YA). (gr. 6 up). 18.95 (978-1-888767-40-7(5)) Dragonhawk Publishing.

Becker, Helaine. Are You Psychic? The Official Guide for Kids. 2005. (Illus.). 64p. pap. 9.95 (978-1-897066-21-8(X)) Maple Tree Pr. CAN. *Dist:* Perseus Distribution.

—Are You Psychic? The Official Guide for Kids. Davila, Claudia, illus. 2005. 64p. (ps-7). 16.95 (978-1-897066-20-1(1)) Maple Tree Pr. CAN. *Dist:* Perseus Distribution.

Blackwood, Gary L. Extraordinary Events & Oddball Occurrences. 1999. (Secrets of the Unexplained Ser.). (Illus.). 80p. (J). (gr. 5-9). lib. bdg. 29.93 (978-0-7614-0748-5(0) , Benchmark Bks.) Cavendish, Marshall Corp.

—Paranormal Powers. 1998. (Secrets of the Unexplained Ser.). (Illus.). 80p. (J). (gr. 5-9). lib. bdg. 28.50 (978-0-7614-0468-2(6) , Benchmark Bks.) Cavendish, Marshall Corp.

Doherty, Gillian, et al, eds. The Usborne Book of the Paranormal. 2000. (Paranormal Guides Ser.). (Illus.). 192p. (YA). (gr. 4 up). pap. 16.95 (978-0-7460-3390-6(7)) EDC Publishing.

Friedrich, Peter, et al. Roadstrip: A Graphic Journey Across America. 2005. (Illus.). 128p. pap. 22.95 (978-0-8118-4742-1(X)) Chronicle Bks. LLC.

Gardner, Robert. What's So Super about the Supernatural? 1998. (Single Titles Ser.). 80p. (YA). (gr. 4-7). lib. bdg. 24.90 (978-0-7613-3228-2(6) , Twenty-First Century Bks.) Lerner Publishing Group.

Herbst, Judith. Vanished. (Unexplained Ser.). (Illus.). 48p. (J). 2005. (gr. 5-12). lib. bdg. 26.60 (978-0-8225-1631-6(4)); 2004. pap. 7.95 (978-0-8225-2404-5(X) , Lerner Pubns.) Lerner Publishing Group.

Kalisher, Jesse & Greenwald, Jeff. Peekabuddha. Kalisher, Jesse, photos by. 2006. (Illus.). 128p. 16.95 (978-0-8118-4814-5(0)) Chronicle Bks. LLC.

Lassiter, Rhiannon. The Supernatural. 2006. (Illus.). 36p. (J). lib. bdg. 24.67 (978-0-8368-6267-6(8)) Stevens, Gareth Inc.

Marcovitz, Hal. Teens & the Supernatural & Paranormal. 2005. (Gallup Youth Survey, Major Issues & Trends Ser.). (Illus.). 112,128p. (YA). (gr. 7-9). lib. bdg. 22.95 (978-1-59084-876-0(4)) Mason Crest Pubs.

Netzley, Patricia D. Paranormal Phenomena. 2000. (Overview Ser.). (Illus.). 96p. (YA). (gr. 6-9). lib. bdg. 29.95 (978-1-56006-622-4(9) , LML00902-177977, Lucent Bks.) Thomson Gale.

Schneck, Robert Damon. Are You Psychic? 2007. (Illus.). 96p. (J). pap., pap., spiral bd. 4.95 (978-1-4027-3233-1(3)) Sterling Publishing Co., Inc.

Steiger, Sherry Hansen. Face to Face with the Unknown. 2001. (gr. 5-8). lib. bdg. 14.15 (978-0-613-17215-8(9)) Tandem Library Bks.

Townsend. Mysterious Disappearances. 2004. (Out There Ser.). (Illus.). pap. 8.95 (978-1-4109-0962-6(X)) Raintree.

Townsend, John. Mysteries of the Body & Mind. 2004. (Out There Ser.). (Illus.). 56p. (J). 28.56 (978-1-4109-0560-4(8)) Raintree.

Weil, Ann. Disappearances. 2007. (J). (***978-1-4109-2977-8(9)***) Steck-Vaughn.

White, Michael. Mind & Matter. 1999. (Illus.). 128p. (J). 7.95 (978-0-14-130017-7(5)) Penguin Bks., Ltd. GBR. *Dist:* Trafalgar Square Publishing.

PARAPSYCHOLOGY—FICTION

Garcia, Richard. Los Espiritus de Mi Tia Otilia. ed. 2004. (ENG & SPA., Illus.). (J). (gr. k-3). spiral bd. (978-0-616-14606-4(X)) Canadian National Institute for the Blind/Institut National Canadien pour les Aveugles.

Hapka, Cathy. Over the Top. 2005. 140p. (J). (978-1-4155-7730-1(7) , Aladdin) Simon & Schuster Children's Publishing.

Poryes, Michael & Sherman, Susan. Dueling Divas. 2005. (That's So Raven Ser.: Vol. 8). (Illus.). 137p. (J). (***978-1-4156-0366-6(9)***) Disney Pr.

—Psyched. 2005. (That's So Raven Ser.: Vol. 10). (Illus.). 136p. (J). (***978-1-4156-2557-6(3)***) Disney Pr.

—Showtime! 2005. (That's So Raven Ser.: Vol. 9). (Illus.). 134p. (J). (***978-1-4156-1643-7(4)***) Disney Pr.

Wright, Nina. Homefree. 2006. 240p. (J). pap. 8.95 (978-0-7387-0927-7(1) , Flux) Llewellyn Pubns.

Wright, Nina. Sensitive. 2007. 240p. (J). (gr. 4-7). pap. 9.95 (***978-0-7387-1170-6(5)*** , Flux) Llewellyn Pubns.

PARASITES

see also Bacteriology; Insects, Injurious and Beneficial

Allman, Toney. Guinea Worms (Parasites) 2004. (Parasites Ser.). (Illus.). 32p. (J). (gr. 4-7). 24.95 (978-0-7377-2634-3(2)) Thomson Gale.

Artell, Mike. Backyard Bloodsuckers: Questions, Facts & Tongue Twisters about Creepy Crawlers. 2004. (Illus.). 80p. pap. (978-0-673-59248-4(0)) Good Year Bks.

Birch, Robin. Head Lice Up Close. 2004. (Minibeasts up Close Ser.). (Illus.). 32p. (J). (gr. 3-5). 26.36 (978-1-4109-1140-7(3)) Harcourt Schl. Pubs.

Caffey, Don. Yikes-Lice! Girouard, Patrick, illus. 2003. 24p. (J). (ps-5). reprint ed. pap. 5.95 (978-0-8075-9375-2(3)) Whitman, Albert & Co.

Davies, Nicola. What's Eating You? Parasites—The Inside Story. Layton, Neal, illus. 2007. (Maisy Ser.). 64p. (J). (gr. 3). 12.99 (***978-0-7636-3460-5(3)***) Candlewick Pr.

Fleisher, Paul. Parasites: Latching on to a Free Lunch. 2006. (Discovery! Ser.). (Illus.). 112p. (J). (gr. 6-12). 29.27 (978-0-8225-3415-0(0) , Twenty-First Century Bks.) Lerner Publishing Group.

Harrison, Paul. Micro Bugs. 2007. (Up Close Ser.). (Illus.). 24p. (J). (gr. 3-5). lib. bdg. 23.95 (***978-1-4042-3760-5(7)*** , PowerKids Pr.) Rosen Publishing Group, Inc., The.

Houston, Rob. Feeders. 2003. (Parasites & Partners Ser.). (Illus.). 32p. (J). pap. 7.50 (978-1-4109-0355-6(9)); lib. bdg. (978-0-7398-6988-8(4)) Raintree.

Lice. 2003. (Illus.). 24.95 (978-0-7377-1784-6(X)) Thomson Gale.

Martin, James W. R. Killers. 2003. (Parasites & Partners Ser.). (Illus.). 32p. (J). pap. 7.50 (978-1-4109-0357-0(5)); lib. bdg. 25.70 (978-0-7398-6990-1(6)) Raintree.

—Killers. 2003. (gr. 5-8). lib. bdg. 15.90 (978-0-613-78250-0(X)) Tandem Library Bks.

McGinty, Alice B. Scavengers & Parasites in the Food Chain. 2002. (Library of Food Chains & Food Webs). (Illus.). 24p. (J). lib. bdg. 18.75 (978-0-8239-5755-2(1) , PowerKids Pr.) Rosen Publishing Group, Inc., The.

Parasites & Partners, 6 vols. 2003. (Illus.). (978-0-7398-6992-5(2)) Raintree.

Parasites & Partners 6 Pack, Set. 2004. pap. 243.00 (978-1-4109-1271-8(X)) Raintree.

Parker, Barbara Keevil. Ticks. 2007. (Early Bird Nature Books). (J). 25.26 (978-0-8225-6464-5(5) , Lerner Pubns.) Lerner Publishing Group.

Rundquist, Eric M. Reptile & Amphibian Parasites. 1999. (Basic Domestic Reptile & Amphibian Library). (Illus.). 64p. (YA). (gr. 4-7). lib. bdg. 19.75 (978-0-7910-5080-4(7) , Chelsea Hse.) Facts On File, Inc.

Schaefer, Lola M. Leeches. 2002. (Ooey-Gooey Animals Ser.). (Illus.). 24p. (J). (ps-1). pap. 5.25 (978-1-58810-715-2(9) , 91368); lib. bdg. 17.08 (978-1-58810-506-6(7)) Heinemann Library.

Szpirglas, Jeff. Gross Universe: Your Guide to All Disgusting Things under the Sun. Cho, Michael, tr. Cho, Michael, illus. 2004. 64p. (J). (gr. 3-7). 21.95 (978-1-894379-64-9(0)); pap. 12.95 (978-1-894379-65-6(9)) Maple Tree Pr. CAN. *Dist:* Firefly Bks., Ltd.

Szpirglas, Jeff & Cho, Michael. Gross Universe: Your Guide to All Disgusting Things under the Sun. 2005. (Illus.). 64p. (J). pap. 9.95 (978-1-897066-39-3(2)) Maple Tree Pr. CAN. *Dist:* Perseus Distribution.

Tsubakiyama, Margaret. Lice Are Lousy: All about Headlice. 1999. 3. (Illus.). 32p. (gr. k-3). lib. bdg. 23.90 (978-0-7613-1316-8(8) , Millbrook Pr.) Lerner Publishing Group.

Woodward, John. Pesky Parasites. 2003. (Amazing Nature Ser.). (Illus.). 32p. (J). pap. (978-1-4034-5403-4(5)); lib. bdg. (978-1-4034-4707-4(1)) Heinemann Library.

Woodward, John. What Lives on Other Animals? 2006. (J). lib. bdg. (***978-0-8368-7860-8(4)***) Stevens, Gareth Inc.

PARATROOPS

see Parachute Troops

PARCEL POST

see Postal Service

PAREJA, JUAN DE, 1606-1670—FICTION

De Trevino, Elizabeth Borton. I, Juan de Pareja. 2008. 192p. (J). pap. 6.99 (***978-0-312-38005-2(4)***) Square Fish.

de Trevino, Elizabeth Borton. I, Juan de Pareja. l.t. ed. 2005. 244p. 20.95 (978-0-7862-7666-0(5)) Thorndike Pr.

I, Juan de Pareja. 3rd ed. (J). pap., stu. ed. (978-0-13-667452-8(6)) Prentice Hall (Schl. Div.).

PARENT AND CHILD

see also Child Rearing; Father and Child; Mother and Child

Afflick, Lloyd E. Teenager's Guide to Success. 2002. (gr. 7-12). lib. bdg. 20.50 (978-0-613-74662-5(7)) Tandem Library Bks.

Aigner-Clark, Julie. 365 Days of Baby Einstein. 2003. (Illus.). 176p. (ps-17). 16.99 (978-0-7868-1908-9(1) , Disney Editions) Disney Pr.

Arquette, Kerry. Daddy Promises. McCain, Kevin, illus. 32p. 2005. (ENG.). (J). pap. 6.99 (978-0-7586-0905-2(1)); 1999. 12.99 (978-0-570-05554-9(7) , 56-1971) Concordia Publishing Hse.

Auld, Mary. My Mom. 2004. (Meet the Family Ser.). (Illus.). 24p. (J). (gr. 1 up). lib. bdg. 20.67 (978-0-8368-3927-2(7)) Stevens, Gareth Inc.

Barbara, Diane & Bloch, Serge. Dad & Me: A Special Book for You & Your Dad to Fill in Together & Share with Each Other. 2005. (Illus.). 52p. (J). (gr. k-5). 16.95 (978-0-8109-5881-4(3)) Abrams, Harry N. , Inc.

Baron, Larry. A Day with My Dad. 2002. (PowerPhonics Ser.). (Illus.). 23p. (J). lib. bdg. (978-0-8239-8247-9(5)) Rosen Publishing Group, Inc., The.

—A Day with My Dad: Learning the D Sound. 2002. (PowerPhonics Ser.). (Illus.). 24p. (J). (gr. 1). lib. bdg. 18.00 (978-0-8239-5902-0(3) , PowerKids Pr.) Rosen Publishing Group, Inc., The.

Bayliss, Peg. Mom... Dad... This Is What I've Been Trying To Tell You: A Book for Kids to Read to Their Parents. Miele, Bob, illus. 1999. 24p. (YA). (gr. 7-12). pap. 6.95 (978-1-57543-078-2(9)) MAR*CO Products, Inc.

Beisswenger, Iffer & Eldred, Margaret. The Way We See Things: Middle Schoolers Look at Themselves & Issues They Face Everyday. Krusi, Carolynne, ed. 2004. 96p. pap. 14.95 (978-0-9759264-0-6(3)) Rope Ferry Pr.

Berry, Joy Wilt. Teach Me about Separation: A Growing up Book. Fitzpatrick, Roey, illus. rev. ed. 1999. (Teach Me about Ser.: Vol. 4). 32p. (J). (ps). bds. 5.95 (978-1-58634-007-0(7) , 01-0102-04) Goldstar Publishing, Inc.

Beyer, Kay. Coping with Teen Parenting. rev. ed. 1999. (Coping Ser.). (Illus.). 209p. (YA). (gr. 7-12). lib. bdg. 26.50 (978-0-8239-3035-7(1) , COTEPA) Rosen Publishing Group, Inc., The.

Bode, Janet. Heartbreak & Roses: Real Life Stories of Troubled Love. 2000. (YA). (978-0-606-19403-7(7)) Tandem Library Bks.

Bolam, Emily & Ehrlich, Fred. Does a Duck Have a Daddy? Early Experiences. 2007. (Illus.). 28p. pap. 5.95 (978-1-59354-590-1(8)) Blue Apple Bks.

—Does a Mouse Have a Mommy? Early Experiences. 2007. (Illus.). 28p. pap. 5.95 (978-1-59354-589-5(4)) Blue Apple Bks.

Bradford-Vernon, Jennifer R. How to Be Your Child's First Teacher: Insights for Parent Involvement. 2003. (Illus.). 176p. (gr. k-1). 14.99 (978-1-56822-998-0(4) , IF27018) School Specialty Publishing.

Bradley, Michael J. Yes, Your Parents Are Crazy! A Teen Survival Handbook. Glasbergen, Randy, illus. 2004. 432p. pap. 14.95 (978-0-936197-48-7(X)) Harbor Pr., Inc.

Brown, Roman & Brown, Ramsey. 101 Ways Kids Can Spoil Their Parents . . . Gift Book: And Increase Their Allowance. Davis, Rich, illus. 1998. 128p. (J). (gr. k-10). 5.99 (978-1-881830-92-4(6)) Garborg's, Inc.

Burgen, Jim. What's the Big Deal about My Parents? Reeves, Dale, ed. 2006. (What's the Big Deal Ser.). 160p. (gr. 7 up). pap. 10.99 (978-0-7847-1252-8(2) , 23335) Standard Publishing.

Burton, Margie, et al. With My Mom & Dad. Evento, Susan, ed. 1998. (Early Connections Ser.). 16p. (J). (gr. k-2). pap. 4.25 (978-1-892393-46-3(8)) Benchmark Education Co.

Combs, Bobbie. ABC a Family Alphabet Book. Keane, Desiree & Rappa, Brian, illus. 2001. 32p. (J). pap. 8.95 (978-0-9674468-1-3(3)) Two Lives Publishing.

Damm, Antje. Ask Me. rev. ed. 2003. (Illus.). 224p. (J). 14.95 (978-0-7613-1845-3(3)) Roaring Brook Pr.

Daniel, Becky. The Playful Child: 130+ Quick Brain-Boosting Activities for 5- & 6-Year Olds. 2000. (Illus.). 176p. (Orig.). (J). (ps-1). pap. 14.99 (978-1-56822-956-0(9) , IF19623-E4, Instructional Fair) Schaffer, Frank Pubns.

—The Playful Preschooler: 130+ Quick Brain-Boosting Activities for 3- & 4-Year-Olds. 2000. (Growing & Learning Ser.). (Illus.). 176p. (J). (gr. 4 up). pap. 14.99 (978-1-56822-955-3(0) , IF19622) School Specialty Publishing.

—The Playful Toddler: 130+ Quick Brain-Boosting Activities for 18 to 36 Months. 2000. (Growing & Learning Ser.). (Illus.). 176p. (J). (gr. 4 up). pap. 16.99 (978-1-56822-954-6(2) , IF19621) School Specialty Publishing.

Drake, Jane & Love, Ann. My Mother & Me. Ritchie, Scot, illus. unabr. ed. 2000. (Memory Scrapbks. for Kids). 32p. (J). (gr. k-3). (978-1-55074-635-8(9)) Kids Can Pr., Ltd.

Ellis, Deborah. Our Stories, Our Songs: African Children Talk About AIDS. 2005. (Illus.). 112p. (YA). (978-1-55041-913-9(7)) Fitzhenry & Whiteside, Ltd.

Feltes, Kim & Chen, Grace. Yo, Yolanda! Advice from an Expert. 2002. (Read 180 Ser.). (Illus.). 70p. (J). (978-0-439-12333-4(X)) Scholastic, Inc.

Flaherty, Patrick F. & Harper, Steven. Life's Lessons from Dad: Quotes for Life Book Series. McLaughlin, Patrick, ed. 2004. per. 12.95 (978-0-9724178-5-3(0)) Teckni-Corp. Ltd.

Fox-Lee, Kyme & Fox-Lee, Susan. What Are Parents? Daddys Edition. Jennings, Randy, illus. 2007. 32p. 15.95 (978-0-9753699-1-3(1)) StoryTyme Publishing.

Garwood, Ben & Garwood, Mary. Not Like You. 2004. 172p. (YA). per. 11.95 (978-1-933094-00-7(1)) Tarbutton Pr.

Gellman, Marc. "Always Wear Clean Underwear!" And Other Ways Parents Say "I Love You" 2000. (Illus.). (J). 11.79 (978-0-606-22049-1(6)) Tandem Library Bks.

—Always Wear Clean Underwear! And Other Ways Parents Say I Love You. Tilley, Debbie, illus. 2000. 112p. (J). (gr. 3-7). pap. 4.99 (978-0-688-17112-4(5) , Harper Trophy) HarperCollins Pubs.

Gellman, Marc. Someday You'll Thank Me for This! And Other Annoying (But True) Life Lessons. Tilley, Debbie, illus. 2007. 144p. (J). (gr. 3-7). 12.99 (***978-0-316-01234-8(3)***) Little, Brown Bks. for Young Readers.

Grollman, Earl A. Talking about Divorce & Separation: A Dialogue Between Parent & Child. Pitzer, Suzanne, illus. 2005. (J). (978-1-56123-155-3(X)) Centering Corp.

Hamada, Leslie. Pee Wee's Adventure in the Woods. 2006. (ENG.). 32p. per. 13.95 (***978-1-4259-6172-5(X)***) AuthorHouse.

Helmer, Diana Star. Let's Talk about When Your Mom or Dad Is Unhappy. 1999. (Let's Talk Library). (Illus.). 24p. (J). (gr. 3). lib. bdg. 18.75 (978-0-8239-5192-5(8) , PowerKids Pr.) Rosen Publishing Group, Inc., The.

Hill, Mary. Let's Go to a Baseball Game. 2004. (Weekend Fun Ser.). (Illus.). 24p. (J). 18.00 (978-0-516-23997-2(X)); pap. 4.95 (978-0-516-25916-1(4)) Scholastic Library Publishing. (Children's Pr.).

Hilton, Marilyn Copley. The Christian Girl's Guide to Your Mom. 2004. (Illus.). 176p. (J). pap. 9.99 (978-1-58411-045-3(7) , Legacy Pr.) Rainbow Pubs. & Legacy Pr.

Hughes, Lynne. You Are Not Alone: Teens Talk about Life after the Loss of a Parent. 2005. (You Are Not Alone Ser.). (Illus.). 208p. (J). pap. 16.99 (978-0-439-58590-3(2) , Scholastic Pr.) Scholastic, Inc.

Jareaux, Marlena. 26 Things to Teach Your Parents. 2007. (Illus.). 76p. (YA). per. 10.95 (***978-0-9790415-1-8(1)***) Inspired By the Beach Publishing.

Kerley, Barbara. You & Me Together: Moms, Dads, & Kids Around the World. 2005. (Illus.). 32p. (J). 16.95 (978-0-7922-8297-6(3) , National Geographic Children's Bks.) National Geographic Society.

—You & Me Together: Moms, Dads, & Kids Arounds the World. 2005. (Illus.). 32p. (J). 25.90 (978-0-7922-8298-3(1) , National Geographic Children's Bks.) National Geographic Society.

Klein, David & Klein, Marymae E. Your Parents & Your Self: Alike, Unlike, Agreeing, Disagreeing. 1999. 166p. (YA). (gr. 7-10). reprint ed. 20.00 (978-0-7881-6843-7(6)) DIANE Publishing Co.

Krohn, Katherine E. Everything You Need to Know about Birth Order. 2005. (Need to Know Library). (Illus.). 64p. (YA). (gr. 7-12). 25.25 (978-0-8239-3228-3(1) , NTBIOR) Rosen Publishing Group, Inc., The.

Leeb, Valorie. My Dad, the Guardian Angel. Tift, Jeanne, ed. Coomes, Sean, illus. 2002. 44p. (YA). (gr. 3 up). 15.95 (978-0-9721872-0-6(0)) Midnight Pr.

Lindsay, Jeanne Warren & McCullough, Sally. Discipline from Birth to Three: How Teen Parents Can Prevent & Deal with Discipline Problems with Babies & Toddlers. Crawford, David, photos by. 3rd ed. 2004. (Teen Pregnancy & Parenting Series Ser.). 224p. (J). 18.95 (978-1-932538-10-6(0)); pap. 12.95 (978-1-932538-09-0(7)) Morning Glory Pr., Inc.

Lovegrove, Emily. Help! I'm Being Bullied. 2007. (Illus.). 167p. pap. 16.95 (***978-1-905170-34-0(3)***) Accent Pr. GBR. *Dist:* Dufour Editions, Inc.

Mancini, Richard E. Everything You Need to Know about Living with a Single Parent. rev. ed. 1999. (Need to Know Library). (Illus.). 64p. (YA). (gr. 7-12). lib. bdg. 25.25 (978-0-8239-3039-5(4) , NTSIPA) Rosen Publishing Group, Inc., The.

Martin-Finks, Nancy. Custody Battle: A Workbook for Children. 2005. (Illus.). 68p. (J). per. 19.95 (978-1-931636-42-1(7)) National Center For Youth Issues.

Martinez, Victor. Parrot in the Oven: Mi Vida. Scott, Steve, illus. rev. ed. 1998. 240p. (J). (gr. 7 up). pap. 5.99 (978-0-06-447186-2(1) , Harper Trophy) HarperCollins Pubs.

McGraw, Jay. Closing the Gap: A Strategy for Bringing Parents & Teens Together. 2001. (gr. 7-12). lib. bdg. 23.45 (978-0-613-84519-9(6)) Tandem Library Bks.

Moore, M. Meet My Mom: Learning the M Sound. 2002. (PowerPhonics Ser.). (Illus.). 24p. (J). (gr. 1). lib. bdg. 18.00 (978-0-8239-5913-6(9) , PowerKids Pr.) Rosen Publishing Group, Inc., The.

Moore-Mallinos, Jennifer & Roca, Nuria. Lost & Found. Fabrega, Marta, illus. 2006. (Let's Talk about It Bks.). 32p. (J). pap. 6.99 (978-0-7641-3510-1(4)) Barron's Educational Series, Inc.

—Perdida y Ecnontrada: Lost & Found, Spanish Edition. Fabrega, Marta, illus. 2006. (Let's Talk about It Bks.). (SPA.). 32p. (J). pap. 6.99 (978-0-7641-3511-8(2)) Barron's Educational Series, Inc.

Moore-Mallions, Jennifer & Roca, Nuria. Mi Papa se Casa: Daddy's Getting Married, Spanish Edition. Fabrega, Marta, illus. 2006. (Let's Talk about It Bks.). (SPA.). 32p. (J). pap. 6.99 (978-0-7641-3505-7(8)) Barron's Educational Series, Inc.

Moore, Sharon. Meet My Mom: Learning the M Sound. 2002. (PowerPhonics Ser.). (Illus.). 23p. (J). lib. bdg. (978-0-8239-8258-5(0) , PowerKids Pr.) Rosen Publishing Group, Inc., The.

Moses, Brian. It Wasn't Me. 2000. (gr. k-3). lib. bdg. 14.45 (978-0-613-30524-2(8)) Tandem Library Bks.

Nuestros Padres 6 Packs. Individual Title. (Coleccion Pm Ser.).Tr. of Our parents. (SPA.). 16p. (gr. 1 up). 26.00 (978-0-7578-3028-0(5)) Rigby Education.

Parents: Growing Closer. ldr.'s ed. 1998. (Cross Training Ser.: Vol. 4). 56p. (YA). (gr. 10-12). pap. 15.00 incl. VHS (978-1-57405-034-9(6)) CharismaLife Pubs.

Peltier, Sylvia M. Nanny & I. Peltier, Sylvia M., illus. 2003. (Illus.). 32p. (YA). (ps up). 16.95 (978-0-9724394-0-4(4)) Sylables.

Pike, Sargente. Everything That Parents Know about Teenagers, Vol. 2. 2001. (YA). (gr. 7-12). pap. 10.00 (978-0-9708655-1-9(1)) IronDream.

Polacco, Patricia. Betty Doll. Polacco, Patricia, illus. (Illus.). (J). (ps-3). 2001. 1p. 16.99 (978-0-399-23638-9(4) , Philomel); 2004. 40p. reprint ed. pap. 6.99 (978-0-14-240196-5(X) , Puffin) Penguin Group (USA) Inc.

Powell, Jillian. Me & My Family. 2007. (J). (***978-1-59771-088-6(1)***) Sea-To-Sea Pubns.

Ramnath, Vianna. Daddy Loves You! 2006. 22p. 11.99 (978-1-4116-8867-4(8)) Lulu.com.

Rice, Wayne & Zondervan. Read This Book or You're Grounded! A Secret Guide to Surviving Home. 2003. (Studentware Ser.). (Illus.). 160p. (J). pap. 9.99 (978-0-310-25049-4(8)) Zondervan.

Richmond, Marianne R. Dear Daughter. 2004. (Illus.). 40p. (YA). 7.95 (978-0-9753528-0-9(6)) Marianne Richmond Studios, Inc.

—Dear Son. 2005. (Illus.). 40p. (J). 7.95 (978-0-9763101-1-2(2)) Marianne Richmond Studios, Inc.

—It's a Boy. 2004. (Illus.). 40p. (YA). 7.95 (978-0-9753528-3-0(0)) Marianne Richmond Studios, Inc.

—It's a Girl. 2004. (Illus.). 40p. (YA). 7.95 (978-0-9753528-2-3(2)) Marianne Richmond Studios, Inc.

Rigby Education Staff. Visiting My Mom's Office. (Illus.). 8p. (J). bds. 3.95 (978-0-7635-6452-0(4) , 764524C99) Rigby Education.

Roark, Walter. Keeping Your Toddler on Track till Mommy Gets Back: The Toddler Survival Guide for 21st-Century Dads. 2003. (Illus.). 224p. (J). pap. 15.95 (978-0-9707937-1-3(5)) Clearing Skies Pr.

Ross, Allison J. Coping When a Parent Is Mentally Ill. 2005. (Coping Ser.). (Illus.). 192p. (YA). (gr. 7-12). lib. bdg. 26.50 (978-0-8239-3359-4(8)) Rosen Publishing Group, Inc., The.

Rotner, Shelley & Kelly, Sheila M. Something's Different. Rotner, Shelley, photos by. 2002. (Contemporary Issues for Young Children Ser.). (Illus.). 32p. (gr. k-3). lib. bdg. 22.90 (978-0-7613-1923-8(9) , Millbrook Pr.) Lerner Publishing Group.

Saunders-Smith, Gail. Parents. 1998. (J). pap. 13.25 (978-0-516-21239-5(7) , Children's Pr.) Scholastic Library Publishing.

Sawyer, Louise. ABC & ASL. 2002. (YA). 6.95 (978-0-9719842-9-5(8)) Martin & Brothers.

Schaefer, Lola M. Fathers. Saunders-Smith, Gail, ed. 1999. (Families Ser.). (Illus.). 24p. (J). (gr. k-1). lib. bdg. 15.93 (978-0-7368-0256-7(8) , Pebble Bks.) Capstone Pr., Inc.

—Mothers. Saunders-Smith, Gail, ed. 1999. (Families Ser.). (Illus.). 24p. (J). (gr. k-1). lib. bdg. 15.93 (978-0-7368-0259-8(2) , Pebble Bks.) Capstone Pr., Inc.

Searching for the Words. 2nd ed. 2003. (J). spiral bd. (978-0-9718626-2-3(1)) Holofcener, Mark.

Shakespeare, William. The Tempest. Ermitage, Kathleen, ed. 2002. (Simply Shakespeare Ser.). (Illus.). 288p. pap. 8.99 (978-0-7641-2087-9(5)) Barron's Educational Series, Inc.

Sheldon, Annette. Big Sister Now: A Story about Me & Our New Baby. Maizel, Karen, illus. 2005. 32p. (J). (ps). 14.95 (978-1-59147-243-8(1)); pap. 8.95 (978-1-59147-244-5(X)) American Psychological Assn. (Magination Pr.).

Sidman, Joyce & Swan, Susan. Just Us Two: Poems about Dads. 2003. (Single Titles Ser.: Vol. 3). 32p. pap. 7.95 (978-0-7613-1833-0(X) , Millbrook Pr.) Lerner Publishing Group.

Smith, Andrea Joy. Gladys Blackmon-Morrow: Let the Words from My Mouth... Be Acceptable in Thy Sight, O Lord... Psalms 19:14: the Woman, the Wife, the Mother. 2005. (YA). per. 14.95 (978-0-9764396-1-5(1)) Smith, Andrea Joy.

Snow, Judith E. How It Feels to Have a Gay or Lesbian Parent: A Book by Kids for Kids of All Ages. 2004. (Illus.). (J). 1p. pap. 12.95 (978-1-56023-420-3(2)); 123p. 19.95 (978-1-56023-419-7(9)) Haworth Pr., Inc., The. (Harrington Park Pr.).

Sportelli-Rehak, Angela. Uncle Sam's Kids: When Duty Calls. Hinlicky, Gregg, illus. 2004. (Uncle Sam's Kids Ser.: Bk. 1). 40p. (gr. k-6). 15.95 (978-0-9714515-1-3(6)) Abidenme Bks.

Stuchin, Mallory. We're in This Together: 15 Teens Reveal How They Get Along with Their Parents (And Other Sanity-Saving Insights) 2003. 112p. (J). pap. 14.95 (978-1-932181-03-6(2)) Personhood Pr.

Sullivan, James Kevin, illus. What Went RIght Today? Journal: WWRT Journal. 2007. 72p. (J). spiral bd. 12.95 (***978-0-9766990-1-9(X)***) Buz-Land Presentations, Inc.

Thumann, Robin K. Peaceful Thoughts: An Interactive Journey in Positive Thinking for Children & Their Parents. Thumann, Robin K., illus. 2003. (Illus.). 44p. (J). (ps-4). 19.95 (978-0-9725118-0-3(6)) Peaceful Thoughts Pr.

PARENT AND CHILD—FICTION

Abegg, Rainbow G. Peaches & Prayers. 2004. (Illus.). 17.95 (978-1-59156-049-4(7)) Covenant Communications, Inc.

Abel, Kathleen. Smile So Big. 2008. (J). 16.00 (978-0-15-200671-6(0)) Harcourt Trade Pubs.

Acker, Rick. The Case of the Autumn Rose. 2003. (Davis Detective Mysteries Ser.). 192p. pap. 7.99 (978-0-8254-2004-7(0)) Kregel Pubns.

Ada, Alma Flor. A Surprise for Mother Rabbit. 2000. (gr. k-3). lib. bdg. 17.60 (978-0-613-79391-9(9)) Tandem Library Bks.

Adler, David A. The Babe & I. Widener, Terry, illus. 1999. 32p. (J). (gr. k-4). 17.00 (978-0-15-201378-3(4) , Gulliver Bks.) Harcourt Children's Bks.

Ahlberg, Janet & Ahlberg, Allan. Adios Pequeño! Ahlberg, Janet & Ahlberg, Allan, illus. (Historias Para Dormir Ser.). (SPA., Illus.). 28p. (J). (gr. k-3). 9.95 (978-968-19-1039-6(7)) Aguilar Editorial MEX. *Dist:* Santillana USA Publishing Co., Inc.

Albert, Louise. Less Than Perfect. 2003. 224p. (J). (gr. 7 up). tchr. ed. 17.95 (978-0-8234-1688-2(7)) Holiday Hse., Inc.

Alborough, Jez. Hug. Alborough, Jez, illus. 2001. (Illus.). 32p. (J). (gr. k-ps). bds. 6.99 (978-0-7636-1576-5(5)) Candlewick Pr.

—Some Dogs Do. Alborough, Jez, illus. 2003. (Illus.). 40p. (J). (ps-2). 15.99 (978-0-7636-2201-5(X)) Candlewick Pr.

Alcott, Louisa May. Little Women: Two Books in One. 2003. (gr. 3-6). lib. bdg. 22.25 (978-0-613-77101-6(X)) Tandem Library Bks.

Aldis, Dorothy & Collins, Heather. Hiding. (FRE.). (J). pap. 7.99 (978-0-590-24195-3(8)) Scholastic, Inc.

Alexander, Jason. Dad, Are You the Tooth Fairy? Spears, Ron, illus. 2005. 32p. (J). pap. 16.95 (978-0-439-66745-6(3)) Scholastic, Inc.

Alfonsi, Alice. Trust Your Heart. novel rev. ed. 2007. (W. I. T. C. H. Ser.: Bk. 24). 144p. (gr. 3-7). pap. 4.99 (***978-1-4231-0288-5(6)***) Hyperion Pr.

Algeo, Kristie. When Daddy Comes Home. 2006. (ENG., Illus.). 36p. per. 21.99 (978-1-4141-0667-0(X)) Pleasant Word.

—When Daddy Goes Away. 2006. (ENG., Illus.). 36p. (J). per. 21.99 (978-1-4141-0643-4(2)) Pleasant Word.

Amaral, Gayla. Hooray for Mommies! Babies & BarneyTM. Full, Dennis, photos by. 2002. (Barney Ser.). (Illus.). 22p. (J). (ps-k). bds. 5.99 (978-1-58668-220-0(2)) Scholastic, Inc.

Ambrosio, Michael. It Takes a Lot of Love. Awes, Jennifer, illus. 2007. 32p. (J). 14.95 (***978-0-9716085-4-2(7)***) LionX Publishing.

Amollo, Regina. When Mother Leaves Home. 2004. (Illus.). 35p. pap. 9.95 (978-9970-02-435-3(3)) Fountain Pubs. Ltd. UGA. *Dist:* Michigan State Univ. Pr.

Anastas, Margaret. A Hug for You. Winter, Susan, photos by. 2005. (Illus.). 32p. (J). (ps-1). 15.99 (978-0-06-623613-1(4)) HarperCollins Pubs.

—Mommy's Best Kisses. Winter, Susan, illus. 32p. (J). (ps-1). 2003. 15.99 (978-0-06-623601-8(0)); 2000. reprint ed. pap. 6.99 (978-0-06-443839-1(2)) HarperCollins Pubs.

Anderson, Laurie Halse. Catalyst. 2003. 240p. (YA). (gr. 6). pap. 7.99 (978-0-14-240001-2(7) , Puffin) Penguin Group (USA) Inc.

—Catalyst. 2003. (gr. 7-12). lib. bdg. 15.30 (978-0-613-70575-2(0)) Tandem Library Bks.

—Time to Fly. 2003. (Wild at Heart Ser.). (Illus.). 113p. (J). (gr. 4 up). lib. bdg. 23.33 (978-0-8368-3262-4(0)) Stevens, Gareth Inc.

Andreae, Giles. Keep Love in Your Heart, Little One. Vulliamy, Clara, illus. 2007. 32p. (J). (ps-2). 15.95 (***978-1-58925-066-6(4)*** , tiger tales) ME Media LLC.

Annunziata, Jane & Nemiroff, Marc A. Why Am I an Only Child? Scott, Margaret, illus. 1998. 36p. (J). (ps-3). 19.95 (978-1-55798-506-4(5) , 441-5065) American Psychological Assn.

Appelt, Kathi. Siempre Pienso en Ti. Dyer, Jane, illus. 2002. (SPA.). 40p. (J). (gr. k-2). 19.99 (978-84-261-3173-7(5) , JV30139) Juventud, Editorial ESP. *Dist:* Lectorum Pubns., Inc.

Araki, Mie. Kitten's Big Adventure. 2005. (Illus.). 40p. (J). 15.00 (978-0-15-216738-7(2)) Harcourt Trade Pubs.

Asch, Frank. Good Night, Baby Bear. Asch, Frank, illus. 2001. (Illus.). 32p. (J). (ps-k). pap. 7.00 (978-0-15-216368-6(9) , Voyager Bks./Libros Viajeros) Harcourt Children's Bks.

—Good Night, Baby Bear. 2001. 12.80 (978-0-606-22600-4(1)); lib. bdg. 14.15 (978-0-613-53034-7(9)) Tandem Library Bks.

Aston, Dianna Hutts. When You Were Born. Lewis, Earl, illus. 2004. 32p. (J). (ps up). 15.99 (978-0-7636-1438-6(6)) Candlewick Pr.

Auerbach, Annie. No Parent's Day. 2001. (gr. k-3). lib. bdg. 11.25 (978-0-613-43945-9(7)) Tandem Library Bks.

Augustine, Kristen. Can I Tell You? 2005. 9.00 (978-0-8059-8071-4(7)) Dorrance Publishing Co., Inc.

Avi. Abigail Takes the Wheel. Bolognese, Don, illus. 1999. (I Can Read Bks.). 64p. (J). (gr. 3 up). 14.95 (978-0-06-027662-1(2)); lib. bdg. 17.89 (978-0-06-027663-8(0)) HarperCollins Pubs.

—Abigail Takes the Wheel. 2000. (Illus.). (J). (978-0-606-18672-8(7)) Tandem Library Bks.

—Ereth's Birthday. Floca, Brian, illus. 2000. (Tales from Dimwood Forest Ser.). 192p. (J). (gr. 4-7). 17.99 (978-0-380-97734-5(6)) HarperCollins Pubs.

Baer, Julie. Love Me Later. 2005. (Illus.). 28p. (J). (ps-ps). 16.99 (978-1-932188-03-5(7)) Bollix Bks.

Baggette, Susan K. Jonathan Goes to the Doctor. Moriarty, William J., photos by. 1998. (Jonathan Adventures Ser.). (Illus.). 16p. (J). (ps-k). bds. 5.95 (978-0-9660172-1-2(8)) Brookfield Reader, Inc., The.

Bajaj, Varsha. How Many Kisses Do You Want Tonight? Bates, Ivan, illus. 2004. 28p. (J). (ps-3). 15.99 (978-0-316-82381-4(3)) Little, Brown Bks. for Young Readers.

Ballard, Robin. My Day, Your Day. Ballard, Robin, illus. 2001. (Illus.). 24p. (J). (ps-3). 14.95 (978-0-688-17796-6(4)) HarperCollins Pubs.

Balzac, Honoré de. Le Pere Goriot: Level D. (FRE.). (YA). (gr. 7-12). 8.95 (978-0-88436-043-8(1) , 40280) EMC/Paradigm Publishing.

Bang, Molly. In My Heart. 2006. (Illus.). 32p. (J). (ps-k). 15.99 (978-0-316-79617-0(4)) Little Brown & Co.

Banim, Lisa. Case at Camp Get-Me Outie. 2004. 125p. (J). lib. bdg. 16.92 (***978-1-4242-0680-3(4)***) Fitzgerald Bks.

Banks, Kate. The Night Worker. Hallensleben, Georg, illus. 2000. 40p. (J). (ps-1). 16.00 (978-0-374-35520-3(7) , Farrar, Straus & Giroux (BYR)) Farrar, Straus & Giroux.

Banting, Celia. I Only Said I Didn't Want You Because I Was Terrified. 2006. (I Only Said Ser.: 4). 240p. (YA). pap. 14.99 (***978-0-9786648-3-1(3)***) Wighita Pr.

Barber, Barbara E. Saturday at the New You. Rich, Anna, illus. 2002. (J). 14.66 (978-0-7587-3566-9(9)) Book Wholesalers, Inc.

Barkow, Henriette. That's My Mum. Brazell, Derek, illus. 2004. (J). (ALB & ENG.). 24p. (978-1-85269-595-8(1)); (ENG & YOR.). (978-1-84444-381-9(7)) Mantra Publishing, Ltd.

Barnes, Joyce Annette. Promise Me the Moon. 1999. (978-0-606-14297-7(5)) Tandem Library Bks.

Baronian, Jean-Baptiste. Con Todo Mi Corazon. 2000. (SPA., Illus.). 12p. (J). 16.95 (978-84-488-0686-6(7) , BS8814) Beascoa, Ediciones S.A. ESP. *Dist:* Lectorum Pubns., Inc.

Barrett, Tracy. On Etruscan Time. rev. ed. 2005. 176p. (J). 17.95 (978-0-8050-7569-4(0) , Holt, Henry & Co. Bks. For Young Readers) Holt, Henry & Co.

Baskin, Nora Raleigh. What Every Girl (Except Me) Knows. 2002. 224p. (J). (gr. 5 up). pap. 5.50 (978-0-440-41852-8(6) , Yearling) Random Hse. Children's Bks.

Bateman, Teresa. Hunting the Daddyosaurus. Huang, Benrei, illus. 2004. 29p. (J). (gr. k-4). reprint ed. 16.00 (978-0-7567-7796-8(8)) DIANE Publishing Co.

—Hunting the Daddyosaurus. Huang, Benrei, illus. 2002. 32p. (J). (ps-1). 15.95 (978-0-8075-1433-7(0)) Whitman, Albert & Co.

Battle-Lavert, Gwendolyn. Papa's Mark. Bootman, Colin, illus. 2003. 32p. (J). (gr. k-3). tchr. ed. 16.95 (978-0-8234-1650-9(X)) Holiday Hse., Inc.

Bauer, Cat. Harley, Like a Person. 2007. 288p. (gr. 9). (J). pap. 8.99 (978-0-375-83735-7(3)); (YA). 15.99 (978-0-375-93735-4(8)) Random Hse. Children's Bks. (Knopf Bks. for Young Readers).

—Harley, Like a Person. 2000. (Illus.). (J). 13.60 (978-0-606-20690-7(6)) Tandem Library Bks.

—Harley, Like a Person. 2000. (Illus.). 248p. (J). (gr. 7 up). pap. 5.95 (978-1-58837-005-1(4)) Winslow Pr.

Bauer, Joan. Sticks. 2002. 192p. (YA). 18.99 (978-0-399-23752-2(6) , Putnam Juvenile) Penguin Group (USA) Inc.

Bauer, Marion Dane & Wu, Leslie. The Very Best Daddy of All. 2004. (Illus.). 40p. (J). 12.95 (978-0-689-84178-1(7)) Simon & Schuster Children's Publishing.

Beale, Fleur. I Am Not Esther. 2004. 256p. (gr. 7-17). reprint ed. pap. 6.99 (978-0-7868-1673-6(2)) Hyperion Bks. for Children.

Bechard, Margaret E. Hanging on to Max. rev. ed. 2002. (Single Titles Ser.: 12). 160p. (YA). (gr. 7 up). 16.95 (978-0-7613-1579-7(9)) Roaring Brook Pr.

—Hanging on to Max. 2003. (Illus.). 176p. (YA). pap. 6.99 (978-0-689-86268-7(7) , Simon Pulse) Simon & Schuster Children's Publishing.

—Hanging on to Max. 2003. (gr. 7-12). lib. bdg. 15.30 (978-0-613-70821-0(0)) Tandem Library Bks.

Becker, Christie. You Will Be My Baby Even When. Brayton, Julie, illus. 2003. 32p. (J). (ps-1). 14.95 (978-0-9728116-0-6(5)) Becker, Christie.

Becker, Shari. Horris Grows Down. Petrone, Valeria, illus. 2007. 32p. (J). (ps). 15.99 (978-0-399-24358-5(5) , Putnam Juvenile) Penguin Group (USA) Inc.

Beckerman, Menucha. A Surprise for Mommy. 2003. (My Middos World Ser.: Vol. 4). (Illus.). 34p. (J). (gr. k-5). 5.95 (978-1-931681-10-0(4)) Israel Bk. Shop.

Bedford, David. Touch the Sky, My Little Bear. Chapman, Jane, illus. 2001. 32p. (J). (ps-k). 15.95 (978-1-929766-20-8(3)) Handprint Bks.

Berenstain, Stan & Berenstain, Jan. The Berenstain Bears Play Ball. l.t. ed. 1998. (Berenstain Bears Ser.). (Illus.). 48p. (J). (ps-3). pap. 10.95 (978-0-590-94732-9(X)) Scholastic, Inc.

Bergel, Colin. Mail by the Pail. Koenig, Mark, illus. 2000. (Great Lakes Bks.). (J). pap. 16.95 (978-0-8143-2891-0(1)); 32p. (gr. 1-4). 18.95 (978-0-8143-2890-3(3) , Great Lakes Bks.) Wayne State Univ. Pr.

Berry, Liz. China Garden. 1999. (gr. 5-8). lib. bdg. 15.30 (978-0-613-22975-3(4)) Tandem Library Bks.

Bertram, Debbie & Bloom, Susan. The Best Place to Read. Garland, Michael, illus. 2003. 32p. (J). (ps-1). 14.95 (978-0-375-82293-3(3) , Random Hse. Bks. for Young Readers) Random Hse. Children's Bks.

Bess, Stacey. Planting More Than Pansies: A Fable about Love. Ricks, Melissa, illus. 2003. (J). 14.95 (978-1-57008-893-3(4) , Shadow Mountain) Deseret Bk. Co.

Binch, Caroline. The Princess & the Castle. 2005. (Illus.). 32p. (J). pap. 8.99 (978-0-09-943236-4(6) , Red Fox) Random Hse. Children's Bks. GBR. *Dist:* Trafalgar Square Publishing.

Black, Frank M. A Visit with Daddy. Moses, Robin, photos by. 1999. (Illus.). 20p. (J). pap. 6.95 (978-1-929157-00-6(2)) Inside-OUT Corp.

—A Visit with Mommy. Moses, Robin, photos by. 1999. (Illus.). 20p. (J). pap. 6.95 (978-1-929157-01-3(0)) Inside-OUT Corp.

—Una Visita a Mami. Moses, Robin, photos by. 1999. (SPA., Illus.). 20p. (J). pap. 6.95 (978-1-929157-03-7(7)) Inside-OUT Corp.

—Una Visita a Papi. Moses, Robin, photos by. 1999. (SPA., Illus.). 20p. (J). pap. (978-1-929157-02-0(9)) Inside-OUT Corp.

Black, Sonia W. Hanging Out with Mom. 2000. (Hello Reader! Ser.). (Illus.). (J). 10.79 (978-0-606-18554-7(2)) Tandem Library Bks.

—Hanging Out with Mom: Level. 1. Ford, George C., illus. 2000. (Hello Reader! Ser.). 32p. (J). (ps-3). pap. 3.99 (978-0-590-86636-1(2)) Scholastic, Inc.

Blackaby, Susan. Fishing Trip. Haugen, Ryan, illus. 2005. (Read-It! Readers Ser.). 32p. (J). (gr. k-3). 18.60 (978-1-4048-1004-4(8)) Picture Window Bks.

Bode, N. E. The Slippery Map. 2007. 288p. (J). lib. bdg. 17.89 (***978-0-06-079109-4(8)***) HarperCollins Pubs.

—The Slippery Map. Dorman, Brandon, illus. 2007. 288p. (J). (gr. 3-7). 16.99 (***978-0-06-079108-7(X)***) HarperCollins Pubs.

Bodett, Tom. Norman Tuttle on the Last Frontier. 2004. 208p. (YA). (gr. 7). 15.95 (978-0-679-89031-7(9) , Knopf Bks. for Young Readers) Random Hse. Children's Bks.

—Norman Tuttle on the Last Frontier: A Novel in Stories. 2004. 208p. (J). (gr. 7). lib. bdg. 17.99 (978-0-679-99031-4(3) , Knopf Bks. for Young Readers) Random Hse. Children's Bks.

Boelts, Maribeth. Big Daddy, Frog Wrestler. Huang, Benrei, illus. 2004. 29p. (J). (gr. k-4). reprint ed. (978-0-7567-7797-5(6)) DIANE Publishing Co.

—Looking for Sleepy. Pons, Bernadette, illus. 2004. 24p. (J). (ps-1). 14.95 (978-0-8075-0447-5(5)) Whitman, Albert & Co.

Bogan, Paulette. Goodnight Lulu. 2005. 32p. (YA). pap. 6.95 (978-1-58234-983-1(5) , Bloomsbury Children) Bloomsbury Publishing.

—Goodnight Lulu. Bogan, Paulette, illus. 2003. (Illus.). 32p. (J). (ps-1). 15.95 (978-1-58234-803-2(0) , Bloomsbury Children) Bloomsbury Publishing.

Bond, Katherine Grace. Sleepy-Time Dance. 2002. 12p. 5.99 (978-0-310-70252-8(6)) Zondervan.

Bondoux, Anne-Laure. The Princetta. 2008. 448p. (YA). pap. 8.95 (***978-1-59990-098-8(X)*** , Bloomsbury Children) Bloomsbury Publishing.

—The Princetta. Bell, Anthea, tr. from FRE. 2006. 500p. (YA). 17.95 (978-1-58234-924-4(X) , Bloomsbury Children) Bloomsbury Publishing.

Bongiorno, Patti Lynn. Daddy, Look at Me! 2002. (Illus.). (J). spiral bd. (978-0-9715819-6-8(7)) Bongiorno Bks.

Bonnell, Kris. A Walk with Dad. 2006. (J). 3.95 (***978-1-933727-43-1(8)***) Reading Reading Bks., LLC.

Borden, Louise. Little Ships: The Heroic Rescue at Dunkirk in World War II. 2003. (gr. 3-6). lib. bdg. 15.30 (978-0-613-61639-3(1)) Tandem Library Bks.

Borden, Louise & Foreman, Michael. The Little Ships. 2003. (Illus.). 32p. (J). (gr. 4 up). pap. 6.99 (978-0-689-85396-8(3) , Aladdin) Simon & Schuster Children's Publishing.

Borntrager, Mary Christner. Polly. l.t. ed. 2002. 165p. (J). 25.95 (978-0-7862-4030-2(X)) Thomson Gale.

Bottner, Barbara. Marsha Makes Me Sick. 1999. (J). (978-0-606-16139-8(2)) Tandem Library Bks.

Boyd, David. Closer to Hamlet. 2003. 120p. (YA). pap. 4.95 (978-0-921156-93-2(6)) Rubicon Publishing, Inc. CAN. *Dist:* International Publishers Marketing.

—Closer to Hamlet. 2003. (gr. 7-12). lib. bdg. 12.95 (978-0-613-77672-1(0)) Tandem Library Bks.

Boynton, Sandra. Snuggle Puppy! A Love Song. 2003. (Illus.). 24p. (J). bds. 6.95 (978-0-7611-3067-3(5) , 13067) Workman Publishing Co., Inc.

Bradley, Kimberly Brubaker. Halfway to the Sky. 2002. 176p. (gr. 3-7). 15.95 (978-0-385-72960-4(X) , Delacorte Bks. for Young Readers) Random Hse. Children's Bks.

Brand, A. Lee the Jewel Thief. 2000. 192p. (J). pap. 7.99 (978-0-7459-4053-3(6) , Lion) Lion Hudson plc GBR. *Dist:* Independent Pubs. Group.

Brave Irene. 2004. pap. 32.75 incl. audio (978-1-55592-195-8(7)); (J). 24.95 incl. audio (978-1-56008-006-0(X)) Weston Woods Studios, Inc.

Bridges, Margaret Park. Am I Big or Little? Dockray, Tracy, illus. 2002. 32p. (J). (ps-2). pap. 5.95 (978-1-58717-147-5(3) , SeaStar Bks.) Chronicle Bks. LLC.

—If I Were Your Father. Denton, Kady MacDonald, illus. 1999. 32p. (J). (ps-3). 16.00 (978-0-688-15192-8(2)) HarperCollins Pubs.

—If I Were Your Mother. Denton, Kady MacDonald, illus. 1999. 32p. (J). (ps-3). 15.95 (978-0-688-15190-4(6)) HarperCollins Pubs.

—Will You Take Care of Me? Sweet, Melissa, illus. 1998. 32p. (J). (ps-k). 15.89 (978-0-688-15195-9(7)) HarperCollins Pubs.

Bridges, Margaret Park & Dockray, Tracy. Am I Big or Little? 2000. (Illus.). 32p. (J). (ps-3). 16.50 (978-1-58717-020-1(5) , SeaStar Bks.) Chronicle Bks. LLC.

Brinkerhoff, Shirley. Mysterious Love. 1998. (Nikki Sheridan Ser.: Bk. 2). 192p. (J). (gr. 4-7). pap. (978-1-56179-485-0(6)) Focus on the Family Publishing.

Brisson, Pat. The Summer My Father Was Ten. Shine, Andrea, illus. 1999. (J). (ps-ps). lib. bdg. 17.60 (978-0-613-23818-2(4)) Tandem Library Bks.

Brooks, Bertha. The Big Fishing Trip. 2004. (Illus.). 32p. (J). 12.00 (978-1-58374-086-6(4)) Chicago Spectrum Pr.

Brooks, Martha. Bone Dance. 2005. 184p. (J). (gr. 7-16). pap. 6.95 (978-0-88899-336-6(6)) Groundwood Bks. CAN. *Dist:* Perseus Distribution.

—The Bone Dance. 1999. (J). (978-0-606-16716-1(1)) Tandem Library Bks.

Brown, Alan. I Am a Dog. Allen, Jonathan, illus. 2002. 32p. (J). pap. 7.95 (978-1-929132-37-9(9)) Kane/Miller Bk. Pubs., Inc.

—I Am a Dog. 2002. (gr. k-3). lib. bdg. 16.40 (978-0-613-62780-1(6)) Tandem Library Bks.

Brown, Jo. Where's My Mommy? 2004. (Illus.). 32p. (J). tchr. ed. 14.95 (978-1-58925-019-2(2) , tiger tales) ME Media LLC.

Brown, Marc. Arthur's Computer Disaster. 1999. (Arthur Adventure Ser.). (J). (gr. k-3). pap. 5.95 (978-0-316-12373-0(0)) Little, Brown Bks. for Young Readers.

—Arthur's Computer Disaster. Brown, Marc, illus. 1999. (Arthur Adventure Ser.). (Illus.). 32p. (J). (ps-3). pap. 6.99 (978-0-316-10534-7(1)) Little, Brown Bks. for Young Readers.

—Arturo y el Negocio de Mascotas. 2001. (SPA.). (gr. k-3). lib. bdg. 15.25 (978-0-613-35901-6(1)) Tandem Library Bks.

Brown, Margaret Wise. The Little Scarecrow Boy. Diaz, David, illus. 1998. 40p. (J). (ps-2). 16.99 (978-0-06-026284-6(2) , Cotler, Joanna Books) HarperCollins Pubs.

—The Runaway Bunny. Hurd, Clement, illus. 2001. 36p. (J). (ps up). bds. 12.99 (978-0-694-01671-6(3)) HarperCollins Pubs.

—The Runaway Bunny. Hurd, Clement, illus. 2000. 40p. (J). (ps-3). pap. 6.95 (978-0-9629298-8-5(3) , MHC-8-3) Minnesota Humanities Commission.

Brown, Susan Taylor. Oliver's Must-Do List. Sullivan, Mary, illus. 2005. 32p. (J). (ps-3). 15.95 (978-1-59078-198-2(8)) Boyds Mills Pr.

Browne, Anthony. Changes. Browne, Anthony, illus. 2002. (Illus.). 32p. (J). (ps-1). reprint ed. pap. 6.95 (978-0-374-41177-0(8) , Sunburst) Farrar, Straus & Giroux.

—Changes. 2002. (ps-2). lib. bdg. 15.25 (978-0-613-71857-8(7)) Tandem Library Bks.

—Into the Forest. Browne, Anthony, illus. 2004. (Illus.). 32p. (J). (gr. k-3). 16.99 (978-0-7636-2511-5(6)) Candlewick Pr.

Brun-Cosme, Nadine. No, I Want Daddy! Backes, Michel, illus. 2004. 32p. (J). (ps-k). tchr. ed. 14.00 (978-0-618-38157-9(0) , Clarion Bks.) Houghton Mifflin Co. Trade & Reference Div.

Bryan, Beth, ed. I Love You. 2006. 144p. (J). pap. 10.99 (978-0-439-84799-5(0) , Cartwheel Bks.) Scholastic, Inc.

Bryant, Louella. Father by Blood. 1999. (Illus.). 160p. (YA). (gr. 6-8). pap. 12.95 (978-1-881535-33-1(9)) New England Pr., Inc., The.

Buchanan, Sue & Hodges, Lynn. I Love You This Much GM. 2006. 32p. (J). 8.99 (978-0-310-60204-0(1)) Zonderkidz.

Buckhout, Nathaniel. My Adventure with Dad. 2003. (Illus.). 27p. pap. 6.95 (978-0-533-14276-7(8)) Vantage Pr., Inc.

Buff, Conrad. Apple & the Arrow. 2001. (gr. 3-6). lib. bdg. 14.10 (978-0-613-35484-4(2)) Tandem Library Bks.

Bullard, Lisa. My Home: Walls, Floors, Ceilings & Doors. Wesley, Omarr, illus. 2004. (All about Me Ser.). 24p. (C). (gr. k-1). 21.26 (978-1-4048-0046-5(8)) Picture Window Bks.

Bunting, Eve. The Day Before Christmas. 2000. (gr. k-3). lib. bdg. 14.10 (978-0-613-29920-6(5)) Tandem Library Bks.

—Flower Garden. 2002. (Illus.). (J). 13.19 (978-0-7587-2519-6(1)) Book Wholesalers, Inc.

—Flower Garden. Hewitt, Kathryn, illus. 2000. 32p. (J). (ps-3). pap. 7.00 (978-0-15-202372-0(0)) Harcourt Children's Bks.

—Flower Garden. Hewitt, Kathryn, illus. 1999. 32p. (J). (ps-3). 25.95 (978-0-15-201968-6(5)) Harcourt Trade Pubs.

—Flower Garden. Hewitt, Kathryn, illus. 2000. (J). (ps-ps). lib. bdg. 14.15 (978-0-613-28490-5(9)) Tandem Library Bks.

—Flower Garden. 2000. 12.80 (978-0-606-17842-6(2)) Tandem Library Bks.

—Flower Garden: Lap-Sized Board Book. Hewitt, Kathryn, illus. 2008. 30p. (J). bds. 10.95 (***978-0-15-206516-4(4)*** , Red Wagon Bks.) Harcourt Children's Bks.

—Hideout. 1999. (J). (gr. 5-8). lib. bdg. 14.15 (978-0-7857-1473-6(1)) Tandem Library Bks.

—My Mom's Wedding. Papp, Lisa, illus. 2006. 32p. (J). (gr. 1-5). 16.95 (978-1-58536-288-2(3)) Sleeping Bear Pr.

Burnett, Frances Hodgson. Editha's Burglar: A Story for Children. Sandham, Henry, illus. 2005. reprint ed. pap. 15.95 (978-1-4179-0135-7(7)) Kessinger Publishing, LLC.

Burnett, Karen Gedig. Katie's Rose: A Tale of Two Late Bloomers. Barrows, Laurie, illus. (Grandma Rose Story). 32p. (J). 2001. pap. 8.50 (978-0-9668530-3-2(2)); 2000. 14.50 (978-0-9668530-2-5(4)) GR Publishing.

Burns, Joanne. No Says the Baby When You Say Yes, a book about the terrible Twos. 2005. 1p. 5.68 (978-1-4116-3386-5(5)) Lulu.com.

Buzzeo, Toni. Dawdle Duckling. Spengler, Margaret, illus. 2003. 32p. (J). (ps). 15.99 (978-0-8037-2731-1(3) , Dial) Penguin Group (USA) Inc.

—Dawdle Duckling. Spengler, Margaret, illus. 2005. 32p. (J). (ps-k). reprint ed. pap. 5.99 (978-0-14-240277-1(X) , Puffin) Penguin Group (USA) Inc.

Byrne, Barbara. Megan's Moon. 2004. 18p. 14.87 (978-1-4116-1008-8(3)) Lulu.com.

Cabrera, Jane. Mommy, Carry Me Please! Cabrera, Jane, illus. 2005. (Illus.). 32p. (J). (ps-1). 16.95 (978-0-8234-1935-7(5)) Holiday Hse., Inc.

Cadnum, Michael. Rundown. Moore, Lisa, ed. 2001. 176p. (YA). pap. 6.99 (978-0-14-131087-9(1) , Puffin) Penguin Group (USA) Inc.

—Rundown. 2001. (J). (978-0-606-20894-9(1)); 168p. (YA). (gr. 8-12). per. 15.30 (978-0-613-33725-0(5)) Tandem Library Bks.

A Cake for Mom: Individual Title Six-Packs. (ps-2). 23.00 (978-0-7635-8997-4(7)) Rigby Education.

Call Me Nikki. 2000. (YA). per. 8.00 (978-1-57861-106-5(7)) Attainment Co., Inc.

Calvert, Patricia. Bigger. 2003. 144p. (J). pap. 8.95 (978-0-689-86003-4(X) , Aladdin) Simon & Schuster Children's Publishing.

Cameron, Ann. Gloria's Way. 2002. (Illus.). 12.34 (978-1-4046-0952-5(0)) Book Wholesalers, Inc.

—Gloria's Way. Toft, Lis, illus. 2000. 112p. (J). (ps-3). 15.00 (978-0-374-32670-8(3) , Farrar, Straus & Giroux (BYR)) Farrar, Straus & Giroux.

Cameron, Ann & Toft, Lis. Gloria's Way. 2001. (Chapters Ser.). (Illus.). 112p. (J). pap. 4.99 (978-0-14-230023-7(3) , Puffin) Penguin Group (USA) Inc.

Campbell, Bebe Moore. Sometimes My Mommy Gets Angry. Lewis, Earl, illus. 2003. 32p. (J). (ps-3). 16.99 (978-0-399-23972-4(3) , Putnam Juvenile) Penguin Group (USA) Inc.

Campos, Tito. Muffler Man/el hombre Mofle. Vigil-Pion, Evangelina, tr. Alvarez, Lamberto & Alvarez, Beto, illus. 2001. Tr. of Hombre Mofle. (ENG & SPA.). 32p. (J). (ps-3). 14.95 (978-1-55885-318-8(9) , Piñata Books) Arte Publico Pr.

Cannon, Ann Edwards. Let the Good Times Roll with Pirate Pete & Pirate Joe. Smith, Elwood, illus. 2004. (Easy-to-Read,Viking Children's Ser.). 32p. (J). (ps-3). 13.99 (978-0-670-03679-0(X) , Viking Juvenile) Penguin Group (USA) Inc.

Caraballo, Samuel. Mis Papitos: Heroes de la Cosecha. (ENG & SPA., Illus.). 32p. (J). (ps-3). 15.95 (978-1-55885-450-5(9) , Piñata Books) Arte Publico Pr.

Carbone, Elisa. Storm Warriors. 2002. (gr. 5-8). lib. bdg. 13.55 (978-0-613-61730-7(4)) Tandem Library Bks.

Carle, Eric. Mister Seahorse. Carle, Eric, illus. 2004. (Illus.). 32p. (J). (ps-2). 17.99 (978-0-399-24269-4(4) , Philomel) Penguin Group (USA) Inc.

Carlson, Lavelle. EEK! I Hear A Squeak & the Scurrying of Little Feet. Loehr, Jenny, illus. 2006. 28p. (J). 19.95 (978-0-9725803-8-0(7)) Children's Publishing.

Carlstrom, Nancy White & Saport, Linda. Before You Were Born. Saport, Linda, illus. 2004. (Illus.). 32p. (ps-k). 17.00 (978-0-8028-5185-7(1)) Eerdmans, William B. Publishing Co.

Carr, Roger. Bird Watching. 2001. (gr. k-3). lib. bdg. 11.65 (978-0-613-33338-2(1)) Tandem Library Bks.

Carrera, Jaume. Santi No Quiere Comer. Vila, Jordi, illus. 2002. (Santi No Quiere... Ser.).Tr. of Santi Doesn't Want to Eat. (SPA & ENG.). 12p. (gr. k-2). pap. 2.95 (978-84-7864-579-4(9)) Combel Editorial, S.A. ESP. *Dist:* Independent Pubs. Group.

—Santi No Quiere Irse a la Cama. Vila, Jordi, illus. 2002. (Santi No Quiere... Ser.).Tr. of Santi Doesn't Want to Go to Bed. (SPA & ENG.). 12p. (gr. k-2). pap. 2.95 (978-84-7864-578-7(0)) Combel Editorial, S.A. ESP. *Dist:* Independent Pubs. Group.

Catalano, Dominic. Hush! Catalano, Dominic, illus. 2003. (Illus.). 32p. (J). (gr. k-3). 14.95 (978-1-57768-679-8(9) , Gingham Dog Pr.) School Specialty Publishing.

Centeio, Tara Jaye. Mommy Loves Her Baby. Date not set. 32p. (J). (ps-1). pap. 5.99 (978-0-06-443715-8(9)) HarperCollins Pubs.

Chaconas, Doris J. Goodnight, Dewberry Bear. 2003. (Illus.). 32p. 17.00 (978-0-687-02691-3(1)) Abingdon Pr.

Charlip, Remy. A Perfect Day. Charlip, Remy, illus. 2007. 40p. (J). lib. bdg. 17.89 (978-0-06-051973-5(8)); 16.99 (978-0-06-051972-8(X)) HarperCollins Pubs.

Chesnut, Sheryl Daane. I'll Be There. Chesnut, Sheryl Daane, illus. 2002. (Illus.). 32p. (J). 14.95 (978-0-689-84181-1(7)) Simon & Schuster Children's Publishing.

Christopher, Matt. Tennis Ace. 2000. (Illus.). 128p. (J). (gr. 3-6). 15.95 (978-0-316-13519-1(4)) Little Brown & Co.

—Tennis Ace. 2000. (978-0-606-18267-6(5)) Tandem Library Bks.

Ciminera, Siobhan. The Silliest Valentine EVER! Petrosino, Tamara, illus. 2007. 16p. (J). (ps-2). pap. 4.99 (***978-0-8431-2678-5(7)*** , Price Stern Sloan) Penguin Group (USA) Inc.

A City Garden, 6 Packs. (ps-2). 27.00 (978-0-7635-9441-1(5)) Rigby Education.

Clark, Catherine. Gilmore Girls No. 1: Like Mother, Like Daughter. 2002. 160p. (YA). mass mkt. 5.99 (978-0-06-009212-2(2)) HarperCollins Pubs.

Clarke, Judith. Al Capsella & Watchdogs. 164p. pap. 9.95 (978-0-7022-2294-8(1)) Univ. of Queensland Pr. AUS. *Dist:* International Specialized Bk. Services.

Cleary, Beverly. Dear Mr. Henshaw. 2002. (Illus.). (J). 13.83 (978-0-7587-9140-5(2)) Book Wholesalers, Inc.

—Dear Mr. Henshaw. Zelinsky, Paul O., illus. 2000. (Cleary Reissue Ser.). 160p. (J). (gr. 5 up). pap. 5.99 (978-0-380-70958-8(9) , Harper Trophy) HarperCollins Pubs.

—Ramona & Her Father. 2002. (Illus.). (J). 13.83 (978-0-7587-5636-7(4)) Book Wholesalers, Inc.

—Ramona & Her Father. (Ramona Quimby Ser.). 186p. (J). (gr. 3-5). pap. 4.99 (978-0-8072-1439-8(6) , Listening Library) Random Hse. Audio Publishing Group.

—Ramona & Her Mother. (Ramona Quimby Ser.). 208p. (J). (gr. 3-5). pap. 4.99 (978-0-8072-1435-0(3) , Listening Library) Random Hse. Audio Publishing Group.

Clements, Andrew. The Janitor's Boy. 2001. 160p. (J). pap. 5.99 (978-0-689-83585-8(X) , Aladdin) Simon & Schuster Children's Publishing.

—The Janitor's Boy. Selznick, Brian, illus. 2000. 144p. (J). (gr. 3-7). 15.95 (978-0-689-81818-9(1)) Simon & Schuster Children's Publishing.

—The Janitor's Boy. 2001. 11.64 (978-0-606-22108-5(5)); (gr. 3-6). lib. bdg. 13.00 (978-0-613-62428-2(9)) Tandem Library Bks.

—The Janitor's Boy. l.t. ed. 2000. 152p. (J). (gr. 4-7). 21.95 (978-0-7862-2903-1(9)) Thorndike Pr.

—The Last Holiday Concert. Selznick, Brian, illus. 2004. 176p. (J). 15.95 (978-0-689-84516-1(2)) Simon & Schuster Children's Publishing.

Clifton, Lucille. Everett Anderson's 1-2-3. Grifalconi, Ann, illus. rev. ed. 2002. 32p. (J). (ps-3). pap. 6.95 (978-0-8050-7048-4(6) , Holt, Henry & Co. Bks. For Young Readers) Holt, Henry & Co.

Cohn, Rachel. Shrimp. 2005. 288p. (YA). (gr. 7 up). 15.95 (978-0-689-86612-8(7) , Simon & Schuster Children's Publishing) Simon & Schuster Children's Publishing.

Cole, Brock. The Facts Speak for Themselves. 2000. (Illus.). (J). (978-0-606-18403-8(1)) Tandem Library Bks.

Cole, Joanna. When Mommy & Daddy Go to Work. Chambliss, Maxie, illus. 2001. (J). lib. bdg. (978-0-06-029603-2(8)) HarperCollins Pubs.

Coleman, Evelyn. Mystery of the Dark Tower. 2000. (History Mysteries Ser.). (978-0-606-18356-7(6)) Tandem Library Bks.

Colfer, Eoin. The Arctic Incident. l.t. ed. 2003. (Artemis Fowl Ser.: Bk. 2). 296p. (J). (gr. 3-6). 16.95 (978-0-7540-7839-5(6) , Galaxy Children's Large Print) BBC Audiobooks America.

—The Arctic Incident. (Artemis Fowl Ser.: Bk. 2). 288p. (ps-17). 2003. (J). pap. 7.99 (978-0-7868-1708-5(9)); 2002. 16.95 (978-0-7868-0855-7(1)) Hyperion Bks. for Children.

—The Arctic Incident. l.t. ed. 2003. (Artemis Fowl Ser.: Bk. 2). 313p. (J). (gr. 3-6). 25.95 (978-0-7862-4825-4(4)) Thorndike Pr.

—Artemis Fowl. (Artemis Fowl Ser.: Bk. 1). (FRE.). pap. 34.95 (978-2-07-054681-7(0)) Gallimard, Editions FRA. *Dist:* Distribooks, Inc.

—Artemis Fowl. 2003. (Artemis Fowl Ser.: Bk. 1). (Illus.). 416p. (ps-17). pap. 5.99 (978-0-7868-1787-0(9)) Hyperion Bks. for Children.

—Artemis Fowl. 2002. (Artemis Fowl Ser.: Bk. 1). 304p. (J). (ps-17). pap. 7.99 (978-0-7868-1707-8(0)) Hyperion Paperbacks for Children.

—Artemis Fowl. 2001. (Artemis Fowl Ser.: Bk. 1). 288p. (gr. 8-17). 16.95 (978-0-7868-0801-4(2)) Miramax Bks.

—Artemis Fowl. abr. ed. 2001. (Artemis Fowl Ser.: Bk. 1). (Illus.). 2p. (J). (gr. 3-6). cd-rom (978-0-14-180286-2(3) , Penguin AudioBooks) Penguin Group (USA) Inc.

—Artemis Fowl. (Artemis Fowl Ser.: Bk. 1). 2003. (gr. 7-12). lib. bdg. 14.15 (978-0-613-75035-6(7)); 2002. (gr. 5-8). lib. bdg. 16.15 (978-0-613-60637-0(X)) Tandem Library Bks.

—Artemis Fowl. l.t. ed. 2001. (Artemis Fowl Ser.: Bk. 1). 312p. (J). (gr. 3-6). 28.95 (978-1-58724-092-8(0) , Wheeler Publishing, Inc.) Thomson Gale.

—Encuentro en el Artico. 2002. (Artemis Fowl Ser.: Bk. 2). (SPA.). 320p. pap. (978-84-8441-173-4(7) , MO32015) Grijalbo Mondadori, S.A.-Montena.

—The Opal Deception. 2005. (Artemis Fowl Ser.: Bk. 4). 352p. (gr. 5-17). 16.95 (978-0-7868-5289-5(5)) Hyperion Bks. for Children.

—The Opal Deception. 2005. (Artemis Fowl Ser.: Bk. 4). (J). pap. 7.99 (978-0-7868-3640-6(7)) Miramax Bks.

Collier, James Lincoln. The Rich & Famous. 2001. (Lost Treasures Ser.: No. 6). (Illus.). 240p. (gr. 3-7). pap. 1.99 (978-0-7868-1519-7(1) , Volo) Hyperion Bks. for Children.

Colshorn, Carl & Colshorn, Theodore. The Porridge Pot. Carls, Claudia, illus. 2007. 32p. (J). (ps). 16.99 (***978-0-698-40073-3(9)*** , Minedition) Penguin Group (USA) Inc.

Come on Rain. 2004. (J). pap. 14.95 incl. audio (978-0-7882-0513-2(7)) Weston Woods Studios, Inc.

Conlon-McKenna, Marita. Under the Hawthorn Tree. 2003. (Illus.). 160p. pap. 5.95 (978-0-86278-206-1(6)) O'Brien Pr., Ltd., The IRL. *Dist:* Independent Pubs. Group.

Conly, Jane Leslie. What Happened on Planet Kid. rev. ed. 2000. (Illus.). 160p. (YA). (gr. 5-9). 16.95 (978-0-8050-6065-2(0) , Holt, Henry & Co. Bks. For Young Readers) Holt, Henry & Co.

Conrad, Pam. Blue Willow. Gallagher, S. Saelig, illus. 2004. 30p. (J). reprint ed. 17.00 (978-0-7567-8262-7(7)) DIANE Publishing Co.

Cooney, Caroline B. The Face on the Milk Carton. l.t. ed. 2006. 225p. (YA). 21.95 (978-0-7862-8504-4(4)) Thorndike Pr.

Corentin, Philippe. Papa! (SPA.). 32p. (978-84-95150-38-7(7)) Corimbo, Editorial S.L.

Cousins, Lucy. Jazzy in the Jungle. Cousins, Lucy, illus. 2002. (Illus.). 32p. (J). (gr. k-k). 14.99 (978-0-7636-1903-9(5)) Candlewick Pr.

Coyle, Carmela LaVigna. Do Princesses Really Kiss Frogs? Gordon, Mike & Gordon, Carl, illus. 2005. 32p. (gr. 1-4). 15.95 (978-0-87358-880-5(0) , Rising Moon Bks. for Young Readers) Northland Publishing.

—Do Princesses Wear Hiking Boots? Gordon, Mike & Gordon, Carl, illus. 2003. 32p. (J). 15.95 (978-0-87358-828-7(2) , Rising Moon Bks. for Young Readers) Northland Publishing.

Craik, Dinah Maria Mulock. The Little Lame Prince & His Traveling Cloak. 2005. reprint ed. pap. 20.95 (978-1-4179-1940-6(X)) Kessinger Publishing, LLC.

Craze, Galaxy. By the Shore. 1999. (gr. 7-12). lib. bdg. 21.10 (978-0-613-28778-4(9)) Tandem Library Bks.

Creech, Sharon. Fishing in the Air. Raschka, Chris, illus. 32p. (J). (ps-3). 2003. pap. 6.99 (978-0-06-051606-2(2) , Harper Trophy); 2000. 15.89 (978-0-06-028112-0(X) , Cotler, Joanna Books) HarperCollins Pubs.

—Fishing in the Air. 2003. (Live Oak Readalong Ser.). (Illus.). (J). pap. 16.95 incl. audio (978-1-59112-224-1(4)) ; pap. 18.95 incl. audio compact disk (978-1-59112-512-9(X)) Live Oak Media.

—Fishing in the Air, 4 bks. Raschka, Chris, illus. 2003. (J). pap. 37.95 incl. audio (978-1-59112-226-5(0)) Live Oak Media.

—Fishing in the Air. Rashka, Chris, illus. 2000. 29p. (J). (ps-3). 28.95 (978-1-59112-513-6(8)) Live Oak Media.

—Fishing in the Air. 2000. (gr. k-3). lib. bdg. 15.30 (978-0-613-66967-2(3)) Tandem Library Bks.

Crew, Gary. Mama's Babies: A Novel. 2002. 160p. (J). (gr. 5-9). pap. 6.95 (978-1-55037-724-8(8)); lib. bdg. 18.95 (978-1-55037-725-5(6)) Annick Pr., Ltd. CAN. *Dist:* Firefly Bks., Ltd.

—Mama's Babies: A Novel. 2002. (gr. 5-8). lib. bdg. 15.25 (978-0-613-58241-4(1)) Tandem Library Bks.

Crilley, Mark. Billy Clikk: Creatch Battler. 2006. (Illus.). 246p. (J). (***978-1-4156-5030-1(6)** , Yearling) Random Hse. Children's Bks.

Crist-Evans, Craig. Amaryllis. (YA). (gr. 9). 2006. 192p. pap. 7.99 (978-0-7636-2990-8(1)); 2003. 208p. 15.99 (978-0-7636-1863-6(2)) Candlewick Pr.

—Moon over Tennessee: A Boy's Civil War Journal. Christensen, Bonnie, illus. 64p. (J). (gr. 4-6). 2003. pap. 6.95 (978-0-618-31107-1(6)); 1999. tchr. ed. 15.00 (978-0-395-91208-9(3)) Houghton Mifflin Co. Trade & Reference Div.

—Moon over Tennessee: A Boy's Civil War Journal. 1999. (gr. 3-6). lib. bdg. 15.25 (978-0-613-60819-0(4)) Tandem Library Bks.

Crites, Susan E. I Love You More Than Rainbows. Jarman, Rosemary & Jarman, Mark, illus. 2008. 32p. (J). 14.99 (***978-1-4003-1089-0(X)**) Nelson, Thomas Inc.

Crowe, Chris. The Mississippi Trial, 1955. Okamura, Tim, illus. 2002. 240p. (YA). (gr. 6-8). 17.99 (978-0-8037-2745-8(3) , Dial) Penguin Group (USA) Inc.

—The Mississippi Trial, 1955. 2003. (gr. 7-12). lib. bdg. 14.15 (978-0-613-86522-7(7)) Tandem Library Bks.

Cruise, Robin. Only You. Chodos-Irvine, Margaret, illus. 2007. 40p. (J). (ps-k). 16.00 (978-0-15-216604-5(1)) Harcourt Children's Bks.

—Top-Secret Journal of Fiona Claire Jardin. 2000. (978-0-606-18192-1(X)) Tandem Library Bks.

Crutcher, Chris. Ironman. 2004. 288p. (J). pap. 6.99 (978-0-06-059840-2(9) , HarperTeen) HarperCollins Pubs.

Curtis, Gavin. Bat Boy & His Violin. 2001. (gr. 3-6). lib. bdg. 15.30 (978-0-613-33669-7(0)) Tandem Library Bks.

Curtis, Jamie Lee. Cuentame Otra Vez la Noche en Que Naci. Cornell, Laura, illus. 1999. (SPA.). (J). (gr. 1-2). 14.95 (978-1-880507-63-6(3) , LC4416) Lectorum Pubns., Inc.

Cusimano, Maryann K. You Are My I Love You. Ichikawa, Satomi, illus. 2001. 32p. (J). (ps-1). 16.99 (978-0-399-23392-0(X) , Philomel) Penguin Group (USA) Inc.

Daddy I Wanna Be A Lawyer: And Make Lots of Money. 2004. lib. bdg. 12.95 (978-1-932762-08-2(6)) Elderberry Press, Inc.

Dahl, Roald. Danny the Champion of the World. 1999. (J). (gr. 5-9). 20.25 (978-0-8446-7025-6(1)) Smith, Peter Pub., Inc.

Daly-Weir, Catherine. Daddy & Me. 1999. (Grossett & Dunlap All Aboard Books & Cassettes Ser.). (Illus.). 32p. (J). (ps-3). pap. 3.49 (978-0-448-41964-0(5) , Grosset & Dunlap) Penguin Group (USA) Inc.

Danziger, Paula. Amber Brown Is Feeling Blue. Ross, Tony, illus. 2002. (Amber Brown Ser.: No. 7). (J). (gr. 3-6). 12.17 (978-0-7587-0418-4(6)) Book Wholesalers, Inc.

—Amber Brown Is Feeling Blue. Ross, Tony, illus. 1998. (Amber Brown Ser.: No. 7). 128p. (J). (gr. 3-6). 14.99 (978-0-399-23179-7(X) , Putnam Juvenile) Penguin Group (USA) Inc.

—Amber Brown Is Feeling Blue. 2004. (Amber Brown Ser.: No. 7). 131p. (J). (gr. 2-4). pap. 17.00 incl. audio (978-0-8072-2063-4(9) , Listening Library) Random Hse. Audio Publishing Group.

—Amber Brown Is Feeling Blue. Ross, Tony & Rogers, Jacqueline, illus. 1999. (Amber Brown Ser.: No. 7). 144p. (J). (gr. 3-6). pap. 3.99 (978-0-439-07168-0(2)) Scholastic, Inc.

—Amber Brown Is Feeling Blue. 1999. (Amber Brown Ser.: No. 7). (J). (gr. 3-6). 10.64 (978-0-606-17275-2(0)); lib. bdg. 11.80 (978-0-613-20096-7(9)) Tandem Library Bks.

—Amber Brown Is Green with Envy. Ross, Tony, illus. 2003. (Amber Brown Ser.: No. 9). 160p. (J). (gr. 2-5). 15.99 (978-0-399-23181-0(1) , Putnam Juvenile) Penguin Group (USA) Inc.

—Amber Brown Is Green with Envy. Ross, Tony, illus. 2004. (Amber Brown Ser.: No. 9). 160p. (J). (gr. 3-6). pap. 4.99 (978-0-439-07171-0(2) , Scholastic Paperbacks) Scholastic, Inc.

—The Divorce Express. 2007. 160p. (J). (gr. 5). pap. 5.99 (978-0-14-240712-7(7) , Puffin) Penguin Group (USA) Inc.

—Everyone Else's Parents Said Yes. 1998. (Matthew Martin Ser.: No. 1). 128p. (J). (gr. 4-7). pap. 5.99 (978-0-698-11687-0(9) , Putnam Juvenile) Penguin Group (USA) Inc.

—I, Amber Brown. Ross, Tony, illus. 1999. (Amber Brown Ser.: No. 8). 144p. (J). (gr. 3-6). 14.99 (978-0-399-23180-3(3) , Putnam Juvenile) Penguin Group (USA) Inc.

—I, Amber Brown. 2004. (Amber Brown Ser.: No. 8). 144p. (J). (gr. 2-4). pap. 17.00 incl. audio (978-0-8072-2064-1(7) , Listening Library) Random Hse. Audio Publishing Group.

—I, Amber Brown. 2000. (Amber Brown Ser.: No. 8). (gr. 3-6). lib. bdg. 11.80 (978-0-613-28528-5(X)) Tandem Library Bks.

—It's a Fair Day, Amber Brown. Ross, Tony, illus. 2003. 28.95 incl. audio compact disk (978-1-59112-565-5(0)); pap. 31.95 incl. audio compact disk (978-1-59112-564-8(2)) Live Oak Media.

—It's a Fair Day, Amber Brown. Ross, Tony, illus. 48p. (J). (gr. k-2). 2003. pap. 3.99 (978-0-698-11982-6(7) , Puffin); 2002. 12.99 (978-0-399-23606-8(6) , Putnam Juvenile) Penguin Group (USA) Inc.

—It's a Fair Day, Amber Brown. 2003. (gr. k-3). lib. bdg. 11.80 (978-0-613-61635-5(9)) Tandem Library Bks.

—Orange You Glad It's Halloween, Amber Brown? Ross, Tony, illus. 2005. 48p. (J). (gr. 2-5). 13.99 (978-0-399-23471-2(3) , Putnam Juvenile) Penguin Group (USA) Inc.

Darlington, Katherine. Gypsy Wind. 2003. 128p. (YA). pap. 12.95 (978-1-59113-417-6(X)) Booklocker.com, Inc.

Davidson, Barbara. Billys Most Difficult Choice. 2007. 49p. 12.95 (***978-1-4241-6153-9(3)**) PublishAmerica, Inc.

Davis, Jennifer. Before You Were Big. Cornell, Laura, illus. 2003. 36p. (J). 11.95 (978-0-7611-2732-1(1) , 12732) Workman Publishing Co., Inc.

Davis, Lambert. Swimming with Dolphins. Davis, Lambert, illus. 2004. (Illus.). 32p. (J). pap. 15.95 (978-0-439-47257-9(1) , Blue Sky Pr., The) Scholastic, Inc.

Davis, Ossie. Just Like Martin. (J). 2002. 176p. 15.99 (978-0-7868-0812-0(8)); 2001. pap. (978-0-7868-1642-2(2)) Hyperion Bks. for Children. (Jump at the Sun).

De Anda, Diane. Dancing Miranda. Castilla, Julia Mercedes, tr. from ENG. Alvarez, Lamberto, illus. 2001. Tr. of Baila, Miranda, Baila. (SPA & ENG.). 32p. (J). (ps-3). 14.95 (978-1-55885-323-2(5) , Piñata Books) Arte Publico Pr.

de Brunhoff, Laurent & de Brunhoff, Jean. Babar Goes to School. 2003. (Illus.). 32p. (J). (ps-1). 9.95 (978-0-8109-4582-1(7)) Abrams, Harry N. , Inc.

De Guzman, Michael. Beekman's Big Deal. 2004. 224p. (J). 16.00 (978-0-374-30672-4(9) , Farrar, Straus & Giroux (BYR)) Farrar, Straus & Giroux.

de Paola, Tomie. Days of the Blackbird: A Tale of Northern Italy. de Paola, Tomie, illus. 2005. (Illus.). 32p. (J). (ps-k). reprint ed. pap. 5.99 (978-0-14-240271-9(0) , Puffin) Penguin Group (USA) Inc.

De Smet, Marian. Anna's Tight Squeeze. Meijer, Marja, illus. 2003. Orig. Title: Op Slot. 32p. (J). pap. 5.95 (978-1-58925-378-0(7) , tiger tales) ME Media LLC.

—Anna's Tight Squeeze. 2003. Orig. Title: Op Slot. (gr. k-3). lib. bdg. 14.10 (978-0-613-84707-0(5)) Tandem Library Bks.

Dean, Zoey. The A-List: A Novel. 2003. (A-List Ser.: Bk. 1). (YA). lib. bdg. 17.60 (978-0-613-70574-5(2)) Tandem Library Bks.

—Tall Cool One, No. 4. 2005. (A-List Ser.: No. 4). 304p. (YA). (gr. 9-17). pap. 9.99 (978-0-316-73508-7(6) , Poppy) Little, Brown Bks. for Young Readers.

Deans, Sis Boulos. Racing the Past. 2005. 160p. (J). (gr. 3-9). reprint ed. pap. 5.99 (978-0-14-240308-2(3) , Puffin) Penguin Group (USA) Inc.

DeKeyser, Stacy. Jump the Cracks. 2008. 216p. (J). pap. 9.95 (***978-0-7387-1274-1(4)** , Flux) Llewellyn Pubns.

Delaney, Mark. Pepperland. 2004. 160p. (J). 14.95 (978-1-56145-317-7(X)) Peachtree Pubs., Ltd.

Desimini, Lisa. My Beautiful Child. Mahurin, Matt, tr. Mahurin, Matt, illus. 2004. 32p. (J). pap. 16.95 (978-0-439-45893-1(5) , Blue Sky Pr., The) Scholastic, Inc.

Dessen, Sarah. This Lullaby. (J). 2002. 304p. 16.99 (978-0-670-03530-4(0) , Viking Juvenile); 2004. 352p. reprint ed. pap. 7.99 (978-0-14-250155-9(7) , Puffin) Penguin Group (USA) Inc.

DeWitt, Dawn Davis. Searching for Blue Bears. Rolando, Cecilia, tr. Rolando, Cecilia, illus. 2003. (J). (978-0-9677057-5-0(4)) Raven Productions, Inc.

Diaz, Enrique Perez. El Nino Que Conversaba Con la Mar. 2000. Tr. of Boy Who Talked to the Sea. (SPA., Illus.). 128p. (J). (gr. 5 up). (978-84-236-5075-0(8) , ED4246) Edebé ESP. *Dist:* Lectorum Pubns., Inc.

—El Nino Que Conversaba Con la Mar. 2000. Tr. of Boy Who Talked to the Sea. (SPA.). (gr. 5-8). lib. bdg. 18.75 (978-0-613-85811-3(5)) Tandem Library Bks.

Doherty, Berlie. Holly Starcross. 2002. 192p. (J). (gr. 7 up). 17.89 (978-0-06-001342-4(7)) HarperCollins Pubs.

Dotlich, Rebecca Kai. Grandpa Loves. Brown, Kathryn, illus. 2005. 32p. (J). (ps-ps). lib. bdg. 16.89 (978-0-06-029406-9(X)) HarperCollins Pubs.

—Mama Loves. Brown, Kathryn, illus. 2004. 32p. (J). (ps-2). 14.99 (978-0-06-029407-6(8)); lib. bdg. 15.89 (978-0-06-029408-3(6)) HarperCollins Pubs.

Dow, Unity. Far & Beyon' 2002. 208p. (YA). (gr. 7 up). pap. 11.95 (978-1-879960-64-0(8)) Aunt Lute Bks.

Downey, Lynn. Most Loved Monster. Davis, Jack E., illus. 2004. 32p. (J). (ps). 16.99 (978-0-8037-2728-1(3) , Dial) Penguin Group (USA) Inc.

—Papa's Birthday Gift. Schuett, Stacey, tr. Schuett, Stacey, illus. 2004. 32p. 16.99 (978-0-8066-4557-5(1) , Augsburg Bks.) Augsburg Fortress, Pubs.

Doyle, Charlotte. It's Twins! Gorton, Julia, illus. 2003. 32p. (J). (ps-1). 10.99 (978-0-399-23718-8(6) , Putnam Juvenile) Penguin Group (USA) Inc.

—Where's Bunny's Mommy? Brown, Rick, illus. 1999. 29p. (J). (ps-k). reprint ed. 14.00 (978-0-7881-6653-2(0)) DIANE Publishing Co.

Doyle, Eugenie. Stray Voltage. 1998. 128p. (YA). (gr. 5-7). 16.95 (978-1-886910-86-7(3) , Lemniscaat) Boyds Mills Pr.

Doyle, Malachy. Antonio on the Other Side of the World, Getting Smaller. Cneut, Carll, illus. 2003. 32p. (J). (ps-3). 15.99 (978-0-7636-2173-5(0)) Candlewick Pr.

Dragonwagon, Crescent. Is This a Sack of Potatoes? Stock, Catherine, illus. 2002. 32p. (J). (ps-k). 15.95 (978-0-7614-5089-4(0)) Cavendish, Marshall Corp.

Duble, Kathi Benner. Pilot Mom. Marks, Alan, illus. 2004. 32p. (J). (gr. k-3). 15.95 (978-1-57091-555-0(5)) Charlesbridge Publishing, Inc.

Duble, Kathleen Benner & Vojnar, Kamil. The Sacrifice. 2005. 224p. (J). (gr. 4-8). 16.99 (978-0-689-87650-9(5) , McElderry, Margaret K.) Simon & Schuster Children's Publishing.

Duksta, Laura. I Love You More. Keesler, Karen, illus. 2007. 34p. (J). (gr. 4-7). 16.99 (***978-1-4022-1126-3(0)** , Sourcebooks Jabberwocky) Sourcebooks, Inc.

Durbin, William. The Broken Blade. 1998. (Illus.). 176p. (J). (gr. 5-9). reprint ed. 5.50 (978-0-440-41184-0(X) , Yearling) Random Hse. Children's Bks.

—The Broken Blade. 1998. (J). 11.64 (978-0-606-13228-2(7)) Tandem Library Bks.

Durrant, George D. Shakespeare's Best Work: A Novel of Unexpected Family Ties & Uncommon Faith. 2003. 130p. (YA). pap. 10.95 (978-1-55517-709-6(3) , 77093, Bonneville Bks.) Cedar Fort, Inc./CFI Distribution.

Dwyer, Mindy. Quilt of Dreams. 2000. (Illus.). 32p. (J). (gr. 2-4). 15.95 (978-0-88240-522-3(5)); pap. 8.95 (978-0-88240-521-6(7)) Graphic Arts Ctr. Publishing Co. (Alaska Northwest Bks.).

—Quilt of Dreams. 2000. (978-0-606-22817-6(9)); (gr. 3-6). lib. bdg. 17.60 (978-0-613-49764-0(3)) Tandem Library Bks.

Egielski, Richard. Jazper. Egielski, Richard, illus. 1998. (Illus.). 32p. (J). (ps-2). 14.95 (978-0-06-027817-5(X)) HarperCollins Pubs.

Ehlert, Lois. Hands: Growing up to be an Artist. 2004. (Illus.). 48p. (J). 14.95 (978-0-15-205107-5(4) , Harcourt Children's Bks) Harcourt Children's Bks.

—Pie in the Sky. 2004. (Illus.). 40p. (J). (ps-2). 16.00 (978-0-15-216584-0(3)) Harcourt Children's Bks.

Eliot, George & West, Clare. Silas Marner: The Weaver of Raveloe, Level 4. 2nd ed. 2000. (Bookworms Ser.). (Illus.). 96p. 6.50 (978-0-19-423044-5(9)) Oxford Univ. Pr., Inc.

Ellis, Sarah. Out of the Blue. 2001. 120p. (J). (gr. 5-9). pap. 5.95 (978-0-88899-236-9(X)) Groundwood Bks. CAN. *Dist:* Perseus Distribution.

—Pick-up Sticks. 2001. (gr. 3-6). lib. bdg. 14.10 (978-0-613-90977-8(1)) Tandem Library Bks.

Emberley, Rebecca. My Mother's Secret Life. Emberley, Rebecca, illus. 1998. (Illus.). 28p. (J). (ps-3). 15.95 (978-0-316-23496-2(6)) Little Brown & Co.

Emmett, Jonathan. I Love You Always & Forever. Howarth, Daniel, illus. 2007. 32p. (J). (ps-3). pap. 14.99 (978-0-439-91654-7(2)) Scholastic, Inc.

Encinas, Carlos. The New Engine: La Maquina Nueva. 2001. (Illus.). (J). 15.95 (978-1-885772-24-4(6)) Kiva Publishing, Inc.

Ethier, Vicki. Papa & the Hen. Ethier, Vicki, illus. 2004. (Illus.). 36p. (J). 7.00 (978-1-928972-12-9(8)) Critter Pubns.

Eubank, Patti Reeder. Count Your Blessings! 2004. (Illus.). 14p. (J). bds. 9.95 (978-0-8249-6544-0(2)) Ideals Pubns.

Ewart, Claire. The Giant. Ewart, Claire, illus. 2003. (Illus.). 32p. (J). (ps-3). 16.95 (978-0-8027-8835-1(1)) Walker & Co.

Falk, Jennifer & Morgan. A Heart Daddy for Chrissie. 2005. 43p. (J). pap. 16.00 (978-1-4116-3585-2(X)) Lulu.com.

Farrell, John. Dear Child. Manning, Maurie, illus. 2008. (J). (***978-1-59078-495-2(2)**) Boyds Mills Pr.

Fearnley, Jan. Colin & the Curly Claw. Fearnley, Jan, illus. 2001. (Blue Bananas Ser.). (Illus.). 48p. (J). (gr. 1-2). (978-0-7787-0840-7(3)); pap. (978-0-7787-0886-5(1)) Crabtree Publishing Co.

—Colin & the Curly Claw. 2002. (gr. k-3). lib. bdg. 12.95 (978-0-613-52821-4(2)) Tandem Library Bks.

—Just Like You. Fearnley, Jan, illus. 2003. (Illus.). 32p. (J). (ps-1). pap. 6.99 (978-0-7636-2207-7(9)) Candlewick Pr.

—Just Like You. 2004. (ps-2). lib. bdg. 15.30 (978-0-613-74824-7(7)) Tandem Library Bks.

—The Search for the Perfect Child. Fearnley, Jan, illus. 2006. (Illus.). 40p. (J). (ps-1). 15.99 (978-0-7636-3231-1(7)) Candlewick Pr.

Fenner, Carol. The King of Dragons. 2000. (J). (978-0-606-19716-8(8)); (gr. 3-6). lib. bdg. 13.00 (978-0-613-28547-6(6)) Tandem Library Bks.

Ferris, Amy Schor. A Greater Goode. 2002. 192p. (YA). (gr. 5-9). 15.00 (978-0-618-13154-9(X)) Houghton Mifflin Co. Trade & Reference Div.

Fine, Anne. Flour Babies. l.t. ed. 2000. 238p. (J). pap. 16.95 (978-0-7540-6110-6(8) , Galaxy Children's Large Print) BBC Audiobooks America.

Finley, Martha. Elsie's Impossible Choice, Bk. 2. Williams, Scott, illus. 1999. (Elsie Dinsmore: Bk. 2). 238p. (YA). (gr. 5-9). 12.99 (978-1-928749-02-8(X)) Zonderkidz.

—Elsie's New Life, Bk. 3. Williams, Scott, illus. Grisco, Michelle, photos by. 1999. (Elsie Dinsmore: Bk. 3). 232p. (YA). (gr. 5-9). 12.99 (978-1-928749-03-5(8)) Zonderkidz.

Fitzhugh, Louise. The Long Secret. 2001. (Illus.). 288p. (J). (gr. 5 up). 15.95 (978-0-385-32784-8(6) , Delacorte Bks. for Young Readers) Random Hse. Children's Bks.

—Long Secret. 2002. (gr. 5-8). lib. bdg. 14.15 (978-0-613-86230-1(9)) Tandem Library Bks.

Flake, Sharon G. Begging for Change. 2003. 240p. (gr. 5-17). 15.99 (978-0-7868-0601-0(X) , Jump at the Sun) Hyperion Bks. for Children.

—Money Hungry. (J). 2003. 208p. (gr. 5-17). pap. 5.99 (978-0-7868-1503-6(5)); 2001. 192p. (gr. 3-7). 15.99 (978-0-7868-0548-8(X) , Jump at the Sun) Hyperion Bks. for Children.

Fleischman, Paul. Seek. braille ed. 2003. (J). (gr. 2). spiral bd. (978-0-616-15870-8(X)) Canadian National Institute for the Blind/Institut National Canadien pour les Aveugles.

—Seek. 2004. 176p. (J). (gr. 7 up). pap. 29.00 incl. audio (978-0-8072-2285-0(2) , Listening Library) Random Hse. Audio Publishing Group.

—Seek. 2003. (Illus.). 176p. (YA). pap. 6.99 (978-0-689-85402-6(1) , Simon Pulse) Simon & Schuster Children's Publishing.

—Seek. 2003. (gr. 7-12). lib. bdg. 15.30 (978-0-613-61813-7(0)) Tandem Library Bks.

Fletcher, Ralph J. Uncle Daddy. rev. ed. 2001. (Illus.). 144p. (J). (gr. 4-6). 16.95 (978-0-8050-6663-0(2) , Holt, Henry & Co. Bks. For Young Readers) Holt, Henry & Co.

Flinn, Alex. Breathing Underwater. 272p. (J). 2002. (gr. 5 up). pap. 8.99 (978-0-06-447257-9(4)); 2001. (gr. 8 up). 18.99 (978-0-06-029198-3(2)) HarperCollins Pubs.

—Breathing Underwater. unabr. ed. 2004. (Young Adult Cassette Librariestm Ser.). 272p. (J). (gr. 7 up). pap. 36.00 incl. audio (978-0-8072-0992-9(9) , S YA 346 SP, Listening Library) Random Hse. Audio Publishing Group.

—Breathing Underwater. 2002. (gr. 7-12). lib. bdg. 16.45 (978-0-613-60383-6(4)) Tandem Library Bks.

Ford, Miela. On My Own. 1999. (Illus.). 16p. (J). (ps-k). pap. 5.95 (978-0-688-16452-2(8)) HarperCollins Pubs.

Foreman, Michael. Hello World. Foreman, Michael, illus. 2003. (Illus.). 48p. (J). (ps). 16.99 (978-0-7636-2112-4(9)) Candlewick Pr.

Fox, Mem. Harriet, You'll Drive Me Wild! Frazee, Marla, illus. 2000. 32p. (J). (ps-2). 16.00 (978-0-15-201977-8(4)) Harcourt Children's Bks.

—Harriet, You'll Drive Me Wild! 2003. (gr. k-3). lib. bdg. 14.15 (978-0-613-59897-2(0)) Tandem Library Bks.

—Koala Lou. 2002. (Illus.). (J). 13.19 (978-0-7587-2941-5(3)) Book Wholesalers, Inc.

—Zoo-Looking. 2001. (ps-2). lib. bdg. 14.15 (978-0-613-86395-7(X)) Tandem Library Bks.

Fox, Mem & Frazee, Marla. Harriet, You'll Drive Me Wild! 2003. (Illus.). 32p. (J). pap. 6.00 (978-0-15-204598-2(8) , Voyager Bks./Libros Viajeros) Harcourt Children's Bks.

Fox, Paula. The Moonlight Man. 2003. (gr. 5-8). lib. bdg. 13.00 (978-0-613-66425-7(6)) Tandem Library Bks.

Frances, Ellen. Looking for Dad. White, Annie, illus. 1999. (Supa Doopers Ser.). 64p. (J). (978-0-7608-3292-9(7)) Sundance/Newbridge Educational Publishing.

—Looking for Dad. 1999. (gr. 3-6). lib. bdg. 12.60 (978-0-613-30565-5(5)) Tandem Library Bks.

Frederick, Heather Vogel. The Voyage of Patience Goodspeed. 2004. (Illus.). 224p. (J). pap. 5.99 (978-0-689-84869-8(2) , Aladdin) Simon & Schuster Children's Publishing.

Freeman, Claire. One Magical Morning. Ho, Louise, illus. 2005. 28p. (J). 16.00 (978-1-56148-472-0(5)) Good Bks.

Freeman, Suzanne. The Cuckoo's Child. 249p. (YA). (gr. 5-8). pap. 5.95 (978-0-8072-1510-4(4) , Listening Library) Random Hse. Audio Publishing Group.

French, Simon. Change the Locks. 2006. 112p. (J). pap. 15.00 (978-0-14-330172-1(1) , Penguin Global) Penguin Group (USA) Inc.

Friend, Natasha. Perfect. 2004. 232p. (J). 16.95 (978-1-57131-652-3(3)); pap. 6.95 (978-1-57131-651-6(5)) Milkweed Editions.

Fritz, April Young. Waiting to Disappear. 2002. 320p. (J). 16.49 (978-0-7868-2624-7(X)) Hyperion Pr.

Gaffney, Linda. My Daddy Does GOOD Things, Too! Dabney, Undra & Goettling, Nickalas, illus. 2006. 55p. per. 10.99 (***978-0-9787501-0-7(1)**) Gaffney, Linda.

Gago, Jenny. Perfect Gift. 2001. (gr. k-3). lib. bdg. 11.80 (978-0-613-82082-0(7)) Tandem Library Bks.

Galluzzi, Edward. Twelve upon A Time... 2005. 270p. per. 18.95 (978-1-59453-625-0(2) , 2871) Airleaf Publishing & Bookselling.

Gandolfi, Silvana & Schwartz, Lynne Sharon. Aldabra, or, the Tortoise Who Loved Shakespeare. 2004. 151p. (J). (978-0-439-49744-2(2) , Levine, Arthur A. Bks.) Scholastic, Inc.

Garisch, Dawn. Babyshoes. 2004. 288p. pap. 9.99 (978-0-689-83778-4(X)) Simon & Schuster, Ltd. GBR. *Dist:* Independent Pubs. Group.

Gasparro, Marie & Falletta, Bernadette. The Magnificent Hole. 2005. 13p. (J). 12.95 (978-1-4116-5924-7(4)) Lulu.com.

Gay, Michel. El Cochecito. 2003. (SPA.). 68p. (978-84-8470-084-5(4)) Corimbo, Editorial S.L.

—Zee. Gay, Michel, illus. 2003. (Illus.). 32p. (J). (gr. k-ps). 15.00 (978-0-618-38148-7(1) , Clarion Bks.) Houghton Mifflin Co. Trade & Reference Div.

Geeslin, Campbell. Elena's Serenade. Juan, Ana, illus. 2004. 40p. (J). 17.95 (978-0-689-84908-4(7) , Atheneum) Simon & Schuster Children's Publishing.

Genechten, Guido van. Because I Love You So Much. 2004. (Illus.). 32p. (J). tchr. ed. 15.95 (978-1-58925-039-0(7) , tiger tales) ME Media LLC.

George, Jean Craighead. Cliff Hanger. Minor, Wendell, illus. 2002. (Outdoor Adventures Ser.). 32p. (J). (ps-4). 15.99 (978-0-06-000260-2(3)) HarperCollins Pubs.

Geras, Adele. My Wishes for You. Wright, Cliff, illus. 2002. 32p. (J). (ps-2). 15.95 (978-0-689-85333-3(5)) Simon & Schuster Children's Publishing.

Gibbs, Dreene. Am I Pretty, Momma? 2nd l.t. ed. 2004. (Illus.). 32p. (J). bds. 12.95 (978-0-9741406-1-2(9) , 0138) Cranberry Quill Publishing Co.

Gikow, Louise. A Day with Daddy. Mazali, Gustavo, tr. Mazali, Gustavo, illus. 2004. (My First Reader Ser.). 31p. (J). 18.50 (978-0-516-24410-5(8) , Children's Pr.) Scholastic Library Publishing.

Giles, Gail. Playing in Traffic. 2006. (Illus.). 176p. (YA). reprint ed. pap. 6.99 (978-1-4169-0926-2(5) , Simon Pulse) Simon & Schuster Children's Publishing.

Gilles, Almira Astudillo. Willie Wins. Angel, Carl, illus. 2001. 32p. (J). (ps-3). 16.00 (978-1-58430-023-6(X)) Lee & Low Bks., Inc.

Girl Who Didn't Mind. 2002. Tr. of Caileag a Bha Coma. 64p. (J). lib. bdg. 17.95 (978-0-9703632-6-8(5)) Wakefield Connection, The.

Gliori, Debi. No Matter What. (Illus.). (J). 2008. 24p. bds. 6.95 (***978-0-15-206343-6(9)*** , Red Wagon Bks.); 1999. 32p. 16.00 (978-0-15-202061-3(6)) Harcourt Children's Bks.

Godwin, Laura. What the Baby Hears. 2002. (Illus.). 32p. (ps-k). 16.49 (978-0-7868-2484-7(0)) Hyperion Bks. for Children.

Goobie, Beth. Kicked Out. 2002. (Orca Soundings Ser.). 96p. (J). (gr. 7-12). pap. 7.95 (978-1-55143-244-1(7)) Orca Bk. Pubs. USA.

—Kicked Out. 2002. (gr. 7-12). lib. bdg. 16.40 (978-0-613-62964-5(7)) Tandem Library Bks.

Gorbachev, Valeri. Nico Y Los Lobos Feroces. 2000. (SPA.). (gr. k-3). lib. bdg. 15.25 (978-0-613-32887-6(6)) Tandem Library Bks.

Gosney, Joy. Naughty Parents. 2000. (Illus.). 32p. (ps-1). lib. bdg. 21.90 (978-0-7613-1823-1(2) , Millbrook Pr.) Lerner Publishing Group.

Gove, Doris. My Mother Talks to Trees. Mallory, Marilynn H., illus. 2005. 32p. (J). pap. 7.95 (978-1-56145-336-8(6) , Q31285) Peachtree Pubs., Ltd.

Graham, Wendy. My Weird Mother. Burgemeestre, Kevin, illus. 1999. (Supa Doopers Ser.). 56p. (J). (978-0-7608-1921-0(1)) Sundance/Newbridge Educational Publishing.

Granowsky, Alvin. At the Park. 2001. 11.79 (978-0-606-22367-6(3)) Tandem Library Bks.

Graver, Elizabeth. Honey Thief. 2000. (gr. 7-12). lib. bdg. 22.25 (978-0-613-36404-1(X)) Tandem Library Bks.

Gray, Keith. The Fearful. 2005. 256p. (J). (978-0-370-32836-2(1)) Random Hse.

—The Runner. 2005. (Illus.). 96p. (J). (gr. 2-4). pap. 7.99 (978-0-440-86656-5(1) , Corgi) Transworld Publishers Ltd. GBR. *Dist:* Trafalgar Square Publishing.

Gray, Kes. Our Twitchy. McQuillan, Mary, illus. rev. ed. 2003. 32p. (J). 15.95 (978-0-8050-7454-3(6) , Holt, Henry & Co. Bks. For Young Readers) Holt, Henry & Co.

Gray, Libba Moore. My Mama Had a Dancing Heart. 1999. (gr. k-3). lib. bdg. 14.10 (978-0-613-28968-9(4)) Tandem Library Bks.

Greban, Quentin. Mommy, I Love You. Greban, Quentin, illus. 2005. (Illus.). 32p. (978-0-689-03922-5(0) , Milk & Cookies) ibooks, Inc.

Greene, Janice. The 75-Cent Son: Set 1. 2002. 32p. (YA). 2.95 (978-1-56254-413-3(6) , SP 4136) Saddleback Educational Publishing.

Greene, Marjorie. Cassie's Big Day. 2003. (Illus.). (J). 16.95 (978-0-9741764-0-6(0)) Greene, Marjorie A.

Greene, Stephanie. Owen Foote, Frontiersman. Weston, Martha, illus. 1999. 96p. (J). (gr. k-3). tchr. ed. 14.00 (978-0-395-61578-2(X) , Clarion Bks.) Houghton Mifflin Co. Trade & Reference Div.

Greenspan, Deborah. Kids' Day. 2004. (J). pap. 10.95 (978-1-59526-197-7(4)) Media Creations, Inc.

Grifalconi, Ann. Tiny's Hat. Grifalconi, Ann, illus. 1999. (Illus.). 32p. (J). (gr. k-3). 14.89 (978-0-06-027655-3(X)) HarperCollins Pubs.

Griffin, Adele. Dive. 2001. (J). 12.64 (978-0-606-21151-2(9)); (gr. 5-8). lib. bdg. 14.15 (978-0-613-46066-8(9)) Tandem Library Bks.

Gunning, Monica. A Shelter in Our Car. Pedlar, Elaine, tr. Pedlar, Elaine, illus. 2004. 32p. (J). 16.95 (978-0-89239-189-9(8)) Children's Bk. Pr.

Gutman, Anne & Hallensleben, Georg. Daddy Cuddles. 2005. (Illus.). 14p. (J). bds. 5.95 (978-0-8118-4674-5(1)) Chronicle Bks. LLC.

Haas, Jessie. Unbroken. 2001. 208p. (J). (gr. 5 up). pap. 6.99 (978-0-380-73313-2(7) , Harper Trophy) HarperCollins Pubs.

—Unbroken. l.t. ed. 2000. (Juvenile Ser.). 248p. (J). (gr. 4-7). 21.95 (978-0-7862-2769-3(9)) Thorndike Pr.

Haddix, Margaret Peterson. The Girl with 500 Middle Names. Hamlin, Janet, illus. 2001. 96p. (J). (gr. 2-5). pap. 4.99 (978-0-689-84136-1(1) , Aladdin) Simon & Schuster Children's Publishing.

—The Girl with 500 Middle Names. 2001. (gr. 3-6). lib. bdg. 11.80 (978-0-613-31244-8(9)); (Illus.). (J). 10.79 (978-0-606-20672-3(8)) Tandem Library Bks.

—The Girl with 500 Middle Names. l.t. ed. 2002. 102p. (J). 21.95 (978-0-7862-4412-6(7)) Thomson Gale.

Haggarty, Holly. Dream Dad. 2001. (gr. 3-6). lib. bdg. 14.10 (978-0-613-62551-7(X)) Tandem Library Bks.

Hague, Kathleen. Good Night, Fairies. Hague, Michael, illus. 2002. 40p. (J). (ps-2). 16.99 (978-1-58717-134-5(1) , SeaStar Bks.) Chronicle Bks. LLC.

Haislip, Phyllis Hall. Lottie's Courage: A Contraband Slave's Story. 2003. (Illus.). 120p. (J). pap. 7.95 (978-1-57249-311-7(9) , White Mane Kids) White Mane Publishing Co., Inc.

Hall, John. What If I Pulled This Thread. Gilpin, Stephen, illus. 2006. 48p. 12.99 (978-1-59379-067-7(8)) White Stone Bks.

Hall, Kirsten. At the Carnival. Rader, Laura, illus. 2003. 32p. (J). pap. 3.99 (978-0-439-59427-1(8) , Scholastic, Inc.) Scholastic, Inc.

Hall, Marjory. The Gold-Lined Box. 2003. 224p. 11.95 (978-0-9714612-6-0(0)) Green Mansion Pr. LLC.

Hallinan, P. K. ABC I Love You. 2003. (Illus.). 26p. (J). bds. 7.95 (978-0-8249-5458-1(0)) Ideals Pubns.

—How Do I Love You? 2006. (Illus.). 32p. (J). pap. 3.95 (978-0-8249-5518-2(8) , Ideals Children's Bks.) Ideals Pubns.

—How Do I Love You/Como Te Amo. 2003. (SPA & ENG., Illus.). 32p. (J). 3.95 (978-0-8249-5471-0(8)) Ideals Pubns.

—My Daddy & I. 2002. (...and I Ser.). (Illus.). 26p. (J). (ps-k). bds. 7.95 (978-0-8249-4217-5(5)) Ideals Pubns.

—We're Very Good Friends, My Mother & I. 24p. (J). 7.95 (978-0-8249-5373-7(8) , Ideals); 5.95 (978-0-8249-5374-4(6)) Ideals Pubns.

Hansen, Sara J. Sand Mermaids. 2004. 122p. pap. 17.95 (978-1-4137-1799-0(3)) PublishAmerica, Inc.

Hanson, Anders. Iguana Mama. Nobens, C. A., illus. (Fact & Fiction Ser.). 24p. (J). 2007. 21.35 (978-1-59928-444-6(8)); 2006. (978-1-59928-445-3(6)) ABDO Publishing Co.

Harcourt School Publishers Staff. A Corn Husk Doll Advanced Level. 3rd ed. 2002. (Trophies Reading Program Ser.). (Illus.). (J). pap. 3.70 (978-0-15-323012-7(6)) Harcourt Schl. Pubs.

—Cross-Country Champ Below Level. 3rd ed. 2002. (Trophies Reading Program Ser.). (Illus.). pap. 5.10 (978-0-15-323404-0(0)) Harcourt Schl. Pubs.

—Dos Familias On Level. 3rd ed. 2002. (Trofeos Ser.).Tr. of Two Families. (SPA., Illus.). pap. 6.80 (978-0-15-324174-1(8)) Harcourt Schl. Pubs.

—From Here to There Below Level. 3rd ed. 2002. (Trophies Reading Program Ser.). (Illus.). pap. 5.10 (978-0-15-323159-9(9)) Harcourt Schl. Pubs.

—Ingredientes Secretos On Level. 3rd ed. 2002. (Trofeos Ser.).Tr. of Secret Ingredients. (SPA., Illus.). pap. 6.80 (978-0-15-324176-5(4)) Harcourt Schl. Pubs.

—Let's Take a Walk. 3rd ed. 2002. (Trophies English Language Learners Ser.). (Illus.). (J). pap. 4.10 (978-0-15-325587-6(1)) Harcourt Schl. Pubs.

—On a Hot, Hot Day Little Book. 3rd ed. 2002. (Trophies Reading Program Ser.). (Illus.). (J). pap. 10.20 (978-0-15-329358-0(6)) Harcourt Schl. Pubs.

—Parent's Night. 3rd ed. 2002. (Trophies English Language Learners Ser.). (Illus.). (J). pap. 3.20 (978-0-15-327574-6(X)) Harcourt Schl. Pubs.

—Rescue from an Avalanche Advanced Level: A Young Girl's Journal. 3rd ed. 2002. (Trophies Reading Program Ser.). (Illus.). pap. 5.10 (978-0-15-323467-5(9)) Harcourt Schl. Pubs.

—Skylark: Reader's Choice Book. 2001. (Collections Ser.). (Illus.). (J). 6.90 (978-0-15-314358-8(4)) Harcourt Schl. Pubs.

—Trish Had a Wish: On Level. 3rd ed. 2002. (Trophies Reading Program Ser.). (Illus.). (J). pap. 4.10 (978-0-15-322984-8(5)) Harcourt Schl. Pubs.

—Trish Had a Wish 5-Pack, On Level. 3rd ed. 2002. (Trophies Reading Program Ser.). (Illus.). (gr. 1). pap. 20.10 (978-0-15-326834-2(4)) Harcourt Schl. Pubs.

Harper, Jo. Como los Perros de la Pradera. 2000. (SPA.). (gr. k-3). lib. bdg. 17.60 (978-0-613-32422-9(6)) Tandem Library Bks.

—I Could Eat You Up! Chorao, Kay, illus. 2007. 32p. (J). (ps-k). 16.95 (978-0-8234-1733-9(6)) Holiday Hse., Inc.

Harper, Jo & Harper, Josephine. Buscando A Papa: Un Cuento Sobre la Epoca de la Gran Depresion. Peluffo, Ana, tr. Mazellan, Ron, illus. 2005. (SPA.). 32p. (J). (ps-17). 16.95 (978-1-890515-32-4(9)) Turtle Bks.

Harris, Joanne. Five Quarters of the Orange. 2002. (gr. 7-12). lib. bdg. 23.40 (978-0-613-62140-3(9)) Tandem Library Bks.

Harris, Robie H. I'm Not Sleepy! Hollander, Nicole, illus. 2005. (Just Being Me Ser.: Vol. 2). 32p. (J). (ps-1). 7.99 (978-0-316-10941-3(X)) Little Brown & Co.

Hasse, John Edward. I Love You When... Obligado, Lilian, illus. 2001. (Pictureback Shape Ser.). 24p. (J). (gr. k-3). pap. 3.25 (978-0-375-81063-3(3) , Random Hse. Bks. for Young Readers) Random Hse. Children's Bks.

Haughton, Emma. Rainy Day. Rinaldi, Angelo, illus. (Carolrhoda Picture Books Ser.). 32p. (J). 2004. pap. 6.95 (978-1-57505-668-5(2)); 2003. 6.95 (978-1-57505-452-0(3) , Carolrhoda Bks.) Lerner Publishing Group.

Hautzig, Esther. A Picture of Grandmother. Peck, Beth, illus. 2002. 80p. (J). (gr. 2-5). 15.00 (978-0-374-35920-1(2) , Farrar, Straus & Giroux (BYR)) Farrar, Straus & Giroux.

Haworth, Margaret. When Daddy Goes Away: Rusty Books. Edwards, Paul, illus. l.t. ed. 2003. (Books That Help Ser.: Vol. 2). 34p. (J). (ps-5). pap. 9.95 (978-0-9740313-1-6(3)) Haworth, Margaret.

Hayes, Geoffrey. A Night-Light for Bunny. Date not set. 32p. (J). (ps-3). pap. 5.99 (978-0-06-443728-8(0)) HarperCollins Pubs.

—A Night-Light for Bunny. Hayes, Geoffrey, illus. 2004. (Illus.). 32p. (J). (ps-3). 14.99 (978-0-06-029163-1(X)) HarperCollins Pubs.

Helakoski, Leslie. Woolbur. Harper, Lee, illus. 2008. 32p. (J). 16.99 (***978-0-06-084726-5(3)***) HarperCollins Pubs.

Henkes, Kevin. Owen. (SPA.). 24p. (J). (gr. k-1). 7.20 (978-84-241-8079-9(8) , EV7342) Everest de Ediciones y Distribucion, S.L. ESP. *Dist:* Lectorum Pubns., Inc.

—Owen. Gil-Toresano, Maria Luz Castela, tr. 2006. (SPA., Illus.). 24p. (J). 8.99 (***978-84-241-1519-7(8)***) Everest de Ediciones y Distribucion, S.L. ESP. *Dist:* Lectorum Pubns., Inc.

Henry, Chad. Dogbreath Victorious. 1999. 192p. (J). (gr. 7 up). tchr. ed. 16.95 (978-0-8234-1458-1(2)) Holiday Hse., Inc.

Henson, Heather. Making the Run. 2002. 240p. (J). (gr. k-4). 15.89 (978-0-06-029797-8(2)); (gr. 10 up). 15.95 (978-0-06-029796-1(4)) HarperCollins Pubs. (HarperTeen).

—Making the Run: A Novel. 2003. (gr. 7-12). lib. bdg. 15.30 (978-0-613-65699-3(7)) Tandem Library Bks.

Hermes, Patricia. Summer Secrets. 2004. (Illus.). 144p. (YA). 15.95 (978-0-7614-5074-0(2)) Cavendish, Marshall Corp.

Hesse, Karen. Come on, Rain. Muth, Jon J., illus. 1999. 32p. (J). (ps-2). pap. 16.95 (978-0-590-33125-8(6)) Scholastic, Inc.

Hest, Amy. Don't You Feel Well, Sam? Jeram, Anita, illus. 2002. 32p. (J). (gr. k-1). 15.99 (978-0-7636-1009-8(7)) Candlewick Pr.

—Remembering Mrs. Rossi. Maione, Heather, illus. 2007. 192p. (J). (gr. 3-7). 14.99 (978-0-7636-2163-6(3)) Candlewick Pr.

Hetzer, Michael. No More Handprints: Your Child's Handprint Completes the Story. Clayton, Kim, illus. 2nd ed. 2005. 32p. (J). 18.95 (978-0-9728222-0-6(8)) Webster Henrietta Publishing.

Hicks, Linda & Ashman, Linda. What Could Be Better Than This? Wingerter, Linda S., illus. 2006. 32p. (J). (ps-2). 16.99 (978-0-525-46954-4(0) , Dutton Juvenile) Penguin Group (USA) Inc.

Hightman, Jason. The Saint of Dragons. (gr. 7 up). 2004. (J). 16.99 (978-0-06-054011-1(7)); 2005. 340p. (YA). reprint ed. pap. 6.99 (978-0-06-054013-5(3)) HarperCollins Pubs.

—Samurai. 2006. 320p. (J). 15.99 (978-0-06-054014-2(1)); lib. bdg. 16.89 (978-0-06-054015-9(X)) HarperCollins Pubs.

Hill, Pamela Smith. Ghost Horses. 1999. 224p. (J). (gr. 4-7). pap. 4.50 (978-0-380-72942-5(3)) HarperCollins Pubs.

—Ghost Horses. 1999. (J). (978-0-606-16340-8(9)) Tandem Library Bks.

Hines, Anna Grossnickle, illus. Whistling. 2003. 40p. (J). 16.89 (978-0-06-050236-2(3)) HarperCollins Pubs.

Ho, Minfong. Peek! A Thai Hide-and-Seek. Ho, Minfong & Meade, Holly, illus. 2004. 40p. (J). (ps-1). 16.99 (978-0-7636-2041-7(6)) Candlewick Pr.

Hobbs, Valerie. Tender. 2001. 256p. (YA). (gr. 7 up). 18.00 (978-0-374-37397-9(3) , Farrar, Straus & Giroux (BYR)) Farrar, Straus & Giroux.

Hodgkins, Fran. If You Were My Baby. Bryant, Laura J., illus. 2007. 26p. (J). (ps-ps). bds. 7.95 (***978-1-58469-090-0(9)***) Dawn Pubns.

Hodgkins, Fran. If You Were My Baby: A Wildlife Lullaby. Bryant, Laura J., illus. 2005. (Sharing Nature with Children Book Ser.). 32p. (J). (ps-2). pap. 8.95 (978-1-58469-075-7(5)); 16.95 (978-1-58469-074-0(7)) Dawn Pubns.

Holburn, Sandra. The Angel & the Bear. 2006. (ENG.). 28p. per. 15.30 (***978-1-4259-4994-5(0)***) AuthorHouse.

Holeman, Linda. Raspberry House Blues. 2000. 238p. (J). (gr. 4-7). per. 15.25 (978-0-613-53300-3(3)) Tandem Library Bks.

—Raspberry House Blues. 2000. 248p. (J). (gr. 6-9). pap. 6.95 (978-0-88776-493-6(2)) Tundra Bks., Inc./Livres Toundra, Inc. CAN. *Dist:* Random Hse., Inc.

Holt, Kimberly Willis. My Louisiana Sky. rev. ed. 1998. 176p. (J). (gr. 4-7). 17.95 (978-0-8050-5251-0(8) , Holt, Henry & Co. Bks. For Young Readers) Holt, Henry & Co.

—My Louisiana Sky. 208p. (YA). (gr. 5 up). 4.99 (978-0-8072-8291-5(X) , Listening Library) Random Hse. Audio Publishing Group.

—My Louisiana Sky. 2000. 200p. (J). (gr. k-9). lib. bdg. 13.55 (978-0-613-22802-2(2)) Tandem Library Bks.

Hong, Denise & Hong, Andrew. Why I Love My Mom: The Ultimate Gift of the Heart. Lopez, Paul & Hong, Denise, illus. 2004. 32p. (J). lib. bdg. 17.95 (978-0-9746503-4-0(X)) Platinum Bks.

Hooks, William H. Little Poss & Horrible Hound. Newsom, Carol, illus. 1998. (Bank Street Reader Collection). 48p. (J). (gr. 2-4). lib. bdg. 22.60 (978-0-8368-1773-7(7)) Stevens, Gareth Inc.

Hopkins, Lee Bennett. Mama. Marchesi, Stephen, illus. 2003. 80p. (YA). (gr. 4-6). pap. 8.95 (978-1-56397-813-5(X)) Boyds Mills Pr.

—Mama. 2000. (gr. 3-6). lib. bdg. 17.60 (978-0-613-78895-3(8)) Tandem Library Bks.

—Mama & Her Boys. Marchesi, Stephen, illus. 2003. 80p. (YA). (gr. 4-6). pap. 8.95 (978-1-56397-814-2(8)) Boyds Mills Pr.

—Mama & Her Boys. 2000. 130p. (J). (gr. 4-7). per. 17.60 (978-0-613-78896-0(6)) Tandem Library Bks.

Horn, Peter. When I Grow Up... 1999. (Illus.). (J). (978-0-606-20987-8(5)) Tandem Library Bks.

—When I Grow Up. 2001. (gr. k-3). lib. bdg. 15.25 (978-0-613-33860-8(X)) Tandem Library Bks.

Horvath, Polly. Everything on a Waffle. 2001. 160p. (J). (gr. 5 up). 16.00 (978-0-374-32236-6(8) , Farrar, Straus & Giroux (BYR)) Farrar, Straus & Giroux.

—Everything on a Waffle. (Illus.). (J). pap. 8.95 (978-0-88899-442-4(7)) Groundwood Bks. CAN. *Dist:* Transition Vendor.

—Everything on a Waffle. 2008. 176p. (J). pap. 6.99 (***978-0-312-38004-5(6)***) Square Fish.

Hossack, Sylvie A. Green Mango Magic. 1998. (Avon Camelot Bks.). 128p. (J). (gr. 3-7). 14.00 (978-0-380-97613-3(7)) HarperCollins Pubs.

How Was Your Day? 2001. 24p. (J). pap. 5.95 (978-0-9713609-0-7(1)) Eagles Publishing.

Hubbell, Patricia. Bouncing Time. Sweet, Melissa, illus. 2000. 32p. (YA). (ps up). 15.95 (978-0-688-17376-0(4)) HarperCollins Pubs.

Hughes, Vi. Aziz the Story Teller. Czernecki, Stefan, illus. 2002. 32p. (J). (ps-3). 15.95 (978-1-56656-456-4(5) , Crocodile Bks.) Interlink Publishing Group, Inc.

Humphrey, Lisa. A Mother's Promise. Danioth, David, illus. 2004. 32p. (J). per. 15.95 (978-0-9701907-9-6(4)) Illumination Arts Publishing Co., Inc.

Hunter, Terri. One Starry Night. 2000. 32p. (J). 16.95 (978-0-9705974-0-3(1)) Baby Star Productions, LLC.

Hurst, Carol Otis & Otis, Rebecca. A Killing in Plymouth Colony. 2003. 160p. (YA). (gr. 5-9). tchr. ed. 15.00 (978-0-618-27597-7(5) , Walter Lorraine) Houghton Mifflin Co. Trade & Reference Div.

I'll Never Find Anything in Here: Coloring Book. 2001. 48p. 4.99 (978-1-893108-15-8(5)) Neighborhood Pr. Publishing.

Inches, Alison. I Love My Papi! Saunders, Zina, tr. Saunders, Zina & Aikins, Dave, illus. 2004. (Ready-to-Read Ser.). 24p. (J). pap. 3.99 (978-0-689-86495-7(7) , Simon Spotlight/Nickelodeon) Simon & Schuster Children's Publishing.

Ingold, Jeanette. Mountain Solo. 320p. (YA). 2005. (gr. 7-17). pap. 6.95 (978-0-15-205358-1(1) , Harcourt Paperbacks); 2003. 17.00 (978-0-15-202670-7(3)) Harcourt Children's Bks.

Jam, Teddy. The Kid Line. Zhang, Ange, illus. 2001. 32p. (J). (gr. k-3). 16.95 (978-0-88899-432-5(X)) Groundwood Bks. CAN. *Dist:* Perseus Distribution.

Janovitz, Marilyn. Can I Help? 1998. (Illus.). 32p. (J). (ps-3). pap. 5.95 (978-1-55858-904-9(X)) North-South Bks., Inc.

Jarrell, Randall. Gingerbread Rabbit. 2004. (gr. k-3). lib. bdg. 15.30 (978-0-613-70970-5(5)) Tandem Library Bks.

Jenkins, Emily. What Happens on Wednesdays. Castillo, Lauren, illus. 2007. 40p. (J). (ps-1). 16.00 (978-0-374-38303-9(0)) Farrar, Straus & Giroux.

Jennings, Patrick. Out Standing in My Field. 2005. (Illus.). 176p. (J). pap. 16.95 (978-0-439-46581-6(8)) Scholastic, Inc.

Jeram, Anita. Bunny, My Honey. Jeram, Anita, illus. 2001. (Illus.). 40p. (J). (gr. k-ps). bds. 6.99 (978-0-7636-1201-6(4)) Candlewick Pr.

—You're All My Favorites Book & Toy Gift Set. Jeram, Anita, illus. 2004. (Illus.). 32p. (J). (ps-2). 15.99 (978-0-7636-2442-2(X)) Candlewick Pr.

Jobling, Brenda. A Foxcub Named Freedom. Anderson, Fred, illus. 1998. (Animal Tales Ser.). 131p. (J). (gr. 3-7). pap. 3.95 (978-0-7641-0600-2(7)) Barron's Educational Series, Inc.

Jobling, Curtis. My Daddy: Mini Edition. Jobling, Curtis, illus. 2007. (Illus.). 32p. (J). (ps). 9.99 (978-0-00-722164-6(9) , HarperCollins Children's Bks.) HarperCollins Pubs. Ltd. GBR. *Dist:* Independent Pubs. Group.

—My Daddy: Mini Edition. 2004. (Illus.). 32p. (J). 19.99 (978-0-00-712254-7(3) , HarperSport) HarperCollins Pubs. Ltd. GBR. *Dist:* Trafalgar Square Publishing.

—My Daddy: My Daddy Is the Best in the Universe! 2006. (Illus.). 32p. (J). (ps-3). pap. pap. 8.99 (978-0-00-712255-4(1)) HarperCollins Pubs. Ltd. GBR. *Dist:* Independent Pubs. Group.

Joel, Billy. Goodnight, My Angel: A Lullabye. Gilbert, Yvonne, illus. 2004. (Goodnight, My Angel Ser.). (J). 32p. pap. 16.95 (978-0-439-55376-6(8) , Scholastic Pr.); pap. (978-0-439-55378-0(4)) Scholastic, Inc.

Johns, Linda. I Can Bowl! 2002. (Rookie Readers Ser.). (J). lib. bdg. 19.00 (978-0-516-22565-4(0) , Children's Pr.) Scholastic Library Publishing.

—I Can Bowl! Caputo, Jim, illus. 2002. (Rookie Readers Ser.). 32p. (J). (gr. 1-2). 19.50 (978-0-516-22374-2(7) , Children's Pr.) Scholastic Library Publishing.

Johnson, Angela. The First Part Last. 144p. (YA). 2003. (Illus.). (gr. 6 up). 15.95 (978-0-689-84922-0(2)); 2004. reprint ed. pap. 5.99 (978-0-689-84923-7(0) , Simon Pulse) Simon & Schuster Children's Publishing.

—The First Part Last. l.t. ed. 241p. 2005. pap. 10.95 (978-0-7862-7379-9(8) , Large Print Pr.); 2004. 22.95 (978-0-7862-6510-7(8)) Thorndike Pr.

—Heaven. 2002. (Illus.). 13.40 (978-0-7587-0359-0(7)) Book Wholesalers, Inc.

—Heaven. 1998. 144p. (YA). (gr. 7-12). 16.95 (978-0-689-82229-2(4)) Simon & Schuster Children's Publishing.

—Heaven. 2000. (gr. 7-12). lib. bdg. 13.00 (978-0-613-28517-9(4)); (Illus.). (YA). 11.64 (978-0-606-18799-2(5)) Tandem Library Bks.

—Heaven. l.t. ed. 2000. 157p. (J). (gr. 7-12). 20.95 (978-0-7862-2463-0(0)) Thorndike Pr.

PQR

Johnson, Angela & Palencar, John Jude. Heaven. 2000. (Illus.). 144p. (YA). (gr. 8-12). pap. 5.99 (978-0-689-82290-2(1) , Simon Pulse) Simon & Schuster Children's Publishing.

Johnson, Lindsay Lee. Soul Moon Soup. 1998. 134p. (J). (gr. 5 up). 15.95 (978-1-886910-87-4(1) , Lemniscaat) Boyds Mills Pr.

Johnson, Maureen G. The Key to the Golden Firebird. 2005. 304p. (YA). reprint ed. pap. 7.99 (978-0-06-054140-8(7) , Harper Trophy) HarperCollins Pubs.

Johnson, Pete. How to Train Your Parents. l.t. ed. 2005. (J). pap. (978-0-7540-7898-2(1) , CLP 466) BBC Audio.

—How to Train Your Parents. 2005. (Illus.). (J). pap. 29.95 incl. audio (978-0-7540-6281-3(3) , Chivers Children's Audio Bks.) BBC Audiobooks America.

—How to Train Your Parents. 2003. (Illus.). 119p. pap. 9.99 (978-0-440-86439-4(9) , Yearling) Transworld Publishers Ltd. GBR. *Dist:* Trafalgar Square Publishing.

Johnston, Tony. Angel City. Byard, Carole M., illus. 2006. 40p. (J). (ps). 15.99 (978-0-399-23405-7(5) , Philomel) Penguin Group (USA) Inc.

Jones, Patrick. Things Change. 2004. 216p. (J). 16.95 (978-0-8027-8901-3(3)) Walker & Co.

Joosse, Barbara M. Mama Do You Love Me? Lavallee, Barbara, illus. 1998. 24p. (J). (ps). bds. 6.95 (978-0-8118-2131-5(5)) Chronicle Bks. LLC.

—Me Quieres, Mama? Lasconi, Diego, tr. from SPA. Lavallee, Barbara, illus. 1998. (SPA.). 32p. (J). (ps-1). 15.95 (978-0-8118-2076-9(9) , CB0769) Chronicle Bks. LLC.

Joosse, Barbara M. & Lavallee, Barbara. Me Quieres, Mama. 2004. (SPA., Illus.). 12p. (J). bds. 6.95 (978-0-8118-4341-6(6)) Chronicle Bks. LLC.

—Papa Do You Love Me? Lavallee, Barbara, illus. 2005. (Illus.). 36p. (J). 15.95 (978-0-8118-4265-5(7)) Chronicle Bks. LLC.

Kasza, Keiko. Don't Laugh, Joe! Kasza, Keiko, illus. 2002. (Illus.). (J). 13.19 (978-0-7587-4978-9(3)) Book Wholesalers, Inc.

—Don't Laugh, Joe! 2000. (gr. k-3). lib. bdg. 14.15 (978-0-613-88870-7(7)) Tandem Library Bks.

Katz, Karen. Daddy & Me. Katz, Karen, illus. 2003. (Illus.). 14p. (J). bds. 6.99 (978-0-689-84906-0(0) , Little Simon) Simon & Schuster Children's Publishing.

Kavanagh, Peter. I Love My Mama. Chapman, Jane, illus. 2003. 32p. (J). (ps-1). 14.99 (978-0-689-85691-4(1)) Simon & Schuster Children's Publishing.

—I Love My Mama. Chapman, Jane, tr. Chapman, Jane, illus. 2003. 32p. (J). 12.95 (978-1-85430-806-1(8) , Simon & Schuster Children's Publishing) Simon & Schuster Children's Publishing.

Kay, Alan N. On the Trail of John Brown's Body. 2001. (Young Heroes of History Ser.: Vol. 2). (Illus.). 175p. (J). (gr. 4-7). pap. 5.95 (978-1-57249-239-4(2) , 1572492406, Burd Street Pr.) White Mane Publishing Co., Inc.

Keehn, Sally M. First Horse I See. 2000. (gr. 3-6). lib. bdg. 14.15 (978-0-613-29957-2(4)) Tandem Library Bks.

Kehret, Peg. I'm Not Who You Think I Am. 2001. 160p. (J). (gr. 5-9). pap. 5.99 (978-0-14-131237-8(8) , Puffin) Penguin Group (USA) Inc.

—I'm Not Who You Think I Am. 2001. (J). (978-0-606-20717-1(1)); (gr. 5-8). lib. bdg. 13.00 (978-0-613-35962-7(3)) Tandem Library Bks.

Keillor, Garrison. Daddy's Girl. Glasser, Robin Preiss, illus. 2005. 40p. (J). (ps-ps). 16.99 incl. audio compact disk (978-0-7868-1986-7(3)) Hyperion Bks. for Children.

Kellerhals-Stewart, Heather. Brave Highland Heart. ed. 2004. (Illus.). (J). (gr. k-3). spiral bd. (978-0-616-01688-6(3)) Canadian National Institute for the Blind/Institut National Canadien pour les Aveugles.

—Brave Highland Heart. Zimmermann, H. Werner, illus. 1998. 15p. (J). (gr. k-3). 15.95 (978-0-7737-3099-1(0)) Stoddart Kids CAN. *Dist:* Fitzhenry & Whiteside, Ltd.

Kennedy, X. J. Owlstone Crown. 2005. 176p. (J). pap. (978-1-932425-35-2(7) , Lemniscaat) Boyds Mills Pr.

Kern, Noris. I Love You with All My Heart. 2002. (Illus.). 26p. (J). bds. 6.95 (978-0-8118-3622-7(3)) Chronicle Bks. LLC.

Khan, Rukshana. Silly Chicken. Kyong, Yunmee, illus. 2005. 32p. (J). (ps-3). 15.99 (978-0-670-05912-6(9) , Viking Juvenile) Penguin Group (USA) Inc.

Kim, Wu-kyung. Su-il vs. Su-il. Park, Jung-eun, tr. from KOR. Kwon, Sawoo, illus. 2005. 164p. (J). pap. 20.00 (978-0-89581-839-3(6)) Jain Publishing Company, Inc.

Kirk, Daniel. Moondogs. 1999. (Illus.). 1p. (J). (ps-3). 16.99 (978-0-399-23128-5(5) , Putnam Juvenile) Penguin Group (USA) Inc.

Kirk, David & Scholastic, Inc. Staff. Miss Spider's Sunny Patch Kids. Rees, Jenifer, ed. 2004. (Illus.). 40p. (J). pap. 14.95 (978-0-439-40870-7(9) , Scholastic Pr.) Scholastic, Inc.

Kita, Joy. Amy's Wish. 2003. 135p. pap. 16.95 (978-1-59286-174-3(1)) PublishAmerica, Inc.

Klass, Sheila S. The Uncivil War. 1999. (978-0-606-17477-0(X)) Tandem Library Bks.

Klingel, Cynthia Fitterer & Noyed, Robert B. Daisy, My Dad & the Letter D. 2003. (Alphaphonics Ser.). (Illus.). 24p. (J). (ps-2). 21.36 (978-1-59296-094-1(4)) Child's World, Inc.

—Muhammad's Monday & the Letter M. 2003. (Alphaphonics Ser.). (Illus.). 24p. (J). (ps-2). 21.36 (978-1-59296-103-0(7)) Child's World, Inc.

—Pablo, His Papa, & the Letter P. 2003. (Alphaphonics Ser.). (Illus.). 24p. (J). (ps-2). 21.36 (978-1-59296-106-1(1)) Child's World, Inc.

Koller, Jackie French. The Promise. Rogers, Jacqueline, illus. 2001. 80p. (gr. 5-8). 4.99 (978-0-440-41658-6(2) , Yearling) Random Hse. Children's Bks.

Krauser, Susan A. Lilith A. Wilith. 2002. (J). lib. bdg. 16.95 (978-0-9717860-0-4(3)) Lilith & Co.

Krauss, Ruth. You're Just What I Need. Noonan, Julia, illus. 1998. 40p. (J). (ps-2). 15.95 (978-0-06-027514-3(6)) HarperCollins Pubs.

Kroll, Steven. That Makes Me Mad! Davenier, Christine, illus. 2002. 32p. (J). (ps-1). 16.50 (978-1-58717-184-0(8)); 15.95 (978-1-58717-183-3(X)) Chronicle Bks. LLC. (SeaStar Bks.).

Kroll, Virginia L. Motherlove. Washburn, Lucia, illus. 1998. 32p. (J). (ps-3). 16.95 (978-1-883220-81-5(5)); pap. 7.95 (978-1-883220-80-8(7)) Dawn Pubns.

Kubler, Annie. Man's Work. 2000. (All in a Day Boardbooks Ser.). (Illus.). 14p. (J). (ps-k). bds. 3.99 (978-0-85953-587-8(8)) Child's Play-International.

Kupchella, Rick. Tell Me What We Did Today. Hanson, Warren, illus. 32p. (J). 15.95 (978-0-9726504-0-3(7)) Tristan Publishing, Inc.

Kurtz, Jane. Rain Romp: Stomping Away a Grouchy Day. Wolcott, Dyanna, illus. 2002. 32p. (J). (ps up). 16.99 (978-0-06-029805-0(7)) HarperCollins Pubs.

Lambert, Marilyn. Franny & Roxxy. 1999. (J). (gr. k-3). pap. 6.95 (978-0-533-12820-4(X)) Vantage Pr., Inc.

Lamm, C. Drew & Sherrow, Victoria. Smithsonian Backyard Cottontail & Chipmunk Box, 4 bks., Set. Davis, Allen, illus. 2002. (Smithsonian Soundprints Mini Book & Plush Ser.). 32p. (J). (ps-2). bds. (978-1-931465-56-4(8)) Soundprints.

Lane, Lindsey. Snuggle Mountain. Iwai, Melissa, illus. 2003. 32p. (J). (gr. k-ps). tchr. ed. 15.00 (978-0-618-04328-6(4) , Clarion Bks.) Houghton Mifflin Co. Trade & Reference Div.

Lang, Greg. Early One Morning. 2000. (gr. k-3). lib. bdg. 11.80 (978-0-613-29605-2(2)) Tandem Library Bks.

Lapid, Koty. The Wild Virtual Enchanted Garden. 2005. 41p. (J). per. 16.18 (978-1-4116-2068-1(2)) Lulu.com.

Lasky, Kathryn. Before I Was Your Mother. Pham, Le Uyen, illus. 2005. 30p. (J). (gr. k-4). reprint ed. 16.00 (978-0-7567-8541-3(3)) DIANE Publishing Co.

—Before I Was Your Mother. Pham, LeUyen, illus. 2003. 40p. (J). 16.00 (978-0-15-201464-3(0)) Harcourt Children's Bks.

Lawler, Janet. If Kisses Were Colors. Jay, Alison, illus. 2003. 32p. (J). (ps). 15.99 (978-0-8037-2617-8(1) , Dial) Penguin Group (USA) Inc.

Lawrence, David. Good Little Girl. 2000. (Illus.). (J). (978-0-606-18784-8(7)) Tandem Library Bks.

Lawrence, Iain. The Wreckers. 1999. (978-0-606-17565-4(2)) Tandem Library Bks.

—Wreckers. 1999. (gr. 5-8). lib. bdg. 13.55 (978-0-613-22807-7(3)) Tandem Library Bks.

—The Wreckers. 1999. (Dell Yearling Book Ser.). 224p. (J). (gr. 5-9). reprint ed. 5.99 (978-0-440-41545-9(4) , Yearling) Random Hse. Children's Bks.

—The Wreckers. unabr. ed. 2000. (YA). (gr. 7). pap., stu. ed. 59.95 incl. audio (978-0-7887-4195-1(0) , 41097) Recorded Bks., LLC.

Lawrence, Michael. Baby Loves. 2000. (Toddlers Storybook Ser.). (Illus.). 24p. (J). (ps). pap. 5.95 (978-0-7894-5744-8(X) , D K Ink) Dorling Kindersley Publishing, Inc.

Layne, Steven L. Over Land & Sea: The Story of International Adoption. Bower, Jan, illus. 2005. 32p. (J). 15.95 (978-1-58980-182-0(2)) Pelican Publishing Co., Inc.

Le, Ny Jeanine. Date. 2008. (Once upon A Prom Ser.). 240p. (J). pap. 5.99 (***978-0-545-03182-0(6)*** , Scholastic Paperbacks) Scholastic, Inc.

Lears, Laurie. Megan's Birthday Tree: A Story about Open Adoption. Farnsworth, Bill, illus. 2005. 32p. (J). (ps-3). 15.95 (978-0-8075-5036-6(1)) Whitman, Albert & Co.

Lee, Tanith. Wolf Queen. 2003. (Claidi Journals: Bk. 3). (gr. 7-12). lib. bdg. 15.30 (978-0-613-70497-7(5)) Tandem Library Bks.

Leon, Georgina Lazaro. El Mejor Es Mi Papa. 2003. (gr. k-3). lib. bdg. 14.10 (978-0-613-79286-8(6)) Tandem Library Bks.

Leonard, Marcia. The Tin Can Man. Handelman, Dorothy, photos by. 1998. (Real Kids Readers Ser.). (Illus.). 32p. (ps-1). lib. bdg. 18.90 (978-0-7613-2012-8(1) , Millbrook Pr.) Lerner Publishing Group.

Leonetti. The Greatest Goal. Thompson, Sean, illus. 2004. (Hockey Heroes Ser.). 32p. pap. 6.95 (978-1-55192-574-5(5)) Raincoast Bk. Distribution CAN. *Dist:* Perseus Distribution.

Lester, Julius. Pharaoh's Daughter: A Novel of Ancient Egypt. 2002. 192p. (J). (gr. 5 up). pap. 5.99 (978-0-06-440969-8(4) , Harper Trophy) HarperCollins Pubs.

—Pharaoh's Daughter: A Novel of Ancient Egypt. 2002. (gr. 5-8). lib. bdg. 14.15 (978-0-613-87835-7(3)) Tandem Library Bks.

—When Dad Killed Mom. 2003. (YA). 216p. pap. 6.95 (978-0-15-204698-9(4)); (gr. 7-12). mass mkt. 6.95 (978-0-15-524698-0(4)) Harcourt Trade Pubs. (Silver Whistle).

—When Dad Killed Mom. 2003. (gr. 7-12). lib. bdg. 15.25 (978-0-613-59932-0(2)) Tandem Library Bks.

Levert, Mireille. An Island in the Soup. 2002. (Illus.). 24p. (J). (ps-k). pap. 5.95 (978-0-88899-505-6(9)) Groundwood Bks. CAN. *Dist:* Perseus Distribution.

Levine, Phyllis. At the Skylight: With Matilda. 2003. pap. 12.95 (978-1-891429-45-3(0)) Armadillo Publishing Corp.

Levy, Elizabeth. My Life As a Fifth-Grade Comedian. 1998. 192p. (J). (ps-7). pap. 5.99 (978-0-06-440723-6(3) , Harper Trophy) HarperCollins Pubs.

—My Life As a Fifth-Grade Comedian. 1999. (J). pap., stu. ed. 41.20 incl. audio (978-0-7887-3180-8(7) , 40915) Recorded Bks., LLC.

—Parents' Night Fright, 6. 1998. (Invisible Ink Ser.). (978-0-606-13526-9(X)) Tandem Library Bks.

Levy, Janice. Totally Uncool. Monroe, Chris, illus. 1999. (Picture Bks.). 32p. (J). (ps-3). 15.95 (978-1-57505-306-6(3) , Carolrhoda Bks.) Lerner Publishing Group.

Lewis, Beverly. Just Like Mama. Bladholm, Cheri, illus. 2002. 32p. (J). 14.99 (978-0-7642-2507-9(3)) Bethany Hse. Pubs.

Lewis, Kim. Quilt for Baby. Lewis, Kim, illus. 2002. (Illus.). 32p. (J). (gr. k-k). 15.99 (978-0-7636-1925-1(6)) Candlewick Pr.

Lewis, Paeony. I'll Always Love You. Ives, Penny, illus. 2004. 32p. (J). pap. 5.95 (978-1-58925-360-5(4) , tiger tales) ME Media LLC.

—I'll Always Love You. 2002. (ps-2). lib. bdg. 14.10 (978-0-613-52270-0(2)) Tandem Library Bks.

L'Heureux, Christine. Caillou, Just Like Daddy. Lapierre, Claude, illus. 2001. 24p. (J). pap. (978-2-89450-256-3(7)) Chouette Publishing CAN. *Dist:* Perseus Distribution.

L'Heureux, Christine & Lapierre, Claude. Caillou Treasury Collection. 2003. (North Star Ser.). (Illus.). 148p. (J). pap. 9.99 (978-2-89450-357-7(1)) Chouette Publishing CAN. *Dist:* Independent Pubs. Group.

Linden, Dianne. Peacekeepers. (J). 82p. stu. ed. 9.95 (978-1-55050-297-8(2)); 2004. (Illus.). 220p. (gr. 4-7). pap. 7.95 (978-1-55050-271-8(9)) Coteau Bks. CAN. *Dist:* Fitzhenry & Whiteside, Ltd.

Lindgren, Astrid. Mio, My Son. Wikland, Ilon, illus. 2003. Tr. of Mio, Min Mio. 179p. (J). 17.95 (978-1-930900-23-3(6)) Purple Hse. Pr.

Lindquist, Susan Hart. Summer Soldiers. 2000. (J). (978-0-606-19132-6(1)) Tandem Library Bks.

Lisle, Janet Taylor. The Crying Rocks. 2003. (Illus.). 208p. (YA). 16.95 (978-0-689-85319-7(X) , Atheneum/Richard Jackson Bks.) Simon & Schuster Children's Publishing.

—The Crying Rocks. l.t. ed. 2004. (Thorndike Press Large Print Literacy Bridge Ser.). 273p. (J). 22.95 (978-0-7862-6140-6(4)) Thorndike Pr.

Little, Jean. Birdie for Now. 2002. (gr. 3-6). lib. bdg. 13.00 (978-0-613-53482-6(4)) Tandem Library Bks.

Little Tiny Good Things. 2002. (Illus.). 28p. (978-0-9726611-0-2(7)) New Leaf Communications.

Living the Life Prequel - Kurtis. 2003. (Living the Life Ser.: Vol. 2). 160p. (YA). pap. 14.00 (978-0-9710398-3-4(6)) Michael-Christopher Bks.

Livsey, John. '38: The Great Hurricane in Quonochontaug, Rhode Island. 2004. 288p. (YA). per. 15.49 (978-0-9754979-2-0(8)) Big Wave Bks.

Lobel, Gillian & Braun, Sebastien. Too Small for Honey Cake. 2006. (Illus.). 32p. (J). 16.00 (978-0-15-206097-8(9)) Harcourt Trade Pubs.

London, Jonathan. Froggy's Day with Dad. Remkiewicz, Frank, illus. 2004. (Froggy Ser.). 32p. (J). (gr. k-2). 15.99 (978-0-670-03596-0(3) , Viking Juvenile) Penguin Group (USA) Inc.

—What Do You Love? Schmidt, Karen Lee, illus. 2004. 30p. (J). bds. 6.95 (978-0-15-205054-2(X) , Red Wagon Bks.) Harcourt Children's Bks.

Loomis, Christine. Across America, I Love You. Kiesler, Kate A., illus. 2000. 32p. (ps-3). 16.49 (978-0-7868-2314-7(3)) Hyperion Bks. for Children.

Lopez Soria, Marisa. Los Colores de Mateo. Rogowicz, Katarzyna, illus. 2002. (Montana Encantada Ser.). (SPA.). 36p. (J). 7.50 (978-84-241-8029-4(1)) Everest de Ediciones y Distribucion, S.L. ESP. *Dist:* Lectorum Pubns., Inc.

Losier, Dave. Fred's Prayer Machine. 2002. (Illus.). 152p. (J). pap. 11.95 (978-1-929039-07-4(7)) Ambassador Bks., Inc.

Lou Weber Staff, ed. Fairly Oddparents: Little Sound Book. 2004. 10p. (J). bds. 9.98 (978-1-4127-3225-3(5) , 7237600) Publications International, Ltd.

Loupy, Christophe. Hugs & Kisses. James, J. Alison, tr. from GER. Tharlet, Eve, illus. 2001. 36p. (J). (ps-k). 15.95 (978-0-7358-1484-4(8)) North-South Bks., Inc.

Love, Angelica. Words Can Break a Heart. Stancil, Mary H., ed. Stancil, Mary H., illus. 1998. 20p. (J). (gr. k-2). pap. 4.95 (978-1-892212-07-8(2)) Love Publishing Co.

Love, Maryann Cusimano. You Are My Miracle. Ichikawa, Satomi, illus. 2005. 32p. (J). (ps-1). 15.99 (978-0-399-24037-9(3) , Philomel) Penguin Group (USA) Inc.

Lowry, Brigid. Guitar Highway Rose. 2003. 208p. (J). (gr. 7 up). tchr. ed. 16.95 (978-0-8234-1790-2(5)) Holiday Hse., Inc.

—Guitar Highway Rose. 2006. 208p. (YA). reprint ed. pap. 8.95 (978-0-312-34296-8(9) , St. Martin's Griffin) St. Martin's Pr.

Lowry, Danielle. What Can I Do? A Book for Children of Divorce. Matthews, Bonnie, illus. 2001. 46p. (J). (gr. 3-7). 14.95 (978-1-55798-769-3(6)); pap. 8.95 (978-1-55798-770-9(X)) American Psychological Assn. (Magination Pr.).

Lucado, Max. A Hat for Ivan. Wenzel, David, illus. 2005. 32p. 15.99 (978-1-58134-414-1(7) , Crossway Bibles) Crossway Bks.

—Just in Case You Ever Wonder. 2007. 24p. (J). 15.99 (978-1-4003-0878-1(X)); 2000. (Illus.). 16p. (YA). bds. 6.99 (978-0-8499-7509-7(3)) Nelson, Thomas Inc.

—Just in Case You Ever Wonder - No Jacket. 2005. 32p. 9.99 (978-1-4003-0740-1(6)) Nelson, Thomas Inc.

Lucashenko, Melissa. Killing D'arcy. 1998. 240p. (YA). (gr. 8-12). pap. 16.95 (978-0-7022-3041-7(3)) Univ. of Queensland Pr. AUS. *Dist:* International Specialized Bk. Services.

Luckett, Kathy. Does Your Father Snore? Chilomwe Version. Nkhoma, Wilson, tr. 1999. (Cambridge Reading Routes Ser.). (Illus.). 16p. pap. 3.70 (978-0-521-66847-7(6)) Cambridge Univ. Pr.

—Does Your Father Snore? Chitumbuka Version. Chirambo, Reuben, tr. 1999. (Cambridge Reading Routes Ser.). (Illus.). 16p. pap. 3.70 (978-0-521-66868-2(9)) Cambridge Univ. Pr.

—Does Your Father Snore? Chiyao Version. Mjaya, Ahmmardouh, tr. 1999. (Cambridge Reading Routes Ser.). (Illus.). 16p. pap. 3.70 (978-0-521-66864-4(6)) Cambridge Univ. Pr.

—Does Your Father Snore? Kiswahili Version. Mhando, Harold, tr. 1999. (Cambridge Reading Routes Ser.). (Illus.). 16p. pap. 3.70 (978-0-521-66890-3(5)) Cambridge Univ. Pr.

Luke's Go-cart: Individual Title Six-Packs. 16p. (gr. 2 up). 35.00 (978-0-7635-9371-1(0)) Rigby Education.

Lupica, Mike. Travel Team. 2004. 288p. (YA). (gr. 3-8). 16.99 (978-0-399-24150-5(7) , Philomel) Penguin Group (USA) Inc.

Ly, Many. Home Is East. 2005. 304p. (J). (gr. 5 up). lib. bdg. 17.99 (978-0-385-73223-9(6) , Delacorte Bks. for Young Readers) Random Hse. Children's Bks.

MacCullough, Carolyn. Stealing Henry. rev. ed. 2005. 208p. (YA). 16.95 (978-1-59643-045-7(1)) Roaring Brook Pr.

MacDonald, George. The History of Gutta-Percha Willie. 2006. pap. (***978-1-4250-0933-5(6)***) Assistedreadingbooks.com Inc.

Mack, Paulette. Cookout at Grandma's House: The Adventures of Mielle & Cheeky. 2006. (ENG., Illus.). 24p. per. 10.95 (***978-1-59800-998-9(2)***) Outskirts Press, Inc.

Mack, Todd. Princess Penelope. Gran, Julia, illus. 2003. 32p. (J). (ps-k). pap. 15.95 (978-0-439-22436-9(5) , Scholastic Pr.) Scholastic, Inc.

Mackall, Dandi Daley. Just Jazz Bk. 3: Blog On! 2006. (Faithgirlz Ser.). (Illus.). 128p. (J). pap. 6.99 (978-0-310-71095-0(2)) Zonderkidz.

Mackel, Kathy. A Season of Comebacks. 1998. (J). (978-0-606-13767-6(X)) Tandem Library Bks.

MacLean, Christine. Even Firefighters Hug Their Moms. Reed, Mike, illus. 2004. 32p. (J). (gr. k-3). pap. 5.99 (978-0-14-240191-0(9) , Puffin) Penguin Group (USA) Inc.

MacLean, Christine Kole. Even Firefighters Hug Their Moms. Reed, Mike, illus. 2002. 32p. (J). 16.99 (978-0-525-46996-4(6) , Dutton Juvenile) Penguin Group (USA) Inc.

Madrigal, Antonio Hernandez. Erandi's Braids. Peskin, Joy, ed. de Paola, Tomie, illus. 2001. 1p. (J). (ps-3). pap. 6.99 (978-0-698-11885-0(5) , Putnam Juvenile) Penguin Group (USA) Inc.

—Erandi's Braids. de Paola, Tomie, illus. 1999. 32p. (J). (ps-3). 15.99 (978-0-399-23212-1(5) , Putnam Juvenile) Penguin Group (USA) Inc.

Magnus, Kellie. Little Lion Goes to School. Robinson, Michael, illus. l.t. ed. 2003. 16p. (J). 9.99 (978-0-9744211-0-0(3)) Media Magic New York.

Mahr, Juli. Mama Tiger, Baba Tiger. 2001. (Illus.). (J). (978-0-606-21314-1(7)) Tandem Library Bks.

Mahy, Margaret. The Catalogue of the Universe. 2002. (gr. 7-12). lib. bdg. 16.45 (978-0-613-57621-5(7)) Tandem Library Bks.

Maier, Inger M. When Fuzzy Was Afraid: Of Losing His Mother. Candon, Jennifer, illus. 2005. 32p. (J). 14.95 (978-1-59147-168-4(0)); pap. 8.95 (978-1-59147-169-1(9)) American Psychological Assn. (Magination Pr.).

Mallat, Kathy. Mama Love. Mallat, Kathy, illus. 2004. (Illus.). 24p. (J). 15.95 (978-0-8027-8902-0(1)) Walker & Co.

Malokas, Ann. Military Dads. 2002. (Illus.). 20p. 6.95 (978-0-9708415-5-1(8)) Guilty Mom Pr.

—Military Moms. 2002. (Illus.). 20p. (J). 6.95 (978-0-9708415-4-4(X)) Guilty Mom Pr.

Marchetta, Melina. Saving Francesca. 2004. 256p. (gr. 7). (J). lib. bdg. 17.99 (978-0-375-92982-3(7)); (YA). 15.95 (978-0-375-82982-6(2)) Random Hse. Children's Bks. (Knopf Bks. for Young Readers).

—Saving Francesca. l.t. ed. 2005. 343p. 22.95 (978-0-7862-7309-6(7) , Large Print Pr.) Thorndike Pr.

Marlowe, Pete. One Arabian Morning. Bell, Charles, illus. 2000. 32p. (J). (gr. k-3). pap. 6.95 (978-1-55037-658-6(6)) Annick Pr., Ltd. CAN. *Dist:* Firefly Bks., Ltd.

Martella, Liz. Izabella & her Wardrobe. 2007. 18p. 12.95 (***978-0-615-14941-7(3)***) Martella, Liz.

Martin, David. Piggy & Dad Play. Remkiewicz, Frank, illus. 2002. (Brand New Readers Ser.). 8p. (J). (ps-2). pap. 5.99 (978-0-7636-1333-4(9)) Candlewick Pr.

Marzollo, Jean. Mama Mama/Papa Papa Flip Board Book. Regan, Laura, illus. 2003. (Flip Boardbks.). 32p. (J). (ps up). 6.99 (978-0-06-051915-5(0) , Harper Festival) HarperCollins Pubs.

Masters, Susan Rowan. Summer Song. 2000. 148p. (YA). (gr. 4-7). pap. 9.95 (978-0-595-14407-5(1)) iUniverse, Inc.

Mayer, Mercer. Beach Day. 2002. (Little Critter First Readers Ser.). (Illus.). 24p. (J). (ps-k). pap. 3.95 (978-1-57768-844-0(9)) School Specialty Publishing.

—Beach Day. 2003. (gr. k-3). lib. bdg. 11.80 (978-0-613-67599-4(1)) Tandem Library Bks.

Mazer, Anne. The No-Nothings & Their Baby. Collins, Ross, illus. 2000. (J). (gr. k-3). 40p. pap. 15.95 (978-0-590-68049-3(8) , Scholastic Paperbacks); (978-0-590-68051-6(X)) Scholastic, Inc.

Mazer, Norma Fox. Girlhearts. 2002. (gr. 7-12). lib. bdg. 15.30 (978-0-613-58571-2(2)) Tandem Library Bks.

—GoodNight, Maman. 1999. (C). 16.00 net. (978-0-15-202677-6(0)) Harcourt College Pubs.

—What I Believe. 176p. 2007. (Illus.). (J). pap. 6.95 (978-0-15-206283-5(1) , Harcourt Paperbacks); 2005. (YA). (gr. 5-9). 16.00 (978-0-15-201462-9(4) , Harcourt Children's Bks) Harcourt Children's Bks.

McBratney, Sam. Guess How Much I Love You. Jeram, Anita, illus. 10th anniv. ed. 2004. 32p. (J). 20.00 (978-0-7636-2435-4(7)) Candlewick Pr.

McCaughrean, Geraldine. Casting the Gods Adrift: A Tale of Ancient Egypt. Ludlow, Patricia D., illus. 2003. 112p. (J). (gr. 4-7). 15.95 (978-0-8126-2684-1(2)) Cricket Bks.

McCloskey, Robert. Blueberries for Sal. McCloskey, Robert, illus. 2002. (Illus.). (J). 14.04 (978-0-7587-0097-1(0)) Book Wholesalers, Inc.

—Blueberries for Sal. 2000. (J). pap. 19.97 incl. audio (978-0-7366-9193-2(6)) Books on Tape, Inc.

—Blueberries for Sal. (J). (ps-k). pap. 12.95 incl. audio Weston Woods Studios, Inc.

McConnaughhay, JoDee. Be Brave, Anna! God Helps Me When I'm Afraid. Caldwell, Lise, ed. Dubin, Jill, illus. 1999. (Happy Day Bks.). 24p. (J). (ps-2). 2.49 (978-0-7847-0895-8(9) , 04268, Bean Sprouts) Standard Publishing.

McCourt, Lisa. I Love You, Stinky Face. Moore, Cyd, illus. (J). 2004. 32p. pap. 15.95 (978-0-439-63571-4(3)); 2004. 16p. bds. 6.99 (978-0-439-63572-1(1)); 2003. 32p. 5.99 (978-0-439-63469-4(5)) Scholastic, Inc.

—I Miss You, Stinky Face. Moore, Cyd, illus. 2004. 32p. (J). pap. 15.95 (978-0-439-63573-8(X)) Scholastic, Inc.

—I Miss You, Stinky Face. 2000. (978-0-606-18667-4(0)) Tandem Library Bks.

—The Most Thankful Thing. Moore, Cyd, illus. 2004. 32p. (J). (gr. k). pap. 15.95 (978-0-439-65083-0(6) , Cartwheel Bks.) Scholastic, Inc.

McCourt, Lisa. My Forever Valentine. Bryant, Laura J., illus. 2008. (J). (***978-0-439-75058-5(X))*** Scholastic, Inc.

McCully, Emily Arnold. Monk Camps Out. McCully, Emily Arnold, illus. 2000. (Illus.). 32p. (J). (ps-4). pap. 15.95 (978-0-439-09976-9(5) , Levine, Arthur A. Bks.) Scholastic, Inc.

—Monk Camps Out. 2000. (Illus.). (J). (978-0-439-09977-6(3)) Scholastic, Inc.

McCully, Emily Arnold & Schertle, Alice. 1, 2, I Love You. 2004. (Illus.). 32p. (J). (ps-k). 16.95 (978-0-8118-3518-3(9)) Chronicle Bks. LLC.

McCurry, Meryl Alyse. The Sea Monster's Darkest Night. McCurry, Meryl Alyse, illus. 1999. (Illus.). 34p. (J). (ps-3). pap. 7.99 (978-1-881524-67-0(1)) Milligan Bks., Inc.

McDonald, Janet. Chill Wind. l.t. ed. 2003. 165p. (J). 24.95 (978-0-7862-5502-3(1)) Thorndike Pr.

McDonough, Alison. Do the Hokey Pokey. Urbanovic, Jackie, illus. 2001. 112p. (J). (gr. 3-7). 14.95 (978-0-8126-2699-5(0)) Cricket Bks.

McKee, David. Not Now, Bernard. 2005. (Illus.). 32p. (J). 6.99 (978-1-84270-456-1(7)) Trafalgar Square Publishing.

McKendrick, Lisa. On a Whim. 2001. 156p. (J). (978-1-57734-896-2(6)) Covenant Communications.

McLean, Jacqueline. Grace from China. 2003. 179p. (J). 16.00 (978-0-9638472-8-7(7)) Yeong & Yeong Bk. Co.

McNeal, Laura & McNeal, Tom. Crooked. 2007. 352p. (J). (gr. 7). pap. 7.99 (978-0-375-84191-0(1) , Knopf Bks. for Young Readers) Random Hse. Children's Bks.

McOmber, Rachel B., ed. McOmber Phonics Storybooks: Mom & Dad Hop-Jig. rev. ed. (Illus.). (J). (978-0-944991-16-9(5)) Swift Learning Resources.

McVeity, Jen. On Different Shores. 1998. (Illus.). 167p. (YA). (gr. 5-9). 17.99 (978-0-531-33115-6(6)); pap. 16.95 (978-0-531-30115-9(X)) Scholastic, Inc. (Orchard Bks.).

Melmed, Laura Krauss. I Love You As Much... Sorensen, Henri, illus. 2005. 24p. (J). (ps-2). pap. 5.99 (978-0-06-000202-2(6) , Harper Festival) HarperCollins Pubs.

Metzger, Steve. I'll Always Come Back! Allen, Joy, illus. 2002. (J). (978-0-439-42922-1(6)) Scholastic, Inc.

Michaels, Kat. Gentle Is the Night. 2008. (J). 15.95 (***978-0-9745052-7-5(7))*** Tree Of Life Publishing.

Middlestadt, Donna. Little Miss No Name. 2004. 218p. pap. 19.95 (978-1-4137-0894-3(3)) PublishAmerica, Inc.

Miller, Kathryn Ann. Did My First Mother Love Me? A Story for an Adopted Child. Moffett, Jamie, illus. 2003. 48p. (J). (ps-3). 12.95 (978-0-930934-85-9(7)); pap. 5.95 (978-0-930934-84-2(9)) Morning Glory Pr., Inc.

Mills, Charles. Stranger in the Shadows. 1998. (Shadow Creek Ranch Ser.: Vol. 11). 151p. (Orig.). (J). (gr. 4-7). pap. 5.99 (978-0-8280-1316-1(0)) Review & Herald Publishing Assn.

Mills, Claudia. Alex Ryan, Stop That! 2003. 160p. (J). 16.00 (978-0-374-34655-3(0) , Farrar, Straus & Giroux (BYR)) Farrar, Straus & Giroux.

—You're a Brave Man, Julius Zimmerman. 2001. 160p. (gr. 3-7). pap. 5.99 (978-0-7868-1448-0(9)) Hyperion Bks. for Children.

Moeri, Louise. The Devil in Ol' Rosie. l.t. ed. 2002. (Juvenile Ser.). 161p. (J). 21.95 (978-0-7862-3808-8(9)) Thomson Gale.

Montgomery, Arch. Hank. 2003. 171p. (YA). 19.95 (978-1-890862-22-0(3)) Bancroft Pr.

Moore, Isabel. Daughter. 1999. (gr. 5-8). lib. bdg. 15.25 (978-0-613-33886-8(3)) Tandem Library Bks.

Moore, Martha A. Matchit. 2003. (Illus.). 208p. (J). (gr. 3-7). pap. 4.99 (978-0-440-41716-3(3) , Yearling) Random Hse. Children's Bks.

Mora, Pat. Maria Paints the Hills. Hesch, Maria, illus. 2002. 32p. 19.95 (978-0-89013-401-6(4)); 1p. pap. 9.95 (978-0-89013-410-8(3)) Museum of New Mexico Pr.

Moran, Alex. Todd's Box. 2004. (ps-2). lib. bdg. 11.80 (978-0-613-81968-8(3)) Tandem Library Bks.

Moran, Alex & Sullivan, Paula. Todd's Box. Westcott, Nadine Bernard, illus. 2004. (Green Light Readers Level 1 Ser.). 24p. (J). 11.95 (978-0-15-205093-1(0)); pap. 3.95 (978-0-15-205094-8(9)) Harcourt Children's Bks. (Green Light Readers).

Moreillon, Judi. Read to Me. Teis, Kyra, illus. 24p. (J). (ps-ps). 2004. per. 6.95 (978-1-59572-014-6(6)); 2003. 6.95 (978-1-932065-49-7(0) , 1-718-794-9112) Star Bright Bks., Inc.

Morgan, Melissa J. Camp Confidential Vol. 4: Alex's Challenge. 2005. (Camp Confidential Ser.). 160p. (gr. 4-7). mass mkt. 4.99 (978-0-448-43876-4(3) , Grosset & Dunlap) Penguin Group (USA) Inc.

—Grace's Twist, Vol. 3. 2005. (Camp Confidential Ser.). 160p. (gr. 4-7). mass mkt. 4.99 (978-0-448-43875-7(5) , Grosset & Dunlap) Penguin Group (USA) Inc.

Morgenroth, Kate. Jude. 2004. 288p. (YA). 16.95 (978-0-689-86479-7(5)) Simon & Schuster Children's Publishing.

Morrow, Tara Jaye. Just Mommy & Me. Bratun, Katy, illus. 2004. 32p. (J). 13.89 (978-0-06-000725-6(7)) HarperCollins Pubs.

—Mommy Loves Her Baby/Daddy Loves His Baby. Beeke, Tiphanie, illus. 2003. 32p. (J). (ps-1). 15.99 (978-0-06-029077-1(3)); lib. bdg. 16.89 (978-0-06-029078-8(1)) HarperCollins Pubs.

Morter, Amanda L. Hush, My Baby. 2006. 28p. per. 12.99 (***978-1-59886-725-1(3))*** Tate Publishing & Enterprises, L.L.C.

Mother-Daughter Literary Social Event Kit. 2000. (J). pap. (978-0-06-449276-8(1) , Harper Trophy) HarperCollins Pubs.

Mouse Works Staff. Dumbo. 2000. (Read-Aloud Storybook Ser.). 64p. (J). 6.99 (978-0-7364-1052-6(X)) Hyperion Bks. for Children.

—Dumbo. 1999. (Disney's Friendly Tales Ser.). (Illus.). 10p. (J). (ps-k). 6.99 (978-0-7364-1012-0(0)) Mouse Works.

Munsch, Robert. Algo Bueno. 2001. (SPA.). (gr. k-3). lib. bdg. 14.10 (978-0-613-78388-0(3)) Tandem Library Bks.

—Lighthouse: A Story of Remembrance. Wilson, Janet, illus. 2004. 28p. (J). pap. 5.95 (978-0-439-49032-0(4)) Scholastic, Inc.

Munson, Derek. Enemy Pie. King, Tara Calahan, illus. 2000. 40p. (J). (gr. k-3). 15.95 (978-0-8118-2778-2(X)) Chronicle Bks. LLC.

Murphy, Mary. I Kissed the Baby! Murphy, Mary, illus. 2003. (Illus.). 24p. (J). (gr. k-k). 14.99 (978-0-7636-2122-3(6)) Candlewick Pr.

—I Like It When ... /Me gusta Cuando ... Campoy, F. Isabel & Ada, Alma Flor, trs. 2008. (Illus.). 22p. (J). bds. 6.95 (***978-0-15-206045-9(6)*** , Voyager Bks./Libros Viajeros) Harcourt Children's Bks.

Murphy, Mary. Please Be Quiet! Murphy, Mary, illus. 1999. (Illus.). 32p. (J). (gr. k-ps). 9.95 (978-0-395-97113-0(6)) Houghton Mifflin Co. Trade & Reference Div.

My Dad Is Great. 2002. (Great Relatives Ser.). 32p. (J). 11.95 (978-1-84250-574-8(2) , Bright Sparks) Parragon, Inc.

My Father the Mad Professor: Individual Title Six-Packs. (Action Packs Ser.). 120p. (gr. 3-5). 44.00 (978-0-7635-8424-5(X)) Rigby Education.

My Mommy & I! 2002. (Illus.). 24p. (J). (ps-k). bds. 7.95 (978-0-8249-4218-2(3)) Ideals Pubns.

My Name Is Really Lucy! 2003. (J). pap. (978-0-9745591-1-7(3)) Roehm, Nancy Jean.

Myers, Anna. The Keeping Room. 1999. (Illus.). 128p. (J). (gr. 3-7). pap. 5.99 (978-0-14-130468-7(5) , Puffin) Penguin Group (USA) Inc.

—The Keeping Room. 1999. (J). (978-0-606-16786-4(2)) Tandem Library Bks.

—Keeping Room. 1999. (gr. 3-6). lib. bdg. 14.15 (978-0-613-19519-5(1)) Tandem Library Bks.

—Tulsa Burning. 2004. 184p. (J). pap. 7.95 (978-0-8027-7696-9(5)); (Illus.). (gr. 3-7). 16.95 (978-0-8027-8829-0(7)) Walker & Co.

Myers, Walter Dean. The Dream Bearer. 2003. 192p. (J). (gr. 5 up). 15.99 (978-0-06-029521-9(X) , Amistad) HarperCollins Pubs.

—The Dream Bearer. l.t. ed. 2003. 207p. (J). 25.95 (978-0-7862-5923-6(X)) Thorndike Pr.

—Somewhere in the Darkness. 2003. (gr. 7-12). lib. bdg. 14.15 (978-0-613-67390-6(X)) Tandem Library Bks.

Napoli, Donna Jo. Crazy Jack. 2000. (YA). pap., stu. ed. 51.95 incl. audio (978-0-7887-4159-3(4) , 41099) Recorded Bks., LLC.

—Crazy Jack. l.t. ed. 2000. 183p. (YA). (gr. 8-12). 20.95 (978-0-7862-3047-1(9)) Thorndike Pr.

—Spinners. 2001. (gr. 7-12). lib. bdg. 14.15 (978-0-613-36016-6(8)) Tandem Library Bks.

Nelson, Annabelle. Angelica's Hope: A Story for Young People & Their Parents about the Need to Talk about Things That No One Talks About. Palomares, Franz, illus. 2003. (SPA.). (978-0-9656732-9-7(4)) WHEEL Council, Inc., The.

Nelson, Theresa. Ruby Electric. 272p. (J). 2003. (Illus.). 16.95 (978-0-689-83852-1(2) , Atheneum/Richard Jackson Bks.); 2004. reprint ed. pap. 5.99 (978-0-689-87146-7(5) , Aladdin) Simon & Schuster Children's Publishing.

Neufeld, John. Edgar Allan. 2007. 136p. (gr. 5-9). per. 11.95 (***978-0-595-45039-8(3)*** , Backinprint.com) iUniverse, Inc.

Neville, Emily Cheney. It's Like This, Cat. 2002. (Illus.). (J). 14.47 (978-0-7587-0195-4(0)) Book Wholesalers, Inc.

—It's Like This, Cat. 1999. (J). 9.95 (978-1-56137-101-3(7)) Novel Units, Inc.

New Pet. l.t. ed. 2005. (Illus.). 32p. (J). lib. bdg. 14.95 (978-0-9658365-8-6(4)) Beetle Bug Bks.

Newman, Leslea. The Boy Who Cried Fabulous. Ferguson, Peter, illus. 32p. (J). (ps-2). 2007. pap. 7.95 (***978-1-58246-224-0(0));*** 2004. 15.95 (978-1-58246-101-4(5)) Ten Speed Pr. (Tricycle Pr.).

Newman, Leslea. Jailbait. 256p. (YA). (gr. 9). 2006. pap. 8.95 (978-0-385-73405-9(0)); 2005. lib. bdg. 17.99 (978-0-385-90230-4(1)) Random Hse. Children's Bks. (Delacorte Bks. for Young Readers).

Nichole, Michelle. Love for Miraye. Nichole, Michelle, illus. l.t. ed. 2002. (Illus.). 26p. per. 16.50 (978-0-9705823-9-3(0)) Pearl Line Pr., Inc.

Nixon, Joan Lowery. John's Story, 1775. 2004. (J). (978-0-87935-228-8(0)) Colonial Williamsburg Foundation.

—Will's Story, 1771. 2004. (J). (978-0-87935-226-4(4)) Colonial Williamsburg Foundation.

Nolan, Han. Born Blue. (YA). 2003. 300p. pap. 6.95 (978-0-15-204697-2(6) , Harcourt Paperbacks); 2001. 288p. (gr. 9 up). 17.00 (978-0-15-201916-7(2)) Harcourt Children's Bks.

—Born Blue. 2003. (gr. 7-12). lib. bdg. 15.25 (978-0-613-59882-8(2)) Tandem Library Bks.

Nolen, Jerdine. Hewitt Anderson's Great Big Life. Nelson, Kadir A., illus. 2005. 40p. (J). 16.95 (978-0-689-86866-5(9) , Simon & Schuster/Paula Wiseman Bks.) Simon & Schuster Children's Publishing.

North, Sherry. Because You Are My Baby. Hall, Marcellus, illus. 2008. 32p. (J). 15.95 (***978-0-8109-9482-9(8)*** , Abrams Bks. for Young Readers) Abrams, Harry N. , Inc.

Noyes, Deborah. Hana in the Time of the Tulips. Ibatoulline, Bagram, illus. 2004. 40p. (J). (gr. 1-6). 16.99 (978-0-7636-1875-9(6)) Candlewick Pr.

Numeroff, Laura Joffe. What Mommies Do Best. Munsinger, Lynn, illus. abr. ed. 2003. (Classic Board Bks.). 22p. (J). bds. 6.99 (978-0-689-85659-4(8) , Little Simon) Simon & Schuster Children's Publishing.

Numeroff, Laura Joffe & Munsinger, Lynn. What Daddies Do Best. 2001. (Illus.). 24p. (J). (ps-3). 6.95 (978-0-689-84466-9(2)) Simon & Schuster Children's Publishing.

Oates, Joyce Carol. Freaky Green Eyes. 2003. 352p. (J). 16.99 (978-0-06-623759-6(9) , HarperTeen); 2003. 352p. (J). lib. bdg. 17.89 (978-0-06-623757-2(2) , HarperTeen); 2003. tchr. ed. (978-0-06-056885-6(2)); 2005. 368p. (YA). reprint ed. pap. 7.99 (978-0-06-447348-4(1) , HarperTeen) HarperCollins Pubs.

Ochiltree, Dianne. Lull-a-Bye, Little One. Takahashi, Hideko, illus. 2006. 32p. (J). (gr. 1-ps). 16.99 (978-0-399-24305-9(4)) Penguin Group (USA) Inc.

O'Connell, Rebecca. The Baby Goes Beep. Wilson-Max, Ken, illus. rev. ed. 2003. 32p. (J). (ps up). 22.90 (978-0-7613-2867-4(X)); 14.95 (978-0-7613-1789-0(9)) Roaring Brook Pr.

O'Connor, Barbara. Beethoven in Paradise. 1999. (Illus.). 160p. (J). (gr. 5-8). pap. 7.95 (978-0-374-40588-5(3) , Sunburst) Farrar, Straus & Giroux.

—Beethoven in Paradise. 1999. (gr. 3-6). lib. bdg. 12.95 (978-0-613-29559-8(5)) Tandem Library Bks.

—Moonpie & Ivy. 160p. (J). 2001. (gr. 5 up). 16.00 (978-0-374-35059-8(0) , Farrar, Straus & Giroux (BYR)); 2004. (Illus.). reprint ed. pap. 7.95 (978-0-374-45320-6(9) , Sunburst) Farrar, Straus & Giroux.

Odanaka, Barbara. Skateboard Mom. Adinolfi, JoAnn, illus. 2004. 32p. (J). (ps-3). 15.99 (978-0-399-23867-3(0) , Putnam Juvenile) Penguin Group (USA) Inc.

Oke, Janette. Ducktails. Munger, Nancy, illus. 2001. (Animal Friends Ser.: Vol. 6). 80p. (J). (ps-3). pap. 6.99 (978-0-7642-2450-8(6)) Bethany Hse. Pubs.

—Ducktails. 2001. (gr. k-3). lib. bdg. 14.15 (978-0-613-82430-9(X)) Tandem Library Bks.

O'Keefe, Susan Heyboer. Love Me, Love You. Spowart, Robin, illus. 2003. 32p. (J). (ps up). 15.95 (978-1-56397-837-1(7)) Boyds Mills Pr.

Olasky, Susan. Will Northaway & the Quest for Liberty. 2005. (Young American Patriots Ser.). 128p. pap. 5.99 (978-1-58134-475-2(9) , Crossway Bibles) Crossway Bks.

Oldham, Mary. No Fire, No Candle. 2001. 217p. (YA). pap. 12.95 (978-1-85902-945-9(0)) Beekman Bks., Inc.

Olsen, Ashley. Just Between Us. 2002. (gr. 5-8). lib. bdg. 13.00 (978-0-613-64741-0(6)) Tandem Library Bks.

On the Job: Individual Title Six-Packs. (ps-2). 27.00 (978-0-7635-9468-8(7)) Rigby Education.

One Starry Night Gift Box. 2000. 32p. 29.95 (978-0-9705974-1-0(X)) Baby Star Productions, LLC.

Orloff, Karen Kaufman. I Wanna Iguana. Catrow, David, illus. 2004. 32p. (J). (ps-3). 16.99 (978-0-399-23717-1(8) , Putnam Juvenile) Penguin Group (USA) Inc.

Ovenell-Carter, Julie. Adam's Daycare. Ohi, Ruth, illus. 2003. 32p. (J). (gr. k-2). pap. 5.95 (978-1-55037-444-5(3)) Annick Pr., Ltd. CAN. *Dist:* Firefly Bks., Ltd.

Owens, Mary Beth. Panda Whispers. 2007. (Illus.). 32p. (J). (ps-2). 16.99 (978-0-525-47171-4(5) , Dutton Juvenile) Penguin Group (USA) Inc.

Page, Josephine. Mommy Loves Her Bunny. Morgan, Mary, illus. 2003. 5p. (J). (ps). bds. 4.99 (978-0-439-44322-7(9) , Cartwheel Bks.) Scholastic, Inc.

Pak, Soyung. A Place to Grow. Truong, Marcelino, illus. 2002. (J). pap. (978-0-439-13017-2(4) , Levine, Arthur A. Bks.) Scholastic, Inc.

—A Place to Grow. Truong, Marcelino, illus. 2002. 32p. (J). (ps-5). pap. 16.95 (978-0-439-13015-8(8) , Levine, Arthur A. Bks.) Scholastic, Inc.

Palmer, Catherine. Fatal Harvest. l.t. ed. 2004. (Matthew 25 Ser.). 496p. (YA). 28.95 (978-0-7862-6259-5(1)) Thorndike Pr.

Pappas, Debra. Mom, Dad, Come Back Soon. Koeller, Carol, illus. 2002. 32p. (J). (ps-2). 14.95 (978-1-55798-799-0(8)); pap. 8.95 (978-1-55798-798-3(X)) American Psychological Assn. (Magination Pr.).

Paradise, Susan. My Mommy. 1998. (Illus.). 32p. (J). (ps-1). 15.95 (978-1-886910-73-7(1) , Lemniscaat) Boyds Mills Pr.

Paratore, Coleen Murtagh. The Wedding Planner's Daughter. 2005. (Wedding Planner's Daughter Ser.). 208p. (J). 15.95 (978-0-689-87340-9(9)) Simon & Schuster Children's Publishing.

Parker, Vicki Sue. The Get Well Soon... Balloon. Beebe, Susan, illus. 2005. 16p. (J). 15.00 (978-1-931117-35-7(7) , BALL) Lash & Assocs. Publishing/Training, Inc.

Parrish, Shelley Berlin. Sharing Grandma's Gift. Petosa-Sigel, Kristi, illus. 2000. 40p. (J). 18.00 (978-0-89716-936-3(0)) Peanut Butter Publishing.

Paterson, Katherine. Marvin One Too Many. Brown, Jane Clark, illus. 2002. (J). 23.98 (978-0-7587-6904-6(0)) Book Wholesalers, Inc.

—Preacher's Boy. 2001. 192p. (J). (gr. 5 up). pap. 5.99 (978-0-06-447233-3(7) , Harper Trophy) HarperCollins Pubs.

—Preacher's Boy. 1999. (Illus.). 176p. (J). (gr. 5-9). tchr. ed. 15.00 (978-0-395-83897-6(5) , Clarion Bks.) Houghton Mifflin Co. Trade & Reference Div.

—Preacher's Boy. 2001. (gr. 5-8). lib. bdg. 12.95 (978-0-613-34906-2(7)) Tandem Library Bks.

—El Signo del Crisantemo. 2003. (SPA., Illus.). 142p. (YA). (gr. 5-8). (978-84-348-6699-7(4) , SM30544) SM Ediciones ESP. *Dist:* Lectorum Pubns., Inc.

Patneaude, David. Deadly Drive. 184p. (J). 2007. pap. 6.95 (***978-0-8075-0845-9(4));*** 2005. (gr. 6-8). 15.95 (978-0-8075-0844-2(6)) Whitman, Albert & Co.

Paton, Alan. Cry, the Beloved Country. 2003. (gr. 7-12). lib. bdg. 23.45 (978-0-613-70981-1(0)) Tandem Library Bks.

Paulsen, Gary. The Glass Cafe: Or the Stripper & the State; How My Mother Started a War with the System That Made Us Kind of Rich & a Little Bit Famous. 2003. 112p. (gr. 5). 12.95 (978-0-385-32499-1(5)); lib. bdg. 14.99 (978-0-385-90121-5(6)) Random Hse. Children's Bks. (Lamb, Wendy).

Paxton, Tom. The Marvelous Toy. 2000. (Metro Reading Program Ser.). (J). (gr. k). 7.98 (978-1-58120-970-9(3)); 45.95 (978-1-58830-028-7(5)) Metropolitan Teaching & Learning Co.

Peck, Robert Newton. Cowboy Ghost. 1999. 208p. (YA). (gr. 7 up). 15.95 (978-0-06-028168-7(5) , Harper Trophy) HarperCollins Pubs.

—Cowboy Ghost. 1999. (YA). pap., stu. ed. 52.95 incl. audio (978-0-7887-3189-1(0) , 40924) Recorded Bks., LLC.

—Cowboy Ghost. 2000. (Illus.). (J). 11.60 (978-0-606-18684-1(0)) Tandem Library Bks.

Pelton, Mindy. When Dad's at Sea. Steele, Robert Gantt, illus. 2004. 32p. (J). (gr. 1-4). 15.95 (978-0-8075-6339-7(0)) Whitman, Albert & Co.

Perl, Erica S. Chicken Bedtime Is Really Early. Bates, George, illus. 2005. 32p. (J). (ps-1). 14.95 (978-0-8109-4926-3(1)) Abrams, Harry N. , Inc.

Perrault, Charles. Las Hadas. Trias, Margarida, tr. Dumas, Philippe, illus. 2002. (SPA.). 52p. (978-84-8470-058-6(5)) Corimbo, Editorial S.L.

Peters, Julie Anne. Define Normal. 2003. (Illus.). 208p. (J). (gr. 7-17). pap. 7.99 (978-0-316-73489-9(6)) Little, Brown Bks. for Young Readers.

—Define "Normal" l.t. ed. 2001. 250p. 22.95 (978-0-7862-3527-8(6)) Thorndike Pr.

Petersen, P. J. White Water. 1999. (978-0-606-16710-9(2)) Tandem Library Bks.

Pete's a Pizza. 2004. (Illus.). 32p. (J). (ps-2). 28.95 (978-1-59112-740-6(8)) Live Oak Media.

Pete's a Pizza. 2004. 24.95 incl. audio (978-1-55592-068-5(3)) Weston Woods Studios, Inc.

Pinkham, Mark Amaru. Love Me Later. 2005. 202p. 14.95 (978-1-932188-02-8(9)) Adventures Unlimited Pr.

Pinocchio: 6 Small Books. (gr. k-2). 23.00 (978-0-7635-8513-6(0)) Rigby Education.

Piper, Sophie. When You Were Very Small. Stephenson, Kristina, illus. 2006. 28p. (J). 7.95 (978-1-56148-515-4(2)) Good Bks.

Platt, Randall Beth. Honor Bright. 1998. (978-0-606-13486-6(7)) Tandem Library Bks.

Polacco, Patricia. Mommies Say Shhh! Polacco, Patricia, illus. 2005. (Illus.). 40p. (J). (ps-1). 16.99 (978-0-399-24341-7(0) , Philomel) Penguin Group (USA) Inc.

Porter-Gaylord, Laurel. I Love My Mommy Because... Wolff, Ashley, illus. 2004. 24p. (J). (ps). bds. 6.99 (978-0-525-47247-6(9) , Dutton Juvenile) Penguin Group (USA) Inc.

Powell. Tribute to Another Dead Rock Star. 2003. (gr. 7-12). lib. bdg. 14.10 (978-0-613-71884-4(4)) Tandem Library Bks.

Powell, Randy. Run If You Dare. 2001. 192p. (YA). (gr. 7 up). 16.00 (978-0-374-39981-8(6) , Farrar, Straus & Giroux (BYR)) Farrar, Straus & Giroux.

—Run If You Dare. l.t. ed. 2001. 216p. (J). 22.95 (978-0-7862-3716-6(3)) Thorndike Pr.

Powers, John. Seymour & the Big Red Rhino. Colavecchio, Alan, illus. 2005. 32p. (J). (ps-ps). 14.95 (978-1-929039-21-0(2)) Ambassador Bks., Inc.

Pressler, Mirjam. Malka. Murdoch, Brian, tr. from GER. 2003. 288p. (YA). (gr. 5-12). 18.99 (978-0-399-23984-7(7) , Philomel) Penguin Group (USA) Inc.

Prins, Piet. Stefan Derksen's Polar Adventure. 2004. (Illus.). 237p. (J). pap. (978-1-894666-67-1(4)) Inheritance Pubns.

Propp, Vera W. When the Soldiers Were Gone. 2001. (gr. 3-6). lib. bdg. 13.00 (978-0-613-36028-9(1)) Tandem Library Bks.

—When the Soldiers Were Gone: A Novel. 2006. 101p. (J). (gr. 4-8). reprint ed. 15.00 (978-1-4223-5310-3(9)) DIANE Publishing Co.

Pure. 2005. 245p. (YA). pap. 7.95 (978-1-896764-96-2(7)) Second Story Pr. CAN. *Dist:* Orca Bk. Pubs. USA.

Quattlebaum, Mary. Grover G. Graham & Me. 2003. 192p. (J). (gr. 3-7). pap. 5.99 (978-0-440-41918-1(2) , Yearling) Random Hse. Children's Bks.

Rabb, Margo. Cures for Heartbreak. 2007. 256p. (YA). (gr. 9). 15.99 (978-0-385-73402-8(6)); lib. bdg. 18.99 (978-0-385-90414-8(2)) Random Hse. Children's Bks. (Delacorte Bks. for Young Readers).

Random House Disney Staff. Best Dad in the Sea. 2003. (gr. k-3). lib. bdg. 11.80 (978-0-613-73685-5(0)) Tandem Library Bks.

—I Love You, Mama. 2002. (gr. k-3). lib. bdg. 11.80 (978-0-613-73727-2(X)) Tandem Library Bks.

Ransom, Candice F. The Christmas Dolls. Fain, Moira, illus. 1998. 32p. (J). (gr. k-3). 15.95 (978-0-8027-8659-3(6)); lib. bdg. 16.85 (978-0-8027-8661-6(8)) Walker & Co.

Ransom, Jeanie Franz. I Don't Want to Talk about It. Finney, Kathryn Kunz, illus. 2000. 28p. (J). (ps-3). (978-1-55798-664-1(9), 441-6649); pap. (978-1-55798-703-7(3), 441-7033) American Psychological Assn. (Magination Pr.).

—I Don't Want to Talk about It. 2000. (gr. k-3). lib. bdg. 17.60 (978-0-613-78683-6(1)) Tandem Library Bks.

Rau, Dana Meachen. In the Yard, Level A. 2001. (Early Reader Ser.). (Illus.). 24p. (J). (gr. k up). lib. bdg. 18.60 (978-0-7565-0116-7(4)) Compass Point Bks.

—My Red Rowboat, Level A. Sagasti, Miriam, illus. 2002. (Compass Point Early Reader Ser.). 24p. (J). (gr. k up). lib. bdg. 18.60 (978-0-7565-0174-7(1)) Compass Point Bks.

Rawlings, Marjorie Kinnan. The Yearling. 1999. (Illus.). 444p. (J). 17.90 (978-0-03-054778-2(4)) Holt, Rinehart & Winston.

—The Yearling. 2002. 480p. pap. 15.00 (978-0-7432-2525-0(2), Scribner) Simon & Schuster.

—The Yearling. 2001. (Aladdin Classics Ser.). 528p. mass mkt. 5.99 (978-0-689-84623-6(1), Aladdin) Simon & Schuster Children's Publishing.

—Yearling. 2001. (gr. 3-6). lib. bdg. 14.15 (978-0-613-90195-6(9)) Tandem Library Bks.

—The Yearling, Level 3. 2001. 64p. (C). pap. 9.00 (978-0-582-34439-6(5)) Pearson ESL.

Ray, Mary Lyn. The Basket Moon. Cooney, Barbara, illus. 1999. 32p. (J). (ps-3). 16.99 (978-0-316-73521-6(3)) Little Brown & Co.

Reichert, Amy. While Mama Had a Quick Little Chat. Boiger, Alexandra, illus. 2005. 40p. (J). 15.95 (978-0-689-85170-4(7), Atheneum) Simon & Schuster Children's Publishing.

Reiser, Lynn. You & Me, Baby. Gentieu, Penny, illus. 2006. 40p. (J). (gr. k-ps). lib. bdg. 17.99 (978-0-375-93401-8(4), Knopf Bks. for Young Readers) Random Hse. Children's Bks.

—You & Me, Baby. Gentieu, Penny, photos by. 2006. (Illus.). 40p. (J). (gr. k-ps). 15.95 (978-0-375-83401-1(X), Knopf Bks. for Young Readers) Random Hse. Children's Bks.

Remkiewicz, Frank, illus. Froggy Bakes a Cake. 2002. (Froggy Ser.). (J). 11.06 (978-0-7587-5541-4(4)) Book Wholesalers, Inc.

—Froggy Learns to Swim. 2002. (Froggy Ser.). (J). 13.19 (978-0-7587-2553-0(1)) Book Wholesalers, Inc.

—Let's Go, Froggy! 2002. (Froggy Ser.). (J). 13.19 (978-0-7587-2975-0(8)) Book Wholesalers, Inc.

Renninson, Lou. Frontalknutschen. pap. 17.95 (978-3-570-30008-4(0)) Bertelsman, Verlagsgruppe C. GmbH DEU. *Dist:* Distribooks, Inc.

Reynolds, Marilyn. Too Soon for Jeff. 2003. 192p. (J). (gr. 7-12). pap. 8.95 (978-0-930934-91-0(1)); 15.95 (978-0-930934-90-3(3)) Morning Glory Pr., Inc.

Richardson, Beverly J. Timbs. Lilly & Me. (Illus.). 2006. (ENG.). 36p. per. 12.95 (978-1-59800-459-5(X)); 2005. 29p. 26.99 (978-1-59800-121-1(3)) Outskirts Press, Inc.

Richmond, Marianne. I Love You So ... Richmond, Marianne, illus. 2004. (Illus.). 40p. (J). 15.95 (978-0-9753528-8-5(1)) Marianne Richmond Studios, Inc.

Rigby Education Staff. Cinderella: Jumbled Tumble. (gr. k-2). 26.00 (978-0-7635-2420-3(4)) Rigby Education.

—Pinocchio: Jumbled Tumble. (gr. k-2). 26.00 (978-0-7635-2419-7(0)) Rigby Education.

—William Tell. (gr. k-2). 21.00 (978-0-7635-2426-5(3)) Rigby Education.

Riley, Walter, Jr. Ozzie Owl: Believe, Achieve & Succeed! 2002. (gr. 7-12). lib. bdg. 24.00 (978-0-613-77912-8(6)) Tandem Library Bks.

Rinaldi, Ann. Mine Eyes Have Seen. 2002. (978-0-606-22271-6(5)) Tandem Library Bks.

—The Secret of Sarah Revere. 2003. (Great Episodes Ser.). 336p. (YA). pap. 6.95 (978-0-15-204684-2(4), Gulliver Bks.) Harcourt Children's Bks.

—The Staircase. 2002. (gr. 7-12). lib. bdg. 14.15 (978-0-613-59929-0(2)) Tandem Library Bks.

Ritter, John. Choosing up Sides. 2000. (gr. 5-8). lib. bdg. 14.15 (978-0-613-28444-8(5)) Tandem Library Bks.

Robberecht, Thierry. Angry Dragon. Goossens, Philippe, illus. 2004. 32p. (J). (gr. k-3). tchr. ed. 15.00 (978-0-618-47430-1(7), Clarion Bks.) Houghton Mifflin Co. Trade & Reference Div.

Roberts, Kristi. My Thirteenth Season. rev. ed. 2005. (Illus.). 160p. (J). 15.95 (978-0-8050-7495-6(3), Holt, Henry & Co. Bks. For Young Readers) Holt, Henry & Co.

Roberts, Mary. Once upon A Monday. Lipe, Barbara, illus. 2004. 48p. (J). per. 19.95 (978-0-9744412-0-7(1)) DinRo.

Robinson, Hilary. Freddie's Fears. Collins, Ross, illus. 2004. (Read-It! Readers Ser.). 32p. (C). (gr. k-3). 18.60 (978-1-4048-0056-4(5)) Picture Window Bks.

Rodowsky, Colby. The Turnabout Shop. 2000. (978-0-606-17885-3(6)) Tandem Library Bks.

Romano, Christy. Grace's Turn. 2006. 272p. (gr. 4-7). 15.99 (978-0-7868-4884-3(7)) Hyperion Pr.

Rosenberg, Liz. We Wanted You. 1999. (J). (978-0-7894-2600-0(5)) Dorling Kindersley Publishing, Inc.

Ross-Rodgers, Martha J. Awakenings. rev. ed. 1998. 120p. (YA). pap. 9.95 (978-0-9653197-0-6(9)) Jireh Pubs.

Rubalcaba, Jill. Place in the Sun. 1998. (Puffin Novel Ser.). 96p. (J). (gr. 3-7). pap. 4.99 (978-0-14-130123-5(6), Puffin) Penguin Group (USA) Inc.

Rue, Nancy N. The Invasion. 1998. (Christian Heritage Ser.). 192p. (J). (gr. 3-7). pap. (978-1-56179-541-3(0)) Focus on the Family Publishing.

—Invasion. 1998. (gr. 3-6). lib. bdg. 14.15 (978-0-613-85284-5(2)) Tandem Library Bks.

—Lily's in London: It's a God Thing! 2003. (gr. 3-6). lib. bdg. 13.00 (978-0-613-71688-8(4)) Tandem Library Bks.

—Sophie Flakes Out, Vol. 9. 2006. (Faithgirlz Ser.). (Illus.). 128p. (J). pap. 6.99 (978-0-310-71024-0(3)) Zonderkidz.

Ruiz-Flores, Lupe. Lupita's Papalote / el Papalote de Lupita. Ventura, Gabriela Baeza, tr. Rodriguez Howard, Pauline, illus. 32p. (J). (gr. k-2). 15.95 (978-1-55885-359-1(6), Piñata Books) Arte Publico Pr.

Rusackas, Francesca. I Love You All Day Long. Burris, Priscilla, illus. 32p. (J). (ps-k). 2002. 12.99 (978-0-06-050276-8(2)); 2004. reprint ed. pap. 6.99 (978-0-06-050278-2(9), Harper Trophy) HarperCollins Pubs.

Rushton, Rosie. What a Week to Break Free. (Illus.). 144p. (J). 7.95 (978-0-14-038762-9(5)) Penguin Bks., Ltd. GBR. *Dist:* Trafalgar Square Publishing.

—What a Week to Make a Stand. 128p. (J). 7.95 (978-0-14-130225-6(9)) Penguin Bks., Ltd. GBR. *Dist:* Trafalgar Square Publishing.

Russell, Barbara Timberlake. The Remembering Stone. Cotts, Claire B., illus. 2004. 32p. (J). 16.00 (978-0-374-36242-3(4), Farrar, Straus & Giroux (BYR)) Farrar, Straus & Giroux.

Russell, Laura Okmin. Mommy Has Cancer. Calvert-Weyant, Lynda, illus. 2003. (J). (978-0-7853-6335-4(1)) Publications International, Ltd.

Russo, Marisabina. When Mama Gets Home. Russo, Marisabina, illus. 1998. (Illus.). 24p. (J). (ps-3). 16.99 (978-0-688-14985-7(5)) HarperCollins Pubs.

Ryan, Susan Jane. Esmeralda & the Enchanted Pond. Cook, Sandra, illus. 2001. 48p. (J). (gr. 2-5). 14.95 (978-1-56164-236-6(3)) Pineapple Pr., Inc.

Ryan, Susan Jane & Cook, Sandra G. Esmeralda & the Enchanted Pond. 2001. (Illus.). 48p. (gr. 4-7). pap., act. bk. ed. 5.00 (978-1-56164-247-2(9)) Pineapple Pr., Inc.

Rylant, Cynthia. Henry & Mudge & the Snowman Plan. Stevenson, Sucie, illus. 2002. (Henry & Mudge Ser.). (J). 11.91 (978-0-7587-4471-5(4)) Book Wholesalers, Inc.

—Puppies & Piggies. Bates, Ivan, illus. 2008. 32p. (J). 16.00 (978-0-15-202321-8(6)) Harcourt Trade Pubs.

Saldana, Rene, Jr. The Jumping Tree. 2002. (Illus.). 192p. (YA). (gr. 5). pap. 5.99 (978-0-440-22881-3(6), Laurel Leaf) Random Hse. Children's Bks.

Salmansohn, Karen, et al. Crashed, Smashed, & Mashed: A Trip to Junkyard Heaven. 2004. (Alexandra Rambles on! Ser.). (Illus.). 32p. (J). (gr. 3-6). 14.95 (978-1-58246-034-5(5), Tricycle Pr.) Ten Speed Pr.

Sammy's Sneeze: Individual Title Six-Packs. (ps-2). 23.00 (978-0-7635-9013-0(4)) Rigby Education.

Santiago, Roberto. El Ultimo Sordo. 2003. (SPA., Illus.). 95p. (978-84-236-3428-6(0), ED7340) Edebé ESP. *Dist:* Lectorum Pubns., Inc.

Santucci, Barbara. Loon Summer. Shine, Andrea, illus. 2004. 32p. (J). (gr. k-3). 16.00 (978-0-8028-5182-6(7)) Eerdmans, William B. Publishing Co.

Sarda, Rosa. I Like Hiding (Me Gusta Esconderme) Randall, Bernice, tr. Curto, Rosa Maria, illus. (SPA & ENG.). (J). (ps-1). pap. 4.95 (978-1-930332-30-0(0), LC5516) Lectorum Pubns., Inc.

Savadier, Elivia. No Haircut Today! Savadier, Elivia, illus. rev. ed. 2005. (Illus.). 32p. (J). 15.95 (978-1-59643-046-4(X)) Roaring Brook Pr.

Sawyer, Louise. Mother's Storybook Signs, Vol. 2. 2004. (YA). spiral bd. 19.95 (978-0-9719842-8-8(X)) Martin & Brothers.

Schecter, Ellen. Swim Like a Fish. Cymerman, John E., illus. 1998. (Bank Street Reader Collection). 48p. (J). (ps-2). lib. bdg. 22.60 (978-0-8368-1767-6(2)) Stevens, Gareth Inc.

Schertle, Alice. Down the Road. Lewis, Earl, illus. 2000. 40p. (J). (gr. k-3). pap. 7.00 (978-0-15-202471-0(9), Harcourt Paperbacks) Harcourt Children's Bks.

—Down the Road. Lewis, E. B., illus. 2000. (J). (ps-17). lib. bdg. 14.15 (978-0-613-29935-0(3)) Tandem Library Bks.

—Down the Road. 2000. 12.80 (978-0-606-20324-1(9)) Tandem Library Bks.

Schick, Alice & Schick, Joel. The Penguin Child & the Albatross Child. 2007. (J). bds. 13.95 (***978-1-59692-228-0(1)***) MacAdam/Cage Publishing, Inc.

Schick, Eleanor. Mama. 2000. (Accelerated Reader Bks.). (Illus.). 32p. (J). (gr. k-3). 15.95 (978-0-7614-5060-3(2), Cavendish Children's Bks.) Cavendish, Marshall Corp.

Schlessinger, Laura. Growing up Is Hard. McFeeley, Daniel, illus. 2003. 40p. (J). (ps-2). pap. 5.99 (978-0-06-052623-8(8), Harper Trophy) HarperCollins Pubs.

—Why Do You Love Me? 2001. (gr. k-3). lib. bdg. 14.10 (978-0-613-36029-6(X)) Tandem Library Bks.

Schlessinger, Laura & Lambert, Martha. Why Do You Love Me? McFeeley, Daniel, illus. 2001. 40p. (J). (ps-2). pap. 6.99 (978-0-06-443654-0(3), Harper Trophy) HarperCollins Pubs.

Schlessinger, Laura & Lambert, Martha L. Why Do You Love Me? Meisel, Paul & McFeeley, Daniel, illus. 1999. 40p. (J). (ps-2). 15.95 (978-0-06-027866-3(8)) HarperCollins Pubs.

Schlessinger, Laura & McFeeley, Daniel. Growing up Is Hard. 2001. (Illus.). 40p. (J). (ps-2). 15.89 (978-0-06-029201-0(6)) HarperCollins Pubs.

Schmidtfranz, Theone. Rules Are for Safety. 2007. (ENG.). 16p. (J). per. 19.99 (***978-1-4141-0887-2(7)***) Pleasant Word.

Scholastic, Inc. Staff & Grimes, Nikki. Day with Daddy. Tadgell, Nicole, illus. 2004. (Just for You! Ser.). 32p. pap. 3.99 (978-0-439-56850-0(1), Teaching Resources) Scholastic, Inc.

Scholastic, Inc. Staff & Taylor-Butler, Christine. Mom Like No Other. Devard, Nancy, illus. 2004. (Just for You! Ser.). 32p. pap. 3.99 (978-0-439-56853-1(6), Teaching Resources) Scholastic, Inc.

Schotter, Roni. Missing Rabbit. Moore, Cyd, illus. 2002. 32p. (J). (gr. k-ps). 15.00 (978-0-618-03432-1(3), Clarion Bks.) Houghton Mifflin Co. Trade & Reference Div.

Schraff, Anne. The Greatest Heroes. 2000. 143p. (J). pap. (978-0-7891-5133-9(2)); (gr. 5-12). lib. bdg. 13.95 (978-0-7807-9271-5(8)) Perfection Learning Corp.

—Hear That Whistle Blow. 1999. (Passages Ser.). 119p. (J). (gr. 5-12). lib. bdg. 13.95 (978-0-7807-8970-8(9)) Perfection Learning Corp.

—The Terrible Orchid Sky. 2001. (PageTurner Adventure Ser.). 80p. (YA). per. 3.95 (978-1-56254-185-9(4), SP 1854) Saddleback Educational Publishing.

Schreiber, Mark. Starcrossed. 2007. 336p. (J). (gr. 9 up). pap. 8.95 (978-0-7387-1001-3(6), Flux) Llewellyn Pubns.

Schwartz, Amy. Some Babies. Schwartz, Amy, illus. 2000. (Illus.). 32p. (J). (ps-k). 16.99 (978-0-531-33287-0(X), Orchard Bks.) Scholastic, Inc.

Sederman, Marty & Epstein, Seymour. The Magic Box: When Parents Can't Be There to Tuck You In. Brooks, Karen Stormer, illus. 2003. 32p. (J). (ps-3). 14.95 (978-1-55798-807-2(2)); pap. 8.95 (978-1-55798-806-5(4)) American Psychological Assn. (Magination Pr.).

Senior, Gregg. Daddy in the Sky. 2004. (J). pap. 7.95 (978-0-533-14783-0(2)) Vantage Pr., Inc.

Seuling, Barbara. Robert & the Back-to-School Special. Brewer, Paul, illus. 2002. (Robert Bks.). 120p. (J). 15.95 (978-0-8126-2662-9(1)) Cricket Bks.

Shaw, Mary. Brady Brady & the Singing Tree, 11 vols. Temple, Chuck, illus. l.t. ed. 2004. 32p. (J). per. (978-0-9735557-3-8(4)) Brady Brady, Inc.

—Brady Brady & the Singing Tree. Temple, Chuck, illus. 2002. 32p. 4.95 (978-0-7737-6272-5(8)) Stoddart Kids CAN. *Dist:* Fitzhenry & Whiteside, Ltd.

Shollar, Leah Perl & Klineman, Harvey. The Key under the Pillow: A Story about Honoring Parents. 2004. (Illus.). 32p. (J). 9.95 (978-1-929628-16-2(1)) Hachai Publishing.

Shreve, Susan. Under the Watsons' Porch. 2006. 208p. (J). (gr. 5-8). reprint ed. pap. 4.99 (978-0-440-41969-3(7), Yearling) Random Hse. Children's Bks.

Shreve, Susan Richards. Under the Watsons' Porch. (J). 2006. 199p. (***978-1-4156-7020-0(X)***, Yearling); 2004. 208p. (gr. 5-8). 15.95 (978-0-375-82630-6(0), Knopf Bks. for Young Readers) Random Hse. Children's Bks.

Shusterman, Neal. Unwind. 2007. 352p. (YA). (gr. 8 up). 16.99 (***978-1-4169-1204-0(5)***, Simon & Schuster Children's Publishing) Simon & Schuster Children's Publishing.

Shyer, Marlene Fanta. The Rainbow Kite. 2002. 208p. (YA). (gr. 7-10). 15.95 (978-0-7614-5122-8(6)) Cavendish, Marshall Corp.

Simmons, Jane. Come along, Daisy! Simmons, Jane, illus. 2002. (Illus.). (J). 19.96 (978-0-7587-2263-8(X)) Book Wholesalers, Inc.

—Come along, Daisy! Simmons, Jane, illus. 1998. (Illus.). 32p. (J). (ps-2). 15.99 (978-0-316-79790-0(1)) Little Brown & Co.

—Come along, Daisy! Simmons, Jane, illus. 2001. (Daisy Bks.). (Illus.). 20p. (J). (ps-ps). 5.95 (978-0-316-79603-3(4)) Little, Brown Bks. for Young Readers.

Simmons, Michael. Pool Boy. 2005. 192p. (YA). (gr. 7). reprint ed. pap. 7.95 (978-0-385-73196-6(5), Delacorte Bks. for Young Readers) Random Hse. Children's Bks.

Simoneau, D. K. We're Having a Tuesday. Cornelius, Brad, illus. 2006. 32p. 16.95 (978-1-933302-13-3(5)) AC Pubns. Group LLC.

Sinykin, Sheri Cooper. A Matter of Time. 1998. (Accelerated Reader Bks.). 208p. (J). (gr. 5-9). lib. bdg. 14.95 (978-0-7614-5019-1(X), Cavendish Children's Bks.) Cavendish, Marshall Corp.

Sirof, Harriet. Real World. 2000. (gr. 7-12). lib. bdg. 21.05 (978-0-613-84103-0(4)) Tandem Library Bks.

Skirvan, Pamela. The Bad Day. Skirvan, Ted, 3rd, illus. 2003. 12p. (J). (gr. k-6). pap. 4.95 (978-0-9742943-0-8(6)) Skirvan, Pamela.

Sklansky, Amy E. My Daddy & Me. Hoyt, Ard, illus. 2005. 24p. (J). 3.50 (978-0-439-74046-3(0), Cartwheel Bks.) Scholastic, Inc.

Skrypuch, Marsha Forchuk. Best Gifts. 1999. (ps-2). lib. bdg. 15.25 (978-0-613-84763-6(6)) Tandem Library Bks.

Small, David. Eulalie & the Hopping Head. Small, David, illus. 2001. (Illus.). 32p. (J). 16.00 (978-0-374-32230-4(9), Farrar, Straus & Giroux (BYR)) Farrar, Straus & Giroux.

—Eulalie & the Hopping Head. (Illus.). (J). 2005. pap. 16.95 incl. audio (978-1-59112-216-6(3)); 2005. pap. 18.95 incl. audio compact disk (978-1-59112-509-9(X)); 2003. 25.95 incl. audio (978-1-59112-217-3(1)) Live Oak Media.

—Eulalie & the Hopping Head. Small, David, illus. 2003. (Illus.). (J). pap. 33.95 incl. audio (978-1-59112-218-0(X)) Live Oak Media.

—Eulalie & the Hopping Head. Small, David, illus. l.t. ed. 2001. (Illus.). 32p. (J). pap. 5.95 (978-0-374-42202-8(8), Sunburst) Farrar, Straus & Giroux.

Smalls, Irene. Kevin & His Dad. Hays, Michael, illus. 1999. 32p. (J). (gr. k-3). 16.99 (978-0-316-79899-0(1)) Little Brown & Co.

Smith, George Harmon. Bayou Boy. 2000. 196p. (gr. 7-12). pap. 11.95 (978-0-595-00755-4(4), Writer's Showcase Pr.) iUniverse, Inc.

Smith, Gordon. The Forest in the Hallway. 2006. 160p. (J). (gr. 5-9). 16.00 (978-0-618-68847-0(1), Clarion Bks.) Houghton Mifflin Co. Trade & Reference Div.

Smucker, Anna Egan. To Keep the South Manitou Light. 2004. (Great Lakes Books Ser.). (Illus.). 144p. 23.95 (978-0-8143-3235-1(8), Painted Turtle) Wayne State Univ. Pr.

Spears, Britney. Mother's Gift. 2003. (gr. 5-8). lib. bdg. 14.15 (978-0-613-72254-4(X)) Tandem Library Bks.

Spillebeen, Geert. Kipling's Choice. Edelstein, Terese, tr. from DUT. 2005. 160p. (YA). (gr. 7-9). 16.00 (978-0-618-43124-3(1)) Houghton Mifflin Co. Trade & Reference Div.

Spinelli, Eileen. When Mama Comes Home Tonight. Dyer, Jane, illus. 1998. 32p. (J). (ps-k). 14.00 (978-0-689-81065-7(2)) Simon & Schuster Children's Publishing.

Springer, Nancy. Outlaw Princess of Sherwood. 2003. (Tales of Rowan Hood Ser.: No. 3). 128p. (J). (gr. 3-6). 16.99 (978-0-399-23721-8(6), Philomel) Penguin Group (USA) Inc.

—Rowan Hood: Outlaw Girl of Sherwood Forest. 2002. (Tales of Rowan Hood Ser.: No. 1). (gr. 5-8). lib. bdg. 14.15 (978-0-613-53860-2(9)) Tandem Library Bks.

—Wild Boy: A Tale of Rowan Hood. 2004. (Tales of Rowan Hood Ser.: No. 4). 128p. (YA). (gr. 5-7). 16.99 (978-0-399-24015-7(2), Philomel) Penguin Group (USA) Inc.

St. Aubin, Bruno. Daddy's a Dinosaur. 1999. (ps-2). lib. bdg. 14.10 (978-0-613-24745-0(0)) Tandem Library Bks.

St. John, Patricia. The Secret at Pheasant Cottage. 2002. (Illus.). 144p. (YA). pap. 5.99 (978-0-8024-6579-5(X)) Moody Pubs.

Staenberg, Bonnie. Present for Mama Bear. 1999. (Hello Reader! Ser.). (978-0-606-16633-1(5)) Tandem Library Bks.

Stamper, Judith Bauer. Up, up, & Away! Ramsey, Marcy Dunn, illus. 2000. (Scholastic At-Home Phonics Reading Program Ser.: Vol. 55). 24p. (J). (978-0-590-68857-4(X)) Scholastic, Inc.

Standish, Burt L. Frank Merriwell's Son. Rudman, Jack, ed. 2003. (Frank Merriwell Ser.). pap. 9.95 (978-0-8373-9137-3(7)) Merriwell, Frank Inc.

Stanley, Diane. A Time Apart. 1999. (Illus.). 256p. (J). (gr. 5 up). 15.95 (978-0-688-16997-8(X)) HarperCollins Pubs.

Steig, William. Pedro Es una Pizza. (Buenas Noches Coleccion). (SPA., Illus.). (J). (ps-5). 7.95 (978-958-04-6034-3(5)) Norma S.A. COL. *Dist:* Distribuidora Norma, Inc., Lectorum Pubns., Inc.

—Pete's a Pizza. Steig, William, illus. 1998. (Illus.). 32p. (J). (ps up). lib. bdg. 16.89 (978-0-06-205158-5(X)); 62nd ed. 16.99 (978-0-06-205157-8(1)) HarperCollins Pubs.

—Pete's a Pizza. Steig, William, illus. (Illus.). pap. 18.95 incl. audio compact disk (978-1-59112-739-0(4)); pap. incl. audio compact disk (978-1-59112-741-3(6)) Live Oak Media.

Sternthal, Sherry. How Do You Get to Heaven? Thornton-Haas, Barbara, illus. 2000. 36p. (J). (gr. 3-9). pap. 11.95 (978-0-9700375-0-3(3)) Schlifer, Sherry.

Stewart, Kymberly M. Play It Again, Rachel. 2003. 74p. (J). pap. 10.95 (978-0-9740653-0-4(7)) Neema's Children Literature Assn., Inc.

Stewart, Paul & Riddell, Chris. Blobheads Go Boing! l.t. ed. 2005. (J). pap. (978-1-4056-6002-0(3)) BBC Audio.

Stoehr, Shelley. Crosses. 2003. (gr. 7-12). lib. bdg. 23.40 (978-0-613-86660-6(6)) Tandem Library Bks.

—Crosses. 2003. 161p. (YA). pap. 13.95 (978-0-595-26952-5(4), Backinprint.com) iUniverse, Inc.

Stolls, Amy. Palms to the Ground. 2005. 256p. (YA). 17.00 (978-0-374-35731-3(5), Farrar, Straus & Giroux (BYR)) Farrar, Straus & Giroux.

The Story of William Tell: Individual Title Six-Packs. (gr. 3 up). 35.00 (978-0-7635-9673-6(6)) Rigby Education.

Stutson, Caroline. Mama Loves You. Segal, John, illus. 2005. 32p. (J). pap. 6.99 (978-0-439-57842-4(6)) Scholastic, Inc.

Sullivan, Therese M. & Bitner, Pamela. A Gift from Valentine. 2007. 24p. (J). per. 12.95 (***978-1-58939-981-5(1)***) Virtualbookworm.com Publishing, Inc.

Sumpolec, Sarah Anne. The Passage. 2005. (Becoming Beka Ser.). 256p. (J). pap. 12.99 (978-0-8024-6453-8(X)) Moody Pubs.

Sundberg, Angela M., et al. The Pottamus Family & the Unhappy Pottamus. Sundberg, Angela M. et al, illus. 2007. (J). pap. 16.00 (***978-0-8059-7478-2(4)***) Dorrance Publishing Co., Inc.

Susi, Geraldine Lee. My Father, My Companion: Life at the Hollow, Chief Justice John Marshall's Boyhood Home in Virginia. 2001. (Illus.). 96p. (J). (gr. 4-9). pap. 10.95 (978-1-889324-22-7(1)) EPM Pubns., Inc.

Swanson, Julie A. Going for the Record. 2004. 223p. (J). pap. 8.00 (978-0-8028-5273-1(4)) Eerdmans, William B. Publishing Co.

Sweeney, Joyce. Spirit Window. 1999. (978-0-606-16717-8(X)) Tandem Library Bks.

—Waiting for June. 2003. 144p. (YA). 15.95 (978-0-7614-5138-9(2)) Cavendish, Marshall Corp.

Tabor, Nancy. Bottles Break. 1999. (Illus.). 32p. (J). (ps-3). 15.95 (978-0-88106-317-2(7)); pap. 6.95 (978-0-88106-318-9(5)) Charlesbridge Publishing, Inc.

Tada, Joni Eareckson. I'll Be with You Always. Nelson, Craig, illus. 2004. 32p. (gr. 8-12). 14.99 (978-1-58134-000-6(1)) Crossway Bks.

Tada, Joni Eareckson & Jensen, Steve. Tell Me the Promises. Dicanni, Ron, illus. 2004. 48p. (gr. 5-7). 17.99 (978-0-89107-904-0(1)) Crossway Bks.

Tafuri, Nancy. I Love You, Little One. 2000. (Illus.). 15p. (J). (ps-k). bds. 7.99 (978-0-439-13746-1(2), Scholastic Reference) Scholastic, Inc.

—You Are Special, Little One. 2005. 15p. (J). bds. 7.99 (978-0-439-68613-6(X)) Scholastic, Inc.

—You Are Special, Little One. Tafuri, Nancy, illus. 2003. (Illus.). 32p. (J). pap. 16.95 (978-0-439-39879-4(7)) Scholastic, Inc.

Tamburri, Pasqualino. Alex & the Trampoline. 2007. 32p. (J). 14.95 (***978-1-60227-473-0(8)***) Above the Clouds Publishing.

Taylor, Ann & HarperCollins Staff. Baby Dance. Van Heerden, Marjorie, illus. 1999. (Growing Tree Ser.). 16p. (J). (ps up). 6.99 (978-0-694-01206-0(8) , Harper Festival) HarperCollins Pubs.

Taylor, Kim. Cissy Funk. 2001. 224p. (J). (gr. 5 up). 15.95 (978-0-06-029041-2(2)); 15.89 (978-0-06-029042-9(0)) HarperCollins Pubs.

Tebbetts, Christopher. Viking Saga Three: Land of the Dead. 2003. (gr. 5-8). lib. bdg. 14.15 (978-0-613-67588-8(6)) Tandem Library Bks.

Thesman, Jean. Singer. l.t. ed. 2005. 384p. (YA). (gr. 8-12). 22.95 (978-0-7862-7919-7(2) , Large Print Pr.) Thorndike Pr.

Thiel, Annie. Cosmos' Mom & Dad Are Moving Apart. 2006. (Playdate Kids Ser.). (Illus.). 32p. 14.95 (978-1-933721-04-0(9)) Playdate Kids Publishing.

Thiesing, Lisa. Me & You: A Mother-Daugher Album. 2000. (ps-2). lib. bdg. 13.00 (978-0-613-31466-4(2)) Tandem Library Bks.

Thomas, Dalandra. Noonimals. 2006. (J). pap. 16.95 (***978-90-78473-02-2(9)***) Nooni Publishing.

Thompson, Lauren. A Christmas Gift for Mama. Burke, Jim, illus. 2003. (J). 48p. pap. 16.95 (978-0-590-30725-3(8)); pap. 16.95 (978-0-590-30726-0(6)) Scholastic, Inc.

Thompson, Vivian L. Neat! Said Jeremy. 2003. 33p. (J). pap. 8.95 (978-0-7414-1579-0(8)) Infinity Publishing.

Tidd, Louise Vitellaro. Let Me Help! Handelman, Dorothy, photos by. 1999. (Real Kids Readers Ser.). (Illus.). 32p. (gr. k-2). lib. bdg. 18.90 (978-0-7613-2067-8(9) , Millbrook Pr.) Lerner Publishing Group.

—Let Me Help! 1999. (J). (978-0-606-19157-9(7)); lib. bdg. 11.80 (978-0-613-18159-4(X)) Tandem Library Bks.

Tidd, Louise Vitellaro & Handelman, Dorothy. Let Me Help! 1999. (Real Kids Readers Ser.: 2). (Illus.). 32p. (J). (gr. k-2). pap. 4.99 (978-0-7613-2092-0(X) , Millbrook Pr.) Lerner Publishing Group.

Tierno, Susan F. I Did My Best. Ramirez, Michael, illus. 1998. (Think-Kids Book Collection). 16p. (J). (gr. 1-4). pap. 2.95 (978-1-58237-011-8(7)) Creative Thinkers, Inc.

—Lo Hice Bien! Alvarado, Ana María, tr. Ramirez, Michael, illus. 2000. (Think-Kids Book Collection).Tr. of I Did My Best Ser.. (SPA.). 16p. (J). pap. 2.95 (978-1-58237-040-8(0)) Creative Thinkers, Inc.

—What's That Mom? What's That? Ramirez, Michael, illus. 1998. (Think-Kids Book Collection). 16p. (J). (gr. 1-4). pap. 2.95 (978-1-58237-010-1(9)) Creative Thinkers, Inc.

Time Slime. 2003. 156p. (YA). (gr. 5-12). pap. 7.95 (978-0-9702176-3-9(3) , 0004) Night Howl Productions.

Tocher, Timothy. Long Shot. 2001. 137p. (J). (978-0-88166-395-2(6)) Meadowbrook Pr.

Todd, John. The Zoo Savers. 2007. 140p. (J). per. (***978-0-9779680-8-4(1)***) Global Authors Pubns.

Tondreau-Levert, Louise. Parents Do the Weirdest Things! Roge, illus. 2005. (Read-It! Readers Ser.). 32p. (J). (gr. k-3). 18.60 (978-1-4048-1031-0(5)) Picture Window Bks.

Townley, Roderick. Sky. 2004. (Illus.). 272p. (J). 16.95 (978-0-689-85712-6(8) , Atheneum/Richard Jackson Bks.) Simon & Schuster Children's Publishing.

Treiber, Jutta & Antoni, Birgit. Porque Siempre Va a Ser Asi. 2004. (SPA., Illus.). 28p. (J). 18.99 (978-84-89804-54-8(0)) Loguez Ediciones ESP. *Dist:* Lectorum Pubns., Inc.

Troncale, Steven L. Yankee Boys of War. 2003. (gr. 7-12). lib. bdg. 30.35 (978-0-613-87921-7(X)) Tandem Library Bks.

Ungerer, Tomi. The Mellops Go Spelunking. Ungerer, Tomi, illus. 1998. (Illus.). 32p. (J). (gr. k-4). pap. 5.95 (978-1-57098-228-6(7)) Rinehart, Roberts Pubs.

—No Kiss for Mother. 1998. (Illus.). 40p. (J). (ps-3). pap. 5.95 (978-1-57098-208-8(2)) Rinehart, Roberts Pubs.

Vail, Rachel. The (Almost) Perfect Mother's Day. Bjorkman, Steve, illus. 2003. (Mama Rex & T Ser.: No. 8). 32p. (J). pap. 14.95 (978-0-439-40718-2(4) , Orchard Bks.) Scholastic, Inc.

—Do-Over. 2005. 176p. (J). (gr. 7 up). pap. 7.99 (978-0-06-058749-9(0) , Harper Trophy) HarperCollins Pubs.

—Homework Trouble. Bjorkman, Steve, illus. 2002. (Mama Rex & T Ser.). 32p. (J). (gr. k-2). pap. 14.95 (978-0-439-40628-4(5)); pap. 4.99 (978-0-439-33281-1(8)) Scholastic, Inc. (Orchard Bks.).

—The Horrible Play Date. Bjorkman, Steve, illus. 2002. (Mama Rex & T Ser.). 32p. (J). pap. 14.95 (978-0-439-40627-7(7)); pap. 4.99 (978-0-439-28335-9(3)) Scholastic, Inc. (Orchard Bks.).

—Mama Rex & T: Lose a Waffle. Bjorkman, Steve, illus. 2000. (Mama Rex & T Ser.). (J). (978-0-439-19918-6(2)) Scholastic, Inc.

—Mama Rex & T: Run Out of Tape. Bjorkman, Steve, illus. 2001. (Mama Rex & T Ser.). (J). (978-0-439-19920-9(4)) Scholastic, Inc.

—Please, Please, Please. (Friendship Ring Ser.: No. 2). 240p. (J). (gr. 4-8). 1999. pap. 3.99 (978-0-439-08762-9(7)); 1998. pap. 14.95 (978-0-590-00327-8(5)); 1998. pap. 4.99 (978-0-590-37452-1(4)) Scholastic, Inc.

Valentine, Johnny. The Daddy Machine. Schmidt, Lynette, illus. 2nd ed. 2004. 32p. (Orig.). pap. 10.95 (978-1-55583-846-1(4)) Alyson Pubns.

—One Dad, Two Dads, Brown Dad, Blue Dads. Sarecky, Melody, illus. 2004. 32p. (J). pap. 10.95 (978-1-55583-848-5(0)) Alyson Pubns.

Valriu, Caterina. Thumbelina: A Bilingual Book. Max, illus. 2004. Tr. of Pulgarcita. (ENG & SPA.). 32p. (J). (gr. k-3). pap. 6.95 (978-0-8118-3928-0(1)) Chronicle Bks. LLC.

—Thumbelina/Pulgarcita: A Bilingual Book. Max, illus. 2004. Tr. of Pulgarcita. (ENG & SPA.). 32p. (J). (gr. k-3). 13.95 (978-0-8118-3927-3(3)) Chronicle Bks. LLC.

Van Fleet, Mara. Mama Loves Me. Gévry, Claudine, illus. 2005. 12p. (J). bds. 12.99 (978-0-7944-0762-9(5)) Reader's Digest Assn., Inc., The.

Van Laan, Nancy. Tickle Tum! Pons, Bernadette, illus. 2005. (Stories to Go! Ser.). 32p. (J). 4.99 (978-1-4169-0836-4(6) , Aladdin) Simon & Schuster Children's Publishing.

Van Meter, Jen. Hopeless Savages, 3 vols., Vol. 1. 2nd ed. 2003. (Illus.). 136p. (YA). (gr. 7 up). pap. 11.95 (978-1-929998-75-3(9)) Oni Pr., Inc.

Van Steenwyk, Elizabeth. Prairie Christmas. Himler, Ronald, illus. 2006. 32p. (J). 17.00 (978-0-8028-5280-9(7) , Eerdmans Bks For Young Readers) Eerdmans, William B. Publishing Co.

Vander Zee, Ruth. Mississippi Morning. Cooper, Floyd, illus. 2004. 32p. (J). 16.00 (978-0-8028-5211-3(4)) Eerdmans, William B. Publishing Co.

Vigna, Judith. When Eric's Mom Fought Cancer. ed. 2004. (J). (gr. 1-5). spiral bd. (978-0-616-03063-9(0)) Canadian National Institute for the Blind/Institut National Canadien pour les Aveugles.

Voigt, Cynthia. A Solitary Blue. 2003. (Tillerman Cycle Ser.: Bk. 3). 256p. (J). pap. 6.99 (978-0-689-86360-8(8) , Aladdin); (YA). mass mkt. 6.99 (978-0-689-86434-6(5) , Simon Pulse) Simon & Schuster Children's Publishing.

—When She Hollers. 2003. 192p. (J). (gr. 7 up). pap. 5.99 (978-0-590-46715-5(8) , Scholastic Paperbacks) Scholastic, Inc.

Waddell, Martin. Las Lechucitas. Benson, Patrick, illus. (SPA.). 28p. (J). (gr. k-3). 14.95 (978-0-88272-137-8(2)) Santillana USA Publishing Co., Inc.

—Owl Babies. 2002. (Illus.). (J). 13.83 (978-1-4046-3008-6(2)) Book Wholesalers, Inc.

—Owl Babies. 2003. (Illus.). 22p. (J). 12.99 (978-0-7636-2157-5(9)) Candlewick Pr.

—Owl Babies. Benson, Patrick, illus. 32p. (J). (ps-2). 2002. pap. 5.99 (978-0-7636-1710-3(5)); 2000. pap. 19.99 (978-0-7636-1283-2(9)) Candlewick Pr.

—Owl Babies. (Illus.). 25p. (J). (CHI, ENG, URD, TUR & VIE.). (978-1-85430-343-1(0) , 93441); (ENG, VIE, URD, TUR & CHI., (978-1-85430-348-6(1) , 93442) Magi Pubns.

—Owl Babies. 2002. (ps-2). lib. bdg. 14.15 (978-0-613-74780-6(1)) Tandem Library Bks.

—Snow Bears. Fox-Davies, Sarah, illus. 2002. 32p. (J). (ps-1). 14.99 (978-0-7636-1906-0(X)) Candlewick Pr.

Wahl, Jan. Christmas Present. McCurdy, Michael, illus. 1999. 64p. (gr. 5-9). 18.00 (978-1-56846-165-6(8) , Creative Editions) Creative Co., The.

Waldorf, Heather. Fighting the Current. Lee, Karen, ed. 2004. 224p. (J). pap. 9.95 (978-1-894222-92-1(X)) Lobster Pr. CAN. *Dist:* Univ. of Toronto Pr.

Wallace, Bill. Skinny-Dipping at Monster Lake. (Illus.). 224p. (J). 2004. pap. 4.99 (978-0-689-85151-3(0) , Aladdin); 2003. 16.95 (978-0-689-85150-6(2)) Simon & Schuster Children's Publishing.

Wallin, Luke. The Redneck Poacher's Son. 2001. 260p. (YA). pap. 17.95 (978-0-595-19244-1(0)) iUniverse, Inc.

Walter, Lee. The Gifts That Are Forgotten. 2006. 60p. pap. 12.95 (978-1-4137-9070-2(4)) PublishAmerica, Inc.

Walter, Mildred Pitts. Ray & the Best Family Reunion Ever. 2001. (Illus.). 128p. (J). (ps-2). 15.95 (978-0-06-623624-7(X) , Amistad) HarperCollins Pubs.

Walvoord, Linda. Razzamadaddy. Yoshikawa, Sachiko, tr. Yoshikawa, Sachiko, illus. 2004. 32p. (J). 14.95 (978-0-7614-5158-7(7)) Cavendish, Marshall Corp.

Ward, Jennifer. Because You Are My Baby. Long, Sylvia, illus. 2007. 32p. 15.95 (***978-0-87358-911-6(4)*** , Rising Moon Bks. for Young Readers) Northland Publishing.

Ward, Ruth. The Adventures of Bloor Bone. 2005. (J). lib. bdg. 18.00 (978-1-59094-105-8(5)) Jawbone Publishing Corp.

Ward, Sally. Dorothy's Visit: Chilomwe Version. Nkhoma, Wilson, tr. 1999. (Cambridge Reading Routes Ser.). (Illus.). 16p. pap. 3.70 (978-0-521-66853-8(0)) Cambridge Univ. Pr.

Wardlaw, Lee. 101 Ways to Bug Your Parents. (gr. k-3). 2005. 208p. pap. 5.99 (978-0-14-240340-2(7) , Puffin); 2002. 160p. (J). pap. (978-0-14-038739-1(0) , Putnam Juvenile) Penguin Group (USA) Inc.

—101 Ways to Bug Your Parents. 1998. (J). (978-0-606-13076-9(4)) Tandem Library Bks.

Ware, Jim. Crazy Jacob. 2000. (Kidwitness Tales Ser.). (Illus.). 128p. (J). (gr. 3-7). pap. 5.99 (978-1-56179-885-8(1)) Bethany Hse. Pubs.

Warnes, Tim. Mommy Mine. Chapman, Jane, illus. 2005. 32p. (J). (ps-k). 15.99 (978-0-06-058947-9(7)); lib. bdg. 16.89 (978-0-06-058948-6(5)) HarperCollins Pubs.

Watts, Irene N. When the Bough Breaks. 2007. 152p. (J). (gr. 4-7). pap. 9.95 (***978-0-88776-821-7(0)***) Tundra Bks., Inc./Livres Toundra, Inc. CAN. *Dist:* Random Hse., Inc.

Watts, Leander. Wild Ride to Heaven. 2003. 176p. (YA). (gr. 5-9). tchr. ed. 16.00 (978-0-618-26805-4(7)) Houghton Mifflin Co. Trade & Reference Div.

Waugh, Sylvia. Space Race. 2001. 256p. (gr. 5 up). 5.50 (978-0-440-41714-9(7) , Yearling) Random Hse. Children's Bks.

—Space Race. 2001. (gr. 5-8). lib. bdg. 13.00 (978-0-613-88327-6(6)) Tandem Library Bks.

—Space Race. l.t. ed. 2001. 300p. (J). 20.95 (978-0-7862-3606-0(X)) Thorndike Pr.

Wax, Wendy. Fairly Odd Funnies. Style Guide Staff, illus. 2005. (Fairly OddParents Ser.). 48p. (J). pap. 3.99 (978-0-689-87599-1(1) , Simon Spotlight) Simon & Schuster Children's Publishing.

Weaver, Will. Hard Ball: A Billy Baggs Novel. l.t. ed. 2000. (Illus.). 270p. (YA). (gr. 8-12). 20.95 (978-0-7862-2752-5(4)) Thorndike Pr.

Webb, Terry. Manning the Light. 2003. 148p. (J). pap. 12.99 (978-1-57921-669-6(2)) Pleasant Word.

Weeks, Sarah. Guy Time. 2001. 176p. (J). (gr. 3-7). pap. 5.99 (978-0-06-440783-0(7) , Harper Trophy) HarperCollins Pubs.

—Guy Wire. 2002. 144p. (J). (gr. 3-7). 16.99 (978-0-06-029492-2(2) , Geringer, Laura Book) HarperCollins Pubs.

—My Guy. 192p. (J). (gr. 3-7). 2003. pap. 6.99 (978-0-06-440781-6(0)); 2001. (Illus.). 14.89 (978-0-06-028370-4(X)) HarperCollins Pubs. (Geringer, Laura Book).

—My Guy. 2003. (gr. 3-6). lib. bdg. 14.15 (978-0-613-67213-9(5)) Tandem Library Bks.

—Regular Guy. 1999. (Illus.). 128p. (J). (gr. 3-7). 14.95 (978-0-06-028367-4(X) , Geringer, Laura Book) HarperCollins Pubs.

—So B. It. 2004. 256p. (J). (gr. 5 up). 16.99 (978-0-06-623622-3(3)); lib. bdg. 16.89 (978-0-06-623623-0(1)) HarperCollins Pubs. (Geringer, Laura Book).

—Without You. Duranceau, Suzanne, illus. 40p. (J). 2007. pap. 6.99 (978-0-06-113998-7(X) , Harper Trophy); 2003. 16.99 incl. audio compact disk (978-0-06-027816-8(1) , Geringer, Laura Book) HarperCollins Pubs.

Weigel, Jeff. Atomic Ace: (He's Just My Dad) Weigel, Jeff, illus. 2004. (Illus.). 32p. (J). (gr. 1-4). pap. 6.95 (978-0-8075-3217-1(7)) Whitman, Albert & Co.

Wells, Rosemary. The Bear Went over the Mountain. Wells, Rosemary, illus. 2007. (Bruno & Boots Book Ser.). (Illus.). 18p. (J). bds. 5.99 (978-0-590-02910-0(X)) Scholastic, Inc.

—Only You. 2003. (SPA., Illus.). 24p. (J). (ps). 14.99 (978-0-670-03634-9(X) , Viking Juvenile) Penguin Group (USA) Inc.

—Only You (Solo Tu) Wells, Rosemary, illus. 2004. (SPA., Illus.). 32p. (J). (ps-k). 14.99 (978-0-670-03692-9(7) , Viking Juvenile) Penguin Group (USA) Inc.

Weninger, Brigitte. A Child Is a Child. Tharlet, Eve, illus. 2004. 32p. (J). (ps-3). 14.99 (978-0-698-40006-1(2) , Minedition) Penguin Group (USA) Inc.

Westerhout, Lynn. Business in Bangkok. McLeod, Chum, illus. 2005. 24p. (J). (ps-3). 11.95 (978-1-896764-48-1(7)) Second Story Pr. CAN. *Dist:* Orca Bk. Pubs. USA.

Weyn, Suzanne. Spa-di-da! A Spa Day with Mom. Mingus, Cathi, illus. 2006. 16p. (J). 9.99 (978-1-4169-0974-3(5) , Little Simon) Simon & Schuster Children's Publishing.

Whelan, Gloria. Jam & Jelly by Holly & Nellie. van Frankenhuyzen, Gijsbert, illus. 2002. 48p. (J). (ps-5). 17.95 (978-1-58536-109-0(7)) Sleeping Bear Pr.

—A Time to Keep Silent. 2004. 144p. (J). pap. 8.00 (978-0-8028-5255-7(6)) Eerdmans, William B. Publishing Co.

—Time to Keep Silent. 2003. (gr. 5-8). lib. bdg. 16.45 (978-0-613-75511-5(1)) Tandem Library Bks.

White, James C. David Goes Fishing. Chapin, Patrick, illus. 2003. 32p. (J). 6.95 (978-0-9747752-0-3(7)) White, James C.

White, Ruth. Belle Prater's Boy. l.t. ed. 2000. (Illus.). 221p. (YA). (gr. 4-7). 21.95 (978-0-7862-2885-0(7)) Thorndike Pr.

Whybrow, Ian. Badness for Beginners: A Little Wolf & Smellybreff Adventure. 2005. (Illus.). 32p. (J). (ps-ps). 16.95 (978-1-57505-861-0(8) , Carolrhoda Bks.) Lerner Publishing Group.

—Malicia para Principiantes: Una Aventura de Lobito y Apestosito. 2005. (Libros Ilustrados (Picture Bks.)). (SPA., Illus.). 32p. (gr. k-2). 16.95 (978-0-8225-3211-8(5) , Ediciones Lerner) Lerner Publishing Group.

Wicke, Ed. Nicklus. Warne, Tom, illus. 2004. 192p. (J). per. (978-0-9677652-4-2(2) , BlacknBlue Pr. UK) Blacknblue Pr.

Wild, Margaret. Kiss, Kiss! Strevens-Marzo, Bridget, illus. 2003. 24p. (J). 12.95 (978-0-689-86279-3(2)) Simon & Schuster Children's Publishing.

—Piglet & Mama. King, Stephen Michael, illus. 2005. 32p. (J). (ps-1). 14.95 (978-0-8109-5869-2(4)) Abrams, Harry N., Inc.

Wilkins, Rose. So Super-Starry. 2004. 208p. (J). pap. (978-0-330-42086-0(0) , Macmillan Children's Bks.) Pan Macmillan.

Willey, Margaret. Finding David Dolores. 2001. (gr. 7-12). lib. bdg. 23.40 (978-0-613-85102-2(1)) Tandem Library Bks.

—Finding David Dolores. 2001. 164p. (YA). (gr. 7-12). pap. 13.95 (978-0-595-19641-8(1)) iUniverse, Inc.

William Tell: 6 Small Books. (gr. k-2). 23.00 (978-0-7635-8506-8(8)) Rigby Education.

Williams, Carol Lynch. A Mother to Embarrass Me. 2003. 144p. (J). (gr. 3-7). pap. 4.99 (978-0-440-41810-8(0) , Yearling) Random Hse. Children's Bks.

—The True Colors of Caitlynne Jackson. 1998. (J). (978-0-606-13873-4(0)) Tandem Library Bks.

Williams, Laura E. Up a Creek. l.t. ed. 2001. 121p. (J). 22.95 (978-0-7862-3728-9(7)) Thorndike Pr.

Williams, Mark London. Ancient Fire. 2004. (Danger Boy Ser.: No. 1). (Illus.). 224p. (J). (gr. 4-8). 12.99 (978-0-7636-2152-0(8)) Candlewick Pr.

Willner-Pardo, Gina. My Mom & Other Mysteries of the Universe. 2004. 176p. (YA). (gr. 4-6). tchr. ed. 15.00 (978-0-618-43020-8(2) , Clarion Bks.) Houghton Mifflin Co. Trade & Reference Div.

Wilson, Jacqueline. The Illustrated Mum. 2005. 288p. (J). (gr. 5). lib. bdg. 17.99 (978-0-385-90263-2(8) , Delacorte Bks. for Young Readers) Random Hse. Children's Bks.

—The Story of Tracy Beaker. Sharratt, Nick, illus. l.t. ed. 1998. 200p. (J). pap. 16.95 (978-0-7540-6021-5(7) , Galaxy Children's Large Print) BBC Audiobooks America.

—The Story of Tracy Beaker. 2002. (gr. 3-6). lib. bdg. 13.00 (978-0-613-58804-1(5)) Tandem Library Bks.

Wilson, Karma. Mama Always Comes Home. Dyer, Brooke, illus. 2005. 32p. (J). (ps-1). 15.99 (978-0-06-057505-2(0)); lib. bdg. 16.89 (978-0-06-057506-9(9)) HarperCollins Pubs.

Winston, Sherri. Acting: A Novel. 2004. 256p. (YA). 15.95 (978-0-7614-5173-0(0)) Cavendish, Marshall Corp.

Wolcott, Joan. When Are Mom & Dad Coming Home? Wolcott, Joan, illus. 1999. (Illus.). v, 26p. (J). (gr. k-3). 15.95 (978-0-9655317-1-9(6)) Small Rain Pr.

Wolf, Erica. I Love You Just the Same. Wolf, Erica, illus. rev. ed. 2003. (Illus.). 32p. (J). 16.95 (978-0-8050-7128-3(8) , Holt, Henry & Co. Bks. For Young Readers) Holt, Henry & Co.

Wolf, Jake. Daddy, Could I Have an Elephant? 1998. (Picture Puffin Ser.). (J). (978-0-606-13303-6(8)) Tandem Library Bks.

Wolfert, Adrienne. Making Tracks. Bell, Justin, illus. 2000. (Adventures in America Ser.). 90p. (J). (gr. 4-7). lib. bdg. 14.95 (978-1-893110-16-8(8)) Silver Moon Pr.

Woods, Ron. The Hero. 2003. 224p. (J). (gr. 4-7). pap. 5.50 (978-0-440-22978-0(2) , Yearling) Random Hse. Children's Bks.

Woodson, Jacqueline. Coming on Home Soon. Lewis, Earl, illus. 2004. 32p. (J). (ps). 16.99 (978-0-399-23748-5(8) , Putnam Juvenile) Penguin Group (USA) Inc.

—Visiting Day. Ransome, James E., illus. 2002. 32p. (J). (ps-3). pap. 15.95 (978-0-590-40005-3(3) , Scholastic Pr.) Scholastic, Inc.

Woodson, Jacqueline & Ransome, James E. Visiting Day. 2001. (Illus.). (J). pap. (978-0-590-55262-2(7)) Scholastic, Inc.

Wright, Betty Ren. Too Many Secrets. 2002. 128p. (J). (gr. 3-7). pap. 4.99 (978-0-439-32665-0(6) , Scholastic Paperbacks) Scholastic, Inc.

Yee, Lisa. So Totally Emily Ebers. 2008. 304p. (J). 5.99 (978-0-439-83848-1(7) , Levine, Arthur A. Bks.) Scholastic, Inc.

—So Totally Emily Embers. 2007. 304p. (J). (gr. 4-7). pap. 16.99 (978-0-439-83847-4(9) , Levine, Arthur A. Bks.) Scholastic, Inc.

Ylvisaker, Anne. Dear Papa. 2002. (Illus.). 192p. (J). (gr. 4-8). 15.99 (978-0-7636-1618-2(4)) Candlewick Pr.

Yolen, Jane. Baby Bear's Chairs. Sweet, Melissa, illus. 2005. 40p. (J). (ps). 16.00 (978-0-15-205114-3(7)) Harcourt Children's Bks.

Yoo, Paula. Good Enough. 2008. 336p. (J). 16.99 (***978-0-06-079085-1(7)***); lib. bdg. 17.89 (***978-0-06-079089-9(X)***) HarperCollins Pubs. (HarperTeen).

Yoo, Paula & Dereske, Jo. Good Enough. 2008. 272p. mass mkt. 6.99 (***978-0-06-079086-8(5)*** , HarperTeen) HarperCollins Pubs.

Young, James. My Bunny. 1999. (Read with Me Paperback Ser.). (Illus.). 32p. (J). (ps-1). pap. 3.25 (978-0-590-18375-8(3)) Scholastic, Inc.

Zagwyn, Deborah Turney. The Pumpkin Blanket. Zagwyn, Deborah Turney, illus. 2004. (Illus.). 32p. (J). (gr. k-3). 7.95 (978-1-883672-59-1(7) , Tricycle Pr.) Ten Speed Pr.

Zemke, Deborah, illus. 35 Uses for a Daughter. 2005. 40p. (J). 12.95 (978-1-59354-099-9(X)) Blue Apple Bks.

Ziefert, Harriet. Home for Navidad. Cohen, Santiago, illus. 2003. 32p. (J). (gr. k-3). tchr. ed. 15.00 (978-0-618-34976-0(6) , Walter Lorraine) Houghton Mifflin Co. Trade & Reference Div.

—Just Like Daddy! Brown, Erik, illus. 2005. 16p. (J). bds. 6.95 (978-1-4027-1789-5(X) , 1241731) Sterling Publishing Co., Inc.

—Just Like Mommy! Brown, Erik, illus. 2005. 16p. (J). bds. 6.95 (978-1-4027-1788-8(1)) Sterling Publishing Co., Inc.

Ziefert, Harriet & Taback, Simms. Where Is My Baby? 2002. (Lift-the-Flap Bks.). (Illus.). 8p. bds. 7.95 (978-1-929766-46-8(7)) Blue Apple Bks.

Ziegler, Jennifer. How Not to Be Popular. 2008. 224p. (YA). (gr. 7). 15.99 (***978-0-385-73465-3(4)***); lib. bdg. 18.99 (***978-0-385-90463-6(0)***) Random Hse. Children's Bks. (Delacorte Bks. for Young Readers).

Zolotow, Charlotte. One Step, Two ... 2001. (J). 16.95 (978-0-8050-6307-3(2) , Holt, Henry & Co. Bks. For Young Readers) Holt, Henry & Co.

Zuckerman, Linda. I Will Hold You 'til You Sleep. Muth, Jon J., illus. 2006. (J). (978-0-439-43421-8(1)); 32p. pap. 16.99 (978-0-439-43420-1(3)) Scholastic, Inc. (Levine, Arthur A. Bks.).

PARENTS AND TEACHERS

see Home and School

PARIS (FRANCE)

Allman, Barbara. Eiffel Tower. 2003. (Building World Landmarks Ser.). (Illus.). 48p. (J). 24.95 (978-1-56711-315-0(X) , Blackbirch Pr., Inc.) Thomson Gale.

Bardhan-Quallen, Sudipta. The Eiffel Tower. 2005. (Great Structures in History Ser.). (Illus.). 48p. (J). (gr. 4-8). 26.20 (978-0-7377-3150-7(8) , Kidhaven) Thomson Gale.

Casas, Roger, photos by. Cool Shops Paris. 2005. (ENG, SPA, FRE, ITA & GER., Illus.). 135p. pap. 16.95 (978-3-8327-9037-0(3)) teNeues Publishing Co.

Davoll, Barbara. High Adventure in Paris. Hockerman, Dennis, illus. 1999. (New Christopher Churchmouse Adventures Ser.: Vol. 3). 24p. (J). (ps-3). 9.99 (978-0-8024-5398-3(8)) Moody Pubs.

Dorling Kindersley Publishing Staff. Paris Pocket Map & Guide. 2006. (Eyewitness Travel Guides Ser.). 448p. (gr. 12). pap. 25.00 (978-0-7566-1547-5(X)) Dorling Kindersley Publishing, Inc.

Evans, June P. Michael in Paris. 2007. 10.00 (***978-0-8059-8933-5(1)***) Dorrance Publishing Co., Inc.

Furstenberg, Gilberte & Levet, Sabine. Dans un Quartier de Paris. 1999. (Yale Language Ser.). (FRE.). 96p. stu. ed., wbk. ed. 20.00 (978-0-300-07850-3(1)) Yale Univ. Pr.

Harcourt School Publishers Staff. At the Eiffel Tower. 3rd ed. 2002. (Horizons Ser.). (Illus.). (J). pap. 3.70 (978-0-15-333158-9(5)) Harcourt Schl. Pubs.

Hatt, Christine. Paris. 2000. (World Cities Ser.). (Illus.). 48p. (J). (gr. 2-6). lib. bdg. 16.95 (978-1-929298-30-3(7)) Chrysalis Education.

Hoban, Sarah. Daily Life in Ancient & Modern Paris. Moulder, Bob, illus. 2005. (Cities Through Time Ser.). 64p. (gr. 5-12). 25.26 (978-0-8225-3222-4(0)) Lerner Publishing Group.

Holmes, Burton. Paris. Schlesinger, Arthur M., Jr. & Isreal, Fred L., eds. 1999. (World 100 Years Ago Ser.). (Illus.). 144p. (YA). (gr. 4-7). lib. bdg. 29.95 (978-0-7910-4662-3(1) , Chelsea Hse.) Facts On File, Inc.

Israel, Fred L. & Schlesinger, Arthur M., Jr., eds. Paris. 1999. (World 100 Years Ago Ser.). (Illus.). 144p. (YA). (gr. 4-7). pap. 19.95 (978-0-7910-4663-0(X) , Chelsea Hse.) Facts On File, Inc.

LeBoutillier, Nate. Eiffel Tower. 2006. (Modern Wonders of the World Ser.). (Illus.). 32p. (J). 18.95 (978-1-58341-438-5(X) , 1262895, Creative Education) Creative Co., The.

Mattern, Joanne. Paris. 2007. (Illus.). 32p. (J). 22.78 (978-1-59679-720-8(7)) ABDO Publishing Co.

Pezzi, Bryan. Eiffel Tower. 2007. (J). ***978-1-59036-719-3(7)); (*978-1-59036-720-9(0))** Weigl Pubs., Inc.

Power-Waters, Alma. St. Catherine Labore & the Miraculous Medal. 2000. (Illus.). 138p. (J). pap. 9.95 (978-0-89870-765-6(X)) Ignatius Pr.

Sasek, Miroslav. This Is Paris. 2004. (Illus.). 64p. (J). (gr. k). 17.95 (978-0-7893-1063-7(5)) Universe Publishing.

Stacey, Gill. Paris. 2004. (Great Cities of the World Ser.). (Illus.). 48p. (J). (gr. 5 up). pap. 11.95 (978-0-8368-5190-8(0)); lib. bdg. 30.00 (978-0-8368-5030-7(0)) Stevens, Gareth Inc. (World Almanac Library).

Tartaglino, Anna Cazzini & Torcellan, Nanda. Medieval Paris. 2001. (Journey to the Past Ser.). (Illus.). 56p. (J). (gr. 6-8). lib. bdg. 27.12 (978-0-7398-1956-2(9)) Raintree.

Wright, Rachel. Paris 1789: A Guide to Paris on the Eve of the Revolution. 1999. (Sightseers Ser.). (Illus.). 32p. (J). (gr. 4-6). 8.95 (978-0-7534-5183-0(2) , Kingfisher) Houghton Mifflin Co. Trade & Reference Div.

PARIS (FRANCE)—FICTION

Agunzo, Marianna. Three Peas in a Pod Go to Paris. Rodriguez, Angelo F., illus. 2006. 26p. (J). per. 14.95 (***978-1-59453-909-1(X)** , 2977, Airleaf Publishing) Airleaf Publishing & Bookselling.

Ahern, Carolyn L. Tino Turtle Travels to Paris, France. Burt Sullivan, Neallia, illus. 2007. 36p. (J). 17.95 incl. audio compact disk (***978-0-9793158-1-7(6))** Tino Turtle Travels, LLC.

—Tino Turtle Travels to Paris, France Book & Sing-along Plush Toy Bundle. 2007. (J). 29.95 incl. audio compact disk (***978-0-9793158-6-2(7))** Tino Turtle Travels, LLC.

Baker, Leslie A. Paris Cat. Baker, Leslie A., illus. 1999. (Illus.). 32p. (J). (ps-3). 15.95 (978-0-316-07309-7(1)) Little Brown & Co.

Bemelmans, Ludwig. Madeline. 2007. (Puffin Storytime Ser.). 48p. (J). (ps). pap. 9.99 (978-0-14-240871-1(9) , Puffin) Penguin Group (USA) Inc.

—Madeline & the Bad Hat. Bemelmans, Ludwig, illus. 2002. (Madeline Ser.). (Illus.). (J). 14.04 (978-0-7587-4084-7(0)) Book Wholesalers, Inc.

—Madeline & the Bad Hat. Bemelmans, Ludwig, illus. 2000. (Madeline Ser.). (Illus.). 64p. (J). (ps-3). pap. 7.99 (978-0-14-056648-2(1) , Viking Juvenile) Penguin Group (USA) Inc.

—Madeline & the Gypsies. Bemelmans, Ludwig, illus. 2000. (Madeline Ser.). (Illus.). 64p. (J). (ps-3). pap. 7.99 (978-0-14-056647-5(3) , Viking Juvenile) Penguin Group (USA) Inc.

—Madeline & the Gypsies. 2000. (gr. k-3). lib. bdg. 15.30 (978-0-8085-2352-9(X)) Tandem Library Bks.

—Madeline & the Gypsies. Bemelmans, Ludwig, illus. 2000. (Madeline Ser.). (Illus.). (J). (ps-3). (978-0-606-18428-1(7)) Tandem Library Bks.

—Madeline in America & Other Holiday Tales. Bemelmans, Ludwig, illus. 2002. (Madeline Ser.). (Illus.). (J). 18.68 (978-0-7587-4186-8(3)) Book Wholesalers, Inc.

—Madeline in America & Other Holiday Tales. Marciano, John Bemelmans, illus. 1999. (Madeline Ser.). (J). (ps-3). 112p. pap. 19.95 (978-0-590-03910-9(5) , Levine, Arthur A. Bks.); pap. 125.00 (978-0-439-09633-1(2)) Scholastic, Inc.

—Madeline's Rescue. ed. 2004. (J). (ps-2). spiral bd. (978-0-616-11864-1(3)) Canadian National Institute for the Blind/Institut National Canadien pour les Aveugles.

—Madeline's Rescue. Bemelmans, Ludwig, illus. 2000. (Madeline Ser.). (Illus.). 64p. (J). (ps-3). pap. 7.99 (978-0-14-056651-2(1) , Viking Juvenile) Penguin Group (USA) Inc.

Bemelmans, Ludwig & Wheeler, Jody. Madeline's Birthday. 1999. (Madeline Ser.). (Illus.). 16p. (J). (ps-3). act. bk. ed. 7.99 (978-0-670-88767-5(6) , Viking Juvenile) Penguin Group (USA) Inc.

Bennett, Cherie & Gottesfeld, Jeff. Anne Frank & Me. 2002. 291p. (YA). pap. 6.99 (978-0-698-11973-4(8) , Putnam Juvenile) Penguin Group (USA) Inc.

Cazet, Denys. Minnie & Moo Go to Paris. Cazet, Denys, illus. 2002. (Minnie & Moo Ser.). (Illus.). (J). 11.45 (978-0-7587-1442-8(4)) Book Wholesalers, Inc.

—Minnie & Moo Go to Paris. 2001. (Illus.). (J). (gr. 1-3). 25.95 incl. audio (978-0-87499-767-5(4)) Live Oak Media.

—Minnie & Moo Go to Paris. 1999. (gr. k-3). lib. bdg. 11.80 (978-0-613-22012-5(9)) Tandem Library Bks.

Cazet, Denys & Dorling Kindersley Publishing Staff. Minnie & Moo Go to Paris. 1999. (Minnie & Moo Ser.: Vol. 4). (Illus.). 48p. (J). (gr. 1-3). pap. 3.99 (978-0-7894-3928-4(X)); Vol. 4. 12.99 (978-0-7894-2595-9(5)) Dorling Kindersley Publishing, Inc.

Clarke, Nicole. French Twist. 2007. (Flirt Ser.: Vol. 8). 224p. (YA). pap. 6.99 (978-0-448-44463-5(1) , Grosset & Dunlap) Penguin Group (USA) Inc.

Clements, Bruce. A Chapel of Thieves. 2002. 224p. (J). (gr. 6-9). 16.00 (978-0-374-37701-4(4) , Farrar, Straus & Giroux (BYR)) Farrar, Straus & Giroux.

Cyr, Joe. Magical Trees & Crayons: Great Stories. 2006. (Illus.). pap. 9.95 (***978-0-9778525-6-7(3))** Peppertree Pr., The.

Derrick, Patricia. Rathbone the Rat. 2007. 32p. 18.95 (978-1-933818-17-7(4)) Animalations.

Disney Storybook Artists Staff, ed. Remy's Adventure in Paris: A Magnetic Book. 2007. 10p. (ps-2). 12.99 (***978-1-4231-0655-5(5))** Disney Pr.

Dixon, Franklin W. Passport to Danger. 2005. (Hardy Boys I Ser.: No. 179). 147p. (J). lib. bdg. 15.00 (978-1-59054-847-9(7)) Fitzgerald Bks.

Durrant, Sabine. Bon Voyage, Connie Pickles. 2008. 240p. (J). 16.99 (***978-0-06-085482-9(0));** lib. bdg. 17.89 (***978-0-06-085483-6(9))** HarperCollins Pubs. (HarperTeen).

Eschberger, Beverly. The Elephants Visit Paris: An Elephant Family Adventure. Gower, Jim, illus. 2009. (J). per. 3.99 (978-1-932926-28-6(3) , Kinkajou Pr.) Artemesia Publishing, LLC.

Fagan, Cary. Daughter of the Great Zandini. Young, Cybele, illus. 2001. 64p. (J). (gr. 3-7). 16.95 (978-0-88776-534-6(3)) Tundra Bks., Inc./Livres Toundra, Inc. CAN. *Dist:* Random Hse., Inc.

Friedman, Aimee. French Kiss. 2006. 336p. (J). pap. 8.99 (978-0-439-79281-3(9) , Scholastic Paperbacks) Scholastic, Inc.

Friedman, Michael Jan. Hunchdog of Notre Dame. l.t. ed. 1999. (Adventures of Wishbone Ser.: No. 5). (Illus.). 139p. (J). (gr. 4 up). lib. bdg. 22.60 (978-0-8368-2301-1(X)) Stevens, Gareth Inc.

Gopnik, Adam. The King in the Window. 2005. (Illus.). 416p. (gr. 5-17). 19.95 (978-0-7868-1862-4(X)) Hyperion Bks. for Children.

—The King in the Window. Rayyan, Omar, illus. 2006. 416p. (gr. 5-17). reprint ed. pap. 9.99 (978-0-7868-3894-3(9)) Miramax Bks.

Greene, Bette. Morning Is a Long Time Coming. l.t. ed. 2004. (Beeler Mystery Ser.). 35.95 (978-1-58118-122-7(1)) LRS.

Grimes, Nikki. On the Road to Paris. (Illus.). 224p. (J). 16.99 (978-0-8037-2817-2(4) , Dial) Penguin Group (USA) Inc.

—The Road to Paris. 2006. 160p. (J). (gr. 4-7). 15.99 (978-0-399-24537-4(5) , Dial) Penguin Group (USA) Inc.

Harris, L. Little Girl in Paris. 2004. (Madame Juliette & the Inchanded Crate Ser.: Vol. 1). (Illus.). 330p. (J). pap. 19.95 (978-0-9749950-2-1(9)) Granny's Pub Co.

Hatton, Caroline K. Vero & Philippe. McDaniels, Preston, illus. 2001. 144p. (J). (gr. 3-7). 14.95 (978-0-8126-2940-8(X)) Cricket Bks.

Henty, G. A. At Agincourt: A Story of the White Hoods of Paris. 2006. 296p. pap. 13.99 (978-1-4264-2133-4(8)); 284p. pap. 17.99 (978-1-4264-2201-0(6)) BiblioBazaar.

Horowitz, Anthony. Three of Diamonds. 2005. (Diamond Brothers Ser.). 240p. (J). (gr. 5). pap. 6.99 (978-0-14-240298-6(2) , Puffin); (YA). (gr. 4). 16.99 (978-0-399-24157-4(4) , Philomel) Penguin Group (USA) Inc.

Hugo, Victor. The Hunchback of Notre Dame: Level 2. Solimene, Laura, ed. 1999. (Illus.). 72p. (YA). (gr. 4 up). act. bk. ed. 9.95 (978-1-55576-324-4(3) , EDCTR-208B) AV Concepts Corp.

—The Hunchback of Notre Dame: With a Discussion of Compassion. Butterfield, Ned, tr. Butterfield, Ned, illus. 2003. (Values in Action Illustrated Classics Ser.). (J). (978-1-59203-049-1(1)) Learning Challenge, Inc.

The Hunchback of Notre Dame. (Read-Along Ser.). (J). 7.99 incl. audio (978-1-55723-992-1(4)) Walt Disney Records.

Hunt, Elizabeth Singer. The Mystery of the Mona Lisa. 2007. (Secret Agent Jack Stalwart Ser.). 128p. (J). (gr. 1-4). pap. 4.99 (***978-1-60286-001-8(7))** Weinstein Bks.

Ichikawa, Satomi. La-La Rose. Ichikawa, Satomi, illus. 2004. (Illus.). 40p. (J). (ps). 15.99 (978-0-399-24029-4(2) , Philomel) Penguin Group (USA) Inc.

Jeanne-Marie in Gay Paris. 2003. (Illus.). 32p. (J). mass mkt. 9.99 (978-0-9740599-1-4(9) , 2) Omnibus Publishing.

Johnston, Antony. Three Days in Europe, Vol. 1. 2003. (Illus.). 144p. pap. 14.95 (978-1-929998-72-2(4)) Oni Pr., Inc.

Kalman, Maira. La Ooh La. 2002. (gr. k-3). lib. bdg. 15.30 (978-0-613-43637-3(7)) Tandem Library Bks.

Kelly, Erin. The Mystery at the Eiffel Tower: Paris, France. 2005. (Carole Marsh Mysteries Ser.). (Illus.). 144p. (J). (gr. 3-5). 14.95 (978-0-635-03471-7(9)); pap. 5.95 (978-0-635-03468-7(9)) Gallopade International.

Kimmel, Elizabeth Cody. Lily B. on the Brink of Paris. 2006. 192p. (J). (gr. 5-8). 15.99 (978-0-06-083948-2(1)); lib. bdg. 16.89 (978-0-06-083949-9(X)) HarperCollins Pubs.

Kimmelman, Leslie. Everybody Bonjours! McMenemy, Sarah, illus. 2008. (J). 16.99 (***978-0-375-84443-0(0));** lib. bdg. 19.99 (***978-0-375-94443-7(5))** Knopf, Alfred A. Inc.

Kirby, David & Woodman, Allen. The Cows Are Going to Paris. Demarest, Chris L., illus. 2003. 32p. (J). (gr. k-2). pap. 8.95 (978-1-56397-781-7(8)) Boyds Mills Pr.

La Montagne Secrete/Secret Mountain. A Poodle in Paris. 2006. (Illus.). 36p. 16.95 (978-2-923163-12-3(5)) La Montagne Secrete CAN. *Dist:* National Bk. Network.

Lasky, Kathryn. Dancing Through Fire. 2005. (Portraits Ser.: No. 1). 176p. (J). (gr. 4-7). pap. 9.99 (978-0-439-71009-1(X) , Scholastic Paperbacks) Scholastic, Inc.

Leroux, Gaston. The Phantom of the Opera. Howell, Troy, illus. 2008. (Classic Starts Ser.). 160p. (J). 5.95 (***978-1-4027-4580-5(X))** Sterling Publishing Co., Inc.

Leroux, Gaston. The Phantom of the Opera. l.t. ed. 1999. (Large Print Heritage Ser.). 420p. (J). (gr. 7-12). lib. bdg. 35.95 (978-1-58118-043-5(8) , 22512) LRS.

Leroux, Gaston & Larkin, Rochelle. The Phantom of the Opera. Schoolcraft, Robert, illus. 2005. (Great Illustrated Classics Ser.). 240p. (J). (gr. 3-8). 21.35 (978-1-59679-248-7(5) , ABDO & Daughters) ABDO Publishing Co.

LeTourneau, Marie. The Mice of Bistrot des Sept Freres. LeTourneau, Marie, illus. 2006. (Illus.). 32p. 15.95 (978-0-9749303-6-7(9)) Tanglewood Pr.

Magoon, Scott. Hugo & Miles In: I've Painted Everything! 2007. (Illus.). (J). (***978-1-4287-3565-1(8))** Houghton Mifflin Co.

Magoon, Scott. Hugo & Miles in I've Painted Everything! 2007. (Illus.). 40p. (J). (gr. 3-5). 16.00 (978-0-618-64638-8(8)) Houghton Mifflin Co.

Maxwell, Katie. What's French for EW!? 2004. (YA). mass mkt. 5.99 (978-0-8439-5297-1(0)) Dorchester Publishing Co., Inc.

Mazer, Anne. What Goes up Must Go Down. 2008. (Amazing Days of Abby Hayes Ser.: No. 18). 128p. (J). 4.99 (***978-0-439-82926-7(7)** , Scholastic Paperbacks) Scholastic, Inc.

McClintock, Barbara. The Fantastic Drawings of Danielle. 2004. (Illus.). 32p. (J). (gr. k-3). pap. 5.95 (978-0-618-43230-1(2)) Houghton Mifflin Co. Trade & Reference Div.

McLaren, Chesley. Zat Cat! A Haute Couture Tail. McLaren, Chesley, illus. 2002. (Illus.). 40p. (J). (ps-3). pap. 16.95 (978-0-439-27316-9(1) , Scholastic Pr.) Scholastic, Inc.

Meade, L. T. The Children's Pilgrimage. 2004. reprint ed. pap. 24.95 (978-1-4191-5659-5(4)); pap. 1.99 (978-1-4192-5659-2(9)) Kessinger Publishing, LLC.

Meyer, Carolyn. Marie, Dancing. 2005. (Illus.). 272p. (YA). (gr. 7). 17.00 (978-0-15-205116-7(3) , Gulliver Bks.) Harcourt Children's Bks.

Mighty Fine, Inc. Staff. French Kitty in Kitty Goes to Paris. 2003. (Illus.). 48p. 12.95 (978-0-8109-4447-3(2)) Abrams, Harry N. , Inc.

Minou: Evaluation Guide. 2006. (J). (978-1-55942-416-5(8)) Marsh Media.

Modiano, Patrick. Catherine Certitude. (FRE.). pap. 17.95 (978-2-07-051608-7(3)) Gallimard, Editions FRA. *Dist:* Distribooks, Inc.

—Catherine Certitude. Rodarmor, William, tr. from FRE. Sempe, Jean-Jacques, illus. 2001. 58p. (J). (gr. 4 up). reprint ed. 17.95 (978-0-87923-959-6(X)) Godine, David R. Pub.

Morgenstern, Susie. Secret Letters from 0 to 10. Rosner, Gil, Jr., illus. 2000. 144p. (J). (gr. 3-7). pap. 4.99 (978-0-14-130819-7(2) , Puffin) Penguin Group (USA) Inc.

—Secret Letters from 0 to 10. 2000. (978-0-606-18846-3(0)) Tandem Library Bks.

Nascimbene, Yan. Day in September. 2002. (J). (978-0-89812-328-9(3) , Creative Paperbacks) Creative Co., The.

Osborne, Mary Pope. Night of the New Magicians. Murdocca, Sal, illus. (Magic Tree House Ser.: No. 35). (J). 2007. 144p. (gr. 2-5). pap. 4.99 (978-0-375-83036-5(7)); 2006. 128p. (gr. k-3). 11.95 (978-0-375-83035-8(9)); 2006. 128p. (gr. k-3). lib. bdg. 13.99 (978-0-375-93035-5(3)) Random Hse. Children's Bks. (Random Hse. Bks. for Young Readers).

Ouriou, Katie. Luv Ya Like a Sister: A Story of Friendship. 1999. (gr. 5-8). lib. bdg. 16.40 (978-0-613-77268-6(7)) Tandem Library Bks.

Paterson, Aileen. Maisie Loves Paris. Paterson, Aileen, illus. 2001. (Illus.). 32p. (J). pap. (978-1-871512-05-2(0)) Glowworm Bks., Ltd.

Rabley, Stephen. Marcel & the Mona Lisa. 2002. (Illus.). 16p. pap. (978-0-582-40173-0(9) , Putnam Juvenile) Penguin Group (USA) Inc.

Random House Disney Staff. I Smell a Rat. Disney Storybook Artists Staff, illus. 2007. (Scented Storybook Ser.). 24p. (J). (ps-2). 9.99 (978-0-7364-2467-7(9) , RH/Disney) Random Hse. Children's Bks.

Rees, Douglas. The Janus Gate: An Encounter with John Singer Sargent. 2006. (Art Encounters Ser.). (Illus.). 176p. (YA). 15.95 (978-0-8230-0406-5(6)) Watson-Guptill Pubns., Inc.

Resnick, Mike. Club in Montmartre. 2006. (Art Encounters Ser.). (Illus.). 176p. (YA). 16.95 (978-0-8230-0420-1(1)) Watson-Guptill Pubns., Inc.

Richemont, Enid. For Maritsa, with Love. 2001. 204p. pap. (978-0-689-83636-7(8)) Simon & Schuster.

Roberts, Laura Peyton. Secret Life. 2003. (gr. 7-12). lib. bdg. 14.15 (978-0-613-72716-7(9)) Tandem Library Bks.

Robertson, Bruce. Marguerite Makes a Book. Hewitt, Kathryn, illus. 1999. (Getty Trust Publications). 44p. (gr. 3 up). bds. 19.95 (978-0-89236-372-8(X)) Oxford Univ. Pr., Inc.

Rue, Nancy N. Lily's Passport to Paris. 2003. (gr. 3-6). lib. bdg. 13.00 (978-0-613-71689-5(2)) Tandem Library Bks.

—Lily's Passport to Paris. 2003. (Ywof Library). 160p. (J). pap. 5.99 (978-0-310-70555-0(X)) Zonderkidz.

Smadja, Brigitte. Tarte aux Escargots. pap. 17.95 (978-2-211-03633-7(3)) Archimede Editions FRA. *Dist:* Distribooks, Inc.

Soriano, Osvaldo. El Negro de Paris. (Torre de Papel Ser.). (SPA.). (J). (gr. 4 up). 8.95 (978-958-04-3450-4(6)) Norma S.A. COL. *Dist:* Distribuidora Norma, Inc.

Spirn, Michele Sobel. The Bridges in Paris. 2000. (Going to Ser.). (Illus.). 121p. (J). (gr. 4-8). pap. 6.95 (978-1-893577-04-6(X)) Four Corners Publishing Co., Inc.

Swimpson, Alayne. Murphy's Big Dream. 2006. (ENG.). 36p. per. 19.49 (***978-1-4259-5188-7(0))** AuthorHouse.

A Tale of Two Cities: Abridged. (ARA., Illus.). 48p. (J). 12.00 (978-0-86685-627-0(7)) International Bk. Ctr., Inc.

Thompson, Kay. Eloise en Paris. Knight, Hilary, illus. 2002. (SPA.). 84p. (J). (gr. k-3). 17.00 (978-84-264-3739-6(7) , LM30421) Editorial Lumen ESP. *Dist:* Distribooks, Inc., Lectorum Pubns., Inc.

Thompson, Kay & Knight, Hilary. Eloise in Paris. 1999. (Eloise Ser.). (Illus.). 72p. (J). (ps-3). 18.00 (978-0-689-82704-4(0)) Simon & Schuster Children's Publishing.

Thorpe, Kiki. Rugrats in Paris Movie Storybook. 2000. (Rugrats Ser.). (Illus.). 32p. (J). (ps-2). 5.99 (978-0-689-84198-9(1) , Simon Spotlight/Nickelodeon) Simon & Schuster Children's Publishing.

Wellington, Monica. Crepes by Suzette. Wellington, Monica, illus. 2004. (Illus.). 32p. (J). (ps). 15.99 (978-0-525-46934-6(6) , Dutton Juvenile) Penguin Group (USA) Inc.

Wells, Carolyn. Patty in Paris. 2006. (ENG.). 63.99 (***978-1-4280-1828-0(X))** IndyPublish.com.

—Patty in Paris. 2004. reprint ed. pap. 21.95 (978-1-4191-4034-1(5)); pap. 1.99 (978-1-4192-4034-8(X)) Kessinger Publishing, LLC.

Young, Amy. Belinda in Paris. 2005. (Illus.). 32p. (J). 15.99 (978-0-670-03693-6(5) , Viking Juvenile) Penguin Group (USA) Inc.

Ziefert, Harriet & Bolam, Emily. Murphy Meets Paris. 2005. (Illus.). 40p. 15.95 (978-1-59354-066-1(3)) Blue Apple Bks.

PARIS (FRANCE)—HISTORY—FICTION

Hoestlandt, Jo. Star of Fear, Star of Hope. 1998. Tr. of Grande Peur sous les Etoiles. (J). pap. 3.95 (978-0-439-04457-8(X)) Scholastic, Inc.

—Star of Fear, Star of Hope. 2000. Tr. of Grande Peur sous les Etoiles. (J). (978-0-606-20296-1(X)); (gr. 3-6). lib. bdg. 17.60 (978-0-613-29518-5(8)) Tandem Library Bks.

Hugo, Victor. The Hunchback of Notre- Dame. Famig, Jon L., illus. 1998. (Illustrated Classic Book Ser.). 61p. (J). (gr. 3 up). pap. 4.95 (978-1-56767-247-3(7)) Educational Insights, Inc.

—The Hunchback of Notre- Dame. unabr. ed. 1998. (Wordsworth Classics Ser.). (YA). (gr. 6-12). 5.27 (978-0-89061-068-8(1) , R0681WW) Jamestown.

—The Hunchback of Notre- Dame. (Young Collector's Illustrated Classics Ser.). (Illus.). 192p. (J). (gr. 3-7). 9.95 (978-1-56156-458-3(3)) Kidsbooks, Inc.

—Hunchback of Notre Dame. 2002. (Great Illustrated Classics Ser.). (Illus.). 240p. (J). (gr. 3-8). 21.35 (978-1-57765-813-9(2) , ABDO & Daughters) ABDO Publishing Co.

Hugo, Victor. The Hunchback of Notre Dame. Corvino, Lucy, illus. 2008. (Classic Starts Ser.). 160p. (J). 5.95 (***978-1-4027-4575-1(3))** Sterling Publishing Co., Inc.

Hugo, Victor Marie. The Hunchback of Notre Dame. 2006. (Illus.). 61p. (J). lib. bdg. 30.77 (***978-1-4242-1329-0(0))** Fitzgerald Bks.

The Hunchback of Notre Dame. (Read-Along Ser.). (J). 7.99 incl. audio (978-1-55723-992-1(4)) Walt Disney Records.

Knight, Joan. Charlotte in Paris. Sweet, Melissa, illus. 2003. 52p. (J). 16.95 (978-0-8118-3766-8(1)) Chronicle Bks. LLC.

Lamensdorf, Len. The Raging Dragon. Swingle, Bob, illus. 2000. (Will to Conquer Ser.: Vol. 2). 350p. (YA). (gr. 5-12). 22.95 (978-0-9669741-7-1(4)) SeaScape Pr., Ltd.

McAlpine, Gordon. Mystery Box. 2003. 190p. (YA). 16.95 (978-0-8126-2680-3(X)) Cricket Bks.

McDonough, Yona Zeldis. The Doll with the Yellow Star. Root, Kimberly Bulcken, illus. 2005. 64p. (J). (gr. 3-5). 17.95 (978-0-8050-6337-0(4) , Holt, Henry & Co. Bks. For Young Readers) Holt, Henry & Co.

Meyer, Carolyn. Marie, Dancing. 2007. (Illus.). 272p. (YA). (gr. 7 up). pap. 6.95 (978-0-15-205879-1(6) , Harcourt Paperbacks) Harcourt Children's Bks.

Robertson, Barbara. Rosemary in Paris: Back to 1889. 2001. (Hourglass Adventures Ser.: Bk. 2). (Illus.). 121p. (J). (gr. 4-7). pap. 4.95 (978-1-890817-56-5(2)) Winslow Pr.

Scott, Elaine. Secrets of the Cirque Medrano. 2008. (J). (***978-1-57091-712-7(4))** Charlesbridge Publishing, Inc.

Scott, Elaine. The Spanish Web: An Encounter with Picasso. 2004. (Art Encounters Ser.). (J). 15.95 (978-0-8230-0410-2(4)); pap. 6.99 (978-0-8230-0413-3(9)) Watson-Guptill Pubns., Inc.

Selznick, Brian. The Invention of Hugo Cabret. Selznick, Brian, illus. 2007. (Illus.). 544p. (J). (gr. 4-7). pap. 22.99 (978-0-439-81378-5(6) , Scholastic Pr.) Scholastic, Inc.

PARKS, GORDON, 1912-2006

Parr, Ann. Gordon Parks, No Excuses. 2006. (Illus.). 32p. (J). 15.95 (978-1-58980-411-1(2)) Pelican Publishing Co., Inc.

PARKS, ROSA, 1913-2005

Adler, David A. A Picture Book of Rosa Parks. Casilla, Robert, illus. 2004. 28.95 incl. audio compact disk (978-1-59112-762-8(9)); (J). audio compact disk 18.95 (978-1-59112-761-1(0)) Live Oak Media.

Ashby, Ruth. Rosa Parks: Freedom Rider. 2008. (Sterling Biographies Ser.). (Illus.). 128p. (J). pap. 5.95 (***978-1-4027-4865-3(5))** Sterling Publishing Co., Inc.

Baker, Courtney. Let's Read About— Rosa Parks. Hunt, Robert, illus. 2004. (Scholastic First Biographies Ser.). 29p. (J). pap. (978-0-439-56413-7(1) , Cartwheel Bks.) Scholastic, Inc.

Banting, Erinn. Rosa Parks. 2005. (Great African American Women for Kids Ser.). (Illus.). 24p. (J). (ps-7). pap. 6.95 (978-1-59036-342-3(6)); lib. bdg. 26.00 (978-1-59036-336-2(1)) Weigl Pubs., Inc.

Bjornlund, Lydia. Rosa Parks & the Montgomery Bus Boycott. 2007. (Lucent Library of Black History Ser.). (Illus.). 128p. (J). (gr. 7-10). 28.70 (*978-1-4205-0010-3(4) , Lucent Bks.) Thomson Gale.

Brandt, Keith & Mattern, Joanne. Rosa Parks: Freedom Rider. Griffith, Gershom, illus. 2006. 54p. (J). pap. (*978-0-439-66045-7(9)) Scholastic, Inc.

Brown, Jonatha A. Rosa Parks. 2005. (Illus.). 24p. (J). (ENG & SPA.). pap. (978-0-8368-4769-7(5)); (ENG & SPA., lib. bdg. 19.33 (978-0-8368-4762-8(8)); pap. (978-0-8368-4755-0(5)); lib. bdg. 19.33 (978-0-8368-4748-2(2)) Stevens, Gareth Inc.

Chanko, Pamela. Easy Reader Biographies: Rosa Parks: Bus Ride to Freedom. 2007. 16p. pap. 2.99 (*978-0-439-77420-8(9) , Teaching Resources) Scholastic, Inc.

Collard, Sneed B., III. Rosa Parks: The Courage to Make a Difference. 2006. (American Heroes Ser.). (Illus.). 48p. (J). (gr. 3-5). lib. bdg. 28.50 (978-0-7614-2163-4(7) , Benchmark Bks.) Cavendish, Marshall Corp.

Collins, James. Rosa Parks: Not Giving In with Buffalo Bill & Farley's Raiders. Cox, Brian T., illus. 2006. (Time Traveler's Adventure Ser.). 56p. (J). 13.50 incl. audio compact disk (978-1-932332-17-9(0)) Toy Box Productions.

DeGezelle, Terri. Life in the Time of Rosa Parks & the Civil Rights Movement. 2007. (J). (*978-1-4034-9671-3(4)); pap. (*978-1-4034-9679-9(X)) Heinemann Library.

Donovan, Sandy. Rosa Parks. 2003. (Illus.). 64p. (J). (gr. 4-7). pap. 9.50 (978-1-4109-0320-4(6)); lib. bdg. 28.56 (978-0-7398-7032-7(7)) Raintree.

Dubois, Muriel L. Rosa Parks. 2003. (Photo-Illustrated Biographies Ser.). (Illus.). 24p. (J). (gr. 2-3). lib. bdg. 18.60 (978-0-7368-1607-6(0) , Bridgestone Bks.) Capstone Pr., Inc.

Dubowski, Cathy East. Rosa Parks: Don't Give In! 2005. (Defining Moments Ser.). (Illus.). 32p. (J). lib. bdg. 25.27 (978-1-59716-078-0(4)) Bearport Publishing Co., Inc.

Edwards, Pamela Duncan. The Bus Ride That Changed History: The Story of Rosa Parks. Shanahan, Danny, illus. 2005. 32p. (J). (gr. k-3). 16.00 (978-0-618-44911-8(6)) Houghton Mifflin Co. Trade & Reference Div.

Fine, Edith Hope. Rosa Parks: Meet a Civil Rights Hero. 2004. (Meeting Famous People Ser.). (Illus.). 32p. (J). lib. bdg. 22.60 (978-0-7660-2099-3(1)) Enslow Pubs., Inc.

Giovanni, Nikki. Rosa. Collier, Bryan, illus. rev. ed. 2005. 40p. (J). (gr. 4-7). 16.95 (978-0-8050-7106-1(7) , Holt, Henry & Co. Bks. For Young Readers) Holt, Henry & Co.

—Rosa. Collier, Bryan, illus. 2007. 40p. (J). pap. 7.99 (*978-0-312-37602-4(2)) Square Fish.

Greenfield, Eloise. Rosa Parks. Ashby, Gil, illus. 2002. 12.62 (978-0-7587-0755-0(X)) Book Wholesalers, Inc.

Hull, Mary, et al. Rosa Parks: Civil Rights Leader. 2nd rev. ed. 2006. (Black Americans of Achievement: Ser.). 128p. (J). (gr. 6-12). 30.00 (*978-0-7910-9523-2(1) , Chelsea Hse.) Facts On File, Inc.

Hull, Mary E. Rosa Parks: Civil Rights Leader. (Black Americans of Achievement Ser.). (Illus.). 112p. (J). (gr. 6-12). 2005. pap. 13.25 (978-0-7910-8338-3(1)); 2004. 30.00 (978-0-7910-8164-8(8)) Facts On File, Inc. (Chelsea Hse.).

Kishel, Ann-Marie. Rosa Parks: A Life of Courage. 2006. (Illus.). 32p. (J). pap. 5.95 (978-0-8225-5698-5(7)); 22.60 (978-0-8225-3478-5(9) , Lerner Pubns.) Lerner Publishing Group.

—Rosa Parks: Una Vida de Valentía. 2006. (Libros para Avanzar Ser.). (ENG & SPA.). 32p. (J). lib. bdg. 22.60 (978-0-8225-6239-9(1)) Lerner Publishing Group.

Kudlinski, Kathleen. Rosa Parks: Young Rebel. 2001. (gr. 3-6). lib. bdg. 13.00 (978-0-613-31647-7(9)) Tandem Library Bks.

Kudlinski, Kathleen V. Rosa Parks. Henderson, Meryl, illus. 2001. (Childhood of Famous Americans Ser.). 224p. (gr. 3-7). mass mkt. 5.99 (978-0-689-83925-2(1) , Aladdin) Simon & Schuster Children's Publishing.

—Rosa Parks: Young Rebel. 2001. (Childhood of Famous Americans Ser.). (Illus.). (J). (978-0-606-20891-8(7)) Tandem Library Bks.

Major, Devorah. Rosa Parks: Freedom Fighter. Stemach, Jerry, ed. Ham, Jeff, illus. 2000. 65.00 incl. audio, cd-rom (978-1-893376-74-8(5)); 2002. 150.00 (978-1-58702-027-8(0)); 2000. 50.00 (978-1-58702-448-1(9)) Johnston, Don Inc.

Manolis, Kay. Rosa Parks: A Life of Courage. 2007. (Illus.). 24p. (J). lib. bdg. 19.95 (978-1-60014-088-4(2)) Bellwether Media.

Mara, Wil. Rosa Parks. 2006. (Rookie Biography Ser.). (Illus.). 31p. (J). (978-0-531-12451-2(7)) Children's Pr., Ltd.

—Rosa Parks. (Rookie Biographies Ser.). (Illus.). (J). 2004. 31p. (gr. 1-2). pap. 4.95 (978-0-516-27916-9(5)); 2003. 32p. 19.50 (978-0-516-25876-8(1)) Scholastic Library Publishing. (Children's Pr.).

Marsh, Carole. Rosa Parks. 2002. (One Thousand Readers Ser.). (Illus.). 12p. (J). (gr. k-4). 2.95 (978-0-635-01497-9(1) , 14971) Gallopade International.

—Rosa Parks. 2000. (My Ancestors—My Heroes Ser.: Vol. 24). (J). (gr. 3-4). (978-1-893091-23-8(6)) Parker Publishing Co.

—Rosa Parks: An Ohio Experience Reader. 2001. (J). (gr. k-5). pap. 1.95 (978-0-635-00450-5(X)) Gallopade International.

—The Virginia Reader: Rosa Parks. 2001. (Virginia Experience! Ser.). (Illus.). 12p. (J). (gr. k-4). pap. 2.95 (978-0-635-00359-1(7)) Gallopade International.

McLeese, Don. Rosa Parks. 2002. (Rourke Discovery Library). (Illus.). 24p. (J). lib. bdg. 20.64 (978-1-58952-287-9(7)) Rourke Publishing, LLC.

Miller, Connie Colwell. Rosa Parks & the Montgomery Bus Boycott. 2007. (Graphic Library). (Illus.). 32p. (J). 25.26 (978-0-7368-6495-4(4)) Capstone Pr., Inc.

Morris, Roz. Rosa Parks: Mother of the Civil Rights Movement. 2003. (Alabama Roots Biography Ser.). (Illus.). 109p. (J). (978-1-878561-57-2(X)) Seacoast Publishing, Inc.

Nobleman, Marc Tyler. Rosa Parks. 2002. (Trailblazers of the Modern World Ser.). (Illus.). 48p. (J). (gr. 5 up). pap. 14.95 (978-0-8368-5231-8(1)); lib. bdg. 30.00 (978-0-8368-5071-0(8)) Stevens, Gareth Inc. (World Almanac Library).

—Rosa Parks. 2002. (gr. 3-6). lib. bdg. 19.90 (978-0-613-76804-7(3)) Tandem Library Bks.

Parks, Rosa. I Am Rosa Parks. 2000. (gr. k-3). lib. bdg. 11.80 (978-0-613-22996-8(7)); (Illus.). (J). 10.79 (978-0-606-18410-6(4)) Tandem Library Bks.

—Rosa Parks: My Story. 1999. (Illus.). 200p. (YA). (gr. 5-9). pap. 6.99 (978-0-14-130120-4(1) , Puffin) Penguin Group (USA) Inc.

—Rosa Parks: My Story. 1999. (978-0-606-15995-1(9)); (gr. 5-8). lib. bdg. 15.30 (978-0-613-15120-7(8)) Tandem Library Bks.

Parks, Rosa & Haskins, Jim. I Am Rosa Parks. Clay, Wil, illus. 1999. (Easy-to-Read Ser.). 48p. (J). (gr. 1-3). pap. 3.99 (978-0-14-130710-7(2) , Puffin) Penguin Group (USA) Inc.

Pingry, Patricia A. The Story of Rosa Parks. Walker, Steven, illus. 2007. 24p. (J). (ps-k). bds. 6.99 (*978-0-8249-6687-4(2) , Candy Cane Pr.) Ideals Pubns.

Rinaldo, Denise. Rosa Parks: With a Discussion of Courage. 2003. (Values in Action Ser.). (J). (978-1-59203-061-3(0)) Learning Challenge, Inc.

Ringgold, Faith. If a Bus Could Talk: The Story of Rosa Parks. Ringgold, Faith, illus. (Illus.). 32p. (J). 2003. (gr. k-4). pap. 7.99 (978-0-689-85676-1(8) , Aladdin); 1999. (gr. 1-4). 16.00 (978-0-689-81892-9(0)) Simon & Schuster Children's Publishing.

—If a Bus Could Talk: The Story of Rosa Parks. 2003. (gr. k-3). lib. bdg. 15.30 (978-0-613-61633-1(2)) Tandem Library Bks.

Roop, Peter. Take a Stand, Rosa Parks. 2005. (Illus.). 59p. (J). (*978-0-439-67625-0(8)) Scholastic, Inc.

Rosa Parks. (Photo Illustrated Biographies Ser.). 24p. (J). 6.95 (978-0-7368-3436-0(2)); Vol. 2. 2005. (YA). (978-0-7368-9374-9(1) , Pebble Bks.) Capstone Pr., Inc.

Rosa Parks. (Compass Point Early Biographies Ser.). 32p. (J). 7.95 (978-0-7565-1179-1(8)) Compass Point Bks.

Rosa Parks, 6 vols. (gr. k-2). 28.95 (978-0-7368-9375-6(X)) Red Brick Learning.

Rosa Parks: Una vida de valentía (A Life of Courage) 2007. (J). pap. 5.95 (978-0-8225-6557-4(9) , Ediciones Lerner) Lerner Publishing Group.

Schaefer, Lola M. Rosa Parks. Saunders-Smith, Gail, ed. 2002. (First Biographies Ser.). (Illus.). 24p. (J). (gr. k-1). lib. bdg. 15.93 (978-0-7368-1176-7(1) , Pebble Bks.) Capstone Pr., Inc.

Schraff, Anne E. Rosa Parks: Tired of Giving In. 2005. (African-American Biography Library). (Illus.). 128p. (J). (gr. 6-12). lib. bdg. 31.93 (978-0-7660-2463-2(6)) Enslow Pubs., Inc.

Shone, Rob. Rosa Parks: The Life of a Civil Rights Heroine. Spender, Nik, illus. 2006. 48p. (J). (978-1-4042-0926-8(3)); pap. (978-1-4042-0927-5(1)); (gr. 3-8). lib. bdg. 29.95 (978-1-4042-0864-3(X)) Rosen Publishing Group, Inc., The.

Shores, Erika L. Rosa Parks: Civil Rights Poineer. 2005. (Fact Finders Ser.). (Illus.). 32p. (J). (ps-7). lib. bdg. 22.60 (978-0-7368-3746-0(9)) Capstone Pr., Inc.

Steck-Vaughn Staff. Rosa Parks: Freedom Fighter: New York City Edition. 2002. pap. 100.00 (978-1-58702-973-8(1)) Johnston, Don Inc.

Steele, Phillip. Rosa Parks & Her Protest for Civil Rights. 2002. (Dates with History Ser.). (Illus.). 31p. (J). lib. bdg. 24.25 (978-1-58340-215-3(2)) Smart Apple Media.

Tieck, Sarah. Rosa Parks. 2007. (Buddy Book Ser.). (Illus.). 32p. (J). 22.78 (978-1-59679-788-8(6)) ABDO Publishing Co.

Time for Kids Editors. Rosa Parks: Civil Rights Pioneer. 2007. (Time for Kids Ser.). (Illus.). 48p. (J). 14.99 (978-0-06-057625-7(1)); pap. 3.99 (978-0-06-057624-0(3)) HarperCollins Pubs.

Weidt, Maryann N. Rosa Parks. 2003. (History Maker Bios Ser.). (Illus.). 47p. (J). 26.60 (978-0-8225-4673-3(6) , Lerner Pubns.) Lerner Publishing Group.

Wheeler, Jill C. Rosa Parks, Set II. 2003. (Breaking Barriers Ser.). (Illus.). 64p. (J). (gr. 3-8). lib. bdg. 25.65 (978-1-57765-640-1(7)) ABDO Publishing Co.

Whiting, Jim. Rosa Parks. 2007. (What's So Great About... ? Ser.). (J). lib. bdg. 25.70 (*978-1-58415-573-7(6)) Mitchell Lane Pubs., Inc.

Wilson, Cammie. Rosa Parks: From the Back of the Bus to the Front of a Movement. 2001. (Scholastic Biography Ser.). (Illus.). 88p. (J). (gr. 3-7). pap. 4.50 (978-0-439-16330-9(7)) Scholastic, Inc.

PARKS

Ada, Alma Flor & Compoy, F. Isabel. El Parque. 3rd ed. 2002. (Trofeos Ser.). (SPA.). (gr. k-6). pap. 19.70 (978-0-15-331058-4(8)) Harcourt Schl. Pubs.

Beck, Isabel L., et al. Trophies Kindergarten: The Park. 2003. (Trophies Ser.). (gr. k-6). 13.80 (978-0-15-329533-1(3)) Harcourt Schl. Pubs.

Beylon, Cathy. At the Amusement Park. 2004. (Dover Coloring Bks.). 32p. (J). pap. 2.95 (978-0-486-43322-6(6)) Dover Pubns., Inc.

Bruce, Lisa. Patterns in the Park. 2003. (Raintree Sprouts Ser.). (Illus.). 24p. (J). lib. bdg. 18.56 (978-1-4109-0634-2(5)); pap. 5.50 (978-1-4109-0660-1(4)) Raintree.

—Patterns in the Park. 2003. (ps-2). lib. bdg. 13.55 (978-0-613-78201-2(1)) Tandem Library Bks.

Chessen, Betsey & Chanko, Pamela. What's in a Park? 2000. (Learning Center Emergent Readers Ser.). (J). pap. 2.50 (978-0-439-04582-7(7)) Scholastic, Inc.

Cipriano, Jeri S. At the Park. 2003. (Illus.). 17p. (J). 15.93 (978-0-7368-2907-6(5)); pap. (978-0-7368-2866-6(4)) Yellow Umbrella Pr.

—En el Parque. 2005. Tr. of At the Park. (SPA., Illus.). 16p. (J). (gr. 1 up). lib. bdg. 15.93 (978-0-7368-4172-6(5)) Capstone Pr., Inc.

Costain, Meredith. Park Rangers. 2000. (gr. k-3). lib. bdg. 11.80 (978-0-613-30662-1(7)) Tandem Library Bks.

Dorling Kindersley Publishing Staff. In the Park. 2004. (Dk Readers Ser.). 32p. (J). 12.99 (978-0-7566-0535-3(0)); (Illus.). pap. 3.99 (978-0-7566-0537-7(7)) Dorling Kindersley Publishing, Inc.

Greenberg, Daniel A. Amusement Park Science. 2003. (Science Links Ser.). (Illus.). 32p. (gr. 3-5). 23.00 (978-0-7910-7416-9(1) , Chelsea Hse.) Facts On File, Inc.

Hall, M. C. Big Bend National Park. 2005. (Symbols of Freedom Ser.). (Illus.). 32p. (J). (gr. k-2). lib. bdg. 25.36 (978-1-4034-6697-6(1)) Heinemann Library.

Hall, Margaret. Big Bend National Park. 2005. (Heinemann First Library). (Illus.). 32p. (J). pap. (978-1-4034-6704-1(8)) Heinemann Library.

—Rocky Mountain National Park. 2005. (Heinemann First Library). (Illus.). 32p. (J). pap. (978-1-4034-6708-9(0)); lib. bdg. 25.36 (978-1-4034-6701-0(3)) Heinemann Library.

Hill, Mary. Let's Go to a Park. 2004. (Weekend Fun Ser.). (J). 18.00 (978-0-516-23998-9(8)); pap. 4.95 (978-0-516-25918-5(0)) Scholastic Library Publishing. (Children's Pr.).

—Signs at the Park. 2003. (Welcome Bks.). (Illus.). 24p. (J). (ps-2). pap. 4.95 (978-0-516-24365-8(9) , Children's Pr.) Scholastic Library Publishing.

—Signs at the Park. 2003. (gr. k-3). lib. bdg. 12.95 (978-0-613-59721-0(4)) Tandem Library Bks.

Imagineers Books Staff, ed. Imagineering Field Guide to Disney's Animal Kingdom at Walt Disney World. 2007. 128p. (ps-17). pap. 9.95 (*978-1-4231-0320-2(3) , Disney Editions) Disney Pr.

Lucas, Diane. Walking with the Seasons in Kakadu. Searle, Ken, illus. 2005. 32p. (J). pap. 9.95 (978-1-74114-471-0(X)) Allen & Unwin AUS. *Dist:* Independent Pubs. Group.

Making a Park: First Grade Guided Reading Level E. (On Our Way to English Ser.). (gr. 1 up). 27.75 (978-0-7578-7048-4(1)) Rigby Education.

Medley, Steven P. Antelope, Bison, Cougar: A National Park Wildlife Alphabet Book. San Souci, Robert D., illus. 2001. (J). (ps-5). 14.95 (978-1-930238-03-9(7)) Yosemite Assn.

On a Roll: How Communities Build State Parks. 2005. (Book Treks Ser.). (J). 37.95 (978-0-7652-3254-0(5)) Celebration Pr.

Parks Matter! 2004. (YA). (978-0-88441-673-9(9)) Girl Scouts of the USA.

Procter, Alice. At the Park: Telling Time by the Hour. 2007. (I Can Tell Time Ser.). 24p. (J). (gr. k-2). lib. bdg. 19.93 (*978-0-8368-8389-3(6)) Stevens, Gareth Inc.

Proctor, Alice. At the Park: Telling Time by the Hour. 2007. (J). pap. (*978-0-8368-8394-7(2)) Stevens, Gareth Inc.

Ruffin, Frances E. Creating a City Park: Dividing Three-Digit Numbers by One-Digit Numbers Without Remainders. 2004. (PowerMath Ser.). (Illus.). 24p. (J). lib. bdg. (978-0-8239-8926-3(7)); lib. bdg. 21.25 (978-0-8239-8978-2(X)) Rosen Publishing Group, Inc., The. (PowerKids Pr.).

Stanley, Mandy. In the Park. 2004. (All Aboard Ser.). Orig. Title: Vamos al Parqu. (Illus.). 12p. (J). (ps-k). bds. 3.95 (978-0-7534-5750-4(4) , Kingfisher) Houghton Mifflin Co. Trade & Reference Div.

—Vamos al Parque/In the Park. 2004. (Todos A Bordo Ser.). (ENG & SPA., Illus.). 12p. (J). (ps-k). bds. 3.95 (978-0-7534-5811-2(X) , Kingfisher) Houghton Mifflin Co. Trade & Reference Div.

Stanos, Dimi. Plants in the Park. 2002. (Windows on Literacy Ser.). (Illus.). 8p. (J). (978-0-7922-8463-5(1)) National Geographic Society.

Stewart, Jacqueline. The Glaciers' Treasure Trove: A Field Guide to the Lake Michigan Riviera. 2003. (Illus.). 155p. spiral bd. 19.95 (978-0-9727484-7-6(4)) Lexicus Pr.

Stillerman, Robbie. Amusement Park Stickers. 2004. (Stickers Ser.). (Illus.). 8p. (J). (ps-5). pap. 1.50 (978-0-486-43305-9(6)) Dover Pubns., Inc.

Waters, Jo. A Walk in the Park. 2006. (Raintree Sprouts Ser.). (Illus.). 24p. (J). (978-1-4109-2291-5(X)); pap. (978-1-4109-2296-0(0)) Steck-Vaughn.

Weekly Reader Early Learning Library (Firm) Staff, contrib. by. Things at the Park. 2006. (Things in My World Ser.). (Illus.). 16p. (J). pap. (978-0-8368-6816-6(1)); lib. bdg. (978-0-8368-6809-8(9)) Stevens, Gareth Inc.

—Things at the Park: Las Cosas Del Parque. 2006. (ENG & SPA., Illus.). 16p. (J). pap. (978-0-8368-7228-6(2) , Weekly Reader Early Learning Library) Stevens, Gareth Inc.

—Things at the Park (Las Cosas del Parque) 2006. (ENG & SPA., Illus.). 16p. (J). lib. bdg. 17.27 (978-0-8368-7221-7(5) , Weekly Reader Early Learning Library) Stevens, Gareth Inc.

What Is a Park?, 6 Packs. (Discovery World Ser.). 16p. (gr. 1-2). 28.00 (978-0-7635-8453-5(3)) Rigby Education.

Williams, Colleen Madonna Flood. My Adventure at the Amusement Park. 2007. 44p. (J). 8.99 (978-1-59092-410-5(X) , Orchard Academy Pr.) Windstorm Creative.

Wishinsky, Frieda. The Man Who Made Parks: The Story of Parkbuilder Frederick Law Olmsted. Zhang, Song Nan, illus. 1999. 32p. (J). (gr. k-12). 15.95 (978-0-88776-435-6(5)) Tundra Bks., Inc./Livres Toundra, Inc. CAN. *Dist:* Random Hse., Inc.

PARKS—FICTION

Baker, Keith. More Mr. & Mrs. Green. (Mr. & Mrs. Green Ser.). (Illus.). 68p. (J). 2005. pap. 5.95 (978-0-15-205246-1(1) , Harcourt Paperbacks); 2004. 16.00 (978-0-15-216494-2(4)) Harcourt Children's Bks.

—More Mr. & Mrs. Green. 2007. (Mr. & Mrs. Green Ser.). 72p. (J). (gr. 2-4). 27.07 (*978-1-59961-302-4(6)) Spotlight.

Barringer, William. Gregory & Alexander. LaFave, Kim, illus. 2003. 32p. (J). (ps-2). 15.95 (978-1-55143-252-6(8)) Orca Bk. Pubs. USA.

Baumgarten, Josephine & Baumgarten, Michael. My Baby Monsters & I went to the Park. 2005. 32p. pap. 14.99 (978-1-4116-6348-0(9)) Lulu.com.

Becker, Shari. Maxwell's Mountain. Wong, Nicole, illus. 32p. (J). (ps-2). 2007. pap. 6.95 (*978-1-58089-212-4(4)); 2006. 15.95 (978-1-58089-047-2(4)) Charlesbridge Publishing, Inc.

Berenstain, Stan & Berenstain, Jan. The Berenstain Bear Scouts & the Search for Naughty Ned. 1998. (Berenstain Bear Scouts Ser.). (Illus.). 32p. (J). (gr. 3-6). pap. 3.50 (978-0-590-56509-7(5)) Scholastic, Inc.

—The Berenstain Bear Scouts & the Search for Naughty Ned. 1998. (Berenstain Bear Scouts Ser.). (J). (gr. 3-6). (978-0-606-13193-3(0)) Tandem Library Bks.

Black, Sonia W. Hanging Out with Mom. 2000. (Hello Reader! Ser.). (Illus.). (J). 10.79 (978-0-606-18554-7(2)) Tandem Library Bks.

—Hanging Out with Mom: Level. 1. Ford, George C., illus. 2000. (Hello Reader! Ser.). 32p. (J). (ps-3). pap. 3.99 (978-0-590-86636-1(2)) Scholastic, Inc.

Brooke, Samantha. Oopsy Does It. 2007. (Care Bears 8x8 Ser.). 24p. (J). pap. 3.99 (*978-0-439-02676-5(8)) Scholastic, Inc.

Browne, Anthony. Voces en el Parque. 2001. (Los Especiales de A la Orilla Del Viento Ser.). (SPA., Illus.). 32p. (J). (gr. k-2). 13.99 (978-968-16-6019-2(6) , FC30109) Fondo de Cultura Economica USA.

—Voices in the Park. 2001. (gr. 3-6). lib. bdg. 16.45 (978-0-613-75141-4(8)) Tandem Library Bks.

Browne, Anthony & Dorling Kindersley Publishing Staff. Voices in the Park. 2001. 32p. (J). (gr. 2-6). pap. 7.99 (978-0-7894-8191-7(X)) Dorling Kindersley Publishing, Inc.

Buchanan, Paul. Tidal Wave, Vol. 7. 1998. (Misadventures of Willie Plummett Ser.: Vol. 7). 128p. (J). (gr. 3-7). 5.99 (978-0-570-05086-5(3)) Concordia Publishing Hse.

Butterworth, Nick. One Snowy Night. Butterworth, Nick, illus. 2008. (Percy the Park Keeper Ser.). (Illus.). 32p. (J). 12.95 (*978-0-00-726024-9(5)) HarperCollins Pubs. Ltd. GBR. *Dist:* Independent Pubs. Group.

—One Snowy Night: Hardback plus DVD. Butterworth, Nick, illus. 2007. (Illus.). 32p. (J). 24.00 (*978-0-00-725942-7(5)) HarperCollins Pubs. Ltd. GBR. *Dist:* Independent Pubs. Group.

—Percy the Park Keeper Treasury. 2007. (Percy the Park Keeper Ser.). (Illus.). 240p. (J). 18.99 (*978-0-00-721137-1(6)) HarperCollins Pubs. Ltd. GBR. *Dist:* Independent Pubs. Group.

Calvert, Pam & Torrey, Richard. Clue School: Mysetery at the Ballpark. 2007. 32p. (J). (gr. 1). pap. 6.99 (*978-1-58476-609-4(3) , IKIDS) Innovative Kids.

Campbell, Rod. Buster's Park. 2003. (Illus.). 14p. (J). bds. 6.99 (978-0-333-76645-3(8)) Macmillan Publishers Ltd. GBR. *Dist:* Trafalgar Square Publishing.

Carlson, Melody. Project, Girl Power. 2007. (Faithgirlz!#8482; / Girls of 622 Harbor View Ser.). 144p. (J). pap. 6.99 (978-0-310-71186-5(X)) Zonderkidz.

—Project, Mystery Bus. 2007. (Faithgirlz!#8482; / Girls of 622 Harbor View Ser.). 144p. (J). pap. 6.99 (978-0-310-71187-2(8)) Zonderkidz.

—Project, Take Charge. 2007. (Faithgirlz!#8482; / Girls of 622 Harbor View Ser.). 144p. (J). pap. 6.99 (978-0-310-71189-6(4)) Zonderkidz.

Chenn, Eric. Willie the Wheel. 2006. (Illus.). 40p. (J). 16.95 (978-0-9762056-7-8(X)) Heryin Publishing Corp.

Cote, Denis & Poulin, Stephane. Le Parc aux Sortileges. 2001. (FRE., Illus.). 96p. (J). pap. (978-2-89021-470-5(2)) Diffusion du livre Mirabel.

Cox, Phil Roxbee. Shark in the Park. Cartwright, Stephen, illus. rev. ed. 2006. 16p. (J). pap. 6.99 (978-0-7945-1509-6(6) , Usborne) EDC Publishing.

Cox, Phil Roxbee & Cartwright, Stephen. Shark in the Park. 2004. (Easy Words to Read Ser.). (Illus.). 16p. (J). (gr. 1 up). pap. 6.95 (978-0-7945-0171-6(0) , Usborne) EDC Publishing.

Cox, Phil Roxbee & Tyler, Jenny. Shark in the Park. Cartwright, Stephen, illus. 2002. (Easy Words to Read Ser.). 16p. (J). (978-0-439-52876-4(3)) Scholastic, Inc.

DiSalvo-Ryan, DyAnne. Spaghettti Park. DiSalvo-Ryan, DyAnne, illus. 2002. (Illus.). 32p. (J). (gr. k-3). tchr. ed. 16.95 (978-0-8234-1682-0(8)) Holiday Hse., Inc.

Dye, Stacey. Twinship Is in Your Heart. Stubbs, Charles, illus. 2001. 16p. (J). pap. 5.95 (978-1-891846-24-3(8)) Business Word, The.

Edwards, Nancy. Mom for Mayor. Chesworth, Michael, illus. 2006. 96p. (J). 16.95 (978-0-8126-2743-5(1)) Cricket Bks.

Fun in the Park. 1999. (Tami & Moishy Ser.: Vol. 3). (J). bds. 6.95 (978-1-58330-378-8(2)) Feldheim Pubs.

Gardner, Sally. The Countess's Calamity: Tales from the Box. Gardner, Sally, illus. 2003. (Tales from the Box Ser.). (Illus.). 160p. (J). (gr. 1-6). 14.95 (978-1-58234-812-4(X)); pap. 6.95 (978-1-58234-855-1(3)) Bloomsbury Publishing. (Bloomsbury Children).

Geter, Maurice. My Friend Buddy. Geter, Maurice, illus. 2006. (Illus.). 24p. (J). (978-1-4120-9646-1(4)) Trafford Publishing.

Going to the Park: Individual Title Six-Packs. (ps-2). 23.00 (978-0-7635-9012-3(6)) Rigby Education.

Gonzales, David. Mijos: Save Mijo Park. Gonzales, David, illus. 2005. (Mijos Ser.: No. 2). (Illus.). 96p. (J). pap. 3.99 (978-0-439-56235-5(X) , Scholastic Paperbacks) Scholastic, Inc.

Gordon, Amy. The Gorillas of Gill Park. 2003. 256p. (J). (gr. 4-6). tchr. ed. 16.95 (978-0-8234-1751-3(4)) Holiday Hse., Inc.

—Return to Gill Park. 2006. (Illus.). 240p. (J). (gr. 3-7). 16.95 (978-0-8234-1998-2(3)) Holiday Hse., Inc.

Gosney, Joy. Naughty Parents. 2000. (Illus.). 32p. (ps-1). lib. bdg. 21.90 (978-0-7613-1823-1(2) , Millbrook Pr.) Lerner Publishing Group.

Graf, Mike. Yellowstone: Eye of the Grizzly. Leggitt, Marjorie, illus. 2007. (Adventures with the Parkers Ser.). 93p. (J). (gr. 4-7). pap. 9.95 (978-1-55591-568-1(X)) Fulcrum Publishing.

—Yosemite: Harrowing Ascent of Half Dome. Leggitt, Marjorie, illus. 2007. (Adventures with the Parkers Ser.). 93p. (J). (gr. 4-7). pap. 9.95 (978-1-55591-609-1(0)) Fulcrum Publishing.

Granowsky, Alvin. At the Park. 2001. 11.79 (978-0-606-22367-6(3)) Tandem Library Bks.

Hall, Margaret. Sebastian in Central Park. Wenzel, David, illus. 2001. (Suitcase Bear Adventures Ser.: Vol. 1). (J). (978-0-9713174-0-6(2) , Bear & Co.) Bear & Co.

Hamilton, Tisha. Picnic in the Park. Style Guide Staff, illus. 2006. (Raggedy Ann Ser.). 96p. (J). 2.99 (978-1-4169-1749-6(7) , Simon Scribbles) Simon & Schuster Children's Publishing.

Harcourt School Publishers Staff. Baboon's Park: Below Level. 3rd ed. 2002. (Trophies Reading Program Ser.). (Illus.). (J). pap. 4.10 (978-0-15-322972-5(1)) Harcourt Schl. Pubs.

—Baboon's Park 5-Pack, Below Level. 3rd ed. 2002. (Illus.). (gr. 1). pap. 20.10 (978-0-15-326822-9(0)) Harcourt Schl. Pubs.

—In the City Park: Below Level. 3rd ed. 2002. (Trophies Reading Program Ser.). (Illus.). (J). pap. 3.20 (978-0-15-322952-7(7)) Harcourt Schl. Pubs.

—What a Great Team! 3rd ed. 2002. (Trophies English Language Learners Ser.). (Illus.). (J). pap. 4.10 (978-0-15-327580-7(4)) Harcourt Schl. Pubs.

Haugaard, Kay. No Place. Peterson-Albandoz, Michelle, illus. 1999. 175p. (J). (gr. 3-8). 15.95 (978-1-57131-616-5(7)) Milkweed Editions.

—No Place. 2nd ed. 2007. (Illus.). 140p. pap. 6.95 (***978-1-57131-675-2(2)***) Milkweed Editions.

—No Place. 1999. (J). (978-0-606-19034-3(1)) Tandem Library Bks.

Hensley, Sarah M. At the Park. Crowell, Knox, illus. l.t. ed. 2006. 10p. (J). (ps-k). pap. 10.95 (978-1-57332-354-3(3)) HighReach Learning, Inc.

Heo, Yumi. One Sunday Morning. 1999. (Illus.). 32p. (J). (ps-1). 16.99 (978-0-531-33156-9(3) , Orchard Bks.) Scholastic, Inc.

Hill, Eric. Spot Goes to the Beach. Hill, Eric, illus. 2005. (Illus.). 22p. (J). (ps-1). bds. 6.99 (978-0-399-24362-2(3) , Putnam Juvenile) Penguin Group (USA) Inc.

—Spot Goes to the Park. Hill, Eric, illus. 2003. (Illus.). 24p. (J). pap. 6.99 (978-0-14-250124-5(7) , Puffin) Penguin Group (USA) Inc.

Hurwitz, Johanna. Lexi's Tale. Brewster, Patience, illus. 2002. (Park Pals Adventure Ser.). 112p. (J). (gr. 2-5). pap. 4.95 (978-1-58717-160-4(0) , SeaStar Bks.) Chronicle Bks. LLC.

—Lexi's Tale. 2002. (gr. 3-6). lib. bdg. 11.80 (978-0-613-54420-7(X)) Tandem Library Bks.

Ichikawa, Satomi. La-La Rose. Ichikawa, Satomi, illus. 2004. (Illus.). 40p. (J). (ps). 15.99 (978-0-399-24029-4(2) , Philomel) Penguin Group (USA) Inc.

Jocelyn, Marthe. Over, Under. Slaughter, Tom, illus. 2006. 16p. (J). (gr. k-k). 7.95 (978-0-88776-790-6(7)) Candlewick Pr.

Jones, Lara. Fun at the Park. Jones, Lara, illus. 2003. (Lola & Binky Bks.). (Illus.). 8p. (J). bds. 5.95 (978-0-7641-5689-2(6)) Barron's Educational Series, Inc.

Jones, Ursula. The Witch's Children. Ayto, Russell, illus. 2003. 32p. (J). (ps-2). 16.95 (978-0-8050-7205-1(5) , Holt, Henry & Co. Bks. For Young Readers) Holt, Henry & Co.

Jullie A. Smith. The Magic Carpet Adventures: A Trip to the Park. 2007. (ENG.). 32p. per. 12.99 (***978-1-4259-7358-2(2)***) AuthorHouse.

Kent, Lorna, illus. In the Park. 2004. 8p. (J). bds. 3.99 (978-1-85854-097-9(6)) Brimax Books Ltd. GBR. *Dist:* Byeway Bks.

Klingel, Cynthia Fitterer & Noyed, Robert B. Anna & the Letter A. 2003. (Alphaphonics Ser.). (Illus.). 24p. (J). (ps-2). 21.36 (978-1-59296-091-0(X)) Child's World, Inc.

Knudsen, Michelle. Carl the Complainer. Cocca-Leffler, Maryann, illus. 2005. 32p. (J). lib. bdg. 20.00 (***978-1-4242-1104-3(2)***) Fitzgerald Bks.

—Carl the Complainer. Cocca-Leffler, Maryann, illus. 2005. (Social Studies Connects). 32p. (J). pap. 4.99 (978-1-57565-157-6(2)) Kane Pr., The.

Koury, Jen. Tommy Truck Helps Build a Park. Torgerson, Dell & Reyner, Mark, eds. Koury, Jen, illus. 1999. (John Deere Kids Toybook Ser.). (Illus.). 10p. (J). (ps up). mass mkt. 9.99 (978-1-887327-30-5(4)) Ertl Co., Inc.

Kurusa. The Streets Are Free. Doppert, Monika, illus. 2000. 50p. (J). (gr. k-5). reprint ed. pap. 7.95 (978-1-55037-370-7(6)) Annick Pr., Ltd. CAN. *Dist:* Firefly Bks., Ltd.

Lorenz, Albert & Schleh, Joy. Hero, Hawk, & Open Hand: A Story about Cahokia. 2004. (J). (978-0-8109-4842-6(7)) Abrams, Harry N., Inc.

Luna, Rachel Nickerson. Central Park Activity & Coloring Book. Luna, Rachel Nickerson, illus. 1998. (Illus.). 32p. (J). (ps-3). pap. 4.95 (978-1-886551-02-2(2)) Howard, Emma Bks.

Mathers, Petra. Lottie's New Friend. Mathers, Petra, illus. (Illus.). 32p. (J). (ps-3). 2002. pap. 5.99 (978-0-689-84896-4(X) , Aladdin); 1999. 15.00 (978-0-689-82014-4(3) , Atheneum/Anne Schwartz Bks.) Simon & Schuster Children's Publishing.

—Lottie's New Friend. 2002. (gr. k-3). lib. bdg. 14.15 (978-0-613-73374-8(6)) Tandem Library Bks.

Messer, Celeste M. When Eagles Fly. Hoeffner, Deb, illus. 2004. 82-92p. 4.95 (978-0-9702171-8-9(8)) AshleyAlan Enterprises.

Metrobooks Staff. Peek-a-Boo Park: A Lift-the-Flap-Book. 2000. (Illus.). 18p. (J). (ps-k). 9.99 (978-1-58663-107-9(1)) Friedman, Michael Publishing Group, Inc.

Morozumi, Atsuko. En el Parque. 2000. (SPA.). (J). (ps-k). bds. (978-958-04-4517-3(6)) Norma S.A. COL. *Dist:* Lectorum Pubns., Inc.

Murphy, Stuart J. Safari Park. Bjorkman, Steve, illus. 2001. (MathStart Ser.). 40p. (J). (gr. 2 up). pap. 5.99 (978-0-06-446245-7(5) , Harper Trophy) HarperCollins Pubs.

Napoli, Donna Jo. On Her Own. 1999. (Angelwings Ser.: No. 3). Orig. Title: Room to Grow. (Illus.). 96p. (J). (gr. 2-5). pap. 7.95 (978-0-689-82985-7(X) , Aladdin) Simon & Schuster Children's Publishing.

—On Her Own. 1999. (Angelwings Ser.: No. 3). Orig. Title: Room to Grow. (Illus.). (J). (978-0-606-17906-5(2)) Tandem Library Bks.

Neri, Filippo. Steam Park. Piero, Ruggeri, illus. 2006. 44p. 16.95 (978-1-894965-63-7(9)) Simply Read Bks. CAN. *Dist:* Perseus Distribution.

Noll, Katherine. Haunted Park. 2003. (gr. 3-6). lib. bdg. 13.00 (978-0-613-72479-1(8)) Tandem Library Bks.

Otte, Kathleen M. The Tod Squad Can Go to the Park. 2007. (J). bds. (***978-1-57332-443-4(4)***) HighReach Learning, Inc.

Peto, Judith & Talwar, Robert. Jenny & Benny: Friends, 2005. (Illus.). 28p. (J). per. 16.95 (978-0-9767511-0-6(0)) Lasting Bks. Publishing Co.

Rau, Dana Meachen. At the Park. 2007. (Fun Time Ser.). 24p. (J). lib. bdg. 22.79 (***978-0-7614-2613-4(2)*** , Benchmark Bks.) Cavendish, Marshall Corp.

Ricci, Christine. Dora's Picnic. Hall, Susan, illus. 2003. (Ready-to-Read Ser.: Vol. 1). 24p. (J). pap. 3.99 (978-0-689-85238-1(X) , Simon Spotlight/Nickelodeon) Simon & Schuster Children's Publishing.

—Dora's Picnic. 2003. (gr. k-3). lib. bdg. 11.80 (978-0-613-67079-1(5)) Tandem Library Bks.

Rigby Education Staff. Headline News. (Sails Literacy Ser.). (Illus.). 16p. (gr. 1-2). 27.00 (978-0-7635-9930-0(1) , 699301C99) Rigby Education.

Rodgers, Frank. Mr. Croc's Walk. 2007. (Read-It! Chapter Books). (J). 21.26 (978-1-4048-2729-5(3)) Picture Window Bks.

Rouillard, Wendy W. Barnaby-Seasons in the Park. Rouillard, Wendy W., ed. 2000. (Barnaby Ser.: Vol. 5). (Illus.). 32p. (J). 15.95 (978-0-9642836-9-5(7)) Barnaby & Co.

Rowe, Jeannette. YoYo Goes to the Park. Rowe, Jeannette, illus. 2003. (Illus.). 12p. (J). pap. 5.95 (978-1-58925-369-8(8) , tiger tales) ME Media LLC.

Rylant, Cynthia. Gooseberry Park. Howard, Arthur, illus. 1998. (Apple Signature Ser.). 144p. (J). (gr. 3-7). pap. 4.99 (978-0-590-94715-2(X)) Scholastic, Inc.

—Gooseberry Park. 1999. (Apple Signature Edition Ser.). (Illus.). (J). 11.64 (978-0-606-15554-0(6)) Tandem Library Bks.

Sander, Sonia. Oopsy Saves the Day. 2007. (Care Bears Movie Reader Ser.). 32p. (J). pap. 3.99 (***978-0-439-02675-8(X)***) Scholastic, Inc.

Scripture Teachers: Solomon & Friends Learn about Forgiveness. 2003. pap. (***978-0-9712894-1-3(7)***) Lighthouse Christian Products Co.

Shi, Sharon. The Camera. Jones, David Phillip, illus. 2000. 24p. (J). (gr. k-3). mass mkt. 4.99 (978-0-9702195-0-3(4) , B011, Tattootles Bks.) Tattoo Manufacturing.

The Book Company, ed. Park. (Sparkle Bks.). 10p. (J). bds. 4.99 (978-1-74047-332-3(9)) Book Co. Publishing Pty, Ltd., The AUS. *Dist:* Penton Overseas, Inc.

A Walk in the Park. 2003. (J). per. (978-1-57657-814-8(3)) Paradise Pr., Inc.

The Water Park. 2005. (J). (978-1-932570-38-0(1)) Literacy Footprints Inc.

Weeks, Sarah. Oh My Gosh, Mrs. McNosh. Westcott, Nadine Bernard, illus. 2002. 32p. (J). (ps up). 15.99 (978-0-694-01204-6(1)); lib. bdg. 15.89 (978-0-06-008858-3(3)) HarperCollins Pubs. (Geringer, Laura Book).

Weiss, Ellen. Twins in the Park. Williams, Sam, illus. ed. 2005. (Ready-to-Read Ser. PreLevel 1). 22p. (J). lib. bdg. 15.00 (978-1-59054-963-6(5)) Fitzgerald Bks.

—Twins in the Park. Williams, Sam, illus. 2003. (Ready-to-Read Ser.). 24p. (J). pap. 3.99 (978-0-689-85742-3(X) , Aladdin) Simon & Schuster Children's Publishing.

Wilson, Pauline Hutchens & Dengler, Sandy. The Case of the Monster in the Creek. 2001. (New Sugar Creek Gang Ser.: Vol. 6). 144p. (J). 5.99 (978-0-8024-8666-0(5)) Moody Pubs.

—The Case of the Red Hot Possum: The New Sugar Creek Gang. 2001. (New Sugar Creek Gang Ser.). 144p. (J). (gr. 2-8). 5.99 (978-0-8024-8661-5(4)) Moody Pubs.

Windsor, Jo. Fun Zone: Individual Title Six-Packs. Hawley, Kelvin, illus. (Sails Literacy Ser.). 16p. (gr. 2-3). 27.00 (978-0-7578-0705-3(4)) Rigby Education.

Witting, David. The Goul of the Garden. 2001. 48p. pap. 9.95 (978-0-7414-0789-4(2)) Infinity Publishing.

Yi, Hu Yong. Good Morning China. 2007. (Illus.). 32p. (J). (ps-1). 16.95 (***978-1-59643-240-6(3)***) Roaring Brook Pr.

PARKS—VOCATIONAL GUIDANCE

Firestone, Mary. Park Rangers. 2003. (Community Helpers Ser.). (Illus.). 24p. (J). (gr. 1-2). lib. bdg. 19.93 (978-0-7368-1615-1(1) , Bridgestone Bks.) Capstone Pr., Inc.

Gartner, Bob. Exploring Careers in the National Parks. rev. ed. 1999. (Careers). (Illus.). 192p. (YA). (gr. 7-12). lib. bdg. 26.50 (978-0-8239-2964-1(7) , CANAPA) Rosen Publishing Group, Inc., The.

PARLIAMENTARY PRACTICE

Cipriano, Jeri S. It's a Rule. 2003. (Yellow Umbrella Books). (Illus.). 16p. (J). (gr. 1). lib. bdg. 14.60 (978-0-7368-2027-1(2) , Pebble Bks.) Capstone Pr., Inc.

Parliamentary Procedure. 2000. (YA). cd-rom 125.00 (978-1-57078-300-5(4) , CEV90300) C E V Multimedia, Ltd.

PARODIES

Hysom, Dennis Joe & Walker, Christine. Wooleycat's Musical Rhyme Time Theater. 2003. (Wooleycat's Favorite Nursery Rhymes Ser.). (Illus.). (J). pap. (978-1-889910-26-0(0)) Tortuga Pr.

—Wooleycat's Musical Theater. Walker, Christine, illus. 2003. (Wooleycat's Favorite Nursery Rhymes Ser.). (Illus.). 32p. (J). (ps-2). 18.95 incl. audio compact disk (978-1-889910-25-3(2)) Tortuga Pr.

Jackson, Ellen B. Jean Henry. 1999. (J). 15.00 (978-0-15-202225-9(2)) Assessment Systems, Inc.

PARROTS

Adams, Pam. Parrot. 1999. (Pocket Pals Ser.). (Illus.). 12p. (J). (ps-1). bds. 1.99 (978-0-85953-861-9(3)) Child's Play-International.

Altman, Linda Jacobs. Parrots. 2000. (Perfect Pets Ser.). (Illus.). 32p. (J). (gr. 3-5). lib. bdg. 25.64 (978-0-7614-1102-4(X) , Benchmark Bks.) Cavendish, Marshall Corp.

Barnes, Julia. Pet Parakeets. 2006. (Pet Pals Ser.). (Illus.). 32p. (J). (gr. 2-5). lib. bdg. 23.93 (978-0-8368-6780-0(7)) Stevens, Gareth Inc.

Bonforte, Lisa. Learning about Parrots. 2002. (Learning about Ser.). (Illus.). 16p. (J). pap. 1.50 (978-0-486-42353-1(0)) Dover Pubns., Inc.

Do Parrots Have Pillows? (Animals All Around Ser.). 24p. (J). 7.95 (978-1-4048-0374-9(2)) Picture Window Bks.

Fetty, Margaret. Parrots. 2006. (Smart Animals! Ser.). (Illus.). 32p. (J). lib. bdg. 25.27 (978-1-59716-163-3(2)) Bearport Publishing Co., Inc.

Frost, Helen. Parrots. Saunders-Smith, Gail, ed. 2002. (Rain Forest Animals Ser.). (Illus.). 24p. (J). (gr. k-1). lib. bdg. 15.93 (978-0-7368-1194-1(X) , Pebble Bks.) Capstone Pr., Inc.

Gareth Stevens Publishing Staff, contrib. by. Parrots. 2004. (All about Wild Animals Ser.). (Illus.). 32p. (J). (gr. 2 up). lib. bdg. 23.33 (978-0-8368-4122-0(0)) Stevens, Gareth Inc.

Hanel, Rachael. Parrots. 2008. (J). (***978-1-58341-657-0(9)*** , Creative Education) Creative Co., The.

Harcourt School Publishers Staff. Let's Talk about Parrots On Level. 3rd ed. 2002. (Trophies Reading Program Ser.). (Illus.). pap. 5.10 (978-0-15-323371-5(0)) Harcourt Schl. Pubs.

Howard, Fran. Parrots: Colorful Birds. 2004. (Wild World of Animals Ser.). (Illus.). 24p. (J). lib. bdg. 21.26 (978-0-7368-2615-0(7) , Bridgestone Bks.) Capstone Pr., Inc.

Jackson, Tom. Nature Watch: Parrots, Tropical & Rainforest Birds. 2005. (Illus.). 64p. 15.99 (978-0-7548-1450-4(5) , Lorenz Bks.) Anness Publishing GBR. *Dist:* National Bk. Network.

Johnson, Jinny. Parrot. Woods, Michael, illus. 2006. 32p. (J). (978-1-58340-904-6(1)) Smart Apple Media.

Juaristi, Felipe. El Loro de Haydn. 2004. (SPA.). 112p. (YA). 11.99 (978-84-241-8667-8(2)) Everest de Ediciones y Distribucion, S.L. ESP. *Dist:* Lectorum Pubns., Inc.

Kalz, Jill. Parrots. 2006. (Wild World of Animals Ser.). (Illus.). 32p. (J). (gr. 3-5). lib. bdg. 18.95 (978-1-58341-434-7(7) , Creative Education) Creative Co., The.

Klobuchar, Lisa. Cockatiels & Other Parrots. 2007. (World Book's Animals of the World Ser.). (Illus.). 64p. (J). (978-0-7166-1327-5(1)) World Bk., Inc.

Landau, Elaine. Parrots & Parakeets as Pets. 1998. (True Bks.). (Illus.). 48p. (J). (gr. 3-5). pap. 6.95 (978-0-516-26272-7(6) , Children's Pr.) Scholastic Library Publishing.

Leon, Vicki. A Rainbow of Parrots. 2nd ed. 2006. (Jean-Michel Cousteau Presents Ser.). (Illus.). 48p. pap. 7.95 (978-0-9766134-2-8(5)) London Town Pr.

Macken, JoAnn Early. Parakeets. 2003. (Let's Read about Pets Ser.). (Illus.). 24p. (J). (ps up). lib. bdg. 19.33 (978-0-8368-3800-8(9)); pap. 7.93 (978-0-8368-3847-3(5)) Stevens, Gareth Inc. (Weekly Reader Early Learning Library).

Murray, Julie. Parrots. 2002. (Animal Kingdom Ser.). (Illus.). 24p. (J). (gr. k-4). lib. bdg. 21.35 (978-1-57765-705-7(5)) ABDO Publishing Co.

Parrots. 2006. (Zootles Ser.). (J). 4.95 (978-1-932396-20-1(9)) Wildlife Education, Ltd.

Parrots: Early Level Satellite, 6 Packs. (Sails Literacy Ser.). 16p. (gr. 1-2). 27.00 (978-0-7578-3160-7(5)) Rigby Education.

Rabinowitz, Sima. Parrots. 2001. (Let's Investigate Ser.). (Illus.). 32p. (J). (978-1-58341-196-4(8) , Creative Education) Creative Co., The.

Rauzon, Mark J. Parrots Around the World. 2001. (Animals in Order Ser.). (Illus.). 48p. (J). (gr. 4-6). pap. 6.95 (978-0-531-13958-5(1)); 26.50 (978-0-531-11688-3(3)) Scholastic Library Publishing. (Watts, Franklin).

—Parrots Around the World. 2001. (gr. 3-6). lib. bdg. 15.25 (978-0-613-37490-3(8)) Tandem Library Bks.

Schulte, Mary Knudson. Parrots & Other Birds. 2005. (Scholastic News Nonfiction Readers Ser.). (Illus.). 24p. (J). (gr. 1-2). 19.00 (978-0-516-24931-5(2) , Children's Pr.) Scholastic Library Publishing.

Wildlife Education, Ltd. Staff. Parrots. Boyer, Trevor, illus. 2000. (Zoobooks Ser.). 18p. (YA). (gr. 5 up). pap. 2.95 (978-0-937934-27-2(5)) Wildlife Education, Ltd.

Wildlife Education, Ltd. Staff & Wexo, John Bonnett. Parrots. Boyer, Trevor, illus. 2001. (Zoobooks Ser.). 24p. (J). 15.95 (978-0-937934-84-5(4)) Wildlife Education, Ltd.

Windsor, Jo. Bat & Parrot: Emergent Level Satellite Individual Title Six-Packs. Storey, Jim, illus. (Sails Literacy Ser.). (gr. k-1). 27.00 (978-0-7578-7917-3(9)) Rigby Education.

PARROTS—FICTION

The adventures of officer Byrd. 2007. (J). 16.99 (***978-0-9787322-0-2(0)***) Officer Byrd Publishing Co.

Agee, Jon. Terrific. Agee, Jon, illus. 2005. (Illus.). 32p. (J). (ps-17). (978-0-7868-5184-3(8) , Di Capua, Michael) Scholastic, Inc.

Anderson, Laurie Halse. Time to Fly. 2003. (Wild at Heart Ser.). (Illus.). 113p. (J). (gr. 4 up). lib. bdg. 23.33 (978-0-8368-3262-4(0)) Stevens, Gareth Inc.

Bee, William. And the Train Goes... Bee, William, illus. 2007. (Illus.). 32p. (J). (ps-1). 15.99 (978-0-7636-3248-9(1)) Candlewick Pr.

Cassidy, Anne. The Queen's Dragon. Williamson, Gwyneth, illus. 2004. (Read-It! Readers Ser.). 32p. (C). (gr. k-3). 18.60 (978-1-4048-0553-8(2)) Picture Window Bks.

Chase, Andra, illus. Feathers at Las Flores. 2001. (Key Concepts in Personal Development Ser.). 32p. pap., tchr. ed. 89.95 incl. VHS (978-1-55942-173-7(8) , 9389K3) Marsh Media.

Clawson, Kimberly. Fun O' Licious. Bellomy, Gail, illus. 2007. (ENG.). 56p. per. 12.95 (***978-1-4241-5556-9(8)***) PublishAmerica, Inc.

Cook, Ande, illus. The Rich Man & the Parrot. 2007. 32p. (J). (gr. k-3). 16.95 (978-0-8075-5059-5(0)) Whitman, Albert & Co.

Dent, Jenny. Peter Parrot & His Magic Star. 2001. (Peter Parrot Ser.). (Illus.). 32p. (gr. k-3). 12.95 (978-0-85487-119-3(5)) White Eagle Publishing Trust GBR. *Dist:* De-Vorss & Co.

—Peter Parrot Visits Africa. 2001. (Peter Parrot Ser.). (Illus.). 32p. (gr. k-3). 12.95 (978-0-85487-120-9(9)) White Eagle Publishing Trust GBR. *Dist:* DeVorss & Co.

Doudna, Kelly. Parrot Crackers. Haberstroh, Anne, illus. 2007. (Fact & Fiction Ser.). 24p. (J). pap. (978-1-59928-459-0(6)); 21.35 (978-1-59928-458-3(8)) ABDO Publishing Co.

Feathers at Las Flores - Evaluation Guide: Evaluation Guide. 2006. (J). (978-1-55942-405-9(2)) Marsh Media.

Feathers at Las Flores - Teaching Guide. 2000. 17.95 (978-1-55942-172-0(X)) Marsh Media.

Fontanez, Edwin. En esta hermosa Isla. Fontanez, Edwin, illus. 2005. (SPA., Illus.). 32p. (J). 16.95 (978-0-9640868-7-6(5)) Exit Studio.

Friedman, Laurie. Love, Ruby Valentine. Cravath, Lynne Avril, illus. 2006. 32p. (J). 15.95 (978-1-57505-899-3(5) , Carolrhoda Bks.) Lerner Publishing Group.

Harcourt School Publishers Staff. The Amazing One of a Kind Parrot Below Level. 3rd ed. 2002. (Trophies Reading Program Ser.). (Illus.). pap. 5.10 (978-0-15-323250-3(1)) Harcourt Schl. Pubs.

—The Amazing Parrot: Take-Home Book. 2001. (Collections Ser.). (Illus.). (J). pap. 1.90 (978-0-15-319512-9(6)) Harcourt Schl. Pubs.

Hardway, Margaret. Parachute Clown in the Rain Forest. Smith, Eloise, ed. 1998. (Illus.). 20p. (J). (ps-6). 7.00 (978-0-9664035-1-0(7)) Mask Flight Pr.

Hardway, Margaret, et al. 3 Parrots in an Orange Tree. Smith, Eloise, ed. 1998. (Illus.). 20p. (J). (ps-6). 7.00 (978-0-9664035-0-3(9)) Mask Flight Pr.

Howard, Milly. The Case of the Sassy Parrot. Day, Bruce, illus. 2002. (Crimebusters, Inc Ser.: Bk. 2). 168p. (J). pap. 6.49 (978-1-57924-721-8(0)) Jones, Bob Univ. Pr.

—Case of the Sassy Parrot. 2002. (gr. 3-6). lib. bdg. 14.70 (978-0-613-79328-5(5)) Tandem Library Bks.

Hughes, Frieda. Rent a Friend Colour Storybook. Riddell, Chris, illus. 48p. (J). pap. 9.99 (978-0-340-86580-4(6) , Hodder & Stoughton) Hodder General Publishing Division GBR. *Dist:* Trafalgar Square Publishing.

I Can: Individual Title Six-Packs. (Sails Literacy Ser.). 16p. (gr. k up). 27.00 (978-0-7635-4396-9(9)) Rigby Education.

Jane, Pamela. Winky Blue, Forever. 1999. (gr. 3-6). lib. bdg. 11.80 (978-0-613-28139-3(X)) Tandem Library Bks.

Joosse, Barbara M. Ghost Trap. Truesdell, Sue, illus. 1998. (Wild Willie Mystery Ser.). 80p. (J). (gr. 4-6). tchr. ed. 15.00 (978-0-395-66587-9(6) , Clarion Bks.) Houghton Mifflin Co. Trade & Reference Div.

Kasten, Nancy, illus. First Feather, 2003. 70p. (J). pap. 9.99 (978-0-9744863-0-7(2)) Paulus Publishing.

Kennedy, Kim. Pirate Pete: "Where There's Gold I'm a Goin'" Kennedy, Doug, illus. 2002. 40p. (J). (ps-3). 15.95 (978-0-8109-4356-8(5)) Abrams, Harry N., Inc.

Kennedy, Kim. Pirate Pete's Talk Like a Pirate. Kennedy, Doug, illus. 2007. 40p. (J). (ps-17). 15.95 (***978-0-8109-9348-8(1)*** , Abrams Bks. for Young Readers) Abrams, Harry N., Inc.

Korten, Gerri. The Parakeets & the Ginkgo Tree at Hide Park. l.t. ed. 2006. (Illus.). 36p. (J). 18.85 (***978-0-9785609-7-3(3)***) New Global Publishing.

Krailing, Tessa. The Rude Parrot, Vol. 10. Lewis, Jan & Eastwood, John, illus. 1999. (Petsitters Club Ser.: No. 10). 96p. (J). (gr. 1-4). pap. 3.95 (978-0-7641-1193-8(0)) Barron's Educational Series, Inc.

Lester, Helen. Princess Penelope's Parrot. Munsinger, Lynn M., illus. 2001. 32p. (J). (gr. k-3). reprint ed. pap. 6.95 (978-0-618-13845-6(5) , Walter Lorraine) Houghton Mifflin Co. Trade & Reference Div.

—Princess Penelope's Parrot. 2001. (Illus.). (J). (978-0-606-21387-5(2)) Tandem Library Bks.

Logue, Stephanie. Mango's Revenge. Murphy, Chris, illus. 2006. (J). pap. (978-1-59336-769-5(4)) Mondo Publishing.

Lost: Individual Title, 6 Packs. (Story Steps Ser.). (gr. k-2). 23.00 (978-0-7635-9817-4(8)) Rigby Education.

Martin, Rafe. The Brave Little Parrot. Gaber, Susan, illus. 1998. 1p. (J). (ps-3). 16.99 (978-0-399-22825-4(X) , Putnam Juvenile) Penguin Group (USA) Inc.

Martinez, Victor. Parrot in the Oven: Mi Vida. Scott, Steve, illus. rev. ed. 1998. 240p. (J). (gr. 7 up). pap. 5.99 (978-0-06-447186-2(1) , Harper Trophy) HarperCollins Pubs.

—Parrot in the Oven: Mi Vida. 1998. (978-0-606-13695-2(9)) Tandem Library Bks.

Meissner, David. The Missing Parrot. ed. 2003. (Early Connections Ser.). (J). pap. 35.00 (978-1-4108-1552-1(8)) Benchmark Education Co.

Metzenthen, David. Bay Boys: Big Wave Day, Adrian over the Top, Adrian Goes Out There! 2005. (Triple Play-Yellow Ser.). (Illus.). 48p. (gr. 4-8). 41.85 (978-0-7910-9080-0(9)) Facts On File, Inc.

My Hat: Individual Title Six-Packs. (Sails Literacy Ser.). 16p. (gr. k up). 27.00 (978-0-7635-4436-2(1)) Rigby Education.

Parakeet. 2004. (J). per. (978-1-57657-398-3(2)) Paradise Pr., Inc.

Peck, Dale. Lost Cities: The Second Voyage. Terry, Michael, illus. 2007. 400p. (J). (gr. 5 up). 16.95 (978-1-58234-859-9(6)) Bloomsbury Publishing.

Pippin, Sheila. Katrina: Through Mango's Eyes. 2007. (J). 12.95 (***978-1-56167-956-0(9)***) American Literary Pr.

Pollack, Pam & Belviso, Meg. Krelboyne Parrot. 2001. (Malcolm in the Middle Ser.: No. 7). 112p. (J). (gr. 4-7). pap. 4.99 (978-0-439-26133-3(3)) Scholastic, Inc.

Polly Parrot. 2006. (J). lib. bdg. 14.95 (978-0-9774937-0-8(9)) Wood, Ella Sue.

Punter, R. Stories of Pirates. 2004. (Young Reading Ser.: Vol. 1). 48p. (J). (gr. 2 up). pap. 5.99 (978-0-7945-0583-7(X)) EDC Publishing.

Rawson, Katherine. If You Were A Parrot. Rogers, Sherry, illus. 2006. 32p. (J). 15.95 (978-0-9764943-9-3(6)) Sylvan Dell Pubng.

Reed, Holcomb. Wird Bird. Reed, Holcomb, illus. 2000. (Illus.). 32p. (J). (ps-3). 16.50 (978-0-9670198-1-9(8)) Potser, T.T. , Inc.

—Wird Bird. 2000. (Illus.). 32p. (J). (ps-3). pap. 9.50 (978-0-9670198-2-6(6)); lib. bdg. 18.00 (978-0-9670198-0-2(X)) Potser, T.T. , Inc.

Rey, H. A. Curious George Feeds the Animals. 1998. (Illus.). 24p. (J). (gr. k-3). tchr. ed. 12.95 (978-0-395-91904-0(5)) Houghton Mifflin Co. Trade & Reference Div.

Rey, Margret & Rey, H. A. Curious George Feeds the Animals. 1998. (Curious George Ser.). (Illus.). 24p. (J). (gr. k-3). pap. 3.95 (978-0-395-91910-1(X)) Houghton Mifflin Co. Trade & Reference Div.

Reza, Connie. Leah Ann Adopta un Perico. 2006. (Illus.). 32p. (J). 19.99 incl. audio compact disk (978-0-9714533-2-6(2)) Yo Puedo Publishing.

Riechel, Rosemarie. Percival, the Homeless Parrot. 1998. (Illus.). 16p. (J). (gr. k-3). pap. 7.00 (978-0-8059-4481-5(8)) Dorrance Publishing Co., Inc.

Rigby Education Staff. All Clean. (Sails Literacy Ser.). (Illus.). 16p. (gr. 1-2). 27.00 (978-0-7635-9901-0(8) , 699018C99) Rigby Education.

Roddie, Shen. The Gossipy Parrot. Terry, Michael, tr. Terry, Michael, illus. 2004. 32p. (J). 20.00 (978-0-7475-6079-1(X)) Bloomsbury Publishing Plc GBR. *Dist:* Independent Pubs. Group.

—Gossipy Parrot Pbk. Terry, Michael, illus. 2003. 32p. pap. 9.99 (978 0 7475-6489-8(2)) Bloomsbury Publishing Plc GBR. *Dist:* Independent Pubs. Group.

Rossell, Judith. Jack Jones & the Pirate Curse. 2007. 176p. (J). (gr. 3-6). 15.95 (***978-0-8027-9661-5(3)***) Walker & Co.

Sandilands, Joyce. 3 on a Moonbeam. Padur, Simone, illus. 2004. 64p. (978-0-9734383-1-4(2)) Whitlands Publishing, Ltd.

Scholastic, Inc. Staff. Paco Beanbag Maya & Miguel. 2005. (Paco Beanbag Ser.). (J). 8.99 (978-0-439-72688-7(3) , Sidekicks TM) Scholastic, Inc.

Small, Tanya. What You Say Is What You Are. 2007. pap. 7.50 (***978-0-9705090-1-7(4)***) MorningGlory Publishing.

Talley, Linda & Chase, Andra. Feathers at Las Flores. 2001. (Illus.). 30p. (J). 17.95 (978-1-55942-162-1(2)) Marsh Media.

Tobin, C. La Mascota de la Clase. DeMonico, Rick, illus. 2005. (Maya & Miguel Ser.). (SPA.). 80p. (J). (ps-ps). pap. 5.99 (978-0-439-78347-7(X) , Scholastic en Espanol) Scholastic, Inc.

—Teacher's Pet. DeMonico, Rick, illus. 2005. (Maya & Miguel Ser.). 80p. (J). (ps-ps). pap. 5.99 (978-0-439-73385-4(5)) Scholastic, Inc.

Wahl, Jan. Rosa's Parrot. Howard, Kim, illus. 1999. (J). (ps-3). 15.95 (978-1-58089-011-3(3)) Charlesbridge Publishing, Inc.

West, Tracey. Me & My Robot No.2: The Show-and-Tell Show-off. Revell, Cindy, illus. 2003. (All Aboard Reading Ser.). 48p. (J). 13.89 (978-0-448-43282-3(X) , Grosset & Dunlap) Penguin Group (USA) Inc.

What's New Cockatoo. 2005. (J). (978-0-9767179-3-5(X)) ABC Development, Inc.

Wiebe, Trina. Parrots Don't Make House Calls. Sarrazin, Marisol, tr. Sarrazin, Marisol, illus. 2004. (Abby & Tess Pet-Sitters Ser.: Vol. 7). 96p. (J). pap. 5.95 (978-1-894222-45-7(8)) Lobster Pr. CAN. *Dist:* Univ. of Toronto Pr.

—Parrots Don't Make Housecalls. 2003. (gr. k-3). lib. bdg. 14.10 (978-0-613-84680-6(X)) Tandem Library Bks.

Wilhelm, Hans. With Lots of Love. 2004. (Illus.). 32p. (J). 12.95 (978-0-7641-5767-7(1)) Barron's Educational Series, Inc.

Willis, Jeanne. Be Quiet, Parrot! Birchall, Mark, illus. 2005. (Picture Bks.). 32p. (J). (gr. k-2). 7.25 (978-1-57505-492-6(2)) Lerner Publishing Group.

Witte, Anna. El Loro Tico Tango. Witte, Anna, illus. 2005. (SPA., Illus.). 24p. (J). pap. 6.99 (978-1-84148-971-1(9)) Barefoot Bks., Inc.

—The Parrot Tico Tango. Witte, Anna, illus. (Illus.). 24p. (J). (gr. k-3). 2005. 15.99 (978-1-84148-243-9(9)); 2004. pap. 6.99 (978-1-905236-11-4(5)) Barefoot Bks., Inc.

Zindel, Paul. The Petrified Parrot. Date not set. (P. C. Hawke Mysteries Ser.: Bk. 11). 160p. (J). (gr. 3-7). pap. 4.99 (978-0-7868-1623-1(6)) Disney Pr.

PARTIES

see also Entertaining

Aretha, David. Ecstasy & Other Party Drugs: A MyReportLinks. com Book. 2005. (Drugs Ser.). (Illus.). 48p. (J). lib. bdg. 25.26 (978-0-7660-5278-9(8) , MyReportLinks.com Bks.) Enslow Pubs., Inc.

Barker, Cicely Mary. How to Host a Flower Fairy Tea Party. 2004. (Flower Fairies Ser.). (Illus.). (ps). 48p. (J). 7.99 (978-0-7232-5360-0(9)); 24p. pap. 4.99 (978-0-7232-4992-4(X)) Penguin Group (USA) Inc. (Warne).

Beker, Jeanne. The Big Night Out. Dion, Nathalie, illus. 2005. 80p. (J). (gr. 4). pap. 15.95 (978-0-88776-719-7(2)) Tundra Bks., Inc./Livres Toundra, Inc. CAN. *Dist:* Random Hse., Inc.

Bell, Alison. Let's Party! Chung, Kun-Sung, illus. 2005. 64p. (J). pap. 14.95 (978-1-894222-99-0(7)) Lobster Pr. CAN. *Dist:* Univ. of Toronto Pr.

Bonner, Lori. Putting on a Party: Adventure Parties for Kids. Lee, Fran, illus. 2004. 64p. (YA). (gr. 2-6). pap. 9.95 (978-1-58685-232-0(9)) Gibbs Smith, Publisher.

Boyd, Heidi. Fairy Crafts. 2003. (Illus.). 96p. pap. 14.99 (978-1-58180-430-0(X) , North Light Bks.) F & W Pubns., Inc.

Brian, Sarah Jane. Party Secrets: Who to Invite, Must-Dance Music, Most-Loved Munchies & Foolproof Fun! Dixon, Debra, illus. 2003. (American Girl Library). 96p. (J). 8.95 (978-1-58485-708-2(0)) American Girl Publishing, Inc.

Bruder, Mikyla. The Star Wars Party Book: Recipes & Ideas for Galactic Occasions. Frankeny, Frankie, illus. Frankeny, Frankie, photos by. 2002. (Star Wars Ser.). 60p. (J). (gr. 3-5). 17.95 (978-0-8118-3491-9(3)) Chronicle Bks. LLC.

Bull, Jane. Parties. 2005. (Sticker activity Bks.). 16p. (J). pap. 6.99 (978-0-7566-1223-8(3)) Dorling Kindersley Publishing, Inc.

Bull, Jane & Dorling Kindersley Publishing Staff. The Party Book. 2005. (Illus.). 48p. (J). 12.99 (978-0-7566-1028-9(1)) Dorling Kindersley Publishing, Inc.

Clibbon, Meg. The Fairy Party Book: Magic Meg & Lucy Loveheart. 2005. (Illus.). 32p. (J). (ps-4). pap. 7.95 (978-1-55037-914-3(3)) Annick Pr., Ltd. CAN. *Dist:* Firefly Bks., Ltd.

Co-Ed Howling Noises Mystery Party Kit for 10 Players: Filled with Fun, Games & Laughter. 2004. (YA). 30.00 (978-1-932839-38-8(0)) SimpliFun Studios.

Dorling Kindersley Publishing Staff. Party Time. 2005. (J). bds. 6.99 (978-0-7566-1110-1(5)) Dorling Kindersley Publishing, Inc.

Dorling Kindersley Publishing Staff & Bull, Jane. The Halloween Book: 50 Creepy Crafts for a Hair-Raising Halloween. Crawford, Andy, photos by. 2000. (Illus.). 48p. (J). (gr. 4-7). 12.95 (978-0-7894-6655-6(4)) Dorling Kindersley Publishing, Inc.

Dunnewind, Stephanie. Come to Tea: Fun Tea Party Themes, Recipes, Crafts, Games, Etiquette & More. Mazille, Capucine, illus. 2003. 80p. (J). pap. 7.95 (978-1-4027-0854-1(8)) Sterling Publishing Co., Inc.

—Come to Tea: Fun Tea Party Themes, Recipes, Crafts, Games, Etiquette & More. 2003. (gr. 3-6). lib. bdg. 16.40 (978-0-613-78021-6(3)) Tandem Library Bks.

Enderlein, Cheryl L. Celebrating Birthdays in Australia. 1998. (Birthdays Around the World Ser.). (Illus.). 24p. (J). (gr. k-3). lib. bdg. 14.00 (978-0-531-11544-2(5) , Watts, Franklin) Scholastic Library Publishing.

—Celebrating Birthdays in Brazil. 1998. (Birthdays Around the World Ser.). (Illus.). 24p. (J). (gr. k-3). lib. bdg. 14.00 (978-0-531-11545-9(3) , Watts, Franklin) Scholastic Library Publishing.

—Celebrating Birthdays in China. 1998. (Birthdays Around the World Ser.). (Illus.). 24p. (J). (gr. k-3). lib. bdg. 14.00 (978-0-531-11546-6(1) , Watts, Franklin) Scholastic Library Publishing.

—Celebrating Birthdays in Russia. 1998. (Birthdays Around the World Ser.). (Illus.). 24p. (J). (gr. k-3). lib. bdg. 14.00 (978-0-531-11547-3(X) , Watts, Franklin) Scholastic Library Publishing.

Erwin, Vicki B. Scooby-Doo! Groovy Guide to Party Fun. 2002. (Illus.). 32p. (J). (978-0-439-37462-0(6)) Scholastic, Inc.

Foxx, Kylie & Ledesma, Sophie. Pajama Parties: Truth or Dare. 2001. (Illus.). 16p. (gr. 3-6). tchr. ed. 7.95 (978-0-7611-2388-0(1) , 12388) Workman Publishing Co., Inc.

Gamblin, Rose Tooley. The Birthday Party. 2007. (J). (***978-0-8127-0464-8(9)***) Autumn Hse. Publishing Co.

Gillis, Jennifer Blizin & Jordan, Denise M. Feliz Cumpleanos! 2002. (Fiestas Con Velas (Candle Time) Ser.). (SPA.). 24p. (J). (ps-1). lib. bdg. 18.50 (978-1-58810-870-8(8)); (Illus.). pap. 5.25 (978-1-58810-871-5(6) , 91594) Heinemann Library.

Hands on Crafts for Kids Staff. Perfect Kids' Parties: 12 Fantastic Theme Celebrations. 2006. (Illus.). 128p. pap. 9.95 (978-1-4027-3620-9(7)) Sterling Publishing Co., Inc.

Hogenkamp, Susan. My Birthday: Learning the IR Sound. (PowerPhonics Ser.). (Illus.). (J). 2002. 24p. (gr. 1). lib. bdg. 18.50 (978-0-8239-5948-8(1)); 2001. 23p. pap. 26.40 (978-0-8239-8293-6(9)) Rosen Publishing Group, Inc., The. (PowerKids Pr.).

Jones, Jen. Throwing Parties. 2008. (J). (***978-1-4296-0130-6(2)***) Capstone Pr., Inc.

Kilby, Janice Eaton & Taylor, Terry. The Book of Wizard Parties: In Which the Wizard Shares the Secrets of Creating Enchanted Gatherings. Baggetta, Marla, illus. 2002. 144p. 19.95 (978-1-57990-292-6(8)) Lark Bks.

Krulik, Nancy E. Prom! The Complete Guide to a Truly Spectacular Night. Johnson, Kim, illus. 2003. 96p. (YA). 8.00 (978-0-7567-9038-7(7)) DIANE Publishing Co.

Lambert, Angela, illus. Party. 2005. (All Change! Ser.). 10p. (YA). (ps). 6.99 (978-1-904550-15-0(0)) Child's Play-International.

McGillian, Jamie Kyle. Sleepover Party! Games & Giggles for a Fun Night. 2007. (Illus.). 96p. (J). (gr. 3-5). 14.95 (***978-1-4027-2978-2(2)***) Sterling Publishing Co., Inc.

Moreton, Daniel & Berger, Samantha. It's a Party. 1999. (Learning Center Emergent Readers Ser.). (J). pap. 2.50 (978-0-439-04587-2(8)) Scholastic, Inc.

My Dolly Dressing Book of Party Girls. 2002. 16p. (J). pap. 2.98 (978-0-7525-8044-9(2)) Parragon, Inc.

Radabaugh, Melinda Beth. Sleeping Over. 2003. (First Time Ser.). (Illus.). 24p. (J). (ps-1). lib. bdg. 18.50 (978-1-4034-0231-8(0)); pap. 5.25 (978-1-4034-0470-1(4)) Heinemann Library.

—Sleeping Over. 2003. (ps-2). lib. bdg. 13.30 (978-0-613-60929-6(8)) Tandem Library Bks.

Ripple, Wilhelminia. Valentine School Parties. Anderson, Heather, illus. 1998. (What Do I Do? Ser.). 192p. (J). pap. 19.95 (978-0-9649939-9-0(6)) Oakbrook Publishing Hse.

Rosenberg, Carol & Rosenberg, Gary. Jon & Jayne's Guide to Throwing, Going to, & surviving Parties. 2008. 128p. (YA). pap. 9.95 (***978-0-7573-0726-3(4)***) Health Communications, Inc.

Ross, Kathy. The Best Birthday Parties Ever! A Kid's Do-It-Yourself Guide. 1999. (Illus.). 80p. (J). (gr. 3-6). pap. 9.95 (978-0-7613-0989-5(6) , Millbrook Pr.) Lerner Publishing Group.

—The Best Birthday Parties Ever! A Kid's Do-it-Yourself Guide. Holm, Sharon Lane, illus. 1999. (Crafts from Kathy Ross Ser.). 80p. (gr. 3-6). lib. bdg. 24.90 (978-0-7613-1410-3(5) , Millbrook Pr.) Lerner Publishing Group.

—Best Birthday Parties Ever! A Kid's Do-It-Yourself Guide. Holm, Sharon Lane, illus. 1999. 78p. (J). (ps-7). lib. bdg. 18.75 (978-0-613-16597-6(7)) Tandem Library Bks.

Rue, Nancy N. The Best Bash Book: It's a God Thing! 2001. (Ywof Library). (Illus.). 144p. (J). (gr. 3-7). pap. 7.99 (978-0-310-70065-4(5)) Zonderkidz.

Schamber, Kimberly. Party Stickity-Splits, 12 vols., 0640. Hamaguchi, Carla, ed. 2002. (Illus.). 10p. pap. 6.99 (978-1-57471-889-8(4)) Creative Teaching Pr., Inc.

Souter, Gillian. Perfect Parties. Watson, Clare, illus. Martin, Andre, photos by. 2001. (Handy Crafts Ser.). 48p. (J). (gr. 2 up). lib. bdg. 24.67 (978-0-8368-2822-1(4)) Stevens, Gareth Inc.

Stacy, Lori Moore. It's My Party: How to Throw a Great Bash for Any Occasion. 2000. (All about You Ser.). 144p. (J). (gr. 4-7). pap. 4.50 (978-0-439-16137-4(1)) Scholastic, Inc.

Thomas, Anne & Thomas, Peter. The Children's Party Book: For Birthdays & Other Occasions. Mutsaars, Anjo, illus. 2001. 120p. 20.00 (978-0-86315-229-0(5)) Floris Bks. GBR. *Dist:* SteinerBooks, Inc.

Warner, Penny. Slumber Parties. 2000. (Illus.). 107p. (J). (978-0-88166-365-5(4)) Meadowbrook Pr.

—Slumber Parties. Bradley, Amanda, illus. 2000. 112p. (J). (gr. 3-9). pap. 8.00 (978-0-689-84077-7(2)) Meadowbrook Pr.

Wheeler, Susan & Kortepeter, Paul. Let's Have Tea Together: Recipes & Celebrations for Every Season. 2nd gif. ed. 2002. Orig. Title: Tea with Victoria Rose. (Illus.). 80p. 15.99 (978-0-7369-1043-9(3)) Harvest Hse. Pubs.

Willson, Sarah. The Ultimate Sleepover Book. 2003. (Nick Reference Ser.). (Illus.). 48p. (J). pap. 5.99 (978-0-689-84559-8(6) , Simon Spotlight/Nickelodeon) Simon & Schuster Children's Publishing.

PARTIES—FICTION

Adams, Georgie. The Three Little Witches Storybook. Bolam, Emily, illus. 2002. 96p. (ps-3). 15.99 (978-0-7868-0824-3(1)) Hyperion Bks. for Children.

Advantage Publishers Group & Saidens, Amy. Glamour Girl Sticker Book. 2007. (Illus.). 24p. (J). 14.95 (***978-1-59223-631-2(6)*** , Silver Dolphin Bks.) Advantage Pubs. Group.

Aikins, Dave, illus. The Birthday Dance Party: Daisy's Fiesta de Quinceañera. 2006. (Dora the Explorer Ser.). 24p. (J). pap. 3.99 (978-1-4169-1303-0(3) , Simon Spotlight/Nickelodeon) Simon & Schuster Children's Publishing.

Allen, Francesca & Brooks, Felicity. Busy Truck. Crisp, Dan, illus. 2007. 10p. (J). bds. 10.99 (978-0-7945-1453-2(7) , Usborne) EDC Publishing.

Anfousse, Ginette. Polo et L'anniversaire. Sarrazin, Marisol, tr. 2003. (Polo Baby Board Bks.). (FRE., Illus.). 16p. (J). (-ps). bds. (978-2-89021-656-3(X)) Diffusion du livre Mirabel.

Angeles, Maria. Tortilla for Emilia. 2001. (J). (978-0-7608-2264-7(6)); pap. (978-0-88741-929-4(1)) Sundance/Newbridge Educational Publishing.

Asher, Sandy. What a Party! Graves, Keith, illus. 2007. 32p. (J). (ps-1). 15.99 (978-0-399-24496-4(4) , Philomel) Penguin Group (USA) Inc.

Aunt Nina & Her Nephews & Nieces. 2004. (J). 24.95 incl. audio (978-1-56008-160-9(0)) Weston Woods Studios, Inc.

Averill, Esther Holden. Jenny's Birthday Book. Averill, Esther Holden, illus. 2005. (New York Review Children's Collection). (Illus.). 44p. (J). (ps-ps). reprint ed. pap. 15.95 (978-1-59017-154-7(3) , NYR Children's Collection) New York Review of Bks., Inc., The.

Awdry, Wilbert V. Happy Birthday, Thomas. Bell, Owain, illus. 2003. (Step into Reading Ser.). 32p. (J). (ps-2). 11.99 (978-0-679-90809-8(9) , Random Hse. Bks. for Young Readers) Random Hse. Children's Bks.

Baena, Gloria. Invitacion a la Fiesta del Gran Gorila. Osorno, Laura, illus. 2003. (SPA.). 32p. (J). 8.95 (978-958-04-7072-4(3)) Norma S.A. COL. *Dist:* Distribuidora Norma, Inc., Lectorum Pubns., Inc.

Bailey, Linda. Stanley's party. Slavin, Bill, illus. 32p. (J). (gr. k-3). 2004. (978-1-55337-768-9(0)); 2003. (978-1-55337-382-7(0)) Kids Can Pr., Ltd.

Barbie: Pajama Party. 2001. (Girl Talk Ser.). (Illus.). 56p. (J). (ps-3). 2.29 (978-0-307-28209-5(0) , Golden Bks.) Random Hse. Children's Bks.

Barker, Cicely Mary. Fairy Whispers. 2007. (Flower Fairies Friends Ser.). (Illus.). 32p. (J). pap. 12.99 (978-0-7232-5737-0(X) , Warne) Penguin Group (USA) Inc.

Barn Party: Level M, 6 vols. 128p. (gr. 2-3). 49.95 (978-0-7699-0983-7(3)) Shortland Pubns. (U. S. A.) Inc.

Barra, Nancy. Monica y la Fiesta de Verano. Zuman, John, ed. Deming, Linda, illus. 2002. (Sunflower/Girasol Ser.). (SPA.). 20p. tchr. ed., spiral bd. 5.95 (978-1-58332-055-6(5)) Intercultural Center for Research in Education (I N C R E).

—Monica y la Fiesta de Verano. Deming, Linda, illus. 2002. (Sunflower/Girasol Ser.). (SPA.). 38p. (J). 5.95 (978-1-58332-054-9(7)) Intercultural Center for Research in Education (I N C R E).

Baynes, Pauline, illus. The Elephant's Ball. 2007. 32p. (J). 17.00 (978-0-8028-5316-5(1) , Eerdmans Bks For Young Readers) Eerdmans, William B. Publishing Co.

Beardshaw, Rosalind. I am a Spaceman! 2008. (Illus.). 12p. (J). bds. 12.95 (***978-1-4052-2759-9(1)***) Egmont Bks., Ltd. GBR. *Dist:* Independent Pubs. Group.

Beardshaw, Rosalind, illus. I am a Princess! 2008. 12p. (J). bds. 12.95 (***978-1-4052-2758-2(3)***) Egmont Bks., Ltd. GBR. *Dist:* Independent Pubs. Group.

Beck, Scott. Happy Birthday, Monster! 2007. (Illus.). 32p. (J). (ps-2). 14.95 (***978-0-8109-9363-1(5)*** , Abrams Bks. for Young Readers) Abrams, Harry N. , Inc.

Benchmark Education Staff, compiled by. Celebrations. 2006. spiral bd. 139.00 (***978-1-4108-7039-1(1)***) Benchmark Education Co.

Bentley, Dawn. The Not-So Itsy Bitsy Spider: A Pop-Up Book. Heo, Yumi, illus. 1999. 12p. (J). (ps up). 12.95 (978-1-58117-051-1(3) , Intervisual/Piggy Toes) Dalmatian Pr.

Best, Cari. Three Cheers for Catherine the Great! 2003. (gr. k-3). lib. bdg. 15.25 (978-0-613-71883-7(6)) Tandem Library Bks.

Best, Cari & Potter, Giselle. Three Cheers for Catherine the Great! 2003. (Illus.). 32p. (J). pap. 6.95 (978-0-374-47551-2(2) , Sunburst) Farrar, Straus & Giroux.

Bickel, Karla. Surprise Christmas Birthday Party. Bickel, Karla, illus. l.t. ed. 2004. (Illus.). 16p. (J). (ps-6). pap. 5.00 (978-1-891452-12-3(6) , 3) Heart Arbor Bks.

Birchall, Mark. Rabbit's Birthday Surprise. Birchall, Mark, illus. 2003. (Illus.). 32p. (J). (ps-3). 15.95 (978-0-87614-910-2(7) , Carolrhoda Bks.) Lerner Publishing Group.

The Birthday Party. (Early Intervention Levels Ser.). 23.10 (978-0-7362-0002-8(9)) Hampton-Brown Bks.

Blackwell-Burke, Melissa & Kunkel, Kristen. Rhyme Time Party. 2003. (J). spiral bd. 14.95 (978-1-58605-955-2(6) , LeapFrog Schl. Hse.) LeapFrog Enterprises, Inc.

Blake, Jon. Crazy Party at the House of Fun. 2007. (Illus.). 128p. pap. 7.95 (***978-0-340-88460-7(6)***) Hodder Children's Division GBR. *Dist:* Independent Pubs. Group.

Blanck, Cathy. A Party for Arty. 2004. (Illus.). 32p. (J). pap. (978-0-9753059-0-4(5)) Red Barn Reading Inc.

Bluthenthal, Diana Cain. I'm Not Invited. Bluthenthal, Diana Cain, illus. 2003. (Illus.). 32p. (J). (gr. k-2). 18.99 (978-0-689-84141-5(8) , Atheneum/Richard Jackson Bks.) Simon & Schuster Children's Publishing.

Book Company Staff. Gilbert's Birthday Surprise. 2002. (Magical World of Teddies Ser.). 14p. (J). 12.95 (978-1-74047-161-9(X)) Book Co. Publishing Pty, Ltd., The AUS. *Dist:* Penton Overseas, Inc.

Brennan, Herbie. Nuff Said: Another Tale of Bluebell Wood. Collins, Ross, illus. 2002. 128p. (J). (gr. 2-5). 13.95 (978-1-58234-771-4(9) , Bloomsbury Children) Bloomsbury Publishing.

Brian, Janeen. Party Time! Join Mia in the Mystery & Magic of the Fairy Shop! Norling, Beth, illus. 2006. (Nibbles Ser.). 72p. (J). (gr. 1-4). pap. 3.95 (978-0-7624-2627-0(6) , Running Pr. Kids) Running Pr. Bk. Pubs.

Brian, Kate. Sweet 16. 2007. 288p. (YA). pap. 8.99 (***978-1-4169-0033-7(0)*** , Simon Pulse) Simon & Schuster Children's Publishing.

Brown, Marc. Arthur's First Kiss. Brown, Marc, illus. 2001. (Arthur Ser.). (Illus.). 24p. (J). (gr. k-3). pap. 3.99 (978-0-375-80602-5(4)); lib. bdg. 11.99 (978-0-375-90602-2(9)) Random Hse. Children's Bks. (Random Hse. Bks. for Young Readers).

—Cumpleanos de Arturo. 2000. (SPA.). (gr. k-3). lib. bdg. 15.25 (978-0-613-28287-1(6)) Tandem Library Bks.

—El Cumpleaños de Arturo. Sarfatti, Esther, tr. from ENG. 2000. (Arthur Adventure Ser.). (SPA., Illus.). (J). (ps-3). pap. 6.95 (978-1-880507-78-0(1) , LC7609) Lectorum Pubns., Inc.

Brown, Rick, illus. Halloween Party. 2007. (I'm Going to Read Ser.). 32p. (J). (gr. 1-2). pap. 3.95 (***978-1-4027-4298-9(3)***) Sterling Publishing Co., Inc.

Bryant, Ann. Jack's Party. Henley, Claire, illus. 2004. (Read-It! Readers Ser.). 32p. (C). (gr. k-3). 18.60 (978-1-4048-0060-1(3)) Picture Window Bks.

Bryant, Megan E. The Friendship Trip No. 3: Friendship Club. Thomas, Laura, illus. 2007. (Strawberry Shortcake Ser.). 64p. (J). (gr. 1-3). pap. 3.99 (978-0-448-44557-1(3) , Grosset & Dunlap) Penguin Group (USA) Inc.

Buehner, Caralyn. Snowmen at Christmas. Buehner, Mark, illus. 2005. 32p. (J). (ps). 16.99 (978-0-8037-2995-7(2) , Dial) Penguin Group (USA) Inc.

Butler, Dorothy. My Brown Bear Barney at the Party. Fuller, Elizabeth, illus. 2001. 24p. (J). (ps). 15.89 (978-0-688-17549-8(X)); 15.95 (978-0-688-17548-1(1)) HarperCollins Pubs.

Butler, Kristi T. A Big Surprise. Paparone, Pamela, illus. 2005. (Green Light Readers Level 1 Ser.). 24p. (J). (ps-ps). 12.95 (978-0-15-205142-6(2)); pap. 3.95 (978-0-15-205141-9(4)) Harcourt Trade Pubs.

Butler, Kristi T. Big Surprise. Paparone, Pamela, illus. 2005. 24p. (J). lib. bdg. 10.00 (***978-1-4242-0175-4(6)***) Fitzgerald Bks.

Byrd, Sandra. Make a Wish. 2001. (Hidden Diary Ser.). 112p. (J). (gr. 3-7). reprint ed. pap. 5.99 (978-0-7642-2481-2(6)) Bethany Hse. Pubs.

Cabot, Meg. Party Princess. 2007. (Princess Diaries: Vol. 7). 368p. (J). pap. 6.99 (978-0-06-072455-9(2) , Harper Trophy) HarperCollins Pubs.

—Party Princess. l.t. rev. ed. 2007. (Princess Diaries: Vol. 7). 335p. (YA). 23.95 (***978-0-7862-9273-8(3)***) Thorndike Pr.

Campbell, Philip. Zion's Special Invitation. 2004. 29p. pap. 14.95 (978-1-4137-1483-8(8)) PublishAmerica, Inc.

Carle, Eric. Hello Red Fox. (J). (gr. k-3). 2000. (Illus.). 26p. per. (978-0-689-83492-9(6)); 1998. per. (978-0-689-00581-7(4)) Simon & Schuster Children's Publishing. (Simon & Schuster Children's Publishing).

—Hello Red Fox. Carle, Eric & Beneduce, Ann, illus. 1998. 32p. (J). (ps-3). 19.95 (978-0-689-81775-5(4)) Simon & Schuster Children's Publishing.

—Hello, Red Fox. Carle, Eric, illus. 2001. (Illus.). 32p. (J). pap. 8.99 (978-0-689-84431-7(X) , Aladdin) Simon & Schuster Children's Publishing.

Carrasco, Ledo & Munoz, Norma. Los Cuentos de la Casa del Arbol. Olson, Johan, illus. rev. ed. 2004. (Castillo de la Lectura Blanca Ser.). (SPA.). 72p. (J). pap. 6.95 (978-970-20-0124-9(2)) Castillo, Ediciones, S. A. de C. V. MEX. *Dist:* Macmillan.

Cazet, Denys. Minnie & Moo: Minnie & Moo Go Dancing. Cazet, Denys, illus. 2001. (Live Oak Readalong Ser.). (Illus.). (J). pap. 18.95 incl. audio compact disk (978-1-59112-390-3(9)) Live Oak Media.

—Minnie & Moo Go Dancing. Cazet, Denys, illus. 2001. (Illus.). 25.95 incl. audio (978-0-87499-722-4(4)); 28.95 incl. audio compact disk (978-1-59112-591-4(X)); pap. 29.95 incl. audio (978-0-87499-723-1(2)); pap. 31.95 incl. audio compact disk (978-1-59112-590-7(1)) Live Oak Media.

Chanda, J-P. Happy Birthday, SpongeBob! Martinez, Heather, illus. 2005. (Ready-To-Read Ser.). 24p. (J). pap. 3.99 (978-0-689-87674-5(2) , Simon Spotlight/ Nickelodeon) Simon & Schuster Children's Publishing.

Chato & the Party Animals. 2004. 29.95 incl. audio compact disk (978-1-55592-703-5(3)); 24.95 incl. audio (978-1-55592-693-9(2)); pap. 14.95 incl. audio (978-1-55592-687-8(8)) Weston Woods Studios, Inc.

Chavarria-Chairez, Becky. Magda's Pinata Magic. Ventura, Gabriela Baeza, tr. Vega, Anne, illus. 2001. Tr. of Magda y la Pi?Ata Magica. (ENG & SPA.). 32p. (J). (ps-3). 14.95 (978-1-55885-320-1(0) , Piñata Books) Arte Publico Pr.

Child, Lauren. This is Actually My Party. 2007. (Charlie & Lola Ser.). 32p. (J). (ps-2). pap. 6.99 (***978-0-448-44694-3(4)*** , Grosset & Dunlap) Penguin Group (USA) Inc.

Chloe Cow & the Party. 2004. (Play Pals Ser.). (Illus.). 12p. (J). bds. (978-1-84229-644-8(2)) Top That! Publishing PLC.

Christopher, Matt. On Thin Ice. Koelsch, Michael, illus. 4th ed. 2004. (Extreme Team Ser.: Vol. 4). 64p. (J). (gr. 2-4). pap. 4.99 (978-0-316-73739-5(9)) Little Brown & Co.

Civardi, Anne. Going to a Party. 2007. 16p. (J). pap. 4.99 (978-0-7945-1011-4(6) , Usborne) EDC Publishing.

Clark, Brenda, illus. Franklin's Birthday Party. 2002. (Franklin Ser.). 12.40 (978-1-4046-0323-3(9)) Book Wholesalers, Inc.

—Hurry up, Franklin. 2002. (Franklin Ser.). (J). 12.40 (978-0-7587-4167-7(7)) Book Wholesalers, Inc.

Clark, Eleanor. Mary Elizabeth: Welcome to America. 2007. (Eleanor Jo Ser.). (J). 14.99 (978-0-9753036-7-2(8)) HonorNet.

Clark, Sherryl. Whose Birthday Is It? Smith, Jan, illus. 2004. (Read-It! Readers Ser.). 32p. (C). (gr. k-3). 18.60 (978-1-4048-0554-5(0)) Picture Window Bks.

Claus, Nancy. Santa's Prize. Ferchaud, Steve, illus. 2006. (J). (***978-0-9746747-5-9(3)***) Cypress Bay Publishing.

Conford, Ellen. Annabel the Actress Starring in Gorilla My Dreams. Andriani, Renee W., illus. 2000. (Annabel the Actress Ser.). 64p. (J). (gr. 2-5). pap. 3.99 (978-0-689-83883-5(2) , Aladdin) Simon & Schuster Children's Publishing.

—Annabel the Actress Starring in Gorilla My Dreams. 2000. (Ready-for-Chapters Ser.). (J). 10.79 (978-0-606-20029-5(0)) Tandem Library Bks.

Constantin, Pascale, illus. I'm Going to Read (Level 1): Little Monster. 2007. (I'm Going to Read Ser.). 80p. (J). pap. 3.95 (***978-1-4027-2078-9(5)***) Sterling Publishing Co., Inc.

Coulton, Mia. Danny's Party. Coulton, Mia, photos by. 2004. (J). 4.95 (978-0-9746475-1-7(9)) Maryruth Bks., Inc.

Cousins, Lucy. Maisy Dresses Up. Cousins, Lucy, illus. 1999. (Maisy Bks.). (Illus.). 24p. (J). (gr. k-k). pap. 3.99 (978-0-7636-0909-2(9)) Candlewick Pr.

—Maisy Dresses Up. 1999. (gr. k-3). lib. bdg. 11.00 (978-0-613-21952-5(X)) Tandem Library Bks.

Cumpleanos de Paco. 2001. (Let's Start Teacher's Pets Ser.).Tr. of Desmond's Birthday Party. (SPA., Illus.). 32p. (J). (ps-3). (978-968-5308-19-9(5) , Silver Dolphin en Español) Advanced Marketing, S. de R. L. de C. V.

Cutting, David A., illus. Tasha's Tea Party: A Lift-the-Flap Board Book. 2006. (Backyardigans Ser.). 12p. (J). 5.99 (978-1-4169-1363-4(7) , Simon Spotlight/Nickelodeon) Simon & Schuster Children's Publishing.

de la Cruz, Melissa. Masquerade: A Blue Bloods Novel. 2007. 320p. (YA). (gr. 7 up). 15.99 (***978-0-7868-3893-6(0)***) Hyperion Pr.

de Paola, Tomie. Four Friends in Autumn. 2004. (Illus.). 32p. (J). 14.95 (978-0-689-85980-9(5)) Simon & Schuster Children's Publishing.

Degen, Bruce, illus. Happy Birthday, Jesse Bear! 2002. (J). 14.47 (978-0-7587-2685-8(6)) Book Wholesalers, Inc.

deGroat, Diane. Happy Birthday to You, You Belong in a Zoo. deGroat, Diane, illus. 2007. 32p. (J). pap. 6.99 (978-0-06-001029-4(0) , Harper Trophy) HarperCollins Pubs.

—Happy Birthday to You, You Belong in a Zoo. 1999. (Illus.). 32p. (J). (ps-3). 15.00 (978-0-688-16544-4(3)) HarperCollins Pubs.

—Happy Birthday to You, You Belong in a Zoo. deGroat, Diane, illus. 1999. (Illus.). 32p. (J). (ps-3). lib. bdg. 16.89 (978-0-688-16545-1(1)) HarperCollins Pubs.

Deich, Cheri Bivin. The Messy Monkey Tea Party. Genth, Christina, illus. 2007. 32p. (J). 15.95 (978-1-60108-006-6(9)) Red Cygnet Pr.

Dewin, Howard. Party Savers. 2001. (gr. k-3). lib. bdg. 11.80 (978-0-613-43863-6(9)) Tandem Library Bks.

Dolan, Penny. Mary & the Fairy. Allwright, Deborah, illus. 2004. (Read-It! Readers Ser.). 32p. (C). (gr. k-3). 18.60 (978-1-4048-0066-3(2)) Picture Window Bks.

Dominguez, Kelli Kyle. The Perfect Pinata: La Pinata Perfecta. Mlawer, Teresa, tr. Paterson, Diane, illus. 2002. (ENG & SPA.). 32p. (J). (gr. k-3). 15.95 (978-0-8075-6495-0(8)) Whitman, Albert & Co.

Donaldson, Joan. The Secret of the Red Shoes. Ettlinger, Doris, illus. 2006. 32p. (J). 8.95 (978-0-8249-5522-9(6) , Ideals Children's Bks.) Ideals Pubns.

Dooley, Norah. Everybody Brings Noodles. Thornton, Peter J., illus. (J). (gr. k-2). 2005. 32p. pap. 6.95 (978-1-57505-916-7(9)); 2003. 40p. 15.95 (978-0-87614-455-8(5) , Carolrhoda Bks.) Lerner Publishing Group.

Dorling Kindersley Publishing Staff. Party Fun. 2003. (Dk Readers Ser.). (Illus.). 32p. (J). pap. 3.99 (978-0-7894-9992-9(4)) Dorling Kindersley Publishing, Inc.

—Party Fun. 2003. (ps-2). lib. bdg. 11.80 (978-0-613-75244-2(9)) Tandem Library Bks.

Down, Reg. The Magic Knot: And other Tangles. 2007. (Illus.). 100p. (J). per. 14.95 (***978-0-9794452-0-0(5)***) Lightly Pr.

Driehaus, Cyndy Ann. The Royal Adventures of Princess Daisy & Princess Darcy. Huser, Jessie Ann, illus. 2007. (J). (***978-1-933197-31-9(5)***) Orange Frazer Pr.

Egan, Kate. Pony Party: Fiesta de Disfraces. LoRaso, Carlo, illus. 2006. (My Little Pony Ser.). (SPA.). 24p. (J). pap. 3.99 (978-0-06-112208-8(4)) HarperCollins Pubs.

Eggleton, Jill. Cat Party: Emergent Level Satellite Individual Title Six-Packs. McGrath, Raymond, illus. (Sails Literacy Ser.). (gr. k-1). 27.00 (978-0-7578-7916-6(0)) Rigby Education.

—Lazy Sailor Sam: Early Level Satellite Individual Title Six-Packs. (Sails Literacy Ser.). 16p. (gr. 1-2). 27.00 (978-0-7578-2933-8(3)) Rigby Education.

Ellis, Kim. Bernard & His Dad. 2005. 49p. pap. 12.95 (978-1-4137-7058-2(4)) PublishAmerica, Inc.

Elya, Susan Middleton. F Is for Fiesta. Karas, G. Brian, illus. 2006. 32p. (J). (ps-2). 12.99 (978-0-399-24225-0(2) , Putnam Juvenile) Penguin Group (USA) Inc.

Epstein, Robin. First Pajama Party: Slumberrific Six. 2005. (Groovy Girls Ser.). (Illus.). 80p. (J). pap. 3.99 (978-0-439-81431-7(6)) Scholastic, Inc.

Evans, Cambria. Martha Moth Makes Socks. 2006. (Illus.). 40p. (J). (gr. k-3). 16.00 (978-0-618-55745-5(8)) Houghton Mifflin Co.

Feldman, Thea. Princess Party. 2006. 3p. 5.99 (978-1-932915-33-4(8)) Sandvik Publishing.

Fitz-Gibbon, Sally. Pig in the Middle. Wakelin, Kirsti, illus. 2004. 32p. (J). (978-1-55041-894-1(7)) Fitzhenry & Whiteside, Ltd.

Fleischman, Sid. The Giant Rat of Sumatra: Or Pirates Galore. Hendrix, John, illus. 2005. 208p. (J). (gr. 5 up). 15.99 (978-0-06-074238-6(0)); lib. bdg. 16.89 (978-0-06-074239-3(9)) HarperCollins Pubs.

Foreman, George & Manushkin, Fran. Let George Do It! Martin, Whitney, illus. 2005. 32p. (J). 15.95 (978-0-689-87807-7(9) , Simon & Schuster Children's Publishing) Simon & Schuster Children's Publishing.

Franklin's Birthday Party. 2004. (Franklin Tv Storybooks Ser.). (Illus.). 32p. (J). (ps-ps). (978-1-55074-882-6(3)) Kids Can Pr., Ltd.

Frantz, Jennifer. The World's Biggest Tea Party. Fletcher, Lyn, illus. 2006. (My Little Pony Ser.). 24p. (J). pap. 3.99 (978-0-06-123444-6(3) , Harper Festival) HarperCollins Pubs.

Freeman, Don. Corduroy's Easter Party. McCue, Lisa, illus. 2000. (Corduroy Ser.). 32p. (J). (gr. k-1). pap. 3.49 (978-0-448-42154-4(2) , Grosset & Dunlap) Penguin Group (USA) Inc.

—Corduroy's Easter Party. 2000. (ps-2). lib. bdg. 11.25 (978-0-613-24691-0(8)) Tandem Library Bks.

Freeman, Tor. Hooray, I'm Five Today! Freeman, Tor, illus. 2004. (Illus.). 32p. (J). (gr. k-k). 16.99 (978-0-7636-2452-1(7)) Candlewick Pr.

French, Jackie. Alicia's Happy Day (English/Spanish Bilingual) Van Wright, Cornelius & Hu, Ying-Hwa, illus. 2007. 36p. (J). pap. 5.95 (***978-1-59572-116-7(9)***) Star Bright Bks., Inc.

Fry, Sonali. Let's Have a Tea Party: A Scratch-and-Sniff Storybook. Berry, Bob, illus. 2007. (Holly Hobbie & Friends Ser.). 16p. (J). pap. 5.99 (***978-1-4169-3656-5(4)*** , Little Simon) Simon & Schuster Children's Publishing.

Furgang, Kathy. A Rainbow Party. ed. 2003. (Early Connections Ser.). (J). pap. 33.00 (978-1-4108-1363-3(0)) Benchmark Education Co.

Gambrell, Linda B. & Dorling Kindersley Publishing Staff. Party Fun. 2003. (Readers Ser.). (Illus.). 32p. (J). 12.99 (978-0-7894-9994-3(0)) Dorling Kindersley Publishing, Inc.

Gates, Josephine Scribner. The live dolls' house Party. Keep, Virginia, illus. 2007. 104p. (J). lib. bdg. 59.00 (***978-1-60304-005-1(6)***) Dollworks.

Gibbs, Lynne. Quiet as a Mouse. Mitchell, Melanie, illus. 2003. (Growing Pains Ser.). 32p. (J). pap. 4.95 (978-1-57768-928-7(3)); 12.95 (978-1-57768-481-7(8)) School Specialty Publishing. (Gingham Dog Pr.).

Godbersen, Anna. The Luxe. 2007. (Luxe Ser.). 448p. (J). lib. bdg. 18.89 (***978-0-06-134567-8(9)***); (YA). (gr. 9 up). 17.99 (***978-0-06-134566-1(0)***) HarperCollins Pubs. (HarperTeen).

Golden Books Staff. Dora: Going to a Party. 2001. (Illus.). 32p. (J). (ps-2). pap. 3.99 (978-0-307-20216-1(X) , Golden Bks.) Random Hse. Children's Bks.

—Move to the Beat! 2006. (Illus.). 32p. (J). (ps-2). pap. 3.99 (978-0-375-83623-7(3) , Golden Bks.) Random Hse. Children's Bks.

—Winnie The Boo! Paint Box. 2000. (Illus.). 32p. (ps-3). pap. 3.99 (978-0-307-09237-3(2) , Golden Bks.) Random Hse. Children's Bks.

Gonzalez Bertrand, Diane. The Ruiz Street Kids (Los Muchachos de la Calle Ruiz) Baeza Ventura, Gabriela, tr. (ENG & SPA., Illus.). (J). pap. 9.95 (978-1-55885-321-8(9) , Piñata Books) Arte Publico Pr.

Goodhart, Pippa. Hoppy Birthday, Jo-Jo! Birkett, Georgie, illus. 2005. (Green Bananas Ser.). 48p. (J). (978-0-7787-1025-7(4)) Crabtree Publishing Co.

—Hoppy Birthday, Jo-Jo! 2005. (Green Bananas Ser.). (Illus.). 48p. (J). (ps). pap. (978-0-7787-1041-7(6)) Crabtree Publishing Co.

The Great Redwall Feast. 2002. (Redwall Ser.). (Illus.). (J). 25.47 (978-0-7587-2657-5(0)) Book Wholesalers, Inc.

Gritton, Steve. The Kandy Witch. 2007. (J). 18.95 (***978-0-9795361-0-6(3)***) Bad Frog Art/SMG Bks.

Gruetzke, Mary, ed. Duck Book & Purse. McDonald, Jill, illus. 2006. 8p. (J). bds. 5.99 (978-0-439-73339-7(1) , Cartwheel Bks.) Scholastic, Inc.

Guest, Elissa Haden. Iris & Walter & the Birthday Party. Davenier, Christine, illus. 2008. (Iris & Walter Ser.). 44p. (J). pap. 5.95 (***978-0-15-205388-8(3)*** , Harcourt Paperbacks) Harcourt Children's Bks.

—Iris & Walter & the Birthday Party. Davenier, Christine, illus. 2006. (Iris & Walter Ser.). 44p. (J). 15.00 (978-0-15-205015-3(9)) Harcourt Trade Pubs.

Guy, Ginger Foglesong. Fiesta. Moreno, Rene King, illus. 2007. 32p. (J). pap. 6.99 (***978-0-06-088226-6(3)*** , Rayo) HarperCollins Pubs.

Hale, Natalie. Peanut Butter Party. 2002. (J). spiral bd. 14.95 (978-0-9702698-3-6(8)) Special Reads for Special Needs.

Hall, Kirsten. Birthday Beastie: All about Counting. Luedecke, Bev, illus. 2003. (Beastieville Ser.). 32p. (J). 19.50 (978-0-516-22891-4(9) , Children's Pr.) Scholastic Library Publishing.

Hallinan, P. K. Happy Birthday! 2003. (J). (Illus.). 26p. bds. 7.95 (978-0-8249-5453-6(X)); (978-0-8249-6507-5(8) , Candy Cane Pr.) Ideals Pubns.

Handler, Daniel & Dudley, Dick, illus. The Alphabet Eurps & the Birthday Surprise. 1999. 10p. (J). 7.95 (978-1-892522-02-3(0)) Eurpsville USA, Inc.

The Hannuka Party. 2001. (J). (978-1-58453-139-5(8)) Pioneer Valley Educational Pr., Inc.

Hanson, Warren. Bugtown Boogie. 2008. 32p. (J). 16.99 (***978-0-06-059937-9(5)***); lib. bdg. 17.89 (***978-0-06-059938-6(3)***) HarperCollins Pubs. (Geringer, Laura Book).

Happy Birthday, Thomas. 2002. (Thomas the Tank Engine Ser.). (Illus.). (J). 11.91 (978-0-7587-1242-4(1)) Book Wholesalers, Inc.

Harcourt School Publishers Staff. Block Party! 3rd ed. 2002. (Trophies English Language Learners Ser.). (Illus.). pap. 5.10 (978-0-15-327893-8(5)) Harcourt Schl. Pubs.

—Ingredientes Secretos On Level. 3rd ed. 2002. (Trofeos Ser.).Tr. of Secret Ingredients. (SPA., Illus.). pap. 6.80 (978-0-15-324176-5(4)) Harcourt Schl. Pubs.

—A Party: Take-Home Book. 1999. (Signatures Ser.). (Illus.). (J). pap. 1.70 (978-0-15-314550-6(1)) Harcourt Schl. Pubs.

—Titch & Daisy: Library Book. 1999. (Collections Ser.). (Illus.). pap. 14.90 (978-0-15-313404-3(6)) Harcourt Schl. Pubs.

Hargreaves, Roger. Little Miss Fun. Hargreaves, Roger, illus. 2001. (Mr. Men & Little Miss Ser.). (Illus.). 32p. (J). (ps-3). pap. 3.99 (978-0-8431-7655-1(5) , Price Stern Sloan) Penguin Group (USA) Inc.

—Mr. Birthday. 2007. 32p. (J). pap. 3.99 (978-0-8431-2130-8(0) , Price Stern Sloan) Penguin Group (USA) Inc.

Harley, Bill. Bear's All-Night Party. Ferreira, Melissa, illus. 2001. 32p. (J). (ps-2). 15.95 (978-0-87483-572-4(0)) August Hse. Pubs., Inc.

HarperCollins Staff, ed. Let's Party. 1999. (gr. 3-6). lib. bdg. 13.00 (978-0-613-21888-7(4)) Tandem Library Bks.

Harris, Annmarie. The Countdown to Halloween. Lucas, Margeaux, illus. 2003. 24p. (J). (ps-4). pap. 3.99 (978-0-8431-0462-2(7) , Price Stern Sloan) Penguin Group (USA) Inc.

Harris, Joe. Halloween Ball. 2008. (J). (***978-0-375-84975-6(0)***); (***978-0-375-84373-0(6)***); lib. bdg. (***978-0-375-94975-3(5)***) Random Hse., Inc.

Haworth, Margaret. When Daddy Goes Away: Rusty Books. Edwards, Paul, illus. l.t. ed. 2003. (Books That Help Ser.: Vol. 2). 34p. (J). (ps-5). pap. 9.95 (978-0-9740313-1-6(3)) Haworth, Margaret.

Herman, Gail. Splish! Splash! Basso, Bill, illus. 2003. (Hello Reader Ser.). (J). (978-0-439-44164-3(1)) Scholastic, Inc.

Heurtelou, Maude. Anayiz Al Nan Fet. Louissaint, Louis, illus. 1999. Tr. of Anayiz Goes to a Party. (CRP.). 26p. (J). (gr. 3-5). pap. 19.00 incl. audio (978-1-881839-88-0(5)) Educa Vision.

Hill, Eric. Spot's Birthday Party. Hill, Eric, illus. 2007. 12p. (J). (ps-ps). bds. 6.99 (***978-0-399-24770-5(X)*** , Putnam Juvenile) Penguin Group (USA) Inc.

Hobbs, Leigh. Old Tom's Guide to Being Good. Hobbs, Leigh, illus. 2006. 96p. (gr. 1-3). pap. 3.99 (978-0-7868-5694-7(7)) Hyperion Pr.

Holabird, Katharine. Angelina Ballerina: The Costume Ball. Craig, Helen, illus. 2006. (Angelina Ballerina Ser.). 24p. (J). (ps-1). 3.99 (978-0-448-44334-8(1) , Grosset & Dunlap) Penguin Group (USA) Inc.

Holabird, Katharine. The Nutcracker—Sticker Stories. Craig, Helen, illus. 2007. 16p. (J). (ps-1). pap. 5.99 (***978-0-448-44681-3(2)*** , Grosset & Dunlap) Penguin Group (USA) Inc.

Holmes, Steve, illus. Animales Marinos: Mezcla y Diviertete. 2005. (Mezcla y Diviertete Ser.). (SPA.). 5p. (J). (ps-7). 7.95 (978-970-718-291-2(1) , Silver Dolphin en Español) Advanced Marketing, S. de R. L. de C. V. MEX. *Dist:* Perseus Distribution.

Holub, Joan. The Halloween Queen. Smythe, Theresa, illus. 2004. 32p. (J). (gr. k-3). 15.95 (978-0-8075-3138-9(3)) Whitman, Albert & Co.

Hook, Jacqueline A. You're Going to Be a Flower Girl. 2005. (J). per. (978-0-9664783-3-4(9)) Jacqueline Beverly Hills.

Horowitz, Dave. Twenty-Six Princesses. Horowitz, Dave, illus. 2008. 32p. (J). (ps). 15.99 (***978-0-399-24607-4(X)*** , Putnam Juvenile) Penguin Group (USA) Inc.

Howard, Arthur. The Hubbub Above. 2005. (Illus.). 32p. (J). 16.00 (978-0-15-204592-0(9)) Harcourt Trade Pubs.

Howe, James. Houndsley & Catina & the Birthday Surprise. Gay, Marie-Louise, illus. 2006. 48p. (J). (gr. k-3). 14.99 (978-0-7636-2405-7(5)) Candlewick Pr.

Howe, James. Houndsley & Catina & the Birthday Surprise. Gay, Marie-Louise, illus. 2007. 48p. (J). (gr. k-3). pap. 4.99 (***978-0-7636-3640-1(1)***) Candlewick Pr.

Hughes, Monica. Jan's Awesome Party. Freire, Carlos, illus. 2001. (First Novels Ser.: Vol. 18). 57p. (gr. 1-5). (J). (978-0-88780-533-2(7)); 4.95 (978-0-88780-532-5(9)) Formac Publishing Co., Ltd. CAN. *Dist:* Casemate Pubs. & Bk. Distributors, LLC.

Hughes, Shirley. Alfie & the Birthday Surprise. 1998. (Illus.). 32p. (J). (ps-1). 16.00 (978-0-688-15187-4(6)) HarperCollins Pubs.

—Alfie & the Birthday Surprise. 2007. (Illus.). 32p. (J). pap. 8.95 (***978-0-09-920862-4(8)*** , Red Fox) Random Hse. Children's Bks. GBR. *Dist:* Independent Pubs. Group.

—Alfie & the Birthday Surprise. Hughes, Shirley, illus. 1999. (Illus.). 30p. (J). 9.99 (978-1-58048-086-4(1)) Sandvik Publishing.

Hundal, Nancy. Twilight Fairies. Kilby, Don, illus. 2002. 32p. (J). (gr. k-3). (978-1-55041-645-9(6)) Fitzhenry & Whiteside, Ltd.

—Twilight Fairies. Kilby, Don, illus. 2006. 32p. pap. 7.95 (978-1-55041-961-0(7)) Fitzhenry & Whiteside, Ltd. CAN. *Dist:* F & W Pubns., Inc.

Hutchins, Hazel. Robyn's Party-in-the-Park. Cathcart, Yvonne, illus. 2005. 59p. (J). lib. bdg. 12.00 (***978-1-4242-1203-3(0)***) Fitzgerald Bks.

—Robyn's Party-in-the-Park. Cathcart, Yvonne, illus. 2005. (First Novel Ser.). 64p. (J). (gr. 2-5). (***978-0-88780-663-6(5)***); 4.95 (978-0-88780-662-9(7)) Formac Publishing Co., Ltd. CAN. *Dist:* Casemate Pubs. & Bk. Distributors, LLC.

Jacques, Brian. The Great Redwall Feast. Denise, Christopher, illus. 2000. 64p. (J). (ps-ps). lib. bdg. 15.30 (978-0-613-29968-8(X)) Tandem Library Bks.

Jonell, Lynne. It's My Birthday, Too! 2001. (Illus.). (J). (978-0-606-21256-4(6)) Tandem Library Bks.

Jordan, Apple & S. I. International Staff. Slumberrific Sleepover Party. Yee, Josie, illus. 2007. (Groovy Girls Ser.). 48p. (J). 3.99 (***978-1-4169-3880-4(X)*** , Simon Scribbles) Simon & Schuster Children's Publishing.

Karasyov, Carrie & Kargman, Jill. Bittersweet Sixteen. 2007. 240p. (J). pap. 7.99 (***978-0-06-077846-0(6)*** , HarperTeen) HarperCollins Pubs.

Kargman, Jill & Karasyov, Carrie. Bittersweet Sixteen. 2006. 240p. (J). 15.99 (978-0-06-077844-6(X)); lib. bdg. 16.89 (978-0-06-077845-3(8)) HarperCollins Pubs.

Keenan, Sheila & Burns, Marilyn. Lizzy's Dizzy Day. Snider, Jackie, illus. 2001. (Hello Reader! Math Ser.). (J). (gr. k-2). pap. 3.99 (978-0-439-05963-3(1) , Cartwheel Bks.) Scholastic, Inc.

Keffer, Lois & Haidle, Helen. Ripples Raccoon Shares His Balloon. Spengler, Ken, illus. 1999. (Read-To-Me Puppet Buddies Ser.: Vol. 9). 24p. (J). (ps-1). 9.99 (978-1-57673-438-4(2) , Multnomah) WaterBrook Pr.

Keller, Holly. Brave Horace. 1998. (Illus.). 32p. (J). (ps-3). 14.89 (978-0-688-15408-0(5)) HarperCollins Pubs.

Kempf, Molly. Happy Birthday. Huxtable, Tonja & Huxtable, John, illus. 2008. (Strawberry Shortcake Ser.). 24p. (J). (ps-2). 4.99 (***978-0-448-44714-8(2)*** , Grosset & Dunlap) Penguin Group (USA) Inc.

King, Dorothea. Teddybears' Party. King, Dorothea, illus. 1999. (Teddybears Ser.). (Illus.). 8p. (J). bds. 3.95 (978-1-57717-107-2(1)) New Line Bks.

King, Susan. Amy & the Christmas Party/Amy & the New Year's Goals. King, Susan, illus. 2001. (Illus.). 75p. (J). (ps-6). 7.00 (978-0-9714446-1-4(7)) King RIT - ACKS Pubs.

Kirk, David. The Bug Flu. 2007. 32p. (J). (ps-2). 6.99 (***978-0-448-44691-2(X)***) Callaway Editions, Inc.

Kirk, David. Miss Spider's Tea Party. 2007. 32p. (J). pap. 5.99 (978-0-439-91817-6(0)) Scholastic, Inc.

Klein, Adria F. Max & the Adoption Day Party. 2007. (Read-It! Readers Ser.). (Illus.). 24p. (J). (***978-1-4048-3283-1(1)*** , 1265792) Picture Window Bks.

—Max & the Adoption Day Party. Gallagher-Cole, Mernie, illus. 2006. (Read-It! Readers Ser.). 24p. (J). (gr. k-2). lib. bdg. 19.93 (***978-1-4048-3145-2(2)*** , 1265792) Picture Window Bks.

Kline, Trish & Donev, Mary. It¿s a Party! KA Reader 2. 2007. (Illus.). 32p. (J). per. 20.00 (***978-0-9717234-3-6(5)***) Ghost Hunter Productions.

Kneen, Maggie. Halloween Kittens. Kneen, Maggie, illus. 2004. (Illus.). 20p. (J). 15.95 (978-0-8118-4228-0(2)) Chronicle Bks. LLC.

Knowitt, Holly. Celebrations. 2002. (Smackers Ser.). (Illus.). 48p. (J). (gr. 1-7). pap. 7.99 (978-0-439-32370-3(3)) Scholastic, Inc.

Koda-Callan, Elizabeth, illus. The Squiggly Wigglys. 2003. 24p. (J). (gr. k-3). 14.95 (978-0-7611-2821-2(2) , 12821) Workman Publishing Co., Inc.

Koeppel, Ruth. My Little Pony a Party in Ponyville Book. 2007. (Readers Book & DVD Ser.). 32p. (J). bds. 17.99 incl. DVD (978-0-7944-1226-5(2)) Reader's Digest Assn., Inc., The.

Krishnaswami, Uma. The Big Party. 2006. (Early Explorers Ser.). (J). 36.00 (***978-1-4108-6133-7(3)***) Benchmark Education Co.

Kropf, Latifa Berry & Cohen, Tod. It's Hanukkah Time! 2004. (Illus.). 24p. (J). (ps-1). (978-1-58013-120-9(4)) Kar-Ben Publishing.

Krulik, Nancy E. Wherefore Art Thou Josh? 2000. (gr. 5-8). lib. bdg. 13.00 (978-0-613-31913-3(3)) Tandem Library Bks.

Lady Ginny's Tea Parties. 2007. (Illus.). 32p. (J). (ps-3). (***978-1-55143-398-1(2)***) Orca Bk. Pubs.

Landy, Sarah. Blue's Snack Party. Cardinali, Kevin, illus. 2000. (Blue's Clues Ser.). 16p. (J). (ps-k). 5.99 (978-0-689-83432-5(2) , Simon Spotlight/Nickelodeon) Simon & Schuster Children's Publishing.

Lepp, Royden. Happy Birthday Barnabas. 2008. 32p. (J). pap. 3.99 (***978-0-310-71586-3(5)***) Zondervan.

Lewis, Beverly. Piggy Party. 1999. (Cul-de-Sac Kids Ser.: Vol. 19). (Illus.). 80p. (J). (gr. 2-5). pap. 3.99 (978-0-7642-2124-8(8)) Bethany Hse. Pubs.

Lewis, Paul Owen. P Bear's New Year's Party: A Counting Book. 1999. (ps-2). lib. bdg. 15.25 (978-0-613-86794-8(7)) Tandem Library Bks.

Little, Jean. The Birthday Girl. Lawrason, June, illus. 2004. (Orca Echoes Ser.). 64p. (J). (gr. 2-3). pap. 4.99 (978-1-55143-292-2(7) , 1234535) Orca Bk. Pubs. USA.

The Littles Gave a Party. 2002. (Littles Ser.). (Illus.). (J). 12.17 (978-0-7587-8433-9(3)) Book Wholesalers, Inc.

The live dolls' party Days. 2007. (Illus.). 160p. (J). llb. bdg. 59.00 (***978-1-60304-010-5(2)***) Dollworks.

Ljungkvist, Laura. Toni's Topsy-Turvy Telephone Day. 2001. (Illus.). 32p. (J). (ps-3). 15.95 (978-0-8109-4486-2(3)) Abrams, Harry N. , Inc.

Lynn, Tammy. Happy Birthday Puppy: An I See Puppy Book. Stewart, Elaine, ed. Lynn, Tammy, illus. 2006. (Illus.). 12p. (J). bds. 6.99 (978-0-9774277-0-3(6) , 0-9774277-0-6) I See Puppy, LLP.

Lytle, Robert A. Mackinac Passage: Pirate Party. Bill, Williams, illus. 2006. (J). per. 9.95 (978-0-9749412-5-7(5)) EDCO Publishing, Inc.

Mack, Paulette. Cookout at Grandma's House: The Adventures of Mielle & Cheeky. 2006. (ENG., Illus.). 24p. per. 10.95 (***978-1-59800-998-9(2)***) Outskirts Press, Inc.

Man-Kong, Mary. Play Doh: Party Time! 2002. (Illus.). 10p. (J). 9.99 (978-0-307-20036-5(1) , Golden Bks.) Random Hse. Children's Bks.

—The Princess Party Book. Legramandi, Francesco & Matta, Gabriella, illus. 2005. 32p. (J). (ps-3). pap. 7.99 (978-0-7364-2314-4(1) , RH/Disney) Random Hse. Children's Bks.

Mansfield, Katherine. The Garden Party. l.t. ed. 2006. pap. (***978-1-84702-354-4(1)***) Echo Library.

Marshall, James. Portly McSwine. 2002. (gr. k-3). lib. bdg. 12.95 (978-0-613-89008-3(6)) Tandem Library Bks.

Martin, Jacqueline Briggs. Chicken Joy on Redbean Road: A Bayou Country Romp. Sweet, Melissa, illus. 2007. 32p. (J). (gr. 3-5). 17.00 (978-0-618-50759-7(0)) Houghton Mifflin Co.

Marzollo, Jean. Hip, Hop, Hooray! 2004. (Shanna Show! Ser.). (Illus.). 32p. (ps-1). pap. 3.99 (978-0-7868-1830-3(1)) Hyperion Bks. for Children.

—Shanna's Party Surprise. 2004. (Shanna Show! Ser.). (Illus.). 32p. (ps-1). pap. 3.99 (978-0-7868-1828-0(X)) Hyperion Bks. for Children.

Maxson, H. A. & Young, Claudia H. Tea Party at Chestertown. Kosits, Andrew, illus. 2003. 55p. (J). per. 8.95 (978-0-9741713-0-2(1)) Bay Oak Pubs., Ltd.

Mayer, Mercer. Little Critter's the Best Present. 2000. (Little Critter Ser.). (J). (ps-3). (978-0-606-18923-1(8)) Tandem Library Bks.

—Tiger's Birthday. 2002. (Little Critter First Readers Ser.). (Illus.). 24p. (J). (gr. k-1). pap. 3.95 (978-1-57768-828-0(7)) School Specialty Publishing.

McAllister, Margaret. Tromso the Troll. Cox, Steve, illus. 2006. 24p. (J). lib. bdg. (***978-1-4048-3144-5(4)***) Picture Window Bks.

McConduit, Denise Walter. D. J. & the Debutante Ball. Henriquez, Emile F., illus. 2004. 32p. (J). pap. 15.95 (978-1-58980-173-8(3)) Pelican Publishing Co., Inc.

McDonald, Erin Melodie. My Birthday Party. Hanrahan, Denise, illus. 2002. 24p. (J). per. 9.95 (978-0-9721427-1-7(1)) Talking Hands, Inc.

McDonald, Megan & Payne, Tom. Ant & Honey Bee: What a Pair! Karas, G. Brian, illus. 2005. 32p. (J). (gr. k-3). 13.99 (978-0-7636-1265-8(0)) Candlewick Pr.

McGee, Warner, illus. Monster Halloween Party. 2007. (Backyardigans Ser.). 14p. (J). bds. 6.99 (***978-1-4169-3435-6(9)*** , Simon Spotlight/Nickelodeon) Simon & Schuster Children's Publishing.

McLarey, Kristina Thermaenius, et al. When You Take a Pig to a Party. Wunsch, Marjory, illus. 2000. 32p. (J). (gr. k-4). 16.99 (978-0-531-33257-3(8)); pap. 15.95 (978-0-531-30257-6(1)) Scholastic, Inc. (Orchard Bks.).

McNamara, Margaret. One Hundred Days (Plus One) Gordon, Mike, illus. ed. 2005. 32p. (J). lib. bdg. 15.00 (978-1-59054-968-1(6)) Fitzgerald Bks.

Melton, Lisa Lete. The Giant Bean Burrito: A Funny Fart Fable. Dillard, Travis, illus. 2002. 20p. (J). (gr. k-4). pap. 7.95 (978-0-9721426-0-1(6)) Paragon Publishing.

Meredith Books Staff & Marvel Comics Staff. Spider-Man Party Book. Dahlstrom, Carol, ed. 2004. (Illus.). 96p. (J). pap. 9.95 (978-0-696-21996-2(4)) Meredith Bks.

Miranda, Anne. Alphabet Fiesta. 2001. (ENG & SPA., Illus.). 56p. (J). (ps-3). 12.95 (978-1-890515-30-0(2)) Turtle Bks.

—Alphabet Fiesta: An English/Spanish Alphabet Story. 2001. (ENG & SPA., Illus.). 56p. (J). (ps-3). 18.95 (978-1-890515-29-4(9)) Turtle Bks.

Mitchell, Pratima. Raju's Ride. Waterhouse, Stephen, illus. 2005. 24p. (J). lib. bdg. 22.65 (***978-1-59646-726-2(6)***) Dingles & Co.

Mitton, Tony. Spooky Hour. Parker-Rees, Guy, illus. 2004. 32p. (J). pap. 16.95 (978-0-439-60373-7(0) , Orchard Bks.) Scholastic, Inc.

Modesitt, Jeanne. Mouse's Halloween Party. Spowart, Robin, illus. 2004. 32p. (J). (ps up). 13.95 (978-1-56397-950-7(0)) Boyds Mills Pr.

Moodie, Fiona. Noko's Suprise Party. 2008. (Illus.). 32p. (J). 16.95 (***978-1-84507-587-3(0)***) Lincoln, Frances Ltd. GBR. *Dist:* Perseus Distribution.

Mora, Pat. ¡Marimba! Animales from A to Z. Cushman, Doug, illus. 2006. 32p. (J). (gr. k-3). 16.00 (978-0-618-19453-7(3) , Clarion Bks.) Houghton Mifflin Co. Trade & Reference Div.

Morgan, Anna & Turkienicz, Rachel. My Worst/Best Sleepover Party. 2007. (Illus.). 96p. (J). (gr. 2-4). pap. 7.95 (***978-1-897187-20-3(3)***) Second Story Pr. CAN. *Dist:* Orca Bk. Pubs. USA.

Moulton, Mark Kimball. One Enchanted Evening. Crouch, Karen Hillard, illus. 2003. 32p. (J). 14.95 (978-0-8249-5480-2(7)) Ideals Pubns.

—One Enchanted Evening. Crouch, Karen Hillard, illus. 2000. 32p. (J). (gr. k-3). 18.00 (978-0-7412-0439-4(8)) Lang Graphics, Ltd.

Moulton, Mark Kimball. A Royal Wedding. Good, Karen Hillard, illus. 2007. 32p. (J). (gr. k-3). 14.99 (***978-0-8249-8677-3(6)***) Ideals Pubns.

Moulton, Mark Kimballl. The Annual Snowman's Ball. Hillaard, Karen, illus. 2007. 32p. (J) (ps-3). 14.99 (***978 0 8249-5564-9(1)*** , Ideals Children's Bks.) Ideals Pubns.

Mouse Works Staff, et al. The Masked Ball. Binder, Eric et al, illus. 2001. (Random House Pictureback Book Ser.). 24p. (J). (gr. k-3). pap. 3.25 (978-0-7364-1182-0(8) , RH/Disney) Random Hse. Children's Bks.

Murphy. Rabbit's Pajama Party. 1999. pap., tchr. ed. 2.00 (978-0-7398-2527-3(5)) Steck-Vaughn.

Nikola-Lisa, W. Shake Dem Halloween Bones. Reed, Mike, illus. 2000. 32p. (J). (gr. k-3). 6.95 (978-0-618-07034-3(6)) Houghton Mifflin Co. Trade & Reference Div.

November, Deborah. Sesame Street Big Block Party! Story Cookbook & Recipe Cards. 2006. (Sesame Street Ser.). 32p. (J). pap. 10.99 (978-0-7944-1104-6(5)) Reader's Digest Assn., Inc., The.

O'Brien, Claire. Barn Party. Archbold, Tim, illus. 2005. (I Am Reading Ser.). 48p. (J). (gr. k-3). pap. 3.95 (978-0-7534-5854-9(3) , Kingfisher) Houghton Mifflin Co. Trade & Reference Div.

—Barn Party. Archbold, Tim, illus. 2005. 46p. (J). (ps-ps). lib. bdg. 10.75 (978-0-606-33661-1(3)) Tandem Library Bks.

O'Connor, Jane. Fancy Nancy: Bonjour, Butterfly. Glasser, Robin Preiss, illus. 2008. (Fancy Nancy Ser.). 32p. (J). 16.99 (***978-0-06-123588-7(1)***); lib. bdg. 17.89 (***978-0-06-123589-4(X)***) HarperCollins Pubs.

Olsen, Ashley. Tell Me about It. 2002. (gr. 5-8). lib. bdg. 13.00 (978-0-613-64773-1(4)) Tandem Library Bks.

Oram, Hiawyn. The Best Party of Them All. Su, Lucy, illus. 2004. 32p. (J). pap. 7.95 (978-1-84507-157-8(3)) Lincoln, Frances Ltd. GBR. *Dist:* Perseus Distribution.

Oram, Hiawyn & Su, Lucy. The Best Party of All. 2004. (Illus.). 32p. (J). (978-0-7112-2062-1(X)) Lincoln, Frances Ltd. GBR. *Dist:* Transition Vendor.

Orgel, Doris. The Spaghetti Party. Durrell, Julie, illus. 1999. (Bank Street Reader Collection). 48p. (J). (gr. 1-3). lib. bdg. (978-0-8368-1780-5(X)) Stevens, Gareth Inc.

Orman, Roscoe, illus. Ricky & Mobo. 2007. (J). 14.95 (***978-1-59299-255-3(2)***) Inkwater Pr.

Otis, James. District Messenger Boy & A Necktie Par. 2006. 62.99 (***978-1-4280-3696-3(2)***); pap. 55.99 (***978-1-4280-3690-1(3)***) IndyPublish.com.

Our Princess Party. 2006. (YA). 12.95 (978-1-58117-453-3(5) , Intervisual/Piggy Toes) Dalmatian Pr.

Park, Barbara. Junie B. Jones y el Cumpleanos del Malo de Jim. Brunkus, Denise, illus. 2005. (SPA.). 96p. (J). (ps-ps). pap. 3.99 (978-0-439-56028-3(4) , Scholastic en Espanol) Scholastic, Inc.

Parnell, Robyn. My Closet Threw a Party. Pickering, Jimmy, illus. 2005. 32p. (J). 14.95 (978-1-4027-1298-2(7)) Sterling Publishing Co., Inc.

Parr, Todd. Otto Has a Birthday Party. 2004. (Illus.). 24p. (J). (ps-3). 9.95 (978-0-316-73907-8(3)) Little Brown & Co.

Passen, Lisa. The Incredible Shrinking Teacher. 2008. (Illus.). 32p. (J). pap. 6.99 (***978-0-312-38017-5(8)***) Square Fish.

Paul, Ann Whitford. Manana, Iguana. Long, Ethan, tr. Long, Ethan, illus. 2005. 32p. (J). tchr. ed. 16.95 (978-0-8234-1808-4(1)) Holiday Hse., Inc.

Pearl, Alyson J. Josie & Friends. 2007. (J). per. 9.99 (***978-1-60247-115-3(0)***) Tate Publishing & Enterprises, L.L.C.

Pearlman, Bobby & Gruelle, Johnny. Leaf Dance. Mitter, Kathryn & Winfield, Alison, illus. 2001. (Classic Raggedy Ann & Andy Ser.). 32p. (J). pap. 3.99 (978-0-689-84679-3(7) , Little Simon) Simon & Schuster Children's Publishing.

Peltzman, Adam. Blue's Sleepover Party. Pontillo, Jenine, illus. 2005. (Blue's Clues Ser.). 36p. (J). bds. 8.99 (978-1-4169-0627-8(4) , Simon Spotlight/Nickelodeon) Simon & Schuster Children's Publishing.

Perkins, T J. In the Grand Scheme of Things: A Kim & Kelly Mystery. 2007. (Illus.). 151p. (YA). 10.99 (***978-0-9777538-4-0(0)***) GumShoe Press.

Pfister, Marcus. Just the Way You Are. Pfister, Marcus, illus. 2002. (Illus.). 32p. (J). (gr. k-3). 15.95 (978-0-7358-1615-2(8)) North-South Bks., Inc.

—Somos Como Somos. Almodar, Ariel, tr. Pfister, Marcus, illus. 2002. (SPA., Illus.). 32p. (J). (gr. k-3). 15.95 (978-0-7358-1654-1(9) , NS31596) North-South Bks., Inc.

Pike, Pat. When Chloe Comes to Tea. Zuby, Cindi, illus. 2000. 12p. (J). 7.95 (978-1-886225-60-2(5)) Day of Grace Publishing Services.

Pollack, Pam & Belviso, Meg. Halloween Night on Shivermore Street. DuBurke, Randy, illus. 2004. 32p. (J). 15.95 (978-0-8118-3946-4(X)) Chronicle Bks. LLC.

Polly Piglet's Surprise Party. 2002. (My First Tab Story Ser.). (J). bds. 3.98 (978-0-7525-8956-5(3)) Parragon, Inc.

Pomerantz, Charlotte. The Birthday Letters. Adinolfi, JoAnn, illus. 2000. 32p. (J). (gr. k-3). 15.95 (978-0-688-16335-8(1)); 15.89 (978-0-688-16336-5(X)) HarperCollins Pubs.

The Presents: Individual Title Six-Packs. (Sails Literacy Ser.). 16p. (gr. k up). 27.00 (978-0-7635-4444-7(2)) Rigby Education.

Pretty Princess- Royal Party. 2005. (J). bds. (978-1-4194-0061-2(4)) Paradise Pr., Inc.

Prom Girl. 2nd ed. 2003. (J). pap. 8.95 (978-0-9726917-0-3(7)) Prom Girl Publishing. Inc.

Random House Staff. Baby Party. Barrett, John E., illus. 2006. 12p. (J). (gr. k-ps). bds. 4.99 (978-0-375-83764-7(7) , Random Hse. Bks. for Young Readers) Random Hse. Children's Bks.

Raschka, Chris. New York Is English, Chattanooga Is Creek. 2005. (Illus.). 40p. (J). (gr. k-4). 16.95 (978-0-689-84600-7(2) , Atheneum) Simon & Schuster Children's Publishing.

Rau, Dana Meachen. Hands. Stromoski, Rick, illus. 2000. (Rookie Reader Espanol Ser.). 24p. (J). (gr. k-2). pap. 4.95 (978-0-516-27043-2(5)); 19.50 (978-0-516-22009-3(8)) Scholastic Library Publishing. (Children's Pr.).

—Hands. 2000. (gr. k-3). lib. bdg. 12.95 (978-0-613-54531-0(1)) Tandem Library Bks.

—Manos. 2000. (SPA.). (gr. k-3). lib. bdg. 12.95 (978-0-613-54422-1(6)) Tandem Library Bks.

Raven, Margot Theis. America's White Table. Ellison, Chris, illus. 2005. 32p. (J). 16.95 (978-1-58536-216-5(6)) Sleeping Bear Pr.

Reichert, Amy. While Mama Had a Quick Little Chat. Boiger, Alexandra, illus. 2005. 40p. (J). 15.95 (978-0-689-85170-4(7) , Atheneum) Simon & Schuster Children's Publishing.

Reisfeld, Randi, ed. Zoey 101: Beach Party. 2006. (Teenick Ser.: Bk. 4). 120p. (J). pap. 4.99 (978-0-439-83160-4(1)) Scholastic, Inc.

Rey, Margret. Curious George Goes to a Costume Party. Vipah Interactive Staff, illus. 2001. (Curious George Ser.). 24p. (J). (gr. k-3). tchr. ed. 12.95 (978-0-618-06564-6(4)) Houghton Mifflin Co. Trade & Reference Div.

—Curious George Goes to a Costume Party. 2001. (gr. k-3). lib. bdg. 11.80 (978-0-613-35499-8(0)) Tandem Library Bks.

Rey, Margret, et al. Curious George Goes to a Costume Party. Weston, Martha, illus. 2001. (Curious George Ser.). 24p. (J). (gr. k-3). pap. 3.95 (978-0-618-06569-1(5)) Houghton Mifflin Co. Trade & Reference Div.

Ricci, Christine. Dora's Costume Party. 2006. (J). (ps-2). 21.35 (978-1-59961-071-9(X)) Spotlight.

Riddell, Chris. Platypus & the Birthday Party. 2003. (Platypus Ser.). (Illus.). 32p. (J). 16.00 (978-0-15-204753-5(0)) Harcourt Children's Bks.

Rinck, Maranke. The Prince Child. Linden, Martijn van der, illus. 2004. (ENG & GER.). 32p. (J). 16.95 (978-1-932425-15-4(2) , Lemniscaat) Boyds Mills Pr.

Roberts, Scott. Patty Cake & Friends. 2006. 96p. pap. 12.95 (978-1-59362-030-1(6)) Slave Labor Bks.

Rocklin, Joanne. Just Add Fun! Lemelman, Martin, illus. 2000. (Hello Reader! Math Ser.). 48p. (J). (ps-3). pap. 3.99 (978-0-590-64399-3(1)) Scholastic, Inc.

—Just Add Fun! 2000. (Hello Reader! Ser.). (Illus.). (J). (978-0-606-18572-1(0)) Tandem Library Bks.

Rose, Deborah Lee. Birthday Zoo. Munsinger, Lynn, illus. 2002. 24p. (J). (ps-1). 15.95 (978-0-8075-0776-6(8)) Whitman, Albert & Co.

Rowling, J. K. Harry Potter y la Camara Secreta. 2001. (SPA.). (gr. 3-6). lib. bdg. 18.80 (978-0-613-35959-7(3)) Tandem Library Bks.

Rue, Nancy N. Lily's Ultimate Party. 2001. (gr. 3-6). lib. bdg. 13.00 (978-0-613-71719-9(8)) Tandem Library Bks.

—Lily's Ultimate Party. 2001. (Young Women of Faith Ser.). 128p. (J). (gr. 3-7). pap. 5.99 (978-0-310-23253-7(8)) Zonderkidz.

Rumford, James. Nine Animals & the Well. 2003. (Illus.). 32p. (J). (gr. k-3). tchr. ed. 16.00 (978-0-618-30915-3(2)) Houghton Mifflin Co. Trade & Reference Div.

Ryan, Pam Muñoz. Mice & Beans. Cepeda, Joe, illus. 2001. 32p. (J). (ps-2). pap. 16.95 (978-0-439-18303-1(0) , Levine, Arthur A. Bks.) Scholastic, Inc.

Rylant, Cynthia. Annie & Snowball & the Dress-Up Birthday. Stevenson, Sucie, illus. 2007. (Annie & Snowball Ser.). 40p. (J). (gr. k-3). 14.99 (978-1-4169-0938-5(9) , Simon & Schuster Children's Publishing) Simon & Schuster Children's Publishing.

—Little Whistle's Dinner Party. Bowers, Tim, illus. 2004. 32p. (J). pap. 6.00 (978-0-15-205062-7(0) , Voyager Bks./Libros Viajeros) Harcourt Children's Bks.

—Little Whistle's Dinner Party. Bowers, Tim, illus. 2007. 32p. (J). 24.21 (***978-1-59961-255-3(0)***) Spotlight.

Rylant, Cynthia. Summer Party. Halperin, Wendy Anderson, illus. 2001. (Cobble Street Cousins Ser.: No. 5). 64p. (J). (gr. 2-8). 15.00 (978-0-689-83241-3(9)) Simon & Schuster Children's Publishing.

—Summer Party. 2002. (Cobble Street Cousins Ser.: No. 5). (gr. 3-6). lib. bdg. 11.80 (978-0-613-46174-0(6)) Tandem Library Bks.

Rylant, Cynthia & Halperin, Wendy Anderson. Summer Party. 2002. (Cobble Street Cousins Ser.: No. 5). (Illus.). 64p. (J). (gr. 2-5). pap. 3.99 (978-0-689-83417-2(9) , Aladdin) Simon & Schuster Children's Publishing.

Sage, Angie. Molly & the Birthday Party. 2001. (Illus.). 12p. (J). (ps-1). 9.95 (978-1-56145-248-4(3)) Peachtree Pubs., Ltd.

Salzmann, Mary Elizabeth. Leaping Lizards. Chawla, Neena, illus. (Fact & Fiction Ser.). 24p. (J). 2007. 21.35 (978-1-59928-450-7(2)); 2006. (978-1-59928-451-4(0)) ABDO Publishing Co.

—Robin Hoods. Haberstroh, Anne, illus. 2007. (Fact & Fiction Ser.). 24p. (J). pap. (978-1-59928-467-5(7)); 21.35 (978-1-59928-466-8(9)) ABDO Publishing Co.

Santomero, Angela C. Blue's Big Birthday. 2002. (gr. k-3). lib. bdg. 11.25 (978-0-613-51292-3(8)) Tandem Library Bks.

Scholastic, Inc. Staff & Hooks, Gwendolyn. The Mystery of the Missing Dog. Devard, Nancy, illus. 2004. (Just for You! Ser.). 32p. (gr. k-3). pap. 3.99 (978-0-439-56864-7(1) , Teaching Resources) Scholastic, Inc.

Schraff, Anne. Blackout: Set 2. 2002. 32p. (YA). 2.95 (978-1-56254-417-1(9) , SP 4179) Saddleback Educational Publishing.

Schreiber, Anne. Brent's B-Day Party. Fisher, Cynthia, illus. 2000. (Scholastic At-Home Phonics Reading Program Ser.). 24p. (J). (978-0-590-68837-6(5)) Scholastic, Inc.

Schubert, Ulli. Harry's Got a Girlfriend! 2000. (gr. 3-6). lib. bdg. 14.10 (978-0-613-29976-3(0)) Tandem Library Bks.

Seto, Dietrich, et al, eds. Galaxy Angel Party, Vol. 3. Tajii, Koji, tr. from JPN. Kanan, illus. 2007. (Galaxy Angel Ser.). Orig. Title: Galaxy Angel Anthology. 208p. pap. 9.99 (978-1-932480-28-3(5) , Broccoli Bks. Deluxe) Broccoli International USA, Inc.

Shankman, Ed. I Went to the Party in Kalamazoo. Frank, Dave, illus. l.t. ed. 2002. 36p. per. 14.95 (978-0-615-12092-8(X)) KidStreet LLC.

Shaskan, Trisha Speed. The Three Princesses. Senturk, Burak, illus. 2006. (Read-It! Readers Ser.). (J). 19.93 (978-1-4048-2422-5(7)) Picture Window Bks.

Shulman, Mark. Not Another Tea Party. Nguyen, Vincent, illus. 2006. 32p. (J). 14.95 (978-1-4027-3304-8(6)) Sterling Publishing Co., Inc.

Silver Dolphin en Español Editors. Caritas felices: Winnie the Pooh: Happy Faces: Winnie the Pooh, Spanish-Language Edition. 2007. (Illus.). 8p. (J). bds. 7.95 (***978-970-718-393-3(4)*** , Silver Dolphin en Español) Advanced Marketing, S. de R. L. de C. V. MEX. *Dist:* Perseus Distribution.

Silverhardt, Lauryn. Una Fiesta de Sorpresa. Lee, Josie, illus. 2004. (Dora the Explorer Ser.). (SPA.). 22p. (J). bds. 4.99 (978-0-689-87392-8(1) , Libros Para Ninos) Simon & Schuster Children's Publishing.

—A Surprise Party. Yee, Josie, illus. 2003. (Dora the Explorer Ser.). 22p. (J). bds. 4.99 (978-0-689-85483-5(8) , Simon Spotlight/Nickelodeon) Simon & Schuster Children's Publishing.

Smith, Audrey. The Halloween Misfits. 2004. 23p. (J). pap. 14.95 incl. audio compact disk (978-0-9722673-4-2(4)) Audrey Productions.

Smith, John D. The Best Mariachi in the World/ el mejor mariachi del Mundo. de la Vega, Eida, tr. Jones, Dani, illus. 2008. (J). lib. bdg. 16.95 (978-0-9770906-1-7(2)) Raven Tree Pr.

PQR

Smith, Sherri L. Hot, Sour, Salty, Sweet. 2008. 176p. (J). (*978-0-385-73417-2(4)); lib. bdg. (*978-0-385-90431-5(2)) Dell Publishing. (Delacorte Pr.).

Soto, Gary. Chato & the Party Animals. Guevara, Susan, illus. 25.95 incl. audio (978-1-59112-460-3(3)); 28.95 incl. audio compact disk (978-1-59112-920-2(6)); pap. 37.95 incl. audio (978-1-59112-461-0(1)); pap. 39.95 incl. audio compact disk (978-1-59112-921-9(4)) Live Oak Media.

—Chato & the Party Animals. 2005. (J). pap. 18.95 incl. audio compact disk (978-1-59112-919-6(2)); (Illus.). pap. 16.95 incl. audio (978-1-59112-459-7(X)) Live Oak Media.

—Chato & the Party Animals. Guevara, Susan, illus. 2000. (SPA.). 32p. (J). (ps-3). 16.99 (978-0-399-23159-9(5), Putnam Juvenile) Penguin Group (USA) Inc.

—Chato & the Party Animals. 2004. (gr. k-3). lib. bdg. 15.30 (978-0-613-89799-0(4)) Tandem Library Bks.

—Chato & the Party Animals. Guevara, Susan, illus. 2004. (J). (ps-ps). lib. bdg. 13.79 (978-0-606-29661-8(1)) Tandem Library Bks.

—Chato & the Party Animals. Guevara, Susan, illus. 2004. 32p. (J). (gr. k-3). reprint ed. pap. 6.99 (978-0-14-240032-6(7), Puffin) Penguin Group (USA) Inc.

—Chato y Los Amigos Pachangueros. 2004. (SPA.). (gr. k-3). lib. bdg. 16.45 (978-0-613-82998-4(0)) Tandem Library Bks.

—Chato y los Amigos Pachangueros. Guevara, Susan, illus. 2004. Tr. of Chato & the Party Animals. (SPA.). 32p. (J). (gr. k-3). reprint ed. pap. 7.99 (978-0-14-240033-3(5), Puffin) Penguin Group (USA) Inc.

Sparks, Michal. My Very First Tea Party. 2000. (Illus.). 10p. (ps). 5.99 (978-0-7369-0243-4(0)) Harvest Hse. Pubs.

Stadler, Alexander. Beverly Billingsly Takes the Cake. 2005. (Gulliver Books). (Illus.). 32p. (J). 16.00 (978-0-15-205357-4(3)) Harcourt Trade Pubs.

Starr, Meg. Alicia's Happy Day. Van Wright, Cornelius & Hu, Ying-Hwa, illus. 2003. 36p. (J). pap. 5.95 (978-1-932065-06-0(7)) Star Bright Bks., Inc.

—Alicia's Happy Day. Hu, Ying-Hwa & Van Wright, Cornelius, illus. 2003. 36p. (J). (ps-3). 15.95 (978-1-887734-85-1(6)) Star Bright Bks., Inc.

Starr, Meg. Alicia's Happy Day (English/Spanish Bilingual) Van Wright, Cornelius & Hu, Ying-Hwa, illus. 2007. 36p. (J). 15.95 (*978-1-59572-115-0(0)) Star Bright Bks., Inc.

Stephens, Monique Z. Strawberry Shortcake & the Friendship Party. Bracken, Carolyn, illus. 2003. (Strawberry Shortcake Ser.). 24p. (J). (ps-3). mass mkt. 4.99 (978-0-448-43222-9(6), Grosset & Dunlap) Penguin Group (USA) Inc.

Steptoe, Javaka. The Jones Family Express. 2003. (Illus.). 40p. (J). (ps-4). 17.95 (978-1-58430-047-2(7)) Lee & Low Bks., Inc.

Strickland, Brad. No-Rules Weekend! 2001. (gr. 3-6). lib. bdg. 11.80 (978-0-613-85082-7(3)) Tandem Library Bks.

Sturges, Philemon. This Little Pirate. Walrod, Amy, illus. 2005. 40p. (J). (ps). 16.99 (978-0-525-46440-2(9), Dutton Juvenile) Penguin Group (USA) Inc.

Surprise Party. 2004. (J). (978-1-932570-21-2(7)) Literacy Footprints Inc.

Sweeney, Jacqueline. Luau. Hart, G. K. & Hart, Vikki, illus. Hart, G. K. & Hart, Vikki, photos by. 2002. (We Can Read! Ser.). 32p. (J). 21.36 (978-0-7614-1513-8(0), Benchmark Bks.) Cavendish, Marshall Corp.

—Who Said Boo? Hart, G. K. & Empey, Mark, illus. 2000. (We Can Read! Ser.). 32p. (J). (gr. 1-2). lib. bdg. 21.36 (978-0-7614-0924-3(6), Benchmark Bks.) Cavendish, Marshall Corp.

Tang, Charles, illus. The Mystery of the Empty Safe. 2000. (Boxcar Children Ser.: No. 75). (J). (gr. 2-5). (978-0-606-18768-8(5)) Tandem Library Bks.

—The Mystery of the Empty Safe, Vol. 75. 2004. (Boxcar Children Ser.: No. 75). 120p. (J). (gr. 2-5). pap. 4.50 (978-0-8075-5463-0(4)) Whitman, Albert & Co.

Tegen, Katherine. Dracula & Frankenstein Are Friends. Cushman, Doug, illus. 2003. 32p. (J). (ps-3). 15.99 (978-0-06-000115-5(1)) HarperCollins Pubs.

Teitelbaum, Michael. Party on, America! 2005. (Ready-To-Read Ser.: Vol. 7). (J). pap. 3.99 (978-0-689-86594-7(5), Simon Spotlight/Nickelodeon) Simon & Schuster Children's Publishing.

Thaler, Mike. The Halloween Party from the Black Lagoon. Lee, Jared D., illus. 2004. (Little Apple Ser.). 64p. (J). pap. (978-0-439-68075-2(1)) Scholastic, Inc.

Thompson, Kay. Eloise Takes a Bawth. Knight, Hilary, illus. ltd. ed. 2002. (Eloise Ser.). 300.00 (978-0-689-84694-6(0), Simon & Schuster Children's Publishing) Simon & Schuster Children's Publishing.

Thompson, Kay & Crowley, Mart. Eloise Takes a Bawth. Knight, Hilary, illus. 2002. (Eloise Ser.). 80p. (J). (ps-3). 17.95 (978-0-689-84288-7(0)) Simon & Schuster Children's Publishing.

Thompson, Yvonne. Miss Tilly's Party. Krecskay, Stephen, illus. 2004. (J). per. (978-0-9749561-0-7(4)) My Sunshine Bks.

Trimble, Marcia. Liberty Cafe Is Open. Hayden, Jennifer, illus. ed. 2006. (J). pap. 895.00 (978-1-891577-91-8(3)); 32p. lib. bdg. 15.95 (978-1-891577-90-1(5)) Images Pr.

Tudor, Tasha. The Dolls' Christmas. unabr. ed. 2000. (YA). (ps). pap. 29.95 incl. audio (978-0-7887-3795-4(3), 41039X4) Recorded Bks., LLC.

Turner, Jill. Percival's Party. Townsend, Peter, illus. 2003. (J). pap. 12.95 (978-1-74047-235-7(7)) Book Co. Publishing Pty, Ltd., The AUS. *Dist:* Penton Overseas, Inc.

Upton, Deborah. Barbie: My First Telephone. Wolfson, Tom, illus. Wolfson, Tom, photos by. 2001. (Play-a-Sound Ser.). (J). 16.98 (978-0-7853-4800-9(X)) Publications International, Ltd.

Ure, Jean. Over the Moon. 2006. (Illus.). 192p. (J). pap. 8.99 (978-0-00-716464-6(5), HarperCollins Children's Bks.) HarperCollins Pubs. Ltd. GBR. *Dist:* Independent Pubs. Group.

Van Draanen, Wendelin. Sammy Keyes & the Curse of Moustache Mary. 2001. (Sammy Keyes Ser.: Bk. 5). (gr. 5-8). lib. bdg. 13.00 (978-0-613-35469-1(9)) Tandem Library Bks.

Volker, Kerstin. Lilly's Birthday Party. 2003. (Funny Friends Lift-and-Learn Bks.). (Illus.). 14p. (J). 5.99 (978-1-59384-022-8(5)) Parklane Publishing.

Wade, Barrie. My Birthday Party. Fairclough, Chris, photos by. 2005. (Reading Corner Ser.). (Illus.). 24p. (J). (gr. k-3). lib. bdg. 22.80 (978-1-59771-016-9(4), 1247649) Sea-To-Sea Pubns.

Waldron, Jan L. John Pig's Halloween. 2001. (gr. 3-6). lib. bdg. 15.30 (978-0-613-58416-6(3)) Tandem Library Bks.

Wallace, John. Tiny Rabbit Goes to a Birthday Party. Wallace, John, illus. 2000. (Illus.). 32p. (J). (gr. k-3). 16.95 (978-0-8234-1489-5(2)) Holiday Hse., Inc.

Wallace, Nancy Elizabeth. Tell-a-Bunny. 2007. 32p. (J). pap. 5.99 (*978-0-7614-5369-7(5)) Cavendish, Marshall Corp.

—Tell-a-Bunny. Wallace, Nancy Elizabeth, illus. 2000. (Illus.). 40p. (J). (ps-2). 15.95 (978-1-890817-29-9(5)) Winslow Pr.

Walters, Eric. House Party. 2007. (Orca Soundings Ser.). 112p. (YA). (gr. 7 up). (*978-1-55143-743-9(0)) Orca Bk. Pubs.

Wardlaw, Lee. Bow-Wow Birthday. Johnson-Petrov, Arden, illus. 1998. 32p. (J). (gr. k-3). 14.95 (978-1-56397-489-2(4)) Boyds Mills Pr.

Warner, Gertrude Chandler. The Mystery of the Empty Safe. Tang, Charles, illus. 2000. 120p. (J). (gr. 2-7). lib. bdg. 11.80 (978-0-613-27992-5(1)) Tandem Library Bks.

Warner, Gertrude Chandler, creator. The Mystery of the Empty Safe, Vol. 75. 2004. (Boxcar Children Ser.: No. 75). (Illus.). 120p. (J). (gr. 2-5). 14.95 (978-0-8075-5462-3(6)) Whitman, Albert & Co.

Watanabe, Etsuko. Oscar's Party. 2006. (Illus.). 12p. (J). 14.95 (978-1-58234-697-7(6), Bloomsbury Children) Bloomsbury Publishing.

Webb, Steve. Polly Jean Pyjama Queen. 2006. (Illus.). 32p. (J). pap. 9.99 (*978-0-09-946402-0(0), Red Fox) Random Hse. Children's Bks. GBR. *Dist:* Independent Pubs. Group.

Wegman, William. Surprise Party. Wegman, William, photos by. 2000. (Illus.). 32p. (ps-17). 16.99 (978-0-7868-0585-3(4)) Hyperion Bks. for Children.

Wells, Carolyn. Patty at Home. 2007. (ENG.). 204p. per. 12.95 (*978-1-4218-3321-7(2)) 1st World Publishing, Inc.

Wells, Rosemary. Bunny Party. 2003. (Max & Ruby Ser.). (Illus.). 24p. (J). (ps-k). pap. 5.99 (978-0-14-250162-7(X), Puffin) Penguin Group (USA) Inc.

—Bunny Party. Wells, Rosemary, illus. 2001. (Max & Ruby Ser.). (Illus.). 32p. (J). (gr. k-2). 15.99 (978-0-670-03501-4(7), Viking Juvenile) Penguin Group (USA) Inc.

—The Secret Birthday. Nez, John & Wheeler, Jody, illus. 2002. (Yoko & Friends School Days Ser.: No. 7). 32p. (gr. k-2). 9.99 (978-0-7868-0729-1(6)) Hyperion Bks. for Children.

Weston, Martha. Curious George Goes to a Costume Party. 2001. (Curious George Ser.). (Illus.). (J). 10.75 (978-0-606-21931-0(5)) Tandem Library Bks.

Wilder, Laura Ingalls. Little House Parties. 1999. (gr. 3-6). lib. bdg. 12.10 (978-0-613-15883-1(0)); (Little House Chapter Bks.: No. 14). (J). (978-0-606-16686-7(6)) Tandem Library Bks.

Willems, Mo. I Am Invited to a Party! An Elephant & Piggie Book. Willems, Mo, illus. rev. ed. 2007. 64p. (J). (ps-3). 8.99 (*978-1-4231-0687-6(3)) Hyperion Pr.

Willson, Sarah. My Dress-Up Party. Oxley, Jennifer, illus. 2003. (Ready-to-Read Ser.). 24p. (J). pap. 3.99 (978-0-689-85229-9(0), Simon Spotlight/Nickelodeon) Simon & Schuster Children's Publishing.

—My Dress-Up Party. 2003. (gr. k-3). lib. bdg. 11.80 (978-0-613-58160-8(1)) Tandem Library Bks.

Wilson, Karma. Bear Snores On. Chapman, Jane, illus. 2002. (J). 25.11 (978-0-7587-9751-3(6)) Book Wholesalers, Inc.

—Bear Snores On. Chapman, Jane, illus. (Classic Board Bks.). (J). 2005. 34p. bds. 7.99 (978-1-4169-0272-0(4), Little Simon); 2002. 40p. 16.95 (978-0-689-83187-4(0), McElderry, Margaret K.) Simon & Schuster Children's Publishing.

—Bear Snores On. 2005. (J). (ps-2). 29.95 incl. audio compact disk (978-0-439-76664-7(8), WHCD666); 24.95 incl. audio (978-0-439-76660-9(5), WHRA666) Weston Woods Studios, Inc.

Wingate, Philippa. Hide & Seek in the Castle. Rutherford, Peter, illus. 2005. (Hide & Seek Ser.). 16p. (J). 7.95 (978-1-904613-76-3(4), Buster Bks.) O'Mara, Michael Bks., Ltd. GBR. *Dist:* Independent Pubs. Group.

Wooding, Chris. Crashing. 2003. (gr. 7-12). lib. bdg. 15.30 (978-0-613-72013-7(X)) Tandem Library Bks.

—Crashing. l.t. ed. 2001. (Illus.). 216p. 18.99 (978-0-7089-9539-6(X)) Ulverscroft Large Print Bks. GBR. *Dist:* Ulverscroft Large Print Bks., Ltd.

Wright, Jill. Minnie's Tea Party. Boyd, Anthony, ed. David, Simon, illus. 1999. (Minnie's Adventures Ser.). 32p. (J). (gr. k-2). 12.00 (978-0-9672839-0-6(6)) Starry Puddle Publishing.

Yeomans, Ellen. Jubilee. Ladwig, Tim, illus. 2004. 32p. (J). 16.00 (978-0-8028-5230-4(0)) Eerdmans, William B. Publishing Co.

Ziarko, Greg. The Waylaid: Asheth. ed. 2007. 280p. (YA). (*978-0-9792694-0-0(7)) gaZko Entertainment.

PARTIES, POLITICAL

see Political Parties

PASSIONS

see Emotions

PASSOVER

Berger, Barry W. Passover Haggadah. Hall, Melanie W., illus. 2004. 36p. (978-0-9674319-3-2(X)) Messianic Perspectives.

Bosch, Nicole in den, illus. Let's Ask Four Questions: "Why Is This Night Different?" 2000. 12p. (J). (ps up). 4.95 (978-1-58013-071-4(2)) Kar-Ben Publishing.

Chwast, Seymour, illus. Had Gadya: A Passover Song. rev. ed. 32p. (J). 2007. pap. 7.95 (*978-1-59643-298-7(5)); 2005. 16.95 (978-1-59643-033-4(8)) Roaring Brook Pr.

Cohen, Joan Freeman & Freeman, Jonathan M. In Every Generation: A Model Seder Haggadah. 2005. (J). (978-0-87441-731-9(7)) Behrman Hse., Inc.

Cohen, Tina. Pesach What & Why? 2005. 36p. 14.99 (978-1-4116-6454-8(X)) Lulu.com.

dePaola, Tomie. My First Passover. 2008. 12p. (J). (ps-k). bds. 5.99 (*978-0-448-44791-9(6), Grosset & Dunlap) Penguin Group (USA) Inc.

Doering, Amanda. Passover: Jewish Celebration of Freedom. 2007. (First Facts Ser.). (Illus.). 24p. (J). 21.26 (978-0-7368-6397-1(4), 1258819) Capstone Pr., Inc.

Dorling Kindersley Publishing Staff. My First Passover. 2nd ed. 2006. (My 1st board Bks.). (Illus.). 36p. (J). bds. 5.99 (978-0-7566-0981-8(X)) Dorling Kindersley Publishing, Inc.

—Passover. 2004. (Ultimate Sticker Bks.). 16p. (J). pap. 6.99 (978-0-7566-0285-7(8)) Dorling Kindersley Publishing, Inc.

Douglas, Lloyd G. Let's Get Ready for Passover. 2003. (gr. k-3). lib. bdg. 12.95 (978-0-613-59664-0(1)) Tandem Library Bks.

Fishman, Cathy Goldberg. On Passover. Hall, Melanie W., illus. 2000. 40p. (J). (gr. k-3). 6.99 (978-0-689-83264-2(8), Aladdin) Simon & Schuster Children's Publishing.

—On Passover. 2000. (978-0-606-17932-4(1)); lib. bdg. 15.30 (978-0-613-22129-0(X)) Tandem Library Bks.

—Passover. Marshall, Ann, illus. 2006. (On My Own Holidays Ser.). (J). 48p. 25.26 (978-1-57505-656-2(9)); pap. 5.95 (978-1-57505-695-1(X), First Avenue Editions) Lerner Publishing Group.

Fishman, Cathy Goldberg & Hall, Melanie W. On Passover. 2003. (Illus.). 28p. (J). (gr. k-4). reprint ed. 16.00 (978-0-7567-6988-8(4)) DIANE Publishing Co.

Flanagan, Alice K. Passover. Koffsky, Ann D., illus. 2003. (Holidays & Festivals Ser.). 32p. (J). (gr. 3 up). lib. bdg. 22.60 (978-0-7565-0481-6(3)) Compass Point Bks.

Ganeri, Anita. The Passover Story. Phillips, Rachael, illus. 2004. (Holiday Stories Ser.). (J). lib. bdg. 22.80 (978-1-58340-491-1(0)) Smart Apple Media.

Groner, Judyth Saypol & Wikler, Madeline. All about Passover. Kreiswirth, Kinny, illus. 2003. 32p. (J). (ps-3). pap. 5.95 (978-1-58013-060-8(7)) Kar-Ben Publishing.

Hanft, Joshua. The Miracles of Passover. Chwast, Seymour, illus. 2007. 28p. (ps-3). 15.95 (978-1-59354-600-7(9)) Blue Apple Bks.

Heiligman, Deborah. Celebrate Passover: With Matzah, Maror, & Memories. 2007. (Holidays Around the World Ser.). (Illus.). 32p. (J). (gr. 1-4). 15.95 (978-1-4263-0018-9(2)); lib. bdg. 23.90 (978-1-4263-0019-6(0)) National Geographic Society. (National Geographic Children's Bks.).

Herman, Debbie & Koffsky, Ann D. More Than Matzah: A Passover Feast of Fun, Facts, & Activities. 2006. (Let's Celebrate Ser.). (Illus.). 48p. (J). pap. 8.99 (978-0-7641-3318-3(7)) Barron's Educational Series, Inc.

Hildebrandt, Ziporah. This Is Our Seder. Roraback, Robin, illus. 1999. 32p. (J). (gr. k-3). tchr. ed. 15.95 (978-0-8234-1436-9(1)) Holiday Hse., Inc.

Hoyt-Goldsmith, Diane. Celebrating Passover. Migdale, Lawrence, photos by. (Illus.). 32p. (YA). (gr. 4-6). tchr. ed. 16.95 (978-0-8234-1420-8(5)) Holiday Hse., Inc.

Kimmel, Eric A. Wonders & Miracles: A Passover Companion. 2004. (Wonders & Miracles Ser.). (Illus.). 144p. (J). pap. 18.95 (978-0-439-07175-8(5)) Scholastic, Inc.

Koffsky, Ann D. All about Passover. 1998. (Illus.). 20p. (J). (gr. k-3). spiral bd. 5.99 (978-0-914080-10-7(5)) Shulsinger Sales, Inc.

Kropf, Latifa Berry. It's Seder Time! Cohen, Tod, illus. Cohen, Tod, photos by. 2004. 24p. (J). (ps-1). 12.95 (978-1-58013-092-9(5)) Kar-Ben Publishing.

Lehman-Wilzig, Tami. Passover Around the World. Wolf, Elizabeth, illus. 2007. 48p. (J). (gr. 2-5). lib. bdg., spiral bd. 15.95 (978-1-58013-213-8(8)); pap. 7.95 (*978-1-58013-215-2(4)) Kar-Ben Publishing.

Levy, Barbara Soloff. Learning about Passover. 2002. (Learning about Ser.). (Illus.). 16p. (J). pap. 1.50 (978-0-486-42354-8(9)) Dover Pubns., Inc.

Lupo, Tamar. Passover. 2006. (J). (978-1-59036-462-8(7)); (978-1-59036-465-9(1)) Weigl Pubs., Inc.

Marx, David. Passover. 2001. (gr. k-3). lib. bdg. 14.10 (978-0-613-54632-4(6)) Tandem Library Bks.

Marx, David F. Passover. 2001. (Rookie Read-About Holidays Ser.). (Illus.). 32p. (J). (gr. 1-2). pap. 5.95 (978-0-516-27178-1(4), Children's Pr.) Scholastic Library Publishing.

Musleah, Rahel. Why on This Night? A Passover Haggadah for Family Celebration. August, Louise, illus. 2000. 112p. (J). (gr. k-4). pap. 13.99 (978-0-689-83313-7(X), Simon Pulse) Simon & Schuster Children's Publishing.

—Why on This Night? a Passover Haggadah for Family Celebration. 2000. (gr. 3-6). lib. bdg. 22.25 (978-0-613-35891-0(0)) Tandem Library Bks.

Pirotta, Saviour. Passover. 2007. (J). lib. bdg. (978-1-4042-3707-0(0), PowerKids Pr.) Rosen Publishing Group, Inc., The.

Raabe, Emily. A Passover Holiday Cookbook. 2002. (Festive Foods for the Holidays Ser.). (Illus.). 24p. (J). (gr. 2-5). lib. bdg. 19.95 (978-0-8239-5625-8(3), PowerKids Pr.) Rosen Publishing Group, Inc., The.

Rose, David. Passover. 1999. (World of Holidays Ser.). (Illus.). 32p. (gr. 2-5). pap. 8.95 (978-0-8172-3885-8(9)) Steck-Vaughn.

Rosinsky, Natalie M. Passover. 2004. (Let's See Ser.). 24p. (J). (gr. 1 up). lib. bdg. 19.93 (978-0-7565-0772-5(3)) Compass Point Bks.

Sanders, Nancy I. Passover. 2003. (True Book Ser.). (Illus.). 48p. (J). 25.00 (978-0-516-22765-8(3), Children's Pr.) Scholastic Library Publishing.

—Passover. 2003. (Illus.). 47p. (J). (gr. 3-5). lib. bdg. 15.25 (978-0-613-89016-8(7)) Tandem Library Bks.

Schuh, Mari C. Passover. 2002. (Holidays & Celebrations Ser.). (Illus.). 24p. (J). (gr. k-1). lib. bdg. 15.93 (978-0-7368-1447-8(7), Pebble Bks.) Capstone Pr., Inc.

Segal, Eliezer Lorne. Uncle Eli's Special-for-Kids, Most Fun-ever, under-the-Table Passover Haggadah. Gordon-Lucas, Bonnie, illus. 2004. 61p. (J). (gr. k-4). reprint ed. 13.00 (978-0-7567-8112-5(4)) DIANE Publishing Co.

Silberg, Francis Barry. The Story of Passover. Britt, Stephanie McFetridge, illus. 2001. 26p. (J). bds. 6.95 (978-0-8249-4146-8(2)) Ideals Pubns.

—The Story of Passover for Children. Britt, Stephanie McFetridge, illus. 2001. 24p. (J). (ps-3). 7.95 (978-1-57102-180-9(9)) Warehousing & Fulfillment Specialists, LLC (WFS, LLC).

Simon, Norma. The Story of Passover. Weihs, Erika, illus. 1998. (Trophy Picture Bk.). 32p. (J). (gr. 2-5). pap. 6.99 (978-0-06-443491-1(5), Harper Trophy) HarperCollins Pubs.

—The Story of Passover. 1998. (Trophy Picture Bks.). (978-0-606-13044-8(6)) Tandem Library Bks.

Sper, Emily. The Passover Seder. Sper, Emily, illus. 2003. (ENG & HEB., Illus.). 24p. (J). (ps-2). pap. 9.99 (978-0-439-44312-8(1), Cartwheel Bks.) Scholastic, Inc.

Story of Passover. 2004. pap. 6.95 (978-0-8249-6277-7(X)) Ideals Pubns.

Tabs, Judy & Steinberg, Barbara. Matzah Meals: A Passover Cookbook for Kids. Hauser, Bill, illus. 2004. (Passover Ser.). 64p. (J). (gr. k up). pap. 7.95 (978-1-58013-086-8(0)) Kar-Ben Publishing.

Wark, Mary Ann Barrows. We Tell It to Our Children: The Story of Passover: A Haggadah for Seders with Young Children. Oskow, Craig, illus. 2nd ed. 2002. (HEB.). 116p. spiral bd. 7.95 (978-0-9619880-6-7(1)); 136p. spiral bd. 15.95 (978-0-9619880-7-4(X)) Mensch Makers Pr.

Ziefert, Harriet & Cohen, Santiago. This Is Passover. 2004. (Illus.). 7p. bds. 8.95 (978-1-59354-031-9(0)) Blue Apple Bks.

PASSOVER—FICTION

Chevat, Richie. Pickles Passover. 2003. (gr. k-3). lib. bdg. 11.25 (978-0-613-57553-9(9)) Tandem Library Bks.

Fireside, Bryna J. Private Joel & the Sewell Mountain Seder. Costello, Shawn, illus. 2008. (Passover Ser.). (J). lib. bdg. 16.95 (*978-0-8225-7240-4(0)) Kar-Ben Publishing.

Geras, Adele & Moxley, Sheila. Rebecca's Passover. 2004. (Illus.). 32p. (J). (gr. k-4). pap. 7.95 (978-1-84507-155-4(7)) Lincoln, Frances Ltd. GBR. *Dist:* Perseus Distribution.

Hannigan, Lynne. Sam's Passover. 2004. (Illus.). 32p. pap. 5.95 (978-0-7136-4084-7(7), 93342) A & C Black GBR. *Dist:* Consortium Bk. Sales & Distribution.

Howland, Naomi. The Matzah Man: A Passover Story. 2002. (Illus.). 32p. (J). (gr. k-3). 16.00 (978-0-618-11750-5(4), Clarion Bks.) Houghton Mifflin Co. Trade & Reference Div.

Krulik, Nancy E. No Matzoh for Me. Hendrix, Bryan, illus. 2003. (Reading Railroad Bks.). 32p. (J). (ps-4). pap. 3.49 (978-0-448-43119-2(X), Grosset & Dunlap) Penguin Group (USA) Inc.

—No Matzoh for Me! 2003. (ps-2). lib. bdg. 11.25 (978-0-613-61648-5(0)) Tandem Library Bks.

Levine, Abby. This Is the Matzah. Billin-Frye, Paige, illus. 2005. 32p. (J). (ps-2). 15.95 (978-0-8075-7885-8(1)) Whitman, Albert & Co.

Manushkin, Fran. A Passover Story. Dacey, Bob, illus. 2006. 32p. (J). pap. 5.99 (978-0-439-81111-8(2)) Scholastic, Inc.

Newman, Leslea. Matzo Ball Moon. 1998. 15.00 (978-0-395-71519-2(9)) Houghton Mifflin Co.

—Matzo Ball Moon. Greenstein, Elaine, illus. 32p. (J). (gr. k-3). 2006. 5.95 (978-0-618-60481-4(2)); 1998. tchr. ed. 15.00 (978-0-395-71530-7(X)) Houghton Mifflin Co. Trade & Reference Div. (Clarion Bks.).

O'Connell, Rebecca. Penina Levine Is a Hard-Boiled Egg. Sue, Majella Lue, illus. 2007. 176p. (J). (gr. 4-6). 16.95 (978-1-59643-140-9(7)) Roaring Brook Pr.

Pearlman, Bobby. Passover Is Here! Desmoinaux, Christel, illus. 2005. 16p. (J). pap. 6.99 (978-0-689-86587-9(2), Little Simon) Simon & Schuster Children's Publishing.

Peretz, I. L. & Goldin, Barbara Diamond. The Magician's Visit: A Passover Tale. Parker, Robert Andrew, illus. 2006. 28p. (J). (gr. 4-8). reprint ed. 15.00 (978-1-4223-5408-7(3)); pap. 5.00 (978-1-4223-5400-1(8)) DIANE Publishing Co.

Rauchwerger, Diane Levin. Dinosaur on Passover. 2006. (J). pap. 6.95 (978-1-58013-161-2(1)) Kar-Ben Publishing.

—Dinosaur on Passover. Wolff, Jason, illus. 2006. (J). 15.95 (978-1-58013-156-8(5)) Kar-Ben Publishing.

Rothenberg, Joan. Matzah Ball Soup. Rothenberg, Joan, illus. 2005. (Illus.). 29p. (J). (ps-2). reprint ed. 15.00 (978-0-7567-8930-5(3)) DIANE Publishing Co.

Rouss, Sylvia A. Sammy Spider's First Haggadah. Kahn, Katherine Janus, illus. 2007. 32p. (J). pap. 5.95 (*978-1-58013-230-5(8)) Kar-Ben Publishing.

Schotter, Roni. Passover! Kono, Erin Eitter, illus. 2006. 28p. (J). (ps-1). 12.99 (978-0-316-93991-1(9)) Little Brown & Co.

—Passover Magic. 1998. (J). (978-0-606-13696-9(7)); lib. bdg. 15.25 (978-0-613-71817-2(8)) Tandem Library Bks.

Shulman, Lisa. The Matzo Ball Boy. Litzinger, Rosanne, illus. 32p. (J). 2007. pap. 5.99 (978-0-14-240769-1(0) , Puffin); 2005. 15.99 (978-0-525-47169-1(3) , Dutton Juvenile) Penguin Group (USA) Inc.

Sollish, Ari. Un Toque de Pesaj: A Touch of Passover. Becker, Boruch, illus. 2005. Tr. of Touch of Passover. (SPA.). 12p. (J). bds. 8.00 (978-0-8266-0022-6(0)) Merkos L'Inyonei Chinuch.

—A Touch of Passover: A Touch & Feel Book. Becker, Boruch, illus. 2006. 12p. (J). bds. 7.95 (978-0-8266-0021-9(2)) Merkos L'Inyonei Chinuch.

Zalben, Jane Breskin. Pearl's Passover: A Family Celebration Through Stories, Recipes, Crafts, & Songs. Zalben, Jane Breskin, illus. 2002. (Illus.). 48p. (J). (gr. k-3). 16.00 (978-0-689-81487-7(9)) Simon & Schuster Children's Publishing.

Zolkower, Edie Stoltz. Too Many Cooks: A Passover Parable. 2000. (gr. k-3). lib. bdg. 14.10 (978-0-613-81767-7(2)) Tandem Library Bks.

Zucker, Jonny. Four Special Questions: A Passover Story. Cohen, Jan Barger, illus. 2003. (Festival Time! Ser.). 24p. (J). (ps-2). pap. 6.95 (978-0-7641-2267-5(3)) Barron's Educational Series, Inc.

PASTEL DRAWING

Merberg, Julie & Bober, Suzanne. Dancing with Degas. 2003. (Illus.). 22p. (J). bds. 6.95 (978-0-8118-4047-7(6)) Chronicle Bks. LLC.

PASTEL PAINTING

see Pastel Drawing

PASTELS

see Pastel Drawing

PASTEUR, LOUIS, 1822-1895

Ackerman, Jane. Louis Pasteur & the Founding of Microbiology. 2004. (Profiles in Science Ser.). (Illus.). 144p. (YA). (gr. 6-12). 26.95 (978-1-931798-13-6(3)) Reynolds, Morgan Inc.

Alphin, Elaine Marie. Germ Hunter: A Story about Louis Pasteur. Verstraete, Elaine, illus. 2003. 64p. (J). 6.95 (978-0-87614-929-4(8)); lib. bdg. 22.60 (978-1-57505-179-6(6)) Lerner Publishing Group. (Carolrhoda Bks.).

—Germ Hunter: A Story about Louis Pasteur. 2003. (gr. 3-6). lib. bdg. 14.10 (978-0-613-77207-5(5)) Tandem Library Bks.

Armentrout, David & Armentrout, Patricia. Louis Pasteur. 2002. (Discover Someone Who Made a Difference Discovery Library Ser.). (Illus.). 24p. (gr. 2-5). 14.95 (978-1-58952-056-1(4)) Rourke Publishing, LLC.

—Louis Pasteur. Sarfatti, Esther & de la Vega, Eida, trs. (Personas que Cambiaron la Historia (People Who Made a Difference) Ser.). (SPA., Illus.). 24p. 2002. mass mkt. 5.95 (978-1-58952-251-0(6) , RK31467); 2001. (J). (gr. 1-4). lib. bdg. 19.27 (978-1-58952-170-4(6) , RK5237) Rourke Publishing, LLC.

Bank Street Staff & Jakab, E. A. M. Louis Pasteur: Hunting Killer Germs. 2000. (Ideas on Trial Ser.). (Illus.). 122p. (C). (gr. 5-10). pap. 8.95 (978-0-07-134334-3(2) , 9780071343343) McGraw-Hill Cos., The.

Fandel, Jennifer. Louis Pasteur. 2003. (World Was Never the Same Ser.). (J). (978-1-58417-266-6(5)) Lake Street Pubs.

Fandel, Jennifer. Louis Pasteur & Pasteurization. Wilson, Keith et al, illus. 2007. 32p. (***978-0-7368-6844-0(5))*** Capstone Pr., Inc.

Feinstein, Stephen. Louis Pasteur: The Father of Microbiology. 2008. (Inventors Who Changed the World Ser.). 128p. (J). (gr. 6 up). lib. bdg. 33.27 (***978-1-59845-078-1(6)*** , MyReportLinks.com Bks.) Enslow Pubs., Inc.

Fullick, Ann. Louis Pasteur. (Groundbreakers Ser.). (Illus.). 48p. (J). (gr. 5-7). 2002. pap. 8.50 (978-1-58810-993-4(3) , 91468); 2000. lib. bdg. 25.64 (978-1-57572-373-0(5)) Heinemann Library.

—Louis Pasteur. 2002. (gr. 5-8). lib. bdg. 17.05 (978-0-613-84251-8(0)) Tandem Library Bks.

Gogerly, Liz. Louis Pasteur. 2002. (Scientists Who Made History Ser.). 48p. (J). lib. bdg. 27.12 (978-0-7398-4846-3(1)) Raintree.

Jakab, E. A. M. Louis Pasteur: Hunting Killer Germs. 2000. (gr. 5-8). lib. bdg. 17.60 (978-0-613-71527-0(6)) Tandem Library Bks.

Kjelle, Marylou Morano. Louis Pasteur: Fighter Against Contagious Disease. 2005. (Uncharted, Unexplored, & Unexplained Ser.). (Illus.). 48p. (J). (gr. 4-8). lib. bdg. 29.95 (978-1-58415-363-4(6) , 1244912) Mitchell Lane Pubs., Inc.

Lassieur, Allison. Louis Pasteur: Revolutionary Scientist. 2005. (Great Life Stories Ser.). (Illus.). 123p. (J). 30.50 (978-0-531-16753-3(4) , Watts, Franklin) Scholastic Library Publishing.

MacDonald, Fiona & Birch, Beverley. Louis Pasteur: Father of Modern Medicine. 2001. (Giants of Science Ser.). (Illus.). 64p. (J). (gr. 5-8). 27.44 (978-1-56711-336-5(2) , Blackbirch Pr., Inc.) Thomson Gale.

Robbins, Louise E. Louis Pasteur & the Hidden World of Microbes. 2001. (Oxford Portraits in Science Ser.). (Illus.). 144p. (YA). 30.00 (978-0-19-512227-5(5)) Oxford Univ. Pr., Inc.

Silverthorne, Elizabeth. Louis Pasteur. 2004. (Heroes & Villains Ser.). (Illus.). 112p. (J). (gr. 7-10). 29.95 (978-1-59018-308-3(8) , Lucent Bks.) Thomson Gale.

Smith, Linda Wasmer. Louis Pasteur: Disease Fighter. (Great Minds of Science Ser.). (Illus.). 128p. (gr. 4-10). 2001. (YA). pap. 13.26 (978-0-7660-1874-7(1)); 2007. (J). lib. bdg. 31.93 (***978-0-7660-2792-3(9))*** Enslow Pubs., Inc.

Spengler, Kremena. Louis Pasteur. 2003. (Photo-Illustrated Biographies Ser.). (Illus.). 24p. (J). lib. bdg. 19.93 (978-0-7368-2225-1(9) , Bridgestone Bks.) Capstone Pr., Inc.

PASTIMES

see Amusements; Games; Recreation; Sports

PASTORS

see Clergy

PASTRY

Beery, Barbara. Pink Princess Cookbook. Snortum, Marty, photos by. 2006. (Illus.). 64p. (J). spiral bd. 14.95 (***978-1-4236-0173-9(4))*** Gibbs Smith, Publisher.

Patchett, Fiona. Children's Bk of Baking. 2007. 96p. (J). 17.99 (978-0-7945-1438-9(3) , Usborne) EDC Publishing.

PATHOLOGICAL PSYCHOLOGY

see Psychology, Pathological

PATHOLOGY

see also Bacteriology; Immunity; Medicine

Allman, Toney. The Medical Examiner. 2006. (Crime Scene Investigations Ser.). (Illus.). 112p. (J). (gr. 7-10). 32.45 (978-1-59018-912-2(4) , 1251556, Lucent Bks.) Thomson Gale.

Dudley, William, ed. Epidemics: Opposing Viewpoints. 1998. (Opposing Viewpoints Ser.). (Illus.). 188p. (YA). (gr. 9-12). lib. bdg. 32.45 (978-1-56510-941-4(4) , Greenhaven Pr., Inc.) Thomson Gale.

Gold, Susan Dudley. Sickle Cell Disease. 2001. (Health Watch Ser.). (Illus.). 48p. (YA). (gr. 4-10). lib. bdg. 23.93 (978-0-7660-1662-0(5)) Enslow Pubs., Inc.

Ridgway, Tom. Mad Cow Disease: Bovine Spongiform Encephalopathy (BSE) 2002. (Epidemics Ser.). (Illus.). 64p. (YA). (gr. 7-12). lib. bdg. 26.50 (978-0-8239-3487-4(X)) Rosen Publishing Group, Inc., The.

Royston, Angela. Burns & Blisters. 2004. (Illus.). 32p. (J). lib. bdg. (978-1-4034-4824-8(8)) Heinemann Library.

Underwood, Deborah. Has a Cow Saved Your Life? 2006. (Illus.). 32p. (J). (978-1-4109-2580-0(3)); pap. (978-1-4109-2609-8(5)) Steck-Vaughn.

PATRICK, SAINT, 373?-463?

de Paola, Tomie. Patrick: Patron Saint of Ireland. de Paola, Tomie, illus. (Illus.). 32p. (J). (gr. k-3). 6.95 (978-0-8234-1077-4(3)); tchr. ed. 17.95 (978-0-8234-0924-2(4)) Holiday Hse., Inc.

Freeman, Dorothy Rhodes. St. Patrick's Day. 2008. (Best Holiday Books Ser.). 48p. (J). (gr. 3-4). lib. bdg. 23.93 (***978-0-7660-3046-6(6))*** Enslow Pubs., Inc.

Lynch, Zachary. The Life of St Patrick: Enlightener of the Irish. 2006. (Illus.). 32p. (J). 12.95 (978-1-888212-76-1(4)) Conciliar Pr.

MacGill-Callahan, Sheila. The Last Snake in Ireland: A Story about St. Patrick. Hillenbrand, Will, illus. 1999. 36p. (J). (gr. k-3). tchr. ed. 16.95 (978-0-8234-1425-3(6)) Holiday Hse., Inc.

McHugh, Michael J. Saint Patrick: Pioneer Missionary to Ireland. 1999. (Illus.). 160p. (YA). (gr. 6-12). pap. 8.00 (978-1-930092-14-3(8) , CLP29665) Christian Liberty Pr.

Pingry, Patricia A. The Story of Saint Patrick's Day. Levy, Pamela R., illus. 2001. 26p. (J). bds. 6.95 (978-0-8249-4145-1(4)) Ideals Pubns.

Rock, Lois & Piper, Sophie. Saint Patrick of Ireland. 2005. (Illus.). 24p. (J). pap. 7.50 (978-0-7459-4811-9(1)) Lion Hudson plc GBR. *Dist:* Independent Pubs. Group.

Tompert, Ann. Saint Patrick. Garland, Michael, illus. 2004. 32p. (J). 8.95 (978-1-56397-992-7(6)) Boyds Mills Pr.

PATRIOTIC SONGS

see National Songs

PATRIOTISM

Casey & the Growing Spurt: Learning Patriotism, Citizenship, & Character. 2002. (Kamaron Concept Book). 94p. (J). per. 9.99 (978-0-9715713-2-7(5)) Kamaron Institute Pr.

Catalano, Angela. Community Spirit: Symbols of Citizenship in Communities. 2005. (Communities at Work Ser.). (J). 19.95 (978-1-4042-2784-2(9) , PowerKids Pr.) Rosen Publishing Group, Inc., The.

DeFord, Deborah H. Patriotism. 2003. (Illus.). 32p. (J). pap. 7.50 (978-1-4109-0326-6(5)); lib. bdg. 24.28 (978-0-7398-7007-5(6)) Raintree.

Keene, Gail. Color My Country. Larsen, Dana, illus. 2005. 28p. (gr. k-3). pap. 8.95 (978-1-889658-29-2(4)) New Canaan Publishing Co. LLC.

Kishel, Ann-Marie. U.S. Symbols. 2007. (First Step Nonfiction Ser.). 24p. (J). (gr. k-2). 18.60 (978-0-8225-6394-5(0) , Lerner Pubns.) Lerner Publishing Group.

Kupperstein, Joel. Celebrating Patriotic Holidays No. 4529: Honoring America. Motoyama, Keiko, illus. 1999. 16p. (J). (ps-2). pap. 2.99 (978-1-57471-574-3(7)) Creative Teaching Pr., Inc.

LaMachia, John. So What Is Patriotism Anyway? 2000. (Students Guide to American Civics Ser.). 48p. (YA). lib. bdg. 23.95 (978-0-8239-3447-8(0)); (Illus.). (gr. 5-8). lib. bdg. 23.95 (978-0-8239-3098-2(X) , CVPATR) Rosen Publishing Group, Inc., The. (Rosen Central).

O Say Can You See. . . 2003. bds. 6.99 (978-0-9726762-0-5(1)) Star Spangled Baby, Ltd.

Peter, Val J. & Dowd, Tom. Patriotism. 2004. 80p. pap. 25.95 (978-1-889322-52-0(0) , 48-318T) Boys Town Pr.

Roberts, Cynthia. Patriotism. 2007. (Learn about Values Ser.). 24p. (J). 21.36 (978-1-59296-674-5(8)) Child's World, Inc.

Salas, Macarena, ed. Promesa de Lealtad/The Pledge of Allegiance. 2002. (SPA & ENG., Illus.). 24p. (J). pap. 4.95 (978-0-439-31738-2(X) , Scholastic en Espanol) Scholastic, Inc.

Scheunemann, Pam. Patriotism. 2003. (United We Stand Ser.). (Illus.). 24p. (J). (ps-3). lib. bdg. 19.93 (978-1-57765-880-1(9)) ABDO Publishing Co.

Schuette, Sarah L. I Am Patriotic. 2004. (Character Values Ser.). (Illus.). 24p. (J). lib. bdg. 15.93 (978-0-7368-2571-9(1) , Pebble Bks.) Capstone Pr., Inc.

Stout, Carol A. Proud to Be an American, 1. 2004. (Illus.). 168p. pap. 6.95 (978-1-886161-08-5(5)) Millennium Marketing & Publishing.

Swanson, June. I Pledge Allegiance. Hanson, Rick, illus. 2002. (On My Own History Ser.). 40p. lib. bdg. 23.93 (978-0-87614-925-6(5) , Carolrhoda Bks.) Lerner Publishing Group.

Tames, Richard. Nationalism. 2003. (Ideas of the Modern World Ser.). (Illus.). 64p. (J). lib. bdg. 28.56 (978-0-7398-6417-3(3)) Raintree.

'Tis of Thee: A Son's Search for the Meaning of American Patriotism. 2001. 131p. per. 9.95 (978-1-928734-04-8(9)) WEDDLE's.

United We Stand, Set. 2002. (J). (ps-3). lib. bdg. 119.58 (978-1-57765-876-4(0)) ABDO Publishing Co.

United We Stand. 2001. (Illus.). 16p. 6.95 (978-0-9727833-5-4(0)) Really Big Coloring Bks., Inc.

We Salute the Stars & Stripes: A Children's Book That Puts Meaning into the Pledge of Allegiance to Our Flag. 2001. (Illus.). 16p. (J). (gr. k-6). pap. 10.00 (978-0-9709436-0-6(1)) Michelson, Bettie E.

Webster, Christine. The Pledge of Allegiance. (Cornerstones of Freedomtrade;, Second Ser.). 48p. (J). (gr. 4-6). 2007. pap. 5.95 (***978-0-531-18768-5(3));*** 2003. (Illus.). 26.00 (978-0-516-22674-3(6)) Scholastic Library Publishing. (Children's Pr.).

PATRIOTISM—POETRY

Martin, Bill & Sampson, Michael. I Pledge Allegiance. Raschka, Chris, illus. 2004. 40p. (J). (gr. 1-4). reprint ed. pap. 6.99 (978-0-7636-2527-6(2)) Candlewick Pr.

PATTON, GEORGE S. (GEORGE SMITH), 1885-1945

Anderson, Christopher J. Patton's Third Army. 1999. (G. I. Ser.). (Illus.). 80p. (gr. 5 up). 27.50 (978-0-7910-5374-4(1) , Chelsea Hse.) Facts On File, Inc.

Hatch, Alden. General George Patton: Old Blood & Guts. 2006. (Sterling Point Bks.). (Illus.). 208p. (J). 12.95 (978-1-4027-3186-0(8)); pap. 6.95 (978-1-4027-3614-8(2)) Sterling Publishing Co., Inc.

Rice, Earle. George S. Patton. 2003. (Great Military Leaders of the Twentieth Century Ser.). (Illus.). 112p. (J). (gr. 6-12). 30.00 (978-0-7910-7403-9(X) , Chelsea Hse.) Facts On File, Inc.

Stanley, George E. George S. Patton: War Hero. Henderson, Meryl, illus. 2007. (Childhood of Famous Americans Ser.). 192p. (J). pap. 5.99 (***978-1-4169-1547-8(8)*** , Aladdin) Simon & Schuster Children's Publishing.

Sutcliffe, Jane. George S. Patton Jr. 2005. (History Maker Bios Ser.). (Illus.). 48p. (J). 26.60 (978-0-8225-2436-6(8) , Lerner Pubns.) Lerner Publishing Group.

PAUL, THE APOSTLE, SAINT

Bek, et al. Daniel in the Dangerous Den & Paul & Silas & the Prison Prayer. Bek et al, illus. 2006. (Upside down Bible Stories Ser.). 62p. (J). pap. 7.99 (978-0-7814-4391-3(1)) Cook, David C. Publishing Co.

Bohnet, Eric C. Saul's Conversion: Acts 9:1-22: 21:1-22:21 for Children. Ramsey, Marcy Dunn, illus. 2006. (Arch Books). (ENG.). 16p. (J). 1.99 (978-0-7586-0868-0(3)) Concordia Publishing Hse.

Bostrom, Kathleen Long & McKinsey, Dennis, trs. Paul's Call: How Saul Became a Christian. McKinsey, Dennis, illus. 2004. (Illus.). 48p. 9.95 (978-0-664-22636-7(1)) Westminster John Knox Pr.

Campdepadros, Jorgelina & Campdepadros, Eduardo. El Viaje de Pablo. 2004. (Bible Stories Ser.).Tr. of Paul's Journey. (SPA.). 32p. 3.99 (978-0-8254-1147-2(5) , Editorial Portavoz) Kregel Pubns.

Christian Focus Publishing Staff. The Resurrection: Jesus Is Alive. 2000. (Bible Wise Ser.). (Illus.). 32p. (J). (gr. k-3). pap. (978-1-85792-344-5(8) , Christian Focus) Christian Focus Pubns.

Chronicles of Faith - Paul. 2007. 224p. (J). pap. 4.97 (***978-1-59789-927-7(5))*** Barbour Publishing, Inc.

Fisher, Nancy. Take Your Students on a Cruise: Paul's Journeys Lesson Guide. Witte, Carol, ed. Hall, Beverly H., illus. 2004. 40p. (gr. 4-8). wbk. ed. 9.99 (978-1-890947-00-2(8) , 308X) Rose Publishing.

Harder Tangvald, Christine. Swish, Swish, Went the Giant Fish: And Other Bible Stories about Prayer. Griego, Tony, illus. 1999. (Read Aloud, Read Alone Ser.). 32p. (J). (978-0-7814-0929-2(2)) Cook, David C. Publishing Co.

Hill, Mary Lea. Saint Paul: The Thirteenth Apostle. Archambault, Matthew, illus. 2007. (Encounter the Saints Ser.: 22). (J). pap. 7.95 (***978-0-8198-7102-2(8))*** Pauline Bks. & Media.

The Journey's of Paul. Date not set. (J). stu. ed., act. bk. ed. 1.49 (978-0-88271-232-1(2) , 1748) Regina Pr., Malhame & Co.

Larsen, Dan. Paul. 1998. (Young Reader's Christian Library). (Illus.). 224p. (J). (gr. 4-7). pap. 1.39 (978-1-55748-135-1(0)) Barbour Publishing, Inc.

Miller, Claire. Shipwrecked Paul: The Story of Paul's Journey to Rome: Acts 27:1-44 for Children. Gleiwe, Unada, tr. Gleiwe, Unada, illus. 2002. (ENG.). 16p. (J). 1.99 (978-0-570-07580-6(7)) Concordia Publishing Hse.

Moore, Eva. The Road to Damascus. Simpson, Fiona, ed. 2006. (Read & Learn Bible Story Ser.). (Illus.). 32p. (J). pap. 3.99 (978-0-439-85428-3(8) , Little Shepherd) Scholastic, Inc.

Nederveld, Patricia L. A New Friend: The Story of Paul's Conversion. Stoub, Paul, illus. 1998. (God Loves Me Ser.). 24p. (J). (ps-3). pap. 2.95 (978-1-56212-317-8(3) , 001248, Faith Alive Christian Resources) CRC Pubns.

—Over the Wall: The Story of Paul's Escape in a Basket. 1998. (God Loves Me Ser.). (Illus.). 24p. (J). (ps-4). pap. 2.95 (978-1-56212-318-5(1) , 001249, Faith Alive Christian Resources) CRC Pubns.

—A Ride in the Night: The Story of Paul's Escape on Horseback. 1998. (God Loves Me Ser.). (Illus.). 24p. (J). (ps-4). pap. 2.95 (978-1-56212-320-8(3) , 001242, Faith Alive Christian Resources) CRC Pubns.

—The Shipwreck: The Story of Paul's Rescue at Sea. 1998. (God Loves Me Ser.). (Illus.). 24p. (J). (ps-4). pap. 2.95 (978-1-56212-321-5(1) , 001252, Faith Alive Christian Resources) CRC Pubns.

—A Song in the Night: The Story of Paul & Silas in Prison. 1998. (God Loves Me Ser.). (Illus.). 24p. (J). (ps-4). pap. 2.95 (978-1-56212-319-2(X) , 001250, Faith Alive Christian Resources) CRC Pubns.

Petry, Dan. Hangin' Loose, Holdin' Tight: Paul's Epistles. 1998. (Generation Why Ser.: Vol. 4, Pt. 3). 45p. (YA). (gr. 9-12). pap. 14.95 (978-0-87303-284-1(5)) Faith & Life Pr.

PAVLOVA, ANNA, 1885-1931

Allman, Barbara & Haas, Shelly O. Dance of the Swan: A Story about Anna Pavlova. 2006. (Creative Minds Biographies Ser.). (Illus.). 64p. (gr. 4-8). lib. bdg. 22.60 (978-1-57505-463-6(9)) Lerner Publishing Group.

Degas, Edgar, illus. I Dreamed I Was A Ballerina. 2001. (J). (978-0-87099-988-8(5)) Metropolitan Museum of Art, The.

Pavlova, Anna. I Dreamed I Was A Ballerina. Degas, Edgar, illus. 2001. 32p. (J). (gr. k-2). 16.00 (978-0-689-84676-2(2) , Atheneum) Simon & Schuster Children's Publishing.

PEACE

see also Disarmament; Security, International; War

Berkeley, Laura. The Seeds of Peace. Dexter, Alison, illus. 1999. 32p. (J). (ps-3). 15.95 (978-1-84148-007-7(X)) Barefoot Bks., Inc.

Center for Learning Staff. Justice & Peace. 2007. (Religion Ser.). 124p. (YA). spiral bd. 18.95 (***978-1-56077-795-3(8))*** Ctr. for Learning, The.

Darraj, Susan Muaddi. Mairead Corrigan & Betty Williams: Partners for Peace in Northern Ireland. 2006. (Modern Peacemakers Ser.). (Illus.). 112p. (J). (gr. 9 up). 30.00 (978-0-7910-9001-5(9) , Chelsea Hse.) Facts On File, Inc.

Dower, Laura. Peace. 2001. (J). pap. (978-0-06-440811-0(6) , Harper Trophy) HarperCollins Pubs.

Durrell, Ann & Sachs, Marilyn, eds. The Big Book for Peace. 2002. (Illus.). 120p. (J). (gr. 4-7). reprint ed. 27.00 (978-0-7567-5337-5(6)) DIANE Publishing Co.

Facts on File, Inc. Staff, ed. Modern Peacemakers Set, 6 Vols. 2006. 112p. (gr. 9). 180.00 (978-0-7910-9446-4(4) , Chelsea Hse.) Facts On File, Inc.

Fox, Carol, ed. In Times of War: An Anthology of War & Peace in Children's Literature. 2000. (Illus.). 272p. (J). 27.50 (978-1-86205-446-2(0) , Pavilion Bks., Ltd.) Anova Bks. GBR. *Dist:* Independent Pubs. Group.

Friedman-Brunt, Elyse. Conflict Resolution in American History, Gr. 8: Lessons from the Past, Lessons for Today. Chandler, Terrence, illus. 2003. 48p. (YA). pap., wbk. ed. 19.95 (978-1-878227-89-8(0)) Peace Education Foundation.

—Conflict Resolution in American History, Grade 8: Lessons from the Past, Lessons for Today. Chandler, Terrence, illus. 2003. 200p. pap., instr.'s training gde. ed. 29.95 (978-1-878227-88-1(2)) Peace Education Foundation.

Friends for Peace Fun Book. 1999. (Illus.). 48p. (J). pap. 4.95 (978-0-915678-64-8(0) , Treasure Tower Bks.) World Tribune Pr.

Gilley, Jeremy. Peace One Day. Blessen, Karen, illus. 2005. 48p. (J). (ps). 16.99 (978-0-399-24330-1(5) , Putnam Adult) Penguin Group (USA) Inc.

Gottfried, Ted. The Fight for Peace: A History of Anti-War Movements in America. 2005. (Women at War Ser.). (Illus.). 136p. (YA). (gr. 8-12). lib. bdg. 29.90 (978-0-7613-2932-9(3) , Twenty-First Century Bks.) Lerner Publishing Group.

—Northern Ireland: Peace in Our Time? 2002. (Headliners Ser.). (Illus.). 64p. (gr. 5-8). lib. bdg. 25.90 (978-0-7613-2252-8(3) , Millbrook Pr.) Lerner Publishing Group.

Harcourt School Publishers Staff. Leaders for Peace. 3rd ed. 2003. (Horizons Ser.). (Illus.). (J). (gr. 3). pap. 5.50 (978-0-15-333278-4(6)) Harcourt Schl. Pubs.

Hoffman, Mary. Lines in the Sand: New Writing on War & Peace. 2003. (gr. 3-6). lib. bdg. 17.60 (978-0-613-84768-1(7)) Tandem Library Bks.

Hoffman, Mary & Lassiter, Rhiannon, eds. Lines in the Sand: New Writing on War & Peace. 2003. (Illus.). 288p. (gr. 2 up). pap. 8.95 (978-0-9729529-1-0(8)) Disinformation Co. Ltd., The.

Kerley, Barbara. A Little Peace. 2007. 32p. (J). lib. bdg. 25.90 (978-1-4263-0087-5(5)); (Illus.). 16.95 (***978-1-4263-0086-8(7))*** National Geographic Society. (National Geographic Children's Bks.).

Kivel, Paul. I Can Make My World a Safer Place: A Kid's Book about Stopping Violence. Gorrell, Nancy, illus. 2001. 96p. (J). (gr. 4-7). pap. 11.95 (978-0-89793-291-2(9)) Hunter Hse., Inc.

Kunkel, Jeff, ed. What Scares Me & What I Do about It: Stories & Pictures by Sunday School Kids. 2004. (Illus.). 48p. 12.99 (978-0-8066-4558-2(X) , Augsburg Bks.) Augsburg Fortress, Pubs.

Lampen, John. The Peace Kit. 2nd ed. 2007. (ENG., Illus.). 84p. per. (***978-0-85245-372-8(8))*** Quaker Books.

Libal, Autumn. International Security: Peacekeeping & Peace-Building Around the World. 2007. (United Nations Ser.). 88p. (J). (gr. 5 up). lib. bdg. 21.95 (978-1-4222-0071-1(X)) Mason Crest Pubs.

Najibi, Neda. The Ground I Walk On. Foster, Bob, illus. 1999. 128p. (J). pap. 14.95 (978-0-9672640-0-4(6) , 1966) PEACE By Piece Publishing.

Promoting Peace - Puppet Scripts Manual. 2005. (J). spiral bd. (978-0-9768827-4-9(4)) Prevention Through Puppetry, Inc.

Promoting Peace - Student Workbook. 2005. (J). spiral bd. (978-0-9768827-3-2(6)) Prevention Through Puppetry, Inc.

Radunsky, Vladimir. What Does Peace Feel Like? Radunsky, Vladimir, illus. 2004. (Illus.). 24p. (J). (gr. k-2). 14.95 (978-0-689-86676-0(3) , Atheneum/Anne Schwartz Bks.) Simon & Schuster Children's Publishing.

Rivera, Sheila. Treaties & Resolutions. 2004. (World in Conflict-the Middle East Ser.). (Illus.). 48p. (J). (gr. 4-8). lib. bdg. 25.65 (978-1-59197-420-8(8)) ABDO Publishing Co.

Scheunemann, Pam. Acting with Kindness. 2004. (Keeping the Peace Ser.). (Illus.). 23p. (J). (ps-3). lib. bdg. 19.93 (978-1-59197-557-1(3)) ABDO Publishing Co.

—Being a Peacekeeper. 2004. (Keeping the Peace Ser.). (Illus.). 23p. (J). (ps-3). lib. bdg. 19.93 (978-1-59197-558-8(1)) ABDO Publishing Co.

—Coping with Anger. 2004. (Keeping the Peace Ser.). (Illus.). 23p. (J). (ps-3). lib. bdg. 19.93 (978-1-59197-559-5(X)) ABDO Publishing Co.

—Dealing with Bullies. 2004. (Keeping the Peace Ser.). (Illus.). 23p. (J). (ps-3). lib. bdg. 19.93 (978-1-59197-560-1(3)) ABDO Publishing Co.

—Keeping the Peace. 2004. (Illus.). (J). (ps-3). lib. bdg. 119.58 (978-1-59197-556-4(5) , SandCastle) ABDO Publishing Co.

—Learning about Differences. 2004. (Keeping the Peace Ser.). (Illus.). 23p. (J). (ps-3). lib. bdg. 19.93 (978-1-59197-561-8(1)) ABDO Publishing Co.

—Working Together. 2004. (Keeping the Peace Ser.). (Illus.). 23p. (J). (ps-3). lib. bdg. 19.93 (978-1-59197-562-5(X)) ABDO Publishing Co.

Schmidt, Fran. Youth Peace Ambassadors. 2001. 72p. (YA). pap. (978-1-890276-11-9(1)) Peace Education International.

Skoor, Susan. The Lion & the Lamb. Shipley, Marie, illus. 12.95 (978-0-8309-1068-7(9)) Herald Publishing Hse.

Thomas, Shelley Moore. Somewhere Today: A Book of Peace. Futran, Eric, photos by. 2004. (Illus.). 24p. (J). (gr. k-4). reprint ed. pap. 6.95 (978-0-8075-7544-4(5)) Whitman, Albert & Co.

Walter, Virginia A. War & Peace: A Guide to Literature & New Media, Grades 4-8. 2006. (Children's & Young Adult Literature Reference Ser.). 288p. pap. 40.00 (978-1-59158-271-7(7) , LU2717) Libraries Unlimited, Inc.

Wolf, Aline D. I Offer You Peace. 2000. 24p. (J). spiral bd. 6.00 (978-0-939195-20-6(8) , 311) Parent Child Pr., Inc.

PEACE—FICTION

Avignone, June. A Peek into the Secret Little Ones of Turtle Back Island. My Wolf Dog, illus. 2004. 40p. (J). pap. (978-0-9654628-2-2(X)) Mill Street Forward, The.

Baskwill, Jane. If Peace Is... Carter, Stephanie, illus. 2003. (J). 23p. pap. 7.95 (978-1-59034-449-1(9)); 24p. (gr. 11 up). 15.95 (978-1-59034-448-4(0)) Mondo Publishing.

Crawford, Quinton Douglass. Moochie the Soochie Visits the Peace People. 2007. 27p. 12.50 (***978-0-615-14879-3(4)***) Crawford, Quinton Douglass.

Davis, Benjamin Doron. The Balloon Project. 2004. 75p. pap. 14.95 (978-1-4137-3663-2(7)) PublishAmerica, Inc.

Hoffelt, Jane. We Share One World. Husted, Marty, illus. 2004. 32p. (J). per. 15.95 (978-0-9701907-8-9(6)) Illumination Arts Publishing Co., Inc.

Jacobson, John & Brymer, Mark A. The Quest: Adventure Story & Songs. Wilson, Roberta, illus. 2005. (J). (978-1-4234-0019-6(4)) Leonard, Hal Corp.

Katz, Karen. Can You Say Peace? 2006. (Illus.). 32p. (J). 15.95 (978-0-8050-7893-0(2)) Holt, Henry & Co.

Parr, Todd. The Peace Book. 32p. (J). (ps-ps). 2005. 9.99 (978-0-316-05962-6(5)); 2004. (Illus.). 15.99 (978-0-316-83531-2(5)) Little, Brown Bks. for Young Readers. (Tingley, Megan Bks.).

Rodriguez-Nora, Tere. En busca de la Paz. Gordo, Alex, illus. 2005. (SPA.). 32p. (J). 13.95 (978-84-96046-51-1(6)) Ediciones Norte, Inc.

Skelton, Vonda Skinner. Bitsy & the Mystery at Amelia Island. 2005. (Bitsy Burroughs Mysteries Ser.). 183p. (J). pap. 8.95 (978-1-57072-307-0(9) , Silver Dagger Mysteries) Overmountain Pr.

Sparrow, L. T. All My Relations, a Prayer. 2000. (Illus.). 32p. (YA). (gr. 3 up). 16.95 (978-0-9670171-0-5(6)) Sparrow, L.T. Publishing.

Steinkamp, Mary J. The Bear, the Rug, & the Echo Tree. 2004. (Illus.). 64p. (J). (978-1-55306-661-3(8) , Epic Pr.) Essence Publishing.

Thomas, Shelley Moore. Somewhere Today: A Book of Peace. Futran, Eric, illus. 1998. (J). (ps-2). pap. 13.95 (978-0-8075-7546-8(1)) Whitman, Albert & Co.

Wahl, Jan. How the Children Stopped the Wars. 2007. 112p. pap. 6.95 (***978-1-58246-200-4(3)*** , Tricycle Pr.) Ten Speed Pr.

Williams, Sam. Talk Peace. Moriuchi, Mique, illus. 2005. 32p. (J). 16.95 (978-0-8234-1936-4(3)) Holiday Hse., Inc.

PEACE CORPS (U.S.)

The Peace Corps, 6 Packs. (On Deck Ser.). 24p. (gr. 4-5). 35.00 (978-0-7578-1032-9(2)) Rigby Education.

Peters, Celeste. Peace Corps. 2002. (International Organizations Ser.). (Illus.). 32p. (J). lib. bdg. 16.95 (978-1-59036-023-1(0)) Weigl Pubs., Inc.

Suen, Anastasia. El Cuerpo de Paz. 2004. (Organizaciones de Ayuda Ser.). (SPA & ENG., Illus.). 24p. (J). (gr. 3-6). lib. bdg. 17.25 (978-0-8239-6859-6(6) , Buenas Letra) Rosen Publishing Group, Inc., The.

—The Peace Corps. 2002. (Reading Power Ser.). (Illus.). 24p. (J). (gr. 2). lib. bdg. 17.25 (978-0-8239-6001-9(3) , PowerKids Pr.) Rosen Publishing Group, Inc., The.

Vandegrift, Tom. 24 New Moons. 2003. 429p. (YA). pap. 20.95 (978-0-7414-1503-5(8)) Infinity Publishing.

PEAFOWL

Marsico, Katie. A Peachick Grows Up. 2007. (Scholastic News Nonfiction Readers: Life Cycles Ser.). 24p. (J). pap. 6.95 (***978-0-531-18699-2(7)*** , Children's Pr.) Scholastic Library Publishing.

Orange, Mariama N. How Peacocks Got Their Long & Beautiful Feathers. Weddle, Shamek I., illus. 1999. 40p. (J). (ps-3). pap. 12.95 (978-0-9669600-0-6(9)) Creating Worlds Publishing Co.

Pohl, Kathleen. Peacocks. 2007. (J). pap. (***978-0-8368-8228-5(8)***); 24p. lib. bdg. 19.93 (***978-0-8368-8221-6(0)***) Stevens, Gareth Inc. (Weekly Reader Early Learning Library).

—Peacocks: Pavos Reales. 2007. (SPA & ENG.). (J). pap. (***978-0-8368-8242-1(3)*** , Weekly Reader Early Learning Library) Stevens, Gareth Inc.

—Peacocks/Paos Reales. 2007. (Animals I See at the Zoo/ Animales que Veo en el Zoologico Ser.). (SPA & ENG.). 24p. (J). (gr. k-2). lib. bdg. 19.93 (***978-0-8368-8235-3(0)*** , Weekly Reader Early Learning Library) Stevens, Gareth Inc.

Underwood, Deborah. Peacocks. 2007. (Pull Ahead Books). (Illus.). 32p. (J). 22.60 (978-0-8225-5930-6(7) , Lerner Pubns.) Lerner Publishing Group.

PEAFOWL—FICTION

Curtis, Chary. Fancy & Brandy Peacock. 2005. (J). per. 9.99 (978-1-59879-030-6(7)) Lifevest Publishing, Inc.

Long, Olivia. The Impossible Peacock. Long, Olivia, illus. Date not set. (Kaleidoscope Ser.). (Illus.). 32p. (J). (ps-4). (978-1-880042-04-5(5)) Shelf-Life Bks.

Thoene, Jake & Thoene, Luke. The Jewelled Peacock of Persia. 1998. (Baker Street Mysteries Ser.: Vol. 3). 168p. (J). (gr. 4-7). pap. 5.99 (978-0-7852-7080-5(9)) Nelson, Thomas Inc.

PEALE, CHARLES WILLSON, 1741-1827

Morrison, Taylor. Mastodon Mystery. 2006. (Illus.). 32p. (J). (gr. k-3). pap. 6.95 (978-0-618-77130-1(1)) Houghton Mifflin Co.

PEANUTS

Boten, Wallace. From Farm to Store. 2003. (Compass Point Phonics Readers Ser.). (Illus.). 16p. (J). (gr. 1 up). 13.26 (978-0-7565-0507-3(0)) Compass Point Bks.

Driscoll, Laura. George Washington Carver. Weber, Jill, illus. 2003. (Smart about Scientists Ser.). 32p. (J). (gr. k-5). pap. 5.99 (978-0-448-43243-4(9) , Grosset & Dunlap) Penguin Group (USA) Inc.

Halfmann, Janet. Peanuts. 2001. (Let's Investigate Ser.). (Illus.). 32p. (J). (978-1-58341-191-9(7) , Creative Education) Creative Co., The.

Hall, Margaret. El Cacahuate. 2003. (Alimentos Ser.).Tr. of Peanuts. 32p. (J). (Illus.). lib. bdg. 22.79 (978-1-4034-3737-2(8)); (ENG & SPA.). pap. 6.50 (978-1-4034-3743-3(2)) Heinemann Library.

—El Cacahuate. 2003. Tr. of Peanuts. (SPA.). (gr. k-3). lib. bdg. 14.75 (978-0-613-67072-2(8)) Tandem Library Bks.

—Peanuts. (Food Ser.). 32p. pap. 6.95 (978-1-4034-4049-5(2)) Heinemann Library.

Hall, Margaret C. Peanuts. 2003. (Food Ser.). (Illus.). 32p. (J). (gr. k-2). lib. bdg. 22.79 (978-1-58810-619-3(5)) Heinemann Library.

Julius, Jennifer. I Like Peanuts. 2001. (gr. k-3). lib. bdg. 12.95 (978-0-613-52091-1(2)) Tandem Library Bks.

Keller, Kristin Thoennes. Peanuts to Peanut Butter. 2004. (First Facts Ser.). 24p. (J). lib. bdg. 21.26 (978-0-7368-2637-2(8)) Capstone Pr., Inc.

Lilly, Melinda. Peanuts. 2001. (Around the World with Food & Spices Ser.). (Illus.). 32p. (J). (gr. 3-5). lib. bdg. 26.60 (978-1-58952-046-2(7)) Rourke Publishing, LLC.

Llewellyn, Claire. Peanuts. Cohen, Helaine, ed. 1998. (What's for Lunch? Ser.). (Illus.). 32p. (J). (gr. k-2). pap. 6.95 (978-0-516-26222-2(X) , Children's Pr.) Scholastic Library Publishing.

Micucci, Charles. The Life & Times of the Peanut. 2000. (Illus.). 32p. (J). (gr. k-3). pap. 6.95 (978-0-618-03314-0(9)) Houghton Mifflin Co. Trade & Reference Div.

—The Life & Times of the Peanut. 2000. (Illus.). (J). (978-0-606-18211-9(X)) Tandem Library Bks.

Nelson, Robin. From Peanut to Peanut Butter. 2004. (Start to Finish Ser.). (Illus.). 24p. (J). 18.60 (978-0-8225-0944-8(X) , Lerner Pubns.) Lerner Publishing Group.

PEANUTS—FICTION

Ketch, Ann. There Goes Peanut Butter! Totire, Valerie, illus. 2003. 12p. (J). (gr. k-2). pap. 4.95 (978-1-57874-036-9(3) , 74-036-3) Kaeden Corp.

Koster, Gloria. The Peanut-Free Café. Cocca-Leffler, Maryann, illus. 2006. 32p. (J). 16.95 (978-0-8075-6386-1(2)) Whitman, Albert & Co.

One Pea, Two Pea, I Pee, You Pee. 2005. (J). bds. (978-0-9761228-0-7(4)) World of Imagination.

Schulz, Charles M. A Charlie Brown Christmas. Braddock, Paige, illus. 2004. 28p. (J). (ps-ps). lib. bdg. 12.79 (978-0-606-30053-7(8)) Tandem Library Bks.

PEARL HARBOR (HAWAII), ATTACK ON, 1941

Allen, Thomas B. Remember Pearl Harbor: American & Japanese Survivors Tell Their Stories. 2007. (Remember Ser.). (Illus.). 64p. (J). (gr. 5). 27.90 (***978-0-7922-3635-1(1)*** , National Geographic Children's Bks.) National Geographic Society.

Allen, Thomas B. Remember Pearl Harbor: Japanese & American Survivors Tell Their Stories. 2001. (Illus.). 64p. (J). (gr. 5 up). 17.95 (978-0-7922-6690-7(0) , National Geographic Children's Bks.) National Geographic Society.

Barr, Gary. Pearl Harbor. 2004. (Illus.). 56p. (J). pap. 8.95 (978-1-4034-4577-3(X)); lib. bdg. (978-1-4034-4569-8(9)) Heinemann Library.

Britton, Tamara L. Pearl Harbor. 2005. (Checkerboard History Library). (Illus.). 40p. (J). (gr. k-6). lib. bdg. 22.78 (978-1-57765-851-1(5)) ABDO Publishing Co.

Crewe, Sabrina & Uschan, Michael V. The Bombing of Pearl Harbor. 2003. (Events That Shaped America Ser.). (Illus.). 32p. (J). (gr. 3 up). lib. bdg. 24.67 (978-0-8368-3392-8(9)) Stevens, Gareth Inc.

De Angelis, Therese. Pearl Harbor: Deadly Surprise Attack. 2002. (American Disasters Ser.). (Illus.). 48p. (J). (gr. 4-10). lib. bdg. 23.93 (978-0-7660-1783-2(4)) Enslow Pubs., Inc.

Dowswell, Paul. Pearl Harbor. 2003. (Days That Shook the World Ser.). (Illus.). 47p. (J). lib. bdg. 28.56 (978-0-7398-6051-9(8)) Raintree.

Dunn, Joe. The Bombing of Pearl Harbor. Wight, Joseph & Espinosa, Rod, illus. 2007. (Graphic History Ser.). 32p. (J). (gr. 3-6). lib. bdg. 27.07 (***978-1-60270-074-1(5)*** , Graphic Planet) Magic Wagon.

Fitzgerald, Stephanie. Pearl Harbor: Day of Infamy. 2006. (Snapshots in History Ser.). (Illus.). 96p. (J). (gr. 5-7). 30.60 (978-0-7565-1622-2(6)) Compass Point Bks.

Hasday, Judy L. Pearl Harbor. 2000. (Great Disasters, Reforms & Ramifications Ser.). (Illus.). 112p. (J). (gr. 4-7). 30.00 (978-0-7910-5271-6(0) , Chelsea Hse.) Facts On File, Inc.

Hudson-Goff, Elizabeth & Uschan, Michael V. The Bombing of Pearl Harbor. 2006. (Graphic Histories Ser.). (Illus.). pap. 8.95 (978-0-8368-6258-4(9)); 32p. lib. bdg. 26.00 (978-0-8368-6206-5(6)) Stevens, Gareth Inc. (World Almanac Library).

Klam, Julie. Pearl Harbor & the Rise of Japan. 2002. (Illus.). 48p. (J). lib. bdg. 28.50 (978-1-58340-188-0(1)) Smart Apple Media.

Krensky, Stephen. Pearl Harbor: Ready to Read Level 3. Day, Larry, illus. 2001. (Ready-to-Reads Ser.). 48p. (J). (gr. 1-3). pap. 3.99 (978-0-689-84214-6(7) , Aladdin) Simon & Schuster Children's Publishing.

McGowen, Tom. The Attack on Pearl Harbor. (Cornerstones of Freedomtrade;, Second Ser.). 48p. (J). 2007. pap. 5.95 (***978-0-531-18685-5(7)***); 2002. (Illus.). (gr. 4-6). 26.00 (978-0-516-22586-9(3)) Scholastic Library Publishing. (Children's Pr.).

McNeese, Tim. The Attack on Pearl Harbor: America Enters World War II. 2004. (First Battles Ser.). (Illus.). 112p. (YA). (gr. 6-12). 23.95 (978-1-883846-78-7(1) , First Biographies) Reynolds, Morgan Inc.

Nardo, Don. Pearl Harbor. 2003. (gr. 7-12). lib. bdg. 33.25 (978-0-613-73873-6(X)) Tandem Library Bks.

Pierce, Alan. Bombing of Pearl Harbor. 2005. (American Moments Set Ii Ser.). (Illus.). 48p. (J). (gr. 4-8). lib. bdg. 25.65 (978-1-59197-729-2(0) , ABDO & Daughters) ABDO Publishing Co.

Richard Tames. Pearl Harbor. 2nd ed. 2006. (Point of Impact Ser.). (Illus.). 32p. (J). pap. (***978-1-4034-9151-0(8)***) Heinemann Library.

Santella, Andrew. Pearl Harbor. 2004. 48p. (J). (gr. 4 up). lib. bdg. 22.60 (978-0-7565-0680-3(8)) Compass Point Bks.

Sherman, Josepha. The Story of the Attack on Pearl Harbor. 2005. (Monumental Milestones Ser.). (Illus.). 48p. (YA). (978-1-58415-397-9(0)) Mitchell Lane Pubs., Inc.

Streissguth, Thomas. The Attack on Pearl Harbor. 2001. (At Issue in History Ser.). (Illus.). 104p. (YA). (gr. 7-10). pap. 18.70 (978-0-7377-0751-9(8) , GML12001-176981, Greenhaven Pr., Inc.) Thomson Gale.

Sutcliffe, Jane. The Attack on Pearl Harbor. Lentz, Bob, illus. 2006. (Graphic Library). 32p. (J). (978-0-7368-5477-1(0)) Capstone Pr., Inc.

Tames, Richard. Pearl Harbor: The U. S. Enters World War II. 2001. (Point of Impact Ser.). (Illus.). 32p. (J). (gr. 5-7). lib. bdg. 24.22 (978-1-57572-416-4(2)) Heinemann Library.

—Pearl Harbor: The U. S. Enters World War II. 2001. (gr. 5-8). lib. bdg. 15.90 (978-0-613-36122-4(9)) Tandem Library Bks.

Tames, Richard. Pearl Harbor: The U.S. Enters World War II. 2006. (Point of Impact Ser.). (Illus.). 32p. (YA). (gr. 5-8). lib. bdg. 29.29 (***978-1-4034-9142-8(9)***) Heinemann Library.

Tanaka, Shelley. Attack on Pearl Harbor. Craig, David, illus. 2001. 64p. (gr. 5-17). 19.99 (978-0-7868-0736-9(9)) Hyperion Bks. for Children.

Taylor, Theodore. Air Raid—Pearl Harbor! The Story of December 7, 1941. 2001. (Great Episodes Ser.). (Illus.). 208p. (YA). (gr. 5-9). pap. 6.00 (978-0-15-216421-8(9) , Gulliver Bks.) Harcourt Children's Bks.

Uschan, Michael V. The Bombing of Pearl Harbor. 2003. (Landmark Events in American History Ser.). (Illus.). 48p. (J). (gr. 5 up). pap. 14.95 (978-0-8368-5401-5(2)); lib. bdg. 30.00 (978-0-8368-5373-5(3)) Stevens, Gareth Inc. (World Almanac Library).

Wels, Susan. Pearl Harbor: America's Darkest Day. 2nd ed. 2006. (Illus.). 224p. 34.95 (978-1-887656-78-8(2)) Tehabi Bks.

White, Steve. Day of Infamy: Attack on Pearl Harbor. Spahn, Jerrold, illus. 2007. (Graphic History Ser.). 48p. (YA). (gr. 3). pap. 9.95 (978-1-84603-059-8(5)) Osprey Publishing, Ltd. GBR. *Dist:* Random Hse., Inc.

White, Steve. Pearl Harbor: A Day of Infamy. 2007. (Graphic Battles of World War II Ser.). (Illus.). 48p. (***978-1-4042-7429-7(4)***); pap. (***978-1-4042-7428-0(6)***) Rosen Publishing Group, Inc., The.

White Steve D. Pearl Harbor: A Day of Infamy. 2007. (Graphic Battles of World War II Ser.). (Illus.). 48p. (YA). (gr. 5-8). lib. bdg. 29.25 (978-1-4042-0785-1(6)) Rosen Publishing Group, Inc., The.

PEARL HARBOR (HAWAII), ATTACK ON, 1941—FICTION

Boyd, David. Pearl Harbor. Ng, Drew, illus. 2007. 48p. (J). lib. bdg. 23.08 (***978-1-4242-1640-6(0)***) Fitzgerald Bks.

Denenberg, Barry. Early Sunday Morning: The Pearl Harbor Diary of Amber Billows. 2003. (Dear America Ser.). 160p. (J). 12.95 (978-0-439-55513-5(2)) Scholastic, Inc.

Earle, Joan Zuber, mem. The Children of Battleship Row: Pearl Harbor 1940-1941. 2004. 136p. pap. 16.95 (978-1-57143-095-3(4)) RDR Bks.

Hamilton, Elizabeth L. Surprise at Pearl Harbor. 2004. (Character Mystery Ser.: No. 2). (Illus.). 144p. (J). per. 9.95 (978-0-9754629-2-8(X) , Character-in-Action) Quiet Impact, Inc.

LeSourd, Nancy. The Personal Correspondence of Catherine Clark & Meredith Lyons: Pearl Harbor, 1941. 2004. (Liberty Letters Ser.). (Illus.). 240p. (J). (gr. 5 up). 9.99 (978-0-310-70353-2(0)) Zonderkidz.

Mazer, Harry. A Boy at War: A Novel of Pearl Harbor. (Illus.). 112p. (gr. 5-9). 2002. mass mkt. 4.99 (978-0-689-84160-6(4) , Aladdin); 2001. (J). 16.99 (978-0-689-84161-3(2)) Simon & Schuster Children's Publishing.

—A Boy at War: A Novel of Pearl Harbor. 2002. (gr. 3-6). lib. bdg. 13.00 (978-0-613-65106-6(5)) Tandem Library Bks.

Salisbury, Graham. Under the Blood-Red Sun. 2005. 272p. (YA). (gr. 7-10). pap. 6.50 (978-0-553-49487-7(2) , Laurel Leaf) Random Hse. Children's Bks.

PEARLS

Franck, Irene M. & Brownstone, David M. Pearls. 2003. (Illus.). 32p. (J). (978-0-7172-5719-5(3) , Grolier) Scholastic Library Publishing.

PEARLS—FICTION

Acker, Rick. The Case of the Autumn Rose. 2003. (Davis Detective Mysteries Ser.). 192p. pap. 7.99 (978-0-8254-2004-7(0)) Kregel Pubns.

Johnson, Julia. The Pearl Diver. Al Fakhri, Patricia, illus. 2003. 56p. (J). pap. 15.95 (978-1-900988-58-2(5)) Interlink Publishing Group, Inc.

—The Pearl Diver. Al-Fakhri, Patricia, illus. 2003. (ARA.). 52p. (J). (gr. 3-6). pap. 15.95 (978-1-900988-62-9(3)) Stacey International Pubs. GBR. *Dist:* Interlink Publishing Group, Inc.

Kerven, Rosalind. Sparrow, the Crow & the Pearl. Williamson, Melanie, illus. 2005. 24p. (J). lib. bdg. 22.65 (***978-1-59646-754-5(1)***) Dingles & Co.

Warfel, Elizabeth Stuart. The Blue Pearls. Giarrusso, Veronique, illus. 2001. 32p. (J). (gr. k-4). 16.99 (978-1-902283-78-4(3)) Barefoot Bks., Inc.

PEARY, ROBERT E. (ROBERT EDWIN), 1856-1920

Bedesky, Baron. Peary & Henson: The Race to the North Pole. 2006. (In the Footsteps of Explorers Ser.). (Illus.). 32p. (J). (gr. 3-9). (978-0-7787-2426-1(3)) Crabtree Publishing Co.

Calvert, Patricia, et al. Robert E. Peary: To the Top of the World. 2001. (Great Explorations Ser.). (Illus.). 80p. (J). (gr. 4 up). lib. bdg. 29.93 (978-0-7614-1242-7(5) , Benchmark Bks.) Cavendish, Marshall Corp.

Harcourt School Publishers Staff. To the Top of the World. 3rd ed. 2002. (Trophies English Language Learners Ser.). (Illus.). pap. 5.10 (978-0-15-327878-5(1)) Harcourt Schl. Pubs.

Petrie, Kristin. Robert Peary. 2007. (Rabbit Ears Ser.). (Illus.). 32p. (J). (gr. k-5). 22.78 (978-1-59679-746-8(0)) ABDO Publishing Co.

Warrick, Karen Clemens. The Race for the North Pole & Robert Peary in World History. 2003. (In World History Ser.). (Illus.). 128p. (J). (gr. 5-12). lib. bdg. 26.60 (978-0-7660-1933-1(0)) Enslow Pubs., Inc.

PEASANT ART

see Art Industries and Trade; Folk Art

PEASANTRY

see also Agricultural Laborers; Sociology, Rural

Lilly, Melinda. Peasant. 2002. (People of the Middle Ages Ser.). (Illus.). 32p. (J). lib. bdg. 26.60 (978-1-58952-229-9(X)) Rourke Publishing, LLC.

PEBBLES

see Rocks

PECCARIES

George, Jean Craighead. Summer Moon. 2002. (gr. 3-6). lib. bdg. 14.10 (978-0-613-50513-0(1)) Tandem Library Bks.

Schaefer, Lola M. Javelinas. 2004. (Illus.). 24p. (J). (ps-1). pap. 6.00 (978-1-4034-5734-9(4)); (gr. 1-3). lib. bdg. (978-1-4034-5046-3(3)) Heinemann Library.

PECOS BILL (LEGENDARY CHARACTER)

Blair, Eric. Pecos Bill Tames the Wild West: A Retelling of the Classic Traditional Tale. Chambers-Goldbert, Micah, illus. 2005. (Read-It! Readers Ser.). 32p. (C). (gr. k-3). 18.60 (978-1-4048-0977-2(5)) Picture Window Bks.

Harcourt School Publishers Staff. Trofeos On Level: Pecos Bill. 3rd ed. 2002. (SPA., Illus.). (gr. 3). pap. 6.80 (978-0-15-324093-5(8)) Harcourt Schl. Pubs.

PEDAGOGY

see Education; Education—Study and Teaching; Teaching

PEDDLERS AND PEDDLING—FICTION

Ayres, Katherine. Stealing South: A Story of the Underground Railroad. l.t. ed. 2002. 231p. (J). 22.95 (978-0-7862-4422-5(4)) Thorndike Pr.

Chaconas, Dori. Pennies in a Jar. Lewin, Ted, illus. 2007. 32p. (J). (ps-3). 16.95 (***978-1-56145-422-8(2)*** , Peachtree Junior) Peachtree Pubs., Ltd.

De Gross, Monalisa. Granddaddy's Street Songs. Cooper, Floyd, illus. 1999. (Jump at the Sun Bks.). 32p. (ps-3). 14.99 (978-0-7868-0160-2(3) , Jump at the Sun) Hyperion Bks. for Children.

Derby, Sally. Two Fools & a Horse: An Orginal Tale. Rayevsky, Robert, illus. 2003. 32p. (J). (gr. k-3). 16.95 (978-0-7614-5119-8(6)) Cavendish, Marshall Corp.

Mlawer, Teresa, tr. Se Venden Gorras. unabr. ed. 1999. (SPA., Illus.). (J). (gr. k-3). pap., tchr. ed. 37.95 incl. audio (978-0-87499-514-5(0)) Live Oak Media.

—Se Venden Gorras. Slobodkina, Esphyr, illus. unabr. ed. 1999. (SPA.). (J). (gr. k-3). 25.95 incl. audio (978-0-87499-513-8(2)); pap. 16.95 incl. audio (978-0-87499-512-1(4) , LK3259) Live Oak Media.

Slobodkina, Esphyr. Caps for Sale. 2000. (J). pap. 19.97 incl. audio (978-0-7366-9218-2(5)) Books on Tape, Inc.

—Caps for Sale. 2005. (Illus.). (J). pap. 18.95 incl. audio compact disk (978-1-59112-697-3(5)) Live Oak Media.

—Caps for Sale. Slobodkina, Esphyr, illus. (Illus.). (J). (gr. k-3). 2005. pap. 16.95 incl. audio (978-0-87499-058-4(0)); 2000. 25.95 incl. audio (978-0-87499-059-1(9)) Live Oak Media.

—Caps for Sale, 2 bks. Mlawer, Teresa, tr. Slobodkina, Esphyr, illus. unabr. ed. 1999. (ENG & SPA., Illus.). (J). (gr. k-3). pap. 33.95 incl. audio (978-0-87499-562-6(0)) Live Oak Media.

—Caps for Sale. 2004. (J). 24.95 incl. audio (978-0-89719-863-9(8) , HRA012) Weston Woods Studios, Inc.

—Caps for Sale: A Tale of a Peddler, Some Monkeys, & Their Monkey Business. 2000. (978-0-606-20342-5(7)) Tandem Library Bks.

—Caps for Sale Board Book: A Tale of a Peddler, Some Monkeys & Their Monkey Business. Slobodkina, Esphyr, illus. 2008. 32p. (J). 8.99 (***978-0-06-147453-8(3)*** , Harper Festival) HarperCollins Pubs.

—Circus Caps for Sale. Slobodkina, Esphyr, illus. 2004. (Illus.). 40p. (J). (ps-2). reprint ed. 17.00 (978-0-7567-8345-7(3)) DIANE Publishing Co.

—Circus Caps for Sale. Slobodkina, Esphyr, illus. (Illus.). 48p. (J). (ps-2). 2002. 16.99 (978-0-06-029655-1(0)); 2004. reprint ed. pap. 6.99 (978-0-06-443793-6(0) , Harper Trophy) HarperCollins Pubs.

—Se Venden Gorras. Slobodkina, Esphyr, illus. 1999. (Illus.). 28.95 incl. audio compact disk (978-1-59519-195-3(X)); pap. 39.95 incl. audio compact disk (978-1-59519-194-6(1)); (SPA., (J). pap. 18.95 incl. audio compact disk (978-1-59519-193-9(3)) Live Oak Media.

PEDIATRICS

see Children—Diseases; Children—Health and Hygiene

PEDIGREES

see Heraldry

PEER PRESSURE

Abingdon. The Pressure's On. 2004. (gr. 6-8). pap., stu. ed. 5.00 (978-0-687-06356-7(6)); pap. 12.00 (978-0-687-06346-8(9)) Abingdon Pr.

Auer, Jim. Standing up to Peer Pressure: A Guide to Being True to You. Alley, R. W., illus. 2003. 32p. (J). per. 7.95 (978-0-87029-375-7(3)) Abbey Pr.

Canfield, Jack L., et al. Una 2nd Racion de Sopa de Pollo para el Alma del Adolescente: Mas Relatos Sobre la Vida el Amour y el Aprendizaje. 2nd ed. 2003. Tr. of Chicken Soup for the Teenage Soul. (SPA., Illus.). 350p. (YA). pap. 12.95 (978-0-7573-0134-6(7)) Health Communications, Inc.

Clued in! on Saying No. 2005. (J). 4.95 (978-1-55548-051-6(9) , 675) Human Relations Media.

Feller, Robyn M. Everything You Need to Know about Peer Pressure. rev. ed. 2001. (Need to Know Library). (Illus.). 64p. (YA). (gr. 4-6). lib. bdg. 25.25 (978-0-8239-3440-9(3)) Rosen Publishing Group, Inc., The.

Garland, Ric, et al. Peer Pressure. Slonim, David, illus. rev. ed. 2002. (Teen Pressure Points Ser.). (YA). (gr. 8-12). pap. 8.95 (978-1-931235-39-6(2)) Word of Life Fellowship, Inc.

Havelin, Kate. Peer Pressure: "How Can I Say No?" 1999. (Perspectives on Relationships Ser.). (Illus.). 64p. (J). (gr. 4-6). lib. bdg. 23.93 (978-0-7368-0291-8(6) , LifeMatters Bks.) Capstone Pr., Inc.

Koubek, Christine Wickert. Friends, Cliques & Peer Pressure: Be True to Yourself. 2002. (Teen Issues Ser.). (Illus.). 64p. (YA). (gr. 6-12). lib. bdg. 22.60 (978-0-7660-1669-9(2)) Enslow Pubs., Inc.

Mototsune, Kat. Image: Deal with it from the inside Out. Shannon, Ben, illus. 2007. (Deal with It Ser.). 32p. (J). (gr. 4-8). pap. 12.95 (***978-1-55028-994-7(2)***) Lorimer, James & Co., Ltd., Pubs. CAN. *Dist:* Casemate Pubs. & Bk. Distributors, LLC.

No Thanks, Not for Me. 1999. (SmartReader Ser.). (J). Level 1. pap., tchr. ed. 19.95 incl. audio (978-0-7887-1158-9(X) , 79419T3); Level 2. pap., tchr. ed. 19.95 incl. audio (978-0-7887-0124-5(X) , 79312T3) Recorded Bks., LLC.

Powell, Kara Eckmann & Johnson, Mike, eds. Peer Pressure. 2001. (Pulse Ser.: 13). 96p. (gr. 6-9). 14.99 (978-0-8307-2549-6(0) , Gospel Light) Gospel Light Pubns.

Real Teens Vol. 5: Diary of A Junior Year. 2000. (gr. 7-12). lib. bdg. 13.00 (978-0-613-26722-9(2)) Tandem Library Bks.

Slavens, Elaine. Peer Pressure: Without Losing Your Cool. Shannon, Ben, illus. 2004. (Deal with It Ser.). 32p. (J). (gr. 4-8). 12.95 (978-1-55028-815-5(6)) Lorimer, James & Co., Ltd., Pubs. CAN. *Dist:* Casemate Pubs. & Bk. Distributors, LLC.

Stewart, Gail B. Peer Pressure. 2002. (Understanding Issues Ser.). (Illus.). 48p. (J). (gr. 3-5). 26.20 (978-0-7377-1024-3(1) , Kidhaven) Thomson Gale.

Straight Talk about Peer Pressure. (YA). (gr. 6-8). 69.95 (978-1-55942-199-7(1) , 9241V9) Marsh Media.

Tym, Kate & Worms, Penny. Coping with Friends. 2004. (Illus.). (J). 28.56 (978-1-4109-0576-5(4)) Harcourt Schl. Pubs.

Webber, Diane. Your Space: Dealing with friends & Peers. 2008. (Scholastic Choices Ser.). 112p. (J). pap. 8.95 (***978-0-531-14774-0(6)*** , Watts, Franklin) Scholastic Library Publishing.

PEER PRESSURE—FICTION

Alford, Jan. I Can't Believe I Have to Do This. 1999. (J). (978-0-606-16801-4(X)); (gr. 5-8). lib. bdg. 14.15 (978-0-613-19374-0(1)) Tandem Library Bks.

—I Can't Believe I Have to Do This! 1999. (Illus.). 192p. (J). (gr. 3-7). pap. 5.99 (978-0-698-11785-3(9) , Putnam Juvenile) Penguin Group (USA) Inc.

Apostolina, M. Dark Cindy. 2006. 336p. (YA). pap. 8.99 (978-1-4169-1769-4(1) , Simon Pulse) Simon & Schuster Children's Publishing.

—Meri Strikes Back. 2006. (Hazing Meri Sugarman Ser.). 288p. (YA). pap. 8.99 (978-1-4169-1163-0(4) , Simon Pulse) Simon & Schuster Children's Publishing.

Bertrand, Diane Gonzales. Trino's Choice. (Illus.). 128p. (YA). (gr. 5-11). pap., stu. ed. 9.95 (978-1-55885-268-6(9)); 1999. 124p. (J). (gr. 4-7). 16.95 (978-1-55885-279-2(4)) Arte Publico Pr. (Piñata Books).

—Trino's Choice. 1999. (978-0-606-17956-0(9)); (gr. 5-8). lib. bdg. 18.75 (978-0-613-33660-4(7)) Tandem Library Bks.

Borchard, Therese Johnson. Whitney Stows Away on Noah's Ark: And Learns How to Deal with Peer Pressure. VanNest, Wendy, illus. 2000. (Emerald Bible Collection). 80p. (gr. 3-7). 5.95 (978-0-8091-6674-9(7) , 6674-7) Paulist Pr.

Brightwood, Laura, illus. Left Out. Brightwood, Laura, . 2006. (J). (978-0-9779290-7-8(8)) 3-C Institute for Social Development.

Brumbeau, Jeff. Miss Hunnicutt's Hat. de Marcken, Gail, illus. 2003. 48p. (J). (gr. k-3). pap. 16.95 (978-0-439-31895-2(5) , Orchard Bks.) Scholastic, Inc.

Cabot, Meg. Pants on Fire. 2007. 272p. (gr. 7-10). (J). lib. bdg. 17.89 (978-0-06-088016-3(3)); (YA). 16.99 (978-0-06-088015-6(5)) HarperCollins Pubs. (HarperTeen).

Carlson, Melody. The Day the Circus Came to Town. Butterfield, Ned, illus. 2004. 31p. (ps-3). 14.99 (978-1-58134-158-4(X)) Crossway Bks.

Christopher, Matt. Fairway Phenom. 2003. 144p. (J). (gr. 5-8). pap. 4.99 (978-0-316-07551-0(5)) Little, Brown Bks. for Young Readers.

Cormier, Robert. The Chocolate War. 2002. (Illus.). (J). 13.94 (978-0-7587-4778-5(0)) Book Wholesalers, Inc.

—The Chocolate War. 191p. (YA). (gr. 7 up). pap. 4.99 (978-0-8072-1428-2(0) , Listening Library) Random Hse. Audio Publishing Group.

—The Chocolate War. 30th ed. 2004. 272p. (YA). (gr. 7-12). pap. 8.95 (978-0-375-82987-1(3) , Knopf Bks. for Young Readers) Random Hse. Children's Bks.

—The Chocolate War. 2000. 12.64 (978-0-606-20038-7(X)) Tandem Library Bks.

Friedman, Laurie B. Honestly, Mallory! Pollak, Barbara, illus. 2007. (Mallory Ser.). 160p. (J). (gr. 2-6). 15.95 (***978-0-8225-6193-4(X)*** , Carolrhoda Bks.) Lerner Publishing Group.

Gonzalez, Julie. Ricochet. 2007. 208p. (YA). (gr. 9). 15.99 (978-0-385-73228-4(7)); lib. bdg. 18.99 (978-0-385-90254-0(9)) Random Hse. Children's Bks. (Delacorte Bks. for Young Readers).

Goobie, Beth. The Dream Where the Losers Go. 2006. 256p. (gr. 9-12). pap. 8.95 (978-1-55143-455-1(5)) Orca Bk. Pubs. USA.

—The Dream Where the Losers Go. 1999. 208p. (YA). (gr. 9-12). pap. 6.95 (978-1-896184-62-3(6)) Roussan Pubs., Inc./Roussan Editeur, Inc. CAN. *Dist:* Orca Bk. Pubs. USA.

Hana's Year: Evaluation Guide. 2006. (J). (978-1-55942-408-0(7)) Marsh Media.

Holmes, Elizabeth. Pretty Is. 2007. 224p. (J). (gr. 4-6). 16.99 (978-0-525-47813-3(2) , Dutton Juvenile) Penguin Group (USA) Inc.

Horrocks, Anita. What They Don't Know. braille ed. 2003. (J). (gr. 2). spiral bd. (978-0-616-15267-6(1)) Canadian National Institute for the Blind/Institut National Canadien pour les Aveugles.

—What They Don't Know. 1999. (Illus.). 240p. (YA). (gr. 7-10). pap. 8.95 (978-0-7737-6001-1(6)) Stoddart Kids CAN. *Dist:* Fitzhenry & Whiteside, Ltd.

—What They Don't Know. 1999. (J). (978-0-606-19101-2(1)) Tandem Library Bks.

Koja, Kathe. Buddha Boy. 2003. 128p. (YA). (gr. 7 up). 16.00 (978-0-374-30998-5(1) , Farrar, Straus & Giroux (BYR)) Farrar, Straus & Giroux.

—Buddha Boy. 2004. 128p. (YA). (gr. 6-11). reprint ed. pap. 5.99 (978-0-14-240209-2(5) , Puffin) Penguin Group (USA) Inc.

—Buddha Boy. l.t. ed. 2003. 113p. (J). 24.95 (978-0-7862-6012-6(2)) Thomson Gale.

Korman, Gordon. Jake, Reinvented. 2005. 224p. (gr. 7-17). pap. 5.99 (978-0-7868-5697-8(1)) Hyperion Bks. for Children.

Kropp, Paul. The Countess & Me. 2003. (Illus.). (YA). pap. (978-1-55041-692-3(8)) Fitzhenry & Whiteside, Ltd.

Lachenmeyer, Nathaniel. Searching for Sasquatch. Bradley, Vicki, illus. 2007. 32p. 16.95 (***978-1-57061-442-2(3)***) Sasquatch Bks.

Laser, Michael. Cheater. 2008. 224p. (YA). (gr. 7). 16.99 (***978-0-525-47826-3(4)*** , Dutton Juvenile) Penguin Group (USA) Inc.

Linko, G. J. Rebecca's Return. 2004. (Seekers Ser.). 5.99 (978-0-8066-4181-2(9) , Augsburg Bks.) Augsburg Fortress, Pubs.

—Rebecca's Return: Topical Study. 2004. (Seekers Ser.). 3.99 (978-0-8066-4184-3(3)) Augsburg Fortress, Pubs.

Margolis, Leslie. Fix. 2006. 256p. (YA). pap. 6.99 (978-1-4169-2456-2(6) , Simon Pulse) Simon & Schuster Children's Publishing.

Morales, Maximino. The Wooden Go-Cart (El Carrito de Madera) 2002. (ENG & SPA., Illus.). 24p. (J). (gr. k-3). pap. 6.95 (978-0-9740308-0-7(5)) Maximum Publishing Co.

Moss, Peggy & Tardif, Dee Dee. Our Friendship Rules. Geis, Alissa Imre, illus. 2007. 32p. (J). (***978-0-88448-291-8(X)***) Tilbury Hse. Pubs.

Nigro, D. M. The Wolfman, the Shrink & the Eighth-Grade Election. 2006. 116p. (J). pap. 13.50 (978-1-931201-66-7(8)) Twilight Times Bks.

Peretti, Frank E. Hangman's Curse. movie tie-in ed. 2003. (Veritas Project Ser.). 312p. (YA). pap. 9.99 (978-1-4003-0371-7(0)) Nelson, Thomas Inc.

—Hangman's Curse. 2003. (gr. 3-6). lib. bdg. 18.80 (978-0-613-77934-0(7)) Tandem Library Bks.

Pfister, Marcus. El Pez Arco Iris al Rescate! Pfister, Marcus, illus. 1998. (Rainbow Fish Ser.). Orig. Title: Regenbogenfisch, Komm Hilf Mir!. (SPA., Illus.). 12p. (J). (ps-3). bds. 9.95 (978-1-55858-885-1(X)) North-South Bks., Inc.

Plum-Ucci, Carol. The Body of Christopher Creed. 2000. 256p. (YA). (gr. 7-12). 17.00 (978-0-15-202388-1(7)) Harcourt Children's Bks.

—The Body of Christopher Creed. 2001. 331p. (YA). (gr. 7-17). pap. 6.99 (978-0-7868-1641-5(4) , Volo) Hyperion Bks. for Children.

—The Body of Christopher Creed. 2001. 13.39 (978-0-606-22569-4(2)); (gr. 7-12). lib. bdg. 15.00 (978-0-613-49392-5(3)) Tandem Library Bks.

—The Body of Christopher Creed. l.t. ed. 2001. 352p. (YA). 23.95 (978-0-7862-3509-4(8)) Thorndike Pr.

Rimes, Leann. Jag. Bernal, Richard, illus. 2003. 40p. (J). (gr. k-3). 15.99 (978-0-525-47155-4(3) , Dutton Juvenile) Penguin Group (USA) Inc.

Rountree, Wendy. Lost Soul. 2003. 87p. (J). pap. 14.95 (978-1-59129-975-2(6)) PublishAmerica, Inc.

Rousaki, Maria. Unique Monique. Papanikolaou, Polina, illus. 2004. 32p. (J). 15.95 (978-1-929132-51-5(4)) Kane/Miller Bk. Pubs., Inc.

Schultz Nicholson, Lorna. Northern Star. 2006. (Sports Stories Ser.). 112p. (J). (gr. 3-8). (***978-1-55028-911-4(X));*** 7.95 (978-1-55028-910-7(1)) Lorimer, James & Co., Ltd., Pubs. CAN. *Dist:* Casemate Pubs. & Bk. Distributors, LLC.

Spinelli, Jerry. Wringer. 2004. 256p. (J). (gr. 7 up). pap. 6.99 (978-0-06-059282-0(6) , Harper Trophy) HarperCollins Pubs.

Stolarz, Laurie Faria. Bleed. 2006. 240p. (gr. 7-17). 15.99 (978-0-7868-3854-7(X)) Hyperion Pr.

Varela, Barry. Palmer's Gate. 2006. 112p. (J). 16.95 (978-1-59643-073-0(7)) Roaring Brook Pr.

Wilde, Jerry. Peace in the Halls: Stories & Activities to Manage Anger & Prevent School Violence. 2003. 112p. (YA). (gr. 4-12). pap. 9.95 (978-0-9657610-4-8(5)) LGR Publishing, Inc.

Willson, Sarah. Hocus Focus. Wummer, Amy, illus. 2004. 32p. (J). lib. bdg. 20.00 (***978-1-4242-1093-0(3)***) Fitzgerald Bks.

Wilson, Jacqueline. Girls Out Late. 2003. 224p. (YA). (gr. 7). mass mkt. 5.50 (978-0-440-22959-9(6) , Laurel Leaf) Random Hse. Children's Bks.

—Girls Out Late. Sharratt, Nick, illus. 2003. 192p. (YA). mass mkt. (978-0-552-54523-5(6) , Corgi) Transworld Publishers Ltd. GBR. *Dist:* Random Hse. of Canada, Ltd.

Wilson, Sarah. Hocus Focus. Wummer, Amy, tr. Wummer, Amy, illus. 2004. (Science Solves It! Ser.). (J). pap. 4.99 (978-1-57565-136-1(X)) Kane Pr., The.

PEGASUS (GREEK MYTHOLOGY)

Marzollo, Jean. Let's Go, Pegasus! 2006. (Illus.). 32p. (J). (ps-5). 12.99 (978-0-316-74136-1(1)) Little Brown & Co.

Mason, Jane. The Flying Horse: The Story of Pegasus. Swan, Susan, illus. 1999. (All Aboard Reading Ser.). 32p. (J). (ps-1). pap. 3.99 (978-0-448-41980-0(7) , Grosset & Dunlap) Penguin Group (USA) Inc.

—Flying Horse: The Story of Pegasus. 1999. (gr. k-3). lib. bdg. 11.80 (978-0-613-14728-6(6)) Tandem Library Bks.

Mayer, Marianna. Pegasus. Craft, Kinuko Y., illus. 1998. 40p. (J). (gr. k-3). 16.99 (978-0-688-13382-5(7)) HarperCollins Pubs.

—Pegasus. Craft, Kinuko, illus. 1998. 40p. (J). (gr. k-3). 16.89 (978-0-688-13383-2(5)) HarperCollins Pubs.

PEKING (CHINA)

see Beijing (China)

PELE, 1940-

Buckley, James. Pele. 2007. (DK Biography Ser.). 128p. (J). (gr. 3-8). 14.99 (978-0-7566-2996-0(9)); pap. 4.99 (978-0-7566-2987-8(X)) Dorling Kindersley Publishing, Inc.

Canizares, Susan. Pele: The King of Soccer. 1999. (ps-2). lib. bdg. 10.10 (978-0-613-22165-8(6)) Tandem Library Bks.

Canizares, Susan & Berger, Samantha. Pele: The King of Soccer. 1999. (Social Studies Emergent Readers). (J). 2.50 (978-0-439-04577-3(0)) Scholastic, Inc.

Cline-Ransome, Lesa. Young Pele: Soccer's First Star. Ransome, James E., illus. 2007. 40p. (J). (ps-3). 16.99 (***978-0-375-83599-5(7)*** , Schwartz & Wade Bks.) Random Hse. Children's Bks.

—Young Pele: Soccer's First Star. Ransome, James, illus. 2007. 40p. (J). (ps-3). lib. bdg. 19.99 (***978-0-375-93599-2(1)*** , Schwartz & Wade Bks.) Random Hse. Children's Bks.

Hillstrom, Laurie. Pele. 2007. (Twentieth Century Most Influential Hispanics Ser.). (Illus.). 128p. (gr. 7-10). 31.20 (***978-1-4205-0023-3(6)*** , Lucent Bks.) Thomson Gale.

PELICANS

Boring, Mel. Flamingos, Loons, & Pelicans. Recher, Andrew, illus. 2006. (Take-Along Guide Ser.). 48p. (J). 7.95 (978-1-55971-943-8(5)); 11.95 (978-1-55971-942-1(7)) T&N Children's Publishing. (NorthWord Bks. for Young Readers).

Cussen, Sarah. Those Peculiar Pelicans. 2006. (J). 14.95 (978-1-56164-358-5(0)) Pineapple Pr., Inc.

—Those Peculiar Pelicans. Weaver, Steve, illus. Hammond, Roger, photos by. 2005. 55p. (J). (gr. 3-7). pap. 8.95 (978-1-56164-340-0(8)) Pineapple Pr., Inc.

Pohl, Kathleen. Pelicans. 2006. (Illus.). 24p. (J). pap. (***978-0-8368-7826-4(4));*** lib. bdg. (***978-0-8368-7819-6(1)***) Stevens, Gareth Inc. (Weekly Reader Early Learning Library).

—Pelicans: Pelicanos. 2006. (Illus.). 24p. (J). pap. (***978-0-8368-8015-1(3));*** lib. bdg. (***978-0-8368-8008-3(0)***) Stevens, Gareth Inc. (Weekly Reader Early Learning Library).

Savage, Candace Sherk, et al. Pelicans. 1999. (Getting to Know ... Nature's Children Ser.). (Illus.). 47p. (J). (978-0-7172-8840-3(4) , Grolier) Scholastic Library Publishing.

Swan, Erin Pembrey. Pelicans, Cormorants, & Their Kin. (Animals in Order Ser.). (Illus.). 48p. (J). 2003. (gr. 4-6). pap. 6.95 (978-0-531-16378-8(4)); 2002. (gr. 5-7). pap. 26.50 (978-0-531-11929-7(7)) Scholastic Library Publishing. (Watts, Franklin).

—Pelicans, Cormorants, & Their Kin. 2003. (Illus.). 47p. (J). (gr. 4-7). lib. bdg. 15.25 (978-0-613-59537-7(8)) Tandem Library Bks.

Taylor, Bonnie Highsmith. Mattie: A Brown Pelican. 2001. (Animal Adventures Ser.). (Illus.). (J). 54p. pap. (978-0-7891-5266-4(5)); 56p. (gr. 1-4). lib. bdg. 16.95 (978-0-7807-9671-3(3)) Perfection Learning Corp.

Welsbacher, Anne. Flying Brown Pelicans. Netherton, John, photos by. (Pull Ahead Bks.). (Illus.). 32p. (J). (gr. k-2). 1999. lib. bdg. 22.60 (978-0-8225-3613-0(7) , Lerner Pubns.); 1998. pap. 5.95 (978-0-8225-3619-2(6)) Lerner Publishing Group.

—Flying Brown Pelicans. 1999. (gr. k-3). lib. bdg. 14.10 (978-0-613-43822-3(1)) Tandem Library Bks.

PELICANS—FICTION

Clark, Irene M. Feathery Tales: Benny Penguin, Huffer & Puffer California Quail, Paco Pelican. Clark, Cynthia D., illus. unabr. ed. 2001. 147p. (J). (ps-3). 12.95 incl. cd-rom (978-0-9709843-0-2(8)) Creekside Stories.

Dahl, Roald. The Giraffe, the Pelly & Me. Blake, Quentin, illus. 1998. 80p. (Orig.). (J). (gr. 2-6). pap. 5.99 (978-0-14-130228-7(3) , Puffin) Penguin Group (USA) Inc.

DeYoung, Anita. Thank God the Pelican. 2007. (J). per. 9.99 (***978-1-59886-882-1(9)***) Tate Publishing & Enterprises, L.L.C.

Dorfman, Gladys E. Hannah Mae, the Little Pelican of Sarasota Bay. Dorfman, Gladys E., illus. 1999. (Illus.). (J). (gr. k-6). 10.95 (978-0-9671111-0-0(2)) Hannah Mae Enterprises, Inc.

Froeber, Sarah & Mosher, Kim. Pelican & Pelicant. 2003. (Illus.). 36p. (J). 17.99 (978-0-9744926-0-5(4)) Toucan Pr., Inc.

Glaze, Dave. Waiting for Pelly. 2003. (Pelly Ser.). (Illus.). 240p. (J). (gr. 3-6). pap. 7.95 (978-1-55050-228-2(X)) Coteau Bks. CAN. *Dist:* Fitzhenry & Whiteside, Ltd.

Halfmann, Janet. Pelican's Catch. Dacey, Bob & Bandelin, Debra, illus. 2005. 32p. (J). (ps-2). 4.95 (978-1-59249-286-2(X) , B4076); 15.95 (978-1-59249-287-9(8) , B4026); 8.95 incl. audio (978-1-59249-309-8(2) , SC4026); pap. 6.95 (978-1-59249-285-5(1) , S4026) Soundprints.

—Pelican's Catch: Smithsonian Oceanic. Dacey, Bob & Bandelin, Debra, illus. 2005. 32p. (J). (ps-2). 9.95 (978-1-59249-311-1(4) , PB4076) Soundprints.

Keiser, Frances. The Adventures of Pelican Pete: A Bird Is Born. Keiser, Hugh, illus. 1999. 32p. (J). (ps-3). 15.00 (978-0-9668845-0-0(7)) Sagaponack Bks.

—The Adventures of Pelican Pete: First Discoveries. Keiser, Hugh, illus. 2002. 32p. (J). 15.00 (978-0-9668845-2-4(3)) Sagaponack Bks.

—Preening for Flight: The Adventures of Pelican Pete. Keiser, Hugh, illus. 2001. Orig. Title: The Adventures of Pelican Pete: Preening for Flight. 32p. (J). 17.00 (978-0-9668845-1-7(5)) Sagaponack Bks.

Keiser, Frances R. Annie the River Otter: The Adventures of Pelican Pete. Keiser, Hugh M., illus. l.t. ed. 2006. 32p. (J). 17.00 (978-0-9668845-4-8(X)) Sagaponack Bks.

Parish, Steve, illus. The Proud Pelican's Secret. 2005. 24p. (J). lib. bdg. 20.67 (978-0-8368-5974-4(X)) Stevens, Gareth Inc.

Prelutsky, Jack. The Gargoyle on the Roof. Sis, Peter, illus. 1999. 40p. (J). (gr. 1 up). 16.99 (978-0-688-09643-4(3)) HarperCollins Pubs.

Renaud, Andrea. Sammy the Surfing Pelican Meets Steve the Surf Guru. l.t. ed. 2003. (Illus.). 32p. (J). per. (978-0-9717041-3-8(9)) A Happy Friend, Inc.

Ryan, Mike. Mayda Saves the Day. Ralph, Karin, illus. 2004. 60p. (J). (gr. 1-5). 14.95 (978-0-9701319-3-5(3)) Temenos Pr.

Rylant, Cynthia. The Turtle. McDaniels, Preston, illus. 2005. (Lighthouse Family Ser.). 48p. (J). 14.95 (978-0-689-86244-1(X) , Simon & Schuster Children's Publishing) Simon & Schuster Children's Publishing.

Sargent, Dave & Sargent, David, Jr. Petie Pelican: Be Proud of Yourself, 20, 14. Lenoir, Jane, illus. 2nd ed. 2003. (Feather Tales Ser.: 14). 42p. (J). lib. bdg. 19.95 (978-1-56763-745-8(0)) Ozark Publishing.

Scheunemann, Pam. Pelican's Pouch. Nobens, C. A., illus. 2007. (Fact & Fiction Ser.). 24p. (J). pap. (978-1-59928-463-7(4)); 21.35 (978-1-59928-462-0(6)) ABDO Publishing Co.

P Q R

Sprecher, John. Tori & Cassandra & the Pelican in Peril. Forrest, James, illus. l.t. ed. Date not set. (Special Kids "Special Message" Book Ser.: Vol. 3). 32p. (J). (gr. k-4). pap. 10.00 (978-1-892186-02-7(0)) Anythings Possible, Inc.

PENAL CODES

see Criminal Law

PENAL INSTITUTIONS

see Prisons

PENAL LAW

see Criminal Law

PENCIL DRAWING

Hosley, Maria. Airplanes. 2007. (Illus.). 24p. (J). 21.35 (*978-1-59679-799-4(1)) ABDO Publishing Co.

—Cars. 2007. (Illus.). 24p. (J). 21.35 (*978-1-59679-800-7(9)) ABDO Publishing Co.

—People. 2007. (Illus.). 24p. (J). 21.35 (*978-1-59679-812-0(2)) ABDO Publishing Co.

Levin, Freddie. 1-2-3 Draw People. 2007. (Illus.). 64p. pap. 8.99 (*978-0-939217-63-2(5)) Peel Productions, Inc.

Levin, Freddie & Gordon, Freddie. 1-2-3 Draw Baby Animals. Levin, Freddie, illus. 2006. (Illus.). 64p. pap. 8.99 (978-0-939217-45-8(7)) Peel Productions, Inc.

Make Your Own Pencil Toppers. 2006. (Creative Studio Ser.). (Illus.). 48p. (YA). (978-1-905359-86-8(1)) Top That! Publishing PLC.

PENGUINS

Anderson, Jill. Penguins. 2007. 24p. (J). pap. (*978-1-55971-973-5(7)); (*978-1-55971-972-8(9)) T&N Children's Publishing. (NorthWord Bks. for Young Readers).

Animal Lives: Penguins. 2006. pap. 4.99 (978-1-4206-8163-5(X)) Teacher Created Materials, Inc.

Antarctic Penguins, 6 vols., Pack. 16p. (gr. 3 up). 36.00 (978-0-7635-9685-9(X)) Rigby Education.

Arlington, Jane & Langdon, Sharon. Penguins. 2006. (J). 7.99 (978-1-59939-032-1(9) , Reader's Digest Young Families, Inc.) Reader's Digest Children's Publishing, Inc.

Arnold, Caroline, illus. A Penguin's World. 2006. 24p. (J). (gr. k-2). 23.93 (978-1-4048-1323-6(3) , 1253185) Picture Window Bks.

Baby Penguin. 2005. (Seaworld Animal Library: Vol. 2). (Illus.). 24p. (J). (ps-k). bds. 6.95 (978-0-8249-6616-4(3)) Ideals Pubns.

Barner, Bob. Penguins, Penguins, Everywhere! 2007. (Illus.). 32p. (J). (ps-2). 14.95 (978-0-8118-5664-5(X)) Chronicle Bks. LLC.

Barnett, Michelle Noble, et al. Theme Pockets - January: The Four Seasons; Penguins; Famous Americans. Evans, Marilyn, ed. Larsen, Jo, illus. 1999. (Making Books with Pockets Ser.). 96p. (J). pap., tchr. ed. 12.99 (978-1-55799-698-5(9) , EMC 584) Evan-Moor Educational Pubs.

Behler, Deborah A. & Jango-Cohen, Judith. Penguins. 2001. (Animals Animals Ser.). (Illus.). 48p. (J). (gr. 3-5). lib. bdg. 25.64 (978-0-7614-1260-1(3) , Benchmark Bks.) Cavendish, Marshall Corp.

Berger, Melvin & Berger, Gilda. Do Penguins Get Frostbite? Questions & Answers about Polar Animals. Bond, Higgins, illus. 2000. (J). (978-0-439-19376-4(1)) Scholastic, Inc.

—Penguins. 2002. (Illus.). (J). (978-0-439-44536-8(1)) Scholastic, Inc.

Bernard, Robin. Penguins. 2003. (Learn All About Ser.). (Illus.). 56p. pap. 10.95 (978-0-439-51883-3(0)) Scholastic, Inc.

Black, Sonia W. Plenty of Penguins. MacCombie, Turi, illus. 2000. (Hello Reader! Science Ser.). 32p. (J). (ps-k). pap. 3.99 (978-0-439-09832-8(7)) Scholastic, Inc.

—Plenty of Penguins. (Hello Reader! Ser.). 2000. (J). (978-0-606-19588-1(2)); 1999. lib. bdg. 11.80 (978-0-613-32958-3(9)) Tandem Library Bks.

Books Are Fun 8 Title Animal Lives Set: Penguins. 2006. (J). (978-1-59566-310-8(X)) QEB Publishing Inc.

Bredeson, Carmen. Emperor Penguins up Close. 2006. (Zoom in on Animals! Ser.). (Illus.). 24p. (J). lib. bdg. 21.26 (978-0-7660-2497-7(0) , Enslow Elementary) Enslow Pubs., Inc.

Brennan, Patricia. Penguins & Other Flightless Birds, Vol. 4. 2002. (World Book's Animals of the World Ser.: Set 3). (Illus.). 64p. (J). (978-0-7166-1227-8(5)) World Bk., Inc.

Chester, Jonathan. Splash! A Penguin Counting Book. 2000. (978-0-606-20317-3(6)) Tandem Library Bks.

Chester, Jonathan & Melville, Kirsty. Splash! A Penguin Counting Book. 2004. (Illus.). 24p. (J). (ps-k). 6.95 (978-1-58246-042-0(6) , Tricycle Pr.) Ten Speed Pr.

Child's Play, creator. Penguin. 2005. (Illus.). 12p. (J). (ps-ps). bds. 5.99 (978-0-85953-680-6(7)) Child's Play-International.

Coats, Judith. Penguins: Flightless Birds of the Southern Hemisphere. 2001. (Seaworld Education Ser.). (Illus.). 92p. per. 7.99 (978-1-893698-05-5(X) , B04, SeaWorld Education Dept.) SeaWorld, Inc.

Cousteau Society Staff. Penguins. 1998. (J). 3.95 (978-0-87628-987-7(1)) Ctr. for Applied Research in Education, The.

Cowcher, Helen. Antarctica. 2001. (Illus.). 40p. (VIE, ENG, URD, TUR & CHI.). 16.95 (978-1-84059-006-7(8)); (GRE, ENG, URD, TUR & VIE., (YA). 16.95 (978-1-84059-002-9(5)); (GUJ, ENG, URD, TUR & VIE., (YA). 16.95 (978-1-84059-003-6(3)); (URD, ENG, TUR, VIE & CHI., (YA). 16.95 (978-1-84059-005-0(X)); (BEN, ENG, URD, TUR & VIE., (YA). 16.95 (978-1-84059-000-5(9)); (TUR., (YA). 16.95 (978-1-84059-007-4(6)) Milet Publishing.

Crewe, Sabrina. Life Cycle of the Penguin. 1998. (Life Cycles Ser.). (Illus.). 32p. (J). (gr. 2-5). pap. 6.95 (978-0-8172-6240-2(7)) Steck-Vaughn.

Daigle, Evelyne. The World of Penguins. Wright, Genevieve, tr. from FRE. Grenier, Daniel, illus. 2007. 48p. (J). (gr. 4). 18.95 (978-0-88776-799-9(0)) Tundra Bks., Inc./Livres Toundra, Inc. CAN. *Dist:* Random Hse., Inc.

DK Publishing. Penguin. 2007. (See How They Grow Ser.). 24p. (J). pap. 3.99 (*978-0-7566-3371-4(0)) Dorling Kindersley Publishing, Inc.

Do Penguins Have Puppies? (Animals All Around Ser.). 24p. (J). 7.95 (978-1-4048-0372-5(6)) Picture Window Bks.

Eckart, Edana. Macaroni Penguin. 2005. (Welcome Bookstm Ser.). (Illus.). 24p. (J). (ps-2). 18.00 (978-0-516-25054-0(X)); pap. 4.95 (978-0-516-25165-3(1)) Scholastic Library Publishing. (Children's Pr.).

Edwards, Roberta. Emperor Penguins. Schwartz, Carol, illus. 2007. (All Aboard Science Reader Station Stop Ser.). 48p. (J). (gr. 1-3). pap. 3.99 (*978-0-448-44664-6(2) , Grosset & Dunlap) Penguin Group (USA) Inc.

Fontanel, Béatrice. The Penguin: A Funny Bird. Fatras, Andre, photos by. 2004. (Animal Close-Ups Ser.). (Illus.). 26p. (J). pap. 6.95 (978-1-57091-628-1(4)) Charlesbridge Publishing, Inc.

Gareth Stevens Publishing Staff, contrib. by. Penguins. 2004. (All about Wild Animals Ser.). (Illus.). 32p. (J). lib. bdg. 23.33 (978-0-8368-4186-2(7)) Stevens, Gareth Inc.

Gibson, Deborah C. Penguins & Their Homes. 1999. (Animal Habitats Ser.). (Illus.). 24p. (J). (gr. k-4). lib. bdg. 18.75 (978-0-8239-5311-0(4) , PowerKids Pr.) Rosen Publishing Group, Inc., The.

Guiberson, Brenda Z. The Emperor Lays an Egg. Schonhorst, Elizabeth, ed. Paley, Joan, illus. rev. ed. 2004. 32p. (J). pap. 6.95 (978-0-8050-7636-3(0) , Owlet Paperbacks for Young Readers) Holt, Henry & Co.

Hall, Margaret. Penguins & Their Chicks. 2003. (Animal Offspring Ser.). (Illus.). 24p. (J). lib. bdg. 17.26 (978-0-7368-2109-4(0) , Pebble Bks.) Capstone Pr., Inc.

Hanel, Rachael. Penguins. 2008. (J). (*978-1-58341-658-7(7) , Creative Education) Creative Co., The.

Hewett, Richard, illus. & photos by. A Penguin Chick Grows Up. Hewett, Richard, photos by. Hewett, Joan, photos by. 2004. (Baby Animals Ser.). 32p. (J). (gr. k-3). lib. bdg. 21.27 (978-1-57505-200-7(8)) Lerner Publishing Group.

Hoff, Mary King. Penguins. 2006. (Wild World of Animals Ser.). (Illus.). 32p. 18.95 (978-1-58341-435-4(5) , Creative Education) Creative Co., The.

Hollenbeck, Kathleen. Penguins Family. Stegos, Daniel, illus. 2005. 32p. (J). (ps-2). 4.95 (978-1-59249-348-7(3) , B4077); pap. 6.95 (978-1-59249-347-0(5) , S4027) Soundprints.

How Penguins & Butterflies Grow Set D, 6 vols. (Phonics Readers Ser.). (gr. k-2). 28.95 (978-0-7368-4053-8(2)) Red Brick Learning.

Jacquet, Luc. March of the Penguins. Maison, Jérome, photos by. 2005. (Illus.). 32p. (ps). pap. 5.95 (978-0-7922-6183-4(6) , National Geographic Children's Bks.) National Geographic Society.

—March of the Penguins: The Official Children's Book. Maison, Jérome, photos by. 2005. (Illus.). 32p. (J). (ps). lib. bdg. 22.90 (978-0-7922-6190-2(9) , National Geographic Children's Bks.) National Geographic Society.

Jenkins, Martin. Emperor's Egg. 2003. (Big Books! Ser.). (Illus.). 32p. (J). pap. 19.99 (978-0-7636-2233-6(8)) Candlewick Pr.

—Emperor's Egg. Chapman, Jane, illus. (Read & Wonder Ser.). 32p. (J). (gr. k-3). 2002. pap. 6.99 (978-0-7636-1871-1(3)); 1999. 16.99 (978-0-7636-0557-5(3)) Candlewick Pr.

Johnson, Jinny. Penguin. Woods, Michael, photos by. 2005. (Illus.). 32p. (J). (gr. 2-5). lib. bdg. 27.10 (978-1-58340-641-0(7)) Smart Apple Media.

Jonas, Anne. Little Penguins. 2005. (Born to Be Wild Ser.). (Illus.). 23p. (J). lib. bdg. 22.00 (978-0-8368-4738-3(5)) Stevens, Gareth Inc.

Kalman, Bobbie. El Ciclo de Vida del Pinguino Emperador. 2007. (SPA.). 32p. (J). (gr. 2-3). (*978-0-7787-8672-6(2)) Crabtree Publishing Co.

Kalman, Bobbie & Johnson, Robin. El Ciclo de Vida del Pinguino Emperador. rev. ed. 2007. (SPA.). 32p. (J). (gr. 2-3). pap. (*978-0-7787-8718-1(4)) Crabtree Publishing Co.

—Endangered Penguins. 2007. (Earth's Endangered Animals Ser.). (Illus.). 32p. (J). (gr. 1-7). (*978-0-7787-1863-5(8)); pap. (*978-0-7787-1909-0(X)) Crabtree Publishing Co.

Kalman, Bobbie & Johnson, Robin. The Life Cycle of an Emperor Penguin. 2006. (Life Cycle Ser.). (Illus.). 32p. (J). (gr. 2-3). pap. (978-0-7787-0704-2(0)); lib. bdg. (978-0-7787-0630-4(3)) Crabtree Publishing Co.

Kendell, Patricia. Penguins. 2003. (In the Wild Ser.). (Illus.). 32p. (J). lib. bdg. 25.70 (978-0-7398-6637-5(0)) Raintree.

l@Heureux, J. J. Good Day Book. 2006. spiral bd. (*978-0-9785892-0-2(3)) Jian Media Ltd.

Lang, Aubrey. Baby Penguin. Lynch, Wayne, photos by. (Nature Babies Ser.). (Illus.). 36p. (J). (gr. k-3). 2002. pap. (978-1-55041-693-0(6)); 2001. (978-1-55041-675-6(8)) Fitzhenry & Whiteside, Ltd.

—Baby Penguin. 2002. (gr. k-3). lib. bdg. 14.10 (978-0-613-62593-7(5)) Tandem Library Bks.

Lazourenko, S. Penguin. 2000. (Babies Bks.). (Illus.). 8p. (J). 10.95 (978-0-7641-5235-1(1)) Barron's Educational Series, Inc.

Lynch, Wayne. Penguins! Lynch, Wayne, photos by. 1999. (Illus.). 64p. (J). (gr. 4-7). pap. 9.95 (978-1-55209-424-2(3)); lib. bdg. 19.95 (978-1-55209-421-1(9)) Firefly Bks., Ltd.

—Penguins! 1999. (gr. 3-6). lib. bdg. 18.75 (978-0-613-35367-0(6)) Tandem Library Bks.

Macken, JoAnn Early. Penguins. 2002. (Weekly Reader Early Learning Library). (Illus.). 24p. (J). (ps up). pap. 5.95 (978-0-8368-3286-0(8)); lib. bdg. 19.33 (978-0-8368-3273-0(6)) Stevens, Gareth Inc. (Weekly Reader Early Learning Library).

—Penguins/Los Pinguinos. 2003. (Weekly Reader Early Learning Library). (ENG & SPA., Illus.). 24p. (J). (ps up). pap. 5.95 (978-0-8368-4006-3(2) , Weekly Reader Early Learning Library) Stevens, Gareth Inc.

—Penguins/Los Pinguinos. Coffey, Colleen & Carrillo, Consuelo, trs. from SPA. 2003. (Weekly Reader Early Learning Library). (ENG & SPA., Illus.). 24p. (J). (ps up). lib. bdg. 19.33 (978-0-8368-4001-8(1) , Weekly Reader Early Learning Library) Stevens, Gareth Inc.

Magloff, Lisa & Dorling Kindersley Publishing Staff. Penguin. 2004. (Watch Me Grow Ser.). 24p. (J). (gr. 5). 7.99 (978-0-7566-0263-5(7)) Dorling Kindersley Publishing, Inc.

Markert, Jenny. Penguins. 2007. (New Naturebooks Ser.). 32p. (J). (gr. 1-5). 27.07 (*978-1-59296-850-3(3)) Child's World, Inc.

Markle, Sandra. A Mother's Journey. Marks, Alan, illus. 32p. (J). 2006. pap. 6.95 (978-1-57091-622-9(5)); 2005. 16.95 (978-1-57091-621-2(7)) Charlesbridge Publishing, Inc.

McKenzie, Michelle. Penguin Chick. Tachiera, Andrea, illus. 2000. 12p. (J). bds. 5.95 (978-1-878244-28-4(0)) Monterey Bay Aquarium.

—El Pinguino Polluelo. Bahia Translators Staff & Echibuni, Taro, trs. Tachiera, Andrea, illus. 2000. Tr. of Penguin Chick. (SPA.). 12p. (J). bds. 5.95 (978-1-878244-29-1(9)) Monterey Bay Aquarium.

McLaughlin, Kari Massie. My Adventure with Penguins. 2007. 44p. (J). 8.99 (978-1-59092-461-7(4) , Orchard Academy Pr.) Windstorm Creative.

McMillan, Bruce. Puffins Climb, Penguins Rhyme. 2001. (Illus.). 32p. (J). (ps-k). pap. 6.00 (978-0-15-202443-7(3) , Voyager Bks./Libros Viajeros) Harcourt Children's Bks.

McNeil, Niki, et al. HOCPP 1123 Penguins. 2006. spiral bd. 16.00 (*978-1-60308-123-8(2)) In the Hands of a Child.

Mettler, René. Der Pinguin. 2005. (Meyers Klien Kinderbibliothek Ser.). (GER., Illus.). spiral bd. 14.25 (978-3-411-09611-4(X) , MY611E) Langenscheidt Pubs Inc.

Molter, Carey. Penguins. l.t. ed. 2001. (Zoo Animals Ser.). (Illus.). 24p. (J). (ps-3). lib. bdg. 19.93 (978-1-57765-562-6(1) , SandCastle) ABDO Publishing Co.

Morgan, Sally. Penguins. 2004. (QEB Animal Lives Ser.). (Illus.). 32p. (J). lib. bdg. 18.95 (978-1-59566-037-4(2)) QEB Publishing Inc.

Murray, Julie. Penguins. 2007. (Life Cycles Ser.). (Illus.). 24p. (J). (gr. k-4). lib. bdg. 21.35 (*978-1-59928-709-6(9) , Buddy Bks.) ABDO Publishing Co.

Noahs Ark Penguin. 2004. bds. 6.99 (978-0-8254-7282-4(2)) Kregel Pubns.

Noonan, Diana. The Emperor Penguin. 2002. (Life Cycle Ser.). (Illus.). 32p. (J). (gr. k-2). 23.00 (978-0-7910-6965-3(6) , Chelsea Hse.) Facts On File, Inc.

Nuzzolo, Deborah. Penguin March: SeaWorld Books for Young Learners. 2002. (Illus.). 28p. (J). per. 3.99 (978-1-893698-23-9(8) , E08, SeaWorld Bks. for Young Learners) SeaWorld, Inc.

Nuzzolo, Deborah. Penguins. 2008. (J). (*978-1-4296-0033-0(0) , Pebble Bks.) Capstone Pr., Inc.

O'Connell, Kim A. The Galapagos Penguin: A MyReportLinks. com Book. 2005. (Endangered & Threatened Animals Ser.). (Illus.). 48p. (J). lib. bdg. 25.26 (978-0-7660-5063-1(7) , MyReportLinks.com Bks.) Enslow Pubs., Inc.

Penguins. (Eyes on Nature Ser.). 32p. (J). (gr. 1). pap. (978-1-882210-61-9(1)) Action Publishing, Inc.

Penguins. 2001. (Animals of the Ocean Ser.). (Illus.). (J). lib. bdg. 15.95 (978-1-56674-300-6(1)) Forest Hse. Publishing Co., Inc.

Penguins & Other Polar Animals. 2007. (J). per. 2.99 (*978-1-4037-3234-7(5)) Dalmatian Pr.

Penguins on the Go. 2002. (Illus.). (J). pap. 3.74 (978-0-7398-5855-4(6)) Steck-Vaughn.

Pringle, Laurence P. Penguins! Strange & Wonderful. Henderson, Meryl, illus. 2006. (J). (gr. 2-5). 16.95 (978-1-59078-090-9(6)) Boyds Mills Pr.

Raatma, Lucia. Penguins. 2001. (First Reports). (Illus.). 48p. (J). (gr. 3 up). lib. bdg. 21.26 (978-0-7565-0058-0(3)) Compass Point Bks.

Rau, Dana Meachen. Guess Who Swims. 2008. (J). (*978-0-7614-2974-6(3)) Cavendish, Marshall Bks., Ltd.

Reid, Keith. Penguin. 2000. (Natural World Ser.). (Illus.). 48p. (J). (gr. 4-7). 9.95 (978-0-7398-3128-1(3)) Steck-Vaughn.

—Penguin. 2000. (gr. 3-6). lib. bdg. 20.55 (978-0-613-74054-8(8)) Tandem Library Bks.

—Penguin: Habitats, Life Cycles, Food Chains, Threats. 2000. (Natural World Ser.). (Illus.). 48p. (J). (gr. 4-7). lib. bdg. 27.12 (978-0-7398-2767-3(7)) Raintree.

Robinson, Claire. Penguins. (In the Wild Ser.). (Illus.). 24p. (J). (gr. k-2). 2002. pap. 6.95 (978-1-57572-468-3(5) , 90458); 1998. lib. bdg. 21.36 (978-1-57572-137-8(6)) Heinemann Library.

Schafer, Kevin. Penguins 123. (Penguins Ser.). (Illus.). (ps up). 2004. 28p. (J). bds. 6.95 (978-1-55971-906-3(0)); 2002. 32p. 14.95 (978-1-55971-830-1(7)) T&N Children's Publishing. (NorthWord Bks. for Young Readers).

—Penguins ABC. (Penguins Ser.). (Illus.). (ps up). 2004. 28p. (J). bds. 6.95 (978-1-55971-905-6(2)); 2002. 32p. 14.95 (978-1-55971-831-8(5)) T&N Children's Publishing. (NorthWord Bks. for Young Readers).

Schindel, John. Busy Penguins. Chester, Jonathan, photos by. 2004. (Illus.). 20p. (J). (ps up). bds. 6.95 (978-1-58246-016-1(7) , Tricycle Pr.) Ten Speed Pr.

Scholastic, Inc. Staff. Penguins. 2007. (Scholastic First Discovery Ser.). 24p. (J). (ps-k). pap. 5.99 (*978-0-545-00144-1(7) , Scholastic Reference) Scholastic, Inc.

—Penguins Through the Year. 2000. (Super Science Readers Ser.). (Illus.). 16p. (J). 10.95 (978-0-439-16770-3(1)) Scholastic, Inc.

—Scholastic Word Wall Bulletin Boardsets: Penguins Prepack. 2002. (Scholastic Word Wall Bulletin Boards Ser.). pap. 8.95 (978-0-439-35417-2(X) , Teaching Resources) Scholastic, Inc.

Sierra, Judy. Antarctic Antics: A Book of Penguin Poems. Aruego, Jose & Dewey, Ariane, illus. 1998. 32p. (J). (ps-2). 17.00 (978-0-15-201006-5(8) , Gulliver Bks.) Harcourt Children's Bks.

Sims, Neil Anthony. Penguins. 2003. (Science Links Ser.). (Illus.). 32p. (gr. 3-5). 23.00 (978-0-7910-7428-2(5) , Chelsea Hse.) Facts On File, Inc.

Spilsbury, Louise & Spilsbury, Richard. A Rookery of Penguins. 2004. 32p. (J). 6.95 (978-1-4034-5419-5(1)); (Illus.). lib. bdg. (978-1-4034-4691-6(1)) Heinemann Library.

—Watching Penguins in Antarctica. 2006. (Heinemann First Library). (Illus.). 32p. (J). 25.36 (978-1-4034-7223-6(8)); pap. (978-1-4034-7236-6(X)) Heinemann Library.

Squire, Ann. Penguins. 2006. (True Book Ser.). (Illus.). 47p. (J). (978-0-516-25472-2(3)) Children's Pr., Ltd.

—Penguins. 2006. (True Book Ser.). (J). (978-0-516-22825-9(0) , Children's Pr.) Scholastic Library Publishing.

Stefoff, Rebecca. Penguins. 2005. (Animalways Ser.). (Illus.). 112p. (J). (gr. 3-7). lib. bdg. (978-0-7614-1743-9(5) , Benchmark Bks.) Cavendish, Marshall Corp.

Stone, Lynn M. Penguins. 1998. (Early Bird Nature Bks.). (Illus.). 48p. (J). (gr. 2-4). 25.26 (978-0-8225-3022-0(8) , Lerner Pubns.) Lerner Publishing Group.

Stone, Lynn M., photos by. Penguins. 2002. (Carolrhoda Nature Watch Ser.). (Illus.). 48p. (J). lib. bdg. 25.26 (978-0-87614-907-2(7) , Carolrhoda Bks.) Lerner Publishing Group.

Stonehouse, Bernard. Penguins: A Visual Introduction to Penguins. Camm, Martin, illus. (Animal Watch Ser.). 48p. (J). (gr. 4-9). 16.95 (978-0-8160-4011-7(7) , Checkmark Bks.) Facts On File, Inc.

Swan, Erin Pembrey. Penguins: From Emperors to Macaronis. 2003. (Animals in Order Ser.). 48p. (gr. 4-6). pap. 6.95 (978-0-531-16660-4(0) , Watts, Franklin) Scholastic Library Publishing.

—Penguins: From Emperors to Macaronis. 2003. (gr. 3-6). lib. bdg. 15.25 (978-0-613-67920-6(2)) Tandem Library Bks.

Swanson, Diane. Penguins. 2004. (Welcome to the World of Animals Ser.). (Illus.). 32p. (J). (gr. 3 up). lib. bdg. 23.33 (978-0-8368-4025-4(9)) Stevens, Gareth Inc.

—Penguins. 2003. (gr. k-3). lib. bdg. 14.10 (978-0-613-78591-4(6)) Tandem Library Bks.

—Welcome to the World of Penguins. 2003. (Welcome to the World Ser.). (Illus.). 32p. (J). (ps-2). pap. 5.95 (978-1-55285-450-1(7)) Whitecap Bks., Ltd. CAN. *Dist:* Firefly Bks., Ltd.

Taberski, Sharon. Penguins Are Water Birds. 2002. (Illus.). 24p. (J). (gr. k-3). pap. 6.00 (978-1-59034-009-7(4)) Mondo Publishing.

Taylor, Barbara. Penguins. 2005. (Illus.). 64p. (gr. 4-7). pap. 8.99 (978-1-84476-181-4(9) , Southwater) Anness Publishing GBR. *Dist:* National Bk. Network.

Taylor, Barbara & Chinery, Michael. Penguins. 2004. (Nature Watch Ser.). (Illus.). 64p. 14.99 (978-0-7548-1287-6(1)) Anness Publishing GBR. *Dist:* National Bk. Network.

Townsend, Emily Rose. Penguins. Saunders-Smith, Gail, ed. 2004. (Polar Animals Ser.). (Illus.). 24p. (J). (gr. k-1). lib. bdg. 15.93 (978-0-7368-2357-9(3) , Pebble Bks.) Capstone Pr., Inc.

Trattles, Patricia. Emperor Penguins. 2006. (Pull Ahead Books-Animals Ser.). (Illus.). 32p. (J). 22.60 (978-0-8225-3484-6(3) , Lerner Pubns.) Lerner Publishing Group.

Trumbauer, Lisa. The Life Cycle of a Penguin. 2003. (Life Cycles Ser.). (Illus.). 24p. (J). (gr. k-1). lib. bdg. 15.93 (978-0-7368-2090-5(6) , Pebble Bks.) Capstone Pr., Inc.

Twine, Alice. Penguins. 2008. (J). lib. bdg. (*978-1-4042-4147-3(7)) Rosen Publishing Group, Inc., The.

Vogel, Julia. Polar Animals. McGee, John F., illus. 2004. (Our Wild World Ser.). 192p. (J). (gr. 2-5). ring bd. 16.95 (978-1-55971-832-5(3) , NorthWord Bks. for Young Readers) T&N Children's Publishing.

Webb, Sophie. My Season with Penguins: An Antarctic Journal. (Illus.). 48p. (J). (gr. 4-6). 2000. tchr. ed. 15.00 (978-0-395-92291-0(7)); 2004. reprint ed. pap. 5.95 (978-0-618-43234-9(5)) Houghton Mifflin Co. Trade & Reference Div.

—My Season with Penguins: An Antarctic Journal. 2004. (Illus.). 48p. (J). (gr. 3-7). lib. bdg. 13.15 (978-0-606-30319-4(7)) Tandem Library Bks.

Wexo, John Bonnett. Penguins. 2001. (Zoobooks). (Illus.). 24p. (J). (gr. 1-7). 15.95 (978-1-888153-30-9(X) , 263-7) Wildlife Education, Ltd.

Wildlife Education, Ltd. Staff & Wexo, John Bonnett. Penguins. Stuart, Walter & Boyer, Trevor, illus. 1998. (Zoobooks Ser.). 18p. (YA). (gr. 5 up). pap. 2.95 (978-0-937934-17-3(8)) Wildlife Education, Ltd.

Williams, Kimberly Joan & Stoops, Erik Daniel. The Banded Penguins, 6 vols. 2001. (Young Explorer Series II). (Illus.). 32p. (J). (gr. 3-7). lib. bdg. 4.85 net. (978-1-890475-18-5(1)) Faulkner's Publishing Group.

—The Brush-Tailed Penguins, 6 vols., Set. 2001. (Young Explorer Series II). (Illus.). 32p. (J). (gr. 3-7). lib. bdg. 4.85 net. (978-1-890475-19-2(X)) Faulkner's Publishing Group.

—The Crested Penguins, 6 vols. 2000. (Young Explorer Series II). (Illus.). 32p. (J). (gr. 3-7). lib. bdg. 4.85 net. (978-1-890475-20-8(3)) Faulkner's Publishing Group.

—The Large Penguins, 6 vols., Set. 2000. (Young Explorer Series II). (Illus.). 32p. (J). (gr. 3-7). lib. bdg. 4.85 net. (978-1-890475-21-5(1)) Faulkner's Publishing Group.

—The Little Penguins, 6 vols. 2002. (Young Explorer Series II). (Illus.). 32p. (J). (gr. 3-7). lib. bdg. 4.85 net. (978-1-890475-22-2(X)) Faulkner's Publishing Group.

—The Yellow - Eyed Penguins, 6 vols., Set. 2001. (Young Explorer Series II). (Illus.). 32p. (J). (gr. 3-7). lib. bdg. 4.85 net. (978-1-890475-23-9(8)) Faulkner's Publishing Group.

Winner, Cherie. Penguins. McGee, John F., illus. 2004. (Our Wild World Ser.). 48p. (J). (gr. 2-5). ring bd. 10.95 (978-1-55971-811-0(0)); pap. 7.95 (978-1-55971-810-3(2)) T&N Children's Publishing. (NorthWord Bks. for Young Readers).

—Penguins. 2002. (gr. 3-6). lib. bdg. 16.40 (978-0-613-55881-5(2)) Tandem Library Bks.

Young, Louise O. Penguin Comes Home. 2005. (Soundprints' Amazing Animal Adventures! Ser.). (Illus.). 32p. (J). (ps-2). 19.95 incl. audio (978-1-59249-327-2(0) , BC7108) Soundprints.

Zoehfeld, Kathleen Weidner. Penguins. 2003. (Science Readers Ser.). (Illus.). 32p. (J). pap. 3.99 (978-0-439-42502-5(6) , Scholastic Reference) Scholastic, Inc.

—Penguins. 2003. (gr. k-3). lib. bdg. 11.80 (978-0-613-65132-5(4)) Tandem Library Bks.

PENGUINS—FICTION

Aboff, Marcie. Smile & Wave. 2005. (Madagascar Ser.: No. 3). 32p. (J). 3.99 (978-0-439-69630-2(5)) Scholastic, Inc.

Ackerley, Sarah. Patrick the Somnambulist. Ackerley, Sarah, illus. 2008. (Illus.). 32p. (J). (ps-3). 14.95 ***(978-1-933831-07-7(3))*** Blooming Tree Pr.

Anderson, Derek. Romeo & Lou Blast Off. Anderson, Derek, illus. 2007. 32p. (J). (ps-3). 15.99 ***(978-1-4169-3784-5(6)*** , Simon & Schuster Children's Publishing) Simon & Schuster Children's Publishing.

Arrhenius, Peter. The Penguin Quartet. Peterson, Ingela, illus. 1998. (Picture Bks.). 28p. (J). (ps-3). 15.95 (978-1-57505-252-6(0) , Carolrhoda Bks.) Lerner Publishing Group.

Atwater, Richard. Mr. Popper's Penguins. Lawson, Robert, illus. 2002. (J). 12.30 (978-0-7587-0294-4(9)) Book Wholesalers, Inc.

Auerbach, Annie. The Unauthorized Biography. 2007. (Surf's Up Ser.). 64p. (J). pap. 4.99 ***(978-0-06-115329-7(X)*** , Harper Entertainment) HarperCollins Pubs.

Bachand, Stephen. My Friend Penguin. Bachand, Stephen, illus. 1999. (Booktime Buddies Ser.). (Illus.). (J). (ps-2). 5.00 (978-1-928972-01-3(2)) Critter Pubns.

—Where's Floater? Bachand, Stephen, illus. 2000. (Booktime Buddies Ser.). (Illus.). (J). (ps-2). pap. 5.00 (978-1-928972-05-1(5)) Critter Pubns.

Bauer, Jutta. Madrechillona. 2nd ed. 2003. (Rosa y Manzana Ser.). (SPA., Illus.). 28p. (J). (gr. k-2). (978-84-89804-36-4(2) , LC30478) Loguez Ediciones ESP. *Dist:* Lectorum Pubns., Inc.

Berg & Holland. Tamino Pinguino y el Asunto Del Huevo. 2004. (SPA., Illus.). 202p. (J). 17.99 (978-84-261-3301-4(0)) Juventud, Editorial ESP. *Dist:* Lectorum Pubns., Inc.

Book Buddy: Penguin with Story Book. Orig. Title: Child's Play. (Illus.). 10p. (J). (ps-3). reprint ed. (978-1-881469-45-2(X)) Safari, Ltd.

Boyle, Alison. 1, 2, 3, 4, 5 Once I Caught a Fish Alive! Pichon, Liz, illus. 2000. (Finger Puppet Bks.). 16p. (J). (ps-k). 10.95 (978-1-86233-116-7(2)) Sterling Publishing Co., Inc.

Boynton, Sandra. Your Personal Penguin. 2006. (Illus.). 24p. (J). bds. 6.95 (978-0-7611-4372-7(6)) Workman Publishing Co., Inc.

Brandon, Taylor. The Penguin Who Hated the Cold Because He Was All Dressed Up & Had No Place To Go. Sandow, Paris, illus. 1999. (World's Greatest Children's Bks.). 48p. (J). (gr. k-5). 14.99 (978-1-889945-61-3(7)) Imperius.

Breathed, Berkeley. The Last Basselope: One Ferocious Story. Breathed, Berkeley, illus. 2001. (Illus.). 32p. (J). (ps-17). pap. 6.99 (978-0-316-12664-9(0)) Little Brown & Co.

—Last Basselope: One Ferocious Story. 2001. (gr. 3-6). lib. bdg. 14.10 (978-0-613-35643-5(8)) Tandem Library Bks.

Brookes, Diane & Wood, Audrey. A Novel Study for Grades One & Two Based on Little Penguin's Tale, 25 vols. 1998. (J). pap., tchr. ed. (978-0-9683234-3-4(X)) Raven Rock Publishing.

Brookes, Diane, et al. A Novel Study for Grades One or Grades Three & Four Based on Mr. Popper's Penguins. Lawson, Robert, illus. 1998. (J). pap., tchr. ed. (978-0-9683449-7-2(6)) Raven Rock Publishing.

Burns, John. The Many Adventures of Pengey Penguin. Coles, James, illus. 2005. 207p. (J). per. 17.95 (978-0-9774227-0-8(4)) San Francisco Story Works.

Carr, Paul C. The Adventures of Three Cousins. 2006. 24.00 (978-0-8059-9032-4(1)) Dorrance Publishing Co., Inc.

Chambers, Sally. The Penguin. 1999. (Zippy Animal Bks.). (Illus.). 24p. (J). (ps-k). 6.95 (978-1-86233-020-7(4)) David & Charles Children's Bks. GBR. *Dist:* Sterling Publishing Co., Inc.

Chardiet, Jon. Parker Penguin & the Winter Games. Micucci, Charles, illus. 1999. (Read with Me Ser.), 32p. (J). (gr. k-2). pap. 3.25 (978-0-590-14925-9(3)) Scholastic, Inc.

—Parker Penguin, Big Brother Blues. Micucci, Charles, illus. 1998. (Read with Me Paperback Ser.). (J). (978-0-590-14924-2(5)) Scholastic, Inc.

Clark, Irene M. Feathery Tales: Benny Penguin, Huffer & Puffer California Quail, Paco Pelican. Clark, Cynthia D., illus. unabr. ed. 2001. 147p. (J). (ps-3). 12.95 incl. cd-rom (978-0-9709843-0-2(8)) Creekside Stories.

Cuyler, Margery. Please Say Please! Penguin's Guide to Manners. Hillenbrand, Will, illus. 2005. (J). ***(978-0-439-67874-2(9))*** Scholastic, Inc.

—Please Say Please! Penguin's Guide to Manners. Hillenbrand, Will, illus. Hillenbrand, Will, illus. 2004. 32p. (J). pap. 15.95 (978-0-590-29224-5(2)) Scholastic, Inc.

de Beer, Hans. Leonardo's Dream. Miller, Marisa, tr. from GER. de Beer, Hans, illus. 2007. (Illus.). 32p. (J). (ps-3). pap. 6.95 ***(978-0-7358-2168-2(2))*** North-South Bks., Inc.

Dorling Kindersley Publishing Staff. Happy Feet Essential Guide. 2006. (Illus.). 48p. (J). 12.99 (978-0-7566-2242-8(5)) Dorling Kindersley Publishing, Inc.

Doudna, Kelly. Penguin Suit. Chawla, Neena, illus. 2006. (Fact & Fiction Ser.). 24p. (J). 21.35 (978-1-59679-957-8(9) , SandCastle); pap. (978-1-59679-958-5(7)) ABDO Publishing Co.

Dunbar, Polly. Penguin. Dunbar, Polly, illus. 2007. (Illus.). 40p. (J). (ps-2). 15.99 ***(978-0-7636-3404-9(2))*** Candlewick Pr.

Duracell and the National Center for Missing & Exploited Children (NCMEC), creator. The Great Tomato Adventure: A Story about Smart Safety Choices. 2007. 0.00 ***(978-0-9795307-0-8(9))*** Duracell & the National Ctr. for Missing & Exploited Children (NCMEC).

Dyer, Heather. Tina & the Penguin. Levert, Mireille, illus. 32p. (J). (gr. k-3). 2004. (978-1-55337-767-2(2)); 2002. (978-1-55074-947-2(1)) Kids Can Pr., Ltd.

Friesen, Ray. Lookit!, Vol. 2. 2004. (YA). per. 4.95 (978-0-9728177-3-8(5)) Don't Eat Any Bugs Prodns.

—Lookit! A Cheese Related Mishap Vol. 1: And Other Stories. 2006. 96p. pap. 8.95 (978-0-9728177-6-9(X)) Don't Eat Any Bugs Prodns.

Fromental, Jean-Luc. 365 Penguins. Jolivet, Joelle, illus. 2006. 48p. (J). (ps-3). 17.95 (978-0-8109-4460-2(X)) Abrams, Harry N. , Inc.

Garden, Randa Sue. Penny the Penguin. 2003. 48p. per. 7.95 (978-0-615-12322-6(8)) Garden, Randa.

Garmendia, Salvador. Un Pinguino en Maracaibo. (SPA.). (J). (gr. 2-4). 23.95 (978-980-07-5242-5(0)) Baker & Taylor Bks.

Grant, Sharon. Mr. Special Visits Mrs. Precious' Class. 2004. (J). per. 9.95 (978-1-59427-032-1(5)) Aglob Publishing.

Hale, Bruce. Key Lardo: A Chet Gecko Mystery. Hale, Bruce, illus. 2007. (Chet Gecko Mystery Ser.: No. 12). (Illus.). 128p. (J). (gr. 3-7). pap. 4.95 (978-0-15-205235-5(6) , Harcourt Paperbacks) Harcourt Children's Bks.

—Key Lardo: A Chet Gecko Mystery. 2006. (Chet Gecko Mystery Ser.: No. 12). (Illus.). 128p. (J). (gr. 3-7). 14.00 (978-0-15-205074-0(4)) Harcourt Children's Bks.

Heidenreich, Elke & Buchholz, Quint. Some Folk Say the South Pole's Hot: The Three Tenors Play the Antarctic. 2001. (Illus.). 64p. (J). 17.95 (978-1-56792-170-0(1)) Godine, David R. Pub.

Hinojosa, Francisco. Yanka, Yanka. Hinojosa, Francisco, illus. 2003. (SPA., Illus.). 44p. (J). (gr. k-3). pap. 10.95 (978-968-19-0440-1(0)) Santillana USA Publishing Co., Inc.

Ichikawa, Satomi. I Am Pangoo the Penguin. Ichikawa, Satomi, illus. 2006. (Illus.). 40p. (J). (ps-4). 16.99 (978-0-399-23313-5(X) , Philomel) Penguin Group (USA) Inc.

Jamaldinian, Joe. Bob Winging It. Jamaldinian, Joe, illus. 2005. (Illus.). 32p. (J). 14.00 (978-0-9766657-0-0(0)) Jamaldinian, Yousef.

James, Nathaniel. Debbie Mumm's Mummford Adventures. Mumm, Debbie, illus. 2002. 32p. (gr. k-3). 14.95 (978-1-890621-33-9(1)) Landauer Corp.

Jeffers, Oliver. Lost & Found. Jeffers, Oliver, illus. 2005. (Illus.). 32p. (J). (ps-3). 15.99 (978-0-399-24503-9(0) , Philomel) Penguin Group (USA) Inc.

Jenkin-Pearce, Susie. A Pal for Pugwug. Macnaughton, Tina, illus. 2005. 32p. (J). 14.95 (978-0-7696-4433-2(3) , Gingham Dog Pr.) School Specialty Publishing.

Kellogg, Steven. A Penguin Pup for Pinkerton. 2003. (Picture Puffin Ser.). (Illus.). 32p. (J). (gr. k-3). pap. 6.99 (978-0-14-250170-2(0) , Puffin) Penguin Group (USA) Inc.

—Penguin Pup for Pinkerton. 2003. (gr. k-3). lib. bdg. 15.30 (978-0-613-87825-8(6)) Tandem Library Bks.

Khatibi, Janis. The Adventures of White Tuxedo Penguin. 2006. (ENG.). 48p. per. 18.99 ***(978-1-4259-5769-8(2))*** AuthorHouse.

Kimmel, Elizabeth Cody. Mi Pinguino Oliver. Lewis, H. B., illus. 2004. Tr. of My Penguin Osbert. (SPA.). (J). 15.99 (978-84-88342-68-3(3)) S.A. Kokinos ESP. *Dist:* Lectorum Pubns., Inc.

—My Penguin Osbert. Lewis, H. B., illus. 2004. 40p. (J). (ps-3). 16.99 (978-0-7636-1699-1(0)) Candlewick Pr.

Krasner, Steven. Have a Nice Nap, Humphrey. Griffis, Sandy, illus. 1998. 36p. (J). (gr. k-5). pap. 12.95 (978-0-9642721-2-5(1)) Gorilla Productions.

Lester, Helen. El Pinguino Taky. Munsinger, Lynn, illus. 2001. (SPA.). 32p. (J). (gr. k-3). pap. 5.95 (978-0-618-12531-9(0) , HM30384); tchr. ed. 15.00 (978-0-618-12530-2(2) , HM30383) Houghton Mifflin Co. Trade & Reference Div.

—Pinguino Taky. 2001. (SPA.). (gr. k-3). lib. bdg. 14.10 (978-0-613-35553-7(9)) Tandem Library Bks.

—Tacky & the Emperor. Munsinger, Lynn, illus. 32p. (J). (gr. k-3). 2002. pap. 6.95 (978-0-618-26009-6(9)); 2000. tchr. ed. 15.00 (978-0-395-98120-7(4)) Houghton Mifflin Co. Trade & Reference Div. (Walter Lorraine).

—Tacky & the Emperor. 2002. (gr. k-3). lib. bdg. 14.10 (978-0-613-72914-7(5)) Tandem Library Bks.

—Tacky & the Winter Games. Munsinger, Lynn, illus. 2007. 32p. (J). (ps-3). 6.95 ***(978-0-618-95674-6(3))*** Houghton Mifflin Co. Trade & Reference Div.

—Tacky & the Winter Games. Munsinger, Lynn M., illus. 2005. 32p. (J). (gr. k-3). 16.00 (978-0-618-55659-5(1) , Walter Lorraine) Houghton Mifflin Co. Trade & Reference Div.

—Tacky the Penguin. Munsinger, Lynn, illus. 2002. (J). 13.79 (978-0-7587-3742-7(4)) Book Wholesalers, Inc.

—Tackylocks & the Three Bears. Munsinger, Lynn, illus. 32p. (J). (gr. k-3). 2004. 5.95 (978-0-618-43953-9(6)); 2002. tchr. ed. 15.00 (978-0-618-22490-6(4)) Houghton Mifflin Co. Trade & Reference Div. (Walter Lorraine).

Lewis, Jill. A Mom in a Million. Gulbis, Stephen, illus. 2005. 32p. (J). (978-1-84458-368-3(6)) Chrysalis Children's Bks.

Lin, Grace. Olvina Swims. rev. ed. 2007. (Illus.). 32p. (J). (ps-2). 16.95 (978-0-8050-7661-5(1)) Holt, Henry & Co.

Lumry, Amanda & Hurwitz, Laura. South Pole Penguins. 2007. 36p. 18.95 (978-0-9748411-8-2(8)); 15.95 (978-0-9748411-5-1(3)) Eaglemont Pr.

Malkowski, Paul James. How Penguins Celebrate Christmas. 2007. 20p. pap. 7.95 ***(978-0-533-15661-0(0))*** Vantage Pr., Inc.

Marsh, Carole. Penguin Strut Fashion Show. 2002. (Carole Marsh Bks.). 32p. (J). (gr. 1-6). pap. 7.95 (978-0-635-01357-6(6) , 13576); (Illus.). (gr. 3-9). lib. bdg. 21.95 (978-0-635-01358-3(4) , 13584, Marsh, Carole Bks.) Gallopade International.

Mayfield, Sue & Padua, Rochelle. I Can, You Can, Toucan! 2006. (Green Bananas Ser.). (Illus.). 47p. (J). (978-0-7787-1032-5(7)) Crabtree Publishing Co.

McAuliffe, Nichola. Attila, Loolagax & the Eagle. Collins, Ross, tr. Collins, Ross, illus. 2003. 126p. pap. 10.99 (978-0-7475-6499-7(X)) Bloomsbury Publishing Plc GBR. *Dist:* Independent Pubs. Group.

McGuinness, Jeff. Paddy the Penguin's Adventure. Starr, Lisa, illus. l.t. ed. 2006. 33p. (J). per. 15.95 ***(978-1-59879-229-4(6))*** Lifevest Publishing, Inc.

—Paddy, the Penguin's Adventure. Starr, Lisa, illus. l.t. ed. 2006. 33p. (J). 27.95 ***(978-1-59879-231-7(8))*** Lifevest Publishing, Inc.

Meschenmoser, Sebastian. Learning to Fly. Meschenmoser, Sebastian, illus. 2006. (Illus.). 56p. (J). 8.95 (978-1-929132-93-5(X)) Kane/Miller Bk. Pubs., Inc.

Miles, Ellen. Penguin's Adventure: The Penguin's Peril. 2007. (Taylor-Made Tales Ser.: No. 4). 112p. (J). pap. 4.99 (978-0-439-59711-1(0) , Scholastic Paperbacks) Scholastic, Inc.

Mishica, Clare. Papa Penguin's Surprise. 2000. (Illus.). (J). (gr. k-2). pap. 3.75 (978-1-58323-010-7(6) , Seedling Pubns.) Continental Pr., Inc.

Mitton, Tony. Playful Little Penguins. Parker-Rees, Guy, illus. 2007. 32p. (J). (ps-1). 15.95 ***(978-0-8027-9710-0(5))*** Walker & Co.

Munsinger, Lynn & Lester, Helen. Tacky in Trouble. 1998. (Illus.). 32p. (J). (gr. k-3). tchr. ed. 16.00 (978-0-395-86113-4(6) , Walter Lorraine) Houghton Mifflin Co. Trade & Reference Div.

Murphy, Mary. I Am an Artist. 2000. (Illus.). 14p. (J). (gr. k-ps). bds. 4.95 (978-0-618-03401-7(3)) Houghton Mifflin Co. Trade & Reference Div.

—I Like It When ... /Me gusta Cuando ... Campoy, F. Isabel & Ada, Alma Flor, trs. 2008. (Illus.). 22p. (J). bds. 6.95 ***(978-0-15-206045-9(6)*** , Voyager Bks./Libros Viajeros) Harcourt Children's Bks.

—I Make a Cake. 2000. (Illus.). 14p. (J). (gr. k-ps). bds. 4.95 (978-0-618-00339-6(8)) Houghton Mifflin Co. Trade & Reference Div.

—If... 2000. (Illus.). (J). (gr. k-ps). pap. 4.95 (978-0-618-03399-7(8)) Houghton Mifflin Co. Trade & Reference Div.

—Let's Go! 2005. (Illus.). 16p. (J). bds. 14.99 (978-1-4052-1115-4(6)) Egmont Bks., Ltd. GBR. *Dist:* Trafalgar Square Publishing.

—Please Be Quiet! Murphy, Mary, illus. 1999. (Illus.). 32p. (J). (gr. k-ps). 9.95 (978-0-395-97113-0(6)) Houghton Mifflin Co. Trade & Reference Div.

—You Choose. 2000. (Illus.). (J). (gr. k-ps). pap. 4.95 (978-0-618-00336-5(3)) Houghton Mifflin Co. Trade & Reference Div.

Ned Visits New York. ed. 2006. (J). 15.95 (978-0-9789384-0-6(2)) Kip Kids of New York.

Nixon, Joan Lowery. Gus & Gertie & the Missing Pearl. deGroat, Diane, illus. 2000. 48p. (J). (ps-3). 15.50 (978-1-58717-023-2(X) , SeaStar Bks.) Chronicle Bks. LLC.

O'Neill, Maria. The Penguin Who Wanted to Be Different: A Christmas Wish. Newton, Jill, illus. 2001. 32p. (J). (gr. 4). pap. 3.99 (978-0-439-31809-9(2)) Scholastic, Inc.

Packard, Mary. The Christmas Penguin. Weidner, Teri, illus. 2002. (Hello Reader! Ser.). 32p. (J). pap. 3.99 (978-0-439-32102-0(6) , Cartwheel Bks.) Scholastic, Inc.

Papineau, Lucie. Gilda the Giraffe & Pepin the Penguin. Sarrazin, Marisol, illus. 2005. (Gilda the Giraffe Ser.). 32p. (J). 22.60 (978-1-4048-1296-3(2)) Picture Window Bks.

Perlman, Janet. Penguin & the Pea. Perlman, Janet, illus. 2006. (Illus.). 32p. (978-1-55337-983-6(7)) Kids Can Pr., Ltd.

Perlman, Janet, illus. & retold by. The Penguin & the Pea. Perlman, Janet, retold by. 2005. 32p. (J). (ps-2). (978-1-55074-832-1(7)) Kids Can Pr., Ltd.

Pfister, Marcus. Penguin Pete, Ahoy! 1998. (Illus.). 32p. (J). (ps-3). pap. 6.95 (978-1-55858-907-0(4)) North-South Bks., Inc.

Los pinguinos Listos: Individual Title Six-Packs. (Coleccion Pm Ser.).Tr. of Clever Penguin. (SPA.). 16p. (gr. 1 up). 26.00 (978-0-7578-3044-0(7)) Rigby Education.

Priddy, Roger. Rainbow Rob. 2006. (Illus.). 20p. (J). bds. 12.95 (978-0-312-49791-0(1) , Priddy Bks.) St. Martin's Pr.

Rabe, Tish. Innovative Kids Readers: Penguins Perfect Picnic. Ho, Jannie, illus. 2007. 24p. (J). (ps-1). pap. 6.99 (978-1-58476-542-4(9)) Innovative Kids.

Randall, Ronne. Snuggle up, Little Penguin! Church, Caroline Jayne, illus. 2003. (Little Friends Ser.). 14p. (J). 12.95 (978-1-57145-919-0(7) , Silver Dolphin Bks.) Advantage Pubs. Group.

Rees, Douglas. Uncle Pirate. Auth, Tony, illus. 2008. 112p. (J). ***(978-1-4169-4762-2(0)*** , McElderry, Margaret K.) Simon & Schuster Children's Publishing.

Regan, Dana. Penguin's Big Hill. 2002. (Rhyme Time Readers Ser.). (Illus.). 32p. (J). (978-0-439-44161-2(7)) Scholastic, Inc.

Rey, H. A. & Rey, Margret. Whiteblack the Penguin Sees the World. (Illus.). 32p. (J). (gr. k-3). 2000. tchr. ed. 16.00 (978-0-618-07389-4(2)); 2004. reprint ed. pap. 5.95 (978-0-618-07390-0(6)) Houghton Mifflin Co. Trade & Reference Div.

Rice, Jonathan & Brandreth, Gyles. The Rock Penguins. 2000. (Illus.). 32p. (J). pap. 11.99 (978-0-233-99525-0(0)) Andre Deutsch GBR. *Dist:* Independent Pubs. Group.

Richardson, Justin & Parnell, Peter. And Tango Makes Three. Cole, Henry, illus. 2005. 32p. (J). 15.99 (978-0-689-87845-9(1)) Simon & Schuster Children's Publishing.

Robinson, Hilary. Pippin's Big Jump. Warburton, Sarah, illus. 2004. (Read-It! Readers Ser.). 32p. (C). (gr. k-3). 18.60 (978-1-4048-0555-2(9)) Picture Window Bks.

Rodriguez, Edel. Sergio Makes a Splash. 2008. 40p. 15.99 ***(978-0-316-06616-7(8))*** Little Brown & Co.

Rosario, Joann. The PenguinThat Boom- Booms to a Ferret That Zoom- Zoomed. Rosario, Joann, illus. 2004. (Illus.). 28p. (J). (ps-5). pap. 10.00 (978-0-9758746-4-6(0) , 1246169) J.G.R. Enterprises.

Rose, Bubba. Penguin Adventures. 2005. 44p. pap. 8.95 (978-1-59453-746-2(1) , 3221) Airleaf Publishing & Bookselling.

Salma, Sergio. Penguins on Ice. Hsiung, Hanvey, tr. 2005. (Illus.). 48p. pap. 12.95 (978-1-59687-829-7(0) , ipicturebooks) ibooks, Inc.

Sang, Franchesca Ho, compiled by. Wisdom of Penguins. 2006. (Illus.). 128p. (J). (978-1-59258-254-9(0)) Hylas Publishing.

Schick, Alice & Schick, Joel. The Penguin Child & the Albatross Child. 2007. (J). bds. 13.95 ***(978-1-59692-228-0(1))*** MacAdam/Cage Publishing, Inc.

Scraper, Katherine. Save the Fairy Penguins. 2005. 40.00 ***(978-1-4108-4214-5(2))*** Benchmark Education Co.

Seibold, J. Otto. Penguin Dreams. Walsh, V. L., illus. 2005. 36p. (J). (ps-3). reprint ed. pap. 6.95 (978-0-8118-5100-8(1)) Chronicle Bks. LLC.

Sobel, Marla. The Penguin Who Lost Her Cool: A Story About Controlling Your Anger. Gilgannon, Denise, illus. 2000. (Early Prevention Ser.). 59p. (J). pap. 11.50 (978-1-882732-98-2(7)) Childswork/Childsplay.

St John Taylor, Jeannie & Idle, Molly Schaar. Le Fameux Arbre de Noël de Pingouin. 2007. (FRE., Illus.). 24p. (J). pap. 9.95 ***(978-2-922435-16-0(4))*** Lobster Pr. CAN. *Dist:* National Bk. Network.

Stamper, Judith Bauer. Penguin Puzzle. 2001. (gr. 3-6). lib. bdg. 11.80 (978-0-613-50722-6(3)) Tandem Library Bks.

—Penguin Puzzle, Vol. 8. Enik, Ted, illus. 2001. (Magic School Bus Chapter Bks.: Vol. 8). 96p. (J). (gr. 2-4). pap. 4.99 (978-0-439-20422-4(4) , Scholastic Paperbacks) Scholastic, Inc.

Tatham, Betty. Penguin Chick. Davie, Helen K., illus. 2001. (Let's-Read-and-Find-Out Science Ser.). 40p. (J). (gr. k-4). 15.99 (978-0-06-028594-4(X)); pap. 5.99 (978-0-06-445206-9(9) , Harper Trophy) HarperCollins Pubs.

—Penguin Chick. 2002. (gr. k-3). lib. bdg. 12.95 (978-0-613-56829-6(X)) Tandem Library Bks.

Taylor, Jeannie St. John. Penguin's Special Christmas Tree. Idle, Molly Schaar, illus. 2007. 24p. (J). (ps-1). 16.95 ***(978-1-897073-61-2(5));*** pap. 9.95 ***(978-1-897073-64-3(X))*** Lobster Pr. CAN. *Dist:* National Bk. Network.

Ted in a Red Bed Kid Kit. (Kid Kits Ser.). (Illus.). 10p. (J). 11.95 (978-1-58086-416-9(3)); 2004. bds. 9.95 (978-1-58086-404-6(X)) EDC Publishing.

Tich, Jan. Pope Meets Pin. 2006. (Adventures in Unusual Places Ser.). (Illus.). 28p. (J). 12.95 (978-9974-7925-7-9(6)) Hardenville SA URY. *Dist:* Independent Pubs. Group.

Tomlinson, Jill. The Penguin Who Wanted to Find Out. Howard, Paul, illus. 2005. 96p. (J). reprint ed. pap. 6.99 (978-1-4052-1085-0(0)) Egmont Bks., Ltd. GBR. *Dist:* Trafalgar Square Publishing.

Top That!, ed. One Little Penguin & his Friends. Gevry, Christine, illus. 2007. 10p. (J). (ps). bds. 12.99 ***(978-1-84666-268-3(0)*** , Tide Mill Pr.) Top That! Publishing PLC GBR. *Dist:* Random Hse., Inc.

Ullrich, Hortense. La Aventura de Lorenzo. (SPA.). (J). 7.95 (978-958-04-7447-0(8)) Norma S.A. COL. *Dist:* Distribuidora Norma, Inc.

—La Prueba de Valor de Lorenzo. (SPA.). (J). 7.95 (978-958-04-7069-4(3)) Norma S.A. COL. *Dist:* Distribuidora Norma, Inc.

Vase, Catherine. Penguin Who Wanted to Fly. 2007. 32p. (J). pap. 5.99 ***(978-0-439-85370-5(2)*** , Cartwheel Bks.) Scholastic, Inc.

Warner, Bros. Happy Feet Jr Cine-Manga. 2006. 32p. pap. 3.99 ***(978-1-59816-997-3(1)*** , Tokyopop Kids) TOKYOPOP, Inc.

Watt, Mélanie. Augustine. 2006. (Illus.). 32p. (J). (978-1-55337-885-3(7)) Kids Can Pr., Ltd.

Weare, Tim. I'm a Little Penguin. Weare, Tim, illus. 2002. (Finger Puppet Pals Ser.). (Illus.). 12p. (J). bds. 6.95 (978-0-439-33868-4(9) , Cartwheel Bks.) Scholastic, Inc.

Weeks, Sarah. Without You. Duranceau, Suzanne, illus. 40p. (J). 2007. pap. 6.99 (978-0-06-113998-7(X) , Harper Trophy); 2003. 16.99 incl. audio compact disk (978-0-06-027816-8(1) , Geringer, Laura Book) HarperCollins Pubs.

What I Learned from a Penguin. 2005. (YA). lib. bdg. 19.95 (978-1-886565-42-5(2)) MindWorks Pr.

Willis, Jeanne. Take Turns, Penguin! Birchall, Mark, illus. 2003. (Picture Bks.). 32p. (J). (ps-3). 7.95 (978-1-57505-493-3(0) , Carolrhoda Bks.) Lerner Publishing Group.

Wilson, Karma. Where Is Home, Little Pip? Chapman, Jane, illus. 2008. 40p. (J). (978-0-689-85983-0(X) , McElderry, Margaret K.) Simon & Schuster Children's Publishing.

Winter, Barbara. Penguin Pranks. 2002. (Amazing Dictionary Ser.). (Illus.). 64p. pap. 4.95 (***978-0-921156-98-7(7)***) Rubicon Publishing, Inc. CAN. *Dist:* International Publishers Marketing.

Wood, A. J. The Little Penguin. Boey, Stephanie, illus. 2002. 32p. (J). 15.99 (978-0-525-47023-6(9) , Dutton Juvenile) Penguin Group (USA) Inc.

Wood, Audrey. Little Penguin's Tale. Wood, Audrey, illus. 2002. (Illus.). (J). 13.83 (978-0-7587-3012-1(8)) Book Wholesalers, Inc.

Young, Louise O. Penguin Comes Home. 2005. (Soundprints' Amazing Animal Adventures! Ser.). (Illus.). 36p. (J). (ps-2). 8.95 incl. audio (978-1-59249-328-9(9) , SC7108) Soundprints.

—Penguin Comes Home. Elmore, Larry, illus. 2005. (Amazing Animal Adventures Ser.). (J). (ps-2). 32p. 2.95 incl. cd-rom (978-1-59249-325-8(4) , S7158); 36p. 6.95 (978-1-59249-326-5(2) , S7108); 36p. 15.95 (978-1-59249-324-1(6) , B7108) Soundprints.

PENICILLIN

Bankston, John. Alexander Fleming & the Story of Penicillin. l.t. ed. 2002. (Unlocking the Secrets of Science Ser.). (Illus.). 56p. (gr. 4-10). lib. bdg. 25.70 (978-1-58415-106-7(4)) Mitchell Lane Pubs., Inc.

Birch, Beverley & Fleming, Alexander. Alexander Fleming: Pioneer with Antibiotics. 2002. (Giants of Science Ser.). (Illus.). 64p. (J). 26.20 (978-1-56711-656-4(6) , Blackbirch Pr., Inc.) Thomson Gale.

De la Bédoyère, Guy. The Discovery of Penicillin. 2005. (Milestones in Modern Science Ser.). (Illus.). 48p. (J). pap. (978-0-8368-5859-4(X)); lib. bdg. 30.00 (978-0-8368-5852-5(2)) Stevens, Gareth Inc. (World Almanac Library).

Hantula, Richard. Alexander Fleming. 2003. (Trailblazers of the Modern World Ser.). (Illus.). 48p. (J). (gr. 5 up). pap. 14.95 (978-0-8368-5243-1(5)); lib. bdg. 30.00 (978-0-8368-5083-3(1)) Stevens, Gareth Inc. (World Almanac Library).

Tames, Richard. Penicillin: A Breakthrough in Medicine. (Point of Impact Ser.). (Illus.). 32p. (J). 2006. (***978-1-4034-9141-1(0)***); 2000. (gr. 5-7). lib. bdg. 24.22 (978-1-57572-417-1(0)) Heinemann Library.

Tocci, Salvatore. Alexander Fleming: The Man Who Discovered Penicillin. 2002. (Great Minds of Science Ser.). (Illus.). 128p. (J). (gr. 4-10). lib. bdg. 26.60 (978-0-7660-1998-0(5)) Enslow Pubs., Inc.

PENINSULAR WAR, 1807-1814—FICTION

Henty, G. A. The Young Buglers: A Tale of the Peninsular War. 2006. 270p. pap. 13.99 (***978-1-4264-3587-4(8)***); 300p. pap. 15.99 (***978-1-4264-3638-3(6)***) BiblioBazaar.

Styles, Showell. The Flying Ensign: Greencoats Against Napoleon. 2003. (Budget Bks.). Orig. Title: Greencoat Against Napoleon. 340p. (J). pap. 14.95 (978-1-883937-70-6(1)) Bethlehem Bks.

PENITENTIARIES

see Prisons

PENN, WILLIAM, 1644-1718

Baczynski, Bernadette L. William Penn: Founder of the Pennsylvania Colony. 2004. (Let Freedom Ring Ser.). (Illus.). 48p. (J). 17.95 (978-0-7368-2459-0(6) , Bridgestone Bks.) Capstone Pr., Inc.

Benge, Janet & Benge, Geoff. William Penn: Liberty & Justice for All. 2002. (Illus.). 192p. pap. 8.99 (978-1-883002-82-4(6)) Emerald Bks.

Boothroyd, Jennifer. William Penn: A Life of Tolerance. 2007. (Pull Ahead Books). (Illus.). 32p. (J). 22.60 (978-0-8225-6387-7(8) , Lerner Pubns.) Lerner Publishing Group.

Capstone Press, contrib. by. William Penn. (Colonial America Biographies Ser.). 48p. (YA). pap. 7.95 (978-0-7368-4486-4(4)) Capstone Pr., Inc.

Gillis, Jennifer Blizin. William Penn. 2004. (Illus.). 32p. (J). pap. 7.50 (978-1-4034-5971-8(1)); lib. bdg. 25.64 (978-1-4034-5963-3(0)) Heinemann Library.

Hinman, Bonnie. The Life & Times of William Penn. 2006. (Profiles in American History Ser.). (Illus.). 48p. (J). (gr. 4-8). lib. bdg. 29.95 (978-1-58415-433-4(0) , 1259521) Mitchell Lane Pubs., Inc.

Jacobson, Ryan. William Penn. Stiles, Tim, illus. 2007. (Graphic Library). 32p. (J). 25.26 (978-0-7368-6501-2(2)) Capstone Pr., Inc.

Kroll, Steven. William Penn: Founder of Pennsylvania. Himler, Ronald, illus. 2000. 32p. (J). (gr. 4-6). tchr. ed. 16.95 (978-0-8234-1439-0(6)) Holiday Hse., Inc.

Lerner Publishing Group Staff. Freedom Seeker: A Story about William Penn. 2003. (gr. 3-6). lib. bdg. 14.10 (978-0-613-77143-6(5)) Tandem Library Bks.

Lilly, Melinda. Quakers in Early America. 2003. (Rourke Discovery Library). (Illus.). 24p. (gr. 1-4). 14.95 (978-1-58952-370-8(9)) Rourke Publishing, LLC.

Lutz, Norma Jean. William Penn. (Colonial Leaders Ser.). (Illus.). 80p. (gr. 3 up). 2000. (YA). 27.50 (978-0-7910-5344-7(X)); 1999. (J). pap. 8.95 (978-0-7910-5687-5(2)) Facts On File, Inc. (Chelsea Hse.).

—William Penn: Founder of Democracy. 2000. (gr. 5-8). lib. bdg. 17.60 (978-0-613-43400-3(5)) Tandem Library Bks.

Mountjoy, Shane. Philadelphia. 2007. (Colonial Settlements in America Ser.). (Illus.). 104p. (J). (gr. 5-8). 30.00 (***978-0-7910-9336-8(0)*** , Chelsea Hse.) Facts On File, Inc.

Somervill, Barbara A. William Penn: Founder of Pennsylvania. 2006. (Signature Lives Ser.). (Illus.). 112p. (J). (gr. 5-7). 30.60 (978-0-7565-1598-0(X)) Compass Point Bks.

Stefoff, Rebecca. William Penn. 2000. (Illus.). 112p. (J). (ps-7). lib. bdg. 18.75 (978-0-613-12285-6(2)) Tandem Library Bks.

—William Penn: Pennsylvania's Founder. 1999. (Overcoming Adversity Ser.). (Illus.). 128p. (YA). (gr. 5 up). lib. bdg. 21.95 (978-0-7910-4873-3(X) , Chelsea Hse.) Facts On File, Inc.

Swain, Gwenyth. Freedom Seeker: A Story about William Penn. Harvey, Lisa, illus. 2003. 64p. (J). pap. 6.95 (978-0-87614-931-7(X)); 22.60 (978-1-57505-176-5(1)) Lerner Publishing Group. (Carolrhoda Bks.).

Walsh, Kieran. William Penn. 2005. (Discover the Life of a Colonial American Ser.). (Illus.). 24p. (gr. 2-5). 14.95 (978-1-59515-139-1(7)) Rourke Publishing, LLC.

William Penn, 6 vols. (gr. 2-5). 39.95 (978-0-7368-4575-5(5)) Red Brick Learning.

William Penn's Peaceable Kingdom (NCHS) 52p. (J). (gr. 5-8). spiral bd., tchr.'s planning gde. ed. 11.50 (978-0-382-40930-1(2)) Cobblestone Publishing Co.

PENN, WILLIAM, 1644-1718—FICTION

Jackson, Dave & Jackson, Neta. Hostage on the Nighthawk: William Penn. McLaughlin, Catherine R., illus. 2000. (Trailblazer Bks.: Vol. 32). 144p. (J). (gr. 3-7). pap. 6.99 (978-0-7642-2265-8(1)) Bethany Hse. Pubs.

Maxson, H. A. & Young, Claudia H. William Penn & the Lower Three Counties. Kosits, Andrew, illus. 2002. 64p. (J). per. 8.95 (978-0-9704692-8-1(4)) Bay Oak Pubs., Ltd.

PENNSYLVANIA

Aiken, Eileen. Golden Remembrances: Of Monaca, Pennsylvania. Vetter, Margaret, illus. 1999. (J). (gr. 5-8). 38p. 22.95 (978-0-9667007-2-5(4)); 45p. per. 8.95 (978-0-9667007-3-2(2)) Skeeter Hill Pr.

—A Tract of Land Called Appetite. Vetter, Margaret, illus. 1998. 44p. (J). (gr. 5-8). 22.95 (978-0-9667007-0-1(8)) Skeeter Hill Pr.

—A Tract of Land Called Appetite: The Story of Monaca, Pennsylvania. Vetter, Margaret, illus. 1998. 44p. (J). (gr. 5-8). per. 8.95 (978-0-9667007-1-8(6)) Skeeter Hill Pr.

Capstone Press Staff, contrib. by. Pennsylvania. rev. ed. 2002. (One Nation Ser.). (Illus.). 48p. (J). (gr. 3-4). lib. bdg. 22.60 (978-0-7368-1262-7(8) , Bridgestone Bks.) Capstone Pr., Inc.

Glaser, Jason. Pennsylvania. 2003. (Land of Liberty Ser.). (Illus.). 64p. (J). lib. bdg. 25.26 (978-0-7368-2194-0(5)) Capstone Pr., Inc.

Heinrichs, Ann. Pennsylvania. Kania, Matt, illus. 2005. (Welcome to the USA Ser.). 40p. (J). (gr. 1-5). 27.07 (978-1-59296-480-2(X)) Child's World, Inc.

—Pennsylvania. 2003. (This Land Is Your Land Ser.). (Illus.). 48p. (J). (gr. 3 up). lib. bdg. 22.60 (978-0-7565-0320-8(5)) Compass Point Bks.

—Pennsylvania. 2006. 32p. (gr. 1-2). (YA). pap. 5.95 (978-0-516-26719-7(1)); (Illus.). (J). 20.50 (978-0-516-24967-4(3)) Scholastic Library Publishing. (Children's Pr.).

Ingram, Scott. Pennsylvania: The Keystone State. 2002. (World Almanac Library of the States). (Illus.). 48p. (J). (gr. 5 up). pap. 14.95 (978-0-8368-5291-2(5)); lib. bdg. 30.00 (978-0-8368-5120-5(X)) Stevens, Gareth Inc. (World Almanac Library).

—Pennsylvania: The Keystone State. 2002. (gr. 5-8). lib. bdg. 24.15 (978-0-613-52474-2(8)) Tandem Library Bks.

Kane, Kristen. K Is for Keystone: A Pennsylvania Alphabet. Knorr, Laura, illus. 2003. 40p. (J). 17.95 (978-1-58536-104-5(6)) Sleeping Bear Pr.

Kavanagh, James. Pennsylvania Birds. Leung, Raymond, illus. 2001. (Pocket Naturalist Ser.). 12p. (gr. 9). pap. 5.95 (978-1-58355-009-0(7)) Waterford Pr., Ltd.

Marsh, Carole. My First Book about Pennsylvania. 2004. (Pennsylvania Experience! Ser.). (Illus.). 32p. (J). (gr. k-4). pap. 7.95 (978-0-7933-9587-3(9)) Gallopade International.

—Pennsylvania Classic Christmas Trivia. 2002. (Carole Marsh Pennsylvania Bks.). (Illus.). 32p. pap. 6.95 (978-0-635-01441-2(6) , 14416); lib. bdg. 21.95 (978-0-635-01442-9(4) , 14424) Gallopade International. (Marsh, Carole Bks.).

—Pennsylvania Current Events Projects: 30 Cool, Activities, Crafts, Experiments & More for Kids to Do to Learn about Your State! 2003. (Pennsylvania Experience Ser.). 32p. (gr. k-8). pap. 5.95 (978-0-635-02057-4(2) , Marsh, Carole Bks.) Gallopade International.

—The Pennsylvania Experience Pocket Guide. 2004. (Pennsylvania Experience! Ser.). (Illus.). 96p. (J). (gr. 3-8). pap. 6.95 (978-0-7933-9586-6(0)) Gallopade International.

—Pennsylvania Geography Projects: 30 Cool, Activities, Crafts, Experiments & More for Kids to Do to Learn about Your State! 2003. (Pennsylvania Experience Ser.). 32p. (gr. k-5). pap. 5.95 (978-0-635-01857-1(8) , Marsh, Carole Bks.) Gallopade International.

—Pennsylvania Government Projects: 30 Cool, Activities, Crafts, Experiments & More for Kids to Do to Learn about Your State! 2003. (Pennsylvania Experience Ser.). 32p. (gr. k-5). pap. 5.95 (978-0-635-01957-8(4) , Marsh, Carole Bks.) Gallopade International.

—Pennsylvania Jeopardy! Answers & Questions about Our State! 2004. (Pennsylvania Experience! Ser.). (Illus.). 32p. (J). (gr. 3-8). pap. 7.95 (978-0-7933-9588-0(7)) Gallopade International.

—Pennsylvania "Jography" A Fun Run Thru Our State! 2004. (Pennsylvania Experience! Ser.). (Illus.). 32p. (J). (gr. 3-8). pap. 7.95 (978-0-7933-9589-7(5)) Gallopade International.

—Pennsylvania People Projects: 30 Cool, Activities, Crafts, Experiments & More for Kids to Do to Learn about Your State! 2003. (Pennsylvania Experience Ser.). 32p. (gr. k-5). pap. 5.95 (978-0-635-02007-9(6) , Marsh, Carole Bks.) Gallopade International.

—Pennsylvania Symbols & Facts Projects: 30 Cool, Activities, Crafts, Experiments & More for Kids to Do to Learn about Your State! 2003. (Pennsylvania Experience Ser.). 32p. (gr. k-5). pap. 5.95 (978-0-635-01907-3(8) , Marsh, Carole Bks.) Gallopade International.

—Pennsylvania's Big Activity Book. 2004. (Pennsylvania Experience! Ser.). (Illus.). 96p. (J). (gr. 2-6). pap. 9.95 (978-0-7933-9590-3(9)) Gallopade International.

—The Proud Pennsylvania Coloring Book. 2004. (Pennsylvania Experience! Ser.). (Illus.). 32p. (J). (gr. k-2). pap. 3.95 (978-0-7933-9591-0(7)) Gallopade International.

McAuliffe, Emily. Pennsylvania Facts & Symbols. (States & Their Symbols Ser.). 24p. (J). 1998. (Illus.). (gr. 2-3). lib. bdg. 18.60 (978-0-7368-0086-0(7) , Bridgestone Bks.); 2003. lib. bdg. 19.93 (978-0-7368-2268-8(2)) Capstone Pr., Inc.

McCollough, Susan. Uniquely Pennsylvania. 2003. (State Studies). (Illus.). 48p. (J). pap. 8.50 (978-1-4034-4511-7(7)) Heinemann Library.

McCulloch, Susan H. Uniquely Pennsylvania. 2004. (Heinemann State Studies). (Illus.). 48p. (J). lib. bdg. (978-1-4034-4496-7(X)) Heinemann Library.

McNamara, Connie. My First University of Pittsburgh Words. 2004. (J). bds. 11.95 (978-0-9759703-2-4(1)) Shamrock Publishing, Inc.

Mercer, Henry C., et al. Color Me Pennsylvania: Our Heritage. 2007. (Illus.). 22p. (J). pap. 12.00 (***978-1-4223-1491-3(X)***) DIANE Publishing Co.

El Meson en Belen (The Bethlehem Inn) (SPA.). (J). (978-0-7899-0876-6(X) , 496235) Editorial Unilit.

Murray, Julie. Pennsylvania. 2006. (Illus.). 32p. (J). (gr. k-4). lib. bdg. 22.78 (978-1-59197-697-4(9) , Buddy Bks.) ABDO Publishing Co.

Noble, Trinka Hakes. One for All: A Pennsylvania Number Book. Papp, L. W., illus. 2005. (Count Your Way Across the USA Ser.). 40p. (J). (gr. k-5). 22.95 (978-1-58536-200-4(X)) Sleeping Bear Pr.

Noble, Trinka Hakes. Pennsylvania Reader. Darnell, Kathryn, illus. rev. ed. 2007. (State Readers Ser.). 96p. 12.95 (***978-1-58536-320-9(0)***) Sleeping Bear Pr.

O'Connell, Kim A. Pennsylvania: A MyReportLinks. Com Book. 2003. (States Ser.). (Illus.). 48p. (J). lib. bdg. 25.26 (978-0-7660-5153-9(6) , MyReportLinks.com Bks.) Enslow Pubs., Inc.

Pellow, Randall A. Pennsylvania Geography. 1999. (Illus.). 64p. (J). (gr. 4-8). pap. 8.35 (978-0-931992-55-1(9)) Penns Valley Pubs.

Pennsylvania. 2000. (Switched on Schoolhouse Ser.). (Illus.). (YA). (gr. 7-12). pap. 24.95 incl. cd-rom (978-0-7403-0290-9(6) , SOSPA) Alpha Omega Pubns., Inc.

Peters, Stephen. Pennsylvania. 2000. (Celebrate the States Ser.). (Illus.). 144p. (gr. 4-8). lib. bdg. 37.07 (978-0-7614-0644-0(1) , Benchmark Bks.) Cavendish, Marshall Corp.

Polley, JoAnn & Shekerow, Mark D. My Trip to Gettysburg. 2007. 80p. (J). 14.95 (978-1-58980-456-2(2)) Pelican Publishing Co., Inc.

Robbie, Natasha. A Guide to Pennsylvania. 2001. (American States Ser.). 32p. (J). (Illus.). (gr. 4-7). lib. bdg. 16.95 (978-1-930954-06-9(9)); per. 7.95 (978-1-930954-56-4(5)) Weigl Pubs., Inc.

Somervill, Barbara A. Pennsylvania. 2003. (From Sea to Shining Sea Ser.: 2). (Illus.). 80p. (J). 30.50 (978-0-516-22388-9(7) , Children's Pr.) Scholastic Library Publishing.

Spinelli, Jerry. Knots in My Yo-Yo String: The Autobiography. 1998. (Illus.). 160p. (J). (gr. 5-8). pap. 10.95 (978-0-679-88791-1(1) , Knopf Bks. for Young Readers) Random Hse. Children's Bks.

—Knots in My Yo-Yo String: The Autobiography of a Kid. 1998. (J). (978-0-606-13553-5(7)) Tandem Library Bks.

—Knots in My Yo-Yo String: The Autobiography of a Kid. l.t. ed. 2000. (Illus.). 187p. (J). (gr. 8-12). 21.95 (978-0-7862-2973-4(X)) Thorndike Pr.

Swain, Gwenyth. Pennsylvania. 2nd exp. rev. ed. (Hello U. S. A. Ser.). (Illus.). 84p. (J). (gr. 3-6). 2003. pap. 6.95 (978-0-8225-4147-9(5)); 2002. 25.26 (978-0-8225-4061-8(4) , Lerner Pubns.) Lerner Publishing Group.

—Pennsylvania. 2001. (gr. 3-6). lib. bdg. 15.25 (978-0-613-89182-0(1)) Tandem Library Bks.

Treasure Maps of Clarion County. 2004. per. 19.95 (978-0-9743881-1-3(4)) Hufnagel Software.

Way, Jennifer. Pennsylvania (Pensilvania) 2006. (Bilingual Library of the United States of America: Set 2). (ENG & SPA., Illus.). 32p. (J). (gr. 3-6). lib. bdg. 22.50 (978-1-4042-3103-0(X) , Buenas Letra) Rosen Publishing Group, Inc., The.

Whitehurst, Susan. The Colony of Pennsylvania. 2000. (Library of the Thirteen Colonies & the Lost Colony). (Illus.). 24p. (J). (gr. 3). lib. bdg. 19.95 (978-0-8239-5481-0(1) , PowerKids Pr.) Rosen Publishing Group, Inc., The.

PENNSYLVANIA—FICTION

Alexander, Lloyd. The Philadelphia Adventure. 2002. (Vesper Holly Ser.). (YA). (gr. 5-8). lib. bdg. 14.15 (978-0-613-51463-7(7)) Tandem Library Bks.

Alger, Horatio. Joe the Hotel Boy. 2006. pap. (***978-1-4065-0712-6(1)***) Dodo Pr.

Alger, Horatio. Joe the Hotel Boy: Or, Winning Out by Pluck. unabr. ed. 2002. (Polyglot Press Alger Ser.). (Illus.). (J). pap. 17.95 (978-1-4115-0015-0(6)) Polyglot Pr., Inc.

Anderson, Laurie Halse. Fever 1793. Earley, Lori, illus. 2000. 256p. (J). (gr. 5-9). 17.99 (978-0-689-83858-3(1)) Simon & Schuster Children's Publishing.

—Fever 1793. 2002. (Illus.). 256p. (J). reprint ed. pap. 5.99 (978-0-689-84891-9(9) , Aladdin) Simon & Schuster Children's Publishing.

—Fever 1793. l.t. ed. 2001. 22.95 (978-0-7862-3408-0(3)) Thorndike Pr.

—Prom. 2006. 224p. (YA). (gr. 7). reprint ed. pap. 8.99 (978-0-14-240570-3(1) , Puffin) Penguin Group (USA) Inc.

—Prom. l.t. ed. 2005. 288p. (YA). (gr. 7-12). per. 21.95 (978-0-7862-7813-8(7) , Large Print Pr.) Thorndike Pr.

—Time to Fly. 2003. (Wild at Heart Ser.). (Illus.). 113p. (J). (gr. 4 up). lib. bdg. 23.33 (978-0-8368-3262-4(0)) Stevens, Gareth Inc.

Ashcraft, Shelly & Hunter, Cheryl. Mamaw & the Girls. 2007. per. 10.99 (***978-1-59886-846-3(2)***) Tate Publishing & Enterprises, L.L.C.

Avi. Encounter at Easton. 2000. (Illus.). (J). 12.64 (978-0-606-17969-0(0)) Tandem Library Bks.

—Night Journeys. 2000. (Illus.). 160p. (J). (gr. 3-7). pap. 5.99 (978-0-380-73242-5(4) , Harper Trophy) HarperCollins Pubs.

—Night Journeys. 2000. (978-0-606-17978-2(X)); (gr. 5-8). lib. bdg. 14.15 (978-0-613-22094-1(3)) Tandem Library Bks.

Ayres, Katherine. Macaroni Boy. 2004. 192p. (J). (gr. 3-7). pap. 5.99 (978-0-440-41884-9(4) , Yearling) Random Hse. Children's Bks.

—Voices at Whisper Bend. 1999. (American Girl Collection Ser.). (978-0-606-17521-0(0)) Tandem Library Bks.

Beaudoin, Sean. Going Nowhere Faster. 2007. 240p. (J). (gr. 8 up). 16.99 (***978-0-316-01415-1(X)***) Little, Brown Bks. for Young Readers.

Bender, Carrie. Birch Hollow Schoolmarm. 1999. (gr. 7-12). lib. bdg. 17.60 (978-0-613-81313-6(8)) Tandem Library Bks.

—Hemlock Hill Hideaway: Whispering Brook Series #4. 2007. (Illus.). 168p. pap. 8.99 (***978-1-60126-022-2(9)***) Masthof Pr.

Bender, Carrie. Timber Lane Cove. 2003. (Whispering Brook Ser.: Bk. 6). 144p. (YA). pap. 8.99 (978-0-8361-9202-5(8)) Herald Pr.

Benedict, Helen. Opposite of Love. 2007. 256p. (J). (gr. 6 up). 16.99 (***978-0-670-06135-8(2)*** , Viking Juvenile) Penguin Group (USA) Inc.

Breaker. 2002. (gr. 7-12). lib. bdg. 18.75 (978-0-613-46050-7(2)) Tandem Library Bks.

Carvell, Marlene. Sweetgrass Basket. 2005. 256p. (J). (gr. 3-6). 16.99 (978-0-525-47547-7(8) , Dutton Juvenile) Penguin Group (USA) Inc.

Clark, Clara. Willie & the Rattlesnake King. 1999. (gr. 7-12). lib. bdg. 16.40 (978-0-613-16880-9(1)) Tandem Library Bks.

Clinton, Cathryn. Simeon's Fire. 128p. (J). 2007. (gr. 3-7). pap. 5.99 (978-0-7636-3294-6(5)); 2005. (gr. 5-9). 15.99 (978-0-7636-2707-2(0)) Candlewick Pr.

Coles, William E., Jr. Another Kind of Monday. 1999. 246p. per. 14.64 (978-0-606-16357-6(3)) Tandem Library Bks.

Connolly, Brian A. Hawk. 2007. 156p. 20.95 (***978-1-60264-030-6(0)***); 160p. per. 13.95 (***978-1-60264-029-0(7)***) Virtualbookworm.com Publishing, Inc.

De Angeli, Marguerite. Henner's Lydia. 1998. (Illus.). 74p. (YA). (ps-3). 15.99 (978-0-8361-9093-9(9)) Herald Pr.

Dellasega, Cheryl. Nugrl90 (Sadie) LaPierre, Karina, illus. 2007. (Bloggrls Ser.). (YA). (gr. 7 up). 200p. 15.99 (***978-0-7614-5375-8(X)***); 190p. per. 6.99 (***978-0-7614-5396-3(2)***) Cavendish, Marshall Corp.

Deming, Sarah. Iris, Messenger. 2007. (Illus.). 224p. (YA). (gr. 5-8). 16.00 (978-0-15-205823-4(0)) Harcourt Children's Bks.

Duey, Kathleen & Bale, Karen A. Cave-In, St. Claire, Pennsylvania, 1859. 1998. (Survival! Ser.: No. 7). 160p. (J). (gr. 4-7). pap. 3.99 (978-0-689-82350-3(9) , Simon Pulse) Simon & Schuster Children's Publishing.

Easton, Richard. A Real American. 2002. 160p. (J). (gr. 4-6). 15.00 (978-0-618-13339-0(9) , Clarion Bks.) Houghton Mifflin Co. Trade & Reference Div.

Erskine, Kathryn. Quaking. 2007. 272p. (YA). (gr. 6 up). 16.99 (***978-0-399-24774-3(2)*** , Philomel) Penguin Group (USA) Inc.

Evernden, Margery. Wilderness Boy. 2001. 192p. (J). pap. 9.95 (978-0-8229-5754-6(X)) Univ. of Pittsburgh Pr.

Faigen, Anne G. New World Waiting. 2006. iii, 188p. (J). pap. (978-0-9744715-5-6(0)) Local History Co., The.

Fenton, Edward. Duffy's Rocks. 1999. (gr. 7-12). lib. bdg. 22.20 (978-0-613-76650-0(4)) Tandem Library Bks.

—Duffy's Rocks. l.t. ed. 1999. (Golden Triangle Bks.). 240p. (YA). (gr. 8-12). pap. 9.95 (978-0-8229-5706-5(X)) Univ. of Pittsburgh Pr.

Ferris, Amy Schor. A Greater Goode. 2002. 192p. (YA). (gr. 5-9). 15.00 (978-0-618-13154-9(X)) Houghton Mifflin Co. Trade & Reference Div.

Ficklin, Jonene H. The Garden Gate. 2005. (YA). 14.95 (978-0-9761188-2-4(3)) Victor's Crown Publishing.

Foster, F. Gordon. The Seasons of the Swans. 2006. (Illus.). 203p. (978-0-9760563-3-1(X)) Mechling Bookbindery.

Freeman, Martha. The Year My Parents Ruined My Life. 1999. (978-0-606-16453-5(7)) Tandem Library Bks.

Gerstein, Mordicai. Sparrow Jack. Gerstein, Mordicai, illus. 2003. (Illus.). 32p. (J). 16.00 (978-0-374-37139-5(3) , Farrar, Straus & Giroux (BYR)) Farrar, Straus & Giroux.

Gilbert, Joan. Mule Boy. Burke, Kathryn Schaar, illus. 2004. 248p. (YA). per. 12.95 (978-0-930973-30-8(5)) Moore, Hugh Historical Park & Museums, Inc.

Glass, Andrew. Bewildered for Three Days: As to Why Daniel Boone Never Wore His Coonskin Cap. Glass, Andrew, illus. 2000. (Illus.). 32p. (J). (gr. k-3). tchr. ed. 16.95 (978-0-8234-1446-8(9)) Holiday Hse., Inc.

Gregory, Kristiana. The Winter of Red Snow: The Revolutionary War Story of Abigail Jane Stewart, Valley Forge, Pa, 1777. 2000. (Dear America Ser.). (J). 9.95 (978-0-439-17969-0(6)) Scholastic, Inc.

Haas, Jessie. Chase. 2007. 256p. (J). (gr. 5-9). 16.99 (978-0-06-112850-9(3)); lib. bdg. 17.89 (978-0-06-112851-6(1)) HarperCollins Pubs.

Haile, Carol J. The Christmas Story. Haile, Carol J., illus. 2001. 60p. 27.95 (978-0-9711236-0-1(8)) Firenze Pr.

Heitzmann, Kristen. Chestnut Ridge Acres. 2001. 220p. (J). 25.95 (978-0-7862-3415-8(6) , Five Star) Thomson Gale.

Hershenhorn, Esther. Fancy That. Lloyd, Megan, illus. 2003. 32p. (J). (gr. k-3). tchr. ed. 16.95 (978-0-8234-1605-9(4)) Holiday Hse., Inc.

Hubler, Marsha. Teamwork at Camp Tioga. 2005. (Keystone Stables Ser.). (Illus.). 128p. (J). pap. 4.99 (978-0-310-70575-8(4)) Zonderkidz.

—Trouble Times Two. 2005. (Keystone Stables Ser.). (Illus.). 128p. (J). pap. 4.99 (978-0-310-70574-1(6)) Zondervan.

Hughes, Pat. The Breaker Boys. 2004. (Illus.). 256p. (J). 18.00 (978-0-374-30956-5(6) , Farrar, Straus & Giroux (BYR)) Farrar, Straus & Giroux.

Jensen, Dorothea. Riddle of Penncroft Farm. 2001. (gr. 3-6). lib. bdg. 14.15 (978-0-613-59249-9(2)) Tandem Library Bks.

Kay, Alan. Breaking the Rules. 2007. (Young Heroes of History: 7). (J). pap. 7.95 (*978-1-57249-389-6(5) , White Mane Kids) White Mane Publishing Co., Inc.

Kay, Alan N. Crossroads at Gettysburg. 2005. (Young Heroes of History: 6). (Illus.). 166p. (J). (gr. 3-7). pap. 7.95 (978-1-57249-359-9(3) , White Mane Kids) White Mane Publishing Co., Inc.

Kay, Verla. Homespun Sarah. Rand, Ted, illus. 2003. 32p. (J). (ps-3). 16.99 (978-0-399-23417-0(9) , Putnam Juvenile) Penguin Group (USA) Inc.

Kehret, Peg. Flood Disaster. 1999. (978-0-606-17854-9(6)) Tandem Library Bks.

Knopp, Sue, creator. Study Guide for Wolf Journal: A Novel. 2005. 60p. per. 7.95 (978-1-58939-827-6(0)) Virtualbookworm.com Publishing, Inc.

Konigsburg, E. L. Father's Arcane Daughter. 1999. (J). (978-0-606-19131-9(3)) Tandem Library Bks.

Krensky, Stephen. Hanukkah at Valley Forge. Harlin, Greg, illus. 2006. 32p. (J). (gr. k). 17.99 (978-0-525-47738-9(1) , Dutton Juvenile) Penguin Group (USA) Inc.

Lamba, Marie. What I Meant... 2007. 320p. (gr. 5-11). (J). 16.99 (978-0-375-84091-3(5)); (YA). lib. bdg. 19.99 (978-0-375-94091-0(X)) Random Hse. Children's Bks. (Random Hse. Bks. for Young Readers).

Lamba, Marie. What I Said- 2008. (J). (*978-0-375-84093-7(1)); lib. bdg. (*978-0-375-94093-4(6)) Random Hse., Inc.

Lawhead, Stephen R. & Lawhead, Ross. Hero. 2003. (gr. 7-12). lib. bdg. 18.80 (978-0-613-89617-7(3)) Tandem Library Bks.

Lewis, Beverly. October Song: Lancaster County Is Cloaked in Autumn Splendor, & a Reunion Is in the Air. 2001. (gr. 5-8). lib. bdg. 22.25 (978-0-613-55643-9(7)) Tandem Library Bks.

Lubar, David. Sleeping Freshmen Never Lie. (YA). 2007. 288p. pap. 6.99 (978-0-14-240780-6(1) , Puffin); 2005. 160p. (gr. 6-10). 16.99 (978-0-525-47311-4(4) , Dutton Juvenile) Penguin Group (USA) Inc.

Ly, Many. Roots & Wings. 2008. 256p. (YA). (gr. 7). lib. bdg. 18.99 (*978-0-385-90494-0(0) , Delacorte Bks. for Young Readers) Random Hse. Children's Bks.

Marsh, Carole. The MYST in Chocolate Town... Hershey,Pennsylvania. 2007. 160p. pap. 5.95 (*978-0-635-06333-5(6)) Gallopade International.

McGough, Michael R. The Lincoln Inn. 2004. (YA). per. 14.95 (*978-1-57747-108-0(3)) Thomas Pubns.

Morgan, Melissa J. Camp Confidential Vol. 4: Alex's Challenge. 2005. (Camp Confidential Ser.). 160p. (gr. 4-7). mass mkt. 4.99 (978-0-448-43876-4(3) , Grosset & Dunlap) Penguin Group (USA) Inc.

—Grace's Twist, Vol. 3. 2005. (Camp Confidential Ser.). 160p. (gr. 4-7). mass mkt. 4.99 (978-0-448-43875-7(5) , Grosset & Dunlap) Penguin Group (USA) Inc.

—Natalie's Secret, No. 1. 2005. (Camp Confidential Ser.). 160p. (J). (gr. 4-7). mass mkt. 4.99 (978-0-448-43737-8(6) , Grosset & Dunlap) Penguin Group (USA) Inc.

O'Hara, John. Appointment in Samarra. 2003. (gr. 7-12). lib. bdg. 22.25 (978-0-613-68488-0(5)) Tandem Library Bks.

Perez, Norah A. Breaker. 2002. (Pitt Golden Triangle Bks.). 216p. pap. 9.95 (978-0-8229-5778-2(7) , Golden Triangle Bks.) Univ. of Pittsburgh Pr.

Price, Olive. Three Golden Rivers. l.t. ed. 1999. (Golden Triangle Bks.). 272p. (YA). (gr. 4-7). pap. 9.95 (978-0-8229-5707-2(8)) Univ. of Pittsburgh Pr.

Pryor, Bonnie. Thomas in Danger, 1779. Dodson, Bert, illus. 2000. (American Adventures Ser.). 176p. (J). (gr. 3-7). pap. 4.95 (978-0-380-73212-8(2)) HarperCollins Pubs.

Richter, Conrad. The Light in the Forest. 2005. (Illus.). 176p. 14.95 (978-1-4000-4426-9(X) , Everyman's Library) Knopf Publishing Group.

Rodman, Mary Ann. Jimmy's Stars. 2008. 272p. (J). 16.95 (*978-0-374-33703-2(9)) Farrar, Straus & Giroux.

Rosenswieg, Jay B. & Repka, Janice. The Stupendous Dodgeball Fiasco. Dibley, Glin, illus. 2004. 192p. (J). (gr. 3). 16.99 (978-0-525-47346-6(7) , Dutton Juvenile) Penguin Group (USA) Inc.

Savage, Deborah. Summer Hawk. 1999. 304p. (YA). (gr. 7-12). tchr. ed. 16.00 (978-0-395-91163-1(X)) Houghton Mifflin Co. Trade & Reference Div.

Shuster, Bud. Double Buckeyes: A Story of the Way America Used to Be. (Illus.). vi, 149p. (J). (gr. 4-7). 2000. pap. 7.95 (978-1-57249-177-9(9) , White Mane Kids); 1999. 19.95 (978-1-57249-176-2(0) , White Mane Bks.) White Mane Publishing Co., Inc.

Siegrist, Bonnie. Little Farm down the Lane -Book IV. 2007. pap. 10.99 (*978-1-60034-912-6(9)) Xulon Pr., Inc.

Sonnenblick, Jordan. Zen & the Art of Faking It. 2007. 272p. (J). pap. 16.99 (*978-0-439-83707-1(3) , Scholastic Pr.) Scholastic, Inc.

Spinelli, Jerry. Love, Stargirl. 2007. (J). 192p. (gr. 5-8). lib. bdg. 19.99 (*978-0-375-91375-4(0)); 288p. (gr. 7-8). 16.99 (*978-0-375-81375-7(6)) Random Hse. Children's Bks. (Knopf Bks. for Young Readers).

Sykes, Shelley & Szymanski, Lois. Ghost on Board. 2001. (Gettysburg Ghost Gang Ser.: Vol. 2). (Illus.). 96p. (J). pap. 5.95 (978-1-57249-267-7(8) , White Mane Kids) White Mane Publishing Co., Inc.

Thomas, Joan M. Mimi's Gift. 2004. (Illus.). 112p. (J). (ps-4). pap. 14.95 (978-1-57921-482-1(7)) WinePress Publishing.

Wallace, Rich. Losing Is Not an Option. 2003. 144p. (YA). (gr. 5-9). 15.95 (978-0-375-81351-1(9) , Knopf Bks. for Young Readers) Random Hse. Children's Bks.

Wallace, Rich. One Good Punch. 2007. 128p. (YA). (gr. 7). 15.99 (*978-0-375-81352-8(7)); lib. bdg. 18.99 (*978-0-375-91352-5(1)) Random Hse. Children's Bks. (Knopf Bks. for Young Readers).

Weaver, K. C. For the Sake of the Children. 2007. 75p. 14.95 (*978-1-4241-0647-9(8)) PublishAmerica, Inc.

Welch, Sheila Kelly. The Shadowed Unicorn. 2000. 192p. (J). (gr. 5-9). 15.95 (978-0-8126-2895-1(0)) Cricket Bks.

Woodruff, Elvira. Dear Austin: Letters from the Underground Railroad. 2000. (gr. 5-8). lib. bdg. 13.00 (978-0-613-28463-9(1)) Tandem Library Bks.

PENNSYLVANIA—HISTORY

Ammon, Richard. Valley Forge. Farnsworth, Bill, illus. 2004. 32p. (J). (gr. 4-6). tchr. ed. 16.95 (978-0-8234-1746-9(8)) Holiday Hse., Inc.

Baczynski, Bernadette L. William Penn: Founder of the Pennsylvania Colony. 2004. (Let Freedom Ring Ser.). (Illus.). 48p. (J). 17.95 (978-0-7368-2459-0(6) , Bridgestone Bks.) Capstone Pr., Inc.

Bartoletti, Susan Campbell. Growing up in Coal Country. 1999. (Illus.). 128p. (J). (gr. 4-6). pap. 7.95 (978-0-395-97914-3(5)) Houghton Mifflin Co. Trade & Reference Div.

Boothroyd, Jennifer. William Penn: A Life of Tolerance. 2007. (Pull Ahead Books). (Illus.). 32p. (J). 22.60 (978-0-8225-6387-7(8) , Lerner Pubns.) Lerner Publishing Group.

Burgan, Michael. Valley Forge. 2004. (We the People Ser.). (Illus.). 48p. (J). (gr. 4 up). lib. bdg. 22.60 (978-0-7565-0615-5(8)) Compass Point Bks.

DeFord, Deborah H. Pennsylvania. 2004. (Life in the Thirteen Colonies Ser.). (Illus.). 124p. (J). 36.00 (978-0-516-24577-5(5) , Children's Pr.) Scholastic Library Publishing.

Doeden, Matt. Winter at Valley Forge. Barnett, Charles & Frenz, Ron, illus. 2006. (Graphic Library). 32p. (J). 25.26 (978-0-7368-4975-3(0)) Capstone Pr., Inc.

Doylestown Historical Society Staff. Doylestown: Pennsylvania. 2000. (Images of America Ser.). 128p. pap. 19.99 (978-0-7385-0497-1(1)) Arcadia Publishing.

Fox, Arthur B. Pittsburgh During the American Civil War 1860-1865. ed. 2004. (Illus.). 236p. per. 29.95 (978-0-9760563-0-0(5) , 7526S) Mechling Bookbindery.

Galchefski, Christina, compiled by. Coloring the Pieces of Luzerne County, 2003. (Illus.). 36p. (J). 4.00 (978-0-937537-12-1(8)) Wyoming Historical & Geological Society.

Gallagher, Jim. Johnstown Flood. 1999. (Great Disasters Ser.). (Illus.). 112p. (YA). (gr. 5 up). 30.00 (978-0-7910-5266-2(4) , Chelsea Hse.) Facts On File, Inc.

Gillis, Jennifer Blizin. William Penn. 2004. (Illus.). 32p. (J). pap. 7.50 (978-1-4034-5971-8(1)); lib. bdg. 25.64 (978-1-4034-5963-3(0)) Heinemann Library.

Gow, Mary. Johnstown Flood: The Day the Dam Burst. 2003. (American Disasters Ser.). (Illus.). 48p. (J). (gr. 4-10). lib. bdg. 23.93 (978-0-7660-2109-9(2)) Enslow Pubs., Inc.

Grey, Rochelle, text. My RiverPlace on the Schuylkill Coloring Book. 2006. (Illus.). 12p. (J). (978-0-9785538-0-7(2)) RiverPlace Development Corp.

Harris, Nancy. The Liberty Bell. 2007. (J). (*978-1-4034-9381-1(2)) Heinemann Library.

Hinman, Bonnie. Pennsylvania: William Penn & the City of Brotherly Love. 2006. (Building America Ser.). (Illus.). 48p. (J). (gr. 4-8). lib. bdg. 20.95 (978-1-58415-463-1(2)) Mitchell Lane Pubs., Inc.

Hintz, Martin. The Pennsylvania Colony. 2005. (Fact Finders Ser.). (Illus.). 32p. (J). (ps-7). lib. bdg. 22.60 (978-0-7368-2681-5(5)) Capstone Pr., Inc.

Italia, Bob. The Pennsylvania Colony. 2001. (Colonies Ser.). (Illus.). 32p. (J). (gr. k-6). lib. bdg. 22.78 (978-1-57765-588-6(5) , Checkerboard Library) ABDO Publishing Co.

Jacobson, Ryan. William Penn. Stiles, Tim, illus. 2007. (Graphic Library). 32p. (J). 25.26 (978-0-7368-6501-2(2)) Capstone Pr., Inc.

Jensen, Dorothea. The Riddle of Penncroft Farm. 2001. (Great Episodes Ser.). 272p. (YA). (gr. 5-9). pap. 6.00 (978-0-15-216441-6(3) , Gulliver Bks.) Harcourt Children's Bks.

Kinney Williams, Jean. The Pennsylvania Colony. 2003. (Spirit of America). (Illus.). 40p. (J). (gr. 2-6). 28.50 (978-1-56766-684-7(1)) Child's World, Inc.

Korman, Susan. P Is for Philadelphia. 2005. (Illus.). 64p. 16.95 (978-1-59213-107-5(7)) Temple Univ. Pr.

Kozar, Richard. Fort Duquesne & Fort Pitt. 2004. (American Forts & Their Strategic Importance Ser.). (J). (978-1-59084-719-0(9)) Mason Crest Pubs.

Krebs, Laurie. A Day in the Life of a Colonial Doctor. 2004. (Library of Living & Working in Colonial Times). (Illus.). 24p. (J). lib. bdg. 18.75 (978-0-8239-6228-0(8) , PowerKids Pr.) Rosen Publishing Group, Inc., The.

Kroll, Steven. William Penn: Founder of Pennsylvania. Himler, Ronald, illus. 2000. 32p. (J). (gr. 4-6). tchr. ed. 16.95 (978-0-8234-1439-0(6)) Holiday Hse., Inc.

Leathers, Dan. The Johnstown, Pennsylvania, Flood 1889. 2007. (Natural Disasters Ser.). (J). lib. bdg. 25.70 (*978-1-58415-570-6(1)) Mitchell Lane Pubs., Inc.

Lewis, Noah & Graham, Loretta. Edward Ned Hector. 2005. (ENG., Illus.). 36p. (J). per. 19.99 (*978-1-4208-6817-3(9)) AuthorHouse.

Lilly, Melinda. Quakers in Early America. 2003. (Rourke Discovery Library). (Illus.). 24p. (gr. 1-4). 14.95 (978-1-58952-370-8(9)) Rourke Publishing, LLC.

Lutz, Norma Jean. William Penn. (Colonial Leaders Ser.). (Illus.). 80p. (gr. 3 up). 2000. (YA). 27.50 (978-0-7910-5344-7(X)); 1999. (J). pap. 8.95 (978-0-7910-5687-5(2)) Facts On File, Inc. (Chelsea Hse.).

—William Penn: Founder of Democracy. 2000. (gr. 5-8). lib. bdg. 17.60 (978-0-613-43400-3(5)) Tandem Library Bks.

Marsh, Carole. My First Pocket Guide Pennsylvania. 2000. (Pennsylvania Experience! Ser.). (Illus.). 96p. (J). (gr. 3-8). 12.95 (978-0-635-01328-6(2) , 13282) Gallopade International.

—Pennsylvania History Projects: 30 Cool, Activities, Crafts, Experiments & More for Kids to Do to Learn about Your State! 2003. (Pennsylvania Experience Ser.). 32p. (gr. k-5). pap. 5.95 (978-0-635-01807-6(1) , Marsh, Carole Bks.) Gallopade International.

—Pennsylvania Millionaire. 2001. (GameBook Ser.). 32p. (J). (gr. 3-8). pap., act. bk. ed. 9.95 (978-0-635-00092-7(X)) Gallopade International.

—Pennsylvania Survivor. 2001. (GameBook Ser.). 32p. (J). (gr. 3-8). pap., act. bk. ed. 9.95 (978-0-635-00559-5(X)) Gallopade International.

—Pennsylvania Wheel of Fortune. 2001. (GameBook Ser.). 32p. (J). (gr. 3-8). pap., act. bk. ed. 9.95 (978-0-7933-9692-4(1)) Gallopade International.

—The Survivor: A Class Challenge. 2001. (Carole Marsh Pennsylvania Bks.). (J). lib. bdg. 29.95 (978-0-635-00684-4(7)) Gallopade International.

—Wheel of Fortune. 2001. (Pennsylvania Experience! Ser.). (J). lib. bdg. 29.95 (978-0-7933-9693-1(X)) Gallopade International.

—Who Wants to Be a Millionaire? 2001. (Carole Marsh Pennsylvania Bks.). (J). lib. bdg. 29.95 (978-0-635-00093-4(8)) Gallopade International.

Mis, Melody S. The Colony of Pennsylvania: A Primary Source History. 2007. (Primary Source Library of the Thirteen Colonies & the Lost Colony). (Illus.). 24p. (J). lib. bdg. (978-1-4042-3437-6(3) , PowerKids Pr) Rosen Publishing Group, Inc., The.

—How to Draw Pennsylvania's Sights & Symbols. 2002. (Kids Guide to Drawing America Ser.). 32p. (J). lib. bdg. 25.25 (978-0-8239-6094-1(3) , PowerKids Pr.) Rosen Publishing Group, Inc., The.

Moore, Noreen. Reaching Tidewater: Life on the Delaware Canal. 2004. (Illus.). v, 92p. (J). pap. 5.95 (978-1-57249-358-2(5) , White Mane Kids) White Mane Publishing Co., Inc.

Mountjoy, Shane. Philadelphia. 2007. (Colonial Settlements in America Ser.). (Illus.). 104p. (J). (gr. 5-8). 30.00 (*978-0-7910-9336-8(0) , Chelsea Hse.) Facts On File, Inc.

Murphy, Jim. An American Plague: The True & Terrifying Story of the Yellow Fever Epidemic of 1793. 2003. (Illus.). 176p. (J). (gr. 5-9). tchr. ed. 17.00 (978-0-395-77608-7(2) , Clarion Bks.) Houghton Mifflin Co. Trade & Reference Div.

Nobleman, Marc Tyler. The Johnstown Flood. 2005. (We the People Ser.). (Illus.). 48p. (J). (gr. 4-6). (978-0-7565-1267-5(0)) Compass Point Bks.

O'Hanlon-Lincoln, Ceane. County Chronicles: A Vivid Collection of Fayette County, Pennsylvania Histories. 2004. (County Chronicles Ser.: 1). (Illus.). 420p. 45.95 (978-0-9744657-8-4(X) , 7792) Mechling Bookbindery.

Prentzas, G. S. The Colony of Pennsylvania. 2005. (Primary Sources of the Thirteen Colonies & the Lost Colony Ser.). (Illus.). 64p. (J). (gr. 3-7). pap. 14.60 (978-1-4042-0673-1(6)) Rosen Publishing Group, Inc., The.

—A Primary Source History of the Colony of Pennsylvania. 2005. (Primary Sources of the Thirteen Colonies & the Lost Colony Ser.). (Illus.). 64p. (YA). (gr. 5-8). lib. bdg. 29.25 (978-1-4042-0433-1(4)) Rosen Publishing Group, Inc., The.

Rau, Dana Meachen & Brown, Jonatha A. Pennsylvania. 2005. (Portraits of the States Ser.). (Illus.). 32p. (J). pap. (978-0-8368-4652-2(4)); lib. bdg. 23.33 (978-0-8368-4633-1(8)) Stevens, Gareth Inc.

Reynolds, Patrick M. Pennsylvania's Hectic Heritage. 2000. (gr. 7-12). lib. bdg. 11.80 (978-0-613-77641-7(0)) Tandem Library Bks.

Schiel, Katy. The Whiskey Rebellion: An Early Challenge to America's New Government. 2004. (Life in the New American Nation Ser.). (Illus.). 32p. (YA). lib. bdg. (978-0-8239-4262-6(7)) Rosen Publishing Group, Inc., The.

Simon, Charnan. Milton Hershey: Chocolate King, Town Builder. De Capua, Sarah, ed. 1998. (Community Builders Ser.). (Illus.). 48p. (J). (gr. 3-5). pap. 6.95 (978-0-516-26330-4(7) , Children's Pr.) Scholastic Library Publishing.

Somervill, Barbara A. William Penn: Founder of Pennsylvania. 2006. (Signature Lives Ser.). (Illus.). 112p. (J). (gr. 5-7). 30.60 (978-0-7565-1598-0(X)) Compass Point Bks.

Stefoff, Rebecca. William Penn: Pennsylvania's Founder. 1999. (Overcoming Adversity Ser.). (Illus.). 128p. (YA). (gr. 5 up). lib. bdg. 21.95 (978-0-7910-4873-3(X) , Chelsea Hse.) Facts On File, Inc.

Swain, Gwenyth. Freedom Seeker: A Story about William Penn. Harvey, Lisa, illus. 2003. 64p. (J). pap. 6.95 (978-0-87614-931-7(X)); 22.60 (978-1-57505-176-5(1)) Lerner Publishing Group. (Carolrhoda Bks.).

Trumbauer, Lisa. Pennsylvania, 1643-1776. 2005. (Voices from Colonial America Ser.). (Illus.). 112p. (J). (gr. 5-9). 21.95 (978-0-7922-6596-2(3) , National Geographic Children's Bks.) National Geographic Society.

Trumbauer, Lisa. Pennsylvania, 1643-1776. 2006. (Voices from Colonial America Ser.). (Illus.). 112p. (J). (gr. 5-9). 32.90 (978-0-7922-6854-3(7) , National Geographic Children's Bks.) National Geographic Society.

Varonka, Steve. Hard Coal Times Vol. 3: Early Coal Transportation. 2004. (Illus.). 24p. (YA). 4.72 (978-0-9709630-5-5(X)) Coal Hole Productions.

Walsh, Kieran. William Penn. 2005. (Discover the Life of a Colonial American Ser.). (Illus.). 24p. (gr. 2-5). 14.95 (978-1-59515-139-1(7)) Rourke Publishing, LLC.

Wiener. Pennsylvania 6-Pack. 2004. (13 Colonies Ser.). (Illus.). 51.30 (978-1-4109-0373-0(7)) Harcourt Schl. Pubs.

Wiener, Roberta & Arnold, James R. Pennsylvania. 2004. (Thirteen Colonies Ser.). (Illus.). 64p. (J). 28.56 (978-0-7398-6886-7(1)); 9.50 (978-1-4109-0310-5(9)) Harcourt Schl. Pubs.

PENNSYLVANIA DUTCH

Ammon, Richard. An Amish Year. Patrick, Pamela, illus. 2007. 36p. (J). (ps-3). pap. 10.95 (*978-1-59078-465-5(0)) Boyds Mills Pr.

Williamson, Chet. Pennsylvania Dutch Alphabet. Stacy, Alan Fearl, illus. 2007. 32p. (J). (gr. k-3). 15.95 (*978-1-58980-496-8(1)) Pelican Publishing Co., Inc.

PENNSYLVANIA DUTCH—FICTION

Robinson, Scottie. Ada's Bells. 2001. (Illus.). (J). (978-0-7614-5098-6(X)) Cavendish, Marshall Corp.

PENNSYLVANIA GERMANS

see Pennsylvania Dutch

PENOLOGY

see Prisons

PEOPLE WITH DISABILITIES

see also People with Mental Disabilities; Sick

Abbott, Marcia. My Face. Abbott, Barbara, ed. Westdal, Jamie, photos by. 1998. (Illus.). 44p. (J). (gr. 1-5). 12.50 (978-0-9666097-0-7(0)) Forward Face.

Adler, David A. Helen Keller. Wallner, John C., illus. 32p. (J). (gr. k-3). tchr. ed. 14.95 (978-0-8234-1606-6(2)) Holiday Hse., Inc.

Alter, Judy. Christopher Reeve: Triumph over Tragedy. 2000. (gr. 5-8). lib. bdg. 15.25 (978-0-613-54128-2(6)) Tandem Library Bks.

Apel, Melanie Ann. Let's Talk about Being in a Wheelchair. 2002. (Let's Talk Library). (Illus.). 24p. (J). lib. bdg. 18.75 (978-0-8239-5863-4(9) , PowerKids Pr.) Rosen Publishing Group, Inc., The.

Around the World Resource Guide. 4th ed. 2001. (Disabled Resources Ser.). 366p. spiral bd. 15.00 (978-1-928616-07-8(0)) Access for Disabled Americans.

Barasch, Lynne. Knockin' on Wood: Starring Peg Leg Bates. 2004. (Illus.). 32p. (J). 16.95 (978-1-58430-170-7(8)) Lee & Low Bks., Inc.

Basinger, Carol. Everything You Need to Know about Deafness. 2005. (Need to Know Library). (Illus.). 64p. (J). (gr. 7-12). lib. bdg. 25.25 (978-0-8239-3165-1(X) , NT-DEAF) Rosen Publishing Group, Inc., The.

Beckman, Paula J. My Community, My Family. 2001. (Me, Too! Ser.). (Illus.). 20p. pap. 19.95 (978-1-55766-511-9(7) , 5117) Brookes, Paul H. Publishing Co.

Brocker, Susan. Vision Without Sight: Human Capabilities. 2007. (Shockwave: Life Science & Medicine Ser.). (Illus.). 36p. (J). (gr. 4-6). lib. bdg. 25.00 (*978-0-531-17769-3(6) , Children's Pr.) Scholastic Library Publishing.

Busic, Valerie. Jason's First Day. OI Foundation, ed. Meyers, Jeff, illus. l.t. ed. 2004. 48p. per. 8.50 (978-0-9642189-4-9(1)) Osteogenesis Imperfecta Foundation.

Cruz, Barbara C. Jose Clemente Orozco: Mexican Artist. 1998. (Hispanic Biographies Ser.). (Illus.). 128p. (YA). (gr. 6-12). lib. bdg. 26.60 (978-0-7660-1041-3(4)) Enslow Pubs., Inc.

Derke, Connie Butterfield. Mommy Has 1 Foot: Learning about Numbers - Learning about People. Smith, Tracy, illus. 2003. (Kayla's Learning Books). 24p. (J). (gr. 1-6). pap. 5.95 (978-0-9747063-0-6(2)) Derke, Connie.

Devillier, Christy. Helen Keller. 2004. (First Biographies Set Iv Ser.). (Illus.). 32p. (J). (gr. k-4). lib. bdg. 22.78 (978-1-59197-514-4(X)) ABDO Publishing Co.

Disabilities in Ministry Committee. Ephphatha! Open Up! A Children's Curriculum for Understanding Disabilities. 1999. 80p. pap. 12.95 (978-0-7880-1350-8(5)) CSS Publishing Co.

Esherick, Joan. Breaking down Barriers: Youth with Physical Challenges. 2004. (Youth with Special Needs Ser.). (Illus.). 128p. (J). (978-1-59084-737-4(7)) Mason Crest Pubs.

Fisher, Gary L. The Survival Guide for Kids with LD (Learning Differences) 2002. lib. bdg. 18.00 (978-0-613-65002-1(6)) Tandem Library Bks.

Fisher, Gary L. & Cummings, Rhoda. The Survival Guide for Kids with LD (Learning Differences) rev. ed. 2004. (Illus.). 112p. (YA). (gr. 3 up). pap. 10.95 (978-1-57542-119-3(4)) Free Spirit Publishing, Inc.

Hale, Natalie. Oh, Brother! Growing up with a Special Needs Sibling. Sternberg, Kate, tr. Sternberg, Kate, illus. 2004. 48p. (J). 14.95 (978-1-59147-060-1(9)); pap. 8.95 (978-1-59147-061-8(7)) American Psychological Assn. (Magination Pr.).

Hanson, Marci J. It's Time for Preschool. 2001. (Me, Too! Ser.). (Illus.). 28p. pap. 19.95 (978-1-55766-510-2(9) , 5109) Brookes, Paul H. Publishing Co.

Hanson, Marci J. & Morgan, Maria L. Introducing Me. 2001. (Me, Too! Ser.). (Illus.). pap. 19.95 (978-1-55766-509-6(5) , 5095) Brookes, Paul H. Publishing Co.

—Look What I Can Do Now. 2001. (Me, Too! Ser.). (Illus.). 20p. pap. 19.95 (978-1-55766-514-0(1) , 5141) Brookes, Paul H. Publishing Co.

Hanson, Marci J., et al. My New Friends. 2001. (Me, Too! Ser.). (Illus.). 24p. 19.95 (978-1-55766-512-6(5) , 5125) Brookes, Paul H. Publishing Co.

—On My Best Behavior. 2001. (Me, Too! Ser.). (Illus.). 24p. pap. 19.95 (978-1-55766-513-3(3) , 5133) Brookes, Paul H. Publishing Co.

Health Physically Challenged. (J). (978-0-8136-9354-5(3)) Modern Curriculum Pr.

Heelan, Jamee Riggio. Can You Hear a Rainbow? The Story of a Deaf Boy Named Chris. Simmonds, Nicola, illus. 2002. (Rehabilitation Institute of Chicago Learning Book Ser.). 32p. (J). (gr. 1-5). 14.95 (978-1-56145-268-2(8) , Q34265) Peachtree Pubs., Ltd.

—The Making of My Special Hand: Madison's Story. Simmonds, Nicola, illus. Heelan, Jamee Riggio, photos by. 2000. (Rehabilitation Institute of Chicago Learning Book Ser.). 32p. (J). (gr. 1-5). 14.95 (978-1-56145-186-9(X)) Peachtree Pubs., Ltd.

Jeffrey, Laura S. All about Braille: Reading by Touch. 2004. (Transportation & Communication Ser.). (Illus.). 48p. (J). lib. bdg. 23.93 (978-0-7660-2184-6(X)) Enslow Pubs., Inc.

Keith, Lois. Being in a Wheelchair. 1999. (Think about Ser.). (Illus.). 32p. (J). (gr. 2-5). lib. bdg. 16.95 (978-1-887068-87-1(2)) Smart Apple Media.

Kent, Deborah. Athletes with Disabilities. 2003. (Watts Library). (Illus.). 64p. (J). (gr. 5-7). pap. 8.95 (978-0-531-16664-2(3)); 25.50 (978-0-531-12019-4(8)) Scholastic Library Publishing. (Watts, Franklin).

—Helen Keller: Author & Advocate for the Disabled. 2003. (Spirit of America). (Illus.). 32p. (J). (gr. 2-6). 27.07 (978-1-59296-005-7(7)) Child's World, Inc.

Klein, Steve. The Power of Early Speed. 2006. 144p. pap. 14.95 (978-1-932910-98-8(0)) Daily Racing Form Pr.

Klingel, Cynthia Fitterer & Noyed, Robert B. Helen Keller. 2001. (Wonder Books Level 2: Biographies Ser.). (Illus.). 24p. (J). (ps-3). 22.79 (978-1-56766-952-7(2)) Child's World, Inc.

Koestler-Grack, Rachel A. The Story of Helen Keller. 2003. (Breakthrough Biographies Ser.). (Illus.). 32p. (J). (gr. 3-5). 23.00 (978-0-7910-7315-5(7) , Chelsea Hse.) Facts On File, Inc.

Kovatch, Sarah. Special Helpers. 2005. (Illus.). 16p. (J). (978-0-7367-2854-6(6)) Zaner-Bloser, Inc.

Landau, Elaine. Head & Brain Injuries. 2002. (Diseases & People Ser.). (Illus.). 112p. (YA). (gr. 6-12). lib. bdg. 26.60 (978-0-7660-1473-2(8)) Enslow Pubs., Inc.

—Spinal Cord Injuries. 2001. (Diseases & People Ser.). (Illus.). 128p. (J). (gr. 6-12). lib. bdg. 26.60 (978-0-7660-1474-9(6)) Enslow Pubs., Inc.

Larabie, Gayle. Is My Dad Still My Dad? 2005. (Illus.). 32p. (J). (978-1-55306-873-0(4)) Essence Publishing.

Like Me Like You. 2005. (Illus.). 32p. (gr. 2-4). pap. 138.00 (978-0-7910-8462-5(0) , Chelsea Hse.) Facts On File, Inc.

Lorbiecki, Marybeth. Friendship Book Set: That's Life! Literature Series, 4 vols. Gallop, Jim, photos by. 2004. (Illus.). 18p. (YA). 45.00 (978-0-9666667-3-1(9)) AbleNet, Inc.

Manson, Ainslie. Baboo: The Story of Sir John A. MacDonald's Daughter. Wand, Bill, illus. 1998. (J). (ps-4). (978-0-88899-329-8(3)) Groundwood Bks.

McIntosh, Kenneth & Walker, Ida. Youth with Cultural/Language Differences: Interpreting an Alien World. 2008. (J). (*978-1-4222-0141-1(4)) Mason Crest Pubs.

McMahon, Patricia. Summer Tunes: A Martha's Vineyard Vacation. Simon, Peter, illus. 2003. 48p. (J). (gr. 4-6). 16.95 (978-1-56397-572-1(6)) Boyds Mills Pr.

Meyer, D J. Sibling Slam Book. 2005. (Illus.). 152p. pap. 15.95 (978-1-890627-52-2(6)) Woodbine Hse.

Meyer, Donald J. Living with a Brother or Sister with Special Needs: A Book for Sibs. 2nd exp. rev. ed. 2003. (Illus.). 144p. (ps up). pap. 18.95 (978-0-295-97547-4(4)) Univ. of Washington Pr.

Oleksy, Walter. Christopher Reeve. 1999. (People in the News Ser.). (Illus.). 112p. (YA). (gr. 6-9). 32.45 (978-1-56006-534-0(6) , Lucent Bks.) Thomson Gale.

Owens, Connie S. Special Needs... Special Love: Relating to Children with Disabilities (Tender Topics) 2005. 32p. pap. 6.99 (978-1-59317-098-1(X)) Warner Pr. Pubs.

Powell, Jillian. Disability. 1999. (Talking about Ser.). (Illus.). 32p. (J). (gr. k-4). lib. bdg. 25.70 (978-0-8172-5537-4(0)) Raintree.

—Sam Uses a Wheelchair. 2004. (Like Me Like You Ser.). (Illus.). 32p. (gr. 2-4). 23.00 (978-0-7910-8180-8(X) , Chelsea Hse.) Facts On File, Inc.

Presnall, Judith Janda. Canine Companions. 2003. (Animals with Jobs Ser.). (Illus.). 48p. (J). 26.20 (978-0-7377-2050-1(6) , Greenhaven Pr., Inc.) Thomson Gale.

—Capuchin Monkeys. 2003. (Animals with Jobs Ser.). (Illus.). 48p. (J). (gr. 3-5). 26.20 (978-0-7377-1788-4(2) , Kidhaven) Thomson Gale.

Ratto, Linda Lee. (dis) Ability. 2004. (YA). per. (978-0-9748508-2-5(9)) Power Pr.

Riggs, Stephanie. Never Sell Yourself Short. Youmans, Bill, illus. Youmans, Bill, photos by. 2001. 32p. (J). (gr. 1-5). 15.95 (978-0-8075-5563-7(0)) Whitman, Albert & Co.

Rogers, Fred. Extraordinary Friends. Judkis, Jim, photos by. 2000. (Let's Talk about It Ser.). (Illus.). 32p. (J). (ps-3). pap. 6.99 (978-0-698-11861-4(8) , Putnam Juvenile) Penguin Group (USA) Inc.

—Special Friends. 2000. (Let's Talk about It Ser.). (Illus.). (J). (978-0-606-18417-5(1)) Tandem Library Bks.

Rogers, Fred & Rogers, Fred. Lets Talk about It Extraordinary Friends. Judkis, Jim, photos by. 2000. (Illus.). (J). (ps-ps). lib. bdg. 15.30 (978-0-613-21889-4(2)) Tandem Library Bks.

Royston, Angela. Blindness. 2005. (Illus.). 32p. (J). (978-1-4034-5849-0(9)) Heinemann Library.

—What's It? Deafness. 2005. (Illus.). 32p. (J). (ps-ps). lib. bdg. 25.36 (978-1-4034-5852-0(9)) Heinemann Library.

Sabin, Ellen. The Special Needs Acceptance Book: Being a Friend to Someone with Special Needs. 2007. (Illus.). 64p. (J). 17.95 (*978-0-9759868-5-1(6)) Watering Can.

Sabin, Francene. Helen Keller: Una Chica Valiente. abr. ed. 2007. 64p. (J). pap. 3.99 (*978-0-439-87999-6(X) , Scholastic en Espanol) Scholastic, Inc.

Savage, Jeff. Top 10 Physically Challenged Athletes. 2000. (Sports Top 10 Ser.). (Illus.). 48p. (J). (gr. 4-10). lib. bdg. 23.93 (978-0-7660-1272-1(7)) Enslow Pubs., Inc.

Schaefer, Adam. Herramientas Que Me Ayudan. 2007. (ENG & SPA., Illus.). 24p. (J). (*978-1-60044-305-3(2)) Rourke Publishing, LLC.

—Tools That Help Me. 2007. (Illus.). 24p. (J). (*978-1-59515-996-0(7)) Rourke Publishing, LLC.

Schaefer, Lola M. Some Kids Use Wheelchairs. Saunders-Smith, Gail, ed. 2000. (Understanding Differences Ser.). (Illus.). 24p. (J). (gr. k-1). lib. bdg. 15.93 (978-0-7368-0666-4(0) , Pebble Bks.) Capstone Pr., Inc.

—Some Kids Wear Leg Braces. Saunders-Smith, Gail, ed. 2000. (Understanding Differences Ser.). (Illus.). 24p. (J). (gr. k-1). lib. bdg. 15.93 (978-0-7368-0667-1(9) , Pebble Bks.) Capstone Pr., Inc.

Sirof, Harriet. Road Back: Living with a Physical Disability. 2000. (gr. 7-12). lib. bdg. 22.20 (978-0-613-88319-1(5)) Tandem Library Bks.

Some Kids Use Wheelchairs. (Understanding Differences Ser.). 24p. (J). 5.95 (978-0-7368-8794-6(6)) Capstone Pr., Inc.

Some Kids Use Wheelchairs, 6 vols. (gr. k-2). 28.95 (978-0-7368-8818-9(7)) Red Brick Learning.

Stewart, Gail B. Alexandra Scott, Cancer Research Fundraiser. 2006. 64p. (gr. 4-8). 27.45 (978-0-7377-3613-7(5) , Kidhaven) Thomson Gale.

—Teens with Disabilities. Franzen, Carl G., photos by. 2000. (Other America Ser.). (Illus.). 96p. (J). (gr. 4-12). lib. bdg. 29.95 (978-1-56006-815-0(9) , LML00902-178147, Lucent Bks.) Thomson Gale.

Summer, Paulette. I Am Lucky: The True Story of a Courageous & Inspiring Kitten Born with Disabling Disabilities. Nozik, Ira, photos by. 2000. 64p. (YA). (gr. 5 up). per. 9.95 (978-0-9627610-1-0(X)) Millennium Pubns.

Thomas, Pat. Don't Call Me Special: A First Look at Disability. Harker, Lesley, illus. 2002. (First Look at Bks.). 32p. (J). (ps-2). pap. 6.95 (978-0-7641-2118-0(9)) Barron's Educational Series, Inc.

Thornton, Denise. Physical Disabilities: Ultimat. 2007. (Illus.). 176p. 42.00 (978-0-8108-5300-3(0)) Scarecrow Pr., Inc.

Tubbs, Janet. Disabilities, Set. 2000. (Spud Packs Ser.). 16p. (J). pap. 19.95 (978-1-881185-14-7(1)) Arcadia Pr.

Turkovitz, Karen. What's So Special about Mitchell? Ryan, Linda et al, eds. Marshall, Ian, illus. l.t. ed. 2002. 26p. (J). (gr. k-4). pap. 6.95 (978-0-9679115-5-7(9)) Fivedegressbelowzero Pr.

Westcott, Patsy. Living with Blindness. 1999. (Living with... Ser.). (Illus.). 32p. (J). (gr. 1-5). lib. bdg. 25.69 (978-0-8172-5741-5(1)) Raintree.

White, Peter. Being Blind. 1999. (Think about Ser.). (Illus.). 32p. (J). (gr. 2-5). lib. bdg. 16.95 (978-1-887068-84-0(8)) Smart Apple Media.

PEOPLE WITH DISABILITIES—BIOGRAPHY

Abraham, Philip. Christopher Reeve. 2002. (gr. k-3). lib. bdg. 12.95 (978-0-613-58826-3(6)) Tandem Library Bks.

Adams, Colleen. The Courage of Helen Keller. 2003. (Reading Room Collection). (Illus.). 24p. (J). lib. bdg. 18.75 (978-0-8239-3710-3(0)) Rosen Publishing Group, Inc., The.

All about Me: Growing up with Turner Syndrome & Nonverbal Learning Disabilities. 2004. (J). lib. bdg. 14.95 (978-0-9759850-0-7(0)); per. (978-0-9759850-1-4(9)) Maple Leaf Ctr.

Currie-McGhee, Leanne K. Emmanuel Osofu Yeboah: Champion for Ghana's Disabled. 2006. (Young Heroes Ser.). (Illus.). 64p. (J). (gr. 4-8). lib. bdg. 27.45 (978-0-7377-3614-4(3) , Kidhaven) Thomson Gale.

Edwards, Karen. Christopher Reeve: A Real-Life Superhero. 2005. (Illus.). 32p. (J). (978-0-669-51411-7(X)) Great Source Education Group, Inc.

Feinstein, Stephen. Read about Helen Keller. 2004. (I Like Biographies! Ser.). (Illus.). 24p. (J). lib. bdg. 21.26 (978-0-7660-2299-7(4)) Enslow Pubs., Inc.

Howard, Megan. Christopher Reeve. 1999. (Biography Ser.). (Illus.). 112p. (gr. 6-12). lib. bdg. 27.93 (978-0-8225-4945-1(X)) Lerner Publishing Group.

Kosek, Jane Kelly. Learning about Courage from the Life of Christopher Reeve. 1999. (Character Building Book Ser.). (Illus.). 24p. (J). (gr. 3). lib. bdg. 18.75 (978-0-8239-5346-2(7) , PowerKids Pr.) Rosen Publishing Group, Inc., The.

Lakin, Patricia. Helen Keller & the Big Storm. Magnuson, Diana, illus. 2002. (Ready-to-Read Ser.: Level 2). 32p. (J). pap. 3.99 (978-0-689-84104-0(3) , Aladdin) Simon & Schuster Children's Publishing.

Lewis, Gregg & Lewis, Deborah S. Joni Eareckson Tada. 2002. (Today's Heroes Ser.). (Illus.). 112p. (J). pap. 4.99 (978-0-310-70300-6(X)) Zonderkidz.

Lobb, Nancy. 16 Extraordinary Americans with Disabilities. 2001. (Illus.). 150p. (J). (gr. 6-12). 21.99 (978-0-8251-4249-9(0) , 0-42490) Walch Publishing.

Marsh, Carole. Helen Keller. 2002. (One Thousand Readers Ser.). (Illus.). 12p. (J). (gr. k-4). 2.95 (978-0-635-01478-8(5) , 14785) Gallopade International.

Moore, Sherry. Jason's #16 Dream. 2005. 48p. pap. 12.95 (978-1-4137-6878-7(4)) PublishAmerica, Inc.

Packard, Mary. Beating the Odds: A Chapter Book. (True Tales Ser.). (J). 2005. (Illus.). 48p. (gr. 2-4). pap. 4.95 (978-0-516-24682-6(8)); 2004. 22.50 (978-0-516-23731-2(4)) Scholastic Library Publishing. (Children's Pr.).

Roop, Peter & Roop, Connie. Give Me a Sign, Helen Keller! 2004. (Scholastic Chapter Book Biography Ser.). (Illus.). 55p. (J). (978-0-439-55444-2(6)) Scholastic, Inc.

Sandler, Michael. Jean Driscoll: Dream Big, Work Hard! 2007. (Defining Moments Ser.). (Illus.). 32p. (J). lib. bdg. 25.27 (978-1-59716-268-5(X)) Bearport Publishing Co., Inc.

Sullivan, George. Her Life in Pictures. 2007. (Helen Keller Ser.). 80p. (J). (gr. 2-5). 17.99 (*978-0-439-91815-2(4) , Scholastic Nonfiction) Scholastic, Inc.

Woodhouse, Jayne. Helen Keller. 2002. (Lives & Times Ser.). (Illus.). 24p. (J). (gr. k-3). pap. 6.50 (978-1-4034-0030-7(X) , 91474) Heinemann Library.

—Helen Keller. 2002. (gr. k-3). lib. bdg. 12.95 (978-0-613-88095-4(1)) Tandem Library Bks.

Wren, Laura Lee. Christopher Reeve: Hollywood's Man of Courage. 1999. (People to Know Ser.). (Illus.). 112p. (YA). (gr. 6-12). lib. bdg. 26.60 (978-0-7660-1149-6(6)) Enslow Pubs., Inc.

PEOPLE WITH DISABILITIES—EDUCATION

Bryant, John E. Taking Speech Disorders to School. Schader, Karen, ed. Dineen, Tom, illus. 2004. (Special Kids in School Ser.: Sixteenth). (J). per. 11.95 (978-1-891383-24-3(8) , 70016) JayJo Bks., LLC.

Duckworth, Katie. Education. 2004. (Children's Rights Ser.). (J). lib. bdg. 27.10 (978-1-58340-419-5(8)) Smart Apple Media.

Lawlor, Laurie. Helen Keller, Rebellious Spirit: The Life & Times of Helen Keller. 2001. (Illus.). 176p. (J). (gr. 4-6). tchr. ed. 22.95 (978-0-8234-1588-5(0)) Holiday Hse., Inc.

PEOPLE WITH DISABILITIES—FICTION

Alborghetti, Marci. The Miracle of the Myrrh. Blondon, Herve, illus. 2003. (J). 16.95 (978-0-87946-249-9(3) , 708) ACTA Pubns.

—The Miracle of the Myrrh. Blondon, Herve, illus. 2000. 40p. (J). (ps-3). 16.95 (978-1-890817-16-9(3)) Winslow Pr.

Aronson, Sarah. Head Case. 2007. 192p. (YA). (gr. 9 up). 16.95 (*978-1-59643-214-7(4)) Roaring Brook Pr.

Arterburn, Stephen & Hunt, Angela Elwell. Paige. 2004. (Young Believer on Tour Ser.). (J). pap. 3.99 (978-0-8423-8338-7(7)) Tyndale Hse. Pubs.

Asare, Meshack. Sosu's Call. Asare, Meshack, illus. 2002. (Illus.). 40p. (J). (gr. k-4). 15.95 (978-1-929132-21-8(2)) Kane/Miller Bk. Pubs., Inc.

Atkins, Ben. The Breakaway Kid. 2005. 30p. 14.99 (978-1-4116-2792-5(X)) Lulu.com.

—The Breakaway Kid. Woods, Vanessa, illus. 2nd rev. ed. 2005. (ENG.). 32p. (J). per. 8.00 (978-0-9768653-0-8(0)) Summer Day Publishing, LLC.

Auch, M. J. One-Handed Catch. 2006. 256p. (J). 16.95 (978-0-8050-7900-5(9) , Holt, Henry & Co. Bks. For Young Readers) Holt, Henry & Co.

Aunt Katie's Visit: A Child's First Book on Disabilities. 2003. (J). 16.99 (978-0-9744908-0-9(6)) Access-4-All, Inc.

Avi. Prairie School. Farnsworth, Bill, illus. 2003. (I Can Read Bks.). 48p. (J). (gr. 3 up). pap. 3.99 (978-0-06-051318-4(7)) HarperCollins Pubs.

—Prairie School. 2001. (gr. 3-6). lib. bdg. 11.80 (978-0-613-66991-7(6)) Tandem Library Bks.

Baggette, Susan K. Jonathan & Papa. Moriarty, William J., photos by. 1999. (Jonathan Adventures Ser.). (Illus.). 24p. (J). (ps-3). bds. 7.95 (978-0-9660172-7-4(7)) Brookfield Reader, Inc., The.

—Jonathan Goes to the Grocery Store. Moriarty, William J., photos by. 1998. (Jonathan Adventures Ser.). (Illus.). 16p. (J). (ps-k). bds. 5.95 (978-0-9660172-2-9(6)) Brookfield Reader, Inc., The.

Baker, Julie. Up Molasses Mountain. 2002. 224p. (YA). (gr. 7). lib. bdg. 17.99 (978-0-385-90048-5(1) , Lamb, Wendy) Random Hse. Children's Bks.

Baldwin, Richard L. Unity & the Children. 1999. xiv, 160p. (J). (978-0-9660685-3-5(X)) Buttonwood Pr.

Bang, Molly Garrett. Tiger's Fall. Bang, Molly Garrett, illus. rev. ed. 2001. (Illus.). 112p. (J). (gr. 4-7). 15.95 (978-0-8050-6689-0(6) , Holt, Henry & Co. Bks. For Young Readers) Holt, Henry & Co.

Battisti-Cole, Teresa. Silent One: The Adventure of a Hearing Impaired Heroine. Scharschu, Dotty K., illus. 1998. 38p. (gr. 1 up). reprint ed. (J). pap. 12.00 (978-0-9667227-1-0(X)); (YA). pap. 12.00 (978-0-9667227-0-3(1)) Lonely Blue Coyote, Inc.

Bauer, Marion Dane. The Double-Digit Club. 2004. 126p. (J). (gr. 4-6). tchr. ed. 15.95 (978-0-8234-1805-3(7)) Holiday Hse., Inc.

Beall-Sullivan, Christina. Hi, My Name Is Jack. 2000. (Illus.). 42p. (J). 9.95 (978-0-9759718-0-2(8)) Bopar Bks.

Bertrand, Diane Gonzales. My Pal, Victor/Mi amigo, Víctor. Raven Tree Press Staff, ed. de la Vega, Eida, tr. Sweetland, Robert, illus. 2004. Tr. of Mi amigo, Víctor. (SPA & ENG.). 32p. (J). 16.95 (978-0-9720192-9-3(4) , 626999) Raven Tree Pr.

Best, Cari. Goose's Story. Meade, Holly, illus. 2002. 32p. (J). 16.00 (978-0-374-32750-7(5) , Farrar, Straus & Giroux (BYR)) Farrar, Straus & Giroux.

Bevins, Rose. Coming to Terms. 2004. (Cover-To-Cover Books). (Illus.). (J). 64p. pap. (978-0-7891-6018-8(8)); 56p. (gr. 1-4). lib. bdg. 16.95 (978-0-7569-1371-7(3)) Perfection Learning Corp.

Bingham, Kelly. Shark Girl. 2007. (Illus.). 288p. (YA). (gr. 7 up). 16.99 (*978-0-7636-3207-6(4)) Candlewick Pr.

Bingham, Kelly L. Shark Girl. 2007. 276p. (YA). (*978-1-4287-4705-0(2)) Candlewick Pr.

Blatchford, Claire H. Going with the Flow. 1998. (Illus.). 40p. (J). (gr. 2-4). pap. 7.95 (978-1-57505-284-7(9) , Carolrhoda Bks.) Lerner Publishing Group.

Bloor, Edward. Tangerine. 2006. (Illus.). 324p. (YA). pap. 6.95 (978-0-15-205780-0(3) , Harcourt Paperbacks) Harcourt Children's Bks.

—Tangerine. 1998. (Apple Signature Edition Ser.). 304p. (YA). (gr. 6 up). pap. 4.99 (978-0-590-43277-1(X) , Scholastic Paperbacks) Scholastic, Inc.

Brouwer, Sigmund. Mission 10: Last Stand. 2002. (Mars Diaries Ser.: Mission 10). 144p. (J). mass mkt. 4.99 (978-0-8423-5634-3(7)) Tyndale Hse. Pubs.

—Mission 9: Manchurian Sector. 2002. (Mars Diaries Ser.: Mission 9). 160p. (J). mass mkt. 4.99 (978-0-8423-5633-6(9)) Tyndale Hse. Pubs.

Brudos, Susan E. & Rubino, Alisa A., illus. Wayne's Trail. 2004. (J). pap. (978-0-932991-62-1(9)) Place In The Woods, The.

Brugman, Alyssa. Finding Grace. 2006. 240p. (YA). (gr. 7). mass mkt. 6.50 (978-0-440-23833-1(1) , Laurel Leaf) Random Hse. Children's Bks.

Bryant, Louella. Two Tracks in the Snow. Fargo, Todd, illus. l.t. ed. 2004. (Turtle Bks.). 32p. (J). lib. bdg. 15.95 (978-0-944727-46-1(8)); per. 9.95 (978-0-944727-45-4(X)) Jason & Nordic Pubs. (Turtle Bks.).

Burnett, Frances Hodgson. The Secret Garden. 2008. (Puffin Classics Ser.). 368p. (J). (gr. 3). pap. 4.99 (*978-0-14-132106-6(7) , Puffin) Penguin Group (USA) Inc.

—The Secret Garden. 2002. (Illustrated Children's Library Ser.). (Illus.). 288p. (J). 12.99 (978-0-517-22115-0(2) , Gramercy) Random Hse. Value Publishing.

—The Secret Garden. Corvino, Lucy, illus. 2005. (Classic Starts Ser.). 160p. 4.95 (978-1-4027-1319-4(3)) Sterling Publishing Co., Inc.

—The Secret Garden. Engelbreit, Mary, illus. 2007. (Mary Engelbreit's Classic Library). 368p. (J). (gr. 3-7). 9.99 (*978-0-06-008136-2(8) , Harper Festival) HarperCollins Pubs.

—The Secret Garden: A Young Reader's Edition of the Classic Story. 2005. 332p. 29.95 (978-1-4218-0619-8(3) , 1st World Library - Literary Society) 1st World Publishing, Inc.

—The Secret Garden: A Young Reader's Edition of the Classic Story. (J). 22.95 (978-0-8488-0692-7(1)) Amereon LTD.

—The Secret Garden: A Young Reader's Edition of the Classic Story. ed. 2004. (Illus.). (J). (gr. 1-4). spiral bd. (978-0-616-14566-1(7)); spiral bd. (978-0-616-14565-4(9)) Canadian National Institute for the Blind/Institut National Canadien pour les Aveugles.

—The Secret Garden: A Young Reader's Edition of the Classic Story. Moore, Inga, illus. 2008. 272p. (J). (gr. 1). 21.99 (*978-0-7636-3161-1(2)) Candlewick Pr.

—The Secret Garden: A Young Reader's Edition of the Classic Story. 2005. 132p. per. 5.95 (978-1-4209-2229-5(7)) Digireads.com.

—The Secret Garden: A Young Reader's Edition of the Classic Story. 1999. (Illus.). 256p. (J). (gr. 4-7). pap. 3.00 (978-0-486-40784-5(5)) Dover Pubns., Inc.

—The Secret Garden: A Young Reader's Edition of the Classic Story. Tudor, Tasha, illus. 1998. 368p. (gr. 4 up). (YA). 17.99 (978-0-397-32165-0(1)); (J). reprint ed. pap. 6.99 (978-0-06-440188-3(X) , Harper Trophy) HarperCollins Pubs.

—The Secret Garden: A Young Reader's Edition of the Classic Story. Cockcroft, Jason, illus. 2002. (Kingfisher Classics Ser.). 384p. (J). (gr. k-3). tchr. ed. 15.95 (978-0-7534-5479-4(3) , Kingfisher) Houghton Mifflin Co. Trade & Reference Div.

—The Secret Garden: A Young Reader's Edition of the Classic Story. 2004. reprint ed. pap. 1.99 (978-1-4192-8193-8(3)); pap. 28.95 (978-1-4179-2544-5(2)) Kessinger Publishing, LLC.

—The Secret Garden: A Young Reader's Edition of the Classic Story. (English As a Second Language Bk.). (Illus.). 92p. pap. 4.46 net. (978-0-582-53417-9(8)) Longman Publishing Group.

—The Secret Garden: A Young Reader's Edition of the Classic Story. 1998. 248p. (J). reprint ed. lib. bdg. 25.00 (978-1-58287-069-4(1)) North Bks.

—The Secret Garden: A Young Reader's Edition of the Classic Story. 2002. (Oxford World's Classics Ser.). (Illus.). 368p. 8.95 (978-0-19-283596-3(3)) Oxford Univ. Pr., Inc.

—The Secret Garden: A Young Reader's Edition of the Classic Story. 288p. 2003. (gr. 12). mass mkt. 3.95 (978-0-451-52883-4(2) , Signet Classics); 2002. pap. 8.00 (978-0-14-243705-6(0) , Penguin Classics) Penguin Group (USA) Inc.

—The Secret Garden: A Young Reader's Edition of the Classic Story. 2003. (Modern Library Classics Ser.). 288p. pap. 7.95 (978-0-8129-6998-6(7) , Modern Library) Random House Publishing Group.

—The Secret Garden: A Young Reader's Edition of the Classic Story. Sauber, Robert G., illus. 2001. 56p. (J). (ps up). 9.98 (978-0-7624-0572-5(4) , Courage Bks.) Running Pr. Bk. Pubs.

—The Secret Garden: A Young Reader's Edition of the Classic Story. 2006. (Scholastic Classics Ser.). vi, 222p. (J). (gr. 9-12). 25.00 (978-0-531-16960-5(X) , Watts, Franklin) Scholastic Library Publishing.

—The Secret Garden: A Young Reader's Edition of the Classic Story. 1999. (Illus.). 320p. (J). (gr. 4-7). pap. 4.99 (978-0-439-09939-4(0)) Scholastic, Inc.

—The Secret Garden: A Young Reader's Edition of the Classic Story. Rust, Graham, illus. 1999. (J). pap. 22.95 (978-0-590-24077-2(3)) Scholastic, Inc.

—The Secret Garden: A Young Reader's Edition of the Classic Story. 2005. (ENG.). 24.95 (***978-1-55742-519-5(1)***); pap. 15.95 (***978-1-55742-524-9(8)***) Wildside Pr.

—The Secret Garden: A Young Reader's Edition of the Classic Story. 1998. (Children's Classics). (ENG.). 224p. (YA). (gr. 8-12). pap. (978-1-85326-104-6(1), 1041WW) Wordsworth Editions, Ltd.

—The Secret Garden: With a Discussion of Compassion. Lauter, Richard, illus. 2003. (Values in Action Illustrated Classics Ser.). 191p. (J). (978-1-59203-037-8(8)) Learning Challenge, Inc.

—The Secret Garden Includes Charm. Tudor, Tasha, illus. adapted ed. 1998. (Charming Classics). 368p. (YA). (gr. 5 up). pap. 6.99 (978-0-694-01110-0(X)) HarperCollins Pubs.

Burnett, Frances Hodgson & Cockcroft, Jason. The Secret Garden: A Young Reader's Edition of the Classic Story. 2002. (Kingfisher Classics Ser.). (Illus.). 384p. (J). (978-0-7534-0602-1(0), Kingfisher) Houghton Mifflin Co. Trade & Reference Div.

Burnett, Frances Hodgson & Rust, Graham. The Secret Garden: A Young Reader's Edition of the Classic Story. 2000. (Illus.). 224p. (YA). (gr. 5 up). reprint ed. 18.95 (978-0-87923-649-6(3)) Godine, David R. Pub.

Calhoun, Dia. White Midnight. 2003. 304p. (YA). 18.00 (978-0-374-38389-3(8), Farrar, Straus & Giroux (BYR)) Farrar, Straus & Giroux.

Card, C. Fran. Ceana Has CP. 2007. 16.95 (***978-0-615-13125-2(5)***) Partners Bk. Distributing, Inc.

Carter, Anne Laurel. In the Clear. 2001. 176p. (J). (gr. 3-7). pap. 6.95 (978-1-55143-192-5(0)) Orca Bk. Pubs. USA.

Chaconas, Dori. Dancing with Katya. Bergum, Constance Rummel, illus. 2006. 32p. (J). 16.95 (978-1-56145-376-4(5), Peachtree Junior) Peachtree Pubs., Ltd.

Chase, Diana. Surf's Up. 1999. 200p. (J). pap. 12.95 (978-1-86368-250-3(3)) Fremantle Pr. AUS. *Dist:* International Specialized Bk. Services.

Cheripko, Jan. Rat. (Illus.). 208p. (YA). 2004. pap. 9.95 (978-1-59078-349-8(2)); 2003. (gr. 6-9). 16.95 (978-1-59078-034-3(5)) Boyds Mills Pr.

Christopher, Matt. Wheel Wizards. 2000. 132p. (J). (gr. 3-7). 15.95 (978-0-316-13611-2(5)) Little Brown & Co.

Clark, Dan. Puppies for Sale. 1999. (Illus.). 28p. (J). (gr. k-5). 6.99 (978-1-57759-262-4(X)) Dalmatian Pr.

Clements, Andrew. Things Not Seen. 2006. 272p. (YA). pap. 10.00 (978-0-14-240731-8(3), Puffin); 2002. 176p. (J). (gr. 6-9). 15.99 (978-0-399-23626-6(0), Philomel); 2004. 251p. (J). reprint ed. pap. 6.99 (978-0-14-240076-0(9), Puffin) Penguin Group (USA) Inc.

—Things Not Seen. 2004. 256p. (J). (gr. 4-7). pap. 38.00 incl. audio (978-1-4000-9014-3(8), Listening Library) Random Hse. Audio Publishing Group.

Coolidge, Susan. What Katy Did. 1999. (Illus.). 160p. 19.95 (978-1-85149-705-8(6)) Antique Collectors' Club.

—What Katy Did. 2006. 62.99 (***978-1-4280-3108-1(1)***) IndyPublish.com.

Cormier, Robert. Heroes. 2006. (York Notes Ser.). 112p. pap. (978-1-4058-3559-6(1)) Pearson Education, Ltd.

—Heroes. 2000. 144p. (YA). (gr. 7-12). pap. 5.99 (978-0-440-22769-4(0), Laurel Leaf) Random Hse. Children's Bks.

—Heroes. 2000. 135p. (YA). (gr. 7-12). lib. bdg. 13.55 (978-0-613-23622-5(X)); per. 12.15 (978-0-606-17836-5(8)) Tandem Library Bks.

—Heroes. l.t. ed. 2000. 147p. (YA). (gr. 8-12). 21.95 (978-0-7862-2909-3(8)) Thorndike Pr.

Craik, Dinah Maria Mulock. Little Lame Prince EasyRead Comfort Edit. 2006. pap. (***978-1-4250-2001-9(1)***) Assistedreadingbooks.com Inc.

—Little Lame Prince EasyRead Edition. 2006. pap. (***978-1-4250-1718-7(5)***) Assistedreadingbooks.com Inc.

—Little Lame Prince EasyRead Large Editio. 2006. pap. (***978-1-4250-2260-0(X)***) Assistedreadingbooks.com Inc.

—Little Lame Prince the. 2006. pap. (***978-1-4250-2683-7(4)***) Assistedreadingbooks.com Inc.

Creech, Sharon. Granny Torrelli Makes Soup. Raschka, Chris, illus. 160p. (J). 2003. (gr. 3-6). 15.99 (978-0-06-029290-4(3), HarperChildren's Audio); 2003. (gr. 4-7). lib. bdg. 16.89 (978-0-06-029291-1(1), Cotler, Joanna Books); 2005. reprint ed. pap. 5.99 (978-0-06-440960-5(0), Harper Trophy) HarperCollins Pubs.

Crockett-Blassingame, Linda, illus. See the Ocean. 2006. 32p. (J). 14.95 (978-0-9778143-0-5(0)) Inclusive Books LLC.

Cross, Gillian. Phoning a Dead Man. 2002. 256p. (J). (gr. 7 up). 16.95 (978-0-8234-1685-1(2)) Holiday Hse., Inc.

Crutcher, Chris. Crazy Horse Electric Game. 2003. (gr. 7-12). lib. bdg. 15.30 (978-0-613-66954-2(1)) Tandem Library Bks.

De Anda, Diane. Dancing Miranda. Castilla, Julia Mercedes, tr. from ENG. Alvarez, Lamberto, illus. 2001. Tr. of Baila, Miranda, Baila. (SPA & ENG.). 32p. (J). (ps-3). 14.95 (978-1-55885-323-2(5), Piñata Books) Arte Publico Pr.

DeBear, Kirsten. Be Quiet Marina! Dwight, Laura, photos by. 2001. (Illus.). 40p. (J). (ps-3). 16.95 (978-1-887734-79-0(1)) Star Bright Bks., Inc.

DeGross, Monalisa. Donavans Double Trouble. Bates, Amy, illus. 2008. 192p. (J). 15.99 (***978-0-06-077293-2(X)***) HarperCollins Pubs.

—Donavan's Double Trouble. Bates, Amy June, illus. 2008. 192p. (J). lib. bdg. 16.89 (***978-0-06-077294-9(8)***, Amistad) HarperCollins Pubs.

Denenberg, Barry. Mirror Mirror on the Wall: The Diary of Bess Brennan. 2002. (Dear America Ser.). (Illus.). 144p. (J). (gr. 4-9). pap. 10.95 (978-0-439-19446-4(6)) Scholastic, Inc.

Diaz, Gloria Cecilia. Oyeme con los Ojos. Lucini, Chata, illus. 2001. (Sopa de Libros, Serie Verde: No. 54). (SPA.). 88p. 8.95 (978-84-207-4403-2(4)) Grupo Anaya, S.A. ESP. *Dist:* AIMS International Bks., Inc., Lectorum Pubns., Inc.

Dion. Fishing with Balloons. 2004. (Illus.). 68p. (J). (978-1-881929-34-5(5)) Oxton Hse., Pubs.

Dorris, Michael. Sees Behind Trees. rev. ed. 1999. 128p. (gr. 4-17). pap. 4.99 (978-0-7868-1357-5(1)) Disney Pr.

—Sees Behind Trees. 104p. (J). (gr. 4-6). pap. 4.95 (978-0-8072-1516-6(3)); 1998. pap. 28.00 incl. audio (978-0-8072-7957-1(9), YA949SP) Random Hse. Audio Publishing Group. (Listening Library).

Dowell, Frances O'Roark. Dovey Coe. 192p. (J). 2001. (Illus.). pap. 5.99 (978-0-689-84667-0(3), Aladdin); 2000. (gr. 4-7). 16.99 (978-0-689-83174-4(9), Atheneum) Simon & Schuster Children's Publishing.

—Dovey Coe. 2001. 11.64 (978-0-606-22127-6(1)) Tandem Library Bks.

—Dovey Coe. l.t. ed. 2001. 171p. (J). 22.95 (978-0-7862-3590-2(X)) Thorndike Pr.

Duchesne, Christiane. Peter's Secret. Pratt, Mylene, illus. 2005. (Read-It! Readers Ser.). 32p. (J). (ps). lib. bdg. 18.60 (978-1-4048-1351-9(9)) Picture Window Bks.

Duey, Kathleen. Swamp: Bayou Teche, Louisiana 1850. 1999. (gr. 3-6). lib. bdg. 12.40 (978-0-613-15997-5(7)) Tandem Library Bks.

Duey, Kathleen & Bale, Karen. Swamp, Bayou Teche, Louisiana, 1851. 1999. (Survival! Ser.: No. 11). (978-0-606-16302-6(6)) Tandem Library Bks.

Duey, Kathleen & Bale, Karen A. Swamp: Bayou Teche, Louisiana 1851. Dodge, Bill, illus. 1999. (Survival! Ser.: No. 11). 160p. (J). (gr. 4-7). pap. 4.50 (978-0-689-82929-1(9), 076714004504, Aladdin) Simon & Schuster Children's Publishing.

Durbin, William. The Winter War. 2008. (J). (***978-0-385-90889-4(X)***); 240p. (gr. 7). 15.99 (***978-0-385-74652-6(0)***) Dell Publishing. (Delacorte Pr.).

Dwight, Laura. Nosotros Si Podemos Hacerlo! Fiol, María A., tr. Dwight, Laura, photos by. 1998. (SPA., Illus.). 40p. (J). (gr. k-1). 14.95 (978-1-887734-37-0(6), SK7670) Star Bright Bks., Inc.

—We Can Do It! Dwight, Laura, photos by. (Illus.). 40p. (J). 2005. pap. 5.95 (978-1-59572-033-7(2)); 1998. 14.95 (978-1-887734-34-9(1)) Star Bright Bks., Inc.

Dyer, K. C. Secret of Light. 2004. 200p. pap. 8.99 (978-1-55002-477-7(9)) Dundurn Group, The CAN. *Dist:* Univ. of Toronto Pr.

Dyer, Thomas A. A Way of His Own. 2001. 160p. (J). (gr. 5-9). pap. 6.95 (978-0-618-13132-7(9)) Houghton Mifflin Co. Trade & Reference Div.

Ellis, Deborah. Jackal in the Garden: An Encounter with Bihzad. 2006. (Art Encounters Ser.). (Illus.). 176p. (YA). (gr. 7 up). 16.95 (978-0-8230-0415-7(5)) Watson-Guptill Pubns., Inc.

Epchook, Dorothy M. Ayaruqa. Epchook, Dorothy M. & Shantz, Joy, illus. 1998. Tr. of My Walking Cane. (ESK.). 8p. (J). (gr. k-3). pap. 6.00 (978-1-58084-038-5(8)) Lower Kuskokwim Schl. District.

Farrell, Mame. Marrying Malcolm Murgatroyd. 1998. 128p. (J). (gr. 4-7). pap. 6.95 (978-0-374-44744-1(6), Sunburst) Farrar, Straus & Giroux.

—Marrying Malcolm Murgatroyd. 1998. 122p. (J). (ps-7). per. 12.95 (978-0-613-10517-0(6)) Tandem Library Bks.

Ferris, Jean. Of Sound Mind. 224p. (YA). 2001. (gr. 8 up). 16.00 (978-0-374-35580-7(0), Farrar, Straus & Giroux (BYR)); 2004. reprint ed. pap. 6.95 (978-0-374-45584-2(8), Sunburst) Farrar, Straus & Giroux.

—Of Sound Mind. l.t. ed. 2004. 225p. 21.95 (978-0-7862-7036-1(5), Large Print Pr.) Thorndike Pr.

Finley, Martha. Elsie's Great Hope, Vol. 8. 2006. (Life of Faith': Elsie Dinsmore Ser.). 224p. (J). pap. 7.99 (978-1-928749-87-5(9)) Zonderkidz.

Fleischman, Paul. Mind's Eye. 2001. (J). (978-0-606-20800-0(3)) Tandem Library Bks.

Fletcher, Susan. Shadow Spinner. unabr. ed. 1999. (J). (gr. 5). pap., stu. ed. 59.24 incl. audio (978-0-7887-3007-8(X), 40889) Recorded Bks., LLC.

—Shadow Spinner. Kramer, Dave, illus. 1999. (Jean Karl Bks.). 224p. (J). (gr. 5-9). pap. 5.99 (978-0-689-83051-8(3), Aladdin) Simon & Schuster Children's Publishing.

—Shadow Spinner. 1999. (978-0-606-17195-3(9)); (gr. 5-8). lib. bdg. 13.00 (978-0-613-23034-6(5)) Tandem Library Bks.

Foland, Constance M. A Song for Jeffrey. 1999. (978-0-606-18357-4(4)) Tandem Library Bks.

Foreman, Michael. Seal Surfer. 2007. (Illus.). 36p. (J). pap. 9.95 (978-1-84270-578-0(4)) Andersen GBR. *Dist:* Independent Pubs. Group.

Fournier, Kevin Mark. Sandbag Shuffle. 2007. 240p. (YA). (gr. 9 up). pap. 10.95 (***978-1-897235-22-5(4)***) Thistledown Pr., Ltd. CAN. *Dist:* Fitzhenry & Whiteside, Ltd.

Friedman, Michael Jan. Hunchdog of Notre Dame. l.t. ed. 1999. (Adventures of Wishbone Ser.: No. 5). (Illus.). 139p. (J). (gr. 4 up). lib. bdg. 22.60 (978-0-8368-2301-1(X)) Stevens, Gareth Inc.

Frizzell, Colin. Chill. 2006. 112p. (YA). lib. bdg. 14.95 (978-1-55143-670-8(1)); (gr. 7 up). pap. 8.95 (978-1-55143-507-7(1)) Orca Bk. Pubs. USA.

Getzinger, Donna. Special. 2004. 108p. (J). pap. 7.95 (978-0-87714-530-1(X)) Denlingers Pubs., Ltd.

Giff, Patricia Reilly. All the Way Home. 2003. (Illus.). 176p. (J). (gr. 3-7). pap. 5.99 (978-0-440-41182-6(3), Yearling) Random Hse. Children's Bks.

Gingerich, Neeltje & Peterson, Joyce. The Secret Garden. 1999. 38p. (gr. 1-12). pap. 10.00 (978-0-88734-045-1(8)) Players Pr., Inc.

Gleitzman, Morris. Sticky Beak. l.t. ed. 2005. 200p. (J). pap. (978-0-7540-6180-9(9), CLP 374) BBC Audio.

Greene, Joanne. Lippy the Lion. 2006. per. (***978-1-894936-67-5(1)***) Saga Bks.

Gutman, Dan. The Million Dollar Putt. 2006. 176p. (gr. 3-7). 15.99 (978-0-7868-3641-3(5)) Hyperion Bks. for Children.

Gutman, Dan. Million Dollar Putt. 2007. 176p. (gr. 3-7). pap. 5.99 (***978-0-7868-3642-0(3)***) Hyperion Pr.

Guzman, Lila. Green Slime & Jam. Guzman, Lila, illus. 2001. (Illus.). v, 168p. (J). pap. 11.95 (978-1-57168-555-1(3), Eakin Pr.) Eakin Pr.

—Green Slime & Jam. Guzman, Jenny, illus. 2001. 174p. 16.95 (978-1-57168-483-7(2)) Eakin Pr.

Hagman, Harvey Dixon. Majesty from Assateague. Aiken, David, illus. 2003. 76p. (J). pap. 8.95 (978-0-87033-552-5(9), Tidewater Pubs.) Cornell Maritime Pr., Inc.

Hale, Marian. The Truth about Sparrows. rev. ed. 2004. (Illus.). 272p. (J). 16.95 (978-0-8050-7584-7(4), Holt, Henry & Co. Bks. For Young Readers) Holt, Henry & Co.

—The Truth about Sparrows. 2007. 288p. (J). pap. 6.99 (***978-0-312-37133-3(0)***) Square Fish.

Halliday, John. Shooting Monarchs. 2003. (Illus.). 144p. (YA). 15.95 (978-0-689-84338-9(0), McElderry, Margaret K.) Simon & Schuster Children's Publishing.

—Shooting Monarchs. l.t. ed. 2005. 157p. 20.95 (978-0-7862-7462-8(X)) Thorndike Pr.

Hambrick, Sharon. Tommy's Race. Manning, Maurie, illus. 2004. (Fig Street Kids Ser.). 95p. (J). (gr. 1-2). 7.49 (978-1-59166-286-0(9)) Jones, Bob Univ. Pr.

Hamilton, Bethany. Surfer Girl Rise above 90 Day Devotional. 2007. (Soul Surfer#482; Ser.). 192p. (J). pap. 9.99 (978-0-310-71226-8(2)) Zonderkidz.

Hamilton, Bethany & Bundschuh, Rick. Burned. 2007. (Soul Surfer#482; Ser.). (Illus.). 144p. (J). pap. 6.99 (978-0-310-71223-7(8)) Zonderkidz.

—Clash. 2007. (Soul Surfer#482; Ser.). (Illus.). 144p. (J). pap. 6.99 (978-0-310-71222-0(X)) Zonderkidz.

Hamilton, Virginia. Bluish. Dillon, Leo & Dillon, Diane, illus. 1999. 128p. (J). (gr. 4-9). pap. 16.95 (978-0-590-28879-8(2), Blue Sky Pr., The) Scholastic, Inc.

—Bluish. 2002. (gr. 5-8). lib. bdg. 13.00 (978-0-613-53797-1(1)) Tandem Library Bks.

Harris, Loretta. The Inside Struggle. 2006. (YA). (***978-0-9786681-3-6(8)***) Children's Heart Publishing Co.

Henry, Heather French. Las Zapatas Magicas de Claire. 2007. (Claire's Everyday Adventures Ser Ser.). (SPA., Illus.). 32p. (gr. k-4). pap. 9.95 (978-1-932824-03-2(0)) Cubbie Blue Publishing.

Hill, Elizabeth Starr. Bird Boy. 2003. (gr. 3-6). lib. bdg. 14.10 (978-0-613-71735-9(X)) Tandem Library Bks.

Hodge, Lois L. R. Season of Change. 2002. (gr. 7-12). lib. bdg. 10.60 (978-0-613-88532-4(5)) Tandem Library Bks.

Hoffman, Eric. No Fair to Tigers, 1. 2004. (Anti-Bias Books for Kids). (SPA., Illus.). 32p. (J). (ps-3). pap. 11.95 (978-1-884834-62-2(0)) Redleaf Pr.

Hoobler, Dorothy & Hoobler, Thomas. The 1960's: Rebels. Hoffman, Robin, illus. 2001. (Century Kids Ser.). 160p. (J). (gr. 5-8). lib. bdg. 22.90 (978-0-7613-1606-0(X), Twenty-First Century Bks.) Lerner Publishing Group.

Hooks, Gwendolyn. Nice Wheels. Andriani, Renee, illus. 2005. (My First Reader Ser.). (J). (gr. k-1). 31p. pap. 3.95 (978-0-516-25277-3(1)); 32p. 18.50 (978-0-516-25179-0(1)) Scholastic Library Publishing. (Children's Pr.).

Hubler, Marsha. The Winning Summer. 2005. (Keystone Stables Ser.: Bk. 5). (Illus.). 144p. (J). pap. 4.99 (978-0-310-70798-1(6)) Zonderkidz.

Hugo, Victor. The Hunchback of Notre- Dame. Famig, Jon L., illus. 1998. (Illustrated Classic Book Ser.). 61p. (J). (gr. 3 up). pap. 4.95 (978-1-56767-247-3(7)) Educational Insights, Inc.

—The Hunchback of Notre- Dame. unabr. ed. 1998. (Wordsworth Classics Ser.). (YA). (gr. 6-12). 5.27 (978-0-89061-068-8(1), R0681WW) Jamestown.

—The Hunchback of Notre- Dame. (Young Collector's Illustrated Classics Ser.). (Illus.). 192p. (J). (gr. 3-7). 9.95 (978-1-56156-458-3(3)) Kidsbooks, Inc.

—Hunchback of Notre Dame. 2002. (Great Illustrated Classics Ser.). (Illus.). 240p. (J). (gr. 3-8). 21.35 (978-1-57765-813-9(2), ABDO & Daughters) ABDO Publishing Co.

Hugo, Victor. The Hunchback of Notre Dame. Corvino, Lucy, illus. 2008. (Classic Starts Ser.). 160p. (J). 5.95 (***978-1-4027-4575-1(3)***) Sterling Publishing Co., Inc.

The Hunchback of Notre Dame. (Read-Along Ser.). (J). 7.99 incl. audio (978-1-55723-992-1(4)) Walt Disney Records.

Hunter, Alixander. The Handicapped Squirrel. l.t. ed. 1998. (Illus.). 32p. 19.95 (978-0-9665582-0-3(0)) Alixander Group.

Johnson, Harriet McBryde. Accidents of Nature. rev. ed. 2006. 240p. (YA). 16.95 (978-0-8050-7634-9(4), Holt, Henry & Co. Bks. For Young Readers) Holt, Henry & Co.

Johnson, Tim. Never So Green. 2002. 240p. (YA). 18.00 (978-0-374-35509-8(6), Farrar, Straus & Giroux (BYR)) Farrar, Straus & Giroux.

Johnston, Julie. Hero of Lesser Causes. pap. 6.95 (978-0-7737-5850-6(X)) Stoddart Kids CAN. *Dist:* Fitzhenry & Whiteside, Ltd.

—Hero of Lesser Causes. 2003. 232p. (J). (gr. 6). pap. 9.95 (978-0-88776-649-7(8)) Tundra Bks., Inc./Livres Toundra, Inc. CAN. *Dist:* Random Hse., Inc.

Jordan, Sherryl. The Raging Quiet. l.t. ed. 2005. 416p. 22.95 (978-0-7862-7313-3(5), Large Print Pr.) Thorndike Pr.

Jung, Reinhardt. Bambert's Book of Missing Stories. 2006. 128p. (J). (gr. 4-7). pap. 5.50 (978-0-440-42045-3(8), Yearling) Random Hse. Children's Bks.

Keats, Ezra Jack. Apt. 3. Keats, Ezra Jack, illus. 1999. (Illus.). 32p. (J). (ps-3). 15.99 (978-0-670-88342-4(5), Viking Juvenile) Penguin Group (USA) Inc.

—Apt. 3. 1999. (J). 13.79 (978-0-606-16772-7(2)) Tandem Library Bks.

Kehret, Peg. My Brother Made Me Do It: A Sister Remembers Growing up with the Rev. Dr. Martin Luther King Jr. 144p. (J). 2001. pap. 4.99 (978-0-671-03419-1(7), Aladdin); 2000. (gr. 3-6). 16.00 (978-0-671-03418-4(9)) Simon & Schuster Children's Publishing.

—My Brother Made Me Do It: A Sister Remembers Growing up with the Rev. Dr. Martin Luther King Jr. 2001. (978-0-606-22136-8(0)); (gr. 3-6). lib. bdg. 13.00 (978-0-613-53443-7(3)) Tandem Library Bks.

Kent, Renee Holmes. Robyn Flies Home, Vol. 4. 2004. (Adventures in Misty Falls Ser.: Vol. 4). (Illus.). 100p. (gr. 4-7). pap. 4.99 (978-1-56309-764-5(8), N007106) New Hope Pubs.

Keyes, Daniel. Flores para Algernon. 2003. (SPA.). 224p. (J). (978-84-483-0262-7(1)) Acento Editorial.

Kimmel, Elizabeth Cody. Mary Leaves Little House. 2008. (Little House Ser.). 192p. (J). lib. bdg. 16.89 (***978-0-06-000906-9(3)***); (gr. 3-7). 15.99 (***978-0-06-000905-2(5)***) HarperCollins Pubs.

Kinsey-Warnock, Natalie. Lumber Camp Library. Bernardin, James, illus. 2003. 96p. (J). pap. 4.99 (978-0-06-444292-3(6)) HarperCollins Pubs.

—Lumber Camp Library. 2002. (gr. 3-6). lib. bdg. 13.00 (978-0-613-68447-7(8)) Tandem Library Bks.

Klein, Adria F. Max Learns Sign Language. Gallagher-Cole, Mernie, illus. 2006. (Read-It! Readers Ser.). 24p. (J). (gr. k-2). lib. bdg. 19.93 (***978-1-4048-3148-3(7)***, 1265795) Picture Window Bks.

—Max's Fun Day. 2007. (Read-It! Readers Ser.). (Illus.). 24p. (J). (***978-1-4048-3549-8(0)***, 1265797) Picture Window Bks.

—Max's Fun Day. Gallagher-Cole, Mernie, illus. 2006. (Read-It! Readers Ser.). 24p. (J). (***978-1-4048-3150-6(9)***, 1265797) Picture Window Bks.

Kluger, Jeffrey. Nacky Patcher & the Curse of the Dry-Land Boats. Elliot, David, illus. 2007. 384p. (YA). (gr. 4 up). 18.99 (978-0-399-24604-3(5), Philomel) Penguin Group (USA) Inc.

Kneeland, Linda. Cookie. Fargo, Todd, illus. rev. l.t. ed. 1999. 32p. (J). pap. 9.95 (978-0-944727-38-6(7)); lib. bdg. 14.95 (978-0-944727-39-3(5)) Jason & Nordic Pubs. (Turtle Bks.).

Knight, Jackie. Sparky: A Very Special Teddy Bear. 1998. (Illus.). 99p. (J). (gr. 2-5). 19.95 (978-1-85776-279-2(7)) Book Guild, Ltd. GBR. *Dist:* Trans-Atlantic Pubns., Inc.

Koertge, Ronald. Stoner & Spaz. 176p. (YA). (gr. 9-12). 2002. 15.99 (978-0-7636-1608-3(7)); 2004. reprint ed. pap. 6.99 (978-0-7636-2150-6(1)) Candlewick Pr.

Konigsburg, E. L. Retrato del Sabado. 2002. (SPA., Illus.). 208p. (J). (gr. 4-6). 9.95 (978-84-241-7936-6(6), EV31158) Everest de Ediciones y Distribucion, S.L. ESP. *Dist:* Lectorum Pubns., Inc.

—Retrato del Sabado. 2002. (SPA.). (gr. 3-6). lib. bdg. 18.75 (978-0-613-64589-8(8)) Tandem Library Bks.

—Throwing Shadows. 1998. 160p. (J). (gr. 5-9). pap. 5.99 (978-0-689-82120-2(4), Aladdin) Simon & Schuster Children's Publishing.

—The View from Saturday. Konigsburg, E. L., illus. 2002. (Illus.). (J). 25.11 (978-0-7587-0221-0(3)) Book Wholesalers, Inc.

—The View from Saturday. 2000. (J). 11.95 (978-1-56137-936-1(0)) Novel Units, Inc.

—The View from Saturday. 280p. (YA). (gr. 5 up). pap. 4.95 (978-0-8072-1511-1(2), Listening Library) Random Hse. Audio Publishing Group.

—The View from Saturday. 1998. (Jean Karl Bks.). 176p. (J). (gr. 3-7). reprint ed. pap. 5.99 (978-0-689-81721-2(5), Aladdin) Simon & Schuster Children's Publishing.

—The View from Saturday. 1998. (J). (978-0-606-13063-9(2)) Tandem Library Bks.

L. A. Goal Members, contrib. by. Disabled Fables: Aesop's Fables Retold & Illustrated by Artists with Developmental Disabilities. 2005. (Illus.). 52p. (J). (gr. 1 up). 19.95 (978-1-932065-97-8(0)) Star Bright Bks., Inc.

Laird, Elizabeth & Davidson, Roz. Jungle School. Sim, David, illus. 2006. (Green Bananas Ser.). 48p. (J). (gr. k-2). pap. (978-0-7787-1042-4(4)) Crabtree Publishing Co.

Lasky, Kathryn. The Last Girls of Pompeii. 2007. 160p. (J). (gr. 5 up). 15.99 (978-0-670-06196-9(4), Viking Juvenile) Penguin Group (USA) Inc.

Lears, Laurie. Nathan's Wish: A Story about Cerebral Palsy. Schuett, Stacey, illus. 2005. 32p. (J). (gr. 1-4). 15.95 (978-0-8075-7101-9(6)) Whitman, Albert & Co.

Lester, Julius. Shining. Clapp, John, illus. 2007. 32p. (J). pap. 6.00 (***978-0-15-206077-0(4)***, Voyager Bks./Libros Viajeros) Harcourt Children's Bks.

Levin, Betty. The Unmaking of Duncan Veerick. 2007. 204p. (YA). (gr. 5 up). 16.95 (***978-1-932425-96-3(9)***, Front Street) Boyds Mills Pr.

Lewis, Catherine. Postcards to Father Abraham. Yeomans, Jane, illus. 2000. 304p. (YA). (gr. 7-12). 17.95 (978-0-689-82852-2(7), Atheneum) Simon & Schuster Children's Publishing.

Liao, Jimmy. The Sound of Colors: A Journey of the Imagination. 2006. (Illus.). 80p. (J). (ps-17). 16.99 (978-0-316-93992-8(7)) Little Brown & Co.

Look, Lenore. Ruby Lu, Empress of Everything. Wilsdorf, Anne, illus. 2006. 176p. (J). (gr. 1-5). 15.95 (978-0-689-86460-5(4), Atheneum) Simon & Schuster Children's Publishing.

Lord, Cynthia. Rules. 2006. 208p. (J). (gr. 4-7). pap. 15.99 (978-0-439-44382-1(2), Scholastic Pr.) Scholastic, Inc.

—Rules. rev. l.t. ed. 2007. 200p. (YA). 23.95 (***978-0-7862-9559-3(7)***) Thorndike Pr.

Lorimer, Janet. Ring of Fear, Set 2. 2002. 32p. (YA). 2.95 (978-1-56254-421-8(7) , SP 4217) Saddleback Educational Publishing.

Lowry, Lois. Gathering Blue. 2000. (Illus.). 224p. (YA). (gr. 7 up). 16.00 (978-0-618-05581-4(9) , Mariner Bks.) Houghton Mifflin Co. Trade & Reference Div.

—Gathering Blue. unabr. ed. 2004. (Middle Grade Cassette Librariestm Ser.). 224p. (J). (gr. 5-9). pap. 38.00 incl. audio (978-0-8072-0989-9(9) , S YA 250 SP, Listening Library) Random Hse. Audio Publishing Group.

—Gathering Blue. (YA). (gr. 7). 2006. 240p. pap. 8.95 (978-0-385-73256-7(2) , Delacorte Bks. for Young Readers); 2005. 224p. mass mkt. 6.99 (978-0-553-49478-5(3) , Bantam Bks. for Young Readers); 2002. 224p. mass mkt. 6.50 (978-0-440-22949-0(9) , Laurel Leaf) Random Hse. Children's Bks.

—Gathering Blue. 2002. (gr. 5-8). lib. bdg. 14.75 (978-0-613-57593-5(8)) Tandem Library Bks.

—Gathering Blue. l.t. ed. 2000. 256p. (J). (gr. 8-12). 22.95 (978-0-7862-3048-8(7)) Thorndike Pr.

Macguire, Gregory. Missing Sisters. 1998. (J). (978-0-606-13612-9(6)) Tandem Library Bks.

Madden, Kerry. Gentle's Holler. 2007. 272p. (YA). (gr. 4 up). 6.99 (978-0-14-240751-6(8) , Puffin) Penguin Group (USA) Inc.

Maguire, Arlene. Special People, Special Ways. Bailey, Sheila, illus. 2000. 28p. (gr. k-5). per. 14.95 (978-1-885477-65-1(1)) Future Horizons, Inc.

Martelli, Dawn. Like Me. Wharton, Jennifer Heyd, illus. 2004. (J). (978-1-893516-01-4(6)) Our Child Pr.

Martin, Rafe & Bellm, Dan. Birdwing. (J). 2007. 384p. pap. 6.99 (978-0-439-21168-0(9)); 2005. 368p. pap. 16.99 (978-0-439-21167-3(0)) Scholastic, Inc. (Levine, Arthur A. Bks.).

Matlin, Marlee & Cooney, Doug. Leading Ladies. 2007. 288p. (J). (gr. 3-7). 15.99 (***978-0-689-86987-7(8)*** , Simon & Schuster Children's Publishing) Simon & Schuster Children's Publishing.

Matlin, Marlee & Cooney, Doug. Nobody's Perfect. 2006. (Illus.). 240p. (J). (gr. 3-7). 15.95 (978-0-689-86986-0(X) , Simon & Schuster Children's Publishing) Simon & Schuster Children's Publishing.

McDaniel, Lurlene. To Live Again. 2001. (Dawn Rochelle Ser.: No. 5). (gr. 5-8). lib. bdg. 13.00 (978-0-613-57927-8(5)) Tandem Library Bks.

McElfresh, Lynn E. Can You Feel the Thunder? 1999. (YA). pap., stu. ed. 52.00 incl. audio (978-0-7887-3837-1(2) , 41031) Recorded Bks., LLC.

McGraw-Hill - Jamestown Education Staff. Aliens & UFOs. 1999. (Wordsworth Classics Ser.). (gr. 6-12). pap. 16.64 (978-0-89061-104-3(1) , 9780890611043) Jamestown.

McNeal, Laura & McNeal, Tom. The Decoding of Lana Morris. 2007. 304p. (J). (gr. 7). lib. bdg. 18.99 (978-0-375-93106-2(6)); 15.99 (978-0-375-83106-5(1)) Random Hse. Children's Bks. (Knopf Bks. for Young Readers).

Messer, Celeste M. The Gift. 2004. (Adventures of Andi O'Malley Ser.). (Illus.). 82-92p. (J). (gr. 4-7). 4.95 (978-0-9702171-3-4(7)) AshleyAlan Enterprises.

Meyers, Cindy. Rolling along with Goldilocks & the Three Bears. Morgan, Carol, illus. 1999. 27p. (J). (ps-2). 14.95 (978-1-890627-12-6(7)) Woodbine Hse.

Michelinie, David, et al. Freemind - The Origin. 2003. (Freemind Ser.). (Illus.). 112p. 14.95 (978-0-9744225-0-3(9)) Future Comics.

Mikaelsen, Ben. Petey. 1998. 256p. (gr. 5-17). 15.95 (978-0-7868-0426-9(2)) Disney Pr.

Miller, Sarah Elizabeth. Miss Spitfire: Reaching Helen Keller. 2007. 240p. (J). (gr. 5-9). 16.99 (978-1-4169-2542-2(2)) Simon & Schuster Children's Publishing.

Millman, Isaac. Moses Goes to a Concert. Millman, Isaac, illus. (Moses Goes To Ser.). (Illus.). 40p. (J). 2002. pap. 6.95 (978-0-374-45366-4(7) , Sunburst); 1998. 17.00 (978-0-374-35067-3(1) , Farrar, Straus & Giroux (BYR)) Farrar, Straus & Giroux.

—Moses Goes to a Concert. 2002. (gr. k-3). lib. bdg. 14.10 (978-0-613-53841-1(2)) Tandem Library Bks.

—Moses Goes to School. Millman, Isaac, illus. 2000. (Moses Goes To Ser.). (Illus.). 32p. (J). (gr. k-3). 16.00 (978-0-374-35069-7(8) , Farrar, Straus & Giroux (BYR)) Farrar, Straus & Giroux.

Mitchell, Nancy. Global Warning. Christensen, Edie et al, illus. 1999. (Changing Earth Trilogy Ser.: Bk. 3). 178p. (Orig.). (J). (ps-12). mass mkt. 5.95 (978-1-892713-02-5(0)) Lightstream Pubns.

Moore-Malinos, Jennifer & Roca, Nuria. It's Called Dyslexia. Fabrega, Marta, illus. 2007. (Live & Learn Ser.). 32p. (J). (ps-2). pap. 6.99 (***978-0-7641-3794-5(8)***) Barron's Educational Series, Inc.

Munsch, Robert. Zoom! Martchenko, Michael, tr. Martchenko, Michael, illus. 2004. 32p. (J). pap. 3.99 (978-0-439-52349-3(4) , Cartwheel Bks.) Scholastic, Inc.

My Uncle Has Wheels. 2005. (J). 8.00 (978-0-9767077-1-4(3)) Carson, Tracy.

Myers, Anna. Hoggee. 2004. 160p. (J). 16.95 (978-0-8027-8926-6(9)) Walker & Co.

Napoli, Donna Jo. Friends Everywhere. 1999. (Angelwings Ser.: No. 1). (Illus.). (J). 10.79 (978-0-606-17904-1(6)) Tandem Library Bks.

Napoli, Donna Jo & Ben-Ami, Doron. Friends Everywhere. Klementz-Harte, Lauren, illus. 1999. (Angelwings Ser.: No. 1). 96p. (J). (gr. 2-5). pap. 7.95 (978-0-689-82694-8(X) , Aladdin) Simon & Schuster Children's Publishing.

North, Sharon Rae. My Brand New Leg. 2003. (Illus.). 40p. (J). per. 11.95 (978-0-9741544-0-4(7) , Baby Faye Bks.) Northstar Entertainment Group, LLC.

Northrop, Nancy. Connie - the Three Legged Turtle. Duckworth, Jeff, illus. 2002. 41p. (J). (gr. k-3). 8.25 (978-0-9627894-5-8(3)) LNR Pubns.

Nowhere to Hide, Level 2. 1999. (SmartReader Ser.). (J). pap., tchr. ed. 19.95 incl. audio (978-0-7887-0117-7(7) , 79305T3) Recorded Bks., LLC.

O'Donnell, Liam. Ginger Leads Way. Diefendorf, Cathy, illus. 2005. (Pet Tales Ser.). 32p. (J). (ps-2). 9.95 (978-1-59249-360-9(2) , 1B025); 2.95 (978-1-59249-359-3(9) , 1B024); 4.95 incl. cd-rom (978-1-59249-358-6(0) , 1B023) Soundprints.

O'Neill, Kaney. Dream & Reach. 2003. (Illus.). 29p. (J). pap. (978-0-9747797-0-6(9)) ONeill, Gene & Assoc.

Orr, Wendy. Peeling the Onion. 1999. (Laurel-Leaf Bks.). 176p. (YA). (gr. 7-12). mass mkt. 5.50 (978-0-440-22773-1(9) , Laurel Leaf) Random Hse. Children's Bks.

—Peeling the Onion: A Gripping Story, Told with Honesty & Biting Humour. 1999. (978-0-606-15918-0(5)); (gr. 7-12). lib. bdg. 13.00 (978-0-613-15339-3(1)) Tandem Library Bks.

Pallotta, Jerry. The Hershey's Milk Chocolate Multiplication Book. Bolster, Rob, illus. 2002. 32p. (J). (gr. 1-4). pap. 14.95 (978-0-439-23623-2(1)) Scholastic, Inc.

Petrillo, Genevieve & Lyon, Lea. Keep Your Ear on the Ball. 2007. (Illus.). 32p. (J). (gr. 3-7). 16.95 (***978-0-88448-296-3(0)***) Tilbury Hse. Pubs.

Philbrick, Rodman. Freak, the Mighty. 2001. (Illus.). (J). 12.64 (978-0-606-21199-4(3)) Tandem Library Bks.

Porter, Gene. Freckles. 2006. pap. (***978-1-4250-2281-5(2)***) Assistedreadingbooks.com Inc.

Porter, Pamela. The Crazy Man. 2006. 176p. pap. 6.95 (978-0-88899-695-4(0)) Groundwood Bks. CAN. *Dist:* Perseus Distribution.

Powell, Randy. Tribute to Another Dead Rock Star. 224p. (YA). 2003. pap. 5.95 (978-0-374-47968-8(2) , Sunburst); 1999. (gr. 7-12). 17.00 (978-0-374-37748-9(0) , Farrar, Straus & Giroux (BYR)) Farrar, Straus & Giroux.

—Tribute to Another Dead Rock Star. l.t. ed. 2000. 224p. (J). 21.95 (978-0-7862-2191-2(7)) Thorndike Pr.

Purkapile, Sue. Otto the Blind Otter. Ducommun, Barbara, illus. 2004. (J). 13.95 (978-1-930596-27-6(8)) Amherst Pr.

Ramsby, H. S. Neverlore. Velario, Jackie, illus. 2005. (YA). 16.95 (978-0-9785075-6-5(8) , Ferne Pr.) Nelson Publishing & Marketing.

Ray, Delia. Singing Hands. 2006. (Illus.). 224p. (J). (gr. 5-9). 16.00 (978-0-618-65762-9(2) , Clarion Bks.) Houghton Mifflin Co. Trade & Reference Div.

Recorvits, Helen. Where Heroes Hide. 2002. (Illus.). 144p. (J). (gr. 4-6). 16.00 (978-0-374-33057-6(3) , Farrar, Straus & Giroux (BYR)) Farrar, Straus & Giroux.

Richardson, Faith. Tree Root & River Rat. 2003. (Illus.). 248p. (J). 21.95 (978-0-9744989-4-2(7)); pap. 12.95 (978-0-9744989-5-9(5)) Fox Song Bks.

Riggio, Anita. Secret Signs: An Escape Through the Underground Railroad. Riggio, Anita, illus. 2003. (Illus.). 32p. (J). (gr. k-3). 15.95 (978-1-56397-555-4(6)) Boyds Mills Pr.

Riskind, Mary. Apple Is My Sign. 1999. (J). (gr. 4-7). 21.00 (978-0-8446-7004-1(9)) Smith, Peter Pub., Inc.

Roberts, G. Sillwee Wobbert the Happy Heart Kid. Lucas, Glenn E., illus. 2001. (Sillwsee Wobbert Ser.: 1). 32p. (J). (ps-5). pap. 10.00 (978-0-9704861-1-0(1)) Dream Publishing Co.

Robinet, Harriette Gillem. Forty Acres & Maybe a Mule. 2000. (gr. 3-6). lib. bdg. 13.00 (978-0-613-22986-9(X)) Tandem Library Bks.

Roos, Stephen. The Gypsies Never Came. l.t. ed. 2001. (Juvenile Ser.). 116p. (J). 20.95 (978-0-7862-3469-1(5)) Thorndike Pr.

Rosensweig, Jay B. & Repka, Janice. The Stupendous Dodgeball Fiasco. Dibley, Glin, illus. 2004. 192p. (J). (gr. 3). 16.99 (978-0-525-47346-6(7) , Dutton Juvenile) Penguin Group (USA) Inc.

Sachar, Louis. Small Steps. (YA). 2008. 288p. (gr. 7). pap. 8.99 (***978-0-385-73315-1(1)***); 2006. 272p. (gr. 5). 16.95 (978-0-385-73314-4(3)); 2006. 272p. (gr. 7). lib. bdg. 19.99 (978-0-385-90333-2(2)) Random Hse. Children's Bks. (Delacorte Bks. for Young Readers).

—Small Steps. rev. l.t. ed. 2006. 339p. 23.95 (978-0-7862-8297-5(5)) Thorndike Pr.

Salisbury, Linda G. The Mysterious Jamestown Suitcase: A Bailey Fish Adventure. Grotke, Christopher, illus. 2007. 192p. (J). per. 8.95 (978-1-881539-43-8(1)) Tabby Hse. Bks.

Sand, George. The Wings of Courage. Bloom, Margaret, tr. from FRE. Frasconi, Antonio, illus. 1998. 70p. (gr. 4-7). 12.95 (978-0-8076-1434-1(3)) Braziller, George Inc.

Sanford, Agnes. Melissa & the Little Red Book. Heinen, Sandy, illus. (J). (gr. 1-6). pap. 3.95 (978-0-910924-81-8(3)) Macalester Park Publishing Co., Inc.

Sappey, Maureen S. Dreams of Ships, Dreams of Julia: At Sea with the Monitor & the Merrimack-Virginia, 1862. 1998. (Young American Ser.: Vol. 2). (Illus.). 140p. (YA). (gr. 4-7). 5.99 (978-1-57249-134-2(5)) White Mane Publishing Co., Inc.

Savitz, Harriet May. On the Move. 2000. 148p. (gr. 4-7). pap. 10.95 (978-0-595-09012-9(5)) iUniverse, Inc.

Schneider, Maxwell. Do You Hear Me? Laughs for the Hard of Hearing by the Hard of Hearing. 1. 2003. (Illus.). 138p. per. 8.95 (978-0-9727520-0-8(5) , B555) Harris Communications, Inc.

Scott, Rosanna. Peter & Friends at Camp. Fargo, Todd, illus. l.t. ed. 2006. (Turtle Books). 32p. (J). (gr. k-4). pap. 9.95 (978-0-944727-51-5(4)); lib. bdg. 15.95 (978-0-944727-52-2(2)) Jason & Nordic Pubs. (Turtle Bks.).

Scrimger, Richard. From Charlie's Point of View. 2007. 288p. (YA). (gr. 3). pap. 6.99 (978-0-14-240818-6(2) , Puffin) Penguin Group (USA) Inc.

Seeger, Pete & Jacobs, Paul DuBois. The Deaf Musicians. Christie, Gregory, illus. 2006. 32p. (J). (ps-3). 16.99 (978-0-399-24316-5(X)) Penguin Group (USA) Inc.

Senisi, Ellen B. All Kinds of Friends, Even Green! 2002. (Illus.). 28p. (J). (gr. k-4). 15.95 (978-1-890627-35-5(6)) Woodbine Hse.

Slate, Joseph. Crossing the Trestle. 1999. (Accelerated Reader Bks.). 144p. (J). (gr. 3-7). 14.95 (978-0-7614-5053-5(X) , Cavendish Children's Bks.) Cavendish, Marshall Corp.

Slepian, Jan. The Alfred Summer. 2001. (978-0-606-22507-6(2)) Tandem Library Bks.

Smith, D. James. The Boys of San Joaquin. 2005. (Illus.). 240p. (J). (gr. 3-7). 16.99 (978-0-689-87606-6(8) , Atheneum) Simon & Schuster Children's Publishing.

—Probably the World's Best Story about a Dog & the Girl Who Loved Me. 2006. 240p. (J). (gr. 4-7). 15.95 (978-1-4169-0542-4(1)) Simon & Schuster Children's Publishing.

Smith, Stephen & Caldwell, Lise. Strike Three. 2006. (Game on for Girls Ser.). 128p. (J). pap. 5.99 (978-0-7847-1729-5(X) , 42146) Standard Publishing.

Stauffacher, Sue. Harry Sue. 304p. (J). (gr. 3-7). 2007. pap. 6.50 (978-0-440-42064-4(4) , Yearling); 2005. 15.95 (978-0-375-83274-1(2) , Knopf Bks. for Young Readers); 2005. lib. bdg. 17.99 (978-0-375-93274-8(7) , Knopf Bks. for Young Readers) Random Hse. Children's Bks.

Stewart, Maddie. Peg. Willey, Bee, illus. 2001. (Blue Bananas Ser.). 48p. (J). (gr. 1-2). (978-0-7787-0841-4(1)); pap. (978-0-7787-0887-2(X)) Crabtree Publishing Co.

—Peg. 2002. (gr. k-3). lib. bdg. 12.95 (978-0-613-52895-5(6)) Tandem Library Bks.

Stewart, Shannon. Sea Crow. Milkau, Llz, illus. 2004. 32p. (J). (ps-2). 16.95 (978-1-55143-288-5(9)) Orca Bk. Pubs. USA.

Stratton Porter, Gene. Freckles. 2006. 236p. (YA). 19.95 (***978-1-934169-32-2(3)***); pap. 8.95 (***978-1-934169-33-9(1)***) Norilana Bks.

Stratton-Porter, Gene. Freckles. (J). reprint ed. lib. bdg. 24.95 (978-0-89190-949-1(4) , Rivercity Pr.) Amereon LTD.

—Freckles EasyRead Comfort Edition. 2006. pap. (***978-1-4250-1125-3(X)***) Assistedreadingbooks.com Inc.

—Freckles EasyRead Edition. 2006. pap. (***978-1-4250-0577-1(2)***) Assistedreadingbooks.com Inc.

—Freckles EasyRead Large Edition. 2006. pap. (***978-1-4250-1603-6(0)***) Assistedreadingbooks.com Inc.

Stratton-Porter, Gene & Matthews, Andrew. Freckles. 2000. (Illus.). 32p. (C). pap. 9.00 (978-0-582-42655-9(3)) Pearson ESL.

Striegel, Jana. Homeroom Exercise. 2002. 176p. (J). (gr. 4-6). tchr. ed. 16.95 (978-0-8234-1579-3(1)) Holiday Hse., Inc.

Stuve-Bodeen, Stephanie. Babu's Song. Boyd, Aaron, illus. 2003. 32p. (J). 16.95 (978-1-58430-058-8(2)) Lee & Low Bks., Inc.

Suen, Anastasia. Helping Sophia. Ebbeler, Jeffrey, illus. 2007. (Main Street School - Kids with Character Ser.). 32p. (J). (ps-4). lib. bdg. 27.07 (***978-1-60270-030-7(3)*** , Looking Glass Library) Magic Wagon.

Tada, Joni Eareckson. Meanest Teacher. 2001. (gr. 3-6). lib. bdg. 14.15 (978-0-613-81758-5(3)) Tandem Library Bks.

—Mission Adventure. 2001. (gr. 3-6). lib. bdg. 14.15 (978-0-613-89086-1(8)) Tandem Library Bks.

Tada, Joni Eareckson & Jensen, Steve. The Meanest Teacher. 2005. (Darcy & Friends Ser.). 144p. (gr. 3-6). pap. 5.99 (978-1-58134-256-7(X) , Crossway Bibles) Crossway Bks.

—The Mission Adventure. 2005. (Darcy & Friends Ser.). 143p. (gr. 3-6). pap. 5.99 (978-1-58134-257-4(8) , Crossway Bibles) Crossway Bks.

Tashjian, Janet. Tru Confessions. 1999. (Illus.). 176p. (J). pap. 4.99 (978-0-590-96047-2(4)) Scholastic, Inc.

—Tru Confessions. 2007. 176p. (J). pap. 6.99 (***978-0-312-37273-6(6)***) Square Fish.

—Tru Confessions. 1999. (978-0-606-16611-9(4)) Tandem Library Bks.

Taylor, Theodore. A Sailor Returns. 2002. 160p. (J). (gr. 3-7). pap. 4.99 (978-0-439-24880-8(9) , Scholastic Paperbacks) Scholastic, Inc.

—Timothy of the Cay. 2007. (Illus.). 176p. (YA). pap. 5.95 (978-0-15-206320-7(X) , Harcourt Paperbacks) Harcourt Children's Bks.

—The Weirdo. 2006. (Illus.). 304p. (J). pap. 6.95 (978-0-15-205666-7(1) , Harcourt Paperbacks) Harcourt Children's Bks.

Tildes, Phyllis Limbacher. The Garden Wall. Tildes, Phyllis Limbacher, illus. 2006. (Illus.). (J). 16.95 (978-1-57091-467-6(2) , 1258423); pap. 7.95 (978-1-57091-468-3(0) , 1258423) Charlesbridge Publishing, Inc.

Tomos, Angharad. Y Llipryn Llwyd. 2005. (WEL., Illus.). 48p. pap. (978-0-86243-095-5(X)) Y Lolfa.

Trueman, Terry. Cruise Control. 2004. 160p. (J). 15.99 (978-0-06-623960-6(5)); lib. bdg. 16.89 (978-0-06-623961-3(3)) HarperCollins Pubs.

—Stuck in Neutral. 128p. (J). (gr. 5 up). 2001. pap. 7.99 (978-0-06-447213-5(2) , HarperTeen); 2000. (Illus.). lib. bdg. 16.89 (978-0-06-028518-0(4)) HarperCollins Pubs.

—Stuck in Neutral. 2001. (gr. 7-12). lib. bdg. 15.30 (978-0-613-44419-4(1)) Tandem Library Bks.

Trufant, Robert & Mullins, Tinnesha. Angel Fingers Series: Na'dyd Goes to School. 2004. (Angel Fingers Ser.). (Illus.). 19p. (J). (ps-2). 14.95 (978-0-9760160-0-7(1)) Angel Fingers Foundation.

Turner, Bonnie. Haunted Igloo. 2002. (gr. 7-12). lib. bdg. 24.00 (978-0-613-74646-5(5)) Tandem Library Bks.

Uhlberg, Myron. The Printer. Sorensen, Henri, tr. Sorensen, Henri, illus. 2003. 32p. (J). (gr. 1-5). 16.95 (978-1-56145-221-7(1)) Peachtree Pubs., Ltd.

Ure, Jean. Muddy Four Paws. 1999. (We Love Animals Bks.). (Illus.). 128p. (J). (gr. 4-7). pap. 3.95 (978-0-7641-0968-3(5)) Barron's Educational Series, Inc.

Vaughn Zimmer, Tracie. Reaching for Sun. 2007. 144p. (J). (gr. 7 up). 14.95 (978-1-59990-037-7(8) , Bloomsbury Children) Bloomsbury Publishing.

Vision, Mutiya Sahar. Disabilities?! Alcantara, Ignacio, illus. 2005. 40p. (J). mass mkt. 17.00 (978-0-9659538-9-4(0)) Soul Vision Works Publishing.

Vogelaar, Alie. One Day at a Time, Margreet. VanBrugge, Jeanne, tr. from DUT. Kramer, Jaap, illus. 2004. Orig. Title: Elke Dag Genoeg, Margreet. 124p. (978-0-9670728-6-9(7)) Early Foundations Pubs.

Vogiel, Eva. Invisible Chains. 2000. 288p. (YA). (gr. 8-12). 19.95 (978-1-880582-57-2(0)) Judaica Pr., Inc., The.

Voigt, Cynthia. Izzy, Willy-Nilly. 2005. 336p. (YA). mass mkt. 6.99 (978-1-4169-0339-0(9) , Simon Pulse); (Illus.). 17.95 (978-1-4169-0340-6(2) , Atheneum) Simon & Schuster Children's Publishing.

Wait, Lea. Finest Kind. 2006. 256p. (J). 16.95 (978-1-4169-0952-1(4) , McElderry, Margaret K.) Simon & Schuster Children's Publishing.

—Wintering Well. (Illus.). 192p. (J). 2006. pap. 5.99 (978-0-689-85647-1(4) , Aladdin); 2004. 16.95 (978-0-689-85646-4(6) , McElderry, Margaret K.) Simon & Schuster Children's Publishing.

Wallace, Bill. The Legend of Thunderfoot. 2007. 150p. (J). (gr. 3-7). per. 5.99 (***978-1-4169-0692-6(4)*** , Aladdin) Simon & Schuster Children's Publishing.

Weaver, Elizabeth Nixon. Rooster. 2005. 208p. (J). reprint ed. pap. 5.95 (978-0-7614-5218-8(4)) Cavendish, Marshall Corp.

Weirdo. 2002. stu. ed. (978-1-56137-815-9(1)) Novel Units, Inc.

Werlin, Nancy. Are You Alone on Purpose? 2007. 208p. (YA). (gr. 7). pap. 7.99 (978-0-14-240777-6(1) , Puffin) Penguin Group (USA) Inc.

Whelan, Gloria. Forgive the River, Forgive the Sky. 2004. 96p. (J). pap. 8.00 (978-0-8028-5256-4(4)) Eerdmans, William B. Publishing Co.

—Forgive the River, Forgive the Sky. 2003. (gr. 5-8). lib. bdg. 16.45 (978-0-613-75512-2(X)) Tandem Library Bks.

White, Lee A. What Is Pretty? 1998. 20p. (J). pap. 7.95 (978-1-889745-02-2(2)) Triangle Pubns.

Withers, Pam. Daredevil Club. 2006. 112p. (J). pap. 8.95 (978-1-55143-614-2(0)); lib. bdg. 14.95 (978-1-55143-618-0(3)) Orca Bk. Pubs. USA.

Wolff, Virginia. Probably Still Nick Swansen. 2002. (gr. 5-8). lib. bdg. 16.45 (978-0-613-57323-8(4)) Tandem Library Bks.

Yin & Soentpiet, Chris K. Dear Santa, Please Come to the 19th Floor. Soentpiet, Chris K., illus. 2002. (Illus.). 32p. (J). (gr. k-3). 17.99 (978-0-399-23636-5(8) , Philomel) Penguin Group (USA) Inc.

Zalben, Jane Breskin. Leap. 2007. 272p. (J). (gr. 5). 15.99 (978-0-375-83871-2(6)); lib. bdg. 18.99 (978-0-375-93871-9(0)) Random Hse. Children's Bks. (Knopf Bks. for Young Readers).

Zaugg, Sandra L. The Rock Slide Rescue. Ford, Mark, illus. 1998. (Shoebox Kids Ser.: Vol. 8). 91p. (J). (gr. 2-5). pap. 6.99 (978-0-8163-1387-7(3)) Pacific Pr. Publishing Assn.

PEOPLE WITH MENTAL DISABILITIES

see also Mental Illness; Mentally Ill

Baldwin, Carol. Autism. 2003. (Health Matters Ser.). (Illus.). 32p. (J). (gr. 3-5). lib. bdg. 24.22 (978-1-4034-0250-9(7)) Heinemann Library.

Bryan, Jenny. Living with Down Syndrome. 1999. 32 p. (J). lib. bdg. 27.12 (978-0-8172-5569-5(9)) Raintree.

Edwards, Michele Engel. Autism. 2001. (Diseases & Disorders Ser.). (Illus.). 120p. (YA). (gr. 6-9). 32.45 (978-1-56006-829-7(9) , GML12001-178161, Lucent Bks.) Thomson Gale.

Gordon, Melanie Apel. Let's Talk about Down Syndrome. 1999. (Let's Talk Library). (Illus.). 24p. (J). (gr. 3). lib. bdg. 18.75 (978-0-8239-5197-0(9) , PowerKids Pr.) Rosen Publishing Group, Inc., The.

Hoopmann, Kathy. All Cats Have Asperger Syndrome. 2006. (Illus.). 65p. (J). (978-1-84310-481-0(4)) Kingsley, Jessica Ltd.

Landau, Elaine. Autism. 2001. (Single Title - Science Ser.). (Illus.). 128p. (J). (gr. 8-12). 26.00 (978-0-531-11780-4(4) , Watts, Franklin) Scholastic Library Publishing.

—Head & Brain Injuries. 2002. (Diseases & People Ser.). (Illus.). 112p. (YA). (gr. 6-12). lib. bdg. 26.60 (978-0-7660-1473-2(8)) Enslow Pubs., Inc.

Lennard-Brown, Sarah. Autism. 2003. (Health Issues Ser.). (Illus.). 64p. (J). lib. bdg. 28.56 (978-0-7398-6422-7(X)) Raintree.

MacGowan, Shane & O'Callaghan, Deirdre. Hide That Can: A Photographic Diary of the Men of Arlington House. 2002. (Illus.). 192p. 39.95 (978-0-9542079-8-4(X)) Trolley GBR. *Dist:* D.A.P./Distributed Art Pubs.

Majoli, Alex. Leros: An Island in the Heart of the Aegean. 2002. (Illus.). 112p. 19.95 (978-0-9542079-2-2(0)) Trolley GBR. *Dist:* D.A.P./Distributed Art Pubs.

Martin, Michael J. Teen Depression. 2004. (Illus.). 96p. (YA). (gr. 7-12). per. 32.45 (978-1-59018-502-5(1) , Lucent Bks.) Thomson Gale.

Parent, Lauren. I'm different but I'm Special. Parent, Lauren, illus. l.t. ed. 2006. (Illus.). 24p. (J). per. 10.99 (***978-1-59879-259-1(8)***) Lifevest Publishing, Inc.

Rosenberg, Marsha Sarah. Coping When a Brother or Sister Is Autistic. 2005. (Coping Ser.). (Illus.). 192p. (YA). (gr. 7-12). lib. bdg. 26.50 (978-0-8239-3194-1(3)) Rosen Publishing Group, Inc., The.

—Everything You Need to Know When a Brother or Sister Is Autistic. 2005. (Need to Know Library). (Illus.). 64p. (YA). (gr. 7-12). lib. bdg. 25.25 (978-0-8239-3123-1(4) , NTAUTI) Rosen Publishing Group, Inc., The.

Yoshida. How to Be Yourself in a World That's Different an Asperger's Syndrome Study Guide for Adolescents. 2007. (Illus.). 112p. (J). pap. (978-1-84310-504-6(7)) Kingsley, Jessica Ltd.

PEOPLE WITH MENTAL DISABILITIES—FICTION

Beard, Darleen Bailey. The Babbs Switch Story. 2002. 176p. (J). 16.00 (978-0-374-30475-1(0) , Farrar, Straus & Giroux (BYR)) Farrar, Straus & Giroux.

Brooks, Bruce. Vanishing. 2000. (J). pap. 4.95 (978-0-06-440754-0(3)); 1999. 112p. (YA). (gr. 5 up). 14.89 (978-0-06-028237-0(1) , Geringer, Laura Book) HarperCollins Pubs.

Butler, Geoff. The Hangashore. Butler, Geoff, illus. 1998. (Illus.). 32p. (J). (gr. 3-7). 15.95 (978-0-88776-444-8(4)) Tundra Bks., Inc./Livres Toundra, Inc. CAN. *Dist:* Random Hse., Inc.

Byars, Betsy. The Summer of the Swans. Coconis, Ted, illus. 2002. (J). 13.19 (978-0-7587-0217-3(5)) Book Wholesalers, Inc.

—The Summer of the Swans. CoConis, Ted, illus. l.t. ed. 2000. (LRS Large Print Cornerstone Ser.). 176p. (YA). (gr. 5-12). lib. bdg. 27.95 (978-1-58118-060-2(8) , 23474) LRS.

—The Summer of the Swans. 2004. (Puffin Modern Classics Ser.). 144p. (gr. 3). pap. 5.99 (978-0-14-240114-9(5) , Puffin) Penguin Group (USA) Inc.

Byrd, Lee. Treasure on Gold Street / el T. 2007. (SPA.). 40p. (J). pap. 8.95 (***978-1-933693-11-8(8)***) Cinco Puntos Pr.

Byrd, Lee Merrill. Treasure on Gold Street: A Neighborhood Story in Spanish & English. Castro, Antonio, tr. Castro, Antonio, illus. 2003. Tr. of Tesoro de la Calle Oro. (ENG & SPA.). 40p. (J). 16.95 (978-0-938317-75-3(X)) Cinco Puntos Pr.

Carter, Alden R. Dustin's Big School Day. Young, Dan & Carter, Carol S., illus. 1999. (Concept Book Ser.). 32p. (J). (gr. k-3). lib. bdg. 14.95 (978-0-8075-1741-3(0)) Whitman, Albert & Co.

Chase, L. P. Today Is Tuesday. 2006. (J). pap. 9.00 (***978-0-87426-069-4(8)***) Whitmore Publishing Co.

Curtis, Christopher Paul. Bucking the Sarge. 2006. 288p. (YA). (gr. 7). reprint ed. mass mkt. 6.50 (978-0-440-41331-8(1) , Laurel Leaf) Random Hse. Children's Bks.

Cutler, Jane. Spaceman. 1999. (978-0-606-16980-6(6)) Tandem Library Bks.

DeBear, Kirsten. Be Quiet Marina! Dwight, Laura, photos by. 2001. (Illus.). 40p. (J). (ps-3). 16.95 (978-1-887734-79-0(1)) Star Bright Bks., Inc.

Dodds, Bill. My Sister Annie. Hunt, Judith, illus. 2003. 96p. (YA). (gr. 4-6). pap. 10.95 (978-1-56397-554-7(8)) Boyds Mills Pr.

Fox, Paula. Radiance Descending. 1999. (978-0-606-17838-9(4)) Tandem Library Bks.

Gehret, Jeanne. The Don't-Give-Up Kid: And Learning Differences. DePauw, Sandra A., illus. 3rd rev. ed. 2003. 40p. (J). (gr. 1-5). pap. 9.95 (978-1-884281-10-5(9)) Verbal Images Pr.

—Eagle Eyes: A Child's Guide to Paying Attention. Covert, Susan, illus. 3rd rev. ed. 2003. 40p. (J). (gr. 1-5). pap. 9.95 (978-1-884281-11-2(7)) Verbal Images Pr.

Gifaldi, David. Ben, King of the River. Johnson, Layne, illus. 2001. (Concept Book Ser.). 32p. (J). (gr. k-4). 15.95 (978-0-8075-0635-6(4)) Whitman, Albert & Co.

Gregory, Nan & Lightburn, Ron. How Smudge Came. 1999. (Northern Lights Books for Children Ser.). (Illus.). 32p. (J). (ps-3). (978-0-88995-143-3(8)) Red Deer Pr.

Holt, Kimberly Willis. My Louisiana Sky. rev. ed. 1998. 176p. (J). (gr. 4-7). 17.95 (978-0-8050-5251-0(8) , Holt, Henry & Co. Bks. For Young Readers) Holt, Henry & Co.

—My Louisiana Sky. 208p. (YA). (gr. 5 up). 4.99 (978-0-8072-8291-5(X) , Listening Library) Random Hse. Audio Publishing Group.

—My Louisiana Sky. 2000. 200p. (J). (gr. k-9). lib. bdg. 13.55 (978-0-613-22802-2(2)) Tandem Library Bks.

Hubler, Marsha. Skye's Final Test, Vol. 6. 2005. (Keystone Stables Ser.). (Illus.). 112p. (J). pap. 4.99 (978-0-310-70799-8(4)) Zonderkidz.

Keyes, Daniel. Flowers for Algernon. unabr. ed. 1998. (YA). Class Set. 133.70 incl. audio (978-0-7887-2549-4(1) , 46719); Homework Set. (gr. 7). 67.24 incl. audio (978-0-7887-2244-8(1) , 40728) Recorded Bks., LLC.

King-Smith, Dick. The Crowstarver. l.t. ed. 2000. (J). (Illus.). 243p. pap. (978-0-7540-6095-6(0) , Galaxy Children's Large Print); 216p. pap. incl. audio (978-0-7540-6228-8(7) , RA029, Chivers Children's Audio Bks.) BBC Audiobooks America.

Kneeland, Linda. Cookie. Fargo, Todd, illus. rev. l.t. ed. 1999. 32p. (J). pap. 9.95 (978-0-944727-38-6(7)); lib. bdg. 14.95 (978-0-944727-39-3(5)) Jason & Nordic Pubs. (Turtle Bks.).

Lamstein, Sarah. Hunger Moon. 2004. (Illus.). 112p. (YA). 15.95 (978-1-932425-05-5(5) , Lemniscaat) Boyds Mills Pr.

Maguire, Arlene. Special People, Special Ways. Bailey, Sheila, illus. 2000. 28p. (gr. k-5). per. 14.95 (978-1-885477-65-1(1)) Future Horizons, Inc.

Mazer, Harry. The Wild Kid. 2000. (978-0-606-17946-1(1)) Tandem Library Bks.

Morpurgo, Michael. Private Peaceful. (J). 2006. 176p. pap. 5.99 (978-0-439-63653-7(1) , Scholastic Paperbacks); 2004. 208p. (gr. 7 up). 16.95 (978-0-439-63648-3(5) , Scholastic Pr.) Scholastic, Inc.

—Private Peaceful. l.t. ed. 2006. 225p. (J). 21.95 (978-0-7862-8946-2(5)) Thorndike Pr.

Morse, Linda. Sam's Just Sam. 2002. (Illus.). 32p. (J). pap. 15.95 (978-0-9713567-0-2(X)) Bear Hug Pr.

Nixon-Weaver, Elizabeth. Rooster. 2001. (Illus.). 320p. (J). (gr. 7 up). 16.95 (978-1-58837-001-3(1)) Winslow Pr.

Powell. Tribute to Another Dead Rock Star. 2003. (gr. 7-12). lib. bdg. 14.10 (978-0-613-71884-4(4)) Tandem Library Bks.

Rue, Nancy N. The Mirage. 2001. (Christian Heritage Ser.). (Illus.). 192p. (J). (gr. 3-7). pap. 5.99 (978-1-56179-863-6(0)) Bethany Hse. Pubs.

Shriver, Maria. What's Wrong with Timmy? Speidel, Sandra, illus. 2001. 48p. (J). (ps-3). 14.95 (978-0-316-23337-8(4)) Little, Brown Bks. for Young Readers.

Spain, Susan Rosson. The Deep Cut. 2006. (Illus.). 224p. (J). 16.99 (978-0-7614-5316-1(4)) Cavendish, Marshall Corp.

Stuve-Bodeen, Stephanie. We'll Paint the Octopus Red. DeVito, Pamela, illus. 1998. 25p. (J). (ps-2). 15.95 (978-1-890627-06-5(2)) Woodbine Hse.

Tashjian, Janet. Tru Confessions. 1999. (Illus.). 176p. (J). pap. 4.99 (978-0-590-96047-2(4)) Scholastic, Inc.

—Tru Confessions. 2007. 176p. (J). pap. 6.99 (***978-0-312-37273-6(6)***) Square Fish.

—Tru Confessions. 1999. (978-0-606-16611-9(4)) Tandem Library Bks.

To Kill a Mockingbird. 1998. 44p. (YA). 11.95 (978-1-56137-307-9(9) , NU3079SP) Novel Units, Inc.

vanNiekerk, Clarabelle & Venter, Liezl. Understanding Sam: (and Aspergers Syndrome) vanNiekerk, Clarabelle, illus. 2008. (Illus.). 48p. (J). 17.95 (***978-0-9747217-1-2(9)***) Skeezel Pr.

Wood, June Rae. The Man Who Loved Clowns. 2005. 224p. (J). (gr. 4-7). pap. 5.99 (978-0-14-240422-5(5) , Puffin) Penguin Group (USA) Inc.

Wright, Betty Ren. The Dollhouse Murders. unabr. ed. 1999. (Illus.). (J). (gr. 4-6). 39.95 incl. audio (978-0-87499-521-3(3)); pap. 30.95 incl. audio (978-0-87499-520-6(5)) Live Oak Media.

—The Dollhouse Murders, Grades 4-6. unabr. ed. 1999. (Illus.). (J). pap., tchr. ed. 41.95 incl. audio (978-0-87499-522-0(1)) Live Oak Media.

Yates, Alma J. Sammy's Song: A Novel. 2005. 272p. (J). (***978-1-59156-945-9(1)***) Covenant Communications.

PEOPLE'S DEMOCRACIES

see Communist Countries

PEOPLE'S REPUBLIC OF CHINA

see China

PEPYS, SAMUEL, 1633-1703

Bridge, Frederick. Samuel Pepys, Lover of Musique. 2001. 125p. (YA). reprint ed. 88.00 (978-0-7222-5495-0(4)) Library Reprints, Inc.

PERCEPTION

see also Self-perception

Acredolo, Linda & Gentieu, Penny. My First Baby Signs. Gentieu, Penny & Goodwyn, Susan, illus. 2002. 24p. (J). (ps up). pap. 6.99 (978-0-06-009074-6(X) , Harper Festival) HarperCollins Pubs.

Acredolo, Linda & Goodwyn, Susan. Baby Signs for Mealtime. Gentieu, Penny, illus. 2002. 24p. (J). (ps up). pap. 6.99 (978-0-06-009073-9(1) , Harper Festival) HarperCollins Pubs.

Apel, Melanie Ann. Let's Talk about Feeling Confused. 2001. (Let's Talk Library). (Illus.). 24p. (J). (gr. 3). lib. bdg. 18.75 (978-0-8239-5623-4(7) , PowerKids Pr.) Rosen Publishing Group, Inc., The.

Burstein, John. Geometry: Looking Down on Monster Town. 2003. (Weekly Reader Early Learning Library). (Illus.). 24p. (J). (gr. 1 up). pap. 7.93 (978-0-8368-3824-6(6) , Weekly Reader Early Learning Library) Stevens, Gareth Inc.

—Patterns: What's on the Wall? Destiny Images Staff, illus. 2003. (Math Monsters Ser.). 24p. (YA). (gr. 1 up). lib. bdg. 19.33 (978-0-8368-3816-9(5) , Weekly Reader Early Learning Library) Stevens, Gareth Inc.

Davies. Fun Size. (Illus.). 40p. (J). 19.95 (978-1-85479-230-3(X)) O'Mara, Michael Bks., Ltd. GBR. *Dist:* Trans-Atlantic Pubns., Inc.

Dubowski, Cathy East. Who Are You? 2002. (J). per. 23.95 net. (978-0-9719878-2-1(3)) Depiction Bible.

Freese, Joan. Patterns on Parade. 2007. (J). pap. (***978-0-8368-8482-1(5)***); 24p. (gr. 1-3). lib. bdg. 19.93 (***978-0-8368-8473-9(6)***) Stevens, Gareth Inc. (Weekly Reader Early Learning Library).

Gordon, Sharon. Up Down (Arriba Abajo) 2006. (Bookworms Ser.). (ENG & SPA., Illus.). 24p. (J). lib. bdg. 22.79 (978-0-7614-2449-9(0)) Cavendish, Marshall Corp.

I See Patterns. 2006. (Yellow Umbrella Math Ser.). 8,16p. (J). 6.50 (978-0-7368-1694-6(1)) Red Brick Learning.

Jacobs, Daniel. Patrones en los Animales. 2005. Tr. of Animal Patterns. (SPA., Illus.). 16p. (J). (gr. k-1). lib. bdg. 15.93 (978-0-7368-4148-1(2)) Capstone Pr., Inc.

—Patterns. 2006. 16p. (J). (gr. k-2). 15.93 (978-0-7368-5851-9(2) , Yellow Umbrella Bks.) Capstone Pr., Inc.

Johnson, Tami. Near & Far. 2007. 32p. (J). (978-0-7368-6736-8(8)) Capstone Pr., Inc.

Joyce, Katherine. Optical Illusions. 2000. (gr. 5-8). lib. bdg. 10.60 (978-0-613-75546-7(4)) Tandem Library Bks.

Look at Mealtime. (Look at Me Ser.). (Illus.). (J). bds. 5.95 (978-0-590-24863-1(4)) Scholastic, Inc.

Lowery, Lawrence F. Look & See. 2nd ed. 2004. (J). per. (978-0-9762724-9-6(0)) Educational Research & Applications, LLC.

Marks, James Lynn. That's Bad... No, That's Good (What Does Your Child Think) 2000. (Education Through Creation Ser.: Bk. 6). (Illus.). 16p. (J). (ps-6). pap. 9.95 (978-0-9706412-5-0(7) , 1006) Seventh Sun Productions.

Mealtime. 2003. (J). per. (978-1-57657-893-3(3)) Paradise Pr., Inc.

Olson, Nathan. Animal Patterns. 2007. (Finding Patterns Ser.). 32p. (J). (Illus.). 7.95 (***978-0-7368-7846-3(7)***); 23.93 (978-0-7368-6728-3(7)) Capstone Pr., Inc. (Pebble Bks.).

—City Patterns. 2007. 32p. (J). (978-0-7368-6730-6(9)) Capstone Pr., Inc.

—Farm Patterns. 2007. 32p. (J). (978-0-7368-6732-0(5)) Capstone Pr., Inc.

—Food Patterns. 2007. 32p. (J). (978-0-7368-6729-0(5)) Capstone Pr., Inc.

Piper, Susie S. Perceptions. 1999. (J). pap. 6.00 (978-0-9618280-3-5(X)) Piper, Susie Sansom.

Rivera, Sheila. In & Out. 2004. (First Step Nonfiction Ser.). (J). pap. (978-0-8225-5353-3(8)); lib. bdg. (978-0-8225-2641-4(7)) Lerner Publishing Group. (Lerner Pubns.).

—Near & Far. 2004. (First Step Nonfiction Ser.). (J). pap. (978-0-8225-5354-0(6) , Lerner Pubns.) Lerner Publishing Group.

—Over & Under. 2004. (First Step Nonfiction Ser.). (J). pap. (978-0-8225-5350-2(3) , Lerner Pubns.) Lerner Publishing Group.

School Specialty Publishing. Easy Picture Recognition. 2001. (Phonics Flash Cards Ser.). 104p. (C). 6.99 (978-0-86734-406-6(7) , Schaffer, Frank) Schaffer, Frank Pubns.

West, Tori. A Look at Opposites. West, Tori, illus. 1998. (Illus.). (J). (gr. k-2). (978-1-892800-10-7(1)) Tattoo Manufacturing.

What Comes Next? 2000. (Illus.). 16p. (J). (ps-1). wbk. ed. 3.79 (978-1-889319-80-3(5)) Trend Enterprises, Inc.

Wilcox, Charlotte. The Iroquois. 2007. (Native American Histories Ser.). 56p. (J). 27.93 (978-0-8225-2637-7(9) , Lerner Pubns.) Lerner Publishing Group.

PERCEPTION—FICTION

Banks, Kate. Baboon. Hallensleben, Georg, illus. 2004. 24p. (J). (ps-ps). lib. bdg. 13.75 (978-0-606-30284-5(0)) Tandem Library Bks.

Banyai, Istvan. Zoom. 1998. (Picture Puffin Ser.). (Illus.). 64p. (J). (gr. k-3). pap. 6.99 (978-0-14-055774-9(1) , Puffin) Penguin Group (USA) Inc.

Bell, Hilari. The Wizard Test. 176p. (J). 2006. pap. 5.99 (978-0-06-059942-3(1)); 2005. (gr. 5 up). 15.99 (978-0-06-059940-9(5)); 2005. (gr. 5 up). lib. bdg. 16.89 (978-0-06-059941-6(3)) HarperCollins Pubs.

Hodes, Loren. Too Big, Too Little. . . Just Right! Hodes, Loren, illus. 2002. (Illus.). (J). 9.95 (978-1-880582-72-5(4) , TTTH) Judaica Pr., Inc., The.

Jarrell, Pamela R. Who Does Bobby See? Gillen, Lisa P., illus. l.t. ed. 1999. (Cuddle Bks.). 7p. (J). (ps-k). pap. 10.95 (978-1-57332-133-4(8)) HighReach Learning, Inc.

Margulies, Paul. What Julianna Could See. Zonneveld, Famke, illus. 2004. 32p. (J). pap. 11.95 (978-0-88010-515-6(1)) SteinerBooks, Inc.

Martinez, Rocio. Matias Dibuja el Sol. 2002. (SPA.). 28p. (J). (978-980-257-261-8(6)) Ekare, Ediciones.

McGrory, Anik. Kidogo. 2005. (Illus.). 32p. (J). 15.95 (978-1-58234-974-9(6)) Bloomsbury Publishing.

Montanari, Eva. The Crocodile's True Colors. 2002. (Illus.). 32p. (J). (gr. k-3). 14.95 (978-0-8230-2435-3(0)) Watson-Guptill Pubns., Inc.

Norac, Carl. My Daddy Is a Giant. Godon, Ingrid, illus. 2005. 32p. (J). (ps-k). 16.00 (978-0-618-44399-4(1) , Clarion Bks.) Houghton Mifflin Co. Trade & Reference Div.

Norac, Carl & Gordon, Ingrid. My Daddy Is a Giant. 2004. (Illus.). 32p. (J). (ENG & KOR.). pap. 12.95 (978-1-84444-300-0(0)); (ENG & ALB., pap. 12.95 (978-1-84444-351-2(5)); (ENG & ARA., pap. 12.95 (978-1-84444-352-9(3)); (ENG & BEN., pap. 12.95 (978-1-84444-353-6(1)); (ENG & BUL., pap. 12.95 (978-1-84444-354-3(X)); (ENG & CHI., pap. 12.95 (978-1-84444-355-0(8)); (ENG & CHI., pap. 12.95 (978-1-84444-356-7(6)); (CRO & ENG., pap. 12.95 (978-1-84444-357-4(4)); (ENG, PER & FAR., pap. 12.95 (978-1-84444-358-1(2)); (ENG & FRE., pap. 12.95 (978-1-84444-359-8(0)); (ENG & GER., pap. 12.95 (978-1-84444-360-4(4)); (ENG & GUJ., pap. 12.95 (978-1-84444-361-1(2)); (ENG & HIN., pap. 12.95 (978-1-84444-362-8(0)); (ENG & ITA., pap. 12.95 (978-1-84444-363-5(9)); (JPN & ENG., pap. 12.95 (978-1-84444-364-2(7)); (KUR & ENG., pap. 12.95 (978-1-84444-365-9(5)); (ENG & PAN., pap. 12.95 (978-1-84444-366-6(3)); (ENG & POL., pap. 12.95 (978-1-84444-367-3(1)); (POR & ENG., pap. 12.95 (978-1-84444-368-0(X)); (RUS & ENG., pap. 12.95 (978-1-84444-369-7(8)); (SHO & ENG., pap. 12.95 (978-1-84444-370-3(1)); (ENG & SOM., pap. 12.95 (978-1-84444-371-0(X)); (ENG & SPA., pap. 12.95 (978-1-84444-372-7(8)); (ENG & TAG., pap. 12.95 (978-1-84444-373-4(6)); (TAM & ENG., pap. 12.95 (978-1-84444-374-1(4)); (ENG & TUR., pap. 12.95 (978-1-84444-375-8(2)); (ENG & TWI., pap. 12.95 (978-1-84444-376-5(0)); (ENG & URD., pap. 12.95 (978-1-84444-377-2(9)); (ENG & VIE., pap. 12.95 (978-1-84444-378-9(7)); (YOR & ENG., pap. 12.95 (978-1-84444-379-6(5)) Mantra Lingua GBR. *Dist:* Mantra Publishing, Ltd.

Piggot, Dawn. Gregory & the Magic Line. (Illus.). 32p. (J). pap. 9.99 (978-1-84255-278-0(3)) Dolphin Paperbacks GBR. *Dist:* Trafalgar Square Publishing.

Rogers, Alan. En Forme de Bateau. 2003. (Little Giants Ser.). (FRE., Illus.). 16p. (J). (ps-k). 5.95 (978-1-58728-177-8(5) , Two Can Publishing) T&N Children's Publishing.

Rogers, Karen M. Como Pienso Patrones! Alvarado, Ana María, tr. Ramirez, Michael, illus. 2000. (Think-Kids Book Collection).Tr. of Patterns in My Head. (SPA.). 16p. (J). pap. 2.95 (978-1-58237-054-5(0)) Creative Thinkers, Inc.

Shannon, George. White Is for Blueberry. Dronzek, Laura, illus. 2005. 40p. (J). (ps). 16.99 (978-0-06-029275-1(X)); lib. bdg. 17.89 (978-0-06-029276-8(8)) HarperCollins Pubs.

Shively, Julie. What Belongs? Kurtz, John, illus. 2004. (Baby Looney Toons Ser.). 16p. (J). 6.95 (978-0-8249-6561-7(2)) Ideals Pubns.

Wolkstein, Diane. Little Mouse's Painting. 2002. (gr. k-3). lib. bdg. 14.10 (978-0-613-63049-8(1)) Tandem Library Bks.

PERCUSSION INSTRUMENTS

see also names of percussion instruments, e.g. Drums

Aylmore, Angela. Banging. 2005. (Raintree Sprouts Ser.). (Illus.). 24p. pap. (978-1-4109-1609-9(X)); (J). 20.64 (978-1-4109-1604-4(9)) Steck-Vaughn.

—Shaking. 2005. (Raintree Sprouts Ser.). (Illus.). 24p. pap. (978-1-4109-1612-9(X)); (J). 20.64 (978-1-4109-1607-5(3)) Steck-Vaughn.

Dearling, Robert. Percussion & Electronic Instruments. 2000. (Encyclopedia of Musical Instruments Ser.). (Illus.). 48p. (J). (gr. 4-7). 22.95 (978-0-7910-6093-3(4) , Chelsea Hse.) Facts On File, Inc.

Knight, M. J. Percussion. 2005. (Musical Instruments of the World Ser.). (Illus.). 32p. (J). (gr. 3-7). lib. bdg. 27.10 (978-1-58340-417-1(1)) Smart Apple Media.

—Sound Effects. 2005. (Musical Instruments of the World Ser.). (Illus.). 32p. (J). (gr. 3-7). lib. bdg. 27.10 (978-1-58340-413-3(9)) Smart Apple Media.

Lynch, Wendy. Percussion. 2001. (Musical Instruments Ser.). (Illus.). 32p. (J). (gr. k-2). lib. bdg. 21.36 (978-1-58810-235-5(1)) Heinemann Library.

Thomas, Roger. Percussion. 2001. (Soundbites Ser.). (Illus.). 32p. (YA). (gr. 6-8). lib. bdg. 22.79 (978-1-58810-265-2(3)) Heinemann Library.

Turner, Barrie Carson. Drums, 8 vols., Set. 2000. (Musical Instruments of the World Ser.). (Illus.). 32p. (J). (ps-3). lib. bdg. 16.95 (978-1-58340-061-6(3)) Smart Apple Media.

—Percussion. 1998. (Musical Instruments of the World Ser.). (Illus.). 32p. (J). (ps-3). lib. bdg. 16.95 (978-1-887068-46-8(5)) Smart Apple Media.

—Sound Effects. 2000. (Musical Instruments of the World Ser.). (Illus.). 32p. (J). (ps-3). lib. bdg. 16.95 (978-1-58340-064-7(8)) Smart Apple Media.

Zampino, Phil. Music Theory, Scales & Chords for the Percussion Drum Student: Recommended for All Students & All Instruments. 1998. (Illus.). 130p. (YA). (gr. 4 up). spiral bd. 19.95 (978-0-942253-10-8(0)) PAZ Publishing.

PERFORMING ARTS

see also Theater

also art forms performed on stage or screen, e.g. Ballet

All the World's a Stage! Individual Title Six-Packs. (Action Packs Ser.). 104p. (gr. 3-5). 44.00 (978-0-7635-8406-1(1)) Rigby Education.

Anderson, Janet. Modern Dance. (World of Dance Ser.). (Illus.). (gr. 9-13). 2004. 112p. pap. 30.00 (978-0-7910-7774-0(8)); 2003. 120p. 30.00 (978-0-7910-7644-6(X)) Facts On File, Inc. (Chelsea Hse.).

The Arts. (Britannica Learning Library). (Illus.). (gr. 2-5). 14.95 (978-1-59339-004-4(1) , 049905-EN-REF) Encyclopaedia Britannica, Inc.

Backstage Pass, 6 Packs. (Bookweb Ser.). 32p. (gr. 4 up). 34.00 (978-0-7635-3737-1(3)) Rigby Education.

Bland, Celia. Arts & Entertainment. 1999. (Eyes on America Ser.). (Illus.). 29p. (J). pap. (978-1-56156-711-9(6)) Kidsbooks, Inc.

Dowd, Olympia. A Young Dancer's Apprenticeship. 2003. (Illus.). 128p. (J). (gr. 7 up). pap. 14.95 (978-0-7613-1898-9(4) , Twenty-First Century Bks.) Lerner Publishing Group.

Emmer, Rae. Club de Teatro. 2004. (Actividades Escolares Ser.). (SPA & ENG., Illus.). 24p. (J). lib. bdg. 17.25 (978-0-8239-6898-5(7) , Buenas Letra) Rosen Publishing Group, Inc., The.

Fraser, Fil. Alberta's Camelot Vol. 1: Culture & the Arts in the Lougheed Years. rev. ed. 2003. (Illus.). 240p. (J). (gr. 4). pap. 18.95 (978-1-55105-393-6(4)) Lone Pine Publishing USA.

Hughes, Morgan. Entertainment Hall of Fame. 2000. (Halls of Fame Ser.). (Illus.). 24p. (J). (gr. 2-6). lib. bdg. 23.93 (978-1-55916-267-8(8)) Rourke Publishing, LLC.

Hull, Robert E. Entertainment & the Arts. 2000. (World of Ancient Greece Ser.). (Illus.). 32p. (J). (gr. 4-8). pap. 6.95 (978-0-531-15381-9(9) , Watts, Franklin) Scholastic Library Publishing.

J. G. Ferguson Publishing Company Staff. Discovering Careers for Your Future/Performing Arts. 2000. (Discovering Careers for Your Future Ser.). (Illus.). 94p. (J). (gr. 7-12). lib. bdg. 21.95 (978-0-89434-361-2(0) , F543, Ferguson Publishing Co.) Facts On File, Inc.

Jordan, Denise M. Artistas de Circo. 2002. Tr. of Circus Performers. 24p. (J). (ps-1). pap. 5.25 (978-1-58810-843-2(0) , 91568); (SPA.). lib. bdg. 17.08 (978-1-58810-796-1(5)) Heinemann Library.

Lewis, Tommi. Movie Scrapbook: Prince of Egypt. 1998. (Prince of Egypt Ser.). (Illus.). 64p. (J). (gr. 3-7). pap. 8.99 (978-0-8499-5900-4(4)) Nelson, Thomas Inc.

Mason, Antony. Performing Arts. 2003. (Culture Encyclopedia Ser.). (Illus.). 40p. (J). (gr. 5 up). lib. bdg. (978-1-59084-481-6(5)) Mason Crest Pubs.

Pasternak, Ceel. Cool Careers for Girls in Performing Arts. 2000. (gr. 7-12). lib. bdg. 22.20 (978-0-613-79028-4(6)) Tandem Library Bks.

Pasternak, Ceel & Thornburg, Linda. Cool Careers for Girls in Performing Arts. 2000. (Illus.). viii, 171p. (J). 19.95 (978-1-57023-136-0(2)) Impact Pubns.

Pinky & the Brain in Bubba Bo Bob Brain. (Illus.). 32p. (J). (ps up). pap. 7.89 incl. audio (978-1-56826-759-3(2) , KR2) Rhino Entertainment Co, A Warner Music Group Co.

Stevens, Chambers. Sensational Scenes for Teens: The Scene Study-Guide for Teen Actors! Rolle-Whatley, Renee, ed. 2001. (Hollywood 101 Ser.: Vol. 3). (Illus.). 112p. (YA). (gr. 7-11). per. 14.95 (978-1-883995-10-2(8)) Sandcastle Publishing.

Stoler, Sigmund. TV Scenes for Acting: Selected Short Scenes from the "Golden Age" of TV Drama. 2000. (Illus.). 203p. (YA). (gr. 9 up). pap. 19.99 (978-0-89824-226-3(6), 226-6) Royal Fireworks Publishing Co.

The Talent Contest: Individual Title Six-Packs. (gr. 3 up). 35.00 (978-0-7635-9666-8(3)) Rigby Education.

Ward, Kristin. Rain. 2000. (PowerKids Readers Ser.). (Illus.). 24p. (J). (gr. 1). lib. bdg. 16.00 (978-0-8239-5531-2(1), PKNARA, PowerKids Pr.) Rosen Publishing Group, Inc., The.

Wilson, Wayne. Careers in Entertainment. 2001. (Latinos at Work Ser.). (Illus.). 96p. (gr. 5-12). lib. bdg. 32.75 (978-1-58415-083-1(1)) Mitchell Lane Pubs., Inc.

PERFORMING ARTS—BIOGRAPHY

Abbey, Cherie D., ed. Biography Today: Profiles of People of Interest to Young Readers. 2004. (Business Leaders Ser.: 1). 200p. (YA). lib. bdg. 44.00 (978-0-7808-0751-8(0)); 2004. (Scientists & Inventors Ser.: 10). (YA). lib. bdg. 44.00 (978-0-7808-0712-9(X)); 2004. (Performing Artists Ser.: Vol. 4). (Illus.). 250p. (J). lib. bdg. 39.00 (978-0-7808-0710-5(3)); 2004. (Performing Artists Ser.: Vol. 3). (Illus.). 250p. (J). (gr. 3 up). lib. bdg. (978-0-7808-0709-9(X)); 2003. (Performing Artists Ser.: Vol. 1). (YA). lib. bdg. (978-0-7808-0647-4(6)) Omnigraphics, Inc.

Hunter, Shaun. Visual & Performing Artists. 1999. (Illus.). 48p. (J). (ps-11). lib. bdg. 17.60 (978-0-613-12237-5(2)) Tandem Library Bks.

Olmstead, Mary. Yo Yo Ma: A Biography. 2004. (Asian-American Biographies Ser.). (Illus.). 64p. 28.56 (978-1-4109-1058-5(X)) Raintree.

PERFORMING ARTS—FICTION

Bergen, Lara. Drama Queen. 2007. (Candy Apple Ser.: No. 5). 176p. (J). pap. 4.99 (***978-0-439-92953-0(9)***, Scholastic Paperbacks) Scholastic, Inc.

Crow Boy. 2004. (J). 24.95 incl. audio (978-0-89719-868-4(9)); pap. 32.75 incl. audio (978-1-55592-190-3(6)); pap. 14.95 incl. audio (978-1-56008-050-3(7)) Weston Woods Studios, Inc.

Eggleton, Jill. Rave Reviews: Individual Title Six-Packs. Bennett, John, illus. (Sails Literacy Ser.). 20p. (gr. 2-3). 27.00 (978-0-7578-0724-4(0)) Rigby Education.

Gravdahl, John. The Tale of Dog Giovanni. 2000. (Illus.). 32p. (J). (gr. k-4). 16.95 (978-0-9678577-9-4(1)) Propeller Pr.

Gregory, Deborah. In the House with Mouse! 2001. (gr. 3-6). lib. bdg. 11.80 (978-0-613-74976-3(6)) Tandem Library Bks.

Henkes, Kevin. Wemberly Worried. Henkes, Kevin, illus. 2001. (Illus.). (J). 28.95 incl. audio compact disk (978-1-59112-360-6(7)) Live Oak Media.

Higashi, Sandra & Higashi/Glaser Design Inc. Staff. Hello Kitty, Hello School! Kit: Includes Finger Puppets, Mini Book, & Stage. Hirashima, Jean, illus. 2003. (Hello Kitty Ser.). 16p. (J). (ps-3). 12.95 (978-0-8109-4596-8(7)) Abrams, Harry N., Inc.

Holabird, Katharine. A Day at Miss Lilly's. Craig, Helen, illus. 2007. (Angelina Ballerina Ser.). 24p. (J). (ps-1). pap. 4.99 (978-0-448-44548-9(4), Grosset & Dunlap) Penguin Group (USA) Inc.

—Miss Lilly Is Leaving. Craig, Helen, illus. 2006. (Angelina Ballerina Ser.). 24p. (J). (ps-1). 3.99 (978-0-448-44473-4(9), Grosset & Dunlap) Penguin Group (USA) Inc.

—A Very Special Tea Party. Craig, Helen, illus. 2007. (Angelina Ballerina Ser.). 16p. (J). (ps-1). pap. 4.99 (978-0-448-44549-6(2), Grosset & Dunlap) Penguin Group (USA) Inc.

Krulik, Nancy E. All for One & One for All. 2000. (Moffatts on the Road Ser.: No. 3). (Illus.). 128p. (J). (gr. 3-7). pap. 4.99 (978-0-439-13688-4(1)) Scholastic, Inc.

—All for One & One for All. 2000. (gr. 3-6). lib. bdg. 13.00 (978-0-613-24134-2(7)) Tandem Library Bks.

Rushton, Rosie. I Think I'll Just Curl up & Die. 2005. 176p. (J). pap. 5.99 (978-0-7868-5188-1(0)) Hyperion Bks. for Children.

Song & Dance Man. 1998. (J). (gr. 2). pap. 3.95 (978-0-439-04437-0(5)) HarperCollins Pubs.

PERFUMES

Epstein, Rachel. Estee Lauder: Beauty-Business Success. 2000. (YA). (978-0-606-19783-0(4)) Tandem Library Bks.

PERIODIC LAW

Adair, Rick. Beryllium. 2006. (Understanding the Elements of the Periodic Table Ser.: Set 3). (Illus.). 48p. (YA). (gr. 5-8). lib. bdg. 26.50 (978-1-4042-1003-5(2)) Rosen Publishing Group, Inc., The.

Barber, Ian. Sorting the Elements: The Periodic Table at Work. 2008. (J). (***978-1-60044-607-8(8)***) Rourke Publishing, LLC.

Belval, Brian. Gold. 2006. (Understanding the Elements of the Periodic Table Ser.). (Illus.). 48p. (J). lib. bdg. (978-1-4042-0708-0(2)) Rosen Publishing Group, Inc., The.

Cooper, Sharon Katz & Compass Point Books Staff. The Periodic Table: Mapping the Elements. 2006. 48p. (J). (978-0-7565-1961-2(6)) Compass Point Bks.

Dingle, Adrian & Kingfisher Editors. The Periodic Table: Elements with Style! Basher, Simon, illus. 2007. 128p. (J). (gr. 5 up). pap. 8.95 (978-0-7534-6085-6(8), Kingfisher) Houghton Mifflin Co. Trade & Reference Div.

Ham, Becky. The Periodic Table. 2007. (Essential Chemistry Ser.). 128p. (gr. 6-12). 35.00 (***978-0-7910-9533-1(9)***, Chelsea Hse.) Facts On File, Inc.

Hasan, Heather. Fluorine. 2006. (Understanding the Elements of the Periodic Table Ser.). (Illus.). 48p. (YA). (gr. 5-8). lib. bdg. 26.50 (978-1-4042-1005-9(9)) Rosen Publishing Group, Inc., The.

—Iron. 2005. (Interpreting the Periodic Table Ser.). (Illus.). 48p. (J). (gr. 5-8). lib. bdg. 26.50 (978-1-4042-0157-6(2)) Rosen Publishing Group, Inc., The.

—Nitrogen. 2005. (Interpreting the Periodic Table Ser.). (Illus.). 48p. (J). (gr. 5-8). lib. bdg. 26.50 (978-1-4042-0158-3(0)) Rosen Publishing Group, Inc., The.

Lew, Kristi. Argon. 2008. (***978-1-4042-1409-5(7)***) Rosen Publishing Group, Inc., The.

Roza, Greg. Calcium. 2007. (J). (***978-1-4042-1963-2(3)***) Rosen Publishing Group, Inc., The.

—Potassium. 2007. (J). (***978-1-4042-1964-9(1)***) Rosen Publishing Group, Inc., The.

—Titanium. 2008. (J). (***978-1-4042-1412-5(7)***) Rosen Publishing Group, Inc., The.

Saucerman, Linda. Chlorine. 2007. (J). (***978-1-4042-1962-5(5)***) Rosen Publishing Group, Inc., The.

Saucerman, Linda. Hydrogen: The Fuel for Life. 2005. (Interpreting the Periodic Table Ser.). (Illus.). 48p. (J). (gr. 5-8). lib. bdg. 26.50 (978-1-4042-0156-9(4)) Rosen Publishing Group, Inc., The.

Saunders, Nigel. The Periodic Table, 6 bks., Set 2. 2004. (YA). (gr. 8 up). lib. bdg. 196.71 (978-1-4034-1667-4(2)) Heinemann Library.

Slade, Suzanne. Elements & the Periodic Table. 2007. (Library of Physical Sciences). (Illus.). 24p. (J). (978-1-4042-2355-4(X)); pap. (978-1-4042-2165-9(4)); (gr. 3-6). lib. bdg. 21.25 (978-1-4042-3418-5(7)) Rosen Publishing Group, Inc., The. (PowerKids Pr.).

Strom, Laura Layton. Grab a Seat at the Periodic Table: A Chemical Mystery. 2007. (Shockwave: Earth & Physical Science Ser.). (Illus.). 36p. (J). (gr. 4-6). lib. bdg. 25.00 (***978-0-531-17793-8(9)***, Children's Pr.) Scholastic Library Publishing.

Swertka, Albert. The Elements: A Mini Guide to the Periodic Table. 2007. 128p. 4.95 (978-0-7624-2985-1(2), Running Pr. Miniature Editions) Running Pr. Bk. Pubs.

Thomas, Michele. Oxygen. 2005. (Interpreting the Periodic Table Ser.). (Illus.). 48p. (J). (gr. 5-8). lib. bdg. 26.50 (978-1-4042-0159-0(9)) Rosen Publishing Group, Inc., The.

Tocci, Salvatore. The Periodic Table. (True Bks.). (J). 2005. (Illus.). 48p. (gr. 3-5). pap. 6.95 (978-0-516-27852-0(5)); 2004. 25.00 (978-0-516-22833-4(1)) Scholastic Library Publishing. (Children's Pr.).

Understanding the Elements of the Periodic Table. 2005. (Illus.). 48p. (gr. 5-8). lib. bdg. 159.00 (978-1-4042-0348-8(6)) Rosen Publishing Group, Inc., The.

Understanding the Elements of the Periodic Table, 6 bks., Set 3. Incl. Beryllium. Adair, Rick. (YA). lib. bdg. 26.50 (978-1-4042-1003-5(2)); Boron. Adair, Rick. (YA). lib. bdg. 26.50 (978-1-4042-1004-2(0)); Fluorine. Hasan, Heather. (YA). lib. bdg. 26.50 (978-1-4042-1005-9(9)); Lithium. Johanson, Paula. (YA). lib. bdg. 26.50 (978-1-4042-0940-4(9)); Magnesium. Willett, Edward. (YA). lib. bdg. 26.50 (978-1-4042-1007-3(5)); Neon. Willett, Edward. (J). lib. bdg. 26.50 (978-1-4042-1008-0(3)); (Illus.). 48p. (gr. 5-8). 2006. 2007. Set lib. bdg. 159.00 (***978-1-4042-1043-1(1)***) Rosen Publishing Group, Inc., The.

Wiker, Benjamin. The Mystery of the Periodic Table. 2003. (Living History Library). (Illus.). 170p. (J). pap. 14.95 (978-1-883937-71-3(X)) Bethlehem Bks.

Wu, Ronald W. Carbon. 2005. (Interpreting the Periodic Table Ser.). (Illus.). 48p. (J). (gr. 5-8). lib. bdg. 26.50 (978-1-4042-0155-2(6)) Rosen Publishing Group, Inc., The.

Zannos, Susan. Dmitri Mendeleyev & the Periodic Table. 2004. (Uncharted, Unexplored, & Unexplained Ser.). (Illus.). 48p. (J). (gr. 4-8). lib. bdg. 29.95 (978-1-58415-267-5(2)) Mitchell Lane Pubs., Inc.

PERIODIC TABLE OF ELEMENTS

see Periodic Law

PERIODICALS

see also Newspapers

Botzakis, Stergios. Pretty in Print: Questioning Magazines. 2007. (Fact Finders Ser.). (Illus.). 32p. (J). (gr. 4-7). lib. bdg. 22.60 (978-0-7368-6764-1(3), 1264912, Fact Finders) Capstone Pr., Inc.

Botzakis, Stergios. Pretty in Print: Questioning Magazines. 2007. (Fact Finders Ser.). (Illus.). 32p. (J). (***978-0-7368-7860-9(2)***, 1264912) Capstone Pr., Inc.

Hamilton, John. Magazines. 2005. (Straight to the Source Ser.). (Illus.). 32p. (J). (gr. k-6). lib. bdg. 22.78 (978-1-59197-546-5(8)) ABDO Publishing Co.

Heidrich, Delana S. Create a Magazine, Grades 5-8: A Complete Framework for Students to Use in Creating an Original Magazine. Armstrong, Beverly, illus. 1999. 88p. pap., tchr. ed. 11.99 (978-0-88160-310-1(4), LW-379, Learning Works, The) Creative Teaching Pr., Inc.

Little House Life Magazine, Vol. 2. 2000. (J). pap. (978-0-06-449279-9(6), Harper Trophy) HarperCollins Pubs.

Little House Life Magazine Vol. 2: With Hardware. 2000. (J). pap. (978-0-06-449258-4(3), Harper Trophy) HarperCollins Pubs.

Petley, Julian. Newspapers & Magazines. 2003. (Media Wise Ser.). (Illus.). 64p. (J). lib. bdg. 28.50 (978-1-58340-258-0(6)) Smart Apple Media.

PERRY, MATTHEW CALBRAITH, 1794-1858

Gaines, Ann Graham. Commodore Perry Opens Japan to Trade in World History. 2000. (In World History Ser.). (Illus.). 128p. (YA). (gr. 5-12). lib. bdg. 26.60 (978-0-7660-1462-6(2)) Enslow Pubs., Inc.

PERSEUS (GREEK MYTHOLOGY)

Harkins, Susan and William. Perseus. 2007. (Profiles in American History Ser.). (Illus.). 48p. (J). (gr. 4-9). lib. bdg. 29.95 (***978-1-58415-558-4(2)***) Mitchell Lane Pubs., Inc.

Hepplewhite, Peter. The Adventures of Perseus. Bergin, Mark, illus. 2004. (Ancient Myths Ser.). (J). (978-0-7565-0663-6(8)) Compass Point Bks.

—The Adventures of Perseus. Bergin, Mark, illus. 2004. (Ancient Myths Ser.). 32p. (gr. 3-5). 23.93 (978-1-4048-0901-7(5)) Picture Window Bks.

McCaughrean, Geraldine, retold by. Perseus. 2005. (Heroes Ser.). (Illus.). 160p. (J). (ps-7). 15.95 (978-0-8126-2735-0(0)) Open Court Publishing Co.

Spinner, Stephanie. Snake Hair: The Story of Medusa. 1999. (gr. k-3). lib. bdg. 11.80 (978-0-613-15165-8(8)) Tandem Library Bks.

PERSHING, JOHN J. (JOHN JOSEPH), 1860-1948

McNeese, Tim. John J. Pershing. 2003. (Great Military Leaders of the Twentieth Century Ser.). (Illus.). 112p. (gr. 6-12). 30.00 (978-0-7910-7404-6(8), Chelsea Hse.) Facts On File, Inc.

PERSIAN GULF WAR, 1991

Calvert, John. The Arabian Peninsula in the Age of Oil. 2007. (J). (***978-1-4222-0172-5(4)***) Mason Crest Pubs.

Desert Storm. 2003. (Eye on History Ser.). 32p. (gr. 5-12). 5.99 (978-1-56822-942-3(9), IF2675) School Specialty Publishing.

Gunderson, Cory Gideon. U. N. Weapons Inspectors. 2004. (World in Conflict-the Middle East Ser.). (Illus.). 48p. (J). (gr. 4-8). lib. bdg. 25.65 (978-1-59197-414-7(3)) ABDO Publishing Co.

Hillstrom, Laurie Collier. War in the Persian Gulf: From Operation Desert Storm to Operation Iraqi Freedom Reference Library, 3 vols. Incl. War in the Persian Gulf: Biographies. Hillstrom, Kevin. 200p. (J). 67.00 (978-0-7876-6564-7(9)); War in the Persian Gulf Almanac: From Operation Desert Storm to Operation Iraqi Freedom. Carnagie, Julie, ed. 175p. 67.00 (978-0-7876-6563-0(0)); (Illus.). 600p. 2004. 181.00 (978-0-7876-6562-3(2), GML10504-182625, UXL) Thomson Gale.

Holden, Henry M. The Persian Gulf War: A MyReportLinks.com Book. 2003. (U. S. Wars Ser.). (Illus.). 48p. (J). (gr. 4-10). lib. bdg. 25.26 (978-0-7660-5109-6(9), MyReportLinks.com Bks.) Enslow Pubs., Inc.

Hossell, Karen Price. Kitty Hawk. 2003. (Point of Impact Ser.). 32p. (J). pap. 7.50 (978-1-4034-0714-6(2)) Heinemann Library.

—The Persian Gulf War. 2003. (20th-Century Perspectives Ser.). (Illus.). 48p. (J). lib. bdg. 27.07 (978-1-4034-1143-3(3)) Heinemann Library.

Kent, Zachary. The Persian Gulf War: "The Mother of All Battles" 2000. (American War Ser.). (Illus.). 128p. (YA). (gr. 5-12). pap. 13.26 (978-0-7660-1730-6(3)) Enslow Pubs., Inc.

King, John. The Invasion of Kuwait. 2004. (Days That Shook the World Ser.). (Illus.). 47p. (J). lib. bdg. 28.56 (978-0-7398-6644-3(3)) Raintree.

Martin, Michael. The Persian Gulf War: Saddam's Failed Invasion. 2004. (History's Great Defeats Ser.). (J). (gr. 7-10). 29.95 (978-1-59018-428-8(9), Lucent Bks.) Thomson Gale.

McArthur, Debra. Desert Storm—the First Persian Gulf War in American History. 2004. (In American History Ser.). (Illus.). 128p. (J). lib. bdg. 26.60 (978-0-7660-2149-5(1)) Enslow Pubs., Inc.

Nardo, Don. The War Against Iraq. 2001. (American War Library). (Illus.). 112p. (YA). (gr. 4-12). lib. bdg. 29.95 (978-1-56006-715-3(2), LML00902-178067, Lucent Bks.) Thomson Gale.

Peterson, John. Tensions in the Gulf, 1978-1991. 2007. (J). (***978-1-4222-0175-6(9)***) Mason Crest Pubs.

Press, Skip. Kuwaiti Oil Fires. 2000. (gr. 5-8). lib. bdg. 11.80 (978-0-613-51216-9(2)) Tandem Library Bks.

Price Hossell, Karen. The Persian Gulf War. 2003. (20th Century Perspectives Ser.). 48p. 7.95 (978-1-4034-3856-0(0)) Heinemann Library.

Santella, Andrew. The Persian Gulf War. 2004. (We the People Ser.). (Illus.). 48p. (J). (gr. 4 up). lib. bdg. 22.60 (978-0-7565-0612-4(3)) Compass Point Bks.

Schaffer, David. The Iran-Iraq War. 2002. (World History Ser.). (Illus.). 112p. (J). (gr. 8-11). 32.45 (978-1-59018-184-3(0), Lucent Bks.) Thomson Gale.

Schaffer, Donna & Meyer, Alfred. The Persian Gulf War. 2003. (People at the Center of Ser.). (Illus.). 48p. (J). 24.95 (978-1-56711-767-7(8), Blackbirch Pr., Inc.) Thomson Gale.

Speakman, Jay. Weapons of War. 2000. (American War Library). (Illus.). 112p. (YA). (gr. 4-12). lib. bdg. 29.95 (978-1-56006-649-1(0), LML00902-178003, Lucent Bks.) Thomson Gale.

Strait, Sandy. What Was It Like in Desert Storm? 1998. 312p. (YA). (gr. 7 up). pap. 14.99 (978-0-88092-316-3(4), 3164) Royal Fireworks Publishing Co.

Zeinert, Karen & Miller, Mary. The Brave Women of the Gulf Wars: Operation Desert Storm & Operation Iraqi Freedom. 2006. (Women at War Ser.). (Illus.). 112p. (J). (ps-7). 30.60 (978-0-7613-2705-9(3), Millbrook Pr.) Lerner Publishing Group.

Zwier, Lawrence J. & Weltig, Matthew Scott. The Persian Gulf & Iraqi Wars. 2005. (Chronicle of America's Wars Ser.). (Illus.). 96p. (J). (gr. 5-12). 27.93 (978-0-8225-0848-9(6)) Lerner Publishing Group.

PERSONAL APPEARANCE

see Beauty, Personal; Grooming for Men

PERSONAL DEVELOPMENT

see Personality; Success

PERSONAL FINANCE

see Finance, Personal

PERSONAL GROOMING

see Beauty, Personal; Grooming for Men

PERSONAL IDENTITY

see Identity (Psychology); Personality

PERSONAL LIBERTY

see Liberty

PERSONALITY

see also Identity (Psychology); Individuality

Bayer, Linda N. Personality Disorders. 2000. (Encyclopedia of Psychological Disorders Ser.). (Illus.). 88p. (YA). (gr. 7 up). 35.00 (978-0-7910-5317-1(2), Chelsea Hse.) Facts On File, Inc.

Funston, Sylvia. The Book of You: The Science & Fun! of Why You Look, Feel & Act the Way You Do. Denti, Susanna, illus. Duclos, Gilbert, photos by. 2000. 48p. (J). (gr. 3-7). (978-1-895688-95-5(7)) Maple Tree Pr. CAN. *Dist:* Firefly Bks., Ltd.

—Who Are You? Why You Look, Feel, & Act the Way You Do. 2004. (Illus.). 64p. (J). (gr. 4-8). 21.95 (978-1-894379-58-8(6)) Maple Tree Pr. CAN. *Dist:* Firefly Bks., Ltd.

—Who Are You? Why You Look, Feel, & Act the Way You Do. Denti, Susanna, illus. 2004. 64p. (J). (gr. 4-8). pap. 12.95 (978-1-894379-59-5(4)) Maple Tree Pr. CAN. *Dist:* Firefly Bks., Ltd.

Greenspon, Thomas S. What to Do When Good Enough Isn't Good Enough: The Real Deal on Perfectionism. 2007. (Illus.). 128p. (J). (gr. 4-8). pap. 9.95 (***978-1-57542-234-3(4)***) Free Spirit Publishing, Inc.

Ideal Instructional Fair Staff. Who I Am is Up to Me: Developing Character Education in the Middle School. 1998. 96p. (gr. 5-8). 9.99 (978-1-56822-622-4(5), IF2523) School Specialty Publishing.

Jones, Steven. Journey to Excellence: An Introduction to E4. 2003. 75p. (YA). per. 19.99 (978-0-9729798-0-1(8)) Keytochange Publishing, Inc.

Lewis, Barbara A. What Do You Stand for? for Kids: A Guide to Building Character. 2005. (Illus.). 176p. (J). (gr. 2-7). pap. 14.95 (978-1-57542-174-2(7)) Free Spirit Publishing, Inc.

Nelms, Davis Kenyon. Inner-Fire Kindling: Simple Exercises for the Permanent Establishment of Fulfilling Thoughts. 2004. (Illus.). 128p. per. 19.95 (978-0-9654169-7-9(6)) Billings Worldwide Brain.

Raatma, Lucia. Determination. 2002. (Character Education Ser.). (Illus.). 24p. (J). (gr. 1-2). lib. bdg. 18.60 (978-0-7368-1387-7(X), Bridgestone Bks.) Capstone Pr., Inc.

Relate & React: Skits for Developing Good Character in Real Life Situations in Grades 6-12. 2002. 132p. (YA). per. 18.95 (978-1-931636-02-5(8), Students Taking a Right Stand, (STARS)) National Center For Youth Issues.

Shaw, Tucker. Who Do You Think You Are? A Handbook for Analysing the True You. 2001. (gr. 7-12). lib. bdg. 15.30 (978-0-613-49386-4(9)) Tandem Library Bks.

Soul Secrets. 2000. (Two Grrrls Ser.). (J). 12.95 (978-0-439-22947-0(2)) Scholastic, Inc.

Williams, Jane A. A Bluestocking Guide - Building a Personal Model for Success: Companion Workbook to Richard J. Maybury's Uncle Eric Talks about Personal, Career, & Financial Security. Daniels, Kathryn, ed. 2004. (Bluestocking Guide Ser.). 47p. (YA). pap. 10.95 (978-0-942617-39-9(8)) Bluestocking Pr.

PERSONALITY—FICTION

Heuston, Kimberley Burton. Book of Jude. 2008. (J). (***978-1-932425-26-0(8)***, Front Street) Boyds Mills Pr.

Kay, Catherine. When I'm by Myself. Morgan, Ron, illus. 1998. (Sis & Beezie Ser.: Vol. 1). 32p. (J). (ps-6). 17.95 (978-0-9663651-0-8(0)) Portos Publishing Co.

Lundy, Charlotte. Thank You, Moses. Waldrep, Evelyn L., ed. James, Margaret Ray, illus. 1999. 32p. (ps-3). 15.95 (978-0-9670280-3-3(5)) Bay Light Publishing.

Quinones, Juan Carlos. La Pandilla Bajo el Arbol. 2003. (SPA.). (gr. 3-6). lib. bdg. 14.10 (978-0-613-79282-0(3)) Tandem Library Bks.

Rodgers, Mary. Freaky Friday. 2003. 176p. (J). (gr. 5 up). pap. 5.99 (978-0-06-057010-1(5)) HarperCollins Pubs.

—Freaky Friday. 2003. (gr. 7-12). lib. bdg. 14.15 (978-0-613-68424-8(9)) Tandem Library Bks.

Rodgers, Mary, ed. Freaky Friday. 145p. (J). (gr. 4-6). pap. 4.95 (978-0-8072-1390-2(X), Listening Library) Random Hse. Audio Publishing Group.

Sander, Sonia. Who's Who? Sticker Storybook. del Sur, Duendes, illus. 2003. (Care Bears Ser.). 16p. (J). 5.99 (978-0-439-45544-2(8)) Scholastic, Inc.

Scraper, Katherine. Remember the Rules. 2006. (Early Explorers Ser.). (J). 30.00 (***978-1-4108-6031-6(0)***) Benchmark Education Co.

Vail, Rachel. Ever After. 2005. 192p. (J). (gr. 7-12). pap. 7.99 (978-0-06-058748-2(2), Harper Trophy) HarperCollins Pubs.

PERSONNEL SERVICE IN EDUCATION

see Educational Counseling

PERSPECTIVE

see also Drawing

Cole, Alison. Perspective. 2000. (Eyewitness Bks.). (Illus.). 64p. (J). (gr. 4-7). 15.99 (978-0-7894-5585-7(4)) Dorling Kindersley Publishing, Inc.

Cole, Alison & Dorling Kindersley Publishing Staff. Perspective. 2000. (Eyewitness Bks.). (Illus.). 64p. (J). (gr. 4-7). lib. bdg. 19.99 (978-0-7894-6818-5(2)) Dorling Kindersley Publishing, Inc.

Flux, Paul. Perspective. (Illus.). 32p. (J). 2007. (***978-1-4034-9632-4(3)***); 2001. (gr. 1-3). lib. bdg. 22.79 (978-1-58810-080-1(4)) Heinemann Library.

—Perspective (2nd Edition) 2007. (Illus.). 32p. (J). (***978-1-4034-9638-6(2)***) Heinemann Library.

Hepker, Sue. Cheese! Yummy Cheese! Tadjo, Veronique, tr. from ENG. 1998. (Cambridge African Language Library Ser.). (FRE., Illus.). 16p. pap. 3.75 (978-0-521-64789-2(4)) Cambridge Univ. Pr.

—Cheese! Yummy Cheese! Hausa Version. Bello, Gidado, tr. 1998. (Cambridge African Language Library Ser.). (HAU., Illus.). 16p. pap. 6.60 (978-0-521-64797-7(5)) Cambridge Univ. Pr.

Levy, Janey. Renaissance Paintings: Using Perspective to Represent Three-Dimensional Objects. 2005. (PowerMath Ser.). (Illus.). 32p. (J). 22.50 (978-1-4042-2926-6(4) , PowerKids Pr.); (978-1-4042-5116-8(2) , PowerKids Pr.); pap. (978-1-4042-5115-1(4)) Rosen Publishing Group, Inc., The.

PERSUASION (RHETORIC)

see Public Speaking; Rhetoric

PERU

Annabelle Alpaca Travels to Peru. 2005. (J). per. 7.99 (978-0-9746409-1-4(3)) O'Neill, Jan.

Bingham, Jane. The Inca Empire. 2007. (Time Travel Guides Ser.). (Illus.). 64p. (YA). (gr. 5-8). lib. bdg. 34.29 ***(978-1-4109-2731-6(8))*** Raintree.

—The Inca Empire. 2007. (Time Travel Guides Ser.). (Illus.). 64p. (J). ***(978-1-4109-2738-5(5))*** Steck-Vaughn.

Catherine, Mary & O'Sullivan, MaryCate. Peru. 2000. (Countries: Faces & Places Ser.). (Illus.). 32p. (J). (gr. 1-5). 25.64 (978-1-56766-739-4(2)) Child's World, Inc.

Cavan, Seamus. Peru. 2002. (Steadwell Books World Tour). (Illus.). 48p. (J). lib. bdg. 29.93 (978-0-7398-5755-7(X)) Raintree.

Corona, Laurel. Peru. 2001. (Modern Nations of the World Ser.). (Illus.). 112p. (YA). (gr. 7-10). 28.70 (978-1-56006-862-4(0) , Lucent Bks.) Thomson Gale.

Crespi, Jess. Exploring Peru with the Five Themes of Geography. 2005. (Library of the Western Hemisphere). (Illus.). 24p. (J). 19.95 (978-1-4042-2676-0(1) , PowerKids Pr.); pap. (978-0-8239-4636-5(3)) Rosen Publishing Group, Inc., The.

Croy, Anita. Peru. 2007. (National Geographic Countries of the World Ser.). (Illus.). 64p. (J). (gr. 3-5). lib. bdg. 27.90 (978-1-4263-0031-8(X) , National Geographic Children's Bks.) National Geographic Society.

Dalal, Anita. Peru. 2003. (Nations of the World Ser.). (Illus.). 128p. (J). pap. 34.28 (978-0-7398-7000-6(9)) Steck-Vaughn.

De Capua, Sarah. Peru. 2004. (Discovering Cultures Ser.). (J). 25.64 (978-0-7614-1796-5(6) , Benchmark Bks.) Cavendish, Marshall Corp.

DeLoach, Sylvia & Massey, Barbara. Partners in Peru. 1998. (Child Like Me Ser.). 32p. (J). (gr. 1-4). per. 6.99 (978-1-56309-258-9(1) , N987105) New Hope Pubs.

Dubois, Muriel L. Peru. 2005. (Fact Finders Ser.). (Illus.). 32p. (J). 22.60 (978-0-7368-3758-3(2)) Capstone Pr., Inc.

Fajardo, Sara Andrea. In a Peruvian City. 2002. (Child's Day Ser.). (Illus.). 32p. (J). 15.95 (978-0-7614-1408-7(8) , Benchmark Bks.) Cavendish, Marshall Corp.

Falconer, Kieran & Quek, Lynette. Peru. 2nd ed. 2006. (Cultures of the World Ser.). 144p. (J). lib. bdg. 39.93 (978-0-7614-2068-2(1) , Benchmark Bks.) Cavendish, Marshall Corp.

Fearns, Daisy & Fearns, Les. Argentina. 2003. (Changing Face Of... Ser.). (Illus.). 48p. (J). 28.56 (978-0-7398-6040-3(2)); 28.56 (978-0-7398-5486-0(0)) Raintree.

Giraud, Hervé. Tomasino: A Child of Peru. 2005. (Children of the World Ser.). (Illus.). 24p. (J). (gr. 2-4). 22.45 (978-1-4103-0546-6(5) , Blackbirch Pr., Inc.) Thomson Gale.

Gritzner, Charles & Gritzner, Yvonne. Peru. 2004. (Modern World Nations Ser.). (Illus.). 120p. (J). (gr. 6-12). 30.00 (978-0-7910-7478-7(1) , Chelsea Hse.) Facts On File, Inc.

Heisey, Janet. Peru. 2001. (Countries of the World Ser.). (Illus.). 96p. (J). (gr. 6 up). lib. bdg. 30.00 (978-0-8368-2333-2(8)) Stevens, Gareth Inc.

Italia, Bob. Peru. 2002. (Countries Ser.). (Illus.). 40p. (J). (gr. k-6). lib. bdg. 22.78 (978-1-57765-756-9(X) , Checkerboard Library) ABDO Publishing Co.

Kallen, Stuart A. The Deepest Canyon. 2003. (Extreme Places Ser.). (Illus.). 48p. (J). 26.20 (978-0-7377-1880-5(3) , Greenhaven Pr., Inc.) Thomson Gale.

Kalman, Bobbie. Peru: The Land. 2003. (gr. 3-6). lib. bdg. 16.40 (978-0-613-59094-5(5)) Tandem Library Bks.

—Peru: The People & Culture. 2003. (gr. 3-6). lib. bdg. 16.40 (978-0-613-59095-2(3)) Tandem Library Bks.

—Peru - The Land. 2003. (Lands, Peoples & Cultures Ser.). (Illus.). 32p. (J). (gr. 2-9). rev. ed. pap. (978-0-7787-9709-8(0)); 2nd rev. ed. (978-0-7787-9341-0(9)) Crabtree Publishing Co.

Kalman, Bobbie & Everts, Tammy. Peru - The People & Culture. rev. ed. 2003. (Lands, Peoples & Cultures Ser.). (Illus.). 32p. (J). (gr. 2-9). (978-0-7787-9342-7(7)); pap. (978-0-7787-9710-4(4)) Crabtree Publishing Co.

Knox, Barbara. Peru. 2004. (Many Cultures, One World Ser.). (Illus.). 32p. (J). (gr. 2-3). lib. bdg. 23.93 (978-0-7368-2450-7(2) , Bridgestone Bks.) Capstone Pr., Inc.

Landau, Elaine. Peru. 2000. (True Bks.). (Illus.). 48p. (J). (gr. 3-5). pap. 6.95 (978-0-516-27019-7(2) , Children's Pr.) Scholastic Library Publishing.

—Peru. 2000. (gr. 3-6). lib. bdg. 15.25 (978-0-613-54081-0(6)) Tandem Library Bks.

Lyle, Garry. Peru. 1999. (Major World Nations Ser.). (Illus.). 144p. (YA). (gr. 4-7). lib. bdg. 21.95 (978-0-7910-4971-6(X) , Chelsea Hse.) Facts On File, Inc.

Mann, Elizabeth. Machu Picchu: The Story of the Amazing Inkas & Their City in the Clouds. Crehore, Amy, illus. 2006. (Wonders of the World Book Ser.). 48p. (J). (gr. 4-8). pap. 9.95 (978-1-931414-10-4(6)) Mikaya Pr.

Marquez, Heron. Peru in Pictures. 2nd rev. expurg. ed. 2004. (Visual Geography Ser.). (Illus.). 80p. (J). (gr. 5-12). 27.93 (978-0-8225-1999-7(2)) Lerner Publishing Group.

Shields, Charles J. Peru. 2003. (Discovering South America Ser.). (Illus.). 64p. (J). (gr. 5 up). lib. bdg. (978-1-59084-288-1(X)) Mason Crest Pubs.

Steele, Philip. The Incas: What Life Was Like in the Spectacular South American Empire. 2003. (Find Out about ...Ser.). (Illus.). 64p. (gr. 3-7). pap. 7.99 (978-1-84215-777-0(9) , Southwater) Anness Publishing GBR. *Dist:* National Bk. Network.

Thoennes, Kristin. Peru. 1999. (Countries of the World Ser.). (Illus.). 126p. (J). (gr. 2-3). 18.60 (978-0-7368-0155-3(3) , Bridgestone Bks.) Capstone Pr., Inc.

Yip, Dora & Heisey, Janet. Welcome to Peru. 2002. (Welcome to My Country Ser.). (Illus.). 48p. (J). (gr. 2 up). lib. bdg. 26.00 (978-0-8368-2533-6(0)) Stevens, Gareth Inc.

PERU—ANTIQUITIES

Dean, Arlan. Terra-Cotta Soldiers: Army of Stone. 2005. (High Interest Books Ser.). (Illus.). 48p. (J). (ps-7). 24.00 (978-0-516-25124-0(4) , Children's Pr.) Scholastic Library Publishing.

Lourie, Peter. Lost Treasure of the Inca. 2003. (Illus.). 48p. (J). (gr. 4-6). 18.95 (978-1-56397-743-5(5)); pap. 10.95 (978-1-56397-983-5(7)) Boyds Mills Pr.

—Lost Treasure of the Inca. 2001. (gr. 3-6). lib. bdg. 18.75 (978-0-613-53831-2(5)) Tandem Library Bks.

Peterson, Sheryl. Machu Picchu. 2005. (Ancient Wonders of the World Ser.). (Illus.). 32p. (gr. 4-7). 18.95 (978-1-58341-357-9(X) , Creative Education) Creative Co., The.

Somervill, Barbara A. Machu Picchu: City in the Clouds. 2005. (High Interest Books). (Illus.). 48p. (J). (ps-7). 24.00 (978-0-516-25123-3(6)); (YA). (gr. 7-12). pap. 6.95 (978-0-516-25092-2(2)) Scholastic Library Publishing. (Children's Pr.).

PERU—FICTION

Abelove, Joan. Go & Come Back. 2000. (Illus.). 192p. (J). (gr. 7-12). pap. 5.99 (978-0-14-130694-0(7) , Puffin) Penguin Group (USA) Inc.

—Go & Come Back. 2000. (gr. 7-12). lib. bdg. 14.15 (978-0-613-28498-1(4)); (Illus.). (J). (978-0-606-18406-9(6)) Tandem Library Bks.

Angello, Mary L. Rings of Power. 2001. 108p. (J). (gr. 4-7). pap. 9.95 (978-0-595-20231-7(4) , Writers Club Pr.) iUniverse, Inc.

Diaz, Katacha. Carolina's Gift: A Story of Peru. Landolt, Gredna, illus. 2005. (Make Friends Around the World Ser.). 32p. (J). (gr. k-3). 15.95 (978-1-56899-695-0(0) , B8005); 19.95 incl. audio (978-1-56899-697-4(7) , BC8005); pap. 6.95 (978-1-56899-696-7(9) , S8005) Soundprints.

—Carolina's Gift: A Story of Peru. 2002. (gr. k-3). lib. bdg. 14.10 (978-0-613-70805-0(9)) Tandem Library Bks.

Eby, Wes. Jungle Jeopardy. 2006. 56p. 7.75 (978-0-8341-2228-4(6)) Beacon Hill Pr. of Kansas City.

Garcia, Randolph. The Steamer Trunk Adventures #2: The Ghosts of Machu Picchu. 2006. (ENG.). 88p. per. 14.95 ***(978-1-4241-1843-4(3))*** PublishAmerica, Inc.

Hamilton, Martha. The Stolen Smell. 2007. 32p. (J). pap. 3.95 ***(978-0-87483-838-1(X))*** August Hse. Pubs., Inc.

Horowitz, Anthony. Evil Star. 2006. (Power of Five Ser.: Vol. 2). 320p. (J). pap. 17.99 (978-0-439-67996-1(6) , Scholastic Pr.) Scholastic, Inc.

Kain, Wallace M. The Red Column: A Young Woman's Capture, Imprisonment & Escape in the Amazon Jungle. 2006. (YA). per. 12.95 (978-0-9742148-1-8(7)) Inkberry Pr.

Marcuse, Aida E. Lo Que Cuentan los Incas. 1999. (Cuentamerica Ser.). (SPA.). 64p. (J). (gr. 4-6). pap. (978-950-07-1501-0(5) , SA30063) Editorial Sudamericana S.A. ARG. *Dist:* Lectorum Pubns., Inc.

Merino, Jose Maria. Las Lagrimas del Sol Level 4. 1998. (SPA.). (gr. 7-12). lib. bdg. 15.25 (978-0-613-80717-3(0)) Tandem Library Bks.

Packard, Albert. Cavern of Babel. Boyles, Shawn, illus. 2006. (J). per. 14.95 ***(978-0-9790652-0-0(8))*** Diamond Triple C Ranch.

Ramblin' Rose: The Wire Forests of Peru. 2007. 200p. (YA). pap. 8.99 ***(978-0-9776043-9-5(X))*** Aspirations Media, Inc.

Russell, Elaine. Martin Mcmillan & the Lost Inca City. Cornell du Houx, Emily M. D., illus. 2005. 128p. (gr. 5 up). pap. 10.00 (978-1-882190-86-7(6)) Polar Bear & Co.

PERU—HISTORY

Allison, Amy. Machu Picchu. 2003. (Building History Ser.). (Illus.). 112p. (YA). 32.45 (978-1-59018-020-4(8) , Lucent Bks.) Thomson Gale.

Baer, Suzie. Peru's MRTA: Tupac Amaru Revolutionary Movement. 2005. (Inside the World's Most Infamous Terrorist Organizations Ser.). (Illus.). 64p. (YA). (gr. 7-12). lib. bdg. 26.50 (978-0-8239-3824-7(7)) Rosen Publishing Group, Inc., The.

Byers, Helen. Peru. 2004. (National Geographic Reading Expeditions Ser.). (Illus.). 24p. (J). pap. (978-0-7922-4538-4(5)) National Geographic Society.

Donaldson-Forbes, Jeff. Francisco Pizarro. 2002. (Famous Explorers Ser.). (Illus.). 24p. (J). (gr. 3). lib. bdg. 18.75 (978-0-8239-5831-3(0) , PowerKids Pr.) Rosen Publishing Group, Inc., The.

Hoogenboom, Lynn. Francisco Pizarro: A Primary Source Biography. 2006. (J). lib. bdg. (978-1-4042-3038-5(6) , PowerKids Pr.) Rosen Publishing Group, Inc., The.

Hoyle, R. L. Peru. (SPA., Illus.). 260p. pap. 39.95 (978-84-261-1080-0(0) , JV800) Juventud, Editorial ESP. *Dist:* Continental Bk. Co., Inc.

Ingram, Scott. Francisco Pizarro. 2002. (History's Villains Ser.). (Illus.). 112p. 29.94 (978-1-56711-627-4(2) , Blackbirch Pr., Inc.) Thomson Gale.

Kachurek, Sandra J. Francisco Pizarro: Explorer of South America. 2004. (Explorers! Ser.). (Illus.). 48p. (J). lib. bdg. 23.93 (978-0-7660-2178-5(5)) Enslow Pubs., Inc.

Lassieur, Allison. Peru. 2003. (Countries & Cultures Ser.). (Illus.). 64p. (J). lib. bdg. 25.26 (978-0-7368-2176-6(7) , Bridgestone Bks.) Capstone Pr., Inc.

Manning, Ruth. Francisco Pizarro. (Groundbreakers Ser.). (Illus.). 48p. (J). (gr. 5-7). 2002. pap. 8.50 (978-1-58810-341-3(2) , 91092); 2000. lib. bdg. 25.64 (978-1-57572-369-3(7)) Heinemann Library.

—Francisco Pizarro. 2001. (gr. 5-8). lib. bdg. 17.05 (978-0-613-87922-4(8)) Tandem Library Bks.

Martell, Hazel Mary. Civilizations of Peru Before 1535. 1999. (Looking Back Ser.). (Illus.). 64p. (YA). (gr. 6-9). 19.98 (978-0-8172-5428-5(5)) Raintree.

Mountjoy, Shane. Francisco Pizarro & the Conquest of the Inca. Goetzmann, William H., ed. 2005. (Explorers of New Lands Ser.). (Illus.). 150p. (J). (gr. 4-8). 30.00 (978-0-7910-8614-8(3) , Chelsea Hse.) Facts On File, Inc.

Saunders, Nicholas. Pizarro & the Incas. 2006. (Stories from History Ser.). 48p. (J). pap. 6.95 ***(978-0-7696-4642-8(5))*** School Specialty Publishing.

Saunders, Nicholas J. The Inca City of Cuzco. 2005. (Places in History Ser.). (Illus.). 48p. (J). pap. (978-0-8368-5819-8(0)); lib. bdg. 30.00 (978-0-8368-5812-9(3)) Stevens, Gareth Inc. (World Almanac Library).

Somervill, Barbara A. Francisco Pizarro: Conqueror of the Incas. 2004. (Signature Lives Ser.). (Illus.). 112p. (J). 30.60 (978-0-7565-0815-9(0) , 1240121) Compass Point Bks.

Steele, Phillip. Step Into: The Inca World. 2006. (Illus.). 64p. pap. 12.99 (978-1-84476-304-7(8) , Southwater) Anness Publishing GBR. *Dist:* National Bk. Network.

Worth, Richard. Pizarro & the Conquest of the Incan Empire in World History. 2000. (In World History Ser.). (Illus.). 128p. (YA). (gr. 5-12). lib. bdg. 26.60 (978-0-7660-1396-4(0)) Enslow Pubs., Inc.

Zronik, John Paul. Francisco Pizarro: Journeys Through Peru & South America. 2005. (In the Footsteps of Explorers Ser.). (Illus.). 32p. (J). (ps-9). (978-0-7787-2411-7(5)); pap. (978-0-7787-2447-6(6)) Crabtree Publishing Co.

PESTICIDE POLLUTION

see Pesticides—Environmental Aspects

PESTICIDES—ENVIRONMENTAL ASPECTS

Carson, Rachel Louise. Silent Spring. 2002. (gr. 7-12). lib. bdg. 23.45 (978-0-613-62362-9(2)) Tandem Library Bks.

Kroll, Mary. Cycling Back to Nature: Food Production & Pesticides. Clapp, Katie & Hoff, Mary, eds. 1998. (Illus.). 94p. (J). (gr. k-12). pap. 30.00 (978-0-7881-4297-0(6)) DIANE Publishing Co.

Macfarlane, Katherine. Pesticides. 2007. (Our Environment Ser.). 48p. (J). (gr. 4-8). 26.20 ***(978-0-7377-3619-9(4)*** , Kidhaven) Thomson Gale.

PESTS

see Fungi; Insects, Injurious and Beneficial; Parasites; Zoology, Economic

PETER, THE APOSTLE, SAINT

Brennan, Gerald T. The Man Who Never Died. 2005. (Illus.). viii, 87p. (J). pap. 11.95 (978-1-933184-09-8(4)) Sophia Institute Pr.

Britt, Stephanie. My Name Is Peter. 1999. (Illus.). 16p. (J). (ps). 3.95 (978-0-687-05328-5(5)) Abingdon Pr.

Freed, Shirley & Moon, Louise. Peter on the Water. Morelan, Bill, ed. Butler, Steven, illus. 2003. 16p. (J). (gr. 1 up). pap. 3.99 (978-1-58938-110-0(6)) Concerned Communications.

Gemmen, Heather & McNeil, Mary. No Fear, Level 3. Graham, Alastair, tr. Graham, Alastair, illus. 1999. (Rocket Readers Ser.). 24p. (J). (gr. 3 up). pap., pap. 8.99 (978-0-7814-3988-6(4) , 0781439884) Cook, David C. Publishing Co.

Harrison, Susan. Peter, a Follower of Jesus. 1998. (Illus.). 16p. (J). (gr. 2-3). 3.95 (978-0-687-05329-2(3)) Abingdon Pr.

Kershner, Jan, ed. How Peter Served Jesus. 2004. (Bible Big Bks.). (Illus.). 8p. (ps-k). pap. 15.99 (978-1-55945-427-8(X) , Flagship Church Resources) Group Publishing, Inc.

Konzen, Lisa. The Great Catch of Fish: Luke 5:1-11 for Children. Rooney, Ronnie, illus. 2006. (Arch Books). (ENG.). (J). 1.99 (978-0-7586-0871-0(3)) Concordia Publishing Hse.

Mayhan, Benton. Peter & His Friend Jesus. 1998. (Illus.). 16p. (J). (ps-1). 3.95 (978-0-687-05338-4(2)) Abingdon Pr.

Nederveld, Patricia L. A Prayer for Peter: The Story of Peter in Prison. 1998. (God Loves Me Ser.). (Illus.). 24p. (J). (ps-3). pap. 2.95 (978-1-56212-315-4(7) , 001246, Faith Alive Christian Resources) CRC Pubns.

Nystrom, Carolyn. Fish, Peter! 2004. (Follow Me Bks.). 10.99 (978-0-8254-3332-0(0)) Kregel Pubns.

PETER I, EMPEROR OF RUSSIA, 1672-1725

Greenblatt, Miriam. Peter the Great & Tsarist Russia. 1999. (Rulers & Their Times Ser.). (Illus.). 80p. (J). (gr. 6 up). lib. bdg. 29.93 (978-0-7614-0914-4(9) , Benchmark Bks.) Cavendish, Marshall Corp.

PETER PAN (FICTITIOUS CHARACTER)—FICTION

Barrie, J. M. Peter Pan. 2007. (Illus.). 192p. pap. 14.95 ***(978-0-413-73550-8(8))*** A & C Black GBR. *Dist:* Consortium Bk. Sales & Distribution.

—Peter Pan. Davis, Allen, illus. 2002. (Great Illustrated Classics Ser.). 240p. (J). (gr. 3-8). 21.35 (978-1-57765-820-7(5) , ABDO & Daughters) ABDO Publishing Co.

—Peter Pan. (SPA.). 191p. 15.95 (978-84-206-3689-4(4)) Alianza Editorial, S. A. ESP. *Dist:* Distribooks, Inc.

—Peter Pan. 2002. (Spot the Classics Ser.). (Illus.). 178p. (J). (gr. k-5). 4.99 (978-1-57759-548-9(3)) Dalmatian Pr.

—Peter Pan. 2003. (Illus.). 224p. (J). 5.99 (978-0-7653-4719-0(9) , Starscape) Doherty, Tom Assocs., LLC.

—Peter Pan. Vess, Charles, illus. rev. ed. 2003. 224p. (J). 15.95 (978-0-7653-0809-2(6) , Starscape) Doherty, Tom Assocs., LLC.

—Peter Pan. 1999. (Illus.). 160p. (J). (gr. 4-7). pap. 2.50 (978-0-486-40783-8(7)) Dover Pubns., Inc.

—Peter Pan. 2000. (Charming Classics). 240p. (J). (gr. 4-7). pap. 6.99 (978-0-694-01318-0(8) , Harper Festival) HarperCollins Pubs.

—Peter Pan. (J). pap. (978-0-340-71498-0(0) , Hodder & Stoughton) Hodder General Publishing Division.

—Peter Pan. Hague, Michael, illus. 100th annot. rev. ed. 2003. 176p. (J). 22.50 (978-0-8050-7245-7(4) , Holt, Henry & Co. Bks. For Young Readers) Holt, Henry & Co.

—Peter Pan. (J). 9.95 (978-1-56156-305-0(6)) Kidsbooks, Inc.

—Peter Pan. Bedford, Francis D., illus. 1999. (Children's Classics Ser.). 304p. (J). (gr. 4-7). 6.99 (978-0-517-20577-8(7)) Random Hse. Value Publishing.

—Peter Pan. 2006. (Scholastic Classics Ser.). (Illus.). v, 140p. (J). (gr. 9-12). 25.00 (978-0-531-16993-3(6) , Watts, Franklin) Scholastic Library Publishing.

—Peter Pan. 2003. (Aladdin Classics Ser.). 256p. (J). (gr. 3-7). pap. 4.99 (978-0-689-86691-3(7) , Aladdin) Simon & Schuster Children's Publishing.

—Peter Pan. 2000. (Illus.). 134p. (J). 24.95 (978-1-58479-029-7(6)) Stewart, Tabori & Chang.

—Peter Pan. 2003. (gr. 3-6). lib. bdg. 14.15 (978-0-613-85653-9(8)); lib. bdg. 11.80 (978-0-613-86964-5(8)) Tandem Library Bks.

—Peter Pan. l.t. ed. 2003. (Perennial Bestsellers Ser.). 269p. (J). 29.95 (978-0-7862-5263-3(4)) Thorndike Pr.

—Peter Pan: Peter & Wendy & Peter Pan in Kensington Gardens. 2004. (Illus.). 272p. (gr. 12). pap. 9.00 (978-0-14-243793-3(X) , Penguin Classics) Penguin Group (USA) Inc.

—Peter Pan: The Original Story. 2003. (gr. 3-6). lib. bdg. 13.00 (978-0-613-71839-4(9)) Tandem Library Bks.

—Peter Pan: The Original Tale of Neverland. Jaramillo, Raquel, illus. Jaramillo, Raquel, photos by. unabr. ed. 2003. 135p. (YA). (gr. 5-8). reprint ed. 25.00 (978-0-7567-6883-6(7)) DIANE Publishing Co.

—Peter Pan & Other Plays: The Admirable Crichton; Peter Pan; When Wendy Grew Up; What Every Woman Knows; Mary Rose. Hollindale, Peter, ed. 1999. (Oxford World's Classics Ser.). (Illus.). 384p. 14.95 (978-0-19-283919-0(5)) Oxford Univ. Pr., Inc.

—Peter Pan & Other Plays Vol. 10: The Admirable Crichton; Peter Pan; When Wendy Grew Up; What Every Woman Knows; Mary Rose. (J). reprint ed. 57.50 (978-0-404-08790-6(6)) AMS Pr., Inc.

—Peter Pan & Wendy. Foreman, Michael, illus. 1999. (Abbeville Classics Ser.). 176p. (J). 12.95 (978-0-7892-0560-5(2)); pap. 7.95 (978-0-7892-0550-6(5)) Abbeville Pr., Inc. (Abbeville Kids).

—Peter Pan & Wendy. Foreman, Michael, illus. (J). 2007. 158p. pap. 13.95 ***(978-1-84458-479-6(8))***; 2000. 176p. pap. 8.99 (978-1-85793-909-5(3) , Pavilion Bks., Ltd.) Anova Bks. GBR. *Dist:* Independent Pubs. Group, Trafalgar Square Publishing.

—Peter Pan & Wendy. Foreman, Michael, illus. 2003. (Chrysalis Children's Classics Ser.). 176p. (YA). pap. (978-1-84365-039-3(8)) Chrysalis Children's Bks.

—Peter Pan & Wendy. Carruth, Jane, ed. Johnstone, Anne G., illus. 2000. 92p. (J). (gr. 4-6). reprint ed. 25.00 (978-0-7881-9230-2(2)) DIANE Publishing Co.

—Peter Pan & Wendy. 2004. (Illus.). 96p. (J). 9.99 (978-0-517-22366-6(X) , Gramercy) Random Hse. Value Publishing.

—Peter Pan & Wendy: Centenary Edition. Ingpen, Robert R., illus. 2004. 216p. (J). (978-1-897035-12-2(8) , Blue Heron Bks.) Raincoast Bk. Distribution.

—Peter Pan in Kensington Gardens. (J). 18.95 (978-0-8488-0427-5(9)) Amereon LTD.

—Peter Pan in Kensington Gardens. 2006. pap. ***(978-1-4065-0950-2(7))*** Dodo Pr.

—Peter Pan in Kensington Gardens & Peter & Wendy. Hollingdale, Peter, ed. 1999. (Oxford World's Classics Ser.). (Illus.). 288p. 9.95 (978-0-19-283929-9(2)) Oxford Univ. Pr., Inc.

—Peter Pan y Wendy Great Read. 2005. (Great Classics for Children Ser.). (SPA.). 160p. (J). 5.99 (978-1-4037-1146-5(1)) Dalmatian Pr.

Barrie, J. M. Tommy & Grizel (Illustrated Edition) (2006. (Illus.). pap. ***(978-1-4065-0954-0(X))*** Dodo Pr.

Barrie, J. M. & Hyman, Trina Schart. Peter Pan. 2001. (Scribner Illustrated Classics Ser.). (Illus.). 208p. (J). 27.00 (978-0-689-83078-5(5) , Atheneum) Simon & Schuster Children's Publishing.

Barrie, J. M., et al. Peter Pan. 2000. (Illus.). 176p. (J). (gr. 4-7). 19.95 (978-0-8118-2297-8(4)) Chronicle Bks. LLC.

Barry, Dave & Pearson, Ridley. Peter & the Starcatchers. 2004. 464p. (gr. 5-17). 17.99 (978-0-7868-5445-5(6)) Hyperion Bks. for Children.

Bergen, Lara. Walt Disney's Peter Pan. 2007. 96p. (J). (ps-2). 12.99 ***(978-1-4231-0475-9(7))*** Disney Pr.

Dalmatian Press Staff. Disney's Peter Pan. rev. ed. 2007. 18p. 11.99 ***(978-1-4037-3222-4(1))*** Dalmatian Pr.

Dalmatian Press Staff. Peter Pan/Robin Hood Storybook Treasury. 2006. 64p. pap. 8.99 (978-1-4037-2047-4(9)) Dalmatian Pr.

Dalmatian Press Staff, ed. Peter Pan. 2006. 24p. pap. 3.50 (978-1-4037-2957-6(3)) Dalmatian Pr.

—Peter Pan/Robin Hood. 2006. 64p. pap. 4.99 (978-1-4037-2341-3(9)) Dalmatian Pr.

Driggs, Scout. Peter Pan: Adventures in Neverland. 2003. (gr. 3-6). lib. bdg. 13.00 (978-0-613-71458-7(X)) Tandem Library Bks.

Hart, J. V. Capt. Hook: The Adventures of a Notorious Youth. Helquist, Brett, illus. 2007. 368p. (J). (gr. 5 up). pap. 6.99 (***978-0-06-000222-0(0)***, Harper Trophy) HarperCollins Pubs.

LeapFrog Staff, compiled by. Peter Pan. (J). 2002. (gr. 3-7). 14.95 (978-1-58605-919-4(X), LeapFrog Schl. Hse.); 2001. spiral bd. 14.99 (978-1-58605-046-7(X)) LeapFrog Enterprises, Inc.

McCaughrean, Geraldine. Peter Pan. 2006. 232p. pap. 17.95 (***978-958-704-467-6(3)***) Alfaguara, Ediciones, S.A.- Grupo Santillana ESP. *Dist:* Santillana USA Publishing Co., Inc.

McCaughrean, Geraldine. Peter Pan in Scarlet. Fischer, Scott M., illus. 2006. 320p. (J). (gr. 4-9). 17.99 (978-1-4169-1808-0(6), McElderry, Margaret K.) Simon & Schuster Children's Publishing.

Peter Pan. 2003. (Illus.). 12.99 (978-0-7868-3479-2(X)) Disney Pr.

Peter Pan II: Return to Neverland. 2002. (Illus.). (J). 15.95 (978-0-7853-6003-2(4)) Publications International, Ltd.

Peter Pantm. 2003. (J). 173.68 (978-0-06-056911-2(5)) HarperCollins Pubs.

Random House Disney Staff. Walt Disney's Peter Pan. Dempster, Al, illus. 2007. (Little Golden Book Ser.). 24p. (J). (gr. k-k). 2.99 (978-0-7364-0238-5(1), Golden/Disney) Random Hse. Children's Bks.

PETER RABBIT (FICTITIOUS CHARACTER)—FICTION

Ada, Alma Flor. Dear Peter Rabbit. Tryon, Leslie, illus. 2006. (Stories to Go! Ser.).Tr. of Dear Peter Rabbit. 32p. (J). pap. 4.99 (978-1-4169-1233-0(9), Aladdin) Simon & Schuster Children's Publishing.

Akmon, Nancy C. Peter Rabbit Celebrates Christmas. Akmon, Roni, ed. 1999. (Illus.). 48p. (J). 8.95 (978-1-884807-45-9(3), EC745) Blushing Rose Publishing.

Johnson, Jane. The True Story of Peter Rabbit: How a Letter Became a Beloved Children's Classic. Johnson, Jane, illus. 2006. 40p. (J). (ps). pap. 7.99 (978-0-14-240789-9(5), Puffin) Penguin Group (USA) Inc.

Potter, Beatrix. Baby Grows up with Peter Rabbit: A Record of Babies First Year. 2002. (Illus.). 48p. (J). 9.99 (978-0-7232-4802-6(8), Warne) Penguin Group (USA) Inc.

—The Complete Adventures of Peter Rabbit R/I. 2007. 80p. (J). (ps). 14.99 (***978-0-7232-5916-9(X)***, Warne) Penguin Group (USA) Inc.

—The Complete Tales of Peter Rabbit & Other Favorite Stories. 2001. (Courage Children's Ser.). (Illus.). 56p. (J). 9.98 (978-0-7624-1271-6(2), Courage Bks.) Running Pr. Bk. Pubs.

—The Complete Tales of Peter Rabbit & Plush Toy Gift Set. 2002. (Courage Children's Ser.). (Illus.). 56p. (J). 19.98 (978-0-7624-1272-3(0)) Running Pr. Bk. Pubs.

—Merry Christmas, Peter Rabbit! 2003. (Illus.). 12p. (J). (ps). bds. 6.99 (978-0-7232-4925-2(3), Warne) Penguin Group (USA) Inc.

—My Peter Rabbit Cloth Book R/I. 2007. 8p. (J). 5.99 (***978-0-7232-5960-2(7)***, Warne) Penguin Group (USA) Inc.

—Peter Rabbit: A Lucky Escape. 2008. (J). (gr. k). 16p. 17.99 (***978-0-7232-5988-6(7)***); (Illus.). 18p. 17.99 (***978-0-7232-5927-5(5)***) Penguin Group (USA) Inc. (Warne).

—Peter Rabbit & Friends. ed. 2008. (Potter Ser.). (Illus.). 12p. (J). (ps). pap. 4.99 (***978-0-7232-5888-9(0)***, Warne) Penguin Group (USA) Inc.

—The Peter Rabbit & Friends Treasury. Potter, Beatrix, illus. 2006. (Illus.). 240p. (J). (gr. k-4). reprint ed. 20.00 (978-1-4223-5452-0(0)) DIANE Publishing Co.

—Peter Rabbit & Other Stories. unabr. ed. 2002. (J). pap. incl. audio compact disk (978-1-58472-304-2(1), In Audio) Sound Room Pubs., Inc.

—Peter Rabbit & the Flopsy Bunnies. 2008. (Potter Ser.). 16p. (J). (ps). 9.99 (***978-0-7232-5994-7(1)***, Warne) Penguin Group (USA) Inc.

—Peter Rabbit Bathtime Fun. 2007. (Illus.). 8p. (J). 4.99 (978-0-7232-5926-8(7), Warne) Penguin Group (USA) Inc.

—Peter Rabbit Dot-to-Dot. 2006. 24p. (J). 4.99 (978-0-7232-5780-6(9), Viking Juvenile) Penguin Group (USA) Inc.

—Peter Rabbit Large Shaped Board Book. 2008. 12p. (J). (ps-1). bds. 7.99 (***978-0-7232-5956-5(9)***, Warne) Penguin Group (USA) Inc.

—Peter Rabbit Says. 2007. (Illus.). 14p. (J). pap. 8.99 (978-0-7232-5889-6(9), Warne) Penguin Group (USA) Inc.

—Peter Rabbit Shaped Board Book. 2007. 12p. (J). bds. 3.99 (978-0-7232-5855-1(4), Warne) Penguin Group (USA) Inc.

—Peter Rabbit Tales, 2 vols. 1999. (Potter Special Edition Ser.). (Illus.). 96p. (J). 13.25 (978-0-7232-4483-7(9), Warne) Penguin Group (USA) Inc.

—Peter Rabbit Touch & Feel. 2005. (Illus.). 12p. (J). pap. 9.99 (978-0-7232-5578-9(4), Warne) Penguin Group (USA) Inc.

—Peter Rabbit Who Lives Here? 2008. (Potter Ser.). 12p. (J). (ps). bds. 12.99 (***978-0-7232-5995-4(X)***, Warne) Penguin Group (USA) Inc.

—Peter Rabbit's Christmas Collection, 4 vols. 2003. (Illus.). 272p. (J). pap. 20.00 (978-0-7232-4937-5(7), Warne) Penguin Group (USA) Inc.

—Peter Rabbit's Giant Storybook. 2000. (Illus.). 192p. (J). (ps-3). 15.99 (978-0-7232-4583-4(5), Warne) Penguin Group (USA) Inc.

—Peter Rabbit's Halloween. 2003. (Illus.). 10p. (J). (ps-ps). bds. 4.99 (978-0-7232-4900-9(8), Warne) Penguin Group (USA) Inc.

—Peter Rabbit's Touch & Feel Book. 1999. (Illus.). 12p. (J). (ps-3). 9.99 (978-0-7232-4518-6(5), Warne) Penguin Group (USA) Inc.

—Sleep Tight, Peter Rabbit. 2007. (Illus.). 12p. (J). pap. 12.99 (978-0-7232-5809-4(0), Warne) Penguin Group (USA) Inc.

—Snuggle Time. 2004. (Potter Ser.). (Illus.). 6p. (J). (ps-ps). 8.99 (978-0-7232-4998-6(9), Warne) Penguin Group (USA) Inc.

—The Story of Peter Rabbit. McCue, Lisa, illus. 2005. 20p. (J). bds. 10.99 (978-0-7944-0527-4(4)) Reader's Digest Assn., Inc., The.

—The Tale of Peter Rabbit. Potter, Beatrix, illus. 2002. (Illus.). (J). 11.49 (978-0-7587-3751-9(3)) Book Wholesalers, Inc.

—The Tale of Peter Rabbit. (Potter Ser.). (Illus.). (J). 2007. 24p. pap. 6.99 (978-0-7232-5793-6(0), Warne); 2006. 8p. 15.99 (978-0-7232-5704-2(3)) Penguin Group (USA) Inc.

—The Tale of Peter Rabbit. Vining, Alex, illus. 2004. (Reading Railroad Bks.). 32p. (J). (ps-4). mass mkt. 3.99 (978-0-448-43521-3(7), Grosset & Dunlap) Penguin Group (USA) Inc.

—The Tale of Peter Rabbit. (Illus.). (J). 2003. 32p. 3.99 (978-0-7232-4717-3(X)); 2002. 70p. 6.99 (978-0-7232-4770-8(6)); 1999. 12p. bds. 6.99 (978-0-7232-4432-5(4)) Penguin Group (USA) Inc. (Warne).

—The Tale of Peter Rabbit. (Illus.). 12p. 4.95 (978-1-58989-271-2(2)); 6p. (J). bds. 3.95 (978-1-58989-201-9(1)) Thurman Hse., LLC.

—Tale of Peter Rabbit. l.t. ed. 2004. (Potter Ser.). (Illus.). 80p. (J). (ps). 12.99 (978-0-7232-4986-3(5), Warne) Penguin Group (USA) Inc.

—The Tale of Peter Rabbit. Potter, Beatrix, illus. 2004. (Wee Books for Wee Folks). (Illus.). 64p. (J). (ps-3). reprint ed. 6.95 (978-1-55709-412-4(8)) Applewood Bks.

—The Tale of Peter Rabbit. Hague, Michael, illus. 2003. 29p. (J). (gr. 2-5). reprint ed. 16.00 (978-0-7567-6968-0(X)) DIANE Publishing Co.

—The Tale of Peter Rabbit: Commemorative Edition. movie tie-in ed. 2006. (Illus.). 80p. (J). 6.99 (978-0-7232-5873-5(2), Warne) Penguin Group (USA) Inc.

—Tale of Peter Rabbit Book & Toy. 2006. (Illus.). 80p. (J). 14.99 (978-0-7232-5356-3(0), Warne) Penguin Group (USA) Inc.

—Tale of Peter Rabbit Sticker Story Book. 2006. 24p. (J). pap. 5.99 (978-0-7232-5388-4(9), Warne) Penguin Group (USA) Inc.

—The Tales of Peter Rabbit. 2006. (Illus.). 128p. 4.95 (978-0-7624-2694-2(2), Running Pr. Minature Editions) Running Pr. Bk. Pubs.

—We Both Read-the Tales of Peter Rabbit & Benjamin Bunny. Potter, Beatrix, illus. 1998. (We Both Read Ser.). (Illus.). 44p. (J). (gr. 1-2). 7.99 (978-1-891327-01-8(1)) Treasure Bay, Inc.

—World of Peter Rabbit, 12 vols. 2006. (Potter Ser.). (Illus.). (J). pap. 84.00 (978-0-7232-5790-5(6), Warne) Penguin Group (USA) Inc.

—The World of Peter Rabbit, 12 vols. gif. ed. 2004. (Potter Ser.). (Illus.). (J). 84.00 (978-0-7232-8408-6(3), Warne) Penguin Group (USA) Inc.

—World of Peter Rabbit Miniature Collection, 12 vols. 2007. (Illus.). 780p. (J). pap. 15.00 (978-0-7232-5785-1(X), Warne) Penguin Group (USA) Inc.

—World of Peter Rabbit Presentn 1-23, 23 vols. 2006. (Illus.). (J). pap. 160.00 (978-0-7232-5763-9(9), Warne) Penguin Group (USA) Inc.

Potter, Beatrix & Pomaska, Anna. Peter Rabbit & Friends, 10 bks., Set, incl. stickers. 1999. (Illus.). (J). pap. 10.00 (978-0-486-29463-6(3)) Dover Pubns., Inc.

Potter, Beatrix & Taylor, Judy. The Original Peter Rabbit Baby Book: First Year. 2006. 48p. (J). pap. 10.00 (978-0-7232-5683-0(7), Warne) Penguin Group (USA) Inc.

Potter, Beatrix & Warne, Frederick. The Complete Adventures of Peter Rabbit. 2003. (Illus.). 80p. (J). (ps). 14.99 (978-0-7232-4734-0(X), Warne) Penguin Group (USA) Inc.

Potter, Beatrix, et al. The Tale of Peter Rabbit. Andersen, Alan, illus. 2001. (Little Golden Bks.). 24p. (gr. k-k). 2.99 (978-0-307-03071-9(7), 98039, Golden Bks.) Random Hse. Children's Bks.

Warne, Frederick. Peter Rabbit's Easter. 2004. (Peter Rabbit Seedlings Ser.). (Illus.). 12p. (J). (ps). bds. 6.99 (978-0-7232-4953-5(9), Warne) Penguin Group (USA) Inc.

Warne, Frederick & Potter, Beatrix. Be My Valentine, Peter Rabbit: Surprise Sound Inside! 2002. (Illus.). 10p. (J). bds. 5.99 (978-0-7232-4864-4(8), Warne) Penguin Group (USA) Inc.

PETROLEUM

see also Gasoline

Ball, Jacqueline A. Start the Car. 2003. (Step Back Science Ser.). (Illus.). 48p. (J). 24.95 (978-1-56711-678-6(7), Blackbirch Pr., Inc.) Thomson Gale.

Bedford, Kate. Energy: Oil. 2006. (Illus.). 31p. (978-1-59604-106-6(4)) Stargazer Bks.

Cunningham, Kevin. Gasoline. 2008. (J). lib. bdg. 25.26 (***978-1-60279-121-3(X)***) Cherry Lake Publishing.

Del petroleo a la gasolina (from Oil to Gas) 2007. (J). pap. 4.95 (978-0-8225-6633-5(8), Ediciones Lerner) Lerner Publishing Group.

Del Petroleo a la Gasolina (From Oil to Gas) 2006. (De Principio a Fin Ser.). (SPA.). 24p. (J). 18.60 (978-0-8225-6496-6(3), Ediciones Lerner) Lerner Publishing Group.

Ditchfield, Christin. Oil. (True Bks.). (Illus.). 48p. (J). (gr. 3-5). 2003. pap. 6.95 (978-0-516-29367-7(2)); 2002. pap. 25.00 (978-0-516-22343-8(7)) Scholastic Library Publishing. (Children's Pr.).

—Oil. 2002. (gr. 3-6). lib. bdg. 15.25 (978-0-613-59532-2(7)) Tandem Library Bks.

DuTemple, Lesley A. Oil Spills. 1999. (Overview Ser.). (Illus.). 128p. (YA). (gr. 6-9). lib. bdg. 29.95 (978-1-56006-524-1(9), Lucent Bks.) Thomson Gale.

Edwards, Ron & Edwards, Adrianna. Oil & Gas. 2004. (Rocks, Minerals, & Resources Ser.). (Illus.). 32p. (J). (978-0-7787-1412-5(8)); pap. (978-0-7787-1444-6(6)) Crabtree Publishing Co.

Farndon, John. Oil. 2007. (DK Eyewitness Bks.). 72p. (J). (gr. 3-8). 15.99 incl. cd-rom (978-0-7566-2970-0(5)); (ps-12). lib. bdg. 19.99 (978-0-7566-2969-4(1)) Dorling Kindersley Publishing, Inc.

Franck, Irene M. & Brownstone, David M. Oil. 2003. (Illus.). 32p. (J). (978-0-7172-5718-8(5), Grolier) Scholastic Library Publishing.

Katz Cooper, Sharon. Using Coal, Oil, & Gas. 2007. (Illus.). 24p. (J). (***978-1-4034-9326-2(X)***); lib. bdg. (***978-1-4034-9318-7(9)***) Heinemann.

Manatt, Kathleen. Searching for Oil. 2008. (J). pap. 7.95 (***978-1-60279-100-8(7)***) Cherry Lake Publishing.

Manatt, Kathleen G. Searching for Oil. 2008. (J). lib. bdg. 25.26 (***978-1-60279-043-8(4)***) Cherry Lake Publishing.

McCage, Crystal. Oil. 2006. (Fueling the Future Ser.). (Illus.). 244p. (gr. 10-12). 34.95 (978-0-7377-3588-8(0), 1256646, Greenhaven Pr., Inc.) Thomson Gale.

Morris, Neil. Oil & Gas. 2005. (Illus.). 32p. (J). (gr. 4-7). lib. bdg. 27.10 (978-1-58340-632-8(8)) Smart Apple Media.

Murray, Peter. Oil. 2001. (From the Earth Ser.). (Illus.). 24p. (J). 21.35 (978-1-58340-110-1(5)) Smart Apple Media.

Nakaya, Andrea C. Oil. 2006. 244p. (gr. 10-12). 24.95 (978-0-7377-3328-0(4)); pap. 36.20 (978-0-7377-3327-3(6)) Thomson Gale. (Greenhaven Pr., Inc.).

Oxlade, Chris. Energy Transformation. 2004. (Raintree Freestyle Ser.). (Illus.). 48p. (J). lib. bdg. 29.93 (978-1-4109-0494-2(6)) Raintree.

—How We Use Oil. 2004. (Illus.). 32p. (J). (ps-ps). pap. 7.50 (978-1-4109-0994-7(8)); lib. bdg. 25.70 (978-1-4109-0595-6(0)) Raintree.

Parker, Steve. Oil & Gas. 2004. (Science Files Ser.). (Illus.). 32p. (J). (gr. 3 up). lib. bdg. 24.37 (978-0-8368-4031-5(3)) Stevens, Gareth Inc.

Redmond, Jim. Oil Makes Gasoline Power. 2003. (From Resource to Energy Source Ser.). (J). (978-1-58417-292-5(4)); pap. (978-1-58417-293-2(2)) Lake Street Pubs.

Saunders, Nigel & Chapman, Steven. Energy Transfers. 2004. (Illus.). 48p. (J). (gr. 6-8). pap. 7.95 (978-1-4109-0500-0(4)) Raintree.

Thomas, Mark. The Discoverer Enterprise: World's Largest Offshore Drilling Rig. 2002. (Reading Power Ser.). (Illus.). 24p. (J). (gr. 1). lib. bdg. 17.25 (978-0-8239-5994-5(5), PowerKids Pr.) Rosen Publishing Group, Inc., The.

Zemlicka, Shannon. From Oil to Gas. (From Start to Finish Ser.). (J). 2003. (Illus.). 24p. 18.60 (978-0-8225-0718-5(8), Lerner Pubns.); 2002. pap. 4.95 (978-0-8225-0669-0(6)) Lerner Publishing Group.

PETROLEUM—FICTION

Rice, James, illus. Gaston Drills an Offshore Oil Well. 2nd ed. 2002. 40p. 16.95 (978-1-58980-068-7(0)) Pelican Publishing Co., Inc.

Rucker, Mike. Terry & the Wild Well Blowout. 2002. (Terry the Tractor Ser.: Vol. 10). (Illus.). 72p. (J). (gr. k-4). pap. 3.95 (978-0-9711659-1-5(2)) Univ. Editions.

The Story of Petroleum. 2002. (Illus.). 32p. 6.95 (978-0-9727833-8-5(5)) Really Big Coloring Bks., Inc.

PETROLEUM AS FUEL

Murray, Julie. Oil to Gas. 2007. (J). 21.35 (978-1-59679-913-4(7), Buddy Bks.) ABDO Publishing Co.

PETROLEUM INDUSTRY AND TRADE

Aaseng, Nathan. Business Builders in Oil. 2000. (Business Builders Ser.). (Illus.). 160p. (gr. 5 up). lib. bdg. 22.95 (978-1-881508-56-4(0)) Oliver Pr., Inc.

African-Americans in Oil Drilling. 2000. (My Ancestors—My Heroes Ser.: Vol. 30). (J). (gr. 3-4). (978-1-893091-29-0(5)) Parker Publishing Co.

Calvert, John. The Arabian Peninsula in the Age of Oil. 2007. (J). (***978-1-4222-0172-5(4)***) Mason Crest Pubs.

Franck, Irene M. & Brownstone, David M. Oil. 2003. (Illus.). 32p. (J). (978-0-7172-5718-8(5), Grolier) Scholastic Library Publishing.

Glassman, Bruce. John Paul Getty: Billionaire Oilman. 2001. (Giants of American Industry Ser.). (Illus.). 112p. (J). (gr. 5-8). 27.45 (978-1-56711-513-0(6), Blackbirch Pr., Inc.) Thomson Gale.

Gunderson, Cory Gideon. The Need for Oil. 2004. (World in Conflict-the Middle East Ser.). (Illus.). 48p. (J). (gr. 4-8). lib. bdg. 25.65 (978-1-59197-417-8(8)) ABDO Publishing Co.

Jarnow, Jesse. Oil, Steel, & Railroads: America's Big Businesses in the Late 1800s. 2003. (America's Industrial Society in the Nineteenth Century Ser.). (Illus.). 32p. (J). pap. (978-0-8239-4276-3(7)) Rosen Publishing Group, Inc., The.

King, John. Oil in the Middle East. 2005. (Middle East Ser.). (Illus.). 56p. (J). (978-1-4109-1624-2(3)); pap. (978-1-4109-1630-3(8)) Steck-Vaughn.

McKinney, Gary S. Oil on the Brain: The Discovery of Oil & the Excitement of the Boom in Northwestern Pennsylvania. 2nd rev. ed. 2004. Orig. Title: The Discovery of Oil & the Excitement of the Boom in Clarion County, Pennsylvania, Including the Progression of Oil Discovery from Titusville through Clarion County & onto the Bradford Fields. (Illus.). 309p. 39.95 (978-0-9744657-9-1(8), 7801) Mechling Bookbindery.

PETROLEUM INDUSTRY AND TRADE—FICTION

Dixon, Franklin W. Running on Fumes. 2005. 150p. (J). lib. bdg. 16.92 (***978-1-4242-0384-0(8)***) Fitzgerald Bks.

Winfield, Arthur M. Rover Boys in the Land of Luck or Stirri. 2006. pap. 30.95 (***978-1-4286-4101-3(7)***) Kessinger Publishing, LLC.

PETS

see also Domestic Animals

also names of animals, e.g. Cats; Dogs

About Pets Staff. Hamsters. 2003. (Illus.). 64p. pap. 4.95 (978-0-7434-4542-9(2)) ibooks, Inc.

—Tropical Fish. 2003. (Illus.). 64p. pap. 4.95 (978-0-7434-4543-6(0)) ibooks, Inc.

Adelman, Heidi. Weird Pets. 2007. (Boys Rock! Ser.). 32p. (J). (gr. 1-5). 24.21 (***978-1-59296-862-6(7)***) Child's World, Inc.

Alderton, David. Hamster: Looking after My Pet. 2002. (Illus.). 24p. 7.99 (978-0-7548-1088-9(7), Lorenz Bks.) Anness Publishing GBR. *Dist:* National Bk. Network.

All about Pets, 10 bks. Incl. Birds. Frost, Helen. 2000. lib. bdg. 15.93 (978-0-7368-0654-1(7)); Cats. Frost, Helen. 2000. lib. bdg. 15.93 (978-0-7368-0655-8(5)); Dogs. Frost, Helen. 2000. lib. bdg. 15.93 (978-0-7368-0656-5(3)); Fish. Frost, Helen. 2000. lib. bdg. 15.93 (978-0-7368-0657-2(1)); Guinea Pigs. Rustad, Martha E. H. 2001. lib. bdg. 15.93 (978-0-7368-0975-7(9)); Hamsters. Frost, Helen. 2000. lib. bdg. 15.93 (978-0-7368-0658-9(X)); Horses. Rustad, Martha E. H. 2001. lib. bdg. 15.93 (978-0-7368-0976-4(7)); Rabbits. Frost, Helen. 2000. lib. bdg. 15.93 (978-0-7368-0659-6(8)); Snakes. Rustad, Martha E. H. 2001. lib. bdg. 15.93 (978-0-7368-0977-1(5)); Turtles. Rustad, Martha E. H. 2001. lib. bdg. 15.93 (978-0-7368-0978-8(3)); 24p. (J). (gr. k-1). (Illus.). 2001. Set lib. bdg. 159.30 (978-0-7368-1015-9(3), Pebble Bks.) Capstone Pr., Inc.

All about Pets, Set. (gr. k-2). 288.95 (978-0-7368-9245-2(1)) Red Brick Learning.

All My Pets. (Girls' World Ser.). 16p. (J). (978-2-7643-0142-5(1)) Phidal Publishing, Inc./Editions Phidal, Inc.

All My Pets: What's New? (Girls' Activity Kit Ser.). (J). (978-2-7643-0213-2(4)) Phidal Publishing, Inc./Editions Phidal, Inc.

Altman, Linda Jacobs. Big Dogs. 2000. (Perfect Pets Ser.). (Illus.). 32p. (J). (gr. 3-5). lib. bdg. 25.64 (978-0-7614-1101-7(1), Benchmark Bks.) Cavendish, Marshall Corp.

Andres, Patricia. Maggie: A Savannah Dog. Abbott, Jason, illus. 1998. (J). (gr. k-8). 4.75 (978-0-9703795-0-4(1)) Maggie's D.O.G. Co.

Anness Publishing Staff. Let's Look at Pets. 2000. (Illus.). 12p. (J). (gr. 1-5). bds. 5.00 (978-0-7548-0711-7(8), Lorenz Bks.) Anness Publishing, Inc.

Auch, Alison. Happy Pets, Healthy Pets. 2003. (Spyglass Books). (Illus.). 24p. (J). (gr. 1 up). lib. bdg. 18.60 (978-0-7565-0454-0(6)) Compass Point Bks.

Autrey, Jacquelyn & Yeager, Alice. U.S. Presidents & Their Animal Friends. Passarella, Jennie, illus. 2004. 32p. (J). (978-1-59421-005-1(5)) Seacoast Publishing, Inc.

Axelrod, Herbert R. Your Healthy Puppy. 1999. (Cats & Dogs). (Illus.). 84p. (YA). (gr. 4-7). lib. bdg. 19.95 (978-0-7910-4820-7(9), Chelsea Hse.) Facts On File, Inc.

Bailey, Debbie. Mi Animalito. Huszar, Susan, photos by. 2003. (Hablemos Ser.).Tr. of My Pet. (SPA., Illus.). 14p. (J). (gr. k-ps). bds. 5.95 (978-1-55037-826-9(0)) Annick Pr., Ltd. CAN. *Dist:* Firefly Bks., Ltd.

—My Pet. Huszar, Susan, photos by. 2003. (Talk-about-Bks.). (Illus.). 14p. (J). (gr. k-ps). bds. 5.95 (978-1-55037-816-0(3)) Annick Pr., Ltd. CAN. *Dist:* Firefly Bks., Ltd.

Baker, Charles F., ed. Pets. 2005. (Illus.). 32p. (J). 17.95 (978-0-8126-7925-0(3)) Cobblestone Publishing Co.

Baker, H. K. G. Choosing the Perfect Pet: A Kid's & Parent's Guide to the World of Pets. 2008. (Illus.). 64p. (J). pap. 12.95 (978-1-933317-56-4(6)) Silverleaf Pr.

Barclay, Susan. The Ultimate Guide to Sea-Monkeys. Boyle, Tom, ed. 2002. 175p. pap. 13.95 (978-1-931090-68-1(8)) Street Saint Pubns.

Barnes, Julia, et al. 101 Facts about Goldfish. 2002. (One Hundred One Facts about Pets Ser.). (Illus.). 32p. (J). (gr. 3 up). lib. bdg. 23.33 (978-0-8368-3017-0(2)) Stevens, Gareth Inc.

—101 Facts about Hamsters. 2002. (One Hundred One Facts about Pets Ser.). (Illus.). 32p. (J). (gr. 3 up). lib. bdg. 23.33 (978-0-8368-3018-7(0)) Stevens, Gareth Inc.

—101 Facts about Parakeets. 2002. (One Hundred One Facts about Pets Ser.). (Illus.). 32p. (J). (gr. 3 up). lib. bdg. 23.33 (978-0-8368-3020-0(2)) Stevens, Gareth Inc.

—101 Facts about Terrarium Pets. 2002. (One Hundred One Facts about Pets Ser.). (Illus.). 32p. (J). (gr. 3 up). lib. bdg. 23.33 (978-0-8368-3021-7(0)) Stevens, Gareth Inc.

Barraclough, Sue. Animals in the House. 2005. (J). pap. (978-1-4109-1903-8(X)); lib. bdg. (978-1-4109-1898-7(X)) Steck-Vaughn.

Barron's Educational Editorial Staff. Petsitter's Mix. 1999. pap. 237.00 (978-0-7641-7316-5(2)) Barron's Educational Series, Inc.

Basic Domestic Pet Library. 2005. pap. 220.00 (978-0-7910-9191-3(0), Chelsea Hse.) Facts On File, Inc.

Bass, Rick. Colter: The True Story of the Best Dog I Ever Had. 2001. (Illus.). (J). 16.65 (978-0-606-21720-0(7)) Tandem Library Bks.

Beck, Isabel L., et al. Trophies Kindergarten: Pet Day. 2003. (Trophies Ser.). (gr. k-6). 13.80 (978-0-15-329519-5(8)) Harcourt Schl. Pubs.

Berman, Gina Dalpra. Remembering Pets: A Book for Children Who Have Lost a Special Friend. Schneider, Barbara Hoss, illus. 2004. 32p. (J). (ps-3). 14.95 (978-1-885003-68-3(4)) Reed, Robert D. Pubs.

Berman, Ruth. My Pet Dog. Hustace, Billy, photos by. 2005. (All about Pets Ser.). (Illus.). 64p. (gr. 2-6). lib. bdg. 22.60 (978-0-8225-2259-1(4)) Lerner Publishing Group.

Beylon, Cathy. At the Pet Shop. 2004. 32p. (J). pap. 2.95 (978-0-486-43644-9(6)) Dover Pubns., Inc.

Beylon, Cathy. Favorite Pets. 2007. 32p. (J). pap. 2.95 (***978-0-486-45641-6(2)***) Dover Pubns., Inc.

Biale, Rachel. My Pet Died: A Let's Make a Book about It Book. 2004. (Let's Make a Book about It Ser.). (Illus.). 48p. (ps-3). 7.95 (978-1-883672-51-5(1), Tricycle Pr.) Ten Speed Pr.

Bicknell, Joanna. Googlies: Pet Pals. 2006. (Illus.). 12p. (ps). per. 6.95 (978-1-84610-296-7(0)) Make Believe Ideas GBR. *Dist:* Ingram Pub. Services.

Binns, Tristan Boyer. Hermit Crabs. 2004. (Keeping Unusual Pets Ser.). (Illus.). 48p. (J). (gr. 2-4). lib. bdg. 22.80 (978-1-4034-0825-9(4)) Heinemann Library.

—Potbellied Pigs. 2004. (Keeping Unusual Pets Ser.). (Illus.). 48p. (J). (978-1-4034-0828-0(9)) Heinemann Library.

Blackaby, Susan. A Bird for You: Caring for Your Bird. DeLage, Charlene, illus. 2004. (Pet Care Ser.). 24p. (C). (gr. k-3). 22.60 (978-1-4048-0117-2(0)) Picture Window Bks.

—A Dog for You: Caring for Your Dog. DeLage, Charlene, illus. 2004. (Pet Care Ser.). 24p. (C). (gr. k-3). 22.60 (978-1-4048-0114-1(6)) Picture Window Bks.

—Fish for You: Caring for Your Fish. DeLage, Charlene, illus. 2004. (Pet Care Ser.). 24p. (C). (gr. k-3). 22.60 (978-1-4048-0116-5(2)) Picture Window Bks.

—A Guinea Pig for You: Caring for Your Guinea Pig. DeLage, Charlene, illus. 2004. (Pet Care Ser.). 24p. (C). (gr. k-3). 22.60 (978-1-4048-0119-6(7)) Picture Window Bks.

—Pet Care, 6 bks. DeLage, Charlene, illus. Incl. Bird for You : Caring for Your Bird. 22.60 (978-1-4048-0117-2(0)); Cat for You : Caring for Your Cat. 22.60 (978-1-4048-0115-8(4)); Dog for You : Caring for Your Dog. 22.60 (978-1-4048-0114-1(6)); Fish for You : Caring for Your Fish. 22.60 (978-1-4048-0116-5(2)); Guinea Pig for You : Caring for Your Guinea Pig. 22.60 (978-1-4048-0119-6(7)); Rabbit for You : Caring for Your Rabbit. 22.60 (978-1-4048-0118-9(9)); 24p. (C). (gr. k-3). 2004. (Illus.). 2003. 135.60 (978-1-4048-0113-4(8)) Picture Window Bks.

—A Rabbit for You: Caring for Your Rabbit. DeLage, Charlene, illus. 2004. (Pet Care Ser.). 24p. (C). (gr. k-3). 22.60 (978-1-4048-0118-9(9)) Picture Window Bks.

Boone, Eugene. The Big Book of Pet Names: More Than 10,000 Pet Names - Includes Celebrity Pet Names - the Most Complete Guide to Pet Names & Meanings. 2004. (Illus.). 412p. pap. 15.95 (978-0-930865-54-2(5)) RSVP Pr.

Boyer Binns, Tristan, et al. Keeping Unusual Pets, 5 bks., Set 2. 2004. (J). (gr. 3-5). lib. bdg. 142.50 (978-1-4034-0829-7(7)) Heinemann Library.

Bozzo, Linda. My First Guinea Pig & Other Small Pets. 2007. (My First Pet Library from the American Humane Association Ser.). (Illus.). 32p. (J). (gr. 1-2). lib. bdg. 22.60 (978-0-7660-2752-7(X) , Enslow Elementary) Enslow Pubs., Inc.

Brettle, Jane. My Pets. 1999. (Animal Noises Ser.). (Illus.). 10p. (J). 2.95 (978-1-57717-099-0(7)) New Line Bks.

Brighter Vision Publishing Staff, ed. Pets. 2000. (Little Books to Make & Read). (Illus.). (J). (ps-2). pap. 1.49 (978-1-55254-066-4(9)) Brighter Vision Pubns.

Brownlee, Christen. Cute, Furry, & Deadly: Diseases You Can Catch from Your Pet! 2007. (24/7: Science Behind the Scenes: Medical Files Ser.). 64p. (J). pap. 7.95 (***978-0-531-18737-1(3)*** , Watts, Franklin) Scholastic Library Publishing.

Burton, Margie, et al. Caring for Our Pets. Evento, Susan, ed. 1998. (Early Connections Ser.). 16p. (J). (gr. k-2). pap. 4.25 (978-1-892393-60-9(3)) Benchmark Education Co.

Butterfield, Moira. Pet of My Own: A Caring Guide to Pets. 2000. (Illus.). 128p. (J). (ps up). pap. 4.95 (978-1-902618-22-7(X)) Element Children's Bks.

Calmenson, Stephanie. Shaggy, Waggy Dogs (and Others) Sutcliffe, Justin, illus. 1998. 48p. (J). (gr. k-3). tchr. ed. 15.00 (978-0-395-77605-6(8) , Clarion Bks.) Houghton Mifflin Co. Trade & Reference Div.

—Shaggy, Waggy Dogs (and Others) Sutcliffe, Justin, illus. 2002. 48p. (J). (gr. k-3). pap. 5.95 (978-0-618-19466-7(5) , Clarion Bks.) Houghton Mifflin Co. Trade & Reference Div.

Casado, Dami. Los Ruidos de Las Mascotas. 2005. (SPA.). 12p. 7.99 (978-84-272-8293-3(1)) Molino, Editorial ESP. *Dist:* Santillana USA Publishing Co., Inc.

Chanell, Jim & Greenaway, Theresa. Slugs & Snails. 1999. (Minipets Ser.). (Illus.). 32p. (J). (gr. 1-5). lib. bdg. 25.69 (978-0-8172-5587-9(7)) Raintree.

—Worms. 1999. (Minipets Ser.). (Illus.). 32p. (J). (gr. 1-5) lib. bdg. 25.69 (978-0-8172-5588-6(5)) Raintree.

Chapman, Joan. Pet Pals: Learning the P Sound. 2002. (PowerPhonics Ser.). (Illus.). 24p. (J). (gr. 1). lib. bdg. 18.50 (978-0-8239-5915-0(5) , PowerKids Pr.) Rosen Publishing Group, Inc., The.

—Pet Pals: Learning the Short U Sound. 2001. (PowerPhonics Ser.). (Illus.). 23p. (J). lib. bdg. 26.40 (978-0-8239-8260-8(2) , PowerKids Pr.) Rosen Publishing Group, Inc., The.

Chessen, Betsey. Pet Care. 1999. (Learning Center Emergent Readers Ser.). (J). pap. 2.50 (978-0-439-04589-6(4)) Scholastic, Inc.

Christian, Eleanor & Roth-Singer, Lyzz. Looking at Ants. 2000. (Yellow Umbrella Books). (Illus.). 16p. (J). (gr. 1). lib. bdg. 14.60 (978-0-7368-0725-8(X) , Pebble Bks.) Capstone Pr., Inc.

Clements, Andrew. Dolores & the Big Fire: A True Story. 2003. (gr. k-3). lib. bdg. 11.80 (978-0-613-61549-5(2)) Tandem Library Bks.

—Tara & Tiree, Fearless Friends: A True Story. 2002. (gr. k-3). lib. bdg. 11.80 (978-0-613-66607-7(0)) Tandem Library Bks.

Cole, Lynn. My Cat. 2001. (Pet Pals Ser.). (Illus.). 48p. (J). (gr. 1-5). pap. 8.95 (978-1-55971-792-2(0) , NorthWord Bks. for Young Readers) T&N Children's Publishing.

—My Dog. 2001. (Pet Pals Ser.). (Illus.). 48p. (J). (gr. 1-5). pap. 8.95 (978-1-55971-793-9(9) , NorthWord Bks. for Young Readers) T&N Children's Publishing.

Color All About: A Giant Coloring Book about Loving Our Pets: Pets. 2004. (Illus.). 36p. (J). (978-1-59949-002-1(1)) Food Marketing Consultants, Inc.

Complete Set. (Pet's Point of View Ser.). (gr. 4-6). 135.60 (978-0-7565-0733-6(2)) Compass Point Bks.

Connolly, Randy, et al. Poison Ivy, Pets & People: Scratching the Poison Ivy, Oak & Sumac Itch. 2005. (10thingstoknow about ... Ser.). (Illus.). 104p. pap. 9.95 (978-0-9722400-1-7(2)) 2Lakes Publishing.

Coppendale, Jean. Puppy. 2004. (QEB You & Your Pet Ser.). (Illus.). 32p. (J). lib. bdg. 15.95 (978-1-59566-051-0(8)) QEB Publishing Inc.

Cousins, Lucy. Pet Animals. Cousins, Lucy, illus. 2004. (Illus.). 12p. (J). (gr. k-k). bds. 4.99 (978-0-7636-2305-0(9)) Candlewick Pr.

Craats, Rennay. Caring for Your Frog. 2004. (Caring for Your Pet Ser.). (Illus.). (J). pap. (978-1-59036-218-1(7)); 32p. lib. bdg. 16.95 (978-1-59036-198-6(9)) Weigl Pubs., Inc.

—Caring for Your Gecko. 2004. (Caring for Your Pet Ser.). (J). pap. 7.95 (978-1-59036-154-2(7)); (Illus.). 32p. lib. bdg. 16.95 (978-1-59036-119-1(9)) Weigl Pubs., Inc.

—Caring for Your Snake. 2004. (Caring for Your Pet Ser.). (Illus.). (J). pap. (978-1-59036-216-7(0)); 32p. lib. bdg. 16.95 (978-1-59036-196-2(2)) Weigl Pubs., Inc.

Cunningham, Alan Blain, compiled by. Goodbye My Good Friend: Memories of Lost Animal Companions & Loved Ones. 2007. (ENG., Illus.). 112p. per. 15.95 (***978-0-9777072-2-5(9)***) Agreka Bks., LLC.

Curran, Wanda L. Your Guinea Pig: A Kid's Guide to Raising & Showing. 2003. (Illus.). 151p. (J). (gr. 4-7). pap. 14.95 (978-0-88266-889-5(7) , 66889) Storey Publishing, LLC.

Dahl, Michael. Pets ABC: An Alphabet Book. 2004. (A+ Alphabet Books). (Illus.). 17p. (J). 22.60 (978-0-7368-2607-5(6) , Aplus Bks.) Capstone Pr., Inc.

Dalmatian Press Staff. Caring for Your Pet: Pet Care Guide. 2005. (Illus.). 64p. (J). pap. 5.99 (978-1-4037-0888-5(6)) Dalmatian Pr.

Daronco, Mickey & Ohanesian, Diane. Pets. 2nd rev. ed. 2003. (BuildUp Ser.). (J). pap. 22.00 (978-1-4108-0738-0(X)) Benchmark Education Co.

Davis, Rebecca Fjelland. Counting Pets by Twos. 2007. (A+ Books. Counting Books). (Illus.). 32p. (J). 23.93 (978-0-7368-6375-9(3)) Capstone Pr., Inc.

Denzer, Barbara. The Kids Guide to Petiquette: The Inside Scoop on Pet Behavior. 2007. (J). 7.95 (***978-0-9744749-2-2(4)***) Crazy Pet Pr., The.

Denzer, Barbara & Denzer, Missy. The Crazy Kids Guide to Cooking for Your Pet: Recipes, Jokes, Pet Care Tips & Fun Things to Do with Your Pet Featuring the Back Bones of Character. Rodriguez, Manny, illus. 2004. 64p. (J). (gr. k-7). 12.95 (978-0-9744749-0-8(8)) Crazy Pet Pr., The.

Deschamps, Nicola, ed. Toca y Apprende Mascotas/Touch & Feel Pets. 2005. (TOUCH & FEEL Ser.). (SPA., Illus.). 12p. (J). (ps). bds. 6.99 (978-0-7566-1508-6(9)) Dorling Kindersley Publishing, Inc.

Deverell, Christine. Pop-up Pets. Deverell, Richard & King, Chris, illus. 2005. 12p. (J). (gr. k-4). reprint ed. 20.00 (978-0-7567-8776-9(9)) DIANE Publishing Co.

Dib, Pierre. Guide to Owning a Poodle: AKC Rank #6. 1999. (Popular Dog Library). (Illus.). 64p. (J). (gr. 4-7). 27.50 (978-0-7910-5474-1(8) , Chelsea Hse.) Facts On File, Inc.

Domnauer, Teresa. Peculiar Pets: Level 1. 2006. (Extreme Readers Ser.). (Illus.). 32p. (J). pap. 3.95 (978-0-7696-4334-2(5)) School Specialty Publishing.

Dorling Kindersley Publishing Staff. My Pets: A Barbie Touch-and-Feel Book. 2003. (Barbie Ser.). (Illus.). 12p. (J). bds. 6.99 (978-0-7894-9232-6(6)) Dorling Kindersley Publishing, Inc.

—Small Pet Care: How to Look after Your Rabbit, Guinea Pig, or Hamster. 2005. (Illus.). 48p. (J). 9.99 (978-0-7566-1104-0(0) , 1241699) Dorling Kindersley Publishing, Inc.

Dorling Kindersley Publishing Staff, contrib. by. Pets. 2001. (Touch & Feel Ser.). (Illus.). 12p. (J). bds. 6.99 (978-0-7894-7933-4(8)) Dorling Kindersley Publishing, Inc.

Dover Publications Staff. Full Color Pets Illustrations. 2002. (Illus.). 48p. pap. 19.95 incl. cd-rom (978-0-486-99526-7(7)) Dover Pubns., Inc.

Eck, Kristin. Animals in My House. 2004. (Look-And-Learn Books). (J). lib. bdg. 7.95 (978-1-4042-2701-9(6) , PowerKids Pr.) Rosen Publishing Group, Inc., The.

Edwards, Nicola. A Pet. 2003. (Saying Goodbye to Ser.). (Illus.). 32p. (J). (ps-2). lib. bdg. 16.95 (978-1-932333-19-0(3)) Chrysalis Education.

Engfer, Leeanne. My Pet Lizards. King, Andy, photos by. 1999. (All about Pets Ser.). (Illus.). 64p. (gr. 2-6). lib. bdg. 22.60 (978-0-8225-2263-8(2)) Lerner Publishing Group.

Evans, Mark. Rabbit. 2001. (ASPCA Pet Care Guides for Kids). (Illus.). (J). (978-0-606-21392-9(9)) Tandem Library Bks.

Extreme Pets Handbook. 2007. 164p. (J). pap. 12.99 (***978-0-439-82948-9(8)***) Scholastic, Inc.

Family Pets, 6 vols. (gr. k-2). 28.95 (978-0-7368-8266-8(9)) Red Brick Learning.

Farran, Christopher. Animals To The Rescue! True Stories of Animal Heroes. 2000. (Illus.). (J). (978-0-606-21754-5(1)) Tandem Library Bks.

Feldman, Heather. My Dog: A Book about a Special Pet. 2000. (PowerKids Readers Ser.). (Illus.). 24p. (J). (gr. 1). lib. bdg. 16.00 (978-0-8239-5524-4(9) , PKMYDO, PowerKids Pr.) Rosen Publishing Group, Inc., The.

Fenichel, Marilyn P. Lulu the Potbellied Pig & Other True Animal Hero Stories. 2002. (J). (978-0-9707768-8-4(8)) Moonstone Pr.

Fischer, Jean. God Gives Us Pets. Ring, Laura, ed. Brooks, Nan, illus. 1999. (Handle Board Bks.). 10p. (ps up). 2.99 (978-0-7847-0907-8(6) , 04272, Bean Sprouts) Standard Publishing.

Flanagan, Alice K. Buying a Pet from Ms. Chavez. Rau, Dana, ed. 1998. (Our Neighborhood Ser.). (Illus.). 32p. (J). (gr. 1-2). pap. 6.95 (978-0-516-26293-2(9) , Children's Pr.) Scholastic Library Publishing.

Foran, Jill. Caring for Your Dog. Marshall, Diana & Nault, Jennifer, eds. 2003. (Caring for Your Pet Ser.). (Illus.). 32p. (J). pap. 7.95 (978-1-59036-063-7(X)) Weigl Pubs., Inc.

—Caring for Your Guinea Pig. 2004. (Caring for Your Pet Ser.). (J). pap. 7.95 (978-1-59036-151-1(2)); (Illus.). 32p. lib. bdg. 18.20 (978-1-59036-116-0(4)) Weigl Pubs., Inc.

—Caring for Your Hamster. Marshall, Diana & Nault, Jennifer, eds. 2003. (Caring for Your Pet Ser.). (Illus.). 32p. (J). pap. 7.95 (978-1-59036-066-8(4)) Weigl Pubs., Inc.

—Caring for Your Rabbit. Marshall, Diana & Nault, Jennifer, eds. 2003. (Caring for Your Pet Ser.). (Illus.). 32p. (J). pap. 7.95 (978-1-59036-064-4(8)) Weigl Pubs., Inc.

Foster, Walter, ed. Drawing Pets. Fisher, Diana, illus. 2005. 32p. (J). pap. 12.95 (978-1-56010-938-9(6)) Foster, Walter Publishing, Inc.

Frattini, Stephane. Face-to-Face with the Cat. Klein, Jean-Louis & Hubert, Marie-Luce, illus. 2004. (Face to Face Ser.). 28p. (J). 9.95 (978-1-57091-454-6(0)) Charlesbridge Publishing, Inc.

Fried, Dennis & Genevieve. Memoirs of a Papillon: The Canine Guide to Living with Humans without Going Mad. 2000. (Illus.). 160p. (YA). pap. 13.95 (978-0-9679335-0-4(1) , 418) Eiffel Pr.

Frost, Helen. Birds. 2000. (All about Pets Ser.). (Illus.). 24p. (J). (gr. k-1). lib. bdg. 15.93 (978-0-7368-0654-1(7) , Pebble Bks.) Capstone Pr., Inc.

—Cats. 2000. (All about Pets Ser.). (Illus.). 24p. (J). (gr. k-1). lib. bdg. 15.93 (978-0-7368-0655-8(5) , Pebble Bks.) Capstone Pr., Inc.

—Dogs. 2000. (All about Pets Ser.). (Illus.). 24p. (J). (gr. k-1). lib. bdg. 15.93 (978-0-7368-0656-5(3) , Pebble Bks.) Capstone Pr., Inc.

—Fish. 2000. (All about Pets Ser.). (Illus.). 24p. (J). (gr. k-1). lib. bdg. 15.93 (978-0-7368-0657-2(1) , Pebble Bks.) Capstone Pr., Inc.

—Hamsters. 2000. (All about Pets Ser.). (Illus.). 24p. (J). (gr. k-1). lib. bdg. 15.93 (978-0-7368-0658-9(X) , Pebble Bks.) Capstone Pr., Inc.

Funny Faces: Wacky Pets. (J). (978-1-86091-113-2(7) , 91) Trident Pr. International.

Furstinger, Nancy. Creative Crafts for Critters. Bélla, Philippe, illus. 2001. 48p. (J). (gr. 2-7). pap. 8.95 (978-0-7737-6135-3(7)) Stoddart Kids CAN. *Dist:* Fitzhenry & Whiteside, Ltd.

—Creative Crafts for Critters. 2001. (Hello Reader! Ser.). (Illus.). (J). (978-0-606-21128-4(4)) Tandem Library Bks.

Ganeri, Anita. Cats. 2003. (Heinemann First Library). (Illus.). 32p. (J). pap. (978-1-4034-4269-7(X)) Heinemann Library.

—Dogs. 2003. (Heinemann First Library). (Illus.). 32p. (J). pap. (978-1-4034-4270-3(3)) Heinemann Library.

—Goldfish. 2003. (Heinemann First Library). (Illus.). 32p. (J). pap. (978-1-4034-4271-0(1)) Heinemann Library.

—Guinea Pig. 2003. (Heinemann First Library). (Illus.). 32p. (J). pap. (978-1-4034-4272-7(X)) Heinemann Library.

—Guinea Pig. 2003. (gr. k-3). lib. bdg. 15.25 (978-0-613-87670-4(9)) Tandem Library Bks.

—Hamsters. 2003. (Heinemann First Library). (Illus.). 32p. (J). pap. (978-1-4034-4273-4(8)) Heinemann Library.

—Hamsters. 2003. (gr. k-3). lib. bdg. 15.25 (978-0-613-89653-5(X)) Tandem Library Bks.

—A Pet's Life: Cats. 2003. (Heinemann First Library). (Illus.). 32p. (J). lib. bdg. 22.79 (978-1-4034-3993-2(1)) Heinemann Library.

—A Pet's Life: Dogs. 2003. (Heinemann First Library). (Illus.). 32p. (J). lib. bdg. 22.79 (978-1-4034-3994-9(X)) Heinemann Library.

—A Pet's Life: Goldfish. 2003. (Heinemann First Library). (Illus.). 32p. (J). lib. bdg. 22.79 (978-1-4034-3998-7(2)) Heinemann Library.

—A Pet's Life: Guinea Pigs. 2003. (Heinemann First Library). (Illus.). 32p. (J). lib. bdg. 22.79 (978-1-4034-3996-3(6)) Heinemann Library.

—A Pet's Life: Hamsters. 2003. (Heinemann First Library). (Illus.). 32p. (J). lib. bdg. 22.79 (978-1-4034-3997-0(4)) Heinemann Library.

—Rabbits. 2003. (Heinemann First Library). (Illus.). 32p. (J). pap. (978-1-4034-4274-1(6)) Heinemann Library.

—Rabbits. 2003. (gr. k-3). lib. bdg. 15.25 (978-0-613-86559-3(6)) Tandem Library Bks.

Garwood, Mary. Pawprints upon My Heart II: The Journey Continues. 2004. 132p. (J). per. 11.95 (978-0-9714086-3-0(7)) Tarbutton Pr.

Gelman, Amy. My Pet Ferrets. King, Andy, photos by. 2005. (All about Pets Ser.). (Illus.). 64p. (gr. 2-6). lib. bdg. 22.60 (978-0-8225-2264-5(0)) Lerner Publishing Group.

George, Jean Craighead. How to Talk to Your Cat. Truesdell, Sue & Meisel, Paul, illus. 2000. 40p. (J). (gr. 2-4). 14.99 (978-0-06-027968-4(0)); (ps-4). lib. bdg. 13.89 (978-0-06-027969-1(9)) HarperCollins Pubs.

—How to Talk to Your Dog. Truesdell, Sue, illus. 2000. 40p. (J). (gr. 1-4). 14.99 (978-0-06-027092-6(6)) HarperCollins Pubs.

Get a Pet, Bk. 4. 1999. (McGraw-Hill Junior Academic Ser.). (Illus.). 16p. (J). (gr. 1). pap. 2.99 (978-1-57768-541-8(5)) School Specialty Publishing.

Gogerly, Liz. Pets/By Liz Gogerly. 2004. (Starters Ser.). (Illus.). 24p. (J). lib. bdg. 22.80 (978-1-58340-565-9(8)) Smart Apple Media.

Golden Books Staff. Meet the Wonder Pets! 2008. (Paint Box Book Ser.). (Illus.). 48p. (J). (ps-2). pap. 3.99 (***978-0-375-84211-5(X)*** , Golden Bks.) Random Hse., Inc.

Good Morning Miss Prin. 2002. (J). pap. 7.95 (978-0-9722555-0-9(8)) Sblendido, Barbara.

Good Pets: Big Book, Vol. 3. 2005. (Emergent Library: Vol. 1). (YA). (ps-1). 23.94 (978-0-8215-8910-6(5)) Sadlier, William H. Inc.

Gordon, Wendy. I'm Safe! with My New Pet. 1999. 24p. (ps-3). pap., act. bk. ed. 2.95 (978-1-891596-09-4(8)) Backyard Pub. Co., Inc.

Greenaway. Minipets, 3 vols. 1999. (Illus.). (J). 77.07 (978-0-7398-2775-8(8)) Raintree.

Greenaway, Theresa. Ants. Fairclough, Chris, illus. 1999. (Minipets Ser.). 32p. (J). (gr. 1-5). lib. bdg. 25.69 (978-0-7398-1830-5(9)) Raintree.

—Ants. 2000. (Minipets Ser.). (Illus.). 32p. (J). (gr. 1-5). pap. 7.95 (978-0-7398-2193-0(8)) Steck-Vaughn.

—Centipedes & Millipedes. Fairclough, Chris, illus. 1999. (Minipets Ser.). 32p. (J). (gr. 1-5). lib. bdg. 25.69 (978-0-7398-1829-9(5)) Raintree.

—Centipedes & Millipedes. 2000. (Minipets Ser.). (Illus.). 32p. (J). (gr. 1-5), pap. 7.95 (978-0-7398-2194-7(6)) Steck-Vaughn.

—Centipedes & Millipedes. 2000. (gr. 3-6). lib. bdg. 17.85 (978-0-613-74066-1(1)) Tandem Library Bks.

—Minipets, 9 bks., Set. Incl. Ants. Fairclough, Chris, illus. lib. bdg. 25.69 (978-0-7398-1830-5(9)); Beetles. Chanell, Jim. lib. bdg. 25.69 (978-0-8172-5586-2(9)); Caterpillars. Lafford, Stuart. lib. bdg. 25.69 (978-0-8172-5585-5(0)); Centipedes & Millipedes. Fairclough, Chris, illus. lib. bdg. 25.69 (978-0-7398-1829-9(5)); Grasshoppers & Crickets. Hayward, Tim. lib. bdg. 25.69 (978-0-8172-5590-9(7)); Slugs & Snails. Chanell, Jim. lib. bdg. 25.69 (978-0-8172-5587-9(7)); Spiders. Hayward, Tim. lib. bdg. 25.69 (978-0-8172-5589-3(3)); Tadpoles. Fairclough, Chris, illus. lib. bdg. 25.69 (978-0-7398-1828-2(7)); Worms. Chanell, Jim. lib. bdg. 25.69 (978-0-8172-5588-6(5)); 32p. (J). (gr. 1-5). 1999. (Illus.). 1999. Set lib. bdg. 231.21 (978-0-7398-1831-2(7)) Raintree.

—Tadpoles. Fairclough, Chris, illus. 1999. (Minipets Ser.). 32p. (J). (gr. 1-5). lib. bdg. 25.69 (978-0-7398-1828-2(7)) Raintree.

Gruber, Beth. Lizard & Reptile Style. 2004. (Pet's Point of View Ser.). 32p. (J). (gr. 4 up). lib. bdg. 22.60 (978-0-7565-0699-5(9)) Compass Point Bks.

Gunter, Veronika & Newcomb, Rain. Pet Science: Purr-Fectly Woof-Worthy Activities for You & Your Pets. 2006. (Illus.). 80p. (J). 14.95 (978-1-57990-786-0(5)) Lark Bks.

Gunzi, Christiane. Cuddly Puppies. 2005. (Feels Real Bks.). (Illus.). 10p. (J). bds. 4.95 (978-0-7641-5853-7(8)) Barron's Educational Series, Inc.

—Friendly Pets. 2007. (Feels Real Ser.). 10p. (J). (gr. k-k). bds. 4.99 (978-0-7641-6024-0(9)) Barron's Educational Series, Inc.

Gutman, Bill. Adopting Pets: How to Choose Your New Best Friend. 2001. (Pet Friends Ser.). (Illus.). 64p. (gr. 4-6). lib. bdg. (978-0-7613-1863-7(1) , Millbrook Pr.) Lerner Publishing Group.

—Becoming Best Friends with Your Iguana, Snake or Turtle. Green, Anne Canevari, illus. 2001. (Pet Friends Ser.). 64p. (gr. 4-6). lib. bdg. 24.90 (978-0-7613-1862-0(3) , Millbrook Pr.) Lerner Publishing Group.

Hager, Elizabeth. My Friend Fellow: Pets Are Friends Too. 1998. (Illus.). 36p. (J). (gr. k-2). pap. 4.95 (978-1-881524-25-0(6)) Milligan Bks., Inc.

Hamilton, Lynn. Caring for Your Bird. 2003. (gr. 3-6). lib. bdg. 16.40 (978-0-613-79823-5(6)) Tandem Library Bks.

—Caring for Your Bird. 2002. (Caring for Your Pet Ser.). (Illus.). 32p. (J). lib. bdg. 16.95 (978-1-59036-037-8(0)) Weigl Pubs., Inc.

—Caring for Your Ferret. 2004. (Caring for Your Pet Ser.). (J). pap. 7.95 (978-1-59036-150-4(4)); (Illus.). 32p. lib. bdg. 16.95 (978-1-59036-115-3(6)) Weigl Pubs., Inc.

—Caring for Your Fish. 2002. (Caring for Your Pet Ser.). (Illus.). 32p. (J). lib. bdg. 16.95 (978-1-59036-035-4(4)) Weigl Pubs., Inc.

—Caring for Your Turtle. 2004. (Caring for Your Pet Ser.). (J). pap. 7.95 (978-1-59036-153-5(9)); (Illus.). 32p. lib. bdg. 16.95 (978-1-59036-118-4(0)) Weigl Pubs., Inc.

Hamilton, Lynn A. Caring for Your Bird. Marshall, Diana & Nault, Jennifer, eds. 2003. (Caring for Your Pet Ser.). (Illus.). 32p. (J). pap. 7.95 (978-1-59036-067-5(2)) Weigl Pubs., Inc.

—Caring for Your Fish. Kissock, Heather & Marshall, Diana, eds. 2003. (Caring for Your Pet Ser.). (Illus.). 32p. (J). pap. 7.95 (978-1-59036-065-1(6)) Weigl Pubs., Inc.

Handford, Tom. Chinchillas. 2003. (Keeping Unusual Pets Ser.). (Illus.). 48p. (J). (gr. 3-5). lib. bdg. 25.64 (978-1-4034-0280-6(9)) Heinemann Library.

Harcourt School Publishers Staff. Pets - Grade 1. 3rd ed. 2002. (Trophies English Language Learners Ser.). pap. 3.20 (978-0-15-327563-0(4)) Harcourt Schl. Pubs.

—Pick a Pet: On Level. 3rd ed. 2002. (Trophies Reading Program Ser.). (Illus.). (J). pap. 4.10 (978-0-15-322979-4(9)) Harcourt Schl. Pubs.

—Pick a Pet! 5-Pack, On Level. 3rd ed. 2002. (Trophies Reading Program Ser.). (Illus.). (J). (gr. 1). pap. 20.10 (978-0-15-326829-8(8)) Harcourt Schl. Pubs.

Harte, May. Hide-and-Seek Pets. 2004. (Hide-And-Seek Books). (J). lib. bdg. 15.95 (978-1-4042-2815-3(2) , PowerKids Pr.) Rosen Publishing Group, Inc., The.

Hayward, Tim & Greenaway, Theresa. Grasshoppers & Crickets. 1999. (Minipets Ser.). (Illus.). 32p. (J). (gr. 1-5). lib. bdg. 25.69 (978-0-8172-5590-9(7)) Raintree.

—Grasshoppers & Crickets. 1999. (Minipets Ser.). (Illus.). 32p. (J). (gr. 1-5). pap. 5.95 (978-0-7398-1385-0(4)) Steck-Vaughn.

—Spiders. 1999. (Minipets Ser.). (Illus.). 32p. (J). (gr. 1-5). lib. bdg. 25.69 (978-0-8172-5589-3(3)) Raintree.

Head, Honor. Kittens & Cats. 2007. (QEB Know Your Pet Ser.). (Illus.). 32p. (J). lib. bdg. 19.95 (978-1-59566-217-0(0)) QEB Publishing Inc.

—Ponies & Horses. 2007. (QEB Know Your Pet Ser.). (Illus.). 32p. (J). lib. bdg. 19.95 (978-1-59566-219-4(7)) QEB Publishing Inc.

P
Q
R

Healing Your Heart When Your Animal Friend Is Gone: A Children's Pet Bereavement Workbook. 2004. (J). 14.95 (978-0-9748512-0-4(5)) Bree's Gift Publishing.

Heathcote, Peter. Lizards. 2004. (Keeping Unusual Pets Ser.). (Illus.). 48p. (J). (978-1-4034-0827-3(0)) Heinemann Library.

Heinemann Educational Ltd. Publishing Staff. The Wild Side of Pets Package. 2004. pap. 243.00 (978-1-4109-1387-6(2)) Harcourt Schl. Pubs.

Hernandez-Divers, Sonia. Geckos. 2003. (Keeping Unusual Pets Ser.). (Illus.). 48p. (J). (gr. 3-5). lib. bdg. 25.64 (978-1-4034-0282-0(5)) Heinemann Library.

—Snakes. 2003. (Keeping Unusual Pets Ser.). (Illus.). 48p. (J). (gr. 3-5). lib. bdg. 25.64 (978-1-4034-0284-4(1)) Heinemann Library.

Hibbert, Clare. Fish. 2004. (Illus.). 32p. (J). lib. bdg. (978-1-58340-435-5(X)) Smart Apple Media.

—Hamster. 2004. (Illus.). 32p. (J). lib. bdg. 27.10 (978-1-58340-433-1(3)) Smart Apple Media.

Hillenburg, Amy. Please, Please Can We Have a Pet? 2003. (Illus.). (J). per. 14.95 (978-1-59453-046-3(7) , 1732) Airleaf Publishing & Bookselling.

Hodge, Judith. Surprise Puppy! 1998. (Eyewitness Readers). (Illus.). 32p. (J). (gr. 5-3). pap. 3.99 (978-0-7894-3624-5(8)) Dorling Kindersley Publishing, Inc.

Hodge, Judith & Dorling Kindersley Publishing Staff. Surprise Puppy! 1998. (Eyewitness Readers). (Illus.). 32p. (J). (ps-3). 12.99 (978-0-7894-3765-5(1)) Dorling Kindersley Publishing, Inc.

Hodgman, Ann. The House of a Million Pets. Yelchin, Eugene, illus. 2007. 263p. (J). (gr. 3 up). 16.95 ***(978-0-8050-7974-6(2))*** Holt, Henry & Co.

HOP, LLC. Hooked on Animals Pets Super Activity Kit. 2006. (J). (ps). 9.99 (978-1-933863-20-7(X)) HOP, LLC.

Hopcraft, Xan. How It Was with Dooms: A True Story from Africa. Hopcraft, Carol Cawthra, illus. 2000. 64p. (J). (ps-3). pap. 9.99 (978-0-689-83539-1(6) , Aladdin) Simon & Schuster Children's Publishing.

—How It Was with Dooms: A True Story from Africa. 2000. (Illus.). (J). (978-0-606-17923-2(2)) Tandem Library Bks.

Hopkins, Lee Bennett. A Pet for Me. Manning, Jane, illus. 2004. 44p. (J). (ps-ps). lib. bdg. 12.00 (978-0-613-95122-7(0)) Tandem Library Bks.

Horton-Bussey, Claire, et al. 101 Facts about Ferrets. 2002. (One Hundred One Facts about Pets Ser.). (Illus.). 32p. (J). (gr. 3 up). lib. bdg. 23.33 (978-0-8368-3016-3(4)) Stevens, Gareth Inc.

—101 Facts about Pets, 12 bks. Incl. 101 Facts about Ferrets. 2002. lib. bdg. 23.33 (978-0-8368-3016-3(4)); 101 Facts about Goldfish. 2002. lib. bdg. 23.33 (978-0-8368-3017-0(2)); 101 Facts about Guinea Pigs. 2001. lib. bdg. 23.33 (978-0-8368-2887-0(9)); 101 Facts about Hamsters. 2002. lib. bdg. 23.33 (978-0-8368-3018-7(0)); 101 Facts about Horses & Ponies. 2002. lib. bdg. 23.33 (978-0-8368-3019-4(9)); 101 Facts about Iguanas. 2001. lib. bdg. 23.33 (978-0-8368-2888-7(7)); 101 Facts about Kittens. 2001. lib. bdg. 23.33 (978-0-8368-2889-4(5)); 101 Facts about Parakeets. 2002. lib. bdg. 23.33 (978-0-8368-3020-0(2)); 101 Facts about Puppies. 2001. lib. bdg. 23.33 (978-0-8368-2890-0(9)); 101 Facts about Rabbits. 2001. lib. bdg. 23.33 (978-0-8368-2891-7(7)); 101 Facts about Terrarium Pets. 2002. lib. bdg. 23.33 (978-0-8368-3021-7(0)); 101 Facts about Tropical Fish. 2001. lib. bdg. 23.33 (978-0-8368-2892-4(5)); 32p. (J). (gr. 3 up). (Illus.). Set lib. bdg. 279.96 (978-0-8368-3022-4(9)) Stevens, Gareth Inc.

How to Choose a Pet: Individual Title Six-Packs. (Discovery World Ser.). 24p. (gr. 1-2). 33.00 (978-0-7635-8475-7(4)) Rigby Education.

How to Convince Your Parents You Can..., 5 vols., Set. Incl. Care for a Pet Chameleon. Whiting, Jim. lib. bdg. 25.70 ***(978-1-58415-605-5(8));*** Care for a Pet Chimpanzee. Leavitt, Amie. lib. bdg. 25.70 ***(978-1-58415-607-9(4));*** Care for a Pet Mouse. Leavitt, Amie. lib. bdg. 25.70 ***(978-1-58415-606-2(6));*** Care for a Pet Snake. Whiting, Jim. lib. bdg. 25.70 ***(978-1-58415-604-8(X));*** Care for a Pet Tarantula. Leavitt, Amie. lib. bdg. 25.70 ***(978-1-58415-603-1(1));*** (Illus.). 32p. (J). (gr. 1-4). 2007. 2007. Set lib. bdg. 128.50 ***(978-1-58415-608-6(2))*** Mitchell Lane Pubs., Inc.

Hughes, Sarah. My Dog. 2001. (My Pets Ser.). (Illus.). 24p. (J). (ps-2). 17.00 (978-0-516-23184-6(7) , Children's Pr.) Scholastic Library Publishing.

—My Dog. 2001. (gr. k-3). lib. bdg. 12.95 (978-0-613-58861-4(4)) Tandem Library Bks.

Hunter, Rebecca. My First Pet. 2007. (First Times Ser.). (Illus.). 24p. (J). pap. 10.95 ***(978-0-237-53179-9(8) ,*** Evans Brothers, Limited) Evans Publishing Group GBR. *Dist:* Independent Pubs. Group.

I Have A New Puppy Now What: A Puppy Survival Guide for Kids. 2005. (J). 14.99 (978-0-9769401-0-4(8)) Hunt, J. L. Publishing.

Jeffrey, Laura S. Birds: How to Choose & Care for a Bird. 2004. (American Humane Pet Care Library). (Illus.). 48p. (J). (gr. 3-4). lib. bdg. 23.93 (978-0-7660-2515-8(2)) Enslow Pubs., Inc.

—Cats: How to Choose & Care for a Cat. 2004. (American Humane Pet Care Library). (Illus.). 48p. (J). lib. bdg. 23.93 (978-0-7660-2516-5(0)) Enslow Pubs., Inc.

—Dogs: How to Choose & Care for a Dog. 2004. (American Humane Pet Care Library). (Illus.). 48p. (J). lib. bdg. 23.93 (978-0-7660-2520-2(9)) Enslow Pubs., Inc.

—Fish: How to Choose & Care for a Fish. 2004. (American Humane Pet Care Library). (Illus.). 48p. (J). lib. bdg. 23.93 (978-0-7660-2517-2(9)) Enslow Pubs., Inc.

—Hamsters, Gerbils, Guinea Pigs, Rabbits, Ferrets, Mice, & Rats: How to Choose & Care for a Small Mammal. 2004. (American Humane Pet Care Library). (Illus.). 48p. (J). lib. bdg. 23.93 (978-0-7660-2518-9(7)) Enslow Pubs., Inc.

—Horses: How to Choose & Care for a Horse. 2004. (American Humane Pet Care Library). (Illus.). 48p. (J). lib. bdg. 23.93 (978-0-7660-2519-6(5)) Enslow Pubs., Inc.

Johansen, Heidi Leigh. My Book of Pets. 2005. (J). (978-1-4042-2798-9(9)) Rosen Publishing Group, Inc., The.

Johnston, Tony. It's about Dogs. 2000. (Illus.). 48p. (J). (gr. k-3). 16.98 (978-0-7398-2200-5(4)) Raintree.

Kain, Kathleen. All about Pets. Miyake, Yoshi, illus. 2004. (Treasure Tree Ser.). 32p. (J). (978-0-7166-1626-9(2)) World Bk., Inc.

Kalman, Bobbie & MacAulay, Kelley. Guinea Pigs. Crabtree, Marc, illus. Crabtree, Marc, photos by. 2004. (Pet Care Ser.). 32p. (J). pap. (978-0-7787-1787-4(9)); (978-0-7787-1755-3(0)) Crabtree Publishing Co.

Keenan, Sheila. A History of Pets & People. Waters, Kate, ed. 2007. (Animals in the House Ser.). (Illus.). 112p. (J). (gr. 4-7). pap. 17.99 (978-0-439-69286-1(5)) Scholastic, Inc.

Keeping Unusual Pets Series, 5 vols., Set. 2003. (Illus.). (J). (gr. 3-5). lib. bdg. 121.10 (978-1-4034-0286-8(8)) Heinemann Library.

Khan, Sarah. Pets Lift-the-Flap. 2005. (Luxury Lift-the-Flap Learners Ser.). 16p. (J). (gr. 1 up). 11.95 (978-0-7945-0914-9(2) , Usborne) EDC Publishing.

King-Smith, Dick. I Love Guinea Pigs. 2001. (ps-2). lib. bdg. 14.15 (978-0-613-44218-3(0)) Tandem Library Bks.

Kingfisher Editors, ed. Animal Babies Around the House. 2005. (Animal Babies Ser.). (Illus.). 24p. (J). (ps-k). bds. 6.95 (978-0-7534-5840-2(3) , Kingfisher) Houghton Mifflin Co. Trade & Reference Div.

Kneidel, Sally. More Pet Bugs. 1999. (gr. 3-6). lib. bdg. 22.20 (978-0-613-16528-0(4)) Tandem Library Bks.

Lambilly-Bresson, Elisabeth de. Animals Around the House. 2006. (Illus.). 14p. (J). lib. bdg. ***(978-0-8368-7829-5(9))*** Stevens, Gareth Inc.

Landau, Elaine. Minibeasts as Pets. 1998. (True Bks.). (Illus.). 48p. (J). (gr. 3-5). pap. 6.95 (978-0-516-26268-0(8) , Children's Pr.) Scholastic Library Publishing.

Levy, Barbara Soloff. Invisible Pets Magic Picture Book. 2002. (Invisible Magic Picture Bks.). (Illus.). 16p. (J). (ps-2). pap. 1.50 (978-0-486-42091-2(4)) Dover Pubns., Inc.

Lewis, David, contrib. by. Guinea Pigs. 1999. (Junior Pet Care Ser.). (Illus.). 48p. (gr. 4-7). 18.65 (978-0-7910-4908-2(6) , Chelsea Hse.) Facts On File, Inc.

—Hamsters. 1999. (Junior Pet Care Ser.). (Illus.). 48p. (YA). (gr. 4-7). 18.65 (978-0-7910-4907-5(8) , Chelsea Hse.) Facts On File, Inc.

—Kittens. 1999. (Junior Pet Care Ser.). (Illus.). 48p. (YA). (gr. 4-7). lib. bdg. 18.65 (978-0-7910-4906-8(X) , Chelsea Hse.) Facts On File, Inc.

—Puppies. 1999. (Junior Pet Care Ser.). (Illus.). 48p. (YA). (gr. 4-7). 18.65 (978-0-7910-4905-1(1) , Chelsea Hse.) Facts On File, Inc.

—Rabbits. 1999. (Junior Pet Care Ser.). (Illus.). 48p. (gr. 4-7). 18.65 (978-0-7910-4904-4(3) , Chelsea Hse.) Facts On File, Inc.

—Snakes. 1999. (Junior Pet Care Ser.). (Illus.). 48p. (gr. 4-7). 18.65 (978-0-7910-4910-5(8) , Chelsea Hse.) Facts On File, Inc.

Liss-Levinson, Nechama & Baskette, Molly Phinney. Remembering My Pet: A Kid's Own Spiritual Workbook for When a Pet Dies. 2007. 48p. (J). wbk. ed. 16.99 (978-1-59473-221-8(3)) SkyLight Paths Publishing.

Lodge, Jo. Pets. 1999. (Illus.). 12p. (J). 10.99 (978-0-333-76264-6(9)) Pan Macmillan GBR. *Dist:* Trafalgar Square Publishing.

Lodien, Jennie, des. Cat Tales. 2004. (Illus.). 48p. (YA). ring bd. 16.95 (978-0-9746341-8-0(2)) Chin & A Pr.

—A Doggie Diary: The story of our Dog. 2003. (Illus.). 48p. (YA). ring bd. 16.95 (978-0-9746341-7-3(4)) Chin & A Pr.

—Life on a Leash: My Dog's Story. 2003. (Illus.). 48p. (YA). ring bd. 16.95 (978-0-9746341-6-6(6)) Chin & A Pr.

Lollis, Sylvia & Hogan, Joyce W. Should We Have Pets? A Persuasive Text. 2003. (Illus.). 32p. (J). pap. 6.00 (978-1-59034-044-8(2)) Mondo Publishing.

Lomberg, Michelle. Caring for Your Horse. 2004. (Caring for Your Pet Ser.). (J). pap. 7.95 (978-1-59036-152-8(0)); (Illus.). 32p. lib. bdg. 16.95 (978-1-59036-117-7(2)) Weigl Pubs., Inc.

—Caring for Your Spider. 2004. (Caring for Your Pet Ser.). (J). pap. 7.95 (978-1-59036-155-9(5)); (Illus.). 32p. lib. bdg. 16.95 (978-1-59036-120-7(2)) Weigl Pubs., Inc.

Lorenz Books Staff. Pets. 2002. (Let's Look at...Ser.). (Illus.). 20p. 5.99 (978-0-7548-1052-0(6) , Lorenz Bks.) Anness Publishing GBR. *Dist:* National Bk. Network.

Loves, June. Birds. 2003. (Pets Ser.). (Illus.). 32p. (gr. 2-4). 23.00 (978-0-7910-7547-0(8) , Chelsea Hse.) Facts On File, Inc.

—Cats. 2003. (Pets Ser.). (Illus.). 32p. (gr. 2-4). 23.00 (978-0-7910-7548-7(6) , Chelsea Hse.) Facts On File, Inc.

—Dogs. 2003. (Pets Ser.). (Illus.). 32p. (gr. 2-4). 23.00 (978-0-7910-7549-4(4) , Chelsea Hse.) Facts On File, Inc.

—Fish. 2003. (Pets Ser.). (Illus.). 32p. (gr. 2-4). 23.00 (978-0-7910-7550-0(8) , Chelsea Hse.) Facts On File, Inc.

—Guinea Pigs & Rabbits. 2003. (Pets Ser.). (Illus.). 32p. (gr. 2-4). 23.00 (978-0-7910-7552-4(4) , Chelsea Hse.) Facts On File, Inc.

—Mice & Rats. 2003. (Pets Ser.). (Illus.). 32p. (gr. 2-4). 23.00 (978-0-7910-7551-7(6) , Chelsea Hse.) Facts On File, Inc.

Macken, JoAnn Early. Kittens. 2003. (Let's Read about Pets Ser.). (Illus.). 24p. (J). (ps up). lib. bdg. 19.33 (978-0-8368-3799-5(1)); pap. 7.93 (978-0-8368-3846-6(7)) Stevens, Gareth Inc. (Weekly Reader Early Learning Library).

—Let's Read about Pets, 6 bks. Incl. Goldfish. lib. bdg. 19.33 (978-0-8368-3797-1(5)); Guinea Pigs. lib. bdg. 19.33 (978-0-8368-3798-8(3)); Kittens. lib. bdg. 19.33 (978-0-8368-3799-5(1)); Parakeets. lib. bdg. 19.33 (978-0-8368-3800-8(9)); Puppies. lib. bdg. 19.33 (978-0-8368-3801-5(7)); Rabbits. lib. bdg. 19.33 (978-0-8368-3802-2(5)); 24p. (J). (ps up). (Weekly Reader Early Learning Library). (Illus.). 2003. Set lib. bdg. 115.98 (978-0-8368-3796-4(7)); pap. (978-0-8368-3843-5(2)) Stevens, Gareth Inc. (Weekly Reader Early Learning Library).

—Parakeets. 2003. (Let's Read about Pets Ser.). (Illus.). 24p. (J). (ps up). lib. bdg. 19.33 (978-0-8368-3800-8(9)); pap. 7.93 (978-0-8368-3847-3(5)) Stevens, Gareth Inc. (Weekly Reader Early Learning Library).

—Puppies. 2003. (Let's Read about Pets Ser.). (Illus.). 24p. (J). (ps up). lib. bdg. 19.33 (978-0-8368-3801-5(7)); pap. 7.93 (978-0-8368-3848-0(3)) Stevens, Gareth Inc. (Weekly Reader Early Learning Library).

Macmillan Children's Books Staff. The Little Guide to Pets. 2000. (Little Guides Ser.). (Illus.). 24p. (J). (ps-3). (978-0-333-73421-6(1) , Macmillan Children's Bks.) Pan Macmillan.

Make Your Own Pom Pom Pets. 2004. (Fun Kits Ser.). (Illus.). 48p. (J). (978-1-84229-861-9(5)) Top That! Publishing PLC.

Marshall, Diana. Caring for Your Hamster. 2003. (gr. 3-6). lib. bdg. 16.40 (978-0-613-79820-4(1)) Tandem Library Bks.

Martín Larrañaga, Ana. Playful Pets. 2000. (Ana's Animals Bks.). (Illus.). (J). (ps-k). 3.95 (978-1-58646-001-3(3)) Polka Dot Pr.

Mascotas. 2001. (Look At! Ser.).Tr. of Pets. (SPA., Illus.). 32p. (YA). (ps up). pap. (978-968-5308-04-5(7) , Silver Dolphin en Español) Advanced Marketing, S. de R. L. de C. V.

Mascotas, 6 Packs. (Coleccion Pm Ser.: Vol. 1). Tr. of Pets. (SPA.). 16p. (gr. k-1). 26.00 (978-0-7578-0666-7(X)) Rigby Education.

Mascotas. 2005. (Collection Abre Tus Ojos, Collection Eye Openers Ser.).Tr. of Pets. (SPA.). (J). (gr. k-2). 6.95 (978-950-11-0899-6(6)) Sigmar ARG. *Dist:* Iaconi, Mariuccia Bk. Imports.

Mattern, Joanne. The Abyssinian Cat. 2000. (Learning about Cats Ser.). (Illus.). 48p. (J). (gr. 3-4). lib. bdg. 21.26 (978-0-7368-0564-3(8) , Capstone High-Interest Bks.) Capstone Pr., Inc.

—The American Shorthair Cat. 2002. (Learning about Cats Ser.). (Illus.). 48p. (J). (gr. 3-4). lib. bdg. 21.26 (978-0-7368-1300-6(4) , Capstone High-Interest Bks.) Capstone Pr., Inc.

—The Exotic Cat. 2001. (Learning about Cats Ser.). (Illus.). 48p. (J). (gr. 3-4). lib. bdg. 21.26 (978-0-7368-0896-5(5) , Capstone High-Interest Bks.) Capstone Pr., Inc.

—The Maine Coon Cat. 2000. (Learning about Cats Ser.). (Illus.). 48p. (J). (gr. 3-4). lib. bdg. 21.26 (978-0-7368-0565-0(6) , Capstone High-Interest Bks.) Capstone Pr., Inc.

—The Ocicat. 2002. (Learning about Cats Ser.). (Illus.). 48p. (J). (gr. 3-4). lib. bdg. 21.26 (978-0-7368-1302-0(0) , Capstone High-Interest Bks.) Capstone Pr., Inc.

—The Persian Cat. 2000. (Learning about Cats Ser.). (Illus.). 48p. (J). (gr. 3-4). lib. bdg. 21.26 (978-0-7368-0566-7(4) , Capstone High-Interest Bks.) Capstone Pr., Inc.

—The Ragdoll Cat. 2001. (Learning about Cats Ser.). (Illus.). 48p. (J). (gr. 3-4). lib. bdg. 21.26 (978-0-7368-0897-2(3) , Capstone High-Interest Bks.) Capstone Pr., Inc.

Matthews, Derek, illus. Escucha y Aprende: Mascotas. 2005. (Escucha y Aprende Ser.). (SPA.). 10p. (J). (ps-7). 12.95 (978-970-718-299-8(7) , Silver Dolphin en Español) Advanced Marketing, S. de R. L. de C. V. MEX. *Dist:* Perseus Distribution.

McAllister, Angela. Monster. Middleton, Charlotte, illus. 2005. 32p. (J). ***(978-0-689-86078-2(1))*** Simon & Schuster.

McKay, Sindy. We Both Read-about Pets. 2002. (We Both Read Ser.). (Illus.). 44p. (J). (gr. 1 up). pap. 3.99 (978-1-891327-42-1(9)) Treasure Bay, Inc.

—We Both Read-about Pets Big Book: About Pets Big Book Edition. 2005. 44p. (J). (gr. k-1). 29.95 (978-1-891327-91-9(7)) Treasure Bay, Inc.

McNicholas, June. Ferrets. 2003. (Keeping Unusual Pets Ser.). (Illus.). 48p. (J). (gr. 3-5). lib. bdg. 25.64 (978-1-4034-0281-3(7)) Heinemann Library.

—Rats. 2003. (Keeping Unusual Pets Ser.). (Illus.). 48p. (J). (gr. 3-5). lib. bdg. 25.64 (978-1-4034-0283-7(3)) Heinemann Library.

Meister, Cari. Basset Hounds. l.t. ed. 2001. (Dogs Ser.). (Illus.). 24p. (J). (gr. k-6). lib. bdg. 21.35 (978-1-57765-478-0(1) , Checkerboard Library) ABDO Publishing Co.

—Bulldogs. l.t. ed. 2001. (Dogs Ser.). (Illus.). 24p. (J). (gr. k-6). lib. bdg. 21.35 (978-1-57765-476-6(5) , Checkerboard Library) ABDO Publishing Co.

—Cavalier King Charles Spaniels. l.t. ed. 2001. (Dogs Ser.). (Illus.). 24p. (J). (gr. k-6). lib. bdg. 21.35 (978-1-57765-475-9(7) , Checkerboard Library) ABDO Publishing Co.

Mellentin, Kath & Wood, Tim. Pet Corner, 6 bks. 1998. (Illus.). 8p. (J). (ps-k). 9.95 (978-0-7641-7210-6(7)) Barron's Educational Series, Inc.

Miller, M. Cats. 2002. (Pets Ser.). (Illus.). 24p. (J). (gr. k-3). pap. 6.50 (978-1-57572-477-5(4) , 90466) Heinemann Library.

Miller, Michaela. Goldfish. 1998. (Pets Ser.). (Illus.). 24p. (J). (gr. 1-3). lib. bdg. 21.36 (978-1-57572-574-1(6)) Heinemann Library.

—Hamsters. 1998. (Pets Ser.). (Illus.). 24p. (J). (gr. 1-3). lib. bdg. 21.36 (978-1-57572-576-5(2)) Heinemann Library.

—Puppies & Dogs. 2007. (Illus.). 32p. (J). lib. bdg. 19.95 (978-1-59566-218-7(9)) QEB Publishing Inc.

—Rabbits. 2007. (QEB Everybody Feels Ser.). (Illus.). 32p. (J). lib. bdg. 19.95 (978-1-59566-220-0(0)) QEB Publishing Inc.

Morgan, Sally. Animals as Friends. 1999. (gr. 3-6). lib. bdg. 15.25 (978-0-613-53916-6(8)) Tandem Library Bks.

Mueller, Peter & Creative Team at Walter Foster Publishing Staff. Pets. 2004. (Draw & Color Ser.). (Illus.). 40p. (J). pap. 4.95 (978-1-56010-818-4(5)) Foster, Walter Publishing, Inc.

Mullican, Judy. What Pet Should I Get? Linke, Don, Jr., illus. l.t. ed. 1999. (Big Bks.). 8p. (J). (ps-k). pap. 10.95 (978-1-57332-132-7(X)); pap. 10.95 (978-1-57332-134-1(6)) HighReach Learning, Inc.

Murray, Julie. Mutts. 2002. (Buddy Book Ser.). (Illus.). 24p. (J). (gr. k-4). lib. bdg. 21.35 (978-1-57765-641-8(5)) ABDO Publishing Co.

Nelson, Robin. Pet Fish. (First Step Nonfiction). (J). (gr. k-2). 2003. (Illus.). 24p. lib. bdg. 18.60 (978-0-8225-1267-7(X)); 2002. pap. 3.95 (978-0-8225-1298-1(X)) Lerner Publishing Group.

—Pet Frog. (First Step Nonfiction). (J). (gr. k-2). 2003. (Illus.). 24p. lib. bdg. 18.60 (978-0-8225-1271-4(8)); 2002. pap. 3.95 (978-0-8225-1315-5(3)) Lerner Publishing Group.

—Pet Hamster. (First Step Nonfiction). (J). (gr. k-2). 2003. (Illus.). 24p. lib. bdg. 18.60 (978-0-8225-1269-1(6)); 2002. pap. 3.95 (978-0-8225-1313-1(7)) Lerner Publishing Group.

—Pet Hermit Crab. (First Step Nonfiction). (J). (gr. k-2). 2003. (Illus.). 24p. lib. bdg. 18.60 (978-0-8225-1270-7(X)); 2002. pap. 3.95 (978-0-8225-1314-8(5)) Lerner Publishing Group.

Neye, Emily. All about Cats & Kittens. 1999. (gr. k-3). lib. bdg. 11.25 (978-0-613-21082-9(4)) Tandem Library Bks.

Nichols, Catherine. Animal Masterminds: A Chapter Book. 2003. (True Tales Ser.). (Illus.). 48p. (J). 22.50 (978-0-516-22913-3(3) , Children's Pr.) Scholastic Library Publishing.

Nobens, C. A., illus. Perfect Pets, 12 vols., Set. Incl. Brilliant Birds. Salzmann, Mary Elizabeth. lib. bdg. 19.93 ***(978-1-59928-744-7(7));*** Cuddly Cats. Hanson, Anders. lib. bdg. 19.93 ***(978-1-59928-745-4(5));*** Dandy Dogs. Salzmann, Mary Elizabeth. lib. bdg. 19.93 ***(978-1-59928-746-1(3));*** Flashy Fish. Salzmann, Mary Elizabeth. lib. bdg. 19.93 ***(978-1-59928-747-8(1));*** Frisky Ferrets. Doudna, Kelly. lib. bdg. 19.93 ***(978-1-59928-748-5(X));*** Goofy Guinea Pigs. Salzmann, Mary Elizabeth. lib. bdg. 19.93 ***(978-1-59928-749-2(8));*** Handsome Horses. Hanson, Anders. lib. bdg. 19.93 ***(978-1-59928-750-8(1));*** Hidden Hermit Crabs. Doudna, Kelly. lib. bdg. 19.93 ***(978-1-59928-751-5(X));*** Lively Lizards. Hanson, Anders. lib. bdg. 19.93 ***(978-1-59928-752-2(8));*** Rascally Rabbits. Doudna, Kelly. lib. bdg. 19.93 ***(978-1-59928-753-9(6));*** Running Rats. Doudna, Kelly. lib. bdg. 19.93 ***(978-1-59928-754-6(4));*** Terrific Turtles. Hanson, Anders. lib. bdg. 19.93 ***(978-1-59928-755-3(2));*** (Illus.). 24p. (J). (gr. k-3). 2007. Set lib. bdg. 239.16 ***(978-1-59928-743-0(9)*** , SandCastle) ABDO Publishing Co.

Ogle, Belinda. Cockatiels. 2004. (Keeping Unusual Pets Ser.). (Illus.). 48p. (J). (978-1-4034-0826-6(2)); (978-1-4034-0824-2(6)) Heinemann Library.

O'Keeffe, Mariza, ed. My First Pets. 2005. (My 1st board Bks.). (Illus.). 36p. (J). (ps-3). bds. 5.99 (978-0-7566-0978-8(X)) Dorling Kindersley Publishing, Inc.

Orbell, Carole, et al. Dog. Morley, Christine, illus. rev. ed. 2004. (Me & My Pet Ser.). 32p. (J). (ps-1). pap. 4.95 (978-1-58728-201-0(1) , Two Can Publishing) T&N Children's Publishing.

Packard, Mary. Weird Pet Stories. Zalme, Ron, illus. 2004. 86p. (J). (978-0-439-68778-2(0)) Scholastic, Inc.

Page, Gill. I Am Your Goldfish. 2004. (I Am Your Pet Ser.). (Illus.). 48p. (J). pap. 5.95 (978-0-7696-3388-6(9) , Waterbird Bks.) School Specialty Publishing.

—I Am Your Kitten. 2004. (gr. 3-6). lib. bdg. 14.10 (978-0-613-74928-2(6)) Tandem Library Bks.

—I Am Your Puppy. 2004. (gr. 3-6). lib. bdg. 14.10 (978-0-613-74929-9(4)) Tandem Library Bks.

Patterson, Jordan. Box Turtles: Keeping & Breeding Them in Captivity. 1999. (Basic Domestic Reptile & Amphibian Library). (Illus.). 64p. (YA). (gr. 4-7). 32.00 (978-0-7910-5077-4(7) , Chelsea Hse.) Facts On File, Inc.

Paulsen, Gary. My Life in Dog Years. 1999. (Illus.). 144p. (J). (gr. 5-9). pap. 5.99 (978-0-440-41471-1(7) , Yearling) Random Hse. Children's Bks.

—My Life in Dog Years. 1999. (gr. 7-12). lib. bdg. 13.00 (978-0-613-18320-8(7)) Tandem Library Bks.

—My Life in Dog Years. Paulsen, Ruth Wright, illus. l.t. ed. 2000. (Juvenile Ser.). 176p. (J). (gr. 4-7). 21.95 (978-0-7862-2740-2(0)) Thorndike Pr.

Pearce, Sue & Quin, Caroline. Pets. 2004. (Activities for 3-5 Year Olds Ser.). (Illus.). 32p. pap. 11.00 (978-1-897675-38-0(0)) Brilliant Pubns. GBR. *Dist:* Parkwest Pubns., Inc.

Perfect Pets - Group 1, 4 bks., Set. Incl. Cats. Hinds, Kathryn. lib. bdg. 25.64 (978-0-7614-0794-2(4)); Rabbits. Hinds, Kathryn. lib. bdg. 25.64 (978-0-7614-0793-5(6)); Small Dogs. Altman, Linda Jacobs. lib. bdg. 25.64 (978-0-7614-0795-9(2)); Turtles. Schafer, Susan. lib. bdg. 25.64 (978-0-7614-0796-6(0)); (J). (gr. 3-5). (Illus.). 32p. 1999. Set lib. bdg. 102.57 (978-0-7614-0792-8(8) , Benchmark Bks.) Cavendish, Marshall Corp.

Perfect Pets - Group 2, 4 bks., Set. Incl. Big Dogs. Altman, Linda Jacobs. lib. bdg. 25.64 (978-0-7614-1101-7(1)); Hamsters & Gerbils. Hinds, Kathryn. lib. bdg. 25.64 (978-0-7614-1104-8(6)); Lizards. Schafer, Susan. lib.

bdg. 25.64 (978-0-7614-1103-1(8)); Parrots. Altman, Linda Jacobs. lib. bdg. 25.64 (978-0-7614-1102-4(X)); 32p. (J). (gr. 3-5). 2000. (Illus.). 1999. Set lib. bdg. 102.57 (978-0-7614-1100-0(3) , Benchmark Bks.) Cavendish, Marshall Corp.

Pet Day: Individual Title Six-Packs. (gr. k-1). 23.00 (978-0-7635-8826-7(1)) Rigby Education.

Pet Day at School, 6 Packs. (Story Steps Ser.). (gr. k-2). 32.00 (978-0-7635-9606-4(X)) Rigby Education.

Pet Dictionary: An a to Z of Animal Companions. 2005. (Illus.). 64p. (J). pap. (*978-0-439-75459-0(3)*) Scholastic, Inc.

Pet Perspectives: MainSails Individual Title Six-Packs. (Sails Literacy Ser.). (gr. 5 up). 37.00 (978-0-7578-8055-1(X)) Rigby Education.

Pets. 2004. (Thematic Units Ser.). (Illus.). 80p. 9.99 (978-1-57690-619-4(1)) Teacher Created Materials, Inc.

Pets: Individual Title Six-Packs. (Literatura 2000 Ser.). (gr. k-1). 28.00 (978-0-7635-0062-7(3)) Rigby Education.

Pets & Farm Animals Action Sticker Book. 2002. 12p. (J). pap. 3.98 (978-0-7525-8039-5(6)) Parragon, Inc.

Pets once Wild Hb 5Bks Set 2. 2004. pap. (978-1-4109-1410-1(0)) Harcourt Schl. Pubs.

Pickett, Robert & Pickett, Justine, illus. Cat. Pickett, Robert & Pickett, Justine, photos by. 2004. 32p. (J). lib. bdg. 27.10 (978-1-58340-431-7(7)) Smart Apple Media.

—Dog. Pickett, Robert & Pickett, Justine, photos by. 2004. 32p. (J). lib. bdg. 27.10 (978-1-58340-430-0(9)) Smart Apple Media.

—Rabbit. Pickett, Robert & Pickett, Justine, photos by. 2004. 32p. (J). lib. bdg. (978-1-58340-432-4(5)) Smart Apple Media.

Pienkowski, Jan, illus. Jan Pienkowski's Pets. 1998. (Animal Action Pops Ser.). 10p. (J). (gr. 2 up). 4.95 (978-1-58117-022-1(X) , Intervisual/Piggy Toes) Dalmatian Pr.

Pipe, Jim. Pets. 2007. (J). (*978-1-59604-162-2(5)*) Stargazer Bks.

Playful Pets. (Flip Flap Fun Book Ser.). 10p. (J). bds. (978-2-7643-0182-1(0)) Phidal Publishing, Inc./Editions Phidal, Inc.

Pomerance, Diane. Animal Companions: Your Friends, Teachers & Guides. Mier, Vanessa, illus. 2003. 9.95 (978-0-9708500-2-7(6)) Polaire Pubns.

—When Your Pet Dies. Mier, Vanessa, illus. 2001. pap. 9.95 (978-0-9708500-0-3(X)) Polaire Pubns.

Poole, Susie. God Sees Our Pets. 2004. (Illus.). 18p. (J). 6.99 (978-0-310-70863-6(X)) Zonderkidz.

Pountney, Beth. Playful Pets. 2007. (Lift & Count Ser.). (Illus.). 12p. (ps). per., bds. 5.95 (978-1-84610-459-6(9)) Make Believe Ideas GBR. *Dist:* Ingram Pub. Services.

Priddy, Roger. Bright Baby Touch & Feel Perfect Pets. 2006. 10p. (J). bds. 4.95 (978-0-312-49860-3(8) , Priddy Bks.) St. Martin's Pr.

Purple Walrus & Other Perfect Pets: 6 Each of 1 Anthology, 6 vols. (Wildcatstm Ser.). 32p. (gr. 2-8). (978-0-322-00575-4(2)) Wright Group, The.

Rabe, Tish. The Cat in the Hat's Learning Library: All about Our Animal Friends. Ruiz, Aristides & Mathieu, Joe, illus. 2005. (Cat in the Hat's Learning Library). 48p. (J). (gr. k-3). 8.99 (978-0-375-82278-0(X) , Random Hse. Bks. for Young Readers) Random Hse. Children's Bks.

Raintree. Minipets, 6 bks., Set. 1999. (J). (gr. 1-5). 154.14 (978-0-8172-5591-6(5)) Raintree.

Randolph, Joanne. Classroom Pets, 6 bks., Set. Incl. Fish. lib. bdg. 21.25 (*978-1-4042-3681-3(3)* , 1266091); Guinea Pigs. lib. bdg. 21.25 (978-1-4042-3676-9(7)); Rabbits. lib. bdg. 21.25 (*978-1-4042-3680-6(5));* Snakes. lib. bdg. 21.25 (*978-1-4042-3679-0(1));* Tarantulas. lib. bdg. 21.25 (*978-1-4042-3678-3(3));* Turtles. lib. bdg. 21.25 (978-1-4042-3677-6(5) , 1266096); (Illus.). 24p. (J). (gr. k-5). 2007. 2007. Set lib. bdg. 127.50 (*978-1-4042-3608-0(2)* , PowerKids Pr.) Rosen Publishing Group, Inc., The.

Rankin, Wayne & Walls, Jerry G. Tarantulas & Scorpions. 1999. (Basic Domestic Reptile & Amphibian Library). (Illus.). 64p. (YA). (gr. 4-7). lib. bdg. 19.75 (978-0-7910-5081-1(5) , Chelsea Hse.) Facts On File, Inc.

Rayner, Matthew. I Am Your Pet, 2 vols., Set. Incl. Guinea Pig. lib. bdg. 23.93 (*978-0-8368-8385-6(3));* Rat. lib. bdg. 23.93 (*978-0-8368-8386-2(1));* 32p. (J). (gr. 2-4). 2007. 2007. Set lib. bdg. 47.86 (*978-0-8368-8384-8(5)*) Stevens, Gareth Inc.

Rayner, Matthew & BVetMed MRCVS Staff. Cat. Burton, Jane & Greenaway, Frank, photos by. 2004. (I Am Your Pet Ser.). (Illus.). 32p. (J). (gr. 2 up). lib. bdg. 23.33 (978-0-8368-4102-2(6)) Stevens, Gareth Inc.

—Dog. Burton, Jane & Greenaway, Frank, photos by. 2004. (I Am Your Pet Ser.). (Illus.). 32p. (J). (gr. 2 up). lib. bdg. 23.33 (978-0-8368-4103-9(4)) Stevens, Gareth Inc.

—Hamster. Greenaway, Frank & Burton, Jane, photos by. 2004. (I Am Your Pet Ser.). (Illus.). 32p. (J). (gr. 2 up). lib. bdg. 23.33 (978-0-8368-4104-6(2)) Stevens, Gareth Inc.

—I Am Your Pet, 4 bks. Burton, Jane & Greenaway, Frank, photos by. Incl. Cat. lib. bdg. 23.33 (978-0-8368-4102-2(6)); Dog. lib. bdg. 23.33 (978-0-8368-4103-9(4)); Hamster. lib. bdg. 23.33 (978-0-8368-4104-6(2)); Rabbit. lib. bdg. 23.33 (978-0-8368-4105-3(0)); 32p. (J). (gr. 2 up). (Illus.). 2004. Set lib. bdg. 93.32 (978-0-8368-4101-5(8)) Stevens, Gareth Inc.

—Rabbit. Burton, Jane & Greenaway, Frank, photos by. 2004. (I Am Your Pet Ser.). (Illus.). 32p. (J). (gr. 2 up). lib. bdg. 23.33 (978-0-8368-4105-3(0)) Stevens, Gareth Inc.

Ring, Susan. Caring for Your Cat. 2003. (gr. 3-6). lib. bdg. 16.40 (978-0-613-79819-8(8)) Tandem Library Bks.

—Caring for Your Cat. Kissock, Heather & Marshall, Diana, eds. 2003. (Caring for Your Pet Ser.). (Illus.). 32p. (J). pap. 7.95 (978-1-59036-062-0(1)) Weigl Pubs., Inc.

—Taking Care of Pets. 2006. (Illus.). (J). 16p. (978-0-7368-5988-2(8)); (ENG & SPA., 18p. (978-0-7368-6024-6(X)) Yellow Umbrella Bks.

Rizzati, Lorella. Ladybug/Crab/Turtle/Frog. 1998. (Portable Pets Ser.). (Illus.). 12p. (J). pap. 95.20 (978-0-8109-5099-3(5)) Abrams, Harry N., Inc.

Roberts, Heulwen. Anifeiliaid Anwes. 2005. (WEL., Illus.). 16p. (978-1-85644-778-2(2)) Univ. of Wales, Aberystwyth, Centre for Educational Studies.

Roca, Nuria & Curto, Rosa M. Cuidemos a Nuestro Gatito Nuevo. 2006. (Let's Take Care of Bks.). (SPA.). 36p. (J). pap. 6.99 (978-0-7641-3453-1(1)) Barron's Educational Series, Inc.

—Cuidemos a Nuestro Perrito Nuevo. 2006. (Let's Take Care of Bks.). (SPA.). 36p. (J). pap. 6.99 (978-0-7641-3456-2(6)) Barron's Educational Series, Inc.

Rock, Maxine. Totally Fun Things to Do with Your Dog. 1998. (Play with Your Pet). (Illus.). 128p. (gr. 3-7). pap. 12.95 (978-0-471-19574-0(X) , Frommers) Wiley, John & Sons, Inc.

Rockwell, Anne F. My Pet Hamster. Lum, Bernice, illus. 2002. (Let's-Read-and-Find-Out Science Ser.). 40p. (J). (ps-1). pap. 4.99 (978-0-06-445205-2(0)) HarperCollins Pubs.

—My Pet Hamster. 2002. (gr. k-3). lib. bdg. 13.00 (978-0-613-56071-9(X)) Tandem Library Bks.

Rogers, Fred. When a Pet Dies. Judkis, Jim, photos by. 1998. (First Experience Bks.). (Illus.). 32p. (J). (ps-k). pap. 5.99 (978-0-698-11666-5(6) , Putnam Juvenile) Penguin Group (USA) Inc.

—When a Pet Dies. 1998. (ps-2). lib. bdg. 14.15 (978-0-613-90031-7(6)) Tandem Library Bks.

Ross, Michael Elsohn. Indoor Zoo. Seeley, Tim, illus. 2003. (You Are the Scientist Ser.). 48p. (J). (gr. 3-6). lib. bdg. 23.93 (978-0-87614-621-7(3)) Lerner Publishing Group.

Ross, Veronica. Guinea Pig. 2002. (My First Ser.). (Illus.). 32p. (J). lib. bdg. 24.25 (978-1-930643-74-1(8)) Chrysalis Education.

—Hamster. 2002. (My First Ser.). (Illus.). 32p. (J). lib. bdg. 24.25 (978-1-930643-75-8(6)) Chrysalis Education.

Ryan, Victoria. When Your Pet Dies: A Healing Handbook for Kids. Ryan, Victoria & Alley, R. W., illus. 2003. (Elf-Help Books for Kids). 32p. (J). per. 7.95 (978-0-87029-376-4(1)) Abbey Pr.

Schaefer, Lola M. Family Pets. 2008. (J). (*978-1-4296-1223-4(1)* , Pebble Bks.) Capstone Pr., Inc.

—Family Pets. Saunders-Smith, Gail, ed. 1999. (Families Ser.). (Illus.). 24p. (J). (gr. k-1). lib. bdg. 15.93 (978-0-7368-0255-0(X) , Pebble Bks.) Capstone Pr., Inc.

—What Does Your Pet Do? 2007. (J). (978-1-59515-927-4(4)) Rourke Publishing, LLC.

Scholastic Editorial Staff. Littlest Pet Shop: Official Collector's Sticker Book. 2007. (Littlest Pet Shop Ser.: Bk. 2). 32p. (J). pap. 4.99 (978-0-439-89754-9(8)) Scholastic, Inc.

Scholastic, Inc. Staff. Ultimate Handbook Vol. 2, Vol. 2. 2007. (Littlest Pet Shop Ser.). 64p. (J). pap. 5.99 (*978-0-439-91904-3(5)*) Scholastic, Inc.

Silverstein, Alvin, et al. Beautiful Birds. 2003. (What a Pet! Ser.). (Illus.). 48p. (gr. 5-8). lib. bdg. 23.90 (978-0-7613-2513-0(1) , Millbrook Pr.) Lerner Publishing Group.

—Creepy Crawlies. 2003. (What a Pet! Ser.). (Illus.). 48p. (gr. 5-8). lib. bdg. 23.90 (978-0-7613-2511-6(5) , Millbrook Pr.) Lerner Publishing Group.

—Curious Cats. 2003. (What a Pet! Ser.). (Illus.). 48p. (gr. 5-8). lib. bdg. 23.90 (978-0-7613-2512-3(3) , Millbrook Pr.) Lerner Publishing Group.

—Pocket Pets. 2000. (What a Pet! Ser.). (Illus.). 48p. (gr. 4-7). lib. bdg. 23.90 (978-0-7613-1370-0(2) , Twenty-First Century Bks.) Lerner Publishing Group.

—What a Pet!, 4 vols., Set. 2004. (Science & Technology Ser.). (Illus.). 48p. (YA). (gr. 5-8). (978-0-7613-3107-0(7) , Twenty-First Century Bks.) Lerner Publishing Group.

Simon, Elizabeth. Caring for Your Iguana. 2004. (Caring for Your Pet Ser.). (Illus.). (J). pap. (978-1-59036-215-0(2)); 32p. lib. bdg. 16.95 (978-1-59036-195-5(4)) Weigl Pubs., Inc.

—Caring for Your Rat. 2004. (Caring for Your Pet Ser.). (Illus.). (J). pap. (978-1-59036-217-4(9)); 32p. lib. bdg. 16.95 (978-1-59036-197-9(0)) Weigl Pubs., Inc.

Sjonger, Rebecca & Kalman, Bobbie. Gerbils. Crabtree, Marc, illus. Crabtree, Marc, photos by. 2004. (Pet Care Ser.). 32p. (J). pap. (978-0-7787-1784-3(4)); (978-0-7787-1752-2(6)) Crabtree Publishing Co.

—Hamsters. Crabtree, Marc, illus. Crabtree, Marc, photos by. 2004. (Pet Care Ser.). 32p. (J). pap. (978-0-7787-1785-0(2)); (978-0-7787-1753-9(4)) Crabtree Publishing Co.

—Mice. Crabtree, Marc, illus. Crabtree, Marc, photos by. 2004. (Pet Care Ser.). 32p. (J). pap. (978-0-7787-1786-7(0)); (978-0-7787-1754-6(2)) Crabtree Publishing Co.

—Puppies. (Pet Care Ser.). (Illus.). 32p. (J). 2004. pap. (978-0-7787-1783-6(6)); 2003. (978-0-7787-1751-5(8)) Crabtree Publishing Co.

Sladen, Louisa. My Pets. Rinaldo, Luana, illus. 2005. (Magic Color Bks.). 10p. (J). 3.95 (978-1-4027-2053-6(X) , Sterling/Pinwheel) Sterling Publishing Co., Inc.

Smith, A. G. Fun with Favorite Pets Stencils. 1998. (Illus.). 6p. (J). pap. 1.50 (978-0-486-25451-7(8)) Dover Pubns., Inc.

Solomon, Iris L. & Solomon, Ronald B. My Best Friend: A Pet Owner's Journal. 1999. (Illus.). 50p. (J). spiral bd. 12.95 (978-0-9658167-2-4(9)) Swingset Pr., LLC.

Southwater Staff. Pets: Look & Learn. 2000. (Look & Learn Ser.). (Illus.). 32p. (ps). 7.95 (978-1-84215-167-9(3) , Southwater) Anness Publishing GBR. *Dist:* National Bk. Network.

Stanley, Mandy. Mascotas Maravillosas/Perfect Pets. 2004. (Todos A Bordo Ser.). (ENG & SPA., Illus.). 12p. (J). (ps-k). bds. 4.95 (978-0-7534-5813-6(6) , Kingfisher) Houghton Mifflin Co. Trade & Reference Div.

—Perfect Pets. 2004. (All Aboard Ser.). Orig. Title: Mascotas Maravillosas. (Illus.). 12p. (J). (ps-k). bds. 3.95 (978-0-7534-5748-1(2) , Kingfisher) Houghton Mifflin Co. Trade & Reference Div.

Starosta, Paul. Face-to-Face with the Hamster. 2004. (Illus.). 25p. (J). 9.95 (978-1-57091-456-0(7)) Charlesbridge Publishing, Inc.

Steck-Vaughn Staff. Early Reader Program Level B: A Look at Pets, 6 Pack. 2004. (Illus.). pap. 33.00 (978-0-7398-8251-1(1)) Steck-Vaughn.

—Every Pet Is Special. 2000. (Illus.). (J). pap. (978-0-7398-4457-1(1)); bds. (978-0-7398-4447-2(4)) Steck-Vaughn.

—A House Full of Pets. 2000. (Illus.). (J). pap. (978-0-7398-4456-4(3)); bds. (978-0-7398-4446-5(6)) Steck-Vaughn.

—Pets: Plenty of Pets/Pet of the Day. 1998. (Illus.). (J). pap. (978-0-8172-8635-4(7)) Steck-Vaughn.

Stein, Sara. Great Pets! An Extraordinary Guide to Usual & Unusual Family Pets. 2003. (Illus.). 368p. (gr. 3-7). tchr. ed. 26.95 (978-1-58017-504-3(X) , 67504); (J). (gr. 5 up). pap. 16.95 (978-1-58017-489-3(2) , 67489) Storey Publishing, LLC. (Storey Kids).

Stein, Sara Bonnett. Great Pets! An Extraordinary Guide to More Than 60 Usual & Unusual Family Pets. Judice, Edward, photos by. 2003. (Illus.). 358p. (J). (gr. 3-7). per. 26.85 (978-0-613-70581-3(5)) Tandem Library Bks.

Stevens, Carla. Your First Pet. 1999. (J). pap. 10.01 (978-0-688-16567-3(2)) HarperCollins Pubs.

Stone, Lynn M. Boa Constrictors. 2001. (Illus.). 24p. (J). (gr. 1-4). lib. bdg. 20.64 (978-1-58952-036-3(X)) Rourke Publishing, LLC.

—Box Turtles. 2001. (Weird Pets Ser.). (Illus.). 24p. (J). (gr. 1-4). lib. bdg. 20.64 (978-1-58952-037-0(8)) Rourke Publishing, LLC.

—Ferrets. 2001. (Illus.). 24p. (J). (gr. 1-4). lib. bdg. 20.64 (978-1-58952-038-7(6)) Rourke Publishing, LLC.

—Miniature Horses. 2001. (Weird Pets Ser.). (Illus.). 24p. (J). (gr. 1-4). lib. bdg. 20.64 (978-1-58952-039-4(4)) Rourke Publishing, LLC.

—Poodles. 2003. (Eye to Eye with Dogs Ser.). (Illus.). 24p. (gr. 2-5). 17.95 (978-1-58952-330-2(X)) Rourke Publishing, LLC.

—Pot Bellied Pigs. 2001. (Weird Pets Ser.). (Illus.). 24p. (J). (gr. 1-4). lib. bdg. 20.64 (978-1-58952-040-0(8)) Rourke Publishing, LLC.

—Tarantulas. 2001. (Weird Pets Ser.). (Illus.). 24p. (J). (gr. 1-4). lib. bdg. 20.64 (978-1-58952-041-7(6)) Rourke Publishing, LLC.

Taking Care of Pets. 2006. (Yellow Umbrella Social Studies). 8,16p. (J). 6.50 (978-0-7368-1718-9(2)) Red Brick Learning.

Taking Care of Pets Social Studies, 6 vols. (gr. k-2). 28.95 (978-0-7368-1754-7(9) , Yellow Umbrella Bks.) Capstone Pr., Inc.

Tattam, Mark. Pets: Sticker Activity Book. 2005. (Lift Stick & Learn Ser.). (Illus.). 12p. (J). (ps-3). 4.95 (978-1-905051-70-0(0)) Make Believe Ideas GBR. *Dist:* Ingram Pub. Services.

Temple, Bob. Chihuahuas. l.t. ed. 2000. (Dogs Ser.). (Illus.). 24p. (J). (gr. k-6). lib. bdg. 21.35 (978-1-57765-419-3(6) , Checkerboard Library) ABDO Publishing Co.

—Jack Russell Terriers. l.t. ed. 2000. (Dogs Ser.). (Illus.). 24p. (J). (gr. k-6). lib. bdg. 21.35 (978-1-57765-424-7(2) , Checkerboard Library) ABDO Publishing Co.

—Pugs. 2000. (Dogs Ser.). (Illus.). 24p. (J). (gr. k-6). lib. bdg. 21.35 (978-1-57765-422-3(6) , Checkerboard Library) ABDO Publishing Co.

—Shih Tzus. l.t. ed. 2000. (Dogs Ser.). (Illus.). 24p. (J). (gr. k-6). lib. bdg. 21.35 (978-1-57765-423-0(4) , Checkerboard Library) ABDO Publishing Co.

Time-Life Staff. Animal Friends. 1999. (Illus.). 88p. (J). (ps-4). 14.95 (978-0-8094-4849-4(1)) Time Life, Inc.

Tuxworth, Nicola. Learn-a-Word Picture Book: Pets, 12 vols. 2006. (Learn-A-Word Picture Bks.). (Illus.). 12p. bds. 6.99 (978-0-7548-1461-0(0) , Lorenz Bks.) Anness Publishing GBR. *Dist:* National Bk. Network.

Twist, Clint. Pets. 2006. 64p. (gr. 5-8). 26.20 (978-1-4103-0656-2(9) , Blackbirch Pr., Inc.) Thomson Gale.

Vanase, Jessica, ed. How to Be a Helping Hand for Dogs & Cats. 2001. (SPA., Illus.). 32p. (J). act. bk. ed. 3.00 (978-0-941246-13-2(2) , Humane Society Pr.) National Assn. for Humane & Environmental Education.

Verdick, Elizabeth. Tails Are Not for Pulling. Heinlen, Marieka, illus. 2005. (Best Behavior Ser.). (J). (ps-2). 40p. pap. 11.95 (978-1-57542-181-0(X)); 24p. 7.95 (978-1-57542-180-3(1)) Free Spirit Publishing, Inc.

Vidner, Bradley. All about Your... Rat. 1998. (All about Your...Ser.). (Illus.). 64p. 2.95 (978-1-86054-062-2(7)) Ringpress Bks., Ltd. GBR. *Dist:* 7 Hills Bk. Distributors.

Vincenti, Catherine, ed. & illus. Pet Pals Grades 3-4: A Spanish-English Workbook. Vincenti, Catherine, illus. 2003. Tr. of Mascotas Companeros. (SPA.). 34p. wbk. ed. 3.00 (978-0-941246-21-7(3) , Humane Society Pr.) National Assn. for Humane & Environmental Education.

—Pet Pals Grades 5-6: A Spanish-English Workbook. Vincenti, Catherine, illus. 2003. Tr. of Mascotas Companeros. (SPA.). 34p. wbk. ed. 3.00 (978-0-941246-22-4(1) , Humane Society Pr.) National Assn. for Humane & Environmental Education.

—Pet Pals Grades K-2: A Spanish-English Workbook. Vincenti, Catherine, illus. 2003. Tr. of Mascotas Companeros. (SPA.). 34p. (J). wbk. ed. 3.00 (978-0-941246-20-0(5) , Humane Society Pr.) National Assn. for Humane & Environmental Education.

Viner, Bradley. Guinea Pig. 1999. (All about Your Pet Ser.). (Illus.). 32p. pap. 4.99 (978-0-7641-1013-9(6)) Barron's Educational Series, Inc.

—Hamster. 1999. (All about Your Pet Ser.). (Illus.). 32p. pap. 4.99 (978-0-7641-1014-6(4)) Barron's Educational Series, Inc.

—Rabbit. 1999. (All about Your Pet Ser.). (Illus.). 32p. pap. 4.99 (978-0-7641-1015-3(2)) Barron's Educational Series, Inc.

Walker-Hodge, Judith. Surprise Puppy! 1998. (Illus.). 32p. (J). (ps-ps). lib. bdg. 11.80 (978-0-613-12166-8(X)) Tandem Library Bks.

Walker, Niki & Kalman, Bobbie. Kittens. 2004. (Pet Care Ser.). (Illus.). 32p. (J). pap. (978-0-7787-1782-9(8)) Crabtree Publishing Co.

Walker, Pam. My Parakeet. 2001. (My Pets Ser.). (Illus.). 24p. (J). (ps-2). 17.00 (978-0-516-23187-7(1) , Children's Pr.) Scholastic Library Publishing.

Walker, Pamela. My Parakeet. 2001. (gr. k-3). lib. bdg. 12.95 (978-0-613-58869-0(X)) Tandem Library Bks.

Wallace, Bruce & Make Believe Ideas Staff. Pets. 2005. (Touch & Sparkle Ser.). (Illus.). 12p. (ps-k). bds. 5.95 (978-1-905051-01-4(8)) Make Believe Ideas GBR. *Dist:* Ingram Pub. Services.

Walls, Jerry G. Keeping Poison Frogs. 1998. (Basic Domestic Reptile & Amphibian Library). (Illus.). (J). (gr. 2-5). lib. bdg. 17.95 (978-0-7910-5079-8(3) , Chelsea Hse.) Facts On File, Inc.

Walsh, Melanie. Pets. Walsh, Melanie, illus. 2002. (Tiny Teether Ser.). (Illus.). 14p. (J). (gr. k-ps). bds. 4.99 (978-0-7636-1808-7(X)) Candlewick Pr.

Waters. Pets Once Wild, 6 bks., Set 1. 2004. (Illus.). (J). 154.20 (978-1-4109-1023-3(7)); pap. 40.50 (978-1-4109-1163-6(2)) Raintree.

Waters, Jo. Fish. 2004. (Raintree Perspectives Ser.). (Illus.). 32p. (J). (gr. 6-8). lib. bdg. 25.70 (978-1-4109-1020-2(2)) Harcourt Schl. Pubs.

—The Wild Side of Mice & Rats. 2004. (Raintree Perspectives Ser.). (Illus.). 32p. (J). pap. (978-1-4109-1412-5(7)) Harcourt Schl. Pubs.

—The Wild Side of Pet Cats. 2004. (Raintree Perspectives Ser.). (Illus.). 32p. (J). 7.50 (978-1-4109-1157-5(8)); 25.70 (978-1-4109-1017-2(2)) Harcourt Schl. Pubs.

—The Wild Side of Pet Dogs. 2004. (Raintree Perspectives Ser.). (Illus.). 32p. (J). 7.50 (978-1-4109-1158-2(6)); 25.70 (978-1-4109-1018-9(0)) Harcourt Schl. Pubs.

—The Wild Side of Pet Ferrets. 2004. (Raintree Perspectives Ser.). (Illus.). 32p. (J). pap. 7.50 (978-1-4109-1159-9(4)); (gr. 6-8). lib. bdg. 26.36 (978-1-4109-1019-6(9)) Harcourt Schl. Pubs.

—The Wild Side of Pet Fish. 2004. (Raintree Perspectives Ser.). (Illus.). 32p. (J). pap. 7.50 (978-1-4109-1160-5(8)) Harcourt Schl. Pubs.

—The Wild Side of Pet Guinea Pigs. 2004. (Raintree Perspectives Ser.). (Illus.). 32p. (J). 26.36 (978-1-4109-1021-9(0)); pap. 7.50 (978-1-4109-1161-2(6)) Harcourt Schl. Pubs.

—The Wild Side of Pet Lizards. 2004. (Raintree Perspectives Ser.). (Illus.). 32p. (J). 26.36 (978-1-4109-1022-6(9)); pap. 7.50 (978-1-4109-1162-9(4)) Harcourt Schl. Pubs.

—The Wild Side of Pet Mice & Rats. 2005. (Raintree Perspectives Ser.). (Illus.). 32p. (J). (ps-ps). lib. bdg. 27.50 (978-1-4109-1406-4(2)) Harcourt Schl. Pubs.

Watts, Claire. Pets. 2004. (My First Look at Animals Ser.). (SPA., Illus.). 24p. (ps-2). 9.95 (978-1-58728-857-9(5)); (J). pap. 5.95 (978-1-58728-864-7(8)) T&N Children's Publishing. (Two Can Publishing).

—Pets. 2000. (gr. k-3). lib. bdg. 11.80 (978-0-613-36595-6(X)) Tandem Library Bks.

Webb, Cheryl Renee. Do Pets & Other Animals Go to Heaven? How to Recover from the Loss of an Animal Friend. 2003. (Illus.). 108p. per. 15.95 (978-0-9726363-0-8(7)) Brite Bks.

Weingartz, Jill. Ant Colonies. 2001. (Created Environments Ser.). (Illus.). 24p. (J). 21.35 (978-1-58340-103-3(2)) Smart Apple Media.

—Aquariums. 2001. (Created Environments Ser.). (Illus.). 24p. (J). 21.35 (978-1-58340-104-0(0)) Smart Apple Media.

Where Is My Pet?, 6 Packs. (Chiquilibros Ser.). (gr. k-1). 23.00 (978-0-7635-0438-0(6)) Rigby Education.

Wilcox, Charlotte. The Bloodhound. 2001. (Learning about Dogs Ser.). (Illus.). 48p. (J). (gr. 3-4). lib. bdg. 21.26 (978-0-7368-0761-6(6) , Capstone High-Interest Bks.) Capstone Pr., Inc.

—The Boxer. 2001. (Learning about Dogs Ser.). (Illus.). 48p. (J). (gr. 3-4). lib. bdg. 21.26 (978-0-7368-0762-3(4) , Capstone High-Interest Bks.) Capstone Pr., Inc.

—The Dachshund. 2001. (Learning about Dogs Ser.). (Illus.). 48p. (J). (gr. 3-4). lib. bdg. 21.26 (978-0-7368-0763-0(2) , Capstone High-Interest Bks.) Capstone Pr., Inc.

—The Greyhound. 2001. (Learning about Dogs Ser.). (Illus.). 48p. (J). (gr. 3-4). lib. bdg. 21.26 (978-0-7368-0764-7(0) , Capstone High-Interest Bks.) Capstone Pr., Inc.

Wild Side of Pets Hb 5Bks Set. 2004. pap. (978-1-4109-1416-3(X)) Harcourt Schl. Pubs.

The Wild Side of Pets Package. 2004. pap. (978-1-4109-1422-4(4)) Harcourt Schl. Pubs.

Wilkinson, Doris J. House Pets. Wilkinson, Doris J., ed. Chipping, Oliver, illus. 2000. (Jacob's Magic Box Discovery Ser.). 20p. (J). (ps). pap. 4.95 (978-0-9700386-5-4(8)) Magic Box Pubns.

Willow Creek Press Staff, ed. What Pets Teach Us. 2006. (Illus.). 32p. (J). 12.95 (978-1-59543-393-0(7)) Willow Creek Pr., Inc.

Windsor, Jo. Animals in the City: Early Level Satellite Individual Title Six-Packs. (Sails Literacy Ser.). 16p. (gr. 1-2). 27.00 (978-0-7578-2916-1(3)) Rigby Education.

PETS—FICTION

Abercrombie, Barbara & Gustavson, Adam. Bad Dog, Dodger! 2002. (Illus.). 40p. (J). (gr. 1-5). 14.95 (978-0-689-83782-1(8) , McElderry, Margaret K.) Simon & Schuster Children's Publishing.

Ada, Alma Flor. Daniel's Pet. Karas, G. Brian, illus. 2003. (Green Light Readers Level 1 Ser.). 24p. (J). 11.95 (978-0-15-204825-9(1)); pap. 3.95 (978-0-15-204865-5(0)) Harcourt Children's Bks. (Green Light Readers).

—Daniel's Pet. 2002. (ps-2). lib. bdg. 11.80 (978-0-613-64481-5(6)) Tandem Library Bks.

Ada, Alma Flor. Daniel's Pet: Daniel y Su Mascota. Karas, G. Brian, illus. 2008. (Green Light Readers Level 1 Ser.). (SPA & ENG.). 28p. (J). 12.95 (***978-0-15-206237-8(8)***) Harcourt Trade Pubs.

Addy, Sharon Hart. Lucky Jake. Zahares, Wade, illus. 2007. 40p. (J). (gr. k-3). 17.00 (978-0-618-47286-4(X)) Houghton Mifflin Co.

Ahlberg, Allan. The Cat Who Got Carried Away. McEwen, Katharine, illus. 2003. 96p. (J). (gr. 1-4). 15.99 (978-0-7636-2073-8(4)) Candlewick Pr.

—The Children Who Smelled a Rat. McEwen, Katharine, illus. 2005. 80p. (J). (gr. 2-4). 15.99 (978-0-7636-2870-3(0)) Candlewick Pr.

Albee, Sarah. My New Pet Is the Greatest. 1999. (Road to Reading Ser.). (Illus.). (J). (978-0-606-20816-1(X)) Tandem Library Bks.

—Off to Bed. Ebert, Len, illus. 2006. (Step-By-Step Readers Ser.). (J). pap. (978-1-59939-060-4(4) , Reader's Digest Young Families, Inc.) Reader's Digest Children's Publishing, Inc.

Alsenas, Linas. Peanut. 2007. 32p. (J). (ps-k). pap. 16.99 (***978-0-439-77980-7(4)***) Scholastic, Inc.

Arnold, Tedd. There Was an Old Lady Who Swallowed Fly Guy. 2007. (Fly Guy Ser.). 32p. (J). pap. 5.99 (***978-0-439-63906-4(9)***) Scholastic, Inc.

Arnosky, Jim. Little Lions. 1998. (Illus.). 1p. (J). (ps-1). 17.99 (978-0-399-22944-2(2) , Putnam Juvenile) Penguin Group (USA) Inc.

Arruzza, Rick. No Descanso Para Sparky. Newton, Pilar, illus. 2004. (SPA.). 24p. (J). mass mkt. 7.95 (978-0-9744509-3-3(6)) Three Spots Productions.

—No Rest for Sparky. Newton, Pilar, illus. 2004. 24p. (J). mass mkt. 7.95 (978-0-9744509-2-6(8)) Three Spots Productions.

Ashford, Kathy. Jackdaw Jinx. Kitamura, Satoshi, illus. 2007. (Tiger Ser.). 128p. (J). 9.95 (***978-1-84270-540-7(7)***) Transworld Publishers Ltd. GBR. *Dist:* Independent Pubs. Group.

Auch, Mary Jane & Auch, Herm, illus. I Was a Third Grade Bodyguard. 2003. 80p. (J). (gr. 4-6). tchr. ed. 15.95 (978-0-8234-1775-9(1)) Holiday Hse., Inc.

Baby Pets: Chunky photo Book. 2006. (J). bds. 3.99 (978-1-934004-01-2(4)) Byeway Bks.

Bachelet, Gilles. When the Silliest Cat Was Small. Bachelet, Gilles, illus. 2007. (FRE & ENG., Illus.). 32p. (J). (ps-3). 16.95 (***978-0-8109-9415-7(1)*** , Abrams Bks. for Young Readers) Abrams, Harry N. , Inc.

Baglio, Ben M. Come Back, Buddy! 2004. (Illus.). 118p. (J). pap. (978-0-439-68883-3(3)) Scholastic, Inc.

—The Dog with No Name. 2005. (Illus.). 148p. (J). (978-0-439-74617-5(5)) Scholastic, Inc.

—Kitten in the Cold. McNicholas, Shelagh, illus. 1999. (Animal Ark Ser.). 144p. (J). (gr. 3-5). pap. 3.99 (978-0-439-09698-0(7)) Scholastic, Inc.

—Kitten in the Cold. 1999. (gr. 3-6). lib. bdg. 11.80 (978-0-613-21870-2(1)) Tandem Library Bks.

Baglio, Ben M. Max Is Missing. 2005. (Pet Finders Club Ser.: Vol. 2). (Illus.). 126p. (J). pap. (***978-0-439-68884-0(1)***) Scholastic, Inc.

Banks, Kate. Monkeys & Dog Days. Bogacki, Tomasz, illus. 2008. (J). (***978-0-374-35029-1(9)***) Farrar, Straus & Giroux.

Bartlett, Susan. Seal Island School. Bonnell, J., ed. Tusa, Tricia, illus. 2001. (Chapters Ser.). 80p. (J). (gr. 2-5). pap. 4.99 (978-0-14-131104-3(5) , Puffin) Penguin Group (USA) Inc.

—Seal Island School. Tusa, Tricia, illus. 1999. 80p. (J). (gr. 2-5). 15.99 (978-0-670-88349-3(2) , Viking Juvenile) Penguin Group (USA) Inc.

—Seal Island School. 2001. (gr. 3-6). lib. bdg. 13.00 (978-0-613-63991-0(X)) Tandem Library Bks.

Bartoletti, Susan Campbell. Nobody's Diggier Than a Dog. Giacobbe, Beppe, illus. 2005. 40p. (ps-17). 15.99 (978-0-7868-1824-2(7)) Hyperion Bks. for Children.

Bennett, Kelly. Not Norman: A Goldfish Story. Jones, Noah, illus. 2005. 32p. (J). (ps-3). 15.99 (978-0-7636-2384-5(9)) Candlewick Pr.

Bentley, Dawn. Hoppy Goes to School Micro Bk And. Huerta, Catherine, illus. 2006. 32p. 9.95 (978-1-59249-559-7(1)) Soundprints.

The Best Pet: Individual Title Six-Pack Pouch - Level J. (Lighthouse Ser.). 16p. (gr. 2 up). 28.00 (978-0-7578-0877-7(8)) Rigby Education.

Blackaby, Susan. Wes Gets a Pet. Gallagher-Cole, Mernie, illus. 2005. (Read-It! Readers Ser.). 32p. (J). (gr. k-3). 18.60 (978-1-4048-1060-0(9)) Picture Window Bks.

Blake, Quentin. Loveykins. Blake, Quentin, illus. 2003. (Illus.). 32p. (J). 15.95 (978-1-56145-282-8(3)) Peachtree Pubs., Ltd.

Blance, Ellen & Cook. Monster Buys a Pet. Date not set. (Illus.). 40p. pap. 129.15 (978-0-582-19311-6(7)) Addison-Wesley Longman, Ltd. GBR. *Dist:* Trans-Atlantic Pubns., Inc.

Boegehold, Betty. A Pet for Pippa Mouse. 2000. (Illus.). (J). 2.99 (978-0-679-89340-0(7) , Random Hse. Bks. for Young Readers) Random Hse. Children's Bks.

—A Pet for Pippa Mouse. 1999. (J). lib. bdg. 7.99 (978-0-679-99340-7(1)) Random Hse., Inc.

Boelts, Maribeth. Before You Were Mine. Walker, David, illus. 2007. 32p. (J). (ps). 15.99 (***978-0-399-24526-8(X)*** , Putnam Juvenile) Penguin Group (USA) Inc.

Boland, Janice. Zipers. de la Vega, Eida, tr. Pfeiffer, Judith, illus. 2001. (Books for Young Learners).Tr. of Zippers. (SPA.). 8p. (J). (gr. k-2). pap. 5.00 (978-1-57274-453-0(7) , 2919) Owen, Richard C. Pubs., Inc.

—Zippers. Pfeiffer, Judith, illus. 2003. (Books for Young Learners). 8p. (J). pap. 20.00 net. (978-1-57274-700-5(5) , BB2220) Owen, Richard C. Pubs., Inc.

Bonnell, Kris. Pets for Us. 2007. (J). 3.95 (***978-1-933727-50-9(0)***) Reading Reading Bks., LLC.

—We Love Pets. 2007. (J). 3.95 (***978-1-933727-56-1(X)***) Reading Reading Bks., LLC.

Bostrom, Kathleen Long. The Day Scooter Died: A Book about the Death of a Pet. Bladholm, Cheri, illus. 2005. (Helping Kids Heal Ser.). 32p. (J). 9.99 (978-0-310-70902-2(4)) Zonderkidz.

Bourgeois, Paulette. Franklin Quiere una Mascota. Varela, Alejandra Lopez, tr. from ENG. Clark, Brenda, illus. 1998. (Franklin Ser.). (SPA.). 32p. (J). (ps-3). pap. 5.95 (978-1-880507-49-0(8) , LC8143) Lectorum Pubns., Inc.

—Franklin Wants a Pet. 2000. (Franklin Ser.). (Illus.). 180p. (J). (ps-3). (978-1-55074-795-9(9)) Kids Can Pr., Ltd.

Bowdish, Lynea. A Dog for Each Day. Brooks, Karen Stormer, illus. 2003. (Rookie Reader Ser.). 32p. (J). 19.50 (978-0-516-22849-5(8) , Children's Pr.) Scholastic Library Publishing.

Brewer, Elly. Jerry & the Jannans. 2006. 320p. (J). pap. 11.99 (***978-0-7475-8213-7(0)***) Bloomsbury Publishing Plc GBR. *Dist:* Independent Pubs. Group.

Bridwell, Norman. Clifford. 2006. (Scholastic Reader Collection Level 2 Ser.). 144p. (J). pap. 6.99 (978-0-439-84800-8(8) , Cartwheel Bks.) Scholastic, Inc.

—The Runaway Rabbit. Bridwell, Norman, illus. 2002. (Big Red Readers Ser.). (Illus.). (J). 11.91 (978-0-7587-5219-2(9)) Book Wholesalers, Inc.

Brimner, Larry Dane. Long Way Home. 2000. (gr. k-3). lib. bdg. 12.95 (978-0-613-54739-0(X)) Tandem Library Bks.

Broome, Errol. Drusilla the Lucky Duck. Thompson, Sharon, illus. 2003. (Annick Chapter Bks.). 72p. (J). (gr. 2-4). 16.95 (978-1-55037-799-6(X)); pap. 4.95 (978-1-55037-798-9(1)) Annick Pr., Ltd. CAN. *Dist:* Firefly Bks., Ltd.

Brown, Marc. Arthur & the School Pet. 2003. (Arthur Ser.). (Illus.). 24p. (J). (gr. k-2). pap. 3.99 (978-0-375-81001-5(3)); lib. bdg. 11.99 (978-0-375-91001-2(8)) Random Hse. Children's Bks. (Random Hse. Bks. for Young Readers).

—Arthur & the School Pet. 2003. (Arthur Ser.). (ps-2). lib. bdg. 11.80 (978-0-613-57492-1(3)) Tandem Library Bks.

—Arthur's New Puppy. Brown, Marc, illus. 2002. (Arthur Adventure Ser.). (Illus.). (J). 13.15 (978-0-7587-1984-3(1)) Book Wholesalers, Inc.

—Arthur's New Puppy. Brown, Marc, illus. 2005. (Arthur Adventure Ser.). 32p. (J). (ps-1). pap. 10.99 (978-0-316-05955-8(2)) Little Brown & Co.

—Arthur's New Puppy. (Arthur Adventure Ser.). (J). (gr. k-3). 7.98 incl. audio NewSound, LLC.

—Arthur's Pet Business. Brown, Marc, illus. rev. ed. 2007. (Arthur Adventure Ser.). (Illus.). 32p. (J). (ps-1). pap. 10.99 incl. audio compact disk (***978-0-316-11863-7(X)***) Little, Brown Bks. for Young Readers.

Brown, Marc. Arturo y el Negocio de Mascotas. Sarfatti, Esther, tr. (SPA.). (J). (gr. k-2). pap. 6.95 (978-1-880507-94-0(3) , LC8511) Lectorum Pubns., Inc.

—Arturo y el Negocio de Mascotas. 2001. (Arthur's Adventures in Spanish Ser.). (SPA., Illus.). (J). 13.75 (978-0-606-21045-4(8)) Tandem Library Bks.

Buckeridge, Anthony. Jennings' Little Hut. 2002. 198p. pap. (978-0-7551-1367-5(5)) House of Stratus, Inc.

Buggs, Michael A. Tabard. Buggs, Michael A., illus. (Illus.). 64p. (Orig.). (J). (gr. 2-6). pap. 15.00 (978-0-9657723-0-3(6)) Mogul Comics.

Bunting, Eve. Dear Wish Fairy. Bjhorkman, Steve, illus. 2000. (Hello Reader! Ser.). (J). (978-0-439-20634-1(0)) Scholastic, Inc.

Cahill, Doris. Nina. Blackwell, Anne, illus. John, Chirs, photos by. 2001. 80p. (J). 15.95 (978-0-9713224-0-0(6)) Johnson, J LLC.

Calmenson, Stephanie. May I Pet Your Dog? The How-to Guide for Kids Meeting Dogs (And Dogs Meeting Kids) Ormerod, Jan, illus. 2007. 32p. (J). (gr. k-3). 9.95 (978-0-618-51034-4(6) , Clarion Bks.) Houghton Mifflin Co. Trade & Reference Div.

Calmenson, Stephanie. May I Pet Your Dog? The How-To Guide for Kids Meeting Dogs (and Dogs Meeting Kids) Ormerod, Jan, illus. 2007. 32p. (J). (***978-1-4287-3952-9(1)*** , Clarion Bks.) Houghton Mifflin Co. Trade & Reference Div.

Campbell, Rod. Dear Zoo: A Lift-the-Flap Book. Campbell, Rod, illus. 2007. 18p. (J). 6.99 (***978-1-4169-4737-0(X)*** , Little Simon) Simon & Schuster Children's Publishing.

Campbell, Rod. Dear Zoo: A Pop-up Book. 2004. (Illus.). (J). (ENG & CHI.). (978-1-84444-170-9(9)); (ENG & ARA., bds. (978-1-84444-168-6(7)); (ENG & BEN., 32p. bds. (978-1-84444-169-3(5)); (ENG & ALB., 32p. bds. (978-1-84444-167-9(9)); (ENG & CHI., 32p. bds. (978-1-84444-171-6(7)); (ENG & PER., 32p. bds. (978-1-84444-172-3(5)); (ENG & FRE., 32p. bds. (978-1-84444-173-0(3)); (ENG & GUJ., 32p. bds. (978-1-84444-174-7(1)); (ENG & HIN., 32p. bds. (978-1-84444-175-4(X)); (ENG & PAN., 32p. bds. (978-1-84444-176-1(8)); (POR & ENG., 32p. bds. (978-1-84444-177-8(6)); (RUS & ENG., 32p. bds. (978-1-84444-178-5(4)); (ENG & SPA., 32p. bds. (978-1-84444-179-2(2)); (ENG & SOM., bds. (978-1-84444-180-8(6)); (ENG & TUR., 32p. bds. (978-1-84444-181-5(4)); (ENG & URD., bds. (978-1-84444-182-2(2)); (ENG & VIE., 32p. bds. (978-1-84444-183-9(0)) Mantra Publishing, Ltd.

—Dear Zoo: A Pop-up Book. Campbell, Rod, illus. 2005. (Illus.). 20p. (J). 12.95 (978-0-689-87751-3(X) , Little Simon) Simon & Schuster Children's Publishing.

Cann, Francesca. Sylvester. Hillion, Christopher & Spencer, John, eds. 2001. (Illus.). 96p. (YA). pap. 9.95 (978-1-876268-48-0(4)) Univ. of Western Australia Pr. AUS. *Dist:* International Specialized Bk. Services.

Capucilli, Alyssa Satin. Biscuit's New Trick. Schories, Pat, illus. 2001. (My First I Can Read Bks.). 32p. (J). (ps-k). pap. 3.99 (978-0-06-444308-1(6) , Harper Trophy) HarperCollins Pubs.

—Biscuit's Pet & Play Christmas. Schories, Pat & Young, Mary O'Keefe, illus. 2006. (Biscuit Ser.). 12p. (J). 6.99 (978-0-06-009470-6(2) , Harper Festival) HarperCollins Pubs.

Carney, Karen L. They're Part of the Family: Barklay & Eve Talk to Children about Pet Loss. Carney, Karen L., illus. 2002. (Barklay & Eve Ser.: Bk. 8). (Illus.). (J). pap. 6.95 (978-0-9667820-8-0(9)) Dragonfly Publishing.

Carter, Christine R. The Collie of Castle Hill. Carter, Christine R., illus. 2002. 48p. (J). per. 10.95 (978-0-9717964-1-6(6) , TCCH-PB16); (Illus.). 16.95 (978-0-9717964-0-9(8) , TCCH-HC08) Polt Mountain Pr.

Carvajal, Victor. Chipana. (SPA.). (YA). (gr. 5-8). pap. 7.95 (978-958-04-5044-3(7) , NR3753) Norma S.A. COL. *Dist:* Distribuidora Norma, Inc., Lectorum Pubns., Inc.

Caseley, Judith. Mr. Green Peas. 1998. (Illus.). 32p. (J). (ps-3). pap. 4.95 (978-0-688-16092-0(1)) HarperCollins Pubs.

Chataway, Carol. The Perfect Pet. Holfeld, Greg, illus. unabr. ed. 2002. 32p. (J). (gr. k-3). (978-1-55337-178-6(X)) Kids Can Pr., Ltd.

Child, Lauren. I Want a Pet. 2004. (Illus.). 24p. (J). (ps-3). 13.95 (978-1-883672-82-9(1) , Tricycle Pr.) Ten Speed Pr.

Child, Lauren. I Want Pet. Child, Lauren, illus. 2007. (Illus.). 24p. (J). pap. 7.95 (***978-1-58246-238-7(0)*** , Tricycle Pr.) Ten Speed Pr.

Christopher, Matt. You Lucky Dog. Vasconcellos, Daniel, illus. 8th ed. 2003. (Soccer 'Cats Ser.: No. 8). 64p. (J). (gr. 1-4). pap. 4.99 (978-0-316-73805-7(0)) Little, Brown Bks. for Young Readers.

—You Lucky Dog. 2003. (gr. k-3). lib. bdg. 13.00 (978-0-613-71888-2(7)) Tandem Library Bks.

Cimarusti, Marie Torres. Peek-a-Pet! Peterson, Stephanie, illus. 2004. 12p. (J). (ps). 9.99 (978-0-525-47352-7(1) , Dutton Juvenile) Penguin Group (USA) Inc.

Civardi, Anne. New Puppy. 2001. (gr. k-3). lib. bdg. 12.95 (978-0-613-67655-7(6)) Tandem Library Bks.

Clark, Brenda, illus. Franklin Wants a Pet 2002. (Franklin Ser.). 12.40 (978-1-4046-0320-2(4)) Book Wholesalers, Inc.

Coffey, Maria. A Cat in a Kayak. Fernandes, Eugenie, illus. 2005. 32p. (J). (ps-2). pap. 7.95 (978-1-55037-508-4(3)); lib. bdg. 16.95 (978-1-55037-509-1(1)) Annick Pr., Ltd. CAN. *Dist:* Firefly Bks., Ltd.

Cole, Babette. Mi Amor. Filipetto, Celia, illus. 2003. (Babette Cole Ser.). (SPA.). 28p. (J). (gr. k-2). 18.95 (978-84-233-3283-0(7) , DS30975) Ediciones Destino ESP. *Dist:* AIMS International Bks., Inc., Lectorum Pubns., Inc., Planeta Publishing Corp.

Cole, Stephen. The Adventures of Mr. Bean. 2002. (Illus.). 64p. (J). pap. 6.99 (978-1-84222-660-5(6)) Carlton Bks., Ltd. GBR. *Dist:* Independent Pubs. Group.

Cooney, Doug. The Beloved Dearly: Requiem for Fluffy. DiTerlizzi, Tony, illus. 2002. 192p. (J). 16.00 (978-0-689-83127-0(7)) Simon & Schuster Children's Publishing.

Cooney, Doug & DiTerlizzi, Tony. The Beloved Dearly. 2003. (Illus.). 192p. (J). pap. 5.99 (978-0-689-86354-7(3) , Aladdin) Simon & Schuster Children's Publishing.

Coons, Anita. Graze, Gaze & Saddle Days. 2005. (Illus.). 144p. (J). per. 10.95 (978-1-59713-003-5(6)) Goose River Pr.

Cooper, Ann Goode. Zabordee's Caper. Jessee, Diana, illus. 2002. (J). 9.95 (978-1-887905-60-2(X)) Parkway Pubs., Inc.

Cooper, Melrose. "Pets!" Heo, Yumi, illus. rev. ed. 1998. 32p. (C). (ps-2). pap. 15.95 (978-0-8050-3893-4(0) , Holt, Henry & Co. Bks. For Young Readers) Holt, Henry & Co.

Coplans, Peta. The Perfect Pet. 2001. (Illus.). 25p. (J). pap. 8.99 (978-0-86264-102-3(0)) Andersen GBR. *Dist:* Trafalgar Square Publishing.

Coville, Bruce. Jeremy Thatcher, Dragon Hatcher: A Magic Shop Book. Lippincott, Gary A., illus. 2007. (Magic Shop Book Ser.). 168p. (J). (gr. 3-7). pap. 5.95 (***978-0-15-206252-1(1)*** , Magic Carpet Bks.) Harcourt Children's Bks.

Coxon, Michele. Le Has Dado de Comer Al Gato?/Have You Fed the Cat? Coxon, Michele, illus. 2004. (SPA & ENG., Illus.). 40p. (J). 15.95 (978-1-59572-001-6(4)); pap. 5.95 (978-1-59572-002-3(2)) Star Bright Bks., Inc.

Crictor. 2004. (J). 24.95 incl. audio (978-0-89719-867-7(0)); pap. 32.75 incl. audio (978-1-55592-188-0(4)); pap. 14.95 incl. audio (978-1-56008-020-6(5)) Weston Woods Studios, Inc.

Cullen, Lynn. Moi & Marie Antoinette. Young, Amy, illus. 2006. 32p. (J). 16.95 (978-1-58234-958-9(4)) Bloomsbury Publishing.

—Stink Bomb. 128p. (J). (gr. 3-7). 1999. pap. 3.99 (978-0-380-78507-0(2) , Harper Trophy); 1998. 14.00 (978-0-380-97647-8(1)) HarperCollins Pubs.

Dale, Jenny & Reid, Mick. Puppy School. 2002. (Puppy Patrol Ser.: No. 14). 112p. (J). per. 3.99 (978-0-439-21815-3(2)) Scholastic, Inc.

Daniels, Lucy. Kitten Crowd. Howard, Paul, illus. 1999. (Animal Ark Pets Ser.: No. 2). 128p. (J). (gr. 3-6). pap. 3.99 (978-0-439-05159-0(2)) Scholastic, Inc.

Daniels, Lucy & Baglio, Ben M. Duckling Diary. Howard, Paul, illus. 2000. (Animal Ark Pets Ser.: No. 10). 128p. (J). (gr. 2-5). pap. 3.99 (978-0-439-05167-5(3)) Scholastic, Inc.

—Gerbil Genius. Howard, Paul, illus. 2000. (Animal Ark Pets Ser.: No. 9). 128p. (J). (gr. 3-6). pap. 3.99 (978-0-439-05166-8(5)) Scholastic, Inc.

—Mouse Magic. Howard, Paul, illus. 1999. (Animal Ark Pets Ser.: No. 5). 128p. (J). (gr. 3-6). pap. 3.99 (978-0-439-05162-0(2)) Scholastic, Inc.

Dart, Iris Rainer & Brotman, Joyce. Larry: The King of Rock & Roll. 2007. 176p. (J). (gr. 4-6). 16.99 (978-0-399-24546-6(4) , Putnam Juvenile) Penguin Group (USA) Inc.

Davidson, Ellen Dee. Princess Justina Albertina: A Cautionary Tale. Chesworth, Michael, illus. 2007. (J). (ps-2). 15.95 (978-1-57091-652-6(7)) Charlesbridge Publishing, Inc.

Davis, Caroline, illus. My Pets. 2007. 12p. (J). (ps). bds. 6.95 (***978-1-58925-824-2(X)*** , tiger tales) ME Media LLC.

de Brunhoff, Laurent. Babar & the Wully-Wully. 2001. (Illus.). 40p. (J). (ps-3). 16.95 (978-0-8109-4397-1(2)) Abrams, Harry N. , Inc.

de Paola, Tomie. Little Grunt & the Big Egg: A Prehistoric Fairy Tale. 2007. 27.95 incl. audio (***978-0-8045-6944-6(4)***); 29.95 incl. audio compact disk (***978-0-8045-4158-9(2)***) Spoken Arts, Inc.

de Rham, Mickey. Hey Bossie, You're a Spokescow! Gusterson, Leigh, illus. 2004. 24p. (J). 9.95 (978-0-9755216-0-1(8)) Plaidswede Publishing.

Demas, Corinne. Saying Goodbye to Lulu. Hoyt, Ard, tr. Hoyt, Ard, illus. 2004. 40p. (J). (ps-3). 15.99 (978-0-316-70278-2(1)) Little Brown & Co.

Denega, Danielle. Love & Friendship. 2007. (Littlest Pet Shop Ser.). 56p. (J). pap. 6.99 (978-0-439-89751-8(3)) Scholastic, Inc.

Denson, Robert & Jefferies, Marc John. The Lynx. 2006. 120p. (J). pap. 12.95 (***978-0-9770050-8-6(9)***) Big Smile, Inc.

DePaola, Tomie. Little Grunt & the Big Egg: A Prehistoric Fairy Tale. 2006. 32p. (J). (ps-3). 16.99 (978-0-399-24529-9(4)) Penguin Group (USA) Inc.

Diamond, Shendl, illus. & text. The True Story of Critter Angels by Yani. Diamond, Shendl, text. 2005. (J). 15.95 (978-0-9764724-3-8(0)) LikeMinds Pr.

Dinan, Carolyn. Goodnight, Monster. (Illus.). 32p. (J). pap. 7.95 (978-0-14-038281-5(X)) Penguin Bks., Ltd. GBR. *Dist:* Trafalgar Square Publishing.

DiSalvo-Ryan, DyAnne. A Dog Like Jack. unabr. ed. 2005. (Illus.). (J). (ps-2). pap. 16.95 incl. audio (978-0-87499-758-3(5)) BBC Audiobooks America.

—A Dog Like Jack. DiSalvo-Ryan, DyAnne, illus. 1999. (Illus.). 32p. (J). (gr. k-3). tchr. ed. 16.95 (978-0-8234-1369-0(1)); pap. 6.95 (978-0-8234-1680-6(1)) Holiday Hse., Inc.

—A Dog Like Jack. 2005. (Live Oak Readalong Ser.). (J). pap. 18.95 incl. audio compact disk (978-1-59519-298-1(0)) Live Oak Media.

—A Dog Like Jack. DiSalvo-Ryan, DyAnne, illus. 2001. (Illus.). pap. 25.95 incl. audio (978-0-87499-759-0(3)); pap. 37.95 incl. audio (978-0-87499-760-6(7)) Live Oak Media.

Dodd, Emma. What Pet to Get? 2008. 32p. (J). pap. 16.99 (***978-0-545-03570-5(8)*** , Levine, Arthur A. Bks.) Scholastic, Inc.

Dodds, Dayle Ann. Teacher's Pets. Hafner, Marylin, illus. 2006. 40p. (J). (gr. k-3). 15.99 (978-0-7636-2252-7(4)) Candlewick Pr.

Doyle, Malachy. Sleepy Pendoodle. Vivas, Julie, illus. 2001. 32p. (J). (ps-1). 12.99 (978-0-7636-1561-1(7)) Candlewick Pr.

Dubosarsky, Ursula. Rex. Mackintosh, David, illus. 2006. 32p. (J). 16.95 (978-1-59643-186-7(5)) Roaring Brook Pr.

Duchene-Marshall, Michele A. Shirley's Red Satin Shoes. Marshall, Alan David, ed. Ousley, Clayton Gerard, photos by. l.t. ed. 2003. (Illus.). 17p. (J). spiral bd. 10.00 (978-0-9761675-1-8(4)) Storybook Acres.

Edwards, Sonia. Noson y Llygaid Llachar. 2005. (WEL., Illus.). 88p. 4.99 (978-1-84323-400-5(9)) Gomer Pr. GBR. *Dist:* Gomer Pr.

Elkins, Stephen. Testify to Love: A Very Special Story for Children. Colton, Ellie, illus. 2002. (Dove Award Signature Ser.). 32p. (J). (gr. k up). 14.99 (978-0-8054-2416-4(4)) B&H Publishing Grp.

Emberley, Rebecca. My Animals/Mis Animales. Emberley, Rebecca, illus. 2002. (SPA & ENG., Illus.). 10p. (J). (ps-ps). bds. 6.99 (978-0-316-17343-8(6)) Little, Brown Bks. for Young Readers.

Exelby, Kathy. My Dog Harpo: The Biggest Kid I Know. Wall Darby, Colleen, illus. 2007. (J). per. 20.00 (***978-1-932583-39-7(4)***) digital@batesjackson llc.

Farish, Terry. The Cat Who Liked Potato Soup. Root, Barry, illus. 40p. (J). (gr. 1). 2007. pap. 6.99 (978-0-7636-3297-7(X)); 2003. 16.99 (978-0-7636-0834-7(3)) Candlewick Pr.

Feely, Jenny. Looking for Fang. 1999. (ps-2). lib. bdg. 11.80 (978-0-613-30566-2(3)) Tandem Library Bks.

Feiffer, Jules. A Room with a Zoo. Feiffer, Jules, illus. 2007. (Illus.). 182p. (J). (gr. 2-7). per. 7.99 (***978-0-7868-3703-8(9)***) Hyperion Bks. for Children.

Ferri, Francesca, illus. Pets. 2003. (My First Animals Ser.). 8p. (J). pap. 9.95 (978-0-7641-2599-7(0)) Barron's Educational Series, Inc.

Fischer, Emily. The Dog, the Hog, the Rat, the Ram, the Hen, & the Big, Big Din. Bustard, Ned, illus. 2000. per. 3.00 (978-1-930710-25-2(9)) Veritas Pr., Inc.

Flanagan, Alice K. Buying a Pet from Ms. Chavez. Rau, Dana, ed. 1998. (Our Neighborhood Ser.). (Illus.). 32p. (J). (gr. 1-2). pap. 6.95 (978-0-516-26293-2(9) , Children's Pr.) Scholastic Library Publishing.

Fox, Paula. La Habitacion de Mauricio. 2003. (SPA., Illus.). 96p. (J). (gr. 3-5). (978-84-279-3457-3(2) , NG4695) Noguer y Caralt Editores, S. A. ESP. *Dist:* Lectorum Pubns., Inc.

Fraser, Mary Ann. I. Q. Goes to School. Fraser, Mary Ann, illus. 2004. (Illus.). 32p. (J). (ps-3). pap. 6.95 (978-0-8027-7698-3(1)) Walker & Co.

—I. Q. Goes to the Library. Fraser, Mary Ann, illus. 2003. (Illus.). 32p. (J). (gr. k-3). 15.95 (978-0-8027-8877-1(7)) Walker & Co.

—I. Q., It's Time. Fraser, Mary Ann, illus. 2005. (Illus.). 32p. (J). (ps-3). 16.85 (978-0-8027-8980-8(3)); 15.95 (978-0-8027-8978-5(1)) Walker & Co.

—I.Q. Gets Fit. Fraser, Mary Ann, illus. 2007. (Illus.). 32p. (J). (gr. k-2). 15.95 (978-0-8027-9558-8(7)); 16.85 (978-0-8027-9559-5(5)) Walker & Co.

Frazer, Rebecca. Barbie Loves Pets. An, Jiyoung, illus. 2007. (Pictureback(R) Ser.). 16p. (J). (ps-1). pap. 3.99 ***(978-0-375-84797-4(9)** , Golden Bks.) Random Hse., Inc.

Friedman, Laurie. Mallory vs. Max. Schmitz, Tamara, illus. 2006. (J). pap. 5.95 (978-1-57505-863-4(4) , First Avenue Editions) Lerner Publishing Group.

Gaberman, Judith. A Home Is to Share...and Share...and Share... 2001. 164p. (J). (gr. 4-7). pap. 11.95 (978-0-595-15796-9(3) , Backinprint.com) iUniverse, Inc.

Geringer, Lucy T. Rhymes & Times of Cleo-cat-tra. Kollock, Bernardita Cox, illus. 2002. 34p. (J). (ps-1). pap. 8.95 (978-0-9719483-0-3(5)) Cleo Cat Bks.

Giancamilli, Vanessa. Patches Finds a Home. Hatala, Dan, illus. 2006. (Pet Tales Ser.). 32p. (J). (978-1-59249-641-9(5)); pap. (978-1-59249-640-2(7)); pap. incl. audio compact disk (978-1-59249-639-6(3)) Soundprints.

Gibbel, Mark. Oh, Harry! Massini, Sarah, illus. rev. ed. 2003. 32p. (J). (ps-2). 15.95 (978-0-8050-6851-1(1) , Holt, Henry & Co. Bks. For Young Readers) Holt, Henry & Co.

Gill, Janice. My Pet Zoo. 1998. (ps-3). pap. 4.95 (978-0-89868-402-5(1)); lib. bdg. 10.95 (978-0-89868-320-2(3)) ARO Publishing Co.

Gill, Janie S. My Pet Zoo. Resse, Bob, illus. 1998. 24p. (ps-3). 5.95 (978-0-89868-321-9(1)) ARO Publishing Co.

Goldstein, Alrica, ed. Polly & the Perfect Pets. 2008. 24p. (J). pap. 3.99 ***(978-0-696-23893-2(4))*** Meredith Bks.

—Polly Lodge: Snowed In! 2008. 32p. (J). pap. 3.99 ***(978-0-696-23894-9(2))*** Meredith Bks.

Gomes, Linda Nunes. Special Words: A Story about Multicultural Families & Their Pets. Levine, Lenora D., illus. 2007. (YA). per. 12.99 ***(978-1-934400-02-9(5))*** Rock Village Publishing.

Grambling, Lois G. Big Dog. San Diego, Andy, illus. 2001. 32p. (J). (gr. k-3). 15.95 (978-0-7614-5045-0(9) , Cavendish Children's Bks.) Cavendish, Marshall Corp.

Gray, Sondra. According to Punkin. 2006. 82p. per. 8.95 (978-1-59886-436-6(X)) Tate Publishing & Enterprises, L.L.C.

Gregory, Nan & Lightburn, Ron. How Smudge Came. 1999. (Northern Lights Books for Children Ser.). (Illus.). 32p. (J). (ps-3). (978-0-88995-143-3(8)) Red Deer Pr.

Griffis, Molly. The Buffalo in the Mall. Doner, Kim, illus. 32p. 8.95 (978-1-57168-635-0(5)) Eakin Pr.

Grindley, Sally. Captain Pepper's Pets. Parkins, David, illus. 2004. (I Am Reading Ser.). 48p. (J). (gr. 1-3). pap. 3.95 (978-0-7534-5798-6(9)); pap. ***(978-0-7534-1042-4(7))*** Houghton Mifflin Co. Trade & Reference Div. (Kingfisher).

Grovet, Heather. Petunia the Ugly Pug. 2002. (Julius & Friends Ser.: Vol. 7). (Illus.). 94p. (J). 6.99 (978-0-8163-1871-1(9)) Pacific Pr. Publishing Assn.

Gugler, Laurel Dee. Muddle Cuddle. van Kampen, Vlasta, illus. 2003. 24p. (J). (ps-1). lib. bdg. 16.95 (978-1-55037-435-3(4)) Annick Pr., Ltd. CAN. *Dist:* Firefly Bks., Ltd.

Hall, Kirsten. Slider's Pet: All about Nature. Luedecke, Bev, illus. (Beastieville Ser.). (J). (gr. k-1). 2005. 32p. pap. 3.95 (978-0-516-25522-4(3)); 2004. 19.50 (978-0-516-22898-3(6)) Scholastic Library Publishing. (Children's Pr.).

Hamilton, Richard. Cal & the Amazing Anti-Gravity Machine. Hearn, Sam, illus. 2006. 128p. (J). 14.95 (978-1-58234-723-3(9) , Bloomsbury Children); pap. 5.95 (978-1-58234-714-1(X)) Bloomsbury Publishing.

Hanson, Mary Elizabeth. The Old Man & the Flea. Merrell, David W., illus. 2001. 32p. (gr. k-3). 15.95 (978-0-87358-776-1(6) , Rising Moon Bks. for Young Readers) Northland Publishing.

Hanson, Shelley. K9 Crew Beginnings. 2004. 160p. (J). per. 9.99 (978-0-9752887-0-2(9)) Tail Wagging Productions.

Harcourt School Publishers Staff. I Have a Pet: Library Book. 1999. (Collections Ser.). (Illus.). pap. 14.90 (978-0-15-313397-8(X)) Harcourt Schl. Pubs.

—El Invitado Que No Se Fue Below Level. 3rd ed. 2002. (Trofeos Ser.). (SPA., Illus.). pap. 6.80 (978-0-15-324143-7(8)) Harcourt Schl. Pubs.

—Llona Ya Esta Sola: Take-Home Book. 2001. (Vamos Ser.). (SPA., Illus.). (J). (gr. 5). pap. 2.80 (978-0-15-319945-5(8)) Harcourt Schl. Pubs.

—Lonely No More: Take-Home Book. 2001. (Collections Ser.). (Illus.). (J). (gr. 5). pap. 1.90 (978-0-15-319513-6(4)) Harcourt Schl. Pubs.

—My Pet Project On Level. 3rd ed. 2002. (Trophies Reading Program Ser.). (Illus.). pap. 5.10 (978-0-15-323168-1(8)) Harcourt Schl. Pubs.

—My Pets: Take-Home Book. 1999. (Signatures Ser.). (Illus.). (J). pap. 1.70 (978-0-15-313832-4(7)) Harcourt Schl. Pubs.

—The Perfect Pet: Take-Home Book. 1999. (Signatures Ser.). (Illus.). (J). pap. 1.90 (978-0-15-313861-4(0)) Harcourt Schl. Pubs.

—Pet Day: A Reader. 1999. (Collections Ser.). (Illus.). (J). pap. 2.10 (978-0-15-313437-1(2)) Harcourt Schl. Pubs.

—Pet Day 5 Pack. Advanced Level. 3rd ed. 2002. (Trophies Reading Program Ser.). (Illus.). (gr. 1). pap. 20.10 (978-0-15-326863-2(8)) Harcourt Schl. Pubs.

—Pet Day Advanced Level. 3rd ed. 2002. (Trophies Reading Program Ser.). (Illus.). (J). pap. 3.70 (978-0-15-323013-4(4)) Harcourt Schl. Pubs.

—Pet Lizard On Level. 3rd ed. 2002. (Trophies Reading Program Ser.). (Illus.). 16p. pap. 5.10 (978-0-15-323274-9(9)) Harcourt Schl. Pubs.

Harris, Robie H. Goodbye Mousie. Ormerod, Jan, illus. 2004. 32p. (J). reprint ed. 6.99 (978-0-689-87134-4(1) , Aladdin) Simon & Schuster Children's Publishing.

Hays, Anna Jane. The Pup Speaks Up: A Phonics Reader. Petrone, Valeria, illus. 2003. (Early Step into Reading Ser.). 32p. (J). (ps-1). pap. 3.99 (978-0-375-81232-3(6) , Random Hse. Bks. for Young Readers) Random Hse. Children's Bks.

HB. The Perfect Pet. 99th ed. 1999. (gr. 2). pap. 12.00 (978-0-15-314070-9(4)) Harcourt Schl. Pubs.

Heide, Florence Parry. A Promise Is a Promise. Auth, Tony, illus. 2007. 40p. (J). (gr. k-4). 15.99 (978-0-7636-2285-5(0)) Candlewick Pr.

Heiligman, Deborah. Fun Dog, Sun Dog/Deborah Heiligman ; Illustrated by Tim Bowers. Bowers, Tim, illus. 2005. 32p. (J). 14.95 (978-0-7614-5162-4(5)) Cavendish, Marshall Corp.

Henderson, Lyndsey. Dino. 2001. (Teacher's Pet Ser.). 48p. (J). 4.95 (978-0-439-17344-5(2)) Scholastic, Inc.

Hensley, Sarah M. The Tod Squad Can Learn about Pets. 2006. (J). bds. (978-1-57332-417-5(5)) HighReach Learning, Inc.

—The Tod Squad Can Learn about Pets Book with Game Cards. exp. ed. 2006. (J). bds. (978-1-57332-410-6(8)) HighReach Learning, Inc.

Here Kitty. 2005. 32p. (J). 12.99 (978-0-9758709-3-8(9) , A.W.A. Gang) Journey Stone Creations, LLC.

Hock, Dan. The Afternoon Auction: An Iggy & Igor Mystery. 2004. (Illus.). 48p. (J). per. 4.99 (978-0-9754046-0-7(1)) Anticipation Pr.

Hojel, Barbara & Guy, Ginger F. A Pet for Peter. 1999. (English for Me! Storybooks Ser.: Bk. 4). (Illus.). 16p. (C). pap. 7.66 (978-0-201-35146-0(3)) Longman Publishing Group.

Holmes, Linda. Jazz & Sam. 2002. (Reading Explosion Beginner Readers: Book 2). 32p. (J). pap. 9.95 (978-1-57921-445-6(2)) WinePress Publishing.

Hoosier, Wanda M. Princess Mandisa. McCabe, Pat, illus. 1999. 34p. (J). 15.00 (978-1-56469-070-8(9)) Harmony Hse. Pubs.

Hop to It, Minty! Individual Chapter Book Title Six-Packs. Vol. 28. 32p. (gr. 4 up). 44.00 (978-0-7578-0601-8(5)) Rigby Education.

Hope, Laura Lee. Bunny Brown & His Sister Sue. 2005. 188p. pap. 11.95 (978-1-4218-1165-9(0) , 1st World Library - Literary Society) 1st World Publishing, Inc.

Horowitz, Ruth. Big Surprise in the Bug Tank. Holub, Joan, illus. 2005. (Easy-to-Read, Dial Ser.). 48p. (J). (gr. 1). 14.99 (978-0-8037-2874-5(3) , Dial) Penguin Group (USA) Inc.

Howard, Arthur. Hoodwinked. Howard, Arthur, illus. 2005. (Illus.). 32p. (J). (ps-ps). pap., pap. 6.00 (978-0-15-205386-4(7) , Voyager Bks./Libros Viajeros) Harcourt Children's Bks.

Howe, James. Bunnicula Meets Edgar Allan Crow. Fortune, Eric, illus. 2006. (Bunnicula Ser.). 160p. (J). 15.95 (978-1-4169-1458-7(7) , Ginnee Seo Bks) Simon & Schuster Children's Publishing.

—Pinky & Rex & the Just-Right Pet. 2002. (gr. k-3). lib. bdg. 11.80 (978-0-613-45091-1(4)) Tandem Library Bks.

Howe, James, et al. Pinky & Rex & the Just-Right Pet. 2002. (Ready-to-Read Ser.: Level 3). (Illus.). 48p. (J). (ps-ps). pap. 3.99 (978-0-689-83942-9(1) , Aladdin) Simon & Schuster Children's Publishing.

Hubbard, Coleen. One Golden Year. 1999. (Dog Tales Ser.). (Illus.). 128p. (J). (gr. 3-7). pap. 4.50 (978-0-590-18975-0(1)) Scholastic, Inc.

Hubbard, Sharron/Y. Link & Rosie's Pets. Schleihs, Kristin, illus. 2007. (J). bds. ***(978-0-9762434-3-4(1))*** Link & Rosie Pr.

Hull, Rod. Mr. Betts & Mr. Potts. Davies, Jo, illus. 2000. 32p. (J). (ps-5). 15.99 (978-1-84148-106-7(8)) Barefoot Bks., Inc.

Ichikawa, Satomi. My Pig Amarillo: A Tale from Guatemala. Ichikawa, Satomi, illus. 2003. (Illus.). 32p. (J). (ps-3). 16.99 (978-0-399-23768-3(2) , Philomel) Penguin Group (USA) Inc.

Inkpen, Mick. Great Pet Sale. 1999. (Illus.). 16p. (J). (ps-1). pap. 14.95 (978-0-531-30130-2(3) , Orchard Bks.) Scholastic, Inc.

Ireland, Karin. Don't Take Your Snake for a Stroll. Catrow, David, illus. 2003. 32p. (J). 16.00 (978-0-15-202361-4(5)) Harcourt Children's Bks.

Jackson, Neta. Pet Parables: The Cat Who Smelled Like Cabbage & The Duck Who Quacked Bubbles, Vol. 1. Gavitt, Anne, illus. 2004. 128p. (ps-2). 10.99 (978-0-8254-2938-5(2)) Kregel Pubns.

Jane, Pamela. Winky Blue, Forever. 1999. (gr. 3-6). lib. bdg. 11.80 (978-0-613-28139-3(X)) Tandem Library Bks.

—Winky Blue Goes Wild! Tilley, Debbie, illus. 2003. 64p. (J). 13.95 (978-1-59034-588-7(6)); pap. (978-1-59034-589-4(4)) Mondo Publishing.

Jenck, Heidi Shelton. Pets on Vacation. 2007. (Illus.). 32p. (J). ***(978-1-4048-1236-9(9))*** Picture Window Bks.

—Pets on Vacation. Blanks, Natascha Alex, illus. 2006. 32p. (J). lib. bdg. ***(978-1-4048-3141-4(X))*** Picture Window Bks.

Jenkins, Emily. Cinco Criaturas. Cortes, Eunice, tr. Bogacki, Tomek, illus. 2003. (Picture Bks.).Tr. of Five Creatures. (SPA.). (J). (978-970-690-648-9(7)) Planeta Mexicana Editorial S. A. de C. V.

Jenkins, Jane John. The Adventures of Harry the Hamster. Grenda, Janet W., illus. 2001. (J). (978-0-9674867-2-7(6)) Campbell Hse. Museum.

Jenkins, Jerry B. & Fabry, Chris. Hollywood Holdup. 2006. (Red Rock Mysteries Ser.). 224p. (J). pap. 5.99 (978-1-4143-0151-8(0)) Tyndale Hse. Pubs.

Jennings, Richard W. My Life of Crime. 2002. 160p. (J). (gr. 4-6). tchr. ed. 15.00 (978-0-618-21433-4(X) , Walter Lorraine) Houghton Mifflin Co. Trade & Reference Div.

Jeremy Thatcher, Dragon Hatcher. 2001. (J). pap., stu. ed., wbk. ed. (978-1-56137-878-4(X)) Novel Units, Inc.

Jimenez, Angeles. En Que Se Parecen un Elefante y un Gato? 2000. Tr. of How Are an Elephant & a Cat Alike?. (SPA.). (ps-2). lib. bdg. 15.90 (978-0-613-80615-2(8)) Tandem Library Bks.

Jimenez, Angeles & Prestifilippo, Pablo. En Que Se Parecen un Elefante y un Gato?Tr. of How Are an Elephant & a Cat Alike?. (SPA.). 48p. (J). 6.95 (978-84-241-7904-5(8)) Everest de Ediciones y Distribucion, S.L. ESP. *Dist:* Lectorum Pubns., Inc.

Joey & Scout. 2004. (Illus.). (J). 7.95 (978-0-9753704-0-7(5)) MYHRECO.

Johnson, Angela. Julius. Pilkey, Dav, illus. 2002. (J). 14.74 (978-0-7587-2909-5(X)) Book Wholesalers, Inc.

—Julius. Pilkey, Dav, illus. 1998. 32p. (J). (ps-1). pap. 6.95 (978-0-531-07102-1(2) , Orchard Bks.) Scholastic, Inc.

—Julius. 1998. 13.75 (978-0-606-13546-7(4)) Tandem Library Bks.

Johnson, Sandi. Harold the Hopping Hamster. Johnson, Britt, ed. Sturgeon, Bobbi, illus. l.t. ed. 2003. 34p. (J). (gr. k-5). spiral bd. 8.99 (978-1-929063-91-8(1) , 322) Moons & Stars Publishing For Children.

Johnston, Madeline. A Perfect Pet. Johnston, Madeline, illus. l.t. ed. 2000. 28p. (J). (ps-2). 9.95 (978-1-929115-03-7(2)) Azro Pr., Inc.

Jones, Jolie. Little Kisses. Downing, Julie, illus. 2005. (Julie Andrews Collection). 32p. (J). lib. bdg. 16.89 (978-0-06-058699-7(0) , Julie Andrews Collection) HarperCollins Pubs.

Jones, Marcia Thornton & Dadey, Debbie. Kilmer's Pet Monster. 1999. (Bailey City Monsters Ser.: No. 4). (Illus.). 72p. (J). (gr. 2-4). pap. 3.99 (978-0-590-10847-8(6)) Scholastic, Inc.

Jones, Molly. Something in the Air. Welch, Sheila Kelly, illus. 2005. (J). (978-1-893516-03-8(2)) Our Child Pr.

Joosse, Barbara M. Bad Dog School. Plecas, Jennifer, illus. 2004. 40p. (J). (gr. k-3). 15.00 (978-0-618-13331-4(3) , Clarion Bks.) Houghton Mifflin Co. Trade & Reference Div.

Kalomas, Alice & Kerr, Lenora. Sir Wrinkles Goes to School. Utomo, Gabhor, illus. 2005. (J). 16.95 (978-0-9766639-1-1(0)) Sir Wrinkles Pr.

Kalz, Jill. Tuckerbean at Waggle World. 2007. (Illus.). 32p. (J). ***(978-1-4048-3389-0(7))*** Picture Window Bks.

—Tuckerbean at Waggle World. Mahan, Ben, illus. 2006. 32p. (J). lib. bdg. ***(978-1-4048-3388-3(9))*** Picture Window Bks.

Kawai, Ritsuko. Hamtaro Postcard Book. Kawai, Ritsuko, illus. 2003. (Hamtaro Ser.). (Illus.). 24p. (YA). pap. 7.95 (978-1-56931-845-4(X)) Viz Media.

Keats, Ezra Jack. Pet Show! Keats, Ezra Jack, illus. 2002. (Illus.). (J). 14.04 (978-1-4046-0926-6(1)) Book Wholesalers, Inc.

—Pet Show! 1999. (Metro Reading Program Ser.). (J). (gr. k). 29.95 (978-1-58120-112-3(5)) Metropolitan Teaching & Learning Co.

—Pet Show! 2001. (Illus.). 40p. (J). pap. 6.99 (978-0-14-230000-8(4) , Puffin); 16.99 (978-0-670-03504-5(1) , Viking Juvenile) Penguin Group (USA) Inc.

—Pet Show! 2001. (978-0-606-22504-5(8)) Tandem Library Bks.

—Pet Show! (J). (ps-3). pap. 12.95 incl. audio Weston Woods Studios, Inc.

Keenan, Sheila & Burns, Marilyn. Myrtle's Turtles. Coyle, Laura, illus. 2001. (Hello Reader! Math Ser.). (J). (978-0-439-30472-6(5)) Scholastic, Inc.

Kellogg, Steven. Can I Keep Him? Kellogg, Steven, illus. 2002. (Illus.). (J). 13.60 (978-0-7587-2183-9(8)) Book Wholesalers, Inc.

—The Mysterious Tadpole. Kellogg, Steven, illus. 2002. (Illus.). (J). 14.04 (978-0-7587-3233-0(3)) Book Wholesalers, Inc.

—The Mysterious Tadpole. Kellogg, Steven, illus. 25th anniv. ed. (Illus.). 40p. (J). 2002. (gr. k-3). 16.99 (978-0-8037-2788-5(7) , Dial); 2004. (gr. 1 up). reprint ed. pap. 6.99 (978-0-14-240140-8(4) , Puffin) Penguin Group (USA) Inc.

Kerr, Mike. Mike & a Lynx Named Kitty. Vitt, Karren, illus. 2nd rev. ed. 2006. 112p. per. 13.50 ***(978-1-931195-36-2(6))*** KiwE Publishing, Ltd.

Kerry 6 packs. Individual Title. (gr. 3 up). 35.00 (978-0-7635-9659-0(0)) Rigby Education.

Khan, Rukshana. Silly Chicken. Kyong, Yunmee, illus. 2005. 32p. (J). (ps-3). 15.99 (978-0-670-05912-6(9) , Viking Juvenile) Penguin Group (USA) Inc.

Koontz, Robin Michal. Why a Dog? By A. Cat. 2000. (Hello Reader! Ser.). (978-0-606-18892-0(4)) Tandem Library Bks.

Krailing, Tessa. The Cat Burglar. Lewis, Jan & Eastwood, John, illus. 1998. (Petsitters Club Ser.: No. 2). 96p. (J). (gr. 2-5). pap. 4.99 (978-0-7641-0570-8(1)) Barron's Educational Series, Inc.

—Trixie & the Cyber Pet. Lewis, Jan & Eastwood, John, illus. 1998. (Petsitters Club Ser.: No. 6). 96p. (J). (gr. 1-4). pap. 4.50 (978-0-7641-0614-9(7)) Barron's Educational Series, Inc.

—Where's Iggy? Lewis, Jan & Eastwood, John, illus. 1999. (Petsitters Club Ser.: No. 8). 96p. (J). (gr. 1-4). pap. 3.95 (978-0-7641-0693-4(7)) Barron's Educational Series, Inc.

Krensky Stephen. Paul Bunyan. Orback, Craig, illus. 2007. (On My Own Folklore Ser.). (J). pap. 6.95 ***(978-0-8225-6479-9(3)*** , First Avenue Editions) Lerner Publishing Group.

Kulling, Monica. Go, Stitch, Go! Shimabukuro, Denise & Disney Storybook Artists Staff, illus. 2002. (Step into Reading Ser.). 32p. (J). (ps-1). pap. 3.99 (978-0-7364-1350-3(2) , RH/Disney) Random Hse. Children's Bks.

—Go, Stitch, Go. 2002. (ps-2). lib. bdg. 11.80 (978-0-613-50612-0(X)) Tandem Library Bks.

Lane, Nickel. The Ferret Crusaders: Quest of the Wish A Pod. 2nd ed. 2004. 73p. (J). per. 8.49 (978-1-4116-0459-9(8)) Lulu.com.

Lawson, Sue. Ferret Boy. (Illus.). 256p. pap. (978-0-7344-0465-7(4) , Lothian Bks.) Hachette Livre Australia.

Lee, AnnJeanette. Tales of Tails. 2002. 140p. pap. 12.95 (978-1-888223-30-9(8)) McMillen Publishing.

Lee, Quinlan B. Littlest Pet Shop: Best Friends. 2006. (Scholastic Reader Ser.: Vol. 2). (Illus.). 32p. (J). pap. 3.99 (978-0-439-88776-2(3)) Scholastic, Inc.

Lee, Spike & Lee, Tonya Lewis. Please, Puppy, Please. Nelson, Kadir, illus. 2005. 32p. (J). (ps-k). 16.95 (978-0-689-86804-7(9)) Simon & Schuster Children's Publishing.

Lehman, Seth. The Color Pets. 2006. (Illus.). 52p. (J). 7.00 net. ***(978-0-9787986-0-4(0))*** 4All Ages LLC.

Lewis, Rob. Too Much Trouble for Grandpa. 1998. (Mondo Ser.). (Illus.). 48p. (J). (gr. 1-5). pap. 4.50 (978-1-57255-551-8(3)) Mondo Publishing.

Lindgren, Barbro. Julia Wants a Pet. Dyssegaard, Elisabeth Kallick, tr. Eriksson, Eva, illus. 2003. 32p. (J). (ps-ps). 15.00 (978-91-29-65940-5(X)) R & S Bks. SWE. *Dist:* Macmillan.

Little, Jean. Emma's Strange Pet. Plecas, Jennifer, illus. (I Can Read Bks.). 64p. (J). (gr. k-3). 2004. pap. 3.99 (978-0-06-444259-6(4) , Harper Trophy); 2003. 15.99 (978-0-06-028350-6(5)) HarperCollins Pubs.

Littlest, Pet Shop. Rapunzel. 2008. (Littlest Pet Shop Ser.). 32p. (J). pap. 3.99 ***(978-0-545-00795-5(X)*** , Scholastic) Scholastic, Inc.

Long, Olivia. The Boy & the Dog. Long, Olivia, illus. Date not set. (Pets & Their People Ser.). (Illus.). 32p. (J). (gr. k-5). (978-1-880042-07-6(X)) Shelf-Life Bks.

—Diary of a Dog. Long, Olivia, illus. Date not set. (Pets & Their People Ser.). (Illus.). 32p. (J). (ps-4). 9.95 (978-1-880042-06-9(1) , SL12456) Shelf-Life Bks.

—Too Many Kittens. Long, Olivia, illus. Date not set. (Pets & Their People Ser.). (Illus.). 32p. (J). (ps-4). (978-1-880042-09-0(6)) Shelf-Life Bks.

Loughead, Deb. Pet Fair. Birke, Lisa, illus. 2000. vi, 48p. (J). pap. 5.95 (978-0-9686899-3-6(0)) Hodgepog Bks. CAN. *Dist:* Coteau Bks.

Luthardt, Kevin. Peep! Luthardt, Kevin, illus. 2003. (Illus.). 36p. (J). 15.95 (978-1-56145-046-6(4)) Peachtree Pubs., Ltd.

Maccarone, Grace & Burns, Marilyn. Monster Money. 1998. (Hello Reader! Math Ser.: Level 1). (Illus.). 32p. (J). (ps-3). pap. 3.99 (978-0-590-12007-4(7)) Scholastic, Inc.

MacDonald, Marianne. Princess Josie's Pets. 1998. (Hyperion Chapters Ser.). (978-0-606-13724-9(6)) Tandem Library Bks.

MacDonald, Maryann. Princess Josie's Pets. Bluthenthal, Diana Cain, illus. 1998. (Hyperion Chapters Ser.). 64p. (J). (gr. 2-4). pap. 3.95 (978-0-7868-1134-2(X)) Disney Pr.

MacLachlan, Patricia & MacLachlan, Emily. Bittle. Yaccarino, Dan, illus. 2004. 40p. (J). (ps-3). 16.99 (978-0-06-000961-8(6)); lib. bdg. 16.89 (978-0-06-000962-5(4)) HarperCollins Pubs. (Cotler, Joanna Books).

Maclean, Christine. Mary Margaret & the Perfect Pet Plan. Vicky, Lowe, illus. 2007. 192p. (J). (gr. 3). pap. 5.99 (978-0-14-240767-7(4) , Puffin) Penguin Group (USA) Inc.

Mamatas, Emanuel. By My Side: A Tale of the Heart. 2000. (Illus.). 132p. (YA). (gr. 5-10). pap. 8.95 (978-0-9706247-4-1(3)) Ikarian Pr. Of America.

—By My Side: A Tale of the Heart. 2000. (Illus.). 132p. (YA). (gr. 7-12). pap. 8.95 (978-1-891231-20-9(0)) Word Association Pubs.

Manchester, Deborah M. & Davis, Madeline. Bula's Surprise Visit, 53 vols., Vol. 1. Manchester, Deborah M., ed. Johnson, Brook L., illus. 1999. 32p. (J). 4.95 (978-0-9673099-0-3(5)) Zula Ltd.

Margulies, Teddy Slater & Bridwell, Norman. Clifford & the Runaway Rabbit. Studio Orlando Staff, illus. 2001. (Clifford, the Big Red Dog Ser.). 32p. (J). (gr. k-2). pap. 3.99 (978-0-439-21361-5(4)) Scholastic, Inc.

Marsoli, Lisa Ann. Dinos are Big Babies & Dylan's Pets. Smitherton, Jeb, illus. 2005. (J). bds. 19.99 (978-0-9767325-7-0(2)) Toy Quest.

—Dylan's Pets from A to Z. Santat, Dan, illus. 2005. (J). bds. 14.99 (978-0-9767325-1-8(3)) Toy Quest.

Masaurel, Claire. Ten Dogs in the Window. 2000. (978-0-606-18323-9(X)) Tandem Library Bks.

Massey, Jane, illus. Mascotas. (Coloca y Siente). (SPA.). 10p. (J). (gr. k-2). bds. (978-968-5308-66-3(7) , Silver Dolphin en Español) Advanced Marketing, S. de R. L. de C. V.

—Pets. 2000. (Touch & Fit Ser.). 10p. (J). (ps-k). bds. 12.95 (978-1-57145-414-0(4) , Silver Dolphin Bks.) Advantage Pubs. Group.

P Q R

Masurel, Claire. Diez Perros en la Tienda: Un Libro Para Contar. 2000. (SPA., Illus.). (J). 13.75 (978-0-606-18318-5(3)) Tandem Library Bks.

—Diez Perros en la Tienda: Un Libro para Contar. Moro, Elena, tr. from ENG. Paparone, Pamela, illus. 2000. (SPA.). 32p. (J). (ps-1). pap. 6.95 (978-0-7358-1303-8(5) , NS3643) North-South Bks., Inc.

Mayer, Mercer. Just Me & My Puppy. Mayer, Mercer, illus. 1998. (Little Critter Ser.). (Illus.). 24p. (J). (gr. k-k). pap. 3.99 (978-0-307-11937-7(8) , 11937, Random Hse. Bks. for Young Readers) Random Hse. Children's Bks.

—Show & Tell. 2002. (Little Critter First Readers Ser.). (Illus.). 24p. (J). (ps-k). pap. 3.95 (978-1-57768-835-8(X)) School Specialty Publishing.

—Show & Tell. 2001. (gr. k-3). lib. bdg. 11.80 (978-0-613-67668-7(8)) Tandem Library Bks.

McAllister, Angela. Monster Pet! Middleton, Charlotte, illus. 2005. 32p. (J). 15.95 (978-1-4169-0371-0(2) , McElderry, Margaret K.) Simon & Schuster Children's Publishing.

McCarty, Peter. Hondo & Fabian. McCarty, Peter, illus. rev. ed. 2002. (Illus.). 32p. (J). (ps-1). 16.95 (978-0-8050-6352-3(8) , Holt, Henry & Co. Bks. For Young Readers) Holt, Henry & Co.

—Hondo & Fabian. 2007. (Illus.). 32p. (J). pap. 6.95 (***978-0-312-36747-3(3)***) Square Fish.

McCombie, Karen. Indie Kidd: Are We Having Fun Yet? (Hmmm?) Monks, Lydia, illus. 2008. (J). (***978-0-440-42201-3(9)***); 160p. (gr. 2-5). lib. bdg. 9.99 (***978-0-440-42202-0(7)***) Random Hse. Children's Bks. (Yearling).

McDonald, Brenda. How Do You Love A Big Dog? 2007. 18.00 (***978-0-8059-7314-3(1)***) Dorrance Publishing Co., Inc.

McDonnell, Flora. Sparky. McDonnell, Flora, illus. 2004. (Illus.). 32p. (J). (gr. k-ps). 15.99 (978-0-7636-2208-4(7)) Candlewick Pr.

McKay, Sindy. We Both Read-Ben & Becky Get a Pet. Johnson, Meredith, illus. (We Both Read Ser.). 44p. (J). (gr. 2 up). 1999. pap. 3.99 (978-1-891327-10-0(0)); 1998. 7.99 (978-1-891327-06-3(2)) Treasure Bay, Inc.

McMenemy, Sarah. Waggle! McMenemy, Sarah, illus. 2003. (Illus.). 32p. (J). (gr. k-k). 14.99 (978-0-7636-2059-2(9)) Candlewick Pr.

McOmber, Rachel B., ed. McOmber Phonics Storybooks: Ben Has a Pet. rev. ed. (Illus.). (J). (978-0-944991-26-8(2)) Swift Learning Resources.

MCP Staff. Ben's Pets, Level 3, Bk. 31. (J). (ps-3). 24.50 (978-0-8136-1963-7(7)) Modern Curriculum Pr.

Meadows, Daisy. Pet Fairies #1 Katie the Kitten Fairy. 2008. (Pet Fairies Ser.). 80p. (J). pap. 4.99 (***978-0-545-02816-5(7)*** , Scholastic Paperbacks) Scholastic, Inc.

—Pet Fairies #2 Bella the Bunny Fairy. 2008. (Pet Fairies Ser.). 80p. (J). pap. 4.99 (***978-0-545-04185-0(6)*** , Scholastic Paperbacks) Scholastic, Inc.

—Pet Fairies #3 Georgia the Guinea Pig Fairy. 2008. (Pet Fairies Ser.). 80p. (J). pap. 4.99 (***978-0-545-04186-7(4)*** , Scholastic Paperbacks) Scholastic, Inc.

—Pet Fairies #4 Lauren the Puppy Fairy. 2008. (Pet Fairies Ser.). 80p. (J). pap. 4.99 (***978-0-545-04187-4(2)*** , Scholastic Paperbacks) Scholastic, Inc.

Meredith Books Staff. Polly Pocket. Goldstein, Alrica, ed. 2007. (I Can Find It Ser.). 24p. (J). pap. 4.99 (***978-0-696-23730-0(X)***) Meredith Bks.

Merritt, Kate, illus. My Family: My Sister. 2003. 10p. (J). bds. 3.95 (978-0-8069-8581-7(X)) Sterling Publishing Co., Inc.

Michaels, Vaughn. Dodi's Prince. Rogers, Jacqueline, illus. 2003. 96p. (J). (gr. 2-5). 15.99 (978-0-525-47034-2(4) , Dutton Juvenile) Penguin Group (USA) Inc.

Middleton, Charlotte. Do You Still Love Me? Middleton, Charlotte, illus. 2003. (Illus.). 32p. (J). (gr. k-1). 15.99 (978-0-7636-2254-1(0)) Candlewick Pr.

Miles, Ellen. Dr. Doolittle. 2004. 144p. (J). (gr. 3 up). pap. 3.99 (978-0-439-57425-9(0) , Scholastic Paperbacks) Scholastic, Inc.

Miller, Margaret. Baby Pets. Miller, Margaret, illus. 2003. (Look Baby Books Ser.). (Illus.). 14p. (J). 6.99 (978-0-689-85313-5(0) , Little Simon) Simon & Schuster Children's Publishing.

Mohr, Michale & Geer, Debi. Stephy Lynns' My Puppy. Archambault, A. J., illus. l.t. ed. 2002. 22p. per. 9.95 (978-0-9719597-8-1(1)) Thornton Publishing.

Morningforest, Chris & Raymond, Rebecca. Taking Care of Funny Pets. 2006. 36p. (J). pap. 15.43 (978-1-4116-7710-4(2)) Lulu.com.

Mubiru, Betha. Muzinge the Bird. 2004. (Illus.). 16p. pap. 9.95 (978-9970-02-447-6(7)) Fountain Pubs. Ltd. UGA. *Dist:* Michigan State Univ. Pr.

Muench-Williams, Heather. I Want a Pet. Teeple, Jackie, illus. l.t. ed. 2006. 12p. (J). (ps-k). pap. 10.95 (978-1-57332-353-6(5)) HighReach Learning, Inc.

—I Want a Pet Board Book & Felt Puppet Set. Teeple, Jackie, illus. 2005. (J). bds. (978-1-57332-367-3(5)) HighReach Learning, Inc.

Mullican, Judy. Taking Care of Pets. Ruminski, Jeff, illus. l.t. ed. 2004. (Hrl Big Book Ser.). 8p. (J). (ps-1). pap. 10.95 (978-1-57332-278-2(4)); pap. 10.95 (978-1-57332-279-9(2)) HighReach Learning, Inc.

Murray, Martine. Henrietta: There's No One Better. 2006. (Illus.). (J). 88p. 9.99 (978-0-439-80749-4(2)); 96p. pap. 9.99 (978-0-439-80747-0(6)) Scholastic, Inc. (Levine, Arthur A. Bks.).

Myers, Martha. Nibbles, the Mostly Mischievous Monkey. 2003. (Julius & Friends Ser.: Vol. 10). (Illus.). 91p. (J). 6.99 (978-0-8163-1947-3(2)) Pacific Pr. Publishing Assn.

Namm, Diane. Pick a Pet. Suarez, Maribel, illus. 2004. (My First Readers Ser.). 32p. (J). (gr. k-1). pap. 3.95 (978-0-516-25507-1(X) , Children's Pr.) Scholastic Library Publishing.

—Pick a Pet. Suarez, Maribel, tr. Suarez, Maribel, illus. 2004. (My First Reader Ser.). 31p. (J). 18.50 (978-0-516-24417-4(5) , Children's Pr.) Scholastic Library Publishing.

Napoli, Donna Jo & Furrow, Robert. Sly the Sleuth & the Pet Mysteries. Maione, Heather Harms, illus. 2005. 96p. (J). (gr. 2). 15.99 (978-0-8037-2993-3(6) , Dial) Penguin Group (USA) Inc.

Nash, Andy. Tatum & Her Tiger: For Kids Blessed with Passion. 2007. (J). (***978-0-8127-0451-8(7)***) Autumn Hse. Publishing Co.

Naylor, Phyllis Reynolds. Danny's Desert Rats. 1999. 11.15 (978-0-606-17630-9(6)) Tandem Library Bks.

Naylor, Phyllis Reynolds. Patches & Scratches. Ramsey, Marcy, illus. 2007. (Simply Sarah Ser.). 80p. (J). (gr. 2-4). 14.99 (***978-0-7614-5347-5(4)***) Cavendish, Marshall Corp.

Neumeyer, Peter F. & Gorey, Edward. Donald & The... 2004. (Illus.). 40p. (J). (ps-3). reprint ed. 12.95 (978-0-8109-4836-5(2)) Abrams, Harry N., Inc.

Nimmo, Jenny. Charlie Bone & the Hidden King. 2006. (Children of the Red King Ser.: Bk. 5). 464p. (J). 9.95 (978-0-439-54530-3(7) , Orchard Bks.) Scholastic, Inc.

No Trouble at All! Individual Title Six-Packs. (Action Packs Ser.). 120p. (gr. 3-5). 44.00 (978-0-7635-8397-2(9)) Rigby Education.

Norman, Kimberly E. Jack of All Tails. Clark, David H., illus. 2007. 32p. (J). 15.99 (978-0-525-47793-8(4) , Dutton Juvenile) Penguin Group (USA) Inc.

Numeroff, Laura Joffe. Laura Numeroff's 10-Step Guide to Living with Your Monster. Evans, Nate, illus. 2002. 32p. (J). (ps-2). 16.99 (978-0-06-623822-7(6) , Geringer, Laura Book) HarperCollins Pubs.

Nye, Ann Marie, ed. Pet Store Pest. Johnson, Jay, illus. 2006. (Maya & Miguel Ser.). 24p. (J). pap. 4.99 (978-0-439-78958-5(3)) Scholastic, Inc.

O'Connor, Ilett. Misaiah's Pet Fish - Gerard. Kahn, Alisha, illus. Wells, Wadell, photos by. 2002. 20p. pap. 10.00 (978-0-9717003-2-1(X)) O'Connor, Ilett K.

O'Connor, Jane. The Perfect Puppy for Me! Hartland, Jessie, illus. 32p. (J). (ps-3). 2003. 15.99 (978-0-670-03614-1(5) , Viking Juvenile); 2005. reprint ed. pap. 5.99 (978-0-14-240335-8(0) , Puffin) Penguin Group (USA) Inc.

O'Donnell, Liam. Winston in the City. (Pet Tales Ser.). (Illus.). 32p. (J). (ps-2). 9.95 (978-1-59249-449-1(8) , 1B033) Soundprints.

—Winston in the City. Hatala, Dan, illus. 2005. (Pet Tales Ser.). 32p. (J). (ps-2). 2.95 (978-1-59249-448-4(X) , 1B032) Soundprints.

—Winston in the City. Hatala, Dan, illus. 2005. (Pet Tales Ser.). 32p. (J). (ps-ps). pap. 4.95 (978-1-59249-447-7(1) , 1B031) Soundprints.

Ogden, Charles. Nod's Limbs. Carton, Rick, illus. 2007. (Edgar & Ellen Ser.). (J). 224p. 9.99 (978-1-4169-1501-0(X)); 210p. (***978-1-4287-3214-8(4)***) Simon & Schuster Children's Publishing. (Aladdin).

—Pet's Revenge. Carton, Rick, illus. 2006. (Edgar & Ellen Ser.). 192p. (J). (gr. 3-7). 9.95 (978-1-4169-1408-2(0) , Aladdin) Simon & Schuster Children's Publishing.

—Triple Threat Vols. 1-3, Set: Their First Three Misadventures: Rare Beasts, Tourist Trap, under Town. Carton, Rick, illus. 2007. (Edgar & Ellen Ser.). 464p. (J). 29.99 (978-1-4169-3462-2(6) , Aladdin) Simon & Schuster Children's Publishing.

Oke, Janette. A Cote of Many Colors. Munger, Nancy, illus. rev. ed. 2001. (Animal Friends Ser.). 64p. (Orig.). (J). (gr. 1-5). pap. 6.99 (978-0-7642-2459-1(X)) Bethany Hse. Pubs.

—A Cote of Many Colors. 2001. (Orig.). (gr. k-3). lib. bdg. 14.15 (978-0-613-87251-5(7)) Tandem Library Bks.

Orloff, Karen Kaufman. I Wanna Iguana. Catrow, David, illus. 2004. 32p. (J). (ps-3). 16.99 (978-0-399-23717-1(8) , Putnam Juvenile) Penguin Group (USA) Inc.

Owens, Connie S. Missing Maggie: The Death of a Pet. 2003. (J). pap. 5.99 (978-1-59317-007-3(6)) Warner Pr. Pubs.

Palatini, Margie. The Perfect Pet. Whatley, Bruce, illus. 2003. 32p. (J). (ps-2). 15.99 (978-0-06-000108-7(9)); lib. bdg. 16.89 (978-0-06-000109-4(7)) HarperCollins Pubs.

Paraskevas, Betty. Peter Pepper's Pet Spectacular. Paraskevas, Michael, illus. 2007. 32p. (J). (gr. 2-6). pap. 14.95 (***978-1-60095-257-9(7)***) Carson-Dellosa Publishing Co., Inc.

Parish, Peggy. No More Monsters for Me! 2003. 22.95 (978-0-673-75926-9(1)) Celebration Pr.

Park, Barbara. Junie B. Jones Smells Something Fishy. Brunkus, Denise & Silverpin Studio Staff, illus. 1998. (Junie B. Jones Ser.: No. 12). 80p. (J). (gr. k-3). lib. bdg. 11.99 (978-0-679-99130-4(1) , Random Hse. Bks. for Young Readers) Random Hse. Children's Bks.

—Junie B. Jones Smells Something Fishy. Brunkus, Denise, illus. 1998. (Junie B. Jones Ser.: No. 12). 80p. (J). (gr. 1-4). pap. 3.99 (978-0-679-89130-7(7) , Random Hse. Bks. for Young Readers) Random Hse. Children's Bks.

Perl, Erica S. Ninety-Three in My Family. Lester, Mike, illus. 2006. 32p. (J). (ps-3). 15.95 (978-0-8109-5760-2(4)) Abrams, Harry N., Inc.

Perret, Delphine. The Big Bad Wolf & Me. 2006. (Illus.). 64p. (J). 9.95 (978-1-4027-3725-1(4)) Sterling Publishing Co., Inc.

Persun, Morgan R. No Pets Allowed. Banks, Timothy, illus. 1998. 32p. (J). (ps-1). pap. 5.49 (978-1-57924-077-6(1)) Jones, Bob Univ. Pr.

—No Pets Allowed. 1998. (gr. k-3). lib. bdg. 13.55 (978-0-613-81217-7(4)) Tandem Library Bks.

Pet Stories Set 2 800888, 3 vols. 2005. (J). pap. (978-1-59794-063-4(1)) Environments, Inc.

Pet Stories Set 800887, 3 vols. 2005. (J). pap. (978-1-59794-062-7(3)) Environments, Inc.

Peters, Kathryn. A Pet for Elizabeth Rose. Peters, Kathryn, illus. l.t. ed. 2005. 42p. (J). 8.99 (978-0-9752647-9-9(6)) Proton Arts.

Petrucha, Stefan & Pendleton, Thomas. Teacher's Pet. 2008. (YA). (***978-0-06-113853-9(3)*** , HarperTeen) HarperCollins Pubs.

The Pets: Individual Title Six-Packs. (Sails Literacy Ser.). 16p. (gr. k up). 27.00 (978-0-7635-4420-1(5)) Rigby Education.

Pets Board Book Set 800792, 6. 2005. (J). bds. (978-1-59794-022-1(4)) Environments, Inc.

Phillips, Betty Lou. Emily Goes Wild. Watts, Sharon, illus. 2nd ed. 2003. 32p. (J). (ps-3). reprint ed. 16.95 (978-1-58685-268-9(X)) Gibbs Smith, Publisher.

Pienkowski, Jan, illus. Jan Pienkowski's Pets. 1998. (Animal Action Pops Ser.). 10p. (J). (gr. 2 up). 4.95 (978-1-58117-022-1(X) , Intervisual/Piggy Toes) Dalmatian Pr.

Pintozzi, Nick. Bentley & the Great Fire. Pintozzi, Nick et al, illus. 2004. 16.95 (978-0-9749465-2-8(4)) Bent-DaiSha, LLC.

Pittar, Gill. Milly, Molly & Pet Day. 2004. (Illus.). 28p. (978-1-86972-004-9(0)) Milly Molly Bks.

Plourde, Lynn. Dino Pets. Kendall, Gideon, illus. 2007. 32p. (J). (ps-1). 15.99 (978-0-525-47778-5(0) , Dutton Juvenile) Penguin Group (USA) Inc.

Polak, Monique. Finding Elmo. 2007. (Orca Currents Ser.). 112p. (YA). (gr. 5 up). pap. (***978-1-55143-686-9(8)***); lib. bdg. (***978-1-55143-688-3(4)***) Orca Bk. Pubs.

Preller, James. The Case of the Best Pet Ever. 2003. (Jigsaw Jones Ser.). 80p. (J). pap. 3.99 (978-0-439-55995-9(2) , Scholastic Paperbacks) Scholastic, Inc.

—Case of the Best Pet Ever. 2003. (gr. k-3). lib. bdg. 11.80 (978-0-613-72227-8(2)) Tandem Library Bks.

Prince, Sarah. Sebastian's Special Present. 2000. (gr. k-3). lib. bdg. 11.80 (978-0-613-29742-4(3)) Tandem Library Bks.

Pringle, Laurence P. Naming the Cat. Potter, Katherine, illus. 1999. 32p. (J). (gr. k-3). 15.95 (978-0-8027-8621-0(9)) Walker & Co.

Provencher, Rose-Marie. Slithery Jake. Carter, Abby, illus. 2004. 32p. (J). 15.99 (978-0-06-623820-3(X)) HarperCollins Pubs.

—Slithery Jake. Provencher, Rose-Marie & Carter, Abby, illus. 2004. 32p. (J). lib. bdg. 17.89 (978-0-06-623821-0(8)) HarperCollins Pubs.

Provensen, Alice. A Day in the Life of Murphy. Provensen, Alice, illus. 2003. (Illus.). 40p. (J). (ps-2). 16.95 (978-0-689-84884-1(6)) Simon & Schuster Children's Publishing.

Punnett, Dick. Name Patty's Pets: A Talk-along Book. Punnett, Yvonne, ed. 2nd ed. 2005. (Talk-Along Bks.). (Illus.). 32p. (J). pap. 6.99 (978-0-9657211-5-8(9)) Tomoka Pr.

Queen, Ivana. A Child's Pet Frizzes & Parent Tizzies: Short Story Collection. 2007. 236p. pap. 15.95 (***978-1-4327-0050-8(2)***) Outskirts Press, Inc.

Rau, Dana Meachen. Pet Your Pet, Level B. Scherer, Jeffrey, illus. 2002. (Compass Point Early Reader Ser.). 32p. (J). (gr. k up). lib. bdg. 18.60 (978-0-7565-0175-4(X)) Compass Point Bks.

Reber, Deborah. My Pet Turtle. Cutting, David, illus. 2001. (Blues Clue's Ready to Read Ser.: Vol. 5). 24p. (J). pap. 3.99 (978-0-689-84186-6(8) , Simon Spotlight/Nickelodeon) Simon & Schuster Children's Publishing.

—My Pet Turtle. Cutting, David, illus. 2001. 32p. (gr. k-3). lib. bdg. 11.80 (978-0-613-57427-3(3)) Tandem Library Bks.

Reed, Tom. Pookus & Buckie: A Children's Book Based on a True Story. Carter, Sandy Lewis, illus. l.t. ed. 2005. 36p. (J). per. 11.95 (978-0-9749725-4-1(1) , 10000, Lonestar Abilene Publishing) LoneStar Abilene Publishing, LLC.

Reiche, Dietlof. Freddy in Peril. Brownjohn, John & Cepeda, Joe, trs. from GER. Cepeda, Joe, illus. 2004. (Golden Hamster Saga: Bk. 2). 208p. (J). pap. 16.95 (978-0-439-53155-9(1)) Scholastic, Inc.

—Freddy to the Rescue. Brownjohn, John, tr. from GER. Cepeda, Joe, illus. 2005. (Golden Hamster Saga: Bk. 3). 240p. (J). pap. 16.95 (978-0-439-53157-3(8)) Scholastic, Inc.

—Freddy's Final Quest Book Five in Golden Hamster. 2008. 208p. pap. 5.99 (***978-0-439-87415-1(7)*** , Scholastic Paperbacks) Scholastic, Inc.

—The Haunting of Freddy. 2007. (Golden Hamster Saga Ser.: Bk. 4). 320p. (J). pap. 5.99 (978-0-439-53160-3(8) , Scholastic Paperbacks) Scholastic, Inc.

—I, Freddy, Vol. 1. Brownjohn, John, tr. from GER. Cepeda, Joe, illus. 2003. (Golden Hamster Saga: Bk. 1). 208p. (J). pap. 15.95 (978-0-439-28356-4(6)) Scholastic, Inc.

Reiche, Dietlof & Brownjohn, John. Freddy in Peril: Book Two in the Golden Hamster Saga. Cepeda, Joe, illus. 2004. 202p. (J). pap. (978-0-439-64984-1(6)) Scholastic, Inc.

—Freddy's Final Quest. Cepeda, Joe, illus. 2007. (Golden Hamster Saga Ser.: Bk. 5). 304p. (J). pap. 16.99 (978-0-439-87414-4(9) , Scholastic Pr.) Scholastic, Inc.

—The Haunting of Freddy. Cepeda, Joe, illus. 2006. (Golden Hamster Saga Ser.: Bk. 4). 320p. (J). pap. 16.99 (978-0-439-53159-7(4) , Scholastic Pr.) Scholastic, Inc.

Reid, Michael, illus. The Kingfisher Treasury of Pet Stories. 2003. (Kingfisher Treasury of Stories Ser.). 160p. (J). (gr. k-3). pap. 5.95 (978-0-7534-5668-2(0) , Kingfisher) Houghton Mifflin Co. Trade & Reference Div.

Ries, Lori. Aggie & Ben: Three Stories. Dormer, Frank W., illus. 2006. 48p. (J). 12.95 (978-1-57091-594-9(6)) Charlesbridge Publishing, Inc.

Robare, Jay, illus. Pets in Heaven Activity Book: Children's Companion Book to: Do Pets & Other Animals Go to Heaven? 2003. 86p. (J). per. 12.95 (978-0-9726363-1-5(5) , 6315) Brite Bks.

Robbins, Jacqui. The New Girl ... & Me. Phelan, Matt, illus. 2006. 32p. (J). (ps-2). 16.95 (978-0-689-86468-1(X) , Atheneum) Simon & Schuster Children's Publishing.

Robertson, M. P. Hieronymus Betts & His Unusual Pets. 2005. (Illus.). 32p. (J). (ps-3). 15.95 (978-1-84507-289-6(8)) Lincoln, Frances Ltd. GBR. *Dist:* Perseus Distribution.

—Jeronimo Botas y Sus Extranas Mascotas/Hieronymus Betts & His Unusual Pets. Sarfatti, Esther, tr. 2006. (ENG & SPA., Illus.). 32p. (J). (ps-2). 15.95 (978-1-84507-735-8(0)) Lincoln, Frances Ltd. GBR. *Dist:* Perseus Distribution.

Robinson, Hilary. Mr. Smith's Surprising Pet. Archbold, Tim, illus. 2005. (Lightning Readers Ser.). 32p. (J). (gr. 1-2). pap., pap. 3.95 (978-0-7696-4021-1(4) , Gingham Dog Pr.) School Specialty Publishing.

—La Sorprendente Mascota del Señor Perez. Archbold, Tim, illus. 2005. (Lightning Readers Ser.). (SPA.). 32p. (J). (gr. 1-2). pap. 3.95 (978-0-7696-4061-7(3) , Gingham Dog Pr.) School Specialty Publishing.

Roosevelt, Anna. Scamper: Bunny Who Went to the White House. Flack, Marjorie, illus. 2000. 72p. (J). (gr. 3-6). pap. 11.95 (978-1-888683-20-2(1)) Wooster Bk. Co., The.

Rose, Gill. William & the Guinea-Pig: A Book about Responsibility. Archbold, Tim, illus. 2004. (Making Good Choices Ser.). 24p. (C). (gr. k-3). 22.60 (978-1-4048-0664-1(4)) Picture Window Bks.

Rosen, Michael. Lovely Old Roly. Lamont, Priscilla, illus. 2004. 25p. (J). (978-0-7112-1488-0(3)) Lincoln, Frances Ltd. GBR. *Dist:* Transition Vendor.

Ross, Tony. Mascotas. 2006. (Little Princess Ser.).Tr. of Pets. (SPA.). (J). (ps-k). bds. 7.95 (978-968-19-1485-1(6) , AT33279) Lectorum Pubns., Inc.

Roth, Susan L. Happy Birthday Mr. Kang. 2001. (Illus.). 32p. (J). (ps-3). 16.95 (978-0-7922-7723-1(6) , National Geographic Children's Bks.) National Geographic Society.

Rotner, Shelley, et al. Pick a Pet. 1999. (Illus.). 32p. (J). (ps-k). 16.99 (978-0-531-33147-7(4)); pap. 15.95 (978-0-531-30147-0(8)) Scholastic, Inc. (Orchard Bks.).

Roy, Ron. The Canary Caper. Gurney, John Steven, illus. unabr. ed. 2004. (A to Z Mysteries Ser.: No. 3). 80p. (J). (gr. k-3). pap. 17.00 incl. audio (978-0-8072-1705-4(0) , S FTR 271 SP, Listening Library) Random Hse. Audio Publishing Group.

Rylant, Cynthia. Annie & Snowball & the Pink Surprise. Stevenson, Sucie, illus. 2008. (Annie & Snowball Ser.). (J). (***978-1-4169-0941-5(9)*** , Simon & Schuster Children's Publishing) Simon & Schuster Children's Publishing.

—Henry & Mudge & Annie's Perfect Pet. Stevenson, Sucie, illus. 2002. (Henry & Mudge Ser.). (J). 11.91 (978-0-7587-5054-9(4)) Book Wholesalers, Inc.

—Henry & Mudge & Annie's Perfect Pet. (Henry & Mudge Ser.). 2001. (Illus.). (J). 10.79 (978-0-606-20699-0(X)); 2000. lib. bdg. 11.80 (978-0-613-33701-4(8)) Tandem Library Bks.

—Henry & Mudge & the Funny Lunch. Bracken, Carolyn, illus. 2005. (Henry & Mudge Ser.). 40p. (J). pap. 3.99 (978-0-689-83444-8(6) , Aladdin) Simon & Schuster Children's Publishing.

Sager, Elizabeth R. Clif & Simmons: And Pet the Puppies. Gladden, Dawn, photos by. l.t. ed. 2001. (Illus.). 16p. (J). (ps-3). pap. 9.95 (978-0-9678386-4-9(9)) C.S. Publishing.

Sampson, Michael R. Caddie the Golf Dog. Cooper, Floyd, illus. 2000. 32p. (J). 14.99 (978-0-8499-5823-6(7)) Nelson, Thomas Inc.

Samuels, Barbara. Dolores Meets Her Match. 2007. (Dolores Ser.). (Illus.). 32p. (J). (ps-3). 16.00 (***978-0-374-31758-4(5)*** , Farrar, Straus & Giroux (BYR)) Farrar, Straus & Giroux.

Santillo, LuAnn. Steve & Pete. Santillo, LuAnn, ed. 2003. (Half-Pint Kids Readers Ser.). (Illus.). 7p. (J). (ps-1). pap. (978-1-59256-103-2(9)) Half-Pint Kids, Inc.

—The Vet. Santillo, LuAnn, ed. 2003. (Half-Pint Kids Readers Ser.). (Illus.). 7p. (J). (ps-1). pap. (978-1-59256-123-0(3)) Half-Pint Kids, Inc.

Sarah's Pet: Level L, 6 vols. 128p. (gr. 2-3). 41.95 (978-0-7699-0990-5(6)) Shortland Pubns. (U. S. A.) Inc.

Sargent, Dave & Sargent, Pat. A Puppy for Bobby/un cachorro para Robertito. 10. Robinson, Laura, illus. 2004. (Learn to Read Ser.: 10). (ENG & SPA.). 18p. (J). pap. 9.95 (978-1-56763-982-7(8)) Ozark Publishing.

—Puppy for Bobby/un cachorro para Robertito, 10, 11. Robinson, Laura, illus. 2004. (Learn to Read Ser.: 10). (ENG & SPA.). 18p. (J). lib. bdg. 19.95 (978-1-56763-981-0(X)) Ozark Publishing.

Sarnoff, Lolo. Dara: Autobiography of a Chesapeake Bay Retriever. 1999. (Illus.). 94p. (YA). (gr. 4 up). 16.95 (978-0-9700667-9-4(1)) Dara's Canine Foundation, Inc.

Sayles, Kristi. Jacob's Monkey-the Trouble with Lying. 2005. 38p. (J). pap. 10.29 (978-1-4116-6429-6(9)) Lulu.com.

Schertle, Alice. Jeremy Bean. Slonim, David, illus. 2008. (J). (978-0-8118-5609-6(7)) Chronicle Bks. LLC.

Schlangen, DVM, Mary. Zoe's Good-Bye. 2005. (Illus.). 32p. (J). 17.95 (978-1-59298-110-6(0)) Beaver's Pond Pr., Inc.

Schneider, Howie. Chewy Louie. Schneider, Howie, illus. 2000. (Illus.). 32p. (ps-3). 15.95 (978-0-87358-765-5(0) , Rising Moon Bks. for Young Readers) Northland Publishing.

Scholastic, Inc. Staff. Dear Mrs. Larue. 2005. (J). pap. 550.00 (978-0-439-70787-9(0) , Sidekicks TM) Scholastic, Inc.

—Little Petshop: The Ultimate Handbook. 2006. (Littlest Pet Shop Ser.). 64p. (J). pap. 5.99 (978-0-439-88782-3(8)) Scholastic, Inc.

Scruton, Clive. Where Are Mary's Pets. Scruton, Clive, illus. 1999. (Flip & Find Ser.). (Illus.). 32p. (J). (ps-k). pap. 3.99 (978-0-7636-0760-9(7)) Candlewick Pr.

Sea Star Editors. Pet Stories You Don't Have to Walk. 2000. (Reading Rainbow Readers Ser.). (J). (978-0-606-19628-4(5)) Tandem Library Bks.

Seagreaves, Kelly E. The Best Pet. Zoller, Jayson D., illus. l.t. ed. 2004. 29p. (J). lib. bdg. 14.95 (978-1-932338-56-0(X)); per. 8.99 (978-1-932338-53-9(5)) Lifevest Publishing, Inc.

SeaStar Publishing Staff, ed. Pet Stories You Don't Have to Walk. 2000. (Reading Rainbow Bks.). (Illus.). 64p. (J). (ps-3). 15.50 (978-1-58717-032-4(9) , SeaStar Bks.) Chronicle Bks. LLC.

—Pet Stories You Don't Have to Walk. 2000. (gr. 3-6). lib. bdg. 11.80 (978-0-613-32943-9(0)) Tandem Library Bks.

Seignobosc, Francoise. Springtime for Jeanne-Marie. 2004. (Illus.). (J). mass mkt. 9.99 (978-0-9740599-3-8(5)) Omnibus Publishing.

Seuling, Barbara. Robert & the Attack of the Giant Tarantula. Brewer, Paul, illus. 2003. (Oh No, It's Robert Ser.). 64p. (J). pap. 3.99 (978-0-439-23545-7(6) , Scholastic Paperbacks) Scholastic, Inc.

—Robert & the Great Pepperoni. Brewer, Paul, illus. 2001. (Robert Bks.). 128p. (J). (gr. 2-5). 15.95 (978-0-8126-2825-8(X)) Cricket Bks.

Shadow. 2006. (J). (978-1-933343-17-4(6)) Stabenfeldt Inc.

Shaskan, Trisha Speed. Another Pet. Vincent, Kenneth, illus. 2006. (Read-It! Readers Ser.). (J). 19.93 (978-1-4048-2404-1(9)) Picture Window Bks.

Shreve, Susan Richards. Ghost Cats. 1999. 162p. (J). (gr. 3-7). pap. 14.95 (978-0-590-37131-5(2) , Levine, Arthur A. Bks.) Scholastic, Inc.

Simmons, Lynn Sheffield. Bo, the Famous Retriever. Hampton, Lin, illus. 2004. 128p. (YA). (gr. 3-6). pap. 10.95 (978-1-58980-217-9(9)) Pelican Publishing Co., Inc.

Simon, Charnan. Sam's Pet. Bialke, Gary, illus. 2000. (Rookie Reader Skill Set Ser.). 32p. (J). (gr. k-2). pap. 4.95 (978-0-516-26553-7(9) , Children's Pr.) Scholastic Library Publishing.

—Show-and-Tell Sam. Bialke, Gary, illus. 1998. (Rookie Readers Ser.). 32p. (J). (gr. 1-2). 19.50 (978-0-516-20945-6(0) , Children's Pr.) Scholastic Library Publishing.

—Show-and-Tell Sam. Bialke, Gary, illus. 1999. 31p. (J). (gr. k-3). lib. bdg. 12.95 (978-0-613-37537-5(8)) Tandem Library Bks.

Simont, Marc. The Stray Dog. Simont, Marc, illus. Tr. of El Perro Vagabundo. (Illus.). 2004. pap. 33.95 incl. audio (978-1-59112-092-6(6)); 2002. 28.95 incl. audio compact disk (978-1-59112-357-6(7)); 2002. pap. 37.95 incl. audio (978-0-87499-928-0(6)); 2002. pap. 39.95 incl. audio compact disk (978-1-59112-560-0(X)); 2002. (J). 25.95 incl. audio (978-0-87499-927-3(8)) Live Oak Media.

Skies, Cecile. Totally Talented Pets. 2007. (Littlest Pet Shop Ser.). 32p. (J). pap. 3.99 (978-0-439-89752-5(1)) Scholastic, Inc.

Smith, Anne Warren. Tails of Spring Break. 2005. 136p. (J). (gr. 2-5). 15.95 (978-0-8075-6358-8(7)) Whitman, Albert & Co.

Smith van Frankenhuyzen, Robbyn. Adopted by an Owl: The True Story of Jackson the Owl. van Frankenhuyzen, Gijsbert, illus. 2001. 48p. (J). 17.95 (978-1-58536-070-3(8)) Sleeping Bear Pr.

Sommer, Carl. Tied up in Knots Read-along. 2003. (Another Sommer-Time Story Ser.). (Illus.). 48p. (J). lib. bdg. 23.95 incl. audio compact disk (978-1-57537-703-2(9)); lib. bdg. 23.95 incl. audio (978-1-57537-753-7(5)) Advance Publishing, Inc.

Sophie Maye. 2000. (Illus.). 20p. (J). (gr. k-3). pap. 10.00 (978-0-9679561-1-4(0)); 18.00 (978-0-9679561-0-7(2)) Debbie-Lou Productions.

Spinelli, Eileen. Moe McTooth: An Alley Cat's Tale. Bronson, Linda, illus. 2003. 32p. (J). (gr. k-3). tchr. ed. 15.00 (978-0-618-11760-4(1) , Clarion Bks.) Houghton Mifflin Co. Trade & Reference Div.

Spitz, Mary Y. Mint's Christmas Message. Pierce, Joanne Y., illus. 2003. 32p. 14.95 (978-0-9724570-0-2(3)) Mother Moose Pr.

Spooky Pet, 6 vols., Set D,Pack. (Smart Start Ser.). (gr. k-1). 23.00 (978-0-7635-0455-7(6)) Rigby Education.

Staunton, Ted. Morgan's Pet Plot. Slavin, Bill, illus. 2003. (First Novel Ser.). 64p. (J). (gr. 1-5). 4.95 (978-0-88780-587-5(6)); (***978-0-88780-588-2(4)***) Formac Publishing Co., Ltd. CAN. *Dist:* Casemate Pubs. & Bk. Distributors, LLC.

Steck-Vaughn Staff. Pet Day. 1999. (Illus.). (J). pap. (978-0-8172-8704-7(3)) Steck-Vaughn.

—Plenty of Pets. 1999. (Illus.). pap. (978-0-8172-8703-0(5)) Steck-Vaughn.

Steele, Michael. Superpet. 2006. (Illus.). 24p. (J). pap. 3.50 (978-0-439-72507-1(0)) Scholastic, Inc.

Steingold, Rita Whitman. A Kitten Followed Me Home. 2001. (Jellybean Bks.). (Illus.). (J). (ps). (978-0-375-80667-4(9) , Random Hse. Bks. for Young Readers) Random Hse. Children's Bks.

Stewart, Toni D., illus. Ben Gets a Pet. 1999. 13p. (Orig.). (J). (gr. k-2). pap. 2.50 (978-1-889658-03-2(0)) New Canaan Publishing Co. LLC.

Stine, R. L. The Great Smelling Bee. Park, Trip, illus. 2005. (Rotten School Ser.). 128p. (J). lib. bdg. 14.89 (978-0-06-078590-1(X)); 6.99 (978-0-06-078589-5(6)) HarperCollins Pubs.

Suen, Anastasia & Keats, Ezra Jack. Willie's Birthday. Eitzen, Allan, illus. 2001. (Easy-to-Read Ser.). 32p. (J). (gr. k-3). 13.99 (978-0-670-88943-3(1) , Viking Juvenile) Penguin Group (USA) Inc.

Swain, Cynthia. Can We Have a Pet? 2006. (Early Explorers Ser.). (J). 30.00 (***978-1-4108-6037-8(X)***) Benchmark Education Co.

Thaler, Mike. The Class Pet from the Black Lagoon. Lee, Jared D., illus. 2003. (J). pap. (978-0-439-55718-4(6)) Scholastic, Inc.

Things That Go! (Flip Flap Fun Book Ser.). 10p. (J). bds. (978-2-89393-933-9(3)) Phidal Publishing, Inc./Editions Phidal, Inc.

Thomas, Frances. Polly's Absolutely Worst Birthday Ever. Gardner, Sally, illus. 2003. 96p. (gr. 1-4). lib. bdg. 16.99 (978-0-385-90122-2(4) , Delacorte Bks. for Young Readers) Random Hse. Children's Bks.

Tidd, Louise Vitellaro. The Best Pet Yet. Handelman, Dorothy, photos by. 1998. (Real Kids Readers Ser.). (Illus.). 32p. (gr. k-2). lib. bdg. 18.90 (978-0-7613-2006-7(7)); (J). pap. 4.99 (978-0-7613-2031-9(8)) Lerner Publishing Group. (Millbrook Pr.).

Tidd Louise Vitellaro. La mejor mascota (the Best Pet Yet) 2007. (Lecturas para niños de verdad - Nivel 2 (Real Kids Readers - Level 2) Ser.). (J). pap. 5.95 (***978-0-8225-7804-8(2)*** , Ediciones Lerner) Lerner Publishing Group.

Tisopulos, Tara. Finding a Family. Tokar, Rob, photos by. 1999. (Adventures of Buddi the Greyhound Ser.). (Illus.). 22p. (J). (gr. 1-5). 14.95 (978-0-9678057-0-2(8)) Great Dog Publishing.

Tortorich, Vinnie. Monty: A Friendship Can Lead to a Miracle. 2004. (Illus.). 36p. (J). 16.95 (978-0-9762854-0-3(1) , 2500) National Horseman Publishing Inc., The.

Turcotte, Elise & Franson, Leanne. Guillaume Rioux, le Poisson Orphelin. 2001. (FRE., Illus.). 24p. (J). pap. (978-2-89021-502-3(4)) Diffusion du livre Mirabel.

Ulrich, George. Mrs. Picasso's Polliwog: A Mystery. Ulrich, George, illus. 2003. (Illus.). 32p. pap. 7.95 (978-1-891577-84-0(0)); (J). lib. bdg. 15.95 (978-1-891577-83-3(2)) Images Pr.

Umansky, Kaye. I Don't Like Gloria! Chamberlain, Margaret, illus. 2007. 32p. (J). (ps-1). 15.99 (978-0-7636-3202-1(3)) Candlewick Pr.

Van Wert, Faye. Empty Pockets. Van Wert, Faye, illus. 2000. (J). (ps-1). 16.95 (978-1-880851-61-6(X)) Greene Bark Pr., Inc.

Viselman, Kenn. Li'l Pet Hospital: The Great Race. 2003. 32p. pap. 3.99 (978-0-06-054840-7(1) , Harper Entertainment) HarperCollins Pubs.

Voake, Charlotte. Ginger Finds a Home. Voake, Charlotte, illus. 2003. (Illus.). 40p. (J). (ps-2). 15.99 (978-0-7636-1999-2(X)) Candlewick Pr.

Wallace, Bill. Goosed! Rogers, Jacqueline, illus. 2002. 128p. (J). (gr. 4-6). tchr. ed. 16.95 (978-0-8234-1757-5(3)) Holiday Hse., Inc.

—Goosed! Rogers, Jacqueline, illus. 2004. 128p. (J). pap. 4.99 (978-0-689-86681-4(X) , Aladdin) Simon & Schuster Children's Publishing.

—No Dogs Allowed! 2004. 214p. (J). (gr. 4-6). tchr. ed. 16.95 (978-0-8234-1818-3(9)) Holiday Hse., Inc.

Wallace, Carol. One Nosy Pup. Bjorkman, Steve, illus. 40p. (J). 15.95 (978-0-8234-1917-3(7)) Holiday Hse., Inc.

Warner, Gertrude Chandler. Watch, the Superdog! 2002. (gr. k-3). lib. bdg. 11.80 (978-0-613-70864-7(4)) Tandem Library Bks.

—Watch, the Superdog!, Vol. 10. Life, Kay, illus. 2004. (Adventures of Benny & Watch: Vol. 10). 32p. (J). (ps-2). pap. 3.95 (978-0-8075-0647-9(8)) Whitman, Albert & Co.

Watson, Kim. Elephant on the Loose. 2001. (gr. k-3). lib. bdg. 11.25 (978-0-613-35686-2(1)); (Illus.). (J). 10.30 (978-0-606-21299-1(X)) Tandem Library Bks.

Watson, T. E. I Wanna Iguana. Raptis, John, illus. 3rd l.t. ed. 2001. 32p. (J). 16.95 (978-1-58478-009-0(6) , Paw Prints Pr.) Heather & Highlands Publishing.

Weigelt, Udo. Super Guinea Pig to the Rescue. Spranger, Nina, illus. 2007. 32p. (J). 17.85 (***978-0-8027-9706-3(7)***); 16.95 (***978-0-8027-9705-6(9)***) Walker & Co.

Wesley, Valerie Wilson. How to Lose Your Class Pet. 2003. (gr. 3-6). lib. bdg. 11.80 (978-0-613-68244-2(0)) Tandem Library Bks.

West, Jane. Proper Polly's Perfect Pet. Bakerink, Monique Lujan, illus. 2002. (J). (978-0-9701025-3-9(4)) Haylett Publishing.

Wheatley, Bill. Mr. Bumble & the Hippo: A Story for Anyone Who Has Ever Loved a Pet. Duderstadt, Jane, illus. 2001. 100p. (J). pap. 24.95 (978-1-888683-10-3(4)) Wooster Bk. Co., The.

Which Pet Measures Up? 2003. (J). per. (978-1-932524-02-4(9)) Region IV Education Service Ctr.

Whimsy. Benny's Pets. Meadow, Amy, illus. 2005. 32p. (J). 15.95 (978-0-9702675-0-4(9)) World of Whimsy Productions, LLC.

White, Debra. Nobody's Pets. 2001. (Illus.). 127p. (YA). (gr. 5 up). pap. 8.95 net. (978-0-9707758-0-1(6)) Four Footed Friends.

Wiebe, Trina. Ants Don't Catch Flying Saucers. Sarrazin, Marisol, illus. 2004. (Abby & Tess Pet-Sitters Ser.: Vol. 5). 96p. (J). pap. 5.95 (978-1-894222-31-0(8)) Lobster Pr. CAN. *Dist:* Univ. of Toronto Pr.

—Ants Don't Catch Flying Saucers. 2001. (gr. 3-6). lib. bdg. 14.10 (978-0-613-62546-3(3)) Tandem Library Bks.

—Goats Don't Brush Their Teeth. Pavanel, Jane, ed. Sarrazin, Marisol, illus. 2004. (Abby & Tess Pet-Sitters Ser.). 96p. (J). (gr. 2-4). pap. 5.95 (978-1-894222-59-4(8)) Lobster Pr. CAN. *Dist:* Univ. of Toronto Pr.

—Goats Don't Brush Their Teeth. 2002. (gr. 3-6). lib. bdg. 14.10 (978-0-613-62554-8(4)) Tandem Library Bks.

—Hamsters Don't Glow in the Dark. Pavanel, Jane, ed. Sarrazin, Marisol, illus. 2004. (Abby & Tess Pet-Sitters Ser.: Vol. 4). 96p. (J). (gr. 2-4). pap. 5.95 (978-1-894222-15-0(6)) Lobster Pr. CAN. *Dist:* Univ. of Toronto Pr.

—Hamsters Don't Glow in the Dark. 2000. (gr. 3-6). lib. bdg. 14.10 (978-0-613-62556-2(0)) Tandem Library Bks.

—Piglets Don't Watch Television. Pavanel, Jane, ed. Sarrazin, Marisol, illus. 2004. (Abby & Tess Pet-Sitters Ser.: Vol. 3). 96p. (J). (gr. 2-4). pap. 5.95 (978-1-894222-16-7(4)) Lobster Pr. CAN. *Dist:* Univ. of Toronto Pr.

Williams, Jacklyn. Pick a Pet, Gus! Cushman, Doug, illus. 2006. (Read-It! Readers Ser.). (J). 19.93 (978-1-4048-2712-7(9)) Picture Window Bks.

Williams, Rozanne Lanczak. How Can I Get a Pet? Maio, Barbara & Faulkner, Stacey, eds. Reid, Mick, illus. 2006. (Learn to Write Ser.). (J). 8p. pap. (978-1-59198-290-6(1) , 6184); per. 4.99 (***978-1-59198-363-7(0)***) Creative Teaching Pr., Inc.

Willson, Sarah. Pet Peeves. Nez, John, illus. 2005. 32p. (J). lib. bdg. 20.00 (***978-1-4242-1114-2(X)***) Fitzgerald Bks.

Wilson, Nathan. A Pet for Pat. Ruch, Jen, illus. 2000. per. 3.00 (978-1-930710-21-4(6)) Veritas Pr., Inc.

Winkler, Henry & Oliver, Lin. Day of the Iguana. Heyer, Carol, illus. 2003. (Hank Zipzer Ser.: No. 3). 160p. (J). 13.99 (978-0-448-43288-5(9)); (gr. 3-8). mass mkt. 4.99 (978-0-448-43212-0(9)) Penguin Group (USA) Inc. (Grosset & Dunlap).

—Day of the Iguana. 2004. (Hank Zipzer Ser.: No. 3). 160p. (J). (gr. 2-6). pap. 29.00 incl. audio (978-1-4000-9008-2(3) , Listening Library) Random Hse. Audio Publishing Group.

—Day of the Iguana. 2003. (Hank Zipzer Ser.: No. 3). (gr. 3-6). lib. bdg. 13.00 (978-0-613-72526-2(3)) Tandem Library Bks.

Winstead, Rosie. Ruby & Bubbles. 2006. (Illus.). 32p. (J). (ps). 15.99 (978-0-8037-3024-3(1) , Dial) Penguin Group (USA) Inc.

Winthrop, Elizabeth. The Biggest Parade. Ulriksen, Mark, illus. rev. ed. 2006. 32p. (J). 16.95 (978-0-8050-7685-1(9)) Holt, Henry & Co.

Wise, William. Christopher Mouse. Benson, Patrick, illus. 2006. 160p. (J). pap. 5.95 (978-1-58234-708-0(5) , Bloomsbury Children) Bloomsbury Publishing.

—Christopher Mouse: The Tale of a Small Traveler. Benson, Patrick, tr. Benson, Patrick, illus. 2004. 154p. (J). (gr. 2-5). 15.95 (978-1-58234-878-0(2) , Bloomsbury Children) Bloomsbury Publishing.

Yaccarino, Dan. The Birthday Fish. rev. ed. 2005. (Illus.). 40p. (J). 16.95 (978-0-8050-7493-2(7) , Holt, Henry & Co. Bks. For Young Readers) Holt, Henry & Co.

—New Pet. 2003. (ps-2). lib. bdg. 13.00 (978-0-613-74973-2(1)) Tandem Library Bks.

Ziefert, Harriet. Class Pets. Kreloff, Elliot & Gott, Barry, illus. 2005. (I'm Going to Read Ser.). 48p. (J). (ps-ps). 11.95 (978-1-4027-2710-8(0)) Sterling Publishing Co., Inc.

—Class Pets Level 4. Kreloff, Elliot & Gott, Barry, illus. 2005. (I'm Going to Read Ser.). 48p. (J). pap. 3.95 (978-1-4027-2709-2(7)) Sterling Publishing Co., Inc.

PHANTOM OF THE OPERA (FICTITIOUS CHARACTER)—FICTION

Fearon Staff. The Phantom of the Opera. (YA). (gr. 5-12). pap. 6.50 (978-0-8359-0981-5(6)) Globe Fearon Educational Publishing.

Leroux, Gaston. The Phantom of the Opera. l.t. ed. 1999. (Large Print Heritage Ser.). 420p. (J). (gr. 7-12). lib. bdg. 35.95 (978-1-58118-043-5(8) , 22512) LRS.

Raab, Ben. The Phantom: Death in the Deep Woods. 2005. 120p. (YA). pap. 14.95 (978-1-933076-06-5(2)) Moonstone.

PHANTOMS

see Apparitions; Ghosts

PHARMACEUTICAL CHEMISTRY

see Chemistry, Medical and Pharmaceutical

PHARMACOPOEIAS

see Materia Medica

PHARMACY

see also Botany, Medical; Chemistry, Medical and Pharmaceutical; Drugs; Materia Medica

African American Pharmacists. 2000. (My Ancestors—My Heroes Ser.: Vol. 29). (J). (gr. 3-4). (978-1-893091-28-3(7)) Parker Publishing Co.

Ballard, Carol. The Search for Cures from the Rainforest. 2005. (Science Quest Ser.). (Illus.). 32p. (J). lib. bdg. 24.67 (978-0-8368-4554-9(4)) Stevens, Gareth Inc.

Gibson, Karen Bush. Pharmacists. 2000. (Community Helpers Ser.). (Illus.). 92p. (J). (gr. 1-2). 18.60 (978-0-7368-0624-4(5) , Bridgestone Bks.) Capstone Pr., Inc.

Jaffe, Steven L. Prozac & Other Antidepressants. 1999. (Junior Drug Awareness Ser.). (Illus.). 80p. (J). (gr. 4-8). 32.00 (978-0-7910-5204-4(4) , Chelsea Hse.) Facts On File, Inc.

Ruschmann, Paul. Prescription & Non-prescription Drugs. 2007. (Point/Counterpoint Ser.). 136p. (gr. 9). 32.95 (***978-0-7910-9552-2(5)*** , Chelsea Hse.) Facts On File, Inc.

PHEASANTS

Martin, Michael. Pheasant Hunting. 2008. (J). (***978-1-4296-0823-7(4)***) Capstone Pr., Inc.

Martin, Michael J. Pheasant Hunting. 2002. (Great Outdoors Ser.). (Illus.). 48p. (J). (gr. 3-4). lib. bdg. 21.26 (978-0-7368-1057-9(9) , Capstone High-Interest Bks.) Capstone Pr., Inc.

PHILADELPHIA (PA.)

Ashley, Susan. The Liberty Bell. 2004. (Weekly Reader Early Learning Library). (Illus.). 24p. (J). (gr. 2 up). pap. 5.95 (978-0-8368-4148-0(4)); lib. bdg. 19.33 (978-0-8368-4141-1(7)) Stevens, Gareth Inc. (Weekly Reader Early Learning Library).

Douglas, Lloyd G. The Liberty Bell. 2003. (Welcome Book Ser.). (Illus.). 24p. (J). 18.00 (978-0-516-25852-2(4)); pap. 4.95 (978-0-516-27875-9(4)) Scholastic Library Publishing. (Children's Pr.).

Gamble, Adam. Good Night Philadelphia. Kelly, Cooper, illus. 2006. (Good Night Our World Ser.). 20p. (J). bds. 9.95 (978-0-9777979-4-3(5)) Our World of Books.

James, Lincoln. Making History: The Liberty Bell. 2006. (Tony Stead Nonfiction Independent Reading Collection). (J). pap. (978-1-4042-5587-6(7)) Rosen Publishing Group, Inc., The.

Jango-Cohen, Judith. The Liberty Bell. (Pull Ahead Bks.). 32p. (J). (gr. k-3). 2004. (Illus.). lib. bdg. 22.60 (978-0-8225-3803-5(2)); 2003. pap. 5.95 (978-0-8225-3754-0(0)) Lerner Publishing Group.

Kavanagh, James. Philadelphia Birds: An Introduction to Familiar Species in the Metropolitan Area. Leung, Raymond, illus. 2001. (Pocket Naturalist Ser.). 12p. pap. 5.95 (978-1-58355-013-7(5)) Waterford Pr., Ltd.

Magaziner, Henry Jonas. Our Liberty Bell. O'Brien, John, illus. 2007. 32p. (J). (gr. 1-5). 15.95 (978-0-8234-1892-3(8)); 5.95 (***978-0-8234-2081-0(7)***) Holiday Hse., Inc.

Philadelphia from A to Z Coloring Book. 2001. (Illus.). (J). 10.00 (978-0-9714438-0-8(7)) Marmardesign.

Silate, Jennifer. The Liberty Bell. 2004. (Illus.). 24p. (J). lib. bdg. (978-1-4042-2687-6(7)) Rosen Publishing Group, Inc., The.

PHILADELPHIA (PA.)—FICTION

Alexander, Lloyd. The Gawgon & the Boy. (Illus.). (J). (gr. 5-8). 2003. 208p. pap. 5.99 (978-0-14-250000-2(3) , Puffin); 2001. 256p. 17.99 (978-0-525-46677-2(0) , Dutton Juvenile) Penguin Group (USA) Inc.

—The Gawgon & the Boy. l.t. ed. 2003. 204p. (J). 23.95 (978-0-7862-5433-0(5)) Thorndike Pr.

—The Philadelphia Adventure. 2002. (Vesper Holly Ser.). (Illus.). 160p. (YA). (gr. 5-9). pap. 5.99 (978-0-14-230144-9(2) , Puffin) Penguin Group (USA) Inc.

Alger, Horatio. Timothy Crump's Ward: A Story of American Life. 2006. pap. (***978-1-4250-3339-2(3)***) Assistedreadingbooks.com Inc.

Anderson, Laurie Halse. Fever 1793. Earley, Lori, illus. 2000. 256p. (J). (gr. 5-9). 17.99 (978-0-689-83858-3(1)) Simon & Schuster Children's Publishing.

—Fever 1793. 2002. (Illus.). 256p. (J). reprint ed. pap. 5.99 (978-0-689-84891-9(9) , Aladdin) Simon & Schuster Children's Publishing.

—Fever 1793. l.t. ed. 2001. 22.95 (978-0-7862-3408-0(3)) Thorndike Pr.

Cox, Judy. Mrs. Millie Goes to Philly! Mathieu, Joseph, illus. 2008. (J). (***978-0-7614-5372-7(5)***) Cavendish, Marshall Corp.

Curtis, Alice Turner. A Little Maid of Old Philadelphia. Cook, Edna, illus. 2004. (Little Maid Ser.). 192p. (J). (gr. 4-7). reprint ed. per. 9.95 (978-1-55709-325-7(3)) Applewood Bks.

De Angeli, Marguerite. Thee, Hannah! De Angeli, Marguerite, illus. 2nd ed. 2000. (Illus.). 112p. (J). (gr. 3-7). pap. 15.99 (978-0-8361-9106-6(4)) Herald Pr.

Dixon, Franklin W. Extreme Danger. 2005. 165p. (J). lib. bdg. 16.92 (***978-1-4242-0383-3(X)***) Fitzgerald Bks.

—Extreme Danger. 2005. (Illus.). 165p. (J). (***978-1-4156-0379-6(0)*** , Aladdin) Simon & Schuster Children's Publishing.

Dixon, Franklin W. One False Step. 2005. 150p. (J). (978-1-4155-7722-6(6) , Aladdin) Simon & Schuster Children's Publishing.

Finley, Martha. Mildred's New Daughter, 7 Vols., Vol. 7. (Mildred Classics: Vol. 7). 288p. pap. 6.95 (978-1-58182-233-5(2)) Cumberland Hse. Publishing.

Giff, Patricia Reilly. Let's Go, Philadelphia!, 11. 1998. (Polk Street Special Ser.). (978-0-606-13567-2(7)) Tandem Library Bks.

Gregory, Kristiana. Five Smooth Stones: Hope's Revolutionary War Diary. 2001. (My America Ser.). (Illus.). 112p. (J). (gr. 4-7). pap. 10.95 (978-0-439-14827-6(8) , Scholastic Pr.) Scholastic, Inc.

—Five Smooth Stones Bk. 1: Hope's Revolutionary War Diary. 2002. (My America Ser.). (Illus.). 112p. (J). (gr. 2-5). pap. 4.99 (978-0-439-36905-3(3) , Scholastic Pr.) Scholastic, Inc.

—We Are Patriots: Hope's Revolutionary War Diary. 2002. (gr. 3-6). lib. bdg. 13.00 (978-0-613-45633-3(5)) Tandem Library Bks.

Halley, Marilyn. Apple-Green Eyes. 2005. pap. 8.00 (978-0-8059-6681-7(1)) Dorrance Publishing Co., Inc.

Hoff, Syd. Where's Prancer? 1999. (Illus.). 32p. (J). (ps-2). pap. 5.95 (978-0-06-443594-9(6) , Harper Trophy) HarperCollins Pubs.

—Where's Prancer? 1999. (978-0-606-17304-9(8)) Tandem Library Bks.

Holm, Jennifer L. The Creek. 2003. 240p. (J). (gr. 7 up). 15.99 (978-0-06-000133-9(X)); 16.89 (978-0-06-000134-6(8)) HarperCollins Pubs.

—The Creek. l.t. ed. 2003. 303p. (J). 21.95 (978-0-7862-6143-7(9) , Large Print Pr.) Thorndike Pr.

Johnson, Maureen G. The Key to the Golden Firebird. 2005. 304p. (YA). reprint ed. pap. 7.99 (978-0-06-054140-8(7) , Harper Trophy) HarperCollins Pubs.

Mohsenian, Javad. 9/11 Children. 2006. 113p. pap. 10.95 (978-0-7414-3218-6(8)) Infinity Publishing.

Moore, Robin. The Man with the Silver Oar. 2002. 192p. (J). (gr. 5 up). 15.89 (978-0-06-000048-6(1)) HarperCollins Pubs.

Porter, Connie. Addy's Short Story Collection. Dellosso, Gabriella & Graef, Renee, illus. 2006. 248p. (J). 12.95 (***978-1-59369-122-6(X)***) American Girl Publishing, Inc.

Rinaldi, Ann. Finishing Becca: A Story about Peggy Shippen & Benedict Arnold. 2004. (Great Episodes Ser.). 384p. (YA). pap. 6.95 (978-0-15-205079-5(5) , Gulliver Bks.) Harcourt Children's Bks.

Webb, Leonard. Corinthia: My Name Is Corinthia. 2005. 72p. pap. 11.95 (978-1-59113-693-4(8)) Booklocker.com, Inc.

P Q R

Whittenberg, Allison. Life Is Fine. 2008. 192p. (YA). (gr. 7). 15.99 (***978-0-385-73480-6(8)*** , Delacorte Bks. for Young Readers) Random Hse. Children's Bks.

PHILADELPHIA (PA.)—HISTORY

ABC Travel Guides for Kids-Philadelphia. 2004. (J). per. 12.95 (978-0-9760047-0-7(4)) Rosenberger, Matthew.

Britton, Tamara L. Independence Hall. 2005. (Checkerboard History Library). (Illus.). 32p. (J). (gr. k-6). lib. bdg. 22.78 (978-1-57765-853-5(1)) ABDO Publishing Co.

Burt, Barbara. Colonial Life: The Adventures of Benjamin Wilcox. 2002. (Reading Expeditions Ser.). (Illus.). 40p. (J). (978-0-7922-8678-3(2)) National Geographic Society.

—The Eve of Revolution: The Colonial Adventures of Benjamin Wilcox. 2004. (Illus.). 40p. (J). (gr. 4-8). pap. 7.00 (978-0-7567-8215-3(5)) DIANE Publishing Co.

Cheung, Shu Pui, et al. Walking on Solid Ground. Wei, Deborah & Kodish, Debora, eds. Chau, Ming, photos by. 2004. (ENG & CHI., Illus.). 64p. (J). pap. 12.95 (978-0-9644937-4-2(8) , 09644937-4-8) Philadelphia Folklore Project.

Cooper, Jason. Historic Philadelphia. 2000. (Historic Landmarks Ser.). (Illus.). 24p. (J). (gr. 1-4). lib. bdg. 20.64 (978-1-55916-326-2(7)) Rourke Publishing, LLC.

Douglas, Lloyd G. Liberty Bell. 2003. (gr. k-3). lib. bdg. 12.95 (978-0-613-67738-7(2)) Tandem Library Bks.

Figley, Marty Rhodes. Prisoner for Liberty. Orback, Craig, illus. 2008. (On My Own History Ser.). (J). lib. bdg. 25.26 (***978-0-8225-7280-0(X)*** , Millbrook Pr.) Lerner Publishing Group.

—Salvar a la Campana de la Libertad. Lepp, Kevin, illus. 2005. (Yo Solo - Historia (on My Own - History) Ser.). (SPA.). 48p. (J). (gr. 3-7). lib. bdg. 25.26 (978-0-8225-3094-7(5) , Ediciones Lerner); (gr. 2-5). pap. 5.95 (978-0-8225-3095-4(3)) Lerner Publishing Group.

—Saving the Liberty Bell. Lepp, Kevin, illus. 2004. 48p. (J). (ps-ps). lib. bdg. 12.75 (978-0-606-30522-8(X)) Tandem Library Bks.

Harcourt School Publishers Staff. Philadelphia: Home of the Liberty Bell. 3rd ed. 2002. (Horizons Ser.). (Illus.). (J). pap. 3.70 (978-0-15-333154-1(2)) Harcourt Schl. Pubs.

Harris, Nancy. The Liberty Bell. 2007. (J). pap. (***978-1-4034-9388-0(X)***) Heinemann Library.

Jango-Cohen, Judith. Liberty Bell. 2004. (ps-2). lib. bdg. 14.10 (978-0-613-81868-1(7)) Tandem Library Bks.

McDonald, Megan. Saving the Liberty Bell. Carrington, Marsha Gray, illus. 2005. 32p. (J). 16.95 (978-0-689-85167-4(7) , Atheneum) Simon & Schuster Children's Publishing.

Mountjoy, Shane. Philadelphia. 2007. (Colonial Settlements in America Ser.). (Illus.). 104p. (J). (gr. 5-8). 30.00 (***978-0-7910-9336-8(0)*** , Chelsea Hse.) Facts On File, Inc.

Schaefer, Ted & Schaefer, Lola M. Independence Hall. 2005. (Symbols of Freedom Ser.). (Illus.). 32p. (J). pap. (978-1-4034-6673-0(4)); (gr. 1-3). lib. bdg. 25.36 (978-1-4034-6664-8(5)) Heinemann Library.

Warrick, Karen Clemens. Independence National Historical Park: A MyReportLinks.com Book. 2005. (Virtual Field Trips Ser.). (Illus.). 48p. (J). (gr. 4-10). lib. bdg. 25.26 (978-0-7660-5224-6(9) , MyReportLinks.com Bks.) Enslow Pubs., Inc.

Zschock, Martha Day, creator. Journey Around Philadelphia from A to Z. 2006. (Journey Around Ser.). (J). 17.95 (978-1-933212-28-9(4)) Commonwealth Editions.

PHILADELPHIA (PA.)—HISTORY—FICTION

Alexander, Lloyd. The Gawgon & the Boy. 2003. (gr. 3-6). lib. bdg. 14.15 (978-0-613-59809-5(1)) Tandem Library Bks.

Alger, Horatio. Jack's Ward. 2006. pap. (***978-1-4065-0711-9(3)***) Dodo Pr.

Alger, Horatio. Jack's Ward: Or, The Boy Guardian. 2006. 176p. pap. 13.99 (978-1-4264-0882-3(X)); 168p. pap. 16.99 (978-1-4264-0863-2(3)) BiblioBazaar.

Bruce, Wendy, illus. Grandfather's Ship, The S. S. "United States" 2000. 50p. (J). (gr. 3-5). (978-0-9701870-0-0(9)) Fletcher, Elizabeth Byrd.

Coleman, Evelyn. Shadows on Society Hill: An Addy Mystery. 2007. 192p. (J). 10.95 (***978-1-59369-163-9(7)***); pap. 6.95 (***978-1-59369-162-2(9)***) American Girl Publishing, Inc. (American Girl).

Gerstein, Mordicai. Sparrow Jack. Gerstein, Mordicai, illus. 2003. (Illus.). 32p. (J). 16.00 (978-0-374-37139-5(3) , Farrar, Straus & Giroux (BYR)) Farrar, Straus & Giroux.

Gregory, Kristiana. We Are Patriots Bk. 2: Hope's Revolutionary War Diary. 2002. (My America Ser.). (Illus.). 112p. (J). (gr. 2-5). pap. 10.95 (978-0-439-21039-3(9)); pap. 4.99 (978-0-439-36906-0(1)) Scholastic, Inc. (Scholastic Pr.).

—When Freedom Comes: Hope's Revolutionary War Diary, Bk. 3. 2004. (My America Ser.). (Illus.). 112p. (J). pap. 4.99 (978-0-439-37054-7(X)) Scholastic, Inc.

Gutman, Dan. Qwerty Stevens Stuck in Time with Benjamin Franklin. 2002. (Illus.). 192p. (J). (gr. 5-8). 17.95 (978-0-689-84553-6(7)) Simon & Schuster Children's Publishing.

Haislip, Phyllis Hall. Lili's Gift: A Civil War Healer's Story. 2007. (Illus.). (J). pap. 8.95 (***978-1-57249-392-6(5)*** , White Mane Kids) White Mane Publishing Co., Inc.

Noble, Trinka Hakes. The Scarlet Stockings Spy. Papp, Robert, illus. 2004. 48p. (J). (gr. 1-7). 16.95 (978-1-58536-230-1(1)) Sleeping Bear Pr.

Thomas Jefferson: Letters from a Philadelphia Bookworm. 2002. (Dear Mr. President Ser.). (J). (gr. 4-7). 25.95 incl. audio (978-0-87499-989-1(8)) Live Oak Media.

PHILADELPHIA (PA.)—INDEPENDENCE HALL

see Independence Hall (Philadelphia, Pa.)

PHILADELPHIA (PA.)—SOCIAL LIFE AND CUSTOMS

Loeper, John J. Meet the Webbers of Philadelphia. 1998. (Early American Family Ser.). (Illus.). 64p. (J). (gr. 3 up). lib. bdg. 25.64 (978-0-7614-0843-7(6) , Benchmark Bks.) Cavendish, Marshall Corp.

PHILADELPHIA PHILLIES (BASEBALL TEAM)

Burgoyne, Tom. The Phillie Phanatics Happiest Memories. Epstein, Len, illus. 2005. 32p. (J). (gr. k-3). pap. (978-0-9705804-3-6(6)) Middle Atlantic Pr.

Goodman, Michael E. The History of the Philadelphia Phillies. 1998. (Baseball, the Great American Game Ser.). (Illus.). 32p. (YA). (gr. 3-12). pap. 21.30 (978-0-88682-920-9(8) , Creative Education) Creative Co., The.

—Philadelphia Phillies. 2002. 32p. (J). pap. 5.95 (978-0-89812-353-1(4) , Creative Paperbacks); (Illus.). (978-1-58341-219-0(0) , Creative Education) Creative Co., The.

Savage, Jeff. Ryan Howard. 2008. (Amazing Athletes Ser.). (J). lib. bdg. 23.93 (***978-0-8225-8833-7(1)*** , Lerner Pubns.) Lerner Publishing Group.

PHILANTHROPISTS

Alter, Judy. Henrietta King: Rancher & Philanthropist. Messersmith, Patrick, illus. 2005. (Stars of Texas Ser.). 72p. 17.95 (978-1-880510-98-8(7)) State Hse. Pr.

Belmonte, Kevin Charles. A Journey Through the Life of William Wilberforce: The Abolitionist Who Changed the Face of a Nation. 2006. (Illus.). 122p. (J). (***978-0-89221-671-0(9)***) New Leaf Pr., Inc.

Binns, Tristan Boyer. Alfred Nobel. 2004. (Great Life Stories Ser.). (Illus.). 111p. (J). 30.50 (978-0-531-12328-7(6) , Watts, Franklin) Scholastic Library Publishing.

De Capua, Sarah E. Andrew Carnegie. 2008. (J). lib. bdg. 26.00 (***978-1-60279-067-4(1)***) Cherry Lake Publishing.

De Lorenzo, Dawn. Peanut Butter & Jelly Possibilities: Youthful Inspirations. 2004. 96p. (J). (gr. 5 up). per. 12.95 (978-0-9745190-0-5(6)) Crysalis Publishing, Inc.

Edge, Laura Bufano. Andrew Carnegie. 2004. (Lerner Biographies Ser.). (Illus.). 128p. (J). (gr. 6-12). lib. bdg. 27.93 (978-0-8225-4965-9(4)) Lerner Publishing Group.

Fullwood, Harlow, Jr. & Sledge, Herbert. Love Lifted Me: The Unfinished Journey of Harlow Fullwood Jr. 2001. (Illus.). 275p. (YA). (gr. 8-12). pap. 20.00 (978-0-935132-28-1(7)) Fairfax, C.H. Co., Inc.

Hall, Margaret. H. J. Heinz. 2003. (Illus.). 32p. (J). lib. bdg. 22.79 (978-1-4034-3248-3(1)) Heinemann Library.

Kramer, Barbara. The Founders of Famous Food Companies. 2002. (Collective Biographies Ser.). (Illus.). 112p. (YA). (gr. 6-12). lib. bdg. 26.60 (978-0-7660-1537-1(8)) Enslow Pubs., Inc.

Parker, Lewis K. Andrew Carnegie & the Steel Industry, 6 vols., Pack. (On Deck Ser.: Vol. 2). 24p. (gr. 4-5). 35.00 (978-0-7578-5847-5(3)) Rigby Education.

Peterson, Tiffany. W. K. Kellogg. 2003. (Lives & Times Ser.). (Illus.). (J). 24p. pap. (978-1-4034-4259-8(2)); 32p. lib. bdg. 22.79 (978-1-4034-3249-0(X)) Heinemann Library.

Rau, Dana Meachen. Andrew Carnegie: Captain of Industry. 2005. (Signature Lives Ser.). (Illus.). 112p. (J). (gr. 5-7). (978-0-7565-0995-8(5) , 1244082) Compass Point Bks.

Waxman, Laura Hamilton. W. K. Kellogg. 2007. (History Maker Biographies Ser.). (J). 26.60 (978-0-8225-6578-9(1) , Lerner Pubns.) Lerner Publishing Group.

PHILANTHROPY

see Gifts; Social Service

PHILIPPINE ISLANDS

see Philippines

PHILIPPINES

Corrigan, Jim. Filipino Immigration. 2003. (Changing Face of North America Ser.). (Illus.). 112p. (YA). lib. bdg. (978-1-59084-684-1(2)) Mason Crest Pubs.

Davis, Lucile. The Philippines. 1998. (Countries of the World Ser.). (Illus.). 24p. (J). (gr. 2-3). lib. bdg. 18.60 (978-0-7368-0071-6(9) , Bridgestone Bks.) Capstone Pr., Inc.

Gonzalez, Joaquin L. The Philippines. 2001. (Countries of the World Ser.). (Illus.). 96p. (J). (gr. 6 up). lib. bdg. 30.00 (978-0-8368-2334-9(6)) Stevens, Gareth Inc.

Gordon, Sharon. Philippines. 2003. (Discovering Cultures Ser.). (Illus.). 48p. (J). 25.64 (978-0-7614-1518-3(1) , Benchmark Bks.) Cavendish, Marshall Corp.

Gray, Shirley W. The Philippines. 2003. (True Bks.). (J). (gr. 3-5). pap. 6.95 (978-0-516-27775-2(8)); (Illus.). 48p. 25.00 (978-0-516-24212-5(1)) Scholastic Library Publishing. (Children's Pr.).

—Philippines. 2003. (gr. 3-6). lib. bdg. 15.25 (978-0-613-67979-4(2)) Tandem Library Bks.

Italia, Bob. The Philippines. 2003. (Countries Ser.). (Illus.). 40p. (J). (gr. k-6). lib. bdg. 22.78 (978-1-57765-842-9(6)) ABDO Publishing Co.

Lang, Thomas. The Philippines. 2003. (World Tour Ser.). (Illus.). 48p. (J). lib. bdg. 25.70 (978-0-7398-6815-7(2)) Raintree.

Langellier, John P. Uncle Sam's Little Wars: The Spanish-American War, Philippine Insurrection & Boxer Rebellion. 2001. (G. I. Ser.). (Illus.). 80p. (J). 27.50 (978-0-7910-6674-4(6) , Chelsea Hse.) Facts On File, Inc.

Lieurance, Suzanne. The Philippines: A MyReportLinks. com Book. 2004. (Top Ten Countries of Recent Immigrants Ser.). (Illus.). 48p. (J). lib. bdg. 25.26 (978-0-7660-5175-1(7) , MyReportLinks.com Bks.) Enslow Pubs., Inc.

Mendoza, Lunita. Philippines. 1999. (Festivals of the World Ser.). (Illus.). 32p. (J). (gr. 3 up). lib. bdg. 24.67 (978-0-8368-2025-6(8)) Stevens, Gareth Inc.

Mildenstein, Tammy. Philippines. 2004. (Modern World Nations Ser.). (Illus.). 120p. (J). (gr. 6-12). 30.00 (978-0-7910-8024-5(2) , Chelsea Hse.) Facts On File, Inc.

Nickles, Greg. Philippines: The Culture. 2002. (gr. 3-6). lib. bdg. 16.40 (978-0-613-52987-7(1)) Tandem Library Bks.

—Philippines: The Land. 2002. (gr. 3-6). lib. bdg. 16.40 (978-0-613-52988-4(X)) Tandem Library Bks.

—Philippines: The People. 2002. (gr. 3-6). lib. bdg. 16.40 (978-0-613-52989-1(8)) Tandem Library Bks.

—Philippines - The Culture. 2002. (Lands, Peoples & Cultures Ser.). (Illus.). 32p. (J). (gr. 4-5). (978-0-7787-9354-0(0)); pap. (978-0-7787-9722-7(8)) Crabtree Publishing Co.

—Philippines - The Land. 2002. (Lands, Peoples & Cultures Ser.). (Illus.). 32p. (J). (gr. 4-5). (978-0-7787-9352-6(4)); pap. (978-0-7787-9720-3(1)) Crabtree Publishing Co.

—Philippines - The People. 2002. (Lands, Peoples & Cultures Ser.). (Illus.). 32p. (J). (gr. 4-5). (978-0-7787-9353-3(2)); pap. (978-0-7787-9721-0(X)) Crabtree Publishing Co.

Oleksy, Walter G. The Philippines. 2000. (Enchantment of the World, Second Ser.). (Illus.). 144p. (YA). (gr. 5-9). 36.00 (978-0-516-21010-0(6) , Children's Pr.) Scholastic Library Publishing.

The Philippines. (Countries of the World Ser.). 24p. (J). 6.95 (978-0-7368-8381-8(9)) Capstone Pr., Inc.

The Philippines, 6 vols. (gr. 2-5). 36.95 (978-0-7368-8402-0(5)) Red Brick Learning.

Schraff, Anne. Philippines. (Ticket to Ser.). (Illus.). 48p. 2005. (gr. 2-4). lib. bdg. 22.60 (978-1-57505-124-6(9)); 2000. (J). (gr. 3-5). lib. bdg. 22.60 (978-1-57505-149-9(4) , Carolrhoda Bks.) Lerner Publishing Group.

See Catalogue Staff & Romulo, Liana. My First Book of Tagalog Words: Filipino Rhymes & Verses. 2006. (Illus.). 24p. (J). 10.95 (978-0-8048-3819-1(4) , PeriplusEdition) Tuttle Publishing.

Sexton, Colleen A. Philippines in Pictures. 2006. (Visual Geography Series, Second Ser.). (Illus.). 80p. (J). 27.93 (978-0-8225-2677-3(8) , Twenty-First Century Bks.) Lerner Publishing Group.

Sheen, Barbara. Foods of the Philippines. 2006. (Taste of Culture Ser.). (Illus.). 64p. (J). (gr. 3-6). 27.45 (978-0-7377-3454-6(X) , Greenhaven Pr., Inc.) Thomson Gale.

Wee, Jessie. Philippines. 1999. (Major World Nations Ser.). (Illus.). 144p. (YA). (ps up). 29.95 (978-0-7910-4984-6(1) , Chelsea Hse.) Facts On File, Inc.

Wild, Mary C. Philippines. 2003. (Modern Nations of the World Ser.). (Illus.). 111p. (J). 29.95 (978-1-59018-120-1(4) , Lucent Bks.) Thomson Gale.

World Book, Inc. Staff, contrib. by. The Story of the Philipines. 2001. (Illus.). 153p. (J). (978-0-7166-6466-6(6)) World Bk., Inc.

Wynaden, Jo & Gonzalez, Joaquin L. Welcome to the Philippines. 2002. (Welcome to My Country Ser.). (Illus.). 48p. (J). (gr. 2 up). lib. bdg. 26.00 (978-0-8368-2534-3(9)) Stevens, Gareth Inc.

PHILIPPINES—FICTION

Arcellana, Francisco. The Mats. Alegre, Hermes, illus. 1999. 24p. (J). (ps-3). 13.95 (978-0-916291-86-0(3)) Kane/Miller Bk. Pubs., Inc.

Brown, Fletch. Street Boy. 3rd ed. 2005. 140p. reprint ed. pap. 5.99 (978-1-884543-64-7(2)) Authentic Media.

Hertenstein, Jane. Beyond Paradise. 1999. (Illus.). 168p. (YA). (gr. 7 up). 16.00 (978-0-688-16381-5(5)) HarperCollins Pubs.

Juan of the Philippines. 2001. 9.95 (978-1-888796-24-7(3)) ABWE Publishing.

Orme, David. El Burro Que Fue Muy Rapido, Level 3: Basado en un Cuento Folclorico Filipino. Rivers, Ruth, illus. 2005. (Lightning Readers Ser.). 32p. (J). (gr. 1-2). pap., pap. 3.95 (978-0-7696-4231-4(4) , Gingham Dog Pr.) School Specialty Publishing.

—The Donkey That Went Too Fast, Level 3 Level 3: A Philippine Folktale. Rivers, Ruth, illus. 2005. (Lightning Readers Ser.). 32p. (J). (gr. 1-2). pap., pap. 3.95 (978-0-7696-4211-6(X) , Gingham Dog Pr.) School Specialty Publishing.

Romeu, Emma. Naufragio en las Filipinas. 2003. Tr. of Shipwrecked in the Philippines. (SPA., Illus.). 162p. (J). (gr. 5-8). pap. 9.95 (978-968-19-0555-2(5)) Santillana USA Publishing Co., Inc.

—Naufragio en las Filipinas. 2002. Tr. of Shipwrecked in the Philippines. (SPA.). (gr. 5-8). lib. bdg. 18.75 (978-0-613-71354-2(0)) Tandem Library Bks.

Romulo, Liana. Filipino Friends. Dandan-Albano, Corazon, illus. 2007. 32p. (J). 15.95 (978-0-8048-3822-1(4)) Tuttle Publishing.

PHILOLOGY

see Language and Languages

PHILOSOPHERS

Anderson, Margaret J. & Stephenson, Karen F. Aristotle: Philosopher & Scientist. 2004. (Great Minds of Science Ser.). (Illus.). 112p. (J). lib. bdg. 26.60 (978-0-7660-2096-2(7)) Enslow Pubs., Inc.

Burke. El Descontento Politico. (Fondo 2000 Ser.). (SPA.). (J). 2.99 (978-968-16-5307-1(6)) Fondo de Cultura Economica USA.

Crompton, Samuel Willard. Emanuel Swedenborg. 2004. (Spiritual Leaders & Thinkers Ser.). (Illus.). 120p. (gr. 9-13). 30.00 (978-0-7910-8102-0(8) , Chelsea Hse.) Facts On File, Inc.

Freedman, Russell. Confucius: The Golden Rule. Clement, Frederic, illus. 2002. (Confucius Ser.). 48p. (J). (gr. 3-7). pap. 17.99 (978-0-439-13957-1(0)); pap. (978-0-439-13958-8(9)) Scholastic, Inc. (Levine, Arthur A. Bks.).

Harkins, Susan and William. The Life & Times of Pythagoras. 2007. (Biography from Ancient Civilizations Ser.). (Illus.). 48p. (J). lib. bdg. 29.95 (***978-1-58415-545-4(0)***) Mitchell Lane Pubs., Inc.

Love, D. Anne. Of Numbers & Stars: The Story of Hypatia. Papparone, Pam, illus. 2005. 32p. (J). (ps-3). 16.95 (978-0-8234-1621-9(6)) Holiday Hse., Inc.

Philosophers of the Enlightenment. (Illus.). (YA). (gr. 5-8). 191.70 (978-1-4042-0620-5(5) , Rosen Central) Rosen Publishing Group, Inc., The.

Rodríguez, Ricardo. Walter Benjamin -Salida de Emergencia. 2005. 116p. pap. (978-958-30-1598-4(9)) Panamericana Editorial.

Rosenberg, Aaron. Thomas Hobbes: An English Philosopher in the Age of Reason. 2005. (Leaders of the Enlightenment Ser.). (Illus.). 112p. (J). (ps-7). lib. bdg. 31.95 (978-1-4042-0419-5(9)) Rosen Publishing Group, Inc., The.

Roth, John K., ed. World Philosophers & Their Works, 3 vols., 3 vols. 2000. (Illus.). 2066p. (gr. 10 up). lib. bdg. 331.00 (978-0-89356-878-8(3)) Salem Pr., Inc.

Tracy, Kathleen. The Life & Times of Confucius. 2004. (Biography from Ancient Civilizations Ser.). (Illus.). 48p. (J). (gr. 4-8). lib. bdg. 29.95 (978-1-58415-246-0(X)) Mitchell Lane Pubs., Inc.

Urbina, Manuel Ivan. Soren Kierkegaard -la conciencia de un Desesperado. 2005. 128p. pap. (978-958-30-1701-8(9)) Panamericana Editorial.

Weate, Jeremy. A Young Person's Guide to Philosophy: "I Think, Therefore I Am" Lawman, Peter, illus. 1998. 64p. (J). (ps up). 16.99 (978-0-7894-3074-8(6)) Dorling Kindersley Publishing, Inc.

Whiting, Jim. Plato. 2006. (Biography from Ancient Civilizations Ser.). (Illus.). 48p. (J). lib. bdg. 20.95 (978-1-58415-507-2(8) , 1259591) Mitchell Lane Pubs., Inc.

Williams, Brian. Aristotle. 2002. (Historical Biographies Ser.). (Illus.). 32p. (J). (gr. 2-4). lib. bdg. 22.79 (978 1 58810-563-9(6)) Heinemann Library.

PHILOSOPHY

see also Belief and Doubt; Ethics; God; Good and Evil; Humanism; Knowledge, Theory of; Logic; Mind and Body; Psychology; Universe

also general subjects with the subdivision Philosophy, e.g. History—Philosophy, etc.

Alexander, Dennis & Alexander, Fern. Mayan Reiki. 2002. (YA). cd-rom (978-1-880534-11-3(8)) Alexander Productions.

Bowman, John L. Selected Topics in Philosophy. 2002. 174p. (Orig.). pap. 14.95 (978-0-595-22548-4(9) , Writers Club Pr.) iUniverse, Inc.

Confucianism. 2005. (Religions & Religious Movements Ser.). 239p. (YA). (gr. 10-13). lib. bdg. 36.20 (978-0-7377-2567-4(2) , Greenhaven Pr., Inc.) Thomson Gale.

Franco, Eloise. The Young Look. 2003. (Illus.). 168p. (gr. 3-7). 5.95 (978-0-87516-294-2(0) , Devorss Pubns.) DeVorss & Co.

Heine, Steven. Shifting Shape, Shaping Text: Philosophy & Folklore in Fox Koan. 1999. (Illus.). 312p. 32.00 (978-0-8248-2197-5(1)) Univ. of Hawaii Pr.

Jaeger. Semblanza de Aristoteles. (Fondo 2000 Ser.). (SPA.). (J). 2.99 (978-968-16-5303-3(3)) Fondo de Cultura Economica USA.

Koontz, Robin Michal. T'ai Chi for Fun! 2007. (J). lib. bdg. (***978-0-7565-3288-8(4)***) Compass Point Bks.

Krishnamurti, J. Que Estas Haciendo con Tu Vida: Comentarios Sobre el Vivir para Jovenes. 2003. (Teen Bks. on Living: Vol. 1). (SPA., Illus.). 240p. (978-84-7556-277-3(9) , 1500) Oceano Difusion Editorial, S. A.

Krishnamurti, Jiddu. What Are You Doing with Your Life? Carlson, Dale, ed. Nicklaus, Carol, illus. 2002. (Books on Living for Teens Ser.: Vol. 1). 272p. (gr. 8-12). pap. 14.95 (978-1-888004-24-3(X)) Krishnamurti Pubns. of America.

Phelan, J. W. Philosophy: Themes & Thinkers. 2005. (Illus.). 352p. pap. 27.00 (978-0-521-53742-1(8)) Cambridge Univ. Pr.

Phillips, Christopher. The Philosophers' Club. Doner, Kim, illus. 2004. 44p. (J). (gr. 5-7). tchr. ed. 15.95 (978-1-58246-039-0(6) , Tricycle Pr.) Ten Speed Pr.

Philosophie: Scholastik, Logik, Metaphysik: Einblick in Modelle und Schulen der Philosophie. (Duden-Schuelerduden Ser.). (GER.). 492p. (YA). 27.95 (978-3-411-02206-9(X)) Bibliographisches Institut & F. A. Brockhaus AG DEU. *Dist:* Continental Bk. Co., Inc., International Bk. Import Service, Inc.

Playing with Plato: The Republic as a Lens into Popular Culture. 2004. (YA). per. (978-1-932948-05-9(8)) Student Pr. Initiative.

Roda. Algunos Motivos de Proteo. (Fondo 2000 Ser.). (SPA.). (J). 2.99 (978-968-16-5304-0(1)) Fondo de Cultura Economica USA.

Roth, John K., ed. World Philosophers & Their Works, 3 vols., 3 vols. 2000. (Illus.). 2066p. (gr. 10 up). lib. bdg. 331.00 (978-0-89356-878-8(3)) Salem Pr., Inc.

Sallon, Sarah & Krishnamurti, Jiddu. Beginnings of Learning. 2004. 272p. pap. 7.99 (978-0-7538-1687-5(3) , Phoenix) Orion Publishing Group, Ltd. GBR. *Dist:* Trafalgar Square Publishing.

Stokes, Philip. Philosophy: 100 Essential Thinkers. 2003. (Illus.). 224p. 18.95 (978-1-59270-016-5(0)) Enchanted Lion Bks., LLC.

The Enlightened One, Ramtha. Children's View of Destiny & Purpose, 1. 1998. (Illus.). 50p. 14.95 (978-1-57873-005-6(8)) JZK Publishing.

Todd, Tom, illus. Hooked on Nature: The Wanderings & Wondering of an Amateur Naturalist. 2001. 128p. per. (978-0-9689131-0-9(5)) Wales Village Pr.

Weate, Jeremy. A Young Person's Guide to Philosophy: "I Think, Therefore I Am" Lawman, Peter, illus. 1998. 64p. (J). (ps up). 16.99 (978-0-7894-3074-8(6)) Dorling Kindersley Publishing, Inc.

PHILOSOPHY—DICTIONARIES

Flew, Antony & Priest, Stephen, eds. A Dictionary of Philosophy. 3rd ed. 2005. 433p. pap. 20.00 (978-0-330-48730-6(2) , Pan) Pan Macmillan GBR. *Dist:* Trafalgar Square Publishing.

PHILOSOPHY, MODERN

see also Evolution

Ideas of the Modern World, 4 vols. 2003. (Illus.). (978-0-7398-6418-0(1)); (978-0-7398-6419-7(X)) Raintree.

PHILOSOPHY, MORAL

see Ethics

PHILOSOPHY OF RELIGION

see Religion—Philosophy

PHOENICIA

Fine, Jil. Writing in Ancient Phoenicia. 2003. (Writing in the Ancient World Ser.). (Illus.). 24p. (J). lib. bdg. 17.25 (978-0-8239-6507-6(4) , PowerKids Pr.) Rosen Publishing Group, Inc., The.

Marston, Elsa. The Phoenicians. 2001. (Cultures of the Past Ser.). (Illus.). 80p. (J). (gr. 5 up). lib. bdg. 29.93 (978-0-7614-0309-8(4) , Benchmark Bks.) Cavendish, Marshall Corp.

Reece, Katherine E. The Phoenicians: The Mysterious Sea People. 2005. (Ancient Civilizations Ser.). (Illus.). 48p. (gr. 4-8). 20.95 (978-1-59515-236-7(9)) Rourke Publishing, LLC.

Writing in Ancient Phoenicia: Individual Title Six-Packs. (On Deck Ser.: Vol. 2). 24p. (gr. 4-5). 35.00 (978-0-7578-5869-7(4)) Rigby Education.

PHONETICS

see also Speech; Voice

Acorn's Gold Mine. 2004. (J). cd-rom 39.00 (***978-1-890265-12-0(8)***) Janelle Pubns., Inc.

Actividades de conocimiento fonologico, edicion del Maestro: Phonics. 2001. (McGraw-Hill. Lectura Ser.). (ENG & SPA.). (gr. 1 up). (978-0-02-188549-7(4)) Macmillan/McGraw-Hill Schl. Div.

Activity Worksheets. 2004. (J). spiral bd. 29.95 (978-1-886441-64-4(2)) Zoo-phonics, Inc.

Add-on Components. (Alphachant Phonics Ser.). (ps-k). 7.85 (978-0-7362-2007-1(0)) Hampton-Brown Bks.

The Adventures of Tutankhamen: Level T. Group 2, 6 vols. (Sunshinetm Ser.). 48p. 44.95 (978-0-7802-4175-6(4)) Wright Group, The.

Al Circo, Al Circo! 2003. 35.50 (978-0-8136-8083-5(2)); stu. ed. 35.50 (978-0-8136-8081-1(6)) Modern Curriculum Pr.

Alexander, Ian. Little Book: Do You See A Dozen? 2000. (Sadlier Phonics Reading Program). 8p. (J). (978-0-8215-7307-5(1) , Sadlier-Oxford) Sadlier, William H. Inc.

Alfarrimas Phonics Kit. (J). (gr. k). 767.22 (978-0-7362-2629-5(X)) Hampton-Brown Bks.

Allen, Margaret. ABC Bags. 1999. (ps-2). lib. bdg. 10.65 (978-0-613-34565-1(7)) Tandem Library Bks.

—Dave & Jane's Band. 1999. (ps-2). lib. bdg. 10.65 (978-0-613-34167-7(8)) Tandem Library Bks.

—Draw & Share. 1999. 9.79 (978-0-606-22753-7(9)); lib. bdg. 10.65 (978-0-613-34184-4(8)) Tandem Library Bks.

—Hap & Cap. 1999. 9.79 (978-0-606-22752-0(0)) Tandem Library Bks.

—I Spy. 1999. 9.79 (978-0-606-22758-2(X)); lib. bdg. 10.65 (978-0-613-34275-9(5)) Tandem Library Bks.

—Jet It, Get It. 1999. (ps-2). lib. bdg. 10.65 (978-0-613-34301-5(8)) Tandem Library Bks.

—Jo Jo in Outer Space. 1999. (ps-2). lib. bdg. 10.65 (978-0-613-34304-6(2)) Tandem Library Bks.

—Pete's Street Beat. 1999. (ps-2). lib. bdg. 10.65 (978-0-613-34408-1(1)) Tandem Library Bks.

—Pug's Hugs. 1999. (ps-2). lib. bdg. 10.65 (978-0-613-34423-4(5)) Tandem Library Bks.

—Sad Sam & Blue Sue. 1999. (ps-2). lib. bdg. 10.65 (978-0-613-34448-7(0)) Tandem Library Bks.

—Sing-Song Sid. 1999. (ps-2). lib. bdg. 10.65 (978-0-613-34469-2(3)) Tandem Library Bks.

—Top Job, Mom. 1999. (ps-2). lib. bdg. 10.65 (978-0-613-34510-1(X)) Tandem Library Bks.

—Truck Tricks. 1999. (ps-2). lib. bdg. 10.65 (978-0-613-34511-8(8)) Tandem Library Bks.

—Twice As Nice. 1999. (ps-2). lib. bdg. 10.65 (978-0-613-34519-4(3)) Tandem Library Bks.

Alphabet & Phonemic Awareness Activity Cards (OCR) 2004. (J). 14.95 (978-1-56911-192-5(8)) Learning Resources, Inc.

Alphabet & Phonics. 2004. (Skill Builders for Young Learners Ser.). (Illus.). 96p. 11.99 (978-0-7439-3687-3(6)) Teacher Created Materials, Inc.

Alphasnaps & Snapphonics: Snapphonics Big Book: Eek! Squeak! A Leak! 2003. 36.95 (978-0-673-60206-0(0)) Celebration Pr.

Alphasnaps & Snapphonics: Snapphonics Big Book: Scat the Cat. 2003. 36.95 (978-0-673-60207-7(9)) Celebration Pr.

Alphasnaps & Snapphonics: Snapphonics Package With 4 Big Books. 2003. 499.95 (978-0-673-59265-1(0)) Celebration Pr.

American Education Publishing Staff. Phonics. 2003. (Brighter Child Learning Flash Cards Ser.). (Illus.). 36p. (J). 2.99 (978-1-56189-466-6(4) , 31049, American Education Publishing) School Specialty Publishing.

Ancient Man of the Ice: Level T. Group 2, 6 vols. (Sunshinetm Ser.). 48p. 44.95 (978-0-7802-4182-4(7)) Wright Group, The.

The Ants & the Grasshopper: R-Controlled Review: Level C, 6 vols. (Wright Skills Ser.). 16p. (gr. k-3). 26.50 (978-0-322-01501-2(4)) Wright Group, The.

Armapalabras: Phonics. 2001. (McGraw-Hill. Lectura Ser.). (ENG & SPA.). (gr. k up). (978-0-02-186611-3(2)); (gr. 1 up). (978-0-02-186612-0(0)) Macmillan/McGraw-Hill Schl. Div.

Armapalabras: Phonics/Vocabulary. 2001. (McGraw-Hill. Lectura Ser.). (ENG & SPA.). (gr. 2 up). (978-0-02-186613-7(9)); (gr. 3 up). (978-0-02-186614-4(7)); (gr. 4 up). (978-0-02-186615-1(5)); (gr. 5 up). (978-0-02-186616-8(3)); (gr. 6 up). (978-0-02-186617-5(1)) Macmillan/McGraw-Hill Schl. Div.

Astroword: Complete CD-ROM & Lab Pack Sets. 2003. 499.95 (978-0-7652-0907-8(1)); 1849.95 (978-0-7652-0909-2(8)) Modern Curriculum Pr.

Astroword: Module 1-Phonemic Awareness (K-1) 2003. (978-0-7652-0577-3(7)) Modern Curriculum Pr.

Astroword: Module 10-Vowel Digraphs & Diphthongs (1-3) 2003. 166.95 net. (978-0-7652-0831-6(8)) Modern Curriculum Pr.

Astroword: Module 12-Base Words & Endings (2-6) 2003. 55.50 net. (978-0-7652-0589-6(0)) Modern Curriculum Pr.

Astroword: Module 13-Compound Words (2-6) 2003. 55.50 net. (978-0-7652-0590-2(4)) Modern Curriculum Pr.

Astroword: Module 14-Suffixes (2-6) 2003. 55.50 net. (978-0-7652-0591-9(2)); 158.95 net. (978-0-7652-0835-4(0)) Modern Curriculum Pr.

Astroword: Module 15-Prefixes (2-6) 2003. 55.50 net. (978-0-7652-0592-6(0)); 158.95 net. (978-0-7652-0836-1(9)) Modern Curriculum Pr.

Astroword: Module 6-Consonant Blends & Digraphs (1-2) 2003. 166.95 net. (978-0-7652-0825-5(3)) Modern Curriculum Pr.

Astroword: Module 7-Long Vowels A, I (1-3) 2003. 166.95 net. (978-0-7652-0826-2(1)) Modern Curriculum Pr.

Astroword: Module 8-Long Vowels I, O (1-3) 2003. 166.95 net. (978-0-7652-0828-6(8)) Modern Curriculum Pr.

Astroword: Module 9-Long Vowels E, U (1-3) 2003. 166.95 net. (978-0-7652-0829-3(6)) Modern Curriculum Pr.

Austin, Howard & Howard, Elisabeth. Born to Sing: Vocal Technique. unabr. ed. 1999. cd-rom, audio compact disk 14.95 (978-0-934419-36-9(1)) Vocal Power Inc.

A Avenues Level: Alphachant Phonics Kit. (Avenues Ser.). (ps-k). 599.13 (978-0-7362-2020-0(8)) Hampton-Brown Bks.

Avenues Level B. (gr. 1 up). 921.20 (978-0-7362-2542-7(0)) Hampton-Brown Bks.

Avenues Level C. (gr. 2 up). 815.51 (978-0-7362-2543-4(9)) Hampton-Brown Bks.

Avenues PreK Level. 834.01 (978-0-7362-2540-3(4)) Hampton-Brown Bks.

A Baby Animals Set, 6 vols. (Phonics Readers Ser.). (gr. k-2). 17.50 (978-0-7368-3188-8(6)) Red Brick Learning.

Barbie Kindergarten Learning Pads: Basic Phonics. 2004. (Illus.). 48p. (J). (978-0-7666-0610-4(4) , 49870) Modern Publishing.

Basic Phonics Skills, Level A. 2004. (J). per. 29.99 (978-1-55799-966-5(X)) Evan-Moor Educational Pubs.

Basic Phonics Skills, Level B. 2004. (J). per. 29.99 (978-1-55799-967-2(8) , EMC 3319) Evan-Moor Educational Pubs.

Basic Phonics Skills, Level C. 2004. (J). per. 29.99 (978-1-55799-968-9(6) , EMC 3320) Evan-Moor Educational Pubs.

Basic Phonics Skills, Level D. 2004. (J). per. 29.99 (978-1-55799-969-6(4) , EMC 3321) Evan-Moor Educational Pubs.

Basic Phonograms. 2000. (Phonics Windows Ser.). (J). pap. 0.99 (978-0-88724-837-5(3) , CD-3036); pap. 0.99 (978-0-88724-845-0(4) , CD-3044) Carson-Dellosa Publishing Co., Inc.

Bates, Dianne. Pobblebonk Reading 4. 4 Blowflies & Glow Worms. 2008. pap. (***978-0-521-71067-1(7)***) Cambridge Univ. Pr.

—Pobblebonk Reading 4. 8 Your Teeth. 2008. pap. (***978-0-521-71068-8(5)***) Cambridge Univ. Pr.

—Pobblebonk Reading 5. 5 Whales. 2008. pap. (***978-0-521-71069-5(3)***) Cambridge Univ. Pr.

—Pobblebonk Reading 5. 9 Skin & Bones. 2008. pap. (***978-0-521-71070-1(7)***) Cambridge Univ. Pr.

—Pobblebonk Reading 6. 8 Zoo Animals. 2008. pap. (***978-0-521-71071-8(5)***) Cambridge Univ. Pr.

The Battle of Bowling Street: Level 4, 6 vols. (Fluency Strand Ser.). (gr. 4-8). 45.00 (978-1-4045-1224-5(1)) Wright Group, The.

Beals, Jane & Beals, Graeme. Final Consonant Sounds Vol. 3: Phonics in Action Series, 4 vols. 2001. 56p. pap. 6.95 (978-1-58324-096-0(9) , World Teachers Pr.) Didax Educational Resources, Inc.

Beck, Isabel L., et al. Phonics Practice Book Copying Masters. 2001. (Trophies Ser.). (gr. 1 up). pap. 69.20 (978-0-15-320909-3(7)); (gr. 2 up). pap. 69.20 (978-0-15-320910-9(0)) Harcourt Schl. Pubs.

—Phonics Practice Book Copying Masters: Intermediate. 2001. (Trophies Ser.). (gr. k-6). pap. 69.20 (978-0-15-320911-6(9)) Harcourt Schl. Pubs.

Beginning & Ending Sounds. 2003. (Right Start for Early Learners Ser.). 48p. (J). (ps-1). pap. 7.99 (978-0-7439-3391-9(5)) Teacher Created Materials, Inc.

Beginning Blends & Diagraphs Phonics Windows with Answers. 2002. (Phonics Windows Ser.). (J). pap. 0.99 (978-0-88724-835-1(7) , CD-3034) Carson-Dellosa Publishing Co., Inc.

Beginning Blends & Digraphs. 2000. (Phonics Windows Ser.). (J). pap. 0.99 (978-0-88724-843-6(8) , CD-3042) Carson-Dellosa Publishing Co., Inc.

Beginning Consonants. 2000. (Phonics Windows Ser.). (J). pap. 0.99 (978-0-88724-839-9(X) , CD-3038) Carson-Dellosa Publishing Co., Inc.

Beginning Consonants (Gr. K-1) 2003. (J). (978-1-58232-037-3(3)) Bryan Hse. Pubs., Inc.

Beginning Consonants Phonics Windows with Answers. 2002. (Phonics Windows Ser.). (J). pap. 0.99 (978-0-88724-831-3(4) , CD-3030) Carson-Dellosa Publishing Co., Inc.

Benchmark Education Staff, compiled by. BuildUp Phonics Skill Bag Set. 2006. (Phonics Ser.). (J). spiral bd. 1995.00 (***978-1-4108-6365-2(4)***) Benchmark Education Co.

—Phonetic Connections Program without Professional Development: Start up/Build Up. ed. 2004. (Phonics Ser.). (J). spiral bd., instr.'s gde. ed. 2550.00 (978-1-4108-1485-2(8)) Benchmark Education Co.

—Phonological Awareness. 2005. pap. 47.00 (***978-1-4108-5064-5(1)***) Benchmark Education Co.

—SpiralUp Phonics Kit. 2005. (Phonics Ser.). (J). spiral bd. 615.00 (***978-1-4108-5797-2(2)***) Benchmark Education Co.

—SpiralUp Phonics Lesson Resources. 2005. (Phonics Ser.). spiral bd. 470.00 (***978-1-4108-5832-0(4)***) Benchmark Education Co.

—SpiralUp Phonics Skill Bag Set. 2006. (Phonics Ser.). (J). spiral bd. 825.00 (***978-1-4108-6366-9(2)***) Benchmark Education Co.

—SpiralUp Phonics Support Tools. 2005. (Phonics Ser.). spiral bd. 180.00 (***978-1-4108-5833-7(2)***) Benchmark Education Co.

—Start up Phonics Readers Add to Pack: Set Of 26. ed. 2004. (Phonics Ser.). (J). pap. 98.00 (978-1-4108-1500-2(5)) Benchmark Education Co.

—Start up Phonics Readers Set. ed. 2004. (Phonics Ser.). (J). spiral bd., instr.'s gde. ed. 575.00 (978-1-4108-1489-0(0)) Benchmark Education Co.

Bentley, Linda. Big Book of Quick & Easy Art Activities: More Than 75 Creative Activities with Curriculum Connections That Keep Kids Creating & Learning All Year Long! 2007. 208p. pap. 26.99 (***978-0-439-58060-1(9)*** , Teaching Resources) Scholastic, Inc.

Bergen, Lara. Phonics Comics: Fearless Four - Level 2. Semple, Dave, illus. 2007. 24p. (J). (gr. 1-17). pap. 3.99 (978-1-58476-564-6(X)) Innovative Kids.

The Big Hit. 2004. (Illus.). (J). (978-1-59577-003-5(8)) Starfall Education.

Blaxland, Wendy. Pobblebonk Reading 4. 5 Trick the Trolls. 2008. pap. (***978-0-521-71072-5(3)***) Cambridge Univ. Pr.

—Pobblebonk Reading 4. 9 the Sun & the Wind. 2008. pap. (***978-0-521-71073-2(1)***) Cambridge Univ. Pr.

—Pobblebonk Reading 5. 4 Kiwi. 2008. pap. (***978-0-521-71074-9(X)***) Cambridge Univ. Pr.

—Pobblebonk Reading 5. 8 Pirates. 2008. pap. (***978-0-521-71075-6(8)***) Cambridge Univ. Pr.

—Pobblebonk Reading 6. 1 Grandpa's Farm. 2008. pap. (***978-0-521-71076-3(6)***) Cambridge Univ. Pr.

—Pobblebonk Reading 6. 10 Exercise Is Cool. 2008. pap. (***978-0-521-71078-7(2)***) Cambridge Univ. Pr.

—Pobblebonk Reading 6. 7 the Magic Paintbrush. 2008. pap. (***978-0-521-71077-0(4)***) Cambridge Univ. Pr.

Blends & Digraphs (Gr. 1-2) 2003. (J). (978-1-58232-109-7(4)) Bryan Hse. Pubs., Inc.

Blevins, Wiley. Dinopals Boxed Set. Dodd, Emma, illus. 2006. 16p. (J). 8.99 (978-0-439-68497-2(8) , Cartwheel Bks.) Scholastic, Inc.

—Mapping the World, 6 vols., Set E. (Phonics Readers Ser.). (gr. k-2). 28.95 (978-0-7368-4075-0(3)) Red Brick Learning.

—Phonics from A to Z. 2nd ed. 2006. 240p. pap. 19.99 (978-0-439-84511-3(4) , Teaching Resources) Scholastic, Inc.

Blue Collection. (Elefonetica Ser.). (SPA.). (gr. 1-2). 373.22 (978-0-7362-0795-9(3)) Hampton-Brown Bks.

Blumenfeld, Samuel L. Alpha-Phonics the Book. 2001. (J). stu. ed. 39.95 incl. cd-rom (978-0-941995-18-4(6)) Paradigm Co.

Bradshaw, Georgine & Wrighton, Charlene. Basic Kit - Kindergarten. Clark, Irene, illus. 2005. Orig. Title: Basic Kit II. (J). 249.95 (978-1-886441-31-6(6)) Zoo-phonics, Inc.

—Kindergarten Zoo-per Kit. Clark, Irene, illus. 2005. (J). 499.95 (978-1-886441-34-7(0) , ZOP4219) Zoo-phonics, Inc.

—Preschool Zoo-per Kit. Clark, Irene, illus. 2005. (J). 449.95 (978-1-886441-32-3(4) , ZOP4218) Zoo-phonics, Inc.

Breidahl, Harry. The Zoo on You: Life on Human Skin. 2001. (Life in Strange Places Ser.). (Illus.). 32p. (J). (gr. 4 up). 28.00 (978-0-7910-6619-5(3) , 011006, Chelsea Hse.) Facts On File, Inc.

Brighter Vision Publishing Staff. Math-a-Magic Phonics Magic. 2000. (Math-A-Magic Ser.). (Illus.). (J). pap. 2.25 (978-1-55254-157-9(6)); (gr. 3). pap. 2.25 (978-1-55254-160-9(6)); (ps-3). pap. 2.25 (978-1-55254-158-6(4)); (ps-3). pap. 2.25 (978-1-55254-159-3(2)) Brighter Vision Pubns.

Brown, Jane. Little Book, Who Has Four Feet? 2000. (Sadlier Phonics Reading Program). 8p. (J). (978-0-8215-7300-6(4) , Sadlier-Oxford) Sadlier, William H. Inc.

Buitres En La Playa: Little Books, Level 4, Vol. 19. 2003. (Fonolibros Ser.). (SPA.). 25.50 (978-0-7652-0096-9(1)) Modern Curriculum Pr.

Burch, Marilyn Myers, et al. Phonics Stationery. 2003. 32p. pap. 8.95 (978-0-439-51771-3(0) , Teaching Resources) Scholastic, Inc.

Callella, Kim. Build-a-Skill Instant Books Short & Long Vowels. shiotsu, Vicky & Faulkner, Stacey, eds. Campbell, Jenny & Tom, Darcy, illus. 2007. (J). 4.99 (***978-1-59198-412-2(2)***) Creative Teaching Pr., Inc.

A Can You See It?, 6 vols., Set. (Phonics Readers Ser.). (gr. k-2). 17.50 (978-0-7368-3191-8(6)) Red Brick Learning.

Un Canguro en la Cocina! Little Books, Level 10, Vol. 2. 2003. (Fonolibros Ser.). (SPA.). 25.50 (978-0-7652-0111-9(9)) Modern Curriculum Pr.

Carole, Jane. Get Ready for First Grade! 1,107 Interactive & Educational Exercises for Curriculum-Based Learning That's Fun! 2005. (Illus.). 320p. spiral bd., spiral bd. 17.95 (978-1-57912-461-8(5) , 81461) Black Dog & Leventhal Pubs., Inc.

Carteles de fonetica: Ilustraciones: Phonics. 2001. (McGraw-Hill. Lectura Ser.), (ENG & SPA.). (gr. k-1). (978-0-02-186551-2(5)) Macmillan/McGraw-Hill Schl. Div.

La Casa de Abuelito. 2003. (SPA., Illus.). 35.50 (978-0-8136-8526-7(5)) Modern Curriculum Pr.

Cauldwell, Caroline. Sound Aloud with Austin & Carla & the Sound Twins. 2001. 40p. 5.00 (978-1-890352-16-5(0)) Jackson Harbor Pr.

Cernak, Kim. Build-a-Skill Instant Books Consonant Blends & Digraphs. shiotsu, Vicky & Faulkner, Stacey, eds. Campbell, Jenny & Tom, Darcy, illus. 2007. (J). 4.99 (***978-1-59198-410-8(6)***) Creative Teaching Pr., Inc.

Challenging Phonograms. 2000. (Phonics Windows Ser.). pap. 0.99 (978-0-88724-838-2(1) , CD-3036); (J). pap. 0.99 (978-0-88724-846-7(2) , CD-3045) Carson-Dellosa Publishing Co., Inc.

Classification (Gr. 1-2) 2003. (J). (978-1-58232-040-3(3)) Bryan Hse. Pubs., Inc.

Cole, Kathleen A. Phonics. 2000. (Step Ahead Workbooks Ser.). (Illus.). 64p. (J). (ps-3). pap., wbk. ed. 3.99 (978-0-307-03650-6(2) , 03650, Golden Bks.) Random Hse. Children's Bks.

Cole's Notes: Long Vowel o, CVCe Pattern: Level B, 6 vols. (Wright Skills Ser.). 16p. (gr. k-3). 17.95 (978-0-322-03101-2(X)) Wright Group, The.

Come & Get It: Consonant l: Level A, 6 vols. (Wright Skills Ser.). 12p. (gr. k-3). 17.95 (978-0-322-03116-6(8)) Wright Group, The.

Come on, Dot: Short Vowel o: Level A, 6 vols. (Wright Skills Ser.). 12p. (gr. k-3). 17.95 (978-0-322-03112-8(5)) Wright Group, The.

Como Soy Yo? Little Books, Level 2. 2003. (Fonolibros Ser.). 25.50 (978-0-7652-0077-8(5)) Modern Curriculum Pr.

Complete Phonics Readers Program. (Phonics Readers Ser.). (gr. k-2). 1322.95 (978-0-7368-4098-9(2)) Red Brick Learning.

Consonant Pictures. (gr. k-3). 21.99 (978-1-56451-637-4(7) , ID2721) School Specialty Publishing.

Consonants (Gr. K-1) 2003. (J). (978-1-58232-108-0(6)) Bryan Hse. Pubs., Inc.

Cooper, Terry, ed. Learning Phonics. 2006. (Kindergarten Ser.). 48p. pap. 5.99 (978-0-439-81938-1(5) , Teaching Resources) Scholastic, Inc.

Corner Store. (J). 21.95 (978-0-8136-4337-3(6)) Modern Curriculum Pr.

Courtney, Claudia. Barns of Barley: The Parable of the Rich Fool, Luke 12. 1998. (ps-2). lib. bdg. 10.65 (978-0-613-72817-1(3)) Tandem Library Bks.

—Daniel Blessed: Daniel in the Lion's Den. 1999. (ps-2). lib. bdg. 10.65 (978-0-613-72899-7(8)) Tandem Library Bks.

—Jesus Is Born: Christmas. 1998. (ps-2). lib. bdg. 10.65 (978-0-613-72654-2(5)) Tandem Library Bks.

—Little Is Big: Jesus Feeds the 5,000 John 6. 1998. (ps-2). lib. bdg. 10.65 (978-0-613-72813-3(0)) Tandem Library Bks.

Cox, Phil Roxbee & Grant, Marlynne. Goose on the Loose. Tyler, Jenny, ed. Cartwright, Stephen, illus. 10p. (J). pap. 4.95 (978-0-7460-4486-5(0) , Usborne) EDC Publishing.

Crowther, Terence G. Up & Away in Phonics 3. 1999. (Illus.). 48p. (J). 7.50 (978-0-19-434968-0(3)) Oxford Univ. Pr., Inc.

—Up & Away in Phonics 5. 1999. (Illus.). 48p. (J). 7.50 (978-0-19-434982-6(9)) Oxford Univ. Pr., Inc.

—Up & Away in Phonics 6. 1999. (Illus.). (J). 7.50 (978-0-19-434989-5(6)) Oxford Univ. Pr., Inc.

Cuando Seamos Grandes: Little Books, Level 12, Vol. 4. 2003. (Fonolibros Ser.). 35.50 (978-0-7652-0113-3(5)) Modern Curriculum Pr.

Cuentos de la Luna: Little Books, Level 20, Vol. 12. 2003. (Fonolibros Ser.). 34.95 (978-0-7652-0122-5(4)) Modern Curriculum Pr.

Cummings, Carol. Sing-Along, Phonics Fun: Learning to Read with Rhyme, Rhythm & Repetition. Sheriff, John, illus. 2001. 42p. (J). (ps-3). pap. 6.99 (978-1-881660-06-4(0)) Teaching, Inc.

Cummings, Renee & Goldish, Meish. "Fun"damental Phonics. 2003. (Homework Booklets Ser.). (Illus.). 80p. (gr. 2 up). 2.99 (978-1-56822-839-6(2) , IF0362) School Specialty Publishing.

Cunningham, Patricia M. Making More Words: Multilevel, Hands-on Phonics & Spelling Activities. 2001. (Illus.). 208p. (J). (gr. 1-3). pap. 18.99 (978-1-56417-900-5(1) , GA1588) Schaffer, Frank Pubns.

Cunningham, Patricia Marr. Systematic Sequential Phonics They Use: For Befinning Readers of Any Age. 2000. (Four-Blocks Ser.). 192p. (J). (gr. 1-5). per. 24.99 (978-0-88724-581-7(1) , CD-2409) Carson-Dellosa Publishing Co., Inc.

Dalmatian Press Staff. Phonics - Beginning Sounds. 1998. (Precious Moments Workbooks Ser.). (Illus.). 32p. (J). (ps-3). pap. 2.99 (978-1-57759-114-6(3)) Dalmatian Pr.

Dan & the Fan: Consonants d, f, n, p; Short Vowel a word families: Level A, 6 vols. (Wright Skills Ser.). 12p. (gr. k-3). 17.95 (978-0-322-01446-6(8)) Wright Group, The.

Daniel, Claire, et al. Great Big Book of Fun Phonics Activities. 1999. 352p. (J). pap. 23.95 (978-0-439-08247-1(1)) Scholastic, Inc.

D'Avanzo, Maria. Turn & Talk¿ Vocalic R. 2007. (J). spiral bd. 24.95 (***978-1-58650-708-4(7)***) Super Duper Pubns.

de Diaz, Rosario Ahumada. Juguemos a Leer: Libro de Lectura. (SPA.). (J). 6.95 (978-968-24-1220-2(X) , TRM391) Trillas Editorial, S. A. MEX. *Dist:* Continental Bk. Co., Inc.

Den of Thieves: Level 6, 6 vols. (Fluency Strand Ser.). (gr. 4-8). 45.00 (978-1-4045-1238-2(1)) Wright Group, The.

Un Desastre Monumental Vol. 12: Little Books, Level 4. 2003. (Fonolibros Ser.). 25.50 (978-0-7652-0089-1(9)) Modern Curriculum Pr.

DeShong, Molly & Webber, Thomas, eds. Awesome Artic R Sound Loaded Articulation Worksheets. Barr, Steve et al, illus. 2000. 215p. (J). (gr. k-5). spiral bd. 36.95 (978-1-58650-157-0(7) , BK-282) Super Duper Pubns.

—Awesome Artic S Sound Loaded Artic Activities. Barr, Steve et al, illus. 2000. 201p. (J). spiral bd. 36.95 (978-1-58650-156-3(9) , BK-275) Super Duper Pubns.

Did You Know? Big Book: Level L. Group 1. (Sunshinetm Ser.). 24p. 36.50 (978-0-322-00334-7(2)) Wright Group, The.

Digraph. 2001. pap. 3.25 (978-0-7398-4560-8(8)) Steck-Vaughn.

Digraphs & Diphthongs. 2004. (Basic Skills Ser.). 48p. (J). pap. 6.99 (978-0-88724-148-2(4) , CD-4709) Carson-Dellosa Publishing Co., Inc.

Discovering Phonics. 2005. (978-0-9774310-7-6(X)) Educational Tools, Inc.

Disney Staff & LeapFrog Staff, compiled by. Pooh Gets Stuck. 2001. (J). (ps-1). spiral bd. 14.99 (978-1-58605-001-6(X)) LeapFrog Enterprises, Inc.

DK Publishing. Funny Phonics. 2008. (DK Toys & Games Ser.). (J). (ps-1). 12.99 (***978-0-7566-3746-0(5)***) Dorling Kindersley Publishing, Inc.

DK Publishing Staff. My First Phonics Board Book. 2007. 48p. (J). bds. 12.99 (978-0-7566-2590-0(4)) Dorling Kindersley Publishing, Inc.

Donde Viven? Little Books, Level 8, Vol. 14. 2003. (Fonolibros Ser.). 25.50 (978-0-7652-0091-4(0)) Modern Curriculum Pr.

Dora the Explorer Letter Sounds. 2004. (J). 3.95 (***978-1-58610-907-3(3)***) Learning Horizons, Inc.

Dorling Kindersley Publishing Staff. My First Phonics. 2004. 36p. (J). bds. 5.99 (978-0-7566-0282-6(3)) Dorling Kindersley Publishing, Inc.

—Phonic Finders. 2007. 80p. (J). 9.99 (978-0-7566-2919-9(5)) Dorling Kindersley Publishing, Inc.

Doudna, Kelly. Oo: See It Say It Hear It. l.t. ed. 2001. (Alphabet Ser.). (Illus.). 24p. (J). (ps-3). lib. bdg. 19.93 (978-1-57765-435-3(8) , SandCastle) ABDO Publishing Co.

Douglas, Vincent. The Complete Book of Phonics: Ages 4-9. 2002. (Complete Book Ser.). (Illus.). 352p. (J). (gr. k-6). pap., wbk. ed. 14.95 (978-1-56189-207-5(6) , American Education Publishing) School Specialty Publishing.

Douglas, Vincent & School Specialty Publishing Staff. Phonics. 2003. (Brighter Child Flash Cards Ser.). (Illus.). 54p. (J). (ps up). 2.99 (978-0-7696-2394-8(8) , Brighter Child) School Specialty Publishing.

—Sounds & Letters. 2004. (Kindergarten Bound Ser.). (Illus.). 80p. (J). (ps up). pap. 5.95 (978-0-7696-3438-8(9) , American Education Publishing) School Specialty Publishing.

—Spectrum Phonics, Grade 2. 2002. (Starburst Spectrum Workbook Ser.). (Illus.). 150p. (J). (gr. 2-2). pap. 8.95 (978-1-56189-942-5(9) , American Education Publishing) School Specialty Publishing.

—Spectrum Phonics, Grade 3. 2002. (Starburst Spectrum Ser.). (Illus.). 150p. (J). (gr. 3-3). pap. 8.95 (978-1-56189-943-2(7) , American Education Publishing) School Specialty Publishing.

—Spectrum Phonics, Kindergarten. 2002. (Starburst Spectrum Ser.). (Illus.). 128p. (J). (gr. k up). pap. 8.95 (978-1-56189-940-1(2) , American Education Publishing) School Specialty Publishing.

—Spectrum Word Study & Phonics, Grade 4. 2002. (Starburst Spectrum Workbook Ser.). (Illus.). 150p. (J). (gr. 4-4). pap. 8.95 (978-1-56189-944-9(5) , American Education Publishing) School Specialty Publishing.

—Spectrum Word Study & Phonics, Grade 5. 2002. (Starburst Spectrum Workbook Ser.). (Illus.). 150p. (J). (gr. 5-5). pap. 8.95 (978-1-56189-945-6(3) , American Education Publishing) School Specialty Publishing.

—Spectrum Word Study & Phonics, Grade 6. 2002. (Starburst Spectrum Workbook Ser.). (Illus.). 150p. (J). (gr. 6-6). pap. 8.95 (978-1-56189-946-3(1) , American Education Publishing) School Specialty Publishing.

—Theme-Based Phonics, Grade 1. 2003. (100+ Ser.). (Illus.). 128p. (J). (gr. 1-1). pap. 14.99 (978-0-7424-1911-7(8) , IFG99104, Instructional Fair) Schaffer, Frank Pubns.

—Theme-Based Phonics, Grade 2. 2003. (100+ Ser.). (Illus.). 128p. (J). (gr. 2-2). pap. 14.99 (978-0-7424-1912-4(6) , IFG99105, Instructional Fair) Schaffer, Frank Pubns.

—Theme-Based Phonics, Kindergarten. 2003. (100+ Ser.). (Illus.). 128p. (J). (gr. k up). pap. 14.99 (978-0-7424-1910-0(X) , IFG99107, Instructional Fair) Schaffer, Frank Pubns.

Dr Awkward: Level 6, 6 vols. (Fluency Strand Ser.). (gr. 4-8). 45.00 (978-1-4045-1239-9(X)) Wright Group, The.

Dreaming of Great Ideas Set E, 6 vols. (Phonics Readers Ser.). (gr. k-2). 28.95 (978-0-7368-4064-4(8)) Red Brick Learning.

Dworkin, Brooke. Phonics Puzzles. Snider, Jackie & Harpster, Steve, illus. 2006. (First Word Search Ser.). 64p. (J). pap. 3.95 (978-1-4027-3590-5(1)) Sterling Publishing Co., Inc.

En Busca de Bravo: Little Books, Level 12, Vol. 27. 2003. (Fonolibros Ser.). 35.50 (978-0-7652-0106-5(2)) Modern Curriculum Pr.

En Busca de Unicornios: Little Books, Level 6, 2. 2003. (Fonolibros Ser.). 22.50 (978-0-7652-0078-5(3)) Modern Curriculum Pr.

En el Bano, 6, Pack. (Chiquilibros Ser.). (SPA.). (gr. k-1). 23.00 (978-0-7635-8616-4(1)) Rigby Education.

En el Invierno: Individual Title Six-Packs. (Coleccion Pm Ser.).Tr. of Walking in the winter. (SPA.). 16p. (gr. 1 up). 26.00 (978-0-7578-3056-3(0)) Rigby Education.

En el Mercado, 6, Pack. (Coleccion Pm Ser.: Vol. 1). (SPA.). 16p. (gr. k-1). 26.00 (978-0-7578-0671-1(6)) Rigby Education.

En el Otono, 6 Pks. (Coleccion Pm Ser.).Tr. of Walking in the autumn. (SPA.). 16p. (gr. 1 up). 26.00 (978-0-7578-3055-6(2)) Rigby Education.

En el Supermercado, 6, Pack. (Chiquilibros Ser.). (SPA.). (gr. k-1). 23.00 (978-0-7635-8617-1(X)) Rigby Education.

En la Playa, 6, Pack. (Chiquilibros Ser.). (SPA.). (gr. k-1). 23.00 (978-0-7635-8618-8(8)) Rigby Education.

Ending Blends & Digraphs. 2000. (Phonics Windows Ser.). (J). pap. 0.99 (978-0-88724-836-8(5) , CD-3035); pap. 0.99 (978-0-88724-844-3(6) , CD-3043) Carson-Dellosa Publishing Co., Inc.

Ending Consonants. 2000. (Phonics Windows Ser.). (J). pap. 0.99 (978-0-88724-840-5(3) , CD-3039) Carson-Dellosa Publishing Co., Inc.

Energy Every Day Set F, 6 vols. (Phonics Readers Ser.). (gr. k-2). 28.95 (978-0-7368-4086-6(9)) Red Brick Learning.

Esa Mosca! Little Books, Level 3, Vol. 15. 2003. (Fonolibros Ser.). 25.50 (978-0-7652-0092-1(9)) Modern Curriculum Pr.

Esparza, Thomas, Jr., prod. Esther's Playhouse, Disk C. 2004. (Illus.). (J). cd-rom (978-1-879817-44-9(6) , Children) Star Light Pr.

Evans, Anne. First Phonics. 1999. (Illus.). 31p. (J). (ps-k). Bk. 1. pap. 19.00 (978-0-7217-0700-6(9)); Bk. 2. pap. 19.00 (978-0-7217-0701-3(7)); Bk. 3. pap. 19.00 (978-0-7217-0702-0(5)); Bk. 4. pap. 19.00 (978-0-7217-0703-7(3)) Schofield & Sims Ltd. GBR. *Dist:* State Mutual Bk. & Periodical Service, Ltd.

Evans, Mary. Little Book: Cats! Cat! Cat! Kovalcik, Terry, illus. 2000. (Sadlier Phonics Reading Program). 8p. (J). (978-0-8215-7308-2(X) , Sadlier-Oxford) Sadlier, William H. Inc.

Evens, Mary. Little Book: Good Pets. 2000. (Sadlier Phonics Reading Program). 8p. (J). (978-0-8215-7310-5(1) , Sadlier-Oxford) Sadlier, William H. Inc.

Falletta, Bernadette. Sound-a-Likes Books: Literacy. 1999. (Illus.). 110p. (J). (gr. 1-7). 32.95 (978-0-9675466-0-5(5)) We Love to Read Productions.

The Farm: Individual Title Six-Packs. (Chiquilibros Ser.). (gr. k-1). 23.00 (978-0-7635-0413-7(0)) Rigby Education.

The Farm: Individual Title Two-Packs. (Chiquilibros Ser.). (ps-1). 12.00 (978-0-7635-8529-7(7)) Rigby Education.

Fast Forward! 2003. (Fast Forward! Ser.). Level C. (J). (gr. 1 up). stu. ed., per. 7.95 (978-1-58830-779-8(4)); Level D. (J). (gr. 2 up). stu. ed., per. 67.95 (978-1-58830-334-9(9)); Level D. (J). (gr. 2 up). stu. ed., per. 7.95 (978-1-58830-780-4(8)); Level A. tchr. ed., per., tchr.'s training gde. ed. 39.95 (978-1-58830-783-5(2)); Level A. (J). (gr. 1 up). stu. ed., per. 7.95 (978-1-58830-777-4(8)); Level B. tchr. ed., per., tchr.'s training gde. ed. 39.95 (978-1-58830-784-2(0)); Level B. (J). (gr. 1 up). stu. ed., per. 7.95 (978-1-58830-778-1(6)); Level E. (J). (gr. 1 up). stu. ed., per. 7.95 (978-1-58830-781-1(6)); Level E. (J). (gr. 2 up). stu. ed., per. 67.95 (978-1-58830-335-6(7)); Level F. (J). (gr. 2 up). stu. ed., per. 67.95 (978-1-58830-336-3(5)); Level F. (J). (gr. 2 up). stu. ed., per. 7.95 (978-1-58830-782-8(4)) Metropolitan Teaching & Learning Co.

Flanagan, Alice K. Slip & Slide: The Sound of SL. 2004. (Phonics Readers Ser.). 24p. (J). (ps-3). 21.36 (978-1-59296-159-7(2)) Child's World, Inc.

Flip, Flap, & Fluff: Family Blends: Level B, 6 vols. (Wright Skills Ser.). 16p. (gr. k-3). 17.95 (978-0-322-01459-6(X)) Wright Group, The.

Fluent Reader Audio 10-Pk Phonics Blends & Diagraphs Lvl 2. 0. 2004. cd-rom 39.95 (978-1-59455-143-7(X)) Renaissance Learning, Inc.

Fluent Reader Audio 10-Pk Phonics Long Vowel Word Families Lvl 1. 5. 2004. cd-rom 39.95 (978-1-59455-142-0(1)) Renaissance Learning, Inc.

FLuent Reader Audio 10-Pk Phonics Long Vowels Lvl 2. 5. 2004. cd-rom 39.95 (978-1-59455-145-1(6)) Renaissance Learning, Inc.

Fluent Reader Audio 10-Pk Phonics Short Vowel Word Families Lvl 1. 0. 2004. cd-rom 39.95 (978-1-59455-141-3(3)) Renaissance Learning, Inc.

Fluent Reader Audio 10-Pk Phonics Short Vowels Lvl 2. 5. 2004. cd-rom 39.95 (978-1-59455-144-4(8)) Renaissance Learning, Inc.

Fonetica/Conciencia Fonemica: Phonics. 2001. (McGraw-Hill. Lectura Ser.). (ENG & SPA.). (gr. k up). (978-0-02-186536-9(1)); (gr. 1 up). (978-0-02-186051-7(3)) Macmillan/McGraw-Hill Schl. Div.

Fonetica/Conciencia Fonemica: Phonics/Vocabulary. 2001. (McGraw-Hill. Lectura Ser.). (ENG & SPA.). (gr. 2 up). (978-0-02-186085-2(8)); (gr. 3 up). (978-0-02-186117-0(X)); (gr. 4 up). (978-0-02-186540-6(X)) Macmillan/McGraw-Hill Schl. Div.

Fonetica/Conciencia fonemica (Phonics & Phonemic Awareness Practice Book: Phonics/Vocabulary. 2001. (McGraw-Hill. Lectura Ser.). (ENG & SPA.). (gr. 5 up). (978-0-02-186541-3(8)); (gr. 6 up). (978-0-02-186542-0(6)) Macmillan/McGraw-Hill Schl. Div.

Fonolibros Series: Complete Stage One. 2003. (SPA.). 1230.95 (978-0-7652-1052-4(5)) Modern Curriculum Pr.

Fonolibros Series: Complete Stage Two. 2003. (SPA.). 895.50 (978-0-7652-1053-1(3)) Modern Curriculum Pr.

Fowler, Allan. Sound-a-Likes: Homonyms & Phonics, 4 bks., Set. Cafferata, Sue, illus. (J). (gr. k-4). lib. bdg. 73.80 (978-1-56674-901-5(8)) Forest Hse. Publishing Co., Inc.

The Fox: Consonants q, x, z; -ack, -ick, -ill word families: Level A, 6 vols. (Wright Skills Ser.). 12p. (gr. k-3). 17.95 (978-0-322-01456-5(5)) Wright Group, The.

Funny Faces & Funny Places. (Little Book Practice Reader Ser.). (J). (978-0-8136-0687-3(X)) Modern Curriculum Pr.

Gale, John E. Speedyread: A Phonics-Based Reading & Spelling Program. 2005. 353p. ring bd. 275.00 (978-0-9777683-0-1(9)) Mirror Pond Publishing.

Gallagher, Carole M. Little ABC Phonics Workbook. 2006. 283p. (J). 14.50 (***978-0-9702197-1-8(7)***) Gallagher, Carole M.

El Gato Que Rompio las Reglas: Little Books, Level 18, Vol. 7. 2003. (Fonolibros Ser.). 35.50 (978-0-7652-0117-1(8)) Modern Curriculum Pr.

Gaydos, Nora. Phonics Comics: Pony Tales - Level 1. Hamilton, Pamela, illus. 2007. 24p. (J). (gr. 1-17). pap. 3.99 (978-1-58476-553-0(4)) Innovative Kids.

Gerber, Carole. Reading & Phonics: Grade 1. 2003. (Brighter Child Workbooks Ser.). (Illus.). 24p. (J). (gr. 1). pap. 2.25 (978-1-56189-061-3(8) , 31011, American Education Publishing) School Specialty Publishing.

Gerber, Carole, ed. English & Phonics: Grade K. 2003. (Brighter Child Workbooks Ser.). (Illus.). 24p. (J). pap. 2.25 (978-1-56189-080-4(4) , 51010, American Education Publishing) School Specialty Publishing.

Getting Ready to Read with Mother Goose, Hand Puppet. 2001. (Getting Ready to Read with Mother Goose Ser.). (YA). (ps-k). 63.00 (978-0-8215-6953-5(8)) Sadlier, William H. Inc.

Gifford, Myrna. Talking & Walking: A Read-and-Sing Book. Cooper, Frances, illus. 2005. 12p. (J). 9.95 (978-0-9720763-9-5(5)) Action Factor, Inc.

—Two Little Letters: A Read-and-Sing Book. Cooper, Frances, illus. 2005. 12p. (J). 9.95 (978-0-9720763-8-8(7)) Action Factor, Inc.

—What's That Sound? A Read-and-Sing Book. Cooper, Frances, illus. 2003. 12p. (J). 9.95 (978-0-9720763-3-3(6)) Action Factor, Inc.

Gifford, Myrna Ross. Outlaws: A Read-and-Sing Book. Cooper, Frances, illus. 2005. 12p. (J). 9.95 (978-0-9754618-1-5(8)) Action Factor, Inc.

—Silent E: A Read-and-Sing Book. Cooper, Frances, illus. 2005. 12p. (J). 9.95 (978-0-9754618-0-8(X)) Action Factor, Inc.

Gillis, Jennifer B., et al. Reader's Clubhouse Level 2 Long-Vowel Review Valu-Pak. 2006. (Illus.). 96p. (J). pap. 11.97 (978-0-7641-7970-9(5)) Barron's Educational Series, Inc.

Golden Books Staff. Phonics. 2001. (Step Ahead Ser.). 54p. (J). (ps-3). 2.99 (978-0-307-24956-2(5) , Golden Bks.) Random Hse. Children's Bks.

Goldish, Meish. Little Book: Zack Can Fix It! Scraton, Clive, illus. 2000. (Sadlier Phonics Reading Program). 8p. (J). (978-0-8215-7319-8(5) , Sadlier-Oxford) Sadlier, William H. Inc.

Goldish, Mersh. Little Book: How Many AreHere? Meyerhoff, Jill, illus. 2000. (Sadlier Phonics Reading Program). 8p. (J). (978-0-8215-7304-4(7) , Sadlier-Oxford) Sadlier, William H. Inc.

Green Collection. (Elefonetica Ser.). (SPA.). (gr. 1-2). 324.85 (978-0-7362-0784-3(8)) Hampton-Brown Bks.

Grierson, Arlene. Jolly Jingles. Stephen, Lib, illus. 2001. (Jolly Phonics Ser.). 40p. (J). 36.00 (978-1-870946-22-3(7) , JL227) Jolly Learning, Ltd. GBR. *Dist:* American International Distribution Corp.

Grizzly & the Bumble-bee: Big Book: Level K. Group 1. (Sunshinetm Ser.). 16p. 36.50 (978-0-7802-5789-4(8)) Wright Group, The.

Group/McGraw-Hill, Wright. Phonics & Word Study Complete Kits: Phonics & Word Study: Level A. (gr. k-3). 339.95 (978-0-322-03871-4(5)) Wright Group, The.

—Phonics & Word Study Complete Kits: Phonics & Word Study: Level B. (gr. k-3). 429.50 (978-0-322-03872-1(3)) Wright Group, The.

—Sunshine: Early Emergent - Group 3: 1 Each of 4 Student Books: Level A. 16.95 (978-0-322-03707-6(7)) Wright Group, The.

—Sunshine: Early Emergent - Group 3: 1 Each of 4 Student Books: Level C. 16.95 (978-0-322-03709-0(3)) Wright Group, The.

—Sunshine: Early Emergent - Group 3:1 Each of 4 Student Books: Level B. 16.95 (978-0-322-03708-3(5)) Wright Group, The.

—Sunshine: Upper Emergent - Upper Emergent - Complete Kit, Vol. 2. (gr. 1 up). 486.50 (978-0-322-04211-7(9)) Wright Group, The.

—Upper Emergent Guided Reading Kit 1: Student Books. (gr. 1 up). 79.95 (978-0-322-04215-5(1)) Wright Group, The.

—Upper Emergent Guided Reading Kit 2 Vol. 2: Student Books, (gr. 1 up). 79.95 (978-0-322-04216-2(X)) Wright Group, The.

—The Wright Skills: Level A Sets - 1 Each of 40 Titles (includes Short Vowels) (gr. k-3). (978-0-322-03873-8(1)) Wright Group, The.

—The Wright Skills: Level A Sets - 6 Each of 40 Titles (includes Short Vowels) (gr. k-3). 730.50 (978-0-322-03874-5(X)) Wright Group, The.

—The Wright Skills: Level A Sets - Short Vowels only: 1 Each of 19 Titles. (gr. k-3). 56.95 (978-0-322-06473-7(2)) Wright Group, The.

—The Wright Skills: Level A Sets - Short Vowels only: 6 Each of 19 Titles. (gr. k-3). 122.95 (978-0-322-06474-4(0)) Wright Group, The.

—The Wright Skills: Level B Sets - 1 Each of 40 Titles (includes long Vowels) (gr. k-3). 143.95 (978-0-322-03878-3(2)) Wright Group, The.

—The Wright Skills: Level B Sets - 6 Each of 40 Titles (includes long Vowels) (gr. k-3). 860.50 (978-0-322-03880-6(4)) Wright Group, The.

Growing Things - PowerPhonics Skill Set I, 6 bks. Incl. Cats & Kittens : Learning the Hard C & K Sounds. Barnes, J. Lou. lib. bdg. 18.50 (978-0-8239-5903-7(1)); Every Egg : Learning the Short E Sound. Metz, Lynn. lib. bdg. 18.50 (978-0-8239-5909-9(0)); I Go to the Garden : Learning the Hard G Sound. Sarkisian, Kevin. lib. bdg. 18.50 (978-0-8239-5907-5(4)); Lots of Leaves : Learning the L Sound. Roza, Greg. lib. bdg. 18.50 (978-0-8239-5899-3(X)); Red Rose : Learning the R Sound. Battistoni, Ilse. lib. bdg. 18.50 (978-0-8239-5912-9(0)); So Many Seeds : Learning the S Sound. O'Donnell, Kerri. lib. bdg. 18.50 (978-0-8239-5908-2(2)); 24p. (J). (gr. 1). 2002. (Illus.). 2001. Set lib. bdg. 108.50 (978-0-8239-7203-6(8) , PowerKids Pr.) Rosen Publishing Group, Inc., The.

Grundon, Holly & Novelli, Joan. Smart Pads! Phonics: 40 Fun Games to Help Kids Master Phonics Skills. 2005. 48p. pap. 7.99 (978-0-439-72082-3(6) , Teaching Resources) Scholastic, Inc.

Guardians of the Garden: Level 3, 6 vols. (Fluency Strand Ser.). (gr. 4-8). 45.00 (978-1-4045-1218-4(7)) Wright Group, The.

Guffanti, Stephen & Guffanti, Maureen. Rocket Phonics: The Fast, Fun, Easy Way to Teach Reading! 2005. (J). pap. 98.99 (978-0-89455-871-9(4)) Critical Thinking Bks. & Software.

Hall, Nancy. Beyond the Code 1. 2000. pap. 7.00 (978-0-8388-2401-6(3)) Educators Publishing Service, Inc.

—Beyond the Code 3. 2001. pap. 7.00 (978-0-8388-2403-0(X)) Educators Publishing Service, Inc.

Hands on Consonant Sounds (Gr. K-1) 2003. (J). (978-1-58232-115-8(9)) Bryan Hse. Pubs., Inc.

Hands on Sight Words (Gr. 1-2) 2003. (J). (978-1-58232-118-9(3)) Bryan Hse. Pubs., Inc.

Hands on Vowel Sounds (Gr. 1-2) 2003. (J). (978-1-58232-116-5(7)) Bryan Hse. Pubs., Inc.

Hap & the Hat: Consonant h: Level A, 6 vols. (Wright Skills Ser.). 12p. (gr. k-3). 17.95 (978-0-322-03110-4(9)) Wright Group, The.

Harcourt School Publishers Staff. Aldo's Ice Cream: Library Edition. 1999. (Collections Ser.). (Illus.). (J). 6.90 (978-0-15-314351-9(7)) Harcourt Schl. Pubs.

—Ann Gets a Map: Below Level. 3rd ed. 2002. (Trophies Reading Program Ser.). (Illus.). (J). pap. 4.10 (978-0-15-322958-9(6)) Harcourt Schl. Pubs.

—At the Farm: Phonics Practice Reader. 1999. (Collections Ser.). (Illus.). (J). pap. 2.60 (978-0-15-312926-1(3)) Harcourt Schl. Pubs.

—Bo Peep's Sheep: Phonics Practice Reader. 1999. (Collections Ser.). (Illus.). (J). pap. 2.60 (978-0-15-312922-3(0)) Harcourt Schl. Pubs.

—Una Buena Accion: Take-Home Book. 1999. (Vamos Ser.). (SPA., Illus.). (J). pap. 2.50 (978-0-15-318826-8(X)) Harcourt Schl. Pubs.

—Burrito y Perrito: Phonics Practice Reader. 1999. (Vamos Ser.). (SPA., Illus.). pap. 5.00 (978-0-15-318988-3(6)) Harcourt Schl. Pubs.

—Caballito de Totora: Take-Home Book. 1999. (Vamos Ser.). (SPA., Illus.). (J). pap. 2.50 (978-0-15-318838-1(3)) Harcourt Schl. Pubs.

—The Camping Trip: Phonics Practice Reader. 1999. (Collections Ser.). (Illus.). (J). pap. 2.60 (978-0-15-312936-0(0)) Harcourt Schl. Pubs.

—Can You Spot Me: Phonics Practice Reader. 1999. (Collections Ser.). (Illus.). (J). pap. 2.60 (978-0-15-312920-9(4)) Harcourt Schl. Pubs.

—A Cheer for Mr. Leary: Phonics Practice Reader. 1999. (Collections Ser.). (Illus.). (J). pap. 2.60 (978-0-15-312933-9(6)) Harcourt Schl. Pubs.

—Circus Time: Phonics Practice Reader. 1999. (Collections Ser.). (Illus.). (J). (gr. 2). pap. 2.60 (978-0-15-312944-5(1)) Harcourt Schl. Pubs.

—Coco Con Cuchara: Phonics Practice Reader. 1999. (Vamos Ser.). (SPA., Illus.). pap. 5.00 (978-0-15-318987-6(8)) Harcourt Schl. Pubs.

—Los Cocos de Cuco: Phonics Practice Reader. 1999. (Vamos Ser.). (SPA., Illus.). pap. 5.00 (978-0-15-318950-0(9)) Harcourt Schl. Pubs.

—Collections: Phonics Activity Book. 2003. (First-Place Reading Ser.). (Illus.). (gr. k-6). 6.90 (978-0-15-313423-4(2)) Harcourt Schl. Pubs.

—Collections: Phonics Practice. 1999. (Trophies Ser.). (Illus.). (gr. 1 up). pap. 12.70 (978-0-15-313559-0(X)) Harcourt Schl. Pubs.

—Collections: Phonics Practice Book. 1999. (Trophies Ser.). (Illus.). (gr. 2 up). pap. 12.80 (978-0-15-315212-2(5)) Harcourt Schl. Pubs.

—Collections: Phonics Practice Reader. 1999. (Illus.). Level 1. (gr. 1). pap. 7.00 (978-0-15-314887-3(X)); Level 2. (gr. 1). pap. 7.00 (978-0-15-314888-0(8)); Level 3. (J). pap. 4.40 (978-0-15-314889-7(6)); Level 4. (gr. 1). pap. 7.00 (978-0-15-314890-3(X)); Level 5. (J). pap. 4.20 (978-0-15-314891-0(8)) Harcourt Schl. Pubs.

—Collections: Phonics Practice Readers Collection, 30 vols. 1999. (Harcourt Title I Reading Programs Ser.). (Illus.). (gr. 2 up). pap. 87.20 (978-0-15-313564-4(6)) Harcourt Schl. Pubs.

—Collections: Practice Book. (Illus.). Vol. 1. 1999. (gr. 1). pap. 9.40 (978-0-15-312706-9(6)); Vol. 1. 1999. (J). (gr. 2). pap. 6.50 (978-0-15-312709-0(0)); Vol. 1. 1999. (J). (gr. 3). pap. 6.50 (978-0-15-312712-0(0)); Vol. 1. 2001. (gr. 1). pap. 9.40 (978-0-15-317808-5(6)); Vol. 2. 1999. (J). pap. 6.50 (978-0-15-312711-3(2)); Vol. 2. 1999. (J). pap. 6.50 (978-0-15-312713-7(9)); Vol. 2. 1999. pap. 9.40 (978-0-15-312708-3(2)) Harcourt Schl. Pubs.

—Collections Level 1: Phonics Reader, Level 1. rev. ed. 2000. (Illus.). (gr. 1). pap. 30.70 (978-0-15-317799-6(3)) Harcourt Schl. Pubs.

—Collections Level 1: Together Again: Phonics Practice Reader. 2001. (Illus.). (gr. 1). pap. 6.00 (978-0-15-319816-8(8)) Harcourt Schl. Pubs.

—Collections Level 2: Join In: Phonics Practice Reader. 2001. (Illus.). pap. 6.00 (978-0-15-319817-5(6)) Harcourt Schl. Pubs.

—Collections Level 3: Special Times: Phonics Practice Reader. 2001. (Illus.). pap. 5.60 (978-0-15-319818-2(4)) Harcourt Schl. Pubs.

—Collections, Grade 1 Level B: Phonics Express: Teacher's Guide. 1999. (Trophies Ser.). (gr. 1 up). pap., tchr. ed. 10.70 (978-0-15-314922-1(1)) Harcourt Schl. Pubs.

—Collections, Grade 2 Level C: Phonics Express: Teacher's Guide. 1999. (Trophies Ser.). (gr. 2 up). pap., tchr. ed. 10.70 (978-0-15-314923-8(X)) Harcourt Schl. Pubs.

—Collections, Grade 3 Level D: Phonics Express: Teacher's Guide. 1999. (Trophies Ser.). (gr. 3 up). pap., tchr. ed. 10.70 (978-0-15-314924-5(8)) Harcourt Schl. Pubs.

—Collections, Grade K Level A: Phonics Express. 1999. (Trophies Ser.). (gr. k up). pap., tchr. ed. 10.70 (978-0-15-314921-4(3)) Harcourt Schl. Pubs.

—El Compleanos y Meno: Phonics Practice Reader. 1999. (Vamos Ser.). (SPA., Illus.). pap. 5.00 (978-0-15-318958-6(4)) Harcourt Schl. Pubs.

—Con la B el Con la V: Phonics Practice Reader. 1999. (Vamos Ser.). (SPA., Illus.). pap. 5.00 (978-0-15-318956-2(8)) Harcourt Schl. Pubs.

—Conchita: Phonics Practice Reader. 1999. (Vamos Ser.). (SPA., Illus.). pap. 5.00 (978-0-15-319000-1(0)) Harcourt Schl. Pubs.

—Cuantas Veces... Advanced Level. 3rd ed. 2002. (Trofeos Ser.). (SPA., Illus.). pap. 6.80 (978-0-15-324013-3(X)) Harcourt Schl. Pubs.

—A Day in a Marsh: Phonics Practice Reader. 1999. (Collections Ser.). (Illus.). (J). pap. 2.60 (978-0-15-312927-8(1)) Harcourt Schl. Pubs.

—Decodable Book. 3rd ed. (Trophies Ser.). Bk. 1. 2002. (gr. 2). pap. 7.00 (978-0-15-326748-2(8)); Bk. 2. 2002. pap. 7.00 (978-0-15-326749-9(6)); Bk. 3. 2002. pap. 7.00 (978-0-15-326750-5(X)); Bk. 4. 2002. pap. 7.00 (978-0-15-326751-2(8)); Bk. 5. 2002. pap. 4.00 (978-0-15-326752-9(6)); Bk. 6. 2002. pap. 4.00 (978-0-15-326753-6(4)); Bk. 7. 2002. pap. 9.30 (978-0-15-326754-3(2)); Bk. 9. 2002. pap. 9.30 (978-0-15-326756-7(9)); Bk. 10. 2002. pap. 4.00 (978-0-15-326757-4(7)); Bk. 10. 2002. (J). (gr. 1). pap. 3.30 (978-0-15-326690-4(2)); Bk. 11. 2002. (J). pap. 6.20 (978-0-15-326691-1(0)); Bk. 11. 2002. pap. 9.30 (978-0-15-326758-1(5)); Bk. 12. 2002. (J). pap. 3.30 (978-0-15-326692-8(9)); Bk. 12. 2002. pap. 7.00 (978-0-15-326759-8(3)); Bk. 13. 2002. (J). pap. 6.20 (978-0-15-326693-5(7)); Bk. 14. 2002. (J). pap. 3.30 (978-0-15-326694-2(5)); Bk. 14. 2002. pap. 7.00 (978-0-15-326761-1(5)); Bk. 15. 2002. (J). pap. 6.20 (978-0-15-326695-9(3)); Bk. 15. 2002. pap. 7.00 (978-0-15-326762-8(3)); Bk. 16. 2002. pap. 8.30 (978-0-15-326696-6(1)); Bk. 16. 2002. pap. 7.00 (978-0-15-326763-5(1)); Bk. 17. 2003. pap. 7.00 (978-0-15-326764-2(X)); Bk. 17. 2002. (J). pap. 3.30 (978-0-15-326697-3(X)); Bk. 18. 2002. (J). pap. 6.20 (978-0-15-326698-0(8)); Bk. 18. 2002. pap. 7.00 (978-0-15-326765-9(8)); Bk. 19. 2002. pap. 8.30 (978-0-15-326699-7(6)); Bk. 19. 2002. pap. 7.00 (978-0-15-326766-6(6)); Bk. 20. 2002. pap. 7.00 (978-0-15-326767-3(4)); Bk. 20. 2002. (J). (gr. 1). pap. 3.30 (978-0-15-326700-0(3)); Bk. 21. 2002. (J). pap. 3.30 (978-0-15-326701-7(1)); Bk. 22. 2002. (J). pap. 3.30 (978-0-15-326702-4(X)); Bk. 24. 2002. (J). pap. 6.20 (978-0-15-326704-8(6)); Bk. 25. 2002. (J). pap. 6.20 (978-0-15-326705-5(4)); Bk. 27. 2002. (J). pap. 3.30 (978-0-15-326706-2(2)); Bk. 28. 2002. (J). pap. 6.20 (978-0-15-326707-9(0)); Bk. 29. 2002. (J). pap. 3.30 (978-0-15-326708-6(9)); Bk. 30. 2002. (J). pap. 3.30 (978-0-15-326709-3(7)); Bk. 31. 2002. (J). pap. 6.20 (978-0-15-326710-9(0)); Bk. 32. 2002. (J). pap. 3.30 (978-0-15-326711-6(9)); Bk. 33. 2002. (J). pap. 3.30 (978-0-15-326712-3(7)); Bk. 34. 2002. (J). pap. 3.30 (978-0-15-326713-0(5)) Harcourt Schl. Pubs.

—Una Fabula Moderna: Take-Home Book. 2001. (Vamos Ser.). (SPA., Illus.). (J). pap. 2.80 (978-0-15-319931-8(8)) Harcourt Schl. Pubs.

—Feria las San Felipe: Phonics Practice Reader. 1999. (SPA., Illus.). pap. 5.00 (978-0-15-319001-8(9)) Harcourt Schl. Pubs.

—Fernando En la Fotografo: Phonics Practice Reader. 1999. (Vamos Ser.). (SPA., Illus.). pap. 5.00 (978-0-15-318963-0(0)) Harcourt Schl. Pubs.

—First Place Reading: Phonics Practice Reader. 2nd ed. 2003. (First-Place Reading Ser.). (gr. 1 up). Bk. 1. 4.10 (978-0-15-334590-6(X)); Bk. 2. (Illus.). 4.10 (978-0-15-334591-3(8)); Bk. 3. (Illus.). 4.10 (978-0-15-334592-0(6)); Bk. 4. (Illus.). 4.10 (978-0-15-334593-7(4)); Bk. 5. (Illus.). 4.10 (978-0-15-334594-4(2)); Bk. 6. (Illus.). 4.10 (978-0-15-334595-1(0)) Harcourt Schl. Pubs.

—First Place Reading: Phonics Practice Reader Collection. 2nd ed. 2002. (First-Place Reading Ser.). (Illus.). (gr. 1 up). pap. 27.10 (978-0-15-334589-0(6)) Harcourt Schl. Pubs.

—Fun with Clay: Phonics Practice Reader. 1999. (Collections Ser.). (Illus.). (J). pap. 2.60 (978-0-15-312928-5(X)) Harcourt Schl. Pubs.

—La Gatita Rosita: Phonics Practice Reader. 1999. (SPA., Illus.). pap. 5.00 (978-0-15-318989-0(4)) Harcourt Schl. Pubs.

—Gergorio y el Ogro: Phonics Practice Reader. 1999. (Vamos Ser.). (SPA., Illus.). pap. 5.00 (978-0-15-319002-5(7)) Harcourt Schl. Pubs.

—The Goat's Goal: Phonics Practice Reader. 1999. (Collections Ser.). (Illus.). (J). pap. 2.60 (978-0-15-312924-7(7)) Harcourt Schl. Pubs.

—Golosito el Gatito: Phonics Practice Reader. 1999. (Vamos Ser.). (SPA., Illus.). pap. 5.00 (978-0-15-318952-4(5)) Harcourt Schl. Pubs.

—Una Gota de Agua: Take-Home Book. 1999. (Vamos Ser.). (SPA., Illus.). (J). pap. 2.50 (978-0-15-318812-1(X)) Harcourt Schl. Pubs.

—Grandpa Lou: Phonics Practice Reader. 1999. (Collections Ser.). (Illus.). (J). pap. 2.60 (978-0-15-312943-8(3)) Harcourt Schl. Pubs.

—Guillermina: Phonics Practice Reader. 1999. (Vamos Ser.). (SPA., Illus.). pap. 5.00 (978-0-15-318991-3(6)) Harcourt Schl. Pubs.

—Hadaluna y Hadasol: Phonics Practice Reader. 1999. (Vamos Ser.). (SPA., Illus.). pap. 5.00 (978-0-15-318998-2(3)) Harcourt Schl. Pubs.

—The Horse's Long Day: Phonics Practice Reader. 1999. (Collections Ser.). (Illus.). (J). (gr. 2). pap. 2.60 (978-0-15-312932-2(8)) Harcourt Schl. Pubs.

—The House Downtown: Phonics Practice Reader. 1999. (Collections Ser.). (Illus.). (J). pap. 2.60 (978-0-15-312931-5(X)) Harcourt Schl. Pubs.

—How Much Wood: Phonics Practice Reader. 1999. (Collections Ser.). (Illus.). (J). pap. 2.60 (978-0-15-312946-9(8)) Harcourt Schl. Pubs.

—Joe's Jokes: Phonics Practice Reader. 1999. (Collections Ser.). (Illus.). (J). pap. 2.60 (978-0-15-312925-4(5)) Harcourt Schl. Pubs.

—La Jugar! Phonics Practice Reader. 1999. (Vamos Ser.). (SPA., Illus.). pap. 5.00 (978-0-15-318960-9(6)) Harcourt Schl. Pubs.

—The Jump-Rope Song: Phonics Practice Reader. 1999. (Collections Ser.). (Illus.). (J). pap. 2.60 (978-0-15-312921-6(2)) Harcourt Schl. Pubs.

—Lalo y Lupe: Phonics Practice Reader. 1999. (Vamos Ser.). (SPA., Illus.). (gr. 2). pap. 5.00 (978-0-15-318961-6(4)) Harcourt Schl. Pubs.

—Un Libro Asombroso: Phonics Practice Reader. 1999. (Vamos Ser.). (SPA., Illus.). pap. 5.00 (978-0-15-319004-9(3)) Harcourt Schl. Pubs.

—La Lluvia: Phonics Practice Reader. 1999. (Vamos Ser.). (SPA., Illus.). pap. 5.00 (978-0-15-318990-6(8)) Harcourt Schl. Pubs.

—Madge the Mule: Phonics Practice Reader. 1999. (Collections Ser.). (Illus.). (J). pap. 2.60 (978-0-15-312942-1(5)) Harcourt Schl. Pubs.

—Meet the Beans: Phonics Practice Reader. 1999. (Collections Ser.). (Illus.). (J). pap. 2.60 (978-0-15-312923-0(9)) Harcourt Schl. Pubs.

—Mi Abuela y Yo: Phonics Practice Reader. 1999. (Vamos Ser.). (SPA., Illus.). (gr. 3). pap. 5.00 (978-0-15-319003-2(5)) Harcourt Schl. Pubs.

—Mupi y Mama: Phonics Practice Reader. 1999. (Vamos Ser.). (SPA., Illus.). pap. 5.00 (978-0-15-318948-7(7)) Harcourt Schl. Pubs.

—My Pal Paul: Phonics Practice Reader. 1999. (Collections Ser.). (Illus.). (J). pap. 2.60 (978-0-15-312948-3(4)) Harcourt Schl. Pubs.

—Una Nina Valiente: Take-Home Book. 1999. (Vamos Ser.). (SPA., Illus.). (J). pap. 2.50 (978-0-15-318816-9(2)) Harcourt Schl. Pubs.

—Nina y Natan: Phonics Practice Reader. 1999. (Vamos Ser.). (SPA., Illus.). pap. 5.00 (978-0-15-318957-9(6)) Harcourt Schl. Pubs.

—Un Nuevo Hogar: Take-Home Book. 2001. (Vamos Ser.). (SPA., Illus.). (J). pap. 2.80 (978-0-15-319960-8(1)) Harcourt Schl. Pubs.

—Oo-Pples/Boo-Noo-Noo Song Book. 2nd ed. 2002. (Trophies Ser.). (J). pap. 17.60 (978-0-15-325787-2(3)) Harcourt Schl. Pubs.

—Palomas y Abuelo: Phonics Practice Reader. 1999. (Vamos Ser.). (SPA., Illus.). pap. 5.00 (978-0-15-318999-9(1)) Harcourt Schl. Pubs.

—Papagallo y Pollina: Phonics Practice Reader. 1999. (Vamos Ser.). (SPA., Illus.). pap. 5.00 (978-0-15-318953-1(3)) Harcourt Schl. Pubs.

—Para Ti: Phonics Practice Reader. 1999. (Vamos Ser.). (SPA., Illus.). (gr. 2). pap. 5.00 (978-0-15-318946-3(0)) Harcourt Schl. Pubs.

—Los Patos: Phonics Practice Reader. 1999. (Vamos Ser.). (SPA., Illus.). pap. 5.00 (978-0-15-318947-0(9)) Harcourt Schl. Pubs.

—A Pet to the Vet: Below Level. 3rd ed. 2002. (Trophies Reading Program Ser.). (Illus.). (J). pap. 4.10 (978-0-15-322962-6(4)) Harcourt Schl. Pubs.

—Phil's Photos: Phonics Practice Reader. 1999. (Collections Ser.). (Illus.). (J). pap. 2.60 (978-0-15-312937-7(9)) Harcourt Schl. Pubs.

—Phonemics Write-on/Wipe-off Board. 1999. (Trophies Ser.). (gr. k-6). pap. 7.50 (978-0-15-315006-7(8)) Harcourt Schl. Pubs.

—A Pig in the Wind: Phonics Practice Reader. 1999. (Collections Ser.). (Illus.). (J). (gr. 2). pap. 2.60 (978-0-15-312919-3(0)) Harcourt Schl. Pubs.

—Que Hacer Hoy: Phonics Practice Reader. 1999. (Vamos Ser.). (SPA., Illus.). pap. 5.00 (978-0-15-318964-7(9)) Harcourt Schl. Pubs.

—Las Quesadilla: Phonics Practice Reader. 1999. (Vamos Ser.). (SPA., Illus.). pap. 5.00 (978-0-15-318992-0(4)) Harcourt Schl. Pubs.

—Riddles & Grandma: Phonics Practice Reader. 1999. (Collections Ser.). (Illus.). (J). pap. 2.60 (978-0-15-312935-3(2)) Harcourt Schl. Pubs.

—Sapito y Sapita: Phonics Practice Reader. 1999. (Vamos Ser.). (SPA., Illus.). pap. 5.00 (978-0-15-318949-4(5)) Harcourt Schl. Pubs.

—Sara: Phonics Practice Reader. 1999. (Vamos Ser.). (SPA., Illus.). pap. 5.00 (978-0-15-318951-7(7)) Harcourt Schl. Pubs.

—Set Sail, Grades 1-5. 1999. tchr. ed. 158.50 (978-0-15-312081-7(9)) Harcourt Schl. Pubs.

—Somos los Amigos: Phonics Practice Reader. 1999. (Vamos Ser.). (SPA., Illus.). (gr. 3). pap. 5.00 (978-0-15-318986-9(X)) Harcourt Schl. Pubs.

—Suenos: Phonics Practice Reader. 1999. (Vamos Ser.). (SPA., Illus.). pap. 5.00 (978-0-15-318996-8(7)) Harcourt Schl. Pubs.

—A Tall Tale: Phonics Practice Reader. 1999. (Collections Ser.). (Illus.). (J). pap. 2.60 (978-0-15-312934-6(4)) Harcourt Schl. Pubs.

—Tia Chelita: Phonics Practice Reader. 1999. (Vamos Ser.). (SPA., Illus.). pap. 5.00 (978-0-15-318962-3(2)) Harcourt Schl. Pubs.

—Tim & Mike: Phonics Practice Reader. 1999. (Collections Ser.). (Illus.). (J). pap. 2.60 (978-0-15-312918-6(2)) Harcourt Schl. Pubs.

—Tipi Tipi Ton: Phonics Practice Reader. 1999. (Vamos Ser.). (SPA., Illus.). pap. 5.00 (978-0-15-318955-5(X)) Harcourt Schl. Pubs.

—Tita y Tito: Phonics Practice Reader. 1999. (Vamos Ser.). (SPA., Illus.). pap. 5.00 (978-0-15-318994-4(0)) Harcourt Schl. Pubs.

—A Trip & Trains: Phonics Practice Reader. 1999. (Collections Ser.). (Illus.). (J). pap. 2.60 (978-0-15-312929-2(8)) Harcourt Schl. Pubs.

—Trofeos: A Bordo de un Barco Independent Reader. 3rd ed. 2002. (SPA., Illus.). (J). pap. 3.50 (978-0-15-331357-8(9)) Harcourt Schl. Pubs.

—Trofeos: A la Mesa: Practice Book. 3rd ed. 2002. (SPA., Illus.). (J). pap. 2.20 (978-0-15-332070-5(2)) Harcourt Schl. Pubs.

—Trofeos: Aranas, Abejas y Mariposas Independent Reader. 3rd ed. 2002. (SPA., Illus.). (J). pap. 3.50 (978-0-15-331296-0(3)) Harcourt Schl. Pubs.

—Trofeos: Bajo el Mar Independent Reader. 3rd ed. 2002. (SPA., Illus.). (J). pap. 3.50 (978-0-15-331375-2(7)) Harcourt Schl. Pubs.

—Trofeos: Cachorittos y Lila Independent Reader. 3rd ed. 2002. (SPA., Illus.). (J). pap. 3.50 (978-0-15-331290-8(4)) Harcourt Schl. Pubs.

—Trofeos: Caminan y Caminan Independent Reader. 3rd ed. 2002. (SPA., Illus.). (J). pap. 3.50 (978-0-15-331272-4(6)) Harcourt Schl. Pubs.

—Trofeos: Cerdito Bobo y las Imagen Independent Reader. 3rd ed. 2002. (SPA., Illus.). (J). pap. 3.50 (978-0-15-331358-5(7)) Harcourt Schl. Pubs.

—Trofeos: Cerdos Divertidos Independent Reader. 3rd ed. 2002. (SPA., Illus.). (J). pap. 3.50 (978-0-15-331292-2(0)) Harcourt Schl. Pubs.

—Trofeos: Colina Arriba Independent Reader. 3rd ed. 2002. (SPA., Illus.). (J). pap. 3.50 (978-0-15-331356-1(0)) Harcourt Schl. Pubs.

—Trofeos: El Gatito Rapido Independent Reader. 3rd ed. 2002. (SPA., Illus.). (J). pap. 3.50 (978-0-15-331299-1(8)) Harcourt Schl. Pubs.

—Trofeos: El Gusano y las Mariposa Independent Reader. 3rd ed. 2002. (SPA., Illus.). (J). pap. 3.50 (978-0-15-331298-4(X)) Harcourt Schl. Pubs.

—Trofeos: El Mejor Velero Independent Reader. 3rd ed. 2002. (SPA., Illus.). (J). pap. 3.50 (978-0-15-331376-9(5)) Harcourt Schl. Pubs.

—Trofeos: El Perrito Perdido Independent Reader. 3rd ed. 2002. (SPA., Illus.). (J). pap. 3.50 (978-0-15-331323-3(4)) Harcourt Schl. Pubs.

—Trofeos: En el Mar Big Book. 3rd ed. 2002. (SPA., Illus.). pap. 81.90 (978-0-15-332464-2(3)) Harcourt Schl. Pubs.

—Trofeos: En la Orilla de la Mar Independent Reader. 3rd ed. 2002. (SPA., Illus.). (J). pap. 3.50 (978-0-15-331359-2(5)) Harcourt Schl. Pubs.

—Trofeos: Familias de Animales: Practice Book. 3rd ed. 2002. (SPA., Illus.). (J). pap. 2.20 (978-0-15-332073-6(7)) Harcourt Schl. Pubs.

—Trofeos: Insectos y Sopresas: Practice Book. 3rd ed. 2002. (SPA., Illus.). (J). pap. 2.20 (978-0-15-332074-3(5)) Harcourt Schl. Pubs.

—Trofeos: Jardineros Chicos Independent Reader. 3rd ed. 2002. (SPA., Illus.). (J). pap. 3.50 (978-0-15-331289-2(0)) Harcourt Schl. Pubs.

—Trofeos: La Mejor Casa Independent Reader. 3rd ed. 2002. (SPA., Illus.). (J). pap. 3.50 (978-0-15-331330-1(7)) Harcourt Schl. Pubs.

—Trofeos: La Nena Lula Independent Reader. 3rd ed. 2002. (SPA., Illus.). (J). pap. 3.50 (978-0-15-331262-5(9)) Harcourt Schl. Pubs.

—Trofeos: La Pelota Big Book. 3rd ed. 2002. (SPA., Illus.). pap. 81.90 (978-0-15-332459-8(7)) Harcourt Schl. Pubs.

—Trofeos: La Perra y Cachorrito Independent Reader. 3rd ed. 2002. (SPA., Illus.). (J). pap. 3.50 (978-0-15-331293-9(9)) Harcourt Schl. Pubs.

—Trofeos: La Sirena de las Bomberos Independent Reader. 3rd ed. 2002. (SPA., Illus.). (J). pap. 3.50 (978-0-15-331354-7(4)) Harcourt Schl. Pubs.

—Trofeos: La Tarta y Gallinita Independent Reader. 3rd ed. 2002. (SPA., Illus.). (J). pap. 3.50 (978-0-15-331321-9(8)) Harcourt Schl. Pubs.

—Trofeos: Lazos Familiares: Practice Book. 3rd ed. 2002. (SPA., Illus.). (J). pap. 2.20 (978-0-15-332072-9(9)) Harcourt Schl. Pubs.

—Trofeos: Leo, Bebo y Como Independent Reader. 3rd ed. 2002. (SPA., Illus.). (J). pap. 3.50 (978-0-15-331248-9(3)) Harcourt Schl. Pubs.

—Trofeos: Leo Senales. 3rd ed. 2002. (SPA., Illus.). pap. 81.90 (978-0-15-332467-3(8)) Harcourt Schl. Pubs.

—Trofeos: Los Animales Estan en Mi Cama! Independent Reader. 3rd ed. 2002. (SPA., Illus.). (J). pap. 3.50 (978-0-15-331267-0(X)) Harcourt Schl. Pubs.

—Trofeos: Los Primeros... 3rd ed. 2002. (SPA., Illus.). pap. 6.80 (978-0-15-324322-6(8)) Harcourt Schl. Pubs.

—Trofeos: Los Vecinos/Ayudan Independent Reader. 3rd ed. 2002. (SPA., Illus.). (J). pap. 3.50 (978-0-15-331331-8(5)) Harcourt Schl. Pubs.

—Trofeos: Marcos y Guille Son Amigos. 3rd ed. 2002. (Trofeos Ser.). (SPA., Illus.). (J). pap. 3.50 (978-0-15-331329-5(3)) Harcourt Schl. Pubs.

—Trofeos: Mi Pato Peto Independent Reader. 3rd ed. 2002. (SPA., Illus.). (J). pap. 3.50 (978-0-15-331264-9(5)) Harcourt Schl. Pubs.

—Trofeos: Que Divertido! Practice Book. 3rd ed. 2002. (SPA., Illus.). (J). pap. 2.20 (978-0-15-332071-2(0)) Harcourt Schl. Pubs.

—Trofeos: Que Hacen/Paps/Mams Independent Reader. 3rd ed. 2002. (SPA., Illus.). (J). pap. 3.50 (978-0-15-331355-4(2)) Harcourt Schl. Pubs.

—Trofeos: Sara y Yo Independent Reader. 3rd ed. 2002. (SPA., Illus.). (J). pap. 3.50 (978-0-15-331261-8(0)) Harcourt Schl. Pubs.

—Trofeos: Sopa para las Animales! Independent Reader. 3rd ed. 2002. (SPA., Illus.). (J). pap. 3.50 (978-0-15-331265-6(3)) Harcourt Schl. Pubs.

—Trofeos: Soy Especial: Practice Book. 3rd ed. 2002. (SPA., Illus.). (J). pap. 2.20 (978-0-15-332069-9(9)) Harcourt Schl. Pubs.

—Trofeos: Todas y Buenas Manos Big Book. 3rd ed. 2002. (SPA., Illus.). pap. 81.90 (978-0-15-332462-8(7)) Harcourt Schl. Pubs.

—Trofeos: Todos Pueden. 3rd ed. 2002. (SPA., Illus.). pap. 6.80 (978-0-15-324051-5(2)) Harcourt Schl. Pubs.

—Trofeos: Toni, el Papa Es el Papa Independent Reader. 3rd ed. 2002. (SPA., Illus.). (J). pap. 3.50 (978-0-15-331286-1(6)) Harcourt Schl. Pubs.

—Trofeos: Trabajemos para Cambiar el Mundo. 3rd ed. 2002. (SPA., Illus.). pap. 6.80 (978-0-15-324255-7(8)) Harcourt Schl. Pubs.

—Trofeos: Un Copa/Beso/Papa Independent Reader. 3rd ed. 2002. (SPA.). (J). pap. 3.50 (978-0-15-331268-7(8)) Harcourt Schl. Pubs.

—Trofeos: Un Gusanito Sin Casa Independent Reader. 3rd ed. 2002. (SPA., Illus.). (J). pap. 3.50 (978-0-15-331297-7(1)) Harcourt Schl. Pubs.

—Trofeos: Un Lobo en Mi Saco Independent Reader. 3rd ed. 2002. (SPA.). (J). pap. 3.50 (978-0-15-331274-8(2)) Harcourt Schl. Pubs.

—Trofeos: Un Pastel para Mi Independent Reader. 3rd ed. 2002. (SPA., Illus.). (J). pap. 3.50 (978-0-15-331287-8(4)) Harcourt Schl. Pubs.

—Trofeos: Un Ramito de Rosas Independent Reader. 3rd ed. 2002. (SPA., Illus.). (J). pap. 3.50 (978-0-15-331322-6(6)) Harcourt Schl. Pubs.

—Trofeos: Una Banana Independent Reader. 3rd ed. 2002. (SPA., Illus.). (J). pap. 3.50 (978-0-15-331271-7(8)) Harcourt Schl. Pubs.

—Trofeos: Una Osita Unica Independent Reader. 3rd ed. 2002. (SPA., Illus.). (J). pap. 3.50 (978-0-15-331273-1(4)) Harcourt Schl. Pubs.

—Trofeos: Una Semana y Pinquinos Big Book. 3rd ed. 2002. (SPA., Illus.). pap. 81.90 (978-0-15-332463-5(5)) Harcourt Schl. Pubs.

—Trofeos: Vamos/Concernos: Practice Book. 3rd ed. 2002. (SPA.). (J). pap. 2.20 (978-0-15-332068-2(0)) Harcourt Schl. Pubs.

—Trofeos Advanced Level: Actor Estrellas. 3rd ed. 2002. (SPA., Illus.). pap. 6.80 (978-0-15-324375-2(9)) Harcourt Schl. Pubs.

—Trofeos Advanced Level: Al Fin un Hogar. 3rd ed. 2002. (SPA., Illus.). pap. 6.80 (978-0-15-324395-0(3)) Harcourt Schl. Pubs.

—Trofeos Advanced level: Atrapado en el Futuro. 3rd ed. 2002. (SPA.). pap. 6.80 (978-0-15-324306-6(6)) Harcourt Schl. Pubs.

—Trofeos Advanced Level: Avalanche! 3rd ed. 2002. (SPA., Illus.). pap. 6.80 (978-0-15-324378-3(3)) Harcourt Schl. Pubs.

—Trofeos Advanced Level: Aventura en Egipto. 3rd ed. 2002. (SPA., Illus.). pap. 6.80 (978-0-15-324384-4(8)) Harcourt Schl. Pubs.

—Trofeos Advanced Level: Bailar Sea Como Sea. 3rd ed. 2002. (SPA., Illus.). pap. 6.80 (978-0-15-324301-1(5)) Harcourt Schl. Pubs.

—Trofeos Advanced Level: Cerdito en la Feria. 3rd ed. 2002. (SPA., Illus.). pap. 6.80 (978-0-15-323949-6(2)) Harcourt Schl. Pubs.

—Trofeos Advanced Level: Chuc Mung Nam Moi! Felize Ano Nuevo! 3rd ed. 2002. (SPA., Illus.). pap. 6.80 (978-0-15-324393-6(7)) Harcourt Schl. Pubs.

—Trofeos Advanced Level: Como Adoptar... 3rd ed. 2002. (SPA., Illus.). pap. 6.80 (978-0-15-324200-7(0)) Harcourt Schl. Pubs.

—Trofeos Advanced Level: Como en Casa. 3rd ed. 2002. (SPA., Illus.). pap. 6.80 (978-0-15-324398-1(8)) Harcourt Schl. Pubs.

—Trofeos Advanced Level: Como Se Hace... 3rd ed. 2002. (SPA., Illus.). pap. 6.80 (978-0-15-324211-3(6)) Harcourt Schl. Pubs.

—Trofeos Advanced Level: Cuanta Maxima. 3rd ed. 2002. (SPA., Illus.). pap. 6.80 (978-0-15-324392-9(9)) Harcourt Schl. Pubs.

—Trofeos Advanced Level: Cuanto Vale? 3rd ed. 2002. (SPA., Illus.). pap. 6.80 (978-0-15-324374-5(0)) Harcourt Schl. Pubs.

—Trofeos Advanced Level: Cuatro Joyas. 3rd ed. 2002. (SPA., Illus.). pap. 6.80 (978-0-15-324383-7(X)) Harcourt Schl. Pubs.

—Trofeos Advanced Level: Descubrimiento. 3rd ed. 2002. (SPA., Illus.). pap. 6.80 (978-0-15-324291-5(4)) Harcourt Schl. Pubs.

—Trofeos Advanced Level: Donde Aprendamos. 3rd ed. 2002. (SPA., Illus.). pap. 6.80 (978-0-15-324394-3(5)) Harcourt Schl. Pubs.

—Trofeos Advanced Level: El Arte de Ser un Gato. 3rd ed. 2002. (SPA., Illus.). pap. 6.80 (978-0-15-324202-1(7)) Harcourt Schl. Pubs.

—Trofeos Advanced Level: El Club de Arte. 3rd ed. 2002. (SPA., Illus.). pap. 6.80 (978-0-15-324391-2(0)) Harcourt Schl. Pubs.

—Trofeos Advanced Level: El Concierto de Lana. 3rd ed. 2002. (SPA., Illus.). pap. 6.80 (978-0-15-324284-7(1)) Harcourt Schl. Pubs.

—Trofeos Advanced Level: El Cumpleanos de Meno. 3rd ed. 2002. (SPA., Illus.). pap. 6.80 (978-0-15-324297-7(3)) Harcourt Schl. Pubs.

—Trofeos Advanced Level: El Diario... 3rd ed. 2002. (SPA., Illus.). pap. 6.80 (978-0-15-324193-2(4)) Harcourt Schl. Pubs.

P Q R

—Trofeos Advanced Level: El Encuentro. 3rd ed. 2002. (SPA., Illus.). pap. 6.80 (978-0-15-324296-0(5)) Harcourt Schl. Pubs.

—Trofeos Advanced Level: El Informe de Len Sobre la Democracia. 3rd ed. 2002. (SPA., Illus.). pap. 6.80 (978-0-15-324376-9(7)) Harcourt Schl. Pubs.

—Trofeos Advanced Level: El Nacimiento del Drama. 3rd ed. 2002. (SPA., Illus.). pap. 6.80 (978-0-15-324385-1(6)) Harcourt Schl. Pubs.

—Trofeos Advanced Level: El Ojo de la Menta? Lo Que Sabemos del Brillante Planeta Azul. 3rd ed. 2002. (SPA., Illus.). pap. 6.80 (978-0-15-324401-8(1)) Harcourt Schl. Pubs.

—Trofeos Advanced Level: El Vaquero, el Cowboy. 3rd ed. 2002. (SPA., Illus.). pap. 6.80 (978-0-15-324286-1(8)) Harcourt Schl. Pubs.

—Trofeos Advanced Level: En el Espacio. 3rd ed. 2002. (SPA., Illus.). pap. 6.80 (978-0-15-324399-8(6)) Harcourt Schl. Pubs.

—Trofeos Advanced Level: En el Lago. 3rd ed. 2002. (SPA., Illus.). pap. 6.80 (978-0-15-323951-9(4)) Harcourt Schl. Pubs.

—Trofeos Advanced Level: Eso Me Recuerda una Historia. 3rd ed. 2002. (SPA., Illus.). pap. 6.80 (978-0-15-324303-5(1)) Harcourt Schl. Pubs.

—Trofeos Advanced Level: Estadounidenses Ingeniosos. 3rd ed. 2002. (SPA., Illus.). pap. 6.80 (978-0-15-324309-7(0)) Harcourt Schl. Pubs.

—Trofeos Advanced Level: Figuras de Papel. 3rd ed. 2002. (SPA., Illus.). pap. 6.80 (978-0-15-324206-9(X)) Harcourt Schl. Pubs.

—Trofeos Advanced Level: Hablemos Sobre los Loros. 3rd ed. 2002. (SPA., Illus.). (gr. 5). pap. 6.80 (978-0-15-324282-3(5)) Harcourt Schl. Pubs.

—Trofeos Advanced Level: Heroes Anonimos. 3rd ed. 2002. (SPA., Illus.). pap. 6.80 (978-0-15-324377-6(5)) Harcourt Schl. Pubs.

—Trofeos Advanced Level: Humedales: Tesoros Ocultos. 3rd ed. 2002. (SPA., Illus.). pap. 6.80 (978-0-15-324390-5(2)) Harcourt Schl. Pubs.

—Trofeos Advanced Level: Instrumentos de la Geografia. 3rd ed. 2002. (SPA., Illus.). pap. 6.80 (978-0-15-324373-8(2)) Harcourt Schl. Pubs.

—Trofeos Advanced Level: Jason y Busqueda del Vellocino de Oro. 3rd ed. 2002. (SPA., Illus.). pap. 6.80 (978-0-15-324386-8(4)) Harcourt Schl. Pubs.

—Trofeos Advanced Level: Jazz: El Obsequio Musical de Estados Unidos al Mundo. 3rd ed. 2002. (SPA., Illus.). pap. 6.80 (978-0-15-324300-4(7)) Harcourt Schl. Pubs.

—Trofeos Advanced Level: Klondy Nelson y el Perro Lobo. 3rd ed. 2002. (SPA., Illus.). pap. 6.80 (978-0-15-324290-8(6)) Harcourt Schl. Pubs.

—Trofeos Advanced Level: La Balada De... 3rd ed. 2002. (SPA., Illus.). pap. 6.80 (978-0-15-324035-5(0)) Harcourt Schl. Pubs.

—Trofeos Advanced Level: La Banda de Musicos de Bremen. 3rd ed. 2002. (SPA., Illus.). pap. 6.80 (978-0-15-324208-3(6)) Harcourt Schl. Pubs.

—Trofeos Advanced Level: La Epoca/Botnes. 3rd ed. 2002. (SPA., Illus.). pap. 6.80 (978-0-15-324201-4(9)) Harcourt Schl. Pubs.

—Trofeos Advanced Level: La Evolucion... 3rd ed. 2002. (SPA., Illus.). pap. 6.80 (978-0-15-324287-8(6)) Harcourt Schl. Pubs.

—Trofeos Advanced Level: La Historia... 3rd ed. 2002. (SPA., Illus.). pap. 6.80 (978-0-15-324196-3(9)) Harcourt Schl. Pubs.

—Trofeos Advanced Level: La Historia del Caballo. 3rd ed. 2002. (SPA., Illus.). pap. 6.80 (978-0-15-324396-7(1)) Harcourt Schl. Pubs.

—Trofeos Advanced Level: La Historia en una Maleta. 3rd ed. 2002. (SPA., Illus.). pap. 6.80 (978-0-15-324311-0(2)) Harcourt Schl. Pubs.

—Trofeos Advanced Level: La Leyenda de Hielo Artico. 3rd ed. 2002. (SPA., Illus.). pap. 6.80 (978-0-15-324289-2(2)) Harcourt Schl. Pubs.

—Trofeos Advanced Level: La Manera Mas Rapida de Llegar a la Luna. 3rd ed. 2002. (SPA., Illus.). pap. 6.80 (978-0-15-324295-3(7)) Harcourt Schl. Pubs.

—Trofeos Advanced Level: La Navegacion... 3rd ed. 2002. (SPA., Illus.). pap. 6.80 (978-0-15-324040-9(7)) Harcourt Schl. Pubs.

—Trofeos Advanced Level: La Oruga... 3rd ed. 2002. (SPA., Illus.). pap. 6.80 (978-0-15-324017-1(2)) Harcourt Schl. Pubs.

—Trofeos Advanced Level: La Princesa. 3rd ed. 2002. (SPA., Illus.). pap. 6.80 (978-0-15-324129-1(2)) Harcourt Schl. Pubs.

—Trofeos Advanced Level: La Sorpresa del Mayflower. 3rd ed. 2002. (SPA., Illus.). pap. 6.80 (978-0-15-324307-3(4)) Harcourt Schl. Pubs.

—Trofeos Advanced Level: La Vida de Alvin Ailey. 3rd ed. 2002. (SPA., Illus.). (gr. 6). pap. 6.80 (978-0-15-324388-2(0)) Harcourt Schl. Pubs.

—Trofeos Advanced Level: La Vida En... 3rd ed. 2002. (SPA., Illus.). pap. 6.80 (978-0-15-324036-2(9)) Harcourt Schl. Pubs.

—Trofeos Advanced Level: La Visita. 3rd ed. 2002. (SPA., Illus.). pap. 6.80 (978-0-15-324204-5(3)) Harcourt Schl. Pubs.

—Trofeos Advanced Level: Las Cartas de Lila. 3rd ed. 2002. (SPA., Illus.). pap. 6.80 (978-0-15-324016-4(4)) Harcourt Schl. Pubs.

—Trofeos Advanced Level: Las Escuelas de Ayer. 3rd ed. 2002. (SPA.). (gr. 6). pap. 6.80 (978-0-15-324387-5(2)) Harcourt Schl. Pubs.

—Trofeos Advanced Level: Las Fiestas de Hoppar. 3rd ed. 2002. (SPA., Illus.). pap. 6.80 (978-0-15-324020-1(2)) Harcourt Schl. Pubs.

—Trofeos Advanced Level: Las Foto de Ana. 3rd ed. 2002. (SPA., Illus.). pap. 6.80 (978-0-15-324014-0(8)) Harcourt Schl. Pubs.

—Trofeos Advanced Level: Las Llanuras: Hogar del Bisonte y Muchos Mas. 3rd ed. 2002. (SPA., Illus.). pap. 6.80 (978-0-15-324310-3(4)) Harcourt Schl. Pubs.

—Trofeos Advanced Level: Las Pintura... 3rd ed. 2002. (SPA., Illus.). pap. 6.80 (978-0-15-324400-1(3)) Harcourt Schl. Pubs.

—Trofeos Advanced Level: Las Plantas. 3rd ed. 2002. (SPA., Illus.). pap. 6.80 (978-0-15-324023-2(7)) Harcourt Schl. Pubs.

—Trofeos Advanced Level: Las Serpientes. 3rd ed. 2002. (SPA., Illus.). pap. 6.80 (978-0-15-324027-0(X)) Harcourt Schl. Pubs.

—Trofeos Advanced Level: Las Tormentas. 3rd ed. 2002. (SPA., Illus.). pap. 6.80 (978-0-15-324397-4(X)) Harcourt Schl. Pubs.

—Trofeos Advanced Level: Lo Que No Vio. 3rd ed. 2002. (SPA., Illus.). pap. 6.80 (978-0-15-324028-7(8)) Harcourt Schl. Pubs.

—Trofeos Advanced Level: Los Cometas al Aire. 3rd ed. 2002. (SPA., Illus.). (gr. 6). pap. 6.80 (978-0-15-324372-1(4)) Harcourt Schl. Pubs.

—Trofeos Advanced Level: Los Fuegos Artificiales del 4 de Julio. 3rd ed. 2002. (SPA., Illus.). (gr. 6). pap. 6.80 (978-0-15-324380-6(5)) Harcourt Schl. Pubs.

—Trofeos Advanced Level: Los Huracanes. 3rd ed. 2002. (SPA., Illus.). pap. 6.80 (978-0-15-324294-6(9)) Harcourt Schl. Pubs.

—Trofeos Advanced Level: Los Misterios... 3rd ed. 2002. (SPA., Illus.). pap. 6.80 (978-0-15-324207-6(8)) Harcourt Schl. Pubs.

—Trofeos Advanced Level: Los Perros al Rescate. 3rd ed. 2002. (SPA., Illus.). pap. 6.80 (978-0-15-324379-0(1)) Harcourt Schl. Pubs.

—Trofeos Advanced Level: Los Primeros... 3rd ed. 2002. (SPA., Illus.). pap. 6.80 (978-0-15-324298-4(1)) Harcourt Schl. Pubs.

—Trofeos Advanced Level: Los Rios Dan Forma a la Tierra. 3rd ed. 2002. (SPA., Illus.). pap. 6.80 (978-0-15-324381-3(3)) Harcourt Schl. Pubs.

—Trofeos Advanced Level: Los Secretos. 3rd ed. 2002. (SPA., Illus.). pap. 6.80 (978-0-15-324030-0(X)) Harcourt Schl. Pubs.

—Trofeos Advanced Level: Los Tambores. 3rd ed. 2002. (SPA., Illus.). pap. 6.80 (978-0-15-324034-8(2)) Harcourt Schl. Pubs.

—Trofeos Advanced Level: Manuel. 3rd ed. 2002. (SPA., Illus.). pap. 6.80 (978-0-15-324304-2(X)) Harcourt Schl. Pubs.

—Trofeos Advanced Level: Marjory Stoneman Douglas: Campeano de los Everglades. 3rd ed. 2002. (SPA., Illus.). pap. 6.80 (978-0-15-324292-2(2)) Harcourt Schl. Pubs.

—Trofeos Advanced Level: Me Llama Luci. 3rd ed. 2002. (SPA., Illus.). pap. 6.80 (978-0-15-324305-9(8)) Harcourt Schl. Pubs.

—Trofeos Advanced Level: Muy Bien, Dina! 3rd ed. 2002. (SPA., Illus.). pap. 5.50 (978-0-15-323925-0(5)) Harcourt Schl. Pubs.

—Trofeos Advanced Level: Ni un Pelo de Tonto. 3rd ed. 2002. (SPA., Illus.). pap. 6.80 (978-0-15-324210-6(8)) Harcourt Schl. Pubs.

—Trofeos Advanced Level: No Vayan Alli. 3rd ed. 2002. (SPA., Illus.). pap. 6.80 (978-0-15-324205-2(1)) Harcourt Schl. Pubs.

—Trofeos Advanced Level: Nos Estamos Divirtiendo (de Verdad) en la Colonia Determiniacion. 3rd ed. 2002. (SPA., Illus.). pap. 6.80 (978-0-15-324283-0(3)) Harcourt Schl. Pubs.

—Trofeos Advanced Level: Perros Lazrills. 3rd ed. 2002. (SPA., Illus.). pap. 6.80 (978-0-15-324018-8(0)) Harcourt Schl. Pubs.

—Trofeos Advanced Level: Plantas de Bosque Tropical. 3rd ed. 2002. (SPA., Illus.). pap. 6.80 (978-0-15-324219-9(1)) Harcourt Schl. Pubs.

—Trofeos Advanced Level: Por Que los Gansos Vuelan en Bandadas? 3rd ed. 2002. (SPA., Illus.). pap. 6.80 (978-0-15-324288-5(4)) Harcourt Schl. Pubs.

—Trofeos Advanced Level: Quienes/Las... 3rd ed. 2002. (SPA., Illus.). pap. 6.80 (978-0-15-324302-8(3)) Harcourt Schl. Pubs.

—Trofeos Advanced Level: Rano O Sapo? 3rd ed. 2002. (SPA., Illus.). pap. 6.80 (978-0-15-324015-7(6)) Harcourt Schl. Pubs.

—Trofeos Advanced Level: Sami/Sombrero. 3rd ed. 2002. (SPA., Illus.). (gr. 1). pap. 5.50 (978-0-15-323918-2(2)) Harcourt Schl. Pubs.

—Trofeos Advanced Level: Si Fueras Ilustrador. 3rd ed. 2002. (SPA., Illus.). pap. 6.80 (978-0-15-324299-1(X)) Harcourt Schl. Pubs.

—Trofeos Advanced Level: Sllinky/Venta. 3rd ed. 2002. (SPA., Illus.). pap. 6.80 (978-0-15-324021-8(0)) Harcourt Schl. Pubs.

—Trofeos Advanced Level: Tu Decides... 3rd ed. 2002. (SPA., Illus.). pap. 6.80 (978-0-15-324209-0(4)) Harcourt Schl. Pubs.

—Trofeos Advanced Level: Un Dia en el Parque. 3rd ed. 2002. (SPA., Illus.). pap. 5.50 (978-0-15-323924-3(7)) Harcourt Schl. Pubs.

—Trofeos Advanced Level: Un Mundo de Agua. 3rd ed. 2002. (SPA., Illus.). pap. 6.80 (978-0-15-323948-9(4)) Harcourt Schl. Pubs.

—Trofeos Advanced Level: Un Viaje... 3rd ed. 2002. (SPA., Illus.). pap. 6.80 (978-0-15-324285-4(X)) Harcourt Schl. Pubs.

—Trofeos Advanced Level: Una Entrevista con los Hermanos Grimm. 3rd ed. 2002. (SPA., Illus.). (gr. 6). pap. 6.80 (978-0-15-324382-0(1)) Harcourt Schl. Pubs.

—Trofeos Advanced Level: Vecinos en las Praderas. 3rd ed. 2002. (SPA., Illus.). pap. 6.80 (978-0-15-324203-8(5)) Harcourt Schl. Pubs.

—Trofeos Advanced Level: Viaje en el Tiempo. 3rd ed. 2002. (SPA., Illus.). pap. 6.80 (978-0-15-324389-9(9)) Harcourt Schl. Pubs.

—Trofeos Advanced Level: Vivamos el Dia de la Historia. 3rd ed. 2002. (SPA., Illus.). pap. 6.80 (978-0-15-324308-0(2)) Harcourt Schl. Pubs.

—Trofeos Advanced Level: Voy a Trabajar. 3rd ed. 2002. (SPA., Illus.). pap. 6.80 (978-0-15-323950-2(6)) Harcourt Schl. Pubs.

—Trofeos Advanced Level: Yellostone: Geologica Dinamica. 3rd ed. 2002. (SPA., Illus.). pap. 6.80 (978-0-15-324293-9(0)) Harcourt Schl. Pubs.

—Trofeos Avanced Level: Por el Gran Canon de Colorado. 3rd ed. 2002. (SPA., Illus.). pap. 6.80 (978-0-15-324218-2(3)) Harcourt Schl. Pubs.

—Trofeos Below Level: A Banda en la Barrio. 3rd ed. 2002. (SPA., Illus.). pap. 6.80 (978-0-15-323974-8(3)) Harcourt Schl. Pubs.

—Trofeos Below Level: A Veces Solo. 3rd ed. 2002. (SPA., Illus.). pap. 6.80 (978-0-15-323955-7(7)) Harcourt Schl. Pubs.

—Trofeos Below Level: Alrededor la Hoqra. 3rd ed. 2002. (SPA., Illus.). pap. 6.80 (978-0-15-323968-7(9)) Harcourt Schl. Pubs.

—Trofeos Below Level: Amigos/Dis/Llvia. 3rd ed. 2002. (SPA., Illus.). pap. 5.50 (978-0-15-323877-2(1)) Harcourt Schl. Pubs.

—Trofeos Below Level: Animales/Crias. 3rd ed. 2002. (SPA., Illus.). pap. 5.50 (978-0-15-323878-9(X)) Harcourt Schl. Pubs.

—Trofeos Below Level: Apollo: A la Luna! 3rd ed. 2002. (SPA., Illus.). pap. 6.80 (978-0-15-324235-9(3)) Harcourt Schl. Pubs.

—Trofeos Below Level: Ben el Sabio. 3rd ed. 2002. (SPA., Illus.). pap. 6.80 (978-0-15-324249-6(3)) Harcourt Schl. Pubs.

—Trofeos Below Level: Bizcochitos. 3rd ed. 2002. (SPA., Illus.). (gr. 2). pap. 6.80 (978-0-15-323960-1(3)) Harcourt Schl. Pubs.

—Trofeos Below Level: Buscar Animales. 3rd ed. 2002. (SPA., Illus.). (gr. 2). pap. 6.80 (978-0-15-323952-6(2)) Harcourt Schl. Pubs.

—Trofeos Below Level: Carrera Al... 3rd ed. 2002. (SPA., Illus.). (gr. 6). pap. 6.80 (978-0-15-324320-2(1)) Harcourt Schl. Pubs.

—Trofeos Below Level: Con las Yemas de los Dedos. 3rd ed. 2002. (SPA., Illus.). (gr. 6). pap. 6.80 (978-0-15-324334-9(1)) Harcourt Schl. Pubs.

—Trofeos Below Level: Daniel y el Dia de Bienvinida. 3rd ed. 2002. (SPA., Illus.). (gr. 6). pap. 6.80 (978-0-15-324312-7(0)) Harcourt Schl. Pubs.

—Trofeos Below Level: Dentro/Ocho. 3rd ed. 2002. (SPA., Illus.). pap. 6.80 (978-0-15-323973-1(5)) Harcourt Schl. Pubs.

—Trofeos Below Level: Dia Inilvidable. 3rd ed. 2002. (SPA., Illus.). pap. 6.80 (978-0-15-324251-9(5)) Harcourt Schl. Pubs.

—Trofeos Below Level: Dibujos/Iluviso. 3rd ed. 2002. (SPA., Illus.). pap. 6.80 (978-0-15-323970-0(0)) Harcourt Schl. Pubs.

—Trofeos Below Level: Domar la Tierra. 3rd ed. 2002. (SPA., Illus.). (gr. 5). pap. 6.80 (978-0-15-324236-6(1)) Harcourt Schl. Pubs.

—Trofeos Below Level: El Agua... 3rd ed. 2002. (SPA., Illus.). pap. 6.80 (978-0-15-324233-5(7)) Harcourt Schl. Pubs.

—Trofeos Below Level: El Camino/Marapasas. 3rd ed. 2002. (SPA., Illus.). pap. 6.80 (978-0-15-323981-6(6)) Harcourt Schl. Pubs.

—Trofeos Below Level: el Campeon De... 3rd ed. 2002. (SPA., Illus.). pap. 6.80 (978-0-15-324315-8(5)) Harcourt Schl. Pubs.

—Trofeos Below Level: El Crater. 3rd ed. 2002. (SPA., Illus.). pap. 6.80 (978-0-15-324327-1(9)) Harcourt Schl. Pubs.

—Trofeos Below Level: El Cuanto De... 3rd ed. 2002. (SPA., Illus.). pap. 6.80 (978-0-15-324238-0(8)) Harcourt Schl. Pubs.

—Trofeos Below Level: El Deseo. 3rd ed. 2002. (SPA., Illus.). pap. 6.80 (978-0-15-323956-4(5)) Harcourt Schl. Pubs.

—Trofeos Below Level: El Domador de Caballos. 3rd ed. 2002. (SPA., Illus.). pap. 6.80 (978-0-15-324336-3(8)) Harcourt Schl. Pubs.

—Trofeos Below Level: El Fantastico... 3rd ed. 2002. (SPA., Illus.). pap. 6.80 (978-0-15-324234-2(5)) Harcourt Schl. Pubs.

—Trofeos Below Level: El Hit Numero Uno. 3rd ed. 2002. (SPA., Illus.). pap. 6.80 (978-0-15-324226-7(4)) Harcourt Schl. Pubs.

—Trofeos Below Level: El Mejor... 3rd ed. 2002. (SPA., Illus.). pap. 6.80 (978-0-15-324241-0(8)) Harcourt Schl. Pubs.

—Trofeos Below Level: El Mundo Bajo Los Pies. 3rd ed. 2002. (SPA., Illus.). pap. 6.80 (978-0-15-323969-4(7)) Harcourt Schl. Pubs.

—Trofeos Below Level: El Poderoso Volcan. 3rd ed. 2002. (SPA., Illus.). pap. 6.80 (978-0-15-324337-0(6)) Harcourt Schl. Pubs.

—Trofeos Below Level: El Sueno y Las... 3rd ed. 2002. (SPA., Illus.). pap. 6.80 (978-0-15-324338-7(4)) Harcourt Schl. Pubs.

—Trofeos Below Level: El Sueno/Botresta. 3rd ed. 2002. (SPA., Illus.). pap. 6.80 (978-0-15-324243-4(4)) Harcourt Schl. Pubs.

—Trofeos Below Level: El Viaje a las Piramides. 3rd ed. 2002. (SPA., Illus.). pap. 6.80 (978-0-15-324324-0(4)) Harcourt Schl. Pubs.

—Trofeos Below Level: En el Sotano. 3rd ed. 2002. (SPA., Illus.). pap. 6.80 (978-0-15-324317-2(1)) Harcourt Schl. Pubs.

—Trofeos Below Level: En la Frontera. 3rd ed. 2002. (SPA., Illus.). pap. 6.80 (978-0-15-323962-5(X)) Harcourt Schl. Pubs.

—Trofeos Below Level: Feliz Ano Nuevo. 3rd ed. 2002. (SPA., Illus.). (gr. 2). pap. 6.80 (978-0-15-323976-2(X)) Harcourt Schl. Pubs.

—Trofeos Below Level: Fiesta de la Manzanas. 3rd ed. 2002. (SPA., Illus.). pap. 6.80 (978-0-15-323966-3(2)) Harcourt Schl. Pubs.

—Trofeos Below Level: Fuego del Hielo. 3rd ed. 2002. (SPA., Illus.). pap. 6.80 (978-0-15-324222-9(1)) Harcourt Schl. Pubs.

—Trofeos Below Level: Huracan! 3rd ed. 2002. (SPA., Illus.). pap. 6.80 (978-0-15-323980-9(8)) Harcourt Schl. Pubs.

—Trofeos Below Level: Ideas Brillantes. 3rd ed. 2002. (SPA., Illus.). pap. 6.80 (978-0-15-324329-5(5)) Harcourt Schl. Pubs.

—Trofeos Below Level: Jil/Gigante. 3rd ed. 2002. (SPA., Illus.). pap. 6.80 (978-0-15-323957-1(3)) Harcourt Schl. Pubs.

—Trofeos Below Level: La Ayuda de un Buen Amigo. 3rd ed. 2002. (SPA., Illus.). pap. 6.80 (978-0-15-324229-8(9)) Harcourt Schl. Pubs.

—Trofeos Below Level: La Carrera... 3rd ed. 2002. (SPA., Illus.). pap. 6.80 (978-0-15-324048-5(2)) Harcourt Schl. Pubs.

—Trofeos Below Level: La Chica... 3rd ed. 2002. (SPA., Illus.). pap. 6.80 (978-0-15-324242-7(6)) Harcourt Schl. Pubs.

—Trofeos Below Level: La Exploracion... 3rd ed. 2002. (SPA., Illus.). pap. 6.80 (978-0-15-324231-1(0)) Harcourt Schl. Pubs.

—Trofeos Below Level: La Fauna Urbana. 3rd ed. 2002. (SPA., Illus.). (gr. 4). pap. 6.80 (978-0-15-324144-4(6)) Harcourt Schl. Pubs.

—Trofeos Below Level: La Foca Que... 3rd ed. 2002. (SPA., Illus.). pap. 6.80 (978-0-15-324069-0(5)) Harcourt Schl. Pubs.

—Trofeos Below Level: La Gran Funcion. 3rd ed. 2002. (SPA., Illus.). pap. 6.80 (978-0-15-324223-6(X)) Harcourt Schl. Pubs.

—Trofeos Below Level: La Jordana. 3rd ed. 2002. (SPA., Illus.). pap. 6.80 (978-0-15-324065-2(2)) Harcourt Schl. Pubs.

—Trofeos Below Level: La Narradora. 3rd ed. 2002. (SPA., Illus.). pap. 6.80 (978-0-15-324059-1(8)) Harcourt Schl. Pubs.

—Trofeos Below Level: La Nina Que... 3rd ed. 2002. (SPA., Illus.). pap. 6.80 (978-0-15-324319-6(8)) Harcourt Schl. Pubs.

—Trofeos Below Level: La Parada de Autobus. 3rd ed. 2002. (SPA., Illus.). pap. 6.80 (978-0-15-324332-5(5)) Harcourt Schl. Pubs.

—Trofeos Below Level: La Pequena... 3rd ed. 2002. (SPA., Illus.). pap. 6.80 (978-0-15-324045-4(8)) Harcourt Schl. Pubs.

—Trofeos Below Level: La Pequena. 3rd ed. 2002. (SPA., Illus.). pap. 6.80 (978-0-15-324155-0(1)) Harcourt Schl. Pubs.

—Trofeos Below Level: La Polizon. 3rd ed. 2002. (SPA., Illus.). pap. 6.80 (978-0-15-324246-5(9)) Harcourt Schl. Pubs.

—Trofeos Below Level: La Selva Tropical. 3rd ed. 2002. (SPA., Illus.). pap. 6.80 (978-0-15-324141-3(1)) Harcourt Schl. Pubs.

—Trofeos Below Level: La Siesta. 3rd ed. 2002. (SPA., Illus.). pap. 5.50 (978-0-15-323882-6(8)) Harcourt Schl. Pubs.

—Trofeos Below Level: La Sorpresa. 3rd ed. 2002. (SPA., Illus.). pap. 6.80 (978-0-15-323963-2(8)) Harcourt Schl. Pubs.

—Trofeos Below Level: La Sorpresa para Sara. 3rd ed. 2002. (SPA., Illus.). pap. 6.80 (978-0-15-324053-9(9)) Harcourt Schl. Pubs.

—Trofeos Below Level: La Tierra/Burrs. 3rd ed. 2002. (SPA., Illus.). pap. 6.80 (978-0-15-324068-3(7)) Harcourt Schl. Pubs.

—Trofeos Below Level: La Verde y Malvada Carnivora. 3rd ed. 2002. (SPA., Illus.). pap. 6.80 (978-0-15-324160-4(8)) Harcourt Schl. Pubs.

—Trofeos Below Level: La Visita. 3rd ed. 2002. (SPA., Illus.). pap. 6.80 (978-0-15-324335-6(X)) Harcourt Schl. Pubs.

—Trofeos Below Level: La Voz de la Fiebre del Oro. 3rd ed. 2002. (SPA., Illus.). (gr. 4). pap. 6.80 (978-0-15-324157-4(8)) Harcourt Schl. Pubs.

—Trofeos Below Level: La Vuelta al Mundo de la Musica. 3rd ed. 2002. (SPA., Illus.). pap. 6.80 (978-0-15-324313-4(9)) Harcourt Schl. Pubs.

—Trofeos Below Level: La Vuelta/Lobo. 3rd ed. 2002. (SPA., Illus.). pap. 6.80 (978-0-15-324146-8(2)) Harcourt Schl. Pubs.

—Trofeos Below Level: Lagrimas de Cocodrilo y Otras Sorpresas. 3rd ed. 2002. (SPA., Illus.). pap. 6.80 (978-0-15-324244-1(2)) Harcourt Schl. Pubs.

—Trofeos Below Level: Las Ardillas. 3rd ed. 2002. (SPA., Illus.). pap. 6.80 (978-0-15-323954-0(9)) Harcourt Schl. Pubs.

—Trofeos Below Level: Las Mujeres y el Beisbol. 3rd ed. 2002. (SPA., Illus.). pap. 6.80 (978-0-15-324314-1(7)) Harcourt Schl. Pubs.

—Trofeos Below Level: Las Tormentas. 3rd ed. 2002. (SPA., Illus.). pap. 5.50 (978-0-15-323880-2(1)) Harcourt Schl. Pubs.

—Trofeos Below Level: Llegar/Abuelo. 3rd ed. 2002. (SPA., Illus.). pap. 6.80 (978-0-15-323978-6(6)) Harcourt Schl. Pubs.

—Trofeos Below Level: Los Comerciantes de Seda China. 3rd ed. 2002. (SPA., Illus.). pap. 6.80 (978-0-15-324323-3(6)) Harcourt Schl. Pubs.

—Trofeos Below Level: Los Efectos Especiales: Los Monstuos Hechos en Casa. 3rd ed. 2002. (SPA., Illus.). pap. 6.80 (978-0-15-324330-1(9)) Harcourt Schl. Pubs.

—Trofeos Below Level: Los Tomates... 3rd ed. 2002. (SPA., Illus.). (gr. 4). pap. 6.80 (978-0-15-324132-1(2)) Harcourt Schl. Pubs.

—Trofeos Below Level: Lose Heroes en las Llamas. 3rd ed. 2002. (SPA., Illus.). pap. 6.80 (978-0-15-324232-8(9)) Harcourt Schl. Pubs.

—Trofeos Below Level: Mantenerse. 3rd ed. 2002. (SPA., Illus.). pap. 6.80 (978-0-15-323971-7(9)) Harcourt Schl. Pubs.

—Trofeos Below Level: Mejores Intenciones. 3rd ed. 2002. (SPA., Illus.). pap. 6.80 (978-0-15-324331-8(7)) Harcourt Schl. Pubs.

—Trofeos Below Level: Mi Amigo Tino. 3rd ed. 2002. (SPA., Illus.). (J). pap. 3.50 (978-0-15-323853-6(4)) Harcourt Schl. Pubs.

—Trofeos Below Level: Mi Mayor Deseo. 3rd ed. 2002. (SPA., Illus.). (gr. 3). pap. 6.80 (978-0-15-324134-5(9)) Harcourt Schl. Pubs.

—Trofeos Below Level: Mil Palabras. 3rd ed. 2002. (SPA., Illus.). (gr. 4). pap. 6.80 (978-0-15-324133-8(0)) Harcourt Schl. Pubs.

—Trofeos Below Level: Mis Nuevos Amigos. 3rd ed. 2002. (SPA., Illus.). (gr. 5). pap. 6.80 (978-0-15-324221-2(3)) Harcourt Schl. Pubs.

—Trofeos Below Level: Naufragio. 3rd ed. 2002. (SPA., Illus.). pap. 6.80 (978-0-15-324230-4(2)) Harcourt Schl. Pubs.

—Trofeos Below Level: No Es Justo! 3rd ed. 2002. (SPA., Illus.). (gr. 6). pap. 6.80 (978-0-15-324316-5(3)) Harcourt Schl. Pubs.

—Trofeos Below Level: Nunca Es... 3rd ed. 2002. (SPA., Illus.). pap. 6.80 (978-0-15-323967-0(0)) Harcourt Schl. Pubs.

—Trofeos Below Level: Oxodo/Kansas. 3rd ed. 2002. (SPA., Illus.). pap. 6.80 (978-0-15-324158-1(6)) Harcourt Schl. Pubs.

—Trofeos Below Level: Parque de Babo. 3rd ed. 2002. (SPA., Illus.). pap. 5.50 (978-0-15-323883-3(6)) Harcourt Schl. Pubs.

—Trofeos Below Level: Paul Bunyan. 3rd ed. 2002. (SPA., Illus.). pap. 6.80 (978-0-15-324061-4(X)) Harcourt Schl. Pubs.

—Trofeos Below Level: Pepe Encuentra. 3rd ed. 2002. (SPA., Illus.). pap. 6.80 (978-0-15-323975-5(1)) Harcourt Schl. Pubs.

—Trofeos Below Level: Pequeno Jose. 3rd ed. 2002. (SPA., Illus.). pap. 6.80 (978-0-15-324138-3(1)) Harcourt Schl. Pubs.

—Trofeos Below Level: Pericles y la Primera Democracia. 3rd ed. 2002. (SPA., Illus.). pap. 6.80 (978-0-15-324326-4(0)) Harcourt Schl. Pubs.

—Trofeos Below Level: Personajes... 3rd ed. 2002. (SPA., Illus.). pap. 6.80 (978-0-15-324227-4(2)) Harcourt Schl. Pubs.

—Trofeos Below Level: Picnic en la Parque. 3rd ed. 2002. (SPA., Illus.). pap. 6.80 (978-0-15-323965-6(4)) Harcourt Schl. Pubs.

—Trofeos Below Level: Planeta H2O. 3rd ed. 2002. (SPA., Illus.). (gr. 6). pap. 6.80 (978-0-15-324341-7(4)) Harcourt Schl. Pubs.

—Trofeos Below Level: Plantar/Jardin. 3rd ed. 2002. (SPA., Illus.). pap. 6.80 (978-0-15-324140-6(3)) Harcourt Schl. Pubs.

—Trofeos Below Level: Pony Express. 3rd ed. 2002. (SPA., Illus.). pap. 6.80 (978-0-15-324063-8(6)) Harcourt Schl. Pubs.

—Trofeos Below Level: Por una Cancion. 3rd ed. 2002. (SPA., Illus.). pap. 6.80 (978-0-15-324328-8(7)) Harcourt Schl. Pubs.

—Trofeos Below Level: Que Es el Dinro. 3rd ed. 2002. (SPA., Illus.). pap. 6.80 (978-0-15-324066-9(0)) Harcourt Schl. Pubs.

—Trofeos Below Level: Que Hora Es? 3rd ed. 2002. (SPA., Illus.). pap. 6.80 (978-0-15-323953-3(0)) Harcourt Schl. Pubs.

—Trofeos Below Level: Que Robots... 3rd ed. 2002. (SPA., Illus.). pap. 6.80 (978-0-15-324245-8(0)) Harcourt Schl. Pubs.

—Trofeos Below Level: Querida Abuela. 3rd ed. 2002. (SPA., Illus.). pap. 6.80 (978-0-15-324224-3(8)) Harcourt Schl. Pubs.

—Trofeos Below Level: Quien Es Necsita. 3rd ed. 2002. (SPA., Illus.). pap. 6.80 (978-0-15-324055-3(5)) Harcourt Schl. Pubs.

—Trofeos Below Level: Quien Ha Sido? 3rd ed. 2002. (SPA., Illus.). pap. 5.50 (978-0-15-323879-6(8)) Harcourt Schl. Pubs.

—Trofeos Below Level: Regreso al Pasado. 3rd ed. 2002. (SPA., Illus.). pap. 6.80 (978-0-15-324325-7(2)) Harcourt Schl. Pubs.

—Trofeos Below Level: Ricts/Tres Osos. 3rd ed. 2002. (SPA., Illus.). pap. 5.50 (978-0-15-323881-9(X)) Harcourt Schl. Pubs.

—Trofeos Below Level: Rosa/Pajarito. 3rd ed. 2002. (SPA., Illus.). pap. 6.80 (978-0-15-323972-4(7)) Harcourt Schl. Pubs.

—Trofeos Below Level: Sera Verdad... 3rd ed. 2002. (SPA., Illus.). pap. 6.80 (978-0-15-324237-3(X)) Harcourt Schl. Pubs.

—Trofeos Below Level: Siempre con Estilo. 3rd ed. 2002. (SPA., Illus.). pap. 6.80 (978-0-15-324239-7(6)) Harcourt Schl. Pubs.

—Trofeos Below Level: Socorro! 3rd ed. 2002. (SPA., Illus.). pap. 6.80 (978-0-15-323958-8(1)) Harcourt Schl. Pubs.

—Trofeos Below Level: Susan B. Anthony. 3rd ed. 2002. (SPA., Illus.). pap. 6.80 (978-0-15-324247-2(7)) Harcourt Schl. Pubs.

—Trofeos Below Level: Tara Lipinski. 3rd ed. 2002. (SPA., Illus.). pap. 6.80 (978-0-15-324046-1(6)) Harcourt Schl. Pubs.

—Trofeos Below Level: Terremoto! 3rd ed. 2002. (SPA., Illus.). pap. 6.80 (978-0-15-324318-9(X)) Harcourt Schl. Pubs.

—Trofeos Below Level: Tesoros de Vietnam. 3rd ed. 2002. (SPA., Illus.). (gr. 6). pap. 6.80 (978-0-15-324333-2(3)) Harcourt Schl. Pubs.

—Trofeos Below Level: Tiempo de Paz. 3rd ed. 2002. (SPA., Illus.). pap. 6.80 (978-0-15-324145-1(4)) Harcourt Schl. Pubs.

—Trofeos Below Level: Tierras Sin Agua. 3rd ed. 2002. (SPA., Illus.). pap. 6.80 (978-0-15-324154-3(3)) Harcourt Schl. Pubs.

—Trofeos Below Level: Tomar la Decision. 3rd ed. 2002. (SPA., Illus.). pap. 6.80 (978-0-15-324054-6(7)) Harcourt Schl. Pubs.

—Trofeos Below Level: Trabajor en el Aeroporto. 3rd ed. 2002. (SPA., Illus.). pap. 6.80 (978-0-15-323977-9(8)) Harcourt Schl. Pubs.

—Trofeos Below Level: Tres Fabulas. 3rd ed. 2002. (SPA., Illus.). (gr. 3). pap. 6.80 (978-0-15-324056-0(3)) Harcourt Schl. Pubs.

—Trofeos Below Level: Tres Orbitas. 3rd ed. 2002. (SPA., Illus.). pap. 6.80 (978-0-15-324339-4(2)) Harcourt Schl. Pubs.

—Trofeos Below Level: Tutora Virtual. 3rd ed. 2002. (SPA., Illus.). pap. 6.80 (978-0-15-324340-0(6)) Harcourt Schl. Pubs.

—Trofeos Below Level: Un Diario/Fibre. 3rd ed. 2002. (SPA., Illus.). pap. 6.80 (978-0-15-324064-5(4)) Harcourt Schl. Pubs.

—Trofeos Below Level: Un Viaje. 3rd ed. 2002. (SPA., Illus.). pap. 6.80 (978-0-15-323979-3(4)) Harcourt Schl. Pubs.

—Trofeos Below Level: Una Aventura. 3rd ed. 2002. (SPA., Illus.). pap. 6.80 (978-0-15-324057-7(1)) Harcourt Schl. Pubs.

—Trofeos Below Level: Una Aventura... 3rd ed. 2002. (SPA., Illus.). pap. 6.80 (978-0-15-324228-1(0)) Harcourt Schl. Pubs.

—Trofeos Below Level: Una Entrevista. 3rd ed. 2002. (SPA., Illus.). pap. 6.80 (978-0-15-324150-5(0)) Harcourt Schl. Pubs.

—Trofeos Below Level: Unas Vaciones... 3rd ed. 2002. (SPA., Illus.). pap. 6.80 (978-0-15-324250-2(7)) Harcourt Schl. Pubs.

—Trofeos Below Level: Visita a San Francisco. 3rd ed. 2002. (SPA., Illus.). pap. 6.80 (978-0-15-324044-7(X)) Harcourt Schl. Pubs.

—Trofeos Below Level: Vuela, Catarita. 3rd ed. 2002. (SPA., Illus.). pap. 6.80 (978-0-15-323959-5(X)) Harcourt Schl. Pubs.

—Trofeos Below Level: Ya Soy Estado... 3rd ed. 2002. (SPA., Illus.). pap. 6.80 (978-0-15-324153-6(5)) Harcourt Schl. Pubs.

—Trofeos Below Level: Yo Deseo... 3rd ed. 2002. (SPA., Illus.). pap. 6.80 (978-0-15-324052-2(0)) Harcourt Schl. Pubs.

—Trofeos Below Level: Zapatillas/Pinata. 3rd ed. 2002. (SPA., Illus.). pap. 6.80 (978-0-15-324240-3(X)) Harcourt Schl. Pubs.

—Trofeos Below Level: Zona de Inundacion. 3rd ed. 2002. (SPA., Illus.). pap. 6.80 (978-0-15-324321-9(X)) Harcourt Schl. Pubs.

—Trofeos Ib Kevek: Fuego en la Pradera. 3rd ed. 2002. (SPA., Illus.). pap. 6.80 (978-0-15-324263-2(9)) Harcourt Schl. Pubs.

—Trofeos On Level: 500 Veses Isabel. 3rd ed. 2002. (SPA., Illus.). pap. 6.80 (978-0-15-323983-0(2)) Harcourt Schl. Pubs.

—Trofeos On Level: A Dormir! 3rd ed. 2002. (SPA., Illus.). pap. 6.80 (978-0-15-323916-8(6)) Harcourt Schl. Pubs.

—Trofeos On Level: A Recolectar. 3rd ed. 2002. (SPA., Illus.). pap. 6.80 (978-0-15-324362-2(7)) Harcourt Schl. Pubs.

—Trofeos On Level: Adios al Campo! Hola a la Ciudad! 3rd ed. 2002. (SPA., Illus.). (gr. 5). pap. 6.80 (978-0-15-324252-6(3)) Harcourt Schl. Pubs.

—Trofeos On Level: Animales Que Nos Socorren. 3rd ed. 2002. (SPA., Illus.). pap. 6.80 (978-0-15-324260-1(4)) Harcourt Schl. Pubs.

—Trofeos On Level: Babo en el Zoo. 3rd ed. 2002. (SPA., Illus.). pap. 6.80 (978-0-15-323917-5(4)) Harcourt Schl. Pubs.

—Trofeos On Level: Bello/Renacuajo. 3rd ed. 2002. (SPA., Illus.). pap. 5.50 (978-0-15-323893-2(3)) Harcourt Schl. Pubs.

—Trofeos On Level: Como Cultivar. 3rd ed. 2002. (SPA., Illus.). pap. 6.80 (978-0-15-323993-9(X)) Harcourt Schl. Pubs.

—Trofeos On Level: Como se Forman las Montanas? 3rd ed. 2002. (SPA., Illus.). (gr. 6). pap. 6.80 (978-0-15-324357-8(0)) Harcourt Schl. Pubs.

—Trofeos On Level: Como Ser Popular. 3rd ed. 2002. (SPA., Illus.). pap. 6.80 (978-0-15-324346-2(5)) Harcourt Schl. Pubs.

—Trofeos On Level: Como/Inventaron. 3rd ed. 2002. (SPA., Illus.). pap. 6.80 (978-0-15-324008-9(3)) Harcourt Schl. Pubs.

—Trofeos On Level: Con Carino... 3rd ed. 2002. (SPA., Illus.). pap. 6.80 (978-0-15-324281-6(7)) Harcourt Schl. Pubs.

—Trofeos On Level: Cuando Baja la Marea. 3rd ed. 2002. (SPA., Illus.). pap. 6.80 (978-0-15-324360-8(0)) Harcourt Schl. Pubs.

—Trofeos On Level: Del Este al Oeste Norteamericano: La Historia de John Wesley Powell. 3rd ed. 2002. (SPA., Illus.). pap. 6.80 (978-0-15-324366-0(X)) Harcourt Schl. Pubs.

—Trofeos On Level: Del Sueno/Hombre. 3rd ed. 2002. (SPA., Illus.). pap. 6.80 (978-0-15-324273-1(6)) Harcourt Schl. Pubs.

—Trofeos On Level: Desvan y Beatriz. 3rd ed. 2002. (SPA., Illus.). pap. 6.80 (978-0-15-323908-3(5)) Harcourt Schl. Pubs.

—Trofeos On Level: Diez Osos. 3rd ed. 2002. (SPA., Illus.). pap. 6.80 (978-0-15-323912-0(3)) Harcourt Schl. Pubs.

—Trofeos On Level: Donde Esta La... 3rd ed. 2002. (SPA., Illus.). pap. 6.80 (978-0-15-323997-7(2)) Harcourt Schl. Pubs.

—Trofeos On Level: Donde Viven de Animales? 3rd ed. 2002. (SPA., Illus.). pap. 5.50 (978-0-15-323904-5(2)) Harcourt Schl. Pubs.

—Trofeos On Level: El Atlas de Oro. 3rd ed. 2002. (SPA., Illus.). pap. 6.80 (978-0-15-324367-7(8)) Harcourt Schl. Pubs.

—Trofeos On Level: El Bote. 3rd ed. 2002. (SPA., Illus.). (J). pap. 3.50 (978-0-15-323887-1(9)) Harcourt Schl. Pubs.

—Trofeos On Level: El Caiman/Justin. 3rd ed. 2002. (SPA., Illus.). (gr. 2). pap. 6.80 (978-0-15-323999-1(9)) Harcourt Schl. Pubs.

—Trofeos On Level: El Camino de Oregon: Diario de Viaje de Lucy Bell. 3rd ed. 2002. (SPA., Illus.). pap. 6.80 (978-0-15-324280-9(9)) Harcourt Schl. Pubs.

—Trofeos On Level: El Caso de Derrick y los Invasores de la Mente. 3rd ed. 2002. (SPA., Illus.). pap. 6.80 (978-0-15-324266-3(3)) Harcourt Schl. Pubs.

—Trofeos On Level: El Caso de Estudiante Perdido. 3rd ed. 2002. (SPA., Illus.). pap. 6.80 (978-0-15-324371-4(6)) Harcourt Schl. Pubs.

—Trofeos On Level: El Cruce de Rio: Un Cuento de Patriotas. 3rd ed. 2002. (SPA., Illus.). (gr. 5). pap. 6.80 (978-0-15-324256-4(6)) Harcourt Schl. Pubs.

—Trofeos On Level: El Diario de Josie. 3rd ed. 2002. (SPA., Illus.). pap. 6.80 (978-0-15-324363-9(5)) Harcourt Schl. Pubs.

—Trofeos On Level: El Equipo... 3rd ed. 2002. (SPA., Illus.). pap. 6.80 (978-0-15-324257-1(4)) Harcourt Schl. Pubs.

—Trofeos On Level: El Gran Debate Sobre Franklin. 3rd ed. 2002. (SPA., Illus.). pap. 6.80 (978-0-15-324279-3(5)) Harcourt Schl. Pubs.

—Trofeos On Level: El Guardian. 3rd ed. 2002. (SPA., Illus.). pap. 6.80 (978-0-15-324347-9(3)) Harcourt Schl. Pubs.

—Trofeos On Level: El Mystrio de Sam. 3rd ed. 2002. (SPA., Illus.). pap. 6.80 (978-0-15-324002-7(4)) Harcourt Schl. Pubs.

—Trofeos On Level: El Perro Es Sombra. 3rd ed. 2002. (SPA., Illus.). pap. 6.80 (978-0-15-323985-4(9)) Harcourt Schl. Pubs.

—Trofeos On Level: El Rey del Feria. 3rd ed. 2002. (SPA., Illus.). pap. 6.80 (978-0-15-323996-0(4)) Harcourt Schl. Pubs.

—Trofeos On Level: El Secreto de la Seda de la Antigua China. 3rd ed. 2002. (SPA., Illus.). pap. 6.80 (978-0-15-324353-0(8)) Harcourt Schl. Pubs.

—Trofeos On Level: El Sombrero Rojo y Azul. 3rd ed. 2002. (SPA., Illus.). (gr. 5). pap. 6.80 (978-0-15-324258-8(2)) Harcourt Schl. Pubs.

—Trofeos On Level: El Sotano. 3rd ed. 2002. (SPA., Illus.). pap. 6.80 (978-0-15-323906-9(9)) Harcourt Schl. Pubs.

—Trofeos On Level: El Trabajo/Chicos. 3rd ed. 2002. (SPA., Illus.). pap. 6.80 (978-0-15-323991-5(3)) Harcourt Schl. Pubs.

—Trofeos On Level: El Trofeo. 3rd ed. 2002. (SPA., Illus.). pap. 6.80 (978-0-15-324344-8(9)) Harcourt Schl. Pubs.

—Trofeos On Level: En las Profundidades: Buceemos Con la Dra. Sylvia Earle. 3rd ed. 2002. (SPA., Illus.). pap. 6.80 (978-0-15-324264-9(7)) Harcourt Schl. Pubs.

—Trofeos On Level: Esperame, Capitan. 3rd ed. 2002. (SPA., Illus.). pap. 6.80 (978-0-15-324010-2(5)) Harcourt Schl. Pubs.

—Trofeos On Level: Estimado Amigo. 3rd ed. 2002. (SPA., Illus.). pap. 6.80 (978-0-15-324003-4(2)) Harcourt Schl. Pubs.

—Trofeos On Level: Felicia Toca el Chelo. 3rd ed. 2002. (SPA., Illus.). pap. 6.80 (978-0-15-324343-1(0)) Harcourt Schl. Pubs.

—Trofeos On Level: Frutas Comicas. 3rd ed. 2002. (SPA., Illus.). pap. 6.80 (978-0-15-323995-3(6)) Harcourt Schl. Pubs.

—Trofeos On Level: Hagamos un Pastel. 3rd ed. 2002. (SPA., Illus.). pap. 6.80 (978-0-15-323988-5(3)) Harcourt Schl. Pubs.

—Trofeos On Level: Hormigs y Trabejdors. 3rd ed. 2002. (SPA., Illus.). pap. 6.80 (978-0-15-323909-0(3)) Harcourt Schl. Pubs.

—Trofeos On Level: Hoy Nadare! 3rd ed. 2002. (SPA., Illus.). pap. 5.50 (978-0-15-323894-9(1)) Harcourt Schl. Pubs.

—Trofeos On Level: La Arana Te Vio. 3rd ed. 2002. (SPA., Illus.). pap. 6.80 (978-0-15-324348-6(1)) Harcourt Schl. Pubs.

—Trofeos On Level: La Atleta de Oro. 3rd ed. 2002. (SPA., Illus.). pap. 6.80 (978-0-15-324164-2(0)) Harcourt Schl. Pubs.

—Trofeos On Level: La Bailarina Hace un Trato. 3rd ed. 2002. (SPA., Illus.). (gr. 6). pap. 6.80 (978-0-15-324342-4(2)) Harcourt Schl. Pubs.

—Trofeos On Level: La Camara... 3rd ed. 2002. (SPA., Illus.). pap. 6.80 (978-0-15-324270-0(1)) Harcourt Schl. Pubs.

—Trofeos On Level: La Diversion... 3rd ed. 2002. (SPA., Illus.). pap. 6.80 (978-0-15-324267-0(1)) Harcourt Schl. Pubs.

—Trofeos On Level: La Escuela... 3rd ed. 2002. (SPA., Illus.). (gr. 5). pap. 6.80 (978-0-15-324276-2(0)) Harcourt Schl. Pubs.

—Trofeos On Level: La Panadera y Olga. 3rd ed. 2002. (SPA., Illus.). pap. 6.80 (978-0-15-324185-7(3)) Harcourt Schl. Pubs.

—Trofeos On Level: La Plaza Ghirardelli. 3rd ed. 2002. (SPA., Illus.). pap. 6.80 (978-0-15-324173-4(X)) Harcourt Schl. Pubs.

—Trofeos On Level: La Publicidad en Accion. 3rd ed. 2002. (SPA., Illus.). pap. 6.80 (978-0-15-324272-4(8)) Harcourt Schl. Pubs.

—Trofeos On Level: La Vereda. 3rd ed. 2002. (SPA., Illus.). pap. 5.50 (978-0-15-323891-8(7)) Harcourt Schl. Pubs.

—Trofeos On Level: La Vida de un Carnerotillo. 3rd ed. 2002. (SPA., Illus.). pap. 6.80 (978-0-15-324175-8(6)) Harcourt Schl. Pubs.

—Trofeos On Level: La Vida en el Espacio. 3rd ed. 2002. (SPA., Illus.). pap. 6.80 (978-0-15-324369-1(4)) Harcourt Schl. Pubs.

—Trofeos On Level: La Vida/Vaquero. 3rd ed. 2002. (SPA., Illus.). pap. 6.80 (978-0-15-324005-8(9)) Harcourt Schl. Pubs.

—Trofeos On Level: La Vuelta/Mundo. 3rd ed. 2002. (SPA., Illus.). pap. 6.80 (978-0-15-324007-2(5)) Harcourt Schl. Pubs.

—Trofeos On Level: Las Cuerdas Que Nos Unen. 3rd ed. 2002. (SPA., Illus.). pap. 6.80 (978-0-15-324254-0(X)) Harcourt Schl. Pubs.

—Trofeos On Level: Las Mascotas. 3rd ed. 2002. (SPA., Illus.). pap. 5.50 (978-0-15-323890-1(9)) Harcourt Schl. Pubs.

—Trofeos On Level: Las Pruebas de Resistencia. 3rd ed. 2002. (SPA., Illus.). pap. 6.80 (978-0-15-324358-5(9)) Harcourt Schl. Pubs.

—Trofeos On Level: Lo Que Juegan. 3rd ed. 2002. (SPA., Illus.). (gr. 2). pap. 6.80 (978-0-15-323989-2(1)) Harcourt Schl. Pubs.

—Trofeos On Level: Los Animales del Polo Sur. 3rd ed. 2002. (SPA., Illus.). pap. 6.80 (978-0-15-324350-9(3)) Harcourt Schl. Pubs.

—Trofeos On Level: Los Cocodrilos de Everglades Cove. 3rd ed. 2002. (SPA., Illus.). pap. 6.80 (978-0-15-324262-5(0)) Harcourt Schl. Pubs.

—Trofeos On Level: Los Huevos. 3rd ed. 2002. (SPA., Illus.). pap. 6.80 (978-0-15-324001-0(6)) Harcourt Schl. Pubs.

—Trofeos On Level: Los Recuerdos de un Perro. 3rd ed. 2002. (SPA., Illus.). pap. 6.80 (978-0-15-324349-3(X)) Harcourt Schl. Pubs.

—Trofeos On Level: Los Viajes/Papa. 3rd ed. 2002. (SPA., Illus.). pap. 6.80 (978-0-15-324009-6(1)) Harcourt Schl. Pubs.

—Trofeos On Level: Luis Flecha y los Diana. 3rd ed. 2002. (SPA., Illus.). pap. 6.80 (978-0-15-324253-3(1)) Harcourt Schl. Pubs.

—Trofeos On Level: Mas Alla/Huerto. 3rd ed. 2002. (SPA., Illus.). pap. 6.80 (978-0-15-323911-3(5)) Harcourt Schl. Pubs.

—Trofeos On Level: Mi Nabo Enorme. 3rd ed. 2002. (SPA., Illus.). pap. 6.80 (978-0-15-323987-8(5)) Harcourt Schl. Pubs.

—Trofeos On Level: Mi Viaje a la Edad de Piedra. 3rd ed. 2002. (SPA., Illus.). pap. 6.80 (978-0-15-324352-3(X)) Harcourt Schl. Pubs.

—Trofeos On Level: Mi Vida en un Libra Ilustrado. 3rd ed. 2002. (SPA., Illus.). pap. 6.80 (978-0-15-324269-4(8)) Harcourt Schl. Pubs.

—Trofeos On Level: Mi Visita... 3rd ed. 2002. (SPA., Illus.). pap. 6.80 (978-0-15-324006-5(7)) Harcourt Schl. Pubs.

—Trofeos On Level: Mischa Aprende Ingles. 3rd ed. 2002. (SPA., Illus.). (gr. 3). pap. 6.80 (978-0-15-324073-7(3)) Harcourt Schl. Pubs.

—Trofeos On Level: Momo. 3rd ed. 2002. (SPA., Illus.). (J). (gr. 1). pap. 3.50 (978-0-15-323884-0(4)) Harcourt Schl. Pubs.

—Trofeos On Level: Ninas/Rescates. 3rd ed. 2002. (SPA., Illus.). pap. 6.80 (978-0-15-324359-2(7)) Harcourt Schl. Pubs.

—Trofeos On Level: No Lleva Pilas. 3rd ed. 2002. (SPA., Illus.). pap. 6.80 (978-0-15-324177-2(2)) Harcourt Schl. Pubs.

—Trofeos On Level: No Somos Sucios! 3rd ed. 2002. (SPA., Illus.). pap. 6.80 (978-0-15-323915-1(8)) Harcourt Schl. Pubs.

—Trofeos On Level: Nuestro Escondite Favorito. 3rd ed. 2002. (SPA., Illus.). pap. 6.80 (978-0-15-324345-5(7)) Harcourt Schl. Pubs.

—Trofeos On Level: Operacion Tornado. 3rd ed. 2002. (SPA., Illus.). pap. 6.80 (978-0-15-324361-5(9)) Harcourt Schl. Pubs.

—Trofeos On Level: Pajaro/Abrol. 3rd ed. 2002. (SPA., Illus.). pap. 6.80 (978-0-15-323910-6(7)) Harcourt Schl. Pubs.

—Trofeos On Level: Pajaro/Ciudad. 3rd ed. 2002. (SPA., Illus.). (gr. 1). pap. 5.50 (978-0-15-323903-8(4)) Harcourt Schl. Pubs.

—Trofeos On Level: Palomitas/Maiz. 3rd ed. 2002. (SPA., Illus.). (J). pap. 3.50 (978-0-15-323889-5(5)) Harcourt Schl. Pubs.

—Trofeos On Level: Paul Bunyan. 3rd ed. 2002. (SPA., Illus.). pap. 6.80 (978-0-15-323992-2(1)) Harcourt Schl. Pubs.

—Trofeos On Level: Por Que las Hajas. 3rd ed. 2002. (SPA., Illus.). pap. 6.80 (978-0-15-323984-7(0)) Harcourt Schl. Pubs.

—Trofeos On Level: Por Que Tomas Leche Pasteurizada? Tu Guia de Eponimos. 3rd ed. 2002. (SPA., Illus.). pap. 6.80 (978-0-15-324275-5(2)) Harcourt Schl. Pubs.
—Trofeos On Level: Por Si Acaso. 3rd ed. 2002. (SPA., Illus.). (gr. 2). pap. 6.80 (978-0-15-323982-3(4)) Harcourt Schl. Pubs.
—Trofeos On Level: Principe Eduardo. 3rd ed. 2002. (SPA., Illus.). pap. 6.80 (978-0-15-324365-3(1)) Harcourt Schl. Pubs.
—Trofeos On Level: Que Come? 3rd ed. 2002. (SPA., Illus.). (J). pap. 3.50 (978-0-15-323886-4(0)) Harcourt Schl. Pubs.
—Trofeos On Level: Que Es Eso? 3rd ed. 2002. (SPA., Illus.). pap. 5.50 (978-0-15-323892-5(5)) Harcourt Schl. Pubs.
—Trofeos On Level: Que Hay de Comer, Khufu? 3rd ed. 2002. (SPA., Illus.). pap. 6.80 (978-0-15-324354-7(6)) Harcourt Schl. Pubs.
—Trofeos On Level: Que Mimoso! 3rd ed. 2002. (SPA., Illus.). (J). pap. 3.50 (978-0-15-323885-7(2)) Harcourt Schl. Pubs.
—Trofeos On Level: Que Sorpresa! 3rd ed. 2002. (SPA., Illus.). (J). pap. 3.50 (978-0-15-323888-8(7)) Harcourt Schl. Pubs.
—Trofeos On Level: Reconstruir el Pasado. 3rd ed. 2002. (SPA., Illus.). pap. 6.80 (978-0-15-324355-4(4)) Harcourt Schl. Pubs.
—Trofeos On Level: Rescate en Fox Creek. 3rd ed. 2002. (SPA., Illus.). pap. 6.80 (978-0-15-324261-8(2)) Harcourt Schl. Pubs.
—Trofeos On Level: Rios de Baile. 3rd ed. 2002. (SPA., Illus.). pap. 6.80 (978-0-15-324271-7(X)) Harcourt Schl. Pubs.
—Trofeos On Level: Saludos de la Antigua Grecia. 3rd ed. 2002. (SPA., Illus.). pap. 6.80 (978-0-15-324356-1(2)) Harcourt Schl. Pubs.
—Trofeos On Level: Sigue/Repicar. 3rd ed. 2002. (SPA., Illus.). pap. 6.80 (978-0-15-324004-1(0)) Harcourt Schl. Pubs.
—Trofeos On Level: Silencio Detras de Escenario! 3rd ed. 2002. (SPA., Illus.). pap. 6.80 (978-0-15-324268-7(X)) Harcourt Schl. Pubs.
—Trofeos On Level: Somos Detectives. 3rd ed. 2002. (SPA., Illus.). pap. 6.80 (978-0-15-323913-7(1)) Harcourt Schl. Pubs.
—Trofeos On Level: Soy Estadounidense. 3rd ed. 2002. (SPA., Illus.). pap. 6.80 (978-0-15-324182-6(9)) Harcourt Schl. Pubs.
—Trofeos On Level: Sr. Muy Poderoso. 3rd ed. 2002. (SPA., Illus.). pap. 6.80 (978-0-15-324351-6(1)) Harcourt Schl. Pubs.
—Trofeos On Level: Teddy Se Toma. 3rd ed. 2002. (SPA., Illus.). pap. 6.80 (978-0-15-323998-4(0)) Harcourt Schl. Pubs.
—Trofeos On Level: Tisquantum y los Colonos. 3rd ed. 2002. (SPA., Illus.). pap. 6.80 (978-0-15-324277-9(9)) Harcourt Schl. Pubs.
—Trofeos On Level: Todo Saldra Bien. 3rd ed. 2002. (SPA., Illus.). pap. 6.80 (978-0-15-324172-7(1)) Harcourt Schl. Pubs.
—Trofeos On Level: Tortuga en Casa. 3rd ed. 2002. (SPA., Illus.). pap. 6.80 (978-0-15-324077-5(6)) Harcourt Schl. Pubs.
—Trofeos On Level: Tu Si Pedes, Kerry. 3rd ed. 2002. (SPA., Illus.). pap. 6.80 (978-0-15-323986-1(7)) Harcourt Schl. Pubs.
—Trofeos On Level: Un Arbol/Ano. 3rd ed. 2002. (SPA., Illus.). pap. 6.80 (978-0-15-323994-6(8)) Harcourt Schl. Pubs.
—Trofeos On Level: Un Hogar Digno del President. 3rd ed. 2002. (SPA., Illus.). pap. 6.80 (978-0-15-324278-6(7)) Harcourt Schl. Pubs.
—Trofeos On Level: Un Jardin... 3rd ed. 2002. (SPA., Illus.). (gr. 4). pap. 6.80 (978-0-15-324629-6(4)) Harcourt Schl. Pubs.
—Trofeos On Level: Un Lagarto Como Mascota. 3rd ed. 2002. (SPA., Illus.). (gr. 4). pap. 6.80 (978-0-15-324184-0(5)) Harcourt Schl. Pubs.
—Trofeos On Level: Un Mensaje en el Tiempo Cibernetico. 3rd ed. 2002. (SPA., Illus.). pap. 6.80 (978-0-15-324370-7(8)) Harcourt Schl. Pubs.
—Trofeos On Level: Un Viaje al Observatorio. 3rd ed. 2002. (SPA., Illus.). pap. 6.80 (978-0-15-324265-6(5)) Harcourt Schl. Pubs.
—Trofeos On Level: Un Viaje por Alaska. 3rd ed. 2002. (SPA., Illus.). (gr. 5). pap. 6.80 (978-0-15-324259-5(0)) Harcourt Schl. Pubs.
—Trofeos On Level: Una Adivinanza al Dia. 3rd ed. 2002. (SPA., Illus.). pap. 6.80 (978-0-15-324180-2(2)) Harcourt Schl. Pubs.
—Trofeos On Level: Una Carrera en la Oscuridad: Una Obra para Dos Personajes. 3rd ed. 2002. (SPA., Illus.). pap. 6.80 (978-0-15-324364-6(3)) Harcourt Schl. Pubs.
—Trofeos On Level: Una Conversacion. 3rd ed. 2002. (SPA., Illus.). pap. 6.80 (978-0-15-324368-4(6)) Harcourt Schl. Pubs.
—Trofeos On Level: Una Pizca/Acquillo. 3rd ed. 2002. (SPA., Illus.). pap. 6.80 (978-0-15-323990-8(5)) Harcourt Schl. Pubs.
—Trofeos On Level: Y Que Si... 3rd ed. 2002. (SPA., Illus.). pap. 6.80 (978-0-15-324000-3(8)) Harcourt Schl. Pubs.
—Trofoeos Below Level: A Brillar, Estrella! 3rd ed. 2002. (SPA., Illus.). (gr. 5). pap. 6.80 (978-0-15-324225-0(6)) Harcourt Schl. Pubs.
—Under the Blue Moon: Phonics Practice Reader. 1999. (Collections Ser.). (Illus.). (J). pap. 2.60 (978-0-15-312939-1(5)) Harcourt Schl. Pubs.
—Vale Ser Bueno: Phonics Practice Reader. 1999. (Vamos Ser.). (SPA., Illus.). pap. 5.00 (978-0-15-318995-1(9)) Harcourt Schl. Pubs.
—Vamos de Fiesta: Big Book Collection. 1999. (SPA., Illus.). pap. 1144.30 (978-0-15-315091-3(2)) Harcourt Schl. Pubs.
—Vamos de Fiesta: El Sabio Ben Take-Home Book. 2001. (SPA., Illus.). (J). pap. 2.80 (978-0-15-321320-5(5)) Harcourt Schl. Pubs.
—Vamos de Fiesta: Entre Vaqueros Take-Home Book. 2001. (SPA., Illus.). (J). pap. 2.80 (978-0-15-321322-9(1)) Harcourt Schl. Pubs.
—Vamos de Fiesta: Holistic Reading Assessment. 2001. (SPA., Illus.). (gr. 4). pap. 90.50 (978-0-15-317589-3(3)); (gr. 5). pap. 90.50 (978-0-15-317590-9(7)) Harcourt Schl. Pubs.
—Vamos de Fiesta: Intervention Reader. (SPA., Illus.). 2001. (gr. 4). pap. 29.70 (978-0-15-316615-0(0)); 2001. (gr. 5). pap. 29.70 (978-0-15-316616-7(9)); 2000. (gr. 2). pap. 29.70 (978-0-15-316613-6(4)); 2000. (gr. 3). pap. 29.70 (978-0-15-316614-3(2)) Harcourt Schl. Pubs.
—Vamos de Fiesta: Mai: Benchmark. 2001. (SPA., Illus.). pap. 17.10 (978-0-15-322078-4(3)) Harcourt Schl. Pubs.
—Vamos de Fiesta: Phonics Activity Book. 1999. (Trofeos Ser.). (SPA., Illus.). (gr. 1 up). pap. 13.50 (978-0-15-315937-4(5)); (gr. 2 up). pap. 13.50 (978-0-15-316789-8(0)) Harcourt Schl. Pubs.
—Vamos de Fiesta: Phonics Practice Reader Collection. 1999. (SPA., Illus.). (gr. 2). pap. 95.50 (978-0-15-316777-5(7)); (gr. 3). pap. 95.50 (978-0-15-316778-2(5)) Harcourt Schl. Pubs.
—Vamos de Fiesta: Preparadas...Listas...Ya! Reader's Choice. 2001. (SPA., Illus.). pap. 16.30 (978-0-15-319903-5(2)) Harcourt Schl. Pubs.
—Vamos de Fiesta: Reading Skills Assessment. 2001. (SPA., Illus.). (gr. 4). pap. 86.70 (978-0-15-317578-7(8)); (gr. 5). pap. 86.70 (978-0-15-317579-4(6)) Harcourt Schl. Pubs.
—Vamos de Fiesta: Selection Completion Test with Answer Key. (SPA., Illus.). 2001. (gr. 4). pap. 30.90 (978-0-15-316715-7(7)); 2001. (gr. 5). pap. 30.90 (978-0-15-316716-4(5)); 1999. (gr. 1). pap. 25.00 (978-0-15-316623-5(1)); 1999. (gr. 2). pap. 30.90 (978-0-15-316624-2(X)); 1999. (gr. 3). pap. 30.90 (978-0-15-316625-9(8)) Harcourt Schl. Pubs.
—Vamos de Fiesta: Student Materials Package: Texas Edition. 1999. (SPA., Illus.). (gr. 1). pap. 186.30 (978-0-15-315020-3(3)); (gr. 2). pap. 103.50 (978-0-15-315021-0(1)); (gr. 3). pap. 103.50 (978-0-15-315022-7(X)) Harcourt Schl. Pubs.
—Vamos de Fiesta: Student Materials Package with Translation: Texas Edition. 1999. (SPA & ENG., Illus.). pap. 128.30 (978-0-15-315050-0(5)) Harcourt Schl. Pubs.
—Vamos de Fiesta: Susan B. Anthony Take-Home Book. 2001. (SPA., Illus.). (J). pap. 2.80 (978-0-15-321323-6(X)) Harcourt Schl. Pubs.
—Vamos de Fiesta: Un Grande Dia en Nicodemus Take-Home Book. 2001. (SPA., Illus.). (J). pap. 2.80 (978-0-15-321321-2(3)) Harcourt Schl. Pubs.
—Vamos de Fiesta Below Level: Take-Home Book. 2001. (SPA., Illus.). (gr. 4). pap. 31.60 (978-0-15-317975-4(9)); (gr. 5). pap. 31.60 (978-0-15-317976-1(7)) Harcourt Schl. Pubs.
—Vamos de Fiesta Intermediate Level: Phonics Activity Book. 1999. (Trofeos Ser.). (SPA., Illus.). (gr. k-6). pap. 13.50 (978-0-15-316799-7(8)) Harcourt Schl. Pubs.
—Vamos de Fiesta Level D: Asombrosa Graciela. 2001. (SPA., Illus.). pap. 16.90 (978-0-15-319909-7(1)) Harcourt Schl. Pubs.
—Vamos de Fiesta Level D: Babe. 2001. (SPA., Illus.). pap. 18.80 (978-0-15-319908-0(3)) Harcourt Schl. Pubs.
—Vamos de Fiesta Level D: Barriletes. 2001. (SPA., Illus.). pap. 16.00 (978-0-15-319910-3(5)) Harcourt Schl. Pubs.
—Vamos de Fiesta Level D: Beisbol en los Barrios. 2001. (SPA., Illus.). pap. 15.50 (978-0-15-319925-7(3)) Harcourt Schl. Pubs.
—Vamos de Fiesta Level D: Carlos y el Zorrillo. 2001. (SPA., Illus.). pap. 20.90 (978-0-15-319912-7(1)) Harcourt Schl. Pubs.
—Vamos de Fiesta Level D: Chaikovski Descubre America. 2001. (SPA.). pap. 20.70 (978-0-15-319923-3(7)) Harcourt Schl. Pubs.
—Vamos de Fiesta Level D: Doctor De Soto. 2001. (SPA., Illus.). pap. 16.50 (978-0-15-319913-4(X)) Harcourt Schl. Pubs.
—Vamos de Fiesta Level D: La Musica de Chirimia. 2001. (SPA., Illus.). pap. 20.90 (978-0-15-322074-6(0)) Harcourt Schl. Pubs.
—Vamos de Fiesta Level D: Pepita Habla Dos Veces. 2001. (SPA., Illus.). pap. 16.50 (978-0-15-319911-0(3)) Harcourt Schl. Pubs.
—Vamos de Fiesta Level D: Volcanes. 2001. (SPA., Illus.). (gr. 5). pap. 22.90 (978-0-15-319922-6(9)) Harcourt Schl. Pubs.
—Vamos de Fiesta Set I: Guided Reading Library. 2001. (SPA., Illus.). (gr. 5). 420.20 (978-0-15-319376-7(X)) Harcourt Schl. Pubs.
—Vamos de Fiesta, Grade 1 Level B: Phonics Express Espanol. 2000. (Trofeos Ser.). (SPA.). (gr. 1 up). pap., tchr. ed. 12.30 (978-0-15-318471-0(X)) Harcourt Schl. Pubs.
—Vamos de Fiesta, Grade 2 Level C: Phonics Express Espanol. 2000. (Trofeos Ser.). (SPA.). (gr. 2 up). pap., tchr. ed. 12.30 (978-0-15-318478-9(7)) Harcourt Schl. Pubs.
—Vamos de Fiesta, Grade 2-3: Phonics Practice Readers. 2000. (SPA.). pap., tchr. ed. 25.10 (978-0-15-316779-9(3)) Harcourt Schl. Pubs.
—Vamos de Fiesta, Grade 3: Actividades Foneticas. 1999. (Trofeos Ser.). (SPA.). (gr. k-6). pap., tchr. ed. 26.70 (978-0-15-317978-5(3)) Harcourt Schl. Pubs.
—Vamos de Fiesta, Grade 3 Level D: Phonics Express Espanol. 2000. (Trofeos Ser.). (SPA.). (gr. 3 up). pap., tchr. ed. 12.30 (978-0-15-318485-7(X)) Harcourt Schl. Pubs.
—Vamos de Fiesta, Grade K: Actividades Foneticas. 1999. (Trofeos Ser.). (SPA.). (gr. k-6). pap., tchr. ed. 26.70 (978-0-15-315114-9(5)) Harcourt Schl. Pubs.
—Vamos de Fiesta, Grade K Level A: Phonics Express Espanol. 2000. (Trofeos Ser.). (SPA.). (gr. 1 up). pap., tchr. ed. 12.30 (978-0-15-318465-9(5)) Harcourt Schl. Pubs.
—Vamos Take-Home Book Collection: 30 Titles. 2001. (Vamos Ser.). (SPA., Illus.). pap. 105.60 (978-0-15-319944-8(X)) Harcourt Schl. Pubs.
—Welcome Home Level 4. 1999. (Collections Ser.). (Illus.). 31.50 (978-0-15-312041-1(X)) Harcourt Schl. Pubs.
—Who at the Zoo: Phonics Practice Reader. 1999. (Collections Ser.). (Illus.). (J). pap. 2.60 (978-0-15-312938-4(7)) Harcourt Schl. Pubs.
—Wonder Cat: Phonics Practice Reader. 1999. (Collections Ser.). (Illus.). (J). (gr. 2). pap. 2.60 (978-0-15-312916-2(6)) Harcourt Schl. Pubs.
—Ya No Me Atrapas: Take-Home Book. 1999. (Vamos Ser.). (SPA., Illus.). (J). pap. 2.50 (978-0-15-318817-6(0)) Harcourt Schl. Pubs.
—Zapatos Para Zizi: Phonics Practice Reader. 1999. (Vamos Ser.). (SPA., Illus.). pap. 5.00 (978-0-15-318997-5(5)) Harcourt Schl. Pubs.
—El Zar y la Zarina: Phonics Practice Reader. 1999. (Vamos Ser.). (SPA., Illus.). pap. 5.00 (978-0-15-318959-3(2)) Harcourt Schl. Pubs.
Harpster, Steve, illus. Easy Reader Phonics. 2005. (First Word Search Ser.). 64p. pap. 3.95 (978-1-4027-2297-4(4)) Sterling Publishing Co., Inc.
—Fun First Phonics. 2004. (First Word Search Ser.). 64p. (J). pap. 3.95 (978-1-4027-1321-7(5)) Sterling Publishing Co., Inc.
Hartley, Susan. Buzz, Buzz. 2003. (StartUp Ser.). (J). pap. 22.00 (978-1-4108-0717-5(7)) Benchmark Education Co.
Hasbrouck, Ph.D., Jan, contrib. by. Quick Phonics Assessment. 2007. spiral bd. 200.00 ***(978-1-4108-6802-2(8))*** Benchmark Education Co.
Hayden, Lorelea. Read & Write. Caves, Alisa et al, illus. 2002. 246p. (J). (ps-1). pap. 25.00 (978-0-9723511-0-2(8)) Read & Write Pr.
Headway Level D Real Phonics Workbook A. (J). (gr. 2). (978-0-89688-294-2(2) , 88-294) SRA/McGraw-Hill.
Headway Level F Real Phonic Workbook. (J). (gr. 3). (978-0-89688-295-9(0) , 88-295) SRA/McGraw-Hill.
Hey Diddle Diddle. 2001. (Take-Home Bks.). (YA). (ps-k). 15.00 (978-0-8215-6987-0(2)) Sadlier, William H. Inc.
Hidden Pictures Phonics (Gr. 1-2) 2003. (J). (978-1-58232-064-9(0)) Bryan Hse. Pubs., Inc.
Hiebert, Elfrieda H. & Juel, Connie. Can a Cow Hop? (Little Book Practice Reader Ser.). (J). (978-0-8136-0796-2(5)) Modern Curriculum Pr.
—Flip's Trick. (J). (978-0-8136-2166-1(6)) Modern Curriculum Pr.
—Pat's Perfect Pizza, Level 3, Bk. 14. (J). (ps-3). 24.50 (978-0-8136-1945-3(9)) Modern Curriculum Pr.
—Pop Pops the Popcorn. (J). (978-0-8136-2008-4(2)) Modern Curriculum Pr.
—Red & I Visit the Vet. (Little Book Practice Reader Ser.). (J). (978-0-8136-0881-5(3)) Modern Curriculum Pr.
Hoffman, Joan. Beginning Phonics. rev. ed. 2002. (I Know It! Workbooks Ser.). (Illus.). 32p. (J). (gr. 1-2). pap. 2.49 (978-0-88743-333-7(2) , 02107) School Zone Publishing Co.
Hooked on Phonics - Get Ready to Read - Letter Names. 2005. (J). (ps up). 99.99 (978-1-931020-46-6(9)) HOP, LLC.
Hooked on Phonics - Get Ready to Read - Letter Sounds. 2005. (J). (ps up). 99.99 (978-1-931020-47-3(7)) HOP, LLC.
Hooked on Phonics - Learn to Read. 1998. (Illus.). (J). (ps-3). 952p. pap. 229.95 incl. audio (978-1-887942-88-1(2)); 1658p. pap. 269.95 incl. audio (978-1-887942-90-4(4)) HOP, LLC.
Hooked on Phonics - Learn to Read: Classroom Edition. 1999. (Illus.). 1044p. (J). (ps-3). pap. 594.95 incl. audio (978-1-887942-83-6(1)) HOP, LLC.
Hooked on Phonics - Learn to Read: K-1st Grade. 2000. (Illus.). 266p. (J). (gr. k-1). pap. 49.95 incl. audio (978-1-887942-86-7(6)) HOP, LLC.
Hooked on Phonics Chapter Books. 1998. (Illus.). 594p. (J). (ps-3). pap. 39.95 (978-1-887942-55-3(6)) HOP, LLC.
Hooked on Phonics Staff. Hooked on English. 2007. 199.99 ***(978-1-60143-752-5(8))*** HOP, LLC.
Hooked on Phonics Staff, contrib. by. Hooked on Second Grade Super Workbook. 2007. 320p. (J). pap. 12.99 ***(978-1-60143-468-5(5))*** HOP, LLC.
HOP, LLC. Hooked on Phonics Beginning Reading with Bible Stories. 2006. 29.99 (978-1-931020-80-0(9)) HOP, LLC.
—Hooked on Phonics Learn to Read (Kindergarten & First Grade) 2006. 139.99 (978-1-931020-95-4(7)) HOP, LLC.
—Hooked on Phonics Reading Comprehension. 2006. 64p. 3.79 (978-1-933863-94-8(3)) HOP, LLC.
—Hooked on Phonics Word Games. 2006. 64p. 3.79 (978-1-933863-93-1(5)) HOP, LLC.
HOP LLC Staff. Hooked on Phonics - Learn to Read Kindergarten. 2005. (J). (gr. k up). 69.99 (978-1-931020-29-9(9)) HOP, LLC.
—Hooked on Phonics - Learn to Read Second Grade. 2005. (J). (gr. 2 up). 69.99 (978-1-931020-31-2(0)) HOP, LLC.
HOP LLC Staff, ed. Hooked on Phonics - Learn to Read First Grade. 2005. (J). (gr. 1 up). 69.99 (978-1-931020-30-5(2)) HOP, LLC.
La Hora de Comer, 6 Packs. (Chiquilibros Ser.). (SPA.). (gr. k-1). 23.00 (978-0-7635-8590-7(4)) Rigby Education.
Huggles Can Jungle: Level A. Group 1. (Sunshinetm Ser.). 8p. 20.95 (978-0-7802-5707-8(3)) Wright Group, The.
I Can Say S. (Illus.). 160p. 19.95 (978-0-937857-88-5(2) , 1478) Speech Bin, Inc., The.
I Can Swim. (J). 14.15 (978-0-8136-2035-0(X)) Modern Curriculum Pr.
I'm Learning My Phonics. 2004. (Flash Card + Music CD Learning Kits Ser.). (Illus.). 20p. 18.99 (978-1-894677-61-5(7)) Kidzup Productions.
A Is It Hot? Is It Not? Set, 6 vols. (Phonics Readers Ser.). (gr. k-2). 17.50 (978-0-7368-3186-4(X)) Red Brick Learning.
J My Name Is Jess. 2005. (Emergent Library: Vol. 2). (YA). (ps-1). 23.94 (978-0-8215-8935-9(0)) Sadlier, William H. Inc.
J My Name Is Jess: Take-Home Book. 2005. (Emergent Library: Vol. 2). (YA). (ps-1). 12.60 (978-0-8215-7265-8(2)) Sadlier, William H. Inc.
Jackson, Barbara A. How to Read with Magic Sounds... an Advanced Reading Program Phonics First. 2001. (Illus.). 63p. (J). (ps-6). stu. ed. 10.00 (978-0-9712857-5-0(6)) Educational Innovations, Inc.
—How to Read with Magic Sounds Classic - Continum Collection: Phonics First - Second Guide, 2 vols. 2001. (Illus.). (J). pap. 50.00 (978-0-9712857-0-5(5)) Educational Innovations, Inc.
—How to Read with Magicsounds... a Beginning Reading Program Phonics First, Vol. 2. 2001. (Illus.). 43p. (J). (ps-6). pap., stu. ed. 10.00 (978-0-9712857-4-3(8)) Educational Innovations, Inc.
Jacobson, Jennifer. Easy Word Family Lessons for the Overhead: 12 Transparencies, Reproducibles, & Fun, Interactive Lessons for Teaching Essential Phonics Skills. 2004. 32p. pap. 12.99 (978-0-439-51387-6(1) , Teaching Resources) Scholastic, Inc.
Jake's Big Day: Long Vowel a, CVCe Pattern: Level B, 6 vols. (Wright Skills Ser.). 16p. (gr. k-3). 17.95 (978-0-322-01465-7(4)) Wright Group, The.
Joe's Toe: Long o Digraphs: Level B, 6 vols. (Wright Skills Ser.). 16p. (gr. k-3). 26.50 (978-0-322-01480-0(8)) Wright Group, The.
Jog to the Dam: Consonants g, h, j; Short Vowel o word families: Level A, 6 vols. (Wright Skills Ser.). 12p. (gr. k-3). 17.95 (978-0-322-01448-0(4)) Wright Group, The.
Jones, Shelley V. & Gunn, Barbara. Read Well Magazine Unit 20: Slanted Text. 2003. (Read Well Level K Ser.). (Illus.). 8p. (J). (978-1-59318-104-8(3)) Sopris West Educational Services.
—Shells on the Shore: Read Well Level K Unit 14 Storybook. Jerde, Susan, illus. 2003. (Read Well Level K Ser.). 20p. (J). (978-1-57035-685-8(8) , 55546) Sopris West Educational Services.
Jordan, Sara. Funky Phonics, Vol. 4. 2004. 64p. (J). pap. (978-1-55386-023-5(3)) Crabtree Publishing Co.
—Funky Phonics Volume 1. 2004. 64p. (J). pap. (978-1-55386-005-1(5)) Crabtree Publishing Co.
—Funky Phonics Volume 2. 2004. 64p. (J). pap. (978-1-55386-011-2(X)) Crabtree Publishing Co.
—Funky Phonics Volume 3. 2004. (Illus.). 64p. (J). pap. (978-1-55386-017-4(9)) Crabtree Publishing Co.
Kalar, Bonnie. At Dawn. Spreen, Kathe, illus. Date not set. 8p. (J). (ps-2). pap. (978-1-891619-24-3(1)) Corona Pr.
—At the Lake. Spreen, Kathe, illus. Date not set. 12p. (J). (ps-2). pap. (978-1-891619-34-2(9)) Corona Pr.
—At the Pond. Spreen, Kathe, illus. Date not set. 8p. (J). (ps-2). pap. (978-1-891619-07-6(1)) Corona Pr.
—At the Zoo. Spreen, Kathe, illus. Date not set. 8p. (J). (ps-2). pap. (978-1-891619-18-2(7)) Corona Pr.
—Beth & Thad. Spreen, Kathe, illus. Date not set. 12p. (J). (ps-2). pap. (978-1-891619-17-5(9)) Corona Pr.
—The Bird & the Shirt. Spreen, Kathe, illus. Date not set. 12p. (J). (ps-2). pap. (978-1-891619-30-4(6)) Corona Pr.
—Bob. Spreen, Kathe, illus. 1998. 8p. (J). (ps-2). pap. (978-1-891619-01-4(2)) Corona Pr.
—Burt. Spreen, Kathe, illus. Date not set. 8p. (J). (ps-2). pap. (978-1-891619-31-1(4)) Corona Pr.
—Chuck & the Chick. Spreen, Kathe, illus. Date not set. 8p. (J). (ps-2). pap. (978-1-891619-16-8(0)) Corona Pr.
—The Clown. Spreen, Kathe, illus. Date not set. 12p. (J). (ps-2). pap. (978-1-891619-22-9(5)) Corona Pr.
—The Cook & the Crook. Spreen, Kathe, illus. Date not set. 12p. (J). (ps-2). pap. (978-1-891619-29-8(2)) Corona Pr.
—The Crows. Spreen, Kathe, illus. Date not set. 8p. (J). (ps-2). pap. (978-1-891619-28-1(4)) Corona Pr.
—A Dream. Spreen, Kathe, illus. Date not set. 12p. (J). (ps-2). pap. (978-1-891619-23-6(3)) Corona Pr.
—Early Phonetic Readers - Set A, 5 bks., Set. Spreen, Kathe, illus. Incl. Bob. pap. (978-1-891619-01-4(2)); Cat & the Ant. pap. (978-1-891619-02-1(0)); Gus on the Bus. pap. (978-1-891619-03-8(9)); Hen & the Jet. pap. (978-1-891619-05-2(5)); Tim & Kim. pap. (978-1-891619-04-5(7)); (Illus.). 8p. (J). (ps-2). 1998. 8.25 (978-1-891619-00-7(4)) Corona Pr.
—Early Phonetic Readers - Set B, 5 bks., Set. Spreen, Kathe, illus. Incl. At the Pond. pap. (978-1-891619-07-6(1)); Fran & the Doll. pap. (978-1-891619-09-0(8)); Fred. pap. (978-1-891619-10-6(1)); Stan & His Sled. pap. (978-1-891619-08-3(X)); Trip. pap. (978-1-891619-11-3(X)); (Illus.). 8p. (J). (ps-2). 8.25 (978-1-891619-06-9(3)) Corona Pr.
—Early Phonetic Readers - Set C, 20 bks., Set. Spreen, Kathe, illus. Incl. At Dawn. 8p. pap. (978-1-891619-24-3(1)); At the Zoo. 8p. pap. (978-1-891619-18-2(7)); Beth & Thad. 12p. pap. (978-1-891619-17-5(9)); Bird & the Shirt. 12p. pap. (978-1-891619-30-4(6)); Bright Light. 8p. 5.25 hd (978-1-891619-32-8(2)); Burt. 8p. pap. (978-1-891619-31-1(4)); Chuck & the Chick. 8p. pap. (978-1-891619-16-8(0)); Clown. 12p. pap. (978-1-891619-22-9(5)); Cook & the Crook. 12p. pap. (978-1-891619-29-8(2)); Crows. 8p. pap. (978-1-891619-28-1(4)); Dream. 12p. pap. (978-1-891619-23-6(3)); Gail Sails. 12p. pap. (978-1-891619-20-5(9)); Gay & Jay Play. 8p. pap. (978-1-891619-19-9(5)); Jack. 12p. pap.

(978-1-891619-13-7(6)); Joan's Coat. 12p. pap. (978-1-891619-21-2(7)); Josh & the Fish. 8p. pap. (978-1-891619-14-4(4)); Lew & His New Cap. 8p. pap. (978-1-891619-27-4(6)); Mark at the Farm. 12p. pap. (978-1-891619-25-0(X)); Scouts. 8p. pap. (978-1-891619-26-7(8)); Sheep & the Bee. 8p. pap. (978-1-891619-15-1(2)); (Illus.). (J). (ps-2). 38.50 (978-1-891619-12-0(8)) Corona Pr.

—Early Phonetic Readers - Set D, 3 bks., Set. Spreen, Kathe, illus. Incl. At the Lake. 12p. pap. (978-1-891619-34-2(9)); Mike. 8p. pap. (978-1-891619-35-9(7)); Rose & the Mole. 12p. pap. (978-1-891619-36-6(5)); (Illus.). (J). (ps-2). 6.25 (978-1-891619-33-5(0)) Corona Pr.

—Early Phonetic Readers - Set E, 7 bks., set. Spreen, Kathe, illus. Incl. Ann Paints & Plays. pap. (978-1-891619-40-3(3)); Clair at Home. pap. (978-1-891619-44-1(6)); Good Day. pap. (978-1-891619-41-0(1)); Kirk & the Deer. pap. (978-1-891619-43-4(8)); Miss Lane's Class. pap. (978-1-891619-38-0(1)); Neal Camps Out. pap. (978-1-891619-39-7(X)); Trip to the Beach. pap. (978-1-891619-42-7(X)); 12p. (J). (ps-2). (Illus.). Set pap. 14.50 (978-1-891619-37-3(3)) Corona Pr.

—Fran & the Doll. Spreen, Kathe, illus. Date not set. 8p. (J). (ps-2). pap. (978-1-891619-09-0(8)) Corona Pr.

—Fred. Spreen, Kathe, illus. Date not set. 8p. (J). (ps-2). pap. (978-1-891619-10-6(1)) Corona Pr.

—Gail Sails. Spreen, Kathe, illus. Date not set. 12p. (J). (ps-2). pap. (978-1-891619-20-5(9)) Corona Pr.

—Gay & Jay Play. Spreen, Kathe, illus. Date not set. 8p. (J). (ps-2). pap. (978-1-891619-19-9(5)) Corona Pr.

—Joan's Coat. Spreen, Kathe, illus. Date not set. 12p. (J). (ps-2). pap. (978-1-891619-21-2(7)) Corona Pr.

—Lew & His New Cap. Spreen, Kathe, illus. Date not set. 8p. (J). (ps-2). pap. (978-1-891619-27-4(6)) Corona Pr.

—Mark at the Farm. Spreen, Kathe, illus. Date not set. 12p. (J). (ps-2). pap. (978-1-891619-25-0(X)) Corona Pr.

—Mike. Spreen, Kathe, illus. Date not set. 8p. (J). (ps-2). pap. (978-1-891619-35-9(7)) Corona Pr.

—Rose & the Mole. Spreen, Kathe, illus. Date not set. 12p. (J). (ps-2). pap. (978-1-891619-36-6(5)) Corona Pr.

—The Sheep & the Bee. Spreen, Kathe, illus. Date not set. 8p. (J). (ps-2). pap. (978-1-891619-15-1(2)) Corona Pr.

—Stan & His Sled. Spreen, Kathe, illus. Date not set. 8p. (J). (ps-2). pap. (978-1-891619-08-3(X)) Corona Pr.

—Tim & Kim. Spreen, Kathe, illus. 1998. 8p. (J). (ps-2). pap. (978-1-891619-04-5(7)) Corona Pr.

—The Trip. Spreen, Kathe, illus. Date not set. 8p. (J). (ps-2). pap. (978-1-891619-11-3(X)) Corona Pr.

Kang, Hildi. Phonemic Awareness: Listening Activities for Developing Pre-Reading Skills. 2001. 48p. (J). (gr. k-2). pap. 8.99 (978-1-56417-944-9(3) , FE7944, Fearon Teacher Aids) Schaffer, Frank Pubns.

Kate, Paul. Little Book: The Best Ride. 2000. (Sadlier Phonics Reading Program). 8p. (J). (978-0-8215-7305-1(5) , Sadlier-Oxford) Sadlier, William H. Inc.

Katschke, Judy. Duke & Fang, Level 3. Baumann, Marty, illus. 2006. (Phonics Comics Ser.). 24p. (J). (gr. 1-17). pap. 3.99 (978-1-58476-411-3(2) , IKIDS) Innovative Kids.

Keeping Fit Set D, 6 vols. (Phonics Readers Ser.). (gr. k-2). 28.95 (978-0-7368-4058-3(3)) Red Brick Learning.

Kids Can Press Staff, Press Can. First Phonics. 2004. (Kids Can Learn with Franklin Ser.). (Illus.). 32p. (J). (gr. k-3). (978-1-55337-594-4(7)) Kids Can Pr., Ltd.

Kindergarten Phonics. 2002. (Home Workbooks Ser.). (Illus.). 64p. (J). wbk. ed. 2.49 (978-0-88724-719-4(9) , CD-4521) Carson-Dellosa Publishing Co., Inc.

Kindergarten Reader: Take-Home Version. 2004. (gr. k up). 48.00 (978-0-328-02300-4(0)) Addison-Wesley Educational Pubs., Inc.

Kindergarten Review 1.1: Take-Home Version. 2004. (gr. 1 up). stu. ed. 48.00 (978-0-328-02543-5(7)) Addison-Wesley Educational Pubs., Inc.

Klingel, Cynthia Fitterer & Noyed, Robert B. Dreams: The Sound of DR. 2002. (Wonder Books Phonics: R Blends Ser.). (Illus.). 24p. (J). (ps-3). 21.36 (978-1-56766-049-4(5)) Child's World, Inc.

—In the Crib: The Sound of CR. 2002. (Wonder Books Phonics: R Blends Ser.). (Illus.). 24p. (J). (ps-3). 21.36 (978-1-56766-048-7(7)) Child's World, Inc.

—What Do I Bring? The Sound of BR. 2002. (Wonder Books Phonics: R Blends Ser.). (Illus.). 24p. (J). (ps-3). 21.36 (978-1-56766-047-0(9)) Child's World, Inc.

Kozyrev, Joann. Sound Bites! Pronunciation Activities. 2004. 208p. (YA). pap. 31.96 (978-0-618-25972-4(4) , 330538) Houghton Mifflin College Div.

Kumon Publishing Staff, ed. My Book of Rhyming Words Long Vowels. 2007. 80p. (J). pap. 6.95 ***978-1-933241-37-1(3))** Kumon Publishing North America, Inc.

LaCoste, Gary, illus. First Word Search: Phonics for Beginners. 2007. (First Word Search Ser.). 64p. (J). pap. 3.95 ***(978-1-4027-4662-8(8))*** Sterling Publishing Co., Inc.

Ladd, Ann Frances. Scooby Doo Phonics: 12 Book Reading Program, No. 1. 2005. (Scooby Doo Ser.). 240p. (J). 12.99 (978-0-439-66478-3(0)) Scholastic, Inc.

Lakeshore Learning Materials Staff, contrib. by. Jump, Frog, Jump! Packet. 2000. (J). pap. 34.95 (978-1-929255-45-0(4)) Lakeshore Learning Materials.

—Learning Vowel Sounds Literature Packets - Complete Set, 10 vols., Set. 2000. (J). pap. 179.00 (978-1-929255-36-8(5)) Lakeshore Learning Materials.

Lapin, Gloria & Radtke, Becky. More Sight Word Stories: 57 Reproducible Books for Beginning Readers. 2001. (Illus.). 136p. (J). (gr. 1-3). pap. 15.99 (978-1-56417-969-2(9) , FE7954, Fearon Teacher Aids) Schaffer, Frank Pubns.

Las Estaciones: Individual Title Two-Packs. (Chiquilibros Ser.). (SPA.). (ps-1). 12.00 (978-0-7635-8563-1(7)) Rigby Education.

Laurence, Jo. How to Be a Wizard at Phonics. 48p. (J). (gr. 1-4). pap. (978-1-875739-64-6(5)) Wizard Bks.

Leaney, Cindy. An Amazing Machine. Whitehouse, Patty, ed. King, Sue & Wilks, Peter, illus. 2004. (Friendly Phonics Ser.). 24p. (J). lib. bdg. 14.95 (978-1-59054-194-4(4)) Fitzgerald Bks.

—The Circus. Whitehouse, Patty, ed. King, Sue & Wilks, Peter, illus. 2004. (Friendly Phonics Ser.). 24p. (J). lib. bdg. 14.95 (978-1-59054-114-2(6)) Fitzgerald Bks.

—Desert Dream. Whitehouse, Patty, ed. King, Sue & Wilks, Peter, illus. 2004. (Friendly Phonics Ser.). 24p. (J). lib. bdg. 14.95 (978-1-59054-117-3(0)) Fitzgerald Bks.

—Fish Can Fly. Whitehouse, Patty, ed. King, Sue & Wilks, Peter, illus. 2004. (Friendly Phonics Ser.). 24p. (J). lib. bdg. 14.95 (978-1-59054-106-7(5)) Fitzgerald Bks.

—Fun at the Fair. Whitehouse, Patty, ed. King, Sue & Wilks, Peter, illus. 2004. (Friendly Phonics Ser.). 24p. (J). lib. bdg. 14.95 (978-1-59054-153-1(7)) Fitzgerald Bks.

—The Giant's Garden. Whitehouse, Patty, ed. King, Sue & Wilks, Peter, illus. 2004. (Friendly Phonics Ser.). 24p. (J). lib. bdg. 14.95 (978-1-59054-181-4(2)) Fitzgerald Bks.

—Harry Has Hiccups. Whitehouse, Patty, ed. King, Sue & Wilks, Peter, illus. 2004. (Friendly Phonics Ser.). 24p. (J). lib. bdg. 14.95 (978-1-59054-182-1(0)) Fitzgerald Bks.

—Jungle Journey. Whitehouse, Patty, ed. King, Sue & Wilks, Peter, illus. 2004. (Friendly Phonics Ser.). 24p. (J). lib. bdg. 14.95 (978-1-59054-183-8(9)) Fitzgerald Bks.

—Just Lazy Luke. Whitehouse, Patty, ed. King, Sue & Wilks, Peter, illus. 2004. (Friendly Phonics Ser.). 24p. (J). lib. bdg. 14.95 (978-1-59054-105-0(7)) Fitzgerald Bks.

—A Long List. Whitehouse, Peter, ed. King, Sue & Wilks, Peter, illus. 2004. (Friendly Phonics Ser.). 24p. (J). lib. bdg. 14.95 (978-1-59054-190-6(1)) Fitzgerald Bks.

—Mr. Know-it-all Crow. Whitehouse, Patty, ed. King, Sue & Wilks, Peter, illus. 2004. (Friendly Phonics Ser.). 24p. (J). lib. bdg. 14.95 (978-1-59054-086-2(7)) Fitzgerald Bks.

—Nice News. Whitehouse, Patty, ed. King, Sue & Wilks, Peter, illus. 2004. (Friendly Phonics Ser.). 24p. (J). lib. bdg. 14.95 (978-1-59054-205-7(3)) Fitzgerald Bks.

—Note in a Bottle. Whitehouse, Patty, ed. King, Sue & Wilks, Peter, illus. 2004. (Friendly Phonics Ser.). 24p. (J). lib. bdg. 14.95 (978-1-59054-107-4(3)) Fitzgerald Bks.

—On the Beach. Whitehouse, Patty, ed. King, Sue & Wilks, Peter, illus. 2004. (Friendly Phonics Ser.). 24p. (J). lib. bdg. 14.95 (978-1-59054-108-1(1)) Fitzgerald Bks.

—Oodles of Noodles. Whitehouse, Patty, ed. King, Sue & Wilks, Peter, illus. 2004. (Friendly Phonics Ser.). 24p. (J). lib. bdg. 14.95 (978-1-59054-030-5(1)) Fitzgerald Bks.

—Picnic in the Park. Whitehouse, Patty, ed. King, Sue & Wilks, Peter, illus. 2004. (Friendly Phonics Ser.). 24p. (J). lib. bdg. 14.95 (978-1-59054-217-0(7)) Fitzgerald Bks.

—Rachel the Shy Jellyfish. Whitehouse, Patty, ed. King, Sue & Wilks, Peter, illus. 2004. (Friendly Phonics Ser.). 24p. (J). lib. bdg. 14.95 (978-1-59054-274-3(6)) Fitzgerald Bks.

—Rainy Day Play. Whitehouse, Patty, ed. King, Sue & Wilks, Peter, illus. 2004. (Friendly Phonics Ser.). 24p. (J). lib. bdg. 14.95 (978-1-59054-047-3(6)) Fitzgerald Bks.

—Rescue & Repair. Whitehouse, Patty, ed. King, Sue & Wilks, Peter, illus. 2004. (Friendly Phonics Ser.). 24p. (J). lib. bdg. 14.95 (978-1-59054-225-5(8)) Fitzgerald Bks.

—Station K. I. D. S. Whitehouse, Patty, ed. King, Sue & Wilks, Peter, illus. 2004. (Friendly Phonics Ser.). 24p. (J). lib. bdg. 14.95 (978-1-59054-186-9(3)) Fitzgerald Bks.

—Super Sale. Whitehouse, Patty, ed. King, Sue & Wilks, Peter, illus. 2004. (Friendly Phonics Ser.). 24p. (J). lib. bdg. 14.95 (978-1-59054-231-6(2)) Fitzgerald Bks.

—A Talking Telescope. Whitehouse, Patty, ed. King, Sue & Wilks, Peter, illus. 2004. (Friendly Phonics Ser.). 24p. (J). lib. bdg. 14.95 (978-1-59054-247-7(9)) Fitzgerald Bks.

—What Do You See? Whitehouse, Patty, ed. King, Sue & Wilks, Peter, illus. 2004. (Friendly Phonics Ser.). 24p. (J). lib. bdg. 14.95 (978-1-59054-039-8(5)) Fitzgerald Bks.

LeapFrog Staff, compiled by. Alphabet Adventures. 2002. (J). (ps-2). spiral bd. 14.99 (978-1-58605-738-1(3)) LeapFrog Enterprises, Inc.

—Around the Block. 2001. (J). (ps-2). spiral bd. 11.95 (978-1-58605-066-5(4)) LeapFrog Enterprises, Inc.

—At the Art Mart. 2001. (J). (ps-2). spiral bd. 14.95 (978-1-58605-063-4(X)) LeapFrog Enterprises, Inc.

—At the Lake in June. 2001. (J). (ps-2). spiral bd. 13.95 (978-1-58605-053-5(2)) LeapFrog Enterprises, Inc.

—A Bark in the Dark. 2002. (J). (ps-2). spiral bd. 14.99 (978-1-58605-746-6(4)) LeapFrog Enterprises, Inc.

—A Day at Moss Lake. 2002. (J). (ps-2). spiral bd. 14.99 (978-1-58605-740-4(5)) LeapFrog Enterprises, Inc.

—The Day Leap Ate Olives. 2002. (J). (ps-2). spiral bd. 14.99 (978-1-58605-741-1(3)) LeapFrog Enterprises, Inc.

—Learning Phonics with Leap. 2001. (YA). (ps up). spiral bd. 9.99 (978-1-58605-097-9(4)) LeapFrog Enterprises, Inc.

—Lost & Found. 2002. (J). (ps-2). spiral bd. 14.99 (978-1-58605-742-8(1)) LeapFrog Enterprises, Inc.

—The Mole's Huge Nose. 2002. (J). (ps-2). spiral bd. 14.99 (978-1-58605-744-2(8)) LeapFrog Enterprises, Inc.

—Rainy Day Play. 2002. (J). (ps-2). spiral bd. 14.99 (978-1-58605-745-9(6)) LeapFrog Enterprises, Inc.

—Rhyme & Sing with Mother Goose. 2002. (YA). (ps up). spiral bd. 9.99 (978-1-58605-795-4(2)) LeapFrog Enterprises, Inc.

—Tad's Good Night. 2002. (J). (ps-2). spiral bd. 14.99 (978-1-58605-739-8(1)) LeapFrog Enterprises, Inc.

A Learn about the Past Set, 6 vols. (Phonics Readers Ser.). (gr. k-2). 17.50 (978-0-7368-3189-5(4)) Red Brick Learning.

Leber, Nancy Jolson & Onish, Liane B. We're Ready for Pre-K! Sounds & Letters. 2006. (Clear & Simple Workbooks Ser.). 64p. (J). pap. 4.99 (978-0-448-44305-8(8) , Grosset & Dunlap) Penguin Group (USA) Inc.

Lectura en Familia: Spanish Phonics Grade 1 Combo. (SPA.). (gr. 1 up). 200.04 (978-0-7362-1490-2(9)) Hampton-Brown Bks.

Lectura en Familia: Spanish Phonics Grade 2 Combo. (SPA.). (gr. 2 up). 114.18 (978-0-7362-1491-9(7)) Hampton-Brown Bks.

Lee, Etrulia R. Phonics Is My Way Series, 21 bks. Incl. Blake the Duck. 24p. 1994. pap. (978-1-884876-09-7(9)); Dill. 20p. 1995. pap. (978-1-884876-03-5(X)); Footprints in the Sand. 32p. 1994. pap. (978-1-884876-19-6(6)); Horse on a Porch. 36p. 1994. pap. (978-1-884876-15-8(3)); I Can Jump. 16p. 1994. pap. (978-1-884876-01-1(3)); I Like to Dream. 32p. 1994. pap. (978-1-884876-11-0(0)); Jam, Ham & Yams. 20p. 1994. pap. (978-1-884876-02-8(1)); Mel. 20p. 1994. pap. (978-1-884876-07-3(2)); Mel Is Back. 32p. 1994. pap. (978-1-884876-13-4(7)); Mel's Store. 36p. 1994. pap. (978-1-884876-21-9(8)); Red Beans & Rice. 32p. 1994. pap. (978-1-884876-20-2(X)); Skates & Grapes. 24p. 1994. pap. (978-1-884876-12-7(9)); Space Trip. 24p. 1994. pap. (978-1-884876-18-9(8)); Stuff. 20p. 1994. pap. (978-1-884876-17-2(X)); Team. 24p. 1994. pap. (978-1-884876-08-0(0)); Tiff & His Bone. 28p. 1994. pap. (978-1-884876-04-2(8)); Train Ride. 20p. 1994. pap. (978-1-884876-10-3(2)); Wake up Time. 20p. 1994. pap. What Would You Say? 24p. 1994. pap. (978-1-884876-14-1(5)); Zip-a-Zap Zing. 32p. 1994. pap. (978-1-884876-16-5(1)); (Illus.). (J). (gr. k-2). 149.95 (978-1-884876-00-4(5)) Chamike Pubs.

El Leon Ruge: Little Books, Level 12, 28. 2003. (Fonolibros Ser.). 35.50 (978-0-7652-0107-2(0)) Modern Curriculum Pr.

Let's Read—Letter Sounds. 2003. 16p. (J). 3.79 (978-1-58792-050-9(6)) Trend Enterprises, Inc.

Letters in My World. 2006. (J). pap. ***(978-1-57332-386-4(1))*** HighReach Learning, Inc.

Level a Big Book Program. (Phonics & Friends Ser.). (ps-2). 651.23 (978-0-7362-0355-5(9)) Hampton-Brown Bks.

Level E Classroom Set. (Phonics & Friends Ser.). (ps-2). 682.59 (978-0-7362-0601-3(9)) Hampton-Brown Bks.

Level E Let's Read Little Book Set. (Phonics & Friends Ser.). (ps-2). 14.76 (978-0-7362-1068-3(7)) Hampton-Brown Bks.

Level F Classroom Set. (Phonics & Friends Ser.). (ps-2). 682.59 (978-0-7362-0644-0(2)) Hampton-Brown Bks.

Level F Let's Read Little Book Set. (Phonics & Friends Ser.). (ps-2). 14.76 (978-0-7362-1069-0(5)) Hampton-Brown Bks.

Levels E-F Super Classroom Set. (Phonics & Friends Ser.). (ps-2). 1204.58 (978-0-7362-0596-2(9)) Hampton-Brown Bks.

Lewis, Starin. Phonemic Awareness & Phonics E-Book. 2005. 80p. (J). per. 10.99 (978-1-59441-565-4(X) , CD-104018-EB); per. 10.99 (978-1-59441-566-1(8) , CD-104019-EB) Carson-Dellosa Publishing Co., Inc.

Litle Book: A Party of Nine. 2000. (Sadlier Phonics Reading Program). 8p. (J). (978-0-8215-7309-9(8) , Sadlier-Oxford) Sadlier, William H. Inc.

Little Books, Student Set. 2001. (Getting Ready to Read with Mother Goose Ser.). 32p. (YA). (ps-k). 19.50 (978-0-8215-6958-0(9)) Sadlier, William H. Inc.

Little Celebrations. 2000. (gr. 2 up). 35.00 (978-0-673-58422-9(4)) Addison-Wesley Educational Pubs., Inc.

Little Celebrations Package. 2000. (gr. 1 up). 15.15 (978-0-673-28947-6(8)) Addison-Wesley Educational Pubs., Inc.

Llewellyn, Claire. An Owl at School, 6, Pack. 2000. (Cambridge Reading Ser.). 12p. pap. 28.00 (978-0-521-78763-5(7)) Cambridge Univ. Pr.

Lloyd, Sue. Jolly Phonics Cards (Print Letters), 4 vols. 2001. (Jolly Phonics Ser.). (J). 39.50 (978-1-84414-027-5(X)) Jolly Learning, Ltd. GBR. *Dist:* American International Distribution Corp.

—Jolly Phonics Letter Sound Strips (Print Letters), 30 vols. 2003. (Jolly Phonics Ser.). (J). (gr. k-2). pap. 9.95 (978-1-84414-030-5(X)) Jolly Learning, Ltd. GBR. *Dist:* American International Distribution Corp.

—The Phonics Handbook (print Letters) US English. 2001. (Jolly Phonics Ser.). 218p. (J). spiral bd. 32.50 (978-1-870946-95-7(2)) Jolly Learning, Ltd. GBR. *Dist:* American International Distribution Corp.

Lloyd, Sue & Wernham, Sara. Finger Phonics, 7 vols., Vol. 4, Bk. 4. 2001. (Jolly Phonics Ser.: BIG BOOK 4). (Illus.). 16p. (J). 13.95 (978-1-870946-90-2(1) , JL901) Jolly Learning, Ltd. GBR. *Dist:* American International Distribution Corp.

—Finger Phonics Big Book 1: S, a, t, i, p, N, 7 vols. 2001. (Jolly Phonics Ser.: BIG BOOK 1). (Illus.). 16p. (J). 13.95 (978-1-870946-87-2(1) , JL871) Jolly Learning, Ltd. GBR. *Dist:* American International Distribution Corp.

—Finger Phonics Big Book 2: C, k, e, h, r, m, D, 7 vols. 2001. (Jolly Phonics Ser.: BIG BOOK 2). (Illus.). 16p. (J). 13.95 (978-1-870946-88-9(X) , JL88X) Jolly Learning, Ltd. GBR. *Dist:* American International Distribution Corp.

—Finger Phonics Big Book 3: G, o, u, l, f, B, 7 vols. 2001. (Jolly Phonics Ser.: BIG BOOK 3). (Illus.). 16p. (J). 13.95 (978-1-870946-89-6(8) , JL898) Jolly Learning, Ltd. GBR. *Dist:* American International Distribution Corp.

—Finger Phonics Big Book 5: Z, W, Ng, V, Oo ,Oo, 7 vols. 2001. (Jolly Phonics Ser.: BIG BOOK 5). (Illus.). 16p. (J). 13.95 (978-1-870946-91-9(X) , JL91X) Jolly Learning, Ltd. GBR. *Dist:* American International Distribution Corp.

—Finger Phonics Big Book 6: Y, X, Ch, Sh, Th, Th, 7 vols. 2001. (Jolly Phonics Ser.: BIG BOOK 6). (Illus.). 16p. (J). 13.95 (978-1-870946-92-6(8) , JL928) Jolly Learning, Ltd. GBR. *Dist:* American International Distribution Corp.

—Finger Phonics Big Book 7: Qu, Ou, Oi, Ue, Er, Ar, 7 vols. 2001. (Jolly Phonics Ser.: BIG BOOK 7). (Illus.). 16p. (J). 13.95 (978-1-870946-93-3(6) , JL936) Jolly Learning, Ltd. GBR. *Dist:* American International Distribution Corp.

—Finger Phonics Big Books 1-7 (precursive Letters) Vol. 7: Set of 7 Big Books, 7 vols., Set. Stephen, Lib, illus. 2001. (Jolly Phonics Ser.: BIG BOOK SET 1-7). 16p. (J). 97.65 (978-1-870946-94-0(4) , JL944) Jolly Learning, Ltd. GBR. *Dist:* American International Distribution Corp.

—Jolly Phonics Letter Sound Strips (Precursive Letters), 30 vols. 2002. (Jolly Phonics Ser.). (J). 9.95 (978-1-903619-10-0(6) , JL106) Jolly Learning, Ltd. GBR. *Dist:* American International Distribution Corp.

—Jolly Phonics Tricky Word Wall Flowers (Precursive Letters) Stephen, Lib, illus. 2002. (Jolly Phonics Ser.). (J). 16.50 (978-1-903619-11-7(4) , JL114) Jolly Learning, Ltd. GBR. *Dist:* American International Distribution Corp.

—Jolly Phonics Word Book (Precursive Letters) 2001. (Jolly Phonics Ser.). (Illus.). 48p. (J). 3.50 (978-1-870946-79-7(0) , JL790) Jolly Learning, Ltd. GBR. *Dist:* American International Distribution Corp.

Long Vowels (Gr. 1-2) 2003. (J). (978-1-58232-111-0(6)) Bryan Hse. Pubs., Inc.

Long Vowels Phonics Windows with Answers. 2002. (Phonics Windows Ser.). (J). pap. 0.99 (978-0-88724-834-4(9) , CD-3033) Carson-Dellosa Publishing Co., Inc.

Looking at Lizards: Big Book, Vol. 2. 2005. (Emergent Library: Vol. 1). (YA). (ps-1). 23.94 (978-0-8215-8906-9(7)) Sadlier, William H. Inc.

Los animales se Acostaron: Individual Title-Six Packs. (Chiquilibros Ser.). (SPA.). (gr. k-1). 23.00 (978-0-7635-8623-2(4)) Rigby Education.

Los Tres Deseos: Little Books, Level 20, Vol. 8. 2003. (Fonolibros Ser.). 34.95 (978-0-7652-0118-8(6)) Modern Curriculum Pr.

MacDonald, Kimber. The Misfits, Level 3. Swain, Wilson, illus. 2006. (Phonics Comics Ser.). 24p. (J). (gr. 1-17). pap. 3.99 (978-1-58476-421-2(X) , IKIDS) Innovative Kids.

—Time Travelers, Level 3. Sisk, Clay, illus. 2006. (Phonics Comics Ser.). 24p. (J). (gr. 1-17). pap. 3.99 (978-1-58476-472-4(4) , IKIDS) Innovative Kids.

MacKenzie, Joy & Spangler, Ann. The Growing Reader Book of Prayers. Newton, Jill, illus. 2004. 224p. (J). 12.99 (978-0-8423-8479-7(0)) Tyndale Hse. Pubs.

Madu, Abraham. The Road to take to School Is the Phonics Way: Companion Book for Students. 2003. 98p. pap. 11.95 (978-0-595-27748-3(9)) iUniverse, Inc.

Make Words for First Grade from Month-by-Month Phonics Word Card Set. 2002. (Four-Blocks Ser.). (J). pap. 29.99 (978-0-88724-827-6(6) , CD-2813) Carson-Dellosa Publishing Co., Inc.

Make Words for Second Grade from Month-by-Month Phonics Word Card Set. 2002. (J). pap. 29.99 (978-0-88724-828-3(4) , CD-2814) Carson-Dellosa Publishing Co., Inc.

Make Words for Third Grade from Month-by-Month Phonics Word Card Set. 2002. (J). pap. 29.99 (978-0-88724-829-0(2) , CD-2815) Carson-Dellosa Publishing Co., Inc.

Make Words for Upper Grades from Month-by-Month Phonics Word Card Set. 2002. (Four-Blocks Ser.). (J). pap. 29.99 (978-0-88724-830-6(6) , CD-2816) Carson-Dellosa Publishing Co., Inc.

La Manana: Individual Title Two-Packs. (Chiquilibros Ser.). (SPA.). (ps-1). 12.00 (978-0-7635-8551-8(3)) Rigby Education.

Mandel Morrow, Lesley & Vacca, Richard T. Sadlier Phonics Reading, Phonics. 2001st ed. 2005. (Sadlier Phonics Reading Program). (YA). (ps-3). 69.00 (978-0-8215-7035-7(8)) Sadlier, William H. Inc.

Mapaches Y Mapachitos: Little Books, Level 14, Vol. 22. 2003. (Fonolibros Ser.). 34.95 (978-0-7652-0100-3(3)) Modern Curriculum Pr.

Maps, 6 vols., Set B. (Phonics Readers Ser.). (gr. k-2). 17.50 (978-0-7368-3213-7(0)) Red Brick Learning.

Marcel Meringue: Level 2, 6 vols. (Fluency Strand Ser.). (gr. 4-8). 45.00 (978-1-4045-1212-2(8)) Wright Group, The.

Marks, Melanie. Spooky Sara, Level 3. Ball, Victoria, illus. 2006. (Phonics Comics Ser.). 24p. (J). (gr. 1-17). pap. 3.99 (978-1-58476-473-1(2) , IKIDS) Innovative Kids.

—Super Sam. Collins, Daryll, illus. 2006. (Phonics Comics Ser.). 24p. (J). (gr. 1-17). pap. 3.99 (978-1-58476-420-5(1) , IKIDS) Innovative Kids.

Marrow, Lesley Mandel & Vacca, Richard T. Sadlier Phonics. 2004. (Illus.). (YA). Level C. 2001st ed. (Sadlier Phonics Reading Program). 336p. (gr. 3 up). tchr. ed. 54.00 (978-0-8215-7013-5(7)); Level A. 2001st ed. (Sadlier Phonics Reading Program). 488p. (gr. 1 up). tchr. ed. 54.00 (978-0-8215-7011-1(0)); Level B. (Phonics Pre K-C(3) & Word Study D(4)-F(6) Ser.: Vol. 4). 336p. (gr. 2 up). tchr. ed. 54.00 (978-0-8215-7012-8(9)) Sadlier, William H. Inc.

—Sadlier Phonics Reading, Level K. 2004. (Sadlier Phonics (Pre K-Level C) Ser.). (Illus.). 232p. (YA). (gr. k up). stu. ed. 8.55 (978-0-8215-7000-5(5)) Sadlier, William H. Inc.

—Sadlier Phonics/Reading. 2004. (Illus.). (YA). Level C. 2001st rev. ed. (Sadlier Phonics Reading Program). 224p. (gr. 3 up). stu. ed. 8.97 (978-0-8215-7003-6(X)); Level A. 2001st rev. ed. (Sadlier Phonics Reading Program). 344p. (gr. 1 up). stu. ed. 8.97 (978-0-8215-7001-2(3)); Level B. (Phonics Pre K-C(3) & Word Study D(4)-F(6) Ser.: Vol. 4). 240p. (gr. 2 up). stu. ed. 8.97 (978-0-8215-7002-9(1)) Sadlier, William H. Inc.

—Sadlier Word Study. 2001. (Sadlier Phonics Reading Program). (Illus.). (YA). (gr. 4-6). Level D. 2001st ed. 320p. tchr. ed. 57.00 (978-0-8215-1042-1(8)); Level D. 2001st ed. 224p. stu. ed. 10.65 (978-0-8215-1039-1(8)); Level E. 2001st ed. 224p. stu. ed. 11.97 (978-0-8215-1040-7(1)); Level E. 2002nd ed. 320p. tchr. ed. 57.00 (978-0-8215-1043-8(6)); Level F. 2001st ed. 320p. tchr. ed. 57.00 (978-0-8215-1044-5(4)); Level F. 2001st ed. 224p. stu. ed. 11.97 (978-0-8215-1041-4(X)) Sadlier, William H. Inc.

Martin, Tyler. Little Book: I Have a Question. Williams, Toby, illus. 2000. (Sadlier Phonics Reading Program). 8p. (J). (978-0-8215-7316-7(0) , Sadlier-Oxford) Sadlier, William H. Inc.

Matthews, Cecily. Pobblebonk Reading 4. 1 Playing Shop. 2008. pap. (*978-0-521-71079-4(0)) Cambridge Univ. Pr.

—Pobblebonk Reading 4. 3 the Wild Wind. 2008. pap. (*978-0-521-71080-0(4)) Cambridge Univ. Pr.

—Pobblebonk Reading 4. 7 Going to the Snow. 2008. pap. (*978-0-521-71081-7(2)) Cambridge Univ. Pr.

—Pobblebonk Reading 5. 10 the Plane Crash. 2008. pap. (*978-0-521-71084-8(7)) Cambridge Univ. Pr.

—Pobblebonk Reading 5. 2 Watch Out! 2008. pap. (*978-0-521-71082-4(0)) Cambridge Univ. Pr.

—Pobblebonk Reading 5. 6 Race to the Lake. 2008. pap. (*978-0-521-71083-1(9)) Cambridge Univ. Pr.

—Pobblebonk Reading 6. 3 Leeches & Screeches. 2008. pap. (*978-0-521-71085-5(5)) Cambridge Univ. Pr.

—Pobblebonk Reading 6. 4 the Spooky Chook. 2008. pap. (*978-0-521-71086-2(3)) Cambridge Univ. Pr.

—Pobblebonk Reading 6. 9 Go, Go-Cart, Go! 2008. pap. (*978-0-521-71087-9(1)) Cambridge Univ. Pr.

Max Is Sick: Consonants q, x, z; -ack, -ick, -ill word families: Level A, 6 vols. (Wright Skills Ser.). 12p. (gr. k-3). 17.95 (978-0-322-01457-2(3)) Wright Group, The.

McAdams Moore, Carol. Phonics Comics: Cave Dave - Level 1. Dammer, Mike, illus. 2007. 24p. (J). (gr. 1-17). pap. 3.99 (978-1-58476-552-3(6)) Innovative Kids.

McGraw-Hill Staff. Listen!Listen!Letter Sounds in Rhymes Complt Set. (gr. k-1). 210.95 (978-0-322-02636-0(9)) Wright Group, The.

—Phonics. 2001. (Homework Helpers Activity Bks.). (Illus.). 56p. (J). (gr. 1-1). pap., act. bk. ed. 2.99 (978-0-7682-0703-3(7) , FS109032, Schaffer, Frank) Schaffer, Frank Pubns.

McGraw-Hill Staff, et al. Glencoe Speech. 3rd ed. 2004. stu. ed. 80.00 (978-0-07-861618-1(2) , 9780078616181) Glencoe/McGraw-Hill.

MCP Staff. Baby Bear's Ride, Level A, Bk. 1. (J). (ps-3). 24.50 (978-0-8136-1931-6(9)) Modern Curriculum Pr.

—By the Tree, Level 4, Bk. 22. (J). (ps-3). 24.50 (978-0-8136-0693-4(4)) Modern Curriculum Pr.

—Can a Cow Hop?, Level 4, Bk. 27. (J). (ps-3). 24.50 (978-0-8136-0795-5(7)) Modern Curriculum Pr.

—Cat Chat, 6 bks., set, Level 10, Bk. 35. 2003. (J). (ps-3). 24.50 (978-0-8136-2067-1(8)) Modern Curriculum Pr.

—Dive In!, 6 bks., set, Level 10, Bk. 44. 2003. (J). (ps-3). 33.50 (978-0-8136-2083-1(X)) Modern Curriculum Pr.

—Dragon's Lunch, 6 bks., set, Level 10, Bk. 39. 2003. (J). (ps-3). 33.50 (978-0-8136-2073-2(2)) Modern Curriculum Pr.

—Fast As a Fox, Level 4, Bk. 29. (J). (ps-3). 24.50 (978-0-8136-1961-3(0)) Modern Curriculum Pr.

—Good Girl! (Consonant g), Level K. 2003. ("Plaid" Phonics & Stories Libraries). (ps-3). 24.50 (978-0-8136-5416-4(5)) Modern Curriculum Pr.

—How to Make a Hen House (Consonant h), Level K. 2003. ("Plaid" Phonics & Stories Libraries). (ps-3). 24.50 (978-0-8136-5425-6(4)) Modern Curriculum Pr.

—Jan Can Juggle (Consonant j), Level K. 2003. ("Plaid" Phonics & Stories Libraries). (ps-3). 24.50 (978-0-8136-5427-0(0)) Modern Curriculum Pr.

—Jump Right In, Level 4, Bk. 35. 2000. (J). (ps-3). 24.50 (978-0-8136-0745-0(0)) Modern Curriculum Pr.

—Keys (Consonant k), Level K. 2003. ("Plaid" Phonics & Stories Libraries). (ps-3). 24.50 (978-0-8136-5434-8(3)) Modern Curriculum Pr.

—Let's Move!, Level 2, Bk. 18. (J). (ps-3). 24.50 (978-0-8136-0684-2(5)) Modern Curriculum Pr.

—Look Closer (Consonant l), Level K. 2003. ("Plaid" Phonics & Stories Libraries). (ps-3). 24.50 (978-0-8136-5429-4(7)) Modern Curriculum Pr.

—Lost in the Fog, Level 4, Bk. 25. (J). (ps-3). 24.50 (978-0-8136-1957-6(2)) Modern Curriculum Pr.

—A Mess, Level 4, Bk. 3. (J). (ps-3). 21.95 (978-0-8136-1935-4(1)) Modern Curriculum Pr.

—My Cat, Level 4, Bk. 13. 2003. (J). (ps-3). 24.50 (978-0-8136-0679-8(9)) Modern Curriculum Pr.

—My Monster & Me, Level 2, Bk. 6. (J). (ps-3). 24.50 (978-0-8136-0675-0(6)) Modern Curriculum Pr.

—One Bee Got on the Bus, Level 3, Bk. 9. (J). (ps-3). 21.95 (978-0-8136-0739-9(6)) Modern Curriculum Pr.

—The Party, Level 4, Bk. 4. (J). (ps-3). 24.50 (978-0-8136-1937-8(8)) Modern Curriculum Pr.

—Shell Shopping, 6 bks., set, Level A. 2003. (J). (ps-3). 33.50 (978-0-8136-0797-9(3)) Modern Curriculum Pr.

—Six Go By, Level A. 2003. (J). (ps-3). 21.95 (978-0-8136-0672-9(1)) Modern Curriculum Pr.

—Socks: Consonant N, Level K. 2003. ("Plaid" Phonics & Stories Libraries). (ps-3). 24.50 (978-0-8136-5411-9(4)) Modern Curriculum Pr.

—Ted's Red Sled, Level 4, Bk. 40. (J). (ps-3). 24.50 (978-0-8136-1969-9(6)) Modern Curriculum Pr.

—Too High!, Level 4, Bk. 37. 2003. (J). (ps-3). 24.50 (978-0-8136-0774-0(4)) Modern Curriculum Pr.

—Two Turtles (Consonant t), Level 1, Bk. 15. 2003. ("Plaid" Phonics & Stories Libraries). (ps-3). 24.50 (978-0-8136-5414-0(9)) Modern Curriculum Pr.

—Very Big, Level 4, Bk. 45. 2003. (J). (ps-3). 24.50 (978-0-8136-1447-2(3)) Modern Curriculum Pr.

—Vulture on Vacation, Level 3, Bk. 5. (J). (ps-3). 24.50 (978-0-8136-1939-2(4)) Modern Curriculum Pr.

—What Rhymes with Cat?, Level A, Bk. 2. (J). (978-0-8136-1933-0(5)) Modern Curriculum Pr.

—Where Do They Live?, Level 3, Bk. 17. (J). (ps-3). 24.50 (978-0-8136-1949-1(1)) Modern Curriculum Pr.

—Who Made That?, Level 3, Bk. 15. (J). (ps-3). 24.50 (978-0-8136-1947-7(5)) Modern Curriculum Pr.

—Yes I Can! Consonants j, f, g, l, d, Level 4, Bk. 26. 2003. (J). (ps-3). 24.50 (978-0-8136-0766-5(3)) Modern Curriculum Pr.

—Zebra's Yellow Van (Consonant v), Level K. 2003. ("Plaid" Phonics & Stories Libraries). (ps-3). 24.50 (978-0-8136-5439-3(4)) Modern Curriculum Pr.

Mcree Christen, Nancy. Phonics: Level 1 - Beginning & Ending Consonant Sounds. 1999. (Homework Booklets Ser.). 80p. (C). pap. 2.99 (978-0-88012-970-1(0) , IF0261) School Specialty Publishing.

—Phonics: Level 2 - Long & Short Vowel Sounds. 1999. (Homework Booklets Ser.). 80p. (C). pap. 2.99 (978-0-88012-971-8(9) , IF0262) School Specialty Publishing.

—Phonics: Level 3 - Digraphs, Combinations, Blends, & Consonant Review. 1999. (Homework Booklets Ser.). 80p. (C). pap. 2.99 (978-0-88012-972-5(7) , IF0263) School Specialty Publishing.

Meat-Eating Plants Set E, 6 vols. (Phonics Readers Ser.). (gr. k-2). 28.95 (978-0-7368-4065-1(6)) Red Brick Learning.

Medias, 6 vols., Pack. (Chiquilibros Ser.). (SPA.). (gr. k-1). 23.00 (978-0-7635-8595-2(5)) Rigby Education.

Meow-Meow Gets Out: Diphthongs ou, ow: Level B, 6 vols. (Wright Skills Ser.). 16p. (gr. k-3). 26.50 (978-0-322-01484-8(0)) Wright Group, The.

Mi Casa: Individual Title Six-Packs. (Literatura 2000 Ser.). (SPA.). (gr. 1-2). 28.00 (978-0-7635-1071-8(8)) Rigby Education.

Michaels, David. Little Book: Bye-bye Katy. Platt, Pierre, illus. 2000. (Sadlier Phonics Reading Program). 8p. (J). (978-0-8215-7314-3(4) , Sadlier-Oxford) Sadlier, William H. Inc.

Miller, Wilma H. Phonics First! Ready-to-Use Phonics Worksheets for the Intermediate Grades. 2001. 108p. pap., stu. ed., wbk. ed. 3.95 (978-0-13-041461-8(1) , Jossey-Bass) Wiley, John & Sons, Inc.

—Phonics First! Ready-to-Use Phonics Worksheets for the Primary Grades. 2001. 108p. pap., stu. ed., wbk. ed. 3.95 (978-0-13-041462-5(X) , Jossey-Bass) Wiley, John & Sons, Inc.

Minden, Cecilia. Celine & Cedric Go to the Circus: The Sound of Soft C. 2004. (Phonics Friends Ser.). 24p. (J). (ps). 21.36 (978-1-59296-291-4(2)) Child's World, Inc.

—Isabel's Favorite Things: The Sound of Short I. 2005. (Phonics Friends Ser.). (Illus.). 24p. (J). (ps). 21.36 (978-1-59296-314-0(5)) Child's World, Inc.

—Olivia by the Ocean: The Sound of Long O. 2005. (Phonics Friends Ser.). (Illus.). 24p. (J). (ps). 21.36 (978-1-59296-320-1(X)) Child's World, Inc.

—Umberto's Summer Day: The Sound of Short U. 2005. (Phonics Friends Ser.). (Illus.). 24p. (J). (ps). 21.36 (978-1-59296-316-4(1)) Child's World, Inc.

—Umeko & the Music Show: The Sound of Long U. 2005. (Phonics Friends Ser.). (Illus.). 24p. (J). (ps). 21.36 (978-1-59296-321-8(8)) Child's World, Inc.

Minden-Cupp, Cecilia. Akiko, Miss Alice, & the Dance Class: The Sound of Short A. 2005. (Phonics Friends Ser.). (Illus.). 24p. (J). (ps). 21.36 (978-1-59296-312-6(9)) Child's World, Inc.

—Alex & the Box Shop: The Sound of X. 2004. (Phonics Friends Ser.). 24p. (J). (ps). 21.36 (978-1-59296-309-6(9)) Child's World, Inc.

—Amy's Big Race: The Sound of Long A. 2005. (Phonics Friends Ser.). (Illus.). 24p. (J). (ps). 21.36 (978-1-59296-317-1(X)) Child's World, Inc.

—Erin & Her New Pet: The Sound of Short E. 2005. (Phonics Friends Ser.). (Illus.). 24p. (J). (ps). 21.36 (978-1-59296-313-3(7)) Child's World, Inc.

—Eve's Green Garden: The Sound of Long E. 2005. (Phonics Friends Ser.). (Illus.). 24p. (J). (ps). 21.36 (978-1-59296-318-8(8)) Child's World, Inc.

—Fatima & Fay Find a Bird: The Sound of F. 2004. (Phonics Friends Ser.). 24p. (J). (ps). 21.36 (978-1-59296-293-8(9)) Child's World, Inc.

—G—Soft—Title. 2004. (Phonics Friends Ser.). (Illus.). 24p. (J). (ps). 21.36 (978-1-59296-295-2(5)) Child's World, Inc.

—Isaac on the Farm: The Sound of Long I. 2005. (Phonics Friends Ser.). (Illus.). 24p. (J). (ps). 21.36 (978-1-59296-319-5(6)) Child's World, Inc.

—Jamal's Job: The Sound of J. 2004. (Phonics Friends Ser.). 24p. (J). (ps). 21.36 (978-1-59296-297-6(1)) Child's World, Inc.

—K—Title Tk. 2004. (Phonics Friends Ser.). 24p. (J). (ps). 21.36 (978-1-59296-298-3(X)) Child's World, Inc.

—Marcus & the Mail: The Sound of M. 2004. (Phonics Friends Ser.). 24p. (J). (ps). 21.36 (978-1-59296-300-3(5)) Child's World, Inc.

—Nick & Ned: The Sound of N. 2004. (Phonics Friends Ser.). 24p. (J). (ps). 21.36 (978-1-59296-301-0(3)) Child's World, Inc.

—Oliver's Box: The Sound of Short O. 2005. (Phonics Friends Ser.). (Illus.). 24p. (J). (ps). 21.36 (978-1-59296-315-7(3)) Child's World, Inc.

—Quana & Quinn: The Sound of Q. 2004. (Phonics Friends Ser.). (Illus.). 24p. (J). (ps). 21.36 (978-1-59296-303-4(X)) Child's World, Inc.

—R—Title Tk. 2004. (Phonics Friends Ser.). 24p. (J). (ps). 21.36 (978-1-59296-304-1(8)) Child's World, Inc.

—S—Title Tk. 2004. (Phonics Friends Ser.). 24p. (J). (ps). 21.36 (978-1-59296-305-8(6)) Child's World, Inc.

—Taejon & Terrel: The Sound of T. 2004. (Phonics Friends Ser.). 24p. (J). (ps). 21.36 (978-1-59296-306-5(4)) Child's World, Inc.

—Victor Moves: The Sound of V. 2004. (Phonics Friends Ser.). 24p. (J). (ps). 21.36 (978-1-59296-307-2(2)) Child's World, Inc.

—Wan & the Dog Wash: The Sound of W. 2004. (Phonics Friends Ser.). 24p. (J). (ps). 21.36 (978-1-59296-308-9(0)) Child's World, Inc.

—Zack's Zippers: The Sound of Z. 2004. (Phonics Friends Ser.). 24p. (J). (ps). 21.36 (978-1-59296-311-9(0)) Child's World, Inc.

Minden-Cupp, Cecilia & Meier, Joanne. Gary Gets a Gift: The Sound of Hard G. 2004. (Phonics Friends Ser.). (Illus.). 24p. (J). (ps). 21.36 (978-1-59296-294-5(7)) Child's World, Inc.

—Lilly's Lost Lunch: The Sound of L. 2004. (Phonics Friends Ser.). (Illus.). 24p. (J). (ps). 21.36 (978-1-59296-299-0(8)) Child's World, Inc.

—Pam's Trip to the Park: The Sound of P. 2004. (Phonics Friends Ser.). 24p. (J). (ps). 21.36 (978-1-59296-302-7(1)) Child's World, Inc.

—Yoshi's Yard: The Sound of Y. 2004. (Phonics Friends Ser.). 24p. (J). (ps). 21.36 (978-1-59296-310-2(2)) Child's World, Inc.

Miranda, Anne. Little Book: Looking at Lizards. 2000. (Sadlier Phonics Reading Program). 8p. (J). (978-0-8215-7306-8(3) , Sadlier-Oxford) Sadlier, William H. Inc.

—Little Books: Weather Wise. 2000. (Sadlier Phonics Reading Program). 8p. (J). (978-0-8215-7311-2(X) , Sadlier-Oxford) Sadlier, William H. Inc.

Mischel, Jenny Ann. Animal Alphabet. Bell-Myers, Darcy, illus. 2006. (J). bds. (978-0-9769239-0-9(4)) Perfect 4 Preschool.

Mischitelli, Vincent A. Unpopular Animals. 2002. 24.95 (978-0-9721591-0-4(X)) Collaboration for Literacy for All Children.

Mitzo Thompson, Kim & Carder, Ken. Phonics: Songs That Teach Phonics. 2005. (Sing along Activity Books with CDs Ser.). (Illus.). 32p. (J). pap. 4.99 (978-0-7696-4454-7(6)) School Specialty Publishing.

—Songs That Teach Phonics. 2006. (Songs That Teach Ser.). 72p. (J). pap. 14.95 (978-0-7696-6460-6(1) , American Education Publishing) School Specialty Publishing.

Modern Staff. Day at Our Dairy Farm. (J). (gr. k-1). 38.95 (978-0-8136-1358-1(2)) Modern Curriculum Pr.

Molter, Carey. Ck: See It Say It Hear It. l.t. ed. 2001. (More Blends Ser.). (Illus.). 24p. (J). (ps-3). lib. bdg. 19.93 (978-1-57765-447-6(1) , SandCastle) ABDO Publishing Co.

—Ph: See It Say It Hear It. l.t. ed. 2001. (More Blends Ser.). (Illus.). 24p. (J). (ps-3). lib. bdg. 19.93 (978-1-57765-451-3(X) , SandCastle) ABDO Publishing Co.

Molzan, Janet & Lloyd, Sue. Le Manuel Phonique. 2001. (Jolly Phonics Ser.). (FRE.). 218p. (J). 32.50 (978-1-870946-98-8(7)) Jolly Learning, Ltd. GBR. *Dist:* American International Distribution Corp.

Money Set D, 6 vols. (Phonics Readers Ser.). (gr. k-2). 28.95 (978-0-7368-4052-1(4)) Red Brick Learning.

Un Monstruo Debajo de la Cama: Little Books, Level 28. 2003. (Fonolibros Ser.: Vol. 9). 39.50 (978-0-7652-0119-5(4)) Modern Curriculum Pr.

More Phonics. 2004. (Kids Can Learn with Franklin Ser.). (Illus.). 32p. (J). (gr. k-3). (978-1-55337-599-9(8)) Kids Can Pr., Ltd.

Moreau, Maryellen Rooney & Welch, Brian Scott. Talk to Write, Write to Learn: A Teachers' Manual for Differentiated Instruction & Tiered Intervention. 2007. pap. 60.00 (*978-0-9761393-9-3(1)) Mindwing Concepts, Inc.

Mork, Gretchen. Five Minute Phonics. 1999. (Illus.). (J). pap. 12.00 (978-0-9666477-0-9(X)) Wild Pony Publishing.

Morris, Deborah. Phonics Grade 2. 2003. (Skill Builders Ser.). 80p. (gr. 2 up). 2.95 (978-1-932210-01-9(6)) Rainbow Bridge Publishing.

Moss, Miriam. One Day It Was Wet, 6, Pack. 2000. (Cambridge Reading Ser.). (Illus.). 12p. pap. 26.00 (978-0-521-78689-8(4)) Cambridge Univ. Pr.

Mr Hoot's Room: Variant Vowel Review: Level C, 6 vols. (Wright Skills Ser.). 16p. (gr. k-3). 26.50 (978-0-322-01504-3(9)) Wright Group, The.

Mrs Patches & Her Fudge: Silent Consonants: Level C, 6 vols. (Wright Skills Ser.). 16p. (gr. k-3). 26.50 (978-0-322-01503-6(0)) Wright Group, The.

Mrs. Sheep's Garden (18), Vol. 18. (Early Intervention Levels Ser.). 5.31 (978-0-7362-0607-5(8)) Hampton-Brown Bks.

My First Readers: Hooked on Phonics - Learn to Read. 2000. (Illus.). 128p. (J). (ps-1). pap. 14.95 (978-1-887942-85-0(8)) HOP, LLC.

My First Readers: Hooked on Phonics Companion Books. 1998. (Illus.). 112p. (J). (ps-1). pap. 19.95 (978-1-887942-66-9(1)) HOP, LLC.

My First Sight Words (Gr. K-1) 2003. (J). (978-1-58232-090-8(X)) Bryan Hse. Pubs., Inc.

My Little Take-Home Books. 2002. (Phonics & Friends Ser.). (gr. k-2). Blue Set. 129.00 (978-0-7362-0685-3(X)); Green Set. 129.00 (978-0-7362-0594-8(2)); Orange Set. 129.00 (978-0-7362-0642-6(6)); Purple Set. 129.00 (978-0-7362-0586-3(1)) Hampton-Brown Bks.

Nall, Andrea. Have You Ever... ? 04. Davis, Tim, illus. 2006. (J). (*978-1-58650-582-0(3)) Super Duper Pubns.

—Have You Ever... ? 05. Davis, Tim, illus. 2006. (J). (*978-1-58650-583-7(1)) Super Duper Pubns.

—Have You Ever... ? 06. Davis, Tim, illus. 2006. (J). (*978-1-58650-584-4(X)) Super Duper Pubns.

—Have You Ever... ? 07. Davis, Tim, illus. 2006. (J). (*978-1-58650-585-1(8)) Super Duper Pubns.

—Have You Ever... ? 08. Davis, Tim, illus. 2006. (J). (*978-1-58650-586-8(6)) Super Duper Pubns.

—Have You Ever... ? Book Set. Davis, Tim, illus. 2006. (J). (*978-1-58650-587-5(4)) Super Duper Pubns.

Nathan, Ruth. Letter Sounds: Early Literacy Diagnostic. 2002. (J). (gr. k-1). spiral bd. 1.50 (978-1-58605-926-2(2) , LeapFrog Schl. Hse.) LeapFrog Enterprises, Inc.

—Phonemic Awareness Level 1: Early Literacy Diagnostic. 2002. (J). (gr. k-1). spiral bd. 1.50 (978-1-58605-531-8(3) , LeapFrog Schl. Hse.) LeapFrog Enterprises, Inc.

—Phonemic Awareness Level 2: Early Literacy Diagnostic. 2002. (J). (gr. k-1). spiral bd. 1.50 (978-1-58605-532-5(1) , LeapFrog Schl. Hse.) LeapFrog Enterprises, Inc.

—Phonemic Awareness Level 3: Early Literacy Diagnostic. 2002. (J). (gr. k-1). spiral bd. 1.50 (978-1-58605-533-2(X) , LeapFrog Schl. Hse.) LeapFrog Enterprises, Inc.

—Phonemic Awareness Level 4: Early Literacy Diagnostic. 2002. (J). (gr. k-1). spiral bd. 1.50 (978-1-58605-927-9(0) , LeapFrog Schl. Hse.) LeapFrog Enterprises, Inc.

Nicholas, Melissa. Little Book: Who Is My Mom? Cassel, Jean, illus. 2000. (Sadlier Phonics Reading Program). 8p. (J). (978-0-8215-7301-3(2) , Sadlier-Oxford) Sadlier, William H. Inc.

—Little Book: Pumpkins Days. 2000. (Sadlier Phonics Reading Program). 8p. (J). (978-0-8215-7312-9(8) , Sadlier-Oxford) Sadlier, William H. Inc.

Night Mare Trip: Level 5, 6 vols. (Fluency Strand Ser.). (gr. 4-8). 45.00 (978-1-4045-1230-6(5)) Wright Group, The.

No Sweat! Short e Digraph: Level B, 6 vols. (Wright Skills Ser.). 16p. (gr. k-3). 26.50 (978-0-322-01477-0(8)) Wright Group, The.

Novelli, Joan. Phonics. 2006. 80p. pap. 12.99 (978-0-439-53796-4(7) , Teaching Resources) Scholastic, Inc.

Nutria, Nutria: Student Book. 2003. 33.95 (978-0-8136-8075-0(1)) Modern Curriculum Pr.

Ocho Amigos en Total: Little Books, Level 4, Vol. 2525. 2003. (Fonolibros Ser.). 25.50 (978-0-7652-0104-1(6)) Modern Curriculum Pr.

Olivia, Cynthia. Little Book: In January & June. 2000. (Sadlier Phonics Reading Program). 8p. (J). (978-0-8215-7315-0(2) , Sadlier-Oxford) Sadlier, William H. Inc.

Olo: Level 6, 6 vols. (Fluency Strand Ser.). (gr. 4-8). 45.00 (978-1-4045-1237-5(3)) Wright Group, The.

Once, Twice, Boom: Level 7, 6 vols. (Fluency Strand Ser.). (gr. 4-8). 45.00 (978-1-4045-1240-5(3)) Wright Group, The.

Onish, Liane. Reading Skills Card Games: Beginning & Ending Sounds. 2004. (Reading Skills Card Games Ser.). 48p. pap. 10.99 (978-0-439-46598-4(2) , Teaching Resources) Scholastic, Inc.

Orange Collection. (Elefonetica Ser.). (SPA.). (gr. 1-2). 296.76 (978-0-7362-0790-4(2)) Hampton-Brown Bks.

Orphan Train: Medial Digraphs: Level C, 6 vols. (Wright Skills Ser.). 16p. (gr. k-3). 26.50 (978-0-322-01498-5(0)) Wright Group, The.

Out of the Computer: Level 6, 6 vols. (Fluency Strand Ser.). (gr. 4-8). 45.00 (978-1-4045-1235-1(7)) Wright Group, The.

Out of the Sunless Land: Level T. Group 2, 6 vols. (Sunshinetm Ser.). 48p. 44.95 (978-0-7802-4186-2(X)) Wright Group, The.

La Paleteria: Individual Title Two-Packs. (Chiquilibros Ser.). (SPA.). (ps-1). 12.00 (978-0-7635-8554-9(8)) Rigby Education.

Papil: Level T. Group 1, 6 vols. (Sunshinetm Ser.). 48p. 44.95 (978-0-7802-5600-2(X)) Wright Group, The.

Parker, Andrew & Stamford, Jane. Sound Practice, 5 vols. 1999. (Illus.). 32p. (J). (gr. 1-3). Bk. 1. pap. 20.00 (978-0-7217-0392-3(5)); Bk. 2. pap. 20.00 (978-0-7217-0393-0(3)); Bk. 3. pap. 20.00 (978-0-7217-0394-7(1)); Bk. 4. pap. 20.00 (978-0-7217-0395-4(X)); Bk. 5. pap. 20.00 (978-0-7217-0396-1(8)) Schofield & Sims Ltd. GBR. *Dist:* State Mutual Bk. & Periodical Service, Ltd.

El Pastel de Javier: Little Books, Level 16, Vol. 3. 2003. (Fonolibros Ser.). 25.50 (978-0-7652-0112-6(7)) Modern Curriculum Pr.

El Pato Atascado: Little Books, Level 10, Vol. 20. 2003. (Fonolibros Ser.). 25.50 (978-0-7652-0098-3(8)) Modern Curriculum Pr.

Paws, Jaws, & Claws: Variant Vowels al, au, aw: Level B, 6 vols. (Wright Skills Ser.). 16p. (gr. k-3). 26.50 (978-0-322-01482-4(4)) Wright Group, The.

Penton Overseas, Inc. Staff. My First Words: Early Language Development System. rev. ed. 2007. (Illus.). 12p. (J). (gr. k-5). 10.95 (*978-1-59125-810-0(3) , Smart Kids) Penton Overseas, Inc.

Petter, Constance & Bomberg, Hyman. Funics Vol. 2: A Fun Way to Improve Reading, Writing, Spelling & Thinking: Long Vowels. 1999. (J). (gr. k-12). pap., wbk. ed. 8.33 (978-1-930676-02-2(6)) Funics Publishing.

—Funics Vol. 3: A Fun Way to Improve Reading, Writing, Spelling & Thinking: More Vowels. 2000. (J). (gr. k-12). pap., wbk. ed. 8.33 (978-1-930676-03-9(4)) Funics Publishing.

—Funics...A Fun Way to Improve Reading, Writing, Spellin & Thinking: Complete Set. Petter, Constance, ed. Bohanon, Sheila, illus. unabr. ed. 2000. 358p. (J). (gr. k-12). pap. 65.00 (978-1-930676-05-3(0)) Funics Publishing.

Phonemic Awareness, Level 1. 2003. (Illus.). (J). spiral bd. (978-1-58605-822-7(3) , LeapFrog Schl. Hse.) LeapFrog Enterprises, Inc.

Phonemic Awareness & Phonics Manipulatives Kit. 2000. (SPA.). (gr. k up). suppl. ed. 370.45 (978-0-673-64907-2(5)); (gr. 1 up). suppl. ed. 370.45 (978-0-673-64908-9(3)); (gr. 2 up). 370.45 (978-0-673-64909-6(1)); (gr. 3 up). 370.45 (978-0-673-64910-2(5)) Addison-Wesley Educational Pubs., Inc.

Phonemic Awareness Pack. (Phonemic Awareness Pack Ser.). (ps-k). 523.57 incl. audio compact disk (978-0-7362-0899-4(2)) Hampton-Brown Bks.

Phonemic Awareness Pack with Tapes. (Phonemic Awareness Pack Ser.). (ps-k). 538.88 (978-0-7362-0900-7(X)) Hampton-Brown Bks.

Phonics. 2004. (gr. k-6). tchr. ed., wbk. ed. 48.00 (978-0-673-61433-9(6)); 2004. (gr. k-6). wbk. ed. 5.25 (978-0-673-61428-5(X)); 2004. (gr. k up). suppl. ed., wbk. ed. 1.95 (978-0-328-02433-9(3)); 2004. (gr. k up). wbk. ed. 5.25 (978-0-328-02432-2(5)); 2004. (gr. 1 up). suppl. ed., wbk. ed. 48.00 (978-0-673-61430-8(1)); 2004. (gr. 1 up). wbk. ed. 5.25 (978-0-673-61425-4(5)); 2004. (gr. 2 up). suppl. ed., wbk. ed. 48.00 (978-0-673-61431-5(X)); 2004. (gr. 2 up). wbk. ed. 5.25 (978-0-673-61426-1(3)); 2004. (gr. 3 up). tchr. ed., wbk. ed. 48.00 (978-0-673-61432-2(8)); 2004. (gr. 3 up). wbk. ed. 5.25 (978-0-673-61427-8(1)); 2000. (SPA.). (gr. k up). wbk. ed. 5.50 (978-0-673-60829-1(8)); 2000. (SPA.). (gr. 1 up). wbk. ed. 5.50 (978-0-673-60830-7(1)); 2000. (SPA.). (gr. 2 up). wbk. ed. 5.80 (978-0-673-60831-4(X)); 2000. (SPA.). (gr. 3 up). wbk. ed. 5.50 (978-0-673-60832-1(8)); 2000. (SPA.). (gr. 4-5). wbk. ed. 5.50 (978-0-673-60833-8(6)) Addison-Wesley Educational Pubs., Inc.

Phonics. 2004. (Help with Homework Ser.). 32p. (J). (gr. k-2). wbk. ed. 3.99 (978-1-904586-15-9(5)) Byeway Bks.

Phonics. 1999. (Step Ahead Ser.). 320p. (J). pap., wbk. ed. 4.99 (978-0-307-11253-8(5) , Golden Bks.) Random Hse. Children's Bks.

Phonics. 128p. (gr. 1 up). 12.99 (978-0-88012-805-6(4) , IF8705); 128p. (gr. 2 up). 12.99 (978-0-88012-806-3(2) , IF8706); 1998. (Illus.). 80p. (J). pap., wbk. ed. 2.99 (978-1-57768-220-2(3)); 1998. (Illus.). 80p. (J). (gr. 1). pap., wbk. ed. 2.99 (978-1-57768-221-9(1)); 1998. (Illus.). 80p. (J). (gr. 2). pap., wbk. ed. 2.99 (978-1-57768-222-6(X)) School Specialty Publishing.

Phonics: Level 4 - Controlled Vowels, Vowel Digraphs, & Long & Short Vowel Review. (Homework Booklets Ser.). 80p. 2.99 (978-0-88012-973-2(5) , IF0264) School Specialty Publishing.

Phonics 3-4. 2003. (Gold Stars Workbook Ser.). (Illus.). 32p. (J). 2.98 (978-1-4054-1192-9(9)) Parragon, Inc.

Phonics 4-5. 2003. (Illus.). 32p. (J). 2.98 (978-1-4054-1193-6(7)) Parragon, Inc.

Phonics 5-6. 2003. (Gold Stars Workbook Ser.). (Illus.). 32p. (J). 2.98 (978-1-4054-1194-3(5)) Parragon, Inc.

Phonics 6-7. 2003. (Gold Stars Workbook Ser.). (Illus.). 32p. (J). 2.98 (978-1-4054-1195-0(3)) Parragon, Inc.

Phonics & Friends, Level A+ 2002. (Phonics & Friends Ser.). (ps-2). 1499.47 (978-0-7362-0520-7(9)) Hampton-Brown Bks.

Phonics & Reading Excelerator (Ages 6-10), 4 CDs. 2003. cd-rom 29.99 (978-1-59150-262-3(4)) TOPICS Entertainment.

Phonics & Word Study Complete Kits: Phonics & Word Study: Level C. (gr. k-3). 333.95 (978-0-322-01644-6(4)) Wright Group, The.

Phonics & Word Study Core Kits: Phonics & Word Study: Level A. (gr. k-3). 153.50 (978-0-322-01641-5(X)) Wright Group, The.

Phonics & Word Study Core Kits: Phonics & Word Study: Level B. (gr. k-3). 185.50 (978-0-322-01643-9(6)) Wright Group, The.

Phonics & Word Study Core Kits: Phonics & Word Study: Level C. (gr. k-3). 153.50 (978-0-322-01645-3(2)) Wright Group, The.

Phonics Basics. 2000. (Kelley Wingate Ser.). 80p. (J). pap. 9.99 (978-0-88724-625-8(7) , CD-3635) Carson-Dellosa Publishing Co., Inc.

Phonics Cards, Early Level. (gr. k-2). 69.95 (978-0-7368-1497-3(3) , Pebble Bks.) Capstone Pr., Inc.

Phonics Cards, Emergent Level. (gr. k-2). 69.95 (978-0-7368-1496-6(5) , Pebble Bks.) Capstone Pr., Inc.

Phonics Cards, Fluent Level. (gr. k-2). 69.95 (978-0-7368-1498-0(1) , Pebble Bks.) Capstone Pr., Inc.

Phonics Centers A. 2004. (J). (ps-k). per. 19.99 (978-1-55799-980-1(5) , EMC 3327) Evan-Moor Educational Pubs.

Phonics Centers B. 2004. (J). (gr. k-1). per. 19.99 (978-1-55799-981-8(3) , EMC 3328) Evan-Moor Educational Pubs.

Phonics Centers C. 2004. (J). (gr. 1-2). per. 19.99 (978-1-55799-982-5(1) , EMC 3329) Evan-Moor Educational Pubs.

Phonics Centers D. 2004. (J). (gr. 2-3). per. 19.99 (978-1-55799-983-2(X) , EMC 3330) Evan-Moor Educational Pubs.

Phonics Decodable Reader 1. 2004. (gr. 1 up). suppl. ed. 3.35 (978-0-673-65172-3(X)) Addison-Wesley Educational Pubs., Inc.

Phonics Decodable Reader 2. 2004. (gr. 1 up). suppl. ed. 3.35 (978-0-673-65173-0(8)) Addison-Wesley Educational Pubs., Inc.

Phonics Decodable Reader 3. 2004. (gr. 1 up). suppl. ed. 3.35 (978-0-673-65174-7(6)) Addison-Wesley Educational Pubs., Inc.

Phonics Decodable Reader 33-41. 2004. (gr. 1 up). suppl. ed. 7.75 (978-0-673-65180-8(0)) Addison-Wesley Educational Pubs., Inc.

Phonics Decodable Reader 42-50. 2004. (gr. 1 up). suppl. ed. 7.75 (978-0-673-65181-5(9)) Addison-Wesley Educational Pubs., Inc.

Phonics Decodable Reader 5. 2004. (gr. 1 up). suppl. ed. 3.35 (978-0-673-65176-1(2)) Addison-Wesley Educational Pubs., Inc.

Phonics Excelerator, 2 CDs. 2002. cd-rom 9.99 (978-1-59150-015-5(X)) TOPICS Entertainment.

Phonics Fun - Vowels. 2000. (Wipe-Off Activity Bks.). (Illus.). 16p. (J). (ps-2). wbk. ed. 3.79 (978-1-889319-81-0(3)) Trend Enterprises, Inc.

Phonics Games: Integrated Learning Activities That Build Reading Skills. 240p. (gr. 1-3). 16.99 (978-0-7424-0179-2(0) , IF21002) School Specialty Publishing.

Phonics Kit: Phonics. 2001. (McGraw-Hill. Lectura Ser.). (ENG & SPA.). (gr. k-3). (978-0-02-188388-2(2)) Macmillan/McGraw-Hill Schl. Div.

Phonics Plus Staff. Phonics Plus. 2nd ed. Bk. D. (J). 9.55 (978-0-8136-0394-0(3)); Bk. E. tchr. ed. 9.55 (978-0-8136-0395-7(1)); Bk. F. (J). 9.55 (978-0-8136-0396-4(X)) Modern Curriculum Pr.

Phonics Practice Book. 2000. (Phonics Practice Book Ser.). (gr. 1 up). 5.60 (978-0-673-60143-8(9)); (gr. 2 up). 5.60 (978-0-673-60144-5(7)); (gr. 3 up). 5.60 (978-0-673-60145-2(5)) Addison-Wesley Educational Pubs., Inc.

Phonics Practice Book. (De Canciones A Cuentos Ser.). (SPA.). (gr. k up). 9.13 (978-1-56334-580-7(3)); (gr. 1 up). 9.13 (978-1-56334-895-2(0)); (gr. 2 up). 8.36 (978-0-7362-0073-8(8)) Hampton-Brown Bks.

Phonics Puzzles (Gr. 1) 2003. (J). (978-1-58232-047-2(0)) Bryan Hse. Pubs., Inc.

Phonics Readers Big Books. 2005. (J). pap. 95.00 (978-1-58970-687-3(0)) Lakeshore Learning Materials.

Phonics Readers Bookshelf Collection, 36 bks., Set. 2004. (gr. 1 up). 594.00 (978-0-328-00401-0(4)); 2004. (gr. 2 up). 495.00 (978-0-328-00402-7(2)); 2004. (gr. 3 up). 495.00 (978-0-328-00403-4(0)); 2000. (SPA.). (gr. k up). 665.28 (978-0-328-00404-1(9)); 2000. (SPA.). (gr. 1 up). 665.28 (978-0-328-00405-8(7)); 2000. (SPA.). (gr. 2 up). 554.40 (978-0-328-00406-5(5)); 2000. (SPA.). (gr. 3 up). 554.40 (978-0-328-00407-2(3)) Addison-Wesley Educational Pubs., Inc.

Phonics Readers Student Books. 2005. (J). pap. 29.95 (978-1-58970-685-9(4)) Lakeshore Learning Materials.

Phonics Skills of the Week Flip Chart. 2000. (SPA.). (gr. 1 up). suppl. ed. 116.50 (978-0-673-64115-1(5)); (gr. 2 up). 116.50 (978-0-673-64116-8(3)) Addison-Wesley Educational Pubs., Inc.

Phonics Songs & Rhymes. 2000. (SPA.). (gr. k up). suppl. ed. 116.50 (978-0-673-60597-9(3)) Addison-Wesley Educational Pubs., Inc.

Phonics Songs & Rhymes Flip Chart. 2004. (gr. 1 up). suppl. ed. 109.15 (978-0-673-59716-8(4)) Addison-Wesley Educational Pubs., Inc.

Phonics Strand: Phonics Song Chart Phonics Audio Take-Home Alphabet Books Blackline Master Booklet 65 Word Wall Starters Phonics Teacher's Guide. (On Our Way to English Ser.). (gr. k up). 295.00 incl. audio compact disk (978-0-7578-7314-0(6)) Rigby Education.

Phonics Strand: Phonics Song Chart Phonics Audio Take-Home Phonics & Decodable Stories Blackline Master Booklet 115 Word Wall Starters Phonics Teacher's Guide. (On Our Way to English Ser.). (gr. 1 up). 295.00 incl. audio compact disk (978-0-7578-7315-7(4)) Rigby Education.

Phonics Strand: Phonics Song Chart Phonics Audio Take-Home Phonics Stories Blackline Master Booklet 100 Word Wall Starters Phonics Teacher's Guide. (On Our Way to English Ser.). (gr. 3 up). 295.00 incl. audio compact disk (978-0-7578-7317-1(0)) Rigby Education.

Phonics Strand: Phonics Song Chart Phonics Audio Take-Home Phonics Stories Blackline Master Booklet 124 Word Wall Starters Phonics Teacher's Guide. (On Our Way to English Ser.). (gr. 2 up). 295.00 incl. audio compact disk (978-0-7578-7316-4(2)) Rigby Education.

Phonics Take-Home Readers. 2004. (gr. 1 up). tchr. ed. 48.00 (978-0-673-61258-8(9)); (gr. 2 up). 48.00 (978-0-673-61259-5(7)); (gr. 3 up). 48.00 (978-0-673-61260-1(0)) Addison-Wesley Educational Pubs., Inc.

Pigs & Dogs Play Ball: Consonants b, w; Short Vowel i word families: Level A, 6 vols. (Wright Skills Ser.). 12p. (gr. k-3). 17.95 (978-0-322-01450-3(6)) Wright Group, The.

The Pink Tent: Final Blends -nd, -nk, -nt: Level B, 6 vols. (Wright Skills Ser.). 16p. (gr. k-3). 17.95 (978-0-322-01462-6(X)) Wright Group, The.

La Pizzeria, 2 Packs. (Chiquilibros Ser.). (SPA.). (ps-1). 12.00 (978-0-7635-8555-6(6)) Rigby Education.

Places to Visit, Places to See: Take-Home Book. 2005. (Lee Bennett Hopkins Worlds of Poetry Classroom Library). (YA). (gr. k-3). 13.50 (978-0-8215-0568-7(8)) Sadlier, William H. Inc.

Pocket Chart Phonics: Advanced Consonants. 2000. (J). pap. 9.95 (978-1-56911-794-1(2)) Learning Resources, Inc.

Pocket Chart Phonics: Advanced Vowels. 2000. (J). pap. 9.95 (978-1-56911-792-7(6)) Learning Resources, Inc.

Pocket Chart Phonics: Beginning Consonants. 2000. (J). pap. 9.95 (978-1-56911-793-4(4)) Learning Resources, Inc.

Pocket Chart Phonics: Blends. 2000. (J). pap. 9.95 (978-1-56911-795-8(0)) Learning Resources, Inc.

Pocket Chart Phonics: Long Vowels. 2000. (J). pap. 9.95 (978-1-56911-790-3(X)) Learning Resources, Inc.

Pocket Chart Phonics: Short Vowels. 2002. (J). pap. 9.95 (978-1-56911-791-0(8)) Learning Resources, Inc.

Potts, Cheryl. Ready-to-Go Phonics: Games, Manipulatives, Activites, & Rhymes That Make Teaching Phonics Easy. 1998. pap. 10.95 (978-0-590-11594-0(4)) Scholastic, Inc.

Prefixes & Suffixes: Systematic Sequential Phonics & Spelling. 2002. (Four-Blocks Ser.). 192p. pap. 24.99 (978-0-88724-695-1(8) , CD-2413) Carson-Dellosa Publishing Co., Inc.

Price, Alyson. "Say & Glue" Phonology & Artic Fun Sheets. Bunner, Julie et al, illus. 2000. 108p. (J). (ps). spiral bd. 21.95 (978-1-58650-154-9(2) , BK-283) Super Duper Pubns.

Puedes Subir: Little Books, Level 3, 8. 2003. (Fonolibros Ser.). 25.50 (978-0-7652-0085-3(6)) Modern Curriculum Pr.

Puedo Salir? Student Book. 2003. 35.50 (978-0-8136-8099-6(9)) Modern Curriculum Pr.

Pulse Fun with Phonics. 2006. cd-rom 4.99 (***978-1-60245-039-4(0))** GDL Multimedia, LLC.

Quake: Level 4, 6 vols. (Fluency Strand Ser.). (gr. 4-8). 45.00 (978-1-4045-1226-9(8)) Wright Group, The.

Que Desastre De Cuarto! Little Books, Level 20, Vol. 18. 2003. (Fonolibros Ser.). 39.50 (978-0-7652-0128-7(3)) Modern Curriculum Pr.

Que Es Eso? Little Books, Level 3, Vol. 26. 2003. (Fonolibros Ser.). 25.50 (978-0-7652-0105-8(4)) Modern Curriculum Pr.

Que Es Una Linea? Little Books, Level 6, 3. 2003. 25.50 (978-0-7652-0079-2(1)) Modern Curriculum Pr.

Que Gato! Little Books, Level 16, Vol. 5. 2003. (Fonolibros Ser.). 35.50 (978-0-7652-0114-0(3)) Modern Curriculum Pr.

Que quiere Beto? Individual Title-Six Packs. (Chiquilibros Ser.). (SPA.). (gr. k-1). 23.00 (978-0-7635-8610-2(2)) Rigby Education.

Que Soy? Little Books, Level 4, 9. 2003. (Fonolibros Ser.). 25.50 (978-0-7652-0086-0(4)) Modern Curriculum Pr.

Queen Jelly Bean: Vowel Digraph Review: Level C, 6 vols. (Wright Skills Ser.). 16p. (gr. k-3). 26.50 (978-0-322-01499-2(9)) Wright Group, The.

Queen on a Quilt (Consonant q), Level K. 2003. ("Plaid" Phonics & Stories Libraries). (ps-3). 24.50 (978-0-8136-5437-9(8)) Modern Curriculum Pr.

Quinlan, Heather. Phonics Made Easy. Harpster, Steve, illus. 2005. (First Word Search Ser.). 64p. (ps). pap. 3.95 (978-1-4027-2748-1(8)) Sterling Publishing Co., Inc.

Quit It! Consonant q: Level A, 6 vols. (Wright Skills Ser.). 12p. (gr. k-3). 17.95 (978-0-322-03122-7(2)) Wright Group, The.

Rainbow Bridge Publishing Staff. Phonics First Grade: Skill Builders. 2002. (Skill Builders Ser.). (Illus.). 64p. (gr. 1 up). 2.49 (978-1-887923-43-9(8)) Rainbow Bridge Publishing.

Ramsey, Kimberly. Stories from Somerville. 2002. Vol. 1. 56p. 12.95 (978-1-881929-17-8(5)); Vol. 2. 64p. 12.95 (978-1-881929-18-5(3)) Oxton Hse., Pubs.

—Stories from Somerville: Comprehension Workbook. 2002. Vol. 1. 32p. 5.00 (978-1-881929-24-6(8)); Vol. 1b. 20p. 5.00 (978-1-881929-25-3(6)); Vol. 2. 52p. 7.00 (978-1-881929-26-0(4)) Oxton Hse., Pubs.

Random House Staff. Phonics First Steps! Lieser, Ron, illus. 2004. (Step into Reading Ser.: Set 1). 24p. (J). (ps). 9.99 (978-0-375-82577-4(0) , Random Hse. Bks. for Young Readers) Random Hse. Children's Bks.

Rasinski, Timothy. Daily Word Ladders: 100 Reproducible Word Study Lessons That Help Kids Boost Reading, Vocabulary, Spelling & Phonics Skills-Independently! 2005. (Daily Word Ladders Ser.). (Illus.). 112p. (gr. 4-6). pap. 15.99 (978-0-439-77345-4(8) , Teaching Resources) Scholastic, Inc.

Rawlins, Colette. Phonics Kindergarten. 2003. (Skill Builders Ser.). 80p. (gr. k up). 2.95 (978-1-932210-00-2(8)) Rainbow Bridge Publishing.

Read-Alone Phonics Stories. (gr. 1-2). 7.85 (978-0-7362-1656-2(1)) Hampton-Brown Bks.

Read & Spell with Zoo-phonics. 2004. (J). cd-rom 29.95 (978-1-886441-46-0(4)) Zoo-phonics, Inc.

Read & Spell with Zoo=Phonics Guide for CD-ROM. 2004. (J). 14.95 (978-1-886441-45-3(6)) Zoo-phonics, Inc.

Reading at Home: Phonics Grade 1 Combo. (gr. 1 up). 517.92 (978-0-7362-1401-8(1)) Hampton-Brown Bks.

Reading at Home: Phonics Grade 2 Combo. (gr. 2 up). 368.64 (978-0-7362-1402-5(X)) Hampton-Brown Bks.

Reading Rods Phonemic Awareness: Instruction & Activity Book. 2001. (J). spiral bd. 12.95 (978-1-56911-063-8(8)) Learning Resources, Inc.

Reading Rods Phonemic Awareness Activity Book. 2003. (J). pap. 4.95 (978-1-56911-117-8(0)) Learning Resources, Inc.

Reading Rods Phonemic Awareness Activity Cards, Set 2. 2003. (J). 19.95 (978-1-56911-113-0(8)) Learning Resources, Inc.

Reading Rods Phonemic Awareness Double-Sided Activity Cards. 2001. (J). 12.95 (978-1-56911-070-6(0)) Learning Resources, Inc.

Reading Rods Readers: Phonics Foundation 1 Classpack. 2003. (J). per. 249.95 (978-1-56911-575-6(3)) Learning Resources, Inc.

Reading Rods Readers: Phonics Foundation 2 Classpack. 2003. (J). per. 249.95 (978-1-56911-576-3(1)) Learning Resources, Inc.

Reading Rods Readers: Phonics Foundation Set 1. 2003. (J). pap. 44.95 (978-1-56911-121-5(9)) Learning Resources, Inc.

Reading Rods Readers: Phonics Foundation Set 2. 2003. (J). pap. 44.95 (978-1-56911-122-2(7)) Learning Resources, Inc.

Ready Reader Staff. At the Track, 6 bks., set, Level 8, Bk. 29. 2003. (J). (ps-3). pap. 30.95 (978-0-8136-2063-3(5)) Modern Curriculum Pr.

—Little Frog's Monster Story, 6 bks., set, Level 6, Bk. 12. 2003. (J). (ps-3). pap. 33.50 (978-0-8136-0806-8(6)) Modern Curriculum Pr.

—Something to Munch, 6 bks., set, Level 8, Bk. 38. 2003. (J). (ps-3). pap. 33.50 (978-0-8136-2071-8(6)) Modern Curriculum Pr.

Realtime Associates and Mazer Corporation Staff & LeapFrog Staff, compiled by. Distinguish Initial, Medial, & Final Sounds. 2002. (J). (gr. 2). 66.75 (978-1-58605-318-5(3) , LeapFrog Schl. Hse.) LeapFrog Enterprises, Inc.

—Final Consonant Blends Using L (ld, lp, it) 2002. (J). (gr. k-1). 66.75 (978-1-58605-272-0(1) , LeapFrog Schl. Hse.) LeapFrog Enterprises, Inc.

—Final Consonant Blends Using n (nd, nk, nt) 2002. (J). (gr. k-1). 66.75 (978-1-58605-274-4(8) , LeapFrog Schl. Hse.) LeapFrog Enterprises, Inc.

—Final Consonant Blends Using s (sk, sp, st) 2002. (J). (gr. k-1). 66.75 (978-1-58605-269-0(1) , LeapFrog Schl. Hse.) LeapFrog Enterprises, Inc.

—Identify, Segment, & Combine Spoken Syllables. 2002. (J). (gr. 2). 66.75 (978-1-58605-319-2(1) , LeapFrog Schl. Hse.) LeapFrog Enterprises, Inc.

—Initial Consonant Blends Using L. 2002. (J). (gr. k-1). 66.75 (978-1-58605-271-3(3) , LeapFrog Schl. Hse.) LeapFrog Enterprises, Inc.

—Initial Consonant Blends Using qu. 2002. (J). (gr. k-1). 66.75 (978-1-58605-273-7(X) , LeapFrog Schl. Hse.) LeapFrog Enterprises, Inc.

—Initial Consonant Blends Using r. 2002. (J). (gr. k-1). 66.75 (978-1-58605-270-6(5) , LeapFrog Schl. Hse.) LeapFrog Enterprises, Inc.

—Initial Consonant Blends Using s. 2002. (J). (gr. k-1). 66.75 (978-1-58605-268-3(3) , LeapFrog Schl. Hse.) LeapFrog Enterprises, Inc.

—Long a (a_e) 2002. (J). (gr. k-1). 66.75 (978-1-58605-275-1(6) , LeapFrog Schl. Hse.) LeapFrog Enterprises, Inc.

—Long o. 2002. 66.75 (978-1-58605-277-5(2) , LeapFrog Schl. Hse.) LeapFrog Enterprises, Inc.

—Phonics Complex Vowels ai, ay. 2002. (J). (gr. k-1). 66.75 (978-1-58605-256-0(X) , LeapFrog Schl. Hse.) LeapFrog Enterprises, Inc.

—Phonics Complex Vowels ee, ea. 2002. (J). (gr. k-1). 66.75 (978-1-58605-257-7(8) , LeapFrog Schl. Hse.) LeapFrog Enterprises, Inc.

—Phonics Complex Vowels oa. 2002. (J). (gr. k-1). 66.75 (978-1-58605-259-1(4) , LeapFrog Schl. Hse.) LeapFrog Enterprises, Inc.

—Phonics Complex Vowels oi, oy. 2002. (J). (gr. k-1). 66.75 (978-1-58605-258-4(6) , LeapFrog Schl. Hse.) LeapFrog Enterprises, Inc.

—Phonics Digraph sh. 2002. (J). (gr. k-1). 66.75 (978-1-58605-253-9(5) , LeapFrog Schl. Hse.) LeapFrog Enterprises, Inc.

—Phonics Digraph th. 2002. (J). (gr. k-1). 66.75 (978-1-58605-254-6(3)) LeapFrog Enterprises, Inc.

—Phonics Final Consonant Blends Using L (ld, lp, lt) 2002. (J). (gr. k-1). 66.75 (978-1-58605-245-4(4) , LeapFrog Schl. Hse.) LeapFrog Enterprises, Inc.

—Phonics Final Consonant Blends Using n (nd, nk, nt) 2002. (J). (gr. k-1). 66.75 (978-1-58605-247-8(0) , LeapFrog Schl. Hse.) LeapFrog Enterprises, Inc.

—Phonics Final Consonant Blends Using s (sk, sp, st) 2002. (J). (gr. k-1). 66.75 (978-1-58605-242-3(X) , LeapFrog Schl. Hse.) LeapFrog Enterprises, Inc.

—Phonics Initial Consonant Blends Using L. 2002. (J). (gr. k-1). 66.75 (978-1-58605-244-7(6) , LeapFrog Schl. Hse.) LeapFrog Enterprises, Inc.

—Phonics Initial Consonant Blends Using Qu. 2002. (Illus.). (J). (gr. k-1). 66.75 (978-1-58605-246-1(2) , LeapFrog Schl. Hse.) LeapFrog Enterprises, Inc.

—Phonics Initial Consonant Blends Using r. 2002. (J). (gr. k-1). 66.75 (978-1-58605-243-0(8) , LeapFrog Schl. Hse.) LeapFrog Enterprises, Inc.

—Phonics Initial Consonant Blends Using s. 2002. (J). (gr. k-1). 66.75 (978-1-58605-241-6(1) , LeapFrog Schl. Hse.) LeapFrog Enterprises, Inc.

—Phonics LIL 1 Short A. 2002. (J). (gr. k-1). 66.75 (978-1-58605-236-2(5) , LeapFrog Schl. Hse.) LeapFrog Enterprises, Inc.

—Phonics Long a (a_e) 2002. (J). (gr. k-1). 66.75 (978-1-58605-248-5(9) , LeapFrog Schl. Hse.) LeapFrog Enterprises, Inc.

—Phonics Long i as _ie or _y. 2002. (J). (gr. k-1). 66.75 (978-1-58605-252-2(7)) LeapFrog Enterprises, Inc.

—Phonics Long i (i_e) 2002. (J). (gr. k-1). 66.75 (978-1-58605-249-2(7) , LeapFrog Schl. Hse.) LeapFrog Enterprises, Inc.

—Phonics Long o. 2002. (J). (gr. k-1). 66.75 (978-1-58605-250-8(0) , LeapFrog Schl. Hse.) LeapFrog Enterprises, Inc.

—Phonics Long u. 2002. (J). (gr. k-1). 66.75 (978-1-58605-251-5(9) , LeapFrog Schl. Hse.) LeapFrog Enterprises, Inc.

—Phonics r-Controlled Vowel (ar) 2002. (J). (gr. k-1). 66.75 (978-1-58605-260-7(8) , LeapFrog Schl. Hse.) LeapFrog Enterprises, Inc.

—Phonics r-Controlled Vowels (er, ir, ur) 2002. (J). (gr. k-1). 66.75 (978-1-58605-261-4(6) , LeapFrog Schl. Hse.) LeapFrog Enterprises, Inc.

—Phonics r-Controlled Vowels (or) 2002. (J). (gr. k-1). 66.75 (978-1-58605-262-1(4) , LeapFrog Schl. Hse.) LeapFrog Enterprises, Inc.

—Phonics Short e. 2002. (J). (gr. k-1). 66.75 (978-1-58605-239-3(X) , LeapFrog Schl. Hse.) LeapFrog Enterprises, Inc.

—Phonics Short i. 2002. (J). (gr. k-1). 66.75 (978-1-58605-237-9(3) , LeapFrog Schl. Hse.) LeapFrog Enterprises, Inc.

—Phonics Short o. 2002. (J). (gr. k-1). 66.75 (978-1-58605-238-6(1) , LeapFrog Schl. Hse.) LeapFrog Enterprises, Inc.

—Phonics Short u. 2002. (J). (gr. k-1). 66.75 (978-1-58605-240-9(3) , LeapFrog Schl. Hse.) LeapFrog Enterprises, Inc.

—R-Controlled Vowels (ar) 2002. (J). (gr. k-1). 2002.00 (978-1-58605-287-4(X) , LeapFrog Schl. Hse.) LeapFrog Enterprises, Inc.

—R-Controlled Vowels (er, ir, ur) 2002. (J). (gr. k-1). 66.75 (978-1-58605-288-1(8) , LeapFrog Schl. Hse.) LeapFrog Enterprises, Inc.

—R-Controlled Vowels (or) 2002. (J). (gr. k-1). 66.75 (978-1-58605-289-8(6) , LeapFrog Schl. Hse.) LeapFrog Enterprises, Inc.

—Recognize Regular Consonant Blends. 2002. (J). (gr. 2). 66.75 (978-1-58605-323-9(X) , LeapFrog Schl. Hse.) LeapFrog Enterprises, Inc.

—Recognize Regular Consonant Sounds. 2002. (J). (gr. 2). 66.75 (978-1-58605-321-5(3) , LeapFrog Schl. Hse.) LeapFrog Enterprises, Inc.

—Recognize Regular Long Vowel Sounds. 2002. (J). (gr. 2). 66.75 (978-1-58605-320-8(5) , LeapFrog Schl. Hse.) LeapFrog Enterprises, Inc.

Reid, Donna. Pic-a-Drill R Articulation Fun Sheets. Barr, Steve et al, illus. 2000. 184p. (J). spiral bd. 32.95 (978-1-58650-158-7(5) , BK-284) Super Duper Pubns.

Rice, Charles M. Voice Production with the Aid of Phonetics. 2nd ed. 2001. 87p. (YA). reprint ed. 88.00 (978-0-7222-6212-2(4)) Library Reprints, Inc.

Rider, Cynthia. The Dog & the Bone, 6, Pack. 2000. (Cambridge Reading Ser.). (Illus.). 12p. pap. 26.00 (978-0-521-78691-1(6)) Cambridge Univ. Pr.

Rider, Cynthia & Lynne, Francis. Beginning to Read: Phonics for Reading 2. 2000. (Cambridge Reading Ser.). (Illus.). 8p. pap. 19.00 (978-0-521-79525-8(7)) Cambridge Univ. Pr.

—Beginning to Read: Phonics for Reading 3. 2000. (Cambridge Reading Ser.). (Illus.). 8p. pap. 19.00 (978-0-521-79524-1(9)) Cambridge Univ. Pr.

Rigby. Complete Phonemic Awareness Handbook. 2001. (Rigby Best Teachers Press Ser.). 208p. (gr. k-2). 17.99 (978-0-7635-7347-8(7)) Rigby Education.

—Fabulous Phonics Little Books. 2001. (Rigby Best Teachers Press Ser.). (Illus.). 136p. (gr. k-2). 14.99 (978-0-7635-7339-3(6)) Rigby Education.

El Rio Crece: Little Books, Level 16. 2003. (Fonolibros Ser.). 35.50 (978-0-7652-0110-2(0)) Modern Curriculum Pr.

Ristuccia, Christine. The Entire World of R Instructional Workbook: A Phonemic Approach to /R/ Remediation. l.t. ed. 2002. (Illus.). 200p. per. 34.99 (978-0-9723457-0-5(1)) Say It Right.

Ristuccia, Christine & Ristuccia, James. The Entire World of S & Z Instructional Workbook: A Comprehensive Approach to Remediate Frontal & Lateral Lisps. l.t. ed. 2003. (Illus.). 208p. (J). per. 34.99 (978-0-9723457-4-3(4)) Say It Right.

Rooney Moreau, Maryellen & Welch, Brian Scott. Talk to Write, Write to Learn Kit. 2006. pap. (***978-0-9769527-5-6(0)***) Mindwing Concepts, Inc.

Rosario, Sherwin, illus. Meet the Vowels. 2005. 12p. (J). bds. 7.99 (978-0-9767008-2-1(4)) KRO Publishing.

Rothman, Cynthia Anne. Little Book: I Love to Read. 2000. (Sadlier Phonics Reading Program). 8p. (J). (978-0-8215-7313-6(6) , Sadlier-Oxford) Sadlier, William H. Inc.

—Little Book: What Does Sam Sell? Alley, R. W., illus. 2000. (Sadlier Phonics Reading Program). 8p. (J). (978-0-8215-7302-0(0) , Sadlier-Oxford) Sadlier, William H. Inc.

—Little Book: Violets & Vegatables. 2000. (Sadlier Phonics Reading Program). 8p. (J). (978-0-8215-7317-4(9) , Sadlier-Oxford) Sadlier, William H. Inc.

—Little Book: Yes, You Can. 2000. (Sadlier Phonics Reading Program). 8p. (J). (978-0-8215-7318-1(7) , Sadlier-Oxford) Sadlier, William H. Inc.

Rovetch, Lissa. Ook the Book: And Other Silly Rhymes. McNeill, Shannon, illus. 2006. 32p. (J). pap. 5.95 (978-0-8118-5029-2(3)) Chronicle Bks. LLC.

Salta, Oscar: Little Books, Level 1, 5. 2003. (Fonolibros Ser.). (SPA.). 25.50 (978-0-7652-0081-5(3)) Modern Curriculum Pr.

A Saludar Y A Celebrar: Little Books, Level 4, Vol. 23. 2003. (Fonolibros Ser.). (SPA.). 25.50 (978-0-7652-0101-0(1)) Modern Curriculum Pr.

Salzmann, Mary Elizabeth. Ai: See It Say It Hear It. l.t. ed. 2001. (Vowel Blends Ser.). (Illus.). 24p. (J). (ps-3). lib. bdg. 19.93 (978-1-57765-453-7(6) , SandCastle) ABDO Publishing Co.

—Oa: See It Say It Hear It. l.t. ed. 2001. (Vowel Blends Ser.). (Illus.). 24p. (J). (ps-3). lib. bdg. 19.93 (978-1-57765-456-8(0) , SandCastle) ABDO Publishing Co.

—Oo: See It Say It Hear It. (Long Vowels Ser.). (Illus.). 24p. (J). (ps-3). 2000. lib. bdg. 19.93 (978-1-57765-416-2(1)); 2001. lib. bdg. 19.93 (978-1-57765-457-5(9)) ABDO Publishing Co. (SandCastle).

Santillo, LuAnn. Fun with Phonemes. Santillo, LuAnn, ed. 2004. (Half - Pint Readers Ser.). (Illus.). 36p. (J). (ps-1). pap. 14.99 (978-1-59256-129-2(2)) Half-Pint Kids, Inc.

—Lots More Fun with Phonemes. Santillo, LuAnn, ed. 2004. (Half-Pint Readers Ser.). (Illus.). 36p. (J). (ps-1). pap. 14.99 (978-1-59256-131-5(4)) Half-Pint Kids, Inc.

—More Fun with Phonemes. Santillo, LuAnn, ed. 2004. (Half-Pint Readers Ser.). (Illus.). 36p. (J). (ps-1). pap. 14.99 (978-1-59256-130-8(6)) Half-Pint Kids, Inc.

Santos, Dina. My New Glasses: Learning the GL Sound. 2002. (PowerPhonics Ser.). (Illus.). (J). 23p. pap. (978-0-8239-8290-5(4)); 24p. (gr. 1). lib. bdg. 18.50 (978-0-8239-5945-7(7)) Rosen Publishing Group, Inc., The. (PowerKids Pr.).

Sarkisian, Kevin. You Need Your Nose: Learning the N Sound. 2002. (PowerPhonics Ser.). (Illus.). (J). 23p. lib. bdg. (978-0-8239-8255-4(6)); 24p. (gr. 1). lib. bdg. 18.50 (978-0-8239-5910-5(4) , PowerKids Pr.) Rosen Publishing Group, Inc., The.

Saxton, Brenda, illus. Reading Pals: Alphabet Recognition Gr. Pre K-K. 2007. (J). per. 6.99 (***978-1-59198-435-1(1)***) Creative Teaching Pr., Inc.

Scat! Said the Cat: Big Book: Level D. Group 1. (Sunshinetm Ser.). 8p. 20.95 (978-0-7802-5734-4(0)) Wright Group, The.

Schecter, Deborah. Mother Goose Phonics: Learning to Read Fun with Adorable Activities, Games & Manipulatives. 1999. (Illus.). 64p. pap. 10.95 (978-0-439-12927-5(3)) Scholastic, Inc.

Scheunemann, Pam. Dr: See It Say It Hear It. l.t. ed. 2001. (More Blends Ser.). (Illus.). 24p. (J). (ps-3). lib. bdg. 19.93 (978-1-57765-448-3(X)) ABDO Publishing Co.

—Ght: See It Say It Hear It. l.t. ed. 2001. (More Blends Ser.). (Illus.). 24p. (J). (ps-3). lib. bdg. 19.93 (978-1-57765-449-0(8) , SandCastle) ABDO Publishing Co.

—Sl: See It Say It Hear It. l.t. ed. 2001. (More Blends Ser.). (Illus.). 24p. (J). (ps-3). lib. bdg. 19.93 (978-1-57765-452-0(8) , SandCastle) ABDO Publishing Co.

Schmauss, Judy Kentor, et al. Reader's Clubhouse Level 2 Long-Vowel Valu-Pak. 2006. (Illus.). 120 p. (J). pap. 15.96 (978-0-7641-7969-3(1)) Barron's Educational Series, Inc.

School Specialty Pub. Phonics Sorting Activities. 2004. 56p. (J). (gr. k up). pap. 8.99 (978-0-7424-2740-2(4) , IFG99192); (gr. 1 up). pap. 8.99 (978-0-7424-2741-9(2) , IFG99189); (gr. 2 up). pap. 8.99 (978-0-7424-2742-6(0) , IFG99190) School Specialty Publishing.

—Theme-Based Phonics. 2003. (100+ Seriestm Ser.). 128p. (J). (gr. 3 up). pap. 14.99 (978-0-7424-1913-1(4) , IFG99106) School Specialty Publishing.

School Specialty Publishing. Beginning Consonants. 2001. (Flip-Flashtm Ser.). 160p. (J). (gr. k up). pap. 7.99 (978-1-56451-383-0(1) , ID2422) School Specialty Publishing.

—Blends & Digraphs. 2001. (Flip-Flashtm Ser.). 160p. (J). (gr. k up). pap. 7.99 (978-1-56451-384-7(X) , ID2423) School Specialty Publishing.

—Compounds & Contractions. 2001. (Flip-Flashtm Ser.). 160p. (J). (gr. k up). pap. 7.99 (978-1-56451-385-4(8) , ID2424) School Specialty Publishing.

—Easy Blends & Digraphs. 2001. (Phonics Flash Cards Ser.). 104p. (C). 6.99 (978-0-86734-412-7(1) , Schaffer, Frank) Schaffer, Frank Pubns.

—Flip-Flash Phonics: Homonyms. 2002. (Flip-Flashtm Phonics Ser.). 160p. (J). (gr. 1 up). pap. 7.99 (978-1-56451-392-2(0) , ID2427) School Specialty Publishing.

—Flip-Flash Phonics: Opposites. 2002. (Flip-Flashtm Phonics Ser.). 160p. (J). (gr. 1 up). pap. 7.99 (978-1-56451-394-6(7) , ID2429) School Specialty Publishing.

—Flip-Flash Phonics: Synonyms. 2002. (Flip-Flashtm Phonics Ser.). 160p. (J). (gr. 1 up). pap. 7.99 (978-1-56451-393-9(9) , ID2428) School Specialty Publishing.

—Flip-Flash Phonics & Vocabulary: Prefixes. 2004. 160p. (J). (gr. 3-6). pap. 7.99 (978-0-7424-2686-3(6) , ID99060) School Specialty Publishing.

—Flip-Flash Phonics & Vocabulary: Suffixes. 2004. 160p. (J). (gr. 3-6). pap. 7.99 (978-0-7424-2687-0(4) , ID99061) School Specialty Publishing.

—Flip-Flash Phonics & Vocabulary: Vocabulary. 2004. 160p. (J). (gr. k-1). pap. 7.99 (978-0-7424-2694-8(7) , ID99064); (gr. 2-3). pap. 7.99 (978-0-7424-2695-5(5) , ID99062) School Specialty Publishing.

—I Can Spell & Rhyme. 2006. (Brighter Child I Can... Ser.). 128p. (J). pap. 3.95 (978-0-7696-4898-9(3) , Brighter Child) School Specialty Publishing.

—Long Vowels. 2001. (Flip-Flashtm Ser.). 160p. (J). (gr. k up). pap. 7.99 (978-1-56451-382-3(3) , ID2421) School Specialty Publishing.

—Phonemic Awareness & Beginning Phonics: People. 2004. 96p. (J). pap. 10.99 (978-1-57029-495-2(X) , WPH99045, Totline Pubns.) Schaffer, Frank Pubns.

—Phonemic Awareness & Beginning Phonics: Places. 2004. 96p. (J). pap. 10.99 (978-1-57029-493-8(3) , WPH99043, Totline Pubns.) Schaffer, Frank Pubns.

—Phonemic Awareness & Beginning Phonics: Weather & Seasons. 2004. 96p. (J). pap. 10.99 (978-1-57029-494-5(1) , WPH99044, Totline Pubns.) Schaffer, Frank Pubns.

—Phonics. 2006. (Brighter Child Flash Cards Ser.). 54p. (J). 2.99 (978-0-7696-4749-4(9) , Brighter Child) School Specialty Publishing.

—Phonics Flickers CVC Words. 2003. (C). spiral bd. 15.99 (978-0-7424-2206-3(2) , LDA) Findel Education, Ltd. GBR. *Dist:* School Specialty Publishing.

—Phonics Flickers Onset & Rime. 2003. (C). spiral bd. 15.99 (978-0-7424-2208-7(9) , LDA) Findel Education, Ltd. GBR. *Dist:* School Specialty Publishing.

—Phonics Sorting Activities. 2004. 56p. (J). (gr. 3 up). pap. 8.99 (978-0-7424-2743-3(9) , IFG99191) School Specialty Publishing.

—Picture Recognition. 2001. (Phonics Flash Cards Ser.). 104p. (C). 6.99 (978-0-86734-407-3(5) , Schaffer, Frank) Schaffer, Frank Pubns.

—Picture Recognition Set. 2001. (Phonics Flash Cards Ser.). 208p. (C). 13.90 (978-0-7682-1705-6(9) , Schaffer, Frank) Schaffer, Frank Pubns.

—Short Vowels. 2001. (Flip-Flashtm Ser.). 160p. (J). (gr. k up). pap. 7.99 (978-1-56451-381-6(5) , ID2420) School Specialty Publishing.

—Short Vowels, Grades K-1. 2006. (Frank Schaffer Classic Reproducibles Ser.). 48p. (J). (gr. k-1). pap. 6.99 (978-0-7682-3460-2(3) , Schaffer, Frank) Schaffer, Frank Pubns.

—Sight Words. 2001. (Flip-Flashtm Phonics Ser.). 160p. (J). (gr. k up). pap. 7.99 (978-1-56451-386-1(6) , ID2425) School Specialty Publishing.

—Skills for Scholars-phonics 1. 2007. (Skills for Scholars Ser.). 80p. pap. 4.99 (***978-0-7696-8331-7(2)*** , Schaffer, Frank) Schaffer, Frank Pubns.

—Skills for Scholars-phonics 2. 2007. (Skills for Scholars Ser.). 80p. pap. 4.99 (***978-0-7696-8332-4(0)*** , Schaffer, Frank) Schaffer, Frank Pubns.

—Skills for scholars-phonics K. 2007. (Skills for Scholars Ser.). 80p. pap. 4.99 (***978-0-7696-8330-0(4)*** , Schaffer, Frank) Schaffer, Frank Pubns.

—Skills for scholars-phonics Pk. 2007. (Skills for Scholars Ser.). 80p. pap. 4.99 (***978-0-7696-8329-4(0)*** , Schaffer, Frank) Schaffer, Frank Pubns.

—Words & Pictures. 2002. (Flip-Flashtm Phonics Ser.). 160p. (J). (gr. k up). pap. 7.99 (978-1-56451-391-5(2) , ID2426) School Specialty Publishing.

—1-2-3 Phonics. 2003. (1-2-3 Ser.). 80p. (J). pap. 10.99 (978-1-57029-470-9(4) , WPH99021, Totline Pubns.) Schaffer, Frank Pubns.

School Zone Interactive Staff. Phonics Review. rev. ed. 2003. (On-Track Software Ser.). 64p. (J). (gr. 1-2). pap. 15.99 incl. cd-rom (978-1-58947-844-2(4)) School Zone Publishing Co.

School Zone Publishing. Phonics. 2003. (J). (gr. 2-3). cd-rom 19.99 (978-1-58947-935-7(1)) School Zone Publishing Co.

School Zone Publishing Company Staff. Beginning Sounds Bilingual: Get Ready! 2004. 64p. (J). pap. 3.79 (978-1-58947-974-6(2)) School Zone Publishing Co.

—Phonics. 2000. (Mats Ser.). (J). 3.29 (978-0-88743-722-9(2) , 03111) School Zone Publishing Co.

—Phonics 2-3 Big Get Ready! 1999. (Big Get Ready Ser.). (Illus.). 320p. (J). (ps-3). pap., wbk. ed. 9.90 (978-0-88743-149-4(6) , 06319) School Zone Publishing Co.

—Phonics Made Easy. rev. ed. 1999. (Flash Cards Ser.). 56p. (J). 2.79 (978-0-938256-81-6(5) , 04014) School Zone Publishing Co.

—Phonics Review. (Illus.). (J). 19.99 incl. audio compact disk (978-0-88743-967-4(5)) School Zone Publishing Co.

School Zone Publishing Interactive Staff. Pencil-Pal Phonics. 2002. (Pencil-Pal Software Ser.). (Illus.). 64p. (J). (gr. 1-2). pap. 15.99 incl. cd-rom (978-1-58947-523-6(2) , 08220) School Zone Publishing Co.

—Phonics 2-3. 2001. (On-Track Software Ser.). (Illus.). 32p. (J). wbk. ed. 13.99 incl. cd-rom (978-0-88743-959-9(4) , 08835) School Zone Publishing Co.

Schuepbach, Lynnette. Shhhh!!! Schuepbach, Lynnette, illus. l.t. ed. 2004. (Illus.). 32p. (J). 7.00 net. (978-0-9759613-1-5(4)) Creative Sources.

Scott Foresman Reading: Phonics. 2004. (gr. 1 up). (978-0-328-07389-4(X)); (978-0-328-05636-1(7)); (978-0-328-05637-8(5)); (978-0-328-05638-5(3)); (978-0-328-05639-2(1)); (978-0-328-05640-8(5)); (978-0-328-05641-5(3)); (978-0-328-05642-2(1)); (978-0-328-05643-9(X)); (978-0-328-05645-3(6)); (978-0-328-07405-1(5)) Addison-Wesley Educational Pubs., Inc. (Scott Foresman).

Sesame Street Letter Sounds. 2005. (J). 2.95 (***978-1-58610-980-6(4)***) Learning Horizons, Inc.

Set a Add-on Set. (Phonics Readers Ser.). (gr. k-2). 34.95 (978-0-7368-3222-9(X)) Red Brick Learning.

Set a Complete Program. (Phonics Readers Ser.). (gr. k-2). 209.95 (978-0-7368-3221-2(1)) Red Brick Learning.

Set B Add-on Set. (Phonics Readers Ser.). (gr. k-2). 34.95 (978-0-7368-3224-3(6)) Red Brick Learning.

Set B Complete Program. (Phonics Readers Ser.). (gr. k-2). 209.95 (978-0-7368-3223-6(8)) Red Brick Learning.

Set C Add-on Set. (Phonics Readers Ser.). (gr. k-2). 34.95 (978-0-7368-3226-7(2)) Red Brick Learning.

Set C Complete Program. (Phonics Readers Ser.). (gr. k-2). 209.95 (978-0-7368-3225-0(4)) Red Brick Learning.

Set D Add-on Set. (Phonics Readers Ser.). (gr. k-2). 57.95 (978-0-7368-4091-0(5)) Red Brick Learning.

Set D Complete Program. (Phonics Readers Ser.). (gr. k-2). 328.95 (978-0-7368-4090-3(7)) Red Brick Learning.

Set E Add-on Set. (Phonics Readers Ser.). (gr. k-2). 57.95 (978-0-7368-4093-4(1)) Red Brick Learning.

Set E Complete Program. (Phonics Readers Ser.). (gr. k-2). 328.95 (978-0-7368-4092-7(3)) Red Brick Learning.

Set F Add-on Set. (Phonics Readers Ser.). (gr. k-2). 57.95 (978-0-7368-4095-8(8)) Red Brick Learning.

Set F Complete Program. (Phonics Readers Ser.). (gr. k-2). 328.95 (978-0-7368-4094-1(X)) Red Brick Learning.

Sevaly, Karen, ed. Hands on Learning: Beginning Letter Sounds Dominoes. 2006. 12.99 (978-0-439-82403-3(6) , Teaching Resources) Scholastic, Inc.

Shelly's Shell: Digraph sh: Level B, 6 vols. (Wright Skills Ser.). 16p. (gr. k-3). 17.95 (978-0-322-01471-8(9)) Wright Group, The.

Shems, Ed, illus. First Word Search: Phonics Made Fun. 2007. (First Word Search Ser.). 64p. (J). pap. 3.95 (978-1-4027-4262-0(2)) Sterling Publishing Co., Inc.

Shiotsu, Vicky. Build-a-Skill Instant Books Beginning & Ending Consonant Sounds. Faulkner, Stacey, ed. Campbell, Jenny & Tom, Darcy, illus. 2007. (J). 4.99 (***978-1-59198-416-0(5)***) Creative Teaching Pr., Inc.

—Consonant Blends & Digraphs. 1999. (Monster Phonics Ser.). (Illus.). 48p. (J). (gr. 1-3). pap. 5.95 (978-0-7373-0220-2(8) , 02208W) McGraw-Hill/Contemporary.

—Monster Phonics: Special Vowels for Grades 1-2. Helle, Lucy, illus. 2000. (Monster Phonics Ser.). 48p. (J). (gr. 1-3). pap. 5.95 (978-0-7373-0334-6(4) , 03344W, Roxbury Park Juvenile) Lowell Hse. Juvenile.

—Phonics, Bk. 2. 2000. (Gifted & Talented Ser.). (Illus.). 64p. (J). (gr. 1-3). pap. 4.95 (978-0-7373-0498-5(7)); (ps-1). pap. 4.95 (978-0-7373-0499-2(5)) Lowell Hse. Juvenile.

Shopping: Big Book: Level A. (Sunshinetm Ser.). 8p. 20.95 (978-0-7802-5710-8(3)) Wright Group, The.

Short & Long Vowels (Gr. 1-2) 2003. (J). (978-1-58232-038-0(1)) Bryan Hse. Pubs., Inc.

Short Vowels (Gr. 1-2) 2003. (J). (978-1-58232-110-3(8)) Bryan Hse. Pubs., Inc.

Short Vowels Phonics Windows with Answers. 2002. (Phonics Windows Ser.). 1p. pap. 0.99 (978-0-88724-833-7(0) , CD-3032) Carson-Dellosa Publishing Co., Inc.

Sicinski-Skeans, Sharon & Baron, Lindamichelle. The Write Direction: Hardcover Student Book. 2003. (Illus.). (J). (gr. 4). stu. ed. 18.95 (978-0-7652-0751-7(6)); (gr. 5). stu. ed. 18.95 (978-0-7652-0752-4(4)) Modern Curriculum Pr.

Siede Preis Photography (Firm) Staff & Brian Warling Photography (Firm) Staff, contrib. by. Phonics. 2004. (Active Minds(R) Ser.). (Illus.). 12p. (J). bds. (978-1-4127-0536-3(3) , 3970701) Publications International, Ltd.

The Silly Supper: Medial Consonants: Level C, 6 vols. (Wright Skills Ser.). 16p. (gr. k-3). 26.50 (978-0-322-01491-6(3)) Wright Group, The.

SIPPS Beginning Hand-held Sound Cards. 2004. (978-1-57621-455-8(9)) Developmental Studies Ctr.

SIPPS Beginning Package of Little Books. 2004. (978-1-57621-458-9(3)) Developmental Studies Ctr.

SIPPS Beginning Reproducible Book. 2004. (978-1-57621-459-6(1)) Developmental Studies Ctr.

SIPPS Beginning Sound Wall Cards. 2004. (978-1-57621-454-1(0)) Developmental Studies Ctr.

SIPPS Extension Sound Wall Cards. 2004. (978-1-57621-461-9(3)) Developmental Studies Ctr.

Sloppy Tiger Bedtime: Big Book: Level M. Group 1. (Sunshinetm Ser.). 24p. 36.50 (978-0-7802-5791-7(X)) Wright Group, The.

Snake at the Lake: Long Vowel Review: Level C, 6 vols. (Wright Skills Ser.). 16p. (gr. k-3). 26.50 (978-0-322-01496-1(4)) Wright Group, The.

Sounding Out the Alphabet. 2004. (J). cd-rom, audio compact disk 9.95 (978-1-930006-62-1(4) , Reading Co., The) Rhoades & Assocs.

Sounds. 2005. (J). (ps-3). 956.64 (978-1-59679-120-6(9)) ABDO Publishing Co.

Sounds All Around Us Set C, 6 vols. (Phonics Readers Ser.). (gr. k-2). 17.50 (978-0-7368-3217-5(3)) Red Brick Learning.

Sounds & How We Hear Them Set E, 6 vols. (Phonics Readers Ser.). (gr. k-2). 28.95 (978-0-7368-4069-9(9)) Red Brick Learning.

Sounds & Lettersb Set: Level A. (Sing-along Songs Ser.). (ps-2). audio compact disk 66.18 (978-0-7362-0419-4(9)) Hampton-Brown Bks.

Splink & Splank: 3-letter blends str, scr, spr, spl: Level B, 6 vols. (Wright Skills Ser.). 16p. (gr. k-3). 17.95 (978-0-322-01464-0(6)) Wright Group, The.

Sprick, Marilyn, et al. Read Well Magazine Unit 13: Plain Text. 2004. (Read Well Level K Ser.). (Illus.). 8p. (J). (978-1-57035-743-5(9)) Sopris West Educational Services.

—Read Well Magazine Unit 13: Slanted Text. 2004. (Read Well Level K Ser.). (Illus.). 8p. (J). (978-1-57035-769-5(2)) Sopris West Educational Services.

—Read Well Magazine Unit 14: Slanted Text. 2004. (Read Well Level K Ser.). (Illus.). 8p. (J). (978-1-57035-698-8(X)) Sopris West Educational Services.

—Read Well Magazine Unit 16: Plain Text. 2004. (Read Well Level K Ser.). (Illus.). 8p. (J). (978-1-57035-746-6(3)) Sopris West Educational Services.

—Read Well Magazine Unit 17: Plain Text. 2003. (Read Well Level K Ser.). (Illus.). 8p. (J). (978-1-57035-747-3(1)) Sopris West Educational Services.

—Read Well Magazine Unit 18: Plain Text. 2004. (Read Well Level K Ser.). (Illus.). 8p. (J). (978-1-57035-748-0(X)) Sopris West Educational Services.

—Read Well Magazine Unit 18: Slanted Text. 2003. (Read Well Level K Ser.). (Illus.). 8p. (J). (978-1-59318-102-4(7)) Sopris West Educational Services.

—Read Well Magazine Unit 19: Plain Text. 2003. (Read Well Level K Ser.). (Illus.). 8p. (J). (978-1-57035-749-7(8)) Sopris West Educational Services.

—Read Well Magazine Unit 19: Slanted Text. 2003. (Read Well Level K Ser.). (Illus.). 8p. (J). (978-1-59318-103-1(5)) Sopris West Educational Services.

—Read Well Magazine Unit 2: Plain Text. 2003. (Read Well Level K Ser.). (Illus.). 8p. (J). (978-1-57035-733-6(1)) Sopris West Educational Services.

—Read Well Magazine Unit 2: Slanted Text. 2003. (Read Well Level K Ser.). (Illus.). 8p. (J). (978-1-57035-783-1(8)) Sopris West Educational Services.

—Read Well Magazine Unit 20: Plain Text. 2003. (Read Well Level K Ser.). (Illus.). 8p. (J). (978-1-57035-775-6(7)) Sopris West Educational Services.

—Read Well Magazine Unit 3: Plain Text. 2003. (Read Well Level K Ser.). (Illus.). 8p. (J). (978-1-57035-734-3(X)) Sopris West Educational Services.

—Read Well Magazine Unit 3: Slanted Text. 2003. (Read Well Level K Ser.). (Illus.). 8p. (J). (978-1-57035-784-8(6)) Sopris West Educational Services.

—Read Well Magazine Unit 4: Plain Text. 2003. (Read Well Level K Ser.). (Illus.). 8p. (J). (978-1-57035-732-9(3)) Sopris West Educational Services.

—Read Well Magazine Unit 4: Slanted Text. 2003. (Read Well Level K Ser.). (Illus.). 8p. (J). (978-1-57035-785-5(4)) Sopris West Educational Services.

—Read Well Magazine Unit 5: Plain Text. 2003. (Read Well Level K Ser.). (Illus.). 8p. (J). (978-1-57035-736-7(6)) Sopris West Educational Services.

—Read Well Magazine Unit 5: Slanted Text. 2004. (Read Well Level K Ser.). (Illus.). 6p. (J). (978-1-57035-786-2(2)) Sopris West Educational Services.

—Read Well Magazine Unit 6: Plain Text. 2003. (Read Well Level K Ser.). (Illus.). 8p. (J). (978-1-57035-737-4(4)) Sopris West Educational Services.

—Read Well Magazine Unit 6: Slanted Text. 2003. (Read Well Level K Ser.). (Illus.). 8p. (J). (978-1-57035-787-9(0)) Sopris West Educational Services.

—Read Well Magazine Unit 7: Plain Text. 2003. (Read Well Level K Ser.). (Illus.). 8p. (J). (978-1-57035-738-1(2)) Sopris West Educational Services.
—Read Well Magazine Unit 8: Plain Text. 2003. (Read Well Level K Ser.). (Illus.). 8p. (J). (978-1-57035-726-8(9)) Sopris West Educational Services.
—Read Well Magazine Unit 8: Slanted Text. 2003. (Read Well Level K Ser.). (Illus.). 8p. (J). (978-1-57035-789-3(7)) Sopris West Educational Services.
—Read Well Magazine Unit 9: Plain Text. 2003. (Read Well Level K Ser.). (Illus.). 8p. (J). (978-1-57035-739-8(0)) Sopris West Educational Services.
—Read Well Magazine Unit 9: Slanted Text. 2003. (Read Well Level K Ser.). (Illus.). 8p. (J). (978-1-57035-790-9(0)) Sopris West Educational Services.
—Rescue Workers: Read Well Level K Unit 11 Storybook. Zilis, Tom, illus. 2003. (Read Well Level K Ser.). 20p. (J). (978-1-57035-682-7(3) , 55511) Sopris West Educational Services.
—Spiders: Read Well Level K Unit 1 Storybook. Shupe, Bobbi & Crum, Anna-Maria, illus. 2003. (Read Well Level K Ser.). 20p. (J). (978-1-57035-673-5(4)) Sopris West Educational Services.
—Spiders: Unit 1 Read Well Level K Teacher's Storybook. Shupe, Bobbi & Crum, Anna-Maria, illus. 2003. (Read Well Level K Ser.). 20p. (J). (978-1-57035-696-4(3)) Sopris West Educational Services.
—Student Workbook 1 (Plain Text) Units 1-9 Plus Review Unit. 2003. (Read Well Level K Ser.). (Illus.). 104p. (J). (978-1-59318-166-6(3)) Sopris West Educational Services.
—Student Workbook 1 (Slant Text) Units 1-9 Plus Review Unit. 2003. (Read Well Level K Ser.). (Illus.). 104p. (J). (978-1-59318-169-7(8)) Sopris West Educational Services.
—Student Workbook 2 (Plain Text) Units 10-18 Plus Review Unit. 2003. (Read Well Level K Ser.). (Illus.). 104p. (J). (978-1-59318-167-3(1)) Sopris West Educational Services.
—Student Workbook 2 (Slant Text) Units 10-18 Plus Review Unit. 2003. (Read Well Level K Ser.). (Illus.). 104p. (J). (978-1-59318-170-3(1)) Sopris West Educational Services.
Stamper, Judith Bauer & Blevins, Wiley. The Red Hen. Fritz, Ronald, illus. 1998. (Hello Reader! Science Ser.). 160p. (J). (gr. 1-2). pap. 3.99 (978-0-590-76269-4(9)) Scholastic, Inc.
Starlight. 2001. (Take-Home Bks.). (YA). (ps-k). 15.00 (978-0-8215-6984-9(8)) Sadlier, William H. Inc.
Stckvagn. Erp Lpur Complete Package. 2004. pap. (978-0-7398-9025-7(5)) Harcourt Schl. Pubs.
Steck-Vaughn Staff. Alphabet Phonics Readers, Set. 1998. pap. (978-0-8172-5692-0(X)) Steck-Vaughn.
—Big Box/Yum Yum Yum. 1999. (Take Me Home Ser.). (Illus.). (J). pap. (978-0-7398-2794-9(4)) Steck-Vaughn.
—Complete Phonics Readers. 1999. (Take Me Home Ser.). (Illus.). (J). pap. (978-0-7398-2702-4(2)) Steck-Vaughn.
—Core Skills: At Home with Phonics. 2003. (J). (gr. k). pap. 14.99 (978-0-7398-7955-9(3)); (gr. 1). pap. 14.99 (978-0-7398-7956-6(1)); (gr. 2). pap. 14.99 (978-0-7398-7957-3(X)); (gr. 3). pap. 14.99 (978-0-7398-7958-0(8)) Steck-Vaughn.
—Fire Racer/Jake's Fine Mess. 1999. (Take Me Home Ser.). (Illus.). (J). pap. (978-0-7398-2795-6(2)) Steck-Vaughn.
—Pair-It Classroom Set Stage 1. 1999. (Illus.). (J). pap. (978-0-7398-1588-5(1)) Steck-Vaughn.
—Pair-It Classroom Set Stage 2. 1999. (Illus.). (J). pap. (978-0-7398-1589-2(X)) Steck-Vaughn.
—Pair-It Classroom Set Stage 3. 1999. (Illus.). (J). pap. (978-0-7398-1590-8(3)) Steck-Vaughn.
—Pair-It Classroom Version Stage 1. 1999. (Illus.). (J). pap. (978-0-7398-1705-6(1)) Steck-Vaughn.
—Pair-It Classroom Version Stage 2. 1999. (Illus.). (J). pap. (978-0-7398-1706-3(X)) Steck-Vaughn.
—Pair-It Classroom Version Stage 3. 1999. (Illus.). (J). pap. (978-0-7398-1707-0(8)) Steck-Vaughn.
—Pair-It Lab Pack Stage 1. 1999. (Illus.). (J). pap. incl. cd-rom (978-0-7398-1573-1(3)) Steck-Vaughn.
—Pair It Lab Pack Stage 2. 1999. (Illus.). (J). pap. (978-0-7398-1574-8(1)) Steck-Vaughn.
—Pair-It Lab Pack Stage 3. 1999. (Illus.). (J). pap. (978-0-7398-1575-5(X)) Steck-Vaughn.
—Pair-It Lab Set Stage 1. 1999. (Illus.). (J). pap. (978-0-7398-1591-5(1)) Steck-Vaughn.
—Pair-It Lab Set Stage 2. 1999. (Illus.). (J). pap. (978-0-7398-1592-2(X)) Steck-Vaughn.
—Phonics Decoding Skills. 2004. (Illus.). (gr. k). pap. 14.99 (978-0-7398-8860-5(9)); (gr. 1). pap. 14.99 (978-0-7398-8861-2(7)) Steck-Vaughn.
—Phonics Decoding Skills Handbook. 2004. (Illus.). (gr. 3-6). pap. 14.99 (978-0-7398-8863-6(3)) Steck-Vaughn.
—Phonics Handbook. 1998. (Illus.). (J). (gr. 3-6). pap. (978-0-8172-7249-4(6)) Steck-Vaughn.
—Phonics Reader, Grade K. 1998. pap., tchr. ed. (978-0-8172-5686-9(5)) Steck-Vaughn.
—Phonics Readers Complete Class. 1998. pap. (978-0-8172-5808-5(6)) Steck-Vaughn.
—Phonics Readers Level A Class. 1998. pap. (978-0-8172-5693-7(8)) Steck-Vaughn.
—Phonics Readers Level A Set 1. 1998. pap. (978-0-8172-5695-1(4)) Steck-Vaughn.
—Phonics Readers Level A Set 2. 1998. pap. (978-0-8172-5696-8(2)) Steck-Vaughn.
—Phonics Readers Level B Class LI. 1998. pap. (978-0-8172-5694-4(6)) Steck-Vaughn.
—Phonics Readers Level B Set 1. 1998. pap. (978-0-8172-5698-2(9)) Steck-Vaughn.
—Phonics Readers Level B Set 2. 1998. pap. (978-0-8172-5699-9(7)) Steck-Vaughn.
—Phonics Readers Plus Aa. 1998. (Illus.). (J). pap. (978-0-8172-5600-5(8)) Steck-Vaughn.
—Phonics Readers Plus Bb. 1998. (Illus.). pap. (978-0-8172-5601-2(6)) Steck-Vaughn.
—Phonics Readers Plus Cc. 1998. (Illus.). pap. (978-0-8172-5602-9(4)) Steck-Vaughn.
—Phonics Readers Plus Dd. 1998. (Illus.). pap. (978-0-8172-5603-6(2)) Steck-Vaughn.
—Phonics Readers Plus Ee. 1998. (Illus.). pap. (978-0-8172-5604-3(0)) Steck-Vaughn.
—Phonics Readers Plus Ff. 1998. (Illus.). pap. (978-0-8172-5605-0(9)) Steck-Vaughn.
—Phonics Readers Plus Gg. 1998. (Illus.). pap. (978-0-8172-5606-7(7)) Steck-Vaughn.
—Phonics Readers Plus Hh. 1998. (Illus.). pap. (978-0-8172-5607-4(5)) Steck-Vaughn.
—Phonics Readers Plus Ii. 1998. (Illus.). pap. (978-0-8172-5608-1(3)) Steck-Vaughn.
—Phonics Readers Plus Jj. 1998. (Illus.). pap. (978-0-8172-5609-8(1)) Steck-Vaughn.
—Phonics Readers Plus Kk. 1998. (Illus.). pap. (978-0-8172-5610-4(5)) Steck-Vaughn.
—Phonics Readers Plus Ll. 1998. (Illus.). pap. (978-0-8172-5611-1(3)) Steck-Vaughn.
—Phonics Readers Plus Mm. 1998. (Illus.). pap. (978-0-8172-5612-8(1)) Steck-Vaughn.
—Phonics Readers Plus Nn. 1998. (Illus.). pap. (978-0-8172-5613-5(X)) Steck-Vaughn.
—Phonics Readers Plus Oo. 1998. (Illus.). pap. (978-0-8172-5614-2(8)) Steck-Vaughn.
—Phonics Readers Plus Pp. 1998. (Illus.). (J). pap. (978-0-8172-5615-9(6)) Steck-Vaughn.
—Phonics Readers Plus Qq. 1998. (Illus.). pap. (978-0-8172-5616-6(4)) Steck-Vaughn.
—Phonics Readers Plus Rr. 1998. (Illus.). pap. (978-0-8172-5617-3(2)) Steck-Vaughn.
—Phonics Readers Plus Ss. 1998. (Illus.). pap. (978-0-8172-5618-0(0)) Steck-Vaughn.
—Phonics Readers Plus Tt. 1998. (Illus.). pap. (978-0-8172-5619-7(9)) Steck-Vaughn.
—Phonics Readers Plus Uu. 1998. (Illus.). (J). pap. (978-0-8172-5620-3(2)) Steck-Vaughn.
—Phonics Readers Plus Vv. 1998. (Illus.). pap. (978-0-8172-5621-0(0)) Steck-Vaughn.
—Phonics Readers Plus Ww. 1998. (Illus.). pap. (978-0-8172-5622-7(9)) Steck-Vaughn.
—Phonics Readers Plus Xx. 1998. pap. 3.70 (978-0-8172-5623-4(7)) Harcourt Trade Pubs.
—Phonics Readers Plus Yy. 1998. (Illus.). pap. (978-0-8172-5624-1(5)) Steck-Vaughn.
—Phonics Readers Plus Zz. 1998. (Illus.). pap. (978-0-8172-5625-8(3)) Steck-Vaughn.
—Phonograms-Build-a-Word. 2001. (J). pap., tchr.'s planning gde. ed. (978-0-7398-4657-5(4)) Steck-Vaughn.
—Phonograms Set-Build-a-Word. 2001. (J). pap. (978-0-7398-4664-3(7)) Steck-Vaughn.
—Take Me Home: Complete Collection - Stage 5. 1999. (Illus.). (J). pap. 61.90 (978-0-7398-0964-8(4)) Steck-Vaughn.
—Take Me Home: Complete Pack. 1999. (Pair-It Bks.). (J). pap. (978-0-7398-1833-6(3)) Steck-Vaughn.
—Take Me Home Complete Set. 1998. (J). pap. (978-0-8172-8678-1(0)) Steck-Vaughn.
—Take Me Home Complete Transition. 1999. (Take Me Home Ser.). (J). pap. (978-0-7398-2600-3(X)) Steck-Vaughn.
—Take Me Home Primary, Set. 1998. (J). pap. (978-0-8172-8675-0(6)); (gr. 1). pap. (978-0-8172-8676-7(4)); (gr. 2). pap. (978-0-8172-8677-4(2)) Steck-Vaughn.
—Ten Cents/What Is under My Bed. 1999. (Take Me Home Ser.). (Illus.). (J). pap. (978-0-7398-2676-8(X)) Steck-Vaughn.
Sterling-Orth, Angela. Sound Reading: Literature Lists for Phonology & Articulation. 2005. (Illus.). iv, 43p. (J). pap. (978-1-932054-28-6(6)) Super Duper Pubns.
A Stormy Story: R-Controlled o: Level B, 6 vols. (Wright Skills Ser.). 16p. (gr. k-3). 26.50 (978-0-322-01487-9(5)) Wright Group, The.
The Story of Cat & Rat: Benchmark Assessment Book for Level B: Level B, 6 vols. (Wright Skills Ser.). 16p. (gr. k-3). 26.50 (978-0-322-03099-2(4)) Wright Group, The.
Strange Days: Level 7, 6 vols. (Fluency Strand Ser.). (gr. 4-8). 45.00 (978-1-4045-1241-2(1)) Wright Group, The.
Strawberry Shortcake Grow Better with Phonics. 2004. (J). pap. 2.95 (***978-1-58610-898-4(0)***) Learning Horizons, Inc.
Student Pack. (Cuentacuentos Ser.). (SPA.). (gr. k up). 83.31 (978-1-56334-798-6(9)) Hampton-Brown Bks.
Students of Academy of Mastery and Excellence Staff. Phonics, 20 vols. 2000. 10p. (J). pap., wbk. ed. (978-0-9669902-1-8(9)) MassAward Publishing, Inc.
Sunshine: Early Emergent - 1 Each of 4 Big Books: Level A-D. 82.95 (978-0-7802-6772-5(9)) Wright Group, The.
Sunshine: Early Emergent - Group 1: 1 Each of 8 Student Books: Level A. 33.50 (978-0-7802-7118-0(1)) Wright Group, The.
Sunshine: Early Emergent - Group 1:1 Each of 8 Student Books: Level C. 33.50 (978-0-7802-7122-7(X)) Wright Group, The.
Sunshine: Early Emergent - Group 2: 1 Each of 8 Student Books: Level A. 33.50 (978-0-7802-7119-7(X)) Wright Group, The.
Sunshine: Early Emergent - Group 2:1 Each of 8 Student Books: Level B. 33.50 (978-0-7802-7121-0(1)) Wright Group, The.
Sunshine: Early Emergent - Group 2:1 Each of 8 Student Books: Level C. 33.50 (978-0-7802-7123-4(8)) Wright Group, The.
Sunshine: Early Emergent - Nonfiction 1: 1 Each of 4 Student Books: Level A. 16.95 (978-0-7802-3763-6(3)) Wright Group, The.
Sunshine: Early Emergent - Nonfiction:1 Each of 4 Student Books: Level A. 16.95 (978-0-7802-3772-8(2)) Wright Group, The.
Sunshine: Early Emergent: 1 Each of 8 Student Books: Level B. 24.95 (978-0-7802-7120-3(3)) Wright Group, The.
Super Classroom Set. (Elefonetica Ser.). (SPA.). (gr. 1-2). 939.56 (978-0-7362-0782-9(1)) Hampton-Brown Bks.
Systematic Sequential Phonics Classroom Kit. 2001. (Four-Blocks Ser.). pap. (978-0-88724-783-5(0) , CD-5818) Carson-Dellosa Publishing Co., Inc.
Tarjetas de fonetica: Ilustraciones: Phonics. 2001. (McGraw-Hill. Lectura Ser.). (ENG & SPA.). (gr. k-1). (978-0-02-186550-5(7)) Macmillan/McGraw-Hill Schl. Div.
Tarjetas de Letras: Phonics. 2001. (McGraw-Hill. Lectura Ser.). (ENG & SPA.). (gr. k-1). (978-0-02-186552-9(3)) Macmillan/McGraw-Hill Schl. Div.
Tat Is Sad: Consonant d: Level A, 6 vols. (Wright Skills Ser.). 12p. (gr. k-3). 17.95 (978-0-322-03105-0(2)) Wright Group, The.
Taylor, Beth. Little Book: Tina'a Toys. 2000. (Sadlier Phonics Reading Program). 8p. (J). (978-0-8215-7303-7(9) , Sadlier-Oxford) Sadlier, William H. Inc.
Terror Bear Canyon: Level 5, 6 vols. (Fluency Strand Ser.). (gr. 4-8). 45.00 (978-1-4045-1225-2(X)) Wright Group, The.
TestSMART Plus Phonics, Short Vowels Level K-1. 2004. (J). (978-1-57022-502-4(8)) ECS Learning Systems, Inc.
Thompson-Alexander, Catherine. A Letteration Final & Middle Sounds: Phonemic Awareness Activity. 2002. (Illus.). 92p. (J). spiral bd. 18.95 (978-0-9725422-1-0(3)) Front Line Educ.
Thrills at the Fair: 3-letter blends: Level C, 6 vols. (Wright Skills Ser.). 16p. (gr. k-3). 26.50 (978-0-322-01494-7(8)) Wright Group, The.
Thud! Thump! Thud! Digraph th: Level B, 6 vols. (Wright Skills Ser.). 16p. (gr. k-3). 17.95 (978-0-322-01473-2(5)) Wright Group, The.
La Tienda: Individual Title Two-Packs. (Chiquilibros Ser.). (SPA.). (ps-1). 12.00 (978-0-7635-8559-4(9)) Rigby Education.
Time Warp: Level T. Group 1, 6 vols. (Sunshinetm Ser.). 48p. 44.95 (978-0-7802-5602-6(6)) Wright Group, The.
To Catch a Thief: Level 3, 6 vols. (Fluency Strand Ser.). (gr. 4-8). 45.00 (978-1-4045-1219-1(5)) Wright Group, The.
To the Moon & Beyond: Level T. Group 3, 6 vols. (Sunshinetm Ser.). 48p. 44.95 (978-0-322-01835-8(8)) Wright Group, The.
Together, 6 vols. (Sunshinetm Ser.). 16p. (gr. k up). 29.50 (978-0-7802-5426-8(0)) Wright Group, The.
Tomato: Level 4, 6 vols. (Fluency Strand Ser.). (gr. 4-8). 45.00 (978-1-4045-1223-8(3)) Wright Group, The.
Tongue Twisters to Teach Phonemic Awareness & Phonics: Blends & Digraphs. 2000. (Four-Blocks Ser.). 64p. (J). (gr. k-4). pap. 11.99 (978-0-88724-582-4(X) , CD-2603) Carson-Dellosa Publishing Co., Inc.
Too Many Graphs: Digraph ph: Level B, 6 vols. (Wright Skills Ser.). 16p. (gr. k-3). 17.95 (978-0-322-01475-6(1)) Wright Group, The.
Traill, Lyn. Pobblebonk Reading 4. 10 the Glowing Ball. 2008. pap. (***978-0-521-71090-9(1)***) Cambridge Univ. Pr.
—Pobblebonk Reading 4. 2 It's Fun to Fly. 2008. pap. (***978-0-521-71088-6(X)***) Cambridge Univ. Pr.
—Pobblebonk Reading 4. 6 the Wild Child. 2008. pap. (***978-0-521-71089-3(8)***) Cambridge Univ. Pr.
—Pobblebonk Reading 5. 1 Out of the Cage. 2008. pap. (***978-0-521-71091-6(X)***) Cambridge Univ. Pr.
—Pobblebonk Reading 5. 3 It's Time. 2008. pap. (***978-0-521-71092-3(8)***) Cambridge Univ. Pr.
—Pobblebonk Reading 5. 7 Make Believe. 2008. pap. (***978-0-521-71093-0(6)***) Cambridge Univ. Pr.
—Pobblebonk Reading 6. 2 Yummy Food. 2008. pap. (***978-0-521-71094-7(4)***) Cambridge Univ. Pr.
—Pobblebonk Reading 6. 5 Queen Bee. 2008. pap. (***978-0-521-71095-4(2)***) Cambridge Univ. Pr.
El Truco de Inaki Vol. 29: Little Books, Level 20. 2003. (Fonolibros Ser.). 35.50 (978-0-7652-0108-9(9)) Modern Curriculum Pr.
Turly, Sandy. Phonics: Games & Learning Activities. Wilson, Cheri Macourbrie, illus. 1999. 144p. (gr. k-3). pap., tchr. ed. 14.99 (978-1-57690-354-4(0) , TCA2354) Teacher Created Materials, Inc.
Twtin Sisters Productions, prod. Phonics: Songs That Teach. 2005. (J). per. 12.99 (978-1-57583-820-5(6)) Twin Sisters Productions, LLC.
Unccor: Level 5, 6 vols. (Fluency Strand Ser.). (gr. 4-8). 45.00 (978-1-4045-1231-3(4)) Wright Group, The.
Up in a Tree: Level D. Group 1. (Sunshinetm Ser.). 8p. 20.95 (978-0-7802-5736-8(7)) Wright Group, The.
Upper Emergent Skills Guide. (Sunshine Skills Guides). 25.95 (978-0-7802-9810-1(1)) Wright Group, The.
A Van in the Mud: Consonant v: Level A, 6 vols. (Wright Skills Ser.). 12p. (gr. k-3). 17.95 (978-0-322-03118-0(4)) Wright Group, The.
VanLeeuwen. Phonics Connection Grade 1. 2003. (Phonics Connection Ser.). 160p. (gr. 1 up). 8.95 (978-1-932210-23-1(7)) Rainbow Bridge Publishing.
—Phonics Connection Grade 2. 2003. (Phonics Connection Ser.). 160p. (gr. 2 up). 8.95 (978-1-932210-24-8(5)) Rainbow Bridge Publishing.
—Phonics Connection Grade 3. 2003. (Phonics Connection Ser.). 160p. (gr. 3 up). 8.95 (978-1-932210-25-5(3)) Rainbow Bridge Publishing.
—Phonics Connection Kindergarten. 2003. (Phonics Connection Ser.). 160p. (gr. k up). 8.95 (978-1-932210-22-4(9)) Rainbow Bridge Publishing.
—Phonics Grade 3. 2003. (Skill Builders Ser.). 80p. (gr. 3 up). 2.95 (978-1-932210-02-6(4)) Rainbow Bridge Publishing.
Variant Sounds, Diphthongs, Suffixes & Prefixes Big Book & CD Set: Level F. (Sing-along Songs Ser.). (ps-2). 48.46 incl. audio compact disk (978-0-7362-0678-5(7)) Hampton-Brown Bks.
Vaughan, Marlys K. Cop, Fox & Pops. Vaughan, Marlys K., illus. 2000. (Illus.). 12p. (J). (ps-2). pap. 4.00 (978-1-931315-11-1(6)) Early Phonic Practice.
—Gus the Pup. Vaughan, Marlys K., illus. 2000. (Illus.). 12p. (J). (ps-2). pap. 4.00 (978-1-931315-18-0(3)) Early Phonic Practice.
—Ken & Ben Jet. Vaughan, Marlys K., illus. 2000. (Illus.). 12p. (J). (ps). pap. 4.00 (978-1-931315-15-9(9)) Early Phonic Practice.
—Kim & the Pit. Vaughan, Marlys K., illus. 2000. (Illus.). 12p. (J). (ps-2). pap. 4.00 (978-1-931315-16-6(7)) Early Phonic Practice.
—Kit Hits. Vaughan, Marlys K., illus. 2000. (Illus.). 12p. (J). (ps-2). pap. 4.00 (978-1-931315-10-4(8)) Early Phonic Practice.
—Lots of Tots. Vaughan, Marlys K., illus. 2000. (Illus.). 12p. (J). (ps-2). 4.00 (978-1-931315-17-3(5)) Early Phonic Practice.
—My First Short A Book. Vaughan, Marlys K., illus. 2000. (Illus.). 12p. (J). (ps-2). pap. 4.00 (978-1-931315-02-9(7)) Early Phonic Practice.
—My First Short E Book. Vaughan, Marlys K., illus. 2000. (Illus.). 12p. (J). (ps-2). pap. 4.00 (978-1-931315-03-6(5)) Early Phonic Practice.
—My First Short I Book. Vaughan, Marlys K., illus. 2000. (Illus.). 12p. (J). (ps-2). pap. 4.00 (978-1-931315-04-3(3)) Early Phonic Practice.
—My First Short O Book. Vaughan, Marlys K., illus. 2000. (Illus.). 12p. (J). (ps-2). pap. 4.00 (978-1-931315-05-0(1)) Early Phonic Practice.
—My First Short U Book. Vaughan, Marlys K., illus. 2000. (Illus.). 12p. (J). (ps-2). pap. 4.00 (978-1-931315-06-7(X)) Early Phonic Practice.
—Nub Has Fun. Vaughan, Marlys K., illus. 2000. (Illus.). 12p. (J). (ps-2). pap. 4.00 (978-1-931315-12-8(4)) Early Phonic Practice.
—Pals. Vaughan, Marlys K., illus. 2000. (Illus.). 12p. (J). (ps). pap. 4.00 (978-1-931315-14-2(0)) Early Phonic Practice.
—Set 1 Instructions. Vaughan, Marlys K., illus. 2000. (Illus.). 20p. (J). (ps-2). pap. 4.00 (978-1-931315-00-5(0)) Early Phonic Practice.
—Set 1 Readers, 5 bks. Vaughan, Marlys K., illus. 2000. (Illus.). 60p. (J). (ps-2). pap. 20.00 (978-1-931315-01-2(9)) Early Phonic Practice.
—Set 2 Instructions. Vaughan, Marlys K., illus. 2000. (Illus.). 20p. (J). (ps-2). pap. 4.00 (978-1-931315-19-7(1)) Early Phonic Practice.
—Set 2 Readers, 5 bks. Vaughan, Marlys K., illus. 2000. (Illus.). 60p. (J). (ps-2). pap. 20.00 (978-1-931315-07-4(8)) Early Phonic Practice.
—Set 3 Instructions. Vaughan, Marlys K., illus. 2000. (Illus.). 20p. (J). (ps-2). pap. 4.00 (978-1-931315-20-3(5)) Early Phonic Practice.
—Set 3 Readers, 5 bks. Vaughan, Marlys K., illus. 2000. (Illus.). 60p. (J). (ps-2). pap. 20.00 (978-1-931315-13-5(2)) Early Phonic Practice.
—Tap Tap Tap. Vaughan, Marlys K., illus. 2000. (Illus.). 12p. (J). (ps-2). pap. 4.00 (978-1-931315-08-1(6)) Early Phonic Practice.
—Wes Met Deb. Vaughan, Marlys K., illus. 2000. (Illus.). 12p. (J). (ps-2). pap. 4.00 (978-1-931315-09-8(4)) Early Phonic Practice.
Un Verano en el Lago Zafiro: Little Books, Level 24, Vol. 10. 2003. (Fonolibros Ser.). 34.95 (978-0-7652-0120-1(8)) Modern Curriculum Pr.
Verdadero O Falso? Little Books, Level 16, Vol. 11. 2003. (Fonolibros Ser.). 34.95 (978-0-7652-0121-8(6)) Modern Curriculum Pr.
A Very Fine Time: Long Vowel i, CVCe Pattern: Level B, 6 vols. (Wright Skills Ser.). 16p. (gr. k-3). 17.95 (978-0-322-01467-1(0)) Wright Group, The.
Vigne, Elaine W. Jazzgator. 2001. 32p. (J). pap. 8.00 (978-0-8059-4978-0(X)) Dorrance Publishing Co., Inc.
Wagstaff, Janiel M. Irrestible Sound-Matching Sheets & Lessons That Build Phonemic Awareness: Quick Lessons, Word Lists, & Reproducible Sound-Matching Sheets That Use Favorite Children's Books Quick Lessons, Word Lists, & Reproducible Sound-Matching Sheets That Use Favorite Children's Books to Reinforce Phonemic Awareness-and Delight Emergent Read. 2001. 160p. pap. 14.95 (978-0-439-16517-4(2)) Scholastic, Inc.
Wait for Me. 2005. (Emergent Library: Vol. 2). (YA). (ps-1). 23.94 (978-0-8215-8931-1(8)) Sadlier, William H. Inc.
Wait for Me: Take-Home Book. 2005. (Emergent Library: Vol. 2). (YA). (ps-1). 12.60 (978-0-8215-7261-0(X)) Sadlier, William H. Inc.
Wake Up! Long Vowel a, CVCe Pattern: Level B, 6 vols. (Wright Skills Ser.). 16p. (gr. k-3). 17.95 (978-0-322-03129-6(X)) Wright Group, The.
Wake up, Sleepyheads!, Vol. 2. 2005. (Early Library). (YA). (ps-3). 23.94 (978-0-8215-8955-7(5)) Sadlier, William H. Inc.
Ward-Beech, Linda. Fun Phonics Cut & Paste. 2001. (Joyful Learning Ser.). 48p. pap., tchr. ed. 7.95 (978-0-439-40798-4(2) , Teaching Resources) Scholastic, Inc.
—Fun Phonics Puzzles & Games. 2001. (Joyful Learning Ser.). 48p. pap., tchr. ed. 7.95 (978-0-439-40797-7(4) , Teaching Resources) Scholastic, Inc.
Wax, Wendy. Phonics Comics: Clara the Klutz - Level 2. Mattocks, Tracy & Sullivan, Mary, illus. 2007. 24p. (J). (gr. 1-17). pap. 3.99 (978-1-58476-565-3(8)) Innovative Kids.
We Can! Level A: Consonant W. (Wright Skills Ser.). 12p. (gr. k-3). 17.95 (978-0-322-03114-2(1)) Wright Group, The.

Webber, Sharon G. Webber Artic Fun Sheets - Set 2. Webber, Thomas, ed. 2002. (Illus.). (YA). (ps up). spiral bd. 29.95 (978-1-58650-212-6(3)) Super Duper Pubns.

—Webber Artic Fun Sheets - Set 3. 2002. (Illus.). (J). (ps-5). spiral bd. 32.96 (978-1-58650-227-0(1)) Super Duper Pubns.

Weber, Elizabeth C. Lightning Phonics Program. abr. l.t. ed. 2000. 73p. (J). (ps-8). incl. cd-rom (978-0-9704777-0-5(8)) DEW Pubs.

Weber, Lou, ed. Phonics Fun. 2005. 8p. (J). 4.98 (978-1-4127-3463-9(0) , 7261800) Publications International, Ltd.

Wells, Rosemary. Letters & Sounds, Bk. 1. Wells, Rosemary, illus. 2001. (Get Set for Kindergarten Ser.). (Illus.). 24p. (J). (ps-3). pap. 5.99 (978-0-14-056805-9(0) , Puffin) Penguin Group (USA) Inc.

Wernham, Sara. Jolly Readers Level 1 General Fiction Level 1: 6 Titles in a Pack, 6 vols. 2002. 8p. (J). 8.50 (978-1-903619-60-5(2) , JL602) Jolly Learning, Ltd. GBR. *Dist:* American International Distribution Corp.

—Jolly Readers Level 1 Inky & Friends Level 1: 6 Titles in a Pack, 6 vols. 2002. 8p. (J). 8.50 (978-1-903619-47-6(5) , JL475) Jolly Learning, Ltd. GBR. *Dist:* American International Distribution Corp.

—Jolly Readers Level 1 Nonfiction Level 1: 6 Titles in a Pack, 6 vols. 2002. 8p. (J). 8.50 (978-1-903619-73-5(4) , JL734) Jolly Learning, Ltd. GBR. *Dist:* American International Distribution Corp.

Wernham, Sara & Lloyd, Sue. Jolly Phonics Read & See - Pack 1, 12 vols. Stephen, Lib, illus. 2002. (Jolly Phonics Ser.). 16p. (J). 39.50 (978-1-903619-24-7(6) , JL246) Jolly Learning, Ltd. GBR. *Dist:* American International Distribution Corp.

—Jolly Phonics Read & See - Pack 2, 12 vols., Vol. 2. Stephen, Lib, illus. 2002. (Jolly Phonics Ser.). 16p. (J). 39.50 (978-1-903619-40-7(8) , JL408) Jolly Learning, Ltd. GBR. *Dist:* American International Distribution Corp.

Westermann, John J. Bible Phonics: Letters & Primary Sounds. unabr. ed. 2000. (Illus.). xx, 190p. (J). (gr. 1 up). spiral bd. 50.00 (978-0-9704641-0-1(X)) Disciple Builder Media.

When the Alligator Came to Class: Short a; Consonants c, p; Blends cl, cr, scr, pl, spl, Level A. 2003. ("Plaid" Phonics & Stories Libraries). (gr. 1-2). 38.50 (978-0-8136-9141-1(9)) Modern Curriculum Pr.

Wiley, Kaye. Fast Track Phonics. 2001. (C). pap. 22.33 (978-0-13-091583-2(1)) Pearson ESL.

Wilkes, Shar & Grogan, Jane. The Fantastic Phonics Food Factory. Keene, James A., ed. Hobbs, Patricia, illus. 2000. 101p. (J). (ps-5). pap. 24.95 (978-0-944435-47-2(5)) Glenbridge Publishing, Ltd.

Williams, Richie. There's a Bear with a Pear! 2006. (Illus.). 32p. (J). 19.50 (978-0-9777100-0-3(9)) Geoscience Information Services.

Winget, Kerry. Differential Processing Training Program Acoustic Linguistic Tasks. 2007. per. 32.95 ***(978-0-7606-0723-7(0))*** LinguiSystems, Inc.

—Differential Processing Training Program Acoustic Tasks. 2007. per. 32.95 ***(978-0-7606-0722-0(2))*** LinguiSystems, Inc.

—Differential Processing Training Program Linguistic Tasks. 2007. per. 32.95 ***(978-0-7606-0724-4(9))*** LinguiSystems, Inc.

Wolf, Kathy, ed. Learning Library Phonics, Reading & Spelling. 2002. 128p. 19.95 (978-1-56234-480-1(3)); 19.95 (978-1-56234-481-8(1)); 19.95 (978-1-56234-483-2(8)); 19.95 (978-1-56234-482-5(X)) Education Ctr., Inc. (Mailbox Bks., The).

Woods, Andrew. Pobblebonk Reading 6. 6 Goose Berry Pie. 2008. pap. ***(978-0-521-71096-1(0))*** Cambridge Univ. Pr.

Word Builder Tiles. 2000. (gr. 1-3). suppl. ed. 22.90 (978-0-673-28946-9(X)) Addison-Wesley Educational Pubs., Inc.

Word Families. 2005. (J). ***(978-1-60015-010-4(1))*** Steps To Literacy, LLC.

Word Fun: "R" Controlled Vowels. 2003. (Language Arts Card Games Ser.). (Illus.). (gr. 1-3). 9.99 (978-0-7682-1894-7(2) , J41004) School Specialty Publishing.

Word List Charts. 2000. (gr. 1 up). suppl. ed. 61.90 (978-0-673-30066-9(8)); (gr. 2 up). suppl. ed. 61.90 (978-0-673-61807-8(2)); (gr. 3 up). suppl. ed. 61.90 (978-0-673-30081-2(1)) Addison-Wesley Educational Pubs., Inc.

Word Wall Words. 2004. (gr. k up). suppl. ed. 39.70 (978-0-673-62182-5(0)); (gr. 1 up). suppl. ed. 220.50 (978-0-673-62183-2(9)); (gr. 2 up). suppl. ed. 220.50 (978-0-673-62184-9(7)); (gr. 3 up). suppl. ed. 220.50 (978-0-673-62185-6(5)) Addison-Wesley Educational Pubs., Inc.

A World Worth Keeping: Level T. Group 1, 6 vols. (Sunshinetm Ser.). 48p. 44.95 (978-0-7802-6092-4(9)) Wright Group, The.

The Wrecks: Level T. Group 2, 6 vols. (Sunshinetm Ser.). 48p. 44.95 (978-0-7802-4177-0(0)) Wright Group, The.

Wrestle Mania: Magazine Anthology: Level 5, 6 vols. (Comprehension Strand Ser.). (gr. 4-8). 54.00 (978-0-322-06036-4(2)) Wright Group, The.

The Wright Skills: Level B Sets - Long vowels only: 1 Each of 6 Titles. (gr. k-3). 17.95 (978-0-322-01934-8(6)) Wright Group, The.

The Wright Skills: Level B Sets - Long vowels only: 6 Each of 6 Titles. (gr. k-3). 109.50 (978-0-322-01935-5(4)) Wright Group, The.

The Wright Skills: Level C Sets - 1 Each of 16 Titles. (gr. k-3). 69.95 (978-0-322-00734-5(8)) Wright Group, The.

The Wright Skills: Level C Sets - 6 Each of 16 Titles. (gr. k-3). 322.95 (978-0-322-00813-7(1)) Wright Group, The.

Wrighton, Charlene & Bradshaw, Georgine. Basic Kit - Preschool. Clark, Irene, illus. 2005. Orig. Title: Basis Kit I. (J). 249.95 (978-1-886441-30-9(8)) Zoo-phonics, Inc.

Yamile Y Yo Vol. 21: Little Books, Level 12. 2003. (Fonolibros Ser.). 34.95 (978-0-7652-0099-0(6)) Modern Curriculum Pr.

Yip & Yap: Consonant y: Level A, 6 vols. (Wright Skills Ser.). 12p. (gr. k-3). 17.95 (978-0-322-03120-3(6)) Wright Group, The.

Yo Se Nadar! Little Books, Level 2, Vol. 18. 2003. (Fonolibros Ser.). 25.50 (978-0-7652-0095-2(3)) Modern Curriculum Pr.

York. Phonics. 2004. Level C. pap. 12.40 incl. cd-rom (978-0-7398-9137-7(5)); Level C. pap., tchr. ed. 43.20 incl. cd-rom (978-0-7398-9142-1(1)); Level D. (Illus.). (J). pap. 12.40 incl. cd-rom (978-0-7398-9138-4(3)); Level D. (Illus.). pap., tchr. ed. 43.20 incl. cd-rom (978-0-7398-9143-8(X)); Level A. pap., tchr. ed. 43.20 incl. cd-rom (978-0-7398-9140-7(5)); Level A. (Illus.). pap. 12.40 incl. cd-rom (978-0-7398-9135-3(9)); Level B. pap. 12.40 incl. cd-rom (978-0-7398-9136-0(7)); Level B. pap., tchr. ed. 43.20 incl. cd-rom (978-0-7398-9141-4(3)); Level K. pap., tchr. ed. 43.20 incl. cd-rom (978-0-7398-9139-1(1)); Level K. (Illus.). pap. 10.40 incl. cd-rom (978-0-7398-9134-6(0)) Steck-Vaughn.

Zac the Rat. 2004. (Illus.). (J). (978-1-59577-001-1(1)) Starfall Education.

Zoboomafoo: Beginning Phonics. 2003. 32p. pap., wbk. ed. 14.95 incl. cd-rom (978-1-57791-020-6(6)); pap., wbk. ed. 14.95 incl. cd-rom (978-1-57791-021-3(4)) Brighter Minds Children's Publishing.

Zone Zoomers: Level 2, 6 vols. (Fluency Strand Ser.). (gr. 4-8). 45.00 (978-1-4045-1213-9(6)) Wright Group, The.

Zoo-phonics Quick Tests for the Classroom. 2004. cd-rom (978-1-886441-41-5(3)) Zoo-phonics, Inc.

1st & 2nd Grade Excelerator, 2 CDs. 2002. cd-rom 9.99 (978-1-59150-012-4(5)) TOPICS Entertainment.

1st Phonics Booster. 2005. 64p. (J). per. 1.49 (978-1-59441-340-7(1) , C04016) Carson-Dellosa Publishing Co., Inc.

2nd Phonics Booster. 2005. 64p. (J). per. 1.49 (978-1-59441-344-5(4) , C04020) Carson-Dellosa Publishing Co., Inc.

3rd Phonics Booster. 2005. 64p. (J). per. 1.49 (978-1-59441-348-3(7) , C04023) Carson-Dellosa Publishing Co., Inc.

365 Phonics Activities. 1999. (Homonyms, Phonics & Reading Activities Ser.: No. 4). 240p. (J). (gr. k-4). lib. bdg. 24.95 (978-1-56674-270-2(6)) Forest Hse. Publishing Co., Inc.

PHONICS

see Phonetics

PHONOGRAPH

see also Sound—Recording and Reproducing

Doak, Robin S. The Phonograph. 2005. (Great Inventions Ser.). (Illus.). 48p. (YA). lib. bdg. 30.00 (978-0-8368-5877-8(8) , World Almanac Library) Stevens, Gareth Inc.

Scholes, Percy Alfred. The First Book of the Gramophone Record. 2001. 161p. (YA). reprint ed. 88.00 (978-0-7222-6062-3(8)) Library Reprints, Inc.

—Second Book of the Gramophone Record. 2001. 194p. (YA). reprint ed. 88.00 (978-0-7222-6063-0(6)) Library Reprints, Inc.

PHONOLOGY

see Phonetics

PHOTOGRAPHERS

Acker, Kerry. Dorothea Lange. 2003. (Women in the Arts Ser.). (Illus.). 112p. (gr. 6-12). 30.00 (978-0-7910-7460-2(9) , Chelsea Hse.) Facts On File, Inc.

Anderson, Christopher C. L. Margaret Bourke-White: Daring Photographer. 2005. (Great Life Stories Ser.). (Illus.). 127p. (J). (gr. 6-8). 30.50 (978-0-531-12405-5(3) , Watts, Franklin) Scholastic Library Publishing.

Anderson, William. Les Kelly. Kelly, Leslie A., illus. Date not set. (J). (gr. 3-7). Vol. 1. 9.99 (978-0-06-440851-6(5)); Vol. 2. 9.99 (978-0-06-440850-9(7)) HarperCollins Pubs.

Armstrong, Jennifer. Photo by Brady: A Picture of the Civil War. 2005. (Illus.). 160p. (J). (gr. 4-9). 18.95 (978-0-689-85785-0(3) , Atheneum) Simon & Schuster Children's Publishing.

Arruda, Suzanne Middendorf. From Kansas to Cannibals: The Story of Osa Johnson. 2001. (Illus.). 96p. (J). (gr. 6-12). pap. 19.95 (978-1-888105-50-6(X)) Avisson Pr., Inc.

Bueno, Julian David. Henry Cartier - Bresson- el azar y el Instante. 2005. 132p. pap. (978-958-30-1704-9(3)) Panamericana Editorial.

Clee, Paul. Photography & the Making of the American West. 2002. (Illus.). x, 124p. (J). 27.50 (978-0-208-02512-8(X)) Shoe String Pr., Inc.

Donlan, Leni. Mathew Brady: Photographing the Civil War. 2007. (J). ***(978-1-4109-2699-9(0))*** ; pap. ***(978-1-4109-2710-1(5))*** Steck-Vaughn.

Gaines, Ann Graham. American Photographers: Capturing the Image. 2002. (Collective Biographies Ser.). (Illus.). 112p. (YA). (gr. 6-12). lib. bdg. 26.60 (978-0-7660-1833-4(4)) Enslow Pubs., Inc.

Gold, Becky. What a Job. 2003. (On the Job Ser.). (Illus.). 32p. (gr. 3-5). 23.00 (978-0-7910-7413-8(7) , Chelsea Hse.) Facts On File, Inc.

Hall, Ken. George D. Valentine: A 19th Century Photographer in New Zealand. 2004. (Illus.). 132p. pap. (978-1-877333-12-5(3)) Potton, Craig Publishing Ltd.

Litwin, Laura Baskes. Dorothea Lange: A Life in Pictures. 2007. (People to Know Today Ser.). (Illus.). 128p. (J). (gr. 6). lib. bdg. 31.93 ***(978-0-7660-2697-1(3))*** Enslow Pubs., Inc.

McLeese, Don. Louis Daguerre. 2005. (Inventores Famosos Ser.). (ENG & SPA.). (J). (978-1-59515-672-3(0)) Rourke Publishing, LLC.

Nau, Thomas. Walker Evans: Photographer of America. 2007. (Illus.). 64p. (J). (gr. 5-9). 19.95 (978-1-59643-225-3(X)) Roaring Brook Pr.

Partridge, Elizabeth. Restless Spirit: The Life & Work of Dorothea Lange. (Illus.). 128p. (J). 2001. pap. 12.99 (978-0-14-230024-4(1) , Puffin); 1998. (gr. 4-7). 22.99 (978-0-670-87888-8(X) , Viking Juvenile) Penguin Group (USA) Inc.

—Restless Spirit: The Life & Work of Dorothea Lange. 2001. (gr. 7-12). lib. bdg. 19.95 (978-0-613-44411-8(6)) Tandem Library Bks.

Pascal, Janet B. Jacob Riis: Reporter & Reformer. 2005. (Oxford Portraits Ser.). (Illus.). 176p. (YA). 28.00 (978-0-19-514527-4(5)) Oxford Univ. Pr., Inc.

Pflueger, Lynda. Mathew Brady: Photographer of the Civil War. 2001. (Historical American Biographies Ser.). (Illus.). 128p. (J). (gr. 6-12). lib. bdg. 26.60 (978-0-7660-1444-2(4)) Enslow Pubs., Inc.

Rubiano, Roberto. Robert Capa -Imagenes de Guerra. 2005. 168p. pap. (978-958-30-1905-0(4)) Panamericana Editorial.

Sandler, Martin W. America Through the Lens: Photographers Who Changed the Nation. rev. ed. 2005. (Illus.). 192p. (J). 21.00 (978-0-8050-7367-6(1) , Holt, Henry & Co. Bks. For Young Readers) Holt, Henry & Co.

Schulke, Flip & Schudel, Matt. Witness to Our Times: My Life As a Photojournalist. 2003. (Illus.). 160p. (YA). (gr. 7 up). 19.95 (978-0-8126-2682-7(6)) Cricket Bks.

Sills, Leslie. In Real Life: Stories about Women Photographers. 2005. (J). (978-0-7868-2077-1(2)) Hyperion Pr.

Stone, Amy. Dorothea Lange. 2003. (Raintree Biographies Ser.). (J). 25.70 (978-0-7398-6862-1(4)) Raintree.

—Dorothea Lange. 2003. (gr. 3-6). lib. bdg. 15.90 (978-0-613-78225-8(9)) Tandem Library Bks.

Strangis, Joel. Ansel Adams: American Artist with a Camera. 2002. (People to Know Ser.). (Illus.). 128p. (J). (gr. 6-12). lib. bdg. 26.60 (978-0-7660-1847-1(4)) Enslow Pubs., Inc.

Sullivan, George. Berenice Abbott, Photographer: An Independent Vision. 2006. (Illus.). 176p. (J). (gr. 5-9). 20.00 (978-0-618-44026-9(7) , Clarion Bks.) Houghton Mifflin Co. Trade & Reference Div.

Tanaka, Kazumi. Kazumi Tanaka: Words & Works. 2003. (Illus.). 104p. 14.95 (978-1-878607-84-3(7)) Kent Gallery.

Venezia, Mike. Dorothea Lange. Venezia, Mike, illus. 2001. (Getting to Know the World's Greatest Artists Ser.). (Illus.). 32p. (J). (gr. 3-4). pap. 6.95 (978-0-516-27171-2(7) , Children's Pr.) Scholastic Library Publishing.

—Dorothea Lange. 2000. (Getting to Know the World's Greatest Artists Ser.). (Illus.). 32p. (J). (gr. 3-4). 27.00 (978-0-516-22026-0(8) , Children's Pr.) Scholastic Library Publishing.

—Dorothea Lange. 2000. (gr. 3-6). lib. bdg. 15.25 (978-0-613-50681-6(2)) Tandem Library Bks.

Wooten, Sara McIntosh. Margaret Bourke-White: Daring Photographer. 2002. (People to Know Ser.). (Illus.). 112p. (YA). (gr. 6-12). lib. bdg. 26.60 (978-0-7660-1534-0(3)) Enslow Pubs., Inc.

PHOTOGRAPHY

see also Cameras; Nature Study

About Face: Portraits of Activism. 2004. (YA). per. (978-1-932948-06-6(6)) Student Pr. Initiative.

Ang, Tom. Digital Photographer's Handbook. rev. ed. 2004. (Illus.). 408p. 40.00 (978-0-7566-0346-5(3)) Dorling Kindersley Publishing, Inc.

Bankston, John. Louis Daguerre & the Story of the Daguerreotype. 2004. (Uncharted, Unexplored, & Unexplained Ser.). (Illus.). 48p. (J). (gr. 4-8). lib. bdg. 29.95 (978-1-58415-247-7(8)) Mitchell Lane Pubs., Inc.

Beardsley, Kurt. Under Saharan Skies. 2004. (Illus.). 96p. per. 25.00 (978-0-9761103-0-9(X) , 1000) International Vaquero Productions.

Bidner, Jenni. The Kids' Guide to Digital Photography: How to Shoot, Save, Play with & Print Your Digital Photos. 2004. (Illus.). 96p. (J). (gr. k-9). pap. 9.95 (978-1-57990-643-6(5)); 14.95 (978-1-57990-604-7(4)) Lark Bks.

Bob the Builder: Camera Book. 2003. bds. 15.98 (978-0-7853-7979-9(7)) Publications International, Ltd.

Bodden, Valerie. Photography. 2008. ***(978-1-58341-558-0(0)*** , Creative Education) Creative Co., The.

Brown, Cooling. Digital Photo Magic. 2005. (Illus.). 72p. (J). 19.99 (978-0-7566-1471-3(6)) Dorling Kindersley Publishing, Inc.

Buckley, Annie. Inside Photography. 2007. (Girls Rock! Ser.). 32p. (J). (gr. 1-5). 24.21 ***(978-1-59296-867-1(8))*** Child's World, Inc.

Carey, David. What's Inside? 1998. 24p. (J). pap. (978-0-920486-26-9(6)) Shillingford, J. Gordon Publishing.

Chapp, Belena, et al. Through These Eyes: The Photographs of P. H. Polk. Chapp, Belena, ed. 2nd ed. 2001. (Illus.). 64p. reprint ed. pap. 25.00 (978-1-887421-06-5(8)) University Gallery/Univ. of Delaware.

Chapp, Belena S., et al. Through These Eyes: The Photographs of P. H. Polk. Chapp, Belena S., ed. 2nd ltd. ed. 2001. (Illus.). 64p. 30.00 (978-1-887421-05-8(X)) University Gallery/Univ. of Delaware.

Daley, Robert, et al. The Golden Age: Images from the Klemantaski Collection. Sachs, Peter G., ed. 1999. (Illus.). 32p. (YA). pap. 20.00 (978-0-9641689-2-3(8)) Klemantaski Collection, The.

Dicum, Gregory. Window Seat for Kids. 2007. (J). 16.95 (978-0-8118-5605-8(4)); pap. 12.95 (978-0-8118-5606-5(2)) Chronicle Bks. LLC.

Digital Photo Activity Kit Deluxe Vivitar 3700 series Lab-10. 2005. (J). cd-rom 1790.00 (978-1-933229-02-7(0)) APTE, Inc.

Digital Photo Activity Kit Deluxe Vivitar 3700 series Lab-15. 2005. (J). cd-rom 2610.00 (978-1-933229-03-4(9)) APTE, Inc.

Digital Photo Activity Kit Deluxe Vivitar 3700 series Lab-20. 2005. (J). 3260.00 (978-1-933229-04-1(7)) APTE, Inc.

Digital Photo Activity Kit Deluxe Vivitar 3700 series Lab-25. 2005. (J). 3924.00 (978-1-933229-05-8(5)) APTE, Inc.

Digital Photo Activity Kit Deluxe Vivitar 3700 series Lab-30. 2005. (J). 4585.00 (978-1-933229-06-5(3)) APTE, Inc.

Digital Photo Activity Kit Deluxe Vivitar 3700 series Lab-35. 2005. (J). 5239.00 (978-1-933229-07-2(1)) APTE, Inc.

Digital Photo Activity Kit Deluxe Vivitar 3700 series Lab-5. 2005. (J). cd-rom 648.95 (978-1-933229-01-0(2)) APTE, Inc.

Digital Photo Activity Kit Deluxe Vivitar 3700 Series school Version. 2005. (J). cd-rom 133.95 (978-1-933229-00-3(4)) APTE, Inc.

Digital Photo Activity Kit Deluxe Vivitar 5300 series Lab-2005. (J). 1759.95 (978-1-933229-09-6(8)) APTE, Inc.

Digital Photo Activity Kit Deluxe Vivitar 5300 series Lab-10. 2005. (J). 3469.99 (978-1-933229-10-2(1)) APTE, Inc.

Digital Photo Activity Kit Deluxe Vivitar 5300 series Lab-15. 2005. (J). 5129.95 (978-1-933229-11-9(X)) APTE, Inc.

Digital Photo Activity Kit Deluxe Vivitar 5300 series Lab-25. 2005. (J). 8123.90 (978-1-933229-12-6(8)) APTE, Inc.

Digital Photo Activity Kit Deluxe Vivitar 5300 series Lab-30. 2005. (J). 9624.95 (978-1-933229-14-0(4)) APTE, Inc.

Digital Photo Activity Kit Deluxe Vivitar 5300 series Lab-35. 2005. (J). 11119.95 (978-1-933229-15-7(2)) APTE, Inc.

Digital Photo Activity Kit Deluxe Vivitar 5300 series Single. 2005. (J). 359.99 (978-1-933229-08-9(X)) APTE, Inc.

Dorling Kindersley Publishing Staff, ed. Photography: Discover the Evolving World of Photography from Pinhole Cameras to the Digital Age. 2004. (Dk Eyewitness Books Ser.). (Illus.). 72p. (J). 15.99 (978-0-7566-0543-8(1)); lib. bdg. 19.99 (978-0-7566-0542-1(3)) Dorling Kindersley Publishing, Inc.

Dorling Kindersley Publishing Staff & Buckingham, Alan. It's My Life: Digital Photography Kit. 2005. 48p. (J). 29.99 (978-0-7566-1473-7(2)) Dorling Kindersley Publishing, Inc.

Elton, Candice & Elton, Richard. My Family Album. 2003. (Illus.). 32p. (J). 19.95 (978-1-58685-323-5(6)) Gibbs Smith, Publisher.

—My Vacation Album: Includes: Reusable Camera, Film, Batteries & Glue Stick. Lee, Fran, illus. 2003. 28p. (J). spiral bd. 19.95 (978-1-58685-280-1(9)) Gibbs Smith, Publisher.

Elton, Richard & Elton, Candice. My Birthday Album. Lee, Fran, illus. 2004. 28p. pap. 19.95 (978-1-58685-414-0(3)) Gibbs Smith, Publisher.

—My Christmas Album. 2004. (Illus.). 28p. pap. 19.95 (978-1-58685-582-6(4)) Gibbs Smith, Publisher.

—My Family Album. 2004. (Illus.). 28p. pap. 19.95 (978-1-58685-586-4(7)) Gibbs Smith, Publisher.

—My Vacation Album. 2004. (Illus.). 28p. pap. 19.95 (978-1-58685-584-0(0)) Gibbs Smith, Publisher.

Essential Photography. 2004. (I-Quest Ser.). (Illus.). 48p. (J). per. (978-1-84229-744-5(9)) Top That! Publishing PLC.

Fast, Suellen M. America's Daughters. Fast, Suellen M., photos by. (Illus.). 100p. (Orig.). (J). (gr. k up). pap. 19.00 (978-0-935281-13-2(4)) Daughter Culture Pubns.

Frank, Arthur, photos by. Cowboy Up. 2005. (Illus.). 128p. 35.00 (978-1-57687-258-1(0) , powerHouse Bks.) powerHouse Cultural Entertainment, Inc.

Friedman, Debra. Picture This: Fun Photography & Crafts. 2003. (Illus.). 40p. (J). (ps-7). lib. bdg. 14.10 (978-0-613-86550-0(2)) Tandem Library Bks.

Friedman, Debra & Kurisu, Jane. Picture This: Fun Photography & Crafts. 2004. (Kids Can Do It Ser.). (Illus.). 40p. (J). (gr. 4-6). (978-1-55337-047-5(3)); (978-1-55337-046-8(5)) Kids Can Pr., Ltd.

Gaines, Ann Graham. American Photographers: Capturing the Image. 2002. (Collective Biographies Ser.). (Illus.). 112p. (YA). (gr. 6-12). lib. bdg. 26.60 (978-0-7660-1833-4(4)) Enslow Pubs., Inc.

Gelber, Lisa & Roberts, Jody. P Is for Peanut: A Photographic ABC. 2007. (Getty Trust Publications: J. Paul Getty Museum Ser.). (Illus.). 58p. 9.95 ***(978-0-89236-878-5(0))*** Getty Pubns.

Gold, Becky. What a Job. 2003. (On the Job Ser.). (Illus.). 32p. (gr. 3-5). 23.00 (978-0-7910-7413-8(7) , Chelsea Hse.) Facts On File, Inc.

Greenagel, Frank L., photos by. Think Like a Photographer! How to Take Better Pictures Than Anyone in Your Family. 2006. (J). (978-1-59336-766-4(X)) Mondo Publishing.

Haslam, Andrew. Photography. 2004. (Make It Work! Science Ser.). (Illus.). 48p. (J). (gr. 3-6). 12.95 (978-1-58728-372-7(7) , Two Can Publishing) T&N Children's Publishing.

Haslam, Andrew, et al. Photography. 2004. (Make It Work! Science Ser.). (Illus.). 48p. (J). (gr. 3-6). pap. 6.95 (978-1-58728-358-1(1) , Two Can Publishing) T&N Children's Publishing.

Hedgecoe, John. The New Manual of Photography. 2003. (Illus.). 416p. 40.00 (978-0-7894-9637-9(2)) Dorling Kindersley Publishing, Inc.

Hollander, Jim, photos by & intro. Run to the Sun: Pamplona's Fiesta de San Fermin. Hollander, Jim, intro. 2nd unabr. ed. 2002. Tr. of Fiesta. 316p. (YA). 55.00 net. (978-0-9720778-0-4(4)) MasterArts Pr. LLC.

Horne, Ronald William. Forgotten Faces: A Window into Our Immigrant Past (5x8-Clr-BW) 2004. (Illus.). 120p. per. 24.95 (978-0-9747395-1-9(0) , FF5x8ClrBW) Personal Genesis Publishing.

Hubbard, Vicki L. & Children of Paramount Academy Staff. Kinder Spirits: Children Helping Children in the Fight Against Hunger. Killion, Nance, photos by. 2000. (Illus.). 120p. (gr. 4-7). pap. 9.95 (978-0-595-13542-4(0)) iUniverse, Inc.

Hufford, Deborah. Scrapbooking: Keep Your Memories Special. 2005. (Snap Books Craft Ser.). (Illus.). 32p. (J). (gr. 3-5). 22.60 (978-0-7368-4387-4(6)) Capstone Pr., Inc.

Jackson, Michael. My World - the Official Photobook, Vol. 1. 2006. (Illus.). 40p. (YA). pap. 24.99 (978-0-9768891-1-3(0) , 1103) MJ Licensing LLC.

Kallen, Stuart A. Photography. 2007. (Eye on Art Ser.). 128p. (gr. 7-10). 31.20 (***978-1-59018-986-3(8)*** , Lucent Bks.) Thomson Gale.

Landford, Michael. Photography. Moore, Damien, ed. 2004. (101 Essential Tips Ser.). (Illus.). 72p. pap. 5.00 (978-0-7566-0224-6(6)) Dorling Kindersley Publishing, Inc.

Lang, Greg. Taking Pictures. 1999. (ps-2). lib. bdg. 11.80 (978-0-613-30771-0(2)) Tandem Library Bks.

Lorenz Books Staff, et al. Cameras: Practical Tips & Exciting Projects Inprove Techniques & Understanding. 2000. (Investigations Ser.). (Illus.). 64p. (gr. 3-7). 14.95 (978-0-7548-0455-0(0) , Lorenz Bks.) Anness Publishing GBR. *Dist:* National Bk. Network.

Mauro, Paul & Melton, H. Keith. Crime Scene & Surveillance Photography. 2004. (Detective Academy Ser.). (Illus.). 48p. (J). (978-0-439-57182-1(0)) Scholastic, Inc.

Mosley, Kim, text. Workbook for Black & White Photography, 1 vol. 3rd ed. 2005. 48p. (C). (978-0-9663215-1-7(0)) Mosley, Kim.

Murphy, Patricia J. Discovering Underwater Secrets with a Nature Photographer. 2007. (I Like Science! Ser.). (Illus.). 24p. (J). (gr. 1-3). lib. bdg. 21.26 (***978-0-7660-2816-6(X)*** , Enslow Elementary) Enslow Pubs., Inc.

My Mini Box of Books: Photographic, 4 bks.; set. 2002. (J). bds. 3.98 (978-0-7525-7139-3(7)) Parragon, Inc.

My Photo Journal. 2002. (Illus.). (J). pap. (978-0-7398-5941-4(2)) Steck-Vaughn.

Nanclares, Silvia. La Siesta. 2001. (SPA., Illus.). (J). (gr. k-3). (978-84-88342-23-2(3) , KK4163) S.A. Kokinos ESP. *Dist:* Lectorum Pubns., Inc.

Neptune's Garden 2005 Calendar. 2004. spiral bd. 14.99 (978-0-9764146-0-5(0)) Manta Vision.

Newcomb, Rain & Gaines, Thom. Digital Photo Madness! 50 Weird & Wacky Things to Do with Your Digital Camera. 2006. (Illus.). 128p. (J). pap. 9.95 (978-1-57990-624-5(9)) Lark Bks.

Oxlade, Chris & Morrison, Al. Cameras. 2004. (All about Ser.). (Illus.). 64p. (gr. 3-7). pap. 7.99 (978-1-84215-769-5(8) , Southwater) Anness Publishing GBR. *Dist:* National Bk. Network.

Pelusey, Michael & Pelusey, Jane. Photography (Media) 2005. (Media Ser.). (Illus.). 32p. (J). (ps-8). lib. bdg. 21.95 (978-0-7910-8805-0(7) , Chelsea Hse.) Facts On File, Inc.

Peres, Michael & Davidhazy, Andrew, eds. Images from Science: An Exhibition of Scientific Photography. 2002. (Illus.). 144p. (YA). 19.99 (978-0-9713459-9-7(6)) Rochester Institute of Technology, Cary Graphic Arts Pr.

Photography. (Make it Work Ser.). 42p. (J). (gr. 4-8). pap. (978-1-882210-43-5(3)) Action Publishing, Inc.

Picture This! Individual Title Six-Packs. (Bookweb Ser.). 32p. (gr. 5 up). 34.00 (978-0-7635-3791-3(8)) Rigby Education.

Price, Pamela S. Cool Scrapbooks. 2005. (Cool Crafts Ser.). (Illus.). 32p. (J). (gr. k-6). lib. bdg. 22.78 (978-1-59197-744-5(4)) ABDO Publishing Co.

Rausch, Monica. George Eastman & the Camera. 2006. (Illus.). 24p. (J). pap. (***978-0-8368-7730-4(6)***); lib. bdg. (***978-0-8368-7499-0(4)***) Stevens, Gareth Inc. (Weekly Reader Early Learning Library).

Rayles, Jason. Fair: An Artful Documentation of the Final Day of the 2002 Brockton Fair in Video Stills & Stereophonic Sound with Attention to the Dual Nature of the 12-Hour Event. 2002. (978-0-9725651-0-3(8)) Rayles, Jason.

Richter, Dana. Barbie Picture Perfect Camera. 2002. (Illus.). (J). 16.98 (978-0-7853-6071-1(9)) Publications International, Ltd.

Robert, Francois & Robert, Jean. Find a Face. 2004. (Illus.). 36p. (J). 14.95 (978-0-8118-4338-6(6)) Chronicle Bks. LLC.

Romancing the Rain: A Photographic Journey into the Heart of the Amazon. 2002. 38.00 (978-0-9619353-2-0(4)) Thy Marvelous Works.

Sanderson, Krystyna. Light at Ground Zero: St. Paul's Chapel After 9/11. Bustard, Ned, ed. 2003. (Illus.). 120p. per. 11.99 (978-0-9658798-4-2(4)) Square Halo Bks.

Schaub, Stephen, photos by. Through a Glass Darkly: Photographs by Stephen M. Schaub. 2004. (ENG & FRE., Illus.). 60p. 65.00 (978-0-9669079-1-9(4)) Indian Hill Gallery of Fine Photography.

Senior, Kathryn, et al. Photography. (Make It Work! Ser.). (Illus.). 48p. (J). pap. 16.99 (978-0-590-24912-6(6)); pap. 7.99 (978-0-590-24913-3(4)) Scholastic, Inc.

Spencer, Jeffrey. Building for the Ages: Omaha's Architectural Landmarks. 2003. (Illus.). 208p. (YA). lib. bdg. 39.95 (978-0-9745410-1-3(X)) Omaha Bks.

Sullivan, George E. 100 Years in Photographs. 1999. (Illus.). 96p. (J). (gr. 3-7). pap. 8.99 (978-0-590-22858-9(7)) Scholastic, Inc.

—100 Years in Photographs. 1999. (978-0-606-15661-5(5)) Tandem Library Bks.

Sullivan, Sean. Lines: The Snowboard Photography of Sean Sullivan. 2003. (Illus.). 176p. (YA). pap. 19.95 (978-0-7603-1678-8(3)) MBI Publishing Co. LLC.

Swinburne, Stephen R. Guess Whose Shadow? 2003. (Illus.). 32p. (YA). (gr. k-2). 15.95 (978-1-56397-724-4(9)) Boyds Mills Pr.

Thomas the Tank Baby Camera. 2002. (Illus.). (J). 15.98 (978-0-7853-6414-6(5)) Publications International, Ltd.

Thompson, Gary. Digital Photography & Your PC: A Guide to Using Your PC to Create Your Own Personalized Photo Albums. 2003. (Illus.). 166p. (YA). spiral bd. 29.95 (978-0-9749763-0-3(X)) Guiding Horizons.

Tress, Arthur, photos by. Facing Up: Tress: Facing Up. ltd. ed. 2004. (ENG & FRE.). 1250.00 (978-0-9761396-7-6(7) , Tress-LE1) Top Choice Pr., LLC.

Urrea, Luis Alberto. Vatos. 2000. (gr. 7-12). lib. bdg. 30.35 (978-0-613-45158-1(9)) Tandem Library Bks.

Vander Hook, Sue. Photography. 1999. (Making Contact Ser.). (Illus.). 32p. (YA). (gr. 4 up). lib. bdg. 16.95 (978-1-887068-62-8(7)) Smart Apple Media.

Villalba. Mexican Calendar Girls. 2006. (Illus.). 144p. pap. 19.95 (978-0-8118-5315-6(2)) Chronicle Bks. LLC.

Wanless, Harold R. Book of Aerial Stereo Photographs, 10 bks., Set. (Illus.). (J). (gr. 7-12). spiral bd. 13.50 (978-0-8331-1703-8(3) , 589) Hubbard Scientific, Inc.

Warren, Marion E. Bringing Back the Bay: The Chesapeake in the Photographs of Marion E. Warren & the Voices of Its People. 2002. (Illus.). xvi, 240p. 50.00 (978-1-884878-12-1(1)) Annapolis Publishing Co.

Webber, Diane. Shot & Framed: Photographers at the Crime Scene. 2007. (24/7 - Science Behind the Scenes Ser.). (Illus.). 64p. (J). (gr. 8-12). 25.00 (***978-0-531-12063-7(5)*** , Watts, Franklin) Scholastic Library Publishing.

Weed, Paula & Jimison, Carla. Tricky Pix. 2001. (Illus.). 54p. (J). spiral bd. 19.95 (978-1-57054-652-5(5)) Klutz.

Yeager, Bunny. Bunny Yeager's Pin-up Girls of The 1950s. 2001. (Illus.). 128p. (gr. 10-13). pap. 24.95 (978-0-7643-1473-5(4)) Schiffer Publishing, Ltd.

Zier, Nina. 98 Degrees: Backstage Pass. 1999. (gr. 3-6). lib. bdg. 14.15 (978-0-613-16985-1(9)) Tandem Library Bks.

PHOTOGRAPHY, AERIAL

see Aerial Photography

PHOTOGRAPHY—AESTHETICS

see Photography, Artistic

PHOTOGRAPHY, ARTISTIC

Bower, John. Lingering Spirit: A Photographic Tribute to Indiana's Fading, Forlorn, & Forgotten Places. 2003. (Illus.). 144p. per. 22.00 (978-0-9745186-0-2(3)) Studio Indiana.

Brooke, Charles A. Ten years in Sarbwak, Vol. 2. fac. ed. 2001. 364p. pap. 18.95 (978-1-4021-9329-3(7) , Elibron Classics) Adamant Media.

Burkhard, Balthasar. Click, Said the Camera. 2006. (Illus.). 42p. pap. 30.00 (978-3-907044-56-8(8)) Lars Muller CHE. *Dist:* Chronicle Bks. LLC.

Burnett, Craig. Jeff Wall. 2006. (Modern Artists Ser.). (Illus.). 128p. pap. 24.95 (978-1-85437-611-4(X)) Tate Gallery Publishing, Ltd. GBR. *Dist:* Hachette Bk. Group.

Kallas, Randi & Dougherty, Mike, eds. Rochester, Minnesota: A Visual & Historic Journey. 2003. (Illus.). 136p. pap. 24.95 (978-0-9659875-3-0(1)) Riggott, Dean Photography.

Lynch, Marietta & Perry, Patricia. No More Monkeys: A Photographic Version of the Children's Finger Game. (Orig.). (J). (ps-3). pap. 2.95 (978-0-9610962-0-5(9)) Lynch, Marietta & Patricia Perry.

Roma, Giancarlo T. & Roma, Thomas. Show & Tell. Roma, Thomas, illus. Roma, Giancarlo T., photos by. 2005. (Illus.). 80p. 19.95 (978-1-57687-133-1(9) , powerHouse Bks.) powerHouse Cultural Entertainment, Inc.

PHOTOGRAPHY—FICTION

Alphin, Elaine Marie. Picture Perfect. 2003. (Illus.). 252p. (J). (gr. 7 up). 15.95 (978-0-8225-0535-8(5)) Lerner Publishing Group.

Bailer, Darice. Railroad! A Story of the Transcontinental Railroad. Farnsworth, Bill, illus. 3rd ed. 2005. (Soundprints' Read-and-Discover Ser.). 48p. (J). (gr. 2-4). pap. 3.95 (978-1-59249-017-2(4) , S2007) Soundprints.

Bauer, Joan. Thwonk. 2005. 224p. (YA). (gr. 7). pap. 7.99 (978-0-14-240429-4(2) , Puffin); 2001. 208p. (J). 16.99 (978-0-399-23751-5(8) , Putnam Juvenile) Penguin Group (USA) Inc.

—Thwonk. 2001. (978-0-606-22535-9(8)) Tandem Library Bks.

Berleman, Sean & Salyards, Jeffrey. Camera Contest. Saunders, Zina, illus. 2004. 14p. (J). bds. (978-0-7853-9955-1(0) , 7210000) Publications International, Ltd.

Buckless, Andrea. Class Picture Day. Goodnow, Patti, illus. 2004. 32p. (J). lib. bdg. 15.00 (978-1-59054-379-5(3)) Fitzgerald Bks.

—Class Picture Day, Level 2. Goodnow, Patti, illus. 1999. (Hello Reader! Ser.: Level 2). 32p. (J). (gr. k-2). pap. 3.99 (978-0-590-37975-5(5) , Cartwheel Bks.) Scholastic, Inc.

Busiek, Kurt. Marvels. 2001. (gr. 5-8). lib. bdg. 30.35 (978-0-613-53688-2(6)) Tandem Library Bks.

Cheese, Please! Individual Title Six-Packs. (Story Steps Ser.). (gr. k-2). 29.00 (978-0-7635-9589-0(6)) Rigby Education.

Conford, Ellen. Get the Picture, Jenny Archer? 2000. (J). 11.79 (978-0-606-19838-7(5)) Tandem Library Bks.

Crum, Anna-Maria & Fielder, John, illus. Maria's Mysterious Mission. Fielder, John, photos by. 2007. (J). 12.95 (***978-1-56579-588-4(1)***) Westcliffe Pubs.

Cunliffe, John. Postman Pat Takes a Photo. (Illus.). 20p. (J). 11.99 (978-0-340-73712-5(3) , Hodder & Stoughton) Hodder General Publishing Division GBR. *Dist:* Trafalgar Square Publishing.

da Costa, Deborah. Hanukkah Moon. Mocz, Gosia, illus. 2007. (Hanukkah Ser.). (J). (gr. 1-5). 17.95 (***978-1-58013-244-2(8)***) Kar-Ben Publishing.

—Hanukkah Moon. Mosz, Gosia, illus. 2007. (Hanukkah Ser.). (J). (gr. 1-5). pap. 7.95 (***978-1-58013-245-9(6)***) Kar-Ben Publishing.

DeJong, Jennifer Bailey. Say Cheese! Loopstra, Esther Dawn, illus. 2006. 24p. (J). lib. bdg. (***978-1-4048-2400-3(6)***) Picture Window Bks.

—Say Cheese ! 2007. (Illus.). 24p. (J). (***978-1-4048-2430-0(8)***) Picture Window Bks.

Divine, Jill. Miles Smiles. 2006. pap. (***978-1-84685-513-9(6)*** , Exposure Publishing) Meadow Bks.

Doudna, Kelly. Goat Cheese. Haberstroh, Anne, illus. 2006. (Fact & Fiction Ser.). 24p. (J). 21.35 (978-1-59679-937-0(4) , SandCastle); pap. (978-1-59679-938-7(2)) ABDO Publishing Co.

Dwyer, Cynthia. Can You See Me Now? Schuepbach, Lynnette, illus. 2006. 24p. (J). 12.95 (***978-0-9677685-8-8(6)*** , Thumbprint Pr.) McIntyre, Connie.

Elmo's Talking Camera. 2002. (Illus.). 14p. (J). bds. 15.98 (978-0-7853-6069-8(7) , 7153400) Publications International, Ltd.

Enderle, Judith Ross & Gordon, Stephanie Jacob. Smile, Principessa! Litzinger, Rosanne & Curmi, Serena, illus. 2007. 40p. (J). (ps-3). 16.99 (978-1-4169-1004-6(2) , McElderry, Margaret K.) Simon & Schuster Children's Publishing.

Getzinger, Donna. The Picture Wagon. 2000. 156p. (J). (gr. 4-7). pap. 8.95 (978-0-87714-481-6(8)) Denlingers Pubs., Ltd.

Gray, Dianne E. Tomorrow, the River. Cooper, Stephanie, illus. 2006. 240p. (J). (gr. 5-9). 16.00 (978-0-618-56329-6(6)) Houghton Mifflin Co.

Gregory, Kristiana. Earthquake at Dawn. 2003. (gr. 5-8). lib. bdg. 14.10 (978-0-613-64493-8(X)) Tandem Library Bks.

Gregory, Kristiana & Campbell, Mary Exa Atkins. Earthquake at Dawn. 2003. (Great Episodes Ser.). (Illus.). 224p. (J). pap. 5.95 (978-0-15-204681-1(X)) Harcourt Children's Bks.

Harcourt School Publishers Staff. Grandpa's Camera On Level. 3rd ed. 2002. (Trophies Reading Program Ser.). (Illus.). pap. 5.10 (978-0-15-323359-3(1)) Harcourt Schl. Pubs.

—Mil Palabras: Take-Home Book. 2001. (Vamos Ser.). (SPA., Illus.). (J). pap. 2.80 (978-0-15-319927-1(X)) Harcourt Schl. Pubs.

—My Pet Project On Level. 3rd ed. 2002. (Trophies Reading Program Ser.). (Illus.). pap. 5.10 (978-0-15-323168-1(8)) Harcourt Schl. Pubs.

—That's My Shot: Take-Home Book. 1999. (Collections Ser.). (Illus.). (J). pap. 1.90 (978-0-15-317294-6(0)) Harcourt Schl. Pubs.

—A Thousand Words: Take-Home Book. 2001. (Collections Ser.). (Illus.). (J). pap. 1.90 (978-0-15-319484-9(7)) Harcourt Schl. Pubs.

—A Thousand Words Below Level. 3rd ed. 2002. (Trophies Reading Program Ser.). (Illus.). pap. 5.10 (978-0-15-323222-0(6)) Harcourt Schl. Pubs.

Hidier, Tanuja Desai. Born Confused. 2003. (gr. 7-12). lib. bdg. 16.45 (978-0-613-72235-3(3)) Tandem Library Bks.

Hidier, Tanuja Desai, et al. Born Confused. Hidier, Tanuja Desai, illus. 2002. 432p. (J). pap. 16.95 (978-0-439-35762-3(4) , Scholastic Pr.) Scholastic, Inc.

Jordan, Apple & Random House Staff. Barbie: On Your Toes. Wolcott, Karen, illus. 2005. (Step into Reading Ser.: No. 1). 32p. (J). (ps-1). pap. 3.99 (978-0-375-83142-3(8) , Random Hse. Bks. for Young Readers) Random Hse. Children's Bks.

Kalz, Jill. Galen's Camera. Lee, Ji Sun, illus. 2006. (Read-It! Readers Ser.). 24p. (J). (ps-3). 18.60 (978-1-4048-1610-7(0)) Picture Window Bks.

Kelly, Matt. Scooby-Doo! Camera Clues. Wanhala, Dwight, illus. 2004. 14p. (J). bds. (978-0-7853-9954-4(2) , 7209900) Publications International, Ltd.

Kudlinski, Kathleen V. The Spirit Catchers: An Encounter with Georgia O'Keeffe. 2005. (Art Encounters Ser.). (Illus.). 176p. (YA). 15.95 (978-0-8230-0408-9(2)) Watson-Guptill Pubns., Inc.

Marsh, Carole. The Adventure Diaries of P. J., the Photo-Journalist! l.t. ed. 2002. (Illus.). 48p. (J). lib. bdg. 9.95 (978-0-635-01279-1(0)) Gallopade International.

McCaughrean, Geraldine. Smile! 128p. (J). (gr. 2-6). 2008. 5.50 (***978-0-440-23952-9(4)*** , Yearling); 2006. (Illus.). 14.95 (978-0-375-83640-4(3) , Random Hse. Bks. for Young Readers) Random Hse. Children's Bks.

—Smile. 2006. (Illus.). 128p. (J). (gr. 2-6). lib. bdg. 16.99 (978-0-375-93640-1(8) , Random Hse. Bks. for Young Readers) Random Hse. Children's Bks.

—Smile! 2nd rev. ed. 2004. (Illus.). 128p. (J). (978-0-19-271961-4(0)) Oxford Univ. Pr., Inc.

Mills, Charles. The Bandit of Benson Park. 2003. (Honors Club Story Ser.: Vol. 1). 127p. (J). (978-0-8163-1977-0(4)) Pacific Pr. Pubns.

Perkins, Lynne Rae. Pictures from Our Vacation. Perkins, Lynne Rae, illus. 2007. (Illus.). (J). (gr. 2-5). 40p. 16.99 (***978-0-06-085097-5(3)***); 32p. lib. bdg. 17.89 (***978-0-06-085098-2(1)***) HarperCollins Pubs. (Greenwillow Bks.).

Pizante, Raymond. Ali & His Camera. 2002. (Illus.). 16p. pap. (978-0-582-42774-7(6) , Putnam Juvenile) Penguin Group (USA) Inc.

Reber, Deborah. Meet My Family. 2001. (ps-2). lib. bdg. 11.80 (978-0-613-35671-8(3)) Tandem Library Bks.

Richter, Dana. Pooh's Snapshot Surprise. 2002. (Illus.). 14p. (J). bds. (978-0-7853-8089-4(2) , 7181300) Publications International, Ltd.

Scotton, Rob. Russell & the Lost Treasure. Scotton, Rob, illus. 2006. (Illus.). 32p. (J). 15.99 (978-0-06-059851-8(4)); lib. bdg. 16.89 (978-0-06-059852-5(2)) HarperCollins Pubs.

Seibold, J. Otto. Quincy, the Hobby Photographer. 2006. (Illus.). 64p. 14.95 (978-0-15-101494-1(9)) Harcourt Trade Pubs.

Shi, Sharon. The Camera. Jones, David Phillip, illus. 2000. 24p. (J). (gr. k-3). mass mkt. 4.99 (978-0-9702195-0-3(4) , B011, Tattootles Bks.) Tattoo Manufacturing.

Smith, Cynthia Leitich. Rain Is Not My Indian Name. Earley, Lori, illus. 2001. 144p. (J). (gr. 5-9). 16.99 (978-0-688-17397-5(7)) HarperCollins Pubs.

Tinkham, Kelly. Hair for Mama. Bates, Amy June, illus. 2007. 32p. (J). (ps-3). 16.99 (978-0-8037-2955-1(3) , Dial) Penguin Group (USA) Inc.

Townley, Roderick. The Red Thread: A Novel in Three Incarnations. 2007. 304p. (YA). (gr. 7 up). 17.99 (978-1-4169-0894-4(3) , Atheneum/Richard Jackson Bks.) Simon & Schuster Children's Publishing.

Townley, Roderick. The Red Thread: A Novel in Three Incarnations. 2007. 304p. (YA). 17.99 (***978-1-4169-2930-7(4)*** , Atheneum) Simon & Schuster Children's Publishing.

Trimble, Marcia. Hello Sun: A True African Travel Tale. Arciero, Susan, illus. 2000. 32p. (J). (gr. k-2). 12.95 (978-1-891577-50-5(6)); pap. 6.95 (978-1-891577-51-2(4)) Images Pr.

Vivian, Siobhan. A Little Friendly Advice. 2008. 256p. (J). pap. 16.99 (***978-0-545-00404-6(7)*** , PUSH) Scholastic, Inc.

Wittlinger, Ellen. Razzle. 2001. (Illus.). 256p. (J). (gr. 7-10). 17.00 (978-0-689-83565-0(5)) Simon & Schuster Children's Publishing.

—Razzle. 2003. (gr. 7-12). lib. bdg. 16.45 (978-0-613-61811-3(4)) Tandem Library Bks.

Worcester, Donald E. Cowboy with a Camera: Erwin E. Smith, Cowboy Photograph. Smith, Erwin E., photos by. 1999. (Illus.). 48p. (J). (gr. 4-7). 18.95 (978-0-88360-091-7(9)) Amon Carter Museum.

PHOTOGRAPHY—HISTORY

Aller, Susan Bivin. George Eastman. 2004. (History Maker Bios Ser.). (Illus.). 48p. (J). (gr. 3-5). lib. bdg. 26.60 (978-0-8225-0200-5(3)) Lerner Publishing Group.

Bankston, John. Louis Daguerre & the Story of the Daguerreotype. 2004. (Uncharted, Unexplored, & Unexplained Ser.). (Illus.). 48p. (J). (gr. 4-8). lib. bdg. 29.95 (978-1-58415-247-7(8)) Mitchell Lane Pubs., Inc.

Clee, Paul. Photography & the Making of the American West. 2002. (Illus.). x, 124p. (J). 27.50 (978-0-208-02512-8(X)) Shoe String Pr., Inc.

Ford, Carin T. George Eastman: The Kodak Camera Man. 2004. (Famous Inventors Ser.). (Illus.). 32p. (J). lib. bdg. 22.60 (978-0-7660-2247-8(1)) Enslow Pubs., Inc.

Gillis, Jennifer Blizin. George Eastman. 2004. (Illus.). 32p. (J). pap. 6.50 (978-1-4034-5334-1(9)); lib. bdg. 22.79 (978-1-4034-5326-6(8)) Heinemann Library.

Hall, Ken. George D. Valentine: A 19th Century Photographer in New Zealand. 2004. (Illus.). 132p. pap. (978-1-877333-12-5(3)) Potton, Craig Publishing Ltd.

Mattern, Joanne. George Eastman & Photographic Film. 2004. (Uncharted, Unexplored, & Unexplained Ser.). (Illus.). 48p. (J). (gr. 4-8). lib. bdg. 29.95 (978-1-58415-258-3(3)) Mitchell Lane Pubs., Inc.

Pflueger, Lynda. George Eastman: Bringing Photography to the People. 2002. (Historical American Biographies Ser.). (Illus.). 128p. (YA). (gr. 6-12). lib. bdg. 26.60 (978-0-7660-1617-0(X)) Enslow Pubs., Inc.

Pobst, Sandy. The Camera. 2005. (Great Inventions Ser.). (Illus.). 48p. (YA). lib. bdg. 30.00 (978-0-8368-5801-3(8) , World Almanac Library) Stevens, Gareth Inc.

Sandler, Martin W. Photography: An Illustrated History. 2001. (Oxford Illustrated Histories Ser.). (Illus.). 160p. (YA). (gr. 7 up). 35.00 (978-0-19-512608-2(4)) Oxford Univ. Pr., Inc.

Stefoff, Rebecca. The Camera. 2007. (Great Inventions Ser.). (Illus.). 144p. (YA). (gr. 9 up). lib. bdg. 39.93 (***978-0-7614-2596-0(9)*** , Benchmark Bks.) Cavendish, Marshall Corp.

Vander Hook, Sue. Photography. 1999. (Making Contact Ser.). (Illus.). 32p. (YA). (gr. 4 up). lib. bdg. 16.95 (978-1-887068-62-8(7)) Smart Apple Media.

White, Matt. Cameras on the Battlefield: Photos of War. 2001. (High Five Reading Ser.). (Illus.). 64p. (J). pap. (978-0-7368-9504-0(3)); (gr. 4-5). lib. bdg. 22.60 (978-0-7368-4004-0(4) , Capstone High-Interest Bks.) Capstone Pr., Inc.

PHOTOGRAPHY, JOURNALISTIC

see Photojournalism

PHOTOGRAPHY—VOCATIONAL GUIDANCE

Aaseng, Nathan. Wildshots: The World of the Wildlife Photographer. 2001. (Women at War Ser.). (Illus.). 80p. (gr. 5-8). lib. bdg. 29.90 (978-0-7613-1551-3(9) , Twenty-First Century Bks.) Lerner Publishing Group.

Hodgkins, Fran. Photographers. 2001. (Community Helpers Ser.). (Illus.). 92p. (J). (gr. 1-2). 18.60 (978-0-7368-0809-5(4) , Bridgestone Bks.) Capstone Pr., Inc.

Roza, Greg. Choosing a Career as a Professional Photographer. 2005. (Career Resource Library). (Illus.). 192p. (YA). (gr. 7-12). lib. bdg. 26.50 (978-0-8239-3184-2(6)) Rosen Publishing Group, Inc., The.

Sommers, Michael A. Wildlife Photographers: Life Through a Lens. 2005. (Extreme Careers Ser.). (Illus.). 64p. (YA). (gr. 5-8). 26.50 (978-0-8239-3638-0(4)) Rosen Publishing Group, Inc., The.

PHOTOGRAPHY OF ANIMALS

see also Animal Painting and Illustration

P Q R

Aaseng, Nathan. Wildshots: The World of the Wildlife Photographer. 2001. (Women at War Ser.). (Illus.). 80p. (gr. 5-8). lib. bdg. 29.90 (978-0-7613-1551-3(9) , Twenty-First Century Bks.) Lerner Publishing Group.

Burkhard, Balthasar. Click, Said the Camera. 2006. (Illus.). 42p. pap. 30.00 (978-3-907044-56-8(8)) Lars Muller CHE. *Dist:* Chronicle Bks. LLC.

Humane Society of the U. S. Staff & Sirch, Willow Ann. Careers with Animals. 2004. (Illus.). 128p. (gr. 4-6). 16.95 (978-1-55591-408-0(X)) Fulcrum Publishing.

1@Heureux, J. J. Good Day Book. 2006. spiral bd. (***978-0-9785892-0-2(3)***) Jian Media Ltd.

Stimson, Judith A. Animal & Photography Adventures. Stimson, Judith A., photos by. 1999. (Illus.). 115p. (J). (gr. 3-5). wbk. ed. 25.00 (978-0-9669879-0-4(X)) ABConsulting.

PHOTOGRAPHY OF NATURE

see Nature Photography

PHOTOJOURNALISM

Milich, Zoran. City signs. Milich, Zoran, illus. 2002. (Illus.). 32p. (J). (ps-k). (978-1-55337-003-1(1)) Kids Can Pr., Ltd.

PHOTOPLAYS

see Motion Picture Plays

PHOTOSYNTHESIS

Brown, Harriet. Food from the Sun: How Plants Live & Grow. 2008. (J). (***978-1-60044-600-9(0)***) Rourke Publishing, LLC.

Hopkins, William. Photosynthesis & Respiration. 2006. (Green World Ser.). (Illus.). 176p. (J). (gr. 6-12). 37.50 (978-0-7910-8561-5(9) , Chelsea Hse.) Facts On File, Inc.

Juettner, Bonnie. Photosynethesis. 2005. (KidHaven Science Library). (Illus.). 48p. (J). (gr. 4-8). 26.20 (978-0-7377-2350-2(5) , Greenhaven Pr., Inc.) Thomson Gale.

Kalman, Bobbie. La Fotosintesis: De la luz del sol al Alimento. 2006. (SPA., Illus.). 32p. (gr. 3). pap. (978-0-7787-8386-2(3)) Crabtree Publishing Co.

—Photosynthesis: Changing Sunlight into Food. 2005. (Nature's Changes Ser.). (Illus.). 32p. (J). (978-0-7787-2274-8(0)) Crabtree Publishing Co.

—Photosynthesis: Changing Sunlight into Food. 2005. (Nature's Changes Ser.). (Illus.). 32p. (J). (ps). pap. (978-0-7787-2308-0(9)) Crabtree Publishing Co.

O'Donnell, Liam. Understanding Photosynthesis with Max Axiom, Super Scientist. Dominguez, Richard & Barnett, Charles, illus. 2007. (Graphic Library). 32p. (J). (***978-0-7368-6841-9(0)*** , 1264938) Capstone Pr., Inc.

—Understanding Photosynthesis with Max Axiom, Super Scientist. 2007. (Graphic Library). (Illus.). 32p. (J). (***978-0-7368-7893-7(9)*** , 1264938) Capstone Pr., Inc.

Silverstein, Alvin, et al. Photosynthesis. (Illus.). 2007. (Science Concepts, Second Ser.). 80p. (YA). (gr. 6-8). lib. bdg. 31.93 (978-0-8225-6798-1(9)); 1998. (Science Concepts Ser.: 8). 64p. (gr. 5-8). lib. bdg. 26.90 (978-0-7613-3000-4(3)) Lerner Publishing Group. (Twenty-First Century Bks.).

Staub, Frank. Photosynthesis. 2003. (World of Wonder Ser.). (Illus.). 32p. (J). lib. bdg. (978-1-58341-265-7(4) , Creative Education) Creative Co., The.

PHYSICAL CHEMISTRY

see Chemistry, Physical and Theoretical

PHYSICAL CULTURE

see Physical Education and Training

PHYSICAL EDUCATION AND TRAINING

see also Athletics; Coaching (Athletics); Exercise; Games; Gymnastics; Health Education; Physical Fitness; Sports also names of kinds of exercises, e.g. Fencing; Judo

Behind the Moves, 4 bks. Incl. Extreme Bicycle Stunt Riding Moves. Parr, Danny. 2001. lib. bdg. 21.26 (978-0-7368-0781-4(0)); Extreme Freestyle Motocross Moves. Schaefer, A. R. 2003. lib. bdg. 21.26 (978-0-7368-1512-3(0)); Extreme In-Line Skating Moves. Parr, Danny. 2001. lib. bdg. 21.26 (978-0-7368-0782-1(9)); Extreme Mountain Biking Moves. Deady, Kathleen W. 2003. lib. bdg. 21.26 (978-0-7368-1513-0(9)); Extreme Rock Climbing Moves. Deady, Kathleen W. 2003. lib. bdg. 21.26 (978-0-7368-1514-7(7)); Extreme Skateboarding Moves. Freimuth, Jeri. 2001. lib. bdg. 21.26 (978-0-7368-0783-8(7)); Extreme Snowboarding Moves. Freimuth, Jeri. 2001. lib. bdg. 21.26 (978-0-7368-0784-5(5)); Extreme Wakeboarding Moves. Schaefer, A. R. 2003. lib. bdg. 21.26 (978-0-7368-1515-4(5)); 32p. (J). (gr. 3-4). (Illus.). Set lib. bdg. 170.08 (978-0-7368-1523-9(6) , Capstone High-Interest Bks.) Capstone Pr., Inc.

Body Building: Junior High & Middle School. 1998. (Cross Training Ser.: Vol. 6). 204p. (YA). (gr. 7-9). pap. 99.99 incl. VHS (978-1-57405-110-0(5)) CharismaLife Pubs.

Chaline, Eric. Martial Arts for Athletic Conditioning. 2003. (Martial & Fighting Arts Ser.). (Illus.). 96p. (J). (gr. 7 up). lib. bdg. (978-1-59084-397-0(5)) Mason Crest Pubs.

Compton, Leanne, et al. Jump Start 7 & 8: Health & Physical Education. 2007. pap. 41.00 incl. cd-rom (***978-0-521-70156-3(2)***) Cambridge Univ. Pr.

Costello, Patricia. Legend's of Health & Fitness, 10 vols., Set. 2000. (Illus.). 960p. (gr. 6-10). lib. bdg. 257.00 (978-1-58415-062-6(9)) Mitchell Lane Pubs., Inc.

Cruisin', 22 bks. Incl. BMX Bikes. Carstensen, Karol. 1991. lib. bdg. 21.26 (978-1-56065-076-8(1)); Convertibles. Streissguth, Thomas. 1995. lib. bdg. 21.26 (978-1-56065-256-4(X)); Dragsters. Connolly, Maureen. 1992. lib. bdg. 21.26 (978-1-56065-074-4(5)); Emergency Vehicles. Wolhart, Dayna. 1991. lib. bdg. 21.26 (978-1-56065-079-9(6)); Hot Rods. Pernu, Dennis. 1995. lib. bdg. 21.26 (978-1-56065-253-3(5)); Indy Cars. Young, Jesse. 1995. lib. bdg. 21.26 (978-1-56065-222-9(5)); Jeeps. Streissguth, Thomas. 1995. lib. bdg. 21.26 (978-1-56065-255-7(1)); Jet-Powered Funny Cars. Young, Jesse. 1995. lib. bdg. 21.26 (978-1-56065-220-5(9)); Jet Watercraft. Martin, John. 1994. lib. bdg. 21.26 (978-1-56065-201-4(2)); Karts. Cazin, Lorraine. 1992. lib. bdg. 21.26 (978-1-56065-072-0(9)); Monster Vehicles. Atkinson, E. J. 1991. lib. bdg. 21.26 (978-1-56065-077-5(X)); Motocross Cycles. Carser, S. X. 1992. lib. bdg. 21.26 (978-1-56065-069-0(9)); Motorcycles. Kahaner, Ellen. 1991. lib. bdg. 21.26 (978-1-56065-070-6(2)); Original Monster Truck : Bigfoot. Johnston, Scott. 1994. lib. bdg. 21.26 (978-1-56065-200-7(4)); Race Cars. Stephenson, Sallie. 1991. lib. bdg. 21.26 (978-1-56065-068-3(0)); Roller Coasters. Chandler, Gil. 1995. lib. bdg. 21.26 (978-1-56065-221-2(7)); RVs & Vans. Burt, Stephen. 1992. lib. bdg. 21.26 (978-1-56065-071-3(0)); Sports Cars. Stephenson, Sallie. 1991. lib. bdg. 21.26 (978-1-56065-078-2(8)); Stock Cars. Young, Jesse. 1995. lib. bdg. 21.26 (978-1-56065-223-6(3)); Tractors. Chandler, Gil. 1995. lib. bdg. 21.26 (978-1-56065-254-0(3)); 4x4s & Pickups. Donahue, A. K. 1991. lib. bdg. 21.26 (978-1-56065-075-1(3)); 18-Wheelers. Maifair, Linda Lee. 1991. lib. bdg. 21.26 (978-1-56065-073-7(7)); 48p. (J). (gr. 3-4). (Illus.). Set lib. bdg. 467.72 (978-1-56065-640-1(9) , Capstone High-Interest Bks.) Capstone Pr., Inc.

Davis, Barbara. 404 Deskside Activities for Energetic Kids. 2006. (SmartFun Activity Bks.). (Illus.). 168p. pap. 14.95 (978-0-89793-467-1(9)); spiral bd. 19.95 (978-0-89793-468-8(7)) Hunter Hse., Inc.

Dintiman, George B. Speed Improvement for Young Athletes: How to Sprint Faster in Your Sport in 30 Workouts. 2002. (Illus.). 140p. (YA). (gr. 9 up). mass mkt. 17.95 (978-0-938074-25-0(3) , 2002-23) National Assn. of Speed & Explosion.

Dintiman, George Blough. Speed Improvement for Young Athletes: How to Sprint Faster in Your Sport in 30 Workouts. rev. ed. 2006. Vol. 2. (Illus.). 153p. pap. 17.95 (978-0-938074-26-7(1)) National Assn. of Speed & Explosion.

Entrenamiento Deportivo Series, 6 bks., Set. 2003. (Entrenamiento Deportivo Ser.). (SPA & ENG., Illus.). (J). 103.50 (978-0-8239-6913-5(4) , Buenas Letra) Rosen Publishing Group, Inc., The.

Facts on File, Inc. Staff, contrib. by. Careers in Focus. 2004. (Careers in Focus Ser.). (Illus.). 192p. (J). (gr. 6-12). 22.95 (978-0-8160-5548-7(3) , Ferguson Publishing Co.) Facts On File, Inc.

Fitterman, Lisa. Let's Get Moving: The Joy of Movement for Small Children. 1999. (Funtasy League Ser.). (Illus.). 32p. (J). (ps-3). (978-1-896933-93-1(9)) Cethial & Bossche Co.

Gallagher, R., et al. Addysg Gorfforol Trwy Ddiagramau: Llawlyfr Adolygu TGAU. 2005. (WEL., Illus.). 92p. (978-1-85644-562-7(3)) Univ. of Wales, Aberystwyth, Centre for Educational Studies.

Gifford, Clive. A World-Class Sprinter. 2004. (Making of a Champion Ser.). (J). pap. 8.50 (978-1-4034-5537-6(6)) Heinemann Library.

Glover, Donald R. 40 Years in the Gym: Favorite Physical Education Activities. 2006. (Illus.). 168p. pap. 22.00 (978-0-7360-6271-8(8)) Human Kinetics Pubs.

Golden Books Staff. Fun in the Sun. 2000. (Illus.). 128p. (J). (ps-2). pap. 0.99 (978-0-307-44329-8(9) , Golden Bks.) Random Hse. Children's Bks.

Green, Gerry & Porter, David. Winning Weight Training for Girls. (Winning Sports for Girls Ser.). (Illus.). 224p. (YA). (gr. 9-12). pap. 16.95 (978-0-8160-5186-1(0) , Checkmark Bks.) Facts On File, Inc.

Harcourt School Publishers Staff. Harcourt Physical Education Posters, Grades 3-6. 3rd ed. 2003. (Illus.). 55.20 (978-0-15-339102-6(2)) Harcourt Schl. Pubs.

Hayes, Cheri. Playtime is Exercise! A Fun Story about Exercise & Play. Dineen, Tom, illus. 2001. (Healthy Habits for Kids: Vol. 2). 24p. (J). pap. 6.95 (978-1-891383-14-4(0)) JayJo Bks., LLC.

J. G. Ferguson Publishing Company Staff, contrib. by. Careers in Focus. 2003. (Careers in Focus Ser.). (Illus.). (J). (gr. 6-12). 176p. 22.95 (978-0-8160-5484-8(3)); 3rd ed. 208p. 22.95 (978-0-8160-5486-2(X)) Facts On File, Inc. (Ferguson Publishing Co.).

Lasslett, Sally, et al. Jump Start 9 & 10: Health & Physical Education. 2007. pap. 41.00 incl. cd-rom (***978-0-521-70167-9(8)***) Cambridge Univ. Pr.

Massad, Diane Patterson. Hang On! The Kidskills America Training Series. 2004. (Kidskills America Training Ser.). (YA). spiral bd. 12.95 (978-0-9710641-9-5(9)) Kidskills International.

—Making Muscles! The Kidskills America Training Series. 2004. (Kidskills America Training Ser.). (Illus.). 75p. (J). spiral bd. 12.95 (978-0-9710641-6-4(4)) Kidskills International.

—Up & Over! The Kidskills America Training Series. 2004. (Kidskills America Training Ser.). (Illus.). 75p. (J). spiral bd. 12.95 (978-0-9710641-5-7(6) , Kidskills America) Kidskills International.

Morris, Ann. That's Our Gym Teacher! Linenthal, Peter, illus. 2003. (That's Our School Ser.). 32p. lib. bdg. 22.90 (978-0-7613-2403-4(8) , Millbrook Pr.) Lerner Publishing Group.

Physical Education at Work, High School, 6 vols., Vol. 1. 2001. (At Work High School Ser.: Vol. 1). (YA). cd-rom 69.95 (978-1-929879-17-5(2)) Career Kids.

Power up Starter Set Level 2. 2002. (Illus.). (J). pap. (978-0-7398-5129-6(2)) Steck-Vaughn.

Steadman, Barbara. Gym Class Sticker Activity Book. 2001. 4p. (J). pap. 1.00 (978-0-486-41627-4(5)) Dover Pubns., Inc.

Steck-Vaughn Staff. Power up Workout Book. 2002. (Illus.). (J). Level 1. pap. (978-0-7398-5081-7(4)); Level 2. pap. (978-0-7398-5116-6(0)) Steck-Vaughn.

—Power up Workout Book Set, Level 1. 2002. (Illus.). (J). pap. (978-0-7398-5093-0(8)) Steck-Vaughn.

, Suzanne-Kelly, Suzanne-Kelly. Pilates 4 Kidzz. 2005. 104p. pap. 25.00 (978-1-4116-6266-7(0)) Lulu.com.

PHYSICAL FITNESS

Aliotti, Johnny. Johnny's Simple Dumbbell Workout. 2004. spiral bd. 14.95 (978-0-9740600-1-9(1)); (Illus.). 102p. per. 13.95 (978-0-9740600-0-2(3)) ProTips(TM) Media.

Bauchner, Elizabeth. What Do I Have to Lose? A Teen's Guide to Weight Management. 2004. (Science of Health Ser.). (Illus.). 128p. (YA). (978-1-59084-855-5(1)) Mason Crest Pubs.

Bellenir, Karen, ed. Fitness Information for Teens: Health Tips about Exercise, Physical Well-Being, & Health Maintenance. 2004. (Teen Health Ser.). (Illus.). 425p. (gr. 7 up). 65.00 (978-0-7808-0679-5(4)) Omnigraphics, Inc.

Berton, Judy & Guimond, Rick. Do a Dance Picture Book. 2006. (Illus.). (J). spiral bd. 8.95 (978-0-9761051-1-4(X)) Kidrich Corp.

Burkhead, Frank, Jr. Sports Ministry for Christ. 2005. 49p. (YA). per. 10.25 (978-0-9770043-5-5(X)) New Global Publishing.

Carle, Eric. From Head to Toe. 1999. (Illus.). 32p. (J). (gr. k-3). pap. 6.99 (978-0-06-443596-3(2) , Harper Trophy) HarperCollins Pubs.

—From Head to Toe. Carle, Eric, illus. 1999. (Illus.). 26p. (J). (ps-k). bds. 7.99 (978-0-694-01301-2(3) , Harper Festival) HarperCollins Pubs.

—From Head to Toe. 1999. lib. bdg. 15.30 (978-0-613-22852-7(9)) Tandem Library Bks.

—From Head to Toe Big Book. Carle, Eric, illus. 2007. 32p. (J). pap. 24.99 (***978-0-06-111972-9(5)*** , Harper Festival) HarperCollins Pubs.

Carle, Eric. From Head to Toe (Spanish Edition) De la cabeza a los Pies. Carle, Eric, illus. 2007. (SPA.). 32p. (J). pap. 6.99 (978-0-06-051313-9(6) , Rayo) HarperCollins Pubs.

Christopher, Matt. Run for It. 2002. (#1 Sports Series for Kids). 128p. (J). (gr. 2-4). pap. 4.50 (978-0-316-34914-7(3)) Little, Brown Bks. for Young Readers.

—Run for It. 2002. (gr. 3-6). lib. bdg. 12.40 (978-0-613-50638-0(3)) Tandem Library Bks.

Coleman, Lori & Savage, Jeff. Beginning Strength Training. Clarke, Jimmy, illus. 1998. (Beginning Sports Ser.). 80p. (gr. 3-5). lib. bdg. 22.60 (978-0-8225-3511-9(4)) Lerner Publishing Group.

Compact Guides to Health & Fitness, 17 vols., Set. 2002. (Illus.). 36,52p. (YA). (gr. 8 up). lib. bdg. (978-1-59084-245-4(6)) Mason Crest Pubs.

Constant. Fitness. 2004. (Teen Issues Ser.). (Illus.). 56p. (J). 31.36 (978-1-4109-0612-0(4)); pap. 8.95 (978-1-4109-0883-4(6)) Harcourt Schl. Pubs.

—Fitness 6-Pack. 2004. (Teen Issues Ser.). (Illus.). (YA). pap. 48.30 (978-1-4109-0890-2(9)) Harcourt Schl. Pubs.

CosmoGIRL! Editors. Total Body Workout: Fun Moves to Look & Feel Your Best. 2008. (CosmoGirl! Ser.). (Illus.). 128p. (J). pap. 9.95 (***978-1-58816-663-0(5)***) Hearst Bks.

Costello, Patricia. Legend's of Health & Fitness, 10 vols., Set. 2000. (Illus.). 960p. (gr. 6-10). lib. bdg. 257.00 (978-1-58415-062-6(9)) Mitchell Lane Pubs., Inc.

Cultivating Health Weight Management Resource Guide. 2nd ed. 1998. Orig. Title: Cultivating Health Resource Guide. (Illus.). 69p. 5.00 (978-0-9677134-3-4(9) , NK-011) Kaiser Permanente Northwest/Health Education.

Dee, Janet. A Practical Guide to Everyday Health & Well Being. 2005. (J). 9.95 (978-0-9768403-1-2(6)) Wings Above.

DeLisle, Mark. Navy SEAL Breakthrough to Master Level Fitness: The Ultimate Training System to Incredible Strength & a Body-to-Die-For. 2002. (Illus.). 128p. pap. 19.95 (978-0-9724563-2-6(5) , 801-358-7388) Bronze Bow Publishing.

El-Hewie, Mohamed F. Essentials of Weightlifting & Strength Training. 2nd rev. exp. ed. 2005. (Illus.). 700p. lib. bdg. 85.00 (978-0-9719581-9-7(X)) Shaymaa Publishing Corp.

Evans, Lynette. Move Your Bones. 2007. (Shockwave: the Human Experience Ser.). 36p. (J). (gr. 3-5). pap. 6.95 (***978-0-531-18795-1(0)***); (Illus.). (gr. 4-6). lib. bdg. 25.00 (***978-0-531-17761-7(0)***) Scholastic Library Publishing. (Children's Pr.).

Fisher, Beverly. Mental Toughness for Personal Fitness: Workbook for Life. 2004. (Illus.). 64p. pap. 10.99 (978-0-9745066-0-9(5)) Sports In Mind.

Fraser, K. & Tatchell, Judy. Fitness & Health. 1999. (Introductions Ser.). (Illus.). 48p. (YA). (gr. 6 up). lib. bdg. 15.95 (978-0-88110-234-5(2)) EDC Publishing.

Furgang, Kathy. Tener habitos sanos & Having Healthful Habits. 2005. spiral bd. 84.00 (***978-1-4108-5710-1(7)***) Benchmark Education Co.

Furia, John. Collegiate Fitness. Lt. ed. 2003. 130p. (YA). per. 14.95 (978-1-59453-047-0(5) , 1825) Airleaf Publishing & Bookselling.

Gaff, Jackie. Why Must I... Exercise? Fairclough, Chris, photos by. 2005. (Illus.). 32p. (J). (gr. 2-5). lib. bdg. (978-1-84234-348-7(3) , Cherrytree Books) Evans Publishing Group.

Gedatus, Gus. Bicycling for Fitness. 2000. (Nutrition & Fitness Ser.). (Illus.). 64p. (J). (gr. 4-6). lib. bdg. 23.93 (978-0-7368-0705-0(5) , LifeMatters Bks.) Capstone Pr., Inc.

—Exercise for Weight Management. 2000. (Nutrition & Fitness Ser.). (Illus.). 64p. (J). (gr. 4-6). lib. bdg. 23.93 (978-0-7368-0706-7(3) , LifeMatters Bks.) Capstone Pr., Inc.

—In-Line Skating for Fitness. 2000. (Nutrition & Fitness Ser.). (Illus.). 64p. (J). (gr. 4-6). lib. bdg. 23.93 (978-0-7368-0707-4(1) , LifeMatters Bks.) Capstone Pr., Inc.

—Weight Training. 2000. (Nutrition & Fitness Ser.). (Illus.). 64p. (J). (gr. 4-6). lib. bdg. 23.95 (978-0-7368-0708-1(X) , LifeMatters Bks.) Capstone Pr., Inc.

Get Moving. (Your Health Ser.). 24p. (J). 6.95 (978-0-7368-4449-9(X)) Capstone Pr., Inc.

Gilliam, Thomas & Neill, Jane. Move It. Lose It. Live Healthy: Achieve a Healthier Workplace One Employee at a Time! 2004. (J). per. 19.95 (978-0-9762703-0-0(7)) Gilliam, T. & Associates, LLC.

Glibbery, Caroline. Join the Total Fitness Gang. 1998. (Good Health Guides). (Illus.). 32p. (J). (gr. 4 up). lib. bdg. 22.60 (978-0-8368-2181-9(5)) Stevens, Gareth Inc.

Gno, Hoi & Langley, John. Ultimate Martial Arts Encyclopedia for Kids. 2000. (Illus.). 160p. (J). pap. 9.95 (978-0-7373-0551-7(7) , Roxbury Park) Lowell Hse.

Goodger, Beverley. Exercise. 2005. (It's Your Health Ser.). (Illus.). 45p. (J). (gr. 6-9). lib. bdg. 29.95 (978-1-58340-593-2(3)) Smart Apple Media.

Goulding, Sylvia. Keeping Fit. 2005. (Healthy Kids Ser.). (Illus.). 32p. (gr. 3-6). 19.95 (978-1-59515-201-5(6)) Rourke Publishing, LLC.

Graves, Bonnie. Fitness. 2000. (Perspectives on Physical Health Ser.). (Illus.). 64p. (J). (gr. 4-6). lib. bdg. 23.93 (978-0-7368-0418-9(8) , LifeMatters Bks.) Capstone Pr., Inc.

Green, Emily K. Keeping Fit. 2006. (Blastoff! Readers Ser.). (Illus.). 24p. (J). lib. bdg. 16.95 (978-1-60014-006-8(8)) Bellwether Media.

Hallinan, P. K. Let's Be Fit! 2007. (Illus.). 32p. (J). (ps-2). 8.99 (***978-0-8249-5528-1(5)*** , Candy Cane Pr.) Ideals Pubns.

Harcourt School Publishers Staff. Be Active! Cardiovascular Flipchart. 2nd ed. 2003. (Illus.). (J). (gr. 1-6). 9.20 (978-0-15-340983-7(5)) Harcourt Schl. Pubs.

—Be Active! Flexibility Flipchart. 2nd ed. 2003. (Illus.). (J). (gr. 1-6). 9.20 (978-0-15-340981-3(9)) Harcourt Schl. Pubs.

—Be Active! Movement Flipchart. 2nd ed. 2003. (Illus.). (J). 9.20 (978-0-15-340982-0(7)) Harcourt Schl. Pubs.

—Be Active! Strength Flipchart. 2nd ed. 2003. (Illus.). (J). (gr. 1-6). 9.20 (978-0-15-340980-6(0)) Harcourt Schl. Pubs.

—Be Active! Program: Health & Fitness. 4th ed. 2004. (Illus.). (gr. k-2). 311.60 (978-0-15-341407-7(3)); (gr. 3-6). 314.90 (978-0-15-341408-4(1)) Harcourt Schl. Pubs.

—Health & Fitness: Activity Book. 4th ed. 2003. (ps). pap., act. bk. ed. 4.80 (978-0-15-341170-0(8)) Harcourt Schl. Pubs.

—Health & Fitness: Resources for Spanish Speakers. 4th ed. 2004. (SPA.). (gr. 1). pap. 20.00 (978-0-15-341180-9(5)); (gr. 2). pap. 20.00 (978-0-15-341181-6(3)); (gr. 3). pap. 25.40 (978-0-15-341182-3(1)); (gr. 4). pap. 25.40 (978-0-15-341183-0(X)); (gr. 5). pap. 25.40 (978-0-15-341184-7(8)); (gr. 6). pap. 25.40 (978-0-15-341185-4(6)) Harcourt Schl. Pubs.

—Health & Fitness 2006 - Grade 1. 2nd ed. 2002. tchr. ed. 150.90 (978-0-15-337533-0(7)); stu. ed. 39.80 (978-0-15-337524-8(8)) Harcourt Schl. Pubs.

—Health & Fitness 2006 - Grade 2. 2nd ed. 2002. tchr. ed. 153.10 (978-0-15-337534-7(5)); stu. ed. 39.80 (978-0-15-337525-5(6)) Harcourt Schl. Pubs.

—Health & Fitness 2006 - Grade 3. 2nd ed. 2002. 168.60 (978-0-15-337535-4(3)); stu. ed. 46.70 (978-0-15-337526-2(4)) Harcourt Schl. Pubs.

—Health & Fitness 2006 - Grade 4. 2nd ed. 2002. 50.10 (978-0-15-337527-9(2)); tchr. ed. 171.50 (978-0-15-337536-1(1)) Harcourt Schl. Pubs.

—Health & Fitness 2006 - Grade 5. 2nd ed. 2002. 53.10 (978-0-15-337529-3(9)); tchr. ed. 177.80 (978-0-15-337537-8(X)) Harcourt Schl. Pubs.

—Health & Fitness 2006 - Grade 6. 2nd ed. 2002. 56.20 (978-0-15-337530-9(2)); tchr. ed. 182.70 (978-0-15-337538-5(8)) Harcourt Schl. Pubs.

—Health & Fitness 2006 - Grade K. 2nd ed. 2002. tchr. ed. 137.40 (978-0-15-337531-6(0)) Harcourt Schl. Pubs.

—Health & Fitness 5-Pack: Activity Book. 4th ed. 2003. (ps). act. bk. ed. 23.70 (978-0-15-341171-7(6)) Harcourt Schl. Pubs.

—Health & Fitness, Grade 3-6. 4th ed. 2003. pap., tchr. ed. 88.20 (978-0-15-341101-4(5)) Harcourt Schl. Pubs.

—Health & Fitness, Grade K-2. 4th ed. 2003. pap., tchr. ed. 84.80 (978-0-15-341100-7(7)) Harcourt Schl. Pubs.

Hau, Stephanie. I Can Live To 100! Secrets Just for Kids. Hau, Joseph, illus. 2005. 60p. (J). per. 9.95 (978-0-9767324-0-2(8) , Kids Can) Proactive Publishing.

Heart E Heart & Friends Activity Book: Have Fun the Healthy Way. 2004. (J). per. 11.95 (978-0-9762703-2-4(3)) Gilliam, T. & Associates, LLC.

Heart E Heart & Friends Storybook for Children Ages 2 to 4 Years Old: A Children's Way to a Healthy Lifestyle. 2004. (J). per. 5.95 (978-0-9762703-1-7(5)) Gilliam, T. & Associates, LLC.

Hill, Bert. How to Get in Football Shape: Strength Training. 2003. (Illus.). 144p. per. 19.99 (978-1-59186-005-1(9)) Cool Springs Pr.

Hill, Bert & Watterson, Steve. How to Get in Football Shape: Conditioning. 2003. (Illus.). 144p. pap. 19.99 (978-1-59186-004-4(0)) Cool Springs Pr.

Hoeft, Jen. FUNdamental Fitness: Playground Exercises for Grownups, 1. 2004. 144p. per. 19.95 (978-0-9762868-0-6(7)) Read Publishing.

Hovius, Christopher. The Best You Can Be: A Teen's Guide to Fitness & Nutrition. 2004. (Science of Health Ser.). (Illus.). 128p. (J). (978-1-59084-848-7(9)) Mason Crest Pubs.

Hughes, Mary. The Composite Guide to Bodybuilding. 2000. (Composite Guide Ser.). (Illus.). 64p. (J). pap. 5.95 (978-0-7910-5870-1(0) , Chelsea Hse.) Facts On File, Inc.

Hunt, Charles. The Perfect Diet: The Ultimate Weight Solution for Every Body. 2004. (978-0-9630377-2-5(2)) HeartQuake Publishing.

Hurst, Brooklynn. Fitness for Teens: Getting you Motivated for Life by Providing Principles for Healthy Living. 2nd exp. l.t. ed. 2004. (ENG., Illus.). 108p. (YA). spiral bd. 20.00 (978-0-9746262-3-9(6)) Achieving Corporate Excellence, Inc.

Kalman, Bobbie. Active Kids. 2003. (gr. 3-6). lib. bdg. 17.60 (978-0-613-59126-3(7)) Tandem Library Bks.

Keeping Fit New Food Guide Pyramid. 2006. (Illus.). 24p. (J). (gr. k-2). 18.50 (***978-0-531-17853-9(6)***) Scholastic Library Publishing.

Ketch, Susan & Scraper, Katherine. It's Snack Time! Futrell, Ashley, ed. 2005. 128p. (J). per. 11.99 (978-1-59441-043-7(7) , CD-104043) Carson-Dellosa Publishing Co., Inc.

King, Hazel, et al. Body Needs, 5 bks., Set. 2003. (Illus.). (J). (gr. 4-6). lib. bdg. 135.35 (978-1-4034-0761-0(4)) Heinemann Library.

Kray, Peter. The Monster. 2003. 91p. per. 12.95 (978-0-9715715-1-8(1)) Greenleaf Book Group.

Lee, Ilchi. Home Massage Therapy Book 1: Heal Yourself & Your Loved Ones, 2 vols. 2004. (Dahnhak, the Way to Perfect Health Ser.: Vol. 2). (Illus.). 148p. pap. 17.95 (978-0-9720282-9-5(3)) Healing Society, Inc.

—Meridian Exercise for Self-Healing Bk. 1: Classified by Common Symptoms, 2 vols. 2003. (Dahnhak, the Way to Perfect Health Ser.: Vol. 1). (Illus.). 152p. pap. 17.95 (978-0-9720282-7-1(7)) Healing Society, Inc.

—Meridian Exercise for Self-Healing Book 2: Classified by Common Symptoms, 2 vols., Vol. 2. 2003. (Dahnhak, the Way to Perfect Health Ser.: 2). (Illus.). 196p. pap. 17.95 (978-0-9720282-8-8(5)) Healing Society, Inc.

Libal, Autumn. The Importance of Physical Activity & Exercise: The Fitness Factor. 2005. (Obesity Ser.). (Illus.). 104p. (J). (ps-7). lib. bdg. 23.95 (978-1-59084-945-3(0)) Mason Crest Pubs.

Lockspeiser, Nancy Flanders. Flexible You: 21 Stretches a Day for a 9-Lives Body: a Cat's Quick Guide to Stretching & Self-Massage. Lockspeiser, Nancy Flanders, illus. 2004. (Illus.). 48p. spiral bd. 14.94 (978-0-9752922-0-4(X)) Catamount Publishing LLC.

Mann, Michael. Discover Pilates. 2005. (Illus.). 96p. pap. incl. DVD (978-1-84510-565-5(6)) Top That! Publishing PLC.

Massad, Diane. Go! STOP Go! Vol. 3: The Kidskills America Training Series. 2004. (Kidskills America Training Ser.: Three). (Illus.). 75p. (J). spiral bd. 12.95 (978-0-9710641-3-3(X)) Kidskills International.

Massad, Diane P. Moving Right Along! The Kidskills America Training Series. 2004. (Kidskills America Training Ser.: 2). (Illus.). 71p. (J). spiral bd. 12.95 (978-0-9710641-2-6(1) , Kidskills America) Kidskills International.

McKay, Sindy. We Both Read-Happy & Healthy. 2003. 44p. (J). (gr. 1-2). 7.99 (978-1-891327-47-6(X)) Treasure Bay, Inc.

Miller, Olivia H. The Fitness Ball Deck: 50 Exercises for Toning, Balancing, & Building Core Strength. Kaufman, Nicole, illus. 2005. 14.95 (978-0-8118-4687-5(3)) Chronicle Bks. LLC.

Nagler, Michelle H. Get Fit! Eat Right! Be Active! Girls Guide to Health & Fitness. 2001. (WNBA Ser.). (Illus.). 64p. (gr. 3-9). pap. 5.99 (978-0-439-24113-7(8)) Scholastic, Inc.

Naik, Anita. Wise Guide Health & Fitness. 2005. (Illus.). 128p. (J). pap. (978-0-340-90260-8(4) , Hodder Children's Books) Hodder Children's Division.

Nutrition & Fitness, 8 bks. Incl. Bicycling for Fitness. Gedatus, Gus. lib. bdg. 23.93 (978-0-7368-0705-0(5)); Exercise for Weight Management. Gedatus, Gus. lib. bdg. 23.93 (978-0-7368-0706-7(3)); Food & Emotions. Turck, Mary. lib. bdg. 23.93 (978-0-7368-0711-1(X)); Healthy Eating for Weight Management. Turck, Mary. lib. bdg. 23.95 (978-0-7368-0709-8(8)); Healthy Snack & Fast-Food Choices. Turck, Mary. lib. bdg. 23.93 (978-0-7368-0710-4(1)); In-Line Skating for Fitness. Gedatus, Gus. lib. bdg. 23.93 (978-0-7368-0707-4(1)); Vegetarianism for Teens. Duden, Jane. lib. bdg. 23.93 (978-0-7368-0712-8(8)); Weight Training. Gedatus, Gus. lib. bdg. 23.95 (978-0-7368-0708-1(X)); 64p. (J). (gr. 4-6). 2000. (Illus.). Set lib. bdg. 191.44 (978-0-7368-0719-7(5) , LifeMatters Bks.) Capstone Pr., Inc.

Rainey, Don L., et al. Foundations of Personal Fitness. 2005. (gr. 9-12). stu. ed. 65.32 (978-0-07-845127-0(2) , 9780078451270) Glencoe/McGraw-Hill.

Rodomista, Kim. 101 Cool Pool Games for Children: Fun & Fitness for Swimmers of All Levels. Patterson, Robin, illus. 2006. (Hunter House Smartfun Book Ser.). 160p. pap. 14.95 (978-0-89793-483-1(0)) Hunter Hse., Inc.

Rodomista, Kim & Patterson, Robin. 101 Cool Pool Games for Children: Fun & Fitness for Swimmers of All Levels. 2006. (SmartFun Activity Bks.). 160p. spiral bd. 19.95 (978-0-89793-484-8(9)) Hunter Hse., Inc.

Ross, Veronica. Fit & Well. 2002. (My Healthy Body Ser.). (Illus.). 32p. (J). lib. bdg. 24.25 (978-1-930643-82-6(9)) Chrysalis Education.

Royston, Angela. Get Some Exercise! 2003. (Illus.). 32p. (J). pap. 6.95 (978-1-4034-4449-3(8)); lib. bdg. 22.79 (978-1-4034-4440-0(4)) Heinemann Library.

—A Healthy Body. 1999. (Illus.). 32p. (J). (gr. k-2). lib. bdg. 21.36 (978-1-57572-983-1(0)) Heinemann Library.

—Why Do We Need to Be Active? 2005. (Heinemann Read & Learn Ser.). (Illus.). 24p. (J). (978-1-4034-7609-8(8)); pap. (978-1-4034-7614-2(4)) Heinemann Library.

Sadgrove, Judy. Exercise. 1999. (Health & Fitness Ser.). (Illus.). 48p. (J). (gr. 4-6). lib. bdg. 27.12 (978-0-7398-1347-8(1)) Raintree.

Salzmann, Mary Elizabeth. Being Active. 2004. (Healthy Habits Ser.). (Illus.). 23p. (J). (ps-3). lib. bdg. 19.93 (978-1-59197-550-2(6)) ABDO Publishing Co.

Savage, Jeff. Fundamentals Strength Training. Clarke, Jimmy, photos by. 1998. (Fundamental Sports Ser.). (Illus.). 80p. (gr. 5-9). lib. bdg. 22.60 (978-0-8225-3461-7(4)) Lerner Publishing Group.

School Specialty Publishing. Weekly Workouts, Grade 1. 2007. (Weekly Workouts Ser.). 48p. (J). (gr. 1-5). pap. 6.99 (***978-0-7682-3781-8(5)*** , Schaffer, Frank) Schaffer, Frank Pubns.

—Weekly Workouts, Grade 2. 2007. (Weekly Workouts Ser.). 48p. (J). (gr. k-5). pap. 6.99 (***978-0-7682-3782-5(3)*** , Schaffer, Frank) Schaffer, Frank Pubns.

—Weekly Workouts, Grade 3. 2007. (Weekly Workouts Ser.). 48p. (J). (gr. k-5). pap. 6.99 (***978-0-7682-3783-2(1)*** , Schaffer, Frank) Schaffer, Frank Pubns.

—Weekly Workouts, Grade 4. 2007. (Weekly Workouts Ser.). 48p. (J). (gr. k-5). pap. 6.99 (***978-0-7682-3784-9(X)*** , Schaffer, Frank) Schaffer, Frank Pubns.

—Weekly Workouts, Grade 5. 2007. (Weekly Workouts Ser.). 48p. (J). (gr. k-5). pap. 6.99 (***978-0-7682-3785-6(8)*** , Schaffer, Frank) Schaffer, Frank Pubns.

Schuh, Mari C. Being Active. 2006. (Illus.). 24p. (J). 19.93 (978-0-7368-5368-2(5) , Pebble Bks.) Capstone Pr., Inc.

Schwager, Tina & Schuerger, Michele. The Right Moves to Getting Fit & Feeling Great! Verdick, Elizabeth, ed. Gordon, Mike & Heinlen, Marieka, illus. 1998. Orig. Title: The Right Moves: a Girl's Guide to Getting Fit & Feeling Good. 280p. (YA). (gr. 7 up). pap. 15.95 (978-1-57542-035-6(X)) Free Spirit Publishing, Inc.

Sheen, Barbara. Keeping Fit. 2007. (J). pap. (***978-1-4034-9702-4(8)***); (Illus.). 32p. (gr. 4-7). lib. bdg. (***978-1-4034-9695-9(1)***) Heinemann Library.

Silverstein, Alvin. Physical Fitness. 2002. (gr. 3-6). lib. bdg. 15.25 (978-0-613-54083-4(2)) Tandem Library Bks.

Silverstein, Alvin, et al. Physical Fitness. 2002. (My Health Ser.). (Illus.). 48p. (J). (gr. 3-5). pap. 6.95 (978-0-531-15563-9(3) , Watts, Franklin) Scholastic Library Publishing.

Simmons, Mary Beth, et al. Insparations: A Teen's Guide to Healthy Living Inspired by Today's Top Spas. 2005. (Illus.). 128p. (YA). (gr. 10-12). pap. 14.95 (978-0-8230-2641-8(8)) Watson-Guptill Pubns., Inc.

Smithyman, Kathryn & Kalman, Bobbie. Active Kids: Fun Ways to Be Active. 2003. (Kid Power Ser.). (Illus.). 32p. (J). (gr. 3). (978-0-7787-1253-4(2)); pap. (978-0-7787-1275-6(3)) Crabtree Publishing Co.

Sports & Fitness (Gr. PreK-5) 2003. (J). (978-1-58232-026-7(8)) Bryan Hse. Pubs., Inc.

Strauss, Greg. Eleven Minute Workout: Total Fitness in 11 Minutes a Day. 2003. (Illus.). 124p. per. 11.00 (978-0-9744568-0-5(2) , EMW:0974456802) Motion Fitness LLC.

Tecco, Betsy Dru. Food for Fuel: The Connection Between Food & Physical Activity. 2004. (Library of Nutrition). (Illus.). 48p. (J). lib. bdg. 25.25 (978-1-4042-0303-7(6)) Rosen Publishing Group, Inc., The.

Thomas, Pat. My Amazing Body: A First Look at Health & Fitness. Harker, Lesley, illus. 2002. (First Look at Bks.). 32p. (J). (ps-2). pap. 6.99 (978-0-7641-2119-7(7)) Barron's Educational Series, Inc.

Turck, Mary. Healthy Eating for Weight Management. 2000. (Nutrition & Fitness Ser.). (Illus.). 64p. (J). (gr. 4-6). lib. bdg. 23.95 (978-0-7368-0709-8(8) , LifeMatters Bks.) Capstone Pr., Inc.

Vedral, Joyce L. Toning for Teens: The 20-Minute Workout That Makes You Look Good & Feel Great! 2002. (Illus.). 192p. pap. 15.95 (978-0-446-67815-5(5)) Grand Central Publishing.

Vogel, Elizabeth. A Hacer Ejercicio! 2004. (Limpieza y Salud Todo el Dia Ser.). (SPA & ENG., Illus.). 24p. (J). (gr. 1-2). lib. bdg. 16.00 (978-0-8239-6614-1(3) , Buenas Letra) Rosen Publishing Group, Inc., The.

—Let's Exercise. 2001. (PowerKids Readers Ser.). (Illus.). 24p. (J). (gr. 1). lib. bdg. 16.00 (978-0-8239-5687-6(3) , PKEXER, PowerKids Pr.) Rosen Publishing Group, Inc., The.

—Let's Exercise = a Hacer Ejercicio. 2004. (Limpieza y salud todo el Día Ser.). (ENG & SPA., Illus.). 24p. (J). lib. bdg. 16.00 (978-0-8239-6615-8(1) , Buenas Letra) Rosen Publishing Group, Inc., The.

West, Dorothy F. Nutrition, Food, & Fitness: The Science of Wellness. 2006. (Illus.). 510p. (gr. 9-12). 42.75 (978-1-59070-527-8(0)) Goodheart-Willcox Pub.

Whitehouse, Patricia. What Can Run? 2003. (Heinemann Read & Learn Ser.). (Illus.). 24p. (J). lib. bdg. 18.50 (978-1-4034-4367-0(X)) Heinemann Library.

—What Can Run? 2003. (ps-2). lib. bdg. 28.65 (978-0-613-89470-8(7)) Tandem Library Bks.

Winkler, Peter. Keeping Fit. 2003. (Human Body Ser.). (Illus.). 32p. (J). pap. (978-0-7922-8863-3(7)) National Geographic Society.

PHYSICAL GEOGRAPHY

see also Climate; Earth; Earthquakes; Geophysics; Glaciers; Ice; Icebergs; Lakes; Meteorology; Mountains; Ocean; Rivers; Tides; Volcanoes; Winds

Anderson, Sheila. Plateau. 2008. (First Step Nonfiction - Landforms Ser.). (J). lib. bdg. 18.60 (***978-0-8225-8592-3(8)*** , Lerner Pubns.) Lerner Publishing Group.

—Valley. 2008. (First Step Nonfiction - Landforms Ser.). (J). lib. bdg. 18.60 (***978-0-8225-8591-6(X)*** , Lerner Pubns.) Lerner Publishing Group.

Benchmark Education Staff, compiled by. Cactus & Canyons & Regions. 2005. spiral bd. 225.00 (***978-1-4108-5805-4(7)***) Benchmark Education Co.

Boehm, Richard G., et al. Reading Support & Test Preparation: States & Regions. 1999. (Harcourt Brace Social Studies). (gr. k-7). pap. 32.70 (978-0-15-312383-2(4)) Harcourt Schl. Pubs.

Brimner, Larry Dane. Valleys & Canyons. 2000. (True Bks.). (Illus.). 48p. (J). (gr. 3-5). 25.00 (978-0-516-21569-3(8) , Children's Pr.) Scholastic Library Publishing.

Carnibucci, Patricia. Geography & Society: Over 15 Complete Printable Unit Studies with Interactive Links. 2002. 160p. (gr. k-12). cd-rom 15.95 (978-1-891400-98-8(3)) Champion Pr., Ltd.

Cheryl Striveildi. Continents. 2003. (J). (gr. k-4). lib. bdg. 159.46 (978-1-57765-957-0(0) , Buddy Bks.) ABDO Publishing Co.

Coote, Roger. Earth. 2003. (Knowledge Masters Ser.). (Illus.). 32p. (YA). pap. incl. cd-rom (978-1-903954-11-9(8)) Chrysalis Children's Bks.

The Environment. 2004. (Atlases of the Earth & Its Resources Ser.). (Illus.). 80p. (J). (gr. 5 up). lib. bdg. 34.00 (978-0-8368-5616-3(3) , World Almanac Library) Stevens, Gareth Inc.

Gall, Susan B., ed. Junior Worldmark Encyclopedia of Physical Geography, 5 vols. 2003. (Illus.). (J). 850p. 290.00 (978-0-7876-6265-3(8)); (978-0-7876-6266-0(6)); (978-0-7876-6267-7(4)); (978-0-7876-6268-4(2)); (978-0-7876-6269-1(0)); (978-0-7876-6633-0(5)) Thomson Gale. (UXL).

Green, Emily K. Forests. 2006. (Blastoff! Readers Ser.). (Illus.). 24p. (J). lib. bdg. 16.95 (978-1-60014-036-5(X)) Bellwether Media.

Harcourt School Publishers Staff. Horizons. 3rd ed. 2002. (Harcourt Horizons Ser.). (Illus.). (gr. 3 up). pupil's gde. ed. 53.50 (978-0-15-320180-6(0)); (gr. 1 up). pupil's gde. ed. 46.80 (978-0-15-320178-3(9)) Harcourt Schl. Pubs.

—Horizons: States & Regions. 3rd ed. (Harcourt Horizons Ser.). (gr. 4-7). 2003. (Illus.). pupil's gde. ed. 64.00 (978-0-15-320942-0(9)); Vol. 2. 2002. tchr. ed. 121.80 (978-0-15-321959-7(9)) Harcourt Schl. Pubs.

—Horizons Unit 3: The Land Around Us. 3rd ed. 2001. (Illus.). pap. 169.80 (978-0-15-322571-0(8)) Harcourt Schl. Pubs.

—Horizons Vol. 1: States & Regions. 3rd ed. 2003. (Harcourt Horizons Ser.). (gr. 4-7). tchr. ed. 121.80 (978-0-15-320944-4(5)) Harcourt Schl. Pubs.

—Social Studies, Grade 4: States & Regions: Activity Book. 1999. (Harcourt Brace Social Studies). (gr. k-7). pap., tchr. ed., act. bk. ed. 21.70 (978-0-15-312128-9(9)) Harcourt Schl. Pubs.

—States/Regions Horizons. 3rd ed. 2001. (Harcourt Horizons Ser.). (Illus.). (gr. k-7). pap., tchr. ed., act. bk. ed. 21.80 (978-0-15-322607-6(2)) Harcourt Schl. Pubs.

Holt, Rinehart and Winston Staff. Holt Science & Technology Chapter 2: Earth Science: Maps & Models of the Earth. 5th ed. 2004. (Illus.). pap. 12.86 (978-0-03-030271-8(4)) Holt, Rinehart & Winston.

—Taks Every Day! Activities & Practice for World Geography. 3rd ed. 2002. (Illus.). pap. 45.60 (978-0-03-065429-9(7)) Holt, Rinehart & Winston.

Lewis, J. Earth & You, a Closer View: Nature's Features. 2000. (gr. 3-6). lib. bdg. 16.40 (978-0-613-49730-5(9)) Tandem Library Bks.

Lewis, J. Patrick. Earth & You - A Closer View: Nature's Features. Canyon, Christopher, illus. 2004. (Sharing Nature with Children Book Ser.). 36p. (J). (gr. 4-7). pap. 7.95 (978-1-58469-015-3(1)); (ps-3). 16.95 (978-1-58469-016-0(X)) Dawn Pubns.

Moody, Richard. Atlas of the Evolving Earth. 2001. 75.00 (978-0-02-865632-8(6)) Thomson Gale.

Nadeau, Isaac. Peninsulas. 2006. (Illus.). 24p. (J). lib. bdg. (978-1-4042-3125-2(0) , PowerKids Pr.) Rosen Publishing Group, Inc., The.

Nagel, Rob. UXL Encyclopedia of Landforms & Other Geologic Features, 3 vols. 2003. (Illus.). xxviii, 314p. (J). (978-0-7876-7670-4(5)); (978-0-7876-7671-1(3)); (978-0-7876-7672-8(1)) Thomson Gale. (UXL).

Nathan, Emma. Land. 2002. (Eyeopeners Ser.). (Illus.). 24p. (J). 22.45 (978-1-56711-651-9(5) , Blackbirch Pr., Inc.) Thomson Gale.

People & Their Quality of Life. 2004. (Atlases of the Earth & Its Resources Ser.). (Illus.). 80p. (J). (gr. 5 up). lib. bdg. 34.00 (978-0-8368-5618-7(X) , World Almanac Library) Stevens, Gareth Inc.

Raum, Elizabeth. World's Wonders: Landforms. 2006. (Illus.). 32p. (J). (978-1-4109-2599-2(4)); pap. (978-1-4109-2628-9(1)) Steck-Vaughn.

Sayre, April Pulley. The Seven Continents, 7 vols. 2004. (History & Social Studies Ser.). (Illus.). 64p. (YA). (gr. 5-8). (978-0-7613-3098-1(4) , Twenty-First Century Bks.) Lerner Publishing Group.

Taylor, Barbara. Understanding Landforms. 2007. (J). (***978-1-59920-049-1(X)***) Smart Apple Media.

Tull, Mary. Coasts. 2004. (Illus.). 32p. (J). pap. (978-0-7922-4563-6(6)) National Geographic Society.

—Plains. 2004. (Illus.). 32p. (J). pap. (978-0-7922-4564-3(4)) National Geographic Society.

Webster, Christine. Plains. 2005. (Illus.). 24p. (J). 21.26 (978-0-7368-3715-6(9)) Capstone Pr., Inc.

—Valleys. 2005. (Illus.). 24p. (J). 21.26 (978-0-7368-3716-3(7)) Capstone Pr., Inc.

Zuravicky, Orli. Map Math: Learning about Latitude & Longitude Using Coordinate Systems. 2005. (PowerMath Ser.). (J). 22.50 (978-1-4042-2935-8(3)); pap. 22.50 (978-1-4042-5133-5(2)) Rosen Publishing Group, Inc., The. (PowerKids Pr.).

PHYSICAL GEOGRAPHY—NORTH AMERICA

Harcourt School Publishers Staff. Horizons: Texas Edition. 3rd ed. 2003. (Illus.). (gr. 4). 70.10 (978-0-15-320181-3(9)) Harcourt Schl. Pubs.

—Horizons: US History. 3rd ed. 2003. (Harcourt Horizons Ser.). (Illus.). (gr. 4-7). pupil's gde. ed. 71.00 (978-0-15-320182-0(7)) Harcourt Schl. Pubs.

Stone, Lynn M. America's Landscape. 2003. (Land of Liberty Ser.). (Illus.). 24p. (gr. 2-5). 17.95 (978-1-58952-310-4(5)) Rourke Publishing, LLC.

PHYSICAL STAMINA

see Physical Fitness

PHYSICAL THERAPY—VOCATIONAL GUIDANCE

Hawkins, Trisha. Careers in Physical Therapy. 2005. (Career Resource Library). (Illus.). 192p. (YA). (gr. 7-12). lib. bdg. 26.50 (978-0-8239-3192-7(7)) Rosen Publishing Group, Inc., The.

Moe, Barbara. Careers in Sports Medicine. 2005. (Career Resource Library). (Illus.). 192p. (YA). (gr. 7-12). lib. bdg. 26.50 (978-0-8239-3538-3(8)) Rosen Publishing Group, Inc., The.

Quinlan, Kathryn A. Physical Therapist Assistant. 1998. (Careers Without College Ser.). (Illus.). 48p. (J). (gr. 3-7). pap. 19.00 (978-0-516-21286-9(9) , Children's Pr.) Scholastic Library Publishing.

PHYSICAL TRAINING

see Physical Education and Training

PHYSICALLY CHALLENGED PEOPLE

see People with Disabilities

PHYSICALLY DISABLED PEOPLE

see People with Disabilities

PHYSICALLY HANDICAPPED

see People with Disabilities

PHYSICIANS

see also Women Physicians

also names of specialists, e.g. Surgeons

Ada, Alma Flor & Campoy, F. Isabel, contrib. by. Voces. (Literature Collection of Puertas Al Sol Ser.). (SPA.). 32p. (J). (gr. k-6). pap. 13.95 (978-1-59437-707-5(3)) Santillana USA Publishing Co., Inc.

Adamson, Heather. A Day in the Life of a Doctor. 2003. (First Facts Ser.). (Illus.). 24p. (J). 15.95 (978-0-7368-2506-1(1)) Capstone Pr., Inc.

African-American Doctors. 2000. (My Ancestors—My Heroes Ser.: Vol. 13). (J). (gr. 3-4). (978-1-893091-12-2(0)) Parker Publishing Co.

Anderson, Catherine Corley. John F. Kennedy. 2006. (First Step Nonfiction Ser.). (Illus.). 112p. (J). (gr. 3-7). 27.93 (978-0-8225-2643-8(3) , Lerner Pubns.) Lerner Publishing Group.

Bankston, John. Frederick Banting & the Discovery of Insulin. 2002. (Unlocking the Secrets of Science Ser.). (Illus.). 56p. (gr. 4-10). lib. bdg. 25.70 (978-1-58415-094-7(7)) Mitchell Lane Pubs., Inc.

—Joseph Lister & the Story of Antiseptics. 2004. (Uncharted, Unexplored, & Unexplained Ser.). (Illus.). 48p. (J). (gr. 4-8). lib. bdg. 29.95 (978-1-58415-262-0(1)) Mitchell Lane Pubs., Inc.

Bennett, Howard J. Lions Aren't Scared of Shots: A Story for Children about Visiting the Doctor. Weber, M. S., illus. 2006. 32p. (J). (ps-1). 14.95 (978-1-59147-473-9(6) , 441A473); pap. 8.95 (978-1-59147-474-6(4) , 441A474) American Psychological Assn. (Magination Pr.).

BENSON, Mary Rubec. Follow the Warrior's Path: Life Story of Ohiyesa Better Known As Dr. Eastman. 2003. (YA). pap. 14.95 (978-0-89992-155-6(8)) Council for Indian Education.

Boyd, Nicole. A Doctor's Busy Day. 2002. (Reading Room Collection). (Illus.). 24p. (J). lib. bdg. 18.75 (978-0-8239-3734-9(8)) Rosen Publishing Group, Inc., The.

Brill, Marlene Targ. Doctors. (Pull Ahead Bks.). (Illus.). 32p. (J). 2005. lib. bdg. 22.60 (978-0-8225-1689-7(6)); 2004. pap. 5.95 (978-0-8225-2531-8(3) , Lerner Pubns.) Lerner Publishing Group.

Brooks, Felicity. Daisy Doctor. Litchfield, Jo, illus. 2005. 24p. (J). pap. 6.95 (978-0-7945-0724-4(7) , Usborne) EDC Publishing.

Buckley Jr., James. A Day with a Doctor. 2007. (Girls Rock! Ser.). 32p. (J). (gr. 1-5). 24.21 (***978-1-59296-866-4(X)***) Child's World, Inc.

Catala, Ellen. Who Keeps Us Safe? 2006. (Illus.). 18p. (J). (978-0-7368-5984-4(5)) Capstone Pr., Inc.

—Who Keeps Us Safe? 2006. (Illus.). 8,16p. (J). 6.50 (978-0-7368-1720-2(4)) Red Brick Learning.

—Who Keeps Us Safe. 2006. (ENG & SPA., Illus.). 18p. (J). (978-0-7368-6020-8(7)) Yellow Umbrella Pr.

Christy, Lee Louis. I Go to Work as a Doctor. 2003. (I Go to Work As Ser.). (Illus.). (J). (978-1-58417-042-6(5)); pap. (978-1-58417-107-2(3)) Lake Street Pubs.

Civardi, Anne. Going to the Doctor. rev. ed. 2005. 16p. (J). pap. 4.95 (978-0-7945-1004-6(3) , Usborne) EDC Publishing.

Compass Point Books, contrib. by. Doctors. (Community Workers Ser.). 24p. (J). pap. 7.95 (978-0-7565-1188-3(7)) Compass Point Bks.

Davis, Lucile. The Mayo Brothers: Doctors to the World. 1999. (Community Builders Ser.). (Illus.). 48p. (J). (gr. 3-5). pap. 6.95 (978-0-516-26347-2(1) , Children's Pr.) Scholastic Library Publishing.

DK Publishing Staff. Doctor's Office. 2007. (Illus.). 12p. (J). 6.99 (978-0-7566-2585-6(8)) Dorling Kindersley Publishing, Inc.

La Doctora, 2 Pack. (Chiquilibros Ser.). (SPA.). (ps-1). 12.00 (978-0-7635-8564-8(5)) Rigby Education.

Doctors. (Community Helpers Ser.). 24p. (J). 6.95 (978-0-7368-8453-2(X)) Capstone Pr., Inc.

Doctors, 6 vols. (gr. 2-5). 36.95 (978-0-7368-8468-6(8)) Red Brick Learning.

The Doctor's Office. 2005. (Transportation Ser.). (YA). (gr. k-3). (978-1-56065-836-8(3) , Pebble Bks.) Capstone Pr., Inc.

Doctors Without Borders: Individual Title Six-Packs. (On Deck Ser.). 24p. (gr. 4-5). 35.00 (978-0-7578-1033-6(0)) Rigby Education.

Dornhoffer, Mary K. Doctors. 2000. (Community Workers Ser.). (Illus.). 32p. (J). (gr. 1 up). lib. bdg. 21.26 (978-0-7565-0008-5(7)) Compass Point Bks.

Ehrlich, Fred. Does a Hippo Say Ahh? 2006. (Illus.). 32p. pap. 5.95 (978-1-59354-145-3(7)) Blue Apple Bks.

—Does a Hippo Say Ahh? Bolam, Emily, illus. 2003. (Early Experiences Ser.). 32p. 10.95 (978-1-929766-77-2(7)) Blue Apple Bks.

Elford, Jole Shack. William Harvey & the Mechanics of the Heart. 2005. (Illus.). 141p. (YA). (gr. 6-10). reprint ed. 28.00 (978-0-7567-9712-6(8)) DIANE Publishing Co.

Facts on File, Inc. Staff. Physicians. 2nd rev. ed. 2005. (Careers in Focus Ser.). (Illus.). 204p. (J). (gr. 6-12). 22.95 (978-0-8160-5868-6(7) , Ferguson Publishing Co.) Facts On File, Inc.

Gorman, Jacqueline Laks. Doctor. Andersen, Gregg, photos by. 2002. (People in My Community Ser.). (Illus.). 24p. (J). (ps up). lib. bdg. 19.33 (978-0-8368-3294-5(9) , Weekly Reader Early Learning Library) Stevens, Gareth Inc.

—Doctor/El Medico. Acosta, Tatiana & Gutiérrez, Guillermo, trs. 2002. (Weekly Reader Early Learning Library). (ENG & SPA., Illus.). 24p. (J). (ps up). lib. bdg. 19.33 (978-0-8368-3308-9(2) , Weekly Reader Early Learning Library) Stevens, Gareth Inc.

Gorman, Jacqueline Laks & Macken, JoAnn Early. Doctor. Andersen, Gregg, photos by. 2002. (Weekly Reader Early Learning Library). (Illus.). 24p. (J). (ps up). pap. 7.93 (978-0-8368-3301-0(5) , Weekly Reader Early Learning Library) Stevens, Gareth Inc.

—Doctor/El Medico. Coffey, Colleen & Carrillo, Consuelo, trs. Andersen, Gregg, photos by. 2002. (Weekly Reader Early Learning Library). (ENG & SPA., Illus.). 24p. (J). (ps up). pap. 5.95 (978-0-8368-3342-3(2) , Weekly Reader Early Learning Library) Stevens, Gareth Inc.

Hapka, Cathy. My Little Doctor Bag Book. Sharp, Paul, illus. 2005. (J). (***978-1-57151-754-8(5)***) Playhouse Publishing.

Harcourt School Publishers Staff. Doctors Without Borders. 3rd ed. 2002. (Horizons Ser.). (Illus.). (J). pap. 7.30 (978-0-15-333618-8(8)) Harcourt Schl. Pubs.

—Your Health Reader: The Doctor. 3rd ed. 2003. (Illus.). pap. 9.40 (978-0-15-338776-0(9)) Harcourt Schl. Pubs.

Hayward, Linda. Day in the Life of a Doctor. 2001. (gr. k-3). lib. bdg. 11.80 (978-0-613-43926-8(0)) Tandem Library Bks.

—A Day in the Life of a Doctor: Jobs People Do. 2001. 10.75 (978-0-606-22631-8(1)) Tandem Library Bks.

Hayward, Linda & Dorling Kindersley Publishing Staff. Jobs People Do: A Day in the Life of a Doctor. 2001. (Readers Ser.). (Illus.). 32p. (J). 12.99 (978-0-7894-7950-1(8)); pap. 3.99 (978-0-7894-7951-8(6)) Dorling Kindersley Publishing, Inc.

Hoena, B. A. A Visit to the Doctor's Office. 2004. (Pebble Plus, Let's Visit Ser.). (Illus.). 24p. (J). 13.95 (978-0-7368-2391-3(3) , Pebble Bks.) Capstone Pr., Inc.

Hunter, Shaun. Leaders in Medicine. 1998. (Women in Profile Ser.). (Illus.). 48p. (J). (gr. 4). lib. bdg. (978-0-7787-0010-4(0)) Crabtree Publishing Co.

Jacobs, Lee. The Obstetrician. Zucker, Gale, photos by. 1998. (Doctors in Action Ser.). (Illus.). 24p. (J). (gr. 3-6). 22.45 (978-1-56711-235-1(8) , Blackbirch Pr., Inc.) Thomson Gale.

—The Orthopedist. Zucker, Gale, photos by. 1998. (Doctors in Action Ser.). (Illus.). 24p. (J). (gr. 3-6). 22.45 (978-1-56711-236-8(6) , Blackbirch Pr., Inc.) Thomson Gale.

Keeping You Healthy. (Community Workers Ser.). 24p. (J). 7.95 (978-1-4048-0479-1(X)) Picture Window Bks.

Kirsh, Sharon. Fabulous Female Physicians. 2002. (gr. 5-8). lib. bdg. 16.40 (978-0-613-88449-5(3)) Tandem Library Bks.

Kirsh, Sharon & Kirsh, Florence. Fabulous Female Physicians. 2005. (Illus.). 100p. (YA). (gr. 4-8). pap. 7.95 (978-1-896764-43-6(6)) Second Story Pr. CAN. *Dist:* Orca Bk. Pubs. USA, Univ. of Toronto Pr., Univ. of Toronto Pr.

Kottke, Jan. A Day with a Doctor. 2000. (Welcome Bks.). (Illus.). 24p. (J). (ps-2). pap. 4.95 (978-0-516-23012-2(3)); 17.00 (978-0-516-23087-0(5)) Scholastic Library Publishing. (Children's Pr.).

—Day with a Doctor. 2000. (gr. k-3). lib. bdg. 12.95 (978-0-613-58759-4(6)) Tandem Library Bks.

Krebs, Laurie. A Day in the Life of a Colonial Doctor. 2004. (Library of Living & Working in Colonial Times). (Illus.). 24p. (J). lib. bdg. 18.75 (978-0-8239-6228-0(8) , PowerKids Pr.) Rosen Publishing Group, Inc., The.

Liebman, Dan. Je veux etre Medecin. Lior, Tsipora, tr. from ENG. 2006. (Je veux Etre Ser.).Tr. of I Want to Be A Doctor. (FRE., Illus.). 24p. (J). (ps-2). pap. 5.95 (978-1-55407-108-1(9)) Firefly Bks., Ltd.

—Quiero Ser Doctor. 2000. Tr. of I Want to Be a Doctor. (gr. k-3). (SPA.). lib. bdg. 14.15 (978-0-613-78547-1(9)); (Illus.). 24p. (J). lib. bdg. 12.79 (978-0-606-18143-3(1)) Tandem Library Bks.

Liebman, Daniel. I Want to Be a Doctor. 2000. (I Want to Be Ser.). (Illus.). 24p. (J). (ps-2). pap. 3.99 (978-1-55209-461-7(8)); lib. bdg. 14.95 (978-1-55209-463-1(4)) Firefly Bks., Ltd.

—I Want to Be a Doctor. 2000. (Illus.). (J). 10.79 (978-0-606-18138-9(5)) Tandem Library Bks.

—Quiero Ser un Doctor. 2000. (Coleccion Quierno Ser.).Tr. of I Want to Be a Doctor. (SPA., Illus.). 24p. (J). (ps-2). pap. 5.99 (978-1-55209-473-0(1) , AP4236) Firefly Bks., Ltd.

Lowenstein, Felicia. Lo Que Hacen Los Doctores: What Doctors Do. 2007. (What Does a Community Helper Do? Bilingual Ser.). (ENG & SPA., Illus.). 32p. (J). lib. bdg. 22.60 (978-0-7660-2824-1(0) , Enslow Elementary) Enslow Pubs., Inc.

—What Does a Doctor Do? 2005. (What Does a Community Helper Do? Ser.). (Illus.). 24p. (J). (ps-ps). lib. bdg. 21.26 (978-0-7660-2542-4(X) , Enslow Elementary) Enslow Pubs., Inc.

Manson, Ainslie. House Calls: The True Story of a Pioneer Doctor. Gerber, Mary Jane, illus. 2001. (J). (gr. 3-7). pap. 15.95 (978-0-88899-446-2(X)) Groundwood Bks. CAN. *Dist:* Transition Vendor.

Martin, Oscar, Jr., creator. Doctors, l.t. ed. 2003. (Illus.). 25p. (J). E-Book 19.95 incl. cd-rom (978-0-9748416-5-6(X)) Build Your Story.

Mattern, Joanne. At the Doctor's. 2005. (Daily Math Ser.). (Illus.). 24p. (J). pap. (978-0-8368-4861-8(6)) Stevens, Gareth Inc.

—I Use Math at the Doctor's. 2005. (Daily Math Ser.). (Illus.). 24p. (J). (ps). lib. bdg. 19.33 (978-0-8368-4854-0(3)) Stevens, Gareth Inc.

—Joseph E. Murray & the Story of the First Human Kidney Transplant. l.t. ed. 2002. (Unlocking the Secrets of Science Ser.). (Illus.). 56p. (gr. 4-10). lib. bdg. 25.70 (978-1-58415-136-4(6)) Mitchell Lane Pubs., Inc.

McCauley-Bell, Pamela. Winners Don't Quit. . . Today They Call Me Doctor! 2003. (YA). per. 16.95 (978-0-9729912-6-1(3)) Infinite Possibilities Publishing Group, Inc.

Medicos sin Fronteras, 6 vols., Pack. (On Deck en Espanol Ser.).Tr. of Doctors Without Borders. (SPA.). 24p. (gr. 4-5). 35.00 (978-0-7578-6412-4(0)) Rigby Education.

Miller, Heather. Doctor. 2003. (This Is What I Want to Be Ser.). (Illus.). 24p. (J). (ps-1). lib. bdg. 18.50 (978-1-4034-0367-4(8)); pap. 5.25 (978-1-4034-0589-0(1)) Heinemann Library.

—Medico. (Esto es lo Que Quiero Ser (This Is What I Want to Be) Ser.).Tr. of Doctor. 24p. pap. 5.25 (978-1-4034-0599-9(9)); 2003. (SPA., Illus.). (J). lib. bdg. 18.50 (978-1-4034-0377-3(5)) Heinemann Library.

Murkoff, Heidi. What to Expect When You Go to the Doctor. Rader, Laura, illus. 2000. (What to Expect Kids Ser.). 32p. (J). (ps-k). 8.99 (978-0-694-01324-1(2) , Harper Festival) HarperCollins Pubs.

Olmstead, Mary. Antonia Novella. 2004. (J). pap. 9.50 (978-1-4109-0918-3(2)); (Illus.). lib. bdg. 28.56 (978-1-4109-0712-7(0)) Raintree.

Olson, Karen. Cooper Gets a CT Scan. Pritchett and Hull Associates, Inc., illus. 2002. (J). 4.50 (978-0-939838-87-5(7)) Pritchett & Hull Assocs., Inc.

Omoto, Susan. Hmong Milestones in America: Citizens in a New World. (Contemporary Profiles & Policy Series for the Younger Reader). (Illus.). 64p. (YA). (gr. 8 up). 2002. pap. 15.00 (978-0-934272-56-8(5)); 1999. 27.00 (978-0-934272-57-5(3)) Burke, John Gordon Pub., Inc.

Owen, Ann. Keeping You Healthy: A Book about Doctors. Thomas, Eric, illus. 2004. (Community Workers Ser.). 24p. (C). (gr. k-3). 22.60 (978-1-4048-0085-4(9)) Picture Window Bks.

Parks, Peggy J. Doctor. 2003. (Exploring Careers Ser.). (Illus.). 48p. (J). (gr. 3-5). 26.20 (978-0-7377-1484-5(0) , Kidhaven) Thomson Gale.

QEB Start Reading & Talking National Book Stores Edition: First Experiences: Going to the Doctor. 2006. (J). per. (978-1-59566-253-8(7)) QEB Publishing Inc.

Radabaugh, Melinda Beth. Going to the Doctor. 2003. (First Time Ser.). (J). pap. 5.50 (978-1-4034-0468-8(2)); (Illus.). 24p. lib. bdg. 18.50 (978-1-4034-0229-5(9)) Heinemann Library.

Rau, Dana Meachen. Los Doctores. 2007. (Instrumentos de Trabajo Ser.). (SPA.). 32p. (J). lib. bdg. 22.79 (***978-0-7614-2799-5(6)*** , Benchmark Bks.) Cavendish, Marshall Corp.

—Doctors. 2007. (Tools We Use Ser.). 32p. (J). lib. bdg. 22.79 (***978-0-7614-2659-2(0)*** , Benchmark Bks.) Cavendish, Marshall Corp.

—Doctors/Los Doctors. 2007. (Tools We Use/Instrumentos de Trabajo Ser.). (SPA & ENG.). 32p. (J). lib. bdg. 22.79 (***978-0-7614-2824-4(0)*** , Benchmark Bks.) Cavendish, Marshall Corp.

Ready, Dee. Doctores y Doctoras. Schon, Isabel, ed. Ferrer, Martín Luis Guzman, tr. from ENG. 1998. (Servidores Comunitarios Ser.). (SPA., Illus.). 24p. (J). (gr. 1-2). lib. bdg. 18.60 (978-1-56065-796-5(0) , Bridgestone Bks.) Capstone Pr., Inc.

Rivera, Sheila. Doctor. 2004. (First Step Nonfiction Ser.). (J). pap. (978-0-8225-5357-1(0) , Lerner Pubns.) Lerner Publishing Group.

Rodríguez, Ana María. Edward Jenner: Conqueror of Smallpox. 2006. (Great Minds of Science Ser.). (Illus.). 128p. (J). lib. bdg. 31.93 (978-0-7660-2504-2(7)) Enslow Pubs., Inc.

Saunders-Smith, Gail. Doctors Office. 1998. (Field Trips Ser.). 24p. (J). pap. 13.25 (978-0-516-21318-7(0) , Children's Pr.) Scholastic Library Publishing.

Schaefer, Lola M. Helpers in Our Community: We Need Dentists; We Need Doctors; We Need Farmers; We Need Fire Fighters; We Need Mail Carriers; We Need Nurses; We Need Police Officers; We Need Veterinarians, 8 bks. Saunders-Smith, Gail, ed. 2000. (Illus.). (J). (gr. k-1). lib. bdg. 116.80 (978-0-7368-0451-6(X) , Pebble Bks.) Capstone Pr., Inc.

—We Need Doctors. Saunders-Smith, Gail, ed. 1999. (Helpers in Our Community Ser.). (Illus.). 24p. (J). (gr. k-1). lib. bdg. 15.93 (978-0-7368-0389-2(0) , Pebble Bks.) Capstone Pr., Inc.

—We Need Doctors. 1999. pap. 13.25 (978-0-516-21902-8(2) , Children's Pr.) Scholastic Library Publishing.

Schraff, Anne. Charles Drew: Pioneer in Medicine. 2003. (Famous Inventors Ser.). (Illus.). 32p. (J). (gr. 1-4). lib. bdg. 22.60 (978-0-7660-2008-5(8)) Enslow Pubs., Inc.

Severs, Vesta-Nadine. Oswald Avery & the Story of DNA. l.t. ed. 2002. (Unlocking the Secrets of Science Ser.). (Illus.). 56p. (gr. 4-10). lib. bdg. 25.70 (978-1-58415-110-4(2)) Mitchell Lane Pubs., Inc.

Simon, Charnan. My Mother Is a Doctor. Girouard, Patrick, illus. 2006. (Magic Door to Learning Ser.). 24p. (J). (gr. k-2). 21.36 (978-1-59296-620-2(9)) Child's World, Inc.

Sirett, Dawn & Dorling Kindersley Publishing Staff. Doctor for A Day. 2004. (Illus.). 12p. (J). bds. 12.99 (978-0-7566-0210-9(6)) Dorling Kindersley Publishing, Inc.

Sitford, Mikaela. Serial Killer File: The Doctor of Death Investigation. 2008. (J). lib. bdg. (***978-1-59716-551-8(4)***) Bearport Publishing Co., Inc.

Spielman, Gloria. Janusz Korczak's Children. 2007. (Kar-Ben for Older Readers Ser.). (Illus.). (J). (gr. 2-5). 17.95 (978-1-58013-255-8(3)) Kar-Ben Publishing.

—Janusz Korczak's Children. Archambault, Matthew, illus. 2007. (Kar-Ben for Older Readers Ser.). (J). (gr. 2-5). pap. 7.95 (***978-0-8225-7050-9(5)***) Kar-Ben Publishing.

Storring, Rod. A Doctor's Life: A Visual History of Doctors & Nurses Through the Ages. 2004. (Illus.). 48p. (J). (gr. 2-6). reprint ed. 18.00 (978-0-7567-7870-5(0)) DIANE Publishing Co.

Swanson, Diane. The Doctor & You. 2001. (Illus.). 32p. (J). (ps-2). pap. 7.95 (978-1-55037-672-2(1)) Annick Pr., Ltd. CAN. *Dist:* Firefly Bks., Ltd.

Synder, Inez. Doctor Tools. 2002. (gr. k-3). lib. bdg. 12.95 (978-0-613-58831-7(2)) Tandem Library Bks.

Tracy, Kathleen. Willem Kolff & the Invention of the Dialysis Machine. l.t. ed. 2002. (Unlocking the Secrets of Science Ser.). (Illus.). 56p. (gr. 4-10). lib. bdg. 25.70 (978-1-58415-135-7(8)) Mitchell Lane Pubs., Inc.

Voices: Luis Valdez, Judith Francisca Baca, Carlos Juan Finlay. 2001. (Gateways to the Sun Ser.). (J). (gr. 2-3). pap. 11.95 (978-1-58105-572-6(2)) Santillana USA Publishing Co., Inc.

We Need Doctors, 6 vols. (gr. k-2). 28.95 (978-0-7368-8599-7(4)) Red Brick Learning.

Werther, Scott P. Dr. Jerri Nielsen: Cheating Death in Antarctica. 2003. (High Interest Books Ser.). (Illus.). 48p. (J). 23.00 (978-0-516-24331-3(4) , Children's Pr.) Scholastic Library Publishing.

—Dr. Jerri Nielsen: Cheating Death in Antarctica. 2003. (Illus.). 48p. (J). (gr. 4-7). lib. bdg. 15.25 (978-0-613-67881-0(8)) Tandem Library Bks.

Wheeler, Jill C. E. R. Doctors. 2003. (Everyday Heroes (cb) Ser.). (Illus.). 32p. (J). (gr. k-6). lib. bdg. 22.78 (978-1-57765-859-7(0)) ABDO Publishing Co.

Whiting, Jim. Hippocrates. 2006. (Biography from Ancient Civilizations Ser.). (Illus.). 48p. (J). lib. bdg. 20.95 (978-1-58415-512-6(4) , 1259600) Mitchell Lane Pubs., Inc.

Woods, Samuel G. The Pediatrician. Zucker, Gale, photos by. 1998. (Doctors in Action Ser.). (Illus.). 24p. (J). (gr. 3-6). 21.20 (978-1-56711-237-5(4) , Blackbirch Pr., Inc.) Thomson Gale.

Yen Mah, Adeline. Chinese Cinderella: True Story of an Unwanted Daughter. 2001. (Illus.). 224p. (YA). (gr. 7 up). mass mkt. 6.50 (978-0-440-22865-3(4) , Laurel Leaf) Random Hse. Children's Bks.

Yount, Lisa. William Harvey: Discoverer of How Blood Circulates. 2008. (Great Minds of Science Ser.). 128p. (J). (gr. 5 up). lib. bdg. 31.93 (***978-0-7660-3010-7(5)***) Enslow Pubs., Inc.

PHYSICIANS—FICTION

Adams, Gayle. Safe Harbor. 2002. (gr. 7-12). lib. bdg. 22.85 (978-0-613-74657-1(0)) Tandem Library Bks.

Albee, Sarah. Blue's Checkup. Chernichaw, Ian, illus. 2003. 22p. (J). (ps-3). lib. bdg. 11.25 (978-0-613-66351-9(9)) Tandem Library Bks.

Alcott, Louisa May. Les Quatre Filles du Docteur March.Tr. of Little Women. (FRE.). (J). pap. 19.95 (978-2-07-051516-5(8)) Gallimard, Editions FRA. *Dist:* Distribooks, Inc.

Anderson, Laurie Halse. Manatee Blues, No. 4. 2008. (Vet Volunteers Ser.). 144p. (J). (gr. 3). 6.99 (***978-0-14-241084-6(5)*** , Puffin) Penguin Group (USA) Inc.

Bacon, Joy. Oliver Bean, Doctors Aren't Mean! 2007. (Illus.). 32p. (J). pap. 8.95 (***978-0-9792371-1-9(4)*** , Moo Pr.) Keene Publishing.

Baggette, Susan K. Jonathan Goes to the Doctor. Moriarty, William J., photos by. 1998. (Jonathan Adventures Ser.). (Illus.). 16p. (J). (ps-k). bds. 5.95 (978-0-9660172-1-2(8)) Brookfield Reader, Inc., The.

Banks, Steven. Spongebob Goes to the Doctor. Saunders, Zina, illus. 2005. 22p. (J). lib. bdg. 15.00 (***978-1-4242-0976-7(5)***) Fitzgerald Bks.

Banks, Steven & Hillenburg, Stephen. SpongeBob Goes to the Doctor. Saunders, Zina, illus. 2005. (J). (***978-1-4156-3131-7(X)*** , Simon Spotlight/Nickelodeon) Simon & Schuster Children's Publishing.

Beaty, Andrea. Dr. Ted. Lemaître, Pascal, illus. 2008. 32p. (J). 14.99 (978-1-4169-2820-1(0)) Simon & Schuster Children's Publishing.

Benenfeld, Rikki. I Go to the Doctor. Benenfeld, Rikki, illus. 2004. (Illus.). (J). lib. bdg. 9.95 (978-1-929628-15-5(3)) Hachai Publishing.

Beobi & the Magic Coloring Book A Visit to the Doctor. 2005. (J). 3.99 (978-0-9743847-3-3(9)) Cohn, Tricia.

Bierhorst, John. Doctor Coyote: A Native American Aesop's Fables. 1998. (J). pap. 5.99 (978-0-87628-341-7(5)) Ctr. for Applied Research in Education, The.

Blacker, Terence & Ross, Tony. In Stitches with Ms. Wiz, 4 vols. 2003. (Illus.). 57p. (J). pap. 8.99 (978-0-330-34764-8(0) , Pan) Pan Macmillan GBR. *Dist:* Trafalgar Square Publishing.

Brooks, F. Daisy the Doctor. 24p. (J). lib. bdg. 14.95 (978-1-58086-697-2(2) , Usborne) EDC Publishing.

Cadnum, Michael. Ship of Fire. 2003. 208p. (J). (gr. 7). 16.99 (978-0-670-89907-4(0) , Viking Juvenile) Penguin Group (USA) Inc.

Chase, L. P. Today Is Tuesday. 2006. (J). pap. 9.00 (***978-0-87426-069-4(8)***) Whitmore Publishing Co.

Cipriano, A. G. Bertie. 1999. 294p. (YA). (gr. 6-12). pap. 5.99 (978-0-9672074-0-7(1)) Gold Lace Publishing, LLC.

Civardi, Anne. Going to the Hospital. Cartwright, Stephen, illus. rev. ed. 2005. 16p. (J). pap. 4.99 (978-0-7945-1006-0(X) , Usborne) EDC Publishing.

Cole, Joanna. My Friend the Doctor. Chambliss, Maxie, illus. 2005. 32p. (J). (ps up). 6.99 (978-0-06-050500-4(1)) HarperCollins Pubs.

Compestine, Ying Chang. Revolution Is Not a Dinner Party. 2007. 256p. (YA). (gr. 5 up). 16.95 (***978-0-8050-8207-4(7)*** , Holt, Henry & Co. Bks. For Young Readers) Holt, Henry & Co.

Cushman, Karen. Matilda Bone. 2002. 13.94 (978-1-4046-1906-7(2)) Book Wholesalers, Inc.

—Matilda Bone. 2000. (Illus.). 176p. (J). (gr. 5-9). tchr. ed. 15.00 (978-0-395-88156-9(0) , Clarion Bks.) Houghton Mifflin Co. Trade & Reference Div.

—Matilda Bone. unabr. ed. 2004. (Middle Grade Cassette Librariestm Ser.). 176p. (J). (gr. 5-9). pap. 36.00 incl. audio (978-0-8072-1725-2(5) , S YA 252 SP, Listening Library) Random Hse. Audio Publishing Group.

—Matilda Bone. 2002. 176p. (J). (gr. 5-7). reprint ed. 5.99 (978-0-440-41822-1(4) , Yearling) Random Hse. Children's Bks.

—Matilda Bone. 2002. 167p. (J). (gr. 4-7). lib. bdg. 13.55 (978-0-613-45343-1(3)) Tandem Library Bks.

Dalmatian Press Staff, adapted by. Dr. Jekyll & Mr. Hyde. 2002. (YA). (gr. 9-12). stu. ed. (978-1-58130-785-6(3)) Novel Units, Inc.

—The Strange Case of Dr. Jekyll & Mr. Hyde. 2002. (Spot the Classics Ser.). (Illus.). 171p. (J). (gr. k-5). 4.99 (978-1-57759-552-6(1)) Dalmatian Pr.

Danish, Barbara. The Dragon & the Doctor. 2nd rev. ed. 2004. (Illus.). 40p. (ps-3). pap. 5.95 (978-1-55861-117-7(7)) Feminist Pr. at The City Univ. of New York.

DeFelice, Cynthia. The Apprenticeship of Lucas Whitaker. 2007. 160p. (J). pap. 6.95 (978-0-374-40014-9(8) , Farrar, Straus & Giroux (BYR)) Farrar, Straus & Giroux.

Disney Staff. Pooh Plays Doctor. 1999. (Learn & Grow Ser.). (Illus.). 32p. (J). (ps-3). 11.99 (978-0-7364-0144-9(X)) Mouse Works.

Ehrlich, H. M., et al. Dr. Duck. Rader, Laura, illus. 2000. 36p. (J). (ps-1). pap. 14.95 (978-0-531-30254-5(7) , Orchard Bks.) Scholastic, Inc.

Evans, Jan. Repetitive Rhonda. 2007. (Illus.). 29p. (J). 18.95 (***978-0-9720176-7-1(4)***) Breath & Shadows Productions.

Fine, Anne. Poor Monty. Evans, Kevin, illus. 2004. 32p. 18.00 (978-1-4052-0161-2(4)) Egmont Bks., Ltd. GBR. *Dist:* Trafalgar Square Publishing.

Freeman, Don. Corduroy Goes to the Doctor. McCue, Lisa, illus. 2005. 14p. (J). (ps-ps). pap. 5.99 (978-0-670-06031-3(3) , Viking Juvenile) Penguin Group (USA) Inc.

Ganz, Yaffa. The Travels & Tales of Dr. Emanuel J. Mitzva. 2003. (J). 15.99 (978-1-58330-581-2(5)) Feldheim Pubs.

Gay, Michel. Bibunde. 2003. (SPA.). 40p. (978-84-8470-043-2(7)) Corimbo, Editorial S.L.

—Doctor Bibunde. 2003. (SPA.). 134p. (978-84-8470-045-6(3)) Corimbo, Editorial S.L.

Gerritsen, Tess. Bloodstream: A Novel of Medical Suspense. 1999. (gr. 7-12). lib. bdg. 16.45 (978-0-613-24020-8(0)) Tandem Library Bks.

Going to the Doctor: Individual Title Six-Packs. (ps-2). 27.00 (978-0-7635-9450-3(4)) Rigby Education.

Gold, Becky. Phil & Lil Go to the Doctor. 2001. (gr. k-3). lib. bdg. 11.25 (978-0-613-43948-0(1)) Tandem Library Bks.

Guinter, Bob. A Wonderful, Colorful Adventure at the Doctor's Office. 2000. 46p. (J). bds. 15.00 (978-1-890651-07-7(9) , FamilyFinds) Williford Communications.

Inns, Christopher. Help! 2004. (Illus.). 32p. (J). 14.95 (978-1-84507-004-5(6)) Lincoln, Frances Ltd. GBR. *Dist:* Perseus Distribution.

Jenisch, Betty. Rennie. 2007. 9.00 (***978-0-8059-8947-2(1)***) Dorrance Publishing Co., Inc.

Jensen, Patricia. I Am Sick. Hantel, Johanna, illus. (J). (gr. k-1). 2006. 32p. pap. 3.95 (978-0-516-24970-4(3)); 2005. 31p. 18.50 (978-0-516-24878-3(2)) Scholastic Library Publishing. (Children's Pr.).

Kinsey-Warnock, Natalie. A Doctor Like Papa. Bernardin, James, illus. 2002. 80p. (J). 14.99 (978-0-06-029319-2(5)) HarperCollins Pubs.

—A Doctor Like Papa. 2002. (gr. 3-6). lib. bdg. 13.00 (978-0-613-68417-0(6)) Tandem Library Bks.

Klein, Adria F. Max Goes to the Doctor. Gallagher-Cole, Mernie, illus. 2007. (J). lib. bdg. (***978-1-4048-3680-8(2)***) Picture Window Bks.

Krumrey, Melanie. Bagels, Buddy, & Me: A Story about Gluten Intolerance & Celiac Disease. 2007. (Illus.). 40p. (YA). per. 14.95 (***978-0-9797703-0-2(0)***) Mustard Seed Pr.

Lofting, Hugh. The Story of Doctor Dolittle: #1 Animal Talk. 2007. (Easy Reader Classics Ser.). 32p. (J). (ps-3). 21.35 (***978-1-59961-338-3(7)***) Spotlight.

—The Story of Doctor Dolittle: #2 the Circus Crocodile. 2007. (Easy Reader Classics Ser.). 32p. (J). (ps-3). 21.35 (***978-1-59961-339-0(5)***) Spotlight.

LoGuidice, Mike. Open up & Say Aggh! 2005. (J). pap. 16.00 (978-0-8059-7037-1(1)) Dorrance Publishing Co., Inc.

London, Jonathan. Froggy Goes to the Doctor. ed. 2004. (Illus.). (J). (gr. k-3). spiral bd. (978-0-616-14585-2(3)); spiral bd. (978-0-616-14586-9(1)) Canadian National Institute for the Blind/Institut National Canadien pour les Aveugles.

—Froggy Goes to the Doctor. Remkiewicz, Frank, illus. (Froggy Ser.). 32p. (J). 2004. pap. 5.99 (978-0-14-240193-4(5) , Puffin); 2002. 15.99 (978-0-670-03578-6(5) , Viking Juvenile) Penguin Group (USA) Inc.

MacDonald George. Gutta Percha Willie: The Working Genius. l.t. ed. 2006. 142p. pap. 10.99 (***978-1-4264-3934-6(2)***); 154p. pap. 14.99 (***978-1-4264-3992-6(X)***) BiblioBazaar.

Mackinnon, Debbie & Sieveking, Anthea. What Am I? 2004. (Illus.). 24p. (J). pap. 7.95 (978-1-84507-243-8(X)) Lincoln, Frances Ltd. GBR. *Dist:* Perseus Distribution.

Marsh, Carole. The Adventure Diaries of Dharma, the Dedicated Doctor!, 3 vols. 48p. (J). 2003. (gr. 1-4). pap. 5.95 (978-0-635-01157-2(3)); 2002. (Illus.). lib. bdg. 9.95 (978-0-635-01272-2(3)) Gallopade International.

Marx, David F. Hello Doctor. 2000. (gr. k-3). lib. bdg. 12.95 (978-0-613-54534-1(6)) Tandem Library Bks.

Marzollo, Jean. Doctor Show, No. 2. Evans, Shane W., illus. 2001. 24p. (J). lib. bdg. 13.49 (978-0-7868-2548-6(0) , Jump at the Sun) Hyperion Bks. for Children.

—Shanna's Princess Show. 2003. (ps-2). lib. bdg. 11.25 (978-0-613-91009-5(5)) Tandem Library Bks.

McDonald, Megan. Doctora Judy Moody. Reynolds, Peter H., illus. 2005. (SPA.). 175p. (J). (gr. 3-5). pap. 7.95 (978-1-59820-034-8(8)) Santillana USA Publishing Co., Inc.

Morgan, Nicola. Fleshmarket. 2004. 224p. (YA). (gr. 9). lib. bdg. 17.99 (978-0-385-90192-5(5) , Delacorte Bks. for Young Readers) Random Hse. Children's Bks.

Mullican, Judy. A Check up with Dr. Ling. Middleton, Mikell, illus. 2001. (Little Bks.). 8p. (J). (ps-1). pap. 10.95 (978-1-57332-216-4(4)); pap. 10.95 (978-1-57332-215-7(6)) HighReach Learning, Inc.

My Doctor, My Friend. 2002. (Illus.). 24p. (J). (ps-3). 5.95 (978-0-8249-5389-8(4)) Ideals Pubns.

Oxenbury, Helen. Con el Medico (At the Doctor's) (SPA.). 24p. (J). 7.95 (978-84-261-1998-8(0)) Juventud, Editorial ESP. *Dist:* AIMS International Bks., Inc.

Parkinson, Curtis. Death in Kingsport. 2007. 224p. (J). (gr. 5-9). pap. 11.95 ***(978-0-88776-827-9(X))*** Tundra Bks., Inc./Livres Toundra, Inc. CAN. *Dist:* Random Hse., Inc.

Pasternak, Boris. Doktor Zivago. 32.95 (978-5-04-004105-3(5)) Dksmo-Press, Izdatel'skaja firma RUS. *Dist:* Distribooks, Inc.

Quiller-Couch, Mabel. Kitty Trenire. 2007. 210p. pap. 12.99 ***(*978-1-4264-7475-0(X));*** 230p. pap. 16.99 ***(*978-1-4264-7552-8(7))*** BiblioBazaar.

Rader, Jared. Sandy's Dream. 2007. (J). per. 10.99 ***(*978-1-59879-398-7(5))*** Lifevest Publishing, Inc.

Ramthun, Bonnie. The White Gates. 2008. (J). ***(*978-0-375-84554-3(2));*** pap. ***(*978-0-375-84555-0(0));*** lib. bdg. ***(*978-0-375-94554-0(7))*** Random Hse., Inc.

Record, S. Leo. Not by Chance. 2002. (Illus.). 216p. lib. bdg. 19.95 (978-0-9725007-0-8(7)) Sonship Publishing.

Riefe, Barbara. Amelia Dale Archer Story. 1998. 304p. (YA). (gr. 8 up). 22.95 (978-0-312-86077-6(3) , Forge Bks.) Doherty, Tom Assocs., LLC.

Rigby Education Staff, ed. Going to the Doctor. (Illus.). 8p. (J). bds. 3.95 (978-0-7635-6427-8(3) , 764273C99) Rigby Education.

Rinaldi, Ann. An Acquaintance with Darkness. 2005. (Great Episodes Ser.). 384p. (YA). pap. 6.95 (978-0-15-205387-1(5) , Gulliver Bks.) Harcourt Children's Bks.

—An Acquaintance with Darkness. 1999. (J). 12.65 (978-0-606-16525-9(8)) Tandem Library Bks.

Robbins, Beth. Tom & Ally Visit the Doctor: American Edition. Stuart, Jon, illus. 2001. (It's OK! Ser.). 24p. (J). (ps-k). pap. 3.95 (978-0-7894-7428-5(X) , D K Ink) Dorling Kindersley Publishing, Inc.

Rocheleau, Nicole. Ollie Ollie in Come Free! 2006. 76p. pap. 14.95 (978-1-4241-0433-8(5)) PublishAmerica, Inc.

Salenas, Bobbi. Cinderella Latina - Cinicienta Latina. La Madrid, Enriquee, tr. Salenas, Bobbi, illus. 2003. (SPA.). (YA). (gr. 3-12). 19.95 (978-0-934925-06-8(2)) Pinata Pubns.

Sanschagrin, Joceline. La Visita Al Doctor. 2004. (Caillou Osa Menor Ser.).Tr. of Visit to the Doctor. (SPA., Illus.). 24p. (J). (ps up). bds. 5.95 (978-1-58728-337-6(9) , Creative Publishing International) Quayside.

Sargent, Dave & Sargent, Pat. Gus: (Slate Grullo) Be Thankful, 30, 32. Lenoir, Jane, illus. 2003. (Saddle Up Ser.: Vol. 32). 42p. (J). lib. bdg. 22.60 (978-1-56763-693-2(4)); pap. 6.95 (978-1-56763-694-9(2)) Ozark Publishing.

Steig, William. Doctor De Soto. Steig, William, illus. 1998. (Illus.). pap. 39.95 incl. audio compact disk (978-1-59519-161-8(5)); (SPA., (J). pap. 18.95 incl. audio compact disk (978-1-59519-160-1(7)) Live Oak Media.

Stevenson, Robert Louis. Dr. Jekyll & Mr. Hyde. (Classics Illustrated Ser.). (Illus.). 52p. (YA). pap. 4.95 (978-1-57209-008-8(1)) Classics International Entertainment, Inc.

—Dr. Jekyll & Mr. Hyde. (YA). (gr. 5-12). pap. 6.50 (978-0-8224-9255-9(5)) Globe Fearon Educational Publishing.

—Dr Jekyll & Mr Hyde. abr. ed. 1999. (gr. 7-12). lib. bdg. 15.25 (978-0-613-32488-5(9)) Tandem Library Bks.

—Dr. Jekyll & Mr. Hyde. Redondo, Nestor, illus. 2nd ed. 1998. (Illustrated Classic Book Ser.). 61p. (J). (gr. 3 up). reprint ed. pap. 4.95 (978-1-56767-237-4(X)) Educational Insights, Inc.

—The Strange Case of Dr. Jekyll & Mr. Hyde. (Young Collector's Illustrated Classics Ser.). (Illus.). 192p. (J). (gr. 3-7). 9.95 (978-1-56156-460-6(5)) Kidsbooks, Inc.

Stevenson, Robert Louis & Grant, John. DR JEKYLL & Mister HYDE. 2004. 144p. (J). pap. 4.95 (978-0-7945-0238-6(5) , Usborne) EDC Publishing.

Torrey, Michele. Voyage of Midnight. 2006. 240p. (gr. 5). (J). 17.99 (978-0-375-92382-1(9)); (YA). 15.95 (978-0-375-82382-4(4)) Random Hse. Children's Bks. (Knopf Bks. for Young Readers).

Verne, Jules. The Field of Ice: Part II of the Adventures of Captain Hatteras. 2006. 154p. pap. 11.99 ***(*978-1-4264-3591-1(6));*** 168p. pap. 12.99 ***(*978-1-4264-3642-0(4))*** BiblioBazaar.

Vernon, Louise A. Key to the Prison. Eitzen, Allan, illus. 2nd ed. 2003. (Louise A. Vernon's Religious Heritage Ser.). 146p. (YA). (gr. 4-9). 7.99 (978-0-8361-1698-4(4)) Herald Pr.

Warwick, J. M. An Open Vein. 2007. (YA). per. 12.95 (978-1-933963-96-9(4)) Grove Creek Publishing, LLC.

Whelan, Gloria. Listening for Lions. 208p. (J). 2006. pap. 5.99 (978-0-06-058176-3(X) , Harper Trophy); 2005. (gr. 5 up). 15.99 (978-0-06-058174-9(3)); 2005. (Illus.). (gr. 5 up). lib. bdg. 16.89 (978-0-06-058175-6(1)) HarperCollins Pubs.

Zoehfeld, Kathleen Weidner. Pooh Plays Doctor. 1999. (My Very First Winnie the Pooh Ser.). (Illus.). 32p. (J). (ps-k). pap. 4.99 (978-0-7868-4341-1(1)) Disney Pr.

PHYSICISTS

Allan, Tony. Isaac Newton. (Groundbreakers Ser.). (Illus.). 48p. (J). (gr. 5-7). 2002. pap. 8.50 (978-1-58810-992-7(5) , 91467); 2001. lib. bdg. 25.64 (978-1-58810-053-5(7)) Heinemann Library.

Allison, Amy. Luis Alvarez & the Development of the Bubble Chamber. l.t. ed. 2002. (Unlocking the Secrets of Science Ser.). (Illus.). 56p. (gr. 4-10). lib. bdg. 25.70 (978-1-58415-140-1(4)) Mitchell Lane Pubs., Inc.

Allman, Toney. J. Robert Oppenheimer: Theoretical Physicist, Atomic Pioneer. 2005. (Giants of Science Ser.). (Illus.). 64p. (J). (gr. 5-7). 26.20 (978-1-56711-889-6(5) , Blackbirch Pr., Inc.) Thomson Gale.

Atkinson, Mary. Genius or Madman? Sir Isaac Newton. 2008. (Shockwave: Life Stories Ser.). 32p. (J). pap. 6.95 ***(*978-0-531-18840-8(X)*** , Children's Pr.) Scholastic Library Publishing.

Bankston, John. Albert Einstein & the Theory of Relativity. l.t. ed. 2002. (Unlocking the Secrets of Science Ser.). (Illus.). 56p. (gr. 4-10). lib. bdg. 25.70 (978-1-58415-137-1(4)) Mitchell Lane Pubs., Inc.

—Edward Teller & the Development of the Hydrogen Bomb. l.t. ed. 2002. (Unlocking the Secrets of Science Ser.). (Illus.). 56p. (gr. 4-10). lib. bdg. 25.70 (978-1-58415-108-1(0)) Mitchell Lane Pubs., Inc.

—Stephen Hawking: Breaking the Boundaries of Time & Space. 2005. (Great Minds of Science Ser.). (Illus.). 128p. (J). lib. bdg. 26.60 (978-0-7660-2281-2(1)) Enslow Pubs., Inc.

Boerst, William J. Isaac Newton: Organizing the Universe. 2004. (Great Scientists Ser.). (Illus.). 144p. (YA). (gr. 6-12). 26.95 (978-1-931798-01-3(X)) Reynolds, Morgan Inc.

Brown, Don. Odd Boy Out: Young Albert Einstein. 2004. (Illus.). 32p. (J). (gr. k-3). 16.00 (978-0-618-49298-5(4)) Houghton Mifflin Co. Trade & Reference Div.

—Teedie: The Boyhood Adventures of Teddy Roosevelt. 2008. 32p. (J). (gr. k-3). 16.00 (978-0-618-17999-2(2)) Houghton Mifflin Co. Trade & Reference Div.

Cooper, Dan. Enrico Fermi: And the Revolutions of Modern Physics. Gingerich, Owen, ed. 1998. (Oxford Portraits in Science Ser.). (Illus.). 120p. (YA). (gr. 7 up). 30.00 (978-0-19-511762-2(X)) Oxford Univ. Pr., Inc.

Doak, Robin S. Galileo: Astronomer & Physicist. 2004. (Signature Lives Ser.). (Illus.). 112p. (J). 30.60 (978-0-7565-0813-5(4)) Compass Point Bks.

Ferry, Joseph. Maria Goeppert Mayer. 2003. (Women in Science Ser.). (Illus.). 112p. (J). (gr. 6-12). 30.00 (978-0-7910-7247-9(9) , Chelsea Hse.) Facts On File, Inc.

Frisch, Aaron. Albert Einstein. 2005. (Illus.). 48p. (J). (gr. 5-9). 21.95 (978-1-58341-328-9(6) , Creative Education) Creative Co., The.

Fullick, Ann. Michael Faraday. (Groundbreakers Ser.). (Illus.). 48p. (J). (gr. 5-7). 2002. pap. 8.50 (978-1-58810-995-8(X) , 91470); 2000. lib. bdg. 25.64 (978-1-57572-375-4(1)) Heinemann Library.

Garcia, Kimberly. Wilhelm Roentgen & the Discovery of X-Rays. 2001. (Unlocking the Secrets of Science Ser.). (Illus.). 56p. (gr. 4-10). lib. bdg. 17.95 (978-1-58415-114-2(5)) Mitchell Lane Pubs., Inc.

Gianopoulos, Andrea. Isaac Newton & the Laws of Motion. 2007. 32p. (J). (978-0-7368-6847-1(X)) Capstone Pr., Inc.

Goldenstern, Joyce. Albert Einstein: Physicist & Genius. rev. ed. 2007. (Great Minds of Science Ser.). (Illus.). 128p. (J). (gr. 4-10). lib. bdg. 31.93 ***(*978-0-7660-2838-8(0))*** Enslow Pubs., Inc.

Gomez, Rebecca. Albert Einstein. 2003. (First Biographies Ser.). (Illus.). 32p. (J). (gr. k-4). lib. bdg. 22.78 (978-1-57765-946-4(5)) ABDO Publishing Co.

Hasday, Judy L. Albert Einstein: The Giant of 20th Century Science. 2004. (Nobel Prize-Winning Scientists Ser.). (Illus.). 128p. (J). lib. bdg. 26.60 (978-0-7660-2185-3(8)) Enslow Pubs., Inc.

Heilbron, J. L. Ernest Rutherford: And the Explosion of Atoms. 2003. (Oxford Portraits in Science Ser.). (Illus.). 144p. (YA). 30.00 (978-0-19-512378-4(6)) Oxford Univ. Pr., Inc.

Hightower, Paul. Galileo: Astronomer & Physicist. 2008. (J). ***(*978-0-7660-3008-4(3))*** Enslow Pubs., Inc.

Hilliam, Rachel. Galileo Galilei: Father of Modern Science. 2004. (Rulers, Scholars, & Artists of Renaissance Europe Ser.). (Illus.). 112p. (J). lib. bdg. 31.95 (978-1-4042-0314-3(1)) Rosen Publishing Group, Inc., The.

Krull, Kathleen. Isaac Newton. Kulikov, Boris, illus. 2006. (Giants of Science Ser.: No. 2). 128p. (J). (gr. 3-7). 15.99 (978-0-670-05921-8(8) , Viking Juvenile) Penguin Group (USA) Inc.

Lakin, Patricia. Albert Einstein: Genius of the Twentieth Century. Daniel, Alan & Daniel, Lea, illus. 2005. (Ready-To-Read Ser.). 48p. (J). (ps). pap. 3.99 (978-0-689-87034-7(5)); lib. bdg. 11.89 (978-0-689-87035-4(3)) Simon & Schuster Children's Publishing. (Aladdin).

Lassieur, Allison. Albert Einstein: Genius of the Twentieth Century. 2005. (Great Life Stories Ser.). (Illus.). 127p. (J). (gr. 6-8). 30.50 (978-0-531-12401-7(0) , Watts, Franklin) Scholastic Library Publishing.

MacLeod, Elizabeth. Albert Einstein: A Life of Genius. 2004. (Snapshots Ser.). (Illus.). 32p. (J). (gr. 4-6). (978-1-55337-397-1(9)) Kids Can Pr., Ltd.

—Albert Einstein: A Life of Genius. 2003. (gr. 3-6). lib. bdg. 15.25 (978-0-613-84411-6(4)) Tandem Library Bks.

—Albert Einstein; A Questioning Life. 2004. (Snapshots Ser.). (Illus.). 32p. (J). (gr. 4-6). (978-1-55337-396-4(0)) Kids Can Pr., Ltd.

Mattern, Joanne & Santrey, Laurence. Albert Einstein, Creative Genius. Beier, Ellen, illus. 2005. 45p. (J). pap. (978-0-439-80152-2(4)) Scholastic, Inc.

McLeese, Don. Albert Einstein. (Rourke Discovery Library). (Illus.). 24p. 2006. (gr. 2-5). 14.95 (978-1-59515-433-0(7)); 2005. (SPA & ENG., (J). (978-1-59515-673-0(9)) Rourke Publishing, LLC.

McPherson, Stephanie Sammartino. Albert Einstein. 2004. (History Maker Bios Ser.). (Illus.). 48p. (J). (gr. 3-5). lib. bdg. 26.60 (978-0-8225-0350-7(6)) Lerner Publishing Group.

Meltzer, Milton. Albert Einstein: A Biography. 2007. (Illus.). 48p. (J). (gr. 1-5). 16.95 (978-0-8234-1966-1(5)) Holiday Hse., Inc.

Merkur, Janet. Livewire Real Lives Sir Mark Oliphant. 1999. (Livewires Ser.). (Illus.). 32p. (gr. 6-9). pap. 6.00 (978-0-521-77628-8(7)) Cambridge Univ. Pr.

O'Connell, Diane. Strong Force: The Story of Physicist Shirley Ann Jackson. 2005. (Women's Adventures in Science Ser.). (Illus.). 110p. (YA). (gr. 5-8). 31.00 (978-0-531-16784-7(4) , Watts, Franklin) Scholastic Library Publishing.

O'Donnell, Kerri. Sir Isaac Newton: Using the Laws of Motion to Solve Problems. 2006. (Math for the Real World Ser.). (Illus.). 32p. (J). pap. (978-1-4042-6079-5(X)); lib. bdg. (978-1-4042-3363-8(6)) Rosen Publishing Group, Inc., The.

Oxlade, Chris. Albert Einstein. 2003. (20th Century History Makers Ser.). (Illus.). 112p. (J). lib. bdg. 32.85 (978-0-7398-5259-0(0)) Raintree.

Panchyk, Richard. Galileo for Kids: His Life & Ideas, 25 Activities. 2005. (For Kids Ser.). (Illus.). 184p. (J). pap. 16.95 (978-1-55652-566-7(4)) Chicago Review Pr., Inc.

Pasachoff, Naomi E. Ernest Rutherford: Father of Nuclear Science. 2005. (Great Minds of Science Ser.). (Illus.). 128p. (J). lib. bdg. 26.60 (978-0-7660-2441-0(5)) Enslow Pubs., Inc.

—Niels Bohr: Physicist & Humanitarian. 2003. (Great Minds of Science Ser.). (Illus.). 128p. (J). (gr. 4-10). lib. bdg. 26.60 (978-0-7660-1997-3(7)) Enslow Pubs., Inc.

Randall, Tina. Luis Alvarez. (Hispanic-American Biographies Ser.). (Illus.). 64p. (J). 2005. pap. 9.50 (978-1-4109-1303-6(1)); 2004. (gr. 4-6). 32.86 (978-1-4109-1295-4(7)) Raintree.

Randall, Tina. Luis Walter Alvarez. 2006. (Biografías Hispanoamericanas Ser.). (SPA.). 64p. (J). lib. bdg. 32.86 ***(*978-1-4109-2129-1(8))*** Raintree.

Rau, Dana Meachen. Albert Einstein. 2003. (Compass Point Early Biographies Ser.). (Illus.). 32p. (J). (gr. 2 up). lib. bdg. 21.26 (978-0-7565-0416-8(3)) Compass Point Bks.

Reid, Struan. Albert Einstein. 2002. (Groundbreakers Ser.). (Illus.). 48p. (J). (gr. 5-7). pap. 8.50 (978-1-58810-988-0(7) , 91463) Heinemann Library.

—Albert Einstein. 2002. (gr. 5-8). lib. bdg. 17.05 (978-0-613-89417-3(0)) Tandem Library Bks.

Reid, Struan & Einstein, Albert. Albert Einstein. 2000. (Groundbreakers Ser.). (Illus.). 48p. (J). (gr. 5-7). lib. bdg. 25.64 (978-1-57572-365-5(4)) Heinemann Library.

Rosinsky, Natalie M. Sir Isaac Newton: Brilliant Mathematician & Scientist. 2007. (Signature Lives Ser.). (J). lib. bdg. 31.93 ***(*978-0-7565-2209-4(9))*** Compass Point Bks.

Ross, Stewart. Michael Faraday. 2002. (Scientists Who Made History Ser.). (Illus.). 48p. (J). lib. bdg. 27.12 (978-0-7398-5224-8(8)) Raintree.

Salas, Laura Purdie. Discovering Nature's Laws: A Story about Isaac Newton. Reynolds, Emily C. S., tr. Reynolds, Emily C. S., illus. 2004. (Creative Minds Biography Ser.). 64p. (J). (gr. 4-8). lib. bdg. 22.60 (978-1-57505-183-3(4)) Lerner Publishing Group.

Santrey, Laurence. Albert Einstein. 2007. 48p. (J). pap. 3.99 ***(*978-0-439-87479-3(3)*** , Scholastic en Espanol) Scholastic, Inc.

Schaefer, Lola M. & Schaefer, Wyatt S. Albert Einstein. Saunders-Smith, Gail, ed. 2003. (First Biographies Ser.). (Illus.). 24p. (J). (gr. k-1). lib. bdg. 15.93 (978-0-7368-2079-0(5) , Pebble Bks.) Capstone Pr., Inc.

Scherer, Glenn & Fletcher, Marty. J. Robert Oppenheimer: The Brain Behind the Bomb. 2007. (Inventors Who Changed the World Ser.). (Illus.). 128p. (J). lib. bdg. 33.27 (978-1-59845-050-7(6) , MyReportLinks.com Bks.) Enslow Pubs., Inc.

Sherman, Josepha. J. J. Thomson & the Discovery of Electrons. 2005. (Uncharted, Unexplored, & Unexplained Ser.). (Illus.). 48p. (J). (gr. 4-8). lib. bdg. 29.95 (978-1-58415-370-2(9)) Mitchell Lane Pubs., Inc.

Slade, Suzanne. Albert Einstein: Scientist & Genius. Schultz, Jolene, illus. 2007. (J). lib. bdg. ***(*978-1-4048-3730-0(2))*** Picture Window Bks.

Spangenburg, Ray & Moser, Diane Kit. Chien-Shiung Wu: The Elegance of Experiment. 2008. (Makers of Modern Science Ser.). 160p. (gr. 6-12). 29.95 ***(*978-0-8160-6177-8(7)*** , Chelsea Hse.) Facts On File, Inc.

—Richard Feynman: Quarks, Bombs, & Bongos. 2008. (Makers of Modern Science Ser.). 160p. (gr. 6-12). 29.95 ***(*978-0-8160-6176-1(9)*** , Chelsea Hse.) Facts On File, Inc.

Stux, Erica. Enrico Fermi: Trailblazer in Nuclear Physics. 2004. (Nobel Prize-Winning Scientists Ser.). (Illus.). 128p. (J). lib. bdg. 26.60 (978-0-7660-2177-8(7)) Enslow Pubs., Inc.

Sullivan, Anne Marie. Sir Isaac Newton: Famous English Scientist. 2002. (Great Names Ser.). (Illus.). 32p. (J). (gr. 3 up). lib. bdg. (978-1-59084-139-6(5)) Mason Crest Pubs.

Tobin, William. The Life & Science of Léon Foucault: The Man Who Proved the Earth Rotates. 2003. (Illus.). 352p. 90.00 (978-0-521-80855-2(3)) Cambridge Univ. Pr.

Wishinsky, Frieda. What's the Matter with Albert? A Story of Albert Einstein. 2004. (Illus.). 32p. (J). pap. 6.95 (978-1-897066-15-7(5)) Maple Tree Pr. CAN. *Dist:* Perseus Distribution.

—What's the Matter with Albert? A Story of Albert Einstein. Lamontagne, Jacques, illus. 2002. 32p. (J). (gr. 2-5). 19.95 (978-1-894379-31-1(4)) Maple Tree Pr. CAN. *Dist:* Firefly Bks., Ltd.

Wyborny, Sheila. Albert Einstein. 2002. (Inventors & Creators Ser.). (Illus.). 48p. (J). (gr. 3-5). 23.70 (978-0-7377-1278-0(3) , Kidhaven) Thomson Gale.

Zannos, Susan. Michael Faraday & the Discovery of Electromagnetism. 2004. (Uncharted, Unexplored, & Unexplained Ser.). (Illus.). 48p. (J). (gr. 4-8). lib. bdg. 29.95 (978-1-58415-307-8(5)) Mitchell Lane Pubs., Inc.

PHYSICS

see also Astrophysics; Chemistry, Physical and Theoretical; Dynamics; Electricity; Electronics; Geophysics; Gravitation; Hydrostatics; Light; Liquids; Magnetism; Matter; Mechanics; Nuclear Physics; Optics; Quantum Theory; Radiation; Radioactivity; Relativity (Physics); Sound; Thermodynamics

Active Physics, 6 vols. 2000. stu. ed. (978-1-891629-53-2(0)); pap., stu. ed. (978-1-891629-43-3(3)) It's About Time, Herff Jones Education Diiv.

Active Physics Communications. 2000. stu. ed., per. 26.95 (978-1-891629-00-6(X)); 2000. stu. ed., bds. (978-1-891629-47-1(6)); 1999. tchr. ed., per. (978-1-891629-06-8(9)) It's About Time, Herff Jones Education Diiv.

Active Physics Communications Kits Chapter 1. 2000. bds. (978-1-58591-150-9(X)) It's About Time, Herff Jones Education Diiv.

Active Physics Communications Kits Chapter 2. 2002. bds. (978-1-58591-151-6(8)) It's About Time, Herff Jones Education Diiv.

Active Physics Communications Kits Chapter 3. 2002. bds. (978-1-58591-152-3(6)) It's About Time, Herff Jones Education Diiv.

Active Physics Communications Kits Module. 2000. bds. (978-1-58591-153-0(4)) It's About Time, Herff Jones Education Diiv.

Active Physics Home. 2000. tchr. ed., per. (978-1-891629-07-5(7)); stu. ed., per. 26.95 (978-1-891629-01-3(8)); stu. ed., bds. (978-1-891629-48-8(4)) It's About Time, Herff Jones Education Diiv.

Active Physics Home Kits Chapter 1. 2000. bds. (978-1-58591-154-7(2)) It's About Time, Herff Jones Education Diiv.

Active Physics Home Kits Chapter 2. 2000. bds. (978-1-58591-155-4(0)) It's About Time, Herff Jones Education Diiv.

Active Physics Home Kits Chapter 3. 2000. bds. (978-1-58591-156-1(9)) It's About Time, Herff Jones Education Diiv.

Active Physics Home Kits Chapter 3 with Demo Item. 2000. bds. (978-1-58591-157-8(7)) It's About Time, Herff Jones Education Diiv.

Active Physics Home Kits Demo Item Only. 2000. bds. (978-1-58591-182-0(8)) It's About Time, Herff Jones Education Diiv.

Active Physics Home Kits Module. 2000. bds. (978-1-58591-158-5(5)) It's About Time, Herff Jones Education Diiv.

Active Physics Kits Home Module with Demo Item. 2000. bds. (978-1-58591-159-2(3)) It's About Time, Herff Jones Education Diiv.

Active Physics Light up My Life. 2002. tchr. ed., per. (978-1-58591-118-9(6)); stu. ed., bds. (978-1-58591-117-2(8)) It's About Time, Herff Jones Education Diiv.

Active Physics Medicine. 2000. stu. ed., per. (978-1-891629-02-0(6)); 2000. stu. ed., bds. (978-1-891629-49-5(2)); 1999. tchr. ed., per. (978-1-891629-08-2(5)) It's About Time, Herff Jones Education Diiv.

Active Physics Medicine Kits Chapter 1. 2000. bds. (978-1-58591-160-8(7)) It's About Time, Herff Jones Education Diiv.

Active Physics Medicine Kits Chapter 2. 2000. bds. (978-1-58591-161-5(5)) It's About Time, Herff Jones Education Diiv.

Active Physics Medicine Kits Chapter 3. 2000. bds. (978-1-58591-162-2(3)) It's About Time, Herff Jones Education Diiv.

Active Physics Medicine Kits Module. 2000. bds. (978-1-58591-163-9(1)) It's About Time, Herff Jones Education Diiv.

Active Physics Predictions. 2000. stu. ed., per. (978-1-891629-03-7(4)); 1999. tchr. ed., per. (978-1-891629-09-9(3)) It's About Time, Herff Jones Education Diiv.

Active Physics Predictions Kits Chapter 1. 2000. bds. (978-1-58591-164-6(X)) It's About Time, Herff Jones Education Diiv.

Active Physics Predictions Kits Chapter 2. 2000. bds. (978-1-58591-165-3(8)) It's About Time, Herff Jones Education Diiv.

Active Physics Predictions Kits Chapter 3. 2000. bds. (978-1-58591-166-0(6)) It's About Time, Herff Jones Education Diiv.

Active Physics Predictions Kits Chapter 3 with Demo Item. 2000. bds. (978-1-58591-167-7(4)) It's About Time, Herff Jones Education Diiv.

Active Physics Predictions Kits Demo Item Only. 2000. bds. (978-1-58591-183-7(6)) It's About Time, Herff Jones Education Diiv.

Active Physics Predictions Kits Module. 2000. bds. (978-1-58591-168-4(2)) It's About Time, Herff Jones Education Diiv.

P Q R

Active Physics Predictions Kits Module with Demo Item. 2000. bds. (978-1-58591-169-1(0)) It's About Time, Herff Jones Education Diiv.

Active Physics Predictons. 2000. stu. ed., bds. (978-1-891629-50-1(6)) It's About Time, Herff Jones Education Diiv.

Active Physics Sports Kits Chapter 1. 2000. bds. (978-1-58591-170-7(4)) It's About Time, Herff Jones Education Diiv.

Active Physics Sports Kits Chapter 1 with Demo Item. 2000. bds. (978-1-58591-171-4(2)) It's About Time, Herff Jones Education Diiv.

Active Physics Sports Kits Chapter 2. 2000. bds. (978-1-58591-172-1(0)) It's About Time, Herff Jones Education Diiv.

Active Physics Sports Kits Chapter 3. 2000. bds. (978-1-58591-173-8(9)) It's About Time, Herff Jones Education Diiv.

Active Physics Sports Kits Demo Item Only. 2000. bds. (978-1-58591-184-4(4)) It's About Time, Herff Jones Education Diiv.

Active Physics Sports Kits Module. 2000. bds. (978-1-58591-174-5(7)) It's About Time, Herff Jones Education Diiv.

Active Physics Sports Kits Module with Demo Item. 2000. bds. (978-1-58591-175-2(5)) It's About Time, Herff Jones Education Diiv.

Active Physics Transportation. 2000. stu. ed., per. (978-1-891629-05-1(0)); 2000. stu. ed., bds. (978-1-891629-52-5(2)); 1999. tchr. ed., per. (978-1-891629-11-2(5)) It's About Time, Herff Jones Education Diiv.

Active Physics Transportation Kits Chapter 1. 2000. bds. (978-1-58591-176-9(3)) It's About Time, Herff Jones Education Diiv.

Active Physics Transportation Kits Chapter 1 with Demo Item. 2000. bds. (978-1-58591-177-6(1)) It's About Time, Herff Jones Education Diiv.

Active Physics Transportation Kits Chapter 2. 2000. bds. (978-1-58591-178-3(X)) It's About Time, Herff Jones Education Diiv.

Active Physics Transportation Kits Chapter 3. 2000. bds. (978-1-58591-179-0(8)) It's About Time, Herff Jones Education Diiv.

Active Physics Transportation Kits Demo Item Only. 2000. bds. (978-1-58591-185-1(2)) It's About Time, Herff Jones Education Diiv.

Active Physics Transportation Kits Module. 2000. bds. (978-1-58591-180-6(1)) It's About Time, Herff Jones Education Diiv.

Active Physics Transportation Kits Module with Demo Item. 2000. bds. (978-1-58591-181-3(X)) It's About Time, Herff Jones Education Diiv.

Avp, prod. Physical Processes. (YA). cd-rom 149.95 (978-0-7365-7283-5(X)) Films Media Group.

Barraclough, Sue. Floating & Sinking. 2006. (Illus.). 24p. (J). (978-1-4109-2264-9(2)); (978-1-4109-2259-5(6)) Steck-Vaughn.

Basiswissen Mathematik zur Physik. (Duden Abiturhilfen Ser.). (GER.). 96p. (YA). (gr. 11-13). (978-3-411-04841-0(7)) Bibliographisches Institut & F. A. Brockhaus AG DEU. *Dist:* International Bk. Import Service, Inc.

Benchmark Education Staff, compiled by. Physical Science. 2006. spiral bd. 145.00 (***978-1-4108-6945-6(8));** 2006. spiral bd. 115.00 (***978-1-4108-6922-7(9));** 2006. spiral bd. 170.00 (***978-1-4108-6930-2(X));** 2006. spiral bd. 140.00 (***978-1-4108-6936-4(9));** 2005. spiral bd. 180.00 (***978-1-4108-3845-2(5));** 2005. spiral bd. 110.00 (***978-1-4108-3864-3(1));** 2005. spiral bd. 50.00 (***978-1-4108-3871-1(4));** 2005. spiral bd. 280.00 (***978-1-4108-3916-9(8));** 2005. spiral bd. 140.00 (***978-1-4108-3917-6(6));** 2005. spiral bd. 400.00 (***978-1-4108-4517-7(6));** 2005. spiral bd. 335.00 (***978-1-4108-3844-5(7));** 2005. spiral bd. 385.00 (***978-1-4108-5439-1(6));** 2005. spiral bd. 385.00 (***978-1-4108-5868-9(5));** 2005. spiral bd. 145.00 (***978-1-4108-5869-6(3));** 2005. spiral bd. 750.00 (***978-1-4108-5438-4(8))** Benchmark Education Co.

—Science Theme: Physical Science. 2005. spiral bd. 220.00 (***978-1-4108-5310-3(1))** Benchmark Education Co.

Benjamin, Robert F., et al. Spills & Ripples. Cordel, Betty, ed. Richmond, Brenda, illus. 2001. 138p. (YA). pap. 18.95 (978-1-881431-83-1(5) , 1318) AIMS Education Foundation.

Bingaman, Jay. Physical Science Student Labs & Activities. Matthews, Douglas L., ed. 2003. (Illus.). stu. ed., per., wbk. ed. (978-1-931680-30-1(2) , Expert Systems for Teachers) Teaching Point, Inc.

Boothroyd, Jennifer. What Is a Solid? 2007. (First Step Nonfiction Ser.). 24p. (J). (gr. k-3). 18.60 (978-0-8225-6836-0(5) , Lerner Pubns.) Lerner Publishing Group.

Boydell, Sydney. Cambridge Checkpoints VCE Physics Unit 4 2004. 2003. (Cambridge Checkpoints Ser.). (Illus.). vii, 178p. pap. 11.00 (978-0-521-83336-3(1)) Cambridge Univ. Pr.

—Cambridge Checkpoints VCE Physics Unit 4 2005. 2004. (Cambridge Checkpoints Ser.). 208p. pap., stu. ed. 12.50 (978-0-521-61144-2(X)) Cambridge Univ. Pr.

Breithaupt, Jim. New Understanding Physics for Advanced Level. 4th ed. 1999. (Illus.). 736p. (YA). (gr. 11). pap. 79.50 (978-0-7487-4314-8(6)) Nelson Thornes Ltd. GBR. *Dist:* Trans-Atlantic Pubns., Inc.

Brown, Mark. Solids, Liquids, & Gases. 2005. (J). per. 14.99 (978-1-59441-699-6(0) , K04027) Carson-Dellosa Publishing Co., Inc.

Built for Speed, 8 bks. Incl. World's Fastest Boats. Cook, Nick. 2000. lib. bdg. 21.26 (978-0-7368-0569-8(9)); World's Fastest Cars. Cook, Nick. 2000. lib. bdg. 21.26 (978-0-7368-0570-4(2)); World's Fastest Dragsters. Bledsoe, Glen & Bledsoe, Karen. 2003. lib. bdg. 21.26 (978-0-7368-1500-0(7)); World's Fastest Helicopters. Bledsoe, Glen & Bledsoe, Karen. 2002. lib. bdg. 21.26 (978-0-7368-1059-3(5)); World's Fastest Indy Cars. Bledsoe, Glen & Bledsoe, Karen. 2003. lib. bdg. 21.26 (978-0-7368-1501-7(5)); World's Fastest Military Airplanes. Burgan, Michael. 2000. lib. bdg. 21.26 (978-0-7368-0568-1(0)); World's Fastest Pro Stock Trucks. Savage, Jeff. 2003. lib. bdg. 21.26 (978-0-7368-1502-4(3)); World's Fastest Stock Cars. Savage, Jeff. 2003. lib. bdg. 21.26 (978-0-7368-1503-1(1)); World's Fastest Superbikes. Sievert, Terri. 2002. lib. bdg. 21.26 (978-0-7368-1060-9(9)); World's Fastest Trains. Sievert, Terri. 2002. lib. bdg. 21.26 (978-0-7368-1061-6(7)); World's Fastest Trucks. Bledsoe, Glen & Bledsoe, Karen. 2002. lib. bdg. 21.26 (978-0-7368-1062-3(5)); World's Wildest Roller Coasters. Burgan, Michael. 2000. lib. bdg. 21.26 (978-0-7368-0571-1(0)); 48p. (J). (gr. 3-4). (Illus.). Set lib. bdg. 255.12 (978-0-7368-1520-8(1) , Capstone High-Interest Bks.) Capstone Pr., Inc.

Bundey, Nikki. On the Field. Gray, Virginia, illus. 1999. (First Sports Science Ser.). 32p. (J). (gr. 2-4). lib. bdg. 21.27 (978-1-57505-357-8(8) , Carolrhoda Bks.) Lerner Publishing Group.

Burton, Margie, et al. Water Goes Up! Water Comes Down! Adams, Alison, ed. 1999. (Early Connections Ser.). 16p. (J). (gr. k-2). pap. 4.50 (978-1-58344-085-8(2)) Benchmark Education Co.

Check It Out! 2005. (Check It Out! Ser.). (J). lib. bdg. 79.84 (978-1-59716-091-9(1)) Bearport Publishing Co., Inc.

Cientificos! 8: Ciencias Fisicas. (SPA.). (J). 55.00 (978-958-04-6347-4(6)) Norma S.A. COL. *Dist:* Distribuidora Norma, Inc.

Contemporary Discourse in the Field of Physics, 6 bks., Set. 2006. (YA). lib. bdg. 183.60 (978-1-4042-0630-4(2)) Rosen Publishing Group, Inc., The.

Cooke, Andy & Martin, Jean. Spectrum Physics Class Book. 2004. (Spectrum Key Stage 3 Science Ser.). (Illus.). 184p. pap. 13.50 (978-0-521-54923-3(X)) Cambridge Univ. Pr.

Creighton, Jayne, contrib. by. Boomerangs, Blades & Basketballs: The Science of Sports. 1999. (Science @ Work Ser.). (Illus.). 48p. (J). (gr. 4-6). lib. bdg. 27.12 (978-0-7398-0132-1(5)) Raintree.

Curran, Greg. Homework Helpers: Physics. 2005. (Illus.). 1p. (gr. 9-12). pap. 14.99 (978-1-56414-768-4(1)) Career Pr., Inc.

Curry, Don L. What Is Mass? 2005. (Rookie Read-About Science Ser.). (Illus.). 32p. (J). (gr. 1-2). pap. 4.95 (978-0-516-24666-6(6) , Children's Pr.) Scholastic Library Publishing.

Cutnell, John D. Test Bank to Accompany Physics. 6th ed. 2004. 516p. (YA). (978-0-471-23124-0(X)) Wiley, John & Sons, Inc.

Dahl, Michael. Maquinas Simples (Simple Machines), 2 bks. Schon, Isabel, ed. Ferrer, Martín Luis Guzman, tr. Incl. Palancas. lib. bdg. 18.60 (978-1-56065-793-4(6) , CAP1100); Poleas. lib. bdg. 18.60 (978-1-56065-794-1(4) , CAP1155); 24p. (J). (gr. k-3). 1998. (SPA., Illus.). Set lib. bdg. 37.20 (978-0-7368-0146-1(4) , Bridgestone Bks.) Capstone Pr., Inc.

Degner, David Martin. The N-Particle Model. 2nd ed. 2000. (Illus.). 220p. (YA). (gr. 12 up). pap. 44.95 (978-0-9668628-1-2(3)) Degner Pr.

Diagram Group. Physics: An Illustrated Guide to Science. 2006. (Science Visual Resources Ser.). 208p. (YA). (gr. 6-12). 49.50 (978-0-8160-6167-9(X)) Facts On File, Inc.

Dwyer, Jacqueline, et al, contrib. by. Rainbows. 2001. (PowerKids Readers Ser.). (Illus.). 24p. (J). (gr. 1). lib. bdg. 16.00 (978-0-8239-5676-0(8) , PowerKids Pr.) Rosen Publishing Group, Inc., The.

Earth & Moon, 6 vols. (Sunshinetm Science Ser.). 24p. (gr. 1-2). 31.50 (978-0-7802-0293-1(7)); 36.95 (978-0-7802-0544-4(8)) Wright Group, The.

Earth Science, Physics, Chemistry for 21st Century Kit. 2000. bds. (978-1-58591-121-9(6)) It's About Time, Herff Jones Education Diiv.

Earth Science, Physics, Chemistry for the 21st Century. 2002. tchr. ed., per. (978-1-58591-120-2(8)); stu. ed., bds. (978-1-58591-119-6(4)) It's About Time, Herff Jones Education Diiv.

Ehrlich, Robert, et al. Laboratory Manual to accompany Physics Matters: An Introduction to Conceptual Physics. 2004. 166p. pap., lab manual ed. 23.95 (978-0-471-26154-4(8) , Wiley) Wiley, John & Sons, Inc.

Elson, Lawrence M. The Physics Coloring Book. 2001. (HarperCollins Coloring Books). (Illus.). 256p. (J). (gr. k-5). pap. 20.00 (978-0-06-273719-9(8)) HarperCollins Pubs.

Fakhruddin, Hasan. Physics Demos & Hands-ons. 2006. 188p. pap. 23.30 (978-1-4116-8162-0(2)) Lulu.com.

Frank, Marjorie Slavick, et al. Science Instant Readers: Physical Science Collection. 1999. (Harcourt Science Ser.). (gr. 1 up). pap. 12.40 (978-0-15-316230-5(9)); (gr. 2 up). pap. 12.40 (978-0-15-316233-6(3)) Harcourt Schl. Pubs.

—Science Instant Readers Bk. 9: Sink or Float? 1999. (Harcourt Science Ser.). (gr. 3 up). pap. 15.50 (978-0-15-316207-7(4)) Harcourt Schl. Pubs.

—Science Instant Readers Bk. 11: Push It or Pull It? 1999. (Harcourt Science Ser.). (gr. 1 up). pap. 15.50 (978-0-15-316209-1(0)) Harcourt Schl. Pubs.

Fry, Carmel. Physics VCE, Unit 3. 2002. (Cambridge Wizard Subject Guides). (Illus.). 112p. pap., stu. ed. 8.00 (978-1-876367-77-0(6)) Cambridge Univ. Pr.

Gardner, Robert. Science Projects about the Physics of Sports. 2000. (Science Projects Ser.). (Illus.). 128p. (YA). (gr. 6-12). lib. bdg. 26.60 (978-0-7660-1167-0(4)) Enslow Pubs., Inc.

Glover, David. Ramps & Wedges. 2002. (Simple Machines Ser.). (Illus.). 24p. (J). (gr. 2-4). pap. 6.50 (978-1-4034-0058-1(X) , 91502) Heinemann Library.

Gore, Bryson. Physics: A Hair Is Wider Than a Million Atoms. 2005. (Wow Science Ser.). (Illus.). 32p. (J). (gr. 4-17). lib. bdg. 27.10 (978-1-59604-067-0(X)) Stargazer Bks.

Greenberg, Daniel A. Amusement Park Science. 2003. (Science Links Ser.). (Illus.). 32p. (gr. 3-5). 23.00 (978-0-7910-7416-9(1) , Chelsea Hse.) Facts On File, Inc.

Gribbon, John. Quantum Physics. 2002. (gr. 7-12). lib. bdg. 15.30 (978-0-613-55756-6(5)) Tandem Library Bks.

Griffith, Dave. Physics, Vol. 2. 1999. (Illus.). (J). pap., stu. ed. 15.00 (978-1-886998-09-4(4)) Pasco Scientific.

Grolier Educational Staff. Physics Matters!, 10 vols. 2001. (Illus.). (J). (978-0-7172-5510-8(7)); (978-0-7172-5512-2(3)); (978-0-7172-5513-9(1)); (978-0-7172-5514-6(X)); (978-0-7172-5515-3(8)); (978-0-7172-5516-0(6)); (978-0-7172-5518-4(2)); Set. (978-0-7172-5519-1(0)) Scholastic Library Publishing. (Grolier).

—Physics Matters! Electric Charges, 10 vols., Vol. 6. 2001. (Illus.). (YA). (gr. 5-8). 359.00 (978-0-7172-5509-2(3) , Grolier) Scholastic Library Publishing.

Grolier Educational Staff, contrib. by. Physics Matters!, 10 vols. 2001. (Illus.). (J). (978-0-7172-5511-5(5)); (978-0-7172-5517-7(4)) Scholastic Library Publishing. (Grolier).

Grossman, Marvin C., et al. ARIES Exploring Motion & Forces: Friction, Speed & Acceleration: Science Journal. 2000. (Aries Ser.). (Illus.). (J). (gr. 3-8). pap. 3.80 (978-1-57091-257-3(2)) Charlesbridge Publishing, Inc.

Halliday. Test Bank to Accompany Physics. 5th ed. 2002. 680p. (YA). (978-0-471-20406-0(4)) Wiley, John & Sons, Inc.

Harcourt School Publishers Staff. Harcourt Science, Grade 1 Vol. 3: Physical Science: Tennessee Edition. 2nd ed. 2002. tchr. ed. 106.70 (978-0-15-328336-9(X)) Harcourt Schl. Pubs.

—Harcourt Science, Grade 2 Vol. 3: Physical Science: Louisiana Edition. 2nd ed. 2002. tchr. ed. 100.70 (978-0-15-328358-1(0)) Harcourt Schl. Pubs.

—Harcourt Science, Grade 2 Vol. 3: Physical Science: Tennessee Edition. 2nd ed. 2002. tchr. ed. 106.70 (978-0-15-328339-0(4)) Harcourt Schl. Pubs.

—Harcourt Science, Grade 6 Vol. 3: Physical Science: Louisiana Edition. 2nd ed. 2002. tchr. ed. 113.50 (978-0-15-328370-3(X)) Harcourt Schl. Pubs.

—Harcourt Science, Grade 6 Vol. 3: Physical Science: Tennessee Edition. 2nd ed. 2002. tchr. ed. 120.30 (978-0-15-328351-2(3)) Harcourt Schl. Pubs.

—Physical Science: Instant Reader Standard Package. 2000. (Harcourt Ciencias Ser.). (SPA., Illus.). (gr. 1 up). pap. 17.70 (978-0-15-316954-0(0)); (gr. 2 up). pap. 17.70 (978-0-15-316957-1(5)) Harcourt Schl. Pubs.

Hil, Mcgraw. Sciasmtbk Eltrcty & Mgnti. 2000. (McGraw-Hill Science Ser.). (gr. 4 up). (978-0-02-277759-3(8)) Macmillan/McGraw-Hill Schl. Div.

—Sciasmtbk Forces. 2000. (McGraw-Hill Science Ser.). (gr. 6 up). (978-0-02-277773-9(3)) Macmillan/McGraw-Hill Schl. Div.

Holman. Science Spectacular: Physics: Enhanced Online Edition. 4th ed. 2004. 17.26 (978-0-03-037157-8(0)) Holt, Rinehart & Winston.

—Science Spectacular: Physics: Online Edition Upgrade. 4th ed. 2004. 31.93 (978-0-03-037177-6(5)); 7.93 (978-0-03-037219-3(4)) Holt, Rinehart & Winston.

Holt, Rinehart and Winston Staff. Correlation Physics: Holt Science & Technology: California Edition. 2001. pap. 4.20 (978-0-03-067227-9(9)) Holt, Rinehart & Winston.

—Holt Ciencias y Tecnologia: Physics. 2000. 75.80 (978-0-03-064762-8(2)) Holt, Rinehart & Winston.

—Holt Ciencias y Tecnologia 2001: Physics: Chapter Tests & Assessment. 2000. pap. 19.86 (978-0-03-064767-3(3)) Holt, Rinehart & Winston.

—Holt Physics. 2nd ed. 2001. 79.60 (978-0-03-056544-1(8)); 2000. tchr. ed. 103.86 (978-0-03-056546-5(4)) Holt, Rinehart & Winston.

—Holt Physics: Premier Online Edition. 6th ed. 2005. 19.93 (978-0-03-040089-6(9)) Holt, Rinehart & Winston.

—Holt Science & Technology. 4th ed. 2004. (Illus.). 75.80 (978-0-03-073168-6(2)) Holt, Rinehart & Winston.

—Holt Science & Technology: Physical Science. 5th ed. 2004. tchr. ed. 128.80 (978-0-03-066482-3(9)) Holt, Rinehart & Winston.

—Holt Science & Technology: Physical Science: Enhanced Online Edition. 4th ed. 2004. 17.26 (978-0-03-037152-3(X)) Holt, Rinehart & Winston.

—Holt Science & Technology: Physics: California Edition. annot. ed. 2001. pap., tchr. ed. 136.53 (978-0-03-055699-9(6)) Holt, Rinehart & Winston.

—Holt Science & Technology: Physics, Data Sheets, Lab Book & Worksheets - California Edition. 2000. pap. 18.06 (978-0-03-055714-9(3)) Holt, Rinehart & Winston.

—Holt Science & Technology: Physics: Enhanced Online Edition. 2002. 74.53 (978-0-03-072492-3(9)) Holt, Rinehart & Winston.

—Holt Science & Technology: Physics: Georgia Edition. annot. ed. 2001. tchr. ed. 133.80 (978-0-03-066897-5(2)) Holt, Rinehart & Winston.

—Holt Science & Technology: Physics: Online Edition Upgrade. 4th ed. 2004. 31.93 (978-0-03-037172-1(4)); 7.93 (978-0-03-037214-8(3)) Holt, Rinehart & Winston.

—Holt Science & Technology: Physics: Reinforcement & Vocational Worksheets. 2000. pap. 15.20 (978-0-03-055412-4(8)) Holt, Rinehart & Winston.

—Holt Science & Technology: Physics: Reinforcement & Vocational Worksheets - California Edition. 2001. pap. 14.33 (978-0-03-055703-3(8)) Holt, Rinehart & Winston.

—Holt Science & Technology: Physics: Science Puzzles, Twisters & Teasers - California Edition. 2000. pap. 10.73 (978-0-03-055709-5(7)) Holt, Rinehart & Winston.

—Holt Science & Technology: Physics: Study Guide with Answer Key - California Edition. 2000. pap., stu. ed. 10.80 (978-0-03-055717-0(8)) Holt, Rinehart & Winston.

—Holt Science & Technology Chapter 1: Physical Science: The World of Physical Science. 5th ed. 2004. (Illus.). pap. 12.86 (978-0-03-030356-2(7)) Holt, Rinehart & Winston.

—Holt Science & Technology Chapter 7: Physical Science: Forces in Fluids. 5th ed. 2004. (Illus.). pap. 12.86 (978-0-03-030386-9(9)) Holt, Rinehart & Winston.

—Holt Science & Technology Chapter 8: Physical Science: Work & Machines. 5th ed. 2004. (Illus.). pap. 12.86 (978-0-03-030391-3(5)) Holt, Rinehart & Winston.

—Holt Science & Technology Chptr. 16: Matter & Motion: Chapter Resources - Tennessee Edition. 3rd ed. 2003. (YA). pap. 11.40 (978-0-03-069177-5(X)) Holt, Rinehart & Winston.

—Holt Science & Technology 2001: Physics: Directed Reading Worksheets with Answer Key. 2000. pap. 12.00 (978-0-03-055409-4(8)) Holt, Rinehart & Winston.

—Holt Science & Technology Online Edition. 5th ed. 2004. 15.93 (978-0-03-030581-8(0)); 15.93 (978-0-03-030582-5(9)); 15.93 (978-0-03-030583-2(7)); 15.93 (978-0-03-030586-3(1)); 15.93 (978-0-03-030591-7(8)); 15.93 (978-0-03-030594-8(2)); 15.93 (978-0-03-030596-2(9)); 15.93 (978-0-03-030597-9(7)); 15.93 (978-0-03-030598-6(5)); 15.93 (978-0-03-030599-3(3)); 15.93 (978-0-03-030601-3(9)); 15.93 (978-0-03-030602-0(7)); 15.93 (978-0-03-030603-7(5)); 15.93 (978-0-03-030604-4(3)); 15.93 (978-0-03-030606-8(X)) Holt, Rinehart & Winston.

—Holt Science Spectrum: A Physical Approach - Spanish Study Guide. 4th ed. Date not set. pap. 11.20 (978-0-03-068273-5(8)) Holt, Rinehart & Winston.

—Holt Science Spectrum Chptr. 7: Solutions. 4th ed. Date not set. (Illus.). pap. 11.20 (978-0-03-068584-2(2)) Holt, Rinehart & Winston.

—Holt Science Spectrum Chptr. 11: Forces. 4th ed. Date not set. pap. 11.20 (978-0-03-068583-5(4)) Holt, Rinehart & Winston.

—Physics: High School Science Test Preparation - Georgia Edition. 2001. (Holt Science & Technology Ser.). pap. 13.73 (978-0-03-067803-5(X)) Holt, Rinehart & Winston.

—Physics: Middle School Science Test Preparation - Alabama Edition. 2002. (Holt Science & Technology Ser.). pap. 13.73 (978-0-03-068123-3(5)) Holt, Rinehart & Winston.

—Physics: New York Test Preparation for the Regents Exam. 2nd ed. 2002. pap. 12.20 (978-0-03-070818-3(4)) Holt, Rinehart & Winston.

—Physics: Premier Online Edition. 6th ed. Date not set. 83.93 (978-0-03-036843-1(X)) Holt, Rinehart & Winston.

—Physics: Problem Workbook. 2nd ed. 2001. pap., wbk. ed. 31.00 (978-0-03-057337-8(8)) Holt, Rinehart & Winston.

—Physics: Science Special - Assessments. 4th ed. 2004. (SPA.). pap. 11.20 (978-0-03-068333-6(5)) Holt, Rinehart & Winston.

—Science Spectrum: Physics: Datasheets. 2000. pap. 12.13 (978-0-03-055584-8(1)) Holt, Rinehart & Winston.

—Science Spectrum: Physics Math Skills. 4th ed. 2004. pap., wbk. ed. 11.13 (978-0-03-067084-8(5)) Holt, Rinehart & Winston.

—Science Spectrum: Physics: Spanish Resources. 2000. pap. 114.73 (978-0-03-055594-7(9)) Holt, Rinehart & Winston.

Hyde, Philip, III. Defining Time: Lowering the Wacky Factor in Extending the Three Dimensions - A Linguistic Approach. l.t. ed. 2002. 121p. per. (978-0-9668013-2-3(6)) Groundwork Ideas Pr.

Illingworth, Valerie. Penguin Dictionary of Physics. 2000. (gr. 7-12). lib. bdg. 26.90 (978-0-613-64994-0(X)) Tandem Library Bks.

Integrated Physics & Chemistry, Chapter 1, Activities. 2005. (Illus.). 22p. (YA). pap. 5.00 (978-1-59476-173-7(6)) Paradigm Accelerated Curriculum.

Integrated Physics & Chemistry Chapter 1, Text. 2005. Orig. Title: (Key Topics. (Illus.). 34p. (YA). pap. 7.00 (978-1-59476-161-4(2)) Paradigm Accelerated Curriculum.

Integrated Physics & Chemistry, Chapter 10, Activities. 2005. (Illus.). 32p. (YA). pap. 5.00 (978-1-59476-182-9(5)) Paradigm Accelerated Curriculum.

Integrated Physics & Chemistry, Chapter 10, Text. 2005. (Illus.). 68p. (YA). pap. 7.00 (978-1-59476-170-6(1)) Paradigm Accelerated Curriculum.

Integrated Physics & Chemistry, Chapter 11, Activities. 2005. (Illus.). 40p. (YA). pap. 5.00 (978-1-59476-183-6(3)) Paradigm Accelerated Curriculum.

Integrated Physics & Chemistry, Chapter 11, Text. 2005. (Illus.). 64p. (YA). pap. 7.00 (978-1-59476-171-3(X)) Paradigm Accelerated Curriculum.

Integrated Physics & Chemistry, Chapter 12, Activities. 2005. (Illus.). 32p. (YA). pap. 5.00 (978-1-59476-184-3(1)) Paradigm Accelerated Curriculum.

Integrated Physics & Chemistry, Chapter 12, Text. 2005. (Illus.). 66p. (YA). pap. 7.00 (978-1-59476-172-0(8)) Paradigm Accelerated Curriculum.

Integrated Physics & Chemistry, Chapter 2, Activities. 2005. (Illus.). 42p. (YA). pap. 5.00 (978-1-59476-174-4(4)) Paradigm Accelerated Curriculum.

Integrated Physics & Chemistry, Chapter 2, Text. 2005. (Illus.). 66p. (YA). pap. 7.00 (978-1-59476-162-1(0)) Paradigm Accelerated Curriculum.

Integrated Physics & Chemistry, Chapter 3 Activities. 2005. (Illus.). 32p. (YA). pap. 5.00 (978-1-59476-175-1(2)) Paradigm Accelerated Curriculum.

Integrated Physics & Chemistry, Chapter 3, Text. 2005. (Illus.). 66p. (YA). pap. 7.00 (978-1-59476-163-8(9)) Paradigm Accelerated Curriculum.

Integrated Physics & Chemistry, Chapter 4, Text. 2005. (Illus.). 64p. (YA). pap. 7.00 (978-1-59476-164-5(7)) Paradigm Accelerated Curriculum.

Integrated Physics & Chemistry, Chapter 5, Activities. 2005. (Illus.). 32p. (YA). pap. 5.00 (978-1-59476-177-5(9)) Paradigm Accelerated Curriculum.

Integrated Physics & Chemistry, Chapter 5, Text. 2005. (Illus.). 64p. (YA). pap. 7.00 (978-1-59476-165-2(5)) Paradigm Accelerated Curriculum.

Integrated Physics & Chemistry, Chapter 6, Activities. 2005. (Illus.). 32p. (YA). pap. 5.00 (978-1-59476-178-2(7)) Paradigm Accelerated Curriculum.

Integrated Physics & Chemistry, Chapter 6, Text. 2005. (Illus.). 64p. (YA). pap. 7.00 (978-1-59476-166-9(3)) Paradigm Accelerated Curriculum.

Integrated Physics & Chemistry, Chapter 7, Activities. 2005. (Illus.). 32p. (YA). pap. 5.00 (978-1-59476-179-9(5)) Paradigm Accelerated Curriculum.

Integrated Physics & Chemistry, Chapter 7, Text. 2005. (Illus.). 66p. (YA). pap. 7.00 (978-1-59476-167-6(1)) Paradigm Accelerated Curriculum.

Integrated Physics & Chemistry, Chapter 8, Activities. 2005. (Illus.). 32p. (YA). pap. 5.00 (978-1-59476-180-5(9)) Paradigm Accelerated Curriculum.

Integrated Physics & Chemistry, Chapter 8, Text. 2005. (Illus.). 64p. (YA). pap. 7.00 (978-1-59476-168-3(X)) Paradigm Accelerated Curriculum.

Integrated Physics & Chemistry, Chapter 9, Activities. 2005. (Illus.). 32p. (YA). pap. 5.00 (978-1-59476-181-2(7)) Paradigm Accelerated Curriculum.

Integrated Physics & Chemistry, Chapter 9, Text. 2005. (Illus.). 68p. (YA). pap. 7.00 (978-1-59476-169-0(8)) Paradigm Accelerated Curriculum.

Integrated Physics & Chemistry, Full Course Kit, 25 bks. 2005. (Illus.). 7969p. (YA). 169.00 (978-1-59476-187-4(6)) Paradigm Accelerated Curriculum.

Integrated Physics & Chemistry, Teacher's Resource Kit with CD. 2005. (Illus.). 439p. (YA). pap. 25.00 (978-1-59476-185-0(X)) Paradigm Accelerated Curriculum.

Johnson, Keith & Johnson, B. A. Physics for You. 2nd rev. ed. 2001. (Illus.). 400p. (YA). pap. 36.50 (978-0-7487-6236-1(1)) Nelson Thornes Ltd. GBR. *Dist:* Trans-Atlantic Pubns., Inc.

Johnson, Keith, et al. Advanced Physics for You. 2000. (Illus.). 432p. (YA). pap. 62.50 (978-0-7487-5296-6(X)) Nelson Thornes Ltd. GBR. *Dist:* Trans-Atlantic Pubns., Inc.

Kelder, Karin H. Study & Master Physical Science Grade 10 Learner's Book. 2005. 288p. pap. 16.30 (978-0-521-67358-7(5)) Cambridge Univ. Pr.

—Study & Master Physical Science Grade 10 Learner's Book Afrikaans Translation. 2005. (AFR.). 288p. pap. 16.30 (978-0-521-67360-0(7)) Cambridge Univ. Pr.

Lafferty, Peter & Dorling Kindersley Publishing Staff. Force & Motion. 2000. (Eyewitness Bks.). (Illus.). 64p. (J). (gr. 4-7). lib. bdg. 19.99 (978-0-7894-6712-6(7)) Dorling Kindersley Publishing, Inc.

Lancaster, Juliana. PBIS- Lift, Spin, Drop & Fall. 2005. pap., stu. ed. 8.00 (978-1-58591-564-4(5)) It's About Time, Herff Jones Education Diiv.

Large, Tori. Illustrated Dict of Physics. 2007. 128p. (J). pap. 12.99 (978-0-7945-1561-4(4) , Usborne) EDC Publishing.

Larousse Mexico Staff, ed. Fuerza y Movimiento. 2005. (40 Fantasticos Experimentos Ser.). (SPA.). 40p. (gr. 3-5). pap. 5.95 (978-970-22-0863-1(7)) Larousse, Ediciones, S. A. de C. V. MEX. *Dist:* Houghton Mifflin Co. Trade & Reference Div.

—Luz y Sonido. 2005. (40 Fantasticos Experimentos Ser.). (SPA.). 40p. (gr. 3-5). pap. 5.95 (978-970-22-0866-2(1)) Larousse, Ediciones, S. A. de C. V. MEX. *Dist:* Houghton Mifflin Co. Trade & Reference Div.

The Library of Physics, 6 bk. set. 2005. (YA). (gr. 7-12). lib. bdg. 151.50 (978-1-4042-0381-5(8)) Rosen Publishing Group, Inc., The.

Lord, Roberta. Reflections: English Version. 2003. 200p. 9.95 net. (978-1-931934-23-7(1)) Back Yard Pub.

Malone, Peter. Close to the Wind: The Beaufort Scale. 2007. 32p. (J). (gr. k). 16.99 (978-0-399-24399-8(2) , Putnam Juvenile) Penguin Group (USA) Inc.

Materia: Cuaderno de Evaluacion: Unit 4: Materia (Matter) 2000. (McGraw-Hill Ciencias Ser.). (ENG & SPA.). (gr. 5 up). (978-0-02-278674-8(0)) Macmillan/McGraw-Hill Schl. Div.

Materia en movimiento: Cuaderno de Evaluacion: Unit 2: Materia en movimiento (Matter on the Move) 2000. (McGraw-Hill Ciencias Ser.). (ENG & SPA.). (gr. 4 up). (978-0-02-278661-8(9)) Macmillan/McGraw-Hill Schl. Div.

Materia en movimiento: Recursos para el maestro con clave de Respuestas: Unit 2: Materia en movimiento (Matter on the Move) 2000. (McGraw-Hill Ciencias Ser.). (ENG & SPA.). (gr. 4 up). (978-0-02-278701-1(1)) Macmillan/McGraw-Hill Schl. Div.

Materia: Recursos para el maestro con clave de Respuestas: Unit 4: Materia (Matter) 2000. (McGraw-Hill Ciencias Ser.). (ENG & SPA.). (gr. 5 up). (978-0-02-278711-0(9)) Macmillan/McGraw-Hill Schl. Div.

Materia y energia: Cuaderno de Evaluacion: Unit 3: Materia y energia (Matter & Energy) 2000. (McGraw-Hill Ciencias Ser.). (ENG & SPA.). (gr. 3 up). (978-0-02-278651-9(1)) Macmillan/McGraw-Hill Schl. Div.

Materia y energia: Recursos para el maestro con clave de Respuestas: Unit 3: Materia y energia (Matter & Energy) 2000. (McGraw-Hill Ciencias Ser.). (ENG & SPA.). (gr. 3 up). (978-0-02-278694-6(5)) Macmillan/McGraw-Hill Schl. Div.

Materia y mas materia: Cuaderno de Evaluacion: Unit 3: Materia y mas materia (Matter, Matter Everywhere) 2000. (McGraw-Hill Ciencias Ser.). (ENG & SPA.). (gr. 1 up). (978-0-02-278629-8(5)) Macmillan/McGraw-Hill Schl. Div.

Materia y mas materia: Recursos para el maestro con clave de Respuestas: Unit 3: Materia y mas materia (Matter, Matter Everywhere) 2000. (McGraw-Hill Ciencias Ser.). (ENG & SPA.). (gr. 1 up). (978-0-02-278680-9(5)) Macmillan/McGraw-Hill Schl. Div.

McGraw-Hill Staff. Glencoe Physical Science. 2nd ed. 2004. (C). stu. ed. 85.32 (978-0-07-860051-7(0) , 9780078600517) Glencoe/McGraw-Hill.

—Glencoe Physical Science Reading Essentials. 2004. pap., stu. ed. 34.64 (978-0-07-866089-4(0) , 9780078660894) Glencoe/McGraw-Hill.

—Glencoe Physical Science Reinforcement. 2004. (C). pap., stu. ed. 11.96 (978-0-07-866091-7(2) , 9780078660917) Glencoe/McGraw-Hill.

—Glencoe Science: Physical Science Modules. 2004. pap., stu. ed. 8.64 (978-0-07-867309-2(7) , 9780078673092) Glencoe/McGraw-Hill.

—Glencoe Science: Waves, Sound, & Light. 2004. pap., stu. ed., lab manual ed. 8.64 (978-0-07-867322-1(4) , 9780078673221) Glencoe/McGraw-Hill.

—Glencoe Science: Waves, Sound & Light. 2nd ed. 2004. (C). stu. ed. 20.64 (978-0-07-861776-8(6) , 9780078617768) Glencoe/McGraw-Hill.

—Introduction to Physical Science. 2004. pap., stu. ed. 11.96 (978-0-07-867338-2(0) , 9780078673382); 2nd ed. stu. ed. 85.32 (978-0-07-861704-1(9) , 9780078617041) Glencoe/McGraw-Hill.

—Introduction to Physical Science Standardized Test Practice. 2004. (C). pap., stu. ed. 10.64 (978-0-07-867083-1(7) , 9780078670831) Glencoe/McGraw-Hill.

Milner, Bryan. Science Foundations Presents Physics 1 C. 2004. (YA). cd-rom 120.00 (978-1-84565-017-9(4)) Cambridge Univ. Pr.

Milner, Bryan, et al, eds. Core Science 1: Key Concepts. 1998. (Core Science Ser.). (Illus.). 302p. pap. 30.00 (978-0-521-58850-8(2)) Cambridge Univ. Pr.

—Core Science 2: Consolidation. 1998. (Core Science Ser.). (Illus.). 244p. pap. 24.00 (978-0-521-58849-2(9)) Cambridge Univ. Pr.

Modern Drummer Publications Staff. Solids, Liquids & Gases. 2000. (Starting with Science Ser.). (Illus.). 32p. (J). (gr. k-3). (978-1-55074-401-9(1)) Kids Can Pr., Ltd.

Modules: Physical Science. 2005. (gr. 6-12). lab manual ed. (978-0-618-43729-0(0) , 2-01222) McDougal Littell Inc.

Modules: Physical Science; Electricity & Magnetism PE. 2005. (gr. 6-12). (978-0-618-33440-7(8) , 2-01027) McDougal Littell Inc.

Modules: Physical Science; Matter & Energy. 2005. (gr. 6-12). lab manual ed. (978-0-618-43732-0(0) , 2-01225) McDougal Littell Inc.

Modules: Physical Science; Matter & Energy PE. 2005. (gr. 6-12). (978-0-618-33444-5(0) , 2-01031) McDougal Littell Inc.

Modules: Physical Science; Motion & Forces PE. 2005. (gr. 6-12). (978-0-618-33442-1(4) , 2-01029); lab manual ed. (978-0-618-43733-7(9) , 2-01226) McDougal Littell Inc.

Modules: Physical Science; Waves, Sound, & Light Lab Manual, PE. 2005. (gr. 6-12). (978-0-618-43736-8(3) , 2-01229) McDougal Littell Inc.

Modules: Physical Science; Waves, Sound, & Light PE. 2005. (gr. 6-12). (978-0-618-33446-9(7) , 2-01033) McDougal Littell Inc.

Moreau, Nancy. Physics: Physical Setting STAReview. 2003. (ENG., Illus.). 397p. (YA). per. 15.95 (978-0-935487-76-3(X) , STAReviews) N&N Publishing Co., Inc.

Murphy, Patricia J. Around & Around. 2002. (gr. k-3). lib. bdg. 12.95 (978-0-613-53338-6(0)) Tandem Library Bks.

Nelson. Science Spectacular Physics: Enhanced Online Edition. 6th ed. Date not set. cd-rom 87.33 (978-0-03-040014-8(7)) Holt, Rinehart & Winston.

Nikolo, Martin. Physics for the Rest of Us. 2003. (Illus.). 280p. pap. 79.95 (978-0-9741638-0-2(5)) Copernicus Pr.

Niz, Ellen Sturm. Floating & Sinking. 2005. (First Facts Ser.). (Illus.). 24p. (J). (978-0-7368-5401-6(0)) Capstone Pr., Inc.

Nsrc. Science & Technology for Children Books, Ecosystems. 2004. (Illus.). 64p. (J). (978-1-933008-05-9(9)) National Science Resources Ctr.

—Science & Technology for Children Books, Floating & Sinking. 2004. (Illus.). 64p. (J). (978-1-933008-07-3(5)) National Science Resources Ctr.

—Science & Technology for Children Books, Magnets & Motors. 2004. (Illus.). 64p. (J). (978-1-933008-10-3(5)) National Science Resources Ctr.

O'Connell, Diane. Strong Fence: The Story of Physicist Shirley Ann Jackson. 2006. (Women's Adventures in Science Ser.). (Illus.). 128p. pap. 9.95 (978-0-309-09553-2(0) , Joseph Henry Pr.) National Academies Pr.

Our Physical World. (First Facts Ser.). (Illus.). (J). (gr. 1-2). lib. bdg. 170.08 (978-0-7368-2750-8(1)) Capstone Pr., Inc.

Oxlade, Chris, et al, eds. Illustrated Dictionary of Physics. 2nd rev. ed. 2004. (Illustrated Dictionaries Ser.). (Illus.). 128p. (J). (gr. 7 up). pap. 12.95 (978-0-7460-3796-6(1)) EDC Publishing.

Parker, Vic. Rough or Smooth. 2004. (Raintree Sprouts Ser.). (Illus.). 24p. (J). (ps-ps). lib. bdg. 18.56 (978-1-4109-0764-6(3)) Raintree.

Parker, Victoria. Is It Rough or Smooth? 2004. (J). pap. (978-1-4109-0769-1(4)) Raintree.

Parratore, Phil. Hands-On Physical Science. 2001. (Cool, Awesome, Simple Science Ser.). (Illus.). 64p. (J). pap. 9.99 (978-0-88724-651-7(6) , CD-7322) Carson-Dellosa Publishing Co., Inc.

—Hands-On Physics. 2001. (Cool, Awesome, Simple Science Ser.). (Illus.). 64p. (J). pap. 9.99 (978-0-88724-653-1(2) , CD-7324) Carson-Dellosa Publishing Co., Inc.

Paul, Margaret & Wadsworth, Julie B., eds. Physical Science. 2000. (J). (gr. 4-6). 4.95 (978-1-55708-629-7(X) , MCR744) McDonald Publishing Co.

The People, Places & Principles of Integrated Physics & Chemistry. 2000. (YA). (gr. 7-12). Vol. 1. stu. ed., spiral bd. (978-1-928629-18-4(0)); Vol. 2. stu. ed., spiral bd. (978-1-928629-19-1(9)); Vol. 3. stu. ed., spiral bd. (978-1-928629-20-7(2)); Vol. 4. stu. ed., spiral bd. (978-1-928629-21-4(0)) Paradigm Accelerated Curriculum.

The People, Places & Principles of Integrated Physics & Chemistry: Activities, Quizzes & Tests. 2000. (YA). (gr. 7-12). Vol. 1. spiral bd. (978-1-928629-22-1(9)); Vol. 2. spiral bd. (978-1-928629-23-8(7)); Vol. 3. spiral bd. (978-1-928629-24-5(5)); Vol. 3. spiral bd. (978-1-928629-25-2(3)) Paradigm Accelerated Curriculum.

Pipe, Jim. Balancing. 2007. (J). (***978-1-59604-137-0(4)***) Stargazer Bks.

Randolph, Joanne. Liquids in My World. 2006. (My World of Science Ser.). (J). 16.00 (978-1-4042-3285-3(0) , PowerKids Pr.) Rosen Publishing Group, Inc., The.

—Solids in My World. 2006. (My World of Science Ser.). (Illus.). 24p. (J). 16.00 (978-1-4042-3283-9(4) , PowerKids Pr.) Rosen Publishing Group, Inc., The.

—Solids in My World: Los Solidos en Mi Mundo. 2006. (My World of Science/ Mi mundo y la Ciencia Ser.). (ENG & SPA., Illus.). 24p. (J). 16.00 (978-1-4042-3314-0(8) , PowerKids Pr.) Rosen Publishing Group, Inc., The.

Richards, Roy. En Movimiento. (Coleccion 101 Trucos Cientificos). (SPA., Illus.). (J). (gr. 3-5). pap. (978-950-724-176-5(0) , LMA8753) Lumen ARG. *Dist:* Lectorum Pubns., Inc.

Rivera, Sheila. Is It Heavy or Light? 2004. (First Step Nonfiction Ser.). (J). pap. (978-0-8225-5408-0(9) , Lerner Pubns.) Lerner Publishing Group.

Rookie Read-About Science: Physical Science, 6 bks., Set. Incl. Energy in Motion. Stewart, Melissa. 20.50 (978-0-516-24956-8(8)); Energy Is Everywhere. Young, June. 20.50 (978-0-516-25902-4(4)); Look How It Changes! Young, June. 20.50 (978-0-516-25901-7(6)); What Is Density? Barkan, Joanne. 20.50 (978-0-516-23618-6(0)); What Is Volume? Trumbauer, Lisa. 20.50 (978-0-516-23621-6(0)); Will It Float or Sink? Stewart, Melissa. 20.50 (978-0-516-24955-1(X)); (Illus.). 32p. (J). (gr. 1-2). 2006. 2006. 117.00 (978-0-516-25417-3(0) , Children's Pr.) Scholastic Library Publishing.

Rosinsky, Natalie M. Sinking & Floating. 2004. (Illus.). 32p. (J). (gr. 3 up). lib. bdg. 21.26 (978-0-7565-0598-1(4)) Compass Point Bks.

Royston, Angela. Solids, Liquids & Gasses. (My World of Science Ser.). (Illus.). 32p. (J). (gr. k-2). 2002. pap. 6.95 (978-1-4034-0044-4(X) , 91488); 2001. lib. bdg. 21.36 (978-1-58810-245-4(9)) Heinemann Library.

Ryan, Lawrie, et al. Physics. 2003. (Illus.). 80p. pap. (978-0-7487-6801-1(7)) Nelson Thornes Ltd.

Sang, David. Physics 2. 2001. (Cambridge Advanced Sciences Ser.). (Illus.). 176p. (YA). pap. 24.00 (978-0-521-79715-3(2)) Cambridge Univ. Pr.

Schaefer, Lola M. Start & Stop. Saunders-Smith, Gail, ed. 1999. (Way Things Move Ser.). (Illus.). 24p. (J). (gr. k-1). lib. bdg. 15.93 (978-0-7368-0397-7(1) , Pebble Bks.) Capstone Pr., Inc.

—Start & Stop. 1999. pap. 13.25 (978-0-516-21924-0(3) , Children's Pr.) Scholastic Library Publishing.

—The Way Things Move, 6 bks. Saunders-Smith, Gail, ed. Incl. Back & Forth. lib. bdg. 15.93 (978-0-7368-0398-4(X)); Circular Movement. lib. bdg. 15.93 (978-0-7368-0400-4(5)); Push & Pull. lib. bdg. 15.93 (978-0-7368-0396-0(3)); Start & Stop. lib. bdg. 15.93 (978-0-7368-0397-7(1)); Vibrations. lib. bdg. 15.93 (978-0-7368-0399-1(8)); Zigzag Movement. lib. bdg. 15.93 (978-0-7368-0401-1(3)); 24p. (J). (gr. k-1). 1999. (Illus.). 2000. Set lib. bdg. 95.58 (978-0-7368-0452-3(8) , Pebble Bks.) Capstone Pr., Inc.

School Specialty Publishing. Physics. 2004. (Hands-on Experiments Ser.). 80p. (J). (gr. k-2). pap. 10.99 (978-0-7424-2748-8(X) , IFG99236) School Specialty Publishing.

Science & Technology for Children Books, Ecosystems Set, 8 vols. 2004. (Illus.). (J). (978-1-933008-17-2(2)) National Science Resources Ctr.

Science & Technology for Children Books, Floating & Sinking Set, 8 vols. 2004. (Illus.). 64p. (J). (978-1-933008-19-6(9)) National Science Resources Ctr.

Science & Technology for Children Books, Magnets & Motors Set, 8 vols. 2004. (Illus.). 64p. (J). (978-1-933008-22-6(9)) National Science Resources Ctr.

Serway. Holt Physics: Enhanced Online Edition. 2nd ed. 2002. 76.93 (978-0-03-072486-2(4)) Holt, Rinehart & Winston.

Sian revision gears at Work. 2004. (Science in A Nutshell(R) Ser.). (J). (978-1-59242-037-7(0)) Delta Education, LLC.

Sian revision pulley Power. 2004. (J). (978-1-59242-061-2(3)) Delta Education, LLC.

Sian Solids. 2004. (J). (978-1-59242-073-5(7)) Delta Education, LLC.

Slippery or Sticky?, 6 pack. 2004. (Illus.). lib. bdg. 31.05 (978-1-4109-0777-6(5)) Raintree.

Sonneborn, Liz. Forces in Nature: Understanding Gravitational, Electrical, & Magnetic Force. 2004. (Library of Physics). (Illus.). 48p. (YA). lib. bdg. 25.25 (978-1-4042-0332-7(X)) Rosen Publishing Group, Inc., The.

Spyglass Books-Physical Science Complete Set. (Spyglass Books-Physical Science Ser.). (gr. 1-2). 119.58 (978-0-7565-0785-5(5)) Compass Point Bks.

Stewart, Melissa. Energy in Motion. 2006. 32p. (YA). (gr. 1-2). pap. 4.95 (978-0-516-23736-7(5) , Children's Pr.) Scholastic Library Publishing.

—Will It Float or Sink? 2006. 32p. (gr. 1-2). (YA). pap. 4.95 (978-0-516-23737-4(3)); (Illus.). (J). 20.50 (978-0-516-24955-1(X)) Scholastic Library Publishing. (Children's Pr.).

Stille, Darlene R. Physical Change: Reshaping Matter. 2005. (Exploring Science Ser.). (Illus.). 48p. (J). (gr. 5-7). (978-0-7565-1257-6(3)) Compass Point Bks.

Stockley, Corinne. Dictionary of Physics. 1999. (Illustrated Dictionaries Ser.). (Illus.). 128p. (J). (gr. 7-11). lib. bdg. 20.95 (978-0-88110-308-3(X)) EDC Publishing.

—Usborne Illustrated Dictionary of Science: A Complete Reference Guide to Ph. 2002. (gr. 7-12). lib. bdg. 41.95 (978-0-613-86937-9(0)) Tandem Library Bks.

Tobin, William. The Life & Science of Léon Foucault: The Man Who Proved the Earth Rotates. 2003. (Illus.). 352p. 90.00 (978-0-521-80855-2(3)) Cambridge Univ. Pr.

Tocci, Salvatore. Elements, 6 bks., Set. 2005. (J). 144.00 (978-0-516-25214-8(3) , Children's Pr.) Scholastic Library Publishing.

Townsend, John. Foolish Physics. 2006. (Illus.). 56p. (J). pap. (978-1-4109-2382-0(7)) Steck-Vaughn.

Trumbauer, Lisa. You Can Use a Compass. (Rookie Read-About Science Ser.). (Illus.). (J). 2004. 31p. (gr. 1-2). pap. 4.95 (978-0-516-24610-9(0)); 2003. 32p. 20.50 (978-0-516-22870-9(6)) Scholastic Library Publishing. (Children's Pr.).

Twist, Clint. Force & Motion. 2005. (Check It Out! Ser.). (Illus.). 24p. (J). lib. bdg. 19.96 (978-1-59716-061-2(X)) Bearport Publishing Co., Inc.

—Light & Sound. 2005. (Check It Out! Ser.). (Illus.). 24p. (J). (gr. 3-7). lib. bdg. 19.96 (978-1-59716-060-5(1)) Bearport Publishing Co., Inc.

Unterman, Nathan A. Amusement Park Physics. 2001. 210p. (gr. 9-12). tchr. ed. 24.99 (978-0-8251-4264-2(4) , 0-42644) Walch Publishing.

Usborne Books Staff, ed. Illustrated Dictionary of Physics. rev. ed. 2004. (Illustrated Dictionaries Ser.). (Illus.). 128p. (J). (gr. 7 up). lib. bdg. 20.95 (978-1-58086-283-7(7)) EDC Publishing.

Walker, Sally M. Sound. King, Andy, photos by. 2006. (Early Bird Energy Ser.). (Illus.). 48p. (J). (ps-7). 25.26 (978-0-8225-2634-6(4) , Lerner Pubns.) Lerner Publishing Group.

What Floats? Big Book: Level C. 8p. 20.95 (978-0-322-00370-5(9)) Wright Group, The.

Whitehouse, Patricia. Sliding. 2003. (Illus.). 24p. (J). pap. (978-1-4034-3471-5(9)); lib. bdg. 18.50 (978-1-4034-0906-5(4)) Heinemann Library.

Whiteley, Peter & Bassarath, Haydn. CXC Revision Guide for Physics. 2nd rev. ed. 2007. 128p. pap. 9.50 (978-0-521-69294-6(6)) Cambridge Univ. Pr.

Willett, Edward. The Basics of Quantum Physics: Understanding the Photoelectric Effect & Line Spectra. 2004. (Library of Physics). (Illus.). 48p. (YA). lib. bdg. 25.25 (978-1-4042-0334-1(6)) Rosen Publishing Group, Inc., The.

Williams, Gareth, et al. New Physics for You. 2nd ed. 2006. (Illus.). 400p. (YA). pap., stu. ed. 44.00 (978-0-7487-8328-1(8)) Nelson Thornes Ltd. GBR. *Dist:* Trans-Atlantic Pubns., Inc.

Willis, Shirley. Dime Como Flotan los Barcos. 1999. (Coleccion los Estupendos). (SPA., Illus.). 32p. (J). (gr. 2). 20.00 (978-0-531-11845-0(2) , OD30017, Watts, Franklin) Scholastic Library Publishing.

Wilson, Jim. Gravity Rules! Activity Book & Video. Cordel, Betty, ed. Mason, Renee, illus. 1998. 170p. (YA). (gr. 5-12). pap. 36.95 incl. VHS (978-1-881431-80-0(0) , 4075) AIMS Education Foundation.

Wolf, Jonathan S. How to Prepare for the AP Physics B. 3rd ed. 2003. (Illus.). 480p. pap. 16.95 (978-0-7641-2359-7(9)) Barron's Educational Series, Inc.

Yamamoto, Lani. Albert. Yamamoto, Lani, illus. 2005. (Illus.). 28p. (J). 10.95 (978-1-58536-265-3(4)) Sleeping Bear Pr.

Zoehfeld, Kathleen Weidner. What Is the World Made Of? All about Solids, Liquids, & Gases. Meisel, Paul, illus. 1998. 32p. (J). (ps-ps). lib. bdg. 13.00 (978-0-613-12263-4(1)) Tandem Library Bks.

PHYSICS, ASTRONOMICAL

see Astrophysics

PHYSICS—EXPERIMENTS

Ace Academics, ed. Physics: A Whole Course in a Box! 2007. (Exambusters Ser.). 384p. (gr. 7 up). 12.95 (978-1-881374-87-9(4) , Exambusters) Ace Academics, Inc.

Adams, Richard & Goodwin, Peter. Physics Projects for Young Scientists. 2000. (Illus.). 128p. (YA). (gr. 8-12). lib. bdg. 15.25 (978-0-613-54084-1(0)) Tandem Library Bks.

Adams, Richard C. Physics Projects for Young Scientists. rev. ed. 2000. (J). (978-0-606-19405-1(3)) Tandem Library Bks.

Adams, Richard C. & Goodwin, Peter. Engineering Projects for Young Scientists. rev. ed. (Projects for Young Scientists Ser.). 128p. 2002. (J). pap. (978-0-531-16145-6(5)); 2001. (Illus.). (YA). (gr. 9-12). 23.50 (978-0-531-11668-5(9)) Scholastic Library Publishing. (Watts, Franklin).

—Physics Projects for Young Scientists. 2000. (Projects for Young Scientists Ser.). (Illus.). 128p. (YA). (gr. 9-12). rev. ed. 23.50 (978-0-531-11667-8(0)); 2nd rev. ed. pap. 6.95 (978-0-531-16461-7(6)) Scholastic Library Publishing. (Watts, Franklin).

Almukahhal, Raja. Physics Laboratory Experiments for the Gifted: Middle & High School. 2005. (Illus.). 90p. (978-0-910609-51-7(9)) Gifted Education Pr.

Breckenridge, Judy. Physics Experiments. Gallagher, Jack, illus. 2006. (No Sweat Science Ser.). 128p. pap. 5.95 (978-1-4027-2332-2(6)) Sterling Publishing Co., Inc.

Cobb, Vicki. I Fall Down. Gorton, Julia, illus. 2004. (Science Play Ser.). 40p. (J). (ps-k). 15.99 (978-0-688-17842-0(1)) HarperCollins Pubs.

DiSpezio, Michael A. Awesome Experiments in Electricity & Magnetism. 2006. (Illus.). 160p. pap. 6.95 (978-1-4027-2370-4(9)) Sterling Publishing Co., Inc.

—Awesome Experiments in Force & Motion. 2006. (Illus.). 160p. pap. 6.95 (978-1-4027-2371-1(7)) Sterling Publishing Co., Inc.

Dobson, Ken & Roberts, Martin. Physics. 2nd ed. 2002. (Nelson Science Ser.). (Illus.). 352p. pap., stu. ed. 36.50 (978-0-7487-6240-8(X)) Nelson Thornes Ltd. GBR. *Dist:* Trans-Atlantic Pubns., Inc.

Friedhoffer, Robert. Physics Lab in the Home. 1998. (Physical Science Labs Ser.). (Illus.). (YA). (gr. 5-8). pap. 6.95 (978-0-531-15845-6(4) , Watts, Franklin) Scholastic Library Publishing.

Gardner, Robert. Bicycle Science Projects: Physics on Wheels. 2004. (Science Fair Success Ser.). (Illus.). 112p. (J). lib. bdg. 26.60 (978-0-7660-1630-9(7)) Enslow Pubs., Inc.

—Heavy-Duty Science Projects with Weight: How Much Does It Weigh? 2003. (Sensational Science Experiments Ser.). (Illus.). 48p. (J). (gr. 1-4). lib. bdg. 23.93 (978-0-7660-2013-9(4)) Enslow Pubs., Inc.

—Physics Projects with a Light Box You Can Build. 2007. (Build-a-Lab! Science Experiments Ser.). (Illus.). 128p. (J). (gr. 5). lib. bdg. 31.93 ***(978-0-7660-2810-4(0))*** Enslow Pubs., Inc.

—Science Project Ideas in the House. rev. ed. 2002. (Science Project Ideas Ser.). (Illus.). 128p. (J). (gr. 4-9). lib. bdg. 26.60 (978-0-7660-1705-4(2)) Enslow Pubs., Inc.

—Science Projects about Physics in the Home. 1999. (Science Projects Ser.). (Illus.). 112p. (YA). (gr. 6-12). lib. bdg. 26.60 (978-0-89490-948-1(7)) Enslow Pubs., Inc.

—Science Projects about the Physics of Toys & Games. 2000. (Science Projects Ser.). (Illus.). 128p. (YA). (gr. 6-12). lib. bdg. 26.60 (978-0-7660-1165-6(8)) Enslow Pubs., Inc.

Griffith, Dave. Physics, Vol. 1. 1999. (Illus.). (YA). pap., wbk. ed. 15.00 (978-1-886998-07-0(8)) Pasco Scientific.

Hewitt, Sally. Friction. 2007. (J). ***(978-1-59604-139-4(0))*** Stargazer Bks.

Holt, Rinehart and Winston Staff. Physics: Lab Experiments. 2nd ed. 2000. pap. 11.40 (978-0-03-057358-3(0)); pap., tchr. ed. 42.86 (978-0-03-057359-0(9)) Holt, Rinehart & Winston.

Hopwood, James. Cool Gravity Activities: Fun Science Projects about Balance. 2007. (Cool Science Ser.). (Illus.). 32p. (J). (gr. k-6). lib. bdg. 24.21 ***(978-1-59928-908-3(3)*** , Checkerboard Library) ABDO Publishing Co.

McGraw-Hill Staff. Glencoe Physical Science. 2004. (C). pap., stu. ed., lab manual ed. 11.96 (978-0-07-866084-9(X) , 9780078660849) Glencoe/McGraw-Hill.

Oxlade, Chris. Physics: 50 Great Science Experiments & Projects. 2004. (Hands-On Science Ser.). (Illus.). 64p. pap. 10.99 (978-1-84215-856-2(2) , Southwater) Anness Publishing GBR. *Dist:* National Bk. Network.

Pipe, Jim. Floating & Sinking. 2007. (J). ***(978-1-59604-133-2(1))*** Stargazer Bks.

Popular Science Editors. Fantastic Phenomena. 2007. (Experiment with Science Ser.). 32p. (J). pap. 7.95 ***(978-0-531-18759-3(4));*** (Illus.). (gr. 3-6). lib. bdg. 25.00 ***(978-0-531-18543-8(5))*** Scholastic Library Publishing. (Children's Pr.).

School Specialty Publishing. Physics. 2004. (Hands-on Experiments Ser.). 80p. (J). (gr. 3-5). pap. 10.99 (978-0-7424-2749-5(8) , IFG99235) School Specialty Publishing.

VanCleave, Janice Pratt. Janice VanCleave's A+ Projects in Physics: Winning Experiments for Science Fairs & Extra Credit. 2003. (VanCleave a+ Science Projects Ser.). (Illus.). 240p. 27.95 (978-0-471-39017-6(8) , Wiley) Wiley, John & Sons, Inc.

Whitehouse, Patricia. Rodar. 2003. Tr. of Rolling. 5.25 (978-1-4034-3459-3(X)) Heinemann Library.

Williams, Zella. Experiments with Physical Science. 2007. (Do-It-Yourself Science Ser.). (Illus.). 24p. (J). (gr. 2-5). lib. bdg. 23.95 (978-1-4042-3659-2(7)) Rosen Publishing Group, Inc., The.

PHYSICS—HISTORY

Allan, Tony. Isaac Newton. (Groundbreakers Ser.). (Illus.). 48p. (J). (gr. 5-7). 2002. pap. 8.50 (978-1-58810-992-7(5) , 91467); 2001. lib. bdg. 25.64 (978-1-58810-053-5(7)) Heinemann Library.

Atkinson, Mary. The Earth Is Flat! Science Facts & Fictions. 2007. (Shockwave: Science in Practice Ser.). (Illus.). 36p. (J). (gr. 4-6). lib. bdg. 25.00 ***(978-0-531-17580-4(4)*** , Children's Pr.) Scholastic Library Publishing.

Renn, Jurgen, ed. Einstein's Annalen Papers: The Complete Collection 1901 - 1922. 2005. (ENG & GER., Illus.). 590p. 155.00 (978-3-527-40564-0(X)) Wiley, John & Sons, Inc.

Townsend, John. Foolish Physics. 2006. (Illus.). 56p. (J). (978-1-4109-2377-6(0)) Steck-Vaughn.

PHYSICS, TERRESTRIAL

see Geophysics

PHYSICS—VOCATIONAL GUIDANCE

J. G. Ferguson Publishing Company Staff. Careers in Focus: Mathematics. 2003. (Careers in Focus Ser.). (Illus.). 192p. (YA). (gr. 6-12). 22.95 (978-0-89434-413-8(7) , Ferguson Publishing Co.) Facts On File, Inc.

PHYSIOGRAPHY

see Physical Geography

PHYSIOLOGICAL CHEMISTRY

see Biochemistry

PHYSIOLOGISTS

Bosarge, Jerusha. Inventing Ott: The Legacy of Arthur C. Guyton. 2005. (Illus.). 120p. (J). (gr. 3-7). 10.95 (978-1-893062-78-8(3)) Quail Ridge Pr., Inc.

Elford, Jole Shack. William Harvey & the Mechanics of the Heart. 2005. (Illus.). 141p. (YA). (gr. 6-10). reprint ed. 28.00 (978-0-7567-9712-6(8)) DIANE Publishing Co.

Saunders, Barbara R. Ivan Pavlov: Exploring the Mysteries of Behavior. 2006. (Great Minds of Science Ser.). (Illus.). 112p. (J). (gr. 4-10). lib. bdg. 31.93 (978-0-7660-2506-6(3)) Enslow Pubs., Inc.

Tracy, Kathleen. Friedrich Miescher & the Story of Nucleic Acid. 2005. (Uncharted, Unexplored, & Unexplained Ser.). (Illus.). 48p. (J). (gr. 4-8). lib. bdg. 29.95 (978-1-58415-369-6(5)) Mitchell Lane Pubs., Inc.

Yount, Lisa. William Harvey: Discoverer of How Blood Circulates. 2008. (Great Minds of Science Ser.). 128p. (J). (gr. 5 up). lib. bdg. 31.93 ***(978-0-7660-3010-7(5))*** Enslow Pubs., Inc.

PHYSIOLOGY

see also Anatomy; Blood; Bones; Cells; Digestion; Growth; Nervous System; Nutrition; Old Age; Reproduction; Respiration; Senses and Sensation

also names of organs, e.g. Heart

Allman, Toney. From Bat Sonar to Canes for the Blind. 2005. (Imitating Nature Ser.). (Illus.). 32p. (J). (gr. 3-6). 24.95 (978-0-7377-3191-0(5) , Greenhaven Pr., Inc.) Thomson Gale.

Andrews, Barbara. The Respiratory System. 2006. pap. 39.00 ***(978-1-4108-6511-3(8))*** Benchmark Education Co.

Avison, Brigid. I Wonder Why I Blink: And Other Questions about My Body. 2003. (I Wonder Why Ser.). 32p. (J). (gr. k-3). pap. 6.95 (978-0-7534-5610-1(9) , Kingfisher) Houghton Mifflin Co. Trade & Reference Div.

—I Wonder Why I Blink: And Other Questions about My Body. 2003. (gr. k-3). lib. bdg. 14.10 (978-0-613-63159-4(5)) Tandem Library Bks.

Ballard, Carol. The Skeleton & Muscles. 2005. (Exploring the Human Body Ser.). (Illus.). 32p. (J). (gr. 4-7). lib. bdg. 24.95 (978-0-7377-3022-7(6) , Greenhaven Pr., Inc.) Thomson Gale.

Barron's Educational Editorial Staff. Understanding the Human Body. 1998. (Megascope Ser.). (Illus.). 64p. (J). (gr. 4-7). 6.95 (978-0-7641-5093-7(6)) Barron's Educational Series, Inc.

Beres, Samantha. 101 Things Every Kid Should Know about the Human Body. 2000. (Illus.). 112p. (J). (gr. 3-7). 14.95 (978-0-7373-0329-2(8) , 03298W) Lowell Hse.

Berger, Gilda & Berger, Melvin. Why Don't Haircuts Hurt? Questions & Answers about the Human Body. Barnes, Karen, illus. 1999. (Scholastic Question & Answer Ser.). 48p. (J). (gr. 2-4). pap. 6.99 (978-0-439-08569-4(1) , Scholastic Reference) Scholastic, Inc.

Berger, Melvin. Why Don't Haircuts Hurt? Questions & Answers about Your Body. 1999. (Question & Answer Ser.). (J). (978-0-606-20067-7(3)) Tandem Library Bks.

Berger, Melvin & Berger, Gilda. Why Don't Haircuts Hurt? Questions & Answers about Your Body. Barnes, Karen, illus. 1999. (Scholastic Question & Answer Ser.). 48p. (J). (gr. 2-4). pap. 12.95 (978-0-590-13079-0(X) , Scholastic Reference) Scholastic, Inc.

Bingham, Jane. The Human Body: From Head to Toe. 2004. (Science Answers Ser.). (Illus.). 32p. (J). pap. 7.50 (978-1-4034-5512-3(0)); lib. bdg. 24.22 (978-1-4034-4766-1(7)) Heinemann Library.

Branzei, Sylvia. Hands on Grossology: Really Gross Science Experiments. Keely, Jack, illus. 2003. (Grossology Ser.). 80p. (J). (gr. 3-8). mass mkt. 6.99 (978-0-8431-0305-2(1) , Price Stern Sloan) Penguin Group (USA) Inc.

Bruno, Stephen. The Human Body. 2002. (Nature's Record-Breakers Ser.). (Illus.). 32p. (J). (gr. 3 up). lib. bdg. 23.33 (978-0-8368-2905-1(0)) Stevens, Gareth Inc.

Calabresi, Linda. Human Body. 2008. (Insiders Ser.). 64p. (J). 16.99 ***(978-1-4169-3861-3(3)*** , Simon & Schuster Children's Publishing) Simon & Schuster Children's Publishing.

Caviezel, Giovanni. My Own Human Body. Mesturini, Cristina, illus. 2003. 10p. (J). (ps-2). bds. 10.99 (978-0-7641-5630-4(6)) Barron's Educational Series, Inc.

Center for Learning Network Staff. Demian/the Illustrated Man: Curriculum Unit — Novel Series — Grades 9-12. 2001. (Novel Ser.). 87p. (YA). tchr. ed., spiral bd. 19.95 (978-1-56077-661-1(7)) Ctr. for Learning, The.

Claybourne, Anna. The Human Body. 2006. (Science in Focus Ser.). (Illus.). 48p. (J). 27.00 (978-0-7910-8858-6(8) , Chelsea Hse.) Facts On File, Inc.

Creative Media Applications Staff. The Human Body & Environment: Circulatory & Respiratory Breathing, 4 vols., Vol. 2. 2003. (Middle School Reference Ser.). (Illus.). (J). (978-0-313-32560-1(X)) Greenwood Publishing Group, Inc.

—The Human Body & Environment: Digestive Systems, 4 vols., Vol. 3. 2003. (Middle School Reference Ser.). (Illus.). (J). (978-0-313-32561-8(8)) Greenwood Publishing Group, Inc.

—The Human Body & Environment: Hormonal & Reproductive Systems, 4 vols., Vol. 4. 2003. (Middle School Reference Ser.). (Illus.). (J). (978-0-313-32562-5(6)) Greenwood Publishing Group, Inc.

—The Human Body & Environment: Nervous System & the Sense Organs, Vol. 5. 2003. (978-0-313-32563-2(4)) Greenwood Publishing Group, Inc.

Creative Media Applications Staff, contrib. by. The Human Body & the Environment: How Our Surroundings Affect Our Health, 4 vols. 2003. (Middle School Reference Ser.). 576p. (J). (gr. 6-8). 167.95 (978-0-313-32558-8(8) , MS2558, Middle School Reference) Greenwood Publishing Group, Inc.

D'Amico, Joan & Drummond, Karen Eich. The Healthy Body Cookbook: Over 50 Fun Activities & Delicious Recipes for Kids. Cash-Walsh, Tina, illus. 1998. 192p. (gr. 4-7). pap. 12.95 (978-0-471-18888-9(3) , Wiley) Wiley, John & Sons, Inc.

De la Bédoyère, Camilla. The Discovery of DNA. 2005. (Milestones in Modern Science Ser.). 48p. (J). pap. (978-0-8368-5858-7(1)); (Illus.). lib. bdg. 30.00 (978-0-8368-5851-8(4)) Stevens, Gareth Inc. (World Almanac Library).

Dixon, Malcolm & Smith, Karen. The Body. 1998. (Young Scientists Ser.). (Illus.). 32p. (J). (ps-3). lib. bdg. 16.95 (978-1-887068-69-7(4)) Smart Apple Media.

Dorling Kindersley Publishing Staff. Mi Primer Libro del Cuerpo/My First Body Board Book. 2005. (SPA.). 36p. (J). (ps-3). bds. 5.99 (978-0-7566-1501-7(1)) Dorling Kindersley Publishing, Inc.

Farnsworth, Vesta J. The House We Live in or the Making of the Body. 2004. reprint ed. pap. 24.95 (978-1-4179-2036-5(X)) Kessinger Publishing, LLC.

Fowler, Allan. Knowing about Noses. 1999. (Rookie Read-About Science Ser.). (Illus.). 32p. (gr. 1-2). pap. 4.95 (978-0-516-26480-6(X) , Children's Pr.) Scholastic Library Publishing.

—Knowing about Noses. 1999. (gr. k-3). lib. bdg. 12.95 (978-0-613-54601-0(6)) Tandem Library Bks.

Fredericks, Anthony D. Your Amazing, Fantastic, Incredible Body. 2002. (J). (978-0-531-11699-9(9) , Watts, Franklin) Scholastic Library Publishing.

Fullick, Ann. Body Systems & Health. 2005. (Life Science In-Depth Ser.). (Illus.). 64p. (978-1-4034-7519-0(9)); pap. (978-1-4034-7527-5(X)) Heinemann Library.

Ganeri, Anita. Cells & Life Systems. 2000. (Life Processes Ser.). (Illus.). 32p. (J). lib. bdg. 21.95 (978-1-57572-471-3(5)) Heinemann Library.

Gardner, Robert. Health Science Projects about Anatomy & Physiology. 2001. (Science Projects Ser.). (Illus.). 128p. (YA). (gr. 6-12). lib. bdg. 26.60 (978-0-7660-1440-4(1)) Enslow Pubs., Inc.

Gardner, Robert & Conklin, Barbara Gardner. Health Science Projects about Sports Performance. 2002. (Science Projects Ser.). (Illus.). 112p. (YA). (gr. 6-12). lib. bdg. 26.60 (978-0-7660-1441-1(X)) Enslow Pubs., Inc.

Gareth Stevens Publishing Staff, contrib. by. Major Systems of the Body. 2002. (Twenty-First Century Science Ser.). (Illus.). 64p. (J). (gr. 5 up). lib. bdg. 32.67 (978-0-8368-5007-9(6) , World Almanac Library) Stevens, Gareth Inc.

—The Structure of the Body. 2002. (Twenty-First Century Science Ser.). (Illus.). 64p. (J). (gr. 5 up). lib. bdg. 32.67 (978-0-8368-5008-6(4) , World Almanac Library) Stevens, Gareth Inc.

Goodman, Susan E. The Truth about Poop. Smith, Elwood H., illus. 2004. 40p. (J). (gr. 1). 15.99 (978-0-670-03674-5(9) , Viking Juvenile) Penguin Group (USA) Inc.

Hall, Derek. Being Human. 2000. (J). (978-0-7172-9424-4(2)); (Being Human Ser.: Vol. 1). (Illus.). 48p. (978-0-7172-9420-6(X)) Scholastic Library Publishing. (Grolier).

Halls, Kelly Milner. Cells & Systems. 2006. (J). (978-1-4034-7909-9(7)) Heinemann Library.

Haslam, Andrew, et al. Body. (Make It Work! Ser.). (Illus.). 48p. (J). pap. 15.95 (978-0-590-24333-9(0)); pap. 7.99 (978-0-590-24614-9(3)) Scholastic, Inc.

Hewitt, Sally. Life Processes: What's Inside Me? 2005. (Science Starters Ser.). (Illus.). 32p. (J). (gr. 1-4). lib. bdg. 27.10 (978-1-59604-020-5(3)) Stargazer Bks.

—You & Your Body. 1999. (It's Science! Ser.). (Illus.). 32p. (J). (gr. k-3). 23.50 (978-0-516-21182-4(X) , Children's Pr.) Scholastic Library Publishing.

Holly Wallace. Cells & Systems. 2nd ed. 2006. (Life Processes Ser.). (Illus.). 32p. (J). pap. ***(978-1-4034-8851-0(7))*** Heinemann Library.

Johnson, Rebecca L. Ultra-Organized Cell Systems. Desrocher, Jack, illus. 2007. (Microquests Ser.). 48p. (J). (gr. 3-5). lib. bdg. 29.27 ***(978-0-8225-7138-4(2)*** , Millbrook Pr.) Lerner Publishing Group.

Lauw, Darlene & Puay, Lim Cheng. The Human Body. 2002. (Science Alive! Ser.). (Illus.). 32p. (J). (gr. 4-5). pap. (978-0-7787-0614-4(1)); lib. bdg. (978-0-7787-0568-0(4)) Crabtree Publishing Co.

Libra, Anna. Why Does My Head Hurt? An Inside Look at the Nervous System. 2003. (J). pap. (978-1-58417-065-5(4)) Lake Street Pubs.

—Why Does My Stomach Ache? An Inside Look at the Digestive System. 2003. (J). lib. bdg. (978-1-58417-005-1(0)) Lake Street Pubs.

Little, Marjorie. Endocrine System. 2000. (Illus.). 112p. (J). (gr. 7-12). 36.00 (978-0-7910-5982-1(0) , Chelsea Hse.) Facts On File, Inc.

Macnair, Patricia Ann. Building Blocks: Cells, Organs, & Body Systems. 2005. (Bodyscope Ser.). (Illus.). 40p. (J). (gr. 3-5). 9.95 (978-0-7534-5792-4(X) , Kingfisher) Houghton Mifflin Co. Trade & Reference Div.

Madaras, Lynda. Ready, Set, Grow! A What's Happening to My Body? Book for Younger Girls. Davick, Linda, tr. Davick, Linda, illus. 2003. 128p. (YA). (gr. 3 up). 22.00 (978-1-55704-587-4(9) , Newmarket Shooting Scripts) Newmarket Pr.

Manning, Mick. Under Your Skin: Your Amazing Body. Granstrom, Brita, illus. 2007. 24p. (J). (gr. 1-4). 16.95 ***(978-0-8075-8313-5(8))*** Whitman, Albert & Co.

Margulies, Sheldon. The Fascinating Body: How It Works. 2004. (Illus.). 424p. pap. 34.95 (978-1-57886-076-0(8)) Scarecrow Pr., Inc.

Maynard, Christopher, et al. How Your Body Works. 2004. (Knowledge Masters Plus Ser.). (Illus.). 32p. (YA). pap. incl. cd-rom (978-1-903954-44-7(4)) Chrysalis Children's Bks.

Miles, Elizabeth. Noses. (Animal Parts Ser.). (Illus.). 32p. (J). (gr. k-2). 2003. pap. 6.95 (978-1-4034-0428-2(3)); 2002. lib. bdg. 21.36 (978-1-4034-0019-2(9)) Heinemann Library.

—Noses. 2003. (gr. k-3). lib. bdg. 14.75 (978-0-613-45808-5(7)) Tandem Library Bks.

Morgan, Sally. The Human Body. 2002. (Young Discoverers Ser.). (Illus.). 32p. (J). (gr. k-3). pap. 7.95 (978-0-7534-5501-2(3) , Kingfisher) Houghton Mifflin Co. Trade & Reference Div.

Myers, Jack. On Top of Mount Everest: And Other Explorations of Science in Action. Rice, John, illus. 2005. 64p. (J). (ps-7). 17.95 (978-1-59078-252-1(6)) Boyds Mills Pr.

National Geographic Society Staff. Incredible Voyage: Exploring the Human Body. 1998. (Illus.). 352p. (YA). (gr. 7 up). 35.00 (978-0-7922-7148-2(3) , National Geographic) National Geographic Society.

Newson, Lesley. All about People. Pickering, M. & Smith, Herbert, illus. 2000. (First Encyclopedia Ser.). 96p. (J). (gr. k-4). pap. 7.95 (978-0-590-47526-6(6) , Scholastic Reference) Scholastic, Inc.

O'Brien-Palmer, Michelle. Watch Me Grow: Fun Ways to Learn about Cells, Bones, Muscles, Joints. Lee, Fran, illus. 1999. 144p. (J). (gr. k-4). pap. 14.95 (978-1-55652-367-0(X)) Chicago Review Pr., Inc.

Parker, Steve. Brain. 2003. (Body Focus Ser.). 48p. (J). (Illus.). lib. bdg. 27.07 (978-1-4034-0748-1(7)); pap. (978-1-4034-3296-4(1)) Heinemann Library.

—Your Body. 2006. (Inside & Out Guides Ser.). (Illus.). 32p. (J). pap. (978-1-4034-9093-3(7)); lib. bdg. (978-1-4034-9086-5(4)) Heinemann Library.

Phillips, Carey R., et al. Physiology of the Eye. 2000. (Illus.). (YA). cd-rom (978-0-9759464-0-4(4)) Interactive Knowledge, Inc.

Rice, Christopher. My First Body Book. (Illus.). (J). pap. 22.99 (978-0-590-24611-8(9)) Scholastic, Inc.

Riley, Ange Belle Chandler. The House in Which You Live. 2005. reprint ed. pap. 24.95 (978-1-4191-3533-0(3)) Kessinger Publishing, LLC.

Rinder, Lenore. Bones & Skin. Oszkay, Zulay, tr. Date not set. Tr. of Huesos y Piel. (J). (ps-7). pap. 5.00 (978-0-9678778-1-5(4) , 002) Child Scope Productions.

Romanek, Trudee. Achoo! The Most Interesting Book You'll Ever Read about Germs. 2003. (gr. 5-8). lib. bdg. 15.25 (978-0-613-84416-1(5)) Tandem Library Bks.

Rubin, Alan. Keeping Warm. 2003. (Yellow Umbrella Books). (Illus.). 16p. (J). (gr. 1). lib. bdg. 14.60 (978-0-7368-2019-6(1) , Pebble Bks.) Capstone Pr., Inc.

Scherrer, David L. & Klepacki, Linda M. Celebrating Changes: Everything You Always Wanted to Know about Sex in Middle School. 2004. (Worth Waiting for Ser.). 176p. (YA). (gr. 11 up). 19.99 (978-0-7814-4077-6(7) , 0781440777) Cook, David C. Publishing Co.

Seidlitz, Lauri. Human Body. 2007. (J). ***(978-1-59036-705-6(7)); (978-1-59036-706-3(5))*** Weigl Pubs., Inc.

Seidlitz, Lauri. The Science of the Human Body. 1999. (Living Science Ser.). (Illus.). 32p. (J). (gr. 2 up). lib. bdg. 24.67 (978-0-8368-2570-1(5)) Stevens, Gareth Inc.

Seuling, Barbara. From Head to Toe: The Amazing Human Body & How It Works. Miller, Edward, illus. 2002. 32p. (J). (gr. k-3). tchr. ed. 16.95 (978-0-8234-1699-8(2)) Holiday Hse., Inc.

Shier, David N., et al. Hole's Essentials of Human Anatomy & Physiology with OLC bind-In Card. 8th rev. ed. 2003. 640p. (C). (gr. 6-12). 118.75 (978-0-07-293224-9(4) , 9780072932249) Glencoe/McGraw-Hill.

Silverstein, Alvin, et al. Pains & Strains. 2003. (My Health Ser.). (Illus.). 48p. (J). 25.50 (978-0-531-12174-0(7) , Watts, Franklin) Scholastic Library Publishing.

—Pains & Strains. 2003. (Illus.). 48p. (J). (gr. 4-7). lib. bdg. 15.25 (978-0-613-67919-0(9)) Tandem Library Bks.

Snedden, Robert. Animals: Multicelled Life. 2003. (Cells & Life Ser.). (Illus.). 48p. (gr. 6-8). (J). lib. bdg. 27.86 (978-1-58810-671-1(3)); (YA). pap. 8.50 (978-1-58810-933-0(X)) Heinemann Library.

Spilsbury, Louise & Spilsbury, Richard. Life Processes: From Reproduction to Respiration. 2004. (Science Answers Ser.). (Illus.). 32p. (J). pap. 7.50 (978-1-4034-5513-0(9)); lib. bdg. 24.22 (978-1-4034-4767-8(5)) Heinemann Library.

Stangl, Jean. What Makes You Cough, Sneeze, Burp, Hiccup, Blink, Yawn, Sweat & Shiver? 2001. (My Health Ser.). (Illus.). 48p. (J). (gr. 3-5). pap. 6.95 (978-0-531-16510-2(8) , Watts, Franklin) Scholastic Library Publishing.

Stout, Frankie. Nature's Strongest Animals. 2008. (J). lib. bdg. ***(978-1-4042-4158-9(2)*** , PowerKids Pr.) Rosen Publishing Group, Inc., The.

Szpirglas, Jeff. Gross Universe: Your Guide to All Disgusting Things under the Sun. Cho, Michael, tr. Cho, Michael, illus. 2004. 64p. (J). (gr. 3-7). 21.95 (978-1-894379-64-9(0)); pap. 12.95 (978-1-894379-65-6(9)) Maple Tree Pr. CAN. *Dist:* Firefly Bks., Ltd.

Szpirglas, Jeff & Cho, Michael. Gross Universe: Your Guide to All Disgusting Things under the Sun. 2005. (Illus.). 64p. (J). pap. 9.95 (978-1-897066-39-3(2)) Maple Tree Pr. CAN. *Dist:* Perseus Distribution.

Taylor, Barbara. The Best Book of the Human Body. 2006. (J). ***(978-0-7534-6031-3(9)*** , Kingfisher) Houghton Mifflin Co. Trade & Reference Div.

VanCleave, Janice Pratt. Janice VanCleave's Play & Find Out about the Human Body: Easy Experiments for Young Children. 1998. (Play & Find Out Ser.: Vol. 7). (Illus.). 128p. (ps-2). 32.50 (978-0-471-12934-9(8) , Wiley) Wiley, John & Sons, Inc.

Walker, Denise. Cells & Life Processes. 2006. (Illus.). 48p. (J). (978-1-58340-988-6(2)) Smart Apple Media.

Walker, Richard. Human Body. 2006. (Kingfisher Knowledge Ser.). (Illus.). 64p. (J). ***(978-0-7534-1317-3(5)*** , Kingfisher) Houghton Mifflin Co. Trade & Reference Div.

—The Little Encyclopedia of the Human Body. 2001. (Kingfisher Little Encyclopedias Ser.). (Illus.). 112p. (J). (gr. k-3). pap. 11.95 (978-0-7534-5423-7(8) , Kingfisher) Houghton Mifflin Co. Trade & Reference Div.

—Under the Microscope: The Human Body, 8 vols., Set. 1998. (Illus.). (YA). (gr. 2 up). lib. bdg. 235.00 (978-0-7172-9265-3(7) , Grolier) Scholastic Library Publishing.

Wallace, Holly. Cells & Systems. 2006. (Life Processes Ser.). (Illus.). 32p. (J). (*978-1-4034-8844-2(4)) Heinemann Library.

Weber, Rebecca. The Body's Business. 2004. (Spyglass Books). (Illus.). 24p. (J). (gr. k-1). lib. bdg. 18.60 (978-0-7565-0622-3(0)) Compass Point Bks.

World Book, Inc Staff, contrib. by. My Body. 2007. (J). (*978-0-7166-7727-7(X)) World Bk., Inc.

PHYSIOLOGY, COMPARATIVE

Devaney, Sherri. Super Senses. 2005. (Planet's Most Extreme Ser.). (Illus.). 48p. (J). (gr. 3-7). 24.95 (978-1-4103-0398-1(5) , Blackbirch Pr., Inc.) Thomson Gale.

Stonehouse, Bernard & Bertram, Esther. The Truth about Animal Senses. Francis, John, illus. 2002. (Animals Exposed! Ser.). 48p. (J). pap. (978-0-439-51807-9(5)) Scholastic, Inc.

Woodward, John. Stinkers. 2005. (Planet's Most Extreme Ser.). (Illus.). 48p. (J). (gr. 3-7). 24.95 (978-1-4103-0397-4(7) , Blackbirch Pr., Inc.) Thomson Gale.

PHYSIOLOGY OF PLANTS

see Plant Physiology

PIANISTS

Alexander, Patricia Torn. Van Cliburn: America's Musical Hero. Alexander, Darren Scott, illus. 2001. 39p. (J). (gr. 1-5). pap. 13.95 (978-0-9708457-0-2(7)) Bluebonnet Classics.

Allman, Barbara. Her Piano Sang: A Story about Clara Schumann. 2003. (Creative Minds Biographies Ser.). (Illus.). 64p. (J). (gr. 3-6). pap. 22.60 (978-1-57505-151-2(6)) Lerner Publishing Group.

Arthur, Alexander. Anton Rubenstein: A Biographical Sketch. 2001. 154p. (YA). reprint ed. 88.00 (978-0-7222-5502-5(0)) Library Reprints, Inc.

Ehrlich, A. Celebrated Pianists, Past & Present: A Collection of 116 Biographies of Great Pianoforte Players. 2001. 367p. (YA). reprint ed. 98.00 (978-0-7222-5971-9(9)) Library Reprints, Inc.

Hallett, Charles. The Life & Letters of Sir Charles Halle. 2001. 432p. (YA). reprint ed. 98.00 (978-0-7222-5426-4(0)) Library Reprints, Inc.

Harrah, Madge. Blind Boone: Piano Prodigy. 2004. (Trailblazers Biographies Ser.). (Illus.). 112p. (J). (gr. 5-9). lib. bdg. 30.60 (978-1-57505-057-7(9)) Lerner Publishing Group.

Konieczny, Vladimir. Struggling for Perfection: The Story of Glenn Gould. 2004. (Illus.). 97p. (J). 16.95 (978-0-929141-13-8(X)) Napoleon Publishing/Rendezvous Pr. CAN. *Dist:* AtlasBooks Distribution.

Reich, Susanna. Clara Schumann: Piano Virtuoso. (Illus.). 128p. (J). 2005. (gr. 3-5). pap. 9.95 (978-0-618-55160-6(3)); 1999. (gr. 4-6). tchr. ed. 18.00 (978-0-395-89119-3(1)) Houghton Mifflin Co. Trade & Reference Div. (Clarion Bks.).

Rubinstein, Anton. Autobiography of Anton Rubinstein, 1829-1889. 2001. 171p. (YA). reprint ed. 88.00 (978-0-7222-5501-8(2)) Library Reprints, Inc.

PIANISTS—FICTION

Allison, Jennifer. Gilda Joyce: The Ghost Sonata. 2007. 288p. (J). (gr. 5-8). 15.99 (*978-0-525-47808-9(6) , Dutton Juvenile) Penguin Group (USA) Inc.

Bram, Christopher. Notorious Dr August: His Real Life & Crimes. 2001. (gr. 7-12). lib. bdg. 23.45 (978-0-613-37021-9(X)) Tandem Library Bks.

Coveleskie, Sally, et al. Henry the Steinway & the Piano Recital. Friedman, Laura, illus. 2003. (Henry the Steinway Ser.: Vol. 1). 32p. (J). (gr. k-3). (978-1-931721-05-9(X)) Bright Sky Pr.

de Brunhoff, Laurent. Babar Raconte le Pianiste. (Babar Ser.). (FRE., Illus.). 48p. (J). (ps-3). 19.95 (978-0-7859-8822-9(X)) French & European Pubns., Inc.

Harcourt School Publishers Staff. Le Anne Joins the Show Below Level. 3rd ed. 2002. (Trophies Reading Program Ser.). (Illus.). pap. 5.10 (978-0-15-323132-2(7)) Harcourt Schl. Pubs.

—The Piano Piece On Level. 3rd ed. 2002. (Trophies Reading Program Ser.). (Illus.). pap. 5.10 (978-0-15-323172-8(6)) Harcourt Schl. Pubs.

Johnson, Nora. The World of Henry Orient. 2002. 224p. reprint ed. 12.95 (978-0-9714612-0-8(1) , 01-GMP-001) Green Mansion Pr. LLC.

—The World of Henry Orient. 1998. lib. bdg. 18.95 (978-1-56723-068-0(7)) Yestermorrow, Inc.

PIANO

Barber, Nicola. Should I Play the Piano? 2006. (Learning Musical Instruments Ser.). (Illus.). 32p. (J). (gr. 3-5). lib. bdg. 28.21 (978-1-4034-8189-4(X)) Heinemann Library.

Berr, Bruce. Expeditions in Style. 2004. 24p. pap. 6.95 (978-0-634-08632-8(4) , 0634086324) Leonard, Hal Corp.

Blackwood, Alan. Playing the Piano & Keyboards. 2004. (Young Musician Ser.). (J). lib. bdg. (978-1-932799-59-0(1)) Stargazer Bks.

Brinsmead, Edgar. The History of the Pianoforte. 2001. 201p. (YA). reprint ed. 98.00 (978-0-7222-6335-8(X)) Library Reprints, Inc.

Congratulations: Grade 2 Piano. 9.95 (978-1-85909-813-4(4) , Warner Bros. Pubns.) Alfred Publishing Co., Inc.

Currie, Stephen. Pianos. 2006. 32p. (gr. 3-5). 23.70 (978-1-4103-0721-7(2) , Blackbirch Pr., Inc.) Thomson Gale.

Dearling, Robert. Keyboard Instruments & Ensembles. 2000. (Encyclopedia of Musical Instruments Ser.). (Illus.). 48p. (J). (gr. 4-7). 22.95 (978-0-7910-6094-0(2) , Chelsea Hse.) Facts On File, Inc.

Guy, Suzanne & Lacy, Donna. The Music Box: The Story of Christofori. Lacy, Donna, illus. 1998. (Illus.). 32p. (J). (gr. k-4). pap. 6.95 (978-1-55618-173-3(6)); 15.95 (978-1-55618-172-6(8)) Brunswick Publishing Corp.

Healy, Nick. The Piano. 2005. (What in the World Ser.). (Illus.). 48p. (gr. 5-9). 21.95 (978-1-58341-376-0(6) , Creative Education) Creative Co., The.

Klingel, Cynthia Fitterer & Noyed, Robert B. Pianos. 2002. (Wonder Books Level 1: Musical Instuments Ser.). (Illus.). 24p. (J). (ps-3). 22.79 (978-1-56766-948-0(4)) Child's World, Inc.

Lynch, Wendy. Keyboard. 2001. (Musical Instruments Ser.). (Illus.). 32p. (J). (gr. k-2). lib. bdg. 21.36 (978-1-58810-234-8(3)) Heinemann Library.

Piano Accompaniment. 2003. (Share the Music Ser.). (gr. k up). (978-0-02-295579-3(8)); (gr. 1 up). (978-0-02-295580-9(1)); (gr. 2 up). (978-0-02-295581-6(X)); (gr. 3 up). (978-0-02-295582-3(8)); (gr. 4 up). (978-0-02-295583-0(6)); (gr. 5 up). (978-0-02-295584-7(4)); (gr. 6 up). (978-0-02-295585-4(2)) Macmillan/McGraw-Hill Schl. Div.

Sebba, Jane. Abracadabra Piano 3 Vol. 3: Graded Pieces for the Young Pianist. 2004. (Illus.). 48p. pap. 7.95 (978-0-7136-3726-7(9) , 93115) A & C Black GBR. *Dist:* Consortium Bk. Sales & Distribution.

Suzuki, Shinichi. Suzuki Piano School, Vol. 1. rev. ed. 1999. (Suzuki Piano School Ser.). 32p. (J). (ps-3). 6.95 (978-0-87487-473-0(4) , Warner Bros. Pubns.) Alfred Publishing Co., Inc.

Turner, Barrie Carson. Keyboards. 2000. (Musical Instruments of the World Ser.). (Illus.). 32p. (J). (ps-3). lib. bdg. 16.95 (978-1-58340-062-3(1)) Smart Apple Media.

What Else Can I Play Piano Prep. 2000. 7.95 (978-1-85909-822-6(3) , Warner Bros. Pubns.) Alfred Publishing Co., Inc.

Wollard, H. Making of a Modern Pianoforte. 2001. (YA). reprint ed. 150.00 (978-0-7222-5939-9(5)) Library Reprints, Inc.

Zagwyn, Deborah Turney. The Winter Gift. 2004. (Illus.). 32p. (J). (gr. k-3). 15.95 (978-1-883672-93-5(7) , Tricycle Pr.) Ten Speed Pr.

PIANO—INSTRUCTION AND STUDY

Brown, Mary Martha. My Window. Walters, Shellie, illus. 1999. 24.00 (978-1-891721-55-7(0)) McBrown Songs & Stories.

Celik, Vladislav. You Too Can Play Piano & Organ Without Teacher, Vol. 1. (Music Instructional Ser.). (Illus.). 96p. (J). pap. 12.95 incl. audio (978-0-9624062-1-8(X)) Music Institute of California.

Clark, Frances, et al. The Music Tree: Students' Choice, Pt. 4. pap. 5.95 (978-1-58951-009-8(7) , 00970) Summy-Birchard, Inc.

Fowles, Ernst. Harmony in Pianoforte-Study: A Book for the Individual Student. 2001. 87p. (YA). reprint ed. 88.00 (978-0-7222-5733-3(3)) Library Reprints, Inc.

Griggs, Jermaine. The Secrets to Playing Piano by Ear. 1.t. ed. 2001. (Illus.). 300p. (978-0-9744845-0-1(4)) Hear & Play Music.

Hal Leonard Corporation Staff. Pokemon Piano Fun! 2000. (Pokemon Ser.). (Illus.). 16p. (ps-3). pap. 19.95 (978-1-57560-308-7(X) , 157560308X) Cherry Lane Music Co.

Hambourg, Mark. How to Play the Piano. 2001. 122p. (YA). reprint ed. 88.00 (978-0-7222-5944-3(1)) Library Reprints, Inc.

Hickin, W. Pianoforte Accompaniment. 2001. (YA). reprint ed. 150.00 (978-0-7222-5956-6(5)) Library Reprints, Inc.

Marks, Anthony. Easy Pno Classics - Internet Referenced. 2007. 64p. (J). spiral bd. 18.99 (978-0-7945-1273-6(9) , Usborne) EDC Publishing.

—Learn to Play Keyboards. 1999. (Learn to Play Ser.). (Illus.). 48p. (YA). (gr. 4 up). pap. 9.95 (978-0-7460-2412-6(6)); lib. bdg. 17.95 (978-0-88110-899-6(5)) EDC Publishing.

Matthay, Tobias A. The Act of Touch in All Its Diversity: An Analysis & Synthesis of Pianoforte Tone-Production. 2001. 328p. (YA). reprint ed. 98.00 (978-0-7222-5966-5(2)) Library Reprints, Inc.

Milano, Randy. Learn Piano Chords for Children! Chordy & the Magical Chime Time Clock! 2000. (Learn Piano Chords for Children Ser.: Vol. 1). (Illus.). 36p. (J). (gr. k-7). pap. 12.95 (978-0-9679989-1-6(3)) Empire Publishing Group.

Ortmann, Otto. The Physical Basis of Piano Touch & Tone: An Experimental Investigation of the Effect of the Player's Touch upon the Tone of the Piano. 2001. 188p. (YA). reprint ed. 88.00 (978-0-7222-5967-2(0)) Library Reprints, Inc.

Pauer, Ernst. The Art of Pianoforte Playing. 2001. 88p. (YA). reprint ed. 88.00 (978-0-7222-5950-4(6)) Library Reprints, Inc.

Pokemon Theme. 1999. (Easy Piano Ser.). 4p. (J). pap. 3.95 (978-1-57560-267-7(9)) Cherry Lane Music Co.

Saar, Louis V. The Proficient Pianist: A Course of Fifty Progressive Studies for the Equal Development of the Hands, 2 vols., set. 2001. (YA). reprint ed. 250.00 (978-0-7222-5951-1(4)) Library Reprints, Inc.

Sebba, Jane. Abracadabra Piano, Bk. 1. Edwards, Gunvor & Felstead, Cathie, illus. 48p. (J). pap. 7.95 (978-0-7136-3724-3(2) , 93113) A & C Black GBR. *Dist:* Lubrecht & Cramer, Ltd.

Snead, Ned. How to Play the Piano by Ear. 2003. 12.95 (978-1-891429-50-7(7)) Armadillo Publishing Corp.

Suzuki, Shinichi. Suzuki Piano School, Vol. 3. 2001. (Suzuki Piano School Ser.). (FRE, GER, JPN & SPA.). 32p. (J). (gr. k-12). 6.95 (978-0-87487-162-3(X) , Warner Bros. Pubns.) Alfred Publishing Co., Inc.

Taylor, Franklin. Primer of Pianoforte Playing. 2001. (YA). reprint ed. 150.00 (978-0-7222-5952-8(2)) Library Reprints, Inc.

—Technique & Expression in Pianoforte Playing. 2001. 130p. (YA). reprint ed. 88.00 (978-0-7222-5963-4(8)) Library Reprints, Inc.

Vantyne, S. Modern Pianoforte Technique. 2001. (YA). reprint ed. 150.00 (978-0-7222-5964-1(6)) Library Reprints, Inc.

Wedgwood, Pamela. More Up-Grade Piano. 2000. 24p. (J). (gr. k-1). 6.95 (978-0-571-51956-9(3)) Faber & Faber, Ltd. GBR. *Dist:* Leonard, Hal Corp.

—Up-Grade Piano. 1998. 24p. (J). (gr. k-1). 6.95 (978-0-571-51737-4(4)) Faber & Faber, Ltd. GBR. *Dist:* Leonard, Hal Corp.

Westerby, Herbert. How to Study the Pianoforte Works of the Great Composers. 2001. 302p. (YA). reprint ed. 98.00 (978-0-7222-5953-5(0)) Library Reprints, Inc.

Yazbeck, Peter & Castano, Clara. Learning Cards(tm), the ABCs of Keyboard Musicianship: Fundamentals of Music in Q&A Form, Part I - Secondary Level. 2007. (Illus.). 158p. (J). 9.95 (*978-0-9785118-3-8(2)) CCRiddles.

—Learning Cards(tm), the ABCs of Keyboard Musicianship: Fundamentals of Music in Q&A Form, Part II - Secondary Level. 2007. (Illus.). 146p. (J). 9.95 (*978-0-9785118-4-5(0)) CCRiddles.

—Learning Cards(tm), the ABCs of Keyboard Musicianship: Intervals in Q&A Form - All Levels. 2007. (Illus.). 170p. (J). 12.95 (*978-0-9785118-9-0(1)) CCRiddles.

—Learning Cards(tm), the ABCs of Keyboard Musicianship: Musical Symbols in Q&A Form- Secondary Level, 1. 2007. (Illus.). 130p. (J). 9.95 (*978-0-9785118-5-2(9)) CCRiddles.

—Learning Cards(tm), the ABCs of Keyboard Musicianship: Root Position Triads in Q&A Form - All Levels. 2007. (Illus.). 166p. (J). 12.95 (*978-0-9785118-8-3(3)) CCRiddles.

—Learning Cards(tm), the ABCs of Keyboard Musicianship: Scales in Q&A Form, All Levels. 2007. (Illus.). 156p. (J). 12.95 (*978-0-9785118-7-6(5)) CCRiddles.

—Learning Cards(tm), the ABCs of Keyboard Musicianship: Triad Inversions in Q&A Form - All Levels, 1. 2007. (Illus.). 160p. (J). 12.95 (*978-0-9785118-6-9(7)) CCRiddles.

PIANO MUSIC

Adolphe, Bruce. Piano Puzzlers: Thirty Popular Melodies & Folk Tunes in the Styles of Famous Composers. 2004. 42p. 21.95 (978-0-9701249-2-0(9)) PollyRhythm Productions.

Axford, Elizabeth C., compiled by. My Halloween Fun Book. 2004. (Illus.). 100p. spiral bd. 19.95 (978-1-931844-13-0(5) , PP1025) Piano Pr.

Baker, Ed. Blues Riffs for Piano. Date not set. 30p. (YA). pap. 14.95 incl. audio (978-0-89524-928-9(6)) Cherry Lane Music Co.

Beanstalk - Theory. 2000. (J). Bk. 1. 6.95 (978-0-87718-045-6(8)); Bk. 2. 6.95 (978-0-87718-046-3(6)); Bk. 3. 6.95 (978-0-87718-047-0(4)); Bk. 4. 6.95 (978-0-87718-048-7(2)); Vol. Prep A. 5.95 (978-0-87718-043-2(1)) Willis Music Co.

Bergerac. My First Book of Hymns & Spirituals: 26 Favorite Songs in Easy Piano Arrangements. 1999. (Illus.). 48p. pap. 4.95 (978-0-486-40849-1(3)) Dover Pubns., Inc.

Debussy, Claude. Oeuvres Complete Serie 1 Vol. 2: Images, pour le Piano, Children's Corner. 2001. 152p. pap. 89.95 (978-0-634-08211-5(6) , 0634082116) Leonard, Hal Corp.

Feldstein, Sandy & Clark, Larry. Arietta - Clarinet/Bass Clarinet Solo w/ Piano Acc. w/ CD. 2005. (YA). pap. 9.95 (978-1-932895-18-6(3)) PlayinTime Productions, Inc.

—Arietta - Flute/Oboe Solo w/ Pianio Acc & CD. 2005. (YA). pap. 9.95 (978-1-932895-17-9(5)) PlayinTime Productions, Inc.

—Arietta - Trombone/Bariton/Bassoon Solo w/ Piano Acc. W/CD. 2005. (YA). pap. 9.95 (978-1-932895-23-0(X)) PlayinTime Productions, Inc.

—Arietta - Trumpet/Baritone Solo w/ Piano Acc. W/CD. 2005. (YA). pap. 9.95 (978-1-932895-21-6(3)) PlayinTime Productions, Inc.

—Arietta - Tuba Solo w/Piano Acc. w/ CD. 2005. (YA). pap. 9.95 (978-1-932895-24-7(8)) PlayinTime Productions, Inc.

—Arietta- Keyboard Percussion Solo w/Piano Acc. W/CD. 2005. (YA). pap. (978-1-932895-25-4(6)) PlayinTime Productions, Inc.

—Arrietta - Alto Sax/Bari Sax Solo w/ Piano Acc. w/ CD. 2005. (YA). pap. 9.95 (978-1-932895-19-3(1)) PlayinTime Productions, Inc.

—Bacarolle - Flute/Oboe Solo with Piano Acc. W/CD. 2005. (YA). pap. (978-1-932895-87-2(6)) PlayinTime Productions, Inc.

—Bacarolle - Tenor Sax Solo with Piano Acc. W/CD. 2005. (YA). pap. 10.95 (978-1-932895-90-2(6)) PlayinTime Productions, Inc.

—Barbara Allen - Alto Sax/Bari. Sax Solo with Piano Acc. W/CD. 2005. (YA). pap. 9.95 (978-1-932895-59-9(0)) PlayinTime Productions, Inc.

—Barbara Allen - Clarinet/Bass Clarinet Solo with Piano Acc. W/CD. 2005. (YA). pap. 9.95 (978-1-932895-58-2(2)) PlayinTime Productions, Inc.

—Barbara Allen - Flute/Oboe Solo with Piano Acc. W/CD. 2005. (YA). pap. 9.95 (978-1-932895-57-5(4)) PlayinTime Productions, Inc.

—Barbara Allen - Horn in F Solo with Piano Acc. W/CD. 2005. (YA). pap. 9.95 (978-1-932895-62-9(0)) PlayinTime Productions, Inc.

—Barbara Allen - Keyboard Percussion Solo with Piano Acc. W/CD. 2005. (YA). pap. 9.95 (978-1-932895-65-0(5)) PlayinTime Productions, Inc.

—Barbara Allen - Tenor Sax Solo with Piano Acc. W/CD. 2005. (YA). pap. 9.95 (978-1-932895-60-5(4)); pap. 9.95 (978-1-932895-61-2(2)) PlayinTime Productions, Inc.

—Barbara Allen - Trombone/Baritone/Bassoon Solo with Piano Acc. W/CD. 2005. (YA). pap. 9.95 (978-1-932895-63-6(9)) PlayinTime Productions, Inc.

—Barbara Allen - Tuba Solo with Piano Acc. W/CD. 2005. (YA). pap. 9.95 (978-1-932895-64-3(7)) PlayinTime Productions, Inc.

—Barcarolle - Alto Sax. /Bari. Sax Solo with Piano Acc. 2005. (YA). pap. 10.95 incl. audio compact disk (978-1-932895-89-6(2)) PlayinTime Productions, Inc.

—Barcarolle - Clarinet/Bass Clarinet Solo with Piano Acc. 2005. (YA). pap. 10.95 incl. audio compact disk (978-1-932895-88-9(4)) PlayinTime Productions, Inc.

—Barcarolle - Keyboard Percussion Solo with Piano Acc. 2005. (YA). pap. 10.95 incl. audio compact disk (978-1-932895-95-7(7)) PlayinTime Productions, Inc.

—Barcarolle - Snare Drum Solo with Piano Acc. 2005. (YA). pap. 10.95 (978-1-932895-96-4(5)) PlayinTime Productions, Inc.

—Barcarolle - Tuba Solo with Piano Acc. 2005. (YA). pap. 10.95 incl. audio compact disk (978-1-932895-94-0(9)) PlayinTime Productions, Inc.

—Barcarolle -Trombone/Baritone/Bassoon Solo with Piano Acc. 2005. (YA). pap. 10.95 incl. audio compact disk (978-1-932895-93-3(0)) PlayinTime Productions, Inc.

—Barcarolle-Trumpet/Baritone Solo with Piano Acc. 2005. (YA). pap. 10.95 incl. audio compact disk (978-1-932895-91-9(4)) PlayinTime Productions, Inc.

—Fafare Minuet - Keyboard Percussion Solo with Piano Acc. W/CD. 2005. (YA). pap. 9.95 (978-1-932895-55-1(8)) PlayinTime Productions, Inc.

—Fanfare & Minuet -Flute/Oboe Solo with Piano Acc. W/CD. 2005. (YA). pap. 9.95 (978-1-932895-47-6(7)) PlayinTime Productions, Inc.

—Fanfare Minuet - Alto Sax/Bari. Sax Solo with Piano Acc. W/CD. 2005. (YA). pap. 9.95 (978-1-932895-49-0(3)) PlayinTime Productions, Inc.

—Fanfare Minuet - Clarinet/Bass Clarinet Solo with Piano Acc. 2005. (YA). pap. 9.95 incl. audio compact disk (978-1-932895-48-3(5)) PlayinTime Productions, Inc.

—Fanfare Minuet - Horn in F Solo with Piano Acc. 2005. (YA). pap. 9.95 incl. audio compact disk (978-1-932895-52-0(3)) PlayinTime Productions, Inc.

—Fanfare Minuet - Snare Drim Solo with Piano Acc. 2005. (YA). pap. incl. audio compact disk (978-1-932895-56-8(6)) PlayinTime Productions, Inc.

—Fanfare Minuet - Tenor Sax Solo with Piano Acc. 2005. (YA). pap. 9.95 incl. audio compact disk (978-1-932895-50-6(7)) PlayinTime Productions, Inc.

—Fanfare Minuet - Tuba Solo with Piano Acc. W/CD. 2005. (YA). pap. 9.95 (978-1-932895-54-4(X)) PlayinTime Productions, Inc.

—The Fifers - Alto Sax. /Bari. Sax Solo with Piano Acc. 2005. (YA). pap. 10.95 incl. audio compact disk (978-1-932895-79-7(5)) PlayinTime Productions, Inc.

—The Fifers - Clarinet/Bass Clarinet Solo with Piano Acc. W/CD. 2005. (YA). pap. 10.95 (978-1-932895-78-0(7)) PlayinTime Productions, Inc.

—The Fifers - Flute/Oboe Solo with Piano Acc. 2005. (YA). pap. 10.95 incl. audio compact disk (978-1-932895-77-3(9)) PlayinTime Productions, Inc.

—The Fifers - Horn in F Solo with Piano Acc. 2005. (YA). pap. 10.95 incl. audio compact disk (978-1-932895-82-7(5)) PlayinTime Productions, Inc.

—The Fifers - Keyboard Percussion Solo with Piano Acc. 2005. (YA). pap. 10.95 incl. audio compact disk (978-1-932895-85-8(X)) PlayinTime Productions, Inc.

—The Fifers - Snare Drum Solo with Piano Acc. W/CD. 2005. (YA). pap. 10.95 (978-1-932895-86-5(8)) PlayinTime Productions, Inc.

—The Fifers - Tenor Sax. Solo with Piano Acc. 2005. (YA). pap. 10.95 incl. audio compact disk (978-1-932895-80-3(9)) PlayinTime Productions, Inc.

—The Fifers - Trombone/Baritone/Bassoon Solo with Piano Acc. 2005. (YA). pap. 10.95 incl. audio compact disk (978-1-932895-83-4(3)) PlayinTime Productions, Inc.

—The Fifers - Tuba Solo with Piano Acc. 2005. (YA). pap. 10.95 incl. audio compact disk (978-1-932895-84-1(1)) PlayinTime Productions, Inc.

—Horn in F Solo with Piano Acc. 2005. (YA). pap. 10.95 incl. audio compact disk (978-1-932895-92-6(2)) PlayinTime Productions, Inc.

—Scherzando - Flute Solo with Piano Acc. w/CD. 2005. (YA). pap. 9.95 (978-1-932895-26-1(4)) PlayinTime Productions, Inc.

—Scherzando -Horn in F Solo with Piano Acc. W/CD. 2005. (YA). pap. 9.95 (978-1-932895-31-5(0)) PlayinTime Productions, Inc.

—Schezando - Clarinet/Bass Clarinet Solo with Piano acc. W/CD. 2005. (YA). pap. 9.95 (978-1-932895-27-8(2)) PlayinTime Productions, Inc.

—Sensational Snare - Snare Drum Solo with Piano Acc. W/cd. 2005. (YA). pap. 9.95 (978-1-932895-36-0(1)) PlayinTime Productions, Inc.

—Snarendipity - Snare Drum Solo with Piano Acc. W/CD. 2005. (YA). pap. 9.95 (978-1-932895-66-7(3)) PlayinTime Productions, Inc.

—Sonatina - Alto Sax/Bari. Sax Solo with Piano Acc. W/CD. 2005. (YA). pap. 10.95 (978-1-932895-69-8(8)) PlayinTime Productions, Inc.

—Sonatina - Clarinet/Bass Clarinet Solo with Piano Acc. W/CD. 2005. (YA). pap. 10.95 (978-1-932895-68-1(X)) PlayinTime Productions, Inc.

—Sonatina - Flute/Oboe Solo with Piano Acc. W/CD. 2005. (YA). pap. (978-1-932895-67-4(1)) PlayinTime Productions, Inc.

—Sonatina - Horn in F Solo with Piano Acc. W/CD. 2005. (YA). pap. 10.95 (978-1-932895-72-8(8)) PlayinTime Productions, Inc.

—Sonatina - Keyboard Percussion Solo with Piano Acc. W/CD. 2005. (YA). pap. 10.95 (978-1-932895-75-9(2)) PlayinTime Productions, Inc.

—Sonatina - Snare Drum Solo with Piano Acc. W/CD. 2005. (YA). pap. 10.95 (978-1-932895-76-6(0)) PlayinTime Productions, Inc.

—Sonatina - Tenor Sax Solo with Piano Acc. W/CD. 2005. (YA). pap. 10.95 (978-1-932895-70-4(1)) PlayinTime Productions, Inc.

—Sonatina - Trombone/Baritone/Bassoon Solo with Piano Acc. W/CD. 2005. (YA). pap. 10.95 (978-1-932895-73-5(6)) PlayinTime Productions, Inc.

—Sonatina - Trumpet/Baritone Solo with Piano Acc. W/CD. 2005. (YA). pap. 10.95 (978-1-932895-71-1(X)) PlayinTime Productions, Inc.

—Sonatina - Tuba Solo with Piano Acc. W/CD. 2005. (YA). pap. 10.95 (978-1-932895-74-2(4)) PlayinTime Productions, Inc.

—Variations on a Theme by Greig -Flute Solo w/Piano Acc. W/CD. 2005. (YA). pap. 9.95 (978-1-932895-37-7(X)) PlayinTime Productions, Inc.

—Variations on a Theme by Grieg - Alto Sax/Bari. Sax Solo with Piano Acc. W/CD. 2005. (YA). pap. 9.95 (978-1-932895-39-1(6)) PlayinTime Productions, Inc.

—Variations on a Theme by Grieg - Clarinet/Bass Clarinet Solo with Piano Acc. W/CD. 2005. (YA). pap. 9.95 (978-1-932895-38-4(8)) PlayinTime Productions, Inc.

—Variations on a Theme by Grieg - Keyboard Percussion Solo with Piano Acc. W/CD. 2005. (YA). pap. 9.95 (978-1-932895-45-2(0)) PlayinTime Productions, Inc.

—Variations on a Theme by Grieg - Snare Drum Solo with Piano Acc. W/CD. 2005. (YA). pap. 9.95 (978-1-932895-46-9(9)) PlayinTime Productions, Inc.

—Variations on a Theme by Grieg - Trombone/Baritone/Basson Solo with Piano Acc. W/CD. 2005. (YA). pap. 9.95 (978-1-932895-43-8(4)) PlayinTime Productions, Inc.

—Variations on a Theme by Grieg - Trumpet/Baritone Solo with Piano Acc. W/CD. 2005. (YA). pap. 9.95 (978-1-932895-41-4(8)) PlayinTime Productions, Inc.

—Variations on a Theme by Grieg - Tuba Solo with Piano Acc. W/CD. 2005. (YA). pap. 9.95 (978-1-932895-44-5(2)) PlayinTime Productions, Inc.

—Variations on the theme by Grieg - Horn in F Solo with Piano Acc. W/CD. 2005. (YA). pap. 9.95 (978-1-932895-42-1(6)) PlayinTime Productions, Inc.

—Variatons on a theme by Grieg- Tenor Sax Solo with Piano Acc. W/CD. 2005. (YA). pap. 9.95 (978-1-932895-40-7(X)) PlayinTime Productions, Inc.

Finn, Cheryl. Beanstalk - Theory, Vol. Prep B. 2005. 40p. pap. 6.95 (978-0-87718-044-9(X) , 087718044X) Willis Music Co.

Finn, Cheryl & Morris, Eamonn. Beanstalk's Basics for Piano Bk. 1: Lesson Book Preparatory Book. 2000. 46p. pap. 7.95 (978-0-87718-037-1(7) , 0877180377) Willis Music Co.

—Beanstalk's Basics for Piano Bk. B: Lesson Book Preparatory Book. 2000. 47p. pap. 7.95 (978-0-87718-038-8(5) , 0877180385) Willis Music Co.

Flatau, Carole, ed. Sylvester's Snappy Songs: Primer Level for Early Elementary Students. 1999. (Looney Tunes Piano Library). (J). 59.95 (978-0-7692-8433-0(7) , Warner Bros. Pubns.) Alfred Publishing Co., Inc.

—Taz's Terrific Songs: Level Two for Late Elementary Students. 2000. (Looney Tunes Piano Library). 24p. (J). 5.95 (978-0-7692-8434-7(5) , Warner Bros. Pubns.) Alfred Publishing Co., Inc.

Goss, Louise, ed. Contemporary Piano Literature. pap. 6.95 (978-1-58951-036-4(4)) Summy-Birchard, Inc.

Grieg, Edvard. Larger Piano Compositions. 2001. 149p. (YA). reprint ed. 88.00 (978-0-7222-6349-5(X)) Library Reprints, Inc.

—Piano Lyrics & Shorter Compositions. 2001. 184p. (YA). reprint ed. 88.00 (978-0-7222-6350-1(3)) Library Reprints, Inc.

Iliffe, Frederick. Bach's Forty-Eight Preludes & Fugues, 2 vols., set. 2001. (YA). reprint ed. 250.00 (978-0-7222-6326-6(0)) Library Reprints, Inc.

Jonson, George C. A. A Handbook of Chopin's Works, Giving a Detailed Account of All the Compositions of Chopin, Short Analysis for the Piano Student, & Critical Quotations from the Writings of Well-Known Musical Authors. 2nd ed. 2001. 287p. (YA). reprint ed. 98.00 (978-0-7222-5382-3(6)) Library Reprints, Inc.

Kleczynski, Jan. The Chopin's Greater Works: Preludes, Ballads, Nocturnes, Polonaises, Mazurkas. 2001. 115p. (YA). reprint ed. 88.00 (978-0-7222-5385-4(0)) Library Reprints, Inc.

Lancaster, E. L., et al. Music for Little Mozarts. Date not set. (J). (ps-1). (Music Flashcards Ser.: Bk. 3). (978-0-7390-0646-7(0) , 17183); (Music Discovery Bks.: Bk. 3). pap. (978-0-7390-0645-0(2) , 17182); (Music Lesson Bks.: Bk. 3). pap. (978-0-7390-0644-3(4) , 17180); (Music Flashcards Ser.: Bk. 4). (978-0-7390-0653-5(3) , 17189); (Music Lesson Bks.: Bk. 4). pap. (978-0-7390-0650-4(9) , 17186); (Music Discovery Bks.: Bk. 4). pap. (978-0-7390-0652-8(5) , 17188); (Music Workbks.: No. 4). pap., wbk. ed. (978-0-7390-0651-1(7) , 17187) Alfred Publishing Co., Inc.

Lowe, C. Egerton. Beethoven's Pianoforte Sonatas: Hints on Rendering. 2001. (YA). reprint ed. 150.00 (978-0-7222-5337-3(0)) Library Reprints, Inc.

Lowe, Marilyn & Gordon, Edwin. Music Moves for Piano, 2004. (J). Bk. 1. 56p. 17.95 (978-1-57999-343-6(5) , G-6439); Bk. 2. 55p. 17.95 (978-1-57999-345-0(1) , G-6441) GIA Pubns., Inc.

—Music Moves for Piano Preparatory Book. 2004. 36p. (J). 14.95 (978-1-57999-341-2(9) , G-6437) GIA Pubns., Inc.

Lowe, Marilyn, et al. Music Moves for Piano Boogies & Blues. 2004. 30p. (J). 7.95 (978-1-57999-349-8(4) , G-6445) GIA Pubns., Inc.

Make a Joyful Noise: Play & Sing Piano Book. 2006. 24p. (YA). bds. 16.99 (978-0-7847-1455-3(X) , 04080) Standard Publishing.

Marks, A. Easy Piano Tunes. 2004. (Easy Tunes Ser.). (Illus.). 32p. (J). pap. 8.95 (978-0-7945-0474-8(4)) EDC Publishing.

—Piano Tunes for Children. 2004. (Easy Tunes Ser.). (Illus.). 32p. (J). pap. 8.95 (978-0-7945-0459-5(0)) EDC Publishing.

Martyr, Paula, illus. A Musical Day. 1999. (My First Piano Ser.). 8p. (J). bds. 7.95 (978-1-57717-112-6(8)) New Line Bks.

More What Else Can I Play: Piano Grade 1. (gr. 1). 6.95 (978-1-85909-523-2(2) , Warner Bros. Pubns.) Alfred Publishing Co., Inc.

More What Else Can I Play: Piano Grade 2. (gr. 2). 6.95 (978-1-85909-524-9(0) , Warner Bros. Pubns.) Alfred Publishing Co., Inc.

Music. Gr 6 Stm Te/Piano Accomp. 2003. (Share the Music Ser.). (gr. 6 up). (978-0-02-295593-9(3)) Macmillan/McGraw-Hill Schl. Div.

Okun, Milton, ed. Christmas Carols for Piano Duet. 63p. (YA). pap. 14.95 (978-0-89524-948-7(0) , 02505651) Cherry Lane Music Co.

—From a Distance & Twenty-Four Other Easy Listening Favorites for Easy Piano. 119p. (Orig.). (YA). pap. 12.95 (978-0-89524-871-8(9) , 02505508) Cherry Lane Music Co.

Pauer, Ernst. A Dictionary of Pianists & Composers for the Pianoforte. 2001. 159p. (YA). reprint ed. 88.00 (978-0-7222-5973-3(5)) Library Reprints, Inc.

Radin, Isabel. Spanish Childrens Songs (Solo) Elementary Solo Piano, 12 Favorites to Play & Sing. 1998. (J). 5.95 (978-0-7692-5450-0(0) , Warner Bros. Pubns.) Alfred Publishing Co., Inc.

Ruth, Anita, ed. Music from the Heart. 2004. 116p. pap. 34.95 (978-1-891195-12-9(3) , 1891195123) Time Line Productions, Inc.

Shantz, Cheryl. Folksongs for Piano: A Classical Interpretation, Graded Pieces at the Intermediate Level. 2nd ed. 1998. 24p. (YA). reprint ed. pap. 10.00 (978-0-9645431-2-6(5)) Kallisti Music Pr.

Shedlock, John South. Beethoven's Pianoforte Sonatas: The Origin & Respective Values of Various Readings. 2001. 51p. (YA). reprint ed. 88.00 (978-0-7222-5347-2(8)) Library Reprints, Inc.

Tokarjewa, Viktorija. Der Pianist: Erzaehlungen. (GER.). 176p. (978-3-257-06139-0(0)) Diogenes Verlag AG CHE. *Dist:* International Bk. Import Service, Inc.

Tornquist, Carol. Music in Me: A Piano Method for Young Christian Students. 2006. 32p. pap. 7.95 (978-1-4234-1876-4(X) , 142341876X); 40p. pap. 7.95 (978-1-4234-1877-1(8) , 1423418778); 32p. pap. 7.95 (978-1-4234-1878-8(6) , 1423418786); 32p. pap. 7.95 (978-1-4234-1879-5(4) , 1423418794); 32p. pap. 7.95 (978-1-4234-1880-1(8) , 1423418808); 32p. pap. 7.95 (978-1-4234-1881-8(6) , 1423418816); 40p. pap. 7.95 (978-1-4234-1888-7(3) , 1423418883); 32p. pap. 7.95 (978-1-4234-1889-4(1) , 1423418891); 32p. pap. 7.95 (978-1-4234-1890-0(5) , 1423418905); 32p. pap. 7.95 (978-1-4234-1891-7(3) , 1423418913); 32p. pap. 7.95 (978-1-4234-1892-4(1) , 1423418921); 40p. pap. 7.95 (978-1-4234-1893-1(X) , 142341893X); 32p. pap. 7.95 (978-1-4234-1894-8(8) , 1423418948); 32p. pap. 7.95 (978-1-4234-1895-5(6) , 1423418956); 32p. pap. 7.95 (978-1-4234-1896-2(4) , 1423418964) Leonard, Hal Corp.

Turner, Gary. Progressive's Young Beginner Piano Giant Coloring Book. 2003. (Illus.). 36p. (J). pap. 23.95 incl. audio compact disk (978-1-86469-098-9(4)) Learntoplaymusic.com AUS. *Dist:* Bookworld Trade, Inc.

Unbeaten Tracks: 8 Contemporary Pieces for Trumpet & Piano. 2002. 48p. (J). (gr. 4-7). 10.95 (978-0-571-52005-3(7)) Faber & Faber, Ltd. GBR. *Dist:* Leonard, Hal Corp.

Venable, Mary. The Interpretation of Piano Music. 2001. 252p. (YA). reprint ed. 98.00 (978-0-7222-5959-7(X)) Library Reprints, Inc.

Westerby, Herbert. The History of Pianoforte Music. 2001. 407p. (YA). reprint ed. 98.00 (978-0-7222-5938-2(7)) Library Reprints, Inc.

Wilkinson, Charles W. Well-Known Piano Solos: How to Play Them. 2001. 284p. (YA). reprint ed. 98.00 (978-0-7222-5954-2(9)) Library Reprints, Inc.

Yolen, Jane & Stemple, Adam. Sing Noel. Carpenter, Nancy, illus. 2003. 96p. (J). (gr. 4-6). 17.95 (978-1-56397-420-5(7)) Boyds Mills Pr.

PICASSO, PABLO, 1881-1973

Ada, Alma Flor & Campoy, F. Isabel, contrib. by. Sonrisas. (Literature Collection of Puertas Al Sol Ser.). (SPA.). 32p. (J). (gr. k-6). pap. 13.95 (978-1-59437-701-3(4)) Santillana USA Publishing Co., Inc.

Bargallo, Eva. My Name Is Picasso. Monreal, Violeta, illus. 2006. (My Name Is ... Ser.). 64p. (J). pap. 7.99 (978-0-7641-3393-0(4)) Barron's Educational Series, Inc.

Bennett, Leonie. Life & Work of Pablo Picasso. 2004. (Life & Work Of- Ser.). (Illus.). 32p. (J). pap. 7.25 (978-1-4034-5563-5(5)) Heinemann Library.

—Pablo Picasso. 2004. (Life & Work Of- Ser.). (Illus.). 32p. (J). lib. bdg. 22.79 (978-1-4034-5072-2(2)) Heinemann Library.

Boutan, Mila. Picasso. 1998. (Art Activity Pack Ser.). (Illus.). 13p. (J). (gr. k-7). pap. 9.95 (978-0-8118-2029-5(7)) Chronicle Bks. LLC.

Delpech, Sylvie & Leclerc, Caroline, eds. Pablo Picasso. 2006. (Sticker Art Shapes Ser.). (Illus.). 28p. 7.95 (978-1-84507-676-4(1)) Lincoln, Frances Ltd. GBR. *Dist:* Perseus Distribution.

Fandel, Jennifer. Pablo Picasso. 2005. (Xtraordinary Artists Ser.). (Illus.). 48p. (gr. 5-9). 21.95 (978-1-58341-331-9(6) , Creative Education) Creative Co., The.

Giraudy, Daniele & De Maupeou, Patrick. Picasso & His Times. 1999. (W5 Who, What, Where, When & Why Ser.). 96p. (YA). (gr. 6 up). 19.95 (978-0-8050-5061-5(2)) Holt, Henry & Co.

Gogerly, Liz. Pablo Picasso: Master of Modern Art. Picasso, Pablo, illus. 2004. (Famous Lives Ser.). 48p. (J). (gr. 3-5). lib. bdg. 29.93 (978-0-7398-6628-3(1)) Raintree.

—The Story of Pablo Picasso. 2002. (Lifetimes Ser.). (Illus.). 48p. (J). lib. bdg. 28.50 (978-1-931983-17-4(8)) Chrysalis Education.

Hart, Tony. Picasso. Hellard, Susan, illus. 2002. (Ninos Famosos Ser.). (SPA & ENG.). 24p. (gr. 1-5). pap. 6.95 (978-85-7416-166-2(7)) Callis Editora Ltda BRA. *Dist:* Independent Pubs. Group.

Heslewood, Juliet. Introducing Picasso. 2002. (Introducing Painters Ser.). (Illus.). 32p. (J). lib. bdg. 24.25 (978-1-931983-45-7(3)) Chrysalis Education.

Hodge, Susie & Picasso, Pablo. Pablo Picasso. 2004. (Lives of the Artists Ser.). (Illus.). 48p. (J). (gr. 5 up). pap. 29.26 (978-0-8368-5606-4(6)); lib. bdg. 30.00 (978-0-8368-5601-9(5)) Stevens, Gareth Inc. (World Almanac Library).

Holland, Gini. Pablo Picasso. 2003. (Trailblazers of the Modern World Ser.). (Illus.). 48p. (J). (gr. 5 up). pap. 14.95 (978-0-8368-5244-8(3)); lib. bdg. 30.00 (978-0-8368-5084-0(X)) Stevens, Gareth Inc. (World Almanac Library).

Hyde, Margaret E., ed. Picasso for Kids. 2004. (Great Art for Kids Ser.). (Illus.). 12p. (J). pap. 8.95 (978-1-58980-205-6(5)) Pelican Publishing Co., Inc.

Jacobson, Rick. Picasso: Soul on Fire. Jacobson, Rick & Fernandez, Laura, illus. 2004. 32p. (J). (gr. 5). 15.95 (978-0-88776-599-5(8)) Tundra Bks., Inc./Livres Toundra, Inc. CAN. *Dist:* Random Hse., Inc.

Kelley, True. Pablo Picasso: Breaking All the Rules. Kelley, True, illus. 2002. (Smart about Art Ser.). (Illus.). 32p. (J). pap. 5.99 (978-0-448-42862-8(8) , Grosset & Dunlap) Penguin Group (USA) Inc.

—Pablo Picasso: Breaking All the Rules. 2002. (gr. 3-6). lib. bdg. 14.15 (978-0-613-62151-9(4)) Tandem Library Bks.

Klein, Adam G. & Picasso, Pablo. Pablo Picasso. 2007. (Great Artists Ser.). (Illus.). 32p. (J). (gr. 2-5). lib. bdg. 22.78 (978-1-59679-733-8(9)) ABDO Publishing Co.

Langley, Andrew. Pablo Picasso. 2003. pap. 37.50 (978-1-4109-0290-0(0)); 32p. (J). lib. bdg. 25.70 (978-0-7398-6865-2(9)) Raintree.

—Pablo Picasso. 2003. (gr. 3-6). lib. bdg. 15.90 (978-0-613-78167-1(8)) Tandem Library Bks.

Lebscky, Ibi. Pablito. Cardoni, Paolo, illus. (Coleccion Seran Famosos).Tr. of Little Pablo Picasso. (SPA.). 28p. (J). (gr. 2-4). 14.95 (978-84-233-1265-8(8)) Ediciones Destino ESP. *Dist:* AIMS International Bks., Inc., Lectorum Pubns., Inc.

Lowery, Linda. Pablo Picasso. Porter, Janice Lee, illus. (On My Own Biographies Ser.). 48p. (J). (gr. 1-3). 2003. 5.95 (978-1-57505-370-7(5)); 1999. lib. bdg. 23.93 (978-1-57505-331-8(4) , Carolrhoda Bks.) Lerner Publishing Group.

—Pablo Picasso. 1999. (gr. 3-6). lib. bdg. 14.10 (978-0-613-68275-6(0)); (Illus.). (J). (978-0-606-21958-7(7)) Tandem Library Bks.

Lowery, Linda & Porter, Janice Lee. Pablo Picasso. 2006. (Yo Solo Biografías Ser.). (SPA.). (J). 23.93 (978-0-8225-6259-7(6) , Ediciones Lerner) Lerner Publishing Group.

MacDonald, Patricia. Pablo Picasso: Genius! The Artist & the Process. 1999. (Illus.). 128p. (YA). (gr. 7-9). 20.00 (978-0-7881-6842-0(8)) DIANE Publishing Co.

MacDonald, Patricia & Picasso, Pablo. Pablo Picasso: Greatest Artist of the 20th Century. 2001. (Giants of Art & Culture Ser.). (Illus.). 128p. (J). (gr. 5-8). 29.94 (978-1-56711-504-8(7) , Blackbirch Pr., Inc.) Thomson Gale.

Mason, Antony. El arte Moderna: En los tiempos de Picasso. 2005. (Arte Alrededor del Mundo Ser.). 48p. (J). pap. 9.95 (978-85-7416-217-1(5)) Callis Editora Ltda BRA. *Dist:* Independent Pubs. Group.

—El Arte Moderno: En los Tiempos de Picasso. 2005. (Arte Alrededor del Mundo Ser.). 48p. (J). pap. 9.95 (978-85-7416-240-9(X)) Callis Editora Ltda BRA. *Dist:* Independent Pubs. Group.

—In the Time of Picasso. 2002. (gr. 3-6). lib. bdg. 17.60 (978-0-613-85063-6(7)) Tandem Library Bks.

McNeese, Tim. Pablo Picasso. 2006. (Great Hispanic Heritage Ser.). (Illus.). 128p. (J). 30.00 (978-0-7910-8843-2(X) , Chelsea Hse.) Facts On File, Inc.

Nichols, Catherine. Pablo Picasso. 2006. (Primary Source Library of Famous Artists). (Illus.). 32p. (J). 21.95 (978-1-4042-2764-4(4) , PowerKids Pr.) Rosen Publishing Group, Inc., The.

Pablo Picasso. 2006. (J). pap. 5.95 (978-0-8225-6624-3(9) , Ediciones Lerner) Lerner Publishing Group.

Pfleger, Susanne. A Day with Picasso. Wynne, Christopher, tr. from GER. 1999. (Adventures in Art Ser.). (Illus.). 30p. (gr. 3-10). 14.95 (978-3-7913-2165-3(X)) Prestel Publishing.

Picasso, Pablo. Introducing Pablo Picasso: His Life & Art with 16 Stickers. Negri, Paul, ed. 2001. (Illus.). 16p. (YA). 5.95 (978-0-486-41559-8(7)) Dover Pubns., Inc.

Sateren, Shelley Swanson & Picasso, Pablo. Picasso. 2002. (Masterpieces). (Illus.). 24p. (J). (gr. 2-3). lib. bdg. 18.60 (978-0-7368-1122-4(2) , Bridgestone Bks.) Capstone Pr., Inc.

Scarborough, Kate. Pablo Picasso. 2002. (Artists in Their Time Ser.). (Illus.). (J). (gr. 5-7). 46p. pap. 6.95 (978-0-531-16622-2(8)); 48p. pap. 23.50 (978-0-531-12229-7(8)) Scholastic Library Publishing. (Watts, Franklin).

—Pablo Picasso. 2002. (Illus.). 46p. (J). (gr. 3-7). lib. bdg. 15.25 (978-0-613-54067-4(0)) Tandem Library Bks.

Smiles: Pablo Picasso, Gabriela Mistral, Benito Juarez. 2001. (Gateways to the Sun Ser.). (Illus.). (J). (gr. k-1). pap. 10.95 (978-1-58105-570-2(6)) Santillana USA Publishing Co., Inc.

Spence, David. Picasso: Una Revolucion en el Arte. (Coleccion Grandes Artistas).Tr. of Picasso: Breaking the Rules of Art. (SPA.). 226p. (YA). (gr. 5-8). 12.76 (978-84-8211-134-6(5)) Celeste Ediciones, S.A. ESP. *Dist:* Lectorum Pubns., Inc.

Stephens, Pamela Geiger. Dropping in on Picasso. McNeill, Jim, illus. 2004. (J). (978-1-56290-325-1(X)) Crystal Productions.

Trailblazers of the Modern World: Winston Churchill; Alexander Fleming; Pablo Picasso; Elvis Presley; Venus & Serena Williams; Oprah Winfrey, 6 bks. 2002. (Illus.). (J). (gr. 5 up). pap. 89.70 (978-0-8368-5241-7(9) , World Almanac Library) Stevens, Gareth Inc.

Vila, Carmen. Tracy Knows Picasso: Children's Art History Read-Along Book. (Illus.). 24p. (J). (gr. 1-6). incl. audio (978-0-9635047-0-8(3)) VILA Group, Inc., The.

Wallis, Jeremy. Pablo Picasso. 2001. (Creative Lives Ser.). (Illus.). 64p. (J). (gr. 6-8). lib. bdg. 27.07 (978-1-58810-206-5(8)) Heinemann Library.

PICASSO, PABLO, 1881-1973—FICTION

Anholt, Laurence. Picasso & the Girl with a Ponytail. 2007. (Anholt's Artists Books for Children Ser.). 32p. (J). (ps-3). pap. 7.99 (***978-0-7641-3853-9(7)***) Barron's Educational Series, Inc.

—Picasso & the Girl with a Ponytail: A Story of Pablo Picasso. 1998. (Illus.). 32p. (J). (ps-2). 14.95 (978-0-7641-5031-9(6)) Barron's Educational Series, Inc.

—Picasso y Sylvette: Un Cuento Sobre Pablo Picasso. 2000. (Illus.). (J). (gr. 3-5). (CAT.). 32p. 14.95 (978-84-8488-003-5(6)); (SPA., 200p. 14.95 (978-84-95040-01-5(8)) Serres, Ediciones, S. L. ESP. *Dist:* Lectorum Pubns., Inc.

Maltbie, P. I. Picasso & Minou. Estrada, Pau, illus. 2005. 32p. (J). 15.95 (978-1-57091-620-5(9)) Charlesbridge Publishing, Inc.

Ploss, Skip. If Picasso Were a Fish. Ploss, Skip, illus. 2006. 40p. (gr. k-2). 15.99 (978-1-4116-9220-6(9)) Lulu.com.

Scott, Elaine. Secrets of the Cirque Medrano. 2008. (J). (***978-1-57091-712-7(4)***) Charlesbridge Publishing, Inc.

Scott, Elaine. The Spanish Web: An Encounter with Picasso. 2004. (Art Encounters Ser.). (J). 15.95 (978-0-8230-0410-2(4)); pap. 6.99 (978-0-8230-0413-3(9)) Watson-Guptill Pubns., Inc.

PICKETT, BILL, CA. 1860-1932

Dickinson, Malcolm. Bill Pickett's Great Adventures: The Rodeo King's Legend Lives On. 2002. (Illus.). 100p. 10.95 (978-1-57168-737-1(8)) Eakin Pr.

Landau, Elaine. Bill Pickett: Wild West Cowboy. 2004. (Best of the West Biographies Ser.). (Illus.). 48p. (J). lib. bdg. 23.93 (978-0-7660-2215-7(3)) Enslow Pubs., Inc.

Pinkney, Andrea Davis. Bill Pickett: Rodeo-Ridin' Cowboy. Pinkney, Brian, illus. 1999. (J). (gr. 5-8). lib. bdg. 14.15 (978-0-613-22822-0(7)) Tandem Library Bks.

—Bill Pickett: Rodeo-Ridin' Cowboy. 1999. (J). 12.80 (978-0-606-17356-8(0)) Tandem Library Bks.

PICKLING

see Canning and Preserving

PICNICKING

At the Lake: KinderReaders Individual Title Six-Packs. (Kinderstarters Ser.). 8p. (ps-1). 21.00 (978-0-7635-8663-8(3)) Rigby Education.

Dahl, Michael. Ants at the Picnic: Counting by 10s. Trover, Zachary, illus. 2006. 24p. (J). (ps-2). 22.60 (978-1-4048-1318-2(7)) Picture Window Bks.

La Excursion (The Picnic) (Granja Oso de Miel Ser.). (SPA., Illus.). (J). bds. 4.99 (978-0-7899-0608-3(2) , 495050) Editorial Unilit.

Foley, Cate. Let's Go on a Picnic. 2001. (Welcome Bks.). (Illus.). 24p. (J). (ps-2). pap. 4.95 (978-0-516-29579-4(9) , Children's Pr.) Scholastic Library Publishing.

—Let's Go on a Picnic. 2001. (gr. k-3). lib. bdg. 12.95 (978-0-613-58984-0(X)) Tandem Library Bks.

—Let's Go to a Picnic. 2001. (Weekend Fun Ser.). (Illus.). (J). lib. bdg. (978-0-516-23292-8(4) , Children's Pr.) Scholastic Library Publishing.

Kennedy, Jimmy. Teddy Bears' Picnic. 2000. (gr. k-3). lib. bdg. 14.15 (978-0-613-88163-0(X)) Tandem Library Bks.

Mullican, Judy. Picnic Pals. Middleton, Mikell, illus. 2003. 8p. (J). (ps-1). bds. 10.95 (978-1-57332-251-5(2)) High-Reach Learning, Inc.

—Picnic Pals: Big Book. Middleton, Mikell, illus. 2003. 8p. (J). (ps-1). bds. 10.95 (978-1-57332-244-7(X)) High-Reach Learning, Inc.

Rau, Dana Meachen & Vargus, Nanci Reginelli. At a Picnic. 2007. (Fun Time Ser.). 24p. (J). lib. bdg. 22.79 (***978-0-7614-2607-3(8)*** , Benchmark Bks.) Cavendish, Marshall Corp.

The Special Ride: Individual Title Six-Packs. 16p. (gr. 2 up). 35.00 (978-0-7635-9377-3(X)) Rigby Education.

Walton, Rick & Adams, Jennifer. Packing up a Picnic: Activities & Recipes for Kids. Dixon, Debra Spina, illus. 2006. 64p. (J). (gr. 3-6). pap. 9.95 (978-1-58685-778-3(9) , 1255567) Gibbs Smith, Publisher.

PICNICKING—FICTION

Adams, Gloria. Five Little Skunks. Collier-Morales, Roberta, illus. 2006. (Sing-A-Story Ser.). 16p. (J). bds. 10.95 (978-0-7696-4916-0(5)) School Specialty Publishing.

Alborough, Jez. It's the Bear! Alborough, Jez, illus. 2002. (Illus.). (J). 13.83 (978-0-7587-2879-1(4)) Book Wholesalers, Inc.

—It's the Bear! Alborough, Jez, illus. 2004. (Illus.). 30p. (J). (gr. k-ps). bds. 6.99 (978-0-7636-2316-6(4)) Candlewick Pr.

Benson, Laura. The Mouse's Picnic. Adams Marks, Elizabeth, illus. 2002. (Two Can Read Ser.). 16p. (J). 2.99 (978-1-56472-667-4(3)) Edupress, Inc.

Bertrand, Diane Gonzales. Uncle Chente's Picnic/el picnic de Tío Chente. Castilla, Julia Mercedes, tr. Howard, Pauline Rodriguez, illus. Tr. of Picnic de Tio Chente. (ENG & SPA.). 32p. (J). (ps-3). 15.95 (978-1-55885-337-9(5) , Piñata Books) Arte Publico Pr.

Blackaby, Susan. Classroom Cookout. Muehlenhardt, Amy Bailey, illus. 2004. (Read-It! Readers Classroom Tales Ser.). 32p. (C). (gr. k-3). 18.60 (978-1-4048-0583-5(4)) Picture Window Bks.

Bunting, Eve. A Picnic in October. Carpenter, Nancy, illus. 2004. 32p. (J). reprint ed. pap. 7.00 (978-0-15-205065-8(5) , Voyager Bks./Libros Viajeros) Harcourt Children's Bks.

Capucilli, Alyssa Satin. Biscuit's Picnic. Schories, Pat, illus. 1998. (Biscuit Ser.). 24p. (J). (ps-1). 12.95 (978-0-06-028072-7(7)) HarperCollins Pubs.

Caraballo, Samuel. Estrellita se despide de su isla/Estrellita Says Good-bye to Her Island. Caraballo, Samuel, tr. Torrecilla, Pablo, illus. Tr. of Estrellita Says Good-Bye to Her Island. (ENG & SPA.). 32p. (J). stu. ed. 15.95 (978-1-55885-338-6(3) , Piñata Books) Arte Publico Pr.

Cronin, Doreen. Click, Clack, Quackity-Quack: An Alphabetical Adventure. Lewin, Betsy, illus. 2005. 24p. (J). 12.95 (978-0-689-87715-5(3) , Atheneum) Simon & Schuster Children's Publishing.

—Click, Clack, Quackity-Quack: An Alphabetical Adventure. 2006. (J). (ps-3). 22.78 (978-1-59961-089-4(2)) Spotlight.

Dalmatian Press Staff, ed. A Perfect Picnic. rev. ed. 2005. 24p. (J). pap. 3.50 (978-1-4037-1695-8(1)) Dalmatian Pr.

Davis, Catherine. Abby & Alex Feel Their Hearts' Little. 2006. 57p. pap. 12.95 ***(978-1-4241-4586-7(4))*** PublishAmerica, Inc.

Delittle, Cathy. The Squirrel Who Loved Picnics. Delittle, Cathy, illus. 1998. (Illus.). 9p. (J). (ps-1). spiral bd. 7.95 (978-1-892633-05-7(1) , OOCD209) Delittle Storyteller Co.

Donat, Jaclynne. Ribbons for Randi. 2006. (ENG.). 52p. per. 12.95 ***(978-1-4241-5307-7(7))*** PublishAmerica, Inc.

Dotlich, Rebecca Kai. Peanut & Pearl's Picnic Adventure. Alley, R. W., illus. 2007. (My First I Can Read Bks.). 32p. (J). lib. bdg. 16.89 ***(978-0-06-054921-3(1) ;*** 15.99 ***(978-0-06-054920-6(3))*** HarperCollins Pubs.

Eding, June. Easter Showers. Chauhan, Manhar, illus. 2007. (Puppy Scooby-Doo Ser.). 32p. (J). pap. 3.99 (978-0-448-44485-7(2) , Grosset & Dunlap) Penguin Group (USA) Inc.

Elder, Elizabeth. When I'm with You. Mansmann, Leslie, illus. 2003. (J). per. 15.95 (978-0-9671662-8-5(4)) Islandport Pr., Inc.

Elya, Susan Middleton. Oh No, Gotta Go, No. 2. Cravath, Lynne Woodcock & Avril, Lynne, illus. 2007. 32p. (J). (ps-k). 15.99 (978-0-399-24308-0(9) , Putnam Juvenile) Penguin Group (USA) Inc.

Evans, Lezlie. The Bunnies' Picnic. Chorao, Kay, illus. 2007. 32p. (ps-1). 16.99 (978-0-7868-1612-5(0)) Hyperion Pr.

Ferguson, Sarah. Little Red. Williams, Sam, illus. 2006. 40p. (J). 6.99 (978-1-4169-1853-0(1) , Aladdin) Simon & Schuster Children's Publishing.

Footprints: Individual Title Six-Packs. (Rigby Focus Ser.). 16p. (gr. k up). 28.00 (978-0-7578-5528-3(8)); 26.00 (978-0-7578-5294-7(7)) Rigby Education.

Glassman, Jackie. Berry Best Friends' Picnic. 2003. (gr. k-3). lib. bdg. 11.80 (978-0-613-64020-6(9)) Tandem Library Bks.

—The Berry Best Friends' Picnic: Strawberry Shortcake. S. I. Artists Staff et al, illus. 2003. (All Aboard Reading Station Stop Ser.). 32p. (J). (ps-2). pap. 3.99 (978-0-448-43134-5(3) , Grosset & Dunlap) Penguin Group (USA) Inc.

Goode, Diane. The Most Perfect Spot. Goode, Diane, illus. 2006. (Illus.). 32p. (J). lib. bdg. 17.89 (978-0-06-072698-0(9)); 16.99 (978-0-06-072697-3(0)) HarperCollins Pubs.

Graham, Bob. Oscar's Half Birthday. Graham, Bob, illus. 2005. (Illus.). 32p. (J). (gr. k-1). 16.99 (978-0-7636-2699-0(6)) Candlewick Pr.

Granowsky, Alvin. Can I Help? 2001. 11.79 (978-0-606-22430-7(0)) Tandem Library Bks.

Grindley, Sally. A Little Bit of Trouble. Taylor, Eleanor, illus. 2004. 32p. (J). 16.95 (978-1-58234-882-7(0) , Bloomsbury Children) Bloomsbury Publishing.

—No Trouble at All. 2004. (Illus.). 32p. (J). reprint ed. pap. 6.95 (978-1-58234-894-0(4) , Bloomsbury Children) Bloomsbury Publishing.

Hamilton, Richard & Williams, Sophy. Polly's Picnic. 2003. (Illus.). 32p. (J). (ps-2). 16.95 (978-1-58234-819-3(7) , Bloomsbury Children) Bloomsbury Publishing.

Hamilton, Tisha. Picnic in the Park. Style Guide Staff, illus. 2006. (Raggedy Ann Ser.). 96p. (J). 2.99 (978-1-4169-1749-6(7) , Simon Scribbles) Simon & Schuster Children's Publishing.

Harcourt School Publishers Staff. The Ants Picnic: Take-Home Book. 1999. (Illus.). (J). pap. 1.90 (978-0-15-317191-8(X)) Harcourt Schl. Pubs.

—Collections: Night Picnic Take-Home Book. 1999. (Illus.). (J). (gr. 2). pap. 1.90 (978-0-15-317401-8(3)) Harcourt Schl. Pubs.

—Follow Me: Below Level. 3rd ed. 2002. (Trophies Reading Program Ser.). (Illus.). (J). pap. 3.20 (978-0-15-322954-1(3)) Harcourt Schl. Pubs.

—Jason & the Quest for the Golden Fleece Advanced Level. 3rd ed. 2002. (Trophies Reading Program Ser.). (Illus.). pap. 5.10 (978-0-15-323475-0(X)) Harcourt Schl. Pubs.

—The Picnic in the Park Advanced Level. 3rd ed. 2002. (Trophies Reading Program Ser.). (Illus.). pap. 5.10 (978-0-15-323022-6(3)) Harcourt Schl. Pubs.

—The Picnic in the Park Below Level. 3rd ed. 2002. (Trophies Reading Program Ser.). (Illus.). pap. 5.10 (978-0-15-323054-7(1)) Harcourt Schl. Pubs.

—The Potluck Picnic. 3rd ed. 2002. (Trophies English Language Learners Ser.). (Illus.). pap. 5.10 (978-0-15-327832-7(3)) Harcourt Schl. Pubs.

—Trofeos Advanced Level: Almuerzo en el Parque. 3rd ed. 2002. (SPA., Illus.). pap. 6.80 (978-0-15-323933-5(6)) Harcourt Schl. Pubs.

—Trofeos Below Level: Sigueme, Niki! 3rd ed. 2002. (SPA., Illus.). (J). pap. 3.50 (978-0-15-323865-9(8)) Harcourt Schl. Pubs.

—Turtle at Home On Level. 3rd ed. 2002. (Trophies Reading Program Ser.). (Illus.). pap. 5.10 (978-0-15-323166-7(1)) Harcourt Schl. Pubs.

Hayes, Sarah. El Solo y la Merienda. 2000. (Easy Readers Ser.).Tr. of Bear & the Snack. (SPA., Illus.). 32p. (J). 11.95 (978-84-207-3401-9(2)) Grupo Anaya, S.A. ESP. *Dist:* Distribooks, Inc.

Hojel, Barbara & Guy, Ginger F. Rainy Day Picnic. 1999. Bk. 8. (Illus.). 16p. (C). pap. 7.66 (978-0-201-35139-2(0)) Longman Publishing Group.

Honigsberg, Peter John. Too Much Picnic. Jones, Ryan, illus. 2006. 32p. (J). 16.95 (978-1-57143-154-7(3)) RDR Bks.

Hutchins, Pat. We're Going on a Picnic! Hutchins, Pat, illus. 2002. (Illus.). 32p. (J). 16.99 (978-0-688-16799-8(3)) HarperCollins Pubs.

Inkpen, Mick. Picnic. Inkpen, Mick, illus. 2002. (Kipper Ser.). (Illus.). (J). 12.30 (978-0-7587-6469-0(3)) Book Wholesalers, Inc.

—Picnic. 2001. (978-0-606-22345-4(2)) Tandem Library Bks.

Jarrett, Clare. Best Picnic Ever. Jarrett, Clare, illus. 2004. (Illus.). 32p. (J). (gr. k-k). 16.99 (978-0-7636-2370-8(9)) Candlewick Pr.

Jennings, Sharon. Franklin's Picnic. Jeffrey, Sean et al, illus. 2006. 32p. (J). lib. bdg. 15.38 ***(978-1-4242-1179-1(4))*** Fitzgerald Bks.

Jennings, Sharon, et al. Franklin's Picnic. Southern, Shelley et al, illus. 32p. (978-1-55337-714-6(1)) Kids Can Pr., Ltd.

Jumbo & the Stranger. 2004. (J). per. 15.99 (978-0-9744205-5-4(7)) Golden Eagle Publishing Hse., Inc.

Kelman, Marcy & Higginson, Sheila Sweeny. Hot Dog Day. Disney Storybook Artists Staff, illus. 2007. 64p. (J). (ps-k). 8.99 ***(978-1-4231-0651-7(2))*** Disney Pr.

Kids Can Read Staff, ed. Franklin's Picnic. 2006. (Illus.). 32p. 3.95 (978-1-55337-715-3(X)) Kids Can Pr., Ltd. CAN. *Dist:* Wybel Marketing Group.

Klein, Adria F. Max Goes to a Cookout. 2007. (Read-It! Readers Ser.). (Illus.). 24p. (J). ***(978-1-4048-3290-9(4)*** , 1265793) Picture Window Bks.

—Max Goes to a Cookout. Gallagher-Cole, Mernie, illus. 2006. (Read-It! Readers Ser.). 24p. (J). ***(978-1-4048-3146-9(0)*** , 1265793) Picture Window Bks.

Krishnaswami, Uma. The Ants Have a Picnic. 2006. (Early Explorers Ser.). (J). 34.00 ***(978-1-4108-6115-3(5))*** Benchmark Education Co.

Landstrom, Olof. Boo & Baa in the Woods. 2000. (978-0-606-22354-6(1)) Tandem Library Bks.

Leaney, Cindy. Picnic in the Park. Whitehouse, Patty, ed. King, Sue & Wilks, Peter, illus. 2004. (Friendly Phonics Ser.). 24p. (J). lib. bdg. 14.95 (978-1-59054-217-0(7)) Fitzgerald Bks.

Lies, Brian. Bats at the Beach. 2006. (Illus.). 32p. (J). (gr. k-3). 16.00 (978-0-618-55744-8(X)) Houghton Mifflin Co.

Lindgren, Astrid. Pippi's Extraordinary Ordinary Day. 1999. (Pippi Longstocking Storybooks). (Illus.). 64p. (J). (gr. k-2). 14.99 (978-0-670-88073-7(6) , Viking Juvenile) Penguin Group (USA) Inc.

Lovell, H. N. Wootie's Delightful Picnic. 2006. (J). pap. 12.95 (978-0-9761182-4-4(6)) Alpha Run Pr., LLC.

Lucy's Picnic. 2006. (J). (978-0-9764719-3-6(0)) Mice-Works.

McCully, Emily Arnold. Picnic. McCully, Emily Arnold, illus. 2003. (Illus.). 32p. (J). (ps-k). 16.89 (978-0-06-623855-5(2)); 16.99 (978-0-06-623854-8(4)) HarperCollins Pubs.

Medearis, Angela Shelf. On the Way to the Pond. Cauley, Lorinda Bryan, illus. 2006. (Green Light Readers Level 2 Ser.). 32p. (J). 12.95 (978-0-15-205599-8(1)); pap. 3.95 (978-0-15-205623-0(8)) Harcourt Trade Pubs.

Mello, Alondra. Alanora's Magic Tree: Alanora's Spirit Journey. 2007. 48p. per. 12.97 ***(978-1-932344-77-6(2))*** Thornton Publishing.

Miranda, Anne. Pignic. Hoffman, Rosekrans, illus. 2004. 32p. (J). pap. 7.95 (978-1-59078-328-3(X)) Boyds Mills Pr.

Morton, Christine. Picnic Farm. Barringer, Sarah, illus. 1998. 32p. (J). (ps-k). 15.95 (978-0-8234-1332-4(2)) Holiday Hse., Inc.

Murphy, Mary. Panda Foo & the New Friend. Murphy, Mary, illus. 2007. (Illus.). 32p. (J). (ps-k). 15.99 ***(978-0-7636-3405-6(0))*** Candlewick Pr.

Myott, Lanita. RJ Saves the Day. 2003. 19p. 11.16 (978-1-4116-0354-7(0)) Lulu.com.

Nakagawa, Rieko. Guri & Gura's Picnic Adventure. Yamawaki, Yuriko, illus. 2003. 32p. 10.95 (978-0-8048-3355-4(9)) Tuttle Publishing.

Nash, Andy. Tatum & Her Tiger: For Kids Blessed with Passion. 2007. (J). ***(978-0-8127-0451-8(7))*** Autumn Hse. Publishing Co.

Naylor, Phyllis Reynolds. Please Do Feed the Bears. Escriva, Ana Lopez, illus. 2002. 40p. (J). (ps-2). 16.00 (978-0-689-82561-3(7) , Atheneum) Simon & Schuster Children's Publishing.

Nelson, Jim. Crosstown Crush. 2005. 82p. Vol. 1, Bk. 1. (YA). pap. 9.00 (978-1-4116-5266-8(5)); Vol. 1,Bk. 2. pap. 9.00 (978-1-4116-6654-2(2)) Lulu.com.

Paterson, Brian. The Picnic: Board Book. 2006. (Illus.). 16p. (J). (ps). bds. 6.99 (978-0-00-717421-8(7)) HarperCollins Pubs. Ltd. GBR. *Dist:* Trafalgar Square Publishing.

Patty & Pop's Picnic. 2005. (Emergent Library: Vol. 2). (YA). (ps-1). 23.94 (978-0-8215-8932-8(6)) Sadlier, William H. Inc.

Patty & Pop's Picnic: Take-Home Book. 2005. (Emergent Library: Vol. 2). (YA). (ps-1). 12.60 (978-0-8215-7262-7(8)) Sadlier, William H. Inc.

Penston, Gail. Playful Puppies: Picnic in the Park. Tarbett, Debbie, illus. 2006. 12p. (J). (gr. 3-9). 12.95 (978-1-59125-636-6(4) , Penton Kids) Penton Overseas, Inc.

Picnic. 2000. (P. B. Bear Sticker Books Ser.). (Illus.). 16p. (J). pap. 6.95 (978-0-7894-1565-3(8) , D K Ink) Dorling Kindersley Publishing, Inc.

The Picnic, 6 Packs. (gr. k-1). 23.00 (978-0-7635-8836-6(9)) Rigby Education.

Piggy Toes Press Staff. All the Way's I Love You Mini. Downing, Julie, illus. 2005. 10p. (J). 4.95 (978-1-58117-437-3(3) , Intervisual/Piggy Toes) Dalmatian Pr.

Pig's Picnic. 2001. (ps-2). lib. bdg. 9.80 (978-0-613-32947-7(3)) Tandem Library Bks.

Pittar, Gill. Milly, Molly & the Picnic. Morrell, Cris, illus. 2005. 28p. (ps-ps). pap. (978-1-86972-045-2(8)) Milly Molly Bks.

Rabe, Tish. Innovative Kids Readers: Penguins Perfect Picnic. Ho, Jannie, illus. 2007. 24p. (J). (ps-1). pap. 6.99 (978-1-58476-542-4(9)) Innovative Kids.

Random House Disney Staff & Disney Storybook Artists Staff. Picnic with Pooh. 2006. (Illus.). 32p. (J). (ps-2). pap. 4.99 (978-0-375-87513-7(1) , Golden/Disney) Random Hse. Children's Bks.

Rathmann, Peggy. The Day the Babies Crawled Away. Rathmann, Peggy, illus. 2003. (Illus.). 40p. (J). (ps-2). 16.99 (978-0-399-23196-4(X) , Putnam Juvenile) Penguin Group (USA) Inc.

Ricci, Christine. Dora's Picnic. Hall, Susan, illus. 2003. (Ready-to-Read Ser.: Vol. 1). 24p. (J). pap. 3.99 (978-0-689-85238-1(X) , Simon Spotlight/Nickelodeon) Simon & Schuster Children's Publishing.

—Dora's Picnic. 2003. (gr. k-3). lib. bdg. 11.80 (978-0-613-67079-1(5)) Tandem Library Bks.

Rigby Education Staff. Headline News. (Sails Literacy Ser.). (Illus.). 16p. (gr. 1-2). 27.00 (978-0-7635-9930-0(1) , 699301C99) Rigby Education.

Santillo, LuAnn. The Picnic. Santillo, LuAnn, ed. 2003. (Half-Pint Kids Readers Ser.). (Illus.). 7p. (J). (ps-1). pap. (978-1-59256-090-5(3)) Half-Pint Kids, Inc.

—The Trip. Santillo, LuAnn, ed. 2003. (Half-Pint Kids Readers Ser.). (Illus.). 7p. (J). (ps-1). pap. (978-1-59256-057-8(1)) Half-Pint Kids, Inc.

School Specialty Publishing. My Very Best Coloring & Activity Book: Ladybug Picnic. 2002. 120p. (J). (gr. k-3). pap. 1.99 (978-0-7696-2786-1(2) , American Education Publishing) School Specialty Publishing.

—My Very Best Coloring & Activity Book: Zebra Birthday. 2002. 120p. (J). (gr. k-3). pap. 1.99 (978-0-7696-2787-8(0) , American Education Publishing) School Specialty Publishing.

Schreiber, Anne. Picnics on the Hill. Lewis, Anthony, illus. 2000. (Scholastic At-Home Phonics Reading Program Ser.: Vol. 57). 24p. (J). (978-0-590-68859-8(6)) Scholastic, Inc.

—Word Play. Ong, Cristina, illus. 2000. (Scholastic At-Home Phonics Reading Program Ser.: Vol. 60). 24p. (J). (978-0-590-68864-2(2)) Scholastic, Inc.

Sesame Street Staff. Sesame Street A Perfect Picnic: Happy Tale Storybook. 2005. (Illus.). 24p. (J). pap. 2.99 (978-1-4037-1044-4(9)) Dalmatian Pr.

Shepperson, Rob. No Picnic. Date not set. (J). (978-0-374-39979-5(4) , Farrar, Straus & Giroux (BYR)) Farrar, Straus & Giroux.

Simont, Marc. The Stray Dog. Simont, Marc, illus. (Illus.). 32p. (J). (ps-3). 2003. pap. 6.99 (978-0-06-443669-4(1)); 2001. 15.99 (978-0-06-028933-1(3)) HarperCollins Pubs.

Su, Lucy. Make a Picnic. Su, Lucy, illus. 2003. (Kitten & Baby Kitten Ser.). (Illus.). 32p. (YA). (978-1-85602-445-7(8)) Chrysalis Children's Bks.

van Stockum, Hilda. A Day on Skates: 2007 Commemorative Edition. van Stockum, Hilda, illus. 2007. (Illus.). 44p. (J). 19.95 ***(978-1-932350-18-0(7))*** Bethlehem Bks.

Wang, Margaret. Teddy Bear's Picnic. 2008. 12p. (J). (ps-2). 16.99 ***(978-0-7641-6069-1(9))*** Barron's Educational Series, Inc.

Wax, Wendy. Picnic Day! Artful Doodlers, illus. 2006. 24p. (J). lib. bdg. 15.00 ***(978-1-4242-0952-1(8))*** Fitzgerald Bks.

Wax, Wendy & Artful Doodlers Limited Staff. Picnic Day! 2006. (LazyTown Ser.). (Illus.). 24p. (J). pap. 3.99 (978-1-4169-0076-4(4) , Simon Spotlight/Nickelodeon) Simon & Schuster Children's Publishing.

Wells, Rosemary. Bunny Mail. 2004. (Max & Ruby Ser.). (Illus.). 32p. (J). (ps-3). 15.99 (978-0-670-03630-1(7) , Viking Juvenile) Penguin Group (USA) Inc.

—McDuff Saves the Day. Jeffers, Susan, illus. 2002. 32p. (ps-k). 15.49 (978-0-7868-2311-6(9)) Hyperion Bks. for Children.

Williams, David. The Picnic. Ovresat, Laura, illus. 2006. (Green Light Readers Level 1 Ser.). 24p. (J). 12.95 (978-0-15-205776-3(5)); pap. 3.95 (978-0-15-205782-4(X)) Harcourt Trade Pubs.

Woodson, Jacqueline. We Had a Picnic This Sunday Past. Greenseid, Diane, illus. 1998. 32p. (ps-3). 14.95 (978-0-7868-0242-5(1)) Hyperion Bks. for Children.

Young, Lauren. Ally M. & Ally G. Rooney, Sandra, illus. 2006. 20p. (J). ***(978-1-4120-8518-2(7))*** Trafford Publishing.

Young, Polly G. Pokey Pig's Picnic. Raymond, Janet Y., illus. 2007. (J). pap. 15.00 ***(978-0-8059-7298-6(6))*** Dorrance Publishing Co., Inc.

PICTORIAL WORKS

see Pictures

PICTURE BOOKS

see also Stories without Words

Abrams. Babar Bedtime. 2004. (Illus.). 10p. (J). (ps-ps). bds. 5.95 (978-0-8109-5038-2(3)) Abrams, Harry N., Inc.

Abrams, Harry N., Staff, contrib. by. Snail. 2001. (Portable Pets Ser.). (Illus.). 12p. (J). (ps-ps). bds. 6.95 (978-0-8109-5672-8(1)) Abrams, Harry N., Inc.

Abrams, Pam. Now I Eat My ABCs. Wolf, Bruce, illus. 2004. 14p. (J). (ps up). bds. 7.99 (978-0-439-64942-1(0) , Cartwheel Bks.) Scholastic, Inc.

Abramson, Beverley. Off We Go! 2006. (Illus.). 24p. (J). (ps-k). 15.95 (978-0-88776-728-9(1)) Tundra Bks., Inc./Livres Toundra, Inc. CAN. *Dist:* Random Hse., Inc.

Abramson, Jordan. Masterpieces. 2004. (Start Exploring Ser.). (Illus.). 16p. (J). pap. 19.95 (978-0-7624-1850-3(8) , Running Pr. Kids) Running Pr. Bk. Pubs.

Ackroyd, Dorothea. Bathtime. 1999. (Illus.). bds. 3.95 (978-1-58185-203-5(7)) Quadrillion Media LLC.

Ada, Alma Flor. Yours Truly, Goldilocks. Tryon, Leslie, illus. 2005. (Stories to Go! Ser.). 40p. (J). 4.99 (978-1-4169-0837-1(4) , Aladdin) Simon & Schuster Children's Publishing.

Adam, Winky. Invisible Egyptian Magic Picture Book. 2000. (Dover Little Activity Bks.). (Illus.). 16p. (J). pap. 1.50 (978-0-486-41006-7(4)) Dover Pubns., Inc.

—Little Halloween Sticker Activity Book. 2001. (Illus.). 4p. (J). (ps-3). 1.50 (978-0-486-41676-2(3)) Dover Pubns., Inc.

Adams, Pam. Croaky. rev. ed. 1999. (Real Sound Bath Bks Ser.). (Illus.). 8p. (ps-1). pap. 9.99 (978-0-85953-614-1(9)) Child's Play International Ltd. GBR. *Dist:* Child's Play-International.

—Wally Whale. 2nd ed. 1998. (Real Sound Bath Bks Ser.). (Illus.). 10p. (J). (ps-k). 9.99 (978-0-85953-488-8(X)) Child's Play International Ltd. GBR. *Dist:* Child's Play-International.

Adams, William J. Hate That Thunder/Odio Ese Trueno, 1 vol. Stiglich, Tom, illus. 2006. (ENG & SPA.). 50p. (J). pap. 10.95 ***(978-0-9772757-1-7(X))*** Mandy & Andy Bks., Inc.

Addition: With Re-Usable Stickers. 1999. (Fun to Learn Ser.). (Illus.). 32p. (ps-3). 1.99 (978-1-58279-013-8(2) , 97) Trident Pr. International.

Adler, David A. A Picture Book of Eleanor Roosevelt. Casilla, Robert, illus. 2004. (J). pap. 18.95 incl. audio compact disk (978-1-59112-753-6(X)) Live Oak Media.

—A Picture Book of George Washington. Wallner, John & Wallner, Alexandra, illus. 32p. (J). (gr. k-3). tchr. ed. 17.95 (978-0-8234-0732-3(2)); pap. 6.95 (978-0-8234-0800-9(0)) Holiday Hse., Inc.

—A Picture Book of Martin Luther King, Jr., , Mlawer, Teresa, tr. Casilla, Robert, illus. unabr. ed. 1999. (J). pap. 33.95 incl. audio (978-0-87499-569-5(8)) Live Oak Media.

—A Picture Book of Patrick Henry. Wallner, John et al, illus. 2005. 32p. (J). (gr. k-3). pap. 6.95 (978-0-8234-1678-3(X)) Holiday Hse., Inc.

Advantage Publishers Group Staff, ed. Numbers. 1998. (Find & Fit Ser.). (Illus.). 10p. (J). (ps-k). bds. 14.95 (978-1-57145-356-3(3) , Silver Dolphin Bks.) Advantage Pubs. Group.

Agee, Jon. Terrific. Agee, Jon, illus. 2005. (Illus.). 32p. (J). (ps-17). (978-0-7868-5184-3(8) , Di Capua, Michael) Scholastic, Inc.

Aguilar, Leslie. Florida! Color Me... From A to Z. Clay, Jesse, illus. 2001. 28p. (J). (ps-1). pap. 3.99 (978-0-9715996-0-4(2)) Favorite Places Publishing.

Alarcon, Karen Beaumont. Louella Mae, She's Run Away! Litzinger, Rosanne, illus. rev. ed. 2002. 32p. (J). (ps-1). pap. 7.95 (978-0-8050-6830-6(9) , Holt, Henry & Co. Bks. For Young Readers) Holt, Henry & Co.

—Louella Mae, She's Run Away! 2002. (ps-2). lib. bdg. 15.25 (978-0-613-75399-9(2)) Tandem Library Bks.

Albee, Sarah & Lukas, Catherine. Who's Hiding, Little Bill? Goldberg, Barry, illus. 2001. (Little Bill Ser.). 12p. (J). (gr. k-3). bds. 10.95 (978-0-689-84321-1(6) , Simon Spotlight/Nickelodeon) Simon & Schuster Children's Publishing.

Alberti & Wolfsgruber. Simon y los Animales. 2001. (SPA.). (J). (gr. 3-5). lib. bdg. (978-84-348-2104-0(4)) SM Ediciones.

Alborough, Jez. Duck in the Truck. Alborough, Jez, illus. 2002. (Illus.). 40p. (J). (ps-1). pap. 6.99 (978-0-06-443833-9(3) , Harper Trophy) HarperCollins Pubs.

—Duck's Key: Where Can It Be? Alborough, Jez, illus. 2005. (Illus.). 18p. (J). 14.95 (978-1-929132-72-0(7)) Kane/Miller Bk. Pubs., Inc.

—Fix-It Duck. Alborough, Jez, illus. 2002. (Illus.). 40p. (J). (ps-1). 16.99 (978-0-06-000699-0(4)) HarperCollins Pubs.

—Hug. Alborough, Jez, illus. 2005. (Illus.). 32p. (J). (gr. k-ps). bds. 9.99 (978-0-7636-2893-2(X)) Candlewick Pr.

Alcott, Louisa May. The Little Women Pop-Up Dollhouse. Krystanovich, Vesna, illus. 2000. 8p. (J). 21.95 (978-1-55263-290-1(3)) Key Porter Bks. CAN. *Dist:* Firefly Bks., Ltd.

Alda, Arlene. The Book of ZZZs. 2005. (Illus.). 24p. (J). (gr. k-k). 15.95 (978-0-88776-699-2(4)) Tundra Bks., Inc./Livres Toundra, Inc. CAN. *Dist:* Random Hse., Inc.

—Morning Glory Monday. Kovalski, Maryann, illus. 2003. 32p. (J). (gr. k-3). 17.95 (978-0-88776-620-6(X)) Tundra Bks., Inc./Livres Toundra, Inc. CAN. *Dist:* Random Hse., Inc.

Alko, Selina, illus. My Fathers World. 2006. 36p. (J). 14.99 (978-0-7847-1440-9(1) , 04075) Standard Publishing.

All Set for Fun. 1998. (Fisher-Price Kindergarten Learning Pads Ser.). (Illus.). 48p. (J). (ps). wbk. ed. (978-0-7666-0135-2(8) , 49415) Modern Publishing.

All Set to Discover. 1998. (Fisher-Price Kindergarten Learning Pads Ser.). (Illus.). 48p. (J). (ps). wbk. ed. (978-0-7666-0136-9(6) , 49415) Modern Publishing.

P Q R

All Set to Learn. 1998. (Fisher-Price Kindergarten Learning Pads Ser.). (Illus.). 48p. (J). (ps). wbk. ed. (978-0-7666-0134-5(X) , 49415) Modern Publishing.

Allen, Debbie. Dancing in the Wings. Nelson, Kadir A., illus. (J). (gr. k-2). 2003. 32p. pap. 6.99 (978-0-14-250141-2(7) , Puffin); 2000. 1p. 16.99 (978-0-8037-2501-0(9) , Dial) Penguin Group (USA) Inc.

—Dancing in the Wings. 2003. (gr. k-3). lib. bdg. 15.30 (978-0-613-86700-9(9)) Tandem Library Bks.

Alonso, Fernando. The Little Red Hen (La Gallina Paulina) Gimeno, J. M., illus. 16p. (J). (gr. k-3). pap. 6.95 (978-0-88272-468-3(1)) Santillana USA Publishing Co., Inc.

Alvarez, Lourdes M. Alphabet. Brooks, David, illus. 2005. (My First Book Ser.). 9p. (J). (ps-17). bds. 3.95 (978-1-933050-08-9(X)) Sweetwater Pr.

—Animals. Brooks, David, illus. 2005. (My First Book Ser.). 9p. (J). (ps-ps). bds. 3.95 (978-1-933050-09-6(8)) Sweetwater Pr.

—Colors. Brooks, David, illus. 2005. (My First Book Ser.). 9p. (J). (ps-ps). bds. 3.95 (978-1-933050-07-2(1)) Sweetwater Pr.

—Numbers. Brooks, David, illus. 2005. (My First Book Ser.). 9p. (J). (ps-ps). bds. 3.95 (978-1-933050-06-5(3)) Sweetwater Pr.

—Shapes. Brooks, David, illus. 2005. (My First Book Ser.). 9p. (J). (ps-ps). bds. 3.95 (978-1-933050-11-9(X)) Sweetwater Pr.

The Amazing Body: The Five Senses. 2005. (Illus.). (C). (gr. k-3). 113.00 (978-1-4048-1000-6(5)) Picture Window Bks.

Amery, H. & Cartwright, S. Three Little Pigs. 2004. (First Stories Ser.). 16p. (J). pap. 4.99 (978-0-7945-0609-4(7)) EDC Publishing.

Amery, H. & Cartwright, Stephen. Three Little Pigs. 16p. (J). lib. bdg. 12.95 (978-1-58086-623-1(9) , Usborne) EDC Publishing.

Amery, Heather. Old Steam Train. Tyler, Jenny, ed. Cartwright, Stephen, illus. rev. ed. 1999. 15p. (J). (ps-ps). pap. 4.95 (978-0-7945-0648-3(8) , Usborne) EDC Publishing.

Amos, Janine. Animals. 2004. (Picture Reference Ser.). (SPA., Illus.). 48p. (gr. 3-6). 13.95 (978-1-58728-650-6(5) , Two Can Publishing) T&N Children's Publishing.

Andersen, Hans Christian. The Emperor's New Clothes. Archipowa, Anastassija, illus. 1998. 32p. (J). (ps-4). 15.95 (978-1-56397-699-5(4)) Boyds Mills Pr.

Anderson, Doug. Hadley & the Bean. 2004. (Illus.). (J). 16.95 (978-1-59404-038-2(9)) Peanut Butter Publishing.

Anderson, Sara. Noisy City Day. 2005. (Illus.). 6p. (J). bds. 7.95 (978-1-59354-054-8(X)) Handprint Bks.

—Noisy City Night. 2005. (Illus.). 6p. (J). bds. 7.95 (978-1-59354-055-5(8)) Handprint Bks.

Anderson, William T. Almanzo Picture Book Biography. Date not set. (Illus.). 40p. (J). (ps-3). 15.99 (978-0-06-028975-1(9)); pap. 5.99 (978-0-06-443684-7(5)); lib. bdg. 16.89 (978-0-06-028976-8(7)) HarperCollins Pubs.

Anfousse, Ginette & Sarrazin, Marisol. Polo et le Garde-Manger. 2003. (Polo Ser.). (FRE., Illus.). 32p. (J). (ps-3). bds. (978-2-89021-601-3(2)) Diffusion du livre Mirabel.

Anholt, Laurence. Camille y los Girasoles: Un Cuento Sobre Vincent van Gogh. 2000. (Illus.). (J). (ps-3). (CAT.). 32p. 14.95 (978-84-95040-34-3(4)); (SPA., 28p. 14.95 (978-84-88061-35-5(8)) Serres, Ediciones, S. L. ESP. *Dist:* Lectorum Pubns., Inc.

Anholt, Laurence. The Magical Garden of Claude Monet. 2007. (Anholt's Artists Books for Children Ser.). 32p. (J). (ps-3). pap. 7.99 ***978-0-7641-3855-3(3))** Barron's Educational Series, Inc.

Animal Friends: Point & Learn. 1999. (Point & Learn Ser.). (J). (ps). pap. 6.98 incl. audio (978-0-7634-0586-1(8)) Walt Disney Records.

Anness Publishing Staff & Tuxworth, Nicola. Toys. 2000. (Very First Picture Board Bks.). (Illus.). 20p. bds. 5.00 (978-0-7548-0712-4(6)) Anness Publishing GBR. *Dist:* National Bk. Network.

Anthony, Ross. Please Don't Step on the Ants. Anthony, Ross, illus. 2006. (ENG, CHI, SPA & JPN.). (J). per. ***(*978-0-9727894-4-8(8))** Arizona Blueberry Studios.

Appel, Dee. The Friends in My Garden. Francour, Kathleen, photos by. Date not set. (Tiny Times Board Book Ser.). (Illus.). 10p. (J). bds. 5.99 (978-0-7369-0564-0(2)) Harvest Hse. Pubs.

—Let's Play Dress Up. Francour, Kathleen, photos by. Date not set. (Tiny Times Board Book Ser.). (Illus.). 10p. (J). bds. 5.99 (978-0-7369-0563-3(4)) Harvest Hse. Pubs.

Appelt, Kathi. Toddler Two-Step. 2000. (Growing Tree Ser.). (Illus.). 24p. (J). (ps-k). 9.95 (978-0-694-01244-2(0) , Harper Festival) HarperCollins Pubs.

Ardizzone, Edward. Tim & Lucy Go to Sea. ed. 2006. (Little Tim Ser.). (Illus.). 48p. (J). 15.95 (978-1-84507-457-9(2)) Lincoln, Frances Ltd. GBR. *Dist:* Perseus Distribution.

Arndt, Lauel L. Before I Write. Thier, Cooki, illus. 2000. (Step Ahead Workbooks Ser.). 32p. (J). (ps). pap., wbk. ed. 2.99 (978-0-307-03596-7(4) , 03596, Golden Bks.) Random Hse. Children's Bks.

Arnold, Caroline. Who Has More? Who Has Fewer? Arnold, Caroline, illus. 2004. (Illus.). 18p. (J). bds. 5.95 (978-1-57091-493-5(1)) Charlesbridge Publishing, Inc.

—Who Is Bigger? Who Is Smaller? Arnold, Caroline, illus. 2004. (Illus.). 18p. (J). bds. 5.95 (978-1-57091-495-9(8)) Charlesbridge Publishing, Inc.

Arnold, Nick, et al. Sticker Activity Atlas. (Illus.). 8p. (J). pap. 9.99 (978-0-590-24921-8(5)) Scholastic, Inc.

Arnold, Tedd. No Jumping on the Bed! Arnold, Tedd, illus. 2004. (Illus.). 32p. (J). (ps). 6.99 (978-0-8037-3044-1(6) , Dial) Penguin Group (USA) Inc.

Arnold, Tedd. The Twin Princes. 2007. (Illus.). (J). ***(*978-1-4287-3971-0(8)** , Dial) Penguin Group (USA) Inc.

Arnosky, Jim. Mouse Shapes: A Very First Book. Arnosky, Jim, illus. 2001. (Illus.). 48p. (J). (gr. k-ps). tchr. ed. 5.95 (978-0-618-01522-1(1) , Clarion Bks.) Houghton Mifflin Co. Trade & Reference Div.

Arruzza, Rick. El Paseo de Sparky. Newton, Pilar, illus. 2003. (SPA.). 24p. mass mkt. 7.95 (978-0-9744509-1-9(X)) Three Spots Productions.

—Sparky's Walk. Newton, Pilar, illus. 2003. 24p. (J). mass mkt. 7.95 (978-0-9744509-0-2(1)) Three Spots Productions.

Arthur, Clint. Bleep Blop Bloop, 1. Schedeen, Minnie, illus. 2006. 24p. (J). per. 8.99 net. (978-1-4276-0218-3(2)) Aardvark Global Publishing.

Ashford, Kathy. How to Conker the World. 2004. (Illus.). 64p. (J). pap. 8.99 (978-1-84270-321-2(8)) Andersen GBR. *Dist:* Independent Pubs. Group.

Ashman, Linda. Just Another Morning. Munoz, Claudio, illus. 2004. 32p. (J). (ps-3). 15.99 (978-0-06-029053-5(6)) HarperCollins Pubs.

Asquith, Ros. My Do It! 2000. (Toddlers Storybook Ser.). (Illus.). 24p. (J). (ps-k). pap. 5.95 (978-0-7894-5648-9(6) , D K Ink) Dorling Kindersley Publishing, Inc.

Atkins, Jill. Toad Swims for his Life! Mostyn, David, illus. 2004. 24p. (J). lib. bdg. 22.65 ***(*978-1-59646-712-5(6))*** Dingles & Co.

Atwood, Margaret. Bashful Bob & Doleful Dorinda. Petricic, Dusan, illus. 2006. 32p. (J). (gr. 1-3). ***(*978-1-55263-609-1(7))*** Key Porter Bks.

Auerbach, Annie. Naughty Nautical Neighbors. O'Hare, Mark, illus. 2000. (SpongeBob SquarePants Chapter Bks.: No. 2). 64p. (J). (gr. 2-5). pap. 3.99 (978-0-689-84016-6(0) , Simon Spotlight) Simon & Schuster Children's Publishing.

—Naughty Nautical Neighbors. 2000. (gr. 3-6). lib. bdg. 11.80 (978-0-613-31524-1(3)) Tandem Library Bks.

Austen, Jane. Tiny Tales for Toddlers. Balloon Books Staff, ed. 2000. (Balloon Ser.). (Illus.). 18p. (J). bds. 5.95 (978-0-8069-2903-3(0) , Balloon Bks.) Sterling Publishing Co., Inc.

Avery, Karen. Persevere by Mark & Karen Avery. 2006. 17.00 ***(*978-0-8059-8877-2(7))*** Dorrance Publishing Co., Inc.

Away in a Manger. 2006. 16p. (J). pap. 1.99 (978-0-7847-1547-5(5) , 04363) Standard Publishing.

Away in a Manger Coloring Book. 16p. (J). 1.89 (978-0-7847-1260-3(3)) Standard Publishing.

Aylesworth, Jim. Aunt Pitty Patty's Piggy. McClintock, Barbara, illus. 1999. 32p. (J). (ps-2). pap. 15.95 (978-0-590-89987-1(2)) Scholastic, Inc.

—McGraw's Emporium. 1998. (ps-2). lib. bdg. 16.40 (978-0-613-90149-9(5)) Tandem Library Bks.

Babbitt, Natalie. Ouch! Marcellino, Fred, illus. 1998. 32p. (J). (ps-3). 15.89 (978-0-06-205067-0(2)) HarperCollins Pubs.

Baby Peek. 1999. (J). 4.99 (978-0-679-89418-6(7)) Random Hse., Inc.

Baby Shakespeare. (Illus.). 28p. (J). (ps). pap. 21.95 incl. VHS (978-1-892309-18-1(1)) Baby Einstein Co., LLC, The.

Baby Surprise. 1999. (J). 4.99 (978-0-679-89420-9(9)) Random Hse., Inc.

Baby's Day: Point & Learn. 1999. (Point & Learn Ser.). (J). (ps). pap. 6.98 incl. audio (978-0-7634-0585-4(X)) Walt Disney Records.

Badowich, D. M. Mine. Chapman, Chris, illus. 1999. 16p. (J). (ps-3). pap. (978-1-894303-19-4(9)) Raven Rock Publishing.

Bailer, Darice. ABC Animals: A Bedtime Story. Moffatt, Judith, illus. 2005. 60p. (J). 10.95 (978-0-689-86729-3(8) , Little Simon) Simon & Schuster Children's Publishing.

Bailey, Debbie. My Family. Huszar, Susan, photos by. 1998. (Talk-about-Books: Vol. 11). (Illus.). 14p. (J). (gr. k-ps). bds. 5.95 (978-1-55037-510-7(5)) Annick Pr., Ltd. CAN. *Dist:* Firefly Bks., Ltd.

Bailey, Linda. Goodnight, Sweet Pig. Masse, Josée, illus. 2007. 32p. (J). (ps-k). ***(*978-1-55337-844-0(X))*** Kids Can Pr., Ltd.

Baker, Keith. Little Green. ed. 2005. (Illus.). 30p. (J). bds. 6.95 (978-0-15-205308-6(5) , Red Wagon Bks.) Harcourt Children's Bks.

Baker, Liza. Under the Sea. 2003. (Festival Reader Ser.). (Illus.). 32p. (J). (ps-2). pap. 3.99 (978-0-06-000178-0(X)) HarperCollins Pubs.

Baker, Stacy. Sammy's Secret. 2005. (J). lib. bdg. 19.95 ***(*978-1-933732-03-9(2)*** , Bear Hug Bks.) MidAmerica Publishing Co.

Baldwin, Christy. Remembering Wilma. Barnes, Sarah, illus. l.t. ed. 2005. 22p. (J). per. 15.00 (978-0-9765072-0-8(X)) Tribute Bks.

Ballesteros, Xose & Villan, Oscar. The Little White Rabbit. 2002. (Illus.). 32p. (J). 14.95 (978-84-95730-19-0(7)) Kalandraka Catalunya, Edicions, S.L. ESP. *Dist:* Independent Pubs. Group.

Balloon Books. Make a Farmhouse. 2000. (Press Out & Play Bks.). (Illus.). 20p. (J). (gr. k-3). pap. 5.95 (978-0-8069-2901-9(4) , Balloon Bks.) Sterling Publishing Co., Inc.

Balloon Books Staff. Fun Learning for 3- & 4-Year-Olds. 1999. (Tiny the Mouse Fun Learning Ser.). (Illus.). 20p. (ps). pap. 4.95 (978-0-8069-3940-7(0)) Sterling Publishing Co., Inc.

—Fun Learning for 4- & 5-Year-Olds. 1999. (Tiny the Mouse Fun Learning Ser.). (Illus.). 20p. (ps-k). pap. 4.95 (978-0-8069-3938-4(9)) Sterling Publishing Co., Inc.

—Sticker Book for 3 & 4-Year-Olds: Reusable Stickers. 1999. (Tiny the Mouse Sticker Bks.). (Illus.). 20p. (J). pap. 3.95 (978-0-8069-5759-3(X) , Balloon Bks.) Sterling Publishing Co., Inc.

—Sticker Book for 3-Year-Olds: Reusable Stickers. 1999. (Tiny the Mouse Sticker Bks.). (Illus.). 20p. (J). pap. 3.95 (978-0-8069-5751-7(4) , Balloon Bks.) Sterling Publishing Co., Inc.

—Sticker Book for 4-Year-Olds: Reusable Stickers. 2003. (Tiny the Mouse Sticker Bks.). (Illus.). 20p. (J). pap. 3.95 (978-0-8069-5761-6(1) , Balloon Bks.) Sterling Publishing Co., Inc.

—Tiny the Mouse Sticker Book for 2-Year Olds: Reusable Stickers. 1999. (Tiny the Mouse Sticker Bks.). (Illus.). 20p. (J). pap. 3.95 (978-0-8069-5936-8(3) , Balloon Bks.) Sterling Publishing Co., Inc.

Balloon Books Staff, ed. Buddy Bear Learns about Colors. 2000. (Balloon Ser.). (Illus.). 12p. (J). (ps). bds. 4.95 (978-0-8069-2923-1(5) , Balloon Bks.) Sterling Publishing Co., Inc.

—Katie Cat Goes Shopping. 2000. (Balloon Ser.). (Illus.). 12p. (J). (ps-k). bds. 7.95 (978-0-8069-2905-7(7) , Balloon Bks.) Sterling Publishing Co., Inc.

—Katie Cat Learns Animal Names. 2000. (Balloon Ser.). (Illus.). 16p. (J). bds. 3.95 (978-0-8069-2279-9(6) , Balloon Bks.) Sterling Publishing Co., Inc.

—Katie Cat Learns First Words. 2000. (Balloon Ser.). (Illus.). 16p. (J). bds. 3.95 (978-0-8069-2907-1(3) , Balloon Bks.) Sterling Publishing Co., Inc.

—Rachel Rabbit Learns to Count. 2000. (Plush Learning Bks.). (Illus.). 12p. (J). bds. 4.95 (978-0-8069-2917-0(0) , Balloon Bks.) Sterling Publishing Co., Inc.

Banks, Kate. Baboon. Hallensleben, Georg, illus. 2004. 32p. (J). reprint ed. pap. 6.95 (978-0-374-40473-4(9) , Sunburst) Farrar, Straus & Giroux.

Banyai, Istvan. Zoom. 1998. (Picture Puffin Ser.). (Illus.). 64p. (J). (gr. k-3). pap. 6.99 (978-0-14-055774-9(1) , Puffin) Penguin Group (USA) Inc.

Barbaresi, Nina. Funny Fruits & Vegetables Stickers. 2003. (Dover Little Activity Bks.). (Illus.). 4p. (J). pap. 1.50 (978-0-486-43004-1(9)) Dover Pubns., Inc.

Barber, Nicola. Music: An A-Z Guide. 2001. (Watts Reference Ser.). (Illus.). 128p. (YA). (gr. 6-8). 34.00 (978-0-531-11898-6(3) , Watts, Franklin) Scholastic Library Publishing.

Barber, Tom & Chapman, Lynne. Open Wide! 2004. (Illus.). 32p. 14.95 (978-1-84458-241-9(8)) Chrysalis Children's Bks. GBR. *Dist:* Transition Vendor.

Barker, Cicely Mary. Enchanted Garden Sticker Book. 2004. (Flower Fairies Ser.). (Illus.). 24p. pap. 4.99 (978-0-7232-5232-0(7) , Warne) Penguin Group (USA) Inc.

Barney's ABC Animals! 1999. (Barney Ser.). (Illus.). 32p. (J). (ps-k). 6.95 (978-1-57064-624-9(4)) Scholastic, Inc.

Barrett, Judi. Things That Are Most in the World. Nickle, John, illus. 2001. 32p. (J). 6.99 (978-0-689-84449-2(2) , Aladdin) Simon & Schuster Children's Publishing.

—Things That Are Most in the World. 2001. (ps-2). lib. bdg. 15.30 (978-0-613-73328-1(2)) Tandem Library Bks.

Barry, Frances. Duckie's Rainbow. Barry, Frances, illus. 2004. (Illus.). 14p. (J). (gr. k-ps). 7.99 (978-0-7636-2066-0(1)) Candlewick Pr.

Bartlett, A. Erice the Reindeer. (Illus.). 32p. (J). (978-0-340-65598-6(4) , Hodder & Stoughton) Hodder General Publishing Division.

Barton, Byron. My Car. Barton, Byron, illus. (J). (ps-1). 2003. (Illus.). 36p. bds. 6.99 (978-0-06-056045-4(2)); 2004. 40p. reprint ed. pap. 6.99 (978-0-06-058940-0(X) , Harper Trophy) HarperCollins Pubs.

Bateson, Catherine. The Year It All Happened. 2001. 160p. (YA). pap. 15.95 (978-0-7022-3229-9(7)) Univ. of Queensland Pr. AUS. *Dist:* International Specialized Bk. Services.

Bateson-Hill, Margaret. Shota & the Star Quilt. 1998. (Folk Tales Series Ser.). (Illus.). 32p. (J). (gr. k up). 14.95 (978-1-84089-021-1(5) , Zero to Ten, Limited) Evans Publishing Group GBR. *Dist:* Independent Pubs. Group.

Bauer, Marion Dane. Sleep, Little One, Sleep. Stammen, JoEllen McAllister, illus. 2002. 32p. (J). (ps). pap. 6.99 (978-0-689-85269-5(X) , Aladdin) Simon & Schuster Children's Publishing.

—Sleep, Little One, Sleep. 2002. (gr. k-3). lib. bdg. 15.30 (978-0-613-57328-3(5)) Tandem Library Bks.

Beall, Pamela Conn & Nipp, Susan Hagen. If You're Happy & You Know It. Wittwer, Hala, illus. 2002. (Wee Sing Ser.). 32p. (J). (ps-1). bds. 4.99 (978-0-8431-7759-6(4) , Price Stern Sloan) Penguin Group (USA) Inc.

—Old MacDonald. Wittwer, Hala, illus. 2002. (Wee Sing Ser.). 24p. (J). (ps-1). bds. 4.99 (978-0-8431-7758-9(6) , Price Stern Sloan) Penguin Group (USA) Inc.

Beaton, Clare, illus. Opposites: Los Contrarios. l.t. ed. 1998. (English-Spanish Bilingual First Bks.). (ENG & SPA.). 24p. (J). (ps up). lib. bdg. 14.45 (978-1-56674-252-8(8)) Forest Hse. Publishing Co., Inc.

Beck, Ian. The Christmas Story. 2005. (Illus.). 32p. (J). (gr. 1-2). pap. 9.99 (978-0-552-54937-0(1) , Corgi) Transworld Publishers Ltd. GBR. *Dist:* Independent Pubs. Group.

Beckhorn, Susan. In the Morning of the World: Six Woodland Why Stories. Beckhorn, Susan, illus. 2000. (Illus.). 48p. (gr. 4-7). 15.95 (978-0-89272-503-8(6)) Down East Bks.

Beckler, Bruce. My Daddy Is A Deputy Sheriff. Finney, Simone, illus. l.t. ed. 2004. 14p. (J). per. 5.59 (978-0-9745210-4-6(3)) Myers Publishing Co.

—My Daddy Is A Fire Fighter: My Daddy Is A Fireman. Peek, Jeannette, illus. l.t. ed. 2004. 16p. (J). 5.59 (978-0-9745210-8-4(6)) Myers Publishing Co.

—My Daddy Is a Police Officer: My Daddy Wears a Star. Finney, Simone, illus. l.t. ed. 2004. 14p. (J). per. 5.59 (978-0-9745210-3-9(5)) Myers Publishing Co.

—My Daddy Is A Police Officer: Wears A Badge, 8 bks. Finney, Simone, illus. l.t. ed. 2004. 14p. (J). per. 5.59 (978-0-9745210-2-2(7)) Myers Publishing Co.

—My Mommy Is A Deputy Sheriff. Finney, Simone, illus. l.t. ed. 2004. 14p. (J). 5.59 (978-0-9745210-7-7(8)) Myers Publishing Co.

—My Mommy Is A Nurse. Peek, Jeannette, illus. l.t. ed. 2004. 20p. (J). 5.59 (978-0-9745210-9-1(4)) Myers Publishing Co.

—My Mommy Is A Police Officer: My Mommy Wears A Badge. Finney, Simone, illus. l.t. ed. 2004. 14p. (J). per. 5.59 (978-0-9745210-5-3(1)) Myers Publishing Co.

—My Mommy Is A Police Officer: My Mommy Wears A Star. Finney, Simone, illus. l.t. ed. 2004. 14p. (J). 5.59 (978-0-9745210-6-0(X)) Myers Publishing Co.

Bednar, Martin. Sandy's Vision. 2006. (J). lib. bdg. 19.95 ***(*978-1-933732-15-2(6)*** , Bear Hug Bks.) MidAmerica Publishing Co.

Beer, Hans. Kleiner eisbar wohin fahrst Du. pap. 17.95 (978-3-423-07954-9(1)) Deutscher Taschenbuch Verlag GmbH & Co KG DEU. *Dist:* Distribooks, Inc.

Bell, Cece. Busy Buddies: Silly Stuff That Goes Together. Bell, Cece, illus. 2006. (Board Books). (Illus.). 20p. (J). (gr. k-ps). bds. 5.99 (978-0-7636-2776-8(3)) Candlewick Pr.

—Food Friends: Fun Foods That Go Together. Bell, Cece, illus. 2006. (Illus.). 20p. (J). (gr. k-ps). bds. 5.99 (978-0-7636-2777-5(1)) Candlewick Pr.

Bemelsman, Ludwig. La Sauvetage de Madeleine. 2000. (Adventures of Madeleine Ser.).Tr. of Madeleine's Rescue. (FRE.). (J). pap. 14.95 (978-2-211-02196-8(4)) Archimede Editions FRA. *Dist:* Distribooks, Inc.

Bender, Lionel. Crocodile. 2005. (Illus.). 32p. (J). 18.95 (978-1-59389-192-3(X)) Chrysalis Education.

Bennett, Jeffrey. Max Goes to the Moon. Okamoto, Alan, illus. 2003. (Science Adventures with Max the Dog Ser.). 32p. (J). (ps-7). 16.95 (978-0-9721819-0-7(3)) Big Kid Science.

Bennett, Leonie. Locket Out. Adams, Arlene, illus. 2004. 24p. (J). lib. bdg. 22.65 ***(*978-1-59646-688-3(X))*** Dingles & Co.

—No Problem! Brown, Judy, illus. 2004. 16p. (J). lib. bdg. 22.65 ***(*978-1-59646-680-7(4))*** Dingles & Co.

Bennett, Paul. Catching a Meal. 1999. (Nature's Secrets Ser.). (Illus.). 32p. (ps-4). 21.40 (978-0-8172-5252-6(5)) Raintree.

Bentley, Dawn. Fire Engine Freddie to the Rescue! Wind-Up Fire Engine with Pop-Up Playset. Welply, Michael, illus. 1998. (J). (ps-k). 16.95 (978-1-58117-012-2(2) , Intervisual/Piggy Toes) Dalmatian Pr.

—Gingerbread Man. 2005. (Holiday Sparkler Bks.). (Illus.). 10p. (J). 4.95 (978-1-58117-163-1(3) , Intervisual/Piggy Toes) Dalmatian Pr.

—The Icky Sticky Frog. Yoon, Salina, illus. 18p. (J). (ps-k). 2001. 5.95 (978-1-58117-049-8(1)); 1999. 9.95 (978-1-58117-042-9(4)) Dalmatian Pr. (Intervisual/Piggy Toes).

—Mommy, Is That You? Merer, Laura, illus. 2000. (Move & Play Bks.). 10p. (J). (ps-k). 6.95 (978-1-58117-073-3(4) , Intervisual/Piggy Toes) Dalmatian Pr.

—Where's Daddy? Merer, Laura, illus. 2000. (Move & Play Bks.). 10p. (J). (ps-k). 6.95 (978-1-58117-074-0(2) , Intervisual/Piggy Toes) Dalmatian Pr.

Berenstain, Stan & Berenstain, Jan. The Berenstain Bears & the In-Crowd. Berenstain, Stan & Berenstain, Jan, illus. 2002. (Berenstain Bears First Time Bks.). (Illus.). (J). 11.19 (978-0-7587-0940-0(4)) Book Wholesalers, Inc.

Beresford, Elisabeth. Beautiful Boating Weather. (Illus.). 15p. (J). (gr. k-6). pap. 6.99 (978-0-340-73583-1(X) , Hodder & Stoughton) Hodder General Publishing Division GBR. *Dist:* Trafalgar Square Publishing.

—Chaos on the Common: Wombles. (Illus.). 16p. (J). (gr. k-6). pap. (978-0-340-74674-5(2) , Hodder & Stoughton) Hodder General Publishing Division.

—Deep Space Womble: Wombles. (Illus.). 15p. (J). (gr. k-6). pap. (978-0-340-74671-4(8) , Hodder & Stoughton) Hodder General Publishing Division.

—Wombles Camping & Cloudberries. (Illus.). 15p. (J). (gr. k-6). pap. (978-0-340-73584-8(8) , Hodder & Stoughton) Hodder General Publishing Division.

—Wombles Ghost of Wimbledon Common. (Illus.). 15p. (J). (gr. k-6). pap. (978-0-340-73579-4(1) , Hodder & Stoughton) Hodder General Publishing Division.

—Wombles Tomask to the Rescue. (Illus.). 15p. (J). (gr. k-6). pap. (978-0-340-73581-7(3) , Hodder & Stoughton) Hodder General Publishing Division.

Berg, Brook. What Marion Taught Willis. Alberg, Nathan, illus. 2005. (J). 16.95 (978-1-932146-31-8(8) , 1242215) Highsmith Inc.

Berger, Samantha. Big & Little. 1999. (gr. 3-6). lib. bdg. 10.10 (978-0-613-53959-3(1)) Tandem Library Bks.

Berger, Samantha & Chanko, Pamela. Big & Little. 1999. (Learning Center Emergent Readers Ser.). (J). 2.50 (978-0-439-04597-1(5)) Scholastic, Inc.

Berger, Samantha & Moreton, Daniel. Patterns. 1999. (Learning Center Emergent Readers Ser.). (J). 2.50 (978-0-439-04599-5(1)) Scholastic, Inc.

Bergman, Mara & Monks, Lydia. Glitter Kitty. 2006. (Illus.). 32p. (J). 16.99 (978-0-689-87305-8(0)) Simon & Schuster, Ltd. GBR. *Dist:* Independent Pubs. Group.

Bergna, Monica, illus. Juguemos en el Bosque. 2004. (SPA.). 28p. (J). (gr. k up). pap. 6.50 (978-980-257-282-3(9)) Ekare, Ediciones VEN. *Dist:* Lectorum Pubns., Inc., Iaconi, Mariuccia Bk. Imports.

Berkes, Marianne. Over in the Ocean: In a Coral Reef. Canyon, Jeanette, illus. 2004. (J). (ps-2). 32p. 16.95 (978-1-58469-063-4(1)); 36p. pap. 8.95 (978-1-58469-062-7(3)) Dawn Pubns.

Bernthal, Mark S. Barney's 12 Days of Christmas. 1998. (Barney Ser.). 26p. (J). (ps-k). bds. 13.95 (978-1-57064-241-8(9)) Scholastic, Inc.

Bernthal, Mark S. & Lyrick Publishing Staff. Barney's Book of Shapes. 1998. (Barney Ser.). (Illus.). 22p. (J). (ps). bds. 5.95 (978-1-57064-242-5(7)) Scholastic, Inc.

Best, Cari. What's So Bad about Being an Only Child. Blackall, Sophie, illus. 2007. 32p. (J). (ps-3). 16.00 (978-0-374-39943-6(3)) Farrar, Straus & Giroux.

Bevan, Jan Atchley. Corky the Kitten Who Couldn't Swallow. Yovanovic, Christine, illus. 2001. (J). 14.95 (978-0-9653895-5-6(3)); 48p. pap. 12.95 (978-0-9653895-4-9(5)) Bookmark Publishing.

Beylon, Cathy. Pet Shop Sticker Activity Book. 1998. (Illus.). 4p. (J). (ps-3). pap. 1.50 (978-0-486-40312-0(2)) Dover Pubns., Inc.

—Twelve Bugs Bookmarks. 2004. (Bookmarks Ser.). (Illus.). 6p. (J). (gr. k-3). pap. 1.50 (978-0-486-43498-8(2)) Dover Pubns., Inc.

BHB International Staff. Let's Learn. 1998. (Images Ser.). (Illus.). 136p. (ps-3). pap. 9.95 (978-2-215-06189-2(8)) Continental Enterprises Group, Inc. (CEG).

—My First Picture Book. 1998. (Images Ser.). (Illus.). 136p. (ps-k). pap. 9.95 (978-2-215-06190-8(1)) Continental Enterprises Group, Inc. (CEG).

Big's Big Baby. (Looney Tunes Song & Sound Bks.). (Illus.). 16p. (J). (ps-k). 7.98 (978-0-7853-1608-4(6) , PI10) Publications International, Ltd.

Bilik-Franklin, MidiAna & Griffith, Indigo, photos by. The Carseat Tourist. 2006. (Illus.). (J). bds. 7.95 (978-0-9772825-0-0(3)) Critter Camp Inc.

Birchall, Mark. What Kind of Monster? 2004. (Illus.). 32p. (J). pap. 9.99 (978-1-84270-318-2(8)) Andersen GBR. *Dist:* Independent Pubs. Group.

Biro, Val. Gumdrop Finds a Ghost. (Illus.). 27p. (J). (978-0-340-71062-3(4)); pap. (978-0-340-71063-0(2)) Hodder General Publishing Division. (Hodder & Stoughton).

—Gumdrop Makes a Start. (Illus.). 27p. (J). (978-0-340-71058-6(6)); pap. (978-0-340-71059-3(4)) Hodder General Publishing Division. (Hodder & Stoughton).

—Gumdrop's Merry Christmas. (Illus.). 26p. (J). (978-0-340-71060-9(8) , Hodder & Stoughton) Hodder General Publishing Division.

Bishop, Nic, illus. The Backyard Detective: Critters up Close. 2002. (Backyard Detective Ser.). 48p. (J). (gr. 3-6). pap. 16.95 (978-0-439-17478-7(3) , Scholastic Pr.) Scholastic, Inc.

Black, Jessica L. A Very Special Day. Crowell, Knox, illus. 2001. (Cuddle Bks.). 8p. (J). (ps-1). pap. 10.95 (978-1-57332-207-2(5)) HighReach Learning, Inc.

Blackman, S. A. The Kindergarten Book: If Only You Knew How Your Mommy Missed You When You Left for Kindergarten. Petz, Judith Kneen, illus. 2002. 15p. (J). (ps-1). 18.99 (978-1-929409-09-9(5) , 500) Blade Publishing.

Blackstone, Stella. Baby High, Baby Low. Fraifield, Denise & Azevedo, Fernando, illus. 1998. 24p. (J). (ps-3). 14.95 (978-0-8234-1345-4(4)) Holiday Hse., Inc.

—Bear in a Square. 2000. (J). 12.79 (978-0-606-19702-1(8)) Tandem Library Bks.

—There's a Cow in the Cabbage Patch. Beaton, Clare, illus. (J). (gr. k-2). 2002. 24p. bds. 6.99 (978-1-84148-961-2(1)); 2001. 32p. 14.99 (978-1-84148-333-7(8)) Barefoot Bks., Inc.

—Who Are You, Baby Kangaroo? Beaton, Clare, illus. 2004. 24p. (J). (ps-2). per. 6.99 (978-1-905236-19-0(0)) Barefoot Bks., Inc.

Blake, Jan. Give Me My Yam. Melnyczuk, Peter, illus. 1999. (Reading Together Ser.). 32p. (J). (ps). pap. 3.99 (978-0-7636-0873-6(4)) Candlewick Pr.

Blake, Michel. Off to Bed. Gant, Trish, illus. 2005. 16p. (J). (gr. k-ps). bds. 5.99 (978-0-7636-2766-9(6)) Candlewick Pr.

—Out to Play. Candlewick Press Staff, illus. Gant, Trish, photos by. 2005. 16p. (J). (gr. k-ps). bds. 5.99 (978-0-7636-2767-6(4)) Candlewick Pr.

Blathwayt, Benedict. Little Red Train, Set. ed. 2004. (Illus.). 32p. (J). bds. (978-0-09-189374-3(7) , Hutchinson) Random Hse.

Blazin' Hot: Picture Book (English) NL 9x9 with Snipe. 2007. (J). ***(978-1-933934-46-4(8))*** Educational Adventures.

Blight, Peter. Lonely Giraffe. Terry, Michael, illus. 32p. (J). (ps-k). pap. 12.99 (978-0-7475-7144-5(9)) Bloomsbury Publishing Plc GBR. *Dist:* Trafalgar Square Publishing.

Blume, Judy. The One in the Middle Is the Green Kangaroo. 39p. (J). (gr. k-3). pap. 3.99 (978-0-8072-1337-7(3) , Listening Library) Random Hse. Audio Publishing Group.

Bockol, Leslie. Peek-a-Boo! Larranaga, Ana & Parsons, Jackie, illus. 2006. (IBaby Ser.). 10p. (J). (ps-ps). bds. 10.99 (978-1-58476-416-8(3) , IKIDS) Innovative Kids.

Bodecker, N. M. The Mushroom Center Disaster. Blegvad, Erik & Starr, Branka, illus. 2004. 48p. (J). reprint ed. 14.95 (978-1-931561-98-3(2)) MacAdam/Cage Publishing, Inc.

—Quimble Wood. Starr, Branka, illus. 2004. 32p. (J). reprint ed. 14.95 (978-1-931561-97-6(4)) MacAdam/Cage Publishing, Inc.

Boland, Janice. El Desayuno con Juan. Romo, Alberto, tr. Veno, Joe, illus. 1998. (Books for Young Learners).Tr. of Breakfast with John. (SPA.). 8p. (J). (gr. k-2). pap. 5.00 (978-1-57274-198-0(8) , A2847) Owen, Richard C. Pubs., Inc.

—La Laguna. de la Vega, Eida, tr. Boland, Janice, photos by. 2001. (Books for Young Learners).Tr. of Pond. (SPA., Illus.). 8p. (J). (gr. k-2). pap. 5.00 (978-1-57274-447-9(2) , 2871) Owen, Richard C. Pubs., Inc.

Boldt, Mark. The Force B with U. l.t. ed. 1998. (U-Do Book Ser.). (Illus.). 92p. (J). (gr. k-8). pap. (978-0-9662556-3-8(1)) Boldt.Entertainment.

—It's a MADD House Here. l.t. ed. 1998. (U-Do Book Ser.). (Illus.). 24p. (J). (gr. k-6). pap. (978-0-9662556-1-4(5) , U-DO, 02) Boldt.Entertainment.

Bond, Felicia. The Halloween Play. Bond, Felicia, illus. 2003. Orig. Title: The Halloween Performance. (Illus.). 32p. (J). (ps up). bds. 6.99 (978-0-06-054443-0(0)) HarperCollins Pubs.

Boniface, William. What Do You Want on Your Sundae? Palen, Debbie, illus. 2001. 12p. (J). (ps-3). bds. 9.99 (978-0-8431-7638-4(5) , Price Stern Sloan) Penguin Group (USA) Inc.

Book Company Staff. My Cuddly Book of Colors. 2002. (Novelty Bks.). 6p. (J). 12.95 (978-1-74047-255-5(1)) Book Co. Publishing Pty, Ltd., The AUS. *Dist:* Penton Overseas, Inc.

—My Cuddly Book of Shapes. 2002. (Novelty Bks.). 6p. (J). 12.95 (978-1-74047-253-1(5)) Book Co. Publishing Pty, Ltd., The AUS. *Dist:* Penton Overseas, Inc.

Borgo, Deborah Colvin, illus. Baby Bunny. 1999. (J). (978-0-7853-3353-1(3)) Publications International, Ltd.

Bosak, Susan V. Dream: A Tale of Wonder, Wisdom & Wishes. Dillon, Leo and Diane et al, illus. 2004. 40p. (J). (978-1-896232-04-1(3) , TCP Pr.) Communication Project, The.

Bouchard, David. Nokum Was My Teacher. Sapp, Allen, illus. 2007. (CRE & ENG.). 32p. 21.95 incl. audio compact disk ***(978-0-88995-367-3(8))*** Red Deer Pr. CAN. *Dist:* Fitzhenry & Whiteside, Ltd.

Bourgeois, Paulette. Franklin's Christmas Gift. Clark, Brenda, illus. 1998. (Franklin the Turtle Ser.). 32p. (J). (gr. k-3). (978-1-55074-466-8(6)) Kids Can Pr., Ltd.

—Franklin's Neighborhood. Clark, Brenda, illus. 1999. (Franklin Ser.). 32p. (J). (ps-3). (978-1-55074-704-1(5)) Kids Can Pr., Ltd.

—Franklin's Valentines. Clark, Brenda, illus. 1998. (Franklin the Turtle Ser.). 32p. (J). (gr. k-3). (978-1-55074-480-4(1)) Kids Can Pr., Ltd.

Bourgeois, Paulette, et al. Franklin's Neighborhood. Clark, Brenda, illus. 1999. (Franklin the Turtle Ser.). 32p. (J). (gr. k-3). (978-1-55074-729-4(0)) Kids Can Pr., Ltd.

Bourke, Nike & Danalis, Stella. What the Sky Knows. 2005. (Illus.). 32p. (J). 26.95 (978-0-7022-3501-6(6)) Univ. of Queensland Pr. AUS. *Dist:* International Specialized Bk. Services.

Bowie, C. W. Busy Fingers. Willingham, Fred, illus. 2004. 28p. (J). bds. 6.95 (978-1-58089-048-9(2)) Charlesbridge Publishing, Inc.

Bowman, Crystal. Mommy, May I Hug the Fishes? 2000. 24p. (J). 6.99 (978-0-310-23209-4(0)) Zondervan.

Bowness, Kim. The Brave Engineers. 2007. (Illus.). 30p. (J). lib. bdg. 19.95 ***(978-1-933732-36-7(9)*** , Bear Hug Bks.) MidAmerica Publishing Co.

Boynton, Sandra. Buenas Noches a Todos. Boynton, Sandra, illus. 2004. Tr. of Going to Bed Book. (SPA., Illus.). 14p. (J). bds. 5.99 (978-0-689-86652-4(6) , Libros Para Ninos) Simon & Schuster Children's Publishing.

—Moo Cow Book. Boynton, Sandra, illus. 2004. (Illus.). 10p. (J). 16.95 (978-0-689-87683-7(1) , Little Simon) Simon & Schuster Children's Publishing.

—Perritos: Un Libro para Contar y Ladrar. Boynton, Sandra, illus. 2004. Tr. of Doggies. (SPA., Illus.). 14p. (J). bds. 5.99 (978-0-689-86303-5(9) , Libros Para Ninos) Simon & Schuster Children's Publishing.

Bradley, Kimberly Brubaker. The Perfect Pony. McNicholas, Shelagh, illus. 2007. (J). ***(978-1-4287-3296-4(9)*** , Dial) Penguin Group (USA) Inc.

Brami, Elisabeth & Schamp, Tom. Como Todo lo Que Nace. 2001. (SPA., Illus.). 28p. (J). (gr. k-3). (978-84-88342-29-4(2) , KK30074) S.A. Kokinos ESP. *Dist:* Lectorum Pubns., Inc.

Branford, Henrietta. Little Pig Figwort Can't Get to Sleep. Munoz, Claudio, illus. 2002. 32p. (J). (gr. k-3). 14.00 (978-0-618-15968-0(1) , Clarion Bks.) Houghton Mifflin Co. Trade & Reference Div.

Bray, Jeannine D. Pop Pop: What Do Armadillos Eat? Kenyatta, Imani, ed. Mitchell, Denise B., illus. 1998. 56p. (J). (gr. k-6). 13.95 (978-1-886580-87-9(1)) Pinnacle-Syatt Pubns.

Bredehoft, Linda. Oh, Where Is My Ducky? Big Idea Design Staff, illus. 2005. (Big Idea Books). 10p. (J). (ps-1). 6.99 (978-0-310-70716 2(3)) Zonderkidz.

Brennan, Kevin. Jimmy Jammers/Jaimito Pijama. Raven Tree Press, L. L. C., ed. de la Vega, Eida, tr. Driessen, Elizabeth, illus. 2002. Tr. of Jaimito Pijama. (SPA & ENG.). 32p. (J). (gr. k-3). 16.95 (978-0-9701107-9-4(0) , 626999) Raven Tree Pr.

Brett, Jan. Armadillo Rodeo. Brett, Jan, illus. 2004. (Illus.). 32p. (J). (ps-1). pap. 6.99 (978-0-14-240125-5(0) , Puffin) Penguin Group (USA) Inc.

—The Hat. 1999. (Illus.). 28p. (J). (ps-1). bds. 7.99 (978-0-399-23461-3(6) , Putnam Juvenile) Penguin Group (USA) Inc.

—The Trouble with Trolls. Brett, Jan, illus. 1999. (Illus.). 32p. (J). (ps-3). pap. 6.99 (978-0-698-11791-4(3) , Putnam Juvenile) Penguin Group (USA) Inc.

—The Trouble with Trolls. 1999. (978-0-606-17433-6(8)) Tandem Library Bks.

Brian Wildsmith's Birds. 2004. (J). pap. 14.95 incl. audio (978-1-56008-164-7(3)) Weston Woods Studios, Inc.

Bridwell, Norman & Fry, Sonali. Clifford the Weather Dog. Edwards, Ken & Haefele, Steve, illus. 2002. (Clifford, the Big Red Dog Ser.). 5p. (J). bds. 6.99 (978-0-439-39448-2(1)) Scholastic, Inc.

—Clifford's Scary Halloween. Durk, Jim, illus. 2002. (Clifford, the Big Red Dog Ser.). 16p. (J). pap. 4.99 (978-0-439-39453-6(8)) Scholastic, Inc.

—Take Me to School with You! Thompson Brothers Staff, illus. 2002. (Clifford, the Big Red Dog Ser.). 16p. (J). pap. 3.99 (978-0-439-39454-3(6)) Scholastic, Inc.

Bridwell, Norman, et al. T-Bone Tells the Truth. Binder, Eric & Lloyd, Gita, illus. 2002. (Clifford's Big Red Ideas Ser.). 7p. (J). bds. 4.99 (978-0-439-39450-5(3)) Scholastic, Inc.

Brighter Vision Publishing Staff. Mittens. 1999. (Stick'n Learn Stories Ser.). (Illus.). (J). (ps-1). pap. 2.50 (978-1-55254-070-1(7)) Brighter Vision Pubns.

Brimner, Larry Dane. Cat on Wheels. Peterson, Mary, illus. 2003. 32p. (J). (gr. k-2). 15.95 (978-1-56397-747-3(8)) Boyds Mills Pr.

British Museum of Natural History Staff, contrib. by. What Do Animals Eat Colouring Book. (Illus.). 8p. (J). (ps-6). pap. 2.95 (978-0-565-00808-6(0)) Natural History Museum Pubns. GBR. *Dist:* Parkwest Pubns., Inc.

Brooks, David, illus. The First Noel. 2005. (Soft Shapes Ser.). 8p. (J). (ps). 8.99 (978-1-58476-363-5(9)) Innovative Kids.

—My Shabbat. 2005. (Soft Shapes Ser.). 8p. (J). (ps-ps). 8.99 (978-1-58476-351-2(5)) Innovative Kids.

Brooks, F. & Litchfield, J. Picture Dictionary: A First Alphabetical Word Book. 2004. (Picture Dictionaries Ser.). 96p. (J). lib. bdg. 24.95 (978-1-58086-437-4(6)) EDC Publishing.

Broutin & Stehr. Baldomero Va A la Escuela. (SPA.). 26p. (978-84-95150-47-9(6)) Corimbo, Editorial S.L.

Brown, Jeff. Flat Stanley. Bjorkman, Steve, illus. 2002. (Trophy Chapter Bks.). 64p. (J). (gr. 1-5). pap. 4.25 (978-0-06-442026-6(4) , Harper Trophy) HarperCollins Pubs.

Brown, Jennifer Maze. Hooray! It's a Duck Day. Schaedler, Sally, illus. 1999. 32p. (J). (ps-2). 6.99 (978-0-570-05081-0(2) , 56-1905GJ) Concordia Publishing Hse.

Brown, Marc. Arthur's Perfect Christmas. 2004. (Arthur Adventure Ser.). (Illus.). 40p. (J). (ps-1). pap. 6.99 (978-0-316-00130-4(9) , Tingley, Megan Bks.) Little, Brown Bks. for Young Readers.

—Arthur's Perfect Christmas. Brown, Marc, illus. 2000. (Arthur Adventure Ser.). (Illus.). 48p. (J). (ps-3). 15.95 (978-0-316-11968-9(7)) Little, Brown Bks. for Young Readers.

Brown, Margaret Wise. A Child Is Born: Picture Book. Cooper, Floyd, illus. 2000. 32p. (ps-ps). 16.99 (978-0-7868-0673-7(7)) Hyperion Bks. for Children.

—Goodnight Moon. 2002. (Illus.). 14.47 (978-0-7587-0015-5(6)) Book Wholesalers, Inc.

—Goodnight Moon. Hurd, Clement, illus. 2001. 34p. (J). (ps up). 12.99 (978-0-694-01675-4(6) , Harper Festival) HarperCollins Pubs.

—Goodnight Moon. Hurd, Clement, illus. 2001. 38p. (J). (ps-1). pap. 6.95 (978-0-9629298-7-8(5) , MHC-7-5) Minnesota Humanities Commission.

—Goodnight Moon. Hurd, Clement, illus. (J). pap. 32.75 incl. audio. 24.95 incl. audio. 2004. pap. 14.95 incl. audio (978-0-89719-775-5(5) , PRA298) Weston Woods Studios, Inc.

—Goodnight Moon: Board Book & Baby Socks. Hurd, Clement, illus. 2002. 34p. (J). (ps up). 12.99 (978-0-06-009427-0(3) , Harper Festival) HarperCollins Pubs.

—Goodnight Moon Board Book & Nightlight. Hurd, Clement, illus. 2003. 34p. (J). (ps up). 12.99 (978-0-06-054179-8(2) , Harper Festival) HarperCollins Pubs.

—Je Vais Me Sauver! 2000. Tr. of Runaway Bunny. (FRE.). (J). pap. 19.95 (978-2-87142-177-1(3)) Mijade Editions BEL. *Dist:* Distribooks, Inc.

—A Pussycat's Christmas. 1998. (ps-2). lib. bdg. 14.10 (978-0-613-81428-7(2)) Tandem Library Bks.

Brown, Margaret Wise & Hurd, Clement. Goodnight Moon. unabr. ed. 2000. (J). pap. 7.98 incl. audio Random Hse. Audio Publishing Group.

Brown, Margaret Wise & Kahn, Si. Goodnight Moon. Hurd, Clement, illus. unabr. abr. ed. 1998. (Share a Story Ser.). (J). (ps up). 9.95 (978-0-694-70094-3(0)) HarperCollins Pubs.

Brown, Margaret Wise, et al. The Runaway Bunny: Board Book & Doll. Hurd, Clement, illus. 1999. 18p. (J). (ps up). 14.99 (978-0-694-01214-5(9) , Harper Festival) HarperCollins Pubs.

Brown, Mark & Brown, Mark. Arthur: The Race to Read. 2000. (J). pap. 3.95 (978-0-316-11838-5(9)) Little Brown & Co.

Brown, Ruth. Lion in the Long Grass. Brown, Ken, illus. 2004. 32p. (J). pap. 11.99 (978-1-84270-339-7(0)) Andersen GBR. *Dist:* Independent Pubs. Group.

Browne, Anthony. I Like Books. Browne, Anthony, illus. 2004. (Super Sturdy Picture Books Ser.). (Illus.). 24p. (J). (gr. k). 8.99 (978-0-7636-2162-9(5)) Candlewick Pr.

—King Kong. Segovia, Francisco, tr. 2006. (SPA., Illus.). 92p. (J). (978-968-16-7987-3(3)) Fondo de Cultura Economica.

Browne, Eileen. Handa's Surprise: Read & Share. Browne, Eileen, illus. 1999. (Reading Together Ser.). (Illus.). 32p. (J). (gr. k). pap. 3.99 (978-0-7636-0863-7(7)) Candlewick Pr.

—Handa's Surprise: Read & Share. 2004. (Illus.). 28p. (J). (TAM, SPA, GUJ, PER & URD.). (978-1-85269-473-9(4)); (TAM, SPA, GUJ, PER & URD., (978-1-85269-474-6(2)); (TAM, SPA, GUJ, PER & URD., (978-1-85269-475-3(0)); (TAM, SPA, GUJ, PER & URD., (978-1-85269-477-7(7)); (TAM, SPA, GUJ, PER & URD., (978-1-85269-478-4(5)); (TAM, SPA, GUJ, PER & URD., (978-1-85269-472-2(6)); (TAM, SPA, GUJ, PER & URD., (978-1-85269-508-8(0)); (TAM, SPA, GUJ, PER & URD., (978-1-85269-509-5(9)); (TAM, SPA, GUJ, PER & URD., (978-1-85269-512-5(9)); (TAM, SPA, GUJ, PER & URD., (978-1-85269-513-2(7)); (TAM, SPA, GUJ, PER & URD., (978-1-85269-515-6(3)); (POR, TAM, TWI, SPA & CHI., (978-1-85269-476-0(9)); (TAM, SPA, GUJ, PER & URD., (978-1-85269-514-9(5)) Mantra Publishing, Ltd.

—Handa's Surprise: Read & Share. 2004. (TAM, SPA, GUJ, PER & URD., Illus.). 28p. (J). 13.50 (978-1-85269-511-8(0)); 13.50 (978-1-85269-507-1(2)) Mantra Publishing, Ltd. GBR. *Dist:* AIMS International Bks., Inc.

Browne, Eileen & Habashi, Azza. Handa's Surprise: Read & Share. 2004. (TAM, SPA, GUJ, PER & URD., Illus.). 28p. (J). 13.50 (978-1-85269-471-5(8)) Mantra Publishing, Ltd. GBR. *Dist:* AIMS International Bks., Inc.

Browning, Dave. Marvin Weighs In. 2000. (Illus.). 12p. (J). (ps-3). pap. 6.95 (978-0-688-17735-5(2) , Harper Festival) HarperCollins Pubs.

Bruna, Dick. Farmer John's Seeds. 2004. (Illus.). 12p. pap. 5.99 (978-1-59226-191-8(4)) Big Tent Entertainment, Inc.

—Meet Miffy, 2 vols. 2001. (Illus.). 24p. (J). (ps-k). bds. 5.95 (978-1-56836-309-7(5)) Kodansha America, Inc.

—Miffy at Play: A Flip Book. 1998. (Miffy Ser.). (Illus.). 16p. (J). (ps-k). bds. 5.95 (978-1-56836-223-6(4)) Kodansha America, Inc.

—Miffy Rides a Bike. Bruna, Dick, illus. 1999. (Miffy Ser.). (Illus.). 28p. (ps-k). 4.95 (978-1-56836-280-9(3)) Kodansha America, Inc.

—Miffy's Busy Morning: A Flip Book. Bruna, Dick, illus. 1999. (Miffy Ser.). (Illus.). 16p. (ps-k). bds. 5.95 (978-1-56836-288-5(9)) Kodansha America, Inc.

—Miffy's Counting Book. 2004. (Illus.). 20p. bds. 7.99 (978-1-59226-034-8(9)) Big Tent Entertainment, Inc.

—Miffy's Counting Book. Bruna, Dick, illus. 1999. (Miffy Ser.). (Illus.). 20p. (ps-k). bds. 7.95 (978-1-56836-281-6(1)) Kodansha America, Inc.

—Miffy's First Sleepover. Bruna, Dick, illus. 1999. (Miffy Ser.). (Illus.). 28p. (ps-k). 4.95 (978-1-56836-279-3(X)) Kodansha America, Inc.

—Miffy's House. 2004. 24p. 7.99 (978-1-59226-023-2(3)); (Illus.). pap. 4.99 (978-1-59226-008-9(X)) Big Tent Entertainment, Inc.

—Miffy's Magnifying Glass. 2004. (Illus.). 16p. bds. 5.99 (978-1-59226-031-7(4)) Big Tent Entertainment, Inc.

—Peek-a-Boo, Miffy! A Flip Book. 1998. (Miffy Ser.). (Illus.). 16p. (J). (ps-k). bds. 5.95 (978-1-56836-222-9(6)) Kodansha America, Inc.

—Places to Go. 2004. (Illus.). 12p. 6.99 (978-1-59226-043-0(8)) Big Tent Entertainment, Inc.

—Poppy Pig. 2004. (Illus.). 24p. (J). 7.99 (978-1-59226-029-4(2)) Big Tent Entertainment, Inc.

—Snuffy. 2004. (Illus.). 24p. (J). 7.99 (978-1-59226-028-7(4)) Big Tent Entertainment, Inc.

—What Time Is It Miffy? Bruna, Dick, illus. 1999. (Miffy Ser.). (Illus.). 20p. (ps-k). bds. 7.95 (978-1-56836-282-3(X)) Kodansha America, Inc.

—What's at the Zoo, Miffy? 2004. 16p. bds. 5.99 (978-1-59226-033-1(0)) Big Tent Entertainment, Inc.

Buck, Joanna. My First Shapes & Colors Book. Church, Caroline Jayne, illus. 1999. (My First Bks.). 16p. (J). (ps-1). 16.95 (978-1-57145-361-7(X) , Silver Dolphin Bks.) Advantage Pubs. Group.

Bunting, Eve. The Day Before Christmas. Peck, Beth, illus. 2000. 32p. (J). (gr. k-3). pap. 5.95 (978-0-618-05150-2(3) , Clarion Bks.) Houghton Mifflin Co. Trade & Reference Div.

—Peepers. Ransome, James E., illus. 2001. 32p. (J). (gr. 1-4). 17.00 (978-0-15-260297-0(6)) Harcourt Children's Bks.

Burkhalter, Mary L. Active Children's Literature: Alphabet Story, Colors, Mister Prince. 1998. (Illus.). 50p. (J). (gr. k-4). pap. 20.00 (978-0-934284-09-7(1)) Jolean Publishing Co.

Burnett, Frances Hodgson. A Little Princess. Engelbreit, Mary, illus. 2007. (Mary Engelbreit's Classic Library). 304p. (J). (gr. 3-7). 9.99 (978-0-06-008137-9(6) , Harper Festival) HarperCollins Pubs.

Burnham, Janet Hayward. The Dragoness Mess. 2003. (Illus.). 32p. (J). (gr. k-1). pap. 12.95 (978-0-9740743-1-3(4)) My Little Jessie Pr.

Burningham, John. Mr. Gumpy's Outing. Burningham, John, illus. 2002. (Illus.). (J). 15.49 (978-0-7587-3187-6(6)) Book Wholesalers, Inc.

—Mr. Gumpy's Outing. (Illus.). (J). Date not set. bds. 6.95 (978-0-8050-7373-7(6)); 2001. 34p. bds. 6.95 (978-0-8050-6629-6(2)) Holt, Henry & Co. (Holt, Henry & Co. Bks. For Young Readers).

—Que Prefieres? 2001. (SPA., Illus.). (J). (gr. k-2). (978-84-88342-05-8(5) , KK1285) S.A. Kokinos ESP. *Dist:* Lectorum Pubns., Inc.

Burns, Joanne. What Is Heaven Like? 2005. 35p. (J). 10.99 (978-1-4116-3360-5(1)) Lulu.com.

Burrill, Richard L. Somewhere Behind the Eyes: Images in the Moon & in the Stars Aha! Miskey, Tom et al, illus. 1998. 100p. (YA). (gr. 9-12). pap. 19.95 (978-1-878464-05-7(1)) Anthro Co., The.

Burrows, Terry. Chiquitines Cuentos de las Bunas Noches. 2002. (Toddler's Ser.).Tr. of Stories for Bedtime. (SPA., Illus.). 78p. (J). (978-968-5308-38-0(1) , Silver Dolphin en Español) Advanced Marketing, S. de R. L. de C. V.

Burton, Virginia Lee. The Little House. Burton, Virginia Lee, illus. 2002. (Illus.). (J). 13.79 (978-0-7587-0054-4(7)) Book Wholesalers, Inc.

—The Little House. 1998. (Carry-Along Book & Cassette Favorites Ser.). 1p. (J). (gr. k-3). pap. 9.95 incl. audio (978-0-395-89112-4(4)) Houghton Mifflin Co. Trade & Reference Div.

Bye-Bye, Bottle. 2001. (Illus.). 12p. bds. 4.99 (978-0-307-13476-9(8) , Golden Bks.) Random Hse. Children's Bks.

Bynum, Janie. Altoona Baboona. 2002. (Illus.). 36p. (J). (ps-2). pap. 7.00 (978-0-15-216404-1(9) , Voyager Bks./ Libros Viajeros) Harcourt Children's Bks.

Cabrera, Jane. Creaky Noise. 2004. (Popcorn & Banana Bob Ser.). (Illus.). 32p. 15.99 ***(978-0-689-86057-7(9))*** Simon & Schuster, Ltd. GBR. *Dist:* Independent Pubs. Group.

Cabrera, Jane. Mommy, Carry Me Please! Cabrera, Jane, illus. 2005. (Illus.). 32p. (J). (ps-1). 16.95 (978-0-8234-1935-7(5)) Holiday Hse., Inc.

Cache, Dee. Captain Tugalong. Burns, Howard M., illus. 1999. 30p. (J). (ps-3). 12.95 (978-0-87033-515-0(4)) Cornell Maritime Pr., Inc.

Caffey, Don. Yikes-Lice! Girouard, Patrick, illus. 2003. 24p. (J). (ps-5). reprint ed. pap. 5.95 (978-0-8075-9375-2(3)) Whitman, Albert & Co.

Caldwell, Lise. Please & Thank-You. 2000. (Coloring Bks.). (Illus.). 16p. (J). (ps up). pap. 1.99 (978-0-7847-1109-5(7), 22074) Standard Publishing.

Calmenson, Stephanie. May I Pet Your Dog? The How-To Guide for Kids Meeting Dogs (and Dogs Meeting Kids) Ormerod, Jan, illus. 2007. 32p. (J). (*978-1-4287-3952-9(1)*, Clarion Bks.) Houghton Mifflin Co. Trade & Reference Div.

Cambridge Young Writers Staff. I'm Telling You! 2000. (Cambridge Reading Ser.). (Illus.). 80p. pap. 12.00 (978-0-521-78578-5(2)) Cambridge Univ. Pr.

Campbell, Rod. Dear Santa. Campbell, Rod, illus. 2004. (Illus.). 16p. (J). bds. 7.99 (978-0-689-87415-4(4), Little Simon) Simon & Schuster Children's Publishing.

—It's Mine. 1999. (Illus.). 22p. (J). 9.99 (978-0-333-76278-3(9)) Macmillan Publishers Ltd. GBR. *Dist:* Independent Pubs. Group.

Camping Caper: Picture Book (English) 8x8. 2007. (Illus.). (J). (*978-1-933934-64-8(6)*) Educational Adventures.

Capucilli, Alyssa Satin. Biscuit's Fourth of July. Schories, Pat, illus. 2005. (Biscuit Ser.). 20p. (J). (ps-ps). pap., pap. 6.99 (978-0-06-009464-5(8), Harper Festival) HarperCollins Pubs.

—Biscuit's New Trick. Schories, Pat, illus. 2000. (My First I Can Read Bks.). 32p. (J). (ps-k). 16.99 (978-0-06-028067-3(0)) HarperCollins Pubs.

—Bizcocho. Mlawer, Teresa, tr. Schories, Pat, illus. 2001. (Coleccion Ya Se Leer). (SPA & ENG.). 32p. (J). (ps up). 15.95 (978-0-06-029755-8(7), HC1758) HarperCollins Pubs.

Carle, Eric. The Grouchy Ladybug. Carle, Eric, illus. 1999. (Illus.). 44p. (J). (ps-k). bds. 7.99 (978-0-694-01320-3(X), Harper Festival) HarperCollins Pubs.

—A House for a Hermit Crab. Carle, Eric, illus. 2002. (Illus.). (J). 25.11 (978-0-7587-2754-1(2)) Book Wholesalers, Inc.

—A House for a Hermit Crab. Carle, Eric, illus. (Classic Board Bks.). (Illus.). 32p. (J). 2004. bds. 8.99 (978-0-689-87064-4(7), Little Simon); 2002. pap. 7.99 (978-0-689-84894-0(3), Aladdin) Simon & Schuster Children's Publishing.

—Little Cloud. Carle, Eric, illus. 1998. (Illus.). 28p. (J). (ps-k). bds. 6.99 (978-0-399-23191-9(9), Philomel) Penguin Group (USA) Inc.

—My Very First Book of Shapes. Carle, Eric, illus. 2005. (Illus.). 20p. (J). (ps-1). bds. 5.99 (978-0-399-24387-5(9), Philomel) Penguin Group (USA) Inc.

—Pancakes, Pancakes! Carle, Eric, illus. 2004. (Classic Board Bks.). (Illus.). 32p. (J). bds. 7.99 (978-0-689-87148-1(1), Little Simon) Simon & Schuster Children's Publishing.

—Rooster's off to See the World. Carle, Eric, illus. 1999. (Illus.). 32p. (J). (ps-3). pap. 7.99 (978-0-689-82684-9(2), 076714005990, Aladdin) Simon & Schuster Children's Publishing.

—The Tiny Seed. Carle, Eric, illus. 2005. (Classic Board Bks.). (Illus.). 34p. (J). bds. 7.99 (978-0-689-87149-8(X), Little Simon) Simon & Schuster Children's Publishing.

—1, 2, 3 to the Zoo: A Counting Book. Carle, Eric, illus. 1998. (Illus.). 32p. (J). (ps-k). pap. 6.99 (978-0-698-11645-0(3), Putnam Juvenile) Penguin Group (USA) Inc.

Carlson, Nancy. Think Big! 2005. (Illus.). 28p. (J). (ps-ps). 15.95 (978-1-57505-622-7(4), Carolrhoda Bks.) Lerner Publishing Group.

Carter, Anne Laurel. Under a Prairie Sky. Daniel, Alan & Daniel, Lea, illus. 2004. 32p. (J). (ps-2). 7.95 (978-1-55143-282-3(X)) Orca Bk. Pubs. USA.

Carter, David A. Bed Bugs: A Pop-up Bedtime. 1998. (Bugs in a Box Bks.). (Illus.). 6p. (J). (ps-3). 14.95 (978-0-689-81863-9(7), Little Simon) Simon & Schuster Children's Publishing.

—One Red Dot: A Pop-up Book for Children of All Ages. Carter, David A., illus. 2005. (Classic Collectible Pop-Up Ser.). (Illus.). 18p. (J). 19.95 (978-0-689-87769-8(2), Little Simon) Simon & Schuster Children's Publishing.

Cartwright, Stephen, illus. Apple Tree Farm. 1998. (Usborne Cut-Out Models Ser.). 32p. (J). (gr. 4-7). pap. 9.95 (978-0-7460-3286-2(2)) EDC Publishing.

Cassidy, Sean. Good to Be Small. Cassidy, Sean, illus. 2002. (Illus.). 32p. (J). (ps-k). (978-1-55041-734-0(7)) Fitzhenry & Whiteside, Ltd.

Castor, Daniel. Wondaglop Plot. (Illus.). 61p. (J). pap. 6.99 (978-0-340-63442-4(1), Hodder & Stoughton) Hodder General Publishing Division GBR. *Dist:* Trafalgar Square Publishing.

Catalanotto, Peter. Painter. 1999. (978-0-606-16920-2(2)) Tandem Library Bks.

Caudle, Ruth. Yvette, Annette & Renette. 2007. (Illus.). 32p. (J). 16.99 (*978-0-9793039-0-6(7)*) Haiti World.

Ceelen, Vicky. Baby! Baby! 2008. (Illus.). 24p. (J). (gr. k-ps). bds. 6.99 (*978-0-375-84207-8(1)*, Random Hse. Bks. for Young Readers) Random Hse. Children's Bks.

Celebrating Cat. 2003. (Happy Birthday Pull-Out Card-Bks.). (Illus.). 4.99 (978-1-56148-385-3(0)) Good Bks.

Chandler, Pauline. Mr. Rabbit the Farmer. Smith, Eric, illus. 2005. 24p. (J). lib. bdg. 22.65 (*978-1-59646-736-1(3)*) Dingles & Co.

Chapell, Bryan. I'll Love You Anyway & Always. Jonke, Tim, illus. 2005. 32p. 15.99 (978-1-58134-306-9(X), Crossway Bibles) Crossway Bks.

Chapin, Tom & reader. Mama Don't Allow. Chapin, Tom, reader. 2001. (Live Oak Readalong Ser.). (Illus.). (J). (ps-4). pap. 16.95 incl. audio (978-0-87499-743-9(7)) Live Oak Media.

Charman, Andy. The Snowman They Tried to Ban. Silcock, Sara, illus. 2001. 16p. (ps-k). pap. 5.00 (978-0-7548-0235-8(3)) Anness Publishing, Inc.

Chartrand, Micheline & Desputeaux, Helene. Caillou's Room. Chartrand, Micheline & Desputeaux, Helene, illus. 1998. (Illus.). (J). bds. 4.49 (978-1-58048-034-5(9)) Sandvik Publishing.

Cheng, Andrea. Anna the Bookbinder. Rand, Ted, illus. 2003. 32p. (J). (gr. k-4). 16.95 (978-0-8027-8831-3(9)) Walker & Co.

Cherry, Lynne & Plotkin, Mark J. The Shaman's Apprentice: A Tale of the Amazon Rain Forest. Cherry, Lynne, illus. 1998. (Illus.). 40p. (J). 16.00 (978-0-15-201281-6(8)) Harcourt Children's Bks.

Child, Lauren. Ana Tarambana Me Llaman. 2000. (Illus.). (J). (CAT.). 32p. (gr. 3-5). 17.95 (978-84-95040-37-4(9)); (SPA., 48p. (ps-3). 17.95 (978-84-95040-36-7(0)) Serres, Ediciones, S. L. ESP. *Dist:* Lectorum Pubns., Inc.

Child, Lauren. An Extremely Wintery Winter Activity Kit. 2007. 32p. (J). (ps-k). 19.99 (*978-0-8037-3242-1(2)*, Dial) Penguin Group (USA) Inc.

Christelow, Eileen. Cinco Monitos Brincando en la Cama: Five Little Monkeys Jumping on the Bed. Ortiz, Victoria, tr. 2005. (SPA & ENG., Illus.). 28p. (J). (gr. k-ps). bds. 5.95 (978-0-618-56442-2(X), Clarion Bks.) Houghton Mifflin Co. Trade & Reference Div.

—Not until Christmas, Walter! Christelow, Eileen, illus. 2002. (Illus.). 40p. (J). (gr. k-3). pap. 5.95 (978-0-618-24618-2(5), Clarion Bks.) Houghton Mifflin Co. Trade & Reference Div.

—Not until Christmas, Walter! 2002. (Illus.). 40p. (J). (ps-3). lib. bdg. 14.10 (978-0-613-70984-2(5)) Tandem Library Bks.

Church, Caroline Jayne, illus. My First 123 Book, 4 vols., Set. 1998. (My First Bks.). 16p. (J). (ps-1). 16.95 (978-1-57145-312-9(1), Silver Dolphin Bks.) Advantage Pubs. Group.

—My First ABC Book, 4 vols., Set. 1998. (My First Bks.). 16p. (J). (ps-1). 16.95 (978-1-57145-313-6(X), Silver Dolphin Bks.) Advantage Pubs. Group.

Cioffi, Dom, illus. Digby & the Lake Monster. l.t. ed. 2003. 36p. (J). per. (978-0-9745931-0-4(9)) Vermont Bookworks.

Clanchy, Kate. Our Cat Henry Comes to the Swings. (Illus.). 32p. (978-0-19-279122-1(2)) Oxford Univ. Pr., Inc.

Clanchy, Kate & Bird, Jemima. Our Cat Henry Comes to the Swings. (Illus.). 32p. (978-0-19-272557-8(2)) Oxford Univ. Pr., Inc.

Clark, Kimberly. Three Is the Perfect Number. Hummel, Victoria, illus. 1998. 16p. (J). (ps-k). pap. 5.95 (978-1-891846-01-4(9)) Business Word, The.

Clarke, Jane. I'm Not Wearing That! Mostyn, David, illus. 2005. 24p. (J). lib. bdg. 22.65 (*978-1-59646-716-3(9)*) Dingles & Co.

—Prince Albert's Birthday. Chatterton, Martin, illus. 2005. 24p. (J). lib. bdg. 22.65 (*978-1-59646-748-4(7)*) Dingles & Co.

Clarke, Lyndia A. Tidy up Tommy. Clarke, Lyndia A., illus. 2005. (J). 1700.00 (978-0-9762898-6-9(5)) LightHouse Pr.

Clement, Gary. The Great Poochini. ed. 2004. (J). (gr. 1-4). spiral bd. (978-0-616-03027-1(4)) Canadian National Institute for the Blind/Institut National Canadien pour les Aveugles.

—The Great Poochini. Clement, Gary, illus. 1999. (Illus.). 32p. (J). (ps-3). 15.95 (978-0-88899-331-1(5), Libros Tigrillo) Groundwood Bks. CAN. *Dist:* Perseus Distribution.

Clements, Andrew. Classic Board Book Snowden Raggedy Ann & Andy. 1998. 16p. (J). 4.99 (978-0-689-82367-1(3), Little Simon) Simon & Schuster Children's Publishing.

—Raggedy Ann's Christmas Numbers Snowden Board Book With Plush. 1998. (J). 4.99 (978-0-689-82364-0(9), Little Simon) Simon & Schuster Children's Publishing.

Clerk, Jessica. The Wriggly, Wriggly Baby. Rankin, Laura, illus. 2002. 32p. (J). pap. 16.95 (978-0-590-96067-0(9), Levine, Arthur A. Bks.) Scholastic, Inc.

Coakley, Lena. Mrs. Goodhearth & the Gargoyle. Bailey, Wendy, illus. 2005. 32p. (J). (ps-2). 17.95 (978-1-55143-328-8(1)) Orca Bk. Pubs. USA.

Coates, Jan. Rainbows in the Dark. Priestly, Alice, illus. 2005. 24p. (J). 11.95 (978-1-896764-95-5(9)) Second Story Pr. CAN. *Dist:* Orca Bk. Pubs. USA.

Cochran, Bruce. First Birthday Bear. 10p. (J). (978-1-886386-35-8(8)) Trisar, Inc.

—First Pony: Blue. 10p. (J). (978-1-886386-34-1(X)) Trisar, Inc.

—First Pony: Pink. 10p. (J). (978-1-886386-33-4(1)) Trisar, Inc.

—It's the Big 1: Blue. 10p. (J). (978-1-886386-37-2(4)) Trisar, Inc.

—It's the Big 1: Pink. 10p. (J). (978-1-886386-36-5(6)) Trisar, Inc.

Cofer, Amadeus. Friendship Rules: How to Make & Keep Friends, 1. l.t. ed. 2004. (Illus.). 36p. (J). 14.00 (978-1-932957-00-6(6)) Legacy Pubs.

Cohen, Emma. It's Mine! His. Chambers, Sally, illus. 1998. (Nuk Bks.). 8p. (J). 6.95 (978-0-7641-7232-8(8)) Barron's Educational Series, Inc.

Cohen, Miriam. Wah! Wah! A Backpack Baby Story. l.t. ed. 2001. (Backpack Baby Stories Ser.). (Illus.). 12p. (J). (ps). bds. 5.95 (978-1-887734-81-3(3)) Star Bright Bks., Inc.

Cohn, Arlen. Lacey O'Neal: A Shoelace Book. Cole, Jeff, illus. 1999. (Books-in-Motion Ser.). 32p. (J). 15.99 (978-0-939251-99-5(X)) Accord Publishing, Ltd.

Cole, Babette. Estirar la Pata. 2001. (SPA.). 36p. (J). (gr. 1-3). (978-84-233-2711-9(6)) Ediciones Destino ESP. *Dist:* Lectorum Pubns., Inc.

Cole, Joanna. The Magic School Bus Going Places. Reiter, Cheryl & Reyner, Mark, eds. Bracken, Carol, illus. 2000. (Magic School Bus Ser.). 10p. (J). (gr. 1-4). mass mkt. 9.99 (978-1-887327-37-4(1)) Ertl Co., Inc.

Cole, Sheila. My Big Girl Potty Book. 2000. (J). lib. bdg. 5.89 (978-0-06-029222-5(9)) HarperCollins Pubs.

Cole, Stephen & Gardner, Louise. Cars on Mars. 1998. (Alien Pop-Ups Ser.). (Illus.). 10p. (J). 4.95 (978-1-899607-63-1(3)) Sterling Publishing Co., Inc.

—Mucky Martians. 1998. (Alien Pop-Ups Ser.). (Illus.). 10p. (J). 4.95 (978-1-899607-62-4(5)) Sterling Publishing Co., Inc.

—School on Saturn. 1998. (Alien Pop-Ups Ser.). (Illus.). 10p. (J). 4.95 (978-1-899607-64-8(1)) Sterling Publishing Co., Inc.

Coll, Ivar Da. No, No Fui Yo! 2001. (SPA.). 40p. (J). (gr. 1-3). (978-958-30-0495-7(2)) Panamericana Editorial COL. *Dist:* Lectorum Pubns., Inc.

—Tengo Miedo. 2001. (SPA.). 36p. (J). (gr. k-2). (978-958-30-0523-7(1)) Panamericana Editorial COL. *Dist:* Lectorum Pubns., Inc.

Collings, Julie & Klutz Editors. Rescue Trucks. 2005. (Illus.). 22p. (J). (ps-3). spiral bd. 12.95 (978-1-59174-089-6(4)) Klutz.

Collins, Pat Lowery. I Am a Dancer. Graham, Mark, illus. 2008. (Millbrook Picture Books Ser.). (J). lib. bdg. 22.60 (*978-0-8225-6369-3(X)*, Millbrook Pr.) Lerner Publishing Group.

Collinson, Roger. Get Lavinia Goodbody! Shelley, John, illus. 2002. 122p. pap. 9.99 (978-1-84270-097-6(9)) Andersen GBR. *Dist:* Independent Pubs. Group.

Comissiong, Lynette. The Parrots & Papa Bois. Turner, Avril, illus. 2002. 32p. (J). (ps-3). 12.95 (978-0-333-93062-5(2)) Macmillan Caribbean GBR. *Dist:* Interlink Publishing Group, Inc.

Conley, Deane. Angelino. Hunt, Christy, ed. Thiele, Marcus, illus. 2000. (Butterfly Tree Ser.: Vol. 1). 32p. (J). (ps-3). 17.00 (978-0-9664329-2-3(4)) Buckhead Pr.

—Butterflies. Hunt, Christy, ed. Thiele, Marcus, illus. 2000. (Butterfly Tree Ser.: Vol. 2). 32p. (J). (ps-3). 17.00 (978-0-9664329-4-7(0)) Buckhead Pr.

Conlon, Cynthia Kelly. Postcards from the Lake: A History of Geneva Lake for Children. 2001. (Illus.). iv, 28p. (J). (gr. k-7). 14.95 (978-0-9711736-0-6(5)) Geneva Lake Publishing.

Conover, Chris. Un Tesoro para Compartir. 2002. (SPA., Illus.). 246p. (J). (gr. k-2). 15.95 (978-84-261-3164-5(6), JV30155) Juventud, Editorial ESP. *Dist:* Lectorum Pubns., Inc.

Constantine. Kiquoti & the Coati. 2001. 40p. (J). (gr. k-3). pap. 5.95 (978-0-06-443552-9(0)) HarperCollins Pubs.

Cony, Frances. Old MacDonald Had a Farm. Smyth, Iain, illus. 2002. 12p. (J). (ps-k). bds. 10.95 (978-0-531-30129-6(X), Orchard Bks.) Scholastic, Inc.

Cook, David C. Publishing Staff & Tangvald, Christine. Josiah, the Boy King. 2004. (Pencil Fun Bks.: Vol. 10). 16p. (J). (gr. 1-4). pap. 9.90 (978-1-55513-918-6(3), 1555139183) Cook, David C. Publishing Co.

Cooke, Andy. Wheels on the Bus. Cooke, Andy, illus. 1999. (Read & Share Ser.). (Illus.). 24p. (J). (ps). pap. 3.99 (978-0-7636-0877-4(7)) Candlewick Pr.

Cool by the Pool: Picture Book (English) 8x8. 2007. (J). (*978-1-933934-37-2(9)*) Educational Adventures.

Cool by the Pool: Picture Book (English) NL 9x9 with Snipe. 2007. (J). (*978-1-933934-47-1(6)*) Educational Adventures.

Cooner, Donna D. Barney's Toolbox. Hernandez, Joseph, illus. 1998. (Barney Ser.). 14p. (J). (ps-k). 5.95 (978-1-57064-244-9(3)) Scholastic, Inc.

Cooper, Melrose. "Pets!" Heo, Yumi, illus. rev. ed. 1998. 32p. (C). (ps-2). pap. 15.95 (978-0-8050-3893-4(0), Holt, Henry & Co. Bks. For Young Readers) Holt, Henry & Co.

Corey, Shana. Little Airplane Book. 2000. (J). 4.99 (978-0-679-89480-3(2)) Random Hse., Inc.

Coristine, Philip. Serena & the Wild Doll. Gukova, Julia, illus. 2000. 32p. (J). (ps-2). pap. 6.95 (978-1-55037-648-7(9)) Annick Pr., Ltd. CAN. *Dist:* Firefly Bks., Ltd.

Cosgrove, Stephen. Minikin. James, Robin, illus. 2001. (Serendipity Bks.). 32p. (J). (ps-3). pap. 4.99 (978-0-8431-7629-2(6), Price Stern Sloan) Penguin Group (USA) Inc.

Cottringer, Anne. Hot Dog. Walker, Katherine, illus. 2005. 24p. (J). lib. bdg. 22.65 (*978-1-59646-738-5(X)*) Dingles & Co.

Coulman, Valerie. I Am a Ballerina. Lamb, Sandra, illus. 2004. 32p. (J). (ps-2). pap. 6.95 (978-1-897073-20-9(8)) Lobster Pr. CAN. *Dist:* Univ. of Toronto Pr.

—Rafi et les Cochons Volants. Duchesne, Christiane, tr. from ENG. Girard, Roge, illus. (FRE.). 32p. (J). pap. 6.95 (*978-2-922435-02-3(4)*) Editions Homard CAN. *Dist:* Univ. of Toronto Pr.

Coulman, Valerie. Sink or Swim. 2005. (Illus.). 32p. (J). reprint ed. pap. 6.95 (978-1-894222-96-9(2)) Lobster Pr. CAN. *Dist:* Univ. of Toronto Pr.

Couri, Kathryn A., illus. Goodnight Bear! A Book & Night Light. 1999. 12p. (J). (ps-k). 10.95 (978-1-58117-059-7(9), Intervisual/Piggy Toes) Dalmatian Pr.

Cousins, Lucy. A Maisy le Gusta Conducir. 2002. (Illus.). (J). (CAT.). 14p. bds. 7.95 (978-84-95040-90-9(5)); (SPA., 64p. 8.99 (978-84-95040-89-3(1), RR6349) Serres, Ediciones, S. L. ESP. *Dist:* Lectorum Pubns., Inc.

—Country Animals. Cousins, Lucy, illus. 2004. (Illus.). 12p. (J). (gr. k-k). bds. 4.99 (978-0-7636-2302-9(4)) Candlewick Pr.

—Farm Animals. Cousins, Lucy, illus. 2004. (Illus.). 12p. (J). (gr. k-k). bds. 4.99 (978-0-7636-2303-6(2)) Candlewick Pr.

—Garden Animals. Cousins, Lucy, illus. 2004. (Illus.). 12p. (J). (gr. k-k). bds. 4.99 (978-0-7636-2304-3(0)) Candlewick Pr.

—Maisy's Halloween. Cousins, Lucy, illus. 2004. (Maisy Ser.). (Illus.). 14p. (J). (gr. k-k). bds. 5.99 (978-0-7636-2579-5(5)) Candlewick Pr.

—Noah's Ark. Cousins, Lucy, illus. 2004. (Illus.). 22p. (J). (gr. k-k). bds. 6.99 (978-0-7636-2446-0(2)) Candlewick Pr.

—Pet Animals. Cousins, Lucy, illus. 2004. (Illus.). 12p. (J). (gr. k-k). bds. 4.99 (978-0-7636-2305-0(9)) Candlewick Pr.

—Smile, Maisy! Cousins, Lucy, illus. 2004. (Maisy Ser.). (Illus.). 16p. (J). (gr. k-k). bds. 7.99 (978-0-7636-2368-5(7)) Candlewick Pr.

—Sweet Dreams, Maisy. Cousins, Lucy, illus. 2005. (Illus.). 16p. (J). (ps-k). 12.99 (978-0-7636-2874-1(3)) Candlewick Pr.

Covey, Stephen R. I Know the Alphabet. 2000. (Step Ahead Workbooks Ser.). (Illus.). 64p. (J). (ps). pap., wbk. ed. 3.99 (978-0-307-03669-8(3), 03669, Golden Bks.) Random Hse. Children's Bks.

Covington, Jean. Nanny Planted Love. (J). 2006. per. 11.99 (*978-1-933732-12-1(1)*); 2005. lib. bdg. 19.95 (*978-0-9754728-9-7(5)*) MidAmerica Publishing Co. (Bear Hug Bks.).

Cowen, Fletcher. Baby Angels. 2005. (Illus.). 16p. (J). (gr. k-ps). bds. 6.99 (978-0-7636-2896-3(4)) Candlewick Pr.

Cowling, Douglas. Vivaldi's Ring of Mystery. Fernandez, Laura & Jacobson, Rick, illus. 2004. 49p. (J). pap. (*978-0-439-96904-8(2)*, North Winds Pr) Scholastic Canada, Ltd.

Cox, Phil Roxbee, ed. Find the Duck. Cartwright, Stephen, illus. 2004. (Find It Board Bks.). 10p. (J). (ps up). 3.95 (978-0-7460-3821-5(6)) EDC Publishing.

Crafty Inventions. 2005. (C). (gr. 4-6). 319.20 (978-1-4048-1057-0(9)) Picture Window Bks.

Crews, Donald. Freight Train/Tren de Carga. Crews, Donald, illus. 24p. (J). 2008. pap. 7.99 (*978-0-06-056204-5(8)*); 2003. (SPA., Illus.). 16.99 (978-0-06-056202-1(1)) HarperCollins Pubs. (Rayo).

Crews, Donald. Night at the Fair. Crews, Donald, illus. 1998. (Illus.). 32p. (J). (ps-3). 16.99 (978-0-688-11483-1(0)) HarperCollins Pubs.

Crews, Nina. A High, Low, Near, Far, Loud, Quiet Story. 1999. (Illus.). 24p. (J). (ps-3). 15.89 (978-0-688-16795-0(0)) HarperCollins Pubs.

Cronin, Doreen. Clic, Clac, Muu: Vacas Escritoras. Rioja, Alberto Jiménez, tr. Lewin, Betsy, illus. Tr. of CLICK, CLACK, MOO: COWS THAT TYPE. (SPA.). (J). (gr. k-2). 15.00 (978-1-930332-28-7(9), LC4357) Lectorum Pubns., Inc.

—Clic, Clac, Muu: Vacas Escritoras. 2004. Tr. of CLICK, CLACK, MOO: COWS THAT TYPE. (SPA.). (J). (ps-4). 24.95 incl. audio (978-1-55592-155-2(8)) Weston Woods Studios, Inc.

—Click, Clack, Moo: Cows That Type. braille ed. 2004. (Illus.). (J). (gr. k-3). spiral bd. (978-0-616-07227-1(9)) Canadian National Institute for the Blind/Institut National Canadien pour les Aveugles.

—Dooby Dooby Moo. Lewin, Betsy, illus. 2006. 40p. (J). (ps-2). 16.95 (978-0-689-84507-9(3)) Simon & Schuster Children's Publishing.

—Duck for President. Lewin, Betsy, illus. 2004. 40p. (J). 15.95 (978-0-689-86377-6(2)) Simon & Schuster Children's Publishing.

Cross, Gillian. Sam Sorts It Out. Mier, Colin, illus. 2005. 24p. (J). lib. bdg. 22.65 (*978-1-59646-702-6(9)*) Dingles & Co.

Cullimore, Stan. Alien Swap. Schon, Nick, illus. 2005. 24p. (J). lib. bdg. 22.65 (*978-1-59646-744-6(4)*) Dingles & Co.

Cumpleanos de Paco. 2001. (Let's Start Teacher's Pets Ser.).Tr. of Desmond's Birthday Party. (SPA., Illus.). 32p. (J). (ps-3). (978-968-5308-19-9(5), Silver Dolphin en Español) Advanced Marketing, S. de R. L. de C. V.

Cunliffe, John. Postman Pat & the Goat's Supper. (Illus.). 20p. (J). (978-0-340-71437-9(9), Hodder & Stoughton) Hodder General Publishing Division.

—Postman Pat Makes a Clock. (Illus.). 20p. (J). pap. 11.99 (978-0-340-73718-7(2), Hodder & Stoughton) Hodder General Publishing Division GBR. *Dist:* Trafalgar Square Publishing.

—Postman Pat Surprise Breakfast. (Illus.). 24p. (J). (978-0-340-71433-1(6), Hodder & Stoughton) Hodder General Publishing Division.

—Postman Pats Special Delivery Bind. (Illus.). 94p. (J). 22.99 (978-0-340-71055-5(1), Hodder & Stoughton) Hodder General Publishing Division GBR. *Dist:* Trafalgar Square Publishing.

Curren, Joan E. The Springy, Slingy Sling. Jones, Doug, illus. 1998. (Arch Bks.). (ENG.). 16p. (J). (gr. k-4). 1.99 (978-0-570-07549-3(1), 59-1522GJ) Concordia Publishing Hse.

Currie, Robin. Baby Bible 123. 2005. (Baby Bible Ser.). (Illus.). 48p. (J). bds. 12.99 (978-0-7814-3906-0(X), 078143906X) Cook, David C. Publishing Co.

Curry, Casey. I Remember You Today: An Interactive Picturebook for Children Dealing with the Loss of a Sibling or Parent. 2003. (Illus.). 24p. (J). wbk. ed. (978-1-884878-15-2(6)) Annapolis Publishing Co.

Custer, Jason. Everyday Monsters. 2005. (J). lib. bdg. 19.95 (*978-0-9754728-3-5(6)*, Bear Hug Bks.) MidAmerica Publishing Co.

Cutbill, Andy, illus. Albie & the Big Race. 2004. 32p. (J). pap. 9.99 (978-0-00-712212-7(8)) HarperCollins Pubs. Ltd. GBR. *Dist:* Trafalgar Square Publishing.

—Albie Big Race. 2004. 32p. (J). 20.00 (978-0-00-717895-7(6)) HarperCollins Pubs. Ltd. GBR. *Dist:* Independent Pubs. Group.

Czernecki, Stefan. Lilliput 5357. 2005. (Illus.). 44p. (J). 16.95 (978-1-894965-32-3(9)) Simply Read Bks. CAN. *Dist:* Perseus Distribution.

Daisy Garden, 4 bks. 2002. (J). bds. 7.98 (978-0-7525-8731-8(5)) Parragon, Inc.

Dalmatian Press Staff. Inside My Easter Basket. 2002. (Illus.). 5p. (J). (ps). bds. 6.95 (978-1-57759-640-0(4)) Dalmatian Pr.

Damschroder, Scott. The Crazy Carnival Clown We Call Croc. 2006. (Illus.). 40p. (J). lib. bdg. 19.95 (***978-0-9754728-1-1(X)*** , Blue Foot Pr.) MidAmerica Publishing Co.

D'Andrea, Deborah. Picture Me Letters A,B,C. 2002. (Learning Basics Ser.). 10p. (J). (ps up). bds. 4.99 (978-1-57151-556-8(9)) Playhouse Publishing.

D'Andrea, Deborah, concept. Picture Me Happy Halloween. 2001. (Picture Me Ser.). 10p. (J). (ps up). bds. 4.99 (978-1-57151-593-3(3)) Playhouse Publishing.

Danger Alert: Picture Book (English) 2006. (Illus.). 47p. (J). (978-1-933934-03-7(4)) Educational Adventures.

Danger Alert: Picture Book (English) 8x8. 2007. (J). (***978-1-933934-39-6(5)***) Educational Adventures.

Danger Alert: Picture Book (English) 9x9 with Snipe. 2007. (J). (***978-1-933934-49-5(2)***) Educational Adventures.

Dann, Penny. The Secret Fairy Party Book: Or How to Have Your Own Secret Fairy Party. Dann, Penny, illus. 1999. (Secret Fairy Ser.). (Illus.). 16p. (J). (ps-3). pap. 14.95 (978-0-531-30183-8(4) , Orchard Bks.) Scholastic, Inc.

Davenport, Andrew. Here Come the Teletubbies. ed. 2004. (Illus.). (J). (ps-2). spiral bd. (978-0-616-03029-5(0)); spiral bd. (978-0-616-04551-0(4)) Canadian National Institute for the Blind/Institut National Canadien pour les Aveugles.

David C. Cook. Nursery Time. 2003. 175p. audio compact disk 29.99 (978-0-7814-4055-4(6) , 0781440556) Cook, David C. Publishing Co.

David, Luke. Sight for Sore Eyes. Goldberg, Barry, tr. Goldberg, Barry, illus. 1999. (Rugrats Ser.). 32p. (J). (ps-3). per. 3.50 (978-0-671-02866-4(9) , Simon & Schuster Children's Publishing) Simon & Schuster Children's Publishing.

—Sight for Sore Eyes. 1999. (gr. k-3). lib. bdg. 11.25 (978-0-613-15977-7(2)) Tandem Library Bks.

Davidson, Ellen. I Miss You. Wise, Noreen, ed. Schneider, Rex, illus. 2000. 32p. (YA). (ps). pap. 5.95 (978-1-58584-354-1(7)) Huckleberry Pr.

Davis, Aubrey. The Enormous potato. Petricic, Dusan, illus. 2001. 32p. (J). (gr. k-3). (978-1-55074-669-3(3)) Kids Can Pr., Ltd.

Davis, Caroline, illus. It's Christmas! 2004. (Christmas Wood Tops Ser.). 18p. (J). bds. 4.95 (978-0-7641-5752-3(3)) Barron's Educational Series, Inc.

—Trim the Tree! 2004. (Christmas Wood Tops Ser.). 18p. (J). bds. 4.95 (978-0-7641-5755-4(8)) Barron's Educational Series, Inc.

Davis, Guy. Barney Says "Night-Night" McKee, Darren, illus. 1998. (Barney Ser.). 12p. (J). (ps-k). 6.95 (978-1-57064-455-9(1)) Scholastic, Inc.

Davis, Guy & Valentine-Ruppe, June. Baby Bop's Blankey. 1999. (Barney Ser.). (Illus.). 14p. (J). (ps-k). 5.95 (978-1-57064-613-3(9)) Scholastic, Inc.

Davis, Guy, et al. Barney's Search & Spot Book Set. 2001. (Barney Ser.). 9p. (J). pap. 10.99 (978-1-58668-127-2(3)) Scholastic, Inc.

Davis, Katie. Who Hoots? 2004. (Illus.). 36p. (J). pap. 7.00 (978-0-15-205027-6(2) , Voyager Bks./Libros Viajeros) Harcourt Children's Bks.

Davis, Lee. P. B. Bear's Big Board Book. 2001. (P. B. Bear Board Books Ser.). (Illus.). 12p. (J). (ps). bds. 6.99 (978-0-7894-2858-5(X) , D K Ink) Dorling Kindersley Publishing, Inc.

Davis, Nancy. Who Uses a Wrench? Popular Mechanics Staff, ed. 2004. (Popular Mechanics for Kids Ser.). (Illus.). 10p. (J). bds. 4.95 (978-1-58816-372-1(5)) Hearst Bks.

Davoll, Barbara. Bedtime Snuggles with Christopher. Hockerman, Dennis, illus. 2000. 40p. (J). (ps-3). 9.99 (978-0-8024-5395-2(3)) Moody Pubs.

Day, Alexandra. Carl's Birthday. Day, Alexandra, illus. 2002. (Illus.). (J). 22.13 (978-0-7587-2194-5(3)) Book Wholesalers, Inc.

DC Comics Staff & Simonson, Louise. Superman Returns: Strange Visitor. 2nd novel rev. ed. 2006. 144p. (J). (ps-17). pap. 4.99 (978-0-316-17799-3(7)) Little, Brown Bks. for Young Readers.

de Brunhoff, Laurent. Babar's Counting Book. 2003. (Illus.). 32p. (J). (ps-k). 16.95 (978-0-8109-4243-1(7)) Abrams, Harry N. , Inc.

de Maeyer, Gregie & Vanmechelen, Koen. Juul. 2003. (SPA., Illus.). 204p. (978-84-85334-90-2(6)) Loguez Ediciones ESP. *Dist:* Lectorum Pubns., Inc.

de Paola, Tomie. Days of the Blackbird: A Tale of Northern Italy. de Paola, Tomie, illus. 2005. (Illus.). 32p. (J). (ps-k). reprint ed. pap. 5.99 (978-0-14-240271-9(0) , Puffin) Penguin Group (USA) Inc.

—Marcus Colors: Red, Yellow & Blue. 2003. (SPA., Illus.). 14p. (J). (ps-1). bds. 5.99 (978-0-399-24010-2(1) , Putnam Juvenile) Penguin Group (USA) Inc.

—Nana Upstairs & Nana Downstairs. 2000. (Illus.). 32p. (J). (ps-3). pap. 6.99 (978-0-698-11836-2(7) , Putnam Juvenile) Penguin Group (USA) Inc.

—Nana Upstairs & Nana Downstairs. unabr. ed. 2006. (J). (gr. k-3). pap. 17.95 incl. audio (978-0-8045-6943-9(6)); pap. 19.95 incl. audio compact disk (978-0-8045-4157-2(4)) Spoken Arts, Inc.

—Nana Upstairs & Nana Downstairs. 2000. (gr. k-3). lib. bdg. 15.30 (978-0-8085-2686-5(3)) Tandem Library Bks.

De Roma, Giuseppino. Francis of Assisi. (Illus.). 31p. 7.95 (978-1-875570-64-5(0)) St Pauls Pubns. AUS. *Dist:* Alba Hse.

De Smet, Marian & Meijer, Marja. Encerrada: Anna's Tight Squeeze. Pacheco, Laura Emilia, tr. Uitgeverij, Clavis, illus. 2004. 28p. (J). 14.95 (978-970-29-0665-0(2)) Santillana USA Publishing Co., Inc.

Deedy, Carmen Agra. The Secret of Old Zeb. White, Michael P., illus. 2002. 36p. (J). (gr. 1-5). pap. 8.95 (978-1-56145-280-4(7)) Peachtree Pubs., Ltd.

Degen, Bruce. Degen Picture Book. Date not set. (Illus.). 32p. (J). (ps-1). 5.99 (978-0-06-443579-6(2)) HarperCollins Pubs.

del Sur, Duendes. Search for Scooby Snacks. 2000. (gr. k-3). lib. bdg. 11.80 (978-0-613-26871-4(7)) Tandem Library Bks.

Delittle, Cathy. Jungle Parade. Delittle, Cathy, illus. 1998. (Illus.). 11p. (J). (ps-1). spiral bd. 7.95 (978-1-892633-03-3(5) , OOCD201) Delittle Storyteller Co.

—Peanut Butter Bob. Delittle, Cathy, illus. 1998. (Illus.). 9p. (J). (ps-1). spiral bd. 7.95 (978-1-892633-00-2(0) , OOCD203) Delittle Storyteller Co.

—There's a Skunk in My Diaper. Delittle, Cathy, illus. 1998. (Illus.). 10p. (J). (ps-1). spiral bd. 7.95 (978-1-892633-06-4(X) , OOCD207) Delittle Storyteller Co.

—What Do You See When You Sleep? Book-in-a-Bag. Delittle, Cathy, illus. 1998. (Illus.). 16p. (J). (ps-1). spiral bd. 9.95 (978-1-892633-07-1(8) , OOCD205) Delittle Storyteller Co.

Denou, Violeta. Teo en el Dia del Libro. 2001. (SPA., Illus.). 32p. (J). (gr. k-2). (978-84-480-0351-7(9) , TM1800) Timun Mas, Editorial S.A. ESP. *Dist:* Lectorum Pubns., Inc.

Denver, John. Ancient Rhymes, a Dolphin Lullaby: With Audio CD & Score. Canyon, Christopher, illus. 2004. (Sharing Nature with Children Book Ser.). 36p. (J). (ps-6). 19.95 incl. audio compact disk (978-1-58469-064-1(X)) Dawn Pubns.

DePaola, Tomie. Angels, Angels Everywhere. DePaola, Tomie, illus. 2005. (Illus.). 28p. (J). (ps-3). 14.99 (978-0-399-24370-7(4) , Putnam Juvenile) Penguin Group (USA) Inc.

—Big Anthony & the Magic Ring. DePaola, Tomie, illus. 1999. (Illus.). (J). (ps-17). lib. bdg. 13.40 (978-0-88103-359-5(6)) Tandem Library Bks.

—Tomie's Mother Goose Flies Again. DePaola, Tomie, illus. 2005. (Illus.). 30p. (J). (ps-k). pap. 7.99 (978-0-399-24466-7(2) , Putnam Juvenile) Penguin Group (USA) Inc.

Depisco, Dorothea. Beetle Bugs Party: A Counting Book. Parry, Jo, illus. 2005. 10p. (J). (ps-ps). 10.95 (978-1-58117-415-1(2) , Intervisual/Piggy Toes) Dalmatian Pr.

DePrisco, Dorothea. What Will I Become? A Changing Picture Book. Lunsford, Annie, illus. 2002. (Learning Pictures Ser.). 10p. (ps). 7.95 (978-1-58117-160-0(9) , Intervisual/Piggy Toes) Dalmatian Pr.

—Who Lives Here? A Changing Picture Book. Lunsford, Annie, illus. 2002. (Learning Pictures Ser.). 10p. (J). (ps). 7.95 (978-1-58117-159-4(5) , Intervisual/Piggy Toes) Dalmatian Pr.

Dergachov, Oleg. The Yellow Elves. Andryczyk, Mark, tr. from UKR. 2004. (Illus.). 14p. (J). pap. (***978-0-9735003-0-1(1)***) StudioNib Publishing.

Dewan, Ted. Bing: Go Picnic. 2005. (Illus.). 24p. (J). (gr. k-ps). 5.99 (978-0-385-75056-1(0) , Fickling, David Bks.) Random Hse. Children's Bks.

—Bing: Make Music. 2005. (Illus.). 24p. (J). (gr. k-ps). 5.99 (978-0-385-75057-8(9) , Fickling, David Bks.) Random Hse. Children's Bks.

Dhami, Narinder. Monster under the Stairs. Spoor, Mike, illus. 2005. 24p. (J). lib. bdg. 22.65 (***978-1-59646-718-7(5)***) Dingles & Co.

—Samosa Thief. Blundell, Tony, illus. 2005. 24p. (J). lib. bdg. 22.65 (***978-1-59646-708-8(8)***) Dingles & Co.

Diaper Days Songs. (Baby Looney Tunes Song Bks.). (Illus.). 16p. (J). (ps). 7.98 (978-0-7853-1612-1(4) , PI112) Publications International, Ltd.

Diaz, James, illus. Counting. 1999. (Flip-Pop Ser.). 10p. (J). (ps-k). 9.95 (978-1-58117-068-9(8) , Intervisual/Piggy Toes) Dalmatian Pr.

Dillon, Leo & Dillon, Diane. Rap a Tap Tap: Here's Bojangles - Think of That! Dillon, Leo & Dillon, Diane, illus. 2002. (Illus.). 32p. (J). pap. 15.95 (978-0-590-47883-0(4) , Blue Sky Pr., The) Scholastic, Inc.

DiMare, Loren Spiotta. Rockwell: A Boy & His Dog. Miller, Cliff, illus. 2005. 32p. (J). 14.95 (978-0-7641-5790-5(6)) Barron's Educational Series, Inc.

Dinosaurs. (Illus.). (J). (ps-6). pap. 2.95 (978-0-565-01078-2(6)) Natural History Museum Pubns. GBR. *Dist:* Parkwest Pubns., Inc.

Dinosaurs Lift the Flap. 2000. 10p. (J). 4.99 (978-0-7364-1040-3(6)) Disney Pr.

DiPucchio, Kelly S. Liberty's Journey. Egielski, Richard, illus. 2004. 32p. (ps-2). 15.99 (978-0-7868-1876-1(X)) Hyperion Bks. for Children.

Discovering Animal Habitats: Interactive Playbook. 1998. (Illus.). 10p. (J). (ps-6). 19.99 (978-1-890647-07-0(1)) RC2 Corp.

Disney Press Staff. Book of Pooh Tabbed Board Book, Bk. 1. 2002. 14p. (J). bds. (978-0-7868-3357-3(2)) Hachette Bk. Group.

Disney Staff. Follow the Leader. Disney Staff, illus. 1999. (Pooh's Learn & Grow Ser.: Vol. 2). (Illus.). 12p. (J). 3.49 (978-1-57973-036-9(1)) Advance Pubs. LLC.

—Let's Discover Animals Playtime Learning Box: With Winnie the Pooh & Friends. 2004. (Illus.). 128p. (ps-1). 19.99 (978-0-7868-0934-9(5) , Disney Editions) Disney Pr.

—Mickey Mouse & Minnie Mouse: Story & Illustrations. deluxe ed. 1999. (Illus.). 32p. (J). (ps-3). reprint ed. pap. 100.00 (978-1-55709-215-1(X)) Applewood Bks.

—Pooh's Rainy Day. Disney Staff, illus. 1999. (Pooh's Learn & Grow Ser.: Vol. 10). (Illus.). 12p. (J). 3.49 (978-1-57973-044-4(2)) Advance Pubs. LLC.

Disney Staff, ed. Toy Story 2: Buzz's Story. 1999. (Toy Story 2 Ser.). (Illus.). 48p. (J). (ps-3). 10.99 (978-0-7868-3233-0(9)) Disney Pr.

Dixon, Ann. The Blueberry Shoe. Zerbetz, Evon, illus. 1999. 32p. (J). (ps-3). 22.95 (978-0-88240-518-6(7) , Alaska Northwest Bks.) Graphic Arts Ctr. Publishing Co.

DK Publishing. Baby Loves. 2008. 12p. (J). (ps-3). bds. 6.99 (***978-0-7566-3486-5(5)***) Dorling Kindersley Publishing, Inc.

DK Publishing Staff. Baby ABC. 1998. (Soft-to-Touch Bks.). (Illus.). 16p. (J). (ps-k). bds. 4.99 (978-0-7894-3648-1(5)) Dorling Kindersley Publishing, Inc.

—Fire Truck. 2003. (Wheelies Ser.). (Illus.). 12p. (J). (ps-3). bds. 6.99 (978-0-7894-9712-3(3)) Dorling Kindersley Publishing, Inc.

—Home: Touch & Feel. 1998. (Touch & Feel Ser.). (Illus.). 12p. (J). (ps-k). bds. 6.99 (978-0-7894-2917-9(9)) Dorling Kindersley Publishing, Inc.

—My Big Machine Book. 1999. (Big Tab Board Books Ser.). (Illus.). 8p. (J). (ps-3). bds. 9.99 (978-0-7894-4326-7(0)) Dorling Kindersley Publishing, Inc.

—Wild Animals. 1998. (Touch & Feel Ser.). (Illus.). 12p. (J). (ps-k). bds. 6.99 (978-0-7894-2918-6(7)) Dorling Kindersley Publishing, Inc.

Dobson, Shirley. God Loves You! Coloring Book: A Read-Aloud Coloring Book about God's Plan for Salvation. 1998. 16p. (ps-3). pap. 1.49 (978-0-8307-2329-4(3) , Gospel Light) Gospel Light Pubns.

Dodd, Emma. Grande o Pequena, Es Mi Pelota. 2004. (Imagenes cambiantes Ser.). (SPA., Illus.). 16p. (ps). pap. 13.95 (978-84-7864-816-0(X)) Combel Editorial, S.A. ESP. *Dist:* Independent Pubs. Group.

—Tachan! El Azul, El Amarillo Y El Conejito. 2004. (Imagenes cambiantes Ser.). (SPA., Illus.). 16p. 13.95 (978-84-7864-817-7(8)) Combel Editorial, S.A. ESP. *Dist:* Independent Pubs. Group.

Dodson, Emma. Badly Drawn Dog. 2004. (Illus.). 32p. (J). 14.95 (978-0-7641-5814-8(7)) Barron's Educational Series, Inc.

Doepker, David. Animal Babies. Sterling Publishing Company Staff, ed. 2004. (Illus.). 16p. (J). (ps). bds. 4.95 (978-1-4027-1717-8(2)) Sterling Publishing Co., Inc.

—Farm Babies. Sterling Publishing Company Staff, ed. 2004. (Illus.). 16p. (J). (ps). bds. 4.95 (978-1-4027-1714-7(8)) Sterling Publishing Co., Inc.

Dogi, Fiametta. God Made Animal Families. Dogi, Fiametta, illus. 1999. (God Made Animals Ser.). (Illus.). 10p. (J). (ps). bds. 3.99 (978-0-7847-0883-5(5) , 03760, Bean Sprouts) Standard Publishing.

—God Made Baby Animals. Dogi, Fiametta, illus. 1999. (God Made Animals Ser.). (Illus.). 10p. (J). (ps). bds. 3.99 (978-0-7847-0882-8(7) , 03758, Bean Sprouts) Standard Publishing.

—God Made Jungle Animals. Dogi, Fiametta, illus. 1999. (God Made Animals Ser.). (Illus.). 10p. (J). (ps). bds. 3.99 (978-0-7847-0881-1(9) , 03757, Bean Sprouts) Standard Publishing.

—God Made Sea Animals. Dogi, Fiametta, illus. 1999. (God Made Animals Ser.). (Illus.). 10p. (J). (ps). bds. 3.99 (978-0-7847-0884-2(3) , 03761, Bean Sprouts) Standard Publishing.

Doherty, Gillian. 1001 Animales Que Buscar. 2004. (1001 Things to Spot Ser.).Tr. of 1001 Animals to Spot. (SPA., Illus.). (J). pap. 6.95 (978-0-7460-5081-1(X)) EDC Publishing.

Domm, Kristin. The Hatchling's Journey: A Blanding's Turtle Story. Domm, Jeff, illus. 2003. pap. 8.95 (978-1-55109-438-0(X)) Nimbus Publishing, Ltd. CAN. *Dist:* National Bk. Network.

Dorfman, Craig. I Knew You Could! A Book for All the Stops in Your Life. Ong, Cristina, illus. 2003. (Little Engine That Could Ser.). 32p. (J). (gr. 1-2). 11.99 (978-0-448-43148-2(3) , Grosset & Dunlap) Penguin Group (USA) Inc.

Dorling Kindersley Publishing Staff. Airplane. 2004. (Dk Picture Stickers Ser.). 16p. (J). pap. 3.99 (978-0-7566-0226-0(2)) Dorling Kindersley Publishing, Inc.

—Animal Colors. 2000. (Touch & Feel Ser.). (Illus.). 12p. (J). (ps). bds. 6.99 (978-0-7894-5221-4(9)) Dorling Kindersley Publishing, Inc.

—Baby 1 2 3. 1998. (Soft-To-Touch Book Ser.). (Illus.). 16p. (J). (ps-k). bds. 4.99 (978-0-7894-3649-8(3)) Dorling Kindersley Publishing, Inc.

—Baby Colors. 1998. (Soft-To-Touch Book Ser.). (Illus.). 16p. (J). (ps-k). bds. 4.99 (978-0-7894-3651-1(5)) Dorling Kindersley Publishing, Inc.

—Baby Faces. 1998. (Soft-to-Touch Books Ser.). (Illus.). 16p. (J). (ps). bds. 4.99 (978-0-7894-3650-4(7)) Dorling Kindersley Publishing, Inc.

—Baby Talk. 2005. (Baby Fun Ser.). (Illus.). 20p. (J). (ps-3). bds. 4.99 (978-0-7566-0986-3(0)) Dorling Kindersley Publishing, Inc.

—Beach. 2004. (Dk Picture Stickers Ser.). 16p. (J). pap. 3.99 (978-0-7566-0247-5(5)) Dorling Kindersley Publishing, Inc.

—The Bus. 1999. (Wheelies Ser.). (Illus.). 10p. (J). (gr. k-2). bds. 5.99 (978-0-7894-4731-9(2)) Dorling Kindersley Publishing, Inc.

—Christmas Board Book. 2003. (My First Board Books (Bilingual) Ser.). (Illus.). 36p. (J). bds. 6.99 (978-0-7894-9520-4(1)) Dorling Kindersley Publishing, Inc.

—Los Colores / Colors. 2004. (My 1ST Board Books Ser.). 24p. (J). (ps-3). bds. 3.99 (978-0-7566-0440-0(0)) Dorling Kindersley Publishing, Inc.

—Dump Truck. Deschamps, Nicola, ed. Leeney, Richard, photos by. 2000. (Jumbo Shaped Board Books Ser.). (Illus.). 12p. (J). (ps-k). bds. 6.99 (978-0-7894-6532-0(9)) Dorling Kindersley Publishing, Inc.

—Dump Truck. 1998. (Wheelies Ser.). (Illus.). 10p. (J). bds. 5.99 (978-0-7894-3710-5(4)) Dorling Kindersley Publishing, Inc.

—Excavadores y Volquetas/Diggers & Dumpers. 2004. (Things That Go Board Books Ser.). (ENG & SPA.). 10p. (J). bds. 3.99 (978-0-7566-0443-1(5)) Dorling Kindersley Publishing, Inc.

—Fire Engine. (Touch & Feel Ser.). (Illus.). 12p. (J). 2002. bds. 6.99 (978-0-7894-8855-8(8)); 1998. bds. 5.99 (978-0-7894-3711-2(2)) Dorling Kindersley Publishing, Inc.

—Las Formas / Shapes. 2004. (My 1ST Board Books Ser.). 24p. (J). (ps-3). bds. 3.99 (978-0-7566-0441-7(9)) Dorling Kindersley Publishing, Inc.

—Four Seasons. 2004. (Baby Genius Ser.). (Illus.). 16p. (J). bds. 6.99 (978-0-7566-0266-6(1)) Dorling Kindersley Publishing, Inc.

—Humpty Dumpty. 2004. (Baby Games Ser.). 16p. (J). bds. 5.99 (978-0-7566-0258-1(0)) Dorling Kindersley Publishing, Inc.

—Jungle. 2004. (Dk Picture Stickers Ser.). 16p. (J). pap. 3.99 (978-0-7566-0248-2(3)) Dorling Kindersley Publishing, Inc.

—Maquinas Rescate / Rescue Machines. 2004. (My 1ST Board Books Ser.). 22p. (J). bds. 3.99 (978-0-7566-0445-5(1)) Dorling Kindersley Publishing, Inc.

—Maqunias Rapidas / Speedy Machines. 2004. (My 1ST Board Books Ser.). 24p. (J). bds. 3.99 (978-0-7566-0446-2(X)) Dorling Kindersley Publishing, Inc.

—Monster Truck. 1999. (Wheelies Ser.). (Illus.). 10p. (J). (ps-k). bds. 5.99 (978-0-7894-4734-0(7)) Dorling Kindersley Publishing, Inc.

—The Motorcycle. 1999. (Wheelies Ser.). (Illus.). 10p. (J). (ps-k). bds. 5.99 (978-0-7894-4733-3(9)) Dorling Kindersley Publishing, Inc.

—My First Animal Lift-the-Flap Book. 2000. (My First Bks.). (Illus.). 12p. (J). (ps-3). 9.99 (978-0-7894-6515-3(9)) Dorling Kindersley Publishing, Inc.

—My First Phonics. 2004. 36p. (J). bds. 5.99 (978-0-7566-0282-6(3)) Dorling Kindersley Publishing, Inc.

—My First Vacation. 2004. (Barbie Sticker Books Ser.). 16p. (J). pap. 6.99 (978-0-7566-0336-6(6)) Dorling Kindersley Publishing, Inc.

—My First Word Sticker Book. 1999. (My First Ser.). (Illus.). 16p. (J). (gr. k-2). pap. 6.99 (978-0-7894-4686-2(3)) Dorling Kindersley Publishing, Inc.

—My Little Things That Go Carrying Case. 2003. (Illus.). (J). bds. 9.99 (978-0-7894-9907-3(X)) Dorling Kindersley Publishing, Inc.

—Los Numeros/numbers. 2004. (My 1ST Board Books Ser.). 24p. (J). bds. 3.99 (978-0-7566-0439-4(7)) Dorling Kindersley Publishing, Inc.

—Out & About. 2003. (Baby's World Ser.). (Illus.). 36p. (J). bds. 6.99 (978-0-7894-8578-6(8)) Dorling Kindersley Publishing, Inc.

—Racing Car. 1998. (Wheelies Ser.). (Illus.). 12p. (J). (ps-3). bds. 5.99 (978-0-7894-3712-9(0)) Dorling Kindersley Publishing, Inc.

—Zoo Animals. 2004. (Baby Genius Ser.). (Illus.). 16p. (J). bds. 6.99 (978-0-7566-0271-0(8)) Dorling Kindersley Publishing, Inc.

Dorling Kindersley Publishing Staff, ed. Buenas Noches, Bebe! / Good Night, Baby! 2004. (SPA & ENG., Illus.). 18p. (J). bds. 4.99 (978-0-7566-0438-7(9)) Dorling Kindersley Publishing, Inc.

—Do Cars Fly? 2005. (DK See Through Ser.). (Illus.). 21p. (J). 6.99 (978-0-7566-0774-6(4)) Dorling Kindersley Publishing, Inc.

—Do Gloves Go on Feet? 2005. (Dk See-throughs Ser.). (Illus.). 21p. (J). 6.99 (978-0-7566-0775-3(2)) Dorling Kindersley Publishing, Inc.

—Fairy. 2005. (Make-Believe Ser.). (Illus.). 12p. (J). bds. 6.99 (978-0-7566-1016-6(8)) Dorling Kindersley Publishing, Inc.

—Good Morning, Baby! 2004. (SPA & ENG., Illus.). 18p. (J). bds. 4.99 (978-0-7566-0437-0(0)) Dorling Kindersley Publishing, Inc.

—Jungle. 2004. (Dk Eyewitness Books Ser.). (Illus.). 72p. (J). 15.99 (978-0-7566-0694-7(2)) Dorling Kindersley Publishing, Inc.

—Princess. 2005. (Make-Believe Ser.). (Illus.). 12p. (J). bds. 6.99 (978-0-7566-1017-3(6)) Dorling Kindersley Publishing, Inc.

—Sparkly Ballerina. 2005. (Illus.). 10p. (J). bds. 5.99 (978-0-7566-0995-5(X)) Dorling Kindersley Publishing, Inc.

—Sparkly Princess. 2005. (Illus.). 12p. (J). bds. 5.99 (978-0-7566-0996-2(8)) Dorling Kindersley Publishing, Inc.

Dorling Kindersley Publishing Staff & Millard, Anne. Good Morning. 2002. (Baby's World Shaped Board Bks.). (Illus.). 12p. (J). bds. 4.99 (978-0-7894-8563-2(X)) Dorling Kindersley Publishing, Inc.

—In the Jungle. 2002. (Little Windows Ser.). (Illus.). 16p. (J). bds. 6.95 (978-0-7894-8570-0(2)) Dorling Kindersley Publishing, Inc.

—In the Sea. 2002. (Little Windows Ser.). (Illus.). 16p. (J). 6.99 (978-0-7894-8571-7(0)) Dorling Kindersley Publishing, Inc.

Dougherty, Terri. The Traveling Shoes. Haugen, Ryan, illus. 2006. (Read-It! Readers Ser.). 24p. (J). (ps-3). 18.60 (978-1-4048-1588-9(0)) Picture Window Bks.

Douglas, Vincent & School Specialty Publishing Staff. Dolch Sight Word Activities, Vol. 1. 2002. (Starburst Spectrum Workbook Ser.). (Illus.). 150p. (J). (gr. k-1). pap. 9.95 (978-1-56189-917-3(8) , American Education Publishing) School Specialty Publishing.

—Hidden Pictures. 2003. (Homework Helpers Ser.). (Illus.). 32p. (J). (gr. k-1). pap. 2.99 (978-0-7696-2915-5(6) , American Education Publishing) School Specialty Publishing.

—Numbers Hidden Pictures. 2003. (Homework Helpers Ser.). (Illus.). 32p. (J). (gr. k-1). pap. 2.99 (978-0-7696-2925-4(3) , American Education Publishing) School Specialty Publishing.

P Q R

—The Ugly Duckling. 2004. (Handle Book with CD Ser.). (Illus.). 24p. (J). 3.99 (978-1-58845-730-1(3)) School Specialty Publishing.

Dow, Jill. Hazel & Clover's Great Escape. 1999. (Windy Edge Farm Ser.). (Illus.). 32p. (J). (ps-2). pap. 7.99 (978-0-7112-0732-5(1)) Lincoln, Frances Ltd. GBR. *Dist:* Transition Vendor.

—Moonbeam's Big Splash. Dow, Jill, illus. 1999. (Windy Edge Farm Ser.). (Illus.). 32p. (J). (ps-2). pap. 7.99 (978-0-7112-1028-8(4)) Lincoln, Frances Ltd. GBR. *Dist:* Transition Vendor.

Dower, Laura. Bubble Trouble. 2000. (gr. k-3). lib. bdg. 11.25 (978-0-613-24426-8(5)) Tandem Library Bks.

Dowling, Paul. Beans on Toast: Level Three, Blue. Dowling, Paul, illus. 1999. (Reading Together Ser.). (Illus.). (J). pap. (978-0-7636-0875-0(0)) Candlewick Pr.

—The Night Journey. 2003. 12p. (J). 7.95 (978-1-57717-290-1(6)) New Line Bks.

Doyle, Alfreda C. Alfreda's Coloring Books: A Directory to Reproduce. Doyle, Alfreda C., illus. 1998. (Illus.). 62p. (J). (gr. 4-9). ring bd. 39.95 (978-1-56820-247-1(4)) Story Time Stories That Rhyme.

—ZueToo Masqke Go to the Gallery: Story Rhyme Coloring Book. 1998. (Illus.). 24p. (J). (gr. 3-8). pap. 8.95 (978-1-56820-328-7(4)) Story Time Stories That Rhyme.

Doyle, Charlotte. Supermarket! Westcott, Nadine Bernard, tr. Westcott, Nadine Bernard, illus. 2004. (Super Study Picture Book Ser.). 24p. (J). (gr. k-ps). 8.99 (978-0-7636-2218-3(4)) Candlewick Pr.

Doyle, Charlotte L. You Can't Catch Me. Litzinger, Rosanne, illus. 1998. (Growing Tree Ser.). 24p. (J). (gr. 3 up). 9.95 (978-0-694-01038-7(3) , Harper Festival) HarperCollins Pubs.

Doyle, Malachy. King Donal's Secret. Watson, Richard, illus. 2005. 24p. (J). lib. bdg. 22.65 (*978-1-59646-740-8(1)) Dingles & Co.

—Rory's Lost His Voice. Semple, David, illus. 2005. 24p. (J). lib. bdg. 22.65 (*978-1-59646-714-9(2)) Dingles & Co.

Doyle, Malachy. Storm Cats. Trotter, Stuart, illus. 2002. 32p. (J). (ps-1). 15.95 (978-0-689-84464-5(6) , McElderry, Margaret K.) Simon & Schuster Children's Publishing.

Doyle, Tara. Little Bunny's Easter Surprise. McQueen, Lucinda, illus. 2005. 8p. (J). bds. 1.99 (978-0-439-69682-1(8) , Cartwheel Bks.) Scholastic, Inc.

DPWW. Inspector Gadget Flip Book. 1999. 96p. (ps-3). pap. 3.99 (978-0-7868-4359-6(4)) Disney Pr.

Dracula's Den: Make Hundreds of Funny Faces with Re-Usable Stickers! 1999. (Funny Faces Ser.). (Illus.). 10p. (J). (ps-7). 1.99 (978-1-86091-124-8(2) , 84) Trident Pr. International.

Drops of Water. Date not set. 9.95 (978-0-89868-291-5(6)); pap. 3.95 (978-0-89868-290-8(8)) ARO Publishing Co.

Dugan, Joanne. ABC NYC: A Book about Seeing New York City. 2005. (Illus.). 56p. (J). (ps-1). 15.95 (978-0-8109-5854-8(6)) Abrams, Harry N. , Inc.

Dunbar, Polly. Flyaway Katie. Dunbar, Polly, illus. 2004. (Illus.). 40p. (J). (gr. k-k). 14.99 (978-0-7636-2366-1(0)) Candlewick Pr.

Dunmire, Marjorie S. Faces of the Forests. Dunmire, Marjorie S., illus. 1998. (Illus.). 64p. (Orig.). (J). (gr. 3 up). pap. 5.95 (978-0-942559-08-8(8)) Pegasus Graphics.

Dunn, Charles. Learning with Leonard & Friends: From A to Z. Ovange, Sheila & Groller, Scott, eds. Groller, Matt, illus. l.t. ed. 1998. 64p. (J). (ps-1). 17.95 (978-0-9663240-3-7(X)) Dunn, Charles Camaron.

Dunn, Opal. Little Boat. Paterson, Bettina, illus. rev. ed. 2000. (Track-Me-Back Board Bks.). 12p. (J). (ps-k). 5.95 (978-0-8050-6416-2(8)) , Holt, Henry & Co. Bks. For Young Readers) Holt, Henry & Co.

—Little Plane. Paterson, Bettina, illus. rev. ed. 2000. (Track-Me-Back Board Bks.). 12p. (J). (ps-k). 5.95 (978-0-8050-6418-6(4) , Holt, Henry & Co. Bks. For Young Readers) Holt, Henry & Co.

Durham, Robert. First 1000 Words & Pictures Book. 2000. (Illus.). (J). 9.99 (978-1-57866-092-6(0) , Galahad Bks.) BBS Publishing Corp.

Dwyer, Judy. Storybook Starters. (Illus.). (J). (gr. k-3). pap. (978-1-876367-01-5(6)) Wizard Bks.

Easter Fun. 2003. (Holiday Fun Bks.). 32p. (J). 2.99 (978-0-88724-926-6(4)) Carson-Dellosa Publishing Co., Inc.

Eastman, P. D. The Alphabet Book. 2000. (Bright & Early Board Bks.). (Illus.). 24p. (J). (gr. k-ps). bds. 4.99 (978-0-375-80603-2(2) , Random Hse. Bks. for Young Readers) Random Hse. Children's Bks.

—Ve, Perro, Ve! Go, Dog. Go! Perdomo, Adolfo Perez, tr. 2003. Tr. of Go, Dog, Go!. (SPA & ENG., Illus.). 24p. (J). (gr. k-ps). bds. 4.99 (978-0-375-82361-9(1) , RH Para Ninos) Random Hse. Children's Bks.

Eat! 2002. (Baby Faces Ser.). (Illus.). (J). bds. (978-0-439-33945-2(6)) Scholastic, Inc.

Edens, Cooper. Edens Picture Book, No. 3. Day, Alexandra, illus. Date not set. (J). 14.99 (978-0-06-205153-0(9)) HarperCollins Pubs.

Edgson, Alison, et al. Cinderella. 2006. (Flip up Fairy Tales Ser.). (Illus.). 24p. (J). 9.99 (978-1-904550-46-4(0)) Child's Play-International.

—Hansel & Gretel. 2006. (Illus.). 24p. pap. 5.99 (978-1-904550-73-0(8)); pap. 9.99 (978-1-904550-45-7(2)) Child's Play-International.

Educational Adventures, creator. Blazin' Hot: Picture Book (Spanish) 9x9. 2006. (SPA., Illus.). (J). (*978-0-9770455-4-9(4)) Educational Adventures.

—Cool by the Pool: Picture Book (Spanish) 9x9. 2007. (Illus.). (J). per. (*978-1-933934-72-3(7)) Educational Adventures.

—Danger Alert: Picture Book (Spanish) 9x9. 2006. (Illus.). (J). (*978-1-933934-04-4(2)) Educational Adventures.

—Free Wheelin' Picture Book (Spanish) w/ Snipe. 2006. (Illus.). (J). (*978-0-9770455-6-3(0)) Educational Adventures.

—Poison Patrol: Picture Book (Spanish) 9x9. 2006. (Illus.). (J). (*978-1-933934-00-6(X)) Educational Adventures.

—Street Smarts: Picture Book (Spanish) 9x9. 2007. (Illus.). (J). per. (*978-1-933934-77-8(8)) Educational Adventures.

Edwards, Frank B. A Crowded Ride in the Countryside. Bianchi, John, illus. 1999. (New Reader Ser.). 24p. (J). (ps-1). lib. bdg. 14.95 (978-1-894323-03-1(3)) Pokeweed Pr. CAN. *Dist:* Fitzhenry & Whiteside, Ltd.

—Nightgown Countdown. 1999. (New Reader Ser.). (Illus.). (J). (978-0-606-22035-4(6)) Tandem Library Bks.

—Peek-a-Boo at the Zoo. Bianchi, John, illus. 1999. (New Reader Ser.). 24p. (J). (ps-1). pap. 4.95 (978-1-894323-06-2(8)) Pokeweed Pr. CAN. *Dist:* Fitzhenry & Whiteside, Ltd.

—Snug As a Big Red Bug. Bianchi, John, illus. 1999. (New Reader Ser.). (J). (gr. k-1). Pokeweed Pr.

—Snug As a Big Red Bug. Bianchi, John, illus. 1999. (New Reader Ser.). 24p. (J). (ps-1). lib. bdg. 14.95 (978-1-894323-01-7(7)) Pokeweed Pr. CAN. *Dist:* Fitzhenry & Whiteside, Ltd.

—Snug As a Big Red Bug. 1999. (gr. k-3). lib. bdg. 12.95 (978-0-613-37045-5(7)) Tandem Library Bks.

Edwards, Frank B. & Bianchi, John. A Crowded Ride in the Countryside. 1999. (New Reader Ser.). (Illus.). 24p. (J). (ps-1). pap. 4.95 (978-1-894323-02-4(5)) Pokeweed Pr. CAN. *Dist:* Fitzhenry & Whiteside, Ltd.

—Mortimer Mooner Stopped Taking a Bath. 2000. (Mooner Ser.). (Illus.). 24p. (J). (ps-2). pap. 4.95 (978-1-894323-21-5(1)) Pokeweed Pr. CAN. *Dist:* Fitzhenry & Whiteside, Ltd.

—Nightgown Countdown. 1999. (New Reader Ser.). (Illus.). 24p. (J). (ps-1). pap. 4.95 (978-1-894323-04-8(1)); lib. bdg. 14.95 (978-1-894323-05-5(X)) Pokeweed Pr. CAN. *Dist:* Fitzhenry & Whiteside, Ltd.

—Snug As a Big Red Bug. 1999. (New Reader Ser.). (Illus.). 24p. (J). (ps-1). pap. 4.95 (978-1-894323-00-0(9)) Pokeweed Pr. CAN. *Dist:* Fitzhenry & Whiteside, Ltd.

—The Zookeeper's Sleepers. 1999. (New Reader Ser.). (Illus.). 24p. (J). (ps-1). pap. (978-1-894323-07-9(6)) Pokeweed Pr.

Edwards, Pamela Duncan. Livingstone Mouse. Cole, Henry, illus. 1998. 32p. (J). (ps-2). pap. 6.99 (978-0-06-443508-6(3) , Harper Trophy) HarperCollins Pubs.

Edwards, Richard & Hendra, Sue. Amazing Animal Alphabet: With Fantastic Flaps. 1999. (Illus.). 32p. (J). (ps-k). pap. 14.95 (978-0-531-30123-4(0) , Orchard Bks.) Scholastic, Inc.

Efird, Carrie. Wiggly, Squiggly Bugs. Lent, Marion W., illus. l.t. ed. 1998. (Children's Booklets Ser.). (J). (ps-k). 8p. pap. 10.95 (978-1-57332-116-7(8)); pap. 10.95 (978-1-57332-117-4(6)) HighReach Learning, Inc.

Egan, Lorraine Hopping. Ready, Set, Roll! 25, Fun, Easy-to-Play Games That Build Key Math Skills. 1998. (Illus.). 64p. (J). pap. 12.95 (978-0-590-18736-7(8)) Scholastic, Inc.

Egan, Tim. The Experiments of Doctor Vermin. Egan, Tim, illus. 2002. (Illus.). 32p. (J). (gr. k-3). tchr. ed. 15.00 (978-0-618-13224-9(4)) Houghton Mifflin Co. Trade & Reference Div.

Ehlert, Lois. Growing Vegetable Soup. 2004. (Illus.). 30p. (J). bds. 6.95 (978-0-15-205055-9(8) , Red Wagon Bks.) Harcourt Children's Bks.

Einhorn, Kama. I Can Write My ABC's Mini-Books: 26 Interactive Reproducible Mini-Books That Make Learning to Print the Letters A to Z Easy & Fun. 2001. 64p. (ps). pap. 10.95 (978-0-439-22845-9(X)) Scholastic, Inc.

Eisinger, Judith K. I See! Whatever I Want a Line to Be. Vogel, Steve, ed. Eisinger, Judith K., illus. 1998. (Illus.). 36p. (J). (ps-2). pap. 10.00 (978-0-9662747-0-7(9)) Yudit Publishing, Inc.

Ekker, Ernst A. Mozart: A Musical Picture Book. Eisenburger, Doris, illus. 2006. 32p. (J). 20.00 incl. audio compact disk (978-0-7358-2056-2(2)) North-South Bks., Inc.

Elgar, Rebecca. Is That an Elephant over There? 1998. (Lift-the-Flap Bk.). (Illus.). 10p. (ps-k). 4.95 (978-1-899607-13-6(7)) Sterling Publishing Co., Inc.

—Munch! What Are You Eating? 1999. (Illus.). 10p. (J). (ps-k). bds. 6.95 (978-1-899607-57-0(9)) Sterling Publishing Co., Inc.

—One Lonely Lion. 1998. (Lift-the-Flap Bk.). (Illus.). 10p. (J). (ps-k). bds. 4.95 (978-1-899607-31-0(5)) Sterling Publishing Co., Inc.

Elliott, George. The Boy Who Loved Bananas. Krystoforski, Andrei, illus. 2006. 32p. (978-1-55453-119-6(5)) Kids Can Pr., Ltd.

—The Boy Who Loved Bananas. Krystoforski, Andrej, illus. 2005. 32p. (J). (ps-2). (978-1-55337-744-3(3)) Kids Can Pr., Ltd.

Ellis, Sarah. Ben Over Night. LaFave, Kim, illus. 2005. 32p. (J). (978-1-55041-807-1(6)) Fitzhenry & Whiteside, Ltd.

Elsohn, Michael & Long, Sylvia. Snug as a Bug. 2004. (Illus.). 32p. (J). 13.95 (978-0-8118-4245-7(2)) Chronicle Bks. LLC.

Emberley, Rebecca. Let's Go (Vamos) A Book in Two Languages. 2000. (Illus.). (J). (978-0-606-18259-1(4)) Tandem Library Bks.

—My Animals/Mis Animales. Emberley, Rebecca, illus. 2002. (SPA & ENG., Illus.). 10p. (J). (ps-ps). bds. 6.99 (978-0-316-17343-8(6)) Little, Brown Bks. for Young Readers.

—My Clothes/Mi Ropa. Emberley, Rebecca, illus. 2002. (SPA & ENG., Illus.). 10p. (J). (ps-ps). bds. 6.99 (978-0-316-17454-1(8)) Little, Brown Bks. for Young Readers.

—My Day. 2000. Tr. of Mi Dia. (SPA.). (ps-2). lib. bdg. 14.95 (978-0-613-26312-2(X)) Tandem Library Bks.

—My Food/Mi Comida. Emberley, Rebecca, illus. 2002. (SPA & ENG., Illus.). 10p. (J). (ps-ps). bds. 6.99 (978-0-316-17718-4(0)) Little, Brown Bks. for Young Readers.

—My Mother's Secret Life. Emberley, Rebecca, illus. 1998. (Illus.). 28p. (J). (ps-3). 15.95 (978-0-316-23496-2(6)) Little Brown & Co.

—My Toys/Mis Juguetes. Emberley, Rebecca, illus. 2002. (SPA & ENG., Illus.). 10p. (J). (ps-ps). bds. 6.99 (978-0-316-17494-7(7)) Little, Brown Bks. for Young Readers.

Emerick, Yahiya. Color & Learn Salah. Meehan, Patricia, illus. l.t. ed. 1999. 100p. (J). (gr. k-2). mass mkt. 6.00 (978-1-889720-31-9(3)) Amirah Publishing.

Engel, Christiane. Louis & Bobo. 2007. (Illus.). 28p. (J). pap. 6.99 (*978-1-84458-375-1(9)) Anova Bks. GBR. *Dist:* Independent Pubs. Group.

Engelbreit, Mary. Booky. Engelbreit, Mary, illus. 2002. (Illus.). 14p. (J). (ps up). 6.99 (978-0-06-008133-1(3) , Harper Festival) HarperCollins Pubs.

Englemann-Berner, Beth. The Good Knight Night Book: A Picture Riddle Book. Riggs, Jenna, illus. 2005. 10p. (J). (ps-7). 9.95 (978-1-58117-420-5(9) , Intervisual/Piggy Toes) Dalmatian Pr.

Ericsson, Jennifer A. She Did It! Westcott, Nadine Bernard, illus. 2002. 32p. (J). (ps-3). 16.00 (978-0-374-36776-3(0) , Farrar, Straus & Giroux (BYR)) Farrar, Straus & Giroux.

Erlbruch, Wolf. The Big Question. Reynolds, Michael, tr. from FRE. 2005. (Illus.). 52p. (ps-7). pap. 14.95 (978-1-933372-03-7(6)) Europa Editions, Inc.

Esbensen, Barbara Juster. Jumping Day. Cocca-Leffler, Maryann, illus. 2003. 24p. (J). (ps up). pap. 8.95 (978-1-56397-853-1(9)) Boyds Mills Pr.

—Jumping Day. Cocca-Leffler, Maryann, illus. 2000. (J). 14.75 (978-0-606-19756-4(7)) Tandem Library Bks.

Esmaili, Roza. Zagros & Nature Force: Coloring Book. Sun Rise Illustration and Computer Animation Staff, illus. Date not set. 74p. (J). (gr. k-8). pap. 2.49 (978-0-9656185-1-9(X)) Esmaili, Inc.

Evans, Kristina. Cherish Today: A Celebration of Life's Moments. Collier, Bryan, illus. 2007. (J). (*978-1-4287-3968-0(8) , Jump at the Sun) Hyperion Bks. for Children.

Evans, Sandi Gore. Do You See What I See... Johnston, Becky, ed. (Illus.). 32p. (ps-2). 14.95 (978-1-890621-08-7(0)) Landauer Corp.

Evans, Shane W. Little Stevie Wonder. 2003. (Illus.). 32p. (J). 15.99 (978-0-7868-0682-9(6)) Disney Pr.

Exactly Like Me. 2003. (J). per. 8.95 (978-0-9746151-0-3(2)) Alta Retreat Ctr.

Eyuboglu, Melisa, illus. Angel in a Bubble. Eyuboglu, Melisa, . 2007. 28p. (J). 10.95 (*978-1-933090-48-1(0)) Guardian Angel Publishing, Inc.

Faces. Date not set. (Illus.). 40p. (J). 3.98 (978-1-4054-0174-6(5)) Parragon, Inc.

Fajerman, Deborah. Baa for Beginners. 2005. (Illus.). 32p. (J). pap. 5.95 (978-0-7641-3095-3(1)) Barron's Educational Series, Inc.

—How to Speak Moo! 2002. (Illus.). 32p. (J). (ps-1). pap. 5.99 (978-0-7641-2285-9(1)) Barron's Educational Series, Inc.

Falconer, Ian. Olivia. Falconer, Ian, illus. unabr. ed. 2004. (Olivia Ser.). (Illus.). 34p. (J). bds. 7.99 (978-0-689-87472-7(3) , Atheneum) Simon & Schuster Children's Publishing.

Farnsworth, Bill, illus. The Great Stone Face. 2005. 32p. (J). pap. 8.00 (978-0-8028-5292-2(0)) Eerdmans, William B. Publishing Co.

Faulkner, Keith. Sharing & Caring. James, Rhian Nest, illus. 1998. 4p. (J). bds. 7.99 (978-1-58048-036-9(5)) Sandvik Publishing.

Favorite, Deborah. The Tush People. Arinsberg, Norman, illus. (J). 11.95 (978-0-9722514-0-2(5)) Tush People, The.

Feelings. Date not set. 5.95 (978-0-89868-345-5(9)) ARO Publishing Co.

Feiffer, Jules. Feiffer Picture Book. Feiffer, Jules, illus. 2000. (Illus.). (J). (gr. 4-7). 14.95 (978-0-06-028977-5(5)) HarperCollins Pubs.

Feldman, Heather. My Bedtime: A Book about Getting Ready for Bed. 2000. (PowerKids Readers Ser.). (Illus.). 24p. (J). (gr. 1). lib. bdg. 16.00 (978-0-8239-5522-0(2) , PKMYBE, PowerKids Pr.) Rosen Publishing Group, Inc., The.

Ferri, Francesca, illus. Peek-A-Boo. 2005. 10p. (J). 7.95 (978-0-7641-5851-3(1)) Barron's Educational Series, Inc.

Filipowich, Bob & Hoe, Susan. My Ducky. 2004. (Soft Shapestm Ser.). (Illus.). 8p. (J). (ps-ps). 8.99 (978-1-58476-215-7(2)) Innovative Kids.

Finn, Mitch. NASCAR: Mobil 1 Making Friends. Reiter, Cheryl, ed. Hogan, Jayne, illus. 2000. 12p. (J). (ps). mass mkt. 9.99 (978-1-887327-46-6(0)) Ertl Co., Inc.

Fire Truck. 2000. (ps-2). lib. bdg. 14.15 (978-0-613-28485-1(2)) Tandem Library Bks.

Firefly Books Staff. Bedtime. (Illus.). 10p. bds. (978-1-55209-358-0(1)) Firefly Bks., Ltd.

Fischer, Jean. God Gives Us Beaches. Ring, Laura, ed. Brooks, Nan, illus. 1999. (Handle Board Bks.). 10p. (ps up). 2.99 (978-0-7847-0908-5(4) , 04273, Bean Sprouts) Standard Publishing.

—God Gives Us Pets. Ring, Laura, ed. Brooks, Nan, illus. 1999. (Handle Board Bks.). 10p. (ps up). 2.99 (978-0-7847-0907-8(6) , 04272, Bean Sprouts) Standard Publishing.

—Thank You, God! 2000. (Coloring Bks.). (Illus.). 16p. (J). (ps up). pap. 1.99 (978-0-7847-1107-1(0) , 22072) Standard Publishing.

Fitz-Gibbon, Sally. Pig in the Middle. Wakelin, Kirsti, illus. 2004. 32p. (J). (978-1-55041-894-1(7)) Fitzhenry & Whiteside, Ltd.

Fitzgerald, Joanne. This Is Me & Where I Am. Fitzgerald, Joanne, illus. 2004. (Illus.). 32p. (J). (gr. k-1). (978-1-55041-819-4(X)) Fitzhenry & Whiteside, Ltd.

Fleabite. 2004. (J). 14.95 (978-0-9746710-0-0(2)) Terra Linda Publishing.

Fleming, Denise. The Everything Book. rev. ed. 2004. (Illus.). 64p. (J). bds. 6.95 (978-0-8050-7709-4(X) , Holt, Henry & Co. Bks. For Young Readers) Holt, Henry & Co.

Fleming, Sarah. Do the Lolly Trick, 6, Pack. 2000. (Cambridge Reading Ser.). 12p. pap. 28.00 (978-0-521-78765-9(3)) Cambridge Univ. Pr.

Florian, Douglas. Insectlopedia. 2002. (Illus.). 48p. (J). (gr. k-3). pap. 7.00 (978-0-15-216335-8(2) , Voyager Bks./Libros Viajeros) Harcourt Children's Bks.

—Insectlopedia. 2002. (gr. 3-6). lib. bdg. 15.30 (978-0-613-44304-3(7)) Tandem Library Bks.

—Omnibeasts: Animal Poems & Paintings. 2004. (Illus.). 96p. (J). 18.00 (978-0-15-205038-2(8)) Harcourt Children's Bks.

—A Pig Is Big. Florian, Douglas, illus. 2000. (Illus.). 24p. (J). (gr. 2 up). 16.99 (978-0-688-17125-4(7)); (ps-3). 16.89 (978-0-688-17126-1(5)) HarperCollins Pubs.

Fluent Stage 3. 2005. (Little Celebrations Picture/Text & Literacy Cards Ser.). (J). (gr. k-3). 128.50 (978-0-673-77359-3(0)) Celebration Pr.

Foce, Natalia, tr. from ENG. Daniel, el Príncipe que Oraba, Apps, Fred, illus. l.t. ed. 2004. (SPA.). 36p. (J). 2.99 (978-1-932789-19-5(7)) Editorial Sendas Antiguas, LLC.

—David, el Luchador Valiente, Apps, Fred, illus. l.t. ed. 2004. (SPA.). 36p. (J). 2.99 (978-1-932789-18-8(9)) Editorial Sendas Antiguas, LLC.

—La Historia de Pablo — Viajes de Aventura, 1. Apps, Fred, illus. l.t. ed. 2004. Orig. Title: Journeys of Adventure — the Story of Paul. (SPA.). 36p. (J). 2.99 (978-1-932789-23-2(5)) Editorial Sendas Antiguas, LLC.

—Jesus el Milagroso. Anderson, Jeff, illus. l.t. ed. 2004. Orig. Title: Jesus the Miracle Worker. (SPA.). 24p. (J). 2.99 (978-1-932789-28-7(6)) Editorial Sendas Antiguas, LLC.

—Jesus Maestro. Anderson, Jeff, illus. l.t. ed. 2004. Orig. Title: Jesus the Teacher. (SPA.). 24p. (J). 2.99 (978-1-932789-26-3(X)) Editorial Sendas Antiguas, LLC.

—Jesus Narrador. Anderson, Jeff, illus. l.t. ed. 2004. Orig. Title: Jesus the Storyteller. (SPA.). 24p. (J). 2.99 (978-1-932789-25-6(1)) Editorial Sendas Antiguas, LLC.

—Jesus Niño. Anderson, Jeff, illus. l.t. ed. 2004. Orig. Title: Jesus the Child. (SPA.). 24p. (J). 2.99 (978-1-932789-24-9(3)) Editorial Sendas Antiguas, LLC.

—Jesus Salvador. Anderson, Jeff, illus. l.t. ed. 2004. Orig. Title: Jesus the Saviour. (SPA.). 24p. (J). 2.99 (978-1-932789-29-4(4)) Editorial Sendas Antiguas, LLC.

—Jesus Sanador. Anderson, Jeff, illus. l.t. ed. 2004. Orig. Title: Jesus the Healer. (SPA.). 24p. (J). 2.99 (978-1-932789-27-0(8)) Editorial Sendas Antiguas, LLC.

—El Nacimiento de Jesus: El Niño Prometido, 1. Apps, Fred, illus. l.t. ed. 2004. Orig. Title: The Birth of Jesus — the Promised Child. (SPA.). 36p. (J). 2.99 (978-1-932789-20-1(0)) Editorial Sendas Antiguas, LLC.

—El Plan de Rescate: La Historia de Noe, 1. Apps, Fred, illus. l.t. ed. 2004. Orig. Title: The Rescue Plan. (SPA.). 36p. (J). 2.99 (978-1-932789-15-7(4)) Editorial Sendas Antiguas, LLC.

—La Resurreccion: Jesus Esta Vivo, 1. Apps, Fred, illus. l.t. ed. 2004. Orig. Title: The Resurrection — Jesus Is Alive. (SPA.). 36p. (J). 2.99 (978-1-932789-21-8(9)) Editorial Sendas Antiguas, LLC.

—Samuel, el Niño que Escuchaba. Apps, Fred, illus. l.t. ed. 2004. (SPA.). 36p. (J). 2.99 (978-1-932789-17-1(0)) Editorial Sendas Antiguas, LLC.

—Saul — el Milagro en el Camino, 1. Apps, Fred, illus. l.t. ed. 2004. Orig. Title: Saul — the Miracle on the Road. (SPA.). 36p. (J). 2.99 (978-1-932789-22-5(7)) Editorial Sendas Antiguas, LLC.

—El Soñador de Dios: La Historia de José, Apps, Fred, illus. l.t. ed. 2004. (SPA.). 36p. (J). 2.99 (978-1-932789-16-4(2)) Editorial Sendas Antiguas, LLC.

Fontes, Justine. Who Lives at the Pond? Tagel, Peggy, illus. 2000. (Wiggly Tab Bks.). 6p. (J). (ps-k). bds. 5.99 (978-1-57584-351-3(X)) Reader's Digest Children's Publishing, Inc.

Fontes, Justine & Tagel, Peggy. Who Lives in the Forest? 2000. (Wiggly Tab Bks.). (Illus.). 6p. (J). (ps-k). bds. 5.99 (978-1-57584-352-0(8)) Reader's Digest Children's Publishing, Inc.

Forbes, B. C. Teamwork, Stick-to-Itiveness. 1998. 32p. reprint ed. 9.95 (978-1-55709-452-0(7)) Applewood Bks.

Ford, Christine. Snow! Whitman, Candace, illus. 1999. (Growing Tree Ser.). 24p. (J). (ps up). 9.95 (978-0-694-01199-5(1) , Harper Festival) HarperCollins Pubs.

Fox, Christyan & Fox, Diane. Astronaut PiggyWiggy. 2002. (Illus.). 24p. (J). (ps-k). 9.95 (978-1-929766-41-3(6)) Handprint Bks.

—What Shape Is That, Piggywiggy? 2002. (Illus.). 10p. (J). (ps-k). bds. 5.95 (978-1-929766-44-4(0)) Handprint Bks.

—What's the Opposite, Piggywiggy? 2002. (Illus.). 10p. (J). (ps-k). bds. 5.95 (978-1-929766-43-7(2)) Handprint Bks.

Fox, Mem. Hattie & the Fox. 2002. (Illus.). (J). 15.53 (978-0-7587-2704-6(6)) Book Wholesalers, Inc.

Fraser, Mary Ann. I. Q. Goes to the Library. Fraser, Mary Ann, illus. 2005. (Illus.). 32p. (J). (ps-3). pap. 6.95 (978-0-8027-7727-0(9)) Walker & Co.

Free Wheelin' 1998. (Hot Wheels Ser.). (Illus.). 24p. (J). (ps-2). (978-0-7666-0106-2(4) , 69640) Modern Publishing.

Free Wheelin' Picture Book (English) NL 9x9 with Snipe. 2007. (J). (*978-1-933934-48-8(4)*) Educational Adventures.

Freed, Shirley Ann & Moon, Louise. Angels Care for Me. Morelan, Bill, ed. Harrell, Rob, illus. l.t. ed. 2002. 8p. (J). (ps-k). pap. 3.99 (978-1-58938-005-9(3)) Concerned Communications.

—Impossible! Impossible. Morelan, Bill, ed. Butler, Steven, illus. l.t. ed. 2002. 24p. (J). (gr. 3-4). pap. 3.99 (978-1-58938-046-2(0)) Concerned Communications.

—School Tools. Morelan, Bill, ed. Harrell, Rob, illus. l.t. ed. 2002. 8p. (J). (ps-k). pap. 3.99 (978-1-58938-003-5(7)) Concerned Communications.

Freeman, Don. Corduroy. 2003. (Illus.). (J). bds. (978-0-670-03690-5(0) , Viking Adult) Penguin Group (USA) Inc.

—The Corduroy Giant Shaped. 2002. (Illus.). 5p. (J). bds. 7.99 (978-0-670-03534-2(3) , Viking Juvenile) Penguin Group (USA) Inc.

Fremont, Victoria & Stewart, Pat. Invisible Oz Magic Picture Book. 1998. 16p. (J). (ps-2). pap. 1.50 (978-0-486-40528-5(1)) Dover Pubns., Inc.

—Invisible Witches Magic Picture Book. 1998. (Illus.). 16p. (J). pap. 1.00 (978-0-486-40529-2(X)) Dover Pubns., Inc.

French, Renee. The Soap Lady. unabr. ed. 2001. (Illus.). 112p. 19.95 (978-1-891830-24-2(4)) Top Shelf Productions.

French, Vivian & McDonald, Ronald L. Once upon a Time. Prater, John, illus. 1999. (Read & Share Ser.). 32p. (J). (ps). pap. 3.99 (978-0-7636-0858-3(0)) Candlewick Pr.

Freymann, Saxton, et al. Food for Thought: The Complete Book of Concepts for Growing Minds. Freymann, Saxton, illus. 2005. (Illus.). 64p. (J). pap. 14.95 (978-0-439-11018-1(1) , Levine, Arthur A. Bks.) Scholastic, Inc.

Frogberg, Dennis. Digger Dave & Backhoe Joe. l.t. ed. 2001. (Illus.). (J). (ps-4). 30p. pap. 7.95 (978-1-928632-53-5(X)); audio 10.95 (978-1-928632-54-2(8)) Writers Marketplace:Consulting, Critiquing & Publishing.

Frosty the Snowman: Songs of the Season: 5-Button Song Book. (Illus.). 10p. (J). (ps-2). 7.98 (978-0-7853-2067-8(9) , PI27) Publications International, Ltd.

Fry. Picture Nouns. 2004. (Reading Ser.). (Illus.). 48p. 7.99 (978-1-57690-763-4(5)) Teacher Created Materials, Inc.

Fun & Play. 2002. (First Words & Pictures Book Ser.). (J). bds. 7.95 (978-0-7525-7978-8(9)) Parragon, Inc.

Funari Willever, Lisa. Where Do Snowmen Go? 2002. (Illus.). 32p. 9.95 (978-0-9679227-2-0(0) , 329-012) Franklin Mason Pr.

Funny Friends, LLC Staff. Peek-a-Boo I'm Like You. 1999. (Illus.). 18p. (J). bds. (978-1-929758-00-5(6)) Funny Friends, LLC.

—Peek-a-Boo I'm Like You Value Pack: With Plush Star. 1999. (Illus.). 18p. (J). bds. (978-1-929758-03-6(0)) Funny Friends, LLC.

Futech Interactive Products Staff. Crazy Driver. 1999. (Look, Listen & Learn Ser.). (Illus.). (ps-3). 14.95 (978-1-58224-008-4(6)) Futech Interactive Products, Inc.

—Food Fun. 1999. (Look, Listen & Learn Ser.). (Illus.). (ps-3). 14.95 (978-1-58224-007-7(8)) Futech Interactive Products, Inc.

Gaines, Isabel. Pooh's Leaf Pile Book Club: Special Sales Edition. 1999. 40p. (J). pap. 3.99 (978-0-7868-4387-9(X)) Disney Pr.

Galdone, Paul. Henny Penny. Galdone, Paul, illus. 2002. (Illus.). (J). 14.72 (978-0-7587-2712-1(7)) Book Wholesalers, Inc.

Gardner, Louise, illus. Old MacDonald. 2004. 24p. (J). bds. 6.99 (978-1-85854-901-9(9)) Brimax Books Ltd. GBR. *Dist:* Byeway Bks.

Garfield, Valerie. Harold & the Purple Crayon: The Birthday Present. 2002. (ps-2). lib. bdg. 11.80 (978-0-613-50411-9(9)) Tandem Library Bks.

—Who Stole the Cookies from the Cookie Jar? Manning, Jane, illus. 2001. (Playtime Rhymes Ser.). 12p. (J). (ps up). 7.99 (978-0-694-01515-3(6) , Harper Festival) HarperCollins Pubs.

Gates, Susan. Mole Who was Scared of the Dark. Breakespeare, Andrew, illus. 2005. 24p. (J). lib. bdg. 22.65 (*978-1-59646-710-1(X)*) Dingles & Co.

Gauch, Patricia Lee. Christina Katerina & the Box. Burn, Doris, illus. 1998. 32p. (J). (ps-3). pap. 7.99 (978-0-698-11676-4(3) , Putnam Juvenile) Penguin Group (USA) Inc.

—This Time, Tempe Wick? Tomes, Margot, illus. 2003. 48p. (YA). (gr. 4-6). 16.95 (978-1-59078-179-1(1)); pap. 9.95 (978-1-59078-185-2(6)) Boyds Mills Pr.

—This Time, Tempe Wick? 2003. (gr. 3-6). lib. bdg. 18.75 (978-0-613-79892-1(9)) Tandem Library Bks.

Gautier, Gary. Spaghetti & Peas. Guevara, Linda L., ed. Bailey, Sheila, illus. 2002. 40p. (J). (ps-5). 16.95 (978-0-9700863-6-5(9)) All About Kids Publishing.

Geisert, Arthur. The Giant Ball of String. Geisert, Arthur, illus. 2002. (Illus.). 32p. (J). (gr. k-3). tchr. ed. 16.00 (978-0-618-13221-8(X) , Walter Lorraine) Houghton Mifflin Co. Trade & Reference Div.

George-Brooks, Barbara. Kiss the World Goodnight. Scheraga, Mona, ed. George-Brooks, Barbara, illus. 1998. (Illus.). 32p. (J). (ps-3). pap. 5.00 (978-0-9665086-0-4(2)) Creative Realizations, Inc.

Gerber, Carole. Artic Dreams. Husted, Marty, illus. 2006. 32p. (J). pap. 7.95 (978-1-58089-074-8(1)) Charlesbridge Publishing, Inc.

Gerth, Melanie. All about Me. Thelan, Mary, illus. 2000. 10p. (J). (ps-k). bds. 10.95 (978-1-58117-120-4(X) , Intervisual/Piggy Toes) Dalmatian Pr.

—My First Jumbo Book of Christmas. Diaz, Jim, illus. 2003. (My First Jumbo Book Ser.). 10p. (J). pap. 9.95 (978-0-439-52111-6(4) , Cartwheel Bks.) Scholastic, Inc.

Giesler, Dagmar. Max juega en la Arena. 2004. (Coleccion Max Max Ser.). (SPA.). (J). bds. 11.95 (978-84-261-3295-6(2)) Juventud, Editorial ESP. *Dist:* Distribooks, Inc., Lectorum Pubns., Inc.

Gill, Janie S. Feelings: A Predictable Word Book. 1998. (Illus.). 24p. (gr. 4-7). lib. bdg. 10.95 (978-0-89868-344-8(0)) ARO Publishing Co.

Gill, Jim. May There Always Be Sunshine: A Traditional. Signorino-Richards, Susie, illus. 2001. 32p. (J). (ps-1). 15.00 (978-0-9679038-6-6(6)) Gill, Jim Music.

Gillmor, Don. Yuck, a Love Story. Gay, Marie-Louise, illus. 2001. 26p. (ps-3). 7.95 (978-0-7737-6209-1(4)) Stoddart Kids CAN. *Dist:* Fitzhenry & Whiteside, Ltd.

Gilmore, Dorina Lazo. A Stone in the Soup. Hires, Josh, illus. 2006. 39p. per. 15.00 (*978-0-938911-29-6(5)*) Individualized Education Systems/Poppy Lane Publishing.

Gingras, Charlotte. L' Ecuyere. Dubois, Gérard, illus. 2004. (Picture Bks.). (FRE.). 32p. (J). (ps). (978-2-89021-666-2(7)); pap. (978-2-89021-665-5(9)) Diffusion du livre Mirabel.

Given, Cate. Cartwheeling. Hill-Peterson, Jodi, illus. 2006. (J). (*978-0-9790057-1-8(X)*) Paws In the Sand Publishing.

Gliori, Debi. Mr. Bear Says Are You There, Baby Bear? Gliori, Debi, illus. 1999. (Lift-the-Flap Book Ser.). (Illus.). 22p. (J). (ps-k). pap. 9.95 (978-0-531-30182-1(6) , Orchard Bks.) Scholastic, Inc.

Glover, David. Transportation. 2004. (Picture Reference Ser.). (SPA., Illus.). 48p. (gr. 3-6). (J). pap. 7.95 (978-1-58728-657-5(2)); 13.95 (978-1-58728-654-4(8)) T&N Children's Publishing. (Two Can Publishing).

Gnojewski, Carol & Warren, Jean. Music & Dramatics at Circle Time. Tourtillotte, Barbara, illus. 2001. (Circle Time Book Ser.). 96p. (J). (ps-k). pap. 10.99 (978-1-57029-240-8(X) , WPH04902, Totline Pubns.) Schaffer, Frank Pubns.

Goble, Paul. Legend of the White Buffalo Woman. 2002. (gr. k-3). lib. bdg. 16.40 (978-0-613-81335-8(9)) Tandem Library Bks.

Godwin, Laura. The Ring Bearer. Wallace, John, illus. 2006. 32p. (ps-k). 12.99 (978-0-7868-5510-0(X)) Hyperion Pr.

Golden Books Staff. The Buttercup Came Up. 2001. (Illus.). 24p. 2.29 (978-0-307-96039-9(0) , Golden Bks.) Random Hse. Children's Bks.

—Chain of Power. 2001. 32p. (YA). (ps up). pap. 4.99 (978-0-307-27611-7(2) , Golden Bks.) Random Hse. Children's Bks.

—Fun & Fancy. Disney Productions Staff, illus. 2004. 12p. (J). (ps-2). pap. 3.99 (978-0-7364-2233-8(1) , Golden/Disney) Random Hse. Children's Bks.

—Jeepers, It's the Creeper! 2000. (Scooby-Doo Ser.). (Illus.). 64p. (J). (ps-3). pap. 2.99 (978-0-307-29051-9(4) , 29051, Golden Bks.) Random Hse. Children's Bks.

—Let Love Grow. Butcher, Samuel, illus. 2001. (Precious Moments Ser.). 96p. (J). (ps-2). pap. 2.99 (978-0-307-03216-4(7) , 03216, Golden Bks.) Random Hse. Children's Bks.

—Little Golden Book Collection: Animal Tales. 2004. (Illus.). 320p. (J). (gr. k-k). 14.95 (978-0-375-83128-7(2) , Golden Bks.) Random Hse. Children's Bks.

—Ride along the Countryside. Santanach, Tino, illus. 2004. 32p. (J). (ps-2). pap. 3.99 (978-0-375-82820-1(6) , Golden Bks.) Random Hse. Children's Bks.

—Trouble Ahead. 2000. (Scooby-Doo Ser.). (Illus.). 56p. (J). (ps-3). pap. 3.99 (978-0-307-27610-0(4) , 27610, Golden Bks.) Random Hse. Children's Bks.

—Welcome to the Team! Baker, Darrell, illus. 2006. (Stickerific Ser.). 32p. (J). (ps-2). pap. 2.99 (978-0-375-83483-7(4) , Golden Bks.) Random Hse. Children's Bks.

Golden Books Staff, et al. Little Golden Book Collection: Inspirational Tales. Williams, Garth & Edge, Liz, illus. 2006. (Little Golden Book Ser.). 224p. (J). (gr. k-1). 10.95 (978-0-375-83233-8(5) , Golden Inspirational) Random Hse. Children's Bks.

Good, Phyllis Pellman. Plain Pig's ABC's: A Day on Plain Pig's Amish Farm. Benner, Cheryl A., illus. 1998. 24p. (J). (ps-1). 14.95 (978-1-56148-251-1(X)) Good Bks.

Goodhart, Pippa. House that Jack Built. Parker, Andy, illus. 2004. 24p. (J). lib. bdg. 22.65 (*978-1-59646-700-2(2)*) Dingles & Co.

Goodings, Christina. Around the Year: A Calendar & Counting Rhyme. Lewis, Jan, illus. 2001. 32p. (J). pap. 13.99 (978-0-7459-4451-7(5) , Lion) Lion Hudson plc GBR. *Dist:* Independent Pubs. Group.

Goodspeed, Judy. Saddle Up. 2007. (Illus.). 24p. (J). 7.98 (*978-0-9794660-7-6(5)*); 24.99 (*978-0-9794660-0-7(8)*); per. 12.99 (*978-0-9794660-1-4(6)*) Dragonfly Publishing, Inc.

Gorgas, Paula Blais. The Perfect Purple Present. l.t. ed. 2007. (Illus.). 24p. (J). 24.99 (*978-0-9794660-4-5(0)*); per. 12.99 (*978-0-9794660-5-2(9)*) Dragonfly Publishing, Inc.

Gower, Jeremy, illus. Things That Go. 1998. (Find & Fit Ser.). 10p. (J). (ps-k). bds. 14.95 (978-1-57145-359-4(8) , Silver Dolphin Bks.) Advantage Pubs. Group.

Grace, Nicki Clausen. What Comes First? How a Picture Book Is Printed? 2007. (Illus.). 24p. (J). (978-1-59515-977-9(0)) Rourke Publishing, LLC.

Grace, Roz. Why Is John Special? Srba, Lynne, illus. 1998. 22p. (J). (ps-6). pap. 6.95 (978-0-9659181-0-7(6)) BMF Pr.

Graham, Alistair. Full Moon Soup. Graham, Alistair, illus. 2003. (Full Moon Soup & Full Moon Afloat Ser.). (Illus.). 32p. (YA). pap. (978-1-85602-071-8(1)) Chrysalis Children's Bks.

Graham, Elspeth. Sandwich that Jack Made. Mould, Chris, illus. 2004. 24p. (J). lib. bdg. (*978-1-59646-698-2(7)*) Dingles & Co.

Granfield, Linda. What Am I? Herbert, Jennifer, illus. 2007. 32p. (J). (ps-k). 15.95 (*978-0-88776-812-5(1)*) Tundra Bks., Inc./Livres Toundra, Inc. CAN. *Dist:* Random Hse., Inc.

Grannell, Cynthia. The Chairs Where Pam & Sam Sit. Munson, Deborah, illus. 1998. 16p. (J). (ps-k). pap. 5.95 (978-0-9655442-9-0(X)) Business Word, The.

Gray, Libba Moore. Is There Room on the Feather Bed? ed. 2004. (Illus.). (J). (ps-2). spiral bd. (978-0-616-03037-0(1)); spiral bd. (978-0-616-04555-8(7)) Canadian National Institute for the Blind/Institut National Canadien pour les Aveugles.

—Is There Room on the Feather Bed? Westcott, Nadine Bernard, illus. 1999. 32p. (J). (ps-1). pap. 5.95 (978-0-531-07137-3(5) , Orchard Bks.) Scholastic, Inc.

—Is There Room on the Feather Bed? 1999. (Illus.). (J). (978-0-606-18333-8(7)) Tandem Library Bks.

Gray, Nigel. Oliver Twist Finds a Home. McLean, Andrew, illus. 2002. 32p. (J). 22.50 (978-1-876268-87-9(5) , Cygnet Bks.) Univ. of Western Australia Pr. AUS. *Dist:* International Specialized Bk. Services.

Greene, Rhonda Gowler. When a Line Bends... a Shape Begins. Kaczman, James, illus. 2001. 32p. (J). (gr. k-3). pap. 5.95 (978-0-618-15241-4(5)) Houghton Mifflin Co. Trade & Reference Div.

Greenleaf, E. Who Wants to Nap? (Illus.). 32p. (J). (gr. 2-3). lib. bdg. 9.95 (978-0-87783-050-4(9)) Oddo Publishing, Inc.

Greenstein, Elaine. As Big As You. Greenstein, Elaine, illus. 2004. (Illus.). 32p. (J). (gr. k-ps). pap. 6.99 (978-0-553-11234-4(1) , Dragonfly Bks.) Random Hse. Children's Bks.

Greenstein, Elaine, contrib. by. One Little Lamb. 2004. (Illus.). 32p. (J). 10.99 (978-0-670-03683-7(8) , Viking Juvenile) Penguin Group (USA) Inc.

—One Little Seed. 2004. (Illus.). 32p. (J). (gr. k-1). 10.99 (978-0-670-03633-2(1) , Viking Juvenile) Penguin Group (USA) Inc.

Grigas, Denise. Artic-Pic: A Show & Tell Book for R & S. Grigas, Denise, illus. 1999. (Illus.). 80p. (J). (gr. k-5). pap. 22.95 (978-0-937857-82-3(3) , 1513) Speech Bin, Inc., The.

Grimes, Nikki. Wild, Wild Hair. Ford, George, illus. 2002. (J). 11.91 (978-0-7587-1855-6(1)) Book Wholesalers, Inc.

Grindley, Sally. Cuentos de Ositos. Utton, Peter, illus. 2001. (SPA.). 80p. (J). 15.16 (978-84-480-1130-7(9)) Timun Mas, Editorial S.A. ESP. *Dist:* Lectorum Pubns., Inc.

Grindley, Sally & Foreman, Michael. La Playa de Pedro. 2004. (SPA., Illus.). 32p. (J). 19.99 (978-84-261-3314-4(2)) Juventud, Editorial ESP. *Dist:* Lectorum Pubns., Inc.

Grosset and Dunlap Staff, ed. Storybook Treasury of Dick & Jane & Friends. 2003. (Dick & Jane Ser.). (Illus.). 200p. (J). (ps-3). 10.99 (978-0-448-43340-0(0) , Grosset & Dunlap) Penguin Group (USA) Inc.

Grosset and Dunlap Staff & Lamut, Sonja. At the Bakery. Commander, Bob, illus. 1999. (Sticker Stories Ser.). 16p. (J). (ps-1). pap. 4.99 (978-0-448-42080-6(5) , Grosset & Dunlap) Penguin Group (USA) Inc.

Grosset and Dunlap Staff & Noble, Marty. Costume Ball. Jarnow, Jill, ed. 2001. (Sticker Styles Ser.). (Illus.). 1p. (J). (ps-3). pap. 4.99 (978-0-448-42466-8(5) , Grosset & Dunlap) Penguin Group (USA) Inc.

—Real Life Princesses. Jarnow, Jill, ed. 2001. (Sticker Styles Ser.). (Illus.). 16p. (J). (ps-3). pap. 4.99 (978-0-448-42465-1(7) , Grosset & Dunlap) Penguin Group (USA) Inc.

Grossman, Linda Sky. I'm a Great Little Kid Series Set: (6 Picture Books & Guide) (Illus.). 1p. 79.95 (978-1-896764-75-7(4)); pap. 39.95 (978-1-896764-74-0(6)) Second Story Pr. CAN. *Dist:* Orca Bk. Pubs. USA.

Grossnickle, Anna H. What Can You Do in the Snow? Kliros, Thea, illus. 1999. 10p. (J). (ps-k). pap. 5.95 (978-0-688-16078-4(6)) HarperCollins Pubs.

Gugler, Laurel Dee. There's a Billy Goat in the Garden. Beaton, Clare, illus. 2003. 32p. (J). (ps-2). 14.99 (978-1-84148 089 3(4)) Barefoot Bks., Inc.

Guiberson, Brenda Z. Into the Sea. Berenzy, Alix, illus. rev. ed. 2000. 32p. (J). (ps-k). pap., pap. 7.95 (978-0-8050-6481-0(8) , Holt, Henry & Co. Bks. For Young Readers) Holt, Henry & Co.

Gunson, Christopher. Animal Surprise. 2003. (Illus.). 32p. (J). 19.99 (978-0-385-60223-5(5) , Doubleday); pap. 11.95 (978-0-552-54741-3(7) , Corgi) Transworld Publishers Ltd. GBR. *Dist:* Trafalgar Square Publishing, Independent Pubs. Group.

Gunzi, Christiane. Fluffy Babies. 2006. (Feels Real Bks.). (Illus.). 10p. (J). bds. 4.99 (978-0-7641-5948-0(8)) Barron's Educational Series, Inc.

—In the Jungle. 2006. (Feels Real Bks.). (Illus.). 10p. (J). bds. 4.99 (978-0-7641-5949-7(6)) Barron's Educational Series, Inc.

—Little Ponies. 2005. (Feels Real Bks.). (Illus.). 10p. (J). bds. 4.95 (978-0-7641-5855-1(4)) Barron's Educational Series, Inc.

—On the Farm. 2005. (Feels Real Bks.). (Illus.). 10p. (J). bds. 4.95 (978-0-7641-5856-8(2)) Barron's Educational Series, Inc.

—Under the Sea. 2006. (Feels Real Bks.). (Illus.). 10p. (J). bds. 4.99 (978-0-7641-5951-0(8)) Barron's Educational Series, Inc.

Guo, Jing Jing. Grandpa's Mask. Wu, Di, illus. 2001. 32p. (J). (978-1-876615-05-5(2)) Benchmark Pubns. Pty, Ltd.

Guthrie, Woody. Enviarme a Ti, Level 2. Ada, Alma Flor, tr. Rosenberry, Vera, illus. 2003. (Dejame Leer Ser.). (SPA.). 8p. (J). (ps-1). 6.50 (978-0-673-36301-5(5) , Good Year Bks.) Celebration Pr.

Gutman, Anne. Penelope at the Farm. Hallensleben, Georg, illus. 2005. 12p. (J). (ps-ps). pap. 12.95 (978-0-439-67358-7(5) , Cartwheel Bks.) Scholastic, Inc.

Haan, Linda de & Nijland, Stern. King & King. 2004. (Illus.). 32p. 14.95 (978-1-58246-061-1(2) , Tricycle Pr.) Ten Speed Pr.

Hagin, Karen. Jeremy, the Giraffe Who Was Afraid of Heights. 2005. (J). lib. bdg. 19.95 (*978-0-9754728-8-0(7)* , Bear Hug Bks.) MidAmerica Publishing Co.

A Hair-Raising Tale. 2001. 24p. (J). 12.99 (978-0-307-20048-8(5) , 20048, Golden Bks.) Random Hse. Children's Bks.

Half a Moon & One Whole Star. 1998. (J). pap. 5.99 (978-0-87628-391-2(1)) Ctr. for Applied Research in Education, The.

Half a Moon & One Whole Star. 1999. (J). (gr. k-3). 16.00 (978-0-689-82667-2(2) , Atheneum) Simon & Schuster Children's Publishing.

Halperin, Wendy Anderson. Love Is ... ed. 2005. (Illus.). 32p. (J). 8.95 (978-0-689-87618-9(1)) Simon & Schuster Children's Publishing.

Hamanaka, Sheila. Colours of the Earth. (Illus.). 32p. (J). 2002. (TUR & ENG.). 18.95 (978-1-85269-331-2(2)); 2000. (BEN & ENG.), 19.95 (978-1-85269-326-8(6)) Mantra Publishing, Ltd. GBR. *Dist:* AIMS International Bks., Inc.

Hamilton, Virginia. The People Could Fly: The Picture Book. Dillon, Leo & Dillon, Diane, illus. 32p. (J). 2007. audio compact disk 20.99 (*978-0-375-94553-3(9)*); 2004. 16.95 (978-0-375-82405-0(7)) Random Hse. Children's Bks. (Knopf Bks. for Young Readers).

—The People Could Fly Picture. Dillon, Leo & Dillon, Diane, illus. 2007. 32p. (J). 17.99 incl. audio compact disk (*978-0-375-84553-6(4)* , Knopf Bks. for Young Readers) Random Hse. Children's Bks.

Hands-On Crafts for Kids. How Do You Move? 2002. (Balloon Ser.). (Illus.). 12p. (J). bds. 3.95 (978-1-4027-0176-4(4) , Balloon Bks.) Sterling Publishing Co., Inc.

Hannah, Vickie. There's A Schnoozle in My Closet. 2004. (J). lib. bdg. 19.95 (*978-0-9754728-4-2(4)* , Bear Hug Bks.) MidAmerica Publishing Co.

Hao, K. T. & Kim, Byung-Gyu. The 100th Customer. Ferri, Giuliano, illus. 2005. 32p. (J). (ps-17). 15.95 (978-1-933327-03-7(0)) Purple Bear Bks., Inc.

Happy Halloween, 4 bks., Set. 2002. (Illus.). (J). (ps). bds. 7.99 (978-1-57759-876-3(8)) Dalmatian Pr.

Happy Lemonade. 2003. (Happy Birthday Pull-Out Card-Bks.). (Illus.). 4.99 (978-1-56148-384-6(2)) Good Bks.

Harcourt School Publishers Staff. From Head to Toe Little Book. 3rd ed. 2002. (Trophies Reading Program Ser.). (Illus.). (J). pap. 10.20 (978-0-15-329355-9(1)) Harcourt Schl. Pubs.

—Harcourt Science Big Book Collection. 3rd ed. 2002. (Harcourt Science Ser.). (Illus.). (gr. k-6). pap. 400.00 (978-0-15-335318-5(X)) Harcourt Schl. Pubs.

—Horizons Big Book Collection. 2nd ed. 2003. (Illus.). (gr. 1). pap. 840.00 (978-0-15-337573-6(6)); (gr. 2). pap. 840.00 (978-0-15-337581-1(7)) Harcourt Schl. Pubs.

—Horizons Big Book Collection Unit 1. 2nd ed. 2003. (Illus.). pap. 140.00 (978-0-15-337574-3(4)); pap. 140.00 (978-0-15-337812-6(3)) Harcourt Schl. Pubs.

—Horizons Big Book Collection Unit 2. 2nd ed. 2003. (Illus.). pap. 140.00 (978-0-15-337575-0(2)); pap. 140.00 (978-0-15-337813-3(1)) Harcourt Schl. Pubs.

—Horizons Big Book Collection Unit 3. 2nd ed. 2003. (Illus.). pap. 140.00 (978-0-15-337577-4(9)); pap. 140.00 (978-0-15-337814-0(X)) Harcourt Schl. Pubs.

—Horizons Big Book Collection Unit 4. 2nd ed. 2003. (Illus.). pap. 140.00 (978-0-15-337578-1(7)); pap. 140.00 (978-0-15-337815-7(8)) Harcourt Schl. Pubs.

—Horizons Big Book Collection Unit 5. 2nd ed. 2003. (Illus.). pap. 140.00 (978-0-15-337579-8(5)); (J). pap. 140.00 (978-0-15-337816-4(6)) Harcourt Schl. Pubs.

—Horizons Big Book Collection Unit 6. 2nd ed. 2003. (Illus.). pap. 140.00 (978-0-15-337580-4(9)); pap. 140.00 (978-0-15-337817-1(4)) Harcourt Schl. Pubs.

—How Animals Sleep Big Book. 3rd ed. 2002. (Trophies Ser.). (Illus.). (gr. 1 up). pap. 55.70 (978-0-15-326170-1(6)) Harcourt Schl. Pubs.

—I Read Signs. 3rd ed. 2002. (Trophies Reading Program Ser.). (Illus.). pap. 55.10 (978-0-15-326468-9(3)) Harcourt Schl. Pubs.

—I Read Signs Little Book. 3rd ed. 2002. (Trophies Reading Program Ser.). (Illus.). (J). pap. 10.20 (978-0-15-326504-4(3)) Harcourt Schl. Pubs.

—Trophies Big Book: For English-Language Learners. 3rd ed. 2003. (Trophies Ser.). (Illus.). (gr. k-6). 42.00 (978-0-15-329343-6(8)) Harcourt Schl. Pubs.

—Your Health. 3rd ed. 2002. (Your Health Ser.). (Illus.). (gr. 1 up). pap. 99.10 (978-0-15-334698-9(1)) Harcourt Schl. Pubs.

—Your Health Big Book. 3rd ed. 2002. (Your Health Ser.). (Illus.). (gr. 2 up). pap. 99.10 (978-0-15-334699-6(X)) Harcourt Schl. Pubs.

Harder Tangvald, Christine. God Made Shapes...for Me! 1999. (for Me! Bks.). (Illus.). 16p. (J). (ps). pap. 4.99 (978-0-7642-2284-9(8)) Bethany Hse. Pubs.

—God's 123s...for Me! 1999. (for Me! Bks.). (Illus.). 16p. (J). (ps). pap. 4.99 (978-0-7642-2281-8(3)) Bethany Hse. Pubs.

—So Smart Learning Chart. Regan, Dana, illus. 2001. (J). (ps-k). pap. 5.99 (978-0-570-07099-3(6)) Concordia Publishing Hse.

Hargreaves, Roger. Mr. Slow. Hargreaves, Roger, illus. 2000. (Mr. Men & Little Miss Ser.). (Illus.). 32p. (J). (ps-3). pap. 3.99 (978-0-8431-7601-8(6) , Price Stern Sloan) Penguin Group (USA) Inc.

Haring, Keith. Big. 1998. (Illus.). 14p. (J). pap. 6.95 (978-0-7868-0390-3(8)) Hyperion Bks. for Children.

Harper, Charise Mericle. The Little Book of Not So. 2005. (Illus.). 32p. (J). (ps-k). 9.95 (978-0-618-47319-9(X)) Houghton Mifflin Co. Trade & Reference Div.

HarperCollins Staff. Eric Carle Spinner Signage. 1999. (J). pap. (978-0-694-01353-1(6)) HarperCollins Pubs.

P Q R

—Little House Diecut Standee. 1999. pap. (978-0-06-028429-9(3)) HarperCollins Pubs.

Harriman, Marinell & Harriman, Robert. A Myriad of Minstrels. Harriman, Marinell & Harriman, Robert, illus. (Illus.). 32p. (Orig.). (J). (gr. 5-7). pap. 3.50 (978-0-940920-00-2(X)) Drollery Pr.

Harris, John. Greece! Rome! Monsters! Brown, Calef, illus. 2002. (Books for Young Readers Ser.). 48p. 16.95 (978-0-89236-618-7(4)) Oxford Univ. Pr., Inc.

Harris, Marian. Tuesday in Arizona. Harris, Jim, illus. 1998. 32p. (J). (ps-3). 15.95 (978-1-56554-233-4(9)) Pelican Publishing Co., Inc.

Harris, Peter. The Night Pirates. Allwright, Deborah, illus. 2006. 32p. (J). (ps-2). 16.99 (978-0-439-79959-1(7), Scholastic Pr.) Scholastic, Inc.

Harrison, Carlos. Ruben's Rainbow (El Arco Iris de Ruben) Paz, Grizelle, illus. 2001. (ENG & SPA.). 15.95 incl. audio compact disk (978-0-9706953-0-7(6)) Globo Libros.

Harrison, David L. Dylan the Eagle-Hearted Chicken. Brooks, Karen Stormer, illus. 2003. 32p. (J). (gr. k-2). 15.95 (978-1-56397-982-8(9)) Boyds Mills Pr.

—When Cows Come Home. 2003. (Illus.). 32p. (J). (ps up). pap. 8.95 (978-1-56397-946-0(2)) Boyds Mills Pr.

—When Cows Come Home. 2001. (ps-2). lib. bdg. 16.40 (978-0-613-78920-2(2)) Tandem Library Bks.

Hart, Sue C. Bless Your Little Heart. 2005. (Illus.). 32p. (J). (978-1-55306-932-4(3)) Essence Publishing.

Hartmann, Annabelle. As Big As a Mountain. 2003. (Illus.). 32p. (YA). (978-1-84365-001-0(0)) Chrysalis Children's Bks.

Harvey, Amanda. Dog Eared: Starring Otis. Harvey, Amanda, illus. 2004. (Illus.). 32p. (J). (ps-1). reprint ed. pap. 6.99 (978-0-440-41763-7(5), Dragonfly Bks.) Random Hse. Children's Bks.

Harvey, Damian. Mr. Fox's Socks. Rescek, Sanja, illus. 2004. 16p. (J). lib. bdg. 22.65 ***(978-1-59646-678-4(2))*** Dingles & Co.

Harwood, Beth. One Snowy Night. Ronchi, Susanna, illus. 2005. 12p. (J). ***(978-1-84011-627-4(7))*** Templar Publishing, Dorking.

Hassler, Donald & Hassler, Sara. Loving Marley. Newsom, Carol, illus. 2007. 32p. (J). (ps-3). 14.99 ***(978-0-9766390-7-7(6))*** PugTale Publishing.

Hawes, Alison. School Trip. Mould, Chris, illus. 2004. 24p. (J). lib. bdg. 22.65 ***(978-1-59646-694-4(4))*** Dingles & Co.

Hawkins, Colin & Hawkins, Jacqui. Witch Pigs. 2006. (Illus.). 32p. (J). (gr. 1-2). 19.99 (978-0-224-06467-5(3), Jonathan Cape) Random Hse. Children's Bks. GBR. *Dist:* Trafalgar Square Publishing.

Hayes, Wanda. The Bible & Me Picture Book. Caldwell, Lise, ed. Hook, Frances, illus. rev. ed. 1998. 96p. (J). (ps-1). 8.99 (978-0-7847-0799-9(5), 03567, Bean Sprouts) Standard Publishing.

Hazelwood, Drema. The Apple Orchard Gang: Featuring Red Delicious. l.t. ed. 1999. (Illus.). 20p. (J). (ps-3). pap. 5.95 (978-1-891029-45-5(2)) Henderson Publishing.

Hazen, Barbara Shook. Where Do Bears Sleep? Van Royen, Mary Morgan, illus. 1998. (Growing Tree Ser.). 24p. (J). (ps up). 9.95 (978-0-694-01037-0(5), Harper Festival) HarperCollins Pubs.

Head, Honor. Opposites. Stower, Adam, illus. 1998. (Ed Mouse Finds Out about Ser.). 32p. (J). (ps-2). pap. 5.95 (978-0-8172-8102-1(9)) Steck-Vaughn.

Hedderwick, Mairi. Katie Morag & the Birthdays: A Story, Activity & Birthday Book. 2006. (Illus.). 48p. (J). 20.00 (978-0-370-32850-8(7)) Random Hse. GBR. *Dist:* Independent Pubs. Group.

Heide, Florence Parry. The Little One. Longtemps, Ken, illus. 2002. (J). (gr. k-3). lib. bdg. 7.95 (978-0-87460-138-1(X)) Lion Bks.

Heide, Iris van der. The Red Chalk. Tolman, Marije, tr. from DUT. Tolman, Marije, illus. 2006. 24p. (J). (ps-k). 19.95 (978-1-932425-79-6(9), Lemniscaat) Boyds Mills Pr.

Heine, Helme. The Most Wonderful Egg in the World. 2004. (J). (ps-3). pap. 14.95 incl. audio (978-0-89719-785-4(2), PRA297) Weston Woods Studios, Inc.

Hellen, N. Touch & Peek with Teddy & Me. 2003. (Illus.). 18p. (J). 9.99 (978-1-85292-184-2(6), Campbell Bks.) Pan Macmillan GBR. *Dist:* Trafalgar Square Publishing.

Heller, Ruth. Many Luscious Lollipops: A Book about Adjectives. 1998. (World of Language Ser.). (Illus.). 48p. (J). (gr. k-3). pap. 7.99 (978-0-698-11641-2(0), Putnam Juvenile) Penguin Group (USA) Inc.

Henderson, Felicity. The Adventure Story Picture Bible. 2001. 126p. (J). lib. bdg. 16.95 (978-1-59325-024-9(X)) Word Among Us Pr.

Henderson, Holly E. & Tigelaar, Liz. Lighthouse Legend: Emotional & Spiritual Growth for Midlife & Beyond. 2001. (Dawson's Creek Suspense Ser.: Vol. 1). (Illus.). 224p. (YA). (gr. 7-12). mass mkt. 5.99 (978-0-7434-1694-8(5), Simon Pulse) Simon & Schuster Children's Publishing.

Henkes, Kevin. A Box of Treats: Five Little Picture Books about Lilly & Her Friends. Henkes, Kevin, illus. 2004. (Illus.). (J). 14.99 (978-0-06-073211-0(3), Harper Festival) HarperCollins Pubs.

—Jessica. Henkes, Kevin, illus. 1998. (Illus.). 24p. (J). (ps-ps). pap. 6.99 (978-0-688-15847-7(1), Harper Trophy) HarperCollins Pubs.

—Jessica. 1998. 12.79 (978-0-606-13536-8(7)) Tandem Library Bks.

Henley, Karyn. Twigs Has an Adventure. 2000. (Tails Ser.). (Illus.). 28p. (J). (ps-5). 9.99 (978-0-8054-2284-9(6)) B&H Publishing Grp.

Heo, Yumi. One Afternoon. 1998. (Illus.). 32p. (J). (ps-1). pap. 6.95 (978-0-531-07103-8(0), Orchard Bks.) Scholastic, Inc.

Herder, Ronald. Great Works for Piano Four Hands. Herder, Ronald, ed. 1998. 224p. pap. 16.95 (978-0-486-40173-7(1)) Dover Pubns., Inc.

Hershey, Marilyn K. Oncology, Stupology... I Want to Go Home! Boris, Jill M., illus. Blodgea, Randy, photos by. 1999. 32p. (J). (ps-6). pap. 5.00 (978-0-9673550-0-9(1)) Butterfly Pr.

Hickox, Rebecca. Per & the Dala Horse. Gilbert, Yvonne, illus. 2003. 32p. (J). pap. 8.95 (978-1-57534-034-0(8)) Skandisk, Inc.

Hicks, Barbara Jean. I Like Black & White. Prap, Lila, illus. 2006. 32p. (J). 9.95 (978-1-58925-056-7(7), tiger tales) ME Media LLC.

Hicks, Linda Ashman. Just Another Amazing Morning. Date not set. 32p. (J). (ps-3). pap. 5.99 (978-0-06-443712-7(4)) HarperCollins Pubs.

Hicks, Robert Z. Tommie Turtle's Secret. Rolseth, Ruthie, illus. 2007. 40p. (J). 16.95 ***(978-0-9792031-0-7(4))*** R.Z. Enterprises of Florida.

Higgs, Liz Curtis. The Parable of the Lily. 2003. (Parable Series Board Books). 20p. (J). bds. 6.99 (978-1-4003-0010-5(X)) Nelson, Thomas Inc.

—The Sunflower Parable. 2003. (Parable Series Board Books). 20p. (J). bds. 6.99 (978-1-4003-0009-9(6)) Nelson, Thomas Inc.

Highlights for Children Editorial Staff, compiled by. The Third Jumbo Book of Hidden Pictures, Vol. 3. 2003. (Illus.). 96p. (J). (gr. 6-9). pap. 6.95 (978-1-56397-276-8(X)) Boyds Mills Pr.

Hill, Eric. Spot Goes Splash! Hill, Eric, illus. 2003. (Illus.). 5p. (J). (ps-1). 5.99 (978-0-399-24032-4(2), Putnam Juvenile) Penguin Group (USA) Inc.

—Spot's Christmas. Hill, Eric, illus. 2004. (Illus.). 12p. (J). (ps-1). bds. 5.99 (978-0-399-24320-2(8), Putnam Juvenile) Penguin Group (USA) Inc.

Hill, Sandi. Look & See. Kupperstein, Joel, ed. Jarrett, Michael, photos by. 1998. (Learn to Read Math Ser.: Vol. 4469). (Illus.). 16p. (J). pap. 2.75 (978-1-57471-376-3(0), 4469) Creative Teaching Pr., Inc.

Hill, Susan. Simba's A to Z. 1998. (Disneys Ser.). (Illus.). 32p. (J). (ps-3). 8.95 (978-0-7868-3168-5(5)) Disney Pr.

Hilliker, Amy Warren. Little One, God Loves You. Thompson, Carol, illus. 2004. 12p. (J). 6.99 (978-0-310-70971-8(7)) Zondervan.

—Little One, God Made You. Thompson, Carol, illus. 2004. 12p. (J). 6.99 (978-0-310-70959-6(8)) Zondervan.

Hindley, Judy. Big Red Bus. Benedict, William, illus. 2000. 32p. (J). (ps-3). pap. 6.99 (978-0-7636-1250-4(2)) Candlewick Pr.

—Eyes, Nose, Fingers, & Toes: A First Book All about You. Granstrom, Brita, illus. 2002. (J). 23.40 (978-0-7587-2471-7(3)) Book Wholesalers, Inc.

—Eyes, Nose, Fingers, & Toes: A First Book All about You. Granstrom, Brita, illus. 2004. 24p. (J). (gr. k-k). bds. 6.99 (978-0-7636-2383-8(0)) Candlewick Pr.

—Eyes, Nose, Fingers, & Toes: A First Book All about You. 2002. (ps-2). lib. bdg. 14.15 (978-0-613-74778-3(X)) Tandem Library Bks.

—Ten Bright Eyes. Bartlett, Alison, illus. 1998. 32p. (J). (ps-3). 14.95 (978-1-56145-173-9(8)) Peachtree Pubs., Ltd.

Hiscock, Bruce. The Big Caribou Herd: Life in the Arctic National Wildlife Refuge. Hiscock, Bruce, illus. 2003. (Illus.). 32p. (J). (gr. 2-4). 16.95 (978-1-59078-010-7(8)) Boyds Mills Pr.

Hiscock, Karen, illus. Baby Animals. 1998. (Find & Fit Ser.). 10p. (J). (ps-k). bds. 14.95 (978-1-57145-358-7(X), Silver Dolphin Bks.) Advantage Pubs. Group.

Hissey, Jane. Donde Esta el Osito? 2001. (SPA., Illus.). 32p. (J). (gr. k-2). (978-84-89675-79-7(1)) Zendrera Zariquiey, Editorial ESP. *Dist:* Lectorum Pubns., Inc.

Hoban, Tana. Picture Book. 2001. (J). 15.95 (978-0-688-17193-3(1)); lib. bdg. 15.89 (978-0-688-17194-0(X)) HarperCollins Pubs.

Hoberman, Mary Ann. The Cozy Book. 1999. (gr. k-3). lib. bdg. 14.15 (978-0-613-21379-0(3)) Tandem Library Bks.

—The Seven Silly Eaters. Frazee, Marla, illus. 2000. 40p. (J). (ps-3). pap. 7.00 (978-0-15-202440-6(9), Voyager Bks./Libros Viajeros) Harcourt Children's Bks.

Hoff, Syd. Where's Prancer? 1999. (Illus.). 32p. (J). (ps-2). pap. 5.95 (978-0-06-443594-9(6), Harper Trophy) HarperCollins Pubs.

—Where's Prancer? 1999. (978-0-606-17304-9(8)) Tandem Library Bks.

Hogan, Jayne. Bobby Racer's Tough Race. Reiter, Cheryl, ed. 2000. 12p. (J). (ps). mass mkt. 9.99 (978-1-887327-48-0(7)) Ertl Co., Inc.

—Homer's Big Race. Reiter, Cheryl, ed. 2000. 12p. (J). (ps). pap. 9.99 (978-1-887327-47-3(9)) Ertl Co., Inc.

Holden, Arianne. Words. 2002. (Playschool Ser.). (Illus.). 32p. pap. 5.99 (978-1-84215-727-5(2), Southwater) Anness Publishing GBR. *Dist:* National Bk. Network.

Holden, Robert. The Pied Piper of Hamelin. Zak, Drahos, illus. 2004. 28p. (J). (gr. k-4). reprint ed. 15.00 (978-0-7567-7686-2(4)) DIANE Publishing Co.

Holder, Greg. A Pond Full of Pigs: A Story about the Golden Rule. 2000. (Threads Ser.). (Illus.). 32p. (J). (ps-1). bds. 8.99 (978-0-7847-1239-9(5), 04411, Bean Sprouts) Standard Publishing.

Hollingsworth, Mary. Upside down, Inside-Out, Backwards, Oopsy-Daisy Book. 1999. (Illus.). 32p. (J). (ps-2). 7.99 (978-0-570-05595-2(4)) Concordia Publishing Hse.

Holmes, Andy. If You Give a Boy a Bible. 2004. 32p. 11.99 (978-0-8254-5513-1(8)) Kregel Pubns.

Holtz, Lara Tankel & Sutinis, Beth, eds. My Lift-the-Flap Book. 2001. (Early Learners Ser.). (Illus.). 12p. (J). (ps). bds. 9.95 (978-0-7894-7408-7(5)) Dorling Kindersley Publishing, Inc.

Holub, Joan. Light the Candles: A Hanukkah Lift-the-Flap Book. Cravath, Lynne W., illus. 2000. 16p. (J). (ps-1). pap. 6.99 (978-0-14-056757-1(7), Puffin) Penguin Group (USA) Inc.

Hong, Seonna & Hahn, Shenne. Animus. 2005. (Illus.). 34p. 25.00 (978-0-9729388-5-3(0)) Baby Tattoo Bks.

Hood, Karen Jean Matsko. Angels, Angels, Way up High: A Read Aloud Picture Book. 2003. 24.95 (978-1-930948-81-5(6)) Whispering Pine Pr., Inc.

—Angels, Angels Way up High Read Aloud Picture Book. 2003. pap. 24.95 (978-1-930948-09-9(3)) Whispering Pine Pr., Inc.

Hood, Susan. Pup & Hound Lost & Found. Hendry, Linda, illus. 2006. 32p. (J). lib. bdg. 15.38 ***(978-1-4242-0250-8(7))*** Fitzgerald Bks.

Hope Music. 2006. (J). per. 12.00 ***(978-0-9773608-4-0(9))*** Shiny Red Ball Publishing.

Howard, Pam. Thank You Stan! Crowell, Knox, illus. 2001. (Big Bks.). 8p. (J). (ps-1). pap. 10.95 (978-1-57332-204-1(0)); pap. 10.95 (978-1-57332-205-8(9)) HighReach Learning, Inc.

Howard, Pam & Crowell, Knox. A Flight to Polar Bay. l.t. ed. 2002. (Illus.). 8p. (J). (ps-1). pap. 10.95 (978-1-57332-220-1(2)); pap. 10.95 (978-1-57332-221-8(0)) HighReach Learning, Inc.

Howell, David Sanders, frwd. Seascapes by David Sanders Howell. 2004. (Illus.). 64p. per. 20.00 (978-1-886438-02-6(1), 305-538-1033) Grassfield Pr., Inc.

Howell, Gill. Selkie Child. Keen, Sophie, illus. 2005. 24p. (J). lib. bdg. 22.65 ***(978-1-59646-750-7(9))*** Dingles & Co.

—Snow King. Cann, Helen, illus. 2005. 24p. (J). lib. bdg. 22.65 ***(978-1-59646-742-2(8))*** Dingles & Co.

—Tortoise & the Baboon. Woody, illus. 2004. 16p. (J). lib. bdg. 22.65 ***(978-1-59646-686-9(3))*** Dingles & Co.

HSP. First-Place Reading for Title I: A Picture Book of Benjamin Franklin. 2nd ed. 2002. (Harcourt Title I Reading Programs Ser.). (gr. 4 up). pap. 69.60 (978-0-15-338155-3(8)) Harcourt Schl. Pubs.

Hubbard, Suzanna. Lady Who Lived in a Car. 2007. (Illus.). 24p. (J). pap. 6.99 ***(978-1-84458-055-2(5))*** Anova Bks. GBR. *Dist:* Independent Pubs. Group.

Hudson, Charlotte. In a Little While. 2007. (Illus.). 32p. (J). 19.95 ***(978-0-370-32656-6(3))*** Transworld Publishers Ltd. GBR. *Dist:* Independent Pubs. Group.

Hudson, Sue. I Love You. Watanabe, Kaori, illus. 2004. (My First Taggies Book Ser.). 3p. (J). 12.95 (978-0-439-64947-6(1), Cartwheel Bks.) Scholastic, Inc.

Huelsenkamp, Bill. The Very First Christmas: As Told by Elmo the Elf. 2002. 108p. (J). pap. 10.95 (978-1-58736-100-5(0), Starbound Bks.) Wheatmark.

Hughes, Marghanita. Toffee at Home on the Farm. (Illus.). 20p. 13.95 (978-1-899827-50-3(1)) Scottish Children's Pr. GBR. *Dist:* Wilson & Assocs.

Hughes, Monica. Little Mouse Deer & the Crocodile. Moriuchi, Mique, illus. 2004. 24p. (J). lib. bdg. 22.65 ***(978-1-59646-684-5(7))*** Dingles & Co.

—More Little Mouse Deer Tales. Clemenston, John, illus. 2005. 24p. (J). lib. bdg. 22.65 ***(978-1-59646-730-9(4))*** Dingles & Co.

Hughes, Shirley. Alfie's 123. 2000. (Illus.). 32p. (J). (ps-k). 15.95 (978-0-688-17705-8(0)) HarperCollins Pubs.

Hull, Maureen. Rainy Days with Bear. Franson, Leanne, illus. 2004. 32p. (J). 15.95 (978-1-894222-85-3(7)) Lobster Pr. CAN. *Dist:* Univ. of Toronto Pr.

Humphrey, Melanie Friedersdorf. The Tiny Town. Biddix, Cheryl L., illus. 1999. 48p. (J). (ps-3). 16.00 (978-0-9658061-7-6(0)) Peaceful Village Publishing.

—Where Do Falling Stars Go? 3rd ed. 1999. (Illus.). 48p. (J). (ps-1). pap. 14.95 (978-0-9658061-6-9(2)) Peaceful Village Publishing.

Hundal, Nancy. Twilight Fairies. Kilby, Don, illus. 2002. 32p. (J). (gr. k-3). (978-1-55041-645-9(6)) Fitzhenry & Whiteside, Ltd.

—Twilight Fairies. Kilby, Don, illus. 2006. 32p. pap. 7.95 (978-1-55041-961-0(7)) Fitzhenry & Whiteside, Ltd. CAN. *Dist:* F & W Pubns., Inc.

Hunting for Opposites. 1998. (Fisher-Price Little People Concept Bks.: Vol. 2). (Illus.). 24p. (J). (978-0-7666-0320-2(2), 19615) Modern Publishing.

Hurd, Thacher. Zoom City. 1998. (Growing Tree Ser.). (Illus.). 8p. (J). (ps up). 6.99 (978-0-694-01057-8(X), Harper Festival) HarperCollins Pubs.

Hurricane Harbor: Picture Book (English) 8x8. 2007. (Illus.). (J). ***(978-1-933934-68-6(9))*** Educational Adventures.

Hurst, Carol Otis. Picture Books in the Classroom: Addressing Concepts & Skills throughout the Curriculum Through Literature Kindergarten through Grade 2. 2004. (Illus.). 285p. cd-rom 29.95 (978-0-9748509-1-7(8)) Hurst, Carol Consultants.

Hutchins, Hazel. The List. Van Lieshout, Maria, illus. 2007. 32p. (J). (ps-1). pap. 7.95 ***(978-1-55451-063-4(5))***; lib. bdg. 19.95 ***(978-1-55451-064-1(3))*** Annick Pr., Ltd. CAN. *Dist:* Firefly Bks., Ltd.

Hutchins, Pat. Rosie's Walk. Hutchins, Pat, illus. 32p. (J). 2002. mass mkt. 1.00 (978-0-689-85548-1(6)); 2nd ed. 2005. (Illus.). 4.99 (978-1-4169-0835-7(8)) Simon & Schuster Children's Publishing. (Aladdin).

—The Surprise Party. Hutchins, Pat, illus. 2002. (Illus.). (J). 14.47 (978-0-7587-3736-6(X)) Book Wholesalers, Inc.

—Ten Red Apples. Hutchins, Pat, illus. 2000. (Illus.). 32p. (J). (ps up). 16.99 (978-0-688-16797-4(7)); lib. bdg. 17.89 (978-0-688-16798-1(5)) HarperCollins Pubs.

Hyde, Margaret E., ed. Cassatt for Kids. 2004. (Great Art for Kids Ser.). (Illus.). 10p. (J). pap. 8.95 (978-1-58980-202-5(0)) Pelican Publishing Co., Inc.

I Am. Date not set. 8p. (J). (gr. k-2). pap. 3.75 (978-1-58323-016-9(5), Seedling Pubns.) Continental Pr., Inc.

Ikids. My Giant 123 Bath Book. Delice, Shelly Meredith, illus. 2005. (Soft Shapes Numbers Ser.). 2p. (J). (ps-17). 14.99 (978-1-58476-357-4(4)) Innovative Kids.

—My Giant ABC Bath Book. Hine, Eileen, illus. 2005. (Soft Shapes Numbers Ser.). 2p. (J). (ps-17). 14.99 (978-1-58476-356-7(6)) Innovative Kids.

Imperato, Teresa. Colors All Around: A Turn & Pop Book. Petrone, Valeria, illus. 2005. 10p. (J). bds. 5.95 (978-1-58117-277-5(X), Intervisual/Piggy Toes) Dalmatian Pr.

—Five Little Piggies: Mini. Haskamp, Steve, illus. 2005. 12p. (J). bds. (978-1-58117-317-8(2), Intervisual/Piggy Toes) Dalmatian Pr.

—Good Morning, Good Night. Mitchell, Melanie, illus. 2005. 12p. (J). (ps up). 9.95 (978-1-58117-279-9(6), Intervisual/Piggy Toes) Dalmatian Pr.

—How Many Ducks in a Row? A Turn & Pop Book. Petrone, Valeria, illus. 2005. 10p. (J). bds. 5.95 (978-1-58117-278-2(8), Intervisual/Piggy Toes) Dalmatian Pr.

In-House Staff. Thomas Toddler Board Unit, Vol. 6. 2000. (J). 2.99 (978-0-375-80318-5(1)) Random Hse. Children's Bks.

In My Home. 2002. (First Words & Pictures Book Ser.). 14p. (J). bds. 7.95 (978-0-7525-7980-1(0)) Parragon, Inc.

Inches, Alison. Dora Loves Boots. Saunders, Zina, illus. 2003. (Dora the Explorer Ser.). 24p. (J). pap. 3.99 (978-0-689-86373-8(X), Simon Spotlight/Nickelodeon) Simon & Schuster Children's Publishing.

Inkpen, Mick. Beachmoles & Bellvine. 2006. (Blue Nose Island Ser.: Bk. 2). (Illus.). (J). (ps). 19.99 (978-0-340-87865-1(7), Hodder & Stoughton) Hodder General Publishing Division GBR. *Dist:* Trafalgar Square Publishing.

—Beachmoles & Bellvine, 1 CD. MC, ed. 2006. (Blue Nose Island Ser.: Bk. 2). (Illus.). 34p. (J). (ps). audio compact disk 13.95 (978-1-84456-225-1(5), Hodder & Stoughton) Hodder General Publishing Division GBR. *Dist:* Trafalgar Square Publishing.

Innovative Kids Staff. Goodnight, Baby. Larranaga, Ana, illus. 2006. 12p. (J). (ps-ps). bds. 8.99 (978-1-58476-482-3(1), IKIDS) Innovative Kids.

—Happy Baby: A Book of Emotions. Parsons, Jackie & Larranaga, Ana, illus. 2006. (ibaby - Let's Be Babies Ser.). 10p. (J). (ps-ps). bds. 10.99 (978-1-58476-353-6(1)) Innovative Kids.

—My Easter Basket. Filipowich, Bob, illus. 2006. (Soft Shapes Ser.). 6p. (J). (ps). 9.99 (978-1-58476-469-4(4), IKIDS) Innovative Kids.

—My Fire Truck. Brooks, David, illus. 2006. (Soft Shapes Ser.). 8p. (J). (ps-ps). 8.99 (978-1-58476-349-9(3)) Innovative Kids.

Intrater, Roberta Grobel. Baby Faces. 2002. (Baby Faces Ser.). 10p. (J). bds. 4.95 (978-0-439-42005-1(9), Cartwheel Bks.) Scholastic, Inc.

—Eat! 2002. (Baby Faces Ser.). 10p. (J). bds. 4.95 (978-0-439-42006-8(7), Cartwheel Bks.) Scholastic, Inc.

—Hugs & Kisses. 2002. (Baby Faces Ser.). 10p. (J). bds. 4.95 (978-0-439-42003-7(2), Cartwheel Bks.) Scholastic, Inc.

—Sleep. 2002. (Baby Faces Ser.). (Illus.). 10p. (J). bds. 4.95 (978-0-439-42004-4(0), Cartwheel Bks.) Scholastic, Inc.

Isaacson, Marlys J. Picture Me Learning the Numbers from 0 - 20: With Pictures & Rhymes to Make It Fun. 2001. 10.00 (978-0-9742951-9-0(1), Picture Me...! Pubns.) Picture Me Reading!.

Island, Sylvester, Jr. Li'l Rex. Island, Sylvester, Jr., illus. 1998. (Illus.). (J). (ps-6). 11.95 (978-1-892089-53-3(X)); pap. 6.95 (978-1-892089-50-2(5)) Our Kids Pubn., Inc.

—Li'l Rex Says, Let's Have Fun with Shapes. Island, Sylvester, Jr., illus. 1998. (Illus.). (J). (ps-6). pap. 3.95 (978-1-892089-51-9(3)) Our Kids Pubn., Inc.

Itsy, Bitsy Spider. 2005. (Sign & Signalong Ser.). (Illus.). 10p. (J). (ps). per. 4.99 (978-1-904550-43-3(6)) Child's Play-International.

Jackson, Carolyn. If I Had a Dog. Brassard, France, illus. 2006. 32p. (J). (ps-2). 16.95 (978-0-88776-725-8(7)) Tundra Bks., Inc./Livres Toundra, Inc. CAN. *Dist:* Random Hse., Inc.

Jackson, Marjorie. Los Sombrillas de Shintaro. Romo, Alberto, tr. Finch, Linda, illus. 1998. (Books for Young Learners).Tr. of Shintaro's Umbrellas. (SPA.). 16p. (J). (gr. k-2). pap. 5.00 (978-1-57274-204-8(6), A2905) Owen, Richard C. Pubs., Inc.

James, Diane. Here We Go. 2004. (Jigsaw Rhymes Ser.). (Illus.). 12p. (J). (ps-k). bds. 9.95 (978-1-58728-024-5(8), Two Can Publishing) T&N Children's Publishing.

—Splish Splash. 2004. (Jigsaw Rhymes Ser.). (Illus.). 12p. (J). (ps-k). bds. 9.95 (978-1-58728-022-1(1), Two Can Publishing) T&N Children's Publishing.

—Spots & Stripes. 2004. (Jigsaw Rhymes Ser.). (Illus.). 12p. (J). (ps-k). bds. 9.95 (978-1-58728-021-4(3), Two Can Publishing) T&N Children's Publishing.

James, Mark S. Christopher's Little Airplane Coloring & Activity Fun Book. Smelcer, Harold, illus. 2001. 48p. (J). 3.95 (978-0-9676960-1-0(1)) Chelonian Pr, Inc.

Jandl, Ernst. Ser Quinto. Junge, Norman, illus. 2nd ed. 2002. (SPA.). 32p. (J). (978-84-89804-21-0(4)) Loguez Ediciones ESP. *Dist:* Lectorum Pubns., Inc.

Jarman, Julia. Molly & the Giant. Sholto, Walker, illus. 2005. 24p. (J). lib. bdg. 22.65 ***(978-1-59646-746-0(0))*** Dingles & Co.

Jarrell, Pamela R. The Circus. Cress, Michelle H., illus. l.t. ed. 1998. (Cuddle Bks.). 5p. (J). (ps). pap. 10.95 (978-1-57332-122-8(2)) HighReach Learning, Inc.

—Dr. Danny Checks My Teeth. Bicking, Judith, illus. l.t. ed. 2001. (Big Bks.). 8p. (J). (ps-1). pap. 10.95 (978-1-57332-217-1(2)) HighReach Learning, Inc.

—I Can. Linke, Don, Jr., illus. l.t. ed. 1998. (Cuddle Bks.). 7p. (J). (ps-k). pap. 10.95 (978-1-57332-123-5(0)) HighReach Learning, Inc.

—I Like Fall. Middleton, Mikell, illus. l.t. ed. 2001. (Cuddle Bks.). 7p. (J). (ps-1). pap. 10.95 (978-1-57332-214-0(8)) HighReach Learning, Inc.

—In the Garden. Lent, Marion W., illus. l.t. ed. 1998. (Cuddle Bks.). 8p. (J). (ps-k). pap. 10.95 (978-1-57332-113-6(3)) HighReach Learning, Inc.

—Jennifer & Danny. Linke, Don, Jr., illus. l.t. ed. 1999. (Cuddle Bks.). 7p. (J). (ps-k). pap. 10.95 (978-1-57332-124-2(9)) HighReach Learning, Inc.

—Miss Tammy Is Cool! Gray, Stacy A., illus. l.t. ed. 2001. (Little Bks.). 6p. (J). (ps-1). pap. 10.95 (978-1-57332-210-2(5)) HighReach Learning, Inc.

—See the Car. Carroll, Ken, Jr., illus. l.t. ed. 1998. (Cuddle Bks.). 6p. (J). (ps). pap. 10.95 (978-1-57332-105-1(2)) HighReach Learning, Inc.

Jarrell, Pamela R. & Gray, Stacy A. Carol Paints Everything. l.t. ed. 2001. (Big Bks.). (J). (ps-1). 10.95 (978-1-57332-212-6(1)) HighReach Learning, Inc.

Jay, Larsen. What If Cows Could... ? 2005. (J). lib. bdg. 19.95 (***978-1-933732-01-5(6)*** , Bear Hug Bks.) MidAmerica Publishing Co.

Jennings, Linda. Duna y Dan. Chapman, Jane, illus. (SPA.). 28p. (J). (gr. k-1). (978-84-8418-027-2(1) , ZZ4481) Zendrera Zariquiey, Editorial ESP. *Dist:* Lectorum Pubns., Inc.

Jennings, Linda & Gardener, Louise. Monsters. 1999. (Spooky Pop-Ups Ser.). (Illus.). 12p. (J). 4.95 (978-1-899607-19-8(6)) Sterling Publishing Co., Inc.

Jennings, Linda & Gardner, Louise. Batty Beasts. 1999. (Spooky Pop-Ups Ser.). (Illus.). 12p. (J). 4.95 (978-1-899607-20-4(X)) Sterling Publishing Co., Inc.

—Creepy Crawlies. 1999. (Spooky Pop-Ups Ser.). (Illus.). 12p. (J). 4.95 (978-1-899607-18-1(8)) Sterling Publishing Co., Inc.

—Ghosts. 1999. (Spooky Pop-Ups Ser.). (Illus.). 12p. 4.95 (978-1-899607-21-1(8)) Sterling Publishing Co., Inc.

Jennings, Patti. Rise & Shine. 2002. (Illus.). 6p. (J). 6.95 (978-0-8069-8473-5(2)) Sterling Publishing Co., Inc.

Jennings, Patti, illus. Fleecy Chick. 2003. (Fleecy Friends Ser.). 10p. (J). (ps). 9.99 (978-0-8431-7785-5(3) , Price Stern Sloan) Penguin Group (USA) Inc.

Jennings, Sharon. Franklin & the Tin Flute. Gagnon, Celeste et al, illus. 2005. 32p. (J). lib. bdg. 15.38 (***978-1-4242-1180-7(8)***) Fitzgerald Bks.

Jennings, Sharon, et al. Franklin's Picnic. Southern, Shelley et al, illus. 32p. (978-1-55337-714-6(1)) Kids Can Pr., Ltd.

Jerrell, Pam & Mullican, Judy. Let's Take a Trip to Mexico. Linke, Don, Jr., illus. l.t. ed. 2000. (BB Ser.). 8p. (J). (ps-1). pap. 10.95 (978-1-57332-177-8(X)) HighReach Learning, Inc.

Jesus Is Born: (With Puzzle) 2000. (Illus.). (J). (ps-k). bds. 4.95 (978-0-88271-691-6(3)) Regina Pr., Malhame & Co.

Jesus Loves Me Musical. 2000. (Illus.). (J). (ps-k). bds. 10.95 (978-0-88271-013-6(3)) Regina Pr., Malhame & Co.

Jeunesse, Gallimard. The Battery Discovery Box. 1998. (Discovery Box Ser.). (Illus.). 32p. (J). (gr. 1-5). 11.95 (978-0-590-92682-9(9)) Scholastic, Inc.

Jinkins, Jim. Hide & Seek Hunny Pot. 1999. (P B & J Otter Noodle Stories Ser.). (Illus.). 10p. (J). (ps). 4.99 (978-0-7364-0067-1(2)) Mouse Works.

Jocelyn, Marthe. A Day with Nellie. 2002. (Illus.). 24p. (J). (gr. k-k). 15.95 (978-0-88776-600-8(5)) Tundra Bks., Inc./Livres Toundra, Inc. CAN. *Dist:* Random Hse., Inc.

—Over, Under. Slaughter, Tom, illus. 2005. 24p. (J). (gr. k-k). 15.95 (978-0-88776-708-1(7)) Tundra Bks., Inc./ Livres Toundra, Inc. CAN. *Dist:* Random Hse., Inc.

Johnson, Crockett. Harold & the Purple Crayon: Under the Sea. 2003. (gr. k-3). lib. bdg. 11.80 (978-0-613-69129-1(6)) Tandem Library Bks.

—Magic Beach. 2005. (Illus.). 64p. (J). 18.95 (978-1-932425-27-7(6) , Lemniscaat) Boyds Mills Pr.

Johnson, D. B. Henry Hikes to Fitchburg. 2006. (Illus.). 32p. (J). (gr. k-3). reprint ed. 6.95 (978-0-618-73749-9(9)) Houghton Mifflin Co. Trade & Reference Div.

Johnson, Julia. A Is for Arabia. Styles, Emily, illus. 2004. 32p. 12.95 (978-1-900988-55-1(0)) Stacey International Pubs. GBR. *Dist:* Interlink Publishing Group, Inc.

Johnston, Tony. Day of the Dead. Winter, Jeanette, illus. 2000. 48p. (J). (ps up). pap. 6.00 (978-0-15-202446-8(8) , Voyager Bks./Libros Viajeros) Harcourt Children's Bks.

Jolly Santa. (Illus.). 32p. (J). pap. 1.59 (978-1-55254-195-1(9) , BV24015) Brighter Vision Pubns.

Jonas, Ann. Bird Talk. 1999. (Illus.). 32p. (J). (ps-3). 14.89 (978-0-688-14173-8(0)) HarperCollins Pubs.

Jones-Hughes, Karen, illus. Munch, Munch! Who's There? 2002. (Mini Movers Ser.). 14p. (J). bds. 3.99 (978-0-7641-5570-3(9)) Barron's Educational Series, Inc. .

Jones, Karen, illus. Bang, Bang! Who's There? 2002. (Mini Movers Ser.). 14p. (J). bds. 3.99 (978-0-7641-5571-0(7)) Barron's Educational Series, Inc.

—Tap,Tap! Who's There? 2002. (Mini Movers Ser.). 14p. (J). bds. 2.95 (978-0-7641-5568-0(7)) Barron's Educational Series, Inc.

Jones, Katina. Cool School Story: Little Lucy & Friends. Ottinger, Jon, illus. Zaidan, Rick, photos by. 2001. (Little Lucy & Friends Ser.). 24p. (J). (ps-3). 9.99 (978-1-57151-700-5(6)) Playhouse Publishing.

Jones, Lara. I Love Hugs. Jones, Lara, illus. 2002. (Illus.). 16p. (J). bds. 6.95 (978-0-439-36767-7(0) , Cartwheel Bks.) Scholastic, Inc.

—I Love My Potty. Jones, Lara, illus. 2002. (Illus.). 16p. (J). bds. 6.95 (978-0-439-36768-4(9) , Cartwheel Bks.) Scholastic, Inc.

Joslin, Mary. The Goodbye Boat. St. Louis Little, Claire, illus. 1999. 28p. (ps-k). 16.00 (978-0-8028-5186-4(X)) Eerdmans, William B. Publishing Co.

Joy, Flora. The Pride Piper. Harroll, Pat, illus. 1999. 48p. (J). 7.00 (978-1-884624-10-0(3)) Storytelling World Pr.

Joyce, Bill. Little Spot of Color. 2000. (Rolie Polie Olie Ser.). (Illus.). 18p. (ps). 5.99 (978-0-7868-3319-1(X)) Disney Pr.

Joyful Sunflower. 2003. (Illus.). 4.99 (978-1-56148-383-9(4)) Good Bks.

Julian, Russell. My First Farm Books: Lost Calf/Busy Dog/ Hungry Pig/Happy Cockerel, 4 vols. 2005. (Illus.). 12p. (J). per. 12.50 (978-1-4052-1667-8(0)) Egmont Bks., Ltd. GBR. *Dist:* Trafalgar Square Publishing.

Das Jumbo-Buch von Elmar und Willi. 2000. Tr. of Adventures of Elmer, the Patchwork Elephant. (GER.). (J). pap. 16.95 (978-3-423-07996-9(7)) Deutscher Taschenbuch Verlag GmbH & Co KG DEU. *Dist:* Distribooks, Inc.

Jumbo Toddler Workbook, 1 vol. 1998. (Fisher-Price Jumbo Workbook Ser.). 128p. pap., wbk. ed. (978-0-7666-0307-3(5) , Honey Bear Bks.) Modern Publishing.

Kahl, Virginia. The Duchess Bakes a Cake. Kahl, Virginia, illus. 2002. 32p. 17.95 (978-1-930900-14-1(7)) Purple Hse. Pr.

Kaldor, Connie. A Duck in New York City. 2005. (Illus.). 36p. (J). (ps-3). 16.95 incl. audio compact disk (978-2-923163-02-4(8)) La Montagne Secrete CAN. *Dist:* National Bk. Network.

Kalin, Julia. Brady's Bath: A Reader Illustrated Storybook. unabr. ed. 1999. (Picture-It Storybook Ser.). 16p. (J). (ps-6). pap. 12.95 (978-0-9672430-1-6(7) , 9802) Stay, Play & Learn.

Kalomas, Alice & Kerr, Lenora. Sir Wrinkles. Utomo, Gabhor, illus. 2005. (J). 14.95 (978-0-9766639-0-4(2)) Sir Wrinkles Pr.

Kamke, Bridget. The Story of the Infinipede. Ospital, Genevieve, illus. 2003. (J). 19.95 (978-0-9744306-0-7(9)) You Can Do It! Productions.

Kane, Tracy. The Magic of Color. Kane, Tracy, illus. l.t. ed. 2005. (Illus.). 40p. (J). (gr. 1-3). 17.95 (978-0-9766289-0-3(2)) Light-Beams Publishing.

Karim, Roberta. This Is a Hospital, Not a Zoo! 2002. (gr. k-3). lib. bdg. 14.10 (978-0-613-72912-3(9)) Tandem Library Bks.

Karon, Jan, et al. Violet Comes to Stay. McCully, Emily Arnold, illus. 2006. (Mitford Ser.). 36p. (J). (gr. k). 15.99 (978-0-670-06073-3(9) , Viking Juvenile) Penguin Group (USA) Inc.

Kartinyeri, Doris. Bush Games & Knucklebones. McInerney, Kunyi June-Anne, illus. 2003. 32p. (J). pap. 17.00 (978-1-875641-81-9(5)) Magabala Bks. AUS. *Dist:* International Specialized Bk. Services.

Kaska, Keiko. Choco Encuentra una Mama. 2001. (SPA., Illus.). (J). (ps-3). 8.95 (978-958-04-2582-3(5) , NR6002) Norma S.A. COL. *Dist:* Distribuidora Norma, Inc., Lectorum Pubns., Inc.

Katz, Karen. Grandma & Me. Katz, Karen, illus. 2002. (Illus.). 14p. (J). 6.99 (978-0-689-84905-3(2) , Little Simon) Simon & Schuster Children's Publishing.

—Twelve Hats for Lena: A Book of Months. Katz, Karen, illus. 2002. (Illus.). 34p. (J). (ps-3). 17.99 (978-0-689-84873-5(0) , McElderry, Margaret K.) Simon & Schuster Children's Publishing.

Kellaher, Karen. 101 Picture Prompts to Spark Super Writing Grades 3-5: Reproducible Photographs, Cartoons & Art Masterpiece. 1999. (Illus.). 64p. (J). pap., tchr. ed. 9.95 (978-0-590-63229-4(9)) Scholastic, Inc.

Keller, Holly. That's Mine, Horace. Keller, Holly, illus. 2000. (Illus.). 24p. (J). (ps up). 16.99 (978-0-688-17159-9(1)) HarperCollins Pubs.

Kellerhals-Stewart, Heather. Skookum Sal, Birling Gal. Blaine, Janice, illus. unabr. ed. 32p. (YA). 18.95 (***978-1-55017-285-0(9)***) Harbour Publishing Co., Ltd. CAN. *Dist:* Graphic Arts Ctr. Publishing Co.

Kelley, Brooke H. Beach Fun. Lent, Marion W., illus. l.t. ed. 1998. (Cuddle Bks.). 6p. (J). (ps). pap. 10.95 (978-1-57332-118-1(4)) HighReach Learning, Inc.

Kelly, Sharon L. C. M. Coco's Vineyard Vacation: Double Fun on Martha's Vineyard. Galbraith, Alison L., illus. 2005. 40p. (J). 16.95 (978-0-9766283-0-9(9)) Secret Garden Bookworks.

Kendall, Susanna. Where's the Christmas Party? 2000. (Illus.). 16p. (ps-k). pap. 5.00 (978-0-7548-0705-6(3)) Anness Publishing, Inc.

Kennedy, Marge. The Book of Boo! 2002. (Illus.). 32p. (ps-1). 5.99 (978-0-7868-3364-1(5)) Disney Pr.

Kenney, Cindy. Veggie Tales I Can! And So Can You! 2004. (Illus.). bds. 12.99 (978-0-310-70893-3(1)) Zonderkidz.

Kenny, Sean. Fast-Wing: The Adventures of A Blue-Winged Teal. 1998. (Illus.). 174p. (J). (gr. 3-7). pap. 6.95 (978-0-86327-547-0(8)) Wolfhound Pr. IRL. *Dist:* Irish American Bk. Co.

Kent, Lorna, illus. At the Beach. 2004. 8p. (J). bds. 3.99 (978-1-85854-087-0(9)) Brimax Books Ltd. GBR. *Dist:* Byeway Bks.

Kerr, Judith. Goose in a Hole. Kerr, Judith, illus. 2006. (Illus.). 40p. (J). (ps). pap. 9.99 (978-0-00-720794-7(8) , HarperCollins Children's Bks.) HarperCollins Pubs. Ltd. GBR. *Dist:* Independent Pubs. Group.

—Goose in a Hole. 2005. (Illus.). 40p. (J). 15.99 (978-0-00-720793-0(X)) HarperCollins Pubs. Ltd. GBR. *Dist:* Independent Pubs. Group.

—Mog Collection, 6 vols. Kerr, Judith, illus. 2007. 1p. (J). (gr. k-2). pap., pap., pap. 35.00 (***978-0-00-725944-1(1)***) HarperCollins Pubs. Ltd. GBR. *Dist:* Independent Pubs. Group.

Kerr, Judith. Tiger Who Came to Tea. 2006. pap. (978-0-06-052468-5(5)) HarperCollins Canada, Ltd.

Kerven, Rosalind. Sparrow, the Crow & the Pearl. Williamson, Melanie, illus. 2005. 24p. (J). lib. bdg. 22.65 (***978-1-59646-754-5(1)***) Dingles & Co.

Kessler, Leonard P. Mr. Pine's Purple House: 40th Anniversary Edition. Kessler, Leonard P., illus. 40th anniv. ed. 2005. (Illus.). 64p. (J). 16.00 (978-1-930900-32-5(5)) Purple Hse. Pr.

Keyes, Joan Ross. The Oxford Picture Dictionary for Kids. Springer, Sally, illus. 1998. (Oxford Picture Dictionary for Kids Ser.). (SPA & ENG.). 152p. 14.25 (978-0-19-436662-5(6)) Oxford Univ. Pr., Inc.

Kim, Kelly. My Busy, Busy Day. 2000. 12p. (J). 5.99 (978-0-310-23206-3(6)) Zonderkidz.

Kinast, Susan. Play from A to Z. 2006. (J). lib. bdg. 19.95 (***978-1-933732-11-4(3)*** , Bear Hug Bks.) MidAmerica Publishing Co.

Kinkade, Thomas, illus. Away in a Manger. 2005. 32p. (J). 16.99 (978-0-06-078730-1(9)) Zonderkidz.

Kitamura, Satoshi. When Sheep Can't Sleep (Cuando los Borregos no Pueden Dormir) (SPA.). (J). (gr. 1-6). 19.95 (978-84-372-6605-3(X)) Santillana USA Publishing Co., Inc.

Kitten. (Buggy Buddies Ser.). (Illus.). (J). (ps). bds. (978-1-56021-350-5(7) , 201) W.J. Fantasy, Inc.

Kittler, Robert. Can't Sleep, Count Sheep. Jackson, Nick, illus. 1998. 123p. (gr. 4-7). pap. 9.95 (978-0-9668622-0-1(1)) Count Sheep Publishing.

Kleven, Elisa. Sun Bread. 2004. (Illus.). 32p. (J). reprint ed. pap. 6.99 (978-0-14-240073-9(4) , Puffin) Penguin Group (USA) Inc.

Klies, Kimberly. Sea Treasures. Wise, Noreen, ed. Smith, Philip, illus. 2000. (Book-a-Day Collection). 32p. (YA). (ps). pap. 5.95 (978-1-58584-377-0(6)) Huckleberry Pr.

Klinting, Lars. What Do You Want? Lundin, Maria, tr. from SWE. 2006. (Illus.). 36p. (J). 15.95 (978-0-88899-636-7(5)) Groundwood Bks. CAN. *Dist:* Perseus Distribution.

Klutz Shrinky Dinks Refill Pack. 40p. 8.95 (978-1-57054-585-6(5)) Klutz.

Knopf, Susan. Welcome to Merriweather Farm. Walstead, Curt, illus. 2005. 10p. (J). pap. 11.95 (978-0-7624-2342-2(0) , Running Pr. Kids) Running Pr. Bk. Pubs.

Komaiko, Leah. Earl's Too Cool for Me. 2003. (gr. k-3). lib. bdg. 14.15 (978-0-613-65690-0(3)) Tandem Library Bks.

Koralek, Jenny. The Coat of Many Colors. Baynes, Pauline, illus. 2004. 32p. (J). 16.00 (978-0-8028-5277-9(7)) Eerdmans, William B. Publishing Co.

Korman, Justine. The Grumpy Easter Bunny. McQueen, Lucinda, illus. 2004. 32p. (J). 3.50 (978-0-439-63595-0(0)) Scholastic, Inc.

Kotzwinkle, William & Murray, Glenn. Walter the Farting Dog. Colman, Audrey, illus. 2001. 32p. (J). (ps-2). 15.95 (978-1-58394-053-2(7) , Frog Ltd.) North Atlantic Bks.

Koury, Jen. Barney Backhoe's Waterline. Linden, Pat & Hilko, Steve, eds. Koury, Jen, illus. 1999. (Johnny Tractor Toybooks Ser.). (Illus.). 10p. (J). (ps-1). (978-1-887327-14-5(2)) Ertl Co., Inc.

—Big John on the Big Farm. Linden, Pat & Hilko, Steve, eds. Koury, Jen, illus. 1999. (Johnny Tractor Toybooks Ser.). (Illus.). 10p. (J). (ps-1). (978-1-887327-23-7(1)) Ertl Co., Inc.

—Billy Baler's Hay Day. Linden, Pat & Hilko, Steve, eds. Koury, Jen, illus. 1999. (Johnny Tractor Toybooks Ser.). (Illus.). 10p. (J). (ps-1). (978-1-887327-22-0(3)) Ertl Co., Inc.

—Scotty Skidsteer Helps Build a House. Hilko, Steve & Linden, Pat, eds. Koury, Jen, illus. 1999. (Johnny Tractor Toybooks Ser.). (Illus.). 10p. (J). (ps-1). (978-1-887327-21-3(5)) Ertl Co., Inc.

Kraus, Robert. Leo the Late Bloomer. Aruego, Jose, illus. 1999. (Share a Story Ser.). (J). (ps up). 9.95 incl. reel tape (978-0-694-70098-1(3) , Harper Festival) HarperCollins Pubs.

—Leo the Late Bloomer. 1998. (Illus.). 17p. (J). (ps up). 7.95 (978-0-694-00980-0(6)) HarperCollins Pubs.

—Leo the Late Bloomer. Aruego, Jose, illus. 2000. 32p. (J). (ps-3). pap. 6.95 (978-1-931016-02-5(X) , MHC-2-X) Minnesota Humanities Commission.

—Little Louie the Baby Bloomer. 2000. (Illus.). (J). (978-0-606-18702-2(2)) Tandem Library Bks.

Kraus, Robert, et al. Leo the Late Bloomer, 3 vols. Aruego, Jose, illus. 1998. (My Little Library Board Book Ser.). (J). bds. 19.95 (978-0-694-01183-4(5) , Harper Festival) HarperCollins Pubs.

Krauss, Ruth. Bears. Sendak, Maurice, illus. 2005. 24p. (J). 14.95 (978-0-06-027994-3(X)) HarperCollins Pubs.

—I Want to Paint My Bathroom Blue. Sendak, Maurice, illus. 2001. (Sendak Reissues Ser.). 24p. 15.95 (978-0-06-028634-7(2)) HarperCollins Pubs.

—I'll Be You & You Be Me. Sendak, Maurice, illus. rev. ed. 2001. 40p. (J). (ps-3). 14.89 (978-0-06-028458-9(7)) ; 15.95 (978-0-06-028459-6(5)) HarperCollins Pubs.

Krauss, Ruth & Sendak, Maurice. I Want to Paint My Bathroom Blue. 2001. (Sendak Reissues Ser.). (Illus.). 24p. (J). 14.89 (978-0-06-028635-4(0)) HarperCollins Pubs.

Kregel Publications Staff. The Long Ride. 2004. 32p. 13.99 (978-0-8254-3577-5(3)) Kregel Pubns.

Kreischer, Elsie Karr. Bigger Than a Button. Brandenburg, Claire, illus. 2002. 28p. (J). 14.95 (978-0-9708940-4-5(X)) Gently Worded Bks., LLC.

Krensky, Stephen. Lionel & His Friends. 1999. (Illus.). (J). (978-0-606-18418-2(X)) Tandem Library Bks.

Krudwig, Vickie L., creator. Silly Circles Sketch Pad. 2004. (Illus.). 50p. (J). spiral bd. (978-0-9700127-2-2(1)) Sweet Success Pr.

Krulik, Nancy E. Animal Friends: A Learning-to-Write Book. Baroux, illus. 2004. (My Little Chalkboard Ser.). 16p. (J). pap. 12.95 (978-0-7624-1435-2(9) , Running Pr. Kids) Running Pr. Bk. Pubs.

Krulik, Nancy E. Ice-Cream Dreams. Martinez, Heather, illus. 2004. 22p. (J). lib. bdg. 15.00 (***978-1-4242-0975-0(7)***) Fitzgerald Bks.

Krull. Unspecified Picture Book No. 3. 2000. (Illus.). (J). (978-0-15-201439-1(X)) Harcourt Schl. Pubs.

Kubler, Annie, illus. Teddy Bear, Teddy Bear. 2004. (Sign & Signalong Ser.). 12p. (J). (ps). bds. 4.99 (978-1-904550-40-2(1)) Child's Play-International.

—Twinkle, Twinkle, Little Star. 2002. (Sign & Signalong Ser.). 12p. (J). (ps). bds. 4.99 (978-1-904550-42-6(8)) Child's Play-International.

Kubler, Annie & Adams, Pam. Down by the Station. 2005. 16p. (J). bds. 12.99 (978-0-85953-457-4(X)) Child's Play-International.

Kubler, Annie & Baker, Sue, illus. Before I Was Born. 1999. 32p. (J). (ps-3). (978-0-85953-316-4(6)) Child's Play International Ltd. GBR. *Dist:* Child's Play-International.

Kushner, Tony. Brundibar. Sendak, Maurice, illus. 2003. 56p. (J). (ps-17). (978-0-7868-0904-2(3)) Hyperion Bks. for Children.

Kuskin, Karla. Roar & More. ed. 2004. (Illus.). 48p. (J). (ps up). 11.95 (978-1-59078-249-1(6)) Boyds Mills Pr.

Kuwahara, Ryuichi. In Front of the Ant: Walking with Beetles & Other Insects. Kuribayashi, Satoshi, photos by. 2004. (Illus.). 28p. (J). pap. 8.95 (978-1-929132-63-8(8)) Kane/Miller Bk. Pubs., Inc.

La Jars, David. My Animal Friends. rev. ed. 2004. (Talk Together Ser.). (Illus.). 24p. (J). (ps-k). pap. 5.95 (978-1-58728-017-7(5) , Two Can Publishing) T&N Children's Publishing.

—One, Two, Red & Blue. rev. ed. 2004. (Talk Together Ser.). (Illus.). 24p. (J). (ps-k). 9.95 (978-1-58728-015-3(9) , Two Can Publishing) T&N Children's Publishing.

La Montagne Secrete/Secret Mountain. A Poodle in Paris. 2006. (Illus.). 36p. 16.95 (978-2-923163-12-3(5)) La Montagne Secrete CAN. *Dist:* National Bk. Network.

Labatt, Mary. Sam Gets Lost. Sarrazin, Marisol, illus. 2004. 32p. (J). lib. bdg. 15.38 (***978-1-4242-1159-3(X)***) Fitzgerald Bks.

—Sam Goes to School. Sarrazin, Marisol, illus. 2004. 31p. (J). lib. bdg. 15.38 (***978-1-4242-1160-9(3)***) Fitzgerald Bks.

—Sam's Snowy Day. Sarrazin, Marisol, illus. 2005. 32p. (J). lib. bdg. 10.00 (***978-1-4242-1155-5(7)***) Fitzgerald Bks.

Laden, Nina. El Dia Que Pigasso Conocio a Muutisse. 2000. (Illus.). (J). (gr. 4-7). (CAT.). 36p. 14.95 (978-84-95040-26-8(3)); 2nd ed. (SPA., 48p. 14.95 (978-84-95040-24-4(7) , RR6004) Serres, Ediciones, S. L. ESP. *Dist:* Lectorum Pubns., Inc., Lectorum Pubns., Inc., Libros Sin Fronteras.

—Peek-a-Who? 2000. (Illus.). 11p. (J). (ps). bds. 6.95 (978-0-8118-2602-0(3)) Chronicle Bks. LLC.

—Ready, Set, Go! Laden, Nina, illus. 2000. (Illus.). 11p. (J). (ps). bds. 6.95 (978-0-8118-2601-3(5)) Chronicle Bks. LLC.

Ladybird Books Staff. Picture Book for Baby. (First Picture Bks.: No. 832-1). (Illus.). 52p. (J). (ps). pap. 3.50 (978-0-7214-0749-4(8) , Dutton Juvenile) Penguin Group (USA) Inc.

Lafortune, Claude. The Wonderful Story of Christmas. gif. ed. 2003. (Illus.). 24p. (978-2-89507-438-0(0)) Novalis Publishing.

Lambert, Ian. Perdido y Buscandolo. Lambert, Ian, illus. 2001. (SPA., Illus.). 32p. (J). (ps-3). pap. 7.50 (978-1-59134-016-4(0)) Maval Publishing, Inc.

Laminack, Lester L. The Sunsets of Miss Olivia Wiggins. Bergum, Constance Rummel, illus. 1998. 32p. (J). (gr. 1-5). 15.95 (978-1-56145-139-5(8)) Peachtree Pubs., Ltd.

Lammie, Karen J., illus. Moo! 2005. (On the Farm Ser.). 10p. (J). (ps-ps). bds. 4.95 (978-0-7641-5827-8(9)) Barron's Educational Series, Inc.

Lamson, Sharon. Squiggz Rides the Big Storm: A Story about Overcoming Fear. Barry, Bruce, illus. 2006. 32p. (J). 7.99 (978-0-310-71005-9(7)) Zonderkidz.

Landis, Beth, ed. My First Colors Board Book. 2004. (Illus.). 36p. (J). bds. 5.99 (978-0-7566-0280-2(7)) Dorling Kindersley Publishing, Inc.

—My First Dinosaur Board Book. 2004. (Illus.). 36p. (J). bds. 5.99 (978-0-7566-0281-9(5)) Dorling Kindersley Publishing, Inc.

Landstrom, Olof. Boo & Baa Get Wet. 2000. (978-0-606-22355-3(X)) Tandem Library Bks.

—Boo & Baa in the Woods. 2000. (978-0-606-22354-6(1)) Tandem Library Bks.

Lang, Annie J. Puddle Pals & Butterfly Buddies. 1998. (Illus.). 50p. pap. 10.95 (978-1-57377-040-8(X)) Eas'l Pubns.

Langen, Annette. Felix Travels Back in Time. Droop, Constanza, illus. 2004. 40p. (J). 14.99 (978-1-59384-032-7(2)) Parklane Publishing.

Langford, Jane. Hero. Vince, Dawn, illus. 2005. 24p. (J). lib. bdg. 22.65 (***978-1-59646-720-0(7)***) Dingles & Co.

—An Old Red Hat. Axworthy, Anni, illus. 2004. 24p. (J). lib. bdg. 22.65 (***978-1-59646-676-0(6)***) Dingles & Co.

Larson, Beverly. The Whale's Tale: A Little Bible Playbook about Obedience. Moroney, Tracey, illus. 1999. (Chunky Board Bks.). 18p. (J). (ps-k). 5.99 (978-0-7847-0927-6(0) , 03500, Bean Sprouts) Standard Publishing.

Lasky, Kathryn. Untitled Historical #1: Picturebook Series. 2005. 32p. (J). 14.99 (978-0-7868-0503-7(X)) Hyperion Pr.

—Untitled Historical #1 Picturebook Series. 2005. 32p. (J). 15.49 (978-0-7868-2436-6(0)) Hyperion Pr.

—Untitled Historical #2: Picturebook Series. 2005. 32p. (J). 14.99 (978-0-7868-0504-4(8)) Hyperion Pr.

—Untitled Historical #2 Picturebook Series. 2005. 32p. (J). 15.49 (978-0-7868-2437-3(9)) Hyperion Pr.

—Untitled Historical #3: Picturebook Series. 2005. 32p. (J). 14.99 (978-0-7868-0505-1(6)) Hyperion Pr.

—Untitled Historical #3 Picturebook Series. 2005. 32p. (J). 15.49 (978-0-7868-2438-0(7)) Hyperion Pr.

Law, Felicia. Picture Dictionary: A First See-and-Say Book. Knight, Paula, illus. (Patchwork First Poem Bks.). 24p. (J). (ps-7). 8.95 (978-1-904668-86-2(0)) Mercury Bks. Ltd. GBR. *Dist:* International Publishers Marketing.

Lawson, Julie. Emma & the Silk Train. Mombourquette, Paul, illus. 32p. (J). (gr. k-3). 2002. (978-1-55074-651-8(0)); 1998. (978-1-55074-388-3(0)) Kids Can Pr., Ltd.

—Emma & the Silk Train. 2002. (gr. k-3). lib. bdg. 14.10 (978-0-613-83948-8(X)) Tandem Library Bks.

Layton, Neal. Bartholomew & the Bug. 2006. (Illus.). (J). (ps). pap. 9.99 (978-0-340-87329-8(9) , Hodder & Stoughton) Hodder General Publishing Division GBR. *Dist:* Trafalgar Square Publishing.

Lazo, Dorina. Children of the San Joaquin Valley. Hires, Josh, photos by. 2005. (Illus.). 35p. (YA). (gr. 7-12). pap. 15.00 (978-0-938911-28-9(7)) Individualized Education Systems/Poppy Lane Publishing.

Le Jars, David. Mis Amigos, Los Animales. 2004. (Hablemos Ser.). (SPA., Illus.). 24p. (J). (ps-k). pap. 5.95 (978-1-58728-950-7(4) , Two Can Publishing) T&N Children's Publishing.

—Mis Amigos, Los Animales. 2000. (SPA., Illus.). (J). (978-0-606-20801-7(1)) Tandem Library Bks.

—Uno, Dos, Hola y Adios. 2004. (Hablemos Ser.).Tr. of One, Two, Hello & Goodbye to You. (SPA., Illus.). 24p. (J). (ps-k). 9.95 (978-1-58728-948-4(2)); pap. 5.95 (978-1-58728-952-1(0)) T&N Children's Publishing. (Two Can Publishing).

—Uno, Dos, Hola y Adios. 2000. Tr. of One, Two, Hello & Goodbye to You. (SPA., Illus.). (J). (978-0-606-20965-6(4)) Tandem Library Bks.

Learning Letters. 2003. (Kermit the Frog & Friends Ser.). (Illus.). 16p. (J). (ps-k). pap., act. bk. ed. 4.99 (978-1-57768-704-7(3)) School Specialty Publishing.

Lee, Brenda G. Lunch at the Zoo. 2002. 14.95 (978-0-9728732-0-8(1)) Little Cottage Bks.

Lee, Jeanie. Baby Farm Friends. 2006. (Flips & Flaps Book Ser.). (Illus.). 10p. (J). 12.95 (978-1-4169-0702-2(5) , Little Simon) Simon & Schuster Children's Publishing.

Lee, Mary. My Air Force Mom. 2007. (J). per. 6.99 ***(978-1-60247-341-6(2))*** Tate Publishing & Enterprises, L.L.C.

Lee, Meredith Meade. Sissy & Smooch: A Tale of a Kitten & Her Angel. Tidey, Joel, illus. 2000. (J). (ps-3). 39.95 (978-0-9706254-0-3(5)) Meredith International, LLC.

Lee, Uk-Bae. Sori's Harvest Moon Day: A Story of Korea - Including Doll. Lee, Uk-Bae, illus. 1999. Orig. Title: Sori's Chu-Suk. (Illus.). 32p. (J). (gr. k-3). 25.95 (978-1-56899-690-5(X)) Soundprints.

Lees, Stewart. Runaway Jack. 2004. (Illus.). 32p. (J). 14.95 (978-0-7641-5712-7(4)) Barron's Educational Series, Inc.

Lemke, Horst, illus. Places & Faces. 32p. (J). (ps). 14.95 (978-0-87592-041-2(1)) Scroll Pr., Inc.

Leonard, Marcia. Babies Help Out. Handelman, Dorothy, photos by. 2001. (Illus.). 20p. (J). (ps-k). 7.95 (978-0-694-01369-2(2) , Harper Festival) HarperCollins Pubs.

—Busy Babies. Handelman, Dorothy, photos by. 2000. (Hanna Bks.). (Illus.). 24p. (J). (ps-k). 7.95 (978-0-694-01364-7(1)) HarperCollins Pubs.

—Hop, Skip, Run. Handelman, Dorothy, photos by. 1998. (Real Kids Readers Ser.). (Illus.). 32p. (ps-1). lib. bdg. 18.90 (978-0-7613-2015-9(6)); (J). pap. 4.99 (978-0-7613-2040-1(7)) Lerner Publishing Group. (Millbrook Pr.).

—Peekaboo, Baby! 2000. (Hanna Bks.). (Illus.). 18p. (J). (ps up). 7.95 (978-0-694-01373-9(0) , Harper Festival) HarperCollins Pubs.

—Spots. Handelman, Dorothy, photos by. 1998. (Real Kids Readers Ser.). (Illus.). 32p. (ps-1). lib. bdg. 18.90 (978-0-7613-2016-6(4)); (J). pap. 4.99 (978-0-7613-2041-8(5)) Lerner Publishing Group. (Millbrook Pr.).

Leslie, Amanda. Are Chickens Stripy? A Lift-the-Flap Book. 2000. (Illus.). 16p. (J). (ps). 4.95 (978-1-929766-09-3(2)) Handprint Bks.

Lester, Helen. Tacky & the Emperor. Munsinger, Lynn, illus. 32p. (J). (gr. k-3). 2002. pap. 6.95 (978-0-618-26009-6(9)); 2000. tchr. ed. 15.00 (978-0-395-98120-7(4)) Houghton Mifflin Co. Trade & Reference Div. (Walter Lorraine).

—Tacky & the Emperor. 2002. (gr. k-3). lib. bdg. 14.10 (978-0-613-72914-7(5)) Tandem Library Bks.

Lesynski, Loris. Night School. Lesynski, Loris, illus. 2001. (Illus.). 32p. (J). (ps-2). pap. 5.95 (978-1-55037-584-8(9)); lib. bdg. 18.95 (978-1-55037-585-5(7)) Annick Pr., Ltd. CAN. *Dist:* Firefly Bks., Ltd.

Let's Get Ready! (Illus.). (J). pap. 2.79 (978-0-88743-713-7(3)) School Zone Publishing Co.

Levack, Joseph, photos by. Picture Me Cute As Can Bee. 1998. (Illus.). 10p. (J). (ps up). bds. 4.99 (978-1-57151-546-9(1)) Playhouse Publishing.

Levine, Gail Carson. Betsy Who Cried Wolf. Nash, Scott, illus. 40p. (J). (ps-3). 2002. 15.95 (978-0-06-028763-4(2)); 2002. lib. bdg. 16.89 (978-0-06-028764-1(0)); 2005. reprint ed. pap. 6.99 (978-0-06-443640-3(3)) HarperCollins Pubs.

Levinson Bks Staff. Stack-a-Plane, 3 vols. 1999. (Stack-A-Bks.). (Illus.). 20p. (J). (ps-k). 12.95 (978-1-899607-91-4(9)) Levinson Bks. Ltd. GBR. *Dist:* Sterling Publishing Co., Inc.

Levinson Bks Staff & Moore, Jo. Stack-a-Boat, 3 vols. 2000. (Illus.). 30p. (J). bds. (978-1-899607-56-3(0) , Gullane Children's Bks.) Pinwheel.

Levinson Bks Staff & Sage, Angie. Stack-a-Car, 3 vols., Set. 2000. (Illus.). 24p. (J). bds. (978-1-899607-92-1(7) , Gullane Children's Bks.) Pinwheel.

Levitin, Sonia. Boom Town. Smith, Cat Bowman, illus. 1998. 32p. (J). (gr. k-4). pap. 16.95 (978-0-531-30043-5(9) , Orchard Bks.) Scholastic, Inc.

Lewellyn, Claire. Crocodile. Mendez, Simon, illus. 2004. (Starting Life Ser.). 24p. (ps-3). 16.95 (978-1-55971-900-1(1) , NorthWord Bks. for Young Readers) T&N Children's Publishing.

—Ladybug. Mendez, Simon, illus. 2004. (Starting Life Ser.). 24p. (ps-3). 16.95 (978-1-55971-892-9(7) , NorthWord Bks. for Young Readers) T&N Children's Publishing.

Lewin, Ted. The Storytellers. 1998. (Illus.). 40p. (J). (gr. k-3). 16.00 (978-0-688-15178-2(7)) HarperCollins Pubs.

L'Heureux, Christine & Brignaud, Pierre. Caillou: Just Like Daddy. rev. ed. 2006. (Hand in Hand Ser.). (Illus.). 24p. (J). pap. 5.95 ***(978-2-89450-587-8(6))*** Chouette Publishing CAN. *Dist:* Independent Pubs. Group.

L'Heureux, Christine, et al. Caillou: Good Night! 2006. (Hand in Hand Ser.). (Illus.). 24p. (J). pap. 5.95 ***(978-2-89450-588-5(4))*** Chouette Publishing CAN. *Dist:* Independent Pubs. Group.

Lindbergh, Reeve. The Circle of Days. 2002. (gr. 3-6). lib. bdg. 14.15 (978-0-613-74721-9(6)) Tandem Library Bks.

Linenthal, Peter. Look at the Animals! 2006. (Illus.). 18p. (J). (ps). pap. 6.99 (978-0-525-47582-8(6) , Dutton Juvenile) Penguin Group (USA) Inc.

Litchfield, Jo, illus. First Picture 123. 2005. (First Picture Board Books Ser.). 16p. (J). 11.95 (978-0-7945-0939-2(8) , Usborne) EDC Publishing.

Little Red Riding Pooh: A Fairy Tale Friend a Board Book & Plush Figure. 2004. (Pooh's Fairy Tale Theater Ser.). 12p. (J). 6.99 (978-0-7364-2239-0(0) , RH/Disney) Random Hse. Children's Bks.

Lloyd-Jones, Sally. Who Says That? 2001. 16p. (J). (ps-k). 6.99 (978-0-570-07148-8(8)) Concordia Publishing Hse.

—Who's Hiding? 2001. 16p. (J). (ps-k). 6.99 (978-0-570-07147-1(X)) Concordia Publishing Hse.

Lloyd, Sam. Happy Dog, Sad Dog. 2005. (Illus.). 14p. (J). (ps). 5.95 (978-1-56148-455-3(5)) Good Bks.

—Whose Tail? 2005. (Illus.). 14p. (J). (ps). 5.95 (978-1-56148-454-6(7)) Good Bks.

Lobel, Anita. Potatoes, Potatoes. 2004. 40p. (J). 16.89 (978-0-06-051818-9(9)); 15.99 (978-0-06-023927-5(1)); lib. bdg. 16.89 (978-0-06-023928-2(X)) HarperCollins Pubs.

—Potatoes, Potatoes. Lobel, Anita, illus. 2004. (Illus.). 40p. (J). reprint ed. 15.99 (978-0-06-051817-2(0)) HarperCollins Pubs.

Lobel, Arnold. Arnold Lobel's Mother Goose for Babies. 2004. (Illus.). 20p. (J). (gr. k-ps). bds. 5.99 (978-0-375-82904-8(0) , Knopf Bks. for Young Readers) Random Hse. Children's Bks.

London, Jonathan. Condor's Egg. Chaffee, James, illus. 1999. (Endangered Species Ser.). 32p. (J). (ps-3). pap. 7.95 (978-0-8118-2312-8(1)) Chronicle Bks. LLC.

—Crunch Munch. Rex, Michael, illus. 2002. 22p. (J). bds. 5.95 (978-0-15-216600-7(9) , Red Wagon Bks.) Harcourt Children's Bks.

—Let's Go, Froggy! unabr. ed. 1999. (J). (ps up). pap., stu. ed. 24.24 incl. audio (978-0-7887-3647-6(7) , 41013X4) Recorded Bks., LLC.

—Snuggle Wuggle. Rex, Michael, illus. 2002. 22p. (J). bds. 5.95 (978-0-15-216594-9(0) , Red Wagon Bks.) Harcourt Children's Bks.

—What Do You Love? Schmidt, Karen Lee, illus. 2004. 30p. (J). bds. 6.95 (978-0-15-205054-2(X) , Red Wagon Bks.) Harcourt Children's Bks.

—Wiggle Waggle. Rex, Michael, illus. 2002. 22p. (J). bds. 5.95 (978-0-15-216588-8(6) , Red Wagon Bks.) Harcourt Children's Bks.

Looney Tunes Talk Back to the Movies. (Looney Tunes Song & Sound Bks.). (Illus.). 24p. (J). (ps-6). 14.98 (978-0-7853-1253-6(6) , PI5) Publications International, Ltd.

Lore, Erin, illus. Timmy the Dragon. l.t. ed. 2007. 32p. (J). 8.95 ***(978-0-9741562-7-9(2))*** Yarrow Pr.

Lorenz Books Staff. Dressing Up. 2000. (Sticker Fun Ser.). (Illus.). 16p. (ps-k). pap. 5.00 (978-0-7548-0542-7(5)) Anness Publishing GBR. *Dist:* National Bk. Network.

—Numbers: With Over 50 Reusable Stickers. 1998. (Sticker Fun Ser.). (Illus.). 16p. (ps-k). pap. 4.95 (978-1-85967-772-8(X) , Lorenz Bks.) Anness Publishing, Inc.

—Party. 2000. (Sticker Fun Ser.). (Illus.). 16p. (ps-k). pap. 5.00 (978-0-7548-0538-0(7) , Lorenz Bks.) Anness Publishing GBR. *Dist:* National Bk. Network.

—Patterns. 2000. (Sticker Fun Ser.). (Illus.). 16p. (ps-k). pap. 4.95 (978-0-7548-0437-6(2)) Anness Publishing GBR. *Dist:* National Bk. Network.

—Sums. 2000. (Sticker Fun Ser.). (Illus.). 16p. (ps-k). pap. 4.95 (978-0-7548-0436-9(4)) Anness Publishing GBR. *Dist:* National Bk. Network.

Lorenz Books Staff, ed. Animal Friends: A First Word & Picture Book. 2000. (Point & Say Bks.). (Illus.). 96p. (ps-k). 9.95 (978-1-85967-800-8(9)) Anness Publishing GBR. *Dist:* National Bk. Network.

Lorenz Books Staff & Tuxworth, Nicola. Splish, Splash. 1999. (Very First Picture Bks.). (Illus.). 12p. (ps). bds. 4.95 (978-0-7548-0385-0(6) , Lorenz Bks.) Anness Publishing GBR. *Dist:* National Bk. Network.

Lorenz Editors. Colours in the Garden, 4 vols., Set 1. 2001. (Illus.). 10p. bds. 12.95 (978-0-7548-0824-4(6) , Lorenz Bks.) Anness Publishing GBR. *Dist:* National Bk. Network.

—My Day: With over 50 Reusable Stickers. 2001. (Sticker Fun Ser.). (Illus.). 16p. pap. 2.95 (978-0-7548-0846-6(7) , Lorenz Bks.) Anness Publishing, Inc.

—Shapes & Patterns, 4 vols., Set 4. 2001. (Mini Board Bks.). (Illus.). 12p. bds. 12.95 (978-0-7548-0873-2(4)) Anness Publishing GBR. *Dist:* National Bk. Network.

Losordo, Stephen. Cow Moo Me. Conteh-Morgan, Jane, illus. 1998. (Growing Tree Ser.). 16p. (J). (ps up). 5.95 (978-0-694-01108-7(8) , Harper Festival) HarperCollins Pubs.

Lovasik, Lawrence G. Los Angeles. (Illus.). (J). 1.50 (978-0-89942-465-1(1)) Catholic Bk. Publishing Corp.

Love Library: Guess How Much I Love You, Hug, Love & Kisses, 3 vols. Incl. Guess How Much I Love You. 10th anniv. ed. McBratney, Sam. Jeram, Anita, illus. 20p. 1996. reprint ed. bds. 6.99 (978-0-7636-0013-6(X)); Hug. Alborough, Jez. Alborough, Jez, illus. 32p. 2001. bds. 6.99 (978-0-7636-1576-5(5)); Love & Kisses. Wilson, Sarah & Wilson, Sarah. Sweet, Melissa & Sweet, Melissa, illus. 22p. 2001. bds. 6.99 (978-0-7636-1049-4(6)); (J). (gr. k-ps). 96p. 2002. 15.99 (978-0-7636-1670-0(2)) Candlewick Pr.

Love, Pamela. A Cub Explores. Sykes, Shannon, illus. 2004. 32p. (gr. k-2). 15.95 (978-0-89272-593-9(1)) Down East Bks.

Lovejoy, Sharon. The Little Green Island with a Little Red House: A Book of Colors & Critters. 2005. (Illus.). 32p. 9.95 (978-0-89272-673-8(3)) Down East Bks.

Low, Alice. Mommy's Briefcase. 2002. (gr. k-3). lib. bdg. 14.15 (978-0-613-82495-8(4)) Tandem Library Bks.

Lowell, Susan. Cindy Ellen: A Wild Western Cinderella. Manning, Jane, illus. 2001. 40p. (J). (ps-3). pap. 6.99 (978-0-06-443864-3(3) , Harper Trophy) HarperCollins Pubs.

—Cindy Ellen: A Wild Western Cinderella. 2000. (gr. k-3). lib. bdg. 15.30 (978-0-613-44444-6(2)) Tandem Library Bks.

—Josefina Javelina: A Hairy Tale. MacPherson, Bruce, illus. 2005. 32p. (ps-3). 15.95 (978-0-87358-790-7(1) , Rising Moon Bks. for Young Readers) Northland Publishing.

—The Tortoise & the Jackrabbit. Harris, Jim, illus. 2004. (New Bilingual Picture Book Ser.). (ENG & SPA.). 32p. (J). 7.95 incl. 5.25 hd (978-0-87358-869-0(X) , Rising Moon Bks. for Young Readers) Northland Publishing.

Lowery, Linda. Trick or Treat, It's Halloween! 2000. (gr. k-3). lib. bdg. 10.95 (978-0-613-27266-7(8)) Tandem Library Bks.

Lowry, Mark. Good Ol' Noah Had an Ark. Boyer, Lyn, illus. 2000. 24p. (J). 12.99 (978-0-310-23198-1(1)) Zondervan.

Loyie, Larry & Brissenden, Constance. The Gathering Tree. Holmlund, Heather D., illus. 2006. 48p. (J). bds. 18.95 (978-1-894778-28-2(6)) Theytus Bks., Ltd. CAN. *Dist:* Orca Bk. Pubs. USA.

Lujan, Jorge & Monroy, Manuel. Rooster Gallo. Monroy, Manuel & Amado, Elisa, trs. Lujan, Jorge, illus. 2004. (ENG & SPA., Illus.). 24p. (J). 14.95 (978-0-88899-558-2(X)) Groundwood Bks. CAN. *Dist:* Perseus Distribution.

Luna, Rachel Nickerson. Darinka, the Little Artist Deer. Luna, Rachel Nickerson, illus. 1999. (Illus.). 36p. (J). (gr. 3-4). 12.95 (978-1-886551-06-0(5)) Howard, Emma Bks.

Lund, Evelyn. It Happened on Alphabet Street. 2003. (Illus.). 32p. (J). pap. 12.95 (978-1-878044-50-1(8) , Wild Rose) Mayhaven Publishing.

Lundy, Charlotte. Thank You, Mary. Waldrep, Evelyn L., ed. Overcash, Diane, illus. 2000. 32p. (J). (ps-3). 15.95 (978-0-9670280-6-4(X)) Bay Light Publishing.

—Thank You, Paul. Waldrep, Evelyn L., ed. James, Margaret Ray, illus. 2000. 32p. (J). (ps-3). 15.95 (978-0-9670280-7-1(8)) Bay Light Publishing.

Luongo, Ruth E. Beautiful, Big & Bright: The Journey of Sunny Sunflower Seed. 2005. 48p. pap. 16.99 (978-1-4116-1161-0(6)) Lulu.com.

Lynn, Sara. Jungle Friends. (Illus.). (J). bds. (978-0-7636-0042-6(3)) Candlewick Pr.

Mabee, Kerri. The Lemon Dilemna. Wise, Noreen, ed. Wethington, Liz, illus. 2000. (Book-a-Day Collection). 32p. (YA). (ps up). pap. 5.95 (978-1-58584-430-2(6)) Huckleberry Pr.

Mackenzie, Carine. Sara y Abraham: La maravillosa Promesa. Foce, Natalia C., tr. from ENG. Apps, Fred, illus. 2004. Orig. Title: Sarah & Abraham - the Wonderful Promise. (SPA.). 36p. (J). 2.99 (978-1-932789-14-0(6)) Editorial Sendas Antiguas, LLC.

MacKinnon, Debbie. Find My Boots! Sieveking, Anthea, photos by. 1999. (Illus.). 10p. (J). (978-0-7112-0922-0(7)) Lincoln, Frances Ltd. GBR. *Dist:* Antique Collectors' Club.

—Find My Cake! Sieveking, Anthea, photos by. 1999. (Illus.). 10p. (J). (978-0-7112-0920-6(0)) Lincoln, Frances Ltd. GBR. *Dist:* Antique Collectors' Club.

MacLachlan, Patricia. What You Know First. 1998. (Trophy Picture Bks.). (J). (978-0-606-13905-2(2)) Tandem Library Bks.

Maddern, Eric. Earth Story. (Illus.). 32p. (J). 2004. 19.95 (978-1-84507-184-4(0)); 1998. pap. 7.95 (978-1-84507-185-1(9)) Lincoln, Frances Ltd. GBR. *Dist:* Perseus Distribution.

Maddern, Eric, et al. Earth Story. 2001. (Big Bks.). (Illus.). 32p. (J). (ps-3). pap. 22.95 (978-0-7112-1443-9(3)) Lincoln, Frances Ltd. GBR. *Dist:* Transition Vendor.

Magabala Books Staff. Australian Babies. 2005. (Illus.). 10p. (J). 8.00 (978-1-875641-92-5(0)) Magabala Bks. AUS. *Dist:* International Specialized Bk. Services.

Magee, Wes. Little Dragon. Warburton, Sarah, illus. 2004. 24p. (J). lib. bdg. 22.65 ***(978-1-59646-690-6(1))*** Dingles & Co.

Maloney, Clare. Brendan & the Whale. Dunne, Jeanette, illus. 2005. 24p. pap. 9.94 (978-1-85390-645-9(X)) Veritas Pubns. IRL. *Dist:* STL Distribution North America.

Maltbie, Karen. Just for Being Me. Shubeck, Patricia K., illus. 2000. 30p. (J). (ps-3). 15.00 (978-0-9670934-0-6(6)) Magic Shoes Pr.

Mandel, Peter. Planes at the Airport. Miller, Edward, illus. 2004. 8p. (J). pap. 6.99 (978-0-439-56416-8(6)) Scholastic, Inc.

Mandracchia, Charles, creator. A Wacky Wonder World. l.t. ed. 2005. (Illus.). 24p. (J). 13.95 (978-0-9721957-1-3(8)) Mandracchia, Charles.

Manning, Jane, illus. My First Baby Games. 2001. (Growing Tree Ser.). 16p. (J). (ps up). 6.99 (978-0-694-01435-4(4) , Harper Festival) HarperCollins Pubs.

Manning, Maurie J. The Aunts Go Marching. Manning, Maurie J., illus. 2003. (Illus.). 32p. (J). (ps up). 15.95 (978-1-59078-026-8(4)) Boyds Mills Pr.

Manuel, Lynn. Camels Always Do. Charko, Kasia, illus. 2004. 32p. (J). (ps-2). 7.95 (978-1-55143-470-4(9)) Orca Bk. Pubs. USA.

Marchus, Linda. The Gorilla Who Wanted to Dance. Marchus, Linda, illus. 2003. (Illus.). 32p. (J). lib. bdg. 15.95 (978-0-9723122-1-9(8)) Wee Read Publishing.

Marcus, Leonard S. Side by Side: Five Favorite Picture-Book Teams Go to Work. (Illus.). 64p. (J). 2006. pap. 11.95 (978-0-8027-9616-5(8)); 2001. (gr. 3 up). 22.95 (978-0-8027-8778-1(9)) Walker & Co.

—Ways of Telling: Conversations on the Art of the Picture Book. 2005. (Illus.). 247p. reprint ed. 30.00 (978-0-7567-9704-1(7)) DIANE Publishing Co.

Martin, Bill, Jr. & Archambault, John. Here Are My Hands. Rand, Ted, illus. rev. ed. 1998. 32p. (J). (ps-k). bds. 7.95 (978-0-8050-5911-3(3) , Holt, Henry & Co. Bks. For Young Readers) Holt, Henry & Co.

Martin, Rafe. The Rough-Face Girl. Shannon, David, illus. 1998. 32p. (J). (ps-3). pap. 6.99 (978-0-698-11626-9(7) , Putnam Juvenile) Penguin Group (USA) Inc.

Martin, W. Lyon. An Ordinary Girl, a Magical Child. 2005. (Illus.). (J). per. 16.95 (978-1-59405-515-7(7)) New Age World Publishing.

Marzollo, Jean. Do You Know New? Takabayashi, Mari, illus. 1998. (Growing Tree Ser.). 14p. (J). (ps up). 6.99 (978-0-694-00870-4(2)) HarperCollins Pubs.

—I Spy Little Numbers. Wick, Walter, illus. 1999. (I Spy Bks.). 26p. (J). (ps). bds. 6.99 (978-0-590-68714-0(X) , Cartwheel Bks.) Scholastic, Inc.

—Mama Mama/Papa Papa Flip Board Book. Regan, Laura, illus. 2003. (Flip Boardbks.). 32p. (J). (ps up). 6.99 (978-0-06-051915-5(0) , Harper Festival) HarperCollins Pubs.

Massey, Jane. Sea Creatures. 2000. (Touch & Fit Ser.). (Illus.). 10p. (J). (ps-k). bds. 12.95 (978-1-57145-417-1(9) , Silver Dolphin Bks.) Advantage Pubs. Group.

Masurel, Claire. No, Tito, No! No, No, Titus! Lasconi, Diego, tr. Halpern, Shari, illus. 1999. (SPA.). 32p. (J). (ps-1). pap. 6.95 (978-0-7358-1209-3(8) , NS3707) North-South Bks., Inc.

Mayaprua, Alejandro Taish. Nantu & Auju: How the Moon & the Potoo Bird Came to Be. Youth of the Achuar Tribe of Ecuador, illus. 2005. (J). 15.95 (978-0-9745477-0-1(0)) Arutam Pr.

Mayer, Mercer. Just Go to Bed. Mayer, Mercer, illus. rev. ed. 2001. (Little Critter Ser.). (Illus.). 24p. (J). (ps-2). reprint ed. 3.99 (978-0-307-11940-7(8) , 11940, Random Hse. Bks. for Young Readers) Random Hse. Children's Bks.

—Just Grandpa & Me. Mayer, Mercer, illus. 2001. (Little Critter Ser.). (Illus.). 24p. (J). (gr. k-k). pap. 3.99 (978-0-307-11936-0(X) , 11936, Random Hse. Bks. for Young Readers) Random Hse. Children's Bks.

Mayhew, James. Cluck, Cluck Who's There? Church, Caroline J., illus. 2004. 20p. (J). pap. 9.95 (978-0-439-57737-3(3)) Scholastic, Inc.

—El Museo de Carlota. 38p. (J). (ps-3). 2001. (CAT.). pap. 14.95 (978-84-95040-59-6(X)); 2000. (SPA., Illus.). 14.95 (978-84-88061-57-7(9)) Serres, Ediciones, S. L. ESP. *Dist:* Lectorum Pubns., Inc.

Mayo, Margaret. Choo Choo Clickety-Clack! Ayliffe, Alex, illus. 2005. 32p. (J). (ps-2). 14.95 (978-1-57505-819-1(7)) Lerner Publishing Group.

Mazes & Hidden Pictures Booster. 2005. (J). per. 0.00 (978-1-59441-503-6(X) , C04035) Carson-Dellosa Publishing Co., Inc.

McAllister, Margaret. Emily & the Lamb. Vince, Dawn, illus. 2005. 24p. (J). lib. bdg. 22.65 ***(978-1-59646-756-9(8))*** Dingles & Co.

McBratney, Sam. Just You & Me. Bates, Ivan, illus. 2000. 32p. (J). (gr. k-1). pap. 5.99 (978-0-7636-1078-4(X)) Candlewick Pr.

McBratney, Sam. Tell Me a Story Before I Go to Bed. Braun, Sebastien, illus. 2007. 32p. (J). pap. ***(978-0-00-714180-7(7))*** HarperCollins Canada, Ltd.

McCafferty, Catherine. The Gingerbread Man. Bowles, Doug, illus. 2002. (Brighter Child Keepsake Stories Ser.). 32p. (J). (ps-3). pap. 3.99 (978-1-57768-368-1(4) , Brighter Child) School Specialty Publishing.

McCarthy, Michael. The Story of Daniel in the Lions' Den. Ferri, Giuliano, illus. 2003. 32p. (J). (gr. 1-3). 16.99 (978-1-84148-209-5(9)) Barefoot Bks., Inc.

McCaughrean, Geraldine. My Grandmother's Clock. Lambert, Stephen, illus. 2002. 32p. (J). (gr. k-3). 15.00 (978-0-618-21695-6(2) , Clarion Bks.) Houghton Mifflin Co. Trade & Reference Div.

McCloskey, Robert. Blueberries for Sal. 2004. (Live Oak Readalong Ser.). (Illus.). (J). pap. 18.95 incl. audio compact disk (978-1-59112-693-5(2)) Live Oak Media.

—Blueberries for Sal. 2004. (J). pap. 14.95 incl. audio (978-1-56008-048-0(5) , PRA041) Weston Woods Studios, Inc.

—Lentil. 2000. (J). pap. 3.95 (978-0-590-04411-0(7)) Scholastic, Inc.

—Make Way for Ducklings. 2000. (J). pap. 19.97 incl. audio (978-0-7366-9196-3(0)) Books on Tape, Inc.

—Make Way for Ducklings. 1999. (Illus.). 76p. (J). (ps-3). pap. 7.99 (978-0-14-056434-1(9) , Puffin) Penguin Group (USA) Inc.

—Make Way for Ducklings. 2000. (J). (ps-k). pap. 12.95 incl. audio Weston Woods Studios, Inc.

McCreary, Laura. Stickers 'n Shapes. 2002. (Bear in the Big Blue House Ser.: Bk. 7). (Illus.). 16p. (J). mass mkt. 3.99 (978-0-689-84023-4(3) , Simon Spotlight) Simon & Schuster Children's Publishing.

McCully, Emily Arnold. First Snow. McCully, Emily Arnold, illus. 2004. (Illus.). 32p. (J). (ps-k). 16.99 (978-0-06-623852-4(8)); lib. bdg. 17.89 (978-0-06-623853-1(6)) HarperCollins Pubs.

McDonald, Megan. My House Has Stars. Catalanotto, Peter, illus. 2001. 32p. (J). (gr. k-3). reprint ed. pap. 5.95 (978-0-531-07181-6(2) , Orchard Bks.) Scholastic, Inc.

McFarlane, Arlene. I Hate Celery Soup. Wise, Noreen, ed. 2000. (Book-a-Day Collection). 32p. (YA). (ps up). pap. 5.95 (978-1-58584-428-9(4)) Huckleberry Pr.

—My Auntie Bean, She Is a Scream. Wise, Noreen, ed. Silverman, Karen, illus. 2000. (Lemonade Collection). 64p. (J). (ps-2). pap. 5.95 (978-1-58584-258-2(3)) Huckleberry Pr.

McGrath, Barbara Barbieri. Hershey's Kisses: Counting Board Book, 1. 1998. (978-0-9662445-0-2(8)) Corporate Board Bks.

McKee, David. Cebra Tiene Hippo. 1999. (SPA., Illus.). (J). 14.75 (978-0-606-21665-4(0)) Tandem Library Bks.

—Elmer's New Friend. 2003. (Illus.). 22p. (J). 8.99 (978-1-84270-034-1(0)) Andersen GBR. *Dist:* Trafalgar Square Publishing.

—Mr. Benn, Gladiator. 2002. (Illus.). 32p. (J). (ps-3). 17.99 (978-1-84270-024-2(3)) Andersen GBR. *Dist:* Trafalgar Square Publishing.

McKendry, Sam. Are You Ticklish? A Touch & Tickle Book. Mitchell, Melanie, illus. 2005. 12p. (J). (ps up). 10.95 (978-1-58117-376-5(8) , Intervisual/Piggy Toes) Dalmatian Pr.

McKissack, Patricia C. & McKissack, Fredrick L. Messy Bessey's Closet. Regan, Dana, illus. rev. ed. 2002. (Rookie Reader Espanol Ser.). 32p. (J). (gr. k-2). pap. 4.95 (978-0-516-27081-4(8) , Children's Pr.) Scholastic Library Publishing.

McLaughlin, Julie. Hungry Mr. Gator. McKay, Ann Marie, illus. 2002. 32p. (J). (gr. k-2). pap. (978-0-615-12335-6(X)) JAM Publishers.

—Hungry Mr. Gator. McKay, Ann Marie, illus. 2005. (J). 15.99 (978-0-933101-24-1(4)) Legacy Pubns.

McLean, Wendy & Book Company Staff. Follow an Elf. Worthington, Leonie, illus. 2003. (Sparkle Bks.). 10p. (J). bds. 8.95 (978-1-74047-314-9(0)) Book Co. Publishing Pty, Ltd., The AUS. *Dist:* Penton Overseas, Inc.

McLellan, John. The Adventures of Mike & Tim: A Boy & His Shadow. Draaistra, Sylvia, illus. 2004. 48p. (J). (978-1-55306-679-8(0) , Epic Pr.) Essence Publishing.

McLellan, Stephanie Simpson. Leon's Song. Bonder, Dianna, illus. 2004. 32p. (J). (ps-3). (978-1-55041-813-2(0)) Fitzhenry & Whiteside, Ltd.

—Leon's Song. Bonder, Dianna, illus. 2006. 32p. pap. 7.95 (978-1-55041-815-6(7)) Fitzhenry & Whiteside, Ltd. CAN. *Dist:* F & W Pubns., Inc.

McMullan, Kate. Baby Goose. Lemaitre, Pascal, illus. 2004. 48p. (ps-ps). 15.99 (978-0-7868-0430-6(0)) Hyperion Bks. for Children.

McNaughton, Janet. Brave Jack & the Unicorn. Tooke, Susan, illus. 2005. 32p. (J). (gr. k-3). 15.95 (978-0-88776-677-0(3)) Tundra Bks., Inc./Livres Toundra, Inc. CAN. *Dist:* Random Hse., Inc.

MCP Staff. Zelda's Zipper. 2003. (J). 38.95 (978-0-8136-1323-9(X)) Modern Curriculum Pr.

McPhail, David M. Fix-It. McPhail, David M., illus. 2002. (Illus.). 12p. (J). bds. 6.99 (978-0-525-46849-3(8) , Dutton Juvenile) Penguin Group (USA) Inc.

Meade, David. Shapes & Sharing. Byers, Brian, illus. 2005. 22p. (J). (gr. k-5). bds. 6.95 (978-1-59125-518-5(X) , Penton Kids) Penton Overseas, Inc.

Meister, Cari. What Can I Be? 2004. (Rookie Reader Skill Set Ser.). 23p. (J). (gr. k-2). pap. 4.95 (978-0-516-27810-0(X) , Children's Pr.) Scholastic Library Publishing.

Meister, Wil L. Hearts of Childhood. 2000. (J). (ps-k). pap. 9.95 (978-0-533-13350-5(5)) Vantage Pr., Inc.

Mellentin, Kath & Wood, Tim. Pet Corner, 6 bks. 1998. (Illus.). 8p. (J). (ps-k). 9.95 (978-0-7641-7210-6(7)) Barron's Educational Series, Inc.

Melling, David. The Kiss That Missed. 2002. (Illus.). 32p. (J). (gr. k-2). 14.95 (978-0-7641-5451-5(6)) Barron's Educational Series, Inc.

Mercier, Johanne & Brignaud, Pierre. Caillou on the Subway. rev. ed. 2006. (Out & about Ser.). (Illus.). 24p. (J). pap. 3.95 (***978-2-89450-574-7(1)***) Chouette Publishing CAN. *Dist:* Independent Pubs. Group.

Meredith Books Staff, ed. Buggin' with Ruud. 2007. 48p. pap. 6.99 (***978-0-696-23690-7(7)***) Meredith Bks.

Merrie Melodies. (Looney Tunes Song & Sound Bks.). (Illus.). 24p. (J). (ps-5). 14.98 (978-0-7853-1249-9(8) , PI4) Publications International, Ltd.

Messenger, Norman. Imagine. Messenger, Norman, illus. 2005. (Illus.). 32p. (J). (gr. 1 up). 17.99 (978-0-7636-2757-7(7)) Candlewick Pr.

Metrobooks Staff. My Puppy: A Baby Soft Book. 2000. (Illus.). 8p. (J). (ps-k). 8.99 (978-1-58663-104-8(7)) Friedman, Michael Publishing Group, Inc.

Meyers, Susan. Everywhere Babies. Frazee, Marla, illus. 2004. 30p. (J). bds. 6.95 (978-0-15-205315-4(8) , Red Wagon Bks.) Harcourt Children's Bks.

Meyers, Susan. Kittens! Kittens! Kittens! Walker, David, illus. 2007. (J). (***978-1-4287-3986-4(6)*** , Abrams Bks. for Young Readers) Abrams, Harry N. , Inc.

Michelson, Richard. Too Young for Yiddish. Waldman, Neil, illus. 2002. 32p. (J). (gr. k-4). 15.95 (978-0-88106-118-5(2)) Charlesbridge Publishing, Inc.

Milbourne, Anna. Under the Sea (Picture Book) 2007. (Picture Bks). 24p. (J). 9.99 (***978-0-7945-1801-1(X)*** , Usborne) EDC Publishing.

Miles, Victoria. La Cena del Cachorro. Tachiera, Andrea, illus. 1998. Tr. of Pup's Supper. (SPA.). 12p. (J). (ps-k). bds. 5.95 (978-1-878244-26-0(4)) Monterey Bay Aquarium.

Millard, Anne, et al. My First Farm Touch & Feel. 2002. (My First Ser.). (Illus.). 12p. (J). (ps-k). bds. 9.99 (978-0-7894-8524-3(9)) Dorling Kindersley Publishing, Inc.

Miller, J. Philip & Greene, Sheppard M. We All Sing with the Same Voice. Meisel, Paul, illus. 2005. 40p. (J). (ps-2). reprint ed. pap. 6.99 (978-0-06-073900-3(2) , Harper Trophy) HarperCollins Pubs.

Miller, Margaret. Whats on My Head? Miller, Margaret, photos by. 1998. (Look Baby Books Ser.). (Illus.). 14p. (J). (ps-4). 6.99 (978-0-689-81912-4(9) , Little Simon) Simon & Schuster Children's Publishing.

Miller, Millie. Our World: A Country-by-Country Guide. 2006. (Our World Ser.). (Illus.). 112p. (J). (gr. 3-6). pap. 16.99 (978-0-439-55004-8(1) , Scholastic Reference) Scholastic, Inc.

Miller, Sara Swan. Learn & Grow. Lacome, Susie, illus. 1999. 8p. (J). (ps-1). bds. 15.99 (978-1-57584-348-3(X) , Reader's Digest Young Families, Inc.) Reader's Digest Children's Publishing, Inc.

Milligan, Bryce. Brigid's Cloak: An Ancient Irish Story. Cann, Helen, illus. 2005. 32p. (J). (gr. k-17). pap. 8.00 (978-0-8028-5297-7(1) , Eerdmans Bks For Young Readers) Eerdmans, William B. Publishing Co.

Milton, Ann. Ask Me If I'm a Frog. Chambers, Jill, illus. 1998. (Curious Little Critters Ser.). 40p. (J). (ps-3). pap. 8.95 (978-0-88045-143-7(2)); 16.95 (978-0-88045-140-6(8)) Stemmer Hse. Pubs., Inc. (International Design Library).

Minarik, Else Holmelund. Little Bear Makes a Mask. 2003. (gr. k-3). lib. bdg. 11.80 (978-0-613-69140-6(7)) Tandem Library Bks.

Minchin, Adele. The Caravan Club. 2003. 224p. pap. 12.00 (978-0-7043-4978-0(7)) Women's Pr., Ltd., The GBR. *Dist:* Trafalgar Square Publishing.

Mini My First Picture Dictiona. 2004. (Early Learning Ser.). 18p. (J). bds. 2.99 (978-1-85854-832-6(2)) Brimax Books Ltd. GBR. *Dist:* Byeway Bks.

Miranda, Anne. Beep! Beep! A Vehicle Imagination Book. Murphy, David, illus. 1999. 32p. (J). (ps-k). 15.95 (978-1-890515-14-0(0)) Turtle Bks.

Mitchell, Marianne. Gullywasher Gulch. Chartier, Normand, illus. 2003. 32p. (J). (gr. 2-4). 15.95 (978-1-56397-123-5(2)) Boyds Mills Pr.

Mitchell, Melanie, illus. Good Morning, Good Night Bilingual: Buenos Dias! Buenas Noches! 2005. (ENG & SPA.). 12p. (J). 9.95 (978-1-58117-389-5(X) , Intervisual/Piggy Toes) Dalmatian Pr.

Mitchell, Pratima. Raju's Ride. Waterhouse, Stephen, illus. 2005. 24p. (J). lib. bdg. 22.65 (***978-1-59646-726-2(6)***) Dingles & Co.

Mitchell, Robin & Steedman, Judith, illus. Snowy & Chinook. 2005. 32p. (J). 15.95 (978-0-9688768-9-3(7)) Simply Read Bks. CAN. *Dist:* Perseus Distribution.

Mitter, Matt. Dolly Dolphin Can't Stop Clicking. Goode, Jon, illus. 2003. (Snappy Fun Bks.). 12p. (J). bds. 4.99 (978-0-7944-0123-8(6) , Reader's Digest Children's Bks.) Reader's Digest Children's Publishing, Inc.

—Seymour Sea Turtle Snaps up Lunch. Goode, Jon, illus. 2003. (Snappy Fun Bks.). 12p. (J). bds. 4.99 (978-0-7944-0124-5(4) , Reader's Digest Children's Bks.) Reader's Digest Children's Publishing, Inc.

Mitton, Tony. Tough Trucks. Parker, Ant, illus. 2003. (Amazing Machines Ser.). 24p. (J). (ps-k). tchr. ed. 9.95 (978-0-7534-5600-2(1) , Kingfisher) Houghton Mifflin Co. Trade & Reference Div.

—Tremendous Tractors. Parker, Ant, illus. 2003. (Amazing Machines Ser.). 24p. (J). (ps-k). tchr. ed. 9.95 (978-0-7534-5599-9(4) , Kingfisher) Houghton Mifflin Co. Trade & Reference Div.

Miyazaki, Hayao. Howls Moving Castle Picture Book. Miyazaki, Hayao, illus. 2005. (Howl's Moving Castle Picture Book Ser.). 184p. (YA). 19.99 (978-1-4215-0090-4(6)) Viz Media.

Moday, Jane, illus. God Loves Little Lamb. 1999. (Bend-N-Snuggle Bks.). 18p. (gr. k-ps). 10.99 (978-0-7847-0972-6(6) , 03542, Bean Sprouts) Standard Publishing.

—Little Bunny's Easter Day. 1999. (Bend-N-Snuggle Bks.). 18p. (gr. k-ps). 10.99 (978-0-7847-0971-9(8) , 03541, Bean Sprouts) Standard Publishing.

Modell, Frank. One Zillion Valentines. unabr. ed. 1998. (J). (ps-3). pap. 14.95 incl. audio (978-0-7882-0683-2(4) , PRA378) Weston Woods Studios, Inc.

Moller, Jonathan R. Bath Time: Picture Book. l.t. ed. 2003. (Illus.). 71p. pap. 19.95 (978-0-9740169-0-0(X)) Lemonflavor Productions.

Money Matters. 2005. (C). (gr. 1-3). 67.80 (978-1-4048-0992-5(9)) Picture Window Bks.

Montardre, Helene. The Cat & the Dog. 2003. (Illus.). 8p. (J). bds. 7.95 (978-1-58728-483-0(9) , Two Can Publishing) T&N Children's Publishing.

—Elephant & Mouse. 2004. (Turn & Learn Ser.). (Illus.). 8p. (J). (ps up). bds. 7.95 (978-1-58728-482-3(0) , Two Can Publishing) T&N Children's Publishing.

—Hen & Chick. 2004. (Turn & Learn Ser.). (Illus.). 8p. (J). (ps up). bds. 7.95 (978-1-58728-480-9(4) , Two Can Publishing) T&N Children's Publishing.

—Night & Day. 2003. (Illus.). 8p. (J). bds. 7.95 (978-1-58728-481-6(2) , Two Can Publishing) T&N Children's Publishing.

Moodie, Fiona. Noko's Suprise Party. 2008. (Illus.). 32p. (J). 16.95 (***978-1-84507-587-3(0)***) Lincoln, Frances Ltd. GBR. *Dist:* Perseus Distribution.

Moore, Alan. Alan Moore's Another Suburban Romance. 2003. (Illus.). 64p. (gr. 12 up). pap. 7.95 (978-1-59291-007-6(6)) Avatar Pr., Inc.

—Another Suburban Romance. 2003. (Illus.). 64p. 17.95 (978-1-59291-008-3(4)) Avatar Pr., Inc.

Moore, Brian L. The Story Behind Santa Sacks. Mulligan, Todd, illus. 2004. 32p. (978-0-9732651-0-1(8)) Hills-n-Hollows Publishing.

Moore, Clement C. The Night Before Christmas. 2004. (Illus.). 20p. (J). bds. 6.95 (978-0-8118-3933-4(8)) Chronicle Bks. LLC.

Moore, Lillian & Golden Books Staff. Jingle Smells. Williams, Garth & Greenblatt, Carl, illus. 2003. 16p. (J). (ps-3). pap. 3.99 (978-0-307-10458-8(3) , Golden Bks.) Random Hse. Children's Bks.

Mora, Jo. Budgee Budgee Cottontail. Mora, Jo, illus. 2004. (Jo Mora Titles Ser.). (Illus.). 60p. (gr. 2 up). 15.00 (978-0-922029-23-5(7) , BK-30004) Stoecklein Publishing.

Mora, Pat. Agua Agua Agua, Level 2. Ada, Alma Flor, tr. Ortega, Jose, illus. 3rd ed. 2003. (Dejame Leer Ser.). (SPA.). 16p. (J). (ps-1). 6.50 (978-0-673-36292-6(2) , Good Year Bks.) Celebration Pr.

Moreillon, Judi. Vamos a Leer. Teis, Kyra, illus. 2005. (SPA.). 40p. (J). bds. 6.95 (978-1-59572-015-3(4)) Star Bright Bks., Inc.

—Vamos a Leer (Read to Me) Teis, Kyra, illus. 2003. (SPA.). 24p. (J). 6.95 (978-1-932065-50-3(4)) Star Bright Bks., Inc.

Morgan, Michaela. Band of Friends. Price, Nick, illus. 2005. 24p. (J). lib. bdg. 22.65 (***978-1-59646-734-7(7)***) Dingles & Co.

—Mouse with No Name. Mikhail, Jess, illus. 2004. 24p. (J). lib. bdg. 22.65 (***978-1-59646-682-1(0)***) Dingles & Co.

—Shy Shark. Gomez, Elena, illus. 2005. 24p. (J). lib. bdg. 22.65 (***978-1-59646-722-4(3)***) Dingles & Co.

Morgan, Ruth. Big Liam, Little Liam. Archbold, Tim, illus. 2005. 24p. (J). lib. bdg. 22.65 (***978-1-59646-728-6(2)***) Dingles & Co.

—Jess & the Bean Root. 2005. (Illus.). 24p. (J). lib. bdg. 22.65 (***978-1-59646-732-3(0)***) Dingles & Co.

Morozumi, Atsuko, et al. Santa's Christmas Countdown. Morozumi, Atsuko, illus. 2003. (Illus.). (J). (gr. k-4). 15.95 (978-0-7696-3189-9(4) , Gingham Dog Pr.) School Specialty Publishing.

Morton, Christine. Picnic Farm. Barringer, Sarah, illus. 1998. 32p. (J). (ps-k). 15.95 (978-0-8234-1332-4(2)) Holiday Hse., Inc.

Mouse Works Staff. Doug's Composition Book. 1999. (J). 2.99 (978-0-7364-0182-1(2)) Mouse Works.

—Fantasia. 2000. (Flip Bks.). (Illus.). 40p. (J). 3.95 (978-0-7364-0093-0(1)) Mouse Works.

—Foam Bath Book Friendship Book. 2000. (Foam Bks.). 6p. (J). 7.99 (978-0-7364-1053-3(8)); No. 2. (Illus.). 7.99 (978-0-7364-1054-0(6)) Mouse Works.

—Mickey & Friends Roly Poly. 1998. (J). 9.99 (978-0-7364-0035-0(4)) Mouse Works.

—Pooh Movie Tree House Book: Freindship Book. 2000. (Winnie the Pooh Ser.). 8p. (J). (ps-3). 16.99 (978-0-7364-1049-6(X)) Hyperion Pr.

—Teapot Carry. 2001. (Rolie Polie Olie Ser.). (Illus.). 10p. (J). (ps-3). 6.99 (978-0-7364-0166-1(0)) Mouse Works.

—Toy Story 2. 1999. (Spanish Read-Aloud Storybook Classics). (J). 64p. 6.99 (978-0-7364-0140-1(7)); (Illus.). 96p. pap. 3.99 (978-0-7364-0169-2(5)); 14p. 7.99 (978-0-7364-0171-5(7)) Mouse Works.

—Toy Story 2 Find the Flag Hunny Pot Book. 1999. (Lift the Flaps Bks.). (Illus.). 10p. (J). (ps-k). 4.99 (978-0-7364-0179-1(2)) Mouse Works.

—Winter Trail Shimmer. 1998. (J). 4.98 (978-0-7364-0003-9(6)) Mouse Works.

Muller, Jorg. The Changing Countryside. 2006. (Illus.). 7p. (J). 17.95 (978-0-9762056-4-7(5)) Heryin Publishing Corp.

Mullican, Judy. Kenny & the Poison. Carroll, Ken, Jr., illus. 1998. (Big Bks.). 8p. (Orig.). (J). (ps-k). pap. 10.95 (978-1-57332-089-4(7)); pap. 10.95 (978-1-57332-088-7(9)) HighReach Learning, Inc.

—Listen to the Animals. l.t. ed. 2001. (Cuddle Bks.). (Illus.). 8p. (J). (ps-1). pap. 10.95 (978-1-57332-192-1(3)) HighReach Learning, Inc.

—Looking for a Book. Coates, Jennifer, illus. l.t. ed. 2000. (BB Ser.). 8p. (J). (ps-1). pap. 10.95 (978-1-57332-165-5(6)); pap. 10.95 (978-1-57332-166-2(4)) HighReach Learning, Inc.

—Miss Tammy Is Cool! Gillen, Lisa P., illus. l.t. ed. 2001. (Big Bks.). 11p. (J). (ps-1). pap. 10.95 (978-1-57332-209-6(1)) HighReach Learning, Inc.

—Something New at the Zoo. Ruminski, Jeff, illus. l.t. ed. 2002. (Big Bks.). 8p. (J). (ps). pap. 10.95 (978-1-57332-202-7(4)); pap. 10.95 (978-1-57332-203-4(2)) HighReach Learning, Inc.

—Story Time. Coates, Jennifer, illus. l.t. ed. 2000. (CB Ser.). 7p. (J). (ps-1). pap. 10.95 (978-1-57332-171-6(0)) HighReach Learning, Inc.

—Under the Sea. Carroll, Ken, Jr., illus. 1998. (Big Bks.). 8p. (J). (ps-k). pap. 10.95 (978-1-57332-093-1(5)); pap. 10.95 (978-1-57332-092-4(7)) HighReach Learning, Inc.

—Wheels: Cuddle Book. Middleton, Mikell, illus. 2002. 6p. (J). (ps-1). bds. 10.95 (978-1-57332-223-2(7)) HighReach Learning, Inc.

Mullican, Judy & Coales, Jennifer. Time to Eat. l.t. ed. 2001. (Board Bk.). (Illus.). 12p. (J). (ps-1). 4.99 (978-1-57332-195-2(8)) HighReach Learning, Inc.

Multiplication Tables: With Re-Usable Stickers. 1999. (Fun to Learn Ser.). (Illus.). 32p. (ps-5). 1.99 (978-1-58279-012-1(4) , 99) Trident Pr. International.

Munsch, Robert. Andrew's Loose Tooth. Martchenko, Michael, illus. 1998. 29p. (J). (ps-1). 1.95 (978-0-590-21102-4(1) , Cartwheel Bks.) Scholastic, Inc.

—L' Anniversaire. Martchenko, Michael, illus. 2003. (Droles D'Histories Ser.).Tr. of Moira's Birthday. (FRE.). 24p. (J). (gr. k up). pap. (978-2-89021-114-8(2)) Diffusion du livre Mirabel.

—Le Bebe - Murmel, Murmel, Murmel. Martchenko, Michael, illus. 2002. (Droles D'Histories Ser.). (FRE.). 24p. (J). (gr. k up). pap. (978-2-89021-043-1(X)) Diffusion du livre Mirabel.

—Le Dodo. Martchenko, Michael, illus. 2003. (Droles D'Histories Ser.).Tr. of Mortimer. (FRE.). 24p. (J). (gr. k up). pap. (978-2-89021-055-4(3)) Diffusion du livre Mirabel.

—La Magicienne. Martchenko, Michael, illus. 2002. (Droles D'Histories Ser.). Orig. Title: Wait & See. (FRE.). 24p. (J). (gr. k up). pap. (978-2-89021-214-5(9)) Diffusion du livre Mirabel.

Munton, Gill. I Went Swimming, 6 vols, Pack. 2000. (Cambridge Reading Ser.). 8p. pap. 28.00 (978-0-521-78761-1(0)) Cambridge Univ. Pr.

—Make a Banana Treat, 6, Pack. 2000. (Cambridge Reading Ser.). 8p. pap. 28.00 (978-0-521-78760-4(2)) Cambridge Univ. Pr.

Murphy, Stuart J. Animals on Board. Alley, R. W., illus. 1998. (MathStart Ser.: Level 2). 40p. (J). (gr. 1 up). pap. 5.99 (978-0-06-446716-2(3) , Harper Trophy) HarperCollins Pubs.

Murray, Joe. The Enormous Mister Schmupsle. 2003. (Illus.). 32p. (J). 16.95 (978-1-931290-53-1(9)) Tallfellow Pr.

My First 100 Words in Spanish/English. 2003. 32p. (J). 11.95 (978-0-7525-7769-2(7)) Parragon, Inc.

My First Picture Word Book. 1999. (McGraw-Hill Junior Academic Ser.). (Illus.). 64p. (J). (gr. k-2). pap. 3.99 (978-1-57768-206-6(8)) School Specialty Publishing.

My House of Shapes. 2000. (Point & Peek Books Ser.). (Illus.). 6p. (J). (ps-1). bds. (978-1-57584-362-9(5)) Reader's Digest Children's Publishing, Inc.

Mykowski, Michelle. Explore God's Desert. Ring, Laura, ed. Mykowski, Michelle, illus. 1999. (Shaped Paperback Bks.). (Illus.). 24p. (J). (ps-1). pap. 3.99 (978-0-7847-0898-9(3) , 03788, Bean Sprouts) Standard Publishing.

—Explore God's Jungle. Ring, Laura, ed. Mykowski, Michelle, illus. 1999. (Shaped Paperback Bks.). (Illus.). 24p. (J). (ps-1). pap. 3.99 (978-0-7847-0899-6(1) , 03789, Bean Sprouts) Standard Publishing.

—Explore God's Ocean. Ring, Laura, ed. Mykowski, Michelle, illus. 1999. (Shaped Paperback Bks.). (Illus.). 24p. (J). (ps-1). pap. 3.99 (978-0-7847-0897-2(5) , 03787, Bean Sprouts) Standard Publishing.

Nagy, Krisztina, illus. Dog Days: An Opposites Book. 1999. 10p. (J). (ps-k). 9.95 (978-1-58117-053-5(X) , Intervisual/Piggy Toes) Dalmatian Pr.

Nanji, Shenaaz. An Alien in My House. McLeod, Chum, tr. McLeod, Chum, illus. 2005. 24p. (J). (gr. k-3). 11.95 (978-1-896764-77-1(0)) Second Story Pr. CAN. *Dist:* Orca Bk. Pubs. USA.

Nash, Margaret. Secret in the Mist. 1999. (Illus.). 32p. (ps-2). 14.95 (978-1-899607-98-3(6)) Sterling Publishing Co., Inc.

Nash, Margaret & Lambert, Stephen. Secret in the Mist. 2000. (Illus.). 32p. (J). (ps-2). pap. 6.95 (978-1-86233-057-3(3)) Sterling Publishing Co., Inc.

Natural History. (Illus.). (J). (ps-6). pap., act. bk. ed. 2.95 (978-0-565-00857-4(9)) Natural History Museum Pubns. GBR. *Dist:* Parkwest Pubns., Inc.

Neasi, Barbara J. Como Yo. Hantel, Johanna, illus. 2003. (Rookie Reader Espanol Ser.).Tr. of Just Like Me. (SPA.). 32p. (J). (gr. k-2). pap. 4.95 (978-0-516-27795-0(2) , Children's Pr.) Scholastic Library Publishing.

Neasi, Barbara J., et al. Como Yo. Hantel, Johanna, illus. rev. ed. 2002. (Rookie Readers Ser.).Tr. of Just Like Me. (SPA.). 32p. (J). (gr. k-2). 19.50 (978-0-516-22689-7(4) , Children's Pr.) Scholastic Library Publishing.

Nelson, Mary Beth, tr. & illus. Elmo's World: Animals! Nelson, Mary Beth, illus. Barrett, John E., illus. Barrett, John E., photos by. 2001. (Elmo's World Ser.). 12p. (J). (gr. k-ps). bds. 4.99 (978-0-375-81336-8(5) , Random Hse. Bks. for Young Readers) Random Hse. Children's Bks.

Nelson, Scott. Bye-Bye, Pacifier. 2001. (Illus.). 12p. bds. 4.99 (978-0-307-13475-2(X) , Golden Bks.) Random Hse. Children's Bks.

—Mulch the Lawnmower. 2006. (Illus.). 32p. 15.98 (978-0-9745715-4-6(7)) KRBY Creations, LLC.

Nelson, Steve & Rollins, Jack. Frosty the Snowman. Cowdrey, Richard, illus. 2003. 32p. (J). (ps). 9.99 (978-0-448-43199-4(8) , 53666302, Grosset & Dunlap) Penguin Group (USA) Inc.

Nestorowich, Sherri, illus. Wisdom of the Golden Goose. 2003. (Jataka Tales Ser.). 32p. (J). (ps-4). pap. 7.95 (978-0-89800-320-8(2)) Dharma Publishing.

Neubecker, Robert. Wow! City! 2004. (Illus.). 40p. (ps-2). 16.99 (978-0-7868-0951-6(5)) Hyperion Bks. for Children.

Neumeyer, Peter F. & Gorey, Edward. Donald & The... 2004. (Illus.). 40p. (J). (ps-3). reprint ed. 12.95 (978-0-8109-4836-5(2)) Abrams, Harry N. , Inc.

—Donald Has a Difficulty. 2004. (Illus.). 40p. (J). (ps-3). reprint ed. 12.95 (978-0-8109-4835-8(4)) Abrams, Harry N. , Inc.

Newhouse, Maxwell. Let's Go for a Ride. 2006. (Illus.). 24p. (J). (ps-2). 16.95 (978-0-88776-748-7(6)) Tundra Bks., Inc./Livres Toundra, Inc. CAN. *Dist:* Random Hse., Inc.

Newman, Marjorie. Mole & the Baby Bird. Benson, Patrick, illus. 2004. 32p. (J). bds. 6.95 (978-1-58234-914-5(2) , Bloomsbury Children) Bloomsbury Publishing.

Newman, Nanette. Ben's Book. Birkett, Georgie, illus. 2007. 24p. (J). pap. 8.99 (***978-1-84458-125-2(X)***) Anova Bks. GBR. *Dist:* Independent Pubs. Group.

Nielsen, Gwyn English. Torey the Turkey Goes Skiing. 2003. (Illus.). 24p. (Orig.). (ps-4). pap. 5.99 (978-0-9660726-0-0(X)) C.G.S. Pr.

Niepold, Mil & Verdu, Jeanyves. Ooh! Matisse. 2007. (Illus.). 48p. (J). (ps-k). 14.95 (***978-1-58246-227-1(5)*** , Tricycle Pr.) Ten Speed Pr.

Nigg, Joe & Topsell, John. How to Raise & Keep a Dragon. 2006. (Illus.). 128p. (J). 18.99 (978-0-7641-5920-6(8)) Barron's Educational Series, Inc.

Nishimoto, Keisuke, ed. Haiku Picturebook for Children. Shimizu, Kozo, illus. 2006. 32p. (gr. 3 up). bds. 14.95 (978-0-89346-916-0(5)) Stone Bridge Pr.

No Laughing Matter. 2003. (Illus.). pap. 7.60 (978-0-7398-7531-5(0)) Steck-Vaughn.

No Laughing Matter, 6 vols. (Ragged Island Mysteriestm Ser.). 161p. (gr. 5-7). 42.50 (978-0-322-01653-8(3)) Wright Group, The.

Noble, Marty. Alice in Wonderland Sticker Activity Book. 1998. 4p. (J). pap. 1.50 (978-0-486-40314-4(9)) Dover Pubns., Inc.

—Emerald Isle Sticker Activity Book. 1998. 4p. (J). pap. 1.00 (978-0-486-40315-1(7)) Dover Pubns., Inc.

—Invisible Angels Magic Picture Book. 1998. (Illus.). 16p. (J). pap. 1.50 (978-0-486-40330-4(0)) Dover Pubns., Inc.

—Invisible Irish Magic Picture Book. 1999. (Illus.). 16p. (J). pap. 1.00 (978-0-486-40765-4(9)) Dover Pubns., Inc.

—Invisible Mythological Creatures Magic Picture Book. 1998. 16p. (J). pap. 1.50 (978-0-486-40119-5(7)) Dover Pubns., Inc.

—Invisible Nutcracker Magic Picture Book. 1999. (Dover Little Activity Bks.). (Illus.). 16p. (J). (ps-5). pap. 1.50 (978-0-486-40531-5(1)) Dover Pubns., Inc.

—Invisible Rain Forest Animals Magic Picture Book. 1999. (Illus.). 16p. (J). pap. 1.50 (978-0-486-40766-1(7)) Dover Pubns., Inc.

—Little Advent Calendar Sticker Activity Book. 2001. (Dover Little Activity Bks.). (Illus.). 4p. (J). (ps-5). 1.50 (978-0-486-41746-2(8)) Dover Pubns., Inc.

—Nativity Sticker Activity Book. 2001. (Illus.). 4p. (J). (ps-3). 1.50 (978-0-486-41745-5(X)) Dover Pubns., Inc.

North, Merry. My Grandma & Me: A Picture, Play & Tote Book. 2004. 10p. (J). (ps up). bds. 5.99 (978-1-57151-724-1(3)) Playhouse Publishing.

Novak, Matt. Mouse TV. 1998. (Illus.). 32p. (J). (ps-1). pap. 6.95 (978-0-531-07099-4(9) , Orchard Bks.) Scholastic, Inc.

—Too Many Bunnies. Novak, Matt, illus. rev. ed. 2005. (Illus.). 16p. (J). 7.95 (978-1-59643-038-9(9)) Roaring Brook Pr.

Novick, Mary. The Big Book of Animals & Bugs. Hale, Jenny, illus. 32p. (J). pap. (978-1-877003-38-7(7)) Little Hare Bks.

Numeroff, Laura Joffe. The Chicken Sisters. Collicott, Sharleen, illus. abr. ed. 2002. (J). pap., tchr.'s planning gde. ed. 37.95 incl. audio (978-0-87499-892-4(1)) Live Oak Media.

—Why a Disguise? 1999. (978-0-606-16317-0(4)) Tandem Library Bks.

Nutkis, Phyllis. When the World Was Quiet. Argoff, Patti, illus. 2003. (J). pap. 9.95 (978-1-929628-14-8(5)) Hachai Publishing.

Nye, Naomi Shihab. Baby Radar. Carpenter, Nancy, illus. 2003. 32p. (J). lib. bdg. 16.89 (978-0-688-15949-8(4)) HarperCollins Pubs.

Nye, Penny. My Family. Eargle, Michele, illus. 2000. (Bookmates Ser.). 15p. (J). (ps). pap. 12.00 (978-1-890703-18-9(4) , Bookmates) Penny Laine Papers, Inc.

—Wow, Look What I Can Do! Nye, Penny, illus. 2001. (Illus.). 15p. (J). (ps-2). pap. 12.00 (978-1-890703-21-9(4) , Bookmates) Penny Laine Papers, Inc.

O'Book, Irene. Maybe My Baby. Hible, Paula, illus. 1998. (Growing Tree Ser.). 14p. (J). (ps up). 6.99 (978-0-694-00872-8(9) , Harper Festival) HarperCollins Pubs.

O'Brien, Eileen. Mary Had a Little Lamb. Tyler, Jenny, ed. Edward, Linda, illus. 2004. (Carry-Me Bks.). 16p. (J). 5.95 (978-0-7945-0124-2(9) , Usborne) EDC Publishing.

—Sing a Song of Sixpence. Tyler, Jenny, ed. Edward, Linda, illus. 2004. (Carry-Me Bks.). 16p. (J). (ps). 5.95 (978-0-7945-0122-8(2) , Usborne) EDC Publishing.

—This Little Piggy. Tyler, Jenny, ed. Edward, Linda, illus. 2004. (Carry-Me Bks.). 16p. (J). 5.95 (978-0-7945-0125-9(7) , Usborne) EDC Publishing.

O'Brien, John. Poof! O'Brien, John, illus. 2003. (Illus.). 32p. (J). (gr. k-2). 16.95 (978-1-56397-815-9(6)) Boyds Mills Pr.

O'Brien, Melanie & Runnells, Treesha. Pat Them Gently. 2006. (Illus.). 10p. (J). 8.95 (978-1-58117-462-5(4) , Intervisual/Piggy Toes) Dalmatian Pr.

O'Brien, Patrick. Gigantic! How Big Were the Dinosaurs? rev. ed. 2002. (Illus.). 32p. (J). (gr. k-3). pap. 6.95 (978-0-8050-6899-3(6) , Holt, Henry & Co. Bks. For Young Readers) Holt, Henry & Co.

Ocean. 2002. (Fuzzy Felts Ser.). (J). 4.98 (978-0-7525-5234-7(1)) Parragon, Inc.

Ochiltree, Dianne. Ten Monkey Jamboree. Lanquetin, Anne-Sophie, illus. 2001. 32p. (J). (ps-2). 16.95 (978-0-689-83402-8(0) , McElderry, Margaret K.) Simon & Schuster Children's Publishing.

Offerman, Lynn. Where Is It? Hers. Chambers, Sally, illus. 1998. (Nuk Bks.). 8p. (J). 6.95 (978-0-7641-7233-5(6)) Barron's Educational Series, Inc.

Old MacDonald. (J). 46.95 (978-0-8136-8807-7(8)) Modern Curriculum Pr.

Old MacDonald. (J). (gr. k-3). (978-0-663-46485-2(4) , MD7225) Silver, Burdett & Ginn, Inc.

Omary, Rachel, illus. Animals in Dari. l.t. ed. 2003. 4p. (J). spiral bd. 10.95 (978-0-9740535-3-0(8)) Knight Publishing.

—Animals in Farsi. l.t. ed. 2003. 4p. (J). spiral bd. 10.95 (978-0-9740535-4-7(6)) Knight Publishing.

—Animals in Pashto. l.t. ed. 2003. 4p. (J). spiral bd. 10.95 (978-0-9740535-5-4(4)) Knight Publishing.

On the Road. 1998. (Hot Wheels Ser.). (Illus.). 96p. (J). (ps-1). pap. (978-0-7666-0104-8(8) , Honey Bear Bks.) Modern Publishing.

O'Neill, Elizabeth & McPherson, Missie. Alfred Visits New York City. 2003. (Illus.). 24p. (J). pap. 12.00 (978-1-4120-1338-3(0)) Trafford Publishing CAN. *Dist:* Atlas-Books Distribution.

O'Neill, Michael Patrick. Fishy Friends: A Journey Through the Coral Kingdom. O'Neill, Michael Patrick, photos by. 2003. (Illus.). 64p. (J). 19.95 (978-0-9728653-0-2(6)) Batfish Bks.

Onish, Liane. Alphabet Eurps Meet Bipple. 1999. (Eurps Concept Bks.). (Illus.). (J). 7.95 (978-1-892522-03-0(9)) Eurpsville USA, Inc.

Open Road. 1998. (Hot Wheels Ser.). (Illus.). 24p. (J). (ps-2). (978-0-7666-0105-5(6) , 69640) Modern Publishing.

Oram, Hiawyn. Badger's Bad Mood. Varley, Susan, illus. 32p. (J). (ps-3). 2002. pap. 5.99 (978-0-590-21693-7(7)); 1998. pap. 15.95 (978-0-590-18920-0(4)) Scholastic, Inc.

—King Smelly Feet. Shelley, John, illus. 2002. 32p. (J). (978-1-84270-038-9(3)) Andersen GBR. *Dist:* Random Hse. of Canada, Ltd.

Oravecz, Kathy. La Rana y el Puente. Oravecz, Kathy, illus. 2001. Tr. of Frog & the Footbridge. (SPA., Illus.). 32p. (J). (ps-3). pap. 7.50 (978-1-59134-003-4(9)) Maval Publishing, Inc.

Orleans, Ilo. Animal Orchestra. Gergely, Tibor, illus. 2004. (Little Golden Treasures Ser.). 26p. (J). (gr. k-k). bds. 4.99 (978-0-375-82775-4(7) , Golden Bks.) Random Hse. Children's Bks.

Ormerod, Jan. Story of Chicken Licken: Level 4, Green, 7 vols. Ormerod, Jan, illus. 2nd ed. 1999. (Reading Together Ser.). (Illus.). 32p. (J). pap. (978-0-7636-0871-2(8)) Candlewick Pr.

—Sunshine. 2004. (Illus.). 32p. (J). 15.95 (978-1-84507-048-9(8)) Lincoln, Frances Ltd. GBR. *Dist:* Perseus Distribution.

Ostwinkle, Pamela S. The Little Teardrop. Ostwinkle, Pamela S., illus. 1999. (Illus.). 27p. (J). (ps-4). 15.99 (978-1-889406-16-9(3)) Prell Bks. & Multimedia.

Oswald, Diane. Aggies Are We: Coloring & Activity Book. Vanya, Timothy, illus. 1999. 40p. (J). (ps-4). pap. 9.95 (978-0-9659698-3-3(5) , LW5004) Lacewing Pr.

Otterman, Lynn. Fluffy Bunny. Fletcher, Rusty, illus. 2002. (Animal Snuggles Ser.). 8p. (J). bds. 7.95 (978-0-8069-8403-2(1)) Sterling Publishing Co., Inc.

Over in the Meadow. (J). (gr. 1). stu. ed. 23.50 (978-0-8136-0271-4(8)) Modern Curriculum Pr.

Owens, Katherine. Tree Seasons Ball, 1 bk. l.t. ed. 2004. (Illus.). 40p. (J). per. 19.99 (978-0-9760419-0-0(1) , TREESEASONSBALL) ThatsMyLife Co.

Oxenbury, Helen. Tickle, Tickle. Oxenbury, Helen, illus. 1999. (Board Books Ser.). (Illus.). 10p. (J). (ps-k). pap. 6.99 (978-0-689-81986-5(2) , Little Simon) Simon & Schuster Children's Publishing.

Ozeta, Valerie. Legend of the Red Wolf. 2nd ed. 1999. (Illus.). 34p. (J). (gr. 3-7). pap. 5.95 (978-0-9661687-1-6(2)) Red Wolf Publishing.

Palatini, Margie. Untitled Picture Book. 2005. 32p. (J). 14.99 (978-0-7868-0323-1(1)) Hyperion Pr.

—Zak's Lunch. Fine, Howard, illus. 1998. 32p. (J). (gr. k-3). tchr. ed. 16.00 (978-0-395-81674-5(2) , Clarion Bks.) Houghton Mifflin Co. Trade & Reference Div.

—Zak's Lunch. unabr. ed. 1999. (J). pap., stu. ed. 32.00 incl. audio (978-0-7887-2983-6(7) , 40865) Recorded Bks., LLC.

Pallotta, Jerry. Reese's Pieces Peanut Butter: Counting Board Book. 1998. 4.95 (978-0-9662445-1-9(6)) Corporate Board Bks.

Palmer, Kate S. A Gracious Plenty. Palmer, Kate S., illus. 1998. (Illus.). 32p. (J). (gr. 1-4). reprint ed. pap. 7.95 (978-0-9667114-0-0(8)) Warbranch Pr., Inc.

Pan, Hui-Mei. Piggy in My Pocket/el Cochinito en mi Bolsillo. Pan, Hui-Mei, illus. 2004. (ENG & SPA., Illus.). 16p. (J). bds. 5.95 (978-1-932065-11-4(3)) Star Bright Bks., Inc.

Pan, Hui-Mei, illus. Piggy in My Pocket. 2004. 16p. (J). bds. 5.95 (978-1-887734-96-7(1)) Star Bright Bks., Inc.

—What's in Grandma's Grocery Bag? 2004. 16p. (J). bds. 5.95 (978-1-887734-97-4(X)) Star Bright Bks., Inc.

Paris, Pat. The First Noel: A Holiday Pop-Up Book. 1998. (Illus.). 10p. (J). 16.95 (978-0-8054-1793-7(1)) B&H Publishing Grp.

Parker, Sandy. What Day Is Today? Hofher, Cathy, illus. l.t. ed. 2003. 24p. (gr. k-1). 13.95 (978-0-9643462-3-9(0) , 10, Just Think Bks.) Canary Connect Pubns.

Parry, Alan. Discover Oaktree Woods: A Touch & Feel Book. Parry, Linda, illus. 2004. 9.00 (978-0-687-02741-5(1)) Abingdon Pr.

Parry, Alan & Parry, Linda. The Herald Angels. 2003. (Illus.). 16p. 9.99 (978-1-85608-253-2(9)) Hunt, John Publishing Ltd. GBR. *Dist:* STL Distribution North America.

—Look for the Rainbow: Look Through the Telescope, Lift the Flaps, Work the Puzzles, See the Pop-Ups, & Enjoy Hours of Fun with Noah. 2003. (Illus.). 14p. 12.99 (978-1-85608-212-9(1)) Hunt, John Publishing Ltd. GBR. *Dist:* STL Distribution North America.

Partis, Joanne. Look at Me! 2007. (Illus.). 10p. (J). bds. 4.99 **(*978-1-84458-365-2(1)*)** Anova Bks. GBR. *Dist:* Independent Pubs. Group.

Patricelli, Leslie. Binky. Patricelli, Leslie, illus. 2005. (Illus.). 24p. (J). (gr. k-ps). bds. 6.99 (978-0-7636-2364-7(4)) Candlewick Pr.

—Blankie. Patricelli, Leslie, illus. 2005. (Illus.). 24p. (J). (gr. k-ps). bds. 6.99 (978-0-7636-2363-0(6)) Candlewick Pr.

Patrick, Denise Lewis. Ma Dear's Old Green House. Sadler, Sonia Lynn, illus. 2004. (J). (gr. k-3). 16.95 (978-0-940975-55-2(6) , Sankofa Bks.) Just Us Bks., Inc.

Payne, Tony & Payne, Jan. Plummet. Bolam, Emily, illus. 2004. 32p. (J). 12.95 (978-0-7641-5798-1(1)) Barron's Educational Series, Inc.

Pease, Elaine. I'll Never Leave. MacLean, Kerry Lee, illus. 2000. 32p. (J). (ps-2). 14.95 (978-0-9702275-0-8(7)) Peasepod Bks.

Peck, Jan. The Giant Carrot. Root, Barry, illus. 1998. 32p. (J). (ps-3). 16.99 (978-0-8037-1823-4(3) , Dial) Penguin Group (USA) Inc.

Pedersen, Marika. Mommy Works, Daddy Works. 2000. (J). (978-0-606-20140-7(8)) Tandem Library Bks.

Pendziwol, Jean. No Dragons for Tea. ed. 2004. (Illus.). (J). (gr. k-3). spiral bd. (978-0-616-01755-5(3)); spiral bd. (978-0-616-01756-2(1)) Canadian National Institute for the Blind/Institut National Canadien pour les Aveugles.

—No dragons for tea: Fire safety for kids (and dragons) Gourbault, Martine, illus. 32p. (J). (gr. k-3). 2001. (978-1-55074-571-9(9)); 1999. (978-1-55074-569-6(7)) Kids Can Pr., Ltd.

Penguin Books Staff. Come! Let's Read with Dick & Jane! 12 Book Reading Set. 2005. (Dick & Jane Ser.). 8p. (J). (gr. k-1). 9.99 (978-0-448-43981-5(6) , Grosset & Dunlap) Penguin Group (USA) Inc.

Penney, Ian. Ian Penney's Abc. 1998. (Illus.). 36p. (gr. 8-17). 16.95 (978-0-8109-4350-6(6)) Abrams, Harry N., Inc.

People. Date not set. (I Can Draw Ser.). 32p. (J). 4.98 (978-1-4054-0020-6(X)) Parragon, Inc.

Perkins, Myrna. What Makes Honey? Perkins, William C. & Perkins, Lori L., illus. 32p. (Orig.). (J). (ps-3). pap. 3.95 (978-0-937729-03-8(5)) Markins Enterprises.

Perlman, Janet. Penguin & the Pea. Perlman, Janet, illus. 2006. (Illus.). 32p. (978-1-55337-983-6(7)) Kids Can Pr., Ltd.

Perlman, Janet, illus. & retold by. The Penguin & the Pea. Perlman, Janet, retold by. 2005. 32p. (J). (ps-2). (978-1-55074-832-1(7)) Kids Can Pr., Ltd.

Perry, Rex, illus. Over the River & Through the Woods. 2004. (Jump at the Sun Holiday Classics Ser.). 24p. (ps-2). pap. 3.50 (978-0-7868-0923-3(X)) Hyperion Bks. for Children.

Petricic, Dusan, illus. The Enormous potato. 1998. 32p. (J). (gr. k-3). (978-1-55074-386-9(4)) Kids Can Pr., Ltd.

Petty, Kate. Little Rabbits' First Number Book. Baker, Alan, illus. 1998. 30p. (J). pap. 12.98 (978-1-58048-054-3(3)) Sandvik Publishing.

Pfeffer, Wendy. Light So Bright. Date not set. 40p. (J). (ps-1). 15.99 (978-0-06-029121-1(4)) HarperCollins Pubs.

Pfloog, Jan. Monkey Book. 1999. (ps-2). lib. bdg. 11.00 (978-0-613-87570-7(2)) Tandem Library Bks.

Philip, Neil. The Fish Is Me! Bathtime Rhymes. Henley, Claire, illus. 2002. 32p. (J). (gr. k-3). tchr. ed. 16.00 (978-0-618-15939-0(8) , Clarion Bks.) Houghton Mifflin Co. Trade & Reference Div.

Phillips, Gina & Martin, Stuart. Ants & Caterpillars. 2003. (Busy Bugs Ser.). 12p. (J). bds. 14.95 (978-1-74047-240-1(3)) Book Co. Publishing Pty, Ltd., The AUS. *Dist:* Penton Overseas, Inc.

Pichon, Liz. Bored Bill. Pichon, Liz, illus. 2006. (Illus.). 32p. (J). 15.95 (978-1-58925-053-6(2) , tiger tales) ME Media LLC.

Picture, Play & Tote Counter Diaplay. (J). (978-1-57151-726-5(X)) Playhouse Publishing.

Pienkowski, Jan. Botticelli's Bed & Breakfast. Smith, Rodger & Balmer, Helen, illus. 2000. 8p. (J). (gr. 3-5). 23.00 (978-0-7881-9364-4(3)) DIANE Publishing Co.

Pienkowski, Jan, illus. Jan Pienkowski's Jungle. 1998. (Animal Action Pops Ser.). 10p. (J). (gr. 2 up). 4.95 (978-1-58117-020-7(3) , Intervisual/Piggy Toes) Dalmatian Pr.

Piggy Toes Press Staff & Embleton, Chris. Baby Says. 2006. (Illus.). 6p. (J). 12.95 (978-1-58117-458-8(6) , Intervisual/Piggy Toes) Dalmatian Pr.

Piggy Toes Press Staff & Haskamp, Steve. Five Silly Monkeys: With Handpuppet. 2006. (Illus.). 12p. (J). bds. 12.95 (978-1-58117-460-1(8) , Intervisual/Piggy Toes) Dalmatian Pr.

Pilkey, Dav. Mighty Robot vs. the Uranium Unicorns from Uranus. Ontiveros, Martin, illus. 2005. (Ricky Ricotta Ser.: Bk. 7). 128p. (J). (ps). pap. 3.99 (978-0-439-37647-1(5) , Blue Sky Pr., The) Scholastic, Inc.

—La Navidad de Dragon. 1999. (Dragon's Tales Ser.: Bk. 3). (Illus.). (J). (978-0-606-21667-8(7)) Tandem Library Bks.

Pinkston, Ronald. A Police Officer That's What I'll Be! Rivera, Israel, illus. 1999. 26p. (J). (gr. k-2). 12.99 (978-0-9671708-0-0(X)) Pinkston Publishing.

Pinky & the Brain. (Look & Find Bks.). (Illus.). 24p. (J). (gr. k-5). 7.98 (978-0-7853-1607-7(8) , PI11) Publications International, Ltd.

Piper, Sophie. Little Kitten's Friendship Book. Massey, Jane, illus. 2006. 64p. (J). pap. 6.99 (978-0-7459-4710-5(7) , Lion) Lion Hudson plc GBR. *Dist:* Independent Pubs. Group.

—Little Teddy's Birthday Book. Massey, Jane, illus. 2002. 64p. (J). 6.99 (978-0-7459-4709-9(3) , Lion) Lion Hudson plc GBR. *Dist:* Independent Pubs. Group.

Pirulino. On the Farm. Ferri, Francesca, illus. 2004. 10p. (J). 16.95 (978-0-7641-2947-6(3)) Barron's Educational Series, Inc.

Pittar, Gill. Milly, Molly & Alf. 2005. 28p. (978-1-86972-018-6(0)) Milly Molly Bks.

—Milly, Molly & Aunt Maude. 2004. 28p. (978-1-86972-014-8(8)) Milly Molly Bks.

—Milly, Molly & Different Dads. 2004. 28p. (978-1-86972-019-3(9)) Milly Molly Bks.

—Milly, Molly & Sock Heaven. 2004. 28p. (978-1-86972-015-5(6)) Milly Molly Bks.

—Milly, Molly & Special Friends. 2004. 28p. (978-1-86972-017-9(2)) Milly Molly Bks.

Platt, Richard & Biesty, Stephen. Man-of-War. (Illus.). (J). pap. 21.95 (978-0-590-74610-6(3)) Scholastic, Inc.

Playing Inside the Tubbytronic Superdome. 1999. (Teletubbies Ser.). (Illus.). (J). (ps). 19.99 (978-0-439-10603-0(6)) Scholastic, Inc.

Plourde, Lynn. School Picture Day. Wickstrom, Thor, illus. 2002. 40p. (J). (gr. k-3). 16.99 (978-0-525-46886-8(2) , Dutton Juvenile) Penguin Group (USA) Inc.

Plume, Ilse. The Bremen-Town Musicians. 1998. (Illus.). 32p. (ps-3). reprint ed. pap. 6.99 (978-0-440-41456-8(3) , Dragonfly Bks.) Random Hse. Children's Bks.

Pockets Learning Staff. I Can Do It Myself Book. 1998. (Illus.). 8p. (ps up). 35.00 (978-1-888074-98-7(1)) Pockets of Learning.

Podoshen, Lois. La Dulceria de Abuelo. Romo, Alberto, tr. Finch, Linda, illus. 1998. (Books for Young Learners).Tr. of Grandpa's Candy Store. (SPA.). 12p. (J). (gr. k-2). pap. 5.00 (978-1-57274-200-0(3) , A2850) Owen, Richard C. Pubs., Inc.

—El Regalo de Cumpleanos. Romo, Alberto, tr. Schaedler, Sally, illus. 1998. (Books for Young Learners).Tr. of Birthday Bird. (SPA.). 8p. (J). (gr. k-2). pap. 5.00 (978-1-57274-207-9(0) , A2895) Owen, Richard C. Pubs., Inc.

Poison Patrol: Picture Book 8x8. 2007. (J). **(*978-1-933934-40-2(9)*)** Educational Adventures.

Poison Patrol: Picture Book (English) 9x9 with Snipe. 2007. (J). **(*978-1-933934-50-1(6)*)** Educational Adventures.

Pomaska, Anna. Invisible Easter Magic Picture Book. 1998. 16p. (J). pap. 1.50 (978-0-486-40331-1(9)) Dover Pubns., Inc.

Ponti, Claude. En El Coche. 2003. (SPA.). 32p. 15.95 (978-84-95150-08-0(5)) Corimbo, Editorial S.L. ESP. *Dist:* Distribooks, Inc.

Popper, Garry. Ali in Egypt. Johnson, Andi, illus. 2004. 36p. (ps-7). 4.00 (978-1-84161-078-8(X)) Ravette Publishing, Ltd. GBR. *Dist:* Parkwest Pubns., Inc.

—Billy Joe in the U. S. A. Johnson, Andi, illus. 2004. 36p. (ps-7). 4.00 (978-1-84161-053-5(4)) Ravette Publishing, Ltd. GBR. *Dist:* Parkwest Pubns., Inc.

—James & Jemma in Great Britain. Johnson, Andi, illus. 2004. 36p. (ps-7). 4.00 (978-1-84161-054-2(2)) Ravette Publishing, Ltd. GBR. *Dist:* Parkwest Pubns., Inc.

—Keito in Japan. Johnson, Andi, illus. 2004. 36p. (ps-7). 4.00 (978-1-84161-058-0(5)) Ravette Publishing, Ltd. GBR. *Dist:* Parkwest Pubns., Inc.

—Kez in Australia. Johnson, Andi, illus. 2004. 36p. (ps-7). 4.00 (978-1-84161-055-9(0)) Ravette Publishing, Ltd. GBR. *Dist:* Parkwest Pubns., Inc.

—Lena & Peter in Germany. Johnson, Andi, illus. 2004. 36p. (ps-7). 4.00 (978-1-84161-060-3(7)) Ravette Publishing, Ltd. GBR. *Dist:* Parkwest Pubns., Inc.

—Li & Lilly May in China. Johnson, Andi, illus. 2004. 36p. (ps-7). 4.00 (978-1-84161-057-3(7)) Ravette Publishing, Ltd. GBR. *Dist:* Parkwest Pubns., Inc.

—Mario in Italy. Johnson, Andi, illus. 2004. 36p. (ps-7). 4.00 (978-1-84161-059-7(3)) Ravette Publishing, Ltd. GBR. *Dist:* Parkwest Pubns., Inc.

—Mina in India. Johnson, Andi, illus. 2004. 36p. (ps-7). 4.00 (978-1-84161-079-5(8)) Ravette Publishing, Ltd. GBR. *Dist:* Parkwest Pubns., Inc.

—Paul in France. Johnson, Andi, illus. 2004. 36p. (ps-7). 4.00 (978-1-84161-056-6(9)) Ravette Publishing, Ltd. GBR. *Dist:* Parkwest Pubns., Inc.

Popular Mechanics Staff, ed. Who Uses a Drill? Davis, Nancy, illus. 2004. (Popular Mechanics for Kids Ser.). 10p. (J). bds. 4.95 (978-1-58816-370-7(9)) Hearst Bks.

—Who Uses a Hammer? Davis, Nancy, illus. 2004. (Popular Mechanics for Kids Ser.). 10p. (J). bds. 4.95 (978-1-58816-371-4(7)) Hearst Bks.

—Who Uses a Saw? Davis, Nancy, illus. 2004. (Popular Mechanics for Kids Ser.). 10p. (J). bds. 4.95 (978-1-58816-373-8(3)) Hearst Bks.

Potter, Beatrix. Peter Rabbit Giant Shaped Board Book. abr. ed. 2001. (Illus.). 10p. (J). (ps-k). bds. 7.99 (978-0-7232-4682-4(3) , Warne) Penguin Group (USA) Inc.

—The World of Peter Rabbit, 12 vols. gif. ed. 2004. (Potter Ser.). (Illus.). (J). 84.00 (978-0-7232-8408-6(3) , Warne) Penguin Group (USA) Inc.

Poulsen, Allan. Freezy Breezy Fun. Raymond, Kim, illus. 2000. (Look-Look Bks.). 24p. (J). (ps-3). pap. 3.29 (978-0-307-12891-1(1) , 12891, Golden Bks.) Random Hse. Children's Bks.

Pow, Tom. Tell Me One Thing, Dad. Andrew, Ian, illus. 2004. 32p. (J). (ps-k). 15.99 (978-0-7636-2474-3(8)) Candlewick Pr.

Powell, Richard. Puff & the Long Train. Hawksley, Gerald, illus. 2004. (Softy Wheels Ser.). 18p. (J). bds. 8.95 (978-0-7641-7790-3(7)) Barron's Educational Series, Inc.

—Zoom's Finest Hour. Hawksley, Gerald, illus. 2004. (Softy Wheels Ser.). 18p. (J). bds. 8.95 (978-0-7641-7789-7(3)) Barron's Educational Series, Inc.

Prater, John. Number One, Tickle Your Tum. 1999. (Baby Bear Ser.). (Illus.). 24p. (J). 6.95 (978-0-7641-5185-9(1)) Barron's Educational Series, Inc.

—Oh Where, Oh Where? 1998. (Illus.). 24p. (J). bds. 6.95 (978-0-7641-5109-5(6)) Barron's Educational Series, Inc.

Pratt, Pierre. Marcel et Andre. 2003. (Picture Bks.). (FRE., Illus.). 32p. (J). (ps). (978-2-89021-633-4(0)) Diffusion du livre Mirabel.

Price, Mathew. In the Snow. Augarde, Steve, illus. 2000. (Little Red Car Bks.). 10p. (J). (ps-1). pap. 6.95 (978-0-7892-0674-9(9) , Abbeville Kids) Abbeville Pr., Inc.

—Knock! Knock! Claverie, Jean, illus. 2003. (Peekaboo Board Bks.). 10p. (J). bds. 4.99 (978-0-7696-3158-5(4) , Gingham Dog Pr.) School Specialty Publishing.

—Little Red Car Has an Accident. Augarde, Steve, illus. 2000. (Little Red Car Bks.). 10p. (J). (ps-1). pap. 6.95 (978-0-7892-0673-2(0) , Abbeville Kids) Abbeville Pr., Inc.

—Little Red Car Plays Taxi. Augarde, Steve, illus. 2000. (Little Red Car Bks.). 10p. (J). (ps-1). pap. 6.95 (978-0-7892-0675-6(7) , Abbeville Kids) Abbeville Pr., Inc.

—What Does Baby Do? Morozumi, Atsuko, illus. 2003. (Tommy Board Bks.). 10p. (J). bds., bds. 4.99 (978-0-7696-2958-2(X)) School Specialty Publishing.

—Who Lives Here? Morozumi, Atsuko, illus. 2003. (Tommy Board Bks.). 10p. (J). bds., bds. 4.99 (978-0-7696-2982-7(2)) School Specialty Publishing.

Price, Mathew & Claverie, Jean. Peekaboo! A First Pop-up Book. Claverie, Jean, illus. 2004. (First Pop-Up Book Ser.). (Illus.). 24p. (J). (gr. k-ps). 12.95 (978-0-394-87142-4(1) , Knopf Bks. for Young Readers) Random Hse. Children's Bks.

Priddy Books Staff. Kids Can Time. 2003. (J). bds. (978-0-312-49171-0(9) , Priddy Bks.) St. Martin's Pr.

Priddy, Roger. Happy Baby: Colors. rev. ed. 2001. (Baby Soft-to-Touch Ser.). (Illus.). 28p. (J). bds. 5.95 (978-0-312-49047-8(X) , Priddy Bks.) St. Martin's Pr.

—Happy Baby Words. rev. ed. 2001. (Baby Soft-to-Touch Ser.). (Illus.). 28p. (J). bds. 5.95 (978-0-312-49009-6(7) , Priddy Bks.) St. Martin's Pr.

Prims, Marta & Roca, Nuria. I Am a Little Bat. 2001. (Barron's Little Animal Ser.). (Illus.). 24p. (J). (ps-k). 9.95 (978-0-7641-5346-4(3)) Barron's Educational Series, Inc.

—I Am a Little Spider. 2001. (Barron's Little Animal Ser.). (Illus.). 24p. (J). (ps-k). 9.95 (978-0-7641-5345-7(5)) Barron's Educational Series, Inc.

The Princess & the Magic Locket. 2003. (Illus.). 32p. (J). 5.98 (978-1-4054-1022-9(1)) Parragon, Inc.

Pringle, Laurence P. One Room School. 2003. (Illus.). 32p. (J). (gr. 2-4). 16.95 (978-1-56397-583-7(1)) Boyds Mills Pr.

Pringle, Mary L. & Ellis, Joseph. "We Don't Need Drugs to Be OK," with Gillie the Knowbot & Sis & Chris. rev. ed. 1998. (Educational Story Coloring Book Ser.). Orig. Title: Sis & Chris & the Knowbots in "We Don't Need Drugs to Be OK". (Illus.). 32p. (J). (ps-3). 1.95 (978-0-935847-12-3(X)) Institute for Substance Abuse Research.

Professional Scholastic Staff. Around-The-Year Mini-Books. 1999. (Let's Find Out Bks.). 160p. pap. 14.95 (978-0-590-51308-1(7)) Scholastic, Inc.

Prokofiev, Sergei. Sergei Prokofiev's Peter & the Wolf: With Fully-Orchestrated & Narrated CD. Malone, Peter, illus. 2004. 40p. (J). lib. bdg. 21.99 (978-0-375-92430-9(2) , Knopf Bks. for Young Readers) Random Hse. Children's Bks.

Prokofiev, Sergei & Malone, Peter. Sergei Prokofiev's Peter & the Wolf: With Fully-Orchestrated & Narrated CD. 2004. (Illus.). 40p. (J). 19.95 incl. audio compact disk (978-0-375-82430-2(8) , Knopf Bks. for Young Readers) Random Hse. Children's Bks.

Proysen, Alf. Mrs. Pepperpot at the Bazaar. Offen, Hilda, illus. 2007. 32p. pap. 4.99 (***978-0-09-945158-7(1)***) Transworld Publishers Ltd. GBR. *Dist:* Independent Pubs. Group.

—Mrs. Pepperpot Learns to Swim. 2006. (Illus.). 32p. (J). pap. 8.99 (***978-0-09-945157-0(3)*** , Red Fox) Random Hse. Children's Bks. GBR. *Dist:* Independent Pubs. Group.

Pulver, Robin. Axle Annie. Kane, Cindy, ed. 1999. (Illus.). 32p. (J). (ps-3). 15.99 (978-0-8037-2096-1(3) , Dial) Penguin Group (USA) Inc.

Puttock, Simon. Pig's Prize. 2004. (Illus.). 32p. (J). 17.99 (978-1-4052-0538-2(5)); pap. 17.99 (978-1-4052-0880-2(5)) Egmont Bks., Ltd. GBR. *Dist:* Independent Pubs. Group.

Quadrillion Media Staff. Show Me the Apple! 1999. bds. 3.95 (978-1-58185-214-1(2)) Quadrillion Media LLC.

—Show Me the Ball! 1999. bds. 3.95 (978-1-58185-212-7(6)) Quadrillion Media LLC.

—Show Me the Duck! 1999. bds. 3.95 (978-1-58185-215-8(0)) Quadrillion Media LLC.

—Show Me the Train! 1999. bds. 3.95 (978-1-58185-213-4(4)) Quadrillion Media LLC.

—Toby Discovers Opposites. 1999. bds. 3.95 (978-1-58185-210-3(X)) Quadrillion Media LLC.

Rabe, Tish. I'm a Baby: A Mix & Match Book. Larranaga, Ana, illus. 2006. 14p. (J). (ps-ps). bds. 9.99 (978-1-58476-355-0(8) , IKIDS) Innovative Kids.

Radtke, Becky. Invisible Old MacDonald's Farm Magic Picture Book. 2004. 32p. (J). pap. 1.50 (978-0-486-43421-6(4)) Dover Pubns., Inc.

Raintree Steck-Vaughn Staff. Biggest Sandwich Ever. 2000. (Illus.). (J). (gr. k-1). pap. 19.24 (978-0-8172-6454-3(X)) Steck-Vaughn.

Rainville, Doris I., creator. The Girl Who Never Let Her Mother Brush Her Hair. l.t. ed. 2003. (Illus.). 24p. (J). per. 7.95 (978-0-9744879-0-8(2)) Magical Creations.

—The Power of Love. l.t. ed. 2003. (Illus.). 24p. (J). per. 7.95 (978-0-9744879-1-5(0)) Magical Creations.

Random House Beginners Books Staff. Seek & Find Fun. Zimmerman, Jerry, illus. 2002. (Thomas & Friends Ser.). 16p. (J). (ps-2). pap. 2.99 (978-0-375-81496-9(5) , Golden Bks.) Random Hse. Children's Bks.

Random House Disney Staff. Chicken Little. 2006. (Disney Read-Aloud Board Books). (Illus.). 24p. (J). (gr. k-k). bds. 4.99 (978-0-7364-2290-1(0) , RH/Disney) Random Hse. Children's Bks.

Rathmann, Peggy. Good Night, Gorilla. Rathmann, Peggy, illus. 2004. (Illus.). 34p. (J). (ps-1). bds. 12.99 (978-0-399-24260-1(0) , Putnam Juvenile) Penguin Group (USA) Inc.

Ravishankar, Anushka & Ramanathan, Rathna, contrib. by. Anything but a Grabooberry. 2003. (Illus.). 48p. (J). 9.99 (978-81-86211-43-4(8)) Penguin Group (USA) Inc.

Rea-It! Readers: Gus the Hedgehog. 2005. (Illus.). (C). (gr. k-3). 55.80 (978-1-4048-0995-6(3)) Picture Window Bks.

Read it! Readers: Folk Tales. 2005. (Illus.). (C). (gr. k-3). 130.20 (978-1-4048-0999-4(6)) Picture Window Bks.

Read-It! Readers: Tall Tales. 2005. (Illus.). (C). (gr. k-3). 111.60 (978-1-4048-1081-5(1)) Picture Window Bks.

Ready Reader Staff. What Do We Have to Get?, 6 bks., set, Level 6, Bk. 13. 2003. (J). (ps-3). pap. 33.50 (978-0-8136-2021-3(X)) Modern Curriculum Pr.

—Where Does the Rabbit Hop?, 6 bks., set, Level 8, Bk. 30. 2003. (J). (ps-3). 33.50 (978-0-8136-0793-1(0)) Modern Curriculum Pr.

Redeker, Kent. The Bidding War. Brandt, Elizabeth, illus. 2001. (Angela Anaconda Ser.: Vol. 5). 64p. (J). pap. 3.99 (978-0-689-84183-5(3) , Simon Spotlight) Simon & Schuster Children's Publishing.

Reich, J. J. Deer Dad: Kampp Tales¿ Outdoor Adventures. Johnathan, Kuehl, illus. 2006. (BAT.). 32p. (J). (***978-0-9762971-0-9(8)***) Outdoor Originals LLC.

Reidy, Hannah. Crazy Creature Capers. Mackie, Clare, illus. 2003. (Crazy Creatures Ser.). 26p. (J). pap. (978-1-84089-222-2(6) , Zero to Ten, Limited) Evans Publishing Group.

Reilly, Pauline. Roobook the Owl. 1998. (Picture Roo Bks.). (Illus.). 32p. (ps-3). pap. (978-0-86417-966-1(9) , Kangaroo Pr.) Simon & Schuster Australia.

Reiter, Cheryl. Tonka: Billie's Tough Job. Torgerson, Dell & Hogan, Jayne, eds. Knutson, Doug, illus. 2000. 12p. (J). (ps). mass mkt. 9.99 (978-1-887327-43-5(6)) Ertl Co., Inc.

—Tonka: Mike Lends a Helping Hand. Torgerson, Dell, ed. Knutson, Doug, illus. 2000. 12p. (J). (ps). mass mkt. 9.99 (978-1-887327-41-1(X)) Ertl Co., Inc.

Reiter, Cheryl & Torgerson, Dell. Patti Pig & Friends. Solheim, Kermit, illus. 2000. 10p. (J). (ps). mass mkt. 12.99 (978-1-887327-54-1(1)) Ertl Co., Inc.

—Tonka: Reggie's Big Rescue. Knutson, Doug, illus. 2000. 12p. (J). (ps). mass mkt. 9.99 (978-1-887327-42-8(8)) Ertl Co., Inc.

Renyi Bilingual Picture Dictionaries, 12 vols., Set. Date not set. (Illus.). 2304p. 244.40 (978-1-56674-937-4(9)) Forest Hse. Publishing Co., Inc.

Revell, Cindy, illus. A Sack Full of Feathers. 2007. 32p. pap. (***978-1-55143-863-4(1)***) Orca Bk. Pubs.

Revenge of the Tune Squad. Date not set. (Space Jam Eye Illusion Bks.). (Illus.). 24p. (J). (gr. 1-6). pap. 2.95 (978-1-56144-889-0(3) , SJMO32) Modern Publishing.

Rey, H. A. Curious George Goes to the Hospital. Rey, H. A., illus. 2002. (Curious George Picture Bks.). (J). 13.79 (978-0-7587-2319-2(9)) Book Wholesalers, Inc.

Rey, H. A. & Rey, Margret. Brezel. 1999. (GER., Illus.). 36p. (J). pap. (978-3-257-00854-8(6)) Diogenes Verlag AG CHE. *Dist:* International Bk. Import Service, Inc.

Rey, Margret & Rey, H. A. Curious George Visits a Toy Store. Weston, Martha, illus. 2002. 24p. (J). (gr. k-3). tchr. ed. 12.00 (978-0-618-06398-7(6)) Houghton Mifflin Co. Trade & Reference Div.

Reynolds, Pamela. Silly Soup. Wise, Noreen, ed. Cozart, Jane, illus. 2000. (Book-a-Day Collection). 32p. (YA). (ps up). pap. 5.95 (978-1-58584-434-0(9)) Huckleberry Pr.

Richards, Lucy. Little Farm. 2007. (Illus.). 10p. (J). bds. 4.99 (***978-1-84458-362-1(7)***) Anova Bks. GBR. *Dist:* Independent Pubs. Group.

—Little Garden. 2007. (Illus.). 10p. (J). bds. 4.99 (***978-1-84458-363-8(5)***) Anova Bks. GBR. *Dist:* Independent Pubs. Group.

Richardson, Bill. The Aunts Come Marching. Nugent, Cynthia, illus. 2007. 32p. (J). 15.95 (***978-1-55192-990-3(2)***) Raincoast Bk. Distribution CAN. *Dist:* Perseus Distribution.

Riddell, Chris. Mr. Underbed. 1998. (Illus.). 32p. (J). (ps-1). pap. 9.99 (978-0-86264-786-5(X)) Andersen GBR. *Dist:* Trafalgar Square Publishing.

Rider, Cynthia. Chatterbox Turtle. Petrlik, Andrea, illus. 2004. 24p. (J). lib. bdg. 22.65 (***978-1-59646-696-8(0)***) Dingles & Co.

Rikkers, Doris. Little Jesus, Little Me. Stott, Dorothy, illus. 2000. 12p. (J). 5.99 (978-0-310-23205-6(8)) Zonderkidz.

—Little Jesus, Little Me. 2008. 14p. (J). bds. 4.99 (***978-0-310-71651-8(9)***) Zondervan.

Ringbom, Antonia & Wiklund, Alison. The Hiding Hyena. 2nd ed. 2007. (YA). (***978-0-9789617-1-8(4)***) H.B.P., Inc.

Risk, Mary, et al. Puppy Finds a Friend: Cachorrito Encuentra a un Amigo. Bendall-Brunello, John, illus. 2000. (I Can Read Bks.). (SPA, ENG & FRE.). 28p. (J). (gr. k-2). 6.95 (978-0-7641-5283-2(1)) Barron's Educational Series, Inc.

—Puppy Finds a Friend: Le Petit chien Trouve un Copain. Bendall-Brunello, John, illus. 2000. (I Can Read Bks.). (FRE & ENG.). 28p. (J). (ps-2). 8.99 (978-0-7641-5285-6(8)) Barron's Educational Series, Inc.

Risom, Ole. I Am a Bunny. Scarry, Richard, illus. 2004. 26p. (J). (gr. k-k). bds. 5.99 (978-0-375-82778-5(1) , Golden Bks.) Random Hse. Children's Bks.

Rizzati, Lorella. Crab. 1998. (Portable Pets Ser.). (Illus.). 12p. (J). (ps). bds. 5.95 (978-0-8109-5675-9(6)) Abrams, Harry N. , Inc.

—Frog. 1998. (Portable Pets Ser.). (Illus.). 12p. (J). (ps). bds. 6.95 (978-0-8109-5676-6(4)) Abrams, Harry N. , Inc.

—Ladybug. 1998. (Portable Pets Ser.). (Illus.). 12p. (J). (ps). bds. 6.95 (978-0-8109-5677-3(2)) Abrams, Harry N. , Inc.

—Turtle. 1998. (Portable Pets Ser.). (Illus.). 12p. (J). (ps). bds. 6.95 (978-0-8109-5678-0(0)) Abrams, Harry N. , Inc.

Robb, Andy. Betty Boat, 1. 1999. 12p. (J). (ps-k). 4.00 (978-0-570-05568-6(7)) Concordia Publishing Hse.

—Polly Plane, 1. 1999. (Big Truth Stories Ser.). 12p. (J). (ps-k). 4.00 (978-0-570-05570-9(9)) Concordia Publishing Hse.

—Rory Racer, 1. 1999. (Big Truth Stories Ser.). 12p. (J). (ps-k). 4.00 (978-0-570-05569-3(5)) Concordia Publishing Hse.

—Tommy Tractor, 1. 1999. (Big Truth Stories Ser.). 12p. (J). (ps-k). 4.00 (978-0-570-05571-6(7)) Concordia Publishing Hse.

Robb, Andy, illus. Spot the Mistake, Bk. 1. 2001. 24p. (J). (gr. k up). 2.99 (978-0-8254-7208-4(3)) Kregel Pubns.

Robert, Christi. One Baby, Two Baby, Three Baby, Four! Bischel, Mark, illus. 1998. 16p. (J). (ps). pap. 5.95 (978-1-891846-00-7(0)) Business Word, The.

Roberts, Bethany. Birthday Mice! Cushman, Doug, illus. 2002. 32p. (J). (gr. k-ps). tchr. ed. 13.00 (978-0-618-07772-4(3) , Clarion Bks.) Houghton Mifflin Co. Trade & Reference Div.

Roberts, Phyllis. Teeny Tiny Star. 2007. (Illus.). 30p. (J). lib. bdg. 19.95 (***978-1-933732-40-4(7)*** , Bear Hug Bks.) MidAmerica Publishing Co.

ROBERTSON, M. P. The Sandcastle. 2008. (Illus.). 32p. (J). pap. 7.95 (***978-1-84507-800-3(4)***) Lincoln, Frances Ltd. GBR. *Dist:* Perseus Distribution.

Robleda, Margarita. Maria: Una Nina Latina en Estados Unidos. Ramirez, Danilo, illus. 2005. (SPA.). 36p. pap. 10.95 (978-1-59437-557-6(7) , Alfaguara) Santillana USA Publishing Co., Inc.

Roca, Nuria. Fall. 2004. (Four Seasons Ser.). (Illus.). 36p. (J). pap. 6.95 (978-0-7641-2729-8(2)) Barron's Educational Series, Inc.

—El Invierno. 2004. (Cuatro Estaciones Ser.).Tr. of Winter. (SPA., Illus.). 36p. (J). pap. 6.95 (978-0-7641-2732-8(2)) Barron's Educational Series, Inc.

—El Otono. 2004. (Cuatro Estaciones Ser.).Tr. of Autumn. (SPA., Illus.). 36p. (J). pap. 6.95 (978-0-7641-2730-4(6)) Barron's Educational Series, Inc.

—La Primavera. 2004. (Cuatro Estaciones Ser.).Tr. of Spring. (SPA., Illus.). 36p. (J). pap. 7.99 (978-0-7641-2734-2(9)) Barron's Educational Series, Inc.

—El Verano. 2004. (Cuatro Estaciones Ser.).Tr. of Summer. (SPA., Illus.). 36p. (J). pap. 6.95 (978-0-7641-2736-6(5)) Barron's Educational Series, Inc.

—Winter. 2004. (Four Seasons Ser.). (Illus.). 36p. (J). pap. 6.95 (978-0-7641-2731-1(4)) Barron's Educational Series, Inc.

Roche, Luane. The Proud Tree. Sharp, Chris, illus. 1999. 48p. (J). (gr. 1-5). pap. 11.95 (978-0-7648-0377-2(8)) Liguori Pubns.

Rodriguez, Rachel. Through Georgia's Eyes. Paschkis, Julie, illus. rev. ed. 2006. 32p. (J). 16.95 (978-0-8050-7740-7(5)) Holt, Henry & Co.

Roffey, M. First Words Indoors. 2003. (Illus.). 12p. (J). 3.99 (978-1-85292-227-6(3) , Campbell Bks.) Pan Macmillan GBR. *Dist:* Trafalgar Square Publishing.

Rogalski, Mark. Tickets to Ride: An Alphabetic Amusement. 2006. (Illus.). 64p. (J). 15.95 (978-0-7624-2782-6(5) , Running Pr. Kids) Running Pr. Bk. Pubs.

Rogers. What Can You See. 2000. (Illus.). 20p. (J). pap. 8.95 (978-0-552-54588-4(0)) Transworld Publishers Ltd. GBR. *Dist:* Trafalgar Square Publishing.

Rogers, Alan. Blue Tortoise. 2004. (Little Giants Ser.). (Illus.). 16p. (ps-k). (J). pap. 3.95 (978-1-58728-158-7(9)); 5.95 (978-1-58728-150-1(3)) T&N Children's Publishing. (Two Can Publishing).

—El Hipopotamo Amarillo. 2004. (Pequenos Gigantes Ser.).Tr. of Yellow Hippo. (SPA., Illus.). 16p. (ps-k). (J). pap. 3.95 (978-1-58728-956-9(3)); 5.95 (978-1-58728-142-6(2)) T&N Children's Publishing. (Two Can Publishing).

—El Hipopotamo Amarillo. Rogers, Alan, illus. 2000. (Pequenos Gigantes Ser.).Tr. of Yellow Hippo. (SPA., Illus.). 16p. (J). (ps-ps). lib. bdg. 10.75 (978-0-606-20704-1(X)) Tandem Library Bks.

—El Oso Verde. 2004. (Pequenos Gigantes Ser.).Tr. of Green Bear. (SPA., Illus.). 16p. (ps-k). (J). pap. 3.95 (978-1-58728-957-6(1)); 5.95 (978-1-58728-143-3(0)) T&N Children's Publishing. (Two Can Publishing).

—El Oso Verde. Rogers, Alan, illus. 2000. (Pequenos Gigantes Ser.).Tr. of Green Bear. (Illus.). 15p. (J). (ps-ps). lib. bdg. 10.75 (978-0-606-20836-9(4)) Tandem Library Bks.

—Red Rhino. 2004. (Little Giants Ser.). (Illus.). 16p. (J). (ps-k). pap. 3.95 (978-1-58728-161-7(9) , Two Can Publishing) T&N Children's Publishing.

—El Rinoceronte Rojo. 2004. (Pequenos Gigantes Ser.).Tr. of Red Rhino. (SPA., Illus.). 16p. (ps-k). (J). pap. 3.95 (978-1-58728-958-3(X)); 5.95 (978-1-58728-144-0(9)) T&N Children's Publishing. (Two Can Publishing).

—El Rinoceronte Rojo. Rogers, Alan, illus. 2000. (Pequenos Gigantes Ser.).Tr. of Red Rhino. (Illus.). 15p. (J). (ps-ps). lib. bdg. 10.75 (978-0-606-20885-7(2)) Tandem Library Bks.

—La Tortuga Azul. 2004. (Pequenos Gigantes Ser.). (SPA., Illus.). 16p. (ps-k). (J). pap. 3.95 (978-1-58728-959-0(8)); 5.95 (978-1-58728-145-7(7)) T&N Children's Publishing. (Two Can Publishing).

—Le Vent Tourne! 2003. (Little Giants Ser.). (FRE., Illus.). 16p. (J). (ps-k). 5.95 (978-1-58728-179-2(1) , Two Can Publishing) T&N Children's Publishing.

Rogers, Fred. When a Pet Dies. Judkis, Jim, photos by. 1998. (First Experience Bks.). (Illus.). 32p. (J). (ps-k). pap. 5.99 (978-0-698-11666-5(6) , Putnam Juvenile) Penguin Group (USA) Inc.

—When a Pet Dies. 1998. (ps-2). lib. bdg. 14.15 (978-0-613-90031-7(6)) Tandem Library Bks.

Rohmann, Eric. Clara & Asha. Rohmann, Eric, illus. 2005. (Illus.). 40p. (J). (ps-ps). 16.95 (978-1-59643-031-0(1)) Roaring Brook Pr.

Romeo, Joe & Barnett, LaQuela. Road Trip Survival Kit. Phillips, Karen, illus. 1999. 24p. (J). (ps-2). spiral bd. 9.99 (978-1-929140-00-8(2)) Music, Inc.

Root, Phyllis. Oliver Finds His Way. Denise, Christopher, illus. 2002. 40p. (J). (ps-1). 14.99 (978-0-7636-1383-9(5)) Candlewick Pr.

Rosa-Mendoza, Gladys. Animals at the Farm/Animales de la Granja. Wolff, Jason, illus. 2004. (English-Spanish Foundations Ser.). (SPA & ENG.). 20p. (J). (ps). bds. 6.95 (978-1-931398-13-8(5)) Me+Mi Publishing.

—Cars, Trucks & Planes/Carros, Camiones y Aviones. Tugeau, Jeremy, illus. 2004. (English-Spanish Foundations Ser.). (SPA & ENG.). 20p. (J). (ps). bds. 6.95 (978-1-931398-14-5(3)) Me+Mi Publishing.

—Lupe Lupita, Where Are You?/Lupe Lupita, Donde Estas? Ochoa, Ana, illus. 2005. (English-Spanish Foundations Ser.). (SPA & ENG.). 20p. (J). (ps). bds. 6.95 (978-1-931398-16-9(X)) Me+Mi Publishing.

The Rose. 2001. (Teddy Fairies Ser.). (Illus.). 8p. (J). (ps-k). bds. 4.95 (978-0-439-20851-2(3)) Scholastic, Inc.

Rose, Gerald. Sam's Café ELT Edition. 2004. (Cambridge Storybooks Ser.). 24p. pap. 6.00 (978-0-521-75225-1(6)) Cambridge Univ. Pr.

Rosen, Jeff. How Does Poko Feel? 2005. (Illus.). 12p. (J). 5.95 (978-1-897073-18-6(6)) Lobster Pr. CAN. *Dist:* Univ. of Toronto Pr.

Rosoff, Iris, ed. My First Body Book. 2004. (Illus.). 36p. (J). bds. 5.99 (978-0-7566-0279-6(3)) Dorling Kindersley Publishing, Inc.

Ross, K. K. The Little Red Car. Alley, R. W., illus. 1999. (Jellybean Bks.). 24p. (J). (ps-k). lib. bdg. 7.99 (978-0-375-90142-3(6) , Random Hse. Bks. for Young Readers) Random Hse. Children's Bks.

Ross, Thea. Lucy Loves Winter. 2004. 16p. (J). bds. 4.99 (978-1-59384-077-8(2)) Parklane Publishing.

Ross, Tony. I Want My Present! 2007. (Illus.). 12p. (J). (ps-k). 9.99 (***978-1-84270-481-3(8)***) Andersen GBR. *Dist:* Independent Pubs. Group.

Rosselson, Leon. Tom the Whistling Wonder. Haslam, John, illus. 2005. 24p. (J). lib. bdg. 22.65 (***978-1-59646-758-3(4)***) Dingles & Co.

Roth, Carol. Little Bunny's Sleepless Night. Gorbachev, Valeri, illus. 32p. (J). (ps-2). 2002. pap. 6.95 (978-0-7358-1804-0(5)); 1999. 15.95 (978-0-7358-1069-3(9)); 1999. 16.50 (978-0-7358-1070-9(2)) North-South Bks., Inc.

—The Little School Bus. 2004. (Illus.). 32p. (J). (gr. k-1). pap. 6.95 (978-0-7358-1905-4(X)) North-South Bks., Inc.

—The Little School Bus. Paparone, Pamela, illus. 2002. 32p. (J). (ps-1). 14.95 (978-0-7358-1646-6(8)) North-South Bks., Inc.

Rothstein, Gloria. Real-Life Writing Activities Based on Favorite Picture Books: Super-Fun Activities & Reproducibles That Use Picture Books As Models to Help Kids Practice 11 Kinds of Real-Life Writings. 2002. 80p. pap., tchr. ed. 12.95 (978-0-439-25616-2(X)) Scholastic, Inc.

Rotner, Shelley. Boats Afloat. 1998. (Illus.). 32p. (J). (ps-k). 16.99 (978-0-531-33112-5(1)); pap. 15.95 (978-0-531-30112-8(5)) Scholastic, Inc. (Orchard Bks.).

Rotner, Shelley & Kreisler, Ken. Citybook. 1998. (Illus.). 32p. (J). (ps-1). pap. 6.95 (978-0-531-07106-9(5) , Orchard Bks.) Scholastic, Inc.

Rowe, Jeannette. Whose Ears? Rowe, Jeannette, illus. 1999. (Illus.). 24p. (J). (ps-k). 7.95 (978-0-316-75932-8(5)) Little Brown & Co.

Rudkin, Nancy. A Dragon at School. 2005. 28p. (J). 9.95 (978-1-4116-3877-8(8)) Lulu.com.

Rudner, Barry. Special Ed. 1999. 28p. (J). pap. 7.95 (978-0-9642206-4-5(4)) Windword Pr.

—Special Ed. Trabalka, Peggy, illus. l.t. ed. 2000. 28p. (J). (ps-3). 7.95 (978-0-9642206-6-9(0)) Windword Pr.

Runnells, Treesha. Forest Friends: A Fold-Out Fun Book. Runnells, Treesha, illus. 2005. (Fold-Out Fun Ser.). (Illus.). 10p. (J). 4.95 (978-1-58117-275-1(3) , Intervisual/Piggy Toes) Dalmatian Pr.

—Safari Friends: Fold-Out Fun. Runnells, Treesha, illus. 2005. (Fold Out Fun Ser.). (Illus.). 10p. (J). 4.95 (978-1-58117-276-8(1) , Intervisual/Piggy Toes) Dalmatian Pr.

Running Press Staff. Opposites. 2002. (First Discovery Look-Inside Board Bks.). (Illus.). 10p. (J). bds. 4.95 (978-0-439-35592-6(3) , Cartwheel Bks.) Scholastic, Inc.

Running Press Staff & Newberger, Devra. Busy Days in Deerfield Valley. Wakelin, Bob, illus. 2005. 10p. (J). pap. 11.95 (978-0-7624-2343-9(9) , Running Pr.) Running Pr. Bk. Pubs.

Russell, Naomi. Guess Who's in the Jungle: A Flip-Flap Book. Russell, Naomi, illus. 1999. (Illus.). 32p. (J). (ps-k). pap. 3.99 (978-0-7636-0759-3(2)) Candlewick Pr.

—Guess Who's on the Farm. Russell, Naomi, illus. 2nd ed. 1999. (Flip-the-Flap Book Ser.). (Illus.). 32p. (J). (gr. k-ps). pap. 3.99 (978-0-7636-0689-3(8)) Candlewick Pr.

Russo, Marisabina. The Big Brown Box. Russo, Marisabina, illus. 2000. (Illus.). 32p. (J). (ps up). 16.99 (978-0-688-17096-7(X)) HarperCollins Pubs.

Russo-Stark, Marisabina. The Big Brown Box. 2000. (Illus.). (J). lib. bdg. (978-0-688-17097-4(8)) HarperCollins Pubs.

Ruurs, Margriet. Emma's Eggs. Spurll, Barbara, illus. 1998. 24p. (J). (ps-3). pap. (978-0-7737-5898-8(4)) Stoddart Kids.

—Emma's Eggs. Spurll, Barbara, illus. 2002. 24p. (ps-3). pap. 8.95 (978-0-7737-3334-3(5)) Stoddart Kids CAN. *Dist:* Fitzhenry & Whiteside, Ltd.

Ryan, Darlene & Manchester, Peter. Kisses, Kisses, Kisses. 2004. (Illus.). 24p. (J). (***978-1-55131-092-3(9)***) Univ. of New Brunswick, Dept. of Graphic Services.

Ryan, Pam Muñoz. There Was No Snow on Christmas Eve. Nolan, Dennis, illus. 2005. 32p. (ps-1). 15.99 (978-0-7868-5492-9(8)) Hyperion Pr.

P
Q
R

Rydell, Katy. Wind Says Good Night. Jorgensen, David, illus. 2000. 32p. (J). (gr. k-3). pap. 5.95 (978-0-618-08585-9(8)) Houghton Mifflin Co. Trade & Reference Div.

—Wind Says Good Night. Jorgensen, David, illus. 2000. (ps-ps). lib. bdg. 14.10 (978-0-613-30193-0(5)) Tandem Library Bks.

—Wind Says Good Night. 2000. (Illus.). (J). (978-0-606-21735-4(5)) Tandem Library Bks.

Rylant, Cynthia. The Case of the Fidgety Fox. Karas, G. Brian, illus. 2003. (High-Rise Private Eyes Ser.: No. 6). 56p. (J). (gr. 1 up). lib. bdg. 16.89 (978-0-06-009102-6(9)) HarperCollins Pubs.

—Christmas in the Country. Goode, Diane, illus. 2005. 32p. (J). (ps-3). pap. 5.99 (978-0-439-76985-3(X) , Scholastic Paperbacks) Scholastic, Inc.

—Let's Go Home: The Wonderful Things about a House. Halperin, Wendy Anderson, illus. 2005. 32p. (J). pap. 7.99 (978-1-4169-0839-5(0) , Aladdin) Simon & Schuster Children's Publishing.

—The Stars Will Still Shine. Beeke, Tiphanie, illus. 2005. 40p. (J). (ps-k). 15.99 (978-0-06-054639-7(5)) HarperCollins Pubs.

S. I. Artists Staff, illus. Berry Pretty Fashions. 2004. (Strawberry Shortcake Ser.). 16p. (J). (ps-1). pap. 4.99 (978-0-448-43553-4(5) , Grosset & Dunlap) Penguin Group (USA) Inc.

Sadasivan, Lathika. My First Millennium. Sadasivan, Lathika, illus. 2000. (Illus.). 20p. (J). (ps-3). 14.99 (978-0-9700318-1-5(5)); pap. 7.99 (978-0-9700318-0-8(7)) Peek-A-Bks.

Sage, Angie. No Banana. 2002. (Illus.). (J). mass mkt. 7.50 (978-0-340-77343-7(X) , Hodder & Stoughton) Hodder General Publishing Division GBR. *Dist:* Trafalgar Square Publishing.

Sage, Molly. At the Beach. 2007. (Illus.). 6p. (J). pap. 6.99 (***978-1-85602-497-6(0)***) Anova Bks. GBR. *Dist:* Independent Pubs. Group.

Salisbury, Kent. Color Fun: What Colors Are Your Favorite Things? 1998. (Illus.). 24p. (J). (ps-k). 6.99 (978-0-7681-0084-6(4) , McClanahan Bk.) Learning Horizons, Inc.

Sams, Carl R., II & Stoick, Jean, photos by. Lost in the Woods: A Photographic Fantasy. 2004. (Illus.). 48p. (J). pap. 19.95 (978-0-9671748-8-4(0)) Sams, II, Carl R. Photography, Inc.

Samuel, Stuart. One, Two, Three! This Book 's for Me! 2002. (Illus.). 26p. (J). 11.95 (978-0-9655176-5-2(9)) Jupiter Scientific Publishing Co.

SanAngelo, Ryan. Spaghetti Eddie. Urbanovic, Jackie, illus. 2003. 32p. (J). (gr. k-2). 15.95 (978-1-56397-974-3(8)) Boyds Mills Pr.

Sanchez, Miriam & Fernandez, Federico. Where Did Moon Lose Her Laughter? 2002. (Illus.). 32p. (J). 14.95 (978-84-95730-20-6(0)) Kalandraka Catalunya, Edicions, S.L. ESP. *Dist:* Independent Pubs. Group.

Sandhaus, Ellen. The Runaway Balloon (El Globo Que Se Escapo) Blanco, Osvaldo J., tr. unabr. ed. 1999. (SPA & ENG., Illus.). 24p. (J). (gr. k-4). pap. 4.95 (978-1-893266-01-8(X)) Sandhaus, Paul Assocs., Inc.

—Santa's Scavenger Hunt (Santa Claus en Busca de Regalos Raros) Blanco, Osvaldo J., tr. unabr. ed. 1999. (SPA & ENG., Illus.). 16p. (J). (gr. k-4). pap. 4.95 (978-1-893266-04-9(4)) Sandhaus, Paul Assocs., Inc.

—Stop Rhyming! (Deja de Hablar en Rima!) Blanco, Osvaldo J., tr. unabr. ed. 1999. (SPA & ENG., Illus.). 15p. (J). (ps-3). pap. 4.95 (978-1-893266-03-2(6)) Sandhaus, Paul Assocs., Inc.

—Where Do Lost Balloons Go? (Adonde Van los Globos Perdidos?) Blanco, Osvaldo J., tr. unabr. ed. 1999. (ENG & SPA., Illus.). 24p. (J). (gr. k-4). pap. 4.95 (978-1-893266-00-1(1)) Sandhaus, Paul Assocs., Inc.

Santucci, Barbara. Anna's Corn. Bloom, Lloyd, illus. 2004. 32p. (J). (gr. 1 up). 16.00 (978-0-8028-5119-2(3)) Eerdmans, William B. Publishing Co.

Sarfati, Sonia. Crayons, Chaussons et Grands Espions. 2002. (Premier Roman Ser.). (FRE.). 64p. (J). (gr. 2-5). pap. (978-2-89021-220-6(3)) Diffusion du livre Mirabel.

Sauer, Cat. Gwendolyn the Ghost. Jankowski, Dan, illus. l.t. ed. 2003. (Brown Bag Bedtime Bks.: 1). 29p. (YA). spiral bd. 16.95 (978-0-9704460-9-1(8)) Writer's Ink. Studios, Inc.

Savary, Fabien. Caillou: Que Falta? Tipeo, illus. 2004. Tr. of What's Missing?. (SPA.). 12p. (J). bds. 4.95 (978-1-58728-349-9(2) , Creative Publishing International) Quayside.

Savary, Fabien & Vadeboncoeur, Isabelle. Caillou: Donde Esta? Tipeo, illus. 2004. Tr. of Where Is It?. (SPA.). 12p. (J). bds. 4.95 (978-1-58728-402-1(2) , Creative Publishing International) Quayside.

—Caillou: Los Contrarios. Tipeo, illus. 2004. Tr. of What's the Difference?. (SPA.). 12p. (J). bds. 4.95 (978-1-58728-348-2(4) , Creative Publishing International) Quayside.

—Caillou: Sorpresa! Tipeo, illus. 2004. Tr. of What's Inside?. (SPA.). 12p. (J). bds. 4.95 (978-1-58728-390-1(5) , Creative Publishing International) Quayside.

Say, Allen, illus. Stranger in the Mirror. 1998. 32p. (J). (gr. 4-6). pap. 6.95 (978-0-395-93883-6(X) , Walter Lorraine) Houghton Mifflin Co. Trade & Reference Div.

Scarry, Richard. Best Word Book Ever! Scarry, Richard, illus. 1999. (Richard Scarry's Ser.). (Illus.). 72p. (J). (ps-2). 15.99 (978-0-307-15510-8(2) , 15510, Golden Bks.) Random Hse. Children's Bks.

—Jellybean. 1999. (J). lib. bdg. 7.99 (978-0-375-90077-8(2)) Random Hse., Inc.

Schachner, Judith B. Yo, Vikings! Schachner, Judith B., illus. 2002. (Illus.). 32p. (J). (gr. k-4). 16.99 (978-0-525-46889-9(7) , Dutton Juvenile) Penguin Group (USA) Inc.

Schaefer, Lola M. El Halcon de Cola Roja. de la Vega, Eida, tr. Taylor, Stephen, illus. 2001. (Books for Young Learners).Tr. of Red-Tailed Hawk. (SPA.). 16p. (J). (gr. k-2). pap. 5.00 (978-1-57274-445-5(6) , 2864) Owen, Richard C. Pubs., Inc.

—An Island Grows. Felstead, Cathie, illus. 2006. 40p. (J). (gr. k-2). 16.99 (978-0-06-623930-9(3)); lib. bdg. 17.89 (978-0-06-623931-6(1)) HarperCollins Pubs.

—El Nido de la Tortuga. Romo, Alberto, tr. Becker, Neesa, illus. 1998. (Books for Young Learners).Tr. of Turtle Nest. (SPA.). 16p. (J). (gr. k-2). pap. 5.00 (978-1-57274-205-5(4) , A2883) Owen, Richard C. Pubs., Inc.

—This Is the Rain. Wattenberg, Jane, illus. 2001. 40p. (J). 16.99 (978-0-688-17039-4(0)); 16.89 (978-0-688-17040-0(4)) HarperCollins Pubs.

Schechter, Robert. My First Picture Word Book. del Sur, Duendes & Helbig, Allen, illus. 1999. (McGraw-Hill Junior Academic Ser.). 64p. (J). (gr. k-2). 7.99 (978-1-57768-205-9(X)) School Specialty Publishing.

Schilling, Mickey. Colorado Rockies Coloring & Activity Book. 1998. (Illus.). 48p. (J). (ps-6). pap. (978-0-9663885-0-3(X)) Schilling, Mickey.

Schlesinger, Marian C. San Bao & His Adventures in Peking. 2nd ed. 1998. (Illus.). 75p. (J). (gr. 3-7). reprint ed. pap. 15.00 (978-0-9645809-1-6(8)) Gale Hill Bks.

Schneider, Judy. But Not Quite. Weeks, Mary, illus. 2004. (J). 19.95 (978-1-59404-005-4(2)) Peanut Butter Publishing.

Schoberle, Cecile. Open Wide! a Visit to the Dentist. 2000. (gr. k-3). lib. bdg. 11.25 (978-0-613-22138-2(9)) Tandem Library Bks.

Scholastic, Inc. Staff. Humpty Dumpty Loop Rattle, 12 Pack. 2003. (Sidekicks Ser.). (J). 83.88 (978-0-439-55402-2(0) , Sidekicks TM) Scholastic, Inc.

—Teletubbies: 1999 Edition. 1998. (Teletubbies Ser.). (J). (ps). 10.95 (978-0-590-38611-1(5)) Scholastic, Inc.

Scholastic, Inc. Staff & Gerth, Melanie. My First Jumbo Book of Shapes. Diaz, James, illus. 2004. (My First Jumbo Book Ser.). 10p. (J). pap. 9.95 (978-0-439-62377-3(4) , Cartwheel Bks.) Scholastic, Inc.

School Specialty Publishing. Hablo Ingles! Level 1 - Pictures & Words. 1999. (Homework Booklets Ser.). (SPA.). 80p. (C). pap. 2.99 (978-0-88012-921-3(2) , IF0200, Instructional Fair) Schaffer, Frank Pubns.

School Zone Publishing Company Staff. Whimsy Picture Words. 2001. (Flash Cards Whimsy Ser.). 56p. (J). 2.79 (978-0-88743-672-7(2) , 04063) School Zone Publishing Co.

Schubeck, Carol M. Let's Move Together. Clanuwat, Rinna, illus. 2000. 52p. (J). (ps-6). pap. 15.95 (978-0-9675567-0-3(8)) Suitcase Pr.,The.

Schwartz, David M. At the Seashore. Kuhn, Dwight, photos by. 1998. (Springboards into Science Ser.). (Illus.). 24p. (J). (gr. 1 up). lib. bdg. 19.93 (978-0-8368-2224-3(2)) Stevens, Gareth Inc.

—If You Hopped Like a Frog. Warhola, James, illus. 1999. (If You Ser.). 32p. (J). (gr. k-4). pap. 16.95 (978-0-590-09857-1(8)) Scholastic, Inc.

—In the Desert. Kuhn, Dwight, photos by. 1998. (Springboards into Science Ser.). (Illus.). 24p. (J). (gr. 1 up). lib. bdg. 20.67 (978-0-8368-2220-5(X)) Stevens, Gareth Inc.

—In the Meadow. Kuhn, Dwight, photos by. 1998. (Springboards into Science Ser.). (Illus.). 24p. (J). (gr. 1 up). lib. bdg. 20.67 (978-0-8368-2223-6(4)) Stevens, Gareth Inc.

Scott, Cynthia A. Old Jake's Skirts. Slonim, David, illus. 2003. 36p. (J). 7.95 (978-0-87358-839-3(8) , Rising Moon Bks. for Young Readers) Northland Publishing.

Scott, Foresman and Company Staff. Work & Play, Big & Little, You & Me. (J). 18.82 (978-0-673-21373-0(0) , Scott Foresman) Addison Wesley Schl.

Scott, Vicki. Tweety, Temple of Boom! 1999. (Illus.). (J). (978-0-7853-2724-0(X)) Publications International, Ltd.

Sears, William, et al. Baby on the Way. Andriani, Renee W., illus. 2001. 32p. (J). (ps-3). 12.99 (978-0-316-78767-3(1)) Little, Brown Bks. for Young Readers.

Selway, Martina. So Many Babies: A Fun to Count Book. 2001. (Illus.). 32p. (J). 17.99 (978-0-09-176986-4(8)) Random Hse. GBR. *Dist:* Independent Pubs. Group.

—What Can I Write? Rosie Writes Again. 1998. (Illus.). 32p. (J). pap. 29.99 (978-0-09-926712-6(8)) Random Hse. GBR. *Dist:* Independent Pubs. Group.

Sendak, Maurice. Donde Viven los Monstruos. 2003. (SPA., Illus.). 40p. (J). (gr. k-3). 12.95 (978-84-372-2185-4(4)) Altea, Ediciones, S.A. - Grupo Santillana ESP. *Dist:* Santillana USA Publishing Co., Inc.

—Donde Viven los Monstruos. Mlawer, Teresa, tr. 2001. (SPA., Illus.). (J). 7.96 net. (978-1-56137-544-8(6) , NU5725) Novel Units, Inc.

Sesame Street Staff. Sesame Street Take-Along Box. 1998. (J). 2.22 (978-0-676-76810-7(5)) Random Hse., Inc.

Seuss, Dr. Gerald McBoing Boing. Seuss, Dr., illus. 2004. (Little Golden Book Ser.). (Illus.). 24p. (J). (gr. k-k). 2.99 (978-0-375-82721-1(8) , Golden Bks.) Random Hse. Children's Bks.

—Gerald McBoing Boing. Crawford, Mel, illus. 2000. 32p. (J). (gr. k-3). 12.95 (978-0-679-89140-6(4) , Random Hse. Bks. for Young Readers) Random Hse. Children's Bks.

—Horton Escucha a Quien. Canetti, Yanitzia, tr. from SPA. 2002. (SPA & ENG., Illus.). (J). (gr. k-2). 16.00 (978-1-930332-35-5(1) , LC7301) Lectorum Pubns., Inc.

Seymour, Dorothy Z. & Mills, Dorothy. Ann Likes Red. Meyerhoff, Nancy, illus. 2001. 28p. (J). (ps-1). 8.95 (978-1-930900-12-7(0)) Purple Hse. Pr.

Seymour, Sylvia. Just the Way I Am. Jones, Tanna Lee, illus. 2001. (J). (ps-3). pap. 14.95 (978-0-9651396-4-9(6)) Jawbone Publishing Corp.

Shah, Sapna Jaiswal. Sapna Aunty's Hindi Book of Colors: Rang. 2004. (HIN.). (J). 8.00 (978-0-9741686-0-9(2)) 3N Media Group.

Sharp, N. L. Effie's Image. Rohner, Dorothia, illus. 2006. 32p. (J). 17.95 (978-0-9759829-5-2(8)) Prairieland Pr.

Shaw, Gina. All in a Day's Play. Levin, James, photos by. 1998. (Tonka Board Bks.). (Illus.). 16p. (J). (ps). bds. 4.99 (978-0-590-76344-8(X)) Scholastic, Inc.

Shells. Date not set. (Illus.). 8p. (J). (gr. k-2). pap. 3.75 (978-1-58323-015-2(7) , Seedling Pubns.) Continental Pr., Inc.

Shepard, Ernest H., illus. Tigger: Giant Shaped Board Book. 1999. 10p. (J). (ps-k). bds. 7.99 (978-0-525-46233-0(3) , Dutton Juvenile) Penguin Group (USA) Inc.

Sherwood, Barbara B. Jan & Ann & the Pet Rabbit. Campbell, Nancy T., illus. 1998. 16p. (J). (ps). pap. 5.95 (978-1-891846-03-8(5)) Business Word, The.

—Jan & Ann Are Twins. Campbell, Nancy T., illus. 1998. 16p. (J). (ps). pap. 5.95 (978-1-891846-02-1(7)) Business Word, The.

Shields, Carol Diggory. Colors. Junakovic, Svjetlan, illus. 2000. (Animagicals Ser.). 12p. (J). (ps-1). 9.95 (978-1-929766-04-8(1)) Handprint Bks.

—Food Fight! Gay-Kassel, Doreen, illus. 2002. 32p. (J). (ps-2). 15.95 (978-1-929766-29-1(7)) Handprint Bks.

Shipton, Paul. Clown School. Blake, Beccy, illus. 2005. 24p. (J). lib. bdg. 22.65 (***978-1-59646-752-1(5)***) Dingles & Co.

Shulevitz, Uri. The Man in the Picture. Date not set. (J). (978-0-374-34749-9(2) , Farrar, Straus & Giroux (BYR)) Farrar, Straus & Giroux.

Shulman, Mark. Car & Truck Show. Small, Phillip, illus. 2005. (Storytime Stickers Ser.). 16p. (J). pap. 4.95 (978-1-4027-1807-6(1)) Sterling Publishing Co., Inc.

—Magic Fairy Forest. Wilburn, Kathy, illus. 2005. (Storytime Stickers Ser.). 16p. (J). pap. 4.95 (978-1-4027-1806-9(3)) Sterling Publishing Co., Inc.

—Some Sheep. Bartos, Joe & Nguyen, Vincent, illus. 2003. (Some Animals Ser.). 20p. (J). 5.95 (978-0-7641-5653-3(5)) Barron's Educational Series, Inc.

Siegel, Terri. Goodnight Princess Scharazad. 2005. (J). lib. bdg. 19.95 (***978-0-9754728-5-9(2)*** , Bear Hug Bks.) MidAmerica Publishing Co.

Silver Dolphin en Español Editors. Tesoro de Libros de Calcomanias Princesas. 2004. (Disney Calcomanias Ser.). (SPA., Illus.). 72p. (J). pap. 14.95 (978-970-718-106-9(0) , Silver Dolphin en Español) Advanced Marketing, S. de R. L. de C. V. MEX. *Dist:* Bilingual Pubns. Co., The, Perseus Distribution, Transition Vendor.

Silverhardt, Lauryn. Blue's Friends. 2001. (Blue's Clues Ser.). (Illus.). 14p. (J). 4.99 (978-0-689-84544-4(8) , Simon Spotlight/Nickelodeon) Simon & Schuster Children's Publishing.

—Counting with Blue. 2001. (Blue's Clues Ser.). (Illus.). 14p. (J). bds. 4.99 (978-0-689-84543-7(X) , Simon Spotlight/Nickelodeon) Simon & Schuster Children's Publishing.

Simmons, Steven J. Jasper: The Fish Who Saved a Marriage. Bartkus, Ray, illus. 1998. 32p. (J). (ps-3). 15.95 (978-0-88106-989-1(2)) Charlesbridge Publishing, Inc.

Simon, Francesca. Little Yellow Dog Bites the Builder. Lucas, James E., illus. 2004. (Little Yellow Dog Ser.). 32p. (J). pap. 7.99 (978-1-84255-246-9(5)) Orion Children's Bks. GBR. *Dist:* Independent Pubs. Group.

—Little Yellow Dog Gets a Shock. Lucas, James E., tr. Lucas, James E., illus. 2004. (Little Yellow Dog Ser.). 32p. (J). pap. 7.99 (978-1-84255-243-8(0)) Orion Children's Bks. GBR. *Dist:* Independent Pubs. Group.

—Little Yellow Dog Meets His Match. Lucas, James E., illus. 2004. (Little Yellow Dog Ser.). 32p. (J). pap. 7.99 (978-1-84255-245-2(7)) Orion Children's Bks. GBR. *Dist:* Independent Pubs. Group.

—Little Yellow Dog Says Look at Me. Lucas, James E., illus. 2004. (Little Yellow Dog Ser.). 32p. (J). pap. 7.99 (978-1-84255-244-5(9)) Orion Children's Bks. GBR. *Dist:* Independent Pubs. Group.

Simont, Marc. The Stray Dog. Simont, Marc, illus. (Illus.). 32p. (J). (ps-3). 2003. pap. 6.99 (978-0-06-443669-4(1)); 2001. 15.99 (978-0-06-028933-1(3)) HarperCollins Pubs.

Singer, Mutt & Mitter, Matt. My Little People Safari, 4 bks., Set. S. I. International Staff, illus. 2000. (Fisher-Price Sidesqueaker Playbook Ser.). 14p. (J). (ps-k). bds. (978-1-57584-661-3(6)) Reader's Digest Children's Publishing, Inc.

Siomades, Lorianne. Kangaroo & Cricket. Siomades, Lorianne, illus. 2003. (Illus.). 32p. (J). (ps up). 12.95 (978-1-56397-780-0(X)) Boyds Mills Pr.

Sirett, Dawn. Baby's Busy World. 2005. (Illus.). 26p. (J). 12.99 (978-0-7566-1018-0(4)) Dorling Kindersley Publishing, Inc.

Sis, Peter. Fire Truck. Sis, Peter, illus. 2004. (Illus.). 28p. (J). (ps-1). bds. 6.99 (978-0-06-056259-5(5) , Harper Festival) HarperCollins Pubs.

Sitzenstock, Gabriele. Raising Puppy. 2006. (J). spiral bd. 12.95 (***978-1-59872-721-0(4)***) Instantpublisher.com.

Skorpen, Liesel Moak. Outside My Window. Mayer, Mercer, illus. 2004. 32p. (J). (ps-3). 16.89 (978-0-06-050775-6(6)) HarperCollins Pubs.

Slate, Joseph. Miss Bindergarten Stays Home from Kindergarten. Wolff, Ashley, illus. (J). (ps-2). 2000. 1p. 16.99 (978-0-525-46396-2(8) , Dutton Juvenile); 2004. 48p. reprint ed. pap. 6.99 (978-0-14-230127-2(2) , Puffin) Penguin Group (USA) Inc.

—Who Is Coming to Our House? Wolff, Ashley, illus. 2001. 32p. (J). bds. 6.99 (978-0-399-23410-1(1) , Putnam Juvenile) Penguin Group (USA) Inc.

Sleepyheads. 2002. (Baby Faces Ser.). (Illus.). (J). bds. 4.95 (978-0-439-33946-9(4)) Scholastic, Inc.

Sloat, Teri. There Was an Old Lady Who Swallowed a Trout. Ruffins, Reynold, illus. 2002. (J). 26.47 (978-0-7587-3781-6(5)) Book Wholesalers, Inc.

—There Was an Old Lady Who Swallowed a Trout. Ruffins, Reynold, illus. rev. ed. 32p. (J). (gr. k-2). 2002. pap. 7.95 (978-0-8050-6900-6(3)); 1998. 17.95 (978-0-8050-4294-8(6)) Holt, Henry & Co. (Holt, Henry & Co. Bks. For Young Readers).

—There Was an Old Lady Who Swallowed a Trout. 2002. (ps-2). lib. bdg. 15.25 (978-0-613-88115-9(X)) Tandem Library Bks.

Smart Kids Publishing Staff. Play It Safe. (Illus.). 14p. (J). bds. 12.95 (978-0-8249-6593-8(0)) Ideals Pubns.

—Safe at Home! (Illus.). 14p. (J). bds. 12.95 (978-0-8249-6592-1(2)) Ideals Pubns.

Smee, Nicola. Funny Face. 2006. (Illus.). 24p. (J). 8.95 (978-1-58234-710-3(7) , Bloomsbury Children) Bloomsbury Publishing.

Smith, Beth. Red Bug. Coates, Jennifer, illus. l.t. ed. 2000. (Cardboard Bks.). 12p. (J). (ps-1). pap. 10.95 (978-1-57332-169-3(9)) HighReach Learning, Inc.

Smith, Beth Esh. Off We Go! Linke, Don, Jr., illus. l.t. ed. 1998. (Big Bks.). 8p. (J). (ps-k). pap. 10.95 (978-1-57332-111-2(7)) HighReach Learning, Inc.

Smith, Charles R. Let's Play Basketball! Widener, Terry, illus. 2004. (Super Sturdy Picture Books). 24p. (J). (gr. k-ps). 8.99 (978-0-7636-1691-5(5)) Candlewick Pr.

Smith, Dale. Over Is Not Up! Brooks, Donna, illus. 1998. (It's a Bitsie Book Ser.). 32p. 14.95 (978-1-886864-00-9(4) , Golden Anchor Bks.) Golden Anchor Pr.

Smith, Dana Kessimakis. A Brave Spaceboy: Moving Is an Adventure! Freeman, Laura, illus. 2005. 32p. (ps-1). 15.99 (978-0-7868-0933-2(7)) Hyperion Bks. for Children.

Smith, James D. & Smith, Lauren M. My First Golf Book. Vuong, Tuvinh, illus. 1999. (My First Book Ser.). 44p. (ps-1). 14.95 (978-0-9669116-0-2(1)) C T L Publishing.

Smith, Linda. Smith Picture Book. Date not set. (Illus.). 32p. (J). (ps-3). 5.99 (978-0-06-443621-2(7)) HarperCollins Pubs.

Smith, Michael T. Blue's Halloween Hide-and-Seek: A Lift-the-Flap Story. Cardinali, Kevin, illus. 2000. (Blue's Clues Ser.). 16p. (J). (ps-k). 5.99 (978-0-689-83433-2(0) , Simon Spotlight/Nickelodeon) Simon & Schuster Children's Publishing.

Smithsonian Institution Staff. Bear on His Own. 2000. (Let's Go to the Zoo! Ser.). (Illus.). 16p. (J). (ps-k). bds. 5.95 (978-1-56899-913-5(5) , B9008) Soundprints.

Smothers, Ethel Footman. Auntee Edna. Clay, Wil, illus. 2004. 32p. (J). pap. 8.00 (978-0-8028-5246-5(7)); 16.00 (978-0-8028-5154-3(1)) Eerdmans, William B. Publishing Co.

—Auntee Edna. 2002. (gr. k-3). lib. bdg. 16.45 (978-0-613-75338-8(0)) Tandem Library Bks.

Sobrino, Javier. Me Gusta. Villamuza, Noemí, tr. Villamuza, Noemí, illus. (SPA.). 28p. 20.99 (978-84-88342-35-5(7)) S.A. Kokinos ESP. *Dist:* Lectorum Pubns., Inc.

—Me Gusta. Villamuza, Noemi, illus. 2002. (SPA.). (J). (gr. k-2). 16.95 (978-84-88342-32-4(2) , KK30904) S.A. Kokinos ESP. *Dist:* Lectorum Pubns., Inc.

Sofer, Barbara. Ilan Ramon: Israel's First Astronaut. 2004. (General Jewish Interest Ser.). (J). pap. 6.95 (978-0-929371-49-8(6)) Lerner Publishing Group.

—Shabbat Shalom: Israel's First Astronaut. 2004. (Illus.). 12p. (J). 16.95 (978-0-930494-91-9(1)) Kar-Ben Publishing.

Sommer, Carl. Can You Help Me Find My Smile? 2003. (Another Sommer-Time Story Ser.). (Illus.). 48p. (J). (gr. 1-4). 16.95 incl. audio compact disk (978-1-57537-507-6(9)) Advance Publishing, Inc.

—The Great Royal Race. 2003. (Another Sommer-Time Story Ser.). (Illus.). 48p. (J). (gr. 1-4). 16.95 incl. audio compact disk (978-1-57537-508-3(7)) Advance Publishing, Inc.

—I Am a Lion! 2003. (Another Sommer-Time Story Ser.). (Illus.). 48p. (J). (gr. k-4). lib. bdg. 23.95 incl. audio compact disk (978-1-57537-709-4(8)); (gr. k-4). lib. bdg. 23.95 incl. audio (978-1-57537-759-9(4)); (gr. 1-4). 16.95 incl. audio (978-1-57537-558-8(3)); (gr. 1-4). 16.95 incl. audio compact disk (978-1-57537-509-0(5)) Advance Publishing, Inc.

—I Am a Lion! Budwine, Greg, illus. 1999. (Another Sommer-Time Story Ser.). 48p. (J). (gr. k-4). 9.95 (978-1-57537-009-5(3)); lib. bdg. 16.95 (978-1-57537-059-0(X)) Advance Publishing, Inc.

—If Only I Were. . ., 1 bk. 2003. (Another Sommer-Time Story Ser.). (Illus.). 48p. (J). 16.95 incl. audio compact disk (978-1-57537-502-1(8)); (gr. 1-4). 16.95 incl. audio (978-1-57537-551-9(6)) Advance Publishing, Inc.

—King of the Pond. 2003. (Another Sommer-Time Story Ser.). (Illus.). 48p. (J). (gr. k-4). lib. bdg. 23.95 incl. audio (978-1-57537-766-7(7)); (gr. k-4). lib. bdg. 23.95 incl. audio compact disk (978-1-57537-716-2(0)); (gr. 1-4). 16.95 incl. audio (978-1-57537-565-6(6)); (gr. 1-4). 16.95 incl. audio compact disk (978-1-57537-516-8(8)) Advance Publishing, Inc.

—King of the Pond. Budwine, Greg, illus. 2000. (Another Sommer-Time Story Ser.). 48p. (J). (gr. k-3). lib. bdg. 16.95 (978-1-57537-065-1(4)); 9.95 (978-1-57537-016-3(6)) Advance Publishing, Inc.

—Light Your Candle. 2003. (Another Sommer-Time Story Ser.). (Illus.). 48p. (J). (gr. k-4). lib. bdg. 23.95 incl. audio compact disk (978-1-57537-768-1(3)); 16.95 incl. audio (978-1-57537-567-0(2)); 16.95 incl. audio compact disk (978-1-57537-518-2(4)); lib. bdg. 23.95 incl. audio compact disk (978-1-57537-718-6(7)) Advance Publishing, Inc.

—Light Your Candle. James, Kennon, illus. 2000. (Another Sommer-Time Story Ser.). 48p. (J). (ENG.). (gr. 1-4). 9.95 (978-1-57537-019-4(0)); (ps-4). lib. bdg. 16.95 (978-1-57537-068-2(9)) Advance Publishing, Inc.

—The Little Red Train. 2003. (Another Sommer-Time Story Ser.). (Illus.). 48p. (J). (gr. k-4). lib. bdg. 23.95 incl. audio (978-1-57537-764-3(0)); (gr. k-4). lib. bdg. 23.95 incl. audio compact disk (978-1-57537-714-8(4)); (gr. 1-4). 16.95 incl. audio (978-1-57537-563-2(X)); (gr. 1-4). 16.95 incl. audio compact disk (978-1-57537-514-4(1)) Advance Publishing, Inc.

—The Little Red Train. James, Kennon, illus. (Another Sommer-Time Story Ser.). 48p. (J). (gr. k-3). 2000. lib. bdg. 16.95 (978-1-57537-061-3(1)); 1999. 9.95 (978-1-57537-014-9(X)) Advance Publishing, Inc.

—Mayor for a Day. 2003. (Another Sommer-Time Story Ser.). (Illus.). 48p. (J). (gr. k-4). lib. bdg. 23.95 incl. audio compact disk (978-1-57537-713-1(6)); (gr. 1-4). 16.95 incl. audio (978-1-57537-562-5(1)); (gr. 1-4). 16.95 incl. audio compact disk (978-1-57537-513-7(3)) Advance Publishing, Inc.

—Mayor for a Day. Westbrook, Dick, illus. 1999. (Another Sommer-Time Story Ser.). 48p. (J). (gr. k-4). 9.95 (978-1-57537-013-2(1)); lib. bdg. 16.95 (978-1-57537-057-6(3)) Advance Publishing, Inc.

—No Longer a Dilly Dally, 1 bk. 2003. (Another Sommer-Time Story Ser.). (Illus.). 48p. (J). 16.95 incl. audio (978-1-57537-550-2(8)); (gr. 1-4). 16.95 incl. audio compact disk (978-1-57537-501-4(X)) Advance Publishing, Inc.

—No One Will Ever Know. 2003. (Another Sommer-Time Story Ser.). (Illus.). 48p. (J). (gr. 1-4). 16.95 incl. audio compact disk (978-1-57537-506-9(0)) Advance Publishing, Inc.

—The Sly Fox & the Chicks. 2003. (Another Sommer-Time Story Ser.). (Illus.). 48p. (J). 16.95 incl. audio compact disk (978-1-57537-504-5(4)); (gr. 1-4). 16.95 incl. audio (978-1-57537-553-3(2)) Advance Publishing, Inc.

—The Sly Fox & the Chicks. James, Kennon, illus. 2000. (Another Sommer-Time Story Ser.). 48p. (J). (gr. k-3). lib. bdg. 16.95 (978-1-57537-062-0(X)); 9.95 (978-1-57537-004-0(2)) Advance Publishing, Inc.

—Tied up in Knots. 2003. (Another Sommer-Time Story Ser.). (Illus.). 48p. (J). 14.95 incl. audio compact disk (978-1-57537-503-8(6)); (gr. 1-4). 16.95 incl. audio (978-1-57537-552-6(4)) Advance Publishing, Inc.

—The Ugly Caterpillar. 2003. (Another Sommer-Time Story Ser.). (Illus.). 48p. (J). (gr. 1-4). 16.95 incl. audio compact disk (978-1-57537-515-1(X)); 16.95 incl. audio (978-1-57537-564-9(8)) Advance Publishing, Inc.

—The Ugly Caterpillar. Budwine, Greg, illus. (Another Sommer-Time Story Ser.). 48p. (J). (gr. k-3). 2000. lib. bdg. 16.95 (978-1-57537-058-3(1)); 1999. 9.95 (978-1-57537-015-6(8)) Advance Publishing, Inc.

—You Move, You Lose. 2003. (Another Sommer-Time Story Ser.). (Illus.). 48p. (J). (gr. 1-4). 16.95 incl. audio compact disk (978-1-57537-505-2(2)); 16.95 incl. audio (978-1-57537-554-0(0)) Advance Publishing, Inc.

—You Move, You Lose. James, Kennon, illus. (Another Sommer-Time Story Ser.). 48p. (J). (gr. k-3). 2000. lib. bdg. 16.95 (978-1-57537-056-9(5)); 1999. 9.95 (978-1-57537-005-7(0)) Advance Publishing, Inc.

—Your Job Is Easy. 2003. (Another Sommer-Time Story Ser.). (Illus.). 48p. (J). (gr. 1-4). 16.95 incl. audio compact disk (978-1-57537-517-5(6)); 16.95 incl. audio (978-1-57537-566-3(4)) Advance Publishing, Inc.

—Your Job Is Easy. James, Kennon, illus. 2000. (Another Sommer-Time Story Ser.). 48p. (J). (gr. 2-4). lib. bdg. 16.95 (978-1-57537-067-5(0)); (ps-4). 9.95 (978-1-57537-018-7(2)) Advance Publishing, Inc.

Sondheim, Stephen & Lapine, James. Into the Woods. Talbot, Hudson, illus. 2002. 96p. pap. 20.00 (978-0-7432-3290-6(9) , Touchstone) Simon & Schuster.

Southwater Books Staff. Fabulous Fairytales. 2000. (Superstickers Ser.). (Illus.). 64p. (ps-2). pap. 7.95 (978-1-84215-131-0(2)) Anness Publishing, Inc.

—Funtime Teddy Bear Stickers. 2000. (Superstickers Ser.). (Illus.). 64p. (ps-2). pap. 7.95 (978-1-84215-059-7(6) , Southwater) Anness Publishing GBR. *Dist:* National Bk. Network.

Southwater Staff. Christmas Stories. 2000. (Superstickers Ser.). (Illus.). 64p. (ps-2). pap. 7.95 (978-1-84215-262-1(9) , Southwater) Anness Publishing GBR. *Dist:* National Bk. Network.

—Fun with Photos. 2000. (Superstickers Ser.). (Illus.). 64p. (ps-2). pap. 7.95 (978-1-84215-278-2(5) , Southwater) Anness Publishing GBR. *Dist:* National Bk. Network.

Spafford, Suzy. Tales from Duckport: Back to School? Cool. 2002. (Suzy's Zoo Ser.). 40p. (J). (gr. k-3). pap. 3.99 (978-0-439-38355-4(2)) Scholastic, Inc.

Spann, Mary Beth. Alphabet File-Folder Word Walls, Vol. 3. 2001. 64p. (J). (ps). 10.95 (978-0-439-26078-7(7)) Scholastic, Inc.

Spectrum Dolch Sight Word Activities, Vol. 1. 1999. (McGraw-Hill Learning Materials Spectrum Ser.). (Illus.). 160p. (gr. k-1). pap., wbk. ed. 9.95 (978-1-57768-429-9(X)) School Specialty Publishing.

Spelvin, Justin & Hot Animation Staff, Animation. Star of the Show. 2005. (Rubbadubbers). 24p. (J). pap. 3.99 (978-0-689-87427-7(8)) Simon & Schuster, Inc.

Spinelli, Eileen. Now It Is Winter. DePalma, Mary Newell, illus. 2004. 32p. (J). 16.00 (978-0-8028-5244-1(0)) Eerdmans, William B. Publishing Co.

Spizzirri, Linda, ed. Cats of the Wild. (Illus.). 32p. (J). (gr. 1-8). pap. 4.98 incl. audio (978-0-86545-045-5(5)) Spizzirri Pr., Inc.

—Endangered Species. (Illus.). 32p. (J). (gr. 1-8). pap. 4.98 incl. audio (978-0-86545-041-7(2)) Spizzirri Pr., Inc.

Splish Splash. 2002. (Baby Faces Ser.). (Illus.). (J). bds. (978-0-439-33947-6(2)) Scholastic, Inc.

Spongebob's Backpack Book Proprietary. 2003. (Illus.). 16p. (J). bds. 6.99 (978-0-689-86392-9(6) , Simon Spotlight/ Nickelodeon) Simon & Schuster Children's Publishing.

Stack, Richard L. Steamer & Shelly Go to Pot. Word, Reagan, illus. 2001. (Steamer & Shelly Ser.: Vol. 1). 32p. (J). per. 13.95 (978-0-9628262-9-0(4)) Windmill Pr.

Stampfl, Barbara. No More Eggs. 2001. (Illus.). 32p. (J). (ps-2). pap. 10.00 (978-0-9713219-3-9(0)) Jumping Jack Holidays.

Stanek, Gerald R. Sarah 'n' Dippity. Stanek, Joyce Huntington, illus. 2004. 28p. (J). 14.95 (978-0-9747417-0-3(1)) Shiver Hill Bks.

Stanké, Claudie. Les Bisous. Malépart, Céline, illus. 2004. (Picture Bks.). (FRE.). 32p. (J). (ps). (978-2-89021-694-5(2)); pap. (978-2-89021-693-8(4)) Diffusion du livre Mirabel.

Stanley, Mandy. At the Beach. 2002. (All Aboard Ser.). (Illus.). 12p. (J). (gr. 4-6). bds. 4.95 (978-0-7534-5444-2(0) , Kingfisher) Houghton Mifflin Co. Trade & Reference Div.

—At the Pool. 2004. (All Aboard Ser.). Orig. Title: Vamos a la Piscina. (ENG & SPA., Illus.). 12p. (J). (ps-k). bds. 3.95 (978-0-7534-5747-4(4) , Kingfisher) Houghton Mifflin Co. Trade & Reference Div.

—At the Zoo. Morris, Jennis, ed. 2002. (All Aboard Ser.). (Illus.). 12p. (J). (gr. k-ps). bds. 4.95 (978-0-7534-5446-6(7) , Kingfisher) Houghton Mifflin Co. Trade & Reference Div.

—Baby. 1998. 10p. (J). 16.99 (978-0-7641-5123-1(1)) Barron's Educational Series, Inc.

—First Words. Morris, Jennie, ed. 2002. (All Aboard Ser.). (Illus.). 12p. (J). (gr. k-ps). bds. 3.95 (978-0-7534-5443-5(2) , Kingfisher) Houghton Mifflin Co. Trade & Reference Div.

—In the Park. 2004. (All Aboard Ser.). Orig. Title: Vamos al Parqu. (Illus.). 12p. (J). (ps-k). bds. 3.95 (978-0-7534-5750-4(4) , Kingfisher) Houghton Mifflin Co. Trade & Reference Div.

—Mascotas Maravillosas/Perfect Pets. 2004. (Todos A Bordo Ser.). (ENG & SPA., Illus.). 12p. (J). (ps-k). bds. 4.95 (978-0-7534-5813-6(6) , Kingfisher) Houghton Mifflin Co. Trade & Reference Div.

—On the Farm. 2002. (All Aboard Ser.). (Illus.). 12p. (J). (gr. k-ps). bds. 3.95 (978-0-7534-5445-9(9) , Kingfisher) Houghton Mifflin Co. Trade & Reference Div.

—On the Move. 2004. (All Aboard Ser.). Orig. Title: Vamos de Viaje. (Illus.). 12p. (J). (ps-k). bds. 3.95 (978-0-7534-5749-8(0) , Kingfisher) Houghton Mifflin Co. Trade & Reference Div.

—Perfect Pets. 2004. (All Aboard Ser.). Orig. Title: Mascotas Maravillosas. (Illus.). 12p. (J). (ps-k). bds. 3.95 (978-0-7534-5748-1(2) , Kingfisher) Houghton Mifflin Co. Trade & Reference Div.

—Vamos a la Piscina: Todos a Bordo. 2004. (ENG & SPA., Illus.). 12p. (J). (ps-k). bds. 3.95 (978-0-7534-5810-5(1) , Kingfisher) Houghton Mifflin Co. Trade & Reference Div.

—Vamos al Parque/In the Park. 2004. (Todos A Bordo Ser.). (ENG & SPA., Illus.). 12p. (J). (ps-k). bds. 3.95 (978-0-7534-5811-2(X) , Kingfisher) Houghton Mifflin Co. Trade & Reference Div.

—Vamos de Viaje/On the Move. 2004. (Todos A Bordo Ser.). (ENG & SPA., Illus.). 12p. (J). (ps-k). bds. 4.95 (978-0-7534-5812-9(8) , Kingfisher) Houghton Mifflin Co. Trade & Reference Div.

Stauffacher, Sue. Donuthead. 2003. (Illus.). 160p. (J). (gr. 3-7). 15.95 (978-0-375-82468-5(5)); lib. bdg. 17.99 (978-0-375-92468-2(X)) Random Hse. Children's Bks. (Knopf Bks. for Young Readers).

Steadman, Barbara. Ballet Sticker Activity Book. 1998. (Illus.). 4p. (J). 1.50 (978-0-486-40316-8(5)) Dover Pubns., Inc.

Steptoe, Javaka. Sweet, Sweet Baby! Fabric Petals with Fun Sounds & a Mylar Mirror! Steptoe, Javaka, illus. 2005. (Illus.). 4p. (J). bds. 12.95 (978-0-439-65086-1(0) , Cartwheel Bks.) Scholastic, Inc.

Sterling Publishing Company Staff. Benjamin's First Coloring Book. 1999. (Benjamin's Coloring Bks.). 16p. (ps-k). pap. 1.95 (978-0-8069-5930-6(4)) Sterling Publishing Co., Inc.

—Katie Cat. 2003. (Balloon Ser.). (Illus.). 12p. (J). (ps-k). instr.'s planning gde. ed. 7.95 (978-0-8069-3765-6(3) , Balloon Bks.) Sterling Publishing Co., Inc.

Sterling Publishing Company Staff & Balloon Books Staff. Benjamin's Best Coloring Book. 1999. (Benjamin's Coloring Bks.). 16p. (J). (ps-3). pap. 1.95 (978-0-8069-5931-3(2)) Sterling Publishing Co., Inc.

Stevens, Beverly. This Dog Team Lives in the House. 2005. (J). pap. 9.95 ***(*978-1-57833-317-2(2))*** Todd Communications.

Stevenson, Nancy, illus. The Zubble-Wump! 1999. (Jellybean Bks.). 24p. (J). (ps-k). 1.99 (978-0-375-80233-1(9) , Random Hse. Bks. for Young Readers) Random Hse. Children's Bks.

—The Zumble-Wump! 1999. (Jellybean Bks.). 24p. (J). (ps-k). lib. bdg. 7.99 (978-0-375-90233-8(3) , Random Hse. Bks. for Young Readers) Random Hse. Children's Bks.

Stewart, Josie & Salem, Lynn. Squeaky Clean. Gerner, Kristian, illus. 2000. 8p. (J). (gr. k-2). pap. 3.75 (978-1-58323-011-8(4) , Seedling Pubns.) Continental Pr., Inc.

Stewart, Pat. Invisible Bugs Magic Picture Book. 2003. (Dover Little Activity Bks.). (Illus.). 16p. (J). pap. 1.50 (978-0-486-42635-8(1)) Dover Pubns., Inc.

—Invisible Cats Magic Picture Book. 2002. (Illus.). 16p. (J). pap. 1.50 (978-0-486-42157-5(0)) Dover Pubns., Inc.

—Invisible Desert Animals Magic Picture Book. 2003. (Dover Little Activity Bks.). (Illus.). 16p. (J). pap. 1.50 (978-0-486-43023-2(5)) Dover Pubns., Inc.

—Invisible Dogs Magic Picture Book. 2001. (Invisible Magic Picture Bks.). (Illus.). 16p. (J). (ps up). pap. 1.50 (978-0-486-41848-3(0)) Dover Pubns., Inc.

—Invisible Endangered Animals Magic Picture Book. 2001. (Invisible Magic Picture Bks.). (Illus.). 16p. (J). (ps up). pap. 1.50 (978-0-486-41849-0(9)) Dover Pubns., Inc.

—Invisible Fairy Tales Magic Picture Book. 2003. (Dover Little Activity Bks.). (Illus.). 16p. (J). (ps-2). pap. 1.50 (978-0-486-43022-5(7)) Dover Pubns., Inc.

—Invisible Insects Magic Picture Book. 2000. (Dover Little Activity Bks.). (Illus.). 16p. (J). pap. 1.50 (978-0-486-41008-1(0)) Dover Pubns., Inc.

—Learning about Thanksgiving. 2001. (Illus.). 16p. (J). (ps up). pap. 1.50 (978-0-486-41644-1(5)) Dover Pubns., Inc.

Stimson, Joan. Brave Lion, Scared Lion. Rubio, Esther, tr. Rutherford, Meg, illus. (J). (gr. k-1). pap. (978-0-590-90985-3(1) , SO3690) Scholastic, Inc.

—Brave Lion, Scared Lion. 2000. (ps-2). lib. bdg. 10.45 (978-0-613-83522-0(0)) Tandem Library Bks.

Stinson, Kathy. Those Green Things. Betteridge, Deirdre, illus. 2003. 32p. (J). (ps-1). pap. 4.95 (978-1-55037-376-9(5)) Annick Pr., Ltd. CAN. *Dist:* Firefly Bks., Ltd.

Stockham, Jess. Down by the Station. 2002. (Illus.). 16p. (J). 19.99 (978-0-85953-123-8(6)) Child's Play-International.

Stockham, Jessica, illus. Down by the Station. 2002. 16p. (J). 6.99 (978-0-85953-942-5(3)) Child's Play-International.

Stohs, Anita R. A Very Blessed Easter. 1998. (Illus.). 32p. (J). (ps-2). act. bk. ed. 3.99 (978-0-570-05491-7(5)) Concordia Publishing Hse.

Stop by a Pond. 2005. (Early Library). (YA). (ps-3). 23.94 (978-0-8215-8942-7(3)) Sadlier, William H. Inc.

Storytime for Five Year Olds. 2002. 48p. (J). pap. 4.95 (978-0-7894-8499-4(4)) Dorling Kindersley Publishing, Inc.

Storytime for Four Year Olds. 2002. 48p. (J). pap. 4.95 (978-0-7894-8498-7(6)) Dorling Kindersley Publishing, Inc.

Storytime for Six Year Olds. 2002. 48p. (J). pap. 4.95 (978-0-7894-8500-7(1)) Dorling Kindersley Publishing, Inc.

Storytime for Three Year Olds. 2002. 48p. (J). pap. 4.95 (978-0-7894-8497-0(8)) Dorling Kindersley Publishing, Inc.

Storytime for Two Year Olds. 2002. 48p. (J). pap. 4.95 (978-0-7894-8496-3(X)) Dorling Kindersley Publishing, Inc.

Strachan, Linda. Edinburgh Adventure. 2005. (Illus.). 32p. pap. 9.00 (978-0-9546701-7-7(5)) GW Publishing GBR. *Dist:* Wilson & Assocs.

—Ghost of Glamis. 2005. (Illus.). 32p. pap. 9.00 (978-0-9546701-9-1(1)) GW Publishing GBR. *Dist:* Wilson & Assocs.

—Serach for Loch Ness Monster. 2005. (Illus.). 32p. pap. 9.00 (978-0-9546701-5-3(9)) GW Publishing GBR. *Dist:* Wilson & Assocs.

Strang Communications Company Staff, ed. Ages 1-2 Teaching Pictures: Spring 2002. 2002. (J). pap. 11.99 (978-1-57405-916-8(5)) CharismaLife Pubs.

—Ages 1-2 Teaching Pictures: Summer 2002. 2002. (J). pap. 11.99 (978-1-57405-954-0(8)) CharismaLife Pubs.

—Ages 2-3 Teaching Pictures: Spring 2002. 2002. (J). pap. 11.99 (978-1-57405-922-9(X)) CharismaLife Pubs.

—Ages 2-3 Teaching Pictures: Summer 2002. 2002. (J). pap. 11.99 (978-1-57405-960-1(2)) CharismaLife Pubs.

—Ages 4-5 Teaching Pictures: Summer 2002. 2002. (J). (ps-k). pap. 11.99 (978-1-57405-971-7(8)) CharismaLife Pubs.

—Ages 4-5 Teaching Pictures Spring 2002. 2002. (Illus.). (J). (ps-k). pap. 11.99 (978-1-57405-933-5(5)) CharismaLife Pubs.

Street Machines. 1998. (Hot Wheels Ser.). (Illus.). 24p. (J). (ps-1). (978-0-7666-0108-6(0) , 19605) Modern Publishing.

Street Smarts: Picture Book 9x9 with Snipe. 2006. (Illus.). (J). ***(*978-1-933934-17-4(4))*** Educational Adventures.

Street Smarts: Picture Book (English) 8x8. 2006. (Illus.). (J). ***(*978-1-933934-16-7(6))*** Educational Adventures.

Struble, Maegann M. Where Are the Twins? Barry, Rich, illus. 2000. 16p. (J). pap. 5.95 (978-1-891846-19-9(1)) Business Word, The.

Subtraction: With Re-Usable Stickers. 1999. (Fun to Learn Ser.). (Illus.). 32p. (ps-4). 1.99 (978-1-58279-014-5(0) , 98) Trident Pr. International.

Suen, Anastasia. Dos Anos. Cheon, Winnie, illus. 2002. (SPA.). 20p. (J). (ps). bds. 6.95 (978-1-58430-053-3(1)) Lee & Low Bks., Inc.

Suhay, Lisa. Pardon Me, It's Ham, Not Turkey. Cindy, Huffman, ed. Barcita, Pamela, illus. 2007. (J). (ps-3). lib. bdg. 17.95 ***(*978-1-933982-01-4(2))*** Bumble Bee Publishing.

Superman. 2001. (Look & Find Ser.). (Illus.). (J). lib. bdg. 15.95 (978-1-56674-299-3(4)) Forest Hse. Publishing Co., Inc.

Swain, Gwenyth. I Wonder As I Wander. Himler, Ronald, illus. 2005. 32p. (J). (gr. k-17). pap. 8.00 (978-0-8028-5298-4(X) , Eerdmans Bks For Young Readers) Eerdmans, William B. Publishing Co.

Sweet Dreams Lullabies. (Baby Looney Tunes Song Bks.). (Illus.). 16p. (J). (ps). 7.98 (978-0-7853-1613-8(2) , PI13) Publications International, Ltd.

Swensen, Karen. Catherine the Great & Her Teatime Tagalongs. Kirkman, Kelly, illus. 2005. 28p. (J). (gr. k-3). per. 15.95 (978-1-58980-343-5(4)) Pelican Publishing Co., Inc.

Swicord, Robin. Little Women: The Children's Picture Book. 2004. (Illus.). 96p. (gr. 2 up). 15.95 (978-1-55704-216-3(0)) Newmarket Pr.

Sydor, Colleen. Camilla Chameleon. 2007. 32p. pap. ***(*978-1-55453-164-6(0))*** Kids Can Pr., Ltd.

Symes, Ruth Louise. Mondays at Monster School. Reeve, Rosie, illus. 2007. 32p. (J). (ps). 19.99 (978-1-84255-126-4(4)) Orion Children's Bks. GBR. *Dist:* Independent Pubs. Group.

Tal, Ronit. Animal Story Bk. 2: From Birth to 18 Months. 2000. (J). (978-965-7096-01-7(4)) A Different Story, Ltd.

—A Wild Story Bk. 3: Birth & Up. 2000. (J). (978-965-7096-02-4(2)) A Different Story, Ltd.

Talbott, Shawn M. Springtime Robins. 2006. (J). lib. bdg. 19.95 ***(*978-1-933732-05-3(9)*** , Bear Hug Bks.) MidAmerica Publishing Co.

Talking About..., 10 bks., Set. Incl. Adoption. Powell, Jillian. lib. bdg. 25.69 (978-0-8172-5890-0(6)); Alcohol. Green, Jen. lib. bdg. 25.69 (978-0-8172-5888-7(4)); Animal Rights. Powell, Jillian. lib. bdg. 25.69 (978-0-7398-1374-4(9)); Bullying. Powell, Jillian. lib. bdg. 25.70 (978-0-8172-5535-0(4)); Death. Bryant-Mole, Karen & Dineen, Jacqueline. lib. bdg. 25.69 (978-0-8172-5536-7(2)); Disability. Powell, Jillian. lib. bdg. 25.70 (978-0-8172-5537-4(0)); Drugs. Bryant-Mole, Karen. lib. bdg. 25.69 (978-0-8172-5887-0(6)); Family Breakup. Powell, Jillian. lib. bdg. 25.69 (978-0-8172-5542-8(7)); Our Environment. Penny, Malcolm. lib. bdg. 25.69 (978-0-8172-5889-4(2)); Racism. Green, Jen. lib. bdg. 25.69 (978-0-7398-1375-1(7)); (Illus.). 32p. (J). (gr. k-4). 1999. Set lib. bdg. 256.90 (978-0-7398-1380-5(3)) Raintree.

Tallarico, Tony. Ultimate Hidden Pictures Across America. 2003. (Illus.). 48p. (J). (ps-4). mass mkt. 3.99 (978-0-8431-0265-9(9) , Price Stern Sloan) Penguin Group (USA) Inc.

—Ultimate Hidden Pictures under the Sea. 2003. (Illus.). 48p. (J). (ps-4). mass mkt. 3.99 (978-0-8431-0266-6(7) , Price Stern Sloan) Penguin Group (USA) Inc.

Tanen, Sloane. Where Is Coco Going? Hagen, Stefan, photos by. 2004. (Illus.). 32p. (J). 14.95 (978-1-58234-951-0(7) , Bloomsbury Children) Bloomsbury Publishing.

Tang, Greg. Math Fables. Cahoon, Heather, illus. 2004. 40p. (J). pap. 16.95 (978-0-439-45399-8(2)) Scholastic, Inc.

Tasmanian Devil. (Looney Tunes Look & Find Bks.). (Illus.). 24p. (J). (ps-5). 7.98 (978-0-7853-1186-7(6) , PI1) Publications International, Ltd.

Taylor, Jane, et al. Twinkle Twinkle. King, Dave, illus. King, Dave, photos by. 2004. (Baby Games Ser.). 16p. (J). bds. 5.99 (978-0-7566-0257-4(2)) Dorling Kindersley Publishing, Inc.

Taylor, Jody, selected by. Hidden Pictures 2003-2004: With Picture & Word Clues. 2003. (Hidden Pictures Ser.). (Illus.). 48p. (J). (gr. 6-9). Vol. 1. pap. 4.95 (978-1-59078-030-5(2)); Vol. 2. pap. 4.95 (978-1-59078-031-2(0)); Vol. 3. pap. 4.95 (978-1-59078-032-9(9)); Vol. 4. pap. 4.95 (978-1-59078-033-6(7)) Boyds Mills Pr.

Taylor, Kenneth N. The Picture Bible for Little People. 2004. 256p. (J). 15.99 (978-0-8423-8735-4(8)); (Illus.). 12.99 (978-0-8423-8734-7(X)) Tyndale Hse. Pubs.

Taz TV. (Looney Tunes Song & Sound Bks.). (Illus.). 16p. (J). (ps-k). 7.98 (978-0-7853-1609-1(4) , PI9) Publications International, Ltd.

Teague, Mark. One Halloween Night. Teague, Mark, illus. 2005. (Illus.). 32p. (J). (ps-ps). reprint ed. pap. 5.99 (978-0-439-75538-2(7) , Scholastic Paperbacks) Scholastic, Inc.

Telling the Time: With Re-Usable Stickers. 1999. (Fun to Learn Ser.). (Illus.). 32p. (ps-3). 1.99 (978-1-58279-011-4(6) , 100) Trident Pr. International.

Tesoro de Libros de Calcomanías V. 2004. (Disney Calcomanias Ser.). (SPA., Illus.). 72p. (J). pap. 14.95 (978-970-718-105-2(2) , Silver Dolphin en Español) Advanced Marketing, S. de R. L. de C. V. MEX. *Dist:* Bilingual Pubns. Co., The, Perseus Distribution, Transition Vendor.

Tétro, Marc. I Can Skate. 2005. (Illus.). (978-1-55278-542-3(4)) McArthur & Co. CAN. *Dist:* National Bk. Network.

—My New Hat. 2005. (Illus.). (978-1-55278-543-0(2)) McArthur & Co. CAN. *Dist:* National Bk. Network.

Tetro, Marc. One, Two, Three. 2005. (Illus.). (J). (978-1-55278-434-1(7)) McArthur & Co.

—Opposites. 2006. (Illus.). 6.99 (978-1-55278-503-4(3)) McArthur & Co. CAN. *Dist:* National Bk. Network.

—Where Are You from Little Goose? 2006. (Illus.). 6.99 (978-1-55278-433-4(9)) McArthur & Co. CAN. *Dist:* National Bk. Network.

Thacker, Margaret. Just a Little Farther. Wise, Noreen, ed. Cozart, Jane, illus. 2002. (Book-a-Day Collection). 32p. (J). (ps up). pap. 6.95 (978-1-58584-360-2(1)) Huckleberry Pr.

Thatcher, Fran, illus. Teddy Fairies: A Story about Buttercup. 2001. (Teddy Fairies Ser.). 8p. (J). (ps-k). bds. 4.95 (978-0-439-20852-9(1) , Cartwheel Bks.) Scholastic, Inc.

Thatcher, Frances, tr. & illus. Violet. Thatcher, Frances, illus. 2001. (Teddy Fairies Ser.). 8p. (J). (ps-k). bds. 4.95 (978-0-439-20853-6(X) , Cartwheel Bks.) Scholastic, Inc.

The Book Company, ed. Home. (Sparkle Bks.). (J). bds. 4.99 (978-1-74047-330-9(2)) Book Co. Publishing Pty, Ltd., The AUS. *Dist:* Penton Overseas, Inc.

Thorburn, P. & Cobb, S., contrib. by. Picture Words. 1999. (Illus.). 46p. (J). (ps-2). 24.00 (978-0-7217-0658-0(4)) Schofield & Sims Ltd. GBR. *Dist:* State Mutual Bk. & Periodical Service, Ltd.

Thorup, Bryce. Doctor Matthews' Family Christmas. Muller, Ruth, illus. 2005. (J). 18.95 (978-0-9765964-1-7(5)) Round Tower Pr.

—Two Birthdays. Muller, Daniel, illus. 2005. (J). 18.95 (978-0-9765964-0-0(7)) Round Tower Pr.

Thurber, James. Many Moons. Simont, Marc, illus. 2002. (J). 14.79 (978-0-7587-0084-1(9)) Book Wholesalers, Inc.

—Many Moons. Simont, Marc, illus. 1998. 48p. (J). (ps-3). pap. 7.00 (978-0-15-201895-5(6) , Harcourt Paperbacks) Harcourt Children's Bks.

Tibo, Gilles. Au Boulot les Animaux. ed. 2004. (FRE., Illus.). (J). (ps-k). spiral bd. (978-0-616-11146-8(0)) Canadian National Institute for the Blind/Institut National Canadien pour les Aveugles.

—Busy Critters. 2000. (Illus.). 32p. (J). (ps-3). pap. (978-1-894363-32-7(9)) Dominique & Friends.

—Simon & the Snowflakes. Tibo, Gilles, illus. 1999. (Simon Ser.). (Illus.). 24p. (J). (ps-1). pap. 4.95 (978-0-88776-274-1(3)) Tundra Bks., Inc./Livres Toundra, Inc. CAN. *Dist:* Random Hse., Inc.

Tiere der Nacht. (GER.). (978-3-411-09261-1(0)) Bibliographisches Institut & F. A. Brockhaus AG DEU. *Dist:* i.b.d., Ltd.

Tierney, Tom. Late Victorian Costumes Paper Dolls. 1998. (Illus.). 8p. (J). pap. 4.95 (978-0-486-40371-7(8)) Dover Pubns., Inc.

—Marilyn Monroe Paper Dolls. 1998. (Illus.). 32p. (J). 6.95 (978-0-486-23769-5(9)) Dover Pubns., Inc.

Tildes, Phyllis L. Baby Face. Tildes, Phyllis L., illus. 2004. (Illus.). 10p. (J). bds. 5.95 (978-1-57091-399-0(4)) Charlesbridge Publishing, Inc.

Timothy, Ering. Frog Belly Rat F & G. 2003. (J). bds. 16.99 (978-0-7636-2248-0(6)) Candlewick Pr.

Toft, Kim Michelle. The World That We Want. 2005. (Illus.). 32p. (J). (ps-ps). pap. 6.95 (978-1-58089-115-8(2)) ; bds. 16.95 (978-1-58089-114-1(4)) Charlesbridge Publishing, Inc.

Torres, Laura. November Ever After. 1999. 176p. (J). (gr. 7 up). tchr. ed. 16.95 (978-0-8234-1464-2(7)) Holiday Hse., Inc.

Track Pack. 1998. (Hot Wheels Ser.). (Illus.). 32p. (J). (ps-1). pap. (978-0-7666-0099-7(8) , Honey Bear Bks.) Modern Publishing.

Trailblazers. 1998. (Hot Wheels Ser.). (J). (978-0-7666-0383-7(0) , Honey Bear Bks.) Modern Publishing.

Trapani, Iza. Mary Had a Little Lamb. Trapani, Iza, illus. 2004. (Illus.). 24p. (J). (ps-2). bds. 6.95 (978-1-58089-032-8(6)) Charlesbridge Publishing, Inc.

Tremblay, Marc. Le Petit Frere du Chaperon Rouge. Fil et al, illus. 2004. (était une Fois Ser.). (FRE.). 24p. (J). (ps). pap. (978-2-89021-698-3(5)) Diffusion du livre Mirabel.

Trisler, Alana & Cardiel, Patrice Howe. My April Journal. 1999. (Illus.). 48p. (J). (gr. 1-2). pap., wbk. ed. 1.85 (978-1-56762-102-0(3)) Modern Learning Pr.

—My December Journal. 1999. 48p. (J). (gr. 1-2). pap., wbk. ed. 1.85 (978-1-56762-098-6(1)) Modern Learning Pr.

—My Fall Journal. 1999. 72p. (J). (gr. 2-3). pap., wbk. ed. 2.10 (978-1-56762-104-4(X)) Modern Learning Pr.

—My February Journal. 1999. 48p. (J). (gr. 1-2). pap., wbk. ed. 1.85 (978-1-56762-100-6(7)) Modern Learning Pr.

—My January Journal. 1999. 48p. (J). (gr. 1-2). pap., wbk. ed. 1.85 (978-1-56762-099-3(X)) Modern Learning Pr.

—My March Journal. 1999. 48p. (J). (gr. 1-2). pap., wbk. ed. 1.85 (978-1-56762-101-3(5)) Modern Learning Pr.

—My May Journal. 1999. 48p. (J). (gr. 1-2). pap., wbk. ed. 1.85 (978-1-56762-103-7(1)) Modern Learning Pr.

—My November Journal. 1999. 48p. (J). (gr. 1-2). pap., wbk. ed. 1.85 (978-1-56762-097-9(3)) Modern Learning Pr.

—My October Journal. 1999. 48p. (J). (gr. 1-2). pap., wbk. ed. 1.85 (978-1-56762-096-2(5)) Modern Learning Pr.

—My September Journal. 1999. 48p. (J). (gr. 1-2). pap., wbk. ed. 1.85 (978-1-56762-095-5(7)) Modern Learning Pr.

—My Spring Journal. 1999. 72p. (J). (gr. 2-3). pap., wbk. ed. 2.10 (978-1-56762-106-8(6)) Modern Learning Pr.

—My Summer Journal. 1999. 72p. (J). (gr. 2-3). pap., wbk. ed. 2.10 (978-1-56762-107-5(4)) Modern Learning Pr.

—My Winter Journal. 1999. 72p. (J). (gr. 2-3). pap., wbk. ed. 2.10 (978-1-56762-105-1(8)) Modern Learning Pr.

Trucks. 2004. (Illus.). 18p. (J). bds. 5.99 (978-1-85854-431-1(9)) Brimax Books Ltd. GBR. *Dist:* Byeway Bks.

Tsukirino, Yumi. The Pokemon Watcher's Diary Vol. 2, Pt. 3. Tsukirino, Yumi, illus. 2001. (Magical Pokemon Journey, Part 3 Ser.: No. 2). (Illus.). 40p. (YA). (ps-3). pap. 4.95 (978-1-56931-555-2(8)) Viz Media.

Tudor, Tasha. A Tale for Easter. Tudor, Tasha, illus. 2004. (Illus.). 32p. (J). pap. 5.99 (978-0-689-86694-4(1) , Aladdin) Simon & Schuster Children's Publishing.

Turcotte, Elise. Puce, Ma Famille. 2001. 1. (FRE., Illus.). 16p. (J). bds. (978-2-89021-486-6(9)) Diffusion du livre Mirabel.

—Puce, Ma Maison. 2001. 2. (FRE., Illus.). 16p. (J). bds. (978-2-89021-487-3(7)) Diffusion du livre Mirabel.

—Puce, Mes Douceurs. 2001. 4. (FRE., Illus.). 16p. (J). bds. (978-2-89021-489-7(3)) Diffusion du livre Mirabel.

Tuxworth, Nicola. Farm Animals: A Very First Picture Book. 1999. (Pictures & Words Ser.). (Illus.). 24p. (J). (ps up). lib. bdg. 22.00 (978-0-8368-2271-7(4)) Stevens, Gareth Inc.

—Funny Faces. 2002. (Very First Picture Book Ser.). (Illus.). 20p. 5.99 (978-0-7548-1046-9(1) , Lorenz Bks.) Anness Publishing GBR. *Dist:* National Bk. Network.

—Hop, Skip, & Jump, 12 vols. (Illus.). 2006. 12p. bds. 6.99 (978-0-7548-1364-4(9)); 2002. 20p. 5.95 (978-0-7548-1032-2(1)) Anness Publishing GBR. (Lorenz Bks.). *Dist:* National Bk. Network.

—Learn-a-Word Picture Book: Patterns, 12 vols. 2006. (Learn-A-Word Picture Bks.). (Illus.). 12p. bds. 6.99 (978-0-7548-1460-3(2) , Lorenz Bks.) Anness Publishing GBR. *Dist:* National Bk. Network.

—Learn-a-Word Picture Book: Pets, 12 vols. 2006. (Learn-A-Word Picture Bks.). (Illus.). 12p. bds. 6.99 (978-0-7548-1461-0(0) , Lorenz Bks.) Anness Publishing GBR. *Dist:* National Bk. Network.

—Learn-a-Word Picture Book: Things That Go, 12 vols. 2006. (Learn-A-Word Picture Bks.). (Illus.). 12p. bds. 6.99 (978-0-7548-1462-7(9) , Lorenz Bks.) Anness Publishing GBR. *Dist:* National Bk. Network.

—Learn-a-Word Picture Books: Clothes, 12 vols. 2006. (Learn-A-Word Picture Bks.). (Illus.). 12p. bds. 6.99 (978-0-7548-1458-0(0) , Lorenz Bks.) Anness Publishing GBR. *Dist:* National Bk. Network.

—Machines at Work: A Very First Picture Book. 1999. (Pictures & Words Ser.). (Illus.). 24p. (J). (ps up). lib. bdg. 22.00 (978-0-8368-2432-2(6)) Stevens, Gareth Inc.

—Peek-a-Boo. 2002. (Very First Picture Book Ser.). (Illus.). 20p. 5.95 (978-0-7548-1034-6(8) , Lorenz Bks.) Anness Publishing GBR. *Dist:* National Bk. Network.

—Peek-A-Boo. 2005. (Illus.). 12p. (ps). bds. 6.99 (978-0-7548-1337-8(1) , Lorenz Bks.) Anness Publishing GBR. *Dist:* National Bk. Network.

—Pictures & Words, 10 bks. Incl. Baby Animals : A Very First Picture Book. lib. bdg. 22.00 (978-0-8368-2379-0(6)); Farm Animals : A Very First Picture Book. lib. bdg. 22.00 (978-0-8368-2271-7(4)); Food : A Very First Picture Book. lib. bdg. 22.00 (978-0-8368-2430-8(X)); Funny Faces : A Very First Picture Book. lib. bdg. 22.00 (978-0-8368-2272-4(2)); Hop, Skip, Jump : A Very First Picture Book. lib. bdg. 22.00 (978-0-8368-2431-5(8)); Kittens : A Very First Picture Book. lib. bdg. 22.00 (978-0-8368-2273-1(0)); Machines at Work : A Very First Picture Book. lib. bdg. 22.00 (978-0-8368-2432-2(6)); Puppies : A Very First Picture Book. lib. bdg. 22.00 (978-0-8368-2380-6(X)); Splish, Splash : A Very First Picture Book. lib. bdg. 22.00 (978-0-8368-2433-9(4)); Wild Animals : A Very First Picture Book. lib. bdg. 22.00 (978-0-8368-2274-8(9)); 24p. (J). (ps up). (Illus.). 1999. Set lib. bdg. 110.00 (978-0-8368-2456-8(3)) Stevens, Gareth Inc.

—Puppies, 12 vols. (Illus.). 2006. 12p. bds. 6.99 (978-0-7548-1365-1(7)); 2002. 20p. 5.99 (978-0-7548-1047-6(X)) Anness Publishing GBR. (Lorenz Bks.). *Dist:* National Bk. Network.

—Sizes. 2005. (Illus.). 12p. (gr. 2-13). bds. 6.99 (978-0-7548-1412-2(2) , Lorenz Bks.) Anness Publishing GBR. *Dist:* National Bk. Network.

—Splish Splash, 12 vols. 2006. (Illus.). 12p. bds. 6.99 (978-0-7548-1366-8(5) , Lorenz Bks.) Anness Publishing GBR. *Dist:* National Bk. Network.

—Splish Splash: A Very First Picture Book. 2002. (Very First Picture Book Ser.). (Illus.). 20p. 5.99 (978-0-7548-1048-3(8) , Lorenz Bks.) Anness Publishing GBR. *Dist:* National Bk. Network.

—Teddies. 2002. (Very First Picture Book Ser.). (Illus.). 20p. 5.95 (978-0-7548-1035-3(6) , Lorenz Bks.) Anness Publishing GBR. *Dist:* National Bk. Network.

—Toys, 12 vols. (Illus.). 2006. 12p. bds. 6.99 (978-0-7548-1367-5(3) , Lorenz Bks.); 2001. 20p. 5.95 (978-0-7548-0943-2(9)) Anness Publishing GBR. *Dist:* National Bk. Network.

—Wild Animals: A Very First Picture Book. 1999. (Pictures & Words Ser.). (Illus.). 24p. (J). (ps up). lib. bdg. 22.00 (978-0-8368-2274-8(9)) Stevens, Gareth Inc.

Tuxworth, Nicola & Lorenz Editors. Fruit. 2003. (Illus.). 20p. 5.99 (978-0-7548-1197-8(2)) Anness Publishing GBR. *Dist:* National Bk. Network.

—Opposites. 2001. (Let's Look at... Ser.). (Illus.). 20p. 5.95 (978-0-7548-0949-4(8)) Anness Publishing GBR. *Dist:* National Bk. Network.

—Shapes. 2001. (Let's Look at... Ser.). (Illus.). 20p. 5.95 (978-0-7548-0947-0(1)) Anness Publishing GBR. *Dist:* National Bk. Network.

—Sizes. 2001. (Let's Look at...Ser.). (Illus.). 20p. 5.95 (978-0-7548-0952-4(8) , Lorenz Bks.) Anness Publishing GBR. *Dist:* National Bk. Network.

—Things That Go. 2001. (Let's Look at... Ser.). (Illus.). 20p. 5.95 (978-0-7548-0954-8(4)) Anness Publishing GBR. *Dist:* National Bk. Network.

Twinem, Neecy. Hungry Beasties. 2006. (Illus.). 12p. (J). bds. 6.95 (978-1-55971-944-5(3) , 1259986, NorthWord Bks. for Young Readers) T&N Children's Publishing.

Twinn, Michael. Pocket Hippo. Adams, Pam, illus. 2000. 12p. (J). bds. 1.99 (978-0-85953-880-0(X)) Child's Play-International.

Tyler, Anne. Timothy Tugbottom Says No! Modaressi, Mitra, illus. 2005. 36p. (J). (ps-2). 15.99 (978-0-399-24255-7(4) , Putnam Juvenile) Penguin Group (USA) Inc.

Tyler, Michael. The Skin You Live In. Csicsko, David Lee, illus. 2005. 32p. (J). 14.95 (978-0-9759580-0-1(3)) Chicago Children's Museum.

Tyrrell, Melissa. Bulldozer: Little Vehicle Board Book. 1998. (Little Vehicle Board Bks.). (Illus.). 16p. (J). (ps). bds. 5.95 (978-1-888443-96-7(0) , Intervisual/Piggy Toes) Dalmatian Pr.

—Colors. 1998. (Pull & Look Sliding Board Bks.). (Illus.). 12p. (J). (ps). bds. 4.95 (978-1-888443-85-1(5) , Intervisual/Piggy Toes) Dalmatian Pr.

—Dump Truck: Little Vehicle Board Book. 1998. (Little Vehicle Board Bks.). 16p. (J). (ps). bds. 5.95 (978-1-888443-97-4(9) , Intervisual/Piggy Toes) Dalmatian Pr.

—Fairytale Storybook Playset. Wilson, Phil, illus. 1999. (Classics Ser.). 16p. (J). 19.95 (978-1-58117-036-8(X) , Intervisual/Piggy Toes) Dalmatian Pr.

—Fire Engine: Little Vehicle Board Book. 1998. (Box Cars Ser.). 16p. (J). (ps). bds. 5.95 (978-1-888443-98-1(7) , Intervisual/Piggy Toes) Dalmatian Pr.

—The Gingerbread Man. McMullen, Nigel, illus. 2005. (Fairytale Friends Ser.: Vol. 8). 12p. (J). (ps-k). bds. 5.95 (978-1-58117-154-9(4) , Intervisual/Piggy Toes) Dalmatian Pr.

—Opposites. 1998. (Pull & Look Sliding Board Bks.). (Illus.). 12p. (J). (ps). bds. 4.95 (978-1-888443-87-5(1) , Intervisual/Piggy Toes) Dalmatian Pr.

—School Bus: Little Vehicle Board Book. 1998. (Little Vehicle Board Bks.). 16p. (J). (ps). bds. 5.95 (978-1-888443-99-8(5) , Intervisual/Piggy Toes) Dalmatian Pr.

—Star Light, Star Bright: A Magic Glow Book with Peek-Inside Flaps. 1998. (Illus.). 14p. (J). (gr. 2 up). 6.95 (978-1-58117-000-9(9) , Intervisual/Piggy Toes) Dalmatian Pr.

Uchida, Risako. The Gigantic Turnip. Sato, Churyo, illus. 2006. 28p. (J). 11.95 (978-1-74126-026-7(4)) R.I.C. Pubns. AUS. *Dist:* SCB Distributors.

Uff, Caroline. Hello, Lulu. 2004. (Illus.). 14p. (J). bds. 5.95 (978-0-8027-8928-0(5)) Walker & Co.

—Lulu's Busy Day. Uff, Caroline, illus. 2004. (Illus.). 14p. (J). bds. 5.95 (978-0-8027-8929-7(3)) Walker & Co.

Umansky, Kaye. A Chair for Baby Bear. Fisher, Chris, illus. 2004. 32p. (J). 12.95 (978-0-7641-5789-9(2)) Barron's Educational Series, Inc.

Uncle Wiggily: A Child's First Reading Game. 2000. (Illus.). 16p. (J). 14.95 (978-1-891056-01-7(8)) Winning Moves.

Ungerer, Tomi. Crictor. (J). (ps-3). pap. 12.95 incl. audio Weston Woods Studios, Inc.

—Die Drei Raeuber. Michels, Tilde, tr. from ENG. 1999. (Taschenbuecher Ser.). Orig. Title: The Three Robbers. (GER., Illus.). 48p. (J). pap. 18.95 (978-3-257-25007-7(X)) Diogenes Verlag AG CHE. *Dist:* Distribooks, Inc., International Bk. Import Service, Inc.

Usborne Books Staff. 1001 Cosas Que Buscar en la Granja. 1999. (SPA.). (gr. k-3). lib. bdg. 15.25 (978-0-613-74444-7(6)) Tandem Library Bks.

Vail, Rachel. Homework Trouble. Bjorkman, Steve, illus. 2002. (Mama Rex & T Ser.). 32p. (J). (gr. k-2). pap. 14.95 (978-0-439-40628-4(5) , Orchard Bks.) Scholastic, Inc.

—The Horrible Play Date. Bjorkman, Steve, illus. 2002. (Mama Rex & T Ser.). 32p. (J). pap. 14.95 (978-0-439-40627-7(7)); pap. 4.99 (978-0-439-28335-9(3)) Scholastic, Inc. (Orchard Bks.).

—Over the Moon. Nash, Scott, illus. 1998. 32p. (J). (ps-2). pap. 15.95 (978-0-531-30068-8(4) , Orchard Bks.) Scholastic, Inc.

Van Allsburg, Chris. Zathura: A Space Adventure. Van Allsburg, Chris, illus. 2002. (Illus.). 32p. (J). (gr. k-3). 18.00 (978-0-618-25396-8(3)) Houghton Mifflin Co. Trade & Reference Div.

Van Fleet, Matthew. Dog. Stanton, Brian, photos by. 2007. (Illus.). 20p. (J). (ps up). 14.99 (978-1-4169-4137-8(1) , Simon & Schuster/Paula Wiseman Bks.) Simon & Schuster Children's Publishing.

Van Rynbach, Iris. Five Little Pumpkins. 2003. (Illus.). 24p. (J). (ps up). pap. 8.95 (978-1-59078-087-9(6)) Boyds Mills Pr.

—Five Little Pumpkins. 2003. (ps-2). lib. bdg. 17.60 (978-0-613-79889-1(9)) Tandem Library Bks.

Van West, E. El Hombre de los Cangrejos. Lucas, Cedric, illus. 2001. (SPA.). 40p. (J). (ps-3). pap. 8.95 (978-1-890515-26-3(4)) Turtle Bks.

Vasiliu, Mircea. A Day at the Beach. 2007. (Illus.). 36p. (J). 7.95 ***(978-1-59091-068-9(0))*** Eastern National.

Vaugelade, Anais. The War. Rouffiac, Marie-Christine & Streissguth, Thomas, trs. from FRE. Vaugelade, Anais, illus. 2005. (Picture Bks.). (Illus.). 32p. (J). (gr. k-2). 15.25 (978-1-57505-562-6(7)) Lerner Publishing Group.

Vera, Paula. Compara la Diferecnias: Opuestos. Matthews, Derek, illus. 2001. Tr. of Compare the Differences: Opposites. (SPA.). (J). (978-950-11-1483-6(X)) Sigmar ARG. *Dist:* AIMS International Bks., Inc.

Vereb, Jerome M. & John Paul II. Every Child a Light: The Pope's Message to Young People. 2003. (Illus.). 48p. (YA). (gr. 2-4). 16.95 (978-1-56397-090-0(2)) Boyds Mills Pr.

Verrept, Paul. El Pequeno Soldado. Bourgeois, Elodie, tr. Verrept, Paul, illus. 2004. (SPA., Illus.). 26p. (J). (ps-3). 17.99 (978-84-261-3306-9(1)) Juventud, Editorial ESP. *Dist:* Lectorum Pubns., Inc., Iaconi, Mariuccia Bk. Imports.

Villet, Olivia. Chester's Big Surprise. 2001. (Illus.). 32p. (J). 17.99 (978-0-7475-5247-5(9)) Bloomsbury Publishing Plc GBR. *Dist:* Trafalgar Square Publishing.

Viola, Karen & Reader's Digest Staff. Good Night Sun, Hello Moon. Chung, Chi, illus. 2004. 16p. (J). bds. 12.99 (978-0-7944-0356-0(5) , Reader's Digest Children's Bks.) Reader's Digest Children's Publishing, Inc.

Volke, Gordon. Big World Activity Sticker Book, Vol. 2. 2004. (Illus.). 16p. 7.25 (978-1-84161-130-3(1)) Ravette Publishing, Ltd. GBR. *Dist:* Parkwest Pubns., Inc.

von Konigslow, Andrea Wayne. Bing & Chutney. von Konigslow, Andrea Wayne, illus. 1999. (Bing & Chutney Adventures Ser.). (Illus.). 32p. (J). (gr. k-ps). lib. bdg. 16.95 (978-1-55037-609-8(X)) Annick Pr., Ltd. CAN. *Dist:* Firefly Bks., Ltd.

—Bing & Chutney. 1999. (ps-2). lib. bdg. 14.10 (978-0-613-53145-0(0)) Tandem Library Bks.

Vrato, Elizabeth & Mann, Holly. Trucks. 2003. (Magic Window Bks.). (Illus.). 8p. (J). pap. 4.95 (978-0-7624-1575-5(4) , Running Pr. Kids) Running Pr. Bk. Pubs.

Waber, Bernard. Lovable Lyle. Waber, Bernard, illus. 2002. (Lyle the Crocodile Ser.). (Illus.). (J). 14.74 (978-0-7587-3043-5(8)) Book Wholesalers, Inc.

Waddell, Martin. Something So Big. Canty, Charlotte, illus. 2004. 24p. (J). lib. bdg. 22.65 ***(978-1-59646-706-4(1))*** Dingles & Co.

Waddell, Martin. Webster J. Duck. Parkins, David & Firth, Barbara, illus. 2004. 32p. (J). (gr. k-ps). pap. 6.99 (978-0-7636-2431-6(4)) Candlewick Pr.

Wade, Lee. The Cheerios Animal Play Book. Wade, Lee, illus. 1999. (Illus.). 14p. (J). bds. 7.99 (978-0-689-83014-3(9) , Little Simon) Simon & Schuster Children's Publishing.

—The Cheerios Christmas Play Book. Wade, Lee, illus. 2000. (Illus.). 14p. (J). bds. 6.99 (978-0-689-84008-1(X) , Little Simon) Simon & Schuster Children's Publishing.

Waite, Judy. Ratoncito, Ten Cuidado! Burgin, Norma, illus. 2001. (SPA.). 186p. (J). (gr. k-2). (978-84-89675-71-1(6) , ZZ3131) Zendrera Zariquiey, Editorial ESP. *Dist:* Lectorum Pubns., Inc.

Wakeman, Daniel & Van Stralen, Dirk. Ben's Big Dig. 2005. (Illus.). 32p. (J). (ps-2). 17.95 (978-1-55143-384-4(2)) Orca Bk. Pubs. USA.

Waldman, Neil. The Never-Ending Greenness: We Made Israel Bloom. Waldman, Neil, illus. 2003. (Illus.). 32p. (YA). (gr. k-2). 16.95 (978-1-59078-064-0(7)) Boyds Mills Pr.

Walker, Sylvia. Dream Dresses. 2002. (Sticker Styles Ser.). (Illus.). (J). mass mkt. 12.95 (978-0-448-42841-3(5) , Planet Dexter) Penguin Group (USA) Inc.

Wallace, Karen. I Am a Diplodocus. Bostock, Mike, illus. 2005. (J). (ps-ps). (978-0-340-89381-4(8) , Hodder Children's Books) Hodder Children's Division.

Wallace, Mary. The Inuksuk Book. 2004. (Wow Canada! Collection). (Illus.). 64p. (J). pap. 13.95 (978-1-897066-13-3(9)) Maple Tree Pr. CAN. *Dist:* Perseus Distribution.

Wallace, Nancy Elizabeth. Hora de Dormir del Conejo (Rabbit's Bedtime) Kaplan, Annie Garcia, tr. Wallace, Nancy Elizabeth, illus. 2000. (SPA & ENG., Illus.). 32p. (J). (gr. k-ps). tchr. ed. 9.95 (978-0-618-07708-3(1)) Houghton Mifflin Co. Trade & Reference Div.

Wallner, S. J. Hans & the Golden Stirrup. (Illus.). 48p. (J). (gr. 2-3). lib. bdg. 10.95 (978-0-87783-016-0(9)); pap. 3.94 (978-0-87783-093-1(2)) Oddo Publishing, Inc.

Walsch, Neale Donald. The Little Soul & the Earth: A Children's Parable Adapted from Conversations with God. Riccio, Frank, illus. 2005. (Young Spirit Books). 32p. (J). 17.95 (978-1-57174-451-7(7)) Hampton Roads Publishing Co., Inc.

Walsh, Ellen Stoll. Mouse Paint. Walsh, Ellen Stoll, illus. 2002. (Illus.). (J). 13.70 (978-0-7587-3180-7(9)) Book Wholesalers, Inc.

Walsh, Melanie. My Nose, Your Nose. Walsh, Melanie, illus. 2002. (Illus.). 32p. (J). (gr. k-ps). 15.00 (978-0-618-15077-9(3)) Houghton Mifflin Co. Trade & Reference Div.

—Ocean Animals. Walsh, Melanie, illus. 2002. (Tiny Teether Ser.). (Illus.). 14p. (J). (gr. k-ps). bds. 4.99 (978-0-7636-1807-0(1)) Candlewick Pr.

—Pets. Walsh, Melanie, illus. 2002. (Tiny Teether Ser.). (Illus.). 14p. (J). (gr. k-ps). bds. 4.99 (978-0-7636-1808-7(X)) Candlewick Pr.

—Tienen Raynas los Cerditos? Walsh, Melanie, illus. 2002. Tr. of Do Pigs Have Stripes?. (SPA., Illus.). 14p. (J). (gr. k-ps). bds. 5.95 (978-0-618-20319-2(2)) Houghton Mifflin Co. Trade & Reference Div.

—Wild Animals. Walsh, Melanie, illus. 2002. (Tiny Teether Ser.). (Illus.). 14p. (J). (gr. k-ps). bds. 4.99 (978-0-7636-1809-4(8)) Candlewick Pr.

Walt Disney Records Staff. Tigger Mania, 1. 1998. 22.50 (978-0-7634-0433-8(0)) Walt Disney Records.

Walt Disney Records Staff, prod. A Bug's Life Sing Along. 1998. 22p. (J). pap. 12.98 incl. audio (978-0-7634-0440-6(3)) Walt Disney Home Video.

Walter, Gramela Pamela. A Yeben! Activity Book. Walter, Gramela Pamela, illus. deluxe ed. 1999. (Illus.). 68p. (J). pap. 26.95 (978-1-929110-26-1(X)) Colter Enterprises, Inc.

Walter, Virginia. Hi, Pizza Man! 1998. (Illus.). 32p. (J). (ps-3). pap. 6.95 (978-0-531-07107-6(3) , Orchard Bks.) Scholastic, Inc.

Wang, Margaret. Eency Weency Spider. Rueda, Claudia, illus. 2005. 22p. (J). (ps-ps). 10.95 (978-1-58117-418-2(7) , Intervisual/Piggy Toes) Dalmatian Pr.

—Postcards from Kitty. Silver, Pattie, illus. 2005. 12p. (J). (ps-ps). per. 9.95 (978-1-58117-427-4(6) , Intervisual/ Piggy Toes) Dalmatian Pr.

Ward, Helen. Moon Dog. 2005. (Illus.). 40p. (J). ***(978-1-84011-864-3(4))*** Templar Publishing, Dorking.

Ward, Nick. I Wish. 2007. (Illus.). 24p. (J). pap. 8.99 ***(978-1-84458-126-9(8))*** Anova Bks. GBR. *Dist:* Independent Pubs. Group.

Warner Brothers Staff. Dragon's Tale: A Washable Tattoo Book. 1998. (Quest for Camelot Ser.). (J). pap. 4.98 (978-0-590-02438-9(8)) Scholastic, Inc.

Warren, Jean. Balloons. Cubley, Kathleen, ed. 1998. (Sticker Book Ser.). (Illus.). 32p. (J). (ps). pap. 3.95 (978-1-57029-211-8(6) , WPH 3701, Totline Pubns.) Schaffer, Frank Pubns.

—Birds. Cubley, Kathleen, ed. 1998. (Sticker Book Ser.). (Illus.). 32p. (J). (ps). pap. 3.95 (978-1-57029-212-5(4) , WPH 3702, Totline Pubns.) Schaffer, Frank Pubns.

—Bows. Cubley, Kahtleen, ed. 1998. (Sticker Book Ser.). (Illus.). 32p. (J). (ps). pap. 3.95 (978-1-57029-213-2(2) , WPH 3703, Totline Pubns.) Schaffer, Frank Pubns.

—Bugs. Cubley, Kathleen, ed. 1998. (Sticker Book Ser.). (Illus.). 32p. (J). (ps). pap. 3.95 (978-1-57029-214-9(0) , WPH 3704, Totline Pubns.) Schaffer, Frank Pubns.

—Butterflies. Cubley, Kathleen, ed. 1998. (Sticker Book Ser.). (Illus.). 32p. (J). (ps). pap. 3.95 (978-1-57029-215-6(9) , WPH 3705, Totline Pubns.) Schaffer, Frank Pubns.

—Mittens. Cubley, Kathleen, ed. 1998. (Sticker Book Ser.). (Illus.). 32p. (J). (ps). pap. 3.95 (978-1-57029-222-4(1) , WPH 3712, Totline Pubns.) Schaffer, Frank Pubns.

Watson, Jacqueline. Six Frogs on a Log! 2004. 43p. pap. 19.95 (978-1-4137-2986-3(X)) PublishAmerica, Inc.

Watson, T. E. I Wanna Iguana. Raptis, John, illus. 3rd l.t. ed. 2001. 32p. (J). 16.95 (978-1-58478-009-0(6) , Paw Prints Pr.) Heather & Highlands Publishing.

Watt, Fiona. Este No Es Mi Tren. rev. ed. 2004. (Titles in Spanish Ser.).Tr. of That's Not My Train. 32p. (J). 12.99 (978-1-58086-585-2(2)) EDC Publishing.

Watt, Fiona & Wells, Rachel. Gatitos. 2004. (SPA.). 10p. (J). 11.95 (978-0-7460-5091-0(7)) EDC Publishing.

—Perritos. 2004. (SPA., Illus.). 10p. (J). 11.95 (978-0-7460-5090-3(9)) EDC Publishing.

Weatherford, Carole Boston. Freedom on the Menu: The Greensboro Sit-Ins. Lagarrigue, Jerome Lagarrigue, illus. 2007. 32p. (J). (ps). pap. 5.99 ***(978-0-14-240894-0(8))*** , Puffin) Penguin Group (USA) Inc.

Webber, Helen. Webber Quartet, 4 Vols. deluxe ed. (J). (gr. k-6). 35.00 (978-0-8392-3070-0(2)) Astor-Honor, Inc.

Weber, Jane. The Riches of Rangoberra/Las riquezas de Rangoberra. de la Vega, Eida, tr. Saari, Rijalynne, illus. 2002. Tr. of Las riquezas de Rangoberra. (SPA & ENG.). 32p. (J). (gr. 4-6). 16.95 (978-0-9720192-1-7(9) , 626999) Raven Tree Pr.

Weber, Lou, ed. Tummy Time Animal Babies. 2004. 8p. 6.98 (978-1-4127-3063-1(5)) Publications International, Ltd.

Webster, Jean. Papaito-Piernas-Largas. (SPA.). (YA). (gr. 5-8). pap. (978-950-08-1515-4(X) , AA7255) Atlantida ARG. *Dist:* Lectorum Pubns., Inc.

Wedge, Chris. Bunny: A Picture Book Adapted from the Animated Film. Wedge, Chris, illus. 2004. (Illus.). 30p. (J). (gr. k-4). reprint ed. 19.00 (978-0-7567-7460-8(8)) DIANE Publishing Co.

Weedn, Flavia M. & Weedn, Lisa. I Love You Very. Weedn, Flavia M., illus. 2000. (Illus.). 26p. (ps-k). pap. 7.95 (978-0-7683-2157-9(3)) CEDCO Publishing.

Weeks, Sarah. Mrs. McNosh Hangs up Her Wash. Westcott, Nadine Bernard, illus. 1998. (Growing Tree Ser.). 24p. (J). (ps up). 12.99 (978-0-694-01076-9(6) , Harper Festival) HarperCollins Pubs.

Wehr, Julian. Snow White. 2004. (J). pap. 12.95 (978-0-9748093-0-4(6)) Wehr Animations.

Weiss, Ellen. Minnie's Costume Party Discovery. 2000. (Lift the Flaps Bks.). 16p. (J). 6.99 (978-0-7364-1036-6(8)) Mouse Works.

—Simba's Moon. Cuddy, Robin, illus. Date not set. 32p. (J). (ps-2). 12.99 (978-0-7868-3267-5(3)) Disney Pr.

Weiss, Ellen & Fremont, Elenor. My Little People Busy Town. S. I. International Staff, illus. 2000. (Fisher-Price Little People Mini-Flap PlayBooks Ser.). 10p. (J). (ps-k). bds. 8.99 (978-1-57584-424-4(9) , Reader's Digest Children's Bks.) Reader's Digest Children's Publishing, Inc.

Weitzman, Jacqueline Preiss. You Can't Take a Balloon into the Museum of Fine Arts. Glasser, Robin Preiss, illus. 2002. 40p. (J). (gr. k-4). 18.99 (978-0-8037-2570-6(1) , Dial) Penguin Group (USA) Inc.

—You Can't Take a Balloon into the National Gallery. Glasser, Robin Preiss, illus. 2002. 40p. (J). pap. 7.99 (978-0-14-230131-9(0) , Puffin) Penguin Group (USA) Inc.

—You Can't Take a Balloon into the National Gallery. 2002. (ps-2). lib. bdg. 16.45 (978-0-613-83550-3(6)) Tandem Library Bks.

Wells, Rosemary. McDuff Vuelve a Casa. Jeffers, Susan, illus. 2000. (SPA.). (J). (ps-k). pap. 7.95 (978-958-04-4698-9(9) , NR2656) Norma S.A. COL. *Dist:* Distribuidora Norma, Inc., Lectorum Pubns., Inc.

—McDuff y el Bebe. Jeffers, Susan, illus. 2000. (SPA.). (J). (ps-k). pap. 7.95 (978-958-04-4697-2(0) , NR2673) Norma S.A. COL. *Dist:* Distribuidora Norma, Inc., Lectorum Pubns., Inc.

Wells, Rosemary & Wells, Tom. The House in the Mail. 2004. (Illus.). 48p. (J). pap. 6.99 (978-0-14-240061-6(0) , Puffin) Penguin Group (USA) Inc.

—The House in the Mail. Andreasen, Dan, illus. 2002. 32p. (J). (gr. 1-5). 16.99 (978-0-670-03545-8(9) , Viking Juvenile) Penguin Group (USA) Inc.

Weninger, Brigitte. A Child Is a Child. Tharlet, Eve, illus. 2004. 32p. (J). (ps-3). 14.99 (978-0-698-40006-1(2) , Minedition) Penguin Group (USA) Inc.

—Dany, Mira lo Que Has Hecho! 1999. (gr. k-3). (SPA.). lib. bdg. 15.25 (978-0-613-81373-0(1)); 13.75 (978-0-606-17631-6(4)) Tandem Library Bks.

—Little Apple, a Book of Thanks. 2002. (ps-2). lib. bdg. 14.10 (978-0-613-84070-5(4)) Tandem Library Bks.

Werner, Jane. The Christmas Story. Wilkin, Eloise, illus. 2000. (Little Golden Bks.). 24p. (J). (gr. k-k). 2.99 (978-0-307-98913-0(5) , Golden Bks.) Random Hse. Children's Bks.

West, Colin. Have You Seen the Crocodile. West, Colin, illus. 2003. (Reading Together Ser.). (Illus.). 32p. (J). (ps). pap. 3.99 (978-0-7636-0862-0(9)) Candlewick Pr.

Weston, Martha, illus. Curious George Visits a Toy Store. 2002. 24p. (J). (gr. k-3). pap. 3.95 (978-0-618-06570-7(9)) Houghton Mifflin Co. Trade & Reference Div.

WeWrite Kids Staff. Let's All Have Fun! Swallow, Judy, illus. l.t. ed. 2000. (WeWrite Kids! Ser.). 50p. (J). (gr. 1-7). pap. 3.95 (978-1-57635-056-0(8)) WeWrite LLC.

Wezeman, Phyllis Vos & Liechty, Anna L. Tell Me a Story: 30 Children's Sermons Based on Best-Loved Books. 2005. (New Brown Bag Ser.). (Illus.). 96p. pap. 12.00 (978-0-8298-1635-8(6)) Pilgrim Pr., The/United Church Pr.

Whale Mail. 2003. (J). spiral bd. 9.99 (978-0-89610-126-5(6)) Island Heritage Publishing.

What Shape Is It? 2003. (Bear in the Big Blue House Ser.). (Illus.). 16p. (J). (ps-k). pap., act. bk. ed. 4.99 (978-1-57768-700-9(0)) School Specialty Publishing.

Whatley, Bruce. Cowboy Pirate. 2002. (Illus.). 32p. 14.95 (978-0-207-19891-5(8)) HarperCollins Pubs.

Whelan, Gloria. Jam & Jelly by Holly & Nellie. van Frankenhuyzen, Gijsbert, illus. 2002. 48p. (J). (ps-5). 17.95 (978-1-58536-109-0(7)) Sleeping Bear Pr.

When I Go. 2003. (Illus.). (J). bds. 7.98 (978-0-7525-8657-1(2)) Parragon, Inc.

Where the Leprechauns Hide. 2007. pap. 12.99 (***978-0-9792258-9-5(2)***) Bezalel Bks.

Whippo, Walt. Little White Duck. Paley, Joan, illus. 2002. (J). 20.81 (978-0-7587-3019-0(5)) Book Wholesalers, Inc.

Whippo, Walt & Zaritzky, Bernard. Little White Duck. Paley, Joan, illus. 2005. 22p. (J). (ps-k). bds. 6.99 (978-0-316-73397-7(0)) Little, Brown Bks. for Young Readers.

White, Howard. The Airplane Ride. Guzek, Greta, illus. unabr. ed. 2006. 32p. (J). bds. 14.95 (***978-0-88971-224-9(7)***) Harbour Publishing Co., Ltd. CAN. *Dist:* Graphic Arts Ctr. Publishing Co.

White, Kathryn. When They Fight. Wright, Cliff, illus. 2000. 32p. (J). (ps-1). 14.95 (978-1-890817-46-6(5)) Winslow Pr.

White, Stephen. Barney's Storybook Treasury. Sharp, Chris & McGlothin, David, illus. 1999. (Barney Ser.). 176p. (J). (ps-k). pap. 10.95 (978-1-57064-579-2(5)) Scholastic, Inc.

Whoozit's Many Faces. 2000. (J). bds. (978-0-9676292-4-7(1)) Manhattan Toy.

Whybrow, Ian, et al. Owain A'r Cloc. 2005. (WEL., Illus.). 18p. 6.99 (978-1-84323-366-4(5)) Gomer Pr. GBR. *Dist:* Gomer Pr.

Wild, Margaret. Our Granny. Vivas, Julie, illus. 2002. (J). 13.79 (978-0-7587-3344-3(5)) Book Wholesalers, Inc.

—Our Granny. Vivas, Julie, illus. 1998. 32p. (J). (gr. k-3). pap. 5.95 (978-0-395-88395-2(4)) Houghton Mifflin Co. Trade & Reference Div.

Wild, Margaret. Piglet & Papa. King, Stephen Michael, illus. 2007. (J). (***978-1-4287-4648-0(X)*** , Abrams Bks. for Young Readers) Abrams, Harry N., Inc.

Wilder, Alice. Mrs. Pepper's Special Day. 2001. (Illus.). 8p. (J). mass mkt. (978-0-689-85015-8(8) , Simon Spotlight/Nickelodeon) Simon & Schuster Children's Publishing.

Wildsmith, Brian. Los Animales de la Granja. Wildsmith, Brian, illus. 2001. (SPA., Illus.). 16p. (J). (ps-k). bds. 4.95 (978-1-887734-84-4(8)) Star Bright Bks., Inc.

Wilhelm, Hans. I Am Lost. 2004. 32p. (J). lib. bdg. 15.00 (978-1-59054-352-8(1)) Fitzgerald Bks.

—Jesus Wants Me for a Sunbeam. 2006. (Illus.). 24p. (J). 5.99 (978-0-439-80003-7(X)) Scholastic, Inc.

—The Lord Is My Shepherd. 2006. (Illus.). 24p. (J). 5.99 (978-0-439-80002-0(1)) Scholastic, Inc.

—With Lots of Love. 2004. (Illus.). 32p. (J). 12.95 (978-0-7641-5767-7(1)) Barron's Educational Series, Inc.

Willems, Mo. Don't Let the Pigeon Drive the Bus! 2003. (Illus.). 36p. (J). (ps-1). 12.99 (978-0-7868-1988-1(X)) Hyperion Bks. for Children.

—Knuffle Bunny: A Cautionary Tale. 2004. (Illus.). 36p. (J). (ps-1). 15.99 (978-0-7868-1870-9(0)) Hyperion Bks. for Children.

—The Pigeon Has Feelings, Too! 2005. (Illus.). 10p. (J). (ps-ps). bds. 6.99 (978-0-7868-3650-5(4)) Hyperion Bks. for Children.

—The Pigeon Loves Things That Go! 2005. (Illus.). 10p. (J). (ps-ps). bds. 6.99 (978-0-7868-3651-2(2)) Hyperion Bks. for Children.

Willems, Mo, illus. Don't Let the Pigeon Drive the Bus! 2005. 40p. (J). (978-1-84428-013-1(6)) Walker Bks. Australia Pty, Ltd.

Willhoite, Michael. Daddy's Roommate. Willhoite, Michael, illus. 2004. (Alyson Wonderland Ser.). (Illus.). 32p. (ps-3). reprint ed. pap. 11.95 (978-1-55583-118-9(4)) Alyson Pubns.

Williams, Lee. Sufee Finds a Home. 2001. (Illus.). (J). (ps-3). (978-0-9703178-1-0(6)) RBC Publishing Co., Inc.

Williams, Sam. Talk Peace. Moriuchi, Mique, illus. 2005. 32p. (J). 16.95 (978-0-8234-1936-4(3)) Holiday Hse., Inc.

Williamson, Jennifer. Timmy the Tow Truck, 6 vols. Williamson, Alan, 8th, illus. 2005. 28p. (J). pap. (978-0-9771678-1-4(X)) Theee Hole Punch Publishing.

Willis, Jeanne. The Wind in the Willows. Ross, Tony, illus. 1998. 32p. (J). (ps-1). 15.99 (978-0-86264-782-7(7)) Andersen GBR. *Dist:* Trafalgar Square Publishing.

Willis, Jeanne & Ross, Tony. Dr Xargle's Book of Earth Mobiles. 2004. (Illus.). 32p. (J). pap. 8.99 (978-1-84270-369-4(2)) Andersen GBR. *Dist:* Independent Pubs. Group.

—Dr. Xargles Book of Earthlets. 2003. (Illus.). 32p. (J). pap. 9.99 (978-1-84270-067-9(7)) Andersen GBR. *Dist:* Trafalgar Square Publishing.

—Manky Monkey. 2004. (Illus.). 32p. pap. 11.00 (978-1-84270-329-8(3)) Andersen GBR. *Dist:* Independent Pubs. Group.

Wilson, Troy. Frosty Is a Stupid Name. Griffiths, Dean, illus. 2005. 32p. (J). (ps-2). 17.95 (978-1-55143-382-0(6)) Orca Bk. Pubs. USA.

—Perfect Man. Griffiths, Dean, illus. 2005. 32p. (J). (ps-2). 7.95 (978-1-55143-435-3(0)) Orca Bk. Pubs. USA.

Wingate, P. I Can Waddle, Wriggle, Wave. O'Neil, Rachel, illus. 2004. (My Carry-Around Action Bks.). 16p. (J). bds. 3.95 (978-0-7641-5734-9(5)) Barron's Educational Series, Inc.

—I Can Woof, Quack, Moo. O'Neil, Rachel, illus. 2004. (My Carry-Around Action Bks.). 16p. (J). bds. 3.95 (978-0-7641-5735-6(3)) Barron's Educational Series, Inc.

Winterbotham, Anne, illus. First Words. 1998. (Find & Fit Ser.). 10p. (J). (ps-k). bds. 14.95 (978-1-57145-357-0(1) , Silver Dolphin Bks.) Advantage Pubs. Group.

The Wise Men with Puzzle. 2000. (Illus.). (J). (ps-k). bds. 4.95 (978-0-88271-692-3(1)) Regina Pr., Malhame & Co.

Wishbone Jumbo Fun Book. 1998. (Illus.). (J). pap. (978-0-7666-0176-5(5) , Honey Bear Bks.) Modern Publishing.

Wolf, Gita & Rao, Sirish. In the Dark. 2002. (Illus.). 36p. 9.99 (978-81-86211-54-0(3)) Penguin Group (USA) Inc.

Wolfe, Frances. One Wish. 2004. (Illus.). 32p. (J). (ps-1). 15.95 (978-0-88776-662-6(5)) Tundra Bks., Inc./Livres Toundra, Inc. CAN. *Dist:* Random Hse., Inc.

Wood, David. There's a World in my House. 2005. 36p. (J). per. 13.95 (978-1-933290-90-4(0)) Tate Publishing & Enterprises, L.L.C.

Wood, Jacqueline & Wood, Jakki. Baby Parade. 2003. (Illus.). 32p. (J). 14.95 (978-0-7112-2065-2(4)) Lincoln, Frances Ltd. GBR. *Dist:* Transition Vendor.

Wood, Jakki. Baby Parade. 2004. (Illus.). 32p. (J). reprint ed. pap. 7.95 (978-1-84507-042-7(9)) Lincoln, Frances Ltd. GBR. *Dist:* Perseus Distribution.

—Bumper to Bumper: A Traffic Jam. Wood, Jakki, illus. 1999. (Illus.). 32p. (J). (ps-k). pap. (978-0-7112-1031-8(4)) Lincoln, Frances Ltd. GBR. *Dist:* Transition Vendor.

Wood, Ramona. Now Caitlin Can: A Donated Organ Helps a Child Get Well. 2004. (Illus.). 32p. (J). 16.00 (978-0-9758622-0-9(0)) ABC Pr.

Woodson, Jacqueline. Our Gracie Aunt. Muth, Jon J., illus. 2002. 32p. (J). lib. bdg. 16.49 (978-0-7868-2532-5(4)); 15.99 (978-0-7868-0620-1(6)) Hyperion Bks. for Children.

Word, Reagan. The Windrider. l.t. ed. 2002. (Illus.). 32p. (J). 16.00 (978-0-9717629-0-9(2)) Color Cove Studio.

Wormell, Christopher. The New Alphabet of Animals, Vol. 5. 2002. (Illus.). 64p. (J). (gr. k-3). 18.95 (978-0-7624-1347-8(6) , Running Pr. Kids) Running Pr. Bk. Pubs.

X-Men. 2003. (J). (978-1-57657-859-9(3)) Paradise Pr., Inc.

Yaccarino, Dan. Good Night, Mr. Night. 2004. (Illus.). 26p. (J). bds. 6.95 (978-0-15-205351-2(4) , Red Wagon Bks.) Harcourt Children's Bks.

—Zoom! Zoom! Zoom! I'm off to the Moon. 2001. (978-0-606-22251-8(0)) Tandem Library Bks.

Yamamoto, Lani. Albert III. 2006. (Illus.). 32p. (J). 10.95 (***978-1-84507-135-6(2)***) Lincoln, Frances Ltd. GBR. *Dist:* Perseus Distribution.

Yarnelle, Darlene. Dan the Dog. Sheets, L. K., illus. 1998. (J). (ps-3). 8.50 (978-1-891883-02-6(X)) Make Pretend, Inc.

—Did You Ever? Sheets, L. K., illus. 1998. (J). (ps-3). 8.50 (978-1-891883-01-9(1)) Make Pretend, Inc.

—Snow. Sheets, L. K., illus. 1998. (J). (ps-3). 8.50 (978-1-891883-00-2(3)) Make Pretend, Inc.

Ye, Ting-Xing. Share the Sky. Langlois, Suzane, illus. 1999. 32p. (J). (ps-2). lib. bdg. 17.95 (978-1-55037-579-4(2)) Annick Pr., Ltd. CAN. *Dist:* Firefly Bks., Ltd.

—Share the Sky. 1999. (gr. k-3). lib. bdg. 15.25 (978-0-613-26907-0(1)) Tandem Library Bks.

Yeager, Nancy & Yeager, Doug. A Tiny Little Story. 1999. 32p. (J). (ps). pap. (978-1-879911-01-7(9)) Rams Horn Bks.

Yee, Paul. Roses Sing on New Snow: A Delicious Tale. Chan, Harvey, illus. 2003. 32p. (J). pap. 5.95 (978-0-88899-217-8(3)) Groundwood Bks. CAN. *Dist:* Perseus Distribution.

Yee, Wong Herbert. Fireman Small to the Rescue. 1998. (Illus.). 16p. (J). (gr. k-ps). bds. 4.95 (978-0-395-88122-4(6)) Houghton Mifflin Co. Trade & Reference Div.

Yee, Wong Herbert. Who Likes Rain? 2007. (Illus.). (J). (***978-1-4287-3979-6(3)***) Holt, Henry & Co.

Yoon, Salina. Be My Valentine. Yoon, Salina, illus. 2005. (Illus.). 10p. (J). 5.99 (978-1-4169-0536-3(7) , Little Simon) Simon & Schuster Children's Publishing.

—Black Cat. Yoon, Salina, illus. 2004. (Illus.). 10p. (J). bds. 5.99 (978-0-689-85393-7(9) , Little Simon) Simon & Schuster Children's Publishing.

—Duckling's First Spring. 2006. (Illus.). 10p. (J). (ps-1). bds. 5.99 (978-0-8431-1792-9(3) , Price Stern Sloan) Penguin Group (USA) Inc.

—My Little Shimmery Time for Bed. Yoon, Salina, illus. 2002. (Illus.). 12p. (J). bds. 5.95 (978-1-58117-089-4(0) , Intervisual/Piggy Toes) Dalmatian Pr.

—My Little Shimmery Time for Fun. Yoon, Salina, illus. 2002. (Illus.). 12p. (J). bds. 5.95 (978-1-58117-090-0(4) , Intervisual/Piggy Toes) Dalmatian Pr.

—Santa. 2004. (Illus.). 10p. (J). (ps-1). bds. 5.99 (978-0-8431-1150-7(X) , Price Stern Sloan) Penguin Group (USA) Inc.

—Spooky Pumpkin. Yoon, Salina, illus. 2004. (Illus.). 10p. (J). bds. 5.99 (978-0-689-85392-0(0) , Little Simon) Simon & Schuster Children's Publishing.

—Spring Fever! A Petal Tab Book. Yoon, Salina, illus. 2005. (Illus.). 12p. (J). bds. 6.99 (978-0-689-87424-6(3) , Little Simon) Simon & Schuster Children's Publishing.

—St. Patrick's Day Countdown. 2006. (Illus.). 10p. (J). (ps-1). bds. 5.99 (978-0-8431-1660-1(9) , Price Stern Sloan) Penguin Group (USA) Inc.

Yoon, Salina, illus. My Shimmery Learning Book: Colors, Shapes, Counting, Opposites, Getting Dressed. 1999. 10p. (J). (gr. k up). bds. 8.95 (978-1-58117-060-3(2) , Intervisual/Piggy Toes) Dalmatian Pr.

Yorinks, Arthur. The Alphabet Atlas. Yorinks, Adrienne, illus. 1999. 64p. (J). (ps-3). 19.95 (978-1-890817-14-5(7)) Winslow Pr.

York, Michaela D. Mr. Oodle MaDoodle's Time Around the World. 2002. 15.95 (978-0-9704457-0-4(9)) Chef John Folse & Co.

Young, Ed. Lon Po Po: A Red Riding Hood Story from China. Young, Ed, illus. 2002. (Illus.). (J). 14.04 (978-0-7587-0055-1(5)) Book Wholesalers, Inc.

Young, Marianne, illus. Here We Go 'Round the Mulberry Bush. 16p. (J). (gr. k-3). pap. 4.95 (978-0-88272-449-2(5)) Santillana USA Publishing Co., Inc.

Zarick, Nicole, ed. My First Touch & Feel Baby Animals. 2004. (Illus.). 36p. (J). bds. 5.99 (978-0-7894-9901-1(0)) Dorling Kindersley Publishing, Inc.

Zeifert, Harriet. Go! SAMi, illus. 2006. 24p. bds. 8.95 (978-1-59354-138-5(4)) Blue Apple Bks.

—Yum: Baby Flipaface. SAMi, illus. 2006. 24p. bds. 8.95 (978-1-59354-139-2(2)) Blue Apple Bks.

Zemach, Kaethe. Just Enough & Not Too Much. Zemach, Kaethe, illus. 2003. 32p. (J). pap. 16.95 (978-0-439-37724-9(2) , Levine, Arthur A. Bks.) Scholastic, Inc.

Zeman, Ludmila. The First Red Maple Leaf. Zeman, Ludmila, illus. 1999. (Illus.). 24p. (J). (gr. k-3). reprint ed. pap. 9.95 (978-0-88776-419-6(3)) Tundra Bks., Inc./ Livres Toundra, Inc. CAN. *Dist:* Random Hse., Inc.

Ziefert, Harriet. Baby Animals. Sami, illus. 2005. 24p. (J). (ps). bds. 8.95 (978-1-59354-104-0(X)) Blue Apple Bks.

—Buzzy's Big Bedtime Book. Bolam, Emily, illus. 2004. 40p. 9.95 (978-1-59354-059-3(0)) Blue Apple Bks.

—Buzzy's Booboo. 2004. (Illus.). 24p. 9.95 (978-1-59354-023-4(X)) Blue Apple Bks.

—Knick-Knack Paddywhack. Bolam, Emily, illus. 2005. 16p. (ps-k). bds. 5.95 (978-1-4027-2292-9(3)) Sterling Publishing Co., Inc.

—Simms Taback's Big Book of Words. 2004. (Illus.). 96p. 12.95 (978-1-59354-035-7(3)) Blue Apple Bks.

—Woof-Woof. SAMi, illus. 2006. 12p. (J). bds. 8.95 (978-1-59354-148-4(1)) Blue Apple Bks.

Ziefert, Harriet & Demarest, Chris L. I Need a Valentine! 1999. (Holiday Lift-the-Flap Ser.). (Illus.). 16p. (J). (ps-1). pap. 5.99 (978-0-689-81993-3(5) , Little Simon) Simon & Schuster Children's Publishing.

Zimelman, Nathan. El Dolar. de la Vega, Eida, tr. Zemke, Deborah, illus. 2001. (Books for Young Learners).Tr. of Dollar. (SPA.). 16p. (J). (gr. k-2). pap. 5.00 (978-1-57274-443-1(X) , 2849) Owen, Richard C. Pubs., Inc.

Zobel-Nolan, Allia. Jesus & the Children. MacLean, Moira, illus. 2000. (Baby's First Bible Stories Ser.). 10p. (J). (ps). 9.99 (978-0-7847-1209-2(3) , 04397, Bean Sprouts) Standard Publishing.

Zoehfeld, Kathleen Weidner. Have You Seen My Pot of Honey? 1999. (Learn & Grow Ser.). (Illus.). 12p. (J). (ps-3). 5.99 (978-0-7364-0099-2(0)) Mouse Works.

Zolotow, Charlotte. This Quiet Lady. Lobel, Anita, illus. 2000. 24p. (J). (ps-3). pap. 6.99 (978-0-688-17527-6(9) , Harper Trophy) HarperCollins Pubs.

—This Quiet Lady. 2000. (ps-2). lib. bdg. 14.10 (978-0-613-27232-2(3)) Tandem Library Bks.

—Wake up & Goodnight. Paparone, Pamela, illus. 1998. 24p. (J). (ps up). 9.95 (978-0-694-01032-5(4)) HarperCollins Pubs.

Zolotow, Charlotte & Vitale, Stefano. If You Listen. 2002. (Illus.). 32p. (J). (ps-3). reprint ed. 15.95 (978-0-7624-1335-5(2) , Running Pr. Kids) Running Pr. Bk. Pubs.

Zoo Animals. (Little Tot Dot-to-Dots Ser.). 32p. (gr. k-2). 4.29 (978-0-7647-0383-6(8) , FS30303) Schaffer, Frank Pubns.

Zschock, Martha Day & Zschock, Heather. Journey Around New York from A to Z. Zschock, Martha Day, illus. 2002. (Journey Around Ser.). (Illus.). 32p. (J). (gr. 4-7). 17.95 (978-1-889833-32-3(0)) Commonwealth Editions.

Zunshine, Tatiana. A Little Story about a Big Turnip. Antonenkov, Evgeny, illus. 2004. 32p. (J). 15.95 (978-0-9646010-0-0(1)) Pumpkin Hse., Ltd.

PICTURE FRAMES AND FRAMING

Beauvais, Den, creator. Alien Parade Pt. 1: Animated Flip Book. Beauvais, Den, . 2004. (Illus.). (YA). per. 4.25 (978-0-9745213-1-2(0)) Dragonfly Entertainment.

Hendry, Linda & Rebnord, Lisa. Making Picture Frames. Hendry, Linda, illus. unabr. ed. 1999. (Kids Can Do It Ser.). (Illus.). 40p. (J). (gr. 4-6). (978-1-55074-505-4(0)) Kids Can Pr., Ltd.

Hodge, Susie. Picture Frames. 2006. (Illus.). 32p. (J). (978-1-58340-953-4(X)) Smart Apple Media.

Phillips, Matt. Make Your Own Fun Frames! Jaskiel, Stan, illus. 2001. (Quick Starts for Kids! Ser.). 64p. (YA). (gr. 3 up). pap. 8.95 (978-1-885593-64-1(3) , Williamson Bks.) Ideals Pubns.

Shecter, Lara. Now & Then: The Coolest Scrapbook for School-Aged Children. 2nd ed. 2004. (Illus.). 54p. spiral bd. 22.95 (978-0-9732713-8-6(8)) Raincoast Bk. Distribution CAN. *Dist:* Transition Vendor.

PICTURE GALLERIES

see Art Museums

PICTURE POSTERS

see Posters

PICTURES

see also Cartoons and Comics; Portraits

Brown, Michael S., Jr. Berrien County Michigan - Photos & Memories. 2002. (Illus.). 50p. (J). 14.95 (978-0-9661776-1-9(4)) Bluebird Meadows.

Group/McGraw-Hill, Wright. Picture This! 6 Each of 1 Anthology, 6 vols. (Wildcats Ser.). 32p. (gr. 2-8). (978-0-322-05627-5(6)) Wright Group, The.

Lorenz Books Staff, ed. Words. 2000. (Sticker Fun Ser.). (Illus.). 16p. (ps-k). pap. 4.95 (978-0-7548-0433-8(X)) Anness Publishing GBR. *Dist:* National Bk. Network.

Paragon Publishing Staff, ed. Words. 2003. (J). per. (978-1-884907-41-8(5)) Paradise Pr., Inc.

Parragon Staff, ed. Words. (J). Date not set. (Illus.). bds. 5.98 (978-0-7525-8559-8(2)); 2002. 16p. pap. 2.98 (978-1-84273-837-5(2) , Exclusive Editions) Parragon, Inc.

Rudisill, J. J., et al, illus. Horace's Hidden Pictures. 1999. (Wimzie's House Bks.). 32p. (J). pap. 2.99 (978-0-88724-483-4(1) , CD-4851) Carson-Dellosa Publishing Co., Inc.

PICTURES, HUMOROUS

see Cartoons and Comics

PIERCE, FRANKLIN, 1804-1869

DiConsiglio, John. Franklin Pierce. 2004. (Encyclopedia of Presidents Ser.). (Illus.). 110p. (J). 34.00 (978-0-516-24235-4(0) , Children's Pr.) Scholastic Library Publishing.

Ferry, Steven. Franklin Pierce: Our Fourteenth President. 2001. (Spirit of America: Our Presidents Ser.). (Illus.). 48p. (J). (gr. 2-6). 28.50 (978-1-56766-851-3(8)) Child's World, Inc.

Lazo, Caroline Evensen. Franklin Pierce. 2007. (Presidential Leaders Ser.). 112p. (J). (gr. 6-12). 29.27 (978-0-8225-1492-3(3) , Twenty-First Century Bks.) Lerner Publishing Group.

Somervill, Barbara A. Franklin Pierce. 2002. (Profiles of the Presidents Ser.). (Illus.). 64p. (J). (gr. 4 up). lib. bdg. 23.93 (978-0-7565-0262-1(4)) Compass Point Bks.

Venezia, Mike. Franklin Pierce. Venezia, Mike, illus. 2006. (Illus.). 32p. (J). (gr. 3-4). pap. 7.95 (978-0-516-25485-2(5) , Children's Pr.) Scholastic Library Publishing.

—Franklin Pierce: Fourteenth President. Venezia, Mike, illus. 2005. (Illus.). 32p. (J). (ps-7). 27.00 (978-0-516-22619-4(3) , Children's Pr.) Scholastic Library Publishing.

Welsbacher, Anne. Franklin Pierce. 2001. (United States Presidents Ser.). (Illus.). 32p. (J). (gr. k-6). lib. bdg. 22.78 (978-1-57765-247-2(9) , Checkerboard Library) ABDO Publishing Co.

Young, Jeff C. Franklin Pierce: A MyReportLinks.com Book. 2002. (Presidents Ser.). (Illus.). 48p. (J). (gr. 4-10). lib. bdg. 25.26 (978-0-7660-5073-0(4) , MyReportLinks.com Bks.) Enslow Pubs., Inc.

Zamora, Dulce. How to Draw the Life & Times of Franklin Pierce. 2006. (Kid's Guide to Drawing the Presidents of the United States of America Ser.). (J). 25.25 (978-1-4042-2991-4(4) , PowerKids Pr.) Rosen Publishing Group, Inc., The.

PIGEONS

Blanchard, Lucy M. Chico - the story of a Homing Pigeon in the Great War. 2006. 104p. (YA). per. (978-1-84685-039-4(8) , Diggory Pr. Ltd.) Meadow Bks.

Blanchard, M. Lucy. Chico the Story of A Homing Pigeon. 2006. 62.99 (***978-1-4280-3492-1(7)***); pap. 55.99 (***978-1-4280-3493-8(5)***) IndyPublish.com.

Jackson, John. Pigeons. 2004. (Nature's Children Ser.). (J). (978-0-7172-5971-7(4) , Grolier) Scholastic Library Publishing.

Kalz, Jill. Doves. 2002. (Illus.). 24p. (J). lib. bdg. 21.35 (978-1-58340-128-6(8)) Smart Apple Media.

Presnall, Judith Janda. Carrier Pigeons. 2003. (Animals with Jobs Ser.). (J). 26.20 (978-0-7377-1824-9(2) , Greenhaven Pr., Inc.) Thomson Gale.

University Of Portsmouth, prod. The Pigeon: A Functional Anatomy. (Multimedia Dissection Library). (YA). cd-rom 149.95 (978-0-7365-3855-8(0)) Films Media Group.

PIGEONS—FICTION

Arthur, Anne. The Pigeon with the Sticky Stuck Neck. Liebman, Simean, illus. 2004. (J). per. 7.99 (978-0-9753320-0-9(7)) Riverbank Publishing.

Cutler, Jane. Common Sense & Fowls. Barasch, Lynne, illus. 2005. 144p. (J). 16.00 (978-0-374-32262-5(7) , Farrar, Straus & Giroux (BYR)) Farrar, Straus & Giroux.

Davies, Nicola. Stories from Abergelli Street. 2002. (Illus.). 48p. pap. 11.95 (978-1-84323-075-5(5)) Beekman Bks., Inc.

Dolan, Penny. Plip & Plop. Smith, Lisa, illus. 2004. (Read-It! Readers Ser.). (J). lib. bdg. 18.60 (978-1-4048-0551-4(6)) Picture Window Bks.

Doudna, Kelly. Homing Pigeon. Chawla, Neena, illus. (Fact & Fiction Ser.). 24p. (J). 2007. 21.35 (978-1-59928-440-8(5)); 2006. (978-1-59928-441-5(3)) ABDO Publishing Co.

Edgeworth, Maria. The Basket-Woman, the White Pigeon, the Orphans, Waste Not, Want Not, Forgive & Forget: Stories for Children. fac. ed. 2002. 178p. pap. 15.95 (978-1-4021-6112-4(3) , Elibron Classics) Adamant Media.

Eitzen, Ruth & Eitzen, Allan, illus. Tara's Flight. 2008. (J). (***978-1-59078-563-8(0)***) Boyds Mills Pr.

Erdrich, Louise. Grandmother's Pigeon. 1999. (J). (978-0-606-16663-8(7)) Tandem Library Bks.

Farmer, Nancy. Clever Ali. De Marcken, Gail, illus. 2006. 40p. (J). pap. 17.99 (978-0-439-37014-1(0) , Orchard Bks.) Scholastic, Inc.

Freeman, Don. Fly High, Fly Low. Freeman, Don, illus. 2004. (Illus.). 32p. (J). (ps-3). reprint ed. 16.99 (978-0-670-03685-1(4) , Viking Juvenile) Penguin Group (USA) Inc.

—Fly High, Fly Low (50th Anniversary Ed.) Freeman, Don, illus. 2007. 64p. (J). (ps). pap. 7.99 (978-0-14-240817-9(4) , Puffin) Penguin Group (USA) Inc.

Giff, Patricia Reilly. Mary Moon Is Missing. Cravath, Jill & Cravath, Lynne, illus. 2000. (Adventures of Minnie & Max Ser.: Vol. 2). 80p. (J). (gr. 2-6). pap. 4.99 (978-0-14-130823-4(0) , Puffin) Penguin Group (USA) Inc.

—Mary Moon Is Missing. 2000. (gr. 3-6). lib. bdg. 11.80 (978-0-613-26156-2(9)); (Illus.). (J). 10.79 (978-0-606-18385-7(X)) Tandem Library Bks.

Harder Tangvald, Christine. Dependable Dora Dove. Gambill, Henrietta, ed. Fletcher, Rusty, illus. 1998. (Shaped Paperback Bks.). 24p. (J). (ps-k). pap. 3.99 (978-0-7847-0835-4(5) , 24-03995, Bean Sprouts) Standard Publishing.

Healey, Richard (Dick). Holly the Christmas Dove. 2005. 36p. (J). 13.28 (978-1-4116-5496-9(X)) Lulu.com.

Jennings, Patrick. The Bird Shadow: An Ike & Mem Story. Alter, Anna, illus. 2001. 56p. (J). (gr. k-3). tchr. ed. 15.95 (978-0-8234-1670-7(4)) Holiday Hse., Inc.

Jones, Elizabeth McDavid. The Night Flyers. 1999. (978-0-606-17518-0(0)) Tandem Library Bks.

Macaulay, David. Angelo. 2002. (Illus.). 48p. (J). (gr. 1-4). 16.00 (978-0-618-16826-2(5) , Walter Lorraine) Houghton Mifflin Co. Trade & Reference Div.

Myers, Christopher A. Fly! Myers, Christopher A., illus. 2001. (Illus.). 32p. (ps-17). 16.49 (978-0-7868-2373-4(9) , Jump at the Sun) Hyperion Bks. for Children.

Naylor, Phyllis Reynolds. Cuckoo Feathers. Ramsey, Marcy Dunn, illus. 2006. 96p. (J). 14.95 (978-0-7614-5285-0(0)) Cavendish, Marshall Corp.

Oke, Janette. A Cote of Many Colors. Munger, Nancy, illus. rev. ed. 2001. (Animal Friends Ser.). 64p. (Orig.). (J). (gr. 1-5). pap. 6.99 (978-0-7642-2459-1(X)) Bethany Hse. Pubs.

—A Cote of Many Colors. 2001. (Orig.). (gr. k-3). lib. bdg. 14.15 (978-0-613-87251-5(7)) Tandem Library Bks.

Prince, Sarah. Benny & the Birds. 2001. (gr. k-3). lib. bdg. 11.80 (978-0-613-33334-4(9)) Tandem Library Bks.

Redmond, Shirley-Raye. Pigeon Hero! Ettlinger, Doris, illus. ed. 2005. 32p. (J). lib. bdg. 15.00 (978-1-59054-953-7(8)) Fitzgerald Bks.

Redmond, Shirley-Raye & Ettlinger, Doris. Pigeon Hero! 2003. (Ready-to-Reads Ser.). (Illus.). 32p. (J). pap. 3.99 (978-0-689-85486-6(2) , Aladdin) Simon & Schuster Children's Publishing.

San Souci, Daniel. The Mighty Pigeon Club. 2007. (Illus.). 40p. (J). (ps-2). 15.95 (***978-1-58246-213-4(5)*** , Tricycle Pr.) Ten Speed Pr.

Sargent, Dave & Sargent, David M., Jr. Pammie Pigeon: Keep Your Cool, 19, 12. Lenoir, Jane, illus. 2003. (Feather Tales Ser.: 12). 42p. (J). pap. 6.95 (978-1-56763-742-7(6)); 2nd ed. lib. bdg. 19.95 (978-1-56763-741-0(8)) Ozark Publishing.

—Penny Penguin: Be Kind to Others, 20, 13. Lenoir, Jane, illus. 2nd ed. 2003. (Feather Tales Ser.: 13). 42p. (J). lib. bdg. 19.95 (978-1-56763-743-4(4)) Ozark Publishing.

Schneider, Antonie. Come Back, Pigeon! 2001. (Illus.). (J). (978-0-606-21767-5(3)) Tandem Library Bks.

Selden, George. Chester Cricket's Pigeon Ride. Williams, Garth, illus. 2001. (Chester Cricket Ser.). 64p. (J). (gr. 3-6). pap. 6.95 (978-0-374-41181-7(6) , Sunburst) Farrar, Straus & Giroux.

—Chester Cricket's Pigeon Ride. 2001. (gr. 3-6). lib. bdg. 14.10 (978-0-613-37140-7(2)) Tandem Library Bks.

Simmons, Steven J. Percy to the Rescue. Howard, Kim, illus. 1998. 32p. (J). (ps-3). 15.95 (978-0-88106-390-5(8)) Charlesbridge Publishing, Inc.

Spinelli, Jerry. Wringer. 1998. (HarperClassics Ser.). 240p. (J). (gr. 3-6). pap. 6.99 (978-0-06-440578-2(8) , Harper Trophy) HarperCollins Pubs.

—Wringer. 2000. (J). tchr. ed. 9.95 (978-1-58130-676-7(8)) Novel Units, Inc.

—Wringer. 1999. 15p. (J). pap., tchr.'s training gde. ed. 15.95 (978-1-58303-099-8(9)) Pathways Publishing.

—Wringer. 1998. (J). (978-0-606-13930-4(3)) Tandem Library Bks.

—Wringer. l.t. ed. 2000. (Juvenile Ser.). 223p. (J). (gr. 4-7). 21.95 (978-0-7862-2774-7(5)) Thorndike Pr.

Willems, Mo. Don't Let the Pigeon Stay up Late! 2006. (Illus.). 40p. (ps-1). 12.99 (978-0-7868-3746-5(2)) Hyperion Bks. for Children.

—The Pigeon Finds a Hot Dog! 2004. (Illus.). 40p. (ps-1). 12.99 (978-0-7868-1869-3(7)) Hyperion Bks. for Children.

—The Pigeon Has Feelings, Too! 2005. (Illus.). 10p. (J). (ps-ps). bds. 6.99 (978-0-7868-3650-5(4)) Hyperion Bks. for Children.

—The Pigeon Loves Things That Go! 2005. (Illus.). 10p. (J). (ps-ps). bds. 6.99 (978-0-7868-3651-2(2)) Hyperion Bks. for Children.

Williams-Garcia, Rita. Every Time a Rainbow Dies. (Amistad Ser.). (Illus.). 176p. 2002. (J). pap. 6.99 (978-0-06-447303-3(1) , HarperTeen); 2001. (YA). (gr. 9 up). 15.95 (978-0-688-16245-0(2)) HarperCollins Pubs.

—Every Time a Rainbow Dies. 2002. (gr. 7-12). lib. bdg. 15.25 (978-0-613-62381-0(9)) Tandem Library Bks.

Wyeth, Sharon Dennis. Message in the Sky Bk. 3: Corey's Underground Railroad Diary. 2003. (My America Ser.). 112p. (J). pap. 10.95 (978-0-439-37057-8(4) , Scholastic Pr.) Scholastic, Inc.

Yang, Belle. Always Come Home to Me. Yang, Belle, illus. 2007. (Illus.). 32p. (J). (ps-3). 16.99 (***978-0-7636-2899-4(9)***) Candlewick Pr.

Yang, Belle & Williams, Marcia. Archie's War. Williams, Marcia, illus. 2007. (Illus.). 48p. (J). (gr. 3-7). 17.99 (***978-0-7636-3532-9(4)***) Candlewick Pr.

PIGGLE-WIGGLE, MRS. (FICTITIOUS CHARACTER)—FICTION

MacDonald, Betty Bard. Hello, Mrs. Piggle-Wiggle. 2000. (YA). pap. 40.20 incl. audio (978-0-7887-4171-5(3) , 41089) Recorded Bks., LLC.

—Hello, Mrs Piggle Wiggle. unabr. ed. 2004. 125p. (J). (gr. 2-5). pap. 29.00 incl. audio (978-0-8072-1184-7(2) , S YA 1018 SP, Listening Library) Random Hse. Audio Publishing Group.

—Mrs. Piggle-Wiggle. Knight, Hilary, illus. 2002. (J). 13.40 (978-0-7587-6605-2(X)) Book Wholesalers, Inc.

—Mrs. Piggle-Wiggle. unabr. ed. 1999. (J). (gr. 1 up). pap., stu. ed. 32.20 incl. audio (978-0-7887-3851-7(8) , 41049X4) Recorded Bks., LLC.

—Mrs. Piggle-Wiggle's Magic. 2004. (Illus.). 144p. (J). (gr. 2-5). pap. 29.00 incl. audio (978-1-4000-9001-3(6) , Listening Library) Random Hse. Audio Publishing Group.

—Mrs. Piggle-Wiggle's Magic. 2000. (J). pap., stu. ed. 51.95 incl. audio (978-0-7887-4343-6(0) , 41137) Recorded Bks., LLC.

—The Won't-Pick-up-Toys Cure. Whatley, Bruce, illus. 1998. (Mrs. Piggle-Wiggle Adventure Ser.). (J). lib. bdg. (978-0-06-027629-4(0)) HarperCollins Pubs.

—The Won't-Take-a-Bath-Cure. Whatley, Bruce, illus. 1998. (Mrs. Piggle-Wiggle Adventure Ser.). 40p. (J). (ps-2). lib. bdg. 14.89 (978-0-06-027631-7(2)) HarperCollins Pubs.

MacDonald, Betty Bard, ed. Mrs. Piggle-Wiggle's Bad Table-Manners Cure. Whatley, Bruce, illus. 2000. (Mrs. Piggle-Wiggle Adventure Ser.). (J). 12.95 (978-0-06-027632-4(0)); 12.89 (978-0-06-027633-1(9)) HarperCollins Pubs.

MacDonald, Betty Bard & Canham, Anne Macdonald. Mrs. Piggle-Wiggle. Boiger, Alexandra, illus. 2007. 208p. (J). lib. bdg. 16.89 (***978-0-06-072813-7(2)***) HarperCollins Pubs.

PIGLET (FICTITIOUS CHARACTER)—FICTION

Campbell, Louisa. Biglet. 2002. (Illus.). 32p. (ps-1). 5.99 (978-0-7868-3363-4(7)) Disney Pr.

Claire Freedman Staff, et al. Squabble & Squawk. 2006. (Illus.). 32p. (ps). pap. 9.99 (978-0-689-87308-9(5)) Simon & Schuster, Ltd. GBR. *Dist:* Independent Pubs. Group.

Disney Press Staff. Piglet Feels Small. 2002. (gr. k-3). lib. bdg. 11.80 (978-0-613-73604-6(4)) Tandem Library Bks.

English, D. N. Miss Piglet of Steam Mill Ferry Road: Meets New Friends. Winbush, Danny, photos by. 2002. 8.00 (978-0-9710470-5-1(7) , 75, MSP) Main St Publishing, Inc.

Liberts, Jennifer. Piglet Feels Small. Yee, Josie, illus. 2002. (Early Step into Reading Ser.). 32p. (J). (ps-1). pap. 3.99 (978-0-7364-1226-1(3) , RH/Disney) Random Hse. Children's Bks.

Perera, Hilda. Tomasin y el Cerdito. Montero, Jose Perez, illus. 2001. (SPA.). 48p. (J). (gr. 3-5). 12.95 (978-84-241-3333-7(1)) Everest de Ediciones y Distribucion, S.L. ESP. *Dist:* Lectorum Pubns., Inc.

Uncle Markie. Pigletté & Bobo Go Home. 2002. 22p. (YA). ring bd. 9.95 (978-1-933129-02-0(6)) Studio 403.

—Pigletté & Bobo Go to Costa Rica. 2002. 34p. (YA). ring bd. 9.95 (978-1-933129-03-7(4)) Studio 403.

—Pigletté & Bobo Go to Summer Camp. 2002. 34p. (YA). ring bd. 9.95 (978-1-933129-04-4(2)) Studio 403.

—Pigletté & Bobo Head East. 2002. 36p. (YA). ring bd. 9.95 (978-1-933129-00-6(X)) Studio 403.

—Pigletté & Bobo in the National Parks. 2002. 66p. (YA). ring bd. 9.95 (978-1-933129-01-3(8)) Studio 403.

PIGMENTATION

see Animals—Color; Human Skin Color

PIGS

Allen, Connie. Ap Lab Manual with Fetal Pig Dissection Manual, Set. 2003. (Illus.). 724p. (YA). pap., lab manual ed. 25.00 net. (978-0-471-27068-3(7)) Wiley, John & Sons, Inc.

Barbé-Julien, Colette. Little Pigs. 2006. (Born to Be Wild Ser.). (Illus.). 23p. (J). lib. bdg. (978-0-8368-6698-8(3)) Stevens, Gareth Inc.

Beck, Isabel L., et al. Trophies Kindergarten: My Pig. 2003. (Trophies Ser.). (J). (gr. k-6). 13.80 (978-0-15-329535-5(X)) Harcourt Schl. Pubs.

Bell, Rachael. Pigs. (Farm Animals Ser.). (Illus.). 32p. (J). (gr. k-2). 2001. pap. 6.95 (978-1-58810-366-6(8) , 91090); 2000. pap. 21.36 (978-1-57572-532-1(0)) Heinemann Library.

Binns, Tristan Boyer. Potbellied Pigs. 2004. (Keeping Unusual Pets Ser.). (Illus.). 48p. (J). (978-1-4034-0828-0(9)) Heinemann Library.

Blake, Jon. Stinky Finger's House of Fun. Roberts, David, illus. 2007. 128p. (J). pap. 6.95 (***978-0-340-88459-1(2)***) Hodder Children's Division GBR. *Dist:* Independent Pubs. Group.

Bolam, Emily. Chunky Farm Pig. 2000. (Chunky Farm Bks.). (Illus.). 14p. (J). (ps-k). bds. 5.99 (978-0-7641-5323-5(4)) Barron's Educational Series, Inc.

Brady, Peter. Cerdos. Schon, Isabel, ed. Ferrer, Martín Luis Guzman, tr. from ENG. Munoz, William, illus. 1998. (Coleccion Primeros Lectores). (SPA.). 24p. (J). (gr. k-3). lib. bdg. 18.60 (978-1-56065-789-7(8) , Bridgestone Bks.) Capstone Pr., Inc.

Braidich, Shelby. Little Pigs, Big Pigs: Learning the Short I Sound. (PowerPhonics Ser.). (Illus.). (J). 2002. 24p. (gr. 1). lib. bdg. 18.50 (978-0-8239-5904-4(X)); 2001. 23p. pap. 26.40 (978-0-8239-8249-3(1)) Rosen Publishing Group, Inc., The. (PowerKids Pr.).

Butterfield, Moira. Pig. 2000. (Who Am I? Ser.). (Illus.). 32p. (J). (ps-1). lib. bdg. 16.95 (978-1-929298-91-4(9)) Chrysalis Education.

Dahl, Michael. Pie for Piglets: Counting by 2s. Ouren, Todd, illus. 2004. (Know Your Numbers Ser.). 24p. (C). (gr. k-3). 22.60 (978-1-4048-0943-7(0)) Picture Window Bks.

Dalgleish, Sharon. Pigs. 2005. (Farm Animals Ser.). (Illus.). 32p. (J). (gr. 2-4). 23.00 (978-0-7910-8272-0(5) , Chelsea Hse.) Facts On File, Inc.

Dorling Kindersley Publishing Staff. Pig. 2007. (See How They Grow Ser.). 24p. (J). (ps-1). pap. 3.99 (978-0-7566-3018-8(5)) Dorling Kindersley Publishing, Inc.

Doubleday Entertainment USA - Pigs: Down on the Farm. 2006. (J). per. 6.95 (978-1-59566-228-6(6)) QEB Publishing Inc.

Doudna, Kelly. Piglets. l.t. ed. 1999. (Baby Animals Ser.). (Illus.). 24p. (J). (ps-3). lib. bdg. 19.93 (978-1-57765-185-7(5) , SandCastle) ABDO Publishing Co.

Ganeri, Anita. Pigs & Piglets. 2007. (J). (***978-1-58340-811-7(8)***) Smart Apple Media.

Gibbons, Gail. Pigs. 1999. (Illus.). 32p. (J). (gr. k-3). tchr. ed. 16.95 (978-0-8234-1441-3(8)) Holiday Hse., Inc.

—Pigs. Gibbons, Gail, illus. 1999. (Illus.). 32p. (J). (gr. k-3). pap. 6.95 (978-0-8234-1554-0(6)) Holiday Hse., Inc.

Green, Emily. Pigs. 2007. (Blastoff! Readers Ser.). 24p. (J). (gr. k-2). 18.50 (***978-0-531-17554-5(5)*** , Children's Pr.) Scholastic Library Publishing.

Green, Emily K. Pigs. 2007. (Illus.). 24p. (J). lib. bdg. 16.95 (978-1-60014-068-6(8)) Bellwether Media.

Harcourt School Publishers Staff. All about Pigs: On Level. 3rd ed. 2002. (Trophies Reading Program Ser.). (Illus.). pap. 5.10 (978-0-15-323004-2(5)) Harcourt Schl. Pubs.

—Where Do Pigs Play? Independent Reader. 3rd ed. 2002. (Trophies Reading Program Ser.). (Illus.). (J). pap. 2.90 (978-0-15-325484-0(X)) Harcourt Schl. Pubs.

Hudak, Heather C. Pigs. 2006. (J). (978-1-59036-425-3(2)); (978-1-59036-432-1(5)) Weigl Pubs., Inc.

King-Smith, Dick. All Pigs Are Beautiful. Jeram, Anita, illus. 2nd ed. 2001. (Read & Wonder Ser.). 32p. (J). (ps up). pap. 6.99 (978-0-7636-1433-1(5)) Candlewick Pr.

—All Pigs Are Beautiful. 2001. (Read & Wonder Ser.). (J). 12.79 (978-0-606-20540-5(3)) Tandem Library Bks.

Kishel, Ann-Marie. Pigs & Piglets. 2006. (First Step Nonfiction Ser.). (Illus.). 8p. (J). pap. (978-0-8225-5651-0(0) , Lerner Pubns.) Lerner Publishing Group.

Klingel, Cynthia Fitterer & Noyed, Robert B. Pigs. 2000. (Wonder Books Level 2: Farm Animals Ser.). (Illus.). 24p. (J). (ps-3). 22.79 (978-1-56766-822-3(4)) Child's World, Inc.

Krensky, Stephen. Abe Lincoln & the Muddy Pig. 2002. (gr. k-3). lib. bdg. 11.80 (978-0-613-44998-4(3)) Tandem Library Bks.

Macken, JoAnn Early. Pigs. 2004. (Animals That Live on the Farm Ser.). 24p. (J). pap. (978-0-8368-4282-1(0)); (Illus.). (YA). lib. bdg. 19.33 (978-0-8368-4275-3(8)) Stevens, Gareth Inc.

—Pigs: Los Cerdos. 2004. (ENG & SPA., Illus.). 24p. (J). pap. (978-0-8368-4296-8(0)); lib. bdg. 19.33 (978-0-8368-4289-0(8)) Stevens, Gareth Inc.

McNeil, Niki, et al. HOCPP 1125 Pigs. 2006. spiral bd. 16.00 (***978-1-60308-125-2(9)***) In the Hands of a Child.

Meadows, Graham. Pigs. 1998. (Illus.). 24p. (J). (ps up). lib. bdg. 19.93 (978-0-8368-2254-0(4)) Stevens, Gareth Inc.

Miller, Heather. My Pigs. 2000. (Welcome Bks.). (Illus.). 24p. (J). (ps-2). 17.00 (978-0-516-23109-9(X) , Children's Pr.) Scholastic Library Publishing.

—My Pigs. 2000. (gr. k-3). lib. bdg. 12.95 (978-0-613-58870-6(3)) Tandem Library Bks.

Miller, Sara Swan. Pigs. 2000. (True Bks.). (Illus.). 48p. (J). (gr. 3-5). 25.00 (978-0-516-21579-2(5) , Children's Pr.) Scholastic Library Publishing.

—Pigs. 2000. (gr. 3-6). lib. bdg. 15.25 (978-0-613-54086-5(7)) Tandem Library Bks.

Murray, Julie. Pigs. 2002. (Buddy Book Ser.). (Illus.). 24p. (J). (gr. k-4). lib. bdg. 21.35 (978-1-57765-648-7(2)) ABDO Publishing Co.

Older, Jules. Pig. Severance, Lyn, illus. 2004. 32p. (J). 16.95 (978-0-88106-109-3(3)) Charlesbridge Publishing, Inc.

Penton. My First Phot Book with Peggy Piglet. 2002. 12p. (YA). bds. 19.95 (978-1-56015-945-2(6)) Penton Overseas, Inc.

Pigs. Date not set. (Old MacDonald Stickers Ser.). (Illus.). 16p. (J). 5.98 (978-0-7525-9968-7(2)) Parragon, Inc.

Pigs, 6 Packs. 16p. (gr. 2 up). 36.00 (978-0-7635-9211-0(0)) Rigby Education.

Pigs Have Piglets. (Animals & Their Young Ser.). 24p. (J). 7.95 (978-0-7565-1245-3(X)) Compass Point Bks.

Pigs on the Farm, 6 vols. (gr. k-2). 28.95 (978-0-7368-9230-8(3)) Red Brick Learning.

Powell, Jillian. From Piglet to Pig. 2000. (Illus.). 32p. (J). lib. bdg. 25.69 (978-0-7398-4428-1(8)) Raintree.

Prince, Sarah. Three Little Pigs. 1999. (ps-2). lib. bdg. 11.80 (978-0-613-19472-3(1)) Tandem Library Bks.

Rau, Dana Meachen. Guess Who Grunts. 2008. (J). (***978-0-7614-2906-7(9)***) Cavendish, Marshall Bks., Ltd.

Ray, Hannah. Pigs. Davidson, Chris, illus. 2006. (Down on the Farm Ser.). 24p. (J). (gr. k-2). lib. bdg. 15.95 (978-1-59566-181-4(6)) QEB Publishing Inc.

Royston, Angela. El Conejillo de Indias. Abello, Patricia, tr. from ENG. 2003. (Ciclo de la Vida de... Ser.).Tr. of Guinea Pig. (SPA & ENG., Illus.). 32p. (J). lib. bdg. 22.79 (978-1-4034-3016-8(0)) Heinemann Library.

—El Conejillo de Indias. 2003. Tr. of Guinea Pig. (SPA.). 32p. (J). pap. 6.95 (978-1-4034-3039-7(X)) Heinemann Library.

Schuh, Mari C. Pigs on the Farm. 2001. (On the Farm Ser.). (Illus.). 24p. (J). (gr. k-1). lib. bdg. 15.93 (978-0-7368-0993-1(7) , Pebble Bks.) Capstone Pr., Inc.

—Pigs on the Farm. (On the Farm Ser.). 24p. (J). pap. 5.95 (978-0-7368-9144-8(7)) Capstone Pr., Inc.

Searl, Duncan. Pigs. 2006. (Smart Animals! Ser.). (Illus.). 32p. (J). lib. bdg. 25.27 (978-1-59716-164-0(0)) Bearport Publishing Co., Inc.

Stockland, Patricia M. In the Pig Pen. Ouren, Todd, illus. 2007. (Barnyard Buddies Ser.). 24p. (J). (ps-2). lib. bdg. 25.65 (***978-1-60270-025-3(7)*** , Looking Glass Library) Magic Wagon.

Stone, Lynn M. Pigs Have Piglets. 2000. (Animals & Their Young Ser.). (Illus.). 24p. (J). (gr. 1 up). lib. bdg. 18.60 (978-0-7565-0003-0(6)) Compass Point Bks.

—Pork. 2001. (Harvest to Home Ser.). (Illus.). 24p. (J). (gr. 1-4). lib. bdg. 20.64 (978-1-58952-129-2(3)) Rourke Publishing, LLC.

—Pot Bellied Pigs. 2001. (Weird Pets Ser.). (Illus.). 24p. (J). (gr. 1-4). lib. bdg. 20.64 (978-1-58952-040-0(8)) Rourke Publishing, LLC.

Stone, Tanya Lee. Pigs. 2003. (Wild Wild World Ser.). 24p. (YA). 24.94 (978-1-56711-819-3(4) , Blackbirch Pr., Inc.) Thomson Gale.

Swan, Erin Pembrey. Camels & Pigs: What They Have in Common. (Animals in Order Ser.). (Illus.). 48p. (J). (gr. 4-6). 2000. pap. 6.95 (978-0-531-16400-6(4)); 1999. 26.50 (978-0-531-11585-5(2)) Scholastic Library Publishing. (Watts, Franklin).

Tait, Leia. Caring for Your Potbellied Pig. 2006. (J). (978-1-59036-475-8(9)); lib. bdg. (978-1-59036-474-1(0)) Weigl Pubs., Inc.

Top That Publishing Staff, ed. Wacky Pig. 2004. (Wacky Animals Ser.). (Illus.). 10p. (J). pap. (978-1-84510-090-2(5)) Top That! Publishing PLC.

Wolfman, Judy. Life on a Pig Farm. Winston, David L., illus. 1998. (Carolrhoda Photo Bks.). 48p. (J). (gr. k-4). lib. bdg. 23.93 (978-1-57505-237-3(7) , Carolrhoda Bks.) Lerner Publishing Group.

—Life on a Pig Farm. Winston, David Lorenz, photos by. 2nd ed. 2005. (Life on a Farm Ser.). (Illus.). 48p. (J). (gr. 2-5). lib. bdg. 23.93 (978-1-57505-236-6(9)) Lerner Publishing Group.

PIGS—FICTION

Adams, Jean Ekman. Clarence & the Great Surprise. Adams, Jean Ekman, illus. 2001. (Illus.). 32p. (J). (gr. k-2). 15.95 (978-0-87358-795-2(2) , Rising Moon Bks. for Young Readers) Northland Publishing.

—Clarence & the Purple Horse Bounce into Town. Adams, Jean Ekman, illus. 2003. (Illus.). 32p. (ps-3). 15.95 (978-0-87358-826-3(6) , Rising Moon Bks. for Young Readers) Northland Publishing.

Addy, Sharon Hart. Lucky Jake. Zahares, Wade, illus. 2007. 40p. (J). (gr. k-3). 17.00 (978-0-618-47286-4(X)) Houghton Mifflin Co.

Adventures of the Robber Pig: Level J, 6 vols. (Leveled Books). 128p. (gr. 2-3). 41.95 (978-0-7699-0987-5(6)) Shortland Pubns. (U. S. A.) Inc.

Ahlberg, Allan. Half a Pig. Ahlberg, Allan & Ahlberg, Jessica, trs. Ahlberg, Jessica, illus. 2004. 40p. (J). (gr. k-3). 16.99 (978-0-7636-2373-9(3)) Candlewick Pr.

Albee, Sarah. Where Is Pig? Velez, Walter, illus. 2006. (Step-By-Step Readers Ser.). (J). pap. (978-1-59939-056-7(6) , Reader's Digest Young Families, Inc.) Reader's Digest Children's Publishing, Inc.

Alberts, Nancy Markham & Alley, R. W. Joselina Piggy Goes Out. 2007. (I'm Going to Read Ser.). (Illus.). 32p. (J). pap. 3.95 (978-1-4027-4299-6(1)) Sterling Publishing Co., Inc.

Alex Toys Staff. Alex Toys Finger Puppet Storybooks: The Three Little Pigs. McDonald, Jill, illus. 5th rev. ed. 2006. 8p. (J). (ps-17). 11.99 (978-0-316-15403-1(2)) Little Brown & Co.

Alexander, Lloyd. The Book of Three. 2006. (Chronicles of Prydain Ser.: Bk. 1). 224p. (J). (gr. 3-7). pap. 5.99 (978-0-8050-8048-3(1) , Holt, Henry & Co. Bks. For Young Readers) Holt, Henry & Co.

All Pull Together, 6 vols., Pack. (ps-2). 23.00 (978-0-7635-8789-5(3)) Rigby Education.

Allen, Kathryn Madeline. This Little Piggy's Book of Manners. Wolff, Nancy, illus. rev. ed. 2003. 32p. (J). 15.95 (978-0-8050-6769-9(8) , Holt, Henry & Co. Bks. For Young Readers) Holt, Henry & Co.

Amery, H. Where's Curly? Cartwright, Stephen, illus. 2004. (Treasury of Farmyard Tales Ser.). 16p. (J). (gr. 1 up). pap. 7.95 (978-0-7945-0514-1(7)); lib. bdg. 15.95 (978-1-58086-563-0(1)) EDC Publishing.

Amery, H. & Cartwright, S. Three Little Pigs. 2004. (First Stories Ser.). 16p. (J). pap. 4.99 (978-0-7945-0609-4(7)) EDC Publishing.

Amery, H. & Cartwright, Stephen. Three Little Pigs. 16p. (J). lib. bdg. 12.95 (978-1-58086-623-1(9) , Usborne) EDC Publishing.

Amery, Heather. Curly the Pig Board Book. Cartwright, Stephen, illus. 2004. (Young Farmyard Tales Board Books Ser.). 10p. (J). bds. 3.95 (978-0-7945-0468-7(X) , Usborne) EDC Publishing.

Amery, Heather, ed. Pig Gets Lost, Vol. 9. 1999. (Farmyard Tales Sticker Storybooks Ser.: Vol. 9). (Illus.). 18p. (J). (ps up). pap. 6.95 (978-0-7460-3514-6(4)) EDC Publishing.

—Pig Gets Stuck Book. Cartwright, Stephen, illus. 1998. (Usborne Farmyard Tales Ser.). 16p. (J). (ps-3). pap. 14.95 (978-0-7460-3488-0(1)) EDC Publishing.

Amery, Heather & Howell, Laura. Three Little Pigs Sticker Bk. 2006. 16p. (J). pap. 6.99 (978-0-7945-1386-3(7) , Usborne) EDC Publishing.

Amoss, Berthe. Three Little Cajun Pigs. 1999. (Illus.). (J). pap. 13.95 (978-0-922589-67-8(4)) More Than a Card, Inc.

Anderson, Lena. Hedgehog, Pig, & the Sweet Little Friend. Sandin, Joan, tr. from SWE. 2007. (Illus.). 32p. (J). (ps-1). 16.00 (***978-91-29-66742-4(9)***) R & S Bks. SWE. *Dist:* Macmillan.

Andrews, Roxanna. The Adventures of Super Pig. 2006. (Illus.). 68p. (J). 15.95 (978-1-59879-232-4(6)) Lifevest Publishing, Inc.

Anholt, Laurence. Eco-Wolf & the Three Pigs. 2004. (Illus.). 64p. (C). (gr. 3-5). 13.26 (978-0-7565-0630-8(1)) Compass Point Bks.

Ansley, Frank & Wheeler, Lisa. Invasion of the Pig Sisters. Ansley, Frank, illus. 2006. (Fitch & Chip Ser.). (Illus.). 48p. (J). 14.95 (978-0-689-84953-4(2) , Atheneum) Simon & Schuster Children's Publishing.

—Who's Afraid of Granny Wolf? Ansley, Frank, tr. 2004. (Fitch & Chip Ser.). (Illus.). 48p. (J). 14.95 (978-0-689-84952-7(4) , Atheneum/Richard Jackson Bks.) Simon & Schuster Children's Publishing.

Anson-Weber, Joan. Snuffles Goes to Scotland Yard. Russell, Judith, illus. 2001. (J). 16.95 (978-0-87797-293-8(1)) Cherokee Publishing Co.

Appelt, Kathi. Piggies in a Polka. Pham, LeUyen, illus. 2003. 40p. (J). 16.00 (978-0-15-216483-6(9)) Harcourt Children's Bks.

Apperley, Dawn. Hello Little Piglet. Apperley, Dawn, illus. 2000. (Hello Bks.). (Illus.). 12p. (J). bds. 3.95 (978-1-86233-195-2(2)) David & Charles Children's Bks. GBR. *Dist:* Sterling Publishing Co., Inc.

Artell, Mike. Three Little Cajun Pigs. Harris, Jim, illus. 2006. 32p. (J). (ps-3). 16.99 (978-0-8037-2815-8(8) , Dial) Penguin Group (USA) Inc.

Asch, Frank. Ziggy Piggy & the Three Little Pigs. Asch, Frank, illus. (Illus.). 32p. (J). (gr. k-3). 2001. (978-1-55074-913-7(7)); 1998. (978-1-55074-515-3(8)) Kids Can Pr., Ltd.

Ashman, Linda. Can You Make a Piggy Giggle? Cole, Henry, illus. 2002. 32p. (J). 12.99 (978-0-525-46881-3(1) , Dutton Juvenile) Penguin Group (USA) Inc.

Asquith, Ros & Young, Selina. Mrs. Pig's Night Out. 2003. (Illus.). (J). 32p. 15.95 (978-0-340-81707-0(0)); pap. 7.99 (978-0-340-81708-7(9)) Hodder General Publishing Division GBR. (Hodder & Stoughton). *Dist:* Trafalgar Square Publishing.

Atlas, Ron. Ten Pigs Fiddling. Flint, Stacie, illus. 2006. 32p. (J). 16.00 (978-0-9630243-8-1(8) , 1249130) Amberwood Pr.

—Ten Pigs Fiddling. Flint, Stacie, illus. 2nd rev. ed. 2006. 32p. (J). 17.95 (978-0-9630243-3-6(7)) Amberwood Pr.

Axelrod, Amy. Pigs at Odds: Fun with Math & Games. McGinley-Nally, Sharon, illus. 2000. 40p. (J). (gr. 2-4). 15.95 (978-0-689-81566-9(2)) Simon & Schuster Children's Publishing.

—Pigs at Odds: Fun with Math & Games. 2003. (gr. k-3). lib. bdg. 15.30 (978-0-613-67156-9(2)) Tandem Library Bks.

—Pigs Go to Market: Fun with Math & Shopping. McGinley-Nally, Sharon, illus. 1999. 40p. (J). (ps-3). 6.99 (978-0-689-82553-8(6) , 076714005990, Aladdin) Simon & Schuster Children's Publishing.

—Pigs Go to Market: Halloween Fun with Math & Shopping. 1999. (978-0-606-16330-9(1)); lib. bdg. 14.15 (978-0-613-19419-8(5)) Tandem Library Bks.

—Pigs in the Corner: Fun with Math & Dance. McGinley-Nally, Sharon, illus. 2005. 40p. (J). (ps-ps). pap., pap. 6.99 (978-1-4169-0335-2(6) , Aladdin) Simon & Schuster Children's Publishing.

—Pigs in the Pantry. 1999. (gr. k-3). lib. bdg. 14.15 (978-0-613-19421-1(7)) Tandem Library Bks.

—Pigs in the Pantry: Fun with Math & Cooking. McGinley-Nally, Sharon, illus. 1999. 40p. (J). (ps-3). 6.99 (978-0-689-82555-2(2) , 076714005990, Aladdin) Simon & Schuster Children's Publishing.

—Pigs in the Pantry: Fun with Math & Cooking. 1999. (978-0-606-16329-3(8)) Tandem Library Bks.

—Pigs on a Blanket. McGinley-Nally, Sharon, illus. 1998. 40p. (J). (ps-3). 6.99 (978-0-689-82252-0(9) , Aladdin) Simon & Schuster Children's Publishing.

—Pigs on the Ball: Fun With Math & Sports. 2000. (978-0-606-18800-5(2)) Tandem Library Bks.

—Pigs on the Move: Fun with Math & Travel. McGinley-Nally, Sharon, illus. 1999. (Pigs Will Be Pigs Ser.). 40p. (J). (ps-4). 15.95 (978-0-689-81070-1(9)) Simon & Schuster Children's Publishing.

—Pigs on the Move: Fun with Math & Travel. 1999. (gr. k-3). lib. bdg. 15.30 (978-0-613-67157-6(0)) Tandem Library Bks.

—Pigs Will Be Pigs: Fun with Math & Money. McGinley-Nally, Sharon, illus. 2001. (Fun with Math Ser.). lib. bdg. (978-1-59054-512-6(5)) Fitzgerald Bks.

Axelrod, Amy & McGinley-Nally, Sharon. Pigs at Odds. 2003. (Illus.). 40p. (J). pap. 6.99 (978-0-689-86144-4(3) , Aladdin) Simon & Schuster Children's Publishing.

—Pigs in the Corner. 2001. (Pigs Will Be Pigs Ser.). (Illus.). 40p. (J). (ps-4). 15.95 (978-0-689-82470-8(X)) Simon & Schuster Children's Publishing.

—Pigs on the Move: Fun with Math & Travel. 2002. (Illus.). 40p. (J). pap. 6.99 (978-0-689-85343-2(2) , Aladdin) Simon & Schuster Children's Publishing.

Aylesworth, Jim. Aunt Pitty Patty's Piggy. McClintock, Barbara, illus. 1999. 32p. (J). (ps-2). pap. 15.95 (978-0-590-89987-1(2)) Scholastic, Inc.

Babe Picturebook. 1999. pap. (978-0-679-89155-0(2) , Random Hse. Bks. for Young Readers) Random Hse. Children's Bks.

Baglio, Ben M. Piglet in a Playpen. 1999. (Animal Ark Ser.: No. 9). (J). (gr. 3-5). (978-0-606-19935-3(7)) Tandem Library Bks.

Bailey, Elinor Peace. Pickles Learns to Hide. Bailey, Elinor Peace, illus. 2002. (J). 9.50 (978-0-9716586-3-9(3)) Fairfield Processing Corp.

Balducci, Rita. Scarecrow Mix: Halloween Pigs/Happy Scarecrow. 1999. (Illus.). (J). (ps-3). pap. 4.50 (978-1-55254-089-3(8)) Brighter Vision Pubns.

Bardhan-Quallen, Sudipta. Tightrope Poppy the High-Wire Pig. Dillard, Sarah, illus. 2006. 32p. (J). 14.95 (978-1-4027-2411-4(X)) Sterling Publishing Co., Inc.

Barnum, Richard. Squinty the Comical Pig. 2004. reprint ed. pap. 15.95 (978-1-4191-4865-1(6)); pap. 1.99 (978-1-4192-4865-8(0)) Kessinger Publishing, LLC.

Barnum, Richard. Squinty the Comical Pig Illustrated Edit. 2006. (Illus.). pap. (***978-1-4065-0921-2(3)***) Dodo Pr.

Bartell, Lindy. It's Neat to Eat at the Table. 2006. 16p. (J). bds. 6.95 (978-1-57921-843-0(1)) WinePress Publishing.

Bassede, Francine. A Day with the Bellyflops. Bassede, Francine, illus. 2000. (Illus.). 32p. (J). (ps-2). 15.99 (978-0-531-33242-9(X)); pap. 14.95 (978-0-531-30242-2(3)) Scholastic, Inc. (Orchard Bks.).

—Dia con los Cerditos. (Buenas Noches Coleccion). (SPA.). (J). (gr. 1-3). 8.95 (978-958-04-5626-1(7)) Norma S.A. COL. *Dist:* Distribuidora Norma, Inc., Lectorum Pubns., Inc.

Bateman, Teresa. Will You Be My Valenswine? Stephenson, Kristina, illus. 2005. 24p. (J). (ps-2). lib. bdg. 15.95 (978-0-8075-9195-6(5)) Whitman, Albert & Co.

Bauer, Jutta. Selma. Bauer, Jutta, illus. 2004. (Illus.). 56p. (J). 7.95 (978-1-929132-50-8(6)) Kane/Miller Bk. Pubs., Inc.

Beaton, Clare. How Big Is a Pig? Beaton, Clare, illus. 2004. (Illus.). 24p. (J). pap. 5.99 (978-1-84148-702-1(3)) Barefoot Bks., Inc.

Bentley, Dawn. I'm a Pink Piggy. Tom-Nellis, Susan, illus. 1998. (Baby Buddy Bks.: No. 4). 12p. (YA). (ps up). bds. 4.95 (978-1-888443-70-7(7) , Intervisual/Piggy Toes) Dalmatian Pr.

Bergen, Lara. Get Giggly with Piggley: A Jakers! Joke Book. Entara Ltd. Staff, photos by. 2006. (Jakers! Ser.). 48p. (J). pap. 3.99 (978-0-689-87707-0(2) , Simon Spotlight) Simon & Schuster Children's Publishing.

Berger, Samantha & Viscardi, Lisa Huberman. Junior in the City: A Spinwheels Book. Moreton, Daniel, illus. 2002. (Spinwheels Bk.). 7p. (J). (ps-1). 10.95 (978-0-8109-3497-9(3)) Abrams, Harry N. , Inc.

Between the Lions - Early Literacy Kit - Huff & Puff, 2 bks., 1 cass. 2005. (Between the Lions Ser.). (Illus.). (J). VHS 29.95 (978-1-59375-283-5(0) , WG38613) WGBH Boston Video.

Blackstone, Stella. Cerdota Grandota. Beaton, Clare, illus. 2003. Tr. of How Big Is a Pig. (SPA.). 24p. (J). (gr. k-2). pap. 5.99 (978-1-84148-926-1(3)) Barefoot Bks., Inc.

—Cerdota Grandota. 2003. (SPA.). (gr. k-3). lib. bdg. 14.15 (978-0-613-65688-7(1)) Tandem Library Bks.

—How Big Is a Pig? Beaton, Clare, illus. 24p. (J). (gr. k-2). 2002. bds. 6.99 (978-1-84148-959-9(X)); 2000. 14.99 (978-1-84148-077-0(0)) Barefoot Bks., Inc.

Bloom, Suzanne. No Place for a Pig. Bloom, Suzanne, illus. 2003. (Illus.). 32p. (YA). (gr. k-2). 15.95 (978-1-59078-047-3(7)) Boyds Mills Pr.

—Piggy Monday: A Tale about Manners. Bloom, Suzanne, illus. 2001. (Illus.). 32p. (J). (gr. k-4). 16.95 (978-0-8075-6529-2(6)) Whitman, Albert & Co.

—We Keep a Pig in the Parlor. 2004. (Illus.). 24p. (J). (gr. k-2). reprint ed. pap. 7.95 (978-1-59078-084-8(1)) Boyds Mills Pr.

Bond, Felicia. Poinsettia & the Firefighters. Bond, Felicia, illus. 2003. (Illus.). 32p. (J). (ps-2). 14.99 (978-0-06-053509-4(1)); lib. bdg. 15.89 (978-0-06-053510-0(5)) HarperCollins Pubs. (Geringer, Laura Book).

Bond, Michael. The Tales of Olga da Polga. l.t. ed. 2005. (Illus.). 144p. (J). pap. (978-0-7540-7848-7(5) , CLP 438) BBC Audio.

—The Tales of Olga da Polga. 2004. (J). 24.95 incl. audio (978-0-7540-6268-4(6) , Chivers Children's Audio Bks.) BBC Audiobooks America.

Book Company Staff. Who Am I: Pig. 2003. (Board Bks.). (Illus.). (J). bds. 10.95 (978-1-74047-309-5(4)) Book Co. Publishing Pty, Ltd., The AUS. *Dist:* Penton Overseas, Inc.

Boonen, Stefan. When Pigs Fly! Loufane, illus. 2004. 32p. (J). 6.95 (978-1-58925-384-1(1) , tiger tales) ME Media LLC.

Boynton. Bath Time! 2007. 10p. pap. 7.95 (***978-0-7611-4780-0(2)***) Workman Publishing Co., Inc.

Brandon, Taylor. The Pig Who Didn't Want to Get Dirty. Sandow, Paris, illus. 1999. (World's Greatest Children's Bks.). 48p. (J). (gr. k-5). 14.99 (978-1-889945-63-7(3)) Imperius.

Branford, Henrietta. Little Pig Figwort Can't Get to Sleep. Munoz, Claudio, illus. 2002. 32p. (J). (gr. k-3). 14.00 (978-0-618-15968-0(1) , Clarion Bks.) Houghton Mifflin Co. Trade & Reference Div.

Brave M.A., Kathryn A. & Lavin, Paul J. A Fit ting Fairy Tale. 2006. 60p. pap. 12.95 (978-1-4241-2992-8(3)) PublishAmerica, Inc.

Breakstone, Beth E. The 3 Little Pigs. Breakstone, Beth E., illus. l.t. ed. 2000. (Illus.). 20p. (J). 19.00 (978-1-893467-06-4(6)) Spedial Editions Pr.

Brimner, Larry Dane. Nana's Fiddle. Miller, Susan, illus. 2002. (Rookie Reader Ser.). 32p. (J). (gr. 1-2). 19.50 (978-0-516-22373-5(9) , Children's Pr.) Scholastic Library Publishing.

—Nana's Fiddle. 2002. (gr. k-3). lib. bdg. 12.95 (978-0-613-59521-6(1)) Tandem Library Bks.

—Nana's Hog. Miller, Susan, illus. (Rookie Reader Skill Set Ser.). 32p. (J). 1999. (gr. k-2). pap. 4.95 (978-0-516-26412-7(5)); 1998. (gr. 1-2). 19.50 (978-0-516-20755-1(5)) Scholastic Library Publishing. (Children's Pr.).

Brooks, Nan, illus. This Little Piggy. 2004. (J). 11.99 (978-1-890647-10-0(1)) RC2 Corp.

Brooks, Walter R. Freddy & Mr. Camphor. Wiese, Kurt, illus. 2000. 234p. (J). (gr. 3-7). 23.95 (978-1-58567-027-7(8)) Overlook Pr., The.

—Freddy & Simon the Dictator. 2003. 220p. (J). (gr. 4-7). 23.95 (978-1-58567-359-9(5)) Overlook Pr., The.

—Freddy & the Baseball Team from Mars. Wiese, Kurt, illus. 1999. 256p. (J). (gr. 3-7). 23.95 (978-0-87951-942-1(8)) Overlook Pr., The.

—Freddy & the Baseball Team from Mars. 2000. (J). pap. 67.95 incl. audio (978-0-7887-4461-7(5) , 41150) Recorded Bks., LLC.

—Freddy & the Bean Home News. Wiese, Kurt, illus. 2000. (Freddy Ser.). 230p. (J). (gr. 3-7). 23.95 (978-1-58567-081-9(2)) Overlook Pr., The.

—Freddy & the Dragon. Wiese, Kurt, illus. 2000. 239p. (J). (gr. 3 up). 23.95 (978-1-58567-026-0(X)) Overlook Pr., The.

—Freddy & the Flying Saucer Plans. Wiese, Kurt, illus. 1998. (Freddy Ser.). 243p. (J). (gr. 3-7). 23.95 (978-0-87951-883-7(9)) Overlook Pr., The.

—Freddy & the Flying Saucer Plans. unabr. ed. 2000. (J). pap. 66.95 incl. audio (978-0-7887-3639-1(6) , 41004X4) Recorded Bks., LLC.

—Freddy & the IgnormOus. Wiese, Kurt, illus. 2001. 288p. (J). pap. 6.99 (978-0-14-230043-5(8) , Puffin) Penguin Group (USA) Inc.

—Freddy & the Ignormus. Wiese, Kurt, illus. 1998. (Freddy Ser.). 288p. (J). (gr. 3-7). 23.95 (978-0-87951-882-0(0)) Overlook Pr., The.

—Freddy & the Ignormus. 1999. (J). pap. 66.95 incl. audio (978-0-7887-2996-6(9) , 40878) Recorded Bks., LLC.

—Freddy & the Ignormus. 2001. (gr. 3-6). lib. bdg. 15.30 (978-0-613-43621-2(0)) Tandem Library Bks.

—Freddy & the Men from Mars. Wiese, Kurt, illus. 2002. 246p. (J). 23.95 (978-1-58567-269-1(6)) Overlook Pr., The.

—Freddy & the Perilous Adventure. Wiese, Kurt, illus. 2001. 245p. (J). 23.95 (978-1-58567-178-6(9)) Overlook Pr., The.

—Freddy & the Pilot. Wiese, Kurt, illus. 1999. 288p. (J). (gr. 3-7). 23.95 (978-0-87951-941-4(X)) Overlook Pr., The.

—Freddy & the Popinjay. Wiese, Kurt, illus. 2001. 244p. (J). (gr. 4-7). 23.95 (978-1-58567-134-2(7)) Overlook Pr., The.

—Freddy & the Space Ship. Wiese, Kurt, illus. 2001. 262p. (J). (gr. 3). 23.95 (978-1-58567-105-2(3)) Overlook Pr., The.

—The Freddy Anniversary Collection: Freddy Goes to Florida; Freddy Goes to the North Pole; Freddy the Detective, Wiese, Kurt, illus. 2002. 384p. (J). (gr. 4-6). 35.00 (978-1-58567-346-9(3)) Overlook Pr., The.

—Freddy Goes Camping. Wiese, Kurt, illus. 2001. 258p. (J). 23.95 (978-1-58567-177-9(0)) Overlook Pr., The.

—Freddy Goes Camping. 2003. (gr. 3-6). lib. bdg. 16.45 (978-0-613-61624-9(3)) Tandem Library Bks.

—Freddy Goes to Florida. Wiese, Kurt, illus. 2001. 208p. (J). (gr. 4-7). pap. 7.99 (978-0-14-131233-0(5) , Puffin) Penguin Group (USA) Inc.

—Freddy Goes to Florida. Wiese, Kurt, illus. 2001. 196p. (J). (gr. 4-7). per. 15.30 (978-0-613-36062-3(1)) Tandem Library Bks.

—Freddy Goes to the North Pole. Wiese, Kurt, illus. 2001. 306p. (J). 23.95 (978-1-58567-104-5(5)) Overlook Pr., The.

—Freddy Plays Football. Wiese, Kurt, illus. 2001. 265p. (J). (gr. 4-7). 23.95 (978-1-58567-133-5(9)) Overlook Pr., The.

—Freddy Plays Football. Wiese, Kurt, illus. 2002. 272p. (J). pap. 7.99 (978-0-14-230207-1(4) , Puffin) Penguin Group (USA) Inc.

—Freddy Plays Football. 2002. (gr. 3-6). lib. bdg. 16.45 (978-0-613-54415-3(3)) Tandem Library Bks.

—Freddy Rides Again. Wiese, Kurt, illus. 2002. 240p. (J). 23.95 (978-1-58567-268-4(8)) Overlook Pr., The.

—Freddy Shelf-Talker. 2000. (978-1-58567-097-0(9)) Overlook Pr., The.

—Freddy the Pilot. 2000. (YA). pap. 67.95 incl. audio (978-0-7887-4167-8(5) , 41111) Recorded Bks., LLC.

—Freddy the Pilot. 2001. (978-0-606-22516-8(1)) Tandem Library Bks.

—Freddy's Cousin Weedly. Wiese, Kurt, illus. 2002. 220p. (J). 23.95 (978-1-58567-309-4(9)) Overlook Pr., The.

Brown, E. Jane. Pinkie. 2005. 76p. pap. 10.00 (978-1-4116-3115-1(3)) Lulu.com.

Brown, Janet Allison. Choo! Choo! A Squeak Me Book. Pirie, Janie, illus. 2005. 12p. (J). bds. 5.95 (978-0-7641-5825-4(2)) Barron's Educational Series, Inc.

Brown, Margaret Wise. The Good Little Bad Little Pig. Yaccarino, Dan, illus. 2002. 24p. (ps-2). 15.99 (978-0-7868-0600-3(1)) Hyperion Bks. for Children.

—The Good Little Bad Little Pig. Yaccarino, Dan, illus. 2002. 24p. (ps-k). 16.49 (978-0-7868-2514-1(6)) Hyperion Pr.

Brown, Maureen. The Adventures of Pinky Pig & Friends. 2001. (Illus.). 53p. (J). 14.95 (978-1-85776-598-4(2)) Book Guild, Ltd. GBR. *Dist:* Trans-Atlantic Pubns., Inc.

Browne, Anthony. Piggybook: Pho Ntawv Npua/Phau Ntawv Npua. 2001. (Illus.). 32p. (J). (ps-5). pap. 6.95 (978-0-9629298-9-2(1) , MHC-9-1) Minnesota Humanities Commission.

Bruna, Dick. Poppy Pig. 2004. (Illus.). 24p. (J). 7.99 (978-1-59226-029-4(2)) Big Tent Entertainment, Inc.

Burt, Steven E. In a Pig's Eye. 2002. (J). pap. 9.95 (978-0-9649283-9-8(6)) Burt Creations.

Butler, Ellis Parker. Pigs Is Pigs & Other Favorites. 2004. reprint ed. pap. 20.95 (978-1-4179-2471-4(3)) Kessinger Publishing, LLC.

Byars, Betsy. My Brother, Ant. Simont, Marc, illus. 2005. (Ant Ser.). (J). pap. 18.95 incl. audio compact disk (978-1-59112-626-3(6)) Live Oak Media.

Byers, Rob. The Adventures of Pork & Bean. 2006. (ENG.). 124p. (J). per. 13.99 (***978-1-4141-0769-1(2)***) Pleasant Word.

Bynum, Janie. Otis. 2003. (Illus.). 40p. (J). pap. 7.00 (978-0-15-204604-0(6) , Voyager Bks./Libros Viajeros) Harcourt Children's Bks.

—Otis. 2003. (gr. k-3). lib. bdg. 14.15 (978-0-613-70501-1(7)) Tandem Library Bks.

Caple, Kathy. The Wimp. 2000. (Illus.). 32p. (J). (gr. k-3). pap. 5.95 (978-0-618-05577-7(0) , Walter Lorraine) Houghton Mifflin Co. Trade & Reference Div.

Carlson, Nancy. Get up & Go! 2008. 32p. (J). (ps). pap. 5.99 (***978-0-14-241064-6(0)*** , Puffin) Penguin Group (USA) Inc.

—Henry's Show & Tell. 2004. (Illus.). 32p. (J). (ps-1). 15.99 (978-0-670-03695-0(1) , Viking Juvenile) Penguin Group (USA) Inc.

—How about a Hug? 2003. 32p. (J). pap. 5.99 (978-0-14-250144-3(1) , Puffin) Penguin Group (USA) Inc.

—How about a Hug? Carlson, Nancy, illus. 2001. (Illus.). 32p. (J). (ps-1). 15.99 (978-0-670-03506-9(8) , Viking Juvenile) Penguin Group (USA) Inc.

—How about a Hug? 2003. 32p. (gr. k-3). lib. bdg. 14.15 (978-0-613-87821-0(3)) Tandem Library Bks.

—Louanne Pig in Making the Team. 2005. (Illus.). 32p. (J). (ps-ps). lib. bdg. 15.95 (978-1-57505-914-3(2)); pap. 6.95 (978-1-57505-997-6(5)) Lerner Publishing Group.

—Louanne Pig in the Mysterious Valentine. rev. ed. 2004. (Carolrhoda Picture Books Ser.). (Illus.). 32p. (J). (gr. k-2). 15.95 (978-1-57505-671-5(2)); pap. (978-1-57505-722-4(0)) Lerner Publishing Group.

—Louanne Pig in the Talent Show. 2005. (Illus.). 32p. (J). (ps-ps). pap. 6.95 (978-1-57505-996-9(7)) Lerner Publishing Group.

—Louanne Pig in Witch Lady. 2006. (Illus.). 32p. (J). 15.95 (978-0-8225-6196-5(4) , Carolrhoda Bks.); pap. 6.95 (978-0-8225-6197-2(2) , First Avenue Editions) Lerner Publishing Group.

Carlson, Nancy, tr. & illus. Louanne Pig in the Perfect Family. Carlson, Nancy, illus. 2nd rev. ed. 2004. (Nancy Carlson's Neighborhood Ser.). 32p. (J). (gr. k-2). 15.95 (978-1-57505-611-1(9)); pap. (978-1-57505-616-6(X)) Lerner Publishing Group.

Carlson, Nancy & Inkpen, Mick. It's bedtime, Wibbly Pig! Inkpen, Mick, illus. 2004. (Illus.). 32p. (J). (ps-1). 15.99 (978-0-670-05880-8(7) , Viking Juvenile) Penguin Group (USA) Inc.

Carlson, Nancy L. Louanne Pig in the Talent Show. 2005. (Illus.). 32p. (J). (ps-ps). lib. bdg. 15.95 (978-1-57505-915-0(0)) Lerner Publishing Group.

Carr, Jan. Swine Divine. Bender, Robert, illus. 1999. 32p. (J). (gr. k-3). tchr. ed. 15.95 (978-0-8234-1434-5(5)) Holiday Hse., Inc.

Cartwright, Stephen & Zeff, Claudia. Find the Piglet. 2000. (Kid Kits Ser.). (Illus.). 12p. (J). (ps). 10.95 (978-0-88110-800-2(6)) EDC Publishing.

Castle, Caroline. Funny! 2005. (Illus.). 32p. (J). pap. 11.95 (978-0-09-943302-6(8) , Red Fox) Random Hse. Children's Bks. GBR. *Dist:* Trafalgar Square Publishing.

Cazet, Denys. Will You Read to Me? Cazet, Denys, illus. 2007. 32p. (J). (ps-1). 16.99 (978-1-4169-0935-4(4)) Simon & Schuster Children's Publishing.

Celsi, Teresa. The Fourth Little Pig. (Metro Reading Program Ser.). (J). (gr. k). 2000. 45.95 (978-1-58830-030-0(7)); 1999. 29.95 (978-1-58120-118-5(4)) Metropolitan Teaching & Learning Co.

Chambers, Sally. The Pig. 1999. (Zippy Animal Bks.). (Illus.). 24p. (J). (ps-k). 6.95 (978-1-86233-025-2(5)) David & Charles Children's Bks. GBR. *Dist:* Sterling Publishing Co., Inc.

Chandler, Andrew and Amanda. Gertrude & Abigail (the Adventures Thereof) 2006. 35p. (J). 18.90 (978-1-4116-7572-8(X)) Lulu.com.

Chesterfield, Sadie. Let's Make a Snowman! 2007. (Peppa Pig Ser.). 24p. (J). pap. 6.99 (***978-0-06-117367-7(3)** , Harper Entertainment) HarperCollins Pubs.

The Chicks are Hatching. 2002. (J). (978-1-58453-176-0(2)); (978-1-58453-144-9(4)) Pioneer Valley Educational Pr., Inc.

Chin, Oliver. The Year of the Pig: Tales from the Chinese Zodiac. Alcorn, Miah, illus. 2007. (ENG.). 36p. (J). (gr. 1-3). 15.95 (978-1-59702-007-7(9)) Immedium.

Chocolate, Debbi. Pigs Can Fly! The Adventures of Harriet Pig & Friends. Tryon, Leslie, illus. 2004. 64p. (J). 15.95 (978-0-8126-2706-0(7)) Cricket Bks.

Chorao, Kay. Pig & Crow. rev. ed. (Illus.). (J). 2005. 40p. reprint ed. pap. 6.95 (978-0-8050-7261-7(6)); 2000. 32p. 16.95 (978-0-8050-5863-5(X)) Holt, Henry & Co. (Holt, Henry & Co. Bks. For Young Readers).

Christelow, Eileen. The Great Pig Search. Christelow, Eileen, illus. 2001. (Illus.). 40p. (J). (gr. k-3). tchr. ed. 15.00 (978-0-618-04910-3(X) , Clarion Bks.) Houghton Mifflin Co. Trade & Reference Div.

Chuck, Murphy. Playful Piggy with Toy. 1998. (Read-Along Pals Ser.). (Illus.). 10p. (YA). (ps up). bds. 9.95 (978-1-888443-62-2(6) , Intervisual/Piggy Toes) Dalmatian Pr.

Clark, Nicole K. Pigment the Rainbow Pig. Clark, Nicole K., illus. Date not set. (Illus.). (J). (ps-2). (978-1-892176-18-9(1)) PremaNations Publishing.

Clem, Margaret H. Elbert Ein Swine, Genius Pig. Clem, Margaret H., illus. 2003. (Illus.). 32p. (J). (gr. k-4). pap. 6.95 (978-1-878044-12-9(5)) Mayhaven Publishing.

Colorado School Children & MacLean, Kerry Lee. Pigs Over Colorado Past: The Way It Was. MacLean, Kerry Lee, ed. 2002. (Pigs Over Ser.: Vol. 5). (Illus.). 32p. 15.95 (978-0-9652998-5-5(6)) On the Spot! Bks.

Cook, Sherry & Johnson, Terri. Pressure Pete, 26 vols. Kuhn, Jesse, illus. l.t. ed. 2006. (Quirkles—Exploring Phonics through Science Ser.: 16). 32p. (J). 7.99 (978-1-933815-15-2(9) , Quirkles, The) Creative 3, LLC.

Cooke, James. Pink Pig in a Boat. 2004. 59p. pap. 12.95 (978-1-4137-4338-8(2)) PublishAmerica, Inc.

Copp, Raymond. Old Number Nine. 2003. 21 p. pap. 14.95 (978-1-4137-0682-6(7)) PublishAmerica, Inc.

Corey, Shana. Babe. 1998. (Early Step into Reading Ser.). (J). (978-0-606-13967-0(2)) Tandem Library Bks.

—Babe the Brave. 1999. (Illus.). (J). (978-0-606-18482-3(1)) Tandem Library Bks.

—Babe's La-La-Bye. Gerardi, Jan, illus. 1999. (Jellybean Bks.). 24p. (J). (ps-k). lib. bdg. 7.99 (978-0-375-90144-7(2) , Random Hse. Bks. for Young Readers) Random Hse. Children's Bks.

Coulman, Valerie. When Pigs Fly. Roge, illus. 2004. 32p. (J). pap. 6.95 (978-1-894222-79-2(2)) Lobster Pr. CAN. *Dist:* Univ. of Toronto Pr.

Cousins, Lucy. Ha, Ha, Maisy! Cousins, Lucy, illus. 2005. (Illus.). 14p. (J). (gr. k-k). bds. 4.99 (978-0-7636-2633-4(3)) Candlewick Pr.

—More Fun with Maisy. Cousins, Lucy, illus. 2005. (Illus.). 14p. (J). (gr. k-k). bds. 4.99 (978-0-7636-2632-7(5)) Candlewick Pr.

Cowley, Joy. Mrs. Wishy-Washy's Farm. Fuller, Elizabeth, illus. 32p. (J). (ps). 2006. pap. 5.99 (978-0-14-240299-3(0) , Puffin); 2003. 15.99 (978-0-399-23872-7(7) , Philomel) Penguin Group (USA) Inc.

Cox, Phil Roxbee. Big Pig on A Dig. Cartwright, Stephen, illus. rev. ed. 2006. 16p. (J). pap. 6.99 (978-0-7945-1501-0(0) , Usborne) EDC Publishing.

Cox, Rhonda. Pigs Peek. Cox, Rhonda, photos by. 2003. (Illus.). 12p. (J). pap. 20.00 net. (978-1-57274-698-5(X) , BB2180) Owen, Richard C. Pubs., Inc.

Cresp, Gael. The Biography of Gilbert Alexander Pig. Cox, David, illus. 1999. 30p. (978-1-876615-00-0(1)) Benchmark Pubns. Pty, Ltd.

—The Tale of Gilbert Alexander Pig. Cox, David, illus. 2000. 32p. (J). (ps-1). 15.95 (978-1-84148-215-6(3)) Barefoot Bks., Inc.

Crump, Fred, Jr. Three Little Brown Piggies. 2006. 32p. pap. 9.95 (978-1-932715-83-5(5)) UMI (Urban Ministries, Inc.).

Crump, Fred. Three Little Brown Piggies. 2007. 32p. (J). 12.95 (***978-1-934056-21-9(9)**) UMI (Urban Ministries, Inc.).

Curry, Don, ed. The Three Little Pigs. 2006. (My Turn! Your Turn! Ser.). (ENG.). 24p. (J). pap. 3.99 (978-0-696-22855-1(6)) Meredith Bks.

Dahlin, Bill. The Pig & the Whale. Hohnstadt, Cedric, illus. 1999. 15p. (J). pap. 8.97 (978-0-9678028-0-0(6)) Dahlin, Bill.

Dakos, Kalli & Desmarteau, Alicia. Our Principal Promised to Kiss a Pig. DiRocco, Carl, illus. 2004. 32p. (J). (gr. 2-5). 15.95 (978-0-8075-6629-9(2)) Whitman, Albert & Co.

Dakos, Kalli & Karas, G. Brian. Put Your Eyes up Here: And Other School Poems. 2003. (Illus.). 64p. (J). (gr. 2-5). 16.95 (978-0-689-81117-3(9)) Simon & Schuster Children's Publishing.

Dalmatian Press Staff. The Three LIttle Pigs. 2002. (Illus.). 24p. (J). (gr. k-5). pap. 2.99 (978-1-57759-477-2(0)) Dalmatian Pr.

—Three Little Pigs. 2006. 64p. pap. 11.99 (978-1-4037-2187-7(4)) Dalmatian Pr.

Dalmatian Press Staff, ed. Three Little Pigs (Classic Board Book) 2006. 10p. (J). bds. 5.99 (978-1-4037-2377-2(X)) Dalmatian Pr.

Danner-Walls, Carolyn. Richard Scarry's: Ma Pig's New Car. Reiter, Cheryl, ed. 2000. (Illus.). 10p. (J). (ps). mass mkt. 9.99 (978-1-887327-40-4(1)) Ertl Co., Inc.

Davenier, Christine. Leon & Albertine. Barth, Dominic, tr. 1998. (Illus.). 32p. (J). (ps-1). pap. 15.95 (978-0-531-30072-5(2) , Orchard Bks.) Scholastic, Inc.

Davies, Gill & Freeman, Tina. Two Naughty Piglets. 2004. (Tales from Yellow Barn Farm Ser.). (Illus.). 24p. (J). 3.99 (978-1-85854-325-3(8)) Brimax Books Ltd. GBR. *Dist:* Byeway Bks.

Davis, Donald. The Pig Who Went Home on Sunday: An Appalachian Folktale. 2007. 40p. pap. 7.95 (***978-0-87483-851-0(7)**) August Hse. Pubs., Inc.

de Pennart, Geoffroy. Sofia, la Vaca Que Amaba la Musica. 2005. (SPA.). 40p. (J). (gr. k-2). 22.95 (978-84-8470-027-2(5)) Corimbo, Editorial S.L. ESP. *Dist:* Iaconi, Mariuccia Bk. Imports.

Deal, Carla. A Pig's Tale. 2004. (Illus.). 42p. (J). spiral bd. 22.95 (978-1-932373-65-3(9) , Cedar Hill Pr.) Cedar Hill Publishing.

Denise, Anika. Pigs Love Potatoes. Denise, Christopher, illus. 2007. 40p. (J). (ps-1). 15.99 (978-0-399-24036-2(5) , Philomel) Penguin Group (USA) Inc.

DeSmet, Sara. Scared Silly. DeSmet, Sara, illus. 2006. (Illus.). 32p. (J). 15.95 (978-1-60108-009-7(3)) Red Cygnet Pr.

Dewan, Ted. Crispin: The Pig Who Had It All. 2002. (gr. k-3). lib. bdg. 15.30 (978-0-613-89780-8(3)) Tandem Library Bks.

—Crispin & the 3 Little Piglets. Dewan, Ted, illus. 2003. (Illus.). 32p. (J). (gr. k-3). 15.95 (978-0-385-74633-5(4) , Doubleday Bks. for Young Readers) Random Hse. Children's Bks.

—Crispin, el Cerdito Que lo Tenia Todo. 2003. (SPA., Illus.). 40p. (J). (gr. k-3). 18.99 (978-84-261-3171-3(9) , JV30357) Juventud, Editorial ESP. *Dist:* Lectorum Pubns., Inc.

DiCamillo, Kate. Mercy Watson Goes for a Ride. Van Dusen, Chris, illus. 2006. (Mercy Watson Ser.). 80p. (J). (gr. 1-3). 12.99 (978-0-7636-2332-6(6)) Candlewick Pr.

—Mercy Watson to the Rescue. Van Dusen, Chris, illus. 2005. 80p. (J). (gr. 1-3). 12.99 (978-0-7636-2270-1(2)) Candlewick Pr.

DiCamillo, Kate & Van Dusen, Chris. Mercy Watson: Fights Crime. Van Dusen, Chris, illus. 2006. (Illus.). 80p. (J). (gr. 1-3). 12.99 (978-0-7636-2590-0(6)) Candlewick Pr.

DiCamillo, Kate & Van Dusen, Chris. Princess in Disguise. Van Dusen, Chris, illus. 2007. (Mercy Watson Ser.). (Illus.). 80p. (J). (gr. 1-3). 12.99 (***978-0-7636-3014-0(4)**) Candlewick Pr.

Dillon, Jana. Upsie Downsie, Are You Asleep? Dillon, Jana, illus. 2002. (Illus.). 32p. (J). 15.95 (978-1-56554-941-8(4)) Pelican Publishing Co., Inc.

Dinner Time. 2005. (J). (978-1-58453-298-9(X)) Pioneer Valley Educational Pr., Inc.

DiPucchio, Kelly S. Bed Hogs. Fine, Howard, illus. 2004. 32p. (ps-k). 15.99 (978-0-7868-1884-6(0)) Hyperion Bks. for Children.

DK Publishing. Three Little Pigs: Read-along Paperbacks. 2007. 16p. (J). (ps-5). pap. 4.99 (***978-0-7566-3457-5(1)**) Dorling Kindersley Publishing, Inc.

Dorros, Arthur. When the Pigs Took Over. Greenseid, Diane, illus. 2002. (SPA.). 32p. (J). (ps-2). 15.99 (978-0-525-42030-9(4) , Dutton Juvenile) Penguin Group (USA) Inc.

Dotlich, Rebecca Kai. Mama Loves. Brown, Kathryn, illus. 2004. 32p. (J). (ps-2). 14.99 (978-0-06-029407-6(8)); lib. bdg. 15.89 (978-0-06-029408-3(6)) HarperCollins Pubs.

Doyle, Malachy & Bendall-Brunello, John. Big Pig. (Illus.). 32p. (ps). 2006. (J). 19.95 (978-0-689-87484-0(7)); 2005. pap. 9.99 (978-0-689-87485-7(5)) Simon & Schuster, Ltd. GBR. *Dist:* Independent Pubs. Group.

Duck & Pig: Early Level Satellite Individual Title Six-Packs. (Sails Literacy Ser.). 16p. (gr. 1-2). 27.00 (978-0-7578-2908-6(2)) Rigby Education.

Dunker, Bon. An Almost True Tale of Three Pigs & a Wolf. 2000. (Illus.). vi, 132p. (J). (gr. 2-6). pap. 5.99 (978-0-9701371-0-4(9)) Z 3 Universe.

Dunn, Judy. The Little Pig. Dunn, Phoebe, illus. 2001. (Pictureback Ser.). 32p. (J). (gr. k-k). pap. 3.25 (978-0-394-88774-6(3) , Random Hse. Bks. for Young Readers) Random Hse. Children's Bks.

DuVall, Nell. Cormac & the Coyote. Less, Sally, illus. 2001. 30p. (J). pap. 7.95 (978-0-9706654-2-3(3)) Sprite Pr.

Dykes, Ray. The Three Little Pigs Revisited: How to Build Your Spiritual House of Faith. Flippo, Ty, illus. 2002. 96p. per. 9.95 (978-0-9723884-0-5(0)) Pair'o'Docs Pr.

Edwards, Frank B. A Medley of Mooners: Four Playful Pig Tales. Bianchi, John, illus. anniv. ed. 2001. 120p. (J). (gr. k-2). (978-1-894323-31-4(9)) Pokeweed Pr.

Edwards, Pat. A Visit to Cousin Boris. Selway, Martina, illus. 1999. 24p. (J). (978-0-7608-3196-0(3)) Sundance/Newbridge Educational Publishing.

—What's That? 1999. (gr. k-3). lib. bdg. 10.95 (978-0-613-30867-0(0)) Tandem Library Bks.

Egan, Tim. The Experiments of Doctor Vermin. Egan, Tim, illus. 2002. (Illus.). 32p. (J). (gr. k-3). tchr. ed. 15.00 (978-0-618-13224-9(4)) Houghton Mifflin Co. Trade & Reference Div.

Ehrlich, Fred. Does a Pig Flush? Bolam, Emily, illus. 2005. 32p. (ps-k). pap. 5.95 (978-1-59354-124-8(4)) Blue Apple Bks.

Emmett, Jonathan. Pigs Might Fly. 2005. (Illus.). 32p. (J). (***978-0-14-138086-5(1)** , Puffin) Penguin Group (USA) Inc.

English, D. N. Miss Piglet of Steam Mill Ferry Road: Finds a New Home. Winbush, Danny, photos by. l.t. ed. 2002. (Illus.). 20p. 8.00 (978-0-9710470-9-9(X) , 75, MSP) Main St Publishing, Inc.

Entara Ltd., illus. Piggley Makes a Friend. 2007. (Jakers! Ser.). 24p. (J). pap. 3.99 (***978-1-4169-3581-0(9)** , Simon Spotlight) Simon & Schuster Children's Publishing.

—Piggley's Treasure Hunt. 2007. (Jakers! Ser.). 24p. (J). pap. 3.99 (***978-0-689-87612-7(2)** , Simon Spotlight) Simon & Schuster Children's Publishing.

Entara Ltd. Staff, photos by. Big Brother Piggley. 2007. (Jakers! Ser.). 24p. (J). pap. 3.99 (978-1-4169-2819-5(7) , Simon Spotlight) Simon & Schuster Children's Publishing.

—Ferny Gets a Crush. 2006. (Jakers! Ser.). 16p. (J). pap. 5.99 (978-1-4169-0384-0(4) , Simon Spotlight) Simon & Schuster Children's Publishing.

—Piggley & the Magic Doll. 2006. (Jakers! Ser.). 24p. (J). pap. 3.99 (978-0-689-87611-0(4) , Simon Spotlight) Simon & Schuster Children's Publishing.

—Piggley Helps Out. 2006. (Ready-To-Read Ser.). 24p. (J). pap. 3.99 (978-0-689-87614-1(9) , Simon Spotlight) Simon & Schuster Children's Publishing.

—Piggley's Pals. 2006. (Jakers! Ser.). (Illus.). 14p. (J). 7.99 (978-0-689-87617-2(3) , Simon Spotlight) Simon & Schuster Children's Publishing.

Erickson, John R. The Case of the Missing Bird Dog, Vol. 40. Holmes, Gerald L., illus. 2002. (Hank the Cowdog Ser.: No. 40). 144p. (J). 15.99 (978-0-670-03558-8(0) , Viking Juvenile); pap. 4.99 (978-0-14-230141-8(8) , Puffin) Penguin Group (USA) Inc.

Ernst, Lisa Campbell. Riqui y Marisa. 2000. (SPA., Illus.). 36p. (J). (gr. k-2). 17.50 (978-84-261-3093-8(3) , JV3448) Juventud, Editorial ESP. *Dist:* Lectorum Pubns., Inc.

Escardo Bas, Mercè. Los Tres Cerditos. 2003. (SPA.). 24p. (978-84-246-1939-8(0) , GL30510) La Galera, S.A. Editorial ESP. *Dist:* Lectorum Pubns., Inc.

Escardo i Bas, Mercè. Three Little Pigs. Joan, Pere, illus. 2006. (ENG & SPA.). 32p. (J). pap. 6.95 (978-0-8118-5064-3(1)) Chronicle Bks. LLC.

—Three Little Pigs: Los Tres Cerditos. Joan, Pere, illus. 2006. (ENG & SPA.). 32p. (J). 14.95 (978-0-8118-5063-6(3)) Chronicle Bks. LLC.

Este Cerdito. 2005. Tr. of This Little Piggy. (SPA.). 22p. (J). 9.95 (978-1-58117-328-4(8) , Intervisual/Piggy Toes) Dalmatian Pr.

Fairless, Caroline. Hambone. Edelson, Wendy, illus. 2001. 48p. (J). pap. 10.95 (978-0-89869-361-4(6)) Church Publishing, Inc.

Fairy Tales- Three little Pigs. 2005. (J). bds. (978-1-4194-0044-5(4)) Paradise Pr., Inc.

Falconer, Ian. Olivia. Falconer, Ian, illus. 2002. (Olivia Ser.). (YA). 26.13 (978-1-4046-0034-8(5)) Book Wholesalers, Inc.

—Olivia. ed. 2004. (Olivia Ser.). (J). (gr. k-3). (FRE., Illus.). spiral bd. (978-0-616-14599-9(3)); spiral bd. (978-0-616-07232-5(5)); spiral bd. (978-0-616-07233-2(3)) Canadian National Institute for the Blind/Institut National Canadien pour les Aveugles.

—Olivia. Mlawer, Teresa, tr. (Olivia Ser.). (SPA., Illus.). (J). (gr. k-2). 16.00 (978-1-930332-20-1(3) , LC5675); 2002. 30p. 16.00 (978-1-930332-08-9(4) , LC30181) Lectorum Pubns., Inc.

—Olivia. 2001. (Olivia Ser.). (Illus.). (J). (SPA.). 146p. (978-84-8488-016-5(8)); (CAT., 40p. (978-84-8488-017-2(6)) Serres, Ediciones, S. L. ESP. *Dist:* Lectorum Pubns., Inc.

—Olivia. Falconer, Ian, illus. (Olivia Ser.). (Illus.). (J). (ps-3). 2000. 40p. 16.95 (978-0-689-82953-6(1) , Atheneum/Anne Schwartz Bks.); 2004. 34p. bds. 7.99 (978-0-689-87472-7(3) , Atheneum) Simon & Schuster Children's Publishing.

—Olivia: The Essential Latin Edition. High, Amy, tr. Falconer, Ian, illus. 2007. (Illus.). 40p. (J). (ps-2). 17.99 (***978-1-4169-4218-4(1)** , Atheneum) Simon & Schuster Children's Publishing.

—Olivia & the Missing Toy. Falconer, Ian, illus. 2003. (Olivia Ser.). (Illus.). 42p. (J). (ps up). 16.95 (978-0-689-85291-6(6) , Atheneum) Simon & Schuster Children's Publishing.

—Olivia Counts. 2002. (Olivia Ser.). bds. 6.99 (978-0-689-85447-7(1) , Atheneum) Simon & Schuster Children's Publishing.

—Olivia Counts. Falconer, Ian, illus. 2002. (Olivia Ser.). (Illus.). 12p. (J). (ps-1). bds. 6.99 (978-0-689-85087-5(5) , Atheneum) Simon & Schuster Children's Publishing.

—Olivia fait son Cirque. (Olivia Ser.). 29.95 (978-2-02-051642-6(X)) Editions du Seuil FRA. *Dist:* Distribooks, Inc.

—Olivia Forms a Band. Falconer, Ian, illus. 2006. (Olivia Ser.). (Illus.). 50p. (J). (ps-2). 17.95 (978-1-4169-2454-8(X) , Atheneum) Simon & Schuster Children's Publishing.

—Olivia sait Compter. (Olivia Ser.). 18.95 (978-2-02-056487-8(4)) Editions du Seuil FRA. *Dist:* Distribooks, Inc.

—Olivia Saves the Circus. ed. 2004. (Olivia Ser.). (J). (gr. k-2). spiral bd. (978-0-616-11110-9(X)); spiral bd. (978-0-616-11111-6(8)) Canadian National Institute for the Blind/Institut National Canadien pour les Aveugles.

—Olivia Saves the Circus. Falconer, Ian, illus. (Olivia Ser.). (Illus.). 44p. (J). (ps-2). 2001. 17.95 (978-0-689-82954-3(X) , Atheneum/Anne Schwartz Bks.); 2002. 150.00 (978-0-689-85039-4(5) , Atheneum) Simon & Schuster Children's Publishing.

—Olivia's Opposites. Falconer, Ian, illus. 2002. (Olivia Ser.). (J). bds. 6.99 (978-0-689-85448-4(X)); (Illus.). 12p. bds. 6.99 (978-0-689-85088-2(3)) Simon & Schuster Children's Publishing. (Atheneum).

Farrell, Liam. The True Story of the Three Little Pigs & the Big Bad Wolf. 2002. (Illus.). 64p. (YA). (gr. 1 up). pap. 8.95 (978-1-901737-35-6(7)) Anvil Bks., Ltd. IRL. *Dist:* Dufour Editions, Inc.

Faulkner, Keith. The Long-Nosed Pig. Lambert, Jonathan, illus. 1998. (Pop-Up Bks.). 16p. (J). (ps-2). 13.99 (978-0-8037-2296-5(6) , Dial) Penguin Group (USA) Inc.

Feely, Jenny. Big Pig's Wig. 2001. (gr. k-3). lib. bdg. 11.65 (978-0-613-33336-8(5)) Tandem Library Bks.

—Pig's Skin. 2001. (gr. k-3). lib. bdg. 11.80 (978-0-613-33412-9(4)) Tandem Library Bks.

Fetzner, Mary. Simple Story of the 3 Pigs & the Scientific Wolf. 2000. (Illus.). 64p. (J). (gr. k-3). pap. 11.95 (978-1-880505-78-6(9) , CLC0238) Pieces of Learning.

Field, Matthew S. The Three Pigs, Business School, & Wolf Hash Stew. 2006. (J). pap. 19.95 (978-0-9761528-1-1(9)) Matting Leah Publishing Co.

The Fight on the Hill: Individual Title Six-Pack. (Story Steps Ser.). (gr. k-2). 23.00 (978-0-7635-9837-2(2)) Rigby Education.

Fisher, Karin, adapted by. Pig, Pig, & Pig: The Classic Fable of the Three Little Pigs, Retold in One-syllable Words. 2003. (J). pap. 7.95 (978-0-9744343-0-8(2) , SA-303) Bright Solutions for Dyslexia, LLC.

Florian, Douglas. A Pig Is Big. Florian, Douglas, illus. 2000. (Illus.). 24p. (J). (gr. 2 up). 16.99 (978-0-688-17125-4(7)); (ps-3). 16.89 (978-0-688-17126-1(5)) HarperCollins Pubs.

The Flying Pig & the Daredevil Dog: Individual Title Six-Packs. (Action Packs Ser.). 104p. (gr. 3-5). 44.00 (978-0-7635-2985-7(0)) Rigby Education.

Ford, Bernette. No More Bottles for Bunny! Williams, Sam, illus. 2007. 32p. (J). (ps). 12.95 (978-1-905417-34-6(9)) Boxer Bks., Ltd. GBR. *Dist:* Sterling Publishing Co., Inc.

Fox, Christyan & Fox, Diane. Around the World Piggywiggy. 2002. (Illus.). 24p. (J). 14.95 (978-1-929766-58-1(0)) Handprint Bks.

—Astronaut PiggyWiggy. 2002. (Illus.). 24p. (J). (ps-k). 9.95 (978-1-929766-41-3(6)) Handprint Bks.

—Bathtime PiggyWiggy: A Pull-the-Page Book. 2001. (Illus.). 24p. (J). 12.95 (978-1-929766-32-1(7)) Handprint Bks.

—Pirate PiggyWiggy. 2003. (Illus.). 24p. (J). 11.95 (978-1-929766-76-5(9)) Handprint Bks.

—What Shape Is That, Piggywiggy? 2002. (Illus.). 10p. (J). (ps-k). bds. 5.95 (978-1-929766-44-4(0)) Handprint Bks.

—What's the Opposite, Piggywiggy? 2002. (Illus.). 10p. (J). (ps-k). bds. 5.95 (978-1-929766-43-7(2)) Handprint Bks.

Fox, Diane. Firefighter Piggywiggy. Fox, Christyan, illus. 2001. 24p. (J). (ps-k). 9.95 (978-1-929766-16-1(5)) Handprint Bks.

—What Color Is That, Piggywiggy? Fox, Christyan, illus. 2001. 10p. (J). (ps-k). 5.95 (978-1-929766-17-8(3)) Handprint Bks.

Fox, Diane, et al. Goodnight PiggyWiggy: A Pull-the-Page Book. Fox, Christyan, illus. 2000. 24p. (J). (ps-k). 12.95 (978-1-929766-06-2(8)) Handprint Bks.

French & Melling. Iggy Pig's Skippy Day. (Illus.). 42p. (J). pap. (978-0-340-71360-0(7) , Hodder & Stoughton) Hodder General Publishing Division.

French, Vivian. Cerdito Enamorado, Level 3. Archbold, Tim, illus. 2005. (Lightning Readers Ser.). 32p. (J). (gr. 1-2). pap., pap. 3.95 (978-0-7696-4241-3(1) , Gingham Dog Pr.) School Specialty Publishing.

—Pig in Love, Level 3. Archbold, Tim, illus. 2005. (Lightning Readers Ser.). 32p. (J). (gr. 1-2). pap., pap. 3.95 (978-0-7696-4221-5(7) , Gingham Dog Pr.) School Specialty Publishing.

French/Archbold, Vivian/Tim. Pig in Love. 2005. (Illus.). 32p. (J). lib. bdg. 9.00 (***978-1-4242-0889-0(0)**) Fitzgerald Bks.

Galdone, Paul. The Three Little Pigs. Galdone, Paul, illus. 2002. (Illus.). (J). 13.79 (978-0-7587-3805-9(6)) Book Wholesalers, Inc.

Garis, Howard Roger. Curly & Floppy Twistytail (the Funny P. 2006. 25.99 (***978-1-4280-1724-5(0)**) IndyPublish.com.

Gaudet, Mary Kate. Peppa Pig: Coloring & Activity Book & Crayons. 2007. (Peppa Pig Ser.). 32p. (J). pap. 4.99 (***978-0-06-117374-5(6)** , Harper Entertainment) HarperCollins Pubs.

Gay, Marie-Louise. The Three Little Pigs. 2004. (Illus.). 30p. (J). pap. 5.95 (978-0-88899-639-8(X)) Groundwood Bks. CAN. *Dist:* Perseus Distribution.

Geisert, Arthur. The Giant Ball of String. Geisert, Arthur, illus. 2002. (Illus.). 32p. (J). (gr. k-3). tchr. ed. 16.00 (978-0-618-13221-8(X) , Walter Lorraine) Houghton Mifflin Co. Trade & Reference Div.

—Hogwash. 2008. (J). (***978-0-618-77332-9(0)**) Houghton Mifflin Co.

—Lights Out. 2005. (Illus.). 32p. (J). (gr. k-3). 16.00 (978-0-618-47892-7(2) , Walter Lorraine) Houghton Mifflin Co. Trade & Reference Div.

—Mystery. Geisert, Arthur, illus. 2003. (Illus.). 32p. (J). (gr. k-3). 16.00 (978-0-618-27293-8(3) , Walter Lorraine) Houghton Mifflin Co. Trade & Reference Div.

—Nursery Crimes. (Illus.). 32p. (J). (ps-3). 2007. 6.95 (***978-0-618-95671-5(9));** 2001. tchr. ed. 16.00 (978-0-618-06487-8(7) , Walter Lorraine) Houghton Mifflin Co. Trade & Reference Div.

—Oops! 2006. (Illus.). 32p. (J). (gr. k-3). 16.00 (978-0-618-60904-8(0)) Houghton Mifflin Co.

—Pigaroons. 2004. (Illus.). 32p. (J). (gr. k-3). tchr. ed. 16.00 (978-0-618-41058-3(9) , Walter Lorraine) Houghton Mifflin Co. Trade & Reference Div.

—Pigs from 1 to 10. 2002. (Illus.). 32p. (J). (gr. k-3). pap. 6.95 (978-0-618-21611-6(1) , Walter Lorraine) Houghton Mifflin Co. Trade & Reference Div.

George, Susie. Let's Go on a Treasure Hunt. 2007. (Peppa Pig Ser.). 24p. (J). pap. 3.99 (*978-0-06-117363-9(0) , Harper Entertainment) HarperCollins Pubs.

Gibson, Carol Ann. Loopy. 2003. pap. 16.00 (978-0-8059-6096-9(1)) Dorrance Publishing Co., Inc.

Gilbert the Pig Chapter Books Set 1. 2005. (J). (978-1-58453-296-5(3)) Pioneer Valley Educational Pr., Inc.

Gilbert the Pig Goes on a Diet. 2002. (J). (978-1-58453-178-4(9)) Pioneer Valley Educational Pr., Inc.

Gilbert the Pig Has an Adventure. 2002. (J). (978-1-58453-181-4(9)) Pioneer Valley Educational Pr., Inc.

Gilbert the Pig Set 1. 2002. (J). (978-1-58453-175-3(4)) Pioneer Valley Educational Pr., Inc.

Gilbert the Pig Wears a Dress. 2002. (J). (978-1-58453-180-7(0)) Pioneer Valley Educational Pr., Inc.

Gilbert the Prize Winning Pig. 2002. (J). (978-1-58453-179-1(7)) Pioneer Valley Educational Pr., Inc.

Goldapp, Dolores. A Pig Named Fred. Goldapp, Eric & Goldapp, Karl, illus. 1998. (J). pap. 6.00 (978-1-56763-339-9(0)); lib. bdg. 17.25 (978-1-56763-338-2(2)) Ozark Publishing.

Gomez de Salazar, Carmen & Martilotti, Carla. Pinky Pig: Lost in the City! 2006. (ENG.). 32p. per. 12.95 (978-1-59800-118-1(3)) Outskirts Press, Inc.

Gomez de Salazar, Carmen & Martilotti, Carla. Pinky's Birthday. 2007. (ENG.). 28p. per. 12.95 (*978-1-59800-732-9(7)) Outskirts Press, Inc.

Good, Phyllis Pellman. Plain Pig's ABC's: A Day on Plain Pig's Amish Farm. Benner, Cheryl A., illus. 1998. 24p. (J). (ps-1). 14.95 (978-1-56148-251-1(X)) Good Bks.

Gorbachev, Valeri. The Big Trip. Gorbachev, Valeri, illus. 2004. (Illus.). 32p. (J). 15.99 (978-0-399-23965-6(0) , Philomel) Penguin Group (USA) Inc.

—That's What Friends Are For. Gorbachev, Valeri, illus. 2005. (Illus.). 32p. (J). (ps-3). 15.99 (978-0-399-23966-3(9) , Philomel) Penguin Group (USA) Inc.

Gralley, Jean. Hogula: Dread Pig of Night. rev. ed. 2002. (Illus.). 32p. (J). (ps-3). pap. 6.95 (978-0-8050-7164-1(4) , Holt, Henry & Co. Bks. For Young Readers) Holt, Henry & Co.

—Hogula: Dread Pig of Night. 2002. (gr. k-3). lib. bdg. 15.25 (978-0-613-90145-1(2)) Tandem Library Bks.

Grant, Nicola. Don't Be So Nosy, Posy! Warnes, Tim, illus. 2004. 32p. (J). tchr. ed. 15.95 (978-1-58925-036-9(2) , tiger tales) ME Media LLC.

Greene, Stephanie. Pig Pickin' Mathieu, Joseph, illus. 2006. (Marshall Cavendish Chapter Book Ser.). 64p. (J). 14.99 (978-0-7614-5324-6(5)) Cavendish, Marshall Corp.

Greene, Stephanie. The Show-Off. Mathieu, Joseph, illus. 2007. (Moose & Hildy Ser.). 64p. (J). (gr. 1-4). 14.99 (*978-0-7614-5374-1(1)) Cavendish, Marshall Corp.

Grindley, Sally & Ellis, Andy. Can We Play Too, Piglittle? 2000. (Toddler Bks.). (Illus.). 20p. (J). (ps). pap. 4.95 (978-0-7641-1582-0(0)) Barron's Educational Series, Inc.

Gubacz, Margorie. Piglet's Big Day. Baker, Darrell, illus. 2005. (J). (*978-1-4127-3102-7(X)) Publications International, Ltd.

Guess, Catherine Ritch. Rudy & the Magic Sleigh. 2006. (Illus.). 32p. 14.95 (*978-1-933341-18-7(1)) CRM.

—Rudy el Puerco Rojo. 2006. (Illus.). 32p. 14.95 (*978-1-933341-21-7(1)) CRM.

—Rudy the Red Pig. 2006. (Illus.). 32p. 14.95 (*978-1-933341-13-2(0)) CRM.

Hamilton, Elizabeth L. Pansy Pig's Patience Pit. 2004. (Character Critters Ser.: No. 7). (Illus.). 32p. (J). per. 5.95 (978-0-9754629-3-5(8) , Character-in-Action) Quiet Impact, Inc.

Harcourt School Publishers Staff. Babe the Gallant Pig Level D: Reader. 2001. (Collections Ser.). (Illus.). pap. 12.10 (978-0-15-314381-6(9)) Harcourt Schl. Pubs.

—Giggle & Snort On Level. 3rd ed. 2002. (Trophies Reading Program Ser.). (Illus.). (gr. 3). pap. 5.10 (978-0-15-323161-2(0)) Harcourt Schl. Pubs.

—Little Pig at the State Fair Advanced Level. 3rd ed. 2002. (Trophies Reading Program Ser.). (Illus.). pap. 5.10 (978-0-15-323038-7(X)) Harcourt Schl. Pubs.

—The Pig Is Back: Take-Home Book. rev. ed. 2001. (Collections Ser.: Vol. 5). (Illus.). (J). pap. 1.90 (978-0-15-317818-4(3)) Harcourt Schl. Pubs.

—The Pig Who Cried Help: Take-Home Book. 1999. (Collections Ser.). (Illus.). (J). pap. 1.90 (978-0-15-317311-0(4)) Harcourt Schl. Pubs.

Hawkins, Colin & Hawkins, Jacqui. Here's a Happy Pig. 2004. (Illus.). 8p. (J). 3.95 (978-1-56148-441-6(5)) Good Bks.

—Mig the Pig's Big Book. Hawkins, Colin & Hawkins, Jacqui, illus. 2004. (Illus.). 18p. (J). (gr. k-2). reprint ed. pap. 19.00 (978-0-7567-8168-2(X)) DIANE Publishing Co.

—Witch Pigs. 2006. (Illus.). 32p. (J). (gr. 1-2). 19.99 (978-0-224-06467-5(3) , Jonathan Cape) Random Hse. Children's Bks. GBR. *Dist:* Trafalgar Square Publishing.

—Witch Pigs. 2006. (Illus.). 32p. (J). (gr. 1-2). pap. 9.99 (978-0-09-943429-0(6)) Transworld Publishers Ltd. GBR. *Dist:* Independent Pubs. Group.

Healy, Nick. The Big Pig. Rooney, Ronnie, illus. 2006. 32p. (J). (*978-1-4048-3385-2(4)) Picture Window Bks.

Hearne, Betsy. Wishes, Kisses, & Pigs. 2003. 144p. (J). pap. 4.99 (978-0-689-86347-9(0) , Aladdin) Simon & Schuster Children's Publishing.

—Wishes, Kisses, & Pigs. 2003. (gr. 3-6). lib. bdg. 13.00 (978-0-613-70812-8(1)) Tandem Library Bks.

Heiney, Sue P. Zig the Pig Goes to School. Charles, Akins, illus. l.t. ed. 2004. 32p. (J). 7.00 (978-0-9761700-0-6(0)) Zig the Pig.

Heinlein, Robert A. & Briggs, Anita. Hobart. Rayner, Mary, illus. 2002. 64p. (J). (gr. 3-7). 14.00 (978-0-689-84129-3(9)) Simon & Schuster Children's Publishing.

Heller, Nicholas. Elwood & the Witch. Smith, Jos. A., illus. 2000. 32p. (J). (gr. k-3). 15.89 (978-0-688-16946-6(5)) HarperCollins Pubs.

—Elwood & the Witch. Smith, Jos. A., illus. 2000. 32p. (J). (gr. k-3). 15.95 (978-0-688-16945-9(7)) HarperCollins Pubs.

Herman, Gail. Peppa Pig & Her Best Friend. 2007. (My First I Can Read Bks.). 32p. (J). pap. 3.99 (*978-0-06-117305-9(3) , Harper Trophy) HarperCollins Pubs.

Herman, R. A. This Little Piggy Went to Market. Dobson, Leonard, illus. 2005. 6p. (J). (ps-k). bds. 7.95 (978-1-59354-040-1(X)) Handprint Bks.

Hickerson, Joel, illus. ImagineLand's Bubble Gum Trouble, Vol. 1. l.t. ed. 2004. 32p. (J). (978-0-9765038-0-4(8)) Imagineland, LTD.

Hiebert, Elfrieda H. & Juel, Connie. Three Little Pigs & One Big Pig. (Little Book Practice Reader Ser.). (J). (978-0-8136-0819-8(8)) Modern Curriculum Pr.

Hillert, Margaret. The Three Little Pigs. Wilde, Irma, illus. rev. exp. ed. 2007. (Beginning to Read Ser.). 30p. (J). lib. bdg. (978-1-59953-050-5(3)) Norwood Hse. Pr.

Hobbie, Holly. Charming Opal. Hobbie, Holly, illus. 2003. (Toot & Puddle Ser.). (Illus.). 32p. (J). (ps-3). 16.99 (978-0-316-36633-5(1)) Little Brown & Co.

—I'll Be Home for Christmas. Hobbie, Holly, illus. 2001. (Toot & Puddle Ser.: Bk. 5). (Illus.). 32p. (J). (ps-3). 15.95 (978-0-316-36623-6(4) , Tingley, Megan Bks.) Little, Brown Bks. for Young Readers.

—The New Friend. 2004. (Illus.). 32p. (J). (ps-3). 16.99 (978-0-316-36636-6(6) , Tingley, Megan Bks.) Little, Brown Bks. for Young Readers.

—The One & Only. 2006. (Illus.). 32p. (J). (ps-3). 16.99 (978-0-316-36664-9(1)) Little Brown & Co.

—A Present for Toot. Hobbie, Holly, illus. 1998. (Toot & Puddle Ser.). (Illus.). 32p. (J). (ps-3). 15.99 (978-0-316-36556-7(4)) Little Brown & Co.

—Puddle's ABC. Hobbie, Holly, illus. 2000. (Toot & Puddle Ser.: Bk. 4). (Illus.). 48p. (J). (ps-1). 14.95 (978-0-316-36593-2(9)) Little Brown & Co.

—Toot & Puddle. 2006. (978-0-316-15654-7(X)) Little Brown & Co.

—Toot & Puddle. 2007. 32p. (J). (ps-3). 16.99 (*978-0-316-16702-4(9)) Little, Brown Bks. for Young Readers.

—Toot & Puddle: One & Only. 2006. (Illus.). (J). (*978-1-4287-0431-2(0)) Little Brown & Co.

—Top of the World. Hobbie, Holly, illus. 2002. (Toot & Puddle Ser.). (Illus.). 32p. (J). (ps-3). 15.95 (978-0-316-36513-0(0)) Little, Brown Bks. for Young Readers.

—Wish You Were Here. 2005. (Toot & Puddle Ser.). (Illus.). 32p. (J). (ps-3). 16.99 (978-0-316-36602-1(1)) Little Brown & Co.

—You Are My Sunshine. Hobbie, Holly, illus. 3rd ed. 1999. (Toot & Puddle Ser.). (Illus.). 32p. (J). (ps-3). 16.99 (978-0-316-36562-8(9)) Little Brown & Co.

Holder, Greg. A Pond Full of Pigs: A Story about the Golden Rule. 2000. (Threads Ser.). (Illus.). 32p. (J). (ps-1). bds. 8.99 (978-0-7847-1239-9(5) , 04411, Bean Sprouts) Standard Publishing.

Hollaway, David. Quigley Mccormick: And the Curse of the Polka Dotted Pig, 3 vols. l.t. ed. 2005. (Illus.). 156p. (J). per. 15.95 (978-1-933211-54-1(7)) Quackenworth Publishing.

Huelin, Jodi, adapted by. Piggley's Tough Break. 2008. (Jakers! Ser.). 24p. (J). pap. 3.99 (*978-1-4169-4770-7(1) , Simon Spotlight) Simon & Schuster Children's Publishing.

Hutchins, Pat. Little Pink Pig. 2000. (Illus.). 32p. (J). (ps-3). pap. 5.95 (978-0-688-17516-0(3) , Harper Trophy) HarperCollins Pubs.

—Little Pink Pig. 2000. (Illus.). (J). (978-0-606-18703-9(0)) Tandem Library Bks.

Ichikawa, Satomi. My Pig Amarillo: A Tale from Guatemala. Ichikawa, Satomi, illus. 2003. (Illus.). 32p. (J). (ps-3). 16.99 (978-0-399-23768-3(2) , Philomel) Penguin Group (USA) Inc.

Imperato, Teresa. Five Little Piggies: Mini. Haskamp, Steve, illus. 2005. 12p. (J). bds. (978-1-58117-317-8(2) , Intervisual/Piggy Toes) Dalmatian Pr.

—This Little Piggy. Haskamp, Steve, illus. 2005. 22p. (J). 9.95 (978-1-58117-281-2(8) , Intervisual/Piggy Toes) Dalmatian Pr.

Inches, Alison, adapted by. Piggley Helps Out: Jakers! 2006. (Illus.). 24p. (J). lib. bdg. 15.00 (*978-1-4242-1553-9(6)) Fitzgerald Bks.

Inkpen, Mick. A to Z: An Alphabet Adventure. 2001. (Kipper Ser.). (Illus.). 64p. (J). (ps-2). 16.95 (978-0-15-202594-6(4) , Red Wagon Bks.) Harcourt Children's Bks.

—El Cerdito Wibbly Esta Contento. 2001. (SPA.). (J). (978-84-480-1399-8(9)) Timun Mas, Editorial S.A. ESP. *Dist:* Lectorum Pubns., Inc.

—If I Had a Pig. 2000. (Illus.). (J). 32p. pap. (978-0-333-54461-7(7)); 12p. (978-0-333-72254-1(X)) Pan Macmillan. (Macmillan Children's Bks.).

—Wibbly Pig Is Happy. 2000. (Wibbly Pig Ser.). (Illus.). 16p. (J). (ps). bds. 5.99 (978-0-670-89263-1(7) , Viking Juvenile) Penguin Group (USA) Inc.

—Wibbly Pig Likes Bananas. 2000. (Wibbly Pig Ser.). (Illus.). 16p. (J). (ps). bds. 5.99 (978-0-670-89265-5(3) , Viking Juvenile) Penguin Group (USA) Inc.

Jackson, Brenda. Henrietta & the Pot-Bellied Pig. 2005. (J). 16.95 (978-0-9773146-0-7(X)) Krisaran Publishing Co.

Jackson, Chris. Edmund & Washable: A Tale from China Plate Farm. 2000. (Illus.). 24p. (J). 12.00 (978-0-00-224558-6(2)) HarperCollins Pubs.

Jackson, Jill L. How Does One Address a Pig?, Vol. 2. Kirby, Bertha, illus. deluxe ed. 2001. (Lessons for Lucile Ser.). 104p. (J). (gr. 2-7). 24.95 (978-0-9700692-1-4(9)) Noble Endeaver.

James, Annabelle. The Three Little Pigs Story in a Box. Ackerman, Michele L., illus. 2002. (Story in a Box Ser.). 12p. (J). bds., act. bk. ed. 8.99 (978-1-883043-38-4(7)) Straight Edge Pr., The.

James, Larry W. Captain Petey: An Adventure at Sea. Ramos, Violet M., ed. James, Larry W. & Freshman, Floris R., illus. 2003. 28p. pap. 6.99 (978-0-9742154-0-2(6)) Cross Pointe Printing.

Jennings, Linda. This Little Piggy. 2000. (Illus.). 16p. (J). (ps-1). 6.95 (978-1-86233-101-3(4)) David & Charles Children's Bks. GBR. *Dist:* Sterling Publishing Co., Inc.

Jim Pig Is Mad: Short Vowel i: Level A. 6 vols. (Wright Skills Ser.). 12p. (gr. k-3). 17.95 (978-0-322-03115-9(X)) Wright Group, The.

John, Olivia Newton. Pig Tale. 1999. (978-0-606-17729-0(9)) Tandem Library Bks.

Johns, Linda. The Three Shapely Pigs. ed. 2004. (Shared Connections Ser.). (J). pap., instr.'s gde. ed. 27.00 (978-1-4108-1614-6(1)) Benchmark Education Co.

—The Three Shapley Pigs. ed. 2004. (Shared Connections Ser.). (J). pap. 27.00 (978-1-4108-1638-2(9)) Benchmark Education Co.

Johnson, Angela. Julius. Pilkey, Dav, illus. 2002. (J). 14.74 (978-0-7587-2909-5(X)) Book Wholesalers, Inc.

—Julius. Pilkey, Dav, illus. 1998. 32p. (J). (ps-1). pap. 6.95 (978-0-531-07102-1(2) , Orchard Bks.) Scholastic, Inc.

—Julius. 1998. 13.75 (978-0-606-13546-7(4)) Tandem Library Bks.

Johnson, Paul Brett. A Perfect Pork Stew. 1998. (Illus.). 32p. (J). (gr. k-4). 16.99 (978-0-531-33070-8(2) , Orchard Bks.) Scholastic, Inc.

—The Pig Who Ran a Red Light. 1999. (Illus.). 32p. (J). (ps-2). 16.99 (978-0-531-33136-1(9)); pap. 15.95 (978-0-531-30136-4(2)) Scholastic, Inc. (Orchard Bks.).

Johnson, Richard. The Three Little Pigs. 2004. (Illus.). 24p. (J). 7.99 (978-0-85953-535-9(5)) Child's Play-International.

Johnson, Richard, illus. Three Little Pigs. 24p. pap. (978-1-904550-21-1(5)) Child's Play-International.

Jones, Melanie Davis. Pigs Rock! 2003. (Illus.). 32p. (J). (ps-1). 15.99 (978-0-670-03581-6(5) , Viking Juvenile) Penguin Group (USA) Inc.

Jugran, Jan. Rub-a-Dub-Dub. Larranaga, Ana, illus. 2007. 6p. (J). (ps-ps). 12.99 (978-1-58476-555-4(0) , IKIDS) Innovative Kids.

Julian, Russell. Hungry Pig. 2005. (Farm Board Book Ser.). (Illus.). 12p. (J). bds. 9.99 (978-1-4052-1032-4(X)) Egmont Bks., Ltd. GBR. *Dist:* Trafalgar Square Publishing.

Kaminsky, Jeff & Atwater, Martha. Pig. Kaminsky, Jeff, illus. 2002. (Stickamajigs Ser.: Vol. 1). (Illus.). 8p. (ps-1). 5.99 (978-0-7868-0710-9(5)) Hyperion Bks. for Children.

Kasza, Keiko. El Dia de Campo de Don Chancho. (Buenas Noches Coleccion). (SPA., Illus.). (J). (gr. 1-3). 8.95 (978-958-04-1426-1(2)) Norma S.A. COL. *Dist:* Distribuidora Norma, Inc., Lectorum Pubns., Inc.

—My Lucky Day. Kasza, Keiko, illus. 2005. 30p. (J). pap. 5.99 (978-0-14-240456-0(X) , Puffin) Penguin Group (USA) Inc.

—My Lucky Day. 2003. (Illus.). 32p. (J). (ps-3). 15.99 (978-0-399-23874-1(3) , Putnam Juvenile) Penguin Group (USA) Inc.

—My Lucky Day. 2006. (J). (gr. k-3). incl. audio (978-0-8045-6937-8(1) , SAC6937); 29.95 incl. audio compact disk (978-0-8045-4136-7(1) , SACD4136) Spoken Arts, Inc.

—The Pig's Picnic. Kasza, Keiko, illus. 2002. (Illus.). (J). 14.04 (978-1-4046-0012-6(4)) Book Wholesalers, Inc.

—The Pig's Picnic. Kasza, Keiko, illus. 2001. (Illus.). 32p. (J). pap. 6.99 (978-0-698-11902-4(9) , Putnam Juvenile) Penguin Group (USA) Inc.

—Pigs' Picnic. 2001. (ps-2). lib. bdg. 15.30 (978-0-613-44247-3(4)) Tandem Library Bks.

Kaufmann, Nancy. Bye, Bye! Spetter, Jung-Hee, illus. 2004. 32p. (J). (ps-1). 14.95 (978-1-886910-95-9(2) , Lemniscaat) Boyds Mills Pr.

Kaula, Radhika. Three Little Piglets. Kaula, Radhika, illus. 1999. (Illus.). 24p. (J). (ps-2). pap. 10.00 (978-0-9653862-2-7(8)) Transnational Computing Services.

Keller, Holly. Geraldine & Mrs. Duffy. 2000. (Illus.). (J). (gr. k-3). 24p. 15.95 (978-0-688-16887-2(6)); 32p. 15.89 (978-0-688-16888-9(4)) HarperCollins Pubs.

—Geraldine's Big Snow. 1998. (Illus.). 24p. (J). (ps-3). pap. 4.95 (978-0-688-16164-4(2)) HarperCollins Pubs.

Kellogg, Steven. Three Little Pigs. 2002. (gr. k-3). lib. bdg. 15.30 (978-0-613-62999-7(X)) Tandem Library Bks.

Kelly, John & Tincknell, Cathy. The Mystery of Eatum Hall. Kelly, John & Tincknell, Cathy, illus. 2004. (Illus.). 32p. (J). (gr. k-3). 15.99 (978-0-7636-2594-8(9)) Candlewick Pr.

Kennemore, Tim. Alice's Birthday Pig. 2005. (Illus.). 64p. (J). pap. (978-1-84270-240-6(8)) Andersen.

Kenney, Cindy & Big Idea, Inc. Staff. A Knight to Remember. 2005. (Big Idea Bks.). (Illus.). 40p. (gr. k-3). 9.99 (978-0-310-70730-1(7)) Zonderkidz.

King-Smith, Dick. Babe: The Gallant Pig. Kneen, Maggie, illus. 2005. 144p. (J). (gr. 4-7). 16.95 (978-0-375-82970-3(9) , Knopf Bks. for Young Readers) Random Hse. Children's Bks.

—Clever Lollipop. Barton, Jill, illus. 2003. 144p. (J). (gr. 2-5). 15.99 (978-0-7636-2174-2(9)) Candlewick Pr.

—Lady Lollipop. Barton, Jill, illus. 128p. (J). (gr. 2-5). 2003. pap. 6.99 (978-0-7636-2181-0(1)); 2001. 15.99 (978-0-7636-1269-6(3)) Candlewick Pr.

—Lady Lollipop. 2001. (gr. 3-6). lib. bdg. 14.15 (978-0-613-66589-6(9)) Tandem Library Bks.

—Pigs Might Fly. 2000. (J). (gr. 3-7). 22.25 (978-0-8446-7146-8(0)) Smith, Peter Pub., Inc.

—Spotty Pig. 1999. (978-0-606-16471-9(5)) Tandem Library Bks.

—Traffic. 2003. (Illus.). (gr. 3-6). lib. bdg. 11.80 (978-0-613-88820-2(0)) Tandem Library Bks.

—Triffic: The Extraordinary Pig. 1998. (J). (978-0-606-13869-7(2)) Tandem Library Bks.

Kingsolver, Barbara. Pigs in Heaven. 1999. (978-0-606-18201-0(2)) Tandem Library Bks.

Kline, Trish & Donev, Mary. Coming Home: KA Reader 8. 2007. (Illus.). 32p. (J). per. 20.00 (*978-1-934307-01-4(7)) Ghost Hunter Productions.

Kneen, Maggie. The Christmas Surprise. Kneen, Maggie, illus. 2006. (Illus.). 18p. (J). (gr. k-4). reprint ed. 16.00 (978-0-7567-9837-6(X)) DIANE Publishing Co.

Koenig, Albert. Wood, Hay, & Pigs. Compton, Donna, illus. 2005. (J). 8.99 (978-1-4183-0078-4(0)) Christ Inspired, Inc.

Kooser, Diane S. Potter Pig in Control: Four Stories on Anger Management. Norcross, Harry, illus. 2000. 64p. (J). (gr. 1-3). pap. 12.95 (978-1-57543-084-3(3)) MAR*CO Products, Inc.

Kunhardt Davis, Edith. Tickle the Pig. 2001. (Touch & Feel Bks.). (Illus.). 8p. (J). (gr. k). bds. 9.99 (978-0-307-12007-6(4) , Golden Bks.) Random Hse. Children's Bks.

La Brack, Joy. Babe: Christmas in the Barn. Cuddy, Robbin, illus. 1999. 24p. (J). (ps-1). pap. 3.25 (978-0-375-80216-4(9) , Random Hse. Bks. for Young Readers) Random Hse. Children's Bks.

Laden, Nina. When Pigasso Met Mootisse. 1998. (Illus.). 40p. (J). (ps-5). 16.95 (978-0-8118-1121-7(2)) Chronicle Bks. LLC.

Ladybird Books Staff. Three Little Pigs. (First Fairy Tales Ser.: No. S852-2). (Illus.). (J). (ps-2). pap. 3.95 (978-0-7214-5059-9(8) , Dutton Juvenile) Penguin Group (USA) Inc.

Lai-Ma. The Monster of Palapala Mountain. 2006. (Illus.). 44p. (J). 17.95 (978-0-9762056-5-4(3)) Heryin Publishing Corp.

Laird, Donivee Martin. The Magic Shark Learns to Cook. Johnson, Carol Ann, illus. 2004. 48p. (J). 9.95 (978-1-57306-233-6(2)) Bess Pr., Inc.

Landolf, Diane Wright. Hog & Dog. Harris, Jennifer Beck, illus. 2005. (Step into Reading Ser.: Vol. 1). 32p. (J). (ps-1). pap. 3.99 (978-0-375-83165-2(7) , Random Hse. Bks. for Young Readers) Random Hse. Children's Bks.

Larson, D. J. Pigsley Brew. Larson, D. J., illus. 2003. (Illus.). 39p. (J). (gr. k-2). pap. 5.95 (978-0-9728234-0-1(9)) Don't Look Publishing.

Lee, Taylor & Van Dijk, Peter. Winchell Cuts the Cheese. 2005. (Illus.). 32p. (J). 14.95 (978-1-58246-140-3(6) , Tricycle Pr.) Ten Speed Pr.

Leeuwen, Jeanne Van. Oliver & Albert, Friends Forever. 2002. (gr. k-3). lib. bdg. 11.80 (978-0-613-86258-5(9)) Tandem Library Bks.

Leonard, Barry, ed. The Three Little Pigs. 2003. (Illus.). 12p. (J). (gr. k-4). reprint ed. 17.00 (978-0-7567-6860-7(8)) DIANE Publishing Co.

—Three Little Pigs. 2006. (Illus.). 61p. (J). (gr. k-4). reprint ed. 25.00 (978-1-4223-5245-8(5)) DIANE Publishing Co.

Lester, Helen. Me First. Munsinger, Lynn, illus. 2002. (J). 14.72 (978-0-7587-3116-6(7)) Book Wholesalers, Inc.

Leznoff, Glenda. Pigmalion. Berman, Rachel & King, Susan, illus. 2001. 32p. (J). (ps-3). (978-1-896580-20-3(3)) Tradewind Bks.

Liberts, Jennifer. Piglet Feels Small. Yee, Josie, illus. 2002. (Early Step into Reading Ser.). 32p. (J). (ps-1). pap. 3.99 (978-0-7364-1226-1(3) , RH/Disney) Random Hse. Children's Bks.

Lima, Chely. El Credito Que Amaba el Ballet. Rodriguez, Juan, illus. (SPA.). (J). pap. (978-980-01-1035-5(6)) Monte Avila Editores Latinoamericana CA VEN. *Dist:* Lectorum Pubns., Inc.

Lin, Grace. Olvina Flies. Lin, Grace, illus. rev. ed. 2003. (Illus.). 32p. (J). (ps-2). 15.95 (978-0-8050-6711-8(6) , Holt, Henry & Co. Bks. For Young Readers) Holt, Henry & Co.

Lindgren, Barbro. Benny's Had Enough! Dyssegaard, Elisabeth Kallick, tr. Landstrom, Olof, illus. 2005. 28p. (J). (ps-1). reprint ed. pap. 6.95 (978-91-29-66338-9(5)) R & S Bks. SWE. *Dist:* Macmillan.

Little, Jean. Pippin the Christmas Pig. Zimmermann, H. Werner, illus. 2004. 40p. (J). (ps-3). 16.95 (978-0-439-65062-5(3) , Scholastic Pr.) Scholastic, Inc.

Little Softy Pig. 2002. (J). (978-1-931312-91-2(5)) SoftPlay, Inc.

Lodge, Jo. Pass the Parcel with Pig. 1998. (Illus.). 12p. (J). (ps-3). 5.95 (978-0-7641-5076-0(6)) Barron's Educational Series, Inc.

Losordo, Stephen. Cow Moo Me. Conteh-Morgan, Jane, illus. 1998. (Growing Tree Ser.). 16p. (J). (ps up). 5.95 (978-0-694-01108-7(8) , Harper Festival) HarperCollins Pubs.

Loupy, Christophe. Hugs & Kisses. Tharlet, Eve, illus. 2004. 32p. (J). pap. 6.95 (978-0-7358-1972-6(6)) North-South Bks., Inc.

MacDonald, Alan. The Pig in a Wig. Hess, Paul, illus. 2003. 32p. (J). (gr. k-3). pap. 6.95 (978-1-56145-299-6(8) , Q32523) Peachtree Pubs., Ltd.

—Pig in a Wig. 1999. (gr. k-3). lib. bdg. 16.40 (978-0-613-68926-7(7)) Tandem Library Bks.

MacDonald, Betty Bard. Hello, Mrs. Piggle-Wiggle. 2000. (YA). pap. 40.20 incl. audio (978-0-7887-4171-5(3) , 41089) Recorded Bks., LLC.

—Mrs. Piggle-Wiggle. Knight, Hilary, illus. 2002. (J). 13.40 (978-0-7587-6605-2(X)) Book Wholesalers, Inc.

—Mrs. Piggle-Wiggle's Magic. 2004. (Illus.). 144p. (J). (gr. 2-5). pap. 29.00 incl. audio (978-1-4000-9001-3(6) , Listening Library) Random Hse. Audio Publishing Group.

—Mrs. Piggle-Wiggle's Magic. 2000. (J). pap., stu. ed. 51.95 incl. audio (978-0-7887-4343-6(0) , 41137) Recorded Bks., LLC.

MacDonald, Betty Bard, ed. Mrs. Piggle-Wiggle's Bad Table-Manners Cure. Whatley, Bruce, illus. 2000. (Mrs. Piggle-Wiggle Adventure Ser.). (J). 12.95 (978-0-06-027632-4(0)); 12.89 (978-0-06-027633-1(9)) HarperCollins Pubs.

MacDonald, Betty Bard & Canham, Anne Macdonald. Mrs. Piggle-Wiggle. Boiger, Alexandra, illus. 2007. 208p. (J). lib. bdg. 16.89 (***978-0-06-072813-7(2)***) HarperCollins Pubs.

MacDonald, Margaret Read. The Old Woman & Her Pig: An Appalachian Folktale. Kanzler, John, illus. 2001. 32p. (J). (ps-1). 16.99 (978-0-06-028089-5(1)); lib. bdg. 17.89 (978-0-06-028090-1(5)) HarperCollins Pubs.

MacLean, Kerry Lee. Peaceful Piggy Meditation. MacLean, Kerry Lee, illus. 2004. (Illus.). 32p. (J). (gr. k-4). 16.95 (978-0-8075-6380-9(3)) Whitman, Albert & Co.

MacLean, Kerry Lee, creator. Pigs Ski over Colorado: The Top Ten Reasons Winter Is the Piggies Favorite Season. 2005. (J). per. 15.95 (978-0-9652998-7-9(2)) On the Spot! Bks.

MacLean, Kerry Lee, illus. Piggy Meditation. 2006. 32p. (J). 6.95 (978-0-8075-6381-6(1)) Whitman, Albert & Co.

Mamet, David. Henrietta. Dahlie, Elizabeth, illus. 1999. 32p. (ps-3). tchr. ed. 16.00 (978-0-618-00416-4(5)) Houghton Mifflin Co. Trade & Reference Div.

Mansfield, Howard. Hogwood Steps Out. 2008. (Illus.). 32p. (J). 16.95 (***978-1-59643-269-7(1)***) Roaring Brook Pr.

Marshall, James. Portly McSwine. Marshall, James, illus. 2002. (Illus.). 40p. (J). (gr. k-3). reprint ed. tchr. ed. 15.00 (978-0-618-18381-4(7)); pap. 4.95 (978-0-618-18380-7(9)) Houghton Mifflin Co. Trade & Reference Div.

—Portly McSwine. 2002. (gr. k-3). lib. bdg. 12.95 (978-0-613-89008-3(6)) Tandem Library Bks.

—Swine Lake. ed. 2004. (Illus.). (J). (gr. k-5). spiral bd. (978-0-616-01712-8(X)) Canadian National Institute for the Blind/Institut National Canadien pour les Aveugles.

—Swine Lake. Sendak, Maurice, illus. 2002. 45p. (YA). (gr. 6-8). 16.00 (978-0-7567-5267-5(1)) DIANE Publishing Co.

—Swine Lake. Sendak, Maurice, illus. 1999. (Michael di Capua Bks.). (ps-3). 40p. (J). 15.89 (978-0-06-205172-1(5)); 40p. 16.95 (978-0-06-205171-4(7)); (J). 15.95 (978-0-06-028430-5(7)) HarperCollins Pubs.

—The Three Little Pigs. Marshall, James, illus. 2002. (Illus.). (J). 14.04 (978-0-7587-3804-2(8)) Book Wholesalers, Inc.

—The Three Little Pigs. Marshall, James, illus. 2000. (Reading Railroad Bks.). (Illus.). 32p. (J). (ps-3). pap. 3.99 (978-0-448-42288-6(3) , Grosset & Dunlap) Penguin Group (USA) Inc.

—The Three Little Pigs. 2000. (gr. k-3). lib. bdg. 11.25 (978-0-613-30156-5(0)) Tandem Library Bks.

Martin, David. Five Little Piggies. Meddaugh, Susan, illus. 2002. (J). 14.79 (978-0-7587-2513-4(2)) Book Wholesalers, Inc.

—Five Little Piggies. Meddaugh, Susan, illus. 2000. 40p. (J). (ps-1). pap. 6.99 (978-0-7636-1081-4(X)) Candlewick Pr.

—Five Little Piggies. 2000. (J). 13.79 (978-0-606-19315-3(4)); lib. bdg. 15.30 (978-0-613-28488-2(7)) Tandem Library Bks.

—I, Piggy & Dad. 2000. (Brand New Readers Ser.). (Illus.). (J). (978-0-7636-1328-0(2)) Candlewick Pr.

—Piggy & Dad. Remkiewicz, Frank, illus. 2001. (Brand New Readers Ser.). 32p. (J). (ps-2). pap. 5.99 (978-0-7636-1327-3(4)) Candlewick Pr.

—Piggy & Dad Go Fishing. Remkiewicz, Frank, illus. 2005. (Brand New Readers Ser.). 32p. (J). (ps-1). 14.99 (978-0-7636-2506-1(X)) Candlewick Pr.

—Piggy & Dad Play. Remkiewicz, Frank, illus. 2002. (Brand New Readers Ser.). 8p. (J). (ps-2). pap. 5.99 (978-0-7636-1333-4(9)) Candlewick Pr.

—Piggy's Pictures. 2000. (Illus.). (J). (978-0-7636-1331-0(2)) Candlewick Pr.

Martin, Jacqueline Briggs. The Water Gift & the Pig of the Pig. Wingerter, Linda S., illus. 2003. 32p. (J). (gr. k-3). tchr. ed. 15.00 (978-0-618-07436-5(8)) Houghton Mifflin Co. Trade & Reference Div.

Martin Larrañaga, Ana. Pepo & Lolo & the Red Apple. 2004. (Super Sturdy Picture Bookstm Ser.). (Illus.). 24p. (J). (gr. k-ps). 8.99 (978-0-7636-2036-3(X)) Candlewick Pr.

—Pepo & Lolo Are Friends. 2004. (Super Sturdy Picture Bookstm Ser.). (Illus.). 24p. (J). (gr. k-ps). 8.99 (978-0-7636-1982-4(5)) Candlewick Pr.

Mauterer, Erin Marie, illus. We Both Read-the Three Little Pigs. (We Both Read Ser.). 44p. (J). (gr. 1 up). 1998. 7.99 (978-1-891327-05-6(4)); 2nd ed. 1999. pap. 3.99 (978-1-891327-09-4(7)) Treasure Bay, Inc.

McCarroll, Barbara. There's Always Two Sides to Every Story. 2005. 9.00 (978-0-8059-9917-4(5)) Dorrance Publishing Co., Inc.

McD-Furuichi, Michelle. The Littlest Piggy Went to San Francisco. Watson, Nicole, illus. 2000. 32p. (J). (ps-4). pap. 9.95 (978-0-9660593-2-8(8) , 16018) Kibo.

McGraw-Hill Staff. Three Little Pigs. 2001. (gr. k-3). lib. bdg. 11.80 (978-0-613-83138-3(1)) Tandem Library Bks.

McLarey, Kristina Thermaenius, et al. When You Take a Pig to a Party. Wunsch, Marjory, illus. 2000. 32p. (J). (gr. k-4). 16.99 (978-0-531-33257-3(8)); pap. 15.95 (978-0-531-30257-6(1)) Scholastic, Inc. (Orchard Bks.).

McMullan, Kate. Pig Latin—Not Just for Pigs! 2006. (Dragon Slayers' Academy Ser.: No. 14). (J). (gr. 1-6). 24.21 (978-1-59961-127-3(9)) Spotlight.

McNaughton, Colin. De Repente! (Buenas Noches Coleccion). (SPA.). (J). (gr. 1-3). 8.95 (978-958-04-5627-8(5)) Norma S.A. COL. *Dist:* Distribuidora Norma, Inc., Lectorum Pubns., Inc.

—Oops! 2000. (978-0-606-20332-6(X)); (J). (978-0-606-20169-8(6)) Tandem Library Bks.

—Preston's Goal! 2001. (978-0-606-22599-1(4)) Tandem Library Bks.

—S. W. A. L. K. A Preston Pig Story. 2002. (Illus.). 27p. 17.99 (978-1-84270-098-3(7)) Random Hse. GBR. *Dist:* Trafalgar Square Publishing.

—Suddenly! McNaughton, Colin, illus. 2002. (Illus.). (J). 13.19 (978-0-7587-3725-0(4)) Book Wholesalers, Inc.

—Suddenly! 1998. (Preston Pig Ser.). (Illus.). 32p. (J). (ps-3). pap. 7.00 (978-0-15-201699-9(6) , Harcourt Paperbacks) Harcourt Children's Bks.

McNaughton, Colin, et al. Gol! 2005. (WEL., Illus.). 24p. (978-0-948930-79-9(9)) Cymdeithas Lyfrau Ceredigion.

—Mwsg. 2005. (WEL., Illus.). 28p. (978-1-902416-62-5(7)) Cymdeithas Lyfrau Ceredigion.

—Wps! 2005. (WEL., Illus.). 27p. (978-1-902416-29-8(5)) Cymdeithas Lyfrau Ceredigion.

MCP Staff. That Pig Can't Do a Anything, 6 bks., set, Level 10, Bk. 37. 2003. (J). (ps-3). 24.50 (978-0-8136-1682-7(4)) Modern Curriculum Pr.

McPhail, David M. Big Pig & Little Pig. McPhail, David M., illus. 2002. (Illus.). (J). 11.45 (978-0-7587-5345-8(4)) Book Wholesalers, Inc.

—Big Pig & Little Pig. 2003. (Green Light Readers Level 1 Ser.). (Illus.). 24p. (J). 11.95 (978-0-15-204818-1(9)); pap. 3.95 (978-0-15-204857-0(X)) Harcourt Children's Bks. (Green Light Readers).

—Big Pig & Little Pig. (gr. k-3). 2003. lib. bdg. 11.80 (978-0-613-63254-6(0)); 2001. (Illus.). (J). (978-0-606-21066-9(0)) Tandem Library Bks.

—Pig Pig Grows Up. McPhail, David M., illus. 2002. (Illus.). (J). 13.19 (978-0-7587-3406-8(9)) Book Wholesalers, Inc.

—Pigs Ahoy! 1998. (978-0-606-13705-8(X)) Tandem Library Bks.

—Pigs Aplenty, Pigs Galore! McPhail, David M., illus. 2002. (Illus.). (J). 14.04 (978-0-7587-3412-9(3)) Book Wholesalers, Inc.

—Those Can-Do Pigs. McPhail, David M., illus. 2002. (Illus.). (J). 13.19 (978-0-7587-3795-3(5)) Book Wholesalers, Inc.

—Those Can-Do Pigs. 1999. (Illus.). 32p. (J). (ps-3). pap. 6.99 (978-0-14-056256-9(7) , Puffin) Penguin Group (USA) Inc.

—Those Can-Do Pigs. 1999. (978-0-606-16782-6(X)); lib. bdg. 14.15 (978-0-613-19532-4(9)) Tandem Library Bks.

Mechanimals. 2007. (Illus.). 32p. (J). (ps-3). (***978-1-55143-628-9(0)***) Orca Bk. Pubs.

Meddaugh, Susan. Hog-Eye. 1998. (Illus.). 32p. (J). (gr. k-3). 6.95 (978-0-395-93746-4(9) , Walter Lorraine) Houghton Mifflin Co. Trade & Reference Div.

—Hog-Eye. Meddaugh, Susan, illus. 1998. (Illus.). 32p. (J). (ps-ps). lib. bdg. 14.10 (978-0-613-10513-2(3)) Tandem Library Bks.

The Midnight Pig, 6 vols., Pack. (Action Packs Ser.). 120p. (gr. 3-5). 44.00 (978-0-7635-8399-6(5)) Rigby Education.

Miller, Carol A. Maurice the Mole: Can You Guess Series. Miller, Carol A., illus. 2007. 24p. 18.95 (***978-0-9771641-3-4(6)***) Defiance In Print.

Miller, Edward. 3 Tales Retold & Illustrated: The Three Little Pigs, Goldilocks & the Three Bears, Three Billy Goats Gruff. Miller, Edward, illus. 2007. (Illus.). 48p. (J). (ps-2). 17.95 (978-0-8050-7916-6(5)) Holt, Henry & Co.

Milne, A. A. In Which Piglet Meets a Heffalump. Shepard, Ernest H., illus. unabr. ed. (Winnie-the-Pooh Ser.). (J). incl. audio (978-1-57375-014-1(X) , 70124) Audioscope.

Miranda, Anne. Neat Pete: A Pig's Tale. Callen, Liz, illus. 2002. 16p. (J). (978-0-439-35077-8(8)) Scholastic, Inc.

—Pignic. Hoffman, Rosekrans, illus. 2004. 32p. (J). pap. 7.95 (978-1-59078-328-3(X)) Boyds Mills Pr.

Modesitt, Jeanne. Mouse's Halloween Party. Spowart, Robin, illus. 2004. 32p. (J). (ps up). 13.95 (978-1-56397-950-7(0)) Boyds Mills Pr.

Moerbeck, Kees, illus. & des. Three Little Pigs. Moerbeck, Kees, des. 2006. 9.99 (978-1-84643-018-3(6)) Child's Play-International.

Moller, Linda. The Great Pig Escape. 2nd ed. 2003. (Illus.). 144p. (J). (gr. 3 up). pap. 7.95 (978-0-86278-667-0(3)) O'Brien Pr., Ltd., The IRL. *Dist:* Independent Pubs. Group.

Molly's Magic: Evaluation Guide. 2006. (J). (978-1-55942-417-2(6)) Marsh Media.

Moody-Luther, Jacqui. Word World Pig. 2005. NAp. 11.95 (978-0-7624-2464-1(8)) Running Pr. Bk. Pubs.

Moppet on the Run: Individual Title Six-Packs. 16p. (gr. 2 up). 35.00 (978-0-7635-9230-1(7)) Rigby Education.

Moreland, Marian H. & Moreland, Richard. Wee Three Kings. 1999. (Instant Christmas Pageant Ser.). 48p. (J). (gr. k-6). pap. 24.99 incl. audio compact disk (978-0-7644-2149-5(2)) Group Publishing, Inc.

Mr. Pig & Jumbo's Birthday Cake. 2004. (J). per. 15.99 (978-0-9744205-7-8(3)) Golden Eagle Publishing Hse., Inc.

Munsch, Robert. Pigs. Martchenko, Michael, illus. 2003. (Annikins Ser.: Vol. 14). 32p. (J). (ps-2). pap. 1.25 (978-1-55037-388-2(9)) Annick Pr., Ltd. CAN. *Dist:* Firefly Bks., Ltd.

Muntean, Michaela. Do Not Open This Book! Lemaitre, Pascal, illus. 2006. 40p. (J). (ps-3). pap. 16.99 (978-0-439-69839-9(1) , Scholastic Pr.) Scholastic, Inc.

Nanette. Oinky the Yellow Pig. 2004. (Life on Granny's Farm Ser.). (J). 12.95 (978-0-9741269-4-4(2)) St. Bernard Publishing, LLC.

Never Bring a Pigout Home. Date not set. 5.95 (978-0-89868-355-4(6)) ARO Publishing Co.

Newth, Rebecca. Tinkum's Dog. Primm, Thomas, illus. 2005. 32p. (J). 15.00 (***978-0-9630310-7-5(4)***) Will Hall Bks.

Norac, Carl. Monster, Don't Eat Me! Amado, Elisa, tr. from DUT. Cneut, Carll, illus. 2007. 32p. (J). (ps-1). 18.95 (978-0-88899-800-2(7)) Groundwood Bks. CAN. *Dist:* Perseus Distribution.

Numeroff, Laura Joffe. If You Give a Pig a Pancake. braille ed. 2004. (Illus.). (J). (gr. k-3). spiral bd. (978-0-616-07243-1(0)); spiral bd. (978-0-616-07244-8(9)) Canadian National Institute for the Blind/Institut National Canadien pour les Aveugles.

—If You Give a Pig a Pancake. Bond, Felicia, illus. (J). Date not set. 6.99 (978-0-694-01430-9(3)); 2000. 32p. pap., pap. 24.99 (978-0-06-443663-2(2) , Harper Trophy) HarperCollins Pubs.

—If You Give a Pig a Pancake. Mlawer, Teresa, tr. Bond, Felicia, illus. 1999. (Harper Arco Iris Ser.). (SPA.). 32p. (J). (ps-2). 16.99 (978-0-06-028316-2(5) , HC3165) HarperCollins Pubs.

—If You Give a Pig a Pancake. Bond, Felicia, illus. 1998. (If You Give... Ser.). 32p. (J). (ps-2). 15.99 (978-0-06-026686-8(4)); lib. bdg. 16.89 (978-0-06-026687-5(2)) HarperCollins Pubs. (Geringer, Laura Book).

—If You Give a Pig a Party. Bond, Felicia, illus. 2005. (If You Give... Ser.). 32p. (J). (ps-2). 15.99 (978-0-06-028326-1(2)); lib. bdg. 16.89 (978-0-06-028327-8(0)) HarperCollins Pubs. (Geringer, Laura Book).

—If You Give a Pig a Pumpkin: Book & Doll. Bond, Felicia, illus. Date not set. (J). 19.99 (978-0-694-01432-3(X)) HarperCollins Pubs.

—Pig Stroller Songs. Bond, Felicia, illus. Date not set. (J). 10.99 (978-0-694-01428-6(1)) HarperCollins Pubs.

—Si le haces una fiesta a una Cerdita. Bond, Felicia, illus. 2006. (If You Give... Ser.). (SPA.). 32p. (J). 15.99 (978-0-06-081532-5(9)) HarperCollins Pubs.

Numeroff, Laura Joffe & Bond, Felicia. If You Give a Pig a Pancake. 2000. (J). 11.98 incl. audio Random Hse. Audio Publishing Group.

Nurse Pig: New Heroes Backpack Story. 2002. (J). (978-1-931312-60-8(5)) SoftPlay, Inc.

Ohi, Ruth. The Couch Was a Castle. Ohi, Ruth, illus. 2006. (Ruth Ohi Picture Book Ser.). (Illus.). 24p. (J). (ps-1). pap. 5.95 (978-1-55451-013-9(9)); lib. bdg. 19.95 (978-1-55451-014-6(7)) Annick Pr., Ltd. CAN. *Dist:* Firefly Bks., Ltd.

Oke, Janette. This Little Pig. Munger, Nancy, illus. 2001. (Animal Friends Ser.: Vol. 4). 80p. (Orig.). (J). (ps-3). pap. 6.99 (978-0-7642-2448-5(4)) Bethany Hse. Pubs.

—This Little Pig. 2001. (Orig.). (gr. k-3). lib. bdg. 14.15 (978-0-613-85065-0(3)) Tandem Library Bks.

Old MacDonald's Pigs. 2002. 16p. (J). pap. 2.98 (978-0-7525-7062-4(5)) Parragon, Inc.

Once upon a Time Spanish Version-the Three Little Pigs. 2005. (J). (978-1-57022-565-9(6)) ECS Learning Systems, Inc.

Ondrias, Rachel. There's a Pig in my Fridge. Scarborough, Casey, illus. 2006. 28p. (J). 16.95 (***978-1-933660-30-1(9)*** , Tadpole Pr. 4 Kids) Smooth Sailing Pr.

Oxenbury, Helen. Pig Tale. Oxenbury, Helen, illus. 2005. (Illus.). 32p. (J). 16.95 (978-1-4169-0277-5(5) , McElderry, Margaret K.) Simon & Schuster Children's Publishing.

Paine, Walter. Cousin John: The Story of a Boy & A Small Smart Pig. 2006. 96p. 17.95 (978-1-59373-057-4(8)) Bunker Hill Publishing, Inc.

Palatini, Margie. Oink? Cole, Henry, illus. 2006. 40p. (J). (ps-3). 15.95 (978-0-689-86258-8(X)) Simon & Schuster Children's Publishing.

Pan, Hui-Mei. El Cochinito en Mi Bolsillo. Vernescu, Maritza, tr. from ENG. Pan, Hui-Mei, illus. 2004. (SPA., Illus.). 16p. (J). bds. 5.95 (978-1-932065-04-6(0) , 1-718-784-9112) Star Bright Bks., Inc.

—Piggy in My Pocket/el Cochinito en mi Bolsillo. Pan, Hui-Mei, illus. 2004. (ENG & SPA., Illus.). 16p. (J). bds. 5.95 (978-1-932065-11-4(3)) Star Bright Bks., Inc.

Pan, Hui-Mei, illus. Piggy in My Pocket. 2004. 16p. (J). bds. 5.95 (978-1-887734-96-7(1)) Star Bright Bks., Inc.

Paulson, Michael W. The Baker Street Bunch No. 1: A Double Mystery Book. l.t. ed. 2004. (Illus.). 154p. (J). per. (978-0-9754241-0-0(6)) MiMar Publishing.

—The Baker Street Bunch & the Missing Pig Mystery. l.t. ed. 2004. (Illus.). 90p. (J). per. 3.95 (978-0-9754241-1-7(4)) MiMar Publishing.

PC Treasures, prod. The Three Little Pigs. 2007. (J). (***978-1-60072-016-1(1)***) PC Treasures, Inc.

Penguin Books Staff, ed. The Three Little Pigs. (Fairy Tale Fun Ser.). (J). 3.95 (978-0-7214-5431-3(3) , Dutton Juvenile) Penguin Group (USA) Inc.

Peppe, Rodney. Three Little Pigs. 2000. pap. (978-0-688-17718-8(2)) HarperCollins Pubs.

Petach, Heidi. Wee Three Pigs. Petach, Heidi, illus. 2002. (Reading Railroad Bks.). (Illus.). 32p. (J). (ps-2). pap. 3.49 (978-0-448-42528-3(9) , Grosset & Dunlap) Penguin Group (USA) Inc.

—Wee Three Pigs. 2002. (gr. k-3). lib. bdg. 11.25 (978-0-613-71015-2(0)) Tandem Library Bks.

Petty, Colin, illus. The Three Little Pigs: A Tale about Working Hard. 2006. (J). 6.99 (978-1-59939-016-1(7)) Reader's Digest Young Families, Inc.

Pig in a Blanket. 2004. (J). per. (978-1-57657-517-8(9)) Paradise Pr., Inc.

Pig Wants to Play. 2002. (J). 4.98 (978-0-7525-7217-8(2)) Parragon, Inc.

Pig's Picnic. 2001. (ps-2). lib. bdg. 9.80 (978-0-613-32947-7(3)) Tandem Library Bks.

Pippa Pig's Dirty Day. 2002. (J). 5.98 (978-0-7525-8907-7(5)) Parragon, Inc.

Pittar, Gill. Milly, Molly & Betelgeuse (book W/dolls) 2006. 28p. pap. (978-1-86972-095-7(4)) Milly Molly Bks.

—Milly, Molly & Oink. 28p. 2006. pap. (978-1-86972-093-3(8)); 2004. (Illus.). (978-1-86972-002-5(4)) Milly Molly Bks.

Playland Staff. Playland Three Pigs Book. (J). 13.95 (978-0-698-12073-0(6)) Penguin Group (USA) Inc.

Polacco, Patricia. Ginger & Petunia. Polacco, Patricia, illus. 2007. (Illus.). 40p. (J). (ps-3). 16.99 (978-0-399-24539-8(1) , Philomel) Penguin Group (USA) Inc.

Polly Piglet's Surprise Party. 2002. (My First Tab Story Ser.). (J). bds. 3.98 (978-0-7525-8956-5(3)) Parragon, Inc.

Pooh & Piglet Snow Globe. 1999. (Winnie the Pooh Ser.). (J). (978-1-57082-891-1(1)) Mouse Works.

Poole, Jack. Las Primas de Loreto. 2000. (SPA.). 120p. (gr. 4-7). pap. 7.95 (978-1-58348-610-8(0)) iUniverse, Inc.

Portis, Antoinette. Not a Stick. 2008. 32p. (J). (ps-1). 14.89 (***978-0-06-112326-9(9)***) HarperCollins Pubs.

—Not Stick. 2008. 32p. (J). 12.99 (***978-0-06-112325-2(0)***) HarperCollins Pubs.

Potter, Beatrix. The Tale of Little Pig Robinson. 2002. (Illus.). 128p. (J). 6.99 (978-0-7232-4788-3(9) , Warne) Penguin Group (USA) Inc.

—The Tale of Pigling Bland. Potter, Beatrix, illus. 2002. (Illus.). (J). 15.23 (978-0-7587-3752-6(1)) Book Wholesalers, Inc.

—The Tale of Pigling Bland, Vol. 15. 2002. (Illus.). 88p. (J). 6.99 (978-0-7232-4784-5(6) , Warne) Penguin Group (USA) Inc.

Powell, Richard. Team Pig. Holt, Emma, illus. 2003. (Whizzy Wheels Bks.). 20p. (J). bds. 4.95 (978-0-7641-5586-4(5)) Barron's Educational Series, Inc.

Prap, Lila. 1001 Stories. Prap, Lila, illus. 2006. (Illus.). 32p. (J). 15.95 (978-1-929132-92-8(1)) Kane/Miller Bk. Pubs., Inc.

Price, Mathew. Este Cerdito. (SPA.). pap. 3.95 (978-950-07-2058-8(2)) Editorial Sudamericana S.A. ARG. *Dist:* Distribooks, Inc.

Puttock, Simon & Bartlett, Alison. Pig's Digger. 2002. (Illus.). 32p. (J). pap. 8.99 (978-1-4052-0231-2(9)) Egmont Bks., Ltd. GBR. *Dist:* Independent Pubs. Group.

Quednau, Marion. The Gift of Odin. Mulabdic, Sonja, illus. 2007. 192p. (J). (gr. 4-6). 19.95 (***978-1-55451-076-4(7)***); pap. 9.95 (***978-1-55451-075-7(9)***) Annick Pr., Ltd. CAN. *Dist:* Firefly Bks., Ltd.

R. Friend -Panic in the PigPen. 2007. (J). per. (***978-0-9743627-7-9(8)***) Sunflower Seeds Pr.

Rabe, Tish. Pigs of a Feather. 1998. (J). 7.99 (978-0-679-89089-8(0) , Random Hse. Bks. for Young Readers) Random Hse. Children's Bks.

Ransom, Jeanie Franz. Don't Squeal Unless It's a Big Deal: A Tale of Tattletales. Urbanovic, Jackie, illus. 2005. 32p. (J). 14.95 (978-1-59147-239-1(3)); pap. 8.95 (978-1-59147-240-7(7)) American Psychological Assn. (Magination Pr.).

Reider, Katja. Rosalie & Truffle; A Story of Love. Bucker, Jutta, illus. 2005. (ENG & GER.). 64p. (ps-3). 9.95 (978-0-8109-5984-2(4)) Abrams, Harry N. , Inc.

Rettore, Kenny E. & Rettore, A. S. Cow & Pig. Lyly, Olivia, illus. 2004. (Stroller Softies Ser.). 12p. (J). 11.95 (978-0-7641-7768-2(0)) Barron's Educational Series, Inc.

Richardson, John. Grunt. Rogers, Emma, illus. 2002. 32p. (J). (gr. k-3). 15.00 (978-0-618-15974-1(6) , Clarion Bks.) Houghton Mifflin Co. Trade & Reference Div.

Rigamonti, Justin. The Pigs Went Marching Out! Thatch, Nancy R., ed. Rigamonti, Justin, illus. 1998. (Books for Students by Students). (Illus.). 29p. (J). (ps-3). lib. bdg. 15.95 (978-0-933849-70-9(2)) Landmark Editions, Inc.

Rigby Education Staff. Goodness Me, Mr. Magee! (Sails Literacy Ser.). (Illus.). 16p. (gr. 1-2). 27.00 (978-0-7635-9904-1(2) , 699042C99) Rigby Education.

—The Three Little Pigs. (Illus.). 16p. (J). pap. 30.00 (978-0-7635-6442-1(7) , 764427C99) Rigby Education.

Rius, Maria, illus. Los Tres Cerditos / the Three Little Pigs. 2006. (Bilingual Tales Ser.). 24p. (J). pap. 3.99 (978-0-439-77382-9(2) , Scholastic en Espanol) Scholastic, Inc.

Rius, Roser. The Three Little Pigs. 1998. (Fairy Tale Theater Ser.). (Illus.). 32p. (J). (gr. k-3). pap. 8.95 (978-0-7641-5115-6(0)) Barron's Educational Series, Inc.

Rizzati, Lorella. Pig. 2001. (Portable Pets Ser.). (Illus.). 12p. (J). (ps-ps). bds. 6.95 (978-0-8109-5689-6(6)) Abrams, Harry N. , Inc.

Rock, Brian. Piggies. Hudnall, Kate, illus. 2005. 32p. (J). (ps-3). 14.99 (978-0-9754411-1-4(6)) First Light Publishing.

Roddie, Shen. Simon Says. Lambert, Sally Anne, illus. 32p. (J). (ps-3). 2001. pap. 8.99 (978-0-7112-1532-0(4)); 2000. 19.99 (978-0-7112-1529-0(4)) Lincoln, Frances Ltd. GBR. *Dist:* Transition Vendor, Antique Collectors' Club.

Roddie, Shen & Lambert, Sally Ann. Simon Says. 2004. (Illus.). 32p. (J). pap. 7.95 (978-1-84507-233-9(2)) Lincoln, Frances Ltd. GBR. *Dist:* Perseus Distribution.

Roots, Robert. Prepararse para el Lobo: Los secretos del exito a partir de Los Tres Cerditos. 2005. (SPA.). (YA). (978-0-9715336-2-2(8)) Roots, Robert.

Rosen, Michael & Langley, Jonathan. Ow. 2005. (Illus.). 32p. (J). pap. 9.99 (978-0-00-712443-5(0)) HarperCollins Pubs. Ltd. GBR. *Dist:* Trafalgar Square Publishing.

Rosie & Roger. 2002. (Illus.). 32p. (J). 16.95 (978-1-931290-09-8(1)) Tallfellow Pr.

Rosie's House, 6, Pack. (Literatura 2000 Ser.). (gr. 2-3). 33.00 (978-0-7635-0237-9(5)) Rigby Education.

Rusackas, Francesca. Daddy All Day Long. Burris, Priscilla, tr. Burris, Priscilla, illus. 2004. 32p. (J). (ps-k). lib. bdg. 13.89 (978-0-06-050285-0(1)) HarperCollins Pubs.

—I Love You All Day Long. Burris, Priscilla, illus. 32p. (J). (ps-k). 2002. 12.99 (978-0-06-050276-8(2)); 2004. reprint ed. pap. 6.99 (978-0-06-050278-2(9), Harper Trophy) HarperCollins Pubs.

Rylant, Cynthia. Poppleton. Teague, Mark, illus. 2002. (Poppleton Ser.). (J). 11.91 (978-0-7587-1590-6(0)) Book Wholesalers, Inc.

—Poppleton & Friends. Teague, Mark, illus. 1998. (Poppleton Ser.). 56p. (J). (gr. k-3). pap. 3.99 (978-0-590-84788-9(0), Blue Sky Pr., The) Scholastic, Inc.

—Poppleton & Friends. 1998. (Poppleton Ser.). (J). (gr. k-3). (978-0-606-13716-4(5)) Tandem Library Bks.

—Poppleton Display. 1999. (J). 95.76 (978-0-439-05990-9(9)) Scholastic, Inc.

—Poppleton Everyday. Teague, Mark, illus. 2002. (Poppleton Ser.). (J). 11.91 (978-0-7587-1586-9(2)) Book Wholesalers, Inc.

—Poppleton Everyday. Teague, Mark, illus. 1998. (Poppleton Ser.). (J). (gr. k-3). 48p. pap. 15.95 (978-0-590-84845-9(3), Blue Sky Pr., The); 56p. pap. 3.99 (978-0-590-84853-4(4)) Scholastic, Inc.

—Poppleton Everyday. 1998. (Poppleton Ser.). (J). (gr. k-3). (978-0-606-13717-1(3)) Tandem Library Bks.

—Poppleton Forever. Teague, Mark, illus. 2002. (Poppleton Ser.). (J). 11.91 (978-0-7587-1587-6(0)) Book Wholesalers, Inc.

—Poppleton Forever. Teague, Mark, illus. 1998. (Poppleton Ser.). 56p. (J). (gr. k-3). pap. 14.95 (978-0-590-84843-5(7), Blue Sky Pr., The); pap. 3.99 (978-0-590-84844-2(5)) Scholastic, Inc.

—Poppleton Forever. 1998. (Poppleton Ser.). (J). (gr. k-3). (978-0-606-13718-8(1)) Tandem Library Bks.

—Poppleton Forever. Teague, Mark, illus. 1998. (Poppleton Ser.). 48p. (J). (ps). lib. bdg. 11.80 (978-0-613-11990-0(8)) Tandem Library Bks.

—Poppleton Has Fun. Teague, Mark, illus. 2002. (Poppleton Ser.). (J). 11.91 (978-0-7587-6242-9(9)) Book Wholesalers, Inc.

—Poppleton Has Fun. Teague, Mark, illus. 2000. (Poppleton Ser.). 56p. (J). (gr. k-3). pap. 15.95 (978-0-590-84839-8(9)) Scholastic, Inc.

—Poppleton Has Fun. 2000. (Poppleton Ser.). (J). (gr. k-3). (978-0-606-19603-1(X)) Tandem Library Bks.

—Poppleton in Fall. Teague, Mark, illus. 2002. (Poppleton Ser.). (J). 11.91 (978-0-7587-1588-3(9)) Book Wholesalers, Inc.

—Poppleton in Fall. Teague, Mark, illus. 1999. (Poppleton Ser.). 56p. (J). (gr. k-3). pap. 14.95 (978-0-590-84789-6(9), Blue Sky Pr., The) Scholastic, Inc.

—Poppleton in Fall. 1999. (Poppleton Ser.). (J). (gr. k-3). (978-0-606-17273-8(4)) Tandem Library Bks.

—Poppleton in Spring. Teague, Mark, illus. 2002. (Poppleton Ser.). (J). 11.91 (978-0-7587-1589-0(7)) Book Wholesalers, Inc.

—Poppleton in Spring. Teague, Mark, illus. 1999. (Poppleton Ser.). 48p. (J). (ps-2). pap. 15.95 (978-0-590-84818-3(6), Blue Sky Pr., The) Scholastic, Inc.

—Poppleton in Spring. 1999. (Poppleton Ser.). (J). (gr. k-3). (978-0-606-16594-5(0)) Tandem Library Bks.

—Poppleton in Winter. Teague, Mark, illus. 2002. (Poppleton Ser.). (J). 11.91 (978-0-7587-6873-5(7)) Book Wholesalers, Inc.

—Poppleton in Winter. Teague, Mark, illus. 2001. (Poppleton Ser.). 58p. (J). (ps-2). pap. 15.95 (978-0-590-84837-4(2), Blue Sky Pr., The) Scholastic, Inc.

Saltzberg, Barney. Cornelius P. Mud, Are You Ready for Bed? Saltzberg, Barney, illus. (Illus.). (J). (gr. k-ps). 2007. 26p. bds. 6.99 (978-0-7636-3303-5(8)); 2005. 32p. 15.99 (978-0-7636-2399-9(7)) Candlewick Pr.

—Cornelius P. Mud, Are You Ready for School? Saltzberg, Barney, illus. 2007. (Illus.). 32p. (J). (ps-k). 15.99 (978-0-7636-2913-7(8)) Candlewick Pr.

Santillo, LuAnn. The Pig. Santillo, LuAnn, ed. 2003. (Half-Pint Kids Readers Ser.). (Illus.). 7p. (J). (ps-1). pap. (978-1-59256-064-6(4)) Half-Pint Kids, Inc.

Santore, Charles. Three Hungry Pigs & the Wolf Who Came to Dinner. 2005. (Illus.). 32p. (J). (ps-3). 16.95 (978-0-375-82946-8(6)); lib. bdg. 18.99 (978-0-375-92946-5(0)) Random Hse. Children's Bks. (Random Hse. Bks. for Young Readers).

Sargent, Dave & Sargent, Pat. Lennie Leopard: Making New Friends, 56 vols., 50. Lenoir, Jane, illus. 2001. (Animal Pride Ser.: Vol. 50). 36p. (J). lib. bdg. 19.95 (978-1-56763-543-0(1)) Ozark Publishing.

—Robbie Razorback: Meanie! Meanie!, 56 vols., 35. Huff, Jeane, illus. 2001. (Animal Pride Ser.: 35). 36p. (J). lib. bdg. 19.95 (978-1-56763-386-3(2)) Ozark Publishing.

Sargent, Dave, et al. Lennie Leopard: Making New Friends, 17, 50. 2000. (Animal Pride Ser.). (Illus.). 42p. (J). pap. 6.95 (978-1-56763-544-7(X)) Ozark Publishing.

Schami, Rafik. Alberto Y Lila. 2002. (SPA.). (gr. k-3). lib. bdg. 15.25 (978-0-613-51103-2(4)) Tandem Library Bks.

Scheunemann, Pam. Pig Pens. Nobens, C. A., illus. 2006. (Fact & Fiction Ser.). 24p. (J). 21.35 (978-1-59679-959-2(5), SandCastle); pap. (978-1-59679-960-8(9)) ABDO Publishing Co.

Schindel, John. Busy Piggies. Holt, Steven, illus. Holt, Steven, photos by. 2006. 20p. (J). bds. 6.95 (978-1-58246-169-4(4), Tricycle Pr.) Ten Speed Pr.

Scholastic, Inc. Staff & Berg, Michelle. This Little Piggy: A Hand-Puppet Board Book. 2007. (Little Scholastic Ser.). 6p. (J). bds. 12.99 ***(978-0-545-03038-0(2))*** Scholastic, Inc.

School Specialty Publishing. The Three Little Pigs. Elena, Horacio, illus. 2007. 22p. (J). (ps-k). bds. 12.95 ***(978-0-7696-5268-9(9)***, Gingham Dog Pr.) School Specialty Publishing.

School Zone Publishing Company Staff & Hoenecke, Karen. Poor Polly Pig. 2000. (Start to Read Board Bks.). (Illus.). 10p. (J). (ps-k). bds. 4.99 (978-0-88743-812-7(1), 06814) School Zone Publishing Co.

Scieszka, Jon. The True Story of the 3 Little Pigs. 2002. (Illus.). (J). 14.04 (978-0-7587-5387-8(X)) Book Wholesalers, Inc.

Seibert, Patricia. The Three Little Pigs. Elena, Horacio, illus. 2002. (Brighter Child Keepsake Stories Ser.). 32p. (J). (ps-3). pap. 3.99 (978-1-57768-367-4(6), Brighter Child) School Specialty Publishing.

—The Three Little Pigs: Los tres Cerditos. 2005. (Dual Language Keepsake Stories Ser.). (SPA & ENG., Illus.). 32p. (J). (gr. k-3). pap. 3.99 (978-0-7696-3818-8(X), Brighter Child) School Specialty Publishing.

Seltzer, Eric. Doodle Dog. ed. 2005. (Illus.). 32p. (J). lib. bdg. 15.00 (978-1-59054-979-7(1)) Fitzgerald Bks.

Selway, Martina, illus. Clean Out the Fridge, Fred! 1999. (J). (978-0-7608-3199-1(8)) Sundance/Newbridge Educational Publishing.

—Fred Fixes a Faucet. 1999. (J). (978-0-7608-3193-9(9)) Sundance/Newbridge Educational Publishing.

—Something Nasty! 1999. (J). (978-0-7608-3198-4(X)) Sundance/Newbridge Educational Publishing.

—The Visitor. 1999. (J). (978-0-7608-3194-6(7)) Sundance/Newbridge Educational Publishing.

—What's That? 1999. (J). (978-0-7608-3195-3(5)) Sundance/Newbridge Educational Publishing.

Sendak, Maurice. Higglety Pigglety Pop! Or There Must Be More to Life. Sendak, Maurice, illus. 2001. (Sendak Reissues Ser.). (Illus.). 80p. (J). (ps-3). 16.95 (978-0-06-028479-4(X)) HarperCollins Pubs.

Shipton, Paul. The Pig Scrolls. (J). (gr. 5-9). 2007. (Illus.). 304p. 6.99 ***(978-0-7636-3302-8(X));*** 2005. 288p. 15.99 (978-0-7636-2702-7(X)) Candlewick Pr.

—The Pig Who Saved the World. 2007. (Illus.). 272p. (J). (gr. 5-9). 15.99 ***(978-0-7636-3446-9(8))*** Candlewick Pr.

Shulman, Mark. Some Pigs. Nguyen, Vincent, illus. 2003. (Some Animals Ser.). 24p. (J). 5.95 (978-0-7641-5651-9(9)) Barron's Educational Series, Inc.

Simon, Charnan. A Greedy Little Pig. Ramsey, Marcy Dunn, illus. 2006. (Magic Door to Learning Ser.). 24p. (J). (gr. 1-3). 21.36 (978-1-59296-622-6(5)) Child's World, Inc.

Simpson, Patrica Ann. Flick the little Runt. 2006. (J). lib. bdg. (978-0-9779662-6-4(7)) Creative Bk. Pubs.

Slater, Teddy. Pigs in Love. Boyd, Aaron, illus. 2005. (Cuddle & Read Ser.). 24p. (J). (ps-ps). 6.95 (978-1-4027-1986-8(8)) Sterling Publishing Co., Inc.

Sleator, William. Interstellar Pig. 196p. (J). (gr. 4-6). pap. 4.99 (978-0-8072-1381-0(0), Listening Library) Random Hse. Audio Publishing Group.

Smith, Jeffrey B. Stubby. 2006. 15p. 8.28 (978-1-4116-8215-3(7)) Lulu.com.

Sollinger, Emily. Find the Sheep, Piggley! A Jakers! Counting Book. Entara Ltd. Staff, photos by. 2006. (Jakers! Ser.). 14p. (J). 7.99 (978-1-4169-0613-1(4), Simon Spotlight) Simon & Schuster Children's Publishing.

Sommer, Carl. Three Little Pigs Read-along, 1 bk. 2003. (Another Sommer-Time Story Ser.). (Illus.). 48p. (J). lib. bdg. 23.95 incl. audio compact disk (978-1-57537-711-7(X)) Advance Publishing, Inc.

—Three Little Pigs Read-Along. 2003. (Another Sommer-Time Story Ser.). (Illus.). 48p. (J). lib. bdg. 23.95 incl. audio (978-1-57537-761-2(6)) Advance Publishing, Inc.

Soundprints. This Little Piggy & Other Favorites. (Meet Mother Goose Ser.). (Illus.). 36p. (J). 2005. bds. 10.95 incl. audio compact disk (978-1-931465-27-4(4), MD1103); 2002. bds. 8.95 (978-1-931465-21-2(5), Little Soundprints) Soundprints.

Spaht-Gill, Janie. Pigouts. Reese, Bob, illus. 1998. 24p. (J). (ps-3). 5.95 (978-0-89868-317-2(3)) ARO Publishing Co.

Spelman, Cornelia Maude. When I Feel Good about Myself. Parkinson, Kathy, illus. 2003. (Way I Feel Bks.). 24p. (J). (ps-1). pap. 6.95 (978-0-8075-8901-4(2)) Whitman, Albert & Co.

—When I Miss You. Parkinson, Kathy, illus. 2006. (Way I Feel Ser.). 24p. (J). 6.95 (978-0-8075-8903-8(9)) Whitman, Albert & Co.

Spinelli, Eileen. Six Hogs on a Scooter. Nash, Scott, illus. 2000. 40p. (J). (gr. k-4). 16.99 (978-0-531-33212-2(8)); pap. 15.95 (978-0-531-30212-5(1)) Scholastic, Inc. (Orchard Bks.).

Steig, William. Roland the Minstrel Pig. 1999. 32p. (J). (ps-1). pap. 4.95 (978-0-06-443346-4(3)) HarperCollins Pubs.

Stein, Erin K. Peppa Pig: Family Fun Reusable Sticker Book. 2007. (Peppa Pig Ser.). 12p. (J). pap. 6.99 ***(978-0-06-117373-8(8)***, Harper Entertainment) HarperCollins Pubs.

—Peppa Pig: Paint Book. 2007. (Peppa Pig Ser.). 32p. (J). pap. 4.99 ***(978-0-06-117376-9(2)***, Harper Entertainment) HarperCollins Pubs.

Sterling Publishing Co., Inc. & Fernleigh Books Staff. Step Inside ... the Three Little Pigs: A Magic 3-Dimensional Fairy-Tale World. 2006. (Step Inside Ser.). (Illus.). 12p. (J). 9.95 (978-1-4027-3652-0(5)) Sterling Publishing Co., Inc.

Stevenson, James. No Laughing, No Smiling, No Giggling: Is That Understood? 2004. (Illus.). 32p. (J). 16.00 (978-0-374-31829-1(8), Farrar, Straus & Giroux (BYR)) Farrar, Straus & Giroux.

Stevenson, Peter, illus. The Three Little Pigs. 1999. (Finger Puppet Theater Bks.). 16p. (J). (ps-1). pap. 14.95 (978-0-439-04372-4(7), Cartwheel Bks.) Scholastic, Inc.

Stewart, Dana. God Made My Guinea Pigs. Stewart, Jennifer, ed. Haantz, Carol, illus. 1999. (Tall Shape Board Bks.). 10p. (J). (ps-1). bds. 4.99 (978-0-7847-0964-1(5), 04304, Bean Sprouts) Standard Publishing.

Stolz, Mary. Emmett's Birthday Pig. 32p. (J). (ps-2). Date not set. pap. 5.99 (978-0-06-443633-5(0)); 2003. (Illus.). 16.89 (978-0-06-028747-4(0)) HarperCollins Pubs.

Storad, Conrad J. Don't Ever Cross That Road! An Armadillo Story. Jensen, Nathaniel P., illus. 2003. (Sonoran Desert Tails Ser.). 32p. (J). (gr. k-4). 15.95 (978-1-891795-08-4(2)) RGU Group, The.

Sturges, Philemon. This Little Pirate. Walrod, Amy, illus. 2007. 40p. (J). (ps). pap. 6.99 (978-0-14-240850-6(6), Puffin) Penguin Group (USA) Inc.

Teague, Mark. El Chiquero. 2002. (SPA., Illus.). 32p. (J). (gr. k-2). pap. 5.99 (978-0-439-27000-7(6), SO30911, Scholastic en Espanol) Scholastic, Inc.

—Pigsty. Teague, Mark, illus. 2002. (Illus.). (J). 24.00 (978-0-7587-3417-4(4)) Book Wholesalers, Inc.

—Pigsty. 2004. (Scholastic Bookshelf Ser.). 32p. (J). pap. 6.99 (978-0-439-59843-9(5), Scholastic Paperbacks) Scholastic, Inc.

Teague, Mark. Pigsty Library. 2007. (J). 18.95 ***(*978-0-545-00419-0(5))*** Scholastic, Inc.

Ted in a Red Bed Kid Kit. (Kid Kits Ser.). (Illus.). 10p. (J). 11.95 (978-1-58086-416-9(3)); 2004. bds. 9.95 (978-1-58086-404-6(X)) EDC Publishing.

Tekavec, Heather. What's That Awful Smell? Margaret, Spengler, illus. 2006. 32p. (J). pap. 5.99 (978-0-14-240586-4(8), Puffin) Penguin Group (USA) Inc.

—What's That Awful Smell? Spengler, Margaret, illus. 2004. 32p. (J). (gr. k-3). 15.99 (978-0-8037-2660-4(0), Dial) Penguin Group (USA) Inc.

Thaler, Mike. Pig Little. Miglio, Paige, illus. rev. ed. 2006. 32p. (J). 16.95 (978-0-8050-6977-8(1), Holt, Henry & Co. Bks. For Young Readers) Holt, Henry & Co.

The White Stone Co. Peter Pig Likes to Dig. 1998. (ENG., Illus.). 28p. (J). (gr. 1-2). 7.95 (978-1-880122-05-1(7), Little Shepherd Bks.) White Stone Co., The.

Thiesing, Lisa. All Better. 2000. (Road to Reading Ser.). (Illus.). (J). 10.79 (978-0-606-20539-9(X)) Tandem Library Bks.

—The Scarecrow's New Clothes. Thiesing, Lisa, illus. 2006. (Illus.). 32p. (J). (ps-2). 13.99 (978-0-525-47750-1(0), Dutton Juvenile) Penguin Group (USA) Inc.

This Little Piggy. 2002. (Illus.). (J). bds. (978-1-59069-260-8(8), MS1001) Studio Mouse LLC.

This Little Piggy Kid Kit. (Illus.). 16p. (J). (ps up). 12.95 (978-1-58086-445-9(7)) EDC Publishing.

The Three Little Pigs. 2002. (Puppy Tales Ser.). (Illus.). 24p. (J). (gr. k-3). 1.49 (978-1-57759-221-1(2)) Dalmatian Pr.

The Three Little Pigs. 2001. (SPA., Illus.). 32p. 6.95 (978-0-9727833-2-3(6)) Really Big Coloring Bks., Inc.

The Three Little Pigs. (Read-Along Ser.). (J). 7.99 incl. audio (978-1-55723-015-7(3)) Walt Disney Records.

The Three Little Pigs. 2004. 24.95 incl. audio (978-1-56008-040-4(X)); pap. 32.75 incl. audio (978-1-55592-323-5(2)); pap. 32.75 incl. audio (978-1-55592-324-2(0)); pap. 14.95 incl. audio (978-0-7882-0689-4(3)); pap. 14.95 incl. audio (978-0-7882-0486-9(6)) Weston Woods Studios, Inc.

Three Little Pigs. 2005. (J). bds. 3.99 (978-1-933200-13-2(8)) Family Bks. at Home.

The Three Little Pigs: Lap Book. (Pebble Soup Explorations Ser.). 16p. (ps up). 21.00 (978-0-7578-2111-0(1)) Rigby Education.

The Three Little Pigs: Small Book. (Pebble Soup Explorations Ser.). 16p. (ps up). 5.00 (978-0-7578-2112-7(X)) Rigby Education.

Toast, Sarah & Milne, A. A. Piglet's Not So Small Snowball. Williams, Don, illus. 2002. (Disney's Winnie the Pooh Ser.). (J). (978-0-7853-7617-0(8)) Publications International, Ltd.

Toms, Kate. Funny Faces Cloth Books: Digger Pig. 2006. (Funny Faces (Make Believe Ideas) Ser.). (Illus.). 4p. (ps). 8.95 (978-1-84610-288-2(X)) Make Believe Ideas GBR. *Dist:* Ingram Pub. Services.

The Travels of Jimm Pigg. 2001. 32p. (J). per. 9.95 (978-0-9713900-0-3(2)) Hynes Enterprises, Inc.

I Tre Porcellini. 1999. Tr. of Three Little Pigs. (ITA., Illus.). 24p. (J). (ps-5). pap. 7.95 (978-88-8148-255-9(X)) European Language Institute ITA. *Dist:* Distribooks, Inc., Midwest European Pubns.

Los Tres Cerditos. 2nd ed. 2002. (Troquelados Clasicos Ser.). (ENG & SPA., Illus.). 16p. pap. 2.95 (978-84-7864-326-4(5)) Combel Editorial, S.A. ESP. *Dist:* Independent Pubs. Group.

Los Tres Cerditos. (Coleccion Pequenos Clasicos). (SPA.). (J). (gr. k-3). pap. (978-84-246-2534-4(X), GL5617) La Galera, S.A. Editorial ESP. *Dist:* Lectorum Pubns., Inc.

Los tres Cerditos: Lap Book. (Pebble Soup Exploraciones Ser.). (SPA.). 16p. (ps up). 21.00 (978-0-7578-1674-1(6)) Rigby Education.

Los tres Cerditos: Small Book. (Pebble Soup Exploraciones Ser.). (SPA.). 16p. (ps up). 5.00 (978-0-7578-1714-4(9)) Rigby Education.

Los Tres Cochinitos. 2001. (SPA.). (978-968-6347-33-3(X)) Larousse, Ediciones, S. A. de C. V.

Trivizas, Eugene. The Three Little Wolves & the Big Bad Pig: A Pop-up Storybook. Oxenbury, Helen, illus. 2006. 16p. (J). (gr. k-4). reprint ed. 27.00 (978-0-7567-9913-7(9)) DIANE Publishing Co.

—The Three Little Wolves & the Big Bad Pig: A Pop-Up Storybook with a Twist in the Tale! Oxenbury, Helen, illus. 2004. 16p. (J). 24.95 (978-1-4052-0669-3(1)) Egmont Bks., Ltd. GBR. *Dist:* Trafalgar Square Publishing.

—Los Tres Lobitos y el Cochino Feroz. Oxenbury, Helen, illus. 2003. (SPA.). 32p. (J). (gr. k-3). pap. 12.99 (978-980-257-246-5(2), EK1366) Ekare, Ediciones VEN. *Dist:* Kane/Miller Bk. Pubs., Inc., Lectorum Pubns., Inc.

Les Trois Petits Cochons.Tr. of Three Little Pigs. (FRE.). 48p. (J). pap. 12.95 incl. audio compact disk (978-2-89558-053-9(7)) Coffragants CAN. *Dist:* Penton Overseas, Inc.

Les Trois Petits Cochons. (Musicontes Ser.).Tr. of Three Little Pigs. (FRE.). (J). 24.95 incl. audio (978-2-09-230469-3(0)); 2000. (Illus.). 32p. 13.95 (978-2-09-202103-3(6)) Nathan, Fernand FRA. *Dist:* Distribooks, Inc.

Tudor, Tasha. Dorcus Porkus. 1998. (Illus.). 42p. (J). 6.95 (978-0-446-91247-1(6)) Grand Central Publishing.

Two naughty Piglets. 2006. (J). per. 3.99 (978-1-934004-17-3(0)) Byeway Bks.

Tyler, Jenny. Big Pig on a Dig. Cartwright, Stephen, illus. 2004. (Easy Words to Read Ser.). 16p. (J). (gr. 1 up). pap. 6.99 (978-0-7460-3021-9(5)) EDC Publishing.

—Big Pig on a Dig. 1999. (J). (978-1-58086-182-3(2)) EDC Publishing.

Tyrrell, Melissa. The Three Little Pigs. 1998. (Fairytale Friends Ser.: Vol. 4). (Illus.). 12p. (J). (ps up). bds. 5.95 (978-1-58117-017-7(3), Intervisual/Piggy Toes) Dalmatian Pr.

Uncle Markie. Piglette & BoBo Do Tokyo. l.t. ed. 2002. 28p. 9.95 (978-0-9633943-7-8(1)) Studio 403.

—Piglette & BoBo See Hong Kong. l.t. ed. 2002. 46p. ring bd. 9.95 (978-0-9633943-8-5(X)) Studio 403.

—Piglette Goes Hawaiian. l.t. ed. 2001. 56p. ring bd. 9.95 (978-0-9633943-3-0(9)) Studio 403.

—Piglette Goes to Argentina. l.t. ed. 2001. 66p. ring bd. (978-0-9633943-1-6(2)) Studio 403.

—Piglette Goes to Northern California. l.t. ed. 2001. 36p. (978-0-9633943-2-3(0)) Studio 403.

—Piglette Takes the Concorde! l.t. ed. 2002. 56p. ring bd. 9.95 (978-0-9633943-4-7(7)) Studio 403.

Ungerer, Tomi. Christmas Eve at the Mellops' Ungerer, Tomi, illus. 1998. (Illus.). 32p. (J). (gr. k-4). pap. 5.95 (978-1-57098-227-9(9)) Rinehart, Roberts Pubs.

—The Mellops Go Spelunking. Ungerer, Tomi, illus. 1998. (Illus.). 32p. (J). (gr. k-4). pap. 5.95 (978-1-57098-228-6(7)) Rinehart, Roberts Pubs.

—The Mellops Strike Oil. Ungerer, Tomi, illus. 1999. (Illus.). 32p. (J). (ps-4). reprint ed. pap. 5.95 (978-1-57098-284-2(8)) Rinehart, Roberts Pubs.

Uwe, Timm. Rennschwein Rudi Russel. (GER.). pap. 16.95 (978-3-423-70285-0(0)) Deutscher Taschenbuch Verlag GmbH & Co KG DEU. *Dist:* Distribooks, Inc.

Van Genechten, Guido. Alex & the Tart. 2005. (Illus.). 32p. (J). (ps). 6.95 (978-1-58925-393-3(0), tiger tales) ME Media LLC.

Van Leeuwen, Jean. Amanda Pig & Her Best Friend Lollipop. Schweninger, Ann, illus. 2000. (Puffin-Easy-to-Read Ser.). 48p. (J). (ps-3). pap. 3.99 (978-0-14-037999-0(1), Puffin) Penguin Group (USA) Inc.

—Amanda Pig & Her Best Friend Lollipop. 2000. (gr. k-3). lib. bdg. 11.80 (978-0-613-28401-1(1)); (Illus.). (J). 10.79 (978-0-606-18832-6(0)) Tandem Library Bks.

—Amanda Pig & Her Big Brother Oliver. Schweninger, Ann, illus. (Oliver Pig Ser.). 56p. (J). (gr. k-2). pap. 3.99 (978-0-8072-1341-4(1), Listening Library) Random Hse. Audio Publishing Group.

—Amanda Pig & the Awful, Scary Monster. Schweninger, Ann, illus. 2003. (Easy-to-Read Ser.: Vol. 2). 48p. (J). (ps). 13.99 (978-0-8037-2766-3(6), Dial) Penguin Group (USA) Inc.

—Amanda Pig & the Really Hot Day. Schweninger, Ann, illus. 2007. 48p. (J). pap. 3.99 (978-0-14-240775-2(5), Puffin) Penguin Group (USA) Inc.

—Amanda Pig & the Wiggly Tooth. Schweninger, Ann, illus. 2008. 40p. (J). (ps). 14.99 (978-0-8037-3104-2(3), Dial) Penguin Group (USA) Inc.

—Amanda Pig, First Grader. Schweninger, Ann, illus. 2007. 40p. (J). (ps-1). 14.99 (978-0-8037-3181-3(7), Dial) Penguin Group (USA) Inc.

—Amanda Pig, School Girl. Schweninger, Ann, illus. 1999. (Puffin Easy-to-Read Program Ser.). 48p. (J). (gr. k-3). pap. 3.99 (978 0 14 130357-4(3), Puffin) Penguin Group (USA) Inc.

—Amanda Pig, School Girl. 1999. (ps-2). lib. bdg. 11.80 (978-0-613-19333-7(4)) Tandem Library Bks.

—Amanda Pig, Schoolgirl. 1999. (Puffin Easy-to-Read Ser.). (J). 10.79 (978-0-606-16779-6(X)) Tandem Library Bks.

—Oliver & Albert, Best Friends Forever. Schweninger, Ann, illus. 2002. (Easy-to-Read Ser.). 48p. (J). pap. 3.99 (978-0-14-230084-8(5), Puffin) Penguin Group (USA) Inc.

—Oliver Pig & the Best Fort Ever. Schweninger, Ann, illus. 2006. 40p. (J). (ps). 15.99 (978-0-8037-2888-2(3), Dial) Penguin Group (USA) Inc.

—Oliver the Mighty Pig, Level. 2. Schweninger, Ann, illus. 2004. (Easy-to-Read Ser.). 48p. (J). (gr. k-3). 14.99 (978-0-8037-2886-8(7), Dial) Penguin Group (USA) Inc.

—Tales of Oliver Pig. Schweninger, Ann, illus. (Oliver Pig Ser.). 64p. (J). (gr. k-2). pap. 3.99 (978-0-8072-1334-6(9), Listening Library) Random Hse. Audio Publishing Group.

Van Leeuwen, Jean & Van Leeuwen, Jean. Amanda Pig & the Really Hot Day. Schweninger, Ann, illus. 2005. (Easy-to-Read, Dial Ser.). 48p. (J). (ps-ps). 14.99 (978-0-8037-2887-5(5), Dial) Penguin Group (USA) Inc.

Vaughan, Christina. The Fattest Pig. 2000. (Illus.). 32p. (J). (gr. 1-5). spiral bd. 18.95 (978-0-9641697-9-1(7), You-Draw-It Bks.) Castlebrook Pubns.

—There's a Pig in the Firehouse! 2000. 32p. (J). (gr. 1-5). spiral bd. 18.95 (978-0-9641697-8-4(9), You-Draw-It Bks.) Castlebrook Pubns.

Victoria. Confessions of a Pot Bellied Pig. 2002. 96p. pap. (978-0-9688648-8-3(0)) Parkhurst Publishing, Ltd.

Villanueva Leonard. Hungry Puaa. 2005. 24p. 14.95 (978-1-933067-14-8(4)) Mutual Publishing LLC.

P Q R

Vischer, Phil. Sidney & Norman: A Tale of Two Pigs. Gerard, Justin, illus. 2006. 48p. (J). 15.99 (978-1-4003-0834-7(8)) Nelson, Thomas Inc.

von Konigslow, Andrea Wayne. Bing & Chutney. von Konigslow, Andrea Wayne, illus. 1999. (Bing & Chutney Adventures Ser.). (Illus.). 32p. (J). (gr. k-ps). lib. bdg. 16.95 (978-1-55037-609-8(8)) Annick Pr., Ltd. CAN. *Dist:* Firefly Bks., Ltd.

—Bing & Chutney. 1999. (ps-2). lib. bdg. 14.10 (978-0-613-53145-0(0)) Tandem Library Bks.

Waddell, Martin. The Pig in the Pond. 2002. (Illus.). (J). 13.83 (978-0-7587-3404-4(2)) Book Wholesalers, Inc.

Waldron, Jan L. Angel Pig & the Hidden Christmas. McPhail, David M., illus. 2002. (J). 23.40 (978-0-7587-1947-8(7)) Book Wholesalers, Inc.

—Angel Pig & the Hidden Christmas. 2000. (Illus.). 32p. (J). (ps-3). 6.99 (978-0-14-056591-1(4) , Puffin) Penguin Group (USA) Inc.

—Angel Pig & the Hidden Christmas. 2000. (gr. k-3). lib. bdg. 15.30 (978-0-613-29873-5(X)) Tandem Library Bks.

—John Pig's Halloween. McPhail, David M., illus. 1998. 18p. (J). pap. 14.98 (978-1-58048-045-1(4)) Sandvik Publishing.

—John Pig's Halloween. 2001. (gr. 3-6). lib. bdg. 15.30 (978-0-613-58416-6(3)) Tandem Library Bks.

Wallace, Karen. Marvin, the Blue Pig. Williams, Lisa, illus. 2004. (Read-It! Readers Ser.). 32p. (C). (gr. k-3). 18.60 (978-1-4048-0564-4(8)) Picture Window Bks.

Walt Disney Company Staff, illus. Three Little Pigs. 2004. (Little Golden Book Ser.). 24p. (J). (gr. k-k). 2.99 (978-0-7364-2312-0(5) , Golden/Disney) Random Hse. Children's Bks.

Walton, Rick. Pig, Pigger, Piggest. Holder, Jimmy, illus. 2003. 32p. (J). reprint ed. pap. 6.95 (978-1-58685-318-1(X)) Gibbs Smith, Publisher.

—Pig, Pigger, Piggest. 2003. (gr. k-3). lib. bdg. 15.25 (978-0-613-79635-4(7)) Tandem Library Bks.

Wax, Wendy. Piggley's Colorful World. Entara Ltd. Staff, photos by. 2006. (Jakers! Ser.). 30p. (J). bds. 5.99 (978-1-4169-0347-5(X) , Simon Spotlight) Simon & Schuster Children's Publishing.

Weeks, Sarah. I'm a Pig. Berry, Holly, illus. 2005. 32p. (J). (ps-2). lib. bdg. 16.89 (978-0-06-074344-4(1)); 15.99 (978-0-694-01075-2(8)) HarperCollins Pubs. (Geringer, Laura Book).

Welling, Peter J. Michael le Souffle & the April Fool. Welling, Peter J., illus. 2003. (Illus.). 32p. (J). 15.95 (978-1-58980-105-9(9)) Pelican Publishing Co., Inc.

Wesley, Valerie Wilson. Willimena & Mrs. Sweetly's Guinea Pig. 2005. (Illus.). (J). pap. (978-0-7868-1321-6(0)) Hyperion Bks. for Children.

Weston, Martha. Tuck's Haunted House. Weston, Martha, illus. 2002. (Illus.). 32p. (J). (gr. k-3). tchr. ed. 14.00 (978-0-618-15966-6(5) , Clarion Bks.) Houghton Mifflin Co. Trade & Reference Div.

Whatley, Bruce. Wait! No Paint! Whatley, Bruce, illus. 32p. (J). 2005. pap. 6.99 (978-0-06-443546-8(6) , Harper Trophy); 2001. (Illus.). 15.99 (978-0-06-028270-7(3)); 2001. (Illus.). lib. bdg. 16.89 (978-0-06-028271-4(1)) HarperCollins Pubs.

Wheeler, Lisa. Invasion of the Pig Sisters. Ansley, Frank, illus. 2006. (Fitch & Chip Ser.). 48p. (J). pap. 3.99 (978-0-689-84958-9(3)) Simon & Schuster Children's Publishing.

—New Pig in Town. Ansley, Frank, illus. ed. 2005. 48p. (J). lib. bdg. 15.00 (978-1-59054-997-1(X)) Fitzgerald Bks.

—New Pig in Town. Ansley, Frank, illus. 2005. (Fitch & Chip Ser.). 48p. (J). pap. 3.99 (978-0-689-84955-8(9) , Aladdin) Simon & Schuster Children's Publishing.

—When Pigs Fly. Ansley, Frank, illus. ed. 2005. 48p. (J). lib. bdg. 15.00 (978-1-59054-996-4(1)) Fitzgerald Bks.

—When Pigs Fly. Ansley, Frank, illus. 2005. (Fitch & Chip Ser.). 48p. (J). pap. 3.99 (978-0-689-84956-5(7) , Aladdin) Simon & Schuster Children's Publishing.

Wheeler, Lisa & Ansley, Frank. New Pig in Town. 2003. (Ready-to-Read Ser.). (Illus.). 48p. (J). 14.95 (978-0-689-84950-3(8) , Atheneum/Richard Jackson Bks.) Simon & Schuster Children's Publishing.

White. Tela di Carlotta. pap. 13.95 (978-88-04-46241-5(8)) Mondadori ITA. *Dist:* Distribooks, Inc.

White, E. B. Charlotte's Web. Williams, Garth, illus. 2002. (J). 34.64 (978-0-7587-0178-7(0)) Book Wholesalers, Inc.

—Charlotte's Web. Williams, Garth & Wells, Rosemary, illus. 2001. 192p. (J). (gr. 5 up). pap. 8.99 (978-0-06-441093-9(5) , Harper Trophy) HarperCollins Pubs.

—Charlotte's Web. Williams, Garth, illus. collector's ed. 192p. (J). 1999. (gr. 4-7). 24.99 (978-0-06-028298-1(3)); 2006. mass mkt. 7.99 (978-0-06-122874-2(5) , Harper Trophy) HarperCollins Pubs.

—Charlotte's Web. Williams, Garth & Wells, Rosemary, illus. 50th anniv. ed. 2002. (J). 29.95 (978-0-06-000698-3(6)) HarperCollins Pubs.

—Charlotte's Web. Williams, Garth, illus. l.t. ed. 1999. (LRS Large Print Cornerstone Ser.). 310p. (J). (gr. 2-8). lib. bdg. 29.95 (978-1-58118-050-3(0) , 22772) LRS.

—Charlotte's Web. Williams, Garth, illus. 184p. (J). pap. 5.95 (978-0-8072-8305-9(3) , Listening Library) Random Hse. Audio Publishing Group.

—Charlotte's Web. unabr. ed. 2004. 184p. (J). (gr. 3-7). pap. 36.00 incl. audio (978-0-8072-8304-2(5) , YYA156SP, Listening Library) Random Hse. Audio Publishing Group.

—Charlotte's Web. 2001. (gr. 3-6). lib. bdg. 17.60 (978-0-613-81689-2(7)) Tandem Library Bks.

—Some Pig! A Charlotte's Web Picture Book. Kneen, Maggie, illus. 2006. (Charlotte's Web Ser.). 32p. (J). 16.99 (978-0-06-078161-3(0)); lib. bdg. 17.89 (978-0-06-078162-0(9)) HarperCollins Pubs.

—Wilbur's Adventure. Kneen, Maggie, illus. 2008. (Charlotte's Web Ser.). 32p. (J). (gr. k-2). 16.99 (***978-0-06-078164-4(5)***) HarperCollins Pubs.

—Wilbur's Adventure: A Charlotte's Web Picture Book. Kneen, Maggie, illus. 2008. (Charlotte's Web Ser.). 32p. (J). 17.89 (***978-0-06-078165-1(3)***) HarperCollins Pubs.

Whitfield, Willie. Pig Pen Willie's Inheritance. 2007. (J). 12.95 (***978-1-56167-958-4(5)***) American Literary Pr.

Wiesner, David. The Three Pigs. Wiesner, David, illus. 2001. (Illus.). 40p. (J). (gr. k-3). lib. bdg. 16.00 (978-0-618-00701-1(6) , Clarion Bks.) Houghton Mifflin Co. Trade & Reference Div.

—Los Tres Cerditos. 2004. Tr. of Three Little Pigs. (SPA.). (J). (gr. k-2). 21.95 (978-84-261-3291-8(X)) Juventud, Editorial ESP. *Dist:* Lectorum Pubns., Inc., Iaconi, Mariuccia Bk. Imports.

Wild, Margaret. Nana Vieja. Brooks, Ron, illus. 2000. (SPA.). 32p. (J). (gr. 1-3). 19.50 (978-980-257-234-2(9) , EK30125) Ekare, Ediciones VEN. *Dist:* Lectorum Pubns., Inc.

—Piglet & Mama. King, Stephen Michael, illus. 2005. 32p. (J). (ps-1). 14.95 (978-0-8109-5869-2(4)) Abrams, Harry N. , Inc.

—Piglet & Papa. King, Stephen Michael, illus. 2007. (J). (ps-3). 32p. 14.95 (978-0-8109-1476-6(X)); (***978-1-4287-4648-0(X)***) Abrams, Harry N. , Inc. (Abrams Bks. for Young Readers).

Willems, Mo. I Am Invited to a Party! An Elephant & Piggie Book. Willems, Mo, illus. rev. ed. 2007. 64p. (J). (ps-3). 8.99 (***978-1-4231-0687-6(3)***) Hyperion Pr.

—My Friend Is Sad. 2007. 64p. (ps-3). 8.99 (978-1-4231-0297-7(5)) Hyperion Bks. for Children.

—There Is a Bird on Your Head! An Elephant & Piggie Book. Willems, Mo, illus. rev. ed. 2007. 64p. (J). (ps-3). 8.99 (***978-1-4231-0686-9(5)***) Hyperion Pr.

Willems, Mo. Today I Will Fly! 2007. 64p. (ps-3). 8.99 (978-1-4231-0295-3(9)) Hyperion Bks. for Children.

Williams, Rose. Tres Porculi. L and L Enterprises, ed. Este, James, illus. 2006. (LAT.). spiral bd. 18.00 (978-0-9760046-5-3(8)) L & L Enterprises.

Winslow, Lori. Pigs over Louisville. Winslow, Lori, illus. 2000. (Illus.). (J). (ps-7). pap. 12.95 (978-0-615-11566-5(7)) Winslow, Lori.

Winthrop, Elizabeth. Dumpy la Rue. Lewin, Betsy, illus. rev. ed. 40p. (J). 2004. reprint ed. pap. 7.95 (978-0-8050-7535-9(6)); 2001. 16.95 (978-0-8050-6385-1(4)) Holt, Henry & Co. (Holt, Henry & Co. Bks. For Young Readers).

—Dumpy la Rue. Lewin, Betsy, illus. 2004. 48p. (J). (ps-4). lib. bdg. 14.15 (978-0-606-30292-0(1)) Tandem Library Bks.

Wojtowycz, David. Eat up Dudley! Counting. 2002. (Dudley! Ser.). (Illus.). (J). 3.95 (978-1-58925-669-9(7) , tiger tales) ME Media LLC.

—Get Dressed Dudley! Weather. 2002. (Dudley! Ser.). (Illus.). (J). 3.95 (978-1-58925-670-5(0) , tiger tales) ME Media LLC.

—Let's Play, Dudley! Colors. 2003. (Dudley! Ser.). (Illus.). (J). 3.95 (978-1-58925-667-5(0) , tiger tales) ME Media LLC.

Wolf, Jackie. Picture Me Peek-A-Boo Farm. 2002. (Peek-a-Boo Ser.). (Illus.). 10p. (J). (ps up). bds. 4.99 (978-1-57151-595-7(X)) Playhouse Publishing.

Wood, Audrey. Cerditos. Campoy, F. Isabel, tr. Wood, Don, illus. 2006. 34p. (J). bds. 6.95 (978-0-15-205731-2(5) , Voyager Bks./Libros Viajeros) Harcourt Children's Bks.

—Piggies. Wood, Audrey, illus. 2002. (Illus.). (J). 14.04 (978-0-7587-3407-5(7)) Book Wholesalers, Inc.

—Piggy Pie Po. 2001. (J). 16.00 (978-0-15-202494-9(8)) Harcourt Children's Bks.

Wood, Audrey & Wood, Don. Piggies. Wood, Don, illus. 2000. (Illus.). 16p. (J). (ps-k). bds. 5.95 (978-0-15-202638-7(X) , Red Wagon Bks.) Harcourt Children's Bks.

—Piggies: Book & Musical CD. 2006. (Illus.). 32p. (J). 17.95 (978-0-15-205667-4(X)) Harcourt Children's Bks.

—Piggies: Lap-Sized Board Book. 2005. (Illus.). 32p. (J). (gr. 17-ps). bds. 10.95 (978-0-15-205632-2(7) , Red Wagon Bks.) Harcourt Children's Bks.

Worth, Bonnie. Pigs & Robbers. 1999. (978-0-606-17730-6(2)) Tandem Library Bks.

Yamada, Utako. The Story of Cherry the Pig. Yamada, Utako, illus. 2007. (Illus.). 32p. (J). 15.95 (978-1-933605-25-8(1) , 05258) Kane/Miller Bk. Pubs., Inc.

Young, Polly G. Pokey Pig's Picnic. Raymond, Janet Y., illus. 2007. (J). pap. 15.00 (***978-0-8059-7298-6(6)***) Dorrance Publishing Co., Inc.

Zachel, Gretchen. Butterbean & the Great Escape. Johnson, Marc, illus. 2002. 18p. (J). 14.95 (978-1-931945-00-4(4)) Expert Publishing, Inc.

Zemach, Margot. The Three Little Pigs: An Old Story. Zemach, Margot, illus. 2002. (Illus.). (J). 14.43 (978-0-7587-3806-6(4)) Book Wholesalers, Inc.

Ziefert, Harriet. What's Polite? Brown, Rick & Brown, Richard, illus. 2004. 20p. pap. 6.95 (978-1-4027-1790-1(3)) Sterling Publishing Co., Inc.

—What's Pretend? Brown, Rick & Brown, Richard, illus. 2004. 20p. (J). pap. 6.95 (978-1-4027-1791-8(1)) Sterling Publishing Co., Inc.

PIGS—POETRY

Wohnoutka, Mike, illus. This Little Piggy. 2005. (J). (978-1-58987-106-9(5)) Kindermusik International.

PIKAS

Grolier Educational Staff, contrib. by. Pikas. 2001. (Nature's Children Ser.). (Illus.). 48p. (J). (978-0-7172-5542-9(5) , Grolier) Scholastic Library Publishing.

Miller, Sara Swan. Rabbits, Pikas, & Hares. Gonzales, Jose & Savage, Stephen, illus. 2002. (Animals in Order Ser.). 48p. (J). (gr. 4-6). 26.50 (978-0-531-11634-0(4) , Watts, Franklin) Scholastic Library Publishing.

PIKE, ZEBULON MONTGOMERY, 1779-1813

Calvert, Patricia. Zebulon Pike: Lost in the Rockies. 2003. (Great Explorations Ser.). (J). (978-0-7614-1740-8(0)); 29.93 (978-0-7614-1612-8(9)) Cavendish, Marshall Corp. (Benchmark Bks.).

Doak, Robin S. Zebulon Pike: Explorer & Soldier. 2005. (Signature Lives Ser.). (Illus.). 112p. (J). (gr. 5-7). (978-0-7565-0998-9(X)) Compass Point Bks.

Maynard, Charles W. Zebulon Pike: Soldier Explorer of the American Southwest. 2003. (Famous Explorers of the American West Ser.). (Illus.). 24p. (J). lib. bdg. 18.75 (978-0-8239-6286-0(5) , PowerKids Pr.) Rosen Publishing Group, Inc., The.

Witteman, Barbara. Zebulon Pike: Soldier & Explorer. 2002. (Let Freedom Ring Ser.). (Illus.). 48p. (J). (gr. 3-4). lib. bdg. 22.60 (978-0-7368-1351-8(9) , Bridgestone Bks.) Capstone Pr., Inc.

Zebulon Pike. (Exploring the West Biographies Ser.). 48p. (YA). 7.95 (978-0-7368-4512-0(7)) Capstone Pr., Inc.

Zebulon Pike, 6 vols. (gr. 2-5). 39.95 (978-0-7368-4595-3(X)) Red Brick Learning.

PILATE, PONTIUS, 1ST CENT.

Fontanille, Jean-Philippe & Gosline, Sheldon Lee. The Coins of Pontius Pilate, Vol. 4. 2001. (Marco Polo Monographs: Vol. 4). (FRE & ENG., Illus.). 176p. (C). 39.95 (978-0-9677201-4-2(1)) Shangri-La Pubns.

PILGRIM FATHERS

see Pilgrims (New Plymouth Colony)

PILGRIMS (NEW PLYMOUTH COLONY)

Apel, Melanie Ann. The Pilgrims. 2003. (Daily Life Ser.). (Illus.). 48p. (J). (gr. 3-5). (978-0-7377-0993-3(6) , Kidhaven) Thomson Gale.

Arenstam, Peter, et al. Mayflower 1620: A New Look at a Pilgrim Voyage. 2007. (Illus.). 48p. (J). (gr. 3-7). 6.95 (***978-0-7922-6276-3(X)*** , National Geographic Children's Bks.) National Geographic Society.

—Mayflower 1620: A New Look at a Pilgrim Voyage. Brimberg, Sisse & Coulson, Cotton, illus. Brimberg, Sisse & Coulson, Cotton, photos by. 2003. 48p. (J). (gr. 3-7). 17.95 (978-0-7922-6142-1(9) , National Geographic Children's Bks.) National Geographic Society.

—MayFlower 1620: A New Look at a Pilgrim Voyage. 2004. (Illus.). 47p. (J). (gr. k-4). 18.00 (978-0-7567-7967-2(7)) DIANE Publishing Co.

Armentrout, David & Armentrout, Patricia. The Mayflower Compact. (Documents that Shaped the Nation Ser.). 48p. 2005. (Illus.). (gr. 4-6). 20.95 (978-1-59515-229-9(6)); 2004. pap. 7.95 (978-1-59515-334-0(9)) Rourke Publishing, LLC.

—El Pacto Del Mayflower. 2005. (SPA.). (J). (978-1-59515-648-8(8)) Rourke Publishing, LLC.

Bartlett, Robert Merrill. The Story of Thanksgiving. Comport, Sally Wern, illus. rev. ed. 2004. 30p. (J). (gr. k-4). reprint ed. (978-0-7567-7757-9(7)) DIANE Publishing Co.

—The Story of Thanksgiving. Comport, Sally Wern, illus. Date not set. 40p. (J). (gr. 2-5). 5.99 (978-0-06-446238-9(2)) HarperCollins Pubs.

Black, Sonia W. Let's Read About— Squanto. Doucet, Bob, illus. 2002. (Scholastic First Biographies Ser.). (J). pap. (978-0-439-45952-5(4)) Scholastic, Inc.

Bowen, Gary. Stranded at Plimoth Plantation 1626. Bowen, Gary, illus. 2001. (Illus.). 81p. (J). (gr. 2-5). reprint ed. pap. 10.00 (978-0-7881-9835-9(1)) DIANE Publishing Co.

—Stranded at Plimoth Plantation 1626. Bowen, Gary, illus. 1998. (Trophy Chapter Bks.). (Illus.). 88p. (J). (gr. 3-7). pap. 12.95 (978-0-06-440719-9(5)) HarperCollins Pubs.

Brooks, Philip. The Mayflower Compact. 2004. (Illus.). 48p. (J). (gr. 4 up). lib. bdg. 22.60 (978-0-7565-0681-0(6)) Compass Point Bks.

Carter, E. J. The Mayflower Compact. 2003. (Heinemann Know It Ser.). (Illus.). 48p. (J). pap. 8.50 (978-1-4034-3432-6(8)); lib. bdg. 27.07 (978-1-4034-0803-7(3)) Heinemann Library.

Clark, Mary. Biographical Sketches of the Fathers of New England. 2003. 180p. 89.00 (978-0-7950-4738-1(X)) New Library Press.Net.

Crane, Carol. P Is for Pilgrim: A Thanksgiving Alphabet. Urban, Helle, illus. 2003. 40p. (J). 14.95 (978-1-58536-134-2(8)) Sleeping Bear Pr.

—P Is for Pilgrim: A Thanksgiving Alphabet. rev. ed. 2007. (Holiday Ser.). 40p. pap. 7.95 (***978-1-58536-353-7(7)***) Sleeping Bear Pr.

Crawford, Laura. The Pilgrims' Thanksgiving from A to Z. Hierstein, Judith, illus. 2005. 32p. (J). (ps-k). pap. 7.95 (978-1-58980-238-4(1)) Pelican Publishing Co., Inc.

Davis, Kenneth C. Don't Know Much about the Pilgrims. Schindler, S. D., illus. (Don't Know Much About Ser.). 48p. (J). (gr. 1-4). 2006. pap. 6.99 (978-0-06-446228-0(5)); 2002. 16.99 (978-0-06-028609-5(1)) HarperCollins Pubs.

Dell, Pamela. Plymouth Colony. 2004. (Let Freedom Ring Ser.). (Illus.). 48p. (J). 23.93 (978-0-7368-2463-7(4) , Bridgestone Bks.) Capstone Pr., Inc.

Donaldson-Forbes, Jeff. Famous Explorers - Set 3, 6 bks. Incl. Amerigo Vespucci. lib. bdg. 18.75 (978-0-8239-5833-7(7)); Francisco Pizarro. lib. bdg. 18.75 (978-0-8239-5831-3(0)); Hernan Cortes. lib. bdg. 18.75 (978-0-8239-5832-0(9)); Jacques Cartier. lib. bdg. 18.75 (978-0-8239-5834-4(5)); Jacques Marquette & Louis Jolliet. lib. bdg. 18.75 (978-0-8239-5835-1(3)); La Salle. lib. bdg. 18.75 (978-0-8239-5830-6(2)); 24p. (J). (gr. 3). 2002. (Illus.). Set lib. bdg. 112.50 (978-0-8239-7181-7(3) , PowerKids Pr.) Rosen Publishing Group, Inc., The.

Donnelly, Judy. The Pilgrims & Me. Cocca-Leffler, Maryann, illus. 2002. (Smart about History Ser.). 32p. (J). pap. 5.99 (978-0-448-42699-0(4) , Grosset & Dunlap) Penguin Group (USA) Inc.

—Pilgrims & Me. 2002. (gr. k-3). lib. bdg. 14.15 (978-0-613-68374-6(9)) Tandem Library Bks.

Edwards, Judith. The Plymouth Colony & the Pilgrim Adventure in American History. 2003. (In American History Ser.). (Illus.). 128p. (J). (gr. 5-12). lib. bdg. 26.60 (978-0-7660-1989-8(6)) Enslow Pubs., Inc.

Englar, Mary. The Pilgrims & the First Thanksgiving. 2007. (Graphic Library). (Illus.). 32p. (J). (978-0-7368-5492-4(4)) Capstone Pr., Inc.

—The Pilgrims & the First Thanksgiving. McDonnell, Peter, illus. 2007. (Graphic Library). 32p. (J). (***978-0-7368-9656-6(2)***) Capstone Pr., Inc.

Erickson, Paul. Daily Life in the Pilgrim Colony 1636. 2001. (Illus.). 48p. (J). (gr. 4-6). tchr. ed. 20.00 (978-0-618-05846-4(X)); pap. 9.95 (978-0-395-98841-1(1)) Houghton Mifflin Co. Trade & Reference Div. (Clarion Bks.).

—Daily Life in the Pilgrim Colony 1636. 2001. (gr. 3-6). lib. bdg. 18.75 (978-0-613-35501-8(6)) Tandem Library Bks.

—Daily Life in the Pilgrim Colony,1636. 2001. 16.75 (978-0-606-22581-6(1)) Tandem Library Bks.

Florence, Sarah. Pilgrim Food & Recipes. 2002. (Reading Room Collection). (J). pap. (978-0-8239-8165-6(7)); (Illus.). 24p. lib. bdg. 18.75 (978-0-8239-3728-8(3)) Rosen Publishing Group, Inc., The.

Fradin, Dennis B. The Mayflower Compact. 2006. (Turning Points in U. S. History Ser.). (Illus.). 48p. (J). lib. bdg. 29.93 (978-0-7614-2125-2(4) , Benchmark Bks.) Cavendish, Marshall Corp.

Fritz, Jean. Who's That Stepping on Plymouth Rock? 1998. (Illus.). 32p. (J). (gr. 2-5). pap. 6.99 (978-0-698-11681-8(X) , Putnam Juvenile) Penguin Group (USA) Inc.

—Who's That Stepping on Plymouth Rock? Handelsman, J. B., illus. 1998. 31p. lib. bdg. 14.19 (978-0-606-15766-7(2)); 30p. (J). lib. bdg. 15.30 (978-0-613-10540-8(0)) Tandem Library Bks.

Goodman, Susan E. Pilgrims of Plymouth. (J). 2001. (Illus.). 16p. (gr. 3-7). pap. 5.95 (978-0-7922-6675-4(7) , National Geographic Children's Bks.); 1999. (978-0-7922-9429-0(7)); 1999. (978-0-7922-9424-5(6)) National Geographic Society.

—Pilgrims of Plymouth. 2001. (ps-2). lib. bdg. 14.10 (978-0-613-52164-2(1)) Tandem Library Bks.

Grace, Catherine O'Neill, et al. 1621: A New Look at Thanksgiving. Brimberg, Sisse & Coulson, Cotton, photos by. 2001. (Illus.). 48p. (J). (gr. 3-7). 17.95 (978-0-7922-7027-0(4) , National Geographic Children's Bks.) National Geographic Society.

Griffis, William Elliot. Young People's History of the Pilgrims. 353p. reprint ed. 98.00 (978-0-7222-6679-3(0)) Library Reprints, Inc.

Harness, Cheryl. The Adventurous Life of Myles Standish & the Amazing-But-True Survival Story of the Plymouth Colony. Harness, Cheryl, illus. 2006. (Illus.). 144p. (J). (gr. 5-9). lib. bdg. 25.90 (978-0-7922-5919-0(X) , National Geographic Children's Bks.) National Geographic Society.

—The Adventurous Life of Myles Standish & the Amazing-but-True Survival Story of the Plymouth Colony. Harness, Cheryl, illus. 2006. (Illus.). 144p. (J). (gr. 5-9). 16.95 (978-0-7922-5918-3(1) , National Geographic Children's Bks.) National Geographic Society.

Hirschfelder, Arlene B. Squanto1585-1622. 2004. (American Indian Biographies Ser.). (Illus.). 32p. (J). (gr. 3-4). lib. bdg. 23.93 (978-0-7368-2446-0(4) , Blue Earth Bks.) Capstone Pr., Inc.

Jackson, Garnet N. First Thanksgiving. 2000. (gr. k-3). lib. bdg. 11.80 (978-0-613-35508-7(3)) Tandem Library Bks.

—The First Thanksgiving: Level 3. Croll, Carolyn, illus. 2001. (Hello Reader! Ser.). 40p. (J). (gr. 1-3). pap. 3.99 (978-0-439-20628-0(6) , Cartwheel Bks.) Scholastic, Inc.

Kamma, Anne. First Thanksgiving. Dodson, Bert, illus. 2001. (If You Ser.). 64p. (J). pap. 5.99 (978-0-439-10566-8(8)) Scholastic, Inc.

Kauffman, Dorothy. Two Villages: Two Hundred Years Apart. 2005. (Content Area Readers Ser.). 4.95 (978-0-19-430952-3(5)) Oxford Univ. Pr., Inc.

Kessel, Joyce K. Squanto & the First Thanksgiving. Donze, Lisa, illus. rev. ed. 2004. (On My Own Holidays Ser.). 48p. (J). (gr. 2-4). lib. bdg. 25.26 (978-0-87614-941-6(7)) Lerner Publishing Group.

—Squanto & the First Thanksgiving. 2004. (gr. k-3). lib. bdg. 14.10 (978-0-613-63654-4(6)) Tandem Library Bks.

Kessel Joyce K. Squanto y el primer Día de Accion de Gracias (Squanto & the First Thanksgiving) Donze, Lisa, illus. 2007. (Yo solo Festividades (on My Own Holidays) Ser.). (J). pap. 6.95 (***978-0-8225-7795-9(X)*** , Ediciones Lerner) Lerner Publishing Group.

Kessel, Joyce K. Squanto y el Primer Día de Accion de Gracias (Squanto & the First Thanksgiving) Donze, Lisa, illus. 2007. (Yo Solo Festividades (On My Own Holidays) Ser.). (SPA.). 48p. (J). (gr. 2-4). lib. bdg. 25.26 (***978-0-8225-7792-8(5)*** , Ediciones Lerner) Lerner Publishing Group.

Knowlton, MaryLee & Riehecky, Janet. The Plymouth Colony. 2002. (Events That Shaped America Ser.). (Illus.). 32p. (J). (gr. 3 up). lib. bdg. 24.67 (978-0-8368-3224-2(8)) Stevens, Gareth Inc.

Koestler-Grack, Rachel A. The Pilgrims. 2005. (American Moments Ser.). (Illus.). 48p. (J). (gr. 4-8). lib. bdg. 25.65 (978-1-59197-937-1(4)) ABDO Publishing Co.

Landau, Elaine. Celebrate the First Thanksgiving with Elaine Landau. 2006. (Explore Colonial America with Elaine Landau Ser.). (Illus.). 48p. (J). lib. bdg. 23.93 (978-0-7660-2556-1(X) , Enslow Elementary) Enslow Pubs., Inc.

Lilly, Melinda. Pilgrims in America. 2002. (Rourke Discovery Library). (Illus.). 24p. (J). lib. bdg. 20.64 (978-1-58952-360-9(1)) Rourke Publishing, LLC.

Mackall, Dandi Daley. Off to Plymouth Rock. 2006. 26p. (J). bds. 9.99 (978-1-4003-0822-4(4)) Nelson, Thomas Inc.

McNeese, Tim. Plymouth. 2007. (Colonial Settlements in America Ser.). (Illus.). 112p. (YA). (gr. 5-8). 30.00 **(*978-0-7910-9339-9(5)*** , Chelsea Hse.) Facts On File, Inc.

Metaxas, Eric. Squanto & the First Thanksgiving. Donato, Michael A., illus. 2005. (Rabbit Ears-A Classic Tale Ser.). 40p. (J). (gr. k-5). 25.65 (978-1-59197-771-1(1)) Spotlight.

—Squanto & the First Thanksgiving: The Legendary American Tale. Donato, Michael A., illus. 2004. 36p. (J). (gr. 3-8). reprint ed. 19.00 (978-0-7567-7123-2(4)) DIANE Publishing Co.

Miller, Susan Martins. Miles Standish. 1999. (Colonial Leaders Ser.). (Illus.). 80p. (J). (gr. 3 up). pap. 27.50 (978-0-7910-5693-6(7) , Chelsea Hse.) Facts On File, Inc.

Newman-D'Amico, Fran. The Story of the Pilgrims. 2005. 32p. (J). (ps-3). pap. 2.95 (978-0-486-44430-7(9)) Dover Pubns., Inc.

Osborne, Mary Pope & Boyce, Natalie Pope. Pilgrims. Murdocca, Salvatore, illus. 2005. (Magic Tree House Research Guide Ser.: No. 13). 128p. (J). (gr. k-3). pap. 4.99 (978-0-375-83219-2(X) , Random Hse. Bks. for Young Readers) Random Hse. Children's Bks.

—Pilgrims: A Nonfiction Companion to Thanksgiving on Thursday. Murdocca, Salvatore, illus. 2005. (Magic Tree House Research Guide Ser.: No. 13). 128p. (J). (gr. k-3). lib. bdg. 11.99 (978-0-375-93219-9(4) , Random Hse. Bks. for Young Readers) Random Hse. Children's Bks.

Owens, L. L. Pilgrims in America. 2007. (Events in American History Ser.). 48p. (J). (gr. 4-6). lib. bdg. 29.93 (978-1-60044-122-6(X)) Rourke Publishing, LLC.

Philbrick, Nathaniel. The Mayflower & the Pilgrims' New World. 2008. 304p. (J). (gr. 4-6). 19.99 **(*978-0-399-24795-8(5)*** , Putnam Juvenile) Penguin Group (USA) Inc.

Plymouth Colony. (Colonial America Ser.). 48p. (YA). 7.95 (978-0-7368-4480-2(5)) Capstone Pr., Inc.

Pumphrey, Margaret B. Stories of the Pilgrims. 2005. pap. 27.95 (978-1-4179-1115-8(8)) Kessinger Publishing, LLC.

—Stories of the Pilgrims. Perkins, Lucy Fitch, illus. 2005. 264p. pap. 17.95 (978-1-59462-116-1(0) , 144, Book Jungle) Standard Pubns., Inc.

Pumphrey, Margaret B. Stories of the Pilgrims (Yesterday's Classics) 2006. (J). per. 10.95 **(*978-1-59915-123-6(5)*)** Yesterday's Classics.

Riehecky, Janet. The Plymouth Colony. 2002. (Landmark Events in American History Ser.). (Illus.). 48p. (J). (gr. 5 up). lib. bdg. 30.00 (978-0-8368-5340-7(7)); pap. 14.60 (978-0-8368-5354-4(7)) Stevens, Gareth Inc. (World Almanac Library).

Santella, Andrew. The First Thanksgiving. 2003. (Cornerstones of Freedom). (Illus.). 48p. (J). (gr. 4-6). 26.00 (978-0-516-24204-0(0) , Children's Pr.) Scholastic Library Publishing.

Schmidt, Gary. William Bradford: Plymouth's Faithful Pilgrim. 1999. (gr. 7-12). lib. bdg. 21.10 (978-0-613-29384-6(3)) Tandem Library Bks.

Walsh, Kieran. William Bradford. 2004. (Illus.). 24p. (J). 20.64 (978-1-59515-136-0(2)) Rourke Publishing, LLC.

Whitcraft, Melissa. The Mayflower Compact. 2003. (Cornerstones of Freedom). (Illus.). 48p. (J). (gr. 4-6). 26.00 (978-0-516-24203-3(2) , Children's Pr.) Scholastic Library Publishing.

Whitehurst, Susan. The First Thanksgiving. 2002. (Library of the Pilgrims). (Illus.). 24p. (J). (gr. 3). lib. bdg. 19.95 (978-0-8239-5807-8(8) , PowerKids Pr.) Rosen Publishing Group, Inc., The.

—The Library of the Pilgrims, 6 bks. Incl. First Thanksgiving. lib. bdg. 19.95 (978-0-8239-5807-8(8)); Mayflower. lib. bdg. 19.95 (978-0-8239-5806-1(X)); Pilgrims Before the Mayflower. lib. bdg. 19.95 (978-0-8239-5811-5(6)); Plymouth : Surviving the First Winter. lib. bdg. 19.95 (978-0-8239-5809-2(4)); Plymouth Partnership : Pilgrims & Native Americans. lib. bdg. 19.95 (978-0-8239-5810-8(8)); William Bradford & Plymouth : A Colony Grows. lib. bdg. 19.95 (978-0-8239-5808-5(6)); 24p. (J). (gr. 3). 2002. (Illus.). 2001. Set lib. bdg. 117.00 (978-0-8239-7180-0(5) , PowerKids Pr.) Rosen Publishing Group, Inc., The.

—The Mayflower. 2002. (Library of the Pilgrims). (Illus.). 24p. (J). (gr. 3). lib. bdg. 19.95 (978-0-8239-5806-1(X) , PowerKids Pr.) Rosen Publishing Group, Inc., The.

—The Pilgrims Before the Mayflower. 2002. (Library of the Pilgrims). (Illus.). 24p. (J). (gr. 3). lib. bdg. 19.95 (978-0-8239-5811-5(6) , PowerKids Pr.) Rosen Publishing Group, Inc., The.

—Plymouth: Surviving the First Winter. 2002. (Library of the Pilgrims). (Illus.). 24p. (J). (gr. 3). lib. bdg. 19.95 (978-0-8239-5809-2(4) , PowerKids Pr.) Rosen Publishing Group, Inc., The.

—A Plymouth Partnership: Pilgrims & Native Americans. 2002. (Library of the Pilgrims). (Illus.). 24p. (J). (gr. 3). lib. bdg. 19.95 (978-0-8239-5810-8(8) , PowerKids Pr.) Rosen Publishing Group, Inc., The.

—William Bradford & Plymouth: A Colony Grows. 2002. (Library of the Pilgrims). (Illus.). 24p. (J). (gr. 3). lib. bdg. 19.95 (978-0-8239-5808-5(6) , PowerKids Pr.) Rosen Publishing Group, Inc., The.

Witteman, Barbara. Miles Standish: Colonial Leader. 2004. (Let Freedom Ring Ser.). (Illus.). 48p. (J). 17.95 (978-0-7368-2457-6(X) , Bridgestone Bks.) Capstone Pr., Inc.

Yero, Judith Lloyd. The Mayflower Compact. 2004. (National Geographic Reading Expeditions Ser.). (Illus.). 32p. (J). pap. (978-0-7922-4553-7(9)) National Geographic Society.

PILGRIMS (NEW PLYMOUTH COLONY)—FICTION

Bruchac, Joseph. Squanto's Journey: The Story of the First Thanksgiving. Shed, Greg, illus. 2007. 32p. (J). pap. 6.00 **(*978-0-15-206044-2(8)*** , Voyager Bks./Libros Viajeros) Harcourt Children's Bks.

Greene, Rhonda Gowler. The Very First Thanksgiving Day. Gaber, Susan, illus. 2006. 32p. (J). 6.99 (978-1-4169-1916-2(3) , Aladdin) Simon & Schuster Children's Publishing.

Hennessy, B. G. One Little, Two Little, Three Little Pilgrims. Cravath, Lynne, illus. 2001. 32p. (J). pap. 6.99 (978-0-14-230006-0(3) , Puffin) Penguin Group (USA) Inc.

—One Little, Two Little, Three Little Pilgrims. 2001. (gr. k-3). lib. bdg. 15.30 (978-0-613-85724-6(0)) Tandem Library Bks.

Hillert, Margaret. Why We Have Thanksgiving. Siculan, Dan, illus. rev. exp. ed. 2007. (Beginning to Read Ser.). (J). lib. bdg. (978-1-59953-049-9(X)) Norwood Hse. Pr.

Jackson, Dave & Jackson, Neta. The Mayflower Secret: Governor William Bradford. Jackson, Julian & McLaughlin, Catherine R., illus. 1998. (Trailblazer Bks.: Vol. 26). 160p. (J). (gr. 3-7). pap. 6.99 (978-0-7642-2010-4(1)) Bethany Hse. Pubs.

Lasky, Kathryn. A Journey to the New World: The Diary of Remember Patience Whipple, Mayflower, 1620. 1999. (Dear America Ser.). (J). 9.95 (978-0-439-15601-1(7)) Scholastic, Inc.

Lawton, Wendy. Almost Home: A Story Based on the Life of the Mayflower's Mary Chilton. 2003. (Daughters of the Faith Ser.). 160p. (YA). pap. 6.99 (978-0-8024-3637-5(4)) Moody Pubs.

Lough, Loree. Dream Seekers: Roger William's Stand for Freedom. 1999. (American Adventure Ser.: No. 3). (Illus.). 144p. (J). (gr. 3-7). lib. bdg. 15.95 (978-0-7910-5043-9(2) , Chelsea Hse.) Facts On File, Inc.

Osborne, Mary Pope. Thanksgiving on Thursday. Murdocca, Sal, illus. 2002. (Magic Tree House Ser.: No. 27). 96p. (J). (gr. k-3). lib. bdg. 11.99 (978-0-375-90615-2(0)); mass mkt. 3.99 (978-0-375-80615-5(6)) Random Hse. Children's Bks. (Random Hse. Bks. for Young Readers).

—Thanksgiving on Thursday. 2002. (Magic Tree House Ser. : No. 27). (J). (gr. k-3). lib. bdg. 11.80 (978-0-613-56853-1(2)) Tandem Library Bks.

Peacock, Carol Anto. Pilgrim Cat. Ettlinger, Doris, illus. 2004. 32p. (J). (gr. 2-5). 16.95 (978-0-8075-6532-2(6)) Whitman, Albert & Co.

Peacock, Carol Antoinette. Pilgrim Cat. Ettlinger, Doris, illus. 2006. 32p. (J). (gr. 2-5). 6.95 (978-0-8075-6533-9(4)) Whitman, Albert & Co.

Reece, Colleen L. The Mayflower Adventure. 1999. (American Adventure Ser.: No. 1). 144p. (J). (gr. 3-7). lib. bdg. 15.95 (978-0-7910-5041-5(6) , Chelsea Hse.) Facts On File, Inc.

—Plymouth Pioneers. 1998. (American Adventure Ser.: No. 2). (Illus.). 142p. (J). (gr. 3-7). lib. bdg. 15.95 (978-0-7910-5042-2(4) , Chelsea Hse.) Facts On File, Inc.

Rinaldi, Ann. The Journal of Jasper Jonathan Pierce: A Pilgrim Boy, Plymouth, 1620. 2000. (My Name Is America Ser.). (Illus.). 160p. (J). (gr. 4-8). pap. 10.95 (978-0-590-51078-3(9)) Scholastic, Inc.

Selbo, Jule & Peters, Laura. Pilgrim Girl: Diaries & Recipes of her First Year in the New World. 2005. (Illus.). 132p. (YA). per. 12.95 (978-1-932993-05-9(3)) Star Publish LLC.

Stanley, Diane. Thanksgiving on Plymouth Plantation. Berry, Holly, illus. 2004. (Time-Traveling Twins Ser.). 48p. (J). (gr. k-5). 15.99 (978-0-06-027069-8(1)); lib. bdg. 16.89 (978-0-06-027076-6(4)) HarperCollins Pubs. (Cotler, Joanna Books).

Vernon, Louise A. Peter & the Pilgrims. Eitzen, Allan, illus. 2nd ed. 2002. 128p. (YA). (gr. 4-9). 7.99 (978-0-8361-9226-1(5)) Herald Pr.

Waters, Kate. On the Mayflower: Voyage of the Ship's Apprentice & a Passenger Girl. 1998. (J). 5.99 (978-0-590-67408-9(0)) Scholastic, Inc.

PILOTING (AERONAUTICS)

see Airplanes—Piloting

PILOTS, AIRPLANE

see Air Pilots

PILOTS AND PILOTAGE

see also Navigation

Atkins, Jeannine. Wings & Rockets: The Story of Women in Air & Space. Petricic, Dusan, illus. 2003. 208p. (J). 17.00 (978-0-374-38450-0(9) , Farrar, Straus & Giroux (BYR)) Farrar, Straus & Giroux.

Liebman, Dan. I Want to Be a Pilot. 8th ed. 1999. (I Want to Be Ser.). (Illus.). 24p. (J). (ps-2). lib. bdg. 14.95 (978-1-55209-449-5(9)) Firefly Bks., Ltd.

Pilotos: Individual Title Six-Packs. (On Deck en Espanol Ser.).Tr. of Pilots. (SPA.). 24p. (gr. 4-5). 35.00 (978-0-7578-6407-0(4)) Rigby Education.

Pilots: Individual Title Six-Packs. (On Deck Ser.). 24p. (gr. 4-5). 35.00 (978-0-7578-1028-2(4)) Rigby Education.

Wagner, Heather Lehr. Charles Lindbergh. 2003. (Famous Flyers Ser.). (Illus.). 112p. (gr. 6-12). 30.00 (978-0-7910-7212-7(6)); pap. 30.00 (978-0-7910-7497-8(8)) Facts On File, Inc. (Chelsea Hse.).

Wukovits, John F. Flying Aces. 2002. (American War Library). (Illus.). 112p. (YA). (gr. 4-12). lib. bdg. 29.95 (978-1-56006-810-5(8) , LML00902-178142, Lucent Bks.) Thomson Gale.

Youngblood, Wayne. Mark Twain along the Mississippi. 2006. (In the Footsteps of American Heroes Ser.). (Illus.). 64p. (J). pap. (978-0-8368-6435-9(2)); lib. bdg. 32.67 (978-0-8368-6430-4(1)) Stevens, Gareth Inc. (World Almanac Library).

PINCHOT, GIFFORD, 1865-1946

Hines, Gary. Midnight Forests: A Story of Gifford Pinchot & Our National Forests. Casilla, Robert, illus. 2005. 32p. (J). (ps-17). 16.95 (978-1-56397-148-8(8)) Boyds Mills Pr.

PINCKNEY, ELIZA LUCAS, 1723-1793

Krebs, Laurie. A Day in the Life of a Colonial Indigo Planter. 2004. (Library of Living & Working in Colonial Times). (Illus.). 24p. (J). lib. bdg. 18.75 (978-0-8239-6229-7(6)) Rosen Publishing Group, Inc., The.

PINOCCHIO (FICTITIOUS CHARACTER)—FICTION

Cherubini, E. Pinocchio in Africa. 2007. pap. **(*978-1-4065-1442-1(X)*)** Dodo Pr.

Collodi, C. The Adventures of Pinocchio. Della Chiesa, Carol, tr. 2007. (ENG.). 160p. per. **(*978-1-4065-1463-6(2)*)** Dodo Pr.

—Pinocchio: the Tale of a Puppet. Carsey, Alice, illus. 2007. (ENG.). 196p. per. **(*978-1-4065-1462-9(4)*)** Dodo Pr.

Collodi, Carlo. The Adventures of Pinnochio. 2003. (Spot the Classics Ser.). 192p. (J). 4.99 (978-1-57759-940-1(3)) Dalmatian Pr.

—The Adventures of Pinocchio. Murray, M. A., tr. from ITA. Innocenti, Roberto, illus. rev. ed. 2005. (Creative Editions Ser.). 192p. (J). (gr. 4 up). 24.95 (978-1-56846-190-8(9)) Creative Co., The.

—The Adventures of Pinocchio. (Twelve-Point Ser.). 2003. (J). lib. bdg. 25.00 (978-1-58287-248-3(1)); 2004. 229p. 25.00 (978-1-58287-732-7(7)) North Bks.

—The Adventures of Pinocchio. Lucas, Ann Lawson, tr. from ITA. 2002. (Oxford World's Classics Ser.). (Illus.). 256p. 9.95 (978-0-19-280150-0(3)) Oxford Univ. Pr., Inc.

—The Adventures of Pinocchio. Ghiuselev, Iassen, illus. 2nd unabr. ed. 2002. 160p. 24.95 (978-0-9688768-0-0(3)) Simply Read Bks. CAN. *Dist:* Perseus Distribution.

—The Adventures of Pinocchio. Canepa, Nancy L., tr. from ITA. Lettere, Carmelo, illus. 2004. 150p. reprint ed. pap. 12.95 (978-1-58642-052-9(6) , Steerforth Italia) Steerforth Pr.

—Las Aventuras de Pinocho. (SPA., Illus.). 160p. (YA). 14.95 (978-84-7281-190-4(5) , AF1905) Auriga, Ediciones S.A. ESP. *Dist:* Continental Bk. Co., Inc.

—Las Aventuras de Pinocho. (Coleccion Cuentos Universales). (SPA.). (YA). (gr. 4 up). (978-84-261-3145-4(X) , JV30301) Juventud, Editorial ESP. *Dist:* Lectorum Pubns., Inc.

—Las Aventuras de Pinocho Great Read. 2005. (Great Classics for Children Ser.). (SPA., Illus.). 160p. (J). 5.99 (978-1-4037-1148-9(8)) Dalmatian Pr.

—Le Avventure di Pinocchio, Level B. (ITA.). (J). pap. 8.95 (978-0-88436-050-6(4) , 55254) EMC/Paradigm Publishing.

—Pinocchio. (J). 22.95 (978-0-88411-249-5(7)) Amereon LTD.

—Pinocchio. Fanelli, Sara & Rose, Emma, trs. from ITA. Fanelli, Sara, illus. 2003. 192p. (J). (gr. 2). 18.99 (978-0-7636-2261-9(3)) Candlewick Pr.

—Pinocchio. Bartram, Simon, illus. 2006. (Read & Listen Bks.). 64p. (J). 9.99 (978-0-7566-1829-2(0)) Dorling Kindersley Publishing, Inc.

—Pinocchio. 2000. (ITA.). (J). pap. 15.95 (978-88-452-4182-6(3)) Fabbri - RCS Libri ITA. *Dist:* Distribooks, Inc.

—Pinocchio. (978-1-894998-20-8(0)) Lake, Jack Productions, Inc. CAN. *Dist:* Hushion Hse. Publishing, Ltd.

—Pinocchio. Murray, M. A., tr. from ITA. 2002. (Penguin Classics Ser.). (Illus.). 192p. (gr. 12). pap. 10.00 (978-0-14-243706-3(9) , Penguin Classics) Penguin Group (USA) Inc.

—Pinocchio. Ingpen, Robert R., illus. 2005. 136p. (J). (gr. 2-7). 19.95 (978-1-933327-00-6(6)) Purple Bear Bks., Inc.

—Pinocchio. 2002. (gr. 7-12). lib. bdg. 18.80 (978-0-613-64314-6(3)) Tandem Library Bks.

—Pinocchio. 2005. (WEL., Illus.). 40p. (978-1-899877-05-8(3)) Y Ddraig Fach.

—Pinocchio: A Classic Story about Honesty. 2003. (Illus.). 32p. per. 3.95 (978-0-9747133-2-8(5) , Values to Live By Classic Stories) Thomas, Frederic Inc.

—Pinocho. 2003. Tr. of Pinocchio. (SPA.). 284p. (978-958-30-0803-0(6) , PV30464) Centro de Informacion y Desarrollo de la Comunicacion y la Literatura MEX. *Dist:* Lectorum Pubns., Inc.

Collodi, Carlo & Edens, Cooper. Pinocchio. 2001. (Classic Illustrated Treasury Ser.). (Illus.). 176p. (J). 19.95 (978-0-8118-2283-1(4)) Chronicle Bks. LLC.

Collodi, Carlo & Hildebrandt, Greg. The Adventures of Pinocchio. 2003. (Illus.). 56p. (J). 9.98 (978-0-7624-1713-1(7) , Courage Bks.) Running Pr. Bk. Pubs.

Dalmatian Press Staff. Disney Vintage Pinocchio. rev. ed. 2006. 16p. (J). pap. 3.99 (978-1-4037-2337-6(0)) Dalmatian Pr.

Fairy Tales - Pinocchio. 2005. (J). bds. (978-1-4194-0101-5(7)) Paradise Pr., Inc.

Fairy Tales- Pinocchio. 2005. (J). bds. (978-1-4194-0041-4(X)) Paradise Pr., Inc.

Fairy Tales s/s - Pinocchio. 2005. (J). bds. (978-1-4194-0067-4(3)) Paradise Pr., Inc.

Fletcher, Steffi. Pinocchio. Dempster, Al, illus. 2002. 24p. (J). (gr. k-k). 2.99 (978-0-7364-2152-2(1) , Golden/Disney) Random Hse. Children's Bks.

Hillert, Margaret. Pinocchio. Hamilton, Laurie, illus. rev. ed. 2006. (Beginning to Read Ser.). 32p. (J). lib. bdg. 18.60 (978-1-59953-023-9(6)) Norwood Hse. Pr.

Kunhardt, Dorothy, ed. Pinocchio. deluxe ed. 1999. (J). 100.00 (978-1-55709-341-7(5)) Applewood Bks.

—Pinocchio. (FRE.). 96p. (J). (gr. k-5). pap. 9.95 (978-0-7859-8845-8(9)) French & European Pubns., Inc.

—Pinocchio. 2002. (Illus.). (J). lib. bdg. 14.99 (978-0-7364-8019-2(6) , RH/Disney) Random Hse. Children's Bks.

Leigh, Tom, illus. Pinocchio: A Tale of Honesty. 2006. (J). 6.99 (978-1-59939-005-5(1) , Reader's Digest Young Families, Inc.) Reader's Digest Children's Publishing, Inc.

Leonard, Barry, ed. Pinocchio. 2003. (Illus.). 12p. (J). (gr. k-5). reprint ed. 17.00 (978-0-7567-6862-1(4)) DIANE Publishing Co.

Lockman, Vic, illus. Pinocchio's Quest: Coloring Book. 2000. 40p. (J). (gr. 2-6). pap. 2.00 (978-1-930367-40-1(6) , CLP 29650) Christian Liberty Pr.

Mantovani, Maria & Barsotti, Renzo, illus. Classic Fairy Tales - Pinocchio. 32p. 7.95 (978-1-904668-54-1(2)) Mercury Bks. Ltd. GBR. *Dist:* International Publishers Marketing.

McGraw-Hill Staff. Le Avventure di Pinocchio: Beginning Through Intermediate. abr. ed. 2001. (ITA & ENG., Illus.). 88p. (C). pap. 19.96 (978-0-8442-8023-3(2) , 9780844280233) McGraw-Hill/Contemporary.

Mouse Works Staff. Pinocchio - Toy Story, 2. 75th anniv. ed. 1998. 9.99 (978-0-7364-0088-6(5)) Mouse Works.

Nickel. Pinocchio. Date not set. (J). 4.99 (978-0-7214-5404-7(6)) Nickel Pr.

Pinocchio. 2002. (Puppy Tales Ser.). (Illus.). 24p. (J). (gr. k-3). 1.49 (978-1-57759-260-0(3)) Dalmatian Pr.

Pinocchio. 2003. (Illus.). 12.99 (978-0-7868-3480-8(3)) Disney Pr.

Pinocchio. 1999. (ITA., Illus.). 24p. (J). (ps-3). pap. 7.95 (978-88-8148-258-0(4)) European Language Institute ITA. *Dist:* Distribooks, Inc., Midwest European Pubns.

Pinocchio: The Human Body, Sea Life, The Bedroom. 1999. (FRE & ENG., Illus.). 24p. (J). (ps-5). pap., stu. ed. 7.95 (978-88-8148-243-6(6)) European Language Institute ITA. *Dist:* Distribooks, Inc., Midwest European Pubns.

Pinocchio: The Human Body; Sea Life; The Bedroom. 1999. (Lesen Leicht Germacht Ser.). (GER & ENG., Illus.). 24p. (J). (ps-5). pap. 7.95 (978-88-8148-248-1(7)) European Language Institute ITA. *Dist:* Distribooks, Inc., Midwest European Pubns.

Pinocho: The Human Body, Sea Life, the Bedroom. 1999. Tr. of Pinocchio. (SPA & ENG., Illus.). (J). (ps-5). pap. 7.95 (978-88-8148-253-5(3)) European Language Institute ITA. *Dist:* Distribooks, Inc., Midwest European Pubns.

Random House Disney Staff. Pinocchio. 2002. (Illus.). (J). 2.99 (978-0-7364-2075-4(4) , RH/Disney) Random Hse. Children's Bks.

Random House Disney Staff & Winkelman, Barbara Gaines. Pinocchio's Nose Grows. 2002. (Step into Reading Bks.). (Illus.). 32p. (J). (ps-1). lib. bdg. 11.99 (978-0-7364-8001-7(3) , RH/Disney) Random Hse. Children's Bks.

Rogland, Robert. Pinocchio's Quest. 2000. (Illus.). 216p. (J). (gr. 4-6). pap. 8.95 (978-1-930367-39-5(2) , CLP 29650); 12.95 (978-1-930367-55-5(4) , CLP29651) Christian Liberty Pr.

Tyrrell, Melissa. Pinocchio. McMullen, Nigel, illus. 2005. (Fairytale Friends Ser.: Vol. 7). 12p. (J). (ps-k). bds. 5.95 (978-1-58117-151-8(X) , Intervisual/Piggy Toes) Dalmatian Pr.

Walt Disney's Pinocchio. 2002. (J). spiral bd. (978-0-9720651-2-2(1)) Story Reader, Inc.

PIONEER LIFE

see Frontier and Pioneer Life

PIPE FITTING—VOCATIONAL GUIDANCE

Thomas, Mark. Day with a Plumber. 2001. (gr. k-3). lib. bdg. 12.95 (978-0-613-58763-1(4)) Tandem Library Bks.

PIRATES

see also Privateering; United States—History—Tripolitan War, 1801-1805; Women Pirates

Adkins, Jan. What If You Met a Pirate? Adkins, Jan, illus. 2006. (Illus.). 32p. (J). pap. 6.95 (978-1-59643-182-9(2)) Roaring Brook Pr.

Aprile, Thierry. Piratas. Gonzalez Balle, Jorge, tr. Place, Francois, illus. 2004. (Tras los pasos de ... Ser.). (SPA.). 128p. (J). pap. 14.95 (978-84-95939-68-5(1)) Blume ESP. *Dist:* Independent Pubs. Group.

Barry, Bill. Pirates of the High Seas: Illustrated Adventures in History, 4 vols. Barry, Orpha Harryman, ed. 2002. (Illus.). 64p. (YA). pap. 11.95 (978-0-944099-25-4(4)) Bill Barry's Compass Bks.

Bell, Robin. My Adventure with Pirates. 2007. 44p. (J). 8.99 (978-1-59092-462-4(2) , Orchard Academy Pr.) Windstorm Creative.

Blackwood, Gary L. Pirates. 2001. (Bad Guys Ser.). (Illus.). 72p. (J). (gr. 5 up). lib. bdg. 29.93 (978-0-7614-1019-5(8) , Benchmark Bks.) Cavendish, Marshall Corp.

Brown, Chris. Shiver Me Timbers! A Funbook of Pirates-,Sailors & Other Sea-Farers. 2006. (Illus.). 32p. pap. 8.95 (978-0-7145-3303-2(3)) Consortium Bk. Sales & Distribution.

Bulloch, Ivan. A Pirate. James, Diane, illus. rev. ed. 2004. (I Wish I Were Ser.). 24p. (ps-2). (J). pap. 7.95 (978-1-58728-038-2(8)); 12.95 (978-1-58728-034-4(5)) T&N Children's Publishing. (Two Can Publishing).

Butterfield, Moira. Pirates & Smugglers. 2005. (Kingfisher Knowledge Ser.). (Illus.). 64p. (J). (gr. 5-9). 12.95 (978-0-7534-5864-8(0) , Kingfisher) Houghton Mifflin Co. Trade & Reference Div.

Caviezel, Giovanni. Pirates! Mesturini, Cristina, illus. 2006. 10p. (J). 10.99 (978-0-7641-5993-0(3)) Barron's Educational Series, Inc.

Clibbon, Meg. Imagine You're a Pirate! Clibbon, Lucy, illus. 2002. (Imagine This! Ser.). 32p. (J). (ps-4). pap. 8.95 (978-1-55037-740-8(X)); 19.95 (978-1-55037-741-5(8)) Annick Pr., Ltd. CAN. *Dist:* Firefly Bks., Ltd.

—Imagine You're a Pirate! 2002. (gr. k-3). lib. bdg. 16.40 (978-0-613-56443-4(X)) Tandem Library Bks.

PQR

Currie, Stephen. Pirates. 2000. (World History Ser.). (Illus.). 108p. (YA). (gr. 8-11). 27.45 (978-1-56006-807-5(8) , LML00902-178139, Lucent Bks.) Thomson Gale.

Dalmatian Press Staff. Pirates: Book to Color Plus 3 Toy Pirates. rev. ed. 2007. 48p. 3.99 (***978-1-4037-3204-0(3)***) Dalmatian Pr.

D'Andrea, Deborah. Picture Me As a Pirate. Ayers, Michael B., illus. rev. ed. 2000. 10p. (J). (ps-1). bds. 4.99 (978-1-57151-578-0(X)) Playhouse Publishing.

Davis, Kelly. See-Through Pirates, Vol. 3. Malam, John, illus. 2003. (See-Through Ser.). 32p. (J). 15.95 (978-0-7624-1587-8(8) , Running Pr. Kids) Running Pr. Bk. Pubs.

Deary, Terry. The Handbook of Pirates. 2007. 96p. (J). (gr. 4-7). pap. 5.99 (***978-0-545-03302-2(0)***) Scholastic, Inc.

Dorling Kindersley Publishing Staff. Pirate. 2004. (Eyewitness Books). (J). 72p. lib. bdg. 19.99 (978-0-7566-0712-8(4)); 16p. pap. 6.99 (978-0-7566-0219-2(X)) Dorling Kindersley Publishing, Inc.

Drechsler, Lawrence. The Pirates. (Illus.). (Orig.). (J). (gr. 6 up). pap. (978-0-935143-01-0(7)) Treadle Pr.

Elborough, Travis. Highwayman, Outlaws & Bandits of London. 2004. (... of London Ser.). (Illus.). 96p. 8.99 (978-1-904153-13-9(5)) Watling St., Ltd. GBR. *Dist:* Trafalgar Square Publishing.

Farman, John. The Short & Bloody History of Pirates. 2005. (Short & Bloody Histories Ser.). (Illus.). 96p. (gr. 6-12). lib. bdg. 19.93 (978-0-8225-0843-4(5)) Lerner Publishing Group.

Forester, C. S. Sterling Point Books: the Barbary Pirates. 2007. (Sterling Point Bks.). (Illus.). 176p. (J). 12.95 (978-1-4027-4522-5(2)); pap. 6.95 (978-1-4027-4142-5(1)) Sterling Publishing Co., Inc.

Garwood, Val. Lift the Lid on Pirates: Discover High-Seas Adventure, Build Your Own Pirate Ship, & Learn to Navigate with a 16-Century Compass! 1999. (Illus.). 24p. (J). (gr. 4-7). pap. 22.95 (978-0-7624-0490-2(6) , Running Pr. Kids) Running Pr. Bk. Pubs.

Gilpin, Rebecca. Pirate Things to make & Do. 2005. 32p. (J). pap. 6.95 (978-0-7945-1061-9(2) , Usborne) EDC Publishing.

Hague, Michael. The Book of Pirates. Hague, Michael, illus. 2001. (Illus.). 160p. (J). 25.99 (978-0-688-14003-8(3)) HarperCollins Pubs.

Hamilton, John. A History of Pirates. 2007. (Pirates! Ser.). (Illus.). 32p. (J). (gr. 4-7). lib. bdg. 24.21 (***978-1-59928-761-4(7)*** , ABDO & Daughters) ABDO Publishing Co.

—Pirate Ships & Weapons. 2007. (ENG., Illus.). 32p. (J). lib. bdg. 24.21 (***978-1-59928-763-8(3)*** , ABDO & Daughters) ABDO Publishing Co.

—A Pirate's Life. 2007. (Pirates! Ser.). (Illus.). 32p. (J). (gr. 4-7). lib. bdg. 24.21 (***978-1-59928-762-1(5)*** , ABDO & Daughters) ABDO Publishing Co.

Hamilton, Sue L. Bartholomew Roberts. 2007. (Illus.). 32p. (J). lib. bdg. 24.21 (***978-1-59928-757-7(9)*** , ABDO & Daughters) ABDO Publishing Co.

—Blackbeard. 2007. (Pirates! Ser.). (ENG., Illus.). 32p. (J). (gr. 3-6). 24.21 (***978-1-59928-758-4(7)*** , ABDO & Daughters) ABDO Publishing Co.

—Captain Kidd. 2007. (Pirates! Ser.). (ENG., Illus.). 32p. (J). (gr. 3-6). 24.21 (***978-1-59928-759-1(5)*** , ABDO & Daughters) ABDO Publishing Co.

—Henry Morgan. 2007. (Pirates! Ser.). (ENG., Illus.). 32p. (J). (gr. 3-6). 24.21 (***978-1-59928-760-7(9)*** , ABDO & Daughters) ABDO Publishing Co.

—Pirates!, 8 vols., Set. Incl. Blackbeard. 24.21 (***978-1-59928-758-4(7));*** Captain Kidd. 24.21 (***978-1-59928-759-1(5));*** Henry Morgan. 24.21 (***978-1-59928-760-7(9));*** (Illus.). 32p. (J). (gr. 3-6). 2007. Set lib. bdg. 193.68 (***978-1-59928-756-0(0)*** , ABDO & Daughters) ABDO Publishing Co.

Hanel, Rachael. Pirates. 2007. (J). (978-1-58341-537-5(8) , Creative Education) Creative Co., The.

Hibbert, Clare. Real Pirates: Over 30 True Stories of Seafaring Sculduggery. James, John, illus. 2003. 48p. (J). 15.95 (978-1-59270-018-9(7)) Enchanted Lion Bks., LLC.

Howard, Barnaby. The Best Book of Pirates. (Best Book of... Ser.). (Illus.). 32p. (J). (gr. k-3). 2006. 6.95 (978-0-7534-5936-2(1)); 2002. tchr. ed. 12.95 (978-0-7534-5449-7(1)) Houghton Mifflin Co. Trade & Reference Div. (Kingfisher).

Jordan, Shirley. Pirates & Privateers in the New World: Moments in History. 2001. (Cover-to-Cover Bks.). (Illus.). 72p. (J). pap. 8.95 (978-0-7891-5396-8(3)); (gr. 4-7). lib. bdg. 17.95 (978-0-7807-9803-8(1)) Perfection Learning Corp.

Kallen, Stuart A. Life among the Pirates. 1998. (Way People Live Ser.). (Illus.). 96p. (YA). (gr. 7-10). 28.70 (978-1-56006-393-3(9) , LML00902-177775, Lucent Bks.) Thomson Gale.

Kozar, Richard. Infamous Pirates. 1998. (Costume, Tradition & Culture). (Illus.). 64p. (YA). 12.95 (978-0-7910-5165-8(X) , Chelsea Hse.) Facts On File, Inc.

Langley, Andrew. 100 Things You Should Know about Pirates. 2003. (Illus.). 48p. (J). (gr. 3 up). lib. bdg. (978-1-59084-453-3(X)) Mason Crest Pubs.

Larousse Mexico Staff, ed. Mi Pequena Larousse Enciclopedia Los Piratas. 2006. (Mi Pequena Enciclopedia Ser.). (Illus.). 38p. (ps-k). pap. 3.95 (978-970-22-1192-1(1)) Larousse, Ediciones, S. A. de C. V. MEX. *Dist:* Houghton Mifflin Co. Trade & Reference Div.

Lassieur, Allison. The History of Pirates: From Privateers to Outlaws. 2007. (Edge Books, the Real World of Pirates). (Illus.). 32p. (J). 23.93 (978-0-7368-6423-7(7) , 1258946) Capstone Pr., Inc.

—Pirate Hideouts: Secret Spots & Shelters. 2007. (Edge Books, the Real World of Pirates). (Illus.). 32p. (J). 23.93 (978-0-7368-6426-8(1)) Capstone Pr., Inc.

Less, Emma. Little Scribbles: Pirate Fun. Harpster, Steve, illus. 2007. (Little Scribbles Ser.). 12p. (J). bds. 5.95 (978-1-4027-3804-3(8)) Sterling Publishing Co., Inc.

Lethbridge, Lucy. True Stories of Pirates. 2005. (True Adventure Stories Ser.). (Illus.). 144p. (J). pap. 4.99 (978-0-7945-0875-3(8) , Usborne) EDC Publishing.

Lichtenheld, Tom. Everything I Know about Pirates. Lichtenheld, Tom, illus. 2003. (Illus.). 40p. (J). pap. 7.99 (978-0-689-86009-6(9) , Aladdin) Simon & Schuster Children's Publishing.

—Everything I Know about Pirates. 2000. (Illus.). 40p. (J). (ps-3). 17.95 (978-0-689-82625-2(7)) Simon & Schuster Children's Publishing.

Lincoln, Margarette. The Pirate's Handbook: How to Become a Rogue of the High Seas. (Illus.). (J). pap. 15.99 (978-0-590-24558-6(9)) Scholastic, Inc.

—The Pirate's Handbook: How to Become a Rogue of the High Seas. 1998. (Puffin Book Ser.). (978-0-606-13711-9(4)) Tandem Library Bks.

Lock, Deborah & Dorling Kindersley Publishing Staff. Pirate. 2005. (Eye Wonder Ser.). (Illus.). 48p. (J). 9.99 (978-0-7566-1167-5(9)); lib. bdg. 17.99 (978-0-7566-1168-2(7)) Dorling Kindersley Publishing, Inc.

Lubber, William. Pirateology: The Pirate Hunter's Companion. Steer, Dugald A., ed. Gilbert, Anne Yvonne et al, illus. 2006. (Ologies Ser.). 32p. (J). (gr. 3). 19.99 (978-0-7636-3143-7(4)) Candlewick Pr.

Malam, John. How to Be a Pirate. Antram, Dave, illus. 2005. (How to Be Ser.). 32p. (J). (gr. 3-7). 14.95 (978-0-7922-7448-3(2)); 21.90 (978-0-7922-7497-1(0)) National Geographic Society. (National Geographic Children's Bks.).

—You Wouldn't Want to Be a Pirate's Prisoner! Antram, David, illus. 2002. (You Wouldn't Want to Ser.). 32p. (J). (gr. 2-5). 28.50 (978-0-531-14607-1(3)); pap. 9.95 (978-0-531-16368-9(7)) Scholastic Library Publishing. (Watts, Franklin).

—You Wouldn't Want to Be a Pirate's Prisoner! 2002. (gr. 3-6). lib. bdg. 18.75 (978-0-613-53885-5(4)) Tandem Library Bks.

Mason, Paul. Pirates. 2005. (Illus.). 32p. (J). (gr. 4-7). lib. bdg. 27.10 (978-1-58340-772-1(3)) Smart Apple Media.

Matthews, Gill, et al. Pirates Ahoy! 2007. (I-read Ser.). (Illus.). 48p. pap. (***978-0-521-70487-8(1)***) Cambridge Univ. Pr.

Matthews, John. Pirates. 2006. (Illus.). 32p. (J). (gr. 1-7). 19.95 (978-1-4169-2734-1(4) , Atheneum) Simon & Schuster Children's Publishing.

—Pirates: Most Wanted. 2007. 32p. (J). (gr. 1-7). 16.99 (978-1-4169-3934-4(2) , Atheneum) Simon & Schuster Children's Publishing.

Maynard, Christopher. Pirates: Raiders of the High Seas. 1998. (Eyewitness Readers). (Illus.). 48p. (J). (gr. 3-5). pap. 3.99 (978-0-7894-3443-2(1)) Dorling Kindersley Publishing, Inc.

Maynard, Christopher & Dorling Kindersley Publishing Staff. Pirates: Raiders of the High Seas. 1998. (Eyewitness Readers). (Illus.). 48p. (J). (gr. 4-7). 12.99 (978-0-7894-3768-6(6)) Dorling Kindersley Publishing, Inc.

McDonald, Jill. Alex Toys: My First Pirate Book & Treasure Chest. Silver-Thompson, Pattie, illus. rev. ed. 2007. (Everything... ! Ser.). 46p. (J). (ps-1). 14.99 (***978-0-316-11346-5(8)***) Little, Brown Bks. for Young Readers.

McNeil, Niki, et al. HOCPP 1139 Pirates. 2006. spiral bd. 19.00 (***978-1-60308-139-9(9)***) In the Hands of a Child.

Meltzer, Milton. Piracy & Plunder: A Murderous Business. Waldman, Bruce, illus. 2001. 96p. (J). 24.99 (978-0-525-45857-9(3) , Dutton Juvenile) Penguin Group (USA) Inc.

Menges, Jeff A. Haunted Pirates Tattoos. 2004. (Tattoos Ser.). (Illus.). 2p. (J). pap. 1.50 (978-0-486-43320-2(X)) Dover Pubns., Inc.

Morris, Neil. Pirates. 2007. (J). (***978-1-59920-104-7(6)***) Smart Apple Media.

Nemmers, Tom. Pirates Scratch & Sketch: An Art Activity Book for Adventurous Artists & Explorers of All Ages. 2007. (Illus.). 64p. (YA). 12.99 (***978-1-59359-871-6(8)***) Peter Pauper Pr. Inc.

Niehaus, Alisha & Hecker, Alan. Piratepedia. 2006. (Illus.). 128p. (J). (gr. 2). 12.99 (978-0-7566-2660-0(9)) Dorling Kindersley Publishing, Inc.

Nobleman, Marc Tyler. Pirate. 2007. (J). (***978-1-4109-2966-2(3));*** pap. (***978-1-4109-2987-7(6)***) Steck-Vaughn.

O'Donnell, Liam. The Pirate Code: Life of a Pirate. 2007. (Illus.). 32p. (J). 23.93 (978-0-7368-6424-4(5)) Capstone Pr., Inc.

—Pirate Gear: Cannons, Swords, & the Jolly Roger. 2007. (Edge Books, the Real World of Pirates). (Illus.). 32p. (J). 23.93 (978-0-7368-6425-1(3)) Capstone Pr., Inc.

—Pirate Ships: Sailing the High Seas. 2007. (Edge Books, the Real World of Pirates). (Illus.). 32p. (J). (978-0-7368-6427-5(X)) Capstone Pr., Inc.

—Pirate Treasure: Stolen Riches. 2007. (Edge Books, the Real World of Pirates). (Illus.). 32p. (J). 23.93 (978-0-7368-6428-2(8)) Capstone Pr., Inc.

Osborne, Mary Pope & Osborne, Will. Pirates: A Nonfiction Companion to Pirates Past Noon. 2001. (Magic Tree House Research Guide Ser.: No. 4). (Illus.). (J). (gr. k-3). (978-0-606-21313-4(9)) Tandem Library Bks.

Osborne, Will. Pirates: A Nonfiction Companion to Pirates Past Noon. 2001. (Magic Tree House Research Guide Ser.: No. 4). (J). (gr. k-3). lib. bdg. 13.00 (978-0-613-33774-8(3)) Tandem Library Bks.

Pirates. (Awesome Adventures Ser.). 16p. (J). (978-2-7643-0117-3(0)) Phidal Publishing, Inc./Editions Phidal, Inc.

Pirotta, Saviour. Pirates & Treasure. (Remarkable World Ser.). (Illus.). 48p. (YA). (gr. 3-8). lib. bdg. 24.26 (978-1-56847-366-6(4)) Raintree.

Platt, Richard. Discovering Pirates. 2004. (Illus.). 32p. (YA). pap. 16.95 (978-1-58980-227-8(6)) Pelican Publishing Co., Inc.

—Piratas. Chambers, Tina, photos by. 2005. (Dk eyewitness Bks.). (Illus.). 72p. (J). (gr. 4-7). 15.99 (978-0-7566-1483-6(X)); lib. bdg. 19.99 (978-0-7566-1489-8(9)) Dorling Kindersley Publishing, Inc.

—Pirate. Chambers, Tina, photos by. 2002. (Illus.). 64p. (YA). (gr. 5-7). reprint ed. 16.00 (978-0-7567-5333-7(3)) DIANE Publishing Co.

—Pirate. 2007. (DK Eyewitness Bks.). 72p. (J). (gr. 3-8). 15.99 incl. cd-rom (978-0-7566-3005-8(3)) Dorling Kindersley Publishing, Inc.

Price, Roger & Stern, Leonard. Pirates Mad Libs. 2007. (Mad Libs Ser.). 48p. (J). pap. 3.99 (978-0-8431-2313-5(3) , Price Stern Sloan) Penguin Group (USA) Inc.

Punter, R. Pirates. 2004. (Young Reading Ser.: Vol. 1). 48p. (J). (gr. 2 up). lib. bdg. 13.99 (978-1-58086-608-8(5) , Usborne) EDC Publishing.

Punter, Russell. Pirates Kid Kit. 2004. (Kid Kits Ser.). 48p. (J). 15.99 (978-1-58086-732-0(4)); 15.99 (978-1-58086-735-1(9)) EDC Publishing. (Usborne).

Pyle, Howard. The Book of Pirates. Pyle, Howard, illus. 2000. (Illus.). 320p. (J). (gr. 5-8). pap. 12.95 (978-0-486-41304-4(7)) Dover Pubns., Inc.

Radtke, Becky. Pirates Ahoy! 2006. 64p. (J). pap., act. bk. ed. 1.50 (978-0-486-45170-1(4)) Dover Pubns., Inc.

Richardson, Christopher. Pirates. 2005. (X-Zone Ser.). (Illus.). 30p. (gr. 4-8). 23.00 (978-0-7910-8989-7(4)) Facts On File, Inc.

Rogers, Jon, et al. Pirate Talk: The Quotable Pirates of the Caribbean. 2007. 112p. (gr. 7-17). pap. 9.95 (***978-1-4231-0654-8(7)*** , Disney Editions) Disney Pr.

Sander, Sonia. The Pirates Who Don't Color Anything! Funnypages Productions, illus. 2006. (VeggieTales Ser.). 48p. (J). 3.99 (978-1-4169-1784-7(5) , Simon Scribbles) Simon & Schuster Children's Publishing.

Smith, Helen. Pirates, Swashbucklers & Buccaneers of London. 2004. (... of London Ser.). (Illus.). 96p. 8.99 (978-1-904153-17-7(8)) Watling St., Ltd. GBR. *Dist:* Trafalgar Square Publishing.

Solway, Andrew. A Pirate Adventure: Weather. 2005. (Illus.). 32p. (J). lib. bdg. 28.21 (978-1-4109-1926-7(9)) Raintree.

—A Pirate Adventure: Weather. 2005. (Illus.). 32p. (J). (978-1-4109-1957-1(9)) Steck-Vaughn.

Southwater Staff. Pirates: Skulls & Crossbones. 2000. (Illus.). 64p. pap. 7.95 (978-1-84215-043-6(X)) Anness Publishing, Inc.

Spence, David. Pirates. 2004. (Illus.). 32p. (J). (gr. 4-7). pap. 5.95 (978-1-86007-001-3(9)) Ticktock Media Ltd. GBR. *Dist:* Consortium Bk. Sales & Distribution.

—Pirates! 1999. (Illus.). 24p. (J). (gr. 5-8). (978-0-7881-6469-9(4)) DIANE Publishing Co.

Spenceley, Angela, compiled by. Pirate Coloring & Sticker Book: Your Complete Guide to Famous Pirates. l.t. ed. 2006. (Illus.). 24p. (J). pap. 8.95 (978-0-9702168-6-1(6)) Coconut Pr., LLC.

Steele, Philip. Pirates. 2007. (Inside Access Ser.). (Illus.). 32p. (J). (gr. k-3). 9.95 (978-0-7534-6061-0(0) , Kingfisher) Houghton Mifflin Co. Trade & Reference Div.

—Pirates: With Jake Rattlebones. 2007. (Inside Access Ser.). (Illus.). 32p. (J). (***978-1-4287-3538-5(0)*** , Kingfisher) Houghton Mifflin Co. Trade & Reference Div.

Steele, Philip. The World of Pirates. 2004. (World Of Ser.). (Illus.). 64p. (J). (gr. 4-6). pap. 8.95 (978-0-7534-5786-3(5) , Kingfisher) Houghton Mifflin Co. Trade & Reference Div.

Steele, Philip & Cordingly, David. Pirates. 2003. (Illus.). 64p. 14.99 (978-0-7548-1247-0(2)) Anness Publishing GBR. *Dist:* National Bk. Network.

Stockton, Frank Richard. Buccaneers & Pirates. 2007. (Illus.). 368p. pap. 12.95 (***978-0-486-45425-2(8)***) Dover Pubns., Inc.

—Buccaneers & Pirates of Our Coasts. 2006. pap. (***978-1-4068-3064-4(X)***) Echo Library.

—Buccaneers & Pirates of Our Coasts. 1999. (Notable American Authors Ser.). reprint ed. lib. bdg. 125.00 (978-0-7812-8936-8(X)) Reprint Services Co.

Temple, Bob. The Golden Age of Pirates: An Interactive History Adventure. 2008. (You Choose Bks.). 112p. (J). (gr. 3-7). lib. bdg. 27.23 (***978-1-4296-0162-7(0)***) Capstone Pr., Inc.

Tlock, Andrew. We Are Jolly Pirates. 1999. (Illus.). (J). pap. 12.95 (978-1-57717-126-3(8)) New Line Bks.

Weatherly, Myra. Women Pirates: Eight Stories of Adventure. 1998. (Women Adventurers Ser.). (Illus.). 112p. (YA). (gr. 6-12). 21.95 (978-1-883846-24-4(2) , First Biographies) Reynolds, Morgan Inc.

Weintraub, Aileen. Anne Bonny & Mary Read: Fearsome Female Pirates of the 18th-Century. 2002. (Library of Pirates). (Illus.). 24p. (J). (gr. 3). lib. bdg. 18.75 (978-0-8239-5795-8(0) , PowerKids Pr.) Rosen Publishing Group, Inc., The.

—The Barbarossa Brothers: 16th-Century Pirates of the Barbary Coast. 2002. (Library of Pirates). (Illus.). 24p. (J). (gr. 3). lib. bdg. 18.75 (978-0-8239-5799-6(3) , PowerKids Pr.) Rosen Publishing Group, Inc., The.

—Blackbeard: 18th-Century Pirate of the Spanish Main & the Carolina Coast. 2002. (Library of Pirates). (Illus.). 24p. (J). (gr. 3). lib. bdg. 18.75 (978-0-8239-5794-1(2) , PowerKids Pr.) Rosen Publishing Group, Inc., The.

—Captain Kidd: 17th-Century Pirate of the Indian Ocean & African Coast. 2002. (Library of Pirates). (Illus.). 24p. (J). (gr. 3). lib. bdg. 18.75 (978-0-8239-5797-2(7) , PowerKids Pr.) Rosen Publishing Group, Inc., The.

—Henry Morgan: 17th-Century Buccaneer. 2002. (Library of Pirates). (Illus.). 24p. (J). (gr. 3). lib. bdg. 18.75 (978-0-8239-5798-9(5) , PowerKids Pr.) Rosen Publishing Group, Inc., The.

—Jean Lafitte: Pirate Hero of the War of 1812. 2002. (Library of Pirates). (Illus.). 24p. (J). (gr. 3). lib. bdg. 18.75 (978-0-8239-5796-5(9) , PowerKids Pr.) Rosen Publishing Group, Inc., The.

—The Library of Pirates, 6 bks. Incl. Anne Bonny & Mary Read : Fearsome Female Pirates of the 18th-Century. lib. bdg. 18.75 (978-0-8239-5795-8(0)); Barbarossa Brothers : 16th-Century Pirates of the Barbary Coast. lib. bdg. 18.75 (978-0-8239-5799-6(3)); Blackbeard : 18th-Century Pirate of the Spanish Main & the Carolina Coast. lib. bdg. 18.75 (978-0-8239-5794-1(2)); Captain Kidd : 17th-Century Pirate of the Indian Ocean & African Coast. lib. bdg. 18.75 (978-0-8239-5797-2(7)); Henry Morgan : 17th-Century Buccaneer. lib. bdg. 18.75 (978-0-8239-5798-9(5)); Jean Lafitte : Pirate Hero of the War of 1812. lib. bdg. 18.75 (978-0-8239-5796-5(9)); 24p. (J). (gr. 3). 2002. (Illus.). 112.50 (978-0-8239-7133-6(3) , PowerKids Pr.) Rosen Publishing Group, Inc., The.

Williams, Brian Peter. Pirates. 2005. (First Look at History Ser.). (Illus.). 24p. (J). lib. bdg. 22.00 (978-0-8368-4529-7(3)) Stevens, Gareth Inc.

Wren, Laura Lee. Pirates & Privateers of the High Seas. 2003. (Collective Biographies Ser.). (Illus.). 128p. (J). (gr. 6-12). lib. bdg. 26.60 (978-0-7660-1542-5(4)) Enslow Pubs., Inc.

Wright, Rachel. Pirates. (Illus.). 32p. (YA). (gr. 3 up). lib. bdg. 27.10 (978-1-932889-06-2(X)) Sea-To-Sea Pubns.

PIRATES—FICTION

Abbott, Tony. Pirates of the Purple Dawn. 2007. (Secrets of Droon Ser.: No. 29). 128p. (J). pap. 3.99 (978-0-439-90250-2(9) , Scholastic Paperbacks) Scholastic, Inc.

Abbott, Tony. Race to Doobesh. 2005. (Illus.). 127p. (J). lib. bdg. 15.38 (***978-1-4242-0311-6(2)***) Fitzgerald Bks.

Adkins, Jan E. What If You Met a Pirate? Adkins, Jan E., illus. rev. ed. 2004. (Illus.). 32p. (J). 16.95 (978-1-59643-007-5(9)) Roaring Brook Pr.

Aikins, Dave, illus. Dora's Pirate Adventure. 2005. (Dora the Explorer Ser.). 24p. (J). pap. 3.99 (978-0-689-87583-0(5) , Simon Spotlight/Nickelodeon) Simon & Schuster Children's Publishing.

Andreae, Giles. Captain Flinn & the Pirate Dinosaurs. Ayto, Russell, illus. 2005. 32p. (J). (gr. k-3). 15.95 (978-1-4169-0713-8(0) , McElderry, Margaret K.) Simon & Schuster Children's Publishing.

Archer, Chris. Secret City. 2003. (gr. 3-6). lib. bdg. 12.40 (978-0-613-72030-4(X)) Tandem Library Bks.

Arena, Felice & Kettle, Phil. Pirate Ship: By Felice Arena & Phil Kettle: Illustrated by Susy Boyer. Boyer, Susy, illus. 2004. (J). pap. (978-1-59336-362-8(1)) Mondo Publishing.

Babbitt, Natalie. Jack Plank Tells Tales. 2007. 144p. (J). (gr. 3 up). pap. 15.95 (***978-0-545-00496-1(9)*** , Di Capua, Michael) Scholastic, Inc.

Bailey, Len. Clabbernappers. 2005. (Illus.). 224p. (J). 17.95 (978-0-7653-0981-5(5) , Tor Bks.) Doherty, Tom Assocs., LLC.

Baker, Kage. The Life of the World to Come. rev. ed. 2005. (Company Ser.). 416p. mass mkt. 6.99 (978-0-7653-5432-7(2) , Tor Bks.) Doherty, Tom Assocs., LLC.

Balaban, Mariah, ed. Scooby-doo Pirates Ahoy. 2006. (Scooby-doo 8x8 Video Tie-in Ser.). (J). 24p. pap. 3.99 (978-0-439-83993-8(9)); 64p. pap. 3.99 (978-0-439-83992-1(0)) Scholastic, Inc.

Ballantyne, Michael. Blown to Bits or the Lonely Man of Rakat. 2006. 36.99 (***978-1-4280-4221-6(0));*** pap. 30.99 (***978-1-4280-4226-1(1)***) IndyPublish.com.

Ballantyne, R. The Coral Island. 2006. pap. 14.95 (***978-1-55742-666-6(X)***) Wildside Pr.

Ballantyne, R. M. Blown to Bits; or, the Lonely Man of Rak. 2006. pap. (***978-1-4065-0515-3(3)***) Dodo Pr.

Barry, Dave & Pearson, Ridley. Cave of the Dark Wind: A Never Land Adventure. Call, Greg, illus. 2007. 176p. (gr. 3 up). 9.99 (978-0-7868-3790-8(X)) Hyperion Bks. for Children.

—Escape from the Carnivale: A Never Land Book. Call, Greg, illus. 2006. 144p. (gr. 3-17). 9.99 (978-0-7868-3789-2(6)) Hyperion Bks. for Children.

—Peter & the Shadow Thieves. Call, Greg, illus. 2006. 576p. (gr. 5-17). 18.99 (978-0-7868-3787-8(X)) Hyperion Bks. for Children.

—Peter & the Starcatchers. Call, Greg, illus. 2006. 480p. (gr. 5-17), reprint ed. pap. 7.99 (978-0-7868-4907-9(X) , Disney Editions) Disney Pr.

—Peter & the Starcatchers. 2004. 464p. (gr. 5-17). 17.99 (978-0-7868-5445-5(6)) Hyperion Bks. for Children.

Bateman, Teresa. Fluffy, Scourge of the Sea. Chesworth, Michael, illus. 32p. (J). 2006. pap. 6.95 (978-1-58089-152-3(7)); 2005. 14.95 (978-1-58089-099-1(7)) Charlesbridge Publishing, Inc.

Batson, Wayne Thomas. Isle of Swords. 2007. 352p. (J). 16.99 (***978-1-4003-1018-0(0)***) Nelson, Thomas Inc.

Bauer, Christina. The Pirate Queen: A Timewalker Journey. 2005. 280p. (YA). pap. 14.99 (978-1-59092-224-8(7) , Blue Works) Windstorm Creative.

Beardsley, Martyn. Sir Gadabout Goes Overboard. l.t. ed. 2005. (J). pap. (978-1-4056-6010-5(4)) BBC Audio.

Beeke, Joel & Kleyn, Diana. How God Used the Pirates. Anderson, Jeff, illus. (Building on the Rock Ser.). 176p. (J). pap. (978-1-85792-816-7(4) , Christian Focus) Christian Focus Pubns. GBR. *Dist:* Riverside.

Bell, Rebecca. Capitano Ricco. Bell, Rebecca, illus. 2005. 36p. (J). per. 9.95 (***978-1-934138-06-9(1)***) Bouncing Ball Bks., Inc.

Bellville, Sharyn. The Pirate of Smith Point Beach. 2005. 85p. pap. 14.95 (978-1-4137-8353-7(8)) PublishAmerica, Inc.

Binder, Helga, illus. Wild Wicked Winifred & Horrible Hank. 1999. (J). (978-0-7608-3206-6(4)) Sundance/Newbridge Educational Publishing.

—Wild Wicked Winifred & the Pirates. 1999. (J). (978-0-7608-3207-3(2)) Sundance/Newbridge Educational Publishing.

—Wild Wicked Winifred & the Sea Serpent. 1999. (J). (978-0-7608-3204-2(8)) Sundance/Newbridge Educational Publishing.

—Wild Wicked Winifred & the Treasure Map. 1999. (J). (978-0-7608-3205-9(6)) Sundance/Newbridge Educational Publishing.

Bjerkvold, Belinda & Stevenson, Robert Louis. Treasure Island. Tod, Lluis M. & Andrada, Javier, illus. 2006. 36p. (J). lib. bdg. (***978-0-8368-7665-9(2)***) Stevens, Gareth Inc.

Blain, Christophe. Los Hielos, Vol. 2. 2005. (SPA., Illus.). 48p. (gr. 8-17). 19.95 (978-1-59497-114-3(5)) Public Square Bks.

Brian, Kate. Confessions. 2007. (Private Ser.). 240p. (YA). (gr. 9 up). pap. 9.99 (978-1-4169-1876-9(0) , Simon Pulse) Simon & Schuster Children's Publishing.

Brouillet, Chrystine & Brochard, Philippe. Les Pirates. 2001. (Roman Jeunesse Ser.). (FRE., Illus.). 96p. (J). pap. (978-2-89021-474-3(5)) Diffusion du livre Mirabel.

Brown, Edi. A Pirate Treasure. 2000. ii, 232p. (YA). (gr. 5-10). 5.95 (978-0-9677953-0-0(3)) Red Fox Publishing Co.

Bunting, Eve. Little Badger, Terror of the Seven Seas. Pham, LeUyen, illus. 2006. (Badger Bks.). 32p. (J). pap. 6.00 (978-0-15-205702-2(1) , Voyager Bks./Libros Viajeros) Harcourt Children's Bks.

Cannon, A. E. On the Go with Pirate Pete & Pirate Joe! Smith, Elwood H., illus. 2002. (Puffin Easy-to-Read Ser.). 32p. (J). pap. 3.99 (978-0-14-230136-4(1) , Puffin) Penguin Group (USA) Inc.

—On the Go with Pirate Pete & Pirate Joe. 2002. (gr. k-3). lib. bdg. 11.80 (978-0-613-54424-5(2)) Tandem Library Bks.

—Way Out West with Pirate Pete & Pirate Joe. Smith, Elwood H., illus. 2006. (Viking Easy-To-Read Ser.). 32p. (J). (ps). 13.99 (978-0-670-06080-1(1) , Viking Juvenile) Penguin Group (USA) Inc.

Cannon, Ann Edwards. Let the Good Times Roll with Pirate Pete & Pirate Joe. Smith, Elwood, illus. 2004. (Easy-to-Read,Viking Children's Ser.). 32p. (J). (ps-3). 13.99 (978-0-670-03679-0(X) , Viking Juvenile) Penguin Group (USA) Inc.

Carradice, Phil. The Pirates of Thorne Island. 2002. 109p. pap. 12.95 (978-1-85902-979-4(5)) Beekman Bks., Inc.

Carris, Joan D. A Ghost of a Chance. 2003. (Legends of the Carolinas Ser.). 155p. (J). 8.95 (978-1-928556-40-4(X)) Coastal Carolina Pr.

Chaparro, John E. Pirates Island. 2000. 170p. (J). (gr. 4-7). pap. 11.95 (978-1-891929-32-8(1)) Four Seasons Pubs.

Child, Lauren. I Can Do Anything That's Everything All on My Own. 2008. (Charlie & Lola Ser.). 24p. (J). (ps-1). 3.99 (***978-0-448-44792-6(4)*** , Grosset & Dunlap) Penguin Group (USA) Inc.

Ching, Jacqueline & Bones, Bess. Pirates of the Caribbean: A Storm at Sea. 2007. 32p. (gr. k-2). pap. 3.99 (***978-1-4231-0619-7(9)***) Disney Pr.

Chizuru, Mio. The Pirate & the Princess Volume 1: the Timelight Stone: The Timelight Stone. 2007. 110p. (J). pap. 5.99 (***978-1-933164-43-4(3)***) Seven Seas Entertainment, LLC.

—The Pirate & the Princess Volume 2: the Red Crystal: The Red Crystal. 2007. 110p. (J). pap. 5.99 (***978-1-933164-44-1(1)***) Seven Seas Entertainment, LLC.

Chronicle Books LLC Staff. Castaway Pirates. 2008. (J). 19.99 (978-0-8118-5923-3(1)) Chronicle Bks. LLC.

Clark, Sherryl. The Littlest Pirate: Nicholas Nosh Is off to Sea! Jellett, Tom, illus. 2006. (Nibbles Ser.). 72p. (J). pap. 3.95 (978-0-7624-2654-6(3) , Running Pr. Kids) Running Pr. Bk. Pubs.

Clark, Sherryl. Nibbles: the Littlest Pirate & the Hammerheads: Time to Track down Treasure! rev. ed. 2008. (Nibbles, Bites, & Chomps: Ser.). (Illus.). 72p. (J). pap. 3.95 (***978-0-7624-3064-2(8)*** , Running Pr. Kids) Running Pr. Bk. Pubs.

Colfer, Eoin. The Legend of Captain Crow's Teeth. McCoy, Glenn, illus. 2006. 112p. (gr. 2-6). pap. 4.99 (978-0-7868-5505-6(3)) Miramax Bks.

Come Away from the Water, Shirley. 2004. (J). pap. 14.95 incl. audio (978-1-56008-183 8(X)) Weston Woods Studios, Inc.

Come Away from the Water Shirley, 2004. (J). 24.95 incl. audio (978-1-56008-182-1(1)) Weston Woods Studios, Inc.

Cosson, M. J. & MacPhail, C. The Pirate, Big Fist, & Me. Garvey, Brann, illus. 2007. 112p. (J). (***978-1-59889-279-6(7)***) Stone Arch Bks.

Courtauld, Sarah. On a Pirate Ship. 2007. (Picture Bks). 24p. (J). 9.99 (***978-0-7945-1712-0(9)*** , Usborne) EDC Publishing.

Cowell, Cressida. How to Be a Pirate. 2005. (Illus.). 224p. (J). (gr. 3-7). 10.99 (978-0-316-15598-4(5)) Little Brown & Co.

—How to Speak Dragonese. 2006. (Illus.). 240p. (J). (gr. 3-7). 10.99 (978-0-316-15600-4(0)) Little Brown & Co.

Crimi, Carolyn. Henry & the Buccaneer Bunnies. Manders, John, illus. 2005. 40p. (J). (ps-3). 15.99 (978-0-7636-2449-1(7)) Candlewick Pr.

Croce, Pat. My Pop-Pop Is a Pirate. 2008. 18p. (J). 15.95 (***978-0-7624-2871-7(6)*** , Running Pr. Kids) Running Pr. Bk. Pubs.

Curry, Don, ed. Lucky's Pirate Adventure. 2006. 22p. (J). 14.95 (978-0-696-23423-1(8)) Meredith Bks.

Daffern, Brian. Prince Albert Bk. 3: The Realm Pirates. 2004. 192p. (YA). per. 13.95 (978-0-9709104-7-9(9)) Hickory Tales Publishing.

Dalmatian Press Staff, ed. Scooby Doo Pirates Ahoy! 2006. 48p. (J). 2.99 (978-1-4037-2431-1(8)) Dalmatian Pr.

Davis, Guy. Freddi Fish & the Pirate's Treasure. Winslow, Becky, illus. 2001. (Humongous Ser.). 12p. (J). bds. 9.99 incl. cd-rom (978-1-58668-066-4(8)) Lyrick Studios.

Davis, Mike. Pirates, Bats, & Dragons. Simpson, William, illus. 2004. 174p. (J). 15.95 (978-0-9747078-2-2(1)) Perceval Pr.

Day, Jan. The Pirate, Pink. Mason, Janeen I., illus. 2001. 32p. (J). (gr. k-3). pap. 15.95 (978-1-56554-879-4(5)) Pelican Publishing Co., Inc.

—Pirate Pink & Treasures of the Reef. Mason, Janeen I., illus. 2003. 32p. (J). pap. 14.95 (978-1-58980-086-1(9)) Pelican Publishing Co., Inc.

Dead Man's Chest. 2007. (Pirates of the Caribbean Ser.). 160p. pap. 4.99 (***978-1-4231-1106-1(0)***) Disney Publishing Worldwide.

Defilippis, Nunzio & Weir, Christina. Destiny's Hand, Vol. 1. 2006. (Illus.). 192p. (YA). pap. 10.99 (978-1-933164-11-3(5)) Seven Seas Entertainment, LLC.

Defilippis, Nunzio & Weir, Christina. Destiny's Hand Volume 2. 2007. (Illus.). 192p. pap. 10.99 (***978-1-933164-52-6(2)***) Seven Seas Entertainment, LLC.

Dewin, Howie. The Circus Comes to Town. 2007. (One Piece Ser.: No. 2). 112p. (J). pap. 4.99 (978-0-439-89726-6(2) , Scholastic Paperbacks) Scholastic, Inc.

Disney Press, ed. Pirates of the Caribbean Film - Box Set. rev. ed. 2007. 496p. (gr. 3-7). pap. 12.99 (***978-1-4231-0926-6(0)***) Disney Pr.

—Pirates of the Caribbean: GN - at Worlds End. rev. ed. 2007. 48p. (gr. 1). pap. 3.99 (***978-1-4231-0449-0(8)***) Disney Pr.

Disney Press Staff. The Curse of Davy Jones. 2nd rev. ed. 2006. (Pirates of the Carribean Ser.). (Illus.). 24p. (ps-1). pap. 3.50 (978-1-4231-0026-3(3)) Disney Pr.

—Dead Man's Chest. 2007. 48p. (ps-3). 12.99 incl. audio compact disk (978-1-4231-0368-4(8)) Disney Pr.

—Dead Man's Chest - Swann Song. 2nd rev. ed. 2006. (Pirates of the Carribean Ser.:). (Illus.). 24p. (ps-1). pap. 3.50 (978-1-4231-0027-0(1)) Disney Pr.

Disney Press Staff, ed. Dead Man's Chest. 2007. 48p. (gr. 1-3). pap. 3.99 (***978-1-4231-0370-7(X)***) Disney Pr.

—Pirates of the Caribbean: At World's End Storybook. rev. ed. 2007. 48p. (J). (gr. 1-4). 12.99 (***978-1-4231-0918-1(X)***) Disney Pr.

—Pirates of the Caribbean 3: Swann. 2007. 24p. (J). (ps-2). pap. 3.99 (***978-1-4231-0375-2(0)***) Disney Pr.

Disney Publishing Staff. Playing Pirates, 15 vols. 2003. (It's Fun to Learn Ser.). (Illus.). 32p. (J). (ps-3). 3.99 (978-1-57973-136-6(8)) Advance Pubs. LLC.

Disney Staff. Pirates of the Caribbean: Dead Man's Chest. 2006. pap. 5.99 (978-1-59816-482-4(1) , Tokyopop Adult) TOKYOPOP, Inc.

Donaldson, Julia. Charlie Cook's Favorite Book. Scheffler, Axel, illus. 2008. 32p. (J). (ps-k). pap. 6.99 (***978-0-14-241138-4(8)*** , Puffin) Penguin Group (USA) Inc.

Dora & Diego's Adventures! 2007. (Dora the Explorer Ser.). 80p. (J). 6.99 (***978-1-4169-3532-2(0)*** , Simon Spotlight/Nickelodeon) Simon & Schuster Children's Publishing.

Dorling Kindersley Publishing Staff. Pirates of the Caribbean. 2006. (Ultimate Sticker Bks.). 16p. (J). pap. 6.99 (978-0-7566-2065-3(1)) Dorling Kindersley Publishing, Inc.

—Pirates of the Caribbean Visual Guide. 2006. (Illus.). 80p. (J). 19.99 (978-0-7566-2064-6(3)) Dorling Kindersley Publishing, Inc.

Doudna, Kelly. Parrot Crackers. Haberstroh, Anne, illus. 2007. (Fact & Fiction Ser.). 24p. (J). pap. (978-1-59928-459-0(6)) ; 21.35 (978-1-59928-458-3(8)) ABDO Publishing Co.

Drake, David. Pirates. 2002. (Cricket of Dew Drop Dell Ser.). (Illus.). 32p. (J). 3.49 (978-1-885631-59-6(6) , Family Of Man Pr., The) Hutchison, G.F. Pr.

Duey, Kathleen. Patch. Epstein, Eugene, illus. Gould, Robert, photos by. 2005. (Time Soldiers Ser.: Bk. 3). 96p. (J). (gr. 3-4). pap. 5.95 (978-1-929945-55-9(8)) Big Guy Bks., Inc.

—Patch. 2007. (Illus.). 96p. (J). 24.21 (978-1-59961-226-3(7)) Spotlight.

—Patch. 2003. (gr. k-3). lib. bdg. 17.60 (978-0-613-70790-9(7)) Tandem Library Bks.

Dumas, Alexandre. The Count of Monte Cristo. abr. ed. 2001. (gr. 7-12). lib. bdg. 15.25 (978-0-613-43810-0(8)) Tandem Library Bks.

Dupasquier, Philippe. Tom's Pirate Ship. 2003. (Illus.). 32p. (J). pap. 9.99 (978-1-84270-316-8(1)) Andersen GBR. *Dist:* Independent Pubs. Group.

Eaton, Cathy. Curse of the Pirate's Treasure. 2002. (gr. 7-12). lib. bdg. 29.20 (978-0-613-74589-5(2)) Tandem Library Bks.

Farren, Rick. Grandpa & the Pirate. 2003. (J). per. 9.95 (978-0-9728716-4-8(0)) Journey Pubns., LLC.

Faulkner, Matt. The Pirate Meets the Queen: Two Women of Consequence. Faulkner, Matt, illus. 2005. (Illus.). 32p. (J). (gr. 1-5). 15.99 (978-0-399-24038-6(1) , Philomel) Penguin Group (USA) Inc.

Faye, Thomas. Pirates of the Caribbean: The Secret Files of the East India Trading Company. rev. ed. 2007. 28p. (gr. 8). 19.99 (***978-1-4231-0499-5(4)***) Disney Pr.

Feely, Jenny. Annie & the Pirates. 2001. (gr. k-3). lib. bdg. 11.65 (978-0-613-33328-3(4)) Tandem Library Bks.

Feldman, Thea. Backyard Pirates: Magnix Imagination. 2007. 6p. bds. 5.99 (***978-1-932915-40-2(0)***) Sandvik Innovations, LLC.

Ferrone, John M. Gus & the Pirate Treasure. Ferrone, John M., illus. Date not set. (Illus.). 36p. (J). (ps-5). pap. 16.95 (978-1-928811-01-5(9)) Story Stuff, Inc.

Fienberg, Anna. Horrendo's Curse. Gamble, Kim, illus. 2002. 160p. (J). (gr. 2-6). 18.95 (978-1-55037-773-6(6)) ; pap. 6.95 (978-1-55037-772-9(8)) Annick Pr., Ltd. CAN. *Dist:* Firefly Bks., Ltd.

Finn, Felicity. Jeremy & the Air Pirates. 1998. (Illus.). 219p. (YA). (gr. 3-8). pap. 5.95 (978-1-896764-02-3(9)) Second Story Pr. CAN. *Dist:* Orca Bk. Pubs. USA.

Fleischman, Sid. The Ghost in the Noonday Sun. Sis, Peter, illus. 2007. 256p. (J). pap. 5.99 (***978-0-06-134502-9(4)*** , Harper Trophy) HarperCollins Pubs.

—The Ghost in the Noonday Sun. 1999. (J). (978-0-606-18960-6(2)) Tandem Library Bks.

—The Giant Rat of Sumatra: Or Pirates Galore. Hendrix, John, illus. 2006. 208p. (J). reprint ed. pap. 5.99 (978-0-06-074240-9(2) , Harper Trophy) HarperCollins Pubs.

Fontes, Ron & Fontes, Justine. Captured by Pirates. Witt, David, illus. 2007. (Twisted Journeys Ser.). 112p. (J). (gr. 4-7). lib. bdg. 27.93 (***978-0-8225-6201-6(4)*** , Graphic Universe); pap. 7.95 (***978-0-8225-6202-3(2)***) Lerner Publishing Group.

Fox, Christyan & Fox, Diane. Pirate PiggyWiggy. 2003. (Illus.). 24p. (J). 11.95 (978-1-929766-76-5(9)) Handprint Bks.

French, Jackie. My Mom the Pirate. King, Stephen Michael, illus. 2007. (Funny Families Ser.). (J). (gr. 2-4). 107p. pap. 7.95 (***978-1-59889-438-7(2)***); 112p. lib. bdg. 22.60 (***978-1-59889-345-8(9)***) Stone Arch Bks.

From Ship to Shore. 2007. (Pirates of the Caribbean Ser.). 10p. (ps-3). 12.99 (***978-1-4231-0807-8(8)***) Disney Pr.

Funke, Cornelia. Pirate Girl. Meyer, Kerstin, illus. 2005. (Pirate Girl Ser.). 32p. (J). (ps-ps). pap. 15.95 (978-0-439-71672-7(1)) Scholastic, Inc.

Gaiman, Neil. Dangerous Alphabet. Grimly, Gris, illus. 2008. 32p. (J). 17.99 (***978-0-06-078333-4(8)***); lib. bdg. 18.89 (***978-0-06-078334-1(6)***) HarperCollins Pubs.

Garofoli, Viviana. Pirates! 2008. (J). (***978-0-7614-5455-7(1)***) Cavendish, Marshall Corp.

Gelsey, James. Sunken Ship: Scooby-Doo y el Barco Hundido. 2004. (Scooby-Doo Ser.). (ENG & SPA.). 64p. (J). mass mkt. 3.99 (978-0-439-55116-8(1) , Scholastic en Espanol) Scholastic, Inc.

Gibson, D. W., et al. Fundorado Island. 2006. (Illus.). 224p. (J). (gr. 3). lib. bdg. 16.99 (978-0-385-90284-7(0) , Delacorte Bks. for Young Readers) Random Hse. Children's Bks.

Girard, Geoffrey. Tales of the Atlantic Pirates. 2006. (Illus.). 150p. (YA). per. 13.95 (978-0-9754419-5-4(7)) Middle Atlantic Pr.

Golden Books Staff. Treasure Hunters. 2005. (Illus.). 32p. (J). (ps-2). pap. 4.99 (978-0-375-83474-5(5) , Golden Bks.) Random Hse. Children's Bks.

Gregory, Kristiana. The Stowaway: A Tale of California Pirates. 2003. (Stowaway Ser.). 144p. (J). (gr. 4-7). pap. 4.50 (978-0-590-48823-5(6) , Scholastic Paperbacks) Scholastic, Inc.

Grindley, Sally. Pirate Stories. Utton, Peter, illus. 2002. 93p. (J). pap. 12.00 (978-0-552-54502-0(3) , Corgi) Transworld Publishers Ltd. GBR. *Dist:* Trafalgar Square Publishing.

Grove, Vicki. Rhiannon. 2007. 224p. (YA). (gr. 5). 18.99 (***978-0-399-23633-4(3)*** , Putnam Juvenile) Penguin Group (USA) Inc.

Guard, Dominic. Pirate Fun. 2007. (Fun Packs Ser.). 24p. (J). (gr. k-3). pap. 19.99 (***978-0-7641-9343-9(0)***) Barron's Educational Series, Inc.

Gutteridge, Alex. Pirate Polly Rules the Waves. l.t. ed. 2006. pap. 16.95 (978-1-4056-6050-1(3)) BBC Audio GBR. *Dist:* BBC Audiobooks America.

Hagen, Michael. Sail to Caribee. 1998. 157p. (YA). (gr. 5 up). 9.99 (978-0-88092-410-8(1) , 4101) Royal Fireworks Publishing Co.

Hamilton, Tisha. Disney Pirates of the Caribbean Storybook & Compass Viewer: At World's End. Disney & Reader's Digest, illus. 2007. (RD Innovative Book & Player Format Ser.). 40p. (J). (ps-4). bds. 24.99 (978-0-7944-1283-8(1)) Reader's Digest Assn., Inc., The.

—Disney Pirates of the Carribbean: at Worlds End: A Pirate's Tale Adventure Play Pack. 2007. 24p. (J). bds. 21.99 (***978-0-7944-1349-1(8)***) Reader's Digest Assn., Inc., The.

—Piratas del Caribe. el viaje al fin del Mundo: Pirates of the Caribbean: at the World's End. 2007. (Illus.). 38p. (J). 24.95 (***978-970-718-532-6(5)*** , Silver Dolphin en Español) Advanced Marketing, S. de R. L. de C. V. MEX. *Dist:* Perseus Distribution.

Hamilton, Tisha. The Search for Dead Man's Chest: Storybook with Spyglass. 2006. (Pirates of the Caribbean Ser.). (Illus.). 40p. (J). pap. 24.99 (978-0-7944-1101-5(0)) Reader's Digest Assn., Inc., The.

Hapka, Catherine. Pirates Need Sleep, Too! A Bedtime Book. 1998. (Illus.). 32p. (J). (ps up). pap. 3.99 (978-0-307-10433-5(8) , Golden Bks.) Random Hse. Children's Bks.

Hargreaves, Roger. Mr. Jelly & the Pirates. 2007. (Mr. Men & Little Miss Ser.). 32p. (J). pap. 3.99 (978-0-8431-2492-7(X) , Price Stern Sloan) Penguin Group (USA) Inc.

Harley, Bill. Dirty Joe, the Pirate: A True Story. Davis, Jack E., illus. 2008. 32p. (J). 16.99 (***978-0-06-623780-0(7)***); lib. bdg. 17.89 (***978-0-06-623781-7(5)***) HarperCollins Pubs.

Harris, Peter. The Night Pirates. Allwright, Deborah, illus. 2006. 32p. (J). (ps-2). 16.99 (978-0-439-79959-1(7) , Scholastic Pr.) Scholastic, Inc.

Hart, James V. Capt. Hook: The Adventures of a Notorious Youth. Helquist, Brett, illus. 2nd ed. 2005. 352p. (J). 15.99 (978-0-06-000220-6(4)) HarperCollins Pubs.

Hausman, Gerald. Tom Cringle: Battle on the High Seas. Hills, Tad, illus. 2000. 224p. (J). (gr. 4-6). 28.99 (978-0-689-82810-2(1)) Simon & Schuster Children's Publishing.

Hawes, Charles Boardman. The Dark Frigate. 2005. pap. 27.95 (978-1-4179-3209-2(0)) Kessinger Publishing, LLC.

Hawkins, Colin. Pirate Ship: A Pop-up Adventure. Hawkins, Colin et al, illus. 2006. 28p. (J). (gr. 4-8). reprint ed. 20.00 (978-0-7567-9827-7(2)) DIANE Publishing Co.

Hawkins, Colin & Hawkins, Jacqui. Pirate Treasure Map: A Fairytale Adventure. Hawkins, Colin & Hawkins, Jacqui, illus. 2006. 40p. (J). (gr. k-3). 15.99 (978-0-7636-3205-2(8)) Candlewick Pr.

Hazelton, Jamie. The Grandest Adventure of Captain Goldenears. Hazelton, Jamie, illus. 2001. 14p. 5.00 net. (978-0-9715792-0-0(2)) Fables & Tails.

Helquist, Brett. Roger, the Jolly Pirate. Helquist, Brett, illus. 40p. (J). 2007. pap. 6.99 (***978-0-06-443851-3(1)*** , Harper Trophy); 2004. (Illus.). 16.99 (978-0-06-623805-0(6)); 2004. (Illus.). lib. bdg. 17.89 (978-0-06-623806-7(4)) HarperCollins Pubs.

Hemyng, Bracebridge. Jack Harkaway & His Son's Escape from the Brigand's of Greece. 2006. 342p. pap. 14.99 (978-1-4264-2290-4(3)); 386p. pap. 20.99 (978-1-4264-2325-3(X)) BiblioBazaar.

—Jack Harkaway & His Son's Escape from the Brigands of Greece. 2004. reprint ed. pap. 1.99 (978-1-4192-2705-9(X)) Kessinger Publishing, LLC.

Hooks, William H. Lo-Jack & the Pirates. Tusa, Tricia, illus. 1999. (Bank Street Reader Collection). 48p. (J). (gr. 2-4). lib. bdg. 22.60 (978-0-8368-1782-9(6)) Stevens, Gareth Inc.

Hughes, Carol. Jack Black & the Ship of Thieves. 2001. 240p. (J). (gr. 3-8). 5.99 (978-0-375-80473-1(0) , Yearling) Random Hse. Children's Bks.

—Jack Black & the Ship of Thieves. 1999. 11.64 (978-0-606-21803-0(3)) Tandem Library Bks.

Hunt, Elizabeth Singer. The Search for the Sunken Treasure. 2007. (Secret Agent Jack Stalwart Ser.). 128p. (J). (gr. 1-4). pap. 4.99 (***978-1-60286-002-5(5)***) Weinstein Bks.

Hunter, Derek. Pirate Club Vol. 2: Brainwash Escape Victims. 2006. (Illus.). 144p. (YA). pap. 12.95 (978-1-59362-051-6(9)) Slave Labor Bks.

Hurt-Newton, Tania. Yo-Ho Harvey. Hurt-Newton, Tania, illus. 2007. (Illus.). 14p. (J). 14.95 (***978-0-00-724413-3(4)***) HarperCollins Pubs. Ltd. GBR. *Dist:* Independent Pubs. Group.

Impey, Rose. Who's a Clever Girl? Amstutz, Andre, illus. 2003. (Yellow Bananas Ser.). 48p. (J). (gr. 3-4). pap. (978-0-7787-0976-3(0)) Crabtree Publishing Co.

—Who's a Clever Girl? 2002. (gr. 3-6). lib. bdg. 12.95 (978-0-613-52935-8(9)) Tandem Library Bks.

Jackson, Dave & Jackson, Neta. Hostage on the Nighthawk: William Penn. McLaughlin, Catherine R., illus. 2000. (Trailblazer Bks.: Vol. 32). 144p. (J). (gr. 3-7). pap. 6.99 (978-0-7642-2265-8(1)) Bethany Hse. Pubs.

Jacques, Brian. The Angel's Command. Elliot, David & Schoenherr, Ian, illus. 2005. (Castaways of the Flying Dutchman Ser.: No. 2). 384p. (J). (gr. 5-9). pap. 7.99 (978-0-14-240285-6(0) , Puffin) Penguin Group (USA) Inc.

—The Angel's Command. Elliot, David, illus. 2003. (Castaways of the Flying Dutchman Ser.: No. 2). 384p. (J). (gr. 5-6). 23.99 (978-0-399-23999-1(5) , Philomel) Penguin Group (USA) Inc.

James, Brian. Ahoy, Ghost Ship Ahead!, No. 2. Zivoin, Jennifer, illus. 2007. (Pirate School Ser.). 64p. (J). (gr. 1-3). pap. 3.99 (978-0-448-44625-7(1) , Grosset & Dunlap) Penguin Group (USA) Inc.

James, Brian. Treasure Trouble. Zivoin, Jennifer, illus. 2008. (Pirate School Ser.). 64p. (J). (gr. 1-3). 3.99 (***978-0-448-44782-7(7)*** , Grosset & Dunlap) Penguin Group (USA) Inc.

James, Larry W. Captain Petey: An Adventure at Sea. Ramos, Violet M., ed. James, Larry W. & Freshman, Floris R., illus. 2003. 28p. pap. 6.99 (978-0-9742154-0-2(6)) Cross Pointe Printing.

Jardine, Alan. Sloop John B: A Pirate's Tale. Pickering, Jimmy, illus. 2005. 32p. 17.95 (978-1-59687-181-6(4)); 17.95 (978-0-689-03596-8(9)) ibooks, Inc. (Milk & Cookies).

Jaspersohn, William. The Scrimshaw Ring. Thornblad, Vernon, illus. 2002. (Family Heritage Ser.). 36p. (J). (gr. 4-7). 15.95 (978-0-916718-19-0(0)) Vermont Folklife Ctr.

Johansen, K. V. Torrie & the Firebird. Delezenne, Christine, illus. 2006. (Torrie Quests Ser.). 195p. (J). (gr. 3-5). 18.95 (978-1-55037-961-7(5)); pap. 7.95 (978-1-55037-960-0(7)) Annick Pr., Ltd. CAN. *Dist:* Firefly Bks., Ltd.

Kaneko, Shinya. Culdcept, Vol. 5. 5th rev. ed. 2006. (Illus.). pap. 9.99 (978-1-59816-553-1(4) , Tokyopop Adult) TOKYOPOP, Inc.

Kaserman, James & Kaserman, Sarah Jane. How the Pirates Saved Christmas. ed. 2005. (Illus.). 64p. (J). per. 5.99 (978-0-9674081-2-5(1) , (239)939-4845) Pirate Publishing International.

Kaserman, James F. & Kaserman, Sarah Jane. The Legend of Gasparilla: A Tale for All Ages. 2000. (Illus.). 304p. (J). pap. 14.95 (978-0-9674081-1-8(3)) Pirate Publishing International.

Kay, Julia. Gulliver Snip & the Clipper Ship. 2008. 32p. (J). 16.95 (***978-0-8050-7992-0(0)***) Holt, Henry & Co.

Kelman, Marcy. Disney's Little Einsteins: Pirate's Treasure. rev. ed. 2007. 16p. (ps-1). pap. 4.99 (***978-1-4231-0211-3(8)***) Disney Pr.

Kennedy, Kim. Pirate Pete: "Where There's Gold I'm a Goin'" Kennedy, Doug, illus. 2002. 40p. (J). (ps-3). 15.95 (978-0-8109-4356-8(5)) Abrams, Harry N. , Inc.

—Pirate Pete's Giant Adventure. Kennedy, Doug, illus. 2006. 36p. (J). (ps-3). 15.95 (978-0-8109-5965-1(8)) Abrams, Harry N. , Inc.

Kennedy, Kim. Pirate Pete's Talk Like a Pirate. Kennedy, Doug, illus. 2007. 40p. (J). (ps-17). 15.95 (***978-0-8109-9348-8(1)*** , Abrams Bks. for Young Readers) Abrams, Harry N. , Inc.

Kettle, Shey. Girl Pirates. Thomas, Meredith, illus. 2005. (Girlz Rock! Ser.). (J). pap. (978-1-59336-701-5(5)) Mondo Publishing.

Kidd, Rob. City of Gold. Orpinas, Jean-Paul, illus. 7th rev. ed. 2007. (Pirates of the Caribbean Ser.: Bk. 7). 128p. (gr. 3-7). pap. 4.99 (978-1-4231-0170-3(7)) Disney Pr.

—Jack Sparrow: The Pirate Chase. Orpinas, Jean-Paul, illus. 2006. 119p. (J). lib. bdg. 16.00 (*978-1-4242-1570-6(6)) Fitzgerald Bks.

—Jack Sparrow: The Siren Song. Orpinas, Jean-Paul, illus. 2006. 122p. (J). lib. bdg. 16.00 (*978-1-4242-1571-3(4)) Fitzgerald Bks.

—Pirates of the Caribbean: Sins of the Fathers - Jack Sparrows #10. 10th rev. ed. 2007. 144p. (gr. 2-7). pap. 4.99 (*978-1-4231-0455-1(2)) Disney Pr.

—The Quest for the Sword of Cortes, Set. 2006. (Pirates of the Caribbean Ser.). 528p. (gr. 3-7). pap. 15.99 (978-1-4231-0656-2(3)) Disney Pr.

—The Siren Song. 2nd rev. ed. 2006. (Pirates of the Caribbean Ser.: Vol. 2). (Illus.). 128p. (gr. 3-7). pap. 4.99 (978-1-4231-0019-5(0)) Disney Pr.

Kidd, Rob & Ching, Jacqueline. Ghost Ship. 2007. 32p. (gr. k-2). pap. 3.99 (*978-1-4231-0620-3(2)) Disney Pr.

—Pirates of the Caribbean: The Missing Pirate. Disney Storybook Artists Staff, illus. 2007. 32p. (gr. k-2). pap. 3.99 (*978-1-4231-0621-0(0)) Disney Pr.

Kidd, Rob & Rudnick, Elizabeth M. Pirates of the Caribbean: the Curse of the Black Pearl. 2nd ed. 2006. (Illus.). 176p. (ps-3). pap. 4.99 (978-1-4231-0710-1(1)) Disney Pr.

Kidd, Rob, et al. Pirates of the Caribbean: Escape from Davy Jones. 2007. 32p. (gr. k-2). pap. 3.99 (*978-1-4231-0622-7(9)) Disney Pr.

Kimmel, Eric A. Blackbeard's Last Fight. Fisher, Leonard Everett, illus. 2006. 32p. (J). 17.00 (978-0-374-30780-6(6) , Farrar, Straus & Giroux (BYR)) Farrar, Straus & Giroux.

—The Erie Canal Pirates. Glass, Andrew, illus. 2002. 32p. (J). (gr. k-3). tchr. ed. 16.95 (978-0-8234-1657-8(7)) Holiday Hse., Inc.

—Robin Hook, Pirate Hunter! Dooling, Michael, illus. 2001. 32p. (J). (gr. k-4). pap. 15.95 (978-0-590-68199-5(0)) Scholastic, Inc.

Kimmel, Eric A. & Dooling, Michael. Robin Hook, Pirate Hunter! 2001. (Illus.). (J). pap. (978-0-590-68219-0(9)) Scholastic, Inc.

Kingfisher Editors, ed. How to be a Pirate in 7 Days or Less. 2006. (How to Be a... Ser.). (Illus.). 32p. (J). (gr. k-3). 12.95 (978-0-7534-6041-2(6) , Kingfisher) Houghton Mifflin Co. Trade & Reference Div.

Kress, Adrienne. Alex & the Ironic Gentleman. 2007. 320p. (YA). (gr. 3-7). 16.95 (*978-1-60286-005-6(X)) Weinstein Bks.

Krosoczka, Jarrett J. Bubble Bath Pirates. 2003. (Illus.). 40p. (J). (ps-k). 15.99 (978-0-670-03599-1(8) , Viking Juvenile) Penguin Group (USA) Inc.

Krupinski, Loretta. Pirate Treasure. Krupinski, Loretta, illus. 2006. (Illus.). 32p. (J). (gr. k). 15.99 (978-0-525-47579-8(6) , Dutton Juvenile) Penguin Group (USA) Inc.

Laird, Marnie. Water Rat. Shine, Andrea, illus. 1998. 196p. (J). (gr. 4-7). 15.95 (978-1-890817-08-4(2)) Winslow Pr.

Lamm, Drew. Pirates. Schuett, Stacey, illus. 2001. 40p. (gr. 4-7). 15.99 (978-0-7868-0392-7(4)) Hyperion Bks. for Children.

Lasky, Kathryn. Pirate Bob. Clark, David, illus. 2006. (J). 15.95 (978-1-57091-595-6(4)) Charlesbridge Publishing, Inc.

Laurence, Daniel. Captain & Matey Set Sail. Munoz, Claudio, illus. 2003. (I Can Read Bks.). 64p. (J). (ps-3). pap. 4.99 (978-0-06-444285-5(3)) HarperCollins Pubs.

—Captain & Matey Set Sail, Bk. 2. 2001. (I Can Read Bks.). (Illus.). 64p. (J). (gr. k-3). 15.89 (978-0-06-028957-7(0)) HarperCollins Pubs.

—Captain & Matey Set Sail. 2001. (gr. 3-6). lib. bdg. 11.80 (978-0-613-62134-2(4)) Tandem Library Bks.

Lawlor, Laurie. Dead Reckoning: A Pirate Voyage with Captain Drake. 2007. 336p. (J). pap. 5.99 (978-0-689-86578-7(3) , Aladdin) Simon & Schuster Children's Publishing.

Lawlor, Laurie & Barkat, Jonathan. Dead Reckoning: A Pirate Voyage with Captain Drake. 2005. (Illus.). 272p. (J). 15.95 (978-0-689-86577-0(5) , Simon & Schuster Children's Publishing) Simon & Schuster Children's Publishing.

Lawrence, Caroline. Pirates of Pompeii, Vol. 3. 2004. (Roman Mysteries Ser.: No. 3). (Illus.). 176p. (J). (gr. 3). pap. 5.99 (978-0-14-240227-6(3) , Puffin) Penguin Group (USA) Inc.

Lawrence, Iain. The Buccaneers. (Illus.). 256p. (gr. 5-9). 2003. 5.99 (978-0-440-41671-5(X) , Yearling); 2001. 16.95 (978-0-385-32736-7(6) , Delacorte Bks. for Young Readers) Random Hse. Children's Bks.

—Buccaneers. 2003. (gr. 5-8). lib. bdg. 13.55 (978-0-613-64433-4(6)) Tandem Library Bks.

—The Buccaneers. l.t. ed. 2001. (Illus.). 320p. (J). 23.95 (978-0-7862-3464-6(4)) Thorndike Pr.

—Ghost Boy. 2002. 352p. (YA). (gr. 7). reprint ed. pap. 6.50 (978-0-440-41668-5(X) , Laurel Leaf) Random Hse. Children's Bks.

—Ghost Boy. 2002. (gr. 7-12). lib. bdg. 14.15 (978-0-613-58216-2(0)) Tandem Library Bks.

Lawrenson, Judith. Petunia the Pirate of Port Royal Sound. 2007. (J). 14.95 (*978-0-9767278-0-4(3)) Mrs. L's Reading Room.

Lee, Brian, illus. A Pirate Ship. 2005. (What's Inside? Ser.). (*978-0-7607-6809-9(9)) backpackbook.

Lee, Tanith. Piratica: Being a Daring Tale of a Singular Girl's Adventure upon the High Seas. (Piratica Ser.: Vol. 1). 304p. (gr. 6). 2006. (YA). pap. 6.99 (978-0-14-240644-1(9) , Puffin); 2004. (Illus.). (J). 17.99 (978-0-525-47324-4(6) , Dutton Juvenile) Penguin Group (USA) Inc.

—Return to Parrot Island. (Piratica Ser.: Vol. 2). (YA). (gr. 7). 2008. 368p. 6.99 (*978-0-14-241094-3(2) , Puffin); 2006. 360p. 17.99 (978-0-525-47769-3(1) , Dutton Juvenile) Penguin Group (USA) Inc.

Leigh, S. Uncle Pete's Pirate Adventure. rev. ed. 2004. (Young Puzzle Adventures Ser.). 32p. (J). (gr. 2 up). pap. 4.95 (978-0-7945-0401-4(9)); lib. bdg. 12.95 (978-1-58086-545-6(3)) EDC Publishing.

Leigh, Susannah. Uncle Pete the Pirate. 2004. (Usborne Young Puzzle Adventures Ser.). (Illus.). 32p. (J). (gr. 2 up). pap. 4.95 (978-0-7945-0400-7(0) , Usborne) EDC Publishing.

Leigh, Susannah. Uncle Pete's Pirate Adventure. rev. ed. 2007. (Young Puzzle Adventures Ser.). 32p. (J). pap. 4.99 (*978-0-7945-1848-6(6) , Usborne) EDC Publishing.

Leuck, Laura. I Love My Pirate Papa. Stone, Kyle M., illus. 2007. 32p. (J). (ps-2). 16.00 (978-0-15-205664-3(5)) Harcourt Trade Pubs.

Lewman, David. Pirates of Bikini Bottom. Moore, Harry, illus. 2007. (SpongeBob SquarePants Ser.). 64p. (J). pap. 4.99 (*978-1-4169-3560-5(6) , Simon Spotlight/Nickelodeon) Simon & Schuster Children's Publishing.

Leykamm, Martina. Here Come the Pirates! 2007. (Illus.). 10p. (J). bds. 10.95 (978-0-7358-2131-6(3)) North-South Bks., Inc.

Lindgren, Astrid. Ferien auf Saltkroken. pap. 19.95 (978-3-423-70773-2(9)) Deutscher Taschenbuch Verlag GmbH & Co KG DEU. *Dist:* Distribooks, Inc.

Lloyd-Jones, Robin. See Inside Pirate Ships. 2007. (See Inside Board Bks). 16p. (J). bds. 12.99 (*978-0-7945-1601-7(7) , Usborne) EDC Publishing.

—Story of Pirates. 2007. (Young Reading Series 3 Gift Bks). 64p. (J). 8.99 (*978-0-7945-1618-5(1) , Usborne) EDC Publishing.

Long, Melinda. How I Became a Pirate. Shannon, David, illus. 2003. 44p. (J). (ps-3). 16.00 (978-0-15-201848-1(4)) Harcourt Children's Bks.

—Pirates Don't Change Diapers. Shannon, David, illus. 2007. 44p. (J). (ps-2). 16.00 (978-0-15-205353-6(0)) Harcourt Trade Pubs.

Loof, Jan. Mi Abuelo Es Pirata. 2001. (SPA., Illus.). 40p. (J). 16.76 (978-84-305-7196-3(5) , MN3132) Susaeta Ediciones, S.A. ESP. *Dist:* Lectorum Pubns., Inc.

Lord, Kenniston. The Pirates of Peary Village. 2004. 182p. (J). pap. 9.18 (978-1-4116-7893-4(1)) Lulu.com.

Lubber, William & Steer, Dugald A. Pirateology Guidebook & Model Set. 2007. (Ologies Ser.). (Illus.). 24p. (gr. 3 up). 17.99 (*978-0-7636-3582-4(0)) Candlewick Pr.

Lytle, Robert A. Mackinac Passage: Pirate Party. Bill, Williams, illus. 2006. (J). per. 9.95 (978-0-9749412-5-7(5)) EDCO Publishing, Inc.

MacNeil, Stephen. Woolies & Worms. 2007. 192p. (J). (gr. 2-5). 16.95 (*978-0-8126-2751-0(2)) Cricket Bks.

Maden, Mary. The Great Shark Adventure. Geib, Stephanie K., illus. 1999. (Earth/Ocean Adventures Ser.: Vol. 1). (J). (gr. 1-7). pap. 5.95 (978-1-890479-60-2(8)) Dog & Pony Publishing.

Marcotte, Danielle & Duchesne, Bernard. La Terreur des Mers. 2001. (Roman Jeunesse Ser.). (FRE., Illus.). 96p. (J). pap. (978-2-89021-479-8(6)) Diffusion du livre Mirabel.

Marks, Graham. Radio Radio. 2003. 224p. (YA). pap. 12.99 (978-0-7475-5939-9(2)) Bloomsbury Publishing Plc GBR. *Dist:* Independent Pubs. Group.

Marks, Graham. Radio Radio: Rejacketed. 2007. 219p. (YA). pap. 11.95 (*978-0-7475-9087-3(7)) Bloomsbury Publishing Plc GBR. *Dist:* Independent Pubs. Group.

Marsh, Carole. Mystery of Blackbeard the Pirate. 2003. (gr. 5-8). lib. bdg. 14.10 (978-0-613-73037-2(2)) Tandem Library Bks.

Marzollo, Dan, et al. Pirate Treasure. Mills, Liz, ed. Levin, Jimmy, illus. 2003. (I Spy Ser.). 24p. (J). pap. 3.50 (978-0-439-45525-1(1) , Cartwheel Bks.) Scholastic, Inc.

Masefield, John. Jim Davis. l.t. ed. 2006. 142p. pap. 13.99 (978-1-4264-2384-0(5)) BiblioBazaar.

Masters, Anthony. The Desert Pirates. Buckley, Harriet, illus. 2008. (J). pap. (*978-1-59889-906-1(6)); lib. bdg. (*978-1-59889-870-5(1)) Stone Arch Bks.

Mayhar, Ardath & Dunn, Marylois. Timber Pirates. Richards, Jerri S., ed. ltd. ed. 1998. (YA). (gr. 6-12). pap. (978-1-887303-19-4(7)) Blue Lantern Publishing.

McCafferty, Catherine. Dead Man's Chest. 2nd rev. ed. 2006. (Pirates of the Carribean Ser.). (Illus.). 64p. (gr. 2-5). 8.99 (978-1-4231-0025-6(5)) Disney Pr.

McCaughrean, Geraldine. The Pirate's Son. 1999. 304p. (gr. 5-9). mass mkt. 4.99 (978-0-590-20348-7(7)) Scholastic, Inc.

—Pirate's Son. 1999. (978-0-606-17039-0(1)) Tandem Library Bks.

McClatchy, Lisa. Eloise's Pirate Adventure. Lyon, Tammie, illus. 2007. (Eloise Ser.). 32p. (J). (ps-1). pap. 3.99 (*978-1-4169-4979-4(8) , Aladdin) Simon & Schuster Children's Publishing.

McConnell, Sarah. Don't Mention Pirates. 2006. (Illus.). 32p. (J). 14.99 (978-0-7641-5945-9(3)) Barron's Educational Series, Inc.

McCullagh, Sheila. Pirate Gold. 2007. (Three Pirates Ser.). (Illus.). 48p. 15.95 (*978-1-84560-042-6(8)) Mercury Bks. Ltd. GBR. *Dist:* International Publishers Marketing.

—Shipwrecked. 2007. (Three Pirates Ser.). (Illus.). 48p. 15.95 (*978-1-84560-043-3(6)) Mercury Bks. Ltd. GBR. *Dist:* International Publishers Marketing.

—Wild Pirates Attack. 2007. (Illus.). 48p. 15.95 (*978-1-84560-045-7(2)) Mercury Bks. Ltd. GBR. *Dist:* International Publishers Marketing.

McCully, Emily Arnold. The Pirate Queen. 1998. (978-0-606-13709-6(2)) Tandem Library Bks.

McElligott, Matthew. Backbeard & the Birthday Suit: The Hairiest Pirate Who Ever Lived. 2007. (Illus.). 32p. (J). pap. 6.95 (*978-0-8027-9680-6(X)) Walker & Co.

—Backbeard: Pirate for Hire. McElligott, Matthew, illus. 2007. (Illus.). 32p. (J). 17.85 (*978-0-8027-9633-2(8)); 16.95 (*978-0-8027-9632-5(X)) Walker & Co.

McNaughton, Colin. Captain Abdul's Little Treasure. McNaughton, Colin, illus. 2006. (Illus.). 48p. (J). (gr. k). 14.99 (978-0-7636-3045-4(4)) Candlewick Pr.

—Jolly Roger & the Pirates of Captain Abdul. McNaughton, Colin, illus. 2nd ed. 2004. (Illus.). 40p. (J). (gr. 1 up). pap. 6.99 (978-0-7636-2539-9(6)) Candlewick Pr.

Metaxas, Eric & Kenney, Cindy. Jonah & the Pirates Who Don't Do Anything. Eddy, Ron & Vann, Robert, illus. 2002. 32p. (J). 12.99 (978-0-310-70460-7(X)) Zonderkidz.

Meyer, Kai. Pirate Curse. Crawford, Elizabeth D., tr. from GER. 2006. (Wave Walkers Ser.). 336p. (J). (gr. 5-9). 15.95 (978-1-4169-2421-0(3) , McElderry, Margaret K.) Simon & Schuster Children's Publishing.

Meyer, L. A. Under the Jolly Roger: Being an Account of the Further Nautical Adventures of Jacky Faber. 2007. (Bloody Jack Adventures Ser.). (Illus.). 544p. (YA). pap. 6.95 (978-0-15-205873-9(7) , Harcourt Paperbacks) Harcourt Children's Bks.

—Under the Jolly Roger: Being an Account of the Further Nautical Adventures of Jacky Faber. 2005. (Bloody Jack Adventures Ser.). (Illus.). 528p. (YA). (gr. 7-17). 17.00 (978-0-15-205345-1(X)) Harcourt Trade Pubs.

Meyer, Louis A. Bloody Jack: Being an Account of the Curious Adventures of Mary Jacky Faber, Ship's Boy. 2002. (Bloody Jack Adventures Ser.). (Illus.). 336p. (YA). (gr. 6-9). 17.00 (978-0-15-216731-8(5)) Harcourt Children's Bks.

Miles, Ellen. The Pirate's Plot. 2006. (Taylor-Made Tales Ser.: No. 2). 112p. (J). pap. 4.99 (978-0-439-59709-8(9) , Scholastic Paperbacks) Scholastic, Inc.

Miller, Edward. Captain Barnacle's Aquarium: Filled with Fun, Fishy Facts! 2006. 32p. (J). (ps-1). 14.95 (978-0-8109-5985-9(2)) Abrams, Harry N., Inc.

Monsen, Annie. Captain Blye & the Friendly Fly. 2004. 11p. per. 5.00 (978-1-59453-613-7(9) , 2808) Airleaf Publishing & Bookselling.

Moore, Robin. The Man with the Silver Oar. 2002. 192p. (J). (gr. 5 up). 15.89 (978-0-06-000048-6(1)) HarperCollins Pubs.

Morgan, Allen. Matthew & the Midnight Pirates. Martchenko, Michael, illus. 2005. (First Flight Reader Ser.). 40p. (J). (gr. 1-3). pap. (978-1-55041-904-7(8)); (ps-ps). (978-1-55041-902-3(1)) Fitzhenry & Whiteside, Ltd.

—Matthew & the Midnight Pirates. Martchenko, Michael, illus. 1998. (Matthew's Midnight Adventures Ser.). 32p. (J). (ps-3). 6.99 (978-0-7737-5940-4(9)) Stoddart Kids CAN. *Dist:* Fitzhenry & Whiteside, Ltd.

Morgan, Christopher. Pirates Drive Buses. 2008. 80p. (J). 14.95 (*978-1-59643-313-7(2)) Roaring Brook Pr.

—Pirates Eat Porridge. Curtis, Neil, illus. 2007. 80p. (J). (gr. 2-5). 14.95 (*978-1-59643-304-5(3)) Roaring Brook Pr.

Mowll, Joshua. Operation Red Jericho: The Guide of Specialists Book 1. Heller, Julek & Puttapipat, Niroot, illus. 2007. 288p. (J). (gr. 5). pap. 8.99 (*978-0-7636-3475-9(1)) Candlewick Pr.

O'Brien, Patrick & O'Malley, Kevin. Captain Raptor & the Space Pirates. O'Brien, Patrick, illus. 2007. (Illus.). 32p. (J). (gr. k-3). 17.85 (*978-0-8027-9572-4(2)); 16.95 (*978-0-8027-9571-7(4)) Walker & Co.

Okuda, Hitoshi. No Need for Tenchil, Vol. 8. 2nd ed. 2006. (No Need for Tenchi! Ser.). 208p. (YA). pap. 9.99 (978-1-4215-0591-6(6)) Viz Media.

Oppel, Kenneth. Airborn. (J). 2004. 368p. (gr. 7 up). lib. bdg. 17.89 (978-0-06-053181-2(9)); 2004. (Illus.). 368p. (gr. 7 up). 16.99 (978-0-06-053180-5(0)); 2005. (Illus.). 544p. reprint ed. pap. 7.99 (978-0-06-053182-9(7)) HarperCollins Pubs.

—Airborn. l.t. ed. 525p. 2006. (YA). pap. 10.95 (978-0-7862-8367-5(X)); 2004. 22.95 (978-0-7862-7035-4(7) , Large Print Pr.) Thorndike Pr.

—Skybreaker. (J). 2007. 560p. (gr. 7 up). pap. 6.99 (978-0-06-053229-1(7)); 2005. (Illus.). 384p. (gr. 6-10). 16.99 (978-0-06-053227-7(0)); 2005. (Illus.). 384p. (gr. 6-10). lib. bdg. 17.89 (978-0-06-053228-4(9)) HarperCollins Pubs.

Orme, David. Space Pirates. Savage, Paul, illus. 2006. 40p. (J). (gr. 2-3). lib. bdg. (978-1-59889-016-7(6)) Stone Arch Bks.

Osborne, Mary Pope. Piratas Despues del Mediodia. 2004. (Coleccion la Casa Del Arbol the Magic Tree House Ser.). (SPA.). (J). pap. 4.95 (978-1-930332-52-2(1)) Lectorum Pubns., Inc.

—Pirates Past Noon. unabr. ed. 2000. (Magic Tree House Ser. : No. 4). (J). (gr. k-3). pap. 17.00 incl. audio Random Hse. Audio Publishing Group.

Other. Build Your Own Pirate Ship: A Push-Out-and-Play Book. 2008. 12p. (J). bds. 8.95 (*978-0-385-61114-5(5)) Transworld Publishers Ltd. GBR. *Dist:* Independent Pubs. Group.

Owen, Chris. Hairy Mole the Pirate 1. 2007. (Hairy Mole the Pirate Ser.). (Illus.). 82p. pap. 7.95 (*978-1-84167-562-6(8)) Ransom Publishing Ltd. GBR. *Dist:* International Publishers Marketing.

—Hairy Moles Adventure on the High Seas. 2007. (Hairy Mole the Pirate Ser.). (Illus.). 82p. pap. 7.95 (*978-1-84167-563-3(6)) Ransom Publishing Ltd. GBR. *Dist:* International Publishers Marketing.

Owen, James A. & Owen, Jeremy. Lost Treasures of the Pirates of the Caribbean: Secret Maps, Legends, & Lore Revealed! Owen, James A., illus. 2007. 32p. (J). 16.99 (978-1-4169-3960-3(1)) Simon & Schuster Children's Publishing.

Owens, Greg. Rupert the Wrong-Word Pirate. Beaky, Suzanne, illus. 2006. (J). (978-1-58987-143-4(X)) Kindermusik International.

Panec, D. J. We Both Read-the Mystery of Pirate's Point. Spangler, Brie, illus. 2008. (We Both Read Ser.). 44p. (J). 7.99 (*978-1-60115-009-7(1)); pap. 3.99 (*978-1-60115-010-3(5)) Treasure Bay, Inc.

Parker, Jade. To Catch A Pirate. 2007. 320p. (J). pap. 6.99 (*978-0-439-02694-9(6)) Scholastic, Inc.

Partis, Joanne. All Aboard! Pirate Peephole 1. 2007. (Peephole Pirates Ser.). (Illus.). 12p. (J). (ps-k). 6.99 (*978-1-4052-2305-8(7)) Egmont Bks., Ltd. GBR. *Dist:* Independent Pubs. Group.

—Buried Treasure! 2007. (Peephole Pirates Ser.). (Illus.). 12p. (J). (ps-k). 6.99 (*978-1-4052-2306-5(5)) Egmont Bks., Ltd. GBR. *Dist:* Independent Pubs. Group.

Parus, M. V. The Adventures of Mamma Simone, Jodie & Zed: The Mystery of the Pirate's Lost Treasure. 2006. 115p. (YA). per. 12.95 (*978-1-58374-148-1(8)) Chicago Spectrum Pr.

Peck, Dale. Drift House: The First Voyage. (J). 2006. 448p. pap. 7.95 (978-1-59990-005-6(X)); 2005. 420p. 16.95 (978-1-58234-969-5(X)) Bloomsbury Publishing. (Bloomsbury Children).

Penn, Audrey. Blackbeard & the Gift of Silence. 2007. 355p. (gr. 3-7). 15.95 (*978-1-933718-11-8(0)) Tanglewood Pr.

Perkins, T J. Wound Too Tight. 2006. (Illus.). 141p. (YA). 10.99 (978-0-9777538-5-7(9)) GumShoe Press.

Perry, Fred. Gold Digger Pocket Manga, Vol. 8. 2006. (Illus.). 200p. (YA). pap. 9.99 (978-0-9768043-0-7(1)) Antarctic Pr., Inc.

Peter Pan. 2003. (Illus.). 12.99 (978-0-7868-3479-2(X)) Disney Pr.

Petrie, Glen. Lucy & the Pirates. Harrison, Matilda, illus. 32p. (J). (gr. k-5). 2001. pap. (978-1-896580-38-6(8)); 2000. (978-1-896580-02-9(5)) Tradewind Bks.

Pirates of the Caribbean: The Black Pearl - a Pop-up Pirate Ship. 2007. 4p. (ps-3). 12.99 (*978-1-4231-0808-5(6)) Disney Pr.

Pirates of the Caribbean: Poster Book. 2007. 24p. (ps-17). pap. 7.99 (*978-1-4231-0793-4(4)) Disney Pr.

Platt, Richard. Pirates of the Caribbean Visual Guide: The Complete Visual Guide. 2007. 128p. (J). 19.99 (978-0-7566-2676-1(5)) Dorling Kindersley Publishing, Inc.

Platt, Richard & Ridell, Richard. The Journal of Jake Carpenter. Riddell, Chris, illus. 2005. 64p. (J). (gr. 4 up). pap. 7.99 (978-0-7636-2865-9(4)) Candlewick Pr.

Poth, Karen. The Pirates Who Don't Do Anything & Me! 2004. (Illus.). 32p. 7.99 (978-0-310-70725-7(0)) Zonderkidz.

Prasadam, Smriti & Finn, Rebecca. My Pirate Ship: Through Play Books. 2008. (Illus.). 12p. (J). bds. 6.95 (*978-0-7475-8812-2(0)) Bloomsbury Publishing Plc GBR. *Dist:* Independent Pubs. Group.

Priest, Robert. The Old Pirate of Central Park. Priest, Robert, illus. 1999. (Illus.). 32p. (J). (gr. k-3). tchr. ed. 16.00 (978-0-395-90505-0(2)) Houghton Mifflin Co. Trade & Reference Div.

—The Old Pirate of Central Park PB. 2008. 32p. (J). (ps-3). pap. 6.95 (*978-0-618-99769-5(5)) Houghton Mifflin Co. Trade & Reference Div.

Priest, Robert. Pirate's Eye. 2005. (Illus.). 32p. (J). (gr. k-3). 16.00 (978-0-618-43990-4(0)) Houghton Mifflin Co. Trade & Reference Div.

Pryor, Bonnie. Hannah Pritchard: Girl Pirate of the Revolution. 2008. (Historical Fiction Adventures (HFA) Ser.). (Illus.). 160p. (J). (gr. 3-6). lib. bdg. 27.93 (*978-0-7660-2851-7(8)) Enslow Pubs., Inc.

Punter, R. Stories of Pirates. 2004. (Young Reading Ser.: Vol. 1). 48p. (J). (gr. 2 up). pap. 5.99 (978-0-7945-0583-7(X)) EDC Publishing.

Punter, Russell. Percy & the Pirates. 2007. 48p. (J). 8.99 (*978-0-7945-1545-4(2) , Usborne) EDC Publishing.

Punter, Russell. Pirate Adv. Fox, Christyan, illus. 2007. 48p. (J). pap. 5.99 (978-0-7945-1447-1(2) , Usborne) EDC Publishing.

Pyle, Howard. The Ruby of Kishmoor. 2006. (ENG.). pap. (*978-1-4250-3493-1(4)); pap. (*978-1-4250-3494-8(2)); pap. (*978-1-4250-3542-6(6)); pap. (*978-1-4250-0031-8(2)) Assistedreadingbooks.com Inc.

—The Ruby of Kishmoor. 2004. reprint ed. pap. 15.95 (978-1-4191-8126-9(2)); pap. 1.99 (978-1-4192-8126-6(7)) Kessinger Publishing, LLC.

Pyle, Howard. The Story of Jack Ballister's Fortunes. 2007. (YA). (*978-0-486-45467-2(3)) Dover Pubns., Inc.

Raine, Bonnie. Islands. MacMenamin, John, illus. 2003. 48p. (J). per. (978-1-931456-74-6(7)) Athena Pr.

Ramos, Maria Cristina. Ruedamares Pirata de la Mar Bravia. (Torre de Papel Ser.). (SPA.). (J). (gr. 4 up). 8.95 (978-958-04-3814-4(5)) Norma S.A. COL. *Dist:* Distribuidora Norma, Inc.

Random House Disney Staff. Battle for the High Seas. 2007. (Illus.). 24p. (J). (gr. k-7). pap. 5.99 (*978-0-7364-2461-5(X) , RH/Disney) Random Hse. Children's Bks.

Random House Disney Staff. Pirates of the Caribbean: Dead Man's Chest. 2006. (Illus.). 12p. (J). (ps-1). pap. 6.99 (978-0-7364-2378-6(8) , RH/Disney) Random Hse. Children's Bks.

Ransome, Arthur. Missee Lee. 2002. (Swallows & Amazons Ser.). (Illus.). 352p. (J). pap. 14.95 (978-1-56792-196-0(5)) Godine, David R. Pub.

Reasoner, Charles. Inside Jolly Roger's Pirate Ship. Reasoner, Charles, illus. 2007. 12p. (J). (gr. k). bds. 9.99 (*978-1-84666-149-5(8) , Tide Mill Pr.) Top That! Publishing PLC GBR. *Dist:* Random Hse., Inc.

Redbank, Tennant. Captain Jack's Tale. 2007. (PriatesPirates of the Caribbean Ser.). (Illus.). 32p. (ps-3). pap. 3.99 (978-1-4231-0731-6(4)) Disney Pr.

—Curse of the Black Pearl - A Pirate's Life. 2007. (Pirates of the Caribbean Ser.). (Illus.). 32p. (ps-3). pap. 3.99 (978-1-4231-0732-3(2)) Disney Pr.

—Dead Man's Chest - the Chase Is On. 2nd rev. ed. 2006. (Pirates of the Carribean Ser.). 32p. (gr. k-2). pap. 3.99 (978-1-4231-0089-8(1)) Disney Pr.

Rees, Celia. Pirates. 2003. (Illus.). 368p. (978-0-7475-5950-4(3)) Bloomsbury Publishing Plc GBR. *Dist:* Trafalgar Square Publishing.

—Pirates! 2003. 340p. (J). 16.95 (978-1-58234-816-2(2) , Bloomsbury Children) Bloomsbury Publishing.

Rees, Douglas. Uncle Pirate. Auth, Tony, illus. 2008. 112p. (J). (*978-1-4169-4762-2(0) , McElderry, Margaret K.) Simon & Schuster Children's Publishing.

Reeve, Philip. Larklight: A Rousing Tale of Dauntless Pluck in the Farthest Reaches of Space. Wyatt, David, illus. 2007. 416p. (J). (gr. 5 up). pap. 7.95 (*978-1-59990-145-9(5) , Bloomsbury Children) Bloomsbury Publishing.

Rex, Michael. You Can Do Anything, Daddy! Rex, Michael, illus. 2007. 32p. (J). (ps). 14.99 (978-0-399-24298-4(8) , Putnam Juvenile) Penguin Group (USA) Inc.

Richards, Kitty. Yo Ho Ho & a Bottle of Milk. 2000. (gr. 3-6). lib. bdg. 11.80 (978-0-613-27654-2(X)) Tandem Library Bks.

Richardson, V. A. The Moneylender's Daughter. 2006. (Illus.). 300p. (YA). 17.95 (978-1-58234-885-8(5) , Bloomsbury Children) Bloomsbury Publishing.

Rigby Education Staff. The Treasure. (Sails Literacy Ser.). (Illus.). 16p. (gr. k-1). 27.00 (978-0-7635-9873-0(9)) Rigby Education.

Roberts, Dannel. Me & Uncle Mike & the Pirate Ship. Stolte, F., illus. l.t. ed. 2001. (Me & Uncle Mike Children's Book Ser.: Bk. 2). 36p. (J). (ps-3). per. 14.95 (978-1-893459-01-4(2)) Lions & Tigers & Bears Publishing, Inc.

Romeu, Emma. Gregorio y el Pirata. 2003. Tr. of Gregorio & the Pirate. (SPA., Illus.). 152p. (J). pap. 15.95 (978-968-19-0553-8(9)) Santillana USA Publishing Co., Inc.

Rosen, Michael J. Shakespeare: His Work & His World. Ingpen, Robert R., illus. 2001. 104p. (J). (gr. 7-11). 19.99 (978-0-7636-1568-0(4)) Candlewick Pr.

Ross, Tony, illus. The Kingfisher Treasury of Pirate Stories. 2003. (Kingfisher Treasury of Stories Ser.). 160p. (J). (gr. k-3). pap. 5.95 (978-0-7534-5632-3(X) , Kingfisher) Houghton Mifflin Co. Trade & Reference Div.

Rossell, Judith. Jack Jones & the Pirate Curse. 2007. 176p. (J). (gr. 3-6). 15.95 (*978-0-8027-9661-5(3)) Walker & Co.

Rossiter-McFarland, Lyn. The Pirate's Parrot. McFarland, Jim, illus. 2004. 40p. (J). (gr. k-2). 14.95 (978-1-58246-014-7(0) , Tricycle Pr.) Ten Speed Pr.

Rowe, John Alfred. J. A. Teddy. Rowe, John Alfred, illus. 2006. 32p. (J). (ps-3). 16.99 (978-0-698-40043-6(7) , Minedition) Penguin Group (USA) Inc.

Ryan, John. Captain Pugwash: A Pirate Story. (Illus.). 32p. (J). pap. 8.95 (978-0-09-940874-1(0) , Arrow Bks., Ltd.) Random Hse. GBR. *Dist:* Trafalgar Square Publishing.

Sabatini, Rafael. The King's Messenger. 2004. reprint ed. pap. 15.95 (978-1-4191-6824-6(X)); pap. 1.99 (978-1-4192-6824-3(4)) Kessinger Publishing, LLC.

Saunders, Joanne. The Secret at the Winthrop House, Independence Day: Book 2. 2007. 208p. (YA). per. 13.99 (*978-1-59886-935-4(3)) Tate Publishing & Enterprises, L.L.C.

Scarry, Richard. Richard Scarry's Pie Rats Ahoy. Scarry, Richard, illus. 2002. (Illus.). (J). 11.91 (978-0-7587-6251-1(8)) Book Wholesalers, Inc.

Schaub, Michelle. The Lost Pirate. 2006. (Early Explorers Ser.). (J). 34.00 (*978-1-4108-6109-2(0)) Benchmark Education Co.

Schimel, Lawrence. Little Pirate Goes to Bed. Perez, Sara Rojo, illus. 2007. 12p. (J). (ps-k). bds. 6.99 (978-1-58476-546-2(1)) Innovative Kids.

—Little Pirate Goes to School. Perez, Sara Rojo, illus. 2007. 12p. (J). (ps-k). bds. 6.99 (978-1-58476-545-5(3)) Innovative Kids.

Scieszka, Jon. El Pirata Barbanegra. Smith, Lane, illus. (SPA.). (J). (gr. 5-8). 7.95 (978-958-04-3401-6(8) , NR8584) Norma S.A. COL. *Dist:* Distribuidora Norma, Inc., Lectorum Pubns., Inc.

—South Pole or Bust (an Egg) 2007. (Time Warp Trio). 48p. (J). pap. 3.99 (978-0-06-111640-7(8) , Harper Trophy) HarperCollins Pubs.

Sebastian, Alberto. Capitan Calabrote. Serasols, Carles Rabat, illus. 2002. (Coleccion Libros para Sonar). (SPA.). 36p. (978-84-8464-122-3(8)) Kalandraka Editora, S.L.

Seuling, Barbara. Robert & the Happy Endings. Brewer, Paul, illus. 2007. (Robert Bks.). 160p. (J). (gr. 2-4). 16.95 (978-0-8126-2748-0(2)) Cricket Bks.

Simpson, Howard, illus. Pirates! 2007. (LazyTown Ser.). 24p. (J). pap. 3.99 (978-1-4169-4064-7(2) , Simon Spotlight/Nickelodeon) Simon & Schuster Children's Publishing.

Sinnott, L. Great Grandfather Was a Pirate. 2005. 77p. pap. 14.95 (978-1-4137-8006-2(7)) PublishAmerica, Inc.

Smallcomb, Pam. Camp Buccaneer. Lichtenheld, Tom, illus. 2002. (Ready-for-Chapters Ser.). 64p. (J). (gr. 1-3). lib. bdg. 11.89 (978-0-689-84383-9(6) , Aladdin Library) Simon & Schuster Children's Publishing.

Sobel, June. Shiver Me Letters: A Pirate ABC. Cole, Henry, illus. 2006. 32p. (J). 16.00 (978-0-15-216732-5(3)) Harcourt Trade Pubs.

Somper, Justin. Demons of the Ocean. 2006. 336p. (J). (gr. 3-7). 15.99 (978-0-316-01373-4(0)) Little Brown & Co.

—Demons of the Ocean. 2007. 352p. (J). (gr. 3-7). pap. 5.99 (*978-0-316-01444-1(3)) Little, Brown Bks. for Young Readers.

—Vampirates: Tide of Terror. 2nd rev. ed. 2007. 464p. (J). (gr. 3-7). 15.99 (*978-0-316-01374-1(9)) Little, Brown Bks. for Young Readers.

Spangler, Brie. Peg Leg Peke. 2008. 40p. (J). (ps-1). lib. bdg. 18.99 (*978-0-375-94828-6(0) , Knopf Bks. for Young Readers) Random Hse. Children's Bks.

Spendlove, Owen. Stanley Brambles & the Pirate's Treasure. 2007. 320p. per. 18.95 (*978-0-595-43792-4(3)) iUniverse, Inc.

Steele, Micheal Anthony. Chapter Book: King of the Pirates. 2007. 112p. (J). pap. 4.99 (978-0-439-89719-8(X)) Scholastic, Inc.

Sterling Publishing Co., Inc. Pirates: A Magic 3-Dimensional World of Pirates. Phillips, Francis, illus. 2006. (Step Inside Ser.). 12p. (J). 9.95 (978-1-4027-3989-7(3)) Sterling Publishing Co., Inc.

Stevenson, Robert Louis. La Isla del Tesoro. (Coleccion Clasicos de la Juventud). (SPA., Illus.). 188p. (J). 12.95 (978-84-7189-017-7(8) , ORT301) Ortells, Alfredo Editorial S.L. ESP. *Dist:* Continental Bk. Co., Inc.

—La Isla del Tesoro. (Coleccion Estrella). (SPA., Illus.). 64p. (J). 14.95 (978-950-11-0009-9(X) , SGM009) Sigmar ARG. *Dist:* Continental Bk. Co., Inc.

—La Isla del Tesoro. 2000. (Coleccion "Clasicos Juveniles" Ser.). (SPA., Illus.). 192p. (gr. 4-7). pap. 9.95 (978-1-58348-832-4(4)) iUniverse, Inc.

—Off to Sea Bk. 2. Comport, Sally Wern, illus. 2006. (Easy Reader Classics Ser.). 32p. (J). pap. 3.95 (978-1-4027-3298-0(8)) Sterling Publishing Co., Inc.

—Robert Louis Stevenson's Treasure Island: The Graphic Novel. 2005. (Puffin Graphics Ser.). (Illus.). 176p. (978-1-4156-2620-7(0) , Puffin) Penguin Group (USA) Inc.

—Robert Louis Stevenson/Treasure Island. Cruz, Nardo, illus. 2005. 48p. (J). (gr. 5-8). 25.50 (978-0-7910-9107-4(X)) Facts On File, Inc.

—Secuestrado. 3rd ed. (Coleccion Clasicos en Accion). (SPA., Illus.). 80p. (YA). (gr. 5-8). 15.95 (978-84-241-5781-4(8) , EV1487) Everest de Ediciones y Distribucion, S.L. ESP. *Dist:* Lectorum Pubns., Inc.

—Secuestrado. 2002. (Clover Ser.). (SPA., Illus.). 156p. (YA). 11.50 (978-84-392-8006-4(8) , EV5548) Lectorum Pubns., Inc.

—Treasure Island. McAllister, A. J., illus. 2002. (Great Illustrated Classics Ser.). 240p. (J). (gr. 3-8). 21.35 (978-1-57765-805-4(1) , ABDO & Daughters) ABDO Publishing Co.

—Treasure Island. Todd, Justin, illus. 1999. (Abbeville Classics Ser.). 176p. (J). pap. 7.95 (978-0-7892-0551-3(3) , Abbeville Kids) Abbeville Pr., Inc.

—Treasure Island. Gelev, Penko, illus. 2006. (Graphic Classics Ser.). 48p. (J). (gr. 2-6). pap. 8.99 (978-0-7641-3491-3(4)); 15.99 (978-0-7641-5976-3(3)) Barron's Educational Series, Inc.

—Treasure Island. 2002. (YA). 12.34 (978-0-7587-7947-2(X)) Book Wholesalers, Inc.

—Treasure Island. (Great Classics for Children Ser.). (Illus.). 192p. (J). (978-1-4037-0599-0(2)) Dalmatian Pr.

—Treasure Island. 2005. 116p. per. 5.95 (978-1-4209-2258-5(0)) Digireads.com.

—Treasure Island. 2001. (YA). (gr. 5-12). pap. 8.50 (978-0-8359-0234-2(X)) Globe Fearon Educational Publishing.

—Treasure Island. Lawrence, John, illus. 2001. (Kingfisher Classics Ser.). 352p. (J). (gr. 4-6). tchr. ed. 15.95 (978-0-7534-5380-3(0) , Kingfisher) Houghton Mifflin Co. Trade & Reference Div.

—Treasure Island. (Young Collector's Illustrated Classics Ser.). (Illus.). 192p. (J). (gr. 3-7). 9.95 (978-1-56156-456-9(7)) Kidsbooks, Inc.

—Treasure Island. 2007. (Oxford Children's Classics). (Illus.). 288p. (YA). 9.95 (*978-0-19-271998-0(X)) Oxford Univ. Pr., Inc.

—Treasure Island. Ingpen, Robert, illus. 2006. 192p. (J). 19.95 (978-0-9545103-6-7(4)) Palazzo Editions, Ltd. GBR. *Dist:* Trafalgar Square Publishing.

—Treasure Island. Seelye, John, ed. 1999. (Classics Ser.). (Illus.). 240p. (gr. 12). pap. 7.00 (978-0-14-043768-3(1) , Penguin Classics) Penguin Group (USA) Inc.

—Treasure Island. 1998. (Signet Classic Shakespeare Ser.). 224p. mass mkt. 3.95 (978-0-451-52704-2(6) , Signet Classics) Penguin Group (USA) Inc.

—Treasure Island. Winter, Milo, illus. 2002. (Illustrated Library for Children). 272p. (J). 12.99 (978-0-517-22114-3(4) , Gramercy) Random Hse. Value Publishing.

—Treasure Island. 2006. (Scholastic Classics Ser.). (Illus.). x, 205p. (J). (gr. 9-12). 25.00 (978-0-531-16961-2(8) , Watts, Franklin) Scholastic Library Publishing.

—Treasure Island. Wyeth, N. C., illus. 2000. (Aladdin Classics Ser.). 368p. (gr. 3-7). mass mkt. 5.99 (978-0-689-83212-3(5) , Aladdin) Simon & Schuster Children's Publishing.

—Treasure Island. 2006. (J). (gr. 4-8). 24.21 (978-1-59961-119-8(8)) Spotlight.

—Treasure Island. 1999. (Saddleback Classics). (Illus.). (J). (978-0-606-21576-3(X)) Tandem Library Bks.

—Treasure Island. 1998. (Children's Classics). (ENG., Illus.). 224p. (J). (gr. 3-7). pap. (978-1-85326-103-9(3) , 1033WW) Wordsworth Editions, Ltd.

—Treasure Island. Corvino, Lucy, illus. 2005. (Classic Starts Ser.). 160p. 4.95 (978-1-4027-1318-7(5)) Sterling Publishing Co., Inc.

—Treasure Island. Cruz, Nardo, illus. 2nd ed. 1998. (Illustrated Classic Book Ser.). 61p. (J). (gr. 3 up). reprint ed. pap. 4.95 (978-1-56767-239-8(6)) Educational Insights, Inc.

—Treasure Island. unabr. ed. 1998. (Wordsworth Classics Ser.). (YA). (gr. 6-12). 5.27 (978-0-89061-103-6(3) , R1033WW) Jamestown.

—Treasure Island. 2004. reprint ed. pap. 1.99 (978-1-4192-9097-8(5)) Kessinger Publishing, LLC.

—Treasure Island. 1999. (Illus.). 240p. (YA). (gr. 3 up). reprint ed. 7.95 (978-1-56852-233-3(9) , Konecky & Konecky) Konecky, William S. Assocs., Inc.

—Treasure Island. 1998. (Twelve-Point Ser.). 204p. reprint ed. lib. bdg. 25.00 (978-1-58287-075-5(6)) North Bks.

—Treasure Island: With a Discussion of Courage. 2003. (Values in Action Illustrated Classics Ser.). (J). (978-1-59203-054-5(8)) Learning Challenge, Inc.

—Treasure Island: With Story of the Treasure of Normon Island. Date not set. (J). (gr. 5-6). reprint ed. lib. bdg. 22.95 (978-0-89190-236-2(8) , American Reprint Co.) Amereon LTD.

—Treasure Island Bk. 1: The Treasure Map. Comport, Sally Wern, illus. 2006. (Easy Reader Classics Ser.). 32p. (J). pap. 3.95 (978-1-4027-3297-3(X)) Sterling Publishing Co., Inc.

—Treasure Island #3: on the Island. Comport, Sally Wern, illus. 2007. (Easy Reader Classics Ser.). 32p. (J). pap. 3.95 (978-1-4027-4119-7(7)) Sterling Publishing Co., Inc.

—Treasure Island #4: Pirate Attack. Comport, Sally Wern, illus. 2007. (Easy Reader Classics Ser.). 32p. (J). pap. 3.95 (978-1-4027-4120-3(0)) Sterling Publishing Co., Inc.

Stevenson, Robert Louis. Treausre Island: #1 the Treasure Map. 2007. (Easy Reader Classics Ser.). 32p. (J). (ps-3). 21.35 (*978-1-59961-342-0(5)) Spotlight.

Stevenson, Robert Louis & Brook, Henry. Treasure Island. 2006. 160p. (J). pap. 4.99 (978-0-7945-1230-9(5) , Usborne) EDC Publishing.

Stevenson, Robert Louis & Hitchner, Earle. Treasure Island. 1999. (Illus.). 245p. (J). (978-0-03-054463-7(7)) Holt, Rinehart & Winston.

Stewart, Michael. Pirates of the Caribbean. Evans, Dustin, illus. 2006. 128p. (J). (gr. 3-7). pap. 9.99 (978-0-7868-4714-3(X)) Disney Pr.

Stewart, Paul & Riddell, Chris. Far-Flung Adventures: Fergus Crane. 2006. (Illus.). 240p. (J). (gr. 3-7). 14.95 (978-0-385-75088-2(9) , Fickling, David Bks.) Random Hse. Children's Bks.

Stilton, Geronimo. Attack of the Bandit Cats. Wolf, Matt, illus. 2004. (Geronimo Stilton Ser.: No. 8). 115p. (J). lib. bdg. 10.00 (*978-1-4242-0277-5(9)) Fitzgerald Bks.

—Attack of the Bandit Cats. 2004. (Geronimo Stilton Ser.: No. 8). (Illus.). 128p. (J). pap. 5.99 (978-0-439-55970-6(7) , Scholastic Paperbacks) Scholastic, Inc.

Strickland, Brad. Salty Dog. l.t. ed. 1999. (Adventures of Wishbone Ser.: No. 2). (Illus.). 140p. (J). (gr. 4 up). lib. bdg. 22.60 (978-0-8368-2298-4(6)) Stevens, Gareth Inc.

Strong, Jeremy. The Indoor Pirates on Treasure Island. (Illus.). 96p. (J). 7.95 (978-0-14-038637-0(8)) Penguin Bks., Ltd. GBR. *Dist:* Trafalgar Square Publishing.

—Pirate Pandemonium. Sharratt, Nick, illus. l.t. ed. 2005. 152p. (J). pap. (978-0-7540-7807-4(8) , CLP 398) BBC Audio.

Students in Conjunction with 826 Valencia Staff. Some Things You Should Know about Captain Rick: An Informational Booklet Provided for the Safety of the Republic. 2006. 46p. (J). pap. 8.00 (978-0-9770844-1-8(8)) 826 Valencia.

Sturges, Philemon. This Little Pirate. Walrod, Amy, illus. 40p. (J). (ps). 2007. pap. 6.99 (978-0-14-240850-6(6) , Puffin); 2005. 16.99 (978-0-525-46440-2(9) , Dutton Juvenile) Penguin Group (USA) Inc.

Stutson, Caroline. Pirate Pup. Rayevsky, Robert, illus. 2005. 32p. (J). 15.95 (978-0-8118-4239-6(8)) Chronicle Bks. LLC.

Surrell, Jason. Pirates of the Caribbean: from the Magic Kindom to the Movies. 2006. (Illus.). 148p. (ps-17). pap. 22.95 (978-1-4231-0709-5(8) , Disney Editions) Disney Pr.

Sutherland, T. T. Pirates of the Caribbean 3: At World's End. Disney Press Staff, ed. 2007. 176p. (gr. 4-7). pap. 4.99 (*978-1-4231-0377-6(7)) Disney Pr.

—Pirates of the Caribbean 3: Turner. Disney Press Staff, ed. 2007. 24p. (ps-2). pap. 3.99 (*978-1-4231-0376-9(9)) Disney Pr.

—Pirates of the Caribbean At World's End: Saving Jack Sparrow. Disney Press Staff, ed. 2007. 24p. (ps-2). pap. 3.99 (*978-1-4231-0374-5(2)) Disney Pr.

—Pirates of the Caribbean At World's End: Singapore! Disney Press Staff, ed. 2007. 32p. (gr. 1-4). pap. 3.99 (*978-1-4231-0379-0(3)) Disney Pr.

—Pirates of the Caribbean At World's End: The Movie Storybook. Disney Press Staff, ed. 2007. 64p. (gr. 5-17). 8.99 (*978-1-4231-0378-3(5)) Disney Pr.

—Pirates of the Caribbean At World's End: The Mystic's Journey. Disney Press Staff, ed. 2007. 32p. (gr. 1-4). pap. 3.99 (*978-1-4231-0380-6(7)) Disney Pr.

Taplin, Sam. Pirate's Handbook. Mcnee, Ian, illus. 2007. 80p. (J). 12.99 (978-0-7945-1463-1(4) , Usborne) EDC Publishing.

Taylor, Richard A. Ships of Children. 2nd rev. ed. 2006. (Illus.). 191p. (YA). lib. bdg. 37.95 (978-0-9764403-7-6(7)) Klare Taylor Pubs.

Thompson, Lisa. Diving for the Ghost Galleon. Cantell, Brenda, illus. 2005. (Treasure Trackers Ser.). 80p. (gr. 5-9). 19.00 (978-0-7910-8873-9(1)) Facts On File, Inc.

Torrey, Michele. Bottles of Eight & Pieces of Rum. 1998. 138p. (J). (ps-7). pap. 9.99 (978-0-88092-321-7(0) , 3210) Royal Fireworks Publishing Co.

—Voyage of Plunder. 208p. (J). 2007. (gr. 4-7). pap. 5.99 (978-0-440-41887-0(9) , Yearling); 2005. (gr. 5-7). 15.95 (978-0-375-82383-1(2) , Knopf Bks. for Young Readers) Random Hse. Children's Bks.

ToyBox Innovations, creator. The Curse of the Black Pearl. 2006. (Pirates of the Caribbean (Audio) Ser.). (Illus.). 24p. (J). (ps-3). audio compact disk 7.99 (978-0-7634-2176-2(6)) Walt Disney Records.

—Dead Man's Chest. 2006. (Pirates of the Caribbean (Audio) Ser.). (Illus.). 24p. (J). (ps-3). audio compact disk 7.99 (978-0-7634-2177-9(4)) Walt Disney Records.

Trimble, Irene. Dead Man's Chest. 2nd novel rev. ed. 2006. (Pirates of the Caribbean Ser.). (Illus.). 160p. (gr. 3-7). pap. 4.99 (978-1-4231-0024-9(7)) Disney Pr.

Tryon, Micro, et al. Fundorado Island. 2006. (Illus.). 224p. (J). (gr. 3). 14.95 (978-0-385-73267-3(8) , Delacorte Bks. for Young Readers) Random Hse. Children's Bks.

Tullson, Diane. Red Sea. 2005. 176p. (J). (gr. 7-12). pap. 7.95 (978-1-55143-331-8(1)) Orca Bk. Pubs. USA.

Underwood, Deborah. Pirate Mom. Gilpin, Stephen, illus. 2006. (Step into Reading Ser.). 48p. (J). (gr. 1-3). lib. bdg. 11.99 (978-0-375-93323-3(9)); 3.99 (978-0-375-83323-6(4)) Random Hse. Children's Bks. (Random Hse. Bks. for Young Readers).

Utton, Peter. Duncan & the Pirates. Utton, Peter, illus. 2005. (Read-It! Chapter Bks.). (Illus.). 52p. (J). (ps-k). lib. bdg. 19.95 (978-1-4048-1277-2(6)) Picture Window Bks.

Valdes, Leslie. Dora's Pirate Adventure. Aikins, Dave, illus. ed. 2005. (Dora the Explorer Ser.: No. 12). 22p. (J). lib. bdg. 15.00 (978-1-59054-796-0(9)) Fitzgerald Bks.

Vischer, Lisa. Three Pirates & You! 2004. (Illus.). 32p. 7.99 (978-0-310-70724-0(2)) Zonderkidz.

Walker, Richard. The Barefoot Book of Pirates. Whelan, Olwyn, illus. 64p. (J). 2004. pap. 14.99 (978-1-84148-131-9(9)); 1998. (gr. 4-7). reprint ed. 19.99 (978-1-901223-79-8(5)) Barefoot Bks., Inc.

Wallace, John. Pirate Boy. (Illus.). 32p. (J). 2003. pap. 9.99 (978-0-00-664776-8(6)); 2002. 19.99 (978-0-00-198421-9(7)) HarperCollins Pubs. Ltd. GBR. *Dist:* Independent Pubs. Group, Trafalgar Square Publishing.

Wallace, Lew. Blackbeard & the Topsail Island Pirate. 1999. 112p. (J). (gr. 3-7). pap. 6.95 (978-1-889062-03-7(0)) Artel Publishing.

Walsh, Sheila. The Mystery of Magillicuddy's Gold. 2007. (Will, God's Mighty Warrior Ser.). 32p. (J). 12.99 (*978-1-4003-1028-9(8)) Nelson, Thomas Inc.

Walt Disney Company Staff. Treasure Planet: A Pop-Up Adventure. 2002. 12p. (J). bds. 8.99 (978-0-7364-2014-3(2) , RH/Disney) Random Hse. Children's Bks.

Watt, Fiona. That's not My Pirate. Wells, Rachel, illus. 2007. (Touchy-Feely Board Bks). 10p. (J). bds. 7.99 (*978-0-7945-1702-1(1) , Usborne) EDC Publishing.

Wechter, Nell Wise & Tucker, Bruce. Teach's Light. 1999. (Chapel Hill Book Ser.). (Illus.). 160p. (gr. 4-7). pap. 10.95 (978-0-8078-4793-0(3)) Univ. of North Carolina Pr.

Weise, Selene H. C. Gold for a Boat. 2001. (Illus.). 68p. (J). (gr. 1-6). 5.95 (978-1-57249-270-7(8) , Burd Street Pr.) White Mane Publishing Co., Inc.

Whatley, Bruce. Cowboy Pirate. 2002. (Illus.). 32p. 14.95 (978-0-207-19891-5(8)) HarperCollins Pubs.

Whybrow, Ian. Little Wolf, Terror of the Shivery Sea. Ross, Tony, illus. 2005. (Middle Grade Fiction Ser.). 144p. (J). (gr. 3-6). 14.95 (978-1-57505-629-6(1)) Lerner Publishing Group.

Wickstrom, Lois June & Lorrah, Jean. Nessie & the Living Stone. Strand, Sara Silvestri, illus. 2001. (J). pap. 13.80 (978-1-58338-616-3(5) , CrossroadsPub.Org) CrossroadsPub.com.

Wigington, Patti. Pirate's Alphabet. Umscheid, Kit, illus. 2006. 32p. 15.95 (978-0-9766805-8-1(0) , Moo Pr.) Keene Publishing.

Wilkes, Angela. Treasure Island. 2003. (gr. 3-6). lib. bdg. 14.10 (978-0-613-88963-6(0)) Tandem Library Bks.

Wilkes, Angela & Rawson, Christopher. Treasure Island. 2004. (Young Reading Ser.). (Illus.). 64p. (J). (gr. 2 up). pap. 5.95 (978-0-7945-0411-3(6) , Usborne) EDC Publishing.

Williams, Rozanne Lanczak. Captain Jack's Journal. Maio, Barbara, ed. Grayson, Rick, illus. 2006. (Learn to Write Ser.). (J). 16p. pap. 2.99 (978-1-59198-303-3(7) , 6197); per. 6.99 (*978-1-59198-361-3(4)) Creative Teaching Pr., Inc.

Willson, Sarah. Up & Away, Reptar! Rillo, Cary, illus. 2000. (Ready-to-Read Ser.). 32p. (J). (ps-3). pap. 3.99 (978-0-671-77315-1(1) , Simon & Schuster Children's Publishing) Simon & Schuster Children's Publishing.

—Up & Away, Reptar! 1999. (gr. k-3). lib. bdg. 11.80 (978-0-613-16029-2(0)) Tandem Library Bks.

Wininger, Stephen T. The Adventure of Pirate Pete Moss. 2004. (J). pap. (978-1-59196-466-7(0)) Instantpublisher.com.

Wishinsky, Frieda. Beware, Pirates! Griffiths, Dean, illus. 2007. (Canadian Flyer Adventures Ser.: No. 1). 96p. (J). (gr. 1-4). 16.95 (978-1-897066-79-9(1)); pap. 6.95 (978-1-897066-80-5(5)) Maple Tree Pr. CAN. *Dist:* Perseus Distribution.

Wolf-Tau, Kim & Wolf, Jeanne. The Last Treasure of Pirate's Cove. 2001. (Cliffhanger Adventure Mystery Ser.). 126p. (YA). 24.95 incl. VHS (978-0-9668491-0-3(8)) Mental Interactive Systems.

Wood, Francis. The SnowPeople. Larsen, Dan, illus. 2003. 96p. (YA). per. 14.95 (978-0-9746372-0-4(3)) Tip-Of-The-Moon Publishing Co.

Yolen, Jane. The Ballad of the Pirate Queens. ed. 2004. (J). (gr. k-3). spiral bd. (978-0-616-01821-7(5)) Canadian National Institute for the Blind/Institut National Canadien pour les Aveugles.

—The Ballad of the Pirate Queens. Shannon, David, illus. 1998. 32p. (J). (gr. k-7). pap. 7.00 (978-0-15-201885-6(9) , Voyager Bks./Libros Viajeros) Harcourt Children's Bks.

—The Ballad of the Pirate Queens. Shannon, David, illus. 1998. (J). (ps-7). lib. bdg. 15.30 (978-0-613-09936-3(2)) Tandem Library Bks.

—The Ballad of the Pirate Queens. 1998. (978-0-606-13178-0(7)) Tandem Library Bks.

Yoon, Salina. A Pirate's Life. 2007. (Salina Yoon Bks.). 10p. (J). (ps-2). pap. 8.99 (978-0-8431-2487-3(3) , Price Stern Sloan) Penguin Group (USA) Inc.

Young, Joseph R. Legend of the Lost Josephine Mine: A Fascinating Adventure. 2001. 221p. (J). pap. 13.95 (978-1-55517-550-4(3) , Bonneville Bks.) Cedar Fort, Inc./CFI Distribution.

P Q R

Zucker, Jonny. Cut-Throat Pirates. Smith, Pete, illus. 2007. 33p. (J). pap. (*978-1-59889-428-8(5)); 40p. (YA). (gr. 5-9). lib. bdg. 21.26 (*978-1-59889-332-8(7)) Stone Arch Bks.

PITTSBURGH PIRATES (BASEBALL TEAM)

Campbell, Peter A. Old Time Baseball & the First. 2002. (Illus.). 48p. (gr. 3-6). lib. bdg. 24.90 (978-0-7613-2466-9(6) , Millbrook Pr.) Lerner Publishing Group.

Goodman, Michael E. The History of the Pittsburgh Pirates. 1998. (Baseball, the Great American Game Ser.). (Illus.). 32p. (YA). (gr. 3-12). pap. 21.30 (978-0-88682-921-6(6) , Creative Education) Creative Co., The.

Goodman, Michael E. The Story of the Philadelphia Phillies. 2007. (J). (*978-1-58341-498-9(3) , Creative Education) Creative Co., The.

Stewart, Wayne. Pittsburgh Pirates. 2002. 32p. (J). pap. 5.95 (978-0-89812-354-8(2) , Creative Paperbacks); (Illus.). (978-1-58341-220-6(4) , Creative Education) Creative Co., The.

Winter, Jonah. Roberto Clemente: Pride of the Pittsburgh Pirates. Colon, Raul, illus. 2005. 40p. (J). 17.99 (978-0-689-85643-3(1) , Atheneum) Simon & Schuster Children's Publishing.

PIUS V, SAINT, POPE, 1566-1572

Daughters of St. Paul Staff. No Place for Defeat. Date not set. (Encounter Ser.). 96p. (J). (gr. 3-9). pap. 2.00 (978-0-8198-5100-0(0)) Pauline Bks. & Media.

PIUS XII, POPE, 1876-1958

Marchione, Margherita. Pope Pius XII: Bilingual Coloring Book. Elliott, John, illus. 2004. (SPA & ENG.). 32p. 1.00 (978-0-8091-6721-0(2) , 6721-2) Paulist Pr.

PIZARRO, FRANCISCO, CA. 1475-1541

Bergen, Lara Rice. Francisco Pizarro. 1999. (Illus.). 48p. (J). 136.98 (978-0-7398-1489-5(3)) Raintree.

—The Travels of Francisco Pizarro. 2000. (Explorers & Exploration Ser.). (Illus.). 48p. (J). (gr. 4-7). lib. bdg. 22.83 (978-0-7398-1487-1(7)) Raintree.

DeAngelis, Gina. Francisco Pizarro & the Conquest of the Inca. 2000. (Explorers of the New World Ser.). (Illus.). 63p. (J). (gr. 8-12). 31.00 (978-0-7910-5951-7(0)); (gr. 4-7). pap. 25.00 (978-0-7910-6161-9(2)) Facts On File, Inc. (Chelsea Hse.).

Donaldson-Forbes, Jeff. Francisco Pizarro. 2002. (Famous Explorers Ser.). (Illus.). 24p. (J). (gr. 3). lib. bdg. 18.75 (978-0-8239-5831-3(0) , PowerKids Pr.) Rosen Publishing Group, Inc., The.

Hoogenboom, Lynn. Francisco Pizarro: A Primary Source Biography. 2006. (J). lib. bdg. (978-1-4042-3038-5(6) , PowerKids Pr.) Rosen Publishing Group, Inc., The.

Ingram, Scott. Francisco Pizarro. 2002. (History's Villains Ser.). (Illus.). 112p. 29.94 (978-1-56711-627-4(2) , Blackbirch Pr., Inc.) Thomson Gale.

Kachurek, Sandra J. Francisco Pizarro: Explorer of South America. 2004. (Explorers! Ser.). (Illus.). 48p. (J). lib. bdg. 23.93 (978-0-7660-2178-5(5)) Enslow Pubs., Inc.

Kline, Trish. Francisco Pizarro. 2003. (Rourke Discovery Library). (Illus.). 24p. (gr. 2-5). 14.95 (978-1-58952-297-8(4)) Rourke Publishing, LLC.

—Francisco Pizarro: Descubre la Vida de un Explorador. 2002. (J). lib. bdg. 19.27 (978-1-58952-431-6(4)) Rourke Publishing, LLC.

Manning, Ruth. Francisco Pizarro. (Groundbreakers Ser.). (Illus.). 48p. (J). (gr. 5-7). 2002. pap. 8.50 (978-1-58810-341-3(2) , 91092); 2000. lib. bdg. 25.64 (978-1-57572-369-3(7)) Heinemann Library.

—Francisco Pizarro. 2001. (gr. 5-8). lib. bdg. 17.05 (978-0-613-87922-4(8)) Tandem Library Bks.

Meltzer, Milton. Francisco Pizarro: The Conquest of Peru. 2003. (Great Explorations Ser.). (J). 29.93 (978-0-7614-1607-4(2) , Benchmark Bks.) Cavendish, Marshall Corp.

Mountjoy, Shane. Francisco Pizarro & the Conquest of the Inca. Goetzmann, William H., ed. 2005. (Explorers of New Lands Ser.). (Illus.). 150p. (J). (gr. 4-8). 30.00 (978-0-7910-8614-8(3) , Chelsea Hse.) Facts On File, Inc.

Saunders, Nicholas. Pizarro & the Incas. 2006. (Stories from History Ser.). 48p. (J). 14.95 (978-0-7696-4706-7(5)); pap. 6.95 (*978-0-7696-4642-8(5)) School Specialty Publishing.

Somervill, Barbara A. Francisco Pizarro: Conqueror of the Incas. 2004. (Signature Lives Ser.). (Illus.). 112p. (J). 30.60 (978-0-7565-0815-9(0) , 1240121) Compass Point Bks.

Worth, Richard. Pizarro & the Conquest of the Incan Empire in World History. 2000. (In World History Ser.). (Illus.). 128p. (YA). (gr. 5-12). lib. bdg. 26.60 (978-0-7660-1396-4(0)) Enslow Pubs., Inc.

Zronik, John Paul. Francisco Pizarro: Journeys Through Peru & South America. 2005. (In the Footsteps of Explorers Ser.). (Illus.). 32p. (J). (ps-9). (978-0-7787-2411-7(5)); pap. (978-0-7787-2447-6(6)) Crabtree Publishing Co.

PLACE NAMES

see Names, Geographical

PLAGUE

see also Black Death

Cunningham, Jesse G., ed. The Plague: Readings On. 2001. (Illus.). 176p. (YA). (gr. 8-12). lib. bdg. 34.70 (978-0-613-73782-1(2)) Tandem Library Bks.

De Hahn, Tracee. The Black Death. 2001. (Great Disasters, Reforms & Ramifications Ser.). (Illus.). 112p. (J). 30.00 (978-0-7910-6326-2(7) , Chelsea Hse.) Facts On File, Inc.

Dunn, John M. Life During the Black Death. 1999. (Way People Live Ser.). (Illus.). 96p. (J). (gr. 7-10). 28.70 (978-1-56006-542-5(7) , LML00902-177899, Lucent Bks.) Thomson Gale.

Elliott, Lynne. Medieval Medicine & the Plague. 2005. (Medieval World Ser.). (Illus.). 32p. (J). (gr. 4-9). pap. (978-0-7787-1390-6(3)) Crabtree Publishing Co.

Freed, Shirley & Moon, Louise. Let My People Go. Butler, Steven, illus. 2003. 8p. (J). (-k). pap. 3.99 (978-1-58938-096-7(7)) Concerned Communications.

Gentle, Victor & Perry, Janet. Plagues. 2001. (Natural Disasters Ser.). (Illus.). 24p. (J). (gr. 2 up). lib. bdg. 22.00 (978-0-8368-2835-1(6)) Stevens, Gareth Inc.

Jackson, Kay. Bubonic Plague. 2006. (Natural Disasters Ser.). (Illus.). 32p. (J). (gr. 1-4). lib. bdg. (978-1-58415-494-5(2)) Mitchell Lane Pubs., Inc.

Lynette, Rachel. Bubonic Plague. 2004. (Understanding Diseases & Disorders Ser.). (Illus.). 48p. (J). 26.20 (978-0-7377-2639-8(3) , Greenhaven Pr., Inc.) Thomson Gale.

MacDonald, Fiona. The Plague & Medicine in the Middle Ages. 2005. (World Almanac Library of the Middle Ages). (Illus.). 48p. (J). pap. (978-0-8368-5907-2(3) , World Almanac Library) Stevens, Gareth Inc.

—The Plague & Medicine In the Middle Ages. 2005. (World Almanac' Library of the Middle Ages). (Illus.). 48p. (J). (gr. 10-17). lib. bdg. 30.00 (978-0-8368-5898-3(0) , World Almanac Library) Stevens, Gareth Inc.

Narayan, Natasha. Black Death & Other Putrid Plagues of London. 2004. (... of London Ser.). (Illus.). 96p. 8.99 (978-1-904153-01-6(1)) Watling St., Ltd. GBR. *Dist:* Trafalgar Square Publishing.

Peters, Stephanie True. The Black Death. 2003. (Epidemics Ser.). (J). 29.93 (978-0-7614-1633-3(1) , Benchmark Bks.) Cavendish, Marshall Corp.

Robson, Pam. The Great Plague. 2003. (Illus.). 48p. (J). pap. (978-0-7500-1934-7(4) , Hodder Wayland) Hodder Children's Division.

Shields, Charles J. The Great Plague & Fire of London. 2001. (Great Disasters, Reforms & Ramifications Ser.). (Illus.). 120p. (YA). (gr. 6-10). 21.95 (978-0-7910-6324-8(0) , Chelsea Hse.) Facts On File, Inc.

Walker, Jane. Famine, Drought, & Plagues. 2004. (Natural Disasters Ser.). (J). lib. bdg. 27.10 (978-1-932799-08-8(7)) Stargazer Bks.

Walker, Richard. KFK Epidemics & Plagues. 2007. (Kingfisher Knowledge Ser.). 8.95 (*978-0-7534-6181-5(1) , Kingfisher) Houghton Mifflin Co. Trade & Reference Div.

PLAGUE—FICTION

Barker, M. A. R. Lords of Tsamra, 2003. (Illus.). 296p. (YA). per. 19.95 (978-0-9725880-1-0(9) , 2) Zottola Publishing, Inc.

Case, John. First Horseman. 1999. (gr. 7-12). lib. bdg. 15.30 (978-0-613-29244-3(8)) Tandem Library Bks.

Collins, Suzanne. Gregor & the Curse of the Warmbloods. 368p. 2006. (J). pap. 6.99 (978-0-439-65624-5(9) , Scholastic Paperbacks); 2005. (Underland Chronicles: Bk. 3). pap. 16.95 (978-0-439-65623-8(0) , Scholastic Pr.) Scholastic, Inc.

—Gregor & the Curse of the Warmbloods. l.t. ed. 2006. 297p. (J). 23.95 (978-0-7862-8083-4(2)) Thorndike Pr.

Cullen, Lynn. I Am Rembrandt's Daughter. 2007. 320p. (YA). (gr. 7 up). 16.95 (*978-1-59990-046-9(7)) Bloomsbury Publishing.

Decker, Timothy. Run Far, Run Fast. Decker, Timothy, illus. 2007. (Illus.). 40p. (J). (gr. 5 up). 17.95 (*978-1-59078-469-3(3) , Front Street) Boyds Mills Pr.

Hooper, Mary. At the Sign of the Sugared Plum. (J). 2005. 176p. (gr. 4-7). pap. 6.95 (978-1-58234-695-3(X)); 2003. 200p. 16.95 (978-1-58234-849-0(9)) Bloomsbury Publishing. (Bloomsbury Children).

—Petals in the Ashes. 2004. 200p. (J). (gr. 5 up). 16.95 (978-1-58234-936-7(3) , Bloomsbury Children) Bloomsbury Publishing.

Keeling, Annie E. Andrew Golding A Tale of the Great Plague. 2004. reprint ed. pap. 15.95 (978-1-4191-0694-1(5)); pap. 1.99 (978-1-4192-0694-8(X)) Kessinger Publishing, LLC.

Keeling, E. Annie. Andrew Golding (a Tale of the Great Plag. 2006. 40.99 (*978-1-4280-0516-7(1)); pap. 34.99 (*978-1-4280-0515-0(3)) IndyPublish.com.

LaHaye, Tim & Jenkins, Jerry B. Apollyon: The Destroyer Is Unleashed. 1999. (Left Behind Ser.: Bk. 5). (gr. 7-12). lib. bdg. 24.60 (978-0-613-23100-8(7)) Tandem Library Bks.

Levitin, Sonia. The Cure. 2000. (J). 12.64 (978-0-606-19967-4(5)) Tandem Library Bks.

Napoli, Donna Jo. Breath. 2003. (Illus.). 272p. (YA). 17.95 (978-0-689-86174-1(5) , Atheneum) Simon & Schuster Children's Publishing.

—Breath. l.t. ed. 2005. 251p. 21.95 (978-0-7862-7420-8(4) , Large Print Pr.) Thorndike Pr.

Russell, Christopher. Hunted. 2007. 272p. (J). (gr. 5-8). 15.99 (978-0-06-084119-5(2)); lib. bdg. 16.89 (978-0-06-084120-1(6)) HarperCollins Pubs.

Turnbull, Ann. Forged in the Fire. 2007. 320p. (YA). (gr. 7). 16.99 (978-0-7636-3144-4(2)) Candlewick Pr.

Wooderson, Philip. The Plague. 2006. (My Side of the Story Ser.). 192p. (J). (gr. 5-9). pap. 7.95 (978-0-7534-5990-4(6) , Kingfisher) Houghton Mifflin Co. Trade & Reference Div.

PLANE CRASHES

see Aircraft Accidents

PLANE GEOMETRY

see Geometry

PLANE TRIGONOMETRY

see Trigonometry

PLANETS

see also Life on Other Planets; Solar System; Stars
also names of planets, e.g. Venus (Planet)

Ashby, Ruth. The Outer Planets. 2003. (New Solar System Ser.). (J). lib. bdg. 28.50 (978-1-58340-290-0(X)) Smart Apple Media.

Asimov, Isaac & Hantula, Richard. Marte: Nuestro Misteriosos Vecino, Porras, Carlos & D'Andrea, Patricia, trs. 2003. (Isaac Asimov's Biblioteca del Universo del Siglo XXI). (SPA., Illus.). 32p. (J). (gr. 3 up). lib. bdg. 24.67 (978-0-8368-3856-5(4)); pap. 8.95 (978-0-8368-3869-5(6) , Weekly Reader Early Learning Library) Stevens, Gareth Inc.

—Pluton y Caronte. Porras, Carlos & D'Andrea, Patricia, trs. 2003. (Isaac Asimov's Biblioteca del Universo del Siglo XXI). (SPA., Illus.). 32p. (J). (gr. 3 up). pap. 8.95 (978-0-8368-3872-5(6) , Weekly Reader Early Learning Library) Stevens, Gareth Inc.

—Pluton y Caronte. Porras, Carlos & D'Andrea, Patricia, trs. 2003. (Isaac Asimov's Biblioteca del Universo del Siglo XXI). (SPA., Illus.). 32p. (J). (gr. 3 up). lib. bdg. 24.67 (978-0-8368-3859-6(9)) Stevens, Gareth Inc.

Barner, Bob. Stars! Stars! Stars! 2002. (Illus.). 32p. (J). (ps-3). 14.95 (978-0-8118-3159-8(0)) Chronicle Bks. LLC.

Bell, Trudy E. The Inner Planets. 2003. (New Solar System Ser.). (J). lib. bdg. 28.50 (978-1-58340-288-7(8)) Smart Apple Media.

Berger, Melvin & Berger, Gilda. Do Stars Have Points? Questions & Answers about Stars & Planets. Di Fate, Vincent, illus. 1999. (Scholastic Question & Answer Ser.). 48p. (J). (gr. 2-4). pap. 6.99 (978-0-439-08570-0(5) , Scholastic Reference) Scholastic, Inc.

Bing & Bong's Tiny Planets. (Illus.). 12p. (J). pap. (978-1-84222-875-3(7)) Carlton Bks., Ltd.

Birch, Robin. Planets. 2002. (Space Ser.). (Illus.). 32p. (gr. k-2). 23.00 (978-0-7910-6972-1(9) , Chelsea Hse.) Facts On File, Inc.

—Saturn. 2004. (Solar System Ser.). (Illus.). 32p. (gr. 3-5). 23.00 (978-0-7910-7932-4(5) , Chelsea Hse.) Facts On File, Inc.

Borg, Janet. My Favorite Nature Book: Stars & Planets: Includes an Activity Kit with Posters, Stickers & Glow-in-the-Dark Stars. Weiss, Anne & Estellon, Pascale, illus. 2006. 24p. 9.95 (978-1-57990-923-9(X)) Lark Bks.

Bown, Deni & Becklake, Sue. Space, Stars, Planets, & Spacecraft: See & Explore Library. 1998. (See & Explore Library Ser.). (Illus.). 64p. (J). (gr. 4-7). pap. 7.99 (978-0-7894-2966-7(7)) Dorling Kindersley Publishing, Inc.

Bramwell, Martyn. Mapping the Planets & Space. 1998. (Maps & Mapmakers Ser.). (Illus.). 48p. (J). (gr. 5-7). lib. bdg. 22.60 (978-0-8225-2922-4(X) , Lerner Pubns.) Lerner Publishing Group.

Branley, Franklyn M. The Planets in Our Solar System. O'Malley, Kevin, illus. 1998. (Let's-Read-and-Find-Out Science Ser.). 32p. (J). (gr. k-4). pap. 5.99 (978-0-06-445178-9(X)); Stage 2. 15.95 (978-0-06-027769-7(6)); Stage 2. 15.89 (978-0-06-027770-3(X)) HarperCollins Pubs.

Bredeson, Carmen. The Neptune. 2002. (Watts Library). (Illus.). 64p. (J). (gr. 5-7). pap. 25.50 (978-0-531-12037-8(6) , Watts, Franklin) Scholastic Library Publishing.

Brighter Vision Publishing Staff. Space & the Planets. 2000. (Learning Adventures Kindergarten Ser.). (Illus.). (J). (gr. k-1). pap. 2.25 (978-1-55254-146-3(0)) Brighter Vision Pubns.

Brimner, Larry Dane. Neptune. 1999. (gr. 3-6). lib. bdg. 15.25 (978-0-613-37476-7(2)) Tandem Library Bks.

—Saturn. 1999. (gr. 3-6). lib. bdg. 15.25 (978-0-613-37529-0(7)) Tandem Library Bks.

—Uranus. 1999. (True Bks.). (Illus.). 48p. (J). (gr. 3-5). 25.00 (978-0-516-21156-5(0) , Children's Pr.) Scholastic Library Publishing.

—Uranus. 1999. (gr. 3-6). lib. bdg. 15.25 (978-0-613-37571-9(8)) Tandem Library Bks.

Carroll, Michael W., et al. Space & Time. 2005. (God's Creation Ser.). (Illus.). 40p. (J). 7.99 (978-0-310-70578-9(9)) Zonderkidz.

Carson, Mary Kay. Extreme Planets! QandA. 2008. 48p. (J). 16.99 (*978-0-06-089975-2(1)); pap. 7.99 (*978-0-06-089974-5(3)) HarperCollins Pubs.

The Case of the Missing Planet. 2005. (Book Treks Ser.). (J). (gr. 3 up). stu. ed. 34.95 (978-0-673-62845-9(0)) Celebration Pr.

Cole, Michael D. Galileo Spacecraft: Mission to Jupiter. 1999. (Countdown to Space Ser.). (Illus.). 48p. (YA). (gr. 4-10). lib. bdg. 23.93 (978-0-7660-1119-9(4)) Enslow Pubs., Inc.

—Jupiter: The Fifth Planet. 2001. (Countdown to Space Ser.). (Illus.). 48p. (YA). (gr. 4-10). lib. bdg. 23.93 (978-0-7660-1511-1(4)) Enslow Pubs., Inc.

—Mercury: The First Planet. 2001. (Countdown to Space Ser.). (Illus.). 48p. (YA). (gr. 4-10). lib. bdg. 23.93 (978-0-7660-1512-8(2)) Enslow Pubs., Inc.

—Neptune: The Eighth Planet. 2002. (Countdown to Space Ser.). (Illus.). 48p. (J). (gr. 4-10). lib. bdg. 23.93 (978-0-7660-1951-5(9)) Enslow Pubs., Inc.

—Saturn: The Sixth Planet. 2002. (Countdown to Space Ser.). (Illus.). 48p. (J). (gr. 4-10). lib. bdg. 23.93 (978-0-7660-1950-8(0)) Enslow Pubs., Inc.

—Venus: The Second Planet. 2001. (Countdown to Space Ser.). (Illus.). 48p. (YA). (gr. 4-10). lib. bdg. 23.93 (978-0-7660-1509-8(2)) Enslow Pubs., Inc.

Colson, A. Turbulent Planet, 6 packs.,24 bks., Set. 2004. (Illus.). pap. 183.60 (978-1-4109-1275-6(2)) Raintree.

Coupe, Robert. The Planets. 2002. (Junior Adventure Ser.). (Illus.). 32p. (J). (gr. 3 up). lib. bdg. (978-1-59084-181-5(6)) Mason Crest Pubs.

—The Planets. 1999. (Explorers Ser.). (Illus.). 32p. (J). (978-0-7699-0482-5(3)) Shortland Pubns. (U. S. A.) Inc.

Croswell, Ken. Ten Worlds: Everything That Orbits the Sun. (Illus.). 2007. 56p. (*978-1-59078-531-7(2)); 2006. 60p. (J). 19.95 (978-1-59078-423-5(5)) Boyds Mills Pr.

Deboo, Ana. Mapping the Planets & Space. 2006. (Map Readers Ser.). (Illus.). 32p. (J). (978-1-4034-6791-1(9)); pap. (978-1-4034-6798-0(6)) Heinemann Library.

The Deep Blue Planet, 5 bks., Set. Incl. Along the Coasts. Massa, Renato. Davenport, Neil F., tr. (YA). 1998. lib. bdg. 28.54 (978-0-8172-4654-9(1)); Back to the Sea. Massa, Renato. Davenport, Neil F., tr. (YA). 1998. lib. bdg. 28.54 (978-0-8172-4653-2(3)); Coral Reef. Massa, Renato. Serio, Linda, tr. (YA). 1997. lib. bdg. 28.54 (978-0-8172-4652-5(5)); Ocean Environments. Voglino, Alex & Massa, Renato. Davenport, Neil F., tr. (YA). 1998. lib. bdg. 28.54 (978-0-8172-4651-8(7)); Oceans & Seas. Voglino, Alex. (J). 1997. lib. bdg. 28.54 (978-0-8172-4650-1(9)); 56p. (gr. 6-12). (Illus.). Set lib. bdg. 142.70 (978-0-8172-4655-6(X)) Raintree.

Discovery Channel & Staff. Births. 2004. (Planet's Most Extreme Ser.). (Illus.). 48p. (J). (gr. 4-7). 24.95 (978-1-4103-0380-6(2) , Blackbirch Pr., Inc.) Thomson Gale.

—Strength. 2004. (Planet's Most Extreme Ser.). (Illus.). 48p. (J). (gr. 4-7). 24.95 (978-1-4103-0387-5(X) , Blackbirch Pr., Inc.) Thomson Gale.

—Survivors. 2004. (Planet's Most Extreme Ser.). (Illus.). 48p. (J). (gr. 4-7). 24.95 (978-1-4103-0382-0(9) , Blackbirch Pr., Inc.) Thomson Gale.

DK Publishing Staff. Stars & Planets. 2007. (Eyewitness Workbks.). 48p. (J). pap., wbk. ed. 9.99 (978-0-7566-3034-8(7)) Dorling Kindersley Publishing, Inc.

Dussling, Jennifer. Planets. Ortakales, Denise, illus. 2000. (All Aboard Reading Ser.). 48p. (J). (gr. 1-3). pap. 3.99 (978-0-448-42406-4(1) , Grosset & Dunlap) Penguin Group (USA) Inc.

—Planets. 2000. (All Aboard Reading Ser.). (J). (978-0-606-20269-5(2)); lib. bdg. 11.80 (978-0-613-31592-0(8)); (Illus.). (J). (978-0-606-20405-7(9)) Tandem Library Bks.

Enciclopedia del Planeta Tierra. (SPA.). (YA). (gr. 4). pap. 19.95 (978-0-7460-4527-5(1)) EDC Publishing.

Encyclopaedia Britannica Publishers, ed. New Views of the Solar System, 1. 2007. (ENG., Illus.). 112p. (YA). 28.95 net. (*978-1-59339-340-3(7)) Encyclopaedia Britannica, Inc.

Evert, Laura. Planets, Moons & Stars. Garrow, Linda, illus. (Take-Along Guide Ser.). 48p. (gr. 2-5). 2004. (J). pap. 7.95 (978-1-55971-842-4(0)); 2003. 11.95 (978-1-55971-877-6(3)) T&N Children's Publishing. (North-Word Bks. for Young Readers).

Feely, Jenny. In the Sky. 2001. (gr. k-3). lib. bdg. 11.95 (978-0-613-33381-8(0)) Tandem Library Bks.

Fleming, Sarah. The Moons of Jupiter American English Edition. 2000. (Cambridge Reading Ser.). (Illus.). pap. 5.00 (978-0-521-79898-3(1)) Cambridge Univ. Pr.

—The Moons of Jupiter Pack of 6 American English Edition, 6 bks., Set. 2000. (Cambridge Reading Ser.). (Illus.). 12p. pap. 28.00 (978-0-521-79899-0(X)) Cambridge Univ. Pr.

Fredette, Nathalie & Lafleur, Claude. The Solar System & the Stars. 2001. (Twenty-First Century Science Ser.). (Illus.). 64p. (J). (gr. 5 up). lib. bdg. 32.67 (978-0-8368-5004-8(1) , World Almanac Library) Stevens, Gareth Inc.

Galat, Joan Marie. Dot to Dot in the Sky: Stories in the Planets. 2003. (gr. 3-6). lib. bdg. 22.20 (978-0-613-78525-9(8)) Tandem Library Bks.

—Stories in the Planets. Bennett, Lorna & Yu, Chao, illus. 2003. (Dot to Dot in the Sky Ser.). 64p. (J). (gr. 2-6). pap. 12.95 (978-1-55285-392-4(6)) Whitecap Bks., Ltd. CAN. *Dist:* Firefly Bks., Ltd.

Gallant, Roy A. The Planets. 2000. (Kaleidoscope Ser.). (Illus.). 48p. (J). (gr. 3 up). lib. bdg. 25.64 (978-0-7614-1033-1(3) , Benchmark Bks.) Cavendish, Marshall Corp.

Gibbons, Gail. The Planets. Gibbons, Gail, illus. 2002. (Illus.). (J). 15.47 (978-0-7587-3427-3(1)) Book Wholesalers, Inc.

—The Planets. rev. ed. 2005. (Illus.). 32p. (J). 16.95 (978-0-8234-1957-9(6)); pap. 6.95 (978-0-8234-1958-6(4)) Holiday Hse., Inc.

Goldstein, Margaret J. The Sun. 2005. (Pull Ahead Bks.). (Illus.). 32p. (gr. 2-4). lib. bdg. 22.60 (978-0-8225-4647-4(7)) Lerner Publishing Group.

Goss, Tim. Uranus, Neptune & Pluto. 2003. (Universe Ser.). (Illus.). 32p. (J). (gr. 3-5). lib. bdg. 22.79 (978-1-58810-918-7(6)); pap. 7.50 (978-1-4034-0619-4(7)) Heinemann Library.

Goss, Tim & Gyuk, Geza. The Universe: The Outer Planets. 2007. (J). (*978-1-4329-0168-4(0)); pap. (*978-1-4329-0180-6(X)) Heinemann Library.

Graham, Ian. The Far Planets. 2007. (J). (*978-1-59920-072-9(4)) Smart Apple Media.

—The near Planets. 2007. (J). (*978-1-59920-071-2(6)) Smart Apple Media.

Green, Rod. Bing & Bong's Tiny Planets Activity Book. 2003. (Tiny Planets Ser.). (Illus.). 24p. (J). pap. 6.99 (978-1-84222-879-1(X)) Carlton Bks., Ltd. GBR. *Dist:* Independent Pubs. Group.

Group/McGraw-Hill, Wright. Earth & Physical Science: Our Solar System, 6 vols. (Book2WebTM Ser.). (gr. 4-8). 36.50 (978-0-322-04427-2(8)) Wright Group, The.

Halpern, Paul. Faraway Worlds: Planets Beyond Our Solar System. Cook, Lynette R., illus. 2004. 32p. (J). 16.95 (978-1-57091-616-8(0)); pap. 6.95 (978-1-57091-617-5(9)) Charlesbridge Publishing, Inc.

Harris, Nicholas. Incredible Journey to the Planets. 2003. (Incredible Journey Ser.). 32p. (gr. 3 up). 9.95 (978-1-57768-957-7(7) , Bedrick, Peter Bks.) School Specialty Publishing.

—Stars & Planets. 2006. (First Library of Knowledge). 32p. (J). (gr. 2-4). 23.70 (978-1-4103-0343-1(8) , Blackbirch Pr., Inc.) Thomson Gale.

Hasbrouck, Ellen & McDougall, Scott. Planets a Solar System Stickerbook. 2001. (Illus.). 32p. (J). 9.99 (978-0-689-84414-0(X) , Little Simon) Simon & Schuster Children's Publishing.

Haugen, David M. Jupiter. 2001. (Eyes on the Sky Ser.). (Illus.). 48p. (J). (gr. 3-5). 23.70 (978-0-7377-0716-8(X) , LML00902-178566, Kidhaven) Thomson Gale.

—Saturn. 2001. (Eyes on the Sky Ser.). (Illus.). 48p. (J). (gr. 3-5). 23.70 (978-0-7377-0758-8(5) , LML00902-178560, Kidhaven) Thomson Gale.

Hirschmann, Kris. Space & the Planets. Bollinger, Peter, illus. 2003. (Magic School Bus Fact Finder Ser.). 96p. (J). pap. 4.99 (978-0-439-38175-8(4)) Scholastic, Inc.

Hoffmann, Sara. The Little Book of Space. 2005. (Illus.). 24p. (J). (978-1-58728-517-2(7)); (978-1-58728-485-4(5)) T&N Children's Publishing. (Two Can Publishing).

Holt, Rinehart and Winston Staff. Holt Science & Technology Chapter 21: Earth Science: The Family of Planets. 5th ed. 2004. (Illus.). pap. 12.86 (978-0-03-030346-3(X)) Holt, Rinehart & Winston.

—Holt Science & Technology Chptr. 9: Family of Planets: Chapter Resources - Tennessee Edition. 3rd ed. 2003. (J). (gr. 6). pap. 11.40 (978-0-03-069116-4(8)) Holt, Rinehart & Winston.

Hopping, Lorraine Jean. Space Rocks: The Story of Planetary Geologist Adriana Ocampo. 2006. (Women's Adventures in Science Ser.). (Illus.). 128p. pap. 9.95 (978-0-309-09555-6(7) , Joseph Henry Pr.) National Academies Pr.

Jayawardhana, Ray. Star Factories: Stars & Planets. 1999. (Illus.). (J). pap. (978-0-7398-2494-8(5)) Steck-Vaughn.

—Star Factories: The Birth of Stars & Planets. 1999. (Space Explorer Ser.). (Illus.). 64p. (J). (gr. 6-8). lib. bdg. 28.54 (978-0-7398-2212-8(8)) Raintree.

Journey to the Planets. 2003. (Science Card Games Ser.). (gr. 2-3). 9.99 (978-0-7682-1978-4(7) , J53006) School Specialty Publishing.

Kenah, Katharine. Fantastic Planet. 2004. (Extreme Readers Ser.). (Illus.). 32p. (J). (gr. k-1). pap. 3.95 (978-0-7696-3186-8(X)) School Specialty Publishing.

Kerrod. Exploring the Universe, 6 vols., Set. 1999. (Illus.). (J). lib. bdg. 162.72 (978-0-7398-2821-2(5)) Raintree.

Kerrod, Robin. The Far Planets. 2001. (Exploring the Universe Ser.). (Illus.). 48p. (J). lib. bdg. 27.12 (978-0-7398-2820-5(7)) Raintree.

—Jupiter. 2005. (Planet Library). (Illus.). 32p. (gr. 3-8). lib. bdg. 21.27 (978-0-8225-3907-0(1)) Lerner Publishing Group.

—Mercury & Venus. 2005. (Planet Library). (Illus.). 32p. (gr. 3-8). 21.27 (978-0-8225-3904-9(7)) Lerner Publishing Group.

—The Near Planets. 2001. (Exploring the Universe Ser.). (Illus.). 48p. (J). lib. bdg. 27.12 (978-0-7398-2819-9(3)) Raintree.

—Planet Earth. (Planet Library). 2005. (Illus.). 32p. (gr. 3-8). lib. bdg. 21.27 (978-0-8225-3902-5(0)); 1999. (J). (978-1-57505-381-3(0)) Lerner Publishing Group.

—Planets. 2001. (Illus.). 32p. (J). lib. bdg. 24.25 (978-1-930643-27-7(6)) Chrysalis Education.

—Saturn. 2005. (Planet Library). (Illus.). 32p. (gr. 3-8). lib. bdg. 21.27 (978-0-8225-3909-4(8)) Lerner Publishing Group.

—Uranus, Neptune, & Pluto. 2005. (Planet Library). (Illus.). 32p. (gr. 3-8). lib. bdg. 21.27 (978-0-8225-3908-7(X)) Lerner Publishing Group.

Kranz, Rachel. Our Solar System/el sistema Solar: English/Spanish Pair, 12 texts, 2 titles, Vol. 2. ed. 2004. (Navigators Ser.). (J). pap., instr.'s gde. ed. 84.00 (978-1-4108-1766-2(0) , 17660) Benchmark Education Co.

Lancaster, Juliana. PBIS- Planetary Forecaster. 2005. pap. 8.00 (978-1-58591-567-5(X)) It's About Time, Herff Jones Education Diiv.

Landau, Elaine. Jupiter. (Watts Library). (Illus.). 64p. (J). (gr. 5-7). 2000. pap. 8.95 (978-0-531-16426-6(8)); 1999. 25.50 (978-0-531-20387-3(5)) Scholastic Library Publishing. (Watts, Franklin).

—Jupiter. 2000. (Illus.). 63p. (J). (gr. 5-7). lib. bdg. 17.60 (978-0-613-37421-7(5)) Tandem Library Bks.

—Saturn. 2000. (Illus.). 63p. (J). (gr. 5-7). lib. bdg. 17.60 (978-0-613-29507-9(2)) Tandem Library Bks.

Leigh, Autumn. A Trip Through Our Solar System. 2006. (Rosen Publishing Group's Reading Room Collection). (J). lib. bdg. (978-1-4042-3345-4(8) , PowerKids Pr.) Rosen Publishing Group, Inc., The.

Lomberg, Michelle. Planets. 2002. (Science Matters Ser.). (Illus.). 24p. (J). lib. bdg. 17.10 (978-1-59036-086-6(9)) Weigl Pubs., Inc.

Margaret, Amy. Jupiter. 2001. (Library of the Planets). (Illus.). 24p. (J). lib. bdg. 21.25 (978-0-8239-5647-0(4) , PowerKids Pr.) Rosen Publishing Group, Inc., The.

—Saturn. 2001. (Library of the Planets). (Illus.). 24p. (J). lib. bdg. 21.25 (978-0-8239-5646-3(6)) Rosen Publishing Group, Inc., The.

Mi Planeta, 6 Packs. (Chiquilibros Ser.). (SPA.). (gr. k-1). 23.00 (978-0-7635-8620-1(X)) Rigby Education.

Miller, Ron. Extrasolar Planets. 2002. (Science & Technology Ser.). (Illus.). 96p. (gr. 7 up). lib. bdg. 25.90 (978-0-7613-2354-9(6) , Twenty-First Century Bks.) Lerner Publishing Group.

—Uranus & Neptune. 2003. (Worlds Beyond Ser.). (Illus.). 80p. (gr. 7 up). lib. bdg. (978-0-7613-2357-0(0) , Twenty-First Century Bks.) Lerner Publishing Group.

Mitton, S. Kingdom of the Sun: A Book about the Planets. Mitton, Jacqueline & Balit, Christina, illus. 2001. 32p. (J). (ps-3). 16.95 (978-0-7922-7220-5(X) , National Geographic Children's Bks.) National Geographic Society.

Morris, Rick. Stars & Planets. 2005. (Time for Learning Ser.). (Illus.). 96p. (J). (978-1-4127-1135-7(5) , 7255300) Publications International, Ltd.

Moving & Shaking: Individual Title Six-Packs. (Bookweb Ser.). 32p. (gr. 4 up). 34.00 (978-0-7635-3743-2(8)) Rigby Education.

National Geographic Society Staff. Stars & Planets. 2002. (My First Pocket Guides Ser.). (Illus.). 80p. (J). (gr. 1-5). pap. 5.95 (978-0-7922-6580-1(7) , National Geographic Children's Bks.) National Geographic Society.

Nicolson, Cynthia. Discover the Planets. Slavin, Bill, illus. 2005. 32p. (J). lib. bdg. 15.38 (***978-1-4242-1194-4(8)***) Fitzgerald Bks.

Nicolson, Cynthia Pratt. Discover the Planets. Slavin, Bill, illus. 2005. (Kids Can Read Alone Ser.). 32p. (J). (ps-ps). (978-1-55337-825-9(3)) Kids Can Pr., Ltd.

—The Planets. Slavin, Bill, illus. (Starting with Space Ser.). 40p. (J). (gr. 4-6). 1999. (978-1-55074-716-4(9)); 1998. (978-1-55074-512-2(3)) Kids Can Pr., Ltd.

—The Planets. 1999. (Starting with Space Ser.). (978-0-606-18233-1(0)) Tandem Library Bks.

Nussbaum, Ben. All about Planets: Stitch Explores the Solar System. 2005. (All about Ser.). (Illus.). 40p. (J). (ps-3). 12.99 incl. audio compact disk (978-1-59069-452-7(X) , 1A703) Studio Mouse LLC.

Olien, Rebecca. Exploring the Planets in Our Solar System. 2007. (Objects in the Sky Ser.). (Illus.). 24p. (J). (978-1-4042-2366-0(5)); pap. (978-1-4042-2175-8(1)); (gr. 4-6). lib. bdg. 21.25 (978-1-4042-3467-3(5)) Rosen Publishing Group, Inc., The. (PowerKids Pr.).

Our Solar System. (Jump Ser.). 36p. (J). (gr. 2-7). pap. (978-1-882210-23-7(9)) Action Publishing, Inc.

Our Solar System, 13 bks., Set. 2003. (J). (gr. 2-4). 276.38 (978-0-7565-0461-8(9)) Compass Point Bks.

Our Solar System. 48p. (gr. 4-6). 8.99 (978-1-56417-961-6(3) , GA1604) Schaffer, Frank Pubns.

Parks, Peggy J. Killer Asteroids. 2006. (KidHaven Science Library). (Illus.). 48p. (J). (gr. 4-8). 26.20 (978-0-7377-3056-2(0) , Greenhaven Pr., Inc.) Thomson Gale.

Perez, Miguel. El Sistema Solar. Rius, María, illus. 1998. (Universe Ser.).Tr. of Solar System. (SPA.). 36p. (J). pap. 5.95 (978-0-7641-0759-7(3)) Barron's Educational Series, Inc.

—The Solar System. Rius, María, illus. 1998. (Universe Ser.). 36p. (J). pap. 6.95 (978-0-7641-0685-9(6)) Barron's Educational Series, Inc.

Pitluga, Phyllis, ed. Our Solar System & It's Planets. TNT Stone and Associates Staff & Peterttil Design Partners Staff, illus. 1998. (Powertools for Kids Ser.: No. 12). 4p. (J). (gr. 3-7). pap., wbk. ed. 4.95 (978-1-58220-011-8(4) , 32502, PowerTools for Kids) Navigator Systems, Inc.

Planetas. 2005. 115p. (J). spiral bd. 14.99 (978-1-59441-458-9(0) , K04009) Carson-Dellosa Publishing Co., Inc.

Los Planetas, 6 vols., Vol. 2. (Explorers. Exploradores Nonfiction Sets Ser.). (SPA.). 32p. (gr. 3-6). 44.95 (978-0-7699-0642-3(7)) Shortland Pubns. (U. S. A.) Inc.

Planetas y Satelites. (SPA.). (J). 10.00 (978-84-342-1468-2(7)) Parramon Ediciones S.A. ESP. *Dist:* Distribuidora Norma, Inc.

The Planets. 2000. (Illus.). 16p. (YA). (gr. 2 up). 9.95 (978-1-878427-79-3(2)) Cimino Publishing Group.

The Planets, 6 vols. 2005. (Earth & Outer Space Ser.). (gr. k-2). 28.95 (978-0-7368-3260-1(2)) Red Brick Learning.

The Planets. 2001. (Our World Ser.). (J). (gr. k-12). vinyl bd. 4.95 (978-1-58845-074-6(0)) School Specialty Publishing.

Planets: Level L, 6 vols. (Wonder Worldtm Ser.). 16p. 34.95 (978-0-7802-2020-1(X)) Wright Group, The.

The Planets: Level P, 6 vols., Vol. 2. (Explorers Ser.). 32p. (gr. 3-6). 44.95 (978-0-7699-0606-5(0)) Shortland Pubns. (U. S. A.) Inc.

Planets Set E, 6 vols. (Phonics Readers Ser.). (gr. k-2). 28.95 (978-0-7368-4066-8(4)) Red Brick Learning.

Pratt Nicolson, Cynthia. Discover the Planets. Slavin, Bill, illus. 2005. (Kids Can Read Alone Ser.). 32p. (J). (978-1-55337-826-6(1)) Kids Can Pr., Ltd.

Rau, Dana Meachen. Jupiter. 2002. (Our Solar System Ser.). (Illus.). 32p. (J). (gr. 3 up). lib. bdg. 21.26 (978-0-7565-0198-3(9)) Compass Point Bks.

—Saturn. 2002. (Illus.). 32p. (J). (gr. 3 up). lib. bdg. 21.26 (978-0-7565-0298-0(5)) Compass Point Bks.

—Spinning in Space: A Book about the Planets. Shea, Denise, illus. 2005. (Amazing Science Ser.). 24p. (J). (ps-k). lib. bdg. 22.60 (978-1-4048-1138-6(9)) Picture Window Bks.

—Uranus. 2002. (Illus.). 32p. (J). (gr. 3 up). lib. bdg. 21.26 (978-0-7565-0299-7(3)) Compass Point Bks.

Red Bird Press, creator. Planets. 2005. (Glow in the Dark Ser.). (Illus.). 19p. (J). (ps-ps). 5.95 (978-1-902626-73-4(7)) Red Bird Publishing GBR. *Dist:* Perseus Distribution.

Ride, Sally & O'Shaughnessy, Tam. Exploring Our Solar System. 2003. 112p. (J). (gr. 5). lib. bdg. 21.99 (978-0-375-91204-7(5)); (Illus.). 19.95 (978-0-375-81204-0(0)) Random Hse. Children's Bks. (Crown Books For Young Readers).

Ridpath, Ian. Facts on File Stars & Planets Atlas: New Edition. 3rd ed. (Facts on File Atlas Ser.). 80p. (gr. 4-9). 18.95 (978-0-8160-6294-2(3) , Checkmark Bks.) Facts On File, Inc.

Rockwell, Anne F. Our Stars. 2002. (gr. k-3). lib. bdg. 14.15 (978-0-613-53848-0(X)) Tandem Library Bks.

Rudy, Lisa Jo. Planets! 2005. 32p. (J). lib. bdg. 15.00 (***978-1-4242-0859-3(9)***) Fitzgerald Bks.

Rustad, Martha E. H. The Planets. Saunders-Smith, Gail, ed. 2002. (Out in Space Ser.). (Illus.). 24p. (J). (gr. k-1). lib. bdg. 15.93 (978-0-7368-1178-1(8) , Pebble Bks.) Capstone Pr., Inc.

Ryback, Carol. The Planets. 2006. (Illus.). 24p. (J). pap. (978-0-8368-6349-9(6)); lib. bdg. 19.33 (978-0-8368-6344-4(5)) Stevens, Gareth Inc.

Sachatello-Sawyer, Bonnie. Exploring the Planets! The Latest Information & Out-of-This-World Activities That Teach Kids. 2000. (Illus.). 80p. (J). pap. 11.95 (978-0-590-68573-3(2)) Scholastic, Inc.

School Specialty Publishing. Planets. 2004. (On-File Ser.). 4p. (J). (gr. 3-5). ring bd. 4.99 (978-0-7424-2869-0(9) , Instructional Fair) Schaffer, Frank Pubns.

Schwabacher, Martin. Jupiter. 2001. (Blastoff! Ser.). (Illus.). 32p. (J). (gr. 5 up). lib. bdg. 28.50 (978-0-7614-1236-6(0) , Benchmark Bks.) Cavendish, Marshall Corp.

Sian revision Planets&stars. 2004. (J). (978-1-59242-057-5(5)) Delta Education, LLC.

Simon, Seymour. Destination: Jupiter. (Illus.). 32p. (J). 2000. (gr. k up). pap. 6.99 (978-0-06-443759-2(0) , Harper Trophy); 1998. (gr. 5 up). 15.95 (978-0-688-15620-6(7)) HarperCollins Pubs.

—Destination: Jupiter. 2000. (gr. 3-6). lib. bdg. 15.30 (978-0-613-33691-8(7)) Tandem Library Bks.

—Planets. 2006. (Illus.). 24p. (J). (***978-0-439-77702-5(X)***) Scholastic, Inc.

—Planets Around the Sun. 2002. (See More Readers Ser.). (Illus.). 32p. (J). (gr. k-4). 13.95 (978-1-58717-145-1(7)); pap. 3.95 (978-1-58717-146-8(5)) Chronicle Bks. LLC. (SeaStar Bks.).

—Planets Around the Sun. 2002. (gr. 3-6). lib. bdg. 11.80 (978-0-613-58435-7(X)) Tandem Library Bks.

—Seemore Planetas Alrededor Sol. 2007. 32p. (J). 15.50 (978-0-8118-5765-9(4)) Chronicle Bks. LLC.

Sparrow, Giles. Planets & Moons. 2006. (Illus.). 48p. (J). pap. (978-0-8368-7285-9(1)); lib. bdg. (978-0-8368-7278-1(9)) Stevens, Gareth Inc. (World Almanac Library).

Spinning Through Space: Includes: The Earth; The Moon; The Solar System; The Sun, 4 bks., Set. 2000. (Illus.). (J). (gr. 2-4). 71.92 (978-0-7398-2741-3(3)) Raintree.

Stars & Planets. 2001. 63p. (YA). 8.65 (978-0-7525-4879-1(4)) Parragon, Inc.

Stars & Planets. 2002. (Super Science Activities Ser.). 48p. (J). (gr. 2-5). 7.99 (978-0-7439-3663-7(9) , 3663) Teacher Created Materials, Inc.

Stars! Stars! Stars! 2005. (J). 24.95 incl. audio (978-0-439-80462-2(0)); 29.95 incl. audio compact disk (978-0-439-80468-4(X)) Weston Woods Studios, Inc.

Stewart, Melissa. Uranus. 2002. (Watts Library). (Illus.). 64p. (J). (gr. 5-7). pap. 25.50 (978-0-531-12016-3(3) , Watts, Franklin) Scholastic Library Publishing.

Sutter, Debra, et al. Moons of Jupiter. Klofkorn, Lisa, illus. Hoyt, Richard & Bergman, Lincoln, photos by. 2003. (Great Explorations in Math & Science Ser.). 116p. (J). pap., tchr. ed. 16.00 (978-0-924886-87-4(0) , GEMS) Univ. of California, Berkeley, Lawrence Hall of Science.

Theodorou, Rod. Across the Solar System. 2000. (Amazing Journeys Ser.). 32p. (J). (gr. 3-5). lib. bdg. 22.79 (978-1-57572-486-7(3)) Heinemann Library.

Thompson, Luke. Neptune. 2001. (Library of the Planets). (Illus.). 24p. (J). lib. bdg. 21.25 (978-0-8239-5648-7(2) , PowerKids Pr.) Rosen Publishing Group, Inc., The.

—Uranus. 2001. (Library of the Planets). (Illus.). 24p. (J). lib. bdg. 21.25 (978-0-8239-5649-4(0) , PowerKids Pr.) Rosen Publishing Group, Inc., The.

Time for Kids Editors. Planets! 2005. (Time for Kids Ser.). (Illus.). 32p. (J). 14.99 (978-0-06-078203-0(X)); pap. 3.99 (978-0-06-078202-3(1) , Harper Trophy) HarperCollins Pubs.

Twist, Clint. The Planets. 2006. (Stories of the Sun). 28p. (J). (gr. 3-8). 14.95 (978-0-7696-4491-2(0)) School Specialty Publishing.

Vogt, Gregory L. Jupiter. 2000. (Galaxy Ser.). (Illus.). 24p. (J). (gr. 2-3). lib. bdg. 18.60 (978-0-7368-0512-4(5) , Bridgestone Bks.) Capstone Pr., Inc.

—Jupiter, Saturn, Neptune & Uranus. 2000. (Our Universe Ser.). (Illus.). (J). pap. (978-0-7398-3348-3(0)) Steck-Vaughn.

—Mercury, Venus & Earth. 2000. (Our Universe Ser.). (Illus.). (J). pap. (978-0-7398-3349-0(9)) Steck-Vaughn.

—Mercury, Venus, Earth & Mars. 2000. (Our Universe Ser.). (Illus.). 48p. (J). (gr. 4-7). lib. bdg. 22.83 (978-0-7398-3110-6(0)) Raintree.

—Neptune. 2000. (Galaxy Ser.). (Illus.). 24p. (J). (gr. 2-3). lib. bdg. 18.60 (978-0-7368-0513-1(3) , Bridgestone Bks.) Capstone Pr., Inc.

—Pluto & the Search for New Planets. 2000. (Our Universe Ser.). (Illus.). 48p. (YA). (gr. 5-12). lib. bdg. 22.83 (978-0-7398-3111-3(9)) Raintree.

—Pluto & the Search for New Planets. 2000. (Our Universe Ser.). (Illus.). (J). pap. (978-0-7398-3350-6(2)) Steck-Vaughn.

—Saturn. 2000. (Galaxy Ser.). (Illus.). 24p. (J). (gr. 2-3). lib. bdg. 18.60 (978-0-7368-0515-5(X) , Bridgestone Bks.) Capstone Pr., Inc.

—Uranus. 2000. (Galaxy Ser.). (Illus.). 24p. (J). (gr. 2-3). lib. bdg. 18.60 (978-0-7368-0517-9(6) , Bridgestone Bks.) Capstone Pr., Inc.

Watt, E. Planeta Tierra: Ciencia y Experimentos. (SPA.). (J). pap. (978-950-724-135-2(3)) Lumen.

Whitehouse, Patricia. The Planets. 2004. (J). (ps). (Illus.). 32p. pap. 7.25 (978-1-4034-5657-1(7)); lib. bdg. 24.21 (978-1-4034-5153-8(2)) Heinemann Library.

Whiting, Sue. Science Chapters: Ancient Orbiters: A Guide to the Planets. 2006. (National Geographic Science Chapters Ser.). (Illus.). 48p. (gr. 1-4). 17.90 (978-0-7922-5945-9(9) , National Geographic Children's Bks.) National Geographic Society.

PLANETS, LIFE ON OTHER

see Life on Other Planets

PLANNED PARENTHOOD

see Birth Control

PLANNING, CITY

see City Planning

PLANNING, ECONOMIC

see Economic Policy; Social Policy

see names of countries, states, etc. with the subdivision Economic Policy, e.g. United States—Economic Policy

PLANNING, NATIONAL

see Economic Policy; Social Policy

see names of countries with the subdivision Economic Policy, Social Policy; e.g. United States—Economic Policy; United States—Social policy

PLANNING, REGIONAL

see Regional Planning

PLANS

see Geometrical Drawing; Map Drawing; Maps; Mechanical Drawing

PLANT ANATOMY

Blevins, Wiley. Parts of Plants. 2003. (Compass Point Phonics Readers Ser.). (Illus.). 16p. (J). (gr. 1 up). 13.26 (978-0-7565-0518-9(6)) Compass Point Bks.

Johnson, Rebecca L. Powerful Plant Cells. Desrocher, Jack, illus. 2007. (Microquests Ser.). 48p. (J). (gr. 3-5). 29.27 (***978-0-8225-7141-4(2)*** , Millbrook Pr.) Lerner Publishing Group.

Laskey, Elizabeth. Gross & Gory. 2004. (Heinemann Infosearch Ser.). (Illus.). 32p. (J). lib. bdg. (978-1-4034-4959-7(7)) Heinemann Library.

Snedden, Robert. Plants & Fungi: Multicelled Life. 2003. (Cells & Life Ser.). (Illus.). 48p. (gr. 6-8). (J). lib. bdg. 27.86 (978-1-58810-675-9(6)); (YA). pap. 8.50 (978-1-58810-937-8(2)) Heinemann Library.

Spilsbury, Louise & Spilsbury, Richard. Plant Parts. 2003. (Life of Plants Ser.). (Illus.). 48p. (J). (gr. 3-5). lib. bdg. 25.64 (978-1-4034-0296-7(5)); pap. 8.50 (978-1-4034-0504-3(2)) Heinemann Library.

—What Is a Plant? 2005. (World of Plants Ser.). (Illus.). 32p. (J). (978-1-4034-7361-5(7)); pap. (978-1-4034-7366-0(8)) Heinemann.

Stephens, Nicholas. Plant Cells & Tissues. 2006. (Green World Ser.). (Illus.). 144-152p. (J). (gr. 6-12). 37.50 (978-0-7910-8560-8(0) , Chelsea Hse.) Facts On File, Inc.

Weiss, Ellen. From Bulb to Daffodil. 2007. (Scholastic News Nonfiction Readers: How Things Grow—NEW SUBSET Ser.). 24p. (J). pap. 6.95 (***978-0-531-18787-6(X)***); (Illus.). (gr. 1-2). lib. bdg. 20.00 (***978-0-531-18534-6(6)***) Scholastic Library Publishing. (Children's Pr.).

PLANT DISEASES

Halfmann, Janet. Plant Tricksters. 2003. (Watts Library). (Illus.). 64p. (J). 25.50 (978-0-531-12278-5(6) , Watts, Franklin) Scholastic Library Publishing.

Wright, Russell G. Blight! Investigations in Plant Diseases. (Event-Based Science Ser.). 32p. (gr. 5-9). pap., tchr.'s training gde. ed. 25.95 incl. VHS (978-0-7690-0022-0(3)) Seymour, Dale Pubns.

PLANT ECOLOGY

Aruego, Jose & Dewey, Ariane. Weird Friends: Unlikely Allies in the Animal Kingdom. 2002. (Illus.). 40p. (J). (ps-3). 17.00 (978-0-15-202128-3(0) , Gulliver Bks.) Harcourt Children's Bks.

Boothroyd, Jennifer. Plants & the Environment. 2008. (First Step Nonfiction - Ecology Ser.). (J). lib. bdg. 18.60 (***978-0-8225-8603-6(7)*** , Lerner Pubns.) Lerner Publishing Group.

Claybourne, Anna. Plant Secrets. 2005. (Illus.). 32p. (J). (978-1-4109-1934-2(X)) Steck-Vaughn.

—Plant Secrets: Plant Life Processes. 2005. (Illus.). 32p. (J). (gr. 3-5). pap. 7.85 (978-1-4109-1965-6(X)) Steck-Vaughn.

Exploring the Native Plant World Grades 3-4: Survival. 2004. 74p. (J). pap. 14.95 (978-1-57168-835-4(8) , Eakin Pr.) Eakin Pr.

Gibson, Phil. Plant Ecology. 2006. (Green World Ser.). (Illus.). 200p. (gr. 6-12). 37.50 (978-0-7910-8566-0(X) , Chelsea Hse.) Facts On File, Inc.

Giles, Bridget. Dwellers & Cleaners. 2003. (Parasites & Partners Ser.). (Illus.). 32p. (J). lib. bdg. 25.70 (978-0-7398-6991-8(4)) Raintree.

—Lodgers & Cleaners. 2003. (Parasites & Partners Ser.). (Illus.). 32p. (J). pap. 7.50 (978-1-4109-0358-7(3)) Raintree.

—Lodgers & Cleaners. 2003. (gr. 5-8). lib. bdg. 15.90 (978-0-613-78251-7(8)) Tandem Library Bks.

Harman, Amanda. Farmers & Slavers. 2003. (Parasites & Partners Ser.). (Illus.). 32p. (J). pap. (978-1-4109-0354-9(0)); lib. bdg. 25.70 (978-0-7398-6987-1(6)) Raintree.

—Farmers & Slavers. 2003. (gr. 5-8). lib. bdg. 15.90 (978-0-613-78246-3(1)) Tandem Library Bks.

Hines, James Gary, II. Friendships in Nature. McGuire, Jan Martin, illus. 32p. 2004. (J). (gr. k-3). pap. 7.95 (978-1-55971-902-5(8)); 2002. (gr. 3-7). 15.95 (978-1-55971-791-5(2)) T&N Children's Publishing. (NorthWord Bks. for Young Readers).

Hoare, Ben. Breeders. 2003. (Parasites & Partners Ser.). (Illus.). 32p. (J). pap. 7.50 (978-1-4109-0353-2(2)); lib. bdg. 25.70 (978-0-7398-6986-4(8)) Raintree.

—Breeders. 2003. (gr. 5-8). lib. bdg. 15.90 (978-0-613-78247-0(X)) Tandem Library Bks.

Hoff, Mary. Living Together. 2002. (World of Wonder Ser.). (Illus.). 32p. (J). lib. bdg. (978-1-58341-236-7(0) , Creative Education) Creative Co., The.

Kenah, Katharine. Nature's Amazing Partners. 2004. (Extreme Readers Ser.). (Illus.). 32p. (J). (ps-2). pap. 3.95 (978-0-7696-3182-0(7)) School Specialty Publishing.

Lady Bird Johnson Wildflower Center Staff, Lady Bird Johnson, compiled by. Exploring the Native Plant World Grades 1-2: Changes. 2004. 62p. (J). pap. (978-1-57168-827-9(7) , Eakin Pr.) Eakin Pr.

—Exploring the Native Plant World Grades 5-6: Adaptations. 2004. 72p. (J). pap. 14.95 (978-1-57168-851-4(X) , Eakin Pr.) Eakin Pr.

—Exploring the Native Plant World Pre-K-K: Patterns & Shapes. 2004. 44p. (J). pap. 14.95 (978-1-57168-680-0(0) , Eakin Pr.) Eakin Pr.

Llewellyn, Claire. Plants & Animals. 2007. (J). (978-1-59920-030-9(9)) Smart Apple Media.

Marsh, James. Nature's Wild. 2000. (Info Adventure Ser.). (Illus.). (J). (978-0-606-20819-2(4)) Tandem Library Bks.

Parasites & Partners 6 Pack, Set. 2004. pap. 243.00 (978-1-4109-1271-8(X)) Raintree.

Pascoe, Elaine. The Ecosystem of a Milkweed Patch. 2003. (Library of Small Ecosystems Ser.). (Illus.). 24p. (J). lib. bdg. 21.25 (978-0-8239-6309-6(8)) Rosen Publishing Group, Inc., The.

—Slime, Molds & Fungi. Kuhn, Dwight, photos by. 1998. (Nature Close-Up Ser.). (Illus.). 48p. (J). (gr. 4-8). 23.70 (978-1-56711-182-8(3) , Blackbirch Pr., Inc.) Thomson Gale.

Rhodes, Mary Jo & Hall, David. Partners in the Sea. 2006. (Undersea Encounters Ser.). (Illus.). 48p. (J). (gr. 3-5). pap. 6.95 (978-0-516-25492-0(8) , Children's Pr.) Scholastic Library Publishing.

—Partners in the Sea. Hall, David, photos by. 2005. (Undersea Encounters Ser.). (Illus.). 48p. (J). (ps-7). 27.00 (978-0-516-24397-9(7) , Children's Pr.) Scholastic Library Publishing.

Rotter, Charles. The Prairie. 2002. (LifeViews Ser.). (J). (978-0-89812-329-6(1) , Creative Paperbacks) Creative Co., The.

Silverman, Buffy. You Scratch My Back. 2007. (J). (*978-1-4109-2844-3(6)); pap. (*978-1-4109-2861-0(6)) Steck-Vaughn.

Silverstein, Alvin, et al. Symbiosis. rev. ed. 2007. (Science Concepts, Second Ser.). (Illus.). 96p. (YA). (gr. 6-8). lib. bdg. 31.93 (*978-0-8225-6799-8(7) , Twenty-First Century Bks.) Lerner Publishing Group.

Spilsbury, Louise & Spilsbury, Richard. Plant Habitats. 2003. (Illus.). 48p. (J). (gr. 3-5). lib. bdg. 25.64 (978-1-4034-0295-0(7)); pap. 8.50 (978-1-4034-0503-6(4)) Heinemann Library.

—Where Do Plants Grow? 2005. (World of Plants Ser.). (Illus.). 32p. (J). (978-1-4034-7362-2(5)); pap. (978-1-4034-7367-7(6)) Heinemann.

Stone, Lynn M. Partners. 2001. (Under the Sea Ser.). (Illus.). 24p. (J). (gr. 1-4). lib. bdg. 20.64 (978-1-58952-114-8(5)) Rourke Publishing, LLC.

Woods, Mae. Plants of the Rain Forest. 1999. (Rain Forest Ser.). (Illus.). 24p. (J). (gr. k-6). lib. bdg. 21.35 (978-1-57765-018-8(2) , Checkerboard Library) ABDO Publishing Co.

Woodward, John. Perfect Partners. 2003. (Amazing Nature Ser.). (Illus.). 32p. (J). pap. 7.50 (978-1-4034-5404-1(3)); lib. bdg. (978-1-4034-4708-1(X)) Heinemann Library.

PLANT INTRODUCTION

Batten, Mary. Aliens from Earth: When Animals & Plants Invade Other Ecosystems. Doyle, Beverly, illus. 2003. 32p. (J). 15.95 (978-1-56145-236-1(X)) Peachtree Pubs., Ltd.

PLANT PHYSIOLOGY

see also Growth (Plants)

Blevins, Wiley. Parts of Plants. 2003. (Compass Point Phonics Readers Ser.). (Illus.). 16p. (J). (gr. 1 up). 13.26 (978-0-7565-0518-9(6)) Compass Point Bks.

Holt, Rinehart and Winston Staff. Holt Science & Technology Chapter 13: Life Science: Plant Processes. 5th ed. 2004. (Illus.). pap. 12.86 (978-0-03-030217-6(X)) Holt, Rinehart & Winston.

Julivert, Maria Angels. La Vida de Las Plantas. (SPA.). 288p. (J). 10.00 (978-84-342-1465-1(2)) Parramon Ediciones S.A. ESP. *Dist:* Distribuidora Norma, Inc.

Kalman, Bobbie. Las Plantas de Distintos Habitats. 2006. (SPA., Illus.). 32p. pap. (978-0-7787-8391-6(X)) Crabtree Publishing Co.

Oxlade, Edwin. Plant Physiology: The structure of plants Explained. 2007. Orig. Title: Understanding Plant Physiology. (Illus.). 156p. (C). pap. (*978-1-84285-048-0(2)) Studymates Ltd. GBR. *Dist:* Trans-Atlantic Pubns., Inc.

Royston, Angela. Flowers. (Illus.). 32p. (YA). (gr. 2 up). lib. bdg. 27.10 (978-1-932333-39-8(8)) Chrysalis Education.

Spilsbury, Louise & Spilsbury, Richard. Plant Parts. 2003. (Life of Plants Ser.). (Illus.). 48p. (J). (gr. 3-5). lib. bdg. 25.64 (978-1-4034-0296-7(5)); pap. 8.50 (978-1-4034-0504-3(2)) Heinemann Library.

Walker, Denise. Green Plants. 2006. (Illus.). 48p. (978-1-58340-993-0(9)) Smart Apple Media.

PLANT PROPAGATION

see also Seeds

Carle, Eric. The Tiny Seed. 2001. (Illus.). (J). (978-0-606-20946-5(8)) Tandem Library Bks.

Kudlinski, Kathleen V. Venus Flytraps. Wexler, Jerome, photos by. 1998. (Early Bird Nature Bks.). (Illus.). 48p. (J). (gr. 2-4). lib. bdg. 25.26 (978-0-8225-3015-2(5) , Lerner Pubns.) Lerner Publishing Group.

Morris, Ting & Morris, Neil. Growing Things. Levy, Ruth, illus. 2006. (J). (978-1-59771-026-8(1)) Sea-To-Sea Pubns.

Pipe, Jim. Growing Plants. 2007. (J). (*978-1-59604-140-0(4)) Stargazer Bks.

Spilsbury, Louise & Spilsbury, Richard. Plant Products. 2003. (Life of Plants Ser.). (Illus.). 48p. (J). (gr. 3-5). lib. bdg. 25.64 (978-1-4034-0297-4(3)); pap. 8.50 (978-1-4034-0505-0(0)) Heinemann Library.

PLANT STRUCTURE

see Plant Anatomy

PLANTATION LIFE

Draper, Allison Stark. What People Wore on Southern Plantations. 2001. (Clothing, Costumes & Uniforms Thoughout American History Ser.). (Illus.). 24p. (J). (gr. 3). lib. bdg. 19.95 (978-0-8239-5668-5(7) , PKCLPL, PowerKids Pr.) Rosen Publishing Group, Inc., The.

Erickson, Paul. Daily Life on a Southern Plantation. Gabbey, Terry, illus. Slingsby, Miki, photos by. 2006. 48p. (J). (gr. 2-5). reprint ed. pap. 8.00 (978-1-4223-5727-9(9)) DIANE Publishing Co.

Gullo, Jim. A Travel Guide to the Plantation South. 2005. (Travel Guide To Ser.). (Illus.). 112p. (J). (gr. 5-8). lib. bdg. 29.95 (978-1-59018-360-1(6) , Lucent Bks.) Thomson Gale.

Hill, George. The Fall of Irish Chiefs & Clans & the Plantation of Ulster: Including the Names of Irish Catholics, & Protestant Settlers. 2004. Orig. Title: An Historical Account of the Plantation in Ulster at the Commencement of the 17th Century. (Illus.). 276p. lib. bdg. 39.00 (978-0-940134-42-3(X)) Irish Genealogical Foundation.

Kalman, Bobbie. A Slave Family. 2003. (Colonial People Ser.). (Illus.). 32p. (J). pap. (978-0-7787-0792-9(X)); (gr. 3). (978-0-7787-0746-2(6)) Crabtree Publishing Co.

—Slave Family. 2003. (ps-2). lib. bdg. 17.60 (978-0-613-52908-2(1)) Tandem Library Bks.

Krebs, Laurie. A Day in the Life of a Colonial Indigo Planter. 2004. (Library of Living & Working in Colonial Times). (Illus.). 24p. (J). lib. bdg. 18.75 (978-0-8239-6229-7(6)) Rosen Publishing Group, Inc., The.

Levy, Debbie. Slaves on a Southern Plantation. 2004. (Daily Life Ser.). (Illus.). 48p. (J). 26.20 (978-0-7377-1827-0(7) , Greenhaven Pr., Inc.) Thomson Gale.

Rikson, Paule. Daily Life on a Southern Plantation 1853. 2004. (Illus.). 48p. (J). (gr. 4-8). reprint ed. 17.00 (978-0-7567-7709-8(7)) DIANE Publishing Co.

Worth, Richard. Slave Life on the Plantation: Prisons Beneath the Sun. 2004. (Slavery in American History Ser.). (Illus.). 128p. (J). lib. bdg. 26.60 (978-0-7660-2152-5(1)) Enslow Pubs., Inc.

PLANTING

see Agriculture; Gardening; Tree Planting

PLANTS

see also Desert Plants; Endangered Plants; Flower Gardening; Flowers; Forest Plants; Fresh-Water Plants; Gardening; House Plants; Marine Plants; Shrubs; Weeds also names of plants (e.g. Mosses, etc.)

Akeroyd, John. Plant: An Eyewitness 3-D Book. 2004. (Illus.). 52p. (gr. 4-8). reprint ed. 17.00 (978-0-7567-7415-8(2)) DIANE Publishing Co.

Aldrich, William, et al. Annual for Illinois. rev. ed. 2004. (Illus.). 296p. (gr. 4). pap. 18.95 (978-1-55105-380-6(2)) Lone Pine Publishing USA.

—Perennials for Illinois. rev. ed. 2003. (Illus.). 344p. (J). (gr. 4). pap. 18.95 (978-1-55105-378-3(0)) Lone Pine Publishing USA.

All about Plants, 6 vols., Pack. (gr. k-1). 23.00 (978-0-7635-8839-7(3)) Rigby Education.

Allen, Charles M., et al. Trees, Shrubs, & Woody Vines of Louisiana. 2002. (Illus.). x, 333p. per. 20.00 (978-0-9718625-0-0(8)) Allen's Native Ventures.

Anthony, Joseph. The Dandelion Seed. 1999. (J). 14.75 (978-0-606-16436-8(7)) Tandem Library Bks.

Apple Tree. 2003. stu. ed. 36.95 (978-0-8136-9258-6(X)) Modern Curriculum Pr.

Aprende sobre las plantas: Cuaderno de Actividades: Unit 2: Aprende sobre las plantas (All about Plants) 2000. (McGraw-Hill Ciencias Ser.). (ENG & SPA.). (gr. k up). (978-0-02-278991-6(X)) Macmillan/McGraw-Hill Schl. Div.

Arbel, Ilil. Favorite Perennials. 2006. (Illus.). 32p. (J). pap. 3.95 (978-0-486-44709-4(X)) Dover Pubns., Inc.

Armentrout, David & Armentrout, Patricia. Plants. 2003. (50 Words about Ser.). (Illus.). 32p. (gr. 2-4). 19.95 (978-1-58952-345-6(8)) Rourke Publishing, LLC.

Arnold, Katya R. Let's Find It! My First Nature Guide. Arnold, Katya R., illus. 2002. (Illus.). 32p. (J). (gr. k-3). tchr. ed. 16.95 (978-0-8234-1539-7(2)) Holiday Hse., Inc.

Atwell, Brian. Plants in Action: Adaptation in Nature/Performance in Cultivation. rev. ed. 1999. (Illus.). 664p. (YA). 74.95 (978-0-7329-4439-1(2)) Macmillan Education Australia AUS. *Dist:* Paul & Co. Pubs. Consortium, Inc.

Bailey, Jill. Plants & Plant Life, 10 vols. 2000. (Illus.). 640p. (J). (gr. 5-10). lib. bdg. 279.00 (978-0-7172-9510-4(9) , Grolier) Scholastic Library Publishing.

Baines, Francesca. World of Plants. Platt, Gill, illus. 1998. (Launch Pad Library). 32p. (J). (gr. k-4). 11.95 (978-1-58087-003-0(1)) Stampley, C.D. Enterprises, Inc.

—World of Plants. 2003. (Discovery Guides Ser.). 32p. (J). 11.95 (978-1-58728-228-7(3)); pap. 6.95 (978-1-58728-234-8(8)) T&N Children's Publishing. (Two Can Publishing).

Baker, Wendy & Haslam, Andrew. Plants. (Make It Work! Ser.). (Illus.). (J). pap. 15.95 (978-0-590-74523-9(9)); (FRE., pap. 9.99 (978-0-590-24331-5(4)) Scholastic, Inc.

Barnett, Michelle Noble, et al. Theme Pockets - May: Cinco de Mayo; Dinosaurs; Plants. Evans, Marilyn, ed. Larsen, Jo, illus. 1999. (Making Books with Pockets). 96p. (J). pap., tchr. ed. 12.99 (978-1-55799-702-9(0) , EMC 588) Evan-Moor Educational Pubs.

Bartholomew, Linda & Bartholomew, Al. The Rain Forest Book for Kids. Bartholomew, Linda & Bartholomew, Al, photos by. 2005. 32p. (J). 9.00 (978-0-9764802-0-4(4)) Solutions for Human Services, LLC.

Bateman, Donna M. Deep in the Swamp. Lies, Brian, illus. 2007. 32p. (J). (ps-1). 15.95 (978-1-57091-596-3(2)); pap. 6.95 (*978-1-57091-597-0(0)) Charlesbridge Publishing, Inc.

Bauer, David. Quien depende de las Plantas? 2005. Tr. of Who Needs Plants?. (SPA., Illus.). 16p. (J). (gr. 1 up). lib. bdg. 15.93 (978-0-7368-4140-5(7)) Capstone Pr., Inc.

Beck, Alison & Szerlag, Nancy. Annual for Michigan, Vol. 1. Kubish, Shelagh, ed. rev. ed. 2002. (Illus.). 296p. (J). (gr. 4). pap. 18.95 (978-1-55105-346-2(2)) Lone Pine Publishing USA.

Beck, Alison, et al. Annual for Northern California, Vol. 1. rev. ed. 2002. (Illus.). 304p. (gr. 4). pap. 18.95 (978-1-55105-249-6(0)) Lone Pine Publishing USA.

Benchmark Education Staff, compiled by. Amazing Plants & Plantas Asombrosas. 2005. 52.00 (*978-1-4108-4495-8(1)) Benchmark Education Co.

—Plants. 2006. spiral bd. 179.00 (*978-1-4108-7107-7(X)) Benchmark Education Co.

—Plants & Animals. 2006. spiral bd. 159.00 (*978-1-4108-7063-6(4)); spiral bd. 165.00 (*978-1-4108-7083-4(9)); spiral bd. 159.00 (*978-1-4108-7137-4(1)) Benchmark Education Co.

Berger, Melvin & Berger, Gilda. Life in the Rainforest: Plants, Animals, & People. Brittingham, Geoffrey H., illus. 1999. (Discovery Readers Ser.). 48p. (YA). (ps up). lib. bdg. 15.95 (978-0-7910-5068-2(8) , Chelsea Hse.) Facts On File, Inc.

—Seed to Plant. 2004. (Illus.). (J). (978-0-439-57486-0(2)) Scholastic, Inc.

Bernhard, Durga. Earth, Sky, Wet, Dry: A Book of Opposites. Bernhard, Durga, illus. 2000. (Illus.). 40p. (J). (gr. k-4). 17.99 (978-0-531-33213-9(6) , Orchard Bks.) Scholastic, Inc.

Blackaby, Susan. Buds & Blossoms: A Book about Flowers. DeLage, Charlene, illus. 2004. (Growing Things Ser.). 24p. (C). (gr. k-2). 22.60 (978-1-4048-0112-7(X)) Picture Window Bks.

—Green & Growing: A Book about Plants. DeLage, Charlene, illus. 2004. (Growing Things Ser.). 24p. (C). (gr. k-2). 22.60 (978-1-4048-0107-3(3)) Picture Window Bks.

Blaisdell, Molly. Surprising Beans. Spence, Tom, illus. 2007. (J). lib. bdg. (*978-1-4048-2290-0(9)) Picture Window Bks.

Blashfield, Jean F. Plant Life. 2007. (J). pap. (*978-0-8368-8451-7(5)); 48p. (gr. 5-8). lib. bdg. 26.60 (*978-0-8368-8442-5(6)) Stevens, Gareth Inc.

Bocknek, Jonathan. Plants. 2007. (J). (*978-1-59036-717-9(0)); (*978-1-59036-718-6(9)) Weigl Pubs., Inc.

Bocknek, Jonathan. The Science of Plants. 1999. (Living Science Ser.). (Illus.). 32p. (J). (gr. 2 up). lib. bdg. 23.93 (978-0-8368-2467-4(9)) Stevens, Gareth Inc.

Boring, Mel, et al. More Fun with Nature. Garrow, Linda & McGee, John F., illus. 2004. (Big Books Ser.). 224p. (J). (gr. 2-5). ring bd. 16.95 (978-1-55971-795-3(5) , NorthWord Bks. for Young Readers) T&N Children's Publishing.

Boyston, Angela. Flowers, Fruits & Seeds. 1999. (Plants Ser.). (Illus.). 32p. (J). (gr. k-3). lib. bdg. 21.36 (978-1-57572-822-3(2)) Heinemann Library.

Bradley, Suzannah. Global Warming. 2005. (Your Environment Ser.). (Illus.). 32p. (J). (978-1-59604-063-2(7)) Stargazer Bks.

Branigan, Carrie & Dunne, Richard. All Kinds of Plants. 2005. (World of Plants Ser.). (Illus.). 31p. (J). (gr. 2-5). lib. bdg. 27.10 (978-1-58340-610-6(7)) Smart Apple Media.

—How Plants Grow. 2005. (World of Plants Ser.). (Illus.). 30p. (J). (gr. 2-5). lib. bdg. 27.10 (978-1-58340-611-3(5)) Smart Apple Media.

Brown, Harriet. Food from the Sun: How Plants Live & Grow. 2008. (J). (*978-1-60044-600-9(0)) Rourke Publishing, LLC.

Brown, Ruth. Ten Seeds. Brown, Ruth, illus. 2001. (Illus.). 24p. (J). (gr. k-k). 9.95 (978-0-375-80697-1(0) , Knopf Bks. for Young Readers) Random Hse. Children's Bks.

Brown, Susan. Plantas/Plants. 2006. 80p. (J). per. 9.99 (978-1-59441-641-5(9) , FI-704015) Carson-Dellosa Publishing Co., Inc.

Bryant-Mole, Karen & Ansary, Mir Tamim. Moving. 2002. (Science All Around Me Ser.). (Illus.). 24p. (J). (gr. 1-3). pap. 6.50 (978-1-4034-0054-3(7) , 91498) Heinemann Library.

Brynie, Faith Hickman. What Helps Plants Grow? The Nitrogen Cycle Case. 2003. (J). (978-1-58417-151-5(0)) Lake Street Pubs.

Burnie, David. Plant. 2006. (Google E Guides Ser.). (Illus.). 96p. (J). 17.99 (978-0-7566-1954-1(8)) Dorling Kindersley Publishing, Inc.

Burnie, David & Dorling Kindersley Publishing Staff. Plant. (Eye Wonder Ser.). (Illus.). (J). 2005. 48p. 9.99 (978-0-7566-0618-3(7)); 2004. 72p. lib. bdg. 19.99 (978-0-7566-0714-2(0)) Dorling Kindersley Publishing, Inc.

Burton, Margie & French, Tammy, Cathy - Jones. Las plantas & Plants. 2005. spiral bd. 66.00 (*978-1-4108-5638-8(0)) Benchmark Education Co.

Byles, Monica. Plants. 2004. (Interfact Ser.). (SPA., Illus.). 48p. (J). (gr. 3-6). 14.95 incl. cd-rom (978-1-58728-460-1(X) , Two Can Publishing) T&N Children's Publishing.

Cameron, Ken. La genética de las Plantas. Hanner, Albert & Hortens, Mike, illus. ed. 2004. (SPA.). 32p. (J). pap. 6.00 (978-1-4108-2341-0(5) , A23415) Benchmark Education Co.

—Plant Atlas/Plantas alrededor del Mundo: English/Spanish Pair, 12 texts, 2 titles, Vol. 2. ed. 2004. (Navigators Ser.). (J). pap., instr.'s gde. ed. 84.00 (978-1-4108-1767-9(9) , 17679) Benchmark Education Co.

Capogna, Vera Vullo. Did You Ever Wonder about Things You Find in the Woods? 2000. (Did You Ever Wonder? Ser.). (Illus.). 32p. (J). (gr. k-3). lib. bdg. 22.79 (978-0-7614-0852-9(5) , Benchmark Bks.) Cavendish, Marshall Corp.

—Did You Ever Wonder about Things You Find in Your Backyard? 1999. (Did You Ever Wonder? Ser.). (Illus.). 32p. (J). (gr. k-3). lib. bdg. 22.79 (978-0-7614-0855-0(X) , Benchmark Bks.) Cavendish, Marshall Corp.

Carle, Eric. The Tiny Seed. 2001. (gr. k-3). lib. bdg. 15.30 (978-0-613-35001-3(4)) Tandem Library Bks.

Casterline, L. C. Natural-Born Killers: A Chapter Book. 2004. (True Tales Ser.). (Illus.). 48p. (J). 22.50 (978-0-516-23725-1(X) , Children's Pr.) Scholastic Library Publishing.

Cerullo, Mary M. Sea Soup: Zooplankton. Curtsinger, Bill, photos by. 2005. (Illus.). 40p. (J). (gr. 3-7). 16.95 (978-0-88448-219-2(7)) Tilbury Hse. Pubs.

Charman, Andrew. I Wonder Why Trees Have Leaves: And Other Questions about Plants. 2003. (I Wonder Why Ser.). 32p. (J). (gr. k-3). pap. 6.95 (978-0-7534-5663-7(X) , Kingfisher) Houghton Mifflin Co. Trade & Reference Div.

Claybourne, Anna. Plant Secrets. 2005. (Illus.). 32p. (J). (978-1-4109-1934-2(X)) Steck-Vaughn.

—Plant Secrets: Plant Life Processes. 2005. (Illus.). 32p. (J). (gr. 3-5). pap. 7.85 (978-1-4109-1965-6(X)) Steck-Vaughn.

—Plants. 2003. (Weird Wildlife Ser.). (Illus.). 32p. (J). pap. 7.95 (978-1-4109-0079-1(7)) Raintree.

Collard, Sneed B., III. The Prairie Builders: Reconstructing America's Lost Grasslands. 2005. (Scientists in the Field Ser.). (Illus.). 80p. (J). (gr. 4-6). 17.00 (978-0-618-39687-0(X)) Houghton Mifflin Co. Trade & Reference Div.

—Tough Terminators. 2004. (It's Nature! Ser.). (Illus.). 32p. (J). (gr. 3-6). pap. 7.95 (978-1-55971-633-8(9) , Creative Publishing International) Quayside.

Connolly, Randy, et al. Poison Ivy, Pets & People: Scratching the Poison Ivy, Oak & Sumac Itch. 2005. (10thingstoknow about ... Ser.). (Illus.). 104p. pap. 9.95 (978-0-9722400-1-7(2)) 2Lakes Publishing.

Costain, Meredith. Our Plant Home. 2000. (gr. k-3). lib. bdg. 11.80 (978-0-613-30655-3(4)) Tandem Library Bks.

—Rainforests. 2000. (gr. k-3). lib. bdg. 11.80 (978-0-613-30693-5(7)) Tandem Library Bks.

Dalgleish, Sharon. The Plant Kingdom. 2002. (Junior Adventure Ser.). (Illus.). 32p. (J). (gr. 3 up). lib. bdg. (978-1-59084-182-2(4)) Mason Crest Pubs.

—The Plant Kingdom. 1999. (Explorers Ser.). (Illus.). 32p. (J). (978-0-7699-0481-8(5)) Shortland Pubns. (U. S. A.) Inc.

Daoust, Cindy, ed. Investigating Science - Plants. 2003. 48p. 9.95 (978-1-56234-543-3(5) , Mailbox Bks., The) Education Ctr., Inc.

Dell, Pamela. Rain Forest Plants. 2006. (Life in the World's Biomes Ser.). (Illus.). 24p. (J). (978-0-7368-4324-9(8) , Bridgestone Bks.) Capstone Pr., Inc.

Los Desiertos. (Coleccion Planeta Vivo).Tr. of Deserts. (SPA.). (J). (gr. 5-8). 12.00 (978-84-342-1947-2(6)) Parramon Ediciones S.A. ESP. *Dist:* Distribuidora Norma, Inc., Lectorum Pubns., Inc.

Dewire, Bob. My Guide to America's Animals & Plants. Sullivan, Beth, illus. 2000. 48p. (J). (gr. 1-2). pap. 2.50 (978-1-56762-126-6(0)) Modern Learning Pr.

Discovery Channel School Science Set 1: The Plant & Animal Kingdom, 10 bks. (Illus.). (J). (gr. 5 up). lib. bdg. 246.70 (978-0-8368-3209-9(4)) Stevens, Gareth Inc.

Dixon, Malcolm & Smith, Karen. Plants Around Us. 1998. (Young Scientists Ser.). (Illus.). 32p. (J). (ps-3). lib. bdg. 16.95 (978-1-887068-71-0(6)) Smart Apple Media.

Dorling Kindersley Publishing Staff. Cave Life. 2000. (978-0-606-17799-3(X)) Tandem Library Bks.

—Plant. 2005. (Eye Wonder Ser.). 48p. (J). lib. bdg. 17.99 (978-0-7566-0620-6(9)) Dorling Kindersley Publishing, Inc.

—Water. 2006. (Eye Know Ser.). (Illus.). 24p. (J). 8.99 (978-0-7566-1859-9(2)) Dorling Kindersley Publishing, Inc.

Edom, Helen. Science with Plants. rev. ed. 2007. 24p. (J). pap. 5.99 (978-0-7945-1485-3(5) , Usborne) EDC Publishing.

Edwards, Nicola. Flowers. 2007. (J). lib. bdg. (978-1-4042-3699-8(6)) Rosen Publishing Group, Inc., The.

Engebretson, Don & Williamson, Don. Annual for Minnesota & Wisconsin, Vol. 1. rev. ed. 2004. (Illus.). 296p. (gr. 4). pap. 18.95 (978-1-55105-381-3(0)) Lone Pine Publishing USA.

Equipo Staff. La Zanahoria y Otras Hortalizas. (Coleccion Mundo Maravilloso). (SPA., Illus.). 48p. (J). (gr. 2-4). (978-84-348-4152-9(5) , SM6991) SM Ediciones ESP. *Dist:* Lectorum Pubns., Inc.

Farndon, John. Flowering Plants. 2004. (Illus.). 32p. (J). 23.70 (978-1-4103-0121-5(4) , Blackbirch Pr., Inc.) Thomson Gale.

—Flowers. 2005. 24p. (J). (gr. 2-4). pap. 22.45 (978-1-4103-0517-6(1) , Blackbirch Pr., Inc.) Thomson Gale.

Feely, Jenny. Plants. 1999. (ps-2). lib. bdg. 11.80 (978-0-613-30676-8(7)) Tandem Library Bks.

Flowering Plants. 2001. (Inquiry Science Ser.). 32p. (gr. 2-3). 4.99 (978-1-56822-678-1(0) , IF20849) School Specialty Publishing.

Fowler, Allan. From Seed to Plant. 2001. (Rookie Read-About Science Ser.). (Illus.). 32p. (J). (gr. 1-2). pap. 4.95 (978-0-516-27307-5(8)); 19.50 (978-0-516-21682-9(1)) Scholastic Library Publishing. (Children's Pr.).

—From Seed to Plant. 2001. (gr. k-3). lib. bdg. 12.95 (978-0-613-54501-3(X)) Tandem Library Bks.

—Plants That Eat Animals. 2001. (Rookie Read-About Science Ser.). (Illus.). 32p. (J). (gr. 1-2). 19.50 (978-0-516-21683-6(X) , Children's Pr.) Scholastic Library Publishing.

—Science, Rookie Read-About Science: Plants & Fungi. 2004. (Illus.). 304.00 (978-0-516-29318-9(4)) Scholastic Library Publishing.

—Taking Root. 2000. (Rookie Read-About Science Ser.). (Illus.). 32p. (J). (gr. 1-2). 20.50 (978-0-516-21591-4(4) , Children's Pr.) Scholastic Library Publishing.

Freeman, Marcia S. What Plant Is This? 2005. (Everything Science Ser.). (Illus.). 24p. (gr. 1-4). 14.95 (978-1-59515-124-7(9)) Rourke Publishing, LLC.

La Fresa. (Coleccion Ciclos Vitales). (SPA., Illus.). (J). (gr. 3-5). pap. (978-84-236-2653-3(9) , ED4700) Edebé ESP. *Dist:* Lectorum Pubns., Inc.

Fridell, Ron & Royston, Angela. Life Cycle of a... Series: An In-Depth Look at Some Familiar Plants & Animals, 16 bks., Set. (Illus.). (J). (gr. k-2). lib. bdg. 341.76 (978-1-58810-186-0(X)) Heinemann Library.

Fridell, Ron & Walsh, Patricia. Life Cycle of a... Series: An In-Depth Look at Some Familiar Plants & Animals, 4 bks., Set 4. 2001. (Illus.). 32p. (J). (gr. k-2). lib. bdg. 85.44 (978-1-58810-022-1(7)) Heinemann Library.

Galko, Francine. Flowering Plants. 2003. (Classifying Living Things Ser.). (Illus.). 32p. (J). pap. 6.95 (978-1-4034-3276-6(7)); lib. bdg. 24.22 (978-1-4034-3272-8(4)) Heinemann Library.

—Non-Flowering Plants. 2003. (Classifying Living Things Ser.). (Illus.). 32p. (J). pap. (978-1-4034-3277-3(5)); lib. bdg. 24.22 (978-1-4034-3273-5(2)) Heinemann Library.

Ganeri, Anita. Plant Life Cycles. 2005. (Nature's Patterns Ser.). (Illus.). 32p. (J). (978-1-4109-1319-7(8)); lib. bdg. 16.95 (978-1-4034-5896-4(0)) Heinemann Library.

Garassino, Alessandro. Las Plantas. (SPA.). 40p. (YA). (gr. 5-8). 10.36 (978-84-207-5190-0(1)) Grupo Anaya, S.A. ESP. *Dist:* Lectorum Pubns., Inc.

Gardner, Robert. Science Projects about Plants. 1999. (Science Projects Ser.). (Illus.). 112p. (YA). (gr. 6-12). lib. bdg. 26.60 (978-0-89490-952-8(5)) Enslow Pubs., Inc.

Gareth Stevens Publishing Staff, contrib. by. Plants. 2002. (Discovery Channel School Science Ser.). (Illus.). 32p. (J). (gr. 5 up). lib. bdg. 24.67 (978-0-8368-3218-1(3)) Stevens, Gareth Inc.

Gierecke, Ernestine. Flowers. 1999. (Outside My Window Ser.). (Illus.). 24p. (J). (gr. 1-3). lib. bdg. 21.36 (978-1-57572-683-0(1)) Heinemann Library.

Giesecke, Ernestine. Seashore Plants. 1999. (Plants Ser.). (Illus.). 32p. (J). (gr. k-2). lib. bdg. 21.36 (978-1-57572-828-5(1)) Heinemann Library.

—Seashore Plants. 2002. (gr. k-3). lib. bdg. 15.25 (978-0-613-83972-3(2)) Tandem Library Bks.

—Wetland Plants. 2002. (Plants Ser.). 32p. (J). (gr. k-2). pap. 6.95 (978-1-4034-0529-6(8) , 91833) Heinemann Library.

—Wetlands Plants. 1999. (Plants Ser.). (Illus.). 32p. (J). (gr. k-2). lib. bdg. 21.36 (978-1-57572-830-8(3)) Heinemann Library.

Glover, David. Plants. 2001. (Experiments in Science Ser.). (Illus.). (J). (978-0-7894-7471-1(9)) Dorling Kindersley Publishing, Inc.

Godwin, Sam. A Seed in Need: A First Look at the Plant Cycle. Abel, Simone, illus. 2004. (First Look Science Ser.). 32p. (C). (gr. k-3). 22.60 (978-1-4048-0920-8(1)) Picture Window Bks.

Goodman, Susan E. Seeds, Stems, & Stamens: The Ways Plants Fit into Their World. Doolittle, Michael J., photos by. 2001. (Illus.). 48p. (gr. 2-4). lib. bdg. 22.90 (978-0-7613-1874-3(7) , Millbrook Pr.) Lerner Publishing Group.

Graham, Ian. Plants: A Resource Our World Depends On. 2004. (Illus.). 32p. (J). 27.07 (978-1-4034-5619-9(4)); pap. 7.50 (978-1-4034-5627-4(5)) Heinemann Library.

Green, Jen. Plants. 2002. (Young Library - Weird Wildlife Ser.). (Illus.). 32p. (J). lib. bdg. 25.69 (978-0-7398-4857-9(7)) Raintree.

Greenaway, Theresa. The Plant Kingdom: A Guide to Plant Classification & Biodiversity. 1999. (Classification Ser.). (Illus.). 48p. (YA). (gr. 6-8). lib. bdg. 27.12 (978-0-8172-5886-3(8)) Raintree.

—Plant Life. 2000. (Cycles in Nature Ser.). (Illus.). 32p. (J). (gr. 2-4). lib. bdg. 25.69 (978-0-7398-2729-1(4)) Raintree.

Grieveson, Margaret. Plants. 2005. (Illus.). 32p. (J). (gr. 3-7). lib. bdg. 27.10 (978-1-59604-037-3(8)) Stargazer Bks.

Grolier Educational Staff, contrib. by. Plants, 10 vols. 2000. (Illus.). (J). (978-0-7172-9511-1(7) , Grolier) Scholastic Library Publishing.

Group/McGraw-Hill, Wright. Amazing Plants: Magazine Anthology: Level 3, 6 vols. (Comprehension Strand Ser.). (gr. 4-8). 54.00 (978-0-322-06030-2(3)) Wright Group, The.

—Donde Viven Algunos Animales, 6 vols. (First Explorers. Primeros Exploradores Nonfiction Sets Ser.). (SPA.). (gr. 1-2). 29.95 (978-0-7699-1472-5(1)) Shortland Pubns. (U. S. A.) Inc.

—El Mundo de Las Plantas, 6 vols. (First Explorers. Primeros Exploradores Nonfiction Sets Ser.). (SPA.). (gr. 1-2). 29.95 (978-0-7699-1474-9(8)) Shortland Pubns. (U. S. A.) Inc.

Halfmann, Janet. Plant Tricksters. 2004. (Watts Library). (J). (gr. 5-7). pap. 8.95 (978-0-531-16371-9(7) , Watts, Franklin) Scholastic Library Publishing.

Halpern, Monica. Science Chapters: Venus Flytraps, Bladderworts: And Other Wild & Amazing Plants. 2006. (National Geographic Science Chapters Ser.). (Illus.). 48p. (gr. 1-4). 17.90 (978-0-7922-5957-2(2) , National Geographic Children's Bks.) National Geographic Society.

Hammersmith, Craig. Watch It Grow. 2002. (Spyglass Books). (Illus.). 24p. (J). (gr. 1 up). lib. bdg. 18.60 (978-0-7565-0246-1(2)) Compass Point Bks.

Haslam, Andrew. Plants. 2004. (Make It Work! Science Ser.). (Illus.). 48p. (J). (gr. 3-6). 12.95 (978-1-58728-367-3(0) , Two Can Publishing) T&N Children's Publishing.

Head, Heno. God's World of Plants. Fletcher, Rusty, illus. 2002. (Happy Day Book Ser.). (J). 2.49 (978-0-7847-1394-5(4)) Standard Publishing.

Heller, Ruth. Plants That Never Ever Bloom. 1999. (Ruth Heller's World of Nature Ser.). (Illus.). 48p. (J). (ps-3). pap. 6.99 (978-0-698-11558-3(9) , Putnam Juvenile) Penguin Group (USA) Inc.

—The Reason for a Flower. 1999. (Ruth Heller's World of Nature Ser.). (Illus.). 48p. (J). (ps-3). pap. 6.99 (978-0-698-11559-0(7) , Putnam Juvenile) Penguin Group (USA) Inc.

—The Reason for a Flower. (FRE.). (J). 6.99 (978-0-590-71999-5(8)) Scholastic, Inc.

Hewitt, Sally. Amazing Plants. 2007. 32p. pap. (***978-0-7787-3628-8(8)***) Crabtree Publishing Co.

—Plants. (Illus.). 32p. (YA). (gr. 2 up). lib. bdg. 27.10 (978-1-932333-30-5(4)) Chrysalis Education.

—Plants. 2001. (978-0-606-22381-2(9)); (gr. 5-8). lib. bdg. 17.60 (978-0-613-45214-4(3)) Tandem Library Bks.

—Plants & Flowers. 1999. (Illus.). 30p. (J). (gr. k-3). lib. bdg. 15.25 (978-0-613-37507-8(6)) Tandem Library Bks.

—Sorting Plants: What Is a Flower? 2005. (Science Starters Ser.). (Illus.). 32p. (J). (gr. 1-4). lib. bdg. 27.10 (978-1-59604-010-6(6)) Stargazer Bks.

Hibbert. Life of a Bean 6-Pack. 2004. (Life Cycles Ser.). pap. 40.50 (978-1-4109-0823-0(2)) Harcourt Schl. Pubs.

Hickman, Pamela. Plant Book. 2000. (gr. 3-6). lib. bdg. 14.10 (978-0-613-26616-1(1)) Tandem Library Bks.

—Plant Book: Starting with Nature. 2000. (978-0-606-18231-7(4)) Tandem Library Bks.

—Starting with Nature Plant Book. Collins, Heather, illus. unabr. ed. 2000. (Starting with Nature Ser.). 32p. (J). (gr. 4-6). (978-1-55074-483-5(6)) Kids Can Pr., Ltd.

Hickman, Pamela & Collins, Heather. Plant Book. 2000. (Starting with Nature Ser.). (Illus.). 32p. (J). (gr. 4-6). (978-1-55074-812-3(2)) Kids Can Pr., Ltd.

Hil, Mcgraw. Gr 5 Plants Sci Pe. 2000. (McGraw-Hill Science Ser.). (gr. 5 up). (978-0-02-278223-8(0)) Macmillan/McGraw-Hill Schl. Div.

—Sciasmtbk Plants. 2000. (McGraw-Hill Science Ser.). (gr. 5 up). (978-0-02-277763-0(6)) Macmillan/McGraw-Hill Schl. Div.

—Trfpaswak Plants. 2000. (McGraw-Hill Science Ser.). (gr. 5 up). (978-0-02-277644-2(3)) Macmillan/McGraw-Hill Schl. Div.

Hodge, Judith. Las plantas que usamos & Plants We Use. 2005. spiral bd. 84.00 (***978-1-4108-5708-8(5)***) Benchmark Education Co.

Hodge, Judith. Plants We Use. 2004. (Navigators Ser.). (J). pap. 42.00 (978-1-4108-0435-8(6)) Benchmark Education Co.

Hoff, Mary. Pollination. 2003. (World of Wonder Ser.). (Illus.). 32p. (J). lib. bdg. (978-1-58341-270-1(0) , Creative Education) Creative Co., The.

Holt, Rinehart and Winston Staff. Holt Science & Technology Chapter 12: Life Science: Introduction to Plants. 5th ed. 2004. (Illus.). pap. 12.86 (978-0-03-030216-9(1)) Holt, Rinehart & Winston.

Hopkins, William. Photosynthesis & Respiration. 2006. (Green World Ser.). (Illus.). 176p. (J). (gr. 6-12). 37.50 (978-0-7910-8561-5(9) , Chelsea Hse.) Facts On File, Inc.

How Plants Grow. 2002. 21.95 (978-1-57572-537-6(1)) Heinemann Library.

Howell, Laura. World of Plants. 2002. (gr. 3-6). lib. bdg. 18.75 (978-0-613-75099-8(3)) Tandem Library Bks.

Huggins-Cooper, Lynn. Plants & Flowers. McNicholas, Shelagh & Burroughs, Dave, trs. McNicholas, Shelagh & Burroughs, Dave, illus. 2004. 30p. (J). lib. bdg. (978-1-58340-447-8(3)) Smart Apple Media.

Hunter, Rebecca. The Facts about Flowering Plants. 2004. (Illus.). 32p. (J). lib. bdg. (978-1-58340-454-6(6)) Smart Apple Media.

Iasevoli, Brenda. Plants! 2006. 32p. (J). lib. bdg. 13.85 (***978-1-4242-0398-7(8)***) Fitzgerald Bks.

El Increible Mundo de las Plantas. 1999. Tr. of Incredible World of Plants. (SPA., Illus.). 32p. (J). (gr. 3). (978-0-7910-4012-6(7) , Chelsea Hse.) Facts On File, Inc.

Insect-Eaters! Individual Title Six-Packs. (Rigby Focus Ser.). 16p. (gr. 1 up). 28.00 (978-0-7578-5321-0(8)); 30.00 (978-0-7578-5553-5(9)) Rigby Education.

Jeunesse, Gallimard. In the Garden. Heliadore, illus. 2003. (First Discovery Look-and-Learn Bks.). 24p. (J). bds. 6.95 (978-0-439-33637-6(6) , Cartwheel Bks.) Scholastic, Inc.

Kalman, Bobbie. The ABCs of Plants. 2007. 32p. (J). (gr. 6-10). pap. (***978-0-7787-3433-8(1)***) Crabtree Publishing Co.

—ABCs of Plants. 2007. (Illus.). 32p. (J). (***978-0-7787-3413-0(7)***) Crabtree Publishing Co.

—Le Cycle de Vie. 2001. (FRE., Illus.). 31p. (J). pap. (978-2-920660-73-1(X)) Crabtree Publishing Co.

—Les Plantes. 2003. (FRE., Illus.). 32p. (J). pap. (978-2-920660-96-0(9)) Crabtree Publishing Co.

—Plants Are Living Things. 2007. (Introducing Living Things Ser.). (Illus.). 24p. (J). (gr. 1-4). pap. (***978-0-7787-3257-0(6)***) Crabtree Publishing Co.

—Que son las Plantas? 2005. (Ciencia de los Seres Vivos Ser.).Tr. of What are Plants?. (SPA., Illus.). 32p. (YA). (gr. 7-12). pap. (978-0-7787-8805-8(9)) Crabtree Publishing Co.

—Qué Son las Plantas? 2005. (SPA., Illus.). 32p. (J). (978-0-7787-8759-4(1)) Crabtree Publishing Co.

Kalman, Bobbie & Sjonger, Rebecca. Plants in Different Habitats. 2006. (Nature's Changes Ser.). (Illus.). 32p. (J). (gr. k-6). pap. (978-0-7787-2316-5(X)); (978-0-7787-2282-3(1)) Crabtree Publishing Co.

Katz Cooper, Sharon. Using Plants. 2007. (Illus.). 24p. (J). (***978-1-4034-9324-8(3)***); (***978-1-4034-9316-3(2)***) Heinemann.

Kenah, Katharine. Weird & Wacky Plants. 2004. (Extreme Readers Ser.). (Illus.). 32p. (J). (gr. 1-2). pap. 3.95 (978-0-7696-3184-4(3)) School Specialty Publishing.

Kinsner, Kathy. Amazing Plants (Big Book) ed. 2004. (Shared Connections Ser.). (J). pap., instr.'s gde. ed. 27.00 (978-1-4108-1623-8(0)) Benchmark Education Co.

Kinsner, Kathy, told to. Amazing Plants. ed. 2004. (Shared Connections Ser.). (J). pap. 27.00 (978-1-4108-1647-4(8)) Benchmark Education Co.

Knapke, Debra & Beck, Alison. Annual for Ohio. rev. ed. 2003. (Illus.). 296p. (J). (gr. 4). pap. 18.95 (978-1-55105-388-2(8)) Lone Pine Publishing USA.

—Perennials for Ohio. rev. ed. 2003. (Illus.). 352p. (gr. 4). pap. 18.95 (978-1-55105-386-8(1)) Lone Pine Publishing USA.

Kudlinski, Kathleen V. How Plants Survive. 2003. (Science Links Ser.). (Illus.). 32p. (gr. 3-5). 23.00 (978-0-7910-7422-0(6) , Chelsea Hse.) Facts On File, Inc.

—Venus Flytraps. Wexler, Jerome, photos by. 1998. (Early Bird Nature Bks.). (Illus.). 48p. (J). (gr. 2-4). lib. bdg. 25.26 (978-0-8225-3015-2(5) , Lerner Pubns.) Lerner Publishing Group.

Larousse Staff. The Peter Bedricks Young Peoples Encyclopedia: Plants & Animals. 2000. (Peter Bedrick Young People's Encyclopedia Ser.). (Illus.). 103p. (J). (gr. 5-9). 24.95 (978-0-87226-623-0(0) , 66230B, Bedrick, Peter Bks.) School Specialty Publishing.

Laskey, Elizabeth. Speedy & Slow. 2004. (Heinemann Infosearch Ser.). (Illus.). 32p. (J). pap. 7.50 (978-1-4034-4963-4(5)); lib. bdg. (978-1-4034-4958-0(9)) Heinemann Library.

—Weird & Wonderful. 2004. (Heinemann Infosearch Ser.). (Illus.). 32p. (J). pap. 7.50 (978-1-4034-4965-8(1)); lib. bdg. (978-1-4034-4960-3(0)) Heinemann Library.

Leber, Nancy. What Plants & Animals Need. 2003. (Compass Point Phonics Readers Ser.). (Illus.). 16p. (J). (gr. 1 up). 13.26 (978-0-7565-0529-5(1)) Compass Point Bks.

Legg, Gerald. The World of Plant Life. 2002. (Inside Look Ser.). (Illus.). 48p. (J). (gr. 4 up). lib. bdg. 26.00 (978-0-8368-3180-1(2)) Stevens, Gareth Inc.

Life in the World's Biomes. 2005. (Illus.). (J). (gr. 2-3). lib. bdg. 127.56 (978-0-7368-4419-2(8)) Capstone Pr., Inc.

Lilly, Melinda. Make It Grow. Thompson, Scott M., illus. 2003. (Rourke Discovery Library). 24p. (J). 20.64 (978-1-58952-637-2(6)) Rourke Publishing, LLC.

Lindeen, Carol. Life in a Stream. 2003. (Pebble Plus: Living in a Biome Ser.). (Illus.). 24p. (J). lib. bdg. 17.26 (978-0-7368-2103-2(1) , Pebble Bks.) Capstone Pr., Inc.

Lindsay, Elizabeth, ed. Investigating Science - Plants. 2000. 48p. 9.95 (978-1-56234-401-6(3) , Mailbox Bks., The) Education Ctr., Inc.

Lindstrom, Karin. Tiny Life on Plants. (J). 2006. 32p. (gr. 1-2). pap. 4.95 (978-0-516-25478-4(2)); 2005. (Illus.). 31p. (ps-ps). 20.50 (978-0-516-25297-1(6)) Scholastic Library Publishing. (Children's Pr.).

Llewellyn, Claire. How Plants Grow. 2006. (Illus.). 24p. (J). (978-1-59771-021-3(0)) Sea-To-Sea Pubns.

—The Life of Plants. 2007. (J). (***978-1-59920-033-0(3)***) Smart Apple Media.

—Plants & Animals. 2007. (J). (978-1-59920-030-9(9)) Smart Apple Media.

—Plants of the World. 2007. (J). (978-1-59920-032-3(5)) Smart Apple Media.

Loves, June. Flowers. 2004. (Plants Ser.). (Illus.). 32p. (J). (gr. 2-4). 23.00 (978-0-7910-8265-2(2) , Chelsea Hse.) Facts On File, Inc.

—Succulents. 2004. (Plants Ser.). (Illus.). 32p. (J). (gr. 2-4). 23.00 (978-0-7910-8266-9(0) , Chelsea Hse.) Facts On File, Inc.

Lynch, Wayne. Arctic. Lynch, Wayne, photos by. 2007. (Our Wild World Ecosystems Ser.). (Illus.). 64p. (J). (gr. 3-7). 16.95 (978-1-55971-960-5(5)); pap. 8.95 (978-1-55971-961-2(3)) T&N Children's Publishing. (NorthWord Bks. for Young Readers).

MacLeod, Elizabeth. Grow It Again. Price, Caroline, illus. unabr. ed. 1999. (Kids Can Do It Ser.). 40p. (J). (gr. 4-6). (978-1-55074-558-0(1)) Kids Can Pr., Ltd.

—Grow It Again. Price, Carolyn, illus. 1999. 40p. (J). (ps-ps). lib. bdg. 14.10 (978-0-613-16358-3(3)) Tandem Library Bks.

Madgwick, Wendy. Flowering Plants: The Green World. 2000. (Illus.). 47p. (J). (gr. 5-7). 15.00 (978-0-7881-9436-8(4)) DIANE Publishing Co.

Mann, Rachel. Plants Grow from Seeds. 2003. (Compass Point Phonics Readers Ser.). (Illus.). 16p. (J). (gr. 1 up). 13.26 (978-0-7565-0519-6(4)) Compass Point Bks.

El Manzano. (Coleccion Ciclos Vitales). (SPA., Illus.). (J). (gr. 3-5). pap. 7.96 (978-84-236-2659-5(8) , ED4704) Edebé ESP. *Dist:* Lectorum Pubns., Inc.

La Mariposa y la Oruga. (Coleccion Ciclos Vitales). (SPA., Illus.). (J). (gr. 3-5). pap. 7.96 (978-84-236-2663-2(6) , ED4702) Edebé ESP. *Dist:* Lectorum Pubns., Inc.

La Mariquita. (Coleccion Ciclos Vitales). (SPA., Illus.). (J). (gr. 3-5). pap. 7.96 (978-84-236-2661-8(X) , ED4701) Edebé ESP. *Dist:* Lectorum Pubns., Inc.

Marsh, James. Nature's Wild. 2000. (Info Adventure Ser.). (Illus.). (J). (978-0-606-20819-2(4)) Tandem Library Bks.

Marshall Cavendish Corporation Staff, contrib. by. Wildlife & Plants, 20 Vols., Set. 3rd ed. 2007. (Illus.). 1280p. (J). (gr. 4-8). lib. bdg. 514.21 (***978-0-7614-7693-1(8)***) Cavendish, Marshall Corp.

Mason, Adrienne & Hodge, Deborah. Plants. Boudreau, Ray, illus. 1998. (Starting with Science Ser.). 32p. (J). (gr. k-3). (978-1-55074-193-3(4)) Kids Can Pr., Ltd.

May, Suellen. Invasive Terrestrial Plants. 2006. (Invasive Species Ser.). (Illus.). 112p. (J). (gr. 6-12). 30.00 (978-0-7910-9128-9(7) , Chelsea Hse.) Facts On File, Inc.

McCormick, Rosie. Plants & Art Activities. 2002. (Arty Facts Ser.). (Illus.). 48p. (J). (gr. 3-4). pap. (978-0-7787-1138-4(2)); lib. bdg. (978-0-7787-1110-0(2)) Crabtree Publishing Co.

—Plants & Art Activities. 2002. (gr. 3-6). lib. bdg. 17.60 (978-0-613-82416-3(4)) Tandem Library Bks.

McEvoy, Paul. Flowers. 2003. (Plant Facts Ser.). (Illus.). 24p. (J). (gr. 2-4). 23.00 (978-0-7910-7290-5(8) , Chelsea Hse.) Facts On File, Inc.

—Plants. (Make it Work Ser.). (J). 42p. (gr. 4-8). pap. (978-1-882210-41-1(7)); (Illus.). 32p. (gr. 2-7). pap. 4.95 (978-1-882210-31-2(X)) Action Publishing, Inc.

—Plants. 2003. (Plant Facts Ser.). (Illus.). 24p. (gr. 2-4). 23.00 (978-0-7910-7291-2(6) , Chelsea Hse.) Facts On File, Inc.

—Plants, 6 bks., Set. (J). 2002. (ps-1). lib. bdg. 102.48 (978-1-58810-462-5(1)); 1999. (Illus.). 32p. (gr. 1-6). lib. bdg. 213.60 (978-1-57572-831-5(1)) Heinemann Library.

McLaurin, Thad, ed. Investigating Science - Plants. 2000. 48p. 9.95 (978-1-56234-393-4(9) , Mailbox Bks., The) Education Ctr., Inc.

Meacham, Nancy. Plants: Science Discovery Acivity Book. Zuman, John P. & Barra, Nancy C., eds. Deming, Linda, illus. 2002. (Sunflower/Girasol Ser.). (J). 5.00 (978-1-58332-000-6(8)) Intercultural Center for Research in Education (I N C R E).

Medearis, Angela Shelf. Seeds Grow! 2000. (Hello Reader! Ser.). (978-0-606-18606-3(9)) Tandem Library Bks.

Meucci, Antonella. Plants. Holguin, Paola, illus. 2002. (Nature's Record-Breakers Ser.). 32p. (J). (gr. 3 up). lib. bdg. 23.33 (978-0-8368-2908-2(5)) Stevens, Gareth Inc.

Miller, Connie Colwell. Disgusting Plants. 2007. (J). (978-0-7368-6802-0(X)) Capstone Pr., Inc.

Mitchell, Melanie S. Flowers. 2003. (First Step Nonfiction Ser.). (Illus.). 8p. (J). pap. 3.95 (978-0-8225-3917-9(9) , Lerner Pubns.) Lerner Publishing Group.

—Roots. 2003. (First Step Nonfiction Ser.). (Illus.). 8p. (J). pap. 3.95 (978-0-8225-3919-3(5) , Lerner Pubns.) Lerner Publishing Group.

—Stems. 2003. (First Step Nonfiction Ser.). (Illus.). 8p. (J). pap. 3.95 (978-0-8225-3921-6(7) , Lerner Pubns.) Lerner Publishing Group.

Modern Drummer Publications Staff. Plants. unabr. ed. 2000. (Starting with Science Ser.). (Illus.). 32p. (J). (gr. k-3). (978-1-55074-395-1(3)) Kids Can Pr., Ltd.

Monster Plants. 2004. (I-Quest Ser.). (Illus.). 48p. (J). per. (978-1-84510-192-3(8)) Top That! Publishing PLC.

Moor, Jo Ellen. Plants. Evans, Marilyn, ed. Robison, Don, illus. 1998. (ScienceWorks for Kids Ser.: Vol. 6). 80p. (J). (gr. 1-3). pap., tchr. ed. 9.95 (978-1-55799-687-9(3) , EMC 858) Evan-Moor Educational Pubs.

Moore, Jo Ellen. Learning about Plants. Larsen, Jo & Smith, Phillip, illus. 2000. (ScienceWorks for Kids Ser.). 80p. (J). (gr. k-1). pap. 9.95 (978-1-55799-772-2(1) , EMC 868) Evan-Moor Educational Pubs.

—Plants. Evans, Marilyn, ed. Larsen, Jo, illus. 1998. (Science Picture Cards Ser.: Vol. 2). 24p. (J). (gr. 1-3). pap., tchr. ed. 12.95 (978-1-55799-693-0(8) , 864) Evan-Moor Educational Pubs.

Morgan, Sally. Flowers, Trees, & Fruits. 2002. (Young Discoverers Ser.). (Illus.). 32p. (J). (gr. k-3). pap. 7.95 (978-0-7534-5500-5(5) , Kingfisher) Houghton Mifflin Co. Trade & Reference Div.

—Green Plants. 2005. (Life Science In-Depth Ser.). (Illus.). 64p. (J). (978-1-4034-7522-0(9)); pap. (978-1-4034-7530-5(X)) Heinemann Library.

Morris, Neil. Living & Growing. (Our World Ser.). (Illus.). 32p. (J). lib. bdg. 24.25 (978-1-930643-80-2(2)) Chrysalis Education.

Murphy, Brian. Experiment with Plants. 2001. (Experiment with Ser.). (J). (gr. 2-7). 9.95 (978-1-58728-245-4(3)); pap. 5.95 (978-1-58728-117-4(1)) T&N Children's Publishing. (Two Can Publishing).

Name That Plant. 2002. (Illus.). (J). pap. 5.43 (978-0-7398-5918-6(8)) Steck-Vaughn.

El Nido del Pajaro. (Coleccion Ciclos Vitales). (SPA., Illus.). (J). (gr. 3-5). pap. 7.96 (978-84-236-2651-9(2) , ED4699) Edebé ESP. *Dist:* Lectorum Pubns., Inc.

Nsrc. Science & Technology for Children Books, Experiments with Plants. 2004. (Illus.). 64p. (J). (978-1-933008-08-0(3)) National Science Resources Ctr.

Los Oceanos.Tr. of Oceans. (SPA.). (J). (gr. 5-8). 12.00 (978-84-342-1949-6(2)) Parramon Ediciones S.A. ESP. *Dist:* Distribuidora Norma, Inc., Lectorum Pubns., Inc.

Ohanesian, Diane C. Seeds & Plants: Grades 2 & 3. (Illus.). (J). pap., wbk. ed. 4.99 (978-0-88743-961-2(6)) School Zone Publishing Co.

Olson, Nathan. Plant Patterns. 2007. 32p. (J). (978-0-7368-6727-6(9)) Capstone Pr., Inc.

El Paisaje. (Coleccion Planeta Vivo).Tr. of Topography. (SPA.). (YA). (gr. 5-8). 10.36 (978-84-342-1948-9(4)) Parramon Ediciones S.A. ESP. *Dist:* Lectorum Pubns., Inc.

Parker, Steve. Survival & Change. (Life Processes Ser.). 32p. pap. 7.50 (978-1-4034-4076-1(X)); 2006. (Illus.). (J). (***978-1-4034-8848-0(7)***); 2000. (Illus.). (J). (gr. 4-6). lib. bdg. 21.36 (978-1-57572-340-2(9)) Heinemann Library.

Parsons, Alexandra. Plants. Haslam, Andrew, illus. 2004. (Make It Work! Science Ser.). 48p. (J). (gr. 3-6). pap. 6.95 (978-1-58728-359-8(X) , Two Can Publishing) T&N Children's Publishing.

Parsons, Alexandra & Barnes, Jon. Plants. (Make It Work! Ser.). (Illus.). 48p. (J). pap. 7.95 (978-0-590-24403-9(5)) Scholastic, Inc.

Pascoe, Elaine. Plant Clones. 2003. (Illus.). 48p. (J). 27.45 (978-1-56711-444-7(X) , Blackbirch Pr., Inc.) Thomson Gale.

—Plants with Seeds. Kuhn, Dwight, illus. Kuhn, Dwight, photos by. 2003. (Kids Guide to the Classification of Living Things Ser.). 32p. (J). lib. bdg. 21.25 (978-0-8239-6314-0(4) , PowerKids Pr.) Rosen Publishing Group, Inc., The.

—Plants Without Seeds. Kuhn, Dwight, illus. Kuhn, Dwight, photos by. 2003. (Kids Guide to the Classification of Living Things Ser.). 32p. (J). lib. bdg. 21.25 (978-0-8239-6315-7(2) , PowerKids Pr.) Rosen Publishing Group, Inc., The.

La Patata. (Coleccion Ciclos Vitales). (SPA., Illus.). pap. 7.96 (978-84-236-2657-1(1) , ED4698) Edebé ESP. *Dist:* Lectorum Pubns., Inc.

Paul, Heather. Discovering Scottish Plants. Galloway, Fhiona, illus. 1999. (Scottie Bks.). 40p. (J). (gr. 3-7). pap. 6.95 (978-0-11-495760-5(6)) Stationery Office, The GBR. *Dist:* Balogh International, Inc.

Penguin Books Staff, ed. Plants. (Learners Ser.). (Illus.). 48p. (J). 3.50 (978-0-7214-1709-7(4) , Dutton Juvenile) Penguin Group (USA) Inc.

Perry, Phyllis J. Science Fair Success with Plants. 1999. (Science Fair Success Ser.). (Illus.). 104p. (YA). (gr. 6-12). lib. bdg. 26.60 (978-0-7660-1170-0(4)) Enslow Pubs., Inc.

Petty, Kate & Maizels, Jennie. Global Garden. 2007. (Illus.). 12p. (J). (gr. 2-3). 19.99 ***978-1-903919-16-3(9)*** , Eden Project Books) Transworld Publishers Ltd. GBR. *Dist:* Independent Pubs. Group.

Phillips, Dee. Find It in the Park. 2006. (Illus.). 24p. (J). 22.00 (978-0-8368-6301-7(1)) Stevens, Gareth Inc.

Picture Window Books, contrib. by. Bud & Blossoms. (Growing Things Ser.). 24p. (J). pap. 7.95 (978-1-4048-0388-6(2)) Picture Window Bks.

—Green & Growing. (Growing Things Ser.). 24p. (J). pap. 7.95 (978-1-4048-0383-1(1)) Picture Window Bks.

—Plant Packages. (Growing Things Ser.). 24p. (J). pap. 7.95 (978-1-4048-0384-8(X)) Picture Window Bks.

Plant Facts, 4 vols., Set. 2005. (Illus.). 24p. (gr. 2-4). pap. 92.00 (978-0-7910-7289-9(4) , Chelsea Hse.) Facts On File, Inc.

The Plant Kingdom: Level Q, 6 vols., Vol. 2. (Explorers Ser.). 32p. (gr. 3-6). 44.95 (978-0-7699-0605-8(2)) Shortland Pubns. (U. S. A.) Inc.

Plant Life Classroom Library. (gr. k-2). lib. bdg. 91.95 (978-0-7368-1834-6(0)) Red Brick Learning.

Plant Life Complete Unit. (gr. k-2). 433.95 (978-0-7368-1835-3(9)) Red Brick Learning.

Plant Life Cycles. 2004. (Illus.). lib. bdg. 7.95 (978-0-8225-4786-0(4)) Lerner Publishing Group.

Plantas. 2005. Tr. of Plants. 105p. (J). spiral bd. 14.99 (978-1-59441-456-5(4) , K04007) Carson-Dellosa Publishing Co., Inc.

Plantas, 5 bks., Set. 2002. Tr. of Plants. (SPA.). (J). lib. bdg. 92.50 (978-1-58810-781-7(7)) Heinemann Library.

Las plantas: Cuaderno de Evaluacion: Unit 1: Las Plantas (Plants) 2000. (McGraw-Hill Ciencias Ser.). (ENG & SPA.). (gr. 5 up). (978-0-02-278671-7(6)) Macmillan/McGraw-Hill Schl. Div.

Las plantas: Recursos para el maestro con clave de Respuestas: Unit 1: Las Plantas (Plants) 2000. (McGraw-Hill Ciencias Ser.). (ENG & SPA.). (gr. 5 up). (978-0-02-278707-3(0)) Macmillan/McGraw-Hill Schl. Div.

Las plantas y el agua: Cuaderno de Evaluacion: Unit 1: Las plantas y el agua (Watering Earth's Plants) 2000. (McGraw-Hill Ciencias Ser.). (ENG & SPA.). (gr. 2 up). (978-0-02-278638-0(4)) Macmillan/McGraw-Hill Schl. Div.

Las plantas y el agua: Recursos para el maestro con clave de Respuestas: Unit 1: Las plantas y el agua (Watering Earth's Plants) 2000. (McGraw-Hill Ciencias Ser.). (ENG & SPA.). (gr. 2 up). (978-0-02-278685-4(6)) Macmillan/McGraw-Hill Schl. Div.

Plants & Seeds, 6 vols. (Sunshinetm Science Ser.). 24p. (gr. 1-2). 31.50 (978-0-7802-0291-7(0)) ; 36.95 (978-0-7802-0542-0(1)) Wright Group, The.

Plants Grow from Seeds Set B, 6 vols. (Phonics Readers Ser.). (gr. k-2). 17.50 (978-0-7368-3207-6(6)) Red Brick Learning.

Plants Life Cycles Set. (gr. k-2). 114.95 (978-0-7368-9052-6(1)) Red Brick Learning.

Plants We Use: Second Grade Guided Reading Level J. (On Our Way to English Ser.). (gr. 2 up). 34.50 (978-0-7578-7093-4(7)) Rigby Education.

Platt, Richard. Plants Bite Back! 1999. (Eyewitness Readers). (Illus.). 48p. (J). (gr. 5-3). pap. 3.99 (978-0-7894-4754-8(1)) Dorling Kindersley Publishing, Inc.

—Plants Bite Back! 1999. (J). (978-0-606-18991-0(2)); lib. bdg. 11.80 (978-0-613-22189-4(3)) Tandem Library Bks.

Pocket Chart Science: Plants. 2002. (J). pap. 9.95 (978-1-56911-076-8(X)) Learning Resources, Inc.

Pollination. 2001. (Botany Ser.). (J). (gr. k-12). vinyl bd. 4.95 (978-1-58845-136-1(4)) School Specialty Publishing.

Power-Packed Plants: Individual Title Six-Packs. (Rigby Infoquest Ser.). 24p. (gr. 3 up). 34.00 (978-0-7578-5776-8(0)) Rigby Education.

Pressnall, Deb, ed. Inquiry Investigations: Flowering Plants: Needs & Life Cycles. 2005. 48p. (J). per. 6.99 (978-1-59441-055-0(0) , CD-104028) Carson-Dellosa Publishing Co., Inc.

Questions about Plants. 2003. 62p. pap. (978-7-80051-848-5(5)) Dolphin Books, China.

Quien depende de las plantas? Science, 6 vols.Tr. of Who Needs Plants? Science. (SPA.). (gr. k-2). 28.95 (978-0-7368-3148-2(7) , Yellow Umbrella Bks.) Capstone Pr., Inc.

Raintree. Itlp 2004 Sprouts Pkg (29 Titl. 2004. pap. (978-1-4109-1565-8(4)) Harcourt Schl. Pubs.

Reader dsm-3 classroom plants Ea. 2004. (J). (978-1-59242-521-1(6)) Delta Education, LLC.

Reader dsm-3 plant&animal population Ea. 2004. (J). (978-1-59242-524-2(0)) Delta Education, LLC.

Readman, Jo & Roberts, Ley H. The World Came to My Place Today. 2003. (Illus.). 32p. 19.99 (978-1-903919-01-9(0) , Eden Project Books) Transworld Publishers Ltd. GBR. *Dist:* Trafalgar Square Publishing.

Rigby Education Staff. Bugs on the Menu. (Sails Literacy Ser.). (Illus.). 16p. (gr. 2-3). 27.00 (978-0-7635-9954-6(9) , 699549C99) Rigby Education.

Riggs, Sandy. Lan's Plant. 2006. (Reader's Clubhouse Set A Ser.). (Illus.). 24p. (J). pap. 3.99 (978-0-7641-3287-2(3)) Barron's Educational Series, Inc.

Riley, Peter D. Plants. Moller, Ray, photos by. 2003. (Everyday Science Ser.). (Illus.). 32p. (J). (gr. 1 up). lib. bdg. 23.33 (978-0-8368-3718-6(5)) Stevens, Gareth Inc.

Rivera, Sheila. Wetland. 2005. (First Step Nonfiction Ser.). (Illus.). 23p. (J). (ps-7). 18.60 (978-0-8225-2598-1(4) , Lerner Pubns.) Lerner Publishing Group.

Robertson, Matthew. Aranas. 2002. (SPA.). 64p. (978-970-651-635-0(2) , 1610) Editorial Oceano De Mexico, S.A. DE C.V.

Robinson, Richard. Plants. 2007. (J). lib. bdg. 18.95 (***978-1-59566-364-1(9)***) QEB Publishing Inc.

Robinson, Richard, ed. Plant Sciences, 4 vols., Set. 2000. (Macmillan Science Library). (Illus.). 800p. (J). 460.00 (978-0-02-865434-8(X) , GML00502-170601, Macmillan Reference USA) Thomson Gale.

Rogers, Kirsteen & Henderson, Corinne. World of Plants. Howell, Laura, ed. 2001. (Usborne Internet-Linked Library of Science). (Illus.). 64p. (J). pap. (978-0-439-44148-3(X)) Scholastic, Inc.

Romero, Libby. Characteristics of Plants. 2006. pap. 39.00 (***978-1-4108-6480-2(4)***) Benchmark Education Co.

—Discover Plants. 2006. pap. 39.00 (***978-1-4108-6483-3(9)***) Benchmark Education Co.

Royston, Angela. Plants, Flowers, Fruits & Seeds. 2002. (Plants Ser.). (Illus.). 32p. (J). (ps-1). pap. 6.95 (978-1-58810-449-6(4) , 91175) Heinemann Library.

Rushworth, Gary. What Makes a Plant a Plant. 2006. (Navigators Ser.). (J). pap. 42.00 (***978-1-4108-6229-7(1)***) Benchmark Education Co.

Samson, Suzanne. Fairy Dusters & Blazing Stars: Exploring Wildflowers with Children. Neel, Preston, illus. 1999. 40p. (Orig.). (ps-3). pap. 9.95 (978-1-879373-81-5(5)) Rinehart, Roberts Pubs.

Saunders-Smith, Gail. Plants: Life Cycles, Set. 1998. (J). pap. (978-0-516-29779-8(1) , Children's Pr.) Scholastic Library Publishing.

Schaefer, Lola M. Pick, Pull, Snap! Where Once a Flower Bloomed. George, Lindsay B., illus. 2003. 32p. (J). 15.99 (978-0-688-17834-5(0)) HarperCollins Pubs.

School Specialty Publishing. Plant Life Cycle. 2004. (On-File Ser.). 4p. (J). (gr. k-2). ring bd. 4.99 (978-0-7424-2901-7(6) , Instructional Fair) Schaffer, Frank Pubns.

School Zone Publishing Company Staff. Seeds & Plants. (Illus.). (J). 19.99 incl. audio compact disk (978-0-88743-922-3(5)) School Zone Publishing Co.

School Zone Publishing Company Staff & Hall, Julie. Weather, Seeds, Plants. deluxe ed. 2000. (Deluxe Wkbks.). (Illus.). 64p. (J). (gr. 2-4). pap., wbk. ed. 4.16 (978-0-88743-861-5(X) , 02261) School Zone Publishing Co.

Schussler, Elizabeth S. & Wandersee, James H. Lost Plant! 1999. (Illus.). 40p. (J). (ps-6). spiral bd. (978-1-55212-236-5(0) , Thinking Log Pr.) Trafford Publishing.

Schwartz, David M. In the Meadow. Kuhn, Dwight, photos by. 1998. (Springboards into Science Ser.). (Illus.). 24p. (J). (gr. 1 up). lib. bdg. 20.67 (978-0-8368-2223-6(4)) Stevens, Gareth Inc.

—Plant Blossoms. Kuhn, Dwight, photos by. 1999. (Springboards into Science Ser.). (Illus.). 24p. (J). (gr. 1 up). lib. bdg. 20.67 (978-0-8368-2580-0(2)) Stevens, Gareth Inc.

—Plant Fruits & Seeds. Kuhn, Dwight, photos by. 1999. (Springboards into Science Ser.). (Illus.). 24p. (J). (gr. 1 up). lib. bdg. 20.67 (978-0-8368-2427-8(X)) Stevens, Gareth Inc.

—Plant Leaves. Kuhn, Dwight, photos by. 1999. (Springboards into Science Ser.). (Illus.). 24p. (J). (gr. 1 up). lib. bdg. 20.67 (978-0-8368-2428-5(8)) Stevens, Gareth Inc.

—Plant Stems & Roots. Kuhn, Dwight, photos by. 1999. (Springboards into Science Ser.). (Illus.). 24p. (J). (gr. 1 up). lib. bdg. 20.67 (978-0-8368-2581-7(0)) Stevens, Gareth Inc.

Science & Technology for Children Books, Experiments with Plants, 8 vols. 2004. (Illus.). 64p. (J). (978-1-933008-20-2(2)) National Science Resources Ctr.

Science Stories Foss Spanish New Plants EA CR05. 2005. (J). (978-1-59242-583-9(6)) Delta Education, LLC.

Sian Flowering Plants. 2004. (J). (978-1-59242-030-8(3)) Delta Education, LLC.

Sievert, Terri. Prairie Plants. 2006. (Life in the World's Biomes Ser.). (Illus.). 24p. (J). (978-0-7368-4323-2(X)) Capstone Pr., Inc.

—Wetland Plants. 2006. (Life in the World's Biomes Ser.). (Illus.). 24p. (J). (978-0-7368-4325-6(6) , Bridgestone Bks.) Capstone Pr., Inc.

Silverstein, Alvin & Silverstein, Virginia B. Nature's Champions: The Biggest, the Fastest, the Best. Zallinger, Jean, tr. Zallinger, Jean, illus. 2003. 64p. (J). (gr. 5-8). pap. 5.95 (978-0-486-42888-8(5)) Dover Pubns., Inc.

Snedden, Robert. Northern Forests. 2003. (Illus.). 32p. (J). lib. bdg. (978-1-58340-385-3(X)) Smart Apple Media.

—Plants & Fungi: Multicelled Life. 2003. (Cells & Life Ser.). (Illus.). 48p. (gr. 6-8). (J). lib. bdg. 27.86 (978-1-58810-675-9(6)); (YA). pap. 8.50 (978-1-58810-937-8(2)) Heinemann Library.

Southwater Staff. Look & Learn about Flowers, Fruits & Veg. 2001. (Look & Learn Ser.). (Illus.). 32p. (ps). 7.95 (978-1-84215-283-6(1) , Southwater) Anness Publishing GBR. *Dist:* National Bk. Network.

Souza, Dorothy M. Endangered Plants. 2004. (Watts Library). (J). (gr. 5-7). pap. 8.95 (978-0-531-16248-4(6) , Watts, Franklin) Scholastic Library Publishing.

—Plant Invaders. 2003. (Watts Library). (Illus.). 64p. (J). 25.50 (978-0-531-12211-2(5) , Watts, Franklin) Scholastic Library Publishing.

Spilsbury, Louise. Bean. 2005. (Heinemann Read & Learn Ser.). (Illus.). 24p. (J). pap. (978-1-4034-6774-4(9)); lib. bdg. 14.45 (978-1-4034-6769-0(2)) Heinemann Library.

Spilsbury, Louise & Spilsbury, Richard. Como Crecen las Plantas? DoubleO Publishing Services Staff, tr. 2006. (Mundo de las Plantas Ser.). (SPA., Illus.). 32p. (J). lib. bdg. 7.99 (978-1-4034-9072-8(4)) Heinemann Library.

—Donde Crecen las Plantas? DoubleO Publishing Services Staff, tr. 2006. (Mundo de las Plantas Ser.). (SPA., Illus.). 32p. (J). lib. bdg. 7.99 (978-1-4034-9070-4(8)) Heinemann Library.

—Green Plants: From Roots to Leaves. 2004. (Science Answers Ser.). (Illus.). 32p. (J). (ps-k). pap. 7.50 (978-1-4034-5511-6(2)); lib. bdg. 24.22 (978-1-4034-4765-4(9)) Heinemann Library.

—How Do Plants Grow? 2005. (World of Plants Ser.). (Illus.). 32p. (J). pap. (978-1-4034-7365-3(X)) Heinemann.

—Plant Classification. 2003. (Illus.). 48p. pap. 8.50 (978-1-4034-0501-2(8)) Heinemann Library.

—Plant Habitats. 2003. (Illus.). 48p. (J). (gr. 3-5). lib. bdg. 25.64 (978-1-4034-0295-0(7)); pap. 8.50 (978-1-4034-0503-6(4)) Heinemann Library.

—Plant Reproduction. 2002. (Illus.). 48p. (J). pap. 8.50 (978-1-4034-0506-7(9)) Heinemann Library.

—Por Que las Plantas Tienen Flores? DoubleO Publishing Services Staff, tr. 2006. (Mundo de las Plantas Ser.). (SPA., Illus.). 32p. (J). lib. bdg. 7.99 (978-1-4034-9071-1(6)) Heinemann Library.

—Que Es una Planta? DoubleO Publishing Services Staff, tr. 2006. (Mundo de las Plantas Ser.). (SPA., Illus.). 32p. (J). lib. bdg. 7.99 (978-1-4034-9069-8(4)) Heinemann Library.

—What Is a Plant? 2005. (World of Plants Ser.). (Illus.). 32p. (J). (978-1-4034-7361-5(7)); pap. (978-1-4034-7366-0(8)) Heinemann.

—Why Do Plants Have Flowers? 2005. (World of Plants Ser.). (Illus.). 32p. (J). (978-1-4034-7363-9(3)); pap. (978-1-4034-7368-4(4)) Heinemann.

Spilsbury, Richard & Spilsbury, Louise. How Do Plants Grow? 2005. (World of Plants Ser.). (Illus.). 32p. (J). (gr. k-3). lib. bdg. 25.36 (978-1-4034-7360-8(9)) Heinemann.

—Plant Classification. 2003. (Life of Plants Ser.). (Illus.). 48p. (J). (gr. 3-5). lib. bdg. 25.64 (978-1-4034-0293-6(0)) Heinemann Library.

Stanos, Dimi. Plants in the Park. 2002. (Windows on Literacy Ser.). (Illus.). 8p. (J). (978-0-7922-8463-5(1)) National Geographic Society.

Steck-Vaughn Staff. The Surprising World of Plants. 2002. pap. (978-0-7398-6150-9(6)) Steck-Vaughn.

Stefoff, Rebecca. The Flowering Plant Division. 2005. (Family Trees Ser.). (Illus.). 92p. (J). (gr. 3-7). lib. bdg. (978-0-7614-1817-7(2) , Benchmark Bks.) Cavendish, Marshall Corp.

—Flytrap. 1999. (Living Things Ser.). (Illus.). 32p. (J). (gr. 1-12). lib. bdg. 22.79 (978-0-7614-0445-3(7) , Benchmark Bks.) Cavendish, Marshall Corp.

Stems, 6 vols. (gr. k-2). 28.95 (978-0-7368-8003-9(8)) Red Brick Learning.

Stems. 2001. (Botany Ser.). (J). (gr. k-12). vinyl bd. 4.95 (978-1-58845-133-0(X)) School Specialty Publishing.

Stephens, Catherine. Classification Clues. 2004. (National Geographic Reading Expeditions Ser.). (Illus.). 32p. (J). pap. (978-0-7922-4576-6(8)) National Geographic Society.

Stewart, Melissa. A Parade of Plants. 2004. (Investigate Science Ser.). (Illus.). 32p. (J). (gr. 1 up). lib. bdg. 21.26 (978-0-7565-0592-9(5)) Compass Point Bks.

—Plants. 2003. (Simply Science Ser.). (Illus.). 32p. (J). (gr. 3 up). lib. bdg. 19.93 (978-0-7565-0444-1(9)) Compass Point Bks.

Stille, Darlene R. Plant Cells: The Building Blocks of Plants. 2006. (Exploring Science Ser.). (Illus.). 48p. (J). (gr. 5-7). 25.27 (978-0-7565-1619-2(6)) Compass Point Bks.

Stone, Lynn M. Plant Cycle. 2007. (Illus.). 24p. (J). (978-1-60044-180-6(7)) Rourke Publishing, LLC.

Stradling, Jan. Plants all Around: Level H, 6 vols. (First Explorers Ser.). 24p. (gr. 1-2). 29.95 (978-0-7699-1450-3(0)) Shortland Pubns. (U. S. A.) Inc.

Superlibro de Ampliar sobre las Plantas: Unit 2: Aprende sobre las plantas (All about Plants) 2000. (McGraw-Hill Ciencias Ser.). (ENG & SPA.). (gr. k up). (978-0-02-277158-4(1)) Macmillan/McGraw-Hill Schl. Div.

Superlibro de Las plantas y el Agua: Unit 1: Las plantas y el agua (Watering Earth's Plants) 2000. (McGraw-Hill Ciencias Ser.). (ENG & SPA.). (gr. 2 up). (978-0-02-277171-3(9)) Macmillan/McGraw-Hill Schl. Div.

Swain, Cynthia. A Plant Has Parts. 2006. (Early Explorers Ser.). (J). 30.00 (***978-1-4108-6024-8(8)***) Benchmark Education Co.

Talmadge, Ellen. Unearthing Garden Mysteries Vol. 1: Experiments for Kids. Curtis, Bruce, photos by. 2004. (Illus.). 96p. (gr. 4-7). 17.95 (978-1-55591-993-1(6)) Fulcrum Publishing.

Thomas, Lyndall. Plants. 1999. (Interfact Reference Ser.). (Illus.). 48p. (J). (gr. 2-8). 15.00 (978-0-7166-7239-5(1) , 1544) World Bk., Inc.

Thomson, Ruth. Take My Plant for a Walk? 2001. (Why Can't I Ser.). (Illus.). 30p. (J). lib. bdg. 24.25 (978-1-930643-02-4(0)) Chrysalis Education.

Thriving Plants. 1998. (Eyewitness Fun Fax Inserts Ser.). (Illus.). (J). (gr. 4-8). pap. 2.95 (978-0-7894-3013-7(4)) Dorling Kindersley Publishing, Inc.

Time for Kids Editors. Plants! 2006. (Time for Kids Science Scoops Ser.). (Illus.). 32p. (J). 14.99 (978-0-06-078219-1(6)) HarperCollins Pubs.

Time for Kids Editors & Iasevoli, Brenda. Plants! 2006. (Time for Kids Science Scoops Ser.). (Illus.). 32p. (J). pap. 3.99 (978-0-06-078218-4(8) , Harper Trophy) HarperCollins Pubs.

Tocci, Salvatore. Experiments with Plants. (True Books Ser.). (Illus.). 48p. (J). (gr. 3-5). 2002. pap. 6.95 (978-0-516-27351-8(5)); Set. 2001. 25.00 (978-0-516-22252-3(X)) Scholastic Library Publishing. (Children's Pr.).

—Experiments with Plants. 2002. 13.75 (978-0-606-22880-0(2)); 2001. (gr. 3-6). lib. bdg. 15.25 (978-0-613-54211-1(8)) Tandem Library Bks.

Tommes, Susanne & Ross, Thea. Wally's Big Book of Gardening. 2002. (Illus.). 42p. (J). pap. 14.95 (978-0-7892-0741-8(9)) Abbeville Pr., Inc.

Top That Publishing Staff, ed. Monster Plants. 2004. 48p. (J). pap. (978-1-84510-193-0(6)) Top That! Publishing PLC.

Tornqvist, Carl-Erik. Plant Genetics. 2006. (Green World Ser.). (Illus.). 136p. (J). (gr. 6-12). 37.50 (978-0-7910-8563-9(5) , Chelsea Hse.) Facts On File, Inc.

Trumbauer, Lisa. Who Need Plants? 2003. (J). (978-0-7368-1715-8(8)) Yellow Umbrella Pr.

—Who Needs Plants? 2003. (Yellow Umbrella Books). (Illus.). 16p. (J). (gr. 1). lib. bdg. 14.60 (978-0-7368-2023-3(X) , Pebble Bks.) Capstone Pr., Inc.

Van Manen, Dave. Plants of the Pueblo Mountain Park. 2005. (Illus.). 120p. per. 19.95 (978-0-9743791-7-3(4)) Medici Publishing, Inc.

VanCleave, Janice Pratt. Janice VanCleave's Plants: Mind-Boggling Experiments You Can Turn into Science Fair Projects. 2002. (Janice Vancleave Ser.). (Illus.). (J). 19.72 (978-0-7587-4632-0(6)) Book Wholesalers, Inc.

Wadsworth, Pamela. Golwg Gyntaf Ar Bethau Byw. 2005. (WEL., Illus.). 24p. pap. (978-1-85596-250-7(0)) Dref Wen.

—Golwg Gyntaf Ar Wahanol Blanhigion Ac Anifeiliaid. 2005. (WEL., Illus.). 24p. pap. (978-1-85596-254-5(3)) Dref Wen.

—Gwahanol Blanhigion Ac Anifeiliaid. 2005. (WEL., Illus.). 24p. pap. (978-1-85596-223-1(3)) Dref Wen.

—Rhagor Am Bethau Byw Ar Waith. 2005. (WEL., Illus.). 24p. pap. (978-1-85596-234-7(9)) Dref Wen.

—Rhagor Am Wahanol Blanhigion Ac Anifeiliaid. 2005. (WEL., Illus.). 24p. pap. (978-1-85596-224-8(1)) Dref Wen.

Walker, Colin, et al. Las Differentes Cosas Que Vienende las Plantas. (Coleccion Conceptos de Ciencia en Big Books). (SPA.). (J). (gr. k-3). 12.00 (978-0-8136-6753-9(4)) Modern Curriculum Pr.

Walker, Jane. Las Flores. 2001. (SPA., Illus.). 32p. (J). (ps-5). 10.95 (978-84-263-3169-4(6)) Lectorum Pubns., Inc.

Wallace, Marianne D. America's Seashores: Guide to Plants & Animals. 2005. (Illus.). 46p. (J). (ps-7). pap. 11.95 (978-1-55591-483-7(7) , 1250708) Fulcrum Publishing.

Warren, Howard. The Life Cycle of Plants. 2006. (Navigators Ser.). (J). pap. 38.00 (***978-1-4108-6224-2(0)***) Benchmark Education Co.

Waters, Jo. A Walk in the Park. 2006. (Raintree Sprouts Ser.). (Illus.). 24p. (J). (978-1-4109-2291-5(X)); pap. (978-1-4109-2296-0(0)) Steck-Vaughn.

Watts, Barrie. Bean. 2004. (J). lib. bdg. 27.10 (978-1-58340-503-1(8)) Smart Apple Media.

—El Hamster. (Coleccion Ciclos Vitales). (SPA., Illus.). 32p. (J). (gr. 3-5). (978-84-236-2665-6(2) , ED4704) Edebé ESP. *Dist:* Lectorum Pubns., Inc.

Watts, Claire & Nicholson, Robert. Nature's Wild! 2000. (Info Adventure Ser.). (Illus.). 32p. (J). (gr. 3-6). pap. 3.95 (978-1-58728-112-9(0) , Two Can Publishing) T&N Children's Publishing.

Weekly Reader Early Learning Library (Firm) Staff, contrib. by. Things at the Park. 2006. (Things in My World Ser.). (Illus.). 16p. (J). pap. (978-0-8368-6816-6(1)); lib. bdg. (978-0-8368-6809-8(9)) Stevens, Gareth Inc.

—Things at the Park: Las Cosas Del Parque. 2006. (ENG & SPA., Illus.). 16p. (J). pap. (978-0-8368-7228-6(2) , Weekly Reader Early Learning Library) Stevens, Gareth Inc.

—Things at the Park (Las Cosas del Parque) 2006. (ENG & SPA., Illus.). 16p. (J). lib. bdg. 17.27 (978-0-8368-7221-7(5) , Weekly Reader Early Learning Library) Stevens, Gareth Inc.

Welch, Catherine A. Polar Plants. 2006. (Life in the World's Biomes Ser.). (Illus.). 24p. (J). (978-0-7368-4320-1(5)) Capstone Pr., Inc.

What Makes Plants Grow? Second Grade Newcomer Books. (On Our Way to English Ser.). (gr. 2 up). 29.50 (978-0-7578-7212-9(3)) Rigby Education.

Whitehouse, Patricia. Matematicas con Plantas. (Plantas (Plants) Ser.). (SPA.). 24p. (J). (ps-1). 2003. lib. bdg. 17.08 (978-1-58810-780-0(9)); 2002. (Illus.). pap. 5.25 (978-1-58810-827-2(9) , 91648) Heinemann Library.

—Plant ABC. 2002. (Plants Ser.). (Illus.). 24p. (J). (ps-1). pap. 5.25 (978-1-58810-733-6(7) , 91405); lib. bdg. 17.08 (978-1-58810-522-6(9)) Heinemann Library.

—Plant Math. 2002. (Plants Ser.). 24p. (J). (ps-1). pap. 5.25 (978-1-58810-734-3(5) , 91406); (Illus.). lib. bdg. 17.08 (978-1-58810-523-3(7)) Heinemann Library.

—Plants. 2007. (J). (***978-1-4034-7918-1(6)***) Heinemann Library.

Whitehouse, Patricia. Las Raices. (Plantas (Plants) Ser.). (SPA.). 24p. (J). (ps-1). 2003. lib. bdg. 17.08 (978-1-58810-778-7(7)); 2002. (Illus.). pap. 5.25 (978-1-58810-825-8(2) , 91649) Heinemann Library.

Wickings, Ruth. In the Pond. 2007. (World at Your Feet Ser.). (Illus.). 10p. (J). 9.95 (978-1-84560-026-6(6)) Mercury Bks. Ltd. GBR. *Dist:* International Publishers Marketing.

Wiedenhoeft, Alex C. Plant Nutrition. 2006. (Green World Ser.). (Illus.). 152p. (J). (gr. 6-12). 37.50 (978-0-7910-8564-6(3) , Chelsea Hse.) Facts On File, Inc.

Wildlife & Plants of the World, 17 vols., Set. rev. exp. ed. 1999. (Illus.). 1,000p. (gr. 4-8). 471.36 (978-0-7614-7099-1(9) , Cavendish, Marshall Reference Bks.) Cavendish, Marshall Corp.

Windsor, Jo. Good Ideas for People: Early Level Satellite Individual Title Six-Packs. (Sails Literacy Ser.). 16p. (gr. 1-2). 27.00 (978-0-7578-2930-7(9)) Rigby Education.

Woodward, John. Perfect Partners. 2003. (Amazing Nature Ser.). (Illus.). 32p. (J). pap. 7.50 (978-1-4034-5404-1(3)) Heinemann Library.

—Pesky Parasites. 2003. (Amazing Nature Ser.). (Illus.). 32p. (J). pap. (978-1-4034-5403-4(5)) Heinemann Library.

World Book, Inc Staff, contrib. by. Resources & Cumulative Index. 2005. (World Book's Science & Nature Guides Ser.). 80p. (J). (978-0-7166-4216-9(6)) World Bk., Inc.

Wyatt, Valerie. Wacky Plant Cycles. Jones, Lilith, illus. 2000. 24p. (J). (gr. 3-5). pap. 4.95 (978-1-57255-795-6(8)) Mondo Publishing.

—Wacky Plant Cycles. 2000. (978-0-606-22657-8(5)) Tandem Library Bks.

PLANTS—ANATOMY

see Plant Anatomy

PLANTS, CULTIVATED

see also House Plants; Plants, Edible

MacLeod, Elizabeth. Grow It Again. Price, Caroline, illus. unabr. ed. 1999. (Kids Can Do It Ser.). 40p. (J). (gr. 4-6). (978-1-55074-558-0(1)) Kids Can Pr., Ltd.

—Grow It Again. Price, Carolyn, illus. 1999. 40p. (J). (ps-ps). lib. bdg. 14.10 (978-0-613-16358-3(3)) Tandem Library Bks.

PLANTS—DISEASES

see Plant Diseases

PLANTS—ECOLOGY

see Plant Ecology

PLANTS, EDIBLE

Carl, Elsie. Neryugngaunga Naunerrlugnek (I Can Eat Plants) Brunk, Cara, illus. 1998. (ESK.). 16p. (J). (gr. k-3). pap. 6.00 (978-1-58084-034-7(5)) Lower Kuskokwim Schl. District.

Encyclopaedia Britannica Publishers, Inc. Staff. Food Plants. 2004. (Illus.). 64p. 14.95 (978-1-59339-013-6(0)) Encyclopaedia Britannica, Inc.

Feldman, Sarah. Incredible, Edible Plants. ed. 2003. (Early Connections Ser.). (J). pap. 35.00 (978-1-4108-1541-5(2)) Benchmark Education Co.

Ganeri, Anita. From Bean to Bean Plant. 2006. (Heinemann First Library). (Illus.). 32p. (J). (978-1-4034-7870-2(8)); 28.95 (978-1-4034-7861-0(9)) Heinemann Library.

Hughes, Meredith Sayles, et al. Buried Treasure: Roots & Tubers. 1998. (Plants We Eat Ser.). (Illus.). 96p. (J). (gr. 5-7). 26.60 (978-0-8225-2830-2(4) , Lerner Pubns.) Lerner Publishing Group.

Morgan, Sally. Plants & People. 2002. (Looking at Plants Ser.). (Illus.). 32p. (J). lib. bdg. 24.25 (978-1-931983-13-6(5)) Chrysalis Education.

Ritchie, Fern J. The Incredible Edibles Library, 5 discs. Ritchie, Ralph W., photos by. unabr. ed. 2001. (Incredible Edibles Ser.). (Illus.). 1542p. cd-rom 99.95 (978-0-939656-59-2(0)) Ritchie Unlimited Pubns.

Rockwell, Anne F. One Bean. 1999. (978-0-606-17080-2(4)) Tandem Library Bks.

Sweet, Muriel. Common Edible & Useful Plants of the West. rev. ed. 2003. (Illus.). 64p. (J). pap. 5.95 (978-0-87961-046-3(8)) Naturegraph Pubs., Inc.

Tagliaferro, Linda. The Life Cycle of a Bean. 2007. (Pebble Plus Ser.). (Illus.). 24p. (J). (978-0-7368-6710-8(4) , 1264876, Pebble Bks.) Capstone Pr., Inc.

Youdeowei, Anthony. Look & Learn about Common Food Plants. 2001. (Illus.). 16p. pap. (978-978-156-271-6(4)) Fourth Dimension Publishing Co., Ltd.

PLANTS, EXTINCT

see Plants, Fossil

PLANTS—FICTION

Avery, Najiyyah. My Grandmother's House Plant. 1999. 16p. (J). (gr. k-6). pap. 7.00 (978-0-8059-4539-3(3)) Dorrance Publishing Co., Inc.

Bailey, Linda. How Can a Frozen Detective Stay Hot on the Trail? 2004. (Stevie Diamond Mysteries Ser.). 168p. (YA). (gr. 13 up). (978-1-55337-582-1(3)) Kids Can Pr., Ltd.

Beer, Barbara Vagnozzi. Jack & the Beanstalk. (Illus.). 24p. pap. (978-1-904550-20-4(7)) Child's Play-International.

Bergland, Jeannie. God's Little Bush. 2005. 25p. per. 7.95 (978-1-59453-585-7(X) , 2775) Airleaf Publishing & Bookselling.

Betz, Adrienne. A Deal Is a Deal. Andriani, Vincent, illus. 1999. (Scholastic At-Home Phonics Reading Program Ser.: Vol. 33). 24p. (J). pap. (978-0-590-68782-9(4)) Scholastic, Inc.

Bloom, Stephanie. A Place to Grow. Murphy, Kelly, illus. 2002. 32p. (J). lib. bdg. 16.95 (978-1-931969-07-9(8)) Bloom & Grow Bks.

Brenner, Barbara. The Plant That Kept on Growing. Sweet, Melissa, illus. 1999. (Bank Street Reader Collection). 48p. (J). (ps-2). lib. bdg. (978-0-8368-1776-8(1)) Stevens, Gareth Inc.

Bryan, Marcia. Dandy Lion: The Adventure Begins. Bowden, CeCelia, illus. 2006. (J). 18.95 (***978-1-57736-376-7(0)*** , Hillsboro Pr.) Providence Hse Pubs.

Bulla, Clyde Robert. The Poppy Seeds. unabr. ed. 1998. (J). Class Set. 70.70 incl. audio (978-0-7887-2534-0(3) , 46704); Homework. (gr. 2). 22.24 incl. audio (978-0-7887-2229-5(8) , 40713) Recorded Bks., LLC.

Butler, Mary Nyegard. Palmetto Who?, 4 vols. Butler, Mary Nyegard, illus. 2001. (Illus.). 27p. (J). (ps-3). per. 7.95 (978-0-9701497-9-4(4)) Bay Tree Enterprises.

Cannon, Janell. Little Yau: A Fuzzhead Tale. 2002. (Illus.). 56p. (J). (gr. k-3). 16.00 (978-0-15-201791-0(7)) Harcourt Children's Bks.

Capeci, Anne. Little Lab or Horrors. 2003. (Dexter's Laboratory Science Log Ser.: Vol. 4). (Illus.). 78p. (J). (978-0-439-47242-5(3)) Scholastic, Inc.

Ciencin, Scott. Green Gotham. Burchett, Rick, illus. 2005. (Scholastic Reader Ser.). 40p. (J). (ps-k). pap. 3.99 (978-0-439-47102-2(8) , Cartwheel Bks.) Scholastic, Inc.

Coates, Theresa. Imaginary Time of Life. 2007. 102p. pap. 10.95 (***978-0-7414-4067-9(9)***) Infinity Publishing.

D'Ath, Justin. Terrors of Nature. 2005. (Thrillogy Ser.). (Illus.). 48p. (J). (gr. 4-8). 17.50 (978-0-7910-8892-0(8)) Facts On File, Inc.

Donahue, Jill L. Bliss, Blueberries, & the Butterfly. Ice, D. C., illus. 2006. 32p. (J). lib. bdg. (***978-1-4048-3206-0(8)***) Picture Window Bks.

DuTemple, Lesley A. One Little Balsam Fir: A Northwoods Counting Book. Robinson, Susan, illus. 2006. (J). (***978-1-892384-37-9(X)***) Avery Color Studios, Inc.

Ecton, Ann. Saguaro. Torrisi, Gary, illus. 1998. (Books for Young Learners). 12p. (J). (gr. k-2). pap. 5.00 (978-1-57274-118-8(X) , A2190) Owen, Richard C. Pubs., Inc.

Edwards, Tanille & Edwards, Latoya. Jordan & Justine's Weekend Adventures Pts. 1-2: Plants. 2007. 32p. (J). (gr. k-3). 9.95 (***978-0-9787302-3-9(2)***) Fire Flies Entertainment, LLC.

Ehlert, Lois. Leaf Man. 2005. (Illus.). 40p. (J). (ps-ps). 16.00 (978-0-15-205304-8(2) , Harcourt Children's Bks) Harcourt Children's Bks.

Ering, Timothy Basil. The Story of Frog Belly Rat Bone. Ering, Timothy Basil, illus. 2003. (Illus.). 48p. (J). (ps-2). 16.99 (978-0-7636-1382-2(7)) Candlewick Pr.

Fleischman, Paul. Weslandia. 2002. (Illus.). (J). 23.40 (978-0-7587-3948-3(6)) Book Wholesalers, Inc.

—Weslandia. braille ed. 2004. (Illus.). (J). (gr. k-3). spiral bd. (978-0-616-01641-1(7)) Canadian National Institute for the Blind/Institut National Canadien pour les Aveugles.

—Weslandia. Hawkes, Kevin, illus. 40p. (J). (ps-3). 2002. pap. 6.99 (978-0-7636-1052-4(6)); 1999. 15.99 (978-0-7636-0006-8(7)) Candlewick Pr.

—Weslandia. Hawkes, Kevin, illus. 2001. (J). (gr. k-4). 26.95 incl. audio (978-0-8045-6869-2(3) , 6869) Spoken Arts, Inc.

—Weslandia. 2002. (gr. k-3). lib. bdg. 14.15 (978-0-613-63531-8(0)) Tandem Library Bks.

Friedlander, Eleanor. Mrs. Digger's Roots. Traverso, Laura, illus. 1999. 44p. (J). (ps-3). 17.95 (978-0-9672124-0-1(5)) Jadeda Pr.

Grandma Carol's Plant: Individual Title Six-Packs. (gr. k-1). 23.00 (978-0-7635-9039-0(8)) Rigby Education.

Greenstein, Elaine, contrib. by. One Little Seed. 2004. (Illus.). 32p. (J). (gr. k-1). 10.99 (978-0-670-03633-2(1) , Viking Juvenile) Penguin Group (USA) Inc.

Harcourt School Publishers Staff. The Giant of the Desert 5-Pack, Below Level. 3rd ed. 2002. (Trophies Reading Program Ser.). (Illus.). (gr. 2). pap. 25.60 (978-0-15-326903-5(0)) Harcourt Schl. Pubs.

—The Seed Surprise: Take-Home Book. 1999. (Collections Ser.). (Illus.). (J). pap. 1.90 (978-0-15-317229-8(0)) Harcourt Schl. Pubs.

Hausman, Sid. Cactus Critter Bash. Hausman, Sid, illus. 2007. (Illus.). 32p. (J). 21.95 (***978-1-929115-15-0(6)***) Azro Pr., Inc.

Hayward, Linda. What Homework? O'Rourke, Page Eastburn, illus. 2002. (Science Solves It! Ser.). 32p. (J). (gr. 1-3). 4.99 (978-1-57565-116-3(5)) Kane Pr., The.

—What Homework? 2002. (gr. k-3). lib. bdg. 13.00 (978-0-613-53785-8(8)) Tandem Library Bks.

Hobbie, Holly. Wish You Were Here. 2005. (Toot & Puddle Ser.). (Illus.). 32p. (J). (ps-3). 16.99 (978-0-316-36602-1(1)) Little Brown & Co.

Hofmeister, Alan, et al. The Seed. (Reading for All Learners Ser.). (Illus.). (J). pap. (978-1-56861-112-9(9)) Swift Learning Resources.

Inches, Alison & Freeman, Don. Corduroy's Garden. Eitzen, Allan, illus. 2002. (Viking Easy-to-Read Ser.). 32p. (J). (gr. k-3). 13.99 (978-0-670-03547-2(5) , Viking Juvenile) Penguin Group (USA) Inc.

Ioan, Elwyn. Ici'r Ddol A'r Corrach Coch. 2005. (WEL., Illus.). 36p. pap. (978-0-86243-428-1(9)) Y Lolfa.

Jarrell, Pamela R. Planting a Seed. Meler, Kerry L., illus. l.t. ed. 2006. 12p. (J). (ps-k). pap. 10.95 (978-1-57332-350-5(0)) HighReach Learning, Inc.

Johnson, David. Trapped in Space. Liew, Sonny, illus. 2007. (J). 80p. (***978-1-59889-354-0(8)***); 74p. pap. (***978-1-59889-449-3(8)***) Stone Arch Bks.

Johnson, Richard, illus. The Giant Turnip. 2004. 24p. (J). (TAM, CZE, VIE, SPA & URD.). (978-1-85269-733-4(4)); (TAM, CZE, VIE, SPA & URD.). (978-1-85269-734-1(2)); (TAM, CZE, VIE, SPA & URD.). (978-1-85269-735-8(0)); (TAM, CZE, VIE, SPA & URD.). (978-1-85269-736-5(9)); (TAM, CZE, VIE, SPA & PER.). (978-1-85269-737-2(7)); (TAM, CZE, VIE, SPA & URD.). (978-1-85269-739-6(3)); (TAM, CZE, VIE, SPA & GUJ.). (978-1-85269-740-2(7)); (TAM, CZE, VIE, SPA & URD.). (978-1-85269-741-9(5)); (TAM, CZE, VIE, SPA & URD.). (978-1-85269-742-6(3)); (TAM, CZE, VIE, SPA & URD.). (978-1-85269-743-3(1)); (TAM, CZE, VIE, SPA & URD.). (978-1-85269-744-0(X)); (TAM, CZE, VIE, SPA & SER.). (978-1-85269-745-7(8)); (TAM, CZE, VIE, SPA & URD.). (978-1-85269-746-4(6)); (TAM, CZE, VIE, SPA & URD.). (978-1-85269-747-1(4)); (CZE, TAM, VIE, SPA & URD.). (978-1-85269-748-8(2)); (TAM, CZE, VIE, SPA & URD.). (978-1-85269-749-5(0)); (TAM, CZE, VIE, SPA & POL.). (978-1-85269-750-1(4)); (TAM, CZE, VIE, SPA & URD.). (978-1-85269-788-4(1)); (TAM, CZE, SPA, VIE & URD.). (978-1-85269-789-1(X)) Mantra Publishing, Ltd.

King, Susan. Amy & the World's Best Valentine/Amy & the Four-Leaf Clover. King, Susan, illus. 2002. (Illus.). 105p. (J). (ps-6). spiral bd. 7.00 (978-0-9714446-2-1(5)) King RIT - ACKS Pubs.

Kitami, Yoko. Cactus. 2006. Tr. of Cactus. (SPA.). (J). (gr. 2-3). 8.80 (978-968-16-7386-4(7) , FC15223) Fondo de Cultura Economica MEX. *Dist:* Lectorum Pubns., Inc.

Larsen, Kirsten, et al. Lily's Pesky Plant. Clarke, Judith, illus. 2006. (Stepping Stone Bks.). 128p. (J). (gr. 2-4). 5.99 (978-0-7364-2374-8(5) , RH/Disney) Random Hse. Children's Bks.

The Laughing Lavender Field. 2005. (J). 5.00 (978-0-9765731-0-4(5)) DTJ, LLC.

Loki. Jake Greenthumb. Gaillard, Jason, illus. 2002. 32p. (J). pap. (978-1-59034-037-0(X)); 15.95 (978-1-59034-186-5(4)) Mondo Publishing.

McArthur, Nancy. The Plant That Ate Dirty Socks. (Plant That Ate Dirty Socks Ser.: Bk. 1). 119p. (J). (gr. k-3). pap. 4.50 (978-0-8072-1494-7(9) , Listening Library) Random Hse. Audio Publishing Group.

Meddaugh, Susan. Just Teenie. 2006. (Illus.). 32p. (J). (gr. k-3). 16.00 (978-0-618-68565-3(0)) Houghton Mifflin Co.

Metzger, Steve. My Seeds Won't Grow! Wilhelm, Hans, illus. 2000. (Dinofours Ser.: No. 18). (J). (ps-1). (978-0-439-06329-6(9)) Scholastic, Inc.

Morgan, Ruth. Jess & the Bean Root. 2005. (Illus.). 24p. (J). lib. bdg. 22.65 (***978-1-59646-732-3(0)***) Dingles & Co.

Nolen, Jerdine. Plantzilla. Catrow, David, illus. 2002. 32p. (J). (gr. k-3). 16.00 (978-0-15-202412-3(3) , Silver Whistle) Harcourt Trade Pubs.

—Plantzilla Goes to Camp. Catrow, David, illus. 2006. 32p. (J). (gr. k-3). 16.95 (978-0-689-86803-0(0)) Simon & Schuster Children's Publishing.

Nolen, Jerdine & Keliher, Brian. Plantzilla. Catrow, David, illus. 2005. 32p. (J). (ps-3). pap. reprint ed. pap., pap. 7.00 (978-0-15-205392-5(1) , Voyager Bks./Libros Viajeros) Harcourt Children's Bks.

Olaondo, Susana. Julieta, Que Plantaste? Olaondo, Susana, illus. (SPA., Illus.). 31p. (J). (gr. k-3). pap. 7.95 (978-1-59437-793-8(6)) Santillana USA Publishing Co., Inc.

Pacheco, Maria & Garcia-Martinez, Julia. The Hamburger Tree. Hergenroeder, Ernie, illus. 2006. 24p. (J). (***978-0-9776835-0-5(8)***) Run With Me Publishing.

Pallotta, Jerry. Dory Story. Biedrzycki, David, illus. 2004. (J). (ps-ps). lib. bdg. 14.50 (978-0-606-30230-2(1)) Tandem Library Bks.

Petti, Ken. Zenda 09 Trapped in Time. 2007. 144p. (J). pap. (***978-0-448-44343-0(0)*** , Grosset & Dunlap) Penguin Group (USA) Inc.

Pittar, Gill. Milly, Molly & Jimmy's Seeds. 2004. (Illus.). 28p. (978-1-86972-000-1(8)) Milly Molly Bks.

Pugliano-Martin, Carol. The Great Big Giant Turnip. ed. 2003. (Early Connections Ser.). (J). pap. 35.00 (978-1-4108-1553-8(6)) Benchmark Education Co.

Rader, Laura, illus. Grow, Little Turnip, Grow Big. 2006. (I'm Going to Read Ser.). 24p. (J). pap. 3.95 (978-1-4027-3075-7(6)) Sterling Publishing Co., Inc.

Rey, H. A. Elizabite: Adventures of a Carnivorous Plant. Rey, H. A., illus. 1999. (Illus.). 32p. (J). (gr. k-3). tchr. ed. 15.00 (978-0-395-97702-6(9)) Houghton Mifflin Co. Trade & Reference Div.

—Elizabite: Adventures of A Carnivorous Plant. 1999. (gr. k-3). lib. bdg. 14.10 (978-0-613-21489-6(7)) Tandem Library Bks.

Rey, H. A. & Rey, Margret. CG TV Curious George Plants a Seed Spanish Bilingual Edition. 2007. 24p. (J). (gr. k-3). mass mkt. 3.99 (***978-0-618-89688-2(0)***) Houghton Mifflin Co. Trade & Reference Div.

—Curious George Plants a Seed. 2007. (Illus.). 24p. (J). (ps-k). 3.99 (***978-0-618-77710-5(5)***) Houghton Mifflin Co. Trade & Reference Div.

Rovetch, Lissa. TLC Grow with Me! McLeod, Chum, illus. 2005. (J). (978-1-58987-114-4(6)) Kindermusik International.

The Running of the Leaves. l.t. ed. 2001. 54p. (J). (gr. 4-6). spiral bd. 11.95 (978-0-9714293-0-7(8)) IBD Pr.

Sasso, Sandy Eisenberg. Noah's Wife: The Story of Naamah. Andersen, Bethanne, illus. 2002. 32p. (J). 16.95 (978-1-58023-134-3(9)) Jewish Lights Publishing.

Shivers, Juliette. Brenda Doesn't Like Broccoli. 2004. Tr. of Brenda no le Gusta Broculi. (Illus.). 25p. (J). 6.50 (978-0-9769379-0-6(5)) Ingram's Nutrition Consultations.

Simons, Moya. Nibbles: My Amazing Poo Plant: Can Emma grow the perfect Pet? Rossell, Judith, illus. 2007. 80p. (J). pap. 3.95 (***978-0-7624-2934-9(8)*** , Running Pr. Kids) Running Pr. Bk. Pubs.

Soundprints. Here We Go Round the Mulberry Bush: And Other Favorites. 2002. (Illus.). 36p. (J). bds. 8.95 (978-1-931465-26-7(6)); bds. 10.95 incl. audio compact disk (978-1-931465-32-8(0)) Soundprints. (Little Soundprints).

Swain, Cynthia. Sorting at the Nature Center. 2006. (Early Explorers Ser.). (J). 30.00 (***978-1-4108-6039-2(6)***) Benchmark Education Co.

Switzer, Vern. Lucy the Cantaloupe. Connally, Perry L., Sr., illus. 2005. 32p. (J). 15.95 (***978-0-9753542-1-6(3)***) Rural Farm Productions.

—Puffy the Watermelon. Listokin, David & Connally, Perry L., Sr., illus. 2004. 24p. (J). 15.95 (***978-0-9753542-0-9(5)***) Rural Farm Productions.

Tolstoy, Aleksei. The Gigantic Turnip. Sharkey, Niamh, illus. 2005. 40p. (J). (978-1-905236-58-9(1)) Barefoot Bks., Inc.

PLANTS, FOSSIL

Aspen-Baxter, Linda. Plants. 2004. (Prehistoric Life Ser.). (J). pap. 7.95 (978-1-59036-174-0(1)); (Illus.). 32p. lib. bdg. 15.95 (978-1-59036-114-6(8)) Weigl Pubs., Inc.

Daniels, Frank J. Petrified Wood: The World of Fossilized Wood, Cones, Ferns, & Cycads. 1998. (Illus.). vi, 170p. (YA). (gr. 9-12). 75.00 (978-0-9662938-0-7(0)) Western Colorado Publishing Co.

Henderson, Douglas. Dinosaur Tree. 1999. (J). (978-0-606-17194-6(0)) Tandem Library Bks.

PLANTS—GROWTH

see Growth (Plants)

PLANTS, MEDICINAL

see Botany, Medical

PLANTS—PROPAGATION

see Plant Propagation

PLANTS—STRUCTURE

see Plant Anatomy

PLANTS, USEFUL

see Botany, Economic; Plants, Edible

PLASTIC MATERIALS

see Plastics

PLASTICS

Barraclough, Sue. A Plastic Toy. 2006. (How It's Made Ser.). (Illus.). 32p. (J). lib. bdg. (978-0-8368-6704-6(1)) Stevens, Gareth Inc.

Bedford, Kate. Plastics. 2005. (Illus.). 32p. (J). (gr. 3-7). lib. bdg. 27.10 (978-1-59604-042-7(4)) Stargazer Bks.

Good, Keith. Shape It! Magnificent Projects for Molding Materials. 1999. (Design It! Ser.). (Illus.). 30p. (gr. 4-8). lib. bdg. 21.27 (978-0-8225-3568-3(8)) Lerner Publishing Group.

Goodstein, Madeline P. Plastics & Polymers Science Fair Projects Using Hair Gel, Soda Bottles, & Slimy Stuff. 2004. (Chemistry! Best Science Projects Ser.). (Illus.). 128p. (J). lib. bdg. 26.60 (978-0-7660-2123-5(8)) Enslow Pubs., Inc.

Harry, Cindy Groom. Looney Lanyard Lace. 2000. (Funtastic Kits Ser.). (Illus.). 48p. (J). 12.98 (978-0-7853-3979-3(5)) Publications International, Ltd.

Jennings, Terry. Plastic. 2006. (Illus.). 32p. (YA). (gr. 1 up). lib. bdg. 27.10 (978-1-932333-03-9(7)) Chrysalis Education.

Kachur, Matthew. A un material milagroso & Miracle Material. 2005. spiral bd. 84.00 (***978-1-4108-5717-0(4)***) Benchmark Education Co.

Llewellyn, Claire. Plastic. 2002. (Material World Ser.). (Illus.). (J). (gr. 2-4). 32p. pap. 24.00 (978-0-531-14631-6(6)); 30p. pap. 6.95 (978-0-531-14838-9(6)) Scholastic Library Publishing. (Watts, Franklin).

—Plastic. 2005. (Illus.). 24p. (J). (gr. 1-4). lib. bdg. 22.80 (978-1-932889-53-6(1)) Sea-To-Sea Pubns.

Lucas, Rhonda Donald. Plastic. 2004. (First Facts Ser.). (Illus.). 24p. (J). 15.95 (978-0-7368-2514-6(2)) Capstone Pr., Inc.

Mitchell, Melanie S. Plastic. 2003. (First Step Nonfiction Ser.). (Illus.). 24p. (J). (gr. k-2). lib. bdg. 18.60 (978-0-8225-4620-7(5)) Lerner Publishing Group.

O'Daley, Anne. Solids. 2003. (Illus.). 24p. (J). 22.45 (978-1-4103-0085-0(4) , Blackbirch Pr., Inc.) Thomson Gale.

Oxlade, Chris. How We Use Plastic. 2004. (Illus.). 32p. (J). (ps-1). pap. 7.50 (978-1-4109-0995-4(6)); lib. bdg. 25.70 (978-1-4109-0596-3(9)) Raintree.

—Plastic. (Materials, Materials, Materials Ser.). 32p. pap. 6.95 (978-1-4034-4100-3(6)); 2001. (Illus.). (J). lib. bdg. 21.36 (978-1-58810-157-0(6)) Heinemann Library.

Parker, Steve. Plastics. 2002. (Science Files Ser.). (Illus.). 32p. (J). (gr. 3 up). lib. bdg. 24.67 (978-0-8368-3084-2(9)) Stevens, Gareth Inc.

Plastico. (SPA., Illus.). (J). 12.00 (978-84-342-2269-4(8)) Parramon Ediciones S.A. ESP. *Dist:* Distribuidora Norma, Inc., Lectorum Pubns., Inc.

Royston, Angela. Plastic: Let's Look at a Frisbee. 2005. (Heinemann Read & Learn Ser.). (Illus.). 24p. (J). (978-1-4034-7673-9(X)); pap. (978-1-4034-7682-1(9)) Heinemann Library.

—Plastic: Let's Look at a Frisbee. 2005. (J). (978-1-4109-1820-8(3)); pap. (978-1-4109-1829-1(7)) Steck-Vaughn.

—Plastico: Miremos un Frisbee. 2005. (Heinemann Lee y Aprende Ser.). (ENG & SPA., Illus.). 24p. (978-1-4034-7545-9(8)); pap. (978-1-4034-7554-1(7)) Heinemann Library.

Sterngass, Jon & Kachur, Matthew. Plastics. 2005. (Great Inventions Ser.). (Illus.). 48p. (J). lib. bdg. 30.00 (978-0-8368-5878-5(6) , World Almanac Library) Stevens, Gareth Inc.

Thomson, Ruth. Plastics. 2006. (Illus.). 29p. (J). (978-1-58340-938-1(6)) Smart Apple Media.

Walker, Kate. Plastics. 2004. (Recycle, Reduce, Reuse, Rethink Ser.). (J). lib. bdg. 27.10 (978-1-58340-556-7(9)) Smart Apple Media.

Wallace, Holly. Plastic. 2007. (J). (***978-1-59920-005-7(8)***) Smart Apple Media.

Whyman, Kathryn. Plastics & the Environment. 2004. (J). lib. bdg. (978-1-932799-32-3(X)) Stargazer Bks.

PLATYPUS

Clarke, Ginjer L. Platypus! Mirocha, Paul, illus. 2004. (Step into Reading Ser.). 32p. (J). (gr. k-3). pap. 3.99 (978-0-375-82417-3(0) , Random Hse. Bks. for Young Readers) Random Hse. Children's Bks.

Collard, Sneed B., III. A Platypus, Probably. Plant, Andrew, illus. 2005. 32p. (J). (ps-ps). 16.95 (978-1-57091-583-3(0)); pap. 6.95 (978-1-57091-584-0(9)) Charlesbridge Publishing, Inc.

Gaines, Ann Graham. Platypus. 1999. (Let's Investigate Ser.). (Illus.). 32p. (J). (gr. 1-4). lib. bdg. (978-0-88682-612-3(8) , Creative Education) Creative Co., The.

Grolier Educational Staff, contrib. by. Platypus. 2001. (Nature's Children Ser.). (Illus.). 48p. (J). (978-0-7172-5543-6(3) , Grolier) Scholastic Library Publishing.

PLAY

see also Amusements; Games; Recreation; Sports

Ackroyd, Dorothea. Playtime. 1999. 3.95 (978-1-58185-202-8(9)) Quadrillion Media LLC.

Ajmera, Maya & Ivanko, John D. Come Out & Play. Shakti for Children Staff, ed. 2004. (It's Kid's World Ser.). (Illus.). 32p. (J). (ps-1). 15.95 (978-1-57091-385-3(4)); pap. 6.95 (978-1-57091-386-0(2)) Charlesbridge Publishing, Inc.

Baker, Sue. Sleep Tight! Stockham, Jess, illus. 2006. (Blanket Babies Ser.). 12p. (J). 6.99 (978-1-904550-90-7(8)) Child's Play-International.

Bany-Winters, Lisa, et al. On Stage! Theater Games & Activities for Kids. O'Neill, Sean, illus. 2003. 160p. (J). (gr. 1-7). pap. 14.95 (978-1-55652-324-3(6)) Chicago Review Pr., Inc.

Beaton, Clare, illus. Let's Pretend. l.t. ed. 1998. (Craft & Project Books for Children). 48p. (J). (ps-4). lib. bdg. 17.95 (978-1-56674-243-6(9)) Forest Hse. Publishing Co., Inc.

The Bees & the Bear: Individual Title Six-Packs. (Story Steps Ser.). (gr. k-2). 32.00 (978-0-7635-9806-8(2)) Rigby Education.

Bidder, Jane. Inventions We Use for Play. 2006. 32p. (J). lib. bdg. (978-0-8368-6900-2(1)) Stevens, Gareth Inc.

Brent, Lynnette R. At Play. 2003. (Times Change Ser.). (Illus.). 32p. (J). (978-1-4034-4538-4(9)) Heinemann Library.

—At Play: Long Ago & Today. 2003. (Times Change Ser.). (Illus.). 32p. (J). lib. bdg. 24.22 (978-1-4034-4532-2(X)) Heinemann Library.

Bulloch, Ivan. The Big Play Book. James, Diane, illus. rev. ed. 2000. 12p. (J). (ps-k). bds. 19.95 (978-1-58728-535-6(5) , Two Can Publishing) T&N Children's Publishing.

Burton, Margie, et al. Playground Fun. Evento, Susan, ed. 1998. (Early Connections Ser.). 16p. (J). (gr. k-2). pap. 4.25 (978-1-892393-62-3(X)) Benchmark Education Co.

Carroll, Colleen. How Artists See Play. 1999. (How Artists See Ser.). (Illus.). 48p. (gr. 3-6). 12.95 (978-0-7892-0393-9(6)) Abbeville Pr., Inc.

Cartwright, Mary. Splish, Splash, Splosh Bath Bk. Wells, Rachel, illus. 2007. 8p. (J). 14.99 (978-0-7945-1619-2(X) , Usborne) EDC Publishing.

Castaldo, Nancy F. Winter Day Play! Activities, Crafts, & Games for Indoors & Out. 2001. (Illus.). 176p. (J). pap. 13.95 (978-1-55652-381-6(5)) Chicago Review Pr., Inc.

Chapman, Cindy. Play It Safe! 2003. (Compass Point Phonics Readers Ser.). (Illus.). 16p. (J). (gr. 1 up). 13.26 (978-0-7565-0520-2(8)) Compass Point Bks.

Claycomb, Patty. Places to Play. 2002. (Early Learner Photo Fun Activities Ser.). 8p. (J). 6.95 (978-1-56472-386-4(0)) Edupress, Inc.

Conner, Bobbi. Unplugged Play: No Batteries. No Plugs. Pure Fun. 2007. (Illus.). 432p. (J). pap. 16.95 (978-0-7611-4390-1(4)) Workman Publishing Co., Inc.

Daniel, Becky. The Playful Child: 130+ Quick Brain-Boosting Activities for 5- & 6-Year Olds. 2000. (Illus.). 176p. (Orig.). (J). (ps-1). pap. 14.99 (978-1-56822-956-0(9) , IF19623-E4, Instructional Fair) Schaffer, Frank Pubns.

—The Playful Preschooler: 130+ Quick Brain-Boosting Activities for 3- & 4-Year-Olds. 2000. (Growing & Learning Ser.). (Illus.). 176p. (J). (gr. 4 up). pap. 14.99 (978-1-56822-955-3(0) , IF19622) School Specialty Publishing.

—The Playful Toddler: 130+ Quick Brain-Boosting Activities for 18 to 36 Months. 2000. (Growing & Learning Ser.). (Illus.). 176p. (J). (gr. 4 up). pap. 16.99 (978-1-56822-954-6(2) , IF19621) School Specialty Publishing.

DK Publishing. Playtime. 2008. 14p. (J). (ps-k). bds. 5.99 (*978-0-7566-3834-4(8)) Dorling Kindersley Publishing, Inc.

Dorling Kindersley Publishing Staff. Playtime. 1999. (Bath Bks.). (Illus.). 10p. (J). (ps-k). 6.99 (978-0-7894-4324-3(4)) Dorling Kindersley Publishing, Inc.

Galko, Francine. Earth Friends at Play. 2004. (Heinemann First Library). (Illus.). 32p. (J). pap. 6.95 (978-1-4034-4901-6(5)) Heinemann Library.

—Ecology on the Playground. 2004. (Heinemann First Library). (Illus.). 32p. (J). lib. bdg. 22.79 (978-1-4034-4896-5(5)) Heinemann Library.

Gnojewski, Carol. Playtime Props for Toddlers. Burris, Priscilla, illus. 2001. (Time for Toddlers Ser.). 160p. (J). (ps). pap. 16.99 (978-1-57029-204-0(3) , WPH4701, Totline Pubns.) Schaffer, Frank Pubns.

Goose, Mother. Lets Play. 2005. (Illus.). 36p. (J). bds. 7.95 (978-1-59249-535-1(4) , 1D205) Soundprints.

Hallinan, P. K. Let's Play as a Team! 2001. (Illus.). 24p. (J). (ps-3). pap. 3.25 (978-0-8249-5398-0(3) , Ideals) Ideals Pubns.

Herd, Meg. Learn & Play in the Garden Vol. 7: Games, Crafts & Activities for Children. 1999. (Environmental Bks.). (Illus.). 128p. (J). (ps-6). lib. bdg. 18.95 (978-1-56674-242-9(0) , HTS Bks.) Forest Hse. Publishing Co., Inc.

James, Diane. Let's Hop & Skip! Bulloch, Ivan, illus. rev. ed. 2004. (My Turn Ser.). 12p. (J). (ps-k). bds. 6.95 (978-1-58728-010-8(8) , Two Can Publishing) T&N Children's Publishing.

Knight, Paula & Smith, Jane, illus. I'm a Little Teapot. 2002. (Nursery Rhymes Ser.). 10p. (J). bds. (978-1-59069-287-5(X) , MB1010) Studio Mouse LLC.

Kohl, MaryAnn F. Making Make-Believe: Fun Props, Costumes & Creative Play Ideas. 2004. (Illus.). 192p. (gr. 1-3). pap. 16.95 (978-0-87659-198-7(5) , 19674) Gryphon Hse., Inc.

Kulsa, Wha. Childs Play: Positive Affirmations for Children to Sing & Dramatize. Gardner, Stephen, illus. Date not set. 30p. (J). (gr. 1-7). pap. (978-1-886942-08-0(0)) White Lion Pr.

Lawson, Julia & Browne, Naima. Play Games! Millard, Peter, photos by. 2005. (Stepping Stones Ser.). (Illus.). 24p. (J). (ps). pap. 9.95 (978-0-237-52920-8(3) , Evans Brothers, Limited) Evans Publishing Group GBR. *Dist:* Independent Pubs. Group.

Lee, Quinlan B. I Can Do It. McKee, Darren, illus. 2004. (Barney Ser.). 6p. (J). bds. 5.99 (978-0-439-62498-5(3)) Scholastic, Inc.

Lorenz Editors. Action Play, 4 vols., Set 5. 2001. (Mini Board Bks.). (Illus.). 12p. bds. 12.95 (978-0-7548-0874-9(2)) Anness Publishing GBR. *Dist:* National Bk. Network.

MacKinnon, Debbie. Let's Play: I Can Do It. Sieveking, Anthea, illus. 1999. 8p. (J). (ps). 7.95 (978-0-316-64897-4(3)) Little, Brown Bks. for Young Readers.

Mattox, Wendy Ann. Babysitting Activities: Fun with Kids of All Ages. 2007. (Snap Books). (Illus.). 32p. (J). 25.26 (978-0-7368-6461-9(X)) Capstone Pr., Inc.

McDonough, Jerome. Users: An Ongoing Tragedy. 1999. (Young Adult Awareness Plays Ser.). 32p. (YA). pap. 4.00 (978-0-88680-459-6(0)) Clark, I. E. Pubns.

Meiners, Cheri J. Join in & Play. 2004. (Learning to Get Along Ser.). (Illus.). 40p. (J). (ps-3). pap. 10.95 (978-1-57542-152-0(6)) Free Spirit Publishing, Inc.

Nelson, Esther. Blocks Are to Build. Hirsch, Davida, ed. Behr, Joyce, illus. l.t. ed. 1999. 28p. (Orig.). (J). (gr. k-1). pap. 7.95 (978-0-945110-15-6(4)) Granny Pr.

Nelson, Robin. Playing Safely. 2005. (Pull Ahead Books). (Illus.). 32p. (J). pap. 5.95 (978-0-8225-2770-1(7) , Lerner Pubns.) Lerner Publishing Group.

Oppenheim, Joanne & Oppenheim, Stephanie. ¡A leer y jugar! con bebés y niños Pequeños. Auclair, Joan, illus. 2006. Tr. of Read It! Play It! with Babies & Toddlers. (SPA.). 102p. pap. 10.00 (978-0-9721050-5-7(0)) Oppenheim Toy Portfolio, Inc.

—Read It! Play It! with Babies & Toddlers. 2006. (Illus.). pap. 10.00 (978-0-9721050-4-0(2)) Oppenheim Toy Portfolio, Inc.

Petty, Kate. Playtime. 2006. (Illus.). 32p. (J). 8.95 (978-1-58728-546-2(0)); 14.95 (978-1-58728-549-3(5)) T&N Children's Publishing. (Two Can Publishing).

Pretend & Play Kitty. 2004. 10p. (J). (ps up). bds. (978-1-57151-735-7(9)) Playhouse Publishing.

Prince, Sarah. Playing. 1999. (ps-2). lib. bdg. 11.20 (978-0-613-30679-9(1)) Tandem Library Bks.

The Roach Approach, Don't Miss the Boat! Coloring & Activity Book. 2003. (J). 5.99 (978-0-9742997-3-0(1)) Wacky World Studios LLC.

Schumacher, Bev, creator. Play Action. 2005. (Illus.). (J). lib. bdg. (*978-0-9768706-1-6(4)) Learning Props.

Southwater Staff. Look & Learn: Play at Home. 2000. (Look & Learn Ser.). (Illus.). 32p. (ps). 7.95 (978-1-84215-049-8(9) , Southwater) Anness Publishing GBR. *Dist:* National Bk. Network.

—Outdoor Play: Look & Learn. 2000. (Look & Learn Ser.). (Illus.). 32p. (ps). 7.95 (978-1-84215-168-6(1) , Southwater) Anness Publishing GBR. *Dist:* National Bk. Network.

Stoppard, Miriam. Busy Day. 2006. (Let's Play Ser.). (Illus.). 14p. (J). bds. 8.99 (978-0-7566-1698-4(0)) Dorling Kindersley Publishing, Inc.

Wade, Lee. The Cheerios Halloween Play Book. Wade, Lee, illus. 2001. (Illus.). 14p. (J). 6.99 (978-0-689-84684-7(3) , Little Simon) Simon & Schuster Children's Publishing.

Weekly Reader Early Learning Library (Firm) Staff, contrib. by. Things I Play With. 2006. (Things in My World Ser.). (Illus.). 16p. (J). pap. (978-0-8368-6818-0(8)); lib. bdg. (978-0-8368-6811-1(0)) Stevens, Gareth Inc.

—Things I Play with: Las Cosas con Las Que Juego. 2006. (ENG & SPA.). (J). pap. (978-0-8368-7230-9(4) , Weekly Reader Early Learning Library) Stevens, Gareth Inc.

—Things I Play With (Las Cosas con las Que Juego) 2006. (ENG & SPA.). (J). lib. bdg. 17.27 (978-0-8368-7223-1(1) , Weekly Reader Early Learning Library) Stevens, Gareth Inc.

Wingate, P. I Can Woof, Quack, Moo. O'Neil, Rachel, illus. 2004. (My Carry-Around Action Bks.). 16p. (J). bds. 3.95 (978-0-7641-5735-6(3)) Barron's Educational Series, Inc.

PLAY—FICTION

Albee, Sarah. Clever Trevor. Billin-Frye, Paige, illus. 2003. (Science Solves It! Ser.). 32p. (J). 4.99 (978-1-57565-123-8(X)) Kane Pr., The.

—Clever Trevor. 2003. (gr. k-3). lib. bdg. 13.00 (978-0-613-79229-5(7)) Tandem Library Bks.

—Fun in the Sun. Williams, Sue, illus. 2006. (Step-By-Step Readers Ser.). (J). pap. (978-1-59939-058-1(2) , Reader's Digest Young Families, Inc.) Reader's Digest Children's Publishing, Inc.

Allen, J. J. Hello Kitty's Fun Friend Day! 2003. (Illus.). 32p. (J). pap. (978-0-439-44917-5(0)) Scholastic, Inc.

Allen, Marjorie N. & Rotner, Shelley. Changes. 1998. (J). pap. 4.95 (978-0-87628-168-0(4)) Ctr. for Applied Research in Education, The.

Allen, Marty. Let's Play Ball. Weichselbraun, Judann, illus. 1999. 32p. (J). (ps-6). 14.99 (978-0-9672972-0-0(6)) Kids Bks., Pubs.

Alley, R. W., illus. A Bowlful of Rain. 2006. (I'm Going to Read Ser.). 48p. (J). pap. 3.95 (978-1-4027-3087-0(X)) Sterling Publishing Co., Inc.

Anderson, Lynne. Charlie's Championships. ed. 2003. (Early Connections Ser.). (J). pap. 33.00 (978-1-4108-1370-1(3)) Benchmark Education Co.

Anderson, Peggy Perry. Joe on the Go. 2007. (Illus.). 32p. (J). (gr. 3-5). 16.00 (978-0-618-77331-2(2)) Houghton Mifflin Co.

Anglund, Joan Walsh. The Brave Cowboy. 2000. (Illus.). 40p. (J). (ps-3). 6.99 (978-0-7407-0649-3(7)) Andrews McMeel Publishing.

—Cowboy's Secret Life. Anglund, Joan Walsh, illus. anniv. ed. 2002. (Illus.). 40p. (gr. k-3). 6.95 (978-0-7407-2680-4(3)) Andrews McMeel Publishing.

Anholt, Catherine & Anholt, Laurence. Play. 2007. (Chimp & Zee Ser.). (Illus.). 22p. (J). bds. 3.95 (*978-1-84507-746-4(6)) Lincoln, Frances Ltd. GBR. *Dist:* Perseus Distribution.

Ansley, Frank & Wheeler, Lisa. Invasion of the Pig Sisters. Ansley, Frank, illus. 2006. (Fitch & Chip Ser.). (Illus.). 48p. (J). 14.95 (978-0-689-84953-4(2) , Atheneum) Simon & Schuster Children's Publishing.

April, Elyse. We Like to Move: Exercise Is Fun. Iverson, Diane, illus. 2006. 32p. (J). pap. 9.95 (978-1-890772-60-4(7)) Hohm Pr.

Arena, Felice & Kettle, Phil. Olympics. Cox, David, illus. 2004. (J). pap. (978-1-59336-374-1(5)) Mondo Publishing.

—Pirate Ship: By Felice Arena & Phil Kettle: Illustrated by Susy Boyer. Boyer, Susy, illus. 2004. (J). pap. (978-1-59336-362-8(1)) Mondo Publishing.

—Secret Agent Heroes. Vane, Mitch, illus. 2004. (J). pap. (978-1-59336-355-0(9)) Mondo Publishing.

Ashbe, Jeanne. Eso No Se Hace! 2003. (SPA.). 32p. (978-84-95150-35-6(2)) Corimbo, Editorial S.L.

At Play. 2003. (J). per. (978-1-57657-963-3(8)) Paradise Pr., Inc.

Ayres, Katherine. Matthew's Truck. Takahashi, Hideko, tr. Takahashi, Hideko, illus. 2005. (Super Sturdy Picture Books Ser.). 24p. (J). (gr. k). 8.99 (978-0-7636-2269-5(9)) Candlewick Pr.

Bader, Bonnie. Play Ball. Ruppert, Larry, illus. 2007. 24p. (J). pap. 3.99 (978-0-448-44466-6(6) , Grosset & Dunlap) Penguin Group (USA) Inc.

Baguley, Elizabeth. Meggie Moon. Mabire, Gregoire, illus. 2005. 28p. (J). (ps-ps). 16.00 (978-1-56148-474-4(1)) Good Bks.

Bailey, Debbie. Hagamos de Cuenta! Huszar, Susan, photos by. 1999. (Hablemos Ser.: Vol. 13). (SPA., Illus.). 14p. (J). (gr. k-ps). bds. 5.95 (978-1-55037-574-9(1)) Annick Pr., Ltd. CAN. *Dist:* Firefly Bks., Ltd.

—Let's Pretend. Huszar, Susan, photos by. 1999. (Talk-about-Bks.: Vol. 13). (Illus.). 14p. (J). (gr. k-ps). bds. 5.95 (978-1-55037-558-9(X)) Annick Pr., Ltd. CAN. *Dist:* Firefly Bks., Ltd.

Baker, Karle Wilson. The Garden of the Plynck (Illustrated Ed. 2006. (Illus.). pap. (*978-1-4065-0482-8(3)) Dodo Pr.

The Ball: KinderReaders Individual Title Six-Packs. (Kinderstarters Ser.). 8p. (ps-1). 21.00 (978-0-7635-8645-4(5)) Rigby Education.

Banks, Kate. Max's Dragon. Kulikov, Boris, illus. 2008. 32p. (J). 16.95 (*978-0-374-39921-4(2)) Farrar, Straus & Giroux.

Banyai, Istvan. Re-Zoom. 1998. (Picture Puffin Ser.). (Illus.). 64p. (J). (gr. k-3). pap. 7.99 (978-0-14-055694-0(X) , Puffin) Penguin Group (USA) Inc.

Barwin, Gary. Grandpa's Snowman. Macaulay, Kitty, illus. 2000. 24p. (J). (ps-1). 17.95 (978-1-55037-635-7(7)) Annick Pr., Ltd. CAN. *Dist:* Firefly Bks., Ltd.

Batchelor, Louise. Whoops! (Illus.). 21p. (978-1-84089-079-2(7) , 26143, Zero to Ten, Limited) Evans Publishing Group.

Bauer, Marion Dane. One Brown Bunny. Bates, Ivan, illus. 2008. (J). (*978-0-439-68010-3(7) , Orchard Bks.) Scholastic, Inc.

Baumgarten, Josephine & Baumgarten, Michael. My Baby Monsters & I went to the Park. 2005. 32p. pap. 14.99 (978-1-4116-6348-0(9)) Lulu.com.

Beaty, Andrea. When Giants Come to Play. Hawkes, Kevin, illus. 2006. 32p. (J). (ps-3). 16.95 (978-0-8109-5759-6(0)) Abrams, Harry N. , Inc.

Bedford, David. Big Bears Can! Hansen, Gaby, illus. 2007. 18p. (J). (ps-k). bds. 6.95 (*978-1-58925-826-6(6) , tiger tales) ME Media LLC.

Bedford, David. It's My Turn! 2000. 12.75 (978-0-606-20731-7(7)) Tandem Library Bks.

Bedford, David & Field, Elaine. It's My Turn! 2001. (Illus.). 30p. (J). (ps-k). 5.95 (978-1-58925-351-3(5) , tiger tales) ME Media LLC.

Bella & Rosie Play Hide & Seek. 2003. (J). (978-1-932570-11-3(X)) Literacy Footprints Inc.

Benfanti, Russell. Hide, Clyde! 2002. (Illus.). 160p. (J). 16.95 (978-0-316-91204-4(2)) Little, Brown Bks. for Young Readers.

Bennett, Maureen A. Oliver & Audrey's Big Sand Box. Bennett, Exlus S., illus. 1998. (Oliver & Audrey Otter's Adventures Presents Ser.: Vol. 2). 46p. (J). (ps-6). pap. 14.95 (978-1-929914-02-9(4) , Ruf-Fur Pubns) Megaverse City Studios.

Bernstein, Margery. My Brother, the Pest. Handelman, Dorothy, photos by. 1999. (Real Kids Readers Ser.). (Illus.). 32p. (gr. k-2). (J). pap. 4.99 (978-0-7613-2080-7(6)); lib. bdg. 18.90 (978-0-7613-2055-5(5)) Lerner Publishing Group. (Millbrook Pr.).

—My Brother, the Pest. 1999. (J). (978-0-606-19164-7(X)); lib. bdg. 11.80 (978-0-613-16773-4(2)) Tandem Library Bks.

Black, Robyn Hood. Sir Mike. Murphy, David, illus. (J). (gr. k-2). 2006. 32p. pap. 4.95 (978-0-516-25020-5(5)); 2005. 31p. 19.50 (978-0-516-24862-2(6)) Scholastic Library Publishing. (Children's Pr.).

Blackaby, Susan. Jen Plays. Cole, Mernie Gallagher, illus. 2005. (Read-It! Readers Ser.). 32p. (J). (gr. k-3). 18.60 (978-1-4048-1008-2(0)) Picture Window Bks.

—Juanita Juega. Cole, Mernie Gallagher, illus. 2006. (Read-It! Readers en Espanol Ser.).Tr. of Jen Plays. (SPA.). 32p. (J). (ps-3). 19.95 (978-1-4048-1652-7(6)) Picture Window Bks.

—El Lugar de Luis. Gallagher-Cole, Mernie, illus. 2006. (Read-It! Readers en Espanol Ser.).Tr. of Place for Mike. (SPA.). 32p. (J). (ps-3). 19.95 (978-1-4048-1688-6(7)) Picture Window Bks.

—A Place for Mike. Cole, Mernie Gallagher, illus. 2005. (Read-It! Readers Ser.). 32p. (J). (gr. k-3). 18.60 (978-1-4048-1012-9(9)) Picture Window Bks.

Blake, Michel. Let's Play: Easy-Open Board Book. 2007. (Easy-Open Ser.). (Illus.). 16p. (J). (ps). bds. 5.99 (978-0-7636-3369-1(0)) Candlewick Pr.

—Out to Play. Candlewick Press Staff, illus. Gant, Trish, photos by. 2005. 16p. (J). (gr. k-ps). bds. 5.99 (978-0-7636-2767-6(4)) Candlewick Pr.

Blanchet, Sylvia Roberge. Rachel's Adventure Ring. St. Aubin, Bruno, illus. 2005. (Read-It! Readers Ser.). 32p. (J). (gr. k-3). 18.60 (978-1-4048-1070-9(6)) Picture Window Bks.

Boland, Janice. Zipers. de la Vega, Eida, tr. Pfeiffer, Judith, illus. 2001. (Books for Young Learners).Tr. of Zippers. (SPA.). 8p. (J). (gr. k-2). pap. 5.00 (978-1-57274-453-0(7) , 2919) Owen, Richard C. Pubs., Inc.

—Zippers. Pfeiffer, Judith, illus. 2003. (Books for Young Learners). 8p. (J). pap. 20.00 net. (978-1-57274-700-5(5) , BB2220) Owen, Richard C. Pubs., Inc.

Bonnell, Kris. Playtime. 2005. (J). 3.75 (978-1-933727-13-4(6)) Reading Reading Bks., LLC.

Book Company Staff. Moon Dance. Lassen, Christian R., illus. 2005. (Sparkle Bks.). (J). (gr. 4-11). bds. 14.95 (978-1-74047-355-2(8)) Book Co. Publishing Pty, Ltd., The AUS. *Dist:* Penton Overseas, Inc.

Brabham, Barbara. Donkey Tales — Color with Paco! [English/Spanish Versions]. 2006. (J). 2.95 (*978-1-882185-86-3(2)) Cornerstone Publishing, Inc.

Branson, Terri. Tyler on the Moon. 2007. (Illus.). 24p. (J). 7.98 (*978-0-9794660-9-0(1)) Dragonfly Publishing, Inc.

Breen, Susan. Come Play at the Park! 1999. (Disney Ser.). (Illus.). 16p. (J). (ps). pap. 4.99 (978-0-307-10527-1(X)) Whitman Publishing LLC.

Brennan, Linda Crotta. Flannel Kisses. Takabayashi, Mari, illus. 2006. 32p. (J). (gr. k-3). 6.95 (978-0-618-73752-9(9)) Houghton Mifflin Co. Trade & Reference Div.

Brimner, Larry Dane. Summer Fun. Tripp, Christine, illus. 2003. (Rookie Choices Ser.). 32p. (J). (gr. 1-2). 20.50 (978-0-516-22548-7(0) , Children's Pr.) Scholastic Library Publishing.

Brooks, Regina. Never Finished, Never Done! Borgella, Marjorie, illus. 2004. 32p. (J). lib. bdg. 15.00 (*978-1-4242-0229-4(9)) Fitzgerald Bks.

Brooks, Yvonne & Grant, Steven. Meet the Goat Kids. l.t. ed. 2006. (Illus.). 32p. (J). 14.95 (*978-0-9791021-0-3(3) , 978-0-9791021-0-3) Lotus Pond Media.

Brown, Jo. Hoppity Skip Little Chick. 2005. (Illus.). 32p. (J). 15.95 (978-1-58925-045-1(1) , tiger tales) ME Media LLC.

Brown, Susan Taylor. Oliver's Must-Do List. Sullivan, Mary, illus. 2005. 32p. (J). (ps-3). 15.95 (978-1-59078-198-2(8)) Boyds Mills Pr.

Buchanan, Sue & Shafer, Dana. Mud Pie Annie. 2004. (Illus.). 32p. (J). pap. 6.99 (978-0-310-70816-2(8)) Zonderkidz.

Butler, John. Ten in the Meadow. 2006. (Illus.). 32p. (J). 15.95 (978-1-56145-372-6(2)) Peachtree Pubs., Ltd.

Capucilli, Alyssa Satin. Biscuit & the Little Pup. Schories, Pat, illus. 2008. (My First I Can Read Bks.). 32p. (J). pap. 3.99 (*978-0-06-074172-3(4) , Harper Trophy) HarperCollins Pubs.

—Biscuit Wants to Play. Schories, Pat, illus. (My First I Can Read Bks.). 32p. (J). (ps-k). 2002. pap. 3.99 (978-0-06-444315-9(9) , Harper Trophy); 2001. 15.99 (978-0-06-028069-7(7)); 2001. lib. bdg. 15.89 (978-0-06-028070-3(0)) HarperCollins Pubs.

—Biscuit Wants to Play. 2002. (gr. k-3). lib. bdg. 11.80 (978-0-613-44508-5(2)) Tandem Library Bks.

—Biscuit's Pet & Play Christmas. Schories, Pat & Young, Mary O'Keefe, illus. 2006. (Biscuit Ser.). 12p. (J). 6.99 (978-0-06-009470-6(2) , Harper Festival) HarperCollins Pubs.

Child, Lauren. My School Play. Child, Lauren, illus. 2006. (Charlie & Lola Ser.). 16p. (J). (ps-1). 4.99 (978-0-448-44256-3(6) , Grosset & Dunlap) Penguin Group (USA) Inc.

Church, Caroline Jayne. Woof's Playtime: Woof Touch-and-Feel. Church, Caroline Jayne, illus. 2007. (Illus.). 10p. (J). (ps). 5.95 (*978-0-8027-9621-9(4)) Walker & Co.

Cimarusti, Marie Torres. Peek-a-Moo! Peterson, Stephanie, illus. 1998. (Lift-the-Flap Ser.). 10p. (J). (ps-k). 10.99 (978-0-525-46083-1(7) , Dutton Juvenile) Penguin Group (USA) Inc.

Ciminera, Siobhan. The Coolest Snowman EVER! Petrosino, Tamara, illus. 2007. 16p. (J). (ps-2). pap. 4.99 (*978-0-8431-2677-8(9) , Price Stern Sloan) Penguin Group (USA) Inc.

Clammer, Virginia Grant. The Big Box. Handelman, Dorothy, photos by. 1999. (Real Kids Readers Ser.). (Illus.). 32p. (gr. k-1). (J). pap. 4.99 (978-0-7613-2049-4(0)); lib. bdg. 18.90 (978-0-7613-2024-1(5)) Lerner Publishing Group. (Millbrook Pr.).

—The Big Box. 1999. (J). 11.79 (978-0-606-19146-3(1)) Tandem Library Bks.

—Big Box. 1999. (ps-2). lib. bdg. 13.00 (978-0-613-16606-5(X)) Tandem Library Bks.

Clarke, Lyndia A. Tidy up Tommy. Clarke, Lyndia A., illus. 2006. (Illus.). 28p. (J). per. 19.95 (978-1-59453-971-8(5) , 3513, Airleaf Publishing) Airleaf Publishing & Bookselling.

Cocca-Leffler, Maryann. Princess for a Day. 1998. (All Aboard Reading Ser.: Level 1). (Illus.). 32p. (J). (ps-1). pap. 3.99 (978-0-448-41604-5(2) , Grosset & Dunlap) Penguin Group (USA) Inc.

Come & Play Cat. 2000. (J). (978-1-58453-126-5(6)) Pioneer Valley Educational Pr., Inc.

Come Out to Play. (J). 7.95 (978-0-8126-0082-7(7)) Open Court Publishing Co.

Coristine, Philip. Serena & the Wild Doll. Gukova, Julia, illus. 2000. 32p. (J). (ps-2). pap. 6.95 (978-1-55037-648-7(9)); lib. bdg. 19.95 (978-1-55037-649-4(7)) Annick Pr., Ltd. CAN. *Dist:* Firefly Bks., Ltd.

Costales, A. Lupe Vargas & Her Super Best Friend: Lupe Vargas y su super mejor Amiga. 2006. (ENG & SPA., Illus.). 32p. (J). 15.95 (978-0-87358-888-1(6) , Luna Rising) Northland Publishing.

Coulton, Mia. Danny & Abby Play Tag. Coulton, Mia, photos by. 2004. (J). 4.95 (978-0-9746475-3-1(5)) Maryruth Bks., Inc.

Courtin, Thierry. L imagier de T Choupi. 19.95 (978-2-09-202283-2(0)) Nathan, Fernand FRA. *Dist:* Distribooks, Inc.

Cousineau-Peiffer, Trisha. Have You Ever Heard of a Rainbow Farm. Everett-Hawkes, Bonnie, illus. 2006. 32p. (J). 12.95 ***(*978-0-9792084-1-6(6))*** Dream Ridge Pr.

—Have You Ever Heard of a Rainbow Farm: The Missing Color Kittens. Everett-Hawkes, Bonnie, illus. 2007. 48p. (J). per. 15.95 ***(*978-0-9792084-2-3(4))*** Dream Ridge Pr.

Cousins, Lucy. A Maisy le Gusta Jugar. 2002. (Illus.). (J). (CAT.). 14p. bds. 7.95 (978-84-95040-88-6(3)); (SPA., 64p. 7.99 (978-84-95040-87-9(5) , RR6586) Serres, Ediciones, S. L. ESP. *Dist:* Lectorum Pubns., Inc.

—Jugando con Maisy. 2002. (Illus.). 16p. (J). (SPA.). (978-84-95040-44-2(1) , RR8303); (CAT., 10.95 (978-84-95040-45-9(X)) Serres, Ediciones, S. L. ESP. *Dist:* Lectorum Pubns., Inc.

—Playtime, Maisy! Cousins, Lucy, illus. 2001. (Maisy Bks.). (Illus.). 6p. (J). (gr. k-ps). pap. 6.99 (978-0-7636-1602-1(8)) Candlewick Pr.

Cowell, Cressida. That Rabbit Belongs to Emily Brown. Layton, Neal, illus. 2007. 40p. (ps-2). 16.99 (978-1-4231-0645-6(8)) Hyperion Bks. for Children.

Coyle, Carmela LaVigna. Do Princesses Scrape Their Knees? 2006. (Illus.). 32p. (J). 15.95 (978-0-87358-909-3(2)) Northland Publishing.

Crews, Donald. Cloudy Day Sunny Day. 2003. (Green Light Readers Level 1 Ser.). (Illus.). 24p. (J). pap. 3.95 (978-0-15-204850-1(2) , Green Light Readers) Harcourt Children's Bks.

—Cloudy Day Sunny Day. 1999. (ps-2). lib. bdg. 11.80 (978-0-613-62277-6(4)) Tandem Library Bks.

Curry, Don L. Fall Leaves. Jasinski, Aaron, illus. (Rookie Reader Skill Set Ser.). (J). (gr. k-2). 2005. 24p. pap. 4.95 (978-0-516-26831-6(7)); 2004. 23p. 19.50 (978-0-516-25904-8(0)) Scholastic Library Publishing. (Children's Pr.).

—Fall Leaves. Jasinski, Aaron, illus. 2005. 24p. (J). (ps-ps). lib. bdg. 12.15 (978-0-606-33166-1(2)) Tandem Library Bks.

Dadoo Stops Playing. . . 2003. (J). per. 5.50 (978-0-9742714-0-8(3)) I C Creative, Inc.

Darling, Helen. Hide-n-seek Monday. Glickstein, Jennifer, ed. Sona and Jacob, illus. 2007. (J). 10.00 ***(*978-0-9797674-0-1(7))*** My Darling-Tots Pubns.

Davis, Jacky. Ladybug Girl. Soman, David, illus. 2008. 40p. (J). (ps). 16.99 ***(*978-0-8037-3195-0(7)*** , Dial) Penguin Group (USA) Inc.

Day, Alexandra. Follow Carl! Day, Alexandra, illus. 1998. (Carl Ser.). (Illus.). 32p. (J). (ps-1). 12.95 (978-0-374-34380-4(2) , Farrar, Straus & Giroux (BYR)) Farrar, Straus & Giroux.

DeBear, Kirsten. Be Quiet Marina! Dwight, Laura, photos by. 2001. (Illus.). 40p. (J). (ps-3). 16.95 (978-1-887734-79-0(1)) Star Bright Bks., Inc.

Delval, Marie He. Lili et Mistigri jouent a Cache. (FRE.) pap. 14.95 (978-2-227-75602-1(0)) Bayard Editions FRA. *Dist:* Distribooks, Inc.

Derby, Sally. Mi Escalera. de la Vega, Eida, tr. Burrowes, Adjoa J., illus. 1998. (SPA & ENG.). 32p. (J). (ps-3). 15.95 (978-1-880000-74-8(1) , LW7547); pap. 6.95 (978-1-880000-75-5(X) , LW7771) Lee & Low Bks., Inc.

—My Steps. Burrowes, Adjoa J., illus. 1999. 32p. (J). (gr. 1-4). (978-1-880000-84-7(9)); (ps-4). 15.95 (978-1-880000-40-3(7)) Lee & Low Bks., Inc.

deRubertis, Barbara. Perky Otter. Cockrille, Eva V., illus. 1998. (Let's Read Together Ser.). 32p. (J). (ps-3). pap. 4.95 (978-1-57565-045-6(2)) Kane Pr., The.

Dewan, Ted. Crispin: The Pig Who Had It All. 2002. (gr. k-3). lib. bdg. 15.30 (978-0-613-89780-8(3)) Tandem Library Bks.

Don't Do That, Dexter! 2006. 16p. (J). pap. 1.99 (978-0-7847-1690-8(0) , 02992) Standard Publishing.

Dorling Kindersley Publishing Staff. Bedtime Peekaboo! 2006. (Illus.). 12p. (J). bds. 6.99 (978-0-7566-1622-9(0)) Dorling Kindersley Publishing, Inc.

Doyle, Charlotte. The Bouncing, Dancing, Galloping ABC. Gorton, Julia, illus. 2006. 32p. (J). (ps-1). 10.99 (978-0-399-23778-2(X) , Putnam Juvenile) Penguin Group (USA) Inc.

Doyle, Charlotte L. You Can't Catch Me. Litzinger, Rosanne, illus. 1998. (Growing Tree Ser.). 24p. (J). (gr. 3 up). 9.95 (978-0-694-01038-7(3) , Harper Festival) HarperCollins Pubs.

Earley, Catherine. Outside Fun, 1. Earley, Catherine, ed. Art&Script, illus. 2005. 12p. (J). 6.95 (978-0-9769589-1-8(0)) Naynay Bks.

Eaton, Deborah. The Rainy Day Grump. Handelman, Dorothy, photos by. 1998. (Real Kids Readers Ser.). (Illus.). 32p. (gr. k-2). (J). pap. 4.99 (978-0-7613-2043-2(1)); lib. bdg. 18.90 (978-0-7613-2018-0(0)) Lerner Publishing Group. (Millbrook Pr.).

Eaton, Deborah J. My Wild Woolly. Karas, G. Brian, illus. 2005. (Green Light Readers Level 2 Ser.). 24p. (J). (ps-ps). 12.95 (978-0-15-205148-8(1)); pap. 3.95 (978-0-15-205147-1(3)) Harcourt Trade Pubs.

Eaton, Maxwell. Adventures of Max & Pinky: Best Buds. 2006. (Adventures of Max & Pinky Ser.). (Illus.). 32p. (J). (gr. k-3). 12.99 (978-0-375-83803-3(1) , Knopf Bks. for Young Readers) Random Hse. Children's Bks.

—Best Buds. 2006. (Adventures of Max & Pinky Ser.). (Illus.). 32p. (J). (gr. k-3). lib. bdg. 14.99 (978-0-375-93803-0(6) , Knopf Bks. for Young Readers) Random Hse. Children's Bks.

Ehrlich, H. M. Gotcha, Louie! Bolam, Emily, illus. 2002. 32p. (J). (gr. k-3). 15.00 (978-0-618-19549-7(1) , Walter Lorraine) Houghton Mifflin Co. Trade & Reference Div.

Ellery, Amanda. If I Had a Dragon. Ellery, Tom, illus. 2006. 40p. (J). (ps-2). 14.95 (978-1-4169-0924-8(9) , Simon & Schuster Children's Publishing) Simon & Schuster Children's Publishing.

Ellery, Tom, et al. If I Had a Dragon. Ellery, Tom & Ellery, Amanda, illus. 2006. (ENG & SPA.). (J). 12.99 (978-1-933032-16-0(2)); pap. 3.99 (978-1-933032-17-7(0)) Lectorum Pubns., Inc.

Falwell, Cathryn. Where's Nicky? 1998. (Illus.). 26p. (J). (gr. k-ps). bds. 4.95 (978-0-395-92953-7(9) , Clarion Bks.) Houghton Mifflin Co. Trade & Reference Div.

Faulkenberry, Lauren. What Do Animals Do on the Weekend? Adventures from A to Z. Faulkenberry, Lauren, illus. 2002. (Illus.). 64p. (gr. k-3). 17.95 (978-0-9708972-4-4(3)) Novello Festival Pr.

Ficocelli, Elizabeth. Kid Tea. Dibley, Glin, illus. 2007. 40p. (J). (ps-2). 14.99 (978-0-7614-5333-8(4)) Cavendish, Marshall Corp.

Finger Puppet Playset Pet Store. 2005. (J). (978-1-59292-068-6(3)) SoftPlay, Inc.

Firth, Barbara, illus. You & Me, Little Bear. 2002. (Little Bear Picture Bks.). (J). 14.79 (978-0-7587-4058-8(1)) Book Wholesalers, Inc.

Fleming, Maria. Jumping Jill Went down the Hill. Weissman, Bart, illus. 2002. (Word Family Tales Ser.). 16p. (ps-2). pap. 2.95 (978-0-439-26267-5(4)) Scholastic, Inc.

Fry, Sonali. Homeward Bound! A Magnetic Playbook. Fruchter, Jason, illus. 2004. (Dora the Explorer Ser.). 10p. (J). bds. 9.99 (978-0-689-86509-1(0) , Simon Spotlight/Nickelodeon) Simon & Schuster Children's Publishing.

Fudge, Keith. The Rainy Day Discovery. 2006. (J). per. 11.95 (978-1-889743-37-0(2)) Robbie Dean Pr.

Fuller, Bob. Tea for Two. 2007. (Paddywhack Lane Ser.). 24p. (J). pap. 3.99 (978-0-448-44509-0(3) , Grosset & Dunlap) Penguin Group (USA) Inc.

Gardiner, Lindsey. Here Come Poppy & Max. Gardiner, Lindsey, illus. 2000. (Illus.). 24p. (J). (ps-1). 12.95 (978-0-316-60346-1(5)) Little Brown & Co.

Gates, Josephine Scribner. The live dolls' play Days. Keep, Virginia, illus. 2007. 110p. (J). lib. bdg. 59.00 ***(*978-1-60304-008-2(0))*** Dollworks.

Gauthier, Gail. A Girl, a Boy, & a Monster Cat. Cepeda, Joe, illus. 2007. 96p. (J). (gr. 2-4). 14.99 (978-0-399-24689-0(4) , Putnam Juvenile) Penguin Group (USA) Inc.

Gauthier, Gail. A Girl, A Boy, & Three Robbers. Cepeda, Joe, illus. 2008. 64p. (J). (gr. 1-3). 14.99 ***(*978-0-399-24690-6(8)*** , Putnam Juvenile) Penguin Group (USA) Inc.

Gay, Marie-Louise. Stella, Queen of the Snow. ed. 2004. (J). (ps-1). spiral bd. (978-0-616-08493-9(5)) Canadian National Institute for the Blind/Institut National Canadien pour les Aveugles.

—Stella, Queen of the Snow. Gay, Marie-Louise, illus. 2000. (Stella Ser.). (Illus.). 32p. (J). (ps-k). 15.95 (978-0-88899-404-2(4)) Groundwood Bks. CAN. *Dist:* Perseus Distribution.

—Stella, Reine des Neiges. ed. 2004. (FRE., Illus.). (J). (gr. k-3). spiral bd. (978-0-616-14596-8(9)) Canadian National Institute for the Blind/Institut National Canadien pour les Aveugles.

Gay, Marie-Louise, illus. Stella, Queen of the Snow. braille ed. 2004. (J). (ps-1). spiral bd. (978-0-616-08492-2(7)) Canadian National Institute for the Blind/Institut National Canadien pour les Aveugles.

George, Jean Craighead. Snow Bear. 2003. (gr. k-3). lib. bdg. 14.15 (978-0-613-75033-2(0)) Tandem Library Bks.

Gilbert in the Snow. 2005. (J). (978-1-58453-297-2(1)) Pioneer Valley Educational Pr., Inc.

Gillis, Jennifer B. What Do You Say? 2006. (Reader's Clubhouse Set B Ser.). (Illus.). 24p. (J). pap. 3.99 (978-0-7641-3298-8(9)) Barron's Educational Series, Inc.

Glassman, Jackie. Play Day. 2000. (ps-2). lib. bdg. 11.80 (978-0-613-32924-8(4)) Tandem Library Bks.

Gliori, Debi. Tickly under There. Gliori, Debi, illus. 2002. (Illus.). 4p. (J). (ps-k). bds. 5.95 (978-0-439-24404-6(8) , Orchard Bks.) Scholastic, Inc.

Godwin, Laura. Happy & Honey. Chapman, Jane, illus. 2001. (Happy Honey Ser.: Vol. 1). 32p. (J). pap. 3.99 (978-0-689-84235-1(X) , Aladdin) Simon & Schuster Children's Publishing.

—Happy & Honey. 2001. (gr. k-3). lib. bdg. 11.80 (978-0-613-36968-8(8)) Tandem Library Bks.

—Happy & Honey: Honey Helps. 2001. (gr. k-3). lib. bdg. 11.80 (978-0-613-36969-5(6)) Tandem Library Bks.

Goldsby, Katherine. Digging to China. Wordsworth, Viki, illus. 1999. (Books for Young Learners). 12p. (J). (gr. k-2). pap. 5.00 (978-1-57274-255-0(0)) Owen, Richard C. Pubs., Inc.

Gorbachev, Valeri. Big Little Elephant. 2005. (Illus.). 32p. (J). (ps-ps). 16.00 (978-0-15-205195-2(3) , Harcourt Children's Bks) Harcourt Children's Bks.

Graves, Keith. The Unexpectedly Bad Hair of Barcelona Smith. Graves, Keith, illus. 2006. (Illus.). 32p. (J). (ps). 16.99 (978-0-399-24273-1(2) , Philomel) Penguin Group (USA) Inc.

Gray, Kes. Duperball. Mould, Chris, illus. 2006. (Read-It! Chapter Books). 48p. (J). lib. bdg. ***(*978-1-4048-3118-6(5)*** , 1265805) Picture Window Bks.

Gray, Rita. The Wild Little Horse. Wolff, Ashley, illus. 2005. 32p. (J). (ps-ps). 15.99 (978-0-525-47455-5(2) , Dutton Juvenile) Penguin Group (USA) Inc.

Green, Corey. Managing Stan. 2007. 162p. (J). 16.95 ***(*978-1-934437-01-8(8));*** pap. 7.99 ***(*978-1-934437-02-5(6))*** Abligio Bks.

Grindley, Sally & Ellis, Andy. Can We Play Too, Piglittle? 2000. (Toddler Bks.). (Illus.). 20p. (J). (ps). pap. 4.95 (978-0-7641-1582-0(0)) Barron's Educational Series, Inc.

Gritton, Steve. ... & Then I... 2007. (J). 17.95 ***(*978-0-9795361-1-3(1))*** Bad Frog Art/SMG Bks.

Groves. Mud Cake, Bk. 3A. Date not set. (Illus.). 16p. (J). pap. 129.15 (978-0-582-18794-8(X)) Addison-Wesley Longman, Ltd. GBR. *Dist:* Trans-Atlantic Pubns., Inc.

Gutierrez, Akemi. The Mummy & Other Adventures of Sam & Alice. 2005. (Illus.). 64p. (J). (gr. k-3). 16.00 (978-0-618-50761-0(2)) Houghton Mifflin Co. Trade & Reference Div.

—The Pirate & Other Adventures of Sam & Alice. Gutierrez, Akemi, illus. 2007. (Illus.). 64p. (J). (gr. k-3). 17.00 (978-0-618-73737-6(5)) Houghton Mifflin Co.

Gutman, Dan. Miss Small Is off the Wall! Paillot, Jim, illus. 2005. (My Weird School Ser.). 112p. (J). lib. bdg. 15.89 (978-0-06-074519-6(3)); pap. 3.99 (978-0-06-074518-9(5) , Harper Trophy) HarperCollins Pubs.

—Miss Small Is off the Wall! Paillot, Jim, illus. 2005. 96p. (J). (gr. 2-5). lib. bdg. 11.19 (978-0-606-33326-9(6)) Tandem Library Bks.

Halpern, Julie. Toby & the Snowflakes. Cordell, Matthew R., illus. 2004. 32p. (J). (gr. k-3). tchr. ed. 15.00 (978-0-618-42004-9(5)) Houghton Mifflin Co. Trade & Reference Div.

Hans, Marie-Pierre. Mister William. 2007. (J). bds. 13.50 ***(*978-1-59692-237-2(0))*** MacAdam/Cage Publishing, Inc.

Harcourt School Publishers Staff. Can We Play Now: Take-Home Book. 1999. (Collections Ser.). (Illus.). (J). pap. 1.90 (978-0-15-317206-9(1)) Harcourt Schl. Pubs.

—On a Raft: On Level. 3rd ed. 2002. (Trophies Reading Program Ser.). (Illus.). (J). pap. 3.20 (978-0-15-322976-3(4)) Harcourt Schl. Pubs.

—So Say the Little Monkeys: LIbrary Book. 1999. (Collections Ser.). (Illus.). pap. 14.90 (978-0-15-313405-0(4)) Harcourt Schl. Pubs.

—What a Great Team! 3rd ed. 2002. (Trophies English Language Learners Ser.). (Illus.). (J). pap. 4.10 (978-0-15-327580-7(4)) Harcourt Schl. Pubs.

Harris, Joel Chandler. Jump on Over! The Adventures of Brer Rabbit & His Family. Moser, Barry, illus. 1998. 48p. (J). pap. 8.00 (978-0-15-201707-1(0)) Harcourt Children's Bks.

Hawkins, Karen. Splish, Splash, Splish, Splash. 2002. 15.00 (978-0-8059-5578-1(X)) Dorrance Publishing Co., Inc.

Heap, Sue, illus. What Shall We Play ? 2006. 28p. (J). 9.95 (978-1-59764-215-6(0)) New Line Bks.

Heape, David R. That's What Friends Do. l.t. ed. 2006. (ENG., Illus.). 28p. per. 9.95 ***(*978-1-4327-0177-2(0))*** Outskirts Press, Inc.

Heide, Iris van der. The Red Chalk. Tolman, Marije, tr. from DUT. Tolman, Marije, illus. 2006. 24p. (J). (ps-k). 19.95 (978-1-932425-79-6(9) , Lemniscaat) Boyds Mills Pr.

Henkes, Kevin. Oh! Dronzek, Laura, illus. 1999. 24p. (J). (ps-k). 16.99 (978-0-688-17053-0(6)) HarperCollins Pubs.

Herman, Gail. Chutes & Ladders: The Magical Tree House Adventure. 2003. (Illus.). 12p. (J). pap. 9.95 (978-0-7624-1565-6(7) , Running Pr. Kids) Running Pr. Bk. Pubs.

—School Play Surprise. 2007. (Hello Reader! Ser.). (Illus.). 32p. (J). pap. 3.99 (978-0-439-78809-0(9)) Scholastic, Inc.

Hill, Eric. Spot Goes to the Beach. Hill, Eric, illus. 2005. (Illus.). 22p. (J). (ps-1). bds. 6.99 (978-0-399-24362-2(3) , Putnam Juvenile) Penguin Group (USA) Inc.

Hill, Eric. Spot's Playtime Pop-up. Hill, Eric, illus. 2007. (Spot (Hardcover) Ser.). (Illus.). 12p. (J). (ps-k). 14.99 ***(*978-0-399-25019-4(0)*** , Putnam Juvenile) Penguin Group (USA) Inc.

Hoban, Russell. How Tom Beat Captain Najork. Blake, Quentin, illus. 2006. 32p. (J). pap. 7.95 ***(*978-1-56792-322-3(4))*** Godine, David R. Pub.

Hoffman, Sanford. Too Much Tooting. 2006. (I'm Going to Read Ser.). (Illus.). 32p. (J). pap. 3.95 (978-1-4027-3680-3(0)) Sterling Publishing Co., Inc.

Hofmeister, Alan, et al. Fun with the Sheet. (Reading for All Learners Ser.). (Illus.). (J). pap. (978-1-56861-115-0(3)) Swift Learning Resources.

—In the Mud. (Reading for All Learners Ser.). (Illus.). (J). pap. (978-1-56861-127-3(7)) Swift Learning Resources.

—Will We Win? (Reading for All Learners Ser.). (Illus.). (J). pap. (978-1-56861-110-5(2)) Swift Learning Resources.

Hogan, Mary. Let's Play with Winnie the Pooh. 1999. (Disney's Winnie the Pooh Ser.). (Illus.). 10p. (J). (ps-3). 9.99 (978-0-7364-0185-2(7)) Mouse Works.

Hollon, Frank. Glitter Girl & the Crazy Cheese. Dulemba, Elizabeth O., illus. 2006. 32p. (J). 14.95 (978-1-59692-137-5(4)) MacAdam/Cage Publishing, Inc.

Honeywood, Varnette P., illus. The Best Way to Play. 2002. (Little Bill Ser.). (J). 11.91 (978-0-7587-0983-7(8)) Book Wholesalers, Inc.

Hope, Laura Lee. Freddie & Flossie. 2006. (Ready-To-Read Ser.). (J). (ps-2). 21.35 (978-1-59961-095-5(7)) Spotlight.

—Freddie & Flossie & Snap. Pyle, Chuck, illus. 2005. (Ready-To-Read Ser.). 32p. (J). pap. 3.99 (978-1-4169-0267-6(8) , Aladdin) Simon & Schuster Children's Publishing.

—Freddie & Flossie & Snap. 2006. (Ready-To-Read Ser.). (J). (ps-2). 21.35 (978-1-59961-096-2(5)) Spotlight.

Howard-Parham, Pam. Playing on the Playground. Crowell, Knox, illus. l.t. ed. 2005. (Hrl Little Book Ser.). (J). (gr. k up). pap. 10.95 (978-1-57332-336-9(5)); pap. 10.95 (978-1-57332-335-2(7)) HighReach Learning, Inc.

—Spending Time Outdoors. Teeple, Jackie, illus. l.t. ed. 2005. (Hrl Big Book Ser.). (J). (gr. k up). pap. 10.95 (978-1-57332-333-8(0)); pap. 10.95 (978-1-57332-334-5(9)) HighReach Learning, Inc.

Howe, Deborah & Howe, James. Teddy Bear's Scrapbook. Bush, Timothy, illus. 2001. (Ready-for-Chapters Ser.). 80p. (J). (gr. 2-5). pap. 3.99 (978-0-689-84483-6(2) , Aladdin) Simon & Schuster Children's Publishing.

Hubbell, Patricia. Pots & Pans. deGroat, Diane, illus. 1998. (Growing Tree Ser.). 24p. (J). (ps up). 9.99 (978-0-694-01072-1(3)) HarperCollins Pubs.

Hudelhoff, Allen H. Cats & Kids. 2002. 2. (Illus.). 32p. pap. 4.99 (978-0-7613-1783-8(X) , Millbrook Pr.) Lerner Publishing Group.

—Cats & Kids. Green, Anne Canevari, illus. 2002. (Silly Millies Ser.). 32p. (J). (gr. k-2). pap. 4.99 (978-0-7613-2668-7(5) , Millbrook Pr.) Lerner Publishing Group.

—Cats & Kids. 2002. (gr. k-3). lib. bdg. 13.00 (978-0-613-55805-1(7)) Tandem Library Bks.

Hudson, Cheryl Willis. What Do You Know? Snow! Walker, Sylvia, illus. 2004. 32p. (J). (ps-ps). lib. bdg. 10.79 (978-0-606-30031-5(7)) Tandem Library Bks.

Hudson, Cheryl Willis. What Do You Know? SNOW! Walker, Sylvia, illus. 2004. 32p. (J). lib. bdg. 15.00 ***(*978-1-4242-0233-1(7))*** Fitzgerald Bks.

Hughes, Dean. Brad & Butter Play Ball! 1998. (Stepping Stone Bks.). (J). (978-0-606-13957-1(5)) Tandem Library Bks.

Hulme, Joy N. Bubble Trouble. Cressy, Mike, illus. 1999. (Rookie Reader Skill Set Ser.). 32p. (J). (gr. k-2). pap. 4.95 (978-0-516-26473-8(7)); (gr. 1-2). 19.50 (978-0-516-21584-6(1)) Scholastic Library Publishing. (Children's Pr.).

Hurd, Clement, illus. Johnny Lion's Rubber Boots. 2002. (Johnny Lion Ser.). (J). 12.34 (978-0-7587-5040-2(4)) Book Wholesalers, Inc.

Hurd, Edith Thacher. Johnny Lion's Rubber Boots. Hurd, Clement, illus. 2000. (I Can Read Bks.). 64p. (J). (gr. k-3). 14.95 (978-0-06-029337-6(3)) HarperCollins Pubs.

—Johnny Lion's Rubber Boots. Hurd, Clement, illus. 2001. (I Can Read Bks.). (J). (978-0-606-20746-1(5)) Tandem Library Bks.

Hurston, Nancy. The Enchanted Pixie Gardens: Hide & Seek. 2007. 32p. per. 13.99 ***(*978-1-59886-807-4(1))*** Tate Publishing & Enterprises, L.L.C.

I Love to Play. 2003. (J). per. (978-1-57657-962-6(X)) Paradise Pr., Inc.

I Want to Go to. . . the All-American Soap Box Derby Race. 2003. (Illus.). 40p. (J). per. 9.99 (978-0-9742667-0-1(1)) Creative Image Pubs.

Inches, Alison. Let's Play Sports! A Lift-the-Flap Story. Aikins, Dave, illus. 2007. (Dora the Explorer Ser.). 16p. (J). pap. 6.99 ***(*978-1-4169-3350-2(6)*** , Simon Spotlight/Nickelodeon) Simon & Schuster Children's Publishing.

Intrater, Roberta Grobel. Peek-a-Boo, You! Intrater, Roberta Grobel, photos by. 2nd rev. l.t. ed. 2005. (Illus.). 14p. (J). 14.99 (978-0-9764985-0-6(2)) 1212 Pr.

—Peek-a-Boo, You! Intrater, Roberta Grobel, photos by. 2002. (Illus.). 7p. (J). pap. 9.95 (978-0-439-33961-2(8) , Cartwheel Bks.) Scholastic, Inc.

It's a Bit Tricky: Individual Title Six-Packs. (gr. k-1). 23.00 (978-0-7635-9022-2(3)) Rigby Education.

It's Time to Play. 2002. 12p. (J). bds. 7.95 (978-1-84250-494-9(0) , Bright Sparks) Parragon, Inc.

Jacobson, David, illus. The Big Red Blanket. 2005. (J). (ps-k). lib. bdg. 11.15 (978-0-606-33864-6(0)) Tandem Library Bks.

Jaguar's Jungleberry Jamboree. 2001. (ps-2). lib. bdg. 9.80 (978-0-613-32702-2(0)) Tandem Library Bks.

James, Susan. Giddy-Up! Sing, Dance & Read with Me. 2000. (J). (ps-3). 12p. pap. 9.95 incl. audio (978-1-931127-45-5(X) , 986-001); 12p. pap. 14.95 incl. audio (978-1-931127-44-8(1) , 986-002); pap. 29.95 incl. audio compact disk (978-1-931127-46-2(8) , 986-003) Kindermusik International.

Jarrell, Pamela R. Who Is in the Backyard? Crowell, Knox, illus. l.t. ed. 2004. (Hrl Board Book Ser.). 8p. (J). (ps). pap. 10.95 (978-1-57332-281-2(4)) HighReach Learning, Inc.

Jarrett, Clare. Best Picnic Ever. Jarrett, Clare, illus. 2004. (Illus.). 32p. (J). (gr. k-k). 16.99 (978-0-7636-2370-8(9)) Candlewick Pr.

Jeram, Anita. All Together Now. Jeram, Anita, illus. 2005. (Illus.). 40p. (J). (gr. k-k). reprint ed. pap. 5.99 (978-0-7636-2690-7(2)) Candlewick Pr.

Johnson, Crockett. Ellen's Lion: Twelve Stories by Crockett Johnson. 2003. (Illus.). 64p. (J). (gr. 1-5). 12.95 (978-0-375-82288-9(7)); lib. bdg. 14.99 (978-0-375-92288-6(1)) Random Hse. Children's Bks. (Knopf Bks. for Young Readers).

Johnson, Linda Louisa. Needle in a Haystack. 2003. 78p. (YA). pap. 10.95 (978-0-7414-1541-7(0)) Infinity Publishing.

P Q R

Jolin, Dominique. Toupie Veut Jouer. braille ed. 2004. (FRE.). (J). (gr. 1). spiral bd., bds. (978-0-616-07270-7(8)) Canadian National Institute for the Blind/Institut National Canadien pour les Aveugles.

—Washington Wants to Play. Jolin, Dominique, illus. 1999. (Tickle Ser.). (Illus.). 16p. (J). (ps). bds. (978-1-894363-11-2(6)) Dominique & Friends.

Jones, Christianne C. & McKay, Caroline Jones, illus. Paulette's Friend. 2007. (Read-It! Readers Ser.). (J). 19.93 (978-1-4048-2398-3(0)) Picture Window Bks.

Kalar, Bonnie. Ann Paints & Plays. Spreen, Kathe, illus. Date not set. 12p. (J). (ps-2). pap. (978-1-891619-40-3(3)) Corona Pr.

Kathleen, Jo Ann. Buddy Can't Tie Shoes. l.t. ed. 2006. (ENG., Illus.). 28p. per. 9.95 (***978-1-4327-0238-0(6)***) Outskirts Press, Inc.

Katz, Danny. Little Lunch Four. Vane, Mitch, illus. 2005. (Little Lunch Ser.). 64p. (J). pap. (978-1-876372-84-2(2)) Black Dog Bks.

Kawai, Ritsuko. Balloon Adventure. Kawai, Ritsuko, illus. 2003. (Hamtaro Ser.). (Illus.). 16p. (YA). pap. 7.95 (978-1-56931-815-7(8)) Viz Media.

—Ham-Ham Party Vol. 1. Kawai, Ritsuko, illus. 2003. (Hamtaro Ser.). (Illus.). 16p. (YA). pap. 7.95 (978-1-56931-814-0(X)) Viz Media.

Kettle, Shey. Girl Pirates. Thomas, Meredith, illus. 2005. (Girlz Rock! Ser.). (J). pap. (978-1-59336-701-5(5)) Mondo Publishing.

King, Jennifer. A Bear for Breakfast. King, Jennifer, illus. 2007. (Illus.). 22p. (J). bds. 12.95 (***978-0-7696-5258-0(1)***, Gingham Dog Pr.) School Specialty Publishing.

Klein, Adria F. Max Goes to the Playground. Gallagher-Cole, Mernie, illus. 2007. (J). lib. bdg. (***978-1-4048-3681-5(0)***) Picture Window Bks.

Klingel, Cynthia Fitterer & Ballard, Peg. Fun! The Sound of Short U. 1999. (Wonder Books Phonics: Vowels Ser.). (Illus.). 24p. (J). (ps-3). 21.36 (978-1-56766-725-7(2)) Child's World, Inc.

Klingel, Cynthia Fitterer & Noyed, Robert B. Helen at Home & the Letter H. 2003. (Alphaphonics Ser.). (Illus.). 24p. (J). (ps-2). 21.36 (978-1-59296-098-9(7)) Child's World, Inc.

Koeppel, Ruth. Little Tikes Fun with Friends: Little Tikes Play House. 2006. (Little Tikes Ser.). 10p. (J). bds. 5.99 (978-0-7944-1148-0(7)) Reader's Digest Assn., Inc., The.

Koller, Jackie French. Bouncing on the Bed. Hines, Anna Grossnickle, illus. 1999. 32p. (J). (ps-k). 16.99 (978-0-531-33138-5(5)); pap. 15.95 (978-0-531-30138-8(9)) Scholastic, Inc. (Orchard Bks.).

Krauss, Ruth. I Can Fly. Blair, Mary, illus. 2003. (Little Golden Bks.). (J). (gr. k-k). 24p. 2.99 (978-0-307-00146-7(6), 312-12); 48p. 12.95 (978-0-307-10548-6(2)) Random Hse. Children's Bks. (Golden Bks.).

Labatt, Mary. Sam's Snowy Day. Sarrazin, Marisol, illus. 2005. 32p. (J). lib. bdg. 10.00 (***978-1-4242-1155-5(7)***) Fitzgerald Bks.

Ladd, Debbie. Puddles. Morejon, Tom, illus. 2006. 32p. (J). pap. 8.95 (978-0-9727615-4-3(3)) Deb on Air Bks.

Lakin, Patricia. Rainy Day! Nash, Scott, illus. 2007. 40p. (J). (ps-1). 16.99 (978-0-8037-3092-2(6), Dial) Penguin Group (USA) Inc.

Landolf, Diane Wright. Hog & Dog. Harris, Jennifer Beck, illus. 2005. (Step into Reading Ser.: Vol. 1). 32p. (J). (ps-1). pap. 3.99 (978-0-375-83165-2(7), Random Hse. Bks. for Young Readers) Random Hse. Children's Bks.

Latty, Jasmin. Oh, My Boring Toes! 2005. (J). pap. 12.00 (978-0-8059-6668-8(4)) Dorrance Publishing Co., Inc.

Lawlor, Laurie. The Biggest Pest on Eighth Avenue. Fisher, Cynthia, illus. (Holiday House Reader Ser.). 48p. (J). (gr. k-3). tchr. ed. 14.95 (978-0-8234-1321-8(7)) Holiday Hse., Inc.

Lehman, Barbara. Rainstorm. 2007. (Illus.). (J). (ps-k). 32p. 16.00 (978-0-618-75639-1(6)); 30p. (***978-1-4287-3564-4(X)***) Houghton Mifflin Co.

Leonard, Marcia. Dress-Up. Handelman, Dorothy, photos by. 1999. (Real Kids Readers Ser.). (Illus.). 32p. (J). (ps-1). lib. bdg. 18.90 (978-0-7613-2053-1(9)); pap. 4.99 (978-0-7613-2078-4(4)) Lerner Publishing Group. (Millbrook Pr.).

—Dress-Up. 1999. (J). 11.79 (978-0-606-19154-8(2)) Tandem Library Bks.

—Guess Who? 2000. (Hanna Bks.). (Illus.). 18p. (J). (ps up). 7.95 (978-0-694-01374-6(9), Harper Festival) HarperCollins Pubs.

—Hop, Skip, Run. Handelman, Dorothy, photos by. 1998. (Real Kids Readers Ser.). (Illus.). 32p. (ps-1). lib. bdg. 18.90 (978-0-7613-2015-9(6)); (J). pap. 4.99 (978-0-7613-2040-1(7)) Lerner Publishing Group. (Millbrook Pr.).

Leonard Marcia. Saltar, brincar, correr (Hop, Skip, Run) 2007. (Lecturas para niños de verdad - Nivel 1 (Real Kids Readers - Level 1) Ser.). (J). pap. 5.95 (***978-0-8225-7799-7(2)***, Ediciones Lerner) Lerner Publishing Group.

Leslie, Amanda. Babies Play. 2002. 10p. (J). 5.95 (978-1-58925-672-9(7), tiger tales) ME Media LLC.

—Who's That Scratching at My Door? A Peekaboo Riddle Book. 2001. (Illus.). 24p. (J). (ps-k). pap. 12.95 (978-1-929766-19-2(X)) Handprint Bks.

Let's Pretend: Individual Title Six-Packs. (ps-2). 23.00 (978-0-7635-9001-7(0)) Rigby Education.

Lewis, Edwina. Who Plays? Parker, Ant, illus. 2003. (Who. . . Ser.). 16p. (J). (978-1-85602-469-3(5)) Chrysalis Children's Bks.

Linenthal, Peter. Look Look! 1998. (Illus.). 18p. (J). (ps). bds. 6.99 (978-0-525-42028-6(2), Dutton Juvenile) Penguin Group (USA) Inc.

Linn, Margot. Scratches & Scrapes. Gay-Kassel, Doreen, illus. 2001. 32p. (J). (ps-1). pap. 5.95 (978-0-439-23225-8(2)) Scholastic, Inc.

Little Blue Kite & Friends Activity Book. 2005. (YA). per. (978-1-59872-122-5(4)) Instantpublisher.com.

London, Jonathan. Froggy Plays T-Ball. Remkiewicz, Frank, illus. 2007. (Froggy Ser.). 32p. (J). (ps-1). 15.99 (978-0-670-06187-7(5), Viking Juvenile) Penguin Group (USA) Inc.

Loomis, Christine. Cowboy Bunnies. Eitan, Ora, illus. 2000. (J). (978-0-606-18397-0(3)) Tandem Library Bks.

Lorenz Editors. My Day, 4 vols. 2002. Tr. of Mi dia. (Illus.). 48p. pap. 12.95 (978-0-7548-0876-3(9), Lorenz Bks.) Anness Publishing, Inc.

Loti, Pierre. The Story of a Child. 2006. 200p. pap. 12.99 (***978-1-4264-4968-0(2)***); 210p. pap. 15.99 (***978-1-4264-5269-7(1)***) BiblioBazaar.

—The Story of a Child. 2006. (ENG.). 26.99 (***978-1-4280-4147-9(8)***); pap. 19.99 (***978-1-4280-4149-3(4)***) Indy-Publish.com.

—The Story of a Child. 2004. reprint ed. pap. 20.95 (978-1-4191-8367-6(2)) Kessinger Publishing, LLC.

—The Story of A Child. 2004. reprint ed. pap. 1.99 (978-1-4192-8367-3(7)) Kessinger Publishing, LLC.

Love, Pamela. Dos Pies Suben, Dos Pies Bajan. Chapman, Lynne, illus. 2005. (Rookie Reader Espanol Ser.). (SPA & ESP.). 31p. (J). (gr. k-2). pap. 4.95 (978-0-516-25532-3(0), Children's Pr.) Scholastic Library Publishing.

MacDonald, Ross. Bad Baby. MacDonald, Ross, illus. 2005. (Illus.). 32p. (J). 16.95 (978-1-59643-064-8(8)) Roaring Brook Pr.

Magsamen, Sandra. Little Blossom: Huggable, Lovable, Snuggable Books. 2007. (Messages from the Heart Ser.). (Illus.). 6p. (J). (ps-17). 10.99 (***978-0-316-06593-1(5)***) Little, Brown Bks. for Young Readers.

Maisner, Heather. It's My Turn! Stephenson, Kristina, illus. 2005. (First Time Stories Ser.). 24p. (J). (gr. k-ps). pap. 3.95 (978-0-7534-5740-5(7), Kingfisher) Houghton Mifflin Co. Trade & Reference Div.

Mallat, Kathy. Just Ducky. Mallat, Kathy, illus. 2004. (Illus.). 32p. (J). (ps-k). 15.95 (978-0-8027-8824-5(6)) Walker & Co.

—Just Ducky. 2004. (Illus.). 24p. (J). (ps-1). 16.85 (978-0-8027-8825-2(4)) Walker & Co.

Mann, Paul Z. I Can Jump Higher! 2000. (gr. k-3). lib. bdg. 11.80 (978-0-613-71007-7(X)) Tandem Library Bks.

Matsutani, Miyoko. Peek-a-Boo. Segawa, Yasuo, illus. 2006. 20p. (J). 10.95 (978-1-74126-047-2(7)) R.I.C. Pubns AUS. *Dist:* SCB Distributors.

May, Sophie. Dotty Dimple at Play. 2004. reprint ed. pap. 15.95 (978-1-4191-1661-2(4)); pap. 1.99 (978-1-4192-1661-9(9)) Kessinger Publishing, LLC.

Mayer, Mercer. The Bravest Knight. 2007. (Illus.). 32p. (J). (gr. k-2). 16.99 (978-0-8037-3206-3(6), Dial) Penguin Group (USA) Inc.

—Bubbble Bubble. 2003. (Illus.). (J). pap. (978-1-57768-347-6(1)) School Specialty Publishing.

—No One Can Play. 2002. (Little Critter Ser.). (Illus.). 24p. (J). (ps-2). 10.95 (978-1-57768-608-8(X)); pap. 3.95 (978-1-57768-804-4(X)) School Specialty Publishing.

—No One Can Play. 2000. (gr. k-3). lib. bdg. 11.80 (978-0-613-67656-4(4)) Tandem Library Bks.

—Snow Day. 2002. (gr. k-3). lib. bdg. 11.80 (978-0-613-65135-6(9)) Tandem Library Bks.

Mazer, Norma Fox. Has Anyone Seen My Emily Greene? Davenier, Christine, illus. 2007. (J). (***978-1-4287-4761-6(3)***) Candlewick Pr.

McAllister, Angela. Harry's Box. Jones, Jenny, illus. 2003. 32p. (J). (gr. k-3). 16.95 (978-1-58234-772-1(7), Bloomsbury Children) Bloomsbury Publishing.

McBratney, Sam. The Caterpillow Fight. 2002. (Illus.). (J). 11.23 (978-0-7587-2207-2(9)) Book Wholesalers, Inc.

McClure, Brian D. The Bubble. 2006. (Illus.). 64p. (J). 14.95 (978-1-933426-05-1(5)) Universal Flag Publishing.

McCully, Emily Arnold & Schertle, Alice. 1, 2, I Love You. 2004. (Illus.). 32p. (J). (ps-k). 16.95 (978-0-8118-3518-3(9)) Chronicle Bks. LLC.

McDalton, Magdalena. Qaltayak Aquiyaryugyaaquq. Sparck, Amy & Shantz, Joy, illus. 1998. Tr. of Qaltayak Wants to Play Outside. (ESK.). 8p. (J). (gr. k-3). pap. 6.00 (978-1-58084-037-8(X)) Lower Kuskokwim Schl. District.

McGuire, Leslie. I Get Dressed: A Fun Sticker Book. Espinosa, Leo, illus. 1999. 20p. (J). reprint ed. 7.95 (978-1-892374-22-6(6)) Weldon Owen, Inc.

McKee, David. Elmer y el Clima. 2001. (Coleccion "Elmer" Ser.). (SPA.). (J). (978-968-16-6067-3(6)) Fondo de Cultura Economica MEX. *Dist:* Lectorum Pubns., Inc.

McLerran, Alice. Roxaboxen. Cooney, Barbara, illus. 2004. 32p. (J). (ps-3). pap. 6.99 (978-0-06-052633-7(5), Harper Trophy) HarperCollins Pubs.

McOmber, Rachel B., ed. McOmber Phonics Storybooks: A Nifty Ball of String. rev. ed. (Illus.). (J). (978-0-944991-50-3(5)) Swift Learning Resources.

McPhail, David M. Emma in Charge. McPhail, David M., illus. 2005. (Illus.). 32p. (J). (ps). 12.99 (978-0-525-47411-1(0), Dutton Juvenile) Penguin Group (USA) Inc.

—The Puddle. McPhail, David M., illus. 2002. (Illus.). (J). 13.36 (978-0-7587-3458-7(1)) Book Wholesalers, Inc.

—The Puddle. McPhail, David M., illus. 2000. (Illus.). 32p. (J). (ps-k). pap. 5.95 (978-0-374-46030-3(2), Sunburst) Farrar, Straus & Giroux.

Merritt, Kate, illus. Peekaboo, Baby! A Rhyming Flap Book. 2002. (DK Ladybird Ser.). 12p. (J). bds. 6.95 (978-0-7894-8467-3(6)) Dorling Kindersley Publishing, Inc.

Merz, Jennifer J. Playground Day! Merz, Jennifer J., illus. 2007. (Illus.). 32p. (J). (ps-1). 16.00 (***978-0-618-81696-5(8)***, Clarion Bks.) Houghton Mifflin Co. Trade & Reference Div.

Metzger, Steve. Rain! Rain! Go Away! Wilhelm, Hans, illus. 2002. (J). pap. 3.25 (978-0-439-29572-7(6)) Scholastic, Inc.

—That's My Dino! Wilhelm, Hans, illus. 2002. (J). (978-0-439-32052-8(6)) Scholastic, Inc.

Meyers, Susan. This Is the Way a Baby Rides. Nakata, Hiroe, illus. 2005. 32p. (J). (ps-1). 15.95 (978-0-8109-5763-3(9), Abrams Bks. for Young Readers) Abrams, Harry N., Inc.

Michot, Fabienne, et al. I Love to Play. Michot, Fabienne & Brasset, Doris, illus. 2000. (Maki Ser.). 14p. (J). (ps up). bds. (978-1-894363-34-1(5)) Dominique & Friends.

Milbourne, Anna. The Snowy Day. Temporin, Elena, illus. 2007. (J). (***978-0-439-88988-9(X)***) Scholastic, Inc.

Miller, J. P. Follow Me. 1998. (J). 3.25 (978-0-679-88662-4(1), Random Hse. Bks. for Young Readers) Random Hse. Children's Bks.

Mitton, Tony. Playful Little Penguins. Parker-Rees, Guy, illus. 2007. 32p. (J). (ps-1). 15.95 (***978-0-8027-9710-0(5)***) Walker & Co.

Monroe, Debra. Little Tikes (r) Let's Play: Pretend Play Book. 2002. (Illus.). 10p. (J). (ps up). bds. 4.99 (978-1-57151-596-4(8)) Playhouse Publishing.

Montanari, Eva, illus. Carlo Castlecrusher. 2006. 40p. (J). 16.50 (978-1-933327-16-7(2)); 15.95 (978-1-933327-15-0(4)) Purple Bear Bks., Inc.

Moore-Malinos, Jennifer & Roca, Nuria. Ganar no es Todo! Winning Isn't Everything (Spanish Edition) Fabrega, Marta, illus. 2007. (Vive y Aprende Ser.). (SPA.). 32p. (J). (ps-2). pap. 6.99 (***978-0-7641-3792-1(1)***) Barron's Educational Series, Inc.

Morris, Ann. Play. 1998. (Illus.). 32p. (J). (ps-3). 15.00 (978-0-688-14552-1(3)) HarperCollins Pubs.

Mouse Works Staff. Toy Story 2. 1999. (Toy Story 2 Ser.). (Illus.). 10p. (J). (ps-3). 9.99 (978-0-7364-0186-9(5)) Mouse Works.

Mullican, Judy. Caillou Plays Dinosaur Hide-and-Seek. Storch, Ellen N., illus. 2006. (J). pap. (978-1-57332-376-5(4)) HighReach Learning, Inc.

Munsch, Robert. Playhouse. Martchenko, Michael, illus. 2003. 32p. (J). (ps-2). pap. 3.99 (978-0-439-43690-8(7), Cartwheel Bks.) Scholastic, Inc.

Murphy, Jill. All for One. ed. 2004. (Illus.). (J). (ps-2). spiral bd. (978-0-616-14591-3(8)); spiral bd. (978-0-616-14592-0(6)) Canadian National Institute for the Blind/Institut National Canadien pour les Aveugles.

Murphy, Mary. I Am an Artist. 2000. (Illus.). 14p. (J). (gr. k-ps). bds. 4.95 (978-0-618-03401-7(3)) Houghton Mifflin Co. Trade & Reference Div.

—I Make a Cake. 2000. (Illus.). 14p. (J). (gr. k-ps). bds. 4.95 (978-0-618-00339-6(8)) Houghton Mifflin Co. Trade & Reference Div.

Namm, Diane. Guess Who? Sheldon, David, tr. Sheldon, David, illus. 2004. (My First Reader Ser.). 31p. (J). 18.50 (978-0-516-24412-9(4), Children's Pr.) Scholastic Library Publishing.

Napoli, Donna Jo. Playing Games. Ben-Ami, Doren & Klementz-Harte, Lauren, illus. 2000. (Angelwings Ser.: No. 8). 80p. (J). (gr. 2-5). mass mkt. 7.95 (978-0-689-83208-6(7), Aladdin) Simon & Schuster Children's Publishing.

—Playing Games. 2000. (Angelwings Ser.: No. 8). (Illus.). (J). (978-0-606-20386-9(9)) Tandem Library Bks.

Newman, Leslea. A Fire Engine for Ruthie. Moore, Cyd, illus. 2004. 32p. (J). (gr. k-3). tchr. ed. 16.00 (978-0-618-15989-5(4), Clarion Bks.) Houghton Mifflin Co. Trade & Reference Div.

Niland, Deborah. Let's Play. Niland, Deborah, illus. 2007. (Illus.). 24p. (Orig.). (J). (ps). pap. 4.99 (***978-1-933605-47-0(2)***) Kane/Miller Bk. Pubs., Inc.

Nora Juega Todo el Dia/Nora Plays All Day. 2005. (Libros en Espanol Para Ninos Ser.). (SPA.). (YA). (ps-1). 11.97 (978-0-8215-0994-4(2)); 15.75 (978-0-8215-1204-3(8)) Sadlier, William H. Inc.

Nora Plays All Day. 2005. (Emergent Library: Vol. 2). (YA). (ps-1). 23.94 (978-0-8215-8929-8(6)) Sadlier, William H. Inc.

Nora Plays All Day: Take-Home Book. 2005. (Emergent Library: Vol. 2). (YA). (ps-1). 12.60 (978-0-8215-7259-7(8)) Sadlier, William H. Inc.

Nugent, Penn. Come down & Play. 2004. (Illus.). 40p. (J). 7.95 (978-1-880849-90-3(9)) Chapel Hill Pr.

Ochiltree, Dianne & D'Allance, Mireille. Pillow Pup. 2002. (Illus.). 32p. (J). (gr. k-3). 14.95 (978-0-689-83408-0(X), McElderry, Margaret K.) Simon & Schuster Children's Publishing.

Orgel, Doris. The Spaghetti Party. Durrell, Julie, illus. 1999. (Bank Street Reader Collection). 48p. (J). (gr. 1-3). lib. bdg. (978-0-8368-1780-5(X)) Stevens, Gareth Inc.

Page, Josephine. Always Friends: Clover. Beasley, Roberta, illus. 2005. (Always Friends Ser.). 6p. (J). 5.99 (978-0-439-72225-4(X), Cartwheel Bks.) Scholastic, Inc.

Pagratis, Maggie & Pagratis, Illustrator Liliane, MaggieGrenier. Go Away Booboo! 2005. 29p. (J). 11.88 (978-1-4116-3689-7(9)) Lulu.com.

Partis, Joanne. Ready to Go! 2007. (Illus.). 10p. (J). bds. 4.99 (***978-1-84458-364-5(3)***) Anova Bks. GBR. *Dist:* Independent Pubs. Group.

Pattison, Darcy. 19 Girls & Me. Salerno, Steven, illus. 2006. 32p. (J). (ps). 16.99 (978-0-399-24336-3(4), Philomel) Penguin Group (USA) Inc.

Pete's a Pizza. 2004. (Illus.). 32p. (J). (ps-2). 28.95 (978-1-59112-740-6(8)) Live Oak Media.

Pete's a Pizza. 2004. 24.95 incl. audio (978-1-55592-068-5(3)) Weston Woods Studios, Inc.

Peto, Judith & Talwar, Robert. Jenny & Benny: Friends, 2005. (Illus.). 28p. (J). per. 16.95 (978-0-9767511-0-6(0)) Lasting Bks. Publishing Co.

Pig Wants to Play. 2002. (J). 4.98 (978-0-7525-7217-8(2)) Parragon, Inc.

The Playful Kitten. 2003. (J). per. (978-1-57657-888-9(7)) Paradise Pr., Inc.

Playing with my Cat. 2000. (J). (978-1-58453-093-0(6)) Pioneer Valley Educational Pr., Inc.

Ponko, Cindy A. Busy Busy Days. 2006. (J). (978-0-9768230-1-8(2)) Some Kids I Know.

Portis, Antoinette. Not a Stick. 2008. 32p. (J). (ps-1). 14.89 (***978-0-06-112326-9(9)***) HarperCollins Pubs.

—Not Stick. 2008. 32p. (J). 12.99 (***978-0-06-112325-2(0)***) HarperCollins Pubs.

Prince, Sarah. Betty Boots. 2001. (gr. k-3). lib. bdg. 11.80 (978-0-613-33335-1(7)) Tandem Library Bks.

Quadrillion Media Staff. Show Me the Ball! 1999. bds. 3.95 (978-1-58185-212-7(6)) Quadrillion Media LLC.

Quinn, Lin. The Best Mud Pie. Rooney, Ronnie, illus. 2002. (Rookie Reader Skill Set Ser.). 32p. (J). (gr. k-2). pap. 4.95 (978-0-516-25967-3(9), Children's Pr.) Scholastic Library Publishing.

—The Best Mud Pie Level B. Rooney, Ronnie, illus. 2001. (Rookie Readers Ser.). 32p. (J). (gr. 1-2). 19.50 (978-0-516-22219-6(8), Children's Pr.) Scholastic Library Publishing.

Ramirez, Linda M. & Salcines, Maria Luisa. Maggie's Visit to the Playroom. Llendler, Christine, illus. l.t. ed. 2000. 16p. (Orig.). (J). pap. 6.95 (978-0-945199-22-9(8), 956-668-1516) MarLin Bks.

Rand, Edward A. The Knights of the White Shield: Up-the-Ladder Club Series Round One Play. 2007. 166p. pap. 11.99 (***978-1-4264-8273-1(6)***); 184p. pap. 14.99 (***978-1-4264-8310-3(4)***) BiblioBazaar.

Random House Staff. Baby Play. Barrett, John E., illus. 2007. 12p. (J). (gr. k-ps). bds. 4.99 (978-0-375-83763-0(9), Random Hse. Bks. for Young Readers) Random Hse. Children's Bks.

Rau, Dana Meachen. Sounds Like Fun. 2004. (Compass Point Early Reader Ser.). (J). (978-0-7565-0570-7(4)) Compass Point Bks.

—Sounds Like Fun. Elizalde, Marcelo, illus. 2004. (Read-It! Readers Ser.). 32p. (C). (gr. k-3). 18.60 (978-1-4048-0649-8(0)) Picture Window Bks.

Raudenbush, Amy. Lucy More Needs Less. 2006. 48p. (J). pap. 13.99 (978-1-4116-6120-2(6)) Lulu.com.

Rea, Ba. Monarch! Come Play with Me. Rea, Ba, illus. 2006. (Illus.). 32p. (J). per. 10.95 (978-0-9657472-5-7(5)) Bas Relief Publishing.

Reasoner, Charles. No Peeking! 2003. (Illus.). 14p. bds. 4.99 (978-0-8431-0227-7(6), Price Stern Sloan) Penguin Group (USA) Inc.

Redmond, Shirley-Raye. The Princesses' Lucky Day. 2007. (Illus.). 24p. (J). (***978-1-4048-1242-0(3)***) Picture Window Bks.

—The Princesses' Lucky Day. Rooney, Ronnie, illus. 2006. 24p. (J). (***978-1-4048-3143-8(6)***) Picture Window Bks.

Reidy, Hannah. All Sorts of Numbers. Dodd, Emma, illus. 2005. (All Sort of Things Ser.). 24p. (C). (gr. k-3). 22.60 (978-1-4048-1062-4(5)) Picture Window Bks.

Rey, H. A. and Margret. Curious George Hide-and-Seek CG TV shapedanimal tab Book. 2008. 10p. (J). (ps-k). bds. 6.99 (***978-0-618-89199-3(4)***) Houghton Mifflin Co. Trade & Reference Div.

Rice, R. Hugh. Flip Flop. Romo, Alberto, tr. Becker, Neesa, illus. 1999. (Books for Young Learners). (SPA.). 12p. (J). (gr. k-2). pap. 5.00 (978-1-57274-289-5(5)) Owen, Richard C. Pubs., Inc.

Richter, Dana. Fisher Price Little People Busy Playtime. Nostrant, Judy, illus. 2003. (Busy Box Bks.). (J). bds. (978-0-7853-7978-2(9)) Publications International, Ltd.

Ritchie, Alison. What Bear Likes Best! Kolanovic, Dubravka, illus. 2005. 28p. (J). 16.00 (978-1-56148-473-7(3)) Good Bks.

Rizzon, Roberto. Hunt the Thimble. 1999. (Let's Play Series 2 Ser.). (Illus.). 24p. (J). (ps-3). pap. 3.99 (978-0-85953-710-0(2)) Child's Play-International.

Roche, Hannah. Sandra's Sunhat. 1998. (My First Weather Bks.). (Illus.). 24p. (J). (ps-3). (978-1-84089-032-7(0), Zero to Ten, Limited) Evans Publishing Group.

Rodriguez, Paul. Let's All Play! Character Education/ Anti-Bullying. Rodriguez, Paul, illus. 2003. (Illus.). 32p. (J). lib. bdg. 15.99 (978-0-9744770-0-8(1)) Rodro.

Rogers, Karen M. Que Buena Idea! Alvarado, Ana María, tr. Ahers-Johnson, Patrizia, illus. 2000. (Think-Kids Book Collection).Tr. of Good Thinking. (SPA.). 16p. (J). (gr. 1-4). pap. 2.95 (978-1-58237-058-3(3)) Creative Thinkers, Inc.

Ross, Theodore J. Lucy Wants to Play. 2003. (Illus.). 16p. (J). 3.99 (978-1-59384-029-7(2)) Parklane Publishing.

Rudisill, J. J., et al, illus. The Boys Against the Girls. 1999. (Wimzie's House Bks.). 24p. (J). pap. 3.99 (978-0-88724-515-2(3), CD-4840) Carson-Dellosa Publishing Co., Inc.

—Wimzie's Beach Trip. 1999. (Wimzie's House Bks.). 24p. (J). pap. 3.99 (978-0-88724-543-5(9), CD-4849) Carson-Dellosa Publishing Co., Inc.

Rueda, Claudia. Let's Play in the Forest While the Wolf Is Not Around. 2006. (Illus.). 32p. (J). pap. 16.99 (978-0-439-82323-4(4), Scholastic Pr.) Scholastic, Inc.

Rylant, Cynthia. Henry & Mudge & the Long Weekend. Stevenson, Sucie, illus. 2000. (Henry & Mudge Ser.). 28.95 incl. audio compact disk (978-1-59112-577-8(4)); pap. 18.95 incl. audio compact disk (978-1-59112-376-7(3)); pap. 31.95 incl. audio compact disk (978-1-59112-576-1(6)) Live Oak Media.

—Henry & Mudge & the Long Weekend. 2006. (Henry & Mudge Ser.). (J). (gr. 1-6). 24.21 (978-1-59961-083-2(3)) Spotlight.

Rylant, Cynthia. Puppy Mudge Finds a Friend. Stevenson, Sucie, illus. 2005. (Puppy Mudge Ser.). (J). (***978-1-4156-3675-6(3)***, Aladdin) Simon & Schuster Children's Publishing.

Salem, Lynn & Stewart, Josie. Bridges. Hepting, Scott, illus. 2000. 8p. (J). (gr. k-2). pap. 3.75 (978-1-58323-009-1(2), Seedling Pubns.) Continental Pr., Inc.

Samton, Sheila W. Rosa Stories. Samton, Sheila W., illus. 2001. (Brand New Readers Ser.). (Illus.). 1p. (J). (ps-2). pap. 4.99 (978-0-7636-1121-7(2)) Candlewick Pr.

Santillo, LuAnn. Mike. Santillo, LuAnn, ed. 2003. (Half-Pint Kids Readers Ser.). (Illus.). 7p. (J). (ps-1). pap. (978-1-59256-100-1(4)) Half-Pint Kids, Inc.

Santirso, Liliana. Me Gusta Jugar Con los Libros. Gomez, Patricio & Villagomez, Raul, illus. (SPA.). (J). (gr. k-1). pap. (978-968-6465-48-8(0)) Casa de Estudios de Literatura y Talleres Artisticos Amaquemecan A.C. MEX. *Dist:* Lectorum Pubns., Inc.

Sarda, Rosa. I Like Hiding: Me Gusta Esconderme. 2002. (gr. k-3). lib. bdg. 12.95 (978-0-613-50537-6(9)) Tandem Library Bks.

—I Like Hiding (Me Gusta Esconderme) Randall, Bernice, tr. Curto, Rosa Maria, illus. (SPA & ENG.). (J). (ps-1). pap. 4.95 (978-1-930332-30-0(0) , LC5516) Lectorum Pubns., Inc.

Schertle, Alice. The Adventures of Old Bo Bear. Parkins, David, illus. 2005. (J). 16.95 (978-978-081-183-9(4)) Chronicle Bks. LLC.

Schertle, Alice & Parkins, Schertle. The Adventures of Old Bo Bear. 2006. (Illus.). 32p. (J). 16.95 (978-0-8118-3476-6(X)) Chronicle Bks. LLC.

Schlepp, Tammy J. Games I Play. 2001. (gr. k-3). lib. bdg. 13.00 (978-0-613-45182-6(1)) Tandem Library Bks.

Scholastic, Inc. Staff. Barney's Paint & Play. Amaral, Gayla, ed. McKee, Darren & Winslow, Becky, illus. 2001. (Barney Ser.). 32p. (J). (ps-1). pap., act. bk. ed. 2.99 (978-1-58668-142-5(7)) Scholastic, Inc.

Scholastic, Inc. Staff. Where's Moe? 2007. (Doodlebops Ser.). (J). bds. 5.99 (***978-0-545-01150-1(7)***) Scholastic, Inc.

Scholastic, Inc. Staff & Hudson, Cheryl. Just for You! What Do You Know? Snow! Walker, Sylvia, illus. 2004. (Just for You! Ser.). 32p. pap. 3.99 (978-0-439-56851-7(X) , Teaching Resources) Scholastic, Inc.

Schories, Pat, illus. Biscuit & the Little Pup. 2008. (My First I Can Read Bks.). 32p. (J). 17.89 (***978-0-06-074171-6(6)***); 16.99 (***978-0-06-074170-9(8)***) HarperCollins Pubs.

Schories, Pat, illus. Biscuit Wants to Play. 2002. (Biscuit Ser.). (J). 11.87 (978-0-7587-8903-7(3)) Book Wholesalers, Inc.

Seymour, Tres. We Played Marbles. Andreasen, Dan, illus. 1998. 32p. (J). (gr. k-4). 16.99 (978-0-531-33074-6(5)); pap. 15.95 (978-0-531-30074-9(9)) Scholastic, Inc. (Orchard Bks.).

Shahan, Sherry. A Coat Full of Bubbles. Becker, Neesa, illus. 1998. (Books for Young Learners). 12p. (J). (gr. k-2). pap. 5.00 (978-1-57274-130-0(9) , A2441) Owen, Richard C. Pubs., Inc.

Shepherd, Donna J. OUCH! Sunburn. Collier, Kevin Scott, illus. 2007. 27p. (J). E-Book 9.95 incl. cd-rom (***978-1-933090-60-3(X)***) Guardian Angel Publishing, Inc.

Shulman, Mark. Wacky Weekend. Harris, Jenny B., illus. 2003. (Funny Fingers Ser.). 14p. (J). bds. 3.95 (978-1-4027-0704-9(5)) Sterling Publishing Co., Inc.

Si, Artists, illus. Playtime for Baby Strawberry. 2006. (Strawberry Shortcake Baby Ser.). 10p. (J). (ps-ps). bds. 5.99 (978-0-448-44358-4(9) , Grosset & Dunlap) Penguin Group (USA) Inc.

Siddals, Mary McKenna. I'll Play with You. Wisniewski, David, illus. 2000. 32p. (J). (gr. k-ps). tchr. ed. 14.00 (978-0-395-90373-5(4) , Clarion Bks.) Houghton Mifflin Co. Trade & Reference Div.

Simon, Charnan. The Sillies. Petelinsek, Kathleen, illus. 2006. (Magic Door to Learning Ser.). 24p. (J). 21.36 (978-1-59296-627-1(6)) Child's World, Inc.

Singer, Marilyn. On the Same Day in March: A Tour of the World's Weather. Lessac, Frane, illus. 2002. 40p. (J). (ps-3). pap. 6.99 (978-0-06-443528-4(8) , Harper Trophy) HarperCollins Pubs.

—On the Same Day in March: A Tour of the World's Weather. 2001. (gr. k-3). lib. bdg. 14.15 (978-0-613-44531-3(7)) Tandem Library Bks.

Smalls, Irene. My Nana & Me. Johnson, Cathy Ann, illus. 2005. 24p. (J). (ps-3). 15.99 (978-0-316-16821-2(1)) Little Brown & Co.

Smith, Charles R. Let's Play Baseball! Widener, Terry, illus. 2006. (Super Sturdy Picture Book Ser.). 24p. (J). (gr. k-ps). 8.99 (978-0-7636-1646-5(X)) Candlewick Pr.

Smith, Lois T. Carrie & Carl Play: A Flip-Flap Book. Smith, Lois T., illus. 2007. (Illus.). 32p. (J). (ps-k). pap. 5.99 (978-0-7636-1690-8(7)) Candlewick Pr.

Spaceboy Plays Hide & Seek. 2003. (J). (978-1-932570-05-2(5)) Literacy Footprints Inc.

Spafford, Suzy. Witzy & Zoom-Zoom. Spafford, Suzy, illus. 1998. (Illus.). 32p. (J). (ps). 14.95 (978-0-9643588-1-2(6)) Suzy's Zoo.

—Witzy Plays Hide & Seek. 2001. (Little Suzy's Zoo Ser.). (Illus.). 6p. (J). pap. 5.99 (978-0-439-34358-9(5)) Scholastic, Inc.

Spelvin, George. Jumanji. 2000. (SPA., Illus.). 240p. (J). 11.95 (978-84-406-6197-5(5)) Ediciones B ESP. *Dist:* Distribooks, Inc.

Staunton, Ted. The Puddleman. Clark, Brenda, illus. 2004. 32p. (J). (ps-4). pap. 6.95 (978-0-88995-190-7(X)) Red Deer Pr. CAN. *Dist:* Fitzhenry & Whiteside, Ltd.

Steck-Vaughn Staff. Hide & Seek. 1998. (Illus.). pap. 1.20 (978-0-8172-8689-7(6)) Steck-Vaughn.

—Jamies Play/Amazing Kate. 1999. (Take Me Home Ser.). (Illus.). (J). pap. (978-0-7398-2677-5(8)) Steck-Vaughn.

Steig, William. Pedro Es una Pizza. (Buenas Noches Coleccion). (SPA., Illus.). (J). (ps-5). 7.95 (978-958-04-6034-3(5)) Norma S.A. COL. *Dist:* Distribuidora Norma, Inc., Lectorum Pubns., Inc.

—Pete's a Pizza. Steig, William, illus. 1998. (Illus.). 32p. (J). (ps up). lib. bdg. 16.89 (978-0-06-205158-5(X)); 62nd ed. 16.99 (978-0-06-205157-8(1)) HarperCollins Pubs.

—Pete's a Pizza. Steig, William, illus. (Illus.). pap. 18.95 incl. audio compact disk (978-1-59112-742-0(4)); pap. incl. audio compact disk (978-1-59112-741-3(6)) Live Oak Media.

Stein, David Ezra. Monster Hug! 2007. (Illus.). 40p. (J). (ps-2). 15.99 (***978-0-399-24637-1(1)*** , Putnam Juvenile) Penguin Group (USA) Inc.

Steinberg, David. The Snow Ball. Conrad, Liz, illus. 2007. 10p. (J). (ps-k). bds. 6.99 (***978-0-8431-2680-8(9)*** , Price Stern Sloan) Penguin Group (USA) Inc.

Stern, Shirley. Giddy-Up! 2008. (Franny's Feet Ser.). 32p. (J). (ps-1). 3.99 (***978-1-4169-4916-9(X)*** , Simon Scribbles) Simon & Schuster Children's Publishing.

—Let's Get Moving: Carry-along Coloring Kit. 2008. (Franny's Feet Ser.). 80p. (J). (ps-1). 5.99 (***978-1-4169-4918-3(6)*** , Simon Scribbles) Simon & Schuster Children's Publishing.

—Twinkle Toes. 2008. (Franny's Feet Ser.). 48p. (J). (ps-1). 3.99 (***978-1-4169-4917-6(8)*** , Simon Scribbles) Simon & Schuster Children's Publishing.

Stevenson-Spurgon, Barbara J. Have You Ever Made Mud Pies on A Hot Summer Day? Ruffin, Aurzella, illus. 2006. 37p. (J). per. 19.95 (***978-1-60002-234-0(0)*** , 4073, Airleaf Publishing) Airleaf Publishing & Bookselling.

Stewart, Joel. Dexter Bexley & the Big Blue Beastie. Stewart, Joel, illus. 2007. (Illus.). 32p. (J). (ps-3). 16.95 (***978-0-8234-2068-1(X)***) Holiday Hse., Inc.

Sykes, Julie. Wait for Me, Little Tiger! Warnes, Tim, illus. 2001. 28p. (J). (ps-k). tchr. ed. 14.95 (978-1-58925-009-3(5) , tiger tales) ME Media LLC.

Taylor, Joyce. My Dog & I 6 Packs. Pouch - Level B. Garner, Phil, illus. (Lighthouse Ser.). 12p. (gr. k-1). 24.00 (978-0-7578-0816-6(6)) Rigby Education.

Taylor, Susie. The Upside-Downer Day. Lyon, Tammie, illus. 2004. (Topsy-Turvy Tracy Ser.). 40p. (J). 12.99 (978-0-310-70442-3(1)) Zonderkidz.

Thomas, Janet. Can I Play? Bartlett, Alison, illus. 32p. (J). 2005. 8.99 (978-1-4052-0597-9(0)); 2003. 16.99 (978-1-4052-0537-5(7)) Egmont Bks., Ltd. GBR. *Dist:* Trafalgar Square Publishing, Independent Pubs. Group.

Thompson, Elissa. Tryin' Ryan. 2006. (J). 15.00 (978-0-9787341-0-7(6)) Aidan's Butterfly Pubns.

Thompson, Lauren. Little Quack's Hide & Seek. Anderson, Derek, illus. 2007. (Classic Board Bks.). 34p. (J). 7.99 (978-1-4169-0325-3(9) , Little Simon) Simon & Schuster Children's Publishing.

Thompson, Lauren. Little Quack's New Friend. Anderson, Derek, illus. (Classic Board Bks.). (J). 2008. 34p. bds. 7.99 (***978-1-4169-4923-7(2)*** , Little Simon); 2006. 32p. 14.95 (978-0-689-86893-1(6)) Simon & Schuster Children's Publishing.

Thorpe, Kiki. Donde esta Boots? Cuento para levantar la Tapita. Savitsky, Steven, illus. 2005. (Dora the Explorer Ser.).Tr. of Where Is Boots?. (SPA.). 16p. (J). pap. 5.99 (978-1-4169-0621-6(5) , Libros Para Ninos) Simon & Schuster Children's Publishing.

Tinstman, Gretchen. Meet the Silly Sisters. 2006. 28p. (J). per. 12.99 (***978-1-59886-683-4(4)***) Tate Publishing & Enterprises, L.L.C.

Tomberlin-Hightower, Patricia. Play Pals. 2008. (Illus.). 24p. (J). 15.95 (***978-1-60131-020-0(X)***) Big Tent Bks.

Trujillo Stephens, Kristina. The Tod Squad Can Splish & Splash. 2007. (J). bds. (***978-1-57332-447-2(7)***) HighReach Learning, Inc.

Tuxworth, Nicola. Hop, Skip, Jump: A Very First Picture Book. 1999. (Pictures & Words Ser.). (Illus.). 24p. (J). (ps up). lib. bdg. 22.00 (978-0-8368-2431-5(8)) Stevens, Gareth Inc.

Uff, Caroline. Lulu's Busy Day. 2000. (Illus.). (J). (978-0-8027-8717-0(7)) Walker & Co.

Van Allsburg, Chris. Zathura: A Space Adventure. Van Allsburg, Chris, illus. 2002. (Illus.). 32p. (J). (gr. k-3). 18.00 (978-0-618-25396-8(3)) Houghton Mifflin Co. Trade & Reference Div.

Van Leeuwen, Jean. Oliver the Mighty Pig, Level. 2. Schweninger, Ann, illus. 2004. (Easy-to-Read Ser.). 48p. (J). (gr. k-3). 14.99 (978-0-8037-2886-8(7) , Dial) Penguin Group (USA) Inc.

Vilarrubias, Pia. Juguemos a Volar! (SPA.). 36p. 11.95 (978-84-207-1255-0(8)) Grupo Anaya, S.A. ESP. *Dist:* Distribooks, Inc.

—Lina Tambien Juega. (SPA.). 36p. 11.95 (978-84-207-1251-2(5)) Grupo Anaya, S.A. ESP. *Dist:* Distribooks, Inc.

—A Que Juegan Nico y Max? (SPA.). 36p. 11.95 (978-84-207-1250-5(7)) Grupo Anaya, S.A. ESP. *Dist:* Distribooks, Inc.

Waddell, Martin. Snow Bears. Fox-Davies, Sarah, illus. 2002. 32p. (J). (ps-1). 14.99 (978-0-7636-1906-0(X)) Candlewick Pr.

—You & Me, Little Bear. ed. 2004. (Illus.). (J). (ps-2). spiral bd. (978-0-616-01802-6(9)); spiral bd. (978-0-616-01803-3(7)) Canadian National Institute for the Blind/ Institut National Canadien pour les Aveugles.

Wardlaw. Bubble Mania. 1998. (J). pap. 4.99 (978-0-87628-364-6(4)) Ctr. for Applied Research in Education, The.

Weare, Tim. Hide-and-Seek with Leo. 2001. (Hand Puppet Board Bks.). (Illus.). 10p. (J). (ps). pap., bds. 14.95 (978-0-439-29719-6(2) , Cartwheel Bks.) Scholastic, Inc.

Weatherall, Barry. Jay & the Worm Save the Day. 2005. 40p. 14.28 (978-1-4116-4717-6(3)) Lulu.com.

Weber, Lou, ed. Playtime Peekaboo Baby. 2005. 24p. (J). bds. 10.98 (978-1-4127-3598-8(X) , 9520502) Publications International, Ltd.

—Pooh Color & Play Stories. 2005. 32p. 7.98 (978-1-4127-3393-9(6)) Publications International, Ltd.

A Weeekend with Wendell. 2004. 29.95 incl. cd-rom (978-1-55592-129-3(9)); (J). 24.95 incl. audio (978-1-56008-003-9(5)); (J). pap. 18.95 incl. audio compact disk (978-1-55592-116-3(7)); (J). pap. 32.75 incl. audio (978-1-55592-329-7(1)) Weston Woods Studios, Inc.

A Weekend with Wendell. 2004. (J). pap. 38.75 incl. audio compact disk (978-1-55592-647-2(9)) Weston Woods Studios, Inc.

Weeks, Sarah. Bunny Fun. Williams, Sam, illus. 2008. 40p. (J). (ps-k). 14.00 (978-0-15-205838-8(9)) Harcourt Trade Pubs.

—Overboard! Williams, Sam, illus. 2006. 40p. (J). 14.00 (978-0-15-205046-7(9)) Harcourt Trade Pubs.

Weiner, Brian. Toad Catchers' Creek. Weintraub, Claudia & Frederick, Robin, eds. Cannon, Martin, illus. 2005. 40p. (J). lib. bdg. 17.99 (978-1-932949-58-2(5)) Illusion Factory, The.

Wells, Rosemary. Hide-and-Seek. 2008. (Max & Ruby Ser.). 12p. (J). (ps-k). bds. 7.99 (***978-0-448-44784-1(3)*** , Grosset & Dunlap) Penguin Group (USA) Inc.

—Max & Ruby Play School. Wells, Rosemary, illus. 2003. (All Aboard Reading Ser.). (Illus.). 32p. (J). (ps-1). pap. 3.99 (978-0-448-43182-6(3) , Grosset & Dunlap) Penguin Group (USA) Inc.

—Max & Ruby Play School. 2003. (ps-2). lib. bdg. 11.80 (978-0-613-64064-0(0)) Tandem Library Bks.

—Play with Max & Ruby. Wells, Rosemary, illus. 2002. (All Aboard Reading Ser.). (Illus.). 32p. (J). (ps-1). pap. 3.99 (978-0-448-42854-3(7) , Grosset & Dunlap) Penguin Group (USA) Inc.

Wenger, Brahm. Dewey Doo-It at the Jingle Jangle Jamboree: A Musical Storybook Inspired by Arnold Schwarzenegger to Benefit Inner-City Games. 2006. 32p. 18.95 (978-0-9745143-4-5(9)) RandallFraser Publishing.

Weninger, Brigitte. A Ball for All. Tharlet, Eve, illus. 2006. 32p. (J). (ps-3). 16.99 (978-0-698-40049-8(6) , Minedition) Penguin Group (USA) Inc.

West, Jane. Proper Polly's Playroom. Bakerink, Monique Lujan, illus. 2002. (J). (978-0-9701025-2-2(6)) Haylett Publishing.

What Do You Want to Be? 2002. lib. bdg. (978-1-58970-175-5(5)) Lakeshore Learning Materials.

What Shall We Play. 2004. (J). per. (978-1-57657-459-1(8)) Paradise Pr., Inc.

When the Sun Rose. (J). (978-0-399-22487-4(4) , Philomel) Penguin Group (USA) Inc.

White, Ramy Allison. Sunny Boy & His Playmates. 2006. pap. (***978-1-4068-3390-4(8)***) Echo Library.

Whitehead, Pete, illus. Ink, Wink, & Blink Work Out! 2007. (I'm Going to Read Ser.). 32p. (J). pap. 3.95 (978-1-4027-4242-2(8)) Sterling Publishing Co., Inc.

Whybrow, Ian. Gently Bentley. 2005. (Illus.). (J). (ps-ps). (978-0-340-87561-2(5) , Hodder Children's Books) Hodder Children's Division.

Whybrow, Ian & Melling, David. Gently Bentley. 2005. (Illus.). (J). pap., pap. (978-0-340-87562-9(3) , Hodder Children's Books) Hodder Children's Division.

Wilder, Alice. Magenta's Visit. 1999. (Blue's Clues Ser.). (J). (ps-k). mass mkt. 3.99 (978-0-689-83355-7(5) , Simon Spotlight/Nickelodeon) Simon & Schuster Children's Publishing.

Wilder, Alice & Smith, Michael T. Magenta's Visit. Johnson, Traci Paige & Craig, Karen, illus. 1999. (Blue's Clues Ser.: Vol. 1). 24p. (J). (ps-k). pap. 3.50 (978-0-689-82443-2(2) , 076714003507, Simon Spotlight/ Nickelodeon) Simon & Schuster Children's Publishing.

Willis, Tammy A. The Tod Squad Can Play. 2007. (J). bds. (***978-1-57332-448-9(5)***) HighReach Learning, Inc.

Wojack, Craig. Tommy the Skunk. 2004. 24p. pap. 14.95 (978-1-4137-2120-1(6)) PublishAmerica, Inc.

Wojtowycz, David. Let's Play, Dudley! Colors. 2003. (Dudley! Ser.). (Illus.). (J). 3.95 (978-1-58925-667-5(0) , tiger tales) ME Media LLC.

Wood, Douglas. Nothing to Do. Halperin, Wendy Anderson, illus. 2006. 32p. (J). (ps-3). 16.99 (978-0-525-47656-6(3) , Dutton Juvenile) Penguin Group (USA) Inc.

Yacoubou, Jeanne. Wanna Play? Coloring-Story Book. Stebakova, Elena, illus. 2005. 16p. (J). (978-0-9788737-5-2(0)) Alaafia Kids Co.

Yang, James. Joey & Jet. Yang, James, illus. 2004. (Adventures Ser.: Bk. 1). (Illus.). 32p. (J). 15.95 (978-0-689-86926-6(6) , Atheneum/Richard Jackson Bks.) Simon & Schuster Children's Publishing.

Yolen, Jane. Dimity Duck. Braun, Sebastian, illus. 2006. 32p. (J). (ps). 15.99 (978-0-399-24632-6(0) , Philomel) Penguin Group (USA) Inc.

—How Do Dinosaurs Play with Their Friends? Teague, Mark, illus. 2006. 12p. (J). bds. 6.99 (978-0-439-85654-6(X) , Blue Sky Pr., The) Scholastic, Inc.

—How Do Dinosaurs Play with Their Friends (Como Juegan los Dinosaurios con Sus Amigos) 2006. 12p. (J). bds. 6.99 (978-0-439-87193-8(X) , Scholastic en Espanol) Scholastic, Inc.

—Soft House. Halperin, Wendy Anderson, illus. 2005. 32p. (J). (ps-2). 15.99 (978-0-7636-1697-7(4)) Candlewick Pr.

Yoon, Salina. My Little Shimmery Time for Fun. Yoon, Salina, illus. 2002. (Illus.). 12p. (J). bds. 5.95 (978-1-58117-090-0(4) , Intervisual/Piggy Toes) Dalmatian Pr.

Ziefert, Harriet. Buzzy's Balloon. Bolam, Emily, illus. 2007. 28p. (J). 9.95 (978-1-59354-603-8(3)) Blue Apple Bks.

PLAY CENTERS

see Playgrounds

PLAY DIRECTION (THEATER)

see Theater—Production and Direction

PLAY PRODUCTION

see Theater—Production and Direction

PLAY WRITING

see Drama—Technique

PLAYGROUNDS

Dunn, Opal. Acka Backa Boo! Playground Games from Around the World. Winter, Susan, illus. 2000. 46p. (J). (gr. k-4). reprint ed. 17.00 (978-0-7567-6106-6(9)) DIANE Publishing Co.

Finn, Carrie. Manners on the Playground. Lensch, Chris, illus. 2006. (Way to Be! Ser.). 24p. (J). (ps-2). lib. bdg. 23.93 (***978-1-4048-3154-4(1)***) Picture Window Bks.

Gorman, Jacqueline Laks. The Playground. 2005. (I Like to Visit/Me Gusta Visitar Ser.). (ENG & SPA.). 24p. (J). pap. (978-0-8368-4461-0(0)) Stevens, Gareth Inc.

—The Playground. Acosta, Tatiana & Gutiérrez, Guillermo, trs. 2005. (I Like to Visit Ser.). (ENG & SPA., Illus.). 24p. (YA). lib. bdg. 19.33 (978-0-8368-4454-2(8)) Stevens, Gareth Inc.

—The Playground: El Parque. 2005. (Illus.). 24p. (J). (ENG & SPA.). pap. (978-0-8368-4605-8(2)); (SPA & ENG., lib. bdg. 19.33 (978-0-8368-4598-3(6)) Stevens, Gareth Inc.

Kemper, Bitsy. Out & about at the Stadium. Trover, Zachary, illus. 2006. (Field Trips Ser.). 24p. (J). (gr. 2-4). lib. bdg. 25.26 (978-1-4048-2280-1(1)) Picture Window Bks.

Mattern, Joanne. Playgrounds. 2002. (Illus.). 24p. (J). lib. bdg. 21.35 (978-1-58340-148-4(2)) Smart Apple Media.

Pancella, Peggy. Playground Safety. 2004. (Heinemann First Library). (Illus.). 32p. (J). 6.95 (978-1-4034-4943-6(0)); lib. bdg. 22.79 (978-1-4034-4934-4(1)) Heinemann Library.

The Playground: Individual Title Two-Packs. (Chiquilibros Ser.). (ps-1). 12.00 (978-0-7635-8528-0(9)) Rigby Education.

Raatma, Lucia. Safety on the Playground & Outdoors. 2004. (Living Well Ser.). 32p. (J). (gr. 2-6). 27.07 (978-1-59296-243-3(2)) Child's World, Inc.

Sadler, Wendy. Playground Equipment. 2005. (Heinemann First Library). 32p. (J). pap. (978-1-4034-6834-5(6)) Heinemann Library.

—Playgrounds. 2005. (Heinemann First Library). (Illus.). 32p. (J). (ps-ps). lib. bdg. 28.50 (978-1-4034-6828-4(1)) Heinemann Library.

Weiss, Ellen. Math on the Playground. 2007. (Scholastic News Nonfiction Readers: Everyday Math—NEW SUBSET Ser.). 24p. (J). pap. 6.95 (***978-0-531-18786-9(1)*** , Children's Pr.) Scholastic Library Publishing.

What Happens When You Recycle? Individual Title Six-Packs. (Discovery World Ser.). 16p. (gr. 1-2). 28.00 (978-0-7635-8464-1(9)) Rigby Education.

PLAYGROUNDS—FICTION

Allen, Kit. Slide, Already! 2005. (Illus.). 48p. (J). (gr. k-3). 12.00 (978-0-618-49643-3(2)) Houghton Mifflin Co. Trade & Reference Div.

Bailey, Debbie. The Playground, No. 12. Huszar, Susan, photos by. 1998. (Talk about Book Ser.: Vol. 12). (Illus.). 14p. (J). (gr. k-ps). bds. 5.95 (978-1-55037-511-4(3)) Annick Pr., Ltd. CAN. *Dist:* Firefly Bks., Ltd.

Bedford, David. It's My Turn! 2000. 12.75 (978-0-606-20731-7(7)) Tandem Library Bks.

Bedford, David & Field, Elaine. It's My Turn! 2001. (Illus.). 30p. (J). (ps-k). 5.95 (978-1-58925-351-3(5) , tiger tales) ME Media LLC.

Berk, Sheryl. Barney's Little Lessons: Be My Friend! Valentine-Ruppe, June, illus. 2002. (Barney Ser.). 8p. (J). (ps-1). bds. 5.99 (978-1-58668-293-4(8)) Scholastic, Inc.

Bonnell, Kris. Too Big to Play. 2006. (J). 3.95 (***978-1-933727-35-6(7)***) Reading Reading Bks., LLC.

Clanchy, Kate. Our Cat Henry Comes to the Swings. Bird, Jemima, illus. 2007. 32p. (J). (ps-1). 16.00 (***978-1-56148-563-5(2)***) Good Bks.

Copeland, Cynthia L. What Are You Waiting For? Gordon, Mike, illus. 2003. (Silly Millies Ser.: 1). 32p. lib. bdg. 17.90 (978-0-7613-2804-9(1) , Millbrook Pr) Lerner Publishing Group.

Copeland, Cynthia L. & Gordon, Mike. What Are You Waiting For? 2003. (Silly Millies Ser.: Vol.1). (Illus.). 32p. (J). (ps-1). pap. 4.99 (978-0-7613-1828-6(3) , Millbrook Pr.) Lerner Publishing Group.

Emerson, Carl. Old Oak & the Summer Playground. Doerrfeld, Cori, illus. 2007. (J). (978-1-4048-2626-7(2)) Picture Window Bks.

Feldman, Thea. Fun Around the Town. 2006. 3p. 5.99 (978-1-932915-34-1(6)) Sandvik Publishing.

Hines, Anna Grossnickle. Le Toca a Guillermo. Hines, Anna Grossnickle, illus. (Rookie Reader Espanol Ser.). (Illus.). (J). (gr. k-2). 2002. pap. 4.95 (978-0-516-26304-5(8)); 2001. (SPA., 32p. 19.50 (978-0-516-22357-5(7)) Scholastic Library Publishing. (Children's Pr.).

—Le Toca a Guillermo. 2001. (SPA.). (gr. k-3). lib. bdg. 12.95 (978-0-613-54433-7(1)) Tandem Library Bks.

Howard-Parham, Pam. Playing on the Playground. Crowell, Knox, illus. l.t. ed. 2005. (Hrl Little Book Ser.). (J). (gr. k up). pap. 10.95 (978-1-57332-336-9(5)); pap. 10.95 (978-1-57332-335-2(7)) HighReach Learning, Inc.

Klein, Adria F. Max Goes to the Playground. Gallagher-Cole, Mernie, illus. 2007. (J). lib. bdg. (***978-1-4048-3681-5(0)***) Picture Window Bks.

Leman, Nora. The Alpha Building Crew. Hartmann, April, illus. 2005. (J). (978-1-58987-110-6(3)) Kindermusik International.

Merz, Jennifer. Playground Day. 2007. 32p. 16.00 (***978-978-061-896-4(1)*** , Clarion Bks.) Houghton Mifflin Co. Trade & Reference Div.

Merz, Jennifer J. Playground Day! Merz, Jennifer J., illus. 2007. (Illus.). 32p. (J). (ps-1). 16.00 (***978-0-618-81696-5(8)*** , Clarion Bks.) Houghton Mifflin Co. Trade & Reference Div.

Nobisso, Josephine. Hot-Cha-Cha! Holub, Joan, illus. 1998. 40p. (J). (gr. k-4). 15.95 (978-1-890817-00-8(7)) Winslow Pr.

Playland Staff. Playland Dino Backsheet. (J). (978-0-698-13018-0(9)) Penguin Group (USA) Inc.

Prater, John. On Top of the World. 1998. (Illus.). 32p. (J). (ps-2). 15.95 (978-1-57255-649-2(8)) Mondo Publishing.

Richards, Chuck. Jungle Gym Jitters. Richards, Chuck, illus. 2004. (Illus.). 32p. (J). 17.85 (978-0-8027-8932-7(3)); 16.95 (978-0-8027-8931-0(5)) Walker & Co.

Roselle, Gayle. Moozelville Playground. 2007. (Illus.). 74p. (J). pap. 12.95 (*978-0-9788628-8-6(0)) Just Write Bks.

Schwartz, Corey Rosen & Klein, Tali. Hop! Plop! Dunrea, Olivier, illus. 2006. 32p. (J). 16.85 (978-0-8027-8057-7(1)); 15.95 (978-0-8027-8056-0(3)) Walker & Co.

Tan, Shaun, illus. The Haunted Playground. 2008. (J). lib. bdg. (*978-1-59889-860-6(4)); 80p. pap. (*978-1-59889-916-0(3)) Stone Arch Bks.

Watson-Dubisch, Carolyn. The Giant's Playground. 2001. (Illus.). 36p. (J). (ps-1). 11.95 (978-0-9714740-0-0(1)) Fantastic Visions Studio.

PLAYHOUSES

see Theaters

PLAYING CARDS

see Cards

PLAYS

Ada, Alma Flor & Campoy, F. Isabel. Curtains Up! (Literature Collection of Gateways to the Sun Ser.). 32p. (J). (gr. k-6). pap. 13.95 (978-1-58105-680-8(X)); pap. 13.95 (978-1-58105-679-2(6)) Santillana USA Publishing Co., Inc.

—Escenario de Polichinela. (Puertas al Sol Ser.). (SPA & ENG., Illus.). 32p. (J). (gr. k-6). pap. 13.95 (978-1-58105-654-9(0)) Santillana USA Publishing Co., Inc.

—Rat-a-Tat Cat. (Gateways to the Sun). 32p. (J). (gr. k-6). pap. 13.95 (978-1-58105-677-8(X)) Santillana USA Publishing Co., Inc.

Alcott, Louisa May & Longest, David. Little Women. 1998. 116p. pap. 6.25 (978-0-87129-857-7(0), L95) Dramatic Publishing Co.

Alexander, Sue. Small Plays for Special Days. Huffman, Thomas, illus. 2003. 64p. (J). (gr. k-3). pap. 6.95 (978-0-618-37834-0(0), Clarion Bks.) Houghton Mifflin Co. Trade & Reference Div.

—Small Plays for Special Days. 2003. (gr. k-3). lib. bdg. 15.25 (978-0-613-70566-0(1)) Tandem Library Bks.

—Small Plays for Special Days: Holiday Plays for You & a Friend. Huffman, Tom, illus. 2003. 64p. (J). (gr. k-3). tchr. ed. 15.00 (978-0-618-38145-6(7), Clarion Bks.) Houghton Mifflin Co. Trade & Reference Div.

Alfreda. Taestella A Black Cinderella Folder Leaf Edition. 2007. (YA). 3.25 (*978-1-56820-442-0(6), folder leaf) Story Time Stories That Rhyme.

Alger, Horatio. Seeking His Fortune, & Other Dialogues. unabr. ed. 2002. (Polyglot Press Alger Ser.). (Illus.). (YA). pap. 17.95 (978-1-4115-0044-0(X)) Polyglot Pr., Inc.

Allen, Laurie. Middle School Mania: Comedy Duos for Guy / Girl, 8 bklts. 2003. (YA). pap. 19.95 (978-1-932404-53-1(8), 915) Brooklyn Pubs.

Almond, David. Two Plays. 2005. 240p. (YA). (gr. 3-7). pap. 12.95 (978-0-385-73074-7(8), Delacorte Bks. for Young Readers) Random Hse. Children's Bks.

Amstutz, Beverly. Tiny Wings: A Christmas Play for Children. Amstutz, Beverly, illus. 2000. (Illus.). (YA). (gr. k-12). pap. 5.00 (978-0-937836-12-5(5)) Precious Resources.

Andersen, Hans H. & Christian. The Little Mermaid. 2005. 64p. pap. 16.95 (978-1-84002-487-6(9)) Theatre Communications Group, Inc.

Armitage, Simon & Gill, Peter. Eclipse - Friendly Fire. 2000. (Connections Ser.). (Illus.). 112p. (YA). pap. 17.95 (978-0-7487-4290-5(5)) Nelson Thornes Ltd. GBR. *Dist:* Trans-Atlantic Pubns., Inc.

Armstrong, James. The New Mrs. Jones: A One-Act Comedy Play. 2003. (YA). pap. 4.50 (978-1-932404-62-3(7), 760) Brooklyn Pubs.

Asher, Sandra Fenichel. Blackbirds & Dragons, Mermaids & Mice. 150p. (YA). pap. 9.95 (978-1-58342-174-1(2), BB1) Dramatic Publishing Co.

Aston, Nell, contrib. by. Bailed Up. 22p. pap. (978-1-875739-29-5(7)) Wizard Bks.

Atkinson, Lawrence. Great Ideas. 2003. (YA). 8.00 (978-0-9679552-3-0(8)) Mushroom Cloud Pr. of Orlando.

Averill, Ric. Pixies, Kings & Magical Things. 2002. 56p. (YA). pap. 6.25 (978-1-58342-149-9(1), PA1) Dramatic Publishing Co.

Avi. Acting Out. 2008. 192p. (J). (*978-1-4169-3848-4(6), Simon & Schuster Children's Publishing) Simon & Schuster Children's Publishing.

Ayckbourn, Alan, et al. Gizmo - Don't Eat Little Charlie. 2000. (Connections Ser.). (Illus.). 112p. (YA). pap. 17.95 (978-0-7487-4289-9(1)) Nelson Thornes Ltd. GBR. *Dist:* Trans-Atlantic Pubns., Inc.

Ayliffe, Alex. Daniel & Lions. 2007. 16p. bds. 5.99 (*978-1-56148-559-8(4)) Good Bks.

Bagert, Brod. Elephant Games: And Other Playful Poems to Perform. Ellis, Tim, illus. 2003. 32p. (YA). (gr. 2-4). pap. 9.95 (978-1-56397-862-3(8)) Boyds Mills Pr.

—Elephant Games: And Other Playful Poems to Perform. 2000. (gr. 3-6). lib. bdg. 17.60 (978-0-613-78882-3(6)) Tandem Library Bks.

Bajah, S. T. Stop, Malaria, Stop: Science Drama. 2001. (Illus.). 22p. pap. (978-978-2951-51-9(X)) CSS Bookshops, Ltd., Agency & Publishing Div.

Baker, Thomas. The Fine Lady's Airs. 2006. pap. (*978-1-4065-0502-3(1)) Dodo Pr.

Bany-Winters, Lisa, et al. On Stage! Theater Games & Activities for Kids. O'Neill, Sean, illus. 2003. 160p. (J). (gr. 1-7). pap. 14.95 (978-1-55652-324-3(6)) Chicago Review Pr., Inc.

Baptist, Leona. Daniel Boone. (Illus.). (YA). (gr. 6-12). 6.00 (978-0-87602-118-7(6)) Anchorage Pr.

Barrie, J. M. Peter Pan. unabr. ed. 2000. (Thrift Edition Ser.). (Illus.). vii, 70p. (J). pap. 1.50 (978-0-486-41421-8(3)) Dover Pubns., Inc.

—Peter Pan & Other Plays: The Admirable Crichton; Peter Pan; When Wendy Grew Up; What Every Woman Knows; Mary Rose. Hollindale, Peter, ed. 1999. (Oxford World's Classics Ser.). (Illus.). 384p. 14.95 (978-0-19-283919-0(5)) Oxford Univ. Pr., Inc.

Barrie, Shirley. Shusha & the Story Snatcher. 1999. (Illus.). (J). (ps-5). pap. 4.50 (978-1-57514-354-5(2)) Encore Performance Publishing.

Batista, Robert. Street Angel. 1998. 90p. (Orig.). (YA). (gr. 8 up). pap. (978-1-888097-01-6(9)) Word Is Bond Writers-Pr.

Beaton, Clare, illus. Let's Pretend. l.t. ed. 1998. (Craft & Project Books for Children). 48p. (J). (ps-4). lib. bdg. 17.95 (978-1-56674-243-6(9)) Forest Hse. Publishing Co., Inc.

Beckett, Samuel. Waiting for Godot. unabr. ed. 2005. (Stratford Festival Ser.). (gr. 9-12). 15.95 (978-0-660-17981-0(4)) Canadian Broadcasting Corp./Societe Radio-Canada CAN. *Dist:* Georgetown Terminal Warehouse.

Beissel, Henry. Inuk & the Sun (Inuk et le Soleil) Franciere, Arlette, tr. 2001. (FRE & ENG., Illus.). 80p. (J). pap. 14.95 (978-0-88754-593-1(9)) Theatre Communications Group, Inc.

Benchmark Education Staff. Reader's Theater for Fluency & Comprehension Handbook. 2004. (Reader's Theater Ser.). pap., instr.'s hndbk. ed. 10.00 (978-1-4108-1320-6(7)) Benchmark Education Co.

Benes. The Trial of Mother Goose: An Illustrate. 2006. pap. 29.99 (*978-1-4259-1951-1(0)) AuthorHouse.

Benson, Edmund F. & Benson, Susan. Arise Playlets. 1999. (Illus.). (J). (gr. 3-4). pap. (978-1-58614-103-5(1)) Arise Foundation.

Bergman, Steven. Critic's Carnival: A Ten-Minute Dramatic Monologue. 2003. 12p. (YA). pap. 4.50 (978-1-932404-26-5(0), 279) Brooklyn Pubs.

Bernardi, Philip & Havens, Diane. Twice upon a Time. 2003. (Theater for Young Audiences Ser.). (Illus.). 24p. (J). (gr. k-6). pap. 6.00 (978-0-88734-425-1(9)) Players Pr., Inc.

Bible Drama: 136 Stories to Be Read or Acted as Plays. 2004. pap. 29.95 (978-1-879415-41-6(0), Bearly Cooking) Mountain n' Air Bks.

Birch, Beverley. Shakespeare's Tales: Julius Caesar. 2007. (Illus.). 80p. pap. 8.95 (*978-0-7502-5041-2(0), Hodder Wayland) Hodder Children's Division GBR. *Dist:* Independent Pubs. Group.

—Shakespeare's Tales: Macbeth. 2007. (Illus.). 80p. pap. 8.95 (*978-0-7502-5036-8(4), Hodder Wayland) Hodder Children's Division GBR. *Dist:* Independent Pubs. Group.

—Shakespeare's Tales: Midsummer Night's Dream. 2007. (Illus.). 80p. pap. 8.95 (*978-0-7502-5038-2(0), Hodder Wayland) Hodder Children's Division GBR. *Dist:* Independent Pubs. Group.

—Shakespeare's Tales: Romeo & Juliet. 2007. (Illus.). 80p. pap. 8.95 (*978-0-7502-5037-5(2), Hodder Wayland) Hodder Children's Division GBR. *Dist:* Independent Pubs. Group.

—Shakespeare's Tales: Twelfth Night. 2007. (Illus.). 80p. pap. 8.95 (*978-0-7502-5039-9(9), Hodder Wayland) Hodder Children's Division GBR. *Dist:* Independent Pubs. Group.

—The Tempest. 2007. (Illus.). 80p. pap. 8.95 (*978-0-7502-5040-5(2), Hodder Wayland) Hodder Children's Division GBR. *Dist:* Independent Pubs. Group.

Blackaby, Susan. Pulgarcita: Version del Cuento de Hans Christian Andersen. Delage, Charlene, illus. 2006. (Read-It! Readers en Espanol Ser.).Tr. of Thumbelina: A Retelling of the Hans Christian Andersen Fairy Tale. (SPA.). 32p. (J). (ps-3). 19.95 (978-1-4048-1642-8(9)) Picture Window Bks.

Blatchford, Peter. Warthog of Wartonia: A Play of Young People. ltd. unabr. ed. 1998. 36p. (J). (gr. 3-10). 8.00 (978-1-56439-072-1(1)) Ridgeway Pr.

Blessing, Matt. Wisconsin History on Stage: Scripts for Grades 4 Through 8. 1999. (New Badger History Ser.). (Illus.). 80p. (J). (gr. 4-8). pap. 14.95 (978-0-87020-312-1(6)) Wisconsin Historical Society.

Bloom, Harold. Arthur Miller's Death of a Salesman. 2004. (gr. 7-12). lib. bdg. 18.75 (978-0-613-70827-2(X)) Tandem Library Bks.

Blum, Renon. California Wax Museum. 2003. (Ideal for Teens Ser.). 16p. (J). (gr. 4-8). pap. 5.00 (978-0-88734-518-0(2)) Players Pr., Inc.

Bond, Edward & Mulligan, Jim. Eleven Vests & Tuesday. 2004. 96p. pap. 13.95 (978-0-413-72120-4(5)) Methuen Publishing Ltd. GBR. *Dist:* Consortium Bk. Sales & Distribution.

Bosom, Monica, ed. The Ugly Duckling. Peris, Carme, illus. 1999. 32p. (J). (ps-3). 8.95 (978-0-7641-5149-1(5)) Barron's Educational Series, Inc.

Bowers, Gwen. Read-Aloud Plays: the Iliad, the Odyssey, the Aeneid: Three Classics Adapted into Engaging Plays-Plus Background & Activities-Just for Middle Schoolers. 2007. 80p. pap. 12.99 (978-0-439-62918-8(7), Teaching Resources) Scholastic, Inc.

Brooks, Laurie. Deadly Weapons. 2002. 45p. (YA). pap. 6.25 (978-1-58342-050-8(9)) Dramatic Publishing Co.

—Franklin's Apprentice. 2006. 48p. pap. 6.50 (978-0-8222-2069-5(5)) Dramatists Play Service, Inc.

Brown, Kent R. Ciao, Baby! 35p. (YA). 4.25 (978-1-58342-100-0(9), CCB1) Dramatic Publishing Co.

—Hope 'n Mercy. (Illus.). 35p. (YA). 4.25 (978-1-58342-101-7(7), H80) Dramatic Publishing Co.

—Lover Boy & Other Plays. (Illus.). (YA). 4.25 (978-1-58342-085-0(1), LB1) Dramatic Publishing Co.

Brown, Kevin. Wuthering Heights: 11 Speaking Parts. 1999. (Dramascripts Classic Texts Ser.). (J). (gr. 6-9). pap. 17.95 (978-0-17-432559-8(2)) Nelson Thornes Ltd. GBR. *Dist:* Trans-Atlantic Pubns., Inc.

Brown, Marc. Arturo y el Dia de Accion de Gracias. 2000. (SPA.). (gr. k-3). lib. bdg. 15.25 (978-0-613-28276-5(0)) Tandem Library Bks.

Brown, Richard & O'Neill, Judith. Heroes & Villains, 8 vols. 2000. (Cambridge Reading Ser.). (Illus.). 96p. pap. 54.00 (978-0-521-78631-7(2)) Cambridge Univ. Pr.

Bruchac, Joseph. Pushing up the Sky: Seven Native American Plays for Children. 2000. (Illus.). 96p. (J). (gr. 1-5). 19.99 (978-0-8037-2168-5(4), Dial) Penguin Group (USA) Inc.

Buchanan, Matt. Ernie's Place: A Play for Young Audiences. 2006. 36p. (YA). pap. 5.95 (978-1-60003-200-4(1), 618) Brooklyn Pubs.

—Prince Ugly: One Act Youth Play. rev. ed. 2005. 40p. (YA). pap. 5.95 (978-1-60003-169-4(2), 613) Brooklyn Pubs.

—Sleeping Walter: One Act Youth Play. rev. ed. 2005. 32p. (YA). pap. 5.95 (978-1-60003-170-0(6), 614) Brooklyn Pubs.

Burack, Sylvia K., ed. Great American Events on Stage. 2001. 232p. (J). (gr. 4-9). pap. 15.95 (978-0-8238-0305-7(8)) Kalmbach Publishing Co., Bks. Div.

Burdett, Lois. Hamlet for Kids. 2000. (Shakespeare Can Be Fun Ser.). (Illus.). 64p. (J). (gr. 2-4). pap. 8.95 (978-1-55209-530-0(4)); lib. bdg. 19.95 (978-1-55209-522-5(3)) Firefly Bks., Ltd.

—Hamlet for Kids. 2000. (gr. 3-6). lib. bdg. 17.60 (978-0-613-51149-0(2)); (Illus.). (J). (978-0-606-18136-5(9)) Tandem Library Bks.

—A Midsummer Night's Dream for Kids. 2003. (Shakespeare Can Be Fun Ser.). (Illus.). 64p. (J). (gr. 2-7). pap. 8.95 (978-1-55209-124-1(4)) Firefly Bks., Ltd.

—Romeo & Juliet for Kids. 1998. (Shakespeare Can Be Fun Ser.). (Illus.). 64p. (J). (gr. 2-7). pap. 8.95 (978-1-55209-229-3(1)); lib. bdg. 19.95 (978-1-55209-244-6(5)) Firefly Bks., Ltd.

—Tempest: For Kids. 1999. (gr. 3-6). lib. bdg. 17.60 (978-0-613-27194-3(7)) Tandem Library Bks.

Burningham, Hilary. Henry V. 2000. (Graphic Shakespeare Ser.). (Illus.). 48p. (J). pap., tchr. ed. 35.00 (978-0-237-52158-5(X), Evans Brothers, Limited) Evans Publishing Group GBR. *Dist:* Independent Pubs. Group.

Butler, Dori. The Winter Weather Machine: Reader's Theater Levels F-M (9-28) Wolk-Stanley, Jessica, illus. ed. 2004. (Reader's Theater Ser.). 16p. (J). pap. 22.00 (978-1-4108-2293-2(1), A22931) Benchmark Education Co.

Butterfield, Moira. Little Red Riding Hood. 1998. (Playtales Ser.). 24p. (J). lib. bdg. 19.92 (978-1-57572-650-2(5)) Heinemann Library.

—Puss-in-Boots. 1998. (Playtales Ser.). 24p. (J). lib. bdg. 19.92 (978-1-57572-649-6(1)) Heinemann Library.

—Sleeping Beauty. 1998. (Playtales Ser.). 24p. (J). lib. bdg. 19.92 (978-1-57572-651-9(3)) Heinemann Library.

Calcutt, David. Beowulf. 2001. (Dramascripts Classic Texts Ser.). (Illus.). 104p. (J). (gr. 6-10). pap. 16.95 (978-0-17-432656-4(4)) Nelson Thornes Ltd. GBR. *Dist:* Trans-Atlantic Pubns., Inc.

—Dr. Jekyll & Mr. Hyde: 16 Speaking Parts. 1999. (Dramascripts Classic Texts Ser.). (J). (gr. 6-9). pap. 17.95 (978-0-17-432599-4(1)) Nelson Thornes Ltd. GBR. *Dist:* Trans-Atlantic Pubns., Inc.

—The Island of Dr. Moreau: 16 Speaking Parts. 1999. (Dramascripts Classic Texts Ser.). (J). (gr. 6-9). pap. 17.95 (978-0-17-432600-7(9)) Nelson Thornes Ltd. GBR. *Dist:* Trans-Atlantic Pubns., Inc.

—The Wrath of Achilles. 2001. (Dramascripts Classic Texts Ser.). (Illus.). 104p. (J). (gr. 6-10). pap. 16.95 (978-0-17-432660-1(2)) Nelson Thornes Ltd. GBR. *Dist:* Trans-Atlantic Pubns., Inc.

Cano, Robin B. Estamos Aqui Para la Fiesta! 2000. (SPA.). (J). (gr. 3-5). pap. 5.95 (978-1-56492-274-8(X)) Laredo Publishing Co., Inc.

Carlson, Lori M. Bilingual Plays Anthology. 1999. (J). lib. bdg. (978-0-688-16238-2(5)) HarperCollins Pubs.

—Hurray for Three Kings' Day! 1999. (Illus.). 32p. (J). (ps-3). 16.00 (978-0-688-16239-9(8)); 15.89 (978-0-688-16240-5(1)) HarperCollins Pubs.

Carr, Diane. River Dragon Activity Book: Just Add Kids. 2003. (J). 15.00 (978-1-59094-051-8(2), Jawbreakers for Kids) Jawbone Publishing Corp.

Carriere, Jean-Claude. The Little Black Book. 2003. 86p. pap. 16.95 (978-0-9542330-7-5(7)) Aurora Metro Pubns. Ltd. GBR. *Dist:* Consortium Bk. Sales & Distribution.

Carter, Pip. Double Dare. (Illus.). 128p. (J). (gr. 4-6). (978-1-875739-48-6(3)) Wizard Bks.

—The Little People. (Illus.). 112p. (J). (gr. 3-5). (978-1-875739-70-7(X)) Wizard Bks.

Carter, Richard. A Community Shakespeare Company Edition of the TWO GENTLEMEN of VERONA. 2007. 80p. (J). per. 10.95 (*978-0-595-45825-7(4)) iUniverse, Inc.

Caruso, Sandra & Kosoff, Susan. Young Actors Book of Improvisation: Dramatic Situations from Shakespeare to Spielberg. 1998. (Young Actor's Book of Improvisation Ser.: Vol. 1). 280p. (YA). (gr. 7-11). pap. 22.95 (978-0-325-00049-7(2), E00049); 200p. (gr. 2-6). pap. 19.95 (978-0-325-00048-0(4), E00048) Heinemann.

Catalano, Dominic. Frog Went-a-Courting: A Musical Play in Six Acts. 2004. (Illus.). 32p. (J). (gr. k-2). reprint ed. pap. 8.95 (978-1-59078-285-9(2)) Boyds Mills Pr.

Center for Learning Network Staff. Master Harold ... & the Boys/Fences. 2001. (Novel Ser.). (Illus.). 102p. (YA). (gr. 10-12). tchr. ed., spiral bd. 19.95 (978-1-56077-663-5(3)) Ctr. for Learning, The.

Cerio, Johnathan. The Cathedral. 2003. (YA). 7.99 (978-0-9679552-8-5(9)) Mushroom Cloud Pr. of Orlando.

Chaitin, Joy, et al. The Fourth Wise Man - Play with Music. 1998. 27p. (J). (gr. 1 up). pap. 4.25 (978-0-87129-881-2(3), F09) Dramatic Publishing Co.

Charles, Nancy Linehan. Romeo & Juliet or the Old You-Know-I-Really-Love-You-but-My-Father-Really-Hates-You Blues. 2004. 72p. (YA). pap. 4.50 (978-1-58342-236-6(6), R74) Dramatic Publishing Co.

Charles, Nancy Linehan, adapted by. A Midsummer Night's Dream or the Night They Missed the Forest for the Trees. (Illus.). 78p. (YA). 6.25 (978-1-58342-092-8(4), MD1) Dramatic Publishing Co.

Chorpenning, Charlotte B. The Indian Captive. (Illus.). (YA). (gr. 6-12). 6.00 (978-0-87602-139-2(9)) Anchorage Pr.

Christian Reader's Theater. 2005. 64p. (J). per. 8.99 (978-1-59441-077-2(1), CD-204004) Carson-Dellosa Publishing Co., Inc.

Church, Alfred John. Stories from the Greek Comedians: Aristophanes, Philemon, Diphilus, Mendander & Apollodorus. 1998. (Illus.). 344p. (YA). (gr. 6-12). reprint ed. pap. 20.00 (978-0-8196-2081-1(5)) Biblo & Tannen Booksellers & Pubs., Inc.

Clark, Anthony, et al. Carlo Collodi's Pinocchio. 2005. 12p. pap. 16.95 (978-1-84002-529-3(8)) Theatre Communications Group, Inc.

Clark, Ouida Ouijella. He Planned to Be A Leader: First Drama of Children of the 21st Century. 2006. pap. 25.00 (978-0-9777289-4-7(3)) Clark Productions Ltd. Inc.

Coble, Eric. Cinderella Confidential. 2004. 48p. (YA). pap. 6.50 (978-1-58342-201-4(3), CB5) Dramatic Publishing Co.

—Pecos Bill & the Ghost Stampede. 2003. 48p. (YA). pap. 6.50 (978-1-58342-202-1(1), PA3) Dramatic Publishing Co.

Coburn, Ann. Alex & the Warrior: A Christmas Play in Two Acts. 2005. (Illus.). 78p. pap. 14.95 (978-1-84002-502-6(6)) Theatre Communications Group, Inc.

Cohen, Frumi. The Magic Flute RELOADED: (play Script) 2006. (YA). pap. 7.00 (*978-0-87602-415-7(0), Anchorage Press Plays) Anchorage Pr.

Cohen, Frumi. Try a Little Shakespeare. 2003. (J). pap. 10.00 (978-0-88734-519-7(0)) Players Pr., Inc.

Collette, Paul & Wright, Robert. Huddles: Playscript. 2003. (Musicals for Young Audiences Ser.). 28p. (Orig.). (YA). (gr. 3-12). pap. 7.00 (978-0-88734-512-8(3)) Players Pr., Inc.

Cook, Pat. Murder's Bad But Monday Can Kill You! 1998. 79p. (YA). (gr. 10 up). pap. 6.25 (978-0-87129-866-9(X), MA8) Dramatic Publishing Co.

—Pandora's Revenge. 1998. 27p. (J). pap. 4.25 (978-0-87129-859-1(7), P64) Dramatic Publishing Co.

Cosgrove, Stephen & Higgins, Kitty. The el juicio del pastelero & Tasty Tort Trial. 2005. spiral bd. 76.00 (*978-1-4108-5793-4(X)) Benchmark Education Co.

—Semillas de Estrellamelon Star-Melon Seeds. 2005. spiral bd. 76.00 (*978-1-4108-5791-0(3)) Benchmark Education Co.

Cosgrove, Stephen & Higgins, Kitty. Star-Melon Seeds. ed. 2004. (Reader's Theater Ser.). (J). pap. 22.00 (978-1-4108-1139-4(5)) Benchmark Education Co.

Craddock, Chris. Naked at School: Three Plays for Teens. 2005. (Prairie Plays Ser.). (Illus.). 153p. pap. 12.95 (978-1-896300-46-7(4)) NeWest Pubns., Ltd. CAN. *Dist:* Strauss Consultants.

Craig, David & Craig, Danny S. Danny, King of the Basement. 2004. (Illus.). pap. 15.95 (978-0-88754-726-3(5)) Theatre Communications Group, Inc.

Crawford, Sheryl Ann & Sanders, Nancy I. 15 Easy-to-Read Neighborhood & Community Mini-Book Plays. 2003. 64p. pap. 10.95 (978-0-439-22254-9(0), Teaching Resources) Scholastic, Inc.

Crawley, Brian. Halloween Math: Reader's Theater Levels K-M (20-28) Beckes, Shirley, illus. ed. 2004. (Reader's Theater Ser.). 16p. (J). pap. 22.00 (978-1-4108-2300-7(8), A23008) Benchmark Education Co.

Crebbin, June. The Pyjama Party, 6, Pack. 2000. (Cambridge Reading Ser.). (Illus.). 32p. pap. 39.00 (978-0-521-78626-3(6)) Cambridge Univ. Pr.

Croft, Steven. Othello. Beal, Duncan & Jurksaitis, Dinah, eds. 2004. (Nelson Thornes Shakespeare Ser.). (Illus.). 208p. (YA). pap. 14.95 (978-0-7487-8601-5(5)) Nelson Thornes Ltd. GBR. *Dist:* Trans-Atlantic Pubns., Inc.

Cross, Steve. Haunted Hamlet: Comedy Farce Play. 2002. (YA). pap. 4.25 (978-1-931805-85-8(7), 723) Brooklyn Pubs.

—Riches, Witches, & Mystical Switches: Comedy Play. 2002. (YA). pap. 5.00 (978-1-931805-91-9(1), 823) Brooklyn Pubs.

—Simple Things: Dramatic Play. 2002. (YA). pap. 4.00 (978-1-931805-78-0(4)) Brooklyn Pubs.

Crowe, Marla. Pocketwatch: Dramatic Monologue. 2002. (YA). pap. 4.50 (978-1-931805-62-9(8)) Brooklyn Pubs.

—She Doesn't Sell Seashells: Ten-Minute Dramatic Duet. 2002. (YA). pap. 9.00 (978-1-931805-55-1(5), 136A) Brooklyn Pubs.

Cumming, Peter, et al. TYA5: Theatre for Young Audience. 2000. (Illus.). 268p. pap. 17.95 (978-0-88754-577-1(7)) Theatre Communications Group, Inc.

Cummins, Rick, et al. The Little Prince. 1999. 128p. (YA). pap. 6.95 (978-1-58342-195-6(5), L06) Dramatic Publishing Co.

Curtains! Familiar Plays for Little Actors. 88p. (ps-2). 12.99 (978-0-7682-0051-5(2), FE11001, Totline Pubns.) Schaffer, Frank Pubns.

Dahl, Roald. The BFG: A Set of Plays. Jane, Walmsley, illus. 2007. 128p. (J). 5.99 (978-0-14-240792-9(5) , Puffin) Penguin Group (USA) Inc.

—Charlie & the Chocolate Factory. 2007. 96p. (J). (gr. 2). pap. 5.99 (978-0-14-240790-5(9) , Puffin) Penguin Group (USA) Inc.

David C. Cook. Noah's Park Children's Church Puppet Skits: Green Edition. 2002. (Children's Church Kits Ser.). (J). pap., pap. 14.99 (978-0-7814-3845-2(4) , 0781438454) Cook, David C. Publishing Co.

David, Peter, et al. Cyrano de Bergerac. (Classics Illustrated Ser.). (Illus.). 52p. (YA). pap. 4.95 (978-1-57209-019-4(7)) Classics International Entertainment, Inc.

Davies, Robertson. Fifth Business. abr. ed. 2005. (Deptford Trilogy Ser.: Vol. 1). (gr. 9-12). (978-0-660-18654-2(3)) Canadian Broadcasting Corp./Societe Radio-Canada.

de Lancie, John & Segaloff, Nat. The Wright Brothers First Flight-Radio. 2000. 22p. (YA). 6.25 (978-1-58342-010-2(X) , W87) Dramatic Publishing Co.

de Lancie, John, et al. Journey to the Center of the Earth-Radio Play. 1999. 54p. (YA). 10.95 (978-0-87129-968-0(2) , J34) Dramatic Publishing Co.

—The Lost World. 1999. 54p. (YA). 10.95 (978-0-87129-969-7(0) , LA3) Dramatic Publishing Co.

—The Time Machine. 1999. 56p. (YA). 10.95 (978-0-87129-970-3(4) , TC5) Dramatic Publishing Co.

Dean, Jan. Harry & the Megabyte Brain, 6 vols., Pack. 2000. (Cambridge Reading Ser.). (Illus.). 40p. pap. 44.75 (978-0-521-78629-4(0)) Cambridge Univ. Pr.

Dean, Michael. A Ghost in Love & Other Plays. 2000. (Oxford Bookworms Playscripts Ser.). (Illus.). 48p. 6.50 (978-0-19-422854-1(1)) Oxford Univ. Pr., Inc.

Declare His Name: Missionary Sketches, Dramatic Readings, Dramas. 2001. 96p. pap. 8.95 (978-1-888796-26-1(X)) ABWE Publishing.

Dempsey, Sandra. Legacy: Dramatic Monologue. 2002. (YA). pap. 4.50 (978-1-931805-50-6(4) , 255) Brooklyn Pubs.

Desmarattes, J. Lyonel. Lakol Medam Yo. 2004. Orig. Title: L' Ecole des Femmes. (CRP.). 80p. (YA). per. 15.00 (978-1-58432-170-5(9)) Educa Vision.

DeVita, James. Excavating Mom. 1998. Orig. Title: Dinosaur!. 48p. (YA). (gr. 7 up). pap. 6.25 (978-0-87129-904-8(6) , E40) Dramatic Publishing Co.

Dirksing, Donna. First Stage: A Collection of Musical Plays for Children's First Performances Arranged with Orff Instruments for Grades 1-3. 2006. 24.95 (978-0-89328-020-8(8)) Heritage Music Pr.

Donaldson, Julia. Bombs & Blackberries: A World War Two Play. Dupasquier, Philippe, illus. 48p. (YA). (978-0-7502-4124-3(1) , Hodder Wayland) Hodder Children's Division.

Donaldson, Julie. The Head in the Sand: A Roman Play. Collins, Ross, illus. 48p. (J). (978-0-7502-4126-7(8) , Hodder Wayland) Hodder Children's Division.

Doyle, Alfreda C. Alfreda's Reader's Theatre: Comedy Club. Date not set. (Illus.). (J). spiral bd. 8.95 (978-1-56820-362-1(4)) Story Time Stories That Rhyme.

—Alfreda's Reader's Theatre: Dialogues. Date not set. (Illus.). (J). spiral bd. 10.95 (978-1-56820-361-4(6)) Story Time Stories That Rhyme.

—Alfreda's Reader's Theatre: Public Transportation. Date not set. (Illus.). (J). spiral bd. 8.95 (978-1-56820-360-7(8)) Story Time Stories That Rhyme.

—Alfreda's Readers Theatre; Story Plays That Rhyme. 1998. (Illus.). 38p. (J). (gr. 5-8). ring bd., wbk. ed. 19.95 (978-1-56820-356-0(X)) Story Time Stories That Rhyme.

—Coats. 1998. (Illus.). 12p. (J). 8.95 (978-1-56820-353-9(5)) Story Time Stories That Rhyme.

—The Missing Hammer Oyster Shell. 1998. (Illus.). 20p. (J). (gr. 5-8). pap. 8.95 (978-1-56820-354-6(3)) Story Time Stories That Rhyme.

—The Missing Sugar Beet. Date not set. (Illus.). (J). (gr. 5-8). spiral bd. 8.95 (978-1-56820-355-3(1)) Story Time Stories That Rhyme.

—Murphy the Mistletoe: Adventures from the Garden of Eden to the Garden of Nede. 1998. 20p. (J). 8.95 (978-1-56820-351-5(9)) Story Time Stories That Rhyme.

—Story Course - Mask: Stories, Poetry & Color Therapy. 1998. (Illus.). 40p. (J). pap., wbk. ed. 29.95 (978-1-56820-377-5(2)) Story Time Stories That Rhyme.

—Zuetoo Mask Go to the Gallery. 1998. (Illus.). 10p. (J). 8.95 (978-1-56820-352-2(7)) Story Time Stories That Rhyme.

Doyle, Arthur Conan. Sherlock Holmes: Two Plays. 2000. (Oxford Bookworms Playscripts Ser.). (Illus.). 48p. 6.50 (978-0-19-422853-4(3)) Oxford Univ. Pr., Inc.

Drama Club, 6 Packs. (On Deck Ser.). 24p. (gr. 4-5). 35.00 (978-0-7578-1022-0(5)) Rigby Education.

Duffey, William, Jr. Riddles & Short Stories & Mini Plays. 2002. 32p. pap. 8.00 (978-0-8059-5927-7(0)) Dorrance Publishing Co., Inc.

Duffield, Neil & Burnett, Frances Hodgson. The Secret Garden: A Play. 1999. 54p. (J). (978-0-573-05120-3(8)) French, Samuel Inc.

Dugan, Michael. Life's a Riot! 21p. (J). (gr. 4-6). pap. (978-1-875739-30-1(0)) Wizard Bks.

Dunn, Mark. Frank's Life. 1998. 98p. (YA). (gr. 10 up). pap. 6.25 (978-0-87129-858-4(9) , F66) Dramatic Publishing Co.

Dunster, Mark. Cain: With Help from Lord Byron. 2000. 25p. (YA). pap. 5.00 (978-0-7949-0164-6(6)) Linden Pubs.

Dunster, Mark & Byron, George Gordon. The Count: An Episode. 2000. 16p. (YA). pap. 5.00 (978-0-7949-0166-0(2)) Linden Pubs.

Edcon Staff. As You Like It: Level 3. 2004. 72p. (YA). act. bk. ed. 9.95 (978-1-55576-329-9(4) , EDSC301B) AV Concepts Corp.

—The Tempest Worktext: Level 2. 2004. 72p. (YA). act. bk. ed. 9.95 (978-1-55576-327-5(8) , EDSC-201B) AV Concepts Corp.

Edson, Margaret. Wit: A Play. 1999. (gr. 7-12). lib. bdg. 22.25 (978-0-613-36752-3(9)) Tandem Library Bks.

Ellis, Roger. International Plays for Young Audiences: Contemporary Works from Leading Playwrights. 2000. 384p. (J). (gr. 7 up). pap. 16.95 (978-1-56608-065-1(7) , N-B240) Meriwether Publishing, Ltd.

Ellis, Roger, ed. & intro. New International Plays for Young Audiences: Plays of Cultural Conflict. Ellis, Roger, intro. 2002. (Plays of Cultural Conflict Ser.). (Illus.). 561p. pap. 19.95 (978-1-56608-081-1(9) , N-B257) Meriwether Publishing, Ltd.

Elzbieta. Mimi's Scary Theater: A Play in Nine Scenes for Seven Characters & an Egg. Elzbieta & Hawcock, David, illus. 2004. 20p. (J). (ps-3). reprint ed. 15.00 (978-0-7567-8299-3(6)) DIANE Publishing Co.

Emert, Phyllis Raybin. California Missions: A Play & Debate. 1998. (J). (gr. 5-9). pap. 12.00 (978-1-57960-035-8(2)) History Compass, LLC.

Engelhardt, James. Androcles & the Lion. 1999. 64p. (J). (gr. 1 up). pap. 6.25 (978-0-87129-914-7(3) , A71) Dramatic Publishing Co.

Espinosa, Resurreccion. Don Quijote in America: Plays in English & Spanish, Grades 1-6. 2002. (ENG & SPA.). Illus.). 221p. (J). (gr. 1-6). pap. 38.00 (978-1-56308-927-5(0) , LU9270) Libraries Unlimited, Inc.

Euripides. Helen. Burian, Peter, ed. 2005. (GEC & ENG.). 200p. 70.00 (978-0-85668-650-4(6)); pap. 35.00 (978-0-85668-651-1(4)) Aris & Phillips GBR. *Dist:* Brown, David Bk. Co., The.

Evans, Olive. Secrets of the Forest: Playscript. 2003. (Theater for Young Audiences Ser.). 44p. (YA). (gr. 3-12). reprint ed. pap. 6.00 (978-0-88734-502-9(6)) Players Pr., Inc.

Falconer, Ian. Teatro Olivia: Swan Lake; Romeo & Juliet; Turandot. Falconer, Ian, illus. 2004. (Olivia Ser.). (Illus.). 10p. (J). 19.95 (978-0-689-87816-9(8)) Simon & Schuster, Inc.

Fannon, Cecilia & de Lancie, John. The Halloween Trilogy - Radio Play. 1999. 45p. (YA). 10.95 (978-0-87129-967-3(4) , H74) Dramatic Publishing Co.

Fearon, Mary. 25 Plays Based on the New Testament. 1998. (Scripture Comes Alive Ser.: Vol. 2). (J). (gr. 2 up). pap. 69.95 (978-0-8294-0997-0(1)) Loyola Pr.

Fennessey, Sharon. A Matter of Justice: A Play. 2002. (J). pap. 12.00 (978-1-57960-085-3(9)) History Compass, LLC.

Fleischman, Paul. Zap. 2003. 160p. (YA). (gr. 7-11). 16.95 (978-0-8126-2687-2(7)) Cricket Bks.

—Zap: A Play. 96p. (gr. 9). 2006. (YA). pap. 5.99 (978-0-7636-3234-2(1)); 2005. (J). 16.99 (978-0-7636-2774-4(7)) Candlewick Pr.

Flounders, Anne. The Corps of Discovery: Reader's Theater Levels R-T (40-44) Leon, Karen, illus. ed. 2004. (Reader's Theater Ser.). 16p. (J). 22.00 (978-1-4108-2310-6(5) , A23105) Benchmark Education Co.

Focus on the Family. The Great Follywood Fizzle: Fearless or Fake? 2003. (J). 12.99 incl. VHS (978-0-310-70585-7(1)) Zonderkidz.

Fogg, Scott. Power Skits for Youth & Young Adults: 25 Faith-Awakening, Disciple-Making Drama Presentations. 2006. 175p. pap. (*978-0-8280-1883-8(9)) Review & Herald Publishing Assn.

Foon, Dennis. The Short Tree & the Bird That Could Not Sing. 2003. (Illus.). (gr. 4-7). pap. 10.95 (978-0-921368-79-3(8)) Blizzard Publishing, Inc. CAN. *Dist:* Consortium Bk. Sales & Distribution.

Foster, Cass. Macbeth. 2000. (gr. 7-12). lib. bdg. 17.60 (978-0-613-80142-3(3)) Tandem Library Bks.

France, Anatole. The Man Who Married a Dumb Wife. Landes, William-Alan, ed. 2003. 28p. (YA). (gr. 8-12). pap. 7.00 (978-0-88734-850-1(5)) Players Pr., Inc.

Francis, Mary. Praise Him with Your Very Life: A Collection of Plays. 2005. (Illus.). 173p. spiral bd. 18.95 (978-0-9788376-0-0(6)) Catholic Heritage Curricula.

Frankie Dolan, Ragtime Orphan. 2nd ed. 2006. (YA). pap. (978-1-932663-13-6(4)) History Compass, LLC.

Fuerst, Jeffrey B. How the Hubba-Dubbas Saved Lake Ni-ni: Reader's Theater Levels F-M (9-28) DuFalla, Anita, illus. ed. 2004. (Reader's Theater Ser.). 16p. (J). pap. 22.00 (978-1-4108-2292-5(3) , A22925) Benchmark Education Co.

Gabridge, Pat. Deadly Perfection: Ten-Minute Dramatic Duet. 2002. (YA). pap. 9.00 (978-1-931805-32-2(6) , 118A) Brooklyn Pubs.

—Den of Iniquity: A Ten-Minute Comedy Duet. 2003. 16p. (YA). pap. 4.50 (978-1-932404-19-7(8) , 155A) Brooklyn Pubs.

—Flight: A Ten-Minute Dramatic Duet. 2001. (YA). (gr. 7-12). pap. 4.50 (978-1-931000-74-1(3) , 106A) Brooklyn Pubs.

—Flying the Friendly Skies: A Ten-Minute Dramatic Duet. 2003. 16p. (YA). pap. 4.50 (978-1-932404-20-3(1) , 156A) Brooklyn Pubs.

—The Invisible Husband: A Ten-Minute Dramatic Duet. 2003. 16p. (YA). pap. 4.50 (978-1-931805-99-5(7) , 151A) Brooklyn Pubs.

—It's a Girl! A Ten-Minute Comedy Duet. 2003. (YA). pap. 4.50 (978-1-931805-95-7(4) , 147A) Brooklyn Pubs.

—Lies for the Holidays: Ten-Minute Dramatic Duet. 2002. (YA). pap. 9.00 (978-1-931805-34-6(2) , 120A) Brooklyn Pubs.

—Measuring Matthew: A Ten-Minute Comedy Duet. 2003. (YA). pap. 4.50 (978-1-931805-92-6(X) , 144A) Brooklyn Pubs.

—Phoenix Funeral Draft 3: A Ten-Minute Comedy Duet. 2003. 16p. (YA). pap. 4.50 (978-1-931805-98-8(9) , 150A) Brooklyn Pubs.

—Silent Battle: Ten-Minute Dramatic Duet. 2002. (YA). pap. 9.00 (978-1-931805-29-2(6) , 115A) Brooklyn Pubs.

Gabridge, Patrick. The Sky Is Falling: A One-Act Comedy Play. 2003. (YA). pap. 4.50 (978-1-932404-58-6(9) , 756) Brooklyn Pubs.

Gaudreault, Jean-Rock & Gaboriau, Linda. Two Steps from the Stars: Deux Pas Vers les étoiles. 2007. 96p. pap. 17.95 (*978-0-88754-884-0(9)) Theatre Communications Group, Inc.

Gavin, Jamila, adapted by. Monkeys in the Stars: A Play [for Children]. 2001. (Illus.). 55p. (J). (978-0-573-01528-1(7)) French, Samuel Inc.

Geer, Sheila. Lady in the Jukebox. 2001. (gr. 3-6). lib. bdg. 24.55 (978-0-613-74545-1(0)) Tandem Library Bks.

Getzinger, Donna. A Long Trail: A Play about the Cherokee Trail of Tears. 2002. (J). pap. 12.00 (978-1-57960-089-1(1)) History Compass, LLC.

Giannakeff, Dianne D., adapted by. The Young Actor's Bible: Stories from the Bible. 2004. (J). spiral bd. 39.95 (978-0-9762297-0-4(6)) Lucia Pubs.

Gibson, William. Miracle Worker. 2002. (gr. 5-8). lib. bdg. 14.15 (978-0-613-61040-7(7)) Tandem Library Bks.

Gilleland, Michael S. Macbeth. 2000. 68p. (YA). (gr. 9-12). stu. ed., ring bd. 14.99 (978-1-58609-170-5(0) , 416C) Progeny Pr.

Gingerich, Neeltje & Peterson, Joyce. The Secret Garden. 1999. 38p. (gr. 1-12). pap. 10.00 (978-0-88734-045-1(8)) Players Pr., Inc.

Glavich, Mary Kathleen. Gospel Theater for the Whole Community: 92 Plays for Education & Worship. 2006. 224p. pap. 29.95 (*978-1-58595-563-3(9)) Twenty-Third Pubns./Bayard.

Glennon, William. The Trial of the Arkansas Bear. 2003. 52p. (YA). pap. 6.25 (978-1-58342-158-1(0) , TE5) Dramatic Publishing Co.

Glennon, William, adapted by. The Five Little Peppers & How They Grew. 2000. 59p. (YA). pap. 6.25 (978-0-87129-996-3(8) , F69) Dramatic Publishing Co.

Glore, John. Rhubarb Jam: A Musical Play. 1999. 36p. (YA). (gr. 4 up). pap. 4.00 (978-0-88680-551-7(1)) Clark, I. E. Pubns.

Goetzee, Paul & Ridley, Philip. The Pilgrimage - Brokenville. 2000. (Connections Ser.). (Illus.). 112p. (YA). pap. 17.95 (978-0-7487-4292-9(1)) Nelson Thornes Ltd. GBR. *Dist:* Trans-Atlantic Pubns., Inc.

Goldberg, Moses. Cinderella: A Musical. 1998. (J). (gr. k-5). pap. 6.00 (978-0-87602-357-0(X)) Anchorage Pr.

Goldberg, Moses. Sleeping Beauty (Dornroschen) (Play Script) 2006. (J). pap. 6.00 (*978-0-87602-416-4(9) , Anchorage Press Plays) Anchorage Pr.

Goldenthal, Jolene. The Beautiful Truth: A One-Act Comedy Play. 2003. (YA). pap. 4.50 (978-1-932404-64-7(3) , 762) Brooklyn Pubs.

Gonzales, Jose Cruz. Harvest Moon. (Illus.). 79p. (YA). 6.25 (978-1-58342-097-3(5) , H79) Dramatic Publishing Co.

Goodrich, Hackett, ed. The Diary of Anne Frank: 10 Speaking Parts. 2nd ed. 1998. (Dramascripts Classic Texts Ser.). 96p. (J). (gr. 6-9). pap. 17.95 (978-0-17-432550-5(9)) Nelson Thornes Ltd. GBR. *Dist:* Trans-Atlantic Pubns., Inc.

Gordon, Mick & Teevan, Colin. Monkey: A Tale from China. 2002. 72p. pap. 16.95 (978-1-84002-257-5(4) , Oberon Bks.) Theatre Communications Group, Inc.

Gorky, Maxim. The Lower Depths. Landes, William-Alan, ed. Covan, Jennie, tr. from RUS. unabr. ed. 2003. (Players Press Classic Plays Ser.). 64p. (YA). (gr. 4-12). pap. 7.50 (978-0-88734-815-0(7)) Players Pr., Inc.

Graham, Joseph. Who's Gonna Save Me? It's Time to Tell Your Secrets. 2005. 126p. (YA). pap. 14.00 (978-0-9767778-0-9(0) , 704-724-1683) Alpha & Omega Publishing.

Greenidge, Kirsten. Familiar. 2004. (YA). pap. 6.50 (978-1-58342-175-8(0) , F79) Dramatic Publishing Co.

Gregg, Stephen. S. P. A. R. a play / 2003. 26p. (YA). pap. 4.25 (978-1-58342-157-4(2) , SH5) Dramatic Publishing Co.

Group/McGraw-Hill, Wright. Crabs & Frogs Play 2. Decodable Plays, 6 vols. (Fasttrack Reading Ser.). 24p. (gr. 4-8). 40.95 (978-0-322-06003-6(6)) Wright Group, The.

—The Mascot Play 3: Decodable Plays, 6 vols. (Fasttrack Reading Ser.). 24p. (gr. 4-8). 40.95 (978-0-322-05993-1(3)) Wright Group, The.

—Queen of the Trail Play 8: Decodable Plays, 6 vols. (Fasttrack Reading Ser.). 24p. (gr. 4-8). 40.95 (978-0-322-05999-3(2)) Wright Group, The.

—Saws Don't Pounce Play 9: Decodable Plays, 6 vols. (Fasttrack Reading Ser.). 24p. (gr. 4-8). 40.95 (978-0-322-06001-2(X)) Wright Group, The.

Groves. Six Silly Plays. Date not set. (Illus.). 58p. pap. 65.00 (978-0-582-24379-8(3)) Addison-Wesley Longman, Ltd. GBR. *Dist:* Trans-Atlantic Pubns., Inc.

Guderjahn, Ernie L. A Children's Trilogy: Ali's Flying Rug, the Shadow Workers, & the Magic Cricket (Playscript) 2003. (Theater for Young Audiences Ser.). 32p. (Orig.). (YA). (gr. 3 up). pap. 6.00 (978-0-88734-504-3(2)) Players Pr., Inc.

Haehnel, Alan. The Blender: A One-Act Dark Comedy Play. 2003. (YA). pap. 4.50 (978-1-932404-57-9(0) , 755) Brooklyn Pubs.

—Excuses, Excuses: Comedy Play. 2002. (YA). pap. 4.25 (978-1-931805-81-0(4)) Brooklyn Pubs.

—The Twisting-Turning Death Machine: Ten-Minute Comedy Duet. 2003. (YA). pap. 9.00 (978-1-932404-02-9(3) , 139A) Brooklyn Pubs.

—What the Doctor Ordered: Ten-Minute Comedy Duet. 2003. (YA). pap. 9.00 (978-1-932404-00-5(7) , 137A) Brooklyn Pubs.

Hall, Bevelyn C. Royal Wedding of Sugarland Heights: A Play in Two Acts. 1999. 104p. (J). (gr. k-6). pap. 12.00 (978-0-8059-4536-2(9)) Dorrance Publishing Co., Inc.

Hall, Willis & Waterhouse, Keith. Billy Liar: 8 Speaking Parts. 2nd ed. 1998. (Dramascripts Classic Texts Ser.). 124p. (J). (gr. 6-9). pap. 17.95 (978-0-17-432549-9(5)) Nelson Thornes Ltd. GBR. *Dist:* Trans-Atlantic Pubns., Inc.

Halligan, Terry. Funny Skits & Sketches. Behr, Joyce, illus. unabr. ed. 2003. 128p. (YA). (gr. 4-12). pap. 15.00 (978-0-88734-688-0(X)) Players Pr., Inc.

Hamlett, Christina. Humorous Plays for Teenagers. 2001. (Orig.). (YA). (gr. 7-12). pap. 12.95 (978-0-8238-0276-0(0)) Kalmbach Publishing Co., Bks. Div.

Hannaford, Anne. Pride & Prejudice: 26 Speaking Parts. 1999. (Dramascripts Classic Texts Ser.). (J). (gr. 6-9). pap. 17.95 (978-0-17-432558-1(4)) Nelson Thornes Ltd. GBR. *Dist:* Trans-Atlantic Pubns., Inc.

Harcourt School Publishers Staff. Always in Style: Take-Home Book. 2001. (Collections Ser.). (Illus.). (J). pap. 1.90 (978-0-15-319531-0(2)) Harcourt Schl. Pubs.

—Always in Style Below Level. 3rd ed. 2002. (Trophies Reading Program Ser.). (Illus.). pap. 5.10 (978-0-15-323329-6(X)) Harcourt Schl. Pubs.

—Bus Stop: Take-Home Book. 2001. (Collections Ser.). (Illus.). (J). pap. 1.90 (978-0-15-319563-1(0)) Harcourt Schl. Pubs.

—Bus Stop Below Level. 3rd ed. 2002. (Trophies Reading Program Ser.). (Illus.). pap. 5.10 (978-0-15-323421-7(0)) Harcourt Schl. Pubs.

—How Fire Came into the World Below Level. 3rd ed. 2002. (Trophies Reading Program Ser.). (Illus.). pap. 5.10 (978-0-15-323139-1(4)) Harcourt Schl. Pubs.

—How Fire Came to the World: Take-Home Book. 1999. (Collections Ser.). (Illus.). (J). pap. 1.90 (978-0-15-317296-0(7)) Harcourt Schl. Pubs.

—A Race in the Dark On Level. 3rd ed. 2002. (Trophies Reading Program Ser.). (Illus.). pap. 5.10 (978-0-15-323453-8(9)) Harcourt Schl. Pubs.

—Trying Out On Level. 3rd ed. 2002. (Trophies Reading Program Ser.). (Illus.). pap. 5.10 (978-0-15-323180-3(7)) Harcourt Schl. Pubs.

—Wise Queen Catherine Below Level. 3rd ed. 2002. (Trophies Reading Program Ser.). (Illus.). pap. 5.10 (978-0-15-323226-8(9)) Harcourt Schl. Pubs.

Harder, Eleanor. What'd Ya Do Today, Billy Joe? 2003. 40p. (YA). pap. 4.50 (978-1-58342-188-8(2) , W98) Dramatic Publishing Co.

Harris, Aurand. The Orphan Train. 1998. pap. 6.50 (978-0-87602-360-0(X)) Anchorage Pr.

Harris, Denise. Are You Sleeping. 2008. 48p. pap. 7.50 (*978-0-687-64669-2(3)) Abingdon Pr.

Harris, Valerie. The Saga of Henry Box Brown: A Play for Black History Month. 2004. (Illus.). 35p. spiral bd. 12.95 (978-0-9772126-0-6(2)) BPT Media.

Henderson, Heather H. Flip Side II: 64 More Point-of-View Monologs for Teens. 2001. (gr. 7-12). lib. bdg. 25.70 (978-0-613-87950-7(3)) Tandem Library Bks.

Hendrickson, Clyde. The Altos: A Clyde Hendrickson Joint. 2003. (YA). 7.99 (978-0-9679552-7-8(0)) Mushroom Cloud Pr. of Orlando.

—The Merchandise King: A Parody. 2001. 16p. (YA). 8.50 (978-0-9679552-1-6(1)) Mushroom Cloud Pr. of Orlando.

—Special Places. 2003. (AFR.). 20p. (YA). 8.50 (978-0-9679552-5-4(4)) Mushroom Cloud Pr. of Orlando.

—Squirrel. 2003. (YA). 11.00 (978-0-9679552-6-1(2)) Mushroom Cloud Pr. of Orlando.

Hennessey, Gail Skroback. Will the Real Paul Revere Please Stand Up? And 14 Other American History Plays: Short Guess-Who Plays That Motivate Kids to Learn about Key Figures in American History: Grades 4-8. 2002. 40p. 12.95 (978-0-439-09842-7(4)) Scholastic, Inc.

Henry, O. One Thousand Dollars & Other Plays. 2002. (Oxford Bookworms Playscripts Ser.). (Illus.). 48p. 6.50 (978-0-19-423216-6(6)) Oxford Univ. Pr., Inc.

Henry V & the Disappearing Playhouse: 19 Speaking Parts. 2001. (Dramascripts Classic Texts Ser.). 96p. (J). (gr. 6-10). pap. 16.95 (978-0-17-432666-3(1)) Nelson Thornes Ltd. GBR. *Dist:* Trans-Atlantic Pubns., Inc.

Heslep, William. Tower of London. 2003. 23p. (J). pap. 6.00 (978-0-88734-418-3(6)) Players Pr., Inc.

Heurtelou, Maude. Wowo ak Jilyèt. 2002. (CRP.). 84p. (YA). per. 11.50 (978-1-58432-152-1(0)) Educa Vision.

Hezlep, William. Bigfoot! 2004. (Travelers Ser.). 24p. (J). (gr. 3-6). pap. 5.00 (978-0-88734-485-5(2)) Players Pr., Inc.

—Bog Bodies. 2004. (Travelers Ser.). 20p. (J). pap. 5.00 (978-0-88734-467-1(4)) Players Pr., Inc.

—Cayman Duppy: Playscript. 2003. 16p. (YA). (gr. 5 up). pap. 5.00 (978-0-88734-403-9(8)) Players Pr., Inc.

—Curse of the Tomb Raiders. 2005. (Travelers Ser.). 32p. (J). pap. 6.00 (978-0-88734-565-4(4)) Players Pr., Inc.

—How Come Christmas? 2003. (Theater for Young Audiences Ser.). 18p. (J). pap. 5.00 (978-0-88734-424-4(0)) Players Pr., Inc.

—Kokopelli's Cave. 2003. (Travelers Ser.). 24p. (J). (gr. k-6). pap. 5.00 (978-0-88734-466-4(6)) Players Pr., Inc.

—Merlin's Cave. 2003. (Theater for Young Audiences Ser.). 55p. (Orig.). (YA). (gr. k-12). pap. 6.00 (978-0-88734-420-6(8)) Players Pr., Inc.

—Nessie: Playscript. 2003. 24p. (J). (gr. 3-12). reprint ed. pap. 6.00 (978-0-88734-401-5(1)) Players Pr., Inc.

—Pharaoh's Dagger: Playscript. 2003. 70p. (Orig.). (J). (gr. 3-12). reprint ed. pap. 6.00 (978-0-88734-404-6(6)) Players Pr., Inc.

—Shipwrecked. Landes, William Alan, ed. unabr. ed. 2003. (Ideal for Teens Ser.). 21p. (J). (gr. 3-8). pap. 5.00 (978-0-88734-484-8(4)) Players Pr., Inc.

—Time Travelers, 16 vols. 2006. (Travelers Ser.). 36p. (J). (gr. 3-6). pap. 6.00 (978-0-88734-573-9(5)) Players Pr., Inc.

—Treasure of the Mayans. 2003. 28p. (Orig.). (J). (gr. 3-8). pap. 6.00 (978-0-88734-405-3(4)) Players Pr., Inc.

Higgins, Frank. The Slave Dancer's Choice. 40p. (YA). pap. 6.50 (978-1-58342-166-6(1) , SH6) Dramatic Publishing Co.

Higgins, Kitty. As the Crow Flies: Reader's Theater Levels N-U (30-50) Leon, Karen, illus. ed. 2004. (Reader's Theater Ser.). 16p. (J). pap. 22.00 (978-1-4108-2304-5(0) , A23040) Benchmark Education Co.

—Great Beasts of the Great Plains: Reader's Theater Levels S-U (44-50) Leon, Karen, illus. ed. 2004. (Reader's Theater Ser.). 16p. (J). pap. 22.00 (978-1-4108-2311-3(3) , A23113) Benchmark Education Co.

—The Three Sisters: Reader's Theater Levels S-U (44-50) Corcoran, Mark, illus. ed. 2004. (Reader's Theater Ser.). 16p. (J). pap. 22.00 (978-1-4108-2312-0(1) , A23121) Benchmark Education Co.

Higgins, Kitty & Fuerst, Jeffrey B. Above the Clouds: Reader's Theater Levels R-T (40-44) Leon, Karen, illus. ed. 2004. (Reader's Theater Ser.). 16p. (J). pap. 22.00 (978-1-4108-2309-0(1) , A23091) Benchmark Education Co.

Hodge, Bill. Cyril: Tales of a Teenage Cyrano. 31p. (YA). (gr. 7-12). pap. 4.00 (978-1-57514-153-4(1) , 1160) Encore Performance Publishing.

Holtzman, Willy. Hearts. (Illus.). 66p. (YA). 6.25 (978-1-58342-093-5(2) , H81) Dramatic Publishing Co.

Howard, Annabelle. Alex in Numberland: Reader's Theater Levels O-Q (34-40) DuFalla, Anita, illus. ed. 2004. (Reader's Theater Ser.). 16p. (J). pap. 22.00 (978-1-4108-2303-8(2) , A23032) Benchmark Education Co.

—Battle for the Ballot: Reader's Theater Levels N-U (30-50) Leon, Karen, illus. ed. 2004. (Reader's Theater Ser.). 16p. (J). pap. 22.00 (978-1-4108-2305-2(9) , A23059) Benchmark Education Co.

—The Big Cheese: Reader's Theater Levels F-M (9-28) Leon, Karen, illus. ed. 2004. (Reader's Theater Ser.). 16p. (J). pap. 22.00 (978-1-4108-2294-9(X) , A2294X) Benchmark Education Co.

—The King's New Crown: Reader's Theater Levels I-K (15-20) DuFalla, Anita, illus. ed. 2004. (Reader's Theater Ser.). 16p. (J). pap. 22.00 (978-1-4108-2296-3(6) , A22966) Benchmark Education Co.

Huckel, Oliver. Parsifal (a Drama by Wagner) 2006. pap. 33.99 (***978-1-4219-7292-3(1)***) IndyPublish.com.

Hughes, Anne. Civil War Duos: Collection of Three Duets. 2002. (YA). pap. 19.95 (978-1-931805-75-9(X)) Brooklyn Pubs.

—An Unwelcome Guest: Ten-Minute Comedy Duet. 2002. (YA). pap. 9.00 (978-1-931805-42-1(3) , 127A) Brooklyn Pubs.

Hughes, Ted. Collected Plays for Children. Blake, Quentin, illus. 2001. 144p. (978-0-571-20957-6(2)) Faber & Faber, Inc.

Hurst, Keith. Canterbury Tales: Theatrical Adaptation of Six Tales. 2001. (Superscripts Ser.). (Illus.). 72p. (J). (gr. 6-10). pap. 15.95 (978-0-7487-5694-0(9)) Nelson Thornes Ltd. GBR. *Dist:* Trans-Atlantic Pubns., Inc.

Hutchins, Laurence. I'm the King of the Castle! And Other Plays for Children. Hutchins, Laurence, illus. 2005. (Illus.). 17p. pap. 20.95 (978-1-84002-486-9(0)) Theatre Communications Group, Inc.

I Know What Love Ain't. 2001. 360p. (YA). per. 12.95 (978-0-9709448-0-1(2)) Jade Publishing Co.

Ibsen, Henrik. A Doll's House - Literary Touchstone Edition. 2005. 88p. (YA). per. 3.99 (978-1-58049-598-1(2) , PWH5982) Prestwick Hse., Inc.

In the Mind of the Beholder: A Ten-Minute Dramatic Duet. 2003. (YA). pap. 4.50 (978-1-932404-22-7(8) , 158A) Brooklyn Pubs.

Jackson, R. Eugene. Beauty & the Beast: A Musical Play for Youngsters with a Cajun Flavor. 1999. 64p. (J). (gr. k-12). pap. 4.50 (978-0-88680-460-2(4)) Clark, I. E. Pubns.

James, Steven. 30 New Testament Quick Skits for Kids. 2006. 96p. (YA). pap. 15.99 (978-0-7847-1630-4(7) , 42014) Standard Publishing.

—30 Old Testament Quick Skits for Kids. 2006. (Illus.). 96p. (YA). pap. 15.99 (978-0-7847-1629-8(3) , 42013) Standard Publishing.

Janet & Donald Play 7: Decodable Plays, 6 vols. (Fasttrack Reading Ser.). 24p. (gr. 4-8). 40.95 (978-0-322-05998-6(4)) Wright Group, The.

Jasspon, Ethel Reed. Ritual & Dramatized Folkways. 2006. (Illus.). pap. 24.95 (***978-1-4286-6016-8(X)***) Kessinger Publishing, LLC.

Jeffs, Stephanie. Practical Ways to Christmas Plays: Five Christmas Plays for 7-11s, Complete with 'Beyond the Script' Preapration Material & Photocopy Permission. Taylor, Jane, illus. unexpurg. ed. 2005. 64p. (J). pap. (978-1-84101-225-4(4) , Barnabas) Bible Reading Fellowship.

Jenkins, Diana R. All Year Long! Funny Readers Theatre for Life's Special Times. 2007. 264p. (J). pap. 25.00 (***978-1-59158-436-0(1)*** , TIP4361, Teacher Ideas Pr.) Libraries Unlimited, Inc.

Jenkins, Diana R. Just Deal with It: Funny Readers Theatre for Life's Not-So-Funny Moments. 2004. (Readers Theatre Ser.). (Illus.). 256p. (J). pap. 30.00 (978-1-59158-043-0(9) , LU0439) Libraries Unlimited, Inc.

Jennings, Coleman A. Eight Plays for Children: The New Generation Play Project. 1999. (Illus.). 493p. (J). pap. 24.95 (978-0-292-74057-0(3)) Univ. of Texas Pr.

Jonas, J. J. The Bald & the Beautiful: Dramatic Monologue. 2002. (YA). pap. 4.50 (978-1-931805-52-0(0) , 257) Brooklyn Pubs.

—Conflagration: A Ten-Minute Dramatic Duet. 2003. 20p. pap. 4.50 (978-1-932404-17-3(1) , 153A) Brooklyn Pubs.

—Last of the Lotto Laity: A Ten-Minute Comedy Monologue. 2003. 16p. (YA). pap. 4.50 (978-1-932404-29-6(5) , 282) Brooklyn Pubs.

—Revenge of the Coach's Daughter: A Ten-Minute Comedy Monologue. 2003. 12p. (YA). pap. 4.50 (978-1-932404-28-9(7) , 281) Brooklyn Pubs.

—Running on Empty: A Ten-Minute Dramatic Monologue. 2003. 16p. (YA). pap. 4.50 (978-1-932404-27-2(9) , 280) Brooklyn Pubs.

—Twitcher: A Ten-Minute Dramatic Duet. 2003. (YA). pap. 4.50 (978-1-931805-93-3(8) , 145A) Brooklyn Pubs.

Jordan, Pat. Classic Literature for Teens: Every Teachers Friend Classroom Plays. 2007. (***978-0-88734-692-7(8)***) Players Pr., Inc.

Joyce, William. Rolie Polie Olie Buzy Book. 2001. 14p. (J). Bk. 2. (Illus.). bds. 6.99 (978-0-7364-0223-1(3)); Bk. 3. 6.99 (978-0-7364-0224-8(1)); Bk. 4. 6.99 (978-0-7364-0225-5(X)); No. 1. 6.99 (978-0-7364-0222-4(5)) Mouse Works.

Juwell & Precious. The Absolute Truth. Smith, Joanie et al, eds. 2005. (Platinum Teen Ser.: Vol. 2). 112p. (YA). (gr. 5-11). per. 6.99 (978-0-9729325-4-7(2)) Precioustymes Entertainment, LLC.

Kaczewski, Deborah. Ditzies: Ten-Minute Comedy Duet. 2002. (YA). pap. 9.00 (978-1-931805-40-7(7) , 135A) Brooklyn Pubs.

—Understatement of the Century: Ten-Minute Dramatic Duet. 2002. (YA). pap. 9.00 (978-1-931805-38-4(5) , 124A) Brooklyn Pubs.

Kameni, Jean Claude. The Sky of God in My Dream. 2002. (Illus.). 32p. (YA). pap. 5.00 (978-0-9713093-1-9(0)) Dulan & Assocs.

Kaplan, Gabrielle Suzanne. Extraordinary Jews, Their Lives on Stage: One-Act Plays for Teens. 2001. 196p. (YA). pap. 12.95 (978-0-86705-051-6(9)) Behrman Hse., Inc.

Karczerski, Deborah. Trapped by a Stroke: Dramatic Monologue. 2002. (YA). pap. 4.50 (978-1-931805-59-9(8) , 264) Brooklyn Pubs.

Karczewski, Deborah. Cheerleader Meets the Goth: A Ten-Minute Comedy Monologue. 2003. 16p. (YA). pap. 4.50 (978-1-932404-25-8(2) , 278) Brooklyn Pubs.

—Demon Child: Ten-Minute Comedy Duet. 2002. (YA). pap. 9.00 (978-1-931805-37-7(7) , 123A) Brooklyn Pubs.

—Forensics Nightmare: Comedy Monologue. 2002. (YA). pap. 4.50 (978-1-931805-61-2(X)) Brooklyn Pubs.

—Martial Arts Mama: Ten-Minute Dramatic Duet. 2002. (YA). pap. 9.00 (978-1-931805-48-3(2) , 133A) Brooklyn Pubs.

—The Other Animal Right: Comedy Monologue. 2002. (YA). pap. 4.50 (978-1-931805-64-3(4)) Brooklyn Pubs.

—Post-Mortem: Dramatic Monologue. 2002. (YA). pap. 4.50 (978-1-931805-63-6(6)) Brooklyn Pubs.

—Sassy & the Boss: Dramatic Monologue. 2002. (YA). pap. 4.50 (978-1-931805-67-4(9)) Brooklyn Pubs.

—Schmaltz: Dramatic Monologue. 2002. (YA). pap. 4.50 (978-1-931805-66-7(0)) Brooklyn Pubs.

—A Sobering Laugh: Ten-Minute Dramatic-Comedy Duet. 2002. (YA). pap. 9.00 (978-1-931805-36-0(9) , 122A) Brooklyn Pubs.

—Stand-in Sister: Ten-Minute Dramatic Duet. 2002. (YA). pap. 9.00 (978-1-931805-45-2(8) , 130A) Brooklyn Pubs.

—Two Women Scenes for Teens: Collection of Six Duets for Teen Women. 2002. (YA). pap. 19.95 (978-1-931805-72-8(5)) Brooklyn Pubs.

Katz, Leon. Fables: A Collection for Youth. 2006. 68p. (YA). pap. 5.95 (978-1-60003-159-4(3) , 617) Brooklyn Pubs.

Kaye, David. Rump. 1998. 47p. (J). (gr. k-5). mass mkt. 7.00 (978-1-58193-176-1(X)) Brown Bag Productions.

Kaye, Leon. Cooking on the Street: A Comedy Monologue. 2003. (YA). pap. 4.50 (978-1-932404-33-3(3) , 286) Brooklyn Pubs.

—Eat a Can: A Comedy Skit, 3 Booklets. 2003. (YA). pap. 9.00 (978-1-932404-36-4(8) , 324) Brooklyn Pubs.

Keene, Daniel. Terminus & Other Plays. 2003. (Modern Drama Ser.). 280p. pap. (978-1-876857-18-9(8)) Salt Publishing.

Keens-Douglas, Richardo. The Nutmeg Princess. 2001. (Illus.). 80p. pap. 12.95 (978-0-88754-599-3(8)) Theatre Communications Group, Inc.

Kehret, Peg. Tell It Like It Is: Fifty monologs for talented Teens. 2007. 118p. (J). pap. 15.95 (***978-1-56608-144-3(0)***) Meriwether Publishing, Ltd.

Keltz, Martha. A Medley: Four Plays & Four Adaptations. 2nd rev. ed. 2000. 171p. (YA). pap. 35.00 (978-1-893592-17-9(0) , TC Pubs) Studio Editions/TC Pubs.

Kemp, Robert. The Other Dear Charmer. 2006. 80p. (YA). (gr. 6-12). pap. 6.00 (978-0-88734-566-1(2)) Players Pr., Inc.

Kerven, Rosalind. Coyote Girl, 6 vols. 2000. (Cambridge Reading Ser.). (Illus.). 32p. pap. 39.00 (978-0-521-78627-0(4)) Cambridge Univ. Pr.

Kingsland, Robin. Porky Pies Vol. 8: Photocopiable Plays. unabr. ed. 2003. (Plays & Play Collections). (Illus.). 64p. (J). (gr. 1-6). reprint ed. pap. 15.00 (978-0-7136-5370-0(1)) A & C Black GBR. *Dist:* Empire Publishing Service, Players Pr., Inc.

Kirkeby, Jennifer. Dot & Tot of Merryland - 2004. 80p. (J). pap. 7.50 (978-1-58342-237-3(4) , D04) Dramatic Publishing Co.

Kirkland, Rana. Mad about Monologues for Teens. 2002. (YA). pap. 12.95 (978-1-931805-26-1(1)) Brooklyn Pubs.

Kops, Bernard. The Dreams of Anne Frank: A Play for Young People. 2004. (Methuen Student Edition Ser.). 108p. (YA). pap. (978-0-413-71250-9(8)) Methuen Publishing Ltd.

Korty, Carol. Plays from African Folktales. Landes, William-Alan, ed. unabr. ed. 2003. (International Black Plays & Folk Tales Ser.). (Illus.). 98p. (J). (gr. 3-12). pap. 17.00 (978-0-88734-659-0(6)) Players Pr., Inc.

—Silly Soup. Landes, William-Alan, ed. Colombo, David, illus. Helms, Tina, photos by. 2003. (Plays & Play Collections). 128p. (Orig.). (J). (gr. k-6). pap. 17.00 (978-0-88734-679-8(0)) Players Pr., Inc.

Kral, Brian. Paper Lanterns, Paper Cranes. 2002. 76p. pap. 7.00 (978-0-87602-404-1(5)) Anchorage Pr.

Kramer, Alan. Bajo el mar con Jacques Cousteau & under the Sea with Jacques Cousteau. 2005. spiral bd. 76.00 (***978-1-4108-5789-7(1)***) Benchmark Education Co.

—Escape de la extincion & Path from Extinction. 2005. spiral bd. 76.00 (***978-1-4108-5794-1(8)***) Benchmark Education Co.

Kramer, Alan. Jackie Robinson Breaking Baseball's Barriers: Reader's Theater Levels N-P (30-38) Leon, Karen, illus. ed. 2004. (Reader's Theater Ser.). 16p. (J). pap. 22.00 (978-1-4108-2301-4(6) , A23016) Benchmark Education Co.

Kramer, Alan & Kramer, Candice. The Fifth Grade Votes: Reader's Theater Levels N-U (30-50) Leon, Karen, illus. ed. 2004. (Reader's Theater Ser.). 16p. (J). pap. 22.00 (978-1-4108-2307-6(5) , A23075) Benchmark Education Co.

Kramer, Candice. Why Coyote Stopped Imitating His Friends: Reader's Theater Levels N-P (30-38) Leon, Karen, illus. ed. 2004. (Reader's Theater Ser.). 16p. (J). pap. 22.00 (978-1-4108-2302-1(4) , A23024) Benchmark Education Co.

Kraus, Joanna H. Women of Courage: Five Plays by Joanna H. Kraus. Rubin, Janet E., ed. 2000. ix, 342p. (J). pap. 16.95 (978-0-87129-942-0(9) , W84) Dramatic Publishing Co.

Kroll, Virginia L. The Christmas Cow. 2003. 55p. (Orig.). (J). (gr. 1-6). pap. 5.00 (978-0-88734-481-7(X)) Players Pr., Inc.

Kruh, David. Top of the World, Ma! A Ten-Minute Comedy Duet. 2003. 12p. (YA). pap. 4.50 (978-1-932404-16-6(3) , 152A) Brooklyn Pubs.

Kruse, Jeremy. Lockers: Scenes, Monologues & Short Plays for Young People. 1999. 72p. (YA). pap. 6.25 (978-0-87129-943-7(7) , L99) Dramatic Publishing Co.

Kubler, Annie. Friendly Farm. 1999. (Illus.). 44p. (ps-1). 4.99 (978-0-85953-877-0(X)) Child's Play International Ltd. GBR. *Dist:* Child's Play-International.

Kuglen, Sam. Pinocchio: A Play. 1999. pap. 4.50 (978-1-57514-338-5(0) , 1134) Encore Performance Publishing.

Lamedman, Debbie. Twenty 10-Minute Plays For Teens By Teens, Vol. 3. 2007. 176p. 14.95 (978-1-57525-456-2(5)) Smith and Kraus Publishers, Incorporated.

Landes, William-Alan. Aladdin n' His Magic Lamp. rev. ed. 2003. (Wondrawhopper Ser.). 51p. (J). (gr. 3-12). pap. 6.00 (978-0-88734-102-1(0)) Players Pr., Inc.

—Alice n' Wonderland. 2003. (Wondrawhopper Ser.). 32p. (Orig.). (YA). (gr. 3 up). pap. 6.00 (978-0-88734-112-0(8)) Players Pr., Inc.

—Jack 'n the Beanstalk: Playscript. rev. ed. 2003. (Wondrawhopper Ser.). 40p. (J). (gr. 3-12). pap. 6.00 (978-0-88734-101-4(2)) Players Pr., Inc.

—Peter 'n the Wolf: Acting Edition. rev. ed. 2003. (Wondrawhopper Ser.). 36p. (J). (gr. 3-12). pap. 6.00 (978-0-88734-106-9(3)) Players Pr., Inc.

—Rapunzel 'n the Witch. rev. ed. 2003. (Wondrawhopper Ser.). 48p. (J). (gr. 3-12). pap. 6.00 (978-0-88734-107-6(1)) Players Pr., Inc.

—Rhyme Tyme: Playscript. rev. ed. 2003. (Wondrawhopper Ser.). 40p. (J). (gr. 3-12). pap. 6.00 (978-0-88734-108-3(X)) Players Pr., Inc.

—Rumpelstiltskin: Playscript. rev. ed. 2003. (Wondrawhopper Ser.). 52p. (J). (gr. 3-12). pap. 6.00 (978-0-88734-104-5(7)) Players Pr., Inc.

Landes, William-Alan & Lasky, Mark A. Grandpa's Bedtime Story. rev. ed. 2003. (Theater for Young Audiences Ser.). 36p. (YA). (gr. 3-12). pap. 6.00 (978-0-88734-505-0(0)) Players Pr., Inc.

Landes, William-Alan & Standish, Marilyn. The Wizard of Oz. rev. ed. 2003. (Wondrawhopper Ser.). 40p. (J). (gr. 3-12). pap. 6.00 (978-0-88734-105-2(5)) Players Pr., Inc.

Lanfer, Stefan Graves. Gary Grinkle's Battles with Wrinkles & Other Troubles in Mudgeville. 2002. 50p. (YA). pap. 4.25 (978-1-58342-141-3(6) , G74) Dramatic Publishing Co.

Laurie, Margaret S. Freedom Passage. 2001. (Illus.). 32p. (YA). (gr. 11). incl. VHS (978-0-9711153-2-3(X)); 28p. (J). (gr. 4). pap. incl. VHS (978-0-9711153-0-9(3)); 33p. (YA). (gr. 8). pap. incl. VHS (978-0-9711153-1-6(1)) Western Door Playhouse.

Lavery, Bryony. More Light. 2000. (Connections Ser.). (Illus.). 112p. (YA). pap. 17.95 (978-0-7487-4287-5(5)) Nelson Thornes Ltd. GBR. *Dist:* Trans-Atlantic Pubns., Inc.

Lazarus, John. Not So Dumb: "Secrets," "Schoolyard Games," "Not So Dumb" & "Night Light" 2000. 208p. (gr. 7-12). pap. 17.95 (978-0-88754-578-8(5)) Theatre Communications Group, Inc.

Leaf, Claudia. Radical Will. unabr. ed. 2003. (Shakespeare Ser.). 28p. (YA). (gr. 6-12). pap. 6.00 (978-0-85343-614-0(2)) Miller, J. Garnet Ltd. GBR. *Dist:* Empire Publishing Service.

Leavengood, Bill. Grimm Brothers Present: Puss in Boots. 2000. (Illus.). (J). (gr. 1-7). pap. 5.00 (978-1-57514-359-0(3) , 0001) Encore Performance Publishing.

Leeper Buss, Fran. Journey of the Sparrows: A Play with Music. 1999. 66p. pap. 6.25 (978-0-87129-795-2(7) , J32) Dramatic Publishing Co.

Leese, Joan, et al. Three Plays for Women. 2003. (Full-Length Plays Ser.). 44p. (YA). (gr. 8-12). pap. 6.00 (978-0-88734-932-4(3)) Players Pr., Inc.

LeMaster, David. Sir Saddlesore & the Dragon: One-Act Children's Comedy Play. rev. ed. 2005. 12p. (YA). pap. 4.95 (978-1-60003-094-9(7) , 783) Brooklyn Pubs.

LeMaster, David J. Homeland Insecurity: A Comedy Skit, 4 Booklets. 2003. (YA). pap. 4.50 (978-1-932404-38-8(4) , 322) Brooklyn Pubs.

—Paper, Rock, Scissors, Bomb! A Ten-Minute Comedy Duet. 2003. 16p. (YA). pap. 4.50 (978-1-932404-18-0(X) , 154A) Brooklyn Pubs.

—Shakespeare, Horny Toads & Banana Peels: Ten-Minute Comedy Duet. 2003. (YA). pap. 9.00 (978-1-932404-04-3(X) , 141A) Brooklyn Pubs.

Leon, Karen, illus. Milton the Mole: Reader's Theater Levels G-I (11-16) ed. 2004. (Reader's Theater Ser.). 16p. (J). pap. 22.00 (978-1-4108-2295-6(8) , A22958) Benchmark Education Co.

Levine, Karen & Sher, Emil. Hana's Suitcase on Stage. 2006. (Holocaust Remembrance Ser.). (Illus.). 171p. (YA). (gr. 4 up). pap. 15.95 (978-1-897187-05-0(X)) Second Story Pr. CAN. *Dist:* Orca Bk. Pubs. USA.

Liebenow, Todd, et al. Beyond Words 2. 2003. (Illus.). 56p. (YA). 20.00 (978-1-58302-228-3(7)) One Way St., Inc.

Lippa, Louis. The Dreaming of Aloysius. 2002. 69p. (YA). pap. 6.25 (978-1-58342-139-0(4) , D80) Dramatic Publishing Co.

—The Sorcerer's Apprentice. 2002. 32p. (YA). pap. 4.25 (978-1-58342-140-6(8) , SH3) Dramatic Publishing Co.

Lippa, Louis, adapted by. The True Adventures of Pinocchio. 2002. 80p. (YA). pap. 6.25 (978-1-58342-130-7(0) , TE4) Dramatic Publishing Co.

Literature: Timeless Voices, Timeless Themes, Copper Level 2001. (J). (gr. 6). pap. 15.97 (978-0-13-052396-9(8)) Prentice Hall PTR.

Literature Connections English: Hamlet. 2004. (gr. 6-12). (978-0-395-77554-7(X) , 2-80123) McDougal Littell Inc.

Literature Connections English: The Diary of Anne Frank: the Play. 2004. (gr. 6-12). (978-0-395-83364-3(7) , 2-70787) McDougal Littell Inc.

Literature Connections Spanish: Romeo y Julieta (the Tragedy of Romeo & Juliet) 2004. (gr. 6-12). (978-0-395-81739-1(0) , 2-70489) McDougal Littell Inc.

Little, Mindy M. Spellbound, a Musical Play on Words. 1999. 60p. (J). (gr. 1 up). pap. 6.95 (978-0-87129-893-5(7) , SD3) Dramatic Publishing Co.

Lochhead, Liz & Moxley, Gina. Cuba - Dog House. 2000. (Connections Ser.). (Illus.). 112p. (YA). (gr. 6 up). pap. 17.95 (978-0-7487-4291-2(3)) Nelson Thornes Ltd. GBR. *Dist:* Trans-Atlantic Pubns., Inc.

Loon, Michelle Van. Fairy Tale Academy: Comedy Play. 2002. (YA). pap. 4.75 (978-1-931805-79-7(2)) Brooklyn Pubs.

Lopez, Horacio. La Funcion de Teatro: The Play. 2000. (SPA.). (gr. k-3). lib. bdg. 17.60 (978-0-613-81998-5(5)) Tandem Library Bks.

Lou Weber Staff, ed. Tummy Time Baby Einstein Play. 2004. 8p. (J). 6.98 (978-1-4127-3279-6(4) , 7238400) Publications International, Ltd.

Love, Ann. Ice Cream at the Castle. 1999. (Child's Play Library). (Illus.). 32p. (J). (gr. k-3). 7.99 (978-0-85953-678-3(5)) Child's Play-International.

Lowry, Lois. Anastasia Krupnik: Playscript. 48p. (J). pap. 6.25 (978-1-58342-079-9(7) , A95) Dramatic Publishing Co.

Lundren Smith, Laura. Sending down the Sparrows. 2004. (SPA.). 48p. pap. 16.95 (978-1-903392-11-9(X)) Salmon Publishing IRL. *Dist:* Dufour Editions, Inc.

MacDonald, Margaret. The Skit Book: 101 Skits from Kids. 2006. 160p. (J). pap. 17.95 (978-0-87483-785-8(5)) August Hse. Pubs., Inc.

MacDougal, P. Paullette. Waiting for MacArthur. 58p. (YA). (gr. 10). pap. 6.50 (978-1-58342-183-3(1) , W97) Dramatic Publishing Co.

Mankowski, Sarah. Fallout: An original Screenplay. 2004. (YA). spiral bd. 10.95 (978-0-9745268-6-7(X)) WordThunder Pubns.

Manning, Mick. Mi Primer Libro de Teatro. Granstrom, Brita, illus. Tr. of Drama School. (SPA.). (J). (gr. 3-5). 15.16 (978-84-241-7922-9(6)) Everest de Ediciones y Distribucion, S.L. ESP. *Dist:* Lectorum Pubns., Inc.

Mapleson, Peter & Mapleson, Robyn. Bill the Bunyip. (J). (gr. 3-6). pap. (978-1-875739-82-0(3)) Wizard Bks.

Marlin, Therese. Cindyrella. 2006. 32p. 5.50 (***978-0-87440-254-4(9)*** , 1726-B) Baker's Plays.

Marsh, Carole. The Virginia Experience! A Virginia Mystery Musical! 2000. (Virginia Experience! Ser.). (Illus.). (J). pap. 20.00 (978-0-7933-9496-8(1)) Gallopade International.

Marsh, Marcia. The Prince Who Couldn't Dance: Comedy Play. 2002. (YA). pap. 4.25 (978-1-931805-87-2(3) , 725) Brooklyn Pubs.

Martin, Judith. Out of the Bag: The Paper Bag Players Book of Plays. Chwast, Seymour, illus. 2005. 48p. (J). (gr. k-4). reprint ed. pap. 14.00 (978-0-7567-8530-7(8)) DIANE Publishing Co.

Matthews, Grant. Astro 69. 2000. (Illus.). spiral bd. 13.00 (978-0-9711777-1-0(6)) Drama Tree Pr.

Maupassant, Guy de. The Necklace. Kelley, Gary, illus. 2004. 48p. 19.95 (978-1-56846-193-9(3)) Creative Co., The.

Maxwell-Snyder, Hope. Lullaby for George. 2005. (J). 9.95 (978-0-9753285-4-5(9)) H.B.P., Inc.

McBride-Smith, Barbara. Tell It Together: Foolproof Scripts for Story Theatre. 2002. 192p. (gr. 3-6). 24.95 (978-0-87483-655-4(7)); pap. 17.95 (978-0-87483-650-9(6)) August Hse. Pubs., Inc.

McCaslin, Nellie. Angel of the Battlefield. 2003. (Players Press Nellie McCaslin Ser.). (Illus.). 20p. (YA). (gr. 4-12). pap. 5.00 (978-0-88734-430-5(5)) Players Pr., Inc.

—The Bailiff's Wonderful Coat. 2003. (Players Press Nellie McCaslin Ser.). 55p. (J). (gr. 1-6). pap. 5.00 (978-0-88734-453-4(4)) Players Pr., Inc.

—Bluebonnets. 2003. (Players Press Nellie McCaslin Ser.). 18p. (YA). (gr. 4-12). pap. 5.00 (978-0-88734-439-8(9)) Players Pr., Inc.

—Brave New Banner. 2003. (Players Press Nellie McCaslin Ser.). (Illus.). 20p. (YA). (gr. 6-12). pap. 5.00 (978-0-88734-436-7(4)) Players Pr., Inc.

—Broken Rehearsal. 2006. 16p. (gr. 6-12). pap. 6.00 (978-0-88734-580-7(8)) Players Pr., Inc.

—Cold Face - Warm Heart. 2003. 20p. (J). (gr. k-6). pap. 5.00 (978-0-88734-440-4(2)) Players Pr., Inc.

—The Legend of Minna Lamourrie. 2003. (Players Press Nellie McCaslin Ser.). (Illus.). 20p. (J). (gr. k-6). pap. 5.00 (978-0-88734-438-1(0)) Players Pr., Inc.

—Legends in Action: Ten Plays of Ten Lands. 2003. (Plays & Play Collections). (Illus.). xii, 142p. (J). pap. 20.00 (978-0-88734-633-0(2)) Players Pr., Inc.

—Paul Bunyan: Lumberjack. 2003. (Players Press Nellie McCaslin Ser.). 55p. (Orig.). (J). (gr. 1-6). pap. 5.00 (978-0-88734-477-0(1)) Players Pr., Inc.

—A Straight Shooter (Playscript) 2003. (Players Press Nellie McCaslin Ser.). 16p. (YA). (gr. 6-12). pap. 5.00 (978-0-88734-429-9(1)) Players Pr., Inc.

—Three Meals a Day. 2003. 55p. (J). (gr. 1-7). pap. 5.00 (978-0-88734-445-9(3)) Players Pr., Inc.

—Too Many Cooks. 2003. (Players Press Nellie McCaslin Ser.). (Illus.). 20p. (J). pap. 5.00 (978-0-88734-434-3(8)) Players Pr., Inc.

McClelland, Charles E. Certain Arrangements. 1998. (YA). (gr. 6-12). pap. 6.00 (978-0-87602-356-3(1)) Anchorage Pr.

McCullough, L. E. Classroom Plays for Social Studies America in the 1800s, 4 vols. Mason, Mark, illus. 2003. 48p. (J). per. 7.99 (978-1-56472-242-3(2)) Edupress, Inc.

—Classroom Plays for Social Studies American Biographies, 4. Mason, Mark, illus. 2003. 48p. (J). per. 7.99 (978-1-56472-243-0(0)) Edupress, Inc.

—Classroom Plays for Social Studies Ancient Civilizations, 4 vols. Mason, Mark, illus. 2003. 48p. (J). per. 7.99 (978-1-56472-240-9(6)) Edupress, Inc.

—Classroom Plays for Social Studies Early America, 4 vols. Mason, Mark, illus. 2003. 48p. (J). per. 7.99 (978-1-56472-241-6(4)) Edupress, Inc.

—Israel Reborn: Legends of the Diaspora & Israel's Modern Rebirth. 2001. (Plays for Young Actors Ser.). (Illus.). 204p. (J). (gr. 4-6). pap. 15.95 (978-1-57525-253-7(8)) Smith and Kraus Publishers, Incorporated.

—Plays for Learning: Israel Reborn. 2001. (gr. 3-6). lib. bdg. 25.70 (978-0-613-70613-1(7)) Tandem Library Bks.

—Plays for Learning: Ancient Israel. 2001. (Illus.). 163p. (J). (gr. k-2). pap. 15.95 (978-1-57525-252-0(X)) Smith and Kraus Publishers, Incorporated.

—Plays of Fairy Tales. 1998. (Young Readers Ser.). 2183p. (Orig.). (J). (gr. k-3). pap. 14.95 (978-1-57525-109-7(4)) Smith and Kraus Publishers, Incorporated.

—Plays of People at Work. 1998. 128p. (J). (gr. k-3). pap. 14.95 (978-1-57525-140-0(X)) Smith and Kraus Publishers, Incorporated.

McDonald, Trevy. Brandi Surfs the Web. 2007. (J). 15.00 (***978-0-9670712-2-0(4)***) Reyomi Publishing Co.

McLaren, Maria. Seven with One Blow. 2003. (Theater for Young Audiences Ser.). 24p. (J). (gr. 1-6). pap. 6.00 (978-0-88734-517-3(4)) Players Pr., Inc.

Meadows, Kelly. Chair Wars: Ten-Minute Comedy Duet. 2002. (YA). pap. 9.00 (978-1-931805-30-8(X) , 116A) Brooklyn Pubs.

—Dumping Ground: A Ten-Minute Comedy Duet. 2003. (YA). pap. 4.50 (978-1-931805-94-0(6) , 146A) Brooklyn Pubs.

—Fairy Tales & Lies: Comedy Monologue. 2002. (YA). pap. 4.50 (978-1-931805-51-3(2) , 256) Brooklyn Pubs.

—A Ghost of a Chance: A One-Act Comedy Play. 2003. (YA). pap. 4.50 (978-1-932404-59-3(7) , 757) Brooklyn Pubs.

—Kiss of Death: Haunted Comedy Play. 2002. (YA). pap. 4.25 (978-1-931805-80-3(6)) Brooklyn Pubs.

—Maternity Mayhem: Comedy Monologue. 2002. (YA). pap. 4.50 (978-1-931805-53-7(9) , 258) Brooklyn Pubs.

—Not Ready! A Ten-Minute Comedy Monologue. 2003. 12p. (YA). pap. 4.50 (978-1-932404-31-9(7) , 284) Brooklyn Pubs.

—Prom Night: Comedy Play. 2002. (YA). pap. 5.00 (978-1-931805-90-2(3) , 822) Brooklyn Pubs.

—Starlets in Training: Comedy Skit. 2002. (YA). pap. 9.00 (978-1-931805-69-8(5) , 320) Brooklyn Pubs.

—Teen Comedy Playlets: A Collection of Six Skits: Third Time's a Charm, 8 Booklets. 2003. (YA). pap. 19.95 (978-1-932404-49-4(X) , 911) Brooklyn Pubs.

—Teen Comedy Playlets Too: Collection of Six Skits. 2002. (YA). pap. 19.95 (978-1-931805-70-4(9) , 905) Brooklyn Pubs.

—Ten Easy Steps to Humiliation: A Ten-Minute Comedy Duet. 2003. (YA). pap. 4.50 (978-1-931805-96-4(2) , 148A) Brooklyn Pubs.

—Wrong Side of the Tracks: Comedy Play. 2002. (YA). pap. 4.25 (978-1-931805-83-4(0)) Brooklyn Pubs.

Meissner, David. Lost City of the Inca: Reader's Theater Levels P-R (38-40) Leon, Karen, illus. ed. 2004. (Reader's Theater Ser.). 16p. (J). pap. 22.00 (978-1-4108-2308-3(3) , A23083) Benchmark Education Co.

Melville, Herman. Moby Dick. 1998. 61p. (YA). (gr. 7 up). pap. 6.95 (978-0-87129-782-2(5) , M68) Dramatic Publishing Co.

Mercafi, Cindy. Faces of Freedom. 2003. 48p. (YA). pap. 6.50 (978-1-58342-199-4(8) , F81) Dramatic Publishing Co.

The Merchant of Venice Study Guide. 2003. (Illus.). 48p. (YA). per. 17.95 (978-1-56254-634-2(1) , SP6341) Saddleback Educational Publishing.

Middleton, Alasdair. The Enchanted Pig. 2007. 8p. pap. 18.95 (***978-1-84002-717-4(7)***) Oberon Bks., Ltd. GBR. *Dist:* Consortium Bk. Sales & Distribution.

Middleton, Wesley. Degas' Little Dancer. (Illus.). 75p. (YA). 6.25 (978-1-58342-095-9(9) , D78) Dramatic Publishing Co.

Milgrim, Sally-Anne. Dealing with Life's Dilemmas: Exploring Values Through English & Drama. 2001. (Illus.). ix, 225p. (J). pap. (978-0-89390-537-8(2)) Resource Pubns., Inc.

Millay, Edna St. Vincent. Aria Da Capo. Landes, William-Alan, ed. 2003. (Classic One-Acts Ser.). 20p. (YA). (gr. 8-12). pap. 6.00 (978-0-88734-865-5(3)) Players Pr., Inc.

Miller, Helen L. First Plays for Children. 2001. 295p. (J). (gr. 1-3). pap. 12.95 (978-0-8238-0268-5(X)) Kalmbach Publishing Co., Bks. Div.

Mini Plays & Folktale Plays that Build Reading Skills. 2005. (J). pap. (***978-1-60015-036-4(5)***) Steps To Literacy, LLC.

Mitchell, Adrian & Carroll, Lewis. Alice in Wonderland & Through the Looking-Glass. 2002. (Illus.). 11p. pap. 16.95 (978-1-84002-256-8(6) , Oberon Bks.) Theatre Communications Group, Inc.

Mitchell, Adrian & Potter, Beatrix. Two Beatrix Potter Plays. 2005. 93p. pap. 16.95 (978-1-84002-519-4(0)) Theatre Communications Group, Inc.

Molnar, Ferenc. Liliom. 2003. 68p. (YA). (gr. 4-12). pap. 7.50 (978-0-88734-798-6(3)) Players Pr., Inc.

Montgomery, Claire, contrib. by. Flying Colors. 1998. 40p. (J). pap. 4.00 (978-0-87440-069-4(4)) Baker's Plays.

Morgan, Robert F. The Partners: A Three Act Play. 2007. 20p. (J). (gr. 6). pap. 25.00 (978-1-885679-05-5(X)) Morgan Foundation Pubs.: International Published Innovations.

Morreale, Vin, Jr. The Day the Woods Were One. 2003. (Theater for Young Audiences Ser.). 20p. (Orig.). (YA). (gr. 3 up). pap. 6.00 (978-0-88734-507-4(7)) Players Pr., Inc.

—Nicky's Secret. 2003. 48p. (YA). pap. 6.50 (978-1-58342-186-4(6) , N53) Dramatic Publishing Co.

—Uncool. 1998. 41p. (YA). (gr. 10 up). pap. 4.25 (978-0-87129-828-7(7) , U24) Dramatic Publishing Co.

Morreale, Vin, Jr., adapted by. House of the Seven Gables. 2002. 100p. (YA). (gr. 9). pap. 6.25 (978-1-58342-137-6(8) , H84) Dramatic Publishing Co.

Morris, Deborah. Teens 911: Snowbound. 2002. (gr. 3-6). lib. bdg. 22.20 (978-0-613-88131-9(1)) Tandem Library Bks.

Morris, Mark. Jane Eyre: 40 Speaking Parts. 1999. (Dramascripts Classic Texts Ser.). (J). (gr. 6-9). pap. 17.95 (978-0-17-432597-0(5)) Nelson Thornes Ltd. GBR. *Dist:* Trans-Atlantic Pubns., Inc.

Morton, Carlos. The Drop-Out. Landes, William-Alan, ed. 2003. (Players Press Carlos Morton Collection). 55p. (Orig.). (YA). (gr. 6-12). pap. 5.00 (978-0-88734-443-5(7)) Players Pr., Inc.

—Drug-O. Landes, William-Alan, ed. 2003. (Carlos Morton Collection). 55p. (Orig.). (YA). (gr. 6-12). pap. 6.00 (978-0-88734-444-2(5)) Players Pr., Inc.

—Los Fatherless. Landes, William-Alan, ed. 2003. (Players Press Carlos Morton Collection). 55p. (YA). (gr. 6-12). pap. 5.00 (978-0-88734-376-6(7)) Players Pr., Inc.

Moses, Myra, creator. Jesus Is Still Alive! The Special Occasion Collection. 2002. (J). 4.99 (978-1-931785-05-1(8)) By Faith Theatre Ministries, Inc.

—A Special Christmas Day Gift: The Special Occasion Collection. 2002. (J). 4.99 (978-1-931785-00-6(7)) By Faith Theatre Ministries, Inc.

—The Special Occasion Collection, Vol. 1. 2002. (J). 19.99 (978-1-931785-07-5(4)) By Faith Theatre Ministries, Inc.

—Teens for Christ: The Special Occasion Collection. 2002. (J). 4.99 (978-1-931785-06-8(6)) By Faith Theatre Ministries, Inc.

—Through the Eyes of Our Children: The Special Occasion Collection. 2002. (J). 4.99 (978-1-931785-04-4(X)) By Faith Theatre Ministries, Inc.

—The Time Capsule: The Special Occasion Collection. 2002. (J). 4.99 (978-1-931785-03-7(1)) By Faith Theatre Ministries, Inc.

—What Christmas Means to Me: The Special Occasion Collection. 2002. (J). 4.99 (978-1-931785-02-0(3)) By Faith Theatre Ministries, Inc.

Much Ado about Nothing. 2000. (YA). 9.95 (978-1-56137-925-5(5)) Novel Units, Inc.

Muir, Kerry. Three New Plays for Young Actors: From the Young Actor's Studio. 2004. (Illus.). 200p. (Orig.). pap. 18.95 (978-0-87910-957-8(2) , 0879109572, Amadeus Press) Leonard, Hal Corp.

Murphy, Dallas. Read Aloud Plays Grades 4-8: Pioneers. 1999. (Illus.). 64p. pap., tchr. ed. 9.95 (978-0-590-91811-4(7)) Scholastic, Inc.

Murray, Joel. High Fortune: Ten-Minute Comedy Duet. 2002. (YA). pap. 9.00 (978-1-931805-35-3(0) , 121A) Brooklyn Pubs.

Muschell, David. The Invisible Princess: A Full-Length Comedy-Dramatic Play. 2003. (YA). pap. 5.00 (978-1-932404-67-8(8) , 609) Brooklyn Pubs.

Musselman, Forrest. Point Blank: Comedy Play. 2002. (YA). pap. 4.25 (978-1-931805-86-5(5)) Brooklyn Pubs.

Nesbit, E. Beautiful Stories from Shakespeare (Yesterday's Classics) 2006. (J). per. 11.95 (978-1-59915-029-1(8)) Yesterday's Classics.

Nield, Maureen. How Different from Us. 2003. 28p. (YA). (gr. 4-12). pap. 5.00 (978-0-88734-767-2(3)) Players Pr., Inc.

Nimmo, Paul. Will Shakespeare Save Us! Will Shakespeare Save the King! 2003. (Shakespeare Ser.). 58p. (J). (gr. k-8). pap. 12.00 (978-0-88734-658-3(8)) Players Pr., Inc.

Norden, Barbara. Meteorite. 2004. 63p. pap. 16.95 (978-1-84002-401-2(1)) Theatre Communications Group, Inc.

O'Connor, John, ed. The Canterbury Tales: 39 Speaking Parts. 2001. (Dramascripts Classic Texts Ser.). (Illus.). 80p. (J). (gr. 6-10). pap. 16.95 (978-0-17-432658-8(0)) Nelson Thornes Ltd. GBR. *Dist:* Trans-Atlantic Pubns., Inc.

—Macbeth & the Rebels' Plot: 19 Speaking Parts. 2001. (Dramascripts Classic Texts Ser.). (Illus.). 88p. (J). (gr. 6-10). pap. 16.95 (978-0-17-432664-9(5)) Nelson Thornes Ltd. GBR. *Dist:* Trans-Atlantic Pubns., Inc.

—Silas Marner: 20 Speaking Parts. 1998. (Dramascripts Classic Texts Ser.). 96p. (J). (gr. 6-9). pap. 17.95 (978-0-17-432552-9(5)) Nelson Thornes Ltd. GBR. *Dist:* Trans-Atlantic Pubns., Inc.

—Twelfth Night & Puritans' Revenge: 19 Speaking Parts. 2001. (Dramascripts Classic Texts Ser.). (Illus.). 80p. (J). (gr. 6-10). pap. 16.95 (978-0-17-432662-5(9)) Nelson Thornes Ltd. GBR. *Dist:* Trans-Atlantic Pubns., Inc.

O'Donnell, Ronan & Wang, Xiaoli. In the Bag. 2006. 64p. pap. 18.95 (978-1-85459-874-5(0)) Consortium Bk. Sales & Distribution.

Oliver Twist Study Guide. 2000. (Illus.). 48p. (YA). per. 17.95 (978-1-56254-296-2(6) , SP2966) Saddleback Educational Publishing.

O'Neill, Eugene. Four Plays by Eugene O'Neill: Beyond the Horizon, Anna Christie, The Emperor Jones & The Hairy Ape. 1998. (978-0-606-13398-2(4)) Tandem Library Bks.

—Iceman Cometh. 1999. (gr. 7-12). lib. bdg. 21.10 (978-0-613-29263-4(4)) Tandem Library Bks.

Orel, Gwen & Ward, Sherry, eds. The Young Southern Writers' Project of the Alabama Shakespeare Festival: Anthology of New Plays. 2002. 224p. (YA). pap. 14.95 (978-0-595-25043-1(2) , Writers Club Pr.) iUniverse, Inc.

Osment, Philip. The Palace of Fear. 2006. (Illus.). 96p. pap. 16.95 (978-1-84002-505-7(0)) Consortium Bk. Sales & Distribution.

—Plays for Young People. 2006. 217p. pap. 29.95 (978-1-84002-272-8(8)) Oberon Bks., Ltd. GBR. *Dist:* Consortium Bk. Sales & Distribution.

Ott, John. Waiting: Ten-Minute Dramatic Duet: An Existential Cry of Despair. 2002. (YA). pap. 9.00 (978-1-931805-47-6(4) , 132A) Brooklyn Pubs.

Owens, Christopher. Rules of Engagement. 2000. (Illus.). 22p. (YA). spiral bd. 15.00 (978-0-9711777-5-8(9)) Drama Tree Pr.

Pagnol, Marcel. Manon des Sources, Level C. 2002. (FRE.). (YA). (gr. 7-12). 8.95 (978-0-8219-1865-4(6) , 40341) EMC/Paradigm Publishing.

Pascal, Francine. Sweet Valley High # 2: Secrets. 2008. (Sweet Valley High Ser.). 192p. (gr. 7). mass mkt. 5.99 (***978-0-440-42263-1(9)*** , Laurel Leaf) Random Hse. Children's Bks.

—Sweet Valley High #1: Double Love. 2008. (Sweet Valley High Ser.). 192p. (gr. 7). mass mkt. 5.99 (***978-0-440-42262-4(0)*** , Laurel Leaf) Random Hse. Children's Bks.

Paxton, Kate. Tatyana's Golden Doe: A Musical. 1998. (J). pap. 6.50 (978-0-87602-363-1(4)) Anchorage Pr.

Payne, Dave & Payne, Julie. Little Red Riding Hood & the Magic Dragon: Musical. 2002. 34p. (YA). pap. 6.95 (978-1-58342-151-2(3) , L09) Dramatic Publishing Co.

Pedito, Paul. Sounds of Silents (The Essaday Years) 2002. 106p. (YA). (gr. 9 up). pap. 6.25 (978-1-58342-143-7(2) , SH4) Dramatic Publishing Co.

Per, Sharon Mills. Romiette & Julio. 2001. (gr. 7-12). lib. bdg. 14.15 (978-0-613-33723-6(9)) Tandem Library Bks.

Peris, Carme, illus. Puss 'n Boots. 1999. 32p. (J). (ps-3). 8.95 (978-0-7641-5156-9(8)) Barron's Educational Series, Inc.

Peris, Carmie, illus. Snow White & the Seven Dwarfs. 1999. 32p. (J). (gr. k-3). 8.95 (978-0-7641-5151-4(7)) Barron's Educational Series, Inc.

Perkins, David & Dooley, Caroline. Selfish Giant: A Children's Musical. 2003. xv, 28p. (J). pap. (978-0-573-08123-1(9)) French, Samuel Inc.

Peters, Andrew & Peters, Polly. Angelcake. (Illus.). 64p. pap. 9.99 (978-0-7502-3729-1(5) , Hodder & Stoughton) Hodder General Publishing Division GBR. *Dist:* Trafalgar Square Publishing.

—Dragon Chaser. (Illus.). 61p. 19.99 (978-0-7502-3457-3(1) , Hodder & Stoughton) Hodder General Publishing Division GBR. *Dist:* Trafalgar Square Publishing.

Phaelan, Mike. Necessary Evil: Ten-Minute Dramatic Duet. 2002. (YA). pap. 9.00 (978-1-931805-49-0(0) , 134A) Brooklyn Pubs.

Polsky, Milton. Aquadrama: Acting in Waist-High Water. 2002. (Illus.). 88p. pap. 15.95 (978-0-9712092-0-6(0)) Dramata Editions.

Polsky, Milton, et al. Houdini - The King of Escapes: Playscript. 2003. (Musicals Ser.). 32p. (Orig.). (J). (gr. 3-12). pap. 8.00 (978-0-88734-510-4(7)) Players Pr., Inc.

Pop-Out Play-Pak: Bats. Orig. Title: Child's Play. (Illus.). 14p. (J). (ps-4). reprint ed. (978-1-881469-81-0(6)) Safari, Ltd.

Pop-Out Play-Pak: Butterfly. Orig. Title: Child's Play. (Illus.). 14p. (J). (ps-4). reprint ed. (978-1-881469-78-0(6)) Safari, Ltd.

Pop-Out Play-Pak: Frogs. Orig. Title: Child's Play. (Illus.). 14p. (J). (ps-4). reprint ed. (978-1-881469-82-7(4)) Safari, Ltd.

Pop-Out Play-Pak: Spider. Orig. Title: Child's Play. (Illus.). 14p. (J). (ps-4). reprint ed. (978-1-881469-79-7(4)) Safari, Ltd.

Pop-Out Play-Pak: Time Tunnel. Orig. Title: Child's Play. (Illus.). 24p. (J). (ps-4). (978-1-881469-76-6(X)) Safari, Ltd.

Porter, Steven. The Prairie Man. 2003. 62p. (YA). pap. 6.00 (978-0-9625372-0-2(9)) Phantom Pubns., Inc.

Positive African American Plays for Children Book 2: Building High Self Esteem & Confidence Through Plays. 2005. (J). per. 19.95 (***978-1-884163-92-0(0)***) NetNia Publishing Co.

Post, Sam. Responsibility: A Comedy Skit, 3 Booklets. 2003. (YA). pap. 9.00 (978-1-932404-40-1(6) , 326) Brooklyn Pubs.

Pownall, David. The Dream of Chief Crazy Horse. 2001. (Plays for Young People Ser.). 77p. pap. 16.95 (978-1-84002-075-5(X)) Theatre Communications Group, Inc.

Prentice Hall Literature Timeless Voices Timeless Themes: Mini Anthology Short Dramas/Teleplays. 5th ed. 1999. (J). (gr. 9-12). (978-0-13-437206-8(9)) Prentice Hall (Schl. Div.).

Pritchard, Gretchen Wolff. Go, Tell It on the Mountain: Three Christmas Pageants for Church Schools. 2001. (Illus.). xv, 110p. (J). pap. 25.00 (978-0-89869-365-2(8)) Church Publishing, Inc.

Pugliano, Carol. Just Right Plays: 25 Emergent Reader Plays Around the Year. 1999. 64p. pap. 10.95 (978-0-439-10564-4(1)) Scholastic, Inc.

Pugliano-Martin, Carol. Blackout: Reader's Theater Levels J-L (18-24) DuFalla, Anita, illus. ed. 2004. (Reader's Theater Ser.). 16p. (J). pap. 22.00 (978-1-4108-2298-7(2) , A22982) Benchmark Education Co.

—Read-Aloud Plays: Tall Tales. 2000. 64p. (J). pap. 10.95 (978-0-439-11367-0(9)) Scholastic, Inc.

Pullman, Philip, ed. Sherlock Holmes & the Limehouse Horror. 2001. (Superscripts Ser.). (Illus.). 64p. (J). (gr. 6-10). pap. 15.95 (978-0-7487-4062-8(7)) Nelson Thornes Ltd. GBR. *Dist:* Trans-Atlantic Pubns., Inc.

Quinn, Stephanie. Little Stars Creative Drama for Preschoolers. 2008. 100p. per. 19.95 (***978-0-9773099-5-5(9)***) Quinn Entertainment.

Rabushka, Jerry. The Casket & the Casserole: A Ten-Minute Comedy Duet. 2003. 16p. (YA). pap. 4.50 (978-1-932404-23-4(6) , 159A) Brooklyn Pubs.

—Dramatic Reenactment: Comedy Play. 2002. (YA). pap. 4.25 (978-1-931805-84-1(9) , 721) Brooklyn Pubs.

—The Frying Pan: A Dramatic Skit, 4 Booklets. 2003. (YA). pap. 4.50 (978-1-932404-37-1(6) , 323) Brooklyn Pubs.

—Good Cop, Bad Cop: Ten-Minute Comedy Duet. 2002. (YA). pap. 9.00 (978-1-931805-27-8(X) , 113A) Brooklyn Pubs.

—Jack, the Beanstalk, & Social Services: Comedy Play. 2002. (YA). pap. 4.25 (978-1-931805-82-7(2)) Brooklyn Pubs.

—Jock Talk: Ten-Minute Comedy Duet. 2002. (YA). 9.00 (978-1-931805-28-5(8) , 114a) Brooklyn Pubs.

—My Name Isn't Bro: Dramatic Monologue. 2002. (YA). pap. 4.50 (978-1-931805-58-2(X) , 263) Brooklyn Pubs.

—On Location: A Ten-Minute Comedy Duet. 2003. 16p. (YA). pap. 4.50 (978-1-931805-97-1(0) , 149A) Brooklyn Pubs.

—Organ Recital: Comedy Skit. 2002. (YA). pap. 9.00 (978-1-931805-68-1(7) , 319) Brooklyn Pubs.

—Saucy Mamasita: A Dramatic Monologue. 2003. (YA). pap. 4.50 (978-1-932404-30-2(9) , 283) Brooklyn Pubs.

—White Elephant: Comedy Monologue. 2003. (YA). pap. 4.50 (978-1-932404-08-1(2) , 276) Brooklyn Pubs.

—The World Is Flat: Comedy Monologue. 2002. (YA). pap. 4.50 (978-1-931805-60-5(1) , 265) Brooklyn Pubs.

Rankin, James. Wide, Wide World of Love: Readers Theatre Comedy. 2002. (YA). pap. 4.25 (978-1-931805-88-9(1) , 726) Brooklyn Pubs.

Raspanti, Celeste. The Terezin Promise. 2004. 40p. (YA). pap. 4.50 (978-1-58342-200-7(5) , TF7) Dramatic Publishing Co.

Rearick, John. Ancient Egypt: 5 Short Plays for the Classroom with Background Information, Writing Prompts, & Creative Activities. 2002. (Read Aloud Plays Ser.). (Illus.). 64p. pap. 10.95 (978-0-590-64404-4(1)) Scholastic, Inc.

Rechenspiele. (Duden-Schuelerhilfen Ser.). (GER.). 79p. (J). (gr. 4-5). (978-3-411-02611-1(1)) Bibliographisches Institut & F. A. Brockhaus AG DEU. *Dist:* International Bk. Import Service, Inc.

Redmond, Diane. The Odyssey, Vol. 4. Smith, Barry, illus. unabr. ed. 2003. (Curtain up! Ser.: Vol. 4). 48p. (J). (gr. 1-4). pap. 15.00 (978-0-7136-4628-3(4)) A & C Black GBR. *Dist:* Players Pr., Inc.

Reese, Kevin M., adapted by. Chicken Little Henny Penny (Non-Musical Version) 2004. (J). (978-1-932240-60-3(8)) KMR Scripts.

—The Pied Piper (Non-Musical Version) 2004. (J). 4.00 net. (978-1-932240-62-7(4)) KMR Scripts.

—Santa's Elves & the Shoemaker. 2000. pap. (978-1-932240-43-6(8)) KMR Scripts.

—The True Story of the Tortoise & the Hare (Non-Musical Version) 2005. (J). 4.00 net. (978-1-932240-64-1(0)) KMR Scripts.

Reese, Kevin M., adapted by. Chicken Little Henny Penny. Reese, Kevin M., . 2004. (J). 4.00 (978-1-932240-59-7(4)) KMR Scripts.

—The Pied Piper. Reese, Kevin M., . 2004. (J). 4.00 net. (978-1-932240-61-0(6)) KMR Scripts.

—The True Story of the Tortoise & the Hare. Reese, Kevin M., . 2005. (J). 4.00 net. (978-1-932240-63-4(2)) KMR Scripts.

Reeves, Emma & Bawden, Nina. Carrie's War. 2007. 128p. pap. 18.95 (***978-1-84002-720-4(7)***) Oberon Bks., Ltd. GBR. *Dist:* Consortium Bk. Sales & Distribution.

Reeves, Emma Jane & Montgomery, L. M. Anne of Green Gables. 2006. 14p. pap. 16.95 (978-1-84002-538-5(7)) Consortium Bk. Sales & Distribution.

Relate & React: Skits for Developing Good Character in Real Life Situations in Grades 6-12. 2002. 132p. (YA). per. 18.95 (978-1-931636-02-5(8) , Students Taking a Right Stand, (STARS)) National Center For Youth Issues.

Ribar, Sandy. Operation-Rescue in the Redwoods: Mini-Musical Production Guide. 1999. (Kids on Assignment - The Adventures of Rex & Ruby Ser.: Vol. 1). (Illus.). 40p. (J). (gr. k-5). pap. 7.95 (978-1-893401-00-6(6) , KOA010) Pure & Simple Productions.

—Operation-Rescue in the Redwoods: Mini-Musical Production Pack. Brown, Camille B., illus. 1999. (Kids on Assignment - The Adventures of Rex & Ruby Ser.). 40p. (J). (ps-8). pap. 98.00 (978-1-893401-07-5(3) , KOA00RR) Pure & Simple Productions.

—Operation-Rescue in the Redwoods: Storybook. Brown, Camille B., illus. 1999. (Kids on Assignment - The Adventures of Rex & Ruby Ser.: Vol. 8). 40p. (J). pap. 3.99 (978-1-893401-06-8(5) , KOA081RR) Pure & Simple Productions.

Riosley, Lane. The Attack of the Crab Nebula. (Lucky Hightops & the Cosmic Cat Patrol Ser.: No. 2). (Illus.). (J). (gr. 2-8). pap. 4.00 (978-1-57514-268-5(6) , 1027) Encore Performance Publishing.

—Captives of the Dog Star. (Lucky Hightops & the Cosmic Cat Patrol Ser.: No. 1). (Illus.). (J). (gr. 2-8). pap. 4.00 (978-1-57514-267-8(8) , 1026) Encore Performance Publishing.

—Polaris, the Robot King. (Lucky Hightops & the Cosmic Cat Patrol Ser.: No. 3). (Illus.). (J). (gr. 2-8). pap. 4.00 (978-1-57514-269-2(4) , 1028) Encore Performance Publishing.

—Revenge of the Dog Robber. (Lucky Hightops & the Cosmic Cat Patrol Ser.: No. 4). (Illus.). (J). (gr. 2-8). pap. 4.00 (978-1-57514-270-8(8) , 1116) Encore Performance Publishing.

Rius, Roser, illus. Peter Pan: Peter Pan. 1999. 32p. (J). (ps-3). 8.95 (978-0-7641-5153-8(3)) Barron's Educational Series, Inc.

Rivera, Jose. Maricela de la Luz Lights the World. 1998. 52p. (J). (gr. 1 up). pap. 6.25 (978-0-87129-894-2(5) , MB3) Dramatic Publishing Co.

Rizzo, Joe. On the Same Frequency: A One-Act Comedy Play. 2003. (YA). pap. 4.50 (978-1-932404-63-0(5) , 761) Brooklyn Pubs.

Robbins, Kenneeth. The War Woman of Wauhaptchee Creek. 2000. (Illus.). (J). pap. 4.50 (978-1-57514-360-6(7)) Encore Performance Publishing.

Robertson, Tom G. The Irish Murderer. (Illus.). 29p. (YA). 4.25 (978-1-58342-091-1(6) , I78) Dramatic Publishing Co.

Robinetie, Joseph & Tierney, Thomas. The Fabulous Fable Factory. 2004. 56p. (YA). pap. 6.50 (978-1-58342-216-8(1) , F82) Dramatic Publishing Co.

Robinette, Joseph. The Chocolate War. 111p. (YA). 6.25 (978-1-58342-088-1(6) , CA6) Dramatic Publishing Co.

—Dorothy Meets Alice or the Wizard of Wonderland. 2004. 48p. (YA). pap. 6.50 (978-1-58342-221-2(8) , D82) Dramatic Publishing Co.

—Humpty-Dumpty Is Missing! or: The Mysterious Case of the Fallen Egg. 2002. 46p. (YA). pap. 6.25 (978-1-58342-120-8(3) , H83) Dramatic Publishing Co.

Rocamora, Carol. Chekhov for Teens: Ten Short Plays. 2006. 224p. 19.95 (978-1-57525-457-9(3)) Smith and Kraus Publishers, Incorporated.

Romer, Marcus & Hinton, S. E. Rumble Fish. 62p. pap. 6.25 (978-1-58342-154-3(8) , R69) Dramatic Publishing Co.

Romer, Ruth. The Pattern Hike: Levels F-H (9-14), 6 bks. Dufalla, Anita, illus. ed. 2004. (Reader's Theater Ser.). 16p. (J). pap. 22.00 (978-1-4108-2290-1(7) , A22907) Benchmark Education Co.

Rose, Gerald. Cambridge Plays: The Lion & the Mouse. 2000. (Cambridge Reading Ser.). (Illus.). 24p. pap. 6.00 (978-0-521-78616-4(9)) Cambridge Univ. Pr.

—Cambridge Plays: The Little Red Hen. 2000. (Cambridge Reading Ser.). (Illus.). 24p. pap. 6.00 (978-0-521-66455-4(1)) Cambridge Univ. Pr.

—The Little Red Hen Big Book. 2000. (Cambridge Reading Ser.). (Illus.). 24p. pap. 33.00 (978-0-521-78586-0(3)) Cambridge Univ. Pr.

Rosenberg, Joe, ed. Aplauso! Hispanic Children's Theater. 2nd ed. 2003. (Latin-American Play Anthologies Ser.). (Illus.). 274p. (YA). (gr. 4-10). pap. 12.95 (978-1-55885-127-6(5) , Piñata Books) Arte Publico Pr.

Ross, Kathryn & Pruitt, Kimberly. Artic Skits. Utley, David, illus. 2006. 88p. (J). per. 24.95 (978-0-9725803-9-7(5)) Children's Publishing.

Ruditis, Paul. Everyone's a Critic. 2007. (Drama! Ser.). 243p. (YA). (gr. 7-12). per. 8.99 (***978-1-4169-3392-2(1)** , Simon Pulse) Simon & Schuster Children's Publishing.

Ruditis, Paul. The Four Dorothys. 2007. (Drama! Ser.: No. 1). 256p. (YA). (gr. 7 up). pap. 8.99 (978-1-4169-3391-5(3) , Simon Pulse) Simon & Schuster Children's Publishing.

Rumble, P. Barry. Full Moon. 2003. (One Act Plays Ser.). 14p. (J). pap. 5.00 (978-0-88734-422-0(4)) Players Pr., Inc.

Ryan, Tammy. The Music Lesson. 2003. 72p. (YA). pap. 6.50 (978-1-58342-207-6(2) , MD8) Dramatic Publishing Co.

Sabato, George F. The New Improved Santa. Landes, William-Alan, ed. 2003. (Theater for Young Audiences Ser.). 55p. (Orig.). (J). (gr. k-7). pap. 5.00 (978-0-88734-457-2(7)) Players Pr., Inc.

Sanders, D. J. Metatheatre: A Ten-Minute Comedy Duet. 2003. (YA). pap. 4.50 (978-1-932404-43-2(0) , 131A) Brooklyn Pubs.

Sanders, DJ. C. Greek: Ten-Minute Comedy Duet. 2002. (YA). pap. 9.00 (978-1-931805-33-9(4) , 119A) Brooklyn Pubs.

Sanders, Francesca. I Am a Soundman's Daughter: Dramatic Monologue. 2002. (YA). pap. 4.50 (978-1-931805-65-0(2)) Brooklyn Pubs.

—Look Deeper: Collection of Thre Monologs for Young Women: a Multicultural Collection. 2002. (YA). pap. 16.95 (978-1-931805-74-2(1)) Brooklyn Pubs.

—What's Wrong with Me? Ten-Minute Dramatic Duet. 2002. (YA). pap. 9.00 (978-1-931805-43-8(1) , 128A) Brooklyn Pubs.

Sanderson, Jeanette. Read-aloud Plays. 2002. (Read Aloud Plays Ser.). (Illus.). 64p. (gr. 4-8). pap. 11.95 (978-0-439-25181-5(8)) Scholastic, Inc.

Schappert, Edan. Mechanical Micros: Collection of Three Duets: The Inner Lives of Computers, Elevators & Robots. 2002. (YA). pap. 19.95 (978-1-931805-73-5(3)) Brooklyn Pubs.

Schnitzler, Arthur. Anatol. Landes, William-Alan, ed. unabr. ed. 2003. (Players Press Classic Plays Ser.). (Illus.). 68p. (J). (gr. 4-6). pap. 7.50 (978-0-88734-817-4(3)) Players Pr., Inc.

Schnupp, Al. Censored. 2003. (Full-Length Plays Ser.). 76p. (YA). (gr. 8-12). pap. 15.00 (978-0-88734-868-6(8)) Players Pr., Inc.

Schoenfeld, Jeff. Information: A Ten-Minute Comedy Duet. 2003. 16p. (YA). pap. 4.50 (978-1-932404-24-1(4) , 160A) Brooklyn Pubs.

Scholastic, Inc. Staff. Gingerbread Man Fairy Tale Masks. 2006. 11.99 (***978-0-439-82429-3(X)** , Teaching Resources) Scholastic, Inc.

—Goldilocks & the Three Bears Fairy Tale Masks. 2006. 11.99 (***978-0-439-82428-6(1)** , Teaching Resources) Scholastic, Inc.

—Three Little Pigs Fairy Tale Masks. 2006. 11.99 (***978-0-439-82427-9(3)** , Teaching Resources) Scholastic, Inc.

Scholtz, Pieter. Tokoloshe: An African Zulu Folktale. 1998. (J). pap. 6.00 (978-0-87602-364-8(2)) Anchorage Pr.

Schreibspiele. (Duden-Schuelerhilfen Ser.). (GER.). 79p. (J). (gr. 3-4). (978-3-411-02612-8(X)) Bibliographisches Institut & F. A. Brockhaus AG DEU. *Dist:* International Bk. Import Service, Inc.

Scott, James. Julius Caesar: Dual Edition. 1999. 96p. (YA). (gr. 7-12). pap., wbk. ed. 6.75 (978-1-58049-506-6(0) , DE01) Prestwick Hse., Inc.

—Macbeth: Dual Edition. 1999. 84p. (YA). (gr. 7-12). pap., wbk. ed. 6.75 (978-1-58049-505-9(2) , DE05) Prestwick Hse., Inc.

—Romeo & Juliet: Side by Side. 1999. 104p. (YA). (gr. 7-12). pap., wbk. ed. 6.75 (978-1-58049-504-2(4) , DE04) Prestwick Hse., Inc.

—The Taming of the Shrew: Side by Side. 2002. (YA). (gr. 7-12). pap., wbk. ed. 6.75 (978-1-58049-509-7(5) , DE08A) Prestwick Hse., Inc.

Segaloff, Nat, et al. The First Men in the Moon - Radio Play. 1999. 54p. (YA). 10.95 (978-0-87129-966-6(6) , F68) Dramatic Publishing Co.

—The Invisible Man-Radio Play. 1999. 77p. (YA). 10.95 (978-0-87129-483-8(4) , I76) Dramatic Publishing Co.

Shakespeare, William. Hamlet. Mueller, Jenny, ed. 2002. (Simply Shakespeare Ser.). (Illus.). 346p. pap. 8.99 (978-0-7641-2084-8(0)) Barron's Educational Series, Inc.

—Hamlet. unabr. ed. 1998. (Wordsworth Classics Ser.). (YA). (gr. 6-12). 5.27 (978-0-89061-009-1(6) , R0096WW) Jamestown.

—Henry V. Andrews, Gary, illus. 71p. pap., stu. ed. (978-0-237-52159-2(8) , Evans Brothers, Limited) Evans Publishing Group.

—King Lear. Fraser, Russell A., ed. 1998. 275p. (gr. 7-12). lib. bdg. 11.80 (978-0-613-18207-2(3)) Tandem Library Bks.

—King Lear: The Quarto & the Folio Texts. 2000. (gr. 7-12). lib. bdg. 14.15 (978-0-613-64231-6(7)) Tandem Library Bks.

—Pyramus & Thisbe: A Dramatization Arranged from Shakespeare's A Midsummer Night's Dream. Landes, William-Alan, ed. rev. ed. 2003. (One Act Plays Ser.). 55p. (Orig.). (J). (gr. 4-12). pap. 5.00 (978-0-88734-103-8(9)) Players Pr., Inc.

—Romeo & Juliet. Haum, De Jager, ed. 1999. 132p. (gr. 6-9). pap., stu. ed. 13.00 (978-0-521-78659-1(2)) Cambridge Univ. Pr.

—Shakespeare for Children. 1999. (Storyteller's Version Ser.). (YA). (gr. 2 up). audio compact disk 14.95 (978-1-882513-40-6(1) , 1124-015) Greathall Productions, Inc.

—The Tempest. Ermitage, Kathleen, ed. 2002. (Simply Shakespeare Ser.). (Illus.). 288p. pap. 8.99 (978-0-7641-2087-9(5)) Barron's Educational Series, Inc.

—The Tempest. 2002. (gr. 7-12). lib. bdg. 17.60 (978-0-613-52731-6(3)) Tandem Library Bks.

—The Tempest for Young People. Davidson, Diane, ed. Davidson, Diane, illus. 1998. (Shakespeare for Young People Ser.: Vol. 10). 64p. (J). (gr. 5-8). pap. 5.95 (978-0-934048-27-9(4)) Learning Links Inc.

—Twelfth Night. Higgins, Fitzgerald, ed. 2002. (Simply Shakespeare Ser.). (Illus.). 288p. pap. 8.95 (978-0-7641-2088-6(3)) Barron's Educational Series, Inc.

—Twelfth Night: Classicscript. Landes, William-Alan, ed. abr. ed. 2003. (Shakespeare Ser.: Vol. 3). 68p. (YA). (gr. 4-12). pap. 6.50 (978-0-88734-530-2(1)) Players Pr., Inc.

—Twelfth Night: Or, What You Will. unabr. ed. 1998. (Wordsworth Classics Ser.). (YA). (gr. 6-12). 5.27 (978-0-89061-010-7(X) , R010XWW) Jamestown.

—The Two Gentlemen of Verona. 1999. (Folger Library General Reader's Shakespeare Ser.). (978-0-606-18382-6(5)) Tandem Library Bks.

—The Winter's Tale: Texts & Contexts. 1999. (gr. 7-12). lib. bdg. 12.95 (978-0-613-64238-5(4)) Tandem Library Bks.

Shakespeare, William & Burdett, Lois. The Tempest for Kids. 1999. (Shakespeare Can Be Fun Ser.). (Illus.). 64p. (J). (gr. 2-4). pap. 8.95 (978-1-55209-326-9(3)) Firefly Bks., Ltd.

Shakespeare, William & Roth, Robert R., eds. Macbeth. 2002. (Simply Shakespeare Ser.). (Illus.). 288p. pap. 8.99 (978-0-7641-2086-2(7)) Barron's Educational Series, Inc.

Shakespeare, William & SparkNotes Staff. King Lear. Crowther, John, ed. 2003. (No Fear Shakespeare Ser.). (Illus.). 320p. pap. 6.95 (978-1-58663-853-5(X)) Spark Publishing Group.

—The Taming of the Shrew. 2004. (SparkNotes No Fear Shakespeare Ser.). (Illus.). 256p. pap. 5.95 (978-1-4114-0101-3(8)) Spark Publishing Group.

Shakespeare, William, et al. The Tempest. 2003. (No Fear Shakespeare Ser.). (Illus.). 224p. pap. 5.95 (978-1-58663-849-8(1)) Spark Publishing Group.

Shaw, George Bernard. Annajanska. Landes, William-Alan, ed. 2003. (George Bernard Shaw Collection). 20p. (YA). (gr. 6-12). 8.00 (978-0-88734-863-1(7)) Players Pr., Inc.

—The Dark Lady of the Sonnets. abr. ed. 2005. (Stratford Festival Ser.). (gr. 9-12). (978-0-660-17979-7(2)) Canadian Broadcasting Corp./Societe Radio-Canada.

—The Inca of Perusalem. Landes, William-Alan, ed. 2003. (Players Press G. B. Shaw Collection). 28p. (YA). (gr. 4-12). 8.00 (978-0-88734-864-8(5)) Players Pr., Inc.

—O'Flaherty V. C. Landes, William-Alan, ed. 2003. (George Bernard Shaw Collection). 28p. (YA). (gr. 6-12). pap. 8.00 (978-0-88734-350-6(3)) Players Pr., Inc.

Shearer, Bruce W. Swishwooshtinkle: The Windy Wizard. 1999. (Illus.). (J). (gr. k-4). pap. 4.00 (978-1-57514-351-4(8) , 1184) Encore Performance Publishing.

—Wilburforce Wilson & the Magic Fountain. 1999. (Illus.). (J). (ps-5). pap. 4.00 (978-1-57514-352-1(6) , 1186) Encore Performance Publishing.

Shepard, Aaron. Folktales on Stage: Children's Plays for Reader's Theater (or Readers Theatre), with 16 Play Scripts from World Folk & Fairy Tales & Legends, Including Asian, African, Middle Eastern, European, & Native American. 2004. 180p. pap. 14.00 (978-0-938497-20-2(0)) Shepard Pubns.

Shepherd, C. A., et al. The Sly Fox (Playscript) 2003. (Musicals for Young Audiences Ser.). 32p. (Orig.). (YA). (gr. 3-12). pap. 8.00 (978-0-88734-503-6(4)) Players Pr., Inc.

Shockey, Marilyn. What's a Wolf to Do? (Musical) 42p. (YA). pap. 7.50 (978-1-58342-182-6(3) , WD7) Dramatic Publishing Co.

Siddons, Annie. Rapunzel. 2007. 87p. pap. 18.95 (***978-1-84002-698-6(7)**) Oberon Bks., Ltd. GBR. *Dist:* Consortium Bk. Sales & Distribution.

Siebert, Anne. Celebrating American Heroes Text/Teacher's Book/CD Package: Plays for Students of English. Roach, Marilynne, illus. 2005. pap. 39.00 incl. audio compact disk (978-0-86647-213-5(4)) Pro Lingua Associates, Inc.

Simmonds, Rae N. The Shamrock Road: A Musical. 1998. (J). pap. 6.50 (978-0-87602-362-4(6)) Anchorage Pr.

Slaight, Craig, et al, eds. The Smith & Kraus Index of Plays for Young Actors: A Guide to 500 Plays. 1999. (Index of Plays Ser.). 214p. (YA). (gr. 6 up). pap. 14.95 (978-1-57525-050-2(0)) Smith and Kraus Publishers, Incorporated.

Smith, Grady. A Night at Buckingham Palace: Comedy Play. 2002. (YA). pap. 4.00 (978-1-931805-77-3(6)) Brooklyn Pubs.

Smith, Marisa & Frockt, Deborah L., eds. Seattle Children's Theatre Vol. II: Six Plays for Young Audiences. 2000. 308p. (YA). pap. 16.95 (978-1-57525-158-5(2)) Smith and Kraus Publishers, Incorporated.

Snyder, Geraldine Ann. Johnny Appleseed: Musical. 2003. (Illus.). 41p. (YA). pap. 6.95 (978-1-58342-127-7(0) , J04) Dramatic Publishing Co.

—Red Riding Hood: A Vaudeville Romp! 2002. (Illus.). 62p. (YA). pap. 6.95 (978-1-58342-142-0(4) , R05) Dramatic Publishing Co.

Sophocles. Sophocles: Philoctetes. Affleck, Judith, ed. 2001. (Cambridge Translations from Greek Drama Ser.). (Illus.). 128p. pap. 10.50 (978-0-521-64480-8(1)) Cambridge Univ. Pr.

Soto, Gary. Nerdlandia. 1999. (gr. 7-12). lib. bdg. 14.15 (978-0-613-15028-6(7)) Tandem Library Bks.

—Nerdlandia: A Play. 1999. 96p. (J). (gr. 4-7). pap. 5.99 (978-0-698-11784-6(0) , Putnam Juvenile) Penguin Group (USA) Inc.

—Nerdlandia: A Play. 1999. (978-0-606-16800-7(1)) Tandem Library Bks.

SparkNotes Staff. Macbeth. Shakespeare, William & Crowther, John, eds. 2003. (No Fear Shakespeare Ser.). (Illus.). 240p. pap. 5.95 (978-1-58663-846-7(7)) Spark Publishing Group.

Spiegel, Richard A. & Fisher, Barbara, eds. Streams, No. 14. 2000. (Illus.). 150p. (YA). (gr. 9-12). pap. 10.00 (978-0-934830-67-6(3)) Ten Penny Players, Inc.

Stevenson, Augusta. Children's Classics in Dramatic Form (a. 2006. pap. 35.99 (***978-1-4280-0533-4(1)**) IndyPublish.com.

Stevenson, Robert Louis. Treasure Island. 2003. (More for Teens Ser.). 64p. (Orig.). (YA). (gr. 6-12). pap. 6.00 (978-0-88734-412-1(7)) Players Pr., Inc.

Stickland, Eugene. Two Plays: Sitting on Paradise & a Guide to Mourning. 2003. (Plays & Play Collections). 168p. (YA). (gr. 6-12). pap. 15.00 (978-0-88734-931-7(5)) Players Pr., Inc.

Stickler. Mystery of the Shaking Ground Dramas, Speeches & Recitations for Children. 2006. 48p. pap. 7.25 (978-0-687-49596-2(2)) Abingdon Pr.

Stickler, LeeDell, ed. Busy Boogie: And Other Dramas for Preschool. 2004. 112p. pap. 15.00 (978-0-687-07645-1(5)) Abingdon Pr.

Still, James. Jack Frost. 1998. 43p. (J). pap. 4.25 (978-0-87129-780-8(9) , J29) Dramatic Publishing Co.

—Just Before Sleep. 1998. 69p. pap. 6.25 (978-0-87129-779-2(5) , J30) Dramatic Publishing Co.

Strand, John. The Diaries. 2004. 104p. (J). pap. 6.50 (978-1-58342-232-8(3) , D83) Dramatic Publishing Co.

Sturgill, Beverly. The Enchantress of Ipswich. 1998. (J). pap. 6.50 (978-0-87602-359-4(6)) Anchorage Pr.

Sturkie, Joan & Cassady, Marsh. Acting It Out - Junior. 2003. (Plays & Play Collections). 249p. (YA). (gr. 6-8). pap. 22.00 (978-0-89390-240-7(3)) Resource Pubns., Inc.

Sullivan, T. G. Short Contest Monologs for Teen Women: Collection of Six Monologs. 2002. (YA). pap. 19.95 (978-1-931805-71-1(7)) Brooklyn Pubs.

Swajeski, Donna M. The Revolution Machine: Playscript. rev. ed. 2003. (Musicals Ser.). 55p. (Orig.). (J). (gr. 3-12). pap. 8.00 (978-0-88734-511-1(5)) Players Pr., Inc.

Tall, Jennifer. Mayfair-7: Dramatic Play. 2002. (YA). pap. 4.00 (978-1-931805-76-6(8)) Brooklyn Pubs.

—The Special One: Dramatic Play. 2002. (YA). pap. 4.25 (978-1-931805-89-6(X) , 727) Brooklyn Pubs.

Tasso, Torquato, et al. Aminta: A Pastoral Play. Jernigan, Charles & Jones, Irene Marchegiani, eds. Jernigan, Charles & Jones, Irene Marchegiani, trs. from ITA. 2000. (Dual-Language Poetry Ser.). (ITA & ENG., Illus.). xxxiii, 180p. (J). pap. 15.00 (978-0-934977-65-4(8)) Italica Pr.

Taymor, Julie. The Lion King: Circle of Life Board Book. 1998. (Disneys Ser.). (Illus.). 14p. (J). (ps-3). 6.95 (978-0-7868-3216-3(9)) Disney Pr.

Thane, Adele. Plays from Famous Stories & Fairy Tales. 2001. 463p. (J). (gr. 4-7). pap. 15.00 (978-0-8238-0262-3(0)) Kalmbach Publishing Co., Bks. Div.

Thistle, Louise. Dramatizando Tres Cuentos Clasicos: Los Cuentos para Contrar y Actuar. 2000. (Young Actor Ser.). (SPA & ENG., Illus.). 103p. (J). (gr. k-6). pap. 19.95 (978-1-57525-193-6(0)) Smith and Kraus Publishers, Incorporated.

—Little Red Snares the Wolf. (J). pap. 4.25 (978-1-58342-036-2(3) , L49) Dramatic Publishing Co.

Thurston, Cheryl M. A Frog King's Daughter Is Nothing to Sneeze At: Playscript. 2003. (Musicals for Young Audiences Ser.). 32p. (Orig.). (YA). (gr. k-12). pap. 10.00 (978-0-88734-513-5(1)) Players Pr., Inc.

Top Cat: Individual Title Six-Packs. (Story Steps Ser.). (gr. k-2). 32.00 (978-0-7635-9851-8(8)) Rigby Education.

Troughton, Joanna. Cambridge Plays: The Story of Running Water ELT Edition. 2004. (Cambridge Storybooks Ser.). (Illus.). 24p. pap. 6.00 (978-0-521-75243-5(4)) Cambridge Univ. Pr.

Umansky, Kaye. Cruel Times: A Victorian Play. (Illus.). 48p. pap. (978-0-7502-4121-2(7) , Hodder Wayland) Hodder Children's Division.

—The Emperor's New Clothes. 2003. (Curtain up! Ser.: Vol. 6). (Illus.). 48p. (J). (gr. 1-4). pap. 16.95 (978-0-7136-4624-5(1)) A & C Black GBR. *Dist:* Lubrecht & Cramer, Ltd.

—Humble Tom's Big Trip: A Tudor Play. (Illus.). 48p. (J). pap. (978-0-7502-4123-6(3) , Hodder Wayland) Hodder Children's Division.

—Sleeping Beauty. Crossland, Caroline, illus. 2003. (Plays & Play Collections). 48p. (J). pap. 15.00 (978-0-7136-5371-7(X)) A & C Black GBR. *Dist:* Players Pr., Inc.

Verrier, Steven. Don't Needle Me: A Ten-Minute Comedy Duet. 2003. 16p. (YA). pap. 4.50 (978-1-932404-21-0(X) , 157A) Brooklyn Pubs.

—Ear-Igation Blues: Ten-Minute Comedy Duet. 2002. (YA). pap. 9.00 (978-1-931805-46-9(6) , 131A) Brooklyn Pubs.

—Golf Doctor: A Ten-Minute Comedy Duet. 2003. 16p. (YA). pap. 4.50 (978-1-932404-41-8(4) , 108) Brooklyn Pubs.

—Madam & Steve: Ten-Minute Comedy Duet. 2002. (YA). pap. 9.00 (978-1-931805-39-1(3) , 125A) Brooklyn Pubs.

—Seafood Science Lab: Ten-Minute Comedy Duet. 2002. (YA). pap. 9.00 (978-1-931805-41-4(5) , 126A) Brooklyn Pubs.

Vogel, Larry. Fearless Pharaoh Foofoo & Other Dramas for Children. 1998. 160p. (J). (gr. k-6). 14.99 (978-0-570-05332-3(5)) Concordia Publishing Hse.

Walker, Geof. William Shakespeare's 'A Midsummer Night's Dream' - a playscript for younger Students. 2006. 49p. pap. 19.45 (978-1-4116-4407-6(7)) Lulu.com.

Walker, Jeanne Murray. Inventing Montana. 2002. 79p. (YA). (gr. 10 up). pap. 6.25 (978-1-58342-134-5(3) , I81) Dramatic Publishing Co.

—Tales from the Daily Tabloid. 2002. 82p. (YA). pap. 6.25 (978-1-58342-133-8(5) , TE6) Dramatic Publishing Co.

Wall, Suzy. Our New Home: Reader's Theater Levels K-M (20-28) Leon, Karen, illus. ed. 2004. (Reader's Theater Ser.). 16p. (J). pap. 22.00 (978-1-4108-2299-4(0) , A22990) Benchmark Education Co.

Watts, Cedric. Macbeth. Shakespeare, William, ed. 2001. 118p. audio compact disk (978-1-903342-15-2(5)) Wordsworth Educational.

Way, Charles. Plays for Young People. 2002. 16p. pap. 19.95 (978-0-9536757-1-5(8)) Theatre Communications Group, Inc.

—A Spell of Cold Weather. 2004. 64p. pap. 16.95 (978-0-9542330-8-2(5)) Aurora Metro Pubns. Ltd. GBR. *Dist:* Consortium Bk. Sales & Distribution.

Welch, Fay. The Magic Swap Shop. rev. ed. 2003. 48p. (YA). (gr. 3-12). pap. 6.00 (978-0-88734-509-8(3)) Players Pr., Inc.

West, Keith. Jason Brent. Andrews, Gary, illus. 2001. (Star Plays Ser.). 48p. pap. 8.99 (978-0-237-52190-5(3) , Evans Brothers, Limited) Evans Publishing Group GBR. *Dist:* Independent Pubs. Group.

West, Keith & Dickens, Charles. Oliver Twist. Cruikshank, George, illus. 2003. (Star Plays Ser.). 48p. pap. 8.99 (978-0-237-52192-9(X) , Evans Brothers, Limited) Evans Publishing Group GBR. *Dist:* Independent Pubs. Group.

West, Tracey, et al. Heroes in American History. 2003. (Read-aloud Plays Ser.). (Illus.). 96p. pap., tchr. ed. 13.95 (978-0-439-22264-8(8) , Teaching Resources) Scholastic, Inc.

Wheeler, Jacque & Hartsfield, Mariella G. Tall Betsy & the Crackerbarrel Tales. 2003. 32p. (YA). (gr. k-12). pap. 6.00 (978-0-88734-265-3(5)) Players Pr., Inc.

Wier, Alsion. The Sunmaid Raisins Play Book. 2000. (Illus.). 12p. (J). (gr. k-3). mass mkt. 5.99 (978-0-689-82726-6(1) , Simon & Schuster Children's Publishing) Simon & Schuster Children's Publishing.

Williams, Guy. Billy Budd. 2003. (More for Teens Ser.). 32p. (Orig.). (YA). (gr. 6-12). pap. 5.00 (978-0-88734-415-2(1)) Players Pr., Inc.

—David & Goliath. 2003. (Illus.). 20p. (Orig.). (J). (gr. 3 up). pap. 6.00 (978-0-88734-411-4(9)) Players Pr., Inc.

—Oliver Twist: 30 Speaking Parts. 2nd ed. 1998. (Dramascripts Classic Texts Ser.). 130p. (J). (gr. 6-9). pap. 17.95 (978-0-17-432548-2(7)) Nelson Thornes Ltd. GBR. *Dist:* Trans-Atlantic Pubns., Inc.

Williams, Marcia. More Tales from Shakespeare. Williams, Marcia, illus. 2005. (Illus.). 40p. (J). (gr. 3-7). pap. 7.99 (978-0-7636-2693-8(7)) Candlewick Pr.

Williams, Tennessee. The Glass Menagerie. 1999. 105p. (gr. 7-12). per. 17.60 (978-0-8085-0883-0(0)) Tandem Library Bks.

Winther, Barbara. India, Burma/Thailand, Vietnam. 2004. (Plays from Asian Tales Ser.: No. 1). 52p. (YA). (gr. 3-12). pap. 10.00 (978-0-88734-486-2(0)) Players Pr., Inc.

—India, Indonesia/Malaysia, China. 2004. (Plays from Asian Tales Ser.: No. 2). 60p. (YA). (gr. 3-12). pap. 10.00 (978-0-88734-487-9(9)) Players Pr., Inc.

—Japan & Korea. 2004. (Plays from Asian Tales Ser.: No. 3). 56p. (J). pap. 10.00 (978-0-88734-488-6(7)) Players Pr., Inc.

Wistrand, Carolyn Nur. Beauty in Black Performance: Plays for African American Youth. 2006. (Illus.). (YA). 151p. (978-1-59221-379-5(0)); 158p. pap. (978-1-59221-380-1(4)) Africa World Pr.

Wolak, Camilla H. Squire Gullible & the Dragon. rev. ed. 2003. (Theater for Young Audiences Ser.). 40p. (YA). (gr. 3-12). pap. 6.00 (978-0-88734-508-1(5)) Players Pr., Inc.

Wolf, J. M. Cinderella Outgrows the Glass Slipper & Other Zany Fractured Fairy Tale Plays: 5 Funny Plays with Related Writing Activities & Graphic Organizers That Motivate Kids to Explore Plot, Characters, & Settings. 2002. (Illus.). 72p. (ps). pap. 11.95 (978-0-439-27168-4(1)) Scholastic, Inc.

Wolf, Joan. Leveled Read-Aloud Plays: U. S. Civic Holidays: 5 Short Plays with Multi-Leveled Reading Parts to Build Fluency-and Engage All Students. 2007. (Illus.). 80p. pap. 12.99 (***978-0-439-58288-9(1)*** , Teaching Resources) Scholastic, Inc.

Wong, Elizabeth. Boid & Oscar. 2002. 33p. (YA). pap. 4.25 (978-1-58342-115-4(7) , BA7) Dramatic Publishing Co.

—The Happy Prince. 2002. 47p. (YA). pap. 4.25 (978-1-58342-116-1(5) , H82) Dramatic Publishing Co.

Wood, David. The Twits. 62p. (YA). (gr. 6). pap. 6.25 (978-1-58342-172-7(6) , TD6) Dramatic Publishing Co.

Wood, David & Dahl, Roald. Danny the Champion of the World. 2006. 70p. pap. (***978-0-573-15016-6(8)***) French, Samuel Inc.

Wood, David & Hill, Eric. Spot's Birthday Party. 2002. (Illus.). 58p. (J). (978-0-573-05129-6(1)) French, Samuel Inc.

Wood, Nick. Warrior Square. 2004. 64p. pap. 16.95 (978-0-9546912-0-2(2)) Theatre Communications Group, Inc.

Woyiwada, Allison. The Little Fir Tree: A Musical for Primary Children Based on a Story by Hans Christian Andersen. 2003. (Musicals for Young Audiences Ser.). 16p. (J). (gr. k-6). pap. 5.00 (978-0-88734-428-2(3)) Players Pr., Inc.

Wright, Roosevelt. The Broken Wing Dove. 2002. 6.00 net. (978-0-943751-15-3(2)) Free Pr. Pubs.

Wright, Roosevelt, Jr. Deacon Willie's Last Will & Testament. 2004. (YA). (978-0-943751-36-8(5)) Free Pr. Pubs.

—For Such a Time As This. 2004. (YA). 5.00 (978-0-943751-31-3(4)) Free Pr. Pubs.

—I Wants to Be Free: A Black Heritage Drama in Two Acts. 1999. 54p. (YA). pap. 5.00 (978-0-943751-05-4(5)) Free Pr. Pubs.

Wright, Roosevelt, Sr. The Prodigals. 2004. (YA). (978-0-943751-35-1(7)) Free Pr. Pubs.

Wright, Roosevelt, Jr. Shoe Shine. 2004. (YA). 8.00 (978-0-943751-38-2(1)) Free Pr. Pubs.

Wright, Roosevelt, Jr. & Wright, Roosevelt. Honey Babe's Treasure: A Black Heritage Drama in Two Acts. 2003. 24p. 6.00 (978-0-943751-22-1(5)) Free Pr. Pubs.

Yee, Lauren D. How to Be the Perfect Parent: A Comedy Monologue. 2003. (YA). pap. 4.50 (978-1-932404-35-7(X) , 288) Brooklyn Pubs.

—My Mother's Touch: A Dramatic Monologue. 2003. (YA). pap. 4.50 (978-1-932404-34-0(1) , 287) Brooklyn Pubs.

York, Y. Mask of the Unicorn Warrior. 2002. 48p. (YA). pap. 6.25 (978-1-58342-111-6(4) , MD2) Dramatic Publishing Co.

Zager, James. What You Will. 1998. 40p. (YA). (gr. 10 up). pap. 4.25 (978-0-87129-803-4(1) , W83) Dramatic Publishing Co.

Zindel, Paul. The Effect of Gamma Rays on Man-in-the-Moon Marigolds. 2005. 112p. (J). (gr. 7 up). pap. 6.99 (978-0-06-075738-0(8) , Harper Trophy) HarperCollins Pubs.

Zuber, Diane. The Broken Doll A Musical Play for Christmas. 2006. (J). 29.95 (978-0-9785551-0-8(4)) Zuber Publishing.

Zyromski, Page McKean. Skits from Scripture: 10 Plays from the New Testament. Cannizzo, Karen A., ed. 2001. 36p. (J). pap. 11.95 (978-0-937997-97-0(8)) Pflaum Publishing Group.

—Skits from Scripture: 10 Plays from the Old Testament. Cannizzo, Karen A., ed. 2001. 36p. (J). pap. 11.95 (978-0-937997-96-3(X)) Pflaum Publishing Group.

PLAYS—FICTION

Beck, Ana. Elliot's Bath. 2001. lib. bdg. 14.10 (978-0-613-36327-3(2)) Tandem Library Bks.

The Best Part: Individual Title, 6 Nos., Pck. (gr. 3 up). 35.00 (978-0-7635-9664-4(7)) Rigby Education.

Bryant, Annie. Out of Bounds. 2005. (Beacon Street Girls Ser.). 255p. (J). 7.99 (978-0-9746587-9-7(0) , Beacon Street Girls) B*tween Productions, Inc.

Christopher, Lawrence. The Tickle Fingers: Where Is Pinky? Christopher, Lawrence, illus. 2006. (ENG., Illus.). 24p. (J). (ps up). 9.95 (978-0-9712278-3-5(7)) MF Unlimited.

Crew, Linda. Nekomah Creek Christmas. Robinson, Charles, illus. 1999. 147p. (YA). (gr. 6-9). reprint ed. 15.00 (978-0-7881-6628-0(X)) DIANE Publishing Co.

de Paola, Tomie. The Night of las Posadas. de Paola, Tomie, illus. 2001. (Illus.). 32p. (J). pap. 6.99 (978-0-698-11901-7(0) , Putnam Juvenile) Penguin Group (USA) Inc.

—The Night of las Posadas. 2001. (978-0-606-22500-7(5)) Tandem Library Bks.

—The Night of Las Posadas. de Paola, Tomie, illus. 1999. (Illus.). 32p. (J). (ps-3). 16.99 (978-0-399-23400-2(4) , Putnam Juvenile) Penguin Group (USA) Inc.

—Tomie's Little Christmas Pageant. 2002. (Illus.). 32p. (J). bds. 7.99 (978-0-399-23959-5(6) , Putnam Juvenile) Penguin Group (USA) Inc.

deGroat, Diane. Liar, Liar, Pants on Fire. 2006. (Illus.). 32p. (J). reprint ed. pap. 6.95 (978-0-8118-5453-5(1)) Chronicle Bks. LLC.

Engelbreit, Mary. Queen of the Class. Engelbreit, Mary, illus. 2007. (Illus.). 24p. (J). 16.00 (***978-1-4223-6705-6(3)***) DIANE Publishing Co.

Feely, Jenny. Last One Picked. 2000. (gr. k-3). lib. bdg. 11.80 (978-0-613-29802-5(0)) Tandem Library Bks.

Fox, Mem. Wombat Divine. 2002. (Illus.). (J). 13.19 (978-0-7587-4046-5(8)) Book Wholesalers, Inc.

—Wombat Divine. Argent, Kerry, illus. 1999. 32p. (J). (ps-3). pap. 6.00 (978-0-15-202096-5(9) , Harcourt Paperbacks) Harcourt Children's Bks.

Gilman, Phoebe. Jillian Jiggs & the Secret Surprise. ed. 2004. (J). (ps-2). spiral bd. (978-0-616-01655-8(7)) Canadian National Institute for the Blind/Institut National Canadien pour les Aveugles.

Golden Books Staff. Treasure Hunters. 2005. (Illus.). 32p. (J). (ps-2). pap. 4.99 (978-0-375-83474-5(5) , Golden Bks.) Random Hse. Children's Bks.

Graves, Damien. The Deadly Catch. 2008. (Midnight Library: Vol. 8). 176p. (J). pap. 5.99 (***978-0-439-89395-4(X)*** , Scholastic Paperbacks) Scholastic, Inc.

The Great Race. 2002. (Thomas the Tank Engine Ser.). (Illus.). (J). 11.91 (978-0-7587-4754-9(3)) Book Wholesalers, Inc.

Harcourt School Publishers Staff. How to Write a Play On Level. 3rd ed. 2002. (Trophies Reading Program Ser.). (Illus.). pap. 5.10 (978-0-15-323269-5(2)) Harcourt Schl. Pubs.

—Let's Do a Play. 3rd ed. 2002. (Trophies English Language Learners Ser.). (Illus.). pap. 5.10 (978-0-15-327836-5(6)) Harcourt Schl. Pubs.

—Time for a Play. 3rd ed. 2002. (Trophies English Language Learners Ser.). (Illus.). pap. 5.10 (978-0-15-327825-9(0)) Harcourt Schl. Pubs.

—Trofeos On Level: En Mi Escuela. 3rd ed. 2002. (SPA., Illus.). pap. 5.50 (978-0-15-323900-7(X)) Harcourt Schl. Pubs.

Hoffman, Mary. Starring Grace. Binch, Caroline, illus. (Chapters Ser.). 96p. (J). 2001. (gr. 2-6). pap. 4.99 (978-0-14-230022-0(5) , Puffin); 2000. (gr. k-4). 14.99 (978-0-8037-2559-1(0) , Dial) Penguin Group (USA) Inc.

—Starring Grace. 2001. (gr. 3-6). lib. bdg. 13.00 (978-0-613-44418-7(3)) Tandem Library Bks.

Howe, James. Pinky & Rex & the School Play. 1999. (Pinky & Rex Ser.). (J). (gr. 1-4). pap., stu. ed. 22.24 incl. audio (978-0-7887-2984-3(5) , 40866) Recorded Bks., LLC.

—Pinky & Rex & the School Play. Sweet, Melissa, illus. 1998. (Pinky & Rex Ser.). (J). (gr. 1-4). (978-0-606-13707-2(6)) Tandem Library Bks.

Lawlor, Laurie. The Biggest Pest on Eighth Avenue. Fisher, Cynthia, illus. (Holiday House Reader Ser.). 48p. (J). (gr. k-3). tchr. ed. 14.95 (978-0-8234-1321-8(7)) Holiday Hse., Inc.

Little Engine - Playing Together. 2005. (J). bds. (978-1-4194-0022-3(3)) Paradise Pr., Inc.

Lopetegui, Leqnor. I Muy Bien! (Very Good) Theatre Book, Level B. 2001. (SPA., Illus.). 30p. (J). (gr. 1-3). pap. (978-0-9713381-4-2(0)) Double R Publishing, LLC.

MacDonald, Marianne. Secondhand Star. Christelow, Eileen, illus. 1998. (Lots of O'Leary's Ser.). (978-0-606-13769-0(6)) Tandem Library Bks.

Madonna. A Rose by Any Other Name. Fulvimari, Jeffrey, illus. 2007. (English Roses Ser.). 125p. (J). (gr. 2). 9.99 (***978-0-14-240885-8(9)*** , Puffin) Penguin Group (USA) Inc.

Morozumi, Atsuko. A Jugar. 2000. (Coleccion "Conejito" Ser.). (SPA.). (J). (ps-k). bds. (978-958-04-4518-0(4)) Norma S.A. COL. *Dist:* Lectorum Pubns., Inc.

Rue, Nancy N. Lily!lights, Action. 2002. (gr. 3-6). lib. bdg. 13.00 (978-0-613-71698-7(1)) Tandem Library Bks.

The School Play: Individual Title Six-Packs. (ps-2). 27.00 (978-0-7635-9473-2(3)) Rigby Education.

Schotter, Roni. Purim Play. Hafner, Marylin, illus. 1998. 32p. (J). (ps-3). 15.95 (978-0-316-77518-2(5)) Little Brown & Co.

Siebold, Jan. My Nights at the Improv. 2005. 98p. (YA). (gr. 6-9). lib. bdg. 14.95 (978-0-8075-5630-6(0)) Whitman, Albert & Co.

Steck-Vaughn Staff. We Are All Glad. 2000. pap. (978-0-7398-4474-8(1)) Steck-Vaughn.

Strasser, Todd. How I Changed My Life. 2008. 240p. (YA). mass mkt. 6.99 (***978-1-4169-5409-5(0)*** , Simon Pulse) Simon & Schuster Children's Publishing.

Su, Lucy. Play Hide & Seek. Su, Lucy, illus. 2003. (Kitten & Baby Kitten Ser.). (Illus.). 42p. (J). pap. (978-1-85602-538-6(1)) Chrysalis Children's Bks.

Waber, Bernard. Evie & Margie. 2006. (Illus.). 32p. (J). (gr. k-3). reprint ed. pap. 6.95 (978-0-618-69338-2(6)) Houghton Mifflin Co.

Wells, Victoria. The School Play Picturebook. 2002. 32p. (J). 12.99 (978-0-7868-0650-8(8)) Disney Pr.

Wheeler, Lisa. Invasion of the Pig Sisters. Ansley, Frank, illus. 2006. (Fitch & Chip Ser.). 48p. (J). pap. 3.99 (978-0-689-84958-9(3)) Simon & Schuster Children's Publishing.

PLAYS, CHRISTMAS

see Christmas Plays

PLAYS FOR CHILDREN

see Plays

PLAYWRIGHTS

see Dramatists

PLAYWRITING

see Drama—Technique

PLESKIT (FICTITIOUS CHARACTER)—FICTION

Coville, Bruce. The Attack of the Two-Inch Teacher. unabr. ed. 2000. (I Was a Sixth Grade Alien Ser.). 165p. (J). (gr. 3-5). pap. 28.00 incl. audio (978-0-8072-8354-7(1) , YA170SP, Listening Library) Random Hse. Audio Publishing Group.

—The Attack of the Two-Inch Teacher. 1999. (I Was a Sixth Grade Alien Ser.). (Illus.). (J). 10.64 (978-0-606-18374-1(4)) Tandem Library Bks.

—Don't Fry My Veeblax! Sansekers, Tony, illus. 2000. (I Was a Sixth Grade Alien Ser.: Vol. 6). (J). 10.64 (978-0-606-19849-3(0)) Tandem Library Bks.

—I Lost My Grandfather's Brain. unabr. ed. 2004. (I Was a Sixth Grade Alien Ser.). 160p. (J). (gr. 3-6). pap. 29.00 incl. audio (978-0-8072-8385-1(1) , YA180SP, Listening Library) Random Hse. Audio Publishing Group.

—I Was a Sixth Grade Alien. (I Was a Sixth Grade Alien Ser.). 170p. (J). (gr. 4-6). pap. 3.99 (978-0-8072-8202-1(2)); 2004. (gr. 3-6). pap. 29.00 incl. audio (978-0-8072-8201-4(4) , S YA 138 SP) Random Hse. Audio Publishing Group. (Listening Library).

—I Was a Sixth Grade Alien. 1999. (I Was a Sixth Grade Alien Ser.). (J). 11.64 (978-0-606-17089-5(8)) Tandem Library Bks.

—Peanut Butter Lover Boy. 2000. (I Was a Sixth Grade Alien Ser.). (Illus.). (J). (978-0-606-18307-9(8)) Tandem Library Bks.

—Zombies of the Science Fair. 2000. (I Was a Sixth Grade Alien Ser.). (Illus.). (J). (978-0-606-18308-6(6)) Tandem Library Bks.

PLOT-YOUR-OWN STORIES

Here are entered works of fiction in which the reader chooses from a number of possible options for developing the story.

Becket, Jim. Inca Gold: Choose Your Own Adventure #20. 2007. (Choose Your Own Adventure Ser.: 20). (Illus.). 144p. (J). per. 6.99 (***978-1-933390-20-8(4)*** , CHCL20) Chooseco LLC.

Bugsilocks & the Three Bears. 1999. (McGraw-Hill Junior Academic Ser.). (Illus.). 16p. (J). (gr. k-2). pap. 3.99 (978-1-57768-215-8(7)) School Specialty Publishing.

Busby, Cylin. The Dance Dilemma: A Choose Your Boyfriend Book. 2007. (Date Him or Dump Him? Ser.). 192p. (J). (gr. 5 up). pap. 6.95 (***978-1-59990-084-1(X)*** , Bloomsbury Children) Bloomsbury Publishing.

Charbonneau, Eileen. The Connor Emerald. Williams, Lori, ed. 1999. 170p. (YA). pap. 9.99 (978-1-58365-753-9(3) , Timeless Romance) Sierra Raconteur Publishing.

Cousins, Lucy. Maisy's First Game Book. Cousins, Lucy, illus. 2006. (Illus.). 8p. (J). (ps). bds. 9.99 (978-0-7636-2812-3(3)) Candlewick Pr.

de Beer, Hans, illus. Little Polar Bear Sticker Book. 2001. 12p. (J). pap. 4.99 (978-1-59014-033-8(8)) North-South Bks., Inc.

Dennis, Jeanne Gowen & Seifert, Sheila. Attack! Hohn, David, tr. Hohn, David, illus. 2003. (Strive to Thrive Ser.). 96p. (J). pap., pap. 5.99 (978-0-7814-3894-0(2) , 0781438942) Cook, David C. Publishing Co.

—Deadly Expedition! Hohn, David, tr. Hohn, David, illus. 2003. (Survivor Ser.). 96p. (J). pap., pap. 5.99 (978-0-7814-3897-1(7) , 0781438977) Cook, David C. Publishing Co.

—Escape! Hohn, David, tr. Hohn, David, illus. 2003. (Strive to Thrive Ser.). 96p. (J). pap., pap. 5.99 (978-0-7814-3895-7(0) , 0781438950) Cook, David C. Publishing Co.

—Trapped! Hohn, David, tr. Hohn, David, illus. 2003. (Survivor Ser.). 96p. (J). pap., pap. 5.99 (978-0-7814-3898-8(5) , 0781438985) Cook, David C. Publishing Co.

Denton, Terry. The Golden Udder. Denton, Terry, illus. 2003. (Storymaze Ser.: Vol. 4). (Illus.). 120p. (J). (gr. 3-5). pap. 6.95 (978-1-86508-784-9(X)) Allen & Unwin AUS. *Dist:* Independent Pubs. Group.

Fabregat, Antonio-Manuel. Los Cuentos de Mi Escuela. (SPA.). 128p. (J). (gr. 4-6). (978-84-216-1185-2(2) , BU3866) Bruño, Editorial ESP. *Dist:* Lectorum Pubns., Inc.

Fanning, Kieran. Trapdoor to Treachery. 2000. (Illus.). 128p. (J). (gr. 4-8). per. (978-1-84210-023-3(8)) Mentor Bks.

Gilligan, Shannon. The Case of the Silk King. 2005. 116p. (J). pap. (***978-0-7608-9702-7(6)***) Sundance/Newbridge Educational Publishing.

—Struggle down Under. 2007. (Choose Your Own Adventure Ser.: No. 21). (Illus.). 144p. (J). (gr. 3-7). pap. 6.99 (***978-1-933390-21-5(2)***) Chooseco LLC.

The Gingerbread Fudd. 1999. (McGraw-Hill Junior Academic Ser.). (Illus.). 16p. (J). (gr. k-2). pap. 3.99 (978-1-57768-214-1(9)) School Specialty Publishing.

Goodhart, Pippa & Sharratt, Nick. You Choose! (Illus.). 32p. (J). 19.99 (978-0-385-60176-4(X) , Doubleday) Transworld Publishers Ltd. GBR. *Dist:* Trafalgar Square Publishing.

Grosset and Dunlap Staff & Lamb, Stacey. Winter Wonderland. 2000. (Sticker Stories Ser.). (Illus.). 1p. (J). (ps-3). mass mkt. 4.99 (978-0-448-42408-8(8) , Grosset & Dunlap) Penguin Group (USA) Inc.

Inches, Alison. Dora's Treasure Hunt. Hall, Susan', illus. 2002. (Dora the Explorer Ser.). 12p. (J). 5.99 (978-0-689-84664-9(9) , Simon Spotlight/Nickelodeon) Simon & Schuster Children's Publishing.

Iparraguirre, Sylvia, et al. Terminemos el Cuento. 2003. (SPA., Illus.). 128p. (YA). (gr. 9-12). 9.95 (978-84-204-4965-4(2)) Alfaguara, Ediciones, S.A.- Grupo Santillana ESP. *Dist:* Santillana USA Publishing Co., Inc.

Jackson, Steve. The Citadel of Chaos. 2003. 208p. pap. (978-0-7434-7510-5(0)) ibooks, Inc.

Jackson, Steve & Livingstone, Ian. The Worlock of Firetop Mountain. 2003. 192p. pap. 6.99 (978-0-7434-7511-2(9)) ibooks, Inc.

Leibold, Jay. Secret of the Ninja No. 16: Choose Your Own Adventure #16. 2007. (Choose Your Own Adventure Ser.: Vol. 16). (Illus.). 144p. (J). mass mkt. 5.99 (978-1-933390-16-1(6)) Chooseco LLC.

Livingstone, Ian. Deathtrap Dungeon. 2003. 224p. pap. 6.99 (978-0-7434-7967-7(X)) ibooks, Inc.

Matthews, T. J. The Canoeing Safari. Rheburg, Judy, illus. 2004. (J). (978-0-938978-35-0(7)) Wycliffe Bible Translators.

Montgomery, Anson. Moon Quest: Choose Your Own Adventure #25 - Moon Quest. 2008. (Choose Your Own Adventure Ser.: 25). (Illus.). 144p. (J). per. 5.99 (***978-1-933390-25-3(5)***) Chooseco LLC.

Montgomery, R. A. The Abominable Snowman. 2006. (Choose Your Own Adventure Ser.: No. 1). (Illus.). 144p. (J). mass mkt. 5.99 (978-1-933390-01-7(8) , CHCL01) Chooseco LLC.

—Behind the Wheel. 2008. (Choose Your Own Adventure Ser.: No. 26). (Illus.). 144p. (J). per. 5.99 (***978-1-933390-26-0(3)***) Chooseco LLC.

—Beyond Escape. 2007. (Choose Your Own Adventure Ser.: No. 15). (Illus.). 144p. (J). mass mkt. 5.99 (978-1-933390-15-4(8) , CHCL15) Chooseco LLC.

—The Brilliant Dr. Wogan. 2007. (Choose Your Own Adventure Ser.: No. 17). (Illus.). 144p. (J). mass mkt. 5.99 (978-1-933390-17-8(4) , CHC:17) Chooseco LLC.

—Caravan. 2007. (Choose Your Own Adventure - Dragonlarks Ser.). (Illus.). 64p. (J). pap. 5.99 (***978-1-933390-54-3(9)***) Chooseco LLC.

—Choose Your Own Adventure Four Book Boxed Set #1: The Abominable Snowman, Journey under the Sea, Space & Beyond, the Lost Jewels of Nabooti. 2006. 576p. (J). per. 19.95 (***978-1-933390-94-9(8)***) Chooseco LLC.

—Escape. 2006. (Choose Your Own Adventure Ser.: No. 8). (Illus.). 144p. (J). mass mkt. 5.99 (978-1-933390-08-6(5) , CHCL08) Chooseco LLC.

—Forecast from Stonehenge. 2007. (Choose Your Own Adventure Ser.: No. 19). (Illus.). 144p. (J). mass mkt. 6.99 (***978-1-933390-19-2(0)***) Chooseco LLC.

—The Haunted House. 2007. (Choose Your Own Adventure Ser.). (Illus.). 64p. (J). pap. 5.99 (***978-1-933390-51-2(4)***) Chooseco LLC.

—House of Danger. 2006. (Choose Your Own Adventure Ser.: No. 6). (Illus.). 144p. (J). mass mkt. 5.99 (978-1-933390-06-2(9) , CHCL06) Chooseco LLC.

—House of Danger. 2005. (Illus.). 108p. (J). (***978-0-7608-9694-5(1)***) Sundance/Newbridge Educational Publishing.

—Indian Trail. 2007. (Choose Your Own Adventure - Dragonlarks Ser.). (Illus.). 64p. (J). pap. 5.99 (***978-1-933390-53-6(0)***) Chooseco LLC.

—Journey under the Sea. 2006. (Choose Your Own Adventure Ser.: No. 2). (Illus.). 144p. (J). mass mkt. 5.99 (978-1-933390-02-4(6) , CHCL02) Chooseco LLC.

—Journey under the Sea. 1999. mass mkt. (978-0-553-23229-5(0)) Random Hse., Inc.

—The Lost Jewels of Nabooti. 2006. (Choose Your Own Adventure Ser.: No. 4). (Illus.). 144p. (J). mass mkt. 5.99 (978-1-933390-04-8(2) , CHCL04) Chooseco LLC.

—Mystery of the Maya. 2006. (Choose Your Own Adventure Ser.: No. 5). (Illus.). 144p. (J). (gr. 4-7). mass mkt. 5.99 (978-1-933390-05-5(0) , CHCL05) Chooseco LLC.

—Prisoner of the Ant People. 2006. (Choose Your Own Adventure Ser.: No. 10). (Illus.). 144p. (J). mass mkt. 5.99 (978-1-933390-10-9(7) , CHCL10) Chooseco LLC.

—Race Forever. 2006. (Choose Your Own Adventure Ser.: No. 7). (Illus.). 144p. (J). mass mkt. 5.99 (978-1-933390-07-9(7) , CHCL07) Chooseco LLC.

—Race Forever. 2005. (Illus.). 122p. (J). (***978-0-7608-9695-2(X)***) Sundance/Newbridge Educational Publishing.

—Return to Atlantis. 2007. (Choose Your Own Adventure Ser.: No. 18). (Illus.). 144p. (J). mass mkt. 5.99 (978-1-933390-18-5(2) , CHCL18) Chooseco LLC.

—Space & Beyond. 2006. (Choose Your Own Adventure Ser.: No. 3). (Illus.). 144p. (J). mass mkt. 5.99 (978-1-933390-03-1(4) , CHCL03) Chooseco LLC.

—Tattoo of Death. 2007. (Choose Your Own Adventure Ser.: No. 22). (Illus.). 144p. (J). (gr. 3-7). pap. 6.99 (*978-1-933390-22-2(0)) Chooseco LLC.

—Trouble on Planet Earth. 2005. (Illus.). 113p. (J). pap. (*978-0-7608-9699-0(2)) Sundance/Newbridge Educational Publishing.

—War with the Evil Power Master. 2005. (Illus.). 123p. (J). pap. (*978-0-7608-9700-3(X)) Sundance/Newbridge Educational Publishing.

—Your Very Own Robot. 2007. (Choose Your Own Adventure Ser.). (Illus.). 64p. (J). pap. 5.99 (*978-1-933390-52-9(2)) Chooseco LLC.

Ostrow, Kim & Burnett, Mark. Marquesas. 2005. (Survivor—Outwit, Outplay, Outlast Ser.: Vol. 2). 143p. (J). (978-1-4155-7990-9(3) , Simon Spotlight) Simon & Schuster Children's Publishing.

Packard, Edward. Supercomputer. 1999. (Illus.). 118p. (Orig.). mass mkt. (978-0-553-24678-0(X)) Random Hse., Inc.

Pakulak, Eric. At the Side of Esther: A Multiple-Ending Bible Adventure. Bulanadi, Danny, illus. 2000. 96p. (J). pap. 6.95 (978-0-8198-0769-4(9)) Pauline Bks. & Media.

—At the Side of Moses: A Multiple-Ending Bible Adventure. Fielding, David, illus. 2000. (J). pap. 6.95 (978-0-8198-0770-0(2)) Pauline Bks. & Media.

Pomaska, Anna. Scruffy & Muffin in the Land of Enchantment: A Dot-to-Dot Story Book. 2004. (Dover Coloring Bks.). 32p. (J). pap. 3.95 (978-0-486-43566-4(0)) Dover Pubns., Inc.

Roseman, Kenneth D. Escape from the Holocaust. 1998. (gr. 3-6). lib. bdg. 17.60 (978-0-613-88955-1(X)) Tandem Library Bks.

Ruckdeschel, Liz & James, Sara. What If— You Broke All the Rules? A Choose Your Destiny Novel. 2007. (Illus.). 291p. (YA). (*978-1-4287-5664-9(7) , Delacorte Pr.) Dell Publishing.

Ruckdeschel, Liz & James, Sara. What If ... Everyone Knew Your Name. 2006. 352p. (YA). (gr. 7). pap. 8.95 (978-0-385-73296-3(1)); lib. bdg. 10.99 (978-0-385-90317-2(0)) Random Hse. Children's Bks. (Delacorte Bks. for Young Readers).

Scholastic, Inc. Staff. Create & Trace. Jayatilleke, Ruwan, ed. 2003. (G. I. Joe Ser.). (Illus.). 32p. (J). pap. 2.99 (978-0-439-44929-8(4)) Scholastic, Inc.

Sheldon, Tom. Big Match Manager 2. Burton, Nathaniel, illus. 2006. 288p. (J). pap. 11.99 (*978-0-7475-8205-2(X)) Bloomsbury Publishing Plc GBR. *Dist:* Independent Pubs. Group.

Siefken, Paul. Not Another Buttercup. Cook, Christopher, illus. 2002. (Powerpuff Girls Plus You Club Ser.). 64p. (J). (978-0-439-33267-5(2)) Scholastic, Inc.

Stephens, Helen. Shiny Seaside. Stephens, Helen, illus. 2003. (Baby Dazzlers Ser.). (Illus.). 5p. (J). (ps-ps). bds. 5.99 (978-0-316-81160-6(2)) Little, Brown Bks. for Young Readers.

Stine, R. L. Alone in Snakebite Canyon. 1998. (Give Yourself Goosebumps Ser.: No. 26). 10p. (J). (gr. 3-7). pap. 3.99 (978-0-590-39997-5(7) , Scholastic Paperbacks) Scholastic, Inc.

—Checkout Time at the Dead-End Hotel. 1998. (Give Yourself Goosebumps Ser.: No. 27). 10p. (J). (gr. 3-7). pap. 3.99 (978-0-590-39998-2(5) , Scholastic Paperbacks) Scholastic, Inc.

—Checkout Time at the Dead-End Hotel. 1998. (Give Yourself Goosebumps Ser.: No. 27). (J). (gr. 3-7). (978-0-606-13266-4(X)) Tandem Library Bks.

—Into the Jaws of Doom. 1998. (Give Yourself Goosebumps: No. 1). 10p. (J). (gr. 3-7). pap. 3.99 (978-0-590-39777-3(X)) Scholastic, Inc.

—Night of a Thousand Claws. 1998. (Give Yourself Goosebumps Ser.: No. 28). 137p. (J). (gr. 3-7). pap. 3.99 (978-0-590-40034-3(7) , Scholastic Paperbacks) Scholastic, Inc.

—Return to Terror Tower. 1998. (Give Yourself Goosebumps: No. 2). 135p. (J). (gr. 3-7). pap. 3.99 (978-0-590-39999-9(3) , Scholastic Paperbacks) Scholastic, Inc.

—Scary Birthday to You! 1999. (Give Yourself Goosebumps Ser.: No. 39). 144p. (gr. 3-7). pap. 3.99 (978-0-590-99390-6(9)) Scholastic, Inc.

—Trapped in the Circus of Fear. 1998. (Give Yourself Goosebumps: No. 3). 131p. (J). (gr. 3-7). pap. 3.99 (978-0-590-41920-8(X) , Scholastic Paperbacks) Scholastic, Inc.

—You're Plant Food. 1998. (Give Yourself Goosebumps Ser.: No. 30). 144p. (J). (gr. 3-7). pap. 3.99 (978-0-590-41974-1(9) , Scholastic Paperbacks) Scholastic, Inc.

—You're Plant Food. 1998. (Give Yourself Goosebumps Ser.: No. 30). (J). (gr. 3-7). (978-0-606-13933-5(8)) Tandem Library Bks.

—Zapped in Space. 1998. (Give Yourself Goosebumps Ser.: No. 23). (J). (gr. 3-7). (978-0-606-13072-1(1)) Tandem Library Bks.

West, Tracey. Abracadanger. 2003. (gr. 3-6). lib. bdg. 13.00 (978-0-613-72531-6(X)) Tandem Library Bks.

—Blossom & the Haunted House. Alger, Bill, illus. 2002. (Pick a Powerpuff Path Ser.). 64p. (J). (978-0-439-33264-4(8)) Scholastic, Inc.

—Revenge of the Gargoyle. 2003. (gr. 3-6). lib. bdg. 13.00 (978-0-613-72523-1(9)) Tandem Library Bks.

Wolfe, Jennifer. The Mess. Revell, Cindy, illus. 2002. 32p. (J). (gr. 1-3). pap. 6.95 (978-1-55037-734-7(5)) Annick Pr., Ltd. CAN. *Dist:* Firefly Bks., Ltd.

Zuckerman, Lilla & Zuckerman, Nora. Beauty Queen Blowout. 2003. (Miss Adventures Ser.: Bk. 2). 240p. pap. 9.95 (978-0-7432-3846-5(X) , Fireside) Simon & Schuster.

PLUMBING

Plumbers, 6 vols. (gr. 2-5). 36.95 (978-0-7368-8474-7(2)) Red Brick Learning.

Plumbing, Heating, Air Conditioning & Refrigeration Student Activity. 2004. (YA). cd-rom (978-1-57078-954-0(1) , CEV60033) C E V Multimedia, Ltd.

Thomas, Mark. A Day with a Plumber. 2001. (Welcome Bks.). (Illus.). 24p. (J). (ps-2). pap. 4.95 (978-0-516-23063-4(8) , Children's Pr.) Scholastic Library Publishing.

PLUMBING—FICTION

Klise, Kate. Regarding the Sink: Where, Oh Where, Did Waters Go? Klise, M. Sarah, illus. 2004. (Regarding The ... Ser.). 144p. (YA). 15.00 (978-0-15-205019-1(1) , Gulliver Bks.) Harcourt Children's Bks.

Morgan, Allen. Matthew & the Midnight Flood. Martchenko, Michael, illus. 1998. (Matthew's Midnight Adventures Ser.). 32p. (J). (ps-3). 6.99 (978-0-7737-5941-1(7)) Stoddart Kids CAN. *Dist:* Fitzhenry & Whiteside, Ltd.

—Le Plombier. 1999. (FRE., Illus.). 24p. pap. (978-2-89021-362-3(5)) Diffusion du livre Mirabel.

PLUMBING—VOCATIONAL GUIDANCE

Boraas, Tracey. Plumbers. 1999. (Community Helpers Ser.). (Illus.). 24p. (J). (gr. 1-2). lib. bdg. 18.60 (978-0-7368-0073-0(5) , Bridgestone Bks.) Capstone Pr., Inc.

Frew, Katherine. Plumber. 2004. (High-Great Jobs Ser.). (Illus.). 48p. (J). 24.00 (978-0-516-24088-6(9) , Children's Pr.) Scholastic Library Publishing.

Frost, Helen. We Need Plumbers. 2004. (Helpers in Our Community Ser.). (Illus.). 24p. (J). lib. bdg. 15.93 (978-0-7368-2576-4(2) , Pebble Bks.) Capstone Pr., Inc.

Simon, Charnan. Plumbers. 2003. (Wonder Books Level 3: Careers Ser.). (Illus.). 32p. (J). (ps-2). 22.79 (978-1-56766-471-3(7)) Child's World, Inc.

PLUTO (FICTITIOUS CHARACTER)—FICTION

Disney Staff. The Story of Pluto the Pup. 2004. (Illus.). 96p. (J). 35.00 incl. audio compact disk (978-1-55709-356-1(3)) Applewood Bks.

PLUTO (PLANET)

Adamson, Thomas K. Pluto. 2003. (Exploring the Galaxy Ser.). (Illus.). 24p. (J). lib. bdg. 17.26 (978-0-7368-2116-2(3) , Pebble Bks.) Capstone Pr., Inc.

—Pluto: A Dwarf Planet. 2008. (J). (*978-1-4296-0736-0(X)) Capstone Pr., Inc.

Adamson, Thomas K. Pluton: Pluto. 2006. (ENG & SPA., Illus.). 24p. (J). (978-0-7368-5883-0(0)) Capstone Pr., Inc.

Asimov, Isaac & Hantula, Richard. Pluto & Charon. 2003. (Isaac Asimov's 21st Century Library of the Universe). (Illus.). 32p. (gr. 3 up). pap. 8.95 (978-0-8368-3944-9(7) , Weekly Reader Early Learning Library); (YA). lib. bdg. 24.67 (978-0-8368-3240-2(5)) Stevens, Gareth Inc.

—Pluton y Caronte. Porras, Carlos & D'Andrea, Patricia, trs. 2003. (Isaac Asimov's Biblioteca del Universo del Siglo XXI). (SPA., Illus.). 32p. (J). (gr. 3 up). pap. 8.95 (978-0-8368-3872-5(6) , Weekly Reader Early Learning Library) Stevens, Gareth Inc.

—Pluton y Caronte. Porras, Carlos & D'Andrea, Patricia, trs. 2003. (Isaac Asimov's Biblioteca del Universo del Siglo XXI). (SPA., Illus.). 32p. (J). (gr. 3 up). lib. bdg. 24.67 (978-0-8368-3859-6(9)) Stevens, Gareth Inc.

Birch, Robin. Pluto. 2004. (Solar System Ser.). (Illus.). 32p. (gr. 3-5). 23.00 (978-0-7910-7931-7(7) , Chelsea Hse.) Facts On File, Inc.

Bredeson, Carmen. Pluto. 2001. (Space Ser.). (Illus.). 64p. (J). (gr. 5-7). 25.50 (978-0-531-11784-2(7) , Watts, Franklin) Scholastic Library Publishing.

—Pluto. 2001. (gr. 5-8). lib. bdg. 17.60 (978-0-613-37508-5(4)) Tandem Library Bks.

Cole, Michael D. Pluto: The Ninth Planet. 2002. (Countdown to Space Ser.). (Illus.). 48p. (J). (gr. 4-10). lib. bdg. 23.93 (978-0-7660-1953-9(5)) Enslow Pubs., Inc.

Goldstein, Margaret J. Pluto. 2005. (Pull Ahead Bks.). (Illus.). 32p. (gr. 2-4). lib. bdg. 22.60 (978-0-8225-4656-6(6)) Lerner Publishing Group.

Goss, Tim. Uranus, Neptune & Pluto. 2003. (Universe Ser.). (Illus.). 32p. (J). (gr. 3-5). lib. bdg. 22.79 (978-1-58810-918-7(6)); pap. 7.50 (978-1-4034-0619-4(7)) Heinemann Library.

Hayhurst, Chris. Pluto. 2004. (Library of the Nine Planets). (Illus.). 48p. (J). lib. bdg. 26.50 (978-1-4042-0172-9(6)) Rosen Publishing Group, Inc., The.

Hayhurst, Chris. Pluto & Other Dwarf Planets. 2006. (J). (*978-1-4042-1965-6(X)) Rosen Publishing Group, Inc., The.

Kortenkamp, Steve. Why Isn't Pluto a Planet? A Book about Planets. 2007. 32p. (J). (978-0-7368-6753-5(8)) Capstone Pr., Inc.

Landau, Elaine. Beyond Pluto. 2007. (True Bks.). (Illus.). 48p. (J). (gr. 3-7). lib. bdg. 26.00 (*978-0-531-12565-6(3) , Children's Pr.) Scholastic Library Publishing.

—Beyond Pluto: The Final Frontier in Space. 2008. (True Booktrade;: Space Ser.). 48p. (J). pap. 6.95 (*978-0-531-14787-0(8) , Children's Pr.) Scholastic Library Publishing.

—Is It a Planet? 2007. (True Bks.). (Illus.). 48p. (J). (gr. 3-5). lib. bdg. 26.00 (*978-0-531-12566-3(1) , Children's Pr.) Scholastic Library Publishing.

—Pluto: From Planet to Dwarf. 2008. (True Booktrade;: Space Ser.). 48p. (J). pap. 6.95 (*978-0-531-14794-8(0) , Children's Pr.) Scholastic Library Publishing.

Miller, Ron. Mercury & Pluto. 2003. (Worlds Beyond Ser.). (Illus.). 80p. (gr. 7 up). lib. bdg. 25.26 (978-0-7613-2361-7(9) , Twenty-First Century Bks.) Lerner Publishing Group.

O'Connell, Kim A. Pluto. 2005. (Solar System Ser.). (Illus.). 48p. (J). (gr. 4-7). lib. bdg. 25.26 (978-0-7660-5210-9(9) , MyReportLinks.com Bks.) Enslow Pubs., Inc.

Orme, Helen & Orme, David. Let's Explore Pluto & Beyond. 2006. (J). pap. (*978-0-8368-8130-1(3)); lib. bdg. (*978-0-8368-7945-2(7)) Stevens, Gareth Inc.

Oxlade, Chris. Jupiter, Neptune, & the Outer Planets. 2007. lib. bdg. (*978-1-4042-3736-0(4) , Rosen Central) Rosen Publishing Group, Inc., The.

Pluto. (Galaxy Ser.). 24p. (J). 6.95 (978-0-7368-8890-5(X)) Capstone Pr., Inc.

Pluto, 6 vols. (gr. 2-5). 36.95 (978-0-7368-8972-8(8)) Red Brick Learning.

Potts, Steve. Pluto: Our Solar System. 2001. (Illus.). 23p. (J). lib. bdg. 21.35 (978-1-58340-101-9(6)) Smart Apple Media.

Rau, Dana Meachen. Pluto. 2002. (Illus.). 32p. (J). (gr. 3 up). lib. bdg. 21.26 (978-0-7565-0297-3(7)) Compass Point Bks.

Ring, Susan. Pluto. (Exploring Planets Ser.). (J). 2004. pap. (978-1-59036-228-0(4)); 2003. (Illus.). 24p. lib. bdg. 15.95 (978-1-59036-101-6(6)) Weigl Pubs., Inc.

Rusch, Elizabeth. The Planet Hunter. Francis, Guy, illus. 2007. 32p. 15.95 (*978-0-87358-926-0(2) , Rising Moon Bks. for Young Readers) Northland Publishing.

Sparrow, Giles. Uranus, Neptune & Pluto. (Exploring the Solar System Ser.). (Illus.). (J). (gr. 4-6). 2002. 40p. pap. 7.95 (978-1-58810-966-8(6) , 91449); 2001. 39p. lib. bdg. 24.22 (978-1-57572-397-6(2)) Heinemann Library.

Stefoff, Rebecca. Pluto. 2002. (Blastoff! Ser.). (Illus.). 64p. (J). 28.50 (978-0-7614-1404-9(5)) Cavendish, Marshall Corp.

Stille, Darlene R. Pluto. 2003. (Planets Ser.). (Illus.). 32p. (J). (gr. 2-6). 27.07 (978-1-59296-053-8(7)) Child's World, Inc.

Taylor-Butler, Christine. Pluto: Dwarf Planet. (Scholastic News Nonfiction Readers: Space Science Ser.). 24p. (J). 2008. pap. 6.95 (*978-0-531-14766-5(5)); 2007. (Illus.). (gr. 1-2). lib. bdg. 20.00 (*978-0-531-14751-1(7)) Scholastic Library Publishing. (Children's Pr.).

Thompson, Luke. Pluto. 2001. (Library of the Planets). (Illus.). 24p. (J). lib. bdg. 20.65 (978-0-8239-5650-0(4) , PowerKids Pr.) Rosen Publishing Group, Inc., The.

Tocci, Salvatore. Look at Pluto. 2003. (gr. 7-12). lib. bdg. 24.55 (978-0-613-72689-4(8)) Tandem Library Bks.

Vogt, Gregory L. Pluto. 2000. (Galaxy Ser.). (Illus.). 24p. (J). (gr. 2-3). lib. bdg. 18.60 (978-0-7368-0514-8(1) , Bridgestone Bks.) Capstone Pr., Inc.

Wimmer, Teresa. Pluto. 2007. (J). (978-1-58341-521-4(1) , Creative Education) Creative Co., The.

Winrich, Ralph. Pluto. 2005. (Illus.). 24p. (J). 21.26 (978-0-7368-3693-7(4)) Capstone Pr., Inc.

Winrich, Ralph & Adamson, Thomas K. Pluto: A Dwarf Planet. 2007. (J). (*978-0-7368-7967-5(6)); (*978-1-4296-0727-8(0)) Capstone Pr., Inc.

World Book, contrib. by. Neptune & the Distant Dwarf Planets. 2nd ed. 2006. (World Book's Solar System & Space Exploration Library). (Illus.). 64p. (J). (*978-0-7166-9518-9(9)) World Bk., Inc.

World Book, Inc Staff, contrib. by. Neptune & Pluto. 2006. (World Book's Solar System & Space Exploration Library). (Illus.). 63p. (J). (978-0-7166-9507-3(3)) World Bk., Inc.

PLYMOUTH (MASS.)—HISTORY

Fritz, Jean. Who's That Stepping on Plymouth Rock? 1998. (Illus.). 32p. (J). (gr. 2-5). pap. 6.99 (978-0-698-11681-8(X) , Putnam Juvenile) Penguin Group (USA) Inc.

—Who's That Stepping on Plymouth Rock? Handelsman, J. B., illus. 1998. 31p. lib. bdg. 14.19 (978-0-606-15766-7(2)); 30p. (J). lib. bdg. 15.30 (978-0-613-10540-8(0)) Tandem Library Bks.

Hirschfelder, Arlene B. Squanto1585-1622. 2004. (American Indian Biographies Ser.). (Illus.). 32p. (J). (gr. 3-4). lib. bdg. 23.93 (978-0-7368-2446-0(4) , Blue Earth Bks.) Capstone Pr., Inc.

Peacock, Carol Anto. Pilgrim Cat. Ettlinger, Doris, illus. 2004. 32p. (J). (gr. 2-5). 16.95 (978-0-8075-6532-2(6)) Whitman, Albert & Co.

Riehecky, Janet. The Plymouth Colony. 2002. (Landmark Events in American History Ser.). (Illus.). 48p. (J). (gr. 5 up). lib. bdg. 30.00 (978-0-8368-5340-7(7)); pap. 14.60 (978-0-8368-5354-4(7)) Stevens, Gareth Inc. (World Almanac Library).

Santella, Andrew. The Plymouth Colony. 2000. (We the People Ser.). (Illus.). 48p. (J). (gr. 4 up). lib. bdg. 22.60 (978-0-7565-0046-7(X)) Compass Point Bks.

Who's That Stepping of Plymouth Rock? 2004. (J). pap. 14.95 incl. audio (978-0-7882-0695-5(8)); pap. 32.75 incl. audio (978-1-55592-357-0(7)); pap. 32.75 incl. audio (978-1-55592-358-7(5)) Weston Woods Studios, Inc.

Who's That Stepping on Plymouth Rock? 2004. (J). 24.95 incl. audio (978-1-56008-219-4(4)) Weston Woods Studios, Inc.

POCAHONTAS, D. 1617

Adams, Colleen. Pocahontas: The Life on an Indian Princess. 2006. (Rosen Publishing Group's Reading Room Collection). (Illus.). 16p. (J). lib. bdg. (978-1-4042-3348-5(2) , PowerKids Pr.) Rosen Publishing Group, Inc., The.

Becker, Sandra. Pocahontas. 2003. (Folk Heroes Ser.). (Illus.). 24p. (J). lib. bdg. 15.95 (978-1-59036-074-3(5)) Weigl Pubs., Inc.

Bruchac, Joseph. Pocahontas. 2005. (Illus.). 192p. (YA). (gr. 6-8). pap. 5.95 (978-0-15-205465-6(0) , Harcourt Paperbacks) Harcourt Children's Bks.

—Pocahontas. 2003. (Illus.). 192p. (J). (gr. 6-8). 17.00 (978-0-15-216737-0(4) , Silver Whistle) Harcourt Trade Pubs.

Capstone Press, contrib. by. Pocahontas. (American Indian Biographies Ser.). 48p. (YA). pap. 7.95 (978-0-7368-3290-8(4)) Capstone Pr., Inc.

Edwards, Judith. Jamestown, John Smith, & Pocahontas in American History. 2002. (In American History Ser.). (Illus.). 128p. (YA). (gr. 5-12). lib. bdg. 26.60 (978-0-7660-1842-6(3)) Enslow Pubs., Inc.

Ford, Carin T. Pocahontas: American Indian Princess. 2006. (Heroes of American History Ser.). (Illus.). 32p. (J). lib. bdg. 22.60 (978-0-7660-2604-9(3) , Enslow Elementary) Enslow Pubs., Inc.

Fritz, Jean. The Double Life of Pocahontas. l.t. ed. 2003. (Children's Large Print Ser.). 24.95 (978-1-58118-109-8(4)) LRS.

—The Double Life of Pocahontas. Young, Ed, illus. 2002. 96p. (J). (gr. 3-6). pap. 5.99 (978-0-698-11935-2(5) , Putnam Juvenile) Penguin Group (USA) Inc.

Gosda, Randy T. Pocahontas. 2002. (First Biographies Ser.). (Illus.). 32p. (J). (gr. k-4). lib. bdg. 22.78 (978-1-57765-732-3(2) , Buddy Bks.) ABDO Publishing Co.

Hudson, Margaret. Pocahontas. 2002. (Lives & Times Ser.). (Illus.). 24p. (J). (gr. k-3). pap. 6.50 (978-1-4034-0031-4(8) , 91475) Heinemann Library.

Jenner, Caryn. The Story of Pocahontas, Vol. 2. Martin, Linda, ed. 2000. (Readers Ser.). (Illus.). 32p. (J). (gr. 1-3). pap. 3.99 (978-0-7894-6636-5(8)) Dorling Kindersley Publishing, Inc.

—The Story of Pocahontas. 2000. (Illus.). 32p. (J). (ps-ps). lib. bdg. 11.80 (978-0-613-33108-1(7)) Tandem Library Bks.

Jenner, Caryn & Dorling Kindersley Publishing Staff. The Story of Pocahontas. 2000. (Readers Ser.). (Illus.). 32p. (J). (gr. 1-3). 14.99 (978-0-7894-6637-2(6)) Dorling Kindersley Publishing, Inc.

Krull, Kathleen. Pocahontas: Princess of the New World. Diaz, David, illus. 2007. 40p. (J). (gr. 1-6). 17.85 (978-0-8027-9555-7(2)); 16.95 (978-0-8027-9554-0(4)) Walker & Co.

Marsh, Carole. The Virginia Reader: Pocahontas. 2001. (Virginia Experience! Ser.). (Illus.). 12p. (J). (gr. k-5). pap. 2.95 (978-0-635-00355-3(4)) Gallopade International.

McLeese, Don. Pocahontas. 2003. (Native American Legends Ser.). (Illus.). 32p. (J). (gr. 1-3). lib. bdg. 28.50 (978-1-58952-728-7(3)) Rourke Publishing, LLC.

Milton, Joyce. Pocahontas: An American Princess. Hehenberger, Shelly, illus. 2000. (All Aboard Reading Ser.). 48p. (J). (gr. 2-3). pap. 3.99 (978-0-448-42181-0(X) , Grosset & Dunlap) Penguin Group (USA) Inc.

—Pocahontas: An American Princess. 2000. (gr. k-3). lib. bdg. 11.80 (978-0-613-31596-8(0)) Tandem Library Bks.

Nettleton, Pamela Hill. Pocahontas. Yesh, Jeff, illus. 2004. (Biographies Ser.). 24p. (C). (gr. k-3). 22.60 (978-1-4048-0187-5(1)) Picture Window Bks.

Parim D'Aulaire, Ingri & Parim D'Aulaire, Edgar. Pocahontas. Parim D'Aulaire, Ingri & Parim D'Aulaire, Edgar, illus. 1998. (Illus.). 45p. (J). (gr. k-6). reprint ed. pap. 12.95 (978-0-9643803-6-3(6)) Beautiful Feet Bks.

Picture Window Books, contrib. by. Pochahontas. (Biographies Ser.). 24p. (J). pap. 7.95 (978-1-4048-0460-9(9)) Picture Window Bks.

Pocahontas. (Compass Point Early Biographies Ser.). 32p. (J). 7.95 (978-0-7565-1178-4(X)) Compass Point Bks.

Pocahontas, 6 vols. (gr. k-2). 28.95 (978-0-7368-9373-2(3)) Red Brick Learning.

Polette, Nancy. Pocahontas. 2003. (Rookie Biographies Ser.). (gr. 1-2). pap. 4.95 (978-0-516-27782-0(0)); (Illus.). 32p. (J). 20.50 (978-0-516-22859-4(5)) Scholastic Library Publishing. (Children's Pr.).

—Pocahontas. 2003. (gr. k-3). lib. bdg. 12.95 (978-0-613-67659-5(9)) Tandem Library Bks.

Raatma, Lucia. Pocahontas. 2001. 32p. (J). lib. bdg. (978-0-7565-0154-9(7)); (Illus.). (gr. 2 up). lib. bdg. 21.26 (978-0-7565-0115-0(6)) Compass Point Bks.

Schaefer, Lola M. Pocahontas. Saunders-Smith, Gail, ed. 2002. (First Biographies Ser.). (Illus.). 24p. (J). (gr. k-1). lib. bdg. 15.93 (978-0-7368-1175-0(3) , Pebble Bks.) Capstone Pr., Inc.

—Pocahontas, Vol. 2. 2005. (First Biographies Ser.). 24p. (YA). (gr. k-3). pap. (978-0-7368-9372-5(5) , Pebble Bks.) Capstone Pr., Inc.

Sonneborn, Liz. Pocahontas 1595-1617. 2002. (American Indian Biographies Ser.). (Illus.). 32p. (J). (gr. 3-4). lib. bdg. 23.93 (978-0-7368-1214-6(8) , Blue Earth Bks.) Capstone Pr., Inc.

Sullivan, George. Pocahontas. 2002. (gr. 3-6). lib. bdg. 12.40 (978-0-613-43868-1(X)) Tandem Library Bks.

Sullivan, George E. Pocahontas. 2002. (In Their Own Words Ser.). (Illus.). 128p. (J). (gr. 3-7). 4.99 (978-0-439-16585-3(7)); pap. 12.95 (978-0-439-32668-1(0)) Scholastic, Inc. (Scholastic Reference).

Trumbauer, Lisa. Pocahontas & the Early Colonies. 2007. (J). (*978-1-4034-9666-9(8)); pap. (*978-1-4034-9674-4(9)) Heinemann Library.

Weinberger, Kimberly. Let's Read About— Pocahontas. Marchesi, Stephen, illus. 2003. (Scholastic First Biographies Ser.). (J). pap. (978-0-439-56148-8(5)) Scholastic, Inc.

Zemlicka, Shannon. Pocahontas. Reeves, Jeni, illus. 2002. (On My Own Biographies Ser.). 47p. (J). lib. bdg. 23.93 (978-0-87614-598-2(5) , Carolrhoda Bks.) Lerner Publishing Group.

—Pocahontas. 2002. (gr. 3-6). lib. bdg. 14.10 (978-0-613-52481-0(0)) Tandem Library Bks.

POCAHONTAS, D. 1617—FICTION

Ingoglia, Gina. Pocahontas: Illustrated Classic. Mateu, Franc, illus. 1999. (Libros Buena Vista Ser.). (SPA.). 96p. (J). 15.49 (978-0-7868-5026-6(4)) Disney Pr.

Kudlinski, Kathleen V. My Lady, Pocahontas. 400th anniv. ed. 2006, 208p. (YA). (gr. 6-8). 16.95 (978-0-7614-5293-5(1)) Cavendish, Marshall Corp.

Marsh, Carole. Pocahontas. 2002. (One Thousand Readers Ser.). (Illus.). 12p. (J). (gr. k-4). 2.95 (978-0-635-01506-8(4) , 15064) Gallopade International.

—Pocahontas. (Read-Along Ser.). (J). 7.99 incl. audio (978-1-55723-739-2(5)) Walt Disney Records.

Walt Disney Company Staff. Pocahontas. 2005. (WEL., Illus.). 24p. (978-1-899877-04-1(5)) Y Ddraig Fach.

POE, EDGAR ALLAN, 1809-1849

Amper, Susan. Bloom's How to Write about Edgar Allan Poe. 2007. (Bloom's How to Write about Literature Ser.). 224p. (YA). (gr. 9 up). 45.00 (****978-0-7910-9488-4(X)*** , Chelsea Hse.) Facts On File, Inc.

Binns, Tristan Boyer. Edgar Allan Poe: Master of Suspense. 2005. (Great Life Stories Ser.). (Illus.). 127p. (J). 30.50 (978-0-531-16751-9(8) , Watts, Franklin) Scholastic Library Publishing.

Frisch, Aaron. Edgar Allan Poe. 2005. (Voices in Poetry Ser.). (Illus.). 48p. (gr. 5-9). 21.95 (978-1-58341-344-9(8) , Creative Education) Creative Co., The.

Kent, Zachary. Edgar Allan Poe: Tragic Poet & Master of Mystery. 2001. (Historical American Biographies Ser.). (Illus.). 128p. (J). (gr. 6-12). lib. bdg. 26.60 (978-0-7660-1600-2(5)) Enslow Pubs., Inc.

McArthur, Debra. A Student's Guide to Edgar Allan Poe. 2006. (Understanding Literature Ser.). (Illus.). 160p. (J). lib. bdg. 27.93 (978-0-7660-2437-3(7)) Enslow Pubs., Inc.

Meltzer, Milton. Edgar Allan Poe: A Biography. 2003. (Single Titles Ser.). (Illus.). 144p. (gr. 7 up). lib. bdg. 31.90 (978-0-7613-2910-7(2) , Twenty-First Century Bks.) Lerner Publishing Group.

Peltak, Jennifer. Edgar Allan Poe. 2003. (Who Wrote That? Ser.). (Illus.). 112p. (gr. 6-12). 30.00 (978-0-7910-7622-4(9) , Chelsea Hse.) Facts On File, Inc.

Schoell, William. Mystery & Terror: The Story of Edgar Allan Poe. 2004. (Illus.). 128p. (YA). (gr. 6-12). 23.95 (978-1-931798-39-6(7)) Reynolds, Morgan Inc.

Streissguth, Thomas. Edgar Allan Poe. (Just the Facts Biographies Ser.). (J). 2007. 27.93 (978-0-8225-6800-1(4) , Lerner Pubns.); 2005. (Illus.). 112p. (gr. 6-12). lib. bdg. 27.93 (978-0-8225-4991-8(3)) Lerner Publishing Group.

POE, EDGAR ALLAN, 1809-1849—FICTION

Edgar Allan Poe Collection of Stories Student Packet, Gr. 9-12. 2004. (YA). (978-1-58130-510-4(9)) Novel Units, Inc.

POETICS

Here are entered works on the art and technique of poetry. Works on the appreciation and philosophy of poetry are entered under Poetry.

see also Rhythm; Versification

Appelt, Kathi. Poems from Homeroom: A Writer's Place to Start. rev. ed. 2002. 128p. (YA). (gr. 7-12). 16.95 (978-0-8050-6978-5(X) , Holt, Henry & Co. Bks. For Young Readers) Holt, Henry & Co.

Collins, Janet. Pass Me a Poem. Janacek, Lois, illus. 1999. ix, 87p. (J). (gr. 1-7). 13.95 (978-0-9674824-0-8(2)); pap. 7.50 (978-0-9674824-1-5(0)) Collins, Janet.

Fandel, Jennifer. Metaphors, Similes, & Other Word Pictures: Understanding Poetry. 2005. (Illus.). 48p. (gr. 5-9). 21.95 (978-1-58341-340-1(5) , Creative Education) Creative Co., The.

—Puns, Allusions, & Other Word Secrets: Understanding Poetry. 2005. (Illus.). 48p. (gr. 5-9). 21.95 (978-1-58341-341-8(3) , Creative Education) Creative Co., The.

—Rhyme, Meter, & Other Word Music: Understanding Poetry. 2005. (Illus.). 48p. (gr. 5-9). 21.95 (978-1-58341-342-5(1) , Creative Education) Creative Co., The.

Fisk, Sally. Poetry Plus: Intermediate. 1999. 48p. (J). (gr. 1-5). pap. 5.99 (978-1-56822-280-6(7) , IF8410) School Specialty Publishing.

Fletcher, Ralph J. Poetry Matters: Writing a Poem from the Inside Out. 2002. (gr. 5-8). lib. bdg. 17.95 (978-0-613-64997-1(4)) Tandem Library Bks.

Franco, Betsy. Instant Poetry Frames for Primary Poets: 40 Fun & Easy Reproducible Poetry Frames That Spark the Imagination & Give All Children the Support They Need to Write Terrific Poems. 2001. 48p. pap. 9.95 (978-0-439-30363-7(X)) Scholastic, Inc.

Hirsch, Edward. How to Read a Poem: And Fall in Love with Poetry. 2000. 354p. (gr. 7-12). lib. bdg. 24.60 (978-0-613-25601-8(8)) Tandem Library Bks.

Janeczko, Paul B. How to Write Poetry, Grades. 2001. (Scholastic Guides Ser.). (Illus.). 128p. (J). pap. 8.95 (978-0-590-10078-6(5)) Scholastic, Inc.

—How to Write Poetry, Grades 4 to 9. 1999. (Scholastic Guides Ser.). 128p. pap., tchr. ed. 12.95 (978-0-590-10077-9(7)) Scholastic, Inc.

Janeczko, Paul B., compiled by. Seeing the Blue Between: Advice & Inspiration for Young Poets. 2002. (Illus.). 144p. (J). (gr. 4-8). 18.99 (978-0-7636-0881-1(5)) Candlewick Pr.

Kauffman, Jamie. When I Was Eight... A Children's Guide to Writing Poetry Using Poems by an Eight-Year Old. Kauffman, Lisa, ed. Fountain, Linda, photos by. 2000. (Illus.). 112p. (J). (gr. k-7). pap. 4.95 (978-0-9654604-3-9(6)) Citapei Communications, Inc.

Lesynski, Loris. I Did It Because... How a Poem Happens. Martchenko, Michael, illus. 2006. 64p. (J). (gr. 2-5). pap. 9.95 (978-1-55451-017-7(1)); lib. bdg. 19.95 (978-1-55451-018-4(X)) Annick Pr., Ltd. CAN. *Dist:* Firefly Bks., Ltd.

Lombardo, Mary A. Poetry & Pop-Ups: An Art-Enhanced Approach to Writing Poetry. 2003. (Illus.). 96p. (gr. 4-6). 10.95 (978-1-58683-082-3(1)) Linworth Publishing, Inc.

Lyon, George Ella. Where I'm From. 2004. (Writers & Young Writers Ser.: 2). 98p. pap. 13.95 (978-1-888842-18-0(0)) Absey & Co.

Moore, Jo Ellen. Writing Poetry with Children. Evans, Marilyn, ed. Davis, Cindy & Larsen, Jo, illus. 1999. 96p. (J). (gr. 1-6). pap., tchr. ed. 12.99 (978-1-55799-734-0(9) , EMC 734) Evan-Moor Educational Pubs.

Prelutsky, Jack. Prelutsky Writing Book. 2008. 176p. (J). 16.99 (****978-0-06-143449-5(3));*** pap. 5.99 (****978-0-06-143448-8(5))*** HarperCollins Pubs.

Roza, Greg. Patterns in Poetry: Recognizing & Analyzing Poetic Form & Meter. 2005. (PowerMath Ser.). 22.50 (978-1-4042-2941-9(8)); pap. 22.50 (978-1-4042-5146-5(4)) Rosen Publishing Group, Inc., The. (PowerKids Pr.).

Steck-Vaughn Staff. Comprehension Activities in Poetry. (Illus.). (J). 2000. (gr. 1). pap. (978-0-7398-3389-6(8)); 1999. (gr. 2). pap. (978-0-7398-2046-9(X)); 1999. (gr. 3). pap. 7.99 (978-0-7398-2047-6(8)); 1999. (gr. 4). pap. (978-0-7398-2048-3(6)); 1999. (gr. 5). pap. 7.99 (978-0-7398-2049-0(4)); 1999. (gr. 6). pap. (978-0-7398-2050-6(8)) Steck-Vaughn.

Terban, Marvin. Time to Rhyme: A Rhyming Dictionary. Demarest, Chris L., illus. 2003. 96p. (J). (gr. 2-4). pap. 10.95 (978-1-56397-630-8(7)) Boyds Mills Pr.

POETRY

see also Ballads; Hymns; Love Poetry; Nature in Poetry

also American Poetry; English Poetry, etc.; and general subjects, names of historical events, places and famous persons with the subdivision Poetry, e.g. Animals—poetry

La Abajita que Habla (the Talking Bumblebee) 2003. (J). (978-1-56870-477-7(1)) RonJon Publishing, Inc.

ABC Memory Verses. 2003. 32p. (J). per. 7.99 (978-0-88724-137-6(9)) Carson-Dellosa Publishing Co., Inc.

Abell, Angel Morgan. The Alphabliss of Miss: Poems & Pictures. 2005. (Illus.). 54p. (J). 30.00 (****978-1-885679-20-8(3))*** Morgan Foundation Pubs.: International Published Innovations.

Able and Talented Program Resource Room Students Staff, Able and Talented Program Resource Room, et al. Westerville Kids Celebrate the Written Word Vol. 1: 2000-2001. 2001. 254p. pap. 14.95 (978-0-595-20772-5(3) , Writers Club Pr.) iUniverse, Inc.

Abodehman, Ahmed. El Cinturon. Lovillo, Pilar Ortiz, tr. Sanchez, Andres & Tagle, illus. 2002. (SPA.). 121p. (J). pap. 4.99 (978-968-16-6670-5(4)) Fondo de Cultura Economica USA.

Ada, Alma Flor. Abecedario de los Animales. 8th ed. 2003. (Alma Flor Ada Ser.).Tr. of Animal Alphabet. (SPA., Illus.). 44p. (J). (ps-1). 18.95 (978-84-239-2583-4(8)) Espasa Calpe, S.A. ESP. *Dist:* Lectorum Pubns., Inc., Planeta Publishing Corp., i.b.d., Ltd.

Ada, Alma Flor & Campoy, F. Isabel. Chuchurumbe. (Literature Collection of Puertas Al Sol Ser.). (SPA.). 32p. (J). (gr. k-6). pap. 12.95 (978-1-59437-709-9(X)) Santillana USA Publishing Co., Inc.

—Dreaming Fish. (Literature Collection of Gateways to the Sun Ser.). 32p. (J). (gr. k-6). pap. 12.95 (978-1-59437-712-9(X)) Santillana USA Publishing Co., Inc.

—Flying Dragon. (Literature Collection of Gateways to the Sun Ser.). 32p. (J). (gr. k-6). pap. 12.95 (978-1-59437-721-1(9)) Santillana USA Publishing Co., Inc.

—Laughing Crocodiles. (Literature Collection of Gateways to the Sun Ser.). 32p. (J). (gr. k-6). pap. 12.95 (978-1-59437-715-0(4)) Santillana USA Publishing Co., Inc.

—Mambru. (Literature Collection of Puertas Al Sol Ser.). (SPA.). 32p. (J). (gr. k-6). pap. 12.95 (978-1-59437-706-8(5)) Santillana USA Publishing Co., Inc.

—Pimpon. (Literature Collection of Puertas Al Sol Ser.). (SPA.). 32p. (J). (gr. k-6). pap. 12.95 (978-1-59437-700-6(6)) Santillana USA Publishing Co., Inc.

Ada, Alma Flor, et al. Pio Peep! Escriva, Vivi, illus. 2006. 64p. (J). 16.99 (978-0-06-111666-7(1)) HarperCollins Pubs.

Adams, Phyllis J. & Kronowitz, Ellen L. Pathways to Poetry: Poetry Fun for Grades 1-3. 288p. (J). (gr. 1-3). 20.99 (978-0-86653-914-2(X) , FE0914, Fearon Teacher Aids) Schaffer, Frank Pubns.

Adedjouma, Davida. Palm of My Heart: Poetry by African American Children. (gr. k-3). lib. bdg. 15.25 (978-0-613-11028-0(5)) Tandem Library Bks.

Adedjouma, Davida, ed. The Palm of My Heart: Poetry by African American Children. Christie, Gregory R., illus. 1998. 32p. (J), (ps up) 6.95 (978-1 880000-76-2(8)) Lee & Low Bks., Inc.

Adoff, Arnold. Touch the Poem. Desimini, Lisa, illus. 2000. 32p. (J). (ps-3). pap. 16.95 (978-0-590-47970-7(9) , Blue Sky Pr., The) Scholastic, Inc.

Agard, John. Half Caste. 2005. (Illus.). 80p. (J). 16.99 (978-0-340-89382-1(6) , Hodder & Stoughton) Hodder General Publishing Division GBR. *Dist:* Trafalgar Square Publishing.

—Hello H20 (Poetry) 2004. (Illus.). 80p. (J). pap. (978-0-7502-4290-5(6) , Hodder Wayland) Hodder Children's Division.

—Points of View with Prof Peekaboo. Kitamura, Satoshi, illus. 2001. 64p. (J). pap. 9.99 (978-0-09-941326-4(4)) Random Hse. GBR. *Dist:* Independent Pubs. Group.

Agard, John K. Hello H20. 2003. (Illus.). (J). (978-0-7502-4289-9(2) , Hodder Wayland) Hodder Children's Division.

Ageledis, Ida. First Foil Poetry Seasons, 2 vols. Berg, Michelle, illus. 2005. (First Foil Poetry Haikus Ser.). 10p. (J). 6.95 (978-1-58117-188-4(9) , Intervisual/Piggy Toes) Dalmatian Pr.

Agnon, Shmuel Yosef. Agnon's Alef Bet: Poems. Friend, Robert, tr. from HEB. Zeldich, Arieh, illus. 1998. 72p. 19.95 (978-0-8276-0599-2(4)) Jewish Pubn. Society.

Aigner-Clark, Julie. Poems For Little Ones. Marston, J. D., photos by. 2001. (Baby Einstein Ser.). (Illus.). 12p. (J). (ps-ps). 7.99 (978-0-7868-0807-6(1)) Hyperion Bks. for Children.

Alarcon, Francisco X. Angels Ride Bikes & Other Fall Poems. Gonzalez, Maya Christina, illus. 1999. 32p. (J). pap. 21.27 (978-0-516-21696-6(1) , Children's Pr.) Scholastic Library Publishing.

—Angels Ride Bikes & Other Fall Poems (Los Angeles Andan en Bicicleta y Otros Poemas de Otono) Gonzalez, Maya Christina, illus. 1999. (ENG & SPA.). 32p. (J). (gr. 1 up). 16.95 (978-0-89239-160-8(X)) Children's Bk. Pr.

Alarcon, Francisco X. Angels Ride Bikes/Los Angeles Andan en Bicicleta: And Other Fall Poems/Y Otros Poemas de Otono. Gonzalez, Maya Christina, illus. 2005. 32p. (J). (ps-17). pap. 7.95 (978-0-89239-198-1(7)) Children's Bk. Pr.

—From the Bellybutton of the Moon / del Ombligo de la Luna: And Other Summer Poems / Y Otras Poemas de Verano. Gonzalez, Maya Christina, illus. 2005. 32p. (J). (ps-17). pap. 7.95 (978-0-89239-201-8(0)) Children's Bk. Pr.

—Iguanas in the Snow / Iguanas en la Nieve: And Other Winter Poems / Y Otras Poemas de Invierno. Gonzalez, Maya Christina, illus. 2005. 32p. (J). (ps-17). pap. 7.95 (978-0-89239-202-5(9)) Children's Bk. Pr.

Alarcon, Francisco X. Iguanas in the Snow & Other Winter Poems (Iguanas en la Nieve y Otros Poemas de Invierno) Gonzalez, Maya Christina, illus. 2004. (ENG & SPA.). 32p. (J). (gr. 1 up). 16.95 (978-0-89239-168-4(5)) Children's Bk. Pr.

Alarcon, Francisco X. Laughing Tomatoes/Jitomates Risuenos: And Other Spring Poems/Y Otros Poemas de Primavera. Gonzalez, Maya Christina, illus. 2005. 32p. (J). (ps-17). pap. 7.95 (978-0-89239-199-8(5)) Children's Bk. Pr.

Alarcon, Francisco X. Poems to Dream Together: Poemas para soñar Juntos. Barragan, Paula, illus. 2005. (ENG & SPA.). 32p. (J). (gr. 2-5). 16.95 (978-1-58430-233-9(X)) Lee & Low Bks., Inc.

Alarcon, Francisco X, et al. Border Voices: The San Diego Celebration of Poetry & Music: the 10th Annual Anthology of Poetry. 2003. per. 12.95 (978-0-9719906-1-6(1)) Webb, Jack.

Albert, Toni. I Heard the Willow Weep. Brandt, Margaret, illus. Albert, Robert, photos by. 2000. 32p. (J). (gr. k-5). 15.95 (978-1-929432-00-4(3)); pap. 7.95 (978-1-929432-01-1(1)) Trickle Creek Bks.

Alderson, Sue Ann. The Eco-Diary of Kiran Singer. Ballance, Millie, illus. 2007. 64p. (YA). (gr. 5-9). 15.95 (****978-1-896580-47-0(5))*** Tradewind Bks. CAN. *Dist:* Orca Bk. Pubs. USA.

Alekos. Aroma de Nispero. 2000. (SPA., Illus.). 36p. (J). (978-84-95040-56-5(5)) Serres, Ediciones, S. L. ESP. *Dist:* Lectorum Pubns., Inc.

Alexander, Elizabeth & Nelson, Marilyn. Miss Crandall's School for Young Ladies & Little Misses of Color: Poems. Cooper, Floyd, illus. 2007. 48p. (YA). (gr. 5 up). 17.95 (****978-1-59078-456-3(1)*** , Wordsong) Boyds Mills Pr.

Alexander, Karen. Fly Away Fall. Villanueva, Nelson, illus. 2001. (J). (978-0-9661661-7-0(5)) Write Designs, Ltd.

Alexander, Martha, illus. & selected by. Poems & Prayers for the Very Young. Alexander, Martha, selected by. 32p. (J). Random Hse. Children's Bks.

Alexander, Michael. Beowulf: A Verse Translation. 2003. (gr. 7-12). lib. bdg. 18.80 (978-0-613-64255-2(4)) Tandem Library Bks.

Allen, Scott. Somethin' Pumpkin. Pickering, Jimmy, illus. 1999. 32p. (J). 16.95 (978-1-931290-00-5(8)) Tallfellow Pr.

Allison, Jonathan, ed. William Butler Yeats. Harrington, Glenn, illus. 2002. (Poetry for Young People Ser.). 48p. (gr. 3 up). 14.95 (978-0-8069-6615-1(7)) Sterling Publishing Co., Inc.

Alston, Stanley E. Faith, Love & Life. Sharps, Angelique, ed. Alston, Sheila Y., photos by. 48p. (YA). (gr. 4 up). pap. 12.95 (978-0-9719897-0-2(2)) Magnatic Music.

Ancient Tradition: Soul Poetry. 2000. 150p. (YA). per. 12.95 (978-0-9701711-0-8(2)) Conquering Lion Enterprise.

Andreae, Giles. Cock-a-Doodle-Doo! Barnyard Hullabaloo. Wojtowycz, David, illus. 2004. 32p. (J). reprint ed. pap. 7.95 (978-1-58925-387-2(6) , tiger tales) ME Media LLC.

Andrew, Moira. Paint a Poem. 1999. (Kids' Stuff Ser.). (Illus.). 72p. (J). pap., tchr. ed. (978-0-947882-44-0(8) , Belair Publications) Folens Pubs.

Andrews, Tom. Random Symmetries: The Collected Poems of Tom Andrews. 2002. (Field Poetry Ser.: 13). 265p. pap. 22.95 (978-0-932440-92-1(4)) Oberlin College Pr.

Angelou, Maya. Maya Angelou. Wilson, Edwin Graves, ed. Lagarrigue, Jerome, illus. 2007. (Poetry for Young People Ser.). 48p. (J). (gr. 3 up). 14.95 (978-1-4027-2023-9(8)) Sterling Publishing Co., Inc.

Anonymous. Required Poems for Reading & Memorizing: Third & Fourth Grades, Prescribed by State Courses of Study. l.t. ed. 2006. 168p. pap. 11.99 (****978-1-4264-3925-4(3));*** 200p. pap. 15.99 (****978-1-4264-4013-7(8))*** BiblioBazaar.

Anthology of Poetry by Young Americans. 2005. 176p. (YA). 12.95 (978-1-883931-52-0(5)); pap. 6.95 (978-1-883931-53-7(3)) Anthology of Poetry, Inc.

ap Dafydd, Myrddin & Gwalch, Gwasg Carreg. Mae Modfedd yn Llawer Mewn Trwyn. 2005. (Barddoniaeth Poetry Ser.). (WEL., Illus.). 117p. (978-0-86381-857-8(9)) Gwasg Carreg Gwalch.

Appelt, Kathi. Just People & Paper - Pen - Poem: A Young Writer's Way to Begin. Appelt, Kenneth, photos by. 2004. (Writers & Young Writers Ser.: Vol. 1). (Illus.). 91p. (YA). pap. 11.95 (978-1-888842-07-4(5) , 1020) Absey & Co.

Archer, Peggy. From Dawn to Dreams: Poems for Busy Babies. Wakiyama, Hanako, illus. 2007. 32p. (J). (ps-k). 15.99 (978-0-7636-2467-5(5)) Candlewick Pr.

Argueta, Jorge. A Movie in My Pillow / Una Pelicula en Mi Almohada. Gomez, Elizabeth, illus. 2001. Tr. of Pelicula en Mi Almohada. (ENG & SPA.). 32p. (J). (gr. 1 up). 16.95 (978-0-89239-165-3(0)) Children's Bk. Pr.

—A Movie in My Pillow / una pelicula en mi Almohada. Gomez, Elizabeth, illus. 2007. 32p. (J). pap. 7.95 (978-0-89239-219-3(3)) Children's Bk. Pr.

Art and Poetry Datebook from the InsideOut Writing Project Staff. Feels Like Jazz 2002: Arts & Poetry Datebook. Blackhawk, Terry, ed. 2001. 116p. spiral bd. 15.00 (978-0-9713562-0-7(3)) Inside Out, Inc.

Arturo y el Concurso de Poesia. 2004. Tr. of Arthur & the Poetry Contest. (SPA., Illus.). (J). pap. 4.95 (978-1-930332-61-4(0)) Lectorum Pubns., Inc.

Asher, Sandra Fenichel. Somebody Catch My Homework. 2004. (YA). pap. 4.50 (978-1-58342-171-0(8) , SH8) Dramatic Publishing Co.

Attenborough, Liz. Poetry by Heart: A Child's Book of Poems to Remember. 2001. (Illus.). 128p. (J). (gr. k-4). pap. 17.95 (978-0-439-29657-1(9) , Chicken Hse., The) Scholastic, Inc.

—When All The World's Asleep: A Children's Book of Poems, Prayers & Meditations. 1999. (Illus.). 128p. (YA). (ps up). pap. (978-1-902618-73-9(4)) Oneworld Pubns.

Aubrey, Annette. Flora's Family. 2007. (J). lib. bdg. 16.95 (****978-1-59566-391-7(6))*** QEB Publishing Inc.

—A Place in My Heart. 2007. (J). lib. bdg. 16.95 (****978-1-59566-392-4(4))*** QEB Publishing Inc.

—The Rainbow Club. 2007. (J). lib. bdg. 16.95 (****978-1-59566-393-1(2))*** QEB Publishing Inc.

—There for You. 2007. (J). lib. bdg. 16.95 (****978-1-59566-390-0(8))*** QEB Publishing Inc.

Audet, Martine. Que Ferais-Je du Jour? Sylvestre, Daniel, tr. 2003. (New Poetry Ser.). (FRE.). 36p. (J). (gr. 7). pap. (978-2-89021-621-1(7)) Diffusion du livre Mirabel.

Avery, Carrie L. A String of Pearls. 2003. 68p. (YA). pap. 9.95 (978-0-7414-1540-0(2)) Infinity Publishing.

Ayers, Linda. There's Something in My Sandwich. Hunt, Jane, illus. 50p. (J). 2006. 13.95 (978-0-9760505-7-5(9)); 2005. per. 6.95 (978-0-9760505-5-1(2)) Blue Thistle Pr.

Baa! Baa! 2002. (Little Board Books Ser.). 24p. (J). bds. 3.95 (978-0-7894-8463-5(3)) Dorling Kindersley Publishing, Inc.

Bagent, Brad. Rainbows, Head Lice & Pea-Green Tile: Poems in the Voice of the Classroom Teacher. Doner, Kim, illus. 1999. 64p. (J). 15.95 (978-0-929895-28-4(2)) Maupin Hse. Publishing.

Bagert, Brod. Chicken Socks: And Other Contagious Poems. Ellis, Tim, illus. 2003. 32p. (YA). (gr. 2-4). 9.95 (978-1-56397-861-6(X)) Boyds Mills Pr.

—Chicken Socks: And Other Contagious Poems. 2000. (Illus.). (J). (978-0-606-18012-2(5)) Tandem Library Bks.

—The Gooch Machine: A Collection of Humorous Poems to Perform. Ellis, Tim, illus. 32p. (J). (gr. 2-4). 2004. pap. 9.95 (978-1-59078-315-3(8)); 2003. 15.95 (978-1-56397-294-2(8)) Boyds Mills Pr.

—School Fever. Neubecker, Robert, illus. 2008. 40p. (J). (gr. 1-3). 16.99 (****978-0-8037-3201-8(5)*** , Dial) Penguin Group (USA) Inc.

Bagert, Brod. Shout! Little Poems That Roar. Yoshikawa, Sachiko, illus. 2007. 32p. (J). (gr. k-2). 16.99 (978-0-8037-2972-8(3) , Dial) Penguin Group (USA) Inc.

Baird, Audrey B. A Cold Snap! Frosty Poems. O'Brien, Patrick, illus. 2003. 32p. (J). (gr. 2-4). 15.95 (978-1-56397-633-9(1)) Boyds Mills Pr.

Bakay, Betty J. Mother Moose & Her Whole Caboose. 2003. (J). per. 9.95 (978-1-932301-35-9(6) , 1044) Airleaf Publishing & Bookselling.

—Mother Moose & Her Whole Caboose. 1998. (Illus.). 32p. (J). (gr. k-2). pap. 12.95 (978-0-8059-4358-0(7)) Dorrance Publishing Co., Inc.

Baker, Kenneth, ed. Children's English History in Verse. Stower, Adam, illus. 2007. 289p. pap. 20.00 (****978-1-4223-9012-2(8))*** DIANE Publishing Co.

Baldoceda, Blas Puente. Poetica Narrativa en 'Canto de Sirena' de Gregorio Martinez: Estilo, Narracion e Ideologia. 2002. (Latin America: Interdisciplinary Studies Ser.). (SPA.). 224p. (C). 55.95 (978-0-8204-5001-8(4)) Lang, Peter Publishing, Inc.

Bannatyne, Lesley Pratt. Witches' Night Before Halloween. Tans, Adrian, illus. 2007. 32p. (J). (gr. k-3). 15.95 (****978-1-58980-485-2(6))*** Pelican Publishing Co., Inc.

Barbe, Walter, ed. School Year of Poems. Hockerman, Denni, illus. 2005. 112p. (J). pap. 11.95 (978-1-59078-395-5(6)) Boyds Mills Pr.

Barker, Cicely Mary. Flower Fairies Enchanted Parties. 2008. (Flower Fairies Ser.). (J). (ps). 12.99 (****978-0-7232-6289-3(6)*** , Warne) Penguin Group (USA) Inc.

—Flower Fairies of the Garden. 2008. (Flower Fairies Ser.). 56p. (J). (ps). 6.99 (****978-0-7232-5993-0(3)*** , Warne) Penguin Group (USA) Inc.

—Flower Fairies of the Summer (R/J) 2008. (Flower Fairies Ser.). 48p. (J). (ps). 6.99 (****978-0-7232-6282-4(9)*** , Warne) Penguin Group (USA) Inc.

—Flower Fairies of the Wayside (R/J) 2008. (Flower Fairies Ser.). 48p. (J). (ps). 6.99 (****978-0-7232-6283-1(7)*** , Warne) Penguin Group (USA) Inc.

—A Flower Fairies Treasury. 2007. 14.99 (****978-0-7232-5973-2(9))*** Penguin Group (USA) Inc.

Barker, Cicely Mary. Secret World. 2005. (Illus.). 32p. (J). 12.99 (978-0-7232-5685-4(3) , Warne) Penguin Group (USA) Inc.

Barton, Matthew, compiled by. The Winding Road: A Child's Treasury of Poems, Verses, & Prayers. 2005. (Festivals Ser.). 128p. pap. 23.50 (978-1-903458-47-1(1)) Hawthorn Pr. GBR. *Dist:* SteinerBooks, Inc.

Bauer, Kenneth D. Like a Rabbit in the Rain - Prose, Poems, & Drawing. 2002. (Illus.). 96p. (YA). (gr. 11 up). pap. 20.00 (978-0-9728554-0-2(8)) Be Family Bks.

Bayley, Nicola. Canciones Tontas. 1998. (SPA.). 32p. (J). (gr. 4-7). (978-84-264-3566-8(1)) Editorial Lumen.

Beaton, Clare. Mother Goose Remembers. Beaton, Clare, illus. 2000. (Illus.). 64p. (J). (ps-2). 18.99 (978-1-84148-073-2(8)) Barefoot Bks., Inc.

Beck, Ian. The Jumblies. 2003. (Illus.). 32p. (J). pap. 9.99 (978-0-552-54690-4(9) , Corgi) Transworld Publishers Ltd. GBR. *Dist:* Trafalgar Square Publishing.

Beck, J. My Little Miracle. 2007. (J). bds. 6.99 (978-0-439-90249-6(5) , Cartwheel Bks.) Scholastic, Inc.

Becker, Helaine. Mama Likes to Mambo. Beder, John, illus. 2002. 28p. (J). (ps-3). 15.95 (978-0-7737-3316-9(7)) Stoddart Kids CAN. *Dist:* Fitzhenry & Whiteside, Ltd.

The Beginning of Love. 2005. per. 12.00 net. (978-0-9720046-2-6(9)) Bluestone Bks.

Belloc, Hilaire. Selected Cautionary Verses. 1999. 192p. (J). 3.99 (978-0-14-036756-0(X) , Puffin) Penguin Group (USA) Inc.

A Benji's Pup Set, 6 vols. 32p. (gr. 1-3). 37.50 (978-0-322-00338-5(5)); 31.50 incl. 5.25 hd (978-0-7802-8045-8(8)) Wright Group, The.

Benson, Catherine. It Must Have Been a Sunday. 2005. 32p. pap. (978-1-902382-79-1(X)) Smith/Doorstop Books.

Berman, David. Actual Air. 1999. (gr. 7-12). lib. bdg. 22.20 (978-0-613-33991-9(6)) Tandem Library Bks.

Bernier-Grand, Carmen T. Cesar: Si, Se Puede! Yes, We Can! Diaz, David, illus. 2004. 48p. (YA). 16.95 (978-0-7614-5172-3(2)) Cavendish, Marshall Corp.

Berry, James. A Nest Full of Stars. Bryan, Ashley, illus. 2004. 104p. (J). (gr. 2 up). 16.89 (978-0-06-052748-8(X)) HarperCollins Pubs.

Bethea, Indigo K. Calling Out to Nubia. 2001. (gr. 7-12). lib. bdg. 21.60 (978-0-613-74617-5(1)) Tandem Library Bks.

Bevan, Clare & Gordon, Mike. Poems about Being Jealous: Everyone I See is Luckier Than Me. 2006. (Illus.). (J). pap. 9.99 (978-0-340-91115-0(8) , Hodder & Stoughton) Hodder General Publishing Division GBR. *Dist:* Trafalgar Square Publishing.

Bibisi, Carole. Tails of American Bronte: A Cat's View of Life. 2007. (Illus.). 32p. (***978-1-59849-026-8(5)***) Peanut Butter Publishing.

Bierhorst, John, ed. In the Trail of the Wind: American Indian Poems & Ritual Orations. Bierhorst, Jane B., illus. rev. ed. 1998. 224p. (J). (gr. 7-12). pap. 6.95 (978-0-374-43609-4(6) , Sunburst) Farrar, Straus & Giroux.

Big Keep Books, Rhymes & Songs, 2002. (Illus.). 8p. (J). 20.00 net. (978-1-893986-23-7(3)) Keep Bks.

Bilkan, Ali Fuat. Mathnawi Stories: Selections from Rumi. 2008. 160p. (J). pap. 12.95 (***978-1-59784-124-5(2)***) Light, Inc., The.

Binky's Words. 2003. (Illus.). 68p. (YA). pap. 10.95 (978-0-9703803-2-6(1)) Writers & Poets.com.

Bits & Pieces: The Poems of Melvin E. Giles, 1 vol. 2004. (Illus.). 235p. per. 14.50 (978-0-9656364-1-4(0)) Oakdale Pr.

Bittner, Scott. Measuring Silence. 2002. 70p. (YA). per. 8.99 (978-0-9724680-8-4(0)) Lifevest Publishing, Inc.

Blake, William. William Blake. Maynard, John, ed. Cimatoribus, Alessandra, illus. 2007. (Poetry for Young People Ser.). 48p. (J). (gr. 5-9). 14.95 (978-0-8069-3647-5(9)) Sterling Publishing Co., Inc.

Blanco, Alberto. Tambien Los Insectos Son Perfectos. Radaviciute, Diana, illus. 2005. Tr. of Insects Are Perfect, Too. (SPA.). (J). (gr. k-2). pap. 10.95 (978-968-494-054-3(8)) Centro de Informacion y Desarrollo de la Comunicacion y la Literatura MEX. *Dist:* Iaconi, Mariuccia Bk. Imports.

Bloom, Harold. Stories & Poems for Extremely Intelligent Children of All Ages. 2001. (Illus.). 576p. (gr. 3-8). 30.00 (978-0-684-86873-8(3) , Scribner) Simon & Schuster.

Bloom, Valerie. Let Me Touch the Sky: Selected Poems for Children. 2003. (Illus.). 90p. (J). 19.99 (978-0-333-78067-1(1)) Macmillan Publishers Ltd. GBR. *Dist:* Trafalgar Square Publishing.

Blue Lantern Studio Staff, ed. Green Tigers Illus Childrens P. 2007. (Illus.). 122p. (J). (gr. 4-7). 24.95 (***978-1-59583-139-2(8)*** , Green Tiger Pr.) Laughing Elephant.

Boggess, Ace, ed. Wild Sweet Notes II: More Great Poetry from West Virginia. 2005. (Illus.). 233p. per. 17.00 (978-0-9744785-2-4(0)) Publishers Place, Inc.

Bolding, Clarissa. Life Is A Song Worth Singing. 2005. 88p. per. 12.00 (978-0-9762924-7-0(5)) InnerCircle Publishing.

Bollen, Christine. Three Munch-y Cherries. 2007. (J). per. 11.99 (***978-1-59879-376-5(4)***) Lifevest Publishing, Inc.

Boloz, Sigmund A. Diarrhea, Diarrhea: And Other School Poems for Children. Boloz, Autumn C., ed. Boloz, Antoinette C., illus. 1998. 36p. (J). (gr. 3-12). pap. 6.00 (978-1-886635-15-9(3)) Wooded Hill Productions.

—The Restroom Blues & Other School Poems for Children. Boloz, Antoinette C., illus. 2000. 40p. (J). 6.00 (978-1-886635-17-3(X)) Wooded Hill Productions.

Bond, Felicia. Tumble Bumble. Bond, Felicia, illus. 2002. (Illus.). (J). 14.43 (978-0-7587-3873-8(0)) Book Wholesalers, Inc.

—Tumble Bumble. braille ed. 2004. (Illus.). (J). (gr. 1). spiral bd., bds. (978-0-616-03081-3(9)) Canadian National Institute for the Blind/Institut National Canadien pour les Aveugles.

—Tumble Bumble. Bond, Felicia, illus. (Laura Geringer Bks.). (Illus.). (J). (ps-k). 1999. 18p. bds. 7.99 (978-0-694-01344-9(7) , Harper Festival); 2000. 32p. reprint ed. pap. 6.99 (978-0-06-443585-7(7) , Harper Trophy) HarperCollins Pubs.

—Tumble Bumble. 2000. (978-0-606-18724-4(3)); lib. bdg. 14.10 (978-0-613-28682-4(0)) Tandem Library Bks.

Bornemann, Elsa. Tinke-Tinke. Huadi, illus. 2002. (SPA.). 112p. (J). (gr. 3-5). 10.95 (978-950-511-726-0(4)) Alfaguara S.A. de Ediciones ARG. *Dist:* Santillana USA Publishing Co., Inc.

Bouchard, David. If You're Not from the Prairie. Ripplinger, Henry, illus. 1998. 32p. (J). (gr. 1-5). 6.99 (978-0-689-82035-9(6) , Aladdin) Simon & Schuster Children's Publishing.

Bouchard, David & Ripplinger, Henry. If You're Not from the Prairie. 2nd ed. 2002. (Illus.). 32p. (J). (ps-3). 14.95 (978-1-895714-66-1(4)) Raincoast Bk. Distribution CAN. *Dist:* Perseus Distribution.

Boynton, Sandra. Belly Button Book! 2005. (Illus.). 24p. (J). bds. 6.95 (978-0-7611-3799-3(8) , 13799) Workman Publishing Co., Inc.

—Snuggle Puppy! 2005. (Illus.). 24p. (J). 16.95 (978-0-7611-4061-0(1) , 14061) Workman Publishing Co., Inc.

—Snuggle Puppy! A Love Song. gif. ed. (Illus.). 24p. (J). 83.40 (978-0-7611-3455-8(7) , 23455) Workman Publishing Co., Inc.

Bradbury, Ken & Crowe, Robert. What Are You Doing This Evening? 2000. (J). ring bd. 10.00 (978-0-9644681-5-3(8)) Consortium Publishing Co.

Bradbury, Ken & Crowe, Robert L. Forever, with Reservations. Crowe, Robert L., ed. 2001. (YA). ring bd. 10.00 (978-0-9707173-4-4(2)) Consortium Publishing Co.

—One Act Is Often Too Many. Crowe, Robert L., ed. 2000. (YA). ring bd. 10.00 (978-0-9644681-6-0(6)) Consortium Publishing Co.

—There Are No Small Parts. Crowe, Robert L., ed. 2002. (YA). ring bd. 10.00 (978-0-9707173-6-8(9)) Consortium Publishing Co.

—Wait ... Don't Leave Yet. Crowe, Robert L., ed. 2003. (YA). ring bd. 10.00 (978-0-9707173-7-5(7)) Consortium Publishing Co.

Bradford, Imani. People Can't Save You. 2004. (J). pap. 7.00 (978-0-9671796-0-5(2)) Segue Pubs.

Bravo-Guzman, Pedro. Cantos del Alma. 1998th l.t. ed. 1998. (SPA.). 79p. per. 10.00 (978-0-922665-02-0(8)) Hispanic Publishing Works, Inc.

Breckon, Brett, illus. Dragon Days. 2004. 80p. pap. 17.95 (978-1-84323-301-5(0)) Beekman Bks., Inc.

Breier, Christine A., ed. Goodles & Oodles: A Collection of Short Stories, Drawings & Poetry of Children. 1998. 70p. (J). (ps-12). pap. 25.95 (978-0-7392-0013-1(5)) Morris Publishing.

Brennan, Michael. The Imageless World. 2004. (Illus.). 108p. pap. 14.99 (978-1-84471-005-8(X)) Salt Publishing GBR. *Dist:* SPD-Small Pr. Distribution.

Briggs, Kelly Paul. Lighthouse Lullaby. 2001. (Illus.). 32p. (ps-3). 15.95 (978-0-89272-486-4(2)) Down East Bks.

Brighter Garden. (Illus.). (J). (978-0-399-22391-4(6) , Philomel) Penguin Group (USA) Inc.

Brighter Vision Publishing Staff. About Nursery Rhymes. 1999. (Illus.). 20p. (J). (ps). pap. 3.99 (978-1-55254-054-1(5)) Brighter Vision Pubns.

Brigley, Jude. The Poet's House: An Anthology of Poems. Evans, Fran, illus. 2000. 120p. (J). pap. 14.95 (978-1-85902-602-1(8)) Beekman Bks., Inc.

Brilis, Michael Nicholas. Joy & Tears in Life: Perspectives of a Greek Immigrant. 2004. (GRE.). 49p. pap. 24.95 (978-0-9753454-0-5(0) , CQ-003) ComQwest, LLC.

Britt, Jeanetta. Poems from the Fast: A Triology, 3 bks. 2001. 56p. per. 7.95 (978-0-9712363-0-1(5)) Twelve Stones Publishing.

Brock, Justin. Have You Seen My Pencil? Poems & Musings. Wright, Christopher, illus. 2007. (J). pap. (***978-0-9796210-0-0(3)***) OPUS II Bks.

Brookman, Darin. Where Sagebrush Grows. 2004. per. 20.00 (978-0-9749518-0-5(3)) Pair'a Spurs Pr.

Brooks, Gwendolyn. Bronzeville Boys & Girls. Ringgold, Faith, illus. 2007. 48p. (J). (gr. 2-5). lib. bdg. 17.89 (978-0-06-029506-6(6)) HarperCollins Pubs.

Brooks, Walter R. The Collected Poems of Freddy the Pig. Wiese, Kurt, illus. 2001. 81p. (J). (gr. 3). 23.95 (978-1-58567-136-6(3)) Overlook Pr., The.

Broome, Errol. What a Goat! Thompson, Sharon, illus. 2004. (Annick Chapter Bks.). 72p. (J). (gr. 2-4). pap. 4.95 (978-1-55037-868-9(6)) Annick Pr., Ltd. CAN. *Dist:* Firefly Bks., Ltd.

Brown, Karen. Poems That Build Character. Rogers, Kathy, ed. 2001. 64p. (J). per. 8.95 (978-1-56472-342-0(9)) Edupress, Inc.

Brown, Margaret Wise. The Fathers Are Coming Home. 2001. (J). 17.00 (978-0-689-83345-8(8) , McElderry, Margaret K.) Simon & Schuster Children's Publishing.

—A Margaret Wise Brown. ed. 2001. (Illus.). (ps-2). 31.95 (978-0-06-623846-3(3)) HarperCollins Pubs.

Brown, Richard & Ruttle, Kate. Out & about Big Book. 1998. (Cambridge Reading Ser.). (Illus.). 33p. (ps-1). pap. 30.00 (978-0-521-63746-2(8)) Cambridge Univ. Pr.

Browning, Robert. Robert Browning. Gillooly, Eileen, ed. Spector, Joel, illus. 2003. (Poetry for Young People Ser.). 48p. (gr. 4-8). 14.95 (978-0-8069-5543-8(0)) Sterling Publishing Co., Inc.

—Robert Browning: Selected Poems. 2001. (gr. 7-12). lib. bdg. 21.10 (978-0-613-64318-4(6)) Tandem Library Bks.

Bruce Lansky School Poems. 2005. (J). (978-1-59564-874-7(7)) Steps To Literacy, LLC.

Brush & Paint. 2003. (Gateways to the Sun Ser.). 32p. (J). (gr. 1-2). pap. 11.95 (978-1-58105-575-7(7)) Santillana USA Publishing Co., Inc.

Bryant, "Air Conditioner". A Collection of Stuff: Poetry for Those Who Are Cool! 2001. 220p. (YA). pap. 14.95 (978-0-595-17262-7(8) , Writers Club Pr.) iUniverse, Inc.

Buckmaster, Heath L. Pear in a Bowl, a Whimsical Series: Stories & Poems by Heath l Buckmaster. 2005. (YA). mass mkt. 15.99 (978-0-9771802-0-2(4)) Quadradrillion, llc.

Bull, John. House Stuff. Simon Printing Staff, illus. 2000. 28p. (J). (gr. k-3). 3.00 (978-0-9702615-5-7(1)) Bull, John.

—Little Bits & Pieces. Simon Printing Company Staff, illus. 2001. (Poems by John Bull Ser.: Vol. 10). (J). (gr. 2-6). 2.49 (978-0-9702615-9-5(4)) Bull, John.

Bunnaby Bunny (G) Toddler Reader. 2006. (Illus.). 20p. (J). bds. (978-0-9712816-3-9(7)) Third Week Bks.

Burkholder, Kelly. Poetry. 2000. (Artistic Adventures Ser.). (Illus.). 24p. (J). (gr. 2-6). lib. bdg. 23.93 (978-1-57103-354-3(8)) Rourke Publishing, LLC.

Burroughs, William S. Live Performance, Vol. 1. Hoffman, Kathelin, ed. Phillips, Zelmer, illus. (C). 12.95 incl. audio (978-0-929856-00-1(7)) Caravan of Dreams Productions.

Bush Rage: Collected Verse. 2nd ed. 2005. (978-0-9765948-0-2(3)) Diomo Square Bks.

Bush, Timothy. Ferocious Girls, Steamroller Boys & Other Poems in Between. Bush, Timothy, illus. 2000. (Illus.). 64p. (J). (gr. 1-4). pap. 16.95 (978-0-531-30250-7(4) , Orchard Bks.) Scholastic, Inc.

Butcher, Raegan. Stone Hotel: Poems from Prison. 2002. (Illus.). 100p. pap. 10.00 (978-0-9709101-2-7(6)) CrimethInc. Workers' Collective.

Butler, John. Ten in the Den. 2005. (Illus.). 28p. (J). (ps-ps). per. 15.95 (978-1-56145-344-3(7)) Peachtree Pubs., Ltd.

Cain, Janan. The Way I Feel. Cain, Janan, illus. 2000. (Illus.). 32p. (J). (ps-3). 16.95 (978-1-884734-71-7(5)) Parenting Pr., Inc.

Calmenson, Stephanie. Welcome, Baby! Sweet, Melissa, illus. 2008. 64p. (J). pap. 7.99 (***978-0-06-113610-8(7)*** , Harper Trophy) HarperCollins Pubs.

A Camel Called Bump-Along, 6 vols., Set B. 32p. (gr. 1-3). 31.50 (978-0-7802-8049-6(0)) Wright Group, The.

Canas, Alicia, illus. Federico Garcia Lorca para Ninos. (Coleccion Grandes Autores para Ninos). (SPA.). 154p. (J). (gr. 4-6). 20.76 (978-84-305-9302-6(0) , SU4866) Susaeta Ediciones, S.A. ESP. *Dist:* Lectorum Pubns., Inc.

Canton, William. Invisible Playmate A Story of the Unseen. 2006. pap. 19.95 (***978-1-4286-3869-3(5)***) Kessinger Publishing, LLC.

Carangelo, Audrey. On the Street: Poems about Paintings. 2006. (Illus.). 8p. (J). (***978-0-439-73410-3(X)***) Scholastic, Inc.

Carle, Eric. Eric Carle's Animals: Book & Block Puzzle. 2008. 14p. (J). (ps-1). pap. 9.99 (***978-0-448-44871-8(8)*** , Grosset & Dunlap) Penguin Group (USA) Inc.

—Eric Carle's Animals Animals. 1999. (J). 14.64 (978-0-606-17256-1(4)); (gr. 3-6). lib. bdg. 16.45 (978-0-613-22847-3(2)) Tandem Library Bks.

—Eric Carle's Dragons, Dragons: And Other Creatuers That Never Were. 2004. (Illus.). 68p. (J). (gr. k-3). pap. 11.99 (978-0-14-240103-3(X) , Puffin) Penguin Group (USA) Inc.

Carle, Eric, illus. Eric Carle's Animals Animals. 1999. 96p. (J). (ps-3). pap. 8.99 (978-0-698-11855-3(3) , Putnam Juvenile) Penguin Group (USA) Inc.

Carlisle, Bob & Carlisle, Brooke. Butterfly Kisses. Ewing, Carolyn, illus. 2001. (Little Golden Bks.). 24p. (J). (gr. k-k). 2.99 (978-0-307-98872-0(4) , 98872, Golden Bks.) Random Hse. Children's Bks.

Carlson, Lori Marie. Sol a Sol: Original & Selected Bilingual Poems. Lisker, Emily, illus. rev. ed. 1998. (SPA.). 32p. (J). (ps-2). 17.00 (978-0-8050-4373-0(X) , HH5195, Holt, Henry & Co. Bks. For Young Readers) Holt, Henry & Co.

Carlstrom, Nancy White. Who Said Boo? 1999. (gr. k-3). lib. bdg. 14.15 (978-0-613-22629-5(1)) Tandem Library Bks.

Carney-Nunes, Charisse. I Dream for You a World: A Covenant for Our Children. Williams, Ann Marie, illus. 2007. 32p. (J). (gr. k-5). 16.95 (***978-0-9748142-3-0(7)*** , Brand Nu Words) Nunes Productions, LLC.

Carr, Holly, illus. What Is Pink? 2003. 24p. (J). (ps-1). 14.95 (978-0-921156-92-5(8)) Rubicon Publishing, Inc. CAN. *Dist:* International Publishers Marketing.

Carradice, Phil. Ghostly Riders. 2002. (Illus.). 48p. pap. 12.95 (978-1-84323-088-5(7)) Beekman Bks., Inc.

Carroll, Lewis, pseud. The Nonsense Verse of Lewis Carroll. Hussey, Lorna, illus. 2004. 32p. (J). pap. 12.99 (978-0-7475-5019-8(0)) Bloomsbury Publishing Plc GBR. *Dist:* Independent Pubs. Group.

—The Walrus & the Carpenter. Zalben, Jane Breskin, illus. 1998. 32p. (J). (ps-3). pap. 9.95 (978-1-56397-719-0(2)) Boyds Mills Pr.

Carroll, Lewis, pseud, et al. Lewis Carroll. Mendelson, Edward, ed. Copeland, Eric, illus. 2000. (Poetry for Young People Ser.). 48p. (gr. 3-7). 14.95 (978-0-8069-5541-4(4)) Sterling Publishing Co., Inc.

Cart, Michael. Rush Hour: Reckless. 2006. 224p. (YA). (gr. 9). pap. 10.95 (978-0-385-73034-1(9) , Delacorte Bks. for Young Readers) Random Hse. Children's Bks.

Cart, Michael, et al, eds. 911: The Book of Help. 2002. (Illus.). 192p. (YA). (gr. 6 up). pap. 9.95 (978-0-8126-2676-6(1)) Cricket Bks.

Carver, Rachele M. & Miller, Heather R. I to the World: A Collection of Poems. 2002. 108p. (YA). pap. 10.95 (978-0-595-21477-8(0) , Writers Club Pr.) iUniverse, Inc.

Casey, Barbara. Slightest in the House. 2003. 100p. pap. 12.95 (978-1-932162-23-3(2)) Benoy Publishing.

Cashman, Seamus, ed. Something Beginning with P: New Poems from Irish Poets. Askin, Corrina & Clarke, Alan, illus. 2004. (ENG.). 160p. (978-0-86278-868-1(4)) O'Brien Pr., Ltd., The.

Casilla, Robert, photos by. Daddy Poems. 2003. (Illus.). 32p. (J). (gr. k-3). 15.95 (978-1-56397-735-0(4)) Boyds Mills Pr.

Castro, Michael. Human Rites. 2001. 107p. (YA). (gr. 11 up). per. 12.00 (978-1-931190-25-1(9) , 63146) Neshui Publishing, Inc.

Catalano, Tom. Rhymes for Kids! Poems Children Can Enjoy. 2nd ed. 2000. 48p. (J). (gr. k-6). per. 6.95 (978-1-882646-05-0(3)) Wordsmith Bks.

—Rhymes for Teens: Poems Older Students Can Enjoy. Romango, Jim, illus. 2004. 80p. (YA). per. 9.95 (978-1-882646-48-7(7)) Wordsmith Bks.

Cauley, Lorinda Bryan. Clap Your Hands. Cauley, Lorinda Bryan, illus. 2001. (Illus.). 1p. (J). (ps). bds. 7.99 (978-0-399-23710-2(0) , Putnam Juvenile) Penguin Group (USA) Inc.

Causley, Charles. Selected Poems for Children. 2003. (Illus.). 136p. (J). pap. 13.99 (978-0-330-35404-2(3) , Pan) Pan Macmillan GBR. *Dist:* Trafalgar Square Publishing.

Cawthron, John. Poems by the Dozen. Melville, Ken, illus. 1999. 64p. (J). (gr. 2-4). lib. bdg. 12.95 (978-1-888565-06-5(3)) Trinity Rivers Publishing, Inc.

—Poems by the Dozen. Melville, Ken, illus. 1999. 64p. (J). (gr. 2-4). per. 9.95 (978-1-888565-07-2(1)) Trinity Rivers Publishing, Inc.

Celebrate Freedom: Songs, Symbols, & Sayings of the United States. 2003. (Illus.). 32p. (gr. k-2). (978-0-328-03672-1(2)); 48p. (gr. 3-6). (978-0-328-03674-5(9)) Addison-Wesley Educational Pubs., Inc. (Scott Foresman).

Center for Learning Network Staff. Paradise Lost: Curriculum Unit. 2003. (Novel Ser.). 100p. (YA). tchr. ed., spiral bd. 19.95 (978-1-56077-732-8(X)) Ctr. for Learning, The.

Cerda, Gina. Angels Come & Sleep with Me: A Children's Prayer. Miller, Jessel, illus. 1998. 20p. (J). (gr. k-4). 17.95 (978-0-9665153-0-5(7)) Gina Designs.

Champagne, Elena. Where Do Dreams Go? Sarna, Billy, illus. l.t. ed. 2006. 26p. (J). per. 10.99 (***978-1-59879-233-1(4)***) Lifevest Publishing, Inc.

Champlin, DeeAnn. Eddie E & the Eggs. Champlin, DeeAnn, illus. Date not set. (Little Lyrics Short Vowel Collection: Vol. 2). (Illus.). (J). (gr. k-2). pap. 12.00 (978-1-893429-26-0(1)) Little Lyrics Pubns.

—Five Funny A's. Champlin, DeeAnn, illus. 1998. (Little Lyrics Short Vowel Collection: Vol. 1). (Illus.). (J). (gr. k-2). pap. 12.00 (978-1-893429-25-3(3)) Little Lyrics Pubns.

—Incredible I. 1998. (Little Lyrics Short Vowel Collection: Vol. 3). (Illus.). (J). (gr. k-2). pap. 12.00 (978-1-893429-27-7(X)) Little Lyrics Pubns.

—The Land of U. 1998. (Little Lyrics Short Vowel Collection: Vol. 5). (Illus.). (J). (gr. k-2). pap. 12.00 (978-1-893429-29-1(6)) Little Lyrics Pubns.

—Let's Do the Vowel Sounds. 1998. (Little Lyrics Short Vowel Collection: Vol. 6). (Illus.). 11p. (J). (gr. k-2). pap. 12.00 (978-1-893429-30-7(X)) Little Lyrics Pubns.

—Oliver O & the Olives. Champlin, DeeAnn, illus. 1998. (Little Lyrics Short Vowel Collection: Vol. 4). (Illus.). (J). (gr. k-2). pap. 12.00 (978-1-893429-28-4(8)) Little Lyrics Pubns.

Chandler, Tom. Sad Jazz. 2003. 80p. 18.00 (978-0-9726869-0-7(8)) Table Rock Bks.

Chasing Heaven. 2005. (Illus.). 42p. (YA). per. 9.99 (978-0-9769819-4-7(7)) Mustard Seed Comics.

Chatterley, Cedric N., photos by. Grace: For All the Children. 2003. Tr. of Grace: per Tutti I Bambini. (ITA.). 79p. pap. 35.00 (978-0-9729735-2-6(4)) Luquer St. Pr.

Chaudhuri, Sukanta, ed. The Oxford India Illustrated Children's Tagore. 2006. (Illus.). 130p. 13.95 (***978-0-19-568417-9(6)***) Oxford Univ. Pr., Inc.

Cheng, Ainsley. Being Just Me, Myself, & I! 2006. (J). pap. 16.00 (978-0-8059-7189-7(0)) Dorrance Publishing Co., Inc.

Chiasson, Herménéglide. L' Oiseau Tatoué. Lafrance, David, illus. 2004. (Poetry Ser.). (FRE.). 36p. (J). (gr. 7). pap. (978-2-89021-675-4(6)) Diffusion du livre Mirabel.

A Chicago Winds Set, 6 vols. 32p. (gr. 1-3). 26.50 (978-0-7802-8047-2(4)) Wright Group, The.

Chijindu, Ifeyanyi. A Girl's Life: The Song that Never Ends. 2004. 119p. (YA). pap. 10.95 (978-0-7414-1864-7(9)) Infinity Publishing.

Child, Lydia Marie. Over River & Through Wood. Manson, Christopher, illus. 2007. 0024p. bds. 6.95 (***978-0-7358-2153-8(4)***) North-South Bks., Inc.

Child, Lydia Marie. Over the River & Through the Wood. 1999. (gr. k-3). lib. bdg. 15.25 (978-0-613-36576-5(3)) Tandem Library Bks.

Child Returns Home. 2001. 200p. spiral bd. 18.00 net. (978-0-9663132-4-6(0)) ARA IFA Publishing, Inc.

Child's Treasury of Poetry. 2001. 256p. (J). 25.95 (978-0-7525-4179-2(X)) Parragon, Inc.

Chorao, Kay. The Baby's Bedtime Book. Chorao, Kay, illus. ed. 2004. (Illus.). 64p. (J). (ps). 16.99 (978-0-525-47327-5(0) , Dutton Juvenile) Penguin Group (USA) Inc.

—Baby's Lap Book: A Collection of Classic Nursery Rhymes. 1998. (J). (978-0-606-13158-2(0)) Tandem Library Bks.

A Chorus of Cultures. 2002. (Chorus of Cultures Ser.). (gr. k-6). 250.42 (978-1-56334-405-3(X)); 413.41 (978-1-56334-406-0(8)) Hampton-Brown Bks.

Chronicle Books LLC Staff. Nick Jr. Nursery Rhyme Time: A Touch-and-See Activity Book. (J). 15.95 (978-0-8118-4726-1(8)) Chronicle Bks. LLC.

Chronicle Books LLC Staff & Patrick, Lewis J. The World's Greatest: Poems. 2007. 36p. (J). 16.99 (978-0-8118-5130-5(3)) Chronicle Bks. LLC.

Cirillo, Todd, et al. Roxy: The Girl in the Platform Shoes, with the Black Dress On. 2003. (Illus.). 94p. per. 12.95 (978-0-9722958-0-2(1)) Crow, R.L. Pubns.

Clark, Ann Nolan. In My Mother's House. Herrera, Velino, illus. 2004. 56p. (J). (gr. k-3). reprint ed. pap. 14.00 (978-0-7567-7104-1(8)) DIANE Publishing Co.

Clark, Emma Chichester, illus. Shakespeare's Verse. 2005. 96p. (J). (gr. 5-9). pap. 10.95 (978-0-7534-5920-1(5) , Kingfisher) Houghton Mifflin Co. Trade & Reference Div.

Clarke, Gillian & Pearce, Karen. The Animal Wall & Other Poems. 2001. (Illus.). 60p. pap. 16.95 (978-1-85902-654-0(0)) Beekman Bks., Inc.

Class Pack. (Cuentacuentos Ser.). (SPA.). (gr. k up). 813.22 (978-1-56334-799-3(7)) Hampton-Brown Bks.

P
Q
R

First Rhymes. 2002. (J). bds. 9.98 (978-0-7525-6553-8(2)); bds. 4.98 (978-0-7525-3992-8(2)) Parragon, Inc.

Fisher, Aileen. I Heard a Bluebird Sing. 2003. (gr. 3-6). lib. bdg. 19.90 (978-0-613-59313-7(8)) Tandem Library Bks.

—I Heard a Bluebird Sing: Children Select Their Favorite Poems by Aileen Fisher. Emery, Jennifer, illus. 2003. 64p. (YA). (gr. 4-6). 18.95 (978-1-56397-191-4(7)); pap. 10.95 (978-1-59078-071-8(X)) Boyds Mills Pr.

—Sing of the Earth & Sky: Poems about Our Planet & the Wonders Beyond. Thompson, Karmen, photos by. 2003. (Illus.). 48p. (J). (gr. k-3). 15.95 (978-1-56397-802-9(4)) Boyds Mills Pr.

—The Story Goes On. Moriuchi, Mique, illus. rev. ed. 2005. 32p. (J). 16.95 (978-1-59643-037-2(0)) Roaring Brook Pr.

Fisk, Sally. Poetry Plus: Primary. 1999. 48p. (J). (gr. 1-5). pap. 5.99 (978-1-56822-279-0(3) , IF8409) School Specialty Publishing.

Fitch, Sheree. If You Could Wear My Sneakers! Labrosse, Darcia, illus. 1998. 32p. (J). (gr. k-3). pap. 5.95 (978-1-55209-259-0(3)) Firefly Bks., Ltd.

—No Two Snowflakes. Wilson, Janet, illus. 2002. 32p. (J). (ps-2). 7.95 (978-1-55143-227-4(7)) Orca Bk. Pubs. USA.

—No Two Snowflakes. 2001. (gr. 3-6). lib. bdg. 16.40 (978-0-613-55344-5(6)) Tandem Library Bks.

—Peek-a-Little Boo. Watson, Laura, illus. 2005. 32p. (J). (ps-2). 17.95 (978-1-55143-342-4(7)) Orca Bk. Pubs. USA.

Fleming, Maria. Poem of the Month Flip Chart: 12 Joyful Read-Aloud Poems with Skill-Building Lessons & Writing Springboards. 2005. 24p. 21.99 (978-0-439-47123-7(0)) Scholastic, Inc.

—Poem of the Week: 50 Irresistible Poems with Activities That Teach Key Reading & Writing Skills. 2000. (Illus.). 128p. pap. 14.95 (978-0-439-07751-4(6)) Scholastic, Inc.

Fletcher, Ralph J. Relatively Speaking: Poems about Family. Krudop, Walter L., illus. 1999. 48p. (J). (ps-3). 15.99 (978-0-531-33141-5(5)); (gr. 2-4). pap. 14.95 (978-0-531-30141-8(9)) Scholastic, Inc. (Orchard Bks.).

—Relatively Speaking: Poems about Family. 2001. (J). (978-0-606-21566-4(2)) Tandem Library Bks.

—A Writing Kind of Day: Poems for Young Poets. 2004. (Illus.). 32p. (J). 17.95 (978-1-59078-276-7(3)); pap. 9.95 (978-1-59078-353-5(0)) Boyds Mills Pr.

Fletcher, Ralph J. & Krudop, Walter Lyon. Relatively Speaking: Poems about Family. 2001. (Illus.). 48p. (J). (gr. 3-7). pap. 4.95 (978-0-531-07186-1(3) , Orchard Bks.) Scholastic, Inc.

Fletter, Sharon Sofia. My Guardian Angel. Fletter, Sharon Sofia, illus. l.t. ed. 2007. Tr. of Mi Angel Guardian, il Mio Angelo, Meu Anjo Da Guarda, Mein Schutzengel, Mon Ange Guardian. (SPA, ITA, POR, GER & FRE., Illus.). 44p. (J). per. 17.95 (***978-0-9793113-0-7(6)***) SoulSong Publishing.

Flint, Russ, illus. Barefoot Days: Poems of Childhood. 1999. 88p. (J). (ps-3). 14.00 (978-0-8249-4154-3(3) , Candy Cane Pr.) Ideals Pubns.

Florian, Douglas. Bing Bang Boing. 2007. (Illus.). 144p. (J). (gr. 1-4). pap. 8.00 (978-0-15-205860-9(5) , Harcourt Paperbacks) Harcourt Children's Bks.

—Comets, Stars, the Moon, & Mars: Space Poems & Paintings. Florian, Douglas, illus. 2007. (Illus.). 56p. (J). (gr. k-5). 16.00 (978-0-15-205372-7(7)) Harcourt Children's Bks.

—Handsprings: Poems & Paintings. Florian, Douglas, illus. 2006. (Illus.). 48p. (J). lib. bdg. 16.89 (978-0-06-009281-8(5)) HarperCollins Pubs.

—In the Swim. 2001. (J). 12.80 (978-0-606-20723-2(6)); lib. bdg. 14.15 (978-0-613-34838-6(9)) Tandem Library Bks.

—Laugh-Eteria. Florian, Douglas, illus. 1999. (Illus.). 160p. (J). (gr. 1-4). 17.00 (978-0-15-202084-2(5)) Harcourt Children's Bks.

—Laugh-Eteria. 1999. (J). 10.01 (978-0-15-201859-7(X)) Harcourt Trade Pubs.

—Laugh-Eteria. Florian, Douglas, illus. 2000. (Illus.). 160p. (J). (gr. 2-6). pap. 6.99 (978-0-14-130990-3(3) , Puffin) Penguin Group (USA) Inc.

—Laugh-Eteria. 2000. (978-0-606-20363-0(X)); (gr. 3-6). lib. bdg. 15.30 (978-0-613-33708-3(5)) Tandem Library Bks.

—Lizards, Frogs, & Polliwogs. 2005. (Illus.). 48p. (J). reprint ed. pap. 7.00 (978-0-15-205248-5(8) , Voyager Bks./Libros Viajeros) Harcourt Children's Bks.

Flying Dragons. 2003. (Gateways to the Sun Ser.). 32p. (J). (gr. 3-4). pap. 9.95 (978-1-58105-580-1(3)) Santillana USA Publishing Co., Inc.

Foldvary-Anderson, Carol. A Heart's True Love. Foldvary-Anderson, Carol, illus. 2002. (Illus.). 26p. cd-rom 10.95 (978-0-9706612-4-1(X) , 775-846-1185) JetKor.

Follett, C. B. & Terris, Susan, eds. Runes, a Review of Poetry: Memory. 2003. (Illus.). 162p. pap. 12.00 (978-0-9657015-9-4(X)) Arctos Pr.

Forman, Ruth. Young Cornrows Callin Out the Moon: Poem. Bayoc, Cbabi, illus. 2007. 24p. (J). (gr. 1-3). 16.95 (978-0-89239-218-6(5)) Children's Bk. Pr.

Forrest, George. Echoes with a Western Air. 2007. 192p. (YA). per. 16.95 (***978-0-595-45286-6(8)***) iUniverse, Inc.

Foster, John L. Dead Funny. 2002. (Illus.). 93p. (J). pap. 7.99 (978-0-00-711213-5(0)) HarperCollins Pubs. Ltd. GBR. *Dist:* Independent Pubs. Group.

—Dragon Poems. Paul, Korky, illus. 2nd rev. ed. 2004. 32p. (YA). 9.95 (978-0-19-276307-5(5)) Oxford Univ. Pr., Inc.

—Ridiculous Rhymes. 2001. (Illus.). 89p. (J). pap. 6.99 (978-0-00-711212-8(2)) HarperCollins Pubs. Ltd. GBR. *Dist:* Independent Pubs. Group.

—Teasing Tongue Twisters. 2002. (Illus.). 94p. (J). pap. 7.99 (978-0-00-711214-2(9)) HarperCollins Pubs. Ltd. GBR. *Dist:* Trafalgar Square Publishing.

Foster, John L., ed. Chanting Rhymes. Thompson, Carol, illus. 1998. (First Verses Ser.). 32p. (YA). 10.95 (978-0-19-276143-9(9)) Oxford Univ. Pr., Inc.

Foston, Rebera E. Beyond a Reasonable Doubt. 2003. 96p. (YA). pap. (978-1-930362-04-8(8)) Foston Adolescent Workshop, Inc.

—A New Day. 2003. 96p. (YA). pap. (978-1-930362-03-1(X)) Foston Adolescent Workshop, Inc.

—No Cross, No Crown. 2003. 96p. (YA). per. (978-1-930362-08-6(0)) Foston Adolescent Workshop, Inc.

—No Forwarding Address. 2003. 96p. (YA). per. (978-1-930362-09-3(9)) Foston Adolescent Workshop, Inc.

—Pictures of the Wedding. 2003. 96p. (YA). per. (978-1-930362-11-6(0)) Foston Adolescent Workshop, Inc.

—Sweet Memories. 2003. 96p. (YA). per. (978-1-930362-12-3(9)) Foston Adolescent Workshop, Inc.

—When You Have Been Alone. 2003. 96p. (YA). per. (978-1-930362-14-7(5)) Foston Adolescent Workshop, Inc.

—While You Were Gone. 2003. 96p. (YA). per. (978-1-930362-15-4(3)) Foston Adolescent Workshop, Inc.

Frampton, David. Mr. Ferlinghetti's Poem. 2006. (Illus.). 32p. (J). (gr. k-4). 18.00 (978-0-8028-5290-8(4) , Eerdmans Bks For Young Readers) Eerdmans, William B. Publishing Co.

Franco, Betsy. Bees, Snails, & Peacock Tails Shapes— Naturally. Jenkins, Steve, illus. 2008. 40p. (978-1-4169-0386-4(0) , McElderry, Margaret K.) Simon & Schuster Children's Publishing.

—Counting Caterpillars..., 1 vol. 1998. 64p. pap. 9.95 (978-0-590-64210-1(3)) Scholastic, Inc.

—You Hear Me? Poems & Writings by Teenage Boys. 2001. (gr. 7-12). lib. bdg. 15.30 (978-0-613-36033-3(8)) Tandem Library Bks.

—100 Riddle Poems for Pocket Charts: Delightful Guess-Me Poems with Ready-to-Go Pictures That Build Important Early Reading & Phonics Skills. 2001. 80p. (ps). pap. 11.95 (978-0-439-25614-8(3)) Scholastic, Inc.

Franco, Betsy, et al. Whatever the Weather. 2001. (Thematic Poetry Ser.). (Illus.). 32p. (J). (gr. k-2). pap. 6.95 (978-0-439-21620-3(6)) Scholastic, Inc.

Franco, Betty. Things I Have to Tell You: Poems & Writing by Teenage Girls. 2001. (Illus.). (J). (978-0-606-21486-5(0)) Tandem Library Bks.

—You Hear Me? Poems & Writing by Teenage Boys. 2001. (Illus.). (YA). (978-0-606-21538-1(7)) Tandem Library Bks.

Froh, Joanne. Imagine This! Plagens, Frances, illus. 2006. 32p. (J). 19.95 (978-0-9777640-0-6(1)) Joanne Frances Pr.

Frost, Helen. Keesha's House. 2003. (Illus.). 128p. (YA). 16.00 (978-0-374-34064-3(1) , Farrar, Straus & Giroux (BYR)) Farrar, Straus & Giroux.

—Keesha's House. 2007. (Illus.). 128p. (YA). pap. 8.00 (978-0-374-40012-5(1) , Farrar, Straus & Giroux (BYR)) Farrar, Straus & Giroux.

Frost, Robert. The Cow in Apple Time. Yeagle, Dean, illus. 2005. 32p. (J). 15.95 (978-0-9758970-1-0(2)) Beekman & Hathaway.

—Robert Frost's Poems. 2002. (gr. 7-12). lib. bdg. 14.15 (978-0-613-46204-4(1)) Tandem Library Bks.

—The Runaway. Lang, Glenna, illus. Date not set. 32p. pap. 9.95 (978-1-56792-243-1(0)) Godine, David R. Pub.

—Stopping by the Woods on a Snowy Evening. Jeffers, Susan, illus. 2001. 32p. (J). (ps). 16.99 (978-0-525-46734-2(3) , Dutton Juvenile) Penguin Group (USA) Inc.

—You Come Too: Favorite Poems for All Ages. 2002. (gr. 3-6). lib. bdg. 19.90 (978-0-613-51100-1(X)) Tandem Library Bks.

—You Come Too: Favorite Poems for Readers of All Ages. rev. ed. 2002. 96p. (J). pap. 11.95 (978-0-8050-6985-3(2) , Owl Bks.) Holt, Henry & Co.

Frost, Robert & Lang, Glenna. The Runaway. 1998. (Illus.). 32p. (J). (ps-4). 17.95 (978-1-56792-006-2(3)) Godine, David R. Pub.

Fuertes, Gloria. Diccionario Estrafalario. 2003. (SPA.). 168p. (978-84-305-8462-8(5) , SU3166) Susaeta Ediciones, S.A. ESP. *Dist:* Lectorum Pubns., Inc.

Fulk, Dvon. Signs in the Earth: A Collection of Poems. Galloway, Annette, ed. Fulk, Dvon, photos by. l.t. ed. 2001. 154p. per. 14.00 (978-0-9710470-2-0(2)) Main St Publishing, Inc.

Fusek Peters Staff & Fusek, Andrew. Mad, Bad & Dangerously Haddock: The Best from the Very Tall Poet. 2006. (Illus.). 96p. (J). (gr. 3-4). pap. 8.99 (978-0-7459-6021-0(9) , Lion Children's) Lion Hudson plc GBR. *Dist:* Independent Pubs. Group.

Fyleman, Rose. Mary Middling & Other Silly Folk: Nursery Rhymes & Nonsense Poems. Bandlow, Katja, illus. 2004. 32p. (J). (gr. k-3). tchr. ed. 16.00 (978-0-618-38141-8(4) , Clarion Bks.) Houghton Mifflin Co. Trade & Reference Div.

Gaban, Jesus, illus. Rafael Alberti para Ninos. (SPA.). 164p. (J). (gr. 4-6). 20.76 (978-84-305-9290-6(3) , SU0175) Susaeta Ediciones, S.A. ESP. *Dist:* Lectorum Pubns., Inc.

García Lorca, Federico. Canciones (1921-1924) (SPA.). 96p. (J). 13.25 (978-84-206-6106-3(6) , AZ6106) Alianza Editorial, S. A. ESP. *Dist:* Continental Bk. Co., Inc.

—Canciones y Poemas para Ninos. (Coleccion Poemas Juvenil). (SPA., Illus.). 96p. (J). 9.50 (978-84-335-8401-4(4) , DD4014) Labor, Editorial S. A. ESP. *Dist:* Continental Bk. Co., Inc.

—Canciones y Poemas para Ninos. (SPA., Illus.). 64p. (J). (gr. 4-6). pap. 5.95 (978-1-887578-59-2(5) , SQ0128) SpanPr., Inc.

—Mi Primer Libro de Poemas. 2001. (SPA.). (gr. 3-6). lib. bdg. 15.70 (978-0-613-80552-0(6)) Tandem Library Bks.

García Ordaz, Daniel. You Know What I'm Sayin'? Poetry Drama. 2nd exp. rev. ed. 2006. (ENG & SPA.). (YA). per. 9.00 (***978-0-9789954-1-6(4)***) El Zarape Pr.

Garcia Vino, Manuel. Juan Ramon Jimenez para Ninos. 1999. (Introduction to Hispanic Poets for Children Ser.). (SPA., Illus.). 114p. 9.95 (978-84-7960-242-0(2)) Ediciones de la Torre ESP. *Dist:* Libros Sin Fronteras.

Gasca, Theresa & Juarez, Amanda. Mere Words Can Only Say... 2003. 162p. (YA). pap. 14.95 (978-0-595-27669-1(5)) iUniverse, Inc.

Gatell, Angelina. Mis Primeras Lecturas Poeticas. (SPA.). 256p. (YA). (gr. 5-8). (978-84-7175-180-5(1) , EN1279) Twenty-Nine Ediciones ESP. *Dist:* Lectorum Pubns., Inc.

Gbala, Deswin R. Rock University: A Collection of Short Stories & Poems. Gbala, Deswin R., illus. Date not set. (Illus.). 51p. (Orig.). (J). (gr. 3-10). pap. 8.50 (978-0-9650629-2-3(9)) Coulee Region Pubns., Inc.

Gedichte Analysieren. (Duden Abiturhilfen Ser.). (GER.). 112p. (YA). (gr. 12-13). (978-3-411-70141-4(2)) Bibliographisches Institut & F. A. Brockhaus AG DEU. *Dist:* International Bk. Import Service, Inc.

George, Elizabeth. A Little Girl after God's Own Heart: Learning God's Ways in My Early Days. Luenebrink, Judy, illus. 2006. 15.99 (978-0-7369-1545-8(1)) Harvest Hse. Pubs.

George, Kristine O'Connell. Book! Smith, Maggie, illus. 2001. 32p. (J). (gr. k-ps). tchr. ed. 9.95 (978-0-395-98287-7(1) , Clarion Bks.) Houghton Mifflin Co. Trade & Reference Div.

—The Great Frog Race: And Other Poems. Kiesler, Kate, illus. 2005. 48p. (J). (gr. k-3). reprint ed. 5.95 (978-0-618-60478-4(2) , Clarion Bks.) Houghton Mifflin Co. Trade & Reference Div.

—Old Elm Speaks: Tree Poems. Kiesler, Kate, illus. 2007. 48p. (J). (gr. k-3). 5.95 (978-0-618-75242-3(0) , Clarion Bks.) Houghton Mifflin Co. Trade & Reference Div.

Gershator, Phillis & Gershator, David. Summer Is Summer. Blackall, Sophie, illus. rev. ed. 2006. 32p. (J). 16.95 (978-0-8050-7444-4(9) , Holt, Henry & Co. Bks. For Young Readers) Holt, Henry & Co.

Ghigna, Charles. Animal Tracks: Wild Poems to Read Aloud. Speirs, John, tr. Speirs, John, illus. 2004. 36p. (J). (ps-1). 14.95 (978-0-8109-4841-9(9)) Abrams, Harry N. , Inc.

—A Fury of Motion: Poems for Boys. 2003. (Illus.). 64p. (YA). (gr. 6-9). 16.95 (978-1-59078-066-4(3)); pap. 6.95 (978-1-59078-188-3(0)) Boyds Mills Pr.

—Fury of Motion: Poems for Boys. 2003. (gr. 7-12). lib. bdg. 15.25 (978-0-613-70820-3(2)) Tandem Library Bks.

—Halloween Night. 2006. (Illus.). 128p. 4.95 (978-0-7624-2820-5(1)) Running Pr. Bk. Pubs.

Ghigna, Charles. Score! Fifty Poems That Make the Goal. Gorton, Julia, illus. 2008. 56p. (J). 15.95 (***978-0-8109-9488-1(7)*** , Abrams Bks. for Young Readers) Abrams, Harry N. , Inc.

Ghigna, Charles & Ghigna, Debra. Christmas Is Coming! Young, Mary O'Keefe, illus. 2005. 30p. (J). (gr. k-4). reprint ed. 16.00 (978-0-7567-9290-9(8)) DIANE Publishing Co.

Ghigna, Charles & McCauley, Adam. Halloween Night: Twenty-One Spooktacular Poems. rev. ed. 2003. (Illus.). 32p. (J). (gr. k-3). 15.95 (978-0-7624-1552-6(5) , Running Pr. Kids) Running Pr. Bk. Pubs.

Gibbs, Susie & Chatterton, Martin. Revolting Poems to Make You Squirm. 2006. (Illus.). 64p. (YA). 9.95 (978-0-19-272606-3(4)) Oxford Univ. Pr., Inc.

Gibson, Flo. Three Tales in Verse. 2006. pap. 7.95 (978-0-533-15158-5(9)) Vantage Pr., Inc.

Giles, W. Marie. Open Your Mind, Open Your Heart: A Collection of Words of Wisdom, Heartfelt Thoughts, & Original Poetry. 2003. 112p. per. 19.95 (978-0-9728944-0-1(3)) Giles, W. Marie.

Gillespie, Esther A. & Clark, Thomas Curtis, eds. A Child's Thought of God: Religious Poems for Children. 2006. (ENG.). 136p. per. 20.95 (***978-1-4286-2999-8(8)***) Kessinger Publishing, LLC.

Gilmartin, Erin. Stretched into Shadow with No End: A Collection of Poems, 1 book. 2004. (Illus.). 88p. (YA). pap. 11.95 (978-0-9702497-0-8(5) , Meister-Home Pr.) Meister-Home, Inc.

Givens, Florence Rosie. A Little More Cream Please Poem Collection by Florence Rosie Givens. 2003. (Illus.). 232p. per. 12.95 (978-0-9705819-3-8(9)) FloBound Poems Publications.

Glaser, Linda. Our Big Home: An Earth Poem. Kleven, Elisa, illus. 32p. (gr. k-3). 2002. (J). pap. 7.95 (978-0-7613-1776-0(7)); 2000. (978-0-7613-1292-5(7)); 2000. lib. bdg. (978-0-7613-1650-3(7)) Lerner Publishing Group. (Millbrook Pr.).

Glenn, Mel. Who Killed Mr Chippendale? a Mystery in Poems. 1999. (gr. 7-12). lib. bdg. 14.15 (978-0-613-18290-4(1)) Tandem Library Bks.

Godden, Rumer. Cockcrow to Starlight: A Day Full of Poetry. Kneen, Maggie, illus. 2003. 125p. (J). pap. 13.99 (978-0-330-34302-2(5) , Pan) Pan Macmillan GBR. *Dist:* Trafalgar Square Publishing.

Godula, Ellen Kjelgaard & Godula, Brian. Queen Mab, Musical Verses Volume 3. 2007. (J). audio compact disk 16.99 (***978-0-9764109-3-5(1)***) Pillar Rock Publishing.

Goldstone, Bruce. Great Estimations. rev. ed. 2006. (Illus.). 32p. (J). 16.95 (978-0-8050-7446-8(5) , Holt, Henry & Co. Bks. For Young Readers) Holt, Henry & Co.

Gonzalez, Ray. El Conejito Claudio (G) Para Bebés de 1 a 3 Años. Giannini, Claudia, tr. 2006. (SPA., Illus.). 20p. (J). bds. (978-0-9712816-4-6(5)) Third Week Bks.

Goodhart. Row Your Boat - Sound Book. 2007. (Illus.). 16p. (J). (ps). bds. 9.95 (***978-1-4052-2553-3(X)***) Egmont Bks., Ltd. GBR. *Dist:* Independent Pubs. Group.

Goodman, Joan Elizabeth. Woodland Lullabies. Goodman, Joan Elizabeth, illus. 1998. 1. (Illus.). 24p. (ps-1). lib. bdg. 18.40 (978-0-7613-0350-3(2) , Millbrook Pr.) Lerner Publishing Group.

Goodridge, Walt F. J. Lyrics for Living Vol. 2: Just Because I Am. Owens-Waters, Zelda, ed. 2003. 64p. (C). 10.00 (978-0-9629202-5-7(8) , LL002) Passion Profit Co., The/NicheMarket.

Goose, Mother. Old MacDonald & Other Sing Along Rhymes. 2005. (Illus.). 36p. (J). bds. 15.95 incl. audio compact disk (978-1-59249-526-9(5) , 1D029) Soundprints.

Gorey, Edward & Belloc, Hilaire. Cautionary Tales for Children. 2002. (Illus.). 72p. 16.00 (978-0-15-100715-8(2)) Harcourt Trade Pubs.

Gould, Flagg Hannah. The Youth's Coronal. 2006. 94.99 (***978-1-4280-0682-9(6)***); pap. 88.99 (***978-1-4280-0671-3(0)***) IndyPublish.com.

Graham, Bob, illus. Poems for the Very Young. 2004. 80p. (J). (ps-ps). lib. bdg. 17.15 (978-0-606-30325-5(1)) Tandem Library Bks.

Graham, Joan. Splish Splash. 2001. (gr. k-3). lib. bdg. 14.10 (978-0-613-35574-2(1)) Tandem Library Bks.

Graham, Joan Bransfield. Splish Splash. Scott, Steven M., illus. 2001. 40p. (J). (gr. k-3). reprint ed. pap. 6.95 (978-0-618-11123-7(9)) Houghton Mifflin Co. Trade & Reference Div.

Granados, Antonio. Poemas de Juguete 1. 2003. (SPA., Illus.). 191p. 8.95 (978-968-19-0627-6(6)) Aguilar, Altea, Taurus, Alfaguara, S.A. de C.V MEX. *Dist:* Santillana USA Publishing Co., Inc.

—Versos de Dulce y de Sal. (SPA.). 166p. (J). pap. 13.95 (978-968-7205-28-1(8) , AIM288) Amaquemecan, Editorial MEX. *Dist:* Continental Bk. Co., Inc.

Granados, Jose Luis Diaz. Cuaderno Matinal: Poesias para Ninos. (SPA.). 48p. (J). (gr. k-2). (978-958-30-0583-1(5)) Panamericana Editorial COL. *Dist:* Lectorum Pubns., Inc.

Grandits, John. Blue Lipstick: Concrete Poems. 2007. (Illus.). 48p. (J). (gr. 5-9). 15.00 (978-0-618-56860-4(3) , Clarion Bks.) Houghton Mifflin Co. Trade & Reference Div.

—Blue Lipstick: Concrete Poems. Grandits, John, illus. 2007. (Illus.). 48p. (J). (gr. 5-9). 5.95 (***978-0-618-85132-4(1)*** , Clarion Bks.) Houghton Mifflin Co. Trade & Reference Div.

Green, Mischa P., creator. Stream Keepa Runnin Through My Soul: Poetry for Life. 2004. (YA). per. 20.00 (978-0-9754191-1-3(0)) Morals & Values Pr.

Green, Paula & 50 Children. Flamingo Bendalingo: Poems from the Zoo. Hight, Michael, illus. 2006. 100p. 24.95 (978-1-86940-353-9(3)) Auckland Univ. Pr. NZL. *Dist:* Independent Pubs. Group.

Greenberg, Jan, ed. Treasure Hunt: Poetry Inspired by Art from Around Our World. 2008. 88p. (J). 19.95 (***978-0-8109-9471-3(2)*** , Abrams Bks. for Young Readers) Abrams, Harry N. , Inc.

Greenfield Educational Center Staff. Words Through Poetry. (Illus.). (J). Level 1. 2000. (CHI.). 31p. pap. 7.99 (978-962-563-027-4(9)); Level 1. 2000. pap., wbk. ed. 4.99 (978-962-563-028-1(7)); Level 2. 2005. (CHI., 31p. pap. 7.99 (978-962-563-029-8(5)); Level 2. 2005. (CHI., 31p. pap., wbk. ed. 4.99 (978-962-563-030-4(9)); Level 3. 2000. (CHI., 31p. pap. 7.99 (978-962-563-243-8(3)); Level 3. 2000. (CHI., pap., wbk. ed. 4.99 (978-962-563-244-5(1)) Greenfield Enterprises, Ltd. HKG. *Dist:* Cheng & Tsui Co.

Greenfield, Eloise. The Friendly Four. Gilchrist, Jan Spivey, illus. 2006. 48p. (J). 16.99 (978-0-06-000759-1(1)); lib. bdg. 17.89 (978-0-06-000760-7(5)) HarperCollins Pubs.

—When the Horses Ride By: Children in the Times of War. Gilchrist, Jan Spivey, illus. 2006. 40p. (J). (gr. 2-6). 17.95 (978-1-58430-249-0(6)) Lee & Low Bks., Inc.

Grimes, Nikki. Danitra Brown Leaves Town. Cooper, Floyd, illus. 2002. 32p. (J). (gr. 3 up). 15.99 (978-0-688-13155-5(7)); 16.89 (978-0-688-13156-2(5)) HarperCollins Pubs. (Amistad).

—It's Raining Laughter: Poems. Pinkney, Myles C., photos by. 2004. (Illus.). 32p. (J). pap. 10.95 (978-1-59078-077-0(9)) Boyds Mills Pr.

—Stepping Out with Grandma Mac. Angelo, illus. 2001. 48p. (J). (gr. 3 up). pap. 16.95 (978-0-531-30320-7(9) , Orchard Bks.) Scholastic, Inc.

—Thanks a Million. Cabrera, Cozbi A., illus. 2006. 32p. (J). 16.99 (978-0-688-17292-3(X)); lib. bdg. 17.89 (978-0-688-17293-0(8)) HarperCollins Pubs.

—When Daddy Prays. Ladwig, Tim, illus. 2004. 32p. (J). pap. 8.00 (978-0-8028-5266-3(1)); 16.00 (978-0-8028-5152-9(5)) Eerdmans, William B. Publishing Co.

Grommersch, Kevin. Quotes, Poems, & Words That Flow. 2002. 118p. (YA). pap. 9.95 (978-0-595-26146-8(9) , Writers Club Pr.) iUniverse, Inc.

Grossman, Bill. My Little Sister Ate One Hare. Hawkes, Kevin, illus. 1998. 32p. (J). (gr. k-3). pap. 6.99 (978-0-517-88576-5(X) , Dragonfly Bks.) Random Hse. Children's Bks.

—My Little Sister Ate One Hare. Hawkes, Kevin, illus. 1998. (J). (ps-ps). lib. bdg. 15.30 (978-0-613-10521-7(4)) Tandem Library Bks.

Guillén, Nicolas. Por el Mar de las Antillas Anda un Barco de Papel. 3rd ed. 2003. (Rosa y Manzana Ser.). (SPA., Illus.). 44p. (978-84-85334-32-2(9) , LG1397) Loguez Ediciones ESP. *Dist:* Lectorum Pubns., Inc.

Gunning, Monica. Not a Copper Penny in Me House: Poems from the Caribbean. Lessac, Frane, illus. 2003. 32p. (J). (gr. 2-4). pap. 10.95 (978-1-56397-793-0(1)) Boyds Mills Pr.

—Not a Copper Penny in My House. 1999. (gr. 3-6). lib. bdg. 19.90 (978-0-613-16783-3(X)) Tandem Library Bks.

—Under the Breadfruit Tree: Island Poems. 2003. (Illus.). 48p. (J). (gr. 2-5). 15.95 (978-1-56397-539-4(4)) Boyds Mills Pr.

Gutmann, Bessie P. I Love You: Verses & Sweet Sayings. 2007. 32p. (J). (ps-2). 6.99 ***(978-0-448-44659-2(6)*** , Grosset & Dunlap) Penguin Group (USA) Inc.

Hablandole A Tu Corazon. 2005. (SPA.). (YA). 11.99 (978-0-9765663-1-1(1)) Guevara, Alexis.

Haiku Baby. 2008. (Illus.). 14p. (J). (gr. k-ps). bds. 6.99 ***(*978-0-375-84395-2(7)*** , Random Hse. Bks. for Young Readers) Random Hse. Children's Bks.

Hajdusiewicz, Babs Bell. Peaceful Me: Poems & Activities to Help Children Resolve Conflicts Peacefully. l.t. ed. 2002. 32p. (J). (978-0-9665568-1-0(X)) Reading Realm.

Hall, Donald. The Oxford Illustrated Book of American Children's Poems. 2001. (Illus.). (J). (978-0-606-21375-2(9)) Tandem Library Bks.

Hall, Melanie, illus. Christmas Presents Holiday Poetry. 2004. 32p. (J). lib. bdg. 13.85 ***(*978-1-4242-0512-7(3))*** Fitzgerald Bks.

Halstead, Virginia. illus. Spectacular Science: A Book of Poems. 2002. 40p. (J). (gr. k up). 6.99 (978-0-689-85120-9(0) , Aladdin) Simon & Schuster Children's Publishing.

Hamburger, Maria. The Story of Aum. 2006. (J). ***(*978-0-9759226-1-3(0))*** BrainFriendly Learning.

Hamilton, Carol. I'm Not from Neptune. 2003. 117p. (YA). (gr. 4-5). pap. 9.99 (978-0-88092-537-2(X)) Royal Fireworks Publishing Co.

Hammar, Travis. Street Dreams: A Collection of Poems. 2000. (J). (gr. 1-8). pap. 8.95 (978-1-891658-06-8(9) , Captains Log Printing) Mountain Hse. Publishing Co.

Harcourt School Publishers Staff. The Days of Exodusters Below Level. 3rd ed. 2002. (Trophies Reading Program Ser.). (Illus.). pap. 5.10 (978-0-15-323247-3(1)) Harcourt Schl. Pubs.

—Extra Innings, Level D. 2001. (Collections Ser.). (Illus.). pap., lib. bdg. 12.10 (978-0-15-314438-7(6)) Harcourt Schl. Pubs.

—Mean, Green Carnivore: Take-Home Book. 2001. (Collections Ser.). (Illus.). (J). pap. 1.90 (978-0-15-319511-2(8)) Harcourt Schl. Pubs.

—The Mean, Green Carnivore Below Level. 3rd ed. 2002. (Trophies Reading Program Ser.). (Illus.). pap. 5.10 (978-0-15-323249-7(8)) Harcourt Schl. Pubs.

—Music Makes Joy Below Level, 3rd ed. 2002. (Trophies Reading Program Ser.). (Illus.). pap. 5.10 (978-0-15-323316-8(4)) Harcourt Schl. Pubs.

—The 3,000th Hit: Take-Home Book. 2001. (Collections Ser.). (Illus.). (J). pap. 1.90 (978-0-15-319518-1(5)) Harcourt Schl. Pubs.

—The 3000th Hit Below Level. 3rd ed. 2002. (Trophies Reading Program Ser.). (Illus.). pap. 5.10 (978-0-15-323316-6(8)) Harcourt Schl. Pubs.

Harley, Avis. Fly with Poetry: An ABC of Poetry. Harley, Avis, photos by. 2003. (Illus.). 48p. (J). (gr. 2-4). pap. 13.95 (978-1-56397-798-5(2)) Boyds Mills Pr.

—Fly with Poetry: An ABC of Poetry. 2000. (gr. 3-6). lib. bdg. 23.40 (978-0-613-51073-8(9)) Tandem Library Bks.

—Leap into Poetry: More ABCs of Poetry. Harley, Avis, illus. 2003. (Illus.). 48p. (J). (gr. 2-4). 19.95 (978-1-56397-673-5(0)) Boyds Mills Pr.

—Leap into Poetry: More ABC's of Poetry. 2001. (gr. 3-6). lib. bdg. 23.40 (978-0-613-83340-0(6)) Tandem Library Bks.

Harrison, David L. Connecting the Dots. Cousineau, Kelley, illus. 2004. 64p. (J). (gr. 4-6). 16.95 (978-1-59078-260-6(7)) Boyds Mills Pr.

—Farmer's Garden: Rhymes for Two Voices. Johnson-Petrov, Arden, illus. 32p. (J). (gr. k-2). pap. 9.95 (978-1-59078-177-7(5)) Boyds Mills Pr.

—Wild Country: Outdoor Poems for Young People. 2003. 48p. (YA). (gr. 4-6). 14.95 (978-1-56397-784-8(2)) Boyds Mills Pr.

Harrison, Michael. Oxford Treasury of Children's Poems. 1999. (978-0-606-18338-3(8)) Tandem Library Bks.

—The Young Oxford Book of Christmas Poems. 2000. (Illus.). 160p. (J). (978-0-19-276252-8(4)) Oxford Univ. Pr., Inc.

Harrison, Michael & Stuart-Clark, Christopher. One Hundred Years of Poetry for Children. rev. ed. 2007. (Illus.). 192p. (YA). 11.95 ***(*978-0-19-276350-1(4))*** Oxford Univ. Pr., Inc.

—The Oxford Book of Story Poems. 2007. (Illus.). 176p. (YA). 17.95 ***(*978-0-19-276344-0(X))*** Oxford Univ. Pr., Inc.

Harrison, Randolph R. The Frog King of Lily Pond World: Children's Short Stories & Poems. 2002. 131p. (J). pap. 10.95 (978-0-595-22480-7(6) , Writers Club Pr.) iUniverse, Inc.

Harrison, Roosevelt, VI. Faith That Moves Mountains. 2001. (YA). per. 9.99 (978-0-9707536-1-8(6)) Chosen Word Publishing.

Hart, Louise. The Illustrated Book of Trees. 2002. cd-rom 24.95 (978-1-930889-42-2(9)) Sirius Pubns.

Hass, Robert, ed. 2000 River of Words: The Natural World As Viewed by Young People. 2000. (River of Words Ser.). (Illus.). 64p. (YA). (gr. k-12). pap. 7.00 (978-0-9662771-4-2(7)) International Rivers Network.

Havill, Juanita. I Heard It from Alice Zucchini: Poems about the Garden. Davenier, Christine, illus. 2006. 32p. (J). (gr. k-6). 15.95 (978-0-8118-3962-4(1)) Chronicle Bks. LLC.

Hayford, James. Knee-Deep in Blazing Snow: Growing up in Vermont. McCurdy, Michael, illus. 2005. 59p. (J). (gr. 5-17). 17.95 (978-1-59078-338-2(7)) Boyds Mills Pr.

Headstream, John H. Bright Stories & Little Literature for Children. 2007. pap. 10.00 ***(*978-0-8059-7028-9(2))*** Dorrance Publishing Co., Inc.

Heard, Georgia. Creatures of Earth, Sea, & Sky: Poems. Dewey, Jennifer Owings, illus. 2003. 32p. (J). (gr. 2-4). pap. 10.95 (978-1-56397-635-3(8)) Boyds Mills Pr.

Heard, Georgia, ed. This Place I Know: Poems of Comfort. gif. ed. 2006. (Illus.). 48p. (J). (gr. 1). 12.99 (978-0-7636-2875-8(1)) Candlewick Pr.

Heart of the Moment. 2005. (YA). per. (978-1-59872-142-3(9)) Instantpublisher.com.

Heidbreder, Robert. Eenie Meenie Manitoba: Playful Poems from Coast to Coast. Ritchie, Scot, illus. 2000. 130p. (J). (ps-4). (978-1-55074-818-5(1)) Kids Can Pr., Ltd.

—Lickety-Split. Petricic, Dusan, illus. 2007. 32p. (J). (ps-2). ***(*978-1-55337-710-8(9))*** Kids Can Pr., Ltd.

—A Sea-Wishing Day. Denton, Kady MacDonald, illus. 2007. 32p. (J). (ps-3). ***(*978-1-55337-707-8(9))*** Kids Can Pr., Ltd.

Heidbreder, Robert. See Saw Saskatchewan: More Playful Poems from Coast to Coast. Ritchie, Scot, illus. 2003. 32p. (J). (ps-4). (978-1-55337-392-6(8)) Kids Can Pr., Ltd.

Henderson, Kathy. Pets Pets Pets. 2004. (Illus.). 32p. (J). 14.95 (978-1-84507-021-2(6)) Lincoln, Frances Ltd. GBR. *Dist:* Perseus Distribution.

Henderson, Kathy, ed. The Bedtime Book. Ives, Penny, illus. 2004. 72p. (J). pap. 10.95 (978-1-84507-139-4(5)) Lincoln, Frances Ltd. GBR. *Dist:* Perseus Distribution.

Henderson, Stewart. All Things Weird & Wonderful. 2004. (Illus.). 96p. (J). pap. 8.99 (978-0-7459-4898-0(7) , Lion) Lion Hudson plc GBR. *Dist:* Independent Pubs. Group.

—All Things Weird & Wonderful. Baines, Nigel, illus. 2003. 96p. (J). pap. 19.99 (978-0-7459-4678-8(X) , Lion) Lion Hudson plc GBR. *Dist:* Independent Pubs. Group.

—Who Left Grandad at the Chip Shop? And Other Poems. Baines, Nigel, illus. 96p. (J). 2001. pap. 8.99 (978-0-7459-4551-4(1)); 2000. 16.99 (978-0-7459-4412-8(4)) Lion Hudson plc GBR. (Lion). *Dist:* Independent Pubs. Group.

Henri, Adrian. Robocat: New Poems. Smith, Wendy, illus. 1998. 64p. (J). pap. 8.99 (978-0-7475-3863-9(8)) Bloomsbury Publishing Plc GBR. *Dist:* Independent Pubs. Group.

—The World's Your Lobster. 2000. (Illus.). 64p. (J). pap. 7.99 (978-0-7475-3864-6(6)) Bloomsbury Publishing Plc GBR. *Dist:* Trafalgar Square Publishing.

Herbert, Terry. Love Tides & Golden Isles Lore. Layton, AnnaGitana et al, illus. 2002. 130p. (YA). pap. 21.95 (978-0-9653831-2-7(1)) BHouse Publishing Co.

—Love Tides & Golden Isles Lore: (Audio Book on Cd) 2002. (YA). cd-rom 24.95 (978-0-9653831-4-1(8)) BHouse Publishing Co.

Herrick, Steven. Love Poems & Leg Spinners. 2001. (Illus.). 88p. (YA). pap. 13.95 (978-0-7022-3200-8(9)) Univ. of Queensland Pr. AUS. *Dist:* International Specialized Bk. Services.

Hines, Anna Grossnickle. Winter Lights: A Season in Poems & Quilts. Hines, Anna Grossnickle, illus. 2005. (Illus.). 32p. (J). 16.99 (978-0-06-000817-8(2)); lib. bdg. 17.89 (978-0-06-000818-5(0)) HarperCollins Pubs.

Hines, Anna Grossnickle. 1, 2, Buckle My Shoe. 2008. (J). ***(*978-0-15-206305-4(6))*** Harcourt Trade Pubs.

Hirsch, Edward. How to Read a Poem: And Fall in Love with Poetry. 2000. 354p. (gr. 7-12). lib. bdg. 24.60 (978-0-613-25601-8(8)) Tandem Library Bks.

Hirschman, Jessica Elin & Cole, Jennifer Elin. I Love You All the Time. Bright, Bonnie, illus. 2000. 16p. (J). (ps-2). pap. 3.95 (978-0-9701155-1-5(2)) Cookie Bear Pr., Inc.

Hirstein, Christian. Inner Simplicity. 1998. (Illus.). 56p. (YA). (gr. 9-12). pap. 8.00 (978-0-8059-4282-8(3)) Dorrance Publishing Co., Inc.

Hittleman, Carol G. & Hittleman, Daniel R., eds. A Grand Celebration: Grandparents in Poetry. Life, Kay, illus. 2003. 32p. (YA). (ps up). 16.95 (978-1-56397-901-9(2)) Boyds Mills Pr.

Hoberman, Mary Ann. The Llama Who Had No Pajama. 100 Favorite Poems. Fraser, Betty, illus. 2006. 68p. (J). pap. 8.00 (978-0-15-205571-4(1) , Harcourt Paperbacks) Harcourt Children's Bks.

—You Read to Me, I'll Read to You: Very Short Scary Tales to Read Together. Emberley, Michael, illus. 2007. 32p. (J). (ps-1). 16.99 (978-0-316-01733-6(7)) Little Brown & Co.

Hockerman, Dennis, illus. A School Year of Poems: 180 Favorites from Highlights. 2005. 116p. (J). (gr. k-3). 17.95 (978-1-59078-313-9(1)) Boyds Mills Pr.

Hoffman, Barbara. Cliffs of Fall. Enders, Lori, illus. 2002. 28p. per. 7.95 (978-0-9719837-1-7(2)) Enders' Family Publishing.

Hoffman, Heinrich & Blyth, Colin. Struwwelpeter 2000. Hoffman, Heinrich et al, illus. 2000. (ENG & GER.). 64p. (J). (ps-5). (978-0-9641804-2-0(1)) Iolair Publishing.

Holbrook, Sara. Am I Naturally This Crazy? Martin, Reuben, illus. 2003. 48p. (J). (gr. 4-6). pap. 7.95 (978-1-56397-640-7(4)) Boyds Mills Pr.

—The Dog Ate My Homework. Martin, Reuben, illus. 2nd rev. ed. 2003. 48p. (J). (gr. 4-6). pap. 8.95 (978-1-56397-638-4(2)) Boyds Mills Pr.

—I Never Said I Wasn't Difficult. Martin, Reuben, illus. rev. ed. 2003. 48p. (J). (gr. 4-6). pap. 8.95 (978-1-56397-639-1(0)) Boyds Mills Pr.

—Walking on the Boundaries of Change: Poems of Transition. 2003. (Illus.). 64p. (YA). (gr. 6-9). pap. 9.95 (978-1-56397-737-4(0)) Boyds Mills Pr.

—Wham! It's a Poetry Jam: Discovering Performance Poetry. 2003. (Illus.). 64p. (YA). (gr. 2-4). 16.95 (978-1-56397-998-9(5)); pap. 9.95 (978-1-59078-011-4(6)) Boyds Mills Pr.

—Wham! It's a Poetry Jam: Discovering Performance Poetry. 2002. (gr. 3-6). lib. bdg. 18.75 (978-0-613-79875-4(9)) Tandem Library Bks.

—Which Way to the Dragon! Poems for the Coming on Strong. Martin, Reuben, illus. 2003. 48p. (J). (gr. 4-6). pap. 8.95 (978-1-56397-641-4(2)) Boyds Mills Pr.

Holman, Doris Anne. Come with Me to the Sea. Holman, Doris Anne, illus. 1998. (Illus.). 22p. (J). (gr. 2-4). pap. (978-0-9667192-0-8(4)) Holman, Doris Anne.

Homer. The Odyssey. Fagles, Robert, tr. 2006. 560p. (gr. 12). pap. 15.00 (978-0-14-303995-2(4) , Penguin Classics) Penguin Group (USA) Inc.

Hood, Karen Jean Matsko. Haiku Poems: A Collection of haiku Poetry. 2006. spiral bd. 22.95 (978-1-59649-018-5(7)) Whispering Pine Pr., Inc.

—Under the Lilacs: A Book of Children's Poetry. 2002. 24.95 (978-1-930948-51-8(4) , 1-930948-51-4); pap. 15.95 (978-1-930948-52-5(2) , 1-930948-52-2) Whispering Pine Pr., Inc.

Hopkins, Lee Bennett. Alphathoughts: Alphabet Poems from A to Z. Baggetta, Marla, illus. 2003. 32p. (J). (gr. k-2). 15.95 (978-1-56397-979-8(9)) Boyds Mills Pr.

—Been to Yesterdays: Poems of a Life. 2003. (Illus.). 64p. (YA). (gr. 4-6). 9.95 (978-1-56397-808-1(3)) Boyds Mills Pr.

—Been to Yesterdays: Poems of a Life. 1999. (gr. 3-6). lib. bdg. 18.75 (978-0-613-78892-2(3)) Tandem Library Bks.

—Behind the Museum Door: Poems to Celebrate the Wonders of Museums. Dressen-McQueen, Stacey, illus. 2007. (J). ***(*978-1-4287-3985-7(8)*** , Abrams Bks. for Young Readers) Abrams, Harry N. , Inc.

—Dino-Roars. Fisher, Cynthia, illus. 1999. (Road to Reading Ser.). 10.95 (978-0-307-26304-9(5)) Whitman Publishing LLC.

—Got Geography! Stanton, Philip, illus. 2006. 32p. (J). 15.99 (978-0-06-055601-3(3)); lib. bdg. 16.89 (978-0-06-055602-0(1)) HarperCollins Pubs.

—Hamsters, Shells, & Spelling Bees: School Poems. Yoshikawa, Sachiko, illus. 2008. (I Can Read Bks.). 48p. (J). 16.99 ***(*978-0-06-074112-9(0));*** lib. bdg. 17.89 ***(*978-0-06-074113-6(9))*** HarperCollins Pubs.

—Marvelous Math: A Book of Poems. 2001. (gr. k-3). lib. bdg. 15.30 (978-0-613-73325-0(8)); (Illus.). (J). (978-0-606-21316-5(3)) Tandem Library Bks.

—School Supplies: A Book of Poems. 2000. (978-0-606-17937-9(2)) Tandem Library Bks.

—Spectacular Science: A Book of Poems. 2002. (gr. k-3). lib. bdg. 15.30 (978-0-613-45108-6(2)) Tandem Library Bks.

—Valentine Hearts: Holiday Poetry. Adinolfi, JoAnn, illus. 2005. (I Can Read Bks.). 32p. (J). reprint ed. pap. 3.99 (978-0-06-008059-4(0) , Harper Trophy) HarperCollins Pubs.

—Worlds of Poetry, 9 bks. 2005. (YA). (gr. k-3). 270.00 (978-0-8215-0539-7(4)) Sadlier, William H. Inc.

Hopkins, Lee Bennett, selected by. Me, Myself & I! Theme 1. l.t. ed. 1998. (Sadlier Phonics Reading Program). (Illus.). 16p. (YA). (gr. k-3). 29.85 (978-0-8215-0500-7(9)) Sadlier, William H. Inc.

Hopkins, Lee Bennett & Alcorn, Stephen. Little Bill: Extra Thankful Thanksgiving. 2004. (Illus.). (J). pap. 3.99 (978-0-439-35244-4(4) , Orchard Bks.) Scholastic, Inc.

Hopkins, Lee Bennett & Dressen-McQueen, Stacey. Behind the Museum Door: Poems to Celebrate the Wonders of Museums. 2007. (Illus.). 32p. (J). (ps-2). 16.95 (978-0-8109-1204-5(X) , Abrams Bks. for Young Readers) Abrams, Harry N. , Inc.

Hopwood, Mererid, et al. Byd Llawn Hud. 2005. (WEL., Illus.). 32p. 4.99 (978-1-84323-342-8(8)); 12.99 (978-1-84323-343-5(6)) Gomer Pr. GBR. *Dist:* Gomer Pr.

Horton, Joan. I Brought My Rat for Show-and-Tell. Siegel, Melanie, tr. Siegel, Melanie, illus. 2004. (All Aboard Poetry Reader Ser.). 48p. (J). (gr. 1-4). pap. 3.99 (978-0-448-43364-6(8) , Grosset & Dunlap) Penguin Group (USA) Inc.

Hotaling, Gwenn. A Child's Book of Seasons. 2003. (Illus.). 64p. 19.95 (978-0-9728838-0-1(0)) Little Bird Publishing.

Hubbard, Vicki L. & Children of Paramount Academy Staff. Kinder Spirits: Children Helping Children in the Fight Against Hunger. Killion, Nance, photos by. 2000. (Illus.). 120p. (gr. 4-7). pap. 9.95 (978-0-595-13542-4(0)) iUniverse, Inc.

Hudson, Cheryl Willis. Many Colors of Mother Goose. 2004. (Illus.). 32p. (J). (ps-3). pap. 7.95 (978-0-940975-91-0(2) , Sankofa Bks.) Just Us Bks., Inc.

Hudson, Wade. The Pioneers. Hudson, Stephen J., illus. 2004. (Poetry from the Masters Ser.). 88p. (J). pap. 9.95 (978-0-940975-96-5(3) , Sankofa Bks.) Just Us Bks., Inc.

Hughes, Shirley. Rhymes for Annie Rose. Hughes, Shirley, illus. 2006. (Illus.). 48p. (J). (ps-2). reprint ed. 16.99 (978-0-7636-2940-3(5)) Candlewick Pr.

Hugo, Victor. Victor Hugo: Selected Poems. 2002. (gr. 7-12). lib. bdg. 21.10 (978-0-613-64331-3(3)) Tandem Library Bks.

Hulme, Joy N. & Guthrie, Donna. How to Write, Recite, & Delight in All Kinds of Poetry. 2003. (Single Titles Ser.: Vol. 8). 96p. (J). (gr. 3-6). pap. 9.95 (978-0-7613-1831-6(3) , Millbrook Pr.) Lerner Publishing Group.

Hutchins, Hazel J. A Second Is a Hiccup: A Child's Book of Time. Denton, Kady MacDonald, illus. 2004. 29p. (J). pap. ***(*978-0-439-97400-4(3)*** , North Winds Pr) Scholastic Canada, Ltd.

Hyppolite, Michel-Ange. Zile Nou: Poetry in Three Languages. 2001. (CRP & FRE.). 104p. (YA). (gr. 4 up). pap. 11.00 (978-1-58432-090-6(7)) Educa Vision.

If You're Happy & You Know It & Other Favorites. 2005. (Meet Mother Goose Ser.). (Illus.). 36p. (J). bds. 10.95 incl. audio compact disk (978-1-59069-211-0(X) , MD1108) Studio Mouse LLC.

Illustrated Poetry Anthology. 2005. pap. 330.00 (978-0-7910-9136-4(8) , Chelsea Hse.) Facts On File, Inc.

Ingalls, Marjorie. Mr. Moon Man Goes to Japan. 2001. 44p. (YA). pap. (978-1-881533-02-3(6)) Jones, Edward-Lynne & Assocs.

Intermediate School, Parkview, compiled by. School Memories. 2006. per. 19.95 (978-0-9768391-3-2(X)) Pen & Publish Inc.

Isaac, Denise. Agape to You. 2003. (YA). per. 12.99 (978-1-59352-038-0(7)) Christian Services Publishing.

Jackson, Anna. Catullus for Children. 2004. 64p. pap. 12.95 (978-1-86940-308-9(8)) Auckland Univ. Pr. NZL. *Dist:* Independent Pubs. Group.

Jackson, Demond, Sr. The Turnaround Book of Poetry: Complete Series. 2004. (YA). per. 20.00 (978-0-9753028-6-6(8) , TA-04) Turnaround Bk. Publishing Corp.

Jackson, Kathryn & Jackson, Byron. Pirates, Ships, & Sailors. Tenggren, Gustaf, illus. 2006. 72p. (J). (gr. k-k). 14.95 (978-0-375-83665-7(9)); lib. bdg. 16.99 (978-0-375-93665-4(3)) Random Hse. Children's Bks. (Golden Bks.).

Jackson, Robb. Animal Mischief. Jacobsen, Laura, illus. 2006. 32p. (J). (gr. 1-5). 15.95 (978-1-59078-254-5(2) , Wordsong) Boyds Mills Pr.

Jager, Phyllis. Introducing Myself. Jager, Korin Elizabeth, illus. 2005. (J). 9.95 (978-1-59571-080-2(9)) Word Association Pubs.

Jam, Teddy. The New Baby. Reczuch, Karen, illus. 1999. 32p. (J). (ps-3). pap. 16.95 (978-0-88899-327-4(7)) Groundwood Bks. CAN. *Dist:* Transition Vendor.

James, Simon, illus. & compiled by. Days Like This: A Collection of Small Poems. James, Simon, compiled by. 2005. 48p. (J). (gr. 1-5). reprint ed. pap. 6.99 (978-0-7636-2314-2(8)) Candlewick Pr.

Jandrey, Gayle Davies. The Millipede & Other Less Embraceable Friends. Larson, Justin, illus. 2001. 60p. (YA). pap. 16.00 (978-0-9715484-0-4(4)) Cascabel Pr.

Janeczko, Paul B. How to Write Poetry, Grades 4 to 9. 1999. (Scholastic Guides Ser.). 128p. pap., tchr. ed. 12.95 (978-0-590-10077-9(7)) Scholastic, Inc.

—How to Write Poetry, Grades 4 to 9. 2001. 15.75 (978-0-606-21239-7(6)) Tandem Library Bks.

—Worlds Afire. 2007. (Illus.). 112p. (YA). (gr. 7 up). pap. 6.99 (978-0-7636-3400-1(X)) Candlewick Pr.

Janeczko, Paul B., compiled by. Seeing the Blue Between: Advice & Inspiration for Young Poets. 2006. 144p. (J). (gr. 4-8). pap. 7.99 (978-0-7636-2909-0(X)) Candlewick Pr.

Jeffs, Stephanie. Come into the Ark with Noah. Saunderson, Chris, illus. 2007. (J). 5.99 (978-0-9789056-6-8(0)) New Day Publishing, Inc.

—Follow the Star with the Wise Men. Saunderson, Chris, illus. 2007. (J). 5.99 (978-0-9789056-3-7(6)) New Day Publishing, Inc.

—March Around the Walls with Joshua. Saunderson, Chris, illus. 2007. (J). 5.99 (978-0-9789056-7-5(9)) New Day Publishing, Inc.

Jenkins, Mike. Poems for Underage Thinkers. 2004. (Illus.). 32p. pap. 12.95 (978-1-84323-359-6(2)) Beekman Bks., Inc.

Jenkins-Tate, Nesha L. The 10 Love Poems to Empower Young Souls: A Gift Book to Encourage Young People You Love. 2004. 56p. (YA). per. 21.00 (978-0-9753245-0-9(0) , BBR) BBR: Books for Brilliance & Resilience.

Jenny, Alexander. You Are What You.. The Untied Shoelace & Other Revealing Poems. Maynard, Jenn, illus. 2000. 159p. (J). (gr. 2-7). 16.95 (978-0-9674227-4-9(4)) Fumblefingers Press, Inc.

Jihad, Renay. Angels in the Forest. 2001. per. 10.00 (978-0-9716290-1-1(3) , Beatstellar Bks.) Essentials Educational Services.

Jiménez, Juan Ramon. Canta Pajaro Lejano. 14th ed. (SPA., Illus.). 128p. (J). (gr. 4-6). 14.95 (978-84-239-8892-1(9) , EC2591) Espasa Calpe, S.A. ESP. *Dist:* Distribooks, Inc., Lectorum Pubns., Inc.

Jimenez, Juan Ramon. Platero & I Paperback: Platero & I. 2003. (gr. 3-6). lib. bdg. 14.10 (978-0-613-73021-1(6)) Tandem Library Bks.

Joan, Pere, illus. Poemas de Navidad.Tr. of Christmas Poems. (SPA.). 126p. (J). (gr. 3-5). 10.36 (978-84-246-1944-2(7)) La Galera, S.A. Editorial ESP. *Dist:* Lectorum Pubns., Inc.

John Blake UK. Pound A Poem. 2007. (Illus.). 256p. 19.95 ***(*978-1-84454-436-3(2))*** Blake, John Publishing, Ltd. GBR. *Dist:* Independent Pubs. Group.

Johnson, Angela. The Other Side: Shorter Poems. 2000. (Illus.). 64p. (J). (gr. 5-9). pap. 6.95 (978-0-531-07167-0(7) , Orchard Bks.) Scholastic, Inc.

Johnson, Dave, ed. Movin' Teen Poets Take Voice. Raschka, Chris, illus. 2000. ix, 52p. (J). (gr. 5-9). pap. 15.95 (978-0-531-30258-3(X)); pap. 6.95 (978-0-531-07171-7(5)) Scholastic, Inc. (Orchard Bks.).

Johnson-Hall, Wanda. You Can Be: Yes! He Can! 2005. 16p. (YA). 10.00 (978-1-59633-000-9(7)) Goose Creek Pubs.

Johnson, Merdelin V. Joyful Echoes: Original Poems & Prayers for the Growing Years. Bonk, Shirley, illus. 2002. (J). per. 12.99 (978-0-9640025-2-4(3)) Twilight Pr.

Johnson, Tommy L. My Book of Poems. Holston, Larry, illus. 2nd rev. ed. 1999. 80p. (J). pap. 8.00 (978-1-892196-00-2(X)) D J Enterprises.

Johnson, W. Macaulay. Words Unsaid. 2001. (Illus.). (YA). reprint ed. pap. 20.00 (978-0-9740538-0-6(5)) Lost Words Publishing.

Johnston, Tony. My Mexico-Mexico Mio. 1999. Tr. of Spanish). (SPA.). (gr. k-3). lib. bdg. 15.30 (978-0-613-15023-1(6)) Tandem Library Bks.

P Q R

Jones, Betty M. A Child's Seasonal Treasury. Jones, Betty M. & Crowther, Catherine R., illus. 2004. 154p. (J). (ps-2). 24.95 (978-1-883672-30-0(9) , Tricycle Pr.) Ten Speed Pr.

Jones, Susan Smith & Warren, Dianne. Vegetable Soup - The Fruit Bowl. Lindman, Amy Sorvaag, illus. rev. ed. 2006. 64p. (J). (ps-3). per. 14.95 (978-0-9652736-0-2(1)) Oasis Pubns.

Joyce, Hale. Faerys, Dragons & Unicorns. Hale, Joyce & Kirk, Joan, illus. 2002. (J). 12.95 (978-0-9715926-3-6(2)) Passage Publishing.

Joyner, A. Bernard. Out of the Mouths of Babes! A Book of Childrenrsquo;s Poetry. 2007. (ENG.). 68p. per. 12.95 (***978-1-4241-6643-5(8)***) PublishAmerica, Inc.

Kahla, Robert. Mr. X from Planet X: And Other Animules. (Animules Ser.). (Illus.). 64p. (J). pap. 8.95 (978-1-882820-00-9(2)) Cracked Egg Brand Pr.

Kalin, Julia. Peek-a-Boo Moon: A Reader Illustrated Storybook. unabr. ed. 1999. (Picture-It Storybook Ser.). 8p. (J). (ps-3). pap. 10.95 (978-0-9672430-3-0(3) , 9904) Stay, Play & Learn.

—Runaway Balloon: A Picture-It Storybook; A Reader Illustrated Storybook. unabr. ed. 1999. 12p. (J). (ps-3). pap. 12.95 (978-0-9672430-4-7(1) , 9905) Stay, Play & Learn.

Kammeraad, Kevin. A Curious Glimpse of Michigan. 2004. (Illus.). (J). 19.95 (978-0-9712692-9-3(7)) EDCO Publishing, Inc.

—I Remember . . . Memories of Growing Up. 2001. 56p. (J). pap. 7.95 (978-0-9669504-2-7(9)) Cooperfly Bks.

Kanaan. Literati: A Revolution of Living. 2003. 230p. (YA). pap. 18.95 (978-0-595-30381-6(1)) iUniverse, Inc.

Kapell, Dave & Steenland, Sally. The Kids' Magnetic Poetry Book & Creativity Kit. 1998. (Illus.). 64p. (J). (gr. 3-7). spiral bd. 16.95 (978-0-7611-1357-7(6) , 11357) Workman Publishing Co., Inc.

Kaplan, Shelley. Songs for Scratching Mosquito Bites & Petting the Cat. Hutchison, Robert W., illus. 1998. 32p. (J). (ps-8). 16.00 (978-0-9631833-1-6(1)) Kaplan Pr.

Kasper, Catherine. Field Stone: Poems. 2005. 57p. per. 14.00 (978-0-9764726-0-5(0) , 1A) Winnow Pr.

Katz, Alan. Oops! Koren, Edward, illus. 2008. 144p. (J). 17.99 (978-1-4169-0204-1(X) , McElderry, Margaret K.) Simon & Schuster Children's Publishing.

Katz, Bobbi. Once Around the Sun: A Year of Poems. Pham, LeUyen, illus. 2006. 40p. (J). 16.00 (978-0-15-216397-6(2)) Harcourt Trade Pubs.

—Partner Poems for Building Fluency: 25 Original Poems with Research-Based Lessons That Help Students Improve Their Fluency & Comprehension. 2007. 64p. pap. 11.99 (978-0-439-55437-4(3) , Teaching Resources) Scholastic, Inc.

—Trailblazers: Poems of Exploration. Berger, Carin, illus. 2007. 224p. (J). (gr. 3-8). 18.99 (978-0-688-16533-8(8)) HarperCollins Pubs.

Katz, Susan. Oh, Theodore! Guinea Pig Poems. Schuett, Stacey, illus. 2007. 40p. (J). (ps-3). 16.00 (***978-0-618-70222-0(9)*** , Clarion Bks.) Houghton Mifflin Co. Trade & Reference Div.

Kay, Francesca. One Busy Book. Glynn, Chris, illus. 2004. 32p. pap. 12.95 (978-1-84323-344-2(4)) Beekman Bks., Inc.

Kearney, Meg. The Secret of Me. 2005. 128p. (YA). 17.95 (978-0-89255-322-8(7)) Persea Bks., Inc.

Kelfer, Russell. Wait: A Journey to Discovering the Heart of God. Richmond, Marianne, illus. 2002. (YA). 12.99 (978-1-59177-030-5(0)) Marianne Richmond Studios, Inc.

Keller-Miller, LeAnn Marie, illus. When I Grow Up: An A-Z Poem Book for Children & Their Dreams. 2005. (***978-0-9711480-4-8(X)***) ICanPublish.

Kelman, Louise & Kelman, Suzanne. Big Purple Undies. Dowling, Jane, ed. Baker, Penny, illus. 2004. 64p. (J). pap. (978-0-9580869-6-7(6)) Inhoa Publishing.

Kennedy, Caroline. A Family of Poems: My Favorite Poetry for Children. Muth, Jon J., illus. 2005. 144p. (ps-17). 19.95 (978-0-7868-5111-9(2)) Hyperion Pr.

Kennedy, X. J. Talking Like the Rain: A Read-to-Me Book of Poems. 2002. (gr. k-3). lib. bdg. 18.45 (978-0-613-44915-1(0)) Tandem Library Bks.

Kennedy, X. J. & Kennedy, Dorothy M. Knock at a Star: A Child's Introduction to Poetry. Baker, Karen Lee, illus. rev. ed. 1999. 192p. (J). (gr. 5-17). pap. 12.99 (978-0-316-48800-6(3)) Little Brown & Co.

—Talking Like the Rain: A Read-to-Me Book of Poems. Dyer, Jane, illus. 2002. 96p. (J). (ps-3). pap. 10.99 (978-0-316-38491-9(7)) Little, Brown Bks. for Young Readers.

Khan, Shahthureen. Thureen's Emotion: Poems. Khan, Shaima & Khan, Sabiha, eds. Khan, Shahnawaz, illus. Khan, Shahnawaz, photos by. l.t. ed. 1999. 20p. (YA). (gr. 5-12). spiral bd. 12.75 (978-1-928840-00-8(0)) DewDrop Arts & Technology.

Kids: Sagebrush Prairie. 2004. (J). 1.00 (978-1-888631-34-0(1)) Watercourse, The.

Kimble, George J. Poetry for the Road, 1. annot. ed. 2005. (Illus.). 157p. per. 15.00 (978-0-9767024-0-5(1)) Kimble, George J.

King, Michael Riano, Jr. Let's Learn Together. 2007. (J). 8.00 (***978-0-8059-7295-5(1)***) Dorrance Publishing Co., Inc.

Klein, A. M. Doctor Dwarf & Other Poems for Children. Date not set. (Illus.). 32p. 12.95 (978-0-919627-41-3(2)); pap. 6.95 (978-0-919627-43-7(9)) Quarry Pr. CAN. *Dist:* LPC/InBook.

Klunder, Barbara Wyn. Other Goose: Recycled Rhymes for Our Fragile Times. 2007. (Illus.). 48p. (J). (gr. 2 up). 17.95 (***978-0-88899-829-3(5)***) Groundwood Bks. CAN. *Dist:* Perseus Distribution.

Klyde, Barbara. If Giraffes Wore Necklaces. Martinez, Isaac, illus. 1998. 32p. (J). (ps-3). 9.95 (978-1-56492-251-9(0)) Laredo Publishing Co., Inc.

Knowlton, Laurie Lazzaro. God Be in My Heart: Poems & Prayers for Children. 2003. (Illus.). 24p. (J). (ps up). 11.95 (978-1-56397-646-9(3)) Boyds Mills Pr.

—Red, White, & Blue. 2002. (Illus.). 32p. (J). (gr. k-3). 15.95 (978-1-58980-067-0(2)); pap. 7.95 (978-1-58980-055-7(9)) Pelican Publishing Co., Inc.

—Red, White, & Blue. 2002. (gr. k-3). lib. bdg. 24.55 (978-0-613-65328-2(9)) Tandem Library Bks.

Koertge, Ronald. The Brimstone Journals. 2004. (Illus.). 128p. (YA). (gr. 9 up). pap. 6.99 (978-0-7636-1742-4(3)) Candlewick Pr.

—The Brimstone Journals. 2004. (gr. 7-12). lib. bdg. 15.30 (978-0-613-74769-1(0)) Tandem Library Bks.

Koziara, Colleen. Thirteen Silver Moons. Koziara, Colleen, illus. 2004. (Illus.). (J). per. (978-0-9763205-0-0(9)) Mystical Willow Productions.

Kram, T. Gooey Desserts & Messy Shirts Poetry F. 2007. 125p. pap. 17.95 (***978-1-4241-6072-3(3)***) PublishAmerica, Inc.

Kumuhana High, Kukulu. The Hala Grove of Wakiu, Vol. II. 2005. (YA). per. 19.95 (978-1-59571-047-5(7)) Word Association Pubs.

Kurkela, Robert W. Lilies on the Moon. Kurkela, Cassidy S., illus. 2005. 32p. (J). 16.95 (978-0-9760220-0-8(1)) Kidzpoetz Publishing.

Kurzweil, Sonya & Kurzweil, Amy. Forever Poems for Now & Then. 2004. (Illus.). 56p. (J). 15.95 (978-1-932100-39-6(3)) BenBella Bks.

Kusen, Michael. Chess Poems. Kusen, Michael, illus. 2000. (Illus.). 32p. (J). (gr. k-7). pap. 4.50 (978-0-9704640-1-9(0) , CP1) Tandem Publishing.

Lach, William, ed. Curious Cats: In Art & Poetry for Children. 1999. (Illus.). 48p. (J). (978-0-87099-897-3(8)) Metropolitan Museum of Art, The.

Laing, Robin. The Whisky Muse: Collected & Introduced by Robin Laing. Dewar, Bob, illus. 2nd ed. 2004. (ENG.). 224p. per. 14.95 (978-1-84282-041-4(9)) Luath Pr. Ltd. GBR. *Dist:* Ingram Pub. Services.

Lane, Leena. Climb up the Tree with Zacchaeus. Saunderson, Chris, illus. 2007. (J). 5.99 (978-0-9789056-2-0(8)) New Day Publishing, Inc.

Lang, Tiffany. Mango Leaves Strings in Your Teeth. 2003. (J). per. (978-1-59196-409-4(1)) Instantpublisher.com.

Language Through Poetry (Gr. PreK-5) 2003. (J). (978-1-58232-119-6(1)) Bryan Hse. Pubs., Inc.

Lanksy, Bruce. Rolling in the Aisles: A Collection of Laugh-Out-Loud Poems. Carpenter, Stephen, illus. 2004. 116p. (J). (978-0-88166-473-7(1)) Meadowbrook Pr.

Lansky, Bruce. Funny Little Poems for Funny Little People. 2002. (Illus.). 101p. (J). (978-0-88166-426-3(X)); mass mkt. 5.95 (978-0-689-02454-2(1)) Meadowbrook Pr.

—If Pigs Could Fly... & Other Deep Thoughts. 2006. (Illus.). 83p. (J). pap. 9.95 (978-0-689-04976-7(5)) Meadowbrook Pr.

—Lighten Up! Bk. 2: 101 More Funny Little Poems. 1999. 128p. pap. 5.95 (978-0-671-31772-0(5)) Meadowbrook Pr.

—Peter Peter Pizza Eater. 2006. (Illus.). 32p. (J). 15.95 (978-0-684-03166-8(3)) Meadowbrook Pr.

Lansky, Bruce, ed. Dinner with Dracula. Gordon, Mike & Gordon, Carl, illus. 2006. 32p. (J). (978-0-88166-512-3(6)) Meadowbrook Pr.

Lansky, Bruce & Meadowbrook Press Staff. Mary Had A Little Jam. Carpenter, Stephen, illus. 2004. 32p. (J). 9.95 (978-0-689-03392-6(3)) Meadowbrook Pr.

Larios, Julie Hofstrand. Yellow Elephant: A Bright Bestiary. Paschkis, Julie, illus. 2006. 32p. (J). (gr. k-5). 16.00 (978-0-15-205422-9(7)) Harcourt Trade Pubs.

Larrick, Nancy. Piping Down the Valleys Wild. 1999. (Illus.). 272p. (J). (gr. 4-7). pap. 5.99 (978-0-440-41582-4(9) , Yearling) Random Hse. Children's Bks.

—Piping down the Valleys Wild: A Merry Mix of Verse for All Ages. 1999. (gr. 3-6). lib. bdg. 14.15 (978-0-613-16179-4(3)) Tandem Library Bks.

Larsen, Alison. What Makes You Smile? 2006. (J). per. 13.95 (***978-1-60002-094-0(1)*** , Airleaf Publishing) Airleaf Publishing & Bookselling.

Lassiter, Gianna Bari. Rosy Proses: Whimsical Verses & Sanity Journal for Big People Who Have Little People in Their Lives. gif. ed. 2005. (Illus.). 40p. (YA). spiral bd. 10.00 (978-0-9773324-0-3(3)) MentorSource, LLC.

Laughing Crocodiles. 2003. (Gateways to the Sun Ser.). 32p. (J). (gr. 1-2). lib. bdg. 9.95 (978-1-58105-578-8(1)) Santillana USA Publishing Co., Inc.

Lawrie, Robin, illus. Children's Classic Poetry. 1998. 96p. (J). reprint ed. 20.00 (978-0-7567-5619-2(7)) DIANE Publishing Co.

Lawson, Carol, et al, illus. Once upon a Poem: Favorite Poems That Tell Stories. 2004. 128p. (J). (gr. 3 up). pap. 18.95 (978-0-439-65108-0(5) , Chicken Hse., The) Scholastic, Inc.

Lawson, Jonardo. Man in the Moon Fixers Mask. 2004. (Illus.). 88p. (J). (978-0-9732140-9-3(0)) Pedlar Pr.

Lawson, JonArno. Black Stars in a White Night Sky. Tjia, Sherwin, illus. 2008. (J). (***978-1-59078-521-8(5)*** , Wordsong) Boyds Mills Pr.

Layne, Steve. The Principal's Night Before Christmas. Rice, James, illus. 2004. 32p. (J). pap. 15.95 (978-1-58980-252-0(7)) Pelican Publishing Co., Inc.

Layne, Steven L. The Teachers' Night Before Christmas. Rice, James, illus. 2004. 32p. (J). (gr. 3-6). pap. 15.95 (978-1-56554-833-6(7)) Pelican Publishing Co., Inc.

Layton, Carol. ABC Memory Verses E-Book. 2003. (J). per. 7.99 (978-1-59441-569-2(2) , CD-2033-EB) Carson-Dellosa Publishing Co., Inc.

Le, Le Pham. From Where the Wind Blows. Arbuthnot, Nancy, tr. 2003. Tr. of Gio Thoi Phuong Nao. (VIE.). per. 12.00 (978-0-9746300-0-7(4)) Vietnamese International Poetry Society.

Lear, Edward. An Edward Lear Alphabet. Radunsky, Vladimir, illus. 1999. 32p. (J). (ps-2). 14.89 (978-0-06-028114-4(6)) HarperCollins Pubs.

—The Jumblies & Other Nonsense Verse. (Classic Verse Ser.). (Illus.). 56p. (J). 3.50 (978-0-7214-1756-1(6) , Dutton Juvenile) Penguin Group (USA) Inc.

—Nonsense Drolleries: The Owl & the Pussy-Cat, the Duck & the Kangaroo. Foster, William, illus. 2007. 32p. pap. 10.95 (***978-1-60355-050-5(X)***) Juniper Grove.

—The Owl & the Pussycat. 2000. (Illus.). 32p. (J). (ps-2). pap. 12.95 (978-0-552-20560-3(5) , Corgi) Transworld Publishers Ltd. GBR. *Dist:* Trafalgar Square Publishing.

—The Owl & the Pussycat. Mortimer, Anne, illus. 2006. 32p. (J). (ps-4). 15.99 (978-0-06-027228-9(7) , Tegen, Katherine Bks); lib. bdg. 16.89 (978-0-06-027229-6(5)) HarperCollins Pubs.

Leclerc, Rachel. L' Ourse. Sylvestre, Daniel, illus. 2002. (New Poetry Ser.). (FRE.). 36p. (YA). (gr. 7). pap. (978-2-89021-556-6(3)) Diffusion du livre Mirabel.

Lee Bates, Katharine. America the Beautiful. Waldman, Neil, illus. 2004. 27p. (J). reprint ed. 17.00 (978-0-7567-8236-8(8)) DIANE Publishing Co.

Lee, Dennis. Bubblegum Delicious. McPhail, David M., illus. 2001. 32p. (J). (gr. k-4). 15.95 (978-0-06-029773-2(5)) HarperCollins Pubs.

—Bubblegum Delicious. McPhail, David M., illus. 2000. 30p. (J). (ps-2). 19.95 (978-1-55263-159-1(1)) Key Porter Bks. CAN. *Dist:* Firefly Bks., Ltd.

—The Cat & the Wizard. ed. 2004. (Illus.). (J). (gr. k-3). spiral bd. (978-0-616-11115-4(0)); spiral bd. (978-0-616-11116-1(9)) Canadian National Institute for the Blind/Institut National Canadien pour les Aveugles.

—So Cool. Kovalski, Maryann, illus. rev. ed. 2004. 80p. (978-1-55263-613-8(5)) Key Porter Bks.

Lehman, David. Great American Prose Poems: From Poe to the Present. 2003. 352p. pap. 16.00 (978-0-7432-4350-6(1) , Scribner) Simon & Schuster.

Leopold, Niki Clark. K Is for Kitten. Jeffers, Susan, illus. 2002. 32p. (J). 15.99 (978-0-399-23563-4(9) , Putnam Juvenile) Penguin Group (USA) Inc.

Lessie, Pat. Fablesauce. Gaudette, Karen, illus. 1999. 80p. (gr. 4-7). pap. 9.95 (978-1-884540-46-2(5)); (J). 16.95 (978-1-884540-48-6(1)) Haley's.

Lesynski, Loris. Cabbagehead. Lesynski, Loris, illus. 2003. (Illus.). 32p. (J). (gr. k-3). pap. 6.95 (978-1-55037-804-7(X)); lib. bdg. 18.95 (978-1-55037-805-4(8)) Annick Pr., Ltd. CAN. *Dist:* Firefly Bks., Ltd.

—Gatomagico. Canetti, Yanitzia, tr. from ENG. Lesynski, Loris, illus. 2004. (SPA., Illus.). 32p. (J). (ps-2). pap. 5.95 (978-1-55037-874-0(0)) Annick Pr., Ltd. CAN. *Dist:* Firefly Bks., Ltd.

—Nothing Beats a Pizza. Lesynski, Loris, illus. 2001. (Illus.). 32p. (J). (gr. k-3). pap. 7.95 (978-1-55037-700-2(0)); lib. bdg. 18.95 (978-1-55037-701-9(9)) Annick Pr., Ltd. CAN. *Dist:* Firefly Bks., Ltd.

—Nothing Beats a Pizza. 2001. (gr. k-3). lib. bdg. 15.25 (978-0-613-51118-6(2)) Tandem Library Bks.

—Shoe Shakes. Martchenko, Michael, illus. 2007. 32p. (J). (ps-k). pap. 9.95 (***978-1-55451-105-1(4)***); lib. bdg. 19.95 (***978-1-55451-106-8(2)***) Annick Pr., Ltd. CAN. *Dist:* Firefly Bks., Ltd.

Lesynski, Loris. Zigzag: Zoems for Zindergarten. Lesynski, Loris, illus. 2004. (Illus.). 32p. (J). (ps-1). pap. 8.95 (978-1-55037-882-5(1)); lib. bdg. 19.95 (978-1-55037-875-7(9)) Annick Pr., Ltd. CAN. *Dist:* Firefly Bks., Ltd.

Let's Make-Believe. 2002. (Illus.). 32p. 16.95 (978-0-9712675-1-0(0)) Grammy Time Bks.

Levin, Vadim. Silly Horse. Wolfson, Tanya & Zunshine, Tatiana, trs. from RUS. Antonenkov, Evgeny, illus. 2005. 32p. (J). 15.95 (978-0-9646010-1-7(X) , 1241074) Pumpkin Hse., Ltd.

Levithan, David. You Are Here This Is Now: Poems, Stories Essays, & Art from the Best Young Wriiters & Artists in America. 2002. (gr. 7-12). lib. bdg. 15.30 (978-0-613-72042-7(3)) Tandem Library Bks.

Levithan, David, ed. Where We Are, What We See. 2005. (Illus.). 288p. (J). pap. 7.99 (978-0-439-73646-6(3) , PUSH) Scholastic, Inc.

Lewis, J. Patrick. Blackbeard: The Pirate King. 2006. (Illus.). 32p. (J). (gr. 2-5). 25.90 (978-0-7922-5586-4(0) , National Geographic Children's Bks.) National Geographic Society.

—Blackbeard the Pirate King. 2006. (Illus.). 32p. (J). (gr. 2-5). 16.95 (978-0-7922-5585-7(2) , National Geographic Children's Bks.) National Geographic Society.

—God Made the Skunk: And Other Animal Poems. King, Jerry, illus. 2005. 60p. (J). 14.95 (978-0-9722820-1-7(7)) Doggerel Daze.

—Under the Kissletoe: Christmastime Poems. Shepperson, Rob, illus. 2007. 32p. (J). (gr. 1-3). 16.95 (***978-1-59078-438-9(3)*** , Wordsong) Boyds Mills Pr.

Lewis, J. Patrick. Vherses: A Celebration of Outstanding Women. Summer, Mark, illus. 2005. (Creative Editions Ser.). 32p. (J). (gr. 4-7). 18.95 (978-1-56846-185-4(2)) Creative Co., The.

Lewis, J. Patrick & Thompson, John. Freedom Like Sunlight. 2005. (Illus.). pap. 7.95 (978-0-89812-382-1(8)) Creative Co., The.

Lewis, Ophelia S. My Dear Liberia: Recollections, Poetic Memoirs from My Heart. 2004. (YA). per. 9.95 (978-0-9753609-0-3(6)) Village Tales Publishing.

Lewis, Richard. Cave: An Evocation of the Beginnings of Art. Crawford, Elizabeth, illus. Hirose, George, photos by. 2003. 56p. pap. 14.00 (978-1-929299-03-4(6)) Touchstone Ctr. Pubns.

—A Tree Lives. 2006. (Illus.). 48p. pap. 12.00 (978-1-929299-04-1(4)) Touchstone Ctr. Pubns.

Lewis, Sian & Glynn, Chris. Dim Mwnci'n y Dosbarth. 2005. (WEL., Illus.). 64p. 4.99 (978-1-84323-427-2(0)) Gomer Pr. GBR. *Dist:* Gomer Pr.

Literature Connections English: Dogsong. 2004. (gr. 6-12). (978-0-395-77527-1(2) , 2-80096) McDougal Littell Inc.

Little, Jean. I Gave My Mom a Castle. Denton, Kady MacDonald, illus. 2003. 80p. (J). pap. 7.95 (978-1-55143-253-3(6)) Orca Bk. Pubs. USA.

Lloyd, Glynis & Montgomery, Karen. Big Book of a Poetry Box. 2000. (Cambridge Reading Routes Ser.). (Illus.). 32p. pap. 14.25 (978-0-521-77887-9(5)) Cambridge Univ. Pr.

—A Poetry Box. 2000. (Cambridge Reading Routes Ser.). (Illus.). 32p. pap. 6.00 (978-0-521-77907-4(3)) Cambridge Univ. Pr.

Lockheart, Susan, illus. If You See a Fairy Ring. 2007. 24p. (J). (ps up). 16.99 (***978-0-7641-6028-8(1)***) Barron's Educational Series, Inc.

Longfellow, Henry Wadsworth. The Children's Own Longfellow. 2001. (Illus.). 96p. (J). (gr. 3). pap. 5.95 (978-0-618-11854-0(3)) Houghton Mifflin Co. Trade & Reference Div.

—Children's Own Longfellow. 2001. (gr. 3-6). lib. bdg. 14.10 (978-0-613-35496-7(6)) Tandem Library Bks.

—Henry Wadsworth Longfellow. Schoonmaker, Frances, ed. Wallace, Chad, illus. 1998. (Poetry for Young People Ser.). 48p. (gr. 4-7). 14.95 (978-0-8069-9417-8(7)) Sterling Publishing Co., Inc.

—Hiawatha & Megissogwon. Thompson, Jeffrey, illus. 2001. 32p. (J). (gr. 3-7). 16.95 (978-0-7922-6676-1(5) , National Geographic Children's Bks.) National Geographic Society.

—The Midnight Ride of Paul Revere. Thompson, Jeffrey, illus. 2002. 32p. (J). (gr. 1). pap. 7.95 (978-0-7922-6558-0(0) , National Geographic Children's Bks.) National Geographic Society.

—Paul Revere's Ride. Vachula, Monica, illus. 2003. 32p. (J). (gr. 4-6). 16.95 (978-1-56397-799-2(0)) Boyds Mills Pr.

—Paul Revere's Ride: The Landlord's Tale. Santore, Charles, illus. 2005. 28p. (J). (gr. 4-8). reprint ed. 17.00 (978-0-7567-9202-2(9)) DIANE Publishing Co.

—Paul Revere's Ride: The Landlord's Tale. Santore, Charles, illus. 2003. 40p. (J). lib. bdg. 17.89 (978-0-06-623747-3(5)) HarperCollins Pubs.

Longfellow, Henry Wadsworth & Bing, Christopher H. The Midnight Ride of Paul Revere. 2001. (Illus.). 40p. (J). (gr. 3 up). 18.95 (978-1-929766-13-0(0)) Handprint Bks.

Loudin, Jan. Whispers from God. 2002. (gr. 7-12). lib. bdg. 23.40 (978-0-613-74658-8(9)) Tandem Library Bks.

Louise, Ann. Birthday Boy. 1999. (Illus.). (J). pap. 9.95 (978-0-9661451-0-6(0)) Chadko Publishing.

Luby, Chris A. On the Silver Screen: Poetry from the Original Crip. 2002. 136p. pap. 12.95 (978-0-595-22754-9(6) , Writer's Showcase Pr.) iUniverse, Inc.

Lucas, Katherine, illus. Around the World in 80 Poems. 2002. 96p. (J). 19.95 (978-0-8118-3506-0(5)) Chronicle Bks. LLC.

Lucca, Carmen D. Maboiti - El Tallador de Pajaros. Maier, Julia, ed. Maier, Julia & Alvarado, Eli S., illus. 2000. Tr. of Maboiti - The Carver of Birds. (SPA.). 120p. (J). (gr. 3-8). pap. 13.95 (978-0-9623968-2-3(6)) Poets' Refuge.

Lujan, Jorge Elias. Beyond my hand. Amado, Elisa, tr. from SPA. Quintana, Georgina, illus. 2002. 24p. (J). (ps-k). 14.95 (978-0-88899-460-8(5)) Groundwood Bks. CAN. *Dist:* Perseus Distribution.

—Daybreak, Nightfall. Simon, John Oliver & Parfitt, Rebecca R., trs. from SPA. Monroy, Manuel, illus. 2003. 32p. (J). 15.95 (978-0-88899-486-8(9)) Groundwood Bks. CAN. *Dist:* Perseus Distribution.

Lynette, Shannon. A Place with No Name. 2003. 120p. (YA). pap. 14.95 (978-0-7414-1534-9(8)) Infinity Publishing.

Lyons, Anna. The Bunny Meets Ann Peacock. 1998. (Illus.). 16p. (J). (gr. k-3). pap. 6.00 (978-0-8059-4362-7(5)) Dorrance Publishing Co., Inc.

M. Hollenbeck, Kathleen. The Big Book of Classroom Poems. 2004. 176p. pap. 19.99 (978-0-439-43826-1(8) , Teaching Resources) Scholastic, Inc.

MacCormick SEcure Center, Residents. Another Sad Inning: Incarcerated Youth Reveal Their Trials, Tribulations & Loves. MacCormick Secure Center, Residents, illus. 2003. 90p. (YA). per. 17.00 (978-0-9740184-1-6(4) , MAC-2) Durland Alternatives Library.

MacGregor, Kim. Button, Buckle, Tie. Snider, Sharon & Reny, Todd, trs. 2004. (Illus.). 24p. (978-0-9731301-4-0(8)); pap. (978-0-9731301-3-3(X)) Beautiful Beginnings Youth, Inc.

—Yummy Yummy Nummy Nummy, Should I Put This in My Tummy? Ioannou, Gregory Phillip, ed. Snider, Sharon & Reny, Todd, illus. 2004. 24p. (978-0-9731301-0-2(5)) Beautiful Beginnings Youth, Inc.

Macmillan, Lesley. Draw me a Picture. 2006. (Illus.). 46p. (J). per. 12.90 (***978-1-59879-301-7(2)***) Lifevest Publishing, Inc.

Madore, Debbie. Time Shares. 2002. (Illus.). 80p. (YA). per. 8.95 (978-1-930648-23-4(5) , 207-832-6665) Goose River Pr.

Maine: The Way Life Is: A Year of Wicked Good Poetry. 2001. 32p. (J). 7.95 (978-0-9709569-0-3(8)) Blue Lobster Pr.

Major, Kevin. Ann & Seamus. Blackwood, David, illus. 2004. 128p. (J). 16.95 (978-0-88899-561-2(X)) Groundwood Bks. CAN. *Dist:* Perseus Distribution.

Make a Joyful Sound. 2003. (J). 13.95 (978-0-590-28205-5(0)) Scholastic, Inc.

Malenfant, Paul Chanel. Si Tu Allais Quelque Part. 2003. (New Poetry Ser.). (FRE.). 36p. (J). (gr. 7). pap. (978-2-89021-622-8(5)) Diffusion du livre Mirabel.

Manley, Molly. On a Vineyard Veranda. Marshall, Janet, illus. 2007. (J). 12.95 (***978-1-933212-46-3(2)***) Commonwealth Editions.

Mann, Kirk. If Dogs Could Talk & Other Animal Poems. Lanz, Lucille, ed. Mann, Kirk, illus. 1998. (Illus.). 128p. (J). (gr. 2-4). pap. 12.95 (978-1-892517-00-5(0)) Flying Snail Pr.

—Playful Poems That Build Reading Skills. 2000. 96p. (J). pap. 12.95 (978-0-439-11370-0(9)) Scholastic, Inc.

Manna, Giovanni, illus. First Morning: Poems about Time. 2001. 40p. (J). (gr. 1-5). 16.99 (978-1-84148-337-5(0)) Barefoot Bks., Inc.

Mannis, Celeste Davidson. One Leaf Rides the Wind: Counting in a Japanese Garden. Hartung, Susan Kathleen, illus. 2005. 32p. (J). (ps-ps). lib. bdg. 12.79 (978-0-606-33113-5(1)) Tandem Library Bks.

Marcamo, Thais. Vivencias & Despertar. Vilma Muises, ed. 2004. Tr. of Spanish. (SPA., Illus.). 96p. (YA). pap. 15.00 (978-1-931481-34-2(2)) LiArt-Literature & Art.

Marjorie, as told by. A Flower Unfolds: Inspirational Teachings in Verse from Kwan Yin, Bodhisattva of Mercy & Compassion. l.t. ed. 2003. (Illus.). 52p. 12.95 (978-0-9745712-0-1(2)) Sun Sprite Publishing.

Mark, Jan. A Jetblack Sunrise: Poems about War & Conflict. Yates, John, illus. 2005. (J). (ps-7). mass mkt. (978-0-340-89379-1(6) , Hodder Children's Books) Hodder Children's Division.

—A Jetblack Sunrise: Poems about War & Conflict. 2005. (Illus.). (J). 16.99 (978-0-7502-4293-6(0) , Hodder & Stoughton) Hodder General Publishing Division GBR. *Dist:* Trafalgar Square Publishing.

Marrero, Rafelito. Amar sin decir Nada. 1000th l.t. ed. 2003. 137p. per. 14.95 net. (978-0-9747569-0-5(3)) Marrero, Rafael.

Marston, J. D., photos by. The Poems for Pequenines (Poemas Para Pequenines) 2004. (Baby Einstein Ser.). (SPA., Illus.). 12p. (J). bds. 7.95 (978-970-718-159-5(1) , Silver Dolphin en Español) Advanced Marketing, S. de R. L. de C. V. MEX. *Dist:* Perseus Distribution.

Mary Had a Little Lamb. 2004. 24.95 incl. audio (978-0-7882-0582-8(X)); pap. 14.95 incl. audio (978-0-7882-0650-4(8)) Weston Woods Studios, Inc.

Marzollo, Jean. Home Sweet Home. 1998. (Illus.). 32p. (J). (ps-3). pap. 5.95 (978-0-06-443501-7(6)) HarperCollins Pubs.

—Home Sweet Home. 1998. (978-0-606-13483-5(2)) Tandem Library Bks.

Marzollo, Jean & MacDonald, Suse. I Love You: A Rebus Poem. MacDonald, Suse, illus. 2000. (Illus.). 40p. (J). (ps-1). pap. 7.95 (978-0-590-37656-3(X) , Cartwheel Bks.) Scholastic, Inc.

Mattingly, Virginia & Dann, Penny. The Classic Treasury of Best-Loved Children's Poems. gif. ed. 2004. (Illus.). 56p. (J). 9.98 (978-0-7624-2028-5(6) , Courage Bks.) Running Pr. Bk. Pubs.

Maxey, Ann. Country Style Oklahoma. 2005. (Illus.). 71p. (YA). per. 15.95 (978-0-9771939-1-2(8) , 0001) New World Publishing.

Mayhew, James, illus. Classic Poems to Read Aloud. 2003. (Classic Collections). 256p. (J). (gr. 3-5). pap. 8.95 (978-0-7534-5688-0(5) , Kingfisher) Houghton Mifflin Co. Trade & Reference Div.

Maynard, John, ed. Poetry for Young People: Alfred, Lord Tennyson. Garns, Allen, illus. 2003. (Poetry for Young People Ser.). 48p. (J). 14.95 (978-0-8069-6612-0(2)) Sterling Publishing Co., Inc.

Mbabuike, Michael C. Remembering the Baobab. Hollingsworth, A. C. & Mbabuike, Onyebuchi Jeffrey, illus. 2000. 80p. (YA). (gr. 3 up). 15.50 (978-0-9678460-5-7(6)) Timbuktu Pubs.

McClarrin Vaupel, Lynn. The Queen of Hearts. 2007. 9.00 (***978-0-8059-8378-4(3)***) Dorrance Publishing Co., Inc.

McClellan, Cheryl. Bunny Flu Flu Gets Well. 2004. (J). per. 7.99 (978-0-9719241-9-2(8)) Chosen Word Publishing.

McDevitt, Brian. Ode to General George Washington. 2003. 20p. (YA). 6.00 (978-1-888032-14-7(6)) Library Sales of N.J.

McDougall, Jill & Taylor, Jenny J. Anna the Goanna & Other Poems. 2000. (Illus.). 48p. (J). 26.95 (978-0-85575-344-3(7)) Aboriginal Studies Pr. AUS. *Dist:* International Specialized Bk. Services.

Mcgough, Roger. Wicked Poems. 2004. (Illus.). 208p. (gr. 4-8). pap. 15.00 (978-0-7475-6195-8(8)) Bloomsbury Publishing Plc GBR. *Dist:* Independent Pubs. Group.

McKeown, Theresa. The ABCs of Being Me. 2007. (J). 17.00 (***978-0-8059-7235-1(8)***) Dorrance Publishing Co., Inc.

McLeod, Eleanor. Poems for Children to Enjoy - & Teachers Too. 2005. 100p. (J). per. 10.99 (978-1-905363-49-0(4) , Exposure Publishing) Meadow Bks. GBR. *Dist:* Ingram Bk. Co.

Me, Myself, & I! Take-Home Book. 2005. (Lee Bennett Hopkins Worlds of Poetry Classroom Library). (YA). (gr. k-3). 13.50 (978-0-8215-0565-6(3)) Sadlier, William H. Inc.

Meadowbrook Press Staff & Carpenter, Stephen. My Teacher's in Detention: More Kids' Favorite Funny School Poems. 2006. (Illus.). 80p. (J). pap. 8.95 (978-0-689-05245-3(6)) Meadowbrook Pr.

Medearis, Angela Shelf. Skin Deep: And other Teenage Reflections. 2005. (Illus.). 48p. pap. 10.00 (978-0-916727-22-2(X)) Wings Pr.

Medina, Jane. The Dream on Blanca's Wall: Poems in English & Spanish. Casilla, Robert, illus. 2004. 48p. (YA). (gr. 2-4). 16.95 (978-1-56397-740-4(0)) Boyds Mills Pr.

Medina, Tony. Deshawn Days. Christie, Gregory R., illus. 2001. 32p. (J). (gr. 1 up). 16.95 (978-1-58430-022-9(1)) Lee & Low Bks., Inc.

Meilner, Shauna L. It Will Come Back to You. 2004. (ENG., Illus.). 40p. (J). per. (978-1-4141-0273-3(9)) Pleasant Word.

Melmed, Laura Krauss. This First Thanksgiving Day: A Counting Story. 2003. (gr. k-3). lib. bdg. 14.15 (978-0-613-68468-2(0)) Tandem Library Bks.

Memoirs on Love & Life: A Poetic Expression, 4. 2003. (YA). per. 13.00 (978-0-9742010-0-9(6)) KNK Bks.

Mendel, Kathleen Lee. Greeting the Moon. 2000. 27p. (YA). spiral bd. 11.00 incl. trans. (978-1-878142-62-7(3)) Telstar.

Merrell, Billy. Talking in the Dark. 2003. 144p. (J). pap. 7.99 (978-0-439-49036-8(7) , Scholastic Paperbacks) Scholastic, Inc.

—Talking in the Dark. 2003. (gr. 7-12). lib. bdg. 15.30 (978-0-613-72010-6(5)) Tandem Library Bks.

Merrell, Patrick, illus. Maze Halloween. 2002. 32p. (J). (978-0-439-42972-6(2)) Scholastic, Inc.

Mesmer, Edric S. The Best Poems Ever: A Collection of Poetry's Greatest Voices. 2002. (Scholastic Classics Ser.). (Illus.). 80p. (J). (gr. 4-7). pap. 3.99 (978-0-439-29674-8(9)) Scholastic, Inc.

Mesmer, Edric S., ed. The Best Poems Ever: A Collection of Poetry's Greatest Voices. 2001. 74p. (J). pap. (978-0-439-32901-9(9)) Scholastic, Inc.

Michelson, Richard. A Book of Flies: Real or Otherwise. Baskin, Leonard, illus. 1999. (Accelerated Reader Bks.). 56p. (J). (ps up). 18.95 (978-0-7614-5050-4(5) , Cavendish Children's Bks.) Cavendish, Marshall Corp.

Micklos, John. Daddy Poems. 2003. (Illus.). 32p. (YA). (gr. 2-4). pap. 8.95 (978-1-56397-870-8(9)) Boyds Mills Pr.

Middleton, Peter. Aftermath. 2003. (Modern Poets Ser.). 188p. pap. (978-1-876857-63-9(3)) Salt Publishing.

Mike. Lemon Drop Rain: Poems & Drawings by Mr. Mike. Mike, illus. l.t. ed. 2003. (Illus.). 180p. (J). pap. 14.95 (978-0-9658365-6-2(8)) Beetle Bug Bks.

Milam, Mary Kay. The Waiting Place. Milam, Angila Hilt, illus. 2000. 32p. (J). pap. 8.95 (978-1-58597-027-8(1)) Leathers Publishing.

Miller, Ann. Proverbs, Prayers, Poems for Children & Teens. 2005. (J). lib. bdg. 14.95 (978-0-9748165-1-7(5)) Jaylil Publishing Co.

Miller, Megan. Balance Gained Through Poetry. 2002. 200p. (YA). pap. 13.95 (978-0-595-26023-2(3) , Writers Club Pr.) iUniverse, Inc.

Millman, Selena. Ever Notice. 2006. (Illus.). (J). 11.18 (***978-1-4243-2354-8(1)***) Independent Publisher Services.

Mills, Lois. Saddles & Sails. 2005. reprint ed. pap. 15.95 (978-1-4191-0458-9(6)) Kessinger Publishing, LLC.

Milne, A. A. When We Were Very Young Deluxe Edition. 2008. 128p. (J). (gr. 4). 19.99 (***978-0-525-47930-7(9)*** , Tarcher) Penguin Group (USA) Inc.

Milnes, Gerald. Granny Will Your Dog Bite? And Other Mountain Rhymes. Root, Kimberly B., illus. 1999. 60p. (ps-3). reprint ed. pap. 9.95 (978-0-87483-560-1(7)) August Hse. Pubs., Inc.

Minter, Peter. Blue Grass. 2006. (ENG.). 128p. per. (***978-1-84471-246-5(X)***) Salt Publishing.

Miracles Can Happen. 2003. 96p. (YA). per. (978-1-930362-07-9(2)) Foston Adolescent Workshop, Inc.

Mistral, Gabriela. Poesia Infantil. (Coleccion Poemas Juvenil). (SPA.). (J). (gr. 2-4). pap. 9.50 (978-956-13-1083-4(X) , AB0120) Bello, Andres CHL. *Dist:* AIMS International Bks., Inc., Continental Bk. Co., Inc., Lectorum Pubns., Inc.

Mitchell, Christine. Welcome Home, Forever Child: a Celebration of Children Adopted As. 2006. (ENG., Illus.). 32p. per. 13.95 (***978-1-4259-6304-0(8)***) AuthorHouse.

Mitchell, Gail A. Learning English the Cultural Way. Mitchell, Gail A., photos by. 2004. (Illus.). 40p. per. 20.00 (978-0-9653308-9-3(3)) Africana Homestead Legacy Pubs.

Mitchell, Stephen. The Wishing Bone, & Other Poems. Pohrt, Tom, illus. 2003. 56p. (J). (gr. 3-7). 16.99 (978-0-7636-1118-7(2)) Candlewick Pr.

Mitton, Tony. Poems about Being Angry: I Want to Shout & Stamp About. Gordon, Mike, illus. 2006. (Poemotions Ser.). (J). pap. 9.99 (978-0-340-91117-4(4) , Hodder & Stoughton) Hodder General Publishing Division GBR. *Dist:* Trafalgar Square Publishing.

Montale, Eugenio. Selected Poems. Galassi, Jonathan & Wright, Charles, trs. from ITA. 2004. (Field Translation Ser.: 26). 142p. pap. 19.95 (978-0-932440-98-3(3)) Oberlin College Pr.

Montgomery, L. M. The Way to Slumbertown. Bédard, Rachel, illus. 2005. 24p. (J). (ps-2). 14.95 (978-1-894222-98-3(9)) Lobster Pr. CAN. *Dist:* Univ. of Toronto Pr.

Moore, Clement C. Night Before Christmas. Spirin, Gennady, illus. rev. ltd. ed. 2006. 24p. 125.00 (978-0-7614-5315-4(6)) Cavendish, Marshall Corp.

—The Night Before Christmas Gift Box. Engelbreit, Mary, illus. 2007. 40p. (J). (ps-3). 25.00 (***978-0-06-136495-2(9)*** , Harper Festival) HarperCollins Pubs.

—Night Before Christmas Read Along. 2006. (J). 9.95 (978-0-439-89557-6(X)) Scholastic, Inc.

Moore, Clement C. A Scratch & Sniff Night Before Christmas. Swanson, Maggie, illus. 2007. 24p. (J). (ps-2). 9.95 (***978-1-4027-4215-6(0)***) Sterling Publishing Co., Inc.

Moore, Clement Clarke. Night Before Christmas -library. 2006. (J). 18.95 (978-0-439-89843-0(9)) Scholastic, Inc.

Moore, Lilian. Beware, Take Care. Fine, Howard, illus. rev. ed. 2006. 32p. (J). 16.95 (978-0-8050-6917-4(8) , Holt, Henry & Co. Bks. For Young Readers) Holt, Henry & Co.

Mora, Pat. Confeti: Poemas para Ninos. Sanchez, Enrique O., illus. 2006. (SPA.). (J). pap. 7.95 (978-1-58430-270-4(4)) Lee & Low Bks., Inc.

—Confetti: Poems for Children. Sanchez, Enrique O., illus. 1999. 32p. (J). (gr. 2 up). pap. 6.95 (978-1-880000-85-4(7)); (YA). (ps up). 15.95 (978-1-880000-25-0(3)) Lee & Low Bks., Inc.

—Listen to the Desert. 2001. Tr. of Oye Al Desierto. (J). (978-0-606-21298-4(1)) Tandem Library Bks.

—My Own True Name: New & Selected Poems for Young Adults, 1984-1999. 2000. (Illus.). 96p. (YA). (gr. 9 up). pap. 11.95 (978-1-55885-292-1(1) , Piñata Books) Arte Publico Pr.

—My Own True Name: New & Selected Poems for Young Adults, 1984-1999. 2000. (gr. 7-12). lib. bdg. 21.05 (978-0-613-27990-1(5)) Tandem Library Bks.

Mora, Pat, ed. Love to Mama: A Tribute to Mothers. Barragan, Paula S., illus. 2001. 32p. (J). (gr. k up). 16.95 (978-1-58430-019-9(1)) Lee & Low Bks., Inc.

Mordhorst, Heidi. Squeeze: Poems from a Juicy Universe. Torrey, Jesse, photos by. 2005. (Illus.). 32p. (J). (gr. 3-7). 16.95 (978-1-59078-292-7(5)) Boyds Mills Pr.

More, Francisco J., Sr. Carousel de Fantasias, 1. 2000th l.t. ed. 2003. (SPA., Illus.). 26p. (J). lib. bdg. 4.95 (978-0-9747851-0-3(5)) More, Francisco J.

Moreillon, Judi. Vamos a Leer. Teis, Kyra, illus. 2005. (SPA.). 40p. (J). bds. 6.95 (978-1-59572-015-3(4)) Star Bright Bks., Inc.

—Vamos a Leer (Read to Me) Teis, Kyra, illus. 2003. (SPA.). 24p. (J). 6.95 (978-1-932065-50-3(4)) Star Bright Bks., Inc.

Morenz, Justin, creator. Cardlings. 2004. (Illus.). 30p. (YA). 10.95 (978-0-9760108-0-7(1)) Cardlings.

Morgan, Gaby. The Word Party: A World Book Day Poetry Book. Eccles, Jane, illus. 63p. (J). pap. 5.99 (978-0-330-38996-9(3) , Pan) Pan Macmillan GBR. *Dist:* Trafalgar Square Publishing.

Morgenstern, Constance, contrib. by. Waking Day: A poem by Constance Morgenstern with fine art by Monet & Friends. 2006. (Picture Book Ser.). (Illus.). 32p. (J). 17.95 (978-1-55971-919-3(2) , Two Can Publishing) T&N Children's Publishing.

Mornard, Germaine & Farish, Catherine. La Fille Orange. 2003. (New Poetry Ser.). (FRE., Illus.). 36p. (J). (gr. 7). pap. (978-2-89021-623-5(3)) Diffusion du livre Mirabel.

Morris, Jackie. Barefoot Book of Classic Poems. 2006. (Illus.). 128p. (YA). (gr. 3 up). 19.99 (978-1-905236-56-5(5)) Barefoot Bks., Inc.

Morris, Willie. Prayer for the Opening of the Little League Season. 1999. (gr. k-3). lib. bdg. 13.00 (978-0-613-81698-4(6)) Tandem Library Bks.

Morrison, Lillian. Guess Again! Riddle Poems. Hale, Christy, illus. 2006. 48p. (J). 16.95 (978-0-87483-730-8(8)) August Hse. Pubs., Inc.

—Way to Go! Sports Poems. Spellman, Susan, illus. 2003. 48p. (J). (gr. 6-9). 16.95 (978-1-56397-961-3(6)) Boyds Mills Pr.

Mortensen, Lyn. My Favorite Flower Is the Daisy... & other Silly Poems. Mortensen, Lyn, illus. 2005. (Illus.). 48p. (J). per. (978-0-9767570-0-9(1)) Whitegate Bks.

Morton, Jim. Let's Make Memories ... 2004. 100p. per. 9.00 net. (978-0-9763253-0-7(6) , 004) Windchimes Publishing.

Moses, Brian. The Secret Lives of Teachers. Maddison, Lucy, illus. 64p. (J). pap. 8.99 (978-0-330-34265-0(7) , Pan) Pan Macmillan GBR. *Dist:* Trafalgar Square Publishing.

Moses, Brian, contrib. by. Minibeasts. 2003. (Illus.). 65p. (J). pap. 6.99 (978-0-330-37057-8(X) , Pan) Pan Macmillan GBR. *Dist:* Trafalgar Square Publishing.

Moses, Brian & Gordon, Mike. Poems about Being Scared: Is There Anything There at the Top of the Stair? 2006. (Illus.). (J). pap. 9.99 (978-0-340-91118-1(2) , Hodder & Stoughton) Hodder General Publishing Division GBR. *Dist:* Trafalgar Square Publishing.

Moses, Will. Mother Goose. Moses, Will, illus. 2003. (Illus.). 64p. (J). (ps-1). 17.99 (978-0-399-23744-7(5) , Philomel) Penguin Group (USA) Inc.

Moss, Renea L. In Your Face. rev. l.t. ed. 2000. 84p. (YA). per. 12.99 (978-0-9678805-0-1(5) , Attitude Publishing) Moss, Renea L.

MotorVation. 2002. (Illus.). (YA). per. 8.99 (978-0-9660215-4-7(1)) Teal, Joyce Willard.

Moxley, Sheila, illus. All the Colours of the Earth: A Multi-Cultural Treasury. 2004. 48p. (J). (978-1-84507-014-4(3)) Lincoln, Frances Ltd.

Moyer, Bernedette A., creator. Caesar Salad & I Like It! A Copulation of Poetry for Children & by Children. 1999. (Illus.). 80p. (J). (gr. 1-12). pap. 11.95 (978-0-9666183-3-4(5)) Two Bee-A-TwinBee Publishing, LLC.

Mudra, Michele K. What If Camels Wore Lipstick? Mudra, Michele K., illus. 1998. (Illus.). 64p. (J). (ps-3). pap. 6.95 (978-1-888676-06-8(X)) Ardara Hse., Pubs.

Multicultural Poetry Theme Pack, 4 vols. 2001. (Illus.). (J). (gr. 8-9). 31.95 (978-1-56762-147-1(3)) Modern Learning Pr.

Muše, Daphne. The Entrance Place of Wonders: Poems of the Harlem Renaissance. Riley-Webb, Charlotte, illus. 2005. 32p. (J). (ps-17). 16.95 (978-0-8109-5997-2(6)) Abrams, Harry N. , Inc.

Mutuku, Mueni E. Solitude & the Soul. 2002. 80p. (YA). pap. 16.95 (978-1-58597-138-1(3)) Leathers Publishing.

My Voice Matters. 2004. (J). 5.00 (978-0-9664455-6-5(2)) Rhode Island State Council, International Reading Assn.

Myers, Walter & Myers, Christopher, illus. Tribute. 2008. 32p. (J). 16.99 (***978-0-06-052308-4(5)***) HarperCollins Pubs.

Myers, Walter Dean. Angel to Angel: A Mother's Gift of Love. 1998. (Illus.). 40p. (J). (ps-3). 15.95 (978-0-06-027721-5(1)); 15.89 (978-0-06-027722-2(X)) HarperCollins Pubs.

—Angel to Angel: A Mother's Gift of Love. 2000. (Illus.). (J). (ps-3). (978-0-606-18673-5(5)) Tandem Library Bks.

—Blues Journey. Myers, Christopher, illus. 48p. (YA). pap. 8.95 (***978-0-8234-2079-7(5)***) Holiday Hse., Inc.

—Blues Journey. 2003. (Illus.). 44p. (J). (ps-3). 28.95 incl. audio compact disk (978-1-59519-433-6(9)) Live Oak Media.

Myers, Walter Dean & Myers, Christopher. Blues Journey. 2005. (J). 25.95 incl. audio (978-1-59519-429-9(0)) Live Oak Media.

Myrddin ap Dafydd. Briwsion Yn y Clustiau: Cyfrol o Farddoniaeth I Blant. 2005. (WEL., Illus.). 73p. (978-0-86381-300-9(3)) Gwasg Carreg Gwalch.

—Mul Bach Ar Gefn Ei Geffyl: Cerddi Am Greaduriaid. 2005. (WEL., Illus.). 73p. (978-0-86381-314-6(3)) Gwasg Carreg Gwalch.

Myrddin ap Dafydd & Morris, Sion. Armadilo Ar Fy Mhen. 2005. (WEL., Illus.). 64p. (978-0-86381-625-3(8)) Gwasg Carreg Gwalch.

—Chwarae Plant. 2005. (WEL., Illus.). 68p. (978-0-86381-431-0(X)) Gwasg Carreg Gwalch.

—Sach Gysgu Yn Llawn o Greision. 2005. (WEL., Illus.). 80p. (978-0-86381-626-0(6)) Gwasg Carreg Gwalch.

—Tabledi-Gwneud-'chi-Wenu: Dos Arbennig o Farddoniaeth Loerig Am Salwch Ac Afiechydon. 2005. (WEL., Illus.). 72p. (978-0-86381-678-9(9)) Gwasg Carreg Gwalch.

Myrddin ap Dafydd, et al. Caneuon y Coridorau: Barddoniaeth Ar Gyfer Pobl Ifanc. 2005. (WEL., Illus.). 83p. (978-0-86381-970-4(2)) Gwasg Carreg Gwalch.

Nathan, Jeff. Calling All Animals: The First Book of PunOETRY. Ball, Liz, illus. 2003. 92p. (J). per. 9.95 (978-0-9702730-1-7(0)) Chucklebks. Publishing.

—There's a Bear in My Shoe. Ball, Liz, illus. 2005. (J). pap. 9.95 (978-0-9702730-2-4(9)) Chucklebks. Publishing.

National Museum of American Art Staff. Celebrate America in Poetry & Art. 1999. (J). 19.54 (978-0-606-16668-3(8)) Tandem Library Bks.

Nesbitt, Ken. When the Teacher Isn't Looking: And Other Funny School Poems. 2005. (Illus.). 80p. (J). (ps-7). pap. 8.95 (978-0-684-03128-6(0)) Meadowbrook Pr.

Nesbitt, Kenn. Revenge of the Lunch Ladies: The Hilarious Book of School Poetry. Gordon, Mike & Gordon, Carl, illus. 2007. 80p. (***978-0-88166-527-7(4)***) Meadowbrook Pr.

Nesbitt, Kenn. When the Teacher Isn't Looking: And Other Funny School Poems. Gordon, Mike, illus. 2005. 80p. (J). (978-0-88166-489-8(8)) Meadowbrook Pr.

New, W. H. Dream Helmet. Bevis, Vivian, illus. 2005. 32p. (J). pap. 11.95 (978-1-55380-021-7(4)) Ronsdale Pr. CAN. *Dist:* Literary Pr. Group of Canada.

—Llamas in the Laundry. Bevis, Vivian, illus. 2005. 32p. (J). 12.95 (978-0-921870-97-5(3)) Ronsdale Pr. CAN. *Dist:* Literary Pr. Group of Canada.

Newbold, Dale L. Funny Facts & Fun Facts! 2006. 20.00 (978-0-8059-9019-5(4)) Dorrance Publishing Co., Inc.

Newell, Peter. The Slant Book. 2007. (Illus.). 52p. per. (***978-1-4065-3053-7(0)***) Dodo Pr.

Newsome, Effie Lee. Wonders: The Best Children's Poems of Effie Lee Newsome. Bishop, R. S., ed. Jones, Lois Mailou, illus. 2003. 40p. (J). (gr. 2-4). pap. 8.95 (978-1-56397-825-8(3)) Boyds Mills Pr.

—Wonders: The Best Children's Poems of Effie Lee Newsome. Jones, Lois Mailou, illus. 2003. 40p. (J). (gr. 2-4). 14.95 (978-1-56397-786-2(5)) Boyds Mills Pr.

Nichol, Barbara. Biscuits in the Cupboard. Béha, Philippe, illus. 32p. 1999. 6.95 (978-0-7737-5936-7(0)); 1998. (J). 12.95 (978-0-7737-3025-0(7)) Stoddart Kids CAN. *Dist:* Fitzhenry & Whiteside, Ltd.

Nicholls, Judith, ed. The Sun in Me: Poems about the Planet. Krommes, Beth, illus. 2003. 40p. (J). pap. 16.99 (978-1-84148-058-9(4)) Barefoot Bks., Inc.

Nicolson, Paula. The Love Book Healing Poems for Broken Hearts. (Illus.). 40p. (J). 9.95 (978-1-880976-18-0(8)) Brookshire Pubns., Inc.

Nikola-Lisa, W. La Alegria de Ser Tu y Yo. Bryant, Michael, illus. 1999. (SPA.). (J). pap. 18.95 incl. audio compact disk (978-1-59519-124-3(0)) Live Oak Media.

—How We Are Smart. 2006. (Illus.). 32p. (YA) 16.95 (978-1-58430-254-4(2)) Lee & Low Bks., Inc.

Niño, Jairo Aníbal. El Jardin de las Ilusiones. 2003. (SPA.). 84p. (978-958-30-0701-9(3) , PV12806) Panamericana Editorial COL. *Dist:* Lectorum Pubns., Inc.

—Paloma Mensajera. 2003. (SPA.). 68p. (978-958-30-0809-2(5) , PV31143) Centro de Informacion y Desarrollo de la Comunicacion y la Literatura MEX. *Dist:* Lectorum Pubns., Inc.

—Los Papeles de Miguela. 2003. (SPA.). 80p. (978-958-30-0336-3(0) , PV30462) Centro de Informacion y Desarrollo de la Comunicacion y la Literatura MEX. *Dist:* Lectorum Pubns., Inc.

—Preguntario. 2003. (SPA.). 188p. (978-958-30-0497-1(9) , PV30461) Centro de Informacion y Desarrollo de la Comunicacion y la Literatura MEX. *Dist:* Lectorum Pubns., Inc.

Noda, Takayo. Dear World. 2005. (Illus.). 32p. (J). (gr. k-3). reprint ed. pap. 6.99 (978-0-14-240280-1(X) , Puffin) Penguin Group (USA) Inc.

Nursery Rhymes. 2000. (Learning Fun for Little Ones Ser.). (Illus.). 64p. (ps-1). pap. 8.99 (978-0-88724-572-5(2) , CD-6403) Carson-Dellosa Publishing Co., Inc.

Nursery Rhymes. 2001. (Early Learning Ser.). (J). (gr. k-12). vinyl bd. 4.95 (978-1-58845-053-1(8)) School Specialty Publishing.

Nuttall, Neil & Hawkins, Andy, eds. Words on the Wind. Fell, Jenny, illus. 2004. 64p. pap. 14.95 (978-1-84323-046-5(1)) Beekman Bks., Inc.

Nye, Naomi Shihab. Flag of Childhood: Poems from the Middle East. 2002. (gr. 3-6). lib. bdg. 11.80 (978-0-613-45041-6(8)) Tandem Library Bks.

—Honeybee. 2008. 176p. (J). 16.99 (***978-0-06-085390-7(5)***); lib. bdg. 17.89 (***978-0-06-085391-4(3)***) HarperCollins Pubs. (Greenwillow Bks.).

P Q R

—Salting the Ocean: 100 Poems by Young Poets. Bryan, Ashley, illus. 2000. 128p. (J). (gr. 3 up). 17.99 (978-0-688-16193-4(6)) HarperCollins Pubs.

—The Tree Is Older Than You Are: A Bilingual Gathering of Poems & Stories from Mexico with Paintings by Mexican Artists. 1998. (ENG & SPA.). (J). (978-0-606-13867-3(6)) Tandem Library Bks.

—What Have You Lost? 2001. (gr. 7-12). lib. bdg. 18.75 (978-0-613-36027-2(3)); (Illus.). (J). (978-0-606-21517-6(4)) Tandem Library Bks.

—19 Varieties of Gazelle: Poems of the Middle East. 2002. (Illus.). 160p. (J). (gr. 6 up). 16.99 (978-0-06-009765-3(5)) HarperCollins Pubs.

Nye, Naomi Shihab & Mansour, Suleiman. The Flag of Childhood: Poems from the Middle East. 2002. Orig. Title: The Space Between Our Footsteps. 112p. (J). (gr. 3-7). pap. 5.99 (978-0-689-85172-8(3) , Aladdin) Simon & Schuster Children's Publishing.

Ode, Eric. Tall Tales of the Wild West: A Humorous Collection of Cowboy Poems & Songs. Crane, Ben, illus. 2007. 32p. (*978-0-88166-524-6(X)) Meadowbrook Pr.

Of Love Expressed. 2005. per. 8.50 (978-0-9770594-2-3(1)) Grimes, Richard.

Olaleye, Isaac. Distant Talking Drum: Poems from Nigeria. 2001. (gr. k-3). lib. bdg. 17.60 (978-0-613-78918-9(0)) Tandem Library Bks.

—The Distant Talking Drum: Poems from Nigeria. 2003. (Illus.). 32p. (J). (gr. 2-4). pap. 9.95 (978-1-56397-941-5(1)) Boyds Mills Pr.

The Open Door. 2004. per. (978-0-9747704-0-6(X)) Writers in the Schools (WITS).

Opie, Ian, ed. My Very First Mother Goose. Wells, Rosemary, illus. 2004. 107p. (J). reprint ed. 17.00 (978-0-7567-8384-6(4)) DIANE Publishing Co.

Opie, Iona. I Saw Esau: A Schoolchild's Pocket Book. 2000. (gr. 3-6). lib. bdg. 18.80 (978-0-613-32075-7(1)) Tandem Library Bks.

Ortiz, Michelle. You are a Child of God. 2006. (ENG.). 40p. (J). per. 17.99 (978-1-4141-0604-5(1)) Pleasant Word.

Osundare, Niyi. Early Birds: Poems for Junior Secondary Schools. 2004. (Illus.). 100p. pap. 12.95 (978-978-029-530-1(5)) Spectrum Bks., Ltd. NGA. *Dist:* Michigan State Univ. Pr.

Pace, Yolantha. Wing-Plucked Butterfly: A Survivor Speaks: One Woman's War on Hate Crimes Against Women & Children. 2004. 146p. (YA). per. 15.00 (978-0-9747017-8-3(5)) Neshee Pubn.

Padgett, Ron. Scribners Poets for Students, 3 vols. 2000. (Scribner Writers Ser.). (Illus.). (YA). 100.00 (978-0-684-80592-4(8)); 3rd ed. 100.00 (978-0-684-80610-5(X)) Simon & Schuster.

Padgett, Ron, ed. World Poets, 3 vols., Set. 2000. (Scribner Writers Ser.). (Illus.). 1396p. (YA). (gr. 9 up). 360.00 (978-0-684-80591-7(X) , GML00502-169492, Charles Scribner's Sons) Thomson Gale.

Page, P. K. A Brazilian Alphabet for the Younger Reader. 2005. (Illus.). 64p. (J). (ps-ps). pap. 16.95 (978-0-88984-265-6(5)) Porcupine's Quill, Inc. CAN. *Dist:* Univ. of Toronto Pr.

Paolilli, Paul. Silver Seeds: A Book of Nature Poems. 2003. (gr. k-3). lib. bdg. 15.30 (978-0-613-61657-7(X)) Tandem Library Bks.

Paolilli, Paul & Brewer, Dan. Silver Seeds: A Book of Nature Poems. Fancher, Lou & Johnson, Steve, illus. 2003. 32p. (J). (gr. k-4). pap. 6.99 (978-0-14-250010-1(0) , Puffin) Penguin Group (USA) Inc.

—Silver Seeds: A Book of Nature Poems. Johnson, Steve & Fancher, Lou, illus. 2001. 32p. (J). (gr. k-4). 15.99 (978-0-670-88941-9(5) , Viking Juvenile) Penguin Group (USA) Inc.

Park, Linda Sue. Tap Dancing on the Roof: Sijo (Poems) Banyai, Istvan, illus. 2007. 40p. (J). (gr. k-3). 16.00 (*978-0-618-23483-7(7) , Clarion Bks.) Houghton Mifflin Co. Trade & Reference Div.

Parmenter, Wayne, illus. Mother Goose Bedtime Rhymes. 2002. 40p. (J). bds. 12.98 (978-0-7853-7818-1(9) , 7176200) Publications International, Ltd.

Patten, Brian, ed. Puffin Utterly Brilliant Book of Poetry. (Illus.). 144p. (J). pap. 15.00 (978-0-14-038421-5(9)) Penguin Bks., Ltd. GBR. *Dist:* Trafalgar Square Publishing.

Paul, Julia Marian. Song of the Teapot: Poems about Little Babies, Little Jerry, Little Susie, & Other Things. 2007. (ENG.). 60p. per. 12.95 (*978-1-4241-4299-6(7)) PublishAmerica, Inc.

Paul, Korky, illus. Dinosaur Poems. 2nd rev. ed. 2004. 32p. (YA). 9.95 (978-0-19-276305-1(9)) Oxford Univ. Pr., Inc.

—Magic Poems. 2006. 32p. (YA). 9.95 (978-0-19-276304-4(0)) Oxford Univ. Pr., Inc.

—Monster Poems. 2004. 32p. (YA). 9.95 (978-0-19-276306-8(7)) Oxford Univ. Pr., Inc.

Payne Crystian, Carol. Jas & Poetic Lucy. l.t. ed. 2006. (Illus.). 21p. (J). per. 10.99 (978-1-59879-154-9(0)) Lifevest Publishing, Inc.

Paz, Octavio. La Rama. Kitora, Tetsuo, illus. 2005. Tr. of Branch. (SPA.). (J). (gr. k-2). pap. 10.95 (978-968-494-046-8(7)) Centro de Informacion y Desarrollo de la Comunicacion y la Literatura MEX. *Dist:* Iaconi, Mariuccia Bk. Imports.

Pearson, Debora. Leo's Tree. Hilb, Nora, illus. 2004. 24p. (J). (ps-1). 19.95 (978-1-55037-845-0(7)); pap. 5.95 (978-1-55037-844-3(9)) Annick Pr., Ltd. CAN. *Dist:* Firefly Bks., Ltd.

Pearson, Susan. Grimericks. Grimly, Gris, illus. 2005. 32p. (J). 15.95 (978-0-7614-5230-0(3)) Cavendish, Marshall Corp.

—Who Swallowed Harold?: And Other Poems About Pets. Slonim, David, illus. 2005. 32p. (J). 16.95 (978-0-7614-5193-8(5)) Cavendish, Marshall Corp.

Peoples, Rick. Poetry with a Porpoise. 1998. (J). (gr. 1-6). 12.95 (978-0-9668328-0-8(9)) Appenzell Pr.

Perkins, Jill E. Cherubs Chatter: A Collection of Original Songs & Poems. 2004. (Illus.). 88p. (J). per. 7.95 (978-0-9749862-2-7(4)) Theragogy.com.

Perlow, Ann. The Story of Me. Perlow, Ann & Pacheco, Gabe, eds. Pacheco, Gabe, illus. 2001. 36p. (J). (ps-6). 14.95 (978-0-9714999-0-4(X)) Gabann Enterprises.

Perry, Andrea. The Snack Smasher: And Other Reasons Why It's Not My Fault. Snow, Alan, illus. 2007. 40p. (J). 16.99 (978-0-689-85469-9(2) , Atheneum) Simon & Schuster Children's Publishing.

Perry, Andrea. The Snack Smasher & Other Reason Why It's Not My Fault. 2007. (Illus.). 33p. (J). (*978-1-4287-2351-1(X)) Simon & Schuster Children's Publishing.

Perry, Rex, illus. Over the River & Through the Woods. 2004. 24p. (J). lib. bdg. 8.00 (*978-1-4242-0640-7(5)) Fitzgerald Bks.

Perry, Robert. The Ferryboat Ride. Guzek, Greta, illus. unabr. ed. 32p. (J). (978-0-88971-155-6(0)) Harbour Publishing Co., Ltd.

Peters, Andrew & Peters, Polly. Crash. 2004. 112p. (J). (978-0-340-88468-3(1) , Hodder Children's Books) Hodder Children's Division.

—Love, Hate & My Best Mate: Poems about Love & Relationships. 2004. (Illus.). 128p. (J). (978-0-7502-4420-6(8) , Hodder Wayland) Hodder Children's Division.

—Poems with Attitude. 2003. 96p. pap. (978-0-7502-4189-2(6) , Hodder Wayland) Hodder Children's Division.

Peters, Andrew Fusek & Peters, Polly. Poetry Anthol Elemental Earth. 2006. 32p. (J). 19.95 (*978-0-237-52780-8(4) , Evans Brothers, Limited) Evans Publishing Group GBR. *Dist:* Independent Pubs. Group.

—Poetry Anthol Elemental Water. 2006. 32p. (J). 19.95 (*978-0-237-52779-2(0) , Evans Brothers, Limited) Evans Publishing Group GBR. *Dist:* Independent Pubs. Group.

Peters, Andrew Fusek & Peters, Polly, compiled by. Poetry Anthol Elemental Earth. 2007. (Elements in Poetry Ser.). (Illus.). 32p. (J). 18.95 (*978-0-237-52887-4(8) , Evans Brothers, Limited) Evans Publishing Group GBR. *Dist:* Independent Pubs. Group.

Peters, Lisa Westberg. Earthshake: Poems from the Ground Up. Felstead, Cathie, illus. 2003. 32p. (J). (gr. k-6). 16.99 (978-0-06-029265-2(2)) HarperCollins Pubs.

Peters, Polly & Peters, Andrew Fusek. Love Hate My Best Mate. 2005. (Illus.). 128p. (J). pap. (978-0-340-89387-6(7) , Hodder Children's Books) Hodder Children's Division.

Petway, Jessie. A Child's Book of Poetry. 2007. per. 12.00 (*978-0-9791154-5-5(0) , MSP) Main St Publishing, Inc.

Phelps, Leonard. Biblical Reflections: For Children & Young Adults. 2002. (Illus.). (YA). pap. (978-0-7951-0297-4(6)) Watermark Pr.

Philip, Neil, ed. The New Oxford Book of Children's Verse. 1998. (Oxford Books of Verse). (Illus.). 416p. reprint ed. pap. 19.95 (978-0-19-288107-6(8)) Oxford Univ. Pr., Inc.

Phinn, Gervase. What I Like! Poems for the Very Young. Eccles, Jane, illus. 2005. 32p. pap. 7.99 (978-1-904550-12-9(6)) Child's Play-International.

Pickard, Ben & Pickard, Carolyn. A Fish! Don't You Wish. 2003. 265p. 29.95 (978-0-595-65747-6(8)); pap. 19.95 (978-0-595-28229-6(6)) iUniverse, Inc.

Pickard, Deanna. In Dreams We Kiss Ourselves Good-Bye: Poems. 2003. 67p. pap. 14.00 (978-0-9729735-0-2(8) , 199-1) Luquer St. Pr.

Pied Poetry. 2001. 32p. (J). 17.95 (978-0-9711931-1-6(8)) A Child's Voice.

Pirie, Mark. Gallery: A Selection. 2003. (Modern Poets Ser.). 116p. pap. (978-1-876857-24-0(2)) Salt Publishing.

Plaza, José María. Alibaru: La Ronda de las Estaciones. (SPA.). 120p. (978-84-392-8119-1(6)) Gaviota Ediciones ESP. *Dist:* Lectorum Pubns., Inc.

—Pajaruli: Poemas para Sequir Andando. Villamuza, Noemi, illus. (SPA.). (J). (978-84-392-8120-7(X) , EV0782) Gaviota Ediciones ESP. *Dist:* Lectorum Pubns., Inc.

—Tungaira: Miss Primeras Poesias. Lucini, Carmen, illus. (SPA.). 96p. (J). 8.99 (978-84-392-8115-3(3) , EV4870) Gaviota Ediciones ESP. *Dist:* Lectorum Pubns., Inc.

Pockell, Leslie. 100 Best Poems of All Time. 2001. (gr. 7-12). lib. bdg. 21.05 (978-0-613-51060-8(7)) Tandem Library Bks.

Podwal, Mark. Jerusalem Sky: Stars, Crosses & Crescents. Podwal, Mark, illus. 2005. (Illus.). 32p. (J). (ps-7). lib. bdg. 17.99 (978-0-385-90927-3(6) , Doubleday Bks. for Young Readers) Random Hse. Children's Bks.

Poear, Allan. Raven & Other Poems. 2000. (gr. 7-12). lib. bdg. 10.65 (978-0-613-66730-2(1)) Tandem Library Bks.

Poemas y Cantares de America y el Mundo. (SPA.). (YA). (gr. 5-8). pap. (978-956-13-1606-5(4) , AB2725) Bello, Andres CHL. *Dist:* Lectorum Pubns., Inc.

Poems & Rhymes (Gr. 1-2) 2003. (J). (978-1-58232-070-0(5)) Bryan Hse. Pubs., Inc.

The Poet Speaks in Black. 2002. Vol. 1. 104p. vinyl bd. (978-0-9679446-4-7(3)) Motion Pubns.

Poetry Ala Carte. 2002. (J). per. 16.95 (978-1-883055-49-3(0)) Dandy Lion Pubns.

Poetry & Rhymes. Date not set. 256p. (J). 5.98 (978-0-7525-7690-9(9)) Parragon, Inc.

Poetry Power ESL: Complete Set. 2003. (SPA., Illus.). 225.50 (978-0-8136-0715-3(9)) Modern Curriculum Pr.

Poetry Tapes & Small Books. (Dias y Dias de Poesia Ser.). (SPA.). (ps-6). 182.43 (978-1-56334-281-3(2)) Hampton-Brown Bks.

Poetry Works! Complete Set. 2003. (SPA., Illus.). (J). (ps-k). 183.95 (978-0-8136-0719-1(1)) Modern Curriculum Pr.

Polk, James G. Gift of Love, Vol. 2. Rudkin, Shawn, ed. Rudkin, Tracy, illus. (YA). (978-0-9727753-1-1(5)) New Wave Bks. & CD.

Pollack, Dorothy B. A Medley of Myths. (Illus.). 149p. (YA). (gr. 7-12). spiral bd. 4.75 (978-0-939507-46-7(3) , B206) American Classical League, The.

Pollsar, Barry L. Insect Soup: Bug Poems. Clark, David, illus. 1999. (Rainbow Morning Music Picture Bks.). 32p. (J). (gr. 1-7). 14.95 (978-0-938663-22-5(4)) Rainbow Morning Music Alternatives.

Poole, Susie, illus. Whispering in God's Ear. 2004. 96p. (J). pap. 9.99 (978-0-7459-3672-7(5) , Lion) Lion Hudson plc GBR. *Dist:* Independent Pubs. Group.

Popper, Garry. Big World. Johnson, Andi, illus. 2004. 36p. (ps-7). 4.00 (978-1-84161-052-8(6)) Ravette Publishing, Ltd. GBR. *Dist:* Parkwest Pubns., Inc.

Pottle, Robert. I'm Allergic to School: Funny Poems & Songs about School. Gordon, Mike & Gordon, Carl, illus. 2007. 32p. (978-0-88166-522-2(3)) Meadowbrook Pr.

—Maine: A Wicked Good Book of Verse: the Way Wildlife Should Be. Hardwick, Holly, illus. 2005. 64p. (J). per. 8.95 (978-0-9709569-3-4(2)) Blue Lobster Pr.

—Moxie Day & Family: A Laugh & Learn Book of Poetry. Siruno, Jonathan, illus. 2002. (J). per. 9.95 (978-0-9709569-1-0(6) , (207) 565-4476) Blue Lobster Pr.

—Moxie Day the Prankster: Another Laugh & Learn Book of Poetry. Jonathan Siruno, illus. 2004. 64p. (J). per. 8.95 (978-0-9709569-2-7(4) , MDTP) Blue Lobster Pr.

Pottle, Robert. Poems with Moxie: Funny Poems & Funny Songs. 2008. (Illus.). 96p. (J). per. 9.95 (*978-0-9709569-4-1(0)) Blue Lobster Pr.

Potts, Cheryl. Poetry Play Any Day with Jane Yolen. 1999. (Illus.). 64p. (J). (gr. 2-5). pap. 14.95 (978-1-57950-038-2(2) , Upstart Bks.) Highsmith Inc.

Poulson, Joan. Sling a Jammy Doughnut: Poems about Food. Waldek, Kelly, illus. 2002. 32p. pap. 9.99 (978-0-7502-3260-9(9) , Hodder & Stoughton) Hodder General Publishing Division GBR. *Dist:* Trafalgar Square Publishing.

Powell, Amy. Me. 2006. (J). pap. 15.00 (*978-0-9773608-3-3(0)) Shiny Red Ball Publishing.

Powers, Lillian. Girl Child: (The Transition - in Poetic Form) 2004. 64p. (YA). per. 9.95 (978-0-9761523-2-3(0)) Mama Incense Publishing.

Prelutsky, Jack. Behold the Bold Umbrellaphant: And Other Poems. Berger, Carin, illus. 2006. 40p. (J). 16.99 (978-0-06-054317-4(5)); lib. bdg. 17.89 (978-0-06-054318-1(3)) HarperCollins Pubs.

—It's Raining Pigs & Noodles. Stevenson, James, illus. 160p. (J). 2000. (gr. k up). lib. bdg. 18.89 (978-0-06-029195-2(8)); 2000. (gr. 5 up). 17.99 (978-0-06-029194-5(X)); 2005. reprint ed. pap. 9.99 (978-0-06-076390-9(6) , Harper Trophy) HarperCollins Pubs.

—It's Snowing! It's Snowing! Winter Poems. Abolafia, Yossi, illus. 2006. (I Can Read Bks.). 48p. (J). (gr. k-3). 15.99 (978-0-06-053715-9(9)); lib. bdg. 16.89 (978-0-06-053716-6(7)) HarperCollins Pubs.

—Me I Am! Davenier, Christine, illus. 2007. 32p. (J). (ps-1). 16.00 (978-0-374-34902-8(9) , Farrar, Straus & Giroux (BYR)) Farrar, Straus & Giroux.

—My Dog May Be a Genius: Poems. Stevenson, James, illus. 2008. 160p. (J). 18.99 (*978-0-06-623862-3(5)); lib. bdg. 19.89 (*978-0-06-623863-0(3)) HarperCollins Pubs. (Greenwillow Bks.).

—My Parents Think I'm Sleeping. Abolafia, Yossi, illus. (I Can Read Bks.). 48p. (J). 2008. pap. 3.99 (*978-0-06-053722-7(1) , Harper Trophy); 2007. 15.99 (978-0-06-053720-3(5)); 2007. lib. bdg. 16.89 (978-0-06-053721-0(3)) HarperCollins Pubs.

—Scranimals. Sis, Peter, illus. 48p. (J). (gr. k-3). 2002. 17.99 (978-0-688-17819-2(7)); 2002. lib. bdg. 18.89 (978-0-688-17820-8(0)); 2006. reprint ed. pap. 6.99 (978-0-06-075368-9(4) , Harper Trophy) HarperCollins Pubs.

—Tyrannosaurus Was a Beast: Dinosaur Poems. unabr. ed. 1999. (Follow the Reader Ser.). (J). (gr. 1-3). pap. 17.00 incl. audio (978-0-8072-0226-5(6) , EFTR169SP, Listening Library) Random Hse. Audio Publishing Group.

—What a Day It Was at School! Cushman, Doug, illus. 2006. 40p. (J). lib. bdg. 17.89 (978-0-06-082336-8(4)) HarperCollins Pubs.

Pre'Smith, Judith Grand. Don't Fight, Forgive. Johnson, Mildred D., ed. Purnell, Cheryl Martin & Carter, Steve, Jr., illus. 2002. (J). (gr. k-8). pap. 14.95 (978-0-9711291-0-8(X)) Positive Purpose Pr.

Prévert, Jacques. How to Paint the Portrait of a Bird. Gerstein, Mordicai, illus. 2007. 40p. (J). 16.95 (*978-1-59643-215-4(2)) Roaring Brook Pr.

Price, Erika. The Turnaround: Book of Poetry, , 2004. (YA). per. 7.00 (978-0-9753028-0-4(9)) Turnaround Bk. Publishing Corp.

Price, Erika, contrib. by. The Turnaround: Book of Poetry. 2004. (YA). per. 7.00 (978-0-9753028-1-1(7)); per. 7.00 (978-0-9753028-2-8(5)) Turnaround Bk. Publishing Corp.

Prince, Sarah. Pet for Me. 1999. (ps-2). lib. bdg. 11.80 (978-0-613-19416-7(0)) Tandem Library Bks.

Pritchard, Brenda-Joy. Children's Poems of the Living ECK Master's Stories. Klemp, Joan et al, eds. 2001. (Illus.). 18p. (J). 18.00 (978-1-57043-174-6(4) , 017659) Eckankar.

Proquest Information & Learnin, prod. English Poetry Plus. (YA). cd-rom 349.95 (978-0-7365-0237-5(8)) Films Media Group.

Pujari, M. Nathalie. 20 Umbrellas. Sananmuang, Chatree, illus. 2007. (J). (*978-0-9715865-0-5(0)) Abuzz Bks.

Quattlebaum, Mary. Family Reunion. Shine, Andrea, illus. 2004. 32p. 16.00 (978-0-8028-5237-3(8)) Eerdmans, William B. Publishing Co.

—Winter Friends. Nakata, Hiroe, illus. 2005. 32p. (J). (gr. k-k). 15.95 (978-0-385-74626-7(1)); lib. bdg. 17.99 (978-0-385-90868-9(7)) Random Hse. Children's Bks. (Doubleday Bks. for Young Readers).

Quintero, Aramis. Todo el Cielo un Juguete Poemas para Ninos. 2003. (J). (978-956-240-374-0(2)) Arrayan Editores S.A.

Raccah, Dominique, et al, eds. Poetry Speaks to Children. Love, Judy et al, illus. 2005. 112p. (J). (gr. 4-7). 19.95 incl. audio compact disk (978-1-4022-0329-9(2) , Sourcebooks MediaFusion) Sourcebooks, Inc.

Radunsky, Eugenia. Yucka Drucka Droni. Radunsky, Vladimir, illus. 1998. 40p. (J). (ps-1). pap. 15.95 (978-0-590-09837-3(3)) Scholastic, Inc.

Raintree Steck-Vaughn Staff. All by Herself. 2000. 40p. (J). (ps-3). 24.26 (978-0-7398-1378-2(1)) Raintree.

—P.W. Cracker Sees the World. 1999. (Illus.). (J). pap. 35.60 (978-0-7398-0917-4(2)) Steck-Vaughn.

Ramos, Maria Cristina. Un Sol para Tu Sombrero. 2002. (SPA.). 32p. (J). pap. 8.95 (978-1-4000-0052-4(1)) Random Hse., Inc.

Raschka, Chris, illus. A Kick in the Head: An Everyday Guide to Poetic Forms. 2005. 64p. (J). (gr. 3-7). 17.99 (978-0-7636-0662-6(6)) Candlewick Pr.

Rash, Andy. The Robots Are Coming & Other Problems. Rash, Andy, illus. 2000. (Illus.). 40p. (J). (gr. 4-6). pap. 15.95 (978-0-439-06306-7(X) , Levine, Arthur A. Bks.) Scholastic, Inc.

Reflections of a Fool. 2004. (Illus.). 115p. (YA). per. 14.95 (978-1-931084-33-8(5)) Balloon Magic.

Rex, Adam. Frankenstein Makes a Sandwich. 2006. (Illus.). 40p. (J). 16.00 (978-0-15-205766-4(8)) Harcourt Trade Pubs.

Reynolds, Aaron. The Nineteenth of Maquerk: Based on Proverbs 13:4. Whitehead, Peter, illus. 2005. (Insect-Inside Ser.). 40p. (J). 9.99 (978-0-310-70954-1(7)) Zonderkidz.

—The Tale of the Poisonous Yuck-Bugs: Based on Proverbs 12:18. Whitehead, Peter, illus. 2005. (Insect-Inside Ser.). 40p. (J). 9.99 (978-0-310-70955-8(5)) Zonderkidz.

Reynolds, Laureen L. Sight Word Poetry. 2004. 48p. (gr. k-2). pap. 7.99 (978-0-7439-3507-4(1)) Teacher Created Materials, Inc.

Rhodes, Sam. Native American Rhymes: The People of the Far North, 9 vols. Howard, Kimberley, ed. Haas, Deborah, illus. 2003. 92p. (J). (gr. 3-5). mass mkt. 7.50 (978-0-9743214-0-0(0)) Rhodes Educational Pubns.

Richardson, Euralaye. My Cup Runneth Over. 2001. 92p. per. 12.95 (978-1-930908-06-2(7)) AGB Publishing.

Richmond, Marianne. The Gift of an Angel Vol. 1: A Keepsake for Parents Welcoming a New Child. l.t. ed. 2003. (Illus.). 40p. (YA). 15.95 (978-0-9741465-2-2(8)) Marianne Richmond Studios, Inc.

Riley, James Whitcomb. Riley Child Rhymes with Hoosier Pictures. 2006. (Illus.). 188p. (J). reprint ed. 20.00 (978-1-878208-17-0(9)) Emmis Bks.

Roberts, Emrys. Pwdin Semolina: Cerddi Cynganeddol I Blant. 2005. (WEL.). 74p. (978-0-86381-402-0(6)) Gwasg Carreg Gwalch.

Rodda, Geri. Lyme in Rhyme. 2005. (J). 7.50 (*978-0-9793602-1-3(8)) Pumpkin Hill Productions.

Roemer, Heidi. Come to My Party: And Other Shape Poems. Takahashi, Hideko, tr. Takahashi, Hideko, illus. rev. ed. 2004. 32p. (J). 17.95 (978-0-8050-6620-3(9) , Holt, Henry & Co. Bks. For Young Readers) Holt, Henry & Co.

Roessel, David & Rampersad, Arnold, eds. Langston Hughes. Andrews, Benny, illus. 2006. (Poetry for Young People Ser.). 48p. (J). 14.95 (978-1-4027-1845-8(4)) Sterling Publishing Co., Inc.

Rogasky, Barbara. Leaf by Leaf: Autumn Poems. Tauss, Marc, illus. Tauss, Marc, photos by. 2001. 40p. (J). (gr. 2 up). pap. 16.95 (978-0-590-25347-5(6)) Scholastic, Inc.

Rogers, Bertha, ed. Every Infant's Blood: New & Selected Poems. 2002. (Bright Hill Press Poetry Ser.: 1). 152p. (J). 14.95 (978-1-892471-08-6(6)) Bright Hill Pr.

Rojas, Emilio. Poemas de Amor de un Adolescente. 2003. (SPA.). 66p. (YA). 9.95 (978-968-5432-09-2(0)) EDITER'S Publishing Hse. MEX. *Dist:* EDITER'S Publishing Hse.

Romantic Poetry. l.t. ed. 2002. 96p. (YA). per. 10.00 (978-0-9657083-2-6(2)) ANUP Research & Multimedia LP.

Rose, Dilys. When I Wear My Leopard Hat: Poems for Young Children. Allan, Gill, illus. 40p. pap. 6.95 (978-1-899827-70-1(6)) Scottish Children's Pr. GBR. *Dist:* Wilson & Assocs.

Rosen, Michael. Alphabet Poem. Tullet, Herve, illus. 2004. 40p. (J). 15.95 (978-1-84059-393-8(8)) Milet Publishing.

—Classic Poetry: An Illustrated Collection. Howard, Paul, illus. 1998. 160p. (J). (gr. 4-7). 21.99 (978-1-56402-89-7(9)) Candlewick Pr.

—Michael Rosen's Book of Nonsense. Mackie, Clare, illus. 2003. 48p. pap. (978-0-7500-2671-0(5) , Hodder Wayland) Hodder Children's Division.

—Mustard, Custard, Grumble Belly & Gravy. Blake, Quentin, illus. 2008. 100p. (J). 12.95 incl. audio compact disk (*978-0-7475-8738-5(8)) Bloomsbury Publishing Plc GBR. *Dist:* Independent Pubs. Group.

Rosen, Michael. No Breathing in Class. Paul, Korky, illus. 2002. (Colour Young Puffin Ser.). 64p. (J). pap. (978-0-14-130022-1(1) , Puffin) Penguin Group (USA) Inc.

Rosenberg, Liz & November, Deena, eds. I Just Hope It's Lethal: Poems of Sadness, Madness, & Joy. 2005. 208p. (YA). (gr. 7 up). pap. 7.99 (978-0-618-56452-1(7) , Graphia) Houghton Mifflin Co. Trade & Reference Div.

Rosenblatt, Danielle. The Ant in the Cellar. Kirk, Jacqueline, illus. 2007. 138p. (J). per. 19.95 (978-0-9788985-3-3(2)) A Better Be Write Pub.

Rosenthal, Betsy R. My House Is Singing. Chodos-Irvine, Margaret, illus. 2004. 40p. (J). 16.00 (978-0-15-216293-1(3)) Harcourt Children's Bks.

Ross, H. K., ed. & intro. Great American Story Poems. Ross, H. K., intro. 160p. (YA). (gr. 5-12). lib. bdg. 13.95 (978-0-87460-363-7(3)) Lion Bks.

Ross, Mandy. Wake Up Sleepyhead. Kalanovic, Dubravka, illus. 2005. 32p. (J). (ps). pap. 7.99 (978-1-904550-33-4(9)) Child's Play-International.

Routman, Regie. Teaching First Graders to Love Writing Poetry. 2000. (Illus.). 80p. pap. 12.99 (978-0-590-22734-6(3)) Scholastic, Inc.

—Teaching Third & Fourth Graders to Love Writing Poetry. 2000. (Illus.). 88p. (J). (gr. 3-4). pap. 15.99 (978-0-590-22735-3(1)) Scholastic, Inc.

Rovetch, Gerda. There Was a Man Who Loved a Rat & Other Vile Little Poems. Rovetch, Lissa, illus. 2008. 32p. (J). (gr. k). 14.99 (***978-0-399-25014-9(X)*** , Philomel) Penguin Group (USA) Inc.

Rowell, Patricia. Patricia's Poetry of Life. 2003. (YA). per. 14.50 (978-1-59453-010-4(6) , 1485) Airleaf Publishing & Bookselling.

Roza, Greg. Patterns in Poetry: Recognizing & Analyzing Poetic Form & Meter. 2005. (PowerMath Ser.). 22.50 (978-1-4042-2941-9(8)); pap. 22.50 (978-1-4042-5146-5(4)) Rosen Publishing Group, Inc., The. (PowerKids Pr.).

Rumble, Coral. Breaking the Rules. 2004. (Illus.). 96p. (J). pap. 8.99 (978-0-7459-4857-7(X) , Lion) Lion Hudson plc GBR. *Dist:* Independent Pubs. Group.

Rumble, Coral. My Teacher's As Wild As a Bison. 2005. (Illus.). 96p. (J). pap. 8.99 (***978-0-7459-4954-3(1)***) Lion Hudson plc GBR. *Dist:* Independent Pubs. Group.

Ruurs, Margriet. Animal Alphabed. Emery, Jennifer, illus. 2005. 32p. (J). (ps-ps). 15.95 (978-1-59078-200-2(3)) Boyds Mills Pr.

—Virtual Maniac: Silly & Serious Poems for Kids. Tanselle, Eve, illus. 2000. 56p. (J). (gr. 3-5). pap. 7.95 (978-0-929895-43-7(6)) Maupin Hse. Publishing.

Rylant, Cynthia. Baby Face: A Book of Love for Baby. 2008. 40p. (J). 16.99 (***978-1-4169-4909-1(7)***) Simon & Schuster Children's Publishing.

—God Went to Beauty School. 2006. 64p. (J). reprint ed. pap. 4.99 (978-0-06-009435-5(4) , HarperTeen) HarperCollins Pubs.

—Waiting to Waltz: A Childhood. Gammell, Stephen, illus. 2001. 48p. (J). 18.95 (978-0-689-84292-4(9) , Atheneum/Richard Jackson Bks.) Simon & Schuster Children's Publishing.

S., Amaya. The Heart's Medicine. 2001. 108p. (YA). pap. 10.95 (978-0-595-18238-1(0) , Writers Club Pr.) iUniverse, Inc.

S., LaTisha & Lee, Mykle. One Giant Leap: Love Poems. Blob, Anjali & Beverly-Patterson, Sylvia Dianne, eds. 2003. 72p. (YA). per. 8.95 (978-0-9744929-0-2(6)) Leeway Pubs.

Sage, Angie. Yellow Ice. Sage, Angie, illus. 1998. (Colors Board Book Ser.). (Illus.). 12p. (J). (gr. k-ps). bds. 4.95 (978-1-55209-207-1(0)) Firefly Bks., Ltd.

Sakaki, Nanao. Inch by Inch: 45 Haiku by Issa. 1999. (gr. 7-12). lib. bdg. 21.10 (978-0-613-34004-5(3)) Tandem Library Bks.

Salas, Laura Purdie. And Then There Were Eight: Poems about Space. 2008. (***978-1-4296-1207-4(X)***) Capstone Pr., Inc.

Salerno, Joe. Only Here: Poems. 1998. (Illus.). 96p. (J). pap. 7.00 (978-1-886841-07-9(1) , Ars Poetica) Skylands Writers & Artists Assn., Inc.

Salomon, Diana. Duke, the Babysitter. Salomon, Udo, photos by. l.t. ed. 2002. (Illus.). 16p. (J). 6.95 (978-0-9704581-1-7(8) , 1,000, Free Song) LeBlanc, Doreen.

Sandburg, Carl. Not Everyday an Aurora Borealis for Your Birthday: A Love Poem. 1998. pap. 13.00 (978-0-679-88169-8(7) , Random Hse. Bks. for Young Readers) Random Hse. Children's Bks.

Sarreshtedari, Mehdi, narrated by. Hasht Ketab/ Sohrab Sepehri: Eight Books, 1DVD. 2005. (YA). 42.99 (978-1-933429-00-7(3)) Ketabe Gooya Publishing LLC.

Sauvageau, Juan. Stories, Fables & Poems for You, Vol. 1. 1998. Tr. of Cuentos, Fabulas y Poemas para Ti. (ENG & SPA., Illus.). 100p. (J). (gr. 3-5). pap. 9.95 (978-1-893493-00-1(8)) National Educational Systems, Inc.

Sawicki, Lori. Because Sometimes a Miracle Is a Pussy Willow Tree. (J). 2002. 91p. 16.95 (978-0-936389-78-3(8)); 1999. (Illus.). pap. 15.95 (978-0-936389-61-5(3)) Tudor Pubs., Inc.

Sawyer, Louise. My Daddy Was a Vagabond. 2002. (YA). spiral bd. 16.50 (978-0-9719842-3-3(9)) Martin & Brothers.

Schaffer, Angel Boi. Blessed Child. 2004. (YA). per. 29.99 (978-0-9755352-0-2(X)) Angel's Boy Enterprises.

Schertle, Alice. Good Night, Hattie, My Dearie, My Dove. Rand, Ted, illus. rev. ed. 2002. 32p. (J). (ps-3). 15.95 (978-0-688-16022-7(0)) HarperCollins Pubs.

—A Lucky Thing: Poems & Paintings. Minor, Wendell, illus. 2006. 28p. (J). (gr. 4-8). reprint ed. 17.00 (978-1-4223-5417-9(2)) DIANE Publishing Co.

Schiffner, Frederick A. My Back Yard: Poems to Read to Your Children. Guenther, Kim, illus. 2004. 32p. (J). 14.95 (978-0-9765782-0-8(4)) Schiffner, Frederick A.

Schkolnik, Saul. Poemas para Volar. 1999. (J). (978-956-240-272-9(X)) Arrayan Editores S.A.

Schlabach, Mary. Noah's Ark. l.t. ed. 2002. (Illus.). 24p. (J). 4.95 (978-0-9667622-0-4(7)) Schlabach Printers.

Scholastic, Inc. Staff. Best Love Poems Ever. 2003. (gr. 3-6). lib. bdg. 11.80 (978-0-613-72288-9(4)) Tandem Library Bks.

—It's Halloween! Neusner, Dena, ed. 2003. (Barney Ser.). (Illus.). 64p. (J). 2.99 (978-0-439-52452-0(0)) Scholastic, Inc.

Schubeck, Carol M. Personal Peaks. Clanuwat, Rinna, illus. aut. ed. 2002. 56p. (YA). pap. (978-0-9675567-1-0(6)) Suitcase Pr.,The.

Schutz, Samantha. I Don't Want to Be Crazy. 2007. 288p. (YA). (gr. 7 up). pap. 7.99 (***978-0-439-80519-3(8)***) Scholastic, Inc.

Schwartz, Stephen. Through Heaven's Eyes: Prince of Egypt. 1998. (Illus.). 32p. (J). (gr. k-3). 14.99 (978-0-8499-5897-7(0)) Nelson, Thomas Inc.

Searles, H. Louise. Sit Down little Sister & Let me Talk to You Vol. 1: The Voices of the Sparkletts. 84p. (Orig.). (J). pap. (978-0-9706187-0-2(0)) As Sparkle Speaks & Informs/ASSI.

Sehmi, Amritpal Kaur. Punjabi Numbers & Stickers. Sehmi, Amritpal Kaur & Sarch, Oren, eds. Sarch, Gagan Kaur, illus. 2002. (PAN.). 18p. bds. 8.95 (978-0-9709736-0-3(8)) Small People Publishing.

Self, David. The Lion Children's Treasury of Classic Verse. Firmin, Hannah, illus. 2001. 96p. (J). pap. 24.99 (978-0-7459-3980-3(5) , Lion) Lion Hudson plc GBR. *Dist:* Independent Pubs. Group.

Senchyne, Jonathan & Sikorskyj, Jerod, eds. Living Forge. 2003. (YA). per. 10.00 (978-1-932583-05-2(X)) digital@batesjackson llc.

Serio, John N., ed. The Seasons. Crockett, Robert, illus. 2005. (Poetry for Young People Ser.). 48p. (J). (gr. 3-7). 14.95 (978-1-4027-1254-8(5)) Sterling Publishing Co., Inc.

Shabazz, Phillip. XYZoom: Poems. 2004. 145p. per. 12.95 (978-1-890349-17-2(8)) Big Drum Pr.

Shannon, George. Busy in the Garden. Williams, Sam, illus. 2006. 40p. (J). 15.99 (978-0-06-000464-4(9)); lib. bdg. 16.89 (978-0-06-000465-1(7)) HarperCollins Pubs.

Shapiro, Karen Jo. I Must Go down to the Beach Again: And Other Poems. Love, Judy, illus. 2007. 48p. (J). (gr. 4-7). pap. 5.95 (***978-1-58089-144-8(6)***) Charlesbridge Publishing, Inc.

Sherman, Erica. The Mists of Eden: Nature's Last Paradise. Thatch, Nancy R., ed. Sherman, Erica, illus. 1998. (Books for Students by Students). (Illus.). 29p. (J). (ps-3). lib. bdg. 15.95 (978-0-933849-69-3(9)) Landmark Editions, Inc.

Sherrington, Abichal. The Plasmic Bubbler. 2001. 19p. per. 7.00 net. (978-0-9700002-6-2(X)) Light24.

Shields, Carol Diggory. Almost Late to School: And More School Poems. Meisel, Paul, illus. 2005. 48p. (J). (gr. 1-3). pap. 6.99 (978-0-14-240328-0(8) , Puffin) Penguin Group (USA) Inc.

—Lunch Money: And Other Poems about School. Meisel, Paul, illus. 1998. (Picture Puffin Ser.). 40p. (J). (ps-3). pap. 6.99 (978-0-14-055890-6(X) , Puffin) Penguin Group (USA) Inc.

Shihab-Nye, Naomi. 19 Varieties of Gazelle: Poems of the Middle East. 2005. 160p. (J). reprint ed. pap. 6.99 (978-0-06-050404-5(8) , HarperTeen) HarperCollins Pubs.

Shiner, Jack. Raking Leaves: Poems. 2004. 148p. (YA). per. 14.95 (978-0-922224-12-8(9)) Tonepoet Publishing.

Shore, Diane ZuHone & Alexander, Jessica. This Is the Dream. Ransome, James E., illus. 2006. 40p. (J). 16.99 (978-0-06-055519-1(X) , Amistad); lib. bdg. 17.89 (978-0-06-055520-7(3)) HarperCollins Pubs.

Shortridge, Geraldine. Poems of Tribute, Patriotism & Memories. 2002. 132p. 17.00 (978-1-891029-36-3(3)) Henderson Publishing.

Showell, Isaiah, Sr. Faith Found New, 1. Nichols, Clayton, illus. 2004. 82p. (YA). per. 15.00 incl. audio compact disk (978-0-9754489-0-8(0)) Divine Intertwine Publishing.

Shrout, Lois G., ed. Winners: Poems & Stories. 2001. 40p. (YA). (gr. 6 up). pap. 5.00 (978-0-9702646-0-2(7)) New Sweden Pr.

Shurin, Masha. A Great Time: Children's Poems in Russian & English. Morris, Brian, ed. Barton, Alica, tr. Ginukov, Valentin, illus. 2007. (RUS & ENG.). 32p. (J). 19.95 (***978-0-9792583-2-9(4)***) White Stag Pr.

Shuttleworth, Cathie, illus. The Children's Treasury of Classic Poetry. 176p. (J). pap. (978-1-84322-143-2(8)) Bookmart Ltd.

Sidman, Joyce. Butterfly Eyes & Other Secrets of the Meadow: Poems. Krommes, Beth, illus. 2006. 48p. (J). (gr. 3-5). 16.00 (978-0-618-56313-5(X)) Houghton Mifflin Co.

—This Is Just to Say: Poems of Apology & Forgiveness. Zagarenski, Pamela, illus. 2007. 48p. (J). (gr. 4-6). 16.00 (978-0-618-61680-0(2)) Houghton Mifflin Co.

Siebert, Diane. Rhyolite: The True Story of a Ghost Town. Frampton, David, illus. 2003. 32p. (J). (gr. k-3). tchr. ed. 16.00 (978-0-618-09673-2(6) , Clarion Bks.) Houghton Mifflin Co. Trade & Reference Div.

—Spring, Summer, Autumn, Winter. Burckhardt, Marc, illus. 2005. (J). (978-1-59336-299-7(4)); pap. (978-1-59336-300-0(1)) Mondo Publishing.

Sierra, Judy. Antarctic Antics: A Book of Penguin Poems. Aruego, Jose & Dewey, Ariane, illus. 1998. 32p. (J). (ps-2). 17.00 (978-0-15-201006-5(8) , Gulliver Bks.) Harcourt Children's Bks.

—Monster Goose. Davis, Jack E., illus. 56p. (J). (ps-ps). 2005. pap., pap. 7.00 (978-0-15-205417-5(0) , Voyager Bks./Libros Viajeros); 2001. 16.00 (978-0-15-202034-7(9) , Gulliver Bks.) Harcourt Children's Bks.

Silliman, Ron. Tjanting. 2002. (Modern Classics Ser.). 212p. pap. 17.95 (978-1-876857-19-6(6)) Salt Publishing GBR. *Dist:* SPD-Small Pr. Distribution.

Silvano, Wendi J. What Does the Wind Say? Delehanty, Joan, illus. 2006. 32p. 15.95 (978-1-55971-954-4(0) , NorthWord Bks. for Young Readers) T&N Children's Publishing.

Silverstein, Shel. Batacazos: Poemas para Reirse. Aquirre, Daniel, tr. 2000. (Escritura desatada Ser.). (SPA., Illus.). 178p. (J). (gr. 4-6). 13.95 (978-84-406-9295-5(1) , EB4865) Ediciones B ESP. *Dist:* Independent Pubs. Group, Lectorum Pubns., Inc.

—Don't bump The. Silverstein, Shel, illus. 2008. 64p. lib. bdg. 18.89 (***978-0-06-149619-6(7)***) HarperCollins Pubs.

—A Light in the Attic. Silverstein, Shel, illus. 2001. (Illus.). 176p. 22.99 incl. cd-rom (978-0-06-623617-9(7)) HarperCollins Pubs.

—Runny Babbit. Silverstein, Shel, illus. abr. ed. 2006. 96p. 22.99 incl. audio compact disk (978-0-06-113047-2(8)) HarperCollins Pubs.

—Runny Babbit: A Billy Sook. 2005. (Illus.). 96p. (J). 18.99 (978-0-06-025653-1(2)) HarperCollins Pubs.

Simmons, Kenneth. Mr Ken's Rhymes. 2007. 184p. per. 15.95 (***978-0-595-44328-4(1)***) iUniverse, Inc.

Simmons, Lynne Sheffield. Sugar Lump, the Orphan Calf's Night Before Christmas. Ward, Sue Marshall, illus. 2007. 48p. (J). (gr. k-3). 14.95 (***978-1-58980-439-5(2)***) Pelican Publishing Co., Inc.

Simmons, Sukether Williams. Deep in My Soul Poems by Sukether Simmons. 2003. pap. 10.00 (978-0-9678182-1-4(4)) Shrewsbury Publishing.

Simms, B. D. A Place in My Heart. 2003. 38p. (YA). pap. 10.95 (978-0-7414-1681-0(6)) Infinity Publishing.

Simpson, Patricia Ann. The Twinkle Collection. 2006. 19.95 (978-0-9779662-4-0(0)) Creative Bk. Pubs.

Singing Horse. 2003. (Gateways to the Sun Ser.). 32p. (J). (gr. 2-3). lib. bdg. 9.95 (978-1-58105-579-5(X)) Santillana USA Publishing Co., Inc.

Skene, Pat. Rhyme Stones. Ross, Graham, illus. 2007. (Orca Echoes Ser.). 64p. (J). (gr. 2-4). pap. (***978-1-55143-636-4(1)***) Orca Bk. Pubs.

Skevington, Andrea. Poems to Help You Through the Week. 2004. 128p. 16.99 (978-0-7459-4853-9(7) , Lion) Lion Hudson plc GBR. *Dist:* Independent Pubs. Group.

Skinner, Ada & Wickes, Frances. A Child's Own Book of Verse, Book One (Yesterday's Classics) Petersham, Maud and Miska, illus. 2006. (J). pap. 8.95 (***978-1-59915-051-2(4)***) Yesterday's Classics.

—A Child's Own Book of Verse, Book Three (Yesterday's Classics) Petersham, Maud and Miska, illus. 2006. (J). pap. 8.95 (***978-1-59915-053-6(0)***) Yesterday's Classics.

—A Child's Own Book of Verse, Book Two (Yesterday's Classics) Petersham, Maud and Miska, illus. 2006. (J). pap. 8.95 (***978-1-59915-052-9(2)***) Yesterday's Classics.

Slattery, Zara, tr. & illus. Dark as a Midnight Dream: Poetry Collection, Vol. 2. Slattery, Zara, illus. 2003. 288p. 19.99 (978-0-237-52586-6(0) , Evans Brothers, Limited) Evans Publishing Group GBR. *Dist:* Independent Pubs. Group.

Smeeton, Miles. Alligator Tales (& Crocodiles Too) Grantvedt, Eric, illus. 3rd ed. 2000. 48p. (J). (ps-3). pap. 4.95 (978-1-56554-847-3(7)) Pelican Publishing Co., Inc.

Smith, Charles R., Jr. Hoop Queens. 2003. (Illus.). 40p. (J). (gr. 3 up). 14.99 (978-0-7636-1422-5(X)) Candlewick Pr.

Smith, Ernest Lynnwood. Raw Poetry & Prose in Transition. 2005. 50p. 25.00 (978-0-9729154-2-7(7)) Smith, Ernest.

—The Road to Oneness. 2003. 56p. 25.00 (978-0-9729154-1-0(9)) Smith, Ernest.

Smith, Hope Anita. Keeping the Night Watch. Lewis, E. B., illus. rev. ed. 2008. 80p. (J). 18.95 (978-0-8050-7202-0(0) , Holt, Henry & Co. Bks. For Young Readers) Holt, Henry & Co.

Smith, Simon. Reverdy Road. 2003. (Modern Poets Ser.). 252p. pap. (978-1-84471-027-0(0)) Salt Publishing.

Smith, Vivian. Along the Line. 2006. (ENG.). 132p. per. (***978-1-84471-066-9(1)***) Salt Publishing.

Snell, Gordon. The Wonderful Thursday Club. 2002. (Illus.). 96p. (J). pap. 7.99 (978-1-84255-030-4(6)) Orion Bks. Ltd. GBR. *Dist:* Trafalgar Square Publishing.

Snuggly Bear's Book of Poems. 2002. 32p. (J). 16.95 (978-1-930758-80-3(4) , Yeva Kids) Yeva Corp.

Sones, Sonya. Stop Pretending: What Happened When My Big Sister Went Crazy. 2001. (J). (978-0-606-20416-3(4)); (gr. 5-8). lib. bdg. 15.25 (978-0-613-34979-6(2)) Tandem Library Bks.

Soto, Gary. Canto Familiar. Nelson, Annika, illus. 2007. 96p. (J). pap. 5.95 (978-0-15-205885-2(0) , Harcourt Paperbacks) Harcourt Children's Bks.

—A Fire in My Hands: A Book of Poems. rev. exp. ed. 2006. (Illus.). 96p. (YA). 16.00 (978-0-15-205564-6(9)) Harcourt Children's Bks.

—Neighborhood Odes. Diaz, David, illus. 2005. 80p. (J). pap. 5.95 (978-0-15-205364-2(6) , Harcourt Paperbacks) Harcourt Children's Bks.

—Partly Cloudy: Poems of Love & Longing. 2008. (Illus.). 144p. (YA). 16.00 (978-0-15-206301-6(3)) Harcourt Children's Bks.

Soundprints. If You're Happy & You Know It & Other Favorites. 2005. (Meet Mother Goose Ser.). (Illus.). 36p. (J). bds. 14.95 incl. audio compact disk (978-1-59069-213-4(6) , MPD1108) Studio Mouse LLC.

—Little Miss Muffet & Other Favorites. 2005. (Meet Mother Goose Ser.). (Illus.). 36p. (J). bds. 10.95 incl. audio compact disk (978-1-59069-215-8(2)) Studio Mouse LLC.

Soy de dos lugares: Poesia Juvenil: 6 Small Books. (Saludos Ser.: Vol. 2). (SPA.). (gr. 3-5). 31.00 (978-0-7635-1767-0(4)) Rigby Education.

Soy de dos lugares: Poesia Juvenil: Big Book. (Saludos Ser.: Vol. 2). (SPA.). (gr. 3-5). 31.00 (978-0-7635-3162-1(6)) Rigby Education.

Spanish Poetry Packs: Combo Pack. (SPA.). (gr. k-2). 61.62 (978-1-56334-415-2(7)) Hampton-Brown Bks.

Spanish Poetry Packs: Jumbo Pack, (SPA.). (gr. k-2). 332.75 (978-1-56334-414-5(9)) Hampton-Brown Bks.

Sparkle Little One!, 2004. (Illus.). 28p. (J). 6.95 (978-0-9746779-0-3(6)) Children of Color/The Indra Collection.

Sparshott, Francis. The Naming of the Beasts. 2003. (Illus.). 80p. pap. 4.95 (978-0-88753-055-5(9)) Black Moss Pr. CAN. *Dist:* LitDistCo.

Spensley, Joe. Home Thoughts from A Broader Perspective. 2005. 96p. (YA). per. 12.00 (978-1-932496-26-0(2)) Penman Publishing, Inc.

Spicer, Maggee & Thompson, Richard. We'll All Go Flying. LaFave, Kim, illus. 32p. (J). (978-1-55041-698-5(7)) Fitzhenry & Whiteside, Ltd.

A Spicy-Herby Day, 6 vols.; set. 32p. (gr. 1-3). 26.50 (978-0-7802-8044-1(X)) Wright Group, The.

Spinelli, Eileen. Where Is the Night Train Going? Bedtime Poems. Moore, Cyd, illus. 2004. 32p. (J). pap. 9.95 (978-1-59078-331-3(X)) Boyds Mills Pr.

Spink, John & Jones, Mairwen, eds. Are You Talking to Me? 2nd ed. 1998. 86p. (YA). (gr. 6). reprint ed. pap. 11.95 (978-0-8464-4817-4(3)) Beekman Bks., Inc.

Spireng, Matthew J. Inspiration Point: Poems. 2002. (Bright Hill Press Chapbook Award Ser.). x, 38p. (YA). pap. 6.00 (978-1-892471-13-0(2)) Bright Hill Pr.

Sprick, Marilyn, et al. Write Well Big Book of Alphabet Poems. 2000. (Write Well Curriculum Ser.). (Illus.). 36p. (J). (gr. 1-3). pap., stu. ed. (978-1-57035-315-4(8) , 193POEM) Sopris West Educational Services.

Sproule, Gail. Singing the Dark. Lott, Sheena, illus. 2001. 32p. (J). (gr. 2). (978-1-55041-648-0(0)) Fitzhenry & Whiteside, Ltd.

St. Anthony, Jane. The Summer Sherman Loved Me. 2006. 144p. (J). 16.00 (978-0-374-37289-7(6)) Farrar, Straus & Giroux.

St. Pierre, Todd-Michael. A Woolly Mammoth on Amelia Street: Read Aloud Poems4Kids (and Grownups Too!) Douglas, Keith Cartoon Man, illus. 2003. 164p. (J). mass mkt. 15.95 (978-0-9742602-0-4(7)) Amelia Street Pr.

Steck-Vaughn Staff. Rhymes/Poems: Hide & Seek/Kinds. 1998. (Illus.). (J). pap. (978-0-8172-8632-3(2)) Steck-Vaughn.

Steele, Wendi L. The Enchanting Mrs. Hattie Pence: Bite-Size Morsels of God's Word with Poems for Pint-Size People. Siemers, Cade, illus. 1998. viii, 88p. (J). (ps-6). 20.00 (978-0-9660868-0-5(5)) WindowBox Pr.

Steinberg, David. Caveman Manners & Other Polite Poems: All Aboard Poetry Reader Station Stop. Sinnott, Adrian C., illus. 2006. (All Aboard Poetry Reader Ser.). 48p. (J). (gr. 2-4). pap. 3.99 (978-0-448-44109-2(8) , Grosset & Dunlap) Penguin Group (USA) Inc.

—Grasshopper Pie & Other Poems: All Aboard Poetry Reader. Sinnott, Adrian C., tr. Sinnott, Adrian C., illus. 2004. (All Aboard Poetry Reader Ser.). 48p. (J). (gr. 1-4). pap. 3.99 (978-0-448-43347-9(8) , Grosset & Dunlap) Penguin Group (USA) Inc.

Stephens, Christopher S. Rapping on the Window. Carpenter, Suzanne, illus. 2004. 48p. pap. 12.95 (978-1-84323-360-2(6)) Beekman Bks., Inc.

Steptoe, Javaka. In Daddy's Arms I Am Tall: African Americans Celebrating Fathers. 2001. (Illus.). (J). 13.75 (978-0-606-20487-3(3)) Tandem Library Bks.

Steptoe, Javaka, illus. In Daddy's Arms I Am Tall: African Americans Celebrating Fathers. 2001. 32p. (J). 6.95 (978-1-58430-016-8(7)) Lee & Low Bks., Inc.

Stevenson, D. E. Alister & Co. & It's Nice to Be Me: Children's Poems. 2002. (Illus.). 45p. (J). pap. 12.50 (978-0-9716612-1-9(9)) Anglophile Bks.

Stevenson, James. Candy Corn: Poems. Stevenson, James, illus. 1999. (Illus.). 56p. (J). (gr. 3 up). 16.99 (978-0-688-15837-8(4)) HarperCollins Pubs.

Stevenson, Robert. Little Land. Fernandes, Kim, illus. 2004. 24p. (J). (ps-k). (978-1-55337-765-8(6)) Kids Can Pr., Ltd.

Stevenson, Robert Louis. Block City. Kirk, Daniel, illus. 2005. 32p. (J). 14.95 (978-0-689-86964-8(9)) Simon & Schuster Children's Publishing.

—A Child's Garden of Verses. Fujikawa, Gyo, illus. 2007. 104p. (J). (ps-2). 9.95 (***978-1-4027-5062-5(5)***) Sterling Publishing Co., Inc.

—A Child's Garden of Verses. l.t. ed. 2005. 64p. pap. (978-1-84637-255-1(0)) Echo Library.

—A Child's Garden of Verses Vol. 2: A Collection of Scriptures, Prayers & Poems. Stevenson, Robert Louis, ed. 2003. (Illus.). 20p. (J). bds. 6.95 (978-0-8118-4168-9(5)) Chronicle Bks. LLC.

—A Child's Garden of Verses - Selected Poems: Digital Classics. 2002. cd-rom 5.00 (978-1-931457-08-8(5)) Stargate Electronic Library, Inc.

—The Little Land. Fernandes, Kim, illus. 2002. 24p. (J). (ps-k). (978-1-55337-385-8(5)) Kids Can Pr., Ltd.

—Poetry For Young People: Robert Louis Stevenson. 2003. cd-rom 19.00 (978-0-931968-62-4(3)) B & R Samizdat Express.

—Robert Louis Stevenson. Schoonmaker, Frances, ed. Corvino, Lucy, illus. 2000. (Poetry for Young People Ser.). 48p. (gr. 3-7). 14.95 (978-0-8069-4956-7(2)) Sterling Publishing Co., Inc.

Stewart, Joel, illus. Sea Dream: Poems from under the Waves. 2002. 40p. (J). (gr. 1-5). 16.99 (978-1-84148-905-6(0)) Barefoot Bks., Inc.

Stewart, Mattie M. Poetry for Children. 2001. (J). pap. (978-1-58235-956-4(3)) Watermark Pr.

Storad, Conrad J. Don't Ever Cross That Road! An Armadillo Story. Jensen, Nathaniel P., illus. 2003. (Sonoran Desert Tails Ser.). 32p. (J). (gr. k-4). 15.95 (978-1-891795-08-4(2)) RGU Group, The.

—Lizards for Lunch: A Roadrunner's Tale. 1999. (Sonoran Desert Tails Ser.). (Illus.). 32p. (J). (gr. k-4). 6.95 (978-1-891795-00-8(7)) RGU Group, The.

Strang Communications Company Staff, ed. Ages 2-3 Take-Home Papers Spring 2002: Discovering Together. 2002. (J). pap. 14.99 (978-1-57405-920-5(3)) CharismaLife Pubs.

Stuart, Kelly. Lullaby of the Virgin of Guadalupe. Caban, Carlos, illus. 2003. Tr. of Cancion de cuna de la Virgen. 32p. (J). (978-1-931721-07-3(6)) Bright Sky Pr.

Students of Fletcher Hills Elementary School. Many Voices: Where Dreams Take Flight II. 2007. 131p. pap. 13.95 (***978-0-7414-3748-8(1)***) Infinity Publishing.

Stutson, Caroline. On the River ABC. Crum, Anna-Maria, illus. 2000. 32p. (gr. k-3). 12.95 (978-1-879373-46-4(7)) Rinehart, Roberts Pubs.

Suarez, Nora & Gertz, Mercedes, concepts. When Words Dream, Cuando las Palabras Sueñan: Children's Poetry, Poesía Infantil. 1000th ed. 2006. (ENG & SPA., Illus.). 36p. lib. bdg. 25.95 (978-0-9789544-0-6(8)) Hundred Ways LLC, A.

Sullivan, Kevin. Best Hawaiian Style Mother Goose Ever. Aoki, Deb, illus. 2006. 40p. 16.95 incl. cd-rom (***978-0-9644149-6-9(1)***) Hawaya, Inc.

SunRaSon, Tehut-Nine. The Fire in Me. 1999. 88p. (YA). per. 12.00 (978-0-9677644-0-5(8)) SunRaSon Production Co.

Swados, Elizabeth. Sidney's Animal Rescue Store. Wilson, Anne, illus. 2005. (J). (978-0-439-55477-0(2) , Levine, Arthur A. Bks.) Scholastic, Inc.

Swinwood, Laurie. Rainbows & Other Promises. Carrie, Kabak, illus. 2001. 89p. (gr. 3-7). pap. 7.95 (978-1-889658-12-4(X)) New Canaan Publishing Co. LLC.

Swisher, Clarice. Red Pony. 2000. (gr. 7-12). lib. bdg. 34.70 (978-0-613-73807-1(1)) Tandem Library Bks.

Swisher, Ron. The Mail Must Go Through - A Canyon Adventure. Swisher, Gary, illus. 1999. 32p. (J). (gr. k-6). 16.95 (978-0-9677729-0-5(7)) T.R.B. Publishing.

Tadjo, Veronique. If I Were a King, If I Were a Queen. 2002. (Illus.). 32p. (J). 11.95 (978-1-84059-339-6(3)) Milet Publishing.

Tadjo, Veronique, ed. Talking Drums: A Selection of Poems from Africa South of the Sahara. 2004. (Illus.). 96p. (J). 15.95 (978-1-58234-813-1(8) , Bloomsbury Children) Bloomsbury Publishing.

Tagel, Peggy, illus. Twinkle Twinkle Little Star: I Squeak! 2005. (***978-1-4127-3573-5(4)***) Publications International, Ltd.

Tagore, Rabindranath. The Crescent Moon: Child Poems. 2006. 124p. pap. 11.95 (978-1-59462-241-0(8) , 275, Book Jungle) Standard Pubns., Inc.

The Talking Bumblebee. 2003. (J). (978-1-56870-476-0(3)) RonJon Publishing, Inc.

Tamplin, Sam. Christmas Poems. 2006. 96p. (J). 12.99 (978-0-7945-1471-6(5) , Usborne) EDC Publishing.

Taplin, Sam. Poems for Little Children. Furukawa, Masumi, illus. 2007. 48p. (J). 11.99 (978-0-7945-1426-6(X) , Usborne) EDC Publishing.

Taplin, Sam, compiled by. Poems for Young Children. 2005. (Poems for Young Children Ser.). 96p. (J). 14.95 (978-0-7945-0924-8(X) , Usborne) EDC Publishing.

Tarantino, Christine. The Rock Needs the Tree. 1998. (Illus.). 28p. (J). (ps-2). spiral bd. 5.00 (978-1-887480-98-7(6)) Words of Light International Publishing.

Tavares, Gary Gene. Inspirational & Educational Poems. 2007. 60p. per. 9.95 (***978-0-595-45911-7(0)***) iUniverse, Inc.

Taylor, Judy. Hidden Pictures 2005: With Pictures & Word Clues. 2004. (Illus.). 48p. (J). (gr. 6-9). Vol. 1. pap., act. bk. ed. 5.95 (978-1-59078-294-1(1)); Vol. 2. pap., act. bk. ed. 5.95 (978-1-59078-295-8(X)); Vol. 3. pap., act. bk. ed. 5.95 (978-1-59078-296-5(8)) Boyds Mills Pr.

Taylor, Linda. Poems Throughout the Year 2nd Beyond. 2000. (J). (gr. 1-2). pap. 15.00 (978-0-533-13437-3(4)) Vantage Pr., Inc.

Taylor, Michelle A. If Bees Rode Shiny Bicycles. 2003. (Illus.). 152p. (J). pap. 13.95 (978-0-7022-3382-1(X)) Univ. of Queensland Pr. AUS. *Dist:* International Specialized Bk. Services.

Taylor, Minnie. MEAT with the TEAM: AGB & S Writers' Guild Anthology 2002. 2002. (Illus.). 170p. per. 12.95 (978-1-930908-17-8(2)) AGB Publishing.

Teacher's Selection: Anthology of Eighth Grade Poetry. 2005. 158p. (YA). 16.95 (978-1-883931-57-5(6)) Anthology of Poetry, Inc.

Tegnér, Esaias. Fritiofs Saga. ANDREW A. STOMBERG, ed. 2006. 258p. pap. 13.99 (978-1-4264-3043-5(4)); 304p. pap. 17.99 (978-1-4264-3108-1(2)) BiblioBazaar.

Temple, John. Collected Poems. 2003. (Salt Modern Poets). 196p. pap. (978-1-876857-56-1(0)) Salt Publishing.

Tennyson, Alfred Lord. The Lady of Shalott. Cote, Genevieve, illus. 2005. 48p. (YA). (gr. 7 up). (978-1-55337-874-7(1)) Kids Can Pr., Ltd.

Tenuta, Lisa. Rhymes 'n Rhythms Text/CD Package: For the ESL Classroom. 2003. pap. 27.00 incl. audio compact disk (978-0-86647-179-4(0)) Pro Lingua Assocs., Inc.

Testa, Maria. Something about America. Nickles, Nina, illus. 2005. 96p. (YA). (gr. 7 up). 14.99 (978-0-7636-2528-3(0)) Candlewick Pr.

Thomas, Heather, compiled by. A Journey Through Time in Verse & Rhyme. rev. ed. 2001. 368p. (J). (gr. 1-9). pap. 34.95 (978-0-86315-271-9(6)) Floris Bks. GBR. *Dist:* Gryphon Hse., Inc., SteinerBooks, Inc.

Thomas, Joyce Carol. The Blacker the Berry: Poems. Joysmith, Brenda, illus. 2000. 32p. (J). 16.99 (978-0-06-025375-2(4)); lib. bdg. 17.89 (978-0-06-025376-9(2)) HarperCollins Pubs.

—Cherish Me. Bennett, Nneka, illus. 1998. (Growing Tree Ser.). 24p. (J). (ps up). 9.95 (978-0-694-01097-4(9) , Harper Festival) HarperCollins Pubs.

Thomas, Patricia. Nature's Paintbox: A Seasonal Gallery of Art & Verse. Orback, Craig, illus. 2007. (Millbrook Picture Books Ser.). 32p. (J). (gr. 2-5). 16.95 (***978-0-8225-6807-0(1)*** , Millbrook Pr.) Lerner Publishing Group.

Thomas, Shelley Moore. Somewhere Today: A Book of Peace. Futran, Eric, photos by. 2004. (Illus.). 24p. (J). (gr. k-4). reprint ed. pap. 6.95 (978-0-8075-7544-4(5)) Whitman, Albert & Co.

Thompson, Richard & Spicer, Margaret. We'll All Go Exploring. LaFave, Kim, illus. 32p. (J). (978-1-55041-732-6(0)) Fitzhenry & Whiteside, Ltd.

Thou Good & Faithful Servants. 2000. 16p. (YA). (gr. 6-12). pap. (978-1-930695-94-8(2)) Sparrowgrass Poetry Forum, Inc.

Thunder from the Earth, 6, Pack. (Greetings Ser.: Vol. 2). (gr. 3-5). 31.00 (978-0-7635-2062-5(4)) Rigby Education.

TIZE. Twin Poems. 2005. (YA). per. 21.95 (978-0-9766770-1-7(6)) BAU PUBLISHING GROUP.

To Light A Match. 2004. (Illus.). 88p. (YA). spiral bd. 11.95 (978-1-931084-37-6(8)); per. 11.95 (978-1-931084-10-9(6)) Balloon Magic.

Toczek, Nick & Gordon, Mike. Can Anyone Be As Gloomy As Me. 2006. (Illus.). (J). pap. 9.99 (978-0-340-91116-7(6) , Hodder & Stoughton) Hodder General Publishing Division GBR. *Dist:* Trafalgar Square Publishing.

Torices, Jose Gonzalez. Poemas para la Paz. Noriega, Fernando, illus. 2004. Tr. of Poems for Peace. (SPA.). (J). 14.99 (978-84-241-8726-2(1)) Everest de Ediciones y Distribucion, S.L. ESP. *Dist:* Lectorum Pubns., Inc.

—Poesia Infantil. (SPA., Illus.). 72p. (J). 7.50 (978-84-241-7891-8(2)) Everest de Ediciones y Distribucion, S.L. ESP. *Dist:* Lectorum Pubns., Inc.

Torren, Janet. I Am. l.t. ed. 2002. (Illus.). 44p. per. 9.95 (978-1-932344-00-4(4)) Thornton Publishing.

Torribio, Penelope. The Rain Is Coming - Songs & Poems of the Rainforest: Includes Lyric Coloring Book. Ross, Suzanne, illus. 2000. 32p. (J). (gr. k-6). pap. 16.95 incl. cd-rom (978-0-9704516-0-6(1) , 001) One World Publishing.

Totline. Food: Poems Good Enough to Eat. 2002. (Read-to-Me Rhymes Ser.). (J). pap. 10.99 (978-1-57029-307-8(4) , WPH56102, Totline Pubns.) Schaffer, Frank Pubns.

Tracy, Kathleen. The Life & Times of Homer. 2004. (Biography from Ancient Civilizations Ser.). (Illus.). 48p. (J). (gr. 4-8). lib. bdg. 29.95 (978-1-58415-260-6(5)) Mitchell Lane Pubs., Inc.

Trapani, Iza. Row, Row, Row Your Boat. 2004. (Illus.). 32p. (J). (ps-3). 15.95 (978-1-58089-022-9(9)) Charlesbridge Publishing, Inc.

Treasury of Poetry & Rhymes. 2001. (Little Treasuries Ser.). 256p. (J). 11.95 (978-0-7525-4515-8(9)) Parragon, Inc.

Tripp, Wallace. Roses Are Red, Violets Are Blue. 1999. (J). (978-0-316-84433-8(0)) Little Brown & Co.

Tuggle, Le Ann. Let's Go Fishing. 2005. (J). 16.95 (978-0-9770912-7-0(9) , Blue Marble Bks.) Indigo Custom Publishing.

Tully, Sandra M. Cherry Pie Charlie & More Poems for Children. Sadowski, Jeff, illus. 2007. (J). 15.00 (***978-1-933556-86-4(2)***) Publishers' Graphics, L.L.C.

Turcotte, Elise. Voyages Autour de Mon Lit. Bouchard, Elmyna, illus. 2002. (New Poetry Ser.). (FRE.). 36p. (YA). (gr. 7). pap. (978-2-89021-558-0(X)) Diffusion du livre Mirabel.

Turner, Steve. I Was Only Asking. 2004. (Illus.). 96p. (J). pap. 9.99 (978-0-7459-4822-5(7) , Lion) Lion Hudson plc GBR. *Dist:* Independent Pubs. Group.

—I Was Only Asking: Poems about Life's Big Questions. Baines, Nigel, illus. 2004. 96p. pap. 20.00 (978-0-7459-4821-8(9) , Lion) Lion Hudson plc GBR. *Dist:* Independent Pubs. Group.

Turner, Steve & Mostyn, David. Don't Take Your Elephant to School: All Kinds of Alphabet Poems. 2006. (Illus.). 96p. (J). (gr. 3-4). pap. 8.99 (978-0-7459-6020-3(0) , Lion Children's) Lion Hudson plc GBR. *Dist:* Independent Pubs. Group.

Turner, Steve & Winter, Rebecca. Poems. 2002. 192p. (J). pap. 14.99 (978-0-7459-4802-7(2) , Lion) Lion Hudson plc GBR. *Dist:* Independent Pubs. Group.

Tyler, Michael. The Skin You Live In. Csicsko, David Lee, illus. 2005. 32p. (J). 14.95 (978-0-9759580-0-1(3)) Chicago Children's Museum.

Uhlig, Elizabeth. Rainwalk & Other Poems of the Seasons. 2006. (J). pap. 12.95 (978-0-9677047-9-1(0)) Marble House Editions.

Unblocked! Dysgraphia Workbook with Bible Verses. 2000. (Illus.). 110p. spiral bd. 29.95 (978-1-931203-00-5(8)) Inspired Idea.

Unobagha, Uzoamaka Chinyelu. Off to the Sweet Shores of Africa & Other Talking Drum Rhymes. Cairns, Julia, illus. 2000. 56p. (J). (ps-3). 16.95 (978-0-8118-2378-4(4)) Chronicle Bks. LLC.

Updike, John. A Child's Calendar. 2004. (Live Oak Readalong Ser.). (Illus.). (J). pap. 16.95 incl. audio (978-1-59112-471-9(9)) Live Oak Media.

—A Child's Calendar, 4 bks. Hyman, Trina Schart, illus. 2004. (J). (gr. k-4). pap. 37.95 incl. audio (978-1-59112-473-3(5)); pap. 18.95 incl. audio compact disk (978-1-59112-931-8(1)) Live Oak Media.

The Valentine Poem Book. 10p. (J). bds. (978-2-89393-865-3(5)) Phidal Publishing, Inc./Editions Phidal, Inc.

Van De Luecht, Susan. Children's Poetry - Dreams & Visons. 2005. 58p. (J). pap. 20.73 (978-1-4116-6469-2(8)) Lulu.com.

Vance, Rodney. De'Monte Love. 2007. (J). per. (***978-1-933156-15-6(5)*** , Visikid Bks.) GSVQ Publishing.

Varikyan, Arpine & Wallace, Dejuanna. From the Inside Out. 2004. (ENG.). 80p. (YA). per. (978-0-595-33149-9(1)) iUniverse, Inc.

Vecchione, Patrice, ed. Truth & Lies: An Anthology of Poems. rev. ed. 2001. 160p. (YA). (gr. 7-10). 17.00 (978-0-8050-6479-7(6) , Holt, Henry & Co. Bks. For Young Readers) Holt, Henry & Co.

VeJauan, Sherea. Realistically Speaking: Speaking What's Real. . . Keeping What's Holy. 2003. 85p. (YA). per. 14.99 (978-0-9727874-0-6(2)) Realistically Speaking Publishing Co.

VERSE! Poetry for Young Children: Lessons for 4 to 6 Year-olds. 2006. spiral bd. (978-0-9727635-9-2(7)) Univ. of Arizona, Poetry Ctr., Arizona Board of Regents.

Vestergaard, Hope. I Don't Want to Clean My Room: A Mess of Poems about Chores. 2007. (Illus.). 32p. (J). (ps-2). 16.99 (978-0-525-47776-1(4) , Dutton Juvenile) Penguin Group (USA) Inc.

Viorst, Judith. Sad Underwear & Other Complications: More Poems for Children & their Parents. 2000. (978-0-606-17936-2(4)); (gr. 3-6). lib. bdg. 14.15 (978-0-613-28629-9(4)) Tandem Library Bks.

—Sad Underwear & Other Complications: More Poems for Children & Their Parents. Hull, Richard, illus. 2000. 80p. (J). (gr. 4-6). pap. 5.99 (978-0-689-83376-2(8) , Aladdin) Simon & Schuster Children's Publishing.

von Rosenberg, Byron. O Christmas Treed. 2006. 30p. (J). 10.95 (978-0-9759858-5-4(X)) Red Mountain Creations.

Vv. Poesia Una Al Dia. (SPA.). 32p. (J). (gr. 3-5). 15.95 (978-84-204-4334-8(4)) Santillana USA Publishing Co., Inc.

Wadsworth, Olive A. Over in the Meadow. Thornhill, Jan, illus. 2004. 32p. (J). (gr. k-2). 16.95 (978-1-897066-08-9(2)) Maple Tree Pr. CAN. *Dist:* Perseus Distribution.

Waldeck, Kelly, illus. Puzzling Poems to Drive You Crazy. 2006. 64p. (YA). 9.95 (978-0-19-272608-7(0)) Oxford Univ. Pr., Inc.

Waldek, Kelly, illus. Funny Poems to Give You the Giggles. 2007. 64p. (YA). 9.95 (978-0-19-272605-6(6)) Oxford Univ. Pr., Inc.

Waldman, Neil, illus. & compiled by. Dream Makers: Young People Share Their Hopes & Aspirations. Waldman, Neil, compiled by. 2003. 32p. (YA). (gr. 2-4). 15.95 (978-1-59078-178-4(3)) Boyds Mills Pr.

Walker, Alice. There Is a Flower at the Tip of My Nose Smelling Me. Vitale, Stefano, illus. 2006. 32p. (J). 16.99 (978-0-06-057080-4(6)); lib. bdg. 17.89 (978-0-06-057081-1(4)) HarperCollins Pubs.

Walker, Kennesha M. A Word in Due Season. 2003. 47p. (YA). pap. 9.95 (978-0-7414-1555-4(0)) Infinity Publishing.

Walking: Individual Title Six-Packs. (Literatura 2000 Ser.). (gr. 2-3). 33.00 (978-0-7635-0215-7(4)) Rigby Education.

Walrus Books. Children's Treasury: Fairy Tales, Nursery Rhymes & Nonsense Verse. 2002. (Illus.). 448p. (J). (gr. k-12). 24.95 (978-1-55285-425-9(6)) Whitecap Bks., Ltd. CAN. *Dist:* Graphic Arts Ctr. Publishing Co.

Walsh, Maria Elena. Tutu Maramba. Fiorini, Nancy, illus. 2001. (SPA.). 96p. (J). (gr. k-6). pap. 12.95 (978-950-511-635-5(7)) Santillana USA Publishing Co., Inc.

Walt Disney Company Staff, illus. Mother Goose. 2004. 24p. (J). (gr. k-k). 2.99 (978-0-7364-2310-6(9) , Golden/Disney) Random Hse. Children's Bks.

Walton, Rick & Teare, Brad. Dance, Pioneer, Dance! 1998. (Illus.). 32p. (J). (ps-3). 14.95 (978-1-57345-243-4(2)) Deseret Bk. Co.

Warren, Jean. Object Rhymes. Bittinger, Gayle & Cubley, Kathleen, eds. Tourtillotte, Barbara, illus. 1998. (Reproducible Rhyme Book Ser.). 80p. (ps). 9.99 (978-1-57029-278-1(7) , WPH48002, Totline Pubns.) Schaffer, Frank Pubns.

Washington, Peter, ed. Eat, Drink, & Be Merry: Poems about Food & Drink. 2003. (Everyman's Library Pocket Poets). 256p. 12.50 (978-1-4000-4023-0(X) , Everyman's Library) Knopf Publishing Group.

Waters, Fiona. Fire & Stone, Wind & Tide: Poems about the Elements. Corfield, Robin Bell, illus. 2006. 43p. (gr. 4-8). reprint ed. 24.00 (978-1-4223-5595-4(0)) DIANE Publishing Co.

Waters, Fiona, compiled by. Footprints on the Page. 2001. (Illus.). 158p. (J). pap. (978-0-237-52341-1(8) , Evans Brothers, Limited) Evans Publishing Group.

—Poems from Many Cultures. 2001. (Illus.). 96p. (J). (gr. 5-9). 24.99 (978-0-237-52104-2(0) , Evans Brothers, Limited) Evans Publishing Group GBR. *Dist:* Independent Pubs. Group.

Waters, Fiona, ed. Cat in the Dark & Other Cat Poems. Williams, Sophy, illus. 1999. 32p. (J). (gr. 1-5). (978-0-7112-1353-1(4)) Lincoln, Frances Ltd.

—Cat in the Dark & Other Cat Poems. Williams, Sophy, illus. 2001. 32p. (J). (gr. k-5). pap. 8.99 (978-0-7112-1476-7(X)) Lincoln, Frances Ltd. GBR. *Dist:* Transition Vendor.

—Dark as a Midnight Dream: Poetry Collection. 1999. (Illus.). 286p. (YA). (gr. 5-8). (978-0-237-51845-5(7) , Evans Brothers, Limited) Evans Publishing Group.

Waters, Fiona & Williams, Sophy. Cat in the Dark. 2004. (Illus.). 32p. (J). pap. 7.95 (978-1-84507-177-6(8)) Lincoln, Frances Ltd. GBR. *Dist:* Perseus Distribution.

Watkins, Bessie. Presidents in Profile: Three Views of One Face. 2003. (Illus.). 60p. (J). per. 11.95 (978-0-9728674-1-2(4)) Written Expressions Enterprise, Inc.

Watson, Esther Pearl. The Pain Tree: And Other Teenage Angst-Ridden Poetry. 2000. (gr. 7-12). lib. bdg. 15.25 (978-0-613-33948-3(7)) Tandem Library Bks.

Watson, Jane Werner. My Big Little Golden Book about God. Wilkin, Eloise, illus. ed. 2006. 32p. (J). (gr. k-k). 8.99 (978-0-375-83551-3(2) , Golden Inspirational) Random Hse. Children's Bks.

Watson, Robert W. The Epic of Gilgamesh: A Poetic Version. 1998. (YA). (gr. 7-12). per. 6.95 (978-0-9663784-2-9(3) , T6004) Smarr Pubs.

Weatherford, Carole Boston. Sidewalk Chalk: Poems of the City. Tokunbo, Dimitrea, illus. 2003. 32p. (J). (gr. 4-6). 15.95 (978-1-56397-084-9(8)) Boyds Mills Pr.

Webb, V, H. Shadows & Passages of the Soul. 2002. 54p. (YA). per. 6.95 (978-1-930648-46-3(4)) Goose River Pr.

Webster, Dennis. Birds, Beasts & Bugs. Cunningham, Kim W., illus. 1998. 32p. (J). (gr. k up). pap. 15.95 (978-0-9666820-0-7(9)) Yak Attack Graphics.

Weil, Jennifer. Marvin's Lump. 2006. (J). 15.95 (978-1-889743-47-9(X)) Robbie Dean Pr.

Weixl, Twyla. Twenty-Two Feelings from Nice to Nasty. Weixl, Twyla, illus. 2004. (Illus.). 45p. (J). (gr. k-3). pap. 11.95 (978-0-929141-70-1(9)) Napoleon Publishing/Rendezvous Pr. CAN. *Dist:* AtlasBooks Distribution.

Wensel, Bill. Waves of a Wayward Sailor: The Poems of Captain Bill. 2002. 62p. per. 8.95 net. (978-1-931934-08-4(8)) Back Yard Pub.

Westcott, Nadine Bernard. The Lady with the Alligator Purse. Westcott, Nadine Bernard, illus. 2002. (Illus.). (J). 13.15 (978-0-7587-2950-7(2)) Book Wholesalers, Inc.

—Peanut Butter & Jelly: A Play Rhyme. 1999. (J). (ps-2). lib. bdg. 14.30 (978-0-8335-8990-3(3)) Tandem Library Bks.

Westcott, Nadine Bernard, ed. & illus. Never Take a Pig to Lunch: And Other Poems about the Fun of Eating. Westcott, Nadine Bernard, illus. 1998. 64p. (J). (ps-3). pap. 7.95 (978-0-531-07098-7(0) , Orchard Bks.) Scholastic, Inc.

Wheeler, Jordan. Chuck in the City. Cohen, Bill, illus. 2001. 1p. (J). (ps-3). pap. 6.95 (978-0-919441-63-7(7)) Theytus Bks., Ltd. CAN. *Dist:* Orca Bk. Pubs. USA.

Where's Doggy, Daddy? 2006. (J). 16.95 (978-0-9760220-1-5(X)) Kidzpoetz Publishing.

Whitaker, Zai. Boastful Centipede & Other Creatures in Verse. 2007. 72p. pap. 6.99 (978-0-14-333534-4(0) , Penguin Global) Penguin Group (USA) Inc.

White, Eleanor Dantzler. Sincere Sentiments. 2003. 180p. (YA). per. (978-0-9679516-2-1(3)) Full Effect Gospel Ministries, Inc.

White, Lee. Poetry 4 YA Mind! A Collection of Poetry & Artwork. 2000. (gr. 7-12). lib. bdg. 16.40 (978-0-613-80275-8(6)) Tandem Library Bks.

Whitehead, Jenny. Holiday Stew: A Kid's Portion of Holiday & Seasonal Poems. Whitehead, Jenny, illus. rev. ed. 2007. (Illus.). 64p. (J). 17.95 (978-0-8050-7715-5(4)) Holt, Henry & Co.

Whitling, Matt. The Grammar of Poetry. 2000. (Imitation in Writing Ser.). 87p. (J). spiral bd. 20.00 (978-1-930443-13-6(7)) Logos Schl.

Whitman, Walt. Nothing but Miracles. Roth, Susan L., illus. 2003. 32p. (J). (ps-3). 15.95 (978-0-7922-6143-8(7) , National Geographic Children's Bks.) National Geographic Society.

Wickings, Ruth. Mermaids. 2007. (Enchanted World Ser.). (Illus.). 10p. (J). (ps-3). 9.95 (***978-1-84560-031-0(2)***) Mercury Bks. Ltd. GBR. *Dist:* International Publishers Marketing.

—Witches. 2007. (Enchanted World Ser.). (Illus.). 10p. (J). (gr. 4-7). 9.95 (***978-1-84560-032-7(0)***) Mercury Bks. Ltd. GBR. *Dist:* International Publishers Marketing.

Wiilson, Gabriella S. Anything on Earth Poems: Children's Poetry. l.t. ed. 2005. (Illus.). 34p. (J). per. 9.99 (978-1-59879-083-2(8)) Lifevest Publishing, Inc.

Wilbur, Richard. The Disappearing Alphabet. 2001. (gr. k-3). lib. bdg. 14.15 (978-0-613-86527-2(8)) Tandem Library Bks.

—Opposites, More Opposites, & a Few Differences. 2006. (Illus.). 96p. (J). 10.95 (978-0-15-205612-4(2) , Harcourt Paperbacks) Harcourt Children's Bks.

Wilkin, Eloise. Eloise Wilkin's Poems to Read to the Very Young. Wilkin, Eloise, illus. 2001. (Lap Library). (Illus.). 26p. (J). (gr. k-ps). bds. 7.99 (978-0-375-80475-5(7) , Random Hse. Bks. for Young Readers) Random Hse. Children's Bks.

Williams, Julie. Escaping Tornado Season: A Story in Poems. 2004. 272p. (J). 16.89 (978-0-06-008640-4(8) , HarperTeen) HarperCollins Pubs.

Williams, Lyndsay. NonSense! It's Banana Cheese! 2007. (ENG.). 84p. per. 14.95 (***978-1-4241-6736-4(1)***) PublishAmerica, Inc.

Williams, Vera B. Amber Was Brave, Essie was Smart: The Story of Amber & Essie, Told Here in Poems & Pictures. 2003. (Live Oak Readalong Ser.). (Illus.). (J). pap. 18.95 incl. audio compact disk (978-1-59112-338-5(0)) Live Oak Media.

Williamson, Kate T. & Soares, Maria Fernanda. Hello Kitty Through the Seasons! Butefish, Jennifer, photos by. 2006. (Illus.). 96p. (J). (gr. 3-7). 14.95 (978-0-8109-5993-4(3)) Abrams, Harry N. , Inc.

Wilmot, Rod. The Meal of Magic Cards. 2003. (Illus.). 41p. pap. 3.75 (978-0-88753-010-4(9)) Black Moss Pr. CAN. *Dist:* LitDistCo.

Wilson, Karma. Bear Hugs: Romantically Ridiculous Animal Rhymes. Watts, Suzanne, illus. 2007. 32p. (J). 6.99 (***978-1-4169-4958-9(5)*** , Aladdin) Simon & Schuster Children's Publishing.

Wilson, Karma. Give Thanks to the Lord: Celebrating Psalm 92. Bates, Amy June, illus. 2007. 32p. (J). (ps-3). 14.99 (978-0-310-71118-6(5)) Zonderkidz.

Wilson, Raymond, ed. The Puffin Book of Classic Verse. Wallis, Diz, illus. 1998. 384p. (J). 13.95 (978-0-14-036816-1(7)) Penguin Bks., Ltd. GBR. *Dist:* Trafalgar Square Publishing.

Wing, Natasha. The Night Before Summer Vacation. Durrell, Julie, illus. 2002. (Reading Railroad Bks.). 32p. (J). pap. 3.99 (978-0-448-42830-7(X) , Grosset & Dunlap) Penguin Group (USA) Inc.

Winners: Poems & Stories, 2003 Spring Writing Contest. 2003. (J). 5.00 (978-0-9702646-2-6(3)); (YA). 5.00 (978-0-9702646-3-3(1)) New Sweden Pr.

Winters, Kay. Did You See What I Saw? Poems about School. Weston, Martha, illus. 2001. 32p. (J). pap. 5.99 (978-0-14-056265-1(6) , Puffin) Penguin Group (USA) Inc.

—Did You See What I Saw? Poems about School. 2001. (Illus.). (J). (978-0-606-21145-1(4)) Tandem Library Bks.

—Did You See What I Saw? Poems about School. 2001. (ps-2). lib. bdg. 14.15 (978-0-613-43815-5(9)) Tandem Library Bks.

Wishinsky, Frieda. No Frogs for Dinner. Hendry, Linda, illus. 1999. (First Flight Ser.). 40p. (J). (gr. 1-3). (978-1-55041-519-3(0)) Fitzhenry & Whiteside, Ltd.

With Love & a Selection of Short Stories & Poems. 2001. pap. 14.00 (978-0-9714968-0-4(3)) Beulah Fox.

Withrow, Sarah. Be a Baby. Monroy, Manuel, illus. 2007. 32p. (J). (ps). 17.95 ***(978-0-88899-776-0(0))*** Groundwood Bks. CAN. *Dist:* Perseus Distribution.

—Se un Bebé. Monroy, Manuel, illus. 2007. (SPA.). 32p. (J). 17.95 ***(978-0-88899-788-3(4))*** Groundwood Bks. CAN. *Dist:* Perseus Distribution.

Wolff, Pat. Noah's Faith: A Children's Poem. 2007. (J). bds. 10.99 ***(978-0-9788324-2-1(6))*** Playing Pig Pr.

Wondrous Tales of Wicked Winston. (Illus.). pap. (978-0-920236-18-5(9)) Annick Pr., Ltd.

Wong, Janet S. Behind the Wheel. Wong, Janet S., photos by. 1999. (Illus.). 48p. (YA). (gr. 7-12). 15.95 (978-0-689-82531-6(5) , McElderry, Margaret K.) Simon & Schuster Children's Publishing.

—Night Garden. Paschkis, Julie, illus. 2000. 32p. (J). (gr. 2-5). 16.95 (978-0-689-82617-7(6) , McElderry, Margaret K.) Simon & Schuster Children's Publishing.

—Twist: Yoga Poems. Paschkis, Julie, illus. 2007. 40p. (J). 17.99 (978-0-689-87394-2(8) , McElderry, Margaret K.) Simon & Schuster Children's Publishing.

Wood, Carol. Color Really Doesn't Matter. Glisson, Joe, illus. 2001. 24p. (J). pap. 9.95 incl. audio compact disk (978-0-9662378-6-3(2)); bds. 14.95 incl. audio compact disk (978-0-9662378-1-8(1)) Astoria Productions.

Wood, Cristyle. Styl. 2002. 44p. per. 7.95 net. (978-1-931934-16-9(9)) Back Yard Pub.

Woodson, Jacqueline. Locomotion. 2004. 112p. (J). reprint ed. pap. 5.99 (978-0-14-240149-1(8) , Puffin) Penguin Group (USA) Inc.

—Locomotion. 2005. 100p. (J). (ps-13). lib. bdg. 13.19 (978-0-606-32475-5(5)) Tandem Library Bks.

Wooldridge, Susan. Bathing with Ants. 2004. 30p. pap. 10.00 (978-0-9719607-4-9(7)) Bear Star Pr.

Woolf-Wade, Sarah J. Nightsong. 2003. (Illus.). 114p. (YA). per. 12.00 (978-1-930648-45-6(6) , 207-832-6665) Goose River Pr.

Wooten, Terry. When the Bear Came Back: The Whole Story. Lechler, Louan, illus. 2006. (J). per. 9.49 (978-1-893972-27-8(5)) Wordsmith Pr.

Worth, Valerie. Animal Poems. Jenkins, Steve, illus. 2007. 48p. (J). (gr. 3-8). 17.00 (978-0-374-38057-1(0)) Farrar, Straus & Giroux.

Wright, Alice & Bridges, LaVon. Alaska Animals We Love You: Chants & Poems for Children. 2005. (J). kivar 16.95 (978-1-59433-028-5(X) , Publishing Consultants) Publication Consultants.

Xinran. Motherbridge of Love. Masse, José, illus. 2007. 32p. (J). (ps-5). 16.99 ***(978-1-84686-047-8(4))*** Barefoot Bks., Inc.

Yang, Huan. Homes. Huang, Hsiao-Yen, illus. 2006. 32p. 15.95 (978-0-9762056-3-0(7)) Heryin Publishing Corp.

Yang-Huan. Where Is Spring? Huang, Hsiao-Yen & Yang, A., illus. 2007. 32p. (J). (ps-k). 15.95 (978-0-9762056-8-5(8)) Heryin Publishing Corp.

Yee, Paul & Wang, Jan Peng. A Song for Ba. 2004. (Illus.). 32p. (J). 16.95 (978-0-88899-492-9(3)) Groundwood Bks. CAN. *Dist:* Perseus Distribution.

Yolen, Jane. Least Things: Poems about Small Natures. Stemple, Jason, photos by. 2003. (Illus.). 32p. (YA). (gr. 4-6). 17.95 (978-1-59078-098-5(1)) Boyds Mills Pr.

—Snow, Snow: Winter Poems for Children. Stemple, Jason, photos by. 2005. (Illus.). 32p. (J). (gr. k-7). pap. 9.95 (978-1-59078-346-7(8)) Boyds Mills Pr.

—Snow, Snow: Winter Poems for Children. Stemple, Jason, illus. 2003. 32p. (J). (gr. 4-6). 16.95 (978-1-56397-721-3(4)) Boyds Mills Pr.

—Water Music. 2004. (Illus.). 40p. (YA). (gr. 4-6). pap. 9.95 (978-1-59078-251-4(8)) Boyds Mills Pr.

Yolen, Jane, ed. This Little Piggy & Other Rhymes to Sing & Play: Lap Songs, Finger Plays, Clapping Games & Pantomime Rhymes. Hillenbrand, Will, illus. 2006. 80p. (J). (gr. k-ps). 19.99 (978-0-7636-1348-8(7)) Candlewick Pr.

Young, Margie. April & Beagle One Monday Morning. 2007. (J). per. 7.99 ***(978-1-59886-928-6(0))*** Tate Publishing & Enterprises, L.L.C.

Young, Wanda. Inspired Spiritual Poems, Vol. 1. l.t. ed. 2004. (Illus.). 60p. per. 10.00 (978-1-933594-00-2(4)) Faith Baptist Church Publns.

Young, Wanda. Joyous Poems for Children. 2007. (YA). per. ***(978-1-933594-66-8(7))*** Faith Baptist Church Publns.

Zager, Jack. Where Do the Tigers Go? A Collection of Children's Poetry. 2004. (Illus.). 32p. (J). lib. bdg. 9.95 (978-1-930580-57-2(6) , Luminary Media Group) Pine Orchard, Inc.

Zemach, Margot. Some from the Moon, Some from the Sun: Poems & Songs for Everyone. Zemach, Margot, illus. 2001. (Illus.). 48p. (J). (ps-2). 17.00 (978-0-374-39960-3(3) , Farrar, Straus & Giroux (BYR)) Farrar, Straus & Giroux.

Zephaniah, Benjamin. Talking Turkeys. (Illus.). 96p. (J). 9.95 (978-0-14-036330-2(0)) Penguin Bks., Ltd. GBR. *Dist:* Trafalgar Square Publishing.

—We Are Britain! Das, Prodeepta, photos by. 2004. (Illus.). 32p. (J). pap. 7.95 (978-1-84507-143-1(3)); 27p. (YA). (978-0-7112-1764-5(5)) Lincoln, Frances Ltd. GBR. *Dist:* Perseus Distribution, Transition Vendor.

Zeringue, Dona. I Am I. Zeringue, Dona, illus. (Illus.). 32p. (Orig.). (YA). (gr. 6-12). pap. 7.50 (978-1-882913-02-2(7)) Thornton Publishing.

Zolotow, Charlotte. Seasons: A Book of Poems. 2003. (gr. k-3). lib. bdg. 11.80 (978-0-613-62189-2(1)) Tandem Library Bks.

—Some Things Go Together. Wolff, Ashley, illus. 1999. (Growing Tree Ser.). 24p. (J). (ps up). 9.99 (978-0-694-01197-1(5) , Harper Festival) HarperCollins Pubs.

100 Verses about Laura Ingalls Wilder. 2005. (YA). 9.99 (978-0-9765951-0-6(9)) Little Hse. Site Tours LLC.

POETRY—COLLECTIONS

see also American Poetry—Collections; English Poetry—Collections

Ada, Alma Flor. Mambru. 2004. (Puertas al Sol Ser.). (SPA., Illus.). 32p. (YA). (gr. 2-3). 9.95 (978-1-58105-405-7(X)) Santillana USA Publishing Co., Inc.

Adams, Michelle Medlock. My Funny Valentine. Johnson, Meredith, illus. 2005. 32p. (J). 12.95 (978-0-8249-5487-1(4)) Ideals Pubns.

Adedjouma, Davida, ed. The Palm of My Heart: Poetry by African American Children. Christie, Gregory R., illus. 1998. 32p. (J). (ps up). 6.95 (978-1-880000-76-2(8)) Lee & Low Bks., Inc.

Agard, John & Nichols, Grace, eds. Under the Moon & over the Sea: A Collection of Caribbean Poems. 2004. (Illus.). 75p. (J). (gr. k-4). reprint ed. 18.00 (978-0-7567-7991-7(X)) DIANE Publishing Co.

Anderson, Marcella F. Reflections from a Mud Puddle: Helping Children Cope & Grow. Wray, Christopher, illus. 2003. 96p. (J). (gr. 4-6). pap. 14.95 (978-1-56397-606-3(4)) Boyds Mills Pr.

Armengol, Zoraida. Las Alas de un Alma. 2001. (SPA.). 100p. (YA). pap. 10.00 (978-1-931481-16-8(4)) LiArt-Literature & Art.

Backlund, Kristina, illus. Seeds of Hope: A Message from Young Voices in the Aftermath of September 11. Lundgren, Jessica, photos by. 2002. 98p. per. 15.00 (978-0-9720435-0-2(0)) World of Hope International, Inc.

Barbour, Karen, illus. Wonderful Words: Poems about Reading, Writing, Speaking, & Listening. 2004. 32p. (J). 16.95 (978-0-689-83588-9(4)) Simon & Schuster Children's Publishing.

Barsotti, Joan B. The Little Green Frog & Other Poems. Mathis, Carol, illus. 1999. (Apple Hill Ser.). 32p. (J). (gr. k-5). pap. 6.95 (978-0-9642112-5-4(4)) Barsotti Bks.

Baxter, Nicola, ed. Children's Classic Poetry Collection. Shuttleworth, Cathie, illus. 2000. 96p. (J). reprint ed. 20.00 (978-0-7881-9044-5(X)) DIANE Publishing Co.

Beaton, Clare, illus. & compiled by. Playtime Rhymes for Little People. Beaton, Clare, compiled by. 2001. 64p. (J). pap. 18.99 (978-1-84148-425-9(3)) Barefoot Bks., Inc.

Bloom, Harold. Stories & Poems for Extremely Intelligent Children of All Ages. Bloom, Harold, ed. 2002. (Illus.). 576p. reprint ed. pap. 16.00 (978-0-684-86874-5(1) , Scribner) Simon & Schuster.

—Stories & Poems for Extremely Intelligent Children of All Ages. 2002. (gr. 3-6). lib. bdg. 25.75 (978-0-613-90932-7(1)) Tandem Library Bks.

Boldes, Gary. Thoughts of a Sailor. 2003. 58p. pap. 7.00 (978-1-4116-0425-4(3)) Lulu.com.

Brenner, Barbara. The Earth Is Painted Green: A Garden of Poems about Our Planet. 2000. (Illus.). 96p. (J). (ps-3). pap. 5.99 (978-0-590-45135-2(9)) Scholastic, Inc.

—The Earth Is Painted Green: A Garden of Poems about Our Planet. 2000. (Illus.). (J). (978-0-606-18538-7(0)) Tandem Library Bks.

Bunyan, John. Lessons from Nature: Poems for Boys & Girls. Sanseri, Gary & Sanseri, Wanda, eds. 1998. (Illus.). 124p. (J). reprint ed. 19.95 (978-1-880045-19-0(2)) Back Home Industries.

Burns, Robert. Selected Burns for Young Readers. 2002. (Illus.). 256p. pap., act. bk. ed. 3.95 (978-1-85534-129-6(8)) Geddes & Grosset, Ltd. GBR. *Dist:* CPG Publishing, Inc.

Canterbury Scho. Canterbury Festivals 2006 Schools Poetry. 2006. pap. ***(978-1-84375-256-1(5))*** Universal Publishing Solutions Online, Limited (UPSO).

Carnell, Ron, ed. Voices on the Web: Passions in Poetry. 2001. per. 39.95 (978-0-9715646-0-2(4)) netpoets.com.

Catalano, Raine Alyssa. Once upon a Dream: A Collection of Children's Poems. 2nd l.t. ed. 2001. 36p. (J). lib. bdg. 21.95 (978-0-9708726-1-6(5)) Shilo Publishing.

Causley, Charles. Collected Poems for Children. Lawrence, John, illus. rev. ed. 2000. 400p. (J). (gr. 2 up). pap. (978-0-330-38980-8(7) , Pan) Pan Macmillan.

Chess, Richard. Tekiah: Poems. 2nd ed. 2002. 85p. pap. 12.00 (978-1-879852-78-5(0)) Univ. of Tampa Pr.

Clarke, Gillian. Kingfisher Book of Scary Poems. 2003. (gr. 3-6). lib. bdg. 18.75 (978-0-613-70569-1(6)) Tandem Library Bks.

Cooling, Wendy, ed. Come to the Great World: Poems from Around the Globe. Moxley, Sheila, tr. Moxley, Sheila, illus. 2004. 48p. (J). (gr. k-3). tchr. ed. 16.95 (978-0-8234-1822-0(7)) Holiday Hse., Inc.

Cordova, Soledad. Poemas de Perros y Gatos. Graullera, Fabiola, illus. 2003. (SPA.). 21p. (J). (gr. 3-5). pap. 7.95 (978-968-19-0987-1(9)) Santillana USA Publishing Co., Inc.

Corman, Cid. One Man's Moon: Poems by Basho & Other Japanese Poets. exp. ed. 2003. 128p. pap. 15.00 (978-0-917788-76-5(1)) Gnomon Pr.

Coville, Bruce. The Unicorn Treasury: Stories, Poems, & Unicorn Lore. 2004. (Illus.). 216p. (J). pap. 5.95 (978-0-15-205216-4(X) , Magic Carpet Bks.) Harcourt Children's Bks.

Cruz-Contarini, Rafael. Zaranda. (SPA., Illus.). 84p. (J). 7.50 (978-84-241-3367-2(6)) Everest de Ediciones y Distribucion, S.L. ESP. *Dist:* Lectorum Pubns., Inc.

—Zaranda. 2000. (SPA.). (gr. k-3). lib. bdg. 16.40 (978-0-613-80623-7(9)) Tandem Library Bks.

Cullen, Carmen. Under the Eye of the Moon: Poems for Children. 2001. (Illus.). 103p. (J). pap. 7.95 (978-1-85635-378-6(8)) Mercier Pr., Ltd., The IRL. *Dist:* Irish Bks. & Media, Inc.

Daly, Catherine. DaDaDa. 2003. (Modern Poets Ser.). 224p. pap. 18.95 (978-1-876857-95-0(1)) Salt Publishing GBR. *Dist:* SPD-Small Pr. Distribution.

Daniels, John. Love & Pain. 2004. 70p. (YA). mass mkt. 14.95 (978-0-9755489-0-5(5)) New Birth Publishing.

de Paola, Tomie. Tomie de Paola's Rhyme Time. 2000. (978-0-606-18459-5(7)) Tandem Library Bks.

Dover Staff. Listen & Color: Favorite Poems for Children. Kliros, Thea, illus. 2004. 48p. (J). pap. 6.95 (978-0-486-43891-7(0)) Dover Pubns., Inc.

Downes, Belinda. Baby Days: A Quilt of Rhymes & Pictures. Downes, Belinda, illus. 2006. (Illus.). 32p. (J). (gr. k-ps). 14.99 (978-0-7636-2786-7(0)) Candlewick Pr.

Doyle, Alfreda C. Story Course - Mask: Stories, Poetry & Color Therapy. 1998. (Illus.). 40p. (J). pap., wbk. ed. 29.95 (978-1-56820-377-5(2)) Story Time Stories That Rhyme.

Eulalie. Buds, Blossoms, & Leaves: Eulalie's Collected Poems. 2003. 200p. lib. bdg. 25.00 (978-0-9708005-3-4(3)) Singing Tree Pr.

Factor. Language Works Jelly Plate. 16p. (J). (978-0-8136-3520-0(9)) Modern Curriculum Pr.

Faith, Queene. Faces of Abstract. 2003. (YA). per. 11.95 (978-1-59453-020-3(3) , 1593) Airleaf Publishing & Bookselling.

Fehler, Gene. The Silly (And Sometimes Serious) Side of Sports: Sports Poems. 1999. 72p. (J). (gr. 3-12). pap. 7.95 (978-0-9650793-1-0(7)) Mailbox Pr.

Flowers, Audrey X. Rhymes of the Times II. (Orig.). (J). reprint ed. pap. 10.00 (978-1-56411-146-3(6)) UBUS Communications Systems.

Follen, Eliza Lee. Hymns, Songs & Fables for Young People. 2003. (gr. 3-6). lib. bdg. 25.75 (978-0-613-74870-4(0)) Tandem Library Bks.

Foster, John. Word Whirls & Other Shape Poems. (Illus.). 96p. (978-0-19-279156-6(7)) Oxford Univ. Pr., Inc.

Franco, Betsy. Caring, Sharing & Getting Along: 50 Perfect Poems for Promoting Good behavior in the Classro. 2000. 64p. pap. 10.95 (978-0-439-20105-6(5)) Scholastic, Inc.

—The Great Big Book of Thematic Poetry: More Than 200 Delightful Poems on Favorite Topics That Will Enrich Your Lessons, Bild Fluency, & Strengthen Reading Skills. 2004. 184p. pap. 15.99 (978-0-439-56729-9(7)) Scholastic, Inc.

Franco, Betsy, ed. You Hear Me? Poems & Writing by Teenage Boys. Nickles, Nina, photos by. 2001. (Illus.). 128p. (J). (gr. 7 up). pap. 6.99 (978-0-7636-1159-0(X)) Candlewick Pr.

Fuchs, A. P. The Hand I've Been Dealt: A Collection of Poetry & Song Streams of Thought & Reflection. 2003. 110p. (YA). 22.95 (978-0-595-66096-4(7)); pap. 12.95 (978-0-595-29976-8(8)) iUniverse, Inc.

Fuente de Cristal. 2001. (SPA., Illus.). 127p. (YA). pap. 10.00 (978-1-931481-45-8(8)) LiArt-Literature & Art.

Fuertes, Gloria. Poesias, Rimas y Disparates: Pienso Mesa y Digo Silla. 2003. (SPA.). 128p. (978-84-305-8535-9(4) , SU4859) Susaeta Ediciones, S.A. ESP. *Dist:* Lectorum Pubns., Inc.

Fujikawa, Gyo, illus. A Child's Book of Poems. 2007. 128p. (J). (ps-2). 9.95 ***(978-1-4027-5061-8(7))*** Sterling Publishing Co., Inc.

Graham, Bob, illus. Poems for the Very Young. 2004. 80p. (J). (ps up). reprint ed. pap. 9.95 (978-0-7534-5816-7(0) , Kingfisher) Houghton Mifflin Co. Trade & Reference Div.

Greenfield, Eloise. Poetry Anthology. Date not set. 32p. (J). (ps-3). pap. 5.99 (978-0-06-443692-2(6)) HarperCollins Pubs.

Haan, Wanda. The Macaroon Moon: A Book of Poems & Rhymes for Children. Christensen, Donald, illus. 2004. 32p. (J). 17.95 (978-0-913337-51 6(X)) Southfarm Pr.

Hairston, Angelica. Did Noah Have Whales on the Ark? Ferguson, Tamara, illus. l.t. ed. 2004. 44p. (J). (978-0-9716136-1-4(3)) Broadcast Quality Productions, Inc.

Hairston, Maya. My Oh Maya: The Writings of Maya Hairston. Miller, Edwin, Jr., illus. l.t. ed. 2002. 30p. (J). (gr. k-6). (978-0-9716136-0-7(5)) Broadcast Quality Productions, Inc.

Hale, Christy, tr. & illus. It Rained All Day That Night: Autograph Album Verses & Inscriptions. Hale, Christy, illus. 2003. 80p. 16.95 (978-0-87483-735-3(9)); pap. 9.95 (978-0-87483-726-1(X)) August Hse. Pubs., Inc.

Hale, Glorya, ed. An Illustrated Treasury of Read-Aloud Poems for Young People. 2003. (Read Aloud Library). (Illus.). 192p. (J). 14.95 (978-1-57912-289-8(2) , 81289) Black Dog & Leventhal Pubs., Inc.

Hall, Donald & Hall, Donald, eds. The Oxford Illustrated Book of American Children's Poems. 2001. (Illus.). 96p. (YA). (ps-7). reprint ed. pap., pap. 12.95 (978-0-19-514578-6(X)) Oxford Univ. Pr., Inc.

Healthy Missions - Health Education Grades 2-4. 2000. 64p. (J). (gr. 4-8). pap. 8.94 (978-1-889369-45-7(4)) Teaching Ink, Inc.

Healy, Randolph. Green 532: Selected Poems 1983-2000. 2002. (Salt Modern Poets). 140p. pap. 15.95 (978-1-876857-44-8(7)) Salt Publishing GBR. *Dist:* SPD-Small Pr. Distribution.

Heard, Georgia. Songs of Myself: An Anthology of Poems & Art. 2000. (Illus.). 32p. (J). (gr. 2-5). 15.95 (978-1-57255-723-9(0)) Mondo Publishing.

Heard, Georgia, compiled by. Songs of Myself: An Anthology of Poems & Art. 2000. (Illus.). 32p. (J). 62.00 (978-1-57255-854-0(7)); pap. 4.95 (978-1-57255-722-2(2)) Mondo Publishing.

Higman, Perry. They Dream, They Cry, They Sing: Poems for Children from Spain & Spanish America. 1998. (SPA.). 148p. (J). (gr. 4-7). pap. 16.00 (978-0-910055-42-0(4)) Eastern Washington Univ. Pr.

Hollander, John, ed. Animal Poems. Mulazzani, Simona, illus. 2004. (Poetry for Young People Ser.). 48p. 14.95 (978-1-4027-0926-5(9)) Sterling Publishing Co., Inc.

Hollander, John, ed. & intro. Committed to Memory: 100 Best Poems to Memorize. Hollander, John, intro. 2003. 160p. (gr. 10). 24.95 (978-1-885983-15-2(8) , 620211, Turtle Point) Turtle Point Pr.

Hopkins, Lee Bennett. Halloween Howls: Holiday Poetry. Schuett, Stacey, illus. 2005. (I Can Read Bks.). 32p. (J). (gr. k-3). 15.99 (978-0-06-008060-0(4)); lib. bdg. 16.89 (978-0-06-008061-7(2)) HarperCollins Pubs.

Hopkins, Lee Bennett, selected by. Around the Neighborhood, Theme 3. l.t. ed. 1998. (Sadlier Phonics Reading Program). (Illus.). 16p. (YA). (gr. k-3). 29.85 (978-0-8215-0520-5(3)) Sadlier, William H. Inc.

—Around the Neighborhood: Theme Pack, Theme 3. l.t. ed. 1998. (Worlds of Poetry Ser.). (Illus.). 16p. (YA). (gr. k-3). 76.50 (978-0-8215-0527-4(0)) Sadlier, William H. Inc.

—Families, Families: Theme 2. l.t. ed. 1998. (Worlds of Poetry Ser.). (Illus.). 16p. (YA). (gr. k-3). 76.50 (978-0-8215-0517-5(3)) Sadlier, William H. Inc.

—Places to Visit, Places to See: Theme 4. l.t. ed. 1998. (Sadlier Phonics Reading Program). (Illus.). 16p. (YA). (gr. k-3). 29.85 (978-0-8215-0530-4(0)); 76.50 (978-0-8215-0537-3(8)) Sadlier, William H. Inc.

Hovey, Kate & Kimber, Murray. Ancient Voices. 2004. (Illus.). 40p. (J). 18.95 (978-0-689-83342-7(3) , McElderry, Margaret K.) Simon & Schuster Children's Publishing.

Hughes, Langston. Carol of the Brown King. Bryan, Ashley, illus. 1998. 32p. (J). (ps-3). 17.95 (978-0-689-81877-6(7) , Atheneum) Simon & Schuster Children's Publishing.

I Am of Two Places: Children's Poetry, Vol. 2. (Greetings Ser.: Vol. 2). 24p. (gr. 3-5). 31.00 (978-0-7635-3163-8(4)) Rigby Education.

I Am of Two Places: Children's Poetry: 6 Small Books. (Greetings Ser.: Vol. 2). 24p. (gr. 3-5). 31.00 (978-0-7635-1762-5(3)) Rigby Education.

Idaho Writers League Coeur d'Alene Chapter. Kaleidoscope: A Collection of Tantalizing Tales. 2003. (Illus.). (YA). (gr. 6 up). pap. 15.00 (978-0-9740481-0-9(0)) Children's Village Foundation, Inc.

James, John. Collected Poems. 2002. (Salt Modern Poets). 380p. (C). pap. (978-1-876857-40-0(4)) Salt Publishing.

Janeczko, Paul B. Dirty Laundry Pile: Poems in Different Voices. Sweet, Melissa, illus. 2001. 40p. (J). (ps-3). 16.99 (978-0-688-16251-1(7)) HarperCollins Pubs.

Jauregui, Patricia. Sentimientos. Jauregui, Reginald, ed. Pineda, Jesus, illus. l.t. ed. 2004. (SPA.). 39p. (YA). pap. 19.95 (978-1-931481-41-0(5)) LiArt-Literature & Art.

Johnson, Angela. In Daddy's Arms, I Am Tall. ed. 2004. (Illus.). (J). (gr. k-3). spiral bd. (978-0-616-03094-3(0)) Canadian National Institute for the Blind/Institut National Canadien pour les Aveugles.

Johnson, Angela & Adedjouma, Davida, contrib. by. In Daddy's Arms, I Am Tall. 2002. (Illus.). (J). (ps). 25.95 incl. audio (978-0-87499-895-5(6)); pap., tchr.'s planning gde. ed. 37.95 incl. audio (978-0-87499-896-2(4)); pap. 16.95 incl. audio (978-0-87499-894-8(8)) Live Oak Media.

Kantor, Stuart. Call Me Collective. 2003. 365p. (YA). pap. 24.95 (978-0-595-27982-1(1)) iUniverse, Inc.

Kassandra, ed. V antologia nuevo Milenio: Narracion (Cuentos) y Poesía. Ramirez, Antonio & Morrissey, Kay, photos by. l.t. ed. 2004. (SPA., Illus.). 100p. (YA). pap. 12.00 (978-1-931481-86-1(5)) LiArt-Literature & Art.

Katsuura, Jaden. Glimpses. 2004. 276p. (YA). pap. 20.95 (978-0-595-30896-5(1)) iUniverse, Inc.

Katz, Susan. Looking for Jaguar: And Other Rain Forest Poems. Christiansen, Lee, illus. 2005. 40p. (J). 15.99 (978-0-06-029791-6(3)); lib. bdg. 16.89 (978-0-06-029793-0(X)) HarperCollins Pubs.

Kendricks, Nikkia. Poetic Confession. 2001. 41p. (YA). (gr. 9-12). per. 10.00 (978-0-9704470-5-0(1)) Siedon Pubns.

Kennedy, Marge. Disney's Book of Poetry. 2002. 192p. (J). 19.99 (978-0-7868-3365-8(3)) Disney Pr.

Kroll, Virginia L. New Friends, True Friends, Stuck-Like-Glue Friends. Rosely, Rose, illus. 2004. 32p. (J). (ps-3). pap. 8.00 (978-0-8028-5202-1(5)) Eerdmans, William B. Publishing Co.

Lansky, Bruce. Funny Little Poems for Funny Little Kids. 2002. (gr. 3-6). lib. bdg. 14.10 (978-0-613-90382-0(X)) Tandem Library Bks.

—Miles of Smiles. Carpenter, Steven, illus. 2004. (Kids Pick the Funniest Poems Ser.). 128p. (J). pap. 9.95 (978-0-689-03461-9(X)) Meadowbrook Pr.

Larcom, March. Date not set. (Illus.). 32p. (J). (ps-3). 14.99 (978-0-06-024307-4(4)); lib. bdg. 15.89 (978-0-06-024308-1(2)) HarperCollins Pubs.

Lee, Dennis. Jelly Belly. Wijngaard, Juan, illus. rev. ed. 2001. 64p. (J). pap. 14.95 (978-1-55263-326-7(8)) Key Porter Bks. CAN. *Dist:* Firefly Bks., Ltd.

Lewis, J. Patrick. Monumental Verses. 2005. (Illus.). 32p. (J). (gr. 3-7). 16.95 (978-0-7922-7135-2(1) , National Geographic Children's Bks.) National Geographic Society.

Liu, Alan, ed. William Wordsworth. Muir, James, illus. 2003. (Poetry for Young People Ser.). 48p. (gr. 3 up). 14.95 (978-0-8069-8277-9(2)) Sterling Publishing Co., Inc.

Lobel, Arnold, illus. The Random House Book of Poetry for Children. 2000. (Random House Book of... Ser.). 256p. (J). (gr. k-3). 22.99 (978-0-394-85010-8(6) , Random Hse. Bks. for Young Readers) Random Hse. Children's Bks.

Loftin, Orrin. Around the Universe in a Day. 2003. 166p. (YA). per. 9.95 (978-1-59453-018-0(1) , 1107) Airleaf Publishing & Bookselling.

MacDonald, Alan. Whispering in God's Ear: Inspirational Poetry for Children. 1998. (Illus.). 96p. (J). (gr. 1-2). 7.99 (978-0-88486-217-8(8) , Arrowood Pr.) BBS Publishing Corp.

Maddox, Nellie Hazel. Grandmother Nellie's Poems, Vol. I. 2004. (Illus.). 200p. per. 24.95 (978-0-9755255-0-0(6)) Fletcher, C J Publishing LLC.

Mann, Kirk. If Dogs Could Talk & Other Animal Poems. Lanz, Lucille, ed. Mann, Kirk, illus. 1998. (Illus.). 128p. (J). (gr. 2-4). pap. 12.95 (978-1-892517-00-5(0)) Flying Snail Pr.

Mannari, Kaitlyn, et al. Out of Order. 2003. 186p. (YA). pap. 16.95 (978-0-595-30045-7(6)) iUniverse, Inc.

March Hares: The Best Poems from Fine Madness, 1. 2002. (Illus.). 404p. (YA). per. 17.95 (978-0-9722988-0-3(0)) Fine Madness.

Marshall, James. Pocketful of Nonsense. 2003. (Illus.). 32p. (J). (gr. k-3). pap. 5.95 (978-0-618-34186-3(2)); tchr. ed. 15.00 (978-0-618-34187-0(0)) Houghton Mifflin Co. Trade & Reference Div.

—Pocketful of Nonsense. 2003. (gr. k-3). lib. bdg. 14.10 (978-0-613-90053-9(7)) Tandem Library Bks.

Mayhew, James. Classic Poems to Read Aloud. 2003. (gr. k-3). lib. bdg. 17.60 (978-0-613-87033-7(6)) Tandem Library Bks.

Mboya, Sharif. Heart Fealt Doses of Reality. Mboya, Sharif, illus. 2004. (Illus.). 148p. (YA). per. 14.99 (978-0-9754024-5-0(5)) Sharif, Mboya.

McCollough, Aaron. Double Venus. 2003. (Modern Poets Ser.). 108p. pap. (978-1-84471-003-4(3)) Salt Publishing.

McKenzie, Richard. Poems from the Playground & Other Places. Gervasi, Christine, illus. 2004. (J). 12.00 (978-0-9725901-0-5(2)) Lekha Pubs., LLC.

Meltzer, Milton. Hour of Freedom: American History in Poetry. Nadel, Marc, illus. 2003. 96p. (YA). (gr. 6-9). 16.95 (978-1-59078-021-3(3)) Boyds Mills Pr.

Micklos, John, Jr. Grandparent Poems. Johnson, Layne, illus. 2004. 32p. (YA). (gr. 2-4). 15.95 (978-1-56397-900-2(4)) Boyds Mills Pr.

Monks, Julie, illus. Soft Hay Will Catch You. 2004. 128p. (J). (gr. 4-6). 17.95 (978-0-689-83460-8(8)) Simon & Schuster Children's Publishing.

Moore, Ralph. Thoughts of Roses: A Collection of Poems by Ralph S. Moore. 2003. (Illus.). 72p. 19.95 (978-0-9741193-1-1(8)) Roland & Eleanor Bergthold.

Moreno, Fanny. Busqueda: Poemas. Moreno, Fanny, ed. 2001. (SPA.). 101p. (YA). pap. 10.00 (978-0-9718874-0-4(3)) Moreno, Fanny.

Morvillo, Mabel, ed. Poemas con Sol y Son: Poesia de America Latina para Ninos. Garcia, Susana, tr. Ramos, Vicky, illus. 2001. Tr. of Poems with Sun & Song. (SPA.). 72p. (YA). (ps-2). 14.50 (978-9968-15-087-3(8)) Ekare, Ediciones VEN. *Dist:* Baker & Taylor Bks.

Mozz. The Pearls of Wisdumb: The Electric Light Verse & Shocking Scribbles of Mozz. 2003. (ENG., Illus.). 176p. (J). lib. bdg. 17.95 (978-0-9726130-0-2(5)) Goofy Guru Publishing.

Nayler, Sarah, illus. Pet Poems. 2001. 116p. (J). pap. (978-0-439-53995-1(1)) Scholastic, Inc.

New, William H. Vanilla Gorilla. Bevis, Vivian, illus. 1998. 32p. (J). (gr. k-3). pap. 12.95 (978-0-921870-57-9(4)) Ronsdale Pr. CAN. *Dist:* Literary Pr. Group of Canada.

Newbery, John & Thomas, Isaiah. Little Pretty Pocket-Book. 2006. (Illus.). 122p. (J). (gr. 4-7). per. 8.95 (978-1-55709-990-7(1)) Applewood Bks.

Newcome, Zita. Head, Shoulders, Knees, & Toes: And Other Action Counting Rhymes. Newcome, Zita, illus. 2002. (Illus.). 64p. (J). (ps). 15.99 (978-0-7636-1899-5(3)) Candlewick Pr.

Nickel, Barbara K. & Thiessen, Kathy. From the Top of a Grain Elevator. 2005. (Illus.). 72p. (YA). (gr. 2-5). pap., tchr. ed. 5.95 (978-0-88878-397-4(3)) Beach Holme Pubs., Ltd. CAN. *Dist:* Literary Pr. Group of Canada, Strauss Consultants.

Nuestro Mundo en la Poesia: Complete Set. 2003. (SPA., Illus.). (J). 225.50 (978-0-8136-0705-4(1)) Modern Curriculum Pr.

Nuñez, Ana R. Antologia de Poesia Infantil. 2001. (Coleccion Antologias). (SPA.). 180p. (Orig.). (gr. 3-12). 12.00 (978-0-89729-369-3(X)) Ediciones Universal.

Nye, Naomi. I Feel a Little Jumpy Around You: A Book of Her Poems & His Poems Collected in Paris. 1999. (Illus.). (gr. 7-12). lib. bdg. 18.80 (978-0-613-11662-6(3)) Tandem Library Bks.

Nye, Naomi Shihab. The Space Between Our Footsteps: Poems & Paintings from the Middle East. 1998. (Illus.). 144p. (J). (gr. 7-12). 22.95 (978-0-689-81233-0(7)) Simon & Schuster Children's Publishing.

—The Tree Is Older Than You Are: A Bilingual Gathering of Poems & Stories from Mexico with Paintings. 1998. (Illus.). 112p. (J). (gr. 3-7). pap. 14.99 (978-0-689-82087-8(9) , Simon Pulse) Simon & Schuster Children's Publishing.

—The Tree Is Older Than You Are: A Bilingual Gathering of Poems & Stories from Mexico with Paintings by Mexican Artists. 1998. (ENG & SPA.). (J). (978-0-606-13867-3(6)) Tandem Library Bks.

Olcott, Frances Jenkins. The Book of Elves & Fairies. 2002. (Illus.). 208p. (J). (gr. 4-7). pap. 8.95 (978-0-486-42364-7(6)) Dover Pubns., Inc.

Orgel, Joseph R. Families, Families: Theme 2. l.t. ed. 1998. (Sadlier Phonics Reading Program). (Illus.). 16p. (YA). (gr. k-3). 29.85 (978-0-8215-0510-6(6)) Sadlier, William H. Inc.

Oxenbury, Helen. The Helen Oxenbury Nursery Collection. 2004. (Illus.). 96p. (J). (gr. k-1). 19.95 (978-0-375-82992-5(X) , Knopf Bks. for Young Readers) Random Hse. Children's Bks.

Patten, Brian, ed. Puffin Book of 20th Century Childrens Verse. 2nd ed. 1999. (Illus.). 416p. (J). 16.95 (978-0-14-037684-5(4)) Penguin Bks., Ltd. GBR. *Dist:* Trafalgar Square Publishing.

Philip, Neil. War & the Pity of War. McCurdy, Michael, illus. 1998. 96p. (YA). (gr. 7-9). 20.00 (978-0-395-84982-8(9) , Clarion Bks.) Houghton Mifflin Co. Trade & Reference Div.

Protopopescu, Orel O. A Thousand Peaks: Poems from China. Liu, Siyu, tr. from CHI. Liu, Siyu, illus. 2003. (CHI & ENG.). 52p. (gr. 7 up). 19.95 (978-1-881896-24-1(2) , THPE) Pacific View Pr.

Renee, Victoria. Feelings: A Book of Teenage Poetry. 2002. (gr. 7-12). lib. bdg. 18.75 (978-0-613-77913-5(4)) Tandem Library Bks.

Replogle, Steve & Carlsen, Wendy Vergoz, eds. From a Kid's Life: A Collection of Poetry by Bromwell Students. 2004. 160p. (J). per. 10.00 (978-0-9753345-0-8(6)) Bromwell Bks.

Rette's Last Stand: Poems by Everette Maddox. 2004. (YA). pap. 15.00 (978-0-9746444-0-0(4)) Tensaw Pr., Inc., The.

Robbins, Michelle. Leaving the Scars Behind. 2004. 114p. (YA). pap. 12.95 (978-0-595-31257-3(8)) iUniverse, Inc.

Rock, Lois. What Will You Wear to Go Swimming? & Other New Poems for the School Year. 2002. 160p. (J). pap. 9.99 (978-0-7459-4574-3(0) , Lion) Lion Hudson plc GBR. *Dist:* Independent Pubs. Group.

Rodgers, Denise. Great Lakes Rhythmn & Rhyme, 2003. (Illus.). 64p. (J). per. 9.95 (978-0-938682-80-6(6)) River Road Pubns., Inc.

Rosen, Michael. A Spider Bought a Bicycle: And Other Poems for Young Children. Moore, Inga, illus. 2005. 120p. (J). (gr. k-3). reprint ed. pap. 10.95 (978-0-7534-5887-7(X) , Kingfisher) Houghton Mifflin Co. Trade & Reference Div.

Rylant, Cynthia & Dyer, Jane. Good Morning, Sweetie Pie: And Other Poems for Little Children. 2004. 32p. (J). reprint ed. pap. 6.99 (978-0-689-87060-6(4) , Aladdin) Simon & Schuster Children's Publishing.

Schneider, Babs. Giggles: Children's Poetry to Tickle Your Funny Bone. Schneider, Babs, illus. 1999. (Illus.). 22p. (J). (ps-1). pap. 7.95 (978-1-890622-98-5(2)) Leathers Publishing.

Shane, Bill. Hey Batter Batter: A Collection of Baseball Poems for Kids. 2003. (Illus.). 88p. (J). (gr. k-9). pap. 7.95 (978-1-931643-20-7(2)) Seven Locks Pr.

—Hey Batter Batter: A Collection of Baseball Poems for Kids. 2003. (gr. 3-6). lib. bdg. 16.40 (978-0-613-89868-3(0)) Tandem Library Bks.

Shapiro, Karen Jo. Because I Could Not Stop My Bike ... & Other Poems. Faulkner, Matt, illus. 2005. 32p. (J). pap. 6.95 (978-1-58089-105-9(5)) Charlesbridge Publishing, Inc.

Shea, Pegi Deitz, ed. African American Picture-Poetry Collection for Children. Date not set. (Illus.). (J). 17.95 (978-0-8050-7377-5(9) , Holt, Henry & Co. Bks. For Young Readers) Holt, Henry & Co.

Siegen Smith, Nikki, compiled by. Welcome to the World: A Celebration of Birth & Babies from Many Cultures. 2005. (Illus.). 48p. (J). 18.99 (978-1-84148-890-5(9)) Barefoot Bks., Inc.

Sierra, Judy. Antarctic Antics. 2003. (gr. k-3). lib. bdg. 14.15 (978-0-613-59876-7(8)) Tandem Library Bks.

Singer, Marilyn. Central Heating: Poems about Fire & Warmth. So, Meilo, illus. 2005. 48p. (J). (gr. 3-7). lib. bdg. 17.99 (978-0-375-92912-0(6) , Knopf Bks. for Young Readers) Random Hse. Children's Bks.

Smith, Philip, ed. Favorite Poems of Childhood. 1998. (Illus.). 96p. (Orig.). (J). (gr. 3-6). pap. 2.00 (978-0-486-27089-0(0)) Dover Pubns., Inc.

Smith, William Jay. Up the Hill & Down: Poems for the Very Young. Eitzen, Allan, illus. 2003. 32p. (J). (ps up). 16.95 (978-1-56397-028-3(7)) Boyds Mills Pr.

Sneve, Virginia Driving Hawk, ed. Dancing Teepees: Poems of American Indian Youth. Gammell, Stephen, illus. 32p. (J). (gr. k-3). tchr. ed. 17.95 (978-0-8234-0724-8(1)) Holiday Hse., Inc.

St. Mark's Community Center Youths Staff. In Due Time: Writings from St. Mark's Community Center Poetry Workshop. Lewis, Ernest, III, ed. Miller, Antoinette, illus. 2001. 24p. (YA). (gr. 3-12). pap. 8.95 (978-0-9708184-0-9(8)) St. Mark's Community Ctr.

Stahl, R. James, ed. Merlyn's Pen: Fiction, Essays & Poems by America's Teenagers, Vol. IV. 2000. 100p. (YA). (gr. 6-12). per. (978-1-886427-50-1(X) , MP4A) Merlyn's Pen, Inc.

Stemple, Jason, photos by. Once upon Ice: And Other Frozen Poems. (Illus.). 40p. (YA). (gr. 4-6). pap. 9.95 (978-1-59078-174-6(0)) Boyds Mills Pr.

Stepping Stones of Life, 1 vol. 2003. (Illus.). 110p. pap. 19.95 (978-0-9743964-0-8(0)) World of Angels, A.

Steptoe, Javaka. In Daddy's Arms I Am Tall. Steptoe, Javaka, illus. 2004. (Illus.). (J). pap. 18.95 incl. audio compact disk (978-1-59112-316-3(X)) Live Oak Media.

—In Daddy's Arms I Am Tall. 2001. (gr. k-3). lib. bdg. 15.25 (978-0-613-33300-9(4)) Tandem Library Bks.

Stutman, Suzanne. All the Power Rests with You. 2005. 185p. (YA). pap. 12.95 (978-0-9648261-7-5(8)) Manor Hse. Pubns.

Tarazona, Oscar, illus. Volando con Alas Propias. l.t. ed. 2004. (SPA.). 116p. (YA). pap. 12.00 (978-1-931481-88-5(1)) LiArt-Literature & Art.

Thomas, Tamara. ABC Poem Book. Thomas, Tamara, illus. 2004. (Illus.). (YA). (gr. 1-6). pap. (978-1-930200-28-9(5)) Martell Publishing Co.

Thou Good & Faithful Servants. 2000. 16p. (YA). (gr. 6-12). pap. (978-1-930695-94-8(2)) Sparrowgrass Poetry Forum, Inc.

Tindall, Adrienne. Sweet Dreams, My Little Ones. Tindall, Adrienne, ed. Seay, Andrew, illus. 2002. 128p. (J). (gr. k-7). pap. 18.95 incl. audio compact disk (978-1-889079-20-2(0)) Darcey Pr.

To Whom It May Concern. 2006. (YA). per. 12.95 (***978-0-9661256-8-9(1)***) Youth Communication - New York Center.

Umansky, Kaye & Chamberlain, Margaret. This Is Jane, Jim. 2002. (Illus.). 32p. (J). pap. 9.99 (978-0-09-940929-8(1)) Random Hse. GBR. *Dist:* Independent Pubs. Group.

Vecchione, Patrice, ed. & tr. Revenge & Forgiveness: An Anthology of Poems. Vecchione, Patrice, tr. rev. ed. 2004. 160p. (J). 17.95 (978-0-8050-7376-8(0) , Holt, Henry & Co. Bks. For Young Readers) Holt, Henry & Co.

Waters, Fiona. Footprints on the Page: Poetry Collection. 1999. (Illus.). 158p. (J). (gr. 3-6). (978-0-237-51844-8(9) , Evans Brothers, Limited) Evans Publishing Group.

Waters, Fiona & Julian-Ottie, Vanessa. Whiskers & Paws. 2003. (Illus.). 24p. (J). (gr. k-3). 12.95 (978-0-7696-3188-2(6) , Gingham Dog Pr.) School Specialty Publishing.

Webb, Kaye, ed. Let the Sun Shine: Stories & Poems for Reading Aloud. 1998. (Illus.). 72p. (J). (ps-3). pap. 9.99 (978-0-7112-1247-3(3)) Lincoln, Frances Ltd. GBR. *Dist:* Transition Vendor.

Whatley, Bruce, illus. My First Nursery Rhymes. 1999. (Growing Tree Ser.). 24p. (J). (ps-k). 9.99 (978-0-694-01205-3(X) , Harper Festival) HarperCollins Pubs.

White, Lee, ed. Poetry 4 Ya Mind: A Collection of Poetry & Artwork from Getting Ready. 1999. (Illus.). 128p. (J). (gr. 7-12). pap. 9.95 (978-1-892194-22-0(8)) Northwest Media, Inc.

Whitman, Walt & Long, Loren. When I Heard the Learn'd Astronomer. 2004. (Illus.). 32p. (J). 16.95 (978-0-689-86397-4(7)) Simon & Schuster Children's Publishing.

Williams, Vera B. Amber Was Brave, Essie Was Smart: The Story of Amber & Essie, Told Here in Poems & Pictures. 2004. (gr. 3-6). lib. bdg. 15.30 (978-0-613-85740-6(2)) Tandem Library Bks.

Woods, Gemal. From the Limbs of My Poetree: Selected Poems by Omekongo Dibinga, 1 disc. 2004. (ENG, FRE & SWA., Illus.). 183p. per. 24.95 incl. DVD (978-0-9760056-0-5(3)) Free Your Mind Publishing.

Worthen, Tom, ed. Broken Hearts... Healing: Young Poets Speak Out on Divorce. Hernandez, Kyle, illus. 2001. 248p. (YA). (gr. 5 up). 26.95 (978-1-58876-150-7(9)) Poet Tree Pr.

Writers Corps Youth Staff, ed. Smart Mouth: Poetry & Prose. Sorrenzo, Joey et al, illus. 2000. 156p. (YA). pap. 12.95 (978-1-888048-05-6(0) , WritersCorps Bks.) San Francisco Art Commission, The.

Yolen, Jane. Color Me a Rhyme: Nature Poems for Young People. Stemple, Jason, photos by. (Illus.). 32p. (YA). (gr. 4-6). pap. 9.95 (978-1-59078-172-2(4)); 2001. 19.95 (978-1-56397-892-0(X)) Boyds Mills Pr.

—Horizons: Poems As Far As the Eye Can See. Stemple, Jason, photos by. 2003. (Illus.). 32p. (YA). (gr. 4-6). 19.95 (978-1-56397-197-6(6)) Boyds Mills Pr.

—Street Rhymes Around the World. 2000. (gr. k-3). lib. bdg. 18.75 (978-0-613-30147-3(1)) Tandem Library Bks.

—Wild Wings: Poems for Young People. Stemple, Jason, photos by. (Illus.). 32p. (YA). (gr. 4-6). pap. 9.95 (978-1-59078-173-9(2)) Boyds Mills Pr.

Yolen, Jane, ed. Street Rhymes Around the World. 2003. (Illus.). 40p. (J). (gr. k-2). pap. 9.95 (978-1-56397-894-4(6)) Boyds Mills Pr.

Zahares, Wade, illus. Big, Bad, & a Little Bit Scary: Poems That Bite Back! 2001. 32p. (J). (gr. 1-5). 16.99 (978-0-670-03513-7(0) , Viking Juvenile) Penguin Group (USA) Inc.

250 Poesias para Ninos. 2000. (SPA.). (J). (gr. 4-6). pap. 6.99 (978-950-08-1514-7(1) , AA7256) Atlantida ARG. *Dist:* Lectorum Pubns., Inc.

POETRY—FICTION

Bagert, Brod. Hormone Jungle: Coming of Age in Middle School. 2006. (Illus.). 121p. (J). (gr. 5-8). 23.95 (978-0-929895-87-1(8)) Maupin Hse. Publishing.

Bennett, Jill. Grandad's Tree: Poems about Families. Cairns, Julia, illus. 2003. 32p. (J). 16.99 (978-1-84148-541-6(1)) Barefoot Bks., Inc.

Blackman, Malorie. Cloud Busting. 2004. (Illus.). 149p. (J). (978-0-385-60796-4(2)) Hudson Hills Pr. LLC.

Bryant, Jen. Call Me Marianne. Johnson, David A., illus. 2006. 32p. (J). 16.00 (978-0-8028-5242-7(4) , Eerdmans Bks For Young Readers) Eerdmans, William B. Publishing Co.

Cattell, Bob & Agard, John. Butter-Finger. Smy, Pam, illus. 2006. 128p. pap. 7.95 (978-1-84507-376-3(2)) Lincoln, Frances Ltd. GBR. *Dist:* Perseus Distribution.

Cazet, Denys. Minnie & Moo: Minnie & Moo: Will You Be My Valentine? Cazet, Denys, illus. 2005. (Live Oak Readalong Ser.). (Illus.). (J). pap. 16.95 incl. audio (978-1-59112-891-5(9)) Live Oak Media.

—Minnie & Moo: Will You Be My Valentine? Cazet, Denys, illus. 2002. (I Can Read Bks.). (Illus.). 48p. (J). (gr. k-3). 15.99 (978-0-06-623754-1(8)) HarperCollins Pubs.

Cazet, Denys, reader. Minnie & Moo: Will You Be My Valentine? (Read-Alongs for Beginning Readers Ser.). (Illus.). (J). (ps-3). 2005. pap. 18.95 incl. audio compact disk (978-1-59112-895-3(1)); 2004. 25.95 incl. audio (978-1-59112-892-2(7)); 2004. pap. 31.95 incl. audio compact disk (978-1-59112-897-7(8)); 2004. pap. 29.95 incl. audio (978-1-59112-893-9(5)) Live Oak Media.

Creech, Sharon. Love That Dog. 112p. (J). 2003. (gr. 3-6). pap. 5.99 (978-0-06-440959-9(7)); 2001. (gr. 3-6). lib. bdg. 16.89 (978-0-06-029289-8(X) , Cotler, Joanna Books); 2001. (gr. 5 up). 15.99 (978-0-06-029287-4(3) , Cotler, Joanna Books) HarperCollins Pubs.

—Love That Dog. 2003. (gr. 3-6). lib. bdg. 14.15 (978-0-613-61715-4(0)) Tandem Library Bks.

Crew, Gary. Troy Thompson's Excellent Poetry Book. Smith, Craig, illus. 2004. 40p. (J). 14.95 (978-1-929132-52-2(2)) Kane/Miller Bk. Pubs., Inc.

Crew, Gary & Smith, Craig. Troy Thompson's Exvellent Peotry Book. 2002. (Illus.). 32p. pap. (978-0-85091-834-2(0) , Lothian Bks.) Hachette Livre Australia.

Danneberg, Julie. Cowboy Slim. Apple, Margot, illus. 2006. (J). 15.95 (978-1-58089-045-8(8)) Charlesbridge Publishing, Inc.

Dean, Carolee. Comfort. (J). (gr. 7 up). 2004. 256p. pap. 6.99 (978-0-618-43912-6(9) , Graphia); 2002. 240p. 15.00 (978-0-618-13846-3(3)) Houghton Mifflin Co. Trade & Reference Div.

Dell, Pamela. Shaky Bones: A Story of the Harlem Renaissance. 2003. (Scrapbooks of America Ser.). (Illus.). 48p. (J). (gr. 2-6). 28.50 (978-1-59187-040-1(2)) Child's World, Inc.

Grimes, Nikki. Bronx Masquerade. 2003. 176p. (YA). (gr. 6-11). pap. 5.99 (978-0-14-250189-4(1) , Puffin) Penguin Group (USA) Inc.

—Bronx Masquerade. Myers, Chris, illus. 2001. 176p. (J). (gr. 7 up). 16.99 (978-0-8037-2569-0(8) , Dial) Penguin Group (USA) Inc.

—Bronx Masquerade. 2003. (gr. 7-12). lib. bdg. 14.15 (978-0-613-81701-1(X)) Tandem Library Bks.

—Jazmin's Notebook. 2002. (Illus.). (J). 12.34 (978-0-7587-0368-2(6)) Book Wholesalers, Inc.

—Jazmin's Notebook. 112p. (J). 1998. (gr. 8-12). 15.99 (978-0-8037-2224-8(9) , Dial); 2000. (gr. 5-9). reprint ed. pap. 5.99 (978-0-14-130702-2(1) , Puffin) Penguin Group (USA) Inc.

—Jazmin's Notebook. 2000. (gr. 7-12). lib. bdg. 14.15 (978-0-613-23623-2(8)); (Illus.). (J). 12.64 (978-0-606-18414-4(7)) Tandem Library Bks.

Haddad, Charles. Calliope Day Falls... in Love? 2003. (Illus.). 160p. (gr. 3-7). lib. bdg. 16.99 (978-0-385-90100-0(3) , Delacorte Bks. for Young Readers) Random Hse. Children's Bks.

Hesse, Karen. Out of the Dust. l.t. ed. 2004. 180p. 22.95 (978-0-7862-7006-4(3) , Large Print Pr.) Thorndike Pr.

Jonsberg, Barry. Am I Right or Am I Right? 2007. 256p. (gr. 7). (J). lib. bdg. 18.99 (978-0-375-93637-1(8)); (YA). 15.99 (978-0-375-83637-4(3)) Random Hse. Children's Bks. (Knopf Bks. for Young Readers).

Kennedy, Frances. The Just-Right, Perfect Present. Aldridge, Sheila, illus. 2006. 32p. (J). (gr. k-2). 14.95 (***978-1-58246-199-1(6)*** , Tricycle Pr.) Ten Speed Pr.

Kephart, Beth. Undercover. 2007. 288p. (gr. 7 up). (J). 16.99 (***978-0-06-123893-2(7)***); (YA). lib. bdg. 17.89 (***978-0-06-123894-9(5)***) HarperCollins Pubs. (HarperTeen).

Koertge, Ronald. Shakespeare Bats Clean-Up. 2003. 128p. (YA). (gr. 7). 15.99 (978-0-7636-2116-2(1)) Candlewick Pr.

Mangum, Kay Lynn. When the Bough Breaks. 2007. 352p. (YA). pap. 15.95 (***978-1-59038-748-1(1)***) Deseret Bk. Co.

Montenegro, Laura Nyman. A Bird about to Sing. 2003. (Illus.). 32p. (J). (gr. k-3). tchr. ed. 15.00 (978-0-618-18865-9(7)) Houghton Mifflin Co. Trade & Reference Div.

Myers, Tim. Basho & the Fox. Han, Oki S., illus. 2000. 32p. (J). (gr. k-3). 15.95 (978-0-7614-5068-9(8) , Cavendish Children's Bks.) Cavendish, Marshall Corp.

—Basho & the River Stones. Han, Oki S., illus. 2004. 32p. (J). 16.95 (978-0-7614-5165-5(X)) Cavendish, Marshall Corp.

Oldham, Mary. No Fire, No Candle. 2001. 217p. (YA). pap. 12.95 (978-1-85902-945-9(0)) Beekman Bks., Inc.

Pearson, Susan. Slugs in Love. O'Malley, Kevin, illus. 2006. 32p. (J). (ps-3). 16.99 (978-0-7614-5311-6(3)) Cavendish, Marshall Corp.

Rosenberg, Liz. Seventeen: A Novel in Prose Poems. 2002. 160p. (YA). (gr. 9 up). 16.95 (978-0-8126-4915-4(X)) Cricket Bks.

Scieszka, Jon. Science Verse. Smith, Lane, illus. 40p. (J). 2007. (ps). pap. 9.99 (***978-0-670-06269-0(3)***); 2004. (gr. 2-8). 16.99 (978-0-670-91057-1(0)) Penguin Group (USA) Inc. (Viking Juvenile).

Spalding, Andrea & Spalding, David A. E. The Klondike Ring. 2003. (Adventure Net Ser.). 128p. (J). (gr. 3-2). pap. 6.95 (978-1-55285-461-7(2)) Whitecap Bks., Ltd. CAN. *Dist:* Firefly Bks., Ltd.

Whybrow, Ian. Little Wolf's Handy Book of Poems. Ross, Tony, illus. 2005. (Little Wolf Adventures Ser.). 80p. (gr. 3-6). pap., lib. bdg. 14.95 (978-0-87614-927-0(1)) Lerner Publishing Group.

—Little Wolf's Handy Book of Poems. 2002. (gr. 3-6). lib. bdg. 12.95 (978-0-613-52430-8(6)) Tandem Library Bks.

Wilcox, Mary. On Location. 2007. (Hollywood Sisters Ser.). 240p. (J). (gr. 5). 7.99 (978-0-385-73355-7(0) , Delacorte Bks. for Young Readers) Random Hse. Children's Bks.

Wilcox, Mary. Truth or Dare. 2008. (J). (***978-0-385-90514-5(9)***); pap. (***978-0-385-73528-5(6)***) Dell Publishing. (Delacorte Pr.).

Wyeth, Sharon Dennis. Orphea Proud. 2006. 208p. (YA). (gr. 9). pap. 5.99 (978-0-440-22706-9(2) , Laurel Leaf) Random Hse. Children's Bks.

POETRY—HISTORY AND CRITICISM

Bloom, Harold. Sylvia Plath. 2000. (Major Poets Ser.). 120p. (YA). (gr. 10 up). 31.95 (978-0-7910-5935-7(9) , Chelsea Hse.) Facts On File, Inc.

Daly, Mary, ed. & illus. Into Deep Eternity: An Introduction to Emily Dickinson. Daly, Mary, illus. 2001. 110p. (YA). per. 20.00 (978-0-9723239-1-8(0)) Ye Hedge Schl.

Fletcher, Ralph J. Poetry Matters: Writing a Poem from the Inside Out. 2002. (Illus.). 160p. (J). (gr. 3-7). pap. 5.99 (978-0-380-79703-5(8) , Harper Trophy) HarperCollins Pubs.

Garcia Vino, Manuel. Juan Ramon Jimenez para Ninos. 1999. (Introduction to Hispanic Poets for Children Ser.). (SPA., Illus.). 114p. 9.95 (978-84-7960-242-0(2)) Ediciones de la Torre ESP. *Dist:* Libros Sin Fronteras.

Granfield, Linda. In Flanders Fields: The Story of the Poem by John Mccree. 2000. (gr. 7-12). lib. bdg. 17.60 (978-0-613-28535-3(2)) Tandem Library Bks.

Harley, Avis. Leap into Poetry: More ABCs of Poetry. Harley, Avis, illus. 2003. (Illus.). 48p. (J). (gr. 2-4). pap. 13.95 (978-1-56397-438-0(X)) Boyds Mills Pr.

Hyppolite, Michel-Ange. Istwa Pwezi Kreyol Ayiti. 2000. (CRP.). 266p. (YA). per. 15050.00 (978-1-58432-150-7(4)) Educa Vision.

Marsh, Carole. Gwendolyn Brooks. 2002. (One Thousand Readers Ser.). (Illus.). 12p. (J). (gr. k-4). 2.95 (978-0-635-01537-2(4) , 15374) Gallopade International.

Streissguth, Thomas. Beowulf. 2003. (Understanding Great Literature Ser.). (Illus.). 112p. (J). 29.95 (978-1-56006-861-7(2) , Lucent Bks.) Thomson Gale.

Wills, Karen & Pesta, Duke. Lord Byron. Bloom, Harold, ed. 2003. (Bloom's BioCritiques Ser.). (Illus.). 112p. (gr. 9-13). 35.00 (978-0-7910-6367-5(4) , 000872, Chelsea Hse.) Facts On File, Inc.

POETRY—PHILOSOPHY

see Poetry

POETRY—SELECTIONS

see Poetry—Collections

POETRY—TECHNIQUE

see Poetics

POETRY FOR CHILDREN

see Nursery Rhymes; Poetry

POETRY OF LOVE

see Love Poetry

POETRY OF NATURE

see Nature in Poetry

POETS

see also Dramatists

Ada, Alma Flor & Campoy, F. Isabel, contrib. by. Paths. (Literature Collection of Gateways to the Sun Ser.). 48p. (J). (gr. k-6). pap. 16.95 (978-1-59437-722-8(7)) Santillana USA Publishing Co., Inc.

Ashby, Ruth. Caedmon's Song. Slavin, Bill, illus. 2006. 32p. (J). 16.00 (978-0-8028-5241-0(6) , Eerdmans Bks For Young Readers) Eerdmans, William B. Publishing Co.

Barber, Nicola & Lee-Browne, Patrick. The Romantic Poets. 2000. (Writers in Britain Ser.). (Illus.). 30p. (J). 24.99 (978-0-237-52118-9(0) , Evans Brothers, Limited) Evans Publishing Group GBR. *Dist:* Independent Pubs. Group.

Berry, S. L. William Carlos Williams. 2003. (Voices of Poetry Ser.). (Illus.). 48p. 19.95 (978-1-58341-284-8(0) , Creative Education) Creative Co., The.

Bloom, Harold. Gwendolyn Brooks. 2004. (Bloom's BioCritiques Ser.). (Illus.). 112p. (YA). (gr. 9-13). 35.00 (978-0-7910-8114-3(1) , Chelsea Hse.) Facts On File, Inc.

Bloom, Harold, ed. & intro. Hilda Doolittle (H. D.) Bloom, Harold, intro. 2002. (Bloom's Major Poets Ser.). 120p. (YA). 31.95 (978-0-7910-6817-5(X) , Chelsea Hse.) Facts On File, Inc.

Bloom, Harold, et al. Bloom's Major Poets. (Illus.). (J). 780.30 (978-0-7910-7387-2(4) , Chelsea Hse.) Facts On File, Inc.

Bloom's Major Poets. 2005. 80-144p. pap. 1278.00 (978-0-7910-7886-0(8) , Chelsea Hse.) Facts On File, Inc.

Bryant, Philip S. Langston Hughes. 2003. (African-American Biographies Ser.). (Illus.). 64p. (J). lib. bdg. 28.56 (978-0-7398-6871-3(3)) Raintree.

Burke, Rick. Phillis Wheatley. 2003. (American Lives Ser.). (Illus.). 32p. (J). lib. bdg. 24.22 (978-1-4034-0730-6(4)); pap. 6.50 (978-1-4034-3105-9(1)) Heinemann Library.

Burleigh, Robert. Langston's Train Ride. Jenkins, Leonard, tr. Jenkins, Leonard, illus. 2004. 32p. (J). (ps-3). pap. 16.95 (978-0-439-35239-0(8) , Orchard Bks.) Scholastic, Inc.

Carmen, Cantaro. Pablo: Decimas sobre la Infancia de Pablo Neruda. 2002. (J). (978-956-240-347-4(5)) Arrayan Editores S.A.

Center for Learning Network Staff. I Know Why the Caged Bird Sings: Curriculum Unit. 2005. (Novel Ser.). 75p. (YA). tchr. ed., spiral bd. 19.95 (978-1-56077-787-8(7)) Ctr. for Learning, The.

Clinton, Catherine, illus. Phillis's Big Test. 2008. 32p. (J). (gr. k-3). 16.00 (*978-0-618-73739-0(1)) Houghton Mifflin Co.

Cuffie, Terrasita A. Maya Angelou. 1999. (Importance of Ser.). (Illus.). 80p. (YA). (gr. 7-10). 27.45 (978-1-56006-532-6(X) , Lucent Bks.) Thomson Gale.

Davis, Rebecca Henry. Fanny Crosby: Queen of Gospel Songs. 2003. (Illus.). 107p. (J). 6.49 (978-1-57924-970-0(1)) Jones, Bob Univ. Pr.

Dennis, John. Heroes of Literature: English Poets, a B. 2006. pap. 34.95 (*978-1-4254-9436-0(6)) Kessinger Publishing, LLC.

Diggory & Terence. Encyclopedia of the New York School of Poets. 2008. (Literary Movements Ser.). 400p. (gr. 9). 75.00 (*978-0-8160-5743-6(5)) Facts On File, Inc.

Doak, Robin S. Phillis Wheatley: Slave & Poet. 2005. (Signature Lives Ser.). (Illus.). 112p. (J). 30.60 (978-0-7565-0984-2(X)) Compass Point Bks.

Engle, Margarita. The Poet Slave of Cuba: A Biography of Juan Francisco Manzano. Qualls, Sean, illus. rev. ed. 2006. 192p. (J). 16.95 (978-0-8050-7706-3(5)) Holt, Henry & Co.

Fine, Anne. An Interview with Anne Fine. (Illus.). 96p. (YA). pap. 5.50 (978-1-4052-0053-0(7)) Egmont Bks., Ltd. GBR. *Dist:* Trafalgar Square Publishing.

Goodnough, David. Pablo Neruda: Nobel Prize-Winning Poet. 1998. (Hispanic Biographies Ser.). (Illus.). 128p. (YA). (gr. 6-12). lib. bdg. 26.60 (978-0-7660-1042-0(2)) Enslow Pubs., Inc.

Great Life Stories: Writers & Poets. 2004. (Illus.). 88.50 (978-0-531-19296-2(2)) Scholastic Library Publishing.

Gregson, Susan R. Francis Scott Key: Patriotic Poet. 2003. (Let Freedom Ring Ser.). (Illus.). 48p. (J). (gr. 3-4). lib. bdg. 22.60 (978-0-7368-1554-3(6) , Bridgestone Bks.) Capstone Pr., Inc.

Haugen, Brenda. Langston Hughes: The Voice of Harlem. 2005. (Signature Lives Ser.). (Illus.). 112p. (J). (gr. 5-7). 30.60 (978-0-7565-0993-4(9)) Compass Point Bks.

Headstrong Interactive, prod. The English Romantic Poets. (YA). cd-rom 149.95 (978-0-7365-4481-8(X)) Films Media Group.

Herrera, Juan Felipe. Calling the Doves: El Canto de las Palomas. 2001. (J). 14.75 (978-0-606-21098-0(9)) Tandem Library Bks.

—The Upside down Boy. Gomez, Elizabeth, illus. Tr. of Nino de Cabeza. 32p. (J). 2006. pap. 7.95 (978-0-89239-217-9(7)); 2000. (ENG & SPA.). (gr. 1-4). 16.95 (978-0-89239-162-2(6)) Children's Bk. Pr.

Herstek, Amy Paulson. Emily Dickinson: Solitary & Celebrated Poet. 2003. (Historical American Biographies Ser.). (Illus.). 128p. (J). lib. bdg. 26.60 (978-0-7660-1977-5(2)) Enslow Pubs., Inc.

Hill, Christine M. Gwendolyn Brooks: Poetry Is Life Distilled. 2005. (African-American Biography Library). (Illus.). 128p. (J). (gr. 6-12). lib. bdg. 31.93 (978-0-7660-2292-8(7)) Enslow Pubs., Inc.

Hoena, B. A. Langston Hughes. 2005. (Fact Finders Ser.). (Illus.). 32p. (J). 22.60 (978-0-7368-3745-3(0)) Capstone Pr., Inc.

Hubbard-Brown, Janet. Chaucer: Celebrated Poet & Author. 2005. (Makers of the Middle Ages & Renaissance Ser.). (Illus.). 144p. (J). (gr. 4-8). 30.00 (978-0-7910-8635-3(6) , Chelsea Hse.) Facts On File, Inc.

Jarnow, Jesse. Phillis Wheatley. 2003. (Primary Sources of Famous People in American History Ser.). (Illus.). 32p. (J). pap. 6.50 (978-0-8239-4191-9(4)) Rosen Publishing Group, Inc., The.

Jones, Veda Boyd. Jazz Age Poet: A Story about Langston Hughes. Kiwak, Barbara, illus. 2006. (Creative Minds Biography Ser.). 64p. (J). (ps-7). 22.60 (978-1-57505-757-6(3) , Carolrhoda Bks.) Lerner Publishing Group.

Jordan, June. Soldier: A Poet's Childhood. 2000. (gr. 7-12). lib. bdg. 22.25 (978-0-613-34957-4(1)) Tandem Library Bks.

Josephson, Judith Pinkerton. Nikki Giovanni: Poet of the People. 2000. (African-American Biographies Ser.). (Illus.). 128p. (J). (gr. 6-12). lib. bdg. 26.60 (978-0-7660-1238-7(7)) Enslow Pubs., Inc.

Kent, Deborah. Phillis Wheatley: First Published African-American Poet. 2003. (Spirit of America). (Illus.). 32p. (J). (gr. 2-6). 27.07 (978-1-59296-009-5(X)) Child's World, Inc.

Kent, Jacqueline C. Phillis Wheatley. 2003. (Women of the Revolution Ser.). (J). pap. (978-1-58417-089-1(1)); lib. bdg. (978-1-58417-026-6(3)) Lake Street Pubs.

Kerley, Barbara. Walt Whitman: Words for America. Selznick, Brian, illus. 2004. 56p. (J). (gr. 2-5). pap. 16.95 (978-0-439-35791-3(8) , Scholastic Pr.) Scholastic, Inc.

Kirkpatrick, Patricia. John Keats. Delessert, Etienne, illus. 2005. (Voices in Poetry Ser.). 48p. (gr. 5-9). 21.95 (978-1-58341-345-6(6) , Creative Education) Creative Co., The.

Kroll, Steven & Kroll, Steven. By the Dawn's Early Light: The Story of the Star-Spangled Banner. Andreasen, Dan, illus. 2000. 40p. (J). (ps-ps). lib. bdg. 14.15 (978-0-613-28433-2(X)) Tandem Library Bks.

Loos, Pamela. Maya Angelou: Author. 1999. (Overcoming Adversity Ser.). (Illus.). 104p. (J). (gr. 3 up). lib. bdg. 21.95 (978-0-7910-4946-4(9)); (gr. 5 up). pap. 6.65 (978-0-7910-4947-1(7)) Facts On File, Inc. (Chelsea Hse.).

Lukes, Bonnie L. Henry Wadsworth Longfellow: America's Beloved Poet. 2nd rev. exp. ed. 2004. (World Writers Ser.). (Illus.). 144p. (YA). (gr. 6-12). 23.95 (978-1-931798-07-5(9)) Reynolds, Morgan Inc.

McLeese, Don. Phillis Wheatley. (Heroes of the American Revolution Ser.). (Illus.). 32p. 2005. (gr. 2-5). 19.95 (978-1-59515-220-6(2)); 2004. (J). (ps-ps). pap. 5.95 (978-1-59515-320-3(9)) Rourke Publishing, LLC.

McLendon, Jacquelyn Y. Phillis Wheatley: A Revolutionary Poet. 2005. (Library of American Lives & Times). (Illus.). 112p. (YA). (gr. 4-8). lib. bdg. 31.95 (978-0-8239-5750-7(0)) Rosen Publishing Group, Inc., The.

Meltzer, Milton. Emily Dickinson: A Biography. 2006. (American Literary Greats Ser.). 128p. (YA). (gr. 7 up). lib. bdg. 31.93 (978-0-7613-2949-7(8) , Millbrook Pr.) Lerner Publishing Group.

Moses, Brian. Favourite Classic Poets. (Illus.). 32p. pap. (978-0-7502-4292-9(2) , Hodder Wayland) Hodder Children's Division.

Naden, Corinne J. & Blue, Rose. Maya Angelou. (African-American Biographies Ser.). (Illus.). (J). 2005. 64p. (gr. 6-9). pap. 9.50 (978-1-4109-1119-3(5)); 2004. 28.56 (978-1-4109-1042-4(3)) Raintree.

Niven, Penelope & Sandburg, Carl. Carl Sandburg: Adventures of a Poet. Nadel, Marc, illus. 2003. 32p. (J). 17.00 (978-0-15-204686-6(0)) Harcourt Children's Bks.

Padgett, Ron. Scribners Poets for Students, 3 vols. 2000. (Scribner Writers Ser.). (Illus.). (YA). 100.00 (978-0-684-80592-4(8)); 100.00 (978-0-684-80609-9(6)); 3rd ed. 100.00 (978-0-684-80610-5(X)) Simon & Schuster.

Padgett, Ron, ed. World Poets, 3 vols., Set. 2000. (Scribner Writers Ser.). (Illus.). 1396p. (YA). (gr. 9 up). 360.00 (978-0-684-80591-7(X) , GML00502-169492, Charles Scribner's Sons) Thomson Gale.

Poets & Playwrights, 5 vols., Set. Incl. Carl Sandburg. Murcia, Rebecca Thatcher. lib. bdg. 37.10 (978-1-58415-430-3(6)); Emily Dickinson. Griskey, Michele. lib. bdg. 37.10 (978-1-58415-429-7(2)); Langston Hughes. Gibson, Karen Bush. lib. bdg. 37.10 (978-1-58415-431-0(4)); Tennessee Williams. Tracy, Kathleen. lib. bdg. 37.10 (978-1-58415-427-3(6)); William Shakespeare. Whiting, Jim. lib. bdg. 37.10 (978-1-58415-426-6(8)); (Illus.). 112p. (YA). (gr. 6-12). 2006. 2007. Set lib. bdg. 185.50 (*978-1-58415-284-2(2)) Mitchell Lane Pubs., Inc.

Powling, Chris. Roger McGough. 2001. (Tell Me about Ser.). (Illus.). 22p. 15.99 (978-0-237-52291-9(8) , Evans Brothers, Limited) Evans Publishing Group GBR. *Dist:* Independent Pubs. Group.

Ray, Deborah Kogan. To Go Singing Through the World: The Childhood of Pablo Neruda. 2006. (Illus.). 40p. (J). 17.00 (978-0-374-37627-7(1) , Farrar, Straus & Giroux (BYR)) Farrar, Straus & Giroux.

Reef, Catherine. E. E. Cummings: A Poet's Life. 2006. (Illus.). 176p. (J). (gr. 7-9). 21.00 (978-0-618-56849-9(2) , Clarion Bks.) Houghton Mifflin Co. Trade & Reference Div.

—Paul Laurence Dunbar: Portrait of a Poet. 2000. (African-American Biographies Ser.). (Illus.). 128p. (J). (gr. 6-12). lib. bdg. 26.60 (978-0-7660-1350-6(2)) Enslow Pubs., Inc.

—Walt Whitman. 2002. (Illus.). 160p. (J). (gr. 4-6). pap. 7.95 (978-0-618-24616-8(9) , Clarion Bks.) Houghton Mifflin Co. Trade & Reference Div.

—Walt Whitman. 2002. (gr. 5-8). lib. bdg. 16.40 (978-0-613-70734-3(6)) Tandem Library Bks.

Rhynes, Martha E. Gwendolyn Brooks: Poet from Chicago. 2004. (World Writers Ser.). (Illus.). 112p. (YA). (gr. 6-12). 23.95 (978-1-931798-05-1(2)) Reynolds, Morgan Inc.

Rhys, Ann Gruffydd & Bryntirion, Gwasg. Nansi Dolwar. 2005. (WEL., Illus.). 31p. (978-1-85049-212-2(3)) Bryntirion Pr.

Salas, Laura Purdie. Phillis Wheatley: Colonial American Poet. 2006. (Fact Finders Ser.). (Illus.). 32p. (J). (978-0-7368-5435-1(5)) Capstone Pr., Inc.

Salem Press Editors, ed. Notable Poets, 3 vols., Vol. 3. 1998. (Magill's Choice Ser.). (Illus.). 1408p. (gr. 9 up). lib. bdg. 188.00 (978-0-89356-967-9(4) , L6, Magill's Choice) Salem Pr., Inc.

Strong, Amy. Lee Bennett Hopkins: A Children's Poet. 2003. (Great Life Stories: Writers & Poets Ser.). (Illus.). 112p. (J). 30.50 (978-0-531-12315-7(4) , Watts, Franklin) Scholastic Library Publishing.

Tracy, Kathleen. The Life & Times of Homer. 2004. (Biography from Ancient Civilizations Ser.). (Illus.). 48p. (J). (gr. 4-8). lib. bdg. 29.95 (978-1-58415-260-6(5)) Mitchell Lane Pubs., Inc.

Walker, Alice. Langston Hughes: American Poet. Deeter, Catherine, illus. 48p. (J). 2006. reprint ed. pap. 7.99 (978-0-06-079889-5(0)); 2002. (gr. 4 up). 16.99 (978-0-06-021518-7(6)) HarperCollins Pubs. (Amistad).

Wallace, Maurice O. Langston Hughes: The Harlem Renaissance. 2007. (Writers & Their Works). 160p. (YA). (gr. 9 up). lib. bdg. 39.93 (*978-0-7614-2591-5(8) , Benchmark Bks.) Cavendish, Marshall Corp.

Wooten, Sara McIntosh. Robert Frost: The Life of America's Poet. 2006. (People to Know Today Ser.). (Illus.). 128p. (YA). lib. bdg. 31.93 (978-0-7660-2627-8(2)) Enslow Pubs., Inc.

POETS—FICTION

Barnes, Henry. Percy MacKaye: Poet of Old Worlds & New. 2000. (Illus.). 127p. (J). pap. 12.50 (978-0-932776-26-6(4)) Adonis Pr.

Bedard, Michael. Emily. Cooney, Barbara, illus. 2008. 40p. (J). (gr. k-3). lib. bdg. 19.99 (*978-0-385-90539-8(4) , Doubleday Bks. for Young Readers) Random Hse. Children's Bks.

Bennett, Veronica. Angelmonster. 2007. (Illus.). 240p. (YA). (gr. 9). pap. 7.99 (*978-0-7636-3407-0(7)) Candlewick Pr.

Byars, Betsy. Keeper of the Doves. (J). 2002. 96p. (gr. 3-7). 14.99 (978-0-670-03576-2(9) , Viking Juvenile); 2004. (Illus.). 128p. reprint ed. pap. 5.99 (978-0-14-240063-0(7) , Puffin) Penguin Group (USA) Inc.

Carney, Jeffrey K. The Adventures of Michael MacInnes. 2006. 256p. (YA). 17.00 (978-0-374-30146-0(8)) Farrar, Straus & Giroux.

Dana, Barbara. Emily Dickinson: Fictionalized Biography. Date not set. (J). (gr. 3-7). 14.99 (978-0-06-028704-7(7)); 15.89 (978-0-06-028705-4(5)); mass mkt. 4.99 (978-0-06-440843-1(4)) HarperCollins Pubs.

Hayward, Linda & Seuss, Dr. Oh, Say Can You Rhyme. 1998. (J). pap. (978-0-679-87084-5(9) , Random Hse. Bks. for Young Readers) Random Hse. Children's Bks.

Hobbs, Valerie. Defiance. 2005. 128p. (J). 16.00 (978-0-374-30847-6(0)) Farrar, Straus & Giroux.

—Defiance. l.t. ed. 2006. 147p. 22.95 (978-0-7862-8667-6(9)) Thorndike Pr.

Maggie's Pets. 2001. (J). (978-1-58453-140-1(1)) Pioneer Valley Educational Pr., Inc.

McCaughrean, Geraldine. Cyrano. 2006. (Illus.). 128p. (J). (gr. 7 up). 16.00 (978-0-15-205805-0(2)) Harcourt Children's Bks.

Mitchell, Minnie Belle. James Whitcomb Riley: Young Poet. 2002. (gr. 3-6). lib. bdg. 18.75 (978-0-613-80166-9(0)) Tandem Library Bks.

Mitchell, Minnie Belle & Dunham, Montrew. James Whitcomb Riley: Young Poet, 6 vols. Mitchell, Minnie Belle & Underdown, Harold, eds. Morrison, Cathy, illus. 2nd ed. 2002. (Young Patriots Ser.: Vol. 5). 112p. (J). (gr. 3-7). 15.95 (978-1-882859-10-8(3)) Patria Pr., Inc.

—James Whitcomb Riley: Young Poet. Underdown, Harold, ed. Morrison, Cathy, illus. 2nd ed. 2002. (Young Patriots Ser.: Vol. 5). 112p. (J). (gr. 3-7). pap. 9.95 (978-1-882859-11-5(1)) Patria Pr., Inc.

Montenegro, Laura Nyman. A Poet's Bird Garden. 2007. (Illus.). 32p. (J). (ps-3). 16.00 (978-0-374-36038-2(3)) Farrar, Straus & Giroux.

Mortenson, R. K. Landon Snow & the Auctor's Riddle. 2005. (Landon Now Ser.). (Illus.). 224p. (J). (gr. 4-7). 9.97 (978-1-59310-881-6(8)) Barbour Publishing, Inc.

Moulton, Mark K. The Visit. Winget, Susan, illus. 2003. 56p. (J). 14.95 (978-0-8249-5475-8(0)) Ideals Pubns.

Moulton, Mark Kimball. The Visit. Winget, Susan, tr. Winget, Susan, illus. 2003. 56p. (J). 14.95 (978-0-8249-5859-6(4)) Ideals Pubns.

—The Visit. Winget, Susan, illus. 2001. 48p. (J). (gr. 3-6). 22.00 (978-0-7412-0866-8(0)) Lang Graphics, Ltd.

Myers, Tim. Basho & the Fox. Han, Oki S., illus. 2000. 32p. (J). (gr. k-3). 15.95 (978-0-7614-5068-9(8) , Cavendish Children's Bks.) Cavendish, Marshall Corp.

The Poet's Basket. 2006. (J). 10.00 (978-0-9769827-0-8(6)) Wren Song Pr.

Rinaldi, Ann. Hang a Thousand Trees with Ribbons: The Story of Phillis Wheatley. 2005. (Great Episodes Ser.). 352p. (YA). pap. 6.95 (978-0-15-205393-2(X) , Gulliver Bks.) Harcourt Children's Bks.

Rodriguez, Luis J. America Is Her Name. Vazquez, Carlos, illus. 2004. 32p. (gr. 4-7). reprint ed. 16.95 (978-1-880684-40-5(3)) Curbstone Pr.

—La Llaman America. Villanueva, Tino, tr. Vazquez, Carlos, illus. 2004. (SPA.). 32p. (gr. 4-7). reprint ed. 16.95 (978-1-880684-41-2(1)) Curbstone Pr.

Tashjian, Janet. Marty Frye, Private Eye. Keller, Laurie, illus. rev. ed. 1998. (Redfeather Bks.). 64p. (J). (gr. 1-3). 15.95 (978-0-8050-5888-8(5) , Holt, Henry & Co. Bks. For Young Readers) Holt, Henry & Co.

—Marty Frye, Private Eye. 2000. (978-0-606-18880-7(0)) Tandem Library Bks.

POINTE DE SABLE, JEAN BAPTISTE, 1745-1818

Marsh, Carole. Jean Baptiste Pointe du Sable. 2002. (One Thousand Readers Ser.). (Illus.). 12p. (J). (gr. k-4). 2.95 (978-0-635-01556-3(0) , 15560) Gallopade International.

POISONOUS PLANTS

Casterline, L. C. Natural-Born Killers: A Chapter Book. 2004. (True Tales Ser.). (Illus.). 48p. (J). 22.50 (978-0-516-23725-1(X) , Children's Pr.) Scholastic Library Publishing.

Casterline, Linda. Natural-Born Killers: A Chapter Book. 2005. (True Tales Ser.). (Illus.). 48p. (J). (gr. 2-4). pap. 4.95 (978-0-516-24687-1(9) , Children's Pr.) Scholastic Library Publishing.

Chinery, Michael. Poisoners & Pretenders. 2000. (Secrets of the Rainforest Ser.). (Illus.). (J). (978-0-606-20859-8(3)) Tandem Library Bks.

Ganeri, Anita. Prickly & Poisonous: The Deadly Defenses of Nature's Strangest Animals & Plants. 1999. (Weird & Wonderful! Ser.). (Illus.). 45p. (YA). (gr. 3 up). pap. 7.99 (978-0-7681-0185-0(9) , 57005, McClanahan Bk.) Learning Horizons, Inc.

Gordon, Melanie Apel, et al, contrib. by. Let's Talk about Poison Ivy. 2000. (Let's Talk Library). (Illus.). 24p. (J). (gr. 3). lib. bdg. 18.75 (978-0-8239-5415-5(3) , PowerKids Pr.) Rosen Publishing Group, Inc., The.

Pike, Katy. Plants That Bite Back. 2005. (Real Deal Ser.). (Illus.). 32p. (J). 18.50 (978-0-7910-8429-8(9) , Chelsea Hse.) Facts On File, Inc.

Platt, Richard. Plants Bite Back! 1999. (Eyewitness Readers). (Illus.). 48p. (J). (gr. 5-3). pap. 3.99 (978-0-7894-4754-8(1)) Dorling Kindersley Publishing, Inc.

—Plants Bite Back! 1999. (J). (978-0-606-18991-0(2)); lib bdg. 11.80 (978-0-613-22189-4(3)) Tandem Library Bks.

POISONS

Dahl, Michael. Poison Evidence. 2004. (Edge Books, Forensic Crime Solvers). (Illus.). 32p. (J). lib. bdg. 22.60 (978-0-7368-2697-6(1)) Capstone Pr., Inc.

Payan, Gregory. Chemical & Biological Weapons: Anthrax & Sarin. 2000. (gr. 7-12). lib. bdg. 15.25 (978-0-613-58692-4(1)) Tandem Library Bks.

Platt. Poisoning. 2004. (True Crime Ser.). (Illus.). 48p. (J). pap. 7.95 (978-1-4109-1174-2(8)) Harcourt Schl. Pubs.

—Poisoning 6-Pack. 2004. (True Crime Ser.). pap. 42.90 (978-1-4109-1180-3(2)) Harcourt Schl. Pubs.

Prokos, Anna. Killer Wallpaper: True Cases of Deadly Poisonings. (24/7 - Science Behind the Scenes Ser.). 64p. (gr. 8-12). 2007. (YA). pap. 7.95 (*978-0-531-15459-5(9)); 2006. (J). 25.00 (978-0-531-12061-3(9)) Scholastic Library Publishing. (Watts, Franklin).

Silverstein, Alvin. Poisoning. 2003. (gr. 3-6). lib. bdg. 15.25 (978-0-613-67924-4(5)) Tandem Library Bks.

Silverstein, Alvin, et al. Poisoning. 2003. (My Health Ser.). (Illus.). 48p. (J). 25.50 (978-0-531-12194-8(1) , Watts, Franklin) Scholastic Library Publishing.

POKEMON (FICTITIOUS CHARACTERS)—FICTION

Aoki, Toshinao & Toda, Akihito. Pikachu's Day. Itoh, Benimaru & Himeno, Kagemaru, illus. 1999. (Pokemon Tales Ser.: No. 4). 18p. (YA). (ps-k). 4.95 (978-1-56931-386-2(5)) Viz Media.

Dewin, Howie. Pokemon 4Ever: The Voice of the Forest. novel ed. 2002. (Pokemon Ser.). (Illus.). 72p. (J). (gr. 2-7). pap. 4.99 (978-0-439-38919-8(4)) Scholastic, Inc.

Dewin, Howie & Howie, Betsy. Mewtwo Returns. movie tie-in ed. 2002. (Pokemon Ser.). (Illus.). 80p. (J). pap. 4.50 (978-0-439-38564-0(4)) Scholastic, Inc.

Hayahibara, Megumi & Toda, Akihito. Jigglypuff's Magic Lullaby. Himeno, Kagemaru, illus. 2000. (Pokemon Tales Ser.: No. 11). 18p. (YA). (ps-k). 4.95 (978-1-56931-442-5(X)) Viz Media.

Heller, Sarah E. Bellossom's Big Battle. 2001. (Pokemon Junior Chapter Bks.: No. 11). (Illus.). 48p. (J). (ps-3). pap. 3.99 (978-0-439-23400-9(X)) Scholastic, Inc.

—Pikachu & Pichu: Pikachu's Apple Company. Batcheller, Keith, illus. 2002. (Pokemon Junior Chapter Bks.: No. 14). 48p. (J). (ps-3). pap. 3.99 (978-0-439-37212-1(7)) Scholastic, Inc.

—A Pokemon Snow-Down. Batcheller, Keith, illus. 2001. (Pokemon Junior Chapter Bks.: No. 8). 48p. (J). (ps-3). pap. 3.99 (978-0-439-20097-4(0)) Scholastic, Inc.

—Snorlax Takes a Stand. Batcheller, Keith, illus. 2001. (Pokemon Junior Chapter Bks.: No. 9). 48p. (J). (ps-3). pap. 3.99 (978-0-439-20098-1(9)) Scholastic, Inc.

—The Snubbull Blues. 2001. (Pokemon Junior Chapter Bks.: No. 12). (Illus.). 48p. (J). (ps-3). pap. 3.99 (978-0-439-23401-6(8) , Cartwheel Bks.) Scholastic, Inc.

—Two of a Kind. Batcheller, Keith, illus. 2000. (Pokemon Junior Chapter Bks.: No. 5). 48p. (J). (ps-3). pap. 3.99 (978-0-439-15431-4(6)) Scholastic, Inc.

Imakuni, Tomoaki & Toda, Akihito. Come Out, Squirtle!, Vol. 2. Kimura, Naoyo & Himeno, Kagemaru, illus. 1999. (Pokemon Tales Ser.: No. 2). 18p. (YA). (ps-k). 4.95 (978-1-56931-384-8(9)) Viz Media.

Johnson, Jennifer. Secrets of the GS Ball. 2001. (Pokemon Chapter Bks.: Vol. 24). (Illus.). 96p. (J). (gr. 2-5). pap. 4.50 (978-0-439-22091-0(2)) Scholastic, Inc.

Kawamura, Kunimi & Toda, Akihito. Lapras Makes a Friend. Aoki, Toshinao & Himeno, Kagemaru, illus. 2000. (Pokemon Tales Ser.: No. 12). 18p. (YA). (ps-k). 4.95 (978-1-56931-443-2(8)) Viz Media.

Kinebuchi, Keiji, et al. Magnemite's Missions. Kinebuchi, Keiji, illus. 2001. (Pokemon Tales Ser.: No. 18). (Illus.). 18p. (YA). (ps-k). 4.95 (978-1-56931-534-7(5)) Viz Media.

Kizuki, Sumiyashi & Toda, Akihito. Snorlax's Snack. Himeno, Kagemaru, illus. 2000. (Pokemon Tales Ser.: No. 10). 18p. (YA). (ps-k). 4.95 (978-1-56931-441-8(1)) Viz Media.

Kusaka, Hidenori. Desperado Pikachu. MATO Staff, illus. 2000. (Pokemon Adventures Ser.: Vol. 1). 206p. (YA). (gr. 4-7). pap. 13.95 (978-1-56931-507-1(8)) Viz Media.

—Legendary Pokemon. MATO Staff, illus. 2000. (Pokemon Adventures Ser.: Vol. 2). 216p. (YA). (gr. 4-7). pap. 14.95 (978-1-56931-508-8(6)) Viz Media.

—Pokemon Yellow Caballero: The Ice Cage. MATO Staff, illus. 2002. (Pokemon Adventures Ser.). 55p. (YA). (gr. 4-7). pap. 3.95 (978-1-56931-562-0(0)) Viz Media.

—Saffron City Siege. 2001. (Pokemon Chapter Bks.). (Illus.). (J). (978-0-606-22062-0(3)) Tandem Library Bks.

—Yellow Caballero: Dragonair of the Deep. MATO Staff, illus. 2002. (Pokemon Adventures Ser.: Vol. 4). 50p. (YA). pap. 4.95 (978-1-56931-725-9(9)) Viz Media.

—Yellow Caballero: Evolution Action. MATO Staff, illus. 2002. (Pokemon Adventures Ser.: Vol. 3). 51p. (YA). pap. 4.95 (978-1-56931-724-2(0)) Viz Media.

—Yellow Caballero: The Cave Campaign. MATO Staff, illus. 2002. (Pokemon Adventures Ser.: No. 6). 200p. (YA). pap. 13.95 (978-1-59116-028-1(6)) Viz Media.

—Yellow Caballero: The S. S. Ann Adventure. MATO Staff, illus. 2002. (Pokemon Adventures Ser.: Vol. 2). 52p. (YA). pap. 4.95 (978-1-56931-723-5(2)) Viz Media.

—Yellow Caballero: To Catch a Caterpie. MATO Staff, illus. 2002. (Pokemon Adventures Ser.: Vol. 1). 48p. (YA). pap. 4.95 (978-1-56931-679-5(1)) Viz Media.

—Yellow Caballero Vol. 7: The Pokemon Elite. MATO Staff, illus. 2003. (Pokemon Adventures Ser.). 208p. (YA). pap. 13.95 (978-1-56931-851-5(4)) Viz Media.

Kusaka, Hidenori & Ono, Toshihiro. Ghastly Ghosts, Vol. 5. MATO Staff, illus. 2000. (Pokemon Adventures Ser.: No. 5). 200p. (YA). (gr. 4-7). pap. 5.95 (978-1-56931-409-8(8)) Viz Media.

—Mysterious Mew, Vol. 1. MATO Staff, illus. 1999. (Pokemon Adventures Ser.: No. 1). 200p. (YA). (gr. 4-7). pap. 5.95 (978-1-56931-387-9(3)) Viz Media.

—The Snorlax Stop. MATO Staff, illus. 1999. (Pokemon Adventures Ser.: No. 4). 200p. (YA). (gr. 4-7). pap. 5.95 (978-1-56931-408-1(X)) Viz Media.

—Wanted Pikachu. MATO Staff, illus. 1999. (Pokemon Adventures Ser.: No. 2). 200p. (YA). (gr. 4-7). pap. 5.95 (978-1-56931-388-6(1)) Viz Media.

Levithan, David. Journey Through the Lost Canyon. 2000. (Pokemon Challenge Ser.: No. 1). 128p. (J). (gr. 4-7). pap. 5.99 (978-0-439-15407-9(3)) Scholastic, Inc.

Michaels, Bill. Meowth, the Big Mouth. Batcheller, Keith, illus. 2000. (Pokemon Junior Chapter Bks.: No. 2). 48p. (J). (ps-3). pap. 3.99 (978-0-439-15417-8(0)) Scholastic, Inc.

—Surf's up, Pikachu! Batcheller, Keith, illus. 2000. (Pokemon Junior Chapter Bks.: No. 1). 48p. (J). (ps-3). pap. 3.99 (978-0-439-15405-5(7)) Scholastic, Inc.

Michaels, Bill & West, Tracey. Bulbasaur's Bad Day. Batcheller, Keith, illus. 2000. (Pokemon Junior Chapter Bks.: No. 4). 48p. (J). (ps-3). pap. 3.99 (978-0-439-15427-7(8)) Scholastic, Inc.

Ono, Toshihiro. Electric Pikachu Boogaloo, Vol. 4. Ono, Toshihiro, illus. 2000. (Pokemon Ser.). (Illus.). 168p. (YA). (gr. 4-7). pap. 12.95 (978-1-56931-436-4(5)) Viz Media.

—Pikachu Shocks Back. Ono, Toshihiro, illus. 1999. (Pokemon Ser.). (Illus.). 168p. (YA). (gr. 4-7). pap. 12.95 (978-1-56931-411-1(X)) Viz Media.

—Surf's up, Pikachu, Vol. 3. Ono, Toshihiro, illus. 1999. (Pokemon Ser.). (Illus.). 167p. (YA). (ps-3). pap. 12.95 (978-1-56931-494-4(2)) Viz Media.

Pokemon Advanced. 2005. 39.98 incl. DVD (978-1-4215-0214-4(3)) Viz Media.

Pokemon movie animation team, et al. The Art of Pokemon: The Movie Spell of the Unkown, Vol. 3. 2001. (Anime Art Gallery Ser.). (Illus.). 64p. (YA). (gr. 4-7). pap. 12.95 (978-1-56931-633-7(3)) Viz Media.

Scholastic, Inc. Staff. Grovyle Trouble. 2007. (Pokemon Ser.). 48p. (J). pap. 3.99 (***978-0-545-00562-3(0)***) Scholastic, Inc.

—Shinnoh Handbook. 2007. (Pokemon Ser.). 128p. (J). pap. 6.99 (***978-0-545-00072-7(6)***) Scholastic, Inc.

Shudo, Takeshi. Pokemon the Movie 2000: The Power of One. Shudo, Takeshi et al, illus. 2001. (Pokemon Ser.). 208p. (YA). (gr. 4-7). pap. 15.95 (978-1-56931-572-9(8)) Viz Media.

Shudo, Takeshi & Sonoda, Hideki. Pokemon the First Movie. 2000. (Pokemon Ser.). (Illus.). 208p. (YA). (gr. 4-7). pap. 15.95 (978-1-56931-505-7(1)) Viz Media.

Sweeny, Sheila. Scyther, Heart of a Champion. 2000. (Pokemon Chapter Bks.: No.12). (Illus.). (J). (gr. 2-7). pap. 128.88 (978-0-439-21190-1(5)); No. 12. 96p. pap. 4.50 (978-0-439-16945-5(3)) Scholastic, Inc.

Tajin, Satoshi, et al. Pokemon Tv Animation Comic: I Choose You! Ono, Toshihiro, illus. 1999. (Pokemon Ser.). 128p. (YA). (gr. 2-7). pap. 10.95 (978-1-56931-455-5(1)) Viz Media.

Tajiri, Satoshi. I Chose You! 1999. (gr. 3-6). lib. bdg. 19.75 (978-0-613-27893-5(3)) Tandem Library Bks.

Takashi, Toshiko & Toda, Akihito. Fly on, Butterfree. Kimura, Naoyo & Himeno, Kagemaru, illus. 1999. (Pokemon Tales Ser.: No. 7). 18p. (YA). (ps-k). 4.95 (978-1-56931-420-3(9)) Viz Media.

Toda, Akihito. Bulbasaur's Trouble, Vol. 3. Itoh, Benimaru & Himeno, Kagemaru, illus. 1999. (Pokemon Tales Ser.: No. 3). 18p. (YA). (ps-k). 4.95 (978-1-56931-385-5(7)) Viz Media.

—Charmander Sees a Ghost. Himeno, Kagemaru, illus. 1999. (Pokemon Tales Ser.: No. 1). 18p. (YA). (ps-k). 4.95 (978-1-56931-383-1(0)) Viz Media.

—Look Out Houndour! Kizuki, Sumiyashi, illus. 2002. (Pokemon Gold & Silver Tales Ser.: Vol. 8). 18p. (YA). 5.50 (978-1-56931-761-7(5)) Viz Media.

—Meet Mew! Himeno, Kagemaru, illus. 2000. (Pokemon Tales Ser.: No. 9). 18p. (YA). (ps-k). 4.95 (978-1-56931-440-1(3)) Viz Media.

—Mewtwo's Watching You! Kusube, Aya & Himeno, Kagemaru, illus. 2001. (Pokemon Tales Ser.: No. 17). 18p. (YA). (ps-k). 4.95 (978-1-56931-533-0(7)) Viz Media.

—Pokemon Gold & Silver Tales Vol. 1: Detective Chikorita. Kizuki, Sumiyashi, illus. 2002. (Pokemon Gold & Silver Tales Ser.). 18p. (YA). 5.50 (978-1-56931-657-3(0)) Viz Media.

—Pokemon Gold & Silver Tales Vol. 2: Cyndaquil & the Mysterious Hole. Aoki, Toshinao & Kizuki, Sumiyashi, illus. 2002. (Pokemon Gold & Silver Tales Ser.). 18p. (YA). 5.50 (978-1-56931-658-0(9)) Viz Media.

—Pokemon Gold & Silver Tales Vol. 3: Totodile's One Gulp, Vol. 3. Ito, Benimaru & Kizuki, Sumiyashi, illus. 2002. (Pokemon Gold & Silver Tales Ser.). 18p. (YA). 5.50 (978-1-56931-729-7(1)) Viz Media.

Toda, Akihito & Wada, Junko. A Star for Tauros: Pokemon Tales. Baba, Yukiko et al, illus. 2001. (Pokemon Tales Ser.: No. 22). 18p. (YA). 4.95 (978-1-56931-652-8(X)) Viz Media.

Tsukirino, Yumi. Bulbasaur's Beau, Vol. 1. Tsukirino, Yumi, illus. 2001. (Magical Pokemon Journey Ser.: Pt. 4, No. 1). (Illus.). 40p. (YA). pap. 4.95 (978-1-56931-666-5(X)) Viz Media.

—Cooking with Jigglypuff. 2000. (gr. k-3). lib. bdg. 12.95 (978-0-613-27776-1(7)) Tandem Library Bks.

—Cooking with Jigglypuff. Tsukirino, Yumi, illus. 2000. (Magical Pokemon Journey Ser.: No. 2). (Illus.). 40p. (YA). (ps-3). pap. 4.95 (978-1-56931-456-2(X)) Viz Media.

—Love Potion Pursuit. Tsukirino, Yumi, illus. 2001. (Magical Pokemon Journey Ser.: Vol. 2). (Illus.). 40p. (YA). pap. 4.95 (978-1-56931-675-7(9)) Viz Media.

—Magic Pokemon Pt. 5, No. 4, Pt. 5. Tsukirino, Yumi, illus. 2002. (Magic Pokemon Ser.). 40p. (YA). pap. 4.95 (978-1-56931-706-8(2)) Viz Media.

—Magical Pokemon: How Do You Do, Pikachu? Tsukirino, Yumi, illus. 2000. (Magical Pokemon Journey Ser.: No. 1). (Illus.). 40p. (YA). (ps-3). pap. 4.95 (978-1-56931-446-3(2)) Viz Media.

—Magical Pokemon Vol. 3: Pokemon Holiday. Tsukirino, Yumi, illus. 2000. (Magical Pokemon Journey Ser.: No. 3). (Illus.). 40p. (YA). (ps-3). pap. 4.95 (978-1-56931-457-9(8)) Viz Media.

—Magical Pokemon Journey. Tsukirino, Yumi, illus. 2002. 40p. (YA). Vol. 1, Pt. 5. (Magical Pokemon Journey Ser.: Part 5). pap. 4.95 (978-1-56931-678-8(3)); Vol. 3,Pt. 5. 3rd ed. (Magic Pokemon Ser.). pap. 4.95 (978-1-56931-705-1(4)) Viz Media.

—Magical Pokemon Journey: From the Heart. Tsukirino, Yumi, illus. 2001. (Magical Pokemon Journey Part 2 Ser.). (Illus.). 168p. (YA). (gr. 4-7). pap. 13.95 (978-1-56931-554-5(X)) Viz Media.

—Magical Pokemon Journey Pt. 5, No. 2, Pt. 5, Vol. 2. Tsukirino, Yumi, illus. 2002. (Magic Pokemon Ser.). 40p. (YA). pap. 4.95 (978-1-56931-704-4(6)) Viz Media.

—One Lone Pikachu, Vol. 1, Pt. 3. Tsukirino, Yumi, illus. 2001. (Magical Pokemon Journey, Part 3 Ser.: No. 1). (Illus.). 40p. (YA). (ps-3). pap. 4.95 (978-1-56931-547-7(7)) Viz Media.

—Passionate Primeape. 2000. (gr. 3-6). lib. bdg. 12.95 (978-0-613-35649-7(7)) Tandem Library Bks.

—Pokemon Sleepover, Pt. 4. Tsukirino, Yumi, illus. 2001. (Magical Pokemon Journey Ser.: Vol. 4). (Illus.). 40p. (YA). pap. 4.95 (978-1-56931-677-1(5)) Viz Media.

Viz Comics Staff & Toda, Akihito. Pokemon Tales Gift Box Set 2: Psyduck's Tongue Twisters; Where's Clefairy's Voice?; Fly on, Butterfree; Dragonite's Christmas. Himeno, Kagemaru, illus. 2000. (Pokemon Tales Ser.: Nos. 5-8). 18p. (YA). (ps-k). pap. 19.95 (978-1-56931-526-2(4)) Viz Media.

Viz Communications Staff. Art of Pokemon: The Third Movie. 2001. (gr. 3-6). lib. bdg. 22.20 (978-0-613-79060-4(X)) Tandem Library Bks.

Viz Media Staff. Pokemon Vol. 1: Pikachu & Friends. 2006. (Pokemon 3D Pop Outs Ser.). 5p. (YA). pap. 9.99 (978-1-4215-1002-6(2)) Viz Media.

—Pokemon 3D Pop Outs Vol. 1: Togepi & Friends. 2006. (Pokemon Ser.). 5p. (YA). pap. 9.99 (978-1-4215-1132-0(0)) Viz Media.

Wada, Junko. I'm Not Pikachu! Pokemon Tales Movie Special. Aoki, Toshinao, illus. 1999. (Pokemon Tales Movie Special Ser.: No. 1). 18p. (YA). (ps-k). 4.95 (978-1-56931-422-7(5)) Viz Media.

Wada, Junko & Ono, Toshihiro. Pikachu Unparalleled Adventure. Aoki, Toshinao, illus. 2000. (Pokemon Tales Movie Special Ser.: No. 2). 200p. (YA). (ps-k). pap. 4.95 (978-1-56931-485-2(3)) Viz Media.

Wada, Junko & Toda, Akihito. Diglett's Birthday Party. Arai, Yasukazu & Himeno, Kagemaru, illus. 2000. (Pokemon Tales Ser.: No. 14). 18p. (YA). (ps-k). 4.95 (978-1-56931-487-6(X)) Viz Media.

—Dragonite's Christmas. Kimura, Naoyo & Himeno, Kagemaru, illus. 1999. (Pokemon Tales Ser.: No. 8). 18p. (YA). (ps-k). 4.95 (978-1-56931-421-0(7)) Viz Media.

—Eevee's Weather Report. Yamashita, Masako & Himeno, Kagemaru, illus. 2000. (Pokemon Tales Ser.: No. 13). 18p. (YA). (ps-k). 4.95 (978-1-56931-486-9(1)) Viz Media.

West, Terry M. The Legend of the Ghost Pokemon. 2000. (Pokemon Challenge Ser.: No. 2). (Illus.). 128p. (YA). (gr. 4-7). pap. 5.99 (978-0-439-15419-2(7)) Scholastic, Inc.

West, Tracey. Ash to the Rescue. 2001. (Pokemon Chapter Bks.: No. 23). 96p. (J). (gr. 2-7). pap. 4.50 (978-0-439-22092-7(0)) Scholastic, Inc.

—Attack of the Prehistoric Pokemon. 1999. (Pokemon Chapter Bks.: No. 3). (Illus.). 80p. (J). (gr. 2-7). pap. 4.99 (978-0-439-13550-4(8)) Scholastic, Inc.

—Attack of the Prehistoric Pokemon. 1999. (gr. 3-6). lib. bdg. 12.40 (978-0-613-22685-1(2)); (Pokemon Chapter Bks.: No. 3). (J). (gr. 2-7). (978-0-606-19535-5(1)) Tandem Library Bks.

—Celebi Rescue. 2007. (Pokemon Junior Chapter Bks.: No. 2). 48p. (J). pap. 3.99 (***978-0-545-00560-9(4)***) Scholastic, Inc.

—Charizard, Go! 2000. (Pokemon Chapter Bks.: No. 6). (Illus.). 96p. (J). (gr. 2-7). pap. 4.50 (978-0-439-15421-5(9)) Scholastic, Inc.

—Deoxys in Danger. 2007. (Pokemon Ser.: No. 4). 48p. (J). pap. 3.99 (***978-0-545-00564-7(7)***) Scholastic, Inc.

—The Four-Star Challenge. 2000. (Pokemon Chapter Bks.: No. 11). (Illus.). 80p. (J). (gr. 2-7). pap. 4.50 (978-0-439-16944-8(5)) Scholastic, Inc.

—Get Well, Pikachu! 2004. (Pokemon Readers Ser.: No. 6). (Illus.). 32p. (J). 3.99 (978-0-439-55991-1(X)) Scholastic, Inc.

—The Haunted Gym. 2003. (Pokemon Readers Ser.: No. 3). 32p. (J). pap. 3.99 (978-0-439-42988-7(9)) Scholastic, Inc.

—Hoothoot's Haunted Forest. 2001. (Pokemon Junior Chapter Bks.: No. 13). (Illus.). 48p. (J). (gr. k-4). pap. 3.99 (978-0-439-32066-5(6)) Scholastic, Inc.

—I Choose You! 1999. (Pokemon Chapter Bks.: No. 1). (J). (gr. 2-7). (978-0-606-19568-3(8)) Tandem Library Bks.

—Island of the Giant Pokemon. 1999. (Pokemon Chapter Bks.: No. 2). (J). (gr. 2-7). (978-0-606-19570-6(X)) Tandem Library Bks.

—Lord of the Unknown Tower. novel movie tie-in ed. 2001. (Pokemon Ser.). (Illus.). 96p. (gr. 1-3). mass mkt. 4.99 (978-0-439-29487-4(8)) Scholastic, Inc.

—Night in the Haunted Tower. 1999. (Pokemon Chapter Bks.: No. 4). (Illus.). 80p. (J). (gr. 2-7). pap. 4.50 (978-0-439-13742-3(X)) Scholastic, Inc.

—Night in the Haunted Tower. 1999. (Pokemon Chapter Bks.: No. 4). (J). (gr. 2-7). (978-0-606-19585-0(8)) Tandem Library Bks.

—Pikachu & Pichu in the City, No. 3. 2001. (Pokemon Ser.). (Illus.). 64p. (J). (gr. 1-3). pap. 4.50 (978-0-439-29488-1(6)) Scholastic, Inc.

—Pikachu in Love. 2003. (gr. k-3). lib. bdg. 11.80 (978-0-613-72182-0(9)) Tandem Library Bks.

—Pokemon: Pokemon Ranger (2007 Dtv Novelization) 2007. 112p. (J). pap. 4.99 (***978-0-545-00993-5(6)***) Scholastic, Inc.

—Pokemon Reader No.6: Get Well, Pikachu! 2004. (gr. k-3). lib. bdg. 11.80 (978-0-613-84568-7(4)) Tandem Library Bks.

—Psyduck Ducks Out. 2000. (Pokemon Chapter Bks.: Vol. 15). (Illus.). 96p. (J). (gr. 2-7). pap. 4.50 (978-0-439-20091-2(1)) Scholastic, Inc.

—Race to Danger. 2000. (Pokemon Chapter Bks.: Vol. 13). (Illus.). 96p. (J). (gr. 2-7). pap. 4.50 (978-0-439-20089-9(X)) Scholastic, Inc.

—Return of the Squirtle Squad. 2000. (Pokemon Chapter Bks.: No. 8). (Illus.). 96p. (J). (gr. 2-7). pap. 4.50 (978-0-439-15429-1(4)) Scholastic, Inc.

—Secret of the Pink Pokemon. 2000. (Pokemon Chapter Bks.: No. 10). (Illus.). 96p. (J). (gr. 2-7). pap. 4.50 (978-0-439-16943-1(7)) Scholastic, Inc.

—Splashdown in Cerulean City. 2000. (Pokemon Chapter Bks.: No. 7). (Illus.). 96p. (J). (gr. 2-7). pap. 4.50 (978-0-439-15426-0(X)) Scholastic, Inc.

—Talent Showdown. 2000. (Pokemon Chapter Bks.: Vol. 14). (Illus.). 96p. (J). (gr. 2-7). pap. 4.50 (978-0-439-20090-5(3)) Scholastic, Inc.

—Team Rocket Truce. 2007. (Pokemon Junior Chapter Bks.: No. 1). 48p. (J). pap. 3.99 (***978-0-545-00073-4(4)***) Scholastic, Inc.

—Teaming up with Totodile. 2001. (Pokemon Chapter Bks.: No. 26). (Illus.). 96p. (J). (gr. 2-7). pap. 4.50 (978-0-439-29574-1(2) , Cartwheel Bks.) Scholastic, Inc.

—Togepi Springs to Action! 2003. (gr. k-3). lib. bdg. 11.80 (978-0-613-72103-5(9)) Tandem Library Bks.

—Tough Enough. 2002. (Pokemon Chapter Bks.: No. 27). (Illus.). 96p. (J). (gr. 2-7). pap. 4.50 (978-0-439-35801-9(9)) Scholastic, Inc.

—Welcome to Sinnoh. 2008. (Pokemon Ser.). 32p. (J). pap. 3.99 (***978-0-545-01414-4(X)***) Scholastic, Inc.

West, Tracey. Winner Takes All. 2002. (Pokemon Chapter Bks.: Vol. 28). (Illus.). 96p. (J). (gr. 4-6). pap. 4.50 (978-0-439-35802-6(7)) Scholastic, Inc.

West, Tracey, adapted by. Bagon Can Fly! 2005. 45p. (***978-0-439-72184-4(9)***) Scholastic, Inc.

—I Choose You! 1999. (Pokemon Chapter Bks.: No. 1). (Illus.). 80p. (J). (gr. 2-7). pap. 4.50 (978-0-439-10464-7(5)) Scholastic, Inc.

—Pikachu in Love. 2003. (Pokemon Readers Ser.). (Illus.). 32p. (J). (gr. k-2). pap. 3.99 (978-0-439-42990-0(0)) Scholastic, Inc.

—Pokémon: I Feel Skitty. 2005. 45p. (***978-0-439-80940-5(1)***) Scholastic, Inc.

West, Tracey, adapted by. Togepi Springs to Action! 2003. (Pokemon Readers Ser.: No. 2). (Illus.). 32p. (J). (gr. k-2). pap. 3.99 (978-0-439-42991-7(9)) Scholastic, Inc.

West, Tracey & Michaels, Bill. Save Our Squirtle! 2000. (Pokemon Junior Chapter Bks.: No. 3). (Illus.). 48p. (J). (ps-3). pap. 3.99 (978-0-439-15420-8(0)) Scholastic, Inc.

Yamamoto, Kazuyuki & Toda, Akihito. First Prize for Starmie. Kimura, Naoyo & Himeno, Kagemaru, illus. 2000. (Pokemon Tales Ser.: No. 15). 18p. (YA). (ps-k). 4.95 (978-1-56931-489-0(6)) Viz Media.

—Seel to the Rescue. Himeno, Kagemaru, illus. 2000. (Pokemon Tales Ser.: No. 16). 18p. (YA). (ps-k). 4.95 (978-1-56931-488-3(8)) Viz Media.

Yume, Hajime & Toda, Akihito. Psyduck's Tongue Twisters. Himeno, Kagemaru, illus. 1999. (Pokemon Tales Ser.: No. 5). 18p. (YA). (ps-k). 4.95 (978-1-56931-418-0(7)) Viz Media.

—Togepi's Tears. Himeno, Kagemaru, illus. 2001. (Pokemon Tales Ser.: No. 21). 18p. (YA). 4.95 (978-1-56931-651-1(1)) Viz Media.

—Where's Clefairy's Voice? Himeno, Kagemaru, illus. 1999. (Pokemon Tales Ser.: No. 6). 18p. (YA). (ps-k). 4.95 (978-1-56931-419-7(5)) Viz Media.

POKEMON (GAME)

Aihara, Kazunori, illus. Let's Find Pokemon, Vol. 2. 2000. (Pokemon Ser.). 30p. (YA). (ps-3). 11.95 (978-1-56931-414-2(4)) Viz Media.

Arnold, J. Douglas & Brokaw, Brian. Pokemon Trading Card Game Player's Guide. 1999. (Illus.). 144p. (J). pap. 12.95 (978-1-884364-50-1(0)) Sandwich Islands Publishing.

Artists From The Pokemon Animated Series & Viz Comics Staff. Pokemon Standees, Vol. 2. 2000. (Pokemon Ser.). 10p. (YA). pap. 14.95 (978-1-56931-504-0(3)) Viz Media.

Artists From The Pokemon Animated Series & Viz Media Staff. Pokeman Standees, Vol. 1. 1999. (Pokemon Ser.). 10p. (YA). pap. 14.95 (978-1-56931-416-6(0)) Viz Media.

Barbo, Maria S. Official Pokemon Collector's Sticker Book. 1999. (Pokemon Ser.). (Illus.). 48p. (J). (gr. 2-5). pap. 5.99 (978-0-439-10659-7(1)) Scholastic, Inc.

—The Official Pokemon Handbook. (Pokemon Ser.). (Illus.). (J). 1999. 144p. (ps up). pap. 9.99 (978-0-439-10397-8(5)); Vol. 1. 1999. 160p. (gr. 2-7). pap. 12.99 (978-0-439-15404-8(9)); Vol. 2. 2000. 64p. (gr. 4-7). pap. 10.99 (978-0-439-15422-2(7)) Scholastic, Inc.

—The Pokemon Collector's Sticker Book No. 2: Gold & Silver Edition. 2000. (Pokemon Ser.). (Illus.). 48p. (J). (gr. 1-7). pap. 5.99 (978-0-439-15424-6(3)) Scholastic, Inc.

Boris, Cynthia. Pokemon Master: Ultimate Quiz! 2000. (Illus.). 128p. (J). pap. 9.99 (978-0-7821-2904-5(8) , Sybex) Wiley, John & Sons, Inc.

MacDonald, Mark, et al. Pokemon Trainer's Guide. rev. ed. 1999. 144p. (J). pap. 12.95 (978-1-884364-25-9(X)) Sandwich Islands Publishing.

Nintendo of America Staff. Official Nintendo Pokemon Stadium Player's Guide. 2000. (Illus.). 208p. (J). pap. 14.95 (978-1-930206-01-4(1) , NES B GD40) Nintendo of America, Inc.

—Official Nintendo Power Pokemon Trading Card Game Player's Guide. 2000. (Illus.). 112p. (J). pap. 14.95 (978-1-930206-00-7(3) , NES B GD44) Nintendo of America, Inc.

Nishida, Ryoko. Pokemon Origami. Aoyama, Minami, illus. (Pokemon Ser.). 80p. (YA). Vol. 1. 1999. (gr. 4-7). pap. 8.95 (978-1-56931-391-6(1)); Vol. 2. 2000. (ps-3). pap. 8.95 (978-1-56931-415-9(2)) Viz Media.

Pokemon Master Adventure Kit. 2000. (J). 23.99 (978-0-307-16304-2(0) , Golden Bks.) Random Hse. Children's Bks.

Psychic II. 2001. (Pokemon Evolvers Ser.). (Illus.). 4p. (YA). (ps up). 3.99 (978-1-57584-736-8(1)) Reader's Digest Children's Publishing, Inc.

Revelation Lugia Staff, et al. The Movie 2000. 2000. (Pokemon Ser.). (Illus.). 64p. (YA). (gr. 4-7). pap. 9.95 (978-1-56931-502-6(7)) Viz Media.

Scholastic, Inc. Staff & Entin, Carli. Pokemon Pop Quiz! 2000. (Pokemon Ser.). (Illus.). 64p. (J). (gr. 2-7). pap. 3.99 (978-0-439-15406-2(5)) Scholastic, Inc.

Shudo, Takeshi & Sonoda, Hideki. The Art of Pokemon, Volume 1 Vol. 1: The 1st Movie. 1999. (Pokemon Ser.). (Illus.). 64p. (YA). (gr. 4-7). pap. 8.95 (978-1-56931-427-2(6)) Viz Media.

Snyder, Jeffrey B., ed. Collecting Pokemon: An Unauthorized Handbook & Price Guide. 2000. (Schiffer Book for Collectors Ser.). (Illus.). 128p. pap. 9.95 (978-0-7643-1075-1(5)) Schiffer Publishing, Ltd.

Teitelbaum, Michael. Extreme Pokemon. 2000. (Pokemon Ser.). (Illus.). 96p. (J). (gr. 3-7). pap. 9.99 (978-0-439-19401-3(6)) Scholastic, Inc.

Tsukirino, Yumi. The Pokemon Watcher's Diary Vol. 2, Pt. 3. Tsukirino, Yumi, illus. 2001. (Magical Pokemon Journey, Part 3 Ser.: No. 2). (Illus.). 40p. (YA). (ps-3). pap. 4.95 (978-1-56931-555-2(8)) Viz Media.

Viz Comics Staff. Stick 'N Play Book, Vol. 1. 2000. (Pokemon Ser.). (Illus.). 10p. (YA). (ps-3). 11.95 (978-1-56931-417-3(9)) Viz Media.

West, Tracey. Top 10 of Everything Handbook. 2007. (Pokemon Ser.). 80p. (J). pap. 6.99 ***(978-0-439-89047-2(0))*** Scholastic, Inc.

West, Tracey & Nolls, Katherine. Official Pokémon Pokédex. 2006. (Illus.). 111p. (J). (978-0-439-85586-0(1)) Scholastic, Inc.

Yume, Hajime & Toda, Akihito. Where's Clefairy's Voice? Himeno, Kagemaru, illus. 1999. (Pokemon Tales Ser.: No. 6). 18p. (YA). (ps-k). 4.95 (978-1-56931-419-7(5)) Viz Media.

POLAND

Anderson, Dale. Polish Americans. 2006. (World Almanac Library of American Immigration). (Illus.). 48p. (J). pap. (978-0-8368-7330-6(0)); lib. bdg. (978-0-8368-7317-7(3)) Stevens, Gareth Inc. (World Almanac Library).

Andronik, Catherine M. Copernicus: Founder of Modern Astronomy. 2002. (Great Minds of Science Ser.). (Illus.). 112p. (J). (gr. 4-10). lib. bdg. 26.60 (978-0-7660-1755-9(9)) Enslow Pubs., Inc.

Ayer, Eleanor H. In the Ghettos: Teens Who Survived the Ghettos of the Holocaust. 1999. (Teen Witnesses to the Holocaust Ser.). (Illus.). 64p. (YA). (gr. 7-12). lib. bdg. 26.50 (978-0-8239-2845-3(4) , TWGHET) Rosen Publishing Group, Inc., The.

Callahan, Kerry P. Mordechai Anielewicz: Hero of the Warsaw Ghetto Uprising. 2005. (Holocaust Biographies Ser.). (Illus.). 112p. (YA). (gr. 7-12). lib. bdg. 26.50 (978-0-8239-3377-8(6)) Rosen Publishing Group, Inc., The.

Corona, Laurel. Poland. 2000. (Modern Nations of the World Ser.). (Illus.). 128p. (YA). (gr. 7-10). 28.70 (978-1-56006-600-2(8) , Lucent Bks.) Thomson Gale.

Dell'Oro, Suzanne Paul. Poland. 2001. (Countries of the World Ser.). (Illus.). 24p. (J). (gr. 2-3). lib. bdg. 18.60 (978-0-7368-0944-3(9) , Bridgestone Bks.) Capstone Pr., Inc.

Docalavich, Heather. Poland. 2006. (European Union Ser.). (Illus.). 88p. (YA). (gr. 5 up). lib. bdg. (978-1-4222-0058-2(2)) Mason Crest Pubs.

Everett, Charles & Everett, Barbara. Poland. 2003. (Changing Face Of... Ser.). (Illus.). 48p. (J). lib. bdg. 28.56 (978-0-7398-6041-0(0)) Raintree.

Furlong, Kate A. Poland. 2001. (Countries Ser.). (Illus.). 40p. (J). (gr. k-6). lib. bdg. 22.78 (978-1-57765-498-8(6) , Checkerboard Library) ABDO Publishing Co.

Grajnert, Paul. Poland. 2002. (Countries of the World Ser.). (Illus.). 96p. (J). (gr. 6 up). lib. bdg. 30.00 (978-0-8368-2345-5(1)) Stevens, Gareth Inc.

Heale, Jay. Poland. 2nd ed. 2005. (Cultures of the World Ser.). (Illus.). 144p. (J). 37.07 (978-0-7614-1847-4(4)) Cavendish, Marshall Corp.

Lobel, Anita. No Pretty Pictures: A Child of War. 2000. (Illus.). 208p. (J). (gr. 5 up). pap. 6.99 (978-0-380-73285-2(8)) HarperCollins Pubs.

—No Pretty Pictures: A Child of War. 2000. (978-0-606-17979-9(8)); (gr. 5-8). lib. bdg. 14.15 (978-0-613-28590-2(5)) Tandem Library Bks.

McCollum, Sean. Poland. 1999. (Ticket to Ser.). (Illus.). 48p. (gr. 2-4). lib. bdg. 22.60 (978-1-57505-131-4(1)); (J). (gr. 3-5). lib. bdg. 22.60 (978-1-57505-106-2(0) , Carolrhoda Bks.) Lerner Publishing Group.

Mulla-Feroze, Umaima & Grajnert, Paul. Welcome to Poland. 2003. (Welcome to My Country Ser.). (Illus.). 48p. (J). (gr. 2 up). lib. bdg. 26.00 (978-0-8368-2545-9(4)) Stevens, Gareth Inc.

Nichols, Jeremy & Trembicka-Nichols, Emilia. Poland. 2005. (Countries of the World Ser.). 64p. (J). (gr. 6-12). 30.00 (978-0-8160-6005-4(3)) Facts On File, Inc.

Parks, Deborah A. John Paul II: The Pope from Poland. 2002. (Gateway Biography Ser.). (Illus.). 48p. (gr. 2-4). lib. bdg. 23.90 (978-0-7613-2320-4(1) , Millbrook Pr.) Lerner Publishing Group.

Ryan, Patrick. Welcome to Poland. 2008. (Welcome to the World Ser.). 32p. (J). (gr. 1-5). 27.07 ***(978-1-59296-974-6(7))*** Child's World, Inc.

Ryan, Patrick & Berendes, Mary. Poland. 2007. (Welcome to the World Ser.). 32p. (J). (gr. 1-5). 27.07 ***(978-1-59296-920-3(8))*** Child's World, Inc.

Ueda, Reed & Stotsky, Sandra, eds. Polish-American Answer Book. 1999. (Ethnic Answer Book Ser.). (Illus.). 136p. (YA). (gr. 5 up). pap. 9.95 (978-0-7910-4802-3(0)); lib. bdg. 8.95 (978-0-7910-4801-6(2)) Facts On File, Inc. (Chelsea Hse.).

Zuehlke, Jeffrey. Poland in Pictures. 2006. (Visual Geography Ser., Second Ser.). (Illus.). 80p. (J). 27.93 (978-0-8225-2676-6(X) , Lerner Pubns.) Lerner Publishing Group.

Zwierzynska-Coldicott, Aldona M. Poland. 1998. (Festivals of the World Ser.). (Illus.). 32p. (J). (gr. 3 up). lib. bdg. 24.67 (978-0-8368-2018-8(5)) Stevens, Gareth Inc.

POLAND—FICTION

Boyne, John. The Boy in the Striped Pajamas. 2006. 224p. (YA). (gr. 7). 15.95 (978-0-385-75106-3(0)); lib. bdg. 17.99 (978-0-385-75107-0(9)) Random Hse. Children's Bks. (Fickling, David Bks.).

Gleitzman, Morris. Once. 2005. 160p. (J). pap. ***(978-0-14-330195-0(0)*** , Puffin) Penguin Group (USA) Inc.

Harcourt School Publishers Staff. Olga's Bakery On Level. 3rd ed. 2002. (Trophies Reading Program Ser.). (Illus.). pap. 5.10 (978-0-15-323275-6(7)) Harcourt Schl. Pubs.

Hautzig, Esther. A Picture of Grandmother. Peck, Beth, illus. 2002. 80p. (J). (gr. 2-5). 15.00 (978-0-374-35920-1(2) , Farrar, Straus & Giroux (BYR)) Farrar, Straus & Giroux.

Kimmel, Eric A. The Jar of Fools: Eight Hanukkah Stories from Chelm. Gerstein, Mordicai, illus. 64p. (J). (gr. 4-6). tchr. ed. 18.95 (978-0-8234-1463-5(9)) Holiday Hse., Inc.

Kirk, Heather. Warsaw Spring. 2004. 244p. (YA). (gr. 9 up). pap. 8.95 (978-0-929141-86-2(5)) Napoleon Publishing/Rendezvous Pr. CAN. *Dist:* AtlasBooks Distribution.

Koons, Jon. A Confused Hanukkah: An Original Story of Chelm. Schindler, S. D., illus. 2004. 40p. (J). (gr. k). 16.99 (978-0-525-46969-8(9) , Dutton Juvenile) Penguin Group (USA) Inc.

Mackall, Dandi Daley. Eva Underground. 2006. (Illus.). 256p. (YA). 17.00 (978-0-15-205462-5(6)) Harcourt Trade Pubs.

Nattel, Lilian. River Midnight. 1999. (978-0-606-17451-0(6)) Tandem Library Bks.

Orlev, Uri. Run Boy, Run. Halkin, Hillel, tr. from HEB. 2003. 192p. (YA). (gr. 5 up). tchr. ed. 15.00 (978-0-618-16465-3(0) , Walter Lorraine) Houghton Mifflin Co. Trade & Reference Div.

Pressler, Mirjam. Malka. Murdoch, Brian, tr. from GER. 2003. 288p. (YA). (gr. 5-12). 18.99 (978-0-399-23984-7(7) , Philomel) Penguin Group (USA) Inc.

Rosner, Mina. I Am a Witness. (Illus.). 112p. (YA). (gr. 3 up). pap. (978-0-920534-92-2(9)) Hyperion Pr., Ltd.

Roy, Jennifer Rozines. Yellow Star. 2006. 256p. (YA). (gr. 5-9). 16.95 (978-0-7614-5277-5(X)) Cavendish, Marshall Corp.

Sasson, Jean. Ester's Child. 2003. (gr. 7-12). lib. bdg. 22.20 (978-0-613-70913-2(6)) Tandem Library Bks.

Wolf, Joan M. Someone Named Eva. 2007. 208p. (J). (gr. 5-9). 16.00 (978-0-618-53579-8(9) , Clarion Bks.) Houghton Mifflin Co. Trade & Reference Div.

Yolen, Jane. The Devil's Arithmetic. 2002. (J). 13.19 (978-0-7587-9594-6(7)) Book Wholesalers, Inc.

—The Devil's Arithmetic. 2004. (Puffin Modern Classics Ser.). 176p. (gr. 3). pap. 6.99 (978-0-14-240109-5(9) , Puffin) Penguin Group (USA) Inc.

POLAR EXPEDITIONS

see Antarctica; Arctic Regions; North Pole; Polar Regions; South Pole

POLAR REGIONS

see also Antarctica; Arctic Regions; North Pole; South Pole

Anderson, Harry S. Exploring the Polar Regions, 10 vols. 2004. (Discovery & Exploration Ser.). (Illus.). 176p. (J). (gr. 6-12). 40.00 (978-0-8160-5259-2(X)) Facts On File, Inc.

Apte, Sunita. Polar Regions: Surviving in Antarctica. 2005. (X-treme Places Ser.). (Illus.). 32p. (J). (gr. 3-7). lib. bdg. 25.27 (978-1-59716-088-9(1)) Bearport Publishing Co., Inc.

Benduhn, Tea. Living in Polar Regions. 2007. (J). pap. ***(978-0-8368-8348-0(9));*** 24p. (gr. 2-4). lib. bdg. 19.93 ***(978-0-8368-8343-5(8))*** Stevens, Gareth Inc. (Weekly Reader Early Learning Library).

Billings. True Tales of Freezing Land. 1999. (Illus.). (J). pap. 13.00 (978-0-7398-2393-4(0)) Steck-Vaughn.

Broderick, Enid. Roald Amundsen. (Great Explorers Ser.). (Illus.). 48p. (J). (gr. 5 up). 2002. pap. 14.60 (978-0-8368-5171-7(4)); 2001. lib. bdg. 30.00 (978-0-8368-5011-6(4)) Stevens, Gareth Inc. (World Almanac Library).

Butz, Christopher. Tundra Animals. 2002. (Animals of the Biomes Ser.). (Illus.). 48p. (J). lib. bdg. 25.70 (978-0-7398-5691-8(X)) Raintree.

—Tundra Animals. 2002. (Animals of the Biomes Ser.). (Illus.). 48p. (J). pap. (978-0-7398-6410-4(6)) Steck-Vaughn.

Byles, Monica. Life in the Polar Lands. 2000. (Two-Can Ecology Bk.). (Illus.). (J). (978-0-606-20765-2(1)) Tandem Library Bks.

—Life in the Polar Lands. 2001. (World Book Ecology Ser.). (Illus.). 32p. (J). (978-0-7166-5223-6(4)) World Bk., Inc.

—Polar Lands. 2004. (Life In... Ser.). (SPA., Illus.). (J). (gr. 3-6). 32p. pap. 6.95 (978-1-58728-572-1(X)); 48p. pap. 14.95 incl. cd-rom (978-1-58728-452-6(9)) T&N Children's Publishing. (Two Can Publishing).

—Polar Lands. Mosley, Francis, illus. 2004. (Life In... Ser.). (SPA.). 32p. (gr. 3-6). 12.95 (978-1-58728-557-8(6) , Two Can Publishing) T&N Children's Publishing.

Champion, Neil. Polar Regions. 2005. (Caring for the Planet Ser.). (Illus.). 48p. (J). (978-1-58340-512-3(7)) Smart Apple Media.

Conlan, Kathy. Under the Ice. Conlan, Kathy, illus. 2002. (Illus.). 56p. (J). (gr. 4-6). (978-1-55337-001-7(5)) Kids Can Pr., Ltd.

Cooper, Wade & Page, Nick. Polar Animals. 2007. (Scholastic Reader Level 1 Ser.). 32p. (J). pap. 3.99 ***(978-0-545-00718-4(6)*** , Cartwheel Bks.) Scholastic, Inc.

Desonie, Dana. Polar Regions. 2007. (Our Fragile Planet Ser.). 176p. (gr. 6-12). 35.00 ***(978-0-8160-6218-8(8)*** , Chelsea Hse.) Facts On File, Inc.

DK Publishing. Polar Life. 2008. 14p. (J). (gr. 3). 12.99 ***(978-0-7566-3531-2(4))*** Dorling Kindersley Publishing, Inc.

Dorling Kindersley Publishing Staff. Arctic & Antarctic. 2006. (Eye Wonder Ser.). (Illus.). 48p. (J). 9.99 (978-0-7566-1980-0(7)); lib. bdg. 17.99 (978-0-7566-1981-7(5)) Dorling Kindersley Publishing, Inc.

Dowswell, Paul. True Polar Adventures. Woodcock, John, illus. 2004. (True Adventure Stories Ser.). 144p. (J). pap. 4.95 (978-0-7945-0404-5(3) , Usborne) EDC Publishing.

First Book about Animals of the Polar Regions. 1999. (First Book about Animals Ser.). (Illus.). 16p. (J). (ps up). lib. bdg. 19.33 (978-0-8368-2652-4(3)) Stevens, Gareth Inc.

Fowler, Allan. Antarctica. 2001. (Rookie Read-About Geography Ser.). (Illus.). 32p. (J). (gr. 1-2). 20.50 (978-0-516-21669-0(4) , Children's Pr.) Scholastic Library Publishing.

Ganeri, Anita. Perishing Poles. 2002. (Horrible Geography Ser.). (Illus.). 128p. (J). pap. (978-0-439-48302-5(6)) Scholastic, Inc.

—Protecting Polar Regions. 2005. (Protecting Habitats Ser.). (J). lib. bdg. 24.67 (978-0-8368-4993-6(0)) Stevens, Gareth Inc.

Goodman, Susan E. Life on the Ice. Doolittle, Michael J., illus. Doolittle, Michael J., photos by. 2006. 32p. (J). 22.60 (978-0-7613-2775-2(4) , Millbrook Pr.) Lerner Publishing Group.

Gritzner, Charles F. Polar Regions. 2007. (Geography of Extreme Environments Ser.). 128p. (J). (gr. 6-12). 24.95 (978-0-7910-9235-4(6) , Chelsea Hse.) Facts On File, Inc.

Hess, Paul, illus. Polar Animals. 1998. (Animal Worlds Ser.). (YA). (ps up) (978-1-84089-009-9(6) , 868229, Zero to Ten, Limited) Evans Publishing Group.

Hodge, Deborah. Polar Animals. Stephens, Pat, illus. 2008. 24p. pap. ***(978-1-55453-044-1(X))*** Kids Can Pr., Ltd.

Hynes, Margaret. Polar Lands. (Science Kids Ser.). (Illus.). 48p. (J). 2007. pap. 6.95 ***(978-0-7534-6166-2(8));*** 2005. 9.95 (978-0-7534-5868-6(3)) Houghton Mifflin Co. Trade & Reference Div. (Kingfisher).

Isn't It Cool? Individual Title Six-Packs. (Action Packs Ser.). 128p. (gr. 3-5). 44.00 (978-0-7635-3307-6(6)) Rigby Education.

Johnson, Allen L. Kayaking Around Iceland: Adventures with Grandchildren. 2003. (Illus.). 196p. 15.00 (978-1-880675-07-6(2)) Creative Enterprises.

Kerr, Jim. Polar Regions. 2007. (J). ***(978-1-4329-0111-0(7));*** pap. ***(978-1-4329-0117-2(6))*** Heinemann Library.

Kingfisher Editors, ed. Animal Babies in Polar Lands. 2006. (Animal Babies Ser.). 24p. (J). (ps-k). bds. 6.95 (978-0-7534-5944-7(2) , Kingfisher) Houghton Mifflin Co. Trade & Reference Div.

Lindeen, Carol. Life in a Polar Region. 2003. (Pebble Plus: Living in a Biome Ser.). (Illus.). 24p. (J). lib. bdg. 17.26 (978-0-7368-2100-1(7) , Pebble Bks.) Capstone Pr., Inc.

Lindeen, Carol K. Life in a Polar Region, Vol. 3. 2005. (Earth & Outer Space Ser.). 24p. (YA). (gr. k-3). pap. (978-0-7368-3401-8(X) , Pebble Bks.) Capstone Pr., Inc.

Macken, JoAnn Early. Polar Animals. Hess, Paul, illus. 2002. (Animal Worlds Ser.). 24p. (J). (ps up). lib. bdg. 20.67 (978-0-8368-3040-8(7)) Stevens, Gareth Inc.

Mason, Paul. Polar Regions. 2004. (Geography Fact Files Ser.). (J). lib. bdg. 28.50 (978-1-58340-428-7(7)) Smart Apple Media.

Mayer, Cassie. Polar Region. 2007. (J). ***(978-1-4034-9426-9(6));*** pap. ***(978-1-4034-9432-0(0))*** Heinemann Library.

McNeil, Niki, et al. HOCPP 1119 Polar Habitats. 2006. spiral bd. 22.50 ***(978-1-60308-119-1(4))*** In the Hands of a Child.

Morgan, Sally. Polar Regions. (Extreme Survival Ser.). (Illus.). 32p. (J). 2004. pap. 7.95 (978-1-4109-0362-4(1)); 2003. lib. bdg. 25.70 (978-1-4109-0003-6(7)) Raintree.

—Polar Regions. 2003. (gr. 3-6). lib. bdg. 16.40 (978-0-613-78256-2(9)) Tandem Library Bks.

Murphy, Brian & Watts, Claire. Polar Lands. 2004. (Discovery Guides Ser.). (SPA., Illus.). 32p. (J). (gr. 2-5). 11.95 (978-1-58728-230-0(5)); pap. 6.95 (978-1-58728-224-9(0)) T&N Children's Publishing. (Two Can Publishing).

Murphy, Bryan. Polar Lands. 2001. (gr. 3-6). lib. bdg. 15.25 (978-0-613-85495-5(0)) Tandem Library Bks.

Murphy, Patricia J. Why Are the North & South Poles So Cold? 2004. (Library of Why). (Illus.). 24p. (J). lib. bdg. 18.75 (978-0-8239-6233-4(4) , PowerKids Pr.) Rosen Publishing Group, Inc., The.

Nichols, Catherine. Polar Adventures. 2004. (True Tales Ser.). (J). (gr. 2-4). pap. 4.95 (978-0-516-24606-2(2) , Children's Pr.) Scholastic Library Publishing.

—Polar Adventures: A Chapter Book. 2003. (True Tales Ser.). (Illus.). 48p. (J). 22.50 (978-0-516-22920-1(6) , Children's Pr.) Scholastic Library Publishing.

NorthWord Books for Young Readers Editors, contrib. by. Polar Babies. 2003. (Animal Babies Ser.). (Illus.). 22p. (J). (ps up). bds. 5.95 (978-1-55971-875-2(7) , NorthWord Bks. for Young Readers) T&N Children's Publishing.

Pipe, Jim. Polar Region Survival. 2007. (Extreme Habitats Ser.). 32p. (J). (gr. 4-6). lib. bdg. 25.27 ***(978-0-8368-8248-3(2))*** Stevens, Gareth Inc.

Polar Exploration Adventures, 6 vols. (gr. 4 up). 39.95 (978-0-7368-9026-7(2)) Red Brick Learning.

Quadrillion Media Staff. Polar Regions, 2000. (Start Me Up Ser.: Vol. 13). (Illus.). (J). 12.95 (978-1-58185-017-8(4)) Quadrillion Media LLC.

Raintree Steck-Vaughn Staff. True Tales from the Polar Regions. 1999. (Illus.). (J). pap. 13.00 (978-0-7398-0855-9(9)) Steck-Vaughn.

Riley, Peter D. The Polar Regions. 2004. (Survivor's Science Ser.). 28.56 (978-1-4109-0228-3(5)) Harcourt Schl. Pubs.

Rootes, David. Polar Regions. 2000. (Exploration Into... Ser.). (Illus.). 48p. (J). (gr. 4-7). 25.00 (978-0-7910-6026-1(8) , Chelsea Hse.) Facts On File, Inc.

Saffer, Barbara. Polar Exploration Adventures. 2000. (Dangerous Adventures Ser.). (Illus.). 48p. (J). (gr. 3-4). lib. bdg. 21.26 (978-0-7368-0572-8(9) , Capstone High-Interest Bks.) Capstone Pr., Inc.

Schofield, Jennifer. Animal Babies in Polar Lands. 2004. (Animal Babies Ser.). (Illus.). 32p. (J). (ps-k). 7.95 (978-0-7534-5755-9(5) , Kingfisher) Houghton Mifflin Co. Trade & Reference Div.

Snedden, Robert. Around the Poles. 2003. (Illus.). 32p. (J). lib. bdg. (978-1-58340-383-9(3)) Smart Apple Media.

Snowden, Maxine. Polar Explorers for Kids: Historic Expeditions to the Arctic & Antarctic with 21 Activities. 2003. (For Kids Ser.). 160p. (J). pap. 16.95 (978-1-55652-500-1(1)) Chicago Review Pr., Inc.

Steger, Will & Bowermaster, Jon. Over the Top of the World. 1999. (Illus.). 64p. (J). (gr. 3-7). pap. 5.99 (978-0-590-84861-9(5)) Scholastic, Inc.

Stonehouse, Bernard. Nature Unfolds the Poles. 2001. (Nature Unfolds Ser.). (Illus.). 40p. (J). (gr. 4). pap. (978-0-7787-0321-1(5)); lib. bdg. (978-0-7787-0309-9(6)) Crabtree Publishing Co.

—Poles. 2001. (gr. 5-8). lib. bdg. 18.75 (978-0-613-89192-9(9)) Tandem Library Bks.

Taylor, Barbara. Polar Habitats. 2006. (Exploring Habitats Ser.). (Illus.). 36p. (J). lib. bdg. (978-0-8368-7256-9(8)) Stevens, Gareth Inc.

—Pole to Pole. 1999. (Natural World Ser.). (Illus.). 31p. (J). (gr. 5-9). pap. 5.95 (978-0-7641-0639-2(2)) Barron's Educational Series, Inc.

Theodorou, Rod. From the Arctic to the Antarctic. 2000. (Amazing Journeys Ser.). (Illus.). 32p. (J). (gr. 3-5). lib. bdg. 22.79 (978-1-57572-485-0(5)) Heinemann Library.

Townsend, Emily Rose. Polar Animals, 4 bks. Incl. Arctic Foxes. lib. bdg. 15.93 (978-0-7368-2356-2(5)); Penguins. Saunders-Smith, Gail, ed. lib. bdg. 15.93 (978-0-7368-2357-9(3)); Polar Bears. Saunders-Smith, Gail, ed. lib. bdg. 15.93 (978-0-7368-2358-6(1)); Seals. lib. bdg. 15.93 (978-0-7368-2359-3(X)); 24p. (J). (gr. k-1). 2004. (Illus.). 2004. Set lib. bdg. 63.72 (978-0-7368-2532-0(0) , Pebble Bks.) Capstone Pr., Inc.

Watts, Claire. Polar Regions. Donohoe, Bill, illus. 1998. (Launch Pad Library). 32p. (J). (gr. k-4). 11.95 (978-1-58087-004-7(X)) Stampley, C.D. Enterprises, Inc.

—Regiones Polares. Sanz, Maria T., tr. Donohoe, Bill, illus. 1998. (Coleccion Descubre Tu Mundo). (SPA.). 32p. (J). (gr. 3-5). 11.95 (978-1-58087-011-5(2) , SY8643) Stampley, C.D. Enterprises, Inc.

Who Grows up in the Snow? (Who Grows up Here? Ser.). 24p. (J). 7.95 (978-1-4048-0210-0(X)) Picture Window Bks.

Wickings, Ruth. Animals on the Ice. 2006. (First Fun Pop-ups Ser.). (Illus.). 12p. bds. 8.95 (978-1-84560-022-8(3)) Mercury Bks. Ltd. GBR. *Dist:* International Publishers Marketing.

Woodford, Arctic Tundra Polar Desert. 2003. (Biomes Atlas Ser.). (Illus.). pap. 48.30 (978-1-4109-0255-9(2)) Raintree.

Woodford, Chris. Arctic Tundra & Polar Deserts. 2002. (Biomes Atlases Ser.). (Illus.). 64p. (J). lib. bdg. 31.40 (978-0-7398-5246-0(9)) Raintree.

—Arctic Tundra & Polar Deserts. 2003. (gr. 5-8). lib. bdg. 18.20 (978-0-613-78192-3(9)) Tandem Library Bks.

POLAR REGIONS—FICTION

Aston, Dianna Hutts. Loony Little. Murphy, Kelly, illus. 2007. 40p. (J). (ps-3). pap. 6.99 ***(978-0-7636-3562-6(6))*** Candlewick Pr.

Ballantyne, R. M. The World of Ice (Illustrated Edition) (2006. pap. ***(978-1-4065-0533-7(1))*** Dodo Pr.

Bastedo, Jamie. On Thin Ice. 2006. 176p. (YA). (gr. 8 up). pap. ***(978-0-88995-337-6(6))*** Red Deer Pr.

Czerneda, Julie E., ed. Polaris: A Celebration of Polar Science. Normand, Jean-Pierre, illus. 2007. 160p. pap. 14.95 ***(978-0-88995-372-7(4))*** Red Deer Pr. CAN. *Dist:* Fitzhenry & Whiteside, Ltd.

de, Beer Hans. Little Polar Bear & Reindeer. de, Beer Hans, illus. 2007. (Illus.). 0032p. pap. 6.95 ***(978-0-7358-2139-2(9))*** North-South Bks., Inc.

deRubertis, Barbara. Wally Walrus. Pyk, Jan, illus. 1998. (Let's Read Together Ser.). 32p. (J). (ps-3). pap. 4.95 (978-1-57565-046-3(0)) Kane Pr., The.

Grindley, Sally. Reve de Glace et Patins Blancs. Duchesne, Christiane, tr. from ENG. Hieta, Heli, illus. (FRE.). 28p. (J). pap. 6.95 ***(978-2-922435-06-1(7))*** Editions Homard CAN. *Dist:* Univ. of Toronto Pr.

Heinz, Brian J. Nanuk, Lord of the Ice. Manchess, Gregory, illus. 2005. (J). (978-0-936335-13-1(0)); pap. (978-0-936335-14-8(9)) Ballyhoo BookWorks, Inc.

Henkel, Donald G. A Legend of Santa & His Brother Fred. Henkel, Donald B., illus. 2000. 46p. (J). 20.50 (978-0-9673504-0-0(9)) Quillpen.

Howard, Pam & Crowell, Knox. A Flight to Polar Bay. l.t. ed. 2002. (Illus.). 8p. (J). (ps-1). pap. 10.95 (978-1-57332-220-1(2)); pap. 10.95 (978-1-57332-221-8(0)) HighReach Learning, Inc.

Lumry, Amanda. Polar Bear Puzzle. 2007. (Adventures of Riley Ser.). 36p. (ps-3). 18.95 ***(978-1-60040-005-6(1));*** 15.95 ***(978-1-60040-004-9(3))*** Eaglemont Pr.

Peake, Mervyn. Letters from a Lost Uncle. 2004. (Illus.). 19.95 (978-0-413-74590-3(2)) Methuen Publishing Ltd. GBR. *Dist:* Consortium Bk. Sales & Distribution.

Plante, Raymond & Favreau, Marie-Claude. Marilou Polaire et l'Iguane des Neiges. 2002. (La Courte Echelle Premier Roman Ser.). (FRE., Illus.). 64p. (J). (gr. 2-5). pap. (978-2-89021-336-4(6)) Diffusion du livre Mirabel.

Richards, Lucy. The Magic Sky. 2004. (Illus.). 32p. (J). (ps). pap. 8.99 (978-1-4052-1335-6(3)) Egmont Bks., Ltd. GBR. *Dist:* Independent Pubs. Group.

P
Q
R

Wheeler, Lisa. Where, Oh Where, Is Santa Claus? Bates, Ivan, illus. 2007. 32p. (J). (ps-2). 16.00 (978-0-15-216408-9(1)) Harcourt Trade Pubs.

White, Andrea. Surviving Antarctica: Reality TV 2083. 2005. 336p. (J). (gr. 7 up). 16.99 (978-0-06-055454-5(1) , HarperCollins); lib. bdg. 16.89 (978-0-06-055455-2(X)) HarperCollins Pubs.

Whybrow, Ian. Say Hello to the Snowy Animals! Touch & Feel Animals on Every Page. Eaves, Edward, illus. rev. ed. 2007. 20p. 22.95 (***978-0-230-01391-9(0)*** , Macmillan Children's Bks.) Pan Macmillan GBR. *Dist:* Trans-Atlantic Pubns., Inc.

POLARITY

see also Good and Evil

Animal Opposites. 2002. (Illus.). (J). pap. 3.74 (978-0-7398-5857-8(2)) Steck-Vaughn.

Bernhard, Durga. Earth, Sky, Wet, Dry: A Book of Opposites. Bernhard, Durga, illus. 2000. (Illus.). 40p. (J). (gr. k-4). pap. 16.95 (978-0-531-30213-2(X) , Orchard Bks.) Scholastic, Inc.

Black, Jessica L. Opposites. Cress, Michelle H., illus. 2001. (Board Bk.). (J). (ps-1). pap. 10.95 (978-1-57332-193-8(1)) HighReach Learning, Inc.

Burningham, John. Opposites. Burningham, John, illus. 2003. (First Steps Board Books Ser.). (Illus.). 24p. (J). (gr. k-k). bds. 5.99 (978-0-7636-2044-8(0)) Candlewick Pr.

Burns Knight, Margy, et al. Who Belongs Here? Sibley O'Brien, Anne, illus. 2nd ed. 2005. 40p. (gr. 3-8). pap., tchr. ed., tchr.'s training gde. ed. 9.95 (978-0-88448-111-9(5)) Tilbury Hse. Pubs.

Christopher, Jennifer R. What if a Fork was a Spoon. 2006. (ENG., Illus.). 30p. per. 19.99 (***978-1-4257-0847-4(1)***) Xlibris Corp.

Coulton, Mia. Danny & Bee's Book of Opposites. Coulton, Mia, photos by. 2005. (J). 4.95 (978-1-933624-02-0(7)) Maryruth Bks., Inc.

Crowther, Robert. Opposites. Crowther, Robert, illus. 2005. (Illus.). 16p. (J). (ps up). 12.99 (978-0-7636-2783-6(6)) Candlewick Pr.

Emberley, Rebecca. My Opposites (Mis Opuestos) braille ed. 2004. (SPA, ENG & FRE.). (J). (gr. 1). spiral bd., bds. (978-0-616-07271-4(6)) Canadian National Institute for the Blind/Institut National Canadien pour les Aveugles.

—My Opposites/Mis Opuestos. Emberley, Rebecca, illus. 2000. (ENG & SPA., Illus.). 10p. (J). (ps-ps). bds. 6.99 (978-0-316-23345-3(5)) Little Brown & Co.

Fun with Opposites. 2007. (Illus.). 10p. bds. 14.95 (***978-1-59125-797-4(2)*** , Penton Kids) Penton Overseas, Inc.

Funny Friends, LLC Staff. Opposites with Funny Friends. 1999. (Illus.). 18p. (J). bds. (978-1-929758-01-2(4)) Funny Friends, LLC.

—Opposites with Funny Friends Value Pack: With Plush Toy. 1999. (Illus.). 18p. (J). bds. (978-1-929758-04-3(9)) Funny Friends, LLC.

Gordon, Sharon. Arriba Abajo. 2006. (Bookworms Ser.). (SPA., Illus.). 24p. (J). lib. bdg. 22.79 (***978-0-7614-2369-0(9)***) Cavendish, Marshall Corp.

—Duro Blando. 2006. (Bookworms Ser.). (SPA & ENG., Illus.). 24p. (J). lib. bdg. 22.79 (978-0-7614-2368-3(0)) Cavendish, Marshall Corp.

—Exactamente lo Opuesto, 6 bks., Set. Incl. Arriba Abajo. (Illus.). 2006. lib. bdg. 22.79 (***978-0-7614-2369-0(9));*** Duro Blando. (Illus.). 2006. lib. bdg. 22.79 (978-0-7614-2368-3(0)); Grande Pequeño. 2007. lib. bdg. 136.71 (***978-0-7614-2364-5(8)*** , Benchmark Bks.); Mojado Seco. (Illus.). 2006. lib. bdg. 22.79 (978-0-7614-2370-6(2)); Rapido Lento. (Illus.). 2006. lib. bdg. 22.79 (978-0-7614-2367-6(2)); Sucio Limpio. 2006. lib. bdg. 22.79 (***978-0-7614-2365-2(6)*** , Benchmark Bks.); 24p. (J). (SPA.). 2007. Set lib. bdg. 136.71 (***978-0-7614-2363-8(X)*** , Benchmark Bks.) Cavendish, Marshall Corp.

—Fast Slow (Rapido Lento) 2006. (Bookworms Ser.). (ENG & SPA., Illus.). 24p. (J). lib. bdg. 22.79 (978-0-7614-2447-5(4)) Cavendish, Marshall Corp.

—Grande Pequeño. 2007. (Bookworms Ser.). (SPA.). 24p. (J). lib. bdg. 136.71 (***978-0-7614-2364-5(8)*** , Benchmark Bks.) Cavendish, Marshall Corp.

—Hard Soft (Duro Blando) 2006. (Bookworms Ser.). (ENG & SPA., Illus.). 24p. (J). lib. bdg. 22.79 (978-0-7614-2448-2(2)) Cavendish, Marshall Corp.

—Just the Opposite (Exactamente lo Opuesto), 6 bks., Set. Incl. Big Small (Grande Pequeño) lib. bdg. 22.79 (***978-0-7614-2445-1(8)***); Dirty Clean (Sucio Limpio) (Illus.). lib. bdg. 22.79 (978-0-7614-2446-8(6)); Fast Slow (Rapido Lento) (Illus.). lib. bdg. 22.79 (978-0-7614-2447-5(4)); Hard Soft (Duro Blando) (Illus.). lib. bdg. 22.79 (978-0-7614-2448-2(2)); Up Down (Arriba Abajo) (Illus.). lib. bdg. 22.79 (978-0-7614-2449-9(0)); Wet Dry (Mojado Seco) (Illus.). lib. bdg. 22.79 (978-0-7614-2450-5(4)); 24p. (J). 2006. 2007. Set lib. bdg. 136.71 (***978-0-7614-2443-7(1)***) Cavendish, Marshall Corp.

—Mojado Seco. 2006. (Bookworms Ser.). (SPA & ENG., Illus.). 24p. (J). lib. bdg. 22.79 (978-0-7614-2370-6(2)) Cavendish, Marshall Corp.

—Rapido Lento. 2006. (Bookworms Ser.). (SPA & ENG., Illus.). 24p. (J). lib. bdg. 22.79 (978-0-7614-2367-6(2)) Cavendish, Marshall Corp.

—Sucio Limpio. 2006. (Bookworms Ser.). (SPA.). 24p. (J). lib. bdg. 22.79 (***978-0-7614-2365-2(6)*** , Benchmark Bks.) Cavendish, Marshall Corp.

Gordon, Sharon. Wet Dry (Mojado Seco) 2006. (Bookworms Ser.). (ENG & SPA., Illus.). 24p. (J). lib. bdg. 22.79 (978-0-7614-2450-5(4)) Cavendish, Marshall Corp.

Gunzi, Christiane. My Very First Look at Sizes. 2006. (Illus.). 22p. (J). bds. 6.95 (978-1-58728-564-6(9) , Two Can Publishing) T&N Children's Publishing.

Harris, Pamela. Hot, cold, shy, bold: Looking at Opposites. unabr. ed. 1998. (Illus.). 32p. (J). (ps-k). (978-1-55074-153-7(5)) Kids Can Pr., Ltd.

Heath, Beverly C. Opposites. Floyd, John, Jr., illus. 2005. (J). bds. 5.95 (***978-0-9752860-3-6(X)***) OurRainbow Pr., LLC.

Huelin, Jodi. Opposites. Murawski, Kevin, illus. 2004. (Harold & the Purple Crayon Ser.). 22p. (J). (ps up). 5.99 (978-0-06-054366-2(3) , Harper Festival) HarperCollins Pubs.

Insera, Rose. Opposites. Insera, Rose, illus. 2005. (Illus.). 15p. (J). (gr. 3-6). 8.95 (978-1-74157-270-4(3)) Hinkler Bks. Pty, Ltd. AUS. *Dist:* Penton Overseas, Inc.

Jim Henson Staff. Bear Loves Opposites! 2000. (Illus.). 20p. (J). (gr. k-3). pap. 4.99 (978-0-671-77447-9(6) , Simon & Schuster Children's Publishing) Simon & Schuster Children's Publishing.

Kalman, Bobbie. Is It the Same or Different? 2007. (Looking at Nature Ser.). (Illus.). 24p. (J). (ps-2). pap. (***978-0-7787-3337-9(8)***) Crabtree Publishing Co.

Kelly, Lorraine. Fun To Learn: Opposites. 2000. (Illus.). 16p. (J). 4.50 (978-0-233-99908-1(6)) Andre Deutsch GBR. *Dist:* Trans-Atlantic Pubns., Inc.

Learning Opposites. 2003. (Kermit the Frog & Friends Ser.). (Illus.). 16p. (J). (gr. k-3). pap., act. bk. ed. 4.99 (978-1-57768-706-1(X)) School Specialty Publishing.

Leonard, Marcia. The Opposite of Stop Is Go. 2000. (Hanna Bks.). (Illus.). 24p. (J). (ps up). 7.95 (978-0-694-01368-5(4) , Harper Festival) HarperCollins Pubs.

Lorenz Books Staff. Opposites: With over 50 Reusable Stickers. 1998. (Sticker Fun Ser.). (Illus.). 16p. (ps-k). pap. 4.95 (978-1-85967-773-5(8)) Anness Publishing GBR. *Dist:* National Bk. Network.

McDonald, Jill. Opposites: A Play-with-Me BK. 2007. 5p. bds. 6.95 (***978-1-58117-605-6(8)*** , Intervisual/Piggy Toes) Dalmatian Pr.

Meyers. Theme Pack: Opposites. 2002. (Pair-It Bks.). (J). pap. (978-0-7398-6371-8(1)) Steck-Vaughn.

Murphy, Chuck. Chuck Murphy's Black Cat, White Cat: A Pop-Up Book of Opposites. 2000. (Illus.). 12p. (J). (gr. k-3). per. (978-0-689-83507-0(8) , Simon & Schuster Children's Publishing) Simon & Schuster Children's Publishing.

Murphy, Stuart J. The Greatest Gymnast of All. Jabar, Cynthia, illus. 1998. (MathStart Ser.). 40p. (J). (ps up). 15.95 (978-0-06-027608-9(8)); 15.89 (978-0-06-027609-6(6)) HarperCollins Pubs.

Nagy, Krisztina, illus. Dog Days: An Opposites Book. 1999. 10p. (J). (ps-k). 9.95 (978-1-58117-053-5(X) , Intervisual/Piggy Toes) Dalmatian Pr.

O'Neill, Cynthia, ed. My First Sizes & Opposites. 2004. (Barbie Sticker Books Ser.). (SPA.). 16p. (J). bds. 6.99 (978-0-7566-0450-9(8)) Dorling Kindersley Publishing, Inc.

Patricelli, Leslie. Grande Pequeño. Rozarena, P., tr. Patricelli, Leslie, illus. 2003. (SPA.). 25p. (J). (ps-k). bds. 7.95 (978-970-29-0988-0(0)) Santillana USA Publishing Co., Inc.

Petty, Colin. Opposites. 2006. (Concept Sliders Ser.). (Illus.). 10p. (J). 5.99 (978-0-7641-5943-5(7)) Barron's Educational Series, Inc.

Pittau, Francesco & Gervais, Bernadette. Los Contrarios. 2005. (SPA., Illus.). 76p. (J). 19.95 (978-84-95939-62-3(2)) Blume ESP. *Dist:* Independent Pubs. Group.

Poitier, Antonine & School Zone Staff. Opposites Spin Wheel Board Books. 2006. (J). (ps-k). bds. 3.99 (***978-0-88743-617-8(X)***) School Zone Publishing Co.

Priddy Books Staff. First Concepts: Opposite. 2003. (Illus.). (J). bds. 8.95 (978-0-312-49231-1(6) , Priddy Bks.) St. Martin's Pr.

Primm III, E. Russell. Opposites. 2006. (Talking Hands Ser.). (SPA & ENG., Illus.). 24p. (J). (ps). 21.36 (978-1-59296-454-3(0)) Child's World, Inc.

Ready Set Learn Staff. Quacks Opposites. 2005. (Illus.). 24p. (J). (ps-2). bds. 15.99 (978-1-59249-520-7(6) , 1C302) Soundprints.

Reinhart, Matthew. Animal Poppposites: A Pop-up Book of Opposites. Reinhart, Matthew, illus. 2002. (Illus.). 12p. (J). (ps-1). 13.95 (978-0-689-84423-2(9) , Little Simon) Simon & Schuster Children's Publishing.

Running Press Staff. Opposites. 2002. (First Discovery Look-Inside Board Bks.). (Illus.). 10p. (J). bds. 4.95 (978-0-439-35592-6(3) , Cartwheel Bks.) Scholastic, Inc.

Savary, Fabien. Caillou: Que Falta? Tipeo, illus. 2004. Tr. of What's Missing?. (SPA.). 12p. (J). bds. 4.95 (978-1-58728-349-9(2) , Creative Publishing International) Quayside.

Savary, Fabien & Vadeboncoeur, Isabelle. Caillou: Los Contrarios. Tipeo, illus. 2004. Tr. of What's the Difference?. (SPA.). 12p. (J). bds. 4.95 (978-1-58728-348-2(4) , Creative Publishing International) Quayside.

Serfozo, Mary. What's What? A Guessing Game. Narahashi, Keiko, illus. 2000. 32p. (J). (ps-3). 6.99 (978-0-689-83322-9(9) , Aladdin) Simon & Schuster Children's Publishing.

—What's What? A Guessing Game. 2000. (978-0-606-17944-7(5)) Tandem Library Bks.

Sesame Building Blocks: Cube Books. 2002. (J). (978-1-931312-81-3(8)) SoftPlay, Inc.

Shulman, Mark. Big Bagel, Little Bagel. Miline, Bill, photos by. 2006. (Illus.). 10p. (J). (gr. k-4). reprint ed. 6.00 (978-1-4223-5709-5(0)) DIANE Publishing Co.

Silver Dolphin en Español Editors. Disney Learning: Contrarios: Disney Learning: Opposites, Spanish-Language Edition. 2006. (Illus.). 20p. (J). 3.99 (***978-970-718-428-2(0)*** , Silver Dolphin en Español) Advanced Marketing, S. de R. L. de C. V. MEX. *Dist:* Perseus Distribution.

—Disney Tesoro de libros de Calcomanias: Disney Sticker Book Treasury, Spanish-Language Edition. 2007. (Illus.). 48p. (J). 14.95 (***978-970-718-447-3(7)*** , Silver Dolphin en Español) Advanced Marketing, S. de R. L. de C. V. MEX. *Dist:* Perseus Distribution.

Swinburne, Stephen R. What's Opposite? Swinburne, Stephen R., photos by. 2003. (Illus.). 32p. (YA). (gr. k-2). 16.95 (978-1-56397-881-4(4)); pap. 8.95 (978-1-56397-905-7(5)) Boyds Mills Pr.

Tetro, Marc. Opposites. 2006. (Illus.). 6.99 (978-1-55278-503-4(3)) McArthur & Co. CAN. *Dist:* National Bk. Network.

Tullet, Herve. Blue & Square. 2002. (Illus.). 24p. (J). 7.99 (978-1-84059-343-3(1)) Milet Publishing.

Tuxworth, Nicola & Lorenz Editors. Opposites. 2001. (Let's Look at... Ser.). (Illus.). 20p. 5.95 (978-0-7548-0949-4(8)) Anness Publishing GBR. *Dist:* National Bk. Network.

Verplancke, Klass & Sanctobin, Veroniek. Que Hace el Bebe? 2002. (Que Hace? Ser.). (SPA & ENG., Illus.). 16p. 4.95 (978-84-7864-388-2(5)) Combel Editorial, S.A. ESP. *Dist:* Independent Pubs. Group.

—Que Hace la Gallina? 2002. (Que Hace? Ser.). (SPA & ENG., Illus.). 16p. 4.95 (978-84-7864-389-9(3)) Combel Editorial, S.A. ESP. *Dist:* Independent Pubs. Group.

—Que Me Pongo? 2002. (Que Hace? Ser.). (SPA & ENG., Illus.). 16p. 4.95 (978-84-7864-386-8(9)) Combel Editorial, S.A. ESP. *Dist:* Independent Pubs. Group.

—Que Veo? 2002. (Que Hace? Ser.). (SPA & ENG., Illus.). 16p. 4.95 (978-84-7864-387-5(7)) Combel Editorial, S.A. ESP. *Dist:* Independent Pubs. Group.

Walsh, Melanie. Big & Little. Walsh, Melanie, illus. 2001. (Illus.). 14p. (J). (ps-k). bds. 4.99 (978-0-7636-1512-3(9)) Candlewick Pr.

Watt, Melanie. Opposites. 2005. (Learning with Animals Board Bks.). (Illus.). 24p. (J). (gr. k up). (978-1-55337-832-7(6)) Kids Can Pr., Ltd.

Yates, Gene. The Dragon Opposites Book. 2005. (Illus.). 14p. (J). (***978-1-58865-283-6(1)***) Kidsbooks, Inc.

POLARITY—FICTION

Barry, Frances. Duckie's Splash. Barry, Frances, illus. 2006. (Illus.). 14p. (J). (gr. k-ps). bds. 5.99 (978-0-7636-2897-0(2)) Candlewick Pr.

Beinstein, Phoebe. Dora's Opposites/Opuestos de Dora. Roper, Robert, illus. 2002. (Dora the Explorer Ser.). 14p. (J). bds. 4.99 (978-0-689-84819-3(6) , Simon Spotlight/Nickelodeon) Simon & Schuster Children's Publishing.

Berenstain, Stan & Berenstain, Jan. Inside, Outside, Upside Down. 2000. (Berenstain Bears Bright & Early Bks.). (J). (ps-3). 7.99 (978-0-375-80253-9(3)) Random Hse., Inc.

Bockol, Leslie. Tie your shoes rocket Style. 2007. 10p. (J). 9.95 (***978-1-59764-292-7(4)***) New Line Bks.

Bridwell, Norman. Clifford y los Opuestos. 2003. (Clifford Ser.).Tr. of Clifford's Opposites. (SPA., Illus.). 7p. (J). bds. 3.95 (978-0-439-55110-6(2) , Scholastic en Espanol) Scholastic, Inc.

Brown, Ruth. Imagine. 2007. (Illus.). 24p. (J). (ps-3). pap. 9.99 (***978-1-84270-564-3(4)***) Andersen GBR. *Dist:* Independent Pubs. Group.

Cousins, Lucy. Maisy Big, Maisy Small. Cousins, Lucy, illus. 2007. (Illus.). 56p. (J). (ps-k). 15.99 (***978-0-7636-3406-3(9)***) Candlewick Pr.

Coward, Fiona. Swing High, Swing Low: A Day of Opposites. Manna, Giovanni, illus. 2005. 32p. (J). 16.99 (978-1-84148-170-8(X)) Barefoot Bks., Inc.

Falconer, Ian. Olivia's Opposites. Falconer, Ian, illus. 2002. (Olivia Ser.). (J). bds. 6.99 (978-0-689-85448-4(X)); (Illus.). 12p. bds. 6.99 (978-0-689-85088-2(3)) Simon & Schuster Children's Publishing. (Atheneum).

Little Simon Staff. Opposites. 2003. (Osh Kosh Ser.). (Illus.). 8p. (J). 12.95 (978-0-689-85723-2(3) , Little Simon) Simon & Schuster Children's Publishing.

Murphy, Chuck. Opposites. Murphy, Chuck, illus. 2001. (Slide 'n' Seek Ser.: Vol. 4). (Illus.). 12p. (J). bds. 5.99 (978-0-689-84476-8(X) , Little Simon) Simon & Schuster Children's Publishing.

Potter, Beatrix. Peter Rabbit Lift-the-flap Shapes, Opposites & Sizes. 2007. (Potter Ser.). 12p. (J). (ps). 14.99 (***978-0-7232-5961-9(5)*** , Warne) Penguin Group (USA) Inc.

Reidy, Hannah. Crazy Creature Contrasts. Mackie, Clare, illus. 2003. (Crazy Creatures Ser.). 26p. (J). pap. (978-1-84089-223-9(4) , Zero to Ten, Limited) Evans Publishing Group.

Rey, H. A. & Rey, Margret, creators. Opuestos con Jorge el Curioso. 2002. (SPA., Illus.). 8p. (J). (gr. k-ps). bds. 5.95 (978-0-618-20317-8(6)) Houghton Mifflin Co. Trade & Reference Div.

Rey, Margret & Rey, H. A. Curious George's Opposites. 1998. (Curious George Ser.). (Illus.). 16p. (J). (gr. k-ps). bds. 5.95 (978-0-395-89923-6(0)) Houghton Mifflin Co. Trade & Reference Div.

Rivoli Group Staff, illus. Hide & Seek Opposites. 2000. (Jay Jay the Jet Plane's Peek-a-Boo Board Bks.). 12p. (J). (ps-k). bds. 6.95 (978-1-58117-100-6(5) , Intervisual/Piggy Toes) Dalmatian Pr.

Running Press Staff. Opposites. 2004. (Sticker Math Ser.). 24p. (J). pap., act. bk. ed. 4.95 (978-0-7945-0042-9(0) , Usborne) EDC Publishing.

—Opposites. 2001. (Early Learning Ser.). (J). (gr. k-12). vinyl bd. 4.95 (978-1-58845-055-5(4)) School Specialty Publishing.

—Opposites. Pinwheel, ed. 2001. (Bounce-Along Bks.). (Illus.). 12p. (J). bds. 4.95 (978-0-8069-8091-1(5)) Sterling Publishing Co., Inc.

Running Press Staff & Lorenz Editors. Opposites, 4 vols., Set 2. 2001. (Mini Board Bks.). (Illus.). 10p. bds. 12.95 (978-0-7548-0826-8(2)) Anness Publishing GBR. *Dist:* National Bk. Network.

Scarry, Richard. Grande y Pequeno. 2003. (Richard Scarry Ser.). (SPA., Illus.). (J). pap. (978-970-690-846-9(3)) Planeta Mexicana Editorial S. A. de C. V.

POLES—UNITED STATES

Greene, Meg. Thaddeus Kosciuszko. 2001. (Revolutionary War Leaders Ser.). (Illus.). 80p. (J). pap. 27.50 (978-0-7910-6399-6(2)); 27.50 (978-0-7910-6398-9(4)) Facts On File, Inc. (Chelsea Hse.).

POLICE

see also Crime and Criminals; Criminal Investigation; Detectives; Secret Service

also names of cities with the subdivision Police, e.g. New York (N. Y.)—Police, etc.

Adamson, Heather. A Day in the Life of a Police Officer. 2003. (First Facts Ser.). (Illus.). 24p. (J). lib. bdg. 21.26 (978-0-7368-2285-5(2)) Capstone Pr., Inc.

Anderson, Sheila. Police Station. 2008. (J). pap. (***978-0-8225-8842-9(0)***) Lerner Publishing Group.

Ashabranner, Brent. Badge of Valor: The National Law Enforcement Officers Memorial. Ashabranner, Jennifer, illus. 2000. (Great American Memorials Ser.). 64p. (gr. 4-8). lib. bdg. (978-0-7613-1522-3(5) , Twenty-First Century Bks.) Lerner Publishing Group.

Asirvatham, Sandy. Police & Policing. 2001. (Crime, Justice & Punishment Ser.). (Illus.). 80p. (J). 30.00 (978-0-7910-4301-1(0) , Chelsea Hse.) Facts On File, Inc.

Beylon, Cathy. Police Station Coloring Book. 2001. (Illus.). 32p. (J). pap. 2.95 (978-0-486-41538-3(4)) Dover Pubns., Inc.

Blashfield, Jean F. Interpol. 2003. (International Organizations Ser.). (Illus.). 48p. (J). (gr. 5 up). lib. bdg. 30.00 (978-0-8368-5520-3(5)); pap. 11.95 (978-0-8368-5529-6(9)) Stevens, Gareth Inc. (World Almanac Library).

Bourgeois, Paulette. Police Officers. LaFave, Kim, illus. (Kids Can Read Ser.). 32p. (J). 2005. (gr. 1-3). (978-1-55337-743-6(5)); 2005. (gr. 1-3). (978-1-55337-742-9(7)); 2000. (gr. k-3). (978-1-55074-787-4(8)) Kids Can Pr., Ltd.

—Police Officers. 2000. (Illus.). (J). 12.75 (978-0-606-18226-3(8)); 1999. lib. bdg. 14.10 (978-0-613-28611-4(1)) Tandem Library Bks.

Bourgeois, Paulette & LaFave, Kim. Police Officers. unabr. ed. 1998. (In My Neighborhood Ser.). (Illus.). 32p. (J). (gr. k-3). (978-1-55074-502-3(6)) Kids Can Pr., Ltd.

Catala, Ellen. Who Keeps Us Safe? 2006. (Illus.). 18p. (J). (978-0-7368-5984-4(5)) Capstone Pr., Inc.

—Who Keeps Us Safe? 2006. (Illus.). 8,16p. (J). 6.50 (978-0-7368-1720-2(4)) Red Brick Learning.

—Who Keeps Us Safe. 2006. (ENG & SPA., Illus.). 18p. (J). (978-0-7368-6020-8(7)) Yellow Umbrella Pr.

Caviezel, Giovanni. Policeman's Saftey Hints. 2007. (Illus.). 10p. (J). (gr. k-2). bds. 10.99 (978-0-7641-6019-6(2)) Barron's Educational Series, Inc.

Christy, Lee Louis. I Go to Work as a Police Officer. 2003. (I Go to Work As Ser.). (Illus.). (J). (978-1-58417-040-2(9)); pap. (978-1-58417-103-4(0)) Lake Street Pubs.

Compass Point Books, contrib. by. Police Officers. (Community Workers Ser.). 24p. (J). pap. 7.95 (978-0-7565-1196-8(8)) Compass Point Bks.

Conrad, David. Law & Order. 2002. (Spyglass Books). (Illus.). 24p. (J). (gr. 1 up). lib. bdg. 18.60 (978-0-7565-0383-3(3)) Compass Point Bks.

Cunningham, Kevin. J. Edgar Hoover: Controversial FBI Director. 2005. (Signature Lives Ser.). (Illus.). 112p. (J). (gr. 5-7). (978-0-7565-0997-2(1)) Compass Point Bks.

Ethan, Eric. Police Cars. Ethan, Eric, photos by. 2002. (Emergency Vehicles Ser.). (Illus.). 24p. (YA). (gr. 1 up). lib. bdg. 20.67 (978-0-8368-3047-7(4)) Stevens, Gareth Inc.

Fine, Jil. Undercover Agents. 2003. (High-Top Secret Ser.). (Illus.). 48p. (J). 23.00 (978-0-516-24315-3(2) , Children's Pr.) Scholastic Library Publishing.

—Undercover Agents. 2003. (gr. 7-12). lib. bdg. 15.25 (978-0-613-59752-4(4)) Tandem Library Bks.

Fitzgerald, Sheila. Police Brutality. 2006. (Illus.). 244p. (YA). (gr. 10-12). 24.95 (978-0-7377-3359-4(4)); pap. 36.20 (978-0-7377-3358-7(6)) Thomson Gale. (Greenhaven Pr., Inc.).

Flanagan, Alice K. Officer Brown Keeps Neighborhoods Safe. Osinski, Christine, ed. Osinski, Christine, illus. 1998. (Our Neighborhood Ser.). 32p. (J). (gr. 1-2). 20.00 (978-0-516-20780-3(6) , Children's Pr.) Scholastic Library Publishing.

—Police Officers. 2000. (Community Workers Ser.). (Illus.). 32p. (J). (gr. 1 up). lib. bdg. 21.26 (978-0-7565-0011-5(7)) Compass Point Bks.

Freeman, Marcia S. Police Cars. Saunders-Smith, Gail, ed. 1999. (Community Vehicles Ser.). (Illus.). 24p. (J). (gr. k-1). lib. bdg. 15.93 (978-0-7368-0103-4(0) , Pebble Bks.) Capstone Pr., Inc.

Gordon, Sharon. ¿Qué Hay Dentro de una Estacion de Policía? 2006. (Bookworms Ser.). (SPA & ENG., Illus.). 32p. (J). lib. bdg. 22.79 (978-0-7614-2398-0(2)) Cavendish, Marshall Corp.

—What's Inside a Police Station? (¿Qué Hay Dentro de una Estacion de Policía?) 2006. (Bookworms Ser.). (ENG & SPA., Illus.). 32p. (J). lib. bdg. 22.79 (978-0-7614-2476-5(8)) Cavendish, Marshall Corp.

Gorman, Jacqueline Laks. Police Officer. Andersen, Gregg, photos by. 2002. (People in My Community Ser.). (Illus.). 24p. (J). (ps up). lib. bdg. 19.33 (978-0-8368-3297-6(3)); pap. 7.93 (978-0-8368-3304-1(X)) Stevens, Gareth Inc. (Weekly Reader Early Learning Library).

—Police Officer/El Policia. Acosta, Tatiana & Gutiérrez, Guillermo, trs. 2002. (Weekly Reader Early Learning Library). (SPA & ENG., Illus.). 24p. (J). (ps up). lib. bdg. 19.33 (978-0-8368-3311-9(2) , Weekly Reader Early Learning Library) Stevens, Gareth Inc.

Gorman, Jacqueline Laks & Macken, JoAnn Early. Police Officer/El Policia. Coffey, Colleen & Carrillo, Consuelo, trs. Andersen, Gregg, photos by. 2002. (Weekly Reader Early Learning Library). (ENG & SPA., Illus.). 24p. (J). (ps up). pap. 7.93 (978-0-8368-3345-4(7) , Weekly Reader Early Learning Library) Stevens, Gareth Inc.

Green, Michael. Bomb Detection Squads. 2000. (Law Enforcement Ser.). (Illus.). 48p. (J). (gr. 3-4). lib. bdg. 21.26 (978-1-56065-755-2(3) , Capstone High-Interest Bks.) Capstone Pr., Inc.

—Bomb Detection Squads. 1998. (Roverfront Law Enforcement Ser.). 48p. (J). lib. bdg. 19.00 (978-0-531-11558-9(5) , Watts, Franklin) Scholastic Library Publishing.

—Mounted Police. 2000. (Law Enforcement Ser.). (Illus.). 48p. (J). (gr. 3-4). lib. bdg. 21.26 (978-1-56065-757-6(X) , Capstone High-Interest Bks.) Capstone Pr., Inc.

—Mounted Police. 1998. (Law Enforcement Ser.). 48p. (J). lib. bdg. 19.00 (978-0-531-11560-2(7) , Watts, Franklin) Scholastic Library Publishing.

—SWAT Teams. 2000. (Law Enforcement Ser.). (Illus.). 48p. (J). (gr. 3-4). lib. bdg. 21.26 (978-1-56065-758-3(8) , Capstone High-Interest Bks.) Capstone Pr., Inc.

—SWAT Teams. 1998. (Law Enforcement Ser.). 48p. (J). lib. bdg. 19.00 (978-0-531-11561-9(5) , Watts, Franklin) Scholastic Library Publishing.

Hayler, Kate. Police Chase! Emergency. Giraffe, Red, illus. 2003. (Tough Stuff Ser.). 10p. (ps-17). 12.99 (978-0-7868-1984-3(7)) Hyperion Bks. for Children.

Hynes, Patricia Freeland. Cyber Cop. 2007. (J). lib. bdg. ***978-1-60279-056-8(6))** Cherry Lake Publishing.

Johnston, Marianne. Let's Visit the Police Station. 2000. (Our Community Ser.). (Illus.). 24p. (J). (gr. 3). lib. bdg. 18.75 (978-0-8239-5434-6(X) , PowerKids Pr.) Rosen Publishing Group, Inc., The.

Kalman, Bobbie. Emergency Workers Are on Their Way! 2004. (My Community & Its Helpers Ser.). (Illus.). (J). 158p. (978-0-7787-2094-2(2)); 32p. pap. (978-0-7787-2122-2(1)) Crabtree Publishing Co.

Katz, Samuel M. Global Counterstrike: International Counterterrorism. 2005. (Terrorist Dossiers Ser.). (Illus.). 72p. (J). (gr. 6-12). 26.60 (978-0-8225-1566-1(0)) Lerner Publishing Group.

—U. S. Counterstrike: American Counterterrorism. 2005. (Terrorist Dossiers Ser.). (Illus.). 72p. (J). (gr. 6-12). 26.60 (978-0-8225-1569-2(5)) Lerner Publishing Group.

Kelly, Zachary A. Law Enforcement. 1998. (Law & Order Ser.). (J). lib. bdg. (978-0-86625-663-6(6)) Rourke Publishing, LLC.

Kerik, Bernard B. Lost Son: A Life in Pursuit of Justice. 2002. (gr. 7-12). lib. bdg. 16.45 (978-0-613-62147-2(6)) Tandem Library Bks.

Kerrigan, Michael. Police Crime Prevention. 2002. (Rescue & Prevention Ser.). (Illus.). 96p. (J). (gr. 6 up). lib. bdg. (978-1-59084-406-9(8)) Mason Crest Pubs.

King, Andrew. Surveillance. 2007. (Crime Scene Investigations Ser.). (Illus.). 128p. (gr. 7-10). 31.20 ***978-1-59018-991-7(4)** , Lucent Bks.) Thomson Gale.

Knudsen, Shannon. Police Officers. 2004. (Pull Ahead Bks.). (Illus.). 32p. (J). pap. (978-0-8225-2534-9(8) , Lerner Pubns.) Lerner Publishing Group.

Kottke, Jan. A Day with Police Officers. 2000. (Welcome Bks.). (Illus.). 24p. (J). (ps-2). pap. 4.95 (978-0-516-23017-7(4) , Children's Pr.) Scholastic Library Publishing.

—Day with Police Officers. 2000. (gr. k-3). lib. bdg. 12.95 (978-0-613-58768-6(5)) Tandem Library Bks.

Liebman, Dan. Je veux etre Policier. Lior, Tsipora, tr. from ENG. 2006. (Je veux Etre Ser.).Tr. of I Want to Be A Police Officer. (FRE., Illus.). 24p. (J). (ps-2). pap. 5.95 (978-1-55407-109-8(7)) Firefly Bks., Ltd.

Liebman, Daniel. I Want to Be a Police Officer. 2000. (I Want to Be Ser.). (Illus.). 24p. (J). (ps-2). pap. 3.99 (978-1-55209-465-5(0)); lib. bdg. 14.95 (978-1-55209-467-9(7)) Firefly Bks., Ltd.

—I Want to Be a Police Officer. 2000. (Illus.). (J). 10.79 (978-0-606-18139-6(3)) Tandem Library Bks.

—Quiero Ser un Oficial de Policia. 2000. (Coleccion Quierno Ser.).Tr. of I Want to be a Police Officer. (SPA., Illus.). 24p. (J). (ps-2). pap. 5.99 (978-1-55209-475-4(8) , AP5120) Firefly Bks., Ltd.

—Quiero Ser un Oficial de Policia. 2000. Tr. of I Want to be a Police Officer. (978-0-606-18144-0(X)) Tandem Library Bks.

Lindeen, Carol K. Patrullas de Policía: Police Cars. 2006. (ENG & SPA.). (J). (978-0-7368-5875-5(X)) Capstone Pr., Inc.

Lowenstein, Felicia. What Does a Police Officer Do? 2005. (What Does a Community Helper Do? Ser.). (Illus.). 24p. (J). lib. bdg. 21.26 (978-0-7660-2541-7(1) , Enslow Elementary) Enslow Pubs., Inc.

Marcovitz, Hal. Guardians of Safety: Law Enforcement at Ground Zero. 2002. (United We Stand: America Responds to the Events of September 11, 2001 Ser.). (Illus.). 64p. (gr. 6-12). 25.00 (978-0-7910-6960-8(5) , Chelsea Hse.) Facts On File, Inc.

Marquez, Heron. George W. Bush. 2006. (First Step Nonfiction Ser.). (Illus.). 112p. (J). (gr. 3-7). 27.93 (978-0-8225-2647-6(6) , Lerner Pubns.) Lerner Publishing Group.

Mattern, Joanne. Mounted Police. 2002. (Reading Power Ser.). (Illus.). 24p. (J). (gr. 1). lib. bdg. 17.25 (978-0-8239-5981-5(3) , PowerKids Pr.) Rosen Publishing Group, Inc., The.

—Policia Montada. 2004. (Trabajo en Grupo Ser.). (SPA & ENG., Illus.). 24p. (J). (gr. 3-6). lib. bdg. 17.25 (978-0-8239-6843-5(X) , Buenas Letras) Rosen Publishing Group, Inc., The.

Meyer, Jared. Homeland Security Officers. 2006. (Extreme Careers Ser.). (Illus.). 64p. (J). (gr. 5-8). lib. bdg. 26.50 (978-1-4042-0945-9(X)) Rosen Publishing Group, Inc., The.

Miller, Connie Colwell. The Border Patrol: Guarding the Nation. 2008. (J). ***978-1-4296-1270-8(3))** Capstone Pr., Inc.

—SWAT Teams: Armed & Ready. 2008. (J). ***978-1-4296-1276-0(2))** Capstone Pr., Inc.

Miller, Heather. Police Officer. 2003. (This Is What I Want to Be Ser.). (Illus.). 24p. (J). (ps-1). lib. bdg. 18.50 (978-1-4034-0371-1(6)); pap. 5.25 (978-1-4034-0593-7(X)) Heinemann Library.

—Police Officer. 2003. (ps-2). lib. bdg. 13.30 (978-0-613-86439-8(5)) Tandem Library Bks.

—Policia. Prieto, Carlos, tr. 2003. (Esto es lo Que Quiero Ser (This Is What I Want to Be) Ser.).Tr. of Police Officer. (SPA., 24p. (J). (ps-1). Illus.). lib. bdg. 18.50 (978-1-4034-0381-0(3)); pap. 5.25 (978-1-4034-0603-3(0)) Heinemann Library.

Mounted Police: Individual Title Six-Packs. (On Deck Ser.). 24p. (gr. 4-5). 35.00 (978-0-7578-1027-5(6)) Rigby Education.

Murphy, Patricia J. The Police Station. 2004. (Visit To Ser.). (Illus.). 24p. (J). lib. bdg. 19.93 (978-0-7368-2581-8(9) , Pebble Bks.) Capstone Pr., Inc.

Niven, Felicia Lowenstein. Lo Que Hacen Los Oficiales de Policía: What Police Officers Do. 2007. (What Does a Community Helper Do? Bilingual Ser.). (ENG & SPA., Illus.). 32p. (J). lib. bdg. 22.60 (978-0-7660-2828-9(3) , Enslow Elementary) Enslow Pubs., Inc.

Olien, Becky. Police Cars. 2001. (Transportation Library). (Illus.). 24p. (J). (gr. 1-2). lib. bdg. 18.60 (978-0-7368-0843-9(4) , Bridgestone Bks.) Capstone Pr., Inc.

Owen, Ann. Keeping You Safe: A Book about Police Officers. Thomas, Eric, illus. 2004. (Community Workers Ser.). 24p. (C). (gr. k-3). 22.60 (978-1-4048-0089-2(1)) Picture Window Bks.

Parks, Peggy J. Police Officer. 2003. (Exploring Careers Ser.). (Illus.). 48p. (J). (gr. 3-5). 26.20 (978-0-7377-1486-9(7) , Kidhaven) Thomson Gale.

Picture Window Books, contrib. by. Keeping You Safe. (Community Workers Ser.). 24p. (J). pap. 7.95 (978-1-4048-0483-8(8)) Picture Window Bks.

Police Officers, (Community Helpers Ser.). 24p. (J). 6.95 (978-0-7368-8460-0(2)) Capstone Pr., Inc.

Police Officers, 6 vols. (gr. 2-5). 36.95 (978-0-7368-8475-4(0)) Red Brick Learning.

Police Work. 2005. (Book Treks Ser.). (J). (gr. 3 up). stu. ed. 34.95 (978-0-673-62839-8(6)) Celebration Pr.

Policia Montada: Individual Title Six-Packs. (On Deck en Espanol Ser.).Tr. of Mounted Police. (SPA.). 24p. (gr. 4-5). 35.00 (978-0-7578-6406-3(6)) Rigby Education.

Randolph, Joanne. Police Cars. 2008. (J). lib. bdg. ***978-1-4042-4153-4(1)** , PowerKids Pr.) Rosen Publishing Group, Inc., The.

Rau, Dana Meachen. Police Officer. 2007. (Jobs in Town Ser.). 24p. (J). lib. bdg. 22.79 ***978-0-7614-2618-9(3)** , Benchmark Bks.) Cavendish, Marshall Corp.

Ready, Dee. Policias. Schon, Isabel, ed. Ferrer, Martín Luis Guzman, tr. from ENG. 1998. (Servidores Comunitarios Ser.). (SPA., Illus.). 24p. (J). (gr. 1-2). lib. bdg. 18.60 (978-1-56065-802-3(9) , Bridgestone Bks.) Capstone Pr., Inc.

Rivera, Sheila. Police Officer. 2004. (First Step Nonfiction Ser.). (J). pap. (978-0-8225-5359-5(7) , Lerner Pubns.) Lerner Publishing Group.

Rockwell, Anne F. At the Police Station. 2005. (978-0-06-056230-4(7)); (978-0-06-056231-1(5)) HarperCollins Canada, Ltd.

Rubinstein, Jonathan. Police Officer: Protector of the Peace. 2001. (978-0-606-22568-7(4)) Tandem Library Bks.

Sanna, Ellyn. Homeland Security Officer. 2002. (Careers with Character Ser.). (Illus.). 96p. (YA). (gr. 7 up). lib. bdg. 22.95 (978-1-59084-315-4(0)) Mason Crest Pubs.

Santillo, LuAnn. The Cop. Santillo, LuAnn, ed. 2003. (Half-Pint Kids Readers Ser.). (Illus.). 7p. (J). (ps-1). pap. (978-1-59256-122-3(5)) Half-Pint Kids, Inc.

Simon, Charnan. Officers Everywhere! Rooney, Ronnie, illus. 2006. (Magic Door to Learning Ser.). 24p. (J). 21.36 (978-1-59296-626-4(8)) Child's World, Inc.

—Police Officers. 2003. (Wonder Books Level 3. Careers Ser.). (Illus.). 32p. (J). (ps-2). 22.79 (978-1-56766-476-8(8)) Child's World, Inc.

Stewart, Gail. Police Brutality. rev. ed. 2005. (Lucent Overview Ser.). (Illus.). 112p. (YA). (gr. 7-10). lib. bdg. 29.95 (978-1-59018-190-4(5) , Lucent Bks.) Thomson Gale.

Stille, Darlene R. Police Cars. 2002. (Illus.). 32p. (J). (gr. 1 up). lib. bdg. 19.93 (978-0-7565-0290-4(X)) Compass Point Bks.

Sweeney, Alyse. Police Officers on the Go! 2006. (Scholastic News Nonfiction Readers Ser.). (Illus.). 24p. (J). (gr. k-2). 19.00 (978-0-531-16810-3(7)) Scholastic Library Publishing.

Thomas, William. Working in Law Enforcement. 2005. (My Future Career Ser.). (J). lib. bdg. 26.00 (978-0-8368-4775-8(X)) Stevens, Gareth Inc.

Torr, James D. Responding to Attack: Firefighters & Police. 2003. (Lucent Library of Homeland Security). (Illus.). 112p. (J). 29.95 (978-1-59018-375-5(4) , Lucent Bks.) Thomson Gale.

Townsend, John. Lawmakers & the Police. 2005. (J). (978-1-4109-2052-2(6)); pap. (978-1-4109-2057-7(7)) Steck-Vaughn.

VanMeter, Larry A. & McNeese, Tim. Miranda v. Arizona: The Rights of the Accused. 2006. (Great Supreme Court Decisions Ser.). (Illus.). 112p. (YA). (gr. 5-8). 30.00 (978-0-7910-9259-0(3) , Chelsea Hse.) Facts On File, Inc.

We Need Police Officers, 6 vols. (gr. k-2). 28.95 (978-0-7368-8604-8(4)) Red Brick Learning.

Zemlicka, Shannon & Knudsen, Shannon. Police Officers. 2005. (Pull Ahead Bks.). (Illus.). 32p. (J). lib. bdg. 22.60 (978-0-8225-1693-4(4)) Lerner Publishing Group.

POLICE—FICTION

The adventures of officer Byrd. 2007. (J). 16.99 ***978-0-9787322-0-2(0))** Officer Byrd Publishing Co.

Auerbach, Annie. Police on Patrol. 2003. (gr. k-3). lib. bdg. 11.25 (978-0-613-66533-9(3)) Tandem Library Bks.

Barney & BJ Go to the Police Station. 2002. (Barney's Go to Ser.). 32p. (J). (ps-k). bds. 5.95 (978-1-58668-231-6(8)) Lyrick Studios.

Becker, Jason Earl. Hero Corps: The Rookie. Moutafis, Greg, illus. 2005. (YA). per. 7.95 (978-0-9765125-0-9(5)) Baby Shark Productions.

Carter, Anne. Under a Prairie Sky. Daniel, Alan & Daniel, Lea, illus. 2001. 32p. (J). (ps-2). 16.95 (978-1-55143-226-7(9)) Orca Bk. Pubs. USA.

Cea, Robert. No Lights, No Sirens: The Corruption & Redemption of an Inner City Cop. 2006. (Illus.). 304p. mass mkt. 7.99 (978-0-06-058713-0(X)) HarperCollins Pubs.

Clasicos Policiales. (Clasicos Juveniles Coleccion). (SPA.). (YA). (gr. 5-8). pap. (978-950-11-1284-9(5) , SG4722) Sigmar ARG. *Dist:* Lectorum Pubns., Inc.

Cormier, Robert. The Rag & Bone Shop. 2001. (Illus.). 160p. (YA). (gr. 7 up). 15.95 (978-0-385-72962-8(6) , Delacorte Bks. for Young Readers) Random Hse. Children's Bks.

—The Rag & Bone Shop. l.t. ed. 2002. 141p. (J). 24.95 (978-0-7862-3873-6(9)) Thomson Gale.

Dale, Jenny. Abandoned! 2000. (Puppy Patrol Ser.: Vol. 3). (Illus.). 112p. (J). (gr. 3-6). pap. 3.99 (978-0-439-11325-0(3)) Scholastic, Inc.

—Abandoned! 2000. (gr. 3-6). lib. bdg. 11.80 (978-0-613-24082-6(0)) Tandem Library Bks.

Dane, James. Hyde & Seek. 2001. iii, 207p. (YA). pap. 14.95 (978-0-9712798-0-3(2)) James Dane Bks.

Deem, Saitofi Anne. Myrtle Learns about Dangerous Situations. 1998. (Teachable Moments Ser.). (Illus.). 8p. (J). (ps-3). pap. 7.95 (978-1-930694-03-3(2)) Myrtle Learns.

Delgado, Linda D. The Visitors. 2006. 169p. (J). per. (978-0-9767861-1-5(7)) Muslim Writers Publishing.

Desimini, Lisa, et al. Policeman Lou & Policewoman Sue. Desimini, Lisa, illus. 2003. (Illus.). 40p. (J). pap. 15.95 (978-0-439-40888-2(1)) Scholastic, Inc.

Educational Adventures, creator. Charlotte Mecklenburg Police Department Coloring Book. 2007. (Illus.). 24p. (J). ***978-1-933934-71-6(9))** Educational Adventures.

Eggleton, Jill. Police Files, 6 Packs. Webb, Philip, illus. (Sails Literacy Ser.). 16p. (gr. 2-3). 27.00 (978-0-7578-0700-8(3)) Rigby Education.

—Police Work: Individual Title Six-Packs. Storey, Jim, illus. (Sails Literacy Ser.). 20p. (gr. 4 up). 27.00 (978-0-7578-0788-6(7)) Rigby Education.

Evans, Nate & Numeroff, Laura Nate. Sherman Crunchley. Bowers, Tim, illus. 2005. 32p. (J). pap. 5.99 (978-0-14-240385-3(7) , Puffin) Penguin Group (USA) Inc.

Flanagan, Alice K. Officer Brown Keeps Neighborhoods Safe. Osinski, Christine, photos by. 1999. (Our Neighborhood Ser.). (Illus.). 32p. (J). (gr. 1-2). pap. 6.95 (978-0-516-26407-3(9) , Children's Pr.) Scholastic Library Publishing.

Gruelle, Johnny & Palmer, Jan. Raggedy Ann & Andy & the Nice Police Officer. 2002. (My First Raggedy Ann Ser.). (Illus.). 40p. (J). pap. 6.99 (978-0-689-85344-9(0) , Aladdin) Simon & Schuster Children's Publishing.

Hess, Joan. Murder@Maggody.com. 2001. (Arly Hanks Mystery Ser.). (gr. 7-12). lib. bdg. 15.30 (978-0-613-36535-2(6)) Tandem Library Bks.

Hinkes, Enid. Police Cat. Rasmussen, Wendy, illus. 2005. 32p. (J). (gr. k-3). 15.95 (978-0-8075-5758-7(7)) Whitman, Albert & Co.

Hodges, David. Flashpoint. 1999. pap. 9.95 (978-1-901442-04-5(7)) Pharaoh Pr. GBR. *Dist:* 7 Hills Bk. Distributors.

Hoffman, Alice. The River King. 2001. (gr. 7-12). lib. bdg. 23.45 (978-0-613-35818-7(X)) Tandem Library Bks.

Lenski, Lois. Policeman Small. 2006. (Illus.) 32p. (J). (gr. k-ps). bds. 6.99 (978-0-375-83569-8(5) , Random Hse. Bks. for Young Readers) Random Hse. Children's Bks.

—Policeman Small. Lenski, Lois, illus. 2001. (Lois Lenski Bks.). (Illus.). 56p. (J). (gr. k-3). 11.95 (978-0-375-81072-5(2) , Random Hse. Bks. for Young Readers) Random Hse. Children's Bks.

Lewman, David, et al. Zoo Day Disaster. Dress, Robert, illus. 2005. (SpongeBob SquarePants Chapter Book Ser.: Vol. 10). 60p. (J). ***978-1-4156-0765-7(6)** , Simon Spotlight/Nickelodeon) Simon & Schuster Children's Publishing.

Lorimer, Janet. Danger on Ice: Set 1. 2003. 32p. (YA). 2.95 (978-1-56254-406-5(3) , SP 4063) Saddleback Educational Publishing.

Madsen, Wayne. The Case of Stolen Time: The Misadventures of Inspector Moustachio. 2007. (Misadventures of Inspector Moustachio Ser.: Bk. 1). 156p. (J). per. 16.99 ***978-0-9790878-9-9(9))** Community Pr.

Marsh, Carole. The Adventure Diaries of the Perils of Pauline, the Police Officer!, 2 vols. 48p. (J). 2003. (gr. 1-4). pap. 5.95 (978-0-635-01144-2(1)); 2002. (Illus.). lib. bdg. 9.95 (978-0-635-01271-5(5)) Gallopade International.

McCann, David. Garda Gaby: The Danger of Playing Truant. Brundige, Britt, ed. Bauknecht, Julie, illus. l.t. ed. 2003. 14p. (J). (gr. k-5). spiral bd. 5.99 (978-1-929063-92-5(X) , 324) Moons & Stars Publishing For Children.

McClintock, Norah. Tell. 2006. 112p. (YA). (gr. 7 up). pap. 8.95 (978-1-55143-511-4(X)); lib. bdg. 14.95 (978-1-55143-672-2(8)) Orca Bk. Pubs. USA.

McMahon, Kara. Police Officers! Nelson, Mary Beth, illus. 2006. (Elmo's World Ser.). 12p. (J). (gr. k-ps). bds. 4.99 (978-0-375-83371-7(4) , Random Hse. Bks. for Young Readers) Random Hse. Children's Bks.

Mitter, Matt. Fisher Price Let's Meet Police Officer Patrick. SI Artists, illus. 2007. 10p. (J). bds. 6.99 ***978-0-7944-1293-7(9))** Reader's Digest Assn., Inc., The.

Murphy, Barbara Beasley. Tripping the Runner. 2001. 192p. (gr. 4-7). pap. 12.95 (978-0-595-15398-5(4) , Backinprint.com) iUniverse, Inc.

Niemann, Christoph. The Police Cloud. 2007. 40p. (J). (ps-2). 15.99 (978-0-375-83963-4(1)); lib. bdg. 17.99 (978-0-375-93963-1(6)) Random Hse. Children's Bks. (Schwartz & Wade Bks.).

Paulsen, Gary. The Glass Cafe: Or the Stripper & the State; How My Mother Started a War with the System That Made Us Kind of Rich & a Little Bit Famous. 2003. 112p. (gr. 5). 12.95 (978-0-385-32499-1(5)); lib. bdg. 14.99 (978-0-385-90121-5(6)) Random Hse. Children's Bks. (Lamb, Wendy).

Pierce, Tamora. Terrier. 2007. (Beka Cooper Ser.: No. 1). 608p. (YA). (gr. 7-11). pap. 9.99 ***978-0-375-83816-3(3)** , Random Hse. Bks. for Young Readers) Random Hse. Children's Bks.

Pinkston, Ronald. A Police Officer That's What I'll Be! Rivera, Israel, illus. 1999. 26p. (J). (gr. k-2). 12.99 (978-0-9671708-0-0(X)) Pinkston Publishing.

Poe. Breve Ant de Ctos Policiales. (SPA.). pap. 11.95 (978-950-07-1006-0(4)) Editorial Sudamericana S.A. ARG. *Dist:* Distribooks, Inc.

Policeman Dog: New Heroes Backpack Story. 2002. (J). (978-1-931312-59-2(1)) SoftPlay, Inc.

Rathmann, Peggy. Officer Buckle & Gloria. Rathmann, Peggy, illus. 2002. (Illus.). (J). 23.64 (978-0-7587-0061-2(X)) Book Wholesalers, Inc.

Sandoval, Lynda. Who's Your Daddy? 2004. 318p. (YA). (gr. 7). lib. bdg. 15.60 (978-1-4176-4527-5(X)) Tandem Library Bks.

Santillo, LuAnn. Jim & the Thug. Santillo, LuAnn, ed. 2003. (Half-Pint Kids Readers Ser.). (Illus.). 7p. (J). (ps-1). pap. (978-1-59256-078-3(4)) Half-Pint Kids, Inc.

Scarry, Huck & Scarry, Richard. A Day at the Police Station. 2004. (Illus.). 24p. (J). (ps-2). pap. 3.99 (978-0-375-82822-5(2) , Golden Bks.) Random Hse. Children's Bks.

Schott, Kenneth. The (Mis)Adventures of Captain Crazy. 2005. 124p. pap. 17.95 (978-1-4137-8190-8(X)) PublishAmerica, Inc.

Svendsen, Mark. Poison under Their Lips. 2002. 160p. (YA). pap. (978-0-7344-0183-0(3) , Lothian Bks.) Hachette Livre Australia.

—Poison under Their Lips. 2001. (gr. 7-12). lib. bdg. 22.20 (978-0-613-90595-4(4)) Tandem Library Bks.

Thompson, Kate. The New Policeman. 2005. (Illus.). 279p. (J). ***978-0-370-32878-2(7)** , Bodley Head) Random Hse. Children's Bks.

Thoughts Staff. Police Stories: the fight Call. 2005. 16p. 8.99 (978-1-4116-2267-8(7)) Lulu.com.

Turner Sinnenburg, Kris, illus. Aero & Officer Mike: Police Partners. Plummer, Joan & Russell, P., photos by. 2003. 32p. (J). (ps up). 17.95 (978-1-56397-931-6(4)) Boyds Mills Pr.

A Visit to the Police Station. 2003. (J). per. (978-1-57657-901-5(8)) Paradise Pr., Inc.

Wahl, Mats. The Invisible. Tucker, Katarina E., tr. from SWE. 2007. 192p. (YA). (gr. 7 up). 16.00 (978-0-374-33609-7(1) , Farrar, Straus & Giroux (BYR)) Farrar, Straus & Giroux.

Wiess, Laura. Leftovers. 2008. 256p. pap. 12.00 ***978-1-4165-4662-7(6)** , MTV) Simon & Schuster.

Wright, Betty Ren. Princess for a Week. Rogers, Jacqueline, illus. 2007. 160p. (J). (gr. 2-5). pap. 6.95 ***978-0-8234-2111-4(2))** Holiday Hse., Inc.

POLICE—VOCATIONAL GUIDANCE

Boraas, Tracey. Police Detective. 2000. (Career Exploration Ser.). (Illus.). 48p. (J). (gr. 3-4). lib. bdg. 21.26 (978-0-7368-0597-1(4) , LifeMatters Bks.) Capstone Pr., Inc.

Christy, Lee Louis. I Go to Work as a Police Officer. 2003. (I Go to Work As Ser.). (Illus.). (J). (978-1-58417-040-2(9)); pap. (978-1-58417-103-4(0)) Lake Street Pubs.

Ferguson. What Can I Do Now: Safety & Security. 2nd rev. ed. 2007. (What Can I Do Now Ser.). 200p. (gr. 6-12). 29.95 ***978-0-8160-6030-6(4)** , Ferguson Publishing Co.) Facts On File, Inc.

Goldberg, Jan. Security Guard. 1998. (Careers Without College Ser.). (Illus.). 48p. (J). (gr. 3-4). lib. bdg. 21.26 (978-0-7368-0039-6(5) , LifeMatters Bks.) Capstone Pr., Inc.

Goranson, Christopher D. & Goranson, C. D. Police Swat Teams: Life on High Alert. 2005. (Extreme Careers Ser.). (Illus.). 64p. (J). (gr. 5-8). pap., lib. bdg. 26.50 (978-0-8239-3635-9(X)) Rosen Publishing Group, Inc., The.

Hayward, Linda. A Day in the Life of a Police Officer. 2001. (Readers Ser.). (Illus.). 32p. (J). (ps-3). pap. 3.99 (978-0-7894-7955-6(9)) Dorling Kindersley Publishing, Inc.

—Day in the Life of a Police Officer. 2001. (gr. k-3). lib. bdg. 11.80 (978-0-613-43928-2(7)) Tandem Library Bks.

Hayward, Linda & Dorling Kindersley Publishing Staff. Jobs People Do: A Day in the Life of a Police Officer. 2001. (Readers Ser.). (Illus.). 32p. (J). 14.99 (978-0-7894-7954-9(0)) Dorling Kindersley Publishing, Inc.

Liebman, Dan. Quiero Ser Policia. 2000. Tr. of I Want to Be a Police Officer. (SPA.). (gr. k-3). lib. bdg. 14.15 (978-0-613-78544-0(4)) Tandem Library Bks.

Plum, Jennifer. Careers in the Police Department's Search & Rescue Unit. 2005. (Careers in Search & Rescue Operations Ser.). (Illus.). 64p. (YA). (gr. 5-8). lib. bdg. 26.50 (978-0-8239-3834-6(4)) Rosen Publishing Group, Inc., The.

Wirths, Claudine G. Choosing a Career in Law Enforcement. rev. ed. (World of Work Ser.). (Illus.). 64p. (YA). (gr. 7-12). 2005. lib. bdg. 25.25 (978-0-8239-3282-5(6) , WWLAEN); 2000. lib. bdg. 17.95 (978-0-8239-2274-1(X) , WWLAEN) Rosen Publishing Group, Inc., The.

POLICE DOGS

Anderson, Bendix. Security Dogs. 2005. (Dog Heroes Ser.). (Illus.). 32p. (J). lib. bdg. 25.27 (978-1-59716-015-5(6)) Bearport Publishing Co., Inc.

George, Charles & George, Linda. Dogs at Work, 4 bks. Incl. Bomb Detection Dogs. (Illus.). 48p. (J). (gr. 3-4). 1998. lib. bdg. 21.26 (978-1-56065-751-4(0) , Capstone High-Interest Bks.); (Illus.). Set lib. bdg. 85.04 (978-0-7368-0462-2(5) , Capstone High-Interest Bks.) Capstone Pr., Inc.

George, Linda & George, Charles. Police Dogs. 1998. (Dogs at Work Ser.). 48p. (J). pap. 19.00 (978-0-531-11556-5(9) , Watts, Franklin) Scholastic Library Publishing.

McGinty, Alice B. Detector Dogs: Sniffing Out Trouble. 1999. (Dogs Helping People Ser.). 24p. (J). (gr. k-4). lib. bdg. 18.75 (978-0-8239-5217-5(7) , PowerKids Pr.) Rosen Publishing Group, Inc., The.

Miller, Marie-Therese. Police Dogs. 2007. (Dog Tales: True Stories about Amazing Dogs Ser.). 80p. (J). 28.00 (978-0-7910-9036-7(1) , Chelsea Hse.) Facts On File, Inc.

Presnall, Judith Janda. Police Dogs. 2001. (Animals with Jobs Ser.). (Illus.). 48p. (J). (gr. 3-5). 23.70 (978-0-7377-0631-4(7) , LML00902-178555, Kidhaven) Thomson Gale.

Ruffin, Frances E. Police Dogs. 2005. (Dog Heroes Ser.). (Illus.). 32p. (J). lib. bdg. 25.27 (978-1-59716-014-8(8)) Bearport Publishing Co., Inc.

POLIO

see Poliomyelitis

POLIOMYELITIS

Barter, James E. Jonas Salk. 2002. (Importance of Ser.). (Illus.). 120p. (J). (gr. 4-12). 32.45 (978-1-56006-968-3(6) , Lucent Bks.) Thomson Gale.

Draper, Allison Stark. Polio. 2001. (Epidemics Ser.). (Illus.). 64p. (YA). (gr. 4-6). lib. bdg. 26.50 (978-0-8239-3348-8(2)) Rosen Publishing Group, Inc., The.

Durrett, Deanne. Jonas Salk. 2002. (Inventors & Creators Ser.). (Illus.). 48p. (J). (gr. 3-5). 23.70 (978-0-7377-1277-3(5) , LML00902-180219, Kidhaven) Thomson Gale.

Hantula, Richard. Jonas Salk. 2004. (Trailblazers of the Modern World Ser.). (Illus.). 48p. (J). (gr. 5 up). pap. 11.95 (978-0-8368-5260-8(5)); lib. bdg. 30.00 (978-0-8368-5100-7(5)) Stevens, Gareth Inc. (World Almanac Library).

Hecht, Alan D. Polio. 2003. (Deadly Diseases & Epidemics Ser.). (Illus.). 112p. (gr. 9-13). 31.95 (978-0-7910-7462-6(5) , Chelsea Hse.) Facts On File, Inc.

Kehret, Peg. Small Steps: The Year I Got Polio. (Illus.). (J). 2006. 224p. 15.95 (978-0-8075-7459-1(7)); 2004. 184p. (gr. 3-8). pap. 6.95 (978-0-8075-7458-4(9)) Whitman, Albert & Co.

Krohn, Katherine E. Jonas Salk & the Polio Vaccine. Milgrom, A., illus. 2007. (Graphic Library). 32p. (J). 25.26 (978-0-7368-6483-1(0)) Capstone Pr., Inc.

McLeese, Don. Jonas Salk. (Rourke Discovery Library). (Illus.). 24p. 2006. (gr. 2-5). 14.95 (978-1-59515-436-1(1)); 2005. (ENG & SPA., (J). (978-1-59515-676-1(3)) Rourke Publishing, LLC.

Naden, Corinne J. & Blue, Rose. Jonas Salk: Polio Pioneer. 2001. (Gateway Biography Ser.). (Illus.). 48p. (J). (gr. 2-4). lib. bdg. 23.90 (978-0-7613-1804-0(6) , Millbrook Pr.) Lerner Publishing Group.

Parks, Peggy J. Jonas Salk: Polio Vaccine Pioneer. 2003. (Giants of Science Ser.). (Illus.). 64p. (J). 26.20 (978-1-56711-475-1(X) , Blackbirch Pr., Inc.) Thomson Gale.

Peters, Stephanie True. The Battle Against Polio. 2004. (J). 29.93 (978-0-7614-1635-7(8) , Benchmark Bks.) Cavendish, Marshall Corp.

Reis, Ronald A. Jonas Salk: Microbiologist. 2005. (Ferguson Career Biographies Ser.). (Illus.). 128p. (gr. 6-12). 25.00 (978-0-8160-6186-0(6) , Ferguson Publishing Co.) Facts On File, Inc.

Sherrow, Victoria. Jonas Salk: Beyond the Microscope. 2nd rev. ed. 2008. (Makers of Modern Science Ser.). 160p. (J). (gr. 6-12). 29.95 ***(978-0-8160-6180-8(7)*** , Chelsea Hse.) Facts On File, Inc.

Sherrow, Victoria. Polio Epidemic: Crippling Virus Outbreak. 2001. (American Disasters Ser.). (Illus.). 48p. (YA). (gr. 4-10). lib. bdg. 23.93 (978-0-7660-1555-5(6)) Enslow Pubs., Inc.

Silverstein, Alvin, et al. Polio. 2001. (Diseases & People Ser.). (Illus.). 128p. (YA). (gr. 6-12). lib. bdg. 26.60 (978-0-7660-1592-0(0)) Enslow Pubs., Inc.

Tocci, Salvatore. Jonas Salk: Creator of the Polio Vaccine. 2003. (Great Minds of Science Ser.). (Illus.). 128p. (J). (gr. 4-10). lib. bdg. 26.60 (978-0-7660-2097-9(5)) Enslow Pubs., Inc.

POLISH AMERICANS

Anderson, Dale. Polish Americans. 2006. (World Almanac Library of American Immigration). (Illus.). 48p. (J). pap. (978-0-8368-7330-6(0)); lib. bdg. (978-0-8368-7317-7(3)) Stevens, Gareth Inc. (World Almanac Library).

Greene, Meg. Polish Americans. 2003. (Immigrants in America Ser.). (Illus.). 112p. (J). 29.95 (978-1-59018-516-2(1) , Lucent Bks.) Thomson Gale.

Hall, M. C. Polish Americans. 2003. (We Are America Ser.). 32p. pap. 6.95 (978-1-4034-3137-0(X)) Heinemann Library.

Hall, Margaret. Polish Americans. 2003. (We Are America Ser.). (Illus.). 32p. (J). lib. bdg. 24.22 (978-1-4034-0736-8(3)) Heinemann Library.

—Polish Americans. 2003. (gr. 3-6). lib. bdg. 15.25 (978-0-613-67428-7(6)) Tandem Library Bks.

Ingram, Scott & Asher, Robert. Polish Immigrants. 2004. (Immigration to the United States Ser.). (Illus.). 96p. (YA). (gr. 4-9). 35.00 (978-0-8160-5686-6(2)) Facts On File, Inc.

Locke, Donna. The Polish Americans. 2002. (Welcome to America Ser.). (Illus.). 64p. (J). (gr. 5 up). lib. bdg. (978-1-59084-112-9(3)) Mason Crest Pubs.

Nickles, Greg. The Poles. 2001. (We Came to North America Ser.). (Illus.). 32p. (J). (gr. 4). pap. (978-0-7787-0206-1(5)); (978-0-7787-0192-7(1)) Crabtree Publishing Co.

—Poles. 2001. (gr. 3-6). lib. bdg. 17.60 (978-0-613-43492-8(7)) Tandem Library Bks.

—The Poles: We Came to North America. 2006. (Illus.). 32p. (J). (gr. 4-8). reprint ed. 19.00 (978-0-7567-9907-6(4)) DIANE Publishing Co.

Raatma, Lucia. Polish Americans. 2002. (Spirit of America: Our Cultural Heritage Ser.). (Illus.). 32p. (J). (gr. 2-6). 27.07 (978-1-56766-157-6(2)) Child's World, Inc.

Wales, Dirk. Twice A Hero: Polish American Heroes of the American Revolution. Ihsen Peterson, Lynn, illus. 2007. (J). 18.95 ***(978-0-9632459-4-6(5))*** Great Plains Pr.

Wallner, Rosemary & Radzilowski, John. Polish Immigrants, 1890-1920. 2002. (Blue Earth Books). (Illus.). 32p. (J). (gr. 4). lib. bdg. 22.60 (978-0-7368-1208-5(3) , Bridgestone Bks.) Capstone Pr., Inc.

POLISH AMERICANS—FICTION

Armstrong, Jennifer. Theodore Roosevelt: Letters from a Young Coal Miner. 2001. (Dear Mr. President Ser.: Vol. 1). (Illus.). 118p. (J). (gr. 4-7). 8.95 (978-1-890817-27-5(9)) Winslow Pr.

Cushman, Karen. Rodzina. 2003. Tr. of Rodzina. 224p. (J). (gr. 5-9). tchr. ed. 16.00 (978-0-618-13351-2(8) , Clarion Bks.) Houghton Mifflin Co. Trade & Reference Div.

—Rodzina. 2005. Tr. of Rodzina. 224p. (gr. 5). 6.50 (978-0-440-41993-8(X) , Yearling) Random Hse. Children's Bks.

Estes, Eleanor. The Hundred Dresses. Slobodkin, Louis, illus. 2002. (J). 13.19 (978-0-7587-0272-2(8)) Book Wholesalers, Inc.

—The Hundred Dresses. Slobodkin, Louis, illus. anniv. ed. 2004. 96p. (J). pap. 7.00 (978-0-15-205260-7(7) , Harcourt Paperbacks) Harcourt Children's Bks.

Estes, Eleanor & Slobodkin, Louis. The Hundred Dresses. anniv. ed. 2004. (Illus.). 96p. (J). 16.00 (978-0-15-205170-9(8) , Harcourt Children's Bks) Harcourt Children's Bks.

Faigen, Anne G. New World Waiting. 2006. iii, 188p. (J). pap. (978-0-9744715-5-6(0)) Local History Co., The.

Leighton, Maxinne R. An Ellis Island Christmas. Nolan, Dennis, illus. 2005. 32p. (J). (gr. k-3). pap. 6.99 (978-0-14-240506-2(X) , Puffin) Penguin Group (USA) Inc.

Raphael, Marie. Streets of Gold. rev. ed. 2001. (Illus.). 224p. (J). (gr. 5 up). pap. 9.95 (978-0-89255-256-6(5)) Persea Bks., Inc.

Swigut, Bernadetta. First Star: Vigilja- First Star. 2006. (J). 16.99 (978-0-9790026-0-1(5)) Steinschneider, Bernadetta.

POLISH LANGUAGE

Hippocrene Books Staff. Hippocrene Children's Illustrated Polish Dictionary. 2001. (POL & ENG.). (gr. 3-6). lib. bdg. 21.05 (978-0-613-74952-7(9)) Tandem Library Bks.

The Rosetta Stone Language Library: Polish Level 1. 2005. (J). (gr. 1 up). cd-rom 209.00 (978-1-58022-035-4(5)) Fairfield Language Technologies.

POLISH LANGUAGE—DICTIONARIES—ENGLISH

Hippocrene Books, ed. Polish Childrens Picture Dict. 2006. (ENG & POL., Illus.). 108p. (J). pap. 14.95 (978-0-7818-1127-9(9)) Hippocrene Bks., Inc.

Hippocrene Books Staff, ed. Children's Illustrated Polish Dictionary: English-Polish, Polish-English. 1998. (Children's Illustrated Foreign Language Dictionaries Ser.). (ENG & POL., Illus.). 94p. (gr. k-5). 14.95 (978-0-7818-0711-1(5)) Hippocrene Bks., Inc.

Hippocrene Children's Illustrated Polish Dictionary: English-Polish/Polish-English. 2002. (Children's Illustrated Foreign Language Dictionaries Ser.). (ENG & POL., Illus.). 94p. (gr. k-5). pap. 11.95 (978-0-7818-0890-3(1)) Hippocrene Bks., Inc.

Turhan, Sedat. Milet Picture Dictionary: English/Polish. Hagin, Sally, illus. 2005. (Milet Picture Dictionary Ser.). (ENG & POL.). 48p. (J). (ps-ps). 14.95 (978-1-84059-466-9(7)) Milet Publishing.

POLITENESS

see Courtesy; Etiquette

POLITICAL CORRUPTION

Ashby, Ruth. Boss Tweed: And Tammany Hall. 2002. (Notorious Americans & Their Times Ser.). (Illus.). 112p. (YA). (gr. 5 up). 27.45 (978-1-56711-252-8(8) , Blackbirch Pr., Inc.) Thomson Gale.

Gay, Oonagh & Leopold, Patricia, eds. Conduct Unbecoming? The Regulation of Parliamentary Behaviour. Gay, Oonagh & Leopold, Patricia, trs. 2004. 39.95 (978-1-84275-055-1(0)) Politico's Publishing Ltd. GBR. *Dist:* Consortium Bk. Sales & Distribution.

Miller, Debra. Political Corruption. 2007. (Hot Topics Ser.). 128p. (J). (gr. 7-10). 32.45 ***(978-1-59018-982-5(5)*** , Lucent Bks.) Thomson Gale.

Roberts, Russell. Presidents & Scandals. 2000. (History Makers Ser.). (Illus.). 112p. (J). (gr. 7-10). 28.70 (978-1-56006-642-2(3) , Lucent Bks.) Thomson Gale.

Scherer, Randy. Political Scandals. 2007. (Opposing Viewpoints Ser.). (Illus.). 128p. (gr. 10-12). pap. 21.20 ***(978-0-7377-3764-6(6)*** , Greenhaven Pr., Inc.) Thomson Gale.

POLITICAL CORRUPTION—FICTION

Singer, Nicky. GemX. 2008. (YA). ***(978-0-8234-2108-4(2))*** Holiday Hse., Inc.

Skarmeta, Antonio. The Composition. Ruano, Alfonso, illus. 2003. 32p. (J). (gr. 3 up). pap. 5.95 (978-0-88899-550-6(4)) Groundwood Bks. CAN. *Dist:* Perseus Distribution.

—The Composition. Amado, Elisa, tr. from SPA. Ruano, Alfonso, illus. 2000. 32p. (J). (gr. 2-6). 16.95 (978-0-88899-390-8(0) , Libros Tigrillo) Groundwood Bks. CAN. *Dist:* Perseus Distribution.

Sterling, Bruce. Distraction. 1999. (Illus.). 532p. lib. bdg. 13.64 (978-0-606-17995-9(X)) Tandem Library Bks.

POLITICAL CRIMES AND OFFENSES

see also Assassination; Bombings; Concentration Camps; Terrorism

Gedatus, Gus. Hate. 2000. (Perspectives on Violence Ser.). (Illus.). 64p. (J). (gr. 4-6). lib. bdg. 23.93 (978-0-7368-0427-1(7) , LifeMatters Bks.) Capstone Pr., Inc.

Katz, Samuel M. Raging Within: Ideological Terrorism. 2003. (Terrorist Dossiers Ser.). (Illus.). 72p. (J). (gr. 6-12). 26.60 (978-0-8225-4032-8(0)) Lerner Publishing Group.

Kramer, Ann. Mandela: The Rebel Who Led His Nation to Freedom. 2005. (World History Biographies Ser.). (Illus.). 64p. (J). (gr. 3-7). 17.95 (978-0-7922-3658-0(0) , National Geographic Children's Bks.) National Geographic Society.

—Nelson Mandela. 2003. (20th Century History Makers Ser.). (Illus.). 112p. (J). lib. bdg. 32.85 (978-0-7398-5258-3(2)) Raintree.

POLITICAL CRIMES AND OFFENSES—FICTION

Burnham, Sophy. The Dogwalker. 2000. 164p. (gr. 4-7). pap. 11.95 (978-0-595-12939-3(0) , Backinprint.com) iUniverse, Inc.

POLITICAL ECONOMY

see Economics

POLITICAL PARTIES

see also Politics, Practical; Right and Left (Political Science)

also names of parties, e.g. Democratic Party

Heath, David. Elections in the United States. 1998. (American Civics Ser.). (Illus.). 48p. (J). (gr. 3-4). lib. bdg. 22.60 (978-0-7368-0000-6(X) , Bridgestone Bks.) Capstone Pr., Inc.

—Elections in the United States. (American Civics Ser.). 48p. (YA). pap. 6.95 (978-0-7368-8857-8(8)) Capstone Pr., Inc.

Horn, Geoffrey M. Political Parties, Interest Groups & the Media. 2003. (World Almanac Library of American Government). (Illus.). 48p. (J). (gr. 5 up). pap. 14.95 (978-0-8368-5483-1(7)); lib. bdg. 30.00 (978-0-8368-5478-7(0)) Stevens, Gareth Inc. (World Almanac Library).

Klee, Sheila. Volunteering for a Political Campaign. 2000. (High Interest Bks.). (Illus.). 48p. (YA). (gr. 7-12). 23.00 (978-0-516-23398-7(X) , Children's Pr.) Scholastic Library Publishing.

Landau, Elaine. Friendly Foes: A Look at Political Parties. 2004. (How Government Works Ser.). (Illus.). 56p. (J). (gr. 4-8). lib. bdg. 25.26 (978-0-8225-1349-0(8)) Lerner Publishing Group.

Schlesinger, Arthur M., Jr., ed. The History of the Republican Party. 2000. (Your Government Ser.). (Illus.). 64p. (YA). (gr. 4-7). 25.00 (978-0-7910-5540-3(X) , Chelsea Hse.) Facts On File, Inc.

Zilber, Jeremy. Why Mommy Is a Democrat. Firsova, Yuliya, illus. 2005. 28p. (J). 8.00 (978-0-9786688-0-8(4)) Zilber, Jeremy.

POLITICAL SCIENCE

see also Church and State; Citizenship; Civil Rights; Civil Service; Communism; Constitutional Law; Democracy; Government, Resistance to; Kings, Queens, Rulers, etc.; Law; Liberty; Local Government; Municipal Government; Political Parties; Power (Social Sciences); Public Administration; Revolutions; Right and Left (Political Science); Socialism; State Governments; Suffrage; Utopias; World Politics

Adler, Bill, Jr. If I Were President: Kids Talk about Running the Country. 2000. 96p. (YA). pap. 10.00 (978-0-380-80562-4(6)) HarperCollins Pubs.

Baicker, Karen. The Election Activity Book: Dozens of Activities That Help Kids Learn about Voting, Campaigns, Our Government, Presidents, & More. 2004. (Illus.). 32p. pap., tchr. ed. 9.99 (978-0-439-66826-2(3)) Scholastic, Inc.

Barker, Cornelius L. & Searchwell, Claudette J. Government by the Children for the Children. 2000. (Illus.). 35p. (YA). (gr. 7-12). pap. 12.95 (978-0-9678378-1-9(2)) Cordet Bks.

Benchmark Education Staff, compiled by. Power, Authority, & Governance. 2005. spiral bd. 50.00 ***(978-1-4108-4501-6(X));*** spiral bd. 145.00 ***(978-1-4108-5419-3(1))*** Benchmark Education Co.

Branches of Government. (Poster Projects Ser.). (gr. 3-6). 9.99 (978-0-7424-0696-4(2) , IF22453) School Specialty Publishing.

Brown, Alan. The Story Behind George Orwell's Animal Farm. 2006. (History in Literature Ser.). (Illus.). 56p. (YA). (gr. 6-9). lib. bdg. 32.86 (978-1-4034-8203-7(9)) Heinemann Library.

Buehler, Stephanie & Kremer, Kelly Dos Santos. Elections: Primary. 2000. (Illus.). 48p. (Orig.). (J). pap., tchr. ed. 7.99 (978-1-57690-618-7(3) , TCA2618) Teacher Created Materials, Inc.

California 2003-2004 Recall Election Calendar. l.t. ed. 2003. (Illus.). 40p. 14.95 (978-0-9745991-0-6(7)) Princess Ring, LLC.

Campaign Posters. (Poster Projects Ser.). (gr. 3-6). 9.99 (978-0-7424-0695-7(4) , IF22452) School Specialty Publishing.

Cassutto, George. Civics: Student Activities Book. 2003. (Illus.). stu. ed., ring bd., wbk. ed. (978-1-931680-36-3(1) , Expert Systems for Teachers) Teaching Point, Inc.

Cherry Lake Publishing, compiled by. Citizens & their Governments. 2008. lib. bdg. ***(978-1-60279-108-4(2))*** Cherry Lake Publishing.

CQ Press Editors. Public Interest Group Profiles 2004-2005. 11th rev. ed. 2004. 800p. (gr. 9 up). 225.00 (978-1-56802-886-6(5)) CQ Pr.

De Capua, Sarah. Being A Governor. 2004. (True Bks.). 48p. (J). (gr. 3-5). pap. 6.95 (978-0-516-27939-8(4) , Children's Pr.) Scholastic Library Publishing.

Dorling Kindersley Publishing Staff. How Governments Work. 2005. 320p. 30.00 (978-0-7566-2198-8(4)) Dorling Kindersley Publishing, Inc.

Facts on File, Inc. Staff. Politics. 2005. (Careers in Focus Ser.). (Illus.). 172p. (J). (gr. 6-12). 22.95 (978-0-8160-5844-0(X) , Ferguson Publishing Co.) Facts On File, Inc.

Fish, Bruce. Thomas Paine. 1999. (Revolutionary War Leaders Ser.). (Illus.). 80p. (YA). (gr. 3 up). pap. 27.50 (978-0-7910-5699-8(6) , Chelsea Hse.) Facts On File, Inc.

Fridell, Ron. Dictatorship. 2007. (Political Systems of the World Ser.). 160p. (YA). (gr. 9 up). lib. bdg. 39.93 (978-0-7614-2627-1(2) , Benchmark Bks.) Cavendish, Marshall Corp.

Gall, Timothy L. & Gall, Susan B. Junior Worldmark Encyclopedia of the Nations, 10 vols., Set. 5th rev. ed. 2007. 520.00 (978-1-4144-1095-1(6) , UXL) Thomson Gale.

Gall, Timothy L. & Gall, Susan B. Junior Worldmark Encyclopedia of the Nations/[edited By] Timothy L. Gall & Susan Bevan Gall. 5th ed. 2007. ***(978-1-4144-1096-8(4)); (978-1-4144-1097-5(2)); (978-1-4144-1098-2(0)); (978-1-4144-1099-9(9)); (978-1-4144-1100-2(6)); (978-1-4144-1101-9(4)); (978-1-4144-1102-6(2)); (978-1-4144-1103-3(0)); (978-1-4144-1104-0(9)); (978-1-4144-1105-7(7))*** Thomson Gale.

Gall, Timothy L. & Gall, Susan B., eds. Junior Worldmark Encyclopedia of the Nations, 9 vols. 2nd ed. 1999. (Illus.). (J). (978-0-7876-3804-7(8)); (978-0-7876-3805-4(6)) Thomson Gale.

Giesecke, Ernestine. Governments Around the World. 2000. (Kids' Guide Ser.). (Illus.). 32p. (J). (gr. 4-6). lib. bdg. 22.79 (978-1-57572-511-6(8)) Heinemann Library.

Grant, Moyra. Government & Politics. 2005. (Illus.). 232p. (C). pap. 47.50 (978-0-7487-9032-6(2)) Nelson Thornes Ltd. GBR. *Dist:* Trans-Atlantic Pubns., Inc.

Harcourt School Publishers Staff. Horizons Unit 2: Our Government. 3rd ed. 2001. (Illus.). pap. 169.80 (978-0-15-322577-2(7)) Harcourt Schl. Pubs.

—Our Government, No. 2. 2nd ed. 2003. (Illus.). pap. 139.70 (978-0-15-337566-8(3)) Harcourt Schl. Pubs.

Hargrove, Julia. Executive Branch of Government. Mitchell, Judy, ed. Smith, Bron, illus. 2000. (History Speaks Ser.). 32p. (J). (gr. 4-8). pap. 5.95 (978-1-57310-243-8(1)) Teaching & Learning Co.

—Judicial Branch of Government. Mitchell, Judy, ed. Smith, Bron, illus. 2000. (History Speaks Ser.). 32p. (J). (gr. 4-8). pap. 5.95 (978-1-57310-244-5(X)) Teaching & Learning Co.

—Legislative Branch of the Government. Mitchell, Judy, ed. Smith, Bron, illus. 2000. (History Speaks Ser.). 48p. (J). (gr. 4-8). pap., tchr. ed. 6.95 (978-1-57310-245-2(8)) Teaching & Learning Co.

Harris, Nathaniel. Monarchy. 2005. (Systems of Government Ser.). (Illus.). 48p. (J). (978-0-8368-5890-7(5)); lib. bdg. 30.00 (978-0-8368-5885-3(9)) Stevens, Gareth Inc. (World Almanac Library).

Holt, Rinehart and Winston Staff. American Civics: Answer Key for Guided Reading Strategies. 5th ed. 2004. pap. 8.00 (978-0-03-038723-4(X)) Holt, Rinehart & Winston.

—American Civics: Chapter Tutorials for Students. 5th ed. 2004. pap. 26.60 (978-0-03-038719-7(1)) Holt, Rinehart & Winston.

—American Civics: Community Service Handbook. 3rd ed. 2002. pap. 25.80 (978-0-03-067689-5(4)) Holt, Rinehart & Winston.

—American Civics: Guided Reading Strategies. 5th ed. 2004. pap. 25.80 (978-0-03-038716-6(7)) Holt, Rinehart & Winston.

—American Civics: Simulations & Case Studies. 3rd ed. 2002. pap. 25.80 (978-0-03-067704-5(1)) Holt, Rinehart & Winston.

—Holt Researcher: Economics & Government: User Guide for CD-ROM. 1999. pap. 6.73 (978-0-03-051714-3(1)) Holt, Rinehart & Winston.

Ideas of the Modern World, 4 bks., Set. 2001. (Illus.). lib. bdg. 71.92 (978-0-7398-3162-5(3)) Raintree.

Inside Government. (History & Social Studies Ser.). (Illus.). 64p. (J). (978-0-7613-1177-5(7) , Twenty-First Century Bks.) Lerner Publishing Group.

Issues in Focus, Set. (Issues in Focus Ser.). (Illus.). (YA). (gr. 6-12). lib. bdg. (978-0-89490-345-8(4)) Enslow Pubs., Inc.

Issues of Our Time. (Contemporary Issues Ser.). (Illus.). (978-0-7613-3056-1(9) , Twenty-First Century Bks.) Lerner Publishing Group.

Keller, Ellen. Kids Are Citizens. 2002. (National Geographic Reading Expeditions Ser.). (Illus.). 32p. (J). pap. (978-0-7922-8683-7(9)) National Geographic Society.

Kishel, Ann-Marie. What Is Government? 2007. (First Step Nonfiction Ser.). 24p. (J). (gr. k-2). 18.60 (978-0-8225-6393-8(2) , Lerner Pubns.) Lerner Publishing Group.

MacDonald, Fiona. Politics, Society & Leadership. 2001. (Through the Ages Ser.). (Illus.). 96p. (gr. 3-7). 12.95 (978-0-7548-0848-0(3)) Anness Publishing GBR. *Dist:* National Bk. Network.

Marsh, Carole. Pass the Test! Civics & Economics. (Virginia Experience! Ser.). lab manual ed. 195.00 incl. cd-rom (978-0-635-01593-8(5) , 15935); cd-rom 395.00 (978-0-635-01594-5(3) , 15943); 2004. cd-rom 24.95 (978-0-635-01592-1(7) , 15927) Gallopade International.

—Virginia Civics & Economics: Student Workbook. 2004. (Virginia Experience! Ser.). (Illus.). 160p. pap., wbk. ed. 12.95 (978-0-635-01590-7(0) , 15900) Gallopade International.

—Washington Government Projects: 30 Cool, Activities, Crafts, Experiments & More for Kids to Do to Learn about Your State! 2003. (Washington Experience Ser.). 32p. (gr. k-5). pap. 5.95 (978-0-635-01966-0(3) , Marsh, Carole Bks.) Gallopade International.

—West Virginia Government Projects: 30 Cool, Activities, Crafts, Experiments & More for Kids to Do to Learn about Your State! 2003. (West Virginia Experience Ser.). 32p. (gr. k-5). pap. 5.95 (978-0-635-01967-7(1) , Marsh, Carole Bks.) Gallopade International.

—Wisconsin Government Projects: 30 Cool, Activities, Crafts, Experiments & More for Kids to Do to Learn about Your State! 2003. (Wisconsin Experience Ser.). 32p. (gr. k-5). pap. 5.95 (978-0-635-01968-4(X) , Marsh, Carole Bks.) Gallopade International.

—Wyoming Government Projects: 30 Cool, Activities, Crafts, Experiments & More for Kids to Do to Learn about Your State! 2003. (Wyoming Experience Ser.). 32p. (gr. k-5). pap. 5.95 (978-0-635-01969-1(8) , Marsh, Carole Bks.) Gallopade International.

McGraw-Hill Staff. Civics Today. 2002. stu. ed. 85.33 incl. cd-rom (978-0-07-829629-1(3) , 9780078296291) Glencoe/McGraw-Hill.

—Civics Today: Citizenship, Economics & You, Interactive Tutor Self-Assessment. 4th ed. 2007. (C). cd-rom 93.32 (***978-0-07-879108-6(1)*** , 9780078791086) Glencoe/McGraw-Hill.

—Civics Today: Citizenship, Economics & You, Reading Essentials & Note-Taking Guide Workbook. 4th ed. 2007. (C). pap. 18.00 (***978-0-07-877672-4(4)*** , 9780078776724) Glencoe/McGraw-Hill.

—Civics Today, Student Edition. 4th ed. 2007. (C). pap. 86.64 (***978-0-07-874631-4(0)*** , 9780078746314) Glencoe/McGraw-Hill.

McLeese, Don. Thomas Paine. (Heroes of the American Revolution Ser.). 32p. 2005. (Illus.). (gr. 2-5). 19.95 (978-1-59515-215-2(6)); 2004. pap. 5.95 (978-1-59515-319-7(5)) Rourke Publishing, LLC.

Morris, Neil. Modern World Leaders. (Illus.). 48p. (YA). (gr. 5 up). lib. bdg. 29.95 (978-1-932333-79-4(7)) Chrysalis Education.

Othello: Activity Pack. 2003. 156p. (YA). pap. (978-1-58049-631-5(8) , PA6318) Prestwick Hse., Inc.

Perl, Lila. Theocracy. 2007. (Political Systems of the World Ser.). 160p. (YA). (gr. 9 up). lib. bdg. 39.93 (***978-0-7614-2631-8(0)*** , Benchmark Bks.) Cavendish, Marshall Corp.

Political Manipulations. 2004. 28.56 (978-1-4109-1077-6(6)) Raintree.

Prentice-Hall Staff. When Legend. 2nd ed. (J). stu. ed. (978-0-13-717281-8(8)) Prentice Hall (Schl. Div.).

Rees, Peter. Liberty: Blessing or Burden? 2007. (Shockwave: the Human Experience Ser.). (Illus.). 36p. (J). (gr. 4-6). lib. bdg. 25.00 (***978-0-531-17760-0(2)*** , Children's Pr.) Scholastic Library Publishing.

Schlesinger, Arthur M., Jr., ed. How a Bill Is Passed. 2000. (Your Government Ser.). (Illus.). 64p. (YA). (gr. 4-7). 25.00 (978-0-7910-5537-3(X) , Chelsea Hse.) Facts On File, Inc.

—How to Become an Elected Official. 2000. (Your Government Ser.). (Illus.). 64p. (YA). (gr. 4-7). 25.00 (978-0-7910-5536-6(1) , Chelsea Hse.) Facts On File, Inc.

—Major World Leaders, 12 vols., Set. (J). 275.40 (978-0-7910-6938-7(9) , Chelsea Hse.) Facts On File, Inc.

Shafer, Jean. Our Core Democratic Values: Civic Virtue in Action. 1999. (Illus.). 32p. (J). (gr. 3-7). pap., wbk. ed. 14.95 (978-0-938682-54-7(7)) River Road Pubns., Inc.

Sobel, Syl. How the U. S. Government Works. 2001. (United States & Its Flag Ser.). (Illus.). (J). lib. bdg. 14.95 (978-1-56674-289-4(7)) Forest Hse. Publishing Co., Inc.

Steck-Vaughn Staff. Elementary Civics Writing Dictionary. 2002. (J). pap. (978-0-7398-5417-4(8)) Steck-Vaughn.

Stefoff, Rebecca. Monarchy. 2007. (Political Systems of the World Ser.). 160p. (YA). (gr. 9 up). lib. bdg. 39.93 (***978-0-7614-2630-1(2)*** , Benchmark Bks.) Cavendish, Marshall Corp.

A Student's Guide to American Civics, 4 bks. Incl. So What Is Citizenship Anyway? Luthringer, Chelsea. 1999. lib. bdg. 23.95 (978-0-8239-3097-5(1) , CVCITI); So What Is Justice Anyway? Luthringer, Chelsea. 1999. lib. bdg. 23.95 (978-0-8239-3096-8(3) , CVJUST); So What Is Patriotism Anyway? LaMachia, John. 2000. lib. bdg. 23.95 (978-0-8239-3098-2(X) , CVPATR); So What Is Tolerance Anyway? LaMachia, John. 2000. lib. bdg. 23.95 (978-0-8239-3099-9(8) , CVTOLE); 48p. (YA). (gr. 5-8). (Illus.). 2000. Set lib. bdg. 95.80 o.p. (978-0-8239-9049-8(4) , CVAMCI, Rosen Central) Rosen Publishing Group, Inc., The.

Systems of Government. lib. bdg. 120.00 (978-0-8368-5881-5(6)) Stevens, Gareth Inc.

Tears of a Tiger: Activity Pack. 2003. 165p. (YA). pap. (978-1-58049-629-2(6) , PA6296) Prestwick Hse., Inc.

Teets, Ashley Catherine. West Virginia State Government: A Kid's View. 2000. (Illus.). 32p. (J). (gr. 2-10). pap. 4.95 (978-0-929915-27-2(5)) Headline Bks., Inc.

Today's Issues. (Contemporary Issues Ser.). (Illus.). (YA). (978-0-7613-3305-0(3) , Twenty-First Century Bks.) Lerner Publishing Group.

Tripp, Penny. Human Rights. (Illus.). 64p. (YA). (gr. 5 up). lib. bdg. 29.95 (978-1-931983-82-2(8)) Chrysalis Education.

United States, Army Junior ROTC Staff, et al, contrib. by. Army JROTC Leadership Education & Training. 2002. (Illus.). 416p. (J). (978-0-536-67808-9(1)) Pearson Custom Publishing.

Wachtel, Roger. The Donner Party. 2003. (Cornerstones of Freedom, 2ND Ser.). (Illus.). 48p. (J). 26.00 (978-0-516-24218-7(0) , Children's Pr.) Scholastic Library Publishing.

Waxman, Laura Hamilton. An Uncommon Revolutionary: A Story about Thomas Paine. Orback, Craig, illus. 2003. (Creative Minds Biography Ser.). (J). pap. 5.95 (978-1-57505-608-1(9) , Carolrhoda Bks.) Lerner Publishing Group.

Williams, Jane A. A Bluestocking Guide - Political Philosophies: Companion Workbook to Richard J. Maybury's Are You Liberal? Conservative? or Confused? Daniels, Kathryn, ed. 2004. (Bluestocking Guide Ser.). 63p. (YA). pap. 12.95 (978-0-942617-47-4(9)) Bluestocking Pr.

Wilson, Christopher. Understanding A/S Level Government Politics. 2003. (Understanding Politics Ser.). (Illus.). 311p. pap. 21.95 (978-0-7190-6081-6(8)) Manchester Univ. Pr. GBR. *Dist:* Macmillan.

Wise, Rod, et al. Give & Take: An Issues Approach to Civics. 1999. 160p. pap. 18.00 (978-0-521-77653-0(8)) Cambridge Univ. Pr.

Your Government: How It Works. 2005. pap. 625.00 (978-0-7910-9177-7(5) , Chelsea Hse.) Facts On File, Inc.

POLITICIANS

see also Legislators; Presidents; Statesmen

Acker, Kerry. Gerhard Schroeder. 2003. (Major World Leaders Ser.). (Illus.). 112p. (gr. 6-12). 30.00 (978-0-7910-7652-1(0) , Chelsea Hse.) Facts On File, Inc.

Adler, David A. & Adler, Michael S. A Picture Book of Samuel Adams. Himler, Ronald, illus. 2005. 32p. (J). 16.95 (978-0-8234-1846-6(4)) Holiday Hse., Inc.

Alembi, Ezekiel. Jaramogi Oginga Odinga: People's Revolutionary. 2004. (Lion Books). (Illus.). x, 78p. (J). (978-9966-951-24-3(5)) Sasa Sema Publications Ltd.

Anderson, Mercedes Padrino. Benazir Bhutto. 2004. (Women in Politics Ser.). (Illus.). 120p. 30.00 (978-0-7910-7732-0(2)); 110p. pap. 30.00 (978-0-7910-8000-9(5)) Facts On File, Inc. (Chelsea Hse.).

Booth, Lynn. Livewire Real Lives Jack Lang. 1999. (Livewires Ser.). 32p. (gr. 6-9). pap. 6.00 (978-0-521-77633-2(3)) Cambridge Univ. Pr.

Burgan, Michael. Samuel Adams: Patriot & Statesman. 2004. (Signature Lives Ser.). (Illus.). 112p. (J). 30.60 (978-0-7565-0823-4(1) , 1240135) Compass Point Bks.

Doeden, Matt. Samuel Adams: Patriot & Statesman. 2007. (Graphic Library). 32p. (J). 25.26 (978-0-7368-6500-5(4)) Capstone Pr., Inc.

Gillis, Jennifer Blizin. Samuel Adams. 2004. (Illus.). 32p. (J). pap. 7.50 (978-1-4034-5970-1(3)); lib. bdg. 25.64 (978-1-4034-5962-6(2)) Heinemann Library.

Gordon, Janet & Merkur, Janet. Livewire Real Lives John Curtin. 1999. (Livewires Ser.). 32p. (gr. 6-9). pap. 6.00 (978-0-521-77632-5(5)) Cambridge Univ. Pr.

—Livewire Real Lives Sir Robert Menzies. 1999. (Livewires Ser.). 32p. (gr. 6-9). pap. 6.00 (978-0-521-77622-6(8)) Cambridge Univ. Pr.

—Livewire Real Lives William Charles Wentworth. 1999. (Livewire Real Lives Ser.). 32p. (gr. 6-9). pap. 6.00 (978-0-521-77619-6(8)) Cambridge Univ. Pr.

Gorman, Jacqueline Laks. Our Government Leaders. 24p. (YA). 115.98 (978-0-8368-4566-2(8)) Stevens, Gareth Inc.

Great Life Stories: Political Figures. 2004. (Illus.). 88.50 (978-0-531-19330-3(6)) Scholastic Library Publishing.

Haugen, Brenda. Benito Mussolini: Fascist Italian Dictator. 2006. (Illus.). 112p. (J). (978-0-7565-1892-9(X)) Compass Point Bks.

Hughes, Chris. The Constitutional Convention. 2005. (People at the Center of Ser.). (Illus.). 48p. (J). (ps-7). lib. bdg. 24.95 (978-1-56711-918-3(2) , Blackbirch Pr., Inc.) Thomson Gale.

Jakoubek, Robert. Jesse Jackson: Civil Rights Leader & Politician. (Black Americans of Achievement Ser.). (Illus.). 112p. (gr. 6-12). 2005. pap. 13.25 (978-0-7910-8334-5(9)); 2004. (J). 30.00 (978-0-7910-8160-0(5)) Facts On File, Inc. (Chelsea Hse.).

Krakow, Kari. The Harvey Milk Story. Gardner, David, illus. 2002. 32p. (J). 17.95 (978-0-9674468-3-7(X)) Two Lives Publishing.

Lashnits, Tom. Recep Tayyip Erdogan: Prime Minister of Turkey. Schlesinger, Arthur M., Jr., ed. 2005. (Major World Leaders Ser.). (Illus.). 112-144p. (gr. 6-12). 30.00 (978-0-7910-8263-8(6) , Chelsea Hse.) Facts On File, Inc.

Llewellyn-Evans, Teresa. Livewire Real Lives Sir Henry Parkes. 1999. (Livewires Ser.). 32p. (gr. 6-9). pap. 6.00 (978-0-521-77621-9(X)) Cambridge Univ. Pr.

Mallin, Jay. Al Sharpton: Community Activist. 2007. (Great Life Stories Ser.). (Illus.). 111p. (J). (***978-0-531-13672-0(8)*** , Franklin Watts) Hodder Children's Division.

—Al Sharpton: Community Activist. 2006. (Great Life Stories Ser.). (Illus.). 111p. (YA). (gr. 6 up). 30.50 (978-0-531-13872-4(0) , Watts, Franklin) Scholastic Library Publishing.

Mara, Wil. Colin Powell. 2004. (Rookie Biographies Ser.). (Illus.). 31p. (J). (gr. 1-2). pap. 4.95 (978-0-516-27918-3(1) , Children's Pr.) Scholastic Library Publishing.

Marsh, Carole. John Kerry: Successful Senator & 2004 Presidential Candidate. 2004. (J). 24p. pap. 5.95 (978-0-635-02537-1(X)); 24.95 (978-0-635-02542-5(6)) Gallopade International.

—Vel Phillips. 2002. (One Thousand Readers Ser.). (Illus.). 12p. (J). (gr. k-4). 2.95 (978-0-635-01553-2(6) , 15536) Gallopade International.

McCarthy, Pat. Famous Union Generals & Leaders of the North: A MyReportLinks. com Book. 2004. (American Civil War Ser.). (Illus.). 48p. (J). lib. bdg. 25.26 (978-0-7660-5188-1(9) , MyReportLinks.com Bks.) Enslow Pubs., Inc.

McElroy, Lisa Tucker. Alberto Gonzales: Attorney General. 2006. (Gateway Biographies Ser.). (Illus.). 48p. (J). 23.93 (978-0-8225-3418-1(5)) Lerner Publishing Group.

Merkur, Janet. Livewire Real Lives Sir Mark Oliphant. 1999. (Livewires Ser.). (Illus.). 32p. (gr. 6-9). pap. 6.00 (978-0-521-77628-8(7)) Cambridge Univ. Pr.

Sakany, Lois. The Platforms & Policies of America's Reform Politicians. 2004. (Progressive Movement, 1900-1920 Ser.). (Illus.). 32p. (J). lib. bdg. (978-1-4042-0193-4(9)) Rosen Publishing Group, Inc., The.

Sanna, Ellyn. Politician. 2003. (Careers with Character Ser.). (Illus.). 96p. (YA). (gr. 7 up). lib. bdg. 22.95 (978-1-59084-320-8(7)) Mason Crest Pubs.

Somervill, Barbara A. Indira Gandhi: Political Leader in India. 2006. (Illus.). 112p. (J). (978-0-7565-1885-1(7)) Compass Point Bks.

Southwell, David & Twist, Sean. Unsolved Political Mysteries. 2007. (J). (***978-1-4042-1083-7(0)***) Rosen Publishing Group, Inc., The.

Stille, Darlene R. Eva Peron, First Lady of Argentina. 2006. (Signature Lives Ser.). (Illus.). 112p. (J). (gr. 5-7). 30.60 (978-0-7565-1585-0(8)) Compass Point Bks.

Sturgis, James. Adam Beck. (Illus.). 64p. (J). (gr. 5 up). pap. (978-1-55041-828-6(9)) Fitzhenry & Whiteside, Ltd.

Tukan, Jaytoe Antony, Sr. John Reid Edwards: The People's Senator. 2003. per. 19.95 (978-0-9665909-4-4(5)) Kalawantis Publishing Services, Inc.

Walsh, Kieran. Samuel Adams. (Discover the Life of a Colonial American Ser.). 24p. 2005. (Illus.). (gr. 2-5). 14.95 (978-1-59515-135-3(4)); 2004. pap. 4.95 (978-1-59515-336-4(5)) Rourke Publishing, LLC.

Williams, Colleen Madonna Flood. Yasir Arafat. 2002. (gr. 3-6). lib. bdg. 19.90 (978-0-613-85631-7(7)) Tandem Library Bks.

Worth, Richard & Jr. Pervez Musharraf. 2nd rev. ed. 2007. (Modern World Leaders Ser.). 104p. (gr. 6-12). 30.00 (***978-0-7910-9264-4(X)*** , Chelsea Hse.) Facts On File, Inc.

POLITICS, PRACTICAL

see also Elections; Lobbying; Television in Politics

Adler, Bill, Jr. If I Were President: Kids Talk about Running the Country. 2000. 96p. (YA). pap. 10.00 (978-0-380-80562-4(6)) HarperCollins Pubs.

Beyer, Mark. The Election of 1800: Congress Helps Settle a Three-Way Vote. 2004. (Life in the New American Nation Ser.). (Illus.). 32p. (YA). lib. bdg. (978-0-8239-4255-8(4)) Rosen Publishing Group, Inc., The.

Christelow, Eileen. Vote! Christelow, Eileen, illus. (Illus.). 48p. (J). 2004. (gr. 1-5). 47.60 (978-0-618-51723-7(5)); 2003. (gr. 3-5). 16.00 (978-0-618-24754-7(8)) Houghton Mifflin Co. Trade & Reference Div. (Clarion Bks.).

—Vote! 2004. (Illus.). 48p. (J). (gr. 1-5). reprint ed. pap. 6.95 (978-0-618-48606-9(2) , Clarion Bks.) Houghton Mifflin Co. Trade & Reference Div.

De Capua, Sarah. Running for Public Office. 2002. (True Bks.). (Illus.). 48p. (J). (gr. 3-5). pap. 6.95 (978-0-516-27368-6(X)); 25.00 (978-0-516-22333-9(X)) Scholastic Library Publishing. (Children's Pr.).

Decapua, Sarah. Running for Public Office. 2002. (gr. 3-6). lib. bdg. 15.25 (978-0-613-54330-9(0)) Tandem Library Bks.

Donovan, Sandy. Running for Office: A Look at Political Campaigns. 2004. (How Government Works Ser.). (Illus.). 56p. (J). (gr. 4-8). lib. bdg. 25.26 (978-0-8225-4700-6(7)) Lerner Publishing Group.

Engelbert, Phillis. Activists, Rebels & Reformers, 3 vols. Sawinski, Diane M., ed. (Illus.). (J). 2001. 600p. (gr. 6 up). lib. bdg. 181.00 net. (978-0-7876-4847-3(7) , GML00502-114891); 2000. xxx, 596p. (978-0-7876-4848-0(5)); 2000. xxx, 596p. (978-0-7876-4849-7(3)) Thomson Gale. (UXL).

Engelbert, Phillis & Sawinski, Diane M. Activists, Rebels & Reformers, 3 vols., Set. 2000. (Illus.). xxx, 596p. (J). (978-0-7876-4850-3(7)) Visible Ink Pr.

Ferguson. Careers in Focus: Government. 2nd rev. ed. 2007. (Careers in Focus Ser.). 208p. (J). (gr. 6-12). 29.95 (***978-0-8160-6568-4(3)*** , Ferguson Publishing Co.) Facts On File, Inc.

Flanagan, Alice K. Mayors. 2001. (Community Workers Ser.). (Illus.). 32p. (J). (gr. 1 up). lib. bdg. 21.26 (978-0-7565-0064-1(8)) Compass Point Bks.

Hamilton, John. Running for Office. 2005. (Government in Action! Ser.). (J). (gr. k-6). lib. bdg. 22.78 (978-1-59197-822-0(X)) ABDO Publishing Co.

Italia, Bob. Election 2000: A Lesson in Civics. 2001. (United States Presidents Ser.). (Illus.). 32p. (J). (gr. k-6). lib. bdg. 22.78 (978-1-57765-576-3(1) , Checkerboard Library) ABDO Publishing Co.

Kowalski, Kathiann M. Campaign Politics: What's Fair, What's Foul? 2005. (Pro/Con Ser.). (Illus.). 144p. (gr. 6-12). lib. bdg. 25.26 (978-0-8225-2630-8(1)) Lerner Publishing Group.

Lesko, Wendy Schaetzel. Youth: The 26% Solution, 1. 1998. (YA). pap. 14.95 (978-1-878346-47-6(4)) Information U.S.A., Inc.

Lewis, Barbara A. Kid's Guide to Social Action: How to Solve the Social Problems You Choose-A. 1998. (gr. 7-12). lib. bdg. 29.20 (978-0-613-89622-1(X)) Tandem Library Bks.

McGowen, Tom. The 1968 Democratic Convention. 2003. (Cornerstones of Freedom, 2ND Ser.). (Illus.). 48p. (J). 26.00 (978-0-516-24220-0(2) , Children's Pr.) Scholastic Library Publishing.

Ring, Susan. Election Connection: The Official Nick Guide to Electing the President. 2004. (Illus.). 72p. (J). pap. 7.95 (978-0-8118-4175-7(8)) Chronicle Bks. LLC.

Schlesinger, Arthur M., Sr., et al, eds. The Election of 1800. 2003. (Major Presidential Elections & the Administrations That Followed Ser.). (Illus.). 154p. (J). (gr. 7 up). lib. bdg. (978-1-59084-352-9(5)) Mason Crest Pubs.

—The Elections of 1789 & 1792. 2003. (Major Presidential Elections & the Administrations That Followed Ser.). (Illus.). 154p. (J). (gr. 7 up). lib. bdg. (978-1-59084-351-2(7)) Mason Crest Pubs.

Schlesinger, Arthur M., Jr. & Israel, Fred L., eds. Major Presidential Elections, 15 bks., Set. (Illus.). (YA). (gr. 7 up). lib. bdg. (978-1-59084-350-5(9)) Mason Crest Pubs.

Sobel, Syl. Presidential Elections: And Other Cool Facts. Wood, Jill, illus. 2nd ed. 2001. 48p. (J). pap. 6.95 (978-0-7641-1894-4(3)) Barron's Educational Series, Inc.

POLITICS, PRACTICAL—FICTION

Alberto, Daisy. Pete for President! Sims, Blanche, illus. 2004. 32p. (J). lib. bdg. 20.00 (***978-1-4242-1115-9(8)***) Fitzgerald Bks.

—Pete for President! Sims, Blanche, illus. 2004. (Social Studies Connects). 32p. (J). (gr. 1-3). pap. 4.99 (978-1-57565-142-2(4)) Kane Pr., The.

Asturias, Miguel Angel. El Senor Presidente. 1998. (SPA.). (gr. 7-12). lib. bdg. 15.25 (978-0-613-80721-0(9)) Tandem Library Bks.

Bateman, Anya. The Makeover of James Orville Wickenbee. 2007. 262p. (J). pap. (***978-1-59038-707-8(4)***) Deseret Bk. Co.

Bauer, Joan. Hope Was Here. 2000. (Illus.). 192p. (J). (gr. 7-12). 16.99 (978-0-399-23142-1(0) , Putnam Juvenile) Penguin Group (USA) Inc.

Bonners, Susan. Edwina Victorious. Bonners, Susan, illus. (Illus.). 144p. (J). 2007. pap. 5.95 (978-0-374-41960-8(4) , Sunburst); 2000. (gr. 2-5). 16.00 (978-0-374-31968-7(5) , Farrar, Straus & Giroux (BYR)) Farrar, Straus & Giroux.

Buchanan, Paul. Hail to the Chump, Vol. 9. 1998. (Misadventures of Willie Plummett Ser.: Vol. 9). 128p. (J). (gr. 3-7). 5.99 (978-0-570-05088-9(X)) Concordia Publishing Hse.

Card, Orson Scott, ed. Future on Ice. rev. ed. 1998. 432p. (YA). (gr. 7 up). 24.95 (978-0-312-86694-5(1) , Tor Bks.) Doherty, Tom Assocs., LLC.

Cronin, Doreen. Duck for President. Lewin, Betsy, illus. 2004. 40p. (J). 15.95 (978-0-689-86377-6(2)) Simon & Schuster Children's Publishing.

—Duck for President. 2006. (J). (ps-3). 22.78 (978-1-59961-091-7(4)) Spotlight.

Delton, Judy. Molly for Mayor. 1999. (Pee Wee Scouts Ser.: No. 39). (J). (gr. 2-5). (978-0-606-18787-9(1)) Tandem Library Bks.

Duck for President. 2004. 29.95 incl. cd-rom (978-0-7882-0540-8(4)); 24.95 incl. audio (978-0-7882-0539-2(0)) Weston Woods Studios, Inc.

Feiffer, Kate. President Pennybaker. Preiss-Glasser, Robin, illus. 2008. (J). (***978-1-4169-1354-2(8)*** , Simon & Schuster Children's Publishing) Simon & Schuster Children's Publishing.

Fitzgerald, Dawn. Soccer Chick Rules. 2006. 160p. (J). 16.95 (978-1-59643-137-9(7)) Roaring Brook Pr.

FitzGerald, Dawn. Soccer Chick Rules. 2007. 160p. (J). pap. 6.99 (***978-0-312-37662-8(6)***) Square Fish.

Gingras, Charlotte. La Liberte? Connais Pas... 1999. (Roman Plus Ser.). (FRE., Illus.). 160p. (YA). (gr. 8 up). pap. (978-2-89021-343-2(9)) Diffusion du livre Mirabel.

Giunta, Brian. The Seven Presidents. Chapin, Patrick O., illus. l.t. ed. 2003. 24p. (J). 8.95 (978-1-58597-172-5(3)) Leathers Publishing.

Gorman, Carol. Dork on the Run. 192p. (J). 2003. (Illus.). pap. 5.99 (978-0-06-440970-4(8) , Harper Trophy); 2002. (gr. 3-6). 15.99 (978-0-06-029409-0(4)) HarperCollins Pubs.

—Dork on the Run. 2003. (gr. 3-6). lib. bdg. 14.15 (978-0-613-61371-2(6)) Tandem Library Bks.

Gutman, Dan. The Kid Who Became President. 2000. 240p. (J). (gr. 4-8). mass mkt. 4.99 (978-0-590-02376-4(4)) Scholastic, Inc.

—The Kid Who Became President. 1999. (978-0-606-21810-8(6)); (gr. 3-6). lib. bdg. 12.40 (978-0-613-21853-5(1)) Tandem Library Bks.

Haas, Jessie. Will You, Won't You? 2000. 176p. (J). (gr. 5 up). 15.89 (978-0-06-029197-6(4)) HarperCollins Pubs.

Hale, Bruce. The Possum Always Rings Twice: A Chet Gecko Mystery. Hale, Bruce, illus. 2007. (Chet Gecko Mystery Ser.: No. 11). (Illus.). 144p. (J). (gr. 3-7). pap. 4.95 (978-0-15-205233-1(X) , Harcourt Paperbacks) Harcourt Children's Bks.

Hall, Kirsten. Vote for Me: All about Civics. 2004. (Beastieville Ser.). (J). (gr. k-1). pap. 3.95 (978-0-516-24658-1(5) , Children's Pr.) Scholastic Library Publishing.

—Vote for Me: All about Civics. Luedecke, Bev, illus. 2003. (Beastieville Ser.). 32p. (J). 19.50 (978-0-516-22897-6(8) , Children's Pr.) Scholastic Library Publishing.

Kibbe, Pat. My Mother the Mayor, Maybe. Capozzi, Dan, illus. 2001. 184p. (YA). (gr. 4-7). pap. 14.95 (978-0-595-18267-1(4)) iUniverse, Inc.

Levithan, David. Wide Awake. 2006. 240p. (YA). (gr. 9). 16.95 (978-0-375-83466-0(4)); lib. bdg. 18.99 (978-0-375-93466-7(9)) Random Hse. Children's Bks. (Knopf Bks. for Young Readers).

Meek, Nora. Sniffing for Democracy. 2004. (J). per. (978-0-9753852-0-3(8)) PM, INK.

Morgenroth, Kate. Jude. 288p. (YA). 2004. 16.95 (978-0-689-86479-7(5)); 2006. (Illus.). reprint ed. mass mkt. 5.99 (978-1-4169-1267-5(3) , Simon Pulse) Simon & Schuster Children's Publishing.

Parish, Herman. Amelia Bedelia 4 Mayor. Sweat, Lynn, illus. (I Can Read Bks.). (J). 2001. 64p. (gr. k-2). pap. 3.99 (978-0-06-444309-8(4) , Harper Trophy); 1999. 48p. (gr. 1 up). 15.99 (978-0-688-16721-9(7)) HarperCollins Pubs.

Perkins, Mitali. First Daughter: Extreme American Makeover. (YA). (gr. 7). 2008. 288p. pap. 7.99 (*978-0-14-241154-4(X)* , Puffin); 2007. 192p. 16.99 (978-0-525-47800-3(0) , Dutton Juvenile) Penguin Group (USA) Inc.

Sommer, Carl. Mayor for a Day. 2003. (Another Sommer-Time Story Ser.). (Illus.). 48p. (J). (gr. k-4). lib. bdg. 23.95 incl. audio compact disk (978-1-57537-713-1(6)); (gr. 1-4). 16.95 incl. audio (978-1-57537-562-5(1)); (gr. 1-4). 16.95 incl. audio compact disk (978-1-57537-513-7(3)) Advance Publishing, Inc.

—Mayor for a Day. Westbrook, Dick, illus. 1999. (Another Sommer-Time Story Ser.). 48p. (J). (gr. k-4). 9.95 (978-1-57537-013-2(1)); lib. bdg. 16.95 (978-1-57537-057-6(3)) Advance Publishing, Inc.

Tashjian, Janet. Vote for Larry. rev. ed. 2004. (Illus.). 240p. (J). 16.95 (978-0-8050-7201-3(2) , Holt, Henry & Co. Bks. For Young Readers) Holt, Henry & Co.

POLK, JAMES K. (JAMES KNOX), 1795-1849

Behrman, Carol H. James K. Polk. 2005. (Presidential Leaders Ser.). (Illus.). 112p. (J). (gr. 6-12). 29.27 (978-0-8225-1396-4(X)) Lerner Publishing Group.

Bramwell, Neil D. James K. Polk: A MyReportLinks.com Book. 2002. (Presidents Ser.). (Illus.). 48p. (J). (gr. 4-10). lib. bdg. 25.26 (978-0-7660-5052-5(1) , MyReportLinks.com Bks.) Enslow Pubs., Inc.

Gaines, Ann Graham. James Polk: Our Eleventh President. 2001. (Spirit of America: Our Presidents Ser.). (Illus.). 48p. (J). (gr. 2-6). 28.50 (978-1-56766-850-6(X)) Child's World, Inc.

McCollum, Sean. James K. Polk. 2004. (Encyclopedia of Presidents Ser.). (Illus.). 110p. (J). 34.00 (978-0-516-22885-3(4) , Children's Pr.) Scholastic Library Publishing.

Mis, Melody S. How to Draw the Life & Times of James K. Polk. 2006. (Kid's Guide to Drawing the Presidents of the United States of America Ser.). (J). 25.25 (978-1-4042-2988-4(4) , PowerKids Pr.) Rosen Publishing Group, Inc., The.

Somervill, Barbara A. James K. Polk. 2003. (Profiles of the Presidents Ser.). (Illus.). 64p. (J). (gr. 4 up). lib. bdg. 23.93 (978-0-7565-0259-1(4)) Compass Point Bks.

Tibbitts, Alison Davis. James K. Polk. 1999. (United States Presidents Ser.). (Illus.). 128p. (YA). (gr. 5-12). lib. bdg. 26.60 (978-0-7660-1037-6(6)) Enslow Pubs., Inc.

Venezia, Mike. James K. Polk: Eleventh President, 1845-1849. Venezia, Mike, illus. 2005. (Getting to Know the U. S. Presidents Ser.). (Illus.). 32p. (J). (gr. 3-4). pap. 7.95 (978-0-516-27485-0(6) , Children's Pr.) Scholastic Library Publishing.

Venezia, Mike, illus. James K. Polk. 2005. (Getting to Know the U. S. Presidents Ser.). 32p. (J). (gr. 3-4). 27.00 (978-0-516-22616-3(9) , Children's Pr.) Scholastic Library Publishing.

Welsbacher, Anne. James K. Polk. 2001. (United States Presidents Ser.). (Illus.). 32p. (J). (gr. k-6). lib. bdg. 22.78 (978-1-57765-246-5(0) , Checkerboard Library) ABDO Publishing Co.

POLLS, ELECTION

see Elections

POLLUTION

Here are entered works on the condition resulting from the action of environmental contaminants.

see also Air—Pollution; Hazardous Wastes; Refuse and Refuse Disposal; Water—Pollution

Alcraft, Rob. Oil Disasters. 1999. (World's Worst Ser.). 32p. (J). (gr. 4-6). lib. bdg. 22.79 (978-1-57572-990-9(3)) Heinemann Library.

Best, Gerry. Environmental Pollution Studies. 2000. (Illus.). 192p. pap. 20.00 (978-0-85323-923-9(1)) Liverpool Univ. Pr. GBR. *Dist:* Chicago Distribution Ctr.

Binns, Tristan Boyer. Clean Planet: Stopping Litter & Pollution. 2005. (You Can Save the Planet Ser.). (Illus.). 32p. (J). (gr. 3-7). pap. 7.85 (978-1-4034-6852-9(4)); lib. bdg. 28.21 (978-1-4034-6846-8(X)) Heinemann Library.

Brown, Paul. Global Pollution. 2003. (Face the Facts Ser.). (Illus.). 56p. (J). lib. bdg. 28.56 (978-0-7398-6433-3(5)) Raintree.

Bryan, Nichol. Love Canal: Pollution Crisis. 2003. (Environmental Disasters Ser.). (Illus.). 48p. (gr. 5 up). (YA). lib. bdg. 30.00 (978-0-8368-5508-1(6)); (J). pap. 11.95 (978-0-8368-5515-9(9)) Stevens, Gareth Inc. (World Almanac Library).

Capstone Press Editors. Oil Spills. 2002. (Our Planet in Peril Ser.). (Illus.). 48p. (J). (gr. 3-4). lib. bdg. 22.60 (978-0-7368-1363-1(2) , Bridgestone Bks.) Capstone Pr., Inc.

Costain, Meredith. Things We Throw Away. 2000. (gr. k-3). lib. bdg. 11.80 (978-0-613-30788-8(7)) Tandem Library Bks.

—Trash-Free Lunch Day. 2000. (gr. k-3). lib. bdg. 11.80 (978-0-613-30810-6(7)) Tandem Library Bks.

—What Happens to Trash? 2000. (gr. k-3). lib. bdg. 11.80 (978-0-613-30859-5(X)) Tandem Library Bks.

Crelin, Bob. There Once Was a Sky Full of Stars. Ziner, Amie, illus. 2005. 36p. pap. 12.95 (978-1-931559-04-1(X)) Sky Publishing.

Cynthia A. Bily. Pollution. 2006. (Introducing Issues with Opposing Viewpoints Ser.). (Illus.). 244p. (J). (gr. 7-10). 33.70 (978-0-7377-3546-8(5) , Greenhaven Pr., Inc.) Thomson Gale.

Donald, Rhonda Lucas. Air Pollution. 2001. (True Environment Bks.). (Illus.). 48p. (J). (gr. 3-5). 25.00 (978-0-516-22191-5(4) , Children's Pr.) Scholastic Library Publishing.

—Water Pollution. 2001. (True Environment Bks.). (Illus.). 48p. (J). (gr. 3-5). 25.00 (978-0-516-22194-6(9) , Children's Pr.) Scholastic Library Publishing.

Dorion, Christiane. Earth's Garbage Crisis. 2006. (Illus.). 48p. (J). pap. (*978-0-8368-8153-0(2)*); lib. bdg. (*978-0-8368-7753-3(5)*) Stevens, Gareth Inc. (World Almanac Library).

Friedman, Lauri S. Pollution. 2007. (Writing the Critical Essay Ser.). (Illus.). 128p. (gr. 6-10). 29.95 (*978-0-7377-3198-9(2)* , Greenhaven Pr., Inc.) Thomson Gale.

Gifford, Clive. Pollution. 2005. (Planet under Pressure Ser.). (Illus.). 48p. (J). 31.43 (978-1-4034-7742-2(6)) Heinemann Library.

Grant, Pamela & Haswell, Arthur. Air & Energy. 2000. (Earth Strikes Back Ser.). (Illus.). 48p. (J). (gr. 2-6). lib. bdg. 16.95 (978-1-929298-58-7(7)) Chrysalis Education.

Greeley, August. Poisoned Planet: Pollution in Our World. 2003. (Reading Power Ser.). (Illus.). 24p. (J). lib. bdg. 17.25 (978-0-8239-6487-1(6) , PowerKids Pr.) Rosen Publishing Group, Inc., The.

Green, Jen. The Polluted Planet. 2004. (J). lib. bdg. (978-1-59389-140-4(7)) Chrysalis Education.

Halfmann, Janet. Pollution. 2004. (Our Environment Ser.). (Illus.). 48p. (J). (gr. 4-7). 26.20 (978-0-7377-1563-7(4) , Kidhaven) Thomson Gale.

Harlow, Rosie. Pollution & Waste: Environmental Facts & Experiments. 2002. (Young Discoverers Ser.). (Illus.). 32p. (J). (gr. k-3). 7.95 (978-0-7534-5505-0(6) , Kingfisher) Houghton Mifflin Co. Trade & Reference Div.

—Pollution & Waste: Environmental Facts & Experiments. 2002. (gr. k-3). lib. bdg. 16.40 (978-0-613-90577-0(6)) Tandem Library Bks.

Holt, Rinehart and Winston Staff. Decisions for Health Blue, Chptr. 21: Health & Environment. 4th ed. 2004. pap. 11.20 (978-0-03-068057-1(3)) Holt, Rinehart & Winston.

Hunter, Rebecca M. Pollution & Conservation. 2001. (Discovering Science Ser.). (Illus.). 32p. (J). (gr. 3-7). lib. bdg. 25.69 (978-0-7398-3246-2(8)) Raintree.

Leany, Cindy. Pollution. 2005. (Your Environment Ser.). (Illus.). 32p. (J). (978-1-59604-064-9(5)) Stargazer Bks.

Llewellyn, Claire. Let's Recycle. 2005. (Illus.). 32p. (YA). (gr. 1 up). lib. bdg. 27.10 (978-1-932333-22-0(3)) Chrysalis Education.

—Protect Natural Habitats. 2005. (Illus.). 32p. (YA). (gr. 1 up). lib. bdg. 27.10 (978-1-932333-20-6(7)) Chrysalis Education.

Mason, Paul. In the Environment. 2002. (Young Library). (Illus.). 32p. (J). lib. bdg. 25.69 (978-0-7398-6316-9(9)) Raintree.

McGowan, Keith. Hazardous Waste. 2nd rev. ed. 2000. (Overview Ser.). (Illus.). 112p. (J). (gr. 6-9). lib. bdg. 29.95 (978-1-56006-699-6(7) , LML00902-178051, Lucent Bks.) Thomson Gale.

Mercer, Ian. Oils & the Environment. 2004. (J). lib. bdg. (978-1-932799-31-6(1)) Stargazer Bks.

Morrison, Yvonne. Earth Partners: Saving the Planet. 2007. (Shockwave: History & Politics Ser.). (Illus.). 36p. (J). (gr. 4-6). lib. bdg. 25.00 (*978-0-531-17753-2(X)* , Children's Pr.) Scholastic Library Publishing.

Nardo, Don. Ozone. 2005. (Our Environment Ser.). (Illus.). 48p. (J). (gr. 3-8). lib. bdg. 26.20 (978-0-7377-2630-5(X) , Greenhaven Pr., Inc.) Thomson Gale.

Parks, Peggy J. Oil Spills. 2005. (Our Environment Ser.). (Illus.). 48p. (J). (ps-7). lib. bdg. 26.20 (978-0-7377-2629-9(6) , Greenhaven Pr., Inc.) Thomson Gale.

Poisoned Planet: Pollution in Our World: Individual Title Six-Packs. (On Deck Ser.: Vol. 2). 24p. (gr. 4-5). 35.00 (978-0-7578-5832-1(5)) Rigby Education.

Pollution: Level H, 6 vols. (Wonder Worldtm Ser.). 16p. 29.95 (978-0-7802-1233-6(9)) Wright Group, The.

Taylor, Barbara. How to Save the Planet. Anderson, Scoular, illus. 2001. (How to Ser.). 96p. (J). (gr. 5-7). 16.00 (978-0-531-14640-8(5)); pap. 4.95 (978-0-531-14821-1(1)) Scholastic Library Publishing. (Watts, Franklin).

—How to Save the Planet. 2001. (gr. 5-8). lib. bdg. 12.95 (978-0-613-54552-5(4)) Tandem Library Bks.

Thompson, Gare. Take Care of Our Earth. 1998. (Illus.). 32p. (ps-3). pap. 4.95 (978-0-8172-7982-0(2)) Steck-Vaughn.

Watson, Stephanie. Critical Perspectives on Pollution. 2006. (Scientific American Critical Anthologies on Environment & Climate Ser.). (Illus.). 224p. (J). lib. bdg. (978-1-4042-0690-8(6)) Rosen Publishing Group, Inc., The.

World Almanac Library Staff, contrib. by. Climate & the Environment. 2002. (Twenty-First Century Science Ser.). (Illus.). 64p. (J). (gr. 5 up). lib. bdg. 32.67 (978-0-8368-5006-2(8) , World Almanac Library) Stevens, Gareth Inc.

POLLUTION—FICTION

Atwell, Debby. River. Atwell, Debby, illus. 1999. (Illus.). 32p. (J). (gr. k-3). tchr. ed. 16.00 (978-0-395-93546-0(6) , Walter Lorraine) Houghton Mifflin Co. Trade & Reference Div.

—River. 2004. (Illus.). 32p. (J). (gr. k-3). reprint ed. pap. 5.95 (978-0-618-43952-2(8) , Walter Lorraine) Houghton Mifflin Co. Trade & Reference Div.

Base, Graeme. The Sign of the Seahorse: A Tale of Greed & High Adventure in Two Acts. 1998. (Picture Puffin Ser.). (Illus.). 48p. (J). (gr. 1-4). pap. 8.99 (978-0-14-056387-0(3) , Puffin) Penguin Group (USA) Inc.

—Uno's Garden. 2006. (Illus.). 44p. (J). (ps-3). 19.95 (978-0-8109-5473-1(7)) Abrams, Harry N. , Inc.

Berenstain, Stan & Berenstain, Jan. The Berenstain Bears Don't Pollute (Anymore) 1999. (Berenstain Bears First Time Bks.). (Illus.). (J). (ps-2). lib. bdg. 10.95 (978-0-8335-6545-7(1)) Tandem Library Bks.

Brouwer, Sigmund. Cobra Threat: Football. 2007. (Orca Sports Ser.). 176p. (YA). (gr. 5 up). pap. (*978-1-55143-725-5(2)*) Orca Bk. Pubs.

Douglas, Babette. Kiss a Me: To the Rescue. 2004. (J). 9.99 (978-1-890343-11-8(0)) Kiss A Me Productions, Inc.

Ellerbee, Linda. Girl Reporter Blows Lid off Town! 2000. (Get Real Ser.: No. 1). (Illus.). 208p. (J). (gr. 3-7). 14.89 (978-0-06-028245-5(2)) HarperCollins Pubs.

—Girl Reporter Blows Lid off Town! 2000. (Get Real Ser.: No. 1). (Illus.). (J). (978-0-606-18691-9(3)) Tandem Library Bks.

Geiger, Beth & Fuerst, Jeffrey B. Return to Earth: Reader's Theater Levels N-U (30-50) Wolk-Stanley, Jessica, illus. ed. 2004. (Reader's Theater Ser.). 16p. (J). pap. 22.00 (978-1-4108-2306-9(7) , A23067) Benchmark Education Co.

Gratz, Alan M. Something Rotten: A Horatio Wilkes Mystery. 2007. 208p. (J). (gr. 6). 16.99 (*978-0-8037-3216-2(3)* , Dial) Penguin Group (USA) Inc.

Hamilton, Tisha. Oops! I Polluted Again. Noel, Aragon & Hwan, Choi Sung, illus. 2006. (Trollz Ser.). 80p. (J). pap. 3.99 (978-0-439-70003-0(5)) Scholastic, Inc.

Hanson, Janell Marie. The Side-Effects Kid. 2001. (Illus.). 228p. (J). pap. 19.95 (978-0-9662608-0-9(5)) Partae Pr.

Hoobler, Dorothy & Hoobler, Thomas. The 1980s: Earthsong. Hoffman, Robin, illus. 2002. (Century Kids Ser.). 160p. (gr. 5-8). lib. bdg. 22.90 (978-0-7613-1608-4(6) , Twenty-First Century Bks.) Lerner Publishing Group.

Klima, Charlene Hudgins. Give Me Five. 2000. 106p. (YA). (gr. 4-9). pap. 12.00 (978-1-883911-36-2(2)) Brandylane Pubs., Inc.

Liberto, Lorenzo. Save the Planet / Salva el Planeta. Gomez, Rocio, tr. Torres, Irving, illus. 2005. (Matt the Rat Ser. / La Serie de Raton Mateo). (ENG & SPA.). 32p. (J). lib. bdg. 20.00 (978-0-9743668-5-2(4)) Harvest Sun Pr., LLC.

Manos, John. Samantha Saves the Stream. 2006. (Early Explorers Ser.). (J). 36.00 (*978-1-4108-6125-2(2)*) Benchmark Education Co.

Nelson, Bruce M. The Magician's Hat. 2006. 127p. pap. 17.95 (978-1-4241-2301-8(1)) PublishAmerica, Inc.

Pelletier, Maryse. La Chasse au Plomb. Grimard, Gabrielle, illus. 2004. (Roman Jeunesse Ser.). (FRE.). 96p. (J). (gr. 4-7). pap. (978-2-89021-692-1(6)) Diffusion du livre Mirabel.

Petrucha, Stefan. Teen, Inc. 2007. 224p. (YA). (gr. 7 up). 16.95 (*978-0-8027-9650-9(8)*) Walker & Co.

Quinn, Zoe. Totally Toxic. 2006. (Caped 6th Grader Ser.). (Illus.). 160p. (J). (gr. 4-7). pap. 4.99 (978-0-440-42080-4(6) , Yearling) Random Hse. Children's Bks.

Scraper, Katherine. Save the Fairy Penguins. 2005. 40.00 (*978-1-4108-4214-5(2)*) Benchmark Education Co.

Wilson, Barbara. A Clear Spring. 2002. (Girls First! Ser.: Vol. 1). 112p. 12.50 (978-1-55861-277-8(7)) Feminist Pr. at The City Univ. of New York.

Zinsser, Anne. More Dolphin Magic: The Adventure Continues. Sohl, Lee Ellen, illus. 2001. viii, 120p. (J). per. 6.95 (978-0-933951-20-4(5)) Locust Hill Pr.

POLLUTION OF AIR

see Air—Pollution

POLLUTION OF WATER

see Water—Pollution

POLO, MARCO, 1254-1323

Bandon, Alex & O'Brien, Patrick. The Travels of Marco Polo. 1999. (Explorers & Exploration Ser.). (Illus.). 48p. (J). (gr. 4-7). lib. bdg. 22.83 (978-0-7398-1485-7(0)) Raintree.

Boyd, David. Marco Polo & the Roc. Ng, Drew, illus. 2007. 48p. (J). lib. bdg. 23.08 (*978-1-4242-1621-5(4)*) Fitzgerald Bks.

Burgan, Michael. Marco Polo: Marco Polo & the Silk Road to China. 2002. (Exploring the World Ser.). (Illus.). 48p. (J). (gr. 4 up). lib. bdg. 22.60 (978-0-7565-0180-8(6)) Compass Point Bks.

Childress, Diana. Marco Polo's Travels in China. 2006. (Pivotal Moments in History Ser.). 160p. (YA). (gr. 9-12). lib. bdg. 38.60 (978-0-8225-5903-0(X) , Twenty-First Century Bks.) Lerner Publishing Group.

La Extraordinaria Aventura de Marco Polo 10: Leveled Books. 2001. (McGraw-Hill. Lectura Ser.). (ENG & SPA.). (gr. 5 up). (978-0-02-188282-3(7)) Macmillan/McGraw-Hill Schl. Div.

Feeney, Kathy. Marco Polo: Explorer of China. 2004. (Explorers! Ser.). (Illus.). 48p. (J). lib. bdg. 23.93 (978-0-7660-2145-7(9)) Enslow Pubs., Inc.

Freedman, Russell. The Adventures of Marco Polo. Ibatoulline, Bagram, illus. 2006. 64p. (J). (gr. 4-7). pap. 17.99 (978-0-439-52394-3(X) , Levine, Arthur A. Bks.) Scholastic, Inc.

Ganeri, Anita. Marco Polo. 1999. (What Would You Ask...? Ser.). (Illus.). 32p. (J). (gr. 2-6). lib. bdg. 16.95 (978-1-929298-00-6(5)) Chrysalis Education.

Gefen, Keren. Marco Polo. (Great Explorers Ser.). (Illus.). 48p. (J). (gr. 5 up). 2002. pap. 14.60 (978-0-8368-5177-9(3)); 2001. lib. bdg. 30.00 (978-0-8368-5017-8(3)) Stevens, Gareth Inc. (World Almanac Library).

Hain-Jun, Yue & Soldevilla, Juan Manuel. Marco Polo: La Ruta de las Maravillas. 2006. Tr. of Marco Polo & the Route of Wonders. (SPA.). (J). (gr. 6-8). 9.60 (978-84-316-7173-0(4) , W32814) Vicens-Vives, Editorial, S.A. ESP. *Dist:* Lectorum Pubns., Inc.

Herbert, Janis. Marco Polo for Kids: His Marvelous Journey to China, 21 Activities. 2001. (For Kids Ser.). (Illus.). 144p. (J). (gr. 4-7). pap. 16.95 (978-1-55652-377-9(7)) Chicago Review Pr., Inc.

Holub, Joan. Who Was Marco Polo? O'Brien, John & Harrison, Nancy, illus. 2007. (Who Was... ? Ser.). 112p. (J). (gr. 2-6). pap. 4.99 (978-0-448-44540-3(9) , Grosset & Dunlap) Penguin Group (USA) Inc.

MacDonald, Fiona. Marco Polo. 2000. (World in the Time of... Ser.). (Illus.). 48p. (J). (gr. 4-7). 22.95 (978-0-7910-6033-9(0) , Chelsea Hse.) Facts On File, Inc.

Marco Polo. (Exploring the World Ser.). 48p. (YA). 8.95 (978-0-7565-1147-0(X)) Compass Point Bks.

Marcovitz, Hal. Marco Polo & the Wonders of the East. 1999. (Explorers of the New World Ser.). (Illus.). 63p. (J). (gr. 4 up). 31.00 (978-0-7910-5511-3(6) , Chelsea Hse.) Facts On File, Inc.

McCarty, Nick. Marco Polo: The Boy Who Traveled the Medieval World. 2006. (World History Biographies Ser.). (Illus.). 64p. (J). (gr. 3-7). 17.95 (978-0-7922-5893-3(2)); lib. bdg. 27.90 (978-0-7922-5894-0(0)) National Geographic Society. (National Geographic Children's Bks.).

McFarren, Kathleen. Marco Polo. 2004. (Fact Finders Ser.). (Illus.). 32p. (J). 16.95 (978-0-7368-2490-3(1)) Capstone Pr., Inc.

McNeese, Tim. Marco Polo: And the Realm of Kublai Khan. Goetzmann, William H., ed. 2005. (Explorers of New Lands Ser.). (Illus.). 158p. (J). (gr. 4-8). lib. bdg. 30.00 (978-0-7910-8612-4(7) , Chelsea Hse.) Facts On File, Inc.

Otfinoski, Steven. Marco Polo: To China & Back. 2002. (Great Explorations Ser.). (Illus.). 77p. (J). 29.93 (978-0-7614-1480-3(0) , Benchmark Bks.) Cavendish, Marshall Corp.

Petrie, Kristin. Marco Polo. 2007. (Rabbit Ears Ser.). (Illus.). 32p. (J). (gr. k-5). 22.78 (978-1-59679-747-5(9)) ABDO Publishing Co.

Reid, Struan. Marco Polo. (Groundbreakers Ser.). 48p. (J). (gr. 5-7). 2002. pap. 8.50 (978-1-58810-371-0(4) , 91097); 2001. (Illus.). lib. bdg. 25.64 (978-1-58810-047-4(2)) Heinemann Library.

Riddle, John. Marco Polo. 2002. (Great Names Ser.). (Illus.). 32p. (J). (gr. 3 up). lib. bdg. (978-1-59084-136-5(0)) Mason Crest Pubs.

Scheuerman, Richard D. & Ellis, Arthur K. The Travels of Marco Polo & Ibn Battuta: Asian & African Journeys of Discovery. LeGette, James, illus. 1998. 450p. (YA). (gr. 5-8). 79.95 (978-1-885360-21-2(5)) Demco, Inc.

Senker, Cath. Marco Polo's Travels on Asia's Silk Road. 2007. (J). (*978-1-4034-9751-2(6)*) Heinemann Library.

Smalley, Roger. The Adventures of Marco Polo. Carter, Greg, illus. 2005. (Graphic Library). 32p. (J). 22.60 (978-0-7368-3830-6(9)) Capstone Pr., Inc.

—The Adventures of Marco Polo. (Graphic History Ser.). 32p. (YA). pap. 7.95 (978-0-7368-5240-1(9)) Capstone Pr., Inc.

—Las Aventuras de Marco Polo. Lilley, Jessica S., tr. Bascle, Brian, illus. 2006. (Historia Grafica en Espanol Ser.). (SPA.). 32p. (J). lib. bdg. 18.95 (978-0-7368-6054-3(1)) Capstone Pr., Inc.

Strathloch, Robert. Marco Polo. (Historical Biographies Ser.). 32p. 2003. pap. 7.50 (978-1-4034-0147-2(0)); 2002. (Illus.). (J). (gr. 2-4). lib. bdg. 22.79 (978-1-58810-567-7(9)) Heinemann Library.

—Marco Polo. 2002. (gr. 3-6). lib. bdg. 15.25 (978-0-613-45790-3(0)) Tandem Library Bks.

Worth, Richard. The Great Empire of China & Marco Polo in World History. 2003. (In World History Ser.). (Illus.). 112p. (J). lib. bdg. 26.60 (978-0-7660-1939-3(X)) Enslow Pubs., Inc.

Zannos, Susan. The Life & Times of Marco Polo. 2004. (Biography from Ancient Civilizations Ser.). (Illus.). 48p. (J). (gr. 4-8). lib. bdg. 29.95 (978-1-58415-264-4(8)) Mitchell Lane Pubs., Inc.

Zelenyj, Alexander. Marco Polo: Overland to China. 2005. (In the Footsteps of Explorers Ser.). (Illus.). 32p. (J). (gr. 3-9). (978-0-7787-2417-9(4)); pap. (978-0-7787-2453-7(0)) Crabtree Publishing Co.

POLO, MARCO, 1254-1323—FICTION

Johnson, Vargie. Marco Polo the Adventurer: What Made Them Famous? 2006. 156p. (J). per. 15.00 (978-1-931195-98-0(6)) KiwE Publishing, Ltd.

Maisner, Heather. Diary of a Princess: A Tale from Marco Polo's Travels. Moxley, Sheila, illus. 2006. 26p. (gr. k-4). reprint ed. pap. 8.00 (978-1-4223-5302-8(8)) DIANE Publishing Co.

Scieszka, Jon. Marco? Polo. McCauley, Adam, illus. 2006. (Time Warp Trio Ser.: No. 16). 80p. (J). (gr. 2). 14.99 (978-0-670-06104-4(2) , Viking Juvenile) Penguin Group (USA) Inc.

POLTERGEISTS

see Ghosts

POLYMERS AND POLYMERIZATION

see also Plastics

Epp, Diane N. Product Testing: The Chemistry of Ice Cream. 2001. 94p. (J). 12.95 (978-1-883822-25-5(4)) Terrific Science Pr.

Goodstein, Madeline P. Plastics & Polymers Science Fair Projects Using Hair Gel, Soda Bottles, & Slimy Stuff. 2004. (Chemistry! Best Science Projects Ser.). (Illus.). 128p. (J). lib. bdg. 26.60 (978-0-7660-2123-5(8)) Enslow Pubs., Inc.

Woodward, Linda. Polymers All Around You! 2nd ed. 2002. 31p. (Orig.). (J). pap. 7.95 (978-1-883822-26-2(2)) Terrific Science Pr.

POLYNESIA

Currie, Stephen. Polynesians. 1999. (Endangered Cultures Ser.). (Illus.). 32p. (J). (gr. 4-7). lib. bdg. 16.95 (978-1-887068-94-9(5)) Smart Apple Media.

Green, Yuko. Life in Ancient Polynesia. 2001. (Illus.). 48p. (J). (gr. 1 up). pap. 3.95 (978-0-486-41545-1(7)) Dover Pubns., Inc.

Harcourt School Publishers Staff. Close-Up on Tonga. 3rd ed. 2002. (Horizons Ser.). (Illus.). (J). pap. 7.30 (978-0-15-333644-7(7)) Harcourt Schl. Pubs.

Webster, Christine. Polynesians. 2003. (Indigenous Peoples Ser.). (J). pap. 7.95 (978-1-59036-158-0(X)); (Illus.). 32p. lib. bdg. 18.20 (978-1-59036-123-8(7)) Weigl Pubs., Inc.

POLYNESIA—FICTION

Sperry, Armstrong. Call It Courage. 2008. Tr. of Newbery Summer. 128p. (YA). mass mkt. 5.99 (***978-1-4169-5368-5(X)*** , Simon Pulse) Simon & Schuster Children's Publishing.

POMPEII (EXTINCT CITY)

Ball, Karen. Pompeii. Cerisier, Emmanuel, illus. 2006. 64p. (J). 8.99 (978-0-7945-1270-5(4) , Usborne) EDC Publishing.

Bradley, Pamela. Pompeii & Herculaneum. 2005. pap., stu. ed. 23.95 (978-0-521-60895-4(3)) Cambridge Univ. Pr.

Cooley, Alison & Cooley, M. G. L. Pompeii: A Sourcebook. 2004. (Illus.). 272p. 115.00 (978-0-415-26211-8(9)) Routledge.

Deem, James M. Bodies from the Ash: Life & Death in Ancient Pompeii. 2005. (Illus.). 64p. (J). (gr. 4-6). 17.00 (978-0-618-47308-3(4)) Houghton Mifflin Co. Trade & Reference Div.

Dunn, Mary. My Adventure at Pompeii. 2006. 44p. (J). 8.99 (978-1-59092-411-2(8) , Orchard Academy Pr.) Windstorm Creative.

Kaplan, Sarah Pitt. Pompeii: City of Ashes. 2005. (Illus.). 48p. (J). (ps-7). 24.00 (978-0-516-25122-6(8)); (YA). (gr. 7-12). pap. 6.95 (978-0-516-25091-5(4)) Scholastic Library Publishing. (Children's Pr.).

Lindeen, Mary. Ashes to Ashes: Uncovering Pompeii. 2007. (Shockwave: People & Communities Ser.). (Illus.). 36p. (J). (gr. 4-6). lib. bdg. 25.00 (***978-0-531-17745-7(9)*** , Children's Pr.) Scholastic Library Publishing.

Malam, John. You Wouldn't Want to Live in Pompeii! A Volcanic Eruption You'd Rather Avoid. (You Wouldn't Want to... : Ancient Civilization Ser.). 32p. (J). 2008. pap. 9.95 (***978-0-531-16900-1(6)*** , Watts, Franklin); 2007. spiral bd. 29.00 (***978-0-531-18748-7(9)*** , Children's Pr.) Scholastic Library Publishing.

Nardo, Don. Ancient Pompeii. 2004. (Illus.). 112p. (J). (gr. 5-8). lib. bdg. 29.95 (978-1-59018-457-8(2) , Lucent Bks.) Thomson Gale.

Osborne, Mary Pope. Pompeii: Lost & Found. Christensen, Bonnie, illus. 2006. 40p. (J). (gr. 1-5). 16.95 (978-0-375-82889-8(3)); lib. bdg. 18.99 (978-0-375-92889-5(8)) Random Hse. Children's Bks. (Knopf Bks. for Young Readers).

Osborne, Mary Pope & Boyce, Natalie Pope. Ancient Rome & Pompeii. Murdocca, Sal, illus. 2006. (Magic Tree House Research Guide Ser.: No. 14). 128p. (J). (gr. k-3). 4.99 (978-0-375-83220-8(3) , Random Hse. Bks. for Young Readers) Random Hse. Children's Bks.

—Ancient Rome & Pompeii: A Nonfiction Companion to Vacation under the Volcano. Murdocca, Sal, illus. 2006. (Magic Tree House Research Guide Ser.: No. 14). 128p. (J). (gr. k-3). lib. bdg. 11.99 (978-0-375-93220-5(8) , Random Hse. Bks. for Young Readers) Random Hse. Children's Bks.

Parker, Victoria. Pompeii AD 79: A City Buried by a Volcanic Eruption. 2006. (When Disaster Struck Ser.). (Illus.). 56p. (J). (gr. 4-7). lib. bdg. 32.86 (978-1-4109-2276-2(6)) Raintree.

Patent, Dorothy Hinshaw. Lost City of Pompeii. 2000. (Frozen in Time Ser.). (Illus.). (J). (gr. 5-9). lib. bdg. 27.07 (978-0-7614-0785-0(5) , Benchmark Bks.) Cavendish, Marshall Corp.

Platt, Richard. Pompeii. Cappon, Manuela, illus. 2007. (Through Time Ser.). 48p. (J). (gr. 1-5). 16.95 (***978-0-7534-6044-3(0)*** , Kingfisher) Houghton Mifflin Co. Trade & Reference Div.

Roberts, Russell. Mt. Vesuvius & the Destruction of Pompei, A. D. 79. 2005. (Natural Disasters Ser.). (Illus.). 32p. (J). (gr. 1-4). lib. bdg. (978-1-58415-419-8(5)) Mitchell Lane Pubs., Inc.

Sonneborn, Liz. Pompeii. 2008. (J). lib. bdg. (***978-0-8225-7505-4(1)***) Twenty First Century Bks.

POMPEII (EXTINCT CITY)—FICTION

Lasky, Kathryn. The Last Girls of Pompeii. 2007. 160p. (J). (gr. 5 up). 15.99 (978-0-670-06196-9(4) , Viking Juvenile) Penguin Group (USA) Inc.

Osborne, Mary Pope. Vacation under the Volcano, Vol. 13. unabr. ed. 2004. (Magic Tree House Ser. : No. 13). 74p. (J). (gr. k-3). pap. 17.00 incl. audio (978-0-8072-0782-6(9) , LFTR 241 SP, Listening Library) Random Hse. Audio Publishing Group.

—Vacation under the Volcano. Murdocca, Sal, illus. 1998. (Magic Tree House Ser.: No. 13). (J). (gr. k-3). 96p. lib. bdg. 11.99 (978-0-679-99050-5(X)); 80p. mass mkt. 3.99 (978-0-679-89050-8(5)) Random Hse. Children's Bks. (Random Hse. Bks. for Young Readers).

—Vacation under the Volcano, nO. 13. Murdocca, Sal, illus. 1998. (Magic Tree House Ser. : No. 13). (J). (gr. k-3). (978-0-606-13972-4(9)) Tandem Library Bks.

PONCE DE LEON, JUAN, 1460?-1521

Compass Point Books, contrib. by. Ponce de Leon. (Exploring the World Ser.). 48p. (YA). pap. 8.95 (978-0-7565-1148-7(8)) Compass Point Bks.

Crisfield, Deborah. The Travels of Juan Ponce de Leon. 1999. (Explorers & Exploration Ser.). (Illus.). 48p. (J). (gr. 4-7). lib. bdg. 22.83 (978-0-7398-1491-8(5)) Raintree.

Davenport, John. Juan Ponce de Leon: And His Lands of Discovery. Goetzmann, William H., ed. 2005. (Explorers of New Lands Ser.). (Illus.). 142p. (J). (ps-8). lib. bdg. 30.00 (978-0-7910-8607-0(0) , Chelsea Hse.) Facts On File, Inc.

Eagen, Rachel. Ponce de Léon: Exploring Florida & Puerto Rico. 2005. (In the Footsteps of Explorers Ser.). (Illus.). 32p. (J). (gr. 3-9). (978-0-7787-2412-4(3)); pap. (978-0-7787-2448-3(4)) Crabtree Publishing Co.

Green, Tamara. Juan Ponce de Leon. (Great Explorers Ser.). (Illus.). 48p. (J). (gr. 5 up). 2002. pap. 14.60 (978-0-8368-5178-6(1)); 2001. lib. bdg. 30.00 (978-0-8368-5018-5(1)) Stevens, Gareth Inc. (World Almanac Library).

Grohmann, Susan. Ponce de Leon Sails Again. 1999. (Time Travel Adventure Ser.). (Illus.). 80p. (gr. 4 up). pap. 14.95 (978-1-892629-02-9(X)) Tailored Tours Pubns., Inc.

Harmon, Daniel E. Juan Ponce de Leon & the Search for the Fountain of Youth. 1999. (Explorers of the New World Ser.). (Illus.). 63p. (YA). (gr. 4 up). 31.00 (978-0-7910-5517-5(5) , Chelsea Hse.) Facts On File, Inc.

Heinrichs, Ann. Ponce de Leon: Juan Ponce de Leon Searches for the Fountain of Youth. 2002. (Exploring the World Ser.). (Illus.). 48p. (J). (gr. 4 up). lib. bdg. 22.60 (978-0-7565-0181-5(4)) Compass Point Bks.

Hoogenboom, Lynn. Juan Ponce de Leon: A Primary Source Biography. 2006. (Illus.). 24p. (J). lib. bdg. (978-1-4042-3040-8(8) , PowerKids Pr.) Rosen Publishing Group, Inc., The.

Hurwicz, Claude. Juan Ponce de Leon. 2001. (Famous Explorers Ser.). (Illus.). 24p. (J). (gr. 3). lib. bdg. 18.75 (978-0-8239-5563-3(X) , PowerKids Pr.) Rosen Publishing Group, Inc., The.

Kline, Trish. Ponce de Leon. 2001. (Discover the Life of an Explorer Ser.). (Illus.). 24p. (J). (gr. 1-4). lib. bdg. 20.64 (978-1-58952-068-4(8)) Rourke Publishing, LLC.

Manning, Ruth. Juan Ponce de Leon. 2000. (Groundbreakers Ser.). (Illus.). 48p. (J). (gr. 5-7). lib. bdg. 25.64 (978-1-57572-376-1(X)) Heinemann Library.

—Juan Ponce De Leon. 2002. (Groundbreakers Ser.). (Illus.). 48p. (J). (gr. 5-7). pap. 8.50 (978-1-58810-344-4(7) , 91096) Heinemann Library.

Marsh, Carole. Juan Ponce de Leon. 2002. (One Thousand Readers Ser.). (Illus.). 12p. (J). (gr. k-4). 2.95 (978-0-635-01483-2(1) , 14831) Gallopade International.

Molzahn, Arlene Bourgeois. Ponce de Leon: Explorer of Florida. 2003. (Explorers! Ser.). (Illus.). 48p. (J). lib. bdg. 23.93 (978-0-7660-2071-9(1)) Enslow Pubs., Inc.

Nobleman, Marc Tyler. Juan Ponce de Leon. 2004. (Fact Finders Ser.). (Illus.). 32p. (J). lib. bdg. 22.60 (978-0-7368-2667-9(X)) Capstone Pr., Inc.

Otfinoski, Steven. Juan Ponce de Leon: Discoverer of Florida. 2003. (Great Explorations Ser.). (J). (978-0-7614-1741-5(9)); 29.93 (978-0-7614-1610-4(2)) Cavendish, Marshall Corp. (Benchmark Bks.).

Petrie, Kristin. Juan Ponce de Leon. 2007. (Illus.). 32p. (J). 22.78 (978-1-59679-742-0(8)) ABDO Publishing Co.

Sakurai, Gail. Juan Ponce de Leon. (Watts Library). (Illus.). (J). (gr. 5-7). 2002. 64p. pap. 8.95 (978-0-531-16579-9(5)); 2001. 63p. pap. 25.50 (978-0-531-11964-8(5)) Scholastic Library Publishing. (Watts, Franklin).

—Juan Ponce de Leon. 2001. (gr. 3-6). lib. bdg. 17.60 (978-0-613-53516-8(2)) Tandem Library Bks.

Shafer, Susan. Ponce de Leon & the Fountain of Youth. 2005. 40.00 (***978-1-4108-4231-2(2)***) Benchmark Education Co.

Slavicek, Louise Chipley. Juan Ponce de Leon. 2003. (Great Hispanic Heritage Ser.). (Illus.). 112p. (gr. 6-12). 30.00 (978-0-7910-7255-4(X)); pap. 30.00 (978-0-7910-7518-0(4)) Facts On File, Inc. (Chelsea Hse.).

Sutcliffe, Jane. Juan Ponce de Leon. 2006. (History Maker Bios Ser.). (Illus.). 48p. (J). (gr. 3-7). 26.60 (978-0-8225-2944-6(0) , Lerner Pubns.) Lerner Publishing Group.

Whiting, Jim. Juan Ponce de Leon. 2002. (Latinos in American History). (Illus.). 56p. (gr. 4-8). lib. bdg. 29.95 (978-1-58415-149-4(8)) Mitchell Lane Pubs., Inc.

Worth, Richard. Ponce de Leon & the Age of Spanish Exploration in World History. 2003. (In World History Ser.). (Illus.). 112p. (J). (gr. 5-12). lib. bdg. 26.60 (978-0-7660-1940-9(3)) Enslow Pubs., Inc.

POND ECOLOGY

see Fresh-Water Biology

PONIES

see also Horses

Adelman, Beth. The Pony Guide. 2006. (Girls Rock! Ser.). (Illus.). 32p. (J). (gr. 1-5). 24.21 (978-1-59296-749-0(3)) Child's World, Inc.

Andrekson, Judy. Little Squire: The Jumping Pony. Parkins, David, illus. 2007. (True Horse Stories Ser.). 80p. (J). (gr. 3-6). pap. 7.95 (978-0-88776-770-8(2)) Tundra Bks., Inc./Livres Toundra, Inc. CAN. *Dist:* Random Hse., Inc.

Barnes, Julia, et al. 101 Facts about Horses & Ponies. 2002. (One Hundred One Facts about Pets Ser.). (Illus.). 32p. (J). (gr. 3 up). lib. bdg. 23.33 (978-0-8368-3019-4(9)) Stevens, Gareth Inc.

Bell. My Pony Logbook. 2002. (Illus.). 64p. reprint ed. 12.99 (978-0-85131-865-3(7) , Allen, J. A. & Company, Limited) Hale, Robert Ltd. GBR. *Dist:* Independent Pubs. Group.

Binns, Tristan Boyer. Horses & Ponies. 2006. (Keeping Pets Ser.). (Illus.). 48p. (J). (978-1-4034-7703-3(5)) Heinemann Library.

Budd, Jackie. The Best Book of Ponies. 1999. (Best Book of... Ser.). (Illus.). 32p. (J). (gr. k-3). tchr. ed. 12.95 (978-0-7534-5172-4(7) , Kingfisher) Houghton Mifflin Co. Trade & Reference Div.

Curry, Marion. Horse & Pony Basics. 2006. (Illus.). 32p. (J). lib. bdg. (978-0-8368-6831-9(5)) Stevens, Gareth Inc.

—Horse & Pony Care. 2006. (Illus.). 32p. (J). lib. bdg. (978-0-8368-6833-3(1)) Stevens, Gareth Inc.

Dalmatian Press Staff. Ponies & Butterflies: Velvet Bright Book to Color. rev. ed. 2003. (Fuzzy Book to Color Ser.). (Illus.). 4p. (J). pap. 4.49 (978-1-4037-0711-6(1)) Dalmatian Pr.

Dell, Pamela. Shetland Ponies. 2007. (Majestic Horses Ser.). 32p. (J). (gr. k-4). 27.07 (978-1-59296-785-8(X)) Child's World, Inc.

Dickins, Rosie & Pratt, Leonie. Horse & Pony Treasury. 2006. 96p. (J). 19.99 (978-0-7945-1431-0(6) , Usborne) EDC Publishing.

Dorling Kindersley Publishing Staff, ed. Pony. 2004. (Ultimate Sticker Bks.). 16p. (J). (gr. 5). pap. 6.99 (978-0-7566-0562-9(8)) Dorling Kindersley Publishing, Inc.

Draper, Judith. My First Horse & Pony Book. Roberts, Matthew, photos by. 2005. (Illus.). 48p. (J). (gr. k-3). 9.95 (978-0-7534-5878-5(0) , Kingfisher) Houghton Mifflin Co. Trade & Reference Div.

Draper, Judith, et al. My First Horse & Pony Care Book: From Boots & Bedding to Saddles & Stables. Roberts, Matthew, photos by. 2006. (My First Horse & Pony Ser.). (Illus.). 48p. (J). (gr. k-3). 9.95 (978-0-7534-5989-8(2) , Kingfisher) Houghton Mifflin Co. Trade & Reference Div.

Gates, Josephine Scribner. The land of Delight: Child life on a Pony Farm. 2007. (Illus.). 116p. (J). lib. bdg. 59.00 (***978-1-60304-022-8(6)***) Dollworks.

Gentle, Victor & Perry, Janet. Chincoteague Ponies. 2001. (Great American Horses Ser.). (Illus.). 24p. (J). (gr. 1 up). lib. bdg. 22.00 (978-0-8368-2935-8(2)) Stevens, Gareth Inc.

Gunzi, Christiane. Little Ponies. 2005. (Feels Real Bks.). (Illus.). 10p. (J). bds. 4.95 (978-0-7641-5855-1(4)) Barron's Educational Series, Inc.

Harvey, G. & Dickens, R. Riding & Pony Care. 2004. (Complete Book of Riding & Pony Care Ser.). (Illus.). 144p. (J). (gr. 3 up). lib. bdg. 23.95 (978-1-58086-422-0(8)) EDC Publishing.

Head, Honor. Ponies & Horses. 2007. (QEB Know Your Pet Ser.). (Illus.). 32p. (J). lib. bdg. 19.95 (978-1-59566-219-4(7)) QEB Publishing Inc.

Henderson, Carolyn. Horse & Pony Book. 2007. (Illus.). 160p. (J). (gr. 4-7). pap. 10.99 (***978-0-7566-3146-8(7)***) Dorling Kindersley Publishing, Inc.

Henderson, Carolyn. Pony Care: A Young Rider's Guide. 2005. (Illus.). 48p. (J). (ps-7). 9.99 (978-0-7566-1448-5(1)) Dorling Kindersley Publishing, Inc.

Hill, Cherry. Your Pony, Your Horse: A Kid's Guide to Care & Enjoyment. Balmuth, Deborah, ed. 2003. (Storey's Your Ser.). (Illus.). 161p. (Orig.). (J). (gr. 4-7). pap. 14.95 (978-0-88266-908-3(7) , 66908) Storey Publishing, LLC.

Hudak, Heather C. Ponies. 2006. (J). (978-1-59036-426-0(0)); (978-1-59036-433-8(3)) Weigl Pubs., Inc.

Kaster, Pam. Molly the Pony: A True Story. 2008. (J). (***978-0-8071-3320-0(5)***) Louisiana State Univ. Pr.

Krementz, Jill. A Very Young Rider. ed. 2007. 124p. 24.95 (***978-0-9755516-2-2(0)***) DreamHouse Publishing, Inc.

Landau, Elaine. Your Pet Pony. 2006. (True Book Ser.). (Illus.). 47p. (J). (978-0-531-16797-7(6)) Children's Pr., Ltd.

Llewellyn, Claire & Budd, Jackie. The Best Book of Ponies. 2005. (Best Book of... Ser.). (Illus.). 32p. (J). (gr. k-3). pap. 6.95 (978-0-7534-5874-7(8) , Kingfisher) Houghton Mifflin Co. Trade & Reference Div.

MacAulay, Kelley & Kalman, Bobbie. Ponies. Crabtree, Marc, illus. Crabtree, Marc, photos by. 2004. (Pet Care Ser.). 32p. (J). (978-0-7787-1758-4(5)); pap. (978-0-7787-1790-4(9)) Crabtree Publishing Co.

Milbourne, Anna. Horses & Ponies (Level 1) - Internet Referenced. 2007. (Illus.). 32p. (J). 4.99 (978-0-7945-1397-9(2) , Usborne) EDC Publishing.

Needham, Kate. Pony Guide. 2006. (Illus.). 31p. (J). (978-0-439-78703-1(3)) Scholastic, Inc.

Parise-Peterson, Amanda. The Shetland Pony. 2006. (Edge Books, Horses). (Illus.). 32p. (J). (978-0-7368-4374-4(4)) Capstone Pr., Inc.

Parker, Helen. Horse & Pony. 2006. (Lift Stick & Learn Ser.). (Illus.). 12p. (J). (ps-k). pap. 4.95 (978-1-84610-283-7(9)) Make Believe Ideas GBR. *Dist:* Ingram Pub. Services.

Petty, Kate. Ponies & Foals. 2005. (Illus.). 24p. (J). (ps-3). lib. bdg. 22.80 (978-1-59604-031-1(9)) Stargazer Bks.

Pickeral, Tamsin. The Encyclopedia of Horses & Ponies. 2003. 384p. (YA). pap. 19.95 (978-0-7525-8277-1(1)) Parragon, Inc.

Pollack, Pam. Ponies, Vol. 2. Belviso, Meg, illus. 2003. (All Aboard Science Station Stop Ser.: Vol. 2). 32p. (J). (gr. 1-3). mass mkt. 3.99 (978-0-448-42524-5(6) , Grosset & Dunlap) Penguin Group (USA) Inc.

—Ponies. 2003. (gr. k-3). lib. bdg. 11.80 (978-0-613-72385-5(6)) Tandem Library Bks.

Ponies at Play. 12p. (J). (978-2-7643-0191-3(X)) Phidal Publishing, Inc./Editions Phidal, Inc.

Pony. 1999. (Pocket Pals Ser.). (FRE.). (J). (ps-1). pap. 1.99 (978-0-85953-736-0(6)) Child's Play-International.

Pritchard, Louise. I Love Ponies: A First Pony Guide. 2007. 64p. (J). (gr. 2-7). pap. 11.99 (***978-0-7641-3790-7(5)***) Barron's Educational Series, Inc.

Ransford, Sandy. Horse & Pony Breeds. Langrish, Bob, photos by. (Kingfisher Riding Club Ser.). (Illus.). 64p. (J). 2007. (gr. 3-5). pap. 8.95 (978-0-7534-6075-7(0)); 2003. (gr. 5-9). tchr. ed. 14.95 (978-0-7534-5575-3(7)) Houghton Mifflin Co. Trade & Reference Div. (Kingfisher).

—Horse & Pony Care. Langrish, Bob, illus. 2004. (Kingfisher Riding Club Ser.). 64p. (J). (gr. 4-8). pap. 8.95 (978-0-7534-5744-3(X) , Kingfisher) Houghton Mifflin Co. Trade & Reference Div.

—Horse & Pony Care. Langrish, Bob, photos by. 2002. (Kingfisher Riding Club Ser.). (Illus.). 64p. (J). (gr. 4-6). tchr. ed. 14.95 (978-0-7534-5439-8(4) , Kingfisher) Houghton Mifflin Co. Trade & Reference Div.

—Horse & Pony Factfile: An Essential Guide to the World of Horses & Ponies. Kingfisher Publications, Inc. Staff, ed. 2006. (Illus.). 224p. (J). (gr. 3-5). vinyl bd. 12.95 (978-0-7534-6039-9(4) , Kingfisher) Houghton Mifflin Co. Trade & Reference Div.

—Horses & Ponies. Langrish, Bob, photos by. 2001. (Riding Club Ser.). (Illus.). 96p. (J). (gr. 4-6). tchr. ed. 18.95 (978-0-7534-5343-8(6) , Kingfisher) Houghton Mifflin Co. Trade & Reference Div.

—The Kingfisher Illustrated Horse & Pony Encyclopedia. Langrish, Bob, photos by. 2004. (Illus.). 224p. (J). (gr. 5-9). 24.95 (978-0-7534-5781-8(4) , Kingfisher) Houghton Mifflin Co. Trade & Reference Div.

Reid, Struan. Dictionary of horses & ponies - internet Linked. Khan, Aziz, illus. rev. ed. 2004. 128p. (J). pap. 14.95 (978-0-7945-0843-2(X) , Usborne) EDC Publishing.

Rising, Janet. Ponytalk: 50 Ways to Make Friends with Your Pony. 2006. (Illus.). (J). pap. 4.99 (978-0-340-90305-6(8) , Hodder & Stoughton) Hodder General Publishing Division GBR. *Dist:* Trafalgar Square Publishing.

Smith, L. The Usborne Book of Horses & Ponies. rev. ed. 2004. (Young Nature Ser.). (Illus.). 32p. (Orig.). (J). pap. 6.95 (978-0-7945-0850-0(2) , Usborne) EDC Publishing.

Spector, Joanna. Horses & Ponies Sticker Bk. 2007. 24p. (J). pap. 8.99 (978-0-7945-1585-0(1) , Usborne) EDC Publishing.

Van Cleaf, Kristin. Highland Ponies. 2006. (Illus.). 24p. (J). (gr. k-6). 21.35 (978-1-59679-314-9(7) , Checkerboard Library) ABDO Publishing Co.

Walter Foster. Watch Me Draw the Playful World of My Little Pony. 2008. (Watch Me Draw Ser.). (Illus.). 24p. (J). pap. 5.95 (***978-1-60058-030-7(0)***) Foster, Walter Publishing, Inc.

PONIES—FICTION

Alexander, Samantha. Rachel, Vol. 6. 6th ed. 104p. mass mkt. 6.99 (978-0-330-36841-4(9) , Pan) Pan Macmillan GBR. *Dist:* Trafalgar Square Publishing.

Alexander, Sarah. Kate, No. 4. 128p. mass mkt. 6.99 (978-0-330-36839-1(7) , Pan) Pan Macmillan GBR. *Dist:* Trafalgar Square Publishing.

Ambrus, Victor, illus. Horse & Pony Stories. 2003. (Red Hot Reads Ser.). 256p. (gr. 4-8). pap. 6.95 (978-0-7534-5639-2(7) , Kingfisher) Houghton Mifflin Co. Trade & Reference Div.

Anderson, C. W. Blaze Finds the Trail. Anderson, C. W., illus. 2000. (Billy & Blaze Bks.). (Illus.). 32p. (J). (gr. k-3). pap. 5.99 (978-0-689-83520-9(5) , Aladdin) Simon & Schuster Children's Publishing.

—Blaze Finds the Trail. 2001. (gr. 1-4). 22.25 (978-0-8446-7164-2(9)) Smith, Peter Pub., Inc.

—Blaze Finds the Trail. 2000. (gr. k-3). lib. bdg. 13.00 (978-0-613-24380-3(3)); (Illus.). (J). 12.79 (978-0-606-17915-7(1)) Tandem Library Bks.

—Blaze Shows the Way. 2001. (gr. 1-4). 22.25 (978-0-8446-7166-6(5)) Smith, Peter Pub., Inc.

Anderson, R. P. Golden Egg Hunt. Middleton, Gayle, illus. 2006. (My Little Pony Ser.). (J). 24p. pap. 3.99 (978-0-06-079468-2(2)); (***978-1-4156-5114-8(0)***) HarperCollins Pubs. (Harper Festival).

Baglio, Ben M. Ponies at the Point, No. 10. Gregory, Jenny, illus. 1999. (Animal Ark Ser.: No. 10). 144p. (J). (gr. 3-5). mass mkt. 3.99 (978-0-590-66231-4(7)) Scholastic, Inc.

—Ponies at the Point. 1999. (Animal Ark Ser.: No. 10). (J). (gr. 3-5). (978-0-606-19936-0(5)) Tandem Library Bks.

—Ponies at the Point No.10. 1999. (gr. 3-6). lib. bdg. 11.80 (978-0-613-16990-5(5)) Tandem Library Bks.

—Pony in a Package. Baum, Ann, illus. 2003. (Animal Ark Ser.: No. 27). 144p. (J). (gr. 3-6). 3.99 (978-0-439-34388-6(7)) Scholastic, Inc.

—Pony in a Package. 2001. (gr. 3-6). lib. bdg. 11.80 (978-0-613-63333-8(4)) Tandem Library Bks.

—Pony on the Porch. McNicholas, Shelagh, illus. 1998. (Animal Ark Ser.: No. 2). 160p. (J). (gr. 3-5). 3.99 (978-0-590-18750-3(3)) Scholastic, Inc.

—Pony on the Porch. McNicholas, Shelagh, illus. 1998. (Animal Ark Ser.: No. 2). (J). (gr. 3-5). (978-0-606-13130-8(2)) Tandem Library Bks.

Bailey, Scott Arthur. The Tale of Pony Twinkleheels. 2006. pap. 33.99 (***978-1-4280-4093-9(5)***) IndyPublish.com.

Bak, Jenny. My Little Pony Color & Poster Book. Middleton, Gayle & Edwards, Ken, illus. 2006. (My Little Pony Ser.). 32p. (J). pap., pap. 3.99 (978-0-06-079470-5(4) , Harper Festival) HarperCollins Pubs.

—A Very Minty Christmas Reusable Sticker Book. 2005. (My Little Pony Ser.). 12p. (J). pap. 6.99 (978-0-06-084141-6(9) , Harper Festival) HarperCollins Pubs.

Bates, M. The Perfect Pony. 2004. (Sandy Lane Stables Ser.). 128p. (J). pap. 4.99 (978-0-7945-0505-9(8)) EDC Publishing.

Beloat, Betty. The Winged Pony. Schwartz, Wendy, illus. 2005. 32p. (J). (gr. k-5). pap. 5.99 (978-0-9701008-8-7(4)) Bicast, Inc.

Benjamin, Ruth. My Little Pony: A Secret Gift. Middleton, Gayle, illus. 2006. 24p. (J). lib. bdg. 15.00 (***978-1-4242-1536-2(6)***) Fitzgerald Bks.

—My Little Pony: Sleepover Surprise. Yee, Josie, illus. 2006. 24p. (J). lib. bdg. 13.85 (***978-1-4242-0812-8(2)***) Fitzgerald Bks.

—My Little Pony: Ponies on Ice: Ponies on Ice. Lo Raso, Carlo, illus. 2007. (I Can Read Bks.). 24p. (J). pap. 3.99 (***978-0-06-122835-3(4)*** , Harper Trophy) HarperCollins Pubs.

—My Little Pony: Very Lucky Ponies. Fletcher, Lyn, illus. 2008. (I Can Read Bks.). 24p. (J). pap. 3.99 (***978-0-06-122836-0(2)*** , Harper Trophy) HarperCollins Pubs.

—A Secret Gift. Middleton, Gayle, illus. 2006. (I Can Read Bks.). 24p. (J). pap. 3.99 (978-0-06-079474-3(7) , Harper Trophy) HarperCollins Pubs.

—A Secret Gift/el regalo Secreto. Middleton, Gayle, illus. 2006. (I Can Read Bks.). (SPA.). 24p. (J). pap. 3.99 (978-0-06-112391-7(9) , Rayo) HarperCollins Pubs.

—Sleepover Surprise. Yee, Josie, illus. 2006. (I Can Read Bks.). 24p. (J). pap. 3.99 (978-0-06-079469-9(0) , Harper Trophy) HarperCollins Pubs.

Betancourt, Jeanne. Lonely Pony. Bachem, Paul, illus. 2000. (Pony Pals Ser.: No. 25). 144p. (J). (gr. 2-5). pap. 3.99 (978-0-439-06491-0(0)) Scholastic, Inc.

—Lonely Pony. 2000. (Pony Pals Ser.: Vol. 25). (J). (gr. 2-5). (978-0-606-19937-7(3)) Tandem Library Bks.

—Magic Pony. Bachem, Paul, illus. 2002. (Pony Pals Ser.: No. 35). 96p. (J). (gr. 2-5). mass mkt. 3.99 (978-0-439-30645-4(0)) Scholastic, Inc.

—No Ponies in the House! Jones, Richard, illus. 2003. (Pony Pals Ser.: No. 37). 96p. (J). pap. 3.99 (978-0-439-42627-5(8)) Scholastic, Inc.

—The Saddest Pony. 1999. (Pony Pals Ser.: Vol. 18). (J). (gr. 2-5). (978-0-606-19596-6(3)) Tandem Library Bks.

—The Unlucky Pony. Bachem, Paul, illus. 2000. (Pony Pals Ser.: No. 24). 96p. (J). (gr. 2-5). pap. 3.99 (978-0-439-06490-3(2) , Scholastic Paperbacks) Scholastic, Inc.

—The Unlucky Pony. 2000. (Pony Pals Ser.: Vol. 24). (J). (gr. 2-5). (978-0-606-19602-4(1)) Tandem Library Bks.

—What's Wrong with My Pony? 2001. (Pony Pals Ser.: No. 33). (Illus.). 96p. (J). (gr. 2-5). pap. 3.99 (978-0-439-30642-3(6)) Scholastic, Inc.

Betancourt, Jeanne & Winter, Jeannette. Pony-4-Sale. Bachem, Paul, illus. 2001. (Pony Pals Ser.: No. 30). 96p. (J). (gr. 2-5). pap. 3.99 (978-0-439-16573-0(3)) Scholastic, Inc.

Bradley, Kimberly Brubaker. The Perfect Pony. Colon, Raul & McNicholas, Shelagh, illus. 2007. 32p. (J). (ps). 16.99 (978-0-8037-2851-6(4) , Dial) Penguin Group (USA) Inc.

—The Perfect Pony. McNicholas, Shelagh, illus. 2007. (J). (***978-1-4287-3296-4(9)** , Dial) Penguin Group (USA) Inc.

Brooke, Samantha. A Pony Tale. 2008. 32p. (J). (ps-k). pap. 3.99 (***978-0-448-44719-3(3)** , Grosset & Dunlap) Penguin Group (USA) Inc.

Campbell, Donna. An Independent Spirit: The Tale of Betsy Dowdy & Black Bess. 2002. (Legends of the Carolinas Ser.). 200p. (J). 8.95 (978-1-928556-35-0(3)) Coastal Carolina Pr.

—Pale as the Moon. Davis, Debi, illus. 1999. (Carolina Young People Ser.). 104p. (J). (gr. 4-8). pap. 10.95 (978-1-928556-02-2(7)) Coastal Carolina Pr.

Cane, Rochelle & Mada Design Staff. My Little Pony: The Princess Promenade Storybook & Playset. 2006. 10p. (J). 15.99 (978-0-7944-1107-7(X)) Reader's Digest Assn., Inc., The.

Capalija, Ann Marie. Rose Blossom's First Christmas. LoRaso, Carlo, illus. 2005. (J). (***978-1-4156-2255-1(8)** , Harper Festival) HarperCollins Pubs.

Capalija, Ann Marie. Valentine's Day, Up... Up... & Away! Fletcher, Lyn, illus. 2005. (My Little Pony Ser.). 24p. (J). pap. 4.99 (978-0-06-076183-7(0) , Harper Festival) HarperCollins Pubs.

Carlson, Nolan. Lame Eagle & Wind Chaser. 2005. (YA). per. (978-0-9772745-1-2(9)) Mennonite Pr. Inc.

Causton, Linda. Lester's Rainy Lake Pony. l.t. ed. 2004. (Illus.). 32p. (J). 12.00 (978-1-930374-09-6(7)) DeForest Pr.

Chapman, Linda. Dreams Come True. 2006. (My Secret Unicorn Ser.: No. 2). (Illus.). 128p. (J). pap. 4.99 (978-0-439-81383-9(2) , Scholastic Paperbacks) Scholastic, Inc.

—Dreams Come True. Hull, Biz, illus. 2002. 120p. (J). (978-0-439-60010-1(3)) Scholastic, Inc.

—Starlight Surprise. 2007. (My Secret Unicorn Ser.: No. 4). (Illus.). 144p. (J). pap. 4.99 (978-0-439-81385-3(9) , Scholastic Paperbacks) Scholastic, Inc.

Chase, Diana. Daisy Street. Bradley, Vanessa, illus. 2005. 128p. (Orig.). (J). pap. 13.50 (978-1-920731-11-3(3)) Fremantle Pr. AUS. *Dist:* International Specialized Bk. Services.

Chesterfield, Sadie. My Little Pony: Easter Surprise Coloring Book: Easter Surprise Coloring Book. Edwards, Ken, illus. 2007. (My Little Pony Ser.). 32p. (J). pap. 3.99 (978-0-06-121526-1(0) , Harper Festival) HarperCollins Pubs.

Clayton, Elaine. Blue Ribbon for Sugar. Clayton, Elaine, illus. 2006. (Illus.). 32p. (J). 16.95 (978-1-59643-157-7(1)) Roaring Brook Pr.

Clover, Peter. Sheltie & the Stray. 2005. (Illus.). 91p. (J). (978-0-439-68890-1(6)) Scholastic, Inc.

—Sheltie in Trouble. 2005. 89p. (J). (978-0-439-68889-5(2)) Scholastic, Inc.

—Sheltie Saves the Day!, No. 2. 2001. (Sheltie Ser.). (Illus.). (J). (978-0-606-20913-7(1)) Tandem Library Bks.

Cocquyt, Kathryn. A Pony for Luke. Parker, Pam, illus. 1998. (J). 14.95 (978-1-56554-277-8(0)) Pelican Publishing Co., Inc.

Dale, Jenny. Charlie the Champion, Vol. 2. 2002. (Illus.). 58p. incl. audio (978-0-333-90834-1(1)) Ulverscroft Large Print Bks.

Dale, Jenny. Sam the School Pony. 2005. 57p. (***978-0-439-79125-0(1)***) Scholastic, Inc.

—Sam the School Pony, Vol. 1. l.t. ed. 2002. (Illus.). 64p. pap. (978-0-333-90831-0(7)) Ulverscroft Large Print Bks.

Davidson, Susanna. Princess Polly & the Pony. Hill, Dave, illus. 2007. (First Reading Level 4 Ser.). 48p. (J). 8.99 (***978-0-7945-1756-4(0)** , Usborne) EDC Publishing.

—Stories of Magic Ponies. 2007. (Young Reading Series 1 Gift Bks). 48p. (J). 8.99 (***978-0-7945-1790-8(0)** , Usborne) EDC Publishing.

Dawson, JoAnn S. Lady's Big Surprise. 2004. 288p. pap. 8.95 (978-0-9746561-6-8(X)); (Illus.). 15.95 (978-0-9746561-5-1(1)) FT Richards Publishing.

—Star of Wonder. 2005. (Illus.). 268p. pap. 8.95 (978-0-9746561-4-4(3)) FT Richards Publishing.

Demas, Corinne. Perfect Pony. 2000. (Step into Reading Ser.). (978-0-606-18859-3(2)) Tandem Library Bks.

Doty, Jean Slaughter. Summer Pony. Sanderson, Ruth, illus. 2008. (J). (***978-0-375-94709-4(4)***); pap. (***978-0-375-84709-7(X)***) Random Hse. Children's Bks.

—Winter Pony. Sanderson, Ruth, illus. 2008. (J). (***978-0-375-84710-3(3)***); lib. bdg. (***978-0-375-94710-0(8)***) Random Hse., Inc.

Douthwaite, Wendy. Summer Ponies. 2000. (Polly Ser.). (Illus.). 96p. (J). (gr. 2-7). mass mkt. (978-0-330-32540-0(X) , Macmillan Children's Bks.) Pan Macmillan.

Driggs, Scout. Dress-up Day. Middleton, Gayle, illus. 2005. (My Little Pony Ser.). 96p. (J). pap. 2.99 (978-0-06-074448-9(0) , Harper Festival) HarperCollins Pubs.

—Glitter Castle. Edwards, Ken, illus. 2005. (My Little Pony Ser.). 10p. (J). (ps-1). 6.99 (978-0-06-074444-1(8) , Harper Festival) HarperCollins Pubs.

—My Little Pony No. 3: Pony Pop Stars. Fletcher, Lyn, illus. 2005. (My Little Pony Ser.). 24p. (J). (ps-1). pap. 3.99 (978-0-06-074445-8(6) , Harper Festival) HarperCollins Pubs.

—My Little Pony No. 4: Mystery Monster. Fletcher, Lyn, illus. 2005. (My Little Pony Ser.). 24p. (J). (ps-1). pap. 3.99 (978-0-06-074446-5(4) , Harper Festival) HarperCollins Pubs.

Driggs, Scout. Pony Pop Stars. Fletcher, Lynn, illus. 2005. (J). (***978-1-4156-1609-3(4)** , Harper Festival) HarperCollins Pubs.

Earhart, Kristin. Saddle up, Happy! Gurney, John, illus. 2007. (Big Apple Barn Ser.: No. 4). 96p. (J). pap. 3.99 (***978-0-439-90096-6(4)***) Scholastic, Inc.

—Sassy Surprise. 2007. (Big Apple Barn Ser.). 96p. (J). pap. 3.99 (***978-0-439-90095-9(6)** , Scholastic Paperbacks) Scholastic, Inc.

Egan, Kate. Pony Party: Fiesta de Disfraces. LoRaso, Carlo, illus. 2006. (My Little Pony Ser.). (SPA.). 24p. (J). pap. 3.99 (978-0-06-112208-8(4)) HarperCollins Pubs.

Ferris, James Cody. The X Bar X Boys on Big Bison Trail. Rogers, Walter S., illus. 2004. reprint ed. pap. 24.95 (978-1-4179-3953-4(2)) Kessinger Publishing, LLC.

Fisher, Marilyn Anne. Pony Tales. 2005. (Illus.). 75p. (J). per. 20.00 (978-1-890306-90-8(8)) Warwick Hse. Publishing.

Frantz, Jennifer. Hide-and-Seek: My Little Pony. Thompson Brothers Staff, illus. 2005. (Festival Reader Ser.). 24p. (J). (ps-1). pap. 3.99 (978-0-06-073270-7(9) , Harper Festival) HarperCollins Pubs.

—The World's Biggest Tea Party. Fletcher, Lyn, illus. 2006. (My Little Pony Ser.). 24p. (J). pap. 3.99 (978-0-06-123444-6(3) , Harper Festival) HarperCollins Pubs.

Friedrich, Elizabeth. Leah's Pony. 1999. (gr. k-3). lib. bdg. 17.60 (978-0-613-78901-1(6)) Tandem Library Bks.

Gasque, Dale Blackwell. Pony Trouble. 1998. (Hyperion Chapters Ser.). (978-0-606-13714-0(9)) Tandem Library Bks.

Gaydos, Nora. Phonics Comics: Pony Tales - Level 1. Hamilton, Pamela, illus. 2007. 24p. (J). (gr. 1-17). pap. 3.99 (978-1-58476-553-0(4)) Innovative Kids.

Gerver, Jane E. Penny. Papp, Lisa, illus. 2006. (Breyer Stablemates Ser.). 48p. (J). pap. 4.99 (978-0-439-72235-3(7) , Cartwheel Bks.) Scholastic, Inc.

Ghent, Natale. No Small Thing. 2005. 256p. (J). (gr. 5-9). 15.99 (978-0-7636-2422-4(5)) Candlewick Pr.

Grimes, Terri & Timmons, Jasmine. A Pony Named Penny. 2007. 16p. 11.95 (***978-0-615-15990-4(7)***) Dm Productions.

Grovet, Heather. Good As Gold: Discovering What Is Really Important. 2007. (Illus.). 95p. (J). (***978-0-8163-2166-7(3)***) Pacific Pr. Publishing Assn.

—A Perfect Star. 2007. (Illus.). 95p. (J). (***978-0-8163-2164-3(7)***) Pacific Pr. Publishing Assn.

—Prince Prances Again. 2001. (Julius & Friends Ser.: Bk. 9). (Illus.). 94p. (J). 6.99 (978-0-8163-1807-0(7)) Pacific Pr. Publishing Assn.

Grovet, Heather. Zippitty Do Dah: Trusting God in Troubles Great & Small. 2007. (Illus.). 95p. (J). (***978-0-8163-2165-0(5)***) Pacific Pr. Publishing Assn.

Haas, Jessie. Birthday Pony. Apple, Margot, illus. 2004. 80p. (J). (gr. 2 up). 15.99 (978-0-06-057359-1(7)); lib. bdg. 16.89 (978-0-06-057360-7(0)) HarperCollins Pubs.

—Jigsaw Pony. Hu, Ying-Hwa, illus. 2005. 128p. (J). 15.99 (978-0-06-078245-0(5)); (gr. 2-4). lib. bdg. 16.89 (978-0-06-078250-4(1)) HarperCollins Pubs.

Hagman, Harvey Dixon. Majesty from Assateague. Aiken, David, illus. 2003. 76p. (J). pap. 8.95 (978-0-87033-552-5(9) , Tidewater Pubs.) Cornell Maritime Pr., Inc.

Hasbro. Dancing in the Clouds Vol. 3. 2006. (My Little Pony Ser.). (Illus.). 32p. pap. 3.99 (978-1-59816-281-3(0) , Tokyopop Kids) TOKYOPOP, Inc.

Hasbro, creator. Very Minty Christmas. 2005. (Illus.). 32p. pap. 3.99 (978-1-59816-001-7(X) , Tokyopop Kids) TOKYOPOP, Inc.

Haston, Meg. The Thanksgiving Gift. Fletcher, Lyn, illus. 2007. (My Little Pony Ser.). 24p. (J). (ps-2). pap. 4.99 (***978-0-06-123446-0(X)** , Harper Festival) HarperCollins Pubs.

Henry, Marguerite. Misty de Chincoteague. 2001. (978-0-606-22665-3(6)) Tandem Library Bks.

—Misty of Chincoteague. 2002. (Illus.). (J). 13.40 (978-0-7587-0291-3(4)) Book Wholesalers, Inc.

—Misty of Chincoteague. Dennis, Wesley, illus. 2006. 176p. (J). pap. 5.99 (978-1-4169-2783-9(2) , Aladdin) Simon & Schuster Children's Publishing.

—The Misty Treasury: Misty of Chincoteague; Stormy, Misty's Foal; King of the Wind. Dennis, Wesley, illus. 174p. (978-1-4169-0387-1(9)) Simon & Schuster Children's Publishing.

—Sea Star: Orphan of Chincoteague. 2002. 13.40 (978-0-7587-9188-7(7)) Book Wholesalers, Inc.

Henry, Marguerite & Dennis, Wesley. Sea Star: Orphan of Chincoteague. 2007. 176p. (J). pap. 5.99 (978-1-4169-2784-6(0) , Aladdin) Simon & Schuster Children's Publishing.

—Stormy, Misty's Foal. 2007. 224p. (J). pap. 5.99 (978-1-4169-2788-4(3) , Aladdin) Simon & Schuster Children's Publishing.

Herman, R. A. Pal & Sal. Ogden, Betina, illus. 1998. (All Aboard Reading Ser.). 32p. (J). (ps-3). pap. 3.99 (978-0-448-41716-5(2) , Grosset & Dunlap) Penguin Group (USA) Inc.

Heuck, Sidgrid. Poni/Oso/Estrella. 2002. Tr. of Pony/Bear & Star. (SPA., Illus.). 32p. (J). 11.95 (978-84-261-2270-4(1)) Juventud, Editorial ESP. *Dist:* AIMS International Bks., Inc.

Higgenson, Hadley. Keeker & the Horse Show Show-Off. Andersen, Maja, illus. 2006. (Sneaky Pony Ser.: Bk. 2). 48p. (J). pap. 3.95 (978-0-8118-5303-3(9)) Chronicle Bks. LLC.

—Keeker & the Sugar Shack. Andersen, Maja, illus. 2006. (Sneaky Pony Ser.: Bk. 3). 48p. (J). pap. 3.95 (978-0-8118-5456-6(6)) Chronicle Bks. LLC.

Higgenson, Hadley & Andersen, Maja. Keeker & the Sneaky Pony. Andersen, Maja, illus. 2006. (Sneaky Pony Ser.: Bk. 1). (Illus.). 48p. (J). pap. 3.95 (978-0-8118-5217-3(2)) Chronicle Bks. LLC.

Higginson, Hadley. Keeker & Springtime Surprise. Parrett, Lisa, illus. 2007. (Sneaky Pony Ser.: No. 4). 56p. (J). 15.50 (978-0-8118-5598-3(8)) Chronicle Bks. LLC.

—Keeker & Springtime Surprise. Perrett, Lisa, illus. 2007. (Sneaky Pony Ser.: No. 4). 56p. (J). pap. 3.95 (978-0-8118-5599-0(6)) Chronicle Bks. LLC.

—Keeker & the Crazy Upside-Down Day. Perrett, Lisa, illus. 2008. (J). (***978-0-8118-6255-4(0)***); pap. (***978-0-8118-6256-1(9)***) Chronicle Bks. LLC.

—Keeker & the Not-So-Sleepy Hollow. Perrett, Lisa, illus. 2008. (J). (***978-0-8118-6073-4(6)***); 56p. pap. 3.99 (***978-0-8118-6074-1(4)***) Chronicle Bks. LLC.

Higginson, Hadley. Keeker & the Sugar Shack, Bk. 3. Andersen, Maja, illus. 2006. 48p. (J). 15.50 (978-0-8118-5455-9(8)) Chronicle Bks. LLC.

Hurchalla, Elizabeth, ed. Friends Are Never Far Away. 2005. (Illus.). 32p. (ps-7). pap. 3.99 (978-1-59816-000-0(1) , Tokyopop Kids) TOKYOPOP, Inc.

Jeffers, Susan. My Pony. (Illus.). (J). (ps-17). 2003. 28p. 15.99 (978-0-7868-1995-9(2)); 2002. lib. bdg. (978-0-7868-2673-5(8)) Hyperion Bks. for Children.

Johnson, Gwen & Johnson, Carl. The Treasure of Diamond's Shoal. l.t. ed. 2007. (ENG., Illus.). 24p. (J). 8.95 (***978-0-9795860-0-2(3)***) Fish Tales Publishing.

Kalz, Jill. Pony Party. Schultz, Sara, illus. 2006. (Read-It! Readers Ser.). 24p. (J). (ps-3). 18.60 (978-1-4048-1612-1(7)) Picture Window Bks.

Keene, Carolyn. Pony Problems. Pamintuan, Macky, illus. 2006. (Nancy Drew & the Clue Crew Ser.: No. 3). 96p. (J). pap. 3.99 (978-1-4169-1815-8(9) , Aladdin) Simon & Schuster Children's Publishing.

—Pony Problems. 2007. (Nancy Drew & the Clue Crew Ser.). 96p. (J). (gr. 2-4). 24.21 (***978-1-59961-346-8(8)***) Spotlight.

Kelly, Theresa. Tony the Pony. Sampson, Jody, illus. l.t. ed. 2003. 12p. (J). 5.95 (978-1-59466-003-0(4)) Port Town Publishing.

—Tony the Pony: Bugs Are Not Bad. Sampson, Jody, illus. 2005. (J). per. 7.95 (978-1-59466-030-6(1)) Port Town Publishing.

Kent, Deborah. Riding the Pony Express. 2006. (Saddles, Stars, & Stripes Ser.). 176p. (J). (gr. 3-5). 8.95 (978-0-7534-6001-6(7) , Kingfisher) Houghton Mifflin Co. Trade & Reference Div.

Kimpton, Diana. Pony-Crazed Princess No. 7: Princess Ellie Takes Charge. Finlay, Lizzie, illus. 7th rev. ed. 2007. 96p. (gr. 1-4). pap. 3.99 (***978-1-4231-0617-3(2)***) Hyperion Paperbacks for Children.

—Princess Ellie Solves a Mystery. 8th rev. ed. 2007. (Pony Crazed Princess Ser.: No. 8). 96p. (gr. 1-4). pap. 3.99 (***978-1-4231-0901-3(5)***) Disney Pr.

—Princess Ellie to the Rescue. Finlay, Lizzie, illus. 2006. (Pony-Crazed Princess Ser.: Bk. 1). 96p. (gr. 1-4). pap. 3.99 (978-0-7868-4870-6(7)) Hyperion Pr.

—Princess Ellie's Mystery. Finlay, Lizzie, illus. 3rd rev. ed. 2006. (Pony-Crazed Princess Ser.: Bk. 3). 96p. (gr. 1-4). pap. 3.99 (978-0-7868-4872-0(3)) Hyperion Pr.

—Princess Ellie's Secret. Finlay, Lizzie, illus. 2nd rev. ed. 2006. (Pony-Crazed Princess Ser.: Bk. 2). 96p. (gr. 1-4). pap. 3.99 (978-0-7868-4871-3(5)) Hyperion Pr.

—Princess Ellie's Snowy Ride. 9th rev. ed. 2007. (Pony Crazed Princess Ser.: No. 9). 96p. (J). (gr. 1-4). pap. 3.99 (***978-1-4231-0902-0(3)***) Disney Pr.

—Summer Vacation. Finlay, Lizzie, illus. 2007. 144p. (gr. 1-4). pap. 4.99 (***978-1-4231-0616-6(4)***) Hyperion Paperbacks for Children.

Knight, Barbara. The Cowboys with penny the mustang Pony. 2006. (Illus.). 16p. (J). 14.95 net. (***978-0-9766270-1-2(9)***) Mustang BKS.

knight, Barbara. The Rescue, with Penny the Mustang Pony. 2005. (978-0-9766270-0-5(0)) Mustang BKS.

Knight, Barbara Maxine. The Storm. 2007. (Illus.). 32p. (J). 14.95 (***978-0-9766270-2-9(7)***) Mustang BKS.

Koeppel, Ruth. My Little Pony a Party in Ponyville Book. 2007. (Readers Book & DVD Ser.). 32p. (J). bds. 17.99 incl. DVD (978-0-7944-1226-5(2)) Reader's Digest Assn., Inc., The.

—My Little Pony Book & Charm Pony Field Day. 2007. 12p. (J). bds. 9.99 (978-0-7944-1225-8(4)) Reader's Digest Assn., Inc., The.

Lasky, Kathryn. Unicorns? Get Real! 2007. (Camp Princess Ser.). (Illus.). 160p. (J). 15.99 (***978-0-06-058764-2(4)***) HarperCollins Pubs.

Lee, Barbara R. Pookey the Pony. 2004. 35p. pap. 17.95 (978-1-4137-3396-9(4)) PublishAmerica, Inc.

Leigh, S. Runaway Pony. 2004. (Sandy Lane Stables Ser.). 100p. (J). pap. 4.95 (978-0-7945-0507-3(4)); lib. bdg. 12.95 (978-1-58086-575-3(5)) EDC Publishing.

Lester, Alison. The Quicksand Pony. 1998. (Illus.). 144p. (J). (gr. 5-9). tchr. ed. 15.00 (978-0-395-93749-5(3) , Walter Lorraine) Houghton Mifflin Co. Trade & Reference Div.

—The Snow Pony. 208p. (J). (gr. 5-9). 2006. pap. 5.95 (978-0-618-77125-7(5)); 2003. (Illus.). tchr. ed. 15.00 (978-0-618-25404-0(8)) Houghton Mifflin Co. Trade & Reference Div. (Walter Lorraine).

Lindsay, Elizabeth. Annie Saves the Day. Eastwood, John, illus. 2003. 92p. (J). (978-0-439-44651-8(1)) Scholastic, Inc.

Little Softy Pony. 2002. (J). (978-1-931312-92-9(3)) Soft-Play, Inc.

Litty, Julie. Chloe & the Magic Baton. Litty, Julie, illus. 2006. 32p. (J). (ps-3). 16.99 (978-0-698-40039-9(9) , Minedition) Penguin Group (USA) Inc.

Marchesani, Laura. My Little Pony: Easter Celebration Reusable Sticker Book. 2008. (My Little Pony Ser.). 12p. (J). 6.99 (***978-0-06-123467-5(2)** , Harper Festival) HarperCollins Pubs.

Mattern, Joanne. My Little Pony Phonics Fun. Lo Raso, Carlo, illus. 2008. (My First I Can Read Bks.). 12p. (J). pap. 12.99 (***978-0-06-122954-1(7)** , Harper Trophy) HarperCollins Pubs.

Matty & the Problem Ponies. 2006. (J). (978-1-933343-18-1(4)) Stabenfeldt Inc.

McMahon, Kate & Myler, Terry. Timber Twig. 1998. 142p. pap. 10.95 (978-1-901737-01-1(2)) Anvil Bks., Ltd. IRL. *Dist:* Dufour Editions, Inc.

McMillan, Bruce. Gletta the Foal. McMillan, Bruce, photos by. 1998. (Accelerated Reader Bks.). (Illus.). 32p. (J). (ps-3). 14.95 (978-0-7614-5039-9(4) , Cavendish Children's Bks.) Cavendish, Marshall Corp.

Meister, Cari. My Pony Jack. Young, Amy, illus. 2005. (Viking Easy-To-Read Ser.). 32p. (J). (ps-3). 13.99 (978-0-670-05917-1(X) , Viking Adult) Penguin Group (USA) Inc.

—My Pony Jack at Riding Lessons. Young, Amy, illus. 2005. (Viking Easy-To-Read Ser.). 32p. (J). (ps-ps). 13.99 (978-0-670-05918-8(8) , Viking Juvenile) Penguin Group (USA) Inc.

—My Pony Jack at the Horse Show: Viking Easy to Read Level 1. Young, Amy, illus. 2006. (Easy-to-Read,Viking Children's Ser.). 32p. (J). (ps). 13.99 (978-0-670-05919-5(6) , Viking Adult) Penguin Group (USA) Inc.

Miller, Debra J. The Pony Tale: The Truth about Timberlin. 2005. 4.00 (978-0-9776014-1-7(2)) Monogram Booklets.

Mills, Enos A. Cricket, A Mountain Pony: Large Print Edition, 1 vol. l.t. ed. 2006. (Illus.). 67p. 9.95 (978-1-928878-37-7(7)) Temporal Mechanical Pr.

Muschinske, Victoria. Honey Pie Pony's Book: A Fun with Fillies Adventure. 2005. (Illus.). 39p. (***978-0-439-70471-7(5)***) Scholastic, Inc.

My Little Pony. 2003. (J). 144.80 (978-0-06-056336-3(2)); (Illus.). 115.84 (978-0-06-056195-6(5)) HarperCollins Pubs.

Nanette. Pancake the Purple Pony. 2004. (Life on Granny's Farm Ser.). (J). 12.95 (978-0-9741269-8-2(5)) St. Bernard Publishing, LLC.

Newbery, L. El Poni de Mermelada. (Raton de Biblioteca Coleccion). (SPA.). 80p. (J). (gr. 3). 7.95 (978-84-88061-68-3(4)) Serres, Ediciones, S. L. ESP. *Dist:* Lectorum Pubns., Inc.

Nicholas, Sami. My Little Pony Friends Forever Book & Rubber Stamp Set. 2006. (My Little Pony Book & Rubber Stamp Set Ser.). 12p. (J). bds. 15.99 (978-0-7944-1146-6(0)) Reader's Digest Assn., Inc., The.

O'Donnell, Liam. Daisy on the Farm. (Pet Tales Ser.). (Illus.). 32p. (J). (ps-2). 9.95 (978-1-59249-452-1(8) , 1B037) Soundprints.

—Daisy on the Farm. Hatala, Dan, illus. 2005. (Pet Tales Ser.). 32p. (J). (ps-2). 2.95 (978-1-59249-451-4(X) , 1B036) Soundprints.

—Daisy the Farm Pony. Hatala, Dan, illus. 2005. (Pet Tales Ser.). 32p. (J). (ps-ps). pap. 4.95 (978-1-59249-450-7(1) , 1B035) Soundprints.

Oldfield, Jenny. Dawn Light. 2007. (Illus.). 128p. pap. 6.95 (***978-0-340-91078-8(X)***) Hodder Children's Division GBR. *Dist:* Independent Pubs. Group.

—Midnight Snow 4. 2007. (Illus.). 128p. pap. 6.95 (***978-0-340-91076-4(3)***) Hodder Children's Division GBR. *Dist:* Independent Pubs. Group.

—North Star. 2008. (Illus.). 0144p. pap. 6.95 (***978-0-340-91841-8(1)***) Hodder Children's Division GBR. *Dist:* Independent Pubs. Group.

—Pale Moon. 2007. (Illus.). 148p. pap. 6.95 (***978-0-340-91839-5(X)***) Hodder Children's Division GBR. *Dist:* Independent Pubs. Group.

—Sea Haze. 2008. (Illus.). 144p. pap. 6.95 (***978-0-340-91842-5(X)***) Hodder Children's Division GBR. *Dist:* Independent Pubs. Group.

—Summer Shadows 5. 2007. (Illus.). 128p. pap. 6.95 (***978-0-340-91077-1(1)***) Hodder Children's Division GBR. *Dist:* Independent Pubs. Group.

—Summertime Blues. 2008. (Illus.). 0144p. pap. 6.95 (***978-0-340-91840-1(3)***) Hodder Children's Division GBR. *Dist:* Independent Pubs. Group.

Oldfield, Jenny, compiled by. Horse & Pony Stories. 2007. (Illus.). 128p. (J). pap. 9.95 (***978-0-7534-6156-3(0)** , Kingfisher) Houghton Mifflin Co. Trade & Reference Div.

Oldfield, Jenny, compiled by. The Kingfisher Book of Horse & Pony Stories. 2005. (Kingfisher Book of Ser.). (Illus.). 128p. (J). (gr. 4-6). 17.00 (978-0-7534-5850-1(0) , Kingfisher) Houghton Mifflin Co. Trade & Reference Div.

Ongman, Gudrun. Sleep Pony Dreams. l.t. ed. 2006. (Illus.). 32p. (J). pap. 16.95 (978-0-9677204-2-5(7)) Mindcastle Bks., Inc.

Pegg, Laura Wittman. The Patch Quilt Pony. 2006. 17.00 (978-0-8059-7346-4(X)) Dorrance Publishing Co., Inc.

Pelizzari, Nora. Crystal Princess: The Runaway Rainbow. 2006. (My Little Pony Ser.). 12p. (J). pap. 6.99 (978-0-06-111692-6(0) , Harper Festival) HarperCollins Pubs.

—The Princess Promenade. 2006. (My Little Pony Ser.). 24p. (J). pap. 3.99 (978-0-06-111691-9(2)) HarperCollins Pubs.

—Trick or Treat, Friends Are Sweet! Reusable Sticker Book. Fletcher, Lyn, illus. 2007. (My Little Pony Ser.). 12p. (J). (ps-2). pap. 6.99 (***978-0-06-123445-3(1)*** , Harper Festival) HarperCollins Pubs.

Pelizzari, Nora. A Very Pony Place. 2007. (My Little Pony Ser.). 24p. (J). pap. 3.99 (978-0-06-121525-4(2) , Harper Festival) HarperCollins Pubs.

Pelizzari, Nora & Anderson, Robert. The Perfect Pumpkin. Fletcher, Lyn, illus. 2006. (My Little Pony Ser.). 20p. (J). pap. 6.99 (978-0-06-079471-2(2) , Harper Festival) HarperCollins Pubs.

Pennell, Kathleen. The Phantom Stallion. Pennell, Lauren, illus. 2003. (Pony Investigators Ser.: Vol. 4). 118p. (J). (gr. 3-7). pap. 5.95 (978-1-930353-73-2(1)) Masthof Pr.

—The Secret Passage: Pony Investigators. 2005. (Pony Investigators Ser.: 5). (Illus.). 108p. (J). pap. 5.95 (978-1-932864-42-7(3)) Masthof Pr.

Peyton, K. M. The Swallow Tale. l.t. ed. 2005. 216p. (J). pap. (978-0-7540-7837-1(X) , CLP 428) BBC Audio.

—The Swallow Tale. l.t. ed. 2003. (Illus.). (J). pap. 29.95 incl. audio (978-0-7540-6267-7(8) , Galaxy Children's Large Print) BBC Audiobooks America.

Posner-Sanchez, Andrea. A Pony for a Princess. Mateu, Francesc, illus. 2002. (Disney Princess Ser.). 32p. (J). (ps-1). pap. 3.99 (978-0-7364-2045-7(2) , RH/Disney) Random Hse. Children's Bks.

—A Pony for a Princess. 2002. (Disney Princess Ser.). (ps-2). lib. bdg. 11.80 (978-0-613-73659-6(1)) Tandem Library Bks.

Prentice-Hall Staff. The Red Pony. 2nd ed. (J). stu. ed. (978-0-13-717133-0(1)) Prentice Hall (Schl. Div.).

Pullein-Thompson, Christine. Horse & Pony Stories. 2003. (gr. 5-8). lib. bdg. 15.25 (978-0-613-67415-7(4)) Tandem Library Bks.

Redmond, Shirley-Raye. The Princess & Her Pony. 2007. (Illus.). 24p. (J). (***978-1-4048-1238-3(5)***) Picture Window Bks.

—The Princess & Her Pony. Senturk, Burak, illus. 2006. 24p. (J). (***978-1-4048-3142-1(8)***) Picture Window Bks.

Renne. The Ice Horse. 2003. (Illus.). 32p. (J). 17.95 (978-0-86315-384-6(4)) Floris Bks. GBR. *Dist:* SteinerBooks, Inc.

Ruepp, Krista. Runaway Pony PB. 2007. (J). pap. 6.95 (978-0-7358-2106-4(2)) North-South Bks., Inc.

—Winter Pony. James, J. Alison, tr. from GER. Heyne, Ulrike, illus. 2002. 32p. (J). 15.95 (978-0-7358-1691-6(3)) North-South Bks., Inc.

Russell, Anne. Seabiscuit: Wild Pony of the Outer Banks. Halpin, Diane Royder & Pearce, Brooks, illus. 2001. 32p. (J). (gr. k-8). 14.95 (978-1-928556-28-2(0)) Coastal Carolina Pr.

Sargent, Dave & Sargent, Pat. Sweetpea: (Purple Corn Welsh) Be Happy, 30, 58. Lenoir, Jane, illus. 2003. (Saddle Up Ser.: Vol. 58). 42p. (J). pap. 6.95 (978-1-56763-816-5(3)); lib. bdg. 22.60 (978-1-56763-815-8(5)) Ozark Publishing.

Seeley, Bonnie L. Chincoteague Daisy Chain. Lidard, Kelly & Seeley, Douglas A., illus. 2003. 32p. (J). bds. 12.95 (978-0-9728380-0-9(7)) Seelcraft Publishing.

Shepherd, Jodie. Merry Christmas, Rarity! Fletcher, Lyn, illus. 2006. (My Little Pony Ser.). 32p. (J). pap., act. bk. ed. 3.99 (978-0-06-079472-9(0) , Harper Festival) HarperCollins Pubs.

Shire, Poppy. Brightheart the Knight's Pony. Berg, Ron, illus. 2007. (Magic Pony Carousel Ser.: No. 2). 96p. (J). pap. 3.99 (978-0-06-083782-2(9)); 14.99 (978-0-06-083780-8(2)) HarperCollins Pubs. (Harper Trophy).

—Magic Pony Carousel #4: Jewel the Midnight Pony. Berg, Ron, illus. 2008. (Magic Pony Carousel Ser.). 96p. (J). pap. 3.99 (***978-0-06-083788-4(8)*** , Harper Trophy) HarperCollins Pubs.

—Sparkle the Circus Pony. Berg, Ron, illus. 2007. (Magic Pony Carousel Ser.: No. 1). 96p. (J). pap. 3.99 (978-0-06-083779-2(9)); 14.99 (978-0-06-083777-8(2)) HarperCollins Pubs. (Harper Trophy).

Shire, Poppy. Star the Western Pony. Berg, Ron, illus. 2007. (J). (***978-0-06-083783-9(7));*** (Magic Pony Carousel Ser.: No.3). 96p. (gr. 2-5). pap. 3.99 (***978-0-06-083785-3(3)***) HarperCollins Pubs. (Harper Trophy).

Silver Dolphin en Español Staff. Figuras Magicas: Mi Pequeno Pony, Las Maravillosas Estaciones: Magical Magnets: My Little Pony, Sweet Seasons, Spanish-Language Edition. 2006. (Illus.). 8p. (J). bds. 12.95 (978-970-718-359-9(4) , Silver Dolphin en Español) Advanced Marketing, S. de R. L. de C. V. MEX. *Dist:* Perseus Distribution.

—Serie aprendizaje: Mi pequeno pony, dibuja con los Ponys: Learning Series: My Little Pony, Draw with the Ponies, Spanish-Language Edition. 2006. (Illus.). 22p. (J). bds. 16.95 (978-970-718-361-2(6) , Silver Dolphin en Español) Advanced Marketing, S. de R. L. de C. V. MEX. *Dist:* Perseus Distribution.

Simon-Kerr, Julia. Princess Party Paint Book. Edwards, Ken, illus. 2005. (My Little Pony Ser.). 32p. (J). pap. 3.99 (978-0-06-074699-5(8) , Harper Festival) HarperCollins Pubs.

Smith, Donna Campbell. An Independent Spirit: The Tale of Betsy Dowdy & Black Bess. 2006. (Illus.). 182p. (J). per. 11.95 (978-0-9779889-0-7(2)) Faithful Publishing.

Stafford, Liliana. Digger. 2002. 174p. (J). pap. 11.95 (978-1-876268-86-2(7) , Cygnet Bks.) Univ. of Western Australia Pr. AUS. *Dist:* International Specialized Bk. Services.

Stephens, Monique Z. The Easter Bonnet Parade: All Aboard Reading Station Stop 1. S. I. Artists Staff, illus. 2004. (All Aboard Reading Ser.). 32p. (J). (ps-2). mass mkt. 3.99 (978-0-448-43486-5(5) , Grosset & Dunlap) Penguin Group (USA) Inc.

Stewart, Dana. God Made My Pony. Stewart, Jennifer, ed. Haantz, Carol, illus. 1999. (Tall Shape Board Bks.). 10p. (J). (ps-1). bds. 4.99 (978-0-7847-0963-4(7) , 04303, Bean Sprouts) Standard Publishing.

Szymanski, Lois. Sea Feather. 1999. (Illus.). 80p. (J). (gr. 3-7). pap. 3.99 (978-0-380-80566-2(9)) HarperCollins Pubs.

Szymanski, Lois K. Pony Legend. 2008. (Charming Ponies Ser.). 80p. (J). pap. 4.99 (978-0-06-128872-2(1) , Harper Festival) HarperCollins Pubs.

Taylor-Butler, Christine. A Pony to Love. Morgan, Mary, illus. 2005. (Cuddle & Read Ser.). 32p. (ps-ps). 6.95 (978-1-4027-2018-5(1)) Sterling Publishing Co., Inc.

Tirey, Rodney. Coppershoo Saves the Sarge's Saddle! Tirey, Rodney, illus. 2007. (Illus.). 32p. (J). 16.95 (***978-0-9789591-0-4(8)***) MirthMarks Publishing.

Tjornin, Gerta. Ladies & Gentlemen Presenting Gertas B. 2006. pap. 28.00 (***978-1-4259-5915-9(6)***) AuthorHouse.

Tutu el Caballito Volador. 2004. (SPA.). (J). per. (978-0-9744408-6-6(8)) Editorial Busqueda.

Watt, Fiona. That's Not My Pony. 2007. 10p. (J). bds. 7.99 (978-0-7945-1630-7(0) , Usborne) EDC Publishing.

Weber, Lou. My First Library My Little Pony. 2005. 40p. (J). 10.98 (978-1-4127-3566-7(1) , 7265400) Publications International, Ltd.

White, Julie. The Secret Pony. 2005. 140p. (J). (ps-7). pap. 6.95 (978-1-55039-148-0(8)) Sono Nis Pr. CAN. *Dist:* Orca Bk. Pubs. USA.

Zimet, Sara Goodman. Hannah & the Perfect Picture Pony: A Story of the Great Depression. Fuller, Sandy Ferguson, illus. 2005. 24p. (J). lib. bdg. 16.95 (978-0-9645159-2-5(X)) Discovery Pr. Pubns., Inc.

PONY EXPRESS

Brill, Marlene Targ. Bronco Charlie & the Pony Express. Orback, Craig, illus. 2005. (On My Own History Ser.). 48p. (gr. 2-5). lib. bdg. 23.95 (978-1-57505-587-9(2)) Lerner Publishing Group.

—Bronco Charlie & the Pony Express. Orback, Craig, illus. 2004. 46p. (J). (ps-k). lib. bdg. 12.75 (978-0-606-30375-0(8)) Tandem Library Bks.

—Bronco Charlie y el Pony Express. Orback, Craig, illus. 2005. (SPA.). 46p. (J). (ps-k). pap. 5.95 (978-0-8225-3093-0(7)); lib. bdg. 25.26 (978-0-8225-2991-0(2) , Ediciones Lerner) Lerner Publishing Group.

Dolan, Edward F., Jr. The Pony Express. 2002. (Kaleidoscope - American History Ser.). (Illus.). 48p. (J). 25.64 (978-0-7614-1458-2(4) , Benchmark Bks.) Cavendish, Marshall Corp.

Gunderson, Jessica Sarah. Young Riders of the Pony Express. Bascle, Brian, illus. 2006. (Graphic Library). 32p. (J). (978-0-7368-5495-5(9)) Capstone Pr., Inc.

Harness, Cheryl. They're Off! The Story of the Pony Express. Harness, Cheryl, illus. 2002. (Illus.). 32p. (J). (gr. 1 up). pap. 6.99 (978-0-689-85121-6(9) , Aladdin) Simon & Schuster Children's Publishing.

—They're off! the Story of the Pony Express. 2002. (gr. 3-6). lib. bdg. 15.30 (978-0-613-45114-7(7)) Tandem Library Bks.

Hurwitz, Sue. The Pony Express in American History. 1998. (J). (978-0-89490-989-4(4)) Enslow Pubs., Inc.

Isaacs, Sally Senzell. Stagecoaches & the Pony Express. 2004. (Illus.). 32p. (J). pap. 7.50 (978-1-4034-4793-7(4)); lib. bdg. (978-1-4034-2508-9(6)) Heinemann Library.

Kroll, Steven. Pony Express! 2000. (Illus.). 40p. (J). (gr. 4-7). pap. 5.99 (978-0-590-20240-4(5)) Scholastic, Inc.

—Pony Express! 2000. (978-0-606-18589-9(5)) Tandem Library Bks.

Kule, Elaine A. The U. S. Mail. 2002. (Transportation & Communication Ser.). (Illus.). 48p. (J). (gr. 1-4). lib. bdg. 23.93 (978-0-7660-1892-1(X)) Enslow Pubs., Inc.

Landau, Elaine. The Pony Express. 2006. (True Book - Westward Expansion Ser.). (Illus.). 48p. (J). (gr. 3-5). 25.00 (978-0-516-25873-7(7) , Children's Pr.) Scholastic Library Publishing.

Leigh, Autumn. Making History: A Horse Sock Puppet. 2006. (Tony Stead Nonfiction Independent Reading Collection). (J). pap. (978-1-4042-5588-3(5)) Rosen Publishing Group, Inc., The.

Lilly, Melinda. The Pony Express. 2002. (Rourke Discovery Library). (Illus.). 24p. (J). lib. bdg. 20.64 (978-1-58952-364-7(4)) Rourke Publishing, LLC.

McCormick, Anita Louise. The Pony Express in American History. 2001. (In American History Ser.). (Illus.). 104p. (YA). (gr. 5-12). lib. bdg. 26.60 (978-0-7660-1296-7(4)) Enslow Pubs., Inc.

Mercati, Cynthia. The Pony Express. 2000. (Cover-to-Cover Bks.). (Illus.). 56p. (J). pap. (978-0-7891-5041-7(7)); (gr. 1-4). lib. bdg. 16.95 (978-0-7807-9012-4(X)) Perfection Learning Corp.

Ongman, Gudrun. Sleep Pony Dreams. l.t. ed. 2006. (Illus.). 32p. (J). pap. 16.95 (978-0-9677204-2-5(7)) Mindcastle Bks., Inc.

Payment, Simone. The Pony Express. 2005. (Illus.). 64p. (J). (gr. 5-8). lib. bdg. 29.25 (978-1-4042-0181-1(5)) Rosen Publishing Group, Inc., The.

Pierce, Alan. The Pony Express/Alan Pierce. 2005. (American Moments Ser.). (Illus.). 48p. (J). (gr. 4-8). lib. bdg. 25.65 (978-1-59197-938-8(2)) ABDO Publishing Co.

Quasha, Jennifer. The Pony Express: Hands-On Projects about Early Communication. 2001. (Great Social Studies Projects Ser.). (Illus.). 24p. (J). (gr. 3). lib. bdg. 19.95 (978-0-8239-5702-6(0) , PowerKids Pr.) Rosen Publishing Group, Inc., The.

Rau, Margaret. The Mail Must Go Through: The Story of the Pony Express. 2005. (America's Moving Frontier Ser.). (Illus.). 176p. (J). (ps-7). lib. bdg. 26.95 (978-1-931798-63-1(X)) Reynolds, Morgan Inc.

Riddle, John. The Pony Express. 2002. (History of the Old West Ser.). (Illus.). 64p. (YA). (gr. 5 up). lib. bdg. (978-1-59084-061-0(5)) Mason Crest Pubs.

Thompson, Gare. Riding with the Mail: The Story of the Pony Express. 2007. (History Chapters Ser.). 48p. (J). (gr. 1-4). lib. bdg. 17.90 (***978-1-4263-0192-6(8)*** , National Geographic Children's Bks.) National Geographic Society.

Tucker, Mary. History Hands on! Pony Express. Mitchell, Judy, ed. Hierstein, Judith, illus. 2004. 32p. (J). pap. 6.95 (978-1-57310-427-2(2)) Teaching & Learning Co.

Williams, Jean Kinney. The Pony Express. 2002. (We the People Ser.). (Illus.). 48p. (J). (gr. 4 up). lib. bdg. 22.60 (978-0-7565-0301-7(9)) Compass Point Bks.

Yancey, Diane. Life on the Pony Express. 2001. (Way People Live Ser.). (Illus.). 108p. (J). (gr. 7-10). 29.95 (978-1-56006-793-1(4) , LML00902-178131, Lucent Bks.) Thomson Gale.

Young, Jeff C. The Pony Express & Its Death-Defying Mail Carriers. 2006. (Wild History of the American West Ser.). (Illus.). 128p. (J). lib. bdg. 33.27 (978-1-59845-010-1(7) , 1250478, MyReportLinks.com Bks.) Enslow Pubs., Inc.

PONY EXPRESS—FICTION

Bailer, Darice. The Pony Express. Antonishak, Tom, illus. 3rd ed. 2005. (Soundprints' Read-and-Discover Ser.). 48p. (J). (gr. 2-4). pap. 3.95 (978-1-59249-019-6(0) , S2008) Soundprints.

Fuchs, Bernie. Ride Like the Wind: A Tale of the Pony Express. Fuchs, Bernie, illus. 2004. (Illus.). 32p. (J). pap. 16.95 (978-0-439-26645-1(9) , Blue Sky Pr., The) Scholastic, Inc.

Loesch, Joe. The Pony Express. Hutchinson, Cheryl, ed. Cox, Brian T., illus. unabr. ed. 2000. (Backyard Adventure Ser.). 56p. (J). (gr. k-5). reprint ed. 16.95 incl. audio compact disk (978-1-932332-04-9(9)) Toy Box Productions.

McDonald, Brix. Riding on the Wind. 1998. 243p. (YA). (gr. 5-10). pap. 5.95 (978-0-9661306-0-7(X)) Avenue Publishing.

Myers, Stacy Erin. Maremaid: A Pony's Tale. Myers, Stacy Erin, illus. 2000. (Illus.). 32p. (J). (ps-3). pap. 15.95 (978-1-929845-11-8(1)) DeFranco Entertainment.

Potter, Tony. Neigh Neigh Pony. 1998. (J). (978-1-902553-11-5(X)) Grimond.

Sargent, Dave & Sargent, Pat. Jet: (Jet Black) Good Attitude, 30, 36. Lenoir, Jane, illus. 2001. (Saddle Up Ser.: 36). 36p. (J). lib. bdg. 22.60 (978-1-56763-615-4(2)) Ozark Publishing.

Schnetzler, Pattie L. Fast 'n Snappy. Manning, Jane K., tr. Manning, Jane K., illus. 2004. (Carolrhoda Picture Books Ser.). 32p. (J). (gr. k-3). 16.95 (978-1-57505-539-8(2)) Lerner Publishing Group.

Stamper, Judith Bauer. The Pony Express. Lewis, Anthony, illus. 2000. (Scholastic At-Home Phonics Reading Program Ser.: Vol. 54). 24p. (J). (978-0-590-68851-2(0)) Scholastic, Inc.

Tate, Nikki. Jo's Triumph. 2002. (Orca Young Readers Ser.). (Illus.). 160p. (J). (gr. 3-6). pap. 4.99 (978-1-55143-199-4(8)) Orca Bk. Pubs. USA.

—Jo's Triumph. 2002. (gr. 3-6). lib. bdg. 13.00 (978-0-613-86418-3(2)) Tandem Library Bks.

Thomas, Carroll. Riding by Starlight: A Matty Trescott Novel. 2002. (Illus.). ix, 173p. (J). 9.95 (978-1-57525-315-2(1)) Smith and Kraus Publishers, Incorporated.

Wilson, Diane Lee. Black Storm Comin' (J). 2006. 240p. pap. 5.99 (978-0-689-87138-2(4) , Aladdin); 2005. 304p. (gr. 5-9). 17.99 (978-0-689-87137-5(6) , McElderry, Margaret K.) Simon & Schuster Children's Publishing.

POODLES

Dib, Pierre. Guide to Owning a Poodle: AKC Rank #6. 1999. (Popular Dog Library). (Illus.). 64p. (J). (gr. 4-7). 27.50 (978-0-7910-5474-1(8) , Chelsea Hse.) Facts On File, Inc.

Fitzpatrick, Anne. Poodles. 2003. (Dog Breeds Ser.). 24p. (J). lib. bdg. 21.35 (978-1-58340-314-3(0)) Smart Apple Media.

MacAulay, Kelley. Los Caniches o Poodles. 2007. (SPA & ENG.). 32p. (J). (gr. 2-3). (***978-0-7787-8461-6(4)***) Crabtree Publishing Co.

MacAulay, Kelley & Kalman, Bobbie. Los Caniches o Poodles. rev. ed. 2007. (SPA & ENG.). 32p. (J). (gr. 2-3). pap. (***978-0-7787-8483-8(5)***) Crabtree Publishing Co.

MacAulay, Kelley & Kalman, Bobbie. Poodles. 2006. (Pet Care Ser.). (Illus.). 32p. (J). (978-0-7787-1763-8(1) , 1259506) Crabtree Publishing Co.

Stone, Lynn M. Poodles. 2003. (Eye to Eye with Dogs Ser.). (Illus.). 24p. (gr. 2-5). 17.95 (978-1-58952-330-2(X)) Rourke Publishing, LLC.

Trumbauer, Lisa. Poodles. 2006. (Pebble Books). (Illus.). 24p. (J). (978-0-7368-5335-4(9)) Capstone Pr., Inc.

POOH (FICTITIOUS CHARACTER)—FICTION

see Winnie-the-Pooh (Fictitious Character)—Fiction

POPES

Aaseng, Nathan. Pope John Paul II. 2005. (Importance Of Ser.). (Illus.). 112p. (J). (gr. 3-7). lib. bdg. 32.45 (978-1-59018-835-4(7) , Lucent Bks.) Thomson Gale.

Burns, Peggy. Pope John Paul II: Pope for the People. 2000. (Famous Lives Ser.). (Illus.). 48p. (J). (gr. 3-7). lib. bdg. 27.12 (978-0-8172-5714-9(4)) Raintree.

Clarke, Catherine. Our Glorious Popes. 14th ed. 2000. 266p. pap. 12.95 (978-1-930278-02-8(0)) Loreto Pubns.

Daughters of St. Paul Staff. No Place for Defeat. Date not set. (Encounter Ser.). 96p. (J). (gr. 3-9). pap. 2.00 (978-0-8198-5100-0(0)) Pauline Bks. & Media.

Doak, Robin S. Pope Leo X: Opponent of the Reformation. 2006. (Signature Lives Ser.). (Illus.). 112p. (J). (gr. 5-7). 30.60 (978-0-7565-1594-2(7)) Compass Point Bks.

Mainardi, Alessandro. The Life of Pope John Paul II: In Comics! Maresta, Werner, illus. rev. ed. 2006. 96p. (J). (gr. 4-9). 16.95 (978-1-59707-039-3(4)) Papercutz.

Mohan, Claire Jordan. Joseph from Germany: The Life of Pope Benedict XVI for Children. Craig, Charlie, illus. 2007. (J). 8.95 (***978-0-8198-3988-6(4)***) Pauline Bks. & Media.

Parks, Deborah A. John Paul II: The Pope from Poland. 2002. (Gateway Biography Ser.). (Illus.). 48p. (gr. 2-4). lib. bdg. 23.90 (978-0-7613-2320-4(1) , Millbrook Pr.) Lerner Publishing Group.

Stanley, George E. Pope John Paul II: Young Man of the Church. 2005. (Childhood of World Figures Ser.). 176p. (J). pap. 5.99 (978-1-4169-1282-8(7) , Aladdin) Simon & Schuster Children's Publishing.

Stanley, George Edward. Pope John Paul II: Young Man of the Church. 2005. (Childhood of World Figures Ser.). 167p. (J). (978-1-4156-2199-8(3) , Aladdin) Simon & Schuster Children's Publishing.

Wheeler, Jill C. Pope John Paul II. 2003. (Breaking Barriers Ser.). (Illus.). 64p. (J). (gr. 3-8). lib. bdg. 25.65 (978-1-57765-740-8(3)) ABDO Publishing Co.

Wilson, M. Leonora. Karol from Poland: The Life of Pope John Paul II for Children. Koch, Carla, illus. rev. ed. 2006. 38p. (J). pap. 7.95 (978-0-8198-4209-1(5)) Pauline Bks. & Media.

Wilson, Mary L. Karol from Poland: The Life of Pope John Paul II for Children. Koch, Carla, illus. 2000. 40p. (J). (gr. 1-4). pap. 6.95 (978-0-8198-4205-3(2) , 332-160) Pauline Bks. & Media.

POPPLETON (FICTITIOUS CHARACTER)—FICTION

Rylant, Cynthia. Poppleton & Friends. Teague, Mark, illus. 1998. (Poppleton Ser.). 56p. (J). (gr. k-3). pap. 3.99 (978-0-590-84788-9(0) , Blue Sky Pr., The) Scholastic, Inc.

—Poppleton & Friends. 1998. (Poppleton Ser.). (J). (gr. k-3). (978-0-606-13716-4(5)) Tandem Library Bks.

—Poppleton Display. 1999. (J). 95.76 (978-0-439-05990-9(9)) Scholastic, Inc.

—Poppleton Everyday. Teague, Mark, illus. 1998. (Poppleton Ser.). (J). (gr. k-3). 48p. pap. 15.95 (978-0-590-84845-9(3) , Blue Sky Pr., The); 56p. pap. 3.99 (978-0-590-84853-4(4)) Scholastic, Inc.

—Poppleton Everyday. 1998. (Poppleton Ser.). (J). (gr. k-3). (978-0-606-13717-1(3)) Tandem Library Bks.

—Poppleton Forever. Teague, Mark, illus. 1998. (Poppleton Ser.). 56p. (J). (gr. k-3). pap. 14.95 (978-0-590-84843-5(7) , Blue Sky Pr., The); pap. 3.99 (978-0-590-84844-2(5)) Scholastic, Inc.

—Poppleton Forever. 1998. (Poppleton Ser.). (J). (gr. k-3). (978-0-606-13718-8(1)) Tandem Library Bks.

—Poppleton Forever. Teague, Mark, illus. 1998. (Poppleton Ser.). 48p. (J). (ps). lib. bdg. 11.80 (978-0-613-11990-0(8)) Tandem Library Bks.

—Poppleton Has Fun. Teague, Mark, illus. 2000. (Poppleton Ser.). 56p. (J). (gr. k-3). pap. 15.95 (978-0-590-84839-8(9)) Scholastic, Inc.

—Poppleton in Fall. Teague, Mark, illus. 1999. (Poppleton Ser.). 56p. (J). (gr. k-3). pap. 14.95 (978-0-590-84789-6(9) , Blue Sky Pr., The) Scholastic, Inc.

—Poppleton in Fall. 1999. (Poppleton Ser.). (J). (gr. k-3). (978-0-606-17273-8(4)) Tandem Library Bks.

—Poppleton in Spring. Teague, Mark, illus. 1999. (Poppleton Ser.). 48p. (J). (ps-2). pap. 15.95 (978-0-590-84818-3(6) , Blue Sky Pr., The) Scholastic, Inc.

—Poppleton in Spring. 1999. (Poppleton Ser.). (J). (gr. k-3). (978-0-606-16594-5(0)) Tandem Library Bks.

—Poppleton in Winter. Teague, Mark, illus. 2001. (Poppleton Ser.). 58p. (J). (ps-2). pap. 15.95 (978-0-590-84837-4(2) , Blue Sky Pr., The) Scholastic, Inc.

—Poppleton in Winter. 2001. (Poppleton Ser.). (978-0-606-22154-2(9)) Tandem Library Bks.

POPPINS, MARY (FICTITIOUS CHARACTER)—FICTION

Travers, P. L. Mary Poppins & Mary Poppins Comes Back. Shepard, Mary, illus. 2007. 368p. (J). 19.95 (978-0-15-205922-4(9)) Harcourt Children's Bks.

—Mary Poppins in the Kitchen: A Cookery Book with a Story. Shepard, Mary, illus. 2006. 88p. (J). 14.00 (978-0-15-206080-0(4)) Harcourt Children's Bks.

Travers, Pamela L. Mary Poppins. 202p. (J). (gr. 3-5). pap. 6.00 (978-0-8072-1536-4(8)); 1999. (gr. 4-7). pap. 36.00 incl. audio (978-0-8072-8082-9(8) , YA997SP) Random Hse. Audio Publishing Group. (Listening Library).

POPULAR GOVERNMENT

see Democracy

POPULAR MUSIC

Andersen, Neil. Music Madness: Questioning Music & Music Videos. 2007. (Fact Finders Ser.). (Illus.). 32p. (J). (978-0-7368-6765-8(1) , 1264911, Fact Finders) Capstone Pr., Inc.

Andersen, Neil. Music Madness: Questioning Music & Music Videos. 2007. (Fact Finders Ser.). (Illus.). 32p. (J). (***978-0-7368-7861-6(0)*** , 1264911) Capstone Pr., Inc.

Armstrong, Jennifer. What a Song Can Do: 12 Riffs on the Power of Music. 2004. 208p. (J). (gr. 5). lib. bdg. 17.99 (978-0-375-92499-6(X) , Knopf Bks. for Young Readers) Random Hse. Children's Bks.

Aronson, Virginia. The History of Motown. (African American Achievers Ser.). (Illus.). 2001. 112p. (gr. 6-12). 30.00 (978-0-7910-5814-5(X)); 2000. 111p. (J). pap. 9.95 (978-0-7910-5815-2(8)) Facts On File, Inc. (Chelsea Hse.).

Brackett, David. Interpreting Popular Music. 2000. (Illus.). 275p. pap. 21.95 (978-0-520-22541-1(4)) Univ. of California Pr.

Brasch, Nicolas. Pop & Rock Music. 2004. (J). lib. bdg. 27.10 (978-1-58340-546-8(1)) Smart Apple Media.

Dunleavy, Deborah. The Jumbo Book of Music. Phillips, Louise, illus. 2004. (Jumbo Bks.). 208p. (J). (gr. 4-6). (978-1-55074-723-2(1)) Kids Can Pr., Ltd.

Giese, Gayle. Pop Music Play with CD. 1999. 44p. (J). (ps-2). 19.95 incl. audio compact disk (978-0-7692-8421-7(3) , Warner Bros. Pubns.) Alfred Publishing Co., Inc.

Goldsmith, Lynn, photos by. Paul Simon: You're the One. 2004. 76p. 19.95 (978-0-8256-3321-8(4) , PS11500) Music Sales Corp.

Gordon, Keith A., ed. Alt. Culture. Guide: The Journal of (un)Popular Culture. 2003. (Illus.). 148p. (YA). per. 10.00 (978-0-9720455-0-6(3) , Anthem Publishing) Gordon, Rev. Keith A.

Granados, Christine. Christina Aguilera. 2000. (Real Life Reader Biography Ser.). (Illus.). 32p. (J). (gr. 3-8). lib. bdg. 15.95 (978-1-58415-044-2(0)) Mitchell Lane Pubs., Inc.

Hal Leonard Corp., creator. Disney Movie Hits: Tenor Sax. 2003. 19p. pap. 12.95 incl. audio compact disk (978-0-634-04383-3(8) , 0634043838) Leonard, Hal Corp.

—Patriotic Favorites. 2002. (Recorder Fun! Ser.). (Illus.). 16p. (J). pap. 9.95 (978-0-634-04427-4(3) , 0634044273) Leonard, Hal Corp.

Hapka, Catherine. Always Dreamin' 2004. (Star Power Ser.: Vol. 02). (Illus.). 160p. (J). pap. 4.99 (978-0-689-86788-0(3) , Aladdin) Simon & Schuster Children's Publishing.

—Blast from the Past. 2004. (Star Power Ser.: No. 5). 160p. (J). pap. 4.99 (978-0-689-86791-0(3) , Aladdin) Simon & Schuster Children's Publishing.

Hurley, Joe. Music Mania! 2001. (Celebrity Quiz O-Rama Ser.: No. 2). (Illus.). 104p. (J). (gr. 2-6). pap. 3.99 (978-0-439-24409-1(9)) Scholastic, Inc.

Jaques-Dalcroze, Emile. The Eurhythmics. 2001. 64p. (YA). reprint ed. 88.00 (978-0-7222-5810-1(0)) Library Reprints, Inc.

Joseph, Paul. Christina Aguilera. 2000. (Young Profiles Ser.). (Illus.). 32p. (J). (gr. k-6). lib. bdg. 22.78 (978-1-57765-431-5(5) , Checkerboard Library) ABDO Publishing Co.

Kirgiss, Crystal. Folk Music. 2001. (World of Music Ser.). (Illus.). 32p. (J). (gr. 2-7). lib. bdg. 22.60 (978-1-58340-044-9(3)) Smart Apple Media.

Morgan, Sally & Laler, Pauline. Music. 2001. (Behind Media Ser.). (Illus.). 48p. (YA). (gr. 6-8). lib. bdg. 24.22 (978-1-58810-030-6(8)) Heinemann Library.

N Sync: Backstage Pass. 1999. (gr. 3-6). lib. bdg. 14.15 (978-0-613-16983-7(2)) Tandem Library Bks.

Raffi. Everything Grows. 2004. (Illus.). 32p. 15.95 incl. audio compact disk (978-1-57940-097-2(3)) Rounder Bks.

Rauf, Don, et al. Virtual Apprentice: Pop Musician. 2007. (Virtual Apprentice Ser.). 64p. (J). (gr. 6-12). 29.95 (978-0-8160-6752-7(X) , Ferguson Publishing Co.) Facts On File, Inc.

Rodgers, Richard & Hammerstein, Oscar, II. Getting to Know You! Rodgers & Hammerstein Favorites. Wells, Rosemary, illus. 2002. 64p. (J). (ps-3). 20.89 (978-0-06-623845-6(5)) HarperCollins Pubs.

Scholastic, Inc. Staff. Rockin' Your World! 'N Sync. 1999. (Rockin' Your World Ser.). (Illus.). 44p. (J). (gr. 3-7). pap. 4.99 (978-0-439-13549-8(4)) Scholastic, Inc.

Small, Doug. The Story of Good Charlotte. 2004. (Illus.). 96p. pap. 12.95 (978-0-8256-2871-9(7) , OP50061) Omnibus Pr.

The Star Spangled Banner. 2004. pap. 38.75 incl. audio compact disk (978-1-55592-644-1(4)); pap. 14.95 incl. audio (978-0-7882-0310-7(X)) Weston Woods Studios, Inc.

The Star-Spangled Banner. 2004. 24.95 incl. audio (978-0-7882-0563-7(3)); pap. 32.75 incl. audio (978-1-55592-625-0(8)) Weston Woods Studios, Inc.

Talmadge, Morgan. Christina Aguilera. 2001. (Celebrity Bios Ser.). (Illus.). 48p. (J). (gr. 7-12). 23.00 (978-0-516-23422-9(6) , Children's Pr.) Scholastic Library Publishing.

—Usher. 2001. (gr. 7-12). lib. bdg. 15.25 (978-0-613-52213-7(3)) Tandem Library Bks.

Trier, George. Music of Heartohopia. 2003. (Illus.). 240p. (YA). (gr. 2 up). per. 19.95 (978-0-9725184-0-6(1)) Heartohopia Pr.

Unbeaten Tracks: 8 Contemporary Pieces for Trumpet & Piano. 2002. 48p. (J). (gr. 4-7). 10.95 (978-0-571-52005-3(7)) Faber & Faber, Ltd. GBR. *Dist:* Leonard, Hal Corp.

Vernon, Roland. Gershwin: Introducing. 2000. (Introducing Composers Ser.). (Illus.). 32p. (J). (gr. 4-7). 21.95 (978-0-7910-6040-7(3) , Chelsea Hse.) Facts On File, Inc.

POPULAR MUSIC—BIOGRAPHY

Obsessed with the Backstreet Boys, Vol. 2. 2001. 96p. (YA). pap. 9.95 (978-1-931497-44-2(3)) 17th Street Productions, An Alloy Online Inc. Co.

Zymet, Cathy Alter. Backstreet Boys. 1999. (Galaxy of Superstars Ser.). (Illus.). 64p. (J). pap. 8.95 (978-0-7910-5504-5(3)); 25.00 (978-0-7910-5503-8(5)) Facts On File, Inc. (Chelsea Hse.).

POPULAR MUSIC—FICTION

Anonymous. Confessions of a Backup Dancer. l.t. ed. 2005. 360p. (YA). (gr. 8-12). per. 20.95 (978-0-7862-7881-7(1) , Large Print Pr.) Thorndike Pr.

Chotjewitz, David & Orgel, Doris. Crazy Diamond. 2008. 272p. (YA). 17.99 (*978-1-4169-1176-0(6)) Simon & Schuster Children's Publishing.

Disney Press Staff & Alfonsi, Alice. Face-Off. 2nd rev. ed. 2006. (Hannah Montana Ser.: No. 2). 128p. (gr. 3-7). pap. 4.99 (978-1-4231-0222-9(3)) Disney Pr.

Disney Press Staff & Beechwood, Beth. Keeping Secrets. 2006. (Hannah Montana Ser.: No. 1). 128p. (gr. 3-7). pap. 4.99 (978-1-4231-0221-2(5)) Disney Pr.

Disney Press Staff & McElroy, Laurie. Super Sneak. 3rd rev. ed. 2006. (Hannah Montana Ser.: No. 3). 128p. (gr. 3-7). pap. 4.99 (978-1-4231-0276-2(2)) Disney Pr.

Hapka, Catherine. Over the Top. 2005. (Star Power Ser.). 144p. (J). pap. 4.99 (978-0-689-87669-1(6) , Aladdin) Simon & Schuster Children's Publishing.

Harmel, Kristin. When You Wish. 2008. 288p. (J). (*978-0-385-73475-2(1) , Delacorte Pr.) Dell Publishing.

Rayban, Chloe. Hollywood Bliss: My Life Starring Mum. 2007. 304p. (J). pap. 7.95 (*978-1-59990-097-1(1) , Bloomsbury Children) Bloomsbury Publishing.

Rayban, Chloe. My Life Starring Mum. 2006. 250p. (J). 16.95 (978-1-58234-713-4(1) , Bloomsbury Children) Bloomsbury Publishing.

Shaw, Deirdre. Fair Play. 2005. (American Dreams Ser.). 176p. (YA). mass mkt. 5.99 (978-0-689-87850-3(8) , Simon Spotlight Entertainment) Simon & Schuster.

Tanemura, Arina. Full Moon, Vol. 4. 2005. (Full Moon o Sagashite Ser.). (Illus.). 192p. (YA). pap. 8.99 (978-1-4215-0125-3(2)) Viz Media.

POPULARITY

Birtles, Jasmine. A Celebrity's Little Instruction Book. 2003. (Illus.). 128p. pap. 8.99 (978-0-7522-6152-2(5) , Boxtree) Pan Macmillan GBR. *Dist:* Trafalgar Square Publishing.

Harcourt School Publishers Staff. How to Be Popular On Level. 3rd ed. 2002. (Trophies Reading Program Ser.). (Illus.). pap. 5.10 (978-0-15-323435-4(0)) Harcourt Schl. Pubs.

Kemp, Kristen. How to Become Popular Without Losing Your Mind. 2002. (Genny in a Bottle Ser.: No. 1). (Illus.). 160p. (J). (gr. 3-7). pap. 4.50 (978-0-439-21178-9(6) , Scholastic Paperbacks) Scholastic, Inc.

Sheridan, Susan M. Why Don't They Like Me? Helping Your Child Make & Keep Friends. Gebhordt, Suzanne, illus. 1998. 150p. (J). (gr. k-6). pap. 18.50 (978-1-57035-124-2(4) , 25LIKEME) Sopris West Educational Services.

POPULARITY—FICTION

Atkinson, Beth. From Alice to Zen & Everyone in Between: A Novel. 2008. (Exceptional Reading & Language Arts Titles for Intermediate Grades Ser.). (J). 15.95 (*978-0-8225-7271-8(0) , Carolrhoda Bks.) Lerner Publishing Group.

Bateman, Anya. The Makeover of James Orville Wickenbee. 2007. 262p. (J). pap. (*978-1-59038-707-8(4)) Deseret Bk. Co.

Bodi, Sari. The Ghost in Allie's Pool. 2007. 192p. (YA). (gr. 5 up). pap. 8.95 (*978-0-9768126-6-1(5)) Brown Barn Bks.

Breen, Steve. Violet the Pilot. 2008. 32p. (J). (ps). 16.99 (*978-0-8037-3125-7(6) , Dial) Penguin Group (USA) Inc.

Brooks, Jillian. The Makeover. 2003. 157p. (J). (978-0-439-35494-3(3)) Scholastic, Inc.

Cabot, Meg. How to Be Popular. 2008. 320p. (J). pap. 8.99 (*978-0-06-088014-9(7)); 2006. 304p. (J). lib. bdg. 17.89 (978-0-06-088013-2(9)); 2006. 304p. (YA). 16.99 (978-0-06-088012-5(0)) HarperCollins Pubs. (HarperTeen).

Carey, Elizabeth Doyle. Keeping Cool. 3rd ed. 2006. (Callahan Cousins Ser.). (Illus.). 226p. (J). (gr. 3-7). 10.99 (978-0-316-73693-0(7)) Little Brown & Co.

Choldenko, Gennifer. If a Tree Falls at Lunch Period. 2007. (Illus.). 224p. (J). (gr. 5 up). 17.00 (*978-0-15-205753-4(6)) Harcourt Trade Pubs.

Deriso, Christine Hurley. Do-Over. 2006. 192p. (J). (gr. 4-7). 15.95 (978-0-385-73333-5(X)); lib. bdg. 17.99 (978-0-385-90350-9(2)) Random Hse. Children's Bks. (Delacorte Bks. for Young Readers).

Deriso, Christine Hurley. Do-over. 2007. 160p. (J). (gr. 4-7). 5.99 (*978-0-440-42119-1(5) , Yearling) Random Hse. Children's Bks.

Friend, Natasha. Bounce. 2007. 192p. (YA). (gr. 6-8). pap. 16.99 (*978-0-439-85350-7(8) , Scholastic Pr.) Scholastic, Inc.

Frost, Helen. Diamond Willow. 2008. 128p. (J). 16.00 (*978-0-374-31776-8(3)) Farrar, Straus & Giroux.

Garfinkle, D. L. Stuck in the 70's. 2007. 192p. (YA). (gr. 7 up). 16.99 (978-0-399-24663-0(0) , Putnam Juvenile) Penguin Group (USA) Inc.

Giles, Gail. Shattering Glass. 2004. 215p. (J). (gr. 7 up). pap. 37.00 incl. audio (978-1-4000-9013-6(X) , Listening Library) Random Hse. Audio Publishing Group.

—Shattering Glass. rev. ed. 2002. (Single Titles Ser.: 12). 224p. (YA). (gr. 7 up). 17.95 (978-0-7613-1581-0(0)) Roaring Brook Pr.

—Shattering Glass. 2003. 224p. (YA). pap. 7.99 (978-0-689-85800-0(0) , Simon Pulse) Simon & Schuster Children's Publishing.

—Shattering Glass. 2003. (gr. 7-12). lib. bdg. 15.30 (978-0-613-73394-6(0)) Tandem Library Bks.

Gonzalez, Gabriela & Triana, Gaby. Backstage Pass. 2004. (Illus.). 224p. (J). (gr. 7 up). lib. bdg. 16.89 (978-0-06-056018-8(5)) HarperCollins Pubs.

Gorman, Carol. Dork in Disguise. 2000. (J). 12.64 (978-0-606-20049-3(5)) Tandem Library Bks.

—Dork on the Run. 192p. (J). 2003. (Illus.). pap. 5.99 (978-0-06-440970-4(8) , Harper Trophy); 2002. (gr. 3-6). 15.99 (978-0-06-029409-0(4)) HarperCollins Pubs.

—Dork on the Run. 2003. (gr. 3-6). lib. bdg. 14.15 (978-0-613-61371-2(6)) Tandem Library Bks.

—A Midsummer Night's Dork. 224p. (J). 2006. (Illus.). pap. 5.99 (978-0-06-050720-6(9) , Harper Trophy); 2004. 15.99 (978-0-06-050718-3(7)); 2004. lib. bdg. 16.89 (978-0-06-050719-0(5)) HarperCollins Pubs.

Green, Jessica. Diary of a Would-Be Princess: The Journal of Jillian James, 5B. 2007. (Illus.). 236p. (J). (gr. 4-7). 15.95 (978-1-58089-166-0(7)) Charlesbridge Publishing, Inc.

Gunn, Robin Jones. Summer Promise. rev. ed. 1998. (Christy Miller Ser.: Bk. 1). 176p. (J). (gr. 7-12). pap. 6.99 (978-1-56179-597-0(6)) Bethany Hse. Pubs.

Jones, Jasmine. Best Dressed. 2004. 138p. (J). lib. bdg. 16.92 (*978-1-4242-0678-0(2)) Fitzgerald Bks.

Jones, Jasmine. Picture This! 2003. (gr. 3-6). lib. bdg. 13.00 (978-0-613-68277-0(7)) Tandem Library Bks.

Krulik, Nancy E. Boys, Boys, Boys. 2000. (gr. 5-8). lib. bdg. 13.00 (978-0-613-31021-5(7)) Tandem Library Bks.

Lane, Dakota. The Secret Life of It Girls. 2007. 128p. (YA). (gr. 9 up). 14.99 (*978-1-4169-1492-1(7)) Simon & Schuster Children's Publishing.

Larsen, Kirsten. Rise & Fall of the Kate Empire. 2002. (gr. 3-6). lib. bdg. 13.00 (978-0-613-68282-4(3)) Tandem Library Bks.

Levine, Gail Carson. The Wish. 2005. 256p. (J). (gr. 7 up). pap. 6.50 (978-0-06-075911-7(9) , Harper Trophy) HarperCollins Pubs.

—The Wish. 2001. (gr. 3-6). lib. bdg. 14.15 (978-0-613-44274-9(1)); 2000. (978-0-606-22297-6(9)) Tandem Library Bks.

Mackall, Dandi Daley. Upsetting Annie. 2007. (Faithgirlz!#8482; / Blog On! Ser.). 128p. (J). pap. 6.99 (978-0-310-71264-0(5)) Zonderkidz.

MacPhail, Catherine. Get That Ghost to Go! Donnelly, Karen, illus. 2006. (Pathway Books). 83p. (J). 21.26 (978-1-59889-004-4(2)) Stone Arch Bks.

McCourt, Lisa & Grant-Porter, Pat. Della Splatnuk, Birthday Girl. 1999. (Chicken Soup for Little Souls Ser.). (Illus.). 32p. (J). (gr. 4-7). tchr. ed. 14.95 (978-1-55874-600-8(5)) Health Communications, Inc.

McNish, Cliff. Angel. 2008. (Exceptional Reading & Language Arts Titles for Upper Grades Ser.). (J). 16.95 (*978-0-8225-8900-6(1) , Carolrhoda Bks.) Lerner Publishing Group.

Mead, Alice & Weber James, Alice. Madame Squidley & Beanie. 2004. 144p. (J). 16.00 (978-0-374-34688-1(7) , Farrar, Straus & Giroux (BYR)) Farrar, Straus & Giroux.

Mechling, Lauren, et al. The Rise & Fall of a 10th Grade Social Climber. 2005. 304p. (YA). (gr. 7). pap. 7.99 (978-0-618-55519-2(6) , Graphia) Houghton Mifflin Co. Trade & Reference Div.

Mills, Claudia. Lizzie at Last. 2002. 152p. (J). (gr. 4-7). lib. bdg. 14.15 (978-0-613-50150-7(0)) Tandem Library Bks.

—Lizzie Mcguire at Last. 2002. 160p. (gr. 3-7). pap. 5.99 (978-0-7868-1672-9(4)) Hyperion Paperbacks for Children.

Minter, J. Inside Girl: A Novel. 2007. (Insiders Novel Ser.). 240p. (YA). (gr. 7 up). pap. 8.95 (*978-1-59990-086-5(6)) Bloomsbury Publishing.

Myers, Anna. Wart. 2007. 224p. (J). (gr. 5-9). 16.95 (*978-0-8027-8977-8(3)) Walker & Co.

Myers, Bill. My Life As a Busted-Up Basketball Backboard, Vol. 18. 2000. (Incredible Worlds of Wally McDoogle Ser.: No. 18). 128p. (J). (gr. 3-7). pap. 6.99 (978-0-8499-4027-9(3)) Nelson, Thomas Inc.

Myracle, Lauren. Rhymes with Witches. (YA). (gr. 8-17). 2006. 272p. pap. 6.95 (978-0-8109-9215-3(9)); 2005. 224p. 16.95 (978-0-8109-5859-3(7) , Amulet Bks.) Abrams, Harry N. , Inc.

Nigro, D. M. The Wolfman, the Shrink & the Eighth-Grade Election. 2006. 116p. (J). pap. 13.50 (978-1-931201-66-7(8)) Twilight Times Bks.

O'Connor, Barbara. Fame & Glory in Freedom, Georgia. 2003. 112p. (J). 16.00 (978-0-374-32258-8(9) , Farrar, Straus & Giroux (BYR)) Farrar, Straus & Giroux.

Plank, Alex & Plank, Lisa. How Bad Could It Be? 2007. (ENG.). 64p. per. 12.95 (*978-1-4241-6217-8(3)) PublishAmerica, Inc.

Preble, Laura. The Queen Geek Social Club. 2006. 336p. (YA). (gr. 12). pap. 9.99 (978-0-425-21164-9(9) , Berkley Trade) Penguin Group (USA) Inc.

Robbins, Jacqui. Two of a Kind. Phelan, Matt, illus. 2008. (J). (*978-1-4169-2437-1(X)) Simon & Schuster Children's Publishing.

Sachar, Louis. Why Pick on Me? 1999. (Marvin Redpost Ser.: Bk. 2). (J). (gr. k-3). lib. bdg. 11.80 (978-0-7857-0343-3(8)) Tandem Library Bks.

Scott, Kieran. I Was a Non-Blonde Cheerleader. 2007. 272p. (YA). (gr. 7). 7.99 (*978-0-14-240910-7(3) , Puffin); 2006. 272p. (YA). (gr. 7). pap. 6.99 (978-0-14-240641-0(4) , Puffin); 2005. 256p. (J). 15.99 (978-0-399-24279-3(1) , Putnam Juvenile) Penguin Group (USA) Inc.

Scott, Kieran. I was a Non Blonde Cheerleader (Splashproof Edition) 2007. 1p. (J). (gr. 7). pap. 6.99 (978-0-14-240832-2(8) , Puffin) Penguin Group (USA) Inc.

Segal, Zoe. Confessions of a Tenth-Grade Social Climber. 2005. 290p. (YA). (978-0-618-44981-1(7)) Houghton Mifflin Co.

Shannon, David. A Bad Case of Stripes. (J). 2007. 9.95 (978-0-439-92494-8(4)); 1998. (Illus.). 32p. pap. 16.95 (978-0-590-92997-4(6) , Blue Sky Pr., The) Scholastic, Inc.

Shannon, David. Bad Case of Stripes - Library Edition. 2007. (J). 18.95 (*978-0-439-02328-3(9)) Scholastic, Inc.

Shreve, Susan Richards. Kiss Me Tomorrow. 2007. 224p. (YA). (gr. 5-8). pap. 5.99 (978-0-439-68048-6(4)); 2006. 220p. (J). (*978-1-4156-5592-4(8)) Scholastic, Inc. (Levine, Arthur A. Bks.).

Slater, David Michael. Comin' Through. Rooney, Ronnie, illus. 2007. (Missy Swiss & More Ser.). 32p. (J). (ps-4). lib. bdg. 27.07 (*978-1-60270-008-6(7) , Looking Glass Library) Magic Wagon.

Smith, Stephen & Caldwell, Lise. Downhill Challenge. 2006. (Game on for Girls Ser.). 128p. (J). pap. 5.99 (978-0-7847-1735-6(4) , 42145) Standard Publishing.

Sones, Sonya. What My Girlfriend Doesn't Know. 2007. 304p. (YA). (gr. 7 up). 16.99 (978-0-689-87602-8(5)) Simon & Schuster Children's Publishing.

Spinelli, Jerry. Star Girl. 2000. 192p. (J). (gr. 5-8). 15.95 (978-0-679-88637-2(0) , Knopf Bks. for Young Readers) Random Hse. Children's Bks.

—Stargirl. 2002. (EMC Masterpiece Series Access Editions). xiv, 199p. (YA). 10.95 (978-0-8219-2504-1(0) , 35378) EMC/Paradigm Publishing.

—Stargirl. unabr. ed. 2004. 192p. (J). (gr. 7 up). pap. 40.00 incl. audio (978-0-8072-0855-7(8) , LYA 323 SP, Listening Library) Random Hse. Audio Publishing Group.

—Stargirl. (YA). 2004. 208p. (gr. 5). mass mkt. 6.99 (978-0-440-41677-7(9) , Laurel Leaf); 2000. 192p. (gr. 5-8). lib. bdg. 17.99 (978-0-679-98637-9(5) , Knopf Bks. for Young Readers); 2002. 208p. (gr. 7 up). reprint ed. pap. 8.95 (978-0-375-82233-9(X) , Knopf Bks. for Young Readers) Random Hse. Children's Bks.

—Stargirl. Tino, illus. (SPA.). 224p. (J). (gr. 5-8). pap. 9.95 (978-1-59437-815-7(0)) Santillana USA Publishing Co., Inc.

—Stargirl. 2002. (gr. 7-12). lib. bdg. 17.60 (978-0-613-49417-5(2)) Tandem Library Bks.

—Stargirl. l.t. ed. 2001. 240p. (J). (gr. 8-12). 24.95 (978-0-7862-3218-5(8)) Thorndike Pr.

Standish, Burt L. Frank Merriwell's Fame. Rudman, Jack, ed. 2003. (Frank Merriwell Ser.). 29.95 (978-0-8373-9336-0(1)); pap. 9.95 (978-0-8373-9036-9(2)) Merriwell, Frank Inc.

Stone, Phoebe. Deep down Popular. 2008. (J). 288p. pap. 16.99 (*978-0-439-80245-1(8)); (*978-0-439-80244-4(X)) Scholastic, Inc. (Levine, Arthur A. Bks.).

Velde, Vivian Vande. Remembering Raquel. 2007. (Illus.). 160p. (YA). (gr. 7 up). 16.00 (*978-0-15-205976-7(8)) Harcourt Trade Pubs.

Voigt, Cynthia. It's Not Easy Being Bad. Tauss, Marc, illus. 2000. (Bad Girls Ser.). 256p. (J). (gr. 4-7). 16.00 (978-0-689-82473-9(4) , Atheneum/Anne Schwartz Bks.) Simon & Schuster Children's Publishing.

Walde, Christine. The Candy Darlings. 2006. 320p. (YA). (gr. 10). pap. 8.99 (978-0-618-58969-2(4) , Graphia) Houghton Mifflin Co. Trade & Reference Div.

Yoo, David. Girls for Breakfast. 304p. (YA). (gr. 9). 2005. 15.95 (978-0-385-73192-8(2) , Delacorte Bks. for Young Readers); 2005. lib. bdg. 17.99 (978-0-385-90227-4(1) , Delacorte Bks. for Young Readers); 2006. reprint ed. pap. 5.99 (978-0-440-23883-6(8) , Laurel Leaf) Random Hse. Children's Bks.

POPULATION

see also Birth Control; Migration, Internal

also names of countries, cities, etc. with the subdivision Population, e.g. United States—Population

Bowden, Rob. An Overcrowded World? Our Impact on the Planet. 2002. (Twenty-First Century Debates Ser.). (Illus.). 64p. (YA). (gr. 6-8). lib. bdg. 27.12 (978-0-7398-4872-2(0)) Raintree.

Hohm, Charles F. Population. 2000. (Opposing Viewpoints Ser.). (Illus.). 224p. (YA). (gr. 10-12). pap. 21.20 (978-0-7377-0291-0(5) , Greenhaven Pr., Inc.) Thomson Gale.

—Population: Opposing Viewpoints. 2000. (Opposing Viewpoints Ser.). (Illus.). 224p. (YA). 32.45 (978-0-7377-0292-7(3) , Greenhaven Pr., Inc.) Thomson Gale.

Holt, Rinehart and Winston Staff. Holt Science & Technology Chptr. 3: Population Changes over Time: Chapter Resources - Tennessee Edition. 3rd ed. 2003. (J). pap. 11.40 (978-0-03-069108-9(7)) Holt, Rinehart & Winston.

Jakab, Cheryl. Overpopulation. 2007. (J). (*978-1-59920-127-6(5)) Smart Apple Media.

Kent, Deborah. The Changing Face of America: Hispanic Roots, Hispanic Pride. 2004. (Proud Heritage: the Hispanic Library Ser.). (Illus.). 40p. (J). (gr. 3-7). 28.50 (978-1-59296-143-6(6)) Child's World, Inc.

Mason, Paul. Population. 2005. (Planet under Pressure Ser.). (Illus.). 48p. (J). lib. bdg. 31.43 (978-1-4034-7741-5(8)) Heinemann Library.

Peterson, Virginia, et al, eds. Population: Our Growing Planet. rev. ed. 1999. (Information Plus Compact Ser.). (Illus.). 80p. (YA). pap. 28.00 (978-1-57302-104-3(0) , GML00502-172336) Thomson Gale.

Smith, David J. If the World Were a Village: A Book about the World's People. Armstrong, Shelagh, illus. 2004. 32p. (J). (gr. 4-6). (978-1-55074-779-9(7)) Kids Can Pr., Ltd.

Steele, Philip. Population Growth. 2005. (Earth's Changing Landscape Ser.). (Illus.). 46p. (J). lib. bdg. (978-1-58340-480-5(5)) Smart Apple Media.

World Book, Inc. Staff, ed. World Book Special Census Edition. 1 vols. 2001. (Illus.). 160p. (J). (978-0-7166-1294-0(1)) World Bk., Inc.

Zeaman, John. Overpopulation. 2002. (Single Title - Science Ser.). (Illus.). 128p. (YA). (gr. 9-12). 26.00 (978-0-531-11893-1(2) , Watts, Franklin) Scholastic Library Publishing.

POPULATION, FOREIGN

see Emigration and Immigration

POTTER, HARRY (FICTITIOUS CHARACTER)—FICTION

Beahm, George. Fact, Fiction, & Folklore in Harry Potter's World: An Unofficial Guide. Kirk, Tim & McDaniel, Britton, illus. 2005. 256p. (J). (gr. k-10). pap. 16.95 (978-1-57174-440-1(1)) Hampton Roads Publishing Co., Inc.

Bova, Louise. Harry Potter & the Sorcerer's Stone: Stationery Kit. 2000. (Illus.). (J). (gr. 1-5). 10.95 (978-0-439-23658-4(4)) Scholastic, Inc.

Colbert, David. The Hidden Myths in Harry Potter: Spellbinding Map & Book of Secrets. 2005. (Illus.). 32p. (J). (ps-7). 9.95 (978-0-312-34050-6(8) , St. Martin's Griffin) St. Martin's Pr.

—Los Mundos Magicos de Harry Potter: Mitos, Leyendas y Datos Fascinantes. Belaustegui, Ines et al, trs. 2005. (Escritura desatada Ser.). (SPA., Illus.). 232p. (J). (gr. 4-7). 17.95 (978-84-666-1034-6(0)) Ediciones B ESP. *Dist:* Independent Pubs. Group.

Fiona, Simpson, ed. Harry Potter & the Goblet of Fire: Book of Creatures, Create & Trace. 2005. (Harry Potter Ser.). (Illus.). 32p. (J). (gr. 2-5). pap. 3.99 (978-0-439-63296-6(X) , Levine, Arthur A. Bks.) Scholastic, Inc.

—Harry Potter & the Goblet of Fire: Coloring Book. 2005. (Harry Potter Ser.). (Illus.). 48p. (J). (gr. 2-5). pap. 3.99 (978-0-439-63295-9(1) , Levine, Arthur A. Bks.) Scholastic, Inc.

Frankel, Valerie. Henry Potty & the Pet Rock: An Unauthorized Harry Potter Parody. 2006. 112p. (J). pap. 8.99 (978-1-59594-088-9(X) , Wingspan Pr.) WingSpan Publishing.

Harry Potter & the Chamber of Secrets. 2002. (Harry Potter Ser.). (Illus.). (J). 15.23 (978-0-7587-4426-5(9)) Book Wholesalers, Inc.

Hedwig the Owl Vol. 2: Harry Potter Journal. 2000. 144p. (J). pap. 8.99 (978-0-439-23654-6(1)) Scholastic, Inc.

Houghton, John. A Closer Look at Harry Potter. 2001. 92p. pap., pap. 7.99 (978-0-85476-941-4(2) , 0854769412) Cook, David C. Publishing Co.

Magical Movie Scenes from Harry Potter & the Sorcerer's Stone: A Poster Book. movie tie-in ed. 2001. (Illus.). 32p. (YA). (gr. 1 up). mass mkt. 6.99 (978-0-439-34256-8(2)) Scholastic, Inc.

The Magical Worlds of Harry Potter Spellbinding Map & Book of Secrets. 2004. (Illus.). 32p. (J). 8.99 (978-0-9708442-2-4(0)) Lumina Pr. LLC.

Pyne, Erin A. A Fandom of Magical Proportions: S: an Unauthorized History of the Harry Potter Phenomenon. 2007. (Illus.). 84p. (J). per. 8.36 ***(978-0-9788138-8-8(X))*** Nimble Bks. LLC.

Quidditch Through the Ages. 2002. (Harry Potter Ser.). (Illus.). (J). 12.17 (978-0-7587-5135-5(4)) Book Wholesalers, Inc.

Rowling, J. K. Harri Potter Maen yr Athronydd. 2003. (WEL.). 300p. (J). 21.95 (978-1-58234-827-8(8) , Bloomsbury Children) Bloomsbury Publishing.

—Harrius Potter et Camera Secretorum. Needham, Peter, tr. from ENG. 2006. Orig. Title: Harry Potter & the Chamber of Secrets. (LAT., Illus.). 300p. (J). 23.95 (978-1-59990-067-4(X) , Bloomsbury Children) Bloomsbury Publishing.

—Harrius Potter et Philosophi Lapis. Needham, Peter, tr. from ENG. 2003. (Harry Potter Ser.: Year 1). Orig. Title: Harry Potter & the Philosopher's Stone. (LAT., Illus.). 300p. (J). 23.95 (978-1-58234-825-4(1) , Bloomsbury Children) Bloomsbury Publishing.

—Harry Potter agus an Orebloch. 2004. (GAE.). 300p. (J). (gr. 5 up). 21.95 (978-1-58234-828-5(6) , Bloomsbury Children) Bloomsbury Publishing.

—Harry Potter & the Chamber of Secrets. braille ed. 1999. (Harry Potter Ser.: Year 2). 520p. (YA). (gr. 3 up). pap. 17.99 (978-0-939173-35-8(2)) National Braille Pr.

—Harry Potter & the Chamber of Secrets. 2003. 203p. 23.95 (978-7-02-003344-7(X) , HAP02) People's Literature Publishing Hse. CHN. *Dist:* China Bks. & Periodicals, Inc.

—Harry Potter & the Chamber of Secrets. unabr. ed. 2004. (Harry Potter Ser.: Year 2). 352p. (J). (gr. 3 up). pap. 46.00 incl. audio (978-0-8072-8207-6(3) , S YA 137 SP, Listening Library) Random Hse. Audio Publishing Group.

—Harry Potter & the Chamber of Secrets. (RUS., Illus.). 28.95 (978-5-8451-0947-7(7)) Rosmen-Izdat RUS. *Dist:* Distribooks, Inc.

—Harry Potter & the Chamber of Secrets. 2003. (Harry Potter Ser.: Year 2). 352p. (J). 24.95 (978-0-439-55489-3(6) , Levine, Arthur A. Bks.) Scholastic, Inc.

—Harry Potter & the Chamber of Secrets. GrandPré, Mary, illus. (Harry Potter Ser.: Year 2). (J). 2002. 448p. mass mkt. 6.99 (978-0-439-42010-5(5) , Levine, Arthur A. Bks.); 2000. 352p. (gr. 3 up). mass mkt. 8.99 (978-0-439-06487-3(2)) Scholastic, Inc.

—Harry Potter & the Chamber of Secrets. Mark, Mona, illus. 2000. (Harry Potter Ser.: Year 2). 16p. (YA). (gr. 3 up). pap. 5.95 (978-0-439-21114-7(X)) Scholastic, Inc.

—Harry Potter & the Chamber of Secrets. GrandPré, Mary, illus. (Harry Potter Ser.: Year 2). 352p. (J). 1999. (gr. 3 up). 22.99 (978-0-439-06486-6(4)); 2002. 75.00 (978-0-439-20353-1(8)) Scholastic, Inc. (Levine, Arthur A. Bks.).

—Harry Potter & the Chamber of Secrets. 2000. (Harry Potter Ser.: Year 2). (YA). (gr. 3 up). 13.64 (978-0-606-19181-4(X)) Tandem Library Bks.

—Harry Potter & the Chamber of Secrets. l.t. ed. 2003. 464p. 13.95 (978-1-59413-001-4(9)) Thorndike Pr.

—Harry Potter & the Chamber of Secrets. GrandPré, Mary, illus. l.t. ed. 2000. (Harry Potter Ser.: Year 2). 464p. (gr. 3 up). 24.95 (978-0-7862-2273-5(5) , Large Print Pr.) Thorndike Pr.

—Harry Potter & the Deathly Hallows. braille ed. 2007. (Harry Potter Ser.: Year 7). 34.99 ***(978-0-939173-57-0(3))*** National Braille Pr.

—Harry Potter & the Deathly Hallows. GrandPré, Mary, illus. 2007. (Harry Potter Ser.: Year 7). 784p. (J). (gr. 4-7). 34.99 ***(978-0-545-01022-1(5));*** 784p. (YA). (gr. 6 up). 39.99 ***(978-0-545-02936-0(8));*** 816p. (J). 65.00 ***(978-0-545-02937-7(6))*** Scholastic, Inc. (Levine, Arthur A. Bks.).

—Harry Potter & the Deathly Hallows. l.t. ed. 2007. (Harry Potter Ser.: Year 7). (YA). 34.95 ***(978-0-7862-9665-1(8))*** Thorndike Pr.

—Harry Potter & the Goblet of Fire. braille ed. 2000. (Harry Potter Ser.: Year 4). 650p. (YA). (gr. 3 up). pap. 25.95 (978-0-939173-37-2(9)) National Braille Pr.

—Harry Potter & the Goblet of Fire. 2003. 433p. 19.95 (978-7-02-003463-5(2) , HAP04) People's Literature Publishing Hse. CHN. *Dist:* China Bks. & Periodicals, Inc.

—Harry Potter & the Goblet of Fire. 2003. (Harry Potter Ser.: Year 4). 752p. (J). 30.95 (978-0-439-55490-9(X) , Levine, Arthur A. Bks.) Scholastic, Inc.

—Harry Potter & the Goblet of Fire. GrandPré, Mary, illus. 2002. (Harry Potter Ser.: Year 4). 752p. (J). (gr. 3 up). mass mkt. 9.99 (978-0-439-13960-1(0) , Levine, Arthur A. Bks.) Scholastic, Inc.

—Harry Potter & the Goblet of Fire. 2000. (Harry Potter Ser.: Year 4). (Illus.). 16p. (YA). (gr. 3 up). pap. 5.95 (978-0-439-23194-7(9)) Scholastic, Inc.

—Harry Potter & the Goblet of Fire. GrandPré, Mary, illus. 2000. (Harry Potter Ser.: Year 4). 752p. (J). (gr. 3 up). 29.99 (978-0-439-13959-5(7) , Levine, Arthur A. Bks.) Scholastic, Inc.

—Harry Potter & the Goblet of Fire. 2002. (gr. 3-6). lib. bdg. 17.60 (978-0-613-49674-2(4)) Tandem Library Bks.

—Harry Potter & the Goblet of Fire. l.t. ed. 2003. 936p. 14.95 (978-1-59413-003-8(5)) Thorndike Pr.

—Harry Potter & the Goblet of Fire. GrandPré, Mary, illus. l.t. ed. 2000. (Harry Potter Ser.: Year 4). 936p. (gr. 3 up). 25.95 (978-0-7862-2927-7(6) , Large Print Pr.) Thorndike Pr.

—Harry Potter & the Half-Blood Prince, 9 vols. braille ed. 2005. (Harry Potter Ser.: 6). (YA). 29.99 (978-0-939173-39-6(5) , HALF) National Braille Pr.

—Harry Potter & the Half-Blood Prince. 2003. (Harry Potter Ser.). 496p. 24.95 ***(978-7-02-005323-0(8)*** , HAP06) People's Literature Publishing Hse. CHN. *Dist:* China Bks. & Periodicals, Inc.

—Harry Potter & the Half-Blood Prince. GrandPré, Mary, illus. (J). 2005. (Harry Potter Ser.: Year 6). 672p. 34.99 (978-0-439-78677-5(0)); 2005. (Harry Potter Ser.: Year 6). 672p. 29.99 (978-0-439-78454-2(9)); 2005. (Harry Potter Ser.: Year 6). 704p. 60.00 (978-0-439-79132-8(4)); 2006. 672p. reprint ed. pap. 9.99 (978-0-439-78596-9(0)) Scholastic, Inc. (Levine, Arthur A. Bks.).

—Harry Potter & the Half-Blood Prince. l.t. ed. 2005. (Harry Potter Ser.: Year 6). 832p. 29.95 (978-0-7862-7745-2(9) , Large Print Pr.) Thorndike Pr.

—Harry Potter & the Order of the Phoenix, 13 vols. braille ed. 2003. (Harry Potter Ser.: Year 5). (YA). 29.99 (978-0-939173-38-9(7)) National Braille Pr.

—Harry Potter & the Order of the Phoenix. GrandPré, Mary, illus. (Harry Potter Ser.: Year 5). (J). 2004. 896p. (gr. 4-7). mass mkt. 9.99 (978-0-439-35807-1(8) , Scholastic Paperbacks); 2003. 896p. (gr. 3-6). 34.99 (978-0-439-56761-9(0)); 2003. 870p. (gr. 3-6). 29.99 (978-0-439-35806-4(X)); 2003. 896p. (gr. 3-6). 60.00 (978-0-439-56762-6(9)) Scholastic, Inc.

—Harry Potter & the Order of the Phoenix. l.t. ed. 2003. (Harry Potter Ser.: Year 5). 1093p. 29.95 (978-0-7862-5778-2(4) , Large Print Pr.) Thorndike Pr.

—Harry Potter & the Philosopher's Stone. 2004. (GRE & GEC.). 300p. (J). (gr. 3-6). 21.95 (978-1-58234-826-1(X) , Bloomsbury Children) Bloomsbury Publishing.

—Harry Potter & the Prisoner of Azkaban. braille ed. 1999. (Harry Potter Ser.: Year 3). (YA). (gr. 3 up). pap. 19.95 (978-0-939173-36-5(0)) National Braille Pr.

—Harry Potter & the Prisoner of Azkaban. 2000. (J). tchr. ed. 9.95 (978-1-58130-656-9(3)); stu. ed. 11.95 (978-1-58130-657-6(1)) Novel Units, Inc.

—Harry Potter & the Prisoner of Azkaban. 2003. 260p. 15.95 (978-7-02-003345-4(8) , HAP03) People's Literature Publishing Hse. CHN. *Dist:* China Bks. & Periodicals, Inc.

—Harry Potter & the Prisoner of Azkaban. unabr. ed. 2004. (Harry Potter Ser.: Vol. 3). 448p. (J). pap. 52.00 incl. audio (978-0-8072-8316-5(9) , LYA 160 SP, Listening Library) Random Hse. Audio Publishing Group.

—Harry Potter & the Prisoner of Azkaban. (Harry Potter Ser.: Year 3). 2004. 560p. mass mkt. 7.99 (978-0-439-65548-4(X) , Scholastic Paperbacks); 2003. 448p. (J). 24.95 (978-0-439-55492-3(6) , Levine, Arthur A. Bks.) Scholastic, Inc.

—Harry Potter & the Prisoner of Azkaban. GrandPré, Mary, illus. (Harry Potter Ser.: Year 3). 448p. (gr. 3 up). 2001. (YA). mass mkt. 8.99 (978-0-439-13636-5(9) , Levine, Arthur A. Bks.); 1999. (J). 22.99 (978-0-439-13635-8(0)) Scholastic, Inc.

—Harry Potter & the Prisoner of Azkaban. 2001. (gr. 3-6). lib. bdg. 16.45 (978-0-613-37106-3(2)); (Illus.). (J). 14.64 (978-0-606-21584-8(0)) Tandem Library Bks.

—Harry Potter & the Prisoner of Azkaban. l.t. ed. 2003. 592p. 13.95 (978-1-59413-002-1(7)) Thorndike Pr.

—Harry Potter & the Prisoner of Azkaban. GrandPré, Mary, illus. l.t. ed. 2000. (Harry Potter Ser.: Year 3). 592p. (gr. 3 up). 24.95 (978-0-7862-2274-2(3) , Large Print Pr.) Thorndike Pr.

—Harry Potter & the Sorcerer's Stone. 2003. (CHI.). 191p. 13.95 (978-7-02-003343-0(1) , HAP01) People's Literature Publishing Hse. CHN. *Dist:* China Bks. & Periodicals, Inc.

—Harry Potter & the Sorcerer's Stone. unabr. ed. (Harry Potter Ser.: Year 1). 320p. (gr. 3 up). (YA). pap. 62.00 incl. audio (978-0-8072-1547-0(3)); 2004. (J). pap. 46.00 incl. audio (978-0-8072-8119-2(0) , S YA 108 SP) Random Hse. Audio Publishing Group. (Listening Library).

—Harry Potter & the Sorcerer's Stone. GrandPré, Mary, illus. (Harry Potter Ser.: Year 1). (J). 2003. 320p. (ps-17). 24.95 (978-0-439-55493-0(4) , Levine, Arthur A. Bks.); 2001. 400p. (gr. 3 up). mass mkt. 6.99 (978-0-439-36213-9(X)) Scholastic, Inc.

—Harry Potter & the Sorcerer's Stone. 2000. (Harry Potter Ser.: Year 1). (Illus.). 16p. (YA). (gr. 3 up). pap. 5.95 (978-0-439-21116-1(6)) Scholastic, Inc.

—Harry Potter & the Sorcerer's Stone. GrandPré, Mary, illus. (Harry Potter Ser.: Year 1). 320p. (gr. 3 up). 1999. (YA). mass mkt. 8.99 (978-0-590-35342-7(X)); 1998. (J). pap. 22.99 (978-0-590-35340-3(3) , Levine, Arthur A. Bks.) Scholastic, Inc.

—Harry Potter & the Sorcerer's Stone. collector's ed. 2000. (Harry Potter Ser.: Year 1). 320p. (YA). (gr. 3 up). 75.00 (978-0-439-20352-4(X)) Scholastic, Inc.

—Harry Potter & the Sorcerer's Stone. Smith, Rodger, illus. movie tie-in deluxe ed. 2001. (Harry Potter Ser.: Year 1). 12p. (J). (gr. 4-7). pap. 18.95 (978-0-439-29482-9(7)) Scholastic, Inc.

—Harry Potter & the Sorcerer's Stone. 2001. (Illus.). (J). 13.64 (978-0-606-21606-7(5)) Tandem Library Bks.

—Harry Potter & the Sorcerer's Stone. l.t. ed. 2003. 423p. 13.95 (978-1-59413-000-7(0)) Thorndike Pr.

—Harry Potter & the Sorcerer's Stone. GrandPré, Mary, illus. l.t. ed. 1999. (Harry Potter Ser.: Year 1). 422p. (gr. 3 up). 24.95 (978-0-7862-2272-8(7) , Large Print Pr.) Thorndike Pr.

—Harry Potter aur Azkaban ka Qaidi. Khokhar, Darakhshanda Asghar, tr. 2004. 372p. 19.95 (978-0-19-579915-6(1)) Oxford Univ. Pr., Inc.

—Harry Potter Boxed Set, Bks. 1-7. 2007. (Harry Potter Ser.: Years 1-7). (J). 195.00 ***(978-0-545-04425-7(1)*** , Levine, Arthur A. Bks.) Scholastic, Inc.

—Harry Potter Boxed Set: Harry Potter & the Sorcerer's Stone; Harry Potter & the Chamber of Secrets; Harry Potter & the Prisoner of Azkaban, 3 vols. GrandPré, Mary, illus. (Harry Potter Ser.: Years 1-3). (YA). 2002. pap. 21.97 (978-0-439-32466-3(1)); 1999. (gr. 3 up). 55.85 (978-0-439-13316-6(5)) Scholastic, Inc. (Levine, Arthur A. Bks.).

—Harry Potter Boxed Set: Harry Potter & the Sorcerer's Stone; Harry Potter & the Chamber of Secrets; Harry Potter & the Prisoner of Azkaban; Harry Potter & the Goblet of Fire, 4 vols. GrandPré, Mary, illus. 2000. (Harry Potter Ser.: Years 1-4). (YA). (gr. 3 up). 85.80 (978-0-641-06631-3(7) , Levine, Arthur A. Bks.) Scholastic, Inc.

—Harry Potter Coffret. pap. 69.95 (978-2-07-054972-6(0)) Gallimard, Editions FRA. *Dist:* Distribooks, Inc.

—Harry Potter Coffret: Harry Potter a l'Ecole des Sorciers; Harry Potter et la Chambre des Secrets; Harry Potter et le Prisonnier d'Azkaban. 1999. (Harry Potter Ser.: Years 1-3). Tr. of Harry Potter Boxed Set: Harry Potter & the Chamber of Secrets; Harry Potter & the Sorcerer's Stone; Harry Potter & the Prisoner of Azkaban. (FRE.). (YA). (gr. 3 up). pap. 43.95 (978-2-07-052929-2(0)) Gallimard, Editions FRA. *Dist:* Distribooks, Inc.

—Harry Potter Coffret: Harry Potter a l'Ecole des Sorciers; Harry Potter et la Chambre des Secrets; Harry Potter et le Prisonnier d'Azkaban; Harry Potter et la Coupe de Feu. 1999. (Harry Potter Ser.: Years 1-3). Tr. of Harry Potter Boxed Set: Harry Potter & the Chamber of Secrets; Harry Potter & the Sorcerer's Stone; Harry Potter & the Prisoner of Azkaban; Harry Potter et la COupe de Feu. (FRE.). 1400p. (YA). (gr. 3 up). pap. 34.95 (978-0-320-03843-3(2)) French & European Pubns., Inc.

—Harry Potter e a Camara Secreta. (POR.). pap. 28.95 (978-85-325-1166-9(X)) Rocco, Editora, Ltda BRA. *Dist:* Distribooks, Inc.

—Harry Potter e a Pedra Filosofal. (POR.). pap. 28.95 (978-85-325-1101-0(5)) Rocco, Editora, Ltda BRA. *Dist:* Distribooks, Inc.

—Harry Potter e a Prisioneiro de Azkaban. (POR.). pap. 29.95 (978-85-325-1206-2(2)) Rocco, Editora, Ltda BRA. *Dist:* Distribooks, Inc.

—Harry Potter e la Camera dei Segreti. (ITA.). pap. 32.95 (978-88-7782-703-6(3)) Salani ITA. *Dist:* Distribooks, Inc.

—Harry Potter e la Pietra Filosofale. (ITA.). pap. 32.95 (978-88-7782-702-9(5)) Salani ITA. *Dist:* Distribooks, Inc.

—Harry Potter e o Calice de Fogo. (POR.). pap. 38.95 (978-85-325-1252-9(6)) Rocco, Editora, Ltda BRA. *Dist:* Distribooks, Inc.

—Harry Potter et la Chambre des Secrets. 1999. (Harry Potter Ser.: Year 2). Tr. of Harry Potter & the Chamber of Secrets. (FRE.). (YA). (gr. 3 up). pap. 13.95 (978-0-320-03778-8(9)) French & European Pubns., Inc.

—Harry Potter et la Chambre des Secrets. 1999. (Harry Potter Ser.: Year 2). Tr. of Harry Potter & the Chamber of Secrets. (FRE., Illus.). 358p. (YA). (gr. 3 up). pap. 16.95 (978-2-07-052455-6(8)) Gallimard, Editions FRA. *Dist:* Distribooks, Inc.

—Harry Potter et la Coupe de Feu. 2001. Tr. of Harry Potter & the Goblet of Fire. 1173p. pap. 19.95 (978-0-320-04838-8(1)); (Harry Potter Ser.: Year 4). (FRE.). (YA). (gr. 3 up). pap. 34.95 (978-0-320-03932-4(3)) French & European Pubns., Inc.

—Harry Potter et la Coupe de Feu.Tr. of Harry Potter & the Goblet of Fire. (FRE., Illus.). 766p. pap. 19.95 (978-2-07-054351-9(X)) Gallimard, Editions FRA. *Dist:* Distribooks, Inc.

—Harry Potter et le Prisonnier d'Azkaban. 1999. (Harry Potter Ser.: Year 3). Tr. of Harry Potter & the Prisoner of Azkaban. (FRE.). 465p. (YA). (gr. 3 up). pap. 16.95 (978-2-07-052818-9(9)) Gallimard, Editions FRA. *Dist:* Distribooks, Inc.

—Harry Potter et l'Ecole des Sorciers. 3rd ed. 1998. (Harry Potter Ser.: Year 1). Tr. of Harry Potter & the Sorcerer's Stone. (FRE., Illus.). (YA). (gr. 3 up). pap. 14.95 (978-2-07-050142-7(6)) Distribooks, Inc.

—Harry Potter et l'Ecole des Sorciers. 1999. (Harry Potter Ser.: Year 1). Tr. of Harry Potter & the Sorcerer's Stone. (FRE.). (YA). (gr. 3 up). pap. 16.95 (978-0-320-03780-1(0)) French & European Pubns., Inc.

—Harry Potter et l'Ecole des Sorciers.Tr. of Harry Potter & the Sorcerer's Stone. 2007. 311p. pap. 14.95 ***(978-2-07-061236-9(8));*** 2000. (FRE.). (J). pap. 14.95 (978-2-07-051426-7(9)) Gallimard, Editions FRA. *Dist:* Distribooks, Inc.

—Harry Potter I Czara Ognia, Vol. 4. pap. 29.95 (978-83-7278-021-8(8)) Media Rodzina POL. *Dist:* Distribooks, Inc.

—Harry Potter I Kamie D. pap. 18.95 (978-83-7278-000-3(5)) Media Rodzina POL. *Dist:* Distribooks, Inc.

—Harry Potter I Komnata Tajem. pap. 18.95 (978-83-7278-007-2(2)) Media Rodzina POL. *Dist:* Distribooks, Inc.

—Harry Potter I wi Zied Azkab. pap. 29.95 (978-83-7278-014-0(5)) Media Rodzina POL. *Dist:* Distribooks, Inc.

—Harry Potter und der Gefangene von Azkaban. 1999. (Harry Potter Ser.: Year 3). Tr. of Harry Potter & the Prisoner of Azkaban. (GER.). (YA). (gr. 3 up). pap. 34.95 (978-3-551-55169-6(3)) Carlsen Verlag DEU. *Dist:* Distribooks, Inc.

—Harry Potter und der Stein der Weisen. 1999. (Harry Potter Ser.: Year 1). (GER.). 335p. (YA). (gr. 3 up). pap. 34.95 (978-3-551-55167-2(7)) Carlsen Verlag DEU. *Dist:* Distribooks, Inc.

—Harry Potter und die Kammer des Schreckens. 1999. (Harry Potter Ser.: Year 2). Tr. of Harry Potter & Chamber of Secrets. (GER.). (YA). (gr. 3 up). pap. 36.95 (978-3-551-55168-9(5)) Carlsen Verlag DEU. *Dist:* Distribooks, Inc.

—Harry Potter y el Caliz de Fuego. 2001. (SPA.). 640p. (978-84-7888-664-7(8) , 1950) Emece Editores.

—Harry Potter y el Caliz de Fuego. 2004. (Harry Potter Ser.). (SPA., Illus.). (YA). 240p. 19.95 (978-84-7888-645-6(1) , SAL30169); pap. 16.50 (978-84-7888-646-3(X) , SAL30171) Emece Editores ESP. *Dist:* Lectorum Pubns., Inc.

—Harry Potter y el Caliz de Fuego. 2000. 636p. 39.95 (978-0-320-04849-4(7)) French & European Pubns., Inc.

—Harry Potter y el Caliz de Fuego. 2001. (SPA., Illus.). (J). 23.15 (978-0-606-21227-4(2)) Tandem Library Bks.

—Harry Potter y el Prisionero de Azkaban. 2000. (Harry Potter Ser.: Year 3). (SPA.). 359p. (YA). (gr. 3 up). 16.95 (978-84-7888-568-8(4)) Baker & Taylor Bks.

—Harry Potter y el Prisionero de Azkaban. 2002. (SPA.). 362p. (978-84-7888-761-3(X) , 1950) Emece Editores.

—Harry Potter y el Prisionero de Azkaban. 2004. (Harry Potter Ser.). (SPA.). 359p. pap. 12.00 (978-84-7888-655-5(9) , SAL30174); (Illus.). 360p. (gr. 3 up). 17.95 (978-84-7888-519-0(6) , SAL1889) Emece Editores ESP. *Dist:* Lectorum Pubns., Inc.

—Harry Potter y el Prisionero de Azkaban. 2000. (Harry Potter Ser.: Year 3). (SPA.). (YA). (gr. 3 up). 16.95 (978-0-320-03783-2(5)); 360p. 29.95 (978-0-320-04846-3(2)) French & European Pubns., Inc.

—Harry Potter y el Prisionero de Azkaban. 2001. (SPA.). (Harry Potter Ser.: Year 3). (YA). (gr. 3 up). (978-0-606-88519-5(6)); (Illus.). (J). 18.65 (978-0-606-20490-3(3)) Tandem Library Bks.

—Harry Potter y la Caliz de Fuego. 2002. (SPA.). 642p. (978-84-7888-762-0(8) , 1950) Emece Editores.

—Harry Potter y la Camara Secreta. (SPA.). 2002. 290p. (978-84-7888-760-6(1) , 1950); 2000. 288p. (978-84-7888-614-2(1) , 1950) Emece Editores.

—Harry Potter y la Camara Secreta. 2004. (Harry Potter Ser.). (SPA.). (YA). 286p. pap. 9.99 (978-84-7888-656-2(7) , SAL30173); (Illus.). 288p. (gr. 3 up). 15.95 (978-84-7888-495-7(5) , SAL4595) Emece Editores ESP. *Dist:* Lectorum Pubns., Inc.

—Harry Potter y la Camara Secreta. 2000. (SPA.). 290p. (YA). (gr. 7 up). 15.95 (978-950-04-2068-6(6)) Emecé Editores S.A. ARG. *Dist:* Libros Sin Fronteras.

—Harry Potter y la Camara Secreta. 2000. 360p. 29.95 (978-0-320-04847-0(0)); 1999. (Harry Potter Ser.: Year 2). (SPA.). (YA). (gr. 3 up). 14.95 (978-0-320-03781-8(9)) French & European Pubns., Inc.

—Harry Potter y la Camara Secreta. 2001. (SPA.). (Harry Potter Ser.: Year 2). (YA). (gr. 3 up). (978-0-606-88495-2(5)); (Illus.). (J). 16.64 (978-0-606-20491-0(1)) Tandem Library Bks.

—Harry Potter y la Orden del Fenix. 2004. (Harry Potter Ser.). (SPA.). 893p. (YA). 23.99 (978-84-7888-901-3(9)) Emece Editores ESP. *Dist:* Lectorum Pubns., Inc.

—Harry Potter y la Orden del Fenix. Ortega, Gemma Rovira, tr. 2004. (Harry Potter Ser.). (SPA.). 893p. (YA). pap. 17.99 (978-84-7888-884-9(5)) Emece Editores ESP. *Dist:* Lectorum Pubns., Inc.

—Harry Potter y la Orden del Fenix. 2004. 1000p. 69.95 (978-0-320-04850-0(0)) French & European Pubns., Inc.

—Harry Potter y la Piedra Filosofal. (SPA.). 2002. 258p. (978-84-7888-759-0(8) , 1950); 2000. 256p. (978-84-7888-612-8(5) , 1950) Emece Editores.

—Harry Potter y la Piedra Filosofal. 2004. (Harry Potter Ser.). (SPA., Illus.). 256p. (YA). pap. 9.99 (978-84-7888-654-8(0) , SAL30172); (gr. 7 up). 15.95 (978-84-7888-445-2(9) , SAL2819) Emece Editores ESP. *Dist:* Lectorum Pubns., Inc.

—Harry Potter y la Piedra Filosofal. 2000. 254p. 29.95 (978-0-320-04848-7(9)); 1999. (Harry Potter Ser.: Year 1). (SPA.). (YA). (gr. 3 up). 14.95 (978-0-320-03782-5(7)) French & European Pubns., Inc.

—Harry Potter y la Piedra Filosofal. 2001. (SPA.). (Harry Potter Ser.: Year 1). (YA). (gr. 3 up). (978-0-606-88445-7(9)); (Illus.). (J). 16.64 (978-0-606-20489-7(X)) Tandem Library Bks.

—Le Quidditch a Travers les Ages. 2001. 96p. pap. 16.95 (978-0-320-04845-6(4)) French & European Pubns., Inc.

Rowling, J. K. & Dale, Jim. Harry Potter & the Goblet of Fire. unabr. ed. 2004. (Harry Potter Ser.). 752p. (J). pap. 65.00 incl. audio (978-0-8072-1196-0(6) , S YA 270 SP, Listening Library) Random Hse. Audio Publishing Group.

Running Press Staff. Harry Potter Golden Snitch. 2006. 16p. pap. 8.95 (978-0-7624-2821-2(X) , Running Pr.) Running Pr. Bk. Pubs.

Scholastic, Inc. Staff. Flipbook. 2007. (Harry Potter Movie V Ser.). 96p. (J). pap. 3.99 (***978-0-439-02489-1(7)***) Scholastic, Inc.

—Harry Potter & the Prisoner of Azkaban Color & Activity Book: With Stickers. Reisfeld, Randi, ed. 2004. (Harry Potter Ser.). 32p. (J). 3.99 (978-0-439-62561-6(0) , Scholastic Paperbacks) Scholastic, Inc.

—Prisoner of Azkaban Movie Lenticular Poster Book. Reisfeld, Randi, ed. 2004. (Harry Potter Ser.). 16p. (J). pap. 9.99 (978-0-439-62562-3(9) , Scholastic Paperbacks) Scholastic, Inc.

Scott Fuller Graphic Design, des. Hogwarts Journal. deluxe ed. 2000. (Illus.). 64p. (J). pap. 12.95 (978-0-439-23653-9(3)) Scholastic, Inc.

Wizard Academies I: The Heart of Darkness. 2006. 658p. pap. 23.72 (978-1-4116-7787-6(0)) Lulu.com.

Zimmerman, W. Frederick. Unauthorized Harry Potter & the Alchemist's Cell News: Half-Blood Prince Analysis & Speculation. 2006. 160p. per. 14.94 (978-0-9777424-7-9(4)) Nimble Bks. LLC.

—Unauthorized Harry Potter & the Chariots of Light News: Half-Blood Prince Analysis & Speculation. 2006. 160p. per. 14.94 (978-0-9777424-8-6(2)) Nimble Bks. LLC.

POTTERY

see also Porcelain

Ackroyd, Dorothea. Eating & Drinking Bird Book. 1999. 3.95 (978-1-58185-200-4(2)) Quadrillion Media LLC.

Andrews-Goebel, Nancy. The Pot That Juan Built. Diaz, David, illus. 2002. 32p. (J). (gr. 1 up). 16.95 (978-1-58430-038-0(8)) Lee & Low Bks., Inc.

Arima, Elaine. The Kids 'n' Clay Ceramics Book: Hand-building & Wheel-Throwing Projects from the Kids 'n' Clay Pottery Studio. Arima, Curtis, illus. 2004. 128p. (J). (gr. k up). 16.95 (978-1-883672-89-8(9) , Tricycle Pr.) Ten Speed Pr.

Bohera, C. Modela con Barro. (Coleccion Manualidades Divertidas).Tr. of Modeling Clay. (SPA.). 102p. (J). (gr. k-3). 10.00 (978-84-342-1896-3(8)) Parramon Ediciones S.A. ESP. *Dist:* Distribuidora Norma, Inc., Lectorum Pubns., Inc.

Canizares, Susan, et al. Clay Art with Gloria Elliott. 1999. (Learning Center Emergent Readers Ser.). (Illus.). (J). 2.50 (978-0-439-04595-7(9)) Scholastic, Inc.

Clough, Peter. Clay in the Classroom. 2005. (Illus.). 111p. reprint ed. pap. 22.00 (978-0-7567-9594-8(X)) DIANE Publishing Co.

Coe, Debbie & Coe, Randy. Liberty Blue Dinnerware. 2002. (Illus.). 128p. (gr. 10-13). pap. 14.95 (978-0-7643-1543-5(9)) Schiffer Publishing, Ltd.

Ellis, Mary. Ceramics for Kids: Creative Clay Projects to Pinch, Roll, Coil, Slam & Twist. 2004. (Illus.). 144p. pap. 12.95 (978-1-57990-555-2(2)) Lark Bks.

Fisher, Leonard Everett. The Potters. 2000. (Colonial Craftsmen Ser.). (Illus.). 48p. (J). (gr. 4-8). lib. bdg. 21.36 (978-0-7614-1149-9(6) , Benchmark Bks.) Cavendish, Marshall Corp.

Jakab, Cheryl. Clay. 2006. (Illus.). 32p. (J). (978-1-58340-775-2(8)) Smart Apple Media.

Johnson, Donald-Brian, et al. Ceramic Arts Studio: The Legacy of Betty Harrington. 2003. (Illus.). 264p. (gr. 10-13). 59.95 (978-0-7643-1826-9(8)) Schiffer Publishing, Ltd.

Kassinger, Ruth. Ceramics: From Magic Pots to Man-Made Bones. 2003. (Material World Ser.). (Illus.). 80p. (gr. 6-8). lib. bdg. 25.90 (978-0-7613-2108-8(X) , Twenty-First Century Bks.) Lerner Publishing Group.

Leibowitz, Joan. Yellow Ware: The Transitional Ceramic. 3rd rev. ed. 2002. (Illus.). 119p. (gr. 10-13). pap. 24.95 (978-0-7643-1594-7(3)) Schiffer Publishing, Ltd.

Llimos Plomer, Anna. Clay. 2003. (Let's Create! Ser.). (Illus.). 32p. (J). (gr. 2 up). lib. bdg. 23.33 (978-0-8368-3746-9(0)) Stevens, Gareth Inc.

Llimos Plomer, Anna. Easy Clay Crafts in 5 Steps. 2008. (Easy Crafts in 5 Steps Ser.). 32p. (gr. 3-4). lib. bdg. 22.60 (***978-0-7660-3085-5(7)***) Enslow Pubs., Inc.

Oppelt, Norman T. Earth, Water & Fire: The Prehistoric Pottery of Mesa Verde. rev. ed. 1998. (Illus.). 91p. (YA). reprint ed. pap. 14.95 (978-0-9662845-0-8(X)) Oppelt Pubns.

Snyder, Jeffrey B. Collecting Oyster Plates. 2001. (Schiffer Book for Collectors Ser.). (Illus.). 160p. (gr. 10-13). pap. 29.95 (978-0-7643-1481-0(5)) Schiffer Publishing, Ltd.

Zavada, Mary. Lady Head Vases: A Collector's Guide with Prices. 2nd rev. ed. 2003. (Schiffer Book for Collectors Ser.). (Illus.). 112p. (gr. 10-13). pap. 16.95 (978-0-7643-1822-1(5)) Schiffer Publishing, Ltd.

POTTERY—FICTION

Alexander, Lloyd. The Black Cauldron. 2nd rev. ed. 2006. (Chronicles of Prydain Ser.: Bk. 2). 208p. (J). (gr. 3-8). pap. 5.99 (978-0-8050-8049-0(X) , Holt, Henry & Co. Bks. For Young Readers) Holt, Henry & Co.

Camila & Clay-Old-Woman, 6 pack. (Greetings Ser.: Vol. 1). (gr. 3-5). 31.00 (978-0-7635-1745-8(3)) Rigby Education.

Carter, Aubrey Smith. The Enchanted Lizard: La Lagartijita Magica. Nelson, Esther Whitt, ed. Branton, Molly, illus. 2006. (ENG & SPA.). 96p. (J). 18.95 (978-1-893271-38-8(2)) Maverick Publishing Co.

King, Robert A. The Three Lumps of Clay. Vandervoort, Gene, illus. 1999. 16p. (J). (gr. 1-4). pap. 4.95 (978-0-8198-7399-6(3)) Pauline Bks. & Media.

Krug, R. Lyding. The Treasure of Ferson Creek. 2006. 133p. (YA). pap. 9.95 (978-1-4116-3683-5(X)) Lulu.com.

Park, Linda Sue. A Single Shard. braille ed. 2001. (gr. 2). spiral bd. (978-0-616-08848-7(5)) Canadian National Institute for the Blind/Institut National Canadien pour les Aveugles.

—A Single Shard. 2001. (Illus.). 160p. (J). (gr. 5-9). tchr. ed. 15.00 (978-0-395-97827-6(0) , Clarion Bks.) Houghton Mifflin Co. Trade & Reference Div.

—A Single Shard. 2002. (J). (gr. 5-6). stu. ed. (978-1-58130-771-9(3)) Novel Units, Inc.

—A Single Shard. unabr. ed. 2004. (Middle Grade Cassette Librariestm Ser.). (J). (gr. 5-9). pap. 36.00 incl. audio (978-0-8072-1760-3(3) , S YA 349 SP, Listening Library) Random Hse. Audio Publishing Group.

—A Single Shard. 2003. (gr. 5-8). lib. bdg. 14.15 (978-0-613-57327-6(7)) Tandem Library Bks.

POTTINGER, ROSE RITA (FICTITIOUS CHARACTER)—FICTION

Bellairs, John. The Ghost in the Mirror. 2002. (J). (gr. 3 up). 20.75 (978-0-8446-7205-2(X)) Smith, Peter Pub., Inc.

—The House with a Clock in Its Walls. Gorey, Edward, illus. 2004. (Lewis Barnavelt Ser.). 192p. (J). pap. 5.99 (978-0-14-240257-3(5) , Puffin) Penguin Group (USA) Inc.

—The House with a Clock in Its Walls. 179p. (J). (gr. 4-6). pap. 4.50 (978-0-8072-1423-7(X) , Listening Library) Random Hse. Audio Publishing Group.

POULTRY

see also names of domesticated birds, e.g. Ducks; Geese; Turkeys, etc.

Brady, Peter. Pollos. Schon, Isabel, ed. Ferrer, Martin Luis Guzman, tr. from ENG. Munoz, William, illus. 1998. (Coleccion Primeros Lectores).Tr. of Chickens. (SPA.). 24p. (J). (gr. k-3). lib. bdg. 18.60 (978-1-56065-787-3(1) , CAP1683, Bridgestone Bks.) Capstone Pr., Inc.

Chang, Maria L. Early Themes: Life Cycles Butterflies, Chicks, Frogs & More!. 1. 1999. 48p. pap. 9.95 (978-0-590-68572-6(4)) Scholastic, Inc.

Legg, Gerald & Salariya, David. From Egg to Chicken. Scrace, Carolyn, illus. 1998. (Life Cycles Ser.). 32p. (J). (gr. k-2). 25.50 (978-0-531-14490-9(9) , Watts, Franklin) Scholastic Library Publishing.

Oppenlander, Meredith. In the Hen House. Gedeon, Gloria, illus. l.t. ed. 1998. 12p. (J). (gr. k-2). pap. 4.95 (978-1-57874-003-1(7)) Kaeden Corp.

Rauzon, Mark J. Chickens & Peafowl: What They Have in Common. Savage, Stephen et al, illus. 2001. (Animals in Order Ser.). 48p. (J). (gr. 4-6). 26.50 (978-0-531-11689-0(1) , Watts, Franklin) Scholastic Library Publishing.

Richardson, Adele D. Poultry. 2001. (Let's Investigate Ser.). (J). lib. bdg. (978-1-58341-082-0(1) , Creative Education) Creative Co., The.

Saunders-Smith, Gail. Chickens. 1998. (J). pap. 13.25 (978-0-516-21230-2(3) , Children's Pr.) Scholastic Library Publishing.

Stone, Tanya Lee. Chickens. 2003. (Wild Wild World Ser.). 24p. (YA). 24.94 (978-1-56711-812-4(7) , Blackbirch Pr., Inc.) Thomson Gale.

POULTRY—FICTION

Bailey, Scott Arthur. The Tale of Henrietta Hen. 2006. pap. 33.99 (***978-1-4280-4100-4(1)***) IndyPublish.com.

Dalmatian Press Staff. Mother Goose. 2005. (Illus.). 32p. (J). 10.99 (978-1-4037-1606-4(4)) Dalmatian Pr.

Dow, Jill. Bridget's Secret. 2001. (Windy Edge Farm Ser.). (Illus.). 32p. (J). (ps-3). pap. 7.99 (978-0-7112-1780-5(7)) Lincoln, Frances Ltd. GBR. *Dist:* Transition Vendor.

French, Vivian. Henny Penny. Windham, Sophie, illus. 2006. 32p. (J). 16.95 (978-1-58234-706-6(9) , Bloomsbury Children) Bloomsbury Publishing.

Julian, Russell. Happy Cockerel. 2005. (Farm Board Book Ser.). (Illus.). 12p. (J). bds. 9.99 (978-1-4052-1030-0(3)) Egmont Bks., Ltd. GBR. *Dist:* Trafalgar Square Publishing.

Kalar, Bonnie. The Hen & the Jet. Spreen, Kathe, illus. 1998. 8p. (J). (ps-2). pap. (978-1-891619-05-2(5)) Corona Pr.

Ottolenghi, Carol. The Little Red Hen. Holladay, Reggie, illus. 2002. (Brighter Child Keepsake Stories Ser.). 32p. (J). (ps-3). pap. 3.99 (978-1-57768-378-0(1) , Brighter Child) School Specialty Publishing.

POVERTY

see also Homelessness

see also names of countries with the subdivision Economic Conditions and Social Conditions e.g. United States—Economic Conditions; United States—Social Conditions

Bailey, Gerry & Law, Felicia. What's It All Worth? The Value of Money. Phillips, Mike & Brooks, Rosie, illus. 2006. (My Money Ser.). 24p. (J). (gr. 4-6). 27.93 (978-0-7565-1673-4(0)) Compass Point Bks.

Bowden. World Poverty. 2003. (Face the Facts Ser.). 56p. (J). pap. 8.95 (978-1-4109-0049-4(5)) Raintree.

Bowden, Rob. World Poverty. 2003. (Face the Facts Ser.). (Illus.). 56p. (J). lib. bdg. 28.56 (978-0-7398-6436-4(X)) Raintree.

Face the Facts, 6 vols. 2003. (Illus.). (978-0-7398-6853-9(5)); Set 1. (J). pap. 30.60 (978-1-4109-0146-0(7)); Set 2. pap. 24.15 (978-1-4109-0432-4(6)) Raintree.

Garlake, Teresa. Poverty: Changing Attitudes, 1900-2000. 1999. (Twentieth Century Issues Ser.). (Illus.). 64p. (J). (gr. 4-6). lib. bdg. 28.54 (978-0-8172-5894-8(9)) Raintree.

Geist, Ellen, retold by. Not for Me. 2002. (Illus.). 16p. (J). (978-0-439-35081-5(6)) Scholastic, Inc.

Hunnicut, Susan C. World Hunger. 2006. (Illus.). 128p. (J). (gr. 10-12). 21.20 (978-0-7377-2762-3(4) , Greenhaven Pr., Inc.) Thomson Gale.

Information Plus Homeless in America November 2005. 2005. 45.00 (978-1-4144-0418-9(2)) Thomson Gale.

Kowalski, Kathiann M. Poverty in America: Causes & Issues. 2003. (Issues in Focus Ser.). (Illus.). 128p. (J). lib. bdg. 26.60 (978-0-7660-1945-4(4)) Enslow Pubs., Inc.

Kozol, Jonathan. Rachel & Her Children: Homeless Families in America. 2006. 320p. 13.95 (978-0-307-34589-9(0) , Three Rivers Pr.) Crown Publishing Group.

Maddocks, Steven. World Hunger. 2004. (21st Century Issues Ser.). (J). 11.95 (978-0-8368-5663-7(5)); lib. bdg. 30.00 (978-0-8368-5646-0(5)) Stevens, Gareth Inc. (World Almanac Library).

Mason, Paul. Poverty. 2005. (Planet under Pressure Ser.). (Illus.). 48p. (J). 31.43 (978-1-4034-7743-9(4)) Heinemann Library.

Miller, Barbara. Teenage Pregnancy & Poverty: The Economic Realities. rev. ed. 1999. (Teen Pregnancy Prevention Library). (Illus.). 64p. (YA). (gr. 7-12). lib. bdg. 23.95 (978-0-8239-2997-9(3) , TPPRPO) Rosen Publishing Group, Inc., The.

Senker, Cath. Poverty. 2006. (Illus.). 48p. (J). pap. (***978-0-8368-8157-8(5)***); lib. bdg. (***978-0-8368-7757-1(8)***) Stevens, Gareth Inc. (World Almanac Library).

Stearman, Kaye. Poverty. 2002. (World Issues Ser.). (Illus.). 57p. (J). lib. bdg. 28.50 (978-1-931983-26-6(7)) Chrysalis Education.

Wagner, Viqi. Poverty. 2007. (Opposing Viewpoints Ser.). (Illus.). 224p. (gr. 10-12). 36.20 (***978-0-7377-3747-9(6)***); pap. 24.95 (***978-0-7377-3748-6(4)***) Thomson Gale. (Greenhaven Pr., Inc.).

Williams, Mary E. & Munoz, Mercedes. Is Poverty a Serious Threat? 2006. (At Issue Ser.). 80-244*p. (gr. 10-12). 29.95 (978-0-7377-2725-8(X)); pap. 21.20 (978-0-7377-2726-5(8)) Thomson Gale. (Greenhaven Pr., Inc.).

POVERTY—FICTION

Alger, Horatio. Cast upon the Breakers. unabr. ed. 2002. (Polyglot Press Alger Ser.). (Illus.). (J). pap. 17.95 (978-1-931927-81-9(2)) Polyglot Pr., Inc.

—Finding a Fortune. unabr. ed. 2002. (Polyglot Press Alger Ser.). (Illus.). (J). pap. 17.95 (978-1-4115-0089-1(X)) Polyglot Pr., Inc.

Alger Jr. Horatio Staff. Herbert Carter's Legacy. rev. ed. 2006. 264p. 28.95 (978-1-4218-1756-9(X)); pap. 13.95 (978-1-4218-1856-6(6)) 1st World Publishing, Inc. (1st World Library - Literary Society).

Armstrong, William H. Sounder. 2001. (Perennial Classics Ser.). 96p. (gr. 4-7). pap. 7.00 (978-0-06-093548-1(0)) HarperCollins Pubs.

—Sounder. Barkley, James, illus. l.t. ed. 1999. (LRS Large Print Cornerstone Ser.). 230p. (YA). (gr. 6-12). lib. bdg. 27.95 (978-1-58118-054-1(3) , 22768) LRS.

—Sounder. 2001. (gr. 3-6). lib. bdg. 15.30 (978-0-613-85745-1(3)) Tandem Library Bks.

—Sounder. l.t. ed. 2005. 111p. (YA). pap. 10.95 (978-0-7862-7915-9(X)) Thorndike Pr.

Avi. The Traitors' Gate. Raude, Karina, illus. 2007. 368p. (J). (gr. 6-9). 17.99 (978-0-689-85335-7(1) , Atheneum/ Richard Jackson Bks.) Simon & Schuster Children's Publishing.

Ballard, John H. SoulMates: A Novel to End World Hunger, 2 bks. in 1. Ellen, Joan, ed. Litzenger, Roseanne, illus. 1998. (Soul to Soul Adventure Ser.). 524p. (YA). (gr. 7 up). 19.95 (978-0-932279-06-4(6)); (gr. 4-7). pap. 14.95 (978-0-932279-05-7(8)) World Citizens.

Beatty, P. Lupita Manana. 6 vols., Set. 3rd ed. 2000. (J). pap. 29.70 (978-0-13-772484-0(5)) Prentice Hall (Schl. Div.).

Blackwood, Gary L. Moonshine. 1999. (Accelerated Reader Bks.). 160p. (J). (gr. 3-7). 14.95 (978-0-7614-5056-6(4) , Cavendish Children's Bks.) Cavendish, Marshall Corp.

Boelts, Maribeth. Those Shoes. Jones, Noah Z., illus. 2007. 40p. (J). (gr. k-3). 15.99 (***978-0-7636-2499-6(3)***) Candlewick Pr.

Bornstein, Ruth Lercher. Butterflies & Lizards, Beryl & Me. 2002. (Illus.). 160p. (J). (gr. 3-7). 14.95 (978-0-7614-5118-1(8) , Cavendish Children's Bks.) Cavendish, Marshall Corp.

Bowman, Eddie. Gravy on a Bucket Lid. Prater, Howard, illus. 1998. (Silly Songs Ser.). (J). pap. 6.95 (978-1-56763-430-3(3)); lib. bdg. 19.95 (978-1-56763-429-7(X)) Ozark Publishing.

Brown, Don. The Notorious Izzy Fink. 2006. 160p. (J). 16.95 (978-1-59643-139-3(3)) Roaring Brook Pr.

Brown, Fletch. Street Boy. 3rd ed. 2005. 140p. reprint ed. pap. 5.99 (978-1-884543-64-7(2)) Authentic Media.

Conde, Maryse. Reves Amers. pap. 17.95 (978-2-7470-0350-6(7)) Bayard Editions FRA. *Dist:* Distribooks, Inc.

Cousain, Hattie M. When I Was Little. (J). 8.95 (978-0-9640459-0-3(7)) Cole's, C. Consultant & Pubns.

Cullen, Lynn. I Am Rembrandt's Daughter. 2007. 320p. (YA). (gr. 7 up). 16.95 (***978-1-59990-046-9(7)***) Bloomsbury Publishing.

Darrow, Sharon. Painters of Lexieville. 2003. (Illus.). 192p. (YA). (gr. 9). 16.99 (978-0-7636-1437-9(8)) Candlewick Pr.

Dembkoski, Kacey. Believe. 2004. 60p. (YA). pap. 8.95 (978-0-595-30549-0(0)) iUniverse, Inc.

Deuker, Carl. Runner. 224p. (YA). (gr. 7). 2007. pap. 7.99 (***978-0-618-73505-1(4)***, Graphia); 2005. 16.00 (978-0-618-54298-7(1)) Houghton Mifflin Co. Trade & Reference Div.

Falk, Karen. Tacianna & the Endless Ball of String. 2006. 83p. pap. 14.95 (978-1-4241-3287-4(8)) PublishAmerica, Inc.

Fine, Edith Hope & Josephson, Judith Pinkerton. Armando & the Blue Tarp School. Sosa, Hernan, illus. 2007. 32p. (J). (gr. k-4). 16.95 (***978-1-58430-278-0(X)***) Lee & Low Bks., Inc.

Ghent, Natale. No Small Thing. 2005. 256p. (J). (gr. 5-9). 15.99 (978-0-7636-2422-4(5)) Candlewick Pr.

Godby, Ron. The King of Imperial Hill. 2006. 76p. pap. 14.95 (978-1-4241-1061-2(0)) PublishAmerica, Inc.

Hartnett, Sonya. Thursday's Child. 272p. (YA). (gr. 9). 2003. (Illus.). pap. 7.99 (978-0-7636-2203-9(6)); 2002. 15.99 (978-0-7636-1620-5(6)) Candlewick Pr.

—Thursday's Child. 2000. 240p. pap. (978-0-14-029732-4(4)) Penguin Group (USA) Inc.

—Thursday's Child. 2002. (gr. 7-12). lib. bdg. 16.45 (978-0-613-69466-7(X)) Tandem Library Bks.

Hubbard, Suzanna. The Lady Who Lived in a Car. 2004. (Illus.). 32p. (J). (978-1-84458-046-0(6)) Chrysalis Children's Bks.

Lachenmeyer, Nathaniel. Broken Beaks. Ingpen, Robert R., illus. 2005. 32p. (J). 15.95 (978-0-85572-335-4(1)) Warwick Publishing CAN. *Dist:* Perseus Distribution.

Lupita Manana. 3rd ed. (J). pap., stu. ed. (978-0-13-772500-7(0)) Prentice Hall (Schl. Div.).

Madden, Kerry. Gentle's Holler. 2007. 272p. (YA). (gr. 4 up). 6.99 (978-0-14-240751-6(8) , Puffin) Penguin Group (USA) Inc.

McDonald, Joyce. Comfort Creek. 1998. 10.64 (978-0-606-13289-3(9)) Tandem Library Bks.

McGee, Marni. A Song in Bethlehem. Cockcroft, Jason, illus. 2007. 40p. (J). (gr. k-3). 15.99 (***978-0-375-83447-9(8)***); lib. bdg. 18.99 (***978-0-375-93447-6(2)***) Random Hse. Children's Bks. (Knopf Bks. for Young Readers).

Meyer, Carolyn. Marie, Dancing. (Illus.). 272p. (YA). (gr. 7 up). 2007. pap. 6.95 (978-0-15-205879-1(6) , Harcourt Paperbacks); 2005. 17.00 (978-0-15-205116-7(3) , Gulliver Bks.) Harcourt Children's Bks.

Michael, Livi. The Whispering Road. 2006. 336p. (J). (gr. 5). pap. 6.99 (978-0-14-240724-0(0) , Puffin); 2005. 272p. (YA). (gr. 4). 17.99 (978-0-399-24357-8(7) , Putnam Juvenile) Penguin Group (USA) Inc.

Morgan, Nicola. Fleshmarket. 2004. 224p. (YA). (gr. 9). lib. bdg. 17.99 (978-0-385-90192-5(5) , Delacorte Bks. for Young Readers) Random Hse. Children's Bks.

Morpurgo, Michael. Private Peaceful. 2006. 176p. (J). pap. 5.99 (978-0-439-63653-7(1) , Scholastic Paperbacks) Scholastic, Inc.

—Private Peaceful. l.t. ed. 2006. 225p. (J). 21.95 (978-0-7862-8946-2(5)) Thorndike Pr.

Mowry, Jess. Babylon Boyz. Gore, Leonid, illus. 1999. 192p. (YA). (gr. 8-12). mass mkt. 10.95 (978-0-689-82592-7(7) , 076714008007, Simon Pulse) Simon & Schuster Children's Publishing.

—Babylon Boyz. 1999. (J). (978-0-606-16318-7(2)) Tandem Library Bks.

Newton, Robert. Runner. 2007. 224p. (J). (gr. 5). lib. bdg. 18.99 (978-0-375-93744-6(7) , Knopf Bks. for Young Readers) Random Hse. Children's Bks.

Noble, Trinka Hakes. The Orange Shoes. Ettlinger, Doris, illus. rev. ed. 2007. (General Ser.). 40p. (J). (gr. 1-7). 16.95 (***978-1-58536-277-6(8)***) Sleeping Bear Pr.

Qamar, Amjed. Beneath My Mother's Feet. 2008. 208p. (J). (***978-1-4169-4728-8(0)***) Simon & Schuster Children's Publishing.

Roth, Judith L. & Rothshank, Brooke, illus. Cups Held Out. 2006. 40p. (J). (978-0-8361-9316-9(4)) Herald Pr.

Schraff, Anne. Hear That Whistle Blow. 1999. (Passages Ser.). 119p. (J). (gr. 5-12). lib. bdg. 13.95 (978-0-7807-8970-8(9)) Perfection Learning Corp.

Sidney, Margaret. Five Little Peppers & How They Grew. 2006. (Dover Value Editions Ser.). (Illus.). 224p. (J). pap. 5.95 (978-0-486-45267-8(0)) Dover Pubns., Inc.

Smith, Joye. What Does It Mean to Be Poor? 2005. (Illus.). 30p. (J). 8.99 (978-1-56309-880-2(6)) Woman's Missionary Union.

Snicket, Lemony, pseud. Una Funesta Finestra. par. 21.95 (978-88-7782-953-5(2)) Salani ITA. *Dist:* Distribooks, Inc.

St. John, Patricia. Star of Light. 2002. (Illus.). 160p. (YA). pap. 6.99 (978-0-8024-6577-1(3)) Moody Pubs.

Stretton, Hesba. Cassy. Hymper, W. & Stacey, W. S., illus. 2006. (Golden Inheritance Ser.: Vol. 9). 117p. (J). pap. (978-0-921100-94-2(9)) Inheritance Pubns.

—Jessica's First Prayer. 2004. reprint ed. pap. 15.95 (978-1-4191-2751-9(9)); pap. 1.99 (978-1-4192-2751-6(3)) Kessinger Publishing, LLC.

—Little Meg's Children. 2000. (Golden Inheritance Ser.: Vol. 5). (Illus.). 88p. (J). pap. (978-0-921100-92-8(2)) Inheritance Pubns.

—Little Meg's Children. (Early Children's Bks.). (J). reprint ed. 15.00 (978-0-384-56160-1(8)) Johnson Reprint Corp.

—Lost Gip. 2003. (Golden Inheritance Ser.: Vol. 7). (Illus.). 121p. (J). (978-0-921100-93-5(0)) Inheritance Pubns.

Wolf-Sampath, Gita, et al. Elephants Never Forget. 1999. (Illus.). 112p. (978-81-86211-04-5(7)) Tara Publishing.

Wyatt, Leslie J. Poor Is Just a Starting Place. 2005. 192p. (J). (gr. 6-17). 16.95 (978-0-8234-1884-8(7)) Holiday Hse., Inc.

POWELL, JOHN WESLEY, 1834-1902

Harcourt School Publishers Staff. The Story of John Wesley Powell On Level. 3rd ed. 2002. (Trophies Reading Program Ser.). (Illus.). pap. 5.10 (978-0-15-323455-2(5)) Harcourt Schl. Pubs.

Maynard, Charles W. John Wesley Powell: Soldier, Scientist, & Explorer. 2003. (Famous Explorers of the American West Ser.). (Illus.). 24p. (J). lib. bdg. 18.75 (978-0-8239-6290-7(3) , PowerKids Pr.) Rosen Publishing Group, Inc., The.

Powell, John Wesley. The Diary of John Wesley Powell: Exploring the Grand Canyon. Roop, Connie & Roop, Peter, eds. 2000. (In My Own Words Ser.). (Illus.). 96p. (J). (gr. 5 up). lib. bdg. 24.21 (978-0-7614-1013-3(9) , Benchmark Bks.) Cavendish, Marshall Corp.

Ray, Deborah Kogan. Down the Colorado: The Story of John Wesley Powell, the One-Armed Explorer. 2007. (Illus.). 48p. (J). (gr. 3 up). 17.00 (978-0-374-31838-3(7)) Farrar, Straus & Giroux.

Ross, Michael Elsohn. Exploring the Earth with John Wesley Powell. Smith, Wendy, illus. 2006. 48p. (J). (gr. 4-10). reprint ed. 19.00 (978-1-4223-5581-7(0)) DIANE Publishing Co.

—Exploring the Earth with John Wesley Powell. Smith, Wendy, illus. 2005. (Naturalist's Apprentice Biographies Ser.). 48p. (gr. 3-6). lib. bdg. 19.93 (978-1-57505-254-0(7)) Lerner Publishing Group.

Souza, Dorothy M. John Wesley Powell. 2004. (Watts Library). (Illus.). 64p. (J). (gr. 5-7). pap. 8.95 (978-0-531-16653-6(8)); 25.50 (978-0-531-12289-1(1)) Scholastic Library Publishing. (Watts, Franklin).

POWER (MECHANICS)

see also Electric Power; Force and Energy; Machinery; Water Power

Barraclough, Sue. Pushing & Pulling. 2006. (Illus.). 24p. (J). (978-1-4109-2263-2(4)); (978-1-4109-2258-8(8)) Steck-Vaughn.

Farndon, John. Energy. 2002. (Science Experiments Ser.). (J). 25.64 (978-0-7614-1469-8(X) , Benchmark Bks.) Cavendish, Marshall Corp.

Greenberger, Robert. How Do We Know the Nature of Energy. 2005. (Great Scientific Questions & the Scientists Who Answered Them Ser.). (Illus.). 112p. (J). (gr. 7-12). lib. bdg. 26.50 (978-1-4042-0076-0(2)) Rosen Publishing Group, Inc., The.

Grimshaw, Caroline. Energy. 2000. (Invisible Journeys Ser.). (Illus.). 32p. (J). (gr. 3-6). 10.95 (978-1-58728-331-4(X)); pap. 5.95 (978-1-58728-327-7(1)) T&N Children's Publishing. (Two Can Publishing).

Nardo, Don. Kinetic Energy: The Energy of Motion. Schultz, Ashlee & Hossain, Farhana, illus. 2007. (J). lib. bdg. (***978-0-7565-3378-6(3)***) Compass Point Bks.

Parker, Steve. The Science of Forces: Projects with Experiments on Forces & Machines. 2005. (Illus.). 32p. (J). pap. 11.09 (978-1-4034-7292-2(0)); lib. bdg. (978-1-4034-7285-4(8)) Heinemann Library.

Phelan, Glen. Introduction to Energy. 2004. (Illus.). 32p. (J). pap. (978-0-7922-4580-3(6)) National Geographic Society.

Spilsbury, Richard & Spilsbury, Louise. What Is Energy? Exploring Science with Hands-On Activities. 2008. (In Touch with Basic Science Ser.). 32p. (J). (gr. 3-4). lib. bdg. 22.60 (***978-0-7660-3099-2(7)***) Enslow Pubs., Inc.

Webster, Christine. Energy. 2004. (First Facts Ser.). 24p. (J). lib. bdg. 21.26 (978-0-7368-2616-7(5)) Capstone Pr., Inc.

Whitehouse, Patricia. Pulling. 2003. (Illus.). 24p. (J). pap. (978-1-4034-3468-5(9)); lib. bdg. 18.50 (978-1-4034-0909-6(9)) Heinemann Library.

—Pushing. 2003. (Illus.). 24p. (J). pap. (978-1-4034-3469-2(7)); lib. bdg. 18.50 (978-1-4034-0908-9(0)) Heinemann Library.

Woodford, Chris. Power & Energy. 2004. (History of Invention Ser.). (Illus.). 96p. (gr. 6-12). 35.00 (978-0-8160-5440-4(1)) Facts On File, Inc.

—Ships & Submarines. 2004. (History of Invention Ser.). (Illus.). 96p. (YA). (gr. 6-12). 35.00 (978-0-8160-5439-8(8)) Facts On File, Inc.

POWER (SOCIAL SCIENCES)

Kallen, Stuart A. Are America's Wealthy Too Powerful? 2006. (Illus.). 128p. (gr. 10-12). 21.20 (978-0-7377-3430-0(2)); pap. 29.95 (978-0-7377-3429-4(9)) Thomson Gale. (Greenhaven Pr., Inc.).

POWER BOATS

see Motorboats

POWER RESOURCES

see also Electric Power; Fuel; Solar Energy; Water Power

Altman, Paula, ed. Energy Education Resources: Kindergarten through 12th Grade (1999) 2000. 102p. (YA). pap. 20.00 (978-0-7881-8577-9(2)) DIANE Publishing Co.

Ballard, Carol. From Steam Engines to Nuclear Fusion: Discovering Energy. 2007. (Chain Reactions Ser.). (Illus.). 64p. (YA). (gr. 6-9). lib. bdg. 34.29 (***978-1-4034-9554-9(8)***) Heinemann Library.

Bedford, Kate. Energy: Coal. 2006. (J). (978-1-59604-109-7(9)) Stargazer Bks.

—Energy: Oil. 2006. (Illus.). 31p. (978-1-59604-106-6(4)) Stargazer Bks.

Beres, Samantha. Recursos energéticos alrededor del mundo & Energy Resources Around the World. 2005. spiral bd. 88.00 (***978-1-4108-5738-5(7)***) Benchmark Education Co.

Bohn & MacDonald. Energy Technology: Power & Transportation. 4th ed. 1999. (Illus.). 288p. (YA). (gr. 6-12). stu. ed., wbk. ed. 8.87 (978-0-02-675402-6(9)) Glencoe/McGraw-Hill.

Bowden, Rob. Energy: Future Energy. 2006. (Illus.). 32p. (J). (978-1-59604-110-3(2)) Stargazer Bks.

Casper, Julie Kerr. Energy: Powering the Past, Present, & Future. 2007. (Natural Resources Ser.). 224p. (gr. 6-12). 39.50 (***978-0-8160-6354-3(0)*** , Chelsea Hse.) Facts On File, Inc.

Center for Mathematics, Science, and Technology, Illinois State University Staff, contrib. by. Integrated Mathematics, Science & Technology: Energy Transformation. 1999. (Illus.). (YA). (gr. 6-12). stu. ed. 14.99 (978-0-02-647846-5(3)) Glencoe/McGraw-Hill.

Challoner, Jack. Energy. 2000. (Eyewitness Bks.). (Illus.). 64p. (J). (gr. 3-7). 15.99 (978-0-7894-5576-5(5)) Dorling Kindersley Publishing, Inc.

Challoner, Jack & Dorling Kindersley Publishing Staff. Energy. 2000. (Eyewitness Bks.). (Illus.). 64p. (J). (gr. 4-7). lib. bdg. 19.99 (978-0-7894-6710-2(0)) Dorling Kindersley Publishing, Inc.

Chapman, Steven & Saunders, Nigel. Energy Transfers. 2005. (Freestyle Express Ser.). (Illus.). 48p. (J). (gr. 5-8). lib. bdg. 31.43 (978-1-4109-1695-2(2)) Steck-Vaughn.

The Coal Fired Power Facility. 2002. (YA). (gr. 9-12). cd-rom 24.95 (978-0-9703694-8-2(4)) Awesome Guides, Inc.

Cobb, Allan B. Super Science Projects about Energy & Motion. 2005. (Psyched for Science Ser.). (Illus.). 48p. (YA). (gr. 5-8). lib. bdg. 23.95 (978-0-8239-3116-3(1) , SCENMO) Rosen Publishing Group, Inc., The.

Cruden, Gabriel. Energy Alternatives. 2004. (Lucent Library of Science & Technology). (Illus.). 112p. (J). (gr. 7-10). 29.95 (978-1-59018-530-8(7) , Lucent Bks.) Thomson Gale.

Dann, Sarah. The Science of Energy. 2000. (Living Science Ser.). (Illus.). 32p. (J). (gr. 2 up). lib. bdg. 24.67 (978-0-8368-2571-8(3)) Stevens, Gareth Inc.

De Angelis, Therese. Blackout! Cities in Darkness. 2003. (American Disasters Ser.). (Illus.). 48p. (J). (gr. 4-10). lib. bdg. 23.93 (978-0-7660-2110-5(6)) Enslow Pubs., Inc.

de la Garza, Amanda. Biomass: Energy from Plants & Animals. 2006. (Illus.). 244p. (gr. 10-12). 34.95 (978-0-7377-3586-4(4) , Greenhaven Pr., Inc.) Thomson Gale.

Egendorf, Laura K. Energy Alternatives. 2006. 80-244*p. (gr. 7-10). 33.70 (978-0-7377-3458-4(2) , Greenhaven Pr., Inc.) Thomson Gale.

Featherstone, Jane. Energy. 1999. (Ecology Alert Ser.). 32p. (YA). (gr. 3-7). 25.69 (978-0-8172-5374-5(2)) Raintree.

Fix, Alexandra. Energy. 2007. (J). (***978-1-4034-9715-4(X)***); pap. (***978-1-4034-9723-9(0)***) Heinemann Library.

Fullick, Ann. Turning up the Heat: Energy. (Illus.). 56p. (J). 2005. pap. (978-1-4034-6423-1(5)); 2004. lib. bdg. (978-1-4034-4817-0(5)) Heinemann Library.

Geothermal Power. (Energy at Work Ser.). 32p. (J). 7.95 (978-0-7368-5191-6(7)) Capstone Pr., Inc.

Giacobello, John. Nuclear Power of the Future: New Ways of Turning Atoms into Energy. 2005. (Library of Energy of the Future). (Illus.). 64p. (YA). (gr. 7-12). lib. bdg. 26.50 (978-0-8239-3661-8(9)) Rosen Publishing Group, Inc., The.

Gibson, Diane. Fossil Fuels. 2001. (Sources of Energy Ser.). (Illus.). 32p. (J). (gr. 2-7). lib. bdg. 21.30 (978-1-887068-75-8(9)) Smart Apple Media.

—Sources of Energy, 6 vols., Set. 2001. (Illus.). (J). (gr. 2-7). lib. bdg. 127.80 (978-1-58340-029-6(X)) Smart Apple Media.

Gifford, Clive. Energy. 2005. (Planet under Pressure Ser.). (Illus.). 48p. (J). (978-1-4034-7744-6(2)) Heinemann Library.

Gish, Melissa. Energy. 2005. (My First Look at Science Ser.). (Illus.). 24p. (gr. k-3). 15.95 (978-1-58341-372-2(3) , Creative Education) Creative Co., The.

Gold-Dworkin, Heidi, et al. Learn about the Way Things Move. 2000. (Little Science Hands-on Ser.). (Illus.). 58p. (C). (ps-3). pap. 12.95 (978-0-07-134824-9(7) , 9780071348249) McGraw-Hill Cos., The.

Green, Jen. Energy for the Future. 2006. (Illus.). 32p. (YA). (gr. 4 up). lib. bdg. 27.10 (978-1-59389-119-0(9)) Chrysalis Education.

—Why Should I Save Energy? Gordon, Mike, illus. 2005. 32p. (J). (ps-ps). lib. bdg. 13.15 (978-0-606-33633-8(8)) Tandem Library Bks.

Grimshaw, Caroline. Energy. 2000. (Invisible Journeys Ser.). (Illus.). 32p. (J). (gr. 3-6). 10.95 (978-1-58728-331-4(X)); pap. 5.95 (978-1-58728-327-7(1)) T&N Children's Publishing. (Two Can Publishing).

Grossman, Marvin C., et al. ARIES Exploring Energy: Waterwheels, Windmills & Sunlight: Science Journal. 2000. (Illus.). (J). (gr. 3-8). pap. 3.80 (978-1-57091-252-8(1)) Charlesbridge Publishing, Inc.

Gunkel, Darrin. Alternative Energy Sources. 2006. (Illus.). 244p. (gr. 10-12). 24.95 (978-0-7377-3408-9(6)); pap. 36.20 (978-0-7377-3407-2(8)) Thomson Gale. (Greenhaven Pr., Inc.).

Harlow, Rosie. Energy & Power: Environmental Facts & Experiments. 2002. (Young Discoverers Ser.). (Illus.). 32p. (J). (gr. k-3). pap. 7.95 (978-0-7534-5502-9(1) , Kingfisher) Houghton Mifflin Co. Trade & Reference Div.

—Energy & Power: Environmental Facts & Experiments. 2002. (gr. k-3). lib. bdg. 16.40 (978-0-613-90900-6(3)) Tandem Library Bks.

Harman, Rebecca. The Earth's Resources. 2005. (Heinemann Infosearch Ser.). (Illus.). 32p. (J). pap. (978-1-4034-7068-3(5)); lib. bdg. (978-1-4034-7061-4(8)) Heinemann Library.

Hayhurst, Chris. Hydrogen Power: New Ways of Turning Fuel Cells into Energy. 2005. (Library of Future Energy). (Illus.). 64p. (YA). (gr. 7-12). lib. bdg. 26.50 (978-0-8239-3666-3(X)) Rosen Publishing Group, Inc., The.

Hewitt, Sally. Full of Energy. Cohen, Helaine, ed. 1998. (It's Science! Ser.). (Illus.). 32p. (J). (gr. k-3). pap. 6.95 (978-0-516-26391-5(9) , Children's Pr.) Scholastic Library Publishing.

—Jump to the Moon: (Energy) 2002. (Why Can't I Ser.). (Illus.). 32p. (J). lib. bdg. 24.95 (978-1-930643-67-3(5)) Chrysalis Education.

Holt, Rinehart and Winston Staff. Environmental Science Chptr. 17: Nonrenewable Energy. 4th ed. Date not set. pap. 11.20 (978-0-03-068078-6(6)) Holt, Rinehart & Winston.

—Holt Science & Technology Chapter 5: Earth Science: Energy Resources. 5th ed. 2004. (Illus.). pap. 12.86 (978-0-03-030286-2(2)) Holt, Rinehart & Winston.

Jefferis, David. Green Power. 2006. (Science Frontiers Ser.). (Illus.). 32p. (J). (gr. 3-9). pap. (978-0-7787-2871-9(4) , 1253435) Crabtree Publishing Co.

—Green Power: Eco-Energy Without Pollution. 2006. (Science Frontiers Ser.). (Illus.). 32p. (J). (gr. 3-9). (978-0-7787-2857-3(9) , 1253435) Crabtree Publishing Co.

Jones, Susan. Solar Power of the Future: New Ways of Turning Sunlight into Energy. 2005. (Library of Future Energy). (Illus.). 64p. (YA). (gr. 7-12). lib. bdg. 26.50 (978-0-8239-3663-2(5)) Rosen Publishing Group, Inc., The.

Juettner, Bonnie. Energy. 2004. (Our Environment Ser.). (Illus.). 48p. (J). (ps-7). lib. bdg. 26.20 (978-0-7377-1821-8(8) , Greenhaven Pr., Inc.) Thomson Gale.

Kravetz, Jonathan. Learning about Energy with Graphic Organizers. 2007. (Graphic Organizers in Science Ser.). (Illus.). 24p. (J). lib. bdg. (978-1-4042-3409-3(8) , PowerKids Pr.) Rosen Publishing Group, Inc., The.

Lafferty, Peter. Forces & Motion. 2000. (Science Fact Files Ser.). (Illus.). 48p. (J). (gr. 4-7). lib. bdg. 27.12 (978-0-7398-1007-1(3)) Raintree.

Landau, Elaine. The History of Energy. 2006. (Major Inventions Through History Ser.). (Illus.). 56p. (J). (gr. 3-7). 26.60 (978-0-8225-3806-6(7) , Twenty-First Century Bks.) Lerner Publishing Group.

The Library of Future Energy. 2005. (Illus.). (gr. 7-12). lib. bdg. 212.00 (978-0-8239-3901-5(4)) Rosen Publishing Group, Inc., The.

Llewellyn, Claire. Save Energy. 2005. (Illus.). 32p. (YA). (gr. 1 up). lib. bdg. 27.10 (978-1-932333-23-7(1)) Chrysalis Education.

Logan, Michale. Coal. 2007. (Opposing Viewpoints Ser.). (Illus.). 240p. (gr. 10-12). 36.20 (***978-0-7377-3908-4(8)***); pap. 24.95 (***978-0-7377-3909-1(6)***) Thomson Gale. (Greenhaven Pr., Inc.).

Lopatka, Michael. The Natural Gas Power Facility. 2002. (YA). (gr. 9-12). cd-rom 24.95 (978-0-9703694-9-9(2)) Awesome Guides, Inc.

Malnor, Carol. A Teacher's Guide to Nature's Food Chain: Lesson Plans to Teach Nature's Food Chains. 2000. (Illus.). 48p. (J). (gr. 3-6). pap. 7.95 (978-1-58469-007-8(0)) Dawn Pubns.

Mason, Paul. Wackiest Machines Ever: Forms of Energy. 2005. (Illus.). 32p. (J). (978-1-4109-1946-5(3)) Steck-Vaughn.

—Wackiest Machines Ever! Forms of Energy. 2005. (Illus.). 32p. (J). (gr. 3-5). lib. bdg. 28.21 (978-1-4109-1915-1(3)) Steck-Vaughn.

McKinney, Barbara Shaw. Pass the Energy, Please! Wallace, Chad, illus. 2004. (Justin's & Kevin's Great Backyard Adventures Ser.). 32p. (YA). (gr. 1-8). 7.95 (978-1-58469-002-3(X)); pap. 16.95 (978-1-58469-001-6(1)) Dawn Pubns.

—Pass the Energy, Please! 1999. (gr. k-3). lib. bdg. 16.40 (978-0-613-65312-1(2)) Tandem Library Bks.

McLeish, Ewan. Energy Crisis. 2006. (Issues of the World Ser.). (Illus.). 48p. (J). (978-1-59604-091-5(2) , 1262574) Stargazer Bks.

Miller, Kimberly M. What If We Run Out of Fossil Fuels? 2002. (High Interest Bks.). (Illus.). 48p. (YA). (gr. 7-12). pap. 6.95 (978-0-516-23478-6(1) , Children's Pr.) Scholastic Library Publishing.

—What If We Run Out of Fossil Fuels? 2002. (gr. 7-12). lib. bdg. 15.25 (978-0-613-58819-5(3)) Tandem Library Bks.

Moor, Jo Ellen & Norris, Jill. Energy: Heat, Light & Sound: Light, Heat & Sound: Light, Heat & Sound. Evans, Marilyn, ed. Robison, Don, illus. 1998. (ScienceWorks for Kids Ser.: Vol. 9). 80p. (J). (gr. 1-3). pap., tchr. ed. 9.95 (978-1-55799-690-9(3) , EMC 861) Evan-Moor Educational Pubs.

Morgan, Sally. Alternative Energy Sources. 2003. (Science at the Edge Ser.). (Illus.). 64p. (J). (gr. 6-8). lib. bdg. 27.86 (978-1-4034-0322-3(8)) Heinemann Library.

—Energy. 2007. (***978-1-4034-9924-0(1)***); pap. (***978-1-4034-9932-5(2)***) Heinemann Library.

—From Windmills to Hydrogen Fuel Cells: Discovering Alternative Energy. 2007. (Chain Reactions Ser.). (Illus.). 64p. (YA). (gr. 6-9). lib. bdg. 34.29 (***978-1-4034-9555-6(6)***) Heinemann Library.

Morgan, Sally. Future Energy. 2005. (Your Environment Ser.). (Illus.). 32p. (J). (gr. 3-7). lib. bdg. 27.10 (978-1-59604-061-8(0)) Stargazer Bks.

Morris, Neil. Geothermal Power. 2006. (Illus.). 32p. (J). (978-1-58340-906-0(8)) Smart Apple Media.

Muschal, Frank. Biofuels. 2008. (J). lib. bdg. 25.26 (***978-1-60279-045-2(0)***) Cherry Lake Publishing.

Nakaya, Andrea C. Energy Alternatives. 2007. (J). lib. bdg. (***978-1-60152-017-3(4)***) ReferencePoint Pr., Inc.

Nelson, Sara Elizabeth. Let's Save Energy! 2007. (Pebble Books). (Illus.). 24p. (J). 15.93 (978-0-7368-6321-6(4)) Capstone Pr., Inc.

On-Site Power Generation: A Reference Book. 4th ed. 2002. per. 95.00 (978-0-9625949-4-6(6)) Electrical Generating Systems Assn.

Orr, Tamra. Geothermal Energy. 2008. (J). lib. bdg. 25.26 (***978-1-60279-044-5(2)***) Cherry Lake Publishing.

Oxlade, Chris. Energy. 2003. (Science Topics Ser.). (Illus.). 32p. (YA). (gr. 6-8). lib. bdg. 24.22 (978-1-57572-766-0(8)) Heinemann Library.

—Energy. 2004. (Illus.). 44p. (J). lib. bdg. 28.50 (978-1-58340-505-5(4)) Smart Apple Media.

—Renewable Energy. 2004. (Illus.). (J). pap. 7.95 (978-1-4109-0503-1(9)); 48p. lib. bdg. 29.93 (978-1-4109-0497-3(0)); lib. bdg. 42.90 (978-1-4109-0809-4(7)) Raintree.

Passero, Barbara. Energy Alternatives. 2006. (Illus.). 244p. (YA). (gr. 9 up). pap. 24.95 (978-0-7377-3351-8(9)); lib. bdg. 36.20 (978-0-7377-3350-1(0)) Thomson Gale. (Greenhaven Pr., Inc.).

Peters, Celeste, ed. The Energy Dilemma. 2002. (Understanding Global Issues). (Illus.). 56p. (YA). (gr. 10-12). 19.95 (978-1-58340-169-9(5)) Weigl Pubs., Inc.

Povey, Karen D. Energy Alternatives. 2007. (Hot Topics Ser.). 128p. (J). (gr. 7-10). 31.20 (***978-1-59018-980-1(9)*** , Lucent Bks.) Thomson Gale.

Raum, Elizabeth. Potato Clocks & Solar Cars. 2007. (J). (***978-1-4109-2849-8(7)***); (***978-1-4109-2866-5(7)***) Steck-Vaughn.

Redmond, Jim. Oil Makes Gasoline Power. 2003. (From Resource to Energy Source Ser.). (J). (978-1-58417-292-5(4)); pap. (978-1-58417-293-2(2)) Lake Street Pubs.

Riddle, John. Coal Power of the Future: New Ways of Turning Coal into Energy. 2005. (Library of Energy of the Future). (Illus.). 64p. (YA). (gr. 7-12). lib. bdg. 26.50 (978-0-8239-3660-1(0)) Rosen Publishing Group, Inc., The.

Riley, Peter D. Energy. 1998. (Cycles in Science Ser.). (Illus.). 32p. (J). (gr. 4-7). lib. bdg. 21.36 (978-1-57572-617-5(3)) Heinemann Library.

Royston, Angela. Energy of the Future. 2007. (J). pap. (***978-1-4329-0134-9(6)***); lib. bdg. (***978-1-4329-0129-5(X)***) Heinemann Library.

Sadler, Wendy. Energy: Get Moving! 2005. (Raintree Perspectives Ser.). (Illus.). 32p. (J). (978-1-4109-1553-5(0)); pap. (978-1-4109-1561-0(1)) Steck-Vaughn.

Saunders, N. Geothermal Energy. 2007. (J). pap. (***978-0-8368-8409-8(4)***) Stevens, Gareth Inc.

Saunders, N. & Chapman, Steven. Energy Transfers. 2005. (Freestyle Express Ser.). (Illus.). 48p. (J). (978-1-4109-1700-3(2)) Steck-Vaughn.

Saunders, Nigel. Geothermal Energy. 2007. (Energy for the Future & Global Warming Ser.). 24p. (J). (gr. 3-5). lib. bdg. 26.60 (***978-0-8368-8400-5(0)***) Stevens, Gareth Inc.

Savage, Lorraine. Geothermal Power. 2006. (Fueling the Future Ser.). (Illus.). 244p. (J). (gr. 10-12). 34.95 (978-0-7377-3579-6(1) , 1256642, Greenhaven Pr., Inc.) Thomson Gale.

Sherman, Josepha. Energy at Work. (Fact Finders Ser.). (Illus.). (J). (gr. 3-4). lib. bdg. 135.60 (978-0-7368-2557-3(6)) Capstone Pr., Inc.

Smith, Eileen M. ElectriCity Beyond the Curve of Deregulation: Neighborhood Energy Watch Groups & the Ethos of Commerce. 2003. per. (978-0-9741412-9-9(1)) Ethos Of Commerce Pubs., Ltd.

Smith, Trevor. Renewable Energy Resources. King, Nicole Bezic, ed. 2004. (Understanding Global Issues Ser.). (Illus.). 56p. (J). (gr. 10-12). (978-1-58340-361-7(2)) Smart Apple Media.

Snedden, Robert. Energy Alternatives. 2006. (Illus.). 48p. (J). (978-1-4034-8731-5(6)); 2nd ed. pap. (978-1-4034-8736-0(7)) Heinemann Library.

—Energy from Fossil Fuels. (Illus.). 48p. (J). 2006. (978-1-4034-8732-2(4)); 2001. (gr. 5-7). lib. bdg. 24.22 (978-1-57572-442-3(1)); 2nd ed. 2006. pap. (978-1-4034-8737-7(5)) Heinemann Library.

Sobha, Geeta. Green Technology: Earth-Friendly Innovations. 2007. (J). (***978-1-4042-1914-4(5)***) Rosen Publishing Group, Inc., The.

Solway, Andrew. Energy. 2007. (J). lib. bdg. (***978-1-4042-3748-3(8)*** , Rosen Central) Rosen Publishing Group, Inc., The.

Spilsbury, Richard & Spilsbury, Louise. What Is Energy? Exploring Science with Hands-On Activities. 2008. (In Touch with Basic Science Ser.). 32p. (J). (gr. 3-4). lib. bdg. 22.60 (***978-0-7660-3099-2(7)***) Enslow Pubs., Inc.

Stille, Darlene R. Energy. 2004. (Science Around Us Ser.). 32p. (J). (gr. 2-6). 27.07 (978-1-59296-220-4(3)) Child's World, Inc.

—Energy: Heat, Light, & Food. Boyd, Sheree, illus. 2004. (Amazing Science Ser.). 24p. (C). (gr. k-4). 22.60 (978-1-4048-0249-0(5)) Picture Window Bks.

Stringer, John. Energy. 2006. (Sustainable Futures Ser.). (Illus.). 48p. (J). (978-1-58340-979-4(3) , 1262621) Smart Apple Media.

Tecco, Betsy Dru. Wind Power of the Future: New Ways of Turning Wind into Energy. 2003. (Library of Future Energy). (Illus.). 64p. (YA). lib. bdg. 26.50 (978-0-8239-3665-6(1)) Rosen Publishing Group, Inc., The.

Thomas, Isabel. Biomass: The Pros & Cons. 2007. (J). lib. bdg. (***978-1-4042-3742-1(9)***) Rosen Publishing Group, Inc., The.

Tiner, John Hudson. Coal Makes Electric Power. 2003. (From Resource to Energy Source Ser.). (J). (978-1-58417-294-9(0)); (978-1-58417-295-6(9)) Lake Street Pubs.

Top That Publishing Staff, ed. Lets Learn about Energy. 2004. (Fun Kits Ser.). (Illus.). 48p. (J). (978-1-904748-98-4(8)) Top That! Publishing PLC.

VanCleave, Janice Pratt. Energy for Every Kid: Easy Activities That Make Learning Science Fun. 2005. (Science for Every Kid Ser.). (Illus.). 240p. (gr. 3-7). pap. 12.95 (978-0-471-33099-8(X) , Wiley) Wiley, John & Sons, Inc.

Weber, Rebecca. Feel the Power! 2002. (Spyglass Books). (Illus.). 24p. (J). (gr. 1 up). lib. bdg. 18.60 (978-0-7565-0386-4(8)) Compass Point Bks.

Webster, Christine. Energy. 2004. (First Facts Ser.). 24p. (J). lib. bdg. 21.26 (978-0-7368-2616-7(5)) Capstone Pr., Inc.

Wheeler, Jill C. Everyday Conservation. 2007. (Eye on Energy Ser.). (Illus.). 32p. (J). (gr. k-6). lib. bdg. 24.21 (***978-1-59928-804-8(4)*** , Checkerboard Library) ABDO Publishing Co.

—Nature Power. 2007. (Eye on Energy Ser.). (Illus.). 32p. (J). (gr. k-6). lib. bdg. 24.21 (***978-1-59928-806-2(0)*** , Checkerboard Library) ABDO Publishing Co.

—Renewable Fuels. 2007. (Eye on Energy Ser.). (Illus.). 32p. (J). (gr. k-6). lib. bdg. 24.21 (***978-1-59928-808-6(7)*** , Checkerboard Library) ABDO Publishing Co.

Whitehouse, Patricia. Energy Everywhere. 2007. (J). (978-1-60044-189-9(0)) Rourke Publishing, LLC.
Woodford, Chris. Power & Energy. 2004. (History of Invention Ser.). (Illus.). 96p. (gr. 6-12). 35.00 (978-0-8160-5440-4(1)) Facts On File, Inc.
—Ships & Submarines. 2004. (History of Invention Ser.). (Illus.). 96p. (YA). (gr. 6-12). 35.00 (978-0-8160-5439-8(8)) Facts On File, Inc.

POWER SUPPLY

see Power Resources

POWERPUFF GIRLS (FICTITIOUS CHARACTERS)—FICTION

Brewster, Joy, et al. Summer Fun: Sticker Storybook. Binder, Eric & Thompson Brothers Staff, illus. 2003. (Powerpuff Girls Ser.). 24p. (J). pap. 5.99 (978-0-439-44934-2(0)) Scholastic, Inc.
Cartoon Network Staff. Buttercup. 2001. (Powerpuff Girls Ser.). (Illus.). 32p. (J). (ps-3). pap. 3.99 (978-0-307-10802-9(3) , Golden Bks.) Random Hse. Children's Bks.
Cartoon Network Staff & Dower, Laura. Bubble Trouble. 2000. (Powerpuff Girls Ser.: Vol. 2). (Illus.). 32p. (J). (ps-3). pap. 3.50 (978-0-439-17306-3(X)) Scholastic, Inc.
CEDCO Publishing Staff. Powerpuff Girls. 2000. (Gel Pen Blank Bks.). (Illus.). 96p. (J). (gr. 4-7). 9.95 (978-0-7683-2229-3(4)) CEDCO Publishing.
Dalmatian Press Staff. Blossom: Key Chain Book. 2003. (Powerpuff Girls Ser.). (Illus.). 48p. (J). pap. 3.99 (978-1-4037-0192-3(X)) Dalmatian Pr.
—Bubbles: Key Chain Book. 2003. (Powerpuff Girls Ser.). (Illus.). 48p. (J). pap. 3.99 (978-1-4037-0193-0(8)) Dalmatian Pr.
—Buttercup: Key Chain Book. 2003. (Powerpuff Girls Ser.). (Illus.). 48p. (J). pap. 3.99 (978-1-4037-0194-7(6)) Dalmatian Pr.
—Power Play: Glitter Paint Box Book. 2002. (Powerpuff Girls Ser.). (Illus.). 32p. (J). 3.99 (978-1-57759-870-1(9)) Dalmatian Pr.
Dalmatian Press Staff, creator. The Powerpuff Girls: Power Adventure Box. 2003. (Books & Stuff Kits Ser.). (J). pap. 9.99 (978-1-4037-0071-1(0)) Dalmatian Pr.
Denson, Abby. Cover Up. Marderosian, Marc, illus. 2002. (Powerpuff Girls Ser.). 24p. (J). (ps-3). pap. 5.99 (978-0-439-37230-5(5)) Scholastic, Inc.
Dower, Laura. Bubble Trouble. 2000. (gr. k-3). lib. bdg. 11.25 (978-0-613-24426-8(5)) Tandem Library Bks.
—Let the Fur Fly. 2002. (gr. k-3). lib. bdg. 11.25 (978-0-613-64743-4(2)) Tandem Library Bks.
—Mojo Jojo's Rising. 2000. (gr. k-3). lib. bdg. 11.25 (978-0-613-26246-0(8)) Tandem Library Bks.
—Monkey See, Doggy Do. 2000. (ps-2). lib. bdg. 11.25 (978-0-613-32842-5(6)) Tandem Library Bks.
—Paste Makes Waste. 2000. (ps-2). lib. bdg. 11.25 (978-0-613-32931-6(7)) Tandem Library Bks.
—Powerpuff Girls & the Valentine's Day -up. 2002. (gr. k-3). lib. bdg. 14.15 (978-0-613-43951-0(1)) Tandem Library Bks.
—Powerpuff Girls Save Halloween. 2002. (gr. k-3). lib. bdg. 14.15 (978-0-613-50497-3(6)) Tandem Library Bks.
—Powerpuff Girls Save Valentine's Day. 2001. (gr. k-3). lib. bdg. 14.15 (978-0-613-32965-1(1)) Tandem Library Bks.
—Three Girls & a Monster. 2002. (gr. k-3). lib. bdg. 11.25 (978-0-613-43964-0(3)) Tandem Library Bks.
—The Valentine's Day Mix-Up. Ruiz, Art, illus. 2002. (Powerpuff Girls Ser.). 32p. (J). (ps-3). pap. 5.99 (978-0-439-34431-9(X) , Cartwheel Bks.) Scholastic, Inc.
Down N Dirty. 2001. (ps-2). lib. bdg. 14.15 (978-0-613-32487-8(0)) Tandem Library Bks.
Golden Books Staff. Big Terrible Trouble. 2000. (Powerpuff Girls Ser.). (Illus.). (J). (ps-3). bds. 3.99 (978-0-307-16613-5(9)); 16p. bds. 2.99 (978-0-307-99500-1(3)) Random Hse. Children's Bks. (Golden Bks.).
—Dynamo Destruction: The Powerpuff Girls. 2000. (Powerpuff Girls Ser.). (Illus.). 32p. (J). (ps-3). pap. 3.99 (978-0-307-20005-1(1) , 20005, Golden Bks.) Random Hse. Children's Bks.
—Powerpuff Girls: Coloring Book. ed. 2000. (Illus.). 70p. (J). (ps-3). pap. 2.99 (978-0-307-25736-9(3) , Golden Bks.) Random Hse. Children's Bks.
—The Powerpuff Girls: Sugar, Spice & Everything Nice. 2000. (Illus.). 16p. (J). (ps-3). pap. 2.99 (978-0-307-28328-3(3) , Golden Bks.) Random Hse. Children's Bks.
Johnson, Heather Moors. Mojo Jojo's Day Off. 2002. (Pick a Powerpuff Path Ser.). (Illus.). 64p. (J). (978-0-439-33268-2(0)) Scholastic, Inc.
Kindya, Kimberly. Blossom's Bad Hair Day. 2002. (Powerpuff Girls Plus You Club Ser.). (Illus.). 64p. (J). (978-0-439-33263-7(X)) Scholastic, Inc.
Kupperberg, Paul. Buttercup's Terrible Temper Tantrums. 2002. (Illus.). 64p. (J). (978-0-439-33260-6(5)) Scholastic, Inc.
McCracken, Craig. Bubbles Keychain Book. Romano, Lou, illus. 2000. (Powerpuff Girls Ser.). 48p. (J). (ps-3). 3.99 (978-0-307-10241-6(6) , 10241, Golden Bks.) Random Hse. Children's Bks.
McCracken, Craig, creator. The Day is Saved. 2001. (Powerpuff Girls Ser.). (Illus.). 10p. (J). bds. 7.98 (978-0-7853-4754-5(2)) Publications International, Ltd.
Mooney, E. S. Blossom to the Rescue. Alger, Bill, illus. 2001. (Powerpuff Girls Storybks.). 16p. (J). (ps-3). 7.99 (978-0-439-25057-3(9)) Scholastic, Inc.
—Blossoming Out. 2000. (gr. k-3). lib. bdg. 11.80 (978-0-613-32329-1(7)) Tandem Library Bks.
—Cartoon Crazy. 2000. (gr. k-3). lib. bdg. 11.80 (978-0-613-32373-4(4)) Tandem Library Bks.
—Fuzzy Lumpkins Show. 2003. (gr. k-3). lib. bdg. 11.80 (978-0-613-66356-4(X)) Tandem Library Bks.
—Mojo & Mini-Mo. 2003. (gr. k-3). lib. bdg. 11.80 (978-0-613-66424-0(8)) Tandem Library Bks.
—Powerpuff Girls Movie Novelization. 2002. (gr. k-3). lib. bdg. 11.80 (978-0-613-50488-1(7)) Tandem Library Bks.
—Powerpuff Girls Save the Easter Bunny. 2002. (gr. k-3). lib. bdg. 14.15 (978-0-613-50489-8(5)) Tandem Library Bks.
—Shrinky Jinx. 2002. (gr. k-3). lib. bdg. 11.80 (978-0-613-50500-0(X)) Tandem Library Bks.
—Snow Fun. 2002. (gr. k-3). lib. bdg. 11.80 (978-0-613-58168-4(7)) Tandem Library Bks.
Mooney, E. S., et al. Fuzzy Lumpkins Show. Thompson Brothers Staff, illus. 2003. (Powerpuff Girls Ser.). 64p. (J). mass mkt. 3.99 (978-0-439-44226-8(5) , Scholastic Paperbacks) Scholastic, Inc.
Much Ado at the Zoo. 2001. (gr. k-3). lib. bdg. 11.80 (978-0-613-32851-7(5)) Tandem Library Bks.
Powerpuff Girls: A Little Monstrous Problem. 2000. (Golden Super Shape Book Ser.). (Illus.). 24p. (J). (ps-3). pap. 3.29 (978-0-307-13330-4(3) , Golden Bks.) Random Hse. Children's Bks.
Powerpuff Girls Blossom. 2001. (Powerpuff Girls Ser.). (Illus.). 32p. (J). (ps-3). pap. 3.99 (978-0-307-10804-3(X) , Golden Bks.) Random Hse. Children's Bks.
Powerpuff Girls Bubbles. 2001. (Powerpuff Girls Ser.). (Illus.). 32p. (J). (ps-3). pap. 3.99 (978-0-307-10803-6(1) , Golden Bks.) Random Hse. Children's Bks.
Rogers, Amy. The Powerpuff Girls Guide to Being a Hero. 2001. 24p. pap. 3.99 (978-0-307-10773-2(6) , Golden Bks.) Random Hse. Children's Bks.
—Powerpuff Professor. 2000. (gr. k-3). lib. bdg. 11.80 (978-0-613-26655-0(2)) Tandem Library Bks.
Rogers, Amy Keating. Creature Teacher. Faust, Lauren, illus. 2001. (Powerpuff Girls Ser.). 24p. (J). (ps-3). bds. 2.99 (978-0-307-96011-5(0) , Golden Bks.) Random Hse. Children's Bks.
Romano, Lou, illus. Blossom Keychain Book. 2000. (Powerpuff Girls Ser.). 48p. (J). (ps-3). 3.99 (978-0-307-10240-9(8) , 10240, Golden Bks.) Random Hse. Children's Bks.
Super Sisters. 2001. (Powerpuff Girls Ser.). (Illus.). 32p. (J). (ps-3). pap. 4.99 (978-0-307-29950-5(3) , Golden Bks.) Random Hse. Children's Bks.
West, Tracey. Good Monster, Bad Monster. Ruiz, Art, illus. 2002. (Powerpuff Girls Readers: No. 6). 32p. (J). pap. 3.99 (978-0-439-34436-4(0)) Scholastic, Inc.
—Mayor Is Missing. 2003. (gr. 3-6). lib. bdg. 11.80 (978-0-613-58159-2(8)) Tandem Library Bks.
—The Mayor Is Missing. Thompson Brothers Staff, illus. 2003. (Powerpuff Girls Readers: No. 7). 32p. (J). (gr. 1-4). pap. 3.99 (978-0-439-44223-7(0)) Scholastic, Inc.
—No Girls Allowed. Morrow, Cindy, illus. 2001. (Powerpuff Girls Readers: No. 4). 32p. (J). pap. 3.99 (978-0-439-29588-8(2)) Scholastic, Inc.
—No Girls Allowed. 2001. (gr. k-3). lib. bdg. 11.80 (978-0-613-43857-5(4)) Tandem Library Bks.
—Power Pals. Marderosian, Marc, illus. 2002. (Powerpuff Girls Ser.: No. 13). 32p. (J). (gr. 4-6). pap. 3.50 (978-0-439-37229-9(1)) Scholastic, Inc.
—Power Pals. 2002. (gr. k-3). lib. bdg. 11.25 (978-0-613-50486-7(0)) Tandem Library Bks.
—Powerpuff Girls 3-D Book: The Powerpuff Girls Eggs-Traordinary 3-D Adventure. Alger, Bill, illus. 2002. (Powerpuff Girls Ser.). 24p. (J). pap. 5.99 (978-0-439-40790-8(7)) Scholastic, Inc.
—Powerpuff Girls Movie. 2002. (gr. k-3). lib. bdg. 11.25 (978-0-613-50487-4(9)) Tandem Library Bks.
—What's Bugging Bubbles? Thompson Brothers Staff, illus. 2001. (Powerpuff Girls Ser.: Vol. 2). 32p. (J). (ps-1). pap. 3.99 (978-0-439-25054-2(4)) Scholastic, Inc.
—Where Is Chicken Pox? 2001. (gr. k-3). lib. bdg. 11.80 (978-0-613-43911-4(2)) Tandem Library Bks.

PRACTICAL POLITICS

see Politics, Practical

PRAIRIE DOGS

Harcourt School Publishers Staff. La Aldea de los Perros de las Praderas On Level. 3rd ed. 2002. (Trofeos Ser.).Tr. of Village of the Dogs of the Meadows. (SPA., Illus.). pap. 6.80 (978-0-15-324171-0(3)) Harcourt Schl. Pubs.
—Prairie Dog Town On Level. 3rd ed. 2002. (Trophies Reading Program Ser.). (Illus.). pap. 5.10 (978-0-15-323261-9(7)) Harcourt Schl. Pubs.
Ivy, Bill, et al. Bighorn Sheep. 1999. (Getting to Know ... Nature's Children Ser.). (Illus.). 47p. (J). (978-0-7172-8836-6(6) , Grolier) Scholastic Library Publishing.
Kline, Trish. Prairie Dog's Burrow. Smith, Fred, illus. (Read-and-Discover - Great Plains Ser.). 48p. (J). 2005. (ps-1). pap. 3.95 (978-1-56899-904-3(6) , S2013); 2002. (gr. 1-3). 7.95 (978-1-56899-903-6(8) , B2013) Soundprints.
—Prairie Dog's Burrow: Including 8" Toy. Smith, Fred, illus. 2005. (Read-and-Discover - Great Plains Ser.). 48p. (J). (ps-1). 12.95 (978-1-56899-905-0(4) , PS2063) Soundprints.
Markle, Sandra. Prairie Dogs. 2007. (Animal Prey Ser.). 40p. (J). (gr. 4-6). 25.26 (978-0-8225-6438-6(6) , Lerner Pubns.) Lerner Publishing Group.
Murphy, Patricia J. Prairie Dogs. Saunders-Smith, Gail, ed. 2004. (Grassland Animals Ser.). (Illus.). 24p. (J). (gr. k-1). lib. bdg. 15.93 (978-0-7368-2073-8(6) , Pebble Bks.) Capstone Pr., Inc.
Prairie Dogs: MainSails Individual Title, 6 Packs. (Sails Literacy Ser.). (gr. 5 up). 37.00 (978-0-7578-8041-4(X)) Rigby Education.
Prairie Dogs & Their Burrows. (Animal Homes Ser.). 24p. (J). 6.95 (978-0-7368-5128-2(3)) Capstone Pr., Inc.
Rustad, Martha E. H. Prairie Dogs & Their Burrows. 2004. (Animal Homes Ser.). (Illus.). 24p. (J). lib. bdg. 19.93 (978-0-7368-2584-9(3) , Pebble Bks.) Capstone Pr., Inc.
Spilsbury, Louise & Spilsbury, Richard. A Colony of Prairie Dogs. 2004. (Animal Groups Ser.). (Illus.). 32p. (J). lib. bdg. 24.22 (978-1-4034-4693-0(8)) Heinemann Library.
Spilsbury, Richard & Spilsbury, Louise. A Colony of Prairie Dogs. 2004. pap. 6.95 (978-1-4034-5415-7(9)) Heinemann Library.
Staub, Frank. Prairie Dogs. 1998. (Early Bird Nature Bks.). (Illus.). 48p. (J). (gr. 2-4). lib. bdg. 25.26 (978-0-8225-3038-1(4) , Lerner Pubns.) Lerner Publishing Group.
Where Are the Prairie Dogs? Third Grade Guided Reading Level O. (On Our Way to English Ser.). (gr. 3 up). 34.50 (978-0-7578-7143-6(7)) Rigby Education.
Woodward, John. Prairie Dogs. 2003. (Secret World Of... Ser.). (Illus.). 48p. (J). lib. bdg. 27.14 (978-0-7398-7025-9(4)) Raintree.
Zuchora-Walske, Christine. Peeking Prairie Dogs. (Pull Ahead Bks.). (Illus.). 32p. (J). (gr. k-2). 2003. pap. 5.95 (978-0-8225-3622-2(6)); 1999. lib. bdg. 22.60 (978-0-8225-3616-1(1) , Lerner Pubns.) Lerner Publishing Group.
—Peeking Prairie Dogs. 1999. (gr. k-3). lib. bdg. 14.10 (978-0-613-43864-3(7)) Tandem Library Bks.

PRAIRIE DOGS—FICTION

Oke, Janette. Prairie Dog Town. Munger, Nancy, illus. rev. ed. 2001. (Janette Oke's Animal Friends Ser.). 80p. (J). (gr. 1-5). pap. 6.99 (978-0-7642-2455-3(7)) Bethany Hse. Pubs.
Patent, Dorothy Hinshaw. Prairie Dogs. Munoz, William, photos by. 1999. (Illus.). 64p. (J). (gr. 5-9). pap. 7.95 (978-0-395-52601-9(9) , Clarion Bks.) Houghton Mifflin Co. Trade & Reference Div.
Prairie Dog's Town. 2002. (Wild Heritage Collection Mini Bks.). (Illus.). 32p. (J). (978-1-59069-162-5(8) , H3006) Studio Mouse LLC.
Ricci, Christine. Prairie Dog Rescue. Zalme, Ron, illus. 2007. (Go, Diego, Go! Ser.). 24p. (J). pap. 3.99 (***978-1-4169-3363-2(8)*** , Simon Spotlight/Nickelodeon) Simon & Schuster Children's Publishing.
Sargent, Dave & Sargent, Pat. Prater the Prairie Dog: I'm a Worrywart!, 36 vols., 34. Huff, Jeane, illus. 2001. (Animal Pride Ser.: Vol. 34). 36p. (J). pap. 6.95 (978-1-56763-385-6(4)) Ozark Publishing.
Stevens, Janet & Crummel, Susan Stevens. The Great Fuzz Frenzy. 2005. (Illus.). 56p. (J). (ps-ps). 17.00 (978-0-15-204626-2(7) , Harcourt Children's Bks) Harcourt Children's Bks.
—The Great Fuzz Frenzy. unabr. ed. 2006. (J). (gr. k-3). 27.99 incl. audio (***978-0-8045-6940-8(1)*** , SAC6941); 29.95 incl. audio compact disk (***978-0-8045-4154-1(X)*** , SACD4155) Spoken Arts, Inc.
Wheeler, Kathryn. Patty Saves the Day! A Tale in Which Patty Discovers Her True Gift. Myers, Darcy, illus. 2000. (Stories to Grow By Ser.). 19p. (J). (978-0-7424-0012-2(3) , Instructional Fair) Schaffer, Frank Pubns.

PRAIRIES

Baldwin, Carol. Living in a Prairie. 2003. (Living Habitats Ser.). 32p. (J). lib. bdg. 24.22 (978-1-4034-0841-9(6)); (Illus.). pap. 6.95 (978-1-4034-3225-4(2)) Heinemann Library.
Bannatyne, Jo Cugnet. Heartland. Moore, Yvette, illus. 2005. 40p. (J). pap. 9.95 (978-0-88776-722-7(2)) Tundra Bks., Inc./Livres Toundra, Inc. CAN. *Dist:* Random Hse., Inc.
Bradley, Catherine. Life on the Plains. 2001. (World Book Ecology Ser.). (Illus.). 32p. (J). (978-0-7166-5230-4(7)) World Bk., Inc.
Creative Publishing international Editors, et al. Prairie Animals. 2004. (Our Wild World Ser.). (Illus.). 192p. (J). (gr. 2-5). ring bd. 16.95 (978-1-55971-895-0(1) , NorthWord Bks. for Young Readers) T&N Children's Publishing.
Endres, Hollie. Prairies. 2007. (Illus.). 24p. (J). lib. bdg. 19.95 (978-1-60014-114-0(5)) Bellwether Media.
Frisch, Aaron. Prairies. 2008. (J). (***978-1-58341-572-6(6)*** , Creative Education) Creative Co., The.
Geisert, Bonnie. Prairie Town. Geisert, Arthur, illus. 1998. (Small Town U. S. A. Ser.). 32p. (J). (gr. k-3). tchr. ed. 16.00 (978-0-395-85907-0(7) , Walter Lorraine) Houghton Mifflin Co. Trade & Reference Div.
Harcourt School Publishers Staff. At Play on the Plains On Level. 3rd ed. 2002. (Trophies Reading Program Ser.). (Illus.). pap. 5.10 (978-0-15-323356-2(7)) Harcourt Schl. Pubs.
Johnson, Rebecca L. A Walk in the Prairie. Saroff, Phyllis V., illus. Braasch, Gary, photos by. 2005. (Biomes of North America Ser.). 48p. (gr. 3-6). lib. bdg. 23.93 (978-1-57505-153-6(2)) Lerner Publishing Group.
Lee, Evelyn. Bluestem Horizon: A Story of a Tallgrass Prairie. Brauckmann-Towns, Krista, illus. 1998. (Habitat Ser.: Vol. 10). 36p. (J). (gr. 1-4). 19.95 incl. reel tape (978-1-56899-597-7(0) , BC7010) Soundprints.
—Bluestem Horizon: A Story of a Tallgrass Prairie. Braukmann-Towns, Krista, illus. 1998. (Habitat Ser.: Vol. 10). 36p. (J). (gr. 1-4). pap. 10.95 incl. audio (978-1-56899-598-4(9)); Incl. toy. 26.95 (978-1-56899-599-1(7)); Incl. toy. 31.95 incl. audio (978-1-56899-601-1(2)); Incl. toy. pap. 19.95 incl. audio (978-1-56899-602-8(0)) Soundprints.
Lemke, Donald B. The Schoolchildren's Blizzard. Hoover, Dave & Barnett, Charles, illus. 2008. (J). (***978-1-4296-0157-3(4)***) Capstone Pr., Inc.
Levy, Janey. What Lives on a Prairie? 2003. (Reading Room Collection). (Illus.). 24p. (J). lib. bdg. 18.75 (978-0-8239-3701-1(1)) Rosen Publishing Group, Inc., The.
Lion, David C. A Home on the Prairie. 2006. (Scholastic News Nonfiction Readers Ser.). (Illus.). 24p. (J). (gr. 1-3). 19.00 (978-0-516-25346-6(8) , Children's Pr.) Scholastic Library Publishing.
Lynch, Wayne, photos by. Prairie Grasslands. 2006. (Illus.). 64p. 16.95 (978-1-55971-946-9(X)); (J). 8.95 (978-1-55971-947-6(8)) T&N Children's Publishing. (NorthWord Bks. for Young Readers).
Mader, Jan. Living on Prairie. 2004. (Rookie Read-About Geography Ser.). 32p. (J). (gr. 1-2). pap. 5.95 (978-0-516-25932-1(6) , Children's Pr.) Scholastic Library Publishing.
Martin, Patricia A. Fink. Prairies, Fields, & Meadows. (Exploring Ecosystems Ser.). (Illus.). 144p. (YA). (gr. 8-12). pap. 6.95 (978-0-531-16604-8(X) , Watts, Franklin) Scholastic Library Publishing.
Mayer, Cassie. Prairie. 2007. (J). (***978-1-4034-9428-3(2)***); pap. (***978-1-4034-9434-4(7)***) Heinemann Library.
McGehee, Claudia. A Tallgrass Prairie Alphabet. McGehee, Claudia, illus. 2004. (Bur Oak Book Ser.). (Illus.). 32p. (J). 17.95 (978-0-87745-897-5(9)) Univ. of Iowa Pr.
Munson Scullin, Wendy. Young Person's Guide to the Prairie. 2006. (Illus.). 160p. (YA). per. 11.95 (978-0-9770764-0-6(7)) South River Pr.
O'Hara, Megan. Pioneer Farm: A Farm on the Prairie in the 1880s. 1998. 32p. (J). pap. 21.00 (978-0-516-21253-1(2) , Children's Pr.) Scholastic Library Publishing.
Ormsby, Alison. The Prairie. 1999. (Ecosystems of North America Ser.). (Illus.). 64p. (YA). (gr. 6 up). lib. bdg. 28.50 (978-0-7614-0897-0(5) , Benchmark Bks.) Cavendish, Marshall Corp.
Pyers. Prairie Explorer. 2004. (Habitat Explorer Ser.). (Illus.). pap. 7.50 (978-1-4109-0841-4(0)); 6 Pack. lib. bdg. 40.50 (978-1-4109-0847-6(X)) Raintree.
Quigley, Mary. Prairie Explorer. 2004. (Habitat Explorer Ser.). (Illus.). 32p. (J). (gr. ps-ps). lib. bdg. 25.70 (978-1-4109-0513-0(6)) Raintree.
Rotter, Charles. The Prairie. 2002. (LifeViews Ser.). (J). (978-0-89812-329-6(1) , Creative Paperbacks) Creative Co., The.
—The Prairie: An Enduring Spirit. 2001. (Life on Earth Ser.). (Illus.). 32p. (J). lib. bdg. (978-1-58341-029-5(5) , Creative Education) Creative Co., The.
Salzmann, Mary Elizabeth. On a Prairie. l.t. ed. 2001. (What Do You See? Ser.). (Illus.). 24p. (J). (ps-3). lib. bdg. 19.93 (978-1-57765-568-8(0) , SandCastle) ABDO Publishing Co.
Tarbox, A. D. The Prairie. 2008. (J). (***978-1-58341-600-6(5)*** , Creative Education) Creative Co., The.
Wallace, Marianne D. America's Prairies & Grasslands: Guide to Plants & Animals. 2004. (America's EcoSystem Ser.: Vol. 3). (Illus.). 48p. (J). (gr. 3-6). pap. 11.95 (978-1-55591-992-4(8)) Fulcrum Publishing.
—Americas Prairies & Grasslands: Guide to Plants & Animals. 2001. (gr. 5-8). lib. bdg. 26.85 (978-0-613-87963-7(5)) Tandem Library Bks.
Winne, Joanne. Living on a Plain. 2000. (Welcome Bks.). (Illus.). 24p. (J). (ps-2). 17.00 (978-0-516-23304-8(1) , Children's Pr.) Scholastic Library Publishing.

PRAYER

see also Prayers

Alabado, Ceres S. C. God Please Hold Me in Your Hand. Rosal, Felicitas S., ed. Rosal, Carmelita S., illus. 2000. 32p. (J). (gr. 2-5). pap. 7.95 (978-1-887764-55-1(0)) T'Boli Publishing & Distributors.
Anderson, Debby. I Can Talk with God. Anderson, Debby, illus. 2005. (Illus.). 32p. 9.99 (978-1-58134-416-5(3) , Crossway Bibles) Crossway Bks.
Arthur, Kay & Arndt, Janna. The Prayer That Changes Everything. 2002. (Discover 4 Yourself Inductive Bible Studies for Kids Ser.). 176p. pap. 10.99 (978-0-7369-0666-1(5)) Harvest Hse. Pubs.
Atkins, Rosemary & Atkins, Peter. Prayer Bytes: Everyday Prayers for Young People. Jackson-Mee, Olivia, illus. 2006. 40p. (J). pap. 10.95 (978-1-85390-917-7(3)) Veritas Pubns. IRL. *Dist:* STL Distribution North America.
Baden, Robert. Psalms for Kids. 2004. 64p. (J). 6.99 (978-0-570-07141-9(0)) Concordia Publishing Hse.
Bagley, Val Chadwick & Beckstrand, Tamara, trs. My Little Book about Prayer. Bagley, Val Chadwick, illus. 2004. (Illus.). (J). bds. 10.95 (978-1-59156-096-8(9)) Covenant Communications, Inc.
Barker, Dave & Jordan, Lee. Pray Give Go Do. 2004. (Illus.). 192p. pap. 10.99 (978-0-8254-6221-4(5)) Kregel Pubns.
Barrett, Kathy. Jubilee Journal: A Journal & Devotional for Young Prayer Warriors. 2002. 116p. (YA). per. 13.95 (978-1-58930-065-1(3)) Selah Publishing Group, LLC.
Bestmann, Nancy. A Child Said a Prayer Tonight. Bunnell, Gini, illus. 2001. 18p. (J). (ps-5). 12.99 (978-1-890398-00-2(4)) Bestmann, Nancy M.
Bible Visuals International, compiled by. Prayer: New Testament Volume 09. 2006. (Illus.). (J). pap. (978-1-932381-39-9(2) , 1009) Bible Visuals International, Inc.
Bohlmann, Katherine. Grandma, What Is Prayer? 2003. 32p. (J). 14.99 (978-0-7586-0043-1(7)) Concordia Publishing Hse.
Bostrom, Kathleen Long & Kucharik, Elena. What Is Prayer? 2002. (Tyndale Kids Ser.). (Illus.). 80p. (J). 9.99 (978-0-8423-5355-7(0)) Tyndale Hse. Pubs.
Bouchard, Jean-Francois. My First Little Prayer Book. 2002. 52p. 2.95 (978-1-58595-220-5(6)) Twenty-Third Pubns./Bayard.
Bowler, Kathryn C. & Osborne, Rick. I Want to Know, Sam's Club: About God, Jesus, the Bible & Prayer. 2001. 168p. (J). 27.99 (978-0-310-70242-9(9)) Zonderkidz.
Bretherton, Barbara A. Prayer Themes & Guided Meditations for Children. 1998. 96p. (J). pap. 9.95 (978-0-89622-896-2(7)) Twenty-Third Pubns./Bayard.
Britt, Stephanie McFetridge, illus. Mi Primer Libro de Oraciones. 2001. (SPA.). 26p. (J). (ps-k). 6.95 (978-0-8249-4112-3(8)) Ideals Pubns.
Butcher, Sam, illus. Precious Moments: Storybook Bible & Girl Prayer Pal Set. 2003. 14.60 (978-0-7180-0569-6(4)) Nelson, Thomas Inc.

Calderone-Stewart, Lisa-Marie. Prayer Works for Teens, Bk. 2. Samschror, Robert, ed. Korab, Rick, illus. 2003. (Prayer Works for Teens: Vol. 2). 64p. (YA). pap. 12.95 (978-0-88489-433-9(9)) St. Mary's Pr.

—Prayer Works for Teens. Korab, Rick, illus. 2003. (Prayer Works for Teens: Vol. 3). 72p. (YA). Bk. 3. pap. 12.95 (978-0-88489-434-6(7)); Bk. 4. pap. 12.95 (978-0-88489-435-3(5)) St. Mary's Pr.

Callon, Margaret. Praying God's Way. 2003. 204p. (YA). per. 8.95 (978-1-59453-003-6(3) , 1094) Airleaf Publishing & Bookselling.

Case, Steve. Time Out: Quick Devotions for Teens. 2001. 128p. (YA). pap. 10.99 (978-0-8280-1555-4(4) , 240-640) Review & Herald Publishing Assn.

Center for Learning Network Staff. Pentecost, Peanuts, Popcorn, Prayer Bk. 2: Prayer Services for Teens & Young Adults. 2000. (Religion Ser.). 127p. (YA). (gr. 9-12). spiral bd., tchr.'s training gde. ed. 19.95 (978-1-56077-624-6(2)) Ctr. for Learning, The.

Center for Learning Staff. Prayer & Worship. 2007. (Religion Ser.). 138p. (YA). spiral bd. 18.95 (***978-1-56077-785-4(0)***) Ctr. for Learning, The.

Concordia Publishing House, ed. Little Ones Talk with God. Rand, Sue, illus. 2006. (ENG.). 64p. (J). lib. bdg. 9.99 (978-0-7586-1132-1(3)) Concordia Publishing Hse.

Cook, LaVelle. Little Jimmie & the Lord's Prayer. 2005. (J). 14.95 (978-1-882185-45-0(5)) Cornerstone Publishing, Inc.

Daehler, Bridget. Goodnight God, I Love You a Lot. 2002. (J). 12.95 (978-1-58930-066-8(1)) Selah Publishing Group, LLC.

DeGraw, Karin M. God Hears Me! Hershey, Rebecca, illus. 2002. (J). (978-0-8198-3101-9(8)) Pauline Bks. & Media.

Denham, Joyce. A Child's Book of Celtic Prayers. Cann, Helen, illus. 1998. 25p. (ps-3). 14.95 (978-0-8294-1077-8(5)) Loyola Pr.

DeVries, Mike & Murphy, Troy. Exodus: The Sacred Journey. 2003. (No Limits Ser.). 112p. (YA). pap. 12.99 (978-0-8341-5005-8(0)) Beacon Hill Pr. of Kansas City.

Dicianni, Ron. Praying with the Presidents: One Nation's Legacy of Prayer. 2004. 48p. (J). (gr. k-3). 10.99 (978-1-59185-408-1(3) , Charisma Kids) Strang Communications Co.

DiEdwardo, Mary Ann P. & Pasda, Patricia J. Prayer Journal. DiEdwardo, Mary Ann P., illus. 2000. (Illus.). 75p. (J). spiral bd. 19.95 (978-0-9641468-5-3(1)) DiEdwardo, Mary Ann P. Publishing.

Dillon, Sally Pierson. Hugs from Jesus: 180 Devotions & Worship Activities for Preschoolers. 2001. (Illus.). (J). (978-0-8280-1567-7(8)) Review & Herald Publishing Assn.

Elkins, Stephen. Baby's First Book of Blessings. Colton, Ellie, illus. 2002. (Lulla-Bible Ser.). 14p. (J). (ps). 6.99 (978-0-8054-2581-9(0)) B&H Publishing Grp.

—Baby's First Book of Prayers. Colton, Ellie, illus. 2002. (Lulla-Bible Ser.). 14p. (J). (ps). 6.99 (978-0-8054-2580-2(2)) B&H Publishing Grp.

—First Steps in Prayer. Colton, Ellie, illus. 2006. 32p. (J). 9.99 (978-0-8054-2663-2(9)) B&H Publishing Grp.

Esquinaldo, Virginia. Baby, Come to Church! Esquinaldo, Virginia, illus. 2005. (Illus.). (J). 5.95 (978-0-8198-1164-6(5) , 332-027) Pauline Bks. & Media.

Evans, Colleen T. Lord, Teach Us to Pray! A Primer for Children & Adults. Martz, Wendelyn, ed. Davidson, Kate, illus. rev. ed. 2000. 72p. (J). (gr. k-5). 15.95 (978-0-9674105-0-0(9) , 4000) Davidson, Harrison Publishing Hse.

Flamini, Lorella, illus. Thank You, Dear God! Prayers for Little Ones. 2006. Orig. Title: Il mio amico Gesu: Preghierine per tutti i Bambini. (J). 11.95 (978-0-8198-7417-7(5)) Pauline Bks. & Media.

Freed, Shirley & Moon, Louise. I Can Pray. Morelan, Bill, ed. Harrell, Rob, illus. 2003. 16p. (J). (gr. 1 up). pap. 3.99 (978-1-58938-113-1(0)) Concerned Communications.

Galvin, Jennifer. My Catholic Pray & Play. 2002. (Illus.). 32p. act. bk. ed. 6.95 (978-0-8091-6701-2(8) , 6701-8) Paulist Pr.

Ganeri, Martin & Ganeri, Anita. Christian Prayer & Worship. 2007. (J). (***978-1-59771-091-6(1)***) Sea-To-Sea Pubns.

Garrett, Susan R. & Pauw, Amy Plantinga. Making Time for God: Daily Devotions for Children & Families to Share. 2002. 384p. (J). (gr. 2-7). pap. 18.99 (978-0-8010-4505-9(3)) Baker Bks.

Gemmen, Heather & McNeil, Mary. Faithful Friends, Level 1. Swisher, Elizabeth, tr. Swisher, Elizabeth, illus. 2004. (Rocket ReaderT2 Ser.). 40p. (J). (gr. 1 up). pap., pap. 8.99 (978-0-7814-4010-3(6) , 0781440106) Cook, David C. Publishing Co.

George, Elizabeth. A Young Woman after God's Own Heart: A Teen's Guide to Friends, Faith, Family, & the Future. 2003. 224p. (YA). pap. 9.99 (978-0-7369-0789-7(0) , 6907890) Harvest Hse. Pubs.

—A Young Woman's Call to Prayer: Talking with God about Your Life. 2005. 208p. (YA). pap. 9.99 (978-0-7369-1463-5(3)) Harvest Hse. Pubs.

Gold, August. Does God Hear My Prayer? Waller, Diane Hardy, photos by. 2005. (Illus.). 32p. (J). 8.99 (978-1-59473-102-0(0)) SkyLight Paths Publishing.

Gorsky, Jonathan & Ganeri, Anita. Jewish Prayer & Worship. 2007. (J). (***978-1-59771-092-3(X)***) Sea-To-Sea Pubns.

Grandma's Prayer. 2006. (J). 8.00 (978-0-9774822-1-4(9)) Crosam Pr.

Groth, Jeanette L. Prayer: Learning How to Talk to God. rev. ed. 2003. (Illus.). 24p. (J). 5.99 (978-0-570-07188-4(7)) Concordia Publishing Hse.

Grube, Edward C. Teens Pray: Conversations with God. 2003. (ENG.). 96p. (YA). 9.99 (978-0-7586-0035-6(6)) Concordia Publishing Hse.

Hahn, Samuel J. Stories Told under the Sycamore Tree: Bible Plant Object Lessons. Patton, Scott, tr. Patton, Scott, illus. 2003. 191p. (J). pap. 10.95 (978-0-7880-1972-2(4)) CSS Publishing Co.

Harder Tangvald, Christine. I Can Pray. Stewart, Jennifer, ed. Garris, Norma, illus. 1999. (Patty Cake Devotions Ser.). 14p. (J). (ps). bds. 3.99 (978-0-7847-0979-5(3) , 04293, Bean Sprouts) Standard Publishing.

—Tuck Me in God: Doorhanger Set, 5. 1999. (Tuck-Me-In Doorknob Board Bks.). (Illus.). 10p. (J). (ps-k). 9.00 (978-0-570-05578-5(4)) Concordia Publishing Hse.

Henderson, Felicity. The Food We Eat. Donnelly, Strawberrie, illus. 2002. (Pop-Up Prayers Ser.). 16p. (ps-3). 3.99 (978-0-8066-4371-7(4) , Augsburg Bks.) Augsburg Fortress, Pubs.

Henley, Karyn. My Learn-to-Pray Bible. Dippold, Jane, illus. 2004. 66p. (J). bds. 12.99 (978-0-8423-8733-0(1)) Tyndale Hse. Pubs.

—Prayer: The Foundation for Growing Closer to God. Eichenberger, Jim, ed. Koehler, Ed, illus. 2000. (Foundations Curriculum). 96p. (YA). (gr. 3-6). 12.99 (978-0-7847-1216-0(6) , 42065) Standard Publishing.

Hill, Karen. My First Prayer Journal. 2004. (Max Lucado's Hermie & Friends Ser.). 96p. (J). 9.99 (978-1-4003-0494-3(6)) Nelson, Thomas Inc.

I Can Pray! 2006. (J). 16p. pap. 1.99 (978-0-7847-1694-6(3) , 02996); (Illus.). 24p. bds. 6.99 (978-0-7847-1398-3(7) , 04058) Standard Publishing.

Ibrahim, Muhammad & Ganeri, Anita. Muslim Prayer & Worship. 2007. (J). (***978-1-59771-090-9(3)***) Sea-To-Sea Pubns.

Jahsmann, Allan Hart & Simon, Martin. Little Visits with God: Devotions for Families. 4th ed. 2006. (Little Visits Ser.). (ENG.). 256p. (J). pap. 12.99 (978-0-7586-0847-5(0)) Concordia Publishing Hse.

Jelenek, Frank X. Journey to the Heart: Centering Prayer for Children. Boyajian, Ann, illus. 2007. (J). (ps-5). pap. 14.95 (***978-1-55725-482-5(6)***) Paraclete Pr., Inc.

John Paul II, pseud. My Dear Young Friends: Pope John Paul II Speaks to Teens on Life, Love, & Courage. Vitek, John, ed. 2003. 120p. (YA). pap. 6.95 (978-0-88489-724-8(9)) St. Mary's Pr.

Johnson, Kevin W. Pray Hard. 2000. (Early Teen Discipleship Ser.: Vol. 4). 136p. (J). (gr. 6-9). pap. 7.99 (978-1-55661-639-6(2)) Bethany Hse. Pubs.

The Kids Prayed & God Arrived. 2004. (YA). (978-1-59581-083-0(8)) Brentwood Communications Group.

Kirgiss, Crystal & Lyon, Christopher. A Teenager's Daily Prayer Book. 2005. (Illus.). 384p. (978-0-7853-4909-9(X) , 3337100) Publications International, Ltd.

Koch, Carl, et al. Prayerways. 2003. (Illus.). 208p. (gr. 11-12). pap. 15.50 (978-0-88489-258-8(1)) St. Mary's Pr.

Ladwig, Tim. Lord's Prayer. 2002. (gr. k-3). lib. bdg. 17.05 (978-0-613-75339-5(9)) Tandem Library Bks.

Legacy. 7.50 (978-0-8054-5927-2(8)) B&H Publishing Grp.

Legacy Press Staff. Gotta Have God: Devotions for Boys. 2004. (Gotta Have God Ser.). (Illus.). 238p. (J). (gr. 5-7). spiral bd. 12.99 (978-1-885358-98-1(9) , Legacy Pr.) Rainbow Pubs. & Legacy Pr.

Lindbergh, Reeve, ed. In Every Tiny Grain of Sand: A Child's Book of Prayers & Praise. Davenier, Christine et al, illus. 2000. 80p. (J). (ps-3). 22.99 (978-0-7636-0176-8(4)) Candlewick Pr.

Lingo, Susan L. My Good Night Christmas: With Read & Sing-along CD. Parks, Kathy, illus. 2001. 32p. (J). 17.99 incl. audio compact disk (978-0-7847-1205-4(0)) Standard Publishing.

Lingo, Susan L. & Parks, Kathy. My Good Night Devotions: 45 Devotional Stories for Little Ones. 2001. (Illus.). 208p. (J). (ps-1). 12.99 (978-0-7847-1174-3(7)) Standard Publishing.

The Lord's Prayer: Prayer Cards. 2004. (978-0-8294-1406-6(1)) Loyola Pr.

Lounsbury, Pete. Jesus & the Blind Man. 2007. (J). per. 12.95 (***978-1-59879-408-3(6)***) Lifevest Publishing, Inc.

MacArthur, John. My Faith & Prayer Journal. 2004. 64p. (J). pap. 4.99 (978-1-4003-0441-7(5)) Nelson, Thomas Inc.

Mark, Littleton. Through the Bible Devotions. 2006. 384p. (YA). pap. 14.99 (978-0-7847-1474-4(6) , 04151) Standard Publishing.

McIntosh, Kenneth R. Following Aslan: A Book of Devotions for Children Based on the Chronicles of Narnia by C. S. Lewis. 2006. (J). pap. 11.95 (978-1-933630-02-1(7) , Anamchara Bks.) Harding Hse. Publishing Sebice Inc.

McPherson, Miles. Bad to the Bone: Fifteen Young Bible Heroes Who Lived Radical Lives for God. 1999. 224p. (J). (gr. 8-12). reprint ed. pap. 10.99 (978-0-7642-2280-1(5)) Bethany Hse. Pubs.

Meyer, Naama, illus. Siddurchik: Prayer Book for Young Children. 2006. 32p. 12.95 (978-965-229-328-2(8)) Gefen Publishing Hse., Ltd ISR. *Dist:* Gefen Bks.

Michelson, Richard. Grandpa's Gamble. Moser, Barry, illus. 1999. (Accelerated Reader Bks.). 32p. (YA). (ps up). 15.95 (978-0-7614-5034-4(3) , Cavendish Children's Bks.) Cavendish, Marshall Corp.

Miller, Ann. Proverbs, Prayers, Poems for Children & Teens. 2005. (J). lib. bdg. 14.95 (978-0-9748165-1-7(5)) Jaylil Publishing Co.

Mills, Charles. Eyes of the Crocodile: And Other Bite-Sized Devotions for Juniors. 2000. 374p. (J). 12.99 (978-0-8280-1519-6(8) , 059-960) Review & Herald Publishing Assn.

Montgomery Gibson, Jane. Maker of Prayer. Montgomery Gibson, Jane, illus. 2005. (YA). bds. 8.99 (978-1-4183-0047-0(0)) Christ Inspired, Inc.

Murray, Mary. Just Mom & Me Having Tea: A Fun Bible Study for Mothers & Daughters. 2001. (Illus.). 128p. (gr. 4-7). pap. 9.99 (978-0-7369-0426-1(3)) Harvest Hse. Pubs.

Omartian, Stormie. The Power of a Praying Kid. 2005. 112p. (J). (ps-7). pap. 7.99 (978-0-7369-0122-2(1)) Harvest Hse. Pubs.

Oraciones al Acostarse (Prayers for Bedtime) 1998. (Tiempo de Orar Ser.). (SPA.). (J). bds. 3.99 (978-0-7899-0517-8(5) , 495661) Editorial Unilit.

Osborne, Rick & Bowler, K. Christie. I Want to Know about Prayer. 1998. (I Want to Know Ser.). 32p. (J). 9.99 (978-0-310-22091-6(2)) Zondervan.

Panesar, Rajinder Singh & Ganeri, Anita. Sikh Prayer & Worship. 2007. (J). (***978-1-59771-094-7(6)***) Sea-To-Sea Pubns.

Parr, Susan Sherwood. Christopher's Adventures: A Prayer on Angel Wings. Paraschiv, Doina, illus. 2003. 16p. 5.99 (978-0-9728590-3-5(9)) Word Prodns.

—30 Days Out of Depression. 2003. (Illus.). 58p. pap. 4.95 (978-0-9728590-5-9(5)) Word Prodns.

Parry, et al. Orando con los Ositos (Prayers with Bears) El Padre Nuestro (The Lord's Prayer) 2000. (Bears Ser.). (SPA.). (J). bds. 4.50 (978-0-7899-0829-2(8) , 494662) Editorial Unilit.

—Orando con los Ositos (Prayers with Bears) Primera de Corintios 13 (First Corinthians 13) 2000. (Bears Ser.). (SPA.). (J). bds. 4.50 (978-0-7899-0827-8(1) , 494661) Editorial Unilit.

Pearce, Virginia H. & Marsh, Dilleen. Prayer Time. Barnes, Kathleen H., illus. 2001. 32p. (J). (gr. 4-7). pap. 10.95 (978-1-57345-954-9(2)) Deseret Bk. Co.

Perkins, Nicole. I Believe God Will: Book of Devotion & Prayer for Children. Perkins, Nicole & Frisk, Maria, illus. 2008. 32p. (J). 7.00 (***978-0-9755566-1-0(4)***) Azreal Publishing Co.

Peterson, Lorrai. If God Loves Me, Why Can't I Get My Locker Open? exp. ed. 2006. 400p. (YA). pap. 13.99 (978-0-7642-0189-9(1)) Bethany Hse. Pubs.

Pharr, Nancy Elizabeth. When Should I Pray? Rose, Heidi, illus. 2003. 40p. (J). pap. 8.95 (978-0-8198-8304-9(2) , 332-412) Pauline Bks. & Media.

Powell, Darryl. Prayer Journal. 2000. 56p. per. (978-0-9678163-2-6(7)) Diamond Dan Pubns.

Power of Prayer: Senior High. 1998. (Cross Training Ser.: Vol. 6). 80p. (YA). (gr. 10-12). pap., tchr. ed. 15.00 incl. VHS (978-1-57405-107-0(5)) CharismaLife Pubs.

The Prayer for Peace. 2004. 1.75 (978-0-8294-1073-0(2)) Loyola Pr.

Prayer in My Life: Building a Spirit of Devotion. 2004. (Faith Rules Ser.). (Illus.). 96p. (J). pap. 4.99 (978-0-7424-2836-2(2) , In Celebration) Schaffer, Frank Pubns.

The Prayer Jesus Gave Us. (Two Great Ways to Share God's Love Ser.). 16p. (ps-k). 15.00 (978-0-570-00315-1(6)) Concordia Publishing Hse.

Praying. 2002. (Precious Moments Ser.). (Illus.). 11p. (J). bds. 4.99 (978-1-57759-381-2(2)) Dalmatian Pr.

Prothro, Crystaline Joi. I'm a Kid but I'm Not Kiddin' I Love the Lord. Curry, Rosalynn A. & Johnson, Charmaine, eds. Johnson, Bob, photos by. 1998. (Illus.). 100p. (J). (gr. 4-7). pap. 9.95 (978-0-9662919-3-3(X)) Robot Publishing.

Rasamandala Das & Ganeri, Anita. Hindu Prayer & Worship. 2007. (***978-1-59771-093-0(8)***) Sea-To-Sea Pubns.

Redden, Vicki, et al. God's Amazing Creation. 2005. (Review Kids Ser.). 375p. (J). (978-0-8280-1871-5(5)) Review & Herald Publishing Assn.

Reeves, Eira. Oraciones a la Hora de Dormir (Prayers at Bedtime) (SPA.). (J). 1.89 (978-0-7899-0478-2(0) , 498665) Editorial Unilit.

Rivers, Ruth, illus. Thank You Prayers. 2003. 32p. (J). 7.99 (978-0-7459-4650-4(X) , Lion) Lion Hudson plc GBR. *Dist:* Independent Pubs. Group.

Roddy, Lauren S. My Scriptural Rosary. Darrenkamp, Julia M., illus. 1998. 48p. (J). (gr. 2-5). pap. 3.95 (978-0-8198-4797-3(6) , 332-205) Pauline Bks. & Media.

—My Scriptural Rosary. Darrenkamp, Julia Mary, illus. rev. ed. 2006. (J). 4.95 (978-0-8198-4845-1(X)) Pauline Bks. & Media.

The Rosary: Prayer Cards. 2004. (978-0-8294-1403-5(7)) Loyola Pr.

Rose, Kunzler Behncke. Where in the World Is God? Wensell, Ulises, illus. 2006. 26p. (J). 8.95 (978-0-8146-3156-0(8) , Liturgical Pr. Bks.) Liturgical Pr.

Rossel, Seymour. When a Jew Prays, Vol. 1. Weihs, Erika, illus. 192p. (J). (gr. 4-5). pap. 9.50 (978-0-87441-093-8(2)) Behrman Hse., Inc.

Ryan, Gregory. My Happy Heart: Prayer of the Heart. Siqueira, Carlos, illus. 2001. 32p. (J). (gr. 1-7). 12.95 (978-0-9666941-9-2(8)) Medio Media Publishing.

Rylant, Cynthia. Llename de Gracia. Rylant, Cynthia, illus. 2003. (Classic Board Bks.).Tr. of Give Me Grace. (SPA., Illus.). 32p. (J). bds. 6.99 (978-0-689-86305-9(5) , Libros Para Ninos) Simon & Schuster Children's Publishing.

Saxon, Terrill. Now I Lay Me down to Sleep. 2006. (Baby Blessings Ser.). (Illus.). 12p. bds. 11.99 (978-0-7847-1241-2(7) , 04053) Standard Publishing.

Scarfi, Margaret Rose. I Pray the Rosary! Richards, Virginia Helen & Dick, Regina Frances, illus. 2005. 48p. (J). pap. 4.95 (978-0-8198-3689-2(3) , 332-141) Pauline Bks. & Media.

Schmitt, Betsy & Veerman, David. 365 Trivia Twist Devotions: An Almanac of Fun Facts & Spiritual Truth for Every Day of the Year. 2005. (Illus.). 384p. (J). (gr. 3-7). pap. 15.99 (978-0-7847-1737-0(0) , 23350) Standard Publishing.

Setzer, Lee Ann. Tiny Talks #6: I will Trust in Heavenly Father & His Son, Jesus Christ-Their Promises are Sure, Vol. 6. 2005. (YA). pap. 7.99 (978-1-55517-889-5(8) , Cedar Fort, Inc.) Cedar Fort, Inc./CFI Distribution.

Shaw, S. B. Touching Incidents. 1999. (J). (gr. 4-7). pap. 4.95 (978-1-881545-94-1(6)) A B Publishing.

Sheeran, Beth. A Child's Book of Prayer. 2005. 96p. (YA). pap. 14.00 (978-0-14-303567-1(3) , Penguin Global) Penguin Group (USA) Inc.

Silverman, Morris & Silverman, Hillel. Prayer Book for Summer Camps. (J). (gr. 3-12). 8.95 (978-0-87677-060-3(X)); pap. 6.95 (978-0-87677-061-0(8)) Prayer Bk. Pr., Inc.

Simon, Manz Mary. Little Visits with Jesus: Devotions for Families. 4th ed. 2006. (Little Visits Ser.). (ENG.). 256p. (J). pap. 12.99 (978-0-7586-0846-8(2)) Concordia Publishing Hse.

—Little Visits with Toddlers: Devotions for Families. 3rd ed. 2006. (Little Visits Ser.). (ENG.). 256p. (J). pap. 12.99 (978-0-7586-0845-1(4)) Concordia Publishing Hse.

Small Offerings. 2005. 48p. 15.99 (978-1-4003-0563-6(2)) Nelson, Thomas Inc.

Smouse, Phil. Jesus Wants All of Me Prayer Edition. 2007. (Jesus wants all of Me Ser.). 384p. (J). 14.97 (***978-1-59789-675-7(6)***) Barbour Publishing, Inc.

Sorenson, Stephen. Skate Park Swap. 2006. 96p. (YA). pap. 7.99 (978-0-7847-1511-6(4) , 42181) Standard Publishing.

Spraggett, Daphne & Johnston, Jill. Window on the World: Prayer Atlas for Children. 2007. 224p. pap. 16.99 (***978-1-932805-91-8(5)***) Authentic Media.

Stewart, Jennifer, ed. Prayers & Praises. Dubin, Jill, illus. 1999. 48p. (J). (ps-2). 2.99 (978-0-7847-0985-6(8) , 22055, Bean Sprouts) Standard Publishing.

Tamberino, Tony. Pray Your Heart Resource Manual: Music-Based Sessions & Prayer Experiences for Teens. 2003. 32p. (YA). pap. 12.95 (978-0-88489-562-6(9)) St. Mary's Pr.

Tangvald, Christine. Prayer Is. . . for Me! Griego, Tony, illus. 2001. (for Me! Bks.). 24p. (J). pap. 3.99 (978-0-7642-2542-0(1)) Bethany Hse. Pubs.

Tangvald, Christine Harder & DeBoer, Rondi. Finish-the-Picture Book of Prayers. Lewis, Stephen, illus. 2005. (Finish-the-Picture Ser.). 18p. (J). bds. 6.99 (978-0-310-70896-4(6)) Zonderkidz.

Tataryn, Myroslaw. How to Pray with Icons: An Introduction for Children. 2003. (Illus.). 32p. (978-2-89088-348-2(5)) Novalis Publishing.

Taylor, Damon. Times We Pray. 2003. (Child Sockology Ser.). (Illus.). 10p. (J). bds. 6.99 (978-0-8254-3859-2(4)) Kregel Pubns.

Tetz, RosAnne C., told to. God's Big Idea. 2003. 377p. (J). 13.99 (978-0-8280-1762-6(X)) Review & Herald Publishing Assn.

Thank You God 2001. 2004. (My First Prayers Ser.). 10p. (J). bds. 3.99 (978-1-85854-405-2(X)) Brimax Books Ltd. GBR. *Dist:* Byeway Bks.

Thomas Nelson Publishing Staff. My Shining Prayer Book. 2005. 20p. (J). bds. 12.99 (978-1-4003-0591-9(8)) Nelson, Thomas Inc.

Vitek, John. Living the Questions Jesus Asks: A Guide for Teens. 2003. 136p. (YA). per. 6.95 (978-0-88489-782-8(6)) St. Mary's Pr.

Webster, Jennifer Hope. Chat with God: Prayer Journal. 2nd ed. 2002. (Chat with God: Vol. 1). spiral bd., wbk. ed. 11.99 (978-0-9706360-1-0(6)) Webster, Jennifer Hope.

What Happens to Our Prayers? The Story of a Nagging Question. 2002. (Illus.). 22p. (YA). (gr. 5-12). 10.00 (978-0-9722930-0-6(0)) Izraeli, Elana.

Why Prayer Matters. 1998. (Core Belief Bible Study Ser.). (YA). (gr. 10-12). pap. 11.99 (978-0-7644-0893-9(3)) Group Publishing, Inc.

Wunderink, Steve. Work Out! Active Devotions for Teens. 2000. (Devotions Ser.). (Illus.). 131p. 8.25 (978-1-56212-541-7(9) , 160475, Faith Alive Christian Resources) CRC Pubns.

Yagow, James S. Praise Prayers, 1. 1999. (Illus.). 64p. (J). (ps-2). 10.00 (978-0-570-05572-3(5)) Concordia Publishing Hse.

Zardoni, Raffaella. My Rosary. Zardoni, Raffaella, illus. 2006. Tr. of Il Mio Rosario. (Illus.). 32p. pap. 3.95 (***978-0-8189-1235-1(9)*** , St. Pauls) Alba Hse.

PRAYERS

see also Prayer

Abraham, Ken. Jesus Loves Me Bible Storybook & Devotional Combo. 2003. (Illus.). 672p. (J). 24.99 (978-1-4003-0185-0(8)) Nelson, Thomas Inc.

Adams, Carol J. God Listens to Your Care: Prayers for All the Animals of the World. 2006. (Illus.). 48p. (J). 8.00 (978-0-8298-1666-2(6)) Pilgrim Pr., The/United Church Pr.

—God Listens to Your Love: Prayers for Living with Animal Friends. 2005. (God Listens Ser.). 48p. (J). (ps-3). pap. 8.00 (978-0-8298-1665-5(8)) Pilgrim Pr., The/United Church Pr.

—God Listens When You're Afraid: Prayers for When Animals Scare You. 2006. (J). (978-0-8298-1741-6(7)) Pilgrim Pr., The/United Church Pr.

Aiken, Nick, compiled by. Prayers for Teenagers. 2003. 112p. 10.00 (978-0-281-05543-2(2)) SPCK Publishing GBR. *Dist:* Pilgrim Pr., The/United Church Pr.

Alcoholics Anonymous World Services, Inc., Staff. Twenty-Four Hours a Day for Teens: Daily Meditations. 2004. 416p. pap. 10.95 (978-1-59285-078-5(2) , Z2095) Hazelden Publishing & Educational Services.

All Things Bright & Beautiful: A Soft-Edges Touch & Feel Book. 2000. (Baby Blessings Ser.). (Illus.). 10p. (ps-k). bds. 10.99 (978-0-7847-1137-8(2) , 04317) Standard Publishing.

Allen, Joy, illus. Prayers for a Child's Day. 2006. 28p. (J). 7.99 (978-0-7847-1273-3(5) , 04033) Standard Publishing.

Allsopp, Sophie, illus. Dear God: Little Letter Prayers for Little People. 2006. 16p. (J). 12.99 (978-1-4169-1216-3(9) , Little Simon Inspirations) Simon & Schuster Children's Publishing.

PQR

El Alvidadizo David (Bramble Forgets) (Granja Oso de Miel Ser.). (SPA., Illus.). (J). bds. 4.99 (978-0-7899-0610-6(4) , 495052) Editorial Unilit.

Anglund, Joan Walsh. A Little Book of Poems & Prayers. ed. 2005. (Illus.). 32p. (J). 9.99 (978-1-4169-0009-2(8) , Little Simon Inspirations) Simon & Schuster Children's Publishing.

Arthur, Kay & Arndt, Janna. Lord Teach Me to Pray for Kids. 2006. (Discover-4-Yourself for Kids Ser.). 176p. (J). pap. 9.99 (978-1-888655-30-8(5)) Precept Ministries.

Baby's First Prayers. 2002. (J). spiral bd. (978-0-9720158-1-3(7)) Story Reader, Inc.

Banek, Yvette Santiago, illus. New Baby's Prayers. 1999. (Baby's First Bible Collection). 8p. (J). (ps). 12.99 (978-0-7847-0846-0(0) , 03499, Bean Sprouts) Standard Publishing.

Barnhill, Carla. Blessings Every Day: 365 Simple Devotions for the Very Young. Kucharik, Elena, illus. 2001. (Little Blessings Ser.). 384p. (J). 14.99 (978-0-8423-5410-3(7)) Tyndale Hse. Pubs.

Baxter, Leon, illus. Let's Pray! 1998. 128p. (J). (ps-1). 9.99 (978-0-8054-1684-8(6)) B&H Publishing Grp.

Beers, V. Gilbert. El Pequeno Libro Devocional de Dios para Ninos (God's Little Devotional Book for Kids) 2000. (God's Little Devotional Ser.). (SPA.). (J). (gr. 4-7). 10.99 (978-0-7899-0718-9(6) , 498696) Editorial Unilit.

Berger, Alison J. Jesus, Teach Me to Pray; A Catholic Child's Prayerbook. 1999. (Illus.). 124p. (J). (ps-3). 9.95 (978-0-89622-967-9(X)) Twenty-Third Pubns./Bayard.

Bernard, M. My First Mass Book. Date not set. (J). (ps-3). pap. 1.95 (978-0-88271-165-2(2)) Regina Pr., Malhame & Co.

Bicknell, Joanna. Build Your Own Prayers. 2007. (Magnetics Ser.). (Illus.). 14p. (J). (ps-k). 12.95 (978-1-84610-466-4(1)) Make Believe Ideas GBR. *Dist:* Ingram Pub. Services.

Bjorkman, Steve. One Minute Bible Devotions for Kids. 1998. (Illus.). 432p. (ps-3). 16.99 (978-0-8054-9297-2(6)) B&H Publishing Grp.

Boadt, Lawrence. Stations of the Nativity. 2002. (Illus.). 32p. (J). 10.95 (978-0-8091-6699-2(2) , 6699-2) Paulist Pr.

Bogot, Howard I., et al. Gates of Wonder: A Prayerbook for Very Young Children. Waldman, Neil, illus. 2000. 47p. (J). (ps-3). pap. 9.95 (978-0-88123-098-7(7)) Central Conference of American Rabbis/CCAR Pr.

Bowman, Crystal & Kucharik, Elena. The One Year Book of Devotions for Preschoolers. 2004. (Illus.). 384p. (J). 14.99 (978-0-8423-8940-2(7)) Tyndale Hse. Pubs.

Bracy, Linda. Adoration for Children. 2002. (978-0-9723512-1-8(3)) Missionaries of the Blessed Sacrament.

Bratton, Heidi, photos by. Rejoice! Jesus Welcomes Me. 2000. (Walking with God Board Bks.). (Illus.). 16p. (J). (ps-k). bds. 5.95 (978-0-8091-6662-6(3) , 6662-3) Paulist Pr.

Brent, Isabelle, illus. In the House of Happiness: A Book of Prayer & Praise. 2003. 64p. (J). (gr. 7). tchr. ed. 17.00 (978-0-618-23481-3(0) , Clarion Bks.) Houghton Mifflin Co. Trade & Reference Div.

Brewer, Dottie A. Praying 101 for Kids & Teens. 2004. (Illus.). 68p. (J). per. 4.95 (978-0-9707945-2-9(5)) Billion $ Baby Pubns.

Brichto, Mira Pollak. The God Around Us Vol. 2: The Valley of Blessings. Alko, Selina, illus. 2004. 32p. (ps-3). 13.95 (978-0-8074-0738-7(0) , 101074) URJ Pr.

Briscoe, Jill & Children's Bible Hour Staff. The One Year Book of Devotions for Kids, Vol. 3. 2004. (One Year Book of Devotions for Kids Ser.: Vol. 3). 400p. (YA). (gr. 3-7). pap. 12.99 (978-0-8423-4662-7(7)) Tyndale Hse. Pubs.

Britt, Stephanie, illus. My First Book of Prayers. 2007. 32p. pap. 3.99 (***978-0-8249-5570-0(6)** , Ideals Children's Bks.) Ideals Pubns.

—My First Book of Prayers: Mi Primer Libro de Oraciones. 2002. (SPA & ENG.). 30p. (J). 3.95 (978-0-8249-5447-5(5)) Ideals Pubns.

—My Little Prayers. 2005. 96p. (J). 5.99 (978-1-4003-0648-0(5)) Nelson, Thomas Inc.

Britt, Stephanie McFetridge, illus. Mi Primer Libro de Oraciones. 2001. (SPA.). 24p. (J). (gr. 7-10). 12.00 (978-0-7567-5847-9(5)) DIANE Publishing Co.

—My First Book of Prayers. 2001. 26p. (J). (ps-3). bds. 6.95 (978-0-8249-4196-3(9)) Ideals Pubns.

Brooks, Jeremy. A World of Prayers. Gomez, Elena, illus. 2006. 32p. (J). 16.00 (978-0-8028-5285-4(8) , Eerdmans Bks For Young Readers) Eerdmans, William B. Publishing Co.

Brown, Yolanda. Daytime Prayers. Couri, Kathy, illus. 2000. (ENG.). 12p. (J). bds. 6.99 (978-0-570-07121-1(6)) Concordia Publishing Hse.

Browne, Yolanda. Sleepytime Prayers. Couri, Kathy, illus. 2000. (ENG.). 14p. (J). bds. 6.99 (978-0-570-07120-4(8)) Concordia Publishing Hse.

Bulthuis, Lenae. Guess What, Jesus? My Prayer Diary. 1999. (Illus.). 175p. (J). (gr. 3-7). per. 7.95 (978-1-56212-475-5(7) , 160335) CRC Pubns.

—It's Me, Jesus: My Prayer Diary. 1999. (Other Resources Ser.). (Illus.). 175p. (J). (gr. 2-6). 8.25 (978-1-56212-504-2(4) , 160455, Faith Alive Christian Resources) CRC Pubns.

Burnette, Melanie M. 365 Bible Prayers for Children. 2000. (Illus.). 240p. (J). (ps-k). 5.99 (978-0-517-16207-1(5) , Testament) Random Hse. Value Publishing.

—365 Read-To-Me Prayers for Children. 1999. (Illus.). 240p. (J). (ps-2). 10.99 (978-0-8054-9387-0(5)) B&H Publishing Grp.

Burr, Karen Kaslov. A Prayer to Thank You. Wise, Noreen, ed. Wethington, Liz, illus. 2002. (Gold Mixed Collection). 50p. (J). (ps up). pap. 6.95 (978-1-58584-385-5(7)) Huckleberry Pr.

Burrin, Angela M. A Family Journey with Jesus through Lent: Prayers & Activities for Each Day. 2004. (J). pap. 13.95 (978-1-59325-050-8(9)) Word Among Us Pr.

Bus, Sabrina. Hail Mary. Deneux, Xavier, illus. 2006. 12p. (J). bds. 8.00 (978-0-8028-5312-7(9) , Eerdmans Bks For Young Readers) Eerdmans, William B. Publishing Co.

Butcher, Sam, illus. Precious Moments: Angel Kisses & Snuggle Time Prayers with Dolly. 2003. 8.40 (978-0-7180-0575-7(9)) Nelson, Thomas Inc.

—Precious Moments: Angel Kisses & Snuggle Time Prayers with Teddy Bear. 2003. 8.40 (978-0-7180-0567-2(8)) Nelson, Thomas Inc.

Cabrera De Armida, Conception (Conchita). Before the Altar. rev. l.t. ed. 2000. 296p. (YA). per. 12.00 (978-968-7316-08-6(X)) CMJ Marian Pubs.

Calderone-Stewart, Lisa-Marie. Prayer Works for Teens, Bk. 1. Samschror, Robert, ed. Korab, Rick, illus. 2003. (Prayer Work for Teens Ser.: Vol. 1). 72p. (YA). pap. 12.95 (978-0-88489-432-2(0)) St. Mary's Pr.

Cann, Helen, illus. Prayers for Children. 2005. 160p. (J). 14.99 (978-1-56148-470-6(9)) Good Bks.

Carlson, Melody. Baby's First Book of Prayers. 2002. (Illus.). 96p. (J). 6.99 (978-0-310-70287-0(9)) Zonderkidz.

—Piercing Proverbs: Wise Words for Today's Generation. 2002. 96p. pap. 7.99 (978-1-57673-895-5(7) , Multnomah) WaterBrook Pr.

Carlstrom, Nancy White. Thanksgiving Day at Our House: Thanksgiving Poems for the Very Young. Alley, R. W., illus. 2002. 32p. (J). 6.99 (978-0-689-85318-0(1) , Aladdin) Simon & Schuster Children's Publishing.

—Thanksgiving Day at Our House: Thanksgiving Poems for the Very Young. 2002. (ps-2). lib. bdg. 15.30 (978-0-613-90469-8(9)) Tandem Library Bks.

Catholic Baby's Prayers. 2000. (Illus.). (J). (ps-k). bds. 10.99 (978-0-88271-006-8(0)) Regina Pr., Malhame & Co.

Catholic Book Publishing Company Staff, Co Book Publishing. Prayers to My Favorite Saints II. 2002. (gr. k-3). lib. bdg. 21.70 (978-0-613-88792-2(1)) Tandem Library Bks.

Cerda, Gina. Angels Come & Sleep with Me: A Children's Prayer. Miller, Jessel, illus. 1998. 20p. (J). (gr. k-4). 17.95 (978-0-9665153-0-5(7)) Gina Designs.

Child Evangelism Fellowship Staff, prod. The One Year Book of Real Life Encounters with God: 365 Q & A Devotions. 2002. 416p. (J). pap. 12.99 (978-0-8423-7206-0(7)) Tyndale Hse. Pubs.

Children's Bible Hour Staff. The One Year Book of Family Devotions, Vol. 3. 2001. 384p. pap. 12.99 (978-0-8423-2617-9(0)) Tyndale Hse. Pubs.

—Tesoros para Ninos, Vol. 2. 2005. Tr. of Keys for Kids. (SPA.). 368p. pap. 11.99 (978-0-8254-1113-7(0) , Editorial Portavoz) Kregel Pubns.

Children's Bible Hour Staff, prod. The One Year Book of Devotions for Boys, Vol. 2. 2002. 400p. (YA). pap. 13.99 (978-0-8423-6014-2(X)) Tyndale Hse. Pubs.

—The One Year Book of Devotions for Girls, Vol. 2. 2002. (One Year Products Ser.). 400p. (YA). per. 12.99 (978-0-8423-6015-9(8)) Tyndale Hse. Pubs.

Children's Liturgies Made Easy. 1998. Vol. 1. 25.75 (978-0-697-02772-6(4)); Vol. 2. 186p. 25.75 (978-0-697-17595-3(2) , 61-7595-01) Brown & Benchmark.

Children's Missalette. 2006. (J). 2.25 (978-1-933178-40-0(X)) Pflaum Publishing Group.

A Child's First Prayers. 2002. (J). spiral bd. (978-0-9720158-4-4(1)) Story Reader, Inc.

Christenson, Evelyn. What Happens When Children Pray: Learning to Talk & Listen to God. 2005. (Evelyn Christenson Ser.). (Illus.). 32p. 14.99 (978-0-7814-4261-9(3) , 0781442613) Cook, David C. Publishing Co.

Codina, Josep. Hola, Maria! Rius, Roser, illus. 2002. (Praying with Little Ones Ser.: 4). Tr. of I Meet Mary!. (SPA.). 20p. (J). 5.95 (978-0-8198-3683-0(4) , 332-136) Pauline Bks. & Media.

—Prego Com Jesus! Rius, Roser, illus. 2002. (Praying with Little Ones Ser.: 3). Tr. of I Pray Like Jesus!. (SPA.). 20p. (J). 5.95 (978-0-8198-3684-7(2) , 332-137) Pauline Bks. & Media.

—Que N'Ets de Bo! Rius, Roser, illus. 2002. (Praying with Little Ones Ser.: 1). Tr. of I Can Pray!. (SPA.). 20p. 5.95 (978-0-8198-3682-3(6) , 332-135) Pauline Bks. & Media.

—Vull Ser el Teu Amic! Rius, Roser, illus. 2002. (Praying with Little Ones Ser.: 2). Tr. of Jesus Is My Friend!. (SPA.). 20p. (J). 5.95 (978-0-8198-3974-9(4) , 332-150) Pauline Bks. & Media.

Come & See: KIDS, in the Beginning. 2007. (J). per. 9.95 (***978-1-931018-42-5(1)**) Emmaus Road Publishing.

Come & See KIDS, Friends of God. 2006. per. 9.95 (***978-1-931018-41-8(3)**) Emmaus Road Publishing.

Concordia Publishing House, compiled by. Stand Your Ground: Devotions by Teens for Teens. 2001. (ENG.). 128p. (YA). pap. 8.99 (978-0-570-05291-3(2)) Concordia Publishing Hse.

Concordia Publishing House Staff, contrib. by. A Child's Garden of Prayer. 2005. (ENG., Illus.). 80p. (J). 6.99 (978-0-7586-0785-0(7)) Concordia Publishing Hse.

Cook, Cheryl. Kids Prayer Time Series: Lord, Teach me how to pray, Lord, Teach me how to walk by faith, Lord, Teach me how to love others, Lord, Teach me how to take care of the Temple. 2006. (J). 10.99 (***978-0-9746361-5-3(0)**) Heavenly C. Publishing.

Cooper, Emmett. The One Year Make-It-Stick Devotions. Hickerson, Joel, illus. 2007. 416p. (J). pap. 13.99 (***978-1-4143-1551-5(1)**) Tyndale Hse. Pubs.

Cooper, Robert. A World of Wonders: Prayers & Pictures. 2004. (Illus.). 48p. (J). 13.00 (978-0-89869-434-5(5)) Church Publishing, Inc.

Corr, Christopher, illus. A Little Book of Blessings. 2003. 32p. (J). 7.99 (978-0-7459-4674-0(7) , Lion) Lion Hudson plc GBR. *Dist:* Independent Pubs. Group.

Costello, Gwen. Junior-High Prayer Services by Themes & Seasons. 2000. 88p. (YA). (gr. 6-8). pap. 12.95 (978-1-58595-106-2(4)) Twenty-Third Pubns./Bayard.

Cotner, June. House Blessings. 2005. (Illus.). 164p. 15.95 (978-0-9748486-0-0(3)) becker&mayer! books.

—Teen Sunshine Reflections: Words for the Heart & Soul. 2002. (J). (gr. 8 up). (Illus.). 208p. pap. 9.95 (978-0-06-000527-6(0) , Harper Trophy); 160p. 15.89 (978-0-06-000526-9(2)) HarperCollins Pubs.

Creed, C. Patrick, ed. Sanctification of Time in the Third Millennium, Morning & Evening Prayer (with Night Prayer) A Liturgy of the Hours for the Ecclesial Communities of the Local Churches. 2000. 52p. spiral bd. 12.00 (978-0-9715123-0-6(2)) Watchmaker Pr.

Daily Prayers for Foster Children. (YA). 2007. cd-rom 13.95 (978-1-59808-584-6(0)); 2005. 19.95 (978-1-59808-582-2(4)); 2005. ring bd. 24.95 (978-1-59808-159-6(4)); 2005. cd-rom 13.95 (978-1-59808-583-9(2)); 2007. spiral bd. 22.95 (978-1-59808-586-0(7)) Whispering Pine Pr., Inc.

Daizovi, Lonnie G. Cantos Calientes: Musically Accompanied Chants for the Spanish Student. 1998. (SPA.). 76p. (YA). (gr. 7-12). pap. 28.50 incl. audio (978-0-935301-70-0(4)) Vibrante Pr.

Dalfin, Chaim. Davening: Week Day Services. 2000. 120p. (YA). pap. 8.00 (978-1-880880-40-1(7)) Jewish Enrichment Pr.

Dalmatian Press Staff. God Bless Me. (Timeless Treasures Ser.). 28p. (J). bds. 7.99 (978-1-4037-0856-4(8) , Spirit Pr.) Dalmatian Pr.

—My First Prayers: Happy Tale Storybook. 2005. 24p. (J). 2.99 (978-1-4037-1271-4(9) , Spirit Pr.) Dalmatian Pr.

—Prayers for Children. 2006. 15p. 5.99 (978-1-4037-1981-2(0)) Dalmatian Pr.

Darcy-Berube, Francoise & Berube, John Paul. Growing up a Friend of Jesus: A Guide to Discipleship for Children. 2003. (Illus.). 128p. (978-2-89507-041-2(5)) Novalis Publishing.

—Growing up a Friend of Jesus: A Guide to Discipleship for Children. 2000. (Illus.). 128p. (J). (gr. 3-6). 17.95 (978-0-86716-401-5(8)) St. Anthony Messenger Pr. & Franciscan Communications.

Darr, Diane. My Jellybean Prayer Book. Reinbrook Studio, illus. 2002. 20p. (J). pap. 2.99 (978-0-9712618-4-6(9)) C T A, Inc.

Dateno, Maria Grace. I Pray the Stations of the Cross. Rchards, Virginia Helen, illus. 2006. (J). 4.50 (978-0-8198-3691-5(5)) Pauline Bks. & Media.

David C. Cook. Twenty-Third Psalm, 10 vols. 2003. (Jesus Pocket Bks.). (Illus.). 32p. (J). (gr. 5-3). pap., pap. 8.90 (978-1-55513-134-0(4) , 1555131344) Cook, David C. Publishing Co.

Davis, Mary J. My Prayer Journal: A Keepsake for Kids Who Love the Lord. 1998. (Journals Just for Kids Ser.). (Illus.). 144p. (J). (gr. 4-7). pap. 9.99 (978-1-885358-37-0(7) , LP46841, Legacy Pr.) Rainbow Pubs. & Legacy Pr.

Devotionals: Student Devotional, Journal, & Guided Writing. 2004. 104p. (J). (gr. 3-6). pap. 8.99 (978-0-7424-2806-5(0)) School Specialty Publishing.

Dietrich, Amy, illus. First Aid for a Teenager's Soul. 1998. (Charming Petites Ser.). 80p. (YA). 4.95 (978-0-88088-385-6(5)) Peter Pauper Pr. Inc.

Dimensions for Living Staff. Personal Prayers for Children. 2004. 64p. 6.00 (978-0-687-09916-0(1)) Abingdon Pr.

Dobson, S. La Oracion del Padrenuestro (The Lord's Prayer) 1999. (SPA.). (J). pap. 1.69 (978-0-7899-0272-6(9) , 494000) Editorial Unilit.

Douglas, Vincent & School Specialty Publishing Staff. My Little Library of Prayers & Poems. 2003. (My Little Library). (Illus.). 120p. (J). (ps-k). bds. 12.95 (978-1-58845-499-7(1)) School Specialty Publishing.

Edelman, Marian Wright. Guide My Feet: Prayers & Meditations for Our Children. 2000. (Illus.). 240p. pap. 12.00 (978-0-06-095819-0(7)) HarperCollins Pubs.

—I'm Your Child God: Prayers for Our Children. Collier, Bryan, illus. 2002. 112p. (gr. 3-17). 19.99 (978-0-7868-0597-6(8)) Hyperion Bks. for Children.

Edge Ministries Staff, compiled by. One 2 One: Personal Devotions for Youth Camps, Retreats & Trips. 2000. (Essentials for Christian Youth Ser.). (Illus.). 112p. (YA). (gr. 7 up). 15.00 (978-0-687-09561-2(1)) Abingdon Pr.

Egbert, Elaine. Nature in a Nutshell. 2003. 384p. (J). 13.99 (978-0-8280-1669-8(0)) Review & Herald Publishing Assn.

Elkins, Stephen. The Bible Prayer Collection: 30 Life Changing Prayers from the Bible for Children. Colton, Ellie, illus. 2003. 64p. (J). (gr. k-3). 9.99 incl. audio compact disk (978-0-8054-2758-5(9)) B&H Publishing Grp.

—The Jabez Prayer Collection: 30 Life-Changing Prayers from the Bible for Children. Colton, Ellie, illus. 2001. 64p. (J). (ps-3). 14.99 (978-0-8054-2579-6(9)) B&H Publishing Grp.

—Special Times Bible Prayers for Toddlers. Reagan, Susan Joy, illus. 2004. (Special Times Ser.). 32p. (J). (ps up). 9.97 (978-0-8054-2660-1(4)) B&H Publishing Grp.

—Special Times Bible Promises for Toddlers. Reagan, Susan Joy, illus. 2005. (Special Times Ser.). 32p. (J). (ps up). 9.97 (978-0-8054-2678-6(7)) B&H Publishing Grp.

—Stories That End with a Prayer. Menck, Kevin, illus. 32p. (J). (gr. k-8). 12.98 (978-1-56919-003-6(8)) Wonder Workshop.

Ellis, Gwen & Fitchwell, Jennifer. Our Daily Bread. 2006. (Illus.). 10p. (J). bds. 9.99 (978-0-7847-1852-0(0)) Standard Publishing.

Emerick, Yahiya. Color & Learn Salah Textbook & Coloring Book, Meehan, Patricia, illus. l.t. ed. 2000. 91p. (J). pap. 5.95 (978-1-933269-06-1(5)) Noorart, Inc.

Esquinaldo, Virginia, illus. My Book of Prayers. 2006. 48p. (J). 3.95 (978-0-8198-4843-7(3)) Pauline Bks. & Media.

Everyday Prayers for Sleepyheads. 2003. (J). (978-0-7648-0995-8(4)) Liguori Pubns.

Ewald, Thomas. Daily Devotionals. 2004. 192p. pap. (978-1-59441-085-7(2) , CD-204012) Carson-Dellosa Publishing Co., Inc.

Ewen, Caroline, illus. A Prayer a Day: 365 Prayers - One for Every Day of the Year. 1999. 96p. (J). (gr. k-3). 9.99 (978-0-7847-0973-3(4) , 03724, Bean Sprouts) Standard Publishing.

FaithWeaver Children's Messages 3. 2001. 15.99 (978-0-7644-2336-9(3)) Group Publishing, Inc.

Fearon, Mary. Practical Liturgies for the School Year. 1998. 174p. pap. 25.75 (978-0-697-02999-7(9) , WCB/McGraw-Hill) McGraw-Hill Higher Education.

Field, Rachel. Prayer for a Child. Jones, Elizabeth Orton, illus. 2005. 32p. (J). 7.99 (978-0-689-87886-2(9) , Little Simon) Simon & Schuster Children's Publishing.

—Prayer for a Child: Diamond Anniversary Edition. Jones, Elizabeth Orton, illus. anniv. ed. 2004. 32p. (J). 12.00 (978-0-689-87356-0(5)) Simon & Schuster Children's Publishing.

First Prayers. 2003. 192p. 7.98 (978-1-4054-1716-7(1)) Parragon, Inc.

Fishell, Randall Spencer. Supercharged! Fast-Moving, Eye-Popping, Heart-Changing Devotional Stories. 2000. (Illus.). 94p. (J). (gr. 5-9). pap. 7.99 (978-0-8280-1340-6(3) , 197-760) Review & Herald Publishing Assn.

Flanagan, Anne. Come to Jesus: A Kids' Book for Eucharistic Adoration. Cleary, Janice, illus. 2006. (J). 4.50 (978-0-8198-1577-4(2)) Pauline Bks. & Media.

Fletcher, Sarah. My Christmas Prayer Book. Watkins, Bob, illus. 1998. (Arch Bks.). (ENG.). 16p. (J). (gr. k-4). 1.99 (978-0-570-07546-2(7)) Concordia Publishing Hse.

Forte, Bruno & Tarzia, Antonio. My Prayers: To God with Love & Joy. 2003. (Illus.). 65p. (J). pap. 6.95 (978-0-8198-4831-4(X) , 332-222) Pauline Bks. & Media.

Frantz, Jennifer. Bedtime Prayers. Graef, Renee, illus. 2008. (HarperBlessings Ser.). 24p. (J). pap. 3.99 (***978-0-06-083166-0(9)** , Harper Festival) HarperCollins Pubs.

—Everyday Prayers. Graef, Renee, illus. 2008. (HarperBlessings Ser.). 24p. (J). pap. 3.99 (***978-0-06-083167-7(7)** , Harper Festival) HarperCollins Pubs.

Freedman, Claire. My First Book of Bible Prayers. 2004. 32p. 10.99 (978-0-8254-7296-1(2)) Kregel Pubns.

Friedrich, Eliza. Play Pray & Hooray. 2004. 128p. 10.99 (978-0-7586-0117-9(4)) Concordia Publishing Hse.

Frotuna, Stan, told to. U Got 2 Pray. 2004. (Illus.). 255p. (YA). per. 9.95 (978-1-931709-96-5(3)) Our Sunday Visitor, Publishing Div.

Fryar, Jane L. & Varvaris, Cathy. Jesus, Can I Talk with You? A Prayer Journal for Kids. 2003. 32p. (J). pap. 2.99 (978-0-9718985-2-3(9)) C T A, Inc.

Garneau, Jean-Yves. Bedtime Prayers. 2005. (Illus.). 104p. pap. 6.95 (978-0-8146-2890-4(7)) Liturgical Pr.

Garris, Norma. Little Angels Praise Him. 1999. (Illus.). 48p. (J). (ps-2). pap. 2.49 (978-0-7847-0982-5(3) , Bean Sprouts) Standard Publishing.

Gaupin, Linda. The Spirit Sets Us Free: Confirmation Preparation for Youth. 1999. (Illus.). 96p. (YA). (gr. 7-9). pap. 9.45 net. (978-0-8215-5701-3(7)) Sadlier, William H. Inc.

Geisler, Ruth. It's a Great, Awful, In-Between Day: Devotions for Young Readers. 2003. (Illus.). 112p. (J). (gr. 1-4). 9.99 (978-0-7586-0124-7(7)) Concordia Publishing Hse.

Goble, Paul. Song of Creation. Goble, Paul, illus. 2004. (Illus.). 32p. (J). 16.00 (978-0-8028-5271-7(8)) Eerdmans, William B. Publishing Co.

God Made 2001. 2004. (My First Prayers Ser.). 10p. (J). bds. 3.99 (978-1-85854-399-4(1)) Brimax Books Ltd. GBR. *Dist:* Byeway Bks.

God's Awesome Promises. Date not set. (YA). pap. 7.95 (978-0-937347-71-3(X)) C&D International.

Gojoy, Jeanette, ed. My First Prayer Book. Biernacki, Teresa, illus. 1998. 80p. (J). (ps-4). 5.00 (978-1-888765-50-2(X)) Devon Trading Corp.

Golden Books Staff. Prayers for Children. Wilkin, Eloise, illus. 2007. 26p. (J). (gr. k-ps). 4.99 (978-0-375-83927-6(5) , Golden Inspirational) Random Hse. Children's Bks.

Good Night, God Bless. 2002. (J). spiral bd. (978-0-9720158-6-8(8)) Story Reader, Inc.

Goodings, Christina, compiled by. Baby Rhymes & Bedtime Blessings. 1999. (Illus.). 48p. (J). 19.99 (978-0-7459-4166-0(4) , Lion) Lion Hudson plc GBR. *Dist:* Trafalgar Square Publishing.

Goodman, Arnold. A Child's Book of Jewish Prayers. Gill, Daniel, illus. 2001. 48p. (ps-3). 10.95 (978-1-56352-665-7(4)) Longstreet Pr., Inc.

Gospel Light Staff. Big Book of Kid Sermons & Object Talks: 52 Instant Lessons That Children Will Remember. 2004. (Big Book Ser.). 128p. 16.99 (978-0-8307-2516-8(4) , Gospel Light) Gospel Light Pubns.

Grand, Dee Ann. Las Primeras Oraciones del Nino. 2004. (SPA & ENG.). 24p. bds. 12.99 (978-0-8254-5504-9(9) , Editorial Portavoz) Kregel Pubns.

Grant, Larry, ed. Heavenly Father: The Prayers of African-American Children. 1998. (Illus.). 48p. (Orig.). (J). (ps-6). pap. 9.95 (978-1-889851-03-7(5)) SolidGumbo-Works.

Gray, Alice, et al, compiled by. Over One Hundred Treasures to Touch Your Soul. 2002. (Stories for a Teen's Heart Ser.: No. 3). 304p. pap. 12.99 (978-1-57673-974-7(0) , Multnomah) WaterBrook Pr.

Gregg-Schroeder, Susan. For Your Hospital Visit: Prayers & Meditations for Children. 1999. (Illus.). 20p. (J). (gr. 1-6). pap. 2.50 (978-1-57438-033-0(8)) Educational Ministries, Inc.

Griffith, Linda H. Blessings & Prayers for Little Bears. 2002. (Illus.). 32p. (J). 15.95 (978-0-06-623689-6(4)) HarperCollins Pubs.

Groner, Judyth. Thank You, God! A Jewish Child's Book of Prayers. Wikler, Madeline, illus. 2003. 32p. (J). (ps-2). pap. 6.95 (978-1-58013-101-8(8)) Kar-Ben Publishing.

Groome, Thomas H., et al. Acercandote a Dios (Coming to God) 1998. (Acercandote a la Fe Ser.). (SPA & ENG., Illus.). 288p. (J). (gr. 1). pap. (978-0-8215-4461-7(6)) Sadlier, William H. Inc.

—Acercandote a Dios (Coming to God), Grade 1, Guia. 1998. (Acercandote a la Fe Ser.). (SPA & ENG., Illus.). 286p. (J). (gr. 1-2). pap. 20.55 net. (978-0-8215-4471-6(3)) Sadlier, William H. Inc.

—Acercandote a la Iglesias (Coming to the Church) 1998. (Acercandote a la Fe Ser.). (SPA & ENG., Illus.). 288p. (J). (gr. 3). pap. 12.36 net. (978-0-8215-4463-1(2)) Sadlier, William H. Inc.

—Acercandote a la Iglesias (Coming to the Church), Guia. 1998. (Acercandote a la Fe Ser.). (SPA & ENG., Illus.). 286p. (J). (gr. 3). pap. 20.55 net. (978-0-8215-4473-0(X)) Sadlier, William H. Inc.

—Acercandote a la Palabra de Dios (Coming to God's Word), Guia. 1998. (Acercandote a la Fe Ser.). (SPA & ENG., Illus.). 286p. (YA). (gr. 6). pap. 20.55 net. (978-0-8215-4476-1(4)) Sadlier, William H. Inc.

—Acercandote a la Vida de Dios (Coming to God's Life) 1999. (Acercandote a la Fe Ser.). (SPA & ENG., Illus.). 304p. (J). (gr. 5). pap. 12.00 net. (978-0-8215-4465-5(9)) Sadlier, William H. Inc.

—Acercandote a la Vida de Dios (Coming to God's Life), Grade 5, Guia. 1999. (Acercandote a la Fe Ser.). (SPA & ENG., Illus.). 286p. (J). (gr. 5-6). pap. 20.55 net. (978-0-8215-4475-4(6)) Sadlier, William H. Inc.

—Acercandote al Amor de Dios (Coming to God's Love), Guia. 1998. (Acercandote a la Fe Ser.). (SPA & ENG., Illus.). 286p. (J). (gr. 4-5). pap. 19.95 net. (978-0-8215-4474-7(8)) Sadlier, William H. Inc.

Guardian Angel Prayer Book. 2000. 32p. (J). 6.95 (978-0-88271-018-1(4)) Regina Pr., Malhame & Co.

Gutmann, Bessie P., et al. My First Prayers. 2000. 48p. (J). (ps-k). 14.95 (978-1-884807-52-7(6) , EC 752) Blushing Rose Publishing.

Haapala, Christine. Speak Lord I am Listening: A Rosary Book. Maller, Gus, illus. 2nd rev. ed. 2001. 64p. (J). (gr. k-6). pap. 12.00 (978-0-9703996-7-0(7) , 888-652-9494) Suffering Servant Scriptorium.

Haidle, Helen. A Treasury of Children's Prayer. Covington, Neverne, illus. 2002. 192p. (J). 14.99 (978-0-310-70030-2(2)) Zonderkidz.

Hail Mary: Prayer Cards. 2004. (978-0-8294-1405-9(3)) Loyola Pr.

Hamdani, Ibrahim. Salah: The Prescribed Daily Prayers. 2003. 32p. (YA). (978-0-9769245-5-5(2)) Islamic Ctr. of Sacramento, The.

Hardesty, Brian. Closer to God: Prayer Journal, 10 vols. 1998. (gr. 7-12). 15.00 (978-0-687-06820-3(7)) Abingdon Pr.

Harp, Don. Small Blessings: A Book of Prayers for Children. Gill, Daniel, illus. 2001. 48p. (ps-k). 10.95 (978-1-56352-650-3(6)) Longstreet Pr., Inc.

Henderson, Felicity. Day & Night. Donnelly, Strawberrie, illus. 2002. (Pop-Up Prayers Ser.). 18p. (ps-3). 3.99 (978-0-8066-4368-7(4) , Augsburg Bks.) Augsburg Fortress, Pubs.

—People Who Love Us. Donnelly, Strawberrie, illus. 2002. (Pop-Up Prayers Ser.). 16p. (ps-3). 3.99 (978-0-8066-4369-4(2) , Augsburg Bks.) Augsburg Fortress, Pubs.

Henley, Karyn. Day by Day Devotions: A Year of Character Building Devotions for Kids. 2004. 416p. (J). per. 12.99 (978-0-8423-7485-9(X)) Tyndale Hse. Pubs.

Henriques, S. M. My Little Book of Prayer. 2004. 160p. (J). (ps-3). pap. 6.95 (978-1-58334-034-9(3)) Walnut Grove Pr.

Herbert, Christopher, compiled by. Pocket Prayers for Children. 2nd rev. ed. 2006. 96p. 12.00 (***978-0-7151-4040-6(X)***) Church Hse. Pubng. GBR. *Dist:* Church Publishing, Inc.

Hess, Ingrid. Sleep in Peace. 2007. 40p. (J). pap. (***978-0-8361-9381-7(4)***) Herald Pr.

Hill, Karen. All God's Creatures. Johnson, Steven & Fancher, Lou, illus. 2005. 14p. (J). 9.99 (978-0-689-87819-0(2) , Little Simon Inspirations) Simon & Schuster Children's Publishing.

—Prayers for Little Boys. Boldorini, Maria Grazia, illus. 2006. 12p. (J). bds. 6.99 (978-1-4169-0948-4(6) , Little Simon Inspirations) Simon & Schuster Children's Publishing.

—Prayers for Little Girls. Boldorini, Maria Grazia, illus. 2006. 12p. (J). bds. 6.99 (978-1-4169-0949-1(4) , Little Simon Inspirations) Simon & Schuster Children's Publishing.

Hill, Karen & Lucado, Max. You Can Pray, Too! Glueworks Animation, illus. 2005. (Max Lucado's Hermie & Friends Ser.). 22p. (J). (ps-3). bds., bds. 15.99 (978-1-4003-0660-2(4)) Nelson, Thomas Inc.

Hill, Nancy S. The One Year Book of Did You Know Devotions for Kids. 2002. (Illus.). 432p. (J). per. 12.99 (978-0-8423-6184-2(7)) Tyndale Hse. Pubs.

Hodgson, Mona Gansberg. Hide & Seek. 2000. (Critter Creations Devotions Ser.). (Illus.). 144p. (J). (ps-4). 10.99 (978-0-570-07045-0(7)) Concordia Publishing Hse.

The Holy Sacrifice of the Mass. (J). 7.00 (978-1-931555-29-6(5)) Our Lady of Victory Schl.

Hood, Karen Jean Matsko. Daily Prayers for Children: A Collection of Prayers & Bible Verses to Encourage Children in Daily Prayer. 2005. (J). 24.95 (978-1-59210-039-2(2) , 1-59210-039-2) Whispering Pine Pr., Inc.

Horwitz, Brad, ed. & tr. With All Your Heart (A Weekday Prayer Book) Horwitz, Brad, tr. 80p. (J). 14.95 (978-1-58013-144-5(1)) Kar-Ben Publishing.

Hudson, Cheryl Willis. Come by Here Lord: Everyday Prayers for Children. 2004. (Illus.). 32p. (J). (gr. 2). 10.95 (978-0-940975-92-7(0) , Sankofa Bks.) Just Us Bks., Inc.

Inspirio Staff & Zondervan. Promises for Students from the New International Version. 2001. (Promises Ser.). (Illus.). 320p. pap. 4.99 (978-0-310-98263-0(4)) Inspirio.

Jay, Alison. A Child's Book of Graces. 2006. (Illus.). 28p. (J). 5.95 (978-1-56148-514-7(4)) Good Bks.

Jeep, Elizabeth M. Children's Daily Prayer for Summer. 2000. 120p. (J). pap. 8.00 (978-1-56854-356-7(5)) Liturgy Training Pubns.

Jeep, Elizabeth McMahon. Blessings & Prayers through the Year: A Resource for School & Parish. 2004. (J). 49.95 incl. audio compact disk (978-1-56854-369-7(7) , CLASS) Liturgy Training Pubns.

—Children's Daily Prayer 2005 - 2006. 2005. (J). pap. 16.00 (978-1-56854-538-7(X) , CDP06) Liturgy Training Pubns.

Jenkins, J. B. & LaHaye, Tim. De Cara al Futuro. 1999. (Dejados Atras los Chicos Ser.: No. 4). (SPA.). (J). (gr. 4-7). pap. 4.99 (978-0-7899-0557-4(4) , 497523) Editorial Unilit.

—Los Desaparecidos. 1999. (Dejados Atras los Chicos Ser.: No. 1). (SPA.). (J). (gr. 4-7). pap. 4.99 (978-0-7899-0554-3(X) , 497520) Editorial Unilit.

John Paul II, pseud. My Dear Young Friends: Pope John Paul II Speaks to Youth on Life, Love, & Courage. Vitek, John, ed. 2003. (Illus.). 144p. (YA). pap., pap. 9.95 (978-0-88489-748-4(6)) St. Mary's Pr.

Johnson, Barbara. The Pepperoni Parade & the Power of Prayer: A Book about Prayer. Frazier, Victoria Ponikvar, illus. 1999. (Geranium Lady Ser.: Vol. 3). 32p. (J). (ps-2). 4.97 (978-0-8499-5950-9(0)) Nelson, Thomas Inc.

Johnson, Catherine & Kelley, Mary Kay. Give Your Gifts: 40 More Prayer Services for Young People. 2002. 165p. (YA). per. 27.95 (978-1-57999-194-4(7) , G-5437) GIA Pubns., Inc.

Johnson, Kevin. Total Devotion: 365 Days to Hang Tight with Jesus. 2004. 384p. (J). reprint ed. pap. 13.99 (978-0-7642-2884-1(6)) Bethany Hse. Pubs.

Johnson, Lois Walfrid. Burnt Cookies. 2006. 96p. (J). pap. 6.99 (978-0-7847-1510-9(6) , 42180) Standard Publishing.

Joslin, Mary. Our Father: The Prayer Jesus Taught. Newey, Gail, illus. 2004. 24p. (ps-3). 15.95 (978-0-8294-1504-9(1)) Loyola Pr.

Joyner, Rick, ed. The Morning Star Journal Vol. 10. 1999. 96p. (gr. 9 up). pap. 4.00 (978-1-878327-92-5(5) , MSJ10-001) MorningStar Pubns., Inc.

Kast, Michael. What's in Your Locker? 30 Daily Devotions. Reeves, Dale, ed. 2001. 160p. (J). (gr. 7 up). 10.99 (978-0-7847-1253-5(0)) Standard Publishing.

Kendig, Ellen J. Children's Book of Bedtime Blessings. Rockhill, Dennis, illus. 2000. 48p. (ps-3). 5.95 (978-0-8091-6677-0(1) , 6677-1) Paulist Pr.

—Children's Book of Family Blessings. 2000. (Illus.). 48p. (gr. k-3). 7.95 (978-0-8091-6667-1(4) , 6667-4) Paulist Pr.

—Children's Book of Table Blessings. Saroff, Phyllis V., illus. 2001. 48p. (J). (gr. k-3). 6.95 (978-0-8091-6689-3(5) , 6689-5) Paulist Pr.

Kennedy, Anne, illus. Little Prayers & Graces: A Shining Bright Book. 2000. (Baby Blessings Ser.). 12p. (ps-k). bds. 9.99 (978-0-7847-1139-2(9) , 04319) Standard Publishing.

Kid, Penelope. Teach Me to Pray. Goffe, Toni, illus. 2004. (Teach Me Ser.). 24p. (ps-2). 6.95 (978-0-8294-1368-7(5)) Loyola Pr.

Kielbasa, Marilyn. Life Can be a Wild Ride: More Prayers by Young Teens. 2003. (Illus.). 136p. (J). pap. 7.95 (978-0-88489-484-1(3)) St. Mary's Pr.

King, Stephanie. Dear God, It's Me. Mahood, Helen, illus. 2001. 64p. (J). (gr. 4-7). 6.00 (978-0-687-01497-2(2)) Abingdon Pr.

Kitch, Anne. Bless This Way. Conahan, Carolyn Digby, illus. 2003. 20p. 9.95 (978-0-8192-1917-6(7)) Morehouse Publishing.

Kitch, Anne E. Bless This Day: Toddler Prayers. Oeltjenbruns, Joni, illus. 2000. (Toddler Prayers Ser.). 16p. (J). (ps). bds. 6.95 (978-0-8192-1837-7(5) , 6269) Morehouse Publishing.

Kittel, Vernette. Student Daily Devotional: 365 Days. 2003. 388p. (J). pap. 19.99 (978-1-57921-682-5(X)) Pleasant Word.

Knowlton, Laurie Lazzaro. God Be in My Heart: Poems & Prayers for Children. 2003. (Illus.). 24p. (J). (ps up). 11.95 (978-1-56397-646-9(3)) Boyds Mills Pr.

Knox, Lorna Ann. I Came from Joy: Spiritual Affirmations & Activities for Children. 2nd rev. ed. 2003. (Illus.). 172p. (gr. k-7). pap. 19.95 (978-1-56589-146-3(5)) Crystal Clarity Pubs.

Koch, Carl, ed. Dreams Alive: Prayers by Teenagers. 2003. 88p. (YA). (gr. 7-13). pap. 5.95 (978-0-88489-262-5(X)) St. Mary's Pr.

—More Dreams Alive: Prayers by Teenagers. 2003. 112p. (J). (gr. 7-13). pap. 4.95 (978-0-88489-321-9(9)) St. Mary's Pr.

—You Give Me the Sun: Biblical Prayers by Teenagers. 2003. 120p. (YA). (gr. 7-13). per. 5.95 (978-0-88489-615-9(3)) St. Mary's Pr.

Kucharik, Elena. Promesas para Corazoncitos (Promises for Little Hearts) 1999. (Little Hearts Ser.). (SPA.). (J). (gr. 4-7). 7.99 (978-0-7899-0664-9(3) , 497771) Editorial Unilit.

Lach, William & Metropolitan Museum of Art Staff, eds. I Imagine Angels: Poems & Prayers for Parents & Children. 2000. 47p. (J). (978-0-87099-949-9(4)) Metropolitan Museum of Art, The.

Lanciotti, Judi. Prayers with Pizzazz for Junior High Teens. Stamschror, Robert P., ed. 2003. 76p. (YA). spiral bd. 12.95 (978-0-88489-376-9(6)) St. Mary's Pr.

Larkin, Jean K., ed. Prayers & Guidelines for Young Catholics. 2003. 28p. (J). 1.95 (978-0-89837-231-1(3) , 4658) Pflaum Publishing Group.

Larsen, Carolyn. Little Boys Book of Prayers for Toddlers. Turk, Caron, illus. 2002. (Little Boys & Little Girls Storybook Ser.). 32p. (J). (ps). 7.99 (978-0-8010-4501-1(0) , New Kids Media) Baker Bks.

—Little Girls Book of Prayers for Mothers & Daughters. Turk, Caron, illus. 1999. 192p. (J). (ps-2). reprint ed. 12.99 (978-0-8010-4422-9(7) , New Kids Media) Baker Bks.

—Little Girls Book of Prayers for Toddlers. Turk, Caron, illus. 2002. (Little Boys & Little Girls Storybook Ser.). 32p. (J). (ps). 7.99 (978-0-8010-4500-4(2) , New Kids Media) Baker Bks.

—Little Girl's Devotional Storybook. Turk, Caron, illus. 2000. 192p. (J). (ps-2). 16.99 (978-0-8010-4446-5(4) , New Kids Media) Baker Bks.

Lawrence, Greer. Prayers & Meditations for Children. 1998. (Illus.). 64p. (J). 7.95 (978-1-57717-061-7(X)) New Line Bks.

Learning My Prayers: Coloring & Activity Book. 2005. (Illus.). (J). (ps-3). pap. 1.95 (978-0-8198-4518-4(3) , 332-426) Pauline Bks. & Media.

Leclerc, Roland. 365 Prayers for Bedtime. 2001. 300p. (J). (ps-3). pap. (978-1-895919-64-6(9)) Les Editions LOGIQUES.

Lee, Helen, compiled by. Guide's Greatest Prayer Stories. 2002. 142p. (YA). pap. 10.99 (978-0-8280-1647-6(X) , 079-975) Review & Herald Publishing Assn.

Lee, Witness. The Holy Word for Morning Revival: The God-Man Living - a Man of Prayer. 2001. 109p. (J). (gr. 6). per. 7.00 (978-0-7363-1352-0(4) , 13-144-001) Living Stream Ministry.

Legacy Press Staff. Gotta Have God: Devotions for Boys. 2004. (Gotta Have God Ser.). (Illus.). 238p. (J). (gr. 1-4). spiral bd. 12.99 (978-1-885358-97-4(0)); (ps-k). spiral bd. 12.99 (978-1-885358-96-7(2)) Rainbow Pubs. & Legacy Pr. (Legacy Pr.).

Leiser, Bonnie. Angels, Bananas & God's Pajamas: Stories, Rhymes & Bedtime Prayers. 2000. (Illus.). 140p. (ps-3). pap. 10.95 (978-0-595-12183-0(7)) iUniverse, Inc.

Lewis, L. Carol. Little Lumpy's Book of Blessings. Clarke, Christopher B., illus. 2001. 32p. (J). (ps-5). 16.95 (978-0-9702415-0-4(X)) Three Butterflies Entertainment & Pr.

Lewis, Rob, retold by. The Lord Is My Shephard: Psalm 23. 2004. (Illus.). 24p. (ps-3). 12.95 (978-0-8294-1652-7(8)) Loyola Pr.

Lindbergh, Reeve. The Circle of Days. 2002. (gr. 3-6). lib. bdg. 14.15 (978-0-613-74721-9(6)) Tandem Library Bks.

Lingo, Susan L. My Good Night Prayers: 45 Quiet Times with Prayers, Songs, & Rhymes. Parks, Kathy, illus. 2006. 208p. (J). 13.99 (978-0-7847-1365-5(0) , 04026) Standard Publishing.

—My Little Good Night Prayers. Parks, Kathy, illus. 2006. (My Good Night Collection). 108p. (J). 7.99 (978-0-7847-1229-0(8) , 04062) Standard Publishing.

Little Treasury Sac Heart. 15p. pap. (978-0-8198-4461-3(6) , 332-164) Pauline Bks. & Media.

Littleton, Mark. NIRV Kid's Book of Devotions: A 365-Day Adventure in God's Word. 1998. 384p. (J). pap. 9.99 (978-0-310-22130-2(7)) Zonderkidz.

Living Out Christ's Love Prayer Journals, 12 vols. 2005. (YA). 9.95 (978-0-9772313-2-4(1)) Covenant Support Network.

Living the Good News Staff. Kids in Common: A Children's Book of Common Prayer. 2004. (Illus.). 32p. (J). 4.95 (978-1-931960-29-8(1)) Living the Good News.

Lonsdale, Mary, illus. My Prayers for Everyday. 2004. 10p. (J). bds. 7.99 (978-1-85854-438-0(6)) Brimax Books Ltd. GBR. *Dist:* Byeway Bks.

The Lord's Prayer: Forgive Us. 2003. (Illus.). 50p. (J). pap. 6.00 (978-1-58572-052-1(6)) Ambassador Pubns.

The Lord's Prayer: Our Father. 2002. (Illus.). 50p. (J). pap. 6.00 (978-1-58572-048-4(8)) Ambassador Pubns.

Lords Prayer for Children. 2006. 10p. (YA). bds. 11.99 (978-0-7847-1772-1(9) , 04724) Standard Publishing.

Lovasik, Lawrence G. St. Joseph Book of Prayers for Children. 1999. (Pocket-Size Ser.). (Illus.). 64p. (J). (ps-3). pap. 5.95 (978-0-89942-148-3(2) , 148/22) Catholic Bk. Publishing Corp.

Lund, Deborah. All Day Long: A Book of Partner Prayers. Conahan, Carolyn Digby, illus. 2004. 20p. (J). 9.95 (978-0-8192-1961-9(4)) Morehouse Publishing.

—Me & God: A Book of Partner Prayers. Conahan, Carolyn Digby, illus. 2003. 20p. 9.95 (978-0-8192-1911-4(8)) Morehouse Publishing.

Luther's Seal Sticker. 2004. (Illus.). pap. 7.99 (978-0-8066-3720-4(X)) Augsburg Fortress, Pubs.

Lyttle, Marcy. Catching Fireflies: Family Night Devotional Fun. Irwin, Kendra, illus. 2007. 273p. 12.99 (***978-1-932307-77-1(X)*** , Ambassador International) Emerald Hse. Group, Inc.

Maccarone, Grace. A Child's Good Night Prayer. Williams, Sam, illus. 2001. 32p. (J). (ps-1). pap. 10.95 (978-0-439-23505-1(7)) Scholastic, Inc.

—Child's Good Night Prayer. Williams, Sam, illus. 2004. (Bless Me Ser.). 26p. (J). bds. 6.99 (978-0-439-62332-2(4) , Cartwheel Bks.) Scholastic, Inc.

MacDonald, Alan. Whispering in God's Ear: Inspirational Poetry for Children. 1998. (Illus.). 96p. (J). (gr. 1-2). 7.99 (978-0-88486-217-8(8) , Arrowood Pr.) BBS Publishing Corp.

MacKenzie, Joy & Spangler, Ann. The Growing Reader Book of Prayers. Newton, Jill, illus. 2004. 224p. (J). 12.99 (978-0-8423-8479-7(0)) Tyndale Hse. Pubs.

Madero, Pino. My Book of Psalms. Wickenhiser, Mary David, tr. from SPA. Cortesi, Carla, illus. 1999. 56p. (J). (gr. 2-5). mass mkt. 3.95 (978-0-8198-4807-9(7) , 332-207) Pauline Bks. & Media.

—Prayers from My Heart. Wickenhiser, Mary David, tr. from SPA. Cortesi, Carla, illus. 1999. 32p. (J). (gr. 2-5). pap. 3.95 (978-0-8198-5916-7(8) , 332-275) Pauline Bks. & Media.

Make Believe Ideas, Ltd. Build Your Own Prayers: Magnetic Prayer Book. 2007. (Illus.). 14p. (J). (gr. k-3). 12.95 (978-1-59145-554-7(5)) Nelson, Thomas Inc.

Manz Simon, Mary. My First Read & Learn Book of Prayers. 2007. (J). bds. 9.99 (978-0-439-90632-6(6)) Scholastic, Inc.

Martin, Kim. Because You Were Here. Martin, Kim, illus. 2000. (Illus.). 24p. (J). (ps-6). pap. 5.95 (978-0-615-11533-7(0)) Martin Graphics.

Mass, Wendy. Autumn: Poems, Songs, Prayers. 2004. (Weather Windows Ser.). 4.99 (978-0-570-07168-6(2)) Concordia Publishing Hse.

Mass, Wendy, compiled by. Summer: Poems, Songs, Prayers. 2001. (Illus.). 10p. (J). (ps-2). 6.99 (978-0-570-07165-5(8)) Concordia Publishing Hse.

McDaniels, Preston, illus. Now the Day Is Over. 2001. (Hymns for Children Ser.). 32p. (J). (ps-2). 17.95 (978-0-8192-1868-1(5)) Morehouse Publishing.

McDowell, Josh & Stewart, Ed. Friendship 911 Collection: My Friend Is Struggling With... Past Sexual Abuse. 2000. (Friendship 911 Ser.). (Illus.). 64p. (gr. 8-12). pap. 7.98 (978-0-8499-3797-2(3)) Nelson, Thomas Inc.

Medina, Sarah. A Day to Remember. Brecknell, Annie, illus. 41p. pap. 8.99 (978-0-7459-4770-9(0) , Lion) Lion Hudson plc GBR. *Dist:* Trafalgar Square Publishing.

Miller, Cecilia. The Mantra Is a Prayer to God. Trayser, Laura, illus. 2000. 24p. (J). reprint ed. 12.95 (978-0-911307-92-4(3) , 205426, Siddha Yoga Pubn.) SYDA Foundation.

Miller, Steve & Miller, Becky. A Child's Garden of Prayer: Turning Little Hearts Toward God. Fincher, Kathryn Andrews, illus. 1999. 64p. (J). (ps-3). 16.99 (978-0-7369-0117-8(5)) Harvest Hse. Pubs.

Molin, Steve. Game Day: Sports Devotionals for Kids. 2000. 58p. (YA). pap. 5.95 (978-1-929478-20-0(8)) Cross Training Publishing.

Morina, Barbara. Daily Devotions My Gratitude Journal. Morina, Barbara, ed. 2001. (Write It down Ser.). (Illus.). 202p. 19.95 (978-1-892033-36-9(4)) Journals Unlimited, Inc.

Morneau, Robert F., ed. Children's Book of Classic Catholic Prayers. 2000. (Illus.). 32p. (J). (ps-5). 5.95 (978-0-8091-6666-4(6) , 6666-6) Paulist Pr.

Morrow, Lesley Mandel, et al, contrib. by. Discovering God's Love: A Faith Development Program for Five Year Olds. rev. ed. 1999. (Discovering God Ser.). (Illus.). 128p. (J). (gr. k-1). pap. 11.58 net. (978-0-8215-2470-1(4)) Sadlier, William H. Inc.

—Discovering God's World: A Faith Development Program for Four Year Olds. rev. ed. 1999. (Discovering God Ser.). (Illus.). 128p. (J). (ps-k). pap. 11.58 net. (978-0-8215-2460-2(7)) Sadlier, William H. Inc.

Mundy, Michaelene. A Book of Prayers for All Your Cares. Alley, R. W., illus. 2004. (J). per. 7.95 (978-0-87029-382-5(6)) Abbey Pr.

Murphy, Elspeth Campbell. Happy Easter, God. Lewis, Jim, illus. 2001. (Prayer-Poems Ser.). 32p. (J). (ps-3). 7.99 (978-0-7642-2386-0(0)) Bethany Hse. Pubs.

My Prayer Book. 2000. (J). 9.95 (978-0-88271-729-6(4)); 9.95 (978-0-88271-731-9(6)); lthr. 19.95 (978-0-88271-733-3(2)); lthr. 19.95 (978-0-88271-734-0(0)); lthr. 19.95 (978-0-88271-736-4(7)) Regina Pr., Malhame & Co.

Myers, Walter Dean. The Gifts We Bring. 96p. (J). (gr. 3-7). 5. Date not set. 14.99 (978-0-06-027809-0(9)); No. 1. 2001. 14.95 (978-0-06-027805-2(6)); No. 2. 2002. 14.95 (978-0-06-027806-9(4)); No. 6. Date not set. 14.99 (978-0-06-027810-6(2)) HarperCollins Pubs.

Noller & Taylor. Mis Primeras Palabras de la Biblia (My First Bible Words) 2000. (My First... Ser.). (SPA.). (J). 10.99 (978-0-7899-0682-3(1) , 494617) Editorial Unilit.

O'Connor, Francine M. Let's Pray: Catholic Prayers & the Mass. Larkin, Jean, ed. Qvick, Larissa, illus. 1999. (Active Learning for Catholic Kids Ser.). 28p. (J). (gr. 1-3). pap. 7.95 (978-0-937997-54-3(4) , 3403) Pflaum Publishing Group.

O'Dell, Catherine M. & Savitskas, Margaret. Loyola Kids Book of Everyday Prayers. 2004. (Loyola Kids Ser.). (Illus.). 208p. (J). (gr. 3-6). 15.95 (978-0-8294-1509-4(2)) Loyola Pr.

O'Keefe, Susan Heyboer. Angel Prayers: Prayers for All Children. Suzan, Sofia, illus. 2003. 32p. (J). (ps-1). 15.95 (978-1-56397-683-4(8)) Boyds Mills Pr.

O'Malley, William J. More Daily Prayers for Busy People. 1999. 192p. (YA). spiral bd. 10.95 (978-0-88489-634-0(X)) St. Mary's Pr.

O'Neal, Debbie & Satchell, Jonathan. The Big Bedtime Book of Bible Stories & Prayers. 1999. 64p. (J). pap. 22.00 (978-1-85608-356-0(X)) Hunt, John Publishing Ltd. GBR. *Dist:* State Mutual Bk. & Periodical Service, Ltd.

O'Neal, Debbie Trafton. Thank You for This Day: Action Prayers, Songs & Blessings for Every Day. Munger, Nancy, illus. 2000. 32p. (J). (ps up). 7.99 (978-0-8066-4069-3(3) , Augsburg Bks.) Augsburg Fortress, Pubs.

Oraciones de la Biblia (Prayers from the Bible) 1998. (Tiempo de Orar Ser.). (SPA.). (J). bds. 3.99 (978-0-7899-0518-5(3) , 495662) Editorial Unilit.

Oraciones Favoritas (Best-Loved Prayers) 1998. (Tiempo de Orar Ser.). (SPA.). (J). bds. 3.99 (978-0-7899-0520-8(5) , 495664) Editorial Unilit.

Oraciones por Mi Familia (Prayers for My Family) 1998. (Tiempo de Orar Ser.). (SPA.). (J). bds. 3.99 (978-0-7899-0519-2(1) , 495663) Editorial Unilit.

Page, Josephine. Thank You Prayer. Church, Caroline Jayne, illus. 2005. 24p. (J). pap. 8.99 (978-0-439-68099-8(9) , Cartwheel Bks.) Scholastic, Inc.

Paltro, Piera. Learning My Prayers, 8 bks. Daughters of St. Paul Staff, tr. Curti, Anna M., illus. Incl. Angel of God. 16p. 1981. pap. 2.95 (978-0-8198-0739-7(7) , CH0031P); Eternal Rest : A Prayer for People Who Have Died. 15p. 1992. pap. 2.50 (978-0-8198-2332-8(5)); Glory to the Father. 21p. 1987. pap. 2.50 (978-0-8198-3043-2(7) , CH0227); Hail, Holy Queen. 15p. 1992. pap. 2.50 (978-0-8198-3365-5(7)); Hail Mary. 22p. 1992. pap. 2.50 (978-0-8198-3316-7(9)); I Believe : The Profession of Faith or Creed. 29p. 1992. pap. 2.50 (978-0-8198-3664-9(8)); My Mass. 32p. 1992. pap. 2.50 (978-0-8198-4765-2(8)); Our Father. 23p. 1991. pap. 2.95 (978-0-8198-5416-2(6) , CH0416P); (Illus.). (J). (ps-1). Set pap. 18.80 (978-0-8198-4483-5(7)) Pauline Bks. & Media.

Parry, et al. Orando con los Ositos (Prayers with Bears) El Salmo 23 (The 23rd Psalm) 2000. (Bears Ser.). (SPA.). (J). bds. 4.50 (978-0-7899-0830-8(1) , 494664) Editorial Unilit.

—Orando con los Ositos (Prayers with Bears) Las Bienaventuranzas (The Beattitudes) 2000. (Bears Ser.). (SPA.). (J). bds. 4.50 (978-0-7899-0828-5(X) , 494663) Editorial Unilit.

Parry, Alan. Goodnight Prayers. Parry, Linda, illus. 2004. (Oaktree Wood Ser.). 32p. (ps-3). 10.00 (978-0-687-09705-0(3)) Abingdon Pr.

Peralas, Jorge. Oracional Bilingue Para Ninos: A Children's Prayerbook in Spanish-English. 2005. (ENG & SPA., Illus.). 96p. (J). (gr. 3-7). pap. 5.95 (978-0-8146-2459-3(6)) Liturgical Pr.

Petersen, Richard. Santa's Prayer. Vorlicek, Greta N., illus. l.t. ed. 2001. 32p. (YA). (gr. 2 up). pap. 10.00 (978-0-9632180-3-2(4)) Chinaberry Hse.

Pfeiffer, Judith & Tenud, Tish, illus. My First Prayers: Play-a-Sound Book. 1999. (Play-a-Sound Ser.). 12p. (J). (ps-k). 10.99 (978-0-7847-0890-3(8) , 03750, Bean Sprouts) Standard Publishing.

Piper, Sophie. My Baptism Book. Kolanovic, Dubravka, illus. 2007. 64p. 14.95 (978-1-55725-535-8(0)) Paraclete Pr., Inc.

Piper, Sophie. Prayers for the Very Young. 2008. (Illus.). 64p. (J). 7.95 (***978-0-7459-6032-6(4)***) Lion Hudson plc GBR. *Dist:* Independent Pubs. Group.

Pockets Learning Staff. Lord Is My Shepherd Book. 1998. (Illus.). 8p. (ps up). 35.00 (978-1-888074-99-4(X)) Pockets of Learning.

Prayers for Little Hands: My First Treasury. 40p. (J). bds. 7.98 (978-0-7853-5107-8(8) , 7133000) Publications International, Ltd.

Prayers for Sleepyheads, Set. 2003. (J). pap. 10.95 net. (978-0-7648-0994-1(6)) Liguori Pubns.

Prayers of Jesus for Children. (J). (978-0-88271-162-1(8)) Regina Pr., Malhame & Co.

Prayers of the Ages. 2000. (J). 7.95 (978-0-88271-726-5(X)) Regina Pr., Malhame & Co.

Prayers That Avail Much for Teens. (YA). 14.99 (978-0-89274-902-7(4)) Harrison Hse., Inc.

Prayers That Get Results. unabr. ed. 2001. 45p. per. 14.95 (978-0-9710476-0-0(X)) God's Word.

Prothro, Crystaline Joi. I'm a Kid but I'm Not Kiddin' I Love the Lord. Curry, Rosalynn A. & Johnson, Charmaine, eds. Johnson, Bob, photos by. 1998. (Illus.). 100p. (J). (gr. 4-7). pap. 9.95 (978-0-9662919-3-3(X)) Robot Publishing.

Randazzo, Dottie. Praying 101 for Kids & Teens. 2007. 101p. pap. 10.95 (***978-0-615-14725-3(9)***) Creative Dreaming Ltd.

Reese, Kimberly Ingalls. Celebrate Jesus! At Christmas: Family Devotions for Advent Through Epiphany. 2000. (Illus.). 128p. (J). (gr. 1-5). 6.99 (978-0-570-07127-3(5)) Concordia Publishing Hse.

Reeves, Eira. El Padre Nuestro (The Lord's Prayer) (SPA.). (J). 1.89 (978-0-7899-0480-5(2) , 498667) Editorial Unilit.

Regina Press Malhame and Company Staff. My First Prayer Book. 1998. (J). (ps-3). 3.95 (978-0-88271-575-9(5)) Regina Pr., Malhame & Co.

Regina Press Malhame and Company Staff & Company. Catholic Baby's Prayers. 2000. (ps-2). lib. bdg. 19.95 (978-0-613-87509-7(5)) Tandem Library Bks.

Regina Press Staff. Beginner's Bible First Catholic Prayers. 1999. (J). 5.95 (978-0-88271-723-4(5)) Regina Pr., Malhame & Co.

—Catholic Baby's First Prayers. 1999. (J). (ps-k). 10.99 (978-0-88271-715-9(4)) Regina Pr., Malhame & Co.

—Guardian Angel Prayer Book. 2000. 32p. (J). 6.95 (978-0-88271-019-8(2)) Regina Pr., Malhame & Co.

—My First Book of Catholic Prayers. 1999. (J). (ps-k). 5.95 (978-0-88271-753-1(7)) Regina Pr., Malhame & Co.

Reinsma, Carol. Credo Canyon Kids: Stories for Life. 1998. (Devotional Stories for Life Ser.). 255p. (gr. k-2). 9.95 (978-1-56212-342-0(4) , 160305, Faith Alive Christian Resources) CRC Pubns.

—Rooftop Kids: Stories for Life. 1999. (Devotional Stories for Life Ser.). 254p. (gr. k-6). 9.95 (978-1-56212-407-6(2) , 160310, Faith Alive Christian Resources) CRC Pubns.

Ring, Laura, ed. Prayers for a Child's Day. Allen, Joy, illus. 1999. (Happy Day Bks.). 24p. (J). (ps-2). pap. 2.49 (978-0-7847-0891-0(6) , 04264, Bean Sprouts) Standard Publishing.

Rivers, Ruth, illus. This Amazing World: Poems & Prayers about Everything under the Sun. 2002. 48p. (J). (gr. 1-7). 16.00 (978-1-56148-363-1(X)) Good Bks.

Robb, Andy. Kids Say, "Praise God!" 2000. (Illus.). 16p. (J). (ps-k). 8.00 (978-0-687-08342-8(7)) Abingdon Pr.

—Kids Say, "Thank You God!" 2000. (Illus.). 16p. (J). (ps-k). 8.00 (978-0-687-08348-0(6)) Abingdon Pr.

Rock, Lois. Al Final del Dia. Rawlings, Louise, illus. (Coleccion Luz de Noche). (SPA.). (J). (gr. k-3). (978-84-236-5039-2(1)) Edebé ESP. *Dist:* Lectorum Pubns., Inc.

—A Book of Prayers for Baby's Christening. 2008. (Illus.). 48p. (J). 7.95 (***978-0-7459-6044-9(8)***) Lion Hudson plc GBR. *Dist:* Independent Pubs. Group.

—A Child's First Book of Prayers. Jay, Alison, illus. 2002. 224p. (ps-3). 16.99 (978-0-8066-4374-8(9) , Augsburg Bks.) Augsburg Fortress, Pubs.

—Everyday Prayers for Children. 2002. (Illus.). 128p. (J). 14.95 (978-0-86716-501-2(4)) St. Anthony Messenger Pr. & Franciscan Communications.

—The Lion Book of 1000 Prayers for Children. 2003. (Illus.). 540p. (J). 18.00 (978-0-7459-4663-4(1) , Lion) Lion Hudson plc GBR. *Dist:* Independent Pubs. Group.

—My Very First Prayers. Ayliffe, Alex, illus. 2003. (Bestselling Children's Books - Religious Ser.). 158p. (J). 14.99 (978-1-56148-371-6(0)) Good Bks.

—Prayers for Your Confirmation. 2007. (Illus.). 48p. (J). 9.95 (***978-0-7459-6045-6(6)***) Lion Hudson plc GBR. *Dist:* Independent Pubs. Group.

Rock, Lois. Todos los Dias Contigo. Rawlings, Louise, illus. (Coleccion Luz de Noche). (SPA.). (J). (gr. k-3). (978-84-236-4916-7(4)) Edebé ESP. *Dist:* Lectorum Pubns., Inc.

Ross, Michael & Edmondson, Jeff. Radically Plugged In: High-Voltage Devotionals to Ground Your Faith. 1998. (Illus.). 136p. (gr. 8-12). pap. 11.99 (978-0-8341-1707-5(X)) Beacon Hill Pr. of Kansas City.

Rylant, Cynthia. Bless Us All: A Child's Yearbook of Blessings. Rylant, Cynthia, illus. 2001. (Illus.). 32p. (J). pap. 6.99 (978-0-689-84637-3(1) , Aladdin) Simon & Schuster Children's Publishing.

—Bless Us All: A Child's Yearbook of Blessings. 1998. (Illus.). 32p. (J). (ps-3). 14.00 (978-0-689-82370-1(3)) Simon & Schuster Children's Publishing.

—Bless Us All: A Child's Yearbook of Blessings. 2001. (gr. k-3). lib. bdg. 15.30 (978-0-613-73311-3(8)) Tandem Library Bks.

—Give Me Grace: A Child's Daybook of Prayers. Rylant, Cynthia, illus. (Classic Board Bks.). (Illus.). 32p. (J). (ps-k). 2002. bds. 6.99 (978-0-689-85128-5(6) , Little Simon); 1999. 12.95 (978-0-689-82293-3(6)); 2005. 7.99 (978-0-689-87885-5(0) ; Little Simon Inspirations) Simon & Schuster Children's Publishing.

Sabado, Joe, illus. Mommy Teach Us to Pray. Fujii, Jason, photos by. l.t. ed. 2006. 31p. (J). 15.95 (978-1-59879-122-8(2)) Lifevest Publishing, Inc.

Sacraments & Prayer, 6 booklets. 1998. (Illus.). (YA). (gr. 7-10). stu. ed. 12.95 (978-0-89837-213-7(5)) Pflaum Publishing Group.

Sage, Angie, illus. Baby's World. 2000. (Baby Blessings Ser.). 6p. (J). (ps-k). 6.99 (978-0-7847-1131-6(3) , 04311, Bean Sprouts) Standard Publishing.

Savary, Louis M. Rosary for Children. Date not set. (J). (ps-3). pap. 1.25 (978-0-88271-158-4(X)) Regina Pr., Malhame & Co.

—Way of the Cross. Date not set. (J). (ps-3). pap. 1.95 (978-0-88271-160-7(1)) Regina Pr., Malhame & Co.

Sawyer, Kieran. The Faith Difference: Prayers, Lessons, Activities & Crafts for Children. 2004. 160p. (gr. 9-12). tchr. ed., spiral bd. 19.95 (978-0-87793-729-6(X)) Ave Maria Pr.

Sewell, James. Daily Devotionals. 2005. 192p. pap. (978-1-59441-086-4(0) , CD-204013) Carson-Dellosa Publishing Co., Inc.

Sharpe, Sally D. 365 Meditations for Teens. 2000. (gr. 7-12). lib. bdg. 21.10 (978-0-613-73185-0(9)) Tandem Library Bks.

Sharpe, Sally D. & Broderson, Steve. 365 Meditations for Teens. 2004. 244p. (gr. 8-12). 12.00 (978-0-687-08807-2(0)) Abingdon Pr.

Shauers, Margaret. Puzzles & Prayers. 2000. (Illus.). 64p. (gr. 3-6). 5.99 (978-0-570-07032-0(5)) Concordia Publishing Hse.

Sheeran, Beth. A Child's Book of Prayer. 2005. 96p. pap. 14.00 (978-0-7343-0615-9(6) , Penguin Global) Penguin Group (USA) Inc.

Shellenberger, Susie. One Year Devotions for Teens. 2003. (gr. 7-12). lib. bdg. 22.25 (978-0-613-76868-9(X)) Tandem Library Bks.

Sherrer, Quin, Sr. & Garlock, Ruthanne. Abuela, Necesito Tus Oraciones: Blessing Your Grandchildren through the Power of Prayer. 2002. (SPA.). 256p. pap. 9.99 (978-0-8297-3251-1(9)) Vida Pubs.

Shipman, Brian K. WWJD Today? Daily Meditations. 1998. (Illus.). 192p. (J). (gr. 7-12). pap. 10.99 (978-0-8054-1688-6(9)) B&H Publishing Grp.

Shoemaker, H. Stephen. Finding Jesus in His Prayers. 2004. (Illus.). 120p. pap. 14.00 (978-0-687-35253-1(3)) Abingdon Pr.

Singer-Towns, Brian, ed. Catholic Youth Bible: Pray It, Study It, Live It. 2000. (Illus.). 1576p. (YA). (gr. 7-12). im. lthr. 47.95 (978-0-88489-693-7(5)) St. Mary's Pr.

Smith, Barbara. Thank You God. Crowdy, Wendy, illus. 1998. 12p. (J). (ps-k). 8.00 (978-0-687-10370-6(3)) Abingdon Pr.

Smith, Nina. Just Jesus & Me: A Devotional for Boys & Girls. 2002. (Illus.). 144p. (gr. 2-5). 10.99 (978-0-8254-7247-3(4)) Kregel Pubns.

Smouse, Phil A. You Pray for Me, I'll Pray for You! Tummy Tickling Stories & Prayers We Can Read Together. Smouse, Phil A., illus. 2005. (Read Together Ser.). (Illus.). 143p. (J). (ps-2). 12.99 (978-0-7847-1738-7(9) , 04366) Standard Publishing.

Snyder, Margaret. Good Night, God. deluxe ed. 1999. (Talking Pages Deluxe Ser.). (Illus.). 12p. (J). (ps-3). 7.95 (978-1-58224-001-5(9)) Futech Interactive Products, Inc.

Southwater Staff. Prayers for Children. 2003. (Illus.). 64p. pap. 7.99 (978-1-84215-720-6(5) , Southwater) Anness Publishing GBR. *Dist:* National Bk. Network.

Spafford, Suzy, illus. My Little Book of Prayers. gif. ed. 2005. 32p. 9.99 (978-0-7369-1495-6(1)) Harvest Hse. Pubs.

SPCK. I Can Join in Common Worship: A Children's Communion Book. 2003. (Illus.). 24p. 5.00 (978-0-281-05568-5(8)) SPCK Publishing GBR. *Dist:* Pilgrim Pr., The/United Church Pr.

St. John, Patricia. Talking & Listening to God. (Illus.). 128p. (J). pap. 5.99 (978-1-85792-840-2(7) , Christian Focus) Christian Focus Pubns. GBR. *Dist:* Riverside.

Stanton, Sue. Guia Sobre la Misa para Ninos (Child's Guide to the Mass) 2002. (SPA., Illus.). 32p. 9.95 (978-0-8091-6702-9(6) , 6702-6) Paulist Pr.

Stephanie Longfoot Staff. God Bless 2001. 2004. (My First Prayers Ser.). 10p. (J). bds. 3.99 (978-1-85854-403-8(3)) Brimax Books Ltd. GBR. *Dist:* Byeway Bks.

Stevens, Joy. Lots of Hugs in a Lunch Box: 75 Tear-Out Notes to Brighten Your Child's Day. Caldwell, Lise, ed. 2000. (Illus.). 160p. (J). (gr. 1-6). 6.99 (978-0-7847-1065-4(1) , 04324, Bean Sprouts) Standard Publishing.

Stortz, Diane M. Jesus Loves You: A Read-the-Pictures Book. Ebert, Len, illus. 2002. (Heritage Builders Ser.). 32p. (J). 10.99 (978-0-7847-1364-8(2)) Standard Publishing.

Straus, Celia. Prayers on My Pillow: Inspiration for Girls on the Threshold of Change. 1998. 240p. (J). (gr. 4-7). 18.50 (978-0-345-42673-4(8) , Ballantine Bks.) Random House Publishing Group.

Strong, Cynda. Where Do Angels Sleep? Denos, Julia, illus. 2007. 32p. (J). (ps-3). 14.99 (***978-0-7586-1298-4(2)***) Concordia Publishing Hse.

Stuckey, Denise. Jesus, I Feel Close to You. Saroff, Phyllis, illus. 2005. 32p. (J). 10.95 (978-0-8091-6718-0(2) , 6718-2) Paulist Pr.

Suzanne, Rentz. Daughters of Heaven Devotional. 2004. pap. 12.99 (978-1-57794-560-4(3)) Harrison Hse., Inc.

Swamp, Jake. Giving Thanks: A Native American Good Morning Message. braille ed. 2004. (Illus.). (J). (gr. k-3). spiral bd. (978-0-616-03096-7(7)) Canadian National Institute for the Blind/Institut National Canadien pour les Aveugles.

—Giving Thanks: A Native American Good Morning Message. (gr. k-3). lib. bdg. 15.25 (978-0-613-05061-6(4)) Tandem Library Bks.

Swanson, Maggie. Guardian Angel Prayer. 1999. (Maggie Swanson Board Books). (J). (ps-3). 3.95 (978-0-88271-709-8(X)) Regina Pr., Malhame & Co.

—Mary's Prayer. 1999. (Maggie Swanson Board Books). (J). (ps-3). 3.95 (978-0-88271-710-4(3)) Regina Pr., Malhame & Co.

Swarner, Kristina, illus. The Bedtime Sh'ma: A Good Night Book. 2007. (ENG & HEB.). 40p. (J). 17.95 (***978-0-939144-55-6(7)***); pap. 10.95 (***978-0-939144-54-9(9)***) EKS Publishing Co.

Tada, Joni Eareckson. Prayers from a Child's Heart Gift Book: A Delightful Read-a-Long Book That Will Help Young Children Learn. Koechel Peterson and Associates Staff, illus. Henry, Tom, photos by. 1999. 64p. (J). (ps-7). 14.99 (978-1-58375-474-0(1)) Garborg's, Inc.

Talaro, Theresa. Mommy Teach Us to Pray. Sabado, Joe, illus. Fujii, Jason, photos by. l.t. ed. 2006. 31p. (J). per. 12.95 (978-1-59879-121-1(4)) Lifevest Publishing, Inc.

Talaro, Theresa. A Mother's Prayer: A Life-Changing Prayer for Children. Sabado, Joe, illus. French, Petere, photos by. 2007. 44p. (J). 23.99 (***978-1-59879-335-2(7)*** , Lifevest) Lifevest Publishing, Inc.

Tanner, Suzy-Jane, illus. Pick-a-Prayer for Bedtime. 1999. 12p. (ps-1). pap. 4.99 (978-0-8054-2085-2(1)) B&H Publishing Grp.

—Pick-a-Prayer for Every Day. 1999. 12p. (J). (ps-1). pap. 4.99 (978-0-8054-2086-9(X)) B&H Publishing Grp.

—Pick-a-Prayer for Special Days. 1999. 12p. (J). (ps-1). pap. 4.99 (978-0-8054-2087-6(8)) B&H Publishing Grp.

—Pick-a-Prayer to Say Thank You. 1999. 12p. (J). (ps-1). pap. 4.99 (978-0-8054-2088-3(6)) B&H Publishing Grp.

Taylor, Caroline. All Things Bright & Beautiful. Longfoot, Stephanie, illus. 2004. (My First Prayers Ser.). 10p. (J). bds. 3.99 (978-1-85854-238-6(3)) Brimax Books Ltd. GBR. *Dist:* Byeway Bks.

—All Things Wise & Wonderful. Longfoot, Stephanie, illus. 2004. (My First Prayers Ser.). 10p. (J). bds. 3.99 (978-1-85854-239-3(1)) Brimax Books Ltd. GBR. *Dist:* Byeway Bks.

Taylor, Damon. A Child's First Prayers. 2002. 26p. (J). (ps-2). 12.99 (978-0-8254-5500-1(6)) Kregel Pubns.

Taylor, Kenneth N. Right Choices. Shoemaker, Kathryn E., illus. 1999. 64p. (J). 12.99 (978-0-8423-5299-4(6)) Tyndale Hse. Pubs.

Teaching Your Child to Pray. 12.00 (978-0-687-08906-2(9)) Abingdon Pr.

Terrell, Charles. Hey, God, Let's Talk! Teaching Children about Prayer: Keepsake Prayer Journal. 2004. (Illus.). 64p. (gr. 4-6). 5.00 incl. audio compact disk (978-0-687-03379-9(9)) Abingdon Pr.

The Prayer Children. Whispers in God's Ears. 2003. (Illus.). 82p. (J). per. 12.95 (978-0-87029-377-1(X)) Abbey Pr.

Tickle, Phyllis. This Is What I Pray Today: Divine Hours Prayers for Children. Warnick, Elsa, illus. 2007. 32p. (J). (ps). 15.99 (***978-0-525-47828-7(0)*** , Dutton Juvenile) Penguin Group (USA) Inc.

Torres, Elizar. The Gospel for Children. Torres, Anna M., ed. Higgins, Sharon, illus. 2000. 140p. (J). (gr. 3-7). 14.95 (978-0-9678599-2-7(1)) EP PUBS.

Tucker, Terra. Daughter of the King: Daughter of the King: Book with Audio CD. Marsee, Kimberly, illus. ed. 2007. 48p. (J). 19.95 (***978-0-9794578-0-7(7)***) Tucker, Terra.

Tudor, Tasha. First Graces: Life Favors. 1999. (J). 6.99 (978-0-679-88787-4(3) , Random Hse. Bks. for Young Readers) Random Hse. Children's Bks.

—First Prayers. 1998. (Life Favors Ser.). (Illus.). 32p. (J). (ps-3). 6.99 (978-0-679-88786-7(5) , Random Hse. Bks. for Young Readers) Random Hse. Children's Bks.

Vajda, Jaroslav J., ed. God of the Sparrow. McDaniels, Preston, illus. 1999. (Hymns for Children Ser.). 32p. (ps-2). 7.95 (978-0-8192-1745-5(X) , 2102) Morehouse Publishing.

Walker, Celeste Perrino. More Power to Ya. 2001. 373p. (J). 12.99 (978-0-8280-1573-8(2) , 136-730) Review & Herald Publishing Assn.

Walters, David. Children's Prayer Manual: Specially Designed to Turn Children into Serious Prayer Warriors, 5 vols., Vol. 5. Ellis, Jessica, illus. 2nd ed. 2001. 48p. (J). pap. 6.95 (978-1-888081-62-6(7)) Good News Fellowship Ministries.

Warburton, Olivia, compiled by. Prayers to Help You Through the Week. 2003. 128p. 16.99 (978-0-7459-4852-2(9) , Lion) Lion Hudson plc GBR. *Dist:* Independent Pubs. Group.

Warburton, Olivia & White, Jayne. For Your First Holy Communion. Mitchell, Ian, illus. 2004. 48p. pap. 16.99 (978-0-7459-4682-5(8) , Lion) Lion Hudson plc GBR. *Dist:* Independent Pubs. Group.

Ward, Elaine M. Answering Children's Faith Questions: Through Parables, Poetry & Prayer. 1999. 100p. (J). (gr. 1-6). pap. 10.95 (978-1-57438-031-6(1) , 5302) Educational Ministries, Inc.

Watson, Carol. 365 Children's Prayers: Prayers Old & New for Today & Everyday. 2006. (Illus.). 160p. (J). (gr. 1-6). pap. 19.99 (978-0-7459-1454-1(3) , 0745914543, Lion) Lion Hudson plc GBR. *Dist:* Independent Pubs. Group.

Webster, Jennifer Hope. Chat with God: Prayer Journal. 2nd ed. 2002. (Chat with God: Vol. 1). spiral bd., wbk. ed. 11.99 (978-0-9706360-1-0(6)) Webster, Jennifer Hope.

—Molitvennyi Dnevnik: Molitvennoe Pyteshestve Prodolzhaetsya Vechno. . . Chekulaeva, Tatiana, tr. 2003. (RUS.). (J). E-Book 11.99 (978-0-9706360-6-5(7)) Webster, Jennifer Hope.

Wells, Elizabeth. Children's Liturgy of the Word Resource: Cycle A - September-November, Cycle B - November-May. 2002. (Illus.). 76p. (J). (gr. k-5). pap. 18.95 (978-1-893757-31-8(5) , 31-5) Needer, E.T. Publishing.

When Hope Shines Through. 2001. (Illus.). 240p. (YA). pap. 16.95 (978-0-9632180-5-6(0)) Chinaberry Hse.

Widenhouse, Kathy. The Un-Bunny Book. 2004. (Illus.). 168p. (J). pap. 14.99 (978-1-58411-028-6(7) , Legacy Pr.) Rainbow Pubs. & Legacy Pr.

Wiley, Patricia Ann, creator. Time to Change: A Daily Devotinoal. 2nd ed. 2004. Orig. Title: It's Time to Change. (YA). per. 10.00 (978-0-9760734-0-6(4)) Pouring the Oil: Poetic Praise Pubns.

Wilkin, Eloise. Prayers for Children. 1999. (Little Golden Bks.). (Illus.). 24p. (J). (gr. k-1). 2.99 (978-0-307-02106-9(8) , 98016, Golden Inspirational) Random Hse. Children's Bks.

Wilkin, Eloise & Golden Books Staff. Prayers for Children. Wilkin, Eloise, illus. ed. 2006. (Illus.). 32p. (J). (gr. k-k). 8.99 (978-0-375-83553-7(9) , Golden Inspirational) Random Hse. Children's Bks.

Wilkinson, Bruce & Kopp, David. The Prayer of Jabez for Teens. 2001. (Breakthrough Ser.). 96p. (gr. 7 up). bds. 9.99 (978-1-57673-815-3(9) , Multnomah) WaterBrook Pr.

Wilkinson, Bruce H. & Suggs, Rob. The Prayer of Jabez for Young Hearts. Martinez, Sergio, illus. 2004. 32p. (J). (ps-3). 15.99 (978-0-8499-7932-3(3)) Nelson, Thomas Inc.

Will, Julianne, ed. Catholic Prayer Book for Children. 2004. (J). pap. 3.95 (978-1-59276-047-3(3)); per. 10.95 (978-1-59276-046-6(5)) Our Sunday Visitor, Publishing Div.

Wright, Sally Ann, contrib. by. A Child's Book of Prayers. 2007. 96p. 13.99 (***978-1-60255-013-1(1)***) Nelson, Thomas Inc.

PRAYING MANTIS

Brimner, Larry Dane. Praying Mantises. (True Bks.). (Illus.). 48p. (J). (gr. 3-5). 2000. pap. 6.95 (978-0-516-26769-2(8)); 1999. 25.00 (978-0-516-21163-3(3)) Scholastic Library Publishing. (Children's Pr.).

Cooper, Jason. Mantis Religiosas. 2006. (Biblioteca del Descubrimiento de los Insectos Ser.). (ENG & SPA.). (gr. k-2). 14.95 (978-1-59515-655-6(0)) Rourke Publishing, LLC.

Frost, Helen. Praying Mantises. Saunders-Smith, Gail, ed. 2001. (Insects Ser.). (Illus.). 24p. (J). (gr. k-1). lib. bdg. 15.93 (978-0-7368-0853-8(1) , Pebble Bks.) Capstone Pr., Inc.

Hall, Margaret. Praying Mantises. 2004. (Pebble Plus: Bugs, Bugs, Bugs! Ser.). (Illus.). 24p. (J). lib. bdg. 19.93 (978-0-7368-2590-0(8) , Pebble Bks.) Capstone Pr., Inc.

Hipp, Andrew. The Life Cycle of a Praying Mantis. Kuhn, Dwight, illus. Kuhn, Dwight, photos by. 2002. (Life Cycles Library). 24p. (J). lib. bdg. 18.75 (978-0-8239-5867-2(1) , PowerKids Pr.) Rosen Publishing Group, Inc., The.

Jacobs, Liza. Mantises. 2003. (Wild Wild World Ser.). (Illus.). 24p. (J). 22.45 (978-1-4103-0039-3(0) , Blackbirch Pr., Inc.) Thomson Gale.

Markle, Sandra. Praying Mantises: Hungry Insect Heroes. 2008. (Insect World Ser.). (J). lib. bdg. 27.93 (***978-0-8225-7300-5(8)*** , Lerner Pubns.) Lerner Publishing Group.

Miller, Connie Colwell. Praying Mantises. 2005. (Illus.). 24p. (J). 21.26 (978-0-7368-3710-1(8)) Capstone Pr., Inc.

Praying Mantises. (Bugs, Bugs, Bugs! Ser.). 24p. (J). 6.95 (978-0-7368-5098-8(8)) Capstone Pr., Inc.

Sexton, Colleen. Praying Mantises. 2007. (Illus.). 24p. (J). lib. bdg. 16.95 (978-1-60014-053-2(X)) Bellwether Media.

—Praying Mantises. 2007. (Blastoff! Readers Ser.). 24p. (J). (gr. k-2). 18.50 (***978-0-531-17569-9(3)*** , Children's Pr.) Scholastic Library Publishing.

PREACHERS

see Clergy

PRECIOUS STONES

Here are entered mineralogical and technological works on potential and actual engraved stones and jewels. Antiquarian or artistic works on engraved stones and jewels are entered under Gems.

see also Gems

also names of precious stones, e.g. Diamonds

Boekhoff, P. M. & Kallen, Stuart A. Gems. 2002. (Wonders of the World Ser.). (Illus.). 48p. (J). (gr. 3-5). 23.70 (978-0-7377-1028-1(4) , Kidhaven) Thomson Gale.

Cefrey, Holly. Gems. 2003. (Reading Power Ser.). (Illus.). 24p. (J). lib. bdg. 17.25 (978-0-8239-6467-3(1) , PowerKids Pr.) Rosen Publishing Group, Inc., The.

Dayton, Connor. Gemstones. 2007. (Rocks & Minerals Ser.). (Illus.). 24p. (J). (gr. 2-5). lib. bdg. 21.25 (***978-1-4042-3686-8(4)*** , PowerKids Pr.) Rosen Publishing Group, Inc., The.

Edwards, Ron & Dickie, Lisa. Diamonds & Gemstones. 2004. (Rocks, Minerals, & Resources Ser.). (Illus.). 32p. (J). (978-0-7787-1414-9(4)); pap. (978-0-7787-1446-0(2)) Crabtree Publishing Co.

Mercer, Ian. Gemstones & the Environment. Nevett, Louise, illus. 2004. (J). lib. bdg. (978-1-932799-38-5(9)) Stargazer Bks.

Morris, Neil. Diamonds & Other Gems. 2005. (Earth's Resources Ser.). (Illus.). 32p. (J). (gr. 4-7). lib. bdg. 27.10 (978-1-58340-629-8(8)) Smart Apple Media.

Richardson, Adele D. Gems. 1998. (Let's Investigate Ser.: Vol. 12). (Illus.). 32p. (J). (ps-3). lib. bdg. (978-0-88682-993-3(3) , Creative Education) Creative Co., The.

Squire, Ann O. Gemstones. 2002. (True Bks.). (Illus.). 48p. (J). (gr. 3-5). pap. 6.95 (978-0-516-26983-2(6)) Scholastic Library Publishing.

—Gemstones. 2002. (gr. 3-6). lib. bdg. 15.25 (978-0-613-54229-6(0)) Tandem Library Bks.

Symes, R. F. & Harding, R. R. Crystal & Gem. 2007. (DK Eyewitness Bks.). 72p. (J). (gr. 3-8). 15.99 incl. cd-rom (978-0-7566-3001-0(0)) Dorling Kindersley Publishing, Inc.

Symes, R. F. & Harding, Robert. Crystal & Gem: Eyewitness Books. Keates, Colin, photos by. 2004. (Illus.). 63p. (J). (gr. 4-8). reprint ed. 19.00 (978-0-7567-7687-9(2)) DIANE Publishing Co.

Trueit, Trudi Strain. Rocks, Gems, & Minerals. 2003. (Watts Library). 64p. (gr. 5-7). pap. 8.95 (978-0-531-16241-5(9)); (Illus.). (J). 25.50 (978-0-531-12195-5(X)) Scholastic Library Publishing. (Watts, Franklin).

—Rocks, Gems, & Minerals. 2003. (gr. 5-8). lib. bdg. 17.60 (978-0-613-67665-6(3)) Tandem Library Bks.

Ward, Charlotte, ed. Gem Care. Ward, Fred, photos by. 2nd ed. 2003. (Fred Ward Gem Book Ser.). (Illus.). 32p. pap. 9.95 (978-1-887651-07-3(1)) Gem Bk. Pubs.

PREGNANCY

see also Childbirth

Alpern, Michele. Teen Pregnancy. 2002. (Focus on Family Matters Ser.). (Illus.). 64p. (YA). (gr. 5 up). 31.00 (978-0-7910-6695-9(9) , Chelsea Hse.) Facts On File, Inc.

Amos, Janine. Is Helen Pregnant? 2003. (Body Matters Ser.). (Illus.). 32p. (YA). 19.99 (978-1-84234-107-0(3) , Cherrytree Books) Evans Publishing Group GBR. *Dist:* Independent Pubs. Group.

Ayer, Eleanor H. La Paternidad Adolescente. 2002. (Todo lo Que Necesitas Saber Ser.). (SPA & ENG., Illus.). 64p. (YA). lib. bdg. 26.50 (978-0-8239-3585-7(X) , Buenas Letra) Rosen Publishing Group, Inc., The.

Batten, Mary. Who Has a Belly Button? Bond, Higgins, illus. 2004. 32p. (J). (gr. 2-3). 15.95 (978-1-56145-235-4(1)) Peachtree Pubs., Ltd.

Bell, Arlene. Teen Parenthood: It's Not What You Think It Is. 2001. 20p. (YA). pap. 2.95 (978-0-9636426-5-3(0)) Windham Pr.

Beyer, Kay. Coping with Teen Parenting. rev. ed. 1999. (Coping Ser.). (Illus.). 209p. (YA). (gr. 7-12). lib. bdg. 26.50 (978-0-8239-3035-7(1) , COTEPA) Rosen Publishing Group, Inc., The.

Bode, Janet. Kids Still Having Kids: People Talk about Teen Pregnancy. rev. ed. 1999. (Single Titles-Teen Issues Ser.). (Illus.). 160p. (YA). (gr. 8-12). pap. 9.95 (978-0-531-15973-6(6) , Watts, Franklin) Scholastic Library Publishing.

Buck, Nola. How a Baby Grows. 1998. (Growing Tree Ser.). (Illus.). 14p. (J). (ps up). bds. 5.95 (978-0-694-00873-5(7) , Harper Festival) HarperCollins Pubs.

Butler, Dori Hillestad. My Mom's Having a Baby! Thompson, Carol, illus. 32p. (J). 2007. pap. 6.95 (***978-0-8075-5348-0(4));*** 2005. 16.95 (978-0-8075-5344-2(1)) Whitman, Albert & Co.

Byers, Ann. Teens & Pregnancy. 2000. (Hot Issues Ser.). (Illus.). 64p. (YA). (gr. 6-12). lib. bdg. 27.93 (978-0-7660-1365-0(0)) Enslow Pubs., Inc.

Cassidy, Patrice. Teen Pregnancy. 2001. (Teen Issues Ser.). (Illus.). 104p. (J). (gr. 4-12). lib. bdg. 27.45 (978-1-56006-515-9(X) , LML00902-177873, Lucent Bks.) Thomson Gale.

Cooper, Robbi, creator. Help! We're Having a Baby: Solicited Advice from Family & Friends. 2004. 70p. ring bd. 35.00 (978-0-9749643-0-0(1)) Cooper, Robbi.

Cothran, Helen. Teen Pregnancy & Parenting. 2001. (Current Controversies Ser.). (Illus.). 160p. (YA). (gr. 7-12). pap. 36.20 (978-0-7377-0558-4(2) , Greenhaven Pr., Inc.) Thomson Gale.

Cothran, Helen, ed. Teen Pregnancy & Parenting. 2001. (Current Controversies Ser.). (Illus.). 160p. (YA). (gr. 9 up). 24.95 (978-0-7377-0557-7(4) , Greenhaven Pr., Inc.) Thomson Gale.

Diagram Group. Reproductive System. 2005. (Illus.). 112p. (***978-0-8160-5985-0(3)***) Facts On File, Inc.

Dudley, William. Pregnancy. 2001. (Teen Decisions Ser.). (Illus.). 191p. (YA). lib. bdg. 36.20 (978-0-7377-0492-1(6) , Greenhaven Pr., Inc.) Thomson Gale.

Dudley, William, ed. Pregnancy. 2001. (Teen Decisions Ser.). (Illus.). 191p. (YA). (gr. 10 up). pap. 24.95 (978-0-7377-0491-4(8) , Greenhaven Pr., Inc.) Thomson Gale.

Eddelman, Lisa. Math Class Today Lamaze Class Tomorrow. 2003. (gr. 7-12). lib. bdg. 33.80 (978-0-613-77885-5(5)) Tandem Library Bks.

Eddleman, Lisa. Math Class Today Lamaze Class Tomorrow. 2003. 236p. per. 22.95 (978-0-9725461-6-4(2)) Art In The Heartland.

Edelson, Paula. Straight Talk about Teenage Pregnancy. 1998. (Straight Talk Ser.). (Illus.). 144p. (YA). (gr. 6-12). 27.45 (978-0-8160-3717-9(5)) Facts On File, Inc.

Endersbe, Julie. Teen Mothers: Raising a Baby. 1999. (Perspectives on Healthy Sexuality Ser.). (Illus.). 64p. (J). (gr. 4-6). lib. bdg. 23.93 (978-0-7368-0270-3(3) , Life-Matters Bks.) Capstone Pr., Inc.

Englander, Anrenee. Dear Diary, I'm Pregnant: Teenagers Talk about Their Pregnancy. 2003. (Illus.). 160p. (J). (gr. 6 up). pap. 12.95 (978-1-55037-440-7(0)) Annick Pr., Ltd. CAN. *Dist:* Firefly Bks., Ltd.

Flegal, Daphna. A Baby Is Coming. 2002. (J). 5.00 (978-0-687-09649-7(9)) Abingdon Pr.

Goggin, Sherri. Dear Kate. 2007. (Illus.). 160p. 16.95 (***978-1-58818-133-6(2)***) Hill Street Pr., LLC.

Gordon, Lynn. 52 Tips for a Fabulous Pregnancy. Johnson, Karen, illus. 2005. 6.95 (978-0-8118-4470-3(6)) Chronicle Bks. LLC.

Hammerslough, Jane. Everything You Need to Know about Teen Motherhood. rev. ed. 2001. (Need to Know Library). (Illus.). 64p. (YA). (gr. 4-6). lib. bdg. 25.25 (978-0-8239-3441-6(1)) Rosen Publishing Group, Inc., The.

Haskins-Bookser, Laura. Dreams to Reality: Help for Young Moms - Education, Career, & Life Choices. 2006. (Illus.). 160p. (YA). pap. 14.95 (978-1-932538-36-6(4)) Morning Glory Pr., Inc.

Having a Healthy Baby - Planning Your Pregnancy. 2004. (YA). pap. 4.00 net. (978-1-930996-55-7(1)) Planned Parenthood Federation of America, Inc.

Hendersen. What's Behind the Bump? Hendersen, illus. 1998. (Illus.). 32p. (J). (gr. k-2). 14.95 (978-1-890453-14-5(5)) Little Friend Pr.

Hughes, Tracy. Everything You Need to Know about Teen Pregnancy. rev. ed. 1999. (Need to Know Library). (Illus.). 64p. (YA). (gr. 7-12). lib. bdg. 25.25 (978-0-8239-3041-8(6) , NTTEPR) Rosen Publishing Group, Inc., The.

Hurley, Jennifer A. Teen Pregnancy. 2000. (Opposing Viewpoints Digests Ser.). (Illus.). 96p. (YA). (gr. 6-9). pap. 21.20 (978-0-7377-0365-8(2) , Greenhaven Pr., Inc.) Thomson Gale.

Jacobson, Matt. The Amazing Beginning of You. 2002. (Illus.). 40p. (J). 12.99 (978-0-310-70217-7(8)) Zonderkidz.

Jamiolkowski, Raymond M. A Baby Doesn't Make the Man: Alternative Sources of Power & Manhood for Young Men. rev. ed. 2005. (Teen Pregnancy Prevention Library). (Illus.). 64p. (YA). (gr. 7-12). lib. bdg. 23.95 (978-0-8239-3470-6(5)) Rosen Publishing Group, Inc., The.

Juettner, Bonnie. Abortion. 2007. (J). (***978-1-60217-020-9(7)***) Erickson Pr.

Kro Productions, prod. Multimedia Teen Preg Mac Lb. (YA). cd-rom 245.95 (978-0-7365-4353-8(8)) Films Media Group.

Kuklin, Susan. What Do I Do Now? Talking about Teen Pregnancy. 2001. (gr. 7-12). lib. bdg. 26.85 (978-0-613-87320-8(3)) Tandem Library Bks.

—What Do I Do Now? Talking about Teen Pregnancy. 2001. (Illus.). 196p. (YA). (gr. 7-12). pap. 16.95 (978-0-595-17079-1(X)) iUniverse, Inc.

Lamb, Kirsten. Pregnancy. 2001. (Health Issues Ser.). (Illus.). 64p. (YA). (gr. 6-8). lib. bdg. 28.54 (978-0-7398-4418-2(0)) Raintree.

Meister, Deborah. What Catholics Teens Should Know If Pregnant & Panicked. Larkin, Jean K., ed. 2004. (What Catholic Teens Should Know Ser.). (Illus.). 8p. (YA). 7.95 (978-0-89837-237-3(2) , 440710) Pflaum Publishing Group.

Meredith, Susan & Gee, Robyn. Babies. 2005. (Facts of Life Ser.). 48p. (J). pap. 7.95 (978-0-7945-0895-1(2) , Usborne) EDC Publishing.

Miller, Barbara. Teenage Pregnancy & Poverty: The Economic Realities. rev. ed. 1999. (Teen Pregnancy Prevention Library). (Illus.). 64p. (YA). (gr. 7-12). lib. bdg. 23.95 (978-0-8239-2997-9(3) , TPPRPO) Rosen Publishing Group, Inc., The.

Mucciolo, Gary. Everything You Need to Know about Birth Control. rev. ed. 2000. (Need to Know Library). (Illus.). 64p. (YA). (gr. 4-6). lib. bdg. 25.25 (978-0-8239-3301-3(6)) Rosen Publishing Group, Inc., The.

Murkoff, Heidi. What to Expect When Mommy's Having a Baby. Rader, Laura, illus. (What to Expect Kids Ser.). (J). (ps-k). 2004. 24p. pap. 3.99 (978-0-06-053802-6(3)); 2000. 32p. 7.99 (978-0-694-01321-0(8)) HarperCollins Pubs. (Harper Festival).

National Campaign to Prevent Teen Pregnancy Staff, ed. Voices Carry: Teens Speak Out on Sex & Teen Pregnancy. 2000. (Illus.). 35p. (YA). pap. 5.00 (978-1-58671-030-9(3)) National Campaign to Prevent Teen Pregnancy.

Nolan, Mary. Teen Pregnancy. 2002. (Just the Facts Ser.). (Illus.). 56p. (J). (gr. 6-8). lib. bdg. 25.64 (978-1-58810-682-7(9)) Heinemann Library.

Nykiel, Connie, text. After the Loss of Your Baby: For Teen Mothers. 2002. 24p. (Orig.). (YA). 3.50 (978-1-56123-156-0(8) , ALBC) Centering Corp.

Park, Jane & Muller, Kathryn. Just the Facts: What Science Has Found Out about Teenage Sexuality & Pregnancy in the U. S. Card, Josephina T. & Gibson, Anjalique C., eds. 2nd rev. ed. 1998. (Illus.). vii, 133p. (YA). (gr. 6-12). pap. (978-0-9666901-0-1(9)) Sociometrics Corp.

Parker, Gary E. Life Before Birth: A Christian Family Book. 2nd ed. 2003. 85p. (J). (gr. 5-7). 12.95 (978-0-89051-164-0(0) , LIBEBI) Master Bks.

Pringle, Laurence P. Everybody Has a Bellybutton: Your Life Before You Were Born. Wood, Clare, illus. 2003. 32p. (J). (gr. k-2). 14.95 (978-1-56397-009-2(0)) Boyds Mills Pr.

Rauch, Jennifer, et al. Before You Were Born. 1998. (Illus.). 36p. (J). (ps-1). 10.95 (978-0-7611-1200-6(6) , 11200) Workman Publishing Co., Inc.

Rigby Education Staff. Carrying Babies. (Sails Literacy Ser.). (Illus.). 16p. (gr. 1-2). 27.00 (978-0-7635-9886-0(0) , 698860C99) Rigby Education.

Simpson, Carolyn. Coping with an Unplanned Pregnancy. rev. ed. 1999. (Coping Ser.). (Illus.). 174p. (YA). (gr. 7-12). lib. bdg. 26.50 (978-0-8239-2867-5(5) , COUNPR) Rosen Publishing Group, Inc., The.

Smith, Alastair. How are Babies Made. Wheatley, Maria, illus. 2003. 16p. (J). (gr. 2 up). pap. 7.95 (978-0-7945-0641-4(0) , Usborne) EDC Publishing.

Solar, Kay. Where Do Babies Come From? Holden, Chanler, illus. Brignac, Candy, photos by l.t. ed. 1998. 22p. (J). (ps-3). bds. 15.95 (978-0-9666945-0-5(3)) Solar, Kay.

Stroble, Chris. Teen Moms Breaking the Cycle of Teen Pregnancy: A Collection of Inspiring Mother-Daughter Success Stories plus the Handbook for Teen Moms Anonymous. 2006. pap. 14.95 (978-1-933559-00-1(4)) Mental Wellness Pub. Hse.

Surprise in Mommy's Tummy. Date not set. (J). (ps-3). 5.50 (978-0-89259-115-2(3)) American Trust Pubns.

Trapani, Margi. Listen Up! Teenage Mothers Speak Out. rev. ed. 2005. (Teen Pregnancy Prevention Library). (Illus.). 64p. (YA). (gr. 7-12). lib. bdg. 23.95 (978-0-8239-3471-3(3)) Rosen Publishing Group, Inc., The.

—Reality Check: Teenage Fathers Speak Out. rev. ed. 1999. (Teen Pregnancy Prevention Library). (Illus.). 64p. (YA). (gr. 7-12). lib. bdg. 23.95 (978-0-8239-2995-5(7) , TPRECH) Rosen Publishing Group, Inc., The.

Waters, Sophie. The Female Reproductive System. 2007. (J). (***978-1-4042-1950-2(1)***) Rosen Publishing Group, Inc., The.

Winkler, Kathleen. High-Tech Babies: The Debate over Assisted Reproductive Technology. 2006. (Issues in Focus Today Ser.). (Illus.). 104p. (J). lib. bdg. 31.93 (978-0-7660-2528-8(4)) Enslow Pubs., Inc.

Winston, Robert. Getting Pregnant. 2nd ed. 2003. (Illus.). 324p. 15.99 (978-0-330-32766-4(0)) Pan Macmillan GBR. *Dist:* Trafalgar Square Publishing.

Wright, Sally Ann. Where Do Babies Come From? Ayres, Honor, illus. 2007. 29p. (J). 9.95 (978-0-8198-8311-7(5)) Pauline Bks. & Media.

PREGNANCY—FICTION

Adams, Lenora. Baby Girl. 2007. 240p. (YA). pap. 6.99 (978-1-4169-2512-5(0) , Simon Pulse) Simon & Schuster Children's Publishing.

Andreae, Giles. There's a House Inside My Mommy. Cabban, Vanessa, illus. 2002. (Concept Book Ser.). 32p. (J). (ps-3). 15.95 (978-0-8075-7853-7(3)) Whitman, Albert & Co.

Aston, Dianna Hutts. Mama Outside, Mama Inside. Gaber, Susan, illus. rev. ed. 2006. 32p. (J). 15.95 (978-0-8050-7716-2(2)) Holt, Henry & Co.

Atkins, Jill. Cry, Baby. 2004. (Shades Ser.). 62p. (J). pap. 7.99 (978-0-237-52810-2(X) , Evans Brothers, Limited) Evans Publishing Group GBR. *Dist:* Independent Pubs. Group.

Baratz-Logsted, Lauren. Angel's Choice. 2006. 256p. (YA). (gr. 9 up). pap. 6.99 (978-1-4169-2524-8(4) , Simon Pulse) Simon & Schuster Children's Publishing.

Bauer, Cat. Harley's Ninth. 2007. 208p. (YA). (gr. 9). 15.99 (978-0-375-83736-4(1)); lib. bdg. 18.99 (978-0-375-93736-1(6)) Random Hse. Children's Bks. (Knopf Bks. for Young Readers).

Bennett, James W. Faith Wish. 2003. 160p. (J). (gr. 7 up). tchr. ed. 16.95 (978-0-8234-1778-0(6)) Holiday Hse., Inc.

Berenstain, Stan & Berenstain, Jan. The Birds, the Bees, & the Berenstain Bears. 2000. (Berenstain Bears First Time Bks.). (Illus.). 32p. (J). (gr. k-3). pap. 3.99 (978-0-679-88959-5(0) , Random Hse. Bks. for Young Readers) Random Hse. Children's Bks.

Bunting, Eve. Doll Baby. 2000. (Illus.). 48p. (J). (gr. 7-4). tchr. ed. 15.00 (978-0-395-93094-6(4) , Clarion Bks.) Houghton Mifflin Co. Trade & Reference Div.

Butler, Dori Hillestad. Alexandra Hopewell, Labor Coach. 2005. 136p. (J). (gr. 3-6). 15.95 (978-0-8075-0242-6(1)) Whitman, Albert & Co.

Castellarin, Loretta & Roberts, Ken. Spike. 2006. (Degrassi Junior High Ser.). 184p. (YA). (gr. 5-10). 7.95 (978-1-55028-925-1(X)) Lorimer, James & Co., Ltd., Pubs. CAN. *Dist:* Casemate Pubs. & Bk. Distributors, LLC.

Chambers, Aidan. This Is All: The Pillow Book of Cordelia Kenn. 2006. 816p. (J). (gr. 8-17). 19.95 (978-0-8109-7060-1(0) , Amulet Bks.) Abrams, Harry N. , Inc.

Chick, Sandra. Don't Look Back. 2000. (Livewire Ser.). 100p. (J). pap. 11.99 (978-0-7043-4958-2(2)) Women's Pr., Ltd., The GBR. *Dist:* Independent Pubs. Group.

Clarke, Kathryn. The Breakable Vow. 2004. 480p. (YA). (gr. 7 up). 16.89 (978-0-06-051822-6(7)) HarperCollins Pubs.

Clarke, Kathryn Ann. The Breakable Vow. 2004. 480p. (J). (gr. 7 up). pap. 6.99 (978-0-06-051821-9(9)) HarperCollins Pubs.

Coll, Ivar Da. Carlos. Coll, Ivar Da, illus. 2003. (SPA., Illus.). 52p. (J). (gr. k-3). pap. 9.95 (978-958-8061-64-1(4)) Santillana USA Publishing Co., Inc.

Couloumbis, Audrey. Love Me Tender. 2008. (J). (***978-0-375-83839-2(2));*** lib. bdg. (***978-0-375-93839-9(7)***) Random Hse., Inc.

Creech, Sharon. Heartbeat. (J). 2005. 208p. pap. 5.99 (978-0-06-054024-1(9)); 2004. 192p. 15.99 (978-0-06-054022-7(2)); 2004. 192p. lib. bdg. 16.89 (978-0-06-054023-4(0)) HarperCollins Pubs.

—Heartbeat. l.t. ed. 2004. 160p. 23.95 (978-0-7862-6902-0(2) , Large Print Pr.) Thorndike Pr.

Dessen, Sarah. Someone Like You. 1998. 272p. (J). (gr. 7-12). 17.99 (978-0-670-87778-2(6) , Viking Juvenile) Penguin Group (USA) Inc.

—Someone Like You. 2000. (978-0-606-18847-0(9)) Tandem Library Bks.

Draper, Sharon M. November Blues. 2007. 320p. (YA). (gr. 7 up). 16.99 (***978-1-4169-0698-8(3)*** , Atheneum) Simon & Schuster Children's Publishing.

Evans, Mari. I'm Late: The Story of LeNeese & Moonlight & Alisha Who Didn't Have Anyone of Her Own. Honeywood, Varnette P., illus. 2006. 86p. (YA). (gr. 7 up). 14.95 (978-1-933491-00-4(0)) Just Us Bks., Inc.

Fearnley, Jan. A Special Something. 2004. (Illus.). 32p. 7.95 (978-0-7497-4639-1(4)) Egmont Bks., Ltd. GBR. *Dist:* Trafalgar Square Publishing.

—A Special Something. 2000. (Illus.). 32p. (ps-2). 15.99 (978-0-7868-0589-1(7)) Hyperion Pr.

Ferris, Amy Schor. A Greater Goode. 2002. 192p. (YA). (gr. 5-9). 15.00 (978-0-618-13154-9(X)) Houghton Mifflin Co. Trade & Reference Div.

Gray, Nigel. My Dog, My Cat, My Mama, & Me! Graham, Bob, illus. 2007. 24p. (J). (gr. k-ps). 8.99 (***978-0-7636-3639-5(8)***) Candlewick Pr.

Harper, Meg. My Mum & the Gruesome Twosome. 160p. pap. 9.99 (978-0-7459-4829-4(4)); 2001. 144p. pap. 7.50 (978-0-7459-4567-5(8)) Lion Hudson plc GBR. (Lion). *Dist:* Trafalgar Square Publishing.

Hart, Karen. Butterflies in May. 2006. 202p. 16.95 (978-1-890862-44-2(4)) Bancroft Pr.

Hearn, Julie. The Minister's Daughter. 2006. 272p. (YA). pap. 7.99 (978-0-689-87691-2(2) , Simon Pulse) Simon & Schuster Children's Publishing.

Hearn, Julie & Frost, Michael. The Minister's Daughter. 2005. 272p. (YA). (gr. 7 up). 17.99 (978-0-689-87690-5(4) , Atheneum) Simon & Schuster Children's Publishing.

Hooper, Mary. Newes from the Dead: Being a True Story of Anne Green, Hanged for Infanticide at Oxford Assizes in 1650, Restored to the World & Died Again 1665. 2008. 256p. (YA). 15.95 (***978-1-59643-355-7(8)***) Roaring Brook Pr.

Howden, Iris. A Bright Future: Livewire Fiction. 1999. (Livewires Ser.). (Illus.). 48p. pap. (978-0-340-72094-3(8) , Hodder Arnold) Hodder Education.

Hrdlitschka, Shelley. Dancing Naked: A Novel. 2002. 256p. (J). (gr. 7-12). pap. 6.95 (978-1-55143-210-6(2)) Orca Bk. Pubs. USA.

—Dancing Naked: A Novel. 2002. (gr. 7-12). lib. bdg. 15.25 (978-0-613-60545-8(4)) Tandem Library Bks.

Hyde, Diana. Sex Without Love. 2001. 304p. pap. 12.95 (978-0-9705435-4-7(9)) Heicron, Inc.

Johnson, Varian. My Life as a Rhombus. 2008. 312p. (J). pap. 9.95 (***978-0-7387-1160-7(8)*** , Flux) Llewellyn Pubns.

Leavitt, Caroline. Girls in Trouble: A Novel. 2005. 368p. pap. 13.95 (978-0-312-33973-9(9) , St. Martin's Paperbacks) St. Martin's Pr.

Lee, Shelley R. Before I Knew You. Lee, Shelley R., ed. Lehman, Denise, illus. 2006. (J). lib. bdg. 20.00 (978-0-9786757-0-7(3)) Lee, Shelley.

Lohans, Alison. Waiting for the Sun. Mets, Marilyn & Ledwon, Peter, illus. 2004. (Northern Lights Books for Children). 32p. (J). (ps-2). 16.95 (978-0-88995-240-9(X)) Red Deer Pr. CAN. *Dist:* Fitzhenry & Whiteside, Ltd.

MacCullough, Carolyn. Stealing Henry. rev. ed. 2005. 208p. (YA). 16.95 (978-1-59643-045-7(1)) Roaring Brook Pr.

McDaniel, Lurlene. Briana's Gift. 2006. 176p. (YA). (gr. 7). 10.95 (978-0-385-73160-7(4)); lib. bdg. 12.99 (978-0-385-90197-0(6)) Random Hse. Children's Bks. (Delacorte Bks. for Young Readers).

McDonald, Janet. Chill Wind. l.t. ed. 2003. 165p. (J). 24.95 (978-0-7862-5502-3(1)) Thorndike Pr.

McWilliams, Kelly. Doormat. 2006. 144p. (YA). (gr. 7). reprint ed. pap. 5.50 (978-0-440-23875-1(7) , Laurel Leaf) Random Hse. Children's Bks.

Olsen, Sylvia. The Girl with a Baby. 2004. 208p. (J). pap. 7.95 (978-1-55039-142-8(9)) Sono Nis Pr. CAN. *Dist:* Orca Bk. Pubs. USA.

Olshan, Matthew. Finn: A Novel. 2001. (gr. 7-12). lib. bdg. 24.55 (978-0-613-59806-4(7)) Tandem Library Bks.

Orante, Ann-Jeanette P. Best Sisters for Life... 2007. (ENG., Illus.). 36p. (J). per. 11.95 (***978-1-59800-972-9(9)***) Outskirts Press, Inc.

Oughton, Jerrie. Perfect Family. 2000. 208p. (J). (gr. 5-9). tchr. ed. 15.00 (978-0-395-98668-4(0)) Houghton Mifflin Co. Trade & Reference Div.

Paratore, Coleen. Catching the Sun. Catalanotto, Peter, illus. 2008. (J). (***978-1-57091-720-2(5)***) Charlesbridge Publishing, Inc.

Paratore, Coleen Murtagh. Willa by Heart. 2008. (Wedding Planner's Daughter Ser.). 240p. (J). 15.99 (***978-1-4169-4076-0(6)***) Simon & Schuster Children's Publishing.

Pennebaker, Ruth. Don't Think Twice. 1998. (978-0-606-13341-8(0)) Tandem Library Bks.

P Q R

Plummer, Louise. A Dance for Three. 2001. 12.15 (978-0-606-21134-5(9)) Tandem Library Bks.

Poston, Karen. A Baby for Mabel & Frederick. 2005. 20p. (J). 11.28 (978-1-4116-6024-3(2)) Lulu.com.

Reynolds, Marilyn. Detour for Emmy. 2003. 256p. (J). (gr. 7-12). pap. 8.95 (978-0-930934-76-7(8)) Morning Glory Pr., Inc.

Reynolds, Marilyn. No More Sad Goodbyes. 2007. (Hamilton High Ser.). 192p. (YA). 18.95 (***978-1-932538-72-4(0)***); pap. 9.95 (***978-1-932538-71-7(2)***) Morning Glory Pr., Inc.

Ryan, Darlene. Saving Grace. 2006. 112p. (YA). (gr. 7 up). pap. 8.95 (978-1-55143-508-4(X)); lib. bdg. 14.95 (978-1-55143-668-5(X)) Orca Bk. Pubs. USA.

Rylant, Cynthia. A Kindness. Date not set. (Sky Bks.). 104p. pap. 54.75 (978-0-582-08106-2(8)) Addison-Wesley Longman, Ltd. GBR. *Dist:* Trans-Atlantic Pubns., Inc.

Sauer, Tammi. Dear Jack. 2004. 164p. (YA). mass mkt. 6.99 (***978-0-9753367-0-0(3)***) Onstage Publishing, LLC.

Snelson, Brian & Sellars, Rodney. Shaturanga: The Story of Onus. 2003. 244p. pap. 16.95 (978-0-595-29569-2(X)) iUniverse, Inc.

Strong, Jeremy. My Mum's Going to Explode! Clifford, Rowan, illus. l.t. ed. 2005. 80p. (J). pap. (978-0-7540-7824-1(8), CLP 414) BBC Audio.

Sweeney, Joyce. Waiting for June. 2006. 160p. 5.99 (978-0-7614-5329-1(6)); 2003. 144p. (YA). 15.95 (978-0-7614-5138-9(2)) Cavendish, Marshall Corp.

Velasquez, Gloria. Teen Angel. (Roosevelt High School Ser.). 160p. (YA). pap. 9.95 (978-1-55885-391-1(X), Piñata Books) Arte Publico Pr.

Watts, Irene N. When the Bough Breaks. 2007. 152p. (J). (gr. 4-7). pap. 9.95 (***978-0-88776-821-7(0)***) Tundra Bks., Inc./Livres Toundra, Inc. CAN. *Dist:* Random Hse., Inc.

Whelan, Gloria. Chu Ju's House. 2005. 240p. (J). reprint ed. pap. 5.99 (978-0-06-050726-8(8), Harper Trophy) HarperCollins Pubs.

Wild, Margaret. One Night. 2006. 240p. (YA). (gr. 7). mass mkt. 5.99 (978-0-553-49434-1(1), Laurel Leaf) Random Hse. Children's Bks.

Williams, Carol Lynch. A Mother to Embarrass Me. 2003. 144p. (J). (gr. 3-7). pap. 4.99 (978-0-440-41810-8(0), Yearling) Random Hse. Children's Bks.

Wolfer, Dianne. Choices. 2001. 240p. (YA). pap. 13.95 (978-1-86368-317-3(8)) Fremantle Pr. AUS. *Dist:* International Specialized Bk. Services.

PREHISTORIC ANIMALS

see Fossils

PREHISTORIC HUMANS

see Prehistoric Peoples

PREHISTORIC PEOPLES

Brooks, Philip, et al. From the Stone Age to the Space Age. 2003. (Illustrated History Encyclopedia Ser.). (Illus.). 264p. (gr. 3-7). pap. 19.99 (978-0-7548-1202-9(2)) Anness Publishing GBR. *Dist:* National Bk. Network.

Brown, Robin C. The Crafts of Florida's First People. 2003. (Illus.). 64p. (J). pap. 9.95 (978-1-56164-282-3(7)) Pineapple Pr., Inc.

Buell, Janet. Ancient Horsemen of Siberia. 1998. (Time Travelers Ser.: 8). (Illus.). 64p. (gr. 5-8). lib. bdg. 25.90 (978-0-7613-3005-9(4), Twenty-First Century Bks.) Lerner Publishing Group.

Chandler, Fiona. Prehistoric World. 2004. (World History Ser.). (SPA., Illus.). 96p. (J). (gr. 3 up). lib. bdg. 27.95 (978-1-58086-270-7(5)) EDC Publishing.

Chrisp, Peter. Prehistory. 2008. (Dk Online Ser.). 96p. (J). 17.99 (***978-0-7566-3461-2(X)***); pap. 9.99 (***978-0-7566-3460-5(1)***) Dorling Kindersley Publishing, Inc.

Clodd, Edward. Fetish Worship & Idolatry. 2006. pap. 9.95 (***978-1-4286-7861-3(1)***) Kessinger Publishing, LLC.

—Myths about the Earth & Man. 2006. pap. 9.95 (***978-1-4286-7865-1(4)***) Kessinger Publishing, LLC.

De Magalhaes, Roberto Carvalho. Prehistory. 2000. (Art & Civilization Ser.). (Illus.). 40p. (J). (gr. 3 up). 16.95 (978-0-87226-615-5(X), 6615XB, Bedrick, Peter Bks.) School Specialty Publishing.

Deem, James M. Bodies from the Bog. 2003. (Illus.). 48p. (J). (gr. 4-6). pap. 5.95 (978-0-618-35402-3(6)) Houghton Mifflin Co. Trade & Reference Div.

Diagram Group, contrib. by. The First Humans. 2004. (Life on Earth Ser.). (Illus.). 112p. (J). (gr. 4-9). 35.00 (978-0-8160-5050-5(3)) Facts On File, Inc.

Dorling Kindersley Publishing Staff. Early Humans. 2005. (Eyewitness Bks.). (Illus.). 72p. (J). 15.99 (978-0-7566-1067-8(2), 1241898); lib. bdg. 19.99 (978-0-7566-1068-5(0), 1241898) Dorling Kindersley Publishing, Inc.

Douglas, Vincent & School Specialty Publishing Staff. Prehistoric World. 2006. (Just the Facts Ser.). (Illus.). 64p. (J). (gr. 5-8). pap. 9.95 (978-0-7696-4258-1(6)) School Specialty Publishing.

Facchini, Fiorenzo. A Day with Homo Sapiens: Life 15,000 Years Ago. 2003. (Early Humans Ser.). (Illus.). 48p. (gr. 6 up). lib. bdg. 23.90 (978-0-7613-2768-4(1), Twenty-First Century Bks.) Lerner Publishing Group.

—A Day with Neanderthal Man: Life 70,000 Years Ago. Baldanzi, Alessandro, illus. 2003. (Early Humans Ser.). 48p. (gr. 6 up). lib. bdg. 23.90 (978-0-7613-2767-7(3), Twenty-First Century Bks.) Lerner Publishing Group.

Forbes, Claire. Ancient Peoples. 2004. (Discovery Guides Ser.). (SPA., Illus.). 32p. (J). (gr. 2-5). 11.95 (978-1-58728-223-2(2)); pap. 6.95 (978-1-58728-217-1(8)) T&N Children's Publishing. (Two Can Publishing).

—Ancient Peoples. 2001. (gr. 3-6). lib. bdg. 15.25 (978-0-613-43405-8(6)); 2000. (J). 13.75 (978-0-606-20407-1(5)); 2000. (J). (978-0-606-20291-6(9)) Tandem Library Bks.

—Pueblos del Pasado. 2004. (Discovery Guides Ser.). (SPA., Illus.). 32p. (gr. 2-5). (J). pap. 6.95 (978-1-58728-704-6(8)); 11.95 (978-1-58728-647-6(5)) T&N Children's Publishing. (Two Can Publishing).

Gray, Susan Heinrichs. Scholastic News Nonfiction Readers: Prehistoric World, 6 bks., Set. Incl. Dinosaur Armor. 19.00 (978-0-531-17481-4(6)); Dinosaur Dig! 19.00 (***978-0-531-17482-1(4)***); Dinosaur Eggs. 19.00 (***978-0-531-17483-8(2)***); Dinosaur Teeth. 19.00 (978-0-531-17484-5(0)); Dinosaur Tracks. 19.00 (***978-0-531-17485-2(9)***); Is It a Dinosaur? 19.00 (***978-0-531-17486-9(7)***); (Illus.). 24p. (J). (gr. 1-2). 2007. 2007. 114.00 (***978-0-531-12605-9(6)***, Children's Pr.) Scholastic Library Publishing.

Haslam, Andrew. Stone Age People. 2001. (gr. 3-6). lib. bdg. 16.40 (978-0-613-43383-9(1)) Tandem Library Bks.

Hynes, Margaret. The Best Book of Early People. White, Mike, illus. 2003. (Best Book of... Ser.). 32p. (J). (gr. k-3). tchr. ed. 12.95 (978-0-7534-5577-7(3), Kingfisher) Houghton Mifflin Co. Trade & Reference Div.

Lambert, David & Diagram Group. The Field Guide to Early Man. 1999. (Illus.). 256p. (YA). (gr. 8-12). pap. 32.95 (978-0-7351-0215-6(5)) Replica Bks.

Lindsay, William. Prehistoric Life. 2000. (Eyewitness Bks.). (Illus.). 64p. (J). (gr. 4-7). 15.99 (978-0-7894-5868-1(3)) Dorling Kindersley Publishing, Inc.

Lindsay, William & Dorling Kindersley Publishing Staff. Prehistoric Life. Taylor, Harry, photos by. 2000. (Eyewitness Bks.). (Illus.). 63p. (J). (ps-7). lib. bdg. 19.99 (978-0-7894-6601-3(5)) Dorling Kindersley Publishing, Inc.

Lorenz Books Staff & Brooks, Philip. Prehistoric Peoples: Discover the Long-Ago World of the First Humans. 2000. (Exploring History Ser.). (Illus.). 64p. (gr. 3 up). 12.95 (978-0-7548-0442-0(9)) Anness Publishing GBR. *Dist:* National Bk. Network.

MacDonald, Fiona. The Stone Age News. 2001. (History News Ser.). (Illus.). 32p. (J). (gr. 3 up). lib. bdg. 24.67 (978-0-8368-2778-1(3)) Stevens, Gareth Inc.

—The Stone Age News. 2001. (News Ser.). (Illus.). (J). (978-0-606-21468-1(2)) Tandem Library Bks.

Morris, Neil. Everyday Life in Prehistory. 2005. (Uncovering History Ser.). (Illus.). 46p. (J). (gr. 6-9). lib. bdg. 29.95 (978-1-58340-709-7(X)) Smart Apple Media.

Pacchini, Fiorenzo. A Day with Homo Habilis: Life 2,000,000 Years Ago. 2003. (Early Humans Ser.). (Illus.). 48p. (gr. 6 up). lib. bdg. 23.90 (978-0-7613-2765-3(7), Twenty-First Century Bks.) Lerner Publishing Group.

Patent, Dorothy Hinshaw. Secrets of the Ice Man. 1999. (Frozen in Time Ser.). (Illus.). 72p. (gr. 5-9). lib. bdg. 28.50 (978-0-7614-0782-9(0), Benchmark Bks.) Cavendish, Marshall Corp.

People of the Ancient World: Middle School Report Writers Will Experience What is Was Like to Live in the Ancient World, 6 Bks, Set. 2004. (J). 177.00 (978-0-531-19114-9(1), Children's Pr.) Scholastic Library Publishing.

Schomp, Virginia. Prehistoric World, 5 bks., Group 3. Incl. Ceratosaurus : And Other Horned Meat-Eaters. lib. bdg. (978-0-7614-2009-5(6)); Iguanodon : And Other Spiky-Thumbed Plant-Eaters. lib. bdg. (978-0-7614-2005-7(3)); Ornithomimus : And Other Speedy Ostrich Dinosaurs. lib. bdg. (978-0-7614-2006-4(1)); Plateosaurus : And Other Early Long-Necked Plant-Eaters. lib. bdg. (978-0-7614-2008-8(8)); Therizinosaurus : And Other Colossal-Clawed Plant-Eaters. lib. bdg. (978-0-7614-2007-1(X)); (Illus.). 31p. (J). (gr. 3-7). 2005. (978-0-7614-2004-0(5), Benchmark Bks.) Cavendish, Marshall Corp.

Twist, Clint & Kelleher, Pat. Puzzle Quest Through Prehistoric Times. Mendez, Simon, illus. 2006. (Puzzle Quest Ser.). 22p. (J). bds. bds. 22.95 (978-0-7696-4878-1(9), Brighter Child) School Specialty Publishing.

Wilkinson, P. Prehistoric Peoples. 2002. (History Detectives Ser.). (Illus.). 64p. (gr. 3-7). pap. 7.95 (978-1-84215-620-9(9), Southwater) Anness Publishing GBR. *Dist:* National Bk. Network.

Wood, Robert Muir. Discovering Prehistory. 2001. (Inside Look Ser.). (Illus.). 48p. (J). (gr. 4 up). lib. bdg. 26.00 (978-0-8368-2900-6(X)) Stevens, Gareth Inc.

PREHISTORIC PEOPLES—FICTION

Angeletti, Roberta. The Cave Painter of Lascaux. 2004. (Illus.). 32p. (J). (978-1-56290-323-7(3)) Crystal Productions.

Bato, Joseph. The Sorcerer. Donnelly, Katherine Fair, ed. 2001. (Illus.). 192p. (YA). pap. 10.95 (978-0-595-13304-8(5)) iUniverse, Inc.

Brooke, William J. A Is for AARRGH! 1999. 256p. (J). (gr. 5 up). 14.89 (978-0-06-023394-5(X)) HarperCollins Pubs.

Brooks, Mel & Reiner, Carl. The 2000 Year Old Man Goes to School. Bennett, James, illus. 2005. 40p. (J). (ps-3). 17.99 (978-0-06-076676-4(X)); lib. bdg. 18.89 (978-0-06-076677-1(8)) HarperCollins Pubs.

Clark, Patricia Nikolina. In the Shadow of the Mammoth. LeTourneau, Anthony Alex, illus. 2003. 190p. (J). pap. 6.99 (978-0-9674602-4-6(7)) Blue Marlin Pubns.

Dickinson, Peter. The Kin. 2003. (Kin Ser.). (gr. 7-12). lib. bdg. 16.45 (978-0-613-63421-2(7)) Tandem Library Bks.

Dolenz, Micky. Gakky Two-Feet. Clark, David, illus. 2006. (J). (***978-1-4156-8089-6(2)***, Putnam Juvenile) Penguin Group (USA) Inc.

Greenburg, J. C. In the Ice Age. Gerardi, Jan, illus. 2005. (Andrew Lost Ser.: Bk. 12). 96p. (J). (gr. 2-5). pap. 3.99 (978-0-375-82952-9(0)); lib. bdg. 11.99 (978-0-375-92952-6(5)) Random Hse. Children's Bks. (Random Hse. Bks. for Young Readers).

Griffin, Peni R. 11,000 Years Lost. (J). (gr. 5-9). 2006. 368p. pap. 7.95 (978-0-8109-9251-1(5)); 2004. (Illus.). 336p. 18.95 (978-0-8109-4822-8(2)) Abrams, Harry N., Inc.

Harvey, Damian. Oggy & the Dinosaur. Hall, Francois, illus. 2005. (Reading Corner Ser.). 24p. (J). (gr. k-3). lib. bdg. 22.80 (978-1-59771-008-4(3)) Sea-To-Sea Pubns.

Kitamura, Satoshi. Stone Age Boy. Kitamura, Satoshi, illus. 2007. (Illus.). 40p. (J). (ps-3). 15.99 (***978-0-7636-3474-2(3)***) Candlewick Pr.

May, Scott. The Yuggs: A Bird in the Hat. 2000. mass mkt. 8.95 (978-1-931179-07-2(7)) Long Hill Productions, Inc.

—The Yuggs: A Bird in the Hat. Fisher, Brian Patrick, illus. 2000. 24p. (J). (gr. 1-3). pap. (978-0-9701450-3-1(9)) Long Hill Productions, Inc.

Mayhew, James. Boy. 2004. (Illus.). 32p. (J). (gr. k). pap. 15.95 (978-0-439-65106-6(9), Chicken Hse., The) Scholastic, Inc.

Osborne, Mary Pope. Un Tigre Dientes de Sable en el Ocaso. 2004. (Coleccion la Casa Del Arbol the Magic Tree House Ser.).Tr. of Sunset of the Sabretooth. (SPA., Illus.). (J). pap. 4.95 (978-1-930332-68-3(8)) Lectorum Pubns., Inc.

Paver, Michelle. Chronicles of Ancient Darkness #3: Soul Eater. Taylor, Geoff, illus. 2008. (Chronicles of Ancient Darkness). 352p. (J). pap. 6.99 (***978-0-06-072833-5(7)***, Harper Trophy) HarperCollins Pubs.

—Hermano Lobo: Cronicas de la Prehistoria. Anton de vez, Patricia, tr. 2005. (Illus.). 222p. 17.25 (978-84-7888-933-4(7)) Emece Editores ESP. *Dist:* Ediciones Universal.

—Outcast. Taylor, Geoff, illus. 2008. (Chronicles of Ancient Darkness). 336p. (J). 16.99 (***978-0-06-072834-2(5)***); lib. bdg. 17.89 (***978-0-06-072835-9(3)***) HarperCollins Pubs.

—Soul-Eater. Taylor, Geoff, illus. 2007. (Chronicles of Ancient Darkness: No. 3). 336p. (J). (gr. 5 up). 16.99 (978-0-06-072831-1(0), Tegen, Katherine Bks) HarperCollins Pubs.

—Spirit Walker. Taylor, Geoff, illus. (Chronicles of Ancient Darkness: No.2). (J). 2007. 384p. pap. 6.99 (978-0-06-072830-4(2), Harper Trophy); 2006. 368p. 16.99 (978-0-06-072828-1(0), Tegen, Katherine Bks); 2006. 368p. lib. bdg. 17.89 (978-0-06-072829-8(9), Tegen, Katherine Bks) HarperCollins Pubs.

—Wolf Brother. Taylor, Geoff, illus. 2005. (Chronicles of Ancient Darkness). 304p. (J). (gr. 5 up). lib. bdg. 17.89 (978-0-06-072826-7(4)) HarperCollins Pubs.

—Wolf Brother. 2005. (Chronicles of Ancient Darkness: Bk. 1). (Illus.). 304p. (J). (gr. 5 up). 16.99 (978-0-06-072825-0(6)) HarperCollins Pubs.

—Wolf Brother. Taylor, Geoff, illus. 2006. (Chronicles of Ancient Darkness). 320p. (J). reprint ed. pap. 6.99 (978-0-06-072827-4(2), Harper Trophy) HarperCollins Pubs.

Richardson, Faith. The Peacock's Stone. 2003. 192p. (J). 21.95 (978-0-9744989-0-4(4)); (Illus.). pap. 12.95 (978-0-9744989-1-1(2)) Fox Song Bks.

Scieszka, Jon. Your Mother Was a Neanderthal. Smith, Lane, illus. (Time Warp Trio Ser.: No. 4). (J). 2006. 78p. (***978-1-4176-3603-7(3)***); Vol. 4. 2004. 80p. (gr. 2-6). pap. 4.99 (978-0-14-240048-7(3)) Penguin Group (USA) Inc. (Puffin).

Shickman, Allan Richard. Zan-Gah: A Prehistoric Adventure. 2007. 160p. pap. 9.95 (***978-0-9790357-0-8(8)***) Earthshaker Bks.

Shykoff, Henry. Just a Little Later with Eevo & Sm. Mets, Marilyn & Ledwon, Peter, illus. 2004. 132p. pap. 9.95 (978-1-896219-73-8(X), Natural Heritage Bks.) Natural Heritage/Natural History, Inc. CAN. *Dist:* Cardinal Pubs. Group.

Stanley, Diane. A Time Apart. 1999. (Illus.). 256p. (J). (gr. 5 up). 15.95 (978-0-688-16997-8(X)) HarperCollins Pubs.

Turnbull, Ann. Maroo of the Winter Caves. 20th anniv. ed. 2004. (Illus.). 144p. (J). (gr. 4-6). 15.00 (978-0-618-43408-4(9)); (YA). (gr. 3-5). pap. 6.95 (978-0-618-44299-7(5)) Houghton Mifflin Co. Trade & Reference Div. (Clarion Bks.).

Williams, Susan. Wind Rider. 2006. 320p. (J). 16.99 (978-0-06-087236-6(5)); (YA). lib. bdg. 17.89 (978-0-06-087237-3(3)) HarperCollins Pubs.

PREHISTORY

see Archaeology; Prehistoric Peoples; Stone Age

PREJUDICES

see also Antisemitism

Altman, Linda Jacobs. Hate & Racist Groups. 2001. (Hot Issues Ser.). (Illus.). 64p. (J). (gr. 6-12). lib. bdg. 27.93 (978-0-7660-1371-1(5)) Enslow Pubs., Inc.

Caloggero, Lynne. Know Whey Knot Hymn! A Plea to End Prejudice. Higgins, Don, illus. 2001. 64p. (J). (ps-4). per. 7.95 (978-0-9700250-2-9(5)) L. Lemon O'Pea Productions.

Carnes, Jim. Us & Them: A History of Intolerance in America. 1999. (gr. 7-12). lib. bdg. 24.55 (978-0-613-89558-3(4)) Tandem Library Bks.

Chin, Steven A. When Justice Failed: The Fred Korematsu Story. 2001. (Nonfiction Bookbag Ser.). (YA). (gr. 7-8). per. 8.45 (978-1-58830-211-3(3)) Metropolitan Teaching & Learning Co.

Cohn, Janice. The Christmas Menorahs: How a Town Fought Hate. 2000. (J). 13.75 (978-0-606-19688-8(9)) Tandem Library Bks.

Davidson, Tish. Prejudice. (Life Balance Ser.). 2004. (YA). (gr. 5-8). pap. 6.95 (978-0-531-15572-1(2)); 2003. (Illus.). 80p. (J). 20.50 (978-0-531-12252-5(2)) Scholastic Library Publishing. (Watts, Franklin).

Gay, Kathlyn. Cultural Diversity: Conflicts & Challenges: The Ultimate Teen Guide. 2003. (It Happened to Me Ser.: No. 6). (Illus.). 144p. pap. 30.95 (978-0-8108-4805-4(8)) Scarecrow Pr., Inc.

Grant, Rich G. Racism: Changing Attitudes, 1900-2000. 1999. (Twentieth Century Issues Ser.). (Illus.). 64p. (J). (gr. 4-6). lib. bdg. 28.54 (978-0-8172-5567-1(2)) Raintree.

Hanes, Richard Clay, et al. Prejudice in the Modern World. 2007. (J). (***978-1-4144-0205-5(8)***); (***978-1-4144-0206-2(6)***) Thomson Gale.

Kent, Susan. Learning How to Appreciate Differences. 2001. (Violence Prevention Library). (Illus.). 24p. (J). (gr. 3). lib. bdg. 18.75 (978-0-8239-5617-3(2), PowerKids Pr.) Rosen Publishing Group, Inc., The.

Lester, Julius. Let's Talk about Race. Barbour, Karen, illus. 2005. (Amistad Ser.). 32p. (J). (gr. 1-5). 16.99 (978-0-06-028596-8(6)); lib. bdg. 16.89 (978-0-06-028598-2(2)) HarperCollins Pubs. (Amistad).

Levy, Debbie. Bigotry. 2001. (Overview Ser.). (Illus.). 128p. (YA). (gr. 6-9). lib. bdg. 29.95 (978-1-56006-500-5(1), Lucent Bks.) Thomson Gale.

McIntosh, Kenneth & Walker, Ida. Youth with Cultural/Language Differences: Interpreting an Alien World. 2008. (J). (***978-1-4222-0141-1(4)***) Mason Crest Pubs.

Middleton, Don. Dealing with Discrimination. 1999. (Conflict Resolution Library). 24p. (J). lib. bdg. 18.75 (978-0-8239-5270-0(3), PowerKids Pr.) Rosen Publishing Group, Inc., The.

Patrick, Denise Lewis. A Lesson for Martin Luther King, Jr. Pate, Rodney S., illus. 2003. (Ready-to-Read Ser.). 32p. (J). pap. 3.99 (978-0-689-85397-5(1), Aladdin) Simon & Schuster Children's Publishing.

Penchina, Sharon. Dogs & Bugs Go Together, Really They Do! 2007. 28p. 12.95 (978-0-9740684-8-0(9)) 2 Imagine.

Sanders, Bruce. Racism. 2005. (Let's Talk about Ser.). (Illus.). 32p. (J). (gr. 3-7). lib. bdg. 27.10 (978-1-59604-046-5(7)) Stargazer Bks.

Sanders, Pete & Myers, Steve. Dealing with Racism. 2006. (Choices & Decisions Ser.). (Illus.). 32p. (J). (978-1-59604-097-7(1)) Stargazer Bks.

Scheunemann, Pam. Learning about Differences. 2004. (Keeping the Peace Ser.). (Illus.). 23p. (J). (ps-3). lib. bdg. 19.93 (978-1-59197-561-8(1)) ABDO Publishing Co.

—Tolerance. 2003. (United We Stand Ser.). (Illus.). 24p. (J). (ps-3). lib. bdg. 19.93 (978-1-57765-881-8(7)) ABDO Publishing Co.

Senker, Cath. Why Are People Prejudiced? 2002. (Exploring Tough Issues Ser.). 48p. (J). lib. bdg. 25.69 (978-0-7398-4959-0(X)) Raintree.

Stewart, Gail B. Racism. 2002. (Understanding Issues Ser.). (Illus.). 48p. (J). (gr. 3-5). 26.20 (978-0-7377-1025-0(X), Kidhaven) Thomson Gale.

Thomson Gale Staff. Prejudice in the Modern World: Almanac, 2 vols. Hanes, Richard C et al, eds. rev. ed. 2007. (Prejudice Throughout History Reference Library). 462p. (YA). 120.00 (978-1-4144-0204-8(X), UXL) Thomson Gale.

—Prejudice in the Modern World: Biographies. Hanes, Richard C. & Rudd, Kelly, eds. rev. ed. 2007. (Prejudice Throughout History Reference Library). 920p. (YA). 67.00 (978-1-4144-0207-9(4), UXL) Thomson Gale.

—Prejudice in the Modern World: Cumulative Index. Hermsen, Sarah, ed. rev. ed. 2007. (Prejudice Throughout History Reference Library). 34p. (YA). 5.00 (978-1-4144-0209-3(0), UXL) Thomson Gale.

—Prejudice in the Modern World: Primary Sources. Hanes, Sharon M., ed. rev. ed. 2007. (Prejudice Throughout History Reference Library). 214p. (YA). 67.00 (978-1-4144-0208-6(2), UXL) Thomson Gale.

—Prejudice Throughout History Reference Library 4 Vol Set. rev. ed. 2007. (Prejudice Throughout History Reference Library). 235.00 (978-1-4144-0203-1(1), UXL) Thomson Gale.

Wandberg, Robert. Tolerance: Celebrating Differences. 2000. (Contemporary Issues Ser.). (Illus.). 64p. (J). (gr. 4-6). lib. bdg. 23.93 (978-0-7368-1021-0(8), LifeMatters Bks.) Capstone Pr., Inc.

Webber, Diane and Laurie Mandel. Totally Tolerant: Spotting & stopping Prejudice. 2007. (Scholastic Choices Ser.). 112p. (J). spiral bd. 27.00 (***978-0-531-13867-0(4)***, Children's Pr.) Scholastic Library Publishing.

Webster-Doyle, Terrence. Why Is Everybody Always Picking on Us: Understanding the Roots of Prejudice. Cameron, Rod, illus. 2000. 160p. (J). (gr. 3-10). pap. 14.95 (978-0-8348-0435-7(2), Weatherhill, Inc.) Shambhala Pubns., Inc.

Wright, John D. Hate Crimes. 2002. (Crime & Detection Ser.). (Illus.). 96p. (J). (gr. 7 up). lib. bdg. (978-1-59084-379-6(7)) Mason Crest Pubs.

—Race & Crime. 2002. (Crime & Detection Ser.). (Illus.). 96p. (J). (gr. 7 up). lib. bdg. (978-1-59084-378-9(9)) Mason Crest Pubs.

PREJUDICES—FICTION

Armistead, John. The $66 Summer. 2000. (978-0-606-21752-1(5)) Tandem Library Bks.

—The $66 Summer: A Novel of the Segregated South. 2nd ed. 2006. (Milkweed Prize for Children's Literature Ser.). 240p. (J). reprint ed. pap. 6.95 (978-1-57131-663-9(9)) Milkweed Editions.

Atwood, John H. & Atwood, Jenean D. Blue Spots: Yellow Spots! 2000. (Illus.). 32p. (J). (ps-3). pap. 7.99 (978-1-881524-80-9(9)) Milligan Bks., Inc.

Baker, Julie. Up Molasses Mountain. 2002. 224p. (YA). (gr. 7). lib. bdg. 17.99 (978-0-385-90048-5(1), Lamb, Wendy) Random Hse. Children's Bks.

Banks, Jacqueline Turner. A Day for Vincent Chin & Me. 128p. (J). (gr. 5-9). 2005. pap. 5.95 (978-0-618-54879-8(3)); 2001. (Illus.). 15.00 (978-0-618-13199-0(X)) Houghton Mifflin Co. Trade & Reference Div.

Barron, Marietta. Two Worlds. 1999. 94p. (J). (gr. 3-6). 9.99 (978-0-88092-120-6(X), 120-X) Royal Fireworks Publishing Co.

Baskin, Nora Raleigh. The Truth about My Bat Mitzvah. 2008. 144p. (J). 15.99 (***978-1-4169-3558-2(4)***, Simon & Schuster Children's Publishing) Simon & Schuster Children's Publishing.

Bat-Ami, Miriam. Two Suns in the Sky. 1999. 208p. (YA). (gr. 7-12). 17.95 (978-0-8126-2900-2(0)) Cricket Bks.
—Two Suns in the Sky. 2001. 208p. (J). pap. 6.99 (978-0-14-230036-7(5) , Puffin) Penguin Group (USA) Inc.
—Two Suns in the Sky. 2001. (gr. 7-12). lib. bdg. 15.30 (978-0-613-44425-5(6)) Tandem Library Bks.
Bell, Mary Reeves. Secret of Mezuzah. 1999. (J). (978-0-606-18974-3(2)) Tandem Library Bks.
Bell, William. Zack. l.t. ed. 2000. (LRS Large Print Cornerstone Ser.). 256p. (YA). (gr. 5-12). lib. bdg. 28.95 (978-1-58118-072-5(1) , 23656) LRS.
—Zack. 2000. (J). (978-0-606-20095-0(9)) Tandem Library Bks.
Benedict, Helen. Opposite of Love. 2007. 256p. (J). (gr. 6 up). 16.99 (*978-0-670-06135-8(2) , Viking Juvenile) Penguin Group (USA) Inc.
Benge, Judy. My Name Is Sandy. 2004. 152p. pap. 19.95 (978-1-4137-1947-5(3)) PublishAmerica, Inc.
Bernier-Grand, Carmen T. In the Shade of the Nispero Tree. 1999. 192p. (J). (gr. 4-7). 16.99 (978-0-531-33154-5(7)) ; pap. 15.95 (978-0-531-30154-8(0)) Scholastic, Inc. (Orchard Bks.).
Birrer, Cynthia & Birrer, Bill, illus. The Confused Zebra. 1999. (J). 16.95 (978-0-86543-795-1(5)) Africa World Pr.
Blackman, Malorie. Black & White. 2007. 512p. (YA). (gr. 9 up). pap. 7.99 (978-1-4169-0017-7(9) , Simon Pulse) Simon & Schuster Children's Publishing.
—Knife Edge. 2007. 368p. (YA). (gr. 9 up). 16.99 (978-1-4169-0018-4(7) , Simon & Schuster Children's Publishing) Simon & Schuster Children's Publishing.
Blakeslee, Ann R. Summer Battles. 2000. (Illus.). 128p. (YA). (gr. 5-9). 14.95 (978-0-7614-5064-1(5) , Cavendish Children's Bks.) Cavendish, Marshall Corp.
Boedoe, Geefwee. Arrowville. Boedoe, Geefwee, illus. 2004. (Illus.). 40p. (J). (ps-2). 16.89 (978-0-06-055599-3(8) , Geringer, Laura Book) HarperCollins Pubs.
Bradbury, Bianca. Flight into Spring. 2005. 184p. (YA). pap. (*978-1-932350-01-2(2)) Bethlehem Bks.
Brady, Laurel. What Carter Fellows Knew. 1999. 224p. (J). (gr. 5 up). pap. 4.95 (978-0-06-440765-6(9)) HarperCollins Pubs.
Brooks, Kevin. Lucas. 2004. (Push Ser.). 384p. (YA). 6.99 (978-0-439-53063-7(6) , Scholastic Paperbacks) Scholastic, Inc.
Brown, Celease N. & Mubarak, Enoch. The Color Orange. 2004. (Illus.). 32p. (978-1-55306-742-9(8) , Guardian Bks.) Essence Publishing.
Brown, Stephanie. Thea the Yellow Tomato. Brown, Stephanie, illus. l.t. ed. 1998. (Illus.). 32p. (J). (gr. k-4). 14.95 (978-0-9638152-6-2(1)) Freedom Publishing Co.
Bruchac, Joseph. Hidden Roots. 2006. 160p. (J). pap. 5.99 (978-0-439-35359-5(9) , Scholastic Paperbacks) Scholastic, Inc.
Bunting, Eve. Walking to School. Dooling, Michael, illus. 2005. 32p. (J). (gr. k-3). 20.01 (978-0-618-26144-4(3) , Clarion Bks.) Houghton Mifflin Co. Trade & Reference Div.
Burnett, Karen Gedig. If the World Were Blind: A Book about Prejudice & Judgement. Barrows, Laurie, illus. 2001. 48p. 17.00 (978-0-9668530-4-9(0)) GR Publishing.
Byars, Betsy. The Blossoms Meet the Vulture Lady. unabr. ed. 2000. (J). (gr. 4-6). pap. 23.00 incl. audio (978-0-8072-7323-4(6) , YA824SP, Listening Library) Random Hse. Audio Publishing Group.
Calhoun, Dia. Avielle of Rhia. 2006. 400p. (J). 16.99 (978-0-7614-5320-8(2)) Cavendish, Marshall Corp.
—Firegold. Blondon, Herve, illus. 1999. (J). (gr. 7-12). 285p. 15.95 (978-1-890817-10-7(4)); 286p. pap. 9.95 (978-1-890817-28-2(7)) Winslow Pr.
Campbell Hale, Janet. The Owl's Song. 1998. 153p. (C). pap. 13.95 (978-0-8263-1861-9(4)) Univ. of New Mexico Pr.
Cardenas, Teresa. Cartas a Mi Mama. Unger, David, tr. 2006. (SPA.). 96p. (J). 15.95 (978-0-88899-722-7(1)); pap. 6.95 (978-0-88899-723-4(X)) Groundwood Bks. CAN. *Dist:* Perseus Distribution.
Carlson, Margaret. The Canning Season. Smith, Kimanne, illus. 1999. (First Person Ser.). 32p. (J). (gr. 2-4). pap. 7.95 (978-1-57505-283-0(0) , Carolrhoda Bks.) Lerner Publishing Group.
Carlson, Melody. Project, Rescue Chelsea. 2007. (Faithgirlz!#8482; / Girls of 622 Harbor View Ser.). 144p. (J). pap. 6.99 (978-0-310-71188-9(6)) Zonderkidz.
Chotjewitz, David. Daniel, Half Human: And the Good Nazi. Orgel, Doris, tr. from GER. 2004. (Illus.). 304p. (YA). 17.95 (978-0-689-85747-8(0) , Atheneum) Simon & Schuster Children's Publishing.
Chotjewitz, David & Orgel, Doris. Daniel, Half Human: And the Good Nazi. 2004. 298p. (J). (978-3-551-58045-0(6)) Carlsen Verlag DEU. *Dist:* Distribooks, Inc.
Clements, Andrew. The Jacket. Henderson, McDavid, illus. 2003. 96p. (J). pap. 5.99 (978-0-689-86010-2(2) , Aladdin) Simon & Schuster Children's Publishing.
—The Jacket. 2002. (gr. 3-6). lib. bdg. 13.00 (978-0-613-66513-1(9)) Tandem Library Bks.
Clifford, Eth. The Year of the Three-Legged Deer. Cuffari, Richard, tr. Cuffari, Richard, illus. 2003. (Library of Indiana Classics). 176p. (YA). 32.95 (978-0-253-34251-5(1)); pap. 14.95 (978-0-253-21604-5(4)) Indiana Univ. Pr.
Clifton Wisler, G. All for Texas. 2004. 140p. (J). lib. bdg. 16.92 (*978-1-4242-0767-1(3)) Fitzgerald Bks.
Coleman, Evelyn. Circle of Fire. 2001. (American Girl Collection). (Illus.). (J). 12.60 (978-0-606-21249-6(3)) Tandem Library Bks.
Cooney, Caroline B. Burning Up. 2001. 240p. (YA). (gr. 7 up). mass mkt. 5.99 (978-0-440-22687-1(2) , Laurel Leaf) Random Hse. Children's Bks.
Couric, Katie. The Brand New Kid. Priceman, Marjorie, illus. 2000. 32p. (J). (gr. 2-3). 15.95 (978-0-385-50030-2(0) , Doubleday) Doubleday Publishing.
Courtenay, Bryce. The Power of One. 2005. 304p. (J). (gr. 5-12). lib. bdg. 17.99 (978-0-385-90274-8(3) , Delacorte Bks. for Young Readers) Random Hse. Children's Bks.
Cross, Gillian. Pictures in the Dark. 1998. (978-0-606-13703-4(3)) Tandem Library Bks.
Crowther, Kitty. Jack & Jim: Picture Book. Date not set. (Illus.). 32p. (J). pap. 5.99 (978-0-7868-1439-8(X)); 15.99 (978-0-7868-0614-0(1)); 16.49 (978-0-7868-2527-1(8)) Hyperion Bks. for Children.
Curtis, Christopher Paul. The Watsons Go to Birmingham - 1963. 2002. (Illus.). (J). 14.47 (978-0-7587-0328-6(7)) Book Wholesalers, Inc.
—The Watsons Go to Birmingham - 1963. 1998. 15p. pap., stu. ed., tchr.'s training gde. ed. 15.95 (978-1-58303-068-4(9)) Pathways Publishing.
—The Watsons Go to Birmingham - 1963. 210p. (YA). (gr. 5 up). pap. 5.50 (978-0-8072-8336-3(3)); 2004. (J). (gr. 4 up). pap. 38.00 incl. audio (978-0-8072-8335-6(5) , YA166SP) Random Hse. Audio Publishing Group. (Listening Library).
—The Watsons Go to Birmingham - 1963. 2000. 224p. (YA). (gr. 5-7). pap. 6.50 (978-0-440-22800-4(X) , Laurel Leaf) Random Hse. Children's Bks.
—The Watsons Go to Birmingham - 1963. 2000. (gr. 5-8). lib. bdg. 14.15 (978-0-613-85111-4(0)) Tandem Library Bks.
—The Watsons Go to Birmingham - 1963. l.t. ed. 2004. 254p. pap. 10.95 (978-0-7862-6406-3(3)) Thorndike Pr.
Dell, Pamela. Half-Breed: A Story of Two Boys During the Klondike Gold Rush. 2003. (Scrapbooks of America Ser.). (Illus.). 48p. (J). (gr. 2-6). 28.50 (978-1-59187-044-9(5)) Child's World, Inc.
Dorros, Arthur. Under the Sun. (YA). (gr. 5-11). 2006. 240p. pap. 5.95 (978-0-8109-9250-4(7)); 2004. (Illus.). 224p. 16.95 (978-0-8109-4933-1(4)) Abrams, Harry N. , Inc.
DuCharme, Dede Fox. The Treasure in the Tiny Blue Tin. 1998. (Chaparral Books for Young Readers). 144p. (J). (gr. 5-8). pap. 11.95 (978-0-87565-180-4(1)) Texas Christian Univ. Pr.
Fletcher, Susan. Walk Across the Sea. Jakesevic, Nenad, illus. 224p. (J). 2003. pap. 11.95 (978-0-689-85707-2(1) , Aladdin); 2001. (gr. 5-9). 16.95 (978-0-689-84133-0(7) , Atheneum) Simon & Schuster Children's Publishing.
—Walk Across the Sea. 2003. (gr. 3-6). lib. bdg. 13.00 (978-0-613-62227-1(8)) Tandem Library Bks.
—Walk Across the Sea. l.t. ed. 2002. 218p. (J). 22.95 (978-0-7862-4439-3(9)) Thorndike Pr.
Fogelin, Adrian. Crossing Jordan. Schultz, Suzy, illus. (J). 160p. pap. 6.95 (978-1-56145-281-1(5) , Q23381); 2000. 140p. (gr. 3-7). 14.95 (978-1-56145-215-6(7) , Q23381) Peachtree Pubs., Ltd.
—Crossing Jordan. 2002. (gr. 3-6). lib. bdg. 15.25 (978-0-613-54154-1(5)) Tandem Library Bks.
Freedman, Claire. New Kid in Town. Stephenson, Kristina, illus. 2006. 28p. (J). 16.00 (978-1-56148-547-5(0)) Good Bks.
Freschet, Gina. Feet Man & Mr. Tiny. 2006. (Illus.). 32p. (J). 16.00 (978-0-374-32294-6(5)) Farrar, Straus & Giroux.
Fries, Claudia. A Pig Is Moving In! Fries, Claudia, illus. 2000. (Illus.). 32p. (J). (ps-2). 16.99 (978-0-531-33307-5(8)); pap. 15.95 (978-0-531-30307-8(1)) Scholastic, Inc. (Orchard Bks.).
Fuchshuber, Annegert. Carly. Howe, Florence & Kirk, Heidi, trs. from ENG. 2004. (Illus.). 28p. (ps-3). 16.95 (978-1-55861-177-1(0)) Feminist Pr. at The City Univ. of New York.
Fuqua, Jonathan Scott. Darby. 2002. 256p. (J). (gr. 5 up). 16.99 (978-0-7636-1417-1(3)) Candlewick Pr.
Fuqua, Jonathon Scott. Darby. 2006. 256p. (J). (gr. 5). 5.99 (978-0-7636-2290-9(7)) Candlewick Pr.
Gantos, Jack. Desire Lines. 2006. 144p. (YA). reprint ed. pap. 7.95 (978-0-374-41703-1(2)) Macmillan.
Garcia, Maria. Las Aventuras de Connie y Diego. ed. 2004. (ENG & SPA., Illus.). (J). (gr. k-3). spiral bd. (978-0-616-14605-7(1)) Canadian National Institute for the Blind/Institut National Canadien pour les Aveugles.
Garden, Nancy. Holly's Secret. 2000. 144p. (YA). (gr. 3-7). 16.00 (978-0-374-33273-0(8) , Farrar, Straus & Giroux (BYR)) Farrar, Straus & Giroux.
—The Year They Burned the Books. 1999. 256p. (YA). (gr. 7-12). 17.00 (978-0-374-38667-2(6) , Farrar, Straus & Giroux (BYR)) Farrar, Straus & Giroux.
Gershon, Dann. Extra Large. Robinson, David, illus. 1999. (Hangin' with the Hombeez Ser.: Vol. 3). 40p. (J). (gr. k-6). 14.95 (978-0-9656985-5-9(6)) Noware Bks.
Godden, Rumer. Gypsy Girl. 2002. Orig. Title: The Diddakoi. (Illus.). 176p. (J). 15.89 (978-0-06-029192-1(3)) HarperCollins Pubs.
Going, K. L. The Liberation of Gabriel King. 2007. 160p. (J). (gr. 3 up). pap. 6.99 (978-0-14-240766-0(6) , Puffin) Penguin Group (USA) Inc.
Gonzalez, Catherine T. Chacho & Ellie Sanchez, Citizens. 1998. (Illus.). 136p. (gr. 4). 13.95 (978-1-57168-114-0(0)) Eakin Pr.
Gonzalez, Tomas. El Cayo. 2000. (SPA., Illus.). (J). (978-0-606-18242-3(X)) Tandem Library Bks.
Gorman, Carol & Findley, Ron. The Stumptown Kid. 2005. 224p. (J). (gr. 3-7). 14.95 (978-1-56145-337-5(4)) Peachtree Pubs., Ltd.
Greene, Bette. Summer of My German Soldier. 1999. (Illus.). 208p. (J). (gr. 5-9). pap. 6.99 (978-0-14-130636-0(X) , Puffin) Penguin Group (USA) Inc.
—Summer of My German Soldier. 2000. (J). (gr. 6 up). 20.50 (978-0-8446-7144-4(4)) Smith, Peter Pub., Inc.
—Summer of My German Soldier. 1999. (978-0-606-17432-9(X)) Tandem Library Bks.
—Summer of My German Soldier. 2006. (Puffin Modern Classics Ser.). 240p. (J). (gr. 5). pap. 6.99 (978-0-14-240651-9(1) , Puffin) Penguin Group (USA) Inc.
—Summer of My German Soldier. l.t. ed. 2000. (LRS Large Print Cornerstone Ser.). 305p. (YA). (gr. 6-12). lib. bdg. 29.95 (978-1-58118-059-6(4) , 23473) LRS.
Greene, Bette & Hunt, Robert, illus. Summer of My German Soldier. 2003. 256p. (J). (gr. 5). 18.99 (978-0-8037-2869-1(7) , Dial) Penguin Group (USA) Inc.
Grove, Vicki. The Starplace. 2000. (Illus.). 224p. (J). (gr. 5-9). pap. 6.99 (978-0-698-11868-3(5) , Putnam Juvenile) Penguin Group (USA) Inc.
—The Starplace. 2000. (978-0-606-20373-9(7)); (J). (978-0-606-20257-2(9)) Tandem Library Bks.
—Starplace. 2000. (gr. 5-8). lib. bdg. 14.15 (978-0-613-30759-8(3)) Tandem Library Bks.
Haptie, Charlotte. Otto & the Flying Twins: The First Book of the Karmidee. 2004. (Illus.). 320p. (J). (gr. 4-6). 17.95 (978-0-8234-1826-8(X)) Holiday Hse., Inc.
Hay, Barbara. Dusty White Eagle Feather. 2001. 124p. (YA). (gr. 7-11). pap. 9.95 (978-0-595-17008-1(0)) iUniverse, Inc.
Headley, Justina Chen. Nothing but the Truth (And a Few White Lies) 2006. 256p. (J). (gr. 5-9). 16.99 (978-0-316-01128-0(2)) Little Brown & Co.
—Nothing but the Truth (And a Few White Lies) 2007. 256p. (J). (gr. 7 up). pap. 7.99 (*978-0-316-01131-0(2)) Little, Brown Bks. for Young Readers.
Heisel, Sharon E. Precious Gold, Precious Jade. 2000. 192p. (J). (gr. 7 up). tchr. ed. 16.95 (978-0-8234-1432-1(9)) Holiday Hse., Inc.
Hess, Karen. Witness. l.t. ed. 2005. 209p. pap. 10.95 (978-0-7862-7249-5(X) , Large Print Pr.) Thorndike Pr.
Hesse, Karen. Witness. 2004. 168p. (J). (gr. 5-9). pap. 29.00 incl. audio (978-0-8072-2094-8(9) , Listening Library) Random Hse. Audio Publishing Group.
—Witness. (J). (978-0-439-36634-2(8) , Scholastic Pr.); 2003. (Illus.). 176p. (YA). pap. 5.99 (978-0-439-27200-1(9) , Scholastic Paperbacks); 2001. (Illus.). 176p. (YA). (gr. 4-7). pap. 16.95 (978-0-439-27199-8(1)) Scholastic, Inc.
—Witness. 2001. (gr. 5-8). lib. bdg. 14.15 (978-0-613-62503-6(X)) Tandem Library Bks.
Hirsch, Odo. Have Courage, Hazel Green! (J). 2007. (Illus.). 256p. pap. 6.95 (978-1-59990-003-2(3)); 2006. 262p. 15.95 (978-1-58234-659-5(3)) Bloomsbury Publishing. (Bloomsbury Children).
Hoffman, Alice. Incantation. rev. ed. 2007. (Illus.). 166p. (YA). (gr. 7-17). per. 8.99 (*978-0-316-15428-4(8)) Little, Brown Bks. for Young Readers.
Hoffman, Emily Allen. A Friend of the Enemy. 2003. 108p. (J). pap. 7.95 (978-1-57249-312-4(7) , White Mane Kids) White Mane Publishing Co., Inc.
Hoffman, Eric. Play Lady - La Senora Juguentona. 2004. (Anti-Bias Books for Kids). (ENG & SPA., Illus.). 32p. (J). (ps-3). pap. 11.95 (978-1-884834-61-5(2)) Redleaf Pr.
Holland, Isabelle. Paperboy. 1999. 144p. (J). (gr. 7 up). tchr. ed. 16.95 (978-0-8234-1422-2(1)) Holiday Hse., Inc.
Houston, Julian. New Boy. 288p. (J). (gr. 7). 2008. pap. 7.99 (*978-0-618-88405-6(X)); 2005. 16.00 (978-0-618-43253-0(1)) Houghton Mifflin Co. Trade & Reference Div.
Hume, Lachie. Clancy the Courageous Cow. Hume, Lachie, illus. 2007. (Illus.). 32p. (gr. k-1). 16.99 (978-0-06-117249-6(9)) HarperCollins Pubs.
Hurst, Carol Otis. Torchlight. 2006. 160p. (J). (gr. 4-6). 16.00 (978-0-618-27601-1(7)) Houghton Mifflin Co.
Hutchens, Paul. The Battle of the Bees. rev. ed. 1999. (Sugar Creek Gang Ser.: No. 32). (J). (gr. 4-7). 144p. 4.99 (978-0-8024-7035-5(1)); 112p. 4.99 (978-0-8024-7036-2(X)) Moody Pubs.
Ioannides, Mara W. Cohen. A Shout in the Sunshine. 2007. 120p. (J). pap. 12.95 (*978-0-8276-0838-2(1)) Jewish Pubn. Society.
Jones, Carrie. Tips on Having a Gay (ex) Boyfriend. 2008. 264p. (J). pap. 9.95 (*978-0-7387-1341-0(4) , Flux) Llewellyn Pubns.
Jordan, Sherryl. The Raging Quiet. 2004. 368p. (YA). mass mkt. 5.99 (978-0-689-87004-0(3) , Simon Pulse) Simon & Schuster Children's Publishing.
—The Raging Quiet. 2000. (YA). (978-0-606-20093-6(2)) Tandem Library Bks.
—The Raging Quiet. l.t. ed. 2005. 416p. 22.95 (978-0-7862-7313-3(5) , Large Print Pr.) Thorndike Pr.
—The Raging Quiet. l.t. ed. 2000. (Illus.). 464p. (978-0-7089-9535-8(7)) Ulverscroft Large Print Bks.
Kerr, M. E. Someone Like Summer. 2007. 272p. (J). lib. bdg. 17.89 (*978-0-06-114100-3(3)); (YA). (gr. 7 up). 16.99 (*978-0-06-114099-0(6)) HarperCollins Pubs. (HarperTeen).
Ketchum, Liza. Where the Great Hawk Flies. 2005. 272p. (J). (gr. 5-9). 16.00 (978-0-618-40085-0(0) , Clarion Bks.) Houghton Mifflin Co. Trade & Reference Div.
Khatibi, Janis. The Adventures of White Tuxedo Penguin. 2006. (ENG.). 48p. per. 18.99 (*978-1-4259-5769-8(2)) AuthorHouse.
Klass, David. Danger Zone. 1998. (J). 11.64 (978-0-606-13080-6(2)) Tandem Library Bks.
Konigsburg, E. L. T-Backs, T-Shirts, Coat, & Suit. 2003. (Illus.). 176p. (J). pap. 4.99 (978-0-689-85682-2(2) , Aladdin) Simon & Schuster Children's Publishing.
—T-Backs, T-Shirts, Coat, & Suit. 2003. (gr. k-3). lib. bdg. 13.00 (978-0-613-61661-4(8)) Tandem Library Bks.
Krisher, Trudy. Fallout. 2006. 272p. (J). 17.95 (978-0-8234-2035-3(3)) Holiday Hse., Inc.
Lachtman, Ofelia Dumas. Tina & the Scarecrow Skins/Tina y las pieles de Espantapajaros. Colin, Jose Juan, tr. DeLange, Alex Pardo, illus. 2002. (ENG & SPA.). 32p. (J). 14.95 (978-1-55885-373-7(1) , Piñata Books) Arte Publico Pr.
Lawlor, Laurie. Wind on the River. 2004. 156p. (J). lib. bdg. 16.92 (*978-1-4242-0771-8(1)) Fitzgerald Bks.
Lawlor, Laurie. Wind on the River: A Story of the Civil War. 2001. (American Portraits Ser.). (Illus.). iv, 156p. (J). (gr. 5-8). 15.32 (978-0-8092-0582-0(3) , 9780809205820) Jamestown.
—Wind on the River: A Story of the Civil War. 2004. (Jamestown's American Portraits Ser.). (Illus.). 160p. (J). (gr. 5-7). pap. 4.95 (978-0-7696-3425-8(7) , Waterbird Bks.) School Specialty Publishing.
—Wind on the River: A Story of the Civil War. 2000. (978-0-606-21880-1(7)); (gr. 5-8). lib. bdg. 15.70 (978-0-613-36904-6(1)) Tandem Library Bks.
Lawlor, Laurie & McGraw-Hill Staff. Wind on the River: A Story of the Civil War. 2001. (Jamestown Classics Ser.). (Illus.). iv, 156p. (J). (gr. 5-8). pap. 10.00 (978-0-8092-0624-7(2) , 9780809206247) Jamestown.
Leblanc, Louise. Leo's Midnight Rescue. Prud'homme, Jules, illus. 2004. 62p. (J). lib. bdg. 12.00 (*978-1-4242-1217-0(0)) Fitzgerald Bks.
—Leo's Midnight Rescue. Cummins, Sarah, tr. from FRE. Prud'homme, Jules, illus. 2004. (First Novel Ser.). 64p. (J). (gr. 2-5). 4.95 (978-0-88780-640-7(6)); (*978-0-88780-641-4(4)) Formac Publishing Co., Ltd. CAN. *Dist:* Casemate Pubs. & Bk. Distributors, LLC.
Leeds, Constance & Bennett, Constance. The Silver Cup. 2007. 240p. (YA). (gr. 6-9). 16.99 (978-0-670-06157-0(3) , Viking Adult) Penguin Group (USA) Inc.
Les Becquets, Diane. The Stones of Mourning Creek. 2005. 306p. (YA). (gr. 7). reprint ed. pap. 6.95 (978-0-7614-5238-6(9)) Cavendish, Marshall Corp.
—The Stones of Mourning Creek. 2001. (Illus.). 320p. (J). (gr. 7 up). 16.95 (978-1-58837-004-4(6)) Winslow Pr.
Levithan, David. Wide Awake. 2006. 240p. (YA). (gr. 9). 16.95 (978-0-375-83466-0(4)); lib. bdg. 18.99 (978-0-375-93466-7(9)) Random Hse. Children's Bks. (Knopf Bks. for Young Readers).
Levitin, Sonia. The Cure. 1999. 192p. (YA). (gr. 5 up). 16.00 (978-0-15-201827-6(1) , Silver Whistle) Harcourt Trade Pubs.
—The Cure. 2000. 272p. (J). (gr. 7 up). pap. 6.99 (978-0-380-73298-2(X) , Harper Trophy) HarperCollins Pubs.
—Cure. 2000. (gr. 5-8). lib. bdg. 14.15 (978-0-613-29918-3(3)) Tandem Library Bks.
Lisle, Janet Taylor. Sirens & Spies. 2002. (gr. 3-6). lib. bdg. 13.00 (978-0-613-45104-8(X)) Tandem Library Bks.
Lorimer, Janet. Death Grip: Set 3. 2002. 32p. (YA). 2.95 (978-1-56254-427-0(6) , SP 4276) Saddleback Educational Publishing.
Lucado, Max. Best of All. Martinez, Sergio, illus. 2005. (Wemmicks Ser.). 32p. 15.99 (978-1-58134-501-8(1) , Crossway Bibles) Crossway Bks.
—You Are Mine & Best of All, 2 vols. 2006. (Illus.). 64p. (J). 19.99 (978-1-58134-804-0(5)) Crossway Bks.
Mackall, Dandi. Larger-Than-Life Lara. 2006. 195p. (J). (gr. 5). 16.99 (978-0-525-47726-6(8) , Dutton Juvenile) Penguin Group (USA) Inc.
Mamet, David. Henrietta. Dahlie, Elizabeth, illus. 1999. 32p. (ps-3). tchr. ed. 16.00 (978-0-618-00416-4(5)) Houghton Mifflin Co. Trade & Reference Div.
Marsden, Carolyn. The Gold-Threaded Dress. 2006. 80p. (J). (gr. 2-4). reprint ed. pap. 5.99 (978-0-7636-2993-9(6)) Candlewick Pr.
Marsden, Carolyn & Mackler, Carolyn. The Gold-Threaded Dress. 2002. 80p. (J). (gr. 2-4). 14.99 (978-0-7636-1569-7(2)) Candlewick Pr.
Martin, Ann M. Belle Teale. 2004. 224p. (J). pap. 5.99 (978-0-439-09824-3(6) , Scholastic Paperbacks) Scholastic, Inc.
—Here Today. (J). 2005. 336p. (gr. 5-9). pap. 5.99 (978-0-439-57945-2(7) , Scholastic Paperbacks); 2004. 320p. (gr. 4-7). pap. 16.95 (978-0-439-57944-5(9) , Scholastic Pr.) Scholastic, Inc.
Martin, Nora. Flight of the Fisherbird. 2003. (Illus.). 200p. (J). 16.95 (978-1-58234-814-8(6) , Bloomsbury Children) Bloomsbury Publishing.
—A Perfect Snow. 2002. 250p. (J). 16.95 (978-1-58234-788-2(3) , Bloomsbury Children) Bloomsbury Publishing.
—A Perfect Snow. 2004. 144p. (YA). (gr. 7-17). lib. bdg. 14.00 (978-0-606-32848-7(3)) Tandem Library Bks.
Mason, Jo-Anne. Paddy, the Goat That Saved Rainbow Island. 2003. 48p. (ps-3). 13.95 (978-0-333-97062-1(4)) Macmillan Caribbean GBR. *Dist:* Interlink Publishing Group, Inc.
Matas, Carol. Rebecca. 2000. (Illus.). 160p. (J). pap. (978-0-439-98718-9(0)) Scholastic, Inc.
—Sparks Fly Upward. 2002. 192p. (YA). (gr. 5-9). 15.00 (978-0-618-15964-2(9) , Clarion Bks.) Houghton Mifflin Co. Trade & Reference Div.
—The War Within: A Novel of the Civil War. 2002. 160p. (J). pap. 9.95 (978-0-689-84358-7(5) , Aladdin) Simon & Schuster Children's Publishing.
—The War Within: A Novel of the Civil War. l.t. ed. 2003. (J). 22.95 (978-0-7862-5499-6(8)) Thorndike Pr.
Mazer, Anne. The Oxboy. 2000. 112p. reprint ed. pap. 6.95 (978-0-89255-240-5(9)) Persea Bks., Inc.
—The Oxboy. 2000. (gr. 5-8). lib. bdg. 15.25 (978-0-613-90534-3(2)); (YA). (978-0-606-19473-0(8)) Tandem Library Bks.
McAllister, Margaret. The Octave of Angels. 2004. 128p. (J). pap. 8.00 (978-0-8028-5240-3(8)) Eerdmans, William B. Publishing Co.
McGinley, Jerry. Joaquin Strikes Back. 1998. 158p. (YA). (gr. 5-10). 18.95 (978-0-936389-58-5(3)) Tudor Pubs., Inc.
McKissack, Patricia C. Color Me Dark: The Diary of Nellie Lee Love, the Great Migration North, Chicago, Illinois, 1919. 2000. (Dear America Ser.). (J). 9.95 (978-0-439-26653-6(X)) Scholastic, Inc.

PQR

—Color Me Dark: The Diary of Nellie Lee Love, the Great Migration North, Chicago, Illinois, 1919. 2000. (Dear America Ser.). (Illus.). 224p. (J). (gr. 4-9). pap. 10.95 (978-0-590-51159-9(9)) Scholastic, Inc.

Mead, Alice. Girl of Kosovo. 2001. 128p. (J). (gr. 4-7). 16.00 (978-0-374-32620-3(7) , Farrar, Straus & Giroux (BYR)) Farrar, Straus & Giroux.

—Girl of Kosovo. 2003. (Illus.). 128p. (J). (gr. 5). pap. 5.50 (978-0-440-41853-5(4) , Yearling) Random Hse. Children's Bks.

—Girl of Kosovo. 2003. (gr. 3-6). lib. bdg. 13.00 (978-0-613-62205-9(7)) Tandem Library Bks.

Medearis, Michael & Medearis, Angela Shelf. Daisy & the Doll. Johnson, Larry, illus. 2000. (Family Heritage Ser.). 32p. (J). (gr. 1-5). 14.95 (978-0-916718-15-2(8)) Vermont Folklife Ctr.

Miklowitz, Gloria. Secrets in the House of Delgado. 2001. (gr. 5-8). lib. bdg. 15.30 (978-0-613-55662-0(3)) Tandem Library Bks.

Miklowitz, Gloria D. Camouflage. 1998. 166p. (YA). (gr. 7-12). 16.00 (978-0-15-201467-4(5)) Harcourt Trade Pubs.

—Secrets in the House of Delgado. 2004. 192p. (J). (gr. 4 up). pap. 8.00 (978-0-8028-5210-6(6)) Eerdmans, William B. Publishing Co.

Miller, William. Joe Louis, My Champion. Pate, Rodney, tr. Pate, Rodney, illus. 2004. 32p. (J). 16.95 (978-1-58430-161-5(9)) Lee & Low Bks., Inc.

—Night Golf. Lucas, Cedric, illus. 32p. 2002. (YA). pap. 6.95 (978-1-58430-056-4(6)); 1999. (J). (gr. 1-4). 15.95 (978-1-880000-79-3(2)) Lee & Low Bks., Inc.

Mindgue, Frank. Little Horse. Cripe, B. Lee, illus. 1999. 80p. (YA). (gr. 3-12). pap. 9.95 (978-0-932991-59-1(9) , Different Bks.) Place In The Woods, The.

Mochizuki, Ken. Baseball Saved Us. Lee, Dom, illus. (Picture Book Readalong Ser.). 28.95 incl. audio compact disk (978-1-59112-916-5(8)); pap. 39.95 incl. audio compact disk (978-1-59112-917-2(6)) Live Oak Media.

—Baseball Saved Us. 2005. (Picture Book Readalong Ser.). (Illus.). (J). pap. 18.95 incl. audio compact disk (978-1-59112-915-8(X)); pap. 16.95 incl. audio (978-1-59112-455-9(7)) Live Oak Media.

—Baseball Saved Us. Lee, Dom, illus. 2004. (Picture Book Readalong Ser.). (J). (ps-ps). audio 25.95 (978-1-59112-456-6(5)) Live Oak Media.

Moore, Stephanie Perry. True Friends. 2005. (Carmen Browne Ser.). 128p. (YA). pap. 5.99 (978-0-8024-8172-6(8)) Moody Pubs.

Myers, Walter Dean. The Journal of Biddy Owens: The Negro Leagues, Birmingham, Alabama 1948. 2001. (978-0-606-22807-7(1)) Tandem Library Bks.

—Slam! 1998. (Point Signature Ser.). 272p. (YA). (gr. 7-12). 5.99 (978-0-590-48668-2(3) , Scholastic Paperbacks) Scholastic, Inc.

Myers, Walter Dean & Myers, Walter Dean. Slam! 1998. 266p. (YA). (gr. 7-12). lib. bdg. 14.15 (978-0-613-12111-8(2)) Tandem Library Bks.

Namioka, Lensey. An Ocean Apart, a World Away. 2003. (gr. 7-12). lib. bdg. 13.55 (978-0-613-72264-3(7)) Tandem Library Bks.

Nash, Alissa. Markita. 2003. (Illus.). 35p. (J). (gr. k-3). pap. 7.95 (978-0-913543-39-9(X)) African American Images.

Naylor, Phyllis Reynolds. Alice on the Outside. (Alice Ser.). 176p. (gr. 5-9). 2000. (YA). mass mkt. 5.99 (978-0-689-80594-3(2) , Simon Pulse); 1999. (J). 16.00 (978-0-689-80359-8(1) , Atheneum) Simon & Schuster Children's Publishing.

—Alice on the Outside. 2000. (Alice Ser.). (YA). (gr. 5-9). 11.64 (978-0-606-19706-9(0)); (gr. 7-12). lib. bdg. 13.00 (978-0-613-29866-7(7)) Tandem Library Bks.

—Saving Shiloh. 144p. (J). 1999. (Shiloh Ser.: No. 3). (gr. 4-7). reprint ed. pap. 5.99 (978-0-689-81461-7(5)); 2nd ed. 2006. (Illus.). (gr. 3-7). pap. 5.99 (978-1-4169-1422-8(6)) Simon & Schuster Children's Publishing. (Aladdin).

—Saving Shiloh. 1999. (978-0-606-14310-3(6)); (Shiloh Ser.: No. 3). (J). (gr. 3-6). lib. bdg. 13.55 (978-0-613-12073-9(6)) Tandem Library Bks.

—Saving Shiloh. l.t. ed. 2002. 193p. (J). 22.95 (978-0-7862-3713-5(9)) Thorndike Pr.

—Walker's Crossing. 2001. 240p. (J). (gr. 5-9). pap. 4.99 (978-0-689-84261-0(9) , Aladdin) Simon & Schuster Children's Publishing.

Neale, Cynthia. Hope in New York City: The Continuing Story of the Irish Dresser. 2007. (ENG.). 176p. (J). pap. 7.95 (***978-1-57249-387-2(9)** , White Mane Kids) White Mane Publishing Co., Inc.

Nelson, Vaunda Micheaux. Mayfield Crossing. 2002. (gr. 3-6). lib. bdg. 14.15 (978-0-613-43634-2(2)) Tandem Library Bks.

Olivas, Daniel. Benjamin & Word Benjamin Y la Palabra. (SPA & ENG., Illus.). 32p. 15.95 (978-1-55885-413-0(4) , Piñata Books) Arte Publico Pr.

Olsen, Sylvia. White Girl. 2005. (Illus.). 200p. (J). pap. 8.95 (978-1-55039-147-3(X)) Sono Nis Pr. CAN. *Dist:* Orca Bk. Pubs. USA.

Otey Little, Mimi. Yoshiko & the Foreigner. Otey Little, Mimi, illus. 2004. (Illus.). 31p. (J). (gr. 4-8). reprint ed. 16.00 (978-0-7567-7510-0(8)) DIANE Publishing Co.

Park, Linda Sue. Project Mulberry. 2005. 240p. (J). (gr. 5-9). 16.00 (978-0-618-47786-9(1) , Clarion Bks.) Houghton Mifflin Co. Trade & Reference Div.

—Project Mulberry. 2007. 240p. (J). (gr. 4-7). pap. 6.50 (978-0-440-42163-4(2) , Yearling) Random Hse. Children's Bks.

Parker, Robert Andrew. Edenville Owls. 2008. 208p. (YA). (gr. 4-6). pap. 7.99 (***978-0-14-241161-2(2)** , Puffin) Penguin Group (USA) Inc.

Perez, L. King. Remember As You Pass Me By. 2007. 224p. (J). (gr. 4-8). 16.95 (***978-1-57131-677-6(9))** Milkweed Editions.

—Remember as You Pass Me By. 2007. 184p. (J). (gr. 2-7). per. 6.95 (***978-1-57131-678-3(7))** Milkweed Editions.

Peters, Julie Anne. Between Mom & Jo. 2006. 240p. (J). (gr. 7-17). 16.99 (978-0-316-73906-1(5)) Little Brown & Co.

Pinkwater, Daniel M. Go West. Rash, Andy, illus. 2002. (Fat Camp Commandos Ser.). 96p. (J). (gr. 3-8). pap. 14.95 (978-0-439-29772-1(9) , Scholastic Pr.) Scholastic, Inc.

—Go West. 2003. (gr. 3-6). lib. bdg. 12.40 (978-0-613-62511-1(0)) Tandem Library Bks.

Plum-Ucci, Carol. What Happened to Lani Garver. (YA). 2002. 328p. (gr. 9 up). 17.00 (978-0-15-216813-1(3)); 2004. 336p. reprint ed. pap. 6.95 (978-0-15-205088-7(4) , Harcourt Paperbacks) Harcourt Children's Bks.

Polacco, Patricia. Mr. Lincoln's Way. Polacco, Patricia, illus. 2001. (Illus.). 40p. (J). (gr. 1-4). 16.99 (978-0-399-23754-6(2) , Philomel) Penguin Group (USA) Inc.

Porter, James G. Edge of the Rainforest. (Illus.). 180p. pap. 11.95 (978-0-7022-2350-1(6)) Univ. of Queensland Pr. AUS. *Dist:* International Specialized Bk. Services.

Puttock, Simon. Big Bad Wolf Is Good. Chapman, Lynne, illus. 2002. 32p. (J). (ps-2). 12.95 (978-0-8069-0027-8(X)) Sterling Publishing Co., Inc.

Rappaport, Doreen. The Year of the Paper Menorahs. Alcorn, Stephen, illus. 2000. 32p. (J). 15.99 (978-0-7868-0400-9(9)) Hyperion Bks. for Children.

Reece, Colleen L. Saturday Scare. l.t. ed. 2002. (Juli Scott, Super Sleuth Ser.). (Illus.). 211p. (J). 24.95 (978-0-7862-3195-9(5)) Thomson Gale.

Reed, Vernon. Children of the Hollow. 2006. (ENG.). 188p. per. 19.95 (***978-1-4241-3668-1(7))** PublishAmerica, Inc.

Reynolds, Marilyn. Love Rules. (True-to-Life Series from Hamilton High). 224p. (J). (gr. 8 up). 2003. 18.95 (978-1-885356-75-8(7)); 2001. pap. 9.95 (978-1-885356-76-5(5)) Morning Glory Pr., Inc.

Richardson, Faith. The Peacock's Stone. 2003. 192p. (J). 21.95 (978-0-9744989-0-4(4)); (Illus.). pap. 12.95 (978-0-9744989-1-1(2)) Fox Song Bks.

Riefe, Barbara. Amelia Dale Archer Story. 1998. 304p. (YA). (gr. 8 up). 22.95 (978-0-312-86077-6(3) , Forge Bks.) Doherty, Tom Assocs., LLC.

Rinaldi, Ann. The Education of Mary: A Little Miss of Color, 1832. 2000. 256p. (gr. 5-9). 15.99 (978-0-7868-0532-7(3) , Jump at the Sun) Hyperion Bks. for Children.

—The Education of Mary: A Little Miss of Color, 1832. 2005. 176p. (J). pap. (978-0-7868-1377-3(6)) Hyperion Pr.

Rosen, Sybil. Speed of Light. 2001. (J). (978-0-606-20923-6(9)) Tandem Library Bks.

Rue, Nancy. Sophie Tracks a Thief, Vol. 8. 2005. (Faithgirlz Ser.). (Illus.). 144p. (J). pap. 6.99 (978-0-310-71023-3(5)) Zonderkidz.

Rue, Nancy N. The Mirage. 2001. (Christian Heritage Ser.). (Illus.). 192p. (J). (gr. 3-7). pap. 5.99 (978-1-56179-863-6(0)) Bethany Hse. Pubs.

—The Stand. 2001. (Christian Heritage Ser.). 192p. (J). (gr. 3-8). pap. (978-1-56179-893-3(2)) Focus on the Family Publishing.

—The Stunt. 1999. (Christian Heritage Ser.). 208p. (J). (gr. 3-7). pap. 5.99 (978-1-56179-833-9(9)) Bethany Hse. Pubs.

Russ, Tim. Bugsters! 2008. (Illus.). 32p. (J). (***978-0-9795131-7-6(0))** Woods N' Water, Inc.

Schraff, Anne. Darkness. 2000. 119p. (J). pap. (978-0-7891-5183-4(9)); (gr. 5-12). lib. bdg. 13.95 (978-0-7807-9367-5(6)) Perfection Learning Corp.

—Freedom Knows No Color. 2000. 118p. (J). pap. (978-0-7891-5136-0(7)); (gr. 5-12). lib. bdg. 13.95 (978-0-7807-9270-8(X)) Perfection Learning Corp.

—The Hyena Laughs at Night. 1999. 111p. (J). pap. (978-0-7891-4925-1(7)); (gr. 5-12). lib. bdg. 13.95 (978-0-7807-8006-4(X)) Perfection Learning Corp.

—Strawberry Autumn. 1999. (Passages Ser.). (Illus.). 135p. (J). (gr. 5-12). lib. bdg. 13.95 (978-0-7807-8985-2(7)) Perfection Learning Corp.

Scoppettone, Sandra. Happy Endings Are All Alike. 2004. (Alyson Classics Library). 208p. (gr. 8-12). reprint ed. pap. 10.00 (978-1-55583-511-8(2)) Alyson Pubns.

Shyer, Marlene Fanta. The Rainbow Kite. 2002. 208p. (YA). (gr. 7-10). 15.95 (978-0-7614-5122-8(6)) Cavendish, Marshall Corp.

Speck, Nancy. Secret of the Hidden Room. Thomas, Jerry D., ed. Ford, Mark, illus. 1999. (Shoebox Kids Ser.: Vol. 9). 93p. (J). pap. 6.99 (978-0-8163-1682-3(1)) Pacific Pr. Publishing Assn.

Spiegler, Louise. The Amethyst Road. 2005. 336p. (YA). (gr. 7-12). 16.00 (978-0-618-48572-7(4) , Clarion Bks.) Houghton Mifflin Co. Trade & Reference Div.

Staples, Suzanne Fisher. Dangerous Skies. 1998. 12.64 (978-0-606-13312-8(7)) Tandem Library Bks.

Stapleton, E. J. The Calico Buffalo. 2001. 76p. (J). per. 15.95 (978-0-9710283-0-2(3)) BOSC Publishing Co., Inc.

Steele, William O. The Perilous Road. 2004. 156p. (J). (gr. 4-7). per. 13.00 (978-0-606-31268-4(4)) Tandem Library Bks.

Sullivan, Jaqueline Levering. Annie's War. 2007. 190p. (J). (gr. 3-7). 15.00 (***978-0-8028-5325-7(0)** , Eerdmans Bks For Young Readers) Eerdmans, William B. Publishing Co.

Summer of My German Soldier. 1999. (YA). 9.95 (978-1-56137-113-6(0)) Novel Units, Inc.

Swope, Sam. The Araboolies of Liberty Street. Root, Barry, illus. 2001. (Sunburst Bks.). 32p. (J). (ps up). reprint ed. pap. 6.95 (978-0-374-30390-7(8) , Sunburst) Farrar, Straus & Giroux.

—The Araboolies of Liberty Street. 2001. (gr. 3-6). lib. bdg. 14.10 (978-0-613-49713-8(9)) Tandem Library Bks.

Taylor, Bonnie Highsmith. Gypsy in the Cellar. Marks, Dea, illus. 1999. (Cover-to-Cover Bks.). 99p. (J). (gr. 4-6). pap. 5.60 (978-0-7891-5112-4(X)) Perfection Learning Corp.

Taylor, Marilyn. Faraway Home. 2003. 224p. (J). (gr. 5 up). pap. 7.95 (978-0-86278-643-4(6)) O'Brien Pr., Ltd., The IRL. *Dist:* Independent Pubs. Group.

Taylor, Mildred D. The Friendship. Ginsberg, Max, illus. 1998. 56p. (gr. 2-6). pap. 4.99 (978-0-14-038964-7(4) , Puffin) Penguin Group (USA) Inc.

—The Friendship. 1998. 11.79 (978-0-606-12938-1(3)) Tandem Library Bks.

—The Gold Cadillac. Hays, Michael & Ginsberg, Max, illus. 1998. 48p. (YA). (gr. 2-6). pap. 4.99 (978-0-14-038963-0(6) , Puffin) Penguin Group (USA) Inc.

—The Gold Cadillac. 1998. 11.79 (978-0-606-13433-0(6)) Tandem Library Bks.

—The Land. 2003. 400p. (YA). pap. 6.99 (978-0-14-250146-7(8) , Puffin) Penguin Group (USA) Inc.

—The Land. Ginsburg, Max, illus. 2001. 392p. (J). (gr. 7 up). 17.99 (978-0-8037-1950-7(7) , Dial) Penguin Group (USA) Inc.

—Mississippi Bridge. 2002. (J). 12.87 (978-0-7587-9586-1(6)) Book Wholesalers, Inc.

—Mississippi Bridge. Ginsburg, Max, illus. 2000. 64p. (J). (gr. 4-7). pap. 4.99 (978-0-14-130817-3(6) , Puffin) Penguin Group (USA) Inc.

—Mississippi Bridge. 2002. (J). (gr. 2-6). 21.00 (978-0-8446-7213-7(0)) Smith, Peter Pub., Inc.

—Mississippi Bridge. Ginsburg, Max, illus. 2000. 62p. (J). (ps-7). lib. bdg. 13.00 (978-0-8335-9262-0(9)) Tandem Library Bks.

—Mississippi Bridge. 2000. (978-0-606-18434-2(1)) Tandem Library Bks.

—Roll of Thunder, Hear My Cry. 2004. 276p. (gr. 4-8). reprint ed. pap. 10.00 (978-0-7567-7955-9(3)) DIANE Publishing Co.

—Roll of Thunder, Hear My Cry. l.t. ed. 2000. (LRS Large Print Cornerstone Ser.). 348p. (YA). (gr. 5-12). lib. bdg. 32.95 (978-1-58118-057-2(8) , 23471) LRS.

—Roll of Thunder, Hear My Cry. 1999. (Masterpiece Series Access Editions). xvii, 205p. (J). pap. 10.95 (978-0-8219-1985-9(7) , 35335) Paradigm Publishing, Inc.

—Roll of Thunder, Hear My Cry. Pinkney, Jerry, illus. 25th anniv. ed. 2001. 296p. (J). (gr. 5 up). 17.99 (978-0-8037-2647-5(3) , Dial) Penguin Group (USA) Inc.

—Roll of Thunder, Hear My Cry. 1999. 60p. (J). (gr. 6-8). stu. ed., ring bd. 12.99 (978-1-58609-152-1(2)) Progeny Pr.

—Roll of Thunder, Hear My Cry. 1998. (J). (gr. 5). pap. 3.95 (978-0-439-04476-9(6)) Scholastic, Inc.

—The Well: David's Story. 1998. 96p. (J). (gr. 4-7). pap. 5.99 (978-0-14-038642-4(4) , Puffin) Penguin Group (USA) Inc.

Taylor, Theodore. The Cay. 2000. 171p. (J). 15.60 (978-0-03-054604-4(9)) Holt, Rinehart & Winston.

—The Cay. 2003. 144p. (J). (gr. 5). mass mkt. 5.99 (978-0-440-22912-4(X) , Laurel Leaf) Random Hse. Children's Bks.

—Cay. 2003. (gr. 5-8). lib. bdg. 13.55 (978-0-613-72282-7(5)); 2002. (gr. 3-6). lib. bdg. 13.55 (978-0-613-33748-9(4)) Tandem Library Bks.

Townsend, John Rowe. The Islanders. 2006. (J). pap. 9.95 (978-1-932425-69-7(1) , Lemniscaat) Boyds Mills Pr.

Tullos, Matt. Deleting the Net Threat. 1999. (Summit High Ser.: No. 4). 144p. (J). (gr. 7-9). pap. 4.99 (978-0-8054-1766-1(4)) B&H Publishing Grp.

Tuttle, Todd. Spot. Tuttle, Todd, illus. 2007. (Illus.). 20p. (J). 19.95 (***978-1-889829-16-6(1))** Window Bks.

Uchida, Yoshiko. A Jar of Dreams. 1998. (J). pap. 3.95 (978-0-87628-469-8(1)) Ctr. for Applied Research in Education, The.

—Samurai of Gold Hill. Forberg, Ati, illus. 2005. 119p. (J). (gr. 2). pap. 8.95 (978-1-59714-015-7(5)) Heyday Bks.

Uddin, Asma Mobin. My Name Is Bilal. Kiwak, Barbara, illus. 2005. 32p. (J). (ps-17). 15.95 (978-1-59078-175-3(9)) Boyds Mills Pr.

Ulick, Michael Ackerman. Romeo the Rhino's Rocky Romance: A Cautionary Tale about Differences. Guy, Will, illus. 32p. (J). 15.95 (978-0-9679813-0-7(1)) Footprints Pr.

Urban, Betsy. Waiting for Deliverance. 2000. (Illus.). iv, 186p. (J). (gr. 7-12). pap. 17.95 (978-0-531-30310-8(1) , Orchard Bks.) Scholastic, Inc.

Vaught, Susan. Big Fat Manifesto. 2007. 320p. (YA). 16.95 (***978-1-59990-206-7(0)** , Bloomsbury Children) Bloomsbury Publishing.

Velasquez, Gloria. Ankiza. 2000. (Roosevelt High School Ser.). 152p. (J). (gr. 2 up). pap. 9.95 (978-1-55885-309-6(X)); (gr. 8-12). pap. 16.95 (978-1-55885-308-9(1)) Arte Publico Pr. (Piñata Books).

—Ankiza. 2000. (gr. 7-12). lib. bdg. 18.75 (978-0-613-59377-9(4)) Tandem Library Bks.

Velthuijs, Max. Frog & the Stranger. ed. 2006. (Illus.). 32p. (J). 8.99 (***978-1-84270-466-0(4))** Andersen GBR. *Dist:* Independent Pubs. Group.

—Frog & the Stranger. Iqbal, Gulshan, tr. 2005. (Frog Ser.). (URD, ENG, VIE, CHI & BEN., Illus.). 32p. (J). 13.50 (978-1-84059-190-3(0)) Milet Publishing.

—Frog & the Stranger. 2000. (Frog Ser.). (Illus.). 32p. (J). (BEN, ENG, VIE, CHI & URD.). 13.50 (978-1-84059-187-3(0)); (VIE, ENG, CHI, BEN & URD., 13.50 (978-1-84059-191-0(9)); (ALB & ENG., 13.50 (978-1-84059-186-6(2)); (VIE, CHI, BEN, ENG & URD., 13.50 (978-1-84059-189-7(7)) Milet Publishing.

Venkatraman, Padma. Climbing the Stairs. 2008. 256p. (YA). (gr. 7). 15.99 (***978-0-399-24746-0(7)** , Putnam Juvenile) Penguin Group (USA) Inc.

Watts, Irene. Remember Me: A Search for Refuge in Wartime Britain. 2000. (gr. 5-8). lib. bdg. 16.40 (978-0-613-45685-2(8)) Tandem Library Bks.

Watts, Irene N. Remember Me: A Search for Refuge in Wartime Britain. 2000. 192p. (J). (gr. 5 up). pap. 7.95 (978-0-88776-519-3(X)) Tundra Bks., Inc./Livres Toundra, Inc. CAN. *Dist:* Random Hse., Inc.

Waybill, Marjorie. Chinese Eyes. 2002. 32p. pap. 15.99 (978-0-8361-9228-5(1)) Herald Pr.

Weathers, Anah D. Secrets of the Cave. Weathers, Luther, illus. Weathers, Luther, photos by. unabr. ed. 2000. (Treasures from the Past Ser.). x, 104p. (J). (gr. 4-8). pap. 7.98 (978-0-9702584-0-3(2)) Creative Services.

Whelan, Gloria. Miranda's Last Stand. 144p. (J). (gr. 3-7). 2000. pap. 4.95 (978-0-06-442097-6(3) , Harper Trophy); 1999. (Illus.). 14.89 (978-0-06-028252-3(5)) HarperCollins Pubs.

—Miranda's Last Stand. 2000. (J). (978-0-606-19267-5(0)); (978-0-606-19988-9(8)) Tandem Library Bks.

Wildsmith, Brian. The Little Wood Duck. Wildsmith, Brian, illus. 2006. (Illus.). 32p. (J). 16.95 (978-1-59572-042-9(1)); pap. 6.95 (978-1-59572-049-8(9)) Star Bright Bks., Inc.

Wilson, Karma. Sweet Briar Goes to School. Pham, LeUyen, illus. 2003. 32p. (J). (ps). 16.99 (978-0-8037-2767-0(4) , Dial) Penguin Group (USA) Inc.

Wolff, Virginia Euwer. Probably Still Nick Swansen. Katz, illus. 2003. 160p. mass mkt. 10.00 (978-0-689-85227-5(4) , Simon Pulse) Simon & Schuster Children's Publishing.

Woodson, Jacqueline. Feathers. 2007. 128p. (J). (gr. 3-7). 15.99 (978-0-399-23989-2(8) , Putnam Juvenile) Penguin Group (USA) Inc.

Wright, Sue. Davey & Goliath Blind Mans Bluff. 2005. (Davey & Goliath Storybook #2 Ser.). (Illus.). 40p. (J). 3.99 (978-0-439-69832-0(4) , Scholastic Paperbacks) Scholastic, Inc.

Wyeth, Sharon Dennis. The World of Daughter McGuire. 2001. 176p. (gr. 3-7). pap. 12.00 (978-0-375-89502-9(7) , Delacorte Bks. for Young Readers) Random Hse. Children's Bks.

Yep, Laurence. The Traitor: Golden Mountain Chronicles: 1885. (Golden Mountain Chronicles). 320p. (J). (gr. 5 up). 2004. pap. 6.99 (978-0-06-000831-4(8) , Harper Trophy); 2003. 17.99 (978-0-06-027522-8(7)) HarperCollins Pubs.

Yezerski, Thomas F. Together in Pinecone Patch. Date not set. (J). pap. (978-0-374-47579-6(2) , Farrar, Straus & Giroux (BYR)) Farrar, Straus & Giroux.

—Together in Pinecone Patch. Yezerski, Thomas F., illus. 1998. (Illus.). 32p. (J). (gr. k-3). 16.00 (978-0-374-37647-5(6) , Farrar, Straus & Giroux (BYR)) Farrar, Straus & Giroux.

PRESCHOOL EDUCATION

see Nursery Schools

PRESENTS

see Gifts

PRESERVATION OF FOOD

see Food—Preservation

PRESERVATION OF FORESTS

see Forests and Forestry

PRESERVATION OF NATURAL RESOURCES

see Conservation of Natural Resources

PRESERVATION OF NATURAL SCENERY

see Natural Monuments

PRESERVATION OF WILDLIFE

see Wildlife Conservation

PRESERVING

see Canning and Preserving

PRESIDENTS

Abrams, Dennis. Thabo Mbeki. 2007. (Modern World Leaders Ser.). 128p. (J). (gr. 6-12). 30.00 (***978-0-7910-9443-3(X)** , Chelsea Hse.) Facts On File, Inc.

—Viktor Yushchenko. 2007. (Modern World Leaders Ser.). 120p. (J). (gr. 6-12). 30.00 (***978-0-7910-9266-8(6)** , Chelsea Hse.) Facts On File, Inc.

Abrams, Dennis & Jr. Hamid Karzai. 2nd rev. ed. 2007. (Modern World Leaders Ser.). 128p. (gr. 6-12). 30.00 (***978-0-7910-9267-5(4)** , Chelsea Hse.) Facts On File, Inc.

Adi, Hakim. Nelson Mandela: Father of Freedom. 2001. (Famous Lives Ser.). (Illus.). 48p. (J). (gr. 3-7). lib. bdg. 27.12 (978-0-8172-5716-3(0)) Raintree.

Adler, David A. A Picture Book of Abraham Lincoln. Wallner, John & Wallner, Alexandra, illus. 2004. (J). (ps-3). audio compact disk 18.95 (978-1-59112-777-2(7)) Live Oak Media.

—A Picture Book of George Washington. Wallner, John & Wallner, Alexandra, illus. 32p. (J). (gr. k-3). pap. 6.95 (978-0-8234-0800-9(0)) Holiday Hse., Inc.

—A Picture Book of George Washington. Wallner, John & Wallner, Alexandra, illus. 2004. (J). (ps-3). audio compact disk 18.95 (978-1-59112-765-9(3)) Live Oak Media.

Allen, John. Idi Amin. 2003. (History's Villains Ser.). (Illus.). 112p. (J). 28.70 (978-1-56711-759-2(7) , Blackbirch Pr., Inc.) Thomson Gale.

Allport, Alan. Jacques Chirac. 2007. (Modern World Leaders Ser.). 112p. (J). (gr. 6-12). 30.00 (***978-0-7910-9265-1(8)** , Chelsea Hse.) Facts On File, Inc.

Anderson, Dale. Saddam Hussein. 2004. (A&E Biography Ser.). (Illus.). 112p. (J). 29.27 (978-0-8225-5005-1(9) , Lerner Pubns.) Lerner Publishing Group.

Andy Koopmans. Nelson Mandela. 2004. (Heroes & Villains Ser.). (Illus.). 112p. (J). 29.95 (978-1-59018-426-4(2)) Thomson Gale.

Barter, James. Idi Amin. 2004. (Heroes & Villains Ser.). (Illus.). 112p. (J). (gr. 7-10). 29.95 (978-1-59018-553-7(6) , Lucent Bks.) Thomson Gale.

Beecroft, Simon. The Release of Nelson Mandela. 2004. (Days That Changed the World Ser.). (Illus.). 48p. (J). (gr. 5 up). pap. 11.95 (978-0-8368-5578-4(7)); lib. bdg. 30.00 (978-0-8368-5571-5(X)) Stevens, Gareth Inc. (World Almanac Library).

Boothroyd, Jennifer. Nelson Mandela: A Life of Persistence. 2007. (Pull Ahead Books). (Illus.). 32p. (J). 22.60 (978-0-8225-6385-3(1) , Lerner Pubns.) Lerner Publishing Group.

Collin, Grace. Man of Destiny: The Life of Leopold Sedar Senghor. Bostic, Alex, illus. 2006. 32p. (J). lib. bdg. 16.95 (978-1-886366-15-2(2)) Sights Productions.

Connolly, Sean. Nelson Mandela: An Unauthorized Biography. 2000. (Profiles Ser.). (Illus.). 56p. (J). (gr. 4-6). lib. bdg. 24.22 (978-1-57572-225-2(9)) Heinemann Library.

Cooper, Floyd. Mandela: From the Life of the South African Statesman. Cooper, Floyd, illus. 2000. (Illus.). 40p. (J). (gr. k-5). pap. 6.99 (978-0-698-11816-4(2) , Putnam Juvenile) Penguin Group (USA) Inc.

—Mandela: From the Life of the South African Statesman. 2000. (978-0-606-18430-4(9)); lib. bdg. 15.30 (978-0-613-23016-2(7)) Tandem Library Bks.

Cox, Vicki. Hosni Mubarak. 2002. (Major World Leaders Ser.). (Illus.). 112p. (gr. 6-12). 30.00 (978-0-7910-6942-4(7) , Chelsea Hse.) Facts On File, Inc.

Cox, Vicki. Oscar Arias Sanchez: Bringing Peace to Central America. 2007. (Modern Peacemakers Ser.). (Illus.). 128p. (YA). (gr. 9 up). 30.00 (***978-0-7910-8999-6(1)*** , Chelsea Hse.) Facts On File, Inc.

Darraj, Susan Muaddi. Bashar Al-Assad: President of Syria. Schlesinger, Arthur M., Jr., ed. 2005. (Major World Leaders Ser.). (Illus.). 112-144p. (J). (gr. 6-12). 30.00 (978-0-7910-8262-1(8) , Chelsea Hse.) Facts On File, Inc.

Darraj, Susan Muaddi. Hosni Mubarak. 2007. (Modern World Leaders Ser.). 104p. (J). (gr. 6-12). 30.00 (***978-0-7910-9280-4(1)*** , Chelsea Hse.) Facts On File, Inc.

Friedman, Lita. Mary Robinson: Fighter for Human Rights. 2004. (Avisson Young Adult Ser.). (Illus.). 142p. (YA). pap. 19.95 (978-1-888105-65-0(8)) Avisson Pr., Inc.

Gaines, Ann Graham. Vicente Fox: The Road to the Mexican Presidency. 2003. (Proud Heritage-The Hispanic Library). (Illus.). 40p. (J). (gr. 3-7). 28.50 (978-1-56766-177-4(7)) Child's World, Inc.

Giraldo, Paola. Gamal Abdel Nasser -el faraon Rojo. 2005. 112p. pap. (978-958-30-1689-9(6)) Panamericana Editorial.

Gogerly, Liz. Nelson Mandela. 2003. (Leading Lives Ser.). (Illus.). 64p. (J). lib. bdg. 28.50 (978-1-4034-0834-1(3)) Heinemann Library.

Harmon, Daniel E. Pervez Musharraf: President of Pakistan. 2007. (J). (***978-1-4042-1905-2(6)***) Rosen Publishing Group, Inc., The.

Headlam, George. Yasir Arafat. 2004. (A&E Biography Ser.). (Illus.). 112p. (J). 29.27 (978-0-8225-5004-4(0) , Lerner Pubns.) Lerner Publishing Group.

Jones, Gerald Colman. Mary Robinson: Citizen of the World. 2000. (Contemporary Profiles & Policy Series for the Younger Reader). (Illus.). 72p. (J). (gr. 8 up). 24.00 (978-0-934272-63-6(8)); pap. 15.00 (978-0-934272-64-3(6)) Burke, John Gordon Pub., Inc.

Keller, Bill. Tree Shaker: The Story of Nelson Mandela. 2008. (New York Times Ser.). 128p. (J). (gr. 5-9). 17.95 (***978-0-7534-5992-8(2)*** , Kingfisher) Houghton Mifflin Co. Trade & Reference Div.

Koestler-Grack, Rachel A. Kim il Sung & Kim Jong Il. 2003. (Major World Leaders Ser.). (Illus.). 112p. (J). (gr. 6-12). 30.00 (978-0-7910-7648-4(2) , Chelsea Hse.) Facts On File, Inc.

Kraft, Betsy Harvey. Theodore Roosevelt: Champion of the American Spirit. 2003. (Illus.). 192p. (J). (gr. 5-9). tchr. ed. 19.00 (978-0-618-14264-4(9) , Clarion Bks.) Houghton Mifflin Co. Trade & Reference Div.

Kramer, Ann. Mandela: The Rebel Who Led His Nation to Freedom. 2005. (World History Biographies Ser.). (Illus.). 64p. (J). (gr. 3-7). 17.95 (978-0-7922-3658-0(0) , National Geographic Children's Bks.) National Geographic Society.

—Nelson Mandela. 2003. (20th Century History Makers Ser.). (Illus.). 112p. (J). lib. bdg. 32.85 (978-0-7398-5258-3(2)) Raintree.

Kras, Sara Louise. Pervez Musharraf. 2003. (Major World Leaders Ser.). (Illus.). 112p. (gr. 6-12). 30.00 (978-0-7910-7650-7(4) , Chelsea Hse.) Facts On File, Inc.

Kras, Sarah Louise. Anwar Sadat. 2002. (Major World Leaders Ser.). (Illus.). 112p. (gr. 6-12). 30.00 (978-0-7910-6949-3(4) , Chelsea Hse.) Facts On File, Inc.

Landau, Elaine. Warren G. Harding. 2005. (Presidential Leaders Ser.). (Illus.). 120p. (J). 29.27 (978-0-8225-0850-2(8) , Lerner Pubns.) Lerner Publishing Group.

Lange, Brenda. Muammar Qaddafi: President of Libya. Schlesinger, Arthur M., Jr., ed. 2005. (Major World Leaders Ser.). (Illus.). 112-144p. (J). (gr. 6-12). 30.00 (978-0-7910-8258-4(X) , Chelsea Hse.) Facts On File, Inc.

Malam, John. The Release of Nelson Mandela. 2002. (Dates with History Ser.). (Illus.). 31p. (J). lib. bdg. 24.25 (978-1-58340-216-0(0)) Smart Apple Media.

McDonough, Yona Zeldis & Zeldis, Malcah. Peaceful Protest. 2006. (Illus.). 40p. (J). pap. 8.95 (978-0-8027-8948-8(X)) Walker & Co.

Ochester, Betsy. Encyclopedia of Presidents, Second Series, 12 Bks., Set. 2005. (J). 33.00 (978-0-516-25201-8(1)) Scholastic Library Publishing.

O'Hern, Kerri & Holland, Gini. Nelson Mandela. 2006. (Illus.). (J). pap. 8.95 (978-0-8368-6249-2(X)); 32p. lib. bdg. 26.00 (978-0-8368-6197-6(3)) Stevens, Gareth Inc. (World Almanac Library).

O'Hern, Kerri, et al. Nelson Mandela. 2006. (ENG & SPA.). (J). pap. (***978-0-8368-7888-2(4)***); lib. bdg. (***978-0-8368-7881-3(7)***) Stevens, Gareth Inc. (World Almanac Library).

Orr, Tamra. Ronald Reagan: Portrait of an American Hero. 2003. (Illus.). 96p. (978-0-7853-9734-2(5) , 3126701) Publications International, Ltd.

Play Bac Edu-Team, ed. Presidents: From Independence to Now. 2007. (Illus.). 10p. (Orig.). (J). 6.95 (***978-1-60214-006-6(5)***) Play Bac Publishing, USA.

Rausch, Monica. Thomas Jefferson. 2006. (Illus.). 24p. (J). pap. (***978-0-8368-7691-8(1)***); lib. bdg. (***978-0-8368-7684-0(9)***) Stevens, Gareth Inc. (Weekly Reader Early Learning Library).

Rosenberg, Aaron. Vladimir Putin: President of Russia. 2007. (J). (***978-1-4042-1903-8(X)***) Rosen Publishing Group, Inc., The.

Schlesinger, Arthur M., Jr., ed. Kim Dae-Jung: South Korean President. 1999. (World Leaders Past & Present Ser.). (Illus.). 128p. (YA). (gr. 5-9). lib. bdg. 21.95 (978-0-7910-5215-0(X) , Chelsea Hse.) Facts On File, Inc.

Seuling, Barbara. Three Presidents Died on the Fourth of July: And Other Freaky Facts about the First 25 Presidents. Skeens, Matthew, illus. 2007. (J). lib. bdg. (***978-1-4048-3748-5(5)***) Picture Window Bks.

Shields, Charles J. Saddam Hussein. (Major World Leaders Ser.). (Illus.). (gr. 6-12). 2003. 144p. 30.00 (978-0-7910-6943-1(5)); 2003. 144p. pap. 30.00 (978-0-7910-7526-5(5)); 2nd ed. 2005. 162p. (J). pap. 30.00 (978-0-7910-8572-1(4)) Facts On File, Inc. (Chelsea Hse.).

—Saddam Hussein. 2003. (gr. 5-8). lib. bdg. 18.75 (978-0-613-81041-8(4)) Tandem Library Bks.

—Vladimir Putin. (Major World Leaders Ser.). (Illus.). (gr. 6-12). 2003. 144p. pap. 30.00 (978-0-7910-7525-8(7)); 2002. 112p. 30.00 (978-0-7910-6945-5(1)); 2nd rev. ed. 2006. 120p. (J). 30.00 (978-0-7910-9215-6(1)) Facts On File, Inc. (Chelsea Hse.).

—Vladimir Putin. 2003. (gr. 5-8). lib. bdg. 18.75 (978-0-613-86155-7(8)) Tandem Library Bks.

Shields, Charles J. & Koestler-Grack, Rachel A. Saddam Hussein. 2nd ed. 2005. (Major World Leaders Ser.). (Illus.). 112p. (J). 30.00 (978-0-7910-8576-9(7) , Chelsea Hse.) Facts On File, Inc.

Shone, Rob. Nelson Mandela: The Life of an African Statesman. Reed, Neil, illus. 2006. 48p. (J). (978-1-4042-0922-0(0)); pap. (978-1-4042-0923-7(9)) Rosen Publishing Group, Inc., The.

—Nelson Mandela: The Life of an African Statesman. 2006. (Graphic Biographies Ser.). (Illus.). 48p. (J). lib. bdg. 29.95 (978-1-4042-0860-5(7)) Rosen Publishing Group, Inc., The.

Stamper, G. C. Nelson Mandela. 2005. (Illus.). 32p. (J). pap. (***978-0-7367-2922-2(4)***) Zaner-Bloser, Inc.

Steele, Philip. Ho Chi Minh. 2003. (Leading Lives Ser.). (Illus.). 64p. (J). lib. bdg. 28.50 (978-1-4034-0836-5(X)) Heinemann Library.

Stewart, Gail B. Saddam Hussein. 2003. (Heroes & Villains Ser.). (Illus.). 96p. (J). 29.95 (978-1-59018-350-2(9) , Lucent Bks.) Thomson Gale.

Thomson, Sarah L. What Presidents Are Made Of. Piven, Hanoch, illus. 2004. 40p. (J). 17.99 (978-0-689-86880-1(4) , Atheneum) Simon & Schuster Children's Publishing.

Todd, Anne M. Hamid Karzai. 2003. (Major World Leaders Ser.). (Illus.). 112p. (J). (gr. 6-12). 30.00 (978-0-7910-7649-1(0) , Chelsea Hse.) Facts On File, Inc.

Venezia, Mike. Harry S. Truman. Venezia, Mike, illus. 2007. (Getting to Know the U. S. Presidents Ser.). (Illus.). 32p. (J). (gr. 3-4). 27.00 (978-0-516-22637-8(1) , Children's Pr.) Scholastic Library Publishing.

—John F. Kennedy. Venezia, Mike, illus. 2007. (Getting to Know the U. S. Presidents Ser.). (Illus.). 32p. (J). (gr. 3-4). 27.00 (978-0-516-22639-2(8) , Children's Pr.) Scholastic Library Publishing.

—Lyndon B. Johnson. Venezia, Mike, illus. 2007. (Getting to Know the U. S. Presidents Ser.). (Illus.). 32p. (J). (gr. 3-4). 27.00 (978-0-516-22640-8(1) , Children's Pr.) Scholastic Library Publishing.

—Richard M. Nixon. Venezia, Mike, illus. 2007. (Getting to Know the U. S. Presidents Ser.). (Illus.). 32p. (J). (gr. 3-4). 27.00 (978-0-516-22641-5(X) , Children's Pr.) Scholastic Library Publishing.

Wheeler, Jill C. Mary Robinson. 2004. (Women of the World Ser.). (J). (978-1-59197-617-2(0)) ABDO Publishing Co.

—Saddam Hussein. 2004. (War in Iraq Ser.). (Illus.). 48p. (J). (gr. 4-8). lib. bdg. 25.65 (978-1-59197-499-4(2)) ABDO Publishing Co.

Williams, Colleen Madonna Flood. Yasir Arafat. (Major World Leaders Ser.). (Illus.). (gr. 6-12). 2003. 144p. pap. 30.00 (978-0-7910-7186-1(3)); 2002. 112p. 30.00 (978-0-7910-6941-7(9)) Facts On File, Inc. (Chelsea Hse.).

Wolny, Philip. Hamid Karzai: President of Afghanistan. 2007. (J). (***978-1-4042-1902-1(1)***) Rosen Publishing Group, Inc., The.

PRESIDENTS—UNITED STATES

Aaseng, Nathan. The White House. 2001. (Building History Ser.). (Illus.). 96p. (J). (gr. 6-9). 32.45 (978-1-56006-708-5(X) , Lucent Bks.) Thomson Gale.

Abnett, Dan. Abraham Lincoln & the Civil War. 2007. (Jr. Graphic Biographies Ser.). (Illus.). 24p. (J). (978-1-4042-2335-6(5)); pap. (978-1-4042-2145-1(X)); (gr. 2-6). lib. bdg. 21.25 (978-1-4042-3392-8(X)) Rosen Publishing Group, Inc., The. (PowerKids Pr.).

—George Washington & the American Revolution. 2007. (Jr. Graphic Biographies Ser.). (Illus.). 24p. (J). (978-1-4042-2338-7(X)); pap. (978-1-4042-2148-2(4)); (gr. 2-6). lib. bdg. 21.25 (978-1-4042-3395-9(4)) Rosen Publishing Group, Inc., The. (PowerKids Pr.).

Abraham, Philip. How to Draw the Life & Times of George Washington. 2005. (Kid's Guide to Drawing the Presidents of the United States of America Ser.). (J). lib. bdg. 31.95 (978-1-4042-0364-8(8) , PowerKids Pr.) Rosen Publishing Group, Inc., The.

Acker, Kerry. Jimmy Carter. (Major World Leaders Ser.). (Illus.). (gr. 6-12). 2003. 144p. pap. 30.00 (978-0-7910-7523-4(0)); 2002. 112p. 30.00 (978-0-7910-6947-9(8)) Facts On File, Inc. (Chelsea Hse.).

—Jimmy Carter. 2003. (gr. 5-8). lib. bdg. 18.75 (978-0-613-86156-4(6)) Tandem Library Bks.

Adams, Simon. The Presidents. 2004. (Illus.). 96p. (J). (gr. 3-6). pap. 9.95 (978-1-58728-092-4(2) , Two Can Publishing) T&N Children's Publishing.

—Presidents of the United States. rev. ed. 2005. (Illus.). 96p. (J). 9.95 (978-1-58728-528-8(2) , Two Can Publishing) T&N Children's Publishing.

—Presidents of the United States. 2001. (Illus.). (J). (978-0-606-21384-4(8)) Tandem Library Bks.

—The Presidents of the United States: Completely Revised & Updated to Include the 2004 Election. rev. ed. 2005. (Illus.). 96p. (978-1-58728-527-1(4) , Two Can Publishing) T&N Children's Publishing.

Adamsi, Simon. The Presidents. 2004. (Illus.). 96p. (gr. 3-6). 16.95 (978-1-58728-093-1(0) , Two Can Publishing) T&N Children's Publishing.

Adelson, Bruce. Benjamin Harrison. 2007. (Presidential Leaders Ser.). (Illus.). 111p. (J). 29.27 (978-0-8225-1497-8(4) , Lerner Pubns.) Lerner Publishing Group.

Adkins, Jan E. John Adams: Young Revolutionary. 2002. (gr. 3-6). lib. bdg. 13.00 (978-0-613-45074-4(4)) Tandem Library Bks.

Adler, David A. George Washington: An Illustrated Biography. (Illus.). 288p. (J). (gr. 4-6). tchr. ed. 24.95 (978-0-8234-1838-1(3)) Holiday Hse., Inc.

—A Picture Book of Dwight David Eisenhower. 2002. (Illus.). 32p. (J). (gr. k-3). 6.95 (978-0-8234-1830-5(8)); tchr. ed. 16.95 (978-0-8234-1702-5(6)) Holiday Hse., Inc.

—A Picture Book of Thomas Jefferson. Wallner, John, illus. 1999. 28.95 incl. audio compact disk (978-1-59112-770-3(X)); pap. 39.95 incl. audio compact disk (978-1-59112-771-0(8)) Live Oak Media.

—President George Washington. Wallner, John C., illus. 2005. 32p. (J). 14.95 (978-0-8234-1604-2(6)) Holiday Hse., Inc.

Adler, David A. & Adler, Michael S. A Picture Book of John & Abigail Adams. Himler, Ronald, illus. 2007. (J). (978-0-8234-2007-0(8)) Holiday Hse., Inc.

Aldridge, Rebecca. Thomas Jefferson. 2001. (Let Freedom Ring Ser.). (Illus.). 48p. (J). (gr. 3-4). lib. bdg. 22.60 (978-0-7368-1035-7(8) , Bridgestone Bks.) Capstone Pr., Inc.

—The U. S. Government Presidency. 2003. (Let's Investigate Ser.). (Illus.). 32p. (J). lib. bdg. 18.95 (978-1-58341-261-9(1) , Creative Education) Creative Co., The.

Allen, Thomas B. George Washington, Spymaster: How the Americans Outspied the British & Won the Revolutionary War. 2007. (Illus.). 192p. (J). (gr. 5). pap. 5.95 (978-1-4263-0041-7(7) , National Geographic Children's Bks.) National Geographic Society.

Aller, Susan Bivin. Ulysses S. Grant. 2005. (History Maker Bios Ser.). (Illus.). 48p. (J). 26.60 (978-0-8225-2438-0(4) , Lerner Pubns.) Lerner Publishing Group.

Alphin, Elaine Marie & Alphin, Arthur B. Dwight D. Eisenhower. 2005. (History Maker Bios Ser.). (Illus.). 48p. (J). (gr. 3-5). lib. bdg. 26.60 (978-0-8225-1544-9(X)) Lerner Publishing Group.

Alter, Judy. Mirabeau B. Lamar: Second President of Texas. Messersmith, Patrick, illus. 2005. (Stars of Texas Ser.). 72p. (J). (gr. 3-7). 17.95 (978-1-880510-97-1(9)) State Hse. Pr.

American Presidents. 2003. (Middle School Mastery Ser.). 64p. (YA). (gr. 5-8). pap. 3.99 (978-1-56822-458-9(3) , IF2737-E4, Instructional Fair) Schaffer, Frank Pubns.

Anderson, Catherine Corley. John F. Kennedy. 2004. (Presidential Leaders Ser.). (Illus.). 112p. (J). 29.27 (978-0-8225-0812-0(5) , Lerner Pubns.) Lerner Publishing Group.

Anderson, Ken. George Bush: A Lifetime of Service. 2002. (Illus.). v, 150p. (gr. 6-12). 16.95 (978-1-57168-663-3(0)); 12.95 (978-1-57168-600-8(2)) Eakin Pr.

Andryszewski, Tricia. The Reform Party: Ross Perot, Pat Buchanan. 2000. (Headliners Ser.). (Illus.). 64p. (gr. 5-8). lib. bdg. 25.90 (978-0-7613-1906-1(9) , Millbrook Pr.) Lerner Publishing Group.

Ansary, Mir Tamim. El Día de los Presidentes. 2003. (Historias de Fiestas Ser.).Tr. of President's Day. (SPA., 32p. (J). Illus.). lib. bdg. 22.79 (978-1-4034-3006-9(3)); pap. 6.95 (978-1-4034-3029-8(2)) Heinemann Library.

—President's Day. 2002. (Holiday Histories Ser.). (Illus.). 32p. (J). (gr. k-2). pap. 6.95 (978-1-58810-434-2(6) , 91162) Heinemann Library.

Ansary, Mir Tamim. Presidents' Day. 2006. (Illus.). 32p. (J). (***978-1-4034-8891-6(6)***) Heinemann Library.

Armentrout, David & Armentrout, Patricia. Abraham Lincoln. 2002. (People Who Made a Difference Ser.). (Illus.). 24p. (gr. 2-5). 14.95 (978-1-58952-051-6(3)) Rourke Publishing, LLC.

—Abraham Lincoln. Sarfatti, Esther & de la Vega, Eida, trs. from ENG. 2001. (Personas que Cambiaron la Historia Ser.). (SPA., Illus.). 24p. (J). (gr. 1-4). lib. bdg. 19.27 (978-1-58952-167-4(6) , RK7298) Rourke Publishing, LLC.

—The Emancipation Proclamation. 2005. (Documents that Shaped the Nation Ser.). (Illus.). 48p. (gr. 4-6). 20.95 (978-1-59515-233-6(4)) Rourke Publishing, LLC.

—La Proclama de Emancipacion. 2005. (SPA.). (J). (978-1-59515-645-7(3)) Rourke Publishing, LLC.

Aronson, Billy. Abraham Lincoln. 2008. (J). (***978-0-7614-2839-8(9)***) Cavendish, Marshall Bks., Ltd.

—Richard M. Nixon. 2007. (Presidents & Their Times Ser.). 96p. (J). lib. bdg. 32.79 (978-0-7614-2428-4(8) , Benchmark Bks.) Cavendish, Marshall Corp.

—Ulysses S. Grant. 2007. (Presidents & Their Times Ser.). 96p. (J). lib. bdg. 32.79 (978-0-7614-2430-7(X) , Benchmark Bks.) Cavendish, Marshall Corp.

Ashby, Ruth. Abraham & Mary Todd Lincoln. 2004. (Illus.). 48p. (J). pap. 11.95 (978-0-8368-5701-6(1)); lib. bdg. 30.00 (978-0-8368-5695-8(3)) Stevens, Gareth Inc. (World Almanac Library).

—Bill & Hillary Rodham Clinton. 2005. (Illus.). 48p. (J). pap. (978-0-8368-5762-7(3)); lib. bdg. 30.00 (978-0-8368-5756-6(9)) Stevens, Gareth Inc. (World Almanac Library).

—Franklin & Eleanor Roosevelt. 2005. (Illus.). 48p. (J). pap. (978-0-8368-5764-1(X)); lib. bdg. 30.00 (978-0-8368-5758-0(5)) Stevens, Gareth Inc. (World Almanac Library).

—George & Martha Washington. 2005. (Illus.). 48p. (J). pap. (978-0-8368-5703-0(8)); lib. bdg. 30.00 (978-0-8368-5697-2(X)) Stevens, Gareth Inc. (World Almanac Library).

—George W. & Laura Bush. 2004. (Illus.). 48p. (J). pap. (978-0-8368-5699-6(6)); lib. bdg. 30.00 (978-0-8368-5693-4(7)) Stevens, Gareth Inc. (World Almanac Library).

—James & Dolley Madison. 2005. (Illus.). 48p. (J). pap. (978-0-8368-5763-4(1)); lib. bdg. 30.00 (978-0-8368-5757-3(7)) Stevens, Gareth Inc. (World Almanac Library).

—John & Abigail Adams. 2005. (Illus.). 48p. (J). pap. (978-0-8368-5761-0(5)); lib. bdg. 30.00 (978-0-8368-5755-9(0)) Stevens, Gareth Inc. (World Almanac Library).

—John & Jacqueline Kennedy. 2004. (Illus.). 48p. (J). pap. (978-0-8368-5700-9(3)); lib. bdg. 30.00 (978-0-8368-5694-1(5)) Stevens, Gareth Inc. (World Almanac Library).

—Lincoln at War. 2002. (Illus.). 48p. (J). lib. bdg. 28.50 (978-1-58340-183-5(0)) Smart Apple Media.

—Ronald & Nancy Reagan. 2004. (Illus.). 48p. (J). pap. 11.95 (978-0-8368-5702-3(X)); lib. bdg. 30.00 (978-0-8368-5696-5(1)) Stevens, Gareth Inc. (World Almanac Library).

—Woodrow & Edith Wilson. 2005. (Illus.). 48p. (J). pap. (978-0-8368-5765-8(8)); lib. bdg. 30.00 (978-0-8368-5759-7(3)) Stevens, Gareth Inc. (World Almanac Library).

Ashley, Susan. The White House. 2004. (Weekly Reader Early Learning Library). (Illus.). 24p. (J). (gr. 2 up). pap. 5.95 (978-0-8368-4152-7(2)); lib. bdg. 19.33 (978-0-8368-4145-9(X)) Stevens, Gareth Inc. (Weekly Reader Early Learning Library).

Autrey, Jacquelyn & Yeager, Alice. U.S. Presidents & Their Animal Friends. Passarella, Jennie, illus. 2004. 32p. (J). (978-1-59421-005-1(5)) Seacoast Publishing, Inc.

Baldwin, James. Four Great Americans. 2006. pap. (***978-1-4065-0509-2(9)***) Dodo Pr.

Baldwin, James. Four Great Americans: Washington, Franklin, Webster, Lincoln: A Book for Young Americans. 2000. (Illus.). (J). (978-0-89526-203-5(7)) Regnery Publishing, Inc., An Eagle Publishing Co.

Barber, James. Presidents: Discover the Presidents Who Have Shaped American History, from the Founding Fathers to Today's Leaders. rev. ed. 2003. (Eyewitness Bks.). (Illus.). 64p. 15.99 (978-0-7894-8898-5(1)) Dorling Kindersley Publishing, Inc.

Barber, James & Pastan, Amy. Smithsonian Presidents & First Ladies. 2002. (Illus.). 96p. (J). (gr. 4-7). lib. bdg. 22.20 (978-0-613-45619-7(X)) Tandem Library Bks.

Barber, James, et al. The Smithsonian Presidents & First Ladies. 2002. (Illus.). 96p. (J). (gr. 4-6). pap. 12.99 (978-0-7894-8453-6(6)) Dorling Kindersley Publishing, Inc.

Barfell, Judy. Learn & Sign Funtime: The United States Presidents. 2005. (J). per. 29.90 (978-0-9753717-4-9(6)) Learn and Sign Funtime Bks.

Barnes, Peter W. President Adams' Alligator: And Other White House Pets. Barnes, Cheryl Shaw, illus. 2003. 32p. (J). 16.95 (978-1-893622-13-5(4) , VSP Bks.) Vacation Spot Publishing.

Barr, Marilynn G. American Presidents. 1999. (Illus.). 128p. (J). pap. 14.95 (978-1-57612-117-7(8)) Monday Morning Bks., Inc.

Bausum, Ann. Our Country's Presidents. rev. exp. ed. 2005. (Illus.). 208p. (gr. 5). (J). 45.90 (978-0-7922-9330-9(4)); 24.95 (978-0-7922-9329-3(0)) National Geographic Society. (National Geographic Children's Bks.).

Behnke, Alison. Millard Fillmore. 2007. (Presidential Leaders Ser.). (Illus.). 111p. (J). 29.27 (978-0-8225-1495-4(8) , Lerner Pubns.) Lerner Publishing Group.

Behrman, Carol H. Andrew Jackson. (History Maker Bios Ser.). (Illus.). (J). 2005. 48p. (gr. 3-5). 26.60 (978-0-8225-1543-2(1)); 2003. 112p. (gr. 6-12). lib. bdg. 29.27 (978-0-8225-0093-3(0)) Lerner Publishing Group.

—James K. Polk. 2005. (Presidential Leaders Ser.). (Illus.). 112p. (J). (gr. 6-12). 29.27 (978-0-8225-1396-4(X)) Lerner Publishing Group.

—John Adams. 2004. (Presidential Leaders Ser.). (Illus.). 112p. (J). 29.27 (978-0-8225-0820-5(6) , Lerner Pubns.) Lerner Publishing Group.

Benge, Janet. Abraham Lincoln: A New Birth of Freedom. 2001. (gr. 3-6). lib. bdg. 15.30 (978-0-613-83101-7(2)) Tandem Library Bks.

Benge, Janet & Benge, Geoff. George Washington: True Patriot. 2001. (Illus.). 224p. pap. 8.99 (978-1-883002-81-7(8)) Emerald Bks.

—Theodore Roosevelt. 2004. (Illus.). 203p. (J). pap. 8.99 (978-1-932096-10-1(8)) Emerald Bks.

Benson, Michael. William Howard Taft. 2005. (Presidential Leaders Ser.). (Illus.). 112p. (J). 29.27 (978-0-8225-0849-6(4) , Lerner Pubns.) Lerner Publishing Group.

Bergen, Lara Rice, et al. Stuck on the Presidents. Kelleher, Kathie & Milne, Jonathan, illus. rev. ed. 2001. (Books & Stuff Ser.). 1p. (Orig.). (J). (gr. 2 up). pap. 8.99 (978-0-448-41284-9(5) , Grosset & Dunlap) Penguin Group (USA) Inc.

Bernstein, Richard B. Thomas Jefferson: The Revolution of Ideas. 2004. (Oxford Portraits Ser.). (Illus.). 256p. (YA). 28.00 (978-0-19-514368-3(X)) Oxford Univ. Pr., Inc.

Bial, Raymond. Where Lincoln Walked. 1998. (Illus.). 48p. (J). (gr. 2-5). lib. bdg. 17.85 (978-0-8027-8631-9(6)) Walker & Co.

Billman, Hilary Barton. How to Draw the Life & Times of William Henry Harrison. 2006. (Kid's Guide to Drawing the Presidents of the United States of America Ser.). (Illus.). 32p. (J). 25.25 (978-1-4042-2986-0(8) , PowerKids Pr.) Rosen Publishing Group, Inc., The.

Binns, Tristan Boyer. The White House. 2001. (J). (978-0-606-22928-9(0)) Tandem Library Bks.

Blassingame, Wyatt. Presidents. Jonaitis, Alice, ed. rev. ed. 2004. (Look-It-Up Bks.). (Illus.). 184p. (J). (gr. 5-8). lib. bdg. 17.99 (978-0-394-96839-1(5) , Random Hse. Bks. for Young Readers) Random Hse. Children's Bks.

Bober, Natalie S. Thomas Jefferson: Draftsman of a Nation. 2007. 352p. (YA). (gr. 7 up). 22.95 (*978-0-8139-2632-2(7)) Univ. Pr. of Virginia.

Book Studio Staff. Leaders Past & Present: Presidents of the United States of America: Presidents of the United States of America. 2007. (Cool Kits Ser.). 32p. (J). 7.99 (978-0-7566-2664-8(1)) Dorling Kindersley Publishing, Inc.

Bramwell, Neil D. James Madison: A MyReportLinks. Com Book. 2003. (Presidents Ser.). (Illus.). 48p. (J). (gr. 4-10). lib. bdg. 25.26 (978-0-7660-5129-4(3) , MyReportLinks.com Bks.) Enslow Pubs., Inc.

Bredeson, Carmen. George W. Bush: The 43rd President. 2002. (Heroes of American History Ser.). (Illus.). 32p. (J). (gr. 1-4). lib. bdg. 22.60 (978-0-7660-2100-6(9)) Enslow Pubs., Inc.

Brown, Jonatha A. John F. Kennedy. 2005. (J). pap. (978-0-8368-4754-3(7)); (Illus.). 24p. (YA). lib. bdg. 19.33 (978-0-8368-4747-5(4)) Stevens, Gareth Inc.

Brunelli, Carol. Chester A. Arthur: Our Twenty-First President. 2001. (Spirit of America: Our Presidents Ser.). (Illus.). 48p. (J). (gr. 2-6). 28.50 (978-1-56766-858-2(5)) Child's World, Inc.

—James A. Garfield: Our Twentieth President. 2001. (Spirit of America: Our Presidents Ser.). (Illus.). 48p. (J). (gr. 2-6). 28.50 (978-1-56766-857-5(7)) Child's World, Inc.

—Zachary Taylor: Our Twelfth President. 2001. (Spirit of America: Our Presidents Ser.). (Illus.). 48p. (J). (gr. 2-6). 28.50 (978-1-56766-836-0(4)) Child's World, Inc.

Brunelli, Carol & Gaines, Ann Graham. Woodrow Wilson: Our Twenty-Eighth President. 2001. (Spirit of America: Our Presidents Ser.). (Illus.). 48p. (J). (gr. 2-6). 28.50 (978-1-56766-863-6(1)) Child's World, Inc.

Buller, Jon, et al. Smart about the Presidents. Buller, Jon et al, illus. 2004. (Smart about History Ser.). 80p. (J). (gr. k-5). pap. 5.99 (978-0-448-43372-1(9) , Grosset & Dunlap) Penguin Group (USA) Inc.

Burgan, Michael. Andrew Johnson. 2003. (Profiles of the Presidents Ser.). (Illus.). 64p. (J). (gr. 4 up). lib. bdg. 23.93 (978-0-7565-0264-5(0)) Compass Point Bks.

—Franklin D. Roosevelt. 2002. (Profiles of the Presidents Ser.). (Illus.). 64p. (J). (gr. 4 up). lib. bdg. 23.93 (978-0-7565-0203-4(9)) Compass Point Bks.

—George W. Bush. 2003. (Profiles of the Presidents Ser.). (Illus.). 64p. (J). (gr. 4 up). lib. bdg. 23.93 (978-0-7565-0338-3(8)) Compass Point Bks.

—John Adams: Second U. S. President. 2001. (gr. 5-8). lib. bdg. 17.60 (978-0-613-32724-4(1)) Tandem Library Bks.

—John F. Kennedy. 2001. (Trailblazers of the Modern World Ser.). (Illus.). 48p. (J). (gr. 5 up). pap. 14.95 (978-0-8368-5225-7(7)); lib. bdg. 30.00 (978-0-8368-5065-9(3)) Stevens, Gareth Inc. (World Almanac Library).

—John Quincy Adams. 2003. (Profiles of the Presidents Ser.). (Illus.). 64p. (J). (gr. 4 up). lib. bdg. 23.93 (978-0-7565-0254-6(3)) Compass Point Bks.

—Lyndon Baines Johnson. 2003. (Profiles of the Presidents Ser.). (Illus.). 64p. (J). (gr. 4 up). lib. bdg. 23.93 (978-0-7565-0280-5(2)) Compass Point Bks.

—William Howard Taft. 2003. (Profiles of the Presidents Ser.). (Illus.). 64p. (J). (gr. 4 up). lib. bdg. 23.93 (978-0-7565-0273-7(X)) Compass Point Bks.

Burke, Rick. Abraham Lincoln. (American Lives Ser.). (Illus.). 32p. (J). 2003. (gr. 2-4). lib. bdg. (978-1-4034-0155-7(1)); 2002. pap. 6.95 (978-1-4034-0411-4(9)) Heinemann Library.

—Andrew Jackson. (American Lives Ser.). (Illus.). 32p. (J). 2003. (gr. 2-4). lib. bdg. (978-1-4034-0156-4(X)); 2002. pap. 6.95 (978-1-4034-0412-1(7)) Heinemann Library.

—Andrew Jackson. 2003. (gr. 3-6). lib. bdg. 15.25 (978-0-613-60848-0(8)) Tandem Library Bks.

—George W. Bush. (American Lives Ser.). (Illus.). 32p. (J). 2003. (gr. 2-4). lib. bdg. (978-1-4034-0157-1(8)); 2002. pap. 6.95 (978-1-4034-0413-8(5)) Heinemann Library.

—George Washington. (American Lives Ser.). (ENG & SPA., Illus.). 32p. (J). 2003. (gr. 2-4). lib. bdg. (978-1-4034-0158-8(6)); 2002. pap. 6.95 (978-1-4034-0414-5(3)) Heinemann Library.

—George Washington. 2003. (gr. 3-6). lib. bdg. 15.25 (978-0-613-60876-3(3)) Tandem Library Bks.

—Theodore Roosevelt. (American Lives Ser.). (Illus.). 32p. (J). 2003. (gr. 2-4). lib. bdg. (978-1-4034-0159-5(4)); 2002. pap. 6.95 (978-1-4034-0415-2(1)) Heinemann Library.

—Theodore Roosevelt. 2003. (gr. 3-6). lib. bdg. 15.25 (978-0-613-60936-4(0)) Tandem Library Bks.

—Thomas Jefferson. (American Lives Ser.). (Illus.). 32p. (J). 2003. (gr. 2-4). lib. bdg. (978-1-4034-0160-1(8)); 2002. pap. 6.95 (978-1-4034-0416-9(X)) Heinemann Library.

Burton, Alma Holman. Four American Patriots: Patrick Henry, Alexander Hamilton, Andrew Jackson, Ulysses S. Grant: A Book for Young Americans. 2000. (Illus.). (J). (978-0-89526-204-2(5)) Regnery Publishing, Inc., An Eagle Publishing Co.

Button, Beth. Presidents Who Shaped the Nation. Rogers, Kathy, ed. Adams, Elizabeth, illus. 2000. (Famous Faces Ser.). 8p. (J). pap., wbk. ed. 6.95 (978-1-56472-275-1(9)) Edupress, Inc.

Cannarella, Deborah. Harry S. Truman. 2002. (Profiles of the Presidents Ser.). (Illus.). 64p. (J). (gr. 4 up). lib. bdg. 23.93 (978-0-7565-0278-2(0)) Compass Point Bks.

Caplan, Jeremy. Franklin D Roosevelt A Leader in Troubled Times. 2006. 44p. (J). lib. bdg. 15.00 (*978-1-4242-0848-7(3)) Fitzgerald Bks.

Carter, E. J. Jefferson Davis. 2004. (American War Biographies Ser.). (Illus.). 48p. (J). pap. 8.50 (978-1-4034-5089-0(7)); lib. bdg. 27.07 (978-1-4034-5082-1(X)) Heinemann Library.

—Ulysses S. Grant. 2004. (American War Biographies Ser.). (Illus.). 48p. (J). pap. 8.50 (978-1-4034-5087-6(0)); lib. bdg. (978-1-4034-5080-7(3)) Heinemann Library.

Cary, Barbara. Meet Abraham Lincoln. 2001. (gr. 3-6). lib. bdg. 11.80 (978-0-613-84581-6(1)); (Illus.). (J). (978-0-606-20791-1(0)) Tandem Library Bks.

Casciato, Daniel. Expansion & Reform. 2007. (J). (*978-1-59036-741-4(3)); (*978-1-59036-742-1(1)) Weigl Pubs., Inc.

Chandra, Deborah & Comora, Madeleine. George Washington's Teeth. Cole, Brock, illus. 2007. 40p. (J). pap. 6.99 (*978-0-312-37604-8(9)) Square Fish.

Chaneski, John. Presidential Word Search Puzzles. 2004. (Illus.). 112p. pap., pap., spiral bd. 6.95 (978-1-4027-1314-9(2)) Sterling Publishing Co., Inc.

Childress, Diana. George Herbert Walker Bush. 2007. (Presidential Leaders Ser.). 112p. (J). (gr. 6-12). 29.27 (978-0-8225-1510-4(5) , Lerner Pubns.) Lerner Publishing Group.

Colbert, Nancy A. Great Society: The Story of Lyndon Baines Johnson. 2004. (Notable Americans Ser.). (Illus.). 144p. (YA). (gr. 6-12). 23.95 (978-1-883846-84-8(6) , First Biographies) Reynolds, Morgan Inc.

Coleman, Wim & Perrin, Pat. George Washington: Creating a Nation. 2004. (America's Founding Fathers Ser.). (Illus.). 128p. (J). lib. bdg. 26.60 (978-0-7660-2290-4(0)) Enslow Pubs., Inc.

Collard, Sneed B. Abraham Lincoln: A Courageous Leader. 2006. (American Heroes Ser.). (Illus.). 48p. (J). (gr. 3-5). lib. bdg. 28.50 (978-0-7614-2162-7(9) , Benchmark Bks.) Cavendish, Marshall Corp.

Collard, Sneed B., III. John Adams: Our Second President. 2006. (American Heroes Ser.). (Illus.). 48p. (J). lib. bdg. 28.50 (*978-0-7614-2159-7(9) , Benchmark Bks.) Cavendish, Marshall Corp.

Collier, James Lincoln. You Never Knew. Copeland, Greg, illus. 2004. 147.00 (978-0-516-29660-9(4)) Scholastic Library Publishing.

Cooper, Ilene. Jack: The Early Years of John F. Kennedy. 2003. (Illus.). 160p. (J). (gr. 5-9). 22.99 (978-0-525-46923-0(0) , Dutton Juvenile) Penguin Group (USA) Inc.

Copeland, Peter F. American Presidents Coloring Book. 2001. (Illus.). 48p. (J). pap. 3.95 (978-0-486-41324-2(1)) Dover Pubns., Inc.

Cosson, Jody. Civil War & Reconstruction. 2007. (J). (*978-1-59036-743-8(X)); (*978-1-59036-744-5(8)) Weigl Pubs., Inc.

Creative Media Applications Staff. American Presidents in World History, 5 vols. 2003. (Middle School Reference Ser.). (Illus.). (J). Vol. 1. (978-0-313-32565-6(0)); Vol. 2. (978-0-313-32566-3(9)); Vol. 3. (978-0-313-32567-0(7)); Vol. 4. (978-0-313-32568-7(5)); Vol. 5. (978-0-313-32569-4(3)) Greenwood Publishing Group, Inc.

Creative Media Applications Staff, contrib. by. American Presidents in World History, 5 vols. 2003. (Middle School Reference Ser.). (Illus.). 144p. (J). (gr. 6-8). 209.95 (978-0-313-32564-9(2) , MS2564, Middle School Reference) Greenwood Publishing Group, Inc.

Criscione, Rachel. How to Draw the Life & Times of Chester A. Arthur. 2006. (Kid's Guide to Drawing the Presidents of the United States of America Ser.). (J). 25.25 (978-1-4042-2998-3(1) , PowerKids Pr.) Rosen Publishing Group, Inc., The.

Cronkite, Walter, frwd. Great American Presidents. (Illus.). (gr. 4-8). pap. (978-0-7910-8048-1(X) , Chelsea Hse.) Facts On File, Inc.

Darby, Jean. Dwight D. Eisenhower. 2004. (Presidential Leaders Ser.). (Illus.). 112p. (J). (gr. 6-12). lib. bdg. 29.27 (978-0-8225-0813-7(3)) Lerner Publishing Group.

Darraj, Susan Muaddi. John F. Kennedy. (Great American Presidents Ser.). (Illus.). (gr. 4-8). 2004. 112p. pap. 30.00 (978-0-7910-7786-3(1)); 2003. 100p. 30.00 (978-0-7910-7600-2(8)) Facts On File, Inc. (Chelsea Hse.).

Davis, Kenneth C. Don't Know Much about the Presidents. Martin, Pedro, illus. (Don't Know Much About Ser.). 64p. (J). (gr. 1-4). 2002. 16.99 (978-0-06-028615-6(6)); 2004. reprint ed. pap. 6.99 (978-0-06-446231-0(5) , Harper Trophy) HarperCollins Pubs.

—Don't Know Much about the Presidents. 2004. (gr. k-3). lib. bdg. 15.30 (978-0-613-87325-3(4)) Tandem Library Bks.

Davis, Todd & Frey, Marc. The New Big Book of U. S. Presidents. 2005. (Illus.). 56p. 9.98 (978-0-7624-2029-2(4) , Courage Bks.) Running Pr. Bk. Pubs.

Dean, Sheri. Presidents Day/dia De Los Presidentes. 2006. (Illus.). 24p. (J). pap. (978-0-8368-6515-8(4)); (SPA., pap. 5.95 (978-0-8368-6529-5(4)); lib. bdg. 19.33 (978-0-8368-6508-0(1)); (SPA., lib. bdg. 19.33 (978-0-8368-6522-6(7)) Stevens, Gareth Inc.

Deem, James M. Millard Fillmore: A MyReportLinks.com Book. 2003. (Presidents Ser.). 48p. (J). (gr. 4-10). lib. bdg. 25.26 (978-0-7660-5074-7(2) , MyReportLinks.com Bks.) Enslow Pubs., Inc.

DeGezelle, Terri. Franklin D. Roosevelt & the Great Depression. 2007. (J). (*978-1-4034-9670-6(6)); pap. (*978-1-4034-9678-2(1)) Heinemann Library.

DeMauro, Lisa & Time for Kids Editors. Presidents of the United States. 2006. (Time for Kids Ser.). (Illus.). 72p. (J). 17.99 (978-0-06-081554-7(X)); lib. bdg. 18.89 (978-0-06-081555-4(8)) HarperCollins Pubs.

—Theodore Roosevelt: The Adventurous President. 2005. (Time for Kids Ser.). (Illus.). 48p. (J). 14.99 (978-0-06-057606-6(5)); pap. 3.99 (978-0-06-057604-2(9)) HarperCollins Pubs.

Devillier, Christy. Abraham Lincoln. 2001. (First Biographies Ser.). (Illus.). 32p. (J). (gr. k-4). lib. bdg. 22.78 (978-1-57765-591-6(5) , Buddy Bks.) ABDO Publishing Co.

—George Washington. 2001. (First Biographies Ser.). (Illus.). 32p. (J). (gr. k-4). lib. bdg. 22.78 (978-1-57765-593-0(1) , Buddy Bks.) ABDO Publishing Co.

Dicianni, Ron. Praying with the Presidents: One Nation's Legacy of Prayer. 2004. 48p. (J). (gr. k-3). 10.99 (978-1-59185-408-1(3) , Charisma Kids) Strang Communications Co.

DiConsiglio, John. Franklin Pierce. 2004. (Encyclopedia of Presidents Ser.). (Illus.). 110p. (J). 34.00 (978-0-516-24235-4(0) , Children's Pr.) Scholastic Library Publishing.

Doak, Robin S. James A. Garfield. 2003. (Profiles of the Presidents Ser.). (Illus.). 64p. (J). (gr. 4 up). lib. bdg. 23.93 (978-0-7565-0267-6(5)) Compass Point Bks.

—John Tyler. 2003. (Profiles of the Presidents Ser.). (Illus.). 64p. (J). (gr. 4 up). lib. bdg. 23.93 (978-0-7565-0258-4(6)) Compass Point Bks.

—Martin Van Buren. 2003. (Profiles of the Presidents Ser.). (Illus.). 64p. (J). (gr. 4 up). lib. bdg. 23.93 (978-0-7565-0256-0(X)) Compass Point Bks.

—William Henry Harrison. 2003. (Profiles of the Presidents Ser.). (Illus.). 64p. (J). (gr. 4 up). lib. bdg. 23.93 (978-0-7565-0257-7(8)) Compass Point Bks.

—William McKinley. 2003. (Profiles of the Presidents Ser.). (Illus.). 64p. (J). (gr. 4 up). lib. bdg. 23.93 (978-0-7565-0271-3(3)) Compass Point Bks.

—Zachary Taylor. 2003. (Profiles of the Presidents Ser.). (Illus.). 64p. (J). (gr. 4 up). lib. bdg. 23.93 (978-0-7565-0260-7(8)) Compass Point Bks.

Doeden, Matt. George Washington: Leading a New Nation. Martin, Cynthia, illus. 2005. (Graphic Library). 32p. (J). (gr. 3-7). lib. bdg. 25.26 (978-0-7368-4963-0(7)) Capstone Pr., Inc.

—Thomas Jefferson: Great American. Purcell, Gordon & Beatty, Terry, illus. 2006. (Graphic Library). 32p. (J). (978-0-7368-5488-7(6)) Capstone Pr., Inc.

Doherty, Kieran. William Howard Taft. 2004. (Encyclopedia of Presidents Ser.). (Illus.). 110p. (J). 34.00 (978-0-516-22967-6(2) , Children's Pr.) Scholastic Library Publishing.

Dolan, Edward F. George Washington. 2007. (Presidents & Their Times Ser.). 96p. (J). lib. bdg. 32.79 (*978-0-7614-2427-7(X) , Benchmark Bks.) Cavendish, Marshall Corp.

Dommermuth-Costa, Carol. Woodrow Wilson. 2003. (Presidential Leaders Ser.). (Illus.). 112p. (J). 29.27 (978-0-8225-0094-0(9) , Lerner Pubns.) Lerner Publishing Group.

Donlan, Leni. George Washington: Revolution & the New Nation. 2006. (American History Through Primary Sources Ser.). (Illus.). 32p. (J). (978-1-4109-2420-9(3)); pap. (978-1-4109-2431-5(9)) Steck-Vaughn.

Dorling Kindersley Publishing Staff. Presidents. rev. ed. 2003. (Dk Eyewitness Books Ser.). 64p. (J). lib. bdg. 19.99 (978-0-7894-8899-2(X)) Dorling Kindersley Publishing, Inc.

Douglas, Lloyd G. The White House. 2003. (Welcome Book Ser.). (Illus.). 24p. (J). 18.00 (978-0-516-25855-3(9)); pap. 4.95 (978-0-516-27878-0(9)) Scholastic Library Publishing. (Children's Pr.).

Downing, David. John F. Kennedy. (Illus.). 64p. 2003. pap. 8.95 (978-1-4034-3495-1(6)); 2001. (J). (gr. 5-7). lib. bdg. 27.86 (978-1-58810-164-8(9)) Heinemann Library.

Dubois, Muriel L. John Adams. 2003. (Photo-Illustrated Biographies Ser.). (Illus.). 24p. (J). (gr. 2-3). lib. bdg. 18.60 (978-0-7368-1606-9(2) , Bridgestone Bks.) Capstone Pr., Inc.

—The U. S. Presidency. 2003. (First Facts Ser.). (Illus.). 24p. (J). lib. bdg. 21.26 (978-0-7368-2289-3(5)) Capstone Pr., Inc.

Dunn, Joeming W. Abraham Lincoln. Espinosa, Rod, illus. 2007. (Bio-Graphics Ser.). 32p. (J). (gr. 3-6). lib. bdg. 27.07 (*978-1-60270-064-2(8) , Graphic Planet) Magic Wagon.

Durrett, Deanne. George W. Bush. 2002. (Famous People Ser.). (Illus.). 48p. (J). (gr. 3-5). 26.20 (978-0-7377-1371-8(2) , Kidhaven) Thomson Gale.

Edge, Laura Bufano. William McKinley. 2007. (Presidential Leaders Ser.). 112p. (J). (gr. 6-12). 29.27 (978-0-8225-1508-1(3) , Twenty-First Century Bks.) Lerner Publishing Group.

Egan, Tracie. The President & the Executive Branch. 2003. (Primary Source Library of American Citizenship). (Illus.). 32p. (J). pap. (978-1-4042-5091-8(3)) Rosen Publishing Group, Inc., The.

Elish, Dan. Chester A. Arthur. 2004. (Encyclopedia of Presidents Ser.). (Illus.). 110p. (J). 34.00 (978-0-516-22961-4(3) , Children's Pr.) Scholastic Library Publishing.

—James Madison. 2007. (Presidents & Their Times Ser.). 96p. (J). lib. bdg. 32.79 (*978-0-7614-2432-1(6) , Benchmark Bks.) Cavendish, Marshall Corp.

Elish, Dan. Theodore Roosevelt. 2007. (Presidents & Their Times Ser.). 96p. (J). lib. bdg. 32.79 (978-0-7614-2429-1(6) , Benchmark Bks.) Cavendish, Marshall Corp.

Emerson, Judy. John F. Kennedy. Saunders-Smith, Gail, ed. 2004. (First Biographies Ser.). (Illus.). 24p. (J). (gr. k-1). lib. bdg. 15.93 (978-0-7368-2368-5(9) , Pebble Bks.) Capstone Pr., Inc.

—Theodore Roosevelt. Saunders-Smith, Gail, ed. 2004. (First Biographies Ser.). (Illus.). 24p. (J). (gr. k-1). lib. bdg. 15.93 (978-0-7368-2369-2(7) , Pebble Bks.) Capstone Pr., Inc.

—Thomas Jefferson. Saunders-Smith, Gail, ed. 2003. (First Biographies Ser.). (Illus.). 24p. (J). (gr. k-1). lib. bdg. 15.93 (978-0-7368-2088-2(4) , Pebble Bks.) Capstone Pr., Inc.

Encyclopedia of Presidents, Second Series, 10 bks. 2004. (J). 330.00 (978-0-516-23722-0(5) , Children's Pr.); (Illus.). 330.00 (978-0-516-29744-6(9)) Scholastic Library Publishing.

Espinosa, Rod. George Washington. 2007. (Bio-Graphics Ser.). (Illus.). 32p. (J). (gr. 3-6). lib. bdg. 27.07 (*978-1-60270-067-3(2) , Graphic Planet) Magic Wagon.

Famous Americans, Vol. 3. 2005. (First Biographies Ser.). (YA). (gr. k-3). 118.80 (978-0-7368-4197-9(0) , Pebble Bks.) Capstone Pr., Inc.

Favor, Lesli J. Martin Van Buren. 2003. (Encyclopedia of Presidents Ser.). (Illus.). 110p. (J). 34.00 (978-0-516-22770-2(X) , Children's Pr.) Scholastic Library Publishing.

Feder, Chris Welles. Brain Quest Presidents. 2005. (Illus.). 148p. (J). 10.95 (978-0-7611-3998-0(2) , 13998) Workman Publishing Co., Inc.

Feinberg, Barbara Silberdick. John Adams. 2003. (Encyclopedia of Presidents Ser.: Vol. 2). (Illus.). 110p. (J). 34.00 (978-0-516-22680-4(0) , Children's Pr.) Scholastic Library Publishing.

—Woodrow Wilson. 2004. (Encyclopedia of Presidents Ser.). (Illus.). 110p. (J). 34.00 (978-0-516-22968-3(0) , Children's Pr.) Scholastic Library Publishing.

Feinstein, Stephen. Lee sobre Abraham Lincoln/Read about Abraham Lincoln. 2006. (I Like Biographies Ser.!). (ENG & SPA., Illus.). 24p. (J). (gr. 1-3). lib. bdg. 21.26 (978-0-7660-2672-8(8) , Enslow Elementary) Enslow Pubs., Inc.

Feldman, Ruth Tenzer. Chester A. Arthur. 2007. (Presidential Leaders Ser.). 112p. (J). (gr. 6-12). 29.27 (978-0-8225-1512-8(1) , Twenty-First Century Bks.) Lerner Publishing Group.

Ferry, Joseph. Thomas Jefferson. 2003. (Childhood of the Presidents Ser.). (Illus.). 48p. (J). (gr. 4 up). lib. bdg. (978-1-59084-271-3(5)) Mason Crest Pubs.

Ferry, Steven. Franklin Pierce: Our Fourteenth President. 2001. (Spirit of America: Our Presidents Ser.). (Illus.). 48p. (J). (gr. 2-6). 28.50 (978-1-56766-851-3(8)) Child's World, Inc.

—John Tyler: Our Tenth President. 2001. (Spirit of America: Our Presidents Ser.). (Illus.). 48p. (J). (gr. 2-6). 28.50 (978-1-56766-849-0(6)) Child's World, Inc.

Findley, Violet. Easy Reader Biographies: Abraham Lincoln: A Great President, A Great American. 2007. 16p. pap. 2.99 (*978-0-439-77418-5(7) , Teaching Resources) Scholastic, Inc.

Firestone, Mary. The White House. Skeens, Matthew, illus. 2006. 24p. (J). (ps-2). lib. bdg. 23.93 (978-1-4048-2217-7(8)) Picture Window Bks.

First Americans: Large-Format Books. (Rigby Infoquest Ser.). (gr. 4 up). 30.00 (978-0-7578-3906-1(1)) Rigby Education.

Foley, Michael. Harry Truman. 2003. (Great American Presidents Ser.). (Illus.). 100p. (J). (gr. 4-8). 30.00 (978-0-7910-7596-8(6) , Chelsea Hse.) Facts On File, Inc.

Ford, Carin T. Abraham Lincoln: The 16th President. 2003. (Heroes of American History Ser.). (Illus.). 32p. (J). (gr. 1-4). lib. bdg. 22.60 (978-0-7660-2000-9(2)) Enslow Pubs., Inc.

—Franklin D. Roosevelt: The 32nd President. 2006. (Heroes of American History Ser.). (Illus.). 32p. (J). lib. bdg. 22.60 (978-0-7660-2603-2(5) , Enslow Elementary) Enslow Pubs., Inc.

—John F. Kennedy: The 35th President. 2006. (Heroes of American History Ser.). (Illus.). 32p. (J). lib. bdg. 22.60 (978-0-7660-2601-8(9) , Enslow Elementary) Enslow Pubs., Inc.

—Lincoln, Slavery, & the Emancipation Proclamation. 2004. (Civil War Library Ser.). (Illus.). 48p. (J). lib. bdg. 23.93 (978-0-7660-2252-2(8)) Enslow Pubs., Inc.

—Thomas Jefferson: The Third President. 2003. (Heroes of American History Ser.). (Illus.). 32p. (J). (gr. 1-4). lib. bdg. 22.60 (978-0-7660-1861-7(X)) Enslow Pubs., Inc.

Francis, Sandra. Benjamin Harrison: Our Twenty-Third President. 2001. (Spirit of America: Our Presidents Ser.). (Illus.). 48p. (J). (gr. 2-6). 28.50 (978-1-56766-860-5(7)) Child's World, Inc.

—Rutherford B. Hayes: Our Nineteenth President. 2001. (Spirit of America: Our Presidents Ser.). (Illus.). 48p. (J). (gr. 2-6). 28.50 (978-1-56766-856-8(9)) Child's World, Inc.

Frost, Helen. John F. Kennedy. Saunders-Smith, Gail, ed. 2003. (Famous Americans Ser.). (Illus.). 24p. (J). (gr. k-1). lib. bdg. 15.93 (978-0-7368-1642-7(9) , Pebble Bks.) Capstone Pr., Inc.

Fry, Sonali. Let's Read About— George W. Bush. Heyer, Carol, illus. 2003. (Scholastic First Biographies Ser.). (J). pap. (978-0-439-45953-2(2)) Scholastic, Inc.

Gaff, Jackie. George Washington: The Life of an American Patriot. 2005. (Graphic Nonfiction Ser.). (Illus.). 48p. (J). (gr. 4-6). lib. bdg. 26.50 (978-1-4042-0236-8(6)) Rosen Publishing Group, Inc., The.

Gaines, Ann Graham. Andrew Jackson: Our Seventh President. 2001. (Spirit of America: Our Presidents Ser.). (Illus.). 48p. (J). (gr. 2-6). 28.50 (978-1-56766-847-6(X)) Child's World, Inc.

—James Polk: Our Eleventh President. 2001. (Spirit of America: Our Presidents Ser.). (Illus.). 48p. (J). (gr. 2-6). 28.50 (978-1-56766-850-6(X)) Child's World, Inc.

—William Henry Harrison: Our Ninth President. 2001. (Spirit of America: Our Presidents Ser.). (Illus.). 48p. (J). (gr. 2-6). 28.50 (978-1-56766-848-3(8)) Child's World, Inc.

—William J. Clinton: Our Forty-Second President. 2001. (Spirit of America: Our Presidents Ser.). (Illus.). 48p. (J). (gr. 2-6). 28.50 (978-1-56766-876-6(3)) Child's World, Inc.

—Woodrow Wilson. 2003. (Great American Presidents Ser.). (Illus.). 100p. (J). pap. (978-0-7910-7783-2(7)); (gr. 4-8). 30.00 (978-0-7910-7597-5(4)) Facts On File, Inc. (Chelsea Hse.).

Garraty, John A. Sterling Point Books: Teddy Roosevelt: American Rough Rider. 2007. (Sterling Point Bks.). 176p. (J). 12.95 (978-1-4027-4524-9(9)); pap. 6.95 (978-1-4027-4144-9(8)) Sterling Publishing Co., Inc.

Gedacht, Daniel C. George Washington: Leader of a New Nation. 2005. (Library of American Lives & Times). (Illus.). 112p. (J). (gr. 4-8). lib. bdg. 31.95 (978-0-8239-6622-6(4)) Rosen Publishing Group, Inc., The.

George Washington: Una vida de liderazgo (A Life of Leadership) 2007. (J). pap. 5.95 (978-0-8225-6555-0(2) , Ediciones Lerner) Lerner Publishing Group.

George Washington Carver. 2006. (J). 23.93 (978-0-8225-6258-0(8)); pap. 5.95 (978-0-8225-6625-0(7)) Lerner Publishing Group. (Ediciones Lerner).

Getting to Know the U.S. Presidents: The Great Historical Figures of the U.S. Presidency Brought to Life, 6 Bks., Set. 2005. (J). 26.00 (978-0-516-25203-2(8)) Scholastic Library Publishing.

Getting to Know the U.S. Presidents: The Greatest historical Figures on the U.S. Presidency Brought to Life, Bks, Set. 2004. (J). 156.00 (978-0-516-29670-8(1) , Children's Pr.) Scholastic Library Publishing.

Gherman, Beverly. First Son & President: A Story about John Quincy Adams. Bird, Matthew, illus. (Creative Minds Biography Ser.). 64p. (J). (ps-7). 2006. 22.60 (978-1-57505-756-9(5) , Carolrhoda Bks.); 2005. pap. 6.95 (978-0-8225-3091-6(0)) Lerner Publishing Group.

Giblin James Cross. Thomas Jefferson: A Picture Book Biography. 2006. 48p. (J). pap. 5.99 (978-0-439-81067-8(1) , Scholastic Paperbacks) Scholastic, Inc.

Giddens-White, Bryon. Our Government: The President & the Executive Branch. 2005. (Illus.). 32p. (J). 28.21 (978-1-4034-6601-3(7)); pap. (978-1-4034-6606-8(8)) Heinemann Library.

Gillis, Jennifer Blizin. John Adams. 2004. (American Lives Ser.). (Illus.). 32p. (J). pap. 7.50 (978-1-4034-5967-1(3)); lib. bdg. 24.22 (978-1-4034-5959-6(2)) Heinemann Library.

Gitlin, Marty. The Great Depression & World War II. 2007. (J). ***978-1-59036-749-0(9)); (*978-1-59036-750-6(2))*** Weigl Pubs., Inc.

—Postwar United States. 2007. (J). ***(*978-1-59036-751-3(0)); (*978-1-59036-752-0(9))*** Weigl Pubs., Inc.

Goldsmith, Howard. John F. Kennedy & the Stormy Sea. Benoit, Renné, illus. 2006. 32p. (J). lib. bdg. 15.00 ***(*978-1-4242-0958-3(7))*** Fitzgerald Bks.

Gomez, Rebecca. Thomas Jefferson. 2003. (First Biographies Ser.). (Illus.). 32p. (J). (gr. k-4). lib. bdg. 22.78 (978-1-57765-947-1(3)) ABDO Publishing Co.

Gorman, Jacqueline Laks. President. 2005. (Illus.). 24p. (J). pap. (978-0-8368-4578-5(1)); lib. bdg. 19.33 (978-0-8368-4571-6(4)) Stevens, Gareth Inc.

Gormley, Beatrice. President George W. Bush: Our Forty-Third President. 2001. (Illus.). 176p. (J). (gr. 4-8). pap. 4.99 (978-0-689-84123-1(X) , Aladdin) Simon & Schuster Children's Publishing.

—President George W. Bush: Our Forty-Third President. 2001. (gr. 5-8). lib. bdg. 13.00 (978-0-613-70950-7(0)) Tandem Library Bks.

Gottfried, Ted. Millard Fillmore. 2007. (Presidents & Their Times Ser.). 96p. (J). lib. bdg. 32.79 (978-0-7614-2431-4(8) , Benchmark Bks.) Cavendish, Marshall Corp.

Grabowski, John. Abraham Lincoln. 2001. (gr. 5-8). lib. bdg. 17.60 (978-0-613-32238-6(X)) Tandem Library Bks.

Gray, Susan Heinrichs. The White House. 2001. (Let's See Library). 24p. (J). lib. bdg. 18.60 (978-0-7565-0161-7(X)); (Illus.). (gr. 1 up). lib. bdg. 19.93 (978-0-7565-0145-7(8)) Compass Point Bks.

Green, Robert. Richard M. Nixon. 2003. (Profiles of the Presidents Ser.). (Illus.). 64p. (J). (gr. 4 up). lib. bdg. 23.93 (978-0-7565-0281-2(0)) Compass Point Bks.

—Theodore Roosevelt. 2003. (Profiles of the Presidents Ser.). (Illus.). 64p. (J). (gr. 4 up). lib. bdg. 23.93 (978-0-7565-0272-0(1)) Compass Point Bks.

—Woodrow Wilson. 2003. (Profiles of the Presidents Ser.). (Illus.). 64p. (J). (gr. 4 up). lib. bdg. 23.93 (978-0-7565-0274-4(8)) Compass Point Bks.

Greene, Meg. William Henry Harrison. 2007. (Presidential Leaders Ser.). 112p. (J). (gr. 6-12). 29.27 (978-0-8225-1511-1(3) , Twenty-First Century Bks.) Lerner Publishing Group.

Gross, Miriam. How to Draw the Life & Times of James Monroe. 2007. (Kid's Guide to Drawing the Presidents of the United States of America Ser.). (J). 25.25 (978-1-4042-2982-2(5) , PowerKids Pr.) Rosen Publishing Group, Inc., The.

Gross, Miriam J. How to Draw the Life & Times of William Jefferson Clinton. 2007. (Kid's Guide to Drawing the Presidents of the United States of America Ser.). (Illus.). 32p. (J). 25.25 (978-1-4042-3018-7(1) , PowerKids Pr.) Rosen Publishing Group, Inc., The.

Hale, Sarah Elder, ed. Jefferson Davis & the Confederacy. 2005. (Cobblestone the Civil War Ser.). (Illus.). 48p. (J). 17.95 (978-0-8126-7908-3(3)) Cobblestone Publishing Co.

Hancock, Maryann. The White House. 2006. 32p. (J). pap. (978-1-4034-7006-5(5)); (Illus.). lib. bdg. 28.21 (978-1-4034-6999-1(7)) Heinemann Library.

Harcourt School Publishers Staff. A Home for the President On Level. 3rd ed. 2002. (Trophies Reading Program Ser.). (Illus.). pap. 5.10 (978-0-15-323367-8(2)) Harcourt Schl. Pubs.

Harmon, Daniel E. Andrew Jackson. 2003. (Childhoods of the Presidents Ser.). (Illus.). 48p. (J). (gr. 4 up). lib. bdg. (978-1-59084-274-4(X)) Mason Crest Pubs.

—Woodrow Wilson. 2003. (Childhoods of the Presidents Ser.). (Illus.). 48p. (J). (gr. 4 up). lib. bdg. (978-1-59084-277-5(4)) Mason Crest Pubs.

Harness, Cheryl. George Washington. 2000. (Illus.). 48p. (J). (gr. 4-9). 17.95 (978-0-7922-7096-6(7) , National Geographic Children's Bks.) National Geographic Society.

—The Remarkable Rough-Riding Life of Theodore Roosevelt & the Rise of Empire America. 2007. (Illus.). 144p. (J). (gr. 3-7). 16.95 (978-1-4263-0008-0(5)); lib. bdg. 25.90 (978-1-4263-0009-7(3)) National Geographic Society. (National Geographic Children's Bks.).

—The Revolutionary John Adams. 2003. (Illus.). 48p. (J). (gr. 3-7). 17.95 (978-0-7922-6970-0(5) , National Geographic Children's Bks.) National Geographic Society.

—Thomas Jefferson. 2007. (Illus.). 48p. (J). (gr. 3-7). pap. 7.95 (978-1-4263-0043-1(3) , National Geographic Children's Bks.) National Geographic Society.

Harper, Judith E. Andrew Johnson: Our Seventeenth President. 2001. (Spirit of America: Our Presidents Ser.). (Illus.). 48p. (J). (gr. 2-6). 28.50 (978-1-56766-854-4(2)) Child's World, Inc.

—John F. Kennedy: Our Thirty-Fifth President. 2001. (Spirit of America: Our Presidents Ser.). (Illus.). 48p. (J). (gr. 2-6). 28.50 (978-1-56766-869-8(0)) Child's World, Inc.

Harris, Laurie Lanzen, ed. Biography for Beginners: Presidents of the United States. (Illus.). (J). 1998. 467p. (gr. 3-6). lib. bdg. 50.00 (978-0-7808-0262-9(4)); 2nd ed. 2002. x, 484p. (978-1-931360-15-9(4)) Favorable Impressions.

Harris, Nancy. What's a President & Vice President? 2007. ***(*978-1-4034-9465-8(7))***; pap. ***(*978-1-4034-9471-9(1))*** Heinemann Library.

Haugen, Brenda. Abraham Lincoln: Great American President. 2005. (Illus.). 112p. (J). (gr. 5-7). (978-0-7565-0986-6(6) , 1244078) Compass Point Bks.

—Franklin Delano Roosevelt: The New Deal President. 2006. (Signature Lives Ser.). (Illus.). 112p. (J). (gr. 5-7). 30.60 (978-0-7565-1586-7(6)) Compass Point Bks.

—Ulysses S. Grant: Union General & U.S. President. 2004. (Signature Lives Ser.). (Illus.). 112p. (J). 30.60 (978-0-7565-0820-3(7) , 1240145) Compass Point Bks.

Havelin, Kate. Andrew Johnson. 2005. (Presidential Leaders Ser.). (Illus.). 112p. (J). (gr. 6-12). lib. bdg. 29.27 (978-0-8225-1000-0(6)) Lerner Publishing Group.

—John Tyler. 2005. (Presidential Leaders Ser.). (Illus.). 112p. (J). (gr. 6-12). 29.27 (978-0-8225-1395-7(1)) Lerner Publishing Group.

—Ulysses S. Grant. 2004. (Presidential Leaders Ser.). (Illus.). 112p. (J). 29.27 (978-0-8225-0814-4(1) , Lerner Pubns.) Lerner Publishing Group.

Heath, David. The Presidency of the United States. 1998. (American Civics Ser.). (Illus.). 48p. (J). (gr. 3-4). lib. bdg. 22.60 (978-0-7368-0002-0(6) , Bridgestone Bks.) Capstone Pr., Inc.

—The Presidency of the United States, 6 vols. (gr. 2-5). 39.95 (978-0-7368-8924-7(8)) Red Brick Learning.

Heiligman, Deborah. High Hopes: A Photobiography of John F. Kennedy. Feresten, Nancy, ed. 2003. (Illus.). 64p. (J). (gr. 5). 17.95 (978-0-7922-6141-4(0) , National Geographic Children's Bks.) National Geographic Society.

Heinrichs, Ann. Thomas Jefferson. 2002. (Profiles of the Presidents Ser.). (Illus.). 64p. (J). (gr. 4 up). lib. bdg. 23.93 (978-0-7565-0206-5(3)) Compass Point Bks.

Hewson, Martha S. John Quincy Adams. 2003. (Great American Presidents Ser.). (Illus.). 100p. (J). pap. (978-0-7910-7785-6(3)); (gr. 4-8). 30.00 (978-0-7910-7599-9(0)) Facts On File, Inc. (Chelsea Hse.).

Hill, Mary. George W. Bush. 2003. (Welcome Bks.). (Illus.). 24p. (J). (ps-2). pap. 4.95 (978-0-516-27886-5(X) , Children's Pr.) Scholastic Library Publishing.

Hinkle, Donald. Ronald Reagan. A MyReportLinks.com Book. 2003. (Presidents Ser.). (Illus.). 48p. (J). (gr. 4-10). lib. bdg. 25.26 (978-0-7660-5112-6(9) , MyReportLinks.com Bks.) Enslow Pubs., Inc.

Holden, Henry M. Woodrow Wilson: A MyReportLinks.com Book. 2003. (Presidents Ser.). (Illus.). 48p. (J). (gr. 4-10). lib. bdg. 25.26 (978-0-7660-5123-2(4) , MyReportLinks.com Bks.) Enslow Pubs., Inc.

Holford, David M. Herbert Hoover. 1999. (United States Presidents Ser.). (Illus.). 128p. (YA). (gr. 5-12). lib. bdg. 26.60 (978-0-7660-1035-2(X)) Enslow Pubs., Inc.

Hopkinson, Deborah. John Adams Speaks for Freedom. Orback, Craig, illus. 2005. (Ready-To-Read Stories of Famous Americans Ser.). 32p. (J). pap. 3.99 (978-0-689-86907-5(X) , Aladdin) Simon & Schuster Children's Publishing.

Horn, Geoffrey M. The Presidency. 2003. (World Almanac Library of American Government). (Illus.). 48p. (J). (gr. 5 up). pap. 14.95 (978-0-8368-5463-3(2)); lib. bdg. 30.00 (978-0-8368-5458-9(6)) Stevens, Gareth Inc. (World Almanac Library).

—World Almanac Library of American Government: The Armed Forces; Congress; The Presidency; The Supreme Court, 4 bks. 2002. (Illus.). (J). (gr. 5 up). pap. 59.80 (978-0-8368-5460-2(8) , World Almanac Library) Stevens, Gareth Inc.

Ingram, Scott. The President of the United States. 2002. (American Leaders Ser.). (Illus.). 32p. (J). 23.70 (978-1-56711-661-8(2) , Blackbirch Pr., Inc.) Thomson Gale.

Jackson, Garnet N. George Washington: Our First President. Van Wright, Cornelius, illus. 2002. (Hello Reader! Ser.). 32p. (J). pap. 3.99 (978-0-439-09867-0(X)) Scholastic, Inc.

—George Washington: Our First President. 2001. (J). 10.79 (978-0-606-22245-7(6)); 2000. lib. bdg. 11.80 (978-0-613-63543-1(4)) Tandem Library Bks.

January, Brendan. George Washington. 2003. (Encyclopedia of Presidents Ser.: Vol. 1). (Illus.). 110p. (J). 34.00 (978-0-516-24209-5(1) , Children's Pr.) Scholastic Library Publishing.

—James Madison. 2003. (Encyclopedia of Presidents Ser.: Vol. 4). (Illus.). 110p. (J). 34.00 (978-0-516-24210-1(5) , Children's Pr.) Scholastic Library Publishing.

January, Brendan & Seidman, David. Jimmy Carter: Peacemaker & President. 2004. (Great Life Stories Ser.). (Illus.). 127p. (J). 30.50 (978-0-531-12374-4(X) , Watts, Franklin) Scholastic Library Publishing.

Jefferson Davis. (Civil War Biographies Ser.). 48p. (YA). 7.95 (978-0-7368-4523-3(0)) Capstone Pr., Inc.

Jennett, Pamela & Marchant, Sherry. Electing Our President: The Process to Elect the Nation's Leader. Jennett, Pamela, ed. Hillam, Corbin & Grayson, Rick, illus. 2004. 48p. pap. 8.99 (978-0-88160-379-8(1) , LW-436) Creative Teaching Pr., Inc.

Johansen, Heidi Leigh. How to Draw the Life & Times of Calvin Coolidge. 2007. (Kid's Guide to Drawing the Presidents of the United States of America Ser.). (Illus.). 32p. (J). 25.25 (978-1-4042-3006-4(8) , PowerKids Pr.) Rosen Publishing Group, Inc., The.

Johnson, Darv. The Reagan Years. 1999. (World History Ser.). (Illus.). 111p. (YA). (gr. 8-11). 27.45 (978-1-56006-592-0(3) , LML00902-177947, Lucent Bks.) Thomson Gale.

Jones, Lynda. Abe Lincoln. Bolognese, Don, illus. 1999. (Hello Reader! Ser.). (J). 3.99 (978-0-590-87581-3(7)) Scholastic, Inc.

Jones, Rebecca C. The President Has Been Shot! True Stories of the Attacks on Ten U. S. Presidents. 1998. (J). (978-0-606-13720-1(3)) Tandem Library Bks.

Jones, Veda Boyd. George W. Bush. 2nd rev. ed. 2006. (Modern World Leaders Ser.). (Illus.). 128p. (YA). (gr. 6-12). 30.00 (978-0-7910-9217-0(8) , Chelsea Hse.) Facts On File, Inc.

—John F. Kennedy. 2006. 32p. (gr. 1-2). (YA). pap. 4.95 (978-0-516-29797-2(X)); (Illus.). (J). 20.50 (978-0-516-25038-0(8)) Scholastic Library Publishing. (Children's Pr.).

Jordano, Kimberly. Celebrating President's Day: What Is A President? 1999. (ps-2). lib. bdg. 10.65 (978-0-613-34124-0(4)) Tandem Library Bks.

Jordano, Kimberly & Callella, Trisha. Celebrating President's Day No. 4523: What Is a President? Kupperstein, Joel, ed. Lyon, Tammie Speer, illus. 1999. (Learn to Read Read to Learn Holiday Ser.). 16p. (J). (ps-2). pap. 2.99 (978-1-57471-568-2(2)) Creative Teaching Pr., Inc.

Joseph, Paul. Benjamin Harrison. 2000. (United States Presidents Set.). (Illus.). 32p. (J). (gr. k-6). lib. bdg. 22.78 (978-1-57765-243-4(6) , Checkerboard Library) ABDO Publishing Co.

—Bill Clinton. 2001. (United States Presidents Ser.). (Illus.). 32p. (J). (gr. k-6). lib. bdg. 22.78 (978-1-56239-748-7(6) , Checkerboard Library) ABDO Publishing Co.

—Chester Arthur. 1999. (United States Presidents Ser.). (Illus.). 32p. (J). (gr. k-6). lib. bdg. 22.78 (978-1-57765-236-6(3) , Checkerboard Library) ABDO Publishing Co.

—Franklin D. Roosevelt. 2000. (United States Presidents Ser.). (Illus.). 32p. (J). (gr. k-6). lib. bdg. 22.78 (978-1-56239-813-2(X) , Checkerboard Library) ABDO Publishing Co.

—George Bush. 1999. (United States Presidents Ser.). (Illus.). 32p. (J). (gr. k-6). lib. bdg. 22.78 (978-1-56239-816-3(4) , Checkerboard Library) ABDO Publishing Co.

—Gerald Ford. 2000. (United States Presidents Ser.). (Illus.). 32p. (J). (gr. k-6). lib. bdg. 22.78 (978-1-57765-245-8(2) , Checkerboard Library) ABDO Publishing Co.

—Herbert Hoover. 2001. (United States Presidents Ser.). (Illus.). 32p. (J). (gr. k-6). lib. bdg. 22.78 (978-1-57765-301-1(7) , Checkerboard Library) ABDO Publishing Co.

—James A. Garfield. 2000. (United States Presidents Ser.). (Illus.). 32p. (J). (gr. k-6). lib. bdg. 22.78 (978-1-57765-242-7(8) , Checkerboard Library) ABDO Publishing Co.

—James Buchanan. 2000. (United States Presidents Ser.). (Illus.). 32p. (J). (gr. k-6). lib. bdg. 22.78 (978-1-57765-241-0(X) , Checkerboard Library) ABDO Publishing Co.

—John Quincy Adams. 1999. (United States Presidents Ser.). (Illus.). 32p. (J). (gr. k-6). lib. bdg. 22.78 (978-1-57765-231-1(2) , Checkerboard Library) ABDO Publishing Co.

—Lyndon B. Johnson. 2000. (United States Presidents Ser.). (Illus.). 32p. (J). (gr. k-6). lib. bdg. 22.78 (978-1-56239-814-9(8) , Checkerboard Library) ABDO Publishing Co.

—Millard Fillmore. 1999. (United States Presidents Ser.). (Illus.). 32p. (J). (gr. k-6). lib. bdg. 22.78 (978-1-57765-235-9(5) , Checkerboard Library) ABDO Publishing Co.

—Ronald Reagan. 1999. (United States Presidents Ser.). (Illus.). 32p. (J). (gr. k-6). lib. bdg. 22.78 (978-1-56239-815-6(6) , Checkerboard Library) ABDO Publishing Co.

—William H. Harrison. 1999. (United States Presidents Ser.). (Illus.). 32p. (J). (gr. k-6). lib. bdg. 22.78 (978-1-57765-232-8(0) , Checkerboard Library) ABDO Publishing Co.

—William Taft. 2001. (United States Presidents Ser.). (Illus.). 32p. (J). (gr. k-6). lib. bdg. 22.78 (978-1-57765-300-4(9) , Checkerboard Library) ABDO Publishing Co.

—Zachary Taylor. 1999. (United States Presidents Ser.). (Illus.). 32p. (J). (gr. k-6). lib. bdg. 22.78 (978-1-57765-233-5(9) , Checkerboard Library) ABDO Publishing Co.

Judson, Clara Ingram. Abraham Lincoln: Friend of the People. 2007. (Sterling Point Bks.). 208p. (YA). (gr. 7 up). pap. 6.95 ***(*978-1-4027-5117-2(6))*** Sterling Publishing Co., Inc.

Judson, Karen. Abraham Lincoln: "This Nation Shall Have a New Birth of Freedom" 2008. (Americans-the Spirit of a Nation Ser.). (Illus.). 128p. (J). (gr. 5 up). lib. bdg. 31.93 ***(*978-0-7660-3170-8(5))*** Enslow Pubs., Inc.

Jurmain, Suzanne Tripp. George Did It. Day, Larry, illus. 40p. (J). 2007. (ps). pap. 6.99 ***(*978-0-14-240895-7(6)*** , Puffin); 2005. (gr. 1-4). 16.99 (978-0-525-47560-6(5) , Dutton Juvenile) Penguin Group (USA) Inc.

Kallen, Stuart A. George Washington. 2001. (Founding Fathers Ser.). (Illus.). 64p. (J). (gr. 3-8). lib. bdg. 25.65 (978-1-57765-017-1(4) , ABDO & Daughters) ABDO Publishing Co.

—John Adams. 2001. (Founding Fathers Ser.). (Illus.). 64p. (J). (gr. 3-8). lib. bdg. 25.65 (978-1-57765-007-2(7) , ABDO & Daughters) ABDO Publishing Co.

Karr, Kathleen. It Happened Inside the White House: Extraordinary Tales from America's Most Famous Home. Meisel, Paul, illus. 2000. 112p. (gr. 2-5). 16.99 (978-0-7868-0369-9(X)) Hyperion Bks. for Children.

—It Happened Inside the White House: Extraordinary Tales from America's Most Famous Home. 2000. (Illus.). 112p. pap. 5.99 (978-0-7868-1560-9(4)) Hyperion Paperbacks for Children.

Keating, Frank. Theodore. Wimmer, Mike, illus. 2006. 32p. (J). (gr. 1-4). 16.95 (978-0-689-86532-9(5) , Simon & Schuster/Paula Wiseman Bks.) Simon & Schuster Children's Publishing.

Keller, Kristin Thoennes. George Washington. 2000. (Let Freedom Ring Ser.). (Illus.). 48p. (J). (gr. 3-4). lib. bdg. 22.60 (978-0-7368-1034-0(X) , Bridgestone Bks.) Capstone Pr., Inc.

Kelly, Michael. Bill Clinton. 1999. (Overcoming Adversity Ser.). (Illus.). 128p. (YA). (gr. 5 up). pap. 30.00 (978-0-7910-4701-9(6) , Chelsea Hse.) Facts On File, Inc.

—Bill Clinton. 2000. (Illus.). 112p. (J). (ps-7). per. 18.75 (978-0-613-11335-9(7)) Tandem Library Bks.

Kendall, Martha E. Herbert Hoover. 2004. (Encyclopedia of Presidents Ser.). (Illus.). 110p. (J). 34.00 (978-0-516-22963-8(X) , Children's Pr.) Scholastic Library Publishing.

Kent, Deborah. Franklin Delano Roosevelt: Nothing to Fear! 2006. (Defining Moments Ser.). (Illus.). 32p. (J). lib. bdg. 25.27 (978-1-59716-272-2(8)) Bearport Publishing Co., Inc.

—James A. Garfield. 2004. (Encyclopedia of Presidents Ser.). (Illus.). 110p. (J). 34.00 (978-0-516-22886-0(2) , Children's Pr.) Scholastic Library Publishing.

—Warren G. Harding. 2004. (Encyclopedia of Presidents Ser.). (Illus.). 110p. (J). 34.00 (978-0-516-22965-2(6) , Children's Pr.) Scholastic Library Publishing.

Kessler, Paula N. & Segal. Presidents Almanac. 2001. (J). (978-0-606-20863-5(1)) Tandem Library Bks.

Kessler, Paula N. & Segal, Justin. The President's Almanac. rev. ed. 1998. (History Ser.). (Illus.). 112p. (J). (gr. 4-7). pap. 8.95 (978-1-56565-978-0(3) , 09783W) Lowell Hse. Juvenile.

A Kid's Guide to Drawing the Presidents of the United States of America Set 1. 530.25 (978-1-4042-3020-0(3)) Rosen Publishing Group, Inc., The.

King, David C. Have Fun with the Presidents: Activites, Projects & Fascinating Facts. 2007. (Illus.). 128p. pap. 14.95 (978-0-471-67905-9(4) , Wiley) Wiley, John & Sons, Inc.

King, Wilma. Children of the Emancipation. 2005. (Picture the American Past Ser.). (Illus.). 48p. (gr. 2-5). 22.60 (978-1-57505-396-7(9)) Lerner Publishing Group.

Kishel, Ann-Marie. Thomas Jefferson: A Life of Patriotism. 2006. (Pull Ahead Books). (Illus.). 32p. (J). 22.60 (978-0-8225-3480-8(0) , Lerner Pubns.) Lerner Publishing Group.

—Thomas Jefferson: Una Vida de Patriotismo. 2006. (Libros para Avanzar Ser.). (ENG & SPA.). 32p. (J). lib. bdg. 22.60 (978-0-8225-6238-2(3) , Ediciones Lerner) Lerner Publishing Group.

Klingel, Cynthia Fitterer & Noyed, Robert B. Ronald Reagan: Our Fortieth President. 2001. (Spirit of America: Our Presidents Ser.). (Illus.). 48p. (J). (gr. 2-6). 28.50 (978-1-56766-874-2(7)) Child's World, Inc.

Knott, Stephen, et al. Presidential Profiles Set. 2005. (Presidential Profiles Ser.). 528-640p. (gr. 9). 255.00 (978-0-8160-5972-0(1)) Facts On File, Inc.

Knox, Barbara. Abraham Lincoln. Saunders-Smith, Gail, ed. 2004. (First Biographies Ser.). (Illus.). 24p. (J). (gr. k-1). lib. bdg. 15.93 (978-0-7368-2086-8(8) , Pebble Bks.) Capstone Pr., Inc.

—George Washington. Saunders-Smith, Gail, ed. 2003. (First Biographies Ser.). (Illus.). 24p. (J). (gr. k-1). lib. bdg. 15.93 (978-0-7368-2082-0(5) , Pebble Bks.) Capstone Pr., Inc.

Kops, Deborah. Zachary Taylor. 2004. (Encyclopedia of Presidents Ser.). (Illus.). 110p. (J). 34.00 (978-0-516-23442-7(0) , Children's Pr.) Scholastic Library Publishing.

Korman, Justine. Abraham Lincoln: Lawyer, Leader, Legend. 2001. (gr. k-3). lib. bdg. 11.80 (978-0-613-35057-0(X)) Tandem Library Bks.

Koslow, Philip. Famous Presidents. 1999. (Eyes on America Ser.). (Illus.). 29p. (J). (978-1-56156-709-6(4)) Kidsbooks, Inc.

Kozleski, Lisa. James Madison. 2003. (Childhoods of the Presidents Ser.). (Illus.). 48p. (J). (gr. 4 up). lib. bdg. (978-1-59084-269-0(3)) Mason Crest Pubs.

Kramer, Barbara. Jimmy Carter: A Life of Service. 2005. (Awesome Values in Famous Lives Ser.). (Illus.). 48p. (J). (ps-7). lib. bdg. 23.93 (978-0-7660-2379-6(6) , Enslow Elementary) Enslow Pubs., Inc.

Krensky, Stephen. Abe Lincoln & the Muddy Pig. 2002. (gr. k-3). lib. bdg. 11.80 (978-0-613-44998-4(3)) Tandem Library Bks.

—George Washington's First Victory. Dawson Hearn, Diane, illus. ed. 2005. 32p. (J). lib. bdg. 15.00 (978-1-59054-943-8(0)) Fitzgerald Bks.

—George Washington's First Victory. Hearn, Diane Dawson, illus. 2005. (Ready-to-Read Stories of Famous Americans Ser.). 32p. (J). pap. 3.99 (978-0-689-85942-7(2) , Aladdin) Simon & Schuster Children's Publishing.

Krull, Kathleen. Lives of the Presidents: Fame, Shame (And What the Neighbors Thought) annual Hewitt, Kathryn, illus. 1998. (Lives of... Ser.). 96p. (YA). (gr. 3-7). 20.00 (978-0-15-200808-6(X)) Harcourt Children's Bks.

—Lives of the Presidents: Fame, Shame (And What the Neighbors Thought) 1998. (Lives of the... Ser.). (Illus.). 96p. (YA). (gr. 3-8). lib. bdg. 29.97 (978-0-8172-4049-3(7)) Raintree.

—A Woman for President: The Story of Victoria Woodhull. Dyer, Jane, illus. 2006. 32p. (J). reprint ed. pap. 6.95 (978-0-8027-9615-8(X)) Walker & Co.

Landau, Elaine. The Emancipation Proclamation: Would You Do What Lincoln Did? 2008. (What Would You Do? Ser.). (Illus.). 48p. (J). (gr. 3-4). lib. bdg. 23.93 (***978-0-7660-2899-9(2)***, Enslow Elementary) Enslow Pubs., Inc.

—John F. Kennedy, Jr. 2000. (Single Titles Ser.). (Illus.). 128p. (J). (gr. 7 up). lib. bdg. (978-0-7613-1857-6(7), Twenty-First Century Bks.) Lerner Publishing Group.

—The President's Work: The Executive Branch. 2004. (How Government Works Ser.). (Illus.). 56p. (J). (gr. 4-8). lib. bdg. 25.26 (978-0-8225-0811-3(7)) Lerner Publishing Group.

—Warren G. Harding. 2005. (Presidential Leaders Ser.). (Illus.). 120p. (J). 29.27 (978-0-8225-0850-2(8), Lerner Pubns.) Lerner Publishing Group.

Larkin, Tanya. What Was Cooking in Edith Roosevelt's White House? 2001. (Cooking Throughout American History Ser.). (Illus.). 24p. (J). (gr. 3). lib. bdg. 19.95 (978-0-8239-5610-4(5), PowerKids Pr.) Rosen Publishing Group, Inc., The.

Lassieur, Allison. James Buchanan. 2004. (Encyclopedia of Presidents Ser.). (Illus.). 110p. (J). 34.00 (978-0-516-22884-6(6), Children's Pr.) Scholastic Library Publishing.

Lazo, Caroline Evensen. Franklin Pierce. 2007. (Presidential Leaders Ser.). 112p. (J). (gr. 6-12). 29.27 (978-0-8225-1492-3(3), Twenty-First Century Bks.) Lerner Publishing Group.

—Harry S. Truman. 2003. (Presidential Biography Ser.). (Illus.). 112p. (J). (gr. 6-12). lib. bdg. 29.27 (978-0-8225-0096-4(5)) Lerner Publishing Group.

Leighton, Marian. George Washington. Salvador, Martin, illus. 2005. (Heroes of America Ser.). 240p. (J). (gr. 3-8). lib. bdg. 21.35 (978-1-59679-262-3(0)) ABDO Publishing Co.

LeVert, Suzanne. The President. 2003. (Kaleidoscope - Government Ser.). (Illus.). 48p. (J). 25.64 (978-0-7614-1454-4(1), Benchmark Bks.) Cavendish, Marshall Corp.

Levine, Michelle & Waxman, Laura Hamilton. Franklin D. Roosevelt. 2005. (History Maker Bios Ser.). (Illus.). 48p. (J). (gr. 3-5). 26.60 (978-0-8225-1545-6(8)) Lerner Publishing Group.

Levy, Debbie. James Monroe. 2005. (Presidential Leaders Ser.). (Illus.). 112p. (J). 29.27 (978-0-8225-0824-3(9), Lerner Pubns.) Lerner Publishing Group.

—John Quincy Adams. 2005. (Presidential Leaders Ser.). (Illus.). 112p. (J). lib. bdg. 29.27 (978-0-8225-0825-0(7)) Lerner Publishing Group.

—Lyndon B. Johnson. 2003. (Presidential Leaders Ser.). (Illus.). 112p. (J). 29.27 (978-0-8225-0097-1(3), Lerner Pubns.) Lerner Publishing Group.

—Rutherford B. Hayes. 2007. (Presidential Leaders Ser.). (Illus.). 112p. (J). 29.27 (978-0-8225-1493-0(1), Lerner Pubns.) Lerner Publishing Group.

Lewis K., Parker. How to Draw the Life & Times of Richard M. Nixon. 2007. (Kid's Guide to Drawing the Presidents of the United States of America Ser.). (Illus.). 32p. (J). 25.25 (978-1-4042-3013-2(0), PowerKids Pr.) Rosen Publishing Group, Inc., The.

Lillard, David. William Henry Harrison: A MyReportLinks. Com Book. 2003. (Presidents Ser.). (Illus.). 48p. (J). lib. bdg. 25.26 (978-0-7660-5150-8(1), MyReportLinks.com Bks.) Enslow Pubs., Inc.

Lindop, Edmund. Presidents Who Dared. (Biographies Ser.). (Illus.). 64p. (978-0-7613-3084-4(4), Twenty-First Century Bks.) Lerner Publishing Group.

Long, Cathryn J. The Presidents. Nolte, Larry, illus. 2000. (Crossword America Ser.). 64p. (J). (gr. 3-7). pap. 5.95 (978-0-7373-0364-3(6), 03646W, Roxbury Park Juvenile) Lowell Hse. Juvenile.

Lucas, Jerry. States & Capitals & the Presidents: A Fun & Easy Way to Learn Through Pictures! 2000. (Ready - Set - Remember Ser.). (Illus.). 99p. (J). (gr. 1 up). pap. 16.95 (978-1-930853-03-4(3), 967-004) Lucas Educational Systems.

Lukes, Bonnie L. John Adams: Public Servant. 2004. (Notable Americans Ser.). (Illus.). 128p. (J). (gr. 6-12). 23.95 (978-1-883846-80-0(3), First Biographies) Reynolds, Morgan Inc.

—Woodrow Wilson & the Progressive Era. 2006. (World Leaders Ser.). (Illus.). 192p. (J). (gr. 6-10). lib. bdg. 26.95 (978-1-931798-79-2(6)) Reynolds, Morgan Inc.

Lusted, Marcia Amidon. Revolution & the New Nation. 2007. (***978-1-59036-739-1(1)***); (***978-1-59036-740-7(5)***) Weigl Pubs., Inc.

Lynne, Douglas. Contemporary United States. 2007. (J). (***978-1-59036-753-7(7)***); (***978-1-59036-754-4(5)***) Weigl Pubs., Inc.

Magoon, Kekla. Abraham Lincoln. 2007. (Essential Lives Ser.). (ENG., Illus.). 112p. (YA). (gr. 8-12). lib. bdg. 32.79 (***978-1-59928-839-0(7)***, Essential Library) ABDO Publishing Co.

Mara, Wil. Franklin D. Roosevelt. 2004. (Rookie Biographies Ser.). (Illus.). 31p. (J). 20.50 (978-0-516-21844-1(1), Children's Pr.) Scholastic Library Publishing.

—George W. Bush. 2003. (Rookie Biographies Ser.). (gr. 1-2). pap. 4.95 (978-0-516-27838-4(X), Children's Pr.) Scholastic Library Publishing.

—John Adams. 2008. (J). (***978-0-7614-2840-4(2)***) Cavendish, Marshall Bks., Ltd.

—Ronald Reagan. 2005. (Rookie Biographies(R) Ser.). 32p. (J). 20.50 (978-0-516-25271-1(2), Children's Pr.) Scholastic Library Publishing.

—Theodore Roosevelt. 2006. (Illus.). 31p. (J). (978-0-516-29844-3(5)) Children's Pr., Ltd.

Marcovitz, Hal. Bill Clinton. 2003. (Childhoods of the Presidents Ser.). (Illus.). 48p. (J). (gr. 4 up). lib. bdg. (978-1-59084-273-7(1)) Mason Crest Pubs.

—James Monroe. 2003. (Childhoods of the Presidents Ser.). (Illus.). 48p. (J). (gr. 4 up). lib. bdg. (978-1-59084-283-6(9)) Mason Crest Pubs.

—John Adams. 2003. (Childhoods of the Presidents Ser.). (Illus.). 48p. (J). (gr. 4 up). lib. bdg. (978-1-59084-268-3(5)) Mason Crest Pubs.

—John F. Kennedy. 2003. (Childhood of the Presidents Ser.). (Illus.). 48p. (J). (gr. 4 up). lib. bdg. (978-1-59084-272-0(3)) Mason Crest Pubs.

—Theodore Roosevelt. 2003. (Childhood of the Presidents Ser.). (Illus.). 48p. (J). (gr. 4 up). lib. bdg. (978-1-59084-278-2(2)) Mason Crest Pubs.

Margaret, Amy. Franklin D. Roosevelt Library & Museum. 2004. (Presidential Libraries Ser.). (Illus.). 24p. (J). lib. bdg. 18.75 (978-0-8239-6268-6(7), PowerKids Pr.) Rosen Publishing Group, Inc., The.

—John F. Kennedy Library & Museum. 2004. (Presidential Libraries Ser.). (Illus.). 24p. (J). lib. bdg. 18.75 (978-0-8239-6269-3(5), PowerKids Pr.) Rosen Publishing Group, Inc., The.

—Ronald Reagan Presidential Library. 2004. (Presidential Libraries Ser.). (Illus.). 24p. (J). lib. bdg. 18.75 (978-0-8239-6272-3(5), PowerKids Pr.) Rosen Publishing Group, Inc., The.

Markel, Rita J. Grover Cleveland. 2007. (Presidential Leaders Ser.). (Illus.). 112p. (J). 29.27 (978-0-8225-1494-7(X), Lerner Pubns.) Lerner Publishing Group.

Marquez, Heron. George W. Bush. 2007. (Presidential Leaders Ser.). (Illus.). 112p. (J). 29.27 (978-0-8225-1507-4(5), Lerner Pubns.) Lerner Publishing Group.

Marquez, Heron. Richard Nixon. 2003. (Presidential Leaders Ser.). (Illus.). 112p. (J). 29.27 (978-0-8225-0098-8(1), Lerner Pubns.) Lerner Publishing Group.

Marrin, Albert. The Great Adventure: Theodore Roosevelt & the Rise of Modern America. 2007. 256p. (YA). (gr. 7). 30.00 (***978-0-525-47659-7(8)***, Dutton Juvenile) Penguin Group (USA) Inc.

Marrin, Albert. Old Hickory: Andrew Jackson & the American People. 2004. 240p. (J). (gr. 7). 35.00 (978-0-525-47293-3(2), Dutton Juvenile) Penguin Group (USA) Inc.

Marsh, Carole. James Madison. 2002. (One Thousand Readers Ser.). (Illus.). 12p. (J). (gr. k-4). 2.95 (978-0-635-01492-4(0), 14920) Gallopade International.

—James Monroe. 2002. (One Thousand Readers Ser.). (Illus.). 12p. (J). (gr. k-4). 2.95 (978-0-635-01482-5(3), 14823) Gallopade International.

Martin, Justin. Easy Reader Biographies: George Washington: George Washington. 2007. 16p. pap. 2.99 (***978-0-439-92331-6(X)***, Teaching Resources) Scholastic, Inc.

Marx, David. Presidents' Day. 2002. (gr. k-3). lib. bdg. 14.10 (978-0-613-54301-9(7)) Tandem Library Bks.

Matuz, Roger. Complete American Presidents Sourcebook, 5 vols. Baker, Lawrence W., ed. (Illus.). (J). 2001. 1632p. (gr. 6-9). lib. bdg. 290.00 (978-0-7876-4837-4(X), GML00502-114881); 2000. (978-0-7876-4838-1(8)); 2000. (978-0-7876-4839-8(6)); 2000. (978-0-7876-4840-4(X)); 2000. (978-0-7876-4841-1(8)) Thomson Gale. (UXL).

Matuz, Roger & Baker, Lawrence W. Complete American Presidents Sourcebook, 5 vols. 2000. (Illus.). (J). (978-0-7876-4842-8(6)) Thomson Gale.

Maupin, Melissa. Calvin Coolidge: Our Thirtieth President. 2001. (Spirit of America: Our Presidents Ser.). (Illus.). 48p. (J). (gr. 2-6). 28.50 (978-1-56766-864-3(X)) Child's World, Inc.

—William Howard Taft: Our Twenty-Seventh President. 2001. (Spirit of America: Our Presidents Ser.). (Illus.). 48p. (J). (gr. 2-6). 28.50 (978-1-56766-835-3(6)) Child's World, Inc.

Mayer, Cassie. Abraham Lincoln. 2007. (J). (***978-1-4034-9968-4(3)***); pap. (***978-1-4034-9977-6(2)***) Heinemann Library.

—George Washington. 2007. (J). (***978-1-4034-9972-1(1)***); pap. (***978-1-4034-9981-3(0)***) Heinemann Library.

—Thomas Jefferson. 2007. (J). (***978-1-4034-9969-1(1)***); pap. (***978-1-4034-9978-3(0)***) Heinemann Library.

McCollum, Sean. James K. Polk. 2004. (Encyclopedia of Presidents Ser.). (Illus.). 110p. (J). 34.00 (978-0-516-22885-3(4), Children's Pr.) Scholastic Library Publishing.

—John Quincy Adams. 2003. (Encyclopedia of Presidents Ser.). (Illus.). 110p. (J). 34.00 (978-0-516-22867-9(6), Children's Pr.) Scholastic Library Publishing.

—Theodore Roosevelt. 2004. (Encyclopedia of Presidents Ser.). (Illus.). 110p. (J). 34.00 (978-0-516-22964-5(8), Children's Pr.) Scholastic Library Publishing.

McGraw-Hill Staff. The American Journey, Reconstruction to the Present. 2005. (C). stu. ed. 114.00 (978-0-07-867803-5(X), 9780078678035) Glencoe/McGraw-Hill.

—The American Journey, Reconstruction to the President: Active Reading Notetaking Guide. 2004. stu. ed. 18.00 (978-0-07-868547-7(8), 9780078685477) Glencoe/McGraw-Hill.

McLeese, Don. Thomas Jefferson. (Heroes of the American Revolution Ser.). 32p. 2005. (Illus.). (gr. 2-5). 19.95 (978-1-59515-217-6(2)); 2004. pap. 5.95 (978-1-59515-318-0(7)) Rourke Publishing, LLC.

—Ulysses S. Grant. 2006. (Civil War Military Leaders Ser.). (Illus.). 32p. (gr. 3-6). 19.95 (978-1-59515-475-0(2)) Rourke Publishing, LLC.

McPherson, Stephanie Sammartino. Theodore Roosevelt. 2005. (Presidential Leaders Ser.). (Illus.). 112p. (J). 29.27 (978-0-8225-0999-8(7), Lerner Pubns.) Lerner Publishing Group.

Meisner, James, Jr. & Ruth, Amy. American Revolutionaries & Founders of the Nation. 1999. (Collective Biographies Ser.). (Illus.). 112p. (YA). (gr. 6-12). lib. bdg. 26.60 (978-0-7660-1115-1(1)) Enslow Pubs., Inc.

Mello, Tara Baukus. George Washington: First U. S. President. 2000. (gr. 5-8). lib. bdg. 17.60 (978-0-613-43323-5(8)) Tandem Library Bks.

Miller, Brandon Marie. George Washington for Kids: His Life & Times with 21 Activities. 2007. (For Kids Ser.). 144p. (J). pap. 14.95 (***978-1-55652-655-8(5)***) Chicago Review Pr., Inc.

Milton, Joyce. Who Was Ronald Reagan? Harrison, Nancy & Wolf, Elizabeth, illus. 2004. (Who Was... ? Ser.). 112p. (J). (gr. 3-7). lib. bdg. 13.89 (978-0-448-43345-5(1), Grosset & Dunlap) Penguin Group (USA) Inc.

—Who Was Ronald Reagan? Wolf, Elizabeth, illus. 2005. 106p. (J). (gr. 2-6). lib. bdg. 12.19 (978-0-606-33099-2(2)) Tandem Library Bks.

Mir Tamim Ansary. Presidents' Day. 2nd ed. 2006. (Illus.). 32p. (J). pap. (***978-1-4034-8904-3(1)***) Heinemann Library.

Mis, Melody S. How to Draw the Life & Times of Andrew Jackson. 2006. (Kid's Guide to Drawing the Presidents of the United States of America Ser.). (J). 25.25 (978-1-4042-2984-6(1), PowerKids Pr.) Rosen Publishing Group, Inc., The.

—How to Draw the Life & Times of Benjamin Harrison. 2007. (Kid's Guide to Drawing the Presidents of the United States of America Ser.). (Illus.). 32p. (J). 25.25 (978-1-4042-3000-2(9), PowerKids Pr.) Rosen Publishing Group, Inc., The.

—How to Draw the Life & Times of Franklin Delano Roosevelt. 2007. (Kid's Guide to Drawing the Presidents of the United States of America Ser.). (Illus.). 32p. (J). 25.25 (978-1-4042-3008-8(4), PowerKids Pr.) Rosen Publishing Group, Inc., The.

—How to Draw the Life & Times of James Buchanan. 2006. (Kid's Guide to Drawing the Presidents of the United States of America Ser.). (J). 25.25 (978-1-4042-2992-1(2), PowerKids Pr.) Rosen Publishing Group, Inc., The.

—How to Draw the Life & Times of James K. Polk. 2006. (Kid's Guide to Drawing the Presidents of the United States of America Ser.). (J). 25.25 (978-1-4042-2988-4(4), PowerKids Pr.) Rosen Publishing Group, Inc., The.

—How to Draw the Life & Times of Lyndon B. Johnson. 2007. (Kid's Guide to Drawing the Presidents of the United States of America Ser.). (Illus.). 32p. (J). 25.25 (978-1-4042-3012-5(2), PowerKids Pr.) Rosen Publishing Group, Inc., The.

—How to Draw the Life & Times of Ronald Reagan. 2007. (Kid's Guide to Drawing the Presidents of the United States of America Ser.). (Illus.). 32p. (J). 25.25 (978-1-4042-3016-3(5), PowerKids Pr.) Rosen Publishing Group, Inc., The.

—How to Draw the Life & Times of Rutherford B. Hayes. 2006. (Kid's Guide to Drawing the Presidents of the United States of America Ser.). (J). 25.25 (978-1-4042-2996-9(5), PowerKids Pr.) Rosen Publishing Group, Inc., The.

—How to Draw the Life & Times of Thomas Jefferson. 2006. (Kid's Guide to Drawing the Presidents of the United States of America Ser.). (J). 25.25 (978-1-4042-2980-8(9), PowerKids Pr.) Rosen Publishing Group, Inc., The.

—How to Draw the Life & Times of Woodrow Wilson. 2007. (Kid's Guide to Drawing the Presidents of the United States of America Ser.). (Illus.). 32p. (J). 25.25 (978-1-4042-3004-0(1), PowerKids Pr.) Rosen Publishing Group, Inc., The.

Morris, Deborah & Morris, Larry. American History: Presidents: Grade 4-5. Carlson, Andy, illus. 2005. 80p. per. 2.95 (978-1-59441-267-7(7), RB-904000) Carson-Dellosa Publishing Co., Inc.

Morris, Judith. At Home with the Presidents. 1999. (gr. 5-8). lib. bdg. 22.20 (978-0-613-16459-7(8)) Tandem Library Bks.

—At Home with the Presidents. 1999. (Illus.). 176p. (gr. 5-9). pap. 13.95 (978-0-471-25300-6(6), Wiley) Wiley, John & Sons, Inc.

Morrison, John. Luis Inacio Da Silva. 2005. (Major World Leaders Ser.). (Illus.). 112-144p. (J). (gr. 6-12). 30.00 (978-0-7910-8261-4(X), Chelsea Hse.) Facts On File, Inc.

Murphy, Frank. George Washington & the General's Dog. Walz, Richard, illus. 2002. (Step into Reading Ser.). 48p. (J). (gr. 1-3). pap. 3.99 (978-0-375-81015-2(3)); lib. bdg. 11.99 (978-0-375-91015-9(8)) Random Hse. Children's Bks. (Random Hse. Bks. for Young Readers).

—Thomas Jefferson's Feast. Walz, Richard, illus. 2003. 48p. (J). (gr. 2-4). pap. 3.99 (978-0-375-82289-6(5), Random Hse. Bks. for Young Readers) Random Hse. Children's Bks.

—Thomas Jefferson's Feast. 2003. (gr. k-3). lib. bdg. 11.80 (978-0-613-86238-7(4)) Tandem Library Bks.

Murphy, John. The Impeachment Process. 2007. (U. S. Government: How It Works). 104p. (J). (gr. 5-8). 30.00 (***978-0-7910-9465-5(0)***, Chelsea Hse.) Facts On File, Inc.

Murphy, Patricia J. The Presidency. 2001. (Let's See Library). (Illus.). 24p. (J). (gr. 1 up). lib. bdg. 19.93 (978-0-7565-0142-6(3)) Compass Point Bks.

Murray, Julie. President's Day. 2005. (Buddy Book Ser.). (Illus.). 24p. (J). (gr. k-4). lib. bdg. 21.35 (978-1-59197-590-8(5)) ABDO Publishing Co.

Nardo, Don. Andrew Johnson. 2004. (Encyclopedia of Presidents Ser.). (Illus.). 110p. (J). 34.00 (978-0-516-24242-2(3), Children's Pr.) Scholastic Library Publishing.

Nelson, Robin. George Washington: A Life of Leadership. 2006. (Pull Ahead Books). (Illus.). 32p. (J). 22.60 (978-0-8225-3474-7(6), Lerner Pubns.) Lerner Publishing Group.

—George Washington: Una Vida de Liderazgo (A Life of Leadership) 2006. (Libros para Avanzar Ser.). (ENG & SPA.). 32p. (J). lib. bdg. 22.60 (978-0-8225-6235-1(9), Ediciones Lerner) Lerner Publishing Group.

Nixon Resigns. 2002. (History in the Headlines Ser.). 32p. (gr. 6-8). 6.99 (978-0-7682-0470-4(4), GA131695) School Specialty Publishing.

Ochester, Betsy. Grover Cleveland. 2004. (Encyclopedia of Presidents Ser.). (Illus.). 110p. (J). 34.00 (978-0-516-22962-1(1), Children's Pr.) Scholastic Library Publishing.

—John Tyler. 2003. (Encyclopedia of Presidents Ser.). (Illus.). 110p. (J). 34.00 (978-0-516-22850-1(1), Children's Pr.) Scholastic Library Publishing.

O'Connell, Kim A. Slavery, Emancipation, & the Civil War: A MyReportLinks. com Book. 2004. (American Civil War Ser.). (Illus.). 48p. (J). lib. bdg. 25.26 (978-0-7660-5190-4(0), MyReportLinks.com Bks.) Enslow Pubs., Inc.

—William Howard Taft: A MyReportLinks.com Book. 2003. (Presidents Ser.). (Illus.). 48p. (J). (gr. 4-10). lib. bdg. 25.26 (978-0-7660-5078-5(5), MyReportLinks.com Bks.) Enslow Pubs., Inc.

O'Connor, Jane. If the Walls Could Talk: Family Life at the White House. Hovland, Gary, illus. 2004. 48p. (J). 16.95 (978-0-689-86863-4(4), Simon & Schuster/Paula Wiseman Bks.) Simon & Schuster Children's Publishing.

Olson, Nathan. John F. Kennedy: American Visionary. Bascle, Brian, illus. 2007. (J). (978-0-7368-6852-5(6)) Capstone Pr., Inc.

Olson, Nathan. Theodore Roosevelt: Bear of a President. Martin, Cynthia et al, illus. 2007. (Graphic Library). 32p. (J). (gr. 3-5). 25.26 (***978-0-7368-6849-5(6)***, 1264944); pap. 7.95 (***978-0-7368-7901-9(3)***, 1264944) Capstone Pr., Inc.

Olson, Tod & Doherty, Kieran. Andrew Jackson. 2003. (Encyclopedia of Presidents Ser.). (Illus.). 110p. (J). 34.00 (978-0-516-22760-3(2), Children's Pr.) Scholastic Library Publishing.

Orr, Tamra. Ronald Reagan. 2003. (Childhoods of the Presidents Ser.). (Illus.). 48p. (J). (gr. 4 up). lib. bdg. (978-1-59084-280-5(4)) Mason Crest Pubs.

O'Shei, Tim. Bill Clinton: A MyReportLinks. Com Book. 2003. (Presidents Ser.). (Illus.). 48p. (J). lib. bdg. 25.26 (978-0-7660-5149-2(8), MyReportLinks.com Bks.) Enslow Pubs., Inc.

—Gerald R. Ford: A MyReportLinks.com Book. 2003. (Presidents Ser.). (Illus.). 48p. (J). (gr. 5-10). lib. bdg. 25.26 (978-0-7660-5050-1(5), MyReportLinks.com Bks.) Enslow Pubs., Inc.

—Ulysses S. Grant. 2001. (gr. 5-8). lib. bdg. 17.60 (978-0-613-33176-0(1)) Tandem Library Bks.

O'Shei, Tim & Marren, Joe. James Monroe: A MyReportLinks.com Book. 2002. (Presidents Ser.). (Illus.). 48p. (J). (gr. 4-10). lib. bdg. 25.26 (978-0-7660-5076-1(9)) Enslow Pubs., Inc.

Otfinoski, Steven. Calvin Coolidge. 2008. (J). (***978-0-7614-2836-7(4)***) Cavendish, Marshall Bks., Ltd.

Otfinoski, Steven. Rutherford B. Hayes. 2004. (Encyclopedia of Presidents Ser.). (Illus.). 110p. (J). 34.00 (978-0-516-22866-2(8), Children's Pr.) Scholastic Library Publishing.

Our Presidents & First Ladies of the White House. 119.40 (978-0-8249-6046-9(7)) Ideals Pubns.

Owens, L. L. Abraham Lincoln: A Great American Life. 2000. (Cover-to-Cover Bks.). (Illus.). (J). 55p. pap. (978-0-7891-5162-9(6)); 56p. (gr. 1-4). lib. bdg. 16.95 (978-0-7807-9307-1(2)) Perfection Learning Corp.

Panchyk, Richard. Franklin Delano Roosevelt for Kids: His Life & Times with 21 Activities. 2007. (For Kids Ser.). 160p. (J). pap. 14.95 (***978-1-55652-657-2(1)***) Chicago Review Pr., Inc.

Parker, Lewis K. How to Draw the Life & Times of George H. W. Bush. 2007. (Kid's Guide to Drawing the Presidents of the United States of America Ser.). (Illus.). 32p. (J). 25.25 (978-1-4042-3017-0(3), PowerKids Pr.) Rosen Publishing Group, Inc., The.

—How to Draw the Life & Times of Harry S. Truman. 2007. (Kid's Guide to Drawing the Presidents of the United States of America Ser.). (Illus.). 32p. (J). 25.25 (978-1-4042-3009-5(2), PowerKids Pr.) Rosen Publishing Group, Inc., The.

—How to Draw the Life & Times of James A. Garfield. 2006. (Kid's Guide to Drawing the Presidents of the United States of America Ser.). (J). 25.25 (978-1-4042-2997-6(3), PowerKids Pr.) Rosen Publishing Group, Inc., The.

—How to Draw the Life & Times of Warren G. Harding. 2007. (Kid's Guide to Drawing the Presidents of the United States of America Ser.). (Illus.). 32p. (J). 25.25 (978-1-4042-3005-7(X), PowerKids Pr.) Rosen Publishing Group, Inc., The.

—How to Draw the Life & Times of William McKinley. 2007. (Kid's Guide to Drawing the Presidents of the United States of America Ser.). (Illus.). 32p. (J). 25.25 (978-1-4042-3001-9(7), PowerKids Pr.) Rosen Publishing Group, Inc., The.

Parker, Lewis M. George Washington. 2002. (Triangle History of the American Revolution Ser.). (Illus.). 104p. (J). 28.70 (978-1-56711-607-6(8), Blackbirch Pr., Inc.) Thomson Gale.

Patrick, Bethanne Kelly. Ulysses S. Grant. 2003. (Childhoods of the Presidents Ser.). (Illus.). 48p. (J). (gr. 4 up). lib. bdg. (978-1-59084-276-8(6)) Mason Crest Pubs.

Petty, Kate. Abraham Lincoln: The Life of America's Sixteenth President. 2005. (Graphic Nonfiction Ser.). (Illus.). 48p. (J). (gr. 4-6). lib. bdg. 26.50 (978-1-4042-0237-5(4)) Rosen Publishing Group, Inc., The.

Pflueger, Lynda. Thomas Jefferson: Creating a Nation. 2004. (America's Founding Fathers Ser.). (Illus.). 128p. (J). lib. bdg. 26.60 (978-0-7660-2212-6(9)) Enslow Pubs., Inc.

Phillips, Ellen Blue. Sterling Biographies: Abraham Lincoln: From Pioneer to President. 2007. (Sterling Biographies Ser.). (Illus.). 128p. (J). 12.95 (978-1-4027-4745-8(4)) Sterling Publishing Co., Inc.

Pingry, Patricia A. Meet George Washington. 2001. (Meet Ser.). (Illus.). 32p. (J). (ps-3). 9.95 (978-0-8249-4131-4(4)) Ideals Pubns.

—Meet Thomas Jefferson. Johnson, Meredith, ed. Johnson, Meredith, illus. 2003. 32p. (J). 9.95 (978-0-8249-5459-8(9)) Ideals Pubns.

—The Story of Ronald Reagan. 2006. (Illus.). 26p. (J). bds. 6.95 (978-0-8249-6621-8(X) , Candy Cane Pr.) Ideals Pubns.

Pious, Richard M. The Presidency of the United States: A Student Companion. 2nd ed. 2001. (Student Companions to American History Ser.). (Illus.). 320p. (YA). stu. ed., suppl. ed. 60.00 (978-0-19-515006-3(6)) Oxford Univ. Pr., Inc.

Plaut, Michael F. How to Draw the Life & Times of Gerald R. Ford. 2007. (Kid's Guide to Drawing the Presidents of the United States of America Ser.). (Illus.). 32p. (J). 25.25 (978-1-4042-3014-9(9) , PowerKids Pr.) Rosen Publishing Group, Inc., The.

The Presidency of the United States. (American Civics Ser.). 48p. (YA). 6.95 (978-0-7368-8855-4(1)) Capstone Pr., Inc.

Presidential Profiles Set. 2005. (Presidential Profiles Ser.). 528p. (gr. 9). 510.00 (978-0-8160-6514-1(4)) Facts On File, Inc.

Presidents. 1998. (High Q Books Ser.). (Illus.). 60p. (J). (gr. 2-4). pap. 2.99 (978-0-7681-0069-3(0) , McClanahan Bk.) Learning Horizons, Inc.

Presidents. (Mini Question & Answers America Ser.). 32p. Date not set. (J). 3.98 (978-0-7525-9874-1(0)); 2000. (YA). 7.49 (978-0-7525-4643-8(0)) Parragon, Inc.

Presidents. 2005. (Illus.). 96p. 12.98 (978-0-7853-9599-7(7) , 7127401) Publications International, Ltd.

Presidents: Discover the Presidents Who Have Shaped American History, from the Founding Fathers to Today's Leaders. rev. ed. 2001. (Eyewitness Books). (Illus.). 64p. (J). 15.95 (978-0-7894-6285-5(0)) Dorling Kindersley Publishing, Inc.

Presidents: Understanding America's Presidents Through Research-Related Activities. 3rd ed. 176p. (gr. 4 up). 15.99 (978-0-7682-2458-0(6) , GA15017) School Specialty Publishing.

Presidents: U.S. Presidents: Feats & Foul-Ups. 2005. (Illus.). 32p. (J). pap. (***978-0-439-78476-4(X)***) Scholastic, Inc.

Presidents of the U. S. Fact Cards. 2nd ed. 2001. 90p. (J). ring bd. 36.00 (978-1-884925-77-1(4)) Toucan Valley Pubns., Inc.

Price Hossell, Karen. The Emancipation Proclamation. 2005. (Illus.). 48p. (J). (978-1-4034-6813-0(3)); pap. (978-1-4034-6818-5(4)) Heinemann Library.

—John F. Kennedy's Inaugural Speech. 2005. (Illus.). 48p. (J). (978-1-4034-6810-9(9)); pap. (978-1-4034-6815-4(X)) Heinemann Library.

Profiles of the Presidents, 42 bks. Incl. Abraham Lincoln. Blashfield, Jean F. 2002. lib. bdg. 23.93 (978-0-7565-0202-7(0)); Andrew Jackson. Somervill, Barbara A. 2003. lib. bdg. 23.93 (978-0-7565-0255-3(1)); Andrew Johnson. Burgan, Michael. 2003. lib. bdg. 23.93 (978-0-7565-0264-5(0)); Benjamin Harrison. Green, Robert. 2003. lib. bdg. 23.93 (978-0-7565-0270-6(5)); Calvin Coolidge. Doak, Robin S. 2003. lib. bdg. 23.93 (978-0-7565-0276-8(4)); Chester A. Arthur. Santella, Andrew. 2003. lib. bdg. 23.93 (978-0-7565-0268-3(3)); Dwight D. Eisenhower. Raatma, Lucia. 2002. lib. bdg. 23.93 (978-0-7565-0279-9(9)); Franklin D. Roosevelt. Burgan, Michael. 2002. lib. bdg. 23.93 (978-0-7565-0203-4(9)); Franklin Pierce. Somervill, Barbara A. 2002. lib. bdg. 23.93 (978-0-7565-0262-1(4)); George H. W. Bush. Davis, Marc. 2002. lib. bdg. 23.93 (978-0-7565-0285-0(3)); George W. Bush. Burgan, Michael. 2003. lib. bdg. 23.93 (978-0-7565-0338-3(8)); George Washington. Burgan, Michael. 2002. lib. bdg. 23.93 (978-0-7565-0204-1(7)); Gerald R. Ford. Santella, Andrew. 2003. lib. bdg. 23.93 (978-0-7565-0282-9(9)); Grover Cleveland. Williams, Jean Kinney. 2003. lib. bdg. 23.93 (978-0-7565-0269-0(1)); Harry S. Truman. Cannarella, Deborah. 2002. lib. bdg. 23.93 (978-0-7565-0278-2(0)); Herbert Hoover. Teitelbaum, Michael. 2002. lib. bdg. 23.93 (978-0-7565-0277-5(2)); James A. Garfield. Doak, Robin S. 2003. lib. bdg. 23.93 (978-0-7565-0267-6(5)); James Buchanan. Santella, Andrew. 2003. lib. bdg. 23.93 (978-0-7565-0263-8(2)); James Earl Carter, Jr. Santella, Andrew. 2002. lib. bdg. 23.93 (978-0-7565-0283-6(7)); James K. Polk. Somervill, Barbara A. 2003. lib. bdg. 23.93 (978-0-7565-0259-1(4)); James Madison. Santella, Andrew. 2002. lib. bdg. 23.93 (978-0-7565-0252-2(7)); James Monroe. Teitelbaum, Michael. 2002. lib. bdg. 23.93 (978-0-7565-0253-9(5)); John Adams. Santella, Andrew. 2002. lib. bdg. 23.93 (978-0-7565-0251-5(9)); John F. Kennedy. Raatma, Lucia. 2002. lib. bdg. 23.93 (978-0-7565-0205-8(5)); John Quincy Adams. Burgan, Michael. 2003. lib. bdg. 23.93 (978-0-7565-0254-6(3)); John Tyler. Doak, Robin S. 2003. lib. bdg. 23.93 (978-0-7565-0258-4(6)); Lyndon Baines Johnson. Burgan, Michael. 2003. lib. bdg. 23.93 (978-0-7565-0280-5(2)); Martin Van Buren. Doak, Robin S. 2003. lib. bdg. 23.93 (978-0-7565-0256-0(X)); Millard Fillmore. Santella, Andrew. 2003. lib. bdg. 23.93 (978-0-7565-0261-4(6)); Richard M. Nixon. Green, Robert. 2003. lib. bdg. 23.93 (978-0-7565-0281-2(0)); Ronald W. Reagan. Williams, Jean Kinney. 2003. lib. bdg. 23.93 (978-0-7565-0284-3(5)); Rutherford B. Hayes. Santella, Andrew. 2003. lib. bdg. 23.93 (978-0-7565-0266-9(7)); Theodore Roosevelt. Green, Robert. 2003. lib. bdg. 23.93 (978-0-7565-0272-0(1)); Thomas Jefferson. Heinrichs, Ann. 2002. lib. bdg. 23.93 (978-0-7565-0206-5(3)); Ulysses S. Grant. Williams, Jean Kinney. 2002. lib. bdg. 23.93 (978-0-7565-0265-2(9)); Warren G. Harding. Somervill, Barbara A. 2003. lib. bdg. 23.93 (978-0-7565-0275-1(6)); William Henry Harrison. Doak, Robin S. 2003. lib. bdg. 23.93 (978-0-7565-0257-7(8)); William Howard Taft. Burgan, Michael. 2003. lib. bdg. 23.93 (978-0-7565-0273-7(X)); William Jefferson Clinton. Heinrichs, Ann. 2002. lib. bdg. 23.93 (978-0-7565-0207-2(1)); William McKinley. Doak, Robin S. 2003. lib. bdg. 23.93 (978-0-7565-0271-3(3)); Woodrow Wilson. Green, Robert. 2003. lib. bdg. 23.93 (978-0-7565-0274-4(8)); Zachary Taylor. Doak, Robin S. 2003. lib. bdg. 23.93 (978-0-7565-0260-7(8)); 64p. (J). (gr. 4 up). (Illus.). Set lib. bdg. 1005.06 (978-0-7565-0408-3(2)) Compass Point Bks.

Quiri, Patricia Ryon. The Presidency. 1998. (True Bks.). (Illus.). 48p. (J). (gr. 3-5). 25.00 (978-0-516-20674-5(5) , Children's Pr.) Scholastic Library Publishing.

Raatma, Lucia. Dwight D. Eisenhower. 2002. (Profiles of the Presidents Ser.). (Illus.). 64p. (J). (gr. 4 up). lib. bdg. 23.93 (978-0-7565-0279-9(9)) Compass Point Bks.

—Thomas Jefferson. 2001. (Compass Point Early Biographies Ser.). (Illus.). 32p. (J). (gr. 2 up). lib. bdg. 21.26 (978-0-7565-0070-2(2)) Compass Point Bks.

Randolph, Ryan P. How to Draw the Life & Times of Andrew Johnson. 2006. (Kid's Guide to Drawing the Presidents of the United States of America Ser.). (J). 25.25 (978-1-4042-2994-5(9) , PowerKids Pr.) Rosen Publishing Group, Inc., The.

—How to Draw the Life & Times of Dwight D. Eisenhower. (Kid's Guide to Drawing the Presidents of the United States of America Ser.). (Illus.). 32p. (J). 2007. 25.25 (978-1-4042-3010-1(6)); 2006. lib. bdg. (***978-4-04-230106-6(1)***) Rosen Publishing Group, Inc., The. (PowerKids Pr.).

—How to Draw the Life & Times of John Adams. 2006. (Kid's Guide to Drawing the Presidents of the United States of America Ser.). (J). 25.25 (978-1-4042-2979-2(5) , PowerKids Pr.) Rosen Publishing Group, Inc., The.

—How to Draw the Life & Times of Millard Fillmore. 2006. (Kid's Guide to Drawing the Presidents of the United States of America Ser.). (J). 25.25 (978-1-4042-2990-7(6) , PowerKids Pr.) Rosen Publishing Group, Inc., The.

—How to Draw the Life & Times of William Howard Taft. 2007. (Kid's Guide to Drawing the Presidents of the United States of America Ser.). (Illus.). 32p. (J). 25.25 (978-1-4042-3003-3(3) , PowerKids Pr.) Rosen Publishing Group, Inc., The.

Ransom, Candice F. George Washington. 2002. (History Maker Bios Ser.). (Illus.). 47p. (J). pap. 6.95 (978-0-8225-0384-2(0)); (gr. 2-4). 26.60 (978-0-8225-0374-3(3)) Lerner Publishing Group. (Lerner Pubns.).

Rausch, Monica. Andrew Jackson. 2006. (J). (ENG & SPA.). pap. (***978-0-8368-7989-6(9)***); (ENG & SPA.). lib. bdg. (***978-0-8368-7982-7(1)***); (Illus.). 24p. pap. (***978-0-8368-7690-1(3)***); (Illus.). 24p. lib. bdg. (***978-0-8368-7683-3(0)***) Stevens, Gareth Inc. (Weekly Reader Early Learning Library).

—Thomas Jefferson. 2006. (ENG & SPA.). (J). pap. (***978-0-8368-7990-2(2)***); lib. bdg. (***978-0-8368-7983-4(X)***) Stevens, Gareth Inc. (Weekly Reader Early Learning Library).

Renehan, Edward. The Clintons. 2005. (J). (978-0-7910-8526-4(0) , Chelsea Hse.) Facts On File, Inc.

Rice, Earle, Jr. Ulysses S. Grant: Defender of the Union. 2005. (Civil War Leaders Ser.). (Illus.). 176p. (J). (gr. 6-12). 26.95 (978-1-931798-48-8(6)) Reynolds, Morgan Inc.

Riehecky, Janet. Ulysses S. Grant. 2004. (Encyclopedia of Presidents Ser.). (Illus.). 110p. (J). 34.00 (978-0-516-22868-6(4) , Children's Pr.) Scholastic Library Publishing.

—William McKinley. 2004. (Encyclopedia of Presidents Ser.). (Illus.). 110p. (J). 34.00 (978-0-516-22966-9(4) , Children's Pr.) Scholastic Library Publishing.

Riley, Gail Blasser. U. S. Presidents. Blasser-Riley, Gail, illus. 2001. (Homework Booklets Ser.). 60p. (J). (gr. 4-6). pap. 2.99 (978-0-7424-0155-6(3) , IF0239) School Specialty Publishing.

Rinaldo, Denise. White House Q & A. 2008. 48p. (J). (gr. k-4). 16.99 (***978-0-06-089966-0(2)***); pap. 7.99 (***978-0-06-089965-3(4)***) HarperCollins Pubs. (Collins).

Rivera, Sheila. Abraham Lincoln: A Life of Respect. 2006. (Pull Ahead Books). (Illus.). 32p. (J). 22.60 (978-0-8225-3473-0(8) , Lerner Pubns.) Lerner Publishing Group.

—Abraham Lincoln: Una Vida de Respeto. 2006. (Libros para Avanzar Ser.). (ENG & SPA.). 32p. (J). lib. bdg. 22.60 (978-0-8225-6236-8(7)) Lerner Publishing Group.

Robb, Don. Hail to the Chief: The American Presidency. Witschonke, Alan, illus. 2004. 31p. (J). (ps-3). 16.95 (978-0-88106-392-9(4)); pap. 7.95 (978-0-88106-393-6(2)) Charlesbridge Publishing, Inc.

—Hail to the Chief: The American Presidency. Witschonke, Alan, illus. 2000. 31p. (J). (ps-3). lib. bdg. 16.40 (978-0-613-35133-1(9)) Tandem Library Bks.

—Hail to the Chief: The American Presidency. 2000. (J). 14.75 (978-0-606-19328-3(6)) Tandem Library Bks.

Roberts, Jeremy. Franklin D. Roosevelt. 2003. (Presidential Leaders Ser.). (Illus.). 112p. (J). (gr. 6-12). lib. bdg. 29.27 (978-0-8225-0095-7(7)) Lerner Publishing Group.

—George Washington. 2004. (Presidential Leaders Ser.). (Illus.). 112p. (J). (gr. 6-12). lib. bdg. 29.27 (978-0-8225-0818-2(4)) Lerner Publishing Group.

—James Madison. 2004. (Presidential Leaders Ser.). (Illus.). 112p. (J). (gr. 6-12). lib. bdg. 29.27 (978-0-8225-0823-6(0)) Lerner Publishing Group.

Roberts, Russell. Presidents & Scandals. 2000. (History Makers Ser.). (Illus.). 112p. (J). (gr. 7-10). 28.70 (978-1-56006-642-2(3) , Lucent Bks.) Thomson Gale.

Robinson, Tom. The Development of the Industrial United States. 2007. (J). (***978-1-59036-745-2(6)***); (***978-1-59036-746-9(4)***) Weigl Pubs., Inc.

Rockwell, Anne F. Big George. Trueman, Matthew, illus. 2004. (J). 16.00 (978-0-15-216583-3(5) , Silver Whistle) Harcourt Trade Pubs.

Roleff, Tamara. What Limits Should Be Placed on Presidential Powers? 2006. (Illus.). 128p. (gr. 10-12). 21.20 (978-0-7377-3630-4(5)); pap. 29.95 (978-0-7377-3629-8(1)) Thomson Gale. (Greenhaven Pr., Inc.).

Rosinsky, Natalie M. Presidents' Day. 2004. (Let's See Ser.). (Illus.). 24p. (J). (gr. 1 up). lib. bdg. 19.93 (978-0-7565-0773-2(1)) Compass Point Bks.

Rubel, David. Scholastic Encyclopedia of the Presidents & Their Times. 2005. (Illus.). 256p. (J). pap. 19.95 (978-0-439-28323-6(X) , Scholastic Reference) Scholastic, Inc.

Ruffin, Frances E. How to Draw the Life & Times of Theodore Roosevelt. 2007. (Kid's Guide to Drawing the Presidents of the United States of America Ser.). (Illus.). 32p. (J). 25.25 (978-1-4042-3002-6(5) , PowerKids Pr.) Rosen Publishing Group, Inc., The.

Ruth, Amy. Herbert Hoover. 2004. (Presidential Leaders Ser.). (Illus.). 112p. (J). (gr. 6-12). lib. bdg. 29.27 (978-0-8225-0821-2(4)) Lerner Publishing Group.

Saffer, Barbara. Harry S. Truman. 2003. (Childhoods of the Presidents Ser.). (Illus.). 48p. (J). (gr. 4 up). lib. bdg. (978-1-59084-282-9(0)) Mason Crest Pubs.

Sandak, Cass R. The White House. 1999. (American Government Today Ser.). (Illus.). 48p. (J). (gr. 4-7). lib. bdg. 22.83 (978-0-7398-1791-9(4)) Raintree.

Sandifer, Kevin W., ed. History of the United States, Reconstruction-Clinton Era Pt. 2. l.t. ed. 2007. (Illus.). 432p. lib. bdg. (978-0-910653-61-9(5) , 8202U, Red River Pr.) Red River Pr.

Sandler, Martin W. Presidents. 2000. (Library of Congress Classics). (Illus.). 96p. (J). (gr. 3 up). pap. 10.95 (978-0-06-446263-1(3) , Harper Trophy) HarperCollins Pubs.

—Presidents: A Library of Congress Book. 2001. (Illus.). (J). (978-0-606-20862-8(3)) Tandem Library Bks.

Santella, Andrew. Air Force One. 2003. (Illus.). 48p. (gr. 4 up). (J). pap. 8.95 (978-0-7613-1926-9(3)); (Women at War Ser.: up). lib. bdg. 24.90 (978-0-7613-2617-5(0)) Lerner Publishing Group. (Millbrook Pr.).

—Chester A. Arthur. 2003. (Profiles of the Presidents Ser.). (Illus.). 64p. (J). (gr. 4 up). lib. bdg. 23.93 (978-0-7565-0268-3(3)) Compass Point Bks.

—James Earl Carter, Jr. 2002. (Profiles of the Presidents Ser.). (Illus.). 64p. (J). (gr. 4 up). lib. bdg. 23.93 (978-0-7565-0283-6(7)) Compass Point Bks.

—James Madison. 2002. (Profiles of the Presidents Ser.). (Illus.). 64p. (J). (gr. 4 up). lib. bdg. 23.93 (978-0-7565-0252-2(7)) Compass Point Bks.

—James Monroe. 2003. (Encyclopedia of Presidents Ser.). (Illus.). 110p. (J). 34.00 (978-0-516-24200-2(8) , Children's Pr.) Scholastic Library Publishing.

—John Adams. 2002. (Profiles of the Presidents Ser.). (Illus.). 64p. (J). (gr. 4 up). lib. bdg. 23.93 (978-0-7565-0251-5(9)) Compass Point Bks.

—John Kerry. 2004. (Profiles of the Presidents Ser.). (J). (978-0-7565-0858-6(4)) Compass Point Bks.

—Millard Fillmore. 2003. (Profiles of the Presidents Ser.). (Illus.). 64p. (J). (gr. 4 up). lib. bdg. 23.93 (978-0-7565-0261-4(6)) Compass Point Bks.

—Thomas Jefferson: Voice of Liberty. 2000. (Community Builders Ser.). (Illus.). 48p. (J). (gr. 3-5). pap. 6.95 (978-0-516-26514-8(8) , Children's Pr.) Scholastic Library Publishing.

—U. S. Presidential Inaugurations. 2002. (Cornerstones of Freedom). (Illus.). 48p. (J). (gr. 4-6). 26.00 (978-0-516-22533-3(2) , Children's Pr.) Scholastic Library Publishing.

Santow, Dan. Millard Fillmore. 2004. (Encyclopedia of Presidents Ser.). (Illus.). 110p. (J). 34.00 (978-0-516-22888-4(9) , Children's Pr.) Scholastic Library Publishing.

Saunders-Smith, Gail, ed. First Biographies, 8 bks. Incl. Abraham Lincoln. Knox, Barbara. 2004. lib. bdg. 15.93 (978-0-7368-2086-8(8)); Albert Einstein. Schaefer, Lola M. & Schaefer, Wyatt S. 2003. lib. bdg. 15.93 (978-0-7368-2079-0(5)); Alexander Graham Bell. Schaefer, Lola M. 2003. lib. bdg. 15.93 (978-0-7368-1644-1(5)); Amelia Earhart. Schaefer, Lola M. 2002. lib. bdg. 15.93 (978-0-7368-1433-1(7)); Benjamin Franklin. Rustad, Martha E. H. 2001. lib. bdg. 15.93 (978-0-7368-0995-5(3)); Booker T. Washington. Schaefer, Lola M. 2003. lib. bdg. 15.93 (978-0-7368-1647-2(X)); Christopher Columbus. Schaefer, Lola M. 2002. lib. bdg. 15.93 (978-0-7368-1173-6(7)); Clara Barton. Schaefer, Lola M. 2002. lib. bdg. 15.93 (978-0-7368-1434-8(5)); Franklin D. Roosevelt. Emerson, Judy. 2004. lib. bdg. 15.93 (978-0-7368-2087-5(6)); Frederick Douglass. Schaefer, Lola M. 2002. lib. bdg. 15.93 (978-0-7368-1174-3(5)); George Washington. Knox, Barbara. 2003. lib. bdg. 15.93 (978-0-7368-2082-0(5)); George Washington Carver. Rustad, Martha E. H. 2001. lib. bdg. 15.93 (978-0-7368-0996-2(1)); Harriet Tubman. Rustad, Martha E. H. 2001. lib. bdg. 15.93 (978-0-7368-0997-9(X)); Jackie Robinson. Schaefer, Lola M. 2002. lib. bdg. 15.93 (978-0-7368-1435-5(3)); John F. Kennedy. Emerson, Judy. 2004. lib. bdg. 15.93 (978-0-7368-2368-5(9)); Johnny Appleseed. Schaefer, Lola M. 2003. lib. bdg. 15.93 (978-0-7368-1645-8(3)); Mother Teresa. Schaefer, Lola M. 2003. lib. bdg. 15.93 (978-0-7368-1646-5(1)); Paul Revere. Trumbauer, Lisa. 2003. lib. bdg. 15.93 (978-0-7368-2085-1(X)); Pocahontas. Schaefer, Lola M. 2002. lib. bdg. 15.93 (978-0-7368-1175-0(3)); Rosa Parks. Schaefer, Lola M. 2002. lib. bdg. 15.93 (978-0-7368-1176-7(1)); Sam Houston. Trumbauer, Lisa. 2004. lib. bdg. 15.93 (978-0-7368-2370-8(0)); Sitting Bull. Trumbauer, Lisa. 2004. lib. bdg. 15.93 (978-0-7368-2371-5(9)); Susan B. Anthony. Rustad, Martha E. H. 2001. lib. bdg. 15.93 (978-0-7368-0998-6(8)); Theodore Roosevelt. Emerson, Judy. 2004. lib. bdg. 15.93 (978-0-7368-2369-2(7)); Thomas Edison. 2002. lib. bdg. 15.93 (978-0-7368-1436-2(1)); Thomas Jefferson. Emerson, Judy. 2003. lib. bdg. 15.93 (978-0-7368-2088-2(4)); 24p. (J). (gr. k-1). (Illus.). Set lib. bdg. 414.18 (978-0-7368-2535-1(5) , Pebble Bks.) Capstone Pr., Inc.

Schanzer, Rosalyn. George vs. George: The American Revolution As Seen from Both Sides. 2007. (Illus.). 64p. (J). (gr. 4-9). pap. 6.95 (978-1-4263-0042-4(5) , National Geographic Children's Bks.) National Geographic Society.

—George vs. George: The Revolutionary War as Seen by Both Sides. 2004. (Illus.). 64p. (J). (gr. 4-9). 16.95 (978-0-7922-7349-3(4) , National Geographic Children's Bks.) National Geographic Society.

Schlesinger, Arthur M., Jr., ed. Childhood of the Presidents, 16 vols., Set. 2002. (Illus.). 48p. (J). (gr. 4 up). lib. bdg. (978-1-59084-267-6(7)) Mason Crest Pubs.

—The Impeachment Process. 2000. (Your Government Ser.). (Illus.). 64p. (J). (gr. 4-7). 25.00 (978-0-7910-5538-0(8) , Chelsea Hse.) Facts On File, Inc.

Schlesinger, Arthur M., Sr., et al, eds. The Election of 1912 & the Administration of Woodrow Wilson. 2002. (Major Presidential Elections & the Administrations That Followed Ser.). (Illus.). 154p. (YA). (gr. 7 up). lib. bdg. (978-1-59084-358-1(4)) Mason Crest Pubs.

Schlesinger, Arthur M., Jr. & Israel, Fred L., eds. Abraham Lincoln to Herbert Hoover, 3 vols., Vol. 2. 2004. (Illus.). 550p. (YA). lib. bdg. (978-1-59084-548-6(X)) Mason Crest Pubs.

—Franklin D. Roosevelt to George W. Bush, 3 vols., Vol. 3. 2004. (Illus.). 550p. (YA). lib. bdg. 65.00 (978-1-59084-549-3(8)) Mason Crest Pubs.

—George Washington to James Buchanan, 3 vols., Vol. 1. 2004. (Illus.). 550p. (YA). lib. bdg. (978-1-59084-547-9(1)) Mason Crest Pubs.

Schmidt, Roderic. How to Draw the Life & Times of Abraham Lincoln. 2006. (Kid's Guide to Drawing the Presidents of the United States of America Ser.). (J). 25.25 (978-1-4042-2993-8(0) , PowerKids Pr.) Rosen Publishing Group, Inc., The.

—How to Draw the Life & Times of George W. Bush. 2007. (Kid's Guide to Drawing the Presidents of the United States of America Ser.). (Illus.). 32p. (J). 25.25 (978-1-4042-3019-4(X) , PowerKids Pr.) Rosen Publishing Group, Inc., The.

—How to Draw the Life & Times of James Madison. 2006. (Kid's Guide to Drawing the Presidents of the United States of America Ser.). (J). 25.25 (978-1-4042-2981-5(7) , PowerKids Pr.) Rosen Publishing Group, Inc., The.

—How to Draw the Life & Times of Martin Van Buren. 2006. (Kid's Guide to Drawing the Presidents of the United States of America Ser.). (J). 25.25 (978-1-4042-2985-3(X) , PowerKids Pr.) Rosen Publishing Group, Inc., The.

—How to Draw the Life & Times of Zachary Taylor. 2006. (Kid's Guide to Drawing the Presidents of the United States of America Ser.). (J). 25.25 (978-1-4042-2989-1(2) , PowerKids Pr.) Rosen Publishing Group, Inc., The.

School Specialty Publishing. Presidents. 2006. (Brighter Child Flash Cards Ser.). 54p. (J). 2.99 (978-0-7696-7753-8(3) , Brighter Child) School Specialty Publishing.

Schultz, Randy. Dwight D. Eisenhower: A MyReportLinks. Com Book. 2003. (Presidents Ser.). (Illus.). 48p. (J). (gr. 5-10). lib. bdg. 25.26 (978-0-7660-5102-7(1) , MyReportLinks.com Bks.) Enslow Pubs., Inc.

—John F. Kennedy: A MyReportLinks.com Book. 2002. (Presidents Ser.). (Illus.). 48p. (J). (gr. 4-10). lib. bdg. 25.26 (978-0-7660-5012-9(2)) Enslow Pubs., Inc.

—Lyndon B. Johnson: A MyReportLinks.com Book. 2002. (Presidents Ser.). (Illus.). 48p. (J). (gr. 4-10). lib. bdg. 25.26 (978-0-7660-5011-2(4)) Enslow Pubs., Inc.

—Richard M. Nixon: A MyReportLinks. Com Book. 2003. (Presidents Ser.). (Illus.). 48p. (J). (gr. 4-10). lib. bdg. 25.26 (978-0-7660-5104-1(8) , MyReportLinks.com Bks.) Enslow Pubs., Inc.

—Warren G. Harding: A MyReportLinks. Com Book. 2003. (Presidents Ser.). (Illus.). 48p. (J). (gr. 4-10). lib. bdg. 25.26 (978-0-7660-5103-4(X) , MyReportLinks.com Bks.) Enslow Pubs., Inc.

Schuman, Michael A. Bill Clinton. rev. ed. 2003. (United States Presidents Ser.). (Illus.). 128p. (J). (gr. 5-12). lib. bdg. 26.60 (978-0-7660-2032-0(0)) Enslow Pubs., Inc.

—George H. W. Bush. 2002. (United States Presidents Ser.). (Illus.). 128p. (J). (gr. 5-12). lib. bdg. 26.60 (978-0-7660-1702-3(8)) Enslow Pubs., Inc.

—Lyndon B. Johnson. 1998. (United States Presidents Ser.). (Illus.). 128p. (YA). (gr. 5-12). lib. bdg. 26.60 (978-0-89490-938-2(X)) Enslow Pubs., Inc.

Selkirk, Blaine. The Presidents' Rap: Washington to George W. Bush. Stratton, Sara, ed. 2001. (Illus.). 56p. (J). (gr. 3-7). pap. 14.95 incl. audio (978-1-894262-51-4(4) , JMP121K) Jordan Music Productions, Inc.

Sherman, Josepha. Bill Gates: Computer King. 2000. (Gateway Biography Ser.). (Illus.). 48p. (gr. 2-4). lib. bdg. 23.90 (978-0-7613-1771-5(6) , Millbrook Pr.) Lerner Publishing Group.

Sherrow, Victoria. Thomas Jefferson. 2002. (History Maker Bios Ser.). (Illus.). 47p. (J). pap. 6.95 (978-0-8225-0382-8(4)); (gr. 2-4). 26.60 (978-0-8225-0197-8(X)) Lerner Publishing Group. (Lerner Pubns.).

Silate, Jennifer. The White House. 2004. (Illus.). 24p. (J). lib. bdg. (978-1-4042-2695-1(8)) Rosen Publishing Group, Inc., The.

Skarmeas, Nancy J. Our Presidents: Their Lives & Stories. 1998. (United States & Its Flag Ser.: No. 2). (Illus.). 80p. (J). (gr. 4-8). lib. bdg. 16.95 (978-1-56674-223-8(4)) Forest Hse. Publishing Co., Inc.

Slavicek, Louise Chipley. Jimmy Carter. (Great American Presidents Ser.). (Illus.). (gr. 4-8). 2004. 112p. pap. 30.00 (978-0-7910-7790-0(X)); 2003. 100p. 30.00 (978-0-7910-7646-0(6)) Facts On File, Inc. (Chelsea Hse.).

Snyder, Gail. George Washington. 2003. (Childhoods of the Presidents Ser.). (Illus.). 48p. (J). (gr. 4 up). lib. bdg. (978-1-59084-270-6(7)) Mason Crest Pubs.

So You Want to Be President? 2004. pap. 38.75 incl. audio compact disk (978-1-55592-642-7(8)); pap. 32.75 incl. audio (978-1-55592-363-1(1)); pap. 14.95 incl. audio (978-1-55592-167-5(1)) Weston Woods Studios, Inc.

Somervill, Barbara. The Life & Times of James Madison. 2007. (J). lib. bdg. (***978-1-58415-530-0(2)***) Mitchell Lane Pubs., Inc.

Somervill, Barbara A. Andrew Jackson. 2003. (Profiles of the Presidents Ser.). (Illus.). 64p. (J). (gr. 4 up). lib. bdg. 23.93 (978-0-7565-0255-3(1)) Compass Point Bks.

—Franklin Pierce. 2002. (Profiles of the Presidents Ser.). (Illus.). 64p. (J). (gr. 4 up). lib. bdg. 23.93 (978-0-7565-0262-1(4)) Compass Point Bks.

—Warren G. Harding. 2003. (Profiles of the Presidents Ser.). (Illus.). 64p. (J). (gr. 4 up). lib. bdg. 23.93 (978-0-7565-0275-1(6)) Compass Point Bks.

Sommer, Shelley. John F. Kennedy: His Life & Legacy. 2005. (Illus.). 160p. (J). 16.99 (978-0-06-054135-4(0)); lib. bdg. 17.89 (978-0-06-054136-1(9)) HarperCollins Pubs.

Sorensen, Lynda. La Casa Blanca. Palacios, Argentina, tr. 2002. (Simbolos Americanos Ser.). (SPA., Illus.). 24p. (J). mass mkt. 5.95 (978-1-58952-270-1(2) , RK31483) Rourke Publishing, LLC.

Souter, Gerry & Souter, Janet. Herbert Hoover: Our Thirty-First President. 2001. (Spirit of America: Our Presidents Ser.). (Illus.). 48p. (J). (gr. 2-6). 28.50 (978-1-56766-865-0(8)) Child's World, Inc.

—John Quincy Adams: Our Sixth President. 2001. (Spirit of America: Our Presidents Ser.). (Illus.). 48p. (J). (gr. 2-6). 28.50 (978-1-56766-846-9(1)) Child's World, Inc.

—Millard Fillmore: Our Thirteenth President. 2001. (Spirit of America: Our Presidents Ser.). (Illus.). 48p. (J). (gr. 2-6). 28.50 (978-1-56766-838-4(0)) Child's World, Inc.

—Warren G. Harding: Our Twenty-Ninth President. 2001. (Spirit of America: Our Presidents Ser.). (Illus.). 48p. (J). (gr. 2-6). 28.50 (978-1-56766-839-1(9)) Child's World, Inc.

St. George, Judith. In the Line of Fire: Presidents' Lives at Stake. 1999. (Illus.). 144p. (J). (gr. 4-6). tchr. ed. 22.95 (978-0-8234-1428-4(0)) Holiday Hse., Inc.

—Make Your Mark, Franklin Roosevelt! Spencer, Britt, illus. 2007. 40p. (J). (gr. 2-5). 16.99 (978-0-399-24175-8(2) , Philomel) Penguin Group (USA) Inc.

—So You Want to Be President? Small, David, illus. 2000. 56p. (J). (gr. 2-5). 17.99 (978-0-399-23407-1(1) , Philomel) Penguin Group (USA) Inc.

—So You Want to Be President? Small, David, illus. 2004. (J). (gr. 1-6). 29.95 incl. cd-rom (978-1-55592-132-3(9)); 24.95 incl. audio (978-1-55592-094-4(2)) Weston Woods Studios, Inc.

—So You Want to be President? Small, David, illus. 2008. 56p. (J). (gr. 3-7). pap. 9.99 (***978-0-399-25152-8(9)*** , Philomel) Penguin Group (USA) Inc.

—So You Want to Be President? Small, David, illus. rev. ed. 2004. 56p. (J). (gr. 3). 17.99 (978-0-399-24317-2(8) , Philomel) Penguin Group (USA) Inc.

—Stand Tall, Abe Lincoln. Faulkner, Matt, illus. 2008. 48p. (J). (ps). 16.99 (978-0-399-24174-1(4) , Philomel) Penguin Group (USA) Inc.

St. George, Judith & Faulkner, Matt. You're on Your Way, Teddy Roosevelt! 2004. (Illus.). 48p. (J). (gr. 3). 16.99 (978-0-399-23888-8(3) , Philomel) Penguin Group (USA) Inc.

Stanley, George Edward. America in Today's World (1969-2004) 2005. (Illus.). 48p. (J). pap. (978-0-8368-5840-2(9)); lib. bdg. 30.00 (978-0-8368-5831-0(X)) Stevens, Gareth Inc. (World Almanac Library).

Stanley, George Edward. Dwight D. Eisenhower: Young Military Leader. 2006. (Illus.). 117p. (J). (***978-1-4156-7635-6(6)*** , Aladdin) Simon & Schuster Children's Publishing.

Steadwell Books Publishing Staff, ed. The Presidency. 1999. (American Government Today Ser.). (Illus.). 48p. (J). lib. bdg. 22.83 (978-0-7398-1786-5(8)) Raintree.

Steck-Vaughn Staff. The President of the United States. 2002. (J). pap. (978-0-7398-6158-5(1)) Steck-Vaughn.

Stein, R. Conrad. Calvin Coolidge. 2004. (Encyclopedia of Presidents Ser.). (Illus.). 110p. (J). 34.00 (978-0-516-22960-7(5) , Children's Pr.) Scholastic Library Publishing.

Stevenson, Augusta. Abraham Lincoln & George Washington. 2003. (gr. 3-6). lib. bdg. 15.30 (978-0-613-61599-0(9)) Tandem Library Bks.

Stier, Catherine. If I Were President. DiSalvo-Ryan, DyAnne, illus. 2004. (J). (ps-ps). lib. bdg. 13.75 (978-0-606-30350-7(2)) Tandem Library Bks.

—If I Were President. DiSalvo-Ryan, DyAnne, illus. 2004. 32p. (J). (gr. k-3). pap. 6.95 (978-0-8075-3542-4(7)) Whitman, Albert & Co.

Stille, Darlene R. The Emergence of Modern America. 2007. (J). (***978-1-59036-747-6(2)***); (***978-1-59036-748-3(0)***) Weigl Pubs., Inc.

The Story of George Washington. 2000. (Illus.). 24p. (J). (ps-k). 6.95 (978-0-8249-4188-8(8)) Ideals Pubns.

Sullivan, Anne Marie. Franklin D. Roosevelt. 2003. (Childhood of the Presidents Ser.). (Illus.). 48p. (J). (gr. 4 up). lib. bdg. (978-1-59084-279-9(0)) Mason Crest Pubs.

Sullivan, George. Abraham Lincoln. 2000. (gr. 3-6). lib. bdg. 12.40 (978-0-613-32239-3(8)) Tandem Library Bks.

—Mr. President: Book of U. S. Presidents. rev. ed. 2005. (Mr. President Ser.). (Illus.). 192p. (J). pap. 4.99 (978-0-439-70335-2(2) , Scholastic Paperbacks) Scholastic, Inc.

Sullivan, George E. Abraham Lincoln. 2001. (In Their Own Words Ser.). (Illus.). 128p. (J). pap. 12.95 (978-0-439-14750-7(6)) Scholastic, Inc.

—Abraham Lincoln. 2001. (In Their Own Words Ser.). (Illus.). (J). 11.64 (978-0-606-20724-9(4)) Tandem Library Bks.

—Mr. President: A Book of U. S. Presidents. rev. ed. 2001. (Illus.). 176p. (J). (gr. 8). mass mkt. 4.99 (978-0-439-23566-2(9)) Scholastic, Inc.

—Mr. President: A Book of U. S. Presidents. 2000. (J). (978-0-606-19580-5(7)) Tandem Library Bks.

Sutcliffe, Jane. John Adams. 2006. (History Maker Bios Ser.). (Illus.). 48p. (J). 26.60 (978-0-8225-5940-5(4) , Lerner Pubns.) Lerner Publishing Group.

—John F. Kennedy. (History Maker Bios Ser.). (J). 2005. (Illus.). 48p. 26.60 (978-0-8225-1546-3(6)); 2004. pap. (978-0-8225-2540-0(2)) Lerner Publishing Group. (Lerner Pubns.).

Swain, Gwenyth. Theodore Roosevelt. (History Maker Bios Ser.). (J). 2005. (Illus.). 48p. 26.60 (978-0-8225-1548-7(2)); 2004. pap. (978-0-8225-2542-4(9)) Lerner Publishing Group. (Lerner Pubns.).

Taylor-Butler, Christine. The Presidency. (True Booktrade;: American History Ser.). 48p. (J). 2008. pap. 6.95 (***978-0-531-14784-9(3)***); 2007. (Illus.). (gr. 3-5). lib. bdg. 26.00 (***978-0-531-12634-9(X)***) Scholastic Library Publishing. (Children's Pr.).

Taylor, David. Franklin Delano Roosevelt. 2001. (Leading Lives Ser.). (Illus.). 64p. (J). (gr. 5-7). lib. bdg. 27.86 (978-1-58810-161-7(4)) Heinemann Library.

Tecco, Betsy Dru. How to Draw the Life & Times of Grover Cleveland. 2006. (Kid's Guide to Drawing the Presidents of the United States of America Ser.). (J). 25.25 (978-1-4042-2999-0(X) , PowerKids Pr.) Rosen Publishing Group, Inc., The.

—How to Draw the Life & Times of John Quincy Adams. 2006. (Kid's Guide to Drawing the Presidents of the United States of America Ser.). (J). 25.25 (978-1-4042-2983-9(3) , PowerKids Pr.) Rosen Publishing Group, Inc., The.

—How to Draw the Life & Times of Ulysses S. Grant. 2006. (Kid's Guide to Drawing the Presidents of the United States of America Ser.). (J). 25.25 (978-1-4042-2995-2(7) , PowerKids Pr.) Rosen Publishing Group, Inc., The.

Teitelbaum, Michael. Herbert Hoover. 2002. (Profiles of the Presidents Ser.). (Illus.). 64p. (J). (gr. 4 up). lib. bdg. 23.93 (978-0-7565-0277-5(2)) Compass Point Bks.

—James Monroe. 2002. (Profiles of the Presidents Ser.). (Illus.). 64p. (J). (gr. 4 up). lib. bdg. 23.93 (978-0-7565-0253-9(5)) Compass Point Bks.

Thompson, William & Thompson, Dorcas. George W. Bush. 2003. (Childhoods of the Presidents Ser.). (Illus.). 48p. (J). (gr. 4 up). lib. bdg. (978-1-59084-281-2(2)) Mason Crest Pubs.

Thomson, Sarah L. What Presidents Are Made Of. Piven, Hanoch, illus. 2004. 40p. (J). 17.99 (978-0-689-86880-1(4) , Atheneum) Simon & Schuster Children's Publishing.

Thorburn, Mark. The Executive Branch: Leading the Nation. 2008. (Federal Government Ser.). 128p. (J). (gr. 6 up). lib. bdg. 33.27 (***978-1-59845-060-6(3)*** , MyReportLinks.com Bks.) Enslow Pubs., Inc.

Thornton, Brian. Everything Kids' Presidents Book: Puzzles, games & trivia—for hours of presidential Fun! 2007. 144p. pap. 7.95 (978-1-59869-262-4(3)) Adams Media Corp.

Tilton, David, illus. Clipmation: The Presidents. 2002. (J). cd-rom 19.95 (978-1-891405-06-8(3)) FableVision Pr.

Time for Kids Editors. Franklin D. Roosevelt: A Leader in Troubled Times. 2006. (Time for Kids Ser.). (Illus.). 48p. (J). 14.99 (978-0-06-057616-5(2)); pap. 3.99 (978-0-06-057615-8(4)) HarperCollins Pubs.

—Presidents of the United States. 2007. (Time for Kids Ser.). 72p. (J). pap. 7.99 (978-0-06-081556-1(6)) HarperCollins Pubs.

—Ronald Reagan: From Silver Screen to Oval Office. 2006. (Time for Kids Ser.). (Illus.). 48p. (J). 14.99 (978-0-06-057627-1(8)); pap. 3.99 (978-0-06-057626-4(X)) HarperCollins Pubs.

TNT Stone and Associates Staff & Petertil Design Partners Staff, illus. Our Presidents & the White House. 1998. (Powertools for Kids Ser.: No. 14). 4p. (J). (gr. 2-5). pap., wbk. ed. 4.95 (978-1-58220-013-2(0) , 32504, PowerTools for Kids) Navigator Systems, Inc.

Tribble, Mimi. The American Presidents: Everything You Wanted to Know about the 43 Leaders of Our Country. 2004. (Illus.). 48p. (J). (978-1-4027-1794-9(6) , Sterling/Main St.) Sterling Publishing Co., Inc.

Trumbauer, Lisa. Life in the Time of Abraham Lincoln & the Civil War. 2007. (J). (***978-1-4034-9668-3(4)***); pap. (***978-1-4034-9676-8(5)***) Heinemann Library.

—Life in the Time of George Washington & the Revolutionary War. 2007. (J). (***978-1-4034-9667-6(6)***); pap. (***978-1-4034-9675-1(7)***) Heinemann Library.

Trumbauer, Lisa. Set in Stone. 2005. (Yellow Umbrella Ser.). (J). (978-0-7368-5308-8(1)); (Illus.). 17p. (978-0-7368-5272-2(7)) Capstone Pr., Inc.

Turner, Ann Warren. Abe Lincoln Remembers. Minor, Wendell, illus. 2001. 32p. (J). (gr. 1-4). 16.99 (978-0-06-027577-8(4)) HarperCollins Pubs.

Upadhyay, Ritu. John F Kennedy the Making of a Leader. 2005. 44p. (J). lib. bdg. 15.00 (***978-1-4242-0851-7(3)***) Fitzgerald Bks.

Upadhyay, Ritu & Time for Kids Editors. John F. Kennedy: The Making of a Leader. 2005. (Time for Kids Ser.). (Illus.). 48p. (J). 14.99 (978-0-06-057603-5(0)); pap. 3.99 (978-0-06-057602-8(2)) HarperCollins Pubs.

Uschan, Michael V. Abraham Lincoln. 2002. (Beginning Biographies Ser.). (Illus.). 32p. (J). lib. bdg. 25.69 (978-0-7398-5678-9(2)) Raintree.

—Thomas Jefferson. 2002. (Raintree Biographies Ser.). (Illus.). 32p. (J). lib. bdg. 25.69 (978-0-7398-5676-5(6)) Raintree.

Vecchione, Glen. The Little Giant Book of American Presidents. Condrick, Maura, illus. 2007. 352p. (J). pap. 6.95 (978-1-4027-2692-7(9)) Sterling Publishing Co., Inc.

Venezia, Mike. Abraham Lincoln: Sixteenth President. Venezia, Mike, illus. 2005. (Illus.). 32p. (J). (ps-7). 27.00 (978-0-516-22621-7(5) , Children's Pr.) Scholastic Library Publishing.

—Andrew Jackson: Seventh President, 1829-1837. Venezia, Mike, illus. 2005. (Getting to Know the U. S. Presidents Ser.). (Illus.). 32p. (J). (gr. 3-4). pap. 7.95 (978-0-516-27481-2(3) , Children's Pr.) Scholastic Library Publishing.

—Andrew Johnson: Seventeenth President. Venezia, Mike, illus. 2005. (Illus.). 32p. (J). (ps-7). 27.00 (978-0-516-22622-4(3) , Children's Pr.) Scholastic Library Publishing.

—Benjamin Harrison. 2006. (Illus.). 32p. (YA). (gr. 3-4). pap. 7.95 (978-0-516-25400-5(6) , Children's Pr.) Scholastic Library Publishing.

Venezia Mike. Calvin Coolidge. 2006. (J). (978-0-516-22634-7(7)) Children's Pr., Ltd.

Venezia, Mike. Chester A. Arthur. 2006. (Illus.). 32p. (YA). (gr. 3-4). pap. 7.95 (978-0-516-25401-2(4) , Children's Pr.) Scholastic Library Publishing.

—Dwight D. Eisenhower. Venezia, Mike, illus. 2007. (Getting to Know the U. S. Presidents Ser.). 32p. (J). 7.95 (***978-0-531-17944-4(3)***); (Illus.). (gr. 3-4). 27.00 (978-0-516-22638-5(X)) Scholastic Library Publishing. (Children's Pr.).

—Franklin D. Roosevelt. Venezia, Mike, illus. 2007. (Getting to Know the U. S. Presidents Ser.). 32p. (J). 7.95 (***978-0-531-17945-1(1)*** , Children's Pr.) Scholastic Library Publishing.

—Franklin Pierce: Fourteenth President. Venezia, Mike, illus. 2005. (Illus.). 32p. (J). (ps-7). 27.00 (978-0-516-22619-4(3) , Children's Pr.) Scholastic Library Publishing.

—George Bush. 2008. (Getting to Know the U. S. Presidents Ser.). 32p. (J). pap. 7.95 (***978-0-516-25536-1(3)*** , Children's Pr.) Scholastic Library Publishing.

—George W. Bush. (Getting to Know the U. S. Presidents Ser.). 32p. (J). 2008. pap. 7.95 (***978-0-516-25595-8(9)***); 2007. 28.00 (***978-0-516-22649-1(5)***) Scholastic Library Publishing. (Children's Pr.).

—Gerald R. Ford. 2008. (Getting to Know the U. S. Presidents Ser.). 32p. (J). pap. 7.95 (***978-0-516-25597-2(5)*** , Children's Pr.) Scholastic Library Publishing.

—Getting to Know the U. S. Presidents, 6 bks., Set. Venezia, Mike, illus. Incl. Dwight D. Eisenhower. 27.00 (978-0-516-22638-5(X)); Franklin D. Roosevelt. 27.00 (978-0-516-22636-1(3)); Harry S. Truman. 27.00 (978-0-516-22637-8(1)); John F. Kennedy. 27.00 (978-0-516-22639-2(8)); Lyndon B. Johnson. 27.00 (978-0-516-22640-8(1)); Richard M. Nixon. 27.00 (978-0-516-22641-5(X)); (Illus.). 32p. (J). (gr. 3-4). 2007. 2007. 162.00 (***978-0-531-17733-4(5)*** , Children's Pr.) Scholastic Library Publishing.

—Grover Cleveland. 2006. (Illus.). 32p. (YA). (gr. 3-4). pap. 7.95 (978-0-516-25402-9(2) , Children's Pr.) Scholastic Library Publishing.

—Harry S. Truman. Venezia, Mike, illus. 2007. (Getting to Know the U. S. Presidents Ser.). 32p. (J). 7.95 (***978-0-531-17946-8(X)*** , Children's Pr.) Scholastic Library Publishing.

—James A. Garfield. 2006. (Illus.). 32p. (YA). (gr. 3-4). pap. 7.95 (978-0-516-25403-6(0) , Children's Pr.) Scholastic Library Publishing.

—James K. Polk: Eleventh President, 1845-1849. Venezia, Mike, illus. 2005. (Getting to Know the U. S. Presidents Ser.). (Illus.). 32p. (J). (gr. 3-4). pap. 7.95 (978-0-516-27485-0(6) , Children's Pr.) Scholastic Library Publishing.

—John F. Kennedy. Venezia, Mike, illus. 2007. (Getting to Know the U. S. Presidents Ser.). 32p. (J). 7.95 (***978-0-531-17947-5(8)*** , Children's Pr.) Scholastic Library Publishing.

—John Tyler: Tenth President, 1841-1845. Venezia, Mike, illus. 2005. (Getting to Know the U. S. Presidents Ser.). (Illus.). 32p. (J). (gr. 3-4). pap. 7.95 (978-0-516-27484-3(8) , Children's Pr.) Scholastic Library Publishing.

—Lyndon B. Johnson. Venezia, Mike, illus. 2007. (Getting to Know the U. S. Presidents Ser.). 32p. (J). 7.95 (***978-0-531-17948-2(6)*** , Children's Pr.) Scholastic Library Publishing.

—Martin Van Buren: Eighth President, 1937-1841. Venezia, Mike, illus. 2005. (Getting to Know the U. S. Presidents Ser.). (Illus.). 32p. (J). (gr. 3-4). pap. 7.95 (978-0-516-27482-9(1) , Children's Pr.) Scholastic Library Publishing.

—Millard Fillmore. Venezia, Mike, illus. 2006. (Illus.). 32p. (J). (gr. 3-4). pap. 7.95 (978-0-516-25487-6(1) , Children's Pr.) Scholastic Library Publishing.

—Millard Fillmore: Thirteenth President. Venezia, Mike, illus. 2005. (Illus.). 32p. (J). (ps-7). 27.00 (978-0-516-22618-7(5) , Children's Pr.) Scholastic Library Publishing.

—Richard M. Nixon. Venezia, Mike, illus. 2007. (Getting to Know the U. S. Presidents Ser.). 32p. (J). 7.95 (***978-0-531-17949-9(4)*** , Children's Pr.) Scholastic Library Publishing.

—Ronald Reagan. (Getting to Know the U. S. Presidents Ser.). 32p. (J). 2008. pap. 7.95 (***978-0-516-26720-3(5)***); 2007. 28.00 (***978-0-516-22644-6(4)***) Scholastic Library Publishing. (Children's Pr.).

—Rutherford B. Hayes. 2006. (Illus.). 32p. (YA). (gr. 3-4). pap. 7.95 (978-0-516-25404-3(9) , Children's Pr.) Scholastic Library Publishing.

—William Henry Harrison: Ninth President 1841. Venezia, Mike, illus. 2005. (Getting to Know the U. S. Presidents Ser.). (Illus.). 32p. (J). (gr. 3-4). pap. 7.95 (978-0-516-27483-6(X) , Children's Pr.) Scholastic Library Publishing.

—William Mckinley. 2006. (Illus.). 32p. (YA). (gr. 3-4). pap. 7.95 (978-0-516-25405-0(7) , Children's Pr.) Scholastic Library Publishing.

Venezia, Mike, illus. Andrew Jackson. 2005. (Getting to Know the U. S. Presidents Ser.). 32p. (J). (gr. 3-4). 26.00 (978-0-516-22612-5(6) , Children's Pr.) Scholastic Library Publishing.

—Benjamin Harrison. 2006. (Getting to Know the U. S. Presidents Ser.). 32p. (J). (gr. 3-4). 27.00 (978-0-516-22628-6(2) , Children's Pr.) Scholastic Library Publishing.

—Bill Clinton. 2007. 32p. (J). 28.00 (***978-0-516-22646-0(0)*** , Children's Pr.) Scholastic Library Publishing.

—Chester A. Arthur. 2006. (Getting to Know the U. S. Presidents Ser.). 32p. (J). (gr. 3-4). 27.00 (978-0-516-22626-2(6) , Children's Pr.) Scholastic Library Publishing.

—George Bush. 2007. 32p. (J). 28.00 (***978-0-516-22645-3(2)*** , Children's Pr.) Scholastic Library Publishing.

—George Washington. 2004. (Gtk Us Presidents Ser.). (J). 27.00 (978-0-516-22606-4(1) , Children's Pr.) Scholastic Library Publishing.

—Gerald R. Ford. 2007. 32p. (J). 28.00 (***978-0-516-22642-2(8)*** , Children's Pr.) Scholastic Library Publishing.

—Getting to Know the U. S. Presidents, 6 bks., Set. Incl. Benjamin Harrison. 27.00 (978-0-516-22628-6(2)); Chester A. Arthur. 27.00 (978-0-516-22626-2(6)); Grover Cleveland. 27.00 (978-0-516-22627-9(4)); James A. Garfield. 27.00 (978-0-516-22625-5(8)); Rutherford B. Hayes. 27.00 (978-0-516-22624-8(X)); William McKinley. 27.00 (978-0-516-22629-3(0)); (Illus.). 32p. (J). (gr. 3-4). 2006. 2006. Set lib. bdg. 162.00 (978-0-516-25409-8(X) , Children's Pr.) Scholastic Library Publishing.

—Grover Cleveland. 2006. (Getting to Know the U. S. Presidents Ser.). 32p. (J). (gr. 3-4). 27.00 (978-0-516-22627-9(4) , Children's Pr.) Scholastic Library Publishing.

—Herbert Hoover. 2006. 32p. (J). (978-0-516-22635-4(5)) Children's Pr., Ltd.

—James A. Garfield. 2006. (Getting to Know the U. S. Presidents Ser.). 32p. (J). (gr. 3-4). 27.00 (978-0-516-22625-5(8) , Children's Pr.) Scholastic Library Publishing.

—James Buchanan. 2005. 32p. (J). 27.00 (978-0-516-22620-0(7) , Children's Pr.) Scholastic Library Publishing.

—James K. Polk. 2005. (Getting to Know the U. S. Presidents Ser.). 32p. (J). (gr. 3-4). 27.00 (978-0-516-22616-3(9) , Children's Pr.) Scholastic Library Publishing.

—Jimmy Carter. 2007. 32p. (J). 28.00 (***978-0-516-22643-9(6)*** , Children's Pr.) Scholastic Library Publishing.

—John Adams. 2004. (Gtk Us Presidents Ser.). (J). 27.00 (978-0-516-22607-1(X) , Children's Pr.) Scholastic Library Publishing.

—John Tyler. 2005. (Getting to Know the U. S. Presidents Ser.). 32p. (J). (gr. 3-4). 26.00 (978-0-516-22615-6(0) , Children's Pr.) Scholastic Library Publishing.

—Martin Van Buren. 2005. (Getting to Know the U. S. Presidents Ser.). 32p. (J). (gr. 3-4). 27.00 (978-0-516-22613-2(4) , Children's Pr.) Scholastic Library Publishing.

—Rutherford B. Hayes. 2006. (Getting to Know the U. S. Presidents Ser.). 32p. (J). (gr. 3-4). 27.00 (978-0-516-22624-8(X) , Children's Pr.) Scholastic Library Publishing.

—Theodore Roosevelt. 2006. 32p. (J). (978-0-516-22630-9(4)) Children's Pr., Ltd.

—Theodore Roosevelt: Twenty-Sixth President, 1901-1909. 2007. 32p. (J). pap. (***978-0-516-25225-4(9)***) Children's Pr., Ltd.

—Thomas Jefferson. 2004. (Gtk Us Presidents Ser.). (J). 27.00 (978-0-516-22608-8(8) , Children's Pr.) Scholastic Library Publishing.

—Ulysses S. Grant. 2005. 32p. (J). 27.00 (978-0-516-22623-1(1) , Children's Pr.) Scholastic Library Publishing.

—Warren G. Harding. 2006. 32p. (J). (978-0-516-22633-0(9)) Children's Pr., Ltd.

—William Henry Harrison. 2005. (Getting to Know the U. S. Presidents Ser.). 32p. (J). (gr. 3-4). 26.00 (978-0-516-22614-9(2) , Children's Pr.) Scholastic Library Publishing.

—William Howard Taft. 2006. 32p. (J). (978-0-516-22631-6(2)) Children's Pr., Ltd.

—William McKinley. 2006. (Getting to Know the U. S. Presidents Ser.). 32p. (J). (gr. 3-4). 27.00 (978-0-516-22629-3(0) , Children's Pr.) Scholastic Library Publishing.

—Woodrow Wilson. 2006. 32p. (J). (978-0-516-22632-3(0)) Children's Pr., Ltd.

—Zachary Taylor: Twelfth President, 1849-1850. 2005. (Getting to Know the U. S. Presidents Ser.). 32p. (J). (gr. 3-4). 27.00 (978-0-516-22617-0(7) , Children's Pr.) Scholastic Library Publishing.

Venezia, Mike, tr. & illus. James Madison. Venezia, Mike, illus. 2004. (Gtk Us Presidents Ser.). (J). 27.00 (978-0-516-22609-5(6) , Children's Pr.) Scholastic Library Publishing.

—James Monroe. Venezia, Mike, illus. 2004. (Gtk Us Presidents Ser.). (J). 27.00 (978-0-516-22610-1(X) , Children's Pr.) Scholastic Library Publishing.

—John Quincy Adams. Venezia, Mike, illus. 2004. (Gtk Us Presidents Ser.). 32p. (J). 27.00 (978-0-516-22611-8(8) , Children's Pr.) Scholastic Library Publishing.

Vierow, Wendy. The 1864 Presidential Election: A War-Weary Nation Reelects President Abraham Lincoln. 2004. (Headlines from History Ser.). (Illus.). 24p. (J). lib. bdg. 19.95 (978-0-8239-6224-2(5)) Rosen Publishing Group, Inc., The.

Wagner, Heather Lehr. The Presidency. 2nd rev. ed. 2007. (U. S. Government Ser.). (Illus.). 112p. (J). (gr. 5-8). 30.00 (***978-0-7910-9284-2(4)** , Chelsea Hse.) Facts On File, Inc.

Wagner, Heather Lehr. Thomas Jefferson. (Great American Presidents Ser.). (Illus.). (gr. 4-8). 2004. 112p. pap. 30.00 (978-0-7910-7788-7(8)); 2003. 100p. 30.00 (978-0-7910-7602-6(4)) Facts On File, Inc. (Chelsea Hse.).

Waryncia, Lou. Ulysses S. Grant: Confident Leaders & Hero. Hale, Sarah Elder, ed. 2005. (Civil War Ser.). (Illus.). 48p. (J). 17.95 (978-0-8126-7906-9(7)) Cobblestone Publishing Co.

Waryncia, Lou & Hale, Sarah Elder. Abraham Lincoln: Defender of the Union. 2005. (Civil War Ser.). (Illus.). 48p. (J). 17.95 (978-0-8126-7902-1(4)) Cobblestone Publishing Co.

Waxman, Laura Hamilton. Franklin D. Roosevelt. 2004. (History Maker Bios Ser.). (J). pap. 6.95 (978-0-8225-2539-4(9) , Lerner Pubns.) Lerner Publishing Group.

—Jimmy Carter. 2006. (History Makers Bios Ser.). (Illus.). 48p. (J). 26.60 (978-0-8225-5939-9(0) , Lerner Pubns.) Lerner Publishing Group.

—Woodrow Wilson. 2006. (History Maker Bios Ser.). (Illus.). 48p. (J). 26.60 (978-0-8225-6053-1(4) , Lerner Pubns.) Lerner Publishing Group.

Weintraub, Aileen. Lee sobre George Washington/Read about George Washington. 2006. (I Like Biographies! Bilingual Ser.). (ENG & SPA., Illus.). 24p. (J). (gr. 1-3). lib. bdg. 21.26 (978-0-7660-2673-5(6) , Enslow Elementary) Enslow Pubs., Inc.

—Read about George Washington. 2004. (I Like Biographies! Ser.). (Illus.). 24p. (J). lib. bdg. 21.26 (978-0-7660-2301-7(X)) Enslow Pubs., Inc.

Weiss, Ellen & Gormley, Beatrice. President George W. Bush: Our Forty-Third President. 2005. (Illus.). 208p. (J). pap. 4.99 (978-0-689-87834-3(6) , Aladdin) Simon & Schuster Children's Publishing.

Welsbacher, Anne. Andrew Johnson. 2000. (United States Presidents Ser.). (Illus.). 32p. (J). (gr. k-6). lib. bdg. 22.78 (978-1-57765-240-3(1) , Checkerboard Library) ABDO Publishing Co.

—Franklin Pierce. 2001. (United States Presidents Ser.). (Illus.). 32p. (J). (gr. k-6). lib. bdg. 22.78 (978-1-57765-247-2(9) , Checkerboard Library) ABDO Publishing Co.

—James K. Polk. 2001. (United States Presidents Ser.). (Illus.). 32p. (J). (gr. k-6). lib. bdg. 22.78 (978-1-57765-246-5(0) , Checkerboard Library) ABDO Publishing Co.

—John Tyler. 2000. (United States Presidents Ser.). (Illus.). 32p. (J). (gr. k-6). lib. bdg. 22.78 (978-1-57765-239-7(8) , Checkerboard Library) ABDO Publishing Co.

—Martin Van Buren. 2001. (United States Presidents Ser.). (Illus.). 32p. (J). (gr. k-6). lib. bdg. 22.78 (978-1-57765-238-0(X) , Checkerboard Library) ABDO Publishing Co.

—Rutherford B. Hayes. 2001. (United States Presidents Ser.). (Illus.). 32p. (J). (gr. k-6). lib. bdg. 22.78 (978-1-57765-248-9(7) , Checkerboard Library) ABDO Publishing Co.

Whitelaw, Nancy. Andrew Jackson: Frontier President. 2004. (Notable Americans Ser.). (Illus.). 128p. (J). (gr. 6-12). 23.95 (978-1-883846-67-1(6) , First Biographies) Reynolds, Morgan Inc.

Williams, Jean Kinney. Benjamin Harrison. 2004. (Encyclopedia of Presidents Ser.). (Illus.). 110p. (J). 34.00 (978-0-516-22959-1(1) , Children's Pr.) Scholastic Library Publishing.

—Grover Cleveland. 2003. (Profiles of the Presidents Ser.). (Illus.). 64p. (J). (gr. 4 up). lib. bdg. 23.93 (978-0-7565-0269-0(1)) Compass Point Bks.

—Jefferson Davis: President of the Confederate States. 2004. (Signature Lives Ser.). (Illus.). 112p. (J). 30.60 (978-0-7565-0817-3(7) , 1240142) Compass Point Bks.

—Ronald W. Reagan. 2003. (Profiles of the Presidents Ser.). (Illus.). 64p. (J). (gr. 4 up). lib. bdg. 23.93 (978-0-7565-0284-3(5)) Compass Point Bks.

—Ulysses S. Grant. 2002. (Profiles of the Presidents Ser.). (Illus.). 64p. (J). (gr. 4 up). lib. bdg. 23.93 (978-0-7565-0265-2(9)) Compass Point Bks.

Wilson, Natashya. How to Draw the Life & Times of Herbert Hoover. 2007. (Kid's Guide to Drawing the Presidents of the United States of America Ser.). (Illus.). 32p. (J). 25.25 (978-1-4042-3007-1(6) , PowerKids Pr.) Rosen Publishing Group, Inc., The.

Wilson, Natashya & Natashya, Wilson. How to Draw the Life & Times of James Earl Carter Jr. 2007. (Kid's Guide to Drawing the Presidents of the United States of America Ser.). (Illus.). 32p. (J). 25.25 (978-1-4042-3015-6(7) , PowerKids Pr.) Rosen Publishing Group, Inc., The.

Winget, Mary. Gerald R. Ford. 2007. (Presidential Leaders Ser.). 112p. (J). (gr. 6-12). 29.27 (978-0-8225-1509-8(1) , Twenty-First Century Bks.) Lerner Publishing Group.

Winters, Kay. Abe Lincoln: The Boy Who Loved Books. Carpenter, Nancy, illus. 2004. 38p. (J). (ps-3). reprint ed. 17.00 (978-0-7567-7969-6(3)) DIANE Publishing Co.

—Abe Lincoln: The Boy Who Loved Books. Carpenter, Nancy, illus. 2006. 40p. (J). reprint ed. pap. 6.99 (978-1-4169-1268-2(1) , Aladdin) Simon & Schuster Children's Publishing.

Winters, Kay & Carpenter, Nancy. Abe Lincoln: The Boy Who Loved Books. 2003. (Illus.). 40p. (J). (gr. k-3). 16.95 (978-0-689-82554-5(4)) Simon & Schuster Children's Publishing.

Wirth, Crystal. At 1600 Pennsylvania Avenue. Lee, Jared D., illus. 2002. 16p. (J). (978-0-439-35108-9(1)) Scholastic, Inc.

Wood, Ethel, compiled by. The Presidency. 2004. (Historical Reader Ser.). (Illus.). 240p. (gr. 6-12). 13.32 (978-0-618-04821-2(9) , 2-00153) McDougal Littell Inc.

Wooden Teeth & Jelly Beans Adventure Pack. 2000. (J). pap., wbk. ed. 5.00 (978-1-883772-89-5(3)) Flying Rhinoceros, Inc.

World Book, Inc. Staff. World Book of America's Presidents, 2 vols. , Set. 1999. (Illus.). 440p. (YA). (gr. 4-12). (978-0-7166-3695-3(6)) World Bk., Inc.

World Book, Inc. Staff, contrib. by. The World Book of America's Presidents, 2 vols. 2005. (Illus.). (gr. 5-12). 99.00 (978-0-7166-3698-4(0)) World Bk., Inc.

World Book, Inc. Staff, ed. World Book of America's Presidents, 2 vols. 2001. (Illus.). 455p. (J). (gr. 4 up). 79.00 (978-0-7166-3696-0(4) , 20049) World Bk., Inc.

Woronoff, Kristen. American Inaugurals: The Speeches, the Presidents & Their Times. 2002. (Illus.). 320p. (J). (gr. 5 up). 64.94 (978-1-56711-584-0(5) , Blackbirch Pr., Inc.) Thomson Gale.

Wukovits, John F. George W Bush: People in the News. 2004. (Illus.). 111p. (J). (gr. 4-8). reprint ed. 22.00 (978-0-7567-7902-3(2)) DIANE Publishing Co.

Young, Bev. Presidential Cookies. 2nd ed. 2005. Orig. Title: Presidential Cookies the Lure & the Lore. (ENG., Illus.). 168p. (YA). 23.95 (978-0-9729095-3-2(2) , SAN 255-1077) Presidential Publishing.

Young, Jeff C. Chester A. Arthur: A MyReportLinks.com Book. 2002. (Presidents Ser.). (Illus.). 48p. (J). (gr. 4-10). lib. bdg. 25.26 (978-0-7660-5077-8(7)) Enslow Pubs., Inc.

—Dwight D. Eisenhower: Soldier & President. 2004. (Notable Americans Ser.). (Illus.). 128p. (YA). (gr. 6-12). 23.95 (978-1-883846-76-3(5) , First Biographies) Reynolds, Morgan Inc.

—James A. Garfield: A MyReportLinks.com Book. 2003. (Presidents Ser.). (Illus.). 48p. (J). (gr. 5-10). lib. bdg. 25.26 (978-0-7660-5100-3(5) , MyReportLinks.com Bks.) Enslow Pubs., Inc.

—James Buchanan: A MyReportLinks.com Book. 2003. (Presidents Ser.). (Illus.). 48p. (J). (gr. 4-10). lib. bdg. 25.26 (978-0-7660-5101-0(3) , MyReportLinks.com Bks.) Enslow Pubs., Inc.

Zamora, Dulce. How to Draw the Life & Times of Franklin Pierce. 2006. (Kid's Guide to Drawing the Presidents of the United States of America Ser.). (J). 25.25 (978-1-4042-2991-4(4) , PowerKids Pr.) Rosen Publishing Group, Inc., The.

—How to Draw the Life & Times of John Fitzgerald Kennedy. 2007. (Kid's Guide to Drawing the Presidents of the United States of America Ser.). (Illus.). 32p. (J). 25.25 (978-1-4042-3011-8(4) , PowerKids Pr.) Rosen Publishing Group, Inc., The.

—How to Draw the Life & Times of John Tyler. 2006. (Kid's Guide to Drawing the Presidents of the United States of America Ser.). (J). 25.25 (978-1-4042-2987-7(6) , PowerKids Pr.) Rosen Publishing Group, Inc., The.

PRESIDENTS—UNITED STATES—ASSASSINATION

Holzer, Harold. The President Is Shot! The Assassination of Abraham Lincoln. 2004. (Illus.). 184p. (YA). (gr. 4-6). 17.95 (978-1-56397-985-9(3)) Boyds Mills Pr.

Jones, Rebecca C. The President Has Been Shot! True Stories of the Attacks on Ten U. S. Presidents. 1998. (J). (978-0-606-13720-1(3)) Tandem Library Bks.

Salandria, Vincent J. False Mystery: Essays on the Assassination of JFK. Kelin, John, ed. 2004. 25.00 (978-0-9754941-0-3(4)) Square Deal Pr.

St. George, Judith. In the Line of Fire: Presidents' Lives at Stake. 1999. (Illus.). 144p. (J). (gr. 4-6). tchr. ed. 22.95 (978-0-8234-1428-4(0)) Holiday Hse., Inc.

Wilson, Antoine. The Assassination of William McKinley. 2003. (Library of Political Assassinations). (Illus.). 64p. (YA). (gr. 7-12). lib. bdg. 26.50 (978-0-8239-3546-8(9)) Rosen Publishing Group, Inc., The.

PRESIDENTS—UNITED STATES—CHILDREN

Davis, Gibbs. First Kids. Comport, Sally Wern, illus. 2004. (Step into Reading Ser.). 48p. (J). (gr. 2-4). pap. 3.99 (978-0-375-82218-6(6) , Random Hse. Bks. for Young Readers) Random Hse. Children's Bks.

Underwood, Larry. All the Presidents Children. 2002. 120p. (J). per. 15.95 (978-1-886225-85-5(0)) Day of Grace Publishing Services.

PRESIDENTS—UNITED STATES—DRAMA

Kennedy Center Staff. Teddy Roosevelt & the Treasure of Ursa Major (W. T.) Hoyt, Ard, illus. 2008. (Kennedy Center Presidential Ser.). 128p. (J). 10.99 (***978-1-4169-4857-5(0)** , Aladdin) Simon & Schuster Children's Publishing.

PRESIDENTS—UNITED STATES—ELECTION

Beyer, Mark. The Election of 1800: Congress Helps Settle a Three-Way Vote. 2004. (Life in the New American Nation Ser.). (Illus.). 32p. (YA). lib. bdg. (978-0-8239-4255-8(4)) Rosen Publishing Group, Inc., The.

Burgan, Michael. The Electoral College. (Illus.). 48p. (J). 2007. pap. (***978-0-7565-3213-0(2));** 2006. lib. bdg. (***978-0-7565-2455-5(5)**) Compass Point Bks.

Carole Marsh. Presidential Elections. 2004. (Presidents on Parade Ser.). lib. bdg. 29.95 (978-0-635-02221-9(4)); 48p. (gr. 3-8). pap. 7.95 (978-0-635-02220-2(6)) Gallopade International.

Connell, Kate. The Spirit of a New Nation. 2002. (Voices from America's Past Ser.). (Illus.). 40p. (J). (978-0-7922-8684-4(7)) National Geographic Society.

Cunningham, Kevin. The Declaration of Independence. 2004. (Our Government & Citizenship Ser.). 32p. (J). (gr. 2-6). 27.07 (978-1-59296-325-6(0)) Child's World, Inc.

Election 2004: Choosing America's President. 2004. (Illus.). 22p. (J). (978-0-439-68921-2(X)) Scholastic, Inc.

Goldman, David J. Presidential Leaders. 2004. (Middle Grade Nonfiction Ser.). (Illus.). 72p. (J). 25.26 (978-0-8225-0100-8(7) , Carolrhoda Bks.) Lerner Publishing Group.

Gottfried, Ted. The 2000 Election. 2002. (Headliners Ser.). (Illus.). 64p. (gr. 5-8). lib. bdg. 25.90 (978-0-7613-2406-5(2) , Millbrook Pr.) Lerner Publishing Group.

Granfield, Linda. America Votes: How Our President Is Elected. Bjorkman, Steve, illus. (It's Election Year... Get Ready to Make Your Mark! Ser.). 64p. (J). (gr. 4-6). 2005. (978-1-55337-087-1(2)); 2004. (978-1-55337-086-4(4)) Kids Can Pr., Ltd.

—America Votes: How Our President Is Elected. 2003. (gr. 5-8). lib. bdg. 18.75 (978-0-613-89650-4(5)) Tandem Library Bks.

Gunderson, Cory Gideon. The 2000 Presidential Election. 2005. (American Moments Ser.). (Illus.). 48p. (J). (gr. 4-8). lib. bdg. 25.65 (978-1-59197-284-6(1)) ABDO Publishing Co.

Gutman, Dan. Landslide! A Kid's Guide to the U. S. Elections. 2000. (gr. 3-6). lib. bdg. 11.80 (978-0-613-25923-1(8)) Tandem Library Bks.

Havelin, Kate. Victoria Woodhull: Fearless Feminist. 2007. (Trailblazer Biographies Ser.). (Illus.). 112p. (J). 30.60 (978-0-8225-5986-3(2) , Lerner Pubns.) Lerner Publishing Group.

Hewson, Martha S. The Electoral College. 2002. (Your Government Ser.). (Illus.). 64p. (YA). 25.00 (978-0-7910-6790-1(4) , Chelsea Hse.) Facts On File, Inc.

Italia, Bob: Election 2000: A Lesson in Civics. 2001. (United States Presidents Ser.). (Illus.). 32p. (J). (gr. k-6). lib. bdg. 22.78 (978-1-57765-576-3(1) , Checkerboard Library) ABDO Publishing Co.

Krull, Kathleen. A Woman for President: The Story of Victoria Woodhull. Dyer, Jane, illus. 2004. 32p. (J). 16.95 (978-0-8027-8908-2(0)) Walker & Co.

Landau, Elaine. 2000 Presidential Election. 2002. (Cornerstones of Freedom). (Illus.). 48p. (J). (gr. 4-6). 26.00 (978-0-516-22527-2(8) , Children's Pr.) Scholastic Library Publishing.

Morris-Lipsman, Arlene. Presidential Races: The Battle for Power in the United States. 2007. (People's History Ser.). 112p. (YA). (gr. 5-12). lib. bdg. 30.60 (***978-0-8225-6783-7(0)** , Twenty-First Century Bks.) Lerner Publishing Group.

Presidential Elections. 2004. 64p. (J). (gr. 3-5). pap. 9.99 (978-0-7682-2749-9(6) , FS99255) Schaffer, Frank Pubns.

Ring, Susan. Election Connection: The Official Nick Guide to Electing the President. 2004. (Illus.). 72p. (J). pap. 7.95 (978-0-8118-4175-7(8)) Chronicle Bks. LLC.

Ryan, Patrick. George W. Bush. 2001. (United States Presidents Ser.). (Illus.). 32p. (J). (gr. k-6). lib. bdg. 22.78 (978-1-57765-302-8(5) , Checkerboard Library) ABDO Publishing Co.

Saffell, David C., ed. The Encyclopedia of U. S. Presidential Elections. 2004. (Watts Reference Ser.). (J). 39.00 (978-0-531-12051-4(1) , Watts, Franklin) Scholastic Library Publishing.

Schlesinger, Arthur M., Sr., et al, eds. The Election of 1800. 2003. (Major Presidential Elections & the Administrations That Followed Ser.). (Illus.). 154p. (J). (gr. 7 up). lib. bdg. (978-1-59084-352-9(5)) Mason Crest Pubs.

—The Election of 1828. 2003. (Major Presidential Elections & the Administrations That Followed Ser.). (Illus.). 154p. (YA). (gr. 7 up). lib. bdg. (978-1-59084-353-6(3)) Mason Crest Pubs.

—The Election of 1896 & the Administration of William McKinley. 2002. (Major Presidential Elections & the Administrations That Followed Ser.). (Illus.). 154p. (YA). (gr. 7 up). lib. bdg. (978-1-59084-357-4(6)) Mason Crest Pubs.

—The Election of 1932 & the Administration of Franklin D. Roosevelt. 2002. (Major Presidential Elections & the Administrations That Followed Ser.). (Illus.). 154p. (YA). (gr. 7 up). lib. bdg. (978-1-59084-359-8(2)) Mason Crest Pubs.

—The Election of 1948 & the Administration of Harry S. Truman. 2002. (Major Presidential Elections & the Administrations That Followed Ser.). (Illus.). 154p. (YA). (gr. 7 up). lib. bdg. (978-1-59084-360-4(6)) Mason Crest Pubs.

—The Election of 1960 & the Administration of John F. Kennedy. 2002. (Major Presidential Elections & the Administrations That Followed Ser.). (Illus.). 154p. (YA). (gr. 7 up). lib. bdg. (978-1-59084-361-1(4)) Mason Crest Pubs.

—The Election of 1968 & the Administration of Richard Nixon. 2002. (Major Presidential Elections & the Administrations That Followed Ser.). (Illus.). 154p. (YA). (gr. 7 up). lib. bdg. (978-1-59084-362-8(2)) Mason Crest Pubs.

—The Election of 1976 & the Administration of Jimmy Carter. 2002. (Major Presidential Elections & the Administrations That Followed Ser.). (Illus.). 154p. (YA). (gr. 7 up). lib. bdg. (978-1-59084-363-5(0)) Mason Crest Pubs.

—The Election of 1980 & the Administration of Ronald Reagan. 2002. (Major Presidential Elections & the Administrations That Followed Ser.). (Illus.). 154p. (J). (gr. 7 up). lib. bdg. (978-1-59084-364-2(9)) Mason Crest Pubs.

—The Election of 2000 & the Administration of George W. Bush. 2002. (Major Presidential Elections & the Administrations That Followed Ser.). (Illus.). 154p. (YA). (gr. 7 up). lib. bdg. (978-1-59084-365-9(7)) Mason Crest Pubs.

—The Elections of 1789 & 1792. 2003. (Major Presidential Elections & the Administrations That Followed Ser.). (Illus.). 154p. (J). (gr. 7 up). lib. bdg. (978-1-59084-351-2(7)) Mason Crest Pubs.

Schlesinger, Arthur M., Jr. & Israel, Fred L., eds. Major Presidential Elections, 15 bks., Set. (Illus.). (YA). (gr. 7 up). lib. bdg. (978-1-59084-350-5(9)) Mason Crest Pubs.

See, Betty. Electing President: The Electoral Process in Action. 2005. 48p. 10.95 (978-1-59363-067-6(0)) Prufrock Pr.

Sobel, Syl. Presidential Elections: And Other Cool Facts. Wood, Jill, illus. 2nd ed. 2001. 48p. (J). pap. 6.95 (978-0-7641-1894-4(3)) Barron's Educational Series, Inc.

St. George, Judith. So You Want to Be President? Small, David, illus. 2000. 56p. (J). (gr. 2-5). 17.99 (978-0-399-23407-1(1) , Philomel) Penguin Group (USA) Inc.

—So You Want to Be President? Small, David, illus. 2004. (J). (gr. 1-6). 29.95 incl. cd-rom (978-1-55592-132-3(9)); 24.95 incl. audio (978-1-55592-094-4(2)) Weston Woods Studios, Inc.

Stier, Catherine. If I Ran for President. Avril, Lynne, illus. 2007. 32p. (J). (gr. 1-4). 15.95 (***978-0-8075-3543-1(5)**) Whitman, Albert & Co.

Wade, Mary Dodson. George W. Bush: Governor of Texas. 1999. (Illus.). iv, 92p. (J). (gr. 4-8). 15.95 (978-0-87443-173-5(5) , 173-5); pap. 6.95 (978-0-87443-174-2(3) , 174-3) Benson, W. S. & Co., Inc.

Wagner, Heather Lehr. How the President Is Elected. 2007. (U. S. Government: How It Works). 96p. (J). (gr. 5-8). 30.00 (***978-0-7910-9418-1(9)** , Chelsea Hse.) Facts On File, Inc.

PRESIDENTS—UNITED STATES—FAMILY

Davis, Gibbs. First Kids. Comport, Sally Wern, illus. 2004. (Step into Reading Ser.). 48p. (J). (gr. 2-4). pap. 3.99 (978-0-375-82218-6(6) , Random Hse. Bks. for Young Readers) Random Hse. Children's Bks.

George Washington's Mother. 2004. (J). pap. 32.75 incl. audio (978-1-55592-351-8(8)) Weston Woods Studios, Inc.

O'Connor, Jane. If the Walls Could Talk: Family Life at the White House. Hovland, Gary, illus. 2004. 48p. (J). 16.95 (978-0-689-86863-4(4) , Simon & Schuster/Paula Wiseman Bks.) Simon & Schuster Children's Publishing.

PRESIDENTS—UNITED STATES—FICTION

Alger, Horatio. From Canal Boy to President: Or, The Boyhood & Manhood of James A. Garfield. 2006. 78.99 (***978-1-4280-3197-5(9)**) IndyPublish.com.

Bradley, Kimberly Brubaker. The President's Daughter. 2004. (Illus.). 176p. (gr. 3-7). 15.95 (978-0-385-73147-8(7) , Delacorte Bks. for Young Readers) Random Hse. Children's Bks.

Cabot, Meg. Ready or No. 2008. 256p. (J). pap. 7.99 (***978-0-06-147996-0(9)** , HarperTeen) HarperCollins Pubs.

Cabot, Meg. Ready or Not. 2nd ed. 2005. 256p. (YA). (gr. 7 up). 16.99 (978-0-06-072450-4(1)) HarperCollins Pubs.

—Ready or Not. l.t. ed. 2006. 322p. (YA). 23.95 (978-0-7862-8282-1(7)) Thorndike Pr.

Cobot, Meg. All-American Girl. 2004. 416p. (J). (gr. 7 up). pap. 44.00 incl. audio (978-0-8072-2281-2(X) , Listening Library) Random Hse. Audio Publishing Group.

Fritz, Jean. The Great Little Madison. 1998. (J). 12.64 (978-0-606-12956-5(1)) Tandem Library Bks.

Gephart, Donna. As If Being 12 3/4 Isn't Bad Enough, My Mother Is Running for President! 2008. (J). (gr. 3-7). 240p. 15.99 (***978-0-385-73481-3(6)**); 192p. lib. bdg. 18.99 (***978-0-385-90479-7(7)**) Random Hse. Children's Bks. (Delacorte Bks. for Young Readers).

Gutman, Dan. The Kid Who Became President. 2000. 240p. (J). (gr. 4-8). mass mkt. 4.99 (978-0-590-02376-4(4)) Scholastic, Inc.

—The Kid Who Became President. 1999. (978-0-606-21810-8(6)); (gr. 3-6). lib. bdg. 12.40 (978-0-613-21853-5(1)) Tandem Library Bks.

Hoobler, Dorothy & Hoobler, Thomas. The 1960's: Rebels. Hoffman, Robin, illus. 2001. (Century Kids Ser.). 160p. (J). (gr. 5-8). lib. bdg. 22.90 (978-0-7613-1606-0(X) , Twenty-First Century Bks.) Lerner Publishing Group.

Kanehl, Robert. Murder in the Newsroom: Or Andrew Gates, Reporter. Weinberger, Jane, ed. 1998. 164p. (J). (gr. 3-10). pap. 8.00 (978-1-883650-52-0(6)) Windswept Hse. Pubs.

McDonald, Megan. Stink: The Incredible Shrinking Kid. Reynolds, Peter H., illus. 2005. 112p. (J). (gr. k-3). 12.99 (978-0-7636-2025-7(4)) Candlewick Pr.

Roitman, Tanya, illus. I'm Going to Read (Level 1): I'm Going to Washington to Visit the President. 2006. (I'm Going to Read Ser.). 24p. (J). pap. 3.95 (978-1-4027-3408-3(5)) Sterling Publishing Co., Inc.

Schmidt, Gary. First Boy. 2007. 224p. (YA). pap. 6.99 (***978-0-312-37149-4(7)**) Square Fish.

St. George, Judith. The Ghost, the White House, & Me. 2007. 128p. (J). (gr. 3-7). 16.95 (978-0-8234-2045-2(0)) Holiday Hse., Inc.

Stanley, George E. Dwight D. Eisenhower: Young Military Leader. Henderson, Meryl, illus. 2006. (Childhood of Famous Americans Ser.). 192p. (J). pap. 5.99 (978-1-4169-1257-6(6) , Aladdin) Simon & Schuster Children's Publishing.

Twinn, Michael. Countdown to Christmas. 2001. (Illus.). 24p. (J). 11.95 (978-0-85953-844-2(3)) Child's Play-International.

White, Ellen Emerson. The President's Daughter. 2008. (YA). pap. 8.99 (***978-0-312-37488-4(7))*** Feiwel & Friends.

—White House Autumn. 2008. (YA). pap. 8.99 (***978-0-312-37489-1(5))*** Feiwel & Friends.

PRESIDENTS—UNITED STATES—INAUGURATION

Santella, Andrew. U. S. Presidential Inaugurations. 2002. (Cornerstones of Freedom). (Illus.). 48p. (J). (gr. 4-6). 26.00 (978-0-516-22533-3(2) , Children's Pr.) Scholastic Library Publishing.

PRESIDENTS—UNITED STATES—POWER

see Executive Power

PRESIDENTS—UNITED STATES—PROTECTION

Britton, Tamara L. Air Force. 2005. (Symbols, Landmarks & Monuments Ser.). (Illus.). 32p. (J). (gr. k-6). lib. bdg. 22.78 (978-1-59197-520-5(4) , Checkerboard Library) ABDO Publishing Co.

January, Brendan. Air Force One. 2004. (Cornerstones of Freedom Ser.). (Illus.). 48p. (J). 26.00 (978-0-516-24236-1(9) , Children's Pr.) Scholastic Library Publishing.

PRESIDENTS—UNITED STATES—SPOUSES

Adler, David A. & Adler, Michael S. A Picture Book of John & Abigail Adams. Himler, Ronald, illus. 2007. (J). (978-0-8234-2007-0(8)) Holiday Hse., Inc.

Agins, Donna Brown. Jacqueline Kennedy Onassis: Legendary First Lady. 2004. (People to Know Ser.). (Illus.). 128p. (J). lib. bdg. 26.60 (978-0-7660-2186-0(6)) Enslow Pubs., Inc.

Anthony, Carl Sferrazza. America's Most Influential First Ladies. 2003. (Illus.). 160p. (gr. 5 up). lib. bdg. 19.95 (978-1-881508-69-4(2)) Oliver Pr., Inc.

Appelt, Kathi. Miss Lady Bird's Wildflowers: How a First Lady Changed America. Hein, Joy Fisher, illus. 2005. 40p. (J). lib. bdg. 17.89 (978-0-06-001108-6(4)) HarperCollins Pubs.

Ashby, Ruth. Abraham & Mary Todd Lincoln. 2004. (Illus.). 48p. (J). pap. 11.95 (978-0-8368-5701-6(1)); lib. bdg. 30.00 (978-0-8368-5695-8(3)) Stevens, Gareth Inc. (World Almanac Library).

—Bill & Hillary Rodham Clinton. 2005. (Illus.). 48p. (J). pap. (978-0-8368-5762-7(3)); lib. bdg. 30.00 (978-0-8368-5756-6(9)) Stevens, Gareth Inc. (World Almanac Library).

—Franklin & Eleanor Roosevelt. 2005. (Illus.). 48p. (J). pap. (978-0-8368-5764-1(X)); lib. bdg. 30.00 (978-0-8368-5758-0(5)) Stevens, Gareth Inc. (World Almanac Library).

—George & Martha Washington. 2005. (Illus.). 48p. (J). pap. (978-0-8368-5703-0(8)); lib. bdg. 30.00 (978-0-8368-5697-2(X)) Stevens, Gareth Inc. (World Almanac Library).

—George W. & Laura Bush. 2004. (Illus.). 48p. (J). pap. (978-0-8368-5699-6(6)); lib. bdg. 30.00 (978-0-8368-5693-4(7)) Stevens, Gareth Inc. (World Almanac Library).

—John & Abigail Adams. 2005. (Illus.). 48p. (J). pap. (978-0-8368-5761-0(5)); lib. bdg. 30.00 (978-0-8368-5755-9(0)) Stevens, Gareth Inc. (World Almanac Library).

—John & Jacqueline Kennedy. 2004. (Illus.). 48p. (J). pap. (978-0-8368-5700-9(3)); lib. bdg. 30.00 (978-0-8368-5694-1(5)) Stevens, Gareth Inc. (World Almanac Library).

—Ronald & Nancy Reagan. 2004. (Illus.). 48p. (J). pap. 11.95 (978-0-8368-5702-3(X)); lib. bdg. 30.00 (978-0-8368-5696-5(1)) Stevens, Gareth Inc. (World Almanac Library).

—Woodrow & Edith Wilson. 2005. (Illus.). 48p. (J). pap. (978-0-8368-5765-8(8)); lib. bdg. 30.00 (978-0-8368-5759-7(3)) Stevens, Gareth Inc. (World Almanac Library).

Barber, James & Pastan, Amy. Smithsonian Presidents & First Ladies. 2002. (Illus.). 96p. (J). (gr. 4-7). lib. bdg. 22.20 (978-0-613-45619-7(X)) Tandem Library Bks.

Barber, James, et al. The Smithsonian Presidents & First Ladies. 2002. (Illus.). 96p. (J). (gr. 4-6). pap. 12.99 (978-0-7894-8453-6(6)) Dorling Kindersley Publishing, Inc.

Bausum, Ann. Our Country's First Ladies. 2007. (Illus.). 128p. (YA). (gr. 5-9). 19.95 (978-1-4263-0006-6(9)); lib. bdg. 28.90 (978-1-4263-0007-3(7)) National Geographic Society. (National Geographic Children's Bks.).

Blevins, Wiley. Eleanor Roosevelt. 2002. (Illus.). 16p. (J). pap. (978-0-439-35193-5(6)) Scholastic, Inc.

Bober, Natalie S. Abigail Adams: Witness to a Revolution. 1998. (Illus.). 272p. (YA). (gr. 7-12). pap. 9.99 (978-0-689-81916-2(1) , Simon Pulse) Simon & Schuster Children's Publishing.

—Abigail Adams: Witness to a Revolution. 1998. 16.64 (978-0-606-13106-3(X)) Tandem Library Bks.

Bredeson, Carmen. Laura Bush: First Lady. 2002. (Heroes of American History Ser.). (Illus.). 32p. (J). (gr. 1-4). lib. bdg. 22.60 (978-0-7660-2101-3(7)) Enslow Pubs., Inc.

Brown, Don. Dolley Madison Saves George Washington. 2007. 32p. (J). (gr. k-3). 16.00 (978-0-618-41199-3(2)) Houghton Mifflin Co.

Brown, Jonatha A. Eleanor Roosevelt. 2005. (ENG & SPA.). (J). pap. (978-0-8368-4591-4(9)); 2005. (ENG & SPA.). (J). lib. bdg. 19.33 (978-0-8368-4584-6(6)); 2005. (Illus.). 24p. (J). pap. (978-0-8368-4475-7(0)); 2005. (Illus.). 24p. (YA). lib. bdg. 19.33 (978-0-8368-4468-9(8) , Weekly Reader Early Learning Library); 2002. (Illus.). 48p. (J). (gr. 5 up). lib. bdg. 30.00 (978-0-8368-5079-6(3) , World Almanac Library) Stevens, Gareth Inc.

Buller, Jon & Warner, Sally. Smart about the First Ladies: Smart about History. Buller, Jon et al, illus. 2004. (Smart about History Ser.). 78p. (J). (gr. k-5). pap. 5.99 (978-0-448-43724-8(4) , Grosset & Dunlap) Penguin Group (USA) Inc.

Burgan, Michael. Hillary Rodham Clinton: First Lady & Senator. 2005. (J). (978-0-7565-1588-1(2)) Compass Point Bks.

Ching, Jacqueline. Abigail Adams: A Revolutionary Woman. 2005. (Library of American Lives & Times). (Illus.). 112p. (J). (gr. 4-8). lib. bdg. 31.95 (978-0-8239-5723-1(3)) Rosen Publishing Group, Inc., The.

Cohen, Della. Eleanor Roosevelt: Proud & Tall. 2005. (Illus.). 16p. (J). pap. (***978-0-7367-2879-9(1))*** Zaner-Bloser, Inc.

Collier, James Lincoln. The Eleanor Roosevelt You Never Knew. Copeland, Greg, illus. 2004. (You Never Knew Ser.). 80p. (J). 25.50 (978-0-516-24425-9(6) , Children's Pr.) Scholastic Library Publishing.

Cooney, Barbara. Eleanor. Cooney, Barbara, illus. 1999. (Illus.). 32p. (J). (gr. k-3). pap. 6.99 (978-0-14-055583-7(8) , Puffin) Penguin Group (USA) Inc.

—Eleanor. 1999. (J). 13.79 (978-0-606-17255-4(6)) Tandem Library Bks.

Davis, Kate. Abigail Adams. 2002. (Triangle History of the American Revolution Ser.). (Illus.). 104p. (J). 28.70 (978-1-56711-610-6(8) , Blackbirch Pr., Inc.) Thomson Gale.

Donnelly, Shannon. Eleanor Roosevelt. Wolek, Guy, illus. 2005. (Heroes of America Ser.). 240p. (J). (gr. 3-8). lib. bdg. 21.35 (978-1-59679-260-9(4)) ABDO Publishing Co.

Driscoll, Laura. Hillary Clinton: An American Journey. Wood, Judith V., illus. 2007. (All Aboard Reading Ser.). 48p. (J). (gr. 1-3). pap. 3.99 (***978-0-448-44787-2(8)*** , Grosset & Dunlap) Penguin Group (USA) Inc.

Edge, Laura Bufano. Laura Bush: Portrait of a First Lady. 2006. (People to Know Today Ser.). (Illus.). 128p. (J). lib. bdg. 31.93 (978-0-7660-2629-2(9)) Enslow Pubs., Inc.

Eleanor Roosevelt. (Photo Illustrated Biographies Ser.). 24p. (J). 6.95 (978-0-7368-8420-4(3)) Capstone Pr., Inc.

Feinberg, Barbara Silberdick. Eleanor Roosevelt: Everything She Could Be. 2003. (Gateway Biography Ser.: 4). (Illus.). 48p. lib. bdg. 23.90 (978-0-7613-2623-6(5) , Millbrook Pr.) Lerner Publishing Group.

First Ladies. 2003. (Our National Heritage Ser.). 48p. (YA). (gr. 5-8). pap. 5.99 (978-1-56822-918-8(6) , IF2590-E4, Instructional Fair) Schaffer, Frank Pubns.

First Ladies of the White House. 1998. (Illus.). 80p. (J). (gr. k up). lib. bdg. 16.95 (978-1-56674-222-1(6)) Forest Hse. Publishing Co., Inc.

Fleming, Candace. Our Eleanor: A Scrapbook Look at Eleanor Roosevelt's Remarkable Life. 2005. (Illus.). 192p. (J). (gr. 4-8). 21.99 (978-0-689-86544-2(9) , Atheneum) Simon & Schuster Children's Publishing.

Forbes, Dina E. Laura Bush: Teacher, Librarian, & First Lady. 2005. (Ferguson Career Biographies Ser.). (Illus.). 144p. (J). (gr. 6-12). 25.00 (978-0-8160-5886-0(5) , Ferguson Publishing Co.) Facts On File, Inc.

Freedman, Jeri. Hillary Rodham Clinton: Profile of a Leading Democrat. 2007. (J). (***978-1-4042-1910-6(2))*** Rosen Publishing Group, Inc., The.

Fremont, Victoria & Marshall, David. All about the First Ladies Search-a-Word Puzzles. 2001. (Illus.). 64p. (gr. 3). pap. 1.50 (978-0-486-41577-2(5)) Dover Pubns., Inc.

Glass, Maya. Abigail Adams: Famous First Lady. 2003. (Famous People in American History Ser.). (Illus.). 32p. (YA). pap. (978-0-8239-4172-8(8)) Rosen Publishing Group, Inc., The.

Gormley, Beatrice. Jacqueline Kennedy Onassis: Friend of the Arts. 2002. (gr. 3-6). lib. bdg. 13.00 (978-0-613-57576-8(8)) Tandem Library Bks.

—Laura Bush. ed. 2005. 122p. (J). lib. bdg. 15.00 (978-1-59054-921-6(X)) Fitzgerald Bks.

—Laura Bush: America's First Lady. 2003. (Illus.). 128p. (J). pap. 4.99 (978-0-689-85366-1(1) , Aladdin) Simon & Schuster Children's Publishing.

—Laura Bush: America's First Lady. 2003. (gr. 3-6). lib. bdg. 13.00 (978-0-613-61787-1(8)) Tandem Library Bks.

Greenberg, Keith. Bill & Hillary: Working Together in the White House. (gr. 3-6). lib. bdg. 9.25 (978-0-613-09957-8(5)) Tandem Library Bks.

Guernsey, JoAnn B. Hillary Rodham Clinton. 2005. (Biography ' Ser.). (Illus.). 112p. (J). 29.27 (978-0-8225-2372-7(8) , Lerner Pubns.); (gr. 6 up). pap. 7.95 (978-0-8225-9613-4(X)) Lerner Publishing Group.

Gullo, James. Hillary Rodham Clinton. 2003. (Importance of Ser.). (Illus.). 112p. (J). 32.45 (978-1-59018-310-6(X) , Lucent Bks.) Thomson Gale.

Haugen, Brenda. Martha Washington: First Lady of the United States. 2005. (Signature Lives Ser.). (Illus.). 112p. (J). (gr. 5-7). (978-0-7565-0983-5(1)) Compass Point Bks.

Horner, Matina S., intro. Hillary Rodham Clinton: First Lady/Attorney. 1999. (Women of Achievement Ser.). (Illus.). 112p. (YA). (gr. 4-7). 32.00 (978-0-7910-4712-5(1)); pap. 30.00 (978-0-7910-4713-2(X)) Facts On File, Inc. (Chelsea Hse.).

Jacobson, Ryan. Eleanor Roosevelt: First Lady of the World. Purcell, Gordon & Schulz, Barbara, illus. 2005. (Graphic Library). 32p. (J). (gr. 3-7). lib. bdg. 25.26 (978-0-7368-4969-2(6)) Capstone Pr., Inc.

Klingel, Cynthia Fitterer & Noyed, Robert B. Dolley Madison: First Lady. 2002. (Spirit of America: Our People Ser.). (Illus.). 32p. (J). (gr. 2-6). 27.07 (978-1-56766-170-5(X)) Child's World, Inc.

Kramer, Sydelle A. The Look-It-Up Book of First Ladies. 2000. (J). (978-0-606-19901-8(2)) Tandem Library Bks.

Kulling, Monica. Eleanor Everywhere: The Life of Eleanor Roosevelt. 1999. (J). (978-0-606-17177-9(0)) Tandem Library Bks.

Lakin, Patricia. Abigail Adams: First Lady of the American Revolution. Bandelin, Debra & Dacey, Bob, illus. 2006. 48p. (J). lib. bdg. 15.00 (***978-1-4242-1560-7(9))*** Fitzgerald Bks.

—Abigail Adams: First Lady of the American Revolution. Dacey, Bob & Bandelin, Debra, illus. 2006. (Ready-to-read SOFA Ser.). 48p. (J). (gr. 1-3). pap. 3.99 (978-0-689-87032-3(9)); lib. bdg. 11.89 (978-0-689-87033-0(7)) Simon & Schuster Children's Publishing. (Aladdin).

Larkin, Tanya. What Was Cooking in Julia Grant's White House? 2001. (Cooking Throughout American History Ser.). (Illus.). 24p. (J). (gr. 3). lib. bdg. 19.95 (978-0-8239-5611-1(3) , PowerKids Pr.) Rosen Publishing Group, Inc., The.

Lassieur, Allison. Eleanor Roosevelt: Activist for Social Change. 2006. (Great Life Stories Ser.). (Illus.). 111p. (YA). (gr. 5-8). 30.50 (978-0-531-13871-7(2) , Watts, Franklin) Scholastic Library Publishing.

Leininger, Tracy M. Unfading Beauty: The Story of Dolley Madison. Pulley, Kelly & Reed, Lisa, illus. 2000. 64p. (J). 16.00 (978-1-929241-20-0(8)) Vision Forum, Inc., The.

LeVert, Suzanne. Hillary Rodham Clinton: First Lady. 1998. (Gateway Biography Ser.: 4). (Illus.). 48p. (gr. 2-4). pap. (978-1-56294-726-2(5) , Millbrook Pr.) Lerner Publishing Group.

Loewen, Nancy. Hillary Rodham Clinton. 1998. (Ovations Ser.: Vol. 8). (Illus.). 32p. (YA). (gr. 4-7). lib. bdg. (978-0-88682-636-9(5) , Creative Education) Creative Co., The.

MacLeod, Elizabeth. Eleanor Roosevelt: An Inspiring Life. 2006. (Illus.). 32p. (978-1-55337-811-2(3)); (978-1-55337-778-8(8)) Kids Can Pr., Ltd.

Mader, Jan. Dolley Madison. 2007. (J). (978-0-7368-6701-6(5) , Pebble Bks.) Capstone Pr., Inc.

Mara, Wil. Laura Bush. 2003. (Rookie Biographies Ser.). (gr. 1-2). pap. 4.95 (978-0-516-27839-1(8)); (Illus.). 32p. (J). 20.50 (978-0-516-22854-9(4)) Scholastic Library Publishing. (Children's Pr.).

—Laura Bush. 2003. (gr. k-3). lib. bdg. 12.95 (978-0-613-67638-0(6)) Tandem Library Bks.

Mattern, Joanne. Barbara Bush. 2007. (First Ladies Ser.). (Illus.). 32p. (J). (gr. k-6). lib. bdg. 24.21 (***978-1-59928-790-4(0)*** , Checkerboard Library) ABDO Publishing Co.

—Betty Ford. 2007. (First Ladies Ser.). (Illus.). 32p. (J). (gr. k-6). lib. bdg. 24.21 (***978-1-59928-794-2(3)*** , Checkerboard Library) ABDO Publishing Co.

—Dolley Madison. 2007. (First Ladies Ser.). (Illus.). 32p. (J). (gr. k-6). lib. bdg. 24.21 (***978-1-59928-798-0(6)*** , Checkerboard Library) ABDO Publishing Co.

—Eleanor Roosevelt. 2007. (First Ladies Ser.). (Illus.). 32p. (J). (gr. k-6). lib. bdg. 24.21 (***978-1-59928-800-0(1)*** , Checkerboard Library) ABDO Publishing Co.

—Eleanor Roosevelt: More Than a First Lady: Individual Title Six-Packs. (On Deck Ser.: Vol. 2). 24p. (gr. 4-5). 35.00 (978-0-7578-5842-0(2)) Rigby Education.

—First Lady of the United States. 2003. (America's Leaders Ser.). (Illus.). 32p. (J). 23.70 (978-1-56711-264-1(1) , Blackbirch Pr., Inc.) Thomson Gale.

—Grace Coolidge. 2007. (First Ladies Ser.). (Illus.). 32p. (J). (gr. k-6). lib. bdg. 24.21 (***978-1-59928-793-5(5)*** , Checkerboard Library) ABDO Publishing Co.

—Hillary Rodham Clinton. 2007. (First Ladies Ser.). (Illus.). 32p. (J). (gr. k-6). lib. bdg. 24.21 (***978-1-59928-792-8(7)*** , Checkerboard Library) ABDO Publishing Co.

—Jacqueline Kennedy. 2007. (First Ladies Ser.). (Illus.). 32p. (J). (gr. k-6). lib. bdg. 24.21 (***978-1-59928-796-6(X)*** , Checkerboard Library) ABDO Publishing Co.

—Lady Bird Johnson. 2007. (First Ladies Ser.). (Illus.). 32p. (J). (gr. k-6). lib. bdg. 24.21 (***978-1-59928-795-9(1)*** , Checkerboard Library) ABDO Publishing Co.

—Laura Bush. 2007. (First Ladies Ser.). (Illus.). 32p. (J). (gr. k-6). lib. bdg. 24.21 (***978-1-59928-791-1(9)*** , Checkerboard Library) ABDO Publishing Co.

—Martha Washington. 2007. (First Ladies Ser.). (Illus.). 32p. (J). (gr. k-6). lib. bdg. 24.21 (***978-1-59928-801-7(X)*** , Checkerboard Library) ABDO Publishing Co.

—Mary Todd Lincoln. 2007. (First Ladies Ser.). (Illus.). 32p. (J). (gr. k-6). lib. bdg. 24.21 (***978-1-59928-797-3(8)*** , Checkerboard Library) ABDO Publishing Co.

—Nancy Reagan. 2007. (First Ladies Ser.). (Illus.). 32p. (J). (gr. k-6). lib. bdg. 24.21 (***978-1-59928-799-7(4)*** , Checkerboard Library) ABDO Publishing Co.

Mayer, Cassie. Abigail Adams. 2007. (J). (***978-1-4034-9971-4(3)***); pap. (***978-1-4034-9980-6(2))*** Heinemann Library.

McCarthy, Pat. Abigail Adams: First Lady & Patriot. 2002. (Historical American Biographies Ser.). (Illus.). 128p. (YA). (gr. 6-12). lib. bdg. 26.60 (978-0-7660-1618-7(8)) Enslow Pubs., Inc.

McPherson, Stephanie Sammartino. Martha Washington: First Lady. 1998. (Historical American Biographies Ser.). (Illus.). 128p. (YA). (gr. 6-12). lib. bdg. 26.60 (978-0-7660-1017-8(1)) Enslow Pubs., Inc.

Merchant, Peter. Eleanor Roosevelt & the Scary Basement. DiVito, Anna, illus. 2006. (Ready-to-read COFA Ser.). 32p. (J). pap. 3.99 (978-0-689-87205-1(4) , Aladdin); lib. bdg. 11.89 (978-0-689-87206-8(2) , Aladdin Library) Simon & Schuster Children's Publishing.

Our Presidents & First Ladies of the White House. 119.40 (978-0-8249-6046-9(7)) Ideals Pubns.

Pastan, Amy & Dorling Kindersley Publishing Staff. First Ladies. 2001. (Eyewitness Bks.: Vol. 117). (Illus.). 64p. (J). (gr. 4-7). 15.99 (978-0-7894-7397-4(6)) Dorling Kindersley Publishing, Inc.

Patrick, Jean L. S. Dolley Madison. 2002. (History Maker Bios Ser.). (Illus.). (J). 47p. pap. 6.95 (978-0-8225-0379-8(4) , Lerner Pubns.); 48p. (gr. 3-5). lib. bdg. 26.60 (978-0-8225-0194-7(5)) Lerner Publishing Group.

Ransom, Candice. Martha Washington. Ritz, Karen, illus. 2003. 48p. (J). (ps-3). lib. bdg. 14.10 (978-0-613-58928-4(9)) Tandem Library Bks.

Ransom, Candice F. Martha Washington. Ritz, Karen, illus. 2003. (On My Own Biography Ser.). 48p. (J). (gr. 1-3). pap. 5.95 (978-0-87614-107-6(6)); 25.26 (978-0-87614-918-8(2)) Lerner Publishing Group. (Carolrhoda Bks.).

Rinaldo, Denise. Eleanor Roosevelt: With a Discussion of Respect. 2003. (Values in Action Ser.). (J). (978-1-59203-063-7(7)) Learning Challenge, Inc.

Rosenberg, Pam. Eleanor Roosevelt. 2003. (Compass Point Early Biographies Ser.). (Illus.). 32p. (J). (gr. 2 up). lib. bdg. 21.26 (978-0-7565-0417-5(1)) Compass Point Bks.

Ryan, Bernard. Hillary Rodham Clinton: First Lady & Senator. 2004. (Ferguson Career Biographies Ser.). (Illus.). 160p. (J). (gr. 6-12). 25.00 (978-0-8160-5544-9(0) , Ferguson Publishing Co.) Facts On File, Inc.

Slade, Suzanne. Martha Washington: First Lady of the United States. Moore, Frances, illus. 2007. (J). lib. bdg. (***978-1-4048-3727-0(2))*** Picture Window Bks.

Smalley, Roger. Dolley Madison Saves History. Cool, Anna-Maria et al, illus. 2005. (Graphic Library). 32p. (J). (gr. 3-7). lib. bdg. 25.26 (978-0-7368-4972-2(6)) Capstone Pr., Inc.

Somervill, Barbara A. Abigail Adams: Courageous Patriot & First Lady. 2005. (Signature Lives Ser.). (Illus.). 112p. (J). (gr. 5-7). (978-0-7565-0981-1(5)) Compass Point Bks.

—Eleanor Roosevelt: First Lady of the World. 2005. (Signature Lives Ser.). (Illus.). 112p. (J). (gr. 5-7). (978-0-7565-0992-7(0)) Compass Point Bks.

Spengler, Kremena. Eva Peron: First Lady of the People. 2006. (Fact Finders Ser.). 32p. (J). (gr. 1-3). 22.60 (978-0-7368-6415-2(6)) Capstone Pr., Inc.

St. George, Judith. John & Abigail Adams: An American Love Story. 2001. (Illus.). 160p. (J). (gr. 4-6). tchr. ed. 22.95 (978-0-8234-1571-7(6)) Holiday Hse., Inc.

Stone, Tanya Lee. Laura Bush: The First Lady. 2001. (Gateway Biography Ser.). (Illus.). 48p. (J). (gr. 4-8). pap. 9.95 (978-0-7613-1539-1(X) , Millbrook Pr.) Lerner Publishing Group.

—Laura Welch Bush: First Lady. 2001. (Gateway Biography Ser.). (Illus.). 48p. (gr. 2-4). lib. bdg. 23.90 (978-0-7613-2304-4(X) , Millbrook Pr.) Lerner Publishing Group.

—Laura Welch Bush: First Lady. 2001. (J). (978-0-606-22378-2(9)); (gr. 3-6). lib. bdg. 18.75 (978-0-613-44592-4(9)) Tandem Library Bks.

Sutcliffe, Jane. Abigail Adams. 2006. (History Maker Bios Ser.). (Illus.). 48p. (J). 26.60 (978-0-8225-5942-9(0) , Lerner Pubns.) Lerner Publishing Group.

Thompson, Gare. Who Was Eleanor Roosevelt? Wolf, Elizabeth, tr. Wolf, Elizabeth & Harrison, Nancy, illus. 2004. (Who Was...? Ser.). 112p. (J). (gr. 7-7). pap. 4.99 (978-0-448-43509-1(8) , Grosset & Dunlap) Penguin Group (USA) Inc.

—Who Was Eleanor Roosevelt? 2004. (gr. 3-6). lib. bdg. 13.00 (978-0-613-72563-7(8)) Tandem Library Bks.

Time for Kids Editors. Eleanor Roosevelt: First Lady of the World. 2006. (Time for Kids Ser.). (Illus.). 48p. (J). 14.99 (978-0-06-057614-1(6)); pap. 3.99 (978-0-06-057613-4(8)) HarperCollins Pubs.

Trumbauer, Lisa. Eleanor Roosevelt. (First Biographies Ser.). 24p. (J). pap. 5.95 (978-0-7368-5082-7(1)) Capstone Pr., Inc.

—Eleanor Roosevelt. 2004. (First Biographies Ser.). (Illus.). 24p. (J). lib. bdg. 15.93 (978-0-7368-2080-6(9) , Pebble Bks.) Capstone Pr., Inc.

Vaughan, Carolyn. First Ladies. Fandex Family Field Guides Staff, ed. 2003. (Illus.). 50p. (J). (gr. 5 up). 9.95 (978-0-7611-2944-8(8) , 12944) Workman Publishing Co., Inc.

Wagner, Heather Lehr. Hillary Rodham Clinton. 2004. (Women in Politics Ser.). (Illus.). 120p. 30.00 (978-0-7910-7735-1(7)); 110p. pap. 30.00 (978-0-7910-7999-7(6)) Facts On File, Inc. (Chelsea Hse.).

Wallner, Alexandra. Abigail Adams. 2005. (Illus.). 32p. (J). pap. 6.95 (978-0-8234-1942-5(8)) Holiday Hse., Inc.

Welsbacher, Anne. John Adams. 1999. (United States Presidents Ser.). (Illus.). 32p. (J). (gr. k-6). lib. bdg. 22.78 (978-1-56239-738-8(9) , Checkerboard Library) ABDO Publishing Co.

Wheeler, Jill C. Hillary Rodham Clinton. 2003. (Breaking Barriers Ser.). (Illus.). 64p. (J). (gr. 3-8). lib. bdg. 25.65 (978-1-57765-741-5(1)) ABDO Publishing Co.

—Laura Bush. 2003. (Breaking Barriers Ser.). (Illus.). 64p. (J). (gr. 3-8). lib. bdg. 25.65 (978-1-57765-875-7(2)) ABDO Publishing Co.

Whiting, Jim. The Life & Times of Abigail Adams. 2007. (Profiles in American History Ser.). (Illus.). 48p. (J). lib. bdg. 29.95 (***978-1-58415-527-0(2))*** Mitchell Lane Pubs., Inc.

Winget, Mary. Eleanor Roosevelt. (Biography Ser.). (Illus.). 2005. 112p. (gr. 6-12). lib. bdg. 27.93 (978-0-8225-4985-7(9)); 2003. 48p. (J). pap. 6.95 (978-0-8225-4801-0(1) , Lerner Pubns.); 2003. 48p. (J). (gr. 3-5). lib. bdg. 26.60 (978-0-8225-4675-7(2)) Lerner Publishing Group.

—Eleanor Roosevelt. 2003. (gr. 3-6). lib. bdg. 15.25 (978-0-613-84031-6(3)) Tandem Library Bks.

Witteman, Barbara. Dolley Madison: First Lady. 2003. (Let Freedom Ring Ser.). (Illus.). 48p. (J). (gr. 3-4). lib. bdg. 22.60 (978-0-7368-1551-2(1) , Bridgestone Bks.) Capstone Pr., Inc.

PRESIDENTS—UNITED STATES—STAFF

Mattern, Joanne. White House Press Secretary. 2003. (America's Leaders Ser.). (Illus.). 32p. (J). 23.70 (978-1-56711-281-8(1) , Blackbirch Pr., Inc.) Thomson Gale.

Naden, Corinne J. & Blue, Rose. Condoleeza Rice. 2004. (African-American Biographies Ser.). (Illus.). 64p. (J). 28.56 (978-1-4109-1039-4(3)) Raintree.

Ryan, Bernard. Condoleeza Rice: National Security Advisor & Musician. 2003. (Ferguson Career Biographies Ser.). (Illus.). 160p. (J). (gr. 6-12). 25.00 (978-0-8160-5480-0(0) , Ferguson Publishing Co.) Facts On File, Inc.

Wade, Mary. Condoleeza Rice: Being the Best. 2003. (gr. 3-6). lib. bdg. 17.60 (978-0-613-58959-8(9)) Tandem Library Bks.

PRESIDENTS' SPOUSES

see Presidents—United States—Spouses

PRESLEY, ELVIS, 1935-1977

Alagna, Magdalena. Elvis Presley. 2006. (Rock & Roll Hall of Famers Ser.). (Illus.). 112p. (YA). (gr. 5-8). lib. bdg. 29.25 (978-0-8239-3524-6(8)) Rosen Publishing Group, Inc., The.

Brown, Adele Q. Elvis Presley. 2003. (Trailblazers of the Modern World Ser.). (Illus.). 48p. (J). (gr. 5 up). pap. 14.95 (978-0-8368-5245-5(1)); lib. bdg. 30.00 (978-0-8368-5085-7(8)) Stevens, Gareth Inc. (World Almanac Library).

Clayton, Marie. Elvis Presley: Unseen Archives. 2003. (Unseen Archives Ser.). (Illus.). 384p. 29.95 (978-0-7525-8335-8(2)) Parragon, Inc.

Denenberg, Barry. All Shook Up! The Life & Death of Elvis Presley. 2003. (gr. 5-8). lib. bdg. 14.15 (978-0-613-65755-6(1)) Tandem Library Bks.

—All Shook Up: The Life & Death of Elvis Presley. 2003. (All Shook Up Ser.). (Illus.). 192p. (J). (gr. 5-10). pap. 5.99 (978-0-439-52811-5(9)) Scholastic, Inc.

Doll, Susan. Elvis Presley: With Profiles of Muddy Waters & Mick Jagger. 2006. (Biographical Connections Ser.). (Illus.). 112p. (J). (978-0-7166-1823-2(0)) World Bk., Inc.

Eanes, Jim. Elvis in Virginia. 2003. (Illus.). 78p. (YA). per. 15.95 (978-0-9717295-2-0(2)) E & H Publishing Co., Inc.

Edgers, Geoff. Who Was Elvis Presley? Harrison, Nancy & O'Brien, John, illus. 2007. (Who Was... ? Ser.). 112p. (J). (gr. 2-5). pap. 4.99 (***978-0-448-44642-4(1)** , Grosset & Dunlap) Penguin Group (USA) Inc.

Evans, Mike. Elvis: A Celebration: Images of Elvis Presley from the Elvis Presley Archive at Graceland. 2004. (Illus.). 608p. pap. 19.95 (978-0-7566-0769-2(8)) Dorling Kindersley Publishing, Inc.

Gogerly, Liz. Elvis Presley. 2004. (Illus.). 48p. (J). lib. bdg. 28.56 (978-0-7398-6629-0(X)) Raintree.

Hampton, Wilborn. Up Close: Elvis Presley. 2007. 192p. (YA). (gr. 7 up). 16.99 (978-0-670-06166-2(2) , Viking Juvenile) Penguin Group (USA) Inc.

Harper, Betty. Color My World Vol. 1: Early Elvis (Coloring Book) Harper, Betty, illus. 2004. (Illus.). 32p. (J). 4.95 (978-0-932117-42-7(2)) Osborne Enterprises Publishing.

Matthews, Rupert. Elvis Presley. 2001. (Profiles Ser.). (Illus.). 56p. (J). (gr. 6-7). lib. bdg. 24.22 (978-1-58810-056-6(1)) Heinemann Library.

O'Neal, Sean. Elvis Presley Memorabilia: An Unauthorized Collectors Guide. collector's ed. 2001. (Schiffer Book for Collectors Ser.). (Illus.). 160p. (gr. 10-13). pap. 29.95 (978-0-7643-1382-0(7)) Schiffer Publishing, Ltd.

Plantz, Connie. Elvis Presley: Music Legend, Movie Star, the King. 2004. (People to Know Ser.). (Illus.). 128p. (J). lib. bdg. 26.60 (978-0-7660-2103-7(3)) Enslow Pubs., Inc.

Torr, James D., ed. Elvis Presley. 2001. (People Who Made History Ser.). (Illus.). 207p. (YA). (gr. 8-8). pap. (978-0-7377-0643-7(0) , LML00501-176910, Greenhaven Pr., Inc.) Thomson Gale.

Trailblazers of the Modern World: Winston Churchill; Alexander Fleming; Pablo Picasso; Elvis Presley; Venus & Serena Williams; Oprah Winfrey, 6 bks. 2002. (Illus.). (J). (gr. 5 up). pap. 89.70 (978-0-8368-5241-7(9) , World Almanac Library) Stevens, Gareth Inc.

PRESS

see Journalism; Newspapers; Periodicals

PRESS LAW

McGlone, Catherine. New York Times V. Sullivan & the Freedom of the Press Debate. 2005. (Debating Supreme Court Decisions Ser.). (Illus.). 112p. (J). (gr. 5-8). lib. bdg. 26.60 (978-0-7660-2357-4(5)) Enslow Pubs., Inc.

PRESSURE GROUPS

see Lobbying

PRESSURE SUITS

see Astronauts—Clothing

PREVENTION OF ACCIDENTS

see Accidents—Prevention

PREVENTION OF CRUELTY TO ANIMALS

see Animals—Treatment

PREVENTION OF FIRE

see Fire Prevention

PREVENTIVE MEDICINE

see Bacteriology; Health; Immunity; Public Health

PRICE, HOMER (FICTITIOUS CHARACTER)—FICTION

McCloskey, Robert. Centerburg Tales: More Adventures of Homer Price. 1999. (J). (gr. 3-6). lib. bdg. 14.15 (978-0-8085-8462-9(6)) Tandem Library Bks.

—Homer Price. l.t. ed. 2004. (Beeler Mystery Ser.). 158p. 29.95 (978-1-58118-123-4(X)) LRS.

—Homer Price. l.t. ed. (J). (gr. 4-6). reprint ed. 10.00 (978-0-89064-072-2(6)) National Assn. for Visually Handicapped.

PRIESTLEY, JOSEPH, 1733-1804

Bowden, Mary Ellen & Rosner, Linda. Joseph Priestley, Radical Thinker. 2005. 72p. pap. 19.95 (978-0-941901-38-3(6)) AtlasBooks Distribution.

Conley, Kate A. Joseph Priestly & the Discovery of Oxygen. 2005. (Uncharted, Unexplored, & Unexplained Ser.). (Illus.). 48p. (J). (gr. 4-8). lib. bdg. 29.95 (978-1-58415-367-2(9)) Mitchell Lane Pubs., Inc.

PRIMARY EDUCATION

see Education, Elementary

PRIMATES

see also Apes; Human Beings; Lemurs; Monkeys

Banks, Martin. How Monkeys "Talk" 1998. (Nature's Mysteries Ser.). (Illus.). 32p. (J). (gr. 3-5). lib. bdg. 22.79 (978-0-7614-0858-1(4) , Benchmark Bks.) Cavendish, Marshall Corp.

Gorillas & Other Primates. 2002. (Wild, Wild World Ser.). 32p. (J). 9.95 (978-0-7525-4687-2(2)) Parragon, Inc.

Kalman, Bobbie. What Is a Primate? 1999. (Science of Living Things Ser.). (Illus.). 32p. (J). (gr. 2-3). (978-0-86505-922-1(5)); pap. (978-0-86505-950-4(0)) Crabtree Publishing Co.

—What Is a Primate? 1999. (978-0-606-18072-6(9)) Tandem Library Bks.

Kalman, Bobbie & Levigne, Heather. Les Primates. 2005. (FRE., Illus.). 32p. (J). pap. (978-2-89579-051-8(5)) Crabtree Publishing Co.

—What Is a Primate? 1999. (Illus.). 32p. (J). (ps-ps). lib. bdg. 14.10 (978-0-613-19538-6(8)) Tandem Library Bks.

Morgan, Sally. Small Primates. 2004. (J). lib. bdg. (978-1-59389-178-7(4) , Cherrytree Books) Evans Publishing Group.

Morris, Pat, et al. Primates, 10 vols., Vol. 4. 2003. (Illus.). (J). (978-0-7172-5746-1(0) , Grolier) Scholastic Library Publishing.

Paterson, Samantha. Primates. 2007. (J). (***978-1-59036-709-4(X)**); (***978-1-59036-710-0(3)**) Weigl Pubs., Inc.

Paterson, Samantha. The Science of Primates. 2001. (Living Science Ser.). (Illus.). 32p. (J). (gr. 2 up). lib. bdg. 24.67 (978-0-8368-2790-3(2)) Stevens, Gareth Inc.

—The Science of Primates. 2003. (Living Science Ser.). (Illus.). 32p. (J). (gr. 1-3). pap. 7.95 (978-1-930954-36-6(0)) Weigl Pubs., Inc.

Redmond, Ian. Gorilas. Anderson, Peter & Brightling, Geoff, illus. 2003. (SPA.). 64p. 14.95 (978-84-372-2323-0(7)) Altea, Ediciones, S.A. - Grupo Santillana ESP. *Dist:* Santillana USA Publishing Co., Inc.

Sjonger, Rebecca & Kalman, Bobbie. Monkeys & Other Primates. 2005. (What Kind of Animal Is It? Ser.). (Illus.). 32p. (J). (gr. k-6). (978-0-7787-2165-9(5)); pap. (978-0-7787-2223-6(6)) Crabtree Publishing Co.

Stefoff, Rebecca. The Primate Order. 2005. (Family Trees Ser.). (Illus.). 93p. (J). (gr. 3-7). lib. bdg. 32.79 (978-0-7614-1816-0(4) , Benchmark Bks.) Cavendish, Marshall Corp.

Stonehouse, Bernard. Monkeys & Apes: A Visual Introduction to Monkeys & Apes. Camm, Martin & Orr, Richard, illus. (Animal Watch Ser.). 48p. (J). (gr. 4-9). 16.95 (978-0-8160-3927-2(5) , Checkmark Bks.) Facts On File, Inc.

Swan, Erin Pembrey. Primates: From Howler Monkeys to Humans. 1998. (Animals in Order Ser.). (Illus.). 48p. (J). (gr. 4-6). 26.50 (978-0-531-11487-2(2) , Watts, Franklin) Scholastic Library Publishing.

PRIMATES—FICTION

Elliott, David. Evangeline Mudd: And the Golden-Haired Apes of the Ikkinasti Jungle. Wesson, Andrea, tr. Wesson, Andrea, illus. 2004. 208p. (J). (gr. 2-5). 15.99 (978-0-7636-1876-6(4)) Candlewick Pr.

—Evangeline Mudd & the Golden-Haired Apes of the Ikkinasti Jungle. Wesson, Andrea, illus. 2007. 208p. (J). (gr. 2-5). 5.99 (978-0-7636-2614-3(7)) Candlewick Pr.

MacHale, D. J. The Lost City of Faar. 2003. (Pendragon Ser.: Bk. 2). 400p. (J). (gr. 5 up). pap. 6.99 (978-0-7434-3732-5(2) , Aladdin) Simon & Schuster Children's Publishing.

Romines, Greg. Thirteen Rabbit. 2005. 48p. pap. 12.95 (978-1-4137-6507-6(6)) PublishAmerica, Inc.

Star, Nancy. Mystery of the Snow Day Bigfoot. Bernardin, James, illus. 2005. (Calendar Club Mysteries Ser.: Vol. 3). 77p. (J). pap. (***978-0-439-67262-7(7)**) Scholastic, Inc.

PRIME MINISTERS—CANADA

Granatstein, Jack L. W. L. MacKenzie King. rev. ed. 2001. (Canadians Ser.). (Illus.). 64p. (978-1-55041-489-9(5)) Fitzhenry & Whiteside, Ltd.

Hughes, Susan. Lester B. Pearson. (Illus.). 64p. (J). (gr. 5 up). pap. (978-1-55041-504-9(2)) Fitzhenry & Whiteside, Ltd.

Marsh, Carole. Pierre Trudeau: An Ohio Experience Reader. 2001. (J). (gr. k-5). pap. 1.95 (978-0-635-00441-3(0)) Gallopade International.

Selkirk, Blaine & Butts, Ed. Prime Ministers of Canada. Butts, Ed & Zeman, John, eds. 2001. 48p. (J). pap. 14.95 incl. audio (978-1-894262-59-0(X) , JMP122K) Jordan Music Productions, Inc.

Slade, Arthur G. John Diefenbaker: An Appointment with Destiny. 2001. (Illus.). 181p. (J). pap. (978-0-9688166-0-8(6)) X Y Z Publishing.

Waite, P. B. John A. MacDonald. 2000. (Canadians Ser.). 64p. pap. (978-1-55041-479-0(8)) Fitzhenry & Whiteside, Ltd.

PRIME MINISTERS—GREAT BRITAIN

Binns, Tristan Boyer. Winston Churchill: Soldier & Politician. 2004. (Great Life Stories Ser.). (Illus.). 127p. (J). 30.50 (978-0-531-12361-4(8) , Watts, Franklin) Scholastic Library Publishing.

Connolly, Sean. Margaret Thatcher. 2000. (Profiles Ser.). (Illus.). 56p. (J). (gr. 4-6). lib. bdg. 24.22 (978-1-57572-224-5(0)) Heinemann Library.

Daynes, Katie. Winston Churchill. Tomlins, Karen, illus. 2006. 64p. (J). 8.99 (978-0-7945-1258-3(5) , Usborne) EDC Publishing.

Hamilton, Janice. Winston Churchill. 2006. (Illus.). 112p. (J). 27.93 (978-0-8225-3419-8(3) , Twenty-First Century Bks.) Lerner Publishing Group.

Haugen, Brenda. Winston Churchill: British Soldier, Writer, Statesman. 2006. (Signature Lives Ser.). (Illus.). 112p. (J). (gr. 5-7). 30.60 (978-0-7565-1582-9(3)) Compass Point Bks.

Hinman, Bonnie. Tony Blair. (Major World Leaders Ser.). (Illus.). (gr. 6-12). 2003. 144p. pap. 30.00 (978-0-7910-7185-4(5)); 2002. 112p. (YA). 30.00 (978-0-7910-6939-4(7)); 2nd rev. ed. 2006. 120p. (J). 30.00 (978-0-7910-9216-3(X)) Facts On File, Inc. (Chelsea Hse.).

Hughes, Libby. Madam Prime Minister: A Biography of Margaret Thatcher. 2000. (People in Focus Ser.). (Illus.). 152p. (YA). pap. 10.95 (978-0-595-14638-3(4) , Backinprint.com) iUniverse, Inc.

MacDonald, Fiona. Winston Churchill. 2003. (Trailblazers of the Modern World Ser.). (Illus.). 48p. (J). (gr. 5 up). pap. 14.95 (978-0-8368-5242-4(7)); lib. bdg. 30.00 (978-0-8368-5082-6(3)) Stevens, Gareth Inc. (World Almanac Library).

Naden, Corinne J. & Blue, Rose. Tony Blair. 2002. (People in the News Ser.). (Illus.). 112p. (J). (gr. 6-9). 32.45 (978-1-59018-236-9(7) , Lucent Bks.) Thomson Gale.

Reynoldson, Fiona. Winston Churchill. 2001. (Leading Lives Ser.). (Illus.). 64p. (J). (gr. 5-7). lib. bdg. 27.86 (978-1-58810-163-1(0)) Heinemann Library.

Wheeler, Jill C. Margaret Thatcher. 2004. (Women of the World Ser.). (J). (978-1-59197-618-9(9)) ABDO Publishing Co.

Wilson, Wayne. Tony Blair. l.t. ed. 2002. (Real-Life Reader Biography Ser.). (Illus.). 32p. (J). (gr. 3-8). lib. bdg. 15.95 (978-1-58415-143-2(9)) Mitchell Lane Pubs., Inc.

PRIME MINISTERS—ISRAEL

Brackett, Virginia. Menachem Begin. 2002. (Major World Leaders Ser.). (Illus.). 112p. (gr. 6-12). 30.00 (978-0-7910-6946-2(X) , Chelsea Hse.) Facts On File, Inc.

Claybourne, Anna. Golda Meir. 2003. (Leading Lives Ser.). (Illus.). 64p. (J). lib. bdg. 28.50 (978-1-4034-0835-8(1)) Heinemann Library.

Crompton, Samuel Willard. Ariel Sharon. 2nd rev. ed. 2007. (Modern World Leaders Ser.). 112p. (J). (gr. 6-12). 30.00 (***978-0-7910-9263-7(1)** , Chelsea Hse.) Facts On File, Inc.

Marsh, Carole. Golda Meir. 2002. (One Thousand Readers Ser.). (Illus.). 12p. (J). (gr. k-4). 2.95 (978-0-635-01513-6(7) , 15137) Gallopade International.

Sommers, Michael A. Ehud Olmert. 2007. (J). (***978-1-4042-1904-5(8)**) Rosen Publishing Group, Inc., The.

Wheeler, Jill C. Golda Meir. 2004. (Women of the World Ser.). (J). (978-1-59197-615-8(4)) ABDO Publishing Co.

Worth, Richard. Ariel Sharon. 2003. (Major World Leaders Ser.). (Illus.). 112p. (gr. 6-12). 30.00 (978-0-7910-7653-8(9) , Chelsea Hse.) Facts On File, Inc.

PRIMERS

see also Alphabet Books

Ada, Alma Flor & Compoy, F. Isabel. Ahora No. 3rd ed. 2002. (Trofeos Ser.). (SPA.). (gr. k-6). pap. 19.70 (978-0-15-331108-6(8)) Harcourt Schl. Pubs.

—La Caja de Tiguero. 3rd ed. 2002. (Trofeos Ser.). (SPA.). (gr. k-6). pap. 19.70 (978-0-15-331124-6(X)) Harcourt Schl. Pubs.

—Ceferino, Mi Cerdito. 3rd ed. 2002. (Trofeos Ser.). (SPA.). (gr. k-6). pap. 19.70 (978-0-15-330881-9(8)) Harcourt Schl. Pubs.

—Cuantas Ven? 3rd ed. 2002. (Trofeos Ser.). (SPA.). (gr. k-6). pap. 19.70 (978-0-15-331071-3(5)) Harcourt Schl. Pubs.

—Cuso Macaco Come. 3rd ed. 2002. (Trofeos Ser.). (SPA.). (gr. k-6). pap. 19.70 (978-0-15-330698-3(X)) Harcourt Schl. Pubs.

—Dado Nada. 3rd ed. 2002. (Trofeos Ser.). (SPA.). (gr. k-6). pap. 19.70 (978-0-15-330793-5(5)) Harcourt Schl. Pubs.

—Donde Esta Mi Osito? 3rd ed. 2002. (Trofeos Ser.). (SPA.). (gr. k-6). pap. 19.70 (978-0-15-330488-0(X)) Harcourt Schl. Pubs.

—Es Divertido. 3rd ed. 2002. (Trofeos Ser.). (SPA.). (gr. k-6). pap. 19.70 (978-0-15-331129-1(0)) Harcourt Schl. Pubs.

—Es un Pez? 3rd ed. 2002. (Trofeos Ser.). (SPA.). (gr. k-6). pap. 19.70 (978-0-15-331128-4(2)) Harcourt Schl. Pubs.

—La Escurridiza W. 3rd ed. 2002. (Trofeos Ser.). (SPA.). (gr. k-6). pap. 19.70 (978-0-15-331127-7(4)) Harcourt Schl. Pubs.

—La Fiesta. 3rd ed. 2002. (Trofeos Ser.). (SPA.). (gr. k-6). pap. 19.70 (978-0-15-330559-7(2)) Harcourt Schl. Pubs.

—Las Gemelas. 3rd ed. 2002. (Trofeos Ser.). (SPA.). (gr. k-6). pap. 19.70 (978-0-15-330558-0(4)) Harcourt Schl. Pubs.

—Genoveva y Gisela. 3rd ed. 2002. (Trofeos Ser.). (SPA.). (gr. k-6). pap. 19.70 (978-0-15-331032-4(4)) Harcourt Schl. Pubs.

—La Gorra. 3rd ed. 2002. (Trofeos Ser.). (SPA.). (gr. k-6). pap. 19.70 (978-0-15-330749-2(8)) Harcourt Schl. Pubs.

—Un Insecto Va a Poder? 3rd ed. 2002. (Trofeos Ser.). (SPA.). (gr. k-6). pap. 19.70 (978-0-15-332046-0(X)) Harcourt Schl. Pubs.

—Jose Jugo Mucho. 3rd ed. 2002. (Trofeos Ser.). (SPA.). (gr. k-6). pap. 19.70 (978-0-15-330797-3(8)) Harcourt Schl. Pubs.

—Karen la Ocupada. 3rd ed. 2002. (Trofeos Ser.). (SPA.). (gr. k-6). pap. 19.70 (978-0-15-331125-3(8)) Harcourt Schl. Pubs.

—Leti la Libelula. 3rd ed. 2002. (Trofeos Ser.). (SPA.). (gr. k-6). pap. 19.70 (978-0-15-330745-4(5)) Harcourt Schl. Pubs.

—Llego? 3rd ed. 2002. (Trofeos Ser.). (SPA.). (gr. k-6). pap. 19.70 (978-0-15-330839-0(7)) Harcourt Schl. Pubs.

—La Mama Tigre Corre. 3rd ed. 2002. (Trofeos Ser.). (SPA.). (gr. k-6). pap. 19.70 (978-0-15-330748-5(X)) Harcourt Schl. Pubs.

—Mascotas. 3rd ed. 2002. (Trofeos Ser.). (SPA.). (gr. k-6). pap. 19.70 (978-0-15-330499-6(5)) Harcourt Schl. Pubs.

—Mexico Lindo y Querido. 3rd ed. 2002. (Trofeos Ser.). (SPA.). (gr. k-6). pap. 19.70 (978-0-15-331126-0(6)) Harcourt Schl. Pubs.

—Mi Primer Dia de Escuela. 3rd ed. 2002. (Trofeos Ser.). (SPA.). (gr. k-6). pap. 19.70 (978-0-15-329889-9(8)) Harcourt Schl. Pubs.

—Un Muchachito. 3rd ed. 2002. (Trofeos Ser.). (SPA.). (gr. k-6). pap. 19.70 (978-0-15-330795-9(1)) Harcourt Schl. Pubs.

—El Nene Del. 3rd ed. 2002. (Trofeos Ser.). (SPA.). (gr. k-6). pap. 19.70 (978-0-15-330699-0(8)) Harcourt Schl. Pubs.

—La Nina y Su Muneca. 3rd ed. 2002. (Trofeos Ser.). (SPA.). (gr. k-6). pap. 19.70 (978-0-15-330796-6(X)) Harcourt Schl. Pubs.

—Papi y Pepo. 3rd ed. 2002. (Trofeos Ser.). (SPA.). (gr. k-6). pap. 19.70 (978-0-15-330695-2(5)) Harcourt Schl. Pubs.

—El Parque. 3rd ed. 2002. (Trofeos Ser.). (SPA.). (gr. k-6). pap. 19.70 (978-0-15-331058-4(8)) Harcourt Schl. Pubs.

—Que Desazon! 3rd ed. 2002. (Trofeos Ser.). (SPA.). (gr. k-6). pap. 19.70 (978-0-15-331097-3(9)) Harcourt Schl. Pubs.

—Salta O Escala? 3rd ed. 2002. (Trofeos Ser.). (SPA.). (gr. k-6). pap. 19.70 (978-0-15-330747-8(1)) Harcourt Schl. Pubs.

—Sube. 3rd ed. 2002. (Trofeos Ser.). (SPA.). (gr. k-6). pap. 19.70 (978-0-15-330744-7(7)) Harcourt Schl. Pubs.

—El Tesoro. 3rd ed. 2002. (Trofeos Ser.). (SPA.). (gr. k-6). pap. 19.70 (978-0-15-330860-4(5)) Harcourt Schl. Pubs.

—Tortuguita y Aguila. 3rd ed. 2002. (Trofeos Ser.). (SPA.). (gr. k-6). pap. 19.70 (978-0-15-331084-3(7)) Harcourt Schl. Pubs.

—Tu, Tu, Tu. 3rd ed. 2002. (Trofeos Ser.). (SPA.). (gr. k-6). pap. 19.70 (978-0-15-330697-6(1)) Harcourt Schl. Pubs.

—Vamos. 3rd ed. 2002. (Trofeos Ser.). (SPA.). (gr. k-6). pap. 19.70 (978-0-15-330794-2(3)) Harcourt Schl. Pubs.

—Ves la Y? 3rd ed. 2002. (Trofeos Ser.). (SPA.). (gr. k-6). pap. 19.70 (978-0-15-331045-4(6)) Harcourt Schl. Pubs.

—Y Yo, Bebo Cafe? 3rd ed. 2002. (Trofeos Ser.). (SPA.). (gr. k-6). pap. 19.70 (978-0-15-330746-1(3)) Harcourt Schl. Pubs.

Allen, Margaret. Barney Bear's Party (r-Controlled Vowels), Bk. 20. Kupperstein, Joel, ed. Thelen, Mary, illus. 1999. (Dr. Maggie's Phonics Readers Ser.). 15p. (J). (gr. k-3). pap., stu. ed. 2.99 (978-1-57471-595-8(X) , 2920) Creative Teaching Pr., Inc.

—Cat & Dog at the Circus: Question Words, Soft C & G, Bk. 22. Kupperstein, Joel, ed. Leary, Catherine, illus. 1999. (Dr. Maggie's Phonics Readers Ser.). 15p. (J). (gr. k-3). pap., stu. ed. 2.99 (978-1-57471-597-2(6) , 2922) Creative Teaching Pr., Inc.

—Click, Click (qu, ck), Bk. 7. Kupperstein, Joel, ed. Clegg, Dave, illus. 1999. (Dr. Maggie's Phonics Readers Ser.). 15p. (J). (gr. k-3). pap., stu. ed. 2.99 (978-1-57471-582-8(8) , 2907) Creative Teaching Pr., Inc.

—Dave & Jane's Band (long a: ay, a-e, ai), Bk. 12. Kupperstein, Joel, ed. Manders, John, illus. 1999. (Dr. Maggie's Phonics Readers Ser.). 15p. (J). pap., stu. ed. 2.99 (978-1-57471-587-3(9) , 2912) Creative Teaching Pr., Inc.

—Draw & Share (Consonant Digraphs: sh, ch, th), Bk. 10. Kupperstein, Joel, ed. Iwai, Melissa, illus. 1999. (Dr. Maggie's Phonics Readers Ser.). 15p. (J). (gr. k-3). pap., stu. ed. 2.99 (978-1-57471-585-9(2) , 2910) Creative Teaching Pr., Inc.

—Hap & Cap (p, n, short a), Bk. 2. Kupperstein, Joel, ed. Banta, Susan, illus. 1999. (Dr. Maggie's Phonics Readers Ser.). 15p. (J). (gr. k-3). pap., stu. ed. 2.99 (978-1-57471-562-0(3) , 2902) Creative Teaching Pr., Inc.

—I Spy (m, f, s, r, h, t, c, short a), Bk. 1. Kupperstein, Joel, ed. Winston, Jeannie, illus. 1999. (Dr. Maggie's Phonics Readers Ser.). 15p. (J). (gr. k-3). pap., stu. ed. 2.99 (978-1-57471-561-3(5) , 2901) Creative Teaching Pr., Inc.

—Jet It, Get It (z, x, short e), Bk. 6. Kupperstein, Joel, ed. Hehenberger, Shelly, illus. 1999. (Dr. Maggie's Phonics Readers Ser.). 15p. (J). (gr. k-3). pap., stu. ed. 2.99 (978-1-57471-566-8(6) , 2906) Creative Teaching Pr., Inc.

—Jo Jo in Outer Space (Simple Word Endings -er, -ed, -ly, -y), Bk. 23. Kupperstein, Joel, ed. Harris, Jennifer Beck, illus. 1999. (Dr. Maggie's Phonics Readers Ser.). 15p. (J). (gr. k-3). pap., stu. ed. 2.99 (978-1-57471-598-9(4) , 2923) Creative Teaching Pr., Inc.

—The Little Green Man Visits Pine Cone Cove (long o: o-e, oa, ow, ending o; -old), Bk. 15. Kupperstein, Joel, ed. Harris, Jennifer Beck, illus. 1999. (Dr. Maggie's Phonics Readers Ser.). 15p. (J). (gr. k-3). pap., stu. ed. 2.99 (978-1-57471-590-3(9) , 2915) Creative Teaching Pr., Inc.

—Mr. Noisy at the Dude Ranch (long u: u-e; /oi/ sound: oi, oy), Bk. 16. Kupperstein, Joel, ed. Dunne, Kathleen, illus. 1999. (Dr. Maggie's Phonics Readers Ser.). 15p. (J). (gr. k-3). pap., stu. ed. 2.99 (978-1-57471-591-0(7) , 2916) Creative Teaching Pr., Inc.

—Out to Gumball Pond (ew; ou As in out; ow As in Now), Bk. 18. Kupperstein, Joel, ed. Burns, Priscilla, illus. 1999. (Dr. Maggie's Phonics Readers Ser.). 15p. (J). (gr. k-3). pap., stu. ed. 2.99 (978-1-57471-593-4(3) , 2918) Creative Teaching Pr., Inc.

P Q R

—Pete's Street Beat (long e: ee, e-e, ea, ending e), Bk. 13. Kupperstein, Joel, ed. Edwards, Karl, illus. 1999. (Dr. Maggie's Phonics Readers Ser.). 15p. (J). (gr. k-3). pap., stu. ed. 2.99 (978-1-57471-588-0(7) , 2913) Creative Teaching Pr., Inc.

—Pom-Pom's Big Win (w, k, short i), Bk. 4. Kupperstein, Joel, ed. Burris, Priscilla, illus. 1999. (Dr. Maggie's Phonics Readers Ser.). 15p. (J). (gr. k-3). pap., stu. ed. 2.99 (978-1-57471-564-4(X) , 2904) Creative Teaching Pr., Inc.

—Pug's Hugs (v, y, short u), Bk. 5. Kupperstein, Joel, ed. Motoyama, Keiko, illus. 1999. (Dr. Maggie's Phonics Readers Ser.). 15p. (J). (gr. k-3). pap., stu. ed. 2.99 (978-1-57471-565-1(8) , CTP2905) Creative Teaching Pr., Inc.

—The Rainy Day Band (contractions), Bk. 21. Kupperstein, Joel, ed. Banta, Susan, illus. 1999. (Dr. Maggie's Phonics Readers Ser.). 15p. (J). (gr. k-3). pap., stu. ed. 2.99 (978-1-57471-596-5(8) , 2922) Creative Teaching Pr., Inc.

—Riddle & Rhyme with Apron Annie (rhyming words, 2-syllable words), Bk. 24. Kupperstein, Joel, ed. Allen, Joy, illus. 1999. (Dr. Maggie's Phonics Readers Ser.). 15p. (J). (gr. k-3). pap., stu. ed. 2.99 (978-1-57471-599-6(2) , 2924) Creative Teaching Pr., Inc.

—Sad Sam & Blue Sue (oo, ue), Bk. 17. Kupperstein, Joel, ed. Urbanovic, Jackie, illus. 1999. (Dr. Maggie's Phonics Readers Ser.). 15p. (J). (gr. k-3). pap., stu. ed. 2.99 (978-1-57471-592-7(5) , 2917) Creative Teaching Pr., Inc.

—Sing-Song Sid (-ing, -ong, -ang) Kupperstein, Joel, ed. Fujisaki, Tuko, illus. 1999. (Dr. Maggie's Phonics Readers Ser.: Bk. 9). 15p. (J). (gr. k-3). pap., stu. ed. 2.99 (978-1-57471-584-2(4) , 2909) Creative Teaching Pr., Inc.

—Splish, Splash (3-Letter Blends: Str, Spl, Scr), Bk. 19. Kupperstein, Joel, ed. Nobens, Cheryl A., illus. 1999. (Dr. Maggie's Phonics Readers Ser.). 15p. (J). (gr. k-3). pap., stu. ed. 2.99 (978-1-57471-594-1(1) , 2919) Creative Teaching Pr., Inc.

—Top Job, Mom! (b, d, g, l, j, short o), Bk. 3. Kupperstein, Joel, ed. Banta, Susan, illus. 1999. (Dr. Maggie's Phonics Readers Ser.). 15p. (J). (gr. k-3). pap., stu. ed. 2.99 (978-1-57471-563-7(1) , 2903) Creative Teaching Pr., Inc.

—Truck Tricks: Consonant Blends - tr, gr, dr, cr, fl, Bk. 11. Kupperstein, Joel, ed. Winters, Greg, illus. 1999. (Dr. Maggie's Phonics Readers Ser.). 15p. (J). (gr. k-3). pap., stu. ed. 2.99 (978-1-57471-586-6(0) , 2911) Creative Teaching Pr., Inc.

—Twice As Nice (long i: i-e), Bk. 14. Kupperstein, Joel, ed. Halsey, Megan, illus. 1999. (Dr. Maggie's Phonics Readers Ser.). 15p. (J). (gr. k-3). pap., stu. ed. 2.99 (978-1-57471-589-7(5) , 2914) Creative Teaching Pr., Inc.

Augustyn, Brian. Mad Hatter. 2004. (Batman Ser.: No. 3). (Illus.). 40p. (J). pap. 3.99 (978-0-439-47098-8(6) , Cartwheel Bks.) Scholastic, Inc.

—Mad Hatter. 2004. (gr. k-3). lib. bdg. 11.80 (978-0-613-71997-1(2)) Tandem Library Bks.

Baby's First Words. 2003. (Illus.). (J). bds. 7.98 (978-0-7525-8651-9(3)) Parragon, Inc.

Balderstone, Rachel. What Am I? North American Edition. 2002. (Illus.). pap. 0.40 (978-0-521-01571-4(5)) Cambridge Univ. Pr.

—What Am I? North American Edition. Pulles, Elizabeth & Sibbick, John, illus. 2000. (Cambridge Reading Ser.). 8p. (J). pap. 5.00 (978-0-521-80572-8(4)) Cambridge Univ. Pr.

Beake, Lesley, et al. One Dark, Dark Night: Siswati Version. 2002. (Illus.). 16p. pap. 1.75 (978-0-521-52827-6(5)) Cambridge Univ. Pr.

Beck, Isabel L., et al. Trophies Kindergarten: A Big, Big Van. 2003. (Trophies Ser.). (gr. k-6). 13.80 (978-0-15-329546-1(5)) Harcourt Schl. Pubs.

—Trophies Kindergarten: A Bug Can Tug. 2003. (Trophies Ser.). (gr. k-6). 13.80 (978-0-15-329609-3(7)) Harcourt Schl. Pubs.

—Trophies Kindergarten: A Hat I Like. 2003. (Trophies Ser.). (gr. k-6). 13.80 (978-0-15-329551-5(1)) Harcourt Schl. Pubs.

—Trophies Kindergarten: Aa. 2003. (Trophies Ser.). (gr. k-6). 23.40 (978-0-15-329290-3(3)) Harcourt Schl. Pubs.

—Trophies Kindergarten: Bb. 2003. (Trophies Ser.). (gr. k-6). 23.40 (978-0-15-329291-0(1)) Harcourt Schl. Pubs.

—Trophies Kindergarten: But I Can. 2003. (Trophies Ser.). (gr. k-6). 13.80 (978-0-15-329605-5(4)) Harcourt Schl. Pubs.

—Trophies Kindergarten: Cc. 2003. (Trophies Ser.). (gr. k-6). 23.40 (978-0-15-329292-7(X)) Harcourt Schl. Pubs.

—Trophies Kindergarten: Come In. 2003. (Trophies Ser.). (gr. k-6). 13.80 (978-0-15-329547-8(3)) Harcourt Schl. Pubs.

—Trophies Kindergarten: Dd. 2003. (Trophies Ser.). (gr. k-6). 23.40 (978-0-15-329294-1(6)) Harcourt Schl. Pubs.

—Trophies Kindergarten: Ee. 2003. (Trophies Ser.). (gr. k-6). 23.40 (978-0-15-329295-8(4)) Harcourt Schl. Pubs.

—Trophies Kindergarten: Ff. 2003. (Trophies Ser.). (gr. k-6). 23.40 (978-0-15-329296-5(2)) Harcourt Schl. Pubs.

—Trophies Kindergarten: First Day at School. 2003. (Trophies Ser.). (gr. k-6). 13.80 (978-0-15-329516-4(3)) Harcourt Schl. Pubs.

—Trophies Kindergarten: Gg. 2003. (Trophies Ser.). (gr. k-6). 23.40 (978-0-15-329297-2(0)) Harcourt Schl. Pubs.

—Trophies Kindergarten: Hh. 2003. (Trophies Ser.). (gr. k-6). 23.40 (978-0-15-329298-9(9)) Harcourt Schl. Pubs.

—Trophies Kindergarten: Hop In! 2003. (Trophies Ser.). (gr. k-6). 13.80 (978-0-15-329548-5(1)) Harcourt Schl. Pubs.

—Trophies Kindergarten: Hop on Top. 2003. (Trophies Ser.). (gr. k-6). 13.80 (978-0-15-329545-4(7)) Harcourt Schl. Pubs.

—Trophies Kindergarten: I Am. 2003. (Trophies Ser.). (gr. k-6). 13.80 (978-0-15-329525-6(2)) Harcourt Schl. Pubs.

—Trophies Kindergarten: I Can See It! 2003. (Trophies Ser.). (gr. k-6). 13.80 (978-0-15-329543-0(0)) Harcourt Schl. Pubs.

—Trophies Kindergarten: I Have, You Have. 2003. (Trophies Ser.). (gr. k-6). 13.80 (978-0-15-329536-2(8)) Harcourt Schl. Pubs.

—Trophies Kindergarten: I Nap. 2003. (Trophies Ser.). (gr. k-6). 13.80 (978-0-15-329528-7(7)) Harcourt Schl. Pubs.

—Trophies Kindergarten: Ii. 2003. (Trophies Ser.). (gr. k-6). 23.40 (978-0-15-329299-6(7)) Harcourt Schl. Pubs.

—Trophies Kindergarten: In a Sub. 2003. (Trophies Ser.). (gr. k-6). 13.80 (978-0-15-329611-6(9)) Harcourt Schl. Pubs.

—Trophies Kindergarten: Is It a Fish? 2003. (Trophies Ser.). (gr. k-6). 13.80 (978-0-15-329607-9(0)) Harcourt Schl. Pubs.

—Trophies Kindergarten: Is It for Me? 2003. (Trophies Ser.). (gr. k-6). 13.80 (978-0-15-329549-2(X)) Harcourt Schl. Pubs.

—Trophies Kindergarten: It Is Fun. 2003. (Trophies Ser.). (gr. k-6). 13.80 (978-0-15-329608-6(9)) Harcourt Schl. Pubs.

—Trophies Kindergarten: Jj. 2003. (Trophies Ser.). (gr. k-6). 23.40 (978-0-15-329300-9(4)) Harcourt Schl. Pubs.

—Trophies Kindergarten: Kip the Ant. 2003. (Trophies Ser.). (gr. k-6). 13.80 (978-0-15-329539-3(2)) Harcourt Schl. Pubs.

—Trophies Kindergarten: Kk. 2003. (Trophies Ser.). (gr. k-6). 23.40 (978-0-15-329301-6(2)) Harcourt Schl. Pubs.

—Trophies Kindergarten: Little Cat, Big Cat. 2003. (Trophies Ser.). (gr. k-6). 13.80 (978-0-15-329552-2(X)) Harcourt Schl. Pubs.

—Trophies Kindergarten: Ll. 2003. (Trophies Ser.). (gr. k-6). 23.40 (978-0-15-329302-3(0)) Harcourt Schl. Pubs.

—Trophies Kindergarten: Mm. 2003. (Trophies Ser.). (gr. k-6). 23.40 (978-0-15-329304-7(7)) Harcourt Schl. Pubs.

—Trophies Kindergarten: My Bus. 2003. (Trophies Ser.). (gr. k-6). 13.80 (978-0-15-329522-5(8)) Harcourt Schl. Pubs.

—Trophies Kindergarten: My Pig. 2003. (Trophies Ser.). (gr. k-6). 13.80 (978-0-15-329535-5(X)) Harcourt Schl. Pubs.

—Trophies Kindergarten: Nn. 2003. (Trophies Ser.). (gr. k-6). 23.40 (978-0-15-329305-4(5)) Harcourt Schl. Pubs.

—Trophies Kindergarten: Oo. 2003. (Trophies Ser.). (gr. k-6). 23.40 (978-0-15-329306-1(3)) Harcourt Schl. Pubs.

—Trophies Kindergarten: Pet Day. 2003. (Trophies Ser.). (gr. k-6). 13.80 (978-0-15-329519-5(8)) Harcourt Schl. Pubs.

—Trophies Kindergarten: Pp. 2003. (Trophies Ser.). (gr. k-6). 23.40 (978-0-15-329307-8(1)) Harcourt Schl. Pubs.

—Trophies Kindergarten: Pre-decodable/Decodable Books. 3rd ed. 2002. (Trophies Ser.). (gr. k-6). pap. 107.60 (978-0-15-323766-9(X)) Harcourt Schl. Pubs.

—Trophies Kindergarten: Pre-decodable/Decodable Books, Take-Home Version. 3rd ed. 2002. (Trophies Ser.). (gr. k up). pap. 43.70 (978-0-15-325442-0(4)) Harcourt Schl. Pubs.

—Trophies Kindergarten: Qq. 2003. (Trophies Ser.). (gr. k-6). 23.40 (978-0-15-329308-5(X)) Harcourt Schl. Pubs.

—Trophies Kindergarten: Rr. 2003. (Trophies Ser.). (gr. k-6). 23.40 (978-0-15-329309-2(8)) Harcourt Schl. Pubs.

—Trophies Kindergarten: Sid Hid. 2003. (Trophies Ser.). (gr. k-6). 13.80 (978-0-15-329610-9(0)) Harcourt Schl. Pubs.

—Trophies Kindergarten: Sit on My Chair. 2003. (Trophies Ser.). (gr. k-6). 13.80 (978-0-15-329534-8(1)) Harcourt Schl. Pubs.

—Trophies Kindergarten: Soup. 2003. (Trophies Ser.). (gr. k-6). 13.80 (978-0-15-329537-9(6)) Harcourt Schl. Pubs.

—Trophies Kindergarten: Ss. 2003. (Trophies Ser.). (gr. k-6). 23.40 (978-0-15-329310-8(1)) Harcourt Schl. Pubs.

—Trophies Kindergarten: Tap, Tap, Tap. 2003. (Trophies Ser.). (gr. k-6). 13.80 (978-0-15-329532-4(5)) Harcourt Schl. Pubs.

—Trophies Kindergarten: The Big Ram. 2003. (Trophies Ser.). (gr. k-6). 13.80 (978-0-15-329540-9(6)) Harcourt Schl. Pubs.

—Trophies Kindergarten: The Dig. 2003. (Trophies Ser.). (gr. k-6). 13.80 (978-0-15-329538-6(4)) Harcourt Schl. Pubs.

—Trophies Kindergarten: The Mat. 2003. (Trophies Ser.). (gr. k-6). 13.80 (978-0-15-329526-3(0)) Harcourt Schl. Pubs.

—Trophies Kindergarten: The Park. 2003. (Trophies Ser.). (gr. k-6). 13.80 (978-0-15-329533-1(3)) Harcourt Schl. Pubs.

—Trophies Kindergarten: The Party. 2003. (Trophies Ser.). (gr. k-6). 13.80 (978-0-15-329523-2(6)) Harcourt Schl. Pubs.

—Trophies Kindergarten: The Salad. 2003. (Trophies Ser.). (gr. k-6). 13.80 (978-0-15-329524-9(4)) Harcourt Schl. Pubs.

—Trophies Kindergarten: Tt. 2003. (Trophies Ser.). (gr. k-6). 23.40 (978-0-15-329311-5(X)) Harcourt Schl. Pubs.

—Trophies Kindergarten: Up, up, Up. 2003. (Trophies Ser.). (gr. k-6). 13.80 (978-0-15-329606-2(2)) Harcourt Schl. Pubs.

—Trophies Kindergarten: Uu. 2003. (Trophies Ser.). (gr. k-6). 23.40 (978-0-15-329312-2(8)) Harcourt Schl. Pubs.

—Trophies Kindergarten: Vv. 2003. (Trophies Ser.). (gr. k-6). 23.40 (978-0-15-329314-6(4)) Harcourt Schl. Pubs.

—Trophies Kindergarten: We Can Fix. 2003. (Trophies Ser.). (gr. k-6). 13.80 (978-0-15-329550-8(3)) Harcourt Schl. Pubs.

—Trophies Kindergarten: We Go. 2003. (Trophies Ser.). (gr. k-6). 13.80 (978-0-15-329527-0(9)) Harcourt Schl. Pubs.

—Trophies Kindergarten: What Can Hop? 2003. (Trophies Ser.). (gr. k-6). 13.80 (978-0-15-329541-6(4)) Harcourt Schl. Pubs.

—Trophies Kindergarten: What Is in the Box? 2003. (Trophies Ser.). (gr. k-6). 13.80 (978-0-15-329544-7(9)) Harcourt Schl. Pubs.

—Trophies Kindergarten: Where's My Teddy? 2003. (Trophies Ser.). (gr. k-6). 13.80 (978-0-15-329517-1(1)) Harcourt Schl. Pubs.

—Trophies Kindergarten: Write-on/Wipe-off Boards with Phonemic Awareness Disks. 1999. (Trophies Ser.). (gr. k-6). pap. 7.50 (978-0-15-316040-0(3)) Harcourt Schl. Pubs.

—Trophies Kindergarten: Ww. 2003. (Trophies Ser.). (gr. k-6). 23.40 (978-0-15-329315-3(2)) Harcourt Schl. Pubs.

—Trophies Kindergarten: Xx. 2003. (Trophies Ser.). (gr. k-6). 23.40 (978-0-15-329316-0(0)) Harcourt Schl. Pubs.

—Trophies Kindergarten: Yy. 2003. (Trophies Ser.). (gr. k-6). 23.40 (978-0-15-329317-7(9)) Harcourt Schl. Pubs.

—Trophies Kindergarten: Zz. 2003. (Trophies Ser.). (gr. k-6). 23.40 (978-0-15-329319-1(5)) Harcourt Schl. Pubs.

Bednarz, Robert, et al. Grade K Time for Kids Readers: What's the Weather? 3rd ed. 2002. (Harcourt Horizons Ser.). (gr. k up). pap. 19.40 (978-0-15-333113-8(5)) Harcourt Schl. Pubs.

Beech, Linda, et al. Animals. Scholastic, Inc. Staff, ed. 2003. (Sight Word Readers Ser.). (Illus.). 8p. pap. 1.25 (978-0-439-51164-3(X)) Scholastic, Inc.

—City Colors. Scholastic, Inc. Staff, ed. 2003. (Sight Word Readers Ser.). (Illus.). 8p. pap. 1.25 (978-0-439-51158-2(5)) Scholastic, Inc.

—Dinner. Scholastic, Inc. Staff, ed. 2003. (Sight Word Readers). (Illus.). 8p. pap. 1.25 (978-0-439-51176-6(3)) Scholastic, Inc.

—Farm Friends. Scholastic, Inc. Staff, ed. 2003. (Sight Word Readers). 8p. pap. 1.25 (978-0-439-51171-1(2)); (Illus.). pap. 1.25 (978-0-439-51157-5(7)) Scholastic, Inc.

—Find It! Scholastic, Inc. Staff, ed. 2003. (Sight Word Readers Ser.). (Illus.). 8p. pap. 1.25 (978-0-439-51179-7(8)) Scholastic, Inc.

—Fly Away! Scholastic, Inc. Staff, ed. 2003. (Sight Word Readers). (Illus.). 8p. pap. 1.25 (978-0-439-51181-0(X)) Scholastic, Inc.

—Go Go. Scholastic, Inc. Staff, ed. 2003. (Sight Word Readers). (Illus.). 8p. pap. 1.25 (978-0-439-51169-8(0)) Scholastic, Inc.

—Guessing Game. Scholastic, Inc. Staff, ed. 2003. (Sight Word Readers). (Illus.). 8p. pap. 1.25 (978-0-439-51161-2(5)) Scholastic, Inc.

—Helpers. Scholastic, Inc. Staff, ed. 2003. (Sight Word Readers). (Illus.). 8p. pap. 1.25 (978-0-439-51174-2(7)) Scholastic, Inc.

—I Did It! Scholastic, Inc. Staff, ed. 2003. (Sight Word Readers Ser.). (Illus.). 8p. pap. 1.25 (978-0-439-51165-0(8)) Scholastic, Inc.

—Little & Big. Scholastic, Inc. Staff, ed. 2003. (Sight Word Readers). (Illus.). 8p. pap. 1.25 (978-0-439-51177-3(1)) Scholastic, Inc.

—Me Too. Scholastic, Inc. Staff, ed. 2003. (Sight Word Readers Ser.). (Illus.). 8p. pap. 1.25 (978-0-439-51163-6(1)) Scholastic, Inc.

—My Bear. Scholastic, Inc. Staff, ed. 2003. (Sight Word Readers Ser.). (Illus.). 8p. pap. 1.25 (978-0-439-51172-8(0)) Scholastic, Inc.

—My Dog. Scholastic, Inc. Staff, ed. 2003. (Sight Word Readers Ser.). (Illus.). 8p. pap. 1.25 (978-0-439-51180-3(1)) Scholastic, Inc.

—New Socks. Scholastic, Inc. Staff, ed. 2003. (Sight Word Readers Ser.). (Illus.). 8p. pap. 1.25 (978-0-439-51170-4(4)) Scholastic, Inc.

—The Party. Scholastic, Inc. Staff, ed. 2003. (Sight Word Readers). (Illus.). 8p. pap. 1.25 (978-0-439-51160-5(7)) Scholastic, Inc.

—Play Time. Scholastic, Inc. Staff, ed. 2003. (Sight Word Readers Ser.). (Illus.). 8p. pap. 1.25 (978-0-439-51167-4(4)) Scholastic, Inc.

—Ride On! Scholastic, Inc. Staff, ed. 2003. (Sight Word Readers Ser.). (Illus.). 8p. pap. 1.25 (978-0-439-51162-9(3)) Scholastic, Inc.

—Run. Scholastic, Inc. Staff, ed. 2003. (Sight Word Readers Ser.). (Illus.). 8p. pap. 1.25 (978-0-439-51168-1(2)) Scholastic, Inc.

—Sharing. Scholastic, Inc. Staff, ed. 2003. (Sight Word Readers). (Illus.). 8p. pap. 1.25 (978-0-439-51175-9(5)) Scholastic, Inc.

—That Hat. Scholastic, Inc. Staff, ed. 2003. (Sight Word Readers). (Illus.). 8p. pap. 1.25 (978-0-439-51159-9(3)) Scholastic, Inc.

—That Is Funny! Scholastic, Inc. Staff, ed. 2003. (Sight Word Readers Ser.). (Illus.). 8p. pap. 1.25 (978-0-439-51173-5(9)) Scholastic, Inc.

—This Is a Peach. Scholastic, Inc. Staff, ed. 2003. (Sight Word Readers Ser.). (Illus.). 8p. pap. 1.25 (978-0-439-51166-7(6)) Scholastic, Inc.

—Up & Down. Scholastic, Inc. Staff, ed. 2003. (Sight Word Readers Ser.). (Illus.). 8p. pap. 1.25 (978-0-439-51178-0(X)) Scholastic, Inc.

Beginning Reading. 2004. (Skill Builders for Young Learners Ser.). (Illus.). 96p. 11.99 (978-0-7439-3688-0(4)) Teacher Created Materials, Inc.

Bradman, Tony. Here Comes Everyone ELT Edition. 2004. (Cambridge Storybooks Ser.). (Illus.). 16p. pap. 5.00 (978-0-521-75213-8(2)) Cambridge Univ. Pr.

—Heroes & Villains. 1998. (Cambridge Reading Ser.). (Illus.). 124p. pap. 12.00 (978-0-521-57551-5(6)) Cambridge Univ. Pr.

—Please, Miss Miller! ELT Edition. Lamont, Priscilla, illus. 2001. (Cambridge Storybooks Ser.). 16p. pap. 5.00 (978-0-521-00719-1(4)) Cambridge Univ. Pr.

—This Is the Register ELT Edition. 2004. (Cambridge Storybooks Ser.). (Illus.). 16p. pap. 5.00 (978-0-521-75211-4(6)) Cambridge Univ. Pr.

—Well Done Sam! ELT Edition. 2004. (Cambridge Storybooks Ser.). (Illus.). 24p. pap. 6.00 (978-0-521-75215-2(9)) Cambridge Univ. Pr.

—What's the Time?, 6 vols., Pack. 2001. (Cambridge Storybooks Ser.). (Illus.). 16p. pap. 26.00 (978-0-521-00799-3(2)) Cambridge Univ. Pr.

—What's the Time? ELT Edition. Lamont, Priscilla, illus. 2001. (Cambridge Storybooks Ser.). 16p. pap. 5.00 (978-0-521-00716-0(X)) Cambridge Univ. Pr.

Bradman, Tony, ed. Truth or Dare. 1998. (Cambridge Reading Ser.). (Illus.). 112p. pap. 12.00 (978-0-521-57552-2(4)) Cambridge Univ. Pr.

Brown, Jane. Big Book: Who Has Four Feet? l.t. ed. 2005. (Sadlier Phonics Reading Program: Vol. 1). (Illus.). 8p. (YA). (ps-1). 22.50 (978-0-8215-7340-2(3)) Sadlier, William H. Inc.

Brown, Richard. Ben's Amazing Birthday ELT Edition. 2004. (Cambridge Storybooks Ser.). (Illus.). 24p. pap. 6.00 (978-0-521-75259-6(0)) Cambridge Univ. Pr.

—The Moonlit Owl ELT Edition. 2004. (Cambridge Storybooks Ser.). (Illus.). 16p. pap. 5.00 (978-0-521-75257-2(4)) Cambridge Univ. Pr.

Brown, Richard & Ruttle, Kate. Five Little Monkeys: South African Edition. 1998. (Cambridge Reading Routes Ser.). (Illus.). 16p. pap. 5.00 (978-0-521-62819-8(9)) Cambridge Univ. Pr.

—Looking for Dragons ELT Edition. Lewis, Jan, illus. 2001. (Cambridge Storybooks Ser.). 8p. pap. 3.00 (978-0-521-00705-4(4)) Cambridge Univ. Pr.

—Two by Two: South African Edition. 1998. (Cambridge Reading Routes Ser.). (Illus.). 16p. pap. 5.00 (978-0-521-62821-1(0)) Cambridge Univ. Pr.

—Wiggle & Giggle: South African Edition. 1998. (Cambridge Reading Routes Ser.). (Illus.). 16p. pap. 5.00 (978-0-521-62820-4(2)) Cambridge Univ. Pr.

Bruton, Mike. The Four-Legged Fish: South African Edition. Kruger, Bennie, illus. 1999. (Cambridge Reading Routes Ser.). 24p. pap. 5.00 (978-0-521-63655-1(8)) Cambridge Univ. Pr.

—Insects: South African Edition. 1998. (Cambridge Reading Routes Ser.). (Illus.). 24p. pap. 5.00 (978-0-521-63663-6(9)) Cambridge Univ. Pr.

Burroughs, Elizabeth. Elephant: South African Edition. 1998. (Cambridge Reading Routes Ser.). (Illus.). 16p. pap. 5.00 (978-0-521-63668-1(X)) Cambridge Univ. Pr.

—Giraffe: South African Edition. Setterfield, Adrian, illus. 1998. (Cambridge Reading Routes Ser.). 16p. pap. 4.00 (978-0-521-62795-5(8)) Cambridge Univ. Pr.

Burroughs, Elizabeth & Partridge, Juliet. Elephant. 2002. (Illus.). 16p. pap. 0.40 (978-0-521-01438-0(7)) Cambridge Univ. Pr.

Craggs, Marjorie. Rhyming Riddles ELT Edition. 2004. (Cambridge Storybooks Ser.). (Illus.). 16p. pap. 5.00 (978-0-521-75263-3(9)) Cambridge Univ. Pr.

Crawford, Sheryl Ann Saunders & Sanders. Easy-to-Read Mini-Book Plays, 15 bks., Set. 2003. pap. 10.95 (978-0-439-20155-1(1)) Scholastic, Inc.

Crebbin, June. Apples! ELT Edition. 2004. (Cambridge Storybooks Ser.). (Illus.). 24p. pap. 6.00 (978-0-521-75239-8(6)) Cambridge Univ. Pr.

—The Flying Football ELT Edition. 2004. (Cambridge Storybooks Ser.). (Illus.). 24p. pap. 6.00 (978-0-521-75233-6(7)) Cambridge Univ. Pr.

—Nibbles ELT Edition. 2004. (Cambridge Storybooks Ser.). 24p. pap. 6.00 (978-0-521-75237-4(X)) Cambridge Univ. Pr.

Cristaldi, Kathryn. Hide-&-Seek, Level 2. 1998. (Disney's First Readers Ser.: No. 9). (Illus.). 32p. (J). (gr. 1-3). pap. 2.95 (978-0-7868-4074-8(9)) Disney Pr.

Davidson, Rosemary. One Teddy Bear All Alone ELT Edition. Rosato, Amelia, illus. 2001. (Cambridge Storybooks Ser.). 8p. pap. 3.00 (978-0-521-00662-0(7)) Cambridge Univ. Pr.

Davis, Katie. Who Hoots? 2004. (Illus.). 36p. (J). pap. 7.00 (978-0-15-205027-6(2) , Voyager Bks./Libros Viajeros) Harcourt Children's Bks.

Dyer, Dorothy, et al. Radio Days & Other Stories: PRP English Version. 2002. (Illus.). 48p. pap. 0.40 (978-0-521-01482-3(4)) Cambridge Univ. Pr.

Edwards, Fiona. The Lizard's Tail. 2002. (Illus.). 8p. pap. 0.40 (978-0-521-01603-2(7)) Cambridge Univ. Pr.

Evans, Mary. Big Book Vol. 2: Cats! Cats! Cats! Kovalcik, Terry, illus. l.t. ed. 2005. (Sadlier Phonics Reading Program). 8p. (YA). (ps-1). 22.50 (978-0-8215-7348-8(9)) Sadlier, William H. Inc.

—Big Book: Good Pets, Vol. 3. l.t. ed. 2005. (Sadlier Phonics Reading Program). (Illus.). 8p. (YA). (ps-1). 22.50 (978-0-8215-7350-1(0)) Sadlier, William H. Inc.

Fleming, Sarah. Do the Lolly Trick, 6, Pack. 2000. (Cambridge Reading Ser.). 12p. pap. 28.00 (978-0-521-78765-9(3)) Cambridge Univ. Pr.

—I Broke My Arm, 6, Pack. 2000. (Cambridge Reading Ser.). 8p. pap. 28.00 (978-0-521-78771-0(8)) Cambridge Univ. Pr.

—I Made a Map, 6, Pack. 2000. (Cambridge Reading Ser.). 8p. pap. 28.00 (978-0-521-78772-7(6)) Cambridge Univ. Pr.

—The Moons of Jupiter, 6, Pack. 2000. (Cambridge Reading Ser.). 12p. pap. 28.00 (978-0-521-78766-6(1)) Cambridge Univ. Pr.

—The Weather Forecast, 6, Pack. 2000. (Cambridge Reading Ser.). 8p. pap. 28.00 (978-0-521-78770-3(X)) Cambridge Univ. Pr.

Frank, Marjorie Slavick, et al. Prek Program: Little Book Collection. 3rd ed. 2002. (Harcourt Science Ser.). (gr. k-6). pap. 65.30 (978-0-15-335319-2(8)) Harcourt Schl. Pubs.

Fun Wherever We Are. 2004. (Dick & Jane Ser.). (Illus.). 144p. (J). (ps-2). 7.99 (978-0-448-43614-2(0) , Grosset & Dunlap) Penguin Group (USA) Inc.

Gillham, Bill. Dirty Dog. 2002. (Illus.). 8p. pap. 0.40 (978-0-521-01362-8(3)) Cambridge Univ. Pr.

—Dirty Dog ELT Edition. Snow, Alan, illus. 2001. (Cambridge Storybooks Ser.). 8p. pap. 3.00 (978-0-521-00658-3(9)) Cambridge Univ. Pr.

—Two Babies. 2002. (Illus.). 8p. pap. 0.40 (978-0-521-01563-9(4)) Cambridge Univ. Pr.

—What's in the Box? (Illus.). 8p. 2002. pap. 0.40 (978-0-521-01579-0(0)); Pack. 2001. pap. 16.00 (978-0-521-00727-6(5)) Cambridge Univ. Pr.

Glassman, Jackie. The Cherry Pie. Francis, Guy, illus. 2001. (My First Games Readers Ser.). 32p. (J). (ps-1). pap. 3.99 (978-0-439-26465-5(0)) Scholastic, Inc.

Goldish, Meish. Big Book: How Many Are Here? Meyerhoff, Jill, illus. l.t. ed. 2005. (Sadlier Phonics Reading Program). 8p. (YA). (ps-1). 22.50 (978-0-8215-7344-0(6)) Sadlier, William H. Inc.

—Big Book: Zack Can Fix It!, Vol. 4. Scruton, Clive, illus. l.t. ed. 2005. (Sadlier Phonics Reading Program). 8p. (YA). (ps-1). 22.50 (978-0-8215-7359-4(4)) Sadlier, William H. Inc.

—Nice Vine, Quite Fine, Vol. 2. Sargent, Claudia Karabaic, illus. l.t. ed. 2005. (Little Books & Big Bks.: Vol. 7). 8p. (YA). (ps-3). 22.50 (978-0-8215-7516-1(3)) Sadlier, William H. Inc.

Grosset and Dunlap Staff. Away We Go. 2004. (Read with Dick & Jane Ser.: Vol. 7). 32p. (J). (ps-2). pap. 3.99 (978-0-448-43406-3(7) , Grosset & Dunlap) Penguin Group (USA) Inc.

—We Play. 2004. (Read with Dick & Jane Ser.: Vol. 11). 32p. (J). 13.89 (978-0-448-43496-4(2)); pap. 3.99 (978-0-448-43410-0(5)) Penguin Group (USA) Inc. (Grosset & Dunlap).

—We See. 2004. (Read with Dick & Jane Ser.: Vol. 9). 32p. (J). (ps-2). pap. 3.99 (978-0-448-43408-7(3) , Grosset & Dunlap) Penguin Group (USA) Inc.

—We Work. 2004. (Read with Dick & Jane Ser.: Vol. 10). 32p. (J). (ps-2). 13.89 (978-0-448-43495-7(4)); pap. 3.99 (978-0-448-43409-4(1)) Penguin Group (USA) Inc. (Grosset & Dunlap).

—Who Can Help? 2004. (Read with Dick & Jane Ser.: Vol. 8). 32p. (J). (ps-2). 13.89 (978-0-448-43493-3(8)); pap. 3.99 (978-0-448-43407-0(5)) Penguin Group (USA) Inc. (Grosset & Dunlap).

Grosset and Dunlap Staff, ed. Storybook Treasury of Dick & Jane & Friends. 2003. (Dick & Jane Ser.). (Illus.). 200p. (J). (ps-3). 10.99 (978-0-448-43340-0(0) , Grosset & Dunlap) Penguin Group (USA) Inc.

Hallworth, Grace. Dancing to the River ELT Edition. 2004. (Cambridge Storybooks Ser.). 24p. pap. 6.00 (978-0-521-75247-3(7)) Cambridge Univ. Pr.

—Gracie's Cat: South African Edition. 1998. (Cambridge Reading Routes Ser.). (Illus.). 24p. pap. 5.00 (978-0-521-63669-8(8)) Cambridge Univ. Pr.

—Sleep Tight ELT Edition. 2004. (Cambridge Storybooks Ser.). (Illus.). 24p. pap. 6.00 (978-0-521-75249-7(3)) Cambridge Univ. Pr.

Hansen, Penny. Touch. 2002. (Illus.). 16p. pap. 0.40 (978-0-521-01555-4(3)) Cambridge Univ. Pr.

Harcourt School Publishers Staff. Book for All Learners. 2nd ed. 2002. (Trophies Reading Program Ser.). (gr. 2 up). pap., tchr. ed. 63.90 (978-0-15-335747-3(9)); (gr. 6 up). pap., tchr. ed. 63.90 (978-0-15-335751-0(7)); (gr. 1 up). pap., tchr. ed. 70.90 (978-0-15-335746-6(0)); (gr. 3 up). pap., tchr. ed. 63.90 (978-0-15-335748-0(7)); (gr. 4 up). pap., tchr. ed. 63.90 (978-0-15-335749-7(5)); (gr. 5 up). pap., tchr. ed. 63.90 (978-0-15-335750-3(9)) Harcourt Schl. Pubs.

—Horizons, Grade 1: Time for Kids Readers. 3rd ed. 2003. (Harcourt Horizons Ser.). pap., tchr. ed. 51.20 (978-0-15-334646-0(9)) Harcourt Schl. Pubs.

—Horizons, Grade K: Time for Kids Readers. 3rd ed. 2003. (Harcourt Horizons Ser.). pap., tchr. ed. 54.10 (978-0-15-334645-3(0)) Harcourt Schl. Pubs.

—Horizontes, Grade 1: Time for Kids Readers. 3rd ed. 2002. (Harcourt Horizontes Ser.). (SPA.). (gr. 1 up). pap., tchr. ed. 65.80 (978-0-15-334659-0(0)) Harcourt Schl. Pubs.

—Horizontes, Grade 2: Time for Kids Readers. 3rd ed. 2002. (Harcourt Horizontes Ser.). (SPA.). (gr. 2 up). pap., tchr. ed. 65.80 (978-0-15-334660-6(4)) Harcourt Schl. Pubs.

—Horizontes, Grade K: Time for Kids Readers. 3rd ed. 2002. (Harcourt Horizontes Ser.). (SPA.). (gr. k-6). pap., tchr. ed. 69.50 (978-0-15-334658-3(2)) Harcourt Schl. Pubs.

—Trofeos: Libros de Intervencion:Sorpresas Fabulosas. 3rd ed. 2002. (Trofeos Ser.). (SPA., Illus.). (gr. 3 up). pap. 21.30 (978-0-15-326478-8(0)) Harcourt Schl. Pubs.

—Trofeos: Todos a Bordo: Libros de Intervencion. 3rd ed. 2002. (Trofeos Ser.). (SPA., Illus.). (gr. 6 up). pap. 21.30 (978-0-15-326481-8(0)) Harcourt Schl. Pubs.

—Trofeos Coleccion de Superlibros. 3rd ed. 2002. (Trofeos Ser.). (SPA., Illus.). (gr. k-6). pap. 1148.70 (978-0-15-332451-2(1)) Harcourt Schl. Pubs.

—Trofeos Collection, Grade 1. 3rd ed. 2002. (Trofeos Ser.). (SPA.). (gr. 1 up). tchr. ed. 906.60 (978-0-15-334774-0(0)) Harcourt Schl. Pubs.

—Trofeos Collection, Grade 2. 3rd ed. 2002. (Trofeos Ser.). (SPA.). (gr. 2 up). tchr. ed. 597.50 (978-0-15-334780-1(5)) Harcourt Schl. Pubs.

—Trofeos Collection, Grade 3. 3rd ed. 2002. (Trofeos Ser.). (SPA.). (gr. 3 up). tchr. ed. 597.50 (978-0-15-334836-5(4)) Harcourt Schl. Pubs.

—Trofeos, Grade 1. 3rd ed. 2002. (Trofeos Ser.). (SPA.). (gr. 1 up). Bk. 1. tchr. ed. 175.70 (978-0-15-334775-7(9)); Bk. 2. tchr. ed. 175.70 (978-0-15-334776-4(7)); Bk. 3. tchr. ed. 182.80 (978-0-15-334777-1(5)); Bk. 4. tchr. ed. 182.80 (978-0-15-334778-8(3)); Bk. 5. tchr. ed. 189.80 (978-0-15-334779-5(1)) Harcourt Schl. Pubs.

—Trofeos, Grade 2. 3rd ed. 2002. (Trofeos Ser.). (SPA.). Vol. 1, Theme 1. (gr. 1-2). tchr. ed. 99.60 (978-0-15-334781-8(3)); Vol. 1, Theme 2. (gr. 1-2). tchr. ed. 99.60 (978-0-15-334806-8(2)); Vol. 1, Theme 3. (gr. 1-2). tchr. ed. 99.60 (978-0-15-334807-5(0)); Vol. 2, Theme 1. (gr. 2 up). tchr. ed. 99.60 (978-0-15-334808-2(9)); Vol. 2, Theme 2. (gr. 2 up). tchr. ed. 99.60 (978-0-15-334809-9(7)); Vol. 2, Theme 3. (gr. 2 up). tchr. ed. 99.60 (978-0-15-334810-5(0)) Harcourt Schl. Pubs.

—Trofeos Library, Grade 2. 3rd ed. 2002. (Trofeos Ser.). (SPA.). (gr. 2 up). pap., tchr. ed. 19.70 (978-0-15-332060-6(5)) Harcourt Schl. Pubs.

—Trofeos Library, Grade 3. 3rd ed. 2002. (Trofeos Ser.). (SPA.). (gr. 3 up). pap., tchr. ed. 38.60 (978-0-15-332061-3(3)) Harcourt Schl. Pubs.

—Trofeos Library, Grade 4. 3rd ed. 2002. (Trofeos Ser.). (SPA.). (gr. 4 up). pap., tchr. ed. 38.60 (978-0-15-332062-0(1)) Harcourt Schl. Pubs.

—Trofeos Library, Grade 5. 3rd ed. 2002. (Trofeos Ser.). (SPA.). (gr. 5 up). pap., tchr. ed. 38.60 (978-0-15-332063-7(X)) Harcourt Schl. Pubs.

—Trofeos Library, Grade 6. 3rd ed. 2002. (Trofeos Ser.). (SPA.). (gr. 6 up). pap., tchr. ed. 38.60 (978-0-15-332064-4(8)) Harcourt Schl. Pubs.

—Trophies Big Book Collection. 3rd ed. 2002. (Trophies Ser.). (Illus.). (gr. 1 up). 705.30 (978-0-15-327354-4(2)) Harcourt Schl. Pubs.

—Trophies Collection. 3rd ed. 2003. (Trophies Ser.). Grade 1. (gr. 1 up). tchr. ed. 596.00 (978-0-15-327375-9(5)); Grade 2. (gr. 2 up). tchr. ed. 392.80 (978-0-15-327376-6(3)); Grade 3. (gr. 3 up). tchr. ed. 392.80 (978-0-15-327377-3(1)); Grade 4. (gr. 4 up). tchr. ed. 419.20 (978-0-15-327378-0(X)); Grade 5. (gr. 5 up). tchr. ed. 419.20 (978-0-15-327379-7(8)); Theme 6. (gr. 6 up). tchr. ed. 436.00 (978-0-15-329239-2(3)) Harcourt Schl. Pubs.

—Trophies Collection, Grade K. 3rd ed. 2003. (Trophies Ser.). (gr. k-6). tchr. ed. 377.80 (978-0-15-327374-2(7)) Harcourt Schl. Pubs.

—Trophies, Grade 1: For English-Language Learners. 3rd ed. 2002. (Trophies Ser.). (gr. 1 up). pap., tchr. ed. 49.30 (978-0-15-329334-4(9)) Harcourt Schl. Pubs.

—Trophies, Grade 2: For English-Language Learners. 3rd ed. 2002. (Trophies Ser.). (gr. 2 up). pap., tchr. ed. 44.80 (978-0-15-329335-1(7)) Harcourt Schl. Pubs.

—Trophies, Grade 3: For English-Language Learners. 3rd ed. 2002. (Trophies Ser.). (gr. 3 up). pap., tchr. ed. 44.80 (978-0-15-329336-8(5)) Harcourt Schl. Pubs.

—Trophies, Grade 4: For English-Language Learners. 3rd ed. 2002. (Trophies Ser.). (gr. 4 up). pap., tchr. ed. 44.80 (978-0-15-329337-5(3)) Harcourt Schl. Pubs.

—Trophies, Grade K: For English-Language Learners. 3rd ed. 2002. (Trophies Ser.). (Illus.). (gr. k-6). pap., tchr. ed. 42.10 (978-0-15-329331-3(4)) Harcourt Schl. Pubs.

—A Volar! Libros de Intervencion. 3rd ed. 2002. (Trofeos Ser.). (SPA., Illus.). (gr. 5 up). pap. 21.30 (978-0-15-326480-1(2)) Harcourt Schl. Pubs.

HarperCollins Staff, et al. An I Can Read Halloween Treat, Set. Zimmer, Dirk, illus. 2004. (I Can Read Bks.). (J). (gr. k-3). pap. 11.99 (978-0-06-054237-5(3) , Harper Trophy) HarperCollins Pubs.

Heiss, Silke. The Island & the Bay: South African Edition. 1998. (Cambridge Reading Routes Ser.). (Illus.). 24p. pap. 5.00 (978-0-521-63664-3(7)) Cambridge Univ. Pr.

Hiebert, Elfrieda H. Ready Read. (J). (ps-3). pap. 179.95 (978-0-8136-1861-6(4)) Modern Curriculum Pr.

—Ready Read, Stage 1 Take Home Books. (J). (ps-3). pap. 43.50 (978-0-8136-3277-3(3)) Modern Curriculum Pr.

—Ready Read, Stage 2 Take Home Books, 50 bks. , Set. 2003. (J). (ps-3). pap. 48.50 (978-0-8136-3278-0(1)) Modern Curriculum Pr.

Hofmeister, Alan, et al. Dash Has Fun. (Reading for All Learners Ser.). (Illus.). (J). pap. (978-1-56861-145-7(5)) Swift Learning Resources.

Hofmeyr, Dianne. Hic... Hic... Hiccups! Siswati Version. 2002. (Illus.). 16p. pap. 1.75 (978-0-521-52837-5(2)) Cambridge Univ. Pr.

—Mama Mabena's Magic: Siswati Version. 2002. (Illus.). 16p. pap. 1.75 (978-0-521-52842-9(9)) Cambridge Univ. Pr.

Hooper, Meredith. Animals in the Ark American English Edition. 2000. (Cambridge Reading Ser.). pap. 5.00 (978-0-521-79910-2(4)) Cambridge Univ. Pr.

—Dinosaur: South African Edition. Kitchen, Bert, illus. 1998. (Cambridge Reading Routes Ser.). 16p. pap. 5.00 (978-0-521-62826-6(1)) Cambridge Univ. Pr.

—Seal: South African Edition. Kitchen, Bert, illus. 1998. (Cambridge Reading Routes Ser.). 16p. pap. 5.00 (978-0-521-62825-9(3)) Cambridge Univ. Pr.

Horizon Kindergarten Reader, 4 vols., Set. 2000. (Illus.). (J). tchr. ed., stu. ed. 43.80 (978-0-7403-0145-2(4) , KRS01, Horizons) Alpha Omega Pubns., Inc.

Hurst-Nicholson, Janet, et al. Baby Bupe. 2002. (Illus.). 32p. pap. 0.40 (978-0-521-01587-5(1)) Cambridge Univ. Pr.

Jarrell, Pamela R. In the Garden. Lent, Marion W., illus. l.t. ed. 1998. (Cuddle Bks.). 8p. (J). (ps-k). pap. 10.95 (978-1-57332-113-6(3)) HighReach Learning, Inc.

Jensen, Patricia. The Mess. Lewis, Anthony, illus. 2003. (My First Reader Ser.). 32p. (J). 18.50 (978-0-516-22932-4(X) , Children's Pr.) Scholastic Library Publishing.

Kent, Brenda. Hats, Goats & Owls. 2004. (Cambridge Storybooks Ser.). 32p. pap., tchr. ed. (978-0-521-75268-8(X)) Cambridge Univ. Pr.

Leggat, Gillian, et al. Stop That Noise! 2002. (Illus.). 32p. pap. 0.40 (978-0-521-01611-7(8)) Cambridge Univ. Pr.

Lindi, Nkululeko. Three Fat Cats. 2002. (Illus.). 8p. pap. 0.45 (978-0-521-01547-9(2)) Cambridge Univ. Pr.

Liu, Gillian. How Do You Feel? 1998. (Early Words Ser.). (Illus.). 24p. pap. 29.99 (978-0-237-51888-2(0) , Evans Brothers, Limited) Evans Publishing Group GBR. *Dist:* Independent Pubs. Group.

Mapongwana, Nobantu. Naughty Hare: PRP English Version. 2002. (Illus.). 8p. pap. 0.40 (978-0-521-01471-7(9)) Cambridge Univ. Pr.

Marsh, Carole. My First Book: New Edition. 2001. (Kansas Experience! Ser.). pap. 7.95 (978-0-635-00346-1(5) , Marsh, Carole Bks.) Gallopade International.

—My First Book about Canada. 2001. (Canada Experience! Ser.). (Illus.). 32p. (J). (gr. k-4). pap. 7.95 (978-0-635-00519-9(0)) Gallopade International.

Marsh, Robert. Kruger National Park: South African Edition. Meyer, Leo, illus. 1998. (Cambridge Reading Routes Ser.). 16p. pap. 5.00 (978-0-521-63666-7(3)) Cambridge Univ. Pr.

—Thulamela: South African Edition. 1998. (Cambridge Reading Routes Ser.). (Illus.). 24p. pap. 5.00 (978-0-521-63662-9(0)) Cambridge Univ. Pr.

Martin, Tyler. Big Book: I Have a Question, Vol. 4. Williams, Toby, illus. l.t. ed. 2005. (Sadlier Phonics Reading Program). 8p. (YA). (ps-1). 22.50 (978-0-8215-7356-3(X)) Sadlier, William H. Inc.

Martinucci, Suzanne. At Space Camp, Vol. 2. l.t. ed. 2005. (Little Books & Big Bks.: Vol. 6). (Illus.). 8p. (YA). (ps-3). 22.50 (978-0-8215-7515-4(5)) Sadlier, William H. Inc.

Marzollo, Jean. I Spy a Dinosaur's Eye. Wick, Walter, photos by. 2003. (Scholastic Reader Ser.). (Illus.). 32p. (J). pap. 3.99 (978-0-439-52471-1(7) , Cartwheel Bks.) Scholastic, Inc.

Mayer, Mercer. Country Fair. 2003. (Little Critter Ser.). (Illus.). 24p. (J). (ps-2). 10.95 (978-1-57768-633-0(0)) School Specialty Publishing.

—Country Fair. 2001. (gr. k-3). lib. bdg. 11.80 (978-0-613-67607-6(6)) Tandem Library Bks.

—Goodnight, Little Critter. 2001. (gr. k-3). lib. bdg. 11.80 (978-0-613-67624-3(6)) Tandem Library Bks.

—No One Can Play. 2002. (Little Critter Ser.). (Illus.). 24p. (J). (ps-2). 10.95 (978-1-57768-608-8(X)) School Specialty Publishing.

—No One Can Play. 2000. (gr. k-3). lib. bdg. 11.80 (978-0-613-67656-4(4)) Tandem Library Bks.

—A Yummy Lunch. 2002. (Little Critter Ser.). (Illus.). 24p. (J). (ps-2). 10.95 (978-1-57768-627-9(6)) School Specialty Publishing.

MCP Staff. Ready Reader S1. 2003. (J). (ps-3). pap. 227.95 (978-0-8136-1432-8(5)) Modern Curriculum Pr.

—Stage Two - Early. 2003. (J). (ps-3). pap. 227.95 (978-0-8136-1433-5(3)) Modern Curriculum Pr.

Michaels, David. Bye-Bye, Katy, Vol. 3. Platt, Pierre, illus. l.t. ed. 2005. (Sadlier Phonics Reading Program). 8p. (YA). (ps-1). 22.50 (978-0-8215-7354-9(3)) Sadlier, William H. Inc.

Miranda, Anne. The Best Place. l.t. ed. 2005. (Little Books & Big Bks.: Vol. 5). (Illus.). 8p. (YA). (ps-3). 22.50 (978-0-8215-7514-7(7)) Sadlier, William H. Inc.

—Big Book: Looking at Lizards, Vol. 2. l.t. ed. 2005. (Sadlier Phonics Reading Program). (Illus.). 8p. (YA). (ps-1). 22.50 (978-0-8215-7346-4(2)) Sadlier, William H. Inc.

—Big Book: Weather Wise, Vol. 3. l.t. ed. 2005. (Sadlier Phonics Reading Program). (Illus.). 8p. (YA). (ps-1). 22.50 (978-0-8215-7351-8(9)) Sadlier, William H. Inc.

—Peach Tree Street, Vol. 2. Lodge, Katherine, illus. l.t. ed. 2005. (Little Books & Big Bks.: Vol. 10). 8p. (YA). (ps-3). 22.50 (978-0-8215-7519-2(8)) Sadlier, William H. Inc.

Mitton, Tony. The Blob Can Blink! Swift, Gary, illus. 2001. (Cambridge Reading Ser.). 16p. pap. 6.00 (978-0-521-01397-0(6)) Cambridge Univ. Pr.

Moloko, Mpho. The Lost Headband: South African Edition. 1998. (Cambridge Reading Routes Ser.). (Illus.). 16p. pap. 5.00 (978-0-521-62793-1(1)) Cambridge Univ. Pr.

Montardre, Helene. The Cat & the Dog. 2003. (Illus.). 8p. (J). bds. 7.95 (978-1-58728-483-0(9) , Two Can Publishing) T&N Children's Publishing.

—Elephant & Mouse. 2004. (Turn & Learn Ser.). (Illus.). 8p. (J). (ps up). bds. 7.95 (978-1-58728-482-3(0) , Two Can Publishing) T&N Children's Publishing.

—Hen & Chick. 2004. (Turn & Learn Ser.). (Illus.). 8p. (J). (ps up). bds. 7.95 (978-1-58728-480-9(4) , Two Can Publishing) T&N Children's Publishing.

—Night & Day. 2003. (Illus.). 8p. (J). bds. 7.95 (978-1-58728-481-6(2) , Two Can Publishing) T&N Children's Publishing.

Munton, Gill. I Went Swimming, 6 vols, Pack. 2000. (Cambridge Reading Ser.). 8p. pap. 28.00 (978-0-521-78761-1(0)) Cambridge Univ. Pr.

—Make a Banana Treat, 6, Pack. 2000. (Cambridge Reading Ser.). 8p. pap. 28.00 (978-0-521-78760-4(2)) Cambridge Univ. Pr.

Nicholas, Melissa. Big Book: Pumpkin Days, Vol. 3. l.t. ed. 2005. (Sadlier Phonics Reading Program). (Illus.). 8p. (YA). (ps-1). 22.50 (978-0-8215-7352-5(7)) Sadlier, William H. Inc.

—Big Book: Who Is My Mom? Cassels, Jean, illus. l.t. ed. 2005. (Sadlier Phonics Reading Program). 8p. (YA). (ps-1). 22.50 (978-0-8215-7341-9(1)) Sadlier, William H. Inc.

—Stop by a Pond. Gram, Patrick, illus. l.t. ed. 2005. (Little Books & Big Bks.: Vol. 3). 8p. (YA). (ps-3). 22.50 (978-0-8215-7512-3(0)) Sadlier, William H. Inc.

Ockards, Najmiyyah. Water from the Well: South African Edition. 1998. (Cambridge Reading Routes Ser.). (Illus.). 16p. pap. 5.00 (978-0-521-62790-0(7)) Cambridge Univ. Pr.

O'Keefe, Ruth A. Starter One Hundred One, Bk. 8. AEVAC, Inc. Staff, ed. (Structured Beginning Reading Program Ser.). 96p. (J). stu. ed. 3.50 (978-0-913356-14-2(X)) AEVAC, Inc.

Olivia, Cynthia. Big Book: In January & June, Vol. 4. l.t. ed. 2005. (Sadlier Phonics Reading Program: Vol. 16). (Illus.). 8p. (YA). (ps-1). 22.50 (978-0-8215-7355-6(1)) Sadlier, William H. Inc.

Packard, Mary. Surprise! Huang, Benrei, illus. 2003. (My First Reader Ser.). 32p. (J). 18.50 (978-0-516-22937-9(0) , Children's Pr.) Scholastic Library Publishing.

Partridge, Juliet. Blowing Bubbles, Pack of 6. 2001. (Cambridge Storybooks Ser.). (Illus.). 8p. pap. 16.00 (978-0-521-00733-7(X)) Cambridge Univ. Pr.

—Blowing Bubbles ELT Edition. Sweeten, Sami, illus. 2001. (Cambridge Storybooks Ser.). 8p. pap. 3.00 (978-0-521-00669-9(4)) Cambridge Univ. Pr.

—Everyone Is Reading ELT Edition. 2004. (Cambridge Storybooks Ser.). (Illus.). 16p. pap. 5.00 (978-0-521-75205-3(1)) Cambridge Univ. Pr.

—The Picnic ELT Edition. Sweeten, Sami, illus. 2001. (Cambridge Storybooks Ser.). 8p. pap. 3.00 (978-0-521-00686-6(4)) Cambridge Univ. Pr.

Paul, Kate. Big Book: The Best Ride, Vol. 2. l.t. ed. 2005. (Sadlier Phonics Reading Program). (Illus.). 8p. (YA). (ps-1). 22.50 (978-0-8215-7345-7(4)) Sadlier, William H. Inc.

Penguin Books Staff. Fun with Dick & Jane. (J). (ps-2). 2004. (Read with Dick & Jane Ser.: Vol. 12). 32p. pap. 3.99 (978-0-448-43411-7(3)); 2003. (Illus.). bds. 9.99 (978-0-448-43374-5(5)) Penguin Group (USA) Inc. (Grosset & Dunlap).

Perry, Sue & Rose, Jane. Not Yet, Nathan! ELT Edition. 2004. (Cambridge Storybooks Ser.). (Illus.). 16p. pap. 5.00 (978-0-521-75261-9(2)) Cambridge Univ. Pr.

Practice Power School Bus Book: Preschool. 2003. 24p. (J). (ps). spiral bd. (978-1-930355-41-5(6)) Greenbrier/Scentex.

Prater, John. Billy's Box ELT Edition. 2004. (Cambridge Storybooks Ser.). (Illus.). 16p. pap. 5.00 (978-0-521-75253-4(1)) Cambridge Univ. Pr.

—Dan's Box ELT Edition. 2001. (Cambridge Storybooks Ser.). (Illus.). 16p. pap. 5.00 (978-0-521-00713-9(5)) Cambridge Univ. Pr.

—Lucy's Box, 6 vols., Pack. 2001. (Cambridge Storybooks Ser.). (Illus.). 16p. pap. 26.00 (978-0-521-00791-7(7)) Cambridge Univ. Pr.

—Lucy's Box ELT Edition. 2001. (Cambridge Storybooks Ser.). (Illus.). 16p. pap. 5.00 (978-0-521-00710-8(0)) Cambridge Univ. Pr.

—Nishal's Box ELT Edition. 2004. (Cambridge Storybooks Ser.). (Illus.). 24p. pap. 6.00 (978-0-521-75255-8(8)) Cambridge Univ. Pr.

—Wayne's Box ELT Edition. 2004. (Cambridge Storybooks Ser.). (Illus.). 16p. pap. 5.00 (978-0-521-75251-0(5)) Cambridge Univ. Pr.

Preller, Martie & Williams, Nontsikelelo. Grandmother's Medicine & Just Me. 2002. (Illus.). 32p. pap. 0.40 (978-0-521-01493-9(X)) Cambridge Univ. Pr.

Priddy, Roger. My Big Book of Everything. 2000. (Illus.). 64p. (J). (ps-3). 15.95 (978-0-7894-0998-0(4)) Dorling Kindersley Publishing, Inc.

Rankin, Joan. Our House: English Version. 2002. (Illus.). 8p. pap. 0.40 (978-0-521-01461-8(1)) Cambridge Univ. Pr.

Reading Friends Staff. Peanut Single. (J). (978-0-8136-3813-3(5)) Modern Curriculum Pr.

—Run Single. (J). (978-0-8136-3787-7(2)) Modern Curriculum Pr.

Ready Reader Staff. The Ant, Level 6, Bk. 1. 2003. (J). (ps-3). pap. 24.50 (978-0-8136-1983-5(1)) Modern Curriculum Pr.

—Five Little Dinosaurs, 6 bks., set, Level 8, Bk. 34. 2003. (J). (ps-3). pap. 33.50 (978-0-8136-0787-0(6)) Modern Curriculum Pr.

—Let's Go Marching!, Level 6, Bk. 50. 2003. (J). (ps-3). 24.50 (978-0-8136-0779-5(5)) Modern Curriculum Pr.

—Mr. Wink, 6 bks., Set, Level 8, Bk. 48. (J). pap. 24.50 (978-0-8136-0781-8(7)) Modern Curriculum Pr.

Reddy, Deran. Washing Up: South African Edition. Menck, Clare, illus. 1998. (Cambridge Reading Routes Ser.). 16p. pap. 5.00 (978-0-521-62791-7(5)) Cambridge Univ. Pr.

Reid, Carolyn & Edwards, Shirley R. Veld: South African Edition. 1998. (Cambridge Reading Routes Ser.). (Illus.). 16p. pap. 5.00 (978-0-521-62794-8(X)) Cambridge Univ. Pr.

Reid, Carolyn & Hepker, Sue. Busy in the Bush. 2002. (Illus.). 32p. pap. 0.40 (978-0-521-01372-7(0)) Cambridge Univ. Pr.

Ridgway, Dawn, et al. The Magic Flute & Other Stories. 2002. (Illus.). 48p. pap. 0.40 (978-0-521-01531-8(6)) Cambridge Univ. Pr.

Riley, Jeni, ed. Mi Primer Libro de Palabras. Stanley, Mandy, illus. 2002. (SPA.). 48p. (J). (ps-k). pap. 6.95 (978-0-7534-5542-5(0) , Kingfisher) Houghton Mifflin Co. Trade & Reference Div.

P Q R

Robinson, Anthony. Animals in the Jungle, 6, Pack. 2000. (Cambridge Reading Ser.). 8p. pap. 28.00 (978-0-521-78820-5(X)) Cambridge Univ. Pr.

Rose, Gerald. Bad Boy Billy! ELT Edition. 2004. (Cambridge Storybooks Ser.). (Illus.). 16p. pap. 5.00 (978-0-521-75209-1(4)) Cambridge Univ. Pr.

—Cambridge Plays: The Lion & the Mouse. 2004. (Cambridge Storybooks Ser.). (Illus.). 24p. pap. 6.00 (978-0-521-75231-2(0)) Cambridge Univ. Pr.

—Cambridge Plays: The Little Red Hen ELT Edition. 2004. (Cambridge Storybooks Ser.). 24p. pap. 6.00 (978-0-521-75223-7(X)) Cambridge Univ. Pr.

—The Clever Tortoise: ELT Edition. 2004. (Cambridge Storybooks Ser.). (Illus.). 16p. pap. 5.00 (978-0-521-75219-0(1)) Cambridge Univ. Pr.

—The Clever Tortoise: South African Edition. 1998. (Cambridge Reading Routes Ser.). (Illus.). 16p. pap. 5.00 (978-0-521-62829-7(6)) Cambridge Univ. Pr.

—Dad Goes Fishing ELT Edition. 2004. (Cambridge Storybooks Ser.). (Illus.). 24p. pap. 6.00 (978-0-521-75221-3(3)) Cambridge Univ. Pr.

—The Gingerbread Man ELT Edition. 2004. (Cambridge Storybooks Ser.). (Illus.). 16p. pap. 5.00 (978-0-521-75217-6(5)) Cambridge Univ. Pr.

—Little Red Hen: South African Edition. 1998. (Cambridge Reading Routes Ser.). (Illus.). 16p. pap. 5.00 (978-0-521-62827-3(X)) Cambridge Univ. Pr.

—Tiger Dreams: South African Edition. 1998. (Cambridge Reading Routes Ser.). (Illus.). 24p. pap. 5.00 (978-0-521-63670-4(1)) Cambridge Univ. Pr.

—The Tortoise & the Hare: South African Edition. 1998. (Cambridge Reading Routes Ser.). (Illus.). 16p. pap. 5.00 (978-0-521-62747-4(8)) Cambridge Univ. Pr.

—The Tortoise & the Hare ELT Edition. 2004. (Cambridge Storybooks Ser.). (Illus.). 16p. pap. 5.00 (978-0-521-75207-7(8)) Cambridge Univ. Pr.

—We're Going on a Picnic ELT Edition. 2004. (Cambridge Storybooks Ser.). (Illus.). 24p. pap. 6.00 (978-0-521-75227-5(2)) Cambridge Univ. Pr.

—Who's Stealing the Fish? ELT Edition. 2004. (Cambridge Storybooks Ser.). (Illus.). 24p. pap. 6.00 (978-0-521-75229-9(9)) Cambridge Univ. Pr.

Rothman, Cynthia Anne. Big Book. Alley, R. W., illus. l.t. ed. 2005. (Sadlier Phonics Reading Program). 8p. (YA). (ps-1). 22.50 (978-0-8215-7342-6(X)) Sadlier, William H. Inc.

—Big Book Vol. 3: I Love to Read. l.t. ed. 2005. (Sadlier Phonics Reading Program). (Illus.). 8p. (YA). (ps-1). 22.50 (978-0-8215-7353-2(5)) Sadlier, William H. Inc.

—Big Book: Violets & Vegetables, Vol. 4. l.t. ed. 2005. (Sadlier Phonics Reading Program). (Illus.). 8p. (YA). (ps-1). 22.50 (978-0-8215-7357-0(8)) Sadlier, William H. Inc.

—Big Book: Yes, You Can, Vol. 4. l.t. ed. 2005. (Sadlier Phonics Reading Program). (Illus.). 8p. (YA). (ps-1). 22.50 (978-0-8215-7358-7(6)) Sadlier, William H. Inc.

—Funny Bugs. Lester, Mike, illus. l.t. ed. 2005. (Little Books & Big Bks.: Vol. 4). 8p. (YA). (ps-3). 22.50 (978-0-8215-7513-0(9)) Sadlier, William H. Inc.

Schecter, Deborah. My First Little Readers. 2004. 64p. pap. 11.99 (978-0-439-57407-5(2) , Teaching Resources) Scholastic, Inc.

Scheunemann, Pam. Sl: See It Say It Hear It. l.t. ed. 2001. (More Blends Ser.). (Illus.). 24p. (J). (ps-3). lib. bdg. 19.93 (978-1-57765-452-0(8) , SandCastle) ABDO Publishing Co.

School Zone Publishing. Beginning Reading. 2003. (J). cd-rom 19.99 (978-1-58947-921-0(1)); (gr. k-1). cd-rom 19.99 (978-1-58947-923-4(8)); (gr. 1-2). cd-rom 19.99 (978-1-58947-922-7(X)); (gr. 1-2). cd-rom 19.99 (978-1-58947-924-1(6)) School Zone Publishing Co.

Schumacher, Stef. Amazing Blue Animals, Vol. 2. l.t. ed. 2005. (Little Books & Big Bks.: Vol. 9). (Illus.). 8p. (YA). (ps-3). 22.50 (978-0-8215-7518-5(X)) Sadlier, William H. Inc.

Seddon, Tony & Gillham, Bill. What for? & Ostriches. 2002. (Illus.). 16p. pap. 0.40 (978-0-521-01523-5(5)) Cambridge Univ. Pr.

Sikakhane, Nomthandazo. Every Precious Drop: South African Edition. 1998. (Cambridge Reading Routes Ser.). (Illus.). 16p. pap. 5.00 (978-0-521-62789-4(3)) Cambridge Univ. Pr.

Smith, Beth Esh. Off We Go! Linke, Don, Jr., illus. l.t. ed. 1998. (Big Bks.). 8p. (J). (ps-k). pap. 10.95 (978-1-57332-111-2(7)) HighReach Learning, Inc.

Spann, Mary Beth. Word Families: 20 Interactive Word Books That Help Every Child Become a Better Reader, Vol. 1. 1999. (Reading Success Mini-Bks.). (Illus.). 48p. pap. 9.95 (978-0-439-10439-5(4) , Cartwheel Bks.) Scholastic, Inc.

Sprick, Marilyn, et al. Read Well Plain Text Comprehension & Skill Work Masters. 1998. (Read Well Ser.). (Illus.). 256p. (J). (gr. 1-3). ring bd. 39.00 (978-1-57035-165-5(1) , 93SCH/93SLANTED) Sopris West Educational Services.

—Read Well Student Storybooks, 16 vols., Set. 1998. (Read Well Ser.). (Illus.). 72p. (J). (gr. 1-3). pap. 35.00 (978-1-57035-158-7(9) , 93SET) Sopris West Educational Services.

Stanley, Mandy. At the Beach. 2002. (All Aboard Ser.). (Illus.). 12p. (J). (gr. 4-6). bds. 4.95 (978-0-7534-5444-2(0) , Kingfisher) Houghton Mifflin Co. Trade & Reference Div.

—At the Zoo. Morris, Jennis, ed. 2002. (All Aboard Ser.). (Illus.). 12p. (J). (gr. k-ps). bds. 4.95 (978-0-7534-5446-6(7) , Kingfisher) Houghton Mifflin Co. Trade & Reference Div.

—First Words. Morris, Jennie, ed. 2002. (All Aboard Ser.). (Illus.). 12p. (J). (gr. k-ps). bds. 3.95 (978-0-7534-5443-5(2) , Kingfisher) Houghton Mifflin Co. Trade & Reference Div.

—On the Farm. 2002. (All Aboard Ser.). (Illus.). 12p. (J). (gr. k-ps). bds. 3.95 (978-0-7534-5445-9(9) , Kingfisher) Houghton Mifflin Co. Trade & Reference Div.

Steck-Vaughn Staff. At-Home Workbooks: Reading. 2004. (Illus.). (gr. 3). pap., wbk. ed. 5.99 (978-0-7398-8526-0(X)) Steck-Vaughn.

—Early Reader Program Level A: The Puppy That Sniffed Too Much, 6 Pack. 2004. (Illus.). pap. 30.00 (978-0-7398-8151-4(5)) Steck-Vaughn.

—Early Reader Program Level A: Why Cats Hunt at Night, 6 Pack. 2004. (Illus.). pap. 30.00 (978-0-7398-8153-8(1)) Steck-Vaughn.

Stuart, Matt. Who Can Run Fast? l.t. ed. 2005. (Little Books & Big Bks.: Vol. 1). (Illus.). 8p. (YA). (ps-3). 22.50 (978-0-8215-7510-9(4)) Sadlier, William H. Inc.

Taylor, Beth. Big Book: Tina's Toys. l.t. ed. 2005. (Sadlier Phonics Reading Program). (Illus.). 8p. (YA). (ps-1). 22.50 (978-0-8215-7343-3(8)) Sadlier, William H. Inc.

Teacher Created Materials Staff. Apples & Ice Cream. (Go Bks.). 8p. (J). (gr. k-1). pap. 2.49 (978-1-57690-809-9(7)) Teacher Created Materials, Inc.

Thryce, Marc & Robinson, Tim. Look at the Pictures. l.t. ed. 2005. (Little Books & Big Bks.: Vol. 2). (Illus.). 8p. (YA). (ps-3). 22.50 (978-0-8215-7511-6(2)) Sadlier, William H. Inc.

Titzer, Robert C. A Book Your Baby Can Read! Dozier, Brendan et al, photos by. 2003. (Early Language Development Ser.: Vol. 2). (Illus.). 14p. (J). pap. 7.95 (978-0-9657510-5-6(8) , 0-9657510-5-8) Infant Learning Co., The.

—A Book Your Baby Can Read! Dozier, Brendan et al, photos by. 1998. (Early Language Development Ser.: Vol. 1). (Illus.). 14p. (J). (ps). pap. 7.95 (978-0-9657510-1-8(5) , 0-9657510-1-5) Infant Learning Co., The.

—A Book Your Baby Can Read! Early Language Development Series. Dozier, Lisa et al, photos by. 2003. (Early Language Development Ser.: Vol. 3). (Illus.). 14p. (J). pap. 7.95 (978-0-9657510-9-4(0) , 0-9657510-9-0) Infant Learning Co., The.

—A Book Your Baby Can Read! 5 Book Set: Early Language Development Series, 5 vols., Vol. 1. 2003. (Illus.). 80p. (J). pap. 29.95 (978-1-931026-05-5(X) , 1-931026-05-X) Infant Learning Co., The.

—A Book Your Baby Can Read! Review: Early Language Development Series. Dozier, Brendan et al, photos by. 2003. (Early Language Development Ser.). (Illus.). 14p. (J). pap. 7.95 (978-1-931026-04-8(1) , 1-931026-04-1) Infant Learning Co., The.

—A Book Your Baby Can Read! Starter: Early Language Development Series, 1, Starter Book. Dozier, Lisa et al, photos by. 2003. (Book Your Baby Can Read!: Starter Book). (Illus.). 14p. (J). pap. 7.95 (978-1-931026-03-1(3) , 1-931026-03-3) Infant Learning Co., The.

Trisler, Alana & Cardiel, Patrice Howe. My April Journal. 1999. (Illus.). 48p. (J). (gr. 1-2). pap., wbk. ed. 1.85 (978-1-56762-102-0(3)) Modern Learning Pr.

—My December Journal. 1999. 48p. (J). (gr. 1-2). pap., wbk. ed. 1.85 (978-1-56762-098-6(1)) Modern Learning Pr.

—My Fall Journal. 1999. 72p. (J). (gr. 2-3). pap., wbk. ed. 2.10 (978-1-56762-104-4(X)) Modern Learning Pr.

—My February Journal. 1999. 48p. (J). (gr. 1-2). pap., wbk. ed. 1.85 (978-1-56762-100-6(7)) Modern Learning Pr.

—My January Journal. 1999. 48p. (J). (gr. 1-2). pap., wbk. ed. 1.85 (978-1-56762-099-3(X)) Modern Learning Pr.

—My March Journal. 1999. 48p. (J). (gr. 1-2). pap., wbk. ed. 1.85 (978-1-56762-101-3(5)) Modern Learning Pr.

—My May Journal. 1999. 48p. (J). (gr. 1-2). pap., wbk. ed. 1.85 (978-1-56762-103-7(1)) Modern Learning Pr.

—My November Journal. 1999. 48p. (J). (gr. 1-2). pap., wbk. ed. 1.85 (978-1-56762-097-9(3)) Modern Learning Pr.

—My October Journal. 1999. 48p. (J). (gr. 1-2). pap., wbk. ed. 1.85 (978-1-56762-096-2(5)) Modern Learning Pr.

—My September Journal. 1999. 48p. (J). (gr. 1-2). pap., wbk. ed. 1.85 (978-1-56762-095-5(7)) Modern Learning Pr.

—My Spring Journal. 1999. 72p. (J). (gr. 2-3). pap., wbk. ed. 2.10 (978-1-56762-106-8(6)) Modern Learning Pr.

—My Summer Journal. 1999. 72p. (J). (gr. 2-3). pap., wbk. ed. 2.10 (978-1-56762-107-5(4)) Modern Learning Pr.

—My Winter Journal. 1999. 72p. (J). (gr. 2-3). pap., wbk. ed. 2.10 (978-1-56762-105-1(8)) Modern Learning Pr.

Troughton, Joanna. The Animal Wrestlers ELT Edition. 2004. (Cambridge Storybooks Ser.). (Illus.). 24p. pap. 6.00 (978-0-521-75245-9(0)) Cambridge Univ. Pr.

—The Chinese New Year ELT Edition. 2004. (Cambridge Storybooks Ser.). (Illus.). 24p. pap. 6.00 (978-0-521-75241-1(8)) Cambridge Univ. Pr.

Van Heerden, Marjorie. Cave: South African Edition. 1998. (Cambridge Reading Routes Ser.). (Illus.). 16p. pap. 5.00 (978-0-521-62809-9(1)) Cambridge Univ. Pr.

—Frog: Afrikaans Version. 2002. (Illus.). 8p. pap. 0.40 (978-0-521-01386-4(0)) Cambridge Univ. Pr.

Viljoen, Graeme. Eggs Zulu Version. 2002. (Illus.). 8p. pap. 0.40 (978-0-521-01450-2(6)) Cambridge Univ. Pr.

—Fish: South African Edition. 1998. (Cambridge Reading Routes Ser.). (Illus.). 16p. pap. 5.00 (978-0-521-62808-2(3)) Cambridge Univ. Pr.

Walsh, Melanie. Ocean Animals. Walsh, Melanie, illus. 2002. (Tiny Teether Ser.). (Illus.). 14p. (J). (gr. k-ps). bds. 4.99 (978-0-7636-1807-0(1)) Candlewick Pr.

—Pets. Walsh, Melanie, illus. 2002. (Tiny Teether Ser.). (Illus.). 14p. (J). (gr. k-ps). bds. 4.99 (978-0-7636-1808-7(X)) Candlewick Pr.

—Wild Animals. Walsh, Melanie, illus. 2002. (Tiny Teether Ser.). (Illus.). 14p. (J). (gr. k-ps). bds. 4.99 (978-0-7636-1809-4(8)) Candlewick Pr.

Ward, Sally & Dlhomo, Bongi. Dorothy's Visit: Siswati Version. 2002. (Illus.). 16p. pap. 1.75 (978-0-521-52832-0(1)) Cambridge Univ. Pr.

Weizierl, Natasha. The Shoebox Baby: South African Edition. 1998. (Cambridge Reading Routes Ser.). (Illus.). 16p. pap. 5.00 (978-0-521-62788-7(5)) Cambridge Univ. Pr.

Who's Making That Noise? First Words - ABC, 3 bks., 3 disc., Set. 2004. (Make Reading Fun! Ser.: Module 1). (SPA., Illus.). (J). (ps). 49.95 (978-1-58086-178-6(4)) EDC Publishing.

Wildman, Chris & Muwela, Mavis. Try & Catch a Tadpole. 2002. 16p. pap. 0.40 (978-0-521-01595-0(2)) Cambridge Univ. Pr.

Wildman, Chris, et al. Grandfather's Hat & Small Sampa. 2002. (Illus.). 16p. pap. 0.40 (978-0-521-01619-3(3)) Cambridge Univ. Pr.

Wilhelm, Hans. Don't Cut My Hair. 2004. 32p. (J). lib. bdg. 15.00 (978-1-59054-351-1(3)) Fitzgerald Bks.

—I Am Lost. 2004. 32p. (J). lib. bdg. 15.00 (978-1-59054-352-8(1)) Fitzgerald Bks.

Williams, Nontsikelelo. The Worst Taste in the World: South African Edition. 1998. (Cambridge Reading Routes Ser.). (Illus.). 16p. pap. 5.00 (978-0-521-62792-4(3)) Cambridge Univ. Pr.

Winter, Max. Did You Know?, Vol. 2. Rechin, Kevin, illus. l.t. ed. 2005. (Little Books & Big Bks.: Vol. 8). 8p. (YA). (ps-3). 22.50 (978-0-8215-7517-8(1)) Sadlier, William H. Inc.

Wohl, Sharon. Big Tan Van. Bradley, Lisa, illus. 1998. 8p. (J). (gr. k-2). mass mkt. 4.95 (978-0-9665443-5-0(8)) A Better Way of Learning.

—Eat at Joe's. Grainger, Lesley, illus. 1998. 16p. (J). (gr. k-2). mass mkt. 4.95 (978-0-9665443-6-7(6)) A Better Way of Learning.

—It's A Hit. Beeler, Dori, illus. 1998. 16p. (J). (gr. k-2). mass mkt. 4.95 (978-0-9665443-3-6(1)) A Better Way of Learning.

—Matt's Bike. Schaadt, Celeste, illus. 1998. 8p. (J). (gr. k-2). mass mkt. 4.95 (978-0-9665443-9-8(0)) A Better Way of Learning.

The World of Dick & Jane & Friends. 2004. (Dick & Jane Ser.). (Illus.). 192p. (J). (ps-2). 10.99 (978-0-448-43646-3(9) , Grosset & Dunlap) Penguin Group (USA) Inc.

PRIMITIVE ART

see Art, Primitive

PRIMITIVE SOCIETIES

see also Art, Primitive; Indians of North America—Social Life and Customs; Prehistoric Peoples

Fleischman, Paul, ed. Cannibal in the Mirror. Whalen, John, photos by. 2000. (Single Titles Ser.: up). (Illus.). 64p. (gr. 7 up). lib. bdg. 24.90 (978-0-7613-0968-0(3) , Twenty-First Century Bks.) Lerner Publishing Group.

PRINCE EDWARD ISLAND

Campbell, Kumari. Prince Edward Island. 2nd rev. ed. (Hello Canada Ser.). 76p. pap. (978-1-55041-756-2(8)) Fitzhenry & Whiteside, Ltd.

—Prince Edward Island. 1998. (Hello Canada Ser.). (Illus.). (J). (gr. 3-6). pap. 6.95 (978-0-8225-9817-6(5)) Lerner Publishing Group.

Campell, Kumari. Prince Edward Island. 2nd ed. 1999. (Hello Canada Ser.). (Illus.). 72p. pap. (978-1-55041-267-3(1)) Fitzhenry & Whiteside, Ltd.

LeVert, Suzanne. Prince Edward Island. 2000. (Canada in the Twenty First Century Ser.). (Illus.). (J). (gr. 8-12). 29.50 (978-0-7910-6069-8(1) , Chelsea Hse.) Facts On File, Inc.

PRINCE EDWARD ISLAND—FICTION

Chronicles of Avonlea. 2004. 142p. (YA). pap. 7.95 (978-1-57646-893-7(3)) Quiet Vision Publishing.

Dalmatian Press Staff, adapted by. Anne of Green Gables. 2002. (Spot the Classics Ser.). (Illus.). 176p. (J). (gr. k-5). 4.99 (978-1-57759-543-4(2)) Dalmatian Pr.

Dussling, Jennifer. L. M. Montgomery's Anne of Green Gables. 2001. (gr. k-3). lib. bdg. 11.80 (978-0-613-35608-4(X)) Tandem Library Bks.

Dussling, Jennifer & Montgomery, L. M. Anne of Green Gables. Halverson, Lydia, illus. 2001. (All Aboard Reading Ser.). 48p. (J). (gr. 4-7). pap. 3.99 (978-0-448-42459-0(2) , Grosset & Dunlap) Penguin Group (USA) Inc.

Helldorfer, Mary-Claire. Anne of Green Gables. Beier, Ellen, illus. 2003. 40p. (J). (gr. k-3). pap. 6.99 (978-0-440-41614-2(0) , Dragonfly Bks.) Random Hse. Children's Bks.

Manuel, Lynn. The Summer of the Marco Polo. Charko, Kasia, illus. 2007. 32p. (J). (ps-3). ***978-1-55143-330-1(3)*** Orca Bk. Pubs.

McHugh, Fiona, adapted by. Anne of Green Gables Storybook. 2007. (Illus.). 80p. (J). (gr. 2-7). pap. 9.95 (978-0-920668-42-9(9)) Firefly Bks., Ltd.

Montgomery, L. M. Along the Shore: Tales by the Sea. (YA). 22.95 (978-0-8488-2655-0(8)) Amereon LTD.

—Ana la de Isla. 4th ed. (Coleccion "Ana, la de Tejas Verdes"). (SPA., Illus.). 240p. (YA). (gr. 5-8). (978-84-7888-635-7(4) , SAL5036) Emece Editores ESP. *Dist:* Lectorum Pubns., Inc.

—Ana la de Isla. 2001. (SPA.). 240p. (J). (gr. 4-7). 10.95 (978-84-7888-161-1(1)) Scholastic, Inc.

—Ana la de Isla. 2001. (J). (978-0-606-22674-5(5)) Tandem Library Bks.

—Anne of Avonlea. 2006. (Scholastic Classics Ser.). (Illus.). viii, 239p. (J). 25.00 (978-0-531-16979-7(0) , Watts, Franklin) Scholastic Library Publishing.

—Anne of Avonlea. 2005. (Aladdin Classics Ser.). (Illus.). 398p. (J). (gr. 4-7). pap. 4.99 (978-1-4169-0328-4(3) , Aladdin) Simon & Schuster Children's Publishing.

—Anne of Avonlea. unabr. ed. 2002. (Dover Juvenile Classics Ser.). 272p. (J). (gr. 4-7). pap. 3.00 (978-0-486-42239-8(9)) Dover Pubns., Inc.

—Anne of Avonlea. l.t. ed. 2006. (ENG.). pap. ***978-1-4068-3173-3(5)*** Echo Library.

—Anne of Avonlea. l.t. ed. 1998. (Avonlea Ser.: No. 2). 401p. (YA). (gr. 5-8). lib. bdg. 35.95 (978-1-58118-039-8(X) , 22507) LRS.

—Anne of Avonlea. 1998. 270p. (YA). (gr. 5-8). reprint ed. lib. bdg. 25.00 (978-1-58287-013-7(6)) North Bks.

—Anne of Avonlea. l.t. ed. 2000. (Anne of Green Gables Ser.: Vol. 2). 366p. (gr. 5-8). pap. 21.99 (978-1-57646-306-2(0)) Quiet Vision Publishing.

—Anne of Green Gables. 2004. 400p. per. 16.95 (978-1-59540-110-6(5)) 1st World Publishing, Inc.

—Anne of Green Gables. Miralles, Joseph, illus. 2002. (Great Illustrated Classics Ser.). 240p. (J). (gr. 3-8). 21.35 (978-1-57765-816-0(7) , ABDO & Daughters) ABDO Publishing Co.

—Anne of Green Gables. 349p. (978-1-58726-053-7(0)) Ann Arbor Media Group, LLC.

—Anne of Green Gables. 2000. (Avonlea Ser.: No. 1). 280p. (YA). (gr. 5-8). pap. 15.00 (978-0-7881-9155-8(1)) DIANE Publishing Co.

—Anne of Green Gables. 2007. per. 6.99 ***978-1-4209-2922-5(4)*** Digireads.com.

—Anne of Green Gables. 2000. (Avonlea Ser.: No. 1). 320p. (J). (gr. 4-7). pap. 3.50 (978-0-486-41025-8(0)) Dover Pubns., Inc.

—Anne of Green Gables. 2000. (Avonlea Ser.: No. 1). (YA). (gr. 5-8). (978-0-06-028227-1(4)); 1999. (Charming Classics). 400p. (J). (ps up). pap. 6.99 (978-0-694-01251-0(3) , Harper Festival) HarperCollins Pubs.

—Anne of Green Gables. (Avonlea Ser.: No. 1). (YA). (gr. 5-8). pap. (978-0-340-71500-0(6) , Hodder & Stoughton) Hodder General Publishing Division.

—Anne of Green Gables. 2003. 276p. pap. 15.99 ***978-1-4043-6066-2(2)*** IndyPublish.com.

—Anne of Green Gables. Stemach, Jerry, ed. Ham, Jeff, illus. 2000. 65.00 incl. audio, cd-rom (978-1-58702-311-8(3)) Johnston, Don Inc.

—Anne of Green Gables. 1998. 352p. (J). pap. (978-1-55109-249-2(2)) Nimbus Publishing, Ltd.

—Anne of Green Gables. Rubio, Mary & Waterson, Elizabeth, eds. 2006. (Norton Critical Edition Ser.). (Illus.). 400p. (C). pap. 9.00 (978-0-393-92695-8(8)) Norton, W. W. & Co., Inc.

—Anne of Green Gables. (Oxford Children's Classics). 2007. 400p. (YA). 9.95 ***978-0-19-272000-9(7)***; 2004. 8.50 (978-0-19-423273-9(5)) Oxford Univ. Pr., Inc.

—Anne of Green Gables. 2003. 320p. (gr. 12). 4.95 (978-0-451-52882-7(4) , Signet Classics); 2002. (Illus.). (J). pap. 9.99 (978-0-14-250102-3(6) , Puffin) Penguin Group (USA) Inc.

—Anne of Green Gables. 2000. (Anne of Green Gables Ser.: Vol. No. 1). 220p. (gr. 5-8). pap. 12.99 (978-1-57646-300-0(1)); 24.95 (978-1-57646-301-7(X)) Quiet Vision Publishing.

—Anne of Green Gables. Howell, Troy, illus. 2002. 256p. (J). 12.99 (978-0-517-22111-2(X) , Gramercy) Random Hse. Value Publishing.

—Anne of Green Gables. 1998. (Children's Classics Ser.: No. 1). (Illus.). 256p. (J). (gr. 4-7). 6.99 (978-0-517-18968-9(2) , Children's Classics) Random Hse. Value Publishing.

—Anne of Green Gables. 2006. (Scholastic Classics Ser.). (Illus.). viii, 272p. (J). (gr. 9-12). 25.00 (978-0-531-16980-3(4) , Watts, Franklin) Scholastic Library Publishing.

—Anne of Green Gables. 2001. (Aladdin Classics Ser.). (Illus.). 480p. (J). pap. 5.99 (978-0-689-84622-9(3) , Aladdin) Simon & Schuster Children's Publishing.

—Anne of Green Gables. McKowen, Scott, illus. 2004. (Unabridged Classics Ser.). 304p. 9.95 (978-1-4027-1451-1(3)) Sterling Publishing Co., Inc.

—Anne of Green Gables. 2001. (gr. 3-6). lib. bdg. 11.80 (978-0-613-63175-4(7)); (gr. 5-8). lib. bdg. 13.00 (978-0-613-66688-6(7)) Tandem Library Bks.

—Anne of Green Gables. 1999. (Avonlea Ser.: No. 1). (YA). (gr. 5-8). 23.95 (978-0-8057-8090-1(4) , Macmillan Reference USA) Thomson Gale.

—Anne of Green Gables. Fernandez, Laura & Jacobson, Rick, illus. 2000. (Avonlea Ser.: No. 1). 328p. (J). (gr. 5-8). 24.95 (978-0-88776-515-5(7)) Tundra Bks., Inc./Livres Toundra, Inc. CAN. *Dist:* Random Hse., Inc.

—Anne of Green Gables. MQ Publications Staff, ed. 1998. (Little Brown Notebooks Ser.). (Illus.). 256p. (978-1-84072-063-1(8)) Watson-Guptill Pubns., Inc.

—Anne of Green Gables. 2001. (Children's Classics). (ENG.). 288p. (J). pap. (978-1-85326-139-8(4)) Wordsworth Editions, Ltd.

—Anne of Green Gables. Corvino, Lucy, illus. 2005. (Classic Starts Ser.). 160p. 4.95 (978-1-4027-1130-5(1)) Sterling Publishing Co., Inc.

—Anne of Green Gables. l.t. ed. 2006. (ENG.). pap. ***978-1-4068-3174-0(3)*** Echo Library.

—Anne of Green Gables. Stemach, Jerry, ed. Ham, Jeff, illus. l.t. ed. 2002. 150.00 (978-1-58702-021-6(1)); 2000. 50.00 (978-1-58702-502-0(7)) Johnston, Don Inc.

—Anne of Green Gables. 1998. (Avonlea Ser.). 252p. (YA). (gr. 5-8). reprint ed. (978-1-55109-013-9(9)) Nimbus Publishing, Ltd.

—Anne of Green Gables. 1998. 310p. (YA). (gr. 5-8). reprint ed. lib. bdg. 25.00 (978-1-58287-014-4(4)) North Bks.

—Anne of Green Gables. l.t. ed. 2000. (Anne of Green Gables Ser.: Vol. 1). 294p. (gr. 5-8). pap. 17.95 (978-1-57646-302-4(8)) Quiet Vision Publishing.

—Anne of Green Gables. rev. ed. 2002. (Scholastic Classic Ser.). 400p. (J). pap. 4.99 (978-0-439-29577-2(7)) Scholastic, Inc.

—Anne of Green Gables, 100th Anniversary Edition. 2008. 19.95 ***978-0-399-15478-2(7)*** , Putnam Adult) Penguin Group (USA) Inc.

—Anne of Ingleside. 2000. (Avonlea Ser.: No. 10). (YA). (gr. 5-8). 23.95 (978-0-8488-0890-7(8)) Amereon LTD.

—Anne of Ingleside, Vol. 6. 1999. 384p. (J). pap. 3.99 (978-0-14-036801-7(9) , Putnam Juvenile) Penguin Group (USA) Inc.

—Anne of the Island. Date not set. mass mkt. (978-0-8125-6563-8(0) , Tor Bks.) Doherty, Tom Assocs., LLC.

—Anne of the Island. 2006. (ENG.). pap. (***978-1-4068-2171-0(3)***); pap. (***978-1-4068-3175-7(1)***) Echo Library.

—Anne of the Island. 2006. (ENG.). 102.99 (***978-1-4219-3295-8(4)***) IndyPublish.com.

—Anne of the Island. 2004. reprint ed. pap. 1.99 (978-1-4192-0718-1(0)); pap. 30.95 (978-1-4179-0885-1(8)) Kessinger Publishing, LLC.

—Anne of the Island. (Twelve-Point Ser.). 2001. 240p. lib. bdg. 25.00 (978-1-58287-157-8(4)); 2004. 396p. 26.00 (978-1-58287-640-5(1)) North Bks.

—Anne of the Island. abr. ed. 1998. (Avonlea Ser.: No. 4). 304p. (J). (gr. 5-8). pap. 4.99 (978-0-14-036777-5(2) , Puffin) Penguin Group (USA) Inc.

—Anne of the Island. 2000. (Anne of Green Gables Ser.: Vol. No. 3). (gr. 5-8). 182p. 24.95 (978-1-57646-309-3(5)); 182p. pap. 14.99 (978-1-57646-308-6(7)); 336p. pap. 19.99 (978-1-57646-310-9(9)) Quiet Vision Publishing.

—Anne of the Island. 2001. (gr. 7-12). lib. bdg. 30.40 (978-0-613-79774-0(4)) Tandem Library Bks.

—Anne of the Island Book & Charm. 2005. (Charming Classics). 304p. (J). pap. 6.99 (978-0-06-075859-2(7) , Harper Festival) HarperCollins Pubs.

—Anne of Windy Willows, Vol. 4. 1999. 336p. (J). pap. 3.99 (978-0-14-036800-0(0) , Putnam Juvenile) Penguin Group (USA) Inc.

—Anne's House of Dreams. l.t. ed. 1999. (Avonlea Ser.: No. 5). 364p. (YA). (gr. 5-8). lib. bdg. 34.95 (978-1-58118-048-0(9) , 22517) LRS.

—Anne's House of Dreams, Vol. 5. 1999. 320p. (J). 3.99 (978-0-14-036799-7(3) , Putnam Juvenile) Penguin Group (USA) Inc.

—Anne's House of Dreams. 2000. (Anne of Green Gables Ser.: Vol. No. 5). (gr. 5-8). 182p. 24.95 (978-1-57646-313-0(3)); 182p. pap. 14.99 (978-1-57646-312-3(5)); 336p. pap. 19.99 (978-1-57646-314-7(1)) Quiet Vision Publishing.

—The Complete Anne of Green Gables: Anne of Green Gables; Anne of the Island; Anne of Avonlea; Anne of Windy Poplars; Anne's House of Dreams; Anne of Ingleside; Rainbow Valley; Rilla of Ingleside, 8 vols. gif. ed. 1998. (J). (gr. 4-7). mass mkt. 40.43 (978-0-553-60941-7(6) , Starfire) Random Hse. Children's Bks.

—Dreams, Schemes & Mysteries, Bk. 4. 2004. (Story Girl#8482; Ser.). (Illus.). 112p. (J). pap. 4.99 (978-0-310-70601-4(7)) Zonderkidz.

—The Golden Road. 2000. (Sara Stanley of Avonlea Ser.: Vol. 2). 180p. 24.99 (978-1-57646-317-8(6)); 198p. pap. 12.99 (978-1-57646-316-1(8)); 328p. 31.95 (978-1-57646-319-2(2)); 328p. pap. 19.99 (978-1-57646-318-5(4)) Quiet Vision Publishing.

—Kilmeny of the Orchard. 2004. 100p. (YA). pap. 7.95 (978-1-57646-894-4(1)) Quiet Vision Publishing.

—Mary Engelbreit's Classic Library: Anne of Green Gables. Engelbreit, Mary, illus. 2008. (Mary Engelbreit's Classic Library). 464p. (J). 9.99 (***978-0-06-008138-6(4)*** , Harper Festival) HarperCollins Pubs.

—Midnight Madness & Mayhem. Griffin, Jim, illus. 2005. (Story Girl Ser.). 112p. (J). (gr. 3-7). pap. 4.99 (978-0-310-70861-2(3)) Zonderkidz.

—Rainbow Valley. 2004. reprint ed. 210p. pap. 24.95 (978-1-4191-4385-4(9)); pap. 1.99 (978-1-4192-4385-1(3)) Kessinger Publishing, LLC.

—Rainbow Valley. 2005. (Twelve-Point Ser.). lib. bdg. 25.00 (978-1-58287-333-6(X)); lib. bdg. 26.00 (978-1-58287-825-6(0)) North Bks.

—Rainbow Valley. 2004. 184p. (YA). pap. 8.95 (978-1-57646-890-6(9)) Quiet Vision Publishing.

—Rilla of Ingleside. 2002. (ENG.). 272p. 19.99 (***978-1-4043-2710-8(X)***); pap. 14.99 (***978-1-4043-2711-5(8)***) IndyPublish.com.

—Rilla of Ingleside. 2004. 224p. (YA). pap. 10.95 (978-1-57646-891-3(7)) Quiet Vision Publishing.

—The Story Girl. Date not set. 22.95 (978-0-8488-2372-6(9)) Amereon LTD.

—The Story Girl. 2004. reprint ed. pap. 1.99 (978-1-4192-8361-1(8)) Kessinger Publishing, LLC.

—The Story Girl. 2005. (Twelve-Point Ser.). lib. bdg. 24.00 (978-1-58287-336-7(4)); lib. bdg. 25.00 (978-1-58287-828-7(5)) North Bks.

—The Story Girl. 2000. (Sara Stanley of Avonlea Ser.: Vol. vol 1). 178p. 24.95 (978-1-57646-322-2(2)); (Sara Stanley of Avonlea Ser.: Vol. vol 1). 220p. pap. 12.99 (978-1-57646-321-5(4)); (Sara Stanley of Avonlea: Vol. 1). 370p. pap. 21.99 (978-1-57646-323-9(0)) Quiet Vision Publishing.

—Summer Shenanigans, Bk. 3. 2004. (Story Girl Ser.: Bk. 3). (Illus.). 112p. (J). pap. 4.99 (978-0-310-70600-7(9)) Zonderkidz.

—Wedding Wishes & Woes. Griffin, Jim, illus. 2005. (Story Girl#8482; Ser.). 112p. (J). (gr. 3-7). pap. 4.99 (978-0-310-70860-5(5)) Zonderkidz.

—The Winds of Change. 2005. (Story Girl#8482; Ser.). (Illus.). 112p. (J). (gr. 3-7). pap. 4.99 (978-0-310-70862-9(1)) Zonderkidz.

Montgomery, L. M. & Greenwood, Barbara. Anne of Green Gables. Wood, Muriel, illus. rev. ed. 2001. (Avonlea Ser.: No. 1). 94p. (J). (gr. 5-8). pap. 9.95 (978-1-55013-431-5(0)) Key Porter Bks. CAN. *Dist:* Firefly Bks., Ltd.

Montgomery, L. M. & Hedge, Tricia. Anne of Green Gables, Level 2. 2nd abr. ed. 2000. (Bookworms Ser.). (Illus.). 64p. 6.50 (978-0-19-422965-4(3)) Oxford Univ. Pr., Inc.

Peterson. Anne of Green Gables. 1999. (Avonlea Ser.: No. 1). 32p. (YA). (gr. 5-8). pap. 4.95 (978-0-06-443535-2(0)) HarperCollins Pubs.

PRINCES AND PRINCESSES

Ariganello, Lisa. Henry the Navigator: Prince of Portuguese Exploration. 2006. (In the Footsteps of Explorers Ser.). (Illus.). 32p. (J). (gr. 3-9). (978-0-7787-2433-9(6)); pap. (978-0-7787-2469-8(7)) Crabtree Publishing Co.

Billinghurst, Jane. Growing up Royal: Life in the Shadow of the British Throne. 2001. (Illus.). 176p. (J). (gr. 3-7). 22.95 (978-1-55037-623-4(3)); pap. 12.95 (978-1-55037-622-7(5)) Annick Pr., Ltd. CAN. *Dist:* Firefly Bks., Ltd.

Bulloch, Ivan. A Princess. James, Diane, illus. rev. ed. 2004. (I Wish I Were Ser.). 24p. (ps-2). (J). pap. 7.95 (978-1-58728-037-5(X)); 12.95 (978-1-58728-033-7(7)) T&N Children's Publishing. (Two Can Publishing).

Cabot, Meg. Princess Lessons. McLaren, Chesley, illus. 2003. (Princess Diaries). 144p. (J). (gr. 7 up). 12.99 (978-0-06-052677-1(7)) HarperCollins Pubs.

Dalmatian Press Staff. Annabelle: Princess Book to Color with Glitter Paints. 2002. (Illus.). 32p. (J). (ps-3). pap. 2.99 (978-1-57759-810-7(5)) Dalmatian Pr.

—Gabrielle: Princess Book to Color with Glitter Stickers. 2002. (Illus.). 48p. (J). (ps-3). pap. 2.99 (978-1-57759-808-4(3)) Dalmatian Pr.

—Isabel: Princess Book to Color with Glitter Crayons. 2002. (Illus.). 32p. (J). (ps-3). pap. 2.99 (978-1-57759-809-1(1)) Dalmatian Pr.

Davidson, Susanna & Daynes, Katie. Little Princess Treasury. 2006. 96p. (J). 7.99 (978-0-7945-1442-6(1) , Usborne) EDC Publishing.

Dorling Kindersley Publishing Staff, ed. Princess. 2005. (J). 16p. pap. 6.99 (978-0-7566-1133-0(4)); (Illus.). 12p. bds. 6.99 (978-0-7566-1017-3(6)) Dorling Kindersley Publishing, Inc.

—Sparkly Princess. 2005. (Illus.). 12p. (J). bds. 5.99 (978-0-7566-0996-2(8)) Dorling Kindersley Publishing, Inc.

Dougherty, Terri & Dougherty, Denis. Prince William. 2001. (People in the News Ser.). (Illus.). 96p. (YA). (gr. 6-9). 32.45 (978-1-56006-982-9(1) , Lucent Bks.) Thomson Gale.

English Heritage Staff. My Life as a Princess. 2005. (Illus.). 32p. pap. 19.95 (978-1-85074-984-4(1)) English Heritage GBR. *Dist:* Brown, David Bk. Co., The.

Everett, Felicity & Rawson, Christopher. Stories of Princes & Princesses. 2004. (Young Reading Ser.). (Illus.). 48p. (J). (gr. 2 up). pap. 5.95 (978-0-7945-0449-6(3) , Usborne) EDC Publishing.

Fernandes, Lindsay, ed. Princess: The Essential Guide. 2003. (Disney Princess Ser.). (Illus.). 48p. (J). pap. 12.99 (978-0-7894-9830-4(8)) Dorling Kindersley Publishing, Inc.

Grosset and Dunlap Staff & Noble, Marty. Real Life Princesses. Jarnow, Jill, ed. 2001. (Sticker Styles Ser.). (Illus.). 16p. (J). (ps-3). pap. 4.99 (978-0-448-42465-1(7) , Grosset & Dunlap) Penguin Group (USA) Inc.

Hansen, Joyce. African Princess: The Amazing Lives of Africa's Royal Women. McGaw, Laurie, illus. 2004. 48p. (gr. 3-17). 16.99 (978-0-7868-5116-4(3)) Hyperion Bks. for Children.

Klutz Press Staff. Make Your Own Itty-Bitty Princesses. 2005. (Illus.). 32p. (J). (gr. 3 up). 9.95 (978-1-59174-277-7(3)) Klutz.

Landau, Elaine. Prince William: W. O. W., William of Wales. 2002. (Gateway Biography Ser.). (Illus.). 48p. (gr. 2-4). lib. bdg. 23.90 (978-0-7613-2120-0(9) , Millbrook Pr.) Lerner Publishing Group.

Lilly, Melinda. Princess. 2002. (Illus.). 32p. (J). lib. bdg. 26.60 (978-1-58952-231-2(1)) Rourke Publishing, LLC.

McCracken, Kristin. Prince William. 2000. (High Interest Bks.). (Illus.). 48p. (J). (gr. 7-12). 23.00 (978-0-516-23325-3(4)); pap. 6.95 (978-0-516-23525-7(7)) Scholastic Library Publishing. (Children's Pr.).

McDonnell, Peter. The Last Princess. 2005. (Illus.). 16p. (***978-0-7367-2910-9(0)***) Zaner-Bloser, Inc.

My Dolly Dressing Book of Princesses. 2002. 16p. (J). pap. 2.98 (978-0-7525-8045-6(0)) Parragon, Inc.

Priddy, Roger. Sticker Activity Fun Princess. 2007. 48p. (J). bds. 3.95 (978-0-312-49919-8(1) , Priddy Bks.) St. Martin's Pr.

Random House Disney Staff. The Big Book of Princesses. 2007. (Giant Coloring Book Ser.). (Illus.). 40p. (J). (ps-2). pap. 9.99 (***978-0-375-84726-4(X)*** , Golden/Disney) Random Hse. Children's Bks.

Rissik, Maureen. Princess: A Precious Gift to Unlock & Treasure. 1999. (Illus.). 24p. (J). (ps-3). pap. 9.95 (978-0-7624-0539-8(2) , Running Pr. Kids) Running Pr. Bk. Pubs.

Silver Dolphin en Español Staff, ed. Libro de actividades con plantillas: Disney Princess: Disney Princess Stencil. 2007. (Illus.). 20p. (J). bds. 12.95 (***978-970-718-434-3(5)*** , Silver Dolphin en Español) Advanced Marketing, S. de R. L. de C. V. MEX. *Dist:* Perseus Distribution.

Theisen, Gordon. The Mystery of Anastasia Romanov. 2001. (History Channel History Guides Ser.). (Illus.). 40p. (J). pap. 9.99 (978-0-86730-846-4(X)) Lebhar-Friedman Bks.

Wilding, Valerie. Real Princesses: An Inside Look at the Royal Life. 2007. (Illus.). 64p. (J). (gr. 2-6). 16.95 (***978-0-8027-9675-2(3)***) Walker & Co.

Wyborny, Sheila. Prince William. 2002. (Famous People Ser.). (Illus.). 48p. (J). (gr. 3-5). 26.20 (978-0-7377-1401-2(8) , Kidhaven) Thomson Gale.

PRINCES AND PRINCESSES—FICTION

Abbott, Wes, illus. & creator. Dogby Walks Alone. Abbott, Wes, creator. 2006. 192p. pap. 9.99 (978-1-59816-582-1(8) , Tokyopop Adult) TOKYOPOP, Inc.

Abel, Heather & McKnight, Gillian. To Catch a Prince. 2005. 192p. (YA). 14.95 (978-0-689-87733-9(1)) Simon & Schuster Children's Publishing.

Aber, Linda Williams. Princess & the Pauper Jr. Novelization. 2004. (Barbie Ser.). (Illus.). 80p. (J). (ps-3). mass mkt. 3.99 (978-0-439-63600-1(0)) Scholastic, Inc.

Abril, Paco. Sois Vosotros los Reyes Magos? Torcida, María Luisa, illus. Tr. of Are You the Three Kings?. (SPA.). 24p. (J). 5.56 (978-84-246-5411-5(0)) La Galera, S.A. Editorial ESP. *Dist:* Lectorum Pubns., Inc.

Ademola, Lady Kofo. Princess Corn. 1999. (Illus.). 10p. pap. (978-978-2601-95-7(0)) Malthouse Press Ltd, Nigeria.

The Adventures of Marc John Jefferies: The Missing Princess. l.t. ed. 2004. (Illus.). 110p. (YA). per. (978-0-9747218-3-5(2) , 100, Young Women Programming) Young Women Bks.

Aggs, Patrice, illus. The Kingfisher Treasury of Princess Stories. 2003. (Kingfisher Treasury of Stories Ser.). 160p. (J). (gr. k-3). pap. 5.95 (978-0-7534-5633-0(8) , Kingfisher) Houghton Mifflin Co. Trade & Reference Div.

Alberto, Daisy. Barbie as the Island Princess. 2007. (Step into Reading Ser.). (Illus.). 32p. (J). (ps-2). 3.99 (***978-0-375-84353-2(1)***); lib. bdg. 11.99 (***978-0-375-94353-9(6)***) Random Hse. Children's Bks. (Random Hse. Bks. for Young Readers).

Alex Toys Staff. Everything... Princess! My First Tiara & Gemstone Activity Book. Silver-Thompson, Pattie, illus. 2007. (Alex Toys Ser.). 40p. (J). (ps-1). 14.99 (***978-0-316-06520-7(X)***) Little, Brown Bks. for Young Readers.

Alexander, Lloyd. The Castle of Llyr. 3rd rev. ed. 2006. (Chronicles of Prydain Ser.: Bk. 3). 208p. (J). (gr. 5 up). pap. 5.99 (978-0-8050-8050-6(3) , Holt, Henry & Co. Bks. For Young Readers) Holt, Henry & Co.

Alexander, Sy. Pinksta & the Polka Dotted-Pinstriped-Pants-Wearing Princess. Young, Aviance, illus. 2005. (J). per. 9.00 (978-0-9655726-2-0(5)) Proud 2-B Me Publishing!.

Allchin, Rosalind. The Frog Princess. Allchin, Rosalind, illus. 2001. (Illus.). 32p. (J). (gr. k-3). (978-1-55337-000-0(7)) Kids Can Pr., Ltd.

—Frog Princess. 2003. (gr. k-3). lib. bdg. 14.10 (978-0-613-89644-3(0)) Tandem Library Bks.

—The Frog Princess. ed. 2004. (Illus.). (J). (gr. k-3). spiral bd. (978-0-616-14557-9(8)) Canadian National Institute for the Blind/Institut National Canadien pour les Aveugles.

Allchin, Rosalind, illus. The Frog Princess. 2003. 32p. (J). (gr. k-3). (978-1-55337-526-5(2)) Kids Can Pr., Ltd.

Alley, R. W., illus. The Prince's Tooth Is Loose. 2005. (I'm Going to Read Ser.). 28p. (J). (ps-ps). 11.95 (978-1-4027-2722-1(4)) Sterling Publishing Co., Inc.

Alonso, Fernando. Las Estrellas y la Princesa Liwayway (Princess Liwayway & the Stars) (Superbks./Superlibros). (Illus.). 16p. (J). (gr. k-3). pap. 6.95 (978-0-88272-499-7(1)) Santillana USA Publishing Co., Inc.

Amery, H. & Cartwright, S. The Tournament. 2004. (First Stories Ser.). 16p. (J). pap. 4.95 (978-0-7945-0520-2(1)); lib. bdg. 12.95 (978-1-58086-571-5(2)) EDC Publishing.

Andersen, Hans Christian. The Princess & the Pea. Oberdieck, Bernhard, illus. 2007. (Classic Fairy Tale Collection). 24p. (J). (ps-2). 14.95 (978-1-4027-3065-8(9)) Sterling Publishing Co., Inc.

—La Princesse au Petit Pois. 1999. (FRE., Illus.). 32p. (J). (ps-3). 13.95 (978-2-09-202111-8(7)) Nathan, Fernand FRA. *Dist:* Distribooks, Inc.

Andersen, Hans Christian & Davidson, Susanna. Princess & Pea. 2004. 48p. (J). (gr. 2 up). 8.99 (978-0-7945-0812-8(X) , Usborne) EDC Publishing.

Andersen, Hans Christian & Sims, Lesley. Snow Queen. 2004. 64p. (J). (gr. 2 up). 8.99 (978-0-7945-0717-6(4) , Usborne) EDC Publishing.

Anderson, Jodi Lynn. May Bird, Warrior Princess, Bk. 3. 2007. 256p. (J). (gr. 5-9). 16.99 (***978-0-689-86925-9(8)*** , Atheneum) Simon & Schuster Children's Publishing.

Anderson, Ken. The Prince & Princess in Happiness Valley. Woychuk, N. A., ed. Bolt, Eunice, illus. 2000. 58p. (J). (gr. 4-7). pap. 3.50 (978-1-880960-44-8(3)) Scripture Memory Fellowship International.

Andreasen, Dan, et al. Rose Red & the Bear Prince. 2000. (Illus.). 40p. (J). (ps-4). 16.95 (978-0-06-027966-0(4)); 16.89 (978-0-06-027967-7(2)) HarperCollins Pubs.

Ant, Exupery. Giorno con il Piccolo Principe. pap. 13.95 (978-88-451-2269-9(7)) Fabbri - RCS Libri ITA. *Dist:* Distribooks, Inc.

—Journee avec le Petit Prince. pap. 10.95 (978-2-07-054268-0(8)) Gallimard, Editions FRA. *Dist:* Distribooks, Inc.

—L apprends a compter avec Le. pap. 10.95 (978-2-07-054270-3(X)) Gallimard, Editions FRA. *Dist:* Distribooks, Inc.

—Piccolo Principe el Suio. pap. 13.95 (978-88-451-2266-8(2)) Fabbri - RCS Libri ITA. *Dist:* Distribooks, Inc.

Apperley, Dawn. Princess Rosebud: How to Be a Perfect Princess. 2006. (Illus.). 24p. (J). 14.99 (978-0-7641-5938-1(0)) Barron's Educational Series, Inc.

—Princess Rosebud: Perfectly Perfect Princess. 2007. 32p. (J). (gr. k-1). 14.99 (978-0-7641-6033-2(8)) Barron's Educational Series, Inc.

Arias, Carlos Ballesteros. The Magic Forest. 2006. (J). pap. 8.00 (***978-0-8059-7022-7(3)***) Dorrance Publishing Co., Inc.

Arnold, Tedd. More Parts. 2003. (Illus.). 32p. (J). pap. 5.99 (978-0-14-250149-8(2) , Puffin) Penguin Group (USA) Inc.

—More Parts. Arnold, Tedd, illus. 2001. (Illus.). 32p. (J). (ps-3). 16.99 (978-0-8037-1417-5(3) , Dial) Penguin Group (USA) Inc.

—The Twin Princes. Arnold, Tedd, illus. 2007. (Illus.). 32p. (J). (ps-2). 16.99 (978-0-8037-2696-3(1) , Dial) Penguin Group (USA) Inc.

—The Twin Princes. 2007. (Illus.). (J). (***978-1-4287-3971-0(8)*** , Dial) Penguin Group (USA) Inc.

Arredondo, Ines. Historia - Princesa. (SPA.). (J). 12.95 (978-968-494-016-1(5) , CI0802) Centro de Informacion y Desarrollo de la Comunicacion y la Literatura MEX. *Dist:* AIMS International Bks., Inc., Lectorum Pubns., Inc.

Auch, Mary Jane & Auch, Herm. The Princess & the Pizza. 2002. (Illus.). 32p. (J). (gr. k-3). 6.95 (978-0-8234-1798-8(0)) Holiday Hse., Inc.

Auerbach, Annie. Cindy Big Hair: A Twisted (and Teased & Braided) Cinderella Story. Maxey, David, illus. 2005. 16p. (J). 12.95 (978-1-58117-387-1(3) , Intervisual/Piggy Toes) Dalmatian Pr.

Bailey, Sian. My Fairytale Princess Jigsaw Book: With Six 24-Piece Jigsaws. 2005. (Illus.). 14p. (J). (978-1-4050-4061-7(0) , Macmillan Children's Bks.) Pan Macmillan.

Baker, E. D. Dragon's Breath. 2003. 250p. (J). 15.95 (978-1-58234-858-2(8) , Bloomsbury Children) Bloomsbury Publishing.

—Dragon's Breath: Read-Along/Homework Pack. unabr. ed. 2005. (YA). (gr. 5-8). 92.70 incl. audio (978-1-4193-3563-1(4) , 42041) Recorded Bks., LLC.

—The Frog Princess. (J). 2002. 200p. (gr. 3-9). 15.95 (978-1-58234-799-8(9)); 2004. 224p. reprint ed. pap. 6.95 (978-1-58234-923-7(1)) Bloomsbury Publishing. (Bloomsbury Children).

—Once upon a Curse: More Tales of the Frog Princess. 2004. (Illus.). 225p. (J). 15.95 (978-1-58234-892-6(8) , Bloomsbury Children) Bloomsbury Publishing.

—The Salamander Spell. 2007. (Tales of the Frog Princess Ser.). 250p. (J). (gr. 3-7). 16.95 (***978-1-59990-018-6(1)*** , Bloomsbury Children) Bloomsbury Publishing.

—Tales of the Frog Princess, Set. 2007. (Tales of the Frog Princess Ser.). 784p. (J). pap. 20.85 (***978-1-59990-152-7(8)*** , Bloomsbury Children) Bloomsbury Publishing.

Baker, Liza. Disney's 5 Minute Princess Stories. Cuddy, Robbin, illus. 2001. 48p. (J). (ps-2). 12.99 (978-0-7868-3300-9(9)) Disney Pr.

Balague, Lin & Long, Robert. La Dama y el Leon. 2000. (Cuentos y Leyendas Bilingues Ser.).Tr. of Princess & the Lion. (ENG & SPA., Illus.). (J). pap. (978-0-658-01015-6(8)) McGraw-Hill/Contemporary.

Balducci, Rita. Disney Princess Storybook & Movie Projector: Season of Enchantment: Jeweled Collector's Edition. 2007. (RD Innovative Book & Player Format Ser.). 48p. (J). 24.99 (***978-0-7944-1355-2(2)***) Reader's Digest Assn., Inc., The.

Balducci, Rita. Princess Treasury: A Collection of Special Moments from Your Favorite Princess Stories. 2003. (Disney Carryalong(R) Treasuries Ser.). (Illus.). 12p. (J). bds. 14.99 (978-1-57584-979-9(8) , Reader's Digest Children's Bks.) Reader's Digest Children's Publishing, Inc.

Bar-El, Dan. Such a Prince. Manders, John, illus. 2007. 32p. (J). (ps-3). 16.00 (978-0-618-71468-1(5) , Clarion Bks.) Houghton Mifflin Co. Trade & Reference Div.

Barlow, Steve & Skidmore, Steve. Whizzard. 2002. (Tales of the Dark Forest Ser.). (Illus.). 256p. pap. 11.00 (978-0-00-710864-0(8)) HarperCollins Pubs. Ltd. GBR. *Dist:* Independent Pubs. Group.

Barnes, Susan. Kelly Karate: Discovers the Ice Princess. 2004. 138p. (J). (gr. 4-8). pap. 5.95 (978-0-9705777-3-3(7)) McBook Pubs., LLC.

Barnett, Gary W. Princess of the Lights: Fantasy Adventure. 2007. 324p. 29.95 (***978-0-595-68957-6(4)***) iUniverse, Inc.

Bateman, Teresa. The Princesses Have a Ball. Cravath, Lynne W., illus. 2002. 32p. (J). (gr. 2-5). 16.95 (978-0-8075-6626-8(8)) Whitman, Albert & Co.

—The Princesses Have a Ball. Cravath, Lynne, illus. 2005. (Albert Whitman Prairie Bks.). 32p. (J). (gr. 2-5). reprint ed. pap. 6.95 (978-0-8075-6628-2(4)) Whitman, Albert & Co.

—Traveling Tom & the Leprechaun. Potter, Mélisande, illus. 2007. 32p. (J). (ps-3). 16.95 (978-0-8234-1976-0(2)) Holiday Hse., Inc.

Baum, L. Frank. Magic of Oz. 2006. pap. 12.99 (***978-1-4280-2747-3(5)***) IndyPublish.com.

Beddor, Frank. Princess Alyss of Wonderland. Chien, Catia, illus. 2007. 30p. (J). (gr. 4). 19.99 (***978-0-8037-3251-3(1)*** , Dial) Penguin Group (USA) Inc.

Bell, Gillian. The Princess of Veryan. 2005. 263p. pap. 21.95 (978-1-4137-7982-0(4)) PublishAmerica, Inc.

Bell, Hilari. The Prophecy. 208p. (J). 2007. pap. 6.50 (***978-0-06-059945-4(6)*** , Eos); 2006. lib. bdg. 16.89 (978-0-06-059944-7(8)); 2006. (Illus.). 15.99 (978-0-06-059943-0(X)) HarperCollins Pubs.

Bell, Rebecca. Princess Sara. Bell, Rebecca, illus. 2005. 34p. per. 9.95 (***978-1-934138-07-6(X)***) Bouncing Ball Bks., Inc.

Benchmark Education Staff, compiled by. Measuring. 2006. spiral bd. 99.00 (***978-1-4108-7090-2(1)***) Benchmark Education Co.

Bergen, Lara. Dora's I Love You Book. Roper, Robert, illus. 2007. (Dora the Explorer Ser.). 12p. (J). bds. 7.99 (***978-1-4169-4716-5(7)*** , Simon Spotlight/Nickelodeon) Simon & Schuster Children's Publishing.

—The Enchanted Stables. Disney Storybook Artists Staff, illus. rev. ed. 2007. 112p. (ps-1). 14.99 (***978-1-4231-0478-0(1)***) Disney Pr.

—More 5-Minute Princess Stories: A Magical Collection of Princess Tales. Disney Storybook Artists Staff, illus. 2003. 50p. (J). (ps-2). 12.99 (978-0-7868-3470-9(6) , Disney Editions) Disney Pr.

—My Secret Diary by Cinderella. Disney Storybook Artists Staff, illus. 2006. (Disney Princess Ser.). 64p. (ps-2). 14.99 (978-0-7868-4943-7(6)) Disney Pr.

—Walt Disney's Cinderella. 2005. (Illus.). 96p. (ps-2). 12.99 (978-0-7868-3810-3(8)) Disney Pr.

Bergsma, Jody Lynn, et al. Dragon. Bergsma, Jody Lynn, illus. 1999. (Illus.). 32p. (ps-7). 15.95 (978-0-935699-17-3(1)) Illumination Arts Publishing Co., Inc.

Bernhardt, William. Princess Alice & the Dreadful Dragon. McGhee, Kerry, illus. 2007. 36p. (J). 19.95 (***978-1-930709-65-2(X)***) HAWK Publishing Group.

Bianchi, John. Princess Frownsalot. rev. ed. 2001. (Bug & Frogger Ser.). (Illus.). (J). 32p. 14.95 (978-1-894323-28-4(9)); 127p. pap. 4.95 (978-1-894323-25-3(4)) Pokeweed Pr. CAN. *Dist:* Fitzhenry & Whiteside, Ltd.

Birney, Betty G. The Princess & the Peabodys. 2007. 256p. (J). lib. bdg. 16.89 (****978-0-06-084721-0(2)***); (gr. 5 up). 15.99 (****978-0-06-084720-3(4)***) HarperCollins Pubs.

Bishop, Jennie & Henson, Susan. Life Lessons from the Princess & the Kiss. 2004. 8.99 (****978-0-940110-52-6(0)***) Life Action Publishing.

Blackaby, Susan. La Princesa del Guisante: Version del Cuento de los Hermanos Grimm. Delage, Charlene, illus. 2006. (Read-It! Readers en Espanol Ser.).Tr. of Princess & the Pea: A Retelling of the Grimm's Fairy Tale. (SPA.). 32p. (J). (ps-3). 19.95 (978-1-4048-1634-3(8)) Picture Window Bks.

Blair, Eric. La Bella Durmiente: Version del Cuento de los Hermanos Grimm. Ouren, Todd, illus. 2006. (Read-It! Readers en Espanol Ser.).Tr. of Sleeping Beauty: A Retelling of the Grimm's Fairy Tale. (SPA.). 32p. (J). (ps-3). 19.95 (978-1-4048-1639-8(9)) Picture Window Bks.

Blake-Brekke, Carri. Panuk, Princess & Prince. Melton, Jodi, illus. 2002. (J). pap. (978-0-9720549-1-1(X)) Mom's Pride Enterprises.

Boada, Francesc. Cinderella. Surges, James, tr. Fransoy, Monse, illus. 2001. (SPA & ENG.). 32p. (J). (ps-3). pap. 6.95 (978-0-8118-3090-4(X)) Chronicle Bks. LLC.

Bondoux, Anne-Laure. The Princetta. 2008. 448p. (YA). pap. 8.95 (****978-1-59990-098-8(X)*** , Bloomsbury Children) Bloomsbury Publishing.

—The Princetta. Bell, Anthea, tr. from FRE. 2006. 500p. (YA). 17.95 (978-1-58234-924-4(X) , Bloomsbury Children) Bloomsbury Publishing.

Bower, Tamara. How the Amazon Queen Fought the Prince of Egypt. Bower, Tamara, illus. 2005. (Illus.). 40p. (J). (gr. 2-6). 17.99 (978-0-689-84434-8(4) , Atheneum) Simon & Schuster Children's Publishing.

Bradley, Kimberly Brubaker. The Lacemaker & the Princess. 2007. 208p. (J). (gr. 3-7). 16.99 (978-1-4169-1920-9(1) , McElderry, Margaret K.) Simon & Schuster Children's Publishing.

Bray-Moffatt, Naia. Disney Princess Essential Guide. 2006. 48p. (J). 12.99 (978-0-7566-2499-6(1)) Dorling Kindersley Publishing, Inc.

Bredin, Henrietta & McEwen, Priscilla. The Prince & the Goosegirl: A Story with Activities Based on the Opera by Humperdinck. 2006. (Illus.). 30p. (J). (gr. k-4). reprint ed. pap. 17.00 (978-1-4223-5538-1(1)) DIANE Publishing Co.

Brewster, Hugh. Anastasia's Album: The Last Tsar's Youngest Daughter. 1999. 64p. (J). pap. 7.99 (978-0-7868-1395-7(4)) Disney Pr.

Brian, Kate. The Princess & the Pauper. 2004. 272p. (YA). reprint ed. mass mkt. 6.99 (978-0-689-87042-2(6) , Simon Pulse) Simon & Schuster Children's Publishing.

—The Princess & the Pauper. l.t. ed. 2003. 345p. (J). 22.95 (978-0-7862-6101-7(3) , Large Print Pr.) Thorndike Pr.

Brocklehurst, Ruth. Princess Things to Make & Do. 2005. (Illus.). 32p. (J). pap. 6.95 (978-0-7945-0908-8(8) , Usborne) EDC Publishing.

Brookes, Diane. Kailee & the Frog Prince. Brookes, Shelley, illus. 1999. 16p. (J). (ps-5). pap. (978-0-9683640-2-4(0)) Raven Rock Publishing.

Brooks, Amy. Princess Polly's Gay Winter. 2004. reprint ed. pap. 15.95 (978-1-4191-4299-4(2)); pap. 1.99 (978-1-4192-4299-1(7)) Kessinger Publishing, LLC.

—Princess Polly's Playmates. 2004. reprint ed. pap. 19.95 (978-1-4191-4300-7(X)); pap. 1.99 (978-1-4192-4300-4(4)) Kessinger Publishing, LLC.

Brooks, Clint. A Cypress Creek Kid's Letters to His Princess. 2004. 197p. per. 13.95 (978-1-59453-540-6(X)) Airleaf Publishing & Bookselling.

Brothers Grimm Staff. The Frog Prince/ el principe Sapo. 2004. (Illus.). (J). (978-1-933530-21-5(9)) Bingo Bks., Inc.

—Sleeping Beauty/la bella Durmiente. 2004. (Illus.). (J). (978-1-933530-18-5(9)) Bingo Bks., Inc.

Brundage, Frances, illus. Cinderella: A Fairy Story. 2004. reprint ed. pap. 15.95 (978-1-4179-8713-9(8)) Kessinger Publishing, LLC.

Brundage, Jerome. The Princess & the Bear: Book I: the Battle for Aradam. 2007. (ENG.). 148p. per. 19.95 (****978-1-4241-6346-5(3)***) PublishAmerica, Inc.

Bryant, Ann. Dancing Princess. Benton, Tim, illus. 2006. 112p. (J). pap. 4.99 (978-0-7945-1297-2(6) , Usborne) EDC Publishing.

Bryant, Megan E. Berry Princess. MJ Illustrations, M. J. Illustrations, illus. 2005. (Strawberry Shortcake Ser.). 12p. (J). (ps-2). bds. 9.99 (978-0-448-43954-9(9) , Grosset & Dunlap) Penguin Group (USA) Inc.

Burchett, Jan, et al. Exile. 2006. (Lady Grace Mysteries, from the Daybookes of Lady Grace Cavendish Ser.). 208p. (J). (gr. 3-7). 7.95 (978-0-385-73322-9(4)); lib. bdg. 9.99 (978-0-385-90341-7(3)) Random Hse. Children's Bks. (Delacorte Bks. for Young Readers).

Burkart, Jeffrey E., retold by. The Hidden Prince. 2003. (Illus.). 32p. (J). 9.99 incl. audio compact disk (978-0-570-07174-7(7)) Concordia Publishing Hse.

Burke, David. Beauty & the Beast (English to French - Level 3) Learn FRENCH Through Fairy Tales. 2007. (Learn French Through Fairy Tales Ser.). (ENG & FRE., Illus.). (J). per. 14.95 incl. audio compact disk (****978-1-891888-87-8(0)***) Slangman Publishing.

—Beauty & the Beast (English to German - Level 3) Learn GERMAN Through Fairy Tales. 2007. (Learn German Through Fairy Tales Ser.). (ENG & GER., Illus.). (J). per. 14.95 incl. audio compact disk (****978-1-891888-88-5(9)***) Slangman Publishing.

—Beauty & the Beast (English to Italian - Level 3) Learn ITALIAN Through Fairy Tales. 2007. (Learn Italian Through Fairy Tales Ser.). (ENG & ITA., Illus.). (J). per. 14.95 incl. audio compact disk (****978-1-891888-89-2(7)***) Slangman Publishing.

—Beauty & the Beast (English to Spanish - Level 3) Learn SPANISH Through Fairy Tales. 2007. (Learn Spanish Through Fairy Tales Ser.). (ENG & SPA., Illus.). (J). per. 14.95 incl. audio compact disk (****978-1-891888-86-1(2)***) Slangman Publishing.

Burke, David, adapted by. Beauty & the Beast (English to Chinese - Level 3) Learn MANDARIN CHINESE Through Fairy Tales. 2007. (Learn Chinese Through Fairy Tales Ser.). (ENG & CHI., Illus.). (J). per. 14.95 incl. audio compact disk (****978-1-891888-91-5(9)***) Slangman Publishing.

Burnett, Frances Hodgson. A Little Princess. McKowen, Scott, illus. 2004. (Unabridged Classics Ser.). 208p. 9.95 (978-1-4027-1454-2(8)) Sterling Publishing Co., Inc.

—A Little Princess: The Story of Sara Crewe. 2nd ed. 2000. (Oxford Bookworms Ser.). (Illus.). 64p. 6.50 (978-0-19-422944-9(0)) Oxford Univ. Pr., Inc.

—A Little Princess: The Story of Sara Crewe. 2001. (Classics Ser.). (Illus.). 304p. (J). (gr. 3-7). pap. 4.99 (978-0-689-84407-2(7) , Aladdin) Simon & Schuster Children's Publishing.

—A Little Princess: The Story of Sara Crewe. 2003. (ps-2). lib. bdg. 23.40 (978-0-613-83351-6(1)) Tandem Library Bks.

—The Lost Prince. (J). 25.95 (978-0-8488-0691-0(3)) Amereon LTD.

—La Petit Princesse.Tr. of Little Princess. (FRE.). (J). pap. 12.95 (978-2-07-056710-2(9)) Gallimard, Editions FRA. *Dist:* Distribooks, Inc.

—Petite Princess. pap. 19.95 (978-2-07-051994-1(5)) Gallimard, Editions FRA. *Dist:* Distribooks, Inc.

—La Princesita. 2000. Tr. of Little Princess. (SPA., Illus.). 142p. (J). 11.95 (978-84-406-6196-8(7)) Ediciones B ESP. *Dist:* Distribooks, Inc.

—Sara, die Kleine Prinzessin.Tr. of Little Princess. pap. 21.95 (978-3-423-70196-9(X)); 2000. (GER.). (J). pap. 13.95 (978-3-423-70176-1(5)) Deutscher Taschenbuch Verlag GmbH & Co KG DEU. *Dist:* Distribooks, Inc.

Butcher, Nancy. Beauty. 2005. 168p. (YA). (gr. 7-12). lib. bdg. 15.60 (978-1-4176-6053-7(8)) Tandem Library Bks.

Cabal, Graciela Beatriz. Las Hadas Brillan en la Oscuridad. Balzola, Sofia, illus. 3rd ed. 2000. (Tucan Ser.). (SPA.). 58p. (J). (gr. 2-4). (978-84-236-5500-7(8) , ED31150) Edebé ESP. *Dist:* Baker & Taylor Bks., Lectorum Pubns., Inc.

Cabot, Meg. In Love. (Princess Diaries: Vol. 3). (YA). 2003. 288p. (gr. 6 up). pap. 6.99 (978-0-06-447280-7(9)); 2002. 272p. (gr. 7 up). mass mkt. 5.99 (978-0-06-052568-2(1)); 2002. 240p. (gr. 7 up). 16.99 (978-0-06-029467-0(1)) HarperCollins Pubs.

—In Love, Vol. 3. 2004. (Princess Diaries: Vol. 3). 288p. (J). (gr. 7 up). pap. 38.00 incl. audio (978-0-8072-2284-3(4) , Listening Library) Random Hse. Audio Publishing Group.

—In Love. 2002. (Princess Diaries: Vol. 3). (gr. 7-12). lib. bdg. 15.30 (978-0-613-57919-3(4)) Tandem Library Bks.

—In Love. 2003. (Princess Diaries: Vol. 3). (YA). 24.95 (978-0-7862-4844-5(0)) Thorndike Pr.

—Journal d'une Princesse. (FRE.). pap. 13.95 (978-2-01-321853-5(2)) Hachette Groupe Livre FRA. *Dist:* Distribooks, Inc.

—Party Princess. (Princess Diaries: Vol. 7). (J). 2007. 368p. pap. 6.99 (978-0-06-072455-9(2) , Harper Trophy); 2006. 304p. 16.99 (978-0-06-072453-5(6)); 2006. 304p. lib. bdg. 17.89 (978-0-06-072454-2(4)) HarperCollins Pubs.

—Party Princess. l.t. rev. ed. 2007. (Princess Diaries: Vol. 7). 335p. (YA). 23.95 (****978-0-7862-9273-8(3)***) Thorndike Pr.

—Perfect Princess. McLaren, Chesley, illus. 2004. (Princess Diaries). 160p. (J). (gr. 7 up). 12.99 (978-0-06-052679-5(3)) HarperCollins Pubs.

—The Princess Diaries. (Princess Diaries: Vol. I). 2008. 256p. (J). pap. 7.99 (****978-0-06-147993-9(4)*** , HarperTeen); 2000. 240p. (J). (gr. 7 up). lib. bdg. 17.89 (978-0-06-029210-2(5)); 2001. 320p. (YA). (gr. 7 up). pap. 6.99 (978-0-380-81402-2(1) , Harper Trophy); 2000. (Illus.). 240p. (J). (gr. 7 up). 16.99 (978-0-380-97848-9(2)); Vols. 1-3, Set. 2006. (J). pap., pap. 19.99 (978-0-06-115389-1(3) , HarperTeen) HarperCollins Pubs.

—The Princess Diaries. unabr. ed. 2004. (Princess Diaries: Vol. I). 240p. (J). (gr. 7 up). pap. 38.00 incl. audio (978-0-8072-0669-0(5) , Listening Library) Random Hse. Audio Publishing Group.

—The Princess Diaries. 2001. (Princess Diaries: Vol. I). (gr. 7-12). lib. bdg. 15.30 (978-0-613-37165-0(8)); (Illus.). (J). (978-0-606-21844-3(0)) Tandem Library Bks.

—The Princess Diaries. l.t. ed. 2002. (Princess Diaries: Vol. I). 325p. (J). 24.95 (978-0-7862-4058-6(X)) Thomson Gale.

—The Princess Diaries Box Set Vols. I-III: Princess in Love; Princess in the Spotlight; The Princess Diaries. 2003. (Princess Diaries). 304p. (gr. 7 up). pap. 19.99 (978-0-06-058745-1(8)) HarperCollins Pubs.

—The Princess Diaries Collection, 2 bks. 2002. (Princess Diaries). (J). (gr. 7 up). pap. 11.98 (978-0-06-052382-4(4)) HarperCollins Pubs.

—Princess diaries, volume Ii: 2008. (Princess Diaries). 240p. (J). pap. 7.99 (****978-0-06-147994-6(2)*** , HarperTeen) HarperCollins Pubs.

—Princess diaries, volume Iii. 2008. (Princess Diaries). 240p. (J). pap. 7.99 (****978-0-06-147995-3(0)*** , HarperTeen) HarperCollins Pubs.

—The Princess Diaries, Volume IX: Princess Mia (international Edition) 2008. (Princess Diaries). 288p. (J). pap. 12.00 (****978-0-06-156819-0(8)*** , HarperTeen) HarperCollins Pubs.

—Princess in the Spotlight. 2001. (Princess Diaries: Vol. II). 240p. (J). (gr. 7 up). 16.99 (978-0-06-029465-6(5)) HarperCollins Pubs.

—Princess in the Spotlight, unabr. ed. 2004. (Princess Diaries: Vol. II). 272p. (J). (gr. 7 up). pap. 38.00 incl. audio (978-0-8072-1197-7(4) , S YA 332 SP, Listening Library) Random Hse. Audio Publishing Group.

—Princess in Training. (Princess Diaries: Vol. 6). (J). 2006. (Illus.). 320p. pap. 6.99 (978-0-06-009615-1(2) , Harper Trophy); 2005. 288p. (gr. 7 up). lib. bdg. 17.89 (978-0-06-009614-4(4)); 2005. (Illus.). 288p. (gr. 7 up). 16.99 (978-0-06-009613-7(6)) HarperCollins Pubs.

—Princess in Training. l.t. ed. 2005. (Princess Diaries: Vol. 6). 355p. (YA). (gr. 7-12). per. 22.95 (978-0-7862-7753-7(X) , Large Print Pr.) Thorndike Pr.

—Princess in Waiting. 2003. (Princess Diaries: Vol. 4). (Illus.). 240p. (J). (gr. 7 up). 16.99 (978-0-06-009607-6(1)) HarperCollins Pubs.

—Princess in Waiting. l.t. ed. 2003. (Princess Diaries: Vol. 4). 287p. (J). 25.95 (978-0-7862-5682-2(6)) Thorndike Pr.

—Princess Mia. 2008. (Princess Diaries: Vol. 9). 288p. (J). lib. bdg. 17.89 (****978-0-06-072462-7(5)***) HarperCollins Pubs.

—Princess on the Brink. (Princess Diaries: Vol. 8). (J). 2008. 288p. 16.99 (****978-0-06-072461-0(7));*** 2008. 272p. pap. 7.99 (****978-0-06-072460-3(9)*** , Harper Trophy); 2007. 256p. 16.99 (978-0-06-072456-6(0)); 2007. 256p. lib. bdg. 17.89 (978-0-06-072457-3(9)) HarperCollins Pubs.

—The Princess Present. 2004. (Princess Diaries: Vol. 6 1/2). 96p. (J). (gr. 7 up). 8.99 (978-0-06-075433-4(8)) HarperCollins Pubs.

—Project Princess. 2003. (Princess Diaries: Vol. 4 1/2). 64p. (J). (gr. 7 up). pap. 2.99 (978-0-06-057131-3(4)) HarperCollins Pubs.

—Project Princess. 2003. (Princess Diaries: Vol. 4 1/2). (gr. 7-12). lib. bdg. 10.65 (978-0-613-67515-4(0)) Tandem Library Bks.

—Sweet Sixteen Princess. 2006. (Princess Diaries: Vol. 7 1/2). 96p. (J). 8.99 (978-0-06-084716-6(6)) HarperCollins Pubs.

—Valentine Princess. 2006. (Princess Diaries). 96p. (J). 8.99 (978-0-06-084718-0(2) , HarperTeen) HarperCollins Pubs.

Calhoun, Dia. Avielle of Rhia. 2006. 400p. (J). 16.99 (978-0-7614-5320-8(2)) Cavendish, Marshall Corp.

Calvert, Pam. Princess Peepers. Mourning, Tuesday, illus. 2008. (J). (****978-0-7614-5437-3(3)***) Cavendish, Marshall Corp.

Camp, Lindsay & Ross, Tony. Midnight Feast. 2005. (Illus.). 32p. (J). (ps). pap. 9.99 (978-1-84270-489-9(3)) Andersen GBR. *Dist:* Independent Pubs. Group.

Cane, Rochelle & Mada Design Staff. My Little Pony: The Princess Promenade Storybook & Playset. 2006. 10p. (J). 15.99 (978-0-7944-1107-7(X)) Reader's Digest Assn., Inc., The.

Cannon, Sharyn. The Prince of Perfect. Wise, Noreen, ed. Crawford, K. Michael, illus. 2001. (Lemonade Collection). 54p. (J). (ps up). pap. 6.95 (978-1-58584-212-4(5)) Huckleberry Pr.

Cantin, Marc. Princesa Ana. Jarrie, Martin, illus. 2001. (Los Especiales de A la Orilla Del Viento Ser.). (SPA.). 31p. (J). (ps-ps). per. 15.25 (978-968-16-6081-9(1)) Fondo de Cultura Economica USA.

Carey, Janet Lee. Dragon's Keep. (Illus.). 320p. (YA). 2008. pap. 7.95 (****978-0-15-206401-3(X)*** , Magic Carpet Bks.); 2007. (gr. 6-10). 17.00 (978-0-15-205926-2(1)) Harcourt Children's Bks.

—Dragon's Keep. 2007. 302p. (J). (****978-1-4287-3929-1(7)***) Harcourt Trade Pubs.

Carey, Keelin. A Princess, a Tiger, & Other Deaf Tales. 2005. (Illus.). 50p. (J). pap. 7.95 (978-1-896764-90-0(8)) Second Story Pr. CAN. *Dist:* Orca Bk. Pubs. USA.

Carpenter, Ann. The Slumber Girls & the Mystical Dollhouse. 2006. (J). per. 8.99 (978-0-9771030-0-3(5)) Kidz By Dezign Pr., Inc.

Carter, Anne. No Missing Parts: And Other Stories about Real Princesses. 2004. 148p. (YA). (gr. 8 up). pap. 9.95 (978-0-88995-253-9(1)) Red Deer Pr. CAN. *Dist:* Fitzhenry & Whiteside, Ltd.

Cason, Sue. Dragon Trouble. Grimwood, Tracie, illus. 1999. (Supa Doopers Ser.). 64p. (J). (978-0-7608-3289-9(7)) Sundance/Newbridge Educational Publishing.

—Dragon Trouble. 1999. (gr. 3-6). lib. bdg. 12.60 (978-0-613-30364-4(4)) Tandem Library Bks.

Cassidy, Anne. The Crying Princess. Paine, Colin, illus. 2004. (Read-It! Readers Ser.). 32p. (C). (gr. k-3). 18.60 (978-1-4048-0053-3(0)) Picture Window Bks.

—Snow White. 2006. (First Fairy Tales Ser.). (Illus.). 32p. (J). (978-1-59771-074-9(1)) Sea-To-Sea Pubns.

Caveney, Philip. Sebastian Darke: Prince of Fools. 2008. 272p. (YA). (gr. 7). lib. bdg. 18.99 (****978-0-385-90465-0(7)*** , Delacorte Pr.) Dell Publishing.

Chambers, Mark, illus. Build Your Own Fairytale Castle: A Push-Out-and-Play Book. 2008. 12p. (J). bds. 8.95 (****978-0-385-61115-2(3)***) Transworld Publishers Ltd. GBR. *Dist:* Independent Pubs. Group.

Child, Lauren. The Princess & the Pea. Borland, Polly, photos by. 2006. (Illus.). 40p. (gr. k-17). 16.99 (978-0-7868-3886-8(8)) Hyperion Pr.

Chinchinian, Harry. The Princess & the Beggar. 1998. (Heather & Hally Brown Ser.). (Illus.). 152p. (J). (gr. 4-9). 16.95 (978-0-9653535-8-8(3)) Plum Tree Pr.

—The Princess & the Beggar II: Continuing Adventures. Chinchinian, Harry, illus. 2005. (Illus.). 176p. (J). lib. bdg. 18.95 (978-1-892476-11-1(8)) Plum Tree Pr.

Chiu, Harry. Enve Lopt Unfolded. 2007. 268p. per. 17.95 (****978-0-595-44707-7(4)***) iUniverse, Inc.

Chizuru, Mio. The Pirate & the Princess Volume 1: the Timelight Stone: The Timelight Stone. 2007. 110p. (J). pap. 5.99 (****978-1-933164-43-4(3)***) Seven Seas Entertainment, LLC.

—The Pirate & the Princess Volume 2: the Red Crystal: The Red Crystal. 2007. 110p. (J). pap. 5.99 (****978-1-933164-44-1(1)***) Seven Seas Entertainment, LLC.

Chowdhury, Rohini. The Three Princes of Persia. 2005. (Illus.). 176p. (J). pap. 8.00 (978-0-14-333493-4(X) , Penguin Global) Penguin Group (USA) Inc.

Chronicle Books LLC Staff. Snow White (Bilingual) 2008. (SPA & ENG.). (J). 14.95 (978-0-8118-6030-7(2)); pap. 6.95 (978-0-8118-6031-4(0)) Chronicle Bks. LLC.

Clark, Margaret & Malone, Peter. The Classic Treasury of Princess Fairy Tales. 2005. (Illus.). 56p. 9.98 (978-0-7624-1890-9(7) , Courage Bks.) Running Pr. Bk. Pubs.

Clarke, Jane. Prince Albert's Birthday. Chatterton, Martin, illus. 2005. 24p. (J). lib. bdg. 22.65 (****978-1-59646-748-4(7)***) Dingles & Co.

Clausen, Andrew. Prince Caspian. 2003. stu. ed., ring bd. 14.99 (978-1-58609-195-8(6)) Progeny Pr.

Clawson, Kimberly. Fun O' Licious. Bellomy, Gail, illus. 2007. (ENG.). 56p. per. 12.95 (****978-1-4241-5556-9(8)***) PublishAmerica, Inc.

Claybourne, Anna. Don't Kiss the Frog. Waters, Fiona, ed. Burfoot, Ella et al, illus. 2007. 80p. (J). 14.95 (****978-0-7534-5953-9(1)*** , Kingfisher) Houghton Mifflin Co. Trade & Reference Div.

Climo, Shirley. Atlanta's Race: A Greek Myth. 2000. (J). 13.75 (978-0-606-19360-3(X)) Tandem Library Bks.

—A Pride of Princesses: Princess Tales from Around the World. 1999. (Trophy Chapter Bks.). (Illus.). 112p. (J). (gr. 2-5). pap. 4.25 (978-0-06-442102-7(3)) HarperCollins Pubs.

Cohen, Warren Lee. Dragon Baked Bread. Ssebulime, John, illus. 2005. 32p. (J). (978-1-902636-70-2(8)) Clairview Bks.

Coia, Kristina. Lymeria. 2007. 120p. (YA). per. 10.95 (****978-0-595-45268-2(X)***) iUniverse, Inc.

Cole, Babette. Princess Smartypants Rules. Cole, Babette, illus. 2005. (Illus.). 32p. (J). (ps-3). 15.99 (978-0-399-24349-3(6) , Putnam Juvenile) Penguin Group (USA) Inc.

Coleman, Alice Scovell. Engraved in Stone. Armand, Anjale Renee, illus. 2003. 152p. (J). 14.95 (978-0-9729846-0-7(7)) Tiara Bks. LLC.

Combel Editorial Staff. Blancanieves. 2004. (Caballo alado clasicos-Al Trote Ser.). (SPA., Illus.). 24p. 6.95 (978-84-7864-778-1(3)) Combel Editorial, S.A. ESP. *Dist:* Independent Pubs. Group.

Coombs, Kate. The Runaway Princess. 2006. 288p. (J). 17.00 (978-0-374-35546-3(0)) Farrar, Straus & Giroux.

Cooper, Janet E. Three Proud Princesses. 2006. (Illus.). 64p. (J). pap. 19.95 (978-0-913720-86-8(0)) Beil, Frederic C. Pub., Inc.

Cosgrove, Stephen. Morgan & Me. James, Robin, illus. ed. 2002. (Serendipity Ser.). 32p. (J). reprint ed. pap. 4.99 (978-0-8431-4871-8(3) , Price Stern Sloan) Penguin Group (USA) Inc.

—Morgan & Me. 2002. (gr. k-3). lib. bdg. 13.00 (978-0-613-57626-0(8)) Tandem Library Bks.

Courtney, Kateri. Welby & the Knobby King. 2003. pap. 14.95 (978-0-9743588-0-2(0)) Castlegate Pr.

Coventry, Anna. The Princess Who Lost Her Hair. 1998. (Illus.). 28p. pap. 13.95 (978-1-899874-06-4(2)) Goblinshead GBR. *Dist:* Dufour Editions, Inc.

Coville, Bruce. The Dragonslayers. unabr. ed. 2004. (Words Take Wingtm Ser.). 119p. (J). (gr. 3-6). pap. 29.00 incl. audio (978-0-8072-7988-5(9) , S YA 958 SP, Listening Library) Random Hse. Audio Publishing Group.

Coville, Bruce & Shakespeare, William. Hamlet. Gore, Leonid, illus. 2004. 40p. (J). (gr. 3). 18.99 (978-0-8037-2708-3(9) , Dial) Penguin Group (USA) Inc.

Coyle, Carmela LaVigna. Do Princesses Scrape Their Knees? 2006. (Illus.). 32p. (J). 15.95 (978-0-87358-909-3(2)) Northland Publishing.

—Do Princesses Wear Hiking Boots? Gordon, Mike & Gordon, Carl, illus. 2003. 32p. (J). 15.95 (978-0-87358-828-7(2) , Rising Moon Bks. for Young Readers) Northland Publishing.

Craik, Dinah Maria Mulock. The Little Lame Prince & His Traveling Cloak. 2005. reprint ed. pap. 20.95 (978-1-4179-1940-6(X)) Kessinger Publishing, LLC.

—The Little Lame Prince & the Adventures of a Brownie. Date not set. lib. bdg. 25.95 (978-0-8488-2095-4(9)) Amereon LTD.

—Little Lame Prince EasyRead Comfort Edit. 2006. pap. (****978-1-4250-2001-9(1)***) Assistedreadingbooks.com Inc.

—Little Lame Prince EasyRead Edition. 2006. pap. (****978-1-4250-1718-7(5)***) Assistedreadingbooks.com Inc.

—Little Lame Prince EasyRead Large Editio. 2006. pap. (****978-1-4250-2260-0(X)***) Assistedreadingbooks.com Inc.

—Little Lame Prince the. 2006. pap. (****978-1-4250-2683-7(4)***) Assistedreadingbooks.com Inc.

Crump, Fred, Jr. Ebonita & the Seven Boyz. 2007. 32p. (J). 12.95 (****978-1-934056-71-4(5)***) UMI (Urban Ministries, Inc.).

—Marigold & the Dragon. 2007. 32p. (J). 12.95 (****978-1-934056-73-8(1)***) UMI (Urban Ministries, Inc.).

Curtis, Jillian M. The Little Prince & His Magic Wand. 2005. (Illus.). 28p. (J). 24.95 (978-1-59858-015-0(9)); pap. 16.95 (978-1-59858-010-5(8)) Dog Ear Publishing, LLC.

Daffern, Brian. Prince Albert Bk. 2: The Beast School. 2005. 160p. (YA). per. 10.95 (978-0-9709104-6-2(0)) Hickory Tales Publishing.

—Prince Albert Bk. 3: The Realm Pirates. 2004. 192p. (YA). per. 13.95 (978-0-9709104-7-9(9)) Hickory Tales Publishing.
—Prince Albert in a Can, Bk. 1. 2004. 256p. (YA). per. 13.95 (978-0-9709104-5-5(2)) Hickory Tales Publishing.
Dahl, Michael. The Princess & the Tower. Zhurkina, Svetlana A., illus. 2005. (Read-It! Readers Ser.). 32p. (J). (ps). lib. bdg. 18.60 (978-1-4048-1184-3(2)) Picture Window Bks.
Dale, Penny. Princess, Princess. Dale, Penny, illus. (Illus.). 32p. (J). (ps-1). 2007. pap. 4.99 (*978-0-7636-3565-7(0)); 2003. 14.99 (978-0-7636-2212-1(5)) Candlewick Pr.
Dale, Penny & Platt, Richard. Pirate Diary. Ridell, Chris, illus. 2003. 128p. (J). (gr. 4). pap. 6.99 (978-0-7636-2169-8(2)) Candlewick Pr.
Dalmatian Press Staff. Little Princess: Board Book Set, 4 bks., Set. 2003. (Illus.). 80p. (J). bds. 7.99 (978-1-57759-713-1(3)) Dalmatian Pr.
Dalmatian Press Staff, adapted by. A Little Princess. 2003. (Spot the Classics Ser.). 180p. (J). 4.99 (978-1-57759-559-5(9)) Dalmatian Pr.
Dalton, Annie. The Afterdark Princess. l.t. ed. 2005. (Illus.). 144p. (J). pap. (978-0-7540-7834-0(5) , CLP 425) BBC Audio.
—The Afterdark Princess. l.t. ed. 2003. (Illus.). (J). pap. 24.95 incl. audio (978-0-7540-6266-0(X) , Galaxy Children's Large Print) BBC Audiobooks America.
Dancing Princess. 2004. (J). (978-0-9758549-2-1(5)) M.O.R.E.
Danson, Lesley, et al, illus. Snow White. 2006. 24p. pap. 5.99 (978-1-84643-023-7(2)) Child's Play-International.
Daugherty, George. Princess Sheegwa. 2002. (gr. k-3). lib. bdg. 11.80 (978-0-613-50490-4(9)) Tandem Library Bks.
Davidson, Ellen. Princess Justina Albertina. Wise, Noreen, ed. Schneider, Rex, illus. 2000. (Book-a-Day Collection). 32p. (YA). (ps up). pap. 5.95 (978-1-58584-366-4(0)) Huckleberry Pr.
Davidson, Ellen Dee. Princess Justina Albertina: A Cautionary Tale. Chesworth, Michael, illus. 2007. (J). (ps-2). 15.95 (978-1-57091-562-6(7)) Charlesbridge Publishing, Inc.
Davidson, Susanna. Frog Prince. 2005. 48p. (J). (gr. 2 up). 8.95 (978-0-7945-0969-9(X) , Usborne) EDC Publishing.
—Frog Prince Cd Pack. rev. ed. 2007. (Young Reading CD Packs Ser.). 48p. (J). 9.99 (*978-0-7945-1868-4(0) , Usborne) EDC Publishing.
—Princess & the Pea Cd Pack. rev. ed. 2007. (Young Reading CD Packs Ser.). 48p. (J). 9.99 (*978-0-7945-1875-2(3) , Usborne) EDC Publishing.
—Princess Polly & the Pony. Hill, Dave, illus. 2007. (First Reading Level 4 Ser.). 48p. (J). 8.99 (*978-0-7945-1756-4(0) , Usborne) EDC Publishing.
Davidson, Susanna & Von, Preussen Beatrice. Princess Handbook. 2006. 80p. (J). 12.99 (978-0-7945-1329-0(8) , Usborne) EDC Publishing.
Davidts, Jean P. Return of the Little Prince. 1999. (978-1-55192-234-8(7)) Raincoast Bk. Distribution.
Davis, Richard Harding. Princess Aline. 2006. pap. (*978-1-4250-3047-6(5)) Assistedreadingbooks.com Inc.
DC Comics Staff. Wonder Woman Morphing Journal. 2004. (Illus.). 128p. 10.95 (978-0-8118-4197-9(9)) Chronicle Bks. LLC.
De Audrade, Norma. The Frog, the Princess, the Purpurine, & the Silk Threads. 2005. (J). pap. 8.00 (978-0-8059-6524-7(6)) Dorrance Publishing Co., Inc.
De Lafayette, Madame. The Princess de Montpensier. 2004. reprint ed. pap. 1.99 (978-1-4192-7870-9(3)) Kessinger Publishing, LLC.
de Saint-Exupery, Antoine. The Little Prince. l.t. ed. 2005. 100p. (J). 22.95 (978-0-7862-7538-0(3)); pap. 10.95 (978-0-7862-7539-7(1)) Thorndike Pr.
de Saint Exupery, Antoine. El Principito. 2006. (SPA., Illus.). 83p. pap. 4.90 (978-968-7748-04-7(4)) Lectorum, S.A. de C.V. MEX. Dist: LD Bks., Inc.
Dean Wafstet, Cindi. Wings of Light. 2005. 31p. 15.00 (978-1-4116-5567-6(2)) Lulu.com.
DeFelice, Cynthia C. The Real, True Dulcie Campbell. Alley, R. W., illus. 2002. 32p. (J). (gr. k-3). 16.00 (978-0-374-36220-1(3) , Farrar, Straus & Giroux (BYR)) Farrar, Straus & Giroux.
Deisher, Kathleen E. Beyond the Gloesmur: In the Gloesmur Scrolls. Deisher, Kathleen E., illus. 2003. (Gloesmur Scrolls Ser.: Bk. 1). (Illus.). 270p. (J). pap. 13.95 (978-1-892135-00-1(0)) Lamp Post Publishing, Inc.
Del Carril, Bonifacio, tr. from FRE. El Principito. Saint-Exupéry, Antoine de, illus. 2001. (SPA.). 96p. (gr. 5-8). pap. 11.00 (978-0-15-601392-5(4) , HB30634) Harcourt Children's Bks.
Delaney, Kaz. Princesses Don't Sweat. 2004. 208p. (YA). mass mkt. 5.99 (978-0-8439-5325-1(X)) Dorchester Publishing Co., Inc.
Demers, Dominique. Pearl Pennyworth Level Three. Favreau, Marie-Claude, illus. 2000. 32p. (J). (gr. 1-4). pap. (978-1-894363-03-7(5)) Dominique & Friends.
Diaz Studios, illus. Once upon a Dream: Songs. 2004. (Disney Princess Ser.). 14p. (J). bds. 15.98 (978-1-4127-0576-9(2) , 7222500) Publications International, Ltd.
Disney. Disney Princess Treasury. rev. ed. 2007. 576p. 19.99 (*978-1-4231-0754-5(3)) Disney Pr.
Disney Press Staff & Monica, Carol. Princess Mix & Match. Marderosian, Mark, illus. 2006. 12p. (ps-17). 14.99 (978-0-7868-3623-9(7)) Disney Pr.
Disney Press Staff & Richards, Kitty. My Secret Diary by Ariel. Disney Storybook Artists Staff, illus. 2006. (Disney Princess Ser.). 64p. (ps-2). 14.99 (978-0-7868-4954-3(1)) Disney Pr.
Disney Princess Super Activity Fun Storybook Collection. 2005. (J). (978-1-59487-168-9(X)) Artist Studios, Ltd.
Disney Staff. Tales of a Princess. Cardona Studio Staff, illus. 2002. 80p. (J). (ps-3). mass mkt. 2.99 (978-0-7364-1292-6(1) , Golden/Disney) Random Hse. Children's Bks.
Disney Staff & LeapFrog Staff, compiled by. Disney Princesses. 2002. (J). spiral bd. 14.95 (978-1-58605-922-4(X)) LeapFrog Enterprises, Inc.
Disney Storybook Artists Staff. Disney Princess Collection. 2nd ed. 2006. (Illus.). 304p. (ps-17). 15.99 (978-1-4231-0072-0(7)) Disney Pr.
Disney Storybook Artists Staff, contrib. by. Princess Treasury. 2005. (Illus.). 318p. (*978-1-4127-3276-5(X)) Publications International, Ltd.
Disney Studio Archives, illus. My Disney Princess Book: A Book for Keepsakes, Memories & Dreams. 1998. 96p. (J). (gr. 3 up). 10.95 (978-0-7868-3159-3(6)) Disney Pr.
DK Publishing Staff. Fairy Tale Sticker Storybook. 2007. 10p. (J). (ps-2). pap. 4.99 (*978-0-7566-3089-8(4)) Dorling Kindersley Publishing, Inc.
Dodds, Dayle Ann. The Prince Won't Go to Bed. Brooker, Kyrsten, illus. 2007. 32p. (J). (ps-1). 16.00 (978-0-374-36108-2(8)) Farrar, Straus & Giroux.
Dog Artlist Collection Staff, contrib. by. Dog Princess Fairy Tails. 2008. (Illus.). 32p. (J). 16.99 (978-0-06-078310-5(9)); lib. bdg. 17.89 (978-0-06-078311-2(7)) HarperCollins Pubs.
Donaldson, Julia. Princess Mirrorbelle & the Magic Shoes. l.t. ed. 2005. pap. 16.95 (978-1-4056-6038-9(4)) BBC Audio GBR. Dist: BBC Audiobooks America.
Dorling Kindersley Publishing Staff, ed. Make-Believe Princess. 2001. (YA). (gr. 6-12). pap. incl. audio (978-0-8224-3292-0(7)) Globe Fearon Educational Publishing.
Downey, Glen. Rebel Prince. Okum, David, illus. 2007. 48p. (J). lib. bdg. 23.08 (*978-1-4242-1642-0(7)) Fitzgerald Bks.
Driehaus, Cyndy Ann. The Royal Adventures of Princess Daisy & Princess Darcy. Huser, Jessie Ann, illus. 2007. (J). (*978-1-933197-31-9(5)) Orange Frazer Pr.
Dwyer, Mindy. The Salmon Princess: An Alaska Cinderella Story. 2004. (Illus.). 32p. (J). pap. 9.95 (978-1-57061-355-5(9)) Sasquatch Bks.
Easton, Patricia Harrison. Davey's Blue-Eyed Frog. Wohnoutka, Mike, illus. 2003. 112p. (J). (gr. 3-5). tchr. ed. 14.00 (978-0-618-18185-8(7) , Clarion Bks.) Houghton Mifflin Co. Trade & Reference Div.
Edens, Cooper, compiled by. Princess Stories: A Classic Illustrated Edition. 2004. (Illus.). 136p. (J). (gr. 1-5). 19.95 (978-0-8118-4032-3(8)) Chronicle Bks. LLC.
Ehrlich, Amy. Cinderella. Battcock, Gregory, ed. Jeffers, Susan, illus. 2004. 32p. (J). (ps). 16.99 (978-0-525-47345-9(9) , Dutton Juvenile) Penguin Group (USA) Inc.
Eubank, Patti Reeder, illus. The Princess & the Snarls. 2006. 32p. (J). (ps). 16.95 (978-0-8249-5536-6(6) , Ideals Children's Bks.) Ideals Pubns.
Fackrell, David. Princess, the Collection, Vol. 1. 2005. 78p. pap. 19.99 (978-1-4116-5820-2(5)) Lulu.com.
Fairy Tale- Beauty & the Beast. 2005. (J). bds. (978-1-4194-0038-4(X)) Paradise Pr., Inc.
Fairy Tale- Cinderella. 2005. (J). bds. (978-1-4194-0039-1(8)) Paradise Pr., Inc.
Fairy Tales - Beauty & the Beast. 2005. (J). bds. (978-1-4194-0099-5(1)) Paradise Pr., Inc.
Fairy tales - Cinderella. 2005. (J). bds. (978-1-4194-0100-8(9)) Paradise Pr., Inc.
Fairy Tales - Snow White. 2005. (J). bds. (978-1-4194-0102-2(5)) Paradise Pr., Inc.
Fairy Tales- Sleeping Beauty. 2005. (J). bds. (978-1-4194-0042-1(8)) Paradise Pr., Inc.
Fairy Tales- Snow White. 2005. (J). bds. (978-1-4194-0043-8(6)) Paradise Pr., Inc.
Fairy tales s/s - SNow White. 2005. (J). bds. (978-1-4194-0068-1(1)) Paradise Pr., Inc.
Fairy Tales s/s Beauty & the Beast. 2005. (J). bds. (978-1-4194-0065-0(7)) Paradise Pr., Inc.
Fairy talse s/s - CInderella. 2005. (J). bds. (978-1-4194-0066-7(5)) Paradise Pr., Inc.
Fequiere, Marie A. Devil Rain & the Bearded Child of the Desert. 2007. (J). pap. 8.00 (*978-0-8059-7366-2(4)) Dorrance Publishing Co., Inc.
Fiedler, Lisa. Dating Hamlet: Ophelia's Story. rev. ed. 2002. 176p. (YA). (gr. 7 up). 17.95 (978-0-8050-7054-5(0) , Holt, Henry & Co. Bks. For Young Readers) Holt, Henry & Co.
Findlay, Lisa. Puss in Boots. Bowers, Tim, illus. 2008. (J). pap. (*978-0-375-84671-7(9)); 48p. lib. bdg. 11.99 (*978-0-375-94671-4(3)) Random Hse., Inc.
Fine, Judith & Bazilian, Barbara. Princess Lily. Bazilian, Barbara, illus. 1998. (Illus.). 32p. (J). (gr. 1-5). 15.95 (978-1-58089-006-9(7)) Charlesbridge Publishing, Inc.
Finsterbusch, Monika. Princess Lillifee. 2006. (Illus.). 28p. (J). (ps-3). 12.95 (978-0-8109-5722-0(1) , Abrams Bks. for Young Readers) Abrams, Harry N. , Inc.
—Princess Lillifee's Secret. 2006. 28p. (J). (ps-3). 12.95 (978-0-8109-5724-4(8) , Abrams Bks. for Young Readers) Abrams, Harry N. , Inc.
Flaker, Tracey. Around the Corner: Gwenever's Quest. 2006. 55p. pap. 12.95 (978-1-4241-1886-1(7)) PublishAmerica, Inc.
Fletcher, Susan. Alphabet of Dreams. 2008. 432p. (YA). mass mkt. 6.99 (*978-0-689-85152-0(9) , Simon Pulse) Simon & Schuster Children's Publishing.
Floca, Brian, illus. The Hinky Pink. 2008. 48p. (J). (*978-0-689-87588-5(6)) Simon & Schuster Children's Publishing.
Flodin, Louise E. Sherman the Frog Meets the Snow Princess. l.t. ed. 2006. (Illus.). 24p. 15.95 (978-0-9745052-5-1(0) , 1) Tree Of Life Publishing.
Fodi, Edward Lee. Corranda's Crown. 2002. 218p. (YA). (gr. 4-6). 9.99 (978-0-88092-573-0(6) , 5736) Royal Fireworks Publishing Co.
Fowles, Shelley. Climbing Rosa. 2006. (Illus.). 32p. (J). 15.95 (978-1-84507-079-3(8)) Lincoln, Frances Ltd. GBR. Dist: Perseus Distribution.
Fransoy, Monse, illus. Cinderella. 2001. (SPA & ENG.). 32p. (J). (ps-3). 12.95 (978-0-8118-3084-3(5)) Chronicle Bks. LLC.
Franz, Kevin. Into the Hidden Lands: A Castle Rose Adventure. Stigler, Marilyn, illus. 2004. 112p. (J). per. 7.99 (978-0-9747774-0-5(4)) Starbell Bks.
French, Vivian. Princess Alice & the Glass Slipper. Gibb, Sarah, illus. 2007. (J). (*978-0-06-112448-8(6)); 80p. pap. 3.99 (*978-0-06-112447-1(8) , Harper Trophy) HarperCollins Pubs.
—Princess Alice & the Magical Mirror. Gibb, Sarah, illus. 2007. (J). (Tiara Club Ser.: Vol. 4). 80p. pap. 3.99 (978-0-06-112439-6(7) , Harper Trophy); 67p. (*978-1-4287-2734-2(5)) HarperCollins Pubs.
—The Princess Alice & the Magical Mirror. Gibb, Sarah, illus. 2007. (Tiara Club Ser.: Vol. 4). 80p. (J). 15.99 (978-0-06-112440-2(0) , Tegen, Katherine Bks) HarperCollins Pubs.
—Princess Charlotte & the Birthday Ball. Gibb, Sarah, illus. 2007. (Tiara Club Ser.). 80p. (J). (gr. 1-4). pap. 3.99 (978-0-06-112428-0(1) , Harper Trophy); 15.99 (978-0-06-112431-0(1) , Tegen, Katherine Bks) HarperCollins Pubs.
—Princess Charlotte & the Enchanted Rose. Gibb, Sarah, illus. 2007. (Tiara Club Ser.: No. 7). 80p. (J). pap. 3.99 (*978-0-06-112441-9(9) , Harper Trophy) HarperCollins Pubs.
—Princess Chloe & the Primrose Petticoats. Gibb, Sarah, illus. 2008. (Tiara Club Ser.). 80p. (J). pap. 3.99 (*978-0-06-143484-6(1) , Tegen, Katherine Bks) HarperCollins Pubs.
—Princess Daisy & the Dazzling Dragon. Gibb, Sarah, illus. 2007. (Tiara Club Ser.: No.3). 80p. (J). (gr. 1-4). 15.99 (978-0-06-112434-1(6) , Tegen, Katherine Bks); pap. 3.99 (978-0-06-112433-4(8) , Harper Trophy) HarperCollins Pubs.
—Princess Daisy & the Magical Merry-Go-Roun. Gibb, Sarah, illus. 2007. (Tiara Club Ser.: No. 9). 80p. (J). pap. 3.99 (*978-0-06-112445-7(1) , Harper Trophy) HarperCollins Pubs.
—Princess Emily & the Substitute Fairy. Gibb, Sarah, illus. 2007. (Tiara Club Ser.: No. 6). 80p. (J). pap. 3.99 (*978-0-06-112436-5(2) , Harper Trophy) HarperCollins Pubs.
—Princess Emily & the Wishing Star. Gibb, Sarah, illus. 2007. (J). (Tiara Club Ser.: No.12). 80p. pap. 3.99 (*978-0-06-112451-8(6) , Harper Trophy); (*978-0-06-112452-5(4)) HarperCollins Pubs.
—Princess Katie & the Mixed-Up Potion. Gibb, Sarah, illus. 2007. (Tiara Club Ser.: No.8). 80p. (J). pap. 3.99 (*978-0-06-112443-3(5) , Harper Trophy) HarperCollins Pubs.
—Princess Katie & the Silver Pony. Gibb, Sarah, illus. 2007. (Tiara Club Ser.: No.2). 80p. (J). (gr. 1-4). pap. 3.99 (978-0-06-112430-3(3) , Harper Trophy) HarperCollins Pubs.
—Princess Sophia & the Prince's Party. Gibb, Sarah, illus. 2007. (J). (*978-0-06-112450-1(8)); (Tiara Club Ser.: No. 11). 80p. pap. 3.99 (*978-0-06-112449-5(4) , Harper Trophy) HarperCollins Pubs.
—Princess Sophia & the Sparkling Surprise. Gibb, Sarah, illus. 2007. (Tiara Club Ser.: Vol. 5). 80p. (J). pap. 3.99 (978-0-06-112437-2(0) , Harper Trophy) HarperCollins Pubs.
French, Vivian. Tiara Club at Ruby Mansions 2: Princess Jessica & the Best-Friend Bracelet, T. Gibb, Sarah, illus. 2008. (Tiara Club Ser.). 80p. (J). pap. 3.99 (*978-0-06-143485-3(X) , Harper Trophy) HarperCollins Pubs.
Fuenmayor, Morella, illus. El Conde Olinos. 2000. (SPA.). 24p. (J). (ps-1). pap. 6.99 (978-980-257-241-0(1) , EK7598) Ekare, Ediciones VEN. Dist: Kane/Miller Bk. Pubs., Inc., Lectorum Pubns., Inc.
Funke, Cornelia. The Princess Knight. Meyer, Kerstin, illus. 2004. 32p. (J). pap. 15.95 (978-0-439 53630-1(8) , Chicken Hse., The) Scholastic, Inc.
—Princess Pigsty. Wright, Chantal, tr. from GER. Meyer, Kerstin, illus. 2007. 32p. (J). (ps-3). pap. 16.99 (978-0-439-88554-6(X) , Chicken Hse., The) Scholastic, Inc.
Gardner, Sally. Book of Princesses. (Illus.). 96p. (J). 19.95 (978-1-85881-350-9(6)) Orion Bks. Ltd. GBR. Dist: Trafalgar Square Publishing.
—A Book of Princesses: Five Favorite Princess Stories. 2001. (Illus.). pap. 12.00 (978-1-85881-644-9(0)) Dolphin Paperbacks GBR. Dist: Trafalgar Square Publishing.
Garofoli, Viviana. Princess! 2008. (J). (*978-0-7614-5450-2(0)) Cavendish, Marshall Corp.
Gavin, Jamila. Three Indian Princesses: The Stories of Savitri, Damayanti & Sita. 2004. (Illus.). 112p. (Orig.). (J). pap. 7.50 (978-0-7497-4613-1(0)) Egmont Bks., Ltd. GBR. Dist: Trafalgar Square Publishing.
Geras, Adele. Watching the Roses. 2005. (Egerton Hall Novels: Vol. 2). 192p. (YA). (gr. 7-17). pap. 6.95 (978-0-15-205531-8(2) , Harcourt Paperbacks) Harcourt Children's Bks.
Gerver, Jane E. Penny. Papp, Lisa, illus. 2006. (Breyer Stablemates Ser.). 48p. (J). pap. 4.99 (978-0-439-72235-3(7) , Cartwheel Bks.) Scholastic, Inc.
Gherasim, Louise. Grainne: Sailor Princess of Ireland. 1999. 134p. (YA). pap. 9.95 (978-0-7541-0073-7(1)) Irish Bks. & Media, Inc.
Gili, Phillida. Cinderella: A Pop Up Book. 2006. (Illus.). 14p. (J). 17.95 (978-1-58234-712-7(3) , Bloomsbury Children) Bloomsbury Publishing.
Gili, Phillida. Cinderella: A Pop-up Book. Gili, Phillida, illus. 2007. (Illus.). 12p. (J). 25.00 (*978-1-4223-9031-3(4)) DIANE Publishing Co.
Gilman, Phoebe. The Balloon Tree. ed. 2004. (J). (gr. k-3). spiral bd. (978-0-616-01650-3(6)) Canadian National Institute for the Blind/Institut National Canadien pour les Aveugles.
—The Balloon Tree. (Tell Me a Story Ser.). (FRE., Illus.). (J). 13.99 (978-0-590-24399-5(3)) Scholastic, Inc.
Gitomer, Helaine D. & Weinstock, Harriett. The Magic Cow: A Gift. Gitomer, Helaine D. & Weinstock, Harriett, illus. 2000. (Illus.). (J). (978-0-9676205-0-3(3)) Orbin Publishing, Ltd.
Glassman, Jackie. Happy Birthday, Princess Lolly! 2000. (ps-2). lib. bdg. 11.80 (978-0-613-32630-8(X)) Tandem Library Bks.
Golden Books Staff. Barbie in the 12 Dancing Princesses Make Your Own Little Golden Book. 2006. (Illus.). 16p. (J). (gr. k-k). 5.99 (978-0-375-83866-8(X) , Golden Bks.) Random Hse. Children's Bks.
—Journey to Fairytale Land. 2007. (Book & CD Ser.). (Illus.). 24p. (J). (ps-2). 9.99 (978-0-375-84025-8(7) , Golden Bks.) Random Hse. Children's Bks.
—A Perfect Fit. 2006. (Deluxe Coloring Book Ser.). (Illus.). 96p. (J). (ps-2). pap. 3.99 (978-0-375-84004-3(4) , Golden/Disney) Random Hse. Children's Bks.
—A Perfect Match. Duarte, Pamela, illus. 2004. 64p. (J). (ps-2). pap. 3.99 (978-0-375-82937-6(7) , Golden Bks.) Random Hse. Children's Bks.
—Practice Makes Perfect. 2007. (Deluxe Coloring Book Ser.). (Illus.). 96p. (J). (ps-2). pap. 3.99 (*978-0-375-84176-7(8) , Golden/Disney) Random Hse. Children's Bks.
—A True Princess. 2007. (Deluxe Coloring Book Ser.). (Illus.). 96p. (J). (ps-2). 3.99 (*978-0-375-84467-6(8) , Golden Bks.) Random Hse. Children's Bks.
Goodhart, Pippa & Paine, Colin. Arthur's Tractor: A Fairy Tale with Mechanical Parts. 2003. (Illus.). 32p. (J). (ps-3). 15.95 (978-1-58234-847-6(2) , Bloomsbury Children) Bloomsbury Publishing.
Gow, Kailin. Diary of a Discount Donna: A Fashion Fables Book: A Novel. 2005. 274p. (YA). per. 10.95 (978-1-59748-858-7(5)) Sparklesoup Studios, Inc.
Grams, David L. Princess Sarah & the King. French, Sarah, illus. 1999. 56p. (J). 20.00 (978-0-9663002-0-8(3)) Court Jester Ministries, Inc.
Gray, Margaret. The Lovesick Salesman. Cecil, Randy, illus. rev. ed. 2004. 192p. (J). 16.95 (978-0-8050-7558-8(5) , Holt, Henry & Co. Bks. For Young Readers) Holt, Henry & Co.
—The Ugly Princess & the Wise Fool. Cecil, Randy, illus. rev. ed. 2002. 176p. (J). (gr. 3-5). 16.95 (978-0-8050-6847-4(3) , Holt, Henry & Co. Bks. For Young Readers) Holt, Henry & Co.
Greene, Janice. Hamlet's Trap. 2003. (Illus.). 80p. (YA). per. 3.95 (978-1-56254-703-5(8) , SP7038) Saddleback Educational Publishing.
Gregerson, Jonathan, illus. Minerva's Dream. 1999. (J). 30.00 (978-0-8172-7282-1(8)) Steck-Vaughn.
Grey, Chelsea Gillian. Princess Colors. (Early Learning Ser.). (Illus.). 32p. (J). 12.99 incl. audio compact disk (978-1-59069-370-4(1) , 1A102) Studio Mouse LLC.
Grey, Mini. The Very Smart Pea & the Princess-to-Be. 2003. (Illus.). 32p. (J). (ps-3). 14.95 (978-0-375-82626-9(2)); lib. bdg. 16.99 (978-0-375-92626-6(7)) Random Hse. Children's Bks. (Knopf Bks. for Young Readers).
Greycat, Sandy & Cogliandro, Charlotte. Princesses Don't Live in Castles. 2002. (Illus.). 36p. (J). (gr. 1-6). pap. 7.95 (978-0-9717131-2-3(X)) Greycat Tales.
Grimm, Jacob W. Rapunzel. 2000. (gr. k-3). lib. bdg. 15.25 (978-0-613-26715-1(X)) Tandem Library Bks.
Grimm, Wilhelm K. & Grimm, Jacob W. The Golden Goose. Shulevitz, Uri, illus. 1998. 32p. (J). (gr. k-3). pap. 6.95 (978-0-374-42748-1(8) , Sunburst) Farrar, Straus & Giroux.
Grimm. 630 - Cenicienta. 2001. Tr. of Cinderella. (SPA.). (978-968-6347-30-2(5)) Larousse, Ediciones, S. A. de C. V.
Grodin, Elissa. The Happy Prince. Stutzman, Laura, illus. rev. ed. 2006. 48p. (J). 17.95 (978-1-58536-264-6(6)) Sleeping Bear Pr.
Gruffudd, Elena. Gelert. 2005. (WEL., Illus.). 34p. (978-0-86381-291-0(0)) Gwasg Carreg Gwalch.
Guarino, Deborah. If the Shoe Fits. (J). 14.95 (978-0-8118-3774-3(2)) Chronicle Bks. LLC.
Haan, Linda de & Nijland, Stern. King & King. 2004. (Illus.). 32p. 14.95 (978-1-58246-061-1(2) , Tricycle Pr.) Ten Speed Pr.
Haddix, Margaret Peterson. Just Ella. 2000. (J). pap., stu. ed. 61.00 incl. audio (978-0-7887-4337-5(6) , 41132); Class set. (YA). (gr. 7 up). pap. 215.30 incl. audio (978-0-7887-4438-9(0) , 47129) Recorded Bks., LLC.
—Just Ella. 2007. 240p. (YA). mass mkt. 5.99 (978-1-4169-3649-7(1) , Simon Pulse) Simon & Schuster Children's Publishing.
—Just Ella. Milot, René, illus. 2001. 240p. (YA). (gr. 6-9). pap. 5.99 (978-0-689-83128-7(5) , Aladdin) Simon & Schuster Children's Publishing.
—Just Ella. Milot, Rene, illus. 2001. 224p. mass mkt. 4.99 (978-0-689-84917-6(6) , Aladdin) Simon & Schuster Children's Publishing.
—Just Ella. Milot, René, illus. 1999. 192p. (YA). (gr. 7 up). 17.00 (978-0-689-82186-8(7)) Simon & Schuster Children's Publishing.
Haile, Carol J. The Princess Tree: A Tale of Fairies, Elves & Magic. l.t. ed. 2005. (ESK., Illus.). 32p. (J). 19.95 (978-0-9711236-1-8(6)) Firenze Pr.
Hale, Shannon. The Goose Girl. 2003. (Illus.). 300p. (J). (gr. 5 up). 18.95 (978-1-58234-843-8(X)); 2005. 400p. (YA). (gr. 7-17). reprint ed. pap. 8.95 (978-1-58234-990-9(8)) Bloomsbury Publishing. (Bloomsbury Children).

Hale, Shannon. The Princess Academy. (YA). 2007. 336p. pap. 7.95 (*978-1-59990-073-5(4)); 2005. 320p. (gr. 8-12). 16.95 (978-1-58234-993-0(2)) Bloomsbury Publishing. (Bloomsbury Children).

—The Princess Academy. l.t. ed. 2006. 400p. (YA). 23.95 (978-0-7862-8733-8(0)) Thorndike Pr.

Haley, Amanda, illus. A Bath for a Princess. 2007. (I'm Going to Read Ser.). 32p. (J). (gr. 1-2). pap. 3.95 (*978-1-4027-4297-2(5)) Sterling Publishing Co., Inc.

Hall, Kirsten. I'm a Princess. 2004. (My First Reader Ser.). 31p. (J). (gr. k-1). pap. 3.95 (978-0-516-24630-7(5) , Children's Pr.) Scholastic Library Publishing.

—I'm a Princess. DeRosa, Dee, illus. 2003. (My First Reader Ser.). 32p. (J). 18.50 (978-0-516-22928-7(1) , Children's Pr.) Scholastic Library Publishing.

Hamlet. 2002. (Illus.). 48p. (YA). stu. ed., per. 17.95 (978-1-56254-601-4(5) , SP6015) Saddleback Educational Publishing.

Hapka, Cathy. Pretend & Play Kitty: With Real Crown You Can Wear! Borlasca, Hector, illus. 2004. (Role Play Ser.). 10p. (J). (ps up). bds. 6.99 (978-1-57151-742-5(1)) Playhouse Publishing.

Harcourt School Publishers Staff. My Princess: Take-Home Book. 1999. (Signatures Ser.). (Illus.). (J). pap. 1.90 (978-0-15-313909-3(9)) Harcourt Schl. Pubs.

Hargreaves, Roger. Little Miss Splendid & the Princess. 2007. (Mr. Men & Little Miss Ser.). 32p. (J). pap. 3.99 (978-0-8431-2489-7(X) , Price Stern Sloan) Penguin Group (USA) Inc.

Harris, Kandi. Princess, the Future Queen: A Mother's Guidance. Rippon, Jor-El, illus. l.t. ed. 2006. 32p. (J). bds. 12.99 (978-0-9770331-1-9(2)) Harris, K Publishing, Inc.

Harrison, Mette Ivie. The Princess & the Hound. 2007. 416p. (YA). (gr. 7 up). 17.99 (*978-0-06-113187-5(3)); lib. bdg. 18.89 (*978-0-06-113188-2(1)) HarperCollins Pubs. (Eos).

Haskins, Lori. May I Have This Dance? 2005. 16p. (ps-2). 14.99 (978-0-7868-3608-6(3)) Disney Pr.

Havel, Geoff. Punzie, ICQ! Bell, Owen, illus. 1999. 32p. (J). 12.95 (978-1-86368-198-8(1)) Fremantle Pr. AUS. *Dist:* International Specialized Bk. Services.

Hays, Peter D. The Letter Princess. 1998. 41p. (J). (gr. 1-5). pap. 4.95 (978-1-885554-05-5(2)) Hays, Peter D.

Henderson, Kathy. Lugalbanda: The Boy Who Got Caught up in a War. Ray, Jane, illus. 2006. 80p. (J). (gr. 3-5). 16.99 (978-0-7636-2782-9(8)) Candlewick Pr.

Hepworth, David G. The Picture Stone. 2006. (Illus.). 76p. pap. (*978-1-4120-9053-7(9)) Trafford Publishing.

Herbauts, Anne. Prince Silencio. Bedrick, Claudia Z., tr. from FRE. 2006. (Illus.). 28p. (J). 14.95 (978-1-59270-055-4(1)) Enchanted Lion Bks., LLC.

Heyer, Carol. The Sleeping Beauty in the Wood. 2001. (J). (gr. 4-7). 14.95 (978-0-8249-5401-7(7)) Ideals Pubns.

Hibbs, Joan Arlin. Cinderella's Daughter. 2004. 93p. pap. 14.95 (978-1-4137-2935-1(5)) PublishAmerica, Inc.

Hicks, John. Divided World. 2003. 192p. (YA). per. 6.50 (978-0-9742829-1-6(X)) Quiet Man Publishing.

Hiebert, Elfrieda H. & Juel, Connie. The Princess Who Couldn't Cry. (Little Book Practice Reader Ser.). (J). (978-0-8136-0887-7(2)) Modern Curriculum Pr.

—Where Is the Queen? (Little Book Practice Reader Ser.). (J). (978-0-8136-0829-7(5)) Modern Curriculum Pr.

Higgins, James E. Little Prince. Date not set. 136p. (J). 17.95 (978-0-8488-2801-1(1)) Amereon LTD.

Hill, Stuart. The Cry of the Icemark. 2006. (J). 496p. pap. 8.99 (978-0-439-68627-3(X) , Scholastic Paperbacks); 44.95 (978-0-439-87591-2(9)) Scholastic, Inc.

—Cry of the Icemark (library Edition) 2006. (J). 99.95 (978-0-439-87914-9(0)) Scholastic, Inc.

Hillert, Margaret. Cinderella at the Ball. LaSalle, Janet, illus. rev. exp. ed. 2007. (Beginning to Read Ser.). 32p. (J). lib. bdg. (978-1-59953-046-8(5)) Norwood Hse. Pr.

Hindley, Judy. Princess Rosa's Winter. Chamberlain, Margaret, illus. 2005. (I Am Reading Ser.). 48p. (J). (gr. k-3). pap. 3.95 (978-0-7534-5859-4(4) , Kingfisher) Houghton Mifflin Co. Trade & Reference Div.

Hines-Stephens, Sarah & Mason, Jane. Princess School: If the Shoe Fits. 2004. (Princess School Ser.). 144p. (J). pap. 4.99 (978-0-439-54532-7(3) , Scholastic Paperbacks) Scholastic, Inc.

Hoffman, Mary. Princess Grace. Van Wright, Cornelius & Hu, Ying-Hwa, illus. 2008. 32p. (J). (ps). 16.99 (*978-0-8037-3260-5(0) , Dial) Penguin Group (USA) Inc.

Holabird, Katharine. A Party for the Princess #2: Angelina's Diary. Craig, Helen, illus. 2006. (Angelina Ballerina Ser.). 80p. (J). (gr. 1-3). 3.99 (978-0-448-44017-0(2) , Grosset & Dunlap) Penguin Group (USA) Inc.

—The Rose Fairy Princess. Craig, Helen, illus. 2006. (Angelina Ballerina Ser.). 24p. (J). (ps-1). 3.99 (978-0-448-44465-9(8) , Grosset & Dunlap) Penguin Group (USA) Inc.

Hollier, Jo. Roary O'Rourke Challenge of the Trolls, Bk. 3. 2004. pap. 9.95 (978-1-59374-115-0(4)) Whiskey Creek Pr., LLC.

—Roary O'Rourke, Quest for the Secret of Bramble Castle. 2004. (J). pap. 9.95 (978-1-59374-081-8(6)) Whiskey Creek Pr., LLC.

—Roary O'Rourke the Princess & Dooley Do, Bk. 2. 2004. (J). pap. 9.95 (978-1-59374-091-7(3)) Whiskey Creek Pr., LLC.

—Roary O'Rourke Victorious Duo, Bk. 4. 2004. (J). pap. 9.95 (978-1-59374-117-4(0)) Whiskey Creek Pr., LLC.

Holub, Joan. Isabel Saves the Prince: Based on a True Story of Isabel I of Spain. Aleshina, Nonna, illus. 2007. (Young Princesses Around the World Ser.). 48p. (J). pap. 3.99 (*978-0-689-87197-9(X) , Aladdin); lib. bdg. 13.89 (*978-0-689-87198-6(8) , Aladdin Library) Simon & Schuster Children's Publishing.

Holub, Joan. Lydia & the Island Kingdom: A Story Based on the Real Life of Princess Liliuokalani of Hawaii. Aleshina, Nonna, illus. 2007. (Young Princesses Around the World Ser.). 48p. (J). lib. bdg. 13.89 (978-0-689-87200-6(3) , Aladdin Library); pap. 3.99 (*978-0-689-87199-3(6) , Aladdin) Simon & Schuster Children's Publishing.

Hoosier, Wanda M. Princess Mandisa. McCabe, Pat, illus. 1999. 34p. (J). 15.00 (978-1-56469-070-8(9)) Harmony Hse. Pubs.

—Princess Mandisa. 1998. (J). 10.95 (978-0-533-12787-0(4)) Vantage Pr., Inc.

Hopkins, Cathy. The Princess of Pop. 2004. (Truth or Dare Ser.: No. 2). 191p. (YA). (gr. 7-17). per. 14.45 (978-1-4176-2894-0(4)) Tandem Library Bks.

Hopkins, Jackie Mims. The Horned Toad Prince. Austin, Michael, illus. 2000. 32p. (J). (ps-3). 15.95 (978-1-56145-195-1(9) , Q28670) Peachtree Pubs., Ltd.

Hopper, Celia Brashear. Blade & the Story of the Pearl Princess. 2004. (J). 15.95 (978-0-9763093-1-4(9)) Creative Bk. Pubs.

Horowitz, Dave. Twenty-Six Princesses. Horowitz, Dave, illus. 2008. 32p. (J). (ps). 15.99 (*978-0-399-24607-4(X) , Putnam Juvenile) Penguin Group (USA) Inc.

Howard, Peggy Ann. Zorees: Land of Dreams. 2007. (YA). per. 16.95 (*978-0-9795519-0-1(0)) Dream Scape Publishing.

I-Haun. Real Fake Princess Volume 2. 2006. (Illus.). 200p. (YA). pap. 9.95 (*978-1-59796-080-9(2)) DrMaster Pubns. Inc.

—Real Fake Princess Volume 3. 2006. 200p. (YA). pap. 9.95 (*978-1-59796-081-6(0)) DrMaster Pubns. Inc.

—Real/Fake Princess, Vol. 4. 2007. (Illus.). 200p. pap. 9.95 (*978-1-59796-082-3(9)) DrMaster Pubns. Inc.

I-Huan. Real Fake Princess, Vol. 1. 2006. (Illus.). 200p. (YA). pap. 9.95 (*978-1-59796-079-3(9)) DrMaster Pubns. Inc.

Inches, Alison. Dora Saves the Prince. McGee, Brian, illus. 2002. (Dora the Explorer Ser.). 12p. (J). 5.99 (978-0-689-84665-6(7) , Simon Spotlight/Nickelodeon) Simon & Schuster Children's Publishing.

Infante, Francesc, illus. Rumplestiltskin. 2007. (ENG & SPA.). 32p. (J). (ps-3). 14.95 (978-0-8118-5971-4(1)); pap. 6.95 (978-0-8118-5972-1(X)) Chronicle Bks. LLC.

An Inner Child Speaks. 2006. (J). 17.99 (978-0-9779130-0-8(7)) Zy Iman Pubng.

Innovative Kids Staff. Little Princess. Shields, Lori, illus. 2006. (Soft Shapes Ser.). 8p. (J). (ps-ps). 8.99 (978-1-58476-350-5(7) , IKIDS) Innovative Kids.

Irvine, Patricia McCune. Beyond the Greenest Hill: A Fairy Tale. 2003. 136p. (YA). pap. 11.95 (978-0-595-26941-9(9)) iUniverse, Inc.

Isadora, Rachel & Andersen, Han. The Princess & the Pea. Isadora, Rachel, illus. 2007. (Illus.). 32p. (J). (ps-2). 16.99 (978-0-399-24611-1(8) , Putnam Juvenile) Penguin Group (USA) Inc.

Ivanov, Aleksey, illus. The Tall Book of Princesses. 2007. 80p. (J). (ps-2). pap. 6.99 (*978-0-06-085050-0(7) , Harper Festival) HarperCollins Pubs.

Jacques, Brian. The Angel's Command. Elliot, David & Schoenherr, Ian, illus. 2005. (Castaways of the Flying Dutchman Ser.: No. 2). 384p. (J). (gr. 5-9). pap. 7.99 (978-0-14-240285-6(0) , Puffin) Penguin Group (USA) Inc.

Jeffers, Susan. The Nutcracker. Jeffers, Susan, illus. 2007. 40p. (J). (ps-3). lib. bdg. 17.89 (*978-0-06-074387-1(5)); (Illus.). 16.99 (*978-0-06-074386-4(7)) HarperCollins Pubs.

Jensen, Roberta Joan. The Marriage of Princess Winter Bk. 1: Princess Winter. 2005. 64p. pap. 12.95 (978-1-4137-7769-7(4)) PublishAmerica, Inc.

Jocson, Antonio, et al. Richard, Prince of Thieves. Vasquez, Jorge & Romano, Miriam, illus. 1999. 92p. (J). (gr. 1-5). 19.95 (978-1-890963-25-5(9)) Liberty Bell Productions.

Johansen, K. V. Torrie & the Snake-Prince. Delezenne, Christine, illus. 2007. (Torrie Quests Ser.). 192p. (J). (gr. 4-6). 18.95 (*978-1-55451-070-2(8)) Annick Pr., Ltd. CAN. *Dist:* Firefly Bks., Ltd.

John Brown Publishing Ltd. & Murphy, Harriet. Dora's Enchanted Adventure: Follow the Reader Level II. 2007. (Dora the Explorer Ser.). 24p. (J). 24.99 (*978-1-4169-4992-3(5) , Simon Scribbles) Simon & Schuster Children's Publishing.

Johnson, Kylie. Fit for a Princess. 2007. (J). per. 11.99 (*978-1-60247-275-4(0)) Tate Publishing & Enterprises, L.L.C.

Johnson, Vargie. Catherine the Great the Victorious: What Made Them Famous? 2006. 156p. (J). per. 15.00 (978-1-931195-96-6(X)) KiwE Publishing, Ltd.

Jones, Frewin. The Lost Queen. 2007. (Faerie Path Ser.: Bk. 2). 352p. (J). lib. bdg. 17.89 (*978-0-06-087106-2(7)); 335p. (YA). (gr. 7 up). 16.99 (*978-0-06-087105-5(9)) HarperCollins Pubs. (Eos).

—The Sorcerer King. 2008. (Faerie Path Ser.: Bk. 3). 336p. (J). 16.99 (*978-0-06-087108-6(3)); lib. bdg. 17.89 (*978-0-06-087109-3(1)) HarperCollins Pubs. (Eos).

Jones, Jasmine. Enchanted: The Junior Novelization. rev. ed. 2007. 160p. (gr. 3-7). pap. 4.99 (*978-1-4231-0471-1(4)) Disney Pr.

Jordan, Annie Laurie. Bogwaddle Pond. La Grange, Myrtle, illus. 2004. 25p. pap. 14.95 (978-1-4137-2013-6(7)) PublishAmerica, Inc.

Jordan, Apple. The Sweetest Spring. Matta, Gabriella & Legramandi, Francesco, illus. 2008. (Step into Reading Ser.). 32p. (J). (ps-1). lib. bdg. 11.99 (*978-0-375-94810-7(4) , RH/Disney) Random Hse. Children's Bks.

—The Sweetest Spring. Matta, Gabriella & Legramandi, Francesco, illus. 2008. 32p. (J). pap. (*978-0-375-84810-0(X)) Random Hse., Inc.

Jordan, Apple. Winter Wishes. Marrucchi, Elisa, illus. 2006. (Step into Reading Ser.). 32p. (J). (ps-2). pap. 3.99 (978-0-7364-2409-7(1)); lib. bdg. 11.99 (978-0-7364-8049-9(8)) Random Hse. Children's Bks. (RH/Disney).

Joyce, Rita. Wandawillie. 2005. (J). lib. bdg. 17.95 (978-1-59094-095-2(4)) Jawbone Publishing Corp.

Jungman, Ann. The Prince Who Thought He Was a Rooster. 2008. 96p. (J). 14.95 (*978-1-84507-793-8(8)); (Illus.). pap. 7.95 (*978-1-84507-794-5(6)) Lincoln, Frances Ltd. GBR. *Dist:* Perseus Distribution.

Jungman, Ann & Ayto, Russell. Cinderella & the Hot Air Balloon. 1999. (Illus.). 24p. (J). (ps-2). pap. (978-0-7112-1051-6(9)) Lincoln, Frances Ltd. GBR. *Dist:* Transition Vendor.

Kaesshaefer, Charles. The Lost Princess. 2004. (J). mass mkt. 10.00 (978-0-9744407-0-5(1)) Shelbykay Pubilshing Co.

Kale, Ann Stephanian. Marco & Princess Gina. Kale, Ann Stephanian, illus. 2003. (Illus.). 24p. (J). (gr. k-3). pap. 10.00 (978-0-9704131-5-4(7)) Abril BookStore & Publishing.

Katz, Bebe Weinberg. Princess Claudia & the Freckles. 2007. (ENG.). 48p. per. 12.95 (*978-1-4241-6446-2(X)) PublishAmerica, Inc.

Katz, Karen. Princess Baby. 2008. (J). (*978-0-375-84119-4(9)); (Illus.). 32p. lib. bdg. 17.99 (*978-0-375-94119-1(3)) Random Hse. Children's Bks. (Schwartz & Wade Bks.).

Kaye, M. M. The Ordinary Princess. Kaye, M. M., illus. 2002. (Illus.). 128p. (J). (gr. 4-7). reprint ed. pap. 5.99 (978-0-14-230085-5(3) , Puffin) Penguin Group (USA) Inc.

—The Ordinary Princess. 2002. (gr. 7-12). lib. bdg. 14.15 (978-0-613-83544-2(1)) Tandem Library Bks.

Keene, Carolyn. Framed. 2006. 149p. (J). (978-1-4156-4605-2(8) , Aladdin) Simon & Schuster Children's Publishing.

Kemp, Moira. Tell Me a Story, Daddy. 2006. (Illus.). 32p. (J). pap. (978-0-340-87560-5(7) , Hodder Children's Books) Hodder Children's Division.

Kennedy, Mary. Secrets of a South Beach Princess. 2006. 256p. (YA). (gr. 12). pap. 9.99 (978-0-425-21196-0(7) , Berkley Trade) Penguin Group (USA) Inc.

Kim, Mikyung. 11th Cat: Vol. 1. 2005. (Illus.). 180p. (YA). pap. 10.95 (978-89-527-4461-6(6)) Diamond Bk. Distributors.

Kimmel, Eric A. The Three Princes: A Tale from the Middle East. Fisher, Leonard Everett, illus. 2005. (Ala Notable Book Ser.). 32p. (J). (gr. k-3). pap. 6.95 (978-0-8234-1553-3(8)) Holiday Hse., Inc.

Kimpton, Diana. Pony-Crazed Princess No. 7: Princess Ellie Takes Charge. Finlay, Lizzie, illus. 7th rev. ed. 2007. 96p. (gr. 1-4). pap. 3.99 (*978-1-4231-0617-3(2)) Hyperion Paperbacks for Children.

—Princess Ellie Solves a Mystery. 8th rev. ed. 2007. (Pony Crazed Princess Ser.: No. 8). 96p. (gr. 1-4). pap. 3.99 (*978-1-4231-0901-3(5)) Disney Pr.

—Princess Ellie to the Rescue. Finlay, Lizzie, illus. 2006. (Pony-Crazed Princess Ser.: Bk. 1). 96p. (gr. 1-4). pap. 3.99 (978-0-7868-4870-6(7)) Hyperion Pr.

—Princess Ellie's Camping Trip. Finlay, Lizzie, illus. 5th rev. ed. 2006. (Pony-Crazed Princess Ser.). 96p. (gr. 1-4). pap. 3.99 (978-0-7868-4874-4(X)) Hyperion Pr.

—Princess Ellie's Mystery. Finlay, Lizzie, illus. 3rd rev. ed. 2006. (Pony-Crazed Princess Ser.: Bk. 3). 96p. (gr. 1-4). pap. 3.99 (978-0-7868-4872-0(3)) Hyperion Pr.

—Princess Ellie's Secret. Finlay, Lizzie, illus. 2nd rev. ed. 2006. (Pony-Crazed Princess Ser.: Bk. 2). 96p. (gr. 1-4). pap. 3.99 (978-0-7868-4871-3(5)) Hyperion Pr.

—Princess Ellie's Snowy Ride. 9th rev. ed. 2007. (Pony Crazed Princess Ser.: No. 9). 96p. (J). (gr. 1-4). pap. 3.99 (*978-1-4231-0902-0(3)) Disney Pr.

—Princess Ellie's Starlight Adventure. Finlay, Lizzie, illus. 4th rev. ed. 2006. 96p. (gr. 1-4). pap. 3.99 (978-0-7868-4873-7(1)) Hyperion Pr.

—Summer Vacation. Finlay, Lizzie, illus. 2007. 144p. (gr. 1-4). pap. 4.99 (*978-1-4231-0616-6(4)) Hyperion Paperbacks for Children.

Kimpton, Diana. A Surprise for Princess Ellie. Finlay, Lizzie, illus. 6th rev. ed. 2007. 96p. (gr. 1-4). pap. 3.99 (978-0-7868-4875-1(8)) Hyperion Pr.

The Kind Princess. 2005. (J). 6.50 (978-0-9773267-1-6(3)) G Publishing LLC.

King-Smith, Dick. Clever Lollipop. Barton, Jill, illus. 2003. 144p. (J). (gr. 2-5). 15.99 (978-0-7636-2174-2(9)) Candlewick Pr.

—Lady Lollipop. Barton, Jill, illus. 128p. (J). (gr. 2-5). 2003. pap. 6.99 (978-0-7636-2181-0(1)); 2001. 15.99 (978-0-7636-1269-6(3)) Candlewick Pr.

—Lady Lollipop. 2001. (gr. 3-6). lib. bdg. 14.15 (978-0-613-66589-6(9)) Tandem Library Bks.

Kingfisher Publications, Inc. Staff, ed. How to be a Princess in 7 Days or Less. Eckel, Jessie, illus. 2005. (How to Be a... Ser.). 32p. (J). (gr. 3-5). 12.95 (978-0-7534-5921-8(3) , Kingfisher) Houghton Mifflin Co. Trade & Reference Div.

Kirk, David. The Prince, the Princess, & the Bee. 2008. 32p. (J). (ps-2). 17.99 (*978-0-448-44690-5(1)) Penguin Group (USA) Inc.

Kirwan, Anna & Yep, Laurence. Victoria, May Blossom of Britannia, England 1829. 2001. (Royal Diaries Ser.). (Illus.). 224p. (J). (gr. 4-9). pap. 10.95 (978-0-439-21598-5(6)) Scholastic, Inc.

Kiss a Frog, Princess. (Full House Ser.). 96p. (J). (gr. 4-6). pap. 3.25 (978-0-938753-63-6(0) , PP2) Parachute Publishing, LLC.

Klein, Lisa & Shakespeare, William. Ophelia. 2006. 336p. (YA). 16.95 (978-1-58234-801-8(4)) Bloomsbury Publishing.

Kleven, Elisa. Paper Princess. 1998. (Picture Puffin Ser.). (Illus.). 40p. (J). (ps-3). pap. 6.99 (978-0-14-056424-2(1) , Puffin) Penguin Group (USA) Inc.

—Paper Princess. 1998. (978-0-606-13694-5(0)); lib. bdg. 15.30 (978-0-613-85732-1(1)) Tandem Library Bks.

—The Paper Princess Finds Her Way. Kleven, Elisa, illus. 2003. (Illus.). 32p. (J). (gr. k). 16.99 (978-0-525-46911-7(7) , Dutton Juvenile) Penguin Group (USA) Inc.

—The Paper Princess Flies Again: With Her Dog! 2005. (Illus.). 32p. (J). (gr. k-2). 15.95 (978-1-58246-146-5(5) , Tricycle Pr.) Ten Speed Pr.

Koeppel, Ruth. Forever Friends: Storybook. 2006. (Disney Princess Ser.). 32p. (J). 17.99 (978-0-7944-0696-7(3)) Reader's Digest Assn., Inc., The.

Koller, Jackie French. The Wizard's Scepter. 2004. (Keepers Ser.: No. 3). (Illus.). 176p. (J). pap. 4.99 (978-0-689-85593-1(1) , Aladdin) Simon & Schuster Children's Publishing.

Korba, Joanna. Yeh-shen: A Cinderella Tale from China. 2006. 42.00 (*978-1-4108-6162-7(7)) Benchmark Education Co.

Krulik, Nancy E. & Ladybird Books Staff. Yasmin: The Princess Rules. 2003. (Bratz Ser.). (Illus.). 32p. pap. 2.99 (978-1-84422-185-1(7) , Putnam Juvenile) Penguin Group (USA) Inc.

Kurtz, John, illus. Disney Princess: Look & Find. 2004. (Disney Princess Ser.). 24p. (J). 7.98 (978-0-7853-7918-8(5) , 7179200) Publications International, Ltd.

Lafayette, Madame de. The Princess de Montpensier. 2004. reprint ed. pap. 15.95 (978-1-4191-7870-2(9)) Kessinger Publishing, LLC.

Lagonegro, Melissa. Friends for a Princess. Harchy, Atelier Philippe, illus. 2004. (Disney Princess Ser.). 32p. (J). (ps-1). pap. 3.99 (978-0-7364-2208-6(0) , RH/Disney) Random Hse. Children's Bks.

—Friends for a Princess. 2004. (Disney Princess Ser.). (ps-2). lib. bdg. 11.80 (978-0-613-73713-5(X)) Tandem Library Bks.

—A Pet for a Princess. Harchy, Atelier Philippe, illus. 2005. (Step into Reading Ser.). 32p. (J). (ps-2). pap. 3.99 (978-0-7364-2280-2(3) , RH/Disney) Random Hse. Children's Bks.

Lagonegro, Melissa & Random House Disney Staff. Ballerina Princess. 2007. (Step into Reading Ser.). (Illus.). 32p. (J). (ps-2). lib. bdg. 11.99 (978-0-7364-8051-2(X) , RH/Disney) Random Hse. Children's Bks.

—Ballerina Princess. Harding, Niall, illus. 2007. (Step into Reading Ser.). 32p. (J). (ps-2). pap. 3.99 (978-0-7364-2428-8(8) , RH/Disney) Random Hse. Children's Bks.

—A Pet for Princess. 2005. (Step into Reading Ser.). (Illus.). 32p. (J). (ps-2). lib. bdg. 11.99 (978-0-7364-8037-6(4) , RH/Disney) Random Hse. Children's Bks.

Lake, Rosemary. Once upon a Time When the Princess Beat the Dragon. 2001. (Once upon a Time When the Princess...Ser.). (Illus.). 100p. (Orig.). (J). (gr. 4-10). pap. 10.00 (978-0-940918-51-1(X)) Dragon Tree Pr., The.

—Once upon a Time When the Princess Cast the Spell. 2001. (Once upon a Time When the Princess...Ser.). (Illus.). 100p. (J). (gr. 4-10). pap. 10.00 (978-0-940918-52-8(8)) Dragon Tree Pr., The.

—Once upon a Time When the Princess Got the Treasure. 2002. (Once upon a Time When the Princess...Ser.). (Illus.). 100p. (Orig.). (J). (gr. 4-10). pap. 10.00 (978-0-940918-53-5(6)) Dragon Tree Pr., The.

—Once upon a Time When the Princess Rescued the Prince. 2003. (Once upon a Time When the Princess...Ser.: 1). 127p. (J). (gr. 4-10). pap. 12.95 (978-0-940918-50-4(1)) Dragon Tree Pr., The.

LaLumiere, Michael & Messinger, Kim. Princess Caitlin's Tiara. 2006. (J). 14.95 (*978-0-9791006-0-4(7)) Stagger Lee Bks.

Lang, Andrew. Prince Prigio. 2004. reprint ed. pap. 19.95 (978-1-4179-0522-5(0)) Kessinger Publishing, LLC.

LaRochelle, David. The End. Egielski, Richard, illus. (J). (ps-3). 2007. 40p. pap. 16.99 (978-0-439-64011-4(3)); 2006. 16.99 (978-0-439-64012-1(1)) Scholastic, Inc. (Levine, Arthur A. Bks.).

Lascurain, Anna. Apollo in the Moon House. 2006. Orig. Title: The Moonboy. (J). per. 7.99 (978-0-9769612-3-9(7) , Pixiefire) Darker Intentiona Pr.

LaShea, Riley. Bleeding Through Kingdoms: Cinderella's Rebellion. 2005. 256p. (YA). per. 14.95 (978-0-9766130-1-5(8)) Tattered Essence Publishing LLC.

Lasky, Kathryn. Born to Rule. Walton, Tony, illus. 2006. (Camp Princess Ser.: No. 1). 160p. (J). pap. 4.99 (978-0-06-058763-5(6) , Harper Trophy); 15.99 (978-0-06-058761-1(X)) HarperCollins Pubs.

—Humphrey, Albert, & the Flying Machine. Manders, John, illus. 2004. 40p. (J). 16.00 (978-0-15-216235-1(6) , Harcourt Children's Bks) Harcourt Children's Bks.

—Jahanara: Princess of Princesses, India, 1627. 2002. (Royal Diaries Ser.). 192p. (J). (gr. 4-8). pap. 10.95 (978-0-439-22350-8(4) , Scholastic Pr.) Scholastic, Inc.

—Kazunomiya: Prisoner of Heaven, Japan, 1858. 2004. (Royal Diaries). 160p. (J). (gr. 4-7). pap. 10.95 (978-0-439-16485-6(0)) Scholastic, Inc.

Lasky, Kathryn. Unicorns? Get Real! 2007. (Camp Princess Ser.). (Illus.). 160p. (J). 15.99 (*978-0-06-058764-2(4)); pap. 4.99 (*978-0-06-058766-6(0) , Harper Trophy) HarperCollins Pubs.

Lawrence, Peter. The Princess Formerly Known as Snow White. Nino, Alex, illus. 2001. (Twenty-First Century Grimms'). 86p. pap. 9.95 (978-1-930702-02-8(7) , Smart Kids Studio Productions) Literary Assocs. Pr.

Lawrence, R. R. The Starsword. 2005. 416p. pap. 12.99 (978-0-9742549-0-6(8)) nightwares Bks.

Layden, Joseph Lyon. The Other Side of Yore. 2007. 156p. pap. 14.95 (*978-1-60145-122-4(9)) Booklocker.com, Inc.

LeapFrog Staff. Disney Princess Stories - France. 2003. (Illus.). spiral bd. 14.99 (978-1-59319-005-7(0)) LeapFrog Enterprises, Inc.

—Disney Princess Stories - Latin America. 2003. (Illus.). (J). spiral bd. 14.99 (978-1-59319-001-9(8)) LeapFrog Enterprises, Inc.

Lendler, Ian. An Undone Fairy Tale. Martin, Whitney, illus. 2005. 32p. (J). (gr. 1-3). 15.95 (978-0-689-86677-7(1) , Simon & Schuster Children's Publishing) Simon & Schuster Children's Publishing.

Leonhardt, Alice. The Princess & the Castle. 1999. (Illus.). (J). pap. 4.93 (978-0-7398-2414-6(7)) Steck-Vaughn.

Leroe, Ellen. Princess Fun: Count 10 to 1. Takahashi, Hideko, illus. 2005. 12p. (J). 5.99 (978-0-689-86895-5(2) , Little Simon) Simon & Schuster Children's Publishing.

Levine, Gail Carson. The Fairy's Return & Other Princess Tales. 2006. (Princess Tales Ser.). 400p. (J). 14.99 (978-0-06-113061-8(3)) HarperCollins Pubs.

—For Biddle's Sake. Elliott, Mark, illus. 2002. (Princess Tales Ser.). 112p. (J). (gr. 2-6). 9.99 (978-0-06-000094-3(5)) HarperCollins Pubs.

—The Princess Tales, No. 2. Elliott, Mark, illus. 2004. (Princess Tales Ser.). 256p. (J). pap. 6.99 (978-0-06-056043-0(6) , Harper Trophy) HarperCollins Pubs.

—The Princess Test. Elliott, Mark, illus. 1999. (Princess Tales Ser.). 96p. (J). (gr. 2-7). 9.99 (978-0-06-028062-8(X)) HarperCollins Pubs.

—The Two Princesses of Bamarre. (J). 2003. 256p. (gr. 5 up). pap. 6.99 (978-0-06-440966-7(X)); 2004. (Illus.). 304p. (gr. 7 up). reprint ed. pap. 6.99 (978-0-06-057580-9(8)) HarperCollins Pubs.

—The Two Princesses of Bamarre. 2003. (Illus.). (gr. 7-12). lib. bdg. 14.15 (978-0-613-67233-7(X)) Tandem Library Bks.

Lewis, C. S. Prince Caspian. Armstrong, Matthew S., illus. 2007. (Narnia Ser.). 32p. (J). 16.99 ***978-0-06-117327-1(4))**; lib. bdg. 17.89 **(*978-0-06-117328-8(2))** Harper-Collins Pubs.

—Prince Caspian Read-Aloud Edition: The Return to Narnia. Baynes, Pauline, illus. 2008. (Narnia Ser.). 240p. (J). 17.99 **(*978-0-06-122764-6(1))** HarperCollins Pubs.

—The Return to Narnia: The Rescue of Prince Caspian. Armstrong, Matthew, illus. 2006. (Narnia Ser.). 32p. (J). 16.99 (978-0-06-113110-3(5)) ; lib. bdg. 17.89 (978-0-06-113111-0(3)) HarperCollins Pubs.

—La Silla de Plata. 2003. (SPA.). pap. (978-956-13-1672-0(2) , AB3881) Bello, Andres CHL. *Dist:* Lectorum Pubns., Inc.

—The Silver Chair. Baynes, Pauline, illus. 2006. (Narnia Ser.). 256p. (J). 11.99 (978-0-06-112528-7(8)) Harper-Collins Pubs.

Lewison, Wendy Cheyette. The Prince & the Potty. Motoyama, Keiko, illus. 2006. 40p. (J). (ps). 12.95 (978-0-689-87808-4(7) , Simon & Schuster Children's Publishing) Simon & Schuster Children's Publishing.

—The Princess & the Potty. Brown, Rick, illus. 2nd ed. 2005. (Stories to Go! Ser.). 40p. (J). 4.99 (978-0-689-87838-1(9) , Aladdin) Simon & Schuster Children's Publishing.

—Princess Buttercup: A Flower Princess Story. 2001. (ps-2). lib. bdg. 11.80 (978-0-613-35619-0(5)) Tandem Library Bks.

Lewman, David. Bob Esponja y la princesa (SpongeBob & the Princess) Ziegler, Argentina Palacios, tr. Bond, Clint, illus. 2006. (SpongeBob SquarePants Ser.). (SPA.). 24p. (J). pap. 3.99 (978-1-4169-1185-2(5) , Libros Para Ninos) Simon & Schuster Children's Publishing.

—SpongeBob & the Princess. Bond, Clint, illus. 2004. (SpongeBob SquarePants 8 X 8 Paperback ; #5 Ser.). 24p. (J). pap. 3.99 (978-0-689-86581-7(3) , Simon Spotlight/Nickelodeon) Simon & Schuster Children's Publishing.

—Spongebob & the Princess. Bond, Clint, illus. ed. 2005. (SpongeBob Squarepants Ser.: 5). 22p. (J). lib. bdg. 15.00 (978-1-59054-826-4(4)) Fitzgerald Bks.

Liessner, Richard. The Foot Prince. Liessner, Richard, illus. 2006. (Illus.). 24p. (J). 9.95 (978-0-9766129-5-7(X)) Raindrop Bks.

Limke, Jeff & Randall, Ron. Tristan & Isolde: The Warrior & the Princess: A British Legend: Adapted by Jeff Limke from Celtic Mythology & from Sir Thomas Malory's le Morte D'Arthur: Illustrations by Ron Randall. 2008. (Graphic Myths & Legends Ser.). (J). lib. bdg. 26.60 **(*978-0-8225-7526-9(4)** , Graphic Universe) Lerner Publishing Group.

Linamen, Karen Scalf. Princess Madison & the Paisley Puppy. 2007. (Princess Madison Trilogy Ser.). (Illus.). 32p. (J). 12.99 (978-0-8007-1841-1(0)) Revell.

—Princess Madison & the Royal Darling Pageant. 2006. (Princess Madison Trilogy Ser.). (Illus.). 32p. (J). 12.99 (978-0-8007-1840-4(2)) Revell.

—Princess Madison & the Whispering Woods. 2006. (Princess Madison Trilogy Ser.). (Illus.). 32p. 12.99 (978-0-8007-1842-8(9)) Revell.

Linke, Uwe. Princess Moving Book. 2007. (J). bds. 8.95 (978-0-7358-2125-5(9)) North-South Bks., Inc.

Linker, Julie. Disenchanted Princess. 2007. 240p. (YA). (gr. 9 up). pap. 8.99 **(*978-1-4169-3472-1(3)** , Simon Pulse) Simon & Schuster Children's Publishing.

Lionni, Leo. Le Petit Prince. 1999. (FRE.). 123p. (J). (gr. 4-7). pap. 10.95 (978-2-07-051328-4(9)) Schoenhof's Foreign Bks., Inc.

Lisle, Rebecca. Toad Prince. 2005. (Illus.). 64p. (J). 7.99 **(*978-1-84270-315-1(3))** Transworld Publishers Ltd. GBR. *Dist:* Independent Pubs. Group.

Little Princess. 2004. (J). (978-0-9767179-6-6(4)) ABC Development, Inc.

Lodico, Cheryl Madeleine. The Ice Princess Trilogy. 2007. pap. 20.00 **(*978-0-8059-8967-0(6))** Dorrance Publishing Co., Inc.

Losantos, Christina, illus. Beauty & the Beast/La Bella y la Bestia: A Bilingual Book! 2007. (ENG & SPA.). 32p. (J). (ps-3). pap. 6.95 (978-0-8118-5970-7(3)) Chronicle Bks. LLC.

Losantos, Cristina, illus. Beauty & the Beast/La Bella y la Bestia: A Bilingual Book! 2007. (ENG & SPA.). 32p. (J). (ps-3). 14.95 (978-0-8118-5969-1(X)) Chronicle Bks. LLC.

Lost! Individual Title, 6 Packs. (gr. k-1). 23.00 (978-0-7635-9069-7(X)) Rigby Education.

Lost! Set D Individual Title, 6 Packs. (Smart Start Ser.). (gr. k-1). 23.00 (978-0-7635-0450-2(5)) Rigby Education.

Lou Weber Staff, ed. Disney Princess Magic: First Look & Find. 2004. (Illus.). 16p. bds. 7.98 (978-1-4127-3074-7(0) , 7227000) Publications International, Ltd.

Louise, Martha. Why Kings & Queens Don't Wear Crowns. Sevig-Fajardo, Mari Elise, tr. from NOR. Nyhus, Svein, illus. 2005. Orig. Title: Hvorfor de kongelige ikke har krone pa Hodet. 32p. (J). 17.95 (978-1-57534-037-1(2) , CSC 100) Skandisk, Inc.

Love, Ann. A Present for the Prince. Goffe, Toni, illus. 2001. (Selected Stories Published in Other Lands). (J). (gr. k-3). lib. bdg. 17.95 (978-1-56674-290-0(0)) Forest Hse. Publishing Co., Inc.

—Ten Little Monkeys. 2001. (Illus.). 16p. (J). 15.95 (978-0-85953-888-6(5)) Child's Play-International.

Love, D. Anne. The Secret Prince. 2005. 240p. (J). 16.95 (978-0-689-84426-3(3) , McElderry, Margaret K.) Simon & Schuster Children's Publishing.

Low, Vicki. First Emperor. Mayhew, Sara E., illus. 2007. 48p. (J). lib. bdg. 23.08 **(*978-1-4242-1626-0(5))** Fitzgerald Bks.

Lum, Kate. Princesses Are Not Quitters. Hellard, Sue & Hellard, Susan, illus. 2003. 32p. (J). (gr. k-3). 16.95 (978-1-58234-762-2(X) , Bloomsbury Children) Bloomsbury Publishing.

MacDonald, George. The Light Princess. 110p. (J). (gr. 4-5). pap. 5.95 (978-0-8072-1396-4(9) , Listening Library) Random Hse. Audio Publishing Group.

—The Lost Princess. Sadler, Glenn Edward, ed. Oberdieck, Bernhard, illus. 1999. 134p. (J). reprint ed. 25.00 (978-0-7881-6847-5(9)) DIANE Publishing Co.

—The Princess & Curdie. l.t. ed. 2005. 320p. pap. (978-1-84637-020-5(5)) Echo Library.

—The Princess & Curdie. 1998. (Twelve-Point Ser.). 177p. reprint ed. lib. bdg. 24.00 (978-1-58287-059-5(4)) North Bks.

—The Princess & Curdie. Stratton, Helen, illus. 2003. 162p. pap. 12.99 (978-1-57646-634-6(5)) Quiet Vision Publishing.

—The Princess & the Goblin. 2003. (Illus.). 160p. (J). 19.95 (978-1-81514-970-2(1)) Antique Collectors' Club.

—The Princess & the Goblin. 2005. 108p. per. 5.99 (978-1-4209-2557-9(1)) Digireads.com.

—The Princess & the Goblin. 2004. reprint ed. pap. 1.99 (978-1-4192-7868-6(1)) Kessinger Publishing, LLC.

—The Princess & the Goblin. 1998. (Twelve-Point Ser.). 154p. reprint ed. lib. bdg. 24.00 (978-1-58287-060-1(8)) North Bks.

—The Princess & the Goblin. Hughes, Arthur, illus. 2003. 136p. pap. 12.99 (978-1-57646-633-9(7)) Quiet Vision Publishing.

—The Princess & the Goblin Book & Charm. 2004. (Charming Classics). (Illus.). 272p. (J). pap. 6.99 (978-0-06-009552-9(0) , Harper Festival) HarperCollins Pubs.

MacDonald, George & Walton, Nick. The Princess & the Goblin. 1998. (Illus.). 160p. 19.95 (978-1-85149-701-0(3)) Antique Collectors' Club.

MacDonald, Maryann. Princess Josie's Pets. Bluthenthal, Diana Cain, illus. 1998. (Hyperion Chapters Ser.). 64p. (J). (gr. 2-4). pap. 3.95 (978-0-7868-1134-2(X)) Disney Pr.

Mack, Todd. Princess Penelope Takes Charge. Gran, Julia, illus. 2006. 32p. (J). pap. 16.99 (978-0-439-67380-8(1) , Scholastic Pr.) Scholastic, Inc.

Magic Wand Disney Princess. 2005. (Illus.). 10p. (J). bds. 15.98 (978-1-4127-3537-7(8) , 7263500) Publications International, Ltd.

Maisner, Heather. Diary of a Princess: A Tale from Marco Polo's Travels. Moxley, Sheila, illus. 2006. 26p. (gr. k-4). reprint ed. pap. 8.00 (978-1-4223-5302-8(8)) DIANE Publishing Co.

—Diary of a Princess: A Tale from Marco Polo's Travels. Moxley, Sheila, illus. 2004. 32p. (J). (978-0-7112-1854-3(4)); pap. 7.95 (978-1-84507-148-6(4)) Lincoln, Frances Ltd. GBR. *Dist:* Transition Vendor, Perseus Distribution.

Major, Roberta Olsen. The Prince in the Flower Bed. 2001. 147p. (YA). pap. 13.95 (978-1-59088-977-0(0)) Wings ePress, Inc.

Malcolm, Jahnna N. The Diamond Princess & the Magic Ball. 1998. (Jewel Kingdom Ser.: No. 9). (Illus.). (J). (gr. 3-5). pap. 3.99 (978-0-590-11739-5(4) , Scholastic Paperbacks) Scholastic, Inc.

—The Diamond Princess Steps Through the Mirror, No. 12. 1999. (Jewel Kingdom Ser.: No. 12). 80p. (J). (gr. 3-5). pap. 3.99 (978-0-590-97880-4(2)) Scholastic, Inc.

—The Emerald Princess Finds a Fairy. 1998. (Jewel Kingdom Ser.: No. 8). (Illus.). 66p. (J). (gr. 3-5). pap. 3.99 (978-0-590-11738-8(6) , Scholastic Paperbacks) Scholastic, Inc.

—The Emerald Princess Follows a Unicorn. 1999. (Jewel Kingdom Ser.: No. 11). (Illus.). 80p. (J). (gr. 3-5). pap. 3.99 (978-0-590-97879-8(9)) Scholastic, Inc.

—The Jewel Princesses & the Missing Crown. 1998. (Jewel Kingdom Ser.: No. 1). (J). (gr. 3-5). 4.99 (978-0-590-37705-8(1) , Scholastic Paperbacks) Scholastic, Inc.

—The Ruby Princess & the Baby Dragon. 590th ed. 1998. (Jewel Kingdom Ser.: No. 9). (Illus.). 80p. (J). (gr. 3-5). pap. 3.99 (978-0-590-97877-4(2)) Scholastic, Inc.

—The Sapphire Princess Helps a Mermaid. 1999. (Jewel Kingdom Ser.: No. 10). (Illus.). 80p. (J). (gr. 3-5). pap. 3.99 (978-0-590-97878-1(0)) Scholastic, Inc.

—The Sapphire Princess Hunts for Treasure. 1998. (Jewel Kingdom Ser.: No. 6). (J). (gr. 3-5). 3.99 (978-0-590-11714-2(9)) Scholastic, Inc.

Malea. Princess Melia. 2007. 145p. (J). pap. 15.95 **(*978-1-58909-367-6(4))** Bookstand Publishing.

Malone, Peter, illus. The Classic Treasurey of Princess Fairy Tales. 2007. 54p. (J). 7.98 **(*978-0-7624-3162-5(8)** , Courage Bks.) Running Pr. Bk. Pubs.

Man-Kong, Mary. Barbie as the Island Princess. Tormey, Carlotta, illus. 2007. (Picture Book Ser.). 32p. (J). (ps-2). 8.99 **(*978-0-375-84217-7(9)** , Golden Bks.) Random Hse. Children's Bks.

—Barbie as the Island Princess: A Storybook. 2007. (Pictureback(R) Ser.). (Illus.). 24p. (J). (ps-2). 3.99 **(*978-0-375-84218-4(7)** , Random Hse. Bks. for Young Readers) Random Hse. Children's Bks.

—Barbie as the Island Princess:MYOLG. 2007. (Make Your Own LGB Ser.). (Illus.). 16p. (J). (ps-2). 5.99 **(*978-0-375-84219-1(5)** , Golden Bks.) Random Hse. Children's Bks.

Man-Kong, Mary. The Princess Party Book. Legramandi, Francesco & Matta, Gabriella, illus. 2005. 32p. (J). (ps-3). pap. 7.99 (978-0-7364-2314-4(1) , RH/Disney) Random Hse. Children's Bks.

Man-Kong, Mary & Golden Books Staff. Barbie in the Twelve Dancing Princesses. 2006. (Illus.). 24p. (J). (ps-2). pap. 3.99 (978-0-375-83762-3(0) , Golden Bks.) Random Hse. Children's Bks.

—Barbie in the Twelve Dancing Princesses. Tormey, Carlotta, illus. 2006. 32p. (J). (ps-2). 8.99 (978-0-375-83748-7(5) , Golden Bks.) Random Hse. Children's Bks.

Manjula Padmanabhan, illus. Unprincess! 2005. 98p. (J). **(*978-0-14-333495-8(6)** , Puffin) Penguin Group (USA) Inc.

Mann, Pamela. The Frog Princess? (Illus.). (J). 2002. (TUR & ENG.). 24p. 15.95 (978-1-85269-324-4(X)); 2000. (BEN & ENG., 24p. 19.95 (978-1-85269-317-6(7)); 2000. (GUJ & ENG., 25p. 19.95 (978-1-85269-322-0(3)); 2000. (PAN & ENG., 24p. 17.95 (978-1-85269-323-7(1)); 2000. (SOM & ENG., 24p. 15.95 (978-1-85269-319-0(3)); 2000. (URD & ENG., 24p. 17.95 (978-1-85269-321-3(5)) Mantra Publishing, Ltd. GBR. *Dist:* AIMS International Bks., Inc.

Marlowe, Pete. The Trailer Park Princesses. Franson, Leanne, illus. 2000. 32p. (J). (gr. k-2). pap. 6.95 (978-1-55037-616-6(0)); lib. bdg. 16.95 (978-1-55037-617-3(9)) Annick Pr., Ltd. CAN. *Dist:* Firefly Bks., Ltd.

Marrs, Christie, creator. The Promise Keeper. l.t. ed. 2003. (Illus.). 53p. (J). mass mkt. 5.99 (978-1-928890-16-4(4)) I.B. Hoofinit Co.

Martin, Ann M. Karen's Snow Princess. 1998. (Baby-Sitters Little Sister Ser.: No. 94). (J). (gr. 3-7). pap. 3.99 (978-0-590-06592-4(0)) Scholastic, Inc.

—Karen's Snow Princess. 1998. (Baby-Sitters Little Sister Ser.: No. 94). (J). (gr. 3-7). (978-0-606-13170-4(1)) Tandem Library Bks.

Martin, Rafe. The Storytelling Princess. Root, Kimberly Bulcken, illus. 2003. 32p. (J). (ps-17). pap. 6.99 (978-0-14-250085-9(2) , Puffin) Penguin Group (USA) Inc.

—The Storytelling Princess. Root, Kimberly B., illus. 2001. 1p. (J). (gr. k up). 16.99 (978-0-399-22924-4(8) , Putnam Juvenile) Penguin Group (USA) Inc.

—Storytelling Princess. 2003. (gr. 3-6). lib. bdg. 15.30 (978-0-613-67306-8(9)) Tandem Library Bks.

Martin, Rafe & Bellm, Dan. Birdwing. (J). 2007. 384p. pap. 6.99 (978-0-439-21168-0(9)); 2005. 368p. pap. 16.99 (978-0-439-21167-3(0)) Scholastic, Inc. (Levine, Arthur A. Bks.).

Marzollo, Jean. Shanna's Princess Show, No. 1. Evans, Shane W., illus. 2001. 24p. (J). 13.49 (978-0-7868-2549-3(9) , Jump at the Sun) Hyperion Bks. for Children.

Masini, Beatrice. A Brave Little Princess. Handley, Diana, tr. Monaco, Octavia, illus. 2000. 32p. (J). (gr. k-2). lib. bdg. 16.99 (978-1-84148-267-5(6)) Barefoot Bks., Inc.

Mason, Jane & Stevens, Sarah. Princess School. Manzanero, Paula, ed. 2006. (Princess School Ser.). 432p. (J). pap. 9.99 (978-0-439-85198-5(X) , Scholastic) Scholastic, Inc.

Mass, Wendy. Rapunzel: The One with All the Hair. 2006. (Twice upon a Time Ser.: No. 1). 208p. (J). pap. 5.99 (978-0-439-79656-9(3) , Scholastic Paperbacks) Scholastic, Inc.

—Twice upon a Time No. 2: Sleeping Beauty. 2006. (Apple Ser.). (Illus.). 176p. (J). pap. 5.99 (978-0-439-79657-6(1) , Scholastic Paperbacks) Scholastic, Inc.

Matthews, Caitlin. The Barefoot Book of Princesses. Whelan, Olwyn, illus. 1998. 64p. (J). (gr. 4-7). 19.99 incl. audio compact disk (978-1-901223-74-3(4)) Barefoot Bks., Inc.

Maxwell, Miranda. Princess Lola's Wobbly Week. 2005. (Illus.). (J). 20.00 (978-0-340-87848-4(7)); pap. 10.99 (978-0-340-87849-1(5)) Hodder General Publishing Division GBR. (Hodder & Stoughton). *Dist:* Trafalgar Square Publishing.

Mayher, Lauren. The Legend of Darien: A Hero Rises. 2007. pap. 12.95 **(*978-0-9794545-0-9(6))** Blue Eyed Mayhem Publishing.

McAllister, Angela. Digory & the Lost King. Beck, Ian, illus. 2007. 128p. (J). (gr. 3-5). 14.95 **(*978-1-59990-088-9(2))**; pap. 5.95 **(*978-1-59990-089-6(0))** Bloomsbury Publishing.

McAllister, Angela. Felix & the Blue Dragon. Smith, Mary Claire, illus. 2005. 32p. (J). (ps). 16.99 (978-1-84255-182-0(5)) Orion Children's Bks. GBR. *Dist:* Independent Pubs. Group.

McCafferty, Catherine. Rapunzel. Spong, Clive, illus. 2002. (Brighter Child Keepsake Stories Ser.). 32p. (J). (ps-3). pap. 3.99 (978-1-57768-379-7(X) , Brighter Child) School Specialty Publishing.

McCaffrey, Anne. An Exchange of Gifts. 2002. (YA). pap. 7.99 (978-1-880448-44-1(0)) Wildside Pr.

McCaughrean, Geraldine. Beauty & the Beast. Blythe, Gary, illus. 2003. (Picture Bks.). 32p. (J). (ps-3). 15.95 (978-1-57505-491-9(4) , Carolrhoda Bks.) Lerner Publishing Group.

—Princess Stories. 2000. (Illus.). 92p. (J). pap. 22.95 (978-0-385-40783-0(1)) Transworld Publishers Ltd. GBR. *Dist:* Trafalgar Square Publishing.

McClintock. Little Princess Picture Book. Date not set. (Illus.). 40p. (J). (ps-3). pap. 4.99 (978-0-06-443539-0(3)) HarperCollins Pubs.

McClintock, R. Princess & the Goblin. 2000. 40p. (J). (ps-3). pap. 4.95 (978-0-06-443538-3(5)) HarperCollins Pubs.

McGhee, Heather. The Wild Adventures of a Curious Princess. Myers, Shari, illus. 2007. (J). per. 19.95 **(*978-0-9788985-9-5(1))** A Better Be Write Pub.

McKee, David. El Principe Pedro y el oso de Peluche. (SPA.). (J). 7.95 (978-958-04-6258-3(5)) Norma S.A. COL. *Dist:* Distribuidora Norma, Inc.

McKnight, Gillian. The Frog Prince. 2006. 240p. (J). mass mkt. 5.99 (978-0-689-87735-3(8) , Simon Pulse) Simon & Schuster Children's Publishing.

—To Catch a Prince. 2006. 240p. (YA). mass mkt. 5.99 (978-0-689-87734-6(X) , Simon Pulse) Simon & Schuster Children's Publishing.

McMakin, Jordan. Prince Ezrick & the Morpheas Curse, 4 vols. 2005. (Illus.). 304p. (J). per. 11.95 (978-0-9764184-0-5(1)) Canterwine Pr.

McMullan, Kate. A Wedding for Wiglaf? 2003. (Dragon Slayers' Academy Ser.: No. 4). (gr. 3-6). lib. bdg. 13.00 (978-0-613-72540-8(9)) Tandem Library Bks.

Melling, David. Good Knight, Sleep Tight. 2005. (Illus.). 32p. (J). (ps-2). 14.99 (978-0-7641-5878-0(3)) Barron's Educational Series, Inc.

—The Kiss That Missed. 2002. (Illus.). 32p. (J). (gr. k-2). 14.95 (978-0-7641-5451-5(6)) Barron's Educational Series, Inc.

Mendo, Miguel Angel, contrib. by. The Old Princess Armonia. 2002. (Illus.). 56p. 16.00 (978-88-7757-141-0(1)) Hopefulmonster Editore ITA. *Dist:* D.A.P./Distributed Art Pubs.

Metaxas, Eric. Princess Scargo & the Birthday Pumpkin. Barbour, Karen, illus. 2005. (Rabbit Ears-A Classic Tale Ser.). 40p. (J). (gr. k-5). 25.65 (978-1-59197-769-8(X)) Spotlight.

Millman, Selena. More Than a Hero. 2006. 92p. (YA). per. 11.37 **(*978-1-4243-2351-7(7))** Independent Publisher Services.

—The Prince & Me. 2006. 146p. (YA). per. 11.20 **(*978-1-4243-2353-1(3))** Independent Publisher Services.

Mills, Lauren A. The Dog Prince. Mills, Lauren A. & Nolan, Dennis, illus. 2001. 32p. (J). (gr. 1-3). 15.95 (978-0-316-57417-4(1)) Little, Brown Bks. for Young Readers.

Milord, Susan. Willa the Wonderful. (Illus.). 32p. (J). (gr. k-3). 2005. 5.95 (978-0-618-58543-4(5)); 2003. tchr. ed. 15.00 (978-0-618-27522-9(3)) Houghton Mifflin Co. Trade & Reference Div.

Mitchell, N. J. W. The Adventures of Princess Nightshade. 2000. 264p. (J). pap. 13.95 (978-0-595-14024-4(6)) iUniverse, Inc.

Miyazaki, Hayao. Princess Mononoke Film Comics, Vol. 1. 2006. (Princess Mononoke Film Comics Ser.). (YA). 9.99 (978-1-4215-0597-8(5)) Viz Media.

MJ Illustrations Staff, illus. Snow Princess. 2006. (Strawberry Shortcake Ser.). 16p. (J). (ps-1). pap. 4.99 (978-0-448-44410-9(0) , Grosset & Dunlap) Penguin Group (USA) Inc.

Moerbeck, Kees, illus. & des. Cinderella. Moerbeck, Kees, des. 2006. 9.99 (978-1-84643-019-0(4)) Child's Play-International.

Monnar, Ana. Heart of Stone. Michaud, Nancy, illus. 2007. 24p. (J). per. 11.99 **(*978-0-9768035-5-3(0))** Readers Are Leaders U.S.A., Inc.

Montejo, Victor. Blanca Flor; Una princessa Maya, Spanish-Language Edition. Yockteng, Rafael, illus. 2005. (SPA.). 36p. (J). 16.95 (978-0-88899-600-8(4)) Groundwood Bks. CAN. *Dist:* Perseus Distribution.

Montes, Graciela. Había una vez una Princesa. 2006. 26p. 8.95 (978-1-59820-215-1(4) , Alfaguara) Santillana USA Publishing Co., Inc.

Mooney, E. S. Scary Princess. Mardersian, Mark, illus. 2001. (Powerpuff Girls Chapter Bks.: Vol. 7). 64p. (J). (gr. 1-4). pap. 3.99 (978-0-439-25058-0(7)) Scholastic, Inc.

—Scary Princess. 2001. (gr. k-3). lib. bdg. 11.80 (978-0-613-43878-0(7)) Tandem Library Bks.

Morningforest, Chris & Raymond, Rebecca. Princess Underdrawers & the Dragon. 2006. 37p. (J). pap. 15.58 (978-1-4116-8837-7(6)) Lulu.com.

Moser, Cherry. Backyard Adventures. 2005. 51p. pap. 12.95 (978-1-4137-6202-0(6)) PublishAmerica, Inc.

Mowery, Peg K. Once upon A Princess. 2006. 16.50 (978-0-8059-9027-0(5)) Dorrance Publishing Co., Inc.

Moxilada, J. L. Jonty Jones Takes Guard. 2005. 242p. pap. 16.88 (978-1-4116-4126-6(4)) Lulu.com.

Munsch, Robert. The Paper Bag Princess 25th Anniversary Edition: The Story Behind the Story. Martchenko, Michael, illus. 25th anniv. ed. 2005. 64p. (J). (ps-12). 19.95 (978-1-55037-915-0(1)) Annick Pr., Ltd. CAN. *Dist:* Firefly Bks., Ltd.

—La Princesse Dans un Sac. Martchenko, Michael, illus. 2003. (Annikins Ser.). (FRE.). 32p. (J). (ps-2). pap. 0.99 (978-1-55037-391-2(9)) Annick Pr., Ltd. CAN. *Dist:* Firefly Bks., Ltd.

Murphy, Emily. The Princess of Booray. Smith, illus. 2005. (J). (978-0-9742891-2-0(4)) Marriwell Publishing.

Napoli, Donna Jo. Hush: An Irish Princess' Tale. 2007. 320p. (YA). (gr. 7 up). 16.99 **(*978-0-689-86176-5(1))** Simon & Schuster Children's Publishing.

Nathan, Sarah. A Dream Come True. 2007. 32p. (gr. 1). pap. 3.99 (***978-1-4231-0909-9(0)***) Disney Pr.

—Enchanted Storybook. rev. ed. 2007. 48p. (J). (gr. 2-7). 8.99 (***978-1-4231-0911-2(2)***) Disney Pr.

Nef, Count. Princess Navina Visits Nueva Malvolia. Reid, Diana, illus. 1999. 52p. (Orig.). pap. 9.95 (978-0-915728-14-5(1)) Lytton Publishing Co.

Negrin, Fabian. The Princess & the Rainbow Coat. Waters, Fiona, illus. 2005. 32p. (J). (978-1-84458-411-6(9)) Chrysalis Children's Bks.

Negrin, Fabian, illus. Wizard Tales. 2003. 96p. 19.95 (978-1-55285-558-4(9)) Whitecap Bks., Ltd. CAN. *Dist:* Graphic Arts Ctr. Publishing Co.

Newberry, E. Fannie. Sara, a Princess. 2006. 26.99 (***978-1-4280-0737-6(7)***); pap. 20.99 (***978-1-4280-0716-1(4)***) IndyPublish.com.

Nguy, Hoa X. The Bamboo Girl. 2007. 84p. (J). pap. 20.00 (***978-0-8059-7562-8(4)***) Dorrance Publishing Co., Inc.

Novak, Matt. My Froggy Valentine. 2008. (Illus.). 16p. (J). (ps-1). 7.95 (***978-1-59643-204-8(7)***) Roaring Brook Pr.

Noyes, Deborah. Red Butterfly: How a Princess Smuggled the Secret of Silk Out of China. Blackall, Sophie, illus. 2007. 32p. (J). (gr. 1-5). 16.99 (***978-0-7636-2400-2(4)***) Candlewick Pr.

Noyes, Deborah & Haarsma, P. J. Red Butterfly: How a Princess Smuggled the Secret of Silk Out of China. Blackall, Sophie, illus. 2008. (Softwire Ser.). 272p. (J). (gr. 7). 16.99 (***978-0-7636-2710-2(0)***) Candlewick Pr.

Nwokolo, Nwanneka. Zara: The Girl Traveller. 2004. (ENG.). 76p. per. (***978-1-904744-58-0(3)***) Troubador Publishing Ltd.

O'Brien, Kathryn. I'd Be Your Princess. 2006. (Illus.). 32p. (J). 15.99 (978-0-7847-1513-0(0), 04090) Standard Publishing.

O'Connell, Tyne. Dueling Princes: The Calypso Chronicles, Book 3. 2006. 272p. (YA). pap. 7.95 (978-1-58234-900-8(2), Bloomsbury Children) Bloomsbury Publishing.

—Dumping Princes. (YA). 2007. 256p. pap. 7.95 (***978-1-59990-150-3(1)***, Bloomsbury Children); 2006. (Calypso Chronicles Ser.: Bk. 4). (Illus.). 304p. (gr. 7-10). 16.95 (978-1-58234-852-0(9)) Bloomsbury Publishing.

—Pulling Princes. 2005. (Calypso Chronicles : Bk. 1). 224p. (YA). reprint ed. pap. 7.95 (978-1-58234-688-5(7), Bloomsbury Children) Bloomsbury Publishing.

—Stealing Princes. 2006. (Calypso Chronicles Ser.: Bk. 2). 304p. (YA). reprint ed. pap. 7.95 (978-1-58234-905-3(3), Bloomsbury Children) Bloomsbury Publishing.

Oldfield, Jenny. Hollywood Princess. 2005. (Horses of Half Moon Ranch Ser.). (Illus.). (J). pap. (978-0-340-91071-9(2), Hodder Children's Books) Hodder Children's Division.

O'Malley, Kevin. Once upon a Cool Motorcycle Dude. O'Malley, Kevin et al, illus. 2005. 32p. (J). 16.95 (978-0-8027-8947-1(1)) Walker & Co.

Oppenheim, Joanne. The Prince's Bedtime. Latimer, Miriam, illus. 2005. 32p. (J). 16.99 (978-1-84148-597-3(7)) Barefoot Bks., Inc.

Oram, Hiawyn. Princess Chamomile Gets Her Way. 2001. (Illus.). (J). (978-0-606-21386-8(4)) Tandem Library Bks.

Ordal, Stina Langlo. Princess Aasta. 2002. (Illus.). 32p. (J). (ps-3). 16.95 (978-1-58234-783-7(2), Bloomsbury Children) Bloomsbury Publishing.

—Princess Aasta Event Kit. (J). (978-1-58234-806-3(5)) Bloomsbury Publishing.

Ormerod, Jan & Damon, Emma. Frog Princess. (Illus.). 2005. (J). pap. 9.99 (978-0-340-87372-4(8)); 2004. 32p. 17.95 (978-0-340-87371-7(X)) Hodder General Publishing Division GBR. (Hodder & Stoughton). *Dist:* Trafalgar Square Publishing.

Orndorff, John Christian. Prince John's Quest. Orndorff, Debora Morris, illus. 2000. 116p. (J). (gr. 4-8). pap. 7.95 (978-1-893213-01-2(3)) Pensive Bks.

Osmena, J. The Maids of Fairlight. 2004. 86p. pap. 14.95 (978-1-4137-3904-6(0)) PublishAmerica, Inc.

Osterlund, Anne. Aurelia. 2008. 288p. (YA). (gr. 7). pap. 8.99 (***978-0-14-240579-6(5)***, Puffin) Penguin Group (USA) Inc.

Our Princess Party. 2006. (YA). 12.95 (978-1-58117-453-3(5), Intervisual/Piggy Toes) Dalmatian Pr.

Ouren, Todd, illus. The Frog Prince: A Retelling of the Grimms' Fairy Tale. 2004. (Read-It! Readers Ser.). 32p. (C). (gr. k-3). 18.60 (978-1-4048-0313-8(0)) Picture Window Bks.

Page, Nick & Page, Claire. Sleeping Beauty: Ready to Read Level 1. 2007. (Ready to Read: Level 1 (Make Believe Ideas) Ser.). (Illus.). 31p. (J). (gr. k-2). 3.99 (***978-1-84610-441-1(6)***) Make Believe Ideas GBR. *Dist:* Ingram Pub. Services.

Page, Nick & Claire. The Autumn Princess. 2006. (Read with Me (Make Believe Ideas) Ser.). (Illus.). 32p. (J). (gr. k-2). 3.95 (978-1-84610-171-7(9)) Make Believe Ideas GBR. *Dist:* Ingram Pub. Services.

—Snow White: Sticker Activity Book. Willey, Bee, illus. 2006. (Read with Me (Make Believe Ideas) Ser.). 12p. (J). (gr. k-2). pap. 4.95 (978-1-84610-179-3(4)) Make Believe Ideas GBR. *Dist:* Ingram Pub. Services.

—The Winter Prince. 2006. (Read with Me (Make Believe Ideas) Ser.). (Illus.). 31p. (J). (gr. k-2). 3.95 (978-1-84610-172-4(7)) Make Believe Ideas GBR. *Dist:* Ingram Pub. Services.

Panev, Aleksandar. Queen Nzinga. Stefflbauer, Thomas, illus. 2007. 48p. (J). lib. bdg. 23.08 (***978-1-4242-1641-3(9)***) Fitzgerald Bks.

Paper Bag Princess. 1999. (J). 9.95 (978-1-56137-475-5(X)) Novel Units, Inc.

Paterson, Katherine. The Wide-Awake Princess. Vagin, Vladimir Vasil'evich, illus. 2000. 48p. (J). (gr. k-3). tchr. ed. 15.00 (978-0-395-53777-0(0), Clarion Bks.) Houghton Mifflin Co. Trade & Reference Div.

Pef. Belle lisse poire du prince De. pap. 16.95 (978-2-07-054806-4(6)) Gallimard, Editions FRA. *Dist:* Distribooks, Inc.

Pelizzari, Nora. Crystal Princess: The Runaway Rainbow. 2006. (My Little Pony Ser.). 24p. (J). pap. 3.99 (978-0-06-111693-3(9), Harper Festival) HarperCollins Pubs.

—The Princess Promenade. 2006. (My Little Pony Ser.). 24p. (J). pap. 3.99 (978-0-06-111691-9(2)) HarperCollins Pubs.

Perez, Marlene. Princess Rock & the Royal Inches. ed. 2004. (Shared Connections Ser.). (J). pap. 27.00 (978-1-4108-1633-7(8)) Benchmark Education Co.

—Princess Rock & the Royal Inches (Big Book) ed. 2004. (Shared Connections Ser.). (J). pap., instr.'s gde. ed. 27.00 (978-1-4108-1609-2(5)) Benchmark Education Co.

Perez, Vivian. Stolen Stories for My Nieces. 2007. (ENG.). 68p. per. 12.95 (***978-1-4241-6679-4(9)***) PublishAmerica, Inc.

Perlman, Janet, illus. & retold by. The Penguin & the Pea. Perlman, Janet, retold by. 2005. 32p. (J). (ps-2). (978-1-55074-832-1(7)) Kids Can Pr., Ltd.

Perrault, Charles & Grimm, Jacob W. Princess Tales, 4 bks., Set. Deru, Myriam et al, illus. 2007. (Classic Fairy Tales Ser.). 112p. (J). (ps-3). 19.95 (***978-0-7892-0950-4(0)***) Abbeville Pr., Inc.

Perrotti, P. J. Jason & the Enchanted Forest. 2004. 48p. pap. 12.95 (978-1-4137-4593-1(8)) PublishAmerica, Inc.

Peter Pauper Press Staff & Zschock, Heather. Princess Bella: An Art Activity Story Book for Princesses of All Ages. Barbas, Kerren, illus. 2005. (Activity Journal Ser.). 64p. (J). (ps-7). 14.99 (978-1-59359-972-0(2)) Peter Pauper Pr. Inc.

Peters, Stephanie & Hoffmann, E. My First Nutcracker. Bronson, Linda, illus. 2007. 32p. (J). (ps). 16.99 (978-0-525-47687-0(3), Dutton Juvenile) Penguin Group (USA) Inc.

Peters, Stephanie True. A Princess Primer: A Fairy Godmother's Guide to Being a Princess. Oberdieck, Bernhard & Gordeev, Denis, illus. 2006. 32p. (J). (ps). 19.99 (978-0-525-47765-5(9), Dutton Juvenile) Penguin Group (USA) Inc.

Peterseil, Yaacov. Princess Alopecia. Katz, Avi, illus. 1999. 32p. (J). (gr. 1-5). 14.95 (978-0-943706-26-9(2)); pap. 8.95 (978-0-943706-25-2(4)) Pitspopany Pr. (Devora Publishing).

Pierce, Meredith Ann. Birth of the Firebringer. 2003. (gr. 7-12). lib. bdg. 15.30 (978-0-613-67445-4(6)) Tandem Library Bks.

Piggy Toes Press Staff. Princess Palace. 2006. 22.95 (978-1-58117-492-2(6), Intervisual/Piggy Toes) Dalmatian Pr.

Pirotta, Saviour & Marks, Alan. The Lonely Princess. 2007. (J). (***978-1-59771-079-4(2)***) Sea-To-Sea Pubns.

Pomerantz, Charlotte. The Princess & the Admiral. Chen, Tony, illus. 2004. 48p. (gr. 4-7). pap. 8.95 (978-1-55861-061-3(8)) Feminist Pr. at The City Univ. of New York.

Ponti, Claude & Desarthe, Agnes. El Principito Puf. 2003. (SPA.). 102p. (978-84-8470-063-0(1)) Corimbo, Editorial S.L.

Posner, Pat. Princess Fidgety Feet. Norman, Philip, illus. 2003. 32p. (J). 15.95 (978-1-57768-447-3(8), Gingham Dog Pr.) School Specialty Publishing.

Posner-Sanchez, Andrea. A Pony for a Princess. 2002. (Disney Princess Ser.). (ps-2). lib. bdg. 11.80 (978-0-613-73659-6(1)) Tandem Library Bks.

Posner-Sanchez, Andrea & Man-Kong, Mary. Barbie & the Magic of Pegasus: A Storybook. 2005. (Random House Pictureback Book Ser.). (Illus.). (J). (***978-1-4156-2366-4(X)***) Random Hse. Children's Bks.

Prasadam, Smriti & Finn, Rebecca. My Princess Palace. 2008. (Illus.). 12p. (J). bds. 6.95 (***978-0-7475-8808-5(2)***) Bloomsbury Publishing Plc GBR. *Dist:* Independent Pubs. Group.

Pretty Princess- Royal Party. 2005. (J). bds. (978-1-4194-0061-2(4)) Paradise Pr., Inc.

Pretty Princess s/s - Beautiful Princess. 2005. (J). bds. (978-1-4194-0062-9(2)) Paradise Pr., Inc.

Pretty Princess s/s - Fit for a Princess. 2005. (J). bds. (978-1-4194-0060-5(6)) Paradise Pr., Inc.

Pretty Princess s/s - Wedding Day. 2005. (J). bds. (978-1-4194-0064-3(9)) Paradise Pr., Inc.

The Prince & the Pauper. 2000. (Illus.). (YA). 48p. stu. ed., per. 17.95 (978-1-56254-288-7(5), SP2885); 80p. per. 6.95 (978-1-56254-287-0(7), SP2877) Saddleback Educational Publishing.

Prince Apple Head Humpledink. 2006. 38p. (J). 13.68 (978-1-4116-7232-1(1)) Lulu.com.

La Princesa Dora: Magic Wand Adventure. 2005. (Illus.). 10p. (J). bds. 15.98 (978-1-4127-3536-0(X), 7263400) Publications International, Ltd.

Princesa Stephanie. 2005. (SPA.). (YA). per. 9.95 (978-0-9764982-8-5(6)) Legacy Publishing Services, Inc.

Princess & Frog. (Ladybird Bks.). (Illus.). 52p. (J). 12.95 incl. audio (978-0-86685-634-8(X)) International Bk. Ctr., Inc.

The Princess & the Fisherman. 1998. (Illus.). 40p. (YA). pap. 7.99 (978-0-9676090-0-3(3)) Palmer, Lina.

The Princess & the Magic Locket. 2003. (Illus.). 32p. (J). 5.98 (978-1-4054-1022-9(1)) Parragon, Inc.

Princess Aurora: A Special Day in Her Life. l.t. ed. 2005. (Illus.). 32p. (J). 5.95 (978-0-9766640-0-0(3), 212-279-3492) Attitudes in Dressing, Inc.

Princess Petal. 2002. (Dolly Board Book Ser.). bds. 4.98 (978-0-7525-8281-8(X)) Parragon, Inc.

Princess Rosa's Winter: Level M, 6 vols. 128p. (gr. 2-3). 49.95 (978-0-7699-0986-8(3)) Shortland Pubns. (U. S. A.) Inc.

Princesses Are Pretty. 2002. (Little Friends Ser.). 32p. (J). 2.98 (978-1-84273-424-7(5), Exclusive Editions) Parragon, Inc.

The Princess Who Lost Her Smile. 2006. (J). 19.95 (***978-0-9790682-0-1(7)***) Clear Braces L.L.C.

Prokofiev, Sergei & Gozzi, Carlo. The Love for Three Oranges. Gaudasinska, Elzbieta, illus. 2006. (Musical Stories Ser.: Vol. 1). 40p. (J). 16.95 (978-0-9646010-3-1(6)) Pumpkin Hse., Ltd.

Publications International, creator. Disney Princess. 2004. (Disney Princess Ser.). (Illus.). (J). (ps). per. 12.98 (978-0-7853-9019-0(7), 7195600) Publications International, Ltd.

Quindlen, Anna. Happily Ever After. Stevenson, James, illus. 1999. 64p. (J). (gr. 2-5). pap. 4.99 (978-0-14-038706-3(4), Puffin) Penguin Group (USA) Inc.

—Happily Ever After. 1999. (gr. 3-6). lib. bdg. 13.00 (978-0-613-17806-8(8)) Tandem Library Bks.

Rabin, Staton. The Curse of the Romanovs. 2007. 288p. (J). (gr. 7 up). 17.99 (978-1-4169-0208-9(2), McElderry, Margaret K.) Simon & Schuster Children's Publishing.

Rai, Lori. Princess Sheron & the Frog. l.t. ed. 2004. (Illus.). 20p. (J). 10.00 (978-0-9717419-5-9(6)) Law Offices of Harry Glick.

Random House Disney Staff. Cinderella. 2005. (Illus.). 48p. (J). (ps-2). pap. 2.99 (978-0-375-83069-3(3), Golden/Disney) Random Hse. Children's Bks.

—Cinderella. 2002. (gr. k-3). lib. bdg. 10.95 (978-0-613-73670-1(2)) Tandem Library Bks.

—Cinderella III: A Twist in Time. 2006. (Pictureback(R) Ser.). (Illus.). 24p. (J). (gr. k-3). pap. 3.99 (978-0-7364-2429-5(6), RH/Disney) Random Hse. Children's Bks.

—Disney Princess Bookbag. 2006. (Disney Princess Ser.). (Illus.). 32p. (J). (ps-2). pap. 4.99 (978-0-7364-2400-4(8), Golden/Disney) Random Hse. Children's Bks.

—Disney Princess Fun Kit. 2007. (Fun Kit Ser.). (Illus.). 48p. (J). (ps-2). pap. 9.99 (***978-0-7364-2491-2(1)***, Golden/Disney) Random Hse. Children's Bks.

—Dream Castle. Harding, Niall, illus. 2005. (Reusable Sticker Book Ser.). 12p. (J). (ps-3). pap. 6.99 (978-0-7364-2305-2(2), RH/Disney) Random Hse. Children's Bks.

—A Horse to Love: an Enchanted Stables Story. 2007. (Pictureback(R) Ser.). 16p. (J). (ps-2). pap. 3.99 (***978-0-7364-2504-9(7)***, RH/Disney) Random Hse. Children's Bks.

—My Best Friend Is a Princess: A Princess Friendship Treasury. 2007. (Toddler Board Bks.). 30p. (J). (gr. k-k). bds. 11.99 (***978-0-7364-2505-6(5)***, RH/Disney) Random Hse. Children's Bks.

—Pretty Princess Places. 2006. (Disney Princess Ser.). (Illus.). 12p. (J). (ps-k). bds. 5.99 (978-0-7364-2295-6(1), RH/Disney) Random Hse. Children's Bks.

—The Princess Puzzle Book. 2006. (Illus.). 10p. (J). (ps-2). 9.99 (978-0-7364-2406-6(7), RH/Disney) Random Hse. Children's Bks.

—Princess Secrets Collection. 2006. (Illus.). 32p. (J). (ps-2). 15.95 (978-0-7364-2427-1(X), RH/Disney) Random Hse. Children's Bks.

—Princess Story Collection. 2007. (Step into Reading Ser.). (Illus.). 160p. (J). (ps-1). pap. 7.99 (***978-0-7364-2486-8(5)***, RH/Disney) Random Hse. Children's Bks.

—Sweet & Spooky Halloween. Marrucchi, Elisa, illus. 2007. 24p. (J). (ps-2). pap. 3.99 (***978-0-7364-2453-0(9)***, RH/Disney) Random Hse. Children's Bks.

Random House Disney Staff. 12 Princess Stories. 2006. (Illus.). 176p. (J). (ps-2). 10.99 (978-0-7364-2351-9(6), RH/Disney) Random Hse. Children's Bks.

Random House Disney Staff & Berrios, Frank. Princess Vol. II, Vol. II. 2004. (Disney Princess Ser.). (Illus.). 72p. (J). (ps-3). 8.99 (978-0-7364-2241-3(2), RH/Disney) Random Hse. Children's Bks.

Random House Disney Staff & Lagonegro, Melissa. Polite as a Princess. Harding, Niall & Harchy, Atelier Philippe, illus. 2006. 24p. (J). (ps-2). pap. 3.99 (978-0-7364-2367-0(2), RH/Disney) Random Hse. Children's Bks.

Random House Disney Staff & Liberts, Jennifer. Princess Collection 2. 2002. (Illus.). 12p. (J). (ps-3). bds. 9.99 (978-0-7364-2227-7(7), RH/Disney) Random Hse. Children's Bks.

Random House Disney Staff & Posner-Sanchez, Andrea. Lovely Cinderella. 2004. (Illus.). 16p. (J). (gr. k-ps). bds. 3.99 (978-0-7364-2212-3(9), RH/Disney) Random Hse. Children's Bks.

Rao, Chatura. Amie & the Chawl of Colour. Pathak, Ashutosh, illus. 2004. 100p. pap. (978-0-14-333592-4(8), Puffin) Penguin Group (USA) Inc.

Raote, Komilla. The Princess with the Longest Hair. Bist, Vandana, illus. 26p. (J). (978-81-85586-78-6(0)) Katha.

Rawson, Carol & Wilkes, Angela. Stories of Princes & Princesses. 2005. (Illus.). 48p. (J). (ps-7). pap. 9.95 incl. audio compact disk (978-0-7945-0960-6(6), Usborne) EDC Publishing.

Ray, Belinda. Charm Club Collection. Manzanero, Paula, ed. 2006. (Charm Club Ser.). 416p. (J). pap. 9.99 (978-0-439-85199-2(8), Scholastic) Scholastic, Inc.

Reader's Digest Editors. Barbie & the Twelve Dancing Princess. 2006. 12p. (J). bds. 9.99 (978-0-7944-1108-4(8)) Reader's Digest Assn., Inc., The.

—Disney Princess Music Player Storybook. 2004. (Disney Princess Ser.). (Illus.). 32p. (J). 24.99 incl. audio compact disk (978-0-7944-0444-4(8), Reader's Digest Children's Bks.) Reader's Digest Children's Publishing, Inc.

Reader's Digest Staff. Barbie & the Twelve Dancing Princess Panorama Sticker Storybook. 2006. (Barbie Movie Tie-in Ser.). 16p. (J). 7.99 (978-0-7944-1109-1(6)) Reader's Digest Assn., Inc., The.

Reader's Digest Staff. Disney Princess My Pod Storybook & Music Player. Disney & Reader's Digest, illus. 2007. (RD Innovative Book & Player Format Ser.). 40p. 24.99 (***978-0-7944-1301-9(3)***) Reader's Digest Assn., Inc., The.

The Real Princess: 6 Small Books. (gr. k-2). 23.00 (978-0-7635-8505-1(X)) Rigby Education.

Redbank, Tennant. Barbie in the Twelve Dancing Princesses. 2006. (Step into Reading Ser.). (Illus.). 32p. (J). (ps-2). lib. bdg. 11.99 (978-0-375-93780-4(3), Random Hse. Bks. for Young Readers) Random Hse. Children's Bks.

—Enchanted: A Storybook Life. 2nd rev. ed. 2007. 24p. (gr. 1). pap. 3.99 (***978-1-4231-1080-4(3)***) Disney Pr.

—Enchanted: Before the Fall. 2007. 24p. (gr. 1). pap. 3.99 (***978-1-4231-1079-8(X)***) Disney Pr.

Redbank, Tennant & Golden Books Staff. Barbie in the Twelve Dancing Princesses. 2006. (Step into Reading Ser.: No. 2). (Illus.). 32p. (J). (ps-2). pap. 3.99 (978-0-375-83780-7(9), Random Hse. Bks. for Young Readers) Random Hse. Children's Bks.

Redmond, Shirley-Raye. The Princess & Her Pony. 2007. (Illus.). 24p. (J). (***978-1-4048-1238-3(5)***) Picture Window Bks.

—The Princess & Her Pony. Senturk, Burak, illus. 2006. 24p. (J). (***978-1-4048-3142-1(8)***) Picture Window Bks.

—The Princesses' Lucky Day. 2007. (Illus.). 24p. (J). (***978-1-4048-1242-0(3)***) Picture Window Bks.

—The Princesses' Lucky Day. Rooney, Ronnie, illus. 2006. 24p. (J). (***978-1-4048-3143-8(6)***) Picture Window Bks.

Regan, Dian Curtis. Cam's Quest: The Continuing Story of Princess Nevermore & the Wizard's Apprentice. 2007. 256p. (J). (gr. 4-8). 17.95 (***978-1-58196-056-3(5)***) Darby Creek Publishing.

—Princess Nevermore. rev. ed. 2007. (J). 17.95 (***978-1-58196-055-6(7)***) Darby Creek Publishing.

Reis, Erica, illus. Sea Princess Azuri. 2006. 192p. (YA). (gr. 8 up). pap. 4.99 (978-1-59816-401-5(5), Tokyopop Kids) TOKYOPOP, Inc.

Richards, Kitty. The Enchanted Castle. Disney Storybook Artists Staff, illus. rev. ed. 2007. (Disney Princess Ser.). 4p. (ps-1). 12.99 (***978-1-4231-0912-9(0)***) Disney Pr.

Rigby Education Staff. Real Prince: Jumbled Tumble. (gr. k-2). 21.00 (978-0-7635-2423-4(9)) Rigby Education.

Rika, Tanaka. Kilala Princess. 20th rev. ed. 2007. (Illus.). pap. 5.99 (***978-1-59816-768-9(5)***, Tokyopop Kids) TOKYOPOP, Inc.

Rinaldi, Ann. The Redheaded Princess. 2008. 224p. (J). 15.99 (***978-0-06-073374-2(8)***); lib. bdg. 16.89 (***978-0-06-073375-9(6)***) HarperCollins Pubs.

Rizzo, Cynthia Marie. Angela & the Princess. 2006. 89p. pap. 14.95 (978-1-4241-2599-9(5)) PublishAmerica, Inc.

Robinson, Rob. The Princess & the Juggler. 2004. 154p. pap. 12.95 (978-0-595-30831-6(7)) iUniverse, Inc.

Romansky, Sally Rosenberg. Invincible. Ott, Margot Janet, illus. 2006. (J). pap. 8.95 (978-0-9723729-4-7(6)) Imagination Stage, Inc.

Rose, Marie. Princess Silver Tears & One Feather. l.t. ed. 2006. (Illus.). 32p. (J). lib. bdg. (***978-1-934190-07-4(1)***) Ocean Front Bk. Publishing, Inc.

Ross, Jillian. Alissa's Tournament Troubles. Faricy, Patrick, illus. 1999. (Stardust Classics: No. 4). 116p. (J). 12.95 (978-1-889514-31-4(4)); (gr. 2-5). pap. 5.95 (978-1-889514-32-1(2)) Dolls Corp.

Ross, Tony. Figuras. 2006. (Little Princess Ser.).Tr. of Shapes. (SPA.). (J). (ps-k). bds. 7.95 (978-968-19-1486-8(4), AT33280) Lectorum Pubns., Inc.

—Hora de Dormir. 2006. (Little Princess Ser.).Tr. of Bedtime. (SPA.). (J). (ps-k). bds. 7.95 (978-968-19-1488-2(0), AT33282) Lectorum Pubns., Inc.

—I Don't Want to Go to Bed. Ross, Tony, illus. 2004. (Illus.). 28p. (J). pap. 4.95 (978-1-929132-66-9(2)) Kane/Miller Bk. Pubs., Inc.

—I Want My Pacifier. Ross, Tony, illus. 2004. (Illus.). 28p. (J). pap. 4.95 (978-1-929132-65-2(4)) Kane/Miller Bk. Pubs., Inc.

—I Want My Potty. Ross, Tony, illus. 2007. (People Love Little Princess Books! Ser.). (Illus.). 28p. (J). pap. 4.95 (978-1-933605-23-4(5), 05234) Kane/Miller Bk. Pubs., Inc.

—I Want My Present! 2007. (Illus.). 12p. (J). (ps-k). 9.99 (***978-1-84270-481-3(8)***) Andersen GBR. *Dist:* Independent Pubs. Group.

—I Want My Tooth. Ross, Tony, illus. 2005. (Illus.). 28p. (J). (gr. k-2). pap. 4.95 (978-1-929132-85-0(9)) Kane/Miller Bk. Pubs., Inc.

—I Want to Go Home! 2006. (Illus.). 32p. (J). (978-1-84270-585-8(7)) Andersen.

—Mascotas. 2006. (Little Princess Ser.).Tr. of Pets. (SPA.). (J). (ps-k). bds. 7.95 (978-968-19-1485-1(6), AT33279) Lectorum Pubns., Inc.

—Say Please! Ross, Tony, illus. 2006. (People Love Little Princess Books! Ser.: 6). (Illus.). 28p. (J). pap. 4.95 (978-1-933605-16-6(2)) Kane/Miller Bk. Pubs., Inc.

—El Tiempo. 2006. (Little Princess Ser.).Tr. of Weather. (SPA.). (J). (ps-k). bds. 7.95 (978-968-19-1487-5(2), AT33281) Lectorum Pubns., Inc.

—Wash Your Hands. Ross, Tony, illus. 2006. (Illus.). 28p. (J). pap. 4.95 (978-1-933605-03-6(0)) Kane/Miller Bk. Pubs., Inc.

Roy, Ron. The Kidnapped King. Gurney, John Steven, illus. 2000. (A to Z Mysteries Ser.: No. 11). 96p. (J). (gr. k-3). lib. bdg. 11.99 (978-0-679-99459-6(9)); pap. 3.99 (978-0-679-89459-9(4)) Random Hse. Children's Bks. (Random Hse. Bks. for Young Readers).

—The Kidnapped King. Gurney, John Steven, illus. 2000. (A to Z Mysteries Ser.: No. 11). (J). (gr. k-3). lib. bdg. 11.80 (978-0-613-25876-0(2)); (978-0-606-18481-6(3)) Tandem Library Bks.

Ruble, Kam. Princess Annado Tandy's Versery-Rhymes. McMullen, T. C., illus. 2007. (J). per. (***978-0-9779680-4-6(9)***) Global Authors Pubns.

Ryan, Brittney. Holly Claus: The Christmas Princess. Long, Laurel & Bedrick, Jeffrey K., illus. 2007. 48p. (J). lib. bdg. 19.89 (***978-0-06-144023-6(X)***); 18.99 (***978-0-06-144022-9(1)***) HarperCollins Pubs. (Julie Andrews Collection).

—The Legend of Holly Claus. Long, Laurel, illus. 2004. 544p. (J). (gr. 4 up). 16.99 (978-0-06-058511-2(0) , Julie Andrews Collection) HarperCollins Pubs.

—Legend of Holly Claus. Long, Laurel, illus. 2006. 544p. (J). pap. 7.99 (978-0-06-058515-0(3) , Julie Andrews Collection) HarperCollins Pubs.

Sage, Angie. Flyte. Zug, Mark, illus. (Septimus Heap Ser.: Bk. 2). 544p. (J). (gr. 4 up). 2007. pap. 7.99 (978-0-06-057736-0(3) , Harper Trophy); 2006. lib. bdg. 18.89 (978-0-06-057735-3(5)); 2006. 17.99 (978-0-06-057734-6(7) , Tegen, Katherine Bks) HarperCollins Pubs.

—Magyk. Zug, Mark, illus. (Septimus Heap Ser.: Bk. 1). (J). (gr. 4 up). 2005. 576p. 17.99 (978-0-06-057731-5(2) , Tegen, Katherine Bks); 2005. 576p. lib. bdg. 18.89 (978-0-06-057732-2(0)); 2006. 608p. reprint ed. pap. 7.99 (978-0-06-057733-9(9) , Harper Trophy) Harper-Collins Pubs.

—Physik. Zug, Mark, illus. 2007. (Septimus Heap Ser.: Bk. 3). 560p. (J). (gr. 4 up). 17.99 (978-0-06-057737-7(1)); lib. bdg. 18.89 (978-0-06-057738-4(X)) HarperCollins Pubs. (Tegen, Katherine Bks).

Sage, Angie. Septimus Heap Box Set: Books 1 And 2. Zug, Mark, illus. 2007. (Septimus Heap Ser.). (J). pap. 15.99 (***978-0-06-136195-1(X)*** , Harper Trophy) HarperCollins Pubs.

Saint-Exupéry, Antoine de. Der Kleine Prinz. Leitgeb, Grete & Leitgeb, Josef, trs. from FRE. Saint-Exupéry, Antoine de, illus. 2001. Tr. of Petit Prince. (GER., Illus.). 104p. pap. 12.00 (978-0-15-601386-4(X) , Harvest Bks.) Harcourt Trade Pubs.

—The Little Prince. 2001. (Illus.). 109p. (J). reprint ed. pap. 15.00 (978-0-7567-5189-0(6)) DIANE Publishing Co.

—The Little Prince. 2000. (RUS.). pap. 10.95 (978-5-08-003870-9(5)) Detskaja Literatura RUS. *Dist:* Distribooks, Inc.

—The Little Prince. 2003. (Illus.). (J). (978-0-15-204730-6(1)) Harcourt Trade Pubs.

—The Little Prince. Howard, Richard, tr. from FRE. Saint-Exupéry, Antoine de, illus. 2000. (Illus.). 96p. (gr. 4-7). pap. 14.00 (978-0-15-601207-2(3)); pap. 10.00 (978-0-15-601219-5(7)) Harcourt Trade Pubs. (Harvest Bks.).

—The Little Prince. Howard, Richard, tr. from FRE. 2000. (Illus.). 96p. (YA). (gr. 4-7). 19.00 (978-0-15-202398-0(4)) Harcourt Trade Pubs.

—The Little Prince. 2000. (gr. 3-6). lib. bdg. 22.25 (978-0-613-71610-9(8)); (gr. 5-8). lib. bdg. 17.65 (978-0-8085-6337-2(8)); (Illus.). (J). (978-0-606-18806-7(1)) Tandem Library Bks.

—The Little Prince. 1998. (Children's Library). (J). pap. 3.95 Wordsworth Editions, Ltd. GBR. *Dist:* Combined Publishing.

—Le Petit Prince.Tr. of Little Prince. (FRE., Illus.). 64p. (J). (gr. 1-7). audio, audio compact disk 12.95 (978-2-921997-41-6(X)) Coffragants CAN. *Dist:* Penton Overseas, Inc.

—Le Petit Prince. 2000. Tr. of Little Prince. (FRE., Illus.). (J). pap. 15.95 (978-2-07-051578-3(8)) Gallimard, Editions FRA. *Dist:* Distribooks, Inc.

—Le Petit Prince: The Original French Edition. 2001. (FRE., Illus.). 96p. pap. 11.00 (978-0-15-601398-7(3) , Harvest Bks.) Harcourt Trade Pubs.

—Le Petit Prince: The Original French Edition. Saint-Exupéry, Antoine de, illus. rev. ed. 2001. (FRE., Illus.). 96p. 22.00 (978-0-15-216415-7(4)) Harcourt Trade Pubs.

—Il Piccolo Principe. 2000. Tr. of Little Prince. (ITA.). (J). pap. 15.95 (978-88-452-0511-8(8)); pap. 33.95 incl. audio (978-88-452-3835-2(0)) Fabbri - RCS Libri ITA. *Dist:* Distribooks, Inc.

—Piccolo Principe. (ITA.). pap. 17.95 (978-88-452-4741-5(4)) Fabbri - RCS Libri ITA. *Dist:* Distribooks, Inc.

—El Principito. (SPA., Illus.). 120p. (J). 10.95 (978-84-206-3628-3(2) , AZ6282) Alianza Editorial, S. A. ESP. *Dist:* Continental Bk. Co., Inc.

—El Principito. (SPA.). (YA). (gr. 5-8). cd-rom (978-84-415-0621-3(5) , SAL6064) Anaya Multimedia, S.A. ESP. *Dist:* Lectorum Pubns., Inc.

—El Principito. 2002. (SPA., Illus.). 96p. 6.19 (978-956-201-432-8(0) , 1060) Dolmen Ediciones S.A. CHL. *Dist:* Editorial Oceano De Mexico, S.A. DE C.V.

—El Principito. 1998. (SPA.). (J). (ps-3). pap. (978-968-15-0083-2(0)) Editores Mexicanos Unidos.

—El Principito. (SPA.). 10.98 (978-968-13-2180-2(4)) Editorial Diana, S.A. MEX. *Dist:* Continental Bk. Co., Inc.

—El Principito. (Coleccion Centro Literario). (SPA.). (J). pap., stu. ed. 7.95 (978-958-02-0475-6(6) , CAR005) Editorial Voluntad S.A. COL. *Dist:* Continental Bk. Co., Inc.

—El Principito. 2003. (SPA., Illus.). 96p. (YA). (gr. 5-8). (978-84-7888-438-4(6) , SAL7382) Emece Editores ESP. *Dist:* Lectorum Pubns., Inc.

—El Principito. (SPA.). (J). pap. 10.95 (978-950-04-0048-0(0)) Emecé Editores S.A. ARG. *Dist:* Planeta Publishing Corp.

—El Principito. 2001. (SPA.). (gr. 3-6). lib. bdg. 18.80 (978-0-613-71613-0(2)); (978-0-606-22619-6(2)) Tandem Library Bks.

Salas, Macarena, ed. La Bella Durmiente: Sleeping Beauty. 2007. (Bilingual Tales Ser.). (ENG & SPA.). 24p. (J). pap. 3.99 (978-0-439-87199-0(9) , Scholastic en Espanol) Scholastic, Inc.

—La Princesa y el Guisante: The Princess & the Pea. 2007. (Bilingual Tales Ser.). 24p. (J). pap. 3.99 (978-0-439-87197-6(2) , Scholastic en Espanol) Scholastic, Inc.

Santore, Charles. The Silk Princess. 2007. (J). (***978-0-375-83664-0(0));*** 40p. lib. bdg. (***978-0-375-93664-7(5))*** Random Hse. Children's Bks.

Sarfati, Sonia & Merola, Caroline. La Princesse Empoisonnee. 2000. (Roman Jeunesse Ser.). (FRE.). 96p. (J). (gr. 4-7). pap. (978-2-89021-428-6(1)) Diffusion du livre Mirabel.

Saunders, Catherine. The Essential Guide. 2005. (Illus.). 48p. (J). (ps-7). 12.99 (978-0-7566-1333-4(7)) Dorling Kindersley Publishing, Inc.

Saunders, Catherine & Dorling Kindersley Publishing Staff. Barbie Princess Tales. 2005. (Ultimate sticker Bks.). (Illus.). 16p. (J). (ps-7). pap. 6.99 (978-0-7566-1332-7(9)) Dorling Kindersley Publishing, Inc.

Scholastic, Inc. Staff. Elizabeth I: Red Rose of the House of Tudor, England 1544. 2000. (Royal Diaries Ser.). (J). lthr. 9.95 (978-0-439-26654-3(8)) Scholastic, Inc.

Scholastic, Inc. Staff. The Little Mermaid/La Sirenita. Bordoy, Irene, illus. 2007. (Bilingual Tales Ser.). (ENG & SPA.). 24p. (J). pap. 3.99 (***978-0-439-87198-3(0))*** Scholastic, Inc.

School Specialty Publishing, retold by. Princess Tales. 2004. (Handle Book with CD Ser.). 96p. (J). 14.95 (978-1-58845-736-3(2)) School Specialty Publishing.

Schutz, Samantha & Burr, Daniela. Barbie in the Twelve Dancing Princesses. 2006. (Illus.). 80p. (J). pap. 3.99 (978-0-439-87003-0(8) , Scholastic Paperbacks) Scholastic, Inc.

Schwarz, Laurence & KOL (AOL Kids) Staff. Can It: As Seen on Cartoon Network. 5th ed. 2006. (Princess Natasha Ser.: No. 6). (Illus.). 80p. (J). (gr. 3-7). pap. 3.99 (978-0-316-15509-0(8)) Little Brown & Co.

—Game Over: As Seen on Cartoon Network. 3rd ed. 2006. (Princess Natasha Ser.: No. 3). (Illus.). 80p. (J). (gr. 3-7). pap. 3.99 (978-0-316-15506-9(3)) Little Brown & Co.

—Thunderstruck: As Seen on Cartoon Network. 4th ed. 2006. (Princess Natasha Ser.: No. 4). (Illus.). 80p. (J). (gr. 3-7). pap. 3.99 (978-0-316-15508-3(X)) Little Brown & Co.

Scieszka, Jon. The Frog Prince, Continued. 2003. (Live Oak Readalong Ser.). (Illus.). (J). 25.95 incl. audio (978-1-59112-229-6(5)); 28.95 incl. audio compact disk (978-1-59112-515-0(4)); pap. 18.95 incl. audio compact disk (978-1-59112-490-0(5)); pap. 16.95 incl. audio (978-1-59112-228-9(7)) Live Oak Media.

—The Frog Prince, Continued. Johnson, Steve, illus. 2003. pap. 39.95 incl. audio compact disk (978-1-59112-522-8(7)) Live Oak Media.

—The Frog Prince, Continued, 4 bks. 2003. (Live Oak Readalong Ser.). (J). pap. 37.95 incl. audio (978-1-59112-230-2(9)) Live Oak Media.

Scott, Mavis. Magic Palace. Spoor, Mike, illus. 96p. pap. 8.95 (978-0-7022-2528-4(2)) Univ. of Queensland Pr. AUS. *Dist:* International Specialized Bk. Services.

Shanks, Melanie. The Squints. 2007. 116p. per. 10.95 (***978-0-595-44849-4(6))*** iUniverse, Inc.

Shannon, Margaret. The Red Wolf. 2006. 32p. (J). (gr. k-3). 6.95 (978-0-618-73744-4(8)) Houghton Mifflin Co. Trade & Reference Div.

Shaskan, Trisha Speed. Princess Bella's Birthday Cake. Eroglu, Aysin D., illus. 2006. 24p. (J). (***978-1-4048-3166-7(5))*** Picture Window Bks.

—Princess Bella_s Birthday Cake. 2007. (Illus.). 24p. (J). (***978-1-4048-1240-6(7))*** Picture Window Bks.

Shaskan, Trisha Speed. The Three Princesses. Senturk, Burak, illus. 2006. (Read-It! Readers Ser.). (J). 19.93 (978-1-4048-2422-5(7)) Picture Window Bks.

Shulman, Mark. Enchanted Princess Castle. Wenzel, David T., illus. 2005. (Storytime Stickers Ser.). 16p. (J). (gr. k-2). pap. 4.95 (978-1-4027-2747-4(X)) Sterling Publishing Co., Inc.

Siegel, Terri. Goodnight Princess Scharazad. 2005. (J). lib. bdg. 19.95 (***978-0-9754728-5-9(2)*** , Bear Hug Bks.) MidAmerica Publishing Co.

Silver Dolphin en Español Editors. Caritas felices: Cenicienta: Happy faces: Cinderella, Spanish-Language Edition. 2007. (Illus.). 8p. (J). bds. 7.95 (***978-970-718-390-2(X)*** , Silver Dolphin en Español) Advanced Marketing, S. de R. L. de C. V. MEX. *Dist:* Perseus Distribution.

—Disney princesas: Felices para Siempre: Disney Princesses: Happily Ever after, Spanish-Language Editon. 2007. (Illus.). 5p. (J). 14.99 (***978-970-718-448-0(5)*** , Silver Dolphin en Español) Advanced Marketing, S. de R. L. de C. V. MEX. *Dist:* Perseus Distribution.

Silver Dolphin en Español Editors. Tesoros para llevar Disney: Disney Princess CarryAlong Treasury, Spanish-Language Edition. 2004. (SPA., Illus.). 24p. (J). bds. 14.95 (978-970-718-239-4(3) , Silver Dolphin en Español) Advanced Marketing, S. de R. L. de C. V. MEX. *Dist:* Perseus Distribution.

Simon, Charnan. Tressa the Musical Princess. Allen, Joy, illus. 2005. 25p. (J). (978-1-58987-112-0(X)) Kindermusik International.

Sims, Lesley. Stories of Princesses (Combined Volume) 2006. 144p. (J). 14.99 (978-0-7945-1385-6(9) , Usborne) EDC Publishing.

Simson, Dana. Princess Ruby's Rainbow Day. 2003. (Sparkle Bks.). (J). bds. 10.95 (978-1-74047-206-7(3)) Book Co. Publishing Pty, Ltd., The AUS. *Dist:* Penton Overseas, Inc.

Sing-along Disney Princess: Story Reader. 2004. 26p. (J). spiral bd. (978-1-4127-3236-9(0) , 7236800) Publications International, Ltd.

Skinner, Daphne. My Side of the Story Bk. 1: Cinderella & Lady Tremaine. Harchy, Atelier Philippe & Kurtz, John, illus. 3rd ed. 2005. (My Side of the Story Ser.). 72p. (ps-17). 12.99 (978-0-7868-3647-5(4)) Disney Pr.

—Snow White Bk. 2. Kurtz, John & Harchy, Atelier Philippe, illus. 3rd ed. 2005. (My Side of the Story Ser.). 72p. (ps-17). 12.99 (978-0-7868-3648-2(2)) Disney Pr.

The Sleeping Beauty: Individual Title Six-Packs. 32p. (gr. 3 up). 37.00 (978-0-7635-9680-4(9)) Rigby Education.

Smath, Jerry. Flower Princesses. Smath, Jerry, illus. 2000. (Sticker Styles Ser.). (Illus.). 24p. (J). (ps-3). pap. 4.99 (978-0-448-42169-8(0) , Grosset & Dunlap) Penguin Group (USA) Inc.

Snow White & the Seven Dwarfs: Individual Title Six-Packs. 32p. (gr. 2 up). 37.00 (978-0-7635-9401-5(6)) Rigby Education.

Snyder, Laurel. Up & down the Scratchy Mountains, or, the Search for a Suitable Princess. Dorman, Brandon, illus. 2008. (J). (***978-0-375-84719-6(7));*** lib. bdg. (***978-0-375-94719-3(1))*** Random Hse., Inc.

Sommer, Carl. The Great Royal Race. 2003. (Another Sommer-Time Story Ser.). (Illus.). 48p. (J). (gr. k-4). lib. bdg. 23.95 incl. audio compact disk (978-1-57537-708-7(X)); (gr. k-4). lib. bdg. 23.95 incl. audio (978-1-57537-758-2(6)); (gr. 1-4). 16.95 incl. audio (978-1-57537-557-1(5)); (gr. 1-4). 16.95 incl. audio compact disk (978-1-57537-508-3(7)) Advance Publishing, Inc.

Sorenson, Margo. Ambrose & the Princess. Szegedi, Katalin, illus. 2005. 30p. (J). (ps-3). 16.95 (978-0-8146-3043-3(X)) Liturgical Pr.

Souci, Robert D. San. Well at the End of the World. Walsh, Rebecca, illus. 2004. 48p. (J). 16.95 (978-1-58717-212-0(7) , SeaStar Bks.) Chronicle Bks. LLC.

Soundprints. Princess Kindness Counts Pack. rev. ed. (Kindness Counts Ser.). (Illus.). 36p. (J). 12.99 incl. cd-rom (978-1-59069-364-3(7) , 1A500) Studio Mouse LLC.

Springer, Nancy. Outlaw Princess of Sherwood. 2003. (Tales of Rowan Hood Ser.: No. 3). 128p. (J). (gr. 3-6). 16.99 (978-0-399-23721-8(6) , Philomel) Penguin Group (USA) Inc.

Stanley, Diane. Bella at Midnight. Ibatoulline, Ba, illus. 2008. 304p. (J). pap. 6.99 (***978-0-06-077575-9(0)*** , Harper Trophy) HarperCollins Pubs.

—Bella at Midnight. Ibatoulline, Bagram, illus. 2006. 288p. (J). (gr. 5-8). 16.99 (978-0-06-077573-5(4)); lib. bdg. 16.89 (978-0-06-077574-2(2)) HarperCollins Pubs.

Stanton, Mary. Valley of Fear No.3. 1999. (gr. 5-8). lib. bdg. 12.40 (978-0-613-16870-0(4)) Tandem Library Bks.

Staunton, Ted & Gardos, Susan. Princess. 2004. (Monkey Mountain Bks.). (Illus.). 72p. (J). (gr. 2-5). pap. 4.95 (978-0-88995-242-3(6)) Red Deer Pr. CAN. *Dist:* Fitzhenry & Whiteside, Ltd.

Steadman, Barbara. Prince & Princess Sticker Paper Dolls. 2002. (Sticker Paper Dolls Ser.). (Illus.). 4p. (J). pap. 1.50 (978-0-486-42348-7(4)) Dover Pubns., Inc.

Steck-Vaughn Staff. Princess & the Castle. 1999. (Take Me Home Ser.). (Illus.). (J). pap. (978-0-7398-2593-8(3)) Steck-Vaughn.

Sterling Publishing Co., Inc. & Fernleigh Books Staff. Cinderella: A Magic 3-Dimensional Fairy-Tale World. 2006. (Step Inside Ser.). (Illus.). 12p. (J). 9.95 (978-1-4027-3655-1(X)) Sterling Publishing Co., Inc.

Stockham, Jess, et al, illus. The Frog Prince. 2007. 24p. pap. 5.99 (***978-1-84643-077-0(1))*** Child's Play International Ltd. GBR. *Dist:* Child's Play-International.

Stone, David Lee. Illmore Chronicles,the: the Shadewell Shenangans - Book Three. 3rd rev. ed. 2007. 320p. (gr. 2-7). pap. 7.99 (***978-0-7868-3796-0(9))*** Hyperion Pr.

Stowell, Louie. Beauty & the Beast. Tavares, Victor, illus. 2007. 64p. (J). 8.99 (978-0-7945-1456-3(1) , Usborne) EDC Publishing.

Strauss, Linda Leopold. The Princess Gown. Laugesen, Malene, illus. 2008. (J). (***978-0-618-86259-7(5))*** Houghton Mifflin Co.

Strickler, Ashley. Once upon A Time. 2007. 212p. pap. 12.95 (***978-1-4327-0207-6(6))*** Outskirts Press, Inc.

Studio Mouse. Princess ABC's & 123's. rev. ed. 2007. (Disney Princess Ser.). 24p. 4.99 (***978-1-59069-560-9(7))*** Studio Mouse LLC.

Sullivan, Nick. The Seventh Princess. 2001. 112p. (J). (gr. 2-6). pap. 3.99 (978-0-439-26007-7(8) , Scholastic Paperbacks) Scholastic, Inc.

Sundberg, Norma J. An Odd Fable. Leiper, Esther M., illus. 2007. (ENG.). 32p. (J). pap. 13.95 (***978-0-9776958-5-0(9))*** CyPress Pubns.

Swedeen, Staci, Tombi-Ende & the Frog: A Fairy Tale from South Africa. 2006. spiral bd. 42.00 (***978-1-4108-7151-0(7))*** Benchmark Education Co.

Sweet, J.H. & Sierra, Holly. Spiderwort & the Princess of Haiku: The Fairy Chronicles. 2007. (Fairy Chronicles Ser.). (Illus.). 128p. (J). (gr. 2 up). pap. 6.99 (***978-1-4022-1025-9(6)*** , Sourcebooks Jabberwocky) Sourcebooks, Inc.

Swiderska, Barbara. The Fisherman's Bride. Swiderska, Barbara, illus. (Illus.). 32p. (J). (ps-3). 12.95 (978-0-87592-018-4(7)) Scroll Pr., Inc.

Tagore, Rabindranath. The Prince & the Other Modern Fables. 2004. 144p. pap. 10.00 (978-0-14-333570-2(7) , Penguin Global) Penguin Group (USA) Inc.

The Tallest Tower: Individual Title Six-Packs. (Bookweb Ser.). 32p. (gr. 3 up). 34.00 (978-0-7635-3939-9(2)) Rigby Education.

Taniguchi, Tomoko. Princess Prince. Taniguchi, Tomoko, illus. 2003. (Illus.). 336p. pap. 15.95 (978-1-58664-860-2(8) , CMX 62601G, CPM Manhwa) Central Park Media Corp.

Tarcov, Edith H. The Frog Prince. Marshall, James, illus. 2004. 40p. (J). lib. bdg. 15.00 (978-1-59054-506-5(0)) Fitzgerald Bks.

Teis, Kyra, adapted by. The Magic Flute. 2006. 32p. (J). 17.95 (978-1-59572-058-0(8)) Star Bright Bks., Inc.

Tenney, Tommy. Hadassah: The Girl Who Became Queen Esther. 2005. (Illus.). 168p. (J). 9.99 (978-0-7642-2738-7(6)) Bethany Hse. Pubs.

Teply, George. Lost Crown of Meleor. 2000. (gr. k-3). lib. bdg. 15.25 (978-0-613-30013-1(0)) Tandem Library Bks.

Thomas, Becky. The Twelve Dancing Princesses. 2007. (Illus.). 32p. (J). (ps-3). 16.99 (***978-0-399-24744-6(0)*** , Putnam Juvenile) Penguin Group (USA) Inc.

Thomas, Joyce Carol. The Gospel Cinderella. Diaz, David, illus. 2004. 40p. (J). (gr. k-5). 15.99 (978-0-06-025387-5(8) , Amistad) HarperCollins Pubs.

Thorpe, Kiki. My Side of the Story Bk. 4: Sleeping Beauty & Maleficent. Daly, Catherine, ed. 4th rev. ed. 2004. (Disney Princess Ser.). 72p. (ps-17). 12.99 (978-0-7868-3502-7(8)) Disney Pr.

—Princess Magic: Words from the Heart. 2001. (Illus.). 176p. (ps-17). 13.99 (978-0-7868-3296-5(7)) Disney Pr.

Ting, Renee. The Prince's Diary. Dulemba, Elizabeth, illus. 2005. 32p. (J). (978-1-885008-27-5(9)) Shen's Bks.

Tish, Aunty. Kiddiwink Kingdom. 2006. 68p. pap. 19.95 (978-1-59800-587-5(1)) Outskirts Press, Inc.

Tong, Gina. How the Clown Won the Princess' Heart. 2000. (Publish-a-Book Ser.). (Illus.). 24p. (J). (ps-3). pap. 7.95 (978-0-7398-2367-5(1)) Steck-Vaughn.

Townley, Roderick. The Constellation of Sylvie. 2006. (Illus.). 208p. (J). (gr. 5 up). 16.95 (978-0-689-85713-3(6) , Atheneum) Simon & Schuster Children's Publishing.

—The Great Good Thing. 2001. (Illus.). 232p. (J). (gr. 5-9). 17.00 (978-0-689-84324-2(0) , Atheneum/Richard Jackson Bks.) Simon & Schuster Children's Publishing.

—Great Good Thing. 2002. (gr. 5-8). lib. bdg. 13.00 (978-0-613-91045-3(1)) Tandem Library Bks.

—Into the Labyrinth. (Illus.). 272p. (gr. 5-9). 2006. (YA). pap. 5.99 (978-1-4169-1392-4(0) , Aladdin); 2002. (J). 16.95 (978-0-689-84615-1(0) , Atheneum/Richard Jackson Bks.) Simon & Schuster Children's Publishing.

Toy Box Productions Staff, Box, creator. Disney's Read Along Collection: Cinderella; Snow White; Sleeping Beauty. unabr. abr. ed. 2005. (Disney Princess Ser.). (J). audio compact disk 14.99 (978-0-7634-1150-3(7)) Walt Disney Records.

ToyBox Innovations, creator. Disney's Cinderella. 2006. (Disney's Read Along Ser.). (Illus.). 24p. (J). pap. 7.99 incl. audio compact disk (978-0-7634-2171-7(5)) Walt Disney Records.

Traditional Fairy Tale. The Princess & the Pea. Stevenson, Peter, illus. 2001. (Finger Puppet Theater Bks.). 16p. (J). bds. 14.95 (978-0-439-28889-7(4) , Cartwheel Bks.) Scholastic, Inc.

Trapani, Iza. I'm a Little Teapot. 1998. (Illus.). 32p. (J). (gr. 1-5). pap. 6.95 (978-1-58089-010-6(5)) Charlesbridge Publishing, Inc.

Trewellard, J. M. Butterfingers. Beck, Ian, illus. 2007. 208p. (J). (gr. 3-7). 15.99 (***978-0-385-75123-0(0));*** lib. bdg. 18.99 (***978-0-385-75124-7(9))*** Random Hse. Children's Bks. (Fickling, David Bks.).

Twain, Mark. The Prince & the Pauper. (J). 19.95 (978-0-8488-0849-5(5)) Amereon LTD.

—The Prince & the Pauper. 2007. (Bantam Classics Ser.). 224p. (J). (gr. 4-11). pap. 3.95 (978-0-553-21256-3(7) , Bantam Classics) Bantam Bks.

—The Prince & the Pauper. 2000. (Thrift Edition Ser.). 176p. (gr. 6). pap. 2.50 (978-0-486-41110-1(9)) Dover Pubns., Inc.

—The Prince & the Pauper. (YA). (gr. 5-12). pap. 6.50 (978-0-8224-9344-0(6)) Globe Fearon Educational Publishing.

—The Prince & the Pauper. (J). 9.95 (978-1-56156-311-1(0)) Kidsbooks, Inc.

—The Prince & the Pauper. l.t. ed. 2000. (Large Print Heritage Ser.). 364p. (J). lib. bdg. 33.95 (978-1-58118-068-8(3) , 23662) LRS.

—The Prince & the Pauper. 2006. (Aladdin Classics Ser.). 352p. (J). pap. 5.99 (978-1-4169-2805-8(7) , Aladdin) Simon & Schuster Children's Publishing.

—The Prince & the Pauper. 1999. (Bullseye Step into Classics Ser.). (978-0-606-16896-0(6)) Tandem Library Bks.

—The Prince & the Pauper. l.t. ed. 2000. (Perennial Bestsellers Ser.). 307p. (J). 26.95 (978-0-7838-9061-6(3)) Thorndike Pr.

—The Prince & the Pauper. 2001. 186p. pap. 9.95 (978-1-57002-171-8(6)) University Publishing Hse., Inc.

—The Prince & the Pauper. 1998. (Children's Library). 288p. (J). pap. 3.95 (978-1-85326-147-3(5) , 1475WW) Wordsworth Editions, Ltd. GBR. *Dist:* Combined Publishing.

Umansky, Kaye. Big Iggy. l.t. ed. 2005. (J). pap. (978-0-7540-7944-6(9)) BBC Audio.

—Prince Dandypants & the Masked Avenger. Dunton, Trevor, illus. l.t. ed. 2002. 224p. (J). 16.95 (978-0-7540-7825-8(6) , Galaxy Children's Large Print) BBC Audiobooks America.

Vagnozzi, Barbara, illus. Sleeping Beauty. 2007. (First Fairy Tales Ser.). 31p. (J). (***978-1-59771-073-2(3))*** Sea-To-Sea Pubns.

Vande Velde, Vivian. Wizard at Work: A Novel in Stories. 2004. (Illus.). 144p. (J). pap. 5.95 (978-0-15-205309-3(3) , Magic Carpet Bks.) Harcourt Children's Bks.

Vaugelade, Anais. The War. Rouffiac, Marie-Christine & Streissguth, Thomas, trs. from FRE. Vaugelade, Anais, illus. 2005. (Picture Bks.). (Illus.). 32p. (J). (gr. k-2). 15.25 (978-1-57505-562-6(7)) Lerner Publishing Group.

Ventura, Antonio. El Pajaro y la Princesa. (SPA.). 24p. 12.99 (978-968-16-6358-2(6)) Fondo de Cultura Economica USA.

A Very Funny Act, 6 Packs. (gr. k-1). 23.00 (978-0-7635-9050-5(9)) Rigby Education.

Visconti, Guido. The Enchanted Kingdom. Battaglia, Maria, illus. 2000. 30p. (J). (gr. k-2). 16.95 (978-0-86315-333-4(X)) Floris Bks. GBR. *Dist:* SteinerBooks, Inc.

Vize, Dania. My Princess Dress up Storybook. 2005. (Illus.). 12p. (J). (ps-3). bds. 9.95 (978-1-905051-84-7(0)) Make Believe Ideas GBR. *Dist:* Ingram Pub. Services.

Wallace, Karen. King Cudgel's Challenge. Flook, Helen, illus. 2007. (J). lib. bdg. (***978-1-4048-3706-5(X))*** Picture Window Bks.

—Prince Marvin's Great Moment. Flook, Helen, illus. 2007. (J). lib. bdg. (***978-1-4048-3707-2(8))*** Picture Window Bks.

—Princess Gusty Ox's Strange Change. Flook, Helen, illus. 2007. (J). lib. bdg. (***978-1-4048-3708-9(6))*** Picture Window Bks.

Walsh, Sheila. Gigi, No. 4. 2007. (Gigi, God's Little Princess Ser.). (Illus.). 32p. (J). 12.99 (978-1-4003-0804-0(6)) Nelson, Thomas Inc.

—Gigi & the Perfect Christmas Gift. 2006. (Gigi, God's Little Princess Ser.). (Illus.). 32p. (J). 12.99 (978-1-4003-0801-9(1)) Nelson, Thomas Inc.

Walt Disney Company Staff. Happily Ever after Stories Vol. 2. 2004. (Disney Princess Ser.). (Illus.). 320p. (J). (gr. k-5). 15.99 (978-0-7868-3487-7(0) , Disney Editions) Disney Pr.

Walt Disney Records Staff. Disney Princess Holiday: Cinderella So This Is Christmas/Beauty & the Beast One Magical Christmas/Ariel's Christmas under the Sea. unabr. ed. 2005. (Disney's Read along Collection Ser.). (J). audio compact disk 14.99 (978-0-7634-1146-6(9)) Walt Disney Records.

Walt Disney Records Staff, prod. Princess Collection Two: A Dream Come True for Every Little Princess. 1998. (J). 16.98 incl. audio compact disk (978-0-7634-0450-5(0)) Walt Disney Records.

Ward, Nick. The Tadpole Prince. 2003. (Illus.). 32p. (YA). (978-1-84365-016-4(9)) Chrysalis Children's Bks.

Warner Press Staff. Princess & the Kiss: A Story of God's Gift of Purity. 2000. (J). (ps-3). 9.95 (978-0-87162-868-8(6)) Warner Pr. Pubs.

Watanabe, Kaori & Grace, Will. Princess. 2005. 6p. (J). 12.99 (978-0-439-74891-9(7) , Cartwheel Bks.) Scholastic, Inc.

Watt, Fiona. That's Not My Princess. 2006. (Illus.). 10p. (J). bds. 9.99 (978-0-7945-1325-2(5) , Usborne) EDC Publishing.

Watt, J. S. The Hall of Sorrows. 2006. 67p. pap. 14.95 (978-1-4241-2984-3(2)) PublishAmerica, Inc.

Wax, Wendy. Phonics Comics: Clara the Klutz - Level 2. Mattocks, Tracy & Sullivan, Mary, illus. 2007. 24p. (J). (gr. 1-17). pap. 3.99 (978-1-58476-565-3(8)) Innovative Kids.

Wax, Wendy A. Musica en Casa: Libro de Cuentos. de Alba, Arlette, tr. 2005. (SPA., Illus.). 32p. (J), (ps-7). 24.95 (978-970-718-289-9(X) , Silver Dolphin en Español) Advanced Marketing, S. de R. L. de C. V. MEX. *Dist:* Perseus Distribution.

Weaver, Patricia. Ashaki, African Princess. 2001. 164p. (YA). pap. 12.95 (978-0-595-18283-1(6) , Writer's Showcase Pr.) iUniverse, Inc.

Weber, Lou, ed. Colorful Tales. 2004. (Disney Princess Ser.). 32p. (J). 7.98 (978-1-4127-3055-6(4) , 7226300) Publications International, Ltd.

—Disney Princess Look & Find Wipe off 3 Pack. 2004. 72p. (J). spiral bd. 15.98 (978-1-4127-3296-3(4) , 7244700) Publications International, Ltd.

—Dreamy Stories. 2005. (Disney Princess Ser.). 40p. (J). bds. 12.98 (978-1-4127-3479-0(7) , 7259700) Publications International, Ltd.

—Magic Screen Disney Princess. 2005. 14p. (J). bds. 15.98 (978-1-4127-3547-6(5) , 7263700) Publications International, Ltd.

—Musical Disney Princesas. 2004. (ESP & SPA., Illus.). 38p. (J). bds. 12.98 (978-0-7853-8630-8(0) , 7176101) Publications International, Ltd.

Weinberg, Jennifer Liberts. What Is a Princess? Harchy, Atelier Philippe, illus. 2004. 32p. (J). (ps-1). pap. 3.99 (978-0-7364-2238-3(2) , RH/Disney) Random Hse. Children's Bks.

West, Tracey. Mario & the Incredible Rescue. 2006. 76p. (J). pap. (*978-0-439-84366-9(9)) Scholastic, Inc.

Weyn, Suzanne. Water Song: A Retelling of "The Frog Prince" 2006. (Once upon a Time Ser.). 208p. (YA). (gr. 5 up). pap. 5.99 (978-1-4169-4013-5(8) , Simon Pulse) Simon & Schuster Children's Publishing.

White, Annette. The Adventures of Miss Lizzy & Princess Cheeks: Travel to the Land of the Great Instructor. 2005. pap. 7.95 (978-0-533-15052-6(3)) Vantage Pr., Inc.

Wilde, Oscar. The Happy Prince. Muller, Robin, illus. 2002. 20p. (gr. 2-5). 5.95 (978-0-7737-3318-3(3)) Stoddart Kids CAN. *Dist:* Fitzhenry & Whiteside, Ltd.

—The Happy Prince. 2000. (Children's Classics). (ENG.). 80p. (J). pap. (978-1-85326-123-7(8) , 1238WW) Wordsworth Editions, Ltd.

—The Happy Prince & Other Tales. 2006. 56p. per. 4.99 (978-1-4209-2736-8(1)) Digireads.com.

—The Happy Prince & Other Tales. 2004. reprint ed. pap. 15.95 (978-1-4191-6538-2(0)); pap. 1.99 (978-1-4192-6538-9(5)) Kessinger Publishing, LLC.

—The Happy Prince & Other Tales. 2006. per. 4.95 (978-1-57646-987-3(5)) Quiet Vision Publishing.

—The Happy Prince & Other Tales. 2005. pap. 9.95 (978-1-55742-431-0(4)) Wildside Pr.

—Le Prince Hereux. (FRE.). (J). pap. 15.95 (978-2-07-051629-2(6)) Gallimard, Editions FRA. *Dist:* Distribooks, Inc.

Williams, Brenda. The Real Princess. 2006. (J). (978-1-905236-88-6(3)) Barefoot Bks., Inc.

Williams, Julie S. Princess Bernice Pauahi Bishop. Burningham, Robin Y., illus. rev. ed. 1998. (Kamehameha Intermediate Reading Program Ser.). 104p. (J). (gr. 3-7). pap. 13.27 (978-0-87336-057-9(5)) Kamehameha Schools Pr.

Williams, Sophy. Princess Stories from Around the World. Tym, Kate, illus. 2004. 64p. (J). (978-1-84458-142-9(X)) Chrysalis Children's Bks.

Williams, Suzanne. The Awfully Angry Ogre. Gonzales, Chuck, illus. 2007. (Princess Power Ser.). (J). 112p. 15.99 (978-0-06-078303-7(6)); 96p. pap. 4.99 (978-0-06-078302-0(8) , Harper Trophy) HarperCollins Pubs.

—The Charmingly Clever Cousin. Gonzales, Chuck, illus. 2006. (Princess Power Ser.). 128p. (J). (gr. 3-5). 15.99 (978-0-06-078301-3(X)); pap. 4.99 (978-0-06-078300-6(1) , Harper Trophy) HarperCollins Pubs.

—The Gigantic, Genuine Genie. Gonzales, Chuck, illus. 2007. (Princess Power Ser.: No. 6). 128p. (J). 15.99 (*978-0-06-078309-9(5)); (gr. 3-7). pap. 4.99 (*978-0-06-078308-2(7) , Harper Trophy) HarperCollins Pubs.

—The Mysterious, Mournful Maiden. Gonzales, Chuck, illus. 2007. (J). 112p. 15.99 (978-0-06-078305-1(2)); 96p. pap. 4.99 (978-0-06-078304-4(4) , Harper Trophy) HarperCollins Pubs.

—The Perfectly Proper Prince. Gonzales, Chuck, illus. 2006. (Princess Power Ser.). 128p. (J). 15.99 (978-0-06-078299-3(4)); pap. 4.99 (978-0-06-078298-6(6) , Harper Trophy) HarperCollins Pubs.

Williams, Suzanne. The Stubbornly Secretive Servant. Gonzales, Chuck, illus. 2007. (Princess Power Ser.). 128p. (J). 15.99 (*978-0-06-078307-5(9)); pap. 4.99 (*978-0-06-078306-8(0) , Harper Trophy) HarperCollins Pubs.

Williston, Teresa Pierce. The Bamboo Cutter & the Moon Maiden: A Japanese Folk Tale. Marsh, Dilleen, illus. 2006. 32p. (J). 16.95 (978-1-933317-39-7(6)) Silverleaf Pr.

Wilson, George H. The Arrival of Grand Princess Leandria. 2008. (Illus.). 50p. (J). 14.99 (*978-0-9778477-5-4(6)) Storyplus, Inc., A.

Wilson, Karma. Princess Me. Unzner-Fischer, Christa, illus. 2007. 32p. (J). (ps-2). 16.99 (978-1-4169-4098-2(7) , McElderry, Margaret K.) Simon & Schuster Children's Publishing.

Witwer, Julia, illus. The Princess Who Overcame Evil. 2000. (Jataka Tales Ser.). 32p. (J). (gr. k-6). pap. 7.95 (978-0-89800-294-2(X)) Dharma Publishing.

Wood, Audrey. The Princess & the Dragon. 2002. (J). 10p. 9.99 (978-0-85953-717-9(X)); (Illus.). 32p. 7.99 (978-0-85953-716-2(1)) Child's Play-International.

—The Princess & the Dragon. 2003. (gr. k-3). lib. bdg. 16.45 (978-0-613-77050-7(1)) Tandem Library Bks.

—The Princess & the Dragon Storysack. (J). 65.00 (978-0-85953-199-3(6)) Child's Play-International.

—Princess, the Dragon & Scaredy Cats. (J). audio 10.97 (978-0-85953-375-1(1)) Child's Play-International.

—There were Ten in the Bed. 2001. (Illus.). 24p. (J). 11.95 (978-0-85953-897-8(4)) Child's Play-International.

Wood, Maggie. The Princess Mage. 2006. 296p. (YA). pap. 9.95 (978-1-894549-52-3(X)) Sumach Pr. CAN. *Dist:* Orca Bk. Pubs. USA.

Woods, Valerie L. Princess Portia's Enchanted Journey. Agyeman, Janell W., ed. Woods, Valerie L., illus. 2000. (Illus.). 33p. (J). (gr. 1-7). (978-0-615-11490-3(3)) Valikus Publishing Co.

Wormell, Christopher. George, the Dragon & the Princess: 2008. (Illus.). 32p. (J). 16.95 (*978-0-224-07072-0(X)) Transworld Publishers Ltd. GBR. *Dist:* Independent Pubs. Group.

Worrall, Linda, illus. Snow White & the Seven Dwarfs: A Story about Vanity. 2006. (J). 6.99 (978-1-59939-025-3(6) , Reader's Digest Young Families, Inc.) Reader's Digest Children's Publishing, Inc.

Wright, Betty Ren. Princess for a Week. Rogers, Jacqueline, illus. 2007. 160p. (J). (gr. 2-5). pap. 6.95 (*978-0-8234-2111-4(2)) Holiday Hse., Inc.

Wright, Roosevelt. The Wise Prince. 2002. per. 7.95 net. (978-0-943751-14-6(4)) Free Pr. Pubs.

Wright, Sabrina L. & Griffin, Dexter. Kalilah, the Whispered Promise. 2005. (YA). pap. 12.95 (978-0-9770363-0-1(8)) First-Sight Publishing.

Wyatt, Melissa. Raising the Griffin. 2005. 288p. (YA). (gr. 7). 6.50 (978-0-440-23821-8(8) , Laurel Leaf) Random Hse. Children's Bks.

Wyss, Tyan. The Solitaire Prince. 2006. 168p. (YA). 12.95 (978-1-58939-907-5(2)); per. 12.95 (978-1-58939-906-8(4)) Virtualbookworm.com Publishing, Inc.

Yarrow, Reed. Mainu & the Prince of Bakara. 1999. (Illus.). 205p. (J). (gr. 3-7). 14.95 (978-1-893731-04-2(9)) Mandolin Hse.

Yolen, Jane & Harris, Robert J. Girl in a Cage. 2002. (Illus.). 240p. (YA). (gr. 6-10). 18.99 (978-0-399-23627-3(9) , Philomel) Penguin Group (USA) Inc.

Young, Laurie. Princess Polly & the Pea. 2007. 14p. pap. 12.95 (*978-1-58117-558-5(2)) Dalmatian Pr.

YoYo Books. Princess Charlotte Becomes a Magician. 2005. 32p. 9.95 (978-90-5843-459-3(1)) YoYo Bks. BEL. *Dist:* National Bk. Network.

PRINTING

see also Books

Beardsley, Laura E. Benjamin Franklin. 2007. (Essential Lives Ser.). (ENG., Illus.). 112p. (YA). (gr. 8-12). lib. bdg. 32.79 (*978-1-59928-840-6(0) , Essential Library) ABDO Publishing Co.

Boonyadhistarn, Thiranut. Stamping Art: Imprint Your Designs. 2007. (Snap Books Craft Ser.). (Illus.). 31p. (J). (gr. 4-8). lib. bdg. 25.26 (978-0-7368-6477-0(6)) Capstone Pr., Inc.

Childress, Diana. Johannes Gutenberg & the Printing Press. 2008. (YA). lib. bdg. (*978-0-8225-7520-7(5)) Twenty First Century Bks.

Clay, Marie M. No Shoes. 2000. 20p. (J). pap. 9.50 (978-0-325-00236-1(3) , E00236) Heinemann.

Dalmatian Press Staff. Printing Practice: Chalkboard Book. 2003. (Home Learning Tools Ser.). 10p. (J). (gr. 1 up). pap. 3.99 (978-1-4037-0330-9(2)) Dalmatian Pr.

Feinstein, Stephen. Johannes Gutenberg: The Printer Who Gave Words to the World. 2008. (Inventors Who Changed the World Ser.). 128p. (J). (gr. 6 up). lib. bdg. 33.27 (*978-1-59845-077-4(8) , MyReportLinks.com Bks.) Enslow Pubs., Inc.

Fisher, Leonard Everett. The Printers. 1999. (Colonial Craftsmen Ser.). (Illus.). 48p. (J). (gr. 4-8). lib. bdg. 24.21 (978-0-7614-0929-8(7) , Benchmark Bks.) Cavendish, Marshall Corp.

GoBo. Santa Baby: Boxed Set: Boxed Set. 2006. 10p. 9.95 (978-1-932915-37-2(0)) Sandvik Publishing.

Hamilton, John. Books. 2005. (Straight to the Source Ser.). (J). (gr. k-6). lib. bdg. 22.78 (978-1-59197-543-4(3)) ABDO Publishing Co.

Hayward, Linda. I Am a Book. Nicklaus, Carol, illus. (Silly Millies Ser.). 32p. (J). (gr. k-2). 2005. pap. 4.99 (978-0-7613-1826-2(7) , First Avenue Editions); 2004. lib. bdg. 17.90 (978-0-7613-2905-3(6) , Millbrook Pr.) Lerner Publishing Group.

—I Am a Book. 2004. (gr. k-3). lib. bdg. 13.00 (978-0-613-86946-1(X)) Tandem Library Bks.

Linville, Dorothy. Graph-X. Kennedy, Mike, illus. 2000. 33p. (YA). (gr. 5-10). pap. 5.95 (978-0-9701551-0-8(7)) Linville, Dorothy.

Medina, Sarah. Having Fun with Printing. 2007. (J). lib. bdg. (*978-1-4042-3719-3(4) , PowerKids Pr.) Rosen Publishing Group, Inc., The.

Mismas, L. J., Jr. Write on! Printing: Tutor Kit (English) 2005. (JPN & ENG., Illus.). 20p. (J). bds. incl. DVD (978-0-9755836-0-9(3) , 0101) Incredible Kid, LLC.

Nicholson, Sue. Printing, 6 vols. 2005. (QEB Learn Art Ser.). (Illus.). (J). per. 8.95 (978-1-59566-123-4(9)) QEB Publishing Inc.

Oxlade, Chris. Writing & Printing. (Illus.). 32p. (YA). (gr. 3 up). lib. bdg. 27.10 (978-1-932889-08-6(6)) Sea-To-Sea Pubns.

Parks, Peggy J. Benjamin Franklin: Genius Inventor & Electricity Pioneer. 2002. (Giants of Science Ser.). (Illus.). 64p. (J). 26.20 (978-1-56711-658-8(2) , Blackbirch Pr., Inc.) Thomson Gale.

Powell, Michelle. Printing. 2002. (Step-by-Step Ser.). 32p. (J). (gr. 3-5). 7.95 (978-1-4034-0707-8(X)) Heinemann Library.

Printing Practice Booster. 2005. (J). per. 0.00 (978-1-59441-507-4(2) , C04039) Carson-Dellosa Publishing Co., Inc.

The Printing Press: an Information Revolution: Individual Title Six-Packs. (On Deck Ser.: Vol. 2). 24p. (gr. 4-5). 35.00 (978-0-7578-5860-4(0)) Rigby Education.

QEB Let's Start! Art National Book Stores Edition: Printing. 2006. (J). per. (978-1-59566-299-6(5)) QEB Publishing Inc.

Rhatigan, Joe. In Print! 40 Cool Publishing Projects for Kids. 2003. (Illus.). 128p. 19.95 (978-1-57990-359-6(2)) Lark Bks.

Riley, Gail Blasser. Benjamin Franklin & Electricity. 2004. (Cornerstones of Freedom Ser.). (Illus.). 48p. (J). 26.00 (978-0-516-24240-8(7) , Children's Pr.) Scholastic Library Publishing.

Royston, Angela. Book. 2005. (How Are Things Made? Ser.). (Illus.). 32p. (J). pap. (978-0-431-05051-5(1)); tchr. ed. (978-0-431-05044-7(9)) Heinemann Library.

—How Is a Book Made? 2005. (Illus.). 32p. (J). (gr. k-2). lib. bdg. 24.21 (978-1-4034-6639-6(4)); pap. (978-0-431-46646-0(7)); lib. bdg. (978-0-431-46639-2(4)); pap. 7.60 (978-1-4034-6646-4(7)) Heinemann Library.

Time for Kids Editors. Benjamin Franklin: A Man of Many Talents. 2005. (Time for Kids Ser.). (Illus.). 48p. (J). 14.99 (978-0-06-057610-3(3)); pap. 3.99 (978-0-06-057609-7(X)) HarperCollins Pubs.

Wilmore, Kathy. A Day in the Life of a Colonial Printer. 2000. (Library of Living & Working in Colonial Times). (Illus.). 24p. (J). (gr. 3). lib. bdg. 18.75 (978-0-8239-5428-5(5) , PowerKids Pr.) Rosen Publishing Group, Inc., The.

PRINTING—HISTORY

Crompton, Samuel Willard. The Printing Press. 2003. (Transforming Power of Technology Ser.). (Illus.). 112p. (gr. 9-13). 30.00 (978-0-7910-7451-0(X) , Chelsea Hse.) Facts On File, Inc.

Heinrichs, Ann. The Printing Press. 2005. (Inventions That Shaped the World Ser.). (Illus.). 80p. (gr. 5-8). (YA). pap. 9.95 (978-0-531-16722-9(4)); (J). 30.50 (978-0-531-12343-0(X)) Scholastic Library Publishing. (Watts, Franklin).

Inventing the Printing Press. 2007. (Illus.). 32p. (J). (gr. 3-9). (*978-0-7787-2819-1(6)); pap. (*978-0-7787-2841-2(2)) Crabtree Publishing Co.

Krensky, Stephen. Breaking into Print: Before & after the Invention of the Printing Press. Christensen, Bonnie, illus. 2003. 30p. (J). (gr. 3-8). reprint ed. 18.00 (978-0-7567-6843-0(8)) DIANE Publishing Co.

Mattern, Joanne. The Printing Press: An Information Revolution. 2003. (Reading Power Ser.). (Illus.). 24p. (J). lib. bdg. 17.25 (978-0-8239-6488-8(4) , PowerKids Pr.) Rosen Publishing Group, Inc., The.

Olson, Kay. Johann Gutenberg & the Printing Press. 2007. (Graphic Library). (Illus.). 32p. (J). (*978-0-7368-9644-3(9)) Capstone Pr., Inc.

Olson, Kay Melchisedech. Johann Gutenberg & the Printing Press. Smith, Tod, illus. 2007. (Graphic Library). 32p. (J). 25.26 (978-0-7368-6482-4(2)) Capstone Pr., Inc.

Pollard, Michael. Johann Gutenberg: Master of Modern Printing. 2001. (Giants of Science Ser.). (Illus.). 64p. (J). (gr. 5-8). 27.44 (978-1-56711-335-8(4) , Blackbirch Pr., Inc.) Thomson Gale.

Powell, Michelle. Printing. 2002. (Step-by-Step Ser.). 32p. (J). (gr. 3-5). 7.95 (978-1-4034-0707-8(X)) Heinemann Library.

Rees, Fran. Johannes Gutenberg: Inventor of the Printing Press. 2005. (Signature Lives Ser.). (Illus.). 112p. (J). (gr. 5-7). (978-0-7565-0989-7(0)) Compass Point Bks.

Richard Tames. The Printing Press. 2nd ed. 2006. (Illus.). 32p. (J). pap. (*978-1-4034-9152-7(6)) Heinemann Library.

Tames, Richard. Printing Press: A Breakthrough in Communication. 2000. (Point of Impact Ser.). (Illus.). 32p. (J). (gr. 5-7). lib. bdg. 24.22 (978-1-57572-418-8(9)) Heinemann Library.

Tames, Richard. The Printing Press: A Breakthrough in Communication. 2006. (Illus.). 32p. (J). (*978-1-4034-9143-5(7)) Heinemann Library.

Westermann, Karen T. John Peter Zenger: Free Press Advocate. 2000. (Colonial Leaders Ser.). (Illus.). 80p. (J). (gr. 8-12). 27.50 (978-0-7910-5966-1(9) , Chelsea Hse.) Facts On File, Inc.

PRINTING, TEXTILE

see Textile Printing

PRINTING INDUSTRY

Facts on File, Inc. Staff, contrib. by. Discovering Careers for Your Future. 2005. (Discovering Careers for Your Future Ser.). (Illus.). 96p. (J). (gr. 4-9). 21.95 (978-0-8160-5845-7(8) , Ferguson Publishing Co.) Facts On File, Inc.

PRINTS

Finley, Carol. Art of Japan: Wood-Block Color Prints. 1998. (Art Around the World Ser.). (Illus.). 56-64p. (gr. 4-8). 23.93 (978-0-8225-2077-1(X)) Lerner Publishing Group.

PRINTS—TECHNIQUE

Janes, Susan Niner. Printing. Cohen, Helaine, ed. 1998. (Arts & Crafts Skills Ser.). (Illus.). 32p. (J). (gr. 3-6). pap. 6.95 (978-0-516-26213-0(0) , Children's Pr.) Scholastic Library Publishing.

—Printing. 2005. (Illus.). 32p. (J). (gr. 3-7). lib. bdg. 27.10 (978-1-932889-82-6(5) , 1247659) Sea-To-Sea Pubns.

Luxbacher, Irene. 123 I Can Make Prints! 2008. 24p. pap. (*978-1-55453-153-0(5)) Kids Can Pr., Ltd.

PRISON ESCAPES

see Escapes

PRISONS

see also Crime and Criminals; Criminal Law; Escapes

Allen Verbrugge & Friedman, Lauri. Prisons. 2007. (Introducing Issues with Opposing Viewpoints Ser.). 144p. (gr. 7-10). 33.70 (978-0-7377-3578-9(3) , Greenhaven Pr., Inc.) Thomson Gale.

Cooper, Alison. A Punishment to Fit the Crime? 2005. (Illus.). 32p. (J). (gr. 5-9). lib. bdg. 27.10 (978-1-932889-59-8(0)) Sea-To-Sea Pubns.

Costain, Meredith & Antram, David. You Wouldn't Want to Be an 18th-Century British Convict! 2006. (Illus.). 32p. (YA). (gr. 2-5). pap. 9.95 (978-0-531-16998-8(7) , Watts, Franklin) Scholastic Library Publishing.

Elborough, Travis. Dungeons, Gallows, & Severed Heads of London. 2004. (Illus.). 96p. 8.99 (978-1-904153-03-0(8)) Watling St., Ltd. GBR. *Dist:* Trafalgar Square Publishing.

Esherick, Joan. Prisoner Rehabilitation: Success Stories & Failures. 2007. (Incarceration Issues Ser.). (Illus.). 111p. (YA). (gr. 7 up). 22.95 (978-1-59084-994-1(9)) Mason Crest Pubs.

George, Linda. Alcatraz. 1999. (Cornerstones of Freedom Ser.). (Illus.). 32p. (J). (gr. 4-6). pap. 5.95 (978-0-516-26349-6(8) , Children's Pr.) Scholastic Library Publishing.

Hamilton, John. Castles & Dungeons. 2005. (Illus.). 32p. (J). (gr. 4-8). lib. bdg. 24.21 (978-1-59679-335-4(X) , ABDO & Daughters) ABDO Publishing Co.

Hill, Mary K. Prisons. 2006. (Social Issues Firsthand Ser.). (Illus.). 224p. (YA). (gr. 10-12). 29.95 (978-0-7377-3605-2(4) , Greenhaven Pr., Inc.) Thomson Gale.

Incarceration Issues: Punishment, Reform, & Rehabilitation, 11 vols. Set. Incl. Alternatives to Prison : Rehabilitation & Other Programs. Russell, Craig. 111p. (YA). 2006. 22.95 (978-1-59084-991-0(4)); History of Incarceration. Smith, Roger. 111p. (YA). 2007. 22.95 (978-1-59084-985-9(X)); Incarceration Around the World. Russell, Craig. 112p. (J). 2007. 22.95 (978-1-59084-988-0(4)); Inequities of the Justice System. Hunter, David. 112p. (YA). 2006. (978-1-59084-995-8(7)); Political Prisoners. Smith, Roger. 111p. (J). 2007. 22.95 (978-1-59084-987-3(6)); Prison Conditions : Overcrowding, Disease, Violence, & Abuse. Smith, Roger. 111p. (J). 2007. 22.95 (978-1-59084-986-6(8)); Prisoner Rehabilitation : Success Stories & Failures. Esherick, Joan. 111p. (YA). 2007. 22.95 (978-1-59084-994-1(9)); Prisoners on Death Row. Smith, Roger. 111p. (YA). 2006. 22.95 (978-1-59084-989-7(2)); Social, Monetary, & Moral Costs of Prisons. Libal, Autumn. 111p. (J). 2007. 22.95 (978-1-59084-992-7(2)); Women in Prison. Esherick, Joan. 112p. (YA). 2006. (978-1-59084-993-4(0)); Youth in Prison. Smith, Roger & McIntosh, Marsha. 112p. (J). 2006. (978-1-59084-990-3(6)); (gr. 7 up). (Incarceration Issues Ser.). (Illus.). 111p. 2007. 252.45 (*978-1-59084-984-2(1)) Mason Crest Pubs.

Jamuna Carroll. Prisons. 2006. (Illus.). 244p. (gr. 6-10). 29.95 (978-0-7377-3584-0(8) , Greenhaven Pr., Inc.) Thomson Gale.

Kelly, Zachary A. Prisons & Jails. 1998. (Law & Order Ser.). (J). lib. bdg. (978-0-86625-659-9(8)) Rourke Publishing, LLC.

Libal, Autumn. The Social, Monetary, & Moral Costs of Prisons. 2007. (Incarceration Issues Ser.). (Illus.). 111p. (J). (gr. 7 up). 22.95 (978-1-59084-992-7(2)) Mason Crest Pubs.

Lock, Joan. Famous Prisons. 2002. (Crime & Detection Ser.). (Illus.). 96p. (J). (gr. 7 up). lib. bdg. (978-1-59084-380-2(0)) Mason Crest Pubs.

MacDonald, Fiona. You Wouldn't Want to Be in a Medieval Dungeon! 2003. (gr. 3-6). lib. bdg. 18.75 (978-0-613-59559-9(9)) Tandem Library Bks.

—You Wouldn't Want to Be in a Medieval Dungeon! Prisoners You'd Rather Not Meet. Antram, David, illus. 2003. (You Wouldn't Want to Ser.). (J). 28.50 (978-0-531-12312-6(X)); (gr. 2-5). pap. 9.95 (978-0-531-16651-2(1)) Scholastic Library Publishing. (Watts, Franklin).

Maganzini, Christy. Almanac of Dungeons, Prisons & Jails. 1998. (Kidbacks Ser.). (J). pap. 5.99 (978-0-679-88353-1(3) , Random Hse. Bks. for Young Readers) Random Hse. Children's Bks.

Martin, Michael. Life as a POW. 2003. (American War Library). (Illus.). 112p. (J). 29.95 (978-1-59018-260-4(X) , Lucent Bks.) Thomson Gale.

Oliver, Marilyn Tower. Alcatraz Prison in American History. 1998. (In American History Ser.). (Illus.). 128p. (YA). (gr. 5-12). lib. bdg. 26.60 (978-0-89490-990-0(8)) Enslow Pubs., Inc.

Presnall, Judith Janda. Life on Alcatraz. 2000. (Way People Live Ser.). (Illus.). 112p. (J). (gr. 7-10). 28.70 (978-1-56006-639-2(3) , LML00902-177994, Lucent Bks.) Thomson Gale.

Rabiger, Joanna. Daily Prison Life. 2003. (Crime & Detection Ser.). (Illus.). 96p. (J). (gr. 7 up). lib. bdg. (978-1-59084-384-0(3)) Mason Crest Pubs.

Russell, Craig. Incarceration Around the World. 2007. (Incarceration Issues Ser.). (Illus.). 112p. (J). (gr. 7 up). 22.95 (978-1-59084-988-0(4)) Mason Crest Pubs.

Smith, Roger. The History of Incarceration. 2007. (Incarceration Issues Ser.). (Illus.). 111p. (YA). (gr. 7 up). 22.95 (978-1-59084-985-9(X)) Mason Crest Pubs.

—Prison Conditions: Overcrowding, Disease, Violence, & Abuse. 2007. (Incarceration Issues Ser.). (Illus.). 111p. (J). (gr. 7 up). 22.95 (978-1-59084-986-6(8)) Mason Crest Pubs.

Smith, Roger & McIntosh, Marsha. Youth in Prison. 2006. (Incarceration Issues Ser.). (Illus.). 112p. (J). (gr. 7 up). (978-1-59084-990-3(6)) Mason Crest Pubs.

Townsend, John. Prisons & Prisoners. 2005. (Raintree Freestyle Ser.). (Illus.). 48p. (J). (978-1-4109-2053-9(4)); (gr. 6-8). pap. 8.90 (978-1-4109-2058-4(5)) Steck-Vaughn.

Williams, Stanley. Life in Prison. 2001. (gr. 5-8). lib. bdg. 12.95 (978-0-613-33832-5(4)) Tandem Library Bks.

Williams, Stanley T. & Becnel, Barbara Cottman. Life in Prison. 2001. (Illus.). 80p. (J). (gr. 4-7). 14.95 (978-1-58717-093-5(0)); pap. 5.99 (978-1-58717-094-2(9)) Chronicle Bks. LLC. (SeaStar Bks.).

Yaffe, Rebecca M., et al. When a Parent Goes to Jail: A Comprehensive Guide for Counseling Children of Incarcerated Parents. Moody, Barbara S., illus. 2000. 45p. (J). (gr. k-7). 49.95 (978-1-877810-08-4(8)) Rayve Productions, Inc.

PRISONS—FICTION

Black, Frank M. There Are Some Real Special Kids in Our Class. Moses, Robin, photos by. 1999. (Illus.). 24p. (J). pap. 6.95 (978-1-929157-04-4(5)) Inside-OUT Corp.

—A Visit with Daddy. Moses, Robin, photos by. 1999. (Illus.). 20p. (J). pap. 6.95 (978-1-929157-00-6(2)) Inside-OUT Corp.

—A Visit with Mommy. Moses, Robin, photos by. 1999. (Illus.). 20p. (J). pap. 6.95 (978-1-929157-01-3(0)) Inside-OUT Corp.

—Una Visita a Mami. Moses, Robin, photos by. 1999. (SPA., Illus.). 20p. (J). pap. 6.95 (978-1-929157-03-7(7)) Inside-OUT Corp.

—Una Visita a Papi. Moses, Robin, photos by. 1999. (SPA., Illus.). 20p. (J). pap. (978-1-929157-02-0(9)) Inside-OUT Corp.

Burch, Robert. Queenie Peavey. l.t. ed. 2003. (LRS Large Print Cornerstone Ser.). 166p. (J). lib. bdg. 29.95 (978-1-58118-115-9(9)) LRS.

Courtenay, Bryce. The Power of One. 2005. 304p. (J). (gr. 5-12). lib. bdg. 17.99 (978-0-385-90274-8(3) , Delacorte Bks. for Young Readers) Random Hse. Children's Bks.

Davis, Lee. Antietam: The Lost Command. 2001. (Read-Along Radio Dramas Ser.). 45p. ring bd. (978-1-878298-31-7(3)) Balance Publishing Co.

Deary, Terry. Breakout! 2004. (Classified Ser.). 96p. (J). (gr. 5-8). pap. 4.95 (978-0-7534-5826-6(8) , Kingfisher) Houghton Mifflin Co. Trade & Reference Div.

Flynn, Arthur. Luke on Alcatraz. 2001. 128p. (YA). (gr. 5-9). per. (978-1-84210-021-9(1)) Mentor Bks.

Gaffney, Linda. My Daddy Does GOOD Things, Too! Dabney, Undra & Goettling, Nikolas, illus. 2006. 55p. per. 10.99 ***(978-0-9787501-0-7(1))*** Gaffney, Linda.

Hand, Jimmie. Long Way Around. 2003. (gr. 7-12). lib. bdg. 18.75 (978-0-613-77939-5(8)) Tandem Library Bks.

Karr, Kathleen. The Boxer. 2000. (Illus.). 144p. (YA). (gr. 7 up). 17.00 (978-0-374-30921-3(3) , Farrar, Straus & Giroux (BYR)) Farrar, Straus & Giroux.

King, Stephen. The Green Mile: The Complete Serial Novel. 1999. (gr. 7-12). lib. bdg. 16.45 (978-0-613-17261-5(2)) Tandem Library Bks.

Kir-on, Callanitte. The 3-D Files: Prisoner on the Loose. 2003. (Illus.). (J). 10.95 (978-1-931681-47-6(3)) Israel Bk. Shop.

Kline, Suzy. Horrible Harry & the Dungeon. 1998. (Horrible Harry Ser.: No. 7). (J). (gr. 2-4). 10.79 (978-0-606-13490-3(5)) Tandem Library Bks.

Korman, Gordon. Chasing the Falconers. 2005. (On the Run Ser.: No. 1). (Illus.). 160p. (J). pap. 4.99 (978-0-439-65136-3(0) , Scholastic Paperbacks) Scholastic, Inc.

Lawrence, Iain. The Convicts Book I: The Curse of the Jolly Stone Trilogy. 2006. 208p. (YA). (gr. 7). pap. 5.99 (978-0-440-41932-7(8) , Laurel Leaf) Random Hse. Children's Bks.

Morgenroth, Kate. Jude. 288p. (YA). 2004. 16.95 (978-0-689-86479-7(5)); 2006. (Illus.). reprint ed. mass mkt. 5.99 (978-1-4169-1267-5(3) , Simon Pulse) Simon & Schuster Children's Publishing.

Mrs. Richardson's and Mrs. Doyle's 5th Grade Class. Prison - Not Me! Adeniyi, Olu-Jimi, illus. l.t. unabr. ed. 1998. (WeWrite Kids! Ser.: No. 39). 45p. (J). (gr. 3-5). pap. 3.95 (978-1-57635-021-8(5)) WeWrite LLC.

Myers, Walter Dean. Monster. Myers, Christopher A., illus. 1999. (Amistad Ser.). 288p. (J). (gr. 7 up). 16.99 (978-0-06-028077-2(8)) HarperCollins Pubs.

—Monster. Myers, Christopher, illus. (Newbery Honor Roll Ser.). (J). 1999. 288p. (gr. 7 up). lib. bdg. 17.89 (978-0-06-028078-9(6)); 2001. 304p. reprint ed. pap. 7.99 (978-0-06-440731-1(4) , Amistad) HarperCollins Pubs.

—Monster. unabr. ed. 2004. 281p. (J). (gr. 7 up). pap. 29.00 incl. audio (978-0-8072-8363-9(0) , YA188CX, Listening Library) Random Hse. Audio Publishing Group.

—Monster. 2001. (YA). (978-0-606-21336-3(8)) Tandem Library Bks.

Myers, Walter Dean & Myers, Walter Dean. Monster. Myers, Christopher A., illus. 2001. 281p. (YA). (gr. 7-12). per. 15.30 (978-0-613-35985-6(2)) Tandem Library Bks.

Pevsner, Stella & Tang, Fay. Sing for Your Father, Su Phan. 1999. (978-0-606-16709-3(9)) Tandem Library Bks.

Silverman, Erica. The Halloween House. Agee, Jon, illus. 2008. 32p. (J). pap. 6.99 ***(978-0-312-38013-7(5))*** Square Fish.

Stanglin, Jackie A. Mami, ¿ qué es una carcel? (What Is Jail, Mommy? - Spanish Version) 2007. (J). 19.99 ***(978-1-59879-429-8(9));*** per. 11.99 ***(978-1-59879-428-1(0))*** Lifevest Publishing, Inc.

—What Is Jail, Mommy? McGuckie, Cierra Jade, illus. l.t. ed. 2006. 40p. (J). 19.99 ***(978-1-59879-252-2(0));*** per. 11.99 ***(978-1-59879-248-5(2))*** Lifevest Publishing, Inc.

Walker, Jan. An Inmate's Daughter. Leonhard, Herb, illus. 2006. 171p. (J). per. 9.00 (978-0-9714161-9-2(2)) Raven Publishing Inc. of Montana.

Woodson, Jacqueline. Visiting Day. Ransome, James E., illus. 2002. 32p. (J). (ps-3). pap. 15.95 (978-0-590-40005-3(3) , Scholastic Pr.) Scholastic, Inc.

Woodson, Jacqueline & Ransome, James E. Visiting Day. 2001. (Illus.). (J). pap. (978-0-590-55262-2(7)) Scholastic, Inc.

PRISONS—UNITED STATES—FICTION

Wisler, G. Clifton. Red Cap, unabr. ed. 2000. (YA). pap., stu. ed. 41.24 incl. audio (978-0-7887-3629-2(9) , 41018X4) Recorded Bks., LLC.

—Red Cap. 2001. (YA). 20.25 (978-0-8446-7196-3(7)) Smith, Peter Pub., Inc.

PRIVACY, RIGHT OF

Bridegam, Martha. The Right to Privacy. 2003. (Point/Counterpoint Ser.). (Illus.). 112p. (J). (gr. 9-13). 32.95 (978-0-7910-7373-5(4)); pap. 15.95 (978-0-7910-7508-1(7)) Facts On File, Inc. (Chelsea Hse.).

Durrett, Deanne. Teen Privacy Rights. 2001. (Hot Issues Ser.). (Illus.). 64p. (YA). (gr. 6-12). lib. bdg. 27.93 (978-0-7660-1374-2(X)) Enslow Pubs., Inc.

Freedman, Jeri. America Debates Privacy Versus Security. 2007. lib. bdg. ***(978-1-4042-1929-8(3))*** Rosen Publishing Group, Inc., The.

Fridell, Ron. Privacy vs. Security: Your Rights in Conflict. 2004. (Issues in Focus Ser.). (Illus.). 128p. (J). lib. bdg. 26.60 (978-0-7660-2161-7(0)) Enslow Pubs., Inc.

Garrett, Brandon. The Right to Privacy. 2001. (Individual Rights & Civic Responsibility Ser.). (Illus.). 64p. (YA). (gr. 7-12). lib. bdg. 26.50 (978-0-8239-3236-8(2)) Rosen Publishing Group, Inc., The.

Kuhn, Betsy. Prying Eyes: Privacy in the Twenty-First Century. 2008. (J). lib. bdg. ***(978-0-8225-7179-7(X))*** Twenty First Century Bks.

McGwire, Scarlett. Surveillance: The Impact on Our Lives. 2001. (Twenty-First Century Debates Ser.). (Illus.). 64p. (YA). (gr. 6-8). lib. bdg. 27.12 (978-0-7398-3172-4(0)) Raintree.

Morris, Neil. Do We Have a Right to Privacy? 2007. (J). ***(978-1-4329-0354-1(3));*** pap. ***(978-1-4329-0363-3(2))*** Heinemann Library.

Smith, Rich. Fourth Amendment: The Right to Privacy. 2007. (Bill of Rights Ser.). (ENG., Illus.). 32p. (J). (gr. 4-8). lib. bdg. 25.65 ***(978-1-59928-916-8(4)*** , ABDO & Daughters) ABDO Publishing Co.

Stefoff, Rebecca. Security vs. Privacy. 2007. (Open for Debate Ser.). (J). lib. bdg. ***(978-0-7614-2578-6(0)*** , Benchmark Bks.) Cavendish, Marshall Corp.

PRIVATE SCHOOLS—FICTION

Decampi, Alex & Federica Manfredi. Kat & Mouse, Vol. 2. 2007. (Illus.). pap. 5.99 (978-1-59816-549-4(6) , Tokyopop Kids) TOKYOPOP, Inc.

Fisher, Catherine. Darkwater Hall. 2004. 208p. pap. (978-0-340-74383-6(2) , Hodder Children's Books) Hodder Children's Division.

Stanwood Pier, Arthu. The Jester of St. Timothy's. 2006. pap. 14.95 ***(978-1-55742-546-1(9))*** Wildside Pr.

PRIVATEERING

Butterfield, Moira. Pirates & Smugglers. 2005. (Kingfisher Knowledge Ser.). (Illus.). 64p. (J). (gr. 5-9). 12.95 (978-0-7534-5864-8(0) , Kingfisher) Houghton Mifflin Co. Trade & Reference Div.

Hamilton, Sue L. Henry Morgan. 2007. (Pirates! Ser.). (ENG., Illus.). 32p. (J). (gr. 3-6). 24.21 ***(978-1-59928-760-7(9)*** , ABDO & Daughters) ABDO Publishing Co.

PRIZE FIGHTING

see Boxing

PROBABILITIES

Accelerated Math West Virginia State Tagged Probablilty & Statistics Library. 2004. cd-rom 1199.00 (978-1-59455-117-8(0)) Renaissance Learning, Inc.

Benchmark Education Staff, compiled by. Data Analysis & Probability. 2005. spiral bd. 210.00 ***(978-1-4108-3897-1(8));*** spiral bd. 60.00 ***(978-1-4108-3898-8(6));*** spiral bd. 75.00 ***(978-1-4108-3908-4(7));*** spiral bd. 80.00 ***(978-1-4108-3915-2(X));*** spiral bd. 205.00 ***(978-1-4108-4512-2(5));*** spiral bd. 295.00 ***(978-1-4108-5452-0(3));*** spiral bd. 215.00 ***(978-1-4108-5453-7(1));*** spiral bd. 165.00 ***(978-1-4108-5863-4(4));*** spiral bd. 185.00 ***(978-1-4108-5864-1(2))*** Benchmark Education Co.

—Data & Probability. 2005. spiral bd. 185.00 ***(978-1-4108-3901-5(X))*** Benchmark Education Co.

Burrill, Gail F., et al. Probability Models. (Data-Driven Mathematics Ser.). 96p. (YA). (gr. 7-12). pap., stu. ed. 18.95 (978-1-57232-240-0(3)) Seymour, Dale Pubns.

Cushman, Jean. Do You Wanna Bet? Your Chance to Find Out about Probability. Weston, Martha, illus. 2007. 112p. (J). (gr. 4-6). pap. 6.95 ***(978-0-618-82999-6(7)*** , Clarion Bks.) Houghton Mifflin Co. Trade & Reference Div.

Fried, Ellen. What's the Chance? 2004. (National Geographic Reading Expeditions Ser.). (Illus.). 24p. (J). pap. (978-0-7922-4590-2(3)) National Geographic Society.

Leech, Bonnie Coulter. Gregor Mendel's Genetic Theory: Understanding & Applying Concepts of Probability. 2006. (Math for the Real World Ser.). (Illus.). 32p. (J). pap. (978-1-4042-6063-4(3)); lib. bdg. (978-1-4042-3355-3(5)) Rosen Publishing Group, Inc., The.

MathQueue. Using the Standards—Data Analysis & Probability, Grade 1. 2005. (100+ Ser.). (Illus.). 128p. (C). pap. 12.99 (978-0-7424-2991-8(1) , Instructional Fair) Schaffer, Frank Pubns.

—Using the Standards—Data Analysis & Probability, Grade 2. 2005. (100+ Ser.). (Illus.). 128p. (C). pap. 12.99 (978-0-7424-2992-5(X) , Instructional Fair) Schaffer, Frank Pubns.

—Using the Standards—Data Analysis & Probability, Grade 3. 2005. (100+ Ser.). (Illus.). 128p. (C). pap. 12.99 (978-0-7424-2993-2(8) , Instructional Fair) Schaffer, Frank Pubns.

—Using the Standards—Data Analysis & Probability, Grade 4. 2005. (100+ Ser.). (Illus.). 128p. (C). pap. 12.99 (978-0-7424-2994-9(6) , Instructional Fair) Schaffer, Frank Pubns.

—Using the Standards—Data Analysis & Probability, Grade 5. 2005. (100+ Ser.). (Illus.). 128p. (C). pap. 12.99 (978-0-7424-2995-6(4) , Instructional Fair) Schaffer, Frank Pubns.

—Using the Standards—Data Analysis & Probability, Kindergarten. 2005. (100+ Ser.). (Illus.). 128p. (C). pap. 12.99 (978-0-7424-2990-1(3) , Instructional Fair) Schaffer, Frank Pubns.

Moscovich, Ivan. The Probability Games. 2000. (Illus.). 24p. (J). (gr. 3-7). 5.95 (978-0-7611-2017-9(3) , 12017) Workman Publishing Co., Inc.

Murphy, Stuart J. Probably Pistachio. 2001. (gr. k-3). lib. bdg. 13.00 (978-0-613-31611-8(8)) Tandem Library Bks.

—Probably Pistachio: Level 2: Probability. Winborn, Marsha, illus. 2001. (MathStart Ser.). 40p. (J). (gr. 1 up). 15.89 (978-0-06-028029-1(8)) HarperCollins Pubs.

—Probably Pistachio Level 2. Winborn, Marsha, illus. 2001. (MathStart Ser.). 40p. (J). (gr. 1 up). 15.95 (978-0-06-028028-4(X)); pap. 5.99 (978-0-06-446734-6(1) , Harper Trophy) HarperCollins Pubs.

—Probably Pistachio Level 2. 2001. (Math Start Ser.). (Illus.). (J). (978-0-606-20867-3(4)) Tandem Library Bks.

Probability & Statistics. 2003. (Mathematical Mind Ser.). 48p. (gr. 6-8). 5.99 (978-0-7424-0084-9(0) , IF2904) School Specialty Publishing.

Realtime Associates and Mazer Corporation Staff & LeapFrog Staff, compiled by. Identify Events As Certain, Impossible, or Probable. 2002. (J). (gr. 3). 66.75 (978-1-58605-399-4(X) , LeapFrog Schl. Hse.) LeapFrog Enterprises, Inc.

—List Possible Outcomes of a Common Probability Event. 2002. (J). (gr. 5). 66.75 (978-1-58605-516-5(X) , LeapFrog Schl. Hse.) LeapFrog Enterprises, Inc.

—Report Probability as a Fraction. 2002. (J). (gr. 5). 66.75 (978-1-58605-517-2(8) , LeapFrog Schl. Hse.) LeapFrog Enterprises, Inc.

Ring, Susan. Puedes Advinar? 2005. Tr. of Can You Guess?. (SPA., Illus.). 16p. (J). (gr. k-1). lib. bdg. 15.93 (978-0-7368-4149-8(0)) Capstone Pr., Inc.

Roza, Greg. Heads or Tails? 2004. (PowerMath Ser.). (Illus.). 24p. (J). lib. bdg. 21.25 (978-0-8239-8971-3(2) , PowerKids Pr.) Rosen Publishing Group, Inc., The.

School Specialty Publishing. Probability & Logic Gr 6. 2005. (Math 2 Master Ser.). 32p. (J). pap. 3.99 (978-0-7696-3916-1(X) , Brighter Child) School Specialty Publishing.

—Step-by-Step Homework Booklets: Probability. 2003. (Homework Booklets Ser.). 80p. (C). pap. 2.99 (978-0-7682-2646-1(5) , IFG99148) School Specialty Publishing.

Using Cuisenaire Rods: Probability & Statistics. 2002. (J). pap. (978-1-56911-743-9(8)) Learning Resources, Inc.

VanVoorst, Jennifer. Can You Guess? (Math Ser.). (J). 2004. 16p. lib. bdg. 15.93 (978-0-7368-2931-1(8) , Yellow Umbrella Bks.); 2003. pap. (978-0-7368-2890-1(7)) Capstone Pr., Inc.

What Are My Chances? Exploring the Laws of Probability. 2003. 96p. (gr. 5-8). 9.99 (978-1-56822-618-7(7) , IF2507) School Specialty Publishing.

Work with Probability & Statistics. 2004. (Math "How To" Ser.). (Illus.). 48p. (J). (gr. 4-6). 7.99 (978-1-57690-960-7(3)); (YA). (gr. 6-8). 7.99 (978-1-57690-968-3(9)) Teacher Created Materials, Inc.

PROBES, SPACE

see Space Probes

PROBLEM CHILDREN

see also Juvenile Delinquency

Biscontini, Tracey. Youth Violence. 2007. (History of Issues Ser.). (Illus.). 240p. (gr. 10-12). 36.20 (978-0-7377-2877-4(9) , Greenhaven Pr., Inc.) Thomson Gale.

chuta, edith N. Straight Talk to Troubled Kids: Finding Wisdom Underneath Our Pains. 2007. 76p. per. 10.95 ***(978-0-595-43778-8(8))*** iUniverse, Inc.

Corrigan, Eireann. You Remind Me of You: A Poetry Memoir. 2002. (978-0-606-22262-4(6)); (gr. 7-12). lib. bdg. 15.30 (978-0-613-57175-3(4)) Tandem Library Bks.

Day, Roger. Being Mad, Being Glad. 2004. (Kids' Guides Ser.). (Illus.). 32p. (J). (gr. 1-4). lib. bdg. 25.64 (978-1-4109-0570-3(5)) Raintree.

Hames, Annette (Ed). Special Brothers & Sisters. 2005. (Illus.). 96p. pap. (978-1-84310-383-7(4)) Kingsley, Jessica Ltd.

Libal, Autumn. Runaway Train: Youth with Emotional Disturbance. 2004. (Youth with Special Needs Ser.). (Illus.). 128p. (J). (978-1-59084-732-9(6)) Mason Crest Pubs.

McIntyre, Thomas. Behavior Survival Guide for Kids: How to Make Good Choices & Stay Out of Trouble. 2003. (gr. 3-6). lib. bdg. 22.20 (978-0-613-87129-7(4)) Tandem Library Bks.

Nelson, Julie. Families Change: A Book for Children Experiencing Termination of Parental Rights. Gallagher, Mary, illus. 2006. (Kids Are Important Ser.). 32p. (J). pap. 9.95 (978-1-57542-209-1(3)) Free Spirit Publishing, Inc.

Rotner, Shelley. The A. D. D. Book for Kids. 2000. 3. (Illus.). 32p. (gr. k-3). pap. (978-0-7613-1436-3(9) , Millbrook Pr.) Lerner Publishing Group.

Rotner, Shelley & Kelly, Sheila M. The A. D. D. Book for Kids. 2000. (Contemporary Issues for Young Children Ser.). (Illus.). 32p. (gr. k-3). lib. bdg. (978-0-7613-1722-7(8) , Millbrook Pr.) Lerner Publishing Group.

Schmidt, April. Youth Violence. 2006. (Illus.). 244p. (gr. 10-12). 36.20 (978-0-7377-2490-5(0)); pap. 24.95 (978-0-7377-2491-2(9)) Thomson Gale. (Greenhaven Pr., Inc.).

PROBLEM CHILDREN—FICTION

Forde, Catherine. Firestarter. 2006. 160p. (J). pap. 8.99 ***(978-1-4052-1056-0(7))*** Egmont Bks., Ltd. GBR. *Dist:* Independent Pubs. Group.

—Skarrs. 2004. 352p. (J). pap. 8.99 ***(978-1-4052-0947-2(X))*** Egmont Bks., Ltd. GBR. *Dist:* Independent Pubs. Group.

Graver, Elizabeth. Honey Thief. 2000. (gr. 7-12). lib. bdg. 22.25 (978-0-613-36404-1(X)) Tandem Library Bks.

Kennen, Ally. Beast. 2007. 224p. (J). pap. 7.99 ***(978-0-439-86550-0(6))*** Scholastic, Inc.

Mac, Carrie. Charmed. 2006. 112p. (YA). lib. bdg. 14.95 (978-1-55143-578-7(0)) Orca Bk. Pubs. USA.

Weber, Lenora Mattingly. Come Back, Wherever You Are. 1999. (Beany Malone Ser.). 259p. (J). pap. 12.95 (978-1-930009-06-6(2)) Image Cascade Publishing.

PROBLEM SOLVING

Adler, David A. You Can, Toucan, Math: Word Problem-Solving Fun. Miller, Edward, illus. 32p. (J). (ps-3). 16.95 (978-0-8234-1919-7(3)); 2007. 6.95 ***(978-0-8234-2117-6(1))*** Holiday Hse., Inc.

Amos, Janine. Go Away! Spenceley, Annabel, illus. 2002. (Courteous Kids Ser.). 32p. (J). (ps up). lib. bdg. 23.33 (978-0-8368-3607-3(3)) Stevens, Gareth Inc.

—It Won't Work! Spenceley, Annabel, illus. 2002. (Courteous Kids Ser.). 32p. (J). (ps up). lib. bdg. 23.33 (978-0-8368-3608-0(1)) Stevens, Gareth Inc.

—Move Over! Spenceley, Annabel, illus. 2002. (Courteous Kids Ser.). 32p. (J). (ps up). lib. bdg. 23.33 (978-0-8368-3610-3(3)) Stevens, Gareth Inc.

Beckwith, Kathy. If You Choose Not to Hit: A Dozen Skills That Make Kids Powerful Problem Solvers. Henderson, Carol, illus. 2001. 138p. (J). (gr. 2-5). pap. 9.95 (978-1-930572-09-6(3)) Educational Media Corp.

Beers, Jack. Step 1 Student Edition. 1999. (Problem Solving Step by Step Ser.). (J). (gr. 1). stu. ed., per. 7.95 (978-1-58120-701-9(8)) Metropolitan Teaching & Learning Co.

—Step 1 Student Edition 10-Pack. 1999. (Problem Solving Step by Step Ser.). (J). (gr. 1). stu. ed., per. 85.95 (978-1-58830-171-0(0)) Metropolitan Teaching & Learning Co.

—Step 1 Student Edition 6-Pack. 1999. (Problem Solving Step by Step Ser.). (J). (gr. 1). stu. ed., per. 62.95 (978-1-58120-731-6(X)) Metropolitan Teaching & Learning Co.

—Step 2 Student Edition. 1999. (Problem Solving Step by Step Ser.). (J). (gr. 2). stu. ed., per. 7.95 (978-1-58120-702-6(6)) Metropolitan Teaching & Learning Co.

—Step 2 Student Edition 10-Pack. 1999. (Problem Solving Step by Step Ser.). (J). (gr. 2). stu. ed., per. 85.95 (978-1-58830-172-7(9)) Metropolitan Teaching & Learning Co.

—Step 2 Student Edition 6-Pack. 1999. (Problem Solving Step by Step Ser.). (J). (gr. 2). stu. ed., per. 62.95 (978-1-58120-732-3(8)) Metropolitan Teaching & Learning Co.

—Step 2 Teacher Edition. 1999. (Problem Solving Step by Step Ser.). (gr. 2). tchr. ed., per. 9.95 (978-1-58120-712-5(3)) Metropolitan Teaching & Learning Co.

—Step 3 Student Edition. 1999. (Problem Solving Step by Step Ser.). (J). (gr. 3). stu. ed., per. 8.95 (978-1-58120-703-3(4)) Metropolitan Teaching & Learning Co.

—Step 3 Student Edition 10-Pack. 1999. (Problem Solving Step by Step Ser.). (J). (gr. 3). stu. ed., per. 97.95 (978-1-58830-173-4(7)) Metropolitan Teaching & Learning Co.

—Step 3 Student Edition 6-Pack. 1999. (Problem Solving Step by Step Ser.). (J). (gr. 3). stu. ed., per. 69.95 (978-1-58120-733-0(6)) Metropolitan Teaching & Learning Co.

—Step 4 Student Edition 10-Pack. 1999. (Problem Solving Step by Step Ser.). (J). (gr. 4). stu. ed., per. 97.95 (978-1-58830-174-1(5)) Metropolitan Teaching & Learning Co.

—Step 8 Teacher Edition. 1999. (Problem Solving Step by Step Ser.). (gr. 8). tchr. ed., per. 10.95 (978-1-58120-683-8(6)) Metropolitan Teaching & Learning Co.

Bresser, Rusty & Holtzman, Caren. Minilessons for Math Practice, Grades 3-5. 2006. 176p. (gr. 3-5). pap. 19.95 (978-0-941355-75-9(6)) Math Solutions Pubns.

—Minilessons for Math Practice, Grades K-2. 2006. 176p. (gr. k-2). pap. 19.95 (978-0-941355-74-2(8)) Math Solutions Pubns.

Cream of the Crop: Over 50 Fabulous Creative Problem Solving Challenges for Students K-12. 2001. 64p. per. 10.00 (978-0-9715202-0-2(8)) Colorado Seminary.

Cuisenaire Rods Alphabet Book: Problem Solving A to Z. 2000. (J). pap. 9.95 (978-1-56911-061-4(1)) Learning Resources, Inc.

Dalmatian Press Staff & School Zone Publishing Interactive Staff. Same or Different. 2000. (On-Track Software Ser.). 32p. (J). (ps). wbk. ed. 13.99 incl. cd-rom (978-0-88743-926-1(8) , 08802) School Zone Publishing Co.

DeMoss, Glenda & Griffin, Linda. Problem of the Week: A Fresh Approach to Problem-Solving. 1999. 96p. (YA). (gr. 7 up). pap. 9.99 (978-1-56822-620-0(9) , IF2509) School Specialty Publishing.

Fairview Press Staff, ed. Kids Write Through It: Essays from Kids Who've Triumphed over Trouble. 1999. 256p. (gr. 4-7). pap. 9.95 (978-1-57749-081-4(9)) Fairview Pr.

Get Your Hands on Problem Solving. 80p. (gr. 1 up). 8.99 (978-1-56451-254-3(1) , ID7910); (gr. 2 up). 8.99 (978-1-56451-255-0(X) , ID7911); (gr. 3 up). 8.99 (978-1-56451-256-7(8) , ID7912) School Specialty Publishing.

Griffin, Linda & Demos, Glenda. Problem of the Week: A Fresh Approach to Problem-Solving. 1999. 96p. (YA). (gr. 8 up). pap. 9.99 (978-1-56822-621-7(7) , IF2510) School Specialty Publishing.

Griffin, Linda & DeMoss, Glenda. Problem of the Week: A Fresh Approach to Problem-Solving. 1999. 96p. (J). (gr. 6 up). pap. 9.99 (978-1-56822-619-4(5) , IF2508) School Specialty Publishing.

Grishaver, Joel Lurie. You Be the Judge: A Collection of Ethical Cases. 1999. (Family Bet Din Ser.). (Illus.). 128p. (J). (gr. 7-11). pap. 9.95 (978-1-891662-00-3(7)) Torah Aura Productions.

Hoffman, Mary Ann. The History of the Maya: Using Computational Skills in Problem Solving. 2005. (Powermath Ser.). (Illus.). 32p. (J). 22.50 (978-1-4042-2942-6(6)); (978-1-4042-5149-6(9)); pap. (978-1-4042-5148-9(0)) Rosen Publishing Group, Inc., The. (PowerKids Pr.).

Howard, Pat. Word Problems: Building Mathematical Knowledge Through Problem Solving. 2001. (100+ Seriestm Ser.). 128p. (J). (gr. 2-3). pap. 12.99 (978-0-7424-0134-1(0) , IF87140) School Specialty Publishing.

Kent, Susan. Learning How to Ask Someone for Help. 2001. (Violence Prevention Library). (Illus.). 24p. (J). (gr. 3). lib. bdg. 18.75 (978-0-8239-5612-8(1) , PowerKids Pr.) Rosen Publishing Group, Inc., The.

Lin, Jonathon. Exploring Problem Solving. Abouzahr, H. et al, illus. 2002. 32p. cd-rom 19.95 (978-1-59022-005-4(6)) Glory Educational Resource, Inc.

Linde, Barbara M. Math in Our Solar System: Applying Problem-Solving Strategies. 2005. (PowerMath Ser.). (J). 22.50 (978-1-4042-2936-5(1) , PowerKids Pr.); pap. (978-1-4042-5135-9(9)) Rosen Publishing Group, Inc., The.

Maxwell, John C. Las 17 Cualidades Esenciales de un Jugador de Equipo. 2002. (SPA.). 176p. pap. 10.99 (978-0-88113-737-8(5)) Grupo Nelson.

Raintree Steck-Vaughn Staff. Tools for Problem Solving: Level E. 1998. (Illus.). (J). pap., tchr. ed. 6.01 (978-0-8172-8135-9(5)) Steck-Vaughn.

—Tools for Problem Solving: Level F. 1998. (Illus.). (J). pap., tchr. ed. 6.01 (978-0-8172-8136-6(3)) Steck-Vaughn.

Realtime Associates and Mazer Corporation Staff & LeapFrog Staff, compiled by. Choose the Correct Operation to Solve Problems. 2002. (J). (gr. 2). 66.75 (978-1-58605-338-3(8) , LeapFrog Schl. Hse.) LeapFrog Enterprises, Inc.

—Choose the Correct Operations to Solve Problems. 2002. (J). (gr. 4). 66.75 (978-1-58605-457-1(0) , LeapFrog Schl. Hse.) LeapFrog Enterprises, Inc.

—Determine Problem-Solving Strategies. 2002. (J). (gr. 4). 66.75 (978-1-58605-469-4(4) , LeapFrog Schl. Hse.) LeapFrog Enterprises, Inc.

Risby, Bonnie Lou. The Great Honey Robbery: Using Critical Thinking to Solve Problems. 2004. (J). pap. 14.95 (978-1-931334-40-2(4)) Pieces of Learning.

Roza, Greg. The Hoover Dam: Applying Problem-Solving Strategies. 2006. (Math for the Real World Ser.). (Illus.). 32p. (J). pap. (978-1-4042-6065-8(X)); lib. bdg. (978-1-4042-3356-0(3)) Rosen Publishing Group, Inc., The.

Rue, Nancy N. Everything You Need to Know about Peer Mediation. rev. ed. 2001. (Need to Know Library). (Illus.). 64p. (YA). (gr. 4-6). lib. bdg. 25.25 (978-0-8239-3464-5(0)) Rosen Publishing Group, Inc., The.

Ruffin, Frances E. Let's Have a Bake Sale: Calculating Profit & Unit Cost. 2004. (PowerMath Ser.). (Illus.). 24p. (J). lib. bdg. (978-0-8239-8893-8(7)); lib. bdg. 21.25 (978-0-8239-8970-6(4)) Rosen Publishing Group, Inc., The. (PowerKids Pr.).

Sargent, Brian. Guess the Order. 2006. 32p. (gr. 1-2). (YA). pap. 5.95 (978-0-516-29809-2(7)); (Illus.). (J). 20.50 (978-0-516-24963-6(0)) Scholastic Library Publishing. (Children's Pr.).

—Slumber Party Problem Solving. 2006. 32p. (gr. 1-2). (YA). pap. 5.95 (978-0-516-29829-0(1)); (Illus.). (J). 20.50 (978-0-516-24962-9(2)) Scholastic Library Publishing. (Children's Pr.).

Saviola, Joseph A. The Tour de France: Solving Addition Problems Involving Renaming. 2004. (PowerMath Ser.). (Illus.). 24p. (J). lib. bdg. (978-0-8239-8851-8(1) , PowerKids Pr.) Rosen Publishing Group, Inc., The.

—The Tour de France: Solving Addition Problems Using Regrouping. 2004. (PowerMath Ser.). (Illus.). 24p. (J). lib. bdg. 21.25 (978-0-8239-8963-8(1) , PowerKids Pr.) Rosen Publishing Group, Inc., The.

School Specialty Publishing. Pentomino Pattern Cards. 1999. (C). 4.99 (***978-1-56451-862-0(0)** , Ideal School Supply) Schaffer, Frank Pubns.

—Problem Solving Gr 3. 2005. (Math 2 Master Ser.). 32p. (J). pap. 3.99 (978-0-7696-3923-9(2) , Brighter Child) School Specialty Publishing.

—Problems of the Day. 2002. 96p. (J). (gr. 5-8). pap. 9.99 (978-0-7424-0267-6(3) , IF19362) School Specialty Publishing.

—Step-by-Step Homework Booklets: Problem Solving. 2003. (Homework Booklets Ser.). 80p. (C). pap. 2.99 (978-0-7682-2647-8(3) , IFG99149) School Specialty Publishing.

Schwartz, Linda. Brain Stretchers: Using Deductive Reasoning to Problem Solving. Larson, Eric, ed. Kennedy, Kelly, illus. 2002. 48p. (J). (gr. 4-6). pap. 7.99 (978-0-88160-329-3(5) , LW-403, Learning Works, The) Creative Teaching Pr., Inc.

Shea, Therese. Biosphere 2: Solving Word Problems. 2005. (PowerMath Ser.). (Illus.). 32p. (J). 22.50 (978-1-4042-2943-3(4)); (978-1-4042-5151-9(0)); pap. (978-1-4042-5150-2(2)) Rosen Publishing Group, Inc., The. (PowerKids Pr.).

—The Great Barrier Reef: Using Graphs & Charts to Solve Word Problems. 2006. (Math for the Real World Ser.). (Illus.). 32p. (J). pap. (978-1-4042-6071-9(4)); (gr. 4-8). lib. bdg. 23.95 (978-1-4042-3359-1(8)) Rosen Publishing Group, Inc., The.

—The Transcontinental Railroad: Using Proportions to Solve Problems. 2006. (Math for the Real World Ser.). (Illus.). 32p. (J). pap. (978-1-4042-6075-7(7)); (gr. 4-8). lib. bdg. 23.95 (978-1-4042-3361-4(X)) Rosen Publishing Group, Inc., The.

Super 7: Daily Exercises in Mathematical Problem Solving. 2002. (J). per. 19.95 (978-1-883055-51-6(2)) Dandy Lion Pubns.

Torrance, Harold. Word Problems: Building Mathematical Knowledge Through Problem Solving. 2001. (100+ Seriestm Ser.). 128p. (J). (gr. 4-5). pap. 12.99 (978-0-7424-0135-8(9) , IF87141, Instructional Fair) Schaffer, Frank Pubns.

—Word Problems: Building Mathematical Knowledge Through Problem Solving. 2001. (100+ Seriestm Ser.). 128p. (J). (gr. 6-8). pap. 12.99 (978-0-7424-0136-5(7) , IF87142) School Specialty Publishing.

The Violence Prevention Library, 6 bks. Incl. Learning How to Appreciate Differences. Kent, Susan. lib. bdg. 18.75 (978-0-8239-5617-3(2)); Learning How to Ask Someone for Help. Kent, Susan. lib. bdg. 18.75 (978-0-8239-5612-8(1)); Learning How to Be Kind to Others. Kent, Susan. lib. bdg. 18.75 (978-0-8239-5613-5(X)); Learning How to Feel Good about Yourself. Kent, Susan, contrib. by. lib. bdg. 18.75 (978-0-8239-5615-9(6)); Learning How to Say You Are Sorry. Kent, Susan. lib. bdg. 18.75 (978-0-8239-5614-2(8)); Learning How to Stay Safe at School. Kent, Susan. lib. bdg. 18.75 (978-0-8239-5616-6(4)); 24p. (J). (gr. 3). 2001. (Illus.). Set lib. bdg. 103.50 (978-0-8239-7080-3(9) , PowerKids Pr.) Rosen Publishing Group, Inc., The.

Wandberg, Robert. Creative Problem Solving: What's a Better Way? 2000. (Life Skills-Contemporary Issues Ser.). (Illus.). 64p. (J). (gr. 4-6). lib. bdg. 23.93 (978-0-7368-0694-7(6) , LifeMatters Bks.) Capstone Pr., Inc.

Wesley, Sonya L. Game Plan Ethical Decision Making: A Discussion & Activity Tool. 2000. (Illus.). (YA). spiral bd. (978-1-931377-08-9(1)) Game Plan Pubns.

WRITE IT! Problem Solving with Numbers & Words, Grades 5-6. 2004. (J). per. 10.95 (978-1-58123-365-0(5)) Larson Learning, Inc.

WRITE IT! Problem Solving with Numbers & Words, Grades 7-8. 2004. (J). per. 10.95 (978-1-58123-367-4(1)) Larson Learning, Inc.

Youngs, Dave & Pauls, Michelle. Puzzle Play. Pauls, Michelle & Cordel, Betty, eds. Schlotterback, Dave, illus. 2001. 211p. (J). pap. 18.95 (978-1-881431-95-4(9) , 1722) AIMS Education Foundation.

Zuravicky, Orli. Amazing Animals: Multiplying Multidigit Numbers by a One-Digit Number with Renaming. 2004. (PowerMath Ser.). (Illus.). 24p. (J). lib. bdg. (978-0-8239-8861-7(9)); lib. bdg. 21.25 (978-0-8239-8964-5(X)) Rosen Publishing Group, Inc., The. (PowerKids Pr.).

PROCESSIONS

see Parades

PRODUCTION

see Economics; Industry

PRODUCTS, COMMERCIAL

see Commercial Products

PRODUCTS, DAIRY

see Dairy Products

PRODUCTS, WASTE

see Waste Products

PROFESSION, CHOICE OF

see Vocational Guidance

PROFESSIONS

see also Occupations; Vocational Guidance

also names of professions (e.g. Law; Medicine); also Law—Vocational Guidance; music—Vocational guidance

Able to Work Job Outlook: 2002-2003 Edition. 2nd ed. 2001. (Able to Work). 216p. (YA). per. 24.95 (978-1-929879-24-3(5)) Career Kids.

Business Professions: Careers Video Tour, 5 vols., Vol. 2. 2001. (Careers Video Tour: Vol. 2). (J). cd-rom 49.95 (978-1-929879-05-2(9)) Career Kids.

Careers for Me Vol. II: A Career Interest Assessment. 2000. 12p. (J). pap., wbk. ed. (978-1-929879-01-4(6)) Career Kids.

Careers in the Arts: Careers Video Tour, 5 vols. 2001. (Careers Video Tour: Vol. 4). (J). cd-rom 49.95 (978-1-929879-07-6(5)) Career Kids.

Children's Dictionary Of. 2005. (YA). cd-rom 79.95 (978-0-7365-9951-1(7)) Films Media Group.

Discovering Careers for Your Future - Group 1, 8 bks., Set. Incl. Discovering Careers for Your Future/Adventure. J. G. Ferguson Publishing Company Staff. 96p. (gr. 4-9). 2001. 21.95 (978-0-89434-359-9(9) , F540); Discovering Careers for Your Future/Animals. J. G. Ferguson Publishing Company Staff. 94p. (gr. 4-8). 2000. lib. bdg. 21.95 (978-0-89434-360-5(2) , F542); Discovering Careers for Your Future/English. Yehling, Carol B. 94p. (gr. 4-8). 2000. lib. bdg. 21.95 (978-0-89434-321-6(1) , F536); Discovering Careers for Your Future/Performing Arts. J. G. Ferguson Publishing Company Staff. 94p. (gr. 7-12). 2000. lib. bdg. 21.95 (978-0-89434-361-2(0) , F543); Discovering Careers in Your Future/Math. Yehling, Carol B., ed. 96p. (gr. 4-9). 2000. 21.95 (978-0-89434-323-0(8) , F538); (J). (Illus.). 700p. Set lib. bdg. 127.60 (978-0-89434-363-6(7) , Ferguson Publishing Co.) Facts On File, Inc.

Farr, Michael J. 200 Best Jobs for College Graduates. 2003. (gr. 7-12). lib. bdg. 26.85 (978-0-613-58307-7(8)) Tandem Library Bks.

—300 Best Jobs Without a Four-Year Degree. 2003. (gr. 7-12). lib. bdg. 26.85 (978-0-613-58306-0(X)) Tandem Library Bks.

Fiscus, Jim. Careers in the Fashion Industry. rev. ed. 2005. (Career Resource Library). (Illus.). 192p. (YA). (gr. 7-12). lib. bdg. 26.50 (978-0-8239-4082-0(9)) Rosen Publishing Group, Inc., The.

Gillis, Jennifer Blizin. Ayudantes Del Vecindario/Jennifer B. Gillis. 2007. (SPA & ENG., Illus.). 24p. (J). (***978-1-60044-292-6(7)***) Rourke Publishing, LLC.

Gillis, Jennifer Blizin. Neighborhood Helpers. 2007. (Illus.). 24p. (J). (978-1-60044-203-2(X)) Rourke Publishing, LLC.

Harcourt School Publishers Staff. Horizons Unit 6: The Jobs People Do. 3rd ed. 2001. (Illus.). pap. 169.80 (978-0-15-322574-1(2)) Harcourt Schl. Pubs.

—Jobs of the Past. 3rd ed. 2002. (Horizons Ser.). (Illus.). (J). pap. 3.70 (978-0-15-333178-7(X)) Harcourt Schl. Pubs.

—Jobs People Do, No. 6. 2nd ed. 2003. (Illus.). pap. 139.70 (978-0-15-337561-3(2)) Harcourt Schl. Pubs.

—People & Work Big Book No. 6. 2nd ed. 2003. (Illus.). pap. 139.70 (978-0-15-337571-2(X)) Harcourt Schl. Pubs.

—People Working: Little Book. 2000. (Collections Ser.). (Illus.). (J). pap. 10.20 (978-0-15-314503-2(X)) Harcourt Schl. Pubs.

—What Do You Do? 3rd ed. 2002. (Trophies English Language Learners Ser.). (Illus.). pap. 5.10 (978-0-15-327884-6(6)) Harcourt Schl. Pubs.

Health Related Careers: Careers Video Tour. 2001. (Careers Video Tour: Vol. 3). (J). cd-rom 49.95 (978-1-929879-06-9(7)) Career Kids.

If You Were A... - Group 2, 4 bks., Set. Incl. If You Were a Ballplayer. Schomp, Virginia. 2000. lib. bdg. 22.79 (978-0-7614-0917-5(3)); If You Were a Doctor. Schamp, Virginia. 2000. lib. bdg. 22.79 (978-0-7614-1000-3(7)); If You Were a Pilot. Schomp, Virginia. 2000. lib. bdg. 22.79 (978-0-7614-0919-9(X)); If You Were a Teacher. Schomp, Virginia. 2000. lib. bdg. 22.79 (978-0-7614-0916-8(5)); If You Were a Zookeeper. Schomp, Virginia. 1999. lib. bdg. 22.79 (978-0-7614-0918-2(1)); 32p. (J). (gr. 2-4). (Illus.). 2000. Set lib. bdg. 91.14 (978-0-7614-0915-1(7) , Benchmark Bks.) Cavendish, Marshall Corp.

In the Dark Interactive Packages: Nighttime Jobs. (Pebble Soup Explorations Ser.). (SPA.). (ps up). 52.00 (978-0-7578-5250-3(5)) Rigby Education.

J. G. Ferguson Publishing Company Staff. Careers in Focus: Business Managers. 2003. (Careers in Focus Ser.). 192p. (YA). (gr. 6-12). 22.95 (978-0-89434-414-5(5) , Ferguson Publishing Co.) Facts On File, Inc.

Jacobs, Nancy R., et al, eds. Careers & Occupations: Looking to the Future. 1998. (Information Plus Reference Ser.). (Illus.). 172p. (YA). pap. 32.00 (978-1-57302-079-4(6)) Thomson Gale.

Jarrell, Jane & Saathoff, Deborah. Off to Work We Go. 2004. 50p. (ps up). pap., act. bk. ed. 6.99 (978-0-8054-0823-2(1)) B&H Publishing Grp.

JIST Publishing Staff. Your Promising Future. 2004. 208p. (YA). pap. 12.95 (978-1-59357-011-8(2) , JIST Works) JIST Publishing.

Job Connection: Tools to Land the Job. 2nd ed. 2004. (YA). per. 11.95 (978-1-891818-33-2(3) , 01-WB03) Linx Educational Publishing, Inc.

Miller, Heather. This Is What I Want to Be, 14 bks. 2003. (Illus.). (J). (ps-1). Set. lib. bdg. 259.00 (978-1-4034-0986-7(2)); Set 1. lib. bdg. 185.00 (978-1-4034-0385-8(6)); Set 2. lib. bdg. 74.00 (978-1-4034-0914-0(5)) Heinemann Library.

Raintree Steck-Vaughn Staff, ed. I Want to Be... 2000. (J). 81.36 (978-0-7398-2826-7(6)); (Illus.). 51.38 (978-0-7398-1708-7(6)) Raintree.

Reeves, Diane Lindsey. Career Ideas for Kids Who Like Talking. 2nd rev. ed. (Career Ideas for Kids Ser.). (J). (gr. 4-9). 2008. 304p. pap. 18.95 (***978-0-8160-6554-7(3)***); 2007. 192p. 32.95 (***978-0-8160-6553-0(5)***) Facts On File, Inc. (Checkmark Bks.).

Schwartz, Stuart B. Setting Career Goals. 1998. (J). lib. bdg. (978-0-516-21297-5(4) , Children's Pr.) Scholastic Library Publishing.

Step-by-Step Classroom Guide to Careers. 2002. (J). ring bd. 79.95 (978-1-929879-03-8(2)) Career Kids.

Troutman, Kathryn K. Creating Your High School Resume: A Step-by-Step Guide to Preparing an Effective. 2003. (gr. 7-12). lib. bdg. 17.60 (978-0-613-78784-0(6)) Tandem Library Bks.

Zannos, Susan. Latino Entrepreneurs. 2001. (Latinos at Work Ser.). (Illus.). 96p. (gr. 5-12). lib. bdg. 32.75 (978-1-58415-089-3(0)) Mitchell Lane Pubs., Inc.

PROFESSORS

see Teachers

PROGRAMMING (ELECTRONIC COMPUTERS)

see Computer Programming

PROHIBITION

Beyer, Mark. Temperance & Prohibition: The Movement to Pass Anti-Liquor Laws in America. 2006. (Progressive Movement, 1900-1920—Efforts to Reform America's New Industrial Society Ser.). (Illus.). 32p. (J). (978-1-4042-0861-2(5)); lib. bdg. (978-1-4042-0195-8(5)) Rosen Publishing Group, Inc., The.

Graham, Amy. A Look at the Eighteenth & Twenty-First Amendments: The Prohibition & Sale of Intoxicating Liquors. 2007. (Constitution of the United States Ser.). (Illus.). 128p. (J). (gr. 5). lib. bdg. 33.27 (***978-1-59845-063-7(8)*** , MyReportLinks.com Bks.) Enslow Pubs., Inc.

Harvey, Bonnie Carman. Carry A. Nation: Saloon Smasher & Prohibitionist. 2002. (Historical American Biographies Ser.). (Illus.). 128p. (YA). (gr. 6-12). lib. bdg. 26.60 (978-0-7660-1907-2(1)) Enslow Pubs., Inc.

Lieurance, Suzanne. The Prohibition Era in American History. 2003. (In American History Ser.). (Illus.). 112p. (J). (gr. 5-12). lib. bdg. 26.60 (978-0-7660-1840-2(7)) Enslow Pubs., Inc.

Lucas, Eileen. The Eighteenth & Twenty-First Amendments: Alcohol - Prohibition & Repeal. 1998. (Constitution Ser.). (Illus.). 128p. (YA). (gr. 6-12). lib. bdg. 26.60 (978-0-89490-926-9(6)) Enslow Pubs., Inc.

Nishi, Dennis. Prohibition. 2002. (History Firsthand Ser.). (Illus.). 256p. (YA). (gr. 7-10). pap. 24.95 (978-0-7377-1307-7(0)); lib. bdg. 36.20 (978-0-7377-1306-0(2)) Thomson Gale. (Greenhaven Pr., Inc.).

Orr, Tamra. Prohibition. 2003. (People at the Center of Ser.). (Illus.). 48p. (J). 24.95 (978-1-56711-768-4(6) , Blackbirch Pr., Inc.) Thomson Gale.

Rebman, Renee C. Prohibition. 1998. (World History Ser.). (Illus.). 112p. (YA). (gr. 8-11). 31.20 (978-1-56006-444-2(7) , LML00902-177813, Lucent Bks.) Thomson Gale.

Woog, Adam. Prohibition: Banning Alcohol. 2003. (Words That Changed History Ser.). (Illus.). 96p. (J). 32.45 (978-1-56006-595-1(8) , Lucent Bks.) Thomson Gale.

PROHIBITION—FICTION

Doyle, Bill. Nabbed! The 1925 Journal of G. Codd Fitzmorgan. Lewis, Anthony, illus. 2006. 125p. (J). lib. bdg. 18.46 (***978-1-4242-1735-9(0)***) Fitzgerald Bks.

Erickson, John R. Moonshiner's Gold. (J). (gr. 5). 2003. (Illus.). 208p. 7.99 (978-0-14-250023-1(2) , Puffin); 2001. 176p. 15.99 (978-0-670-03502-1(5) , Viking Juvenile) Penguin Group (USA) Inc.

—Moonshiner's Gold. 2003. 199p. (J). (gr. 5-8). lib. bdg. 15.30 (978-0-613-61644-7(8)) Tandem Library Bks.

Lisle, Janet Taylor. Black Duck. (J). (gr. 5 up). 2007. 256p. 6.99 (***978-0-14-240902-2(2)*** , Puffin); 2006. 240p. 15.99 (978-0-399-23963-2(4) , Philomel) Penguin Group (USA) Inc.

PROJECT APOLLO

Aldrin, Buzz, Jr. Reaching for the Moon. Minor, Wendell, illus. 2005. 40p. (J). 16.99 (978-0-06-055445-3(2)); lib. bdg. 17.89 (978-0-06-055446-0(0)) HarperCollins Pubs.

—Reaching for the Moon. Minor, Wendell, illus. unabr. ed. 2006. (Picture Book Readalong Ser.). (J). (gr. k-4). 25.95 incl. audio (978-1-59519-581-4(5)); 28.95 incl. audio compact disk (978-1-59519-582-1(3)) Live Oak Media.

Anderson, Dale. The First Moon Landing. 2003. (Landmark Events in American History Ser.). (Illus.). 48p. (J). (gr. 5 up). pap. 14.95 (978-0-8368-5406-0(3)); lib. bdg. 30.00 (978-0-8368-5378-0(4)) Stevens, Gareth Inc. (World Almanac Library).

Apollo: Stepping Stones to the Moon. (Color & Learn Ser.). 36p. (J). (gr. 1-5). pap. (978-1-882210-14-5(X)) Action Publishing, Inc.

The Apollo Missions: A Giant Leap for Mankind. 2003. (Eye on History Ser.). 32p. (gr. 5-12). 5.99 (978-0-7424-0252-2(5) , IF2678) School Specialty Publishing.

Beyer, Mark. Crisis in Space: Apollo 13. 2002. (Survivors Ser.). (Illus.). 48p. (YA). (gr. 7-12). 24.00 (978-0-516-23903-3(1)); pap. 6.95 (978-0-516-23485-4(4)) Scholastic Library Publishing. (Children's Pr.).

—Crisis in Space: Apollo Thirteen. 2002. (gr. 7-12). lib. bdg. 15.25 (978-0-613-58756-3(1)) Tandem Library Bks.

Bredeson, Carmen. The Moon. 1998. (First Bks.). (Illus.). 64p. (J). (gr. 4-6). 23.00 (978-0-531-20308-8(5) , Watts, Franklin) Scholastic Library Publishing.

Brubaker, Paul E. Apollo 1 Tragedy: Fire in the Capsule. 2002. (American Disasters Ser.). (Illus.). 48p. (J). (gr. 4-10). lib. bdg. 23.93 (978-0-7660-1787-0(7)) Enslow Pubs., Inc.

Crewe, Sabrina & Anderson, Dale. The First Moon Landing. 2004. (Events That Shaped America Ser.). (Illus.). 32p. (J). (gr. 3 up). lib. bdg. 24.67 (978-0-8368-3397-3(X)) Stevens, Gareth Inc.

Dunn, Joeming W. Moon Landing. Wight, Joseph et al, illus. 2007. (Graphic History Ser.). 32p. (J). (gr. 3-6). lib. bdg. 27.07 (***978-1-60270-078-9(8)*** , Graphic Planet) Magic Wagon.

Feinstein, Stephen. Read about Neil Armstrong. 2005. (I Like Biographies! Ser.). (Illus.). 24p. (J). lib. bdg. 21.26 (978-0-7660-2593-6(4) , Enslow Elementary) Enslow Pubs., Inc.

Friend, Robyn C. The Women of Apollo. Katz, David Arthur, illus. l.t. ed. 2006. 80p. (J). 17.95 (978-1-880599-80-8(5)); pap. 12.95 (978-1-880599-79-2(1)) Cascade Pass, Inc.

Getz, David. Moonwalkers. 2003. (Science Links Ser.). (Illus.). 32p. (gr. 3-5). 23.00 (978-0-7910-7417-6(X) , Chelsea Hse.) Facts On File, Inc.

Goldsmith, Mike. Neil Armstrong: The First Man in the Moon. 2001. (Famous Lives Ser.). (Illus.). 48p. (J). (gr. 4-6). lib. bdg. 27.12 (978-0-7398-4431-1(8)) Raintree.

Green, Carl R. Apollo 11 Rockets to First Moon Landing: A MyReportLinks. com Book. 2004. (Space Flight Adventures & Disasters Ser.). (Illus.). 48p. (J). lib. bdg. 25.26 (978-0-7660-5164-5(1) , MyReportLinks.com Bks.) Enslow Pubs., Inc.

Harcourt School Publishers Staff. Apollo Below Level: To the Moon. 3rd ed. 2002. (Trophies Reading Program Ser.). (Illus.). pap. 5.10 (978-0-15-323325-8(7)) Harcourt Schl. Pubs.

Hasday, Judy L. The Apollo 13 Mission: Overcoming Adversity. 2006. (Illus.). 120p. (J). (gr. 4-8). reprint ed. 25.00 (978-1-4223-5546-6(2)) DIANE Publishing Co.

Hehner, Barbara. First on the Moon: What It Was Like When Man Landed on the Moon. 2001. (I Was There Bk.). (Illus.). (J). 14.79 (978-0-606-20659-4(0)) Tandem Library Bks.

Higgins, Nadia. Moon Landing. 2007. (Essential Events Ser.). (ENG., Illus.). 112p. (YA). (gr. 8-12). lib. bdg. 32.79 (***978-1-59928-854-3(0)** , Essential Library) ABDO Publishing Co.

Hilliard, Richard. Neil, Buzz, & Mike Go to the Moon. 2005. (Illus.). 32p. (J). (ps-7). 16.95 (978-1-59078-293-4(3)) Boyds Mills Pr.

Holden, Henry M. Triumph over Disaster Aboard Apollo 13: A MyReportLinks. com Book. 2004. (Space Flight Adventures & Disasters Ser.). (Illus.). 48p. (J). lib. bdg. 25.26 (978-0-7660-5167-6(6) , MyReportLinks.com Bks.) Enslow Pubs., Inc.

Hudson-Goff, Elizabeth & Anderson, Dale. The First Moon Landing. 2006. (Graphic Histories Ser.). (Illus.). pap. 8.95 (978-0-8368-6255-3(4)); 32p. (J). lib. bdg. 26.00 (978-0-8368-6203-4(1)) Stevens, Gareth Inc. (World Almanac Library).

Irwin, James. Destination Moon. 15th anniv. ed. 2004. 52p. 16.00 (978-1-929241-98-9(4)) STL Distribution North America.

Kelly, Nigel. The Moon Landing: The Race into Space. (Illus.). 32p. (J). 2006. (***978-1-4034-9145-9(3));** 2000. (gr. 5-7). lib. bdg. 24.22 (978-1-57572-415-7(4)) Heinemann Library.

—Moon Landing: The Race into Space. 2001. (gr. 5-8). lib. bdg. 15.25 (978-0-613-36110-1(5)) Tandem Library Bks.

—The Moon Landing: The Race into Space, Set 1. 2002. (Point of Impact Ser.). (Illus.). 32p. (J). (gr. 5-7). pap. 7.50 (978-1-58810-356-7(0) , 91115) Heinemann Library.

Koestler-Grack, Rachel A. Moon Landing. 2005. (American Moments Ser.). (Illus.). 48p. (J). (gr. 4-8). lib. bdg. 25.65 (978-1-59197-932-6(3)) ABDO Publishing Co.

Kortenkamp, Steve. The First Moon Landing. 2008. (J). (***978-1-4296-0060-6(8)**) Capstone Pr., Inc.

Kramer, Barbara. Neil Armstrong: Meet the Famous Astronaut. 2003. (Meeting Famous People Ser.). (Illus.). 32p. (J). lib. bdg. 22.60 (978-0-7660-2007-8(X)) Enslow Pubs., Inc.

Malam, John. Man Walks on the Moon. 2003. (Dates with History Ser.). 45p. (J). lib. bdg. 28.50 (978-1-58340-407-2(4)) Smart Apple Media.

Marcovitz, Hal. Reaching for the Moon: The Apollo Astronauts. 2000. (Explorers of the New World Ser.). (Illus.). (J). 63p. (gr. 4-7). pap. 25.00 (978-0-7910-6167-1(1)); 64p. (gr. 8-12). 25.00 (978-0-7910-5957-9(X)) Facts On File, Inc. (Chelsea Hse.).

—Reaching for the Moon: The Apollo Astronauts. 2001. (gr. 3-6). lib. bdg. 17.60 (978-0-613-32989-7(9)) Tandem Library Bks.

Mason, Paul. The Moon Landing. 2002. (Days That Shook the World Ser.). (Illus.). 48p. (J). lib. bdg. 27.12 (978-0-7398-5236-1(1)) Raintree.

Merchant, Peter. The Eagle Has Landed. 2002. (Illus.). 16p. (J). pap. (978-0-439-35140-9(5)) Scholastic, Inc.

Raum, Elizabeth. Edwin "Buzz" Aldrin. 2005. (American Lives Ser.). (Illus.). 32p. (978-1-4034-6939-7(3)); pap. (978-1-4034-6946-5(6)) Heinemann Library.

—Neil Armstrong. 2005. (American Lives Ser.). (Illus.). 32p. (J). (978-1-4034-6938-0(5)); pap. (978-1-4034-6945-8(8)) Heinemann Library.

Schyffert, Bea Uusma. Man Who Went to the Far Side of the Moon: The Story of Apollo 11 Astronaut Michael Collins. 2003. (Illus.). 80p. (J). (gr. 5 up). 14.95 (978-0-8118-4007-1(7)) Chronicle Bks. LLC.

Shearer, Deborah A. Walking on the Moon. 2002. (Explore Space! Ser.). (Illus.). 24p. (J). (gr. 1-2). lib. bdg. 18.60 (978-0-7368-1145-3(1) , Bridgestone Bks.) Capstone Pr., Inc.

Siy, Alexandra. Footprints on the Moon. 2001. (Illus.). (J). 32p. (gr. 1-7). 16.95 (978-1-57091-408-9(7)); (gr. 4-7). pap. 7.95 (978-1-57091-409-6(5)) Charlesbridge Publishing, Inc.

—Footprints on the Moon. 2001. (J). 14.75 (978-0-606-20662-4(0)); (gr. 3-6). lib. bdg. 16.40 (978-0-613-49316-1(8)) Tandem Library Bks.

Tan, Sheri. Handshake in Space: The Apollo-Soyuz Test Project. Bond, Higgins, illus. 1998. (Smithsonian Odyssey Ser.). 32p. (J). (gr. 2-5). 14.95 (978-1-56899-534-2(2) , B6010); pap. 6.95 (978-1-56899-535-9(0) , S6010) Soundprints.

Thimmesh, Catherine. Team Moon: How 400,000 People Landed Apollo 11 on the Moon. 2006. (Illus.). 80p. (J). (gr. 5). 19.95 (978-0-618-50757-3(4)) Houghton Mifflin Co.

Vogt, Gregory L. Apollo Moonwalks: The Amazing Lunar Missions. 2000. (Countdown to Space Ser.). (Illus.). 48p. (YA). (gr. 4-10). lib. bdg. 23.93 (978-0-7660-1306-3(5)) Enslow Pubs., Inc.

Zelon, Helen. Apollo 11 Mission: The First Man to Walk on the Moon. 2002. (Space Missions Ser.). (Illus.). 24p. (J). (gr. 2-4). lib. bdg. 19.95 (978-0-8239-5772-9(1) , PowerKids Pr.) Rosen Publishing Group, Inc., The.

—The Apollo 13 Mission: Surviving an Explosion in Space. 2002. (Space Missions Ser.). (Illus.). 24p. (J). (gr. 2-4). lib. bdg. 19.95 (978-0-8239-5773-6(X) , PowerKids Pr.) Rosen Publishing Group, Inc., The.

Zemlicka, Shannon. Neil Armstrong. (History Maker Bios Ser.). (Illus.). 48p. (J). 2003. (gr. 2-4). 26.60 (978-0-8225-0395-8(6)); 2002. pap. 6.95 (978-0-8225-1563-0(6)) Lerner Publishing Group. (Lerner Pubns.).

PROJECT GEMINI

Green, Carl R. The Gemini 4 Spacewalk Mission: A MyReportLinks. com Book. 2004. (Space Flight Adventures & Disasters Ser.). (Illus.). 48p. (J). lib. bdg. 25.26 (978-0-7660-5163-8(3) , MyReportLinks.com Bks.) Enslow Pubs., Inc.

Sipiera, Diane M. & Sipiera, Paul P. Project Gemini. 1998. (True Bks.). (Illus.). 48p. (J). (gr. 3-5). pap. 6.95 (978-0-516-26274-1(2) , Children's Pr.) Scholastic Library Publishing.

Spangenburg, Ray & Moser, Kit. Project Gemini. 2001. (Out of This World Ser.). (Illus.). 112p. (YA). (gr. 7-9). pap. 14.95 (978-0-531-13973-8(5) , Watts, Franklin) Scholastic Library Publishing.

—Project Gemini. 2001. (Illus.). 112p. (YA). (gr. 8-12). lib. bdg. 24.55 (978-0-613-54304-0(1)) Tandem Library Bks.

Zelon, Helen. The First American Space Walk: The Gemini IV Mission. 2002. (Space Missions Ser.). (Illus.). 24p. (J). lib. bdg. 19.95 (978-0-8239-5771-2(3) , PowerKids Pr.) Rosen Publishing Group, Inc., The.

PROJECT MERCURY

Ashby, Ruth. Rocket Man: The Mercury Adventure of John Glenn. Hunt, Robert, illus. 2004. 144p. (J). 12.95 (978-1-56145-323-8(4)) Peachtree Pubs., Ltd.

Sipiera, Diane M. & Sipiera, Paul P. Project Mercury. 1998. (True Bks.). (Illus.). 48p. (J). (gr. 3-5). pap. 6.95 (978-0-516-26275-8(0) , Children's Pr.) Scholastic Library Publishing.

Spangenburg, Ray. Project Mercury. 2001. (gr. 5-8). lib. bdg. 24.55 (978-0-613-54305-7(X)) Tandem Library Bks.

Spangenburg, Ray & Moser, Kit. Project Mercury. 2001. (Out of This World Ser.). (Illus.). 112p. (YA). (gr. 7-9). pap. 14.95 (978-0-531-13974-5(3) , Watts, Franklin) Scholastic Library Publishing.

Zelon, Helen. The Mercury 6 Mission: The First American Astronaut to Orbit Earth. 2002. (Space Missions Ser.). (Illus.). 24p. (J). (gr. 2-4). lib. bdg. 19.95 (978-0-8239-5770-5(5) , PowerKids Pr.) Rosen Publishing Group, Inc., The.

PROJECT METHOD IN TEACHING

Chard. Project Approach: Developing the Basic Framework. 2003. 63p. pap., tchr. ed. 12.95 (978-0-590-12852-0(3)) Scholastic, Inc.

Chard, Sylvia C. Project Approach: Developing Curriculum with Children. 2003. pap., tchr. ed. 12.95 (978-0-590-12853-7(1)) Scholastic, Inc.

Jaffe, Charlotte & Doherty, Barbara. Create a City: A Complete Framework for Students to Use in Creating an Original City. Armstrong, Beverly, illus. 1999. 88p. (J). (gr. 5-8). pap., stu. ed. 11.99 (978-0-88160-311-8(2) , LW-380, Learning Works, The) Creative Teaching Pr., Inc.

Press, Judy. ArtStarts for Little Hands! 2000. (gr. k-3). lib. bdg. 22.20 (978-0-613-27715-0(5)) Tandem Library Bks.

PROKOFIEV, SERGEI SERGEEVICH, 1891-1953

Lynch, Wendy. Prokofiev. 2000. (Lives & Times Ser.). (Illus.). 24p. (J). lib. bdg. 19.92 (978-1-57572-220-7(8)) Heinemann Library.

PROPAGANDA

see also Advertising

Spangenburg, Ray & Moser, Diane. Propaganda: Understanding the Power of Persuasion. 2002. (Teen Issues Ser.). (Illus.). 64p. (J). (gr. 6-12). lib. bdg. 22.60 (978-0-7660-1664-4(1)) Enslow Pubs., Inc.

PROPAGATION OF PLANTS

see Plant Propagation

PROPHETS

Adil, Hajjah Amina & Sperling, Karima. My Little Lore of Light: A Child's Version of Lore of Light. 2005. (Illus.). x, 193p. (J). 22.00 (978-1-930409-35-4(4)) Islamic Supreme Council of America.

Bible Visuals International, comment. Prophets to God's People Vol. 24: Old Testament. 2006. (Illus.). (J). pap. (978-1-932381-84-9(8) , 2024) Bible Visuals International, Inc.

Bible Visuals International, compiled by. Prophets of the Messiah Vol. 32: Old Testament. 2006. (Illus.). (J). pap. (978-1-932381-91-7(0) , 2032) Bible Visuals International, Inc.

Burrill, Richard L. My Sweet Lord: The Life-Stories of Muhammad & the Five God-Men of History. 2005. (YA). (gr. 9-12). pap. 19.95 (978-1-878464-53-8(1)) Anthro Co., The.

Capstone Press. Nostradamus. 2007. (Illus.). 32p. (J). (***978-0-7368-6760-3(0)** , 1265024) Capstone Pr., Inc.

Cohen, Daniel. Prophets of Doom: Millennium Edition. 1999. (Single Titles Ser.: up). (Illus.). 160p. (gr. 7-12). lib. bdg. 24.90 (978-0-7613-1317-5(6) , Millbrook Pr.) Lerner Publishing Group.

Demi. Muhammad. Demi, illus. 2004. (Illus.). 39p. (J). (gr. 2-5). reprint ed. (978-0-7567-7802-6(6)) DIANE Publishing Co.

—Muhammad. 2003. (Illus.). 48p. (J). 19.95 (978-0-689-85264-0(9) , McElderry, Margaret K.) Simon & Schuster Children's Publishing.

Innes, Brian. Millennium Prophecies. 1999. (Unsolved Mysteries Ser.). (Illus.). 48p. (J). (gr. 3-7). pap. 8.05 (978-0-8172-5848-1(5)) Steck-Vaughn.

Khan, Saniyasnain. Tell Me about the Prophet Musa: What Was the Mission of Musa, What Were His Miracles & What His Life Teaches Me. l.t. ed. 2001. (Tell Me About). (Illus.). 56p. per. 11.50 (978-81-87570-48-6(2)) Goodword Bks. Pvt. Ltd. IND. *Dist:* Lodhia Ctr., The.

Marchant, Kerena. Muhammad & Islam. 2002. (Great Religious Leaders Ser.). (Illus.). 48p. (J). lib. bdg. 28.50 (978-1-58340-217-7(9)) Smart Apple Media.

Oliver, Marilyn Tower. Muhammad. 2003. (Importance of Ser.). (Illus.). 112p. (J). (gr. 7-10). 32.45 (978-1-59018-232-1(4) , Lucent Bks.) Thomson Gale.

Rivetna, Roshan, ed. The Legacy of Zarthushtra: Introduction to the Religion, History & Culture of Zoroastrians. 2002. (Illus.). 100p. (YA). per. 9.00 (978-1-883345-03-7(0)) Federation of Zoroastrian Assns. of North America (FEZANA).

Los Salmos y los Profetas (The Psalms & the Prophets) Quarter 1, Level 4. 2000. (Caminando con Jesus (Walking with Jesus) Series A). (SPA.). (J). (gr. 5-6). stu. ed. 3.50 (978-0-570-05161-9(4) , 16-4811) Concordia Publishing Hse.

Stefoff, Rebecca. Prophets & Prophecy. 2007. (Secrets of the Supernatural Ser.). 96p. (J). lib. bdg. 32.79 (***978-0-7614-2638-7(8)** , Benchmark Bks.) Cavendish, Marshall Corp.

Van Der Veer, Andrew. Bible Lessons for Juniors, Book 2: Kings & Prophets. 2007. (J). (***978-1-60178-013-3(3)**) Reformation Heritage Bks.

PROSODY

see Versification

PROSPECTING

Gintzler, A. S. Rough & Ready Prospectors. Brigman, Chris, illus. 1998. (Rough & Ready Ser.). 46p. (J). lib. bdg. 16.95 (978-1-887238-11-3(5)) Fitzgerald Bks.

Klein, James. Gold Rush! The Young Prospector's Guide to Striking It Rich. Rohani, Michael, illus. 2004. 96p. (J). (gr. 3-7). 9.95 (978-1-883672-64-5(3) , Tricycle Pr.) Ten Speed Pr.

PROSPECTING—FICTION

Mitchell, Marianne. Gullywasher Gulch. Chartier, Normand, illus. 2003. 32p. (J). (gr. 2-4). 15.95 (978-1-56397-123-5(2)) Boyds Mills Pr.

PROTECTION OF ANIMALS

see Animals—Treatment

PROTECTION OF BIRDS

see Birds—Protection

PROTECTION OF CHILDREN

see Child Welfare

PROTECTION OF ENVIRONMENT

see Environmental Protection

PROTECTION OF GAME

see Game Protection

PROTECTION OF NATURAL SCENERY

see Natural Monuments

PROTECTION OF WILDLIFE

see Wildlife Conservation

PROTEST

see Dissent

PROTESTANT REFORMATION

see Reformation

PROTESTANTISM

see also Evangelicalism; Reformation

Brown, Stephen F. Protestantism. (World Religions Ser.). (Illus.). 128p. (J). (gr. 6-12). 2001. 30.00 (978-0-8160-4614-0(X)); 2nd rev. ed. 2006. 30.00 (978-0-8160-6614-8(0)) Facts On File, Inc.

Sullivan, Lawrence Eugene. The Features of Protestantism. 2002. (Religions of Mankind Ser.). (Illus.). 32p. (YA). (gr. 5 up). 21.95 (978-0-7910-6629-4(0) , Chelsea Hse.) Facts On File, Inc.

Woolf, Alex. Fundamentalism. 2003. (Ideas of the Modern World Ser.). (Illus.). 64p. (J). lib. bdg. 28.56 (978-0-7398-6416-6(5)) Raintree.

PROTOZOA

Wyborny, Sheila. The Malaria Parasite. 2005. (Parasites Ser.). (Illus.). 32p. (J). (ps-8). lib. bdg. 24.95 (978-0-7377-3051-7(X) , Greenhaven Pr., Inc.) Thomson Gale.

PROVERBS

Brennan-Nelson, Denise. My Grandma Likes to Say. Donovan, Jane Monroe, illus. rev. ed. 2007. 32p. (J). (ps-3). 16.95 (978-1-58536-284-4(0)) Sleeping Bear Pr.

The Christian Student Compass: KJV Monthly Version with Book of Proverbs. 2003. (YA). spiral bd. (978-0-9725804-2-7(5)) Salt Pubs.

Davis, Mary J. My Wisdom Journal: A Discovering of Proverbs for Kids. 2004. (Journals Just for Kids Ser.). (Illus.). 160p. (J). (gr. 4-7). pap. 9.99 (978-1-885358-73-8(3) , Legacy Pr.) Rainbow Pubs. & Legacy Pr.

Gonzalez, Ralfka & Ruiz, Ana. My First Book of Proverbs. Gonzalez, Ralfka & Ruiz, Ana, illus. 2002. Orig. Title: Mi Primer Libro de Dichos. (SPA & ENG., Illus.). 32p. (J). (gr. 1 up). pap. 7.95 (978-0-89239-200-1(2)) Children's Bk. Pr.

Herrera, J. Ignacio. 125 Refranes Infantiles. Torcida, María Luisa, illus. (SPA.). (J). (gr. 3-5). 12.76 (978-84-305-9180-0(X) , SU6580) Susaeta Ediciones, S.A. ESP. *Dist:* Lectorum Pubns., Inc.

Holt, Daniel D., tr. Tigers, Frogs, & Rice Cakes: A Book of Korean Proverbs. Stickler, Lu Han, illus. 1999. (KOR & ENG.). 32p. (J). 15.95 (978-1-885008-10-7(4)) Shen's Bks.

Libal, Autumn. Folk Proverbs & Riddles. 2003. (North American Folklore Ser.). (Illus.). 112p. (YA). (gr. 7 up). lib. bdg. (978-1-59084-343-7(6)) Mason Crest Pubs.

Longo, Alejandra. Refranes. Chaskielberg, Daniel, illus. 2005. (SPA.). 32p. (J). (ps-3). pap. 3.99 (978-0-439-78346-0(1) , Scholastic en Espanol) Scholastic, Inc.

Mackall, Dandi Daley. I Can Be Happy Because God Blesses Me. Dippold, Jane, illus. 2005. 36p. (J). (ps-7). 9.99 (978-0-7847-1653-3(6) , 04074) Standard Publishing.

Miller, Ann. Proverbs, Prayers, Poems for Children & Teens. 2005. (J). lib. bdg. 14.95 (978-0-9748165-1-7(5)) Jaylil Publishing Co.

Nelson Word Publishing Group Staff. Hand in Hand with Jesus: A Bible Verse for Every Day, to Help Me Live a Better Way. 2000. (Jesus in My Pocket Ser.). (Illus.). 64p. (J). (ps-3). pap. (978-0-7852-0026-0(6)) Nelson/Word Canada.

—Jesus is My Superhero: A Bible Verse for Every Day, to Help Me Live a Better Way, 2000. (Jesus in My Pocket Ser.). (Illus.). 64p. (J). (ps-3). pap. (978-0-7852-0022-2(3)) Nelson/Word Canada.

—My Bible Talks to Me: A Bible Verse for Every Day, to Help Me Live a Better Way, 2000. (Jesus in My Pocket Ser.). (Illus.). 64p. (J). (ps-3). pap. (978-0-7852-0023-9(1)) Nelson/Word Canada.

—Proverbs to Grow By: A Bible Verse for Every Day, to Help Me Live a Better Way. 2000. (Jesus in My Pocket Ser.). (Illus.). 64p. (J). (ps-3). pap. (978-0-7852-0025-3(8)) Nelson/Word Canada.

Proverbs: Wise Guys Are the Best Guys. 1999. (Club 56 Ser.). 160p. (J). (gr. 5-6). tchr. ed., spiral bd. 29.99 (978-1-57405-245-9(4)) CharismaLife Pubs.

Scheffler, Axel, illus. Let Sleeping Dogs Lie & Other Proverbs from Around the World. 2002. 125p. (YA). reprint ed. 13.00 (978-0-7567-5668-0(5)) DIANE Publishing Co.

Snook, Randy, photos by. Many Ideas Open the Way: A Collection of Hmong Proverbs. 2003. (Illus.). 32p. (J). 16.95 (978-1-885008-23-7(6)) Shen's Bks.

Xuan, Yong-Sheng. The Dragon Lover & Other Chinese Proverbs. Xuan, Yong-Sheng, illus. 1999. (CHI & ENG., Illus.). 32p. (J). 16.95 (978-1-885008-11-4(2)) Shen's Bks.

PRYDAIN (IMAGINARY PLACE)—FICTION

Alexander, Lloyd. The Black Cauldron. rev. ed. 1999. (Chronicles of Prydain Ser.: Bk. 2). (Illus.). 224p. (J). (gr. 3-7). 19.95 (978-0-8050-6131-4(2) , Holt, Henry & Co. Bks. For Young Readers) Holt, Henry & Co.

—The Black Cauldron. 2004. (Chronicles of Prydain Ser.: Bk. 2). 240p. (J). (gr. 4-7). pap. 38.00 incl. audio (978-1-4000-8636-8(1) , Listening Library) Random Hse. Audio Publishing Group.

—The Castle of Llyr. rev. ed. 1999. (Chronicles of Prydain Ser.: Bk. 3). (Illus.). 204p. (J). (gr. 3-7). 21.95 (978-0-8050-6133-8(9) , Holt, Henry & Co. Bks. For Young Readers) Holt, Henry & Co.

—The Castle of Llyr. 2004. (Chronicles of Prydain Ser.: Bk. 3). 208p. (J). (gr. 4-7). pap. 36.00 incl. audio (978-1-4000-9019-8(9) , Listening Library) Random Hse. Audio Publishing Group.

—The Chronicles of Prydain. rev. ed. 1999. (Chronicles of Prydain Ser.: Bk. 3). (Illus.). 224p. (J). (gr. 3-7). 19.95 (978-0-8050-6132-1(0) , Holt, Henry & Co. Bks. For Young Readers) Holt, Henry & Co.

—The High King. rev. ed. 1999. (Chronicles of Prydain Ser.: Bk. 5). (Illus.). 288p. (J). (gr. 3-7). 19.95 (978-0-8050-6135-2(5) , Holt, Henry & Co. Bks. For Young Readers) Holt, Henry & Co.

—Taran Wanderer. rev. ed. 1999. (Chronicles of Prydain Ser.: Bk. 4). 256p. (J). (gr. 3-7). 19.95 (978-0-8050-6134-5(7) , Holt, Henry & Co. Bks. For Young Readers) Holt, Henry & Co.

PSALMODY

see Church Music; Hymns

PSYCHIATRISTS

Worth, Richard. Elisabeth Kubler-Ross: Encountering Death & Dying. 2004. (Women in Medicine Ser.). (Illus.). 112p. (gr. 12). 30.00 (978-0-7910-8027-6(7) , Chelsea Hse.) Facts On File, Inc.

PSYCHIATRISTS—FICTION

Henry, April. Shock Point. 2006. 192p. (YA). (gr. 6). 16.99 (978-0-399-24385-1(2) , Putnam Juvenile) Penguin Group (USA) Inc.

Miller, Mary Beth. Aimee. 2004. (Illus.). 288p. (YA). (gr. 9). pap. 6.99 (978-0-14-240025-8(4) , Puffin) Penguin Group (USA) Inc.

—Aimee. 2004. (gr. 7-12). lib. bdg. 15.30 (978-0-613-89043-4(4)) Tandem Library Bks.

PSYCHIATRY

see also Psychotherapy

Brinkerhoff, Shirley. Drug Therapy & Obsessive-Compulsive Disorders. 2003. (Encyclopedia of Psychiatric Drugs & Their Disorders Ser.). (Illus.). 128p. (J). lib. bdg. (978-1-59084-569-1(2)) Mason Crest Pubs.

—Drug Therapy & Schizophrenia. 2003. (Encyclopedia of Psychiatric Drugs & Their Disorders Ser.). (Illus.). 128p. (J). lib. bdg. (978-1-59084-574-5(9)) Mason Crest Pubs.

Carlson, Dale B. & Carlson, Hannah. Where's Your Head? Teenage Psychology. Nicklaus, Carol, illus. 2nd rev. ed. 2000. (Psychology for Teenagers Ser.: Vol. 2). 298p. (gr. 8-12). pap. 14.95 (978-1-884158-19-3(6)) Bick Publishing Hse.

Docalavich, Heather. The Future of Antidepressants: The New Wave of Research. 2006. (Antidepressants Ser.). (Illus.). 120p. (J). (gr. 7 up). (978-1-4222-0103-9(1)) Mason Crest Pubs.

Esherick, Joan. The FDA & Psychiatric Drugs: How a Drug Is Approved. 2003. (Encyclopedia of Psychiatric Drugs & Their Disorders Ser.). (Illus.). 128p. (J). lib. bdg. (978-1-59084-578-3(1)) Mason Crest Pubs.

Libal, Autumn. Drug Therapy & Dissociative Disorders. 2003. (Encyclopedia of Psychiatric Drugs & Their Disorders Ser.). (Illus.). 128p. (J). lib. bdg. (978-1-59084-564-6(1)) Mason Crest Pubs.

—Drug Therapy & Impulse Control Disorders. 2003. (Encyclopedia of Psychiatric Drugs & Their Disorders Ser.). (Illus.). 128p. (J). lib. bdg. (978-1-59084-566-0(8)) Mason Crest Pubs.

Libal, Joyce. Drug Therapy for Mental Disorders Caused by a Medical Condition. 2003. (Encyclopedia of Psychiatric Drugs & Their Disorders Ser.). (Illus.). 128p. (J). lib. bdg. (978-1-59084-567-7(6)) Mason Crest Pubs.

My Name Is Blue, from Me to You, All about PTSD, Vol. 3. 2000. 24p. (J). pap. 6.00 (978-1-929396-02-3(3)) Rain, Blue, & The Crew Pubs.

PSYCHICAL RESEARCH

see Parapsychology

PSYCHOANALYSIS

see also Dreams; Mind and Body; Psychology; Psychology, Pathological

Docalavich, Heather. Antidepressants & Psychology: Talk Therapy vs. Medication. 2006. (Antidepressants Ser.). (Illus.). 120p. (J). (gr. 7 up). (978-1-4222-0096-4(5)) Mason Crest Pubs.

Gogerly, Liz. Sigmund Freud. 2003. (20th Century History Makers Ser.). (Illus.). 112p. (J). lib. bdg. 32.85 (978-0-7398-6142-4(5)) Raintree.

Hitchcock, Susan Tyler. Karen Horney: Pioneer of Feminine Psychology. 2004. (Women in Medicine Ser.). (Illus.). 112p. (gr. 6-12). 30.00 (978-0-7910-8025-2(0) , Chelsea Hse.) Facts On File, Inc.

PSYCHOLOGY

see also Attitude (Psychology); Child Psychology; Educational Psychology; Emotions; Imagination; Individuality; Intellect; Parapsychology; Perception; Personality; Psychoanalysis; Reasoning; Self-acceptance; Senses and Sensation; Social Psychology; Thought and Thinking

Abrahams, George & Ahlbrand, Sheila. Boy v. Girl? How Gender Shapes Who We Are, What We Want, & How We Get Along. 2004. (Illus.). 208p. (YA). (gr. 5-10). pap. 14.95 (978-1-57542-104-9(6)) Free Spirit Publishing, Inc.

Adams, Jessica. Psychic Powers: Do You Have a Secret Sixth Sense? 2004. (Illus.). (J). pap. 7.99 (978-0-340-88205-4(0) , Hodder & Stoughton) Hodder General Publishing Division GBR. *Dist:* Trafalgar Square Publishing.

Anin, Nadia, et al. Essential VCE Psychology, Units 1 and 2. 2004. (Illus.). 360p. pap. 54.00 (978-0-521-53829-9(7)) Cambridge Univ. Pr.

Armstrong, Thomas. You're Smarter Than You Think: A Kid's Guide to Multiple Intelligences. 2004. (Laugh & Learn Ser.). (Illus.). 192p. (YA). (gr. 3-7). pap. 15.95 (978-1-57542-113-1(5)) Free Spirit Publishing, Inc.

—You're Smarter Than You Think: A Kid's Guide to Multiple Intelligences. 2002. (gr. 5-8). lib. bdg. 25.70 (978-0-613-67352-5(2)) Tandem Library Bks.

Ayer, Eleanor H. Everything You Need to Know about Stress. rev. ed. 2001. (Need to Know Library). (Illus.). 64p. (YA). (gr. 4-6). lib. bdg. 25.25 (978-0-8239-3467-6(5)) Rosen Publishing Group, Inc., The.

Bernstein. Bernstein Psychology. 7th ed. 2005. (Illus.). (YA). stu. ed. 3.16 incl. cd-rom (978-0-618-52724-3(9) , 304186) Houghton Mifflin College Div.

—Essentials to Psychology: With Psychology in Context. 3rd ed. 2004. (YA). pap., pap. 98.76 incl. cd-rom (978-0-618-56337-1(7) , 395184) Houghton Mifflin College Div.

—Psychology. 7th ed. 2005. (YA). 118.76 incl. cd-rom (978-0-618-57535-0(9) , 395339) Houghton Mifflin College Div.

Berry, Joy Wilt. Bad Habits: Get over It! Bartholomew, illus. rev. ed. 2000. (Winning Skills Ser.: Vol. 6). 48p. (YA). (gr. 7-12). pap. 2.95 (978-1-58634-165-7(0)) Goldstar Publishing, Inc.

—A Book about Fighting. 2005. (Illus.). (J). (978-0-7172-8584-6(7)) Scholastic, Inc.

—Criticism - Rejection: Get over It! Bartholomew, illus. rev. ed. 2000. (Winning Skills Ser.: Vol. 3). 48p. (YA). (gr. 4-7). pap. 2.95 (978-1-58634-162-6(6)) Goldstar Publishing, Inc.

—Let's Talk about Accepting "No" An Early Social Skills Book. Fitzpatrick, Roey, illus. rev. ed. 2000. (Let's Talk about Ser.: Vol. 5). 36p. (J). (ps-3). pap. 3.95 (978-1-58634-058-2(1)) Goldstar Publishing, Inc.

Block, Joel D. Staying Cool: How to Get a Grip on Anger. 2002. (gr. 7-12). lib. bdg. 22.20 (978-0-613-79731-3(0)) Tandem Library Bks.

Burloux, Gabriel. Body & Its Pain. Woods, Margaret, tr. from FRE. 2005. 295p. pap. 33.95 (978-1-85343-794-6(8)) Free Assn. Bks. Ltd. GBR. *Dist:* International Specialized Bk. Services.

Cardwell, Mike & Flanagan, Cara. Psychology A2: The Complete Companion. 2003. (Illus.). 338p. pap. (978-0-7487-7344-2(4)) Nelson Thornes Ltd.

Carlson, Dale. The Teen Brain Book: Who & What Are You? Teasdale, Nancy, ed. Nicklaus, Carol, illus. 2004. 230p. (gr. 7-12). pap. 14.95 (978-1-884158-29-2(3)) Bick Publishing Hse.

Carlson, Dale B. & Carlson, Hannah. Where's Your Head? Teenage Psychology. Nicklaus, Carol, illus. 2nd rev. ed. 2000. (Psychology for Teenagers Ser.: Vol. 2). 298p. (gr. 8-12). pap. 14.95 (978-1-884158-19-3(6)) Bick Publishing Hse.

Catala, Ellen. Lo que necesitamos y lo que Queremos. 2005. Tr. of Needs & Wants. (SPA., Illus.). 16p. (J) (gr. 1 up). lib. bdg. 15.93 (978-0-7368-4144-3(X)) Capstone Pr., Inc.

Chan, Paul D. Why Is Mommy Sad? A Child's Guide to Parental Depression. Faust, Laurie A., illus. 2006. 12p. (J). pap. 6.99 (978-1-929622-71-9(6)) Current Clinical Strategies Publishing.

Cleveland, Don. How Do We Know How the Brain Works. 2005. (Great Scientific Questions & the Scientists Who Answered Them Ser.). (Illus.). 112p. (J). (gr. 7-12). lib. bdg. 26.50 (978-1-4042-0078-4(9)) Rosen Publishing Group, Inc., The.

Doudna, Kelly. We Have the Nerve, Now Let's Observe. 2007. (Illus.). 24p. (J). 19.93 (978-1-59928-624-2(6) , SandCastle) ABDO Publishing Co.

—We Have the Nerve, Now Let's Observe! 2006. (Illus.). 24p. (J). (978-1-59928-625-9(4)) ABDO Publishing Co.

Eisenpreis, Bettijane. Coping: A Young Woman's Guide to Breast Cancer Prevention. rev. ed. 2005. (Coping Ser.). (Illus.). 192p. (YA). (gr. 7-12). lib. bdg. 26.50 (978-0-8239-2967-2(1) , COBRCA) Rosen Publishing Group, Inc., The.

Esherick, Joan. Balancing Act: A Teen's Guide to Managing Stress. 2004. (Science of Health Ser.). (Illus.). 128p. (J). (978-1-59084-853-1(5)) Mason Crest Pubs.

Espeland, Pamela. Knowing Me, Knowing You: The I-Sight Way to Understand Yourself & Others. 2004. (Illus.). 128p. (YA). (gr. 8-12). pap. 13.95 (978-1-57542-090-5(2)) Free Spirit Publishing, Inc.

Eysenck, Michael W. & Flanagan, Cara. Psychology for A2 Level. 2001. (Illus.). 912p. 29.95 (978-1-84169-251-7(4) , Psychology Press) Taylor & Francis Group GBR. *Dist:* Taylor & Francis, Inc.

Feldman, Heather. My World, 6 bks. Incl. My Bedtime : A Book about Getting Ready for Bed. lib. bdg. 16.00 (978-0-8239-5522-0(2) , PKMYBE); My Best Friend : A Book about Friendship. lib. bdg. 16.00 (978-0-8239-5526-8(5) , PKMYFR); My Breakfast : A Book about a Great Morning Meal. lib. bdg. 16.00 (978-0-8239-5527-5(3) , PKMYBR); My Day at the Baseball Game : A Book about a Special Day. lib. bdg. 16.00 (978-0-8239-5525-1(7) , PKMYBA); My Dog : A Book about a Special Pet. lib. bdg. 16.00 (978-0-8239-5524-4(9) , PKMYDO); My School Bus : A Book about School Bus Safety. lib. bdg. 16.00 (978-0-8239-5523-7(0) , PKMYSC); 24p. (J). (gr. 1). (Illus.). 2000. Set lib. bdg. 88.50 (978-0-8239-7002-5(7) , PKREMW, PowerKids Pr.) Rosen Publishing Group, Inc., The.

Funston, Sylvia & Ingram, Jay. It's All in Your Head: A Guide to Your Brilliant Brain. Clement, Gary, illus. 2nd ed. 2005. 64p. (J). (gr. 4-7). 16.95 (978-1-897066-43-0(0)); pap. 9.95 (978-1-897066-44-7(9)) Maple Tree Pr. CAN. *Dist:* Perseus Distribution.

Girls Know Best, 7 bks. l.t. ed. Incl. Boys Know It All : Wise Thoughts & Wacky Ideas from Guys Like You. Roehm, Michelle, compiled by. 167p. 1999. lib. bdg. 23.33 (978-0-8368-2455-1(5)); Girls Know Best Vol. 2 : Tips on Life & Fun Stuff to Do. Monson-Burton, Marianne, compiled by. 1999. lib. bdg. 23.33 (978-0-8368-2453-7(9)); Girls Know Best Vol. 3 : Your Words, Your World. Monson-Burton, Marianne, compiled by. 153p. 2000. lib. bdg. 23.33 (978-0-8368-2672-2(8)); Girls Knows Best : Advice for Girls from Girls on Just about Everything. Roehm, Michelle, compiled by. 160p. 1999. lib. bdg. 23.33 (978-0-8368-2452-0(0)); Girls Who Rocked the World : Heroines from Sacagawea to Sheryl Swoopes. Welden, Amelie. McCann, Jerry, illus. 117p. 1999. lib. bdg. 23.33 (978-0-8368-2454-4(7)); Girls Who Rocked the World Vol. 2 : Heroines from Harriet Tubman to Mia Hamm. Roehm, Michelle, compiled by. 152p. 2000. lib. bdg. 23.33 (978-0-8368-2673-9(6)); Throw Like a Girl : Discovering the Body, Mind & Spirit of the Athlete in You! Frost, Shelley & Troussieux, Ann. 128p. 2000. lib. bdg. 23.33 (978-0-8368-2674-6(4)); (J). (gr. 3 up). (Illus.). Set lib. bdg. 163.31 (978-0-8368-2741-5(4)) Stevens, Gareth Inc.

Glimm, Adele. Gene Hunter: The Story of Neuropsychologist Nancy Wexler. 2005. (Women's Adventures in Science Ser.). (Illus.). 118p. (YA). (gr. 7-9). 31.00 (978-0-531-16778-6(X) , Watts, Franklin) Scholastic Library Publishing.

Globe-Fearon Staff. Changes. (YA). pap. 12.95 (978-0-8359-0922-8(0)) Globe Fearon Educational Publishing.

Gott, Robert. One in a Million. 2001. (Fact Meets Fiction Ser.). (Illus.). 96p. (J). pap. (978-0-7608-8034-0(4)) Sundance/Newbridge Educational Publishing.

Grolier Educational Staff, contrib. by. Psychology, 6 vols. 2002. (Illus.). 1152p. (YA). 379.00 (978-0-7172-5662-4(6) , Grolier) Scholastic Library Publishing.

Haberman, Lia. Top Tens: Terrific Tips on Friends, Family, Happiness & More! 2001. (All about You Ser.). 128p. (J). (gr. 4-7). per. 4.50 (978-0-439-16138-1(X)) Scholastic, Inc.

Harris, Trudy. Pattern Fish. Green, Anne Canevari, illus. 2000. (Fun Early Math Concepts Ser.). 40p. (J). (gr. k-2). 22.60 (978-0-7613-1712-8(0) , Millbrook Pr.) Lerner Publishing Group.

Helmer, Diana Star. Let's Talk about Feeling Sad. 1999. (Let's Talk Library). (Illus.). 24p. (J). (gr. 3). lib. bdg. 18.75 (978-0-8239-5193-2(6) , PowerKids Pr.) Rosen Publishing Group, Inc., The.

Hess, Lisa L. Acting Assertively: A Seven-Session Assertiveness Program for Use with Students Grades 4-8. Miele, Bob, illus. 1999. 71p. (YA). (gr. 4-8). pap. 13.95 (978-1-57543-073-7(8)) MAR*CO Products, Inc.

Hinkle. Applied Statistics for Behavioral Sciences. 5th ed. 2002. (YA). pap., wbk. ed. 126.36 (978-0-618-37348-2(9) , 386178) Houghton Mifflin College Div.

Hockenbury, Don H. & Hockenbury, Sandra E. Discovering Psychology. stu. ed. (978-0-7167-5705-4(2)) Freeman, W. H. & Co.

Holt, Rinehart and Winston Staff. Psychology: Chapter Review Activities. 3rd ed. 2002. pap. 23.80 (978-0-03-068152-3(9)) Holt, Rinehart & Winston.

—Psychology & Sociology: Study Skills with Reading Guide. 3rd ed. 2002. pap. 23.80 (978-0-03-064652-2(9)) Holt, Rinehart & Winston.

Huebner, Dawn. What to Do When You Grumble Too Much: A Kid's Guide to Overcoming Negativity. Matthews, Bonnie, illus. 2006. ("What to Do" Guides for Kids Ser.). 88p. (J). pap. 14.95 (978-1-59147-450-0(7) , Magination Pr.) American Psychological Assn.

Hyman, Bruce M. & Pedrick, Cherry. Obsessive-Compulsive Disorder. 2003. (Twenty-First Century Medical Library). 96p. (gr. 7 up). lib. bdg. 26.90 (978-0-7613-2758-5(4) , Twenty-First Century Bks.) Lerner Publishing Group.

Jarvis, Matt & Russell, Julia. Key Ideas in Psychology. 2002. (Illus.). 200p. pap. 33.25 (978-0-7487-6564-5(6)) Nelson Thornes Ltd. GBR. *Dist:* International Specialized Bk. Services.

Jarvis, Matt Russell, et al. Angles on Psychology. 2nd ed. 2004. (Illus.). 304p. (YA). pap. 33.25 (978-0-7487-8032-7(7)) Nelson Thornes Ltd. GBR. *Dist:* International Specialized Bk. Services.

Johnson, Spencer. Quién Se Ha Llevado Mi Queso? Para Niños: Una Forma Sorprendente de Cambiar y Ganar ! 2004. (SPA., Illus.). 64p. (978-84-7953-553-7(9)) Ediciones Urano S. A.

Jones, Russell & Jones, Lin. Top Secrets of Success 4 Kids: (Real) Fun Only Lasts When You Know the Secrets... Get Real. Nyman, Steve, illus. 2000. 144p. (YA). (gr. 5-10). pap. 10.99 (978-1-930027-24-4(9)) Insight Publishing Group.

Kahn, Ada P. & Kahn, Ronald. Phobias. 2004. (Life Balance Ser.). (Illus.). 79p. (YA). (gr. 5-8). pap. 6.95 (978-0-531-15575-2(7) , Watts, Franklin) Scholastic Library Publishing.

Kirberger, Kimberly. No Body's Perfect: Stories by Teens about Body Image, Self-Acceptance, & the S. 2003. (gr. 5-8). lib. bdg. 22.20 (978-0-613-61510-5(7)) Tandem Library Bks.

Kuehn, Eileen. After Suicide: Living with the Questions. 2000. (Grief & Loss Ser.). (Illus.). 64p. (J). (gr. 4-6). lib. bdg. 23.93 (978-0-7368-0748-7(9) , LifeMatters Bks.) Capstone Pr., Inc.

Lambillion, Paul. Staying Cool. 2004. (Illus.). 196p. pap. 13.95 (978-0-7171-3598-1(5)) Gill & MacMillan, Ltd. IRL. *Dist:* Hushion Hse. Publishing, Ltd.

Licata, Renora. La Ira. 2002. (Todo lo Que Necesitas Saber Ser.). (SPA & ENG., Illus.). 64p. (YA). lib. bdg. 26.50 (978-0-8239-3587-1(6) , Buenas Letra) Rosen Publishing Group, Inc., The.

Madaras, Lynda. My Feelings, My Self: A Growing-up Guide for Girls. 2001. (gr. 7-12). lib. bdg. 22.20 (978-0-613-45346-2(8)) Tandem Library Bks.

Maitland, Laura Lincoln. Psychology. 2004. (5 Steps to a 5 Ser.). (Illus.). 288p. pap. 16.95 (978-0-07-141277-3(8) , 9780071412773) McGraw-Hill Cos., The.

Matthews, Andrew. Se un Adolescente Feliz. 2002. (SPA.). (gr. 7-12). lib. bdg. 22.20 (978-0-613-71358-0(3)) Tandem Library Bks.

McGraw-Hill Staff. Understanding Psychology. 2006. (C). 90.64 (***978-0-07-874517-1(9)*** , 9780078745171); 2001. stu. ed. 90.64 (978-0-07-828099-3(0) , 9780078280993); 2nd ed. 2002. (C). stu. ed. 90.64 (978-0-07-828571-4(2) , 9780078285714) Glencoe/McGraw-Hill.

McGraw-Hill Staff. Understanding Psychology: Reading Essentials. 2nd ed. 2003. (C). pap., stu. ed. 26.12 (978-0-07-860607-6(1) , 9780078606076) Glencoe/McGraw-Hill.

McMahon, Judith W., et al. Psychology & You. 3rd ed. 2001. (C). stu. ed. 87.16 (978-0-314-14090-6(5) , 9780314140906) Glencoe/McGraw-Hill.

Mental X, 2003. (Illus.). 32p. (YA). pap. 5.50 (978-0-9745066-8-5(0)) Sports In Mind.

Mills, Roger C. & Spittle, Elsie. The Health Realization Primer Vol. 1: Empowering Individuals & Communities. rev. ed. 2003. (Illus.). 72p. (gr. 4). pap. 14.95 (978-1-55105-020-1(X)) Lone Pine Publishing USA.

Monson-Burton, Marianne. Girls Know Best Vol. 3: Your Words, Your World. 1999. (gr. 3-6). lib. bdg. 17.60 (978-0-613-33368-9(3)) Tandem Library Bks.

Monson-Burton, Marianne, compiled by. Girls Know Best Vol. 3: Your Words, Your World. l.t. ed. 2000. (Girls Know Best Ser.). (Illus.). 153p. (J). (gr. 3 up). lib. bdg. 23.33 (978-0-8368-2672-2(8)) Stevens, Gareth Inc.

Moorey, Teresa. Graphology: What Does Your Handwriting Reveal about You? 2004. (Illus.). 128p. (J). pap. 7.99 (978-0-340-88367-9(7) , Hodder & Stoughton) Hodder General Publishing Division GBR. *Dist:* Trafalgar Square Publishing.

Mosatche, Harriet S. Too Old for This, Too Young for That: Your Survival Guide for the Middle-School. 2000. (gr. 5-8). lib. bdg. 24.55 (978-0-613-89619-1(X)) Tandem Library Bks.

Munoz-Kiehnel, Marisol. Since My Brother Died - Desde Que Murio Mi Hermano. Dietrich, Glanda, illus. 2000. (SPA & ENG.). 20p. (J). (gr. k-4). pap. 5.95 (978-1-56123-135-5(5)) Centering Corp.

Murphy, Ed. Cambridge Wizard VCE Psychology Unit 3 Key Card. 2nd rev. ed. 2004. 4p. 4.95 (978-0-521-61546-4(1)) Cambridge Univ. Pr.

—Cambridge Wizard VCE Psychology Unit 4 Key Card. 2004. stu. ed. 2.95 (978-0-521-61294-4(2)); 2nd rev. ed. 4p. 4.95 (978-0-521-61545-7(3)) Cambridge Univ. Pr.

O'Connor, Frances. Frequently Asked Questions about Academic Anxiety. 2007. (J). (***978-1-4042-1937-3(4)***) Rosen Publishing Group, Inc., The.

Pickels, Dwayne E. Psychological Testing & What Those Tests Mean: Am I Okay? 1999. (Encyclopedia of Psychological Disorders Ser.). (Illus.). 98p. (J). (gr. 7 up). 39.00 (978-0-7910-5319-5(9) , Chelsea Hse.) Facts On File, Inc.

Psychologie. (Duden-Schuelerduden Ser.). (GER.). 466p. (YA). (978-3-411-05252-3(X)) Bibliographisches Institut & F. A. Brockhaus AG DEU. *Dist:* International Bk. Import Service, Inc.

Rebman, Renee C. Addictions & Risky Behaviors: Cutting, Bingeing, Snorting, & Other Dangers. 2006. (Issues in Focus Today). (Illus.). 104p. (J). (gr. 6-12). lib. bdg. 31.93 (978-0-7660-2165-5(3)) Enslow Pubs., Inc.

Reisfeld, Randi & Morreale, Marie. Got Issues Much? Celebrities Share Their Traumas & Triumphs. 1999. (Illus.). 144p. (gr. 3-9). pap. 5.99 (978-0-590-63274-4(4)) Scholastic, Inc.

Ring, Susan. Needs & Wants. 2003. (J). (978-0-7368-1725-7(5)) Yellow Umbrella Pr.

Roberts, Ricky. You. 2004. 100p. pap. 10.95 (978-0-9752572-8-9(5)) Tate Publishing & Enterprises, L.L.C.

Roehm, Michelle, ed. Girls Know Best: Advice for Girls on Just about Everything. Roth, Marci Doane, illus. 1999. 160p. (J). (gr. 4-7). 6.98 (978-1-56731-313-0(2) , MJF Bks.) Fine Communications.

Rosen, Marvin. Demystifying Dreams. 2004. 64p. (YA). pap. 9.95 (978-0-595-30290-1(4)) iUniverse, Inc.

Sanders, Pete & Myers, Steve. When People Die. 2005. (Choices & Decisions Ser.). (Illus.). 32p. (J). (gr. 4-7). lib. bdg. 27.10 (978-1-59604-076-2(9)) Stargazer Bks.

Seaward, Brian Luke. Hot Stones & Funny Bones: Teens Helping Teens Cope with Stress & Anger. 2002. 300p. (YA). pap. 12.95 (978-0-7573-0036-3(7)) Health Communications, Inc.

Shoesmith, Geoffrey. Psychology: A Complete GCSE Course. 2004. (Illus.). 200p. pap. 35.00 (978-0-7188-3002-1(4)) Lutherworth Pr., The GBR. *Dist:* Parkwest Pubns., Inc.

Silverman, Robin. Reaching Your Goals. 2004. (Life Balance Ser.). 80p. (YA). (gr. 5-8). pap. 6.95 (978-0-531-16691-8(0) , Watts, Franklin) Scholastic Library Publishing.

Silverman, Robin Landew. Reaching Your Goals. 2004. (Life Balance Ser.). 80p. (J). 20.50 (978-0-531-12342-3(1) , Watts, Franklin) Scholastic Library Publishing.

Slap-Shelton, Laura & Shapiro, Lawrence E. Every Time I Blow My Top I Lose My Head! A Kid's Guide to Keeping Cool under Stress. Beckett, Bob, illus. 1999. Orig. Title: Take a Deep Breath: The Kids' Play-Away Stress Book. 62p. (J). (ps-5). pap. 17.95 (978-1-882732-82-1(0) , 63628) Childswork/Childsplay.

Statt, David A. A Student's Dictionary of Psychology. 2004. (Illus.). 176p. 12.95 (978-1-84169-342-2(1) , Psychology Press) Taylor & Francis Group GBR. *Dist:* Taylor & Francis, Inc.

Steck-Vaughn Staff. Why Me, Level 4, Set. 2002. (J). pap. incl. cd-rom (978-0-7398-6979-6(5)) Steck-Vaughn.

Tallmadge, Alice & Forster, Galyn. Tell It Like It Is: A Resource Guide for Youth in Treatment. Bear, Euan, ed. 1998. 144p. (J). pap. 15.00 (978-1-884444-46-3(6)) Safer Society Pr.

Treays, Rebecca. Understanding Your Brain - Internet Linked. Fox, Christyan, illus. rev. ed. 2004. (Science for Beginners Ser.). 32p. (J). pap. 7.95 (978-0-7945-0853-1(7) , Usborne) EDC Publishing.

—Understanding Your Senses - Internet Linked. Fox, Christyan, illus. rev. ed. 2004. (Science for Beginners Ser.). 32p. (J). pap. 7.95 (978-0-7945-0852-4(9) , Usborne) EDC Publishing.

Von Franz, Marie-Louise. Individuation in Fairy Tales, Vol. 1. rev. ed. 2001. (C. G. Jung Foundation Bks.), 240p. (ps). pap. 24.00 (978-1-57062-613-5(8)) Shambhala Pubns., Inc.

White, Kelly. The Girls' Life Big Book of Quizzes: Your Secret Self Revealed! Montagna, Frank, illus. 2003. 124p. (YA). (978-0-439-44979-3(0)) Scholastic, Inc.

Woodward, John. Daredevils. 2005. (Planet's Most Extreme Ser.). (Illus.). 48p. (J). (gr. 3-7). 24.95 (978-1-4103-0400-1(0) , Blackbirch Pr., Inc.) Thomson Gale.

PSYCHOLOGY, ABNORMAL

see Psychology, Pathological

PSYCHOLOGY, CHILD

see Child Psychology

PSYCHOLOGY, COMPARATIVE

Ehrlich, Fred. Does a Seal Smile? 2006. (Illus.). 32p. 13.50 (978-1-59354-168-2(6)); (J). pap. 5.95 (978-1-59354-169-9(4)) Blue Apple Bks.

Robson, Pam. Body Language. 1998. (Hello Out There! Ser.). (Illus.). 32p. (J). (gr. 2-5). pap. 6.95 (978-0-531-15349-9(5) , Watts, Franklin) Scholastic Library Publishing.

von Kessel, Carola. Understanding Horses with Caddie. Guhe, Irmtraud, illus. 2004. 32p. 22.50 (978-3-86127-948-8(7)) Cadmos Verlag GmbH GBR. *Dist:* Trans-Atlantic Pubns., Inc.

PSYCHOLOGY—DICTIONARIES

Statt, David A. A Student's Dictionary of Psychology. 2004. (Illus.). 176p. 12.95 (978-1-84169-342-2(1) , Psychology Press) Taylor & Francis Group GBR. *Dist:* Taylor & Francis, Inc.

PSYCHOLOGY, EDUCATIONAL

see Educational Psychology

PSYCHOLOGY—EXPERIMENTS

Chahrour, Janet Parks. Zap! Blink! Taste! Think! Exciting Life Science for Curious Minds. Gurvin, Abe, illus. 2003. 200p. (J). (gr. 5-10). pap. 14.95 (978-0-7641-1912-5(5)) Barron's Educational Series, Inc.

Gardner, Robert & Conklin, Barbara Gardner. Health Science Projects about Psychology. 2002. (Science Projects Ser.). (Illus.). 112p. (YA). (gr. 6-12). lib. bdg. 26.60 (978-0-7660-1439-8(8)) Enslow Pubs., Inc.

PSYCHOLOGY, MEDICAL

see Psychology, Pathological

PSYCHOLOGY, PATHOLOGICAL

see also Eating Disorders; Mental Illness; Psychiatry; Psychoanalysis

Brinkerhoff, Shirley. Drug Therapy & Childhood & Adolescent Disorders. 2003. (Encyclopedia of Psychiatric Drugs & Their Disorders Ser.). (Illus.). 128p. (J). lib. bdg. (978-1-59084-563-9(3)) Mason Crest Pubs.

Chou, Joey. Crazy by the Letters. Chou, Joey, illus. 2006. 15.99 (*978-0-9788670-0-3(9)*) Choo Choo Clan.

Van Duyne, Sara. Stress & Anxiety-Related Disorders. 2003. (Diseases & People Ser.). (Illus.). 112p. (J). lib. bdg. 26.60 (978-0-7660-1900-3(4)) Enslow Pubs., Inc.

PSYCHOLOGY, SOCIAL

see Social Psychology

PSYCHOLOGY—VOCATIONAL GUIDANCE

Clayton, Lawrence. Careers in Behavioral Science. 2nd ed. 2001. 201p. (J). (978-0-9709523-5-6(X)) Transcontinental Publishing, Inc.

Riggs, Ernestine G. & Gholar, Cheryl, contrib. by. Psychologist. 2003. (Careers with Character Ser.). (Illus.). 96p. (YA). (gr. 7 up). lib. bdg. 22.95 (978-1-59084-322-2(3)) Mason Crest Pubs.

PSYCHOPATHOLOGISTS

see Psychiatrists

PSYCHOPATHOLOGY

see Psychology, Pathological

PSYCHOPATHY

see Psychology, Pathological

PSYCHOSES

see Mental Illness

PSYCHOTHERAPY

Borenstein, Gerri C. Therapy. 2004. (Life Balance Ser.). (YA). (gr. 5-8). pap. 6.95 (978-0-531-15585-1(4) , Watts, Franklin) Scholastic Library Publishing.

Carter, William Lee. It Happened to Me: A Teen's Guide to Overcoming Sexual Abuse. 2002. (Workbook Ser.). 192p. (gr. 8-12). pap. 21.95 (978-1-57224-279-1(5)) New Harbinger Pubns.

Esherick, Joan. The Journey Toward Recovery: Youth with Brain Injury. 2004. (Youth with Special Needs Ser.). (Illus.). 128p. (J). (978-1-59084-734-3(2)) Mason Crest Pubs.

Fogerty, Ramona. Prince, Labino, & Chrecas from State Parkway. 2005. (YA). per. 24.95 (978-0-9759889-5-4(6)) Potenial Psychotherapy Counseling & Remedial Serv.

Friedl, Susan. Breakfast with Pumpernickel. Shull, Barbara, illus. 2001. 17p. (J). (ps-6). pap. 10.00 (978-0-9717627-0-1(8)) O.A.T.S., Inc. (Offering Alternative Therapy With Smiles).

Heegaard, Marge Eaton. Beyond the Rainbow: A Workbook for Children in the Advanced Stages of a Very Serious Illness. 2003. (Illus.). 32p. pap. 9.95 (978-1-57749-129-3(7)) Fairview Pr.

—Cuando Alguien Muy Especial Muere: Los Ni'os Pueden Aprender a Enfrentar la Adversided. 2003. (SPA.). 32p. pap. 9.95 (978-1-57749-127-9(0)) Fairview Pr.

Presnall, Judith Janda. Horse Therapists. 2001. (Animals with Jobs Ser.). (Illus.). 48p. (J). (gr. 3-5). 23.70 (978-0-7377-0615-4(5) , LML00902-178553, Kidhaven) Thomson Gale.

Rashkin, Rachel. Feeling Better: A Kid's Book about Therapy. Adamson, Bonnie, illus. 2005. 48p. (J). (ps-7). pap. 8.95 (978-1-59147-238-4(5) , Magination Pr.) American Psychological Assn.

—Feeling Better: A Kid's Books about Therapy. Adamson, Bonnie, illus. 2005. 48p. (J). 14.95 (978-1-59147-237-7(7) , Magination Pr.) American Psychological Assn.

Scholastic, Inc. Staff & Martin, Cory. The O C: Novelization, No. 3. 2004. (O C Novelization Ser.). (Illus.). 256p. (J). (gr. 7 up). 6.99 (978-0-439-67702-8(5)) Scholastic, Inc.

Widdifield, Lynn F. A Book about Me: A Place for You to Write about What Happens to You in Therapy. Widdifield, Lynn F., illus. l.t. ed. 1998. (Illus.). 50p. (J). (gr. 2-8). 21.00 (978-0-9668085-0-6(9) , 12160) Weathered Wise Publishing Co.

PTOMAINE POISONING

see Food Poisoning

PUBERTY

see also Adolescence

Blackstone, Margaret. Girl Stuff: A Survival Guide to Growing Up. 2000. (J). 15.60 (978-0-606-19417-4(7)) Tandem Library Bks.

Bourgeois, Paulette & Martyn, Kim. Changes in You & Me: A Book about Puberty Mostly for Girls. Phillips, Louise, illus. rev. ed. 2005. 64p. (J). pap. 16.95 (*978-1-55263-670-1(4)*) Key Porter Bks. CAN. *Dist:* Perseus Distribution.

Bryan, Jenny. Adolescence. 1999. (Health & Fitness Ser.). (Illus.). 48p. (J). (gr. 4-6). lib. bdg. 27.12 (978-0-7398-1346-1(3)) Raintree.

Byers, Ann. Frequently Asked Questions about Puberty. 2006. (Illus.). 64p. (J). (978-1-4042-0966-4(2)) Rosen Publishing Group, Inc., The.

Crump, Marguerite. Don't Sweat It! Everybody's Answers to Questions You Don't Want to Ask: A Guide for Young People. 2004. (Laugh & Learn Ser.). (Illus.). 128p. (YA). (gr. 4-8). pap. 12.95 (978-1-57542-114-8(3)) Free Spirit Publishing, Inc.

De Freitas, Chrystal. Puberty in Boys: Normal Body Changes in Preteens. Clark, Gail & Friedman, Lawrence, eds. Leonardo, Todd, illus. 2000. 24p. (J). (gr. 3-8). pap. 2.95 (978-1-885274-68-7(8) , 1027) Health InfoNet, Inc.

—Puberty in Girls: Normal Body Changes in Preteens. McMillan, Julia & Clark, Gail, eds. Leonardo, Todd, illus. unabr. ed. 2000. 24p. (J). (gr. 3-8). pap. 2.95 (978-1-885274-67-0(X)) Health InfoNet, Inc.

Elliot-Wright, Susan. Puberty. 2003. (Health Issues Ser.). (Illus.). 64p. (J). lib. bdg. 28.56 (978-0-7398-6424-1(6)) Raintree.

Favor, Lesli J. Everything You Need to Know about Growth Spurts & Delayed Growth. 2005. (Need to Know Library). (Illus.). 64p. (YA). (gr. 4-6). lib. bdg. 25.25 (978-0-8239-3549-9(3)) Rosen Publishing Group, Inc., The.

Firth, Alex. What's Happening to Me? (Boys Edition) Larkum, Adam, illus. 2007. 48p. (J). pap. 6.99 (978-0-7945-1514-0(2) , Usborne) EDC Publishing.

Fiscus, James. Coping with Growth Spurts & Delayed Growth. 2005. (Coping Ser.). (Illus.). 192p. (YA). (gr. 7-12). lib. bdg. 26.50 (978-0-8239-3508-6(6)) Rosen Publishing Group, Inc., The.

Gravelle, Karen, et al. Que Pasa Por Alla Abajo? Respuestas Faciles a Preguntas Dificiles para un Adolescente. Leighton, Robert, illus. 2003. (ENG & SPA.). 158p. (YA). (gr. 5-9). pap. 8.95 (978-0-8027-7649-5(3)) Walker & Co.

Jukes, Mavis. The Guy Book: An Owner's Manual: Maintenance, Safety, & Operating Instructions for Boys. 2002. (Illus.). 160p. (YA). (gr. 7 up). 12.95 (978-0-679-89028-7(9) , Crown Books For Young Readers) Random Hse. Children's Bks.

Kelly, Bill. You Ought to Know: A Guy's Guide to Sex. 2005. (Guys' Guides Ser.). (Illus.). 48p. (J). (gr. 5-8). lib. bdg. 23.95 (978-0-8239-3084-5(X) , GUYOSH) Rosen Publishing Group, Inc., The.

Madaras, Lynda & Madaras, Area. My Body, My Self for Boys. (Illus.). 112p. 2nd ed. 2000. (gr. 4-7). reprint ed. 12.95 (978-1-55704-440-2(6) , Newmarket Shooting Scripts); 3rd rev. ed. 2007. (YA). pap. 12.95 (*978-1-55704-767-0(7)*) Newmarket Pr.

—My Body, My Self for Girls. 3rd rev. ed. 2007. (Illus.). 128p. (YA). pap. 12.95 (*978-1-55704-766-3(9)*) Newmarket Pr.

—The What's Happening to My Body Book for Boys. 3rd ed. 2007. (Illus.). 272p. (YA). 24.95 (*978-1-55704-769-4(3)*); pap. 12.95 (*978-1-55704-765-6(0)*) Newmarket Pr.

—The What's Happening to My Body Book for Girls. 3rd rev. ed. 2007. (Illus.). 304p. (YA). 24.95 (*978-1-55704-768-7(5)*); pap. 12.95 (*978-1-55704-764-9(2)*) Newmarket Pr.

Mayle, Peter. What's Happening to Me? The Answers to Some of the World's Most Embarrassing Questions. Walter, Paul & Robins, Arthur, illus. 2000. 1p. (gr. 4-7). pap. 9.95 (978-0-8184-0312-5(8)) Kensington Publishing Corp.

Mejia Soto, Guillermina. Higiene de la Pubertad. 2003. (SPA.). 80p. pap. 12.48 (978-970-661-099-7(5)) Edamex, Editores Asociados Mexicanos, S. A. de C. V. MEX. *Dist:* Giron Bks.

Meredith, Susan. What's Happening to Me? (Girls Edition) Leschnikoff, Nancy, illus. 2006. 48p. (J). pap. 6.99 (978-0-7945-1267-5(4) , Usborne) EDC Publishing.

Saltz, Gail. Changing You! A Guide to Body Changes & Sexuality. Cravath, Lynne Avril, illus. 2007. 48p. (J). (gr. 1). 16.99 (*978-0-525-47817-1(5)* , Dutton Juvenile) Penguin Group (USA) Inc.

Silverstein, Alvin, et al. Puberty. 2000. (Watts Library). (Illus.). 64p. (J). (gr. 5-7). 25.50 (978-0-531-11750-7(2) , Watts, Franklin) Scholastic Library Publishing.

—Puberty. 2001. (Illus.). 63p. (J). (gr. 4-7). lib. bdg. 17.60 (978-0-613-34422-7(7)) Tandem Library Bks.

Smith, Liz. A Girl's Guide to Growing up - Booklet, 10 per packet. Perry, Gala, illus. 2005. (J). 63.95 (978-1-55942-207-9(6)) Marsh Media.

Stubbs, Lori. Fearfully & Wonderfully Made: A Christian Health & Puberty Guide for Preteen Boys & Girls. Stubbs, Robert Earl, illus. 2nd ed. 2005. 40p. (J). (ps-ps). pap. 10.00 (978-1-58597-174-9(X)) Leathers Publishing.

PUBLIC ADMINISTRATION

Kishel, Ann-Marie. Government Services. 2007. (First Step Nonfiction Ser.). 24p. (J). (gr. k-2). 18.60 (978-0-8225-6397-6(5) , Lerner Pubns.) Lerner Publishing Group.

PUBLIC ADMINISTRATION—VOCATIONAL GUIDANCE

J. G. Ferguson Publishing Company Staff. Careers in Focus: Government. 2002. (Careers in Focus Ser.). (Illus.). 192p. (YA). (gr. 9-12). 22.95 (978-0-89434-403-9(X) , F718, Ferguson Publishing Co.) Facts On File, Inc.

PUBLIC FINANCE

see Finance, Public

PUBLIC HEALTH

see also Cemeteries; Communicable Diseases; Hospitals; Noise; Refuse and Refuse Disposal; Sanitation; Sewage Disposal; Vaccination; Water—Pollution; Water-Supply

Amoroso, Gary M. & Klingel, Cynthia Fitterer. Ambulances. 2007. (Machines at Work Ser.). 24p. (J). (ps-2). 22.79 (978-1-59296-826-8(0)) Child's World, Inc.

Begun, Abbey M., et al, eds. Health: A Concern for Every American. 10th rev. ed. 1999. (Reference Ser.). (Illus.). 192p. (J). (gr. 9-12). pap. 32.00 (978-1-57302-086-2(9)) Thomson Gale.

Dudley, William, ed. Epidemics: Opposing Viewpoints. 1998. (Opposing Viewpoints Ser.). (Illus.). 188p. (YA). (gr. 9-12). lib. bdg. 32.45 (978-1-56510-941-4(4) , Greenhaven Pr., Inc.) Thomson Gale.

Foley, Ronan. World Health. 2003. (21st Century Debates Ser.). (Illus.). 64p. (J). lib. bdg. 28.56 (978-0-7398-5507-2(7)) Raintree.

Gordon, Sharon. ¿Qué Hay Dentro de una Ambulancia? 2006. (Bookworms Ser.). (SPA & ENG., Illus.). 32p. (J). lib. bdg. 22.79 (978-0-7614-2390-4(7)) Cavendish, Marshall Corp.

—What's Inside an Ambulance? (Qué Hay Dentro de una Ambulancia?) 2006. (Bookworms Ser.). (ENG & SPA., Illus.). 32p. (J). lib. bdg. 22.79 (978-0-7614-2471-0(7)) Cavendish, Marshall Corp.

Grahame, Deborah A. World Health Organization. 2003. (International Organizations Ser.). (Illus.). 48p. (J). (gr. 5 up). lib. bdg. 30.00 (978-0-8368-5524-1(8)) ; pap. 11.95 (978-0-8368-5533-3(7)) Stevens, Gareth Inc. (World Almanac Library).

Gutman, Howard. Surgeon General. 2003. (America's Leaders Ser.). (Illus.). 32p. (J). 23.70 (978-1-56711-296-2(X) , Blackbirch Pr., Inc.) Thomson Gale.

Health Alert Group 3, 6 bks., Set. Incl. Cerebral Palsy. Bjorklund, Ruth. lib. bdg. 31.36 (978-0-7614-2209-9(9)) ; Down Syndrome. Brill, Marlene Targ. lib. bdg. 31.36 (978-0-7614-2207-5(2)); Epilepsy. Bjorklund, Ruth. lib. bdg. 31.36 (978-0-7614-2206-8(4)); Flu. Hoffmann, Gretchen. lib. bdg. 31.36 (978-0-7614-2208-2(0)); Headaches. Petreycik, Rick. lib. bdg. 31.36 (978-0-7614-2210-5(2)); Meningitis. Klosterman, Lorrie. lib. bdg. 31.36 (978-0-7614-2211-2(0)); (Illus.). 64p. (J). 2006. 2007. Set lib. bdg. 188.14 (*978-0-7614-2205-1(6)* , Benchmark Bks.) Cavendish, Marshall Corp.

Jordan, Anna Louise. What Does an EMT Do? 2005. (What Does a Community Helper Do? Ser.). (Illus.). 24p. (J). lib. bdg. 21.26 (978-0-7660-2540-0(3) , Enslow Elementary) Enslow Pubs., Inc.

Mintzer, Richard. National Institute of Health. 2002. (Your Government Ser.). (Illus.). 64p. (J). 25.00 (978-0-7910-6793-2(9) , Chelsea Hse.) Facts On File, Inc.

Naden, Corinne J. Patients' Rights. 2007. (Open for Debate Ser.). (J). lib. bdg. (978-0-7614-2576-2(4) , Benchmark Bks.) Cavendish, Marshall Corp.

Nygren-Krug, Helena, et al. Right to Health. 2002. (ENG, FRE & SPA., Illus.). 16p. pap. 4.05 (978-92-4-159028-0(9) , 1150474) World Health Organization.

Powell, Jillian. World Health Organization. 2001. (gr. 5-8). lib. bdg. 15.25 (978-0-613-54791-8(8)) Tandem Library Bks.

Stanley, Debbie. New Medications: The Debate over Approval & Access. 2000. (Focus on Science & Society Ser.). (Illus.). 64p. (YA). (gr. 4-6). lib. bdg. 26.50 (978-0-8239-3212-2(5) , FSNEME) Rosen Publishing Group, Inc., The.

Vanase, Jessica, ed. Farms As Factories: Issues in Animal Welfare, Environmental Protection & Public Health. 2000. 32p. (YA). 3.00 (978-0-941246-11-8(6)) National Assn. for Humane & Environmental Education.

Wallerstein, Claire. Health & Disease. 2006. (Planet under Pressure Ser.). (Illus.). 48p. (YA). (gr. 6-8). lib. bdg. 31.43 (978-1-4034-8215-0(2)) Heinemann Library.

Yount, Lisa. Epidemics. 2000. (Overview Ser.). (Illus.). 112p. (YA). (gr. 6-9). lib. bdg. 29.95 (978-1-56006-441-1(2) , LML00902-177810, Lucent Bks.) Thomson Gale.

PUBLIC OPINION

see also Attitude (Psychology); Propaganda

also names of countries with the subdivision Foreign Opinion, e.g., United States—Foreign Opinion

Gallup Youth Survey: Major Issues & Trends, 6 vols., Set. 2004. (YA). 137.70 (978-1-59084-720-6(2)) Mason Crest Pubs.

Kriegel, Otis & McDevitt, Michael. Suggestion. 2005. (Illus.). 416p. pap. 12.95 (978-0-8118-4749-0(7)) Chronicle Bks. LLC.

Robinson, Hilary. E-Mail: Jesus@anytime. Lewis, Anthony, tr. Lewis, Anthony, illus. 2004. 32p. (J). 19.95 (978-0-340-85537-9(1) , Hodder & Stoughton) Hodder General Publishing Division GBR. *Dist:* Trafalgar Square Publishing.

PUBLIC PLAYGROUNDS

see Playgrounds

PUBLIC RELATIONS

Ferguson. Careers in Focus: Public Relations. 2007. (Careers in Focus Ser.). 160p. (J). (gr. 6-12). 29.95 (*978-0-8160-6574-5(8)* , Ferguson Publishing Co.) Facts On File, Inc.

Public Relations. 2004. 28.56 (978-1-4109-1078-3(4)) Raintree.

PUBLIC SCHOOLS

Marzilli, Alan. Religion in Public Schools. 2003. (Point/Counterpoint Ser.). (Illus.). 112p. (gr. 9-13). 32.95 (978-0-7910-7484-8(6) , Chelsea Hse.) Facts On File, Inc.

PUBLIC SERVICE CORPORATIONS

see Public Utilities

PUBLIC SPEAKING

see also Acting; Debates and Debating

Benjamin, Susan. Speak with Success: A Student's Step-by-Step Guide to Fearless Public Speaking. 2nd ed. 2007. 192p. (YA). pap. 14.95 (*978-1-59647-127-6(1)*) Good Year Bks.

Blumstein, Rachel. Everything You Need to Know about Public Speaking. rev. ed. 2005. (Need to Know Library). (Illus.). 64p. (YA). (gr. 7-12). lib. bdg. 25.25 (978-0-8239-3087-6(4) , NTPUSP) Rosen Publishing Group, Inc., The.

Burgett, Cindy. Policy Debate. 2007. (National Forensic League Library of Public Speaking & Debate). (Illus.). 48p. (J). (gr. 5-8). lib. bdg. 26.50 (*978-1-4042-1024-0(5)*) Rosen Publishing Group, Inc., The.

DeForge, Lauretta. Stand & Deliver: A Public Speaking Program. 1999. (Illus.). 35p. (YA). wbk. ed. 6.00 (978-0-9677846-0-1(3)) DeForge Communincations.

Engleberg, Isa N. & Daly, John A. Presentations in Everyday Life: Strategies for Effective Speaking. 2nd ed. 2004. 544p. (YA). pap. 74.36 (978-0-618-26016-4(1) , 313251) Houghton Mifflin College Div.

Ferguson. Mastering Career Skills: Communication Skills. 2nd rev. ed. 2007. (Mastering Career Skills Ser.). (Illus.). 144p. pap. 12.95 (*978-0-8160-7115-9(2)* , Checkmark Bks.) Facts On File, Inc.

Gower, Stephen M. The Missing Lynx: Finally, a Speak-in-Public Learning System for High School Students. 1998. 160p. (YA). (gr. 9 up). 20.00 (978-1-880150-79-5(4)) Lectern Publishing.

Lorusso, Cosmo. Pre-HSPA Success Work-a-Text in Language Arts Literacy. 2002. (YA). 215p. pap. (978-1-56749-535-5(4)); 24p. pap., tchr. ed. (978-1-56749-536-2(2)) Instructivision, Inc.

Marx, Jeff. How to Win a High School Election: Advice & Ideas Collected from over 1,000 High School Seniors. 2003. 180p. (gr. 7-12). pap. 14.95 (978-0-9667824-0-0(2)) Marx, Jeff.

Meany, John & Shuster, Kate. Speak Out: A Guide to Middle School Debate. 2004. (Illus.). 188p. pap. 24.95 (978-1-932716-02-3(5)) International Debate Education Assn.

The National Forensic League Library of Public Speaking & Debate, 6 bks., Set. Incl. Lincoln-Douglas Debate. Woodhouse, Cynthia. (YA). lib. bdg. 26.50 (*978-1-4042-1025-7(3)*); Parliamentary Debate. West, Keith. (YA). lib. bdg. 26.50 (*978-1-4042-1029-5(6)*); Persuasive Speaking. Waldo, Dixie. (YA). lib. bdg. 26.50 (*978-1-4042-1028-8(8)*); Policy Debate. Burgett, Cindy. (J). lib. bdg. 26.50 (*978-1-4042-1024-0(5)*); Public Forum Debate. Kline, Jason. (YA). lib. bdg. 26.50 (*978-1-4042-1027-1(X)*); Student Congress Debate. Jacobi, Adam J. (YA). lib. bdg. 26.50 (*978-1-4042-1026-4(1)*); (Illus.). 48p. (gr. 5-8). 2007. 2007. Set lib. bdg. 159.00 (*978-1-4042-0937-4(9)*) Rosen Publishing Group, Inc., The.

Public Speaking, a Student Guide: 7 Steps to Writing & Delivering a Great Speech. 2002. (J). per. 10.95 (978-1-883055-52-3(0)) Dandy Lion Pubns.

Ryan, Margaret. Extraordinary Oral Presentations. 128p. (YA). (gr. 8-12). 2006. pap. 9.95 (978-0-531-17577-4(4)); 2005. (Illus.). 30.50 (978-0-531-16758-8(5)) Scholastic Library Publishing. (Watts, Franklin).

Taylor, Lacy. Public Speaking Student Activities Book. Matthews, Douglas L., ed. 2003. (Illus.). stu. ed., per., wbk. ed. (978-1-931680-55-4(8) , Expert Systems for Teachers) Teaching Point, Inc.

PUBLIC UTILITIES

see also Railroads; Telegraph; Telephone; Water-Supply

Kallan, Stuart A. The Gas Crisis. 2007. (Ripped from the Headlines Ser.). 64p. (J). (gr. 5). 23.95 (*978-1-60217-001-8(0)*) Erickson Pr.

Nicodemus, Laura Konger. Grandma's House Had No Water, 4 vols. Nicodemus, Laura Konger, illus. 2002. (Illus.). 16p. (J). (gr. 1-4). 3.99 (978-0-9722216-1-0(1)) Grandma's Stories, Inc.

Peters, Craig. Larry Ellison: Database Genius of Oracle. 2003. (Internet Biographies Ser.). (Illus.). 48p. (J). (gr. 4-10). lib. bdg. 23.93 (978-0-7660-1974-4(8)) Enslow Pubs., Inc.

PUBLISHERS AND PUBLISHING

see also Book Industries and Trade; Books; Printing

African-American Publishers. 2000. (My Ancestors—My Heroes Ser.: Vol. 11). (J). (gr. 3-4). (978-1-893091-10-8(4)) Parker Publishing Co.

Asirvatham, Sandy. Katharine Graham. 2001. (Women of Achievement Ser.). (J). pap. (978-0-7910-6311-8(9)); 112p. (YA). (gr. 7 up). 30.00 (978-0-7910-6310-1(0)) Facts On File, Inc. (Chelsea Hse.).

Bradshaw, Anne, et al, contrib. by. Publishing Secrets: A Comprehensive Guide to Getting Your Book Published in the LDS Market. 2004. (Illus.). 194p. pap. 14.95 (978-0-9749241 0 6(5)) Golden Wings Enterprises.

Facts on File, Inc. Staff, contrib. by. Discovering Careers for Your Future. 2005. (Discovering Careers for Your Future Ser.). (Illus.). 96p. (J). (gr. 4-9). 21.95 (978-0-8160-5845-7(8) , Ferguson Publishing Co.) Facts On File, Inc.

Ferguson. Careers in Focus: Publishing. 3rd rev. ed. 2007. (Careers in Focus Ser.). 192p. (YA). (gr. 6-12). 29.95 (*978-0-8160-6572-1(1)* , Ferguson Publishing Co.) Facts On File, Inc.

Freedman, Russell & Elleman, Barbara. Holiday House: The First Sixty-Five Years. 2000. (Illus.). 286p. (J). (gr. 7 up). tchr. ed. 50.00 (978-0-8234-1559-5(7)) Holiday Hse., Inc.

Heidrich, Delana S. Create a Magazine, Grades 5-8: A Complete Framework for Students to Use in Creating an Original Magazine. Armstrong, Beverly, illus. 1999. 88p. pap., tchr. ed. 11.99 (978-0-88160-310-1(4) , LW-379, Learning Works, The) Creative Teaching Pr., Inc.

How a Book Gets Published. 2005. (Book Treks Ser.). (J). (gr. 3 up). stu. ed. 34.95 (978-0-673-62836-7(1)) Celebration Pr.

J. G. Ferguson Publishing Company Staff, contrib. by. Careers in Focus: Publishing. 2nd ed. 2002. (Careers in Focus Ser.). 192p. (YA). (gr. 6-12). 22.95 (978-0-89434-436-7(6) , F515, Ferguson Publishing Co.) Facts On File, Inc.

Lange, Brenda. Edward Stratemeyer. 2003. (Who Wrote That? Ser.). (Illus.). 112p. (gr. 6-12). 30.00 (978-0-7910-7621-7(0) , Chelsea Hse.) Facts On File, Inc.

Marsh, Carole. Robert R. McCormick. 2002. (One Thousand Readers Ser.). (Illus.). 12p. (J). (gr. k-4). 2.95 (978-0-635-01549-5(8) , 15498) Gallopade International.

Mayer, Cassie. Benjamin Franklin. 2007. (J). (*978-1-4034-9970-7(5)*) Heinemann Library.

P Q R

Roberts, Russell. John Newbery & the Story of the Newbery Medal. 2003. (Great Achiever Awards Ser.). (Illus.). 48p. (J). (gr. 4-8). lib. bdg. 29.95 (978-1-58415-201-9(X)) Mitchell Lane Pubs., Inc.

Rocha, Toni L. Careers in Magazine Publishing. 2005. (Career Resource Library). (Illus.). 192p. (J). (gr. 7-12). lib. bdg. 26.50 (978-0-8239-3188-0(9)) Rosen Publishing Group, Inc., The.

Ross, Allison J. Choosing a Career in Desktop Publishing. 2005. (World of Work Ser.). (Illus.). 64p. (J). (gr. 7-12). lib. bdg. 25.25 (978-0-8239-3295-5(8) , WWDEPU) Rosen Publishing Group, Inc., The.

Royston, Angela. Book. 2005. (How Are Things Made? Ser.). (Illus.). 32p. (J). pap. (978-0-431-05051-5(1)); tchr. ed. (978-0-431-05044-7(9)) Heinemann Library.

—How Is a Book Made? 2005. (Illus.). 32p. (J). (gr. k-2). lib. bdg. 24.21 (978-1-4034-6639-6(4)); pap. (978-0-431-46646-0(7)); lib. bdg. (978-0-431-46639-2(4)); pap. 7.60 (978-1-4034-6646-4(7)) Heinemann Library.

Saverwein, Stan. Ma Murray: The Story of Canada's Crusty Queen of Publishing. 2003. (Amazing Stories Ser.). (Illus.). 144p. pap. (978-1-55153-979-9(9)) Altitude Publishing Canada Ltd.

Ventresca, Yvonne. Publishing. 2005. (Careers for the Twenty-First Century Ser.). (Illus.). 112p. (J). (gr. k-8). per. 29.95 (978-1-59018-298-7(7) , Lucent Bks.) Thomson Gale.

Whitelaw, Nancy. Let's Go! Let's Publish! Katharine Graham & the Washington Post. 2004. (Makers of the Media Ser.). (Illus.). 112p. (YA). (gr. 6-12). 21.95 (978-1-883846-37-4(4) , First Biographies) Reynolds, Morgan Inc.

—William Randolph Hearst & the American Century. rev. exp. ed. 2004. (Makers of the Media Ser.). (Illus.). 128p. (YA). (gr. 6-12). 23.95 (978-1-931798-35-8(4)) Reynolds, Morgan Inc.

Wilson, Wayne. Careers in Publishing & Communications. 2001. (Latinos at Work Ser.). (Illus.). 96p. (J). (gr. 5-12). lib. bdg. 22.95 (978-1-58415-088-6(2)) Mitchell Lane Pubs., Inc.

Zoltan, Melanie Barton. A Kid's Guide to Getting Published. 2001. 144p. (J). (gr. 2-10). pap. 12.95 (978-0-940159-66-2(X)) Camino Bks., Inc.

PUBLISHERS AND PUBLISHING—FICTION

Clements, Andrew. The School Story. unabr. ed. 2004. (Middle Grade Cassette Librariestm Ser.). 224p. (J). (gr. 3-7). pap. 29.00 incl. audio (978-0-8072-1000-0(5) , S YA 352 SP, Listening Library) Random Hse. Audio Publishing Group.

—The School Story. Selznick, Brian, illus. (J). 2002. 224p. pap. 5.99 (978-0-689-85186-5(3) , Aladdin); 2001. 160p. (gr. 4-6). 16.00 (978-0-689-82594-1(3)) Simon & Schuster Children's Publishing.

—The School Story. 2002. (gr. 3-6). lib. bdg. 13.00 (978-0-613-54852-6(3)) Tandem Library Bks.

Messina, Lynn. Savvy Girl. 2008. (Illus.). 256p. (YA). pap. 7.95 (***978-0-15-206161-6(4)** , Harcourt Paperbacks) Harcourt Children's Bks.

Spizman, Robyn Freedman & Johnston, Mark. Secret Agent. 240p. (J). 2006. (gr. 4-7). pap. 5.99 (978-1-4169-1862-2(0) , Aladdin); 2005. 16.95 (978-0-689-87044-6(2) , Atheneum) Simon & Schuster Children's Publishing.

Winfield, M. Arthur. The Rover Boys at College or the Right R. 2006. 96.99 (***978-1-4219-7415-6(0)**); pap. 90.99 (***978-1-4219-7402-6(9)**) IndyPublish.com.

PUBLISHING

see Publishers and Publishing

PUERTO RICANS

Conley, Kate A. The Puerto Rican Americans. 2005. (Immigrants in America Ser.). (Illus.). 112p. (YA). (gr. 7-10). lib. bdg. 29.95 (978-1-59018-432-5(7) , Lucent Bks.) Thomson Gale.

PUERTO RICANS—BIOGRAPHY

Ancona, George. Mi Barrio. 2004. (Somos Latino (We Are Latinos) Ser.). 20.00 (978-0-516-23689-6(X) , Watts, Franklin) Scholastic Library Publishing.

Buckley, James, Jr. Roberto Clemente. 2001. (Eyewitness Readers Ser.). (Illus.). (J). (978-0-606-20888-8(7)); (SPA., (978-0-606-20889-5(5)) Tandem Library Bks.

Buckley, James, Jr. & Dorling Kindersley Publishing Staff. Roberto Clemente. 2001. (Readers Ser.). (Illus.). 48p. (J). (ps-3). pap. 3.99 (978-0-7894-7342-4(9)); (SPA., pap. 3.99 (978-0-7894-7344-8(5)) Dorling Kindersley Publishing, Inc.

Fischer, David. Roberto Clemente. 2004. (Trailblazers of the Modern World Ser.). (J). pap. 11.95 (978-0-8368-5264-6(8)); (Illus.). 48p. (YA). lib. bdg. 30.00 (978-0-8368-5495-4(0)) Stevens, Gareth Inc. (World Almanac Library).

Garcia, Kimberly. Roberto Clemente. l.t. ed. 2002. (Real Life Reader Biography Ser.). (Illus.). 32p. (J). (gr. 3-8). lib. bdg. 24.95 (978-1-58415-127-2(7)) Mitchell Lane Pubs., Inc.

Guzman, Lila & Guzman, Rick. Roberto Clemente: Héroe del Béisbol. 2007. (Latinos Famosos Ser.). (SPA., Illus.). 32p. (J). (gr. 3-4). lib. bdg. 22.60 (***978-0-7660-2675-9(2)** , Enslow Elementary) Enslow Pubs., Inc.

Harcourt School Publishers Staff. The Pride of Puerto Rico. 3rd ed. 2002. (Horizons Ser.). (Illus.). (J). pap. 7.30 (978-0-15-333591-4(2)) Harcourt Schl. Pubs.

—Roberto's Dream On Level. 3rd ed. 2002. (Trophies Reading Program Ser.). (Illus.). pap. 5.10 (978-0-15-323173-5(4)) Harcourt Schl. Pubs.

Healy, Nick. Roberto Clemente: Baseball Legend. 2006. (Fact Finders Ser.). (Illus.). 32p. (J). (978-0-7368-5442-9(8)) Capstone Pr., Inc.

Hill, Anne E. Jennifer Lopez. 2000. (Galaxy of Superstars Ser.). (J). pap. 9.95 (978-0-7910-5776-6(3)); 64p. (gr. 4-7). 25.00 (978-0-7910-5775-9(5)) Facts On File, Inc. (Chelsea Hse.).

Joseph, Paul. Ricky Martin. 2000. (Young Profiles Ser.). (Illus.). 32p. (J). (gr. k-6). lib. bdg. 22.78 (978-1-57765-370-7(X) , Checkerboard Library) ABDO Publishing Co.

Macht, Norman L. Roberto Alomar. 1999. (Latinos in Baseball Ser.). (Illus.). 72p. (gr. 4-10). lib. bdg. 18.95 (978-1-883845-84-1(X)) Mitchell Lane Pubs., Inc.

Marquez, Heron. Roberto Clemente. 2005. (Trailblazer Biography Ser.). (Illus.). 112p. (J). (gr. 5-9). 30.60 (978-1-57505-767-5(0)) Lerner Publishing Group.

Mills, Clifford W. Bernie Williams. 2007. (Baseball Superstars Ser.). 128p. (YA). (gr. 6-12). 30.00 (***978-0-7910-9468-6(5)** , Chelsea Hse.) Facts On File, Inc.

Mohr, Nicholasa. All for the Better: A Story of el Barrio. 2001. (Nonfiction Bookbag Ser.). (J). (gr. 3-4). per. 8.45 (978-1-58830-203-8(2)) Metropolitan Teaching & Learning Co.

Newman, Matthew. Ricky Martin. 2000. (Galaxy of Superstars Ser.). (Illus.). 64p. (J). pap. 9.95 (978-0-7910-5772-8(0)); (gr. 4-7). 25.00 (978-0-7910-5771-1(2)) Facts On File, Inc. (Chelsea Hse.).

Olmstead, Mary. Roberto Clemente. 2004. (Hispanic-American Biographies Ser.). (Illus.). 64p. (J). pap. 9.50 (978-1-4109-0917-6(4)) Harcourt Schl. Pubs.

—Roberto Clemente. 2004. (Hispanic-American Biographies Ser.). (Illus.). 64p. (J). (gr. 4-6). 32.86 (978-1-4109-0711-0(2)) Raintree.

Parker, Judy. Ricky Martin. 2001. (gr. 7-12). lib. bdg. 15.25 (978-0-613-58726-6(X)) Tandem Library Bks.

Thornley, Stew. Roberto Alomar: Star Second Baseman. 1999. (Sports Reports). (Illus.). 104p. (YA). (gr. 4-10). lib. bdg. 26.60 (978-0-7660-1079-6(1)) Enslow Pubs., Inc.

Winter, Jonah. Roberto Clemente: Pride of the Pittsburgh Pirates. Colon, Raul, illus. 2005. 40p. (J). 17.99 (978-0-689-85643-3(1) , Atheneum) Simon & Schuster Children's Publishing.

PUERTO RICANS—FICTION

Herrera, Juan Felipe. Cinnamon Girl: Letters Found Inside a Cereal Box. 2006. 176p. (J). pap. 7.99 (978-0-06-057986-9(2) , HarperTeen) HarperCollins Pubs.

Manzano, Sonia & Muth, Jon J. No Dogs Allowed! 2004. (Illus.). 32p. (J). (ps-3). 15.95 (978-0-689-83088-4(2) , Atheneum) Simon & Schuster Children's Publishing.

Ostow, Micol. Emily Goldberg Learns to Salsa. 2007. 288p. (J). (gr. 7). pap. 7.99 (***978-1-59514-144-6(8)** , Razorbill) Penguin Group (USA) Inc.

Padilla, Felix. Mis Dos Luces. Padilla, Rebecca, ed. Gomez, Osvaldo, illus. 1999. (SPA.). 32p. (J). 16.00 (978-0-9675413-1-0(X)) Libros, Encouraging Cultural Literacy.

PUERTO RICANS—NEW YORK (STATE)—NEW YORK—FICTION

Cofer, Judith Ortiz. Call Me Maria. 2006. 144p. (J). pap. 6.99 (978-0-439-38578-7(4) , Scholastic Paperbacks) Scholastic, Inc.

Mohr, Nicholasa. Going Home. 1999. 192p. (J). (gr. 3-7). reprint ed. pap. 5.99 (978-0-14-130644-5(0) , Puffin) Penguin Group (USA) Inc.

—Going Home. 1999. (gr. 3-6). lib. bdg. 14.15 (978-0-8335-2939-8(0)) Tandem Library Bks.

Ortiz Cofer, Judith. Call Me Maria. 2004. (First Person Fiction Ser.). 144p. (J). (gr. 4-7). pap. 16.95 (978-0-439-38577-0(6) , Orchard Bks.) Scholastic, Inc.

Scott, James. When I Was Puerto Rican: Reproducible Teaching Unit. 2001. 55p. (YA). (gr. 7-12). tchr. ed., ring bd. 29.50 (978-1-58049-281-2(9) , TU167) Prestwick Hse., Inc.

Velasquez, Eric. Grandma's Records. Velasquez, Eric, illus. 2004. (Illus.). 32p. (J). pap. 7.95 (978-0-8027-7660-0(4)) Walker & Co.

—Grandma's Records. 2004. (Illus.). 32p. (J). (gr. k-3). 16.95 (978-0-8027-8760-6(6)); 17.85 (978-0-8027-8761-3(4)) Walker & Co.

Velasquez, Eric & de la Vega, Eida. Los Discos de Mi Abuela. 2002. (SPA., Illus.). (J). (gr. 1-3). 16.95 (978-1-930332-21-8(1) , LC7246) Lectorum Pubns., Inc.

PUERTO RICANS—UNITED STATES

Ancona, George. Mi Barrio: My Neighborhood. 2005. (Somos Latinos (We Are Latinos) Ser.). (SPA., Illus.). 32p. (J). (gr. 1-3). pap. 8.95 (978-0-516-25064-9(7) , Children's Pr.) Scholastic Library Publishing.

Hoyt-Goldsmith, Diane. Three Kings Day: A Celebration at Christmastime. Migdale, Lawrence, illus. 32p. (J). (gr. 4-6). tchr. ed. 16.95 (978-0-8234-1839-8(1)) Holiday Hse., Inc.

Nichol, Bryan. Puerto Rican Americans. 2004. (One Nation Ser.). (Illus.). 32p. (J). (gr. k-6). lib. bdg. 22.78 (978-1-59197-532-8(8) , Checkerboard Library) ABDO Publishing Co.

Taus-Bolstad, Stacy. Puerto Ricans in America. 2005. (In America Ser.). (Illus.). 80p. (J). (gr. 5-8). lib. bdg. 27.93 (978-0-8225-3953-7(5)) Lerner Publishing Group.

PUERTO RICANS—UNITED STATES—FICTION

Garcia, Richard. Los Espiritus de Mi Tia Otilia. ed. 2004. (ENG & SPA., Illus.). (J). (gr. k-3). spiral bd. (978-0-616-14606-4(X)) Canadian National Institute for the Blind/Institut National Canadien pour les Aveugles.

Mohr, Nicholasa. Felita. 1999. (J). 12.79 (978-0-606-17413-8(3)); (gr. 3-6). lib. bdg. 13.00 (978-0-8335-4661-6(9)) Tandem Library Bks.

Steptoe, John L. Creativity. Lewis, Earl, illus. 2003. 32p. (J). (gr. k-3). pap. 5.95 (978-0-618-31677-9(9) , Clarion Bks.) Houghton Mifflin Co. Trade & Reference Div.

PUERTO RICO

Banting, Erinn. Puerto Rico: The Land. 2003. (J). lib. bdg. 16.40 (978-0-613-59137-9(2)) Tandem Library Bks.

—Puerto Rico - The Land. 2003. (Lands, Peoples & Cultures Ser.). (Illus.). 32p. (J). (gr. 2-9). (978-0-7787-9333-5(8)); pap. (978-0-7787-9701-2(5)) Crabtree Publishing Co.

Bjorklund, Ruth. Puerto Rico. 2007. (J). (***978-0-7614-2218-1(8)**) Cavendish, Marshall Bks., Ltd.

Boraas, Tracey. Puerto Rico. 2003. (Land of Liberty Ser.). (Illus.). 64p. (J). lib. bdg. 25.26 (978-0-7368-2195-7(3)) Capstone Pr., Inc.

Brown, Jonatha A. Puerto Rico & Other Outlying Areas. 2006. (Portraits of the States Ser.). (Illus.). 32p. (J). pap. (978-0-8368-4693-5(1)); lib. bdg. 23.33 (978-0-8368-4674-4(5)) Stevens, Gareth Inc.

Burgan, Michael. Puerto Rico. 2003. (From Sea to Shining Sea Ser.: 2). (Illus.). 80p. (J). 30.50 (978-0-516-22398-8(4) , Children's Pr.) Scholastic Library Publishing.

—Puerto Rico & Other Outlying Territories. 2003. (World Almanac Library of the States). (Illus.). 48p. (J). (gr. 5 up). pap. 14.95 (978-0-8368-5329-2(6) , World Almanac Library) Stevens, Gareth Inc.

—Puerto Rico & Outlying Territories. 2003. (World Almanac Library of the States). (Illus.). 48p. (J). (gr. 5 up). lib. bdg. 30.00 (978-0-8368-5158-8(7) , World Almanac Library) Stevens, Gareth Inc.

Eagen, Rachel. Ponce de Léon: Exploring Florida & Puerto Rico. 2005. (In the Footsteps of Explorers Ser.). (Illus.). 32p. (J). (gr. 3-9). (978-0-7787-2412-4(3)) Crabtree Publishing Co.

Feeney, Kathy. Puerto Rico Facts & Symbols. (States & Their Symbols Ser.). 24p. (J). 2000. (Illus.). (gr. 2-3). lib. bdg. 18.60 (978-0-7368-0644-2(X) , Bridgestone Bks.); 2003. lib. bdg. 19.93 (978-0-7368-2269-5(0)) Capstone Pr., Inc.

Fein, Eric & Muschinske, Emily. How to Draw Puerto Rico's Sights & Symbols. 2002. (Kid's Guide to Drawing America Ser.). (Illus.). 32p. (J). lib. bdg. 25.25 (978-0-8239-6095-8(1) , PowerKids Pr.) Rosen Publishing Group, Inc., The.

Foster, Leila Merrell. Puerto Rico. (Visit to Ser.). 32p. pap. 6.50 (978-1-4034-4152-2(9)); 2000. (Illus.). (J). lib. bdg. 21.36 (978-1-57572-381-5(6)) Heinemann Library.

—Puerto Rico. 2003. (gr. k-3). lib. bdg. 14.75 (978-0-613-84429-1(7)) Tandem Library Bks.

Fradin, Dennis Brindell. Puerto Rico. 1998. (From Sea to Shining Sea Ser.). (Illus.). 64p. (J). (gr. 3-5). pap. 7.95 (978-0-516-26282-6(3) , Children's Pr.) Scholastic Library Publishing.

George, Marian M. A Little Journey to Puerto Rico. 2004. reprint ed. pap. 1.99 (978-1-4192-0211-7(1)) Kessinger Publishing, LLC.

Heinrichs, Ann. Puerto Rico. Kania, Matt, illus. 2005. (Welcome to the USA Ser.). 40p. (J). (gr. 1-5). 27.07 (978-1-59296-493-2(1)) Child's World, Inc.

Heinrichs, Ann & Labbo, Linda D. Puerto Rico. 2003. (This Land Is Your Land Ser.). (Illus.). 48p. (J). (gr. 3 up). lib. bdg. 22.60 (978-0-7565-0357-4(4)) Compass Point Bks.

Hernandez, Romel. Puerto Rico. 2003. (Discovering Latin America Ser.). (Illus.). 64p. (J). (gr. 5 up). lib. bdg. (978-1-59084-303-1(7)) Mason Crest Pubs.

Johnston, Joyce. Puerto Rico. 2nd exp. rev. ed. (Hello U. S. A. Ser.). (Illus.). 84p. (J). (gr. 3-6). 2003. pap. 6.95 (978-0-8225-4150-9(5)); 2002. 25.26 (978-0-8225-4058-8(4) , Lerner Pubns.) Lerner Publishing Group.

—Puerto Rico. 2001. (gr. 3-6). lib. bdg. 15.25 (978-0-613-89183-7(X)) Tandem Library Bks.

Kummer, Patricia K. Puerto Rico. rev. ed. 2002. (One Nation Ser.). (Illus.). 48p. (J). (gr. 3-4). lib. bdg. 22.60 (978-0-7368-1263-4(6) , Bridgestone Bks.) Capstone Pr., Inc.

LaBrucherie, Roger. Puerto Rico Island in the Sun. LaBrucherie, Roger, photos by. 2002. (Illus.). (J). 20.00 (978-0-939302-38-3(1) , 0939302381) Imagenes Pr.

Landau, Elaine. Puerto Rico. 2000. (True Bks.). (Illus.). 48p. (J). (gr. 3-5). pap. 6.95 (978-0-516-26770-8(1) , Children's Pr.) Scholastic Library Publishing.

—Puerto Rico. 1999. (gr. 3-6). lib. bdg. 15.25 (978-0-613-54307-1(6)) Tandem Library Bks.

Levy, Patricia & Bahrawi, Nazry. Puerto Rico. 2nd ed. 2005. (Cultures of the World Ser.). (Illus.). 144p. (J). (gr. 6-10). lib. bdg. (978-0-7614-1970-9(5) , Benchmark Bks.) Cavendish, Marshall Corp.

Marcus, Amy. Exploring Puerto Rico with the Five Themes of Geography. 2005. (Library of the Western Hemisphere). (J). (Illus.). 24p. 19.95 (978-1-4042-2673-9(7) , PowerKids Pr.); pap. (978-0-8239-4645-7(2)); (Illus.). 24p. pap. (978-0-8239-4633-4(9)) Rosen Publishing Group, Inc., The.

Milivojevic, JoAnn. Puerto Rico. (Ticket to Ser.). (Illus.). 48p. 2005. (gr. 2-4). 22.60 (978-1-57505-144-4(3)); 2000. (J). (gr. 3-5). lib. bdg. 22.60 (978-1-57505-119-2(2) , Carolrhoda Bks.) Lerner Publishing Group.

Puerto Rico. 2006. (Bilingual Library of the United States of America: Set 2). (ENG & SPA., Illus.). 32p. (J). (gr. 3-6). lib. bdg. 22.50 (978-1-4042-3104-7(8) , Buenas Letra) Rosen Publishing Group, Inc., The.

Puerto Rico y Otras Areas Perifericas. (World Almanac Ser.).Tr. of Puerto Rico & Other Outlying Areas. (SPA.). (J). (gr. 3-5). 30.00 (978-0-8368-5726-9(7) , GHS32693) Stevens, Gareth Inc.

Reynolds, Jeff E. Puerto Rico. (to Z Ser.). (Illus.). 40p. (J). 2005. (gr. 2-4). pap. 6.95 (978-0-516-25073-1(6) , Children's Pr.); 2004. 24.50 (978-0-516-23656-8(3) , Watts, Franklin) Scholastic Library Publishing.

Ross, Michael Elsohn. Children of Puerto Rico. Rigau, Felix, illus. Rigau, Felix, photos by. 2001. (World's Children Ser.). 48p. (J). (gr. 3-6). lib. bdg. (978-1-57505-522-0(8) , Carolrhoda Bks.) Lerner Publishing Group.

Schwabacher, Martin. Puerto Rico. 2001. (Celebrate the States Ser.). (Illus.). 144p. (gr. 4-8). lib. bdg. 37.07 (978-0-7614-1313-4(8)); (J). lib. bdg. 35.64 (978-0-7614-1070-6(8)) Cavendish, Marshall Corp. (Benchmark Bks.).

Silva Lee, Alfonso. Mi Isla y Yo: La Naturaleza de Puerto Rico. Hayskar, Bonnie J., ed. Lago, Alexis, illus. 2007. (SPA.). 32p. (J). pap. 8.95 (978-1-929165-19-3(6)) PANGAEA.

—Mi Isla y Yo = My Island & I: La Naturaleza de Puerto Rico = the Nature of Puerto Rico. Hayskar, Bonnie J., ed. Lago, Alexis, illus. 2002. (SPA & ENG.). 32p. (J). (gr. 2-5). 15.95 (978-1-929165-06-3(4)) PANGAEA.

—Mi isla y yo = My Island & I: La naturaleza de Puerto Rico = the Nature of Puerto Rico. Hayskar, Bonnie J., ed. Lago, Alexis, illus. 2003. (SPA & ENG.). 32p. (J). pap. 9.95 (978-1-929165-12-4(9)) PANGAEA.

Tagliaferro, Linda. Puerto Rico in Pictures. 2nd ed. 2004. (Visual Geography Series, Second Ser.). (Illus.). 80p. (J). (gr. 5-12). 27.93 (978-0-8225-0936-3(9)) Lerner Publishing Group.

Winslow, Zachery. Puerto Rico. 1999. (Major World Nations Ser.). (Illus.). 144p. (YA). (ps up). lib. bdg. 21.95 (978-0-7910-4991-4(4) , Chelsea Hse.) Facts On File, Inc.

World Book, Inc. Staff, contrib. by. Christmas in Puerto Rico. 2002. (Christmas Around the World from World Book Ser.). (Illus.). 80p. (gr. 2-8). 24.95 (978-0-7166-0801-1(4)) World Bk., Inc.

Zapata, Elizabeth. Puerto Rico. 2006. (Rookie Read-About Geography Ser.). (Illus.). 32p. (J). (gr. 1-2). 20.50 (***978-0-516-25387-9(5)**) Scholastic Library Publishing.

PUERTO RICO—BIOGRAPHY

Gac-Artigas, Alejandro. Yo, Alejandro: The Story of a Young Latino Boy, My/Our Story. 2nd ed. 2000. (Gutenberg Ser.). 112p. (YA). pap. 11.95 (978-1-930879-21-8(0)) Ediciones Nuevo Espacio.

George, Linda. Luis Munoz Marin: Father of Modern Puerto Rico. 1999. (gr. 3-6). lib. bdg. 15.25 (978-0-613-54744-4(6)) Tandem Library Bks.

George, Linda & George, Charles. Luis Munoz Marin: Father of Modern Puerto Rico. 1999. (Community Builders Ser.). (Illus.). 48p. (J). (gr. 3-5). 25.00 (978-0-516-21586-0(8) , Children's Pr.) Scholastic Library Publishing.

PUERTO RICO—FICTION

Bernier-Grand, Carmen T. In the Shade of the Nispero Tree. 1999. 192p. (J). (gr. 4-7). 16.99 (978-0-531-33154-5(7)); pap. 15.95 (978-0-531-30154-8(0)) Scholastic, Inc. (Orchard Bks.).

Delacre, Lulu. Rafi & Rosi. 2004. (Illus.). 64p. (J). lib. bdg. 13.85 (***978-1-4242-0596-7(4)**) Fitzgerald Bks.

—Rafi & Rosi. Delacre, Lulu, illus. (I Can Read Bks.). 64p. (J). (gr. k-3). 2005. pap. 3.99 (978-0-06-009897-1(X) , Rayo); 2004. (Illus.). lib. bdg. 16.89 (978-0-06-009896-4(1)) HarperCollins Pubs.

—Rafi & Rosi: Carnival! Delacre, Lulu, illus. 2008. (I Can Read Bks.). 64p. (J). 3.99 (***978-0-06-073599-9(6)** , Rayo) HarperCollins Pubs.

—Rafi y Rosi. Delacre, Lulu, illus. 2006. (I Can Read Bks.). (SPA.). 64p. (J). 15.99 (978-0-06-087277-9(2)); pap. 3.99 (978-0-06-087278-6(0)) HarperCollins Pubs. (Rayo).

—Rafi y Rosi: Carnival! Delacre, Lulu, illus. 2006. (I Can Read Bks.). 64p. (J). (SPA.). 15.99 (978-0-06-113134-9(2)); (SPA.). pap. 3.99 (978-0-06-113135-6(0)); (Illus.). 15.99 (978-0-06-073597-5(X)); (Illus.). lib. bdg. 16.89 (978-0-06-073598-2(8)) HarperCollins Pubs. (Rayo).

Enriquez, Jose. Saving the Mango Farm. 2006. 23p. (J). 10.98 (978-1-4116-5917-9(1)) Lulu.com.

Fontanez, Edwin. En esta hermosa Isla. Fontanez, Edwin, illus. 2005. (SPA., Illus.). 32p. (J). 16.95 (978-0-9640868-7-6(5)) Exit Studio.

Garza, Carmen Lomas. Vejigante-Masquerader. (J). (gr. 2-4). (978-0-590-45777-4(2) , SO7640) Scholastic, Inc.

Green, Yuko. Marisol from Puerto Rico Sticker Paper Doll. 1998. (Sticker Paper Dolls Ser.). (Illus.). 4p. (J). (gr. k-5). pap. 1.50 (978-0-486-40319-9(X)) Dover Pubns., Inc.

Hooper, Nancy. Everywhere Coquis. Betancourt, Raymond, illus. 2003. Tr. of En Dondequiera Coquies. (SPA.). 48p. (J). 12.95 (978-0-942929-14-0(4)) Read Street Publishing, Inc.

Jaffe, Nina. Flor de Oro. Sanchez, Enrique, illus. (SPA.). (J). 15.95 (978-1-55885-463-5(0) , Piñata Books) Arte Publico Pr.

—Sing, Little Sack! I Canta, Saquito!: a Folktale from Puerto Rico. Cruz, Ray, illus. 2006. 48p. (J). (gr. 2-3). reprint ed. 19.00 (978-1-4223-5573-2(X)) DIANE Publishing Co.

Mohr, Nicholasa. Going Home. 1999. 192p. (J). (gr. 3-7). reprint ed. pap. 5.99 (978-0-14-130644-5(0) , Puffin) Penguin Group (USA) Inc.

—Going Home. 1999. (gr. 3-6). lib. bdg. 14.15 (978-0-8335-2939-8(0)) Tandem Library Bks.

Montes, Marisa. Get Ready for Gabi No. 5: All in the Familia. Cepeda, Joe, illus. 2004. 112p. (J). (gr. 2-5). (978-0-439-66156-0(0) , Scholastic Paperbacks) Scholastic, Inc.

Nodar, Carmen Santiago. Abuelita's Paradise. Paterson, Diane, illus. unabr. ed. 2001. (J). (gr. k-3). 25.90 incl. audio (978-0-8045-6847-0(2) , 6847) Spoken Arts, Inc.

Padilla, Felix. Mis Dos Luces. Padilla, Rebecca, ed. Gomez, Osvaldo, illus. 1999. (SPA.). 32p. (J). 16.00 (978-0-9675413-1-0(X)) Libros, Encouraging Cultural Literacy.

Romeu, Emma. Gregorio y el Pirata. 2003. Tr. of Gregorio & the Pirate. (SPA., Illus.). 152p. (J). pap. 15.95 (978-968-19-0553-8(9)) Santillana USA Publishing Co., Inc.

Silva Lee, Alfonso. Coqui y Sus Amigos: Los Animales de Puerto Rico. Hayskar, Bonnie J., ed. Silva Lee, Alfonso, photos by. 2000. Tr. of Coqui And His Friends: The Anima. (SPA & ENG., Illus.). 100p. (J). (gr. 3-6). pap. 12.95 (978-1-929165-03-2(X)) PANGAEA.

Trujillo, Rafael E. Mirando y Mirando. Liu, Kimi, illus. 2005. (SPA.). (J). 16.00 (978-0-9765007-0-4(1)) Big Head Fish.

Wallner, Alexandra. Sergio & the Hurricane. 2006. (Illus.). 32p. (J). pap. 6.95 (978-0-8050-7984-5(X) , Holt, Henry & Co. Bks. For Young Readers) Holt, Henry & Co.

—Sergio & the Hurricane. Wallner, Alexandra, illus. rev. ed. 2000. (Illus.). 32p. (J). (ps-2). 17.95 (978-0-8050-6203-8(3) , Holt, Henry & Co. Bks. For Young Readers) Holt, Henry & Co.

PUERTO RICO—HISTORY

Banting, Erinn. Puerto Rico: People & Culture. 2003. (gr. 3-6). lib. bdg. 16.40 (978-0-613-59136-2(4)) Tandem Library Bks.

—Puerto Rico - The People & the Culture. 2003. (Lands, Peoples & Cultures Ser.). (Illus.). 32p. (J). (gr. 2-9). (978-0-7787-9334-2(6)); pap. (978-0-7787-9702-9(3)) Crabtree Publishing Co.

Eagen, Rachel. Ponce de Léon: Exploring Florida & Puerto Rico. 2005. (In the Footsteps of Explorers Ser.). (Illus.). 32p. (J). (gr. 3-9). pap. (978-0-7787-2448-3(4)) Crabtree Publishing Co.

Ebon Research Systems Staff. Dare to Be Vol. 4: Luis Munoz Marion. l.t. ed. 2003. Tr. of Atrevete Ser... Un Heroe Luis Munoz Marin. (ENG & SPA., Illus.). 14p. (J). 3.99 (978-0-9648313-7-7(6)) Ebon Research Systems Publishing, LLC.

Lopez, Jose. Puerto Rico. 2006. (Modern World Nations Ser.). (Illus.). 112p. (J). (gr. 6-12). 30.00 (978-0-7910-8798-5(0) , Chelsea Hse.) Facts On File, Inc.

Maldonado, Ileana. Coloreando y Aprendiendo Con Katsi. 2001. (J). 4.95 (978-0-8477-0123-0(9)) Univ. of Puerto Rico Pr.

Milivojevic, JoAnn. Puerto Rico. (Ticket to Ser.). (Illus.). 48p. 2005. (gr. 2-4). 22.60 (978-1-57505-144-4(3)); 2000. (J). (gr. 3-5). lib. bdg. 22.60 (978-1-57505-119-2(2) , Carolrhoda Bks.) Lerner Publishing Group.

Riddering, Karenlie Anne. Puerto Rico: Encanto Oculto. 2nd ed. 2005. (ENG & SPA.). 60p. (YA). (978-0-9765977-2-8(1)) Ridderíng, Marggie.

Worth, Richard. Puerto Rico in American History. 2008. (From Many Cultures, One History Ser.). (Illus.). 128p. (J). (gr. 5 up). lib. bdg. 31.93 (***978-0-7660-2836-4(4)***) Enslow Pubs., Inc.

PUFFINS

Frost, Helen. Puffins. 2006. (Polar Animals Ser.). (Illus.). 24p. (J). (978-0-7368-4244-0(6)) Capstone Pr., Inc.

McMillan, Bruce. Puffins Climb, Penguins Rhyme. 2001. (Illus.). 32p. (J). (ps-k). pap. 6.00 (978-0-15-202443-7(3) , Voyager Bks./Libros Viajeros) Harcourt Children's Bks.

Quinlan, Susan E. Puffins. Lehnhausen, Bud, photos by. 1998. (Nature Watch Ser.). (Illus.). 48p. (J). (gr. 3-6). lib. bdg. 25.26 (978-1-57505-090-4(0) , Carolrhoda Bks.) Lerner Publishing Group.

Squire, Ann. Puffins. 2006. (True Book Ser.). (Illus.). 47p. (J). (978-0-516-25474-6(X)) Children's Pr., Ltd.

—Puffins. 2006. (True Book Ser.). (J). (978-0-516-22827-3(7) , Children's Pr.) Scholastic Library Publishing.

Zecca, Katherine. A Puffin's Year. 2007. 32p. (gr. k-3). 15.95 (***978-0-89272-742-1(X)***) Down East Bks.

PUGET SOUND (WASH.)—FICTION

Deuker, Carl. Runner. 224p. (YA). (gr. 7). 2007. pap. 7.99 (***978-0-618-73505-1(4)*** , Graphia); 2005. 16.00 (978-0-618-54298-7(1)) Houghton Mifflin Co. Trade & Reference Div.

PUGILISM

see Boxing

PULASKI, KAZIMIERZ, 1748-1779

Marsh, Carole. Casmir Pulaski. 2002. (One Thousand Readers Ser.). (Illus.). 12p. (J). (gr. k-4). 2.95 (978-0-635-01484-9(X) , 1484X) Gallopade International.

PULITZER, JOSEPH, 1847-1911

Whitelaw, Nancy. Joseph Pulitzer & the New York World. rev. exp. ed. 2004. (Makers of the Media Ser.). (Illus.). 128p. (J). lib. bdg. 21.95 (978-1-931798-36-5(2)) Reynolds, Morgan Inc.

PULLMAN, GEORGE MORTIMER, 1831-1897

Stein, R. Conrad. The Pullman Strike & the Labor Movement in American History. 2001. (In American History Ser.). (Illus.). 128p. (YA). (gr. 5-12). lib. bdg. 26.60 (978-0-7660-1300-1(6)) Enslow Pubs., Inc.

PUMAS

Aaseng, Nathan. The Cougar. 2000. (Endangered Animals & Habitats Ser.). (Illus.). 96p. (YA). (gr. 4-12). 28.70 (978-1-56006-730-6(6) , Lucent Bks.) Thomson Gale.

Barret & Allen. El Puma. 2002. (Gatos Salvajes Serie).Tr. of Wild Cats: The Cougar. (SPA.). 24p. (J). (gr. 3-5). 22.45 (978-1-4103-0012-6(9) , Blackbirch Pr., Inc.) Thomson Gale.

Big Cats. 2004. (Explorasaws Ser.). (Illus.). 48p. (J). pap. (978-1-84229-758-2(9)) Top That! Publishing PLC.

Bradley, James V. The Mountain Lion. 2006. (Nature Walk Ser.). (Illus.). 64p. (J). 28.00 (978-0-7910-9119-7(8) , Chelsea Hse.) Facts On File, Inc.

Cooper, Jason. Cougars. 2002. (Illus.). 24p. (J). lib. bdg. 20.64 (978-1-58952-402-6(0)) Rourke Publishing, LLC.

Corrigan, Patricia. Cougars. 2004. (Our Wild World Ser.). (Illus.). 48p. (J). (gr. 2-5). ring bd. 10.95 (978-1-55971-807-3(2) , NorthWord Bks. for Young Readers) T&N Children's Publishing.

—Cougars. McGee, John F., illus. 2004. (Our Wild World Ser.). 48p. (J). (gr. 2-5). pap. 7.95 (978-1-55971-788-5(2) , NorthWord Bks. for Young Readers) T&N Children's Publishing.

—Cougars. 2001. (gr. 3-6). lib. bdg. 16.40 (978-0-613-55819-8(7)) Tandem Library Bks.

Corrigan, Patricia, et al. Big Cats! Exploring the Fascinating Worlds of Cougars, Leopards, Lions, & Tigers. McGee, John F., illus. 2002. (Our Wild World Ser.). 192p. (J). (gr. 2-5). 16.95 (978-1-55971-798-4(X) , NorthWord Bks. for Young Readers) T&N Children's Publishing.

Farentinos, Robert. Winter's Orphans: The Search for a Family of Mountain Lion Cubs, a True Story. Keegan, Shannon, illus. 2001. 64p. (gr. 4-7). pap. 13.95 (978-1-879373-53-2(X)) Rinehart, Roberts Pubs.

Fowler, Allan. Cougar: Lion of the Mountains. 2000. (Rookie Read-About Science Ser.). (Illus.). 32p. (J). (gr. 1-2). pap. 4.95 (978-0-516-26560-5(1) , Children's Pr.) Scholastic Library Publishing.

Gentle, Victor & Perry, Janet. Cougars. 2002. (Big Cats Ser.). (Illus.). 24p. (J). (gr. 2 up). lib. bdg. 22.00 (978-0-8368-3025-5(3)) Stevens, Gareth Inc.

George, Jean Craighead. Summer Moon. 2002. (Seasons of the Moon Ser.). (Illus.). 112p. (J). pap. 5.95 (978-0-06-440995-7(3) , Harper Trophy) HarperCollins Pubs.

—Summer Moon. 2003. (J). (gr. 3-7). 20.75 (978-0-8446-7243-4(2)) Smith, Peter Pub., Inc.

—Summer Moon. 2002. (gr. 3-6). lib. bdg. 14.10 (978-0-613-50513-0(1)) Tandem Library Bks.

Macken, JoAnn Early. Cougars. 2006. (Illus.). 24p. (J). pap. 5.95 (978-0-8368-6324-6(0)); lib. bdg. 19.33 (978-0-8368-6317-8(8)) Stevens, Gareth Inc.

—Cougars: Puma. 2006. (Illus.). 24p. (J). pap. (978-0-8368-6455-7(7)); lib. bdg. 19.33 (978-0-8368-6448-9(4)) Stevens, Gareth Inc.

Middleton, Jon. Pumas. 1999. (PowerKids Readers Ser.). 24p. (J). (gr. k-4). lib. bdg. 18.75 (978-0-8239-5211-3(8) , PowerKids Pr.) Rosen Publishing Group, Inc., The.

St. Pierre, Stephanie. Cougars. 2002. (In the Wild Ser.). (Illus.). 24p. (J). (gr. k-2). pap. 6.95 (978-1-58810-380-2(3) , 91100) Heinemann Library.

—Cougars. 2001. (gr. k-3). lib. bdg. 14.75 (978-0-613-61412-2(7)) Tandem Library Bks.

Stephanie, St Pierre. Cougars. 2001. (In the Wild Ser.). (Illus.). 24p. (J). (ps-3). lib. bdg. 21.36 (978-1-58810-107-5(X)) Heinemann Library.

Swanson, Diane. Wild Cats. 1998. (Welcome to the World of Animals Ser.). (Illus.). 32p. (J). (gr. 3 up). lib. bdg. 23.33 (978-0-8368-2217-5(X)) Stevens, Gareth Inc.

Taylor, Bonnie Highsmith. Ezra: A Mountain Lion. 2001. (Animal Adventures Ser.). (Illus.). (J). 54p. pap. 8.95 (978-0-7891-5166-7(9)); 56p. (gr. 1-4). lib. bdg. 16.95 (978-0-7807-9313-2(7)) Perfection Learning Corp.

Vogel, Elizabeth. Pumas. 2002. (PowerKids Readers Ser.). (Illus.). 24p. (J). (gr. 1). lib. bdg. 16.00 (978-0-8239-6022-4(6) , PowerKids Pr.) Rosen Publishing Group, Inc., The.

Welsbacher, Anne. Cougars. 2002. (Predators in the Wild Ser.). (Illus.). 32p. (J). (gr. 3-4). lib. bdg. 21.26 (978-0-7368-1316-7(0) , Capstone High-Interest Bks.) Capstone Pr., Inc.

—Pumas. 2000. (Wild Cats Ser.). (Illus.). 24p. (J). (gr. k-6). lib. bdg. 21.35 (978-1-57765-091-1(3) , Checkerboard Library) ABDO Publishing Co.

PUMAS—FICTION

Bledsoe, Lucy Jane. Cougar Canyon. 2001. 136p. (J). (gr. 4-6). tchr. ed. 16.95 (978-0-8234-1599-1(6)) Holiday Hse., Inc.

Haig-Brown, Roderick L. Panther. unabr. ed. 2007. 256p. pap. 14.95 (***978-1-55017-341-3(3)*** Harbour Publishing Co., Ltd. CAN. *Dist:* Graphic Arts Ctr. Publishing Co.

Hyndman, Hazel. Puma Secrets. 2006. 84p. (J). per. 9.99 (978-1-84685-037-0(1) , Exposure Publishing) Meadow Bks. GBR. *Dist:* Ingram Bk. Co.

Linklater, Eric. The Wind on the Moon. Bentley, Nicolas, illus. 2004. (New York Review Children's Collection). 376p. (J). 18.95 (978-1-59017-100-4(4) , NYR Children's Collection) New York Review of Bks., Inc., The.

Marlow, Herb. Cougar! l.t. ed. 1998. (Illus.). (J). (gr. k-8). 40p. lib. bdg. 16.95 (978-0-9666858-7-9(3)); 32p. pap. 5.95 (978-0-9666858-0-0(6) , C-1) Four Seasons Bks., Inc.

Mora, Pat. Dona Flor: Un Cuento de una Mujer Gigante con un Gran Corazon. Mora, Pat & Mlawer, Teresa, trs. Colon, Raul, illus. 2005. 32p. (J). (ps-3). lib. bdg. 15.19 (978-0-606-33665-9(6)) Tandem Library Bks.

Sargent, Dave & Sargent, Pat. Kitty Cougar, 60 vols. Huff, Jeane, illus. 2001. (Animal Pride Ser.: Vol. 30). 36p. (J). pap. 19.95 (978-1-56763-377-1(3)) Ozark Publishing.

Sargent, Pat. Cougar Holler, 8, Vol. 4. Lenoir, Jane, illus. 2004. (Barney the Bear Killer Ser.: 6). (J). lib. bdg. 25.25 (978-1-56763-969-8(0)) Ozark Publishing.

PUMPKIN

Berger, Melvin & Berger, Gilda. Calabazas: Pumpkins. 2005. (ENG & SPA., Illus.). (J). pap. (978-0-439-79178-6(2)) Scholastic, Inc.

Burckhardt, Ann L. Calabazas. 1998. (Coleccion Primeros Lectores). (SPA., Illus.). 24p. (J). (gr. k-3). lib. bdg. 18.60 (978-1-56065-786-6(3) , CAP1291, Bridgestone Bks.) Capstone Pr., Inc.

Cave, Kathryn. One Child, One Seed: A South African Counting Book. Wulfsohn, Gisele, photos by. 2003. (Illus.). 32p. (J). (ps-2). 17.95 (978-0-8050-7204-4(7) , Holt, Henry & Co. Bks. For Young Readers) Holt, Henry & Co.

Evangelista, Gloria. In Search of the Perfect Pumpkin. Shea, Shawn, illus. 2004. 32p. (J). (gr. 4-6). 17.95 (978-1-55591-994-8(4)) Fulcrum Publishing.

Farmer, Jacqueline. Calabazas. Tildes, Phyllis Limbacher, illus. 2006. (SPA.). (J). 16.95 (978-1-57091-702-8(7)); pap. 7.95 (978-1-57091-696-0(9)) Charlesbridge Publishing, Inc.

—Pumpkins! Tildes, Phyllis L., illus. 2004. 32p. (J). 16.95 (978-1-57091-557-4(1)); pap. 6.95 (978-1-57091-558-1(X)) Charlesbridge Publishing, Inc.

Fridell, Ron. Pumpkin. 2001. (gr. k-3). lib. bdg. 14.75 (978-0-613-60812-1(7)) Tandem Library Bks.

Fridell, Ron & Walsh, Patricia. Life Cycle of a Pumpkin. 2001. (Heinemann First Library). (Illus.). 32p. (J). (gr. k-2). lib. bdg. 21.36 (978-1-58810-093-1(6)) Heinemann Library.

—Pumpkin. 2002. (Life Cycle of a... Ser.). (Illus.). 32p. (J). (gr. k-2). pap. 6.95 (978-1-58810-395-6(1) , 91141) Heinemann Library.

Gibbons, Gail. The Pumpkin Book. Gibbons, Gail, illus. (Illus.). 32p. (J). (gr. k-3). 6.95 (978-0-8234-1636-3(4)); tchr. ed. 17.95 (978-0-8234-1465-9(5)) Holiday Hse., Inc.

—The Pumpkin Book. Gibbons, Gail, illus. 2002. (Illus.). 28.95 incl. audio compact disk (978-1-59112-940-0(0)); pap. 18.95 incl. audio compact disk (978-1-59112-672-0(X)); pap. 39.95 incl. audio compact disk (978-1-59112-673-7(8)) Live Oak Media.

—The Pumpkin Book. 2002. (Illus.). (J). (ps-3). 25.95 incl. audio (978-0-87499-945-7(6)); pap., tchr.'s planning gde. ed. 37.95 incl. audio (978-0-87499-946-4(4)); pap. 16.95 incl. audio (978-0-87499-944-0(8)) Live Oak Media.

Giesecke, Ernestine. Pumpkins. 2001. (Food Ser.). (Illus.). 32p. (J). (gr. k-2). lib. bdg. 21.36 (978-1-58810-151-8(7)) Heinemann Library.

Harris, Calvin. Pumpkin Harvest. 2008. (J). (***978-1-4296-0026-2(8)***) Capstone Pr., Inc.

Hutchings, Amy & Hutchings, Richard. Growing Apples & Pumpkins. 2001. (Illus.). (J). (978-0-439-22352-2(0)) Scholastic, Inc.

Levenson, George. El Circulo de las Calabazas: Historia de un Huerto. Rioja, Alberto Jiminez, tr. Thaler, Shmuel, photos by. 2004. Tr. of Pumpkin Circle. (SPA., Illus.). 40p. (J). (ps-2). 7.95 (978-1-58246-083-3(3)); 15.95 (978-1-58246-086-4(8)) Ten Speed Pr. (Tricycle Pr.).

McNeil, Niki, et al. HOCPP 1110 Five Little Pumpkins. 2006. spiral bd. 14.00 (***978-1-60308-110-8(0)***) In the Hands of a Child.

Pfeffer, Wendy. From Seed to Pumpkin. Hale, James Graham, illus. 2004. (Let's-Read-and-Find-Out Science Ser.). 40p. (J). (ps-1). 15.99 (978-0-06-028038-3(7)); pap. 5.99 (978-0-06-445190-1(9)); lib. bdg. 16.89 (978-0-06-028039-0(5)) HarperCollins Pubs.

Pumpkins in Fall. 2002. (Illus.). (J). pap. 3.74 (978-0-7398-5834-9(3)) Steck-Vaughn.

Robbins, Ken. Pumpkins. Robbins, Ken, illus. 2006. (Illus.). 32p. (J). (ps-3). 17.95 (978-1-59643-184-3(9)) Roaring Brook Pr.

—Pumpkins. 2007. (Illus.). 32p. (J). pap. 6.99 (***978-0-312-37141-8(1)***) Square Fish.

Stone, Lynn M. Pumpkins. 2001. (Harvest to Home Ser.). (Illus.). 24p. (J). (gr. 1-4). lib. bdg. 20.64 (978-1-58952-130-8(7)) Rourke Publishing, LLC.

Watts, Barrie. Pumpkin. 2002. (Illus.). 32p. (J). (ps-ps). lib. bdg. 24.25 (978-1-58340-199-6(7)) Smart Apple Media.

PUMPKIN—FICTION

The Adventures of the Original Pumpkin Patch Pals. l.t. ed. 2005. (Illus.). 32p. (J). 15.00 (978-0-9770960-1-5(7)) 3 Pals Media, LLC.

Agran, Rick. Pumpkin Shivaree. Anderson, Sara, illus. 2003. 40p. (J). (gr. k-2). 15.95 (978-1-59354-006-7(X)) Handprint Bks.

Alexander, Heather. Allie Gator's Halloween Hayride. 2006. (Illus.). 24p. (J). pap. 3.95 (978-0-7624-2658-4(6)) Running Pr. Bk. Pubs.

Arnold, Marsha D. The Pumpkin Runner. 1998. (Illus.). 32p. (J). (ps-3). 16.99 (978-0-8037-2124-1(2) , Dial) Penguin Group (USA) Inc.

Bang, Betsy. Old Woman & the Red Pumpkin: Level 4, Green, 7 vols. Merriman, Rachel, illus. 2nd ed. 1999. (Reading Together Ser.). 32p. (J). pap. (978-0-7636-0857-6(2)) Candlewick Pr.

Bauer, Joan. Squashed. 2005. 208p. (YA). (gr. 7). pap. 7.99 (978-0-14-240426-3(8) , Puffin) Penguin Group (USA) Inc.

—Squashed. 2001. (978-0-606-22520-5(X)) Tandem Library Bks.

—Squashed! 2001. 208p. (YA). 16.99 (978-0-399-23750-8(X) , Putnam Juvenile) Penguin Group (USA) Inc.

Bleck, Linda. Pepper Picks a Pumpkin. Bleck, Linda, illus. 2007. (Pepper plays, pulls, & Pops! Ser.). 18p. (J). 8.99 (***978-1-4169-1773-1(X)*** , Little Simon) Simon & Schuster Children's Publishing.

Bond, Garnett. The Purple Pumpkin. Zuby, Cindi, illus. 1999. 8p. (J). (gr. k-4). 9.95 (978-1-886225-43-5(5)) Day of Grace Publishing Services.

Boniface, William. The Five Little Pumpkins. Smath, Jerry, illus. 2002. 16p. (J). pap. 5.99 (978-0-8431-4908-1(6) , Price Stern Sloan) Penguin Group (USA) Inc.

Bonnell, Kris. Picking a Pumpkin. 2007. (J). 3.95 (***978-1-933727-51-6(9)***) Reading Reading Bks., LLC.

Bowman, Crystal. My Happy Pumpkin. 2007. (Illus.). 14p. (J). 6.99 (***978-0-310-71160-5(6)***) Zonderkidz.

Boyd, William T. The Pumpkin Fairy. Roberts, Mary Jo, illus. 2003. 32p. (J). (gr. k-1). 14.95 (978-0-9718161-0-7(7)) Wyatt Pr.

Brown, Marc. Buster & the Giant Pumpkin. 2005. (Postcards from Buster Ser.). (Illus.). 32p. (J). (gr. 1-4). 14.99 (978-0-316-15887-9(9)) Little Brown & Co.

Brown, Margaret Wise. The Fierce Yellow Pumpkin. Egielski, Richard, illus. 32p. (J). (ps-1). 2003. 15.99 (978-0-06-024479-8(8)); 2003. lib. bdg. 16.89 (978-0-06-024481-1(X)); 2006. reprint ed. pap. 6.99 (978-0-06-443534-5(2) , Harper Trophy) HarperCollins Pubs.

Burghous, Derrie, illus. Pumpkin & the Pink Bible. 2002. 26p. (J). (gr. 1-6). pap. 12.95 (978-0-9701803-2-2(2)) Xlibris Corp.

Capucilli, Alyssa Satin. Biscuit Visits the Pumpkin Patch. Schories, Pat, illus. 2004. 16p. (J). (ps-1). 4.99 (978-0-06-009466-9(4) , Harper Festival) HarperCollins Pubs.

Chetkowski, Emily. Pumpkin Smile. Peterson, Dawn, illus. 2001. 32p. (J). (gr. k-3). 16.95 (978-0-9700974-2-2(5)); (gr. 1-3). pap. 11.95 (978-0-9700974-3-9(3)) Seven Coin Pr.

Cooper, Helen. Delicious! A Pumpkin Soup Story. 2007. (Illus.). 32p. (J). (ps-3). 16.00 (***978-0-374-31756-0(9)*** , Farrar, Straus & Giroux (BYR)) Farrar, Straus & Giroux.

Cuyler, Margery. The Bumpy Little Pumpkin. Hillenbrand, Will, illus. 2005. 32p. (J). pap. 15.95 (978-0-439-52835-1(6) , Scholastic Pr.) Scholastic, Inc.

Dalmatian Press Staff, ed. Pumpkin Glow. 2006. 176p. (J). 2.99 (978-1-4037-2428-1(8)) Dalmatian Pr.

Donde Esta Belo? (Where's Pipkin?) (Granja Oso de Miel Ser.). (SPA.). (J). bds. 4.99 (978-0-7899-0611-3(2) , 495053) Editorial Unilit.

Duplantis, Marion. The Little Pumpkin. Adams, Charles, illus. 2002. 40p. (J). 24.95 (978-0-9725452-0-4(4)) Mar-Bear Publishing.

Evans, Alwyn & Davis, Anne. Pumpkin in Hollow Countdown. Capelle, Joanna, illus. 16p. (J). pap. 7.49 (978-1-86368-045-5(4)) Fremantle Pr. AUS. *Dist:* International Specialized Bk. Services.

Fall Is Pumpkin Time! 2004. (YA). (978-0-8374-0011-2(2)) Weekly Reader Corp.

Fiorello, Frank. Harvest Song. Fiorello, Frank, illus. 2000. (Illus.). 32p. (J). (ps-6). pap. 7.95 (978-0-9646300-8-6(7)); lib. bdg. 12.95 (978-0-9646300-9-3(5)) Pumpkin Patch Publishing.

—Pumpkinville. Fiorello, Frank, illus. 2001. 40p. (J). pap. 7.95 (978-0-9708400-0-4(4)); lib. bdg. 12.95 (978-0-9708400-1-1(2)) Pumpkin Patch Publishing.

—When I Read. Fiorello, Frank, illus. 2000. (Illus.). 32p. (J). (ps-6). lib. bdg. 12.95 (978-0-9646300-7-9(9)); pap. 7.95 (978-0-9646300-6-2(0)) Pumpkin Patch Publishing.

Gaines, Isabel. Pooh's Halloween Pumpkin: Disney Winnie the Pooh. 2003. (ps-2). lib. bdg. 11.80 (978-0-613-73693-0(1)) Tandem Library Bks.

—Pooh's Pumpkin. 1998. (Winnie the Pooh First Readers Ser.: No. 6). (Illus.). 32p. (J). (ps-3). pap. 3.99 (978-0-7868-4256-8(3)) Disney Pr.

Geisler, Ruth. Shine, Smiling Pumpkin. 2004. (J). 0.99 (978-0-9747923-0-9(6)) C T A, Inc.

Ghigna, Charles. Oh My, Pumpkin Pie! Spengler, Kenneth, illus. 2005. (Step into Reading Ser.). 32p. (J). (ps-2). pap. 3.99 (978-0-375-82945-1(8)); lib. bdg. 11.99 (978-0-375-92945-8(2)) Random Hse. Children's Bks. (Random Hse. Bks. for Young Readers).

—Oh My, Pumpkin Pie! Spengler, Ken, illus. 2005. (J). (ps-2). lib. bdg. 11.19 (978-0-606-33714-4(8)) Tandem Library Bks.

Gilbert, Jeff. Trick or Shriek. 2006. 72p. pap. 5.97 (978-0-9646781-1-8(X)) Hairball Pr.

Gruber, Michael. The Legend of the Brog. Gruber, Michael & Graves, Linda, illus. 2005. (J). per. 9.95 (978-0-9770413-0-5(1)) Gruber Enterprises.

Hall, Zoe. It's Pumpkin Time! Halpern, Shari, illus. 2002. (J). 13.83 (978-0-7587-2878-4(6)) Book Wholesalers, Inc.

—It's Pumpkin Time! Halpern, Sheri, illus. 2002. (SPA.). 40p. (J). (gr. k-1). pap. 5.99 (978-0-439-18731-2(1) , SO30069, Scholastic en Espanol) Scholastic, Inc.

—It's Pumpkin Time! 1999. (ps-2). lib. bdg. 14.15 (978-0-613-22878-7(2)) Tandem Library Bks.

Hansen, T. Cory. The Last Little Pumpkin. Foldvary-Anderson, Carol, illus. l.t. ed. 2002. 38p. (J). cd-rom 11.95 (978-0-9706612-8-9(2)) JetKor.

Harcourt School Publishers Staff. The King of the Pumpkin Fair On Level. 3rd ed. 2002. (Trophies Reading Program Ser.). (Illus.). pap. 5.10 (978-0-15-323085-1(1)) Harcourt Schl. Pubs.

—The Seed Surprise: Take-Home Book. 1999. (Collections Ser.). (Illus.). (J). pap. 1.90 (978-0-15-317229-8(0)) Harcourt Schl. Pubs.

—The Seed Surprise Below Level. 3rd ed. 2002. (Trophies Reading Program Ser.). (Illus.). pap. 5.10 (978-0-15-323052-3(5)) Harcourt Schl. Pubs.

Helton, Dianne. I Like Pumpkins! Me Gustan Las Calabazas! 2006. 32p. per. 13.99 (***978-1-59886-670-4(2)***) Tate Publishing & Enterprises, L.L.C.

Herman, Gail. Spike at Halloween. 2002. (ps-2). lib. bdg. 11.80 (978-0-613-64113-5(2)) Tandem Library Bks.

Hill, Eric. Spot's Thanksgiving. Hill, Eric, illus. 2003. (Spot Ser.). (Illus.). 10p. (J). (ps-1). bds. 5.99 (978-0-399-24186-4(8) , Putnam Juvenile) Penguin Group (USA) Inc.

Hillert, Margaret. Pumpkin, Pumpkin: For the Earliest Reader. 2005. (Illus.). 32p. (J). (978-1-59577-036-3(4)); (978-1-59577-035-6(6)) Starfall Education.

Holub, Joan. The Garden That We Grew. Nakata, Hiroe, illus. 2001. 32p. (J). pap. 3.99 (978-0-14-131198-2(3) , Puffin) Penguin Group (USA) Inc.

—The Garden That We Grew. Nakata, Hiroe, illus. 2001. (J). (ps-3). lib. bdg. 11.80 (978-0-613-35612-1(8)) Tandem Library Bks.

Hubbell, William. Pumpkin Jack. 2003. (gr. k-3). lib. bdg. 15.25 (978-0-613-75725-6(4)) Tandem Library Bks.

—Pumpkin Jack. Hubbell, William, illus. 2000. (Illus.). 32p. (J). (gr. k-3). pap. 6.95 (978-0-8075-6666-4(7)) Whitman, Albert & Co.

Inman, George, Jr., et al. The Bumpy Pumpkin. Lyle, Avis, illus. 2004. 18p. (J). 8.95 (978-0-9754696-0-6(6)) Bumpy Pumpkin.

Jacobson, Jennifer Richard. Andy Shane & the Pumpkin Trick. Carter, Abby, illus. 64p. (J). (gr. k-3). 2007. pap. 4.99 (***978-0-7636-3306-6(2));*** 2006. 13.99 (978-0-7636-2605-1(8)) Candlewick Pr.

Jennings, Sharon. Franklin's Pumkin. McIntyre, Sasha et al, illus. 2004. 32p. (J). lib. bdg. 15.38 (***978-1-4242-1174-6(3)***) Fitzgerald Bks.

Jennings, Sharon, et al. Franklin's Pumpkin. Southern, Shelley et al, illus. 2005. (Kids Can Read Ser.). 32p. (J). (gr. 1-2). (978-1-55337-496-1(7)); (978-1-55337-495-4(9)) Kids Can Pr., Ltd.

Jones, Brien. The Scariest Pumpkin of All. 2003. (Illus.). 63p. (J). (ps-7). per. 9.95 (978-1-59453-014-2(9) , 1670) Airleaf Publishing & Bookselling.

Katz, Karen. Where Is Baby's Pumpkin? Katz, Karen, illus. 2006. 14p. (J). 6.99 (978-1-4169-0970-5(2) , Little Simon) Simon & Schuster Children's Publishing.

Kimmel, Eric A. Pumpkinhead. Haskamp, Steve, illus. 2001. 40p. (J). (ps-3). 15.95 (978-1-890817-33-6(3)) Winslow Pr.

Klein, Abby. The Pumpkin Elf Mystery. McKinley, John, illus. 2007. (Ready, Freddy! Ser.: No. 11). 96p. (J). pap. 3.99 (***978-0-439-89591-0(X)*** , Blue Sky Pr., The) Scholastic, Inc.

Kroll, Steven. Biggest Pumpkin Ever. Bassett, Jeni, illus. 2007. 32p. (J). pap. 4.99 (***978-0-439-92946-2(6))*** Scholastic, Inc.

Kroner, David. Seasons. 2007. 72p. pap. 6.95 (***978-1-882190-54-6(8))*** Polar Bear & Co.

Lardinois, Sandra. Patchy Pumpkin Finds Himself a Home. Gress, Jonna C., ed. Borgo, Deborah C., illus. rev. ed. 22p. (J). (ps-2). reprint ed. pap. 2.99 (978-0-944943-64-9(0)) Current, Inc.

Larsen, Kirsten. Dora's Perfect Pumpkin. Miller, Victoria, illus. 2007. (Dora the Explorer Ser.). 24p. (J). pap. 3.99 (***978-1-4169-3438-7(3)*** , Simon Spotlight/Nickelodeon) Simon & Schuster Children's Publishing.

Lemire, Roger. Pumpkin & Lumpkin. 2005. 17.00 (978-0-8059-9777-4(6)) Dorrance Publishing Co., Inc.

Lenski, Lois. Now It's Fall. Kilgras, Heidi, ed. Lenski, Lois, illus. 2000. (Lois Lenski Bks.). (Illus.). 56p. (J). (ps-1). 9.95 (978-0-375-81069-5(2) , Random Hse. Bks. for Young Readers) Random Hse. Children's Bks.

Levenson, George. Pumpkin Circle: The Story of a Garden. 2004. (Illus.). 40p. (J). (gr. k-3). 15.95 (978-1-58246-004-8(3) , Tricycle Pr.) Ten Speed Pr.

—Pumpkin Circle: The Story of a Garden. Thaler, Shmuel, photos by. 2004. (Illus.). 40p. (J). (ps-2). 7.95 (978-1-58246-078-9(7) , Tricycle Pr.) Ten Speed Pr.

Lewis, Anne Margaret. Hidden Pumpkins. DeWildt, Jim, illus. 2005. 32p. (J). 17.95 (978-0-9749145-5-8(X)) Mackinac Island Pr., Inc.

McKy, Katie & Bernasconi, Pablo. Pumpkin Town! or, Nothing Is Better & Worse Than Pumpkins. McKy, Katie & Bernasconi, Pablo, illus. 2006. (Illus.). 32p. (J). (gr. k-3). 16.00 (978-0-618-60569-9(X)) Houghton Mifflin Co.

McNamara, Margaret. How Many Seeds in a Pumpkin? Karas, G. Brian, illus. 2007. 40p. (J). (ps-2). 14.99 (978-0-375-84014-2(1)); lib. bdg. 17.99 (***978-0-375-94014-9(6))*** Random Hse. Children's Bks. (Schwartz & Wade Bks.).

—The Pumpkin Patch. Gordon, Mike, illus. 2005. (Ready-to-Read Ser. Level 1). 32p. (J). lib. bdg. 15.00 (978-1-59054-932-2(5)) Fitzgerald Bks.

McNamara, Margaret & Gordon, Mike. The Pumpkin Patch. 2003. (Robin Hill School Ser.). (Illus.). 32p. (J). pap. 3.99 (978-0-689-85874-1(4) , Aladdin) Simon & Schuster Children's Publishing.

Metzger, Steve. It's Pumpkin Day! Wilhelm, Hans, illus. 2001. (Dinofours Ser.). (J). (ps-1). pap. 3.25 (978-0-439-29569-7(6)) Scholastic, Inc.

Miglis, Jenny. Return of the Pumpkin Head. Destefano, Stephen & Giles, Mike, illus. ed. 2005. (Adventures of Jimmy Neutron Ser.: 5). 24p. (J). lib. bdg. 15.00 (978-1-59054-785-4(3)) Fitzgerald Bks.

Minor, Wendell. Pumpkin Heads! 2007. 32p. (J). (ps-3). pap. 6.99 (***978-0-590-52138-3(1))*** Scholastic, Inc.

Mitchell, Carolyn. The Tale of the Pumpkin Seed Squad. 2006. (ENG.). 40p. per. 16.99 (***978-1-4259-7004-8(4))*** AuthorHouse.

Moffatt, Judith. The Pumpkin Man. Moffatt, Judith, illus. 1998. (Hello Reader! Ser.). (Illus.). 32p. (J). (gr. k-2). pap. 3.99 (978-0-590-63865-4(3)) Scholastic, Inc.

—Pumpkin Man. 2000. (Hello Reader! Ser.). (978-0-606-18885-2(1)) Tandem Library Bks.

Moulton, Mark Kimball. Miss Fiona's Stupendous Pumpkin Pies. Crouch, Karen Hillard, illus. 2004. 28p. (J). 14.95 (978-0-8249-5489-5(0)) Ideals Pubns.

—Miss Fiona's Stupendous Pumpkin Pies. Crouch, Karen Hillard, illus. 2001. 21p. (J). (gr. k-3). 18.00 (978-0-7412-0865-1(2)) Lang Graphics, Ltd.

Nagler, Michelle H. Haunted Pumpkins. 2001. (gr. k-3). lib. bdg. 11.80 (978-0-613-54532-7(X)) Tandem Library Bks.

Noonan, Julia. My Pumpkin. Lawson, Peter, illus. (J). (gr. k-1). 2006. 32p. pap. 3.95 (978-0-516-24973-5(8)); 2005. 31p. 18.50 (978-0-516-24876-9(6)) Scholastic Library Publishing. (Children's Pr.).

Pasillo, Susan. The Perfect Pumpkin. 2006. (J). lib. bdg. 20.95 (***978-1-933732-14-5(8)*** , Bear Hug Bks.) MidAmerica Publishing Co.

Peter the Pumpkin-Eater: Individual Title Six-Packs. (Action Packs Ser.). 104p. (gr. 3-5). 44.00 (978-0-7635-8401-6(0)) Rigby Education.

Petty, J. T. The Squampkin Patch: A Nasselrogt Adventure. Friend, David Michael, illus. 2006. 256p. (J). (gr. 4-9). 15.95 (978-1-4169-0274-4(0) , Simon & Schuster Children's Publishing) Simon & Schuster Children's Publishing.

Pumpkin Days, Vol. 3. 2005. (Emergent Library: Vol. 1). (YA). (ps-1). 23.94 (978-0-8215-8912-0(1)) Sadlier, William H. Inc.

A Pumpkin Grows. 2005. (Emergent/Early (Prek-2) Science Package Ser.). 12p. (YA). (ps-2). 25.20 (978-0-8215-7837-7(5)) Sadlier, William H. Inc.

The Pumpkin House, 6 Packs. (Literatura 2000 Ser.). (gr. 2-3). 33.00 (978-0-7635-0182-2(4)) Rigby Education.

Regan, Michael. Pimp My Pumpkin. 2006. (Illus.). 32p. pap. 6.95 (978-0-7624-2824-3(4)) Running Pr. Bk. Pubs.

Rockwell, Anne F. Apples & Pumpkins. Rockwell, Lizzy, illus. 2nd ed. 2005. (Stories to Go! Ser.). 24p. (J). 4.99 (978-1-4169-0831-9(5) , Aladdin) Simon & Schuster Children's Publishing.

—Pumpkin Day, Pumpkin Night. Halsey, Megan, illus. 2001. (J). (ps-2). lib. bdg. 15.25 (978-0-613-75433-0(6)) Tandem Library Bks.

—Pumpkin Day, Pumpkin Night. Halsey, Megan, illus. 2001. 32p. (J). (ps-3). pap. 6.95 (978-0-8027-7614-3(0)) Walker & Co.

Rockwell, Anne F. & Rockwell, Lizzy, illus. Apples & Pumpkins. 2nd ed. 2005. (Stories to Go! Ser.). (J). (***978-1-4156-2884-3(X)*** , Aladdin) Simon & Schuster Children's Publishing.

Ross, Katharine. The Little Pumpkin Book. Bratun, Katy, illus. 1999. (Jellybean Bks.). 24p. (J). (ps-k). lib. bdg. 7.99 (978-0-375-90106-5(X) , Random Hse. Bks. for Young Readers) Random Hse. Children's Bks.

Running Press Staff & Deere, John. The Biggest Pumpkin Ever. 2007. (Illus.). 10p. bds. 7.95 (***978-0-7624-3138-0(5)*** , Running Pr. Kids) Running Pr. Bk. Pubs.

Schembri, Pamela & Catalanotto, Peter. No More Pumpkins. 2007. (Second Grade Friends Ser.). (Illus.). 64p. (J). (gr. 2-5). 15.95 (978-0-8050-7839-8(8)) Holt, Henry & Co.

School Zone Publishing Company Staff. Pumpkins! A Book of Opposites. 2000. (Illus.). 16p. (J). bds. 4.99 (978-0-88743-607-9(2) , 06608) School Zone Publishing Co.

Serfozo, Mary. Plumply, Dumply Pumpkin. Petrone, Valeria, illus. 2006. (Classic Board Bks.). 28p. (J). 6.99 (978-0-689-86277-9(6) , Little Simon) Simon & Schuster Children's Publishing.

Shinju, Mariko. A Pumpkin Story. Shinju, Mariko, illus. 1998. (Illus.). 32p. (J). (ps-4). 16.95 (978-1-880851-36-4(9)) Greene Bark Pr., Inc.

Simon, Charnan. Pumpkin Fever. Bryan-Hunt, Jan, illus. 2007. (Rookie Reader Ser.). 30p. (J). pap. (***978-0-531-12488-8(6))*** Children's Pr., Ltd.

Simon, Charnan. Pumpkin Forever. Bryan-Hunt, Jan, illus. 2006. (Rookie Reader Skill Set Ser.). 32p. (J). (gr. k-2). 19.50 (978-0-531-12086-6(4) , Children's Pr.) Scholastic Library Publishing.

Skarmeas, Nancy J. My Jack-o'-Lantern. Levy, Pamela R., illus. 2001. 26p. (J). (ps-k). 6.95 (978-0-8249-4117-8(9)) Ideals Pubns.

Sloat, Teri. Patty's Pumpkin Patch. 1999. (Illus.). 32p. (J). (ps-3). 15.99 (978-0-399-23010-3(6) , Putnam Juvenile) Penguin Group (USA) Inc.

Smath, Jerry. I Like Pumpkins. Smath, Jerry, illus. 2003. (Illus.). 32p. (J). (gr. k-3). pap. 3.50 (978-0-439-52110-9(6) , Cartwheel Bks.) Scholastic, Inc.

—I Like Pumpkins. 2003. (gr. k-3). lib. bdg. 11.25 (978-0-613-72237-7(X)) Tandem Library Bks.

Spurr, Elizabeth. Pumpkin Hill. Martin, Whitney, illus. 32p. (J). 16.95 (978-0-8234-1869-5(3)) Holiday Hse., Inc.

Taylor, Sybil. The Pumpkin Patch: A Traditional Buddhist Tale. Atkin, June, illus. 2004. 32p. 15.95 (978-0-89346-935-1(1)) Heian International Publishing, Inc.

Thompson, Frank. Tim Burton's the Nightmare Before Christmas. 2005. (Illus.). 176p. (J). (gr. 5-17). pap. 8.99 (978-0-7868-3849-3(3)) Disney Pr.

Tim's Pumpkin: Individual Title Six-Packs. (gr. k-1). 23.00 (978-0-7635-9040-6(1)) Rigby Education.

Titherington, Jeanne. Citrouille, Ma Citrouille. l.t. ed. Tr. of Citrouille, Ma Citrouille. (FRE.). (J). bds. 29.99 (978-0-590-73546-9(2)) Scholastic, Inc.

—Pumpkin Pumpkin. l.t. ed. 1999. (J). pap. 19.95 (978-0-590-72452-4(5)) Scholastic, Inc.

Troiano, Joe. The Legend of Spookley the Square Pumpkin. Banta, Susan, illus. 2003. 24p. (J). 6.95 (978-0-7607-4555-7(2)) Sterling Publishing Co., Inc.

—Little Scribbles: Halloween Fun with Spookley the Square Pumpkin. Banta, Susan, illus. 2006. (Little Scribbles Ser.). 12p. (J). bds. 5.95 (978-1-4027-4017-6(4)) Sterling Publishing Co., Inc.

—Storytime Stickers: It's Halloween with Spookley the Square Pumpkin. Banta, Susan, illus. 2006. (Storytime Stickers Ser.). 16p. (J). pap. 4.95 (978-1-4027-4018-3(2)) Sterling Publishing Co., Inc.

Tryon, Leslie. Albert's Halloween: The Case of the Stolen Pumpkins. 2001. 13.79 (978-0-606-22101-6(8)) Tandem Library Bks.

Tucker, Jennifer Herrick. Little Pumpkin. l.t. ed. 2001. 65p. (J). per. 9.95 (978-0-9715198-0-0(3)) PJN & Assocs.

Tudor, Tasha. Pumpkin Moonshine. 1998. (Illus.). 46p. (J). 6.95 (978-0-446-91246-4(8)) Grand Central Publishing.

—Pumpkin Moonshine. Tudor, Tasha, illus. 2000. (Illus.). 40p. (J). (ps-3). 13.95 (978-0-689-82846-1(2)) Simon & Schuster Children's Publishing.

Ure, Jean. Pumpkin Pie. l.t. ed. 2005. (J). pap. (978-0-7540-7886-9(8) , CLP 462) BBC Audio.

Van Rynbach, Iris. Five Little Pumpkins. 2003. (Illus.). 24p. (J). (ps up). pap. 8.95 (978-1-59078-087-9(6)) Boyds Mills Pr.

—Five Little Pumpkins. 2003. (ps-2). lib. bdg. 17.60 (978-0-613-79889-1(9)) Tandem Library Bks.

Wallace, Nancy Elizabeth. Pumpkin Day! 2002. (Illus.). 32p. (J). (ps-2). 16.95 (978-0-7614-5128-0(5)) Cavendish, Marshall Corp.

—Pumpkin Day. Wallace, Nancy Elizabeth, illus. 2006. (Illus.). 32p. 5.99 (978-0-7614-5327-7(X)) Cavendish, Marshall Corp.

Wallace, Nancy Elizabeth, illus. Pumpkins, Pumpkins, Pumpkins. 2002. (J). (978-1-58837-029-7(1)) Winslow Hse. Bks.

Waters, George T. The Perfect Little Pumpkin. Duquet, Guy J., illus. l.t. ed. 2006. 34p. (J). per. 14.95 (***978-1-59879-286-7(5))*** Lifevest Publishing, Inc.

Webb, M. St. John. Knock Three Times. 2003. (Children's Classics). (ENG.). 288p. (J). (gr. 3-6). pap. (978-1-85326-132-9(7)) Wordsworth Editions, Ltd.

White, Linda. Too Many Pumpkins. Lloyd, Megan, illus. 32p. (J). (gr. k-3). tchr. ed. 17.95 (978-0-8234-1245-7(8)); reprint ed. 6.95 (978-0-8234-1320-1(9)) Holiday Hse., Inc.

Whitlock, Matt. Punk 'n Patch. Whitlock, Matt, illus. 2005. (Illus.). 32p. (ps-ps). 16.95 (978-0-9769057-0-7(1)) Little Hero.

Yaccarino, Dan, illus. Five Little Pumpkins. 1998. 16p. (J). bds. 5.99 (978-0-694-01177-3(0) , Harper Festival) HarperCollins Pubs.

Yacowitz, Caryn. Pumpkin Fiesta. Cepeda, Joe, illus. 1998. 32p. (J). (ps-1). 16.99 (978-0-06-027658-4(4)) HarperCollins Pubs.

Zagwyn, Deborah Turney. The Pumpkin Blanket. Zagwyn, Deborah Turney, illus. 2004. (Illus.). 32p. (J). (gr. k-3). 7.95 (978-1-883672-59-1(7) , Tricycle Pr.) Ten Speed Pr.

PUNCH AND JUDY

see Puppets

PUNCHED CARD SYSTEMS

see Information Storage and Retrieval Systems

PUNCTUATION

Beckwith, Carrie, et al. Editor in Chief Book C2: Grammar Disasters & Punctuation Faux Pas. 2001. (Illus.). 140p. (J). (gr. 8 up). pap. 17.99 (978-0-89455-721-7(1) , MP9706) Critical Thinking Bks. & Software.

Bodleian Library Staff, ed. Punctuation Personified, or Pointing Made Easy by Mr. Stops: A Facsimile. 2004. (Illus.). 24p. pap. 10.00 (978-1-85124-194-1(9)) Bodleian Library GBR. *Dist:* Chicago Distribution Ctr.

Breyer, Michelle. How to Punctuate. Buehler, Stephanie J., ed. 1999. (How to Ser.). 48p. (J). (gr. 5-8). pap., act. bk. ed. 7.99 (978-1-57690-488-6(1) , TCA2488) Teacher Created Materials, Inc.

Bridgman, Beth, contrib. by. Apostrophe, Colon, Hyphen. rev. ed. 1998. (Horizons Ser.). (Illus.). 24p. (J). (gr. 4-6). pap. 5.95 (978-1-58086-059-8(1)) EDC Publishing.

—Comma. rev. ed. 1998. (Horizons Ser.). (Illus.). 24p. (J). (gr. 4-6). pap. 5.95 (978-1-58086-061-1(3)) EDC Publishing.

—Period, Question Mark, Exclamation Mark. rev. ed. 1998. (Horizons Ser.). (Illus.). 24p. (J). (gr. 4-6). pap. 5.95 (978-1-58086-058-1(3)) EDC Publishing.

—Quotation Marks, Underlining. rev. ed. 1998. (Horizons Ser.). (Illus.). 24p. (J). (gr. 4-6). pap. 5.95 (978-1-58086-060-4(5)) EDC Publishing.

Capitalization & Punctuation (Gr. 1-3) 2003. (J). (978-1-58232-050-2(0)) Bryan Hse. Pubs., Inc.

Christopher Lee Publications Staff. Webster's Punctuation & Capitalization Made Easy. 2002. (Webster's... Made Easy Flippers Ser.). (Illus.). (J). pap. 7.95 (978-1-59125-168-2(0)) Penton Overseas, Inc.

Cooper, Barbara. Meet the Puncs: A Remarkable Punctuation Family, 6 Vols. 139.98 (978-0-8368-4222-7(7)) Stevens, Gareth Inc.

Douglas, Vincent & School Specialty Publishing Staff. The Complete Book of Grammar & Punctuation. 2005. (Complete Book Ser.). (Illus.). 352p. (J). pap. 14.95 (978-0-7696-4332-8(9) , American Education Publishing) School Specialty Publishing.

Heinrichs, Ann. Punctuation. 2005. (Magic of Language Ser.). (Illus.). 32p. (J). (gr. 1-5). 27.07 (978-1-59296-432-1(X)) Child's World, Inc.

Hockett, M. A. Punctuation Puzzler Bk. 1: Run-Ons. 2003. (J). pap. 9.99 (978-0-89455-818-4(8)) Critical Thinking Bks. & Software.

Irving, Nichole. Improve Your Punctuation - Internet Linked. 2004. (Better English Ser.). 32p. (J). pap. 6.95 (978-0-7945-0879-1(0) , Usborne) EDC Publishing.

Irving, Nicole. Improve Your Punctuation. (Better English Ser.). 32p. (YA). (gr. 5 up). 2004. lib. bdg. 14.95 (978-1-58086-326-1(4)); 2001. (Illus.). pap. 6.95 (978-0-7460-4238-0(8)) EDC Publishing.

Jensen, Frode. Jensen's Punctuation: A Complete Guide to All Your Punctuation Needs. 2000. 184p. (YA). (gr. 6-12). per. 22.00 (978-1-886061-26-2(2)) Wordsmiths.

LD COACH. TEH Learns to Read: Beginning Words & Written Characters, Volume One. 2004. (Illus.). 40p. (J). 34.95 (978-0-9745938-1-4(8)) LD Coach, LLC.

LinguiSystems Staff. 100% Punctuation Lite. 2001. (Illus.). 180p. (J). (gr. 4-9). spiral bd. 34.95 (978-0-7606-0320-8(0) , 0-6320-0) LinguiSystems, Inc.

Petty, Kate. The Perfect Pop-up Punctuation Book. Maizels, Jennie, illus. 2006. 12p. (J). (gr. 2). 14.99 (978-0-525-47772-3(1) , Dutton Juvenile) Penguin Group (USA) Inc.

Practica Galactica. 2000. (SPA.). (gr. k up). cd-rom 69.00 (978-0-673-64018-5(3)); (gr. 1 up). cd-rom 69.00 (978-0-673-63346-0(2)); (gr. 2 up). cd-rom 69.00 (978-0-673-63347-7(0)); (gr. 3 up). cd-rom 69.00 (978-0-673-63348-4(9)) Addison-Wesley Educational Pubs., Inc.

Punctuate & Capitalize. 2003. (Practice Makes Perfect Ser.). (Illus.). 48p. (J). (gr. 3). pap. 4.99 (978-0-7439-3777-1(5)); (gr. 4). pap. 4.99 (978-0-7439-3778-8(3)) Teacher Created Materials, Inc.

Punctuation Made Easy. 2005. (Illus.). 128p. per. (978-0-7853-8844-9(3) , 7192100) Publications International, Ltd.

Salzmann, Mary Elizabeth. Apostrophe. l.t. ed. 2001. (Punctuation Ser.). (Illus.). 24p. (J). (ps-3). lib. bdg. 19.93 (978-1-57765-625-8(3) , SandCastle) ABDO Publishing Co.

—Comma. l.t. ed. 2001. (Punctuation Ser.). (Illus.). 24p. (J). (ps-3). lib. bdg. 19.93 (978-1-57765-620-3(2) , SandCastle) ABDO Publishing Co.

—Exclamation Point. l.t. ed. 2001. (Punctuation Ser.). (Illus.). 24p. (J). (ps-3). lib. bdg. 19.93 (978-1-57765-621-0(0) , SandCastle) ABDO Publishing Co.

—Period. l.t. ed. 2001. (Punctuation Ser.). (Illus.). 24p. (J). (ps-3). lib. bdg. 19.93 (978-1-57765-622-7(9) , SandCastle) ABDO Publishing Co.

—Punctuation, Set. l.t. ed. Incl. Apostrophe. lib. bdg. 19.93 (978-1-57765-625-8(3)); Comma. lib. bdg. 19.93 (978-1-57765-620-3(2)); Exclamation Point. lib. bdg. 19.93 (978-1-57765-621-0(0)); Period. lib. bdg. 19.93 (978-1-57765-622-7(9)); Question Mark. lib. bdg. 19.93 (978-1-57765-623-4(7)); Quotation Marks. lib. bdg. 19.93 (978-1-57765-624-1(5)); 24p. (J). (ps-3). (Illus.). 2001. Set lib. bdg. 119.58 (978-1-57765-517-6(6) , SandCastle) ABDO Publishing Co.

—Question Mark. l.t. ed. 2001. (Punctuation Ser.). (Illus.). 24p. (J). (ps-3). lib. bdg. 19.93 (978-1-57765-623-4(7) , SandCastle) ABDO Publishing Co.

—Quotation Marks. l.t. ed. 2001. (Punctuation Ser.). (Illus.). 24p. (J). (ps-3). lib. bdg. 19.93 (978-1-57765-624-1(5) , SandCastle) ABDO Publishing Co.

Smith, J. L. How to Punctuate. Wally, Barbara M., ed. 1999. (How to Ser.). (Illus.). 48p. (J). (gr. k-3). pap., act. bk. ed. 7.99 (978-1-57690-497-8(0) , TCA2497) Teacher Created Materials, Inc.

Soper, Sandra. Punctuation Practice: Capital. (Illus.). 32p. (J). pap. 4.95 (978-0-330-32083-2(1) , Pan) Pan Macmillan GBR. *Dist:* Trafalgar Square Publishing.

Steck-Vaughn Staff. Middle School Capitalization & Punctuation. 1999. (Illus.). (J). pap. (978-0-7398-1304-1(8)) Steck-Vaughn.

Terban, Marvin. Punctuation Power: Punctuation & How to Use It. 2000. (Illus.). 96p. (J). (gr. 3-9). pap. 12.95 (978-0-590-38673-9(5) , Scholastic Reference) Scholastic, Inc.

—Punctuation Power: Punctuation & How to Use It. 2000. (Illus.). 96p. (J). (ps-9). lib. bdg. 15.25 (978-0-613-45370-7(0)) Tandem Library Bks.

Tracing Punctuation! 2005. (Illus.). 26p. (J). (ps-3). bds. 14.99 incl. audio compact disk (978-1-59069-448-0(1) , 1A603) Studio Mouse LLC.

Truss, Lynne. Eats, Shoots & Leaves: Why, Commas Really Do Make a Difference! Timmons, Bonnie, illus. 2006. 32p. (J). (ps-3). 15.99 (978-0-399-24491-9(3) , Putnam Juvenile) Penguin Group (USA) Inc.

Truss, Lynne. The Girl's Like Spaghetti: Why, You Can't Manage Without Apostrophes! Timmons, Bonnie, illus. 2007. 32p. (J). (gr. 2-5). 16.99 (***978-0-399-24706-4(8)*** , Putnam Juvenile) Penguin Group (USA) Inc.

Turrell, Linda. The Punctuation Book Student Activities Book: Mastering Language Arts Series. Matthews, Douglas L., ed. 2003. (Illus.). stu. ed., wbk. ed. (978-1-931680-75-2(2) , Expert Systems for Teachers) Teaching Point, Inc.

—Punctuation Plus Student Activities Book: Mastering Language Arts Series. Matthews, Douglas L., ed. 2003. (Illus.). stu. ed., wbk. ed. (978-1-931680-77-6(9) , Expert Systems for Teachers) Teaching Point, Inc.

Using Punctuation (Gr. 3+) 2003. (J). (978-1-58232-129-5(9)) Bryan Hse. Pubs., Inc.

Vandyck, William & Burt, Angela V. Punctuation Repair Kit. 2005. (Illus.). (YA). pap. 9.99 (978-0-340-89334-0(6) , Hodder & Stoughton) Hodder General Publishing Division GBR. *Dist:* Trafalgar Square Publishing.

PUPPET MAKING

Bendt, Valerie. Successful Puppet Making. Bendt, Michelle, illus. 1999. 198p. (J). per. 20.00 (978-1-885814-11-1(9)) Bendt Family Ministries.

Bryant, Jill. Making Shadow Puppets. 2002. (gr. 3-6). lib. bdg. 14.10 (978-0-613-87154-9(5)) Tandem Library Bks.

Bryant, Jill & Heard, Catherine. Making Shadow Puppets. Watson, Laura, illus. 2004. (Kids Can Do It Ser.). 40p. (J). (gr. 4-6). (978-1-55337-029-1(5)); (978-1-55337-028-4(7)) Kids Can Pr., Ltd.

Burkholder, Kelly. Puppets. 2000. (Artistic Adventures Ser.). (Illus.). 24p. (J). (gr. 2-6). lib. bdg. 23.93 (978-1-57103-355-0(6)) Rourke Publishing, LLC.

Cummings, Richard. 101 Hand Puppets: A Beginner's Guide to Puppeteering. Cummings, Richard, illus. 2002. (Illus.). 160p. pap. 7.95 (978-0-486-42315-9(8)) Dover Pubns., Inc.

Doney, Meryl. Puppets. 2004. (Crafts from Many Cultures Ser.). (Illus.). 32p. (J). (gr. 3 up). lib. bdg. 23.33 (978-0-8368-4047-6(X)) Stevens, Gareth Inc.

Douglas, Vincent & School Specialty Publishing Staff. Sculpting & Drama. 2003. (Crafty Kids Ser.). (Illus.). 48p. (J). (gr. k-3). 12.95 (978-1-57768-517-3(2) , Waterbird Bks.) School Specialty Publishing.

—Sculpting & Drama. Crafty Kids, ed. 2003. (Crafty Kids Ser.). (Illus.). 48p. (J). (gr. k-3). pap. 6.95 (978-0-7696-3150-9(9) , Waterbird Bks.) School Specialty Publishing.

Haines, Ken & Harvey, Gill. Puppets. Gower, Teri, illus. 1998. (How to Make Ser.). 32p. (J). (gr. 3-7). pap. 7.95 (978-0-7460-2723-3(0)); lthr. 15.95 (978-1-58086-001-7(X)) EDC Publishing.

Hartigan, Karen. Finger Puppet Mania: 64 Pages Includes Patterns to Create 19 Unique Finger Puppets. 1999. (Illus.). 64p. (ps-2). 9.99 (978-0-570-05373-6(0)) Concordia Publishing Hse.

Hodge, Susie. Puppets. 2006. (Illus.). 32p. (J). (978-1-58340-954-1(8)) Smart Apple Media.

Kennedy, John. Puppet Mania! 2004. (Illus.). 80p. pap. 14.99 (978-1-58180-372-3(9) , North Light Bks.) F & W Pubns., Inc.

Lade, Roger. How to Be a Puppeteer. 2006. (Most Excellent Book Of- Ser.). (Illus.). 32p. (978-1-59604-125-7(0)) Stargazer Bks.

Leigh, Autumn. Making History: A Horse Sock Puppet. 2006. (Tony Stead Nonfiction Independent Reading Collection). (J). pap. (978-1-4042-5588-3(5)) Rosen Publishing Group, Inc., The.

Lohnes, Marilyn. Finger Folk. 1999. (Illus.). 102p. (J). (ps-k). pap. 16.95 (978-1-57950-026-9(9) , Upstart Bks.) Highsmith Inc.

Puppets for a Play: Individual Title Six-Packs. (ps-2). 23.00 (978-0-7635-9000-0(2)) Rigby Education.

Regan, Lisa. Fun Kits Make Your Own Finger Puppets. 2005. (Fun Kits Ser.). (Illus.). 48p. (J). (ps-ps). (978-1-84510-312-5(2)) Top That! Publishing PLC.

Sadler, Wendy. Puppets. 2005. (Heinemann First Library). (J). (gr. k-2). (Illus.). 32p. lib. bdg. 25.36 (978-1-4034-7301-1(3)); (978-1-4034-7044-7(8)); pap. (978-1-4034-7045-4(6)); (Illus.). 32p. pap. (978-1-4034-7302-8(1)) Heinemann Library.

Smith, Thomasina. Finger Puppets. 2003. (Fun Factory Ser.). (Illus.). 64p. (gr. k-2). pap. 9.99 (978-1-84215-828-9(7) , Southwater) Anness Publishing GBR. *Dist:* National Bk. Network.

Tandy, Rachel, ed. The Foam Book. 2005. (Chicken Socks). (Illus.). 24p. (J). 9.95 (978-1-59174-350-7(8)) Klutz.

Toler, Violet M. Churchmouse Tales: Puppet Book, 10 vols. Koefler, Leatha, illus. rev. ed. 2004. Orig. Title: Charlie Church Mouse. (J). (ps-6). pap. 10.95 (978-0-9749749-0-3(0)) Wayside Pubns.

—Churchmouse Tales: Puppet Plays, 10 vols., Vol. 2. Koefler, Leatha, illus. 2nd rev. ed. 2004. Orig. Title: "Puppet Plays, Adventures of Charlie & His Friends". (J). (ps-6). pap. 10.95 (978-0-9749749-1-0(9)) Wayside Pubns.

Wolf, Gita & Ravishankar, Anushka. Puppets Unlimited: With Everyday Materials. 2003. (Illus.). 144p. 9.99 (978-81-86211-25-0(X)) Penguin Group (USA) Inc.

PUPPET PLAYS

Benson, Edmund F. & Benson, Susan. Little by Little Puppet Plays. 1999. (Illus.). 16p. (J). (gr. 3-4). pap. 7.49 (978-1-58614-001-4(9)) Arise Foundation.

Bible Application Skits Kids Can Do: Quick & Easy Scripts for Ages 8-12. 2000. (Illus.). 64p. (J). (gr. 3-7). 8.99 (978-0-7847-1075-3(9) , 03396) Standard Publishing.

Butterfield, Moira. Goldilocks & the Three Bears. 1998. (Puppet Play Ser.). 24p. (J). lib. bdg. (978-1-57572-720-2(X)) Heinemann Library.

—The Three Little Pigs. 1998. (Puppet Play Ser.). 24p. (J). lib. bdg. (978-1-57572-719-6(6)) Heinemann Library.

—The Tortoise & the Hare. 1998. (Puppet Play Ser.). 24p. (J). lib. bdg. (978-1-57572-721-9(8)) Heinemann Library.

—The Ugly Duckling. 1998. (Puppet Play Ser.). 24p. (J). lib. bdg. (978-1-57572-722-6(6)) Heinemann Library.

Goldsack, Gaby. Little Camel & Joseph: A Finger Puppet Play & Read Story. 2003. (Snuffleheads Ser.). (Illus.). 14p. (J). 7.99 (978-0-8254-7267-1(9)) Kregel Pubns.

—Little Lion & Daniel: A Finger Puppet Play & Read Story. 2003. (Snuffleheads Ser.). (Illus.). 14p. (J). 7.99 (978-0-8254-7268-8(7)) Kregel Pubns.

Katz, Leon. The Greek Myths: Puppet Plays for Children from Ovid's Metamorphoses. 2004. 160p. pap. 12.95 (978-1-55783-502-4(0) , 1557835020, Applause Theatre & Cinema) Leonard, Hal Corp.

Landes, William-Alan, ed. Punch & Judy. Cruikshank, George, illus. 2003. (Classic Plays Ser.). 24p. (YA). (gr. 4-12). pap. 7.50 (978-0-88734-290-5(6)) Players Pr., Inc.

Lattion, Emmanuelle. Goldilocks & the Three Bears. 1998. (Little Puppet Theaters Ser.). (Illus.). 16p. (ps-3). bds. 19.95 (978-1-57178-076-8(9)) Council Oak Bks.

The Laughing Place: Individual Title Six-Packs. (Story Steps Ser.). (gr. k-2). 32.00 (978-0-7635-9836-5(4)) Rigby Education.

Liebenow, Todd. Sensational Shadows. Washburn, Sue, ed. 2003. 110p. (YA). lib. bdg. 22.00 (978-1-58302-251-1(1)) One Way St., Inc.

Liebenow, Todd, et al. Plug into the Power. Guibord, Charity, illus. 2003. 28p. (YA). spiral bd. 18.00 (978-1-58302-231-3(7)) One Way St., Inc.

Roberts, Lynda S. Mitt Magic: Finger Plays for Finger Puppets. Morris, James, illus. 2004. 89p. (Orig.). (ps-1). pap. 14.95 (978-0-87659-111-6(X) , 10004) Gryphon Hse., Inc.

Rugg, Sharon. Puppet Plays for Grieving Children. Randall, Rebecca, illus. 2000. 74p. (J). (gr. k-6). spiral bd. 25.00 (978-0-9652410-4-5(1)) Rising Sun Ctr. for Loss & Renewal.

Traditional Fairy Tale. The Princess & the Pea. Stevenson, Peter, illus. 2001. (Finger Puppet Theater Bks.). 16p. (J). bds. 14.95 (978-0-439-28889-7(4) , Cartwheel Bks.) Scholastic, Inc.

Ziegler, Sonja, et al. Bible Application Puppet Skits Kids Can Do. Hayes, Theresa, ed. 2000. (Illus.). 64p. (J). (gr. 3-7). pap. 8.99 (978-0-7847-1150-7(X) , 03399) Standard Publishing.

—Bible Story Puppet Skits Kids Can Do. Hayes, Theresa, ed. 2000. (Illus.). 64p. (J). (gr. 3-7). pap. 8.99 (978-0-7847-1153-8(4) , 03398) Standard Publishing.

PUPPET SHOWS

see Puppet Theater

PUPPET THEATER

see also Puppet Plays; Puppets; Shadow Shows

Butterfield, Moira. Goldilocks & the Three Bears. 1998. (Puppet Play Ser.). 24p. (J). lib. bdg. (978-1-57572-720-2(X)) Heinemann Library.

—The Tortoise & the Hare. 1998. (Puppet Play Ser.). 24p. (J). lib. bdg. (978-1-57572-721-9(8)) Heinemann Library.

—The Ugly Duckling. 1998. (Puppet Play Ser.). 24p. (J). lib. bdg. (978-1-57572-722-6(6)) Heinemann Library.

Canizares, Susan & Berger, Samantha. Meet Jim Henson. 1999. (Social Studies Emergent Readers). (J). 2.50 (978-0-439-04575-9(4)) Scholastic, Inc.

—Meet Jim Henson. 1999. (ps-2). lib. bdg. 10.10 (978-0-613-21981-5(3)) Tandem Library Bks.

Carreiro, Carolyn. Make Your Own Puppets & Puppet Theaters. Jourdenais-Martin, Norma Jean, illus. 2005. (Quick Starts for Kids! Ser.). 64p. (YA). (gr. 8-7). pap. 10.95 (978-0-8249-6770-3(4) , 1249275); 10.95 (978-0-8249-6776-5(3) , 1249275) Ideals Pubns. (Williamson Bks.).

Durrett, Deanne. Jim Henson. 2002. (Inventors & Creators Ser.). (Illus.). 48p. (J). (gr. 3-5). 23.70 (978-0-7377-0996-4(0) , LML00902-178605, Kidhaven) Thomson Gale.

Gourse, Leslie. Jim Henson: Young Puppeteer. 2000. (Childhood of Famous Americans Ser.). (Illus.). (J). (978-0-606-17925-6(9)) Tandem Library Bks.

Harcourt School Publishers Staff. The Puppet Show: A Reader. 1999. (Collections Ser.). (Illus.). (J). pap. 2.10 (978-0-15-313448-7(8)) Harcourt Schl. Pubs.

Lade, Roger. How to Be a Puppeteer. 2006. (Most Excellent Book Of- Ser.). (Illus.). 32p. (978-1-59604-125-7(0)) Stargazer Bks.

Roederer, Charlotte. Little Red Riding Hood. 1998. (Little Puppet Theaters Ser.). (Illus.). 444p. (ps-3). bds. 19.95 (978-1-57178-075-1(0)) Council Oak Bks.

Schultz, Terry L. & Sorenson, Linda M. The Organic Puppet Theatre. 6th ed. 2004. (Illus.). 92p. (J). 18.95 (978-0-9749936-0-7(3)) Homelight Pr.

PUPPETRY

see Puppet Making; Puppet Theater

PUPPETS

Adams, Elizabeth. Me & My Shadows: Shadow Puppet Fun for Kids of All Ages. l.t. ed. 2002. (J). spiral bd. 16.96 (978-1-888725-78-0(8) , 1-888725-78-8, MacroPrint-Books) Science & Humanities Pr.

Adams, Elizabeth & Banis, Bud. Me & My Shadows: Shadow Puppet Fun for Kids of All Ages. 2000. (Illus.). 73p. (J). per. 12.95 (978-1-888725-44-5(3) , Beach-House Bks.) Science & Humanities Pr.

Atkinson, Ruth & Atkinson, Brett. Stick Puppet Templates. Atkinson, Ruth & Atkinson, Brett, illus. (J). (gr. k-2). pap. (978-1-875739-72-1(6)) Wizard Bks.

Boase, Petra & Beak, Nick Huckleberry. Crafty Puppets. Freeman, John, photos by. 1999. (Crafty Kids Ser.). (Illus.). 64p. (J). (gr. 3 up). lib. bdg. 26.00 (978-0-8368-2480-3(6)) Stevens, Gareth Inc.

Boyd, Bernadine. Puppets & Puppets. 1998. (Illus.). 72p. (J). pap. 14.00 (978-0-8059-4394-8(3)) Dorrance Publishing Co., Inc.

Briggs, Diane. 101 Fingerplays, Stories & Songs to Use with Finger Puppets. 1999. 144p. 25.00 (978-0-8389-0749-8(0) , 074902270) American Library Assn.

Buckton, Chris & Hammond, Andrew. I-read Year 2 Anthology: Puppet Parade: Volume 0, Part 0. 2007. (I-read Ser.). (Illus.). 40p. pap. (***978-0-521-70484-7(7)***) Cambridge Univ. Pr.

Burkholder, Kelly. Puppets. 2000. (Artistic Adventures Ser.). (Illus.). 24p. (J). (gr. 2-6). lib. bdg. 23.93 (978-1-57103-355-0(6)) Rourke Publishing, LLC.

Canizares, Susan & Berger, Samantha. Puppets. 1999. (ps-2). lib. bdg. 10.10 (978-0-613-22227-3(X)) Tandem Library Bks.

Carreiro, Carolyn. Make Your Own Puppets & Puppet Theaters. Jourdenais-Martin, Norma Jean, illus. 2005. (Quick Starts for Kids! Ser.). 64p. (YA). (gr. 8-7). pap. 10.95 (978-0-8249-6770-3(4) , 1249275, Williamson Bks.) Ideals Pubns.

Cummings, Richard. 101 Hand Puppets: A Beginner's Guide to Puppeteering. Cummings, Richard, illus. 2002. (Illus.). 160p. pap. 7.95 (978-0-486-42315-9(8)) Dover Pubns., Inc.

Doney, Meryl. Puppets. 2004. (Crafts from Many Cultures Ser.). (Illus.). 32p. (J). (gr. 3 up). lib. bdg. 23.33 (978-0-8368-4047-6(X)) Stevens, Gareth Inc.

Geyer, Beth & Geyer, Frank. Teaching Early Concepts with Photos of Kids: Easy Activities Using Snapshots of Students to Build Early Skills, Self-Esteem & Classroom Community. 2005. (Illus.). 48p. (J). pap. 10.99 (978-0-439-51770-6(2) , Teaching Resources) Scholastic, Inc.

Group/McGraw-Hill, Wright. Puppets: 6 Each of 1 Anthology, 6 vols. (Wildcatstm Ser.). 32p. (gr. 2-8). (978-0-322-05632-9(2)) Wright Group, The.

Haines, Ken & Harvey, Gill. Puppets. Gower, Teri, illus. 1998. (How to Make Ser.). 32p. (J). (gr. 3-7). pap. 7.95 (978-0-7460-2723-3(0)); lthr. 15.95 (978-1-58086-001-7(X)) EDC Publishing.

Hodges, Susan. Play & Learn with Puppets. Dieterichs, Shelley, illus. 1998. (Play & Learn Ser.). 48p. (J). (ps-k). pap. 3.95 (978-1-57029-231-6(0) , WPH 02310, Totline Pubns.) Schaffer, Frank Pubns.

Laughlin, Nancy M. Puppet Power. 1998. (Illus.). 128p. (gr. 1-4). pap. (978-0-673-36389-3(9)) Good Year Bks.

Lohnes, Marilyn. Finger Folk. 1999. (Illus.). 102p. (J). (ps-k). pap. 16.95 (978-1-57950-026-9(9) , Upstart Bks.) Highsmith Inc.

The Mad Puppet: Level T. Group 1, 6 vols. (Sunshinetm Ser.). 48p. 44.95 (978-0-7802-5599-9(2)) Wright Group, The.

Nuttall, Gina. Puppets Around the World. 2004. (QEB Start Writing Ser.). (Illus.). 24p. (J). lib. bdg. 15.95 (978-1-59566-017-6(8)) QEB Publishing Inc.

Philpott, V. Know How Book of Puppets. (J). 13.96 (978-0-88110-494-3(9)) EDC Publishing.

The Puppet: First Grade Guided Reading Level A. (On Our Way to English Ser.). (gr. 1 up). 27.75 (978-0-7578-7024-8(4)) Rigby Education.

Puppets, 6 Packs. (Action Packs Ser.). 104p. (gr. 3-5). 44.00 (978-0-7635-8410-8(X)) Rigby Education.

Sadler, Wendy. Puppets. 2005. (Heinemann First Library). (J). (gr. k-2). 32p. lib. bdg. 25.36 (978-1-4034-7301-1(3)); (978-1-4034-7044-7(8)); pap. (978-1-4034-7045-4(6)); (Illus.). 32p. pap. (978-1-4034-7302-8(1)) Heinemann Library.

Shadow Puppets: Individual Title Six-Packs. (Rigby Focus Ser.). 24p. (gr. 2 up). 28.00 (978-0-7578-5342-5(0)); 30.00 (978-0-7578-5572-6(5)) Rigby Education.

Smith, Thomasina. Finger Puppets. 2003. (Fun Factory Ser.). (Illus.). 64p. (gr. k-2). pap. 9.99 (978-1-84215-828-9(7) , Southwater) Anness Publishing GBR. *Dist:* National Bk. Network.

PUPPETS—FICTION

Albee, Sarah. Elmo's Ducky Day. Chartier, Normand, illus. 2005. (Board Books). 24p. (J). (gr. k-ps). bds. 4.99 (978-0-375-83108-9(8) , Random Hse. Bks. for Young Readers) Random Hse. Children's Bks.

—Time for Bed, Elmo. Angelilli, Chris, ed. Swanson, Maggie, illus. 2000. (Sparkle Storybook Ser.). 32p. (J). (gr. k-3). 8.99 (978-0-375-80322-2(X) , Random Hse. Bks. for Young Readers) Random Hse. Children's Bks.

Alex Toys Staff. Alex Toys Finger Puppet Storybooks: The Three Little Pigs. McDonald, Jill, illus. 5th rev. ed. 2006. 8p. (J). (ps-17). 11.99 (978-0-316-15403-1(2)) Little Brown & Co.

—Alex Toys Finger Puppet Storybooks: Goldilocks & the Three Bears. McDonald, Jill, illus. 4th rev. ed. 2006. 8p. (J). (ps-1). 11.99 (978-0-316-15395-9(8)) Little Brown & Co.

Allen, Constance. Elmo's Mother Goose. Swanson, Maggie, illus. 2000. (Big Bird's Favorite Bird Bks.). 12p. (J). (gr. k-ps). bds. 4.99 (978-0-375-80541-7(9) , Random Hse. Bks. for Young Readers) Random Hse. Children's Bks.

Allen, Constance. Guess Who, Abby! Kwiat, Ernie, illus. 2007. (Sesame Street Ser.). 10p. (J). (ps-k). bds. 10.99 (***978-0-7944-1358-3(7)***) Reader's Digest Assn., Inc., The.

Aptekar, Devan. Brain Swap. 2006. (Teen Titans Ser.). (Illus.). 32p. (J). pap. 3.99 (978-0-439-83009-6(5)) Scholastic, Inc.

Book Company Staff. Catch That Hat! 2002. (Magical World of Teddies Ser.). 14p. (J). bds. 12.95 (978-1-74047-162-6(8)) Book Co. Publishing Pty, Ltd., The AUS. *Dist:* Penton Overseas, Inc.

Brunelle, Lynn. Elmo's Movie Star Diary. Walz, Richard, illus. Bridges, James, photos by. 1999. (J). 7.99 (978-0-375-80132-7(4) , Random Hse. Bks. for Young Readers) Random Hse. Children's Bks.

Burns, Kate. Round & Round the Garden. Petrone, Valeria, illus. 2000. 16p. (J). (ps-1). 6.95 (978-1-86233-106-8(5)) Sterling Publishing Co., Inc.

Burns, Kate & Petrone, Valerie. Round & Round the Garden: With Plush Finger Puppet, Lift-the-Flaps & Giant Fold-Out Page. 1998. (Finger Puppet Bks.). (Illus.). 16p. (J). 10.95 (978-1-86233-040-5(9)) Sterling Publishing Co., Inc.

Capalija, Ann Marie. Rose Blossom's First Christmas. LoRaso, Carlo, illus. 2005. (My Little Pony Ser.). 24p. (J). (ps-2). pap. 4.99 (978-0-06-076182-0(2) , Harper Festival) HarperCollins Pubs.

Collodi, C. The Adventures of Pinocchio. 2006. pap. (***978-1-4250-1282-3(5)***) Assistedreadingbooks.com Inc.

—The Adventures of Pinocchio. Della Chiesa, Carol, tr. 2007. (ENG.). 160p. per. (***978-1-4065-1463-6(2)***) Dodo Pr.

—Pinocchio: the Tale of a Puppet. Carsey, Alice, illus. 2007. (ENG.). 196p. per. (***978-1-4065-1462-9(4)***) Dodo Pr.

Collodi, Carlo. The Adventures of Pinocchio. Murray, M. A., tr. from ITA. Innocenti, Roberto, illus. rev. ed. 2005. (Creative Editions Ser.). 192p. (J). (gr. 4 up). 24.95 (978-1-56846-190-8(9)) Creative Co., The.

—The Adventures of Pinocchio. (Twelve-Point Ser.). 2003. (J). lib. bdg. 25.00 (978-1-58287-248-3(1)); 2004. 229p. 25.00 (978-1-58287-732-7(7)) North Bks.

—The Adventures of Pinocchio. Lucas, Ann Lawson, tr. from ITA. 2002. (Oxford World's Classics Ser.). (Illus.). 256p. 9.95 (978-0-19-280150-0(3)) Oxford Univ. Pr., Inc.

—Las Aventuras de Pinocho. (SPA., Illus.). 160p. (YA). 14.95 (978-84-7281-190-4(5) , AF1905) Auriga, Ediciones S.A. ESP. *Dist:* Continental Bk. Co., Inc.

—Las Aventuras de Pinocho. (Coleccion Cuentos Universales). (SPA.). (YA). (gr. 4 up). (978-84-261-3145-4(X) , JV30301) Juventud, Editorial ESP. *Dist:* Lectorum Pubns., Inc.

—Le Aventure di Pinocchio, Level B. (ITA.). (J). pap. 8.95 (978-0-88436-050-6(4) , 55254) EMC/Paradigm Publishing.

—Pinocchio. Fanelli, Sara & Rose, Emma, trs. from ITA. Fanelli, Sara, illus. 2003. 192p. (J). (gr. 2). 18.99 (978-0-7636-2261-9(3)) Candlewick Pr.

—Pinocchio. 2000. (ITA.). (J). pap. 15.95 (978-88-452-4182-6(3)) Fabbri - RCS Libri ITA. *Dist:* Distribooks, Inc.

—Pinocchio. Murray, M. A., tr. from ITA. 2002. (Penguin Classics Ser.). (Illus.). 192p. (gr. 12). pap. 10.00 (978-0-14-243706-3(9) , Penguin Classics) Penguin Group (USA) Inc.

—Pinocchio. Ingpen, Robert R., illus. 2005. 136p. (J). (gr. 2-7). 19.95 (978-1-933327-00-6(6)) Purple Bear Bks., Inc.

—Pinocchio. Grimly, Gris, illus. 2002. 224p. (J). 5.99 (978-0-7653-4458-8(0) , Starscape) Doherty, Tom Assocs., LLC.

—Pinocchio. Ajhar, Brian, illus. 2005. (Rabbit Ears Ser.). 40p. (J). (gr. k-5). 25.65 (978-1-59679-228-9(0)) Spotlight.

—Pinocchio. Grimly, Gris & Grimly, Gus, illus. rev. ed. 2002. 224p. (J). 15.95 (978-0-7653-0591-6(7) , Tor Bks.) Doherty, Tom Assocs., LLC.

Collodi, Carlo & Edens, Cooper. Pinocchio. 2001. (Classic Illustrated Treasury Ser.). (Illus.). 176p. (J). 19.95 (978-0-8118-2283-1(4)) Chronicle Bks. LLC.

Cooper, Susan. The Magician's Boy. Riglietti, Serena, illus. 2006. 112p. (J). (gr. 3-7). pap. 6.99 (978-1-4169-1555-3(9) , Aladdin) Simon & Schuster Children's Publishing.

Cox, Jason. Puppet. 2005. (Illus.). 51p. (YA). per. (978-1-59971-005-1(6)) Aardvark Global Publishing.

Cuno, Sabine. Abre, cierra y Aprende: Open, Close, & Learn, Spanish-Lanaguage Edition. 2007. (Illus.). 12p. (J). 14.95 (***978-970-718-489-3(2)*** , Silver Dolphin en Español) Advanced Marketing, S. de R. L. de C. V. MEX. *Dist:* Perseus Distribution.

Danko, Dan & Mason, Tom. Sidekicks, Vol. 3. 2004. (Illus.). 112p. (J). 13.95 (978-0-316-73426-4(8)) Little Brown & Co.

—Sidekicks 6: Invasion of the Evil Teachers from Planet Buttface. 2005. 128p. (J). pap. 4.99 (978-0-316-15896-1(8)) Little Brown & Co.

Dubarle-Bossy, Philippe. Flutter the Bird. Rinaldo, Luana, illus. 2005. (Playful Puppet Bks.). 10p. (J). 6.95 (978-0-7641-3045-8(5)) Barron's Educational Series, Inc.

Elmo's Christmas. 2000. (J). 9.99 (978-1-931312-29-5(X)) SoftPlay, Inc.

Ernie Gets Lost. (J). 5.58 incl. audio NewSound, LLC.

Escondidos en el Cuarto de Juegos. 2001. (Peek & Find Ser.).Tr. of Hiding in the Playroom. (SPA., Illus.). 12p. (J). (ps-3). (978-968-5308-60-1(8) , Silver Dolphin en Español) Advanced Marketing, S. de R. L. de C. V.

Finger Puppet Playset Farm. 2005. (J). (978-1-59292-069-3(1)) SoftPlay, Inc.

Finger Puppet Playset Pet Store. 2005. (J). (978-1-59292-068-6(3)) SoftPlay, Inc.

Friedman, Kinky. Curse of the Missing Puppet Head. 2003. lib. bdg. 29.95 (978-0-9702383-6-8(3) , CMPH01) Vandam Pr., Inc.

Fuchs, Menucha. The Puppet Show. 2004. (Illus.). 20p. (J). 6.95 (978-1-932443-08-0(8) , PSHH) Judaica Pr., Inc., The.

Gardner, Sally. Boolar's Big Day Out. 2003. (Tales from the Box Ser.: Vol. 2). (Illus.). 128p. (J). 14.95 (978-1-58234-833-9(2) , Bloomsbury Children) Bloomsbury Publishing.

Get Dressed with Elmo. 2000. (Illus.). 8p. (J). (ps). 19.95 (978-1-56156-883-3(X)) Kidsbooks, Inc.

Get Dressed with Elmo. (J). 2003. (978-1-59292-030-3(6)); 2000. (978-1-931312-09-7(5)); 2000. (978-1-931312-04-2(4)) SoftPlay, Inc.

Gikow, Louise. Bye-Bye, Pacifier. 1999. (Naptime Tales Bks.). 14p. (J). bds. 3.49 (978-0-307-13468-4(7) , 13468, Golden Bks.) Random Hse. Children's Bks.

Gubacz, Margorie. The Tigger Show! 2005. (***978-1-4127-3104-1(6)***) Publications International, Ltd.

Hall, Lee & Collodi, Carlo. The Adventures of Pinocchio. 2004. 96p. pap. 13.95 (978-0-413-76720-2(5)) Methuen Publishing Ltd. GBR. *Dist:* Consortium Bk. Sales & Distribution.

Harrison, Barbara Grizzuti. Theo. 1999. 176p. (J). (gr. 5-9). tchr. ed. 15.00 (978-0-89919-959-7(3) , Clarion Bks.) Houghton Mifflin Co. Trade & Reference Div.

Hillert, Margaret. Pinocchio. Hamilton, Laurie, illus. rev. ed. 2006. (Beginning to Read Ser.). 32p. (J). lib. bdg. 18.60 (978-1-59953-023-9(6)) Norwood Hse. Pr.

Ishwaran, Wobine. Spunky Sprout in India. 2006. pap. 19.50 (***978-1-4259-4237-3(7)***) AuthorHouse.

Jennings, Linda & Petrone, Valeria. This Little Piggy. 1998. (Finger Puppet Bks.). (Illus.). 16p. (J). (ps-k). 10.95 (978-1-86233-045-0(X)) Sterling Publishing Co., Inc.

Jugran, Jan. Nose Knows: Puppy Love. Kolanovic, Dubravka, illus. 2007. 10p. (J). (ps-17). 9.99 (978-1-58476-550-9(X)) Innovative Kids.

Keats, Ezra Jack. Louie. Keats, Ezra Jack, illus. 2004. (Illus.). 40p. (J). pap. 6.99 (978-0-14-240080-7(7) , Puffin) Penguin Group (USA) Inc.

—Louie. 2004. 40p. (J). (ps-3). 16.99 (978-0-670-03689-9(7) , Viking Juvenile) Penguin Group (USA) Inc.

Kim, Sun-Min & Horvath, David. The Ugly Guide to the Uglyverse. 2008. (Illus.). 64p. (J). (gr. 1). lib. bdg. 12.99 (***978-0-375-93683-8(1)*** , Random Hse. Bks. for Young Readers) Random Hse. Children's Bks.

Kleinberg, Naomi. It's Naptime, Little One. Moroney, Christopher, illus. 2007. (Sesame Beginnings Ser.). 12p. (J). (gr. k-ps). bds. 6.99 (***978-0-375-84123-1(7)*** , Random Hse. Bks. for Young Readers) Random Hse. Children's Bks.

Koeppel, Ruth. Brought to You by the Number 1. 1999. (gr. k-3). lib. bdg. 10.95 (978-0-613-82501-6(2)) Tandem Library Bks.

Kunhardt, Dorothy, ed. Pinocchio. deluxe ed. 1999. (J). 100.00 (978-1-55709-341-7(5)) Applewood Bks.

LeLeu, Lisa. Frenchy the Frog Story Starter: Puppet Show Book Story Starter. 2004. (Puppet Show Bks.). (Illus.). 14p. 1.50 (978-0-9710537-7-9(4)) LeLeu, Lisa Studios! Inc.

—Miss Moo-Moo the Cow Story Starter: Puppet Book Story Starter. 2004. (Puppet Show Bks.). (Illus.). 14p. 1.50 (978-0-9710537-1-7(5)) LeLeu, Lisa Studios! Inc.

—Scooter the Cat Gift Set: Puppet Book Gift Set with 2 Books. 2004. (Puppet Show Bks.). (Illus.). 30p. 19.95 (978-0-9710537-0-0(7)) LeLeu, Lisa Studios! Inc.

—Scooter the Cat Story Teller: Puppet Book Story Starter. 2004. (Puppet Show Bks.). (Illus.). 14p. 1.50 (978-0-9710537-6-2(6)) LeLeu, Lisa Studios! Inc.

Lincoln, Nan. Cecily's Summer. Wynne, Patricia J., illus. 2005. 40p. 16.95 (978-1-59373-047-5(0)) Bunker Hill Publishing, Inc.

Love, D. Anne. The Puppeteer's Apprentice. 192p. (J). 2003. 16.95 (978-0-689-84424-9(7) , McElderry, Margaret K.); 2004. (Illus.). reprint ed. pap. 4.99 (978-0-689-84425-6(5) , Aladdin) Simon & Schuster Children's Publishing.

Magsamen, Sandra. Butterfly Kisses. rev. ed. 2007. (Snuggle-Me Stories Ser.). 20p. (J). (ps). 7.99 (*978-0-316-06595-5(1)) Little, Brown Bks. for Young Readers.

—Love Bug. rev. ed. 2007. (Snuggle-Me Stories Ser.). 20p. (J). (ps-ps). 7.99 (*978-0-316-06596-2(X)) Little, Brown Bks. for Young Readers.

McCann, Jesse Leon. Scooby-Doo & the Fantastic Puppet Factory. 2000. (gr. k-3). lib. bdg. 11.25 (978-0-613-26852-3(0)) Tandem Library Bks.

McDonald, Megan. When the Library Lights Go Out. Tillotson, Katherine, tr. Tillotson, Katherine, illus. 2005. 40p. (J). 16.95 (978-0-689-86170-3(2) , Atheneum/Richard Jackson Bks.) Simon & Schuster Children's Publishing.

Mitchell, Robin & Steedman, Judith. Sunny. 2003. (Illus.). 40p. 15.95 (978-0-9688768-5-5(4)) Simply Read Bks. CAN. *Dist:* Perseus Distribution.

Mitchell, Robin & Steedman, Judith, illus. Snowy & Chinook. 2005. 32p. (J). 15.95 (978-0-9688768-9-3(7)) Simply Read Bks. CAN. *Dist:* Perseus Distribution.

Nickel. Pinocchio. Date not set. (J). 4.99 (978-0-7214-5404-7(6)) Nickel Pr.

Night of the Living Dummy II. 2004. 120p. (J). (gr. 4-7). lib. bdg. 12.04 (978-0-606-30596-9(3)) Tandem Library Bks.

Nostlinger, Christine. Konrad. 2000. (GER.). (J). pap. 13.95 (978-3-423-70511-0(6)) Deutscher Taschenbuch Verlag GmbH & Co KG DEU. *Dist:* Distribooks, Inc.

Pantuso, Mike & Henson, Jim. Food! 2001. (Illus.). (J). lib. bdg. (978-0-375-91391-4(2) , Random Hse. Bks. for Young Readers) Random Hse. Children's Bks.

—1,2,3 by Elmo. 2001. (Illus.). (J). lib. bdg. (978-0-375-91390-7(4) , Random Hse. Bks. for Young Readers) Random Hse. Children's Bks.

Paterson, Katherine. El Maestro de las Marionetas. (SPA., Illus.). (YA). (gr. 5-8). 9.95 (978-958-04-4382-7(3) , NR8770) Norma S.A. COL. *Dist:* Distribuidora Norma, Inc., Lectorum Pubns., Inc.

—The Master Puppeteer. 3rd ed. (J). pap. 3.95 (978-0-13-800095-0(6)) Prentice Hall (Schl. Div.).

Pilegard, Virginia Walton. The Warlord's Puppeteers. Debon, Nicolas, illus. 2003. (Warlord Ser.: 4). 32p. (J). pap. 14.95 (978-1-58980-077-9(X)) Pelican Publishing Co., Inc.

Pinocchio: The Human Body, Sea Life, The Bedroom. 1999. (FRE & ENG., Illus.). 24p. (J). (ps-5). pap., stu. ed. 7.95 (978-88-8148-243-6(6)) European Language Institute ITA. *Dist:* Distribooks, Inc., Midwest European Pubns.

Pinocho: The Human Body, Sea Life, the Bedroom. 1999. Tr. of Pinocchio. (SPA & ENG., Illus.). (J). (ps-5). pap. 7.95 (978-88-8148-253-5(3)) European Language Institute ITA. *Dist:* Distribooks, Inc., Midwest European Pubns.

Post, Jim & Post, Janet. Jungle Beat. Vasconsellos, Daniel, illus. 2007. 32p. 15.99 (*978-1-57939-352-6(7)) Andrews McMeel Publishing.

The Puppet Show. (Early Intervention Levels Ser.). 21.30 (978-0-7362-0362-3(1)) Hampton-Brown Bks.

Rainey, L. E. Sad Sam, Glad Sam. 2006. (Illus.). 32p. (J). 16.95 (978-0-9785521-0-7(5)) Shoetree Publishers, Inc.

Random House Staff. Baby Party. Barrett, John E., illus. 2006. 12p. (J). (gr. k-ps). bds. 4.99 (978-0-375-83764-7(7) , Random Hse. Bks. for Young Readers) Random Hse. Children's Bks.

—Clap Your Hands. Ewers, Joseph, illus. 2002. (Puppet Book Ser.). 10p. (J). (gr. k-ps). bds. 9.95 (978-0-375-82226-1(7) , Random Hse. Bks. for Young Readers) Random Hse. Children's Bks.

Reader's Digest Staff. Sesame Street I'm a Helper. Moroney, Christopher, illus. 2007. 10p. (J). bds. 12.99 (*978-0-7944-1295-1(5)) Reader's Digest Assn., Inc., The.

Richards, Justin. The Invisible Detective: Double Life. 2005. 160p. (J). (gr. 4). 10.99 (978-0-399-24313-4(5) , Putnam Juvenile) Penguin Group (USA) Inc.

Roberts, Diane. Puppet Pandemonium. 128p. (J). (gr. 3-7). 2007. 5.99 (*978-0-440-42096-5(2) , Yearling); 2006. 15.95 (978-0-385-73309-0(7) , Delacorte Bks. for Young Readers); 2006. lib. bdg. 17.99 (978-0-385-90328-8(6) , Delacorte Bks. for Young Readers) Random Hse. Children's Bks.

Salas, Macarena, ed. Let's Bake Cookies, Pinocchio!/vamos A Hornear Galletas, Pinocho! 2005. (Disney Bil Ser.). (SPA.). 10p. (J). bds. 3.99 (978-0-439-66366-3(0) , Scholastic en Espanol) Scholastic, Inc.

Scholastic, Inc. Staff. Hand Puppet Board Book (Un Libro de Carton Con Titeres) 2007. (Noah's Ark Ser.). 6p. (J). bds. 12.99 (*978-0-439-92274-6(7) , Scholastic en Espanol) Scholastic, Inc.

Scholastic, Inc. Staff. Liz Hand Puppet. 2003. (J). 23.99 (978-0-590-10985-7(5) , Sidekicks TM) Scholastic, Inc.

Schreiber, Elisheva. The Miniature Puppet Theater Book. Pollack, Gadi & Markovitch, Evegeny, illus. (J). 14.95 (978-1-58330-617-8(X)) Feldheim Pubs.

Shepherd, Jodi. Sesame Street When I Grow Up: Storybook & Magnetic Dress-up Dolls. Kwiat, Ernie, illus. 2007. 16p. (J). bds. 14.99 (*978-0-7944-1290-6(4)) Reader's Digest Assn., Inc., The.

Spohn, Kate. Mermaid Swim. 2002. (ps-2). lib. bdg. 14.15 (978-0-613-86240-0(6)) Tandem Library Bks.

Stewart, Josie & Salem, Lynn. The Puppet Show. Dillard, Kristine, illus. 1999. 8p. (J). (gr. k-2). pap. 3.75 (978-1-58323-004-6(1) , Seedling Pubns.) Continental Pr., Inc.

Stine, R. L. Goosebumps: Night of the Living Dummy III. 2005. (Goosebumps Ser.). 144p. (J). 4.99 (978-0-439-66989-4(8) , Scholastic Paperbacks) Scholastic, Inc.

Tattum, Stephan. Fun Pup. 2005. (J). 4.95 (978-1-59792-005-6(3)) F.A.S.T. Learning LLLC.

Trimble, Marcia. Peppy's Shadow. Pellegrini, Will, illus. 2003. 32p. (J). (ps-3). 15.95 (978-1-891577-70-3(0)) ; pap. 7.95 (978-1-891577-71-0(9)) Images Pr.

Vv. Las Cosas Del Jardin. (SPA.). 24p. 7.95 (978-84-488-1109-9(7)) Beascoa, Ediciones S.A. ESP. *Dist:* Distribooks, Inc.

—Las Cosas Del Salon. (SPA.). 24p. 7.95 (978-84-488-1108-2(9)) Beascoa, Ediciones S.A. ESP. *Dist:* Distribooks, Inc.

Weiss, Ellen. Bye-Bye, Diapers. 1998. (Muppets Ser.). 14p. (J). (ps). bds. 3.49 (978-0-307-13467-7(9) , 13467, Golden Bks.) Random Hse. Children's Bks.

Where's Elmo? A Peek-a-boo Book. 1999. (Illus.). (J). (978-1-56156-833-8(3)) Kidsbooks, Inc.

Young, Ed. Pinocchio. Young, Ed, illus. 2002. (Illus.). (J). 25.43 (978-0-7587-3421-1(2)) Book Wholesalers, Inc.

PUPPETS AND PUPPET-PLAYS

see Puppet Plays; Puppet Theater; Puppets

PURCHASING

see Shopping

PURIM

Bredeson, Carmen. Purim. 2003. (Rookie Read. . . Holidays Ser.). (Illus.). (J). 32p. 20.50 (978-0-516-25880-5(X)); 31p. (gr. 1-2). pap. 5.95 (978-0-516-27928-2(9)) Scholastic Library Publishing. (Children's Pr.).

—Purim. 2003. (gr. k-3). lib. bdg. 14.10 (978-0-613-63643-8(0)) Tandem Library Bks.

Groner, Judyth Saypol & Wikler, Madeline. Make Your Own Megillah. Kahn, Katherine Janus, illus. 1998. 32p. (J). (ps-4). pap. 4.95 (978-1-58013-013-4(5)) Kar-Ben Publishing.

Kress, Camille. Purim! Kress, Camille, illus. 2004. (Illus.). 10p. (ps-k). bds. 5.95 (978-0-8074-0654-0(6) , 102555) URJ Pr.

Kropf, Latifa Berry. It's Purim Time! Cohen, Tod, photos by. 2005. (Illus.). 24p. (J). (gr. 2-6). lib. bdg. 12.95 (978-1-58013-153-7(0)) Kar-Ben Publishing.

Pollack, Gadi, illus. & contrib. by. Purimshpiel. Pollack, Gadi, contrib. by. 19.99 (978-1-58330-596-6(3)); (ENG & FRE.). 21.95 (978-1-58330-601-7(3)); (ENG & HEB.). (978-1-58330-611-6(0)) Feldheim Pubs.

Rick, Shoshannah. Hooray! It's Purim! Channen, Don, illus. 2000. 24p. pap. 4.95 (978-965-229-230-8(3)) Gefen Publishing Hse., Ltd ISR. *Dist:* Gefen Bks.

Schram, Peninnah. The Purim Costume. Keiser, Tammy L., illus. 2004. 13.95 (978-0-8074-0874-2(3) , 101312) URJ Pr.

Simon, Norma. Happy Purim Night. Gordon, Ayala, illus. (Festival Series of Picture Storybooks). (J). (ps). vinyl bd. 4.50 (978-0-8381-0706-5(0) , 10-706) United Synagogue of America Bk. Service.

PURIM—FICTION

Adelson, Leone. The Mystery Bear: A Purim Story. Howland, Naomi, illus. 2004. 32p. (J). (gr. k-3). tchr. ed. 15.00 (978-0-618-33725-5(3) , Clarion Bks.) Houghton Mifflin Co. Trade & Reference Div.

—The Mystery Bear: A Purim Story. Howland, Naomi, tr. Howland, Naomi, illus. 2004. 32p. (J). (ps-2). 15.00 (978-0-618-33727-9(X) , Clarion Bks.) Houghton Mifflin Co. Trade & Reference Div.

Cohen, Barbara. Here Come the Purim Players! Mekibel, Shoshana, illus. 1998. (gr. k-3). 13.95 (978-0-8074-0645-8(7) , 101251) URJ Pr.

Geller, Beverly Mach. The Mitzvah Girl. Perel, Rivka-Lisa, illus. 2000. 24p. (J). (ps-3). 12.95 (978-965-229-203-2(6)) Gefen Publishing Hse., Ltd ISR. *Dist:* Gefen Bks.

Rouss, Sylvia A. Lots of Latkes. Kahn, Katherine Janus, illus. 2003. 32p. (J). (ps-3). pap. 6.95 (978-1-58013-061-5(5)) Kar-Ben Publishing.

—Sammy Spider's First Purim. Kahn, Katherine Janus, illus. 2000. 32p. (J). (ps-3). pap. 7.95 (978-1-58013-062-2(3)) Kar-Ben Publishing.

Simpson, Lesley. The Purim Surprise. Church, Peter, illus. 2004. (Purim Ser.). 32p. (J). (ps-3). pap. 6.95 (978-1-58013-090-5(9)) Kar-Ben Publishing.

Watts, Irene N. A Telling Time. Shoemaker, Kathryn E., illus. 2005. 32p. (J). (978-1-896580-39-5(4)) Tradewind Bks.

PURITANS

Allison, Amy. Roger Williams: Founder of Rhode Island. 2000. (Colonial Leaders Ser.). (Illus.). 80p. (J). (gr. 8-12). 27.50 (978-0-7910-5964-7(2) , Chelsea Hse.) Facts On File, Inc.

Aronson, Marc. John Winthrop, Oliver Cromwell, & the Land of Promise. 2004. (Illus.). 224p. (J). (gr. 5-9). tchr. ed. 20.00 (978-0-618-18177-3(6) , Clarion Bks.) Houghton Mifflin Co. Trade & Reference Div.

Burgan, Michael. John Winthrop: First Governor of Massachusetts. 2006. (Signature Lives Ser.). (Illus.). 112p. (J). (gr. 5-7). 30.60 (978-0-7565-1591-1(2)) Compass Point Bks.

—Roger Williams: Founder of Rhode Island. 2006. (Signature Lives Ser.). (Illus.). 112p. (J). (gr. 5-7). 30.60 (978-0-7565-1596-6(3)) Compass Point Bks.

Clark, Beth. Anne Hutchinson. 1999. (Colonial Leaders Ser.). (Illus.). 80p. (J). (gr. 3 up). pap. 27.50 (978-0-7910-5685-1(6) , Chelsea Hse.) Facts On File, Inc.

—Anne Hutchinson: Religious Leader. 2000. (Colonial Leaders Ser.). (Illus.). 80p. (YA). (gr. 3 up). 27.50 (978-0-7910-5342-3(3) , Chelsea Hse.) Facts On File, Inc.

—Anne Hutchinson: Religious Leader. 2000. (gr. 3-6). lib. bdg. 17.60 (978-0-613-83456-8(9)) Tandem Library Bks.

Connelly, Elizabeth Russell. John Winthrop. 2001. (gr. 5-8). lib. bdg. 17.60 (978-0-613-32729-9(2)) Tandem Library Bks.

Gaustad, Edwin S. Roger Williams: Prophet of Liberty. 2001. (Oxford Portraits Ser.). (Illus.). 144p. (YA). (gr. 9 up). 28.00 (978-0-19-513000-3(6)) Oxford Univ. Pr., Inc.

Kiely Miller, Barbara. Anne Hutchinson. 2007. (J). pap. (*978-0-8368-8324-4(1) , Weekly Reader Early Learning Library) Stevens, Gareth Inc.

Knowlton, MaryLee & Riehecky, Janet. The Plymouth Colony. 2002. (Events That Shaped America Ser.). (Illus.). 32p. (J). (gr. 3 up). lib. bdg. 24.67 (978-0-8368-3224-2(8)) Stevens, Gareth Inc.

Lutz, Norma Jean. Cotton Mather. (Colonial Leaders Ser.). (Illus.). 80p. (gr. 3 up). 2000. (J). 27.50 (978-0-7910-5343-0(1)); 1999. (YA). pap. 27.50 (978-0-7910-5686-8(4)) Facts On File, Inc. (Chelsea Hse.).

Mangal, Melina. Anne Hutchinson: Religious Reformer. 2004. (Let Freedom Ring Ser.). (Illus.). 48p. (J). 23.93 (978-0-7368-2454-5(5) , Bridgestone Bks.) Capstone Pr., Inc.

Miller, Barbara Kiely. Anne Hutchinson. 2007. (Great Americans Ser.). 24p. (J). (gr. 2-4). lib. bdg. 19.93 (*978-0-8368-8317-6(9) , Weekly Reader Early Learning Library) Stevens, Gareth Inc.

Owens, L. L. Pilgrims in America. 2007. (Events in American History Ser.). 48p. (J). (gr. 4-6). lib. bdg. 29.93 (978-1-60044-122-6(X)) Rourke Publishing, LLC.

The Puritans, Algonkians & Roger Williams (NCHS) (J). (gr. 5-8). spiral bd., tchr.'s planning gde. ed. 13.50 (978-0-382-44447-0(7)) Cobblestone Publishing Co.

The Puritans, Algonkians & Roger Williams (NCHS) Grades 5-8. (J). tchr. ed. 18.00 (978-0-382-44537-8(6)) Cobblestone Publishing Co.

Raum, Elizabeth. Anne Hutchinson. 2004. (Illus.). 32p. (J). pap. 7.50 (978-1-4034-5966-4(5)); lib. bdg. (978-1-4034-5958-9(4)) Heinemann Library.

—Roger Williams. 2004. (Illus.). 32p. (J). pap. 7.50 (978-1-4034-5969-5(X)); lib. bdg. 25.64 (978-1-4034-5961-9(4)) Heinemann Library.

Stille, Darlene R. Anne Hutchinson: Puritan Protester. 2006. (Signature Lives Ser.). (Illus.). 112p. (J). (gr. 5-7). 30.60 (978-0-7565-1577-5(7)) Compass Point Bks.

Tierney, Tom. Cavalier & Puritan Fashions. 2005. (Illus.). 48p. (J). pap. 3.95 (978-0-486-43655-5(1)) Dover Pubns., Inc.

Walsh, Kieran. Anne Hutchinson. 2005. (Discover the Life of a Colonial American Ser.). (Illus.). 24p. (gr. 2-5). 14.95 (978-1-59515-137-7(0)) Rourke Publishing, LLC.

—Roger Williams. 2005. (Discover the Life of a Colonial American Ser.). (Illus.). 24p. (gr. 2-5). 14.95 (978-1-59515-140-7(0)) Rourke Publishing, LLC.

PURITANS—FICTION

Atkins, Jeannine. Anne Hutchinson's Way. Dooling, Michael, illus. 2007. 32p. (J). (gr. 3 up). 17.00 (978-0-374-30365-5(7)) Farrar, Straus & Giroux.

Duble, Kathleen Benner & Vojnar, Kamil. The Sacrifice. 2005. 224p. (J). (gr. 4-8). 16.99 (978-0-689-87650-9(5) , McElderry, Margaret K.) Simon & Schuster Children's Publishing.

Gilson, Jamie. Stink Alley. 2002. 192p. (J). (gr. 3 up). 15.95 (978-0-688-17864-2(2)); lib. bdg. 15.89 (978-0-06-029217-1(2)) HarperCollins Pubs.

Hawthorne, Nathaniel. The Scarlet Letter. Redondo, Virgilio, illus. 2nd ed. 1998. (Illustrated Classic Book Ser.). 61p. (J). (gr. 3 up). reprint ed. pap. 4.95 (978-1-56767-265-7(5)) Educational Insights, Inc.

Kelley, Nancy J. The Whispering Rod: A Tale of Old Massachusetts. 2002. 160p. (J). lib. bdg. 17.95 (978-1-57249-248-6(1) , White Mane Kids) White Mane Publishing Co., Inc.

Literature Connections English: The Witch of Blackbird Pond. 2004. (gr. 6-12). (978-0-395-78592-8(8) , 2-70293) McDougal Littell Inc.

Noyes, Deborah. Angel & the Apostle. 2006. 304p. pap. 14.95 (978-1-932961-29-4(1)) Unbridled Bks.

Rees, Celia. Witch Child. 272p. (YA). (gr. 7 up). 2002. pap. 8.99 (978-0-7636-1829-2(2)); 2001. (Illus.). 15.99 (978-0-7636-1421-8(1)) Candlewick Pr.

—Witch Child. unabr. ed. 2004. (Young Adult Cassette Librariestm Ser.). 304p. (J). (gr. 5-9). pap. 40.00 incl. audio (978-0-8072-1198-4(2) , S YA 343 SP, Listening Library) Random Hse. Audio Publishing Group.

—Witch Child. 2002. (gr. 7-12). lib. bdg. 16.45 (978-0-613-60740-7(6)) Tandem Library Bks.

—Witch Child. l.t. ed. 2002. 284p. (J). 22.95 (978-0-7862-3896-5(8)) Thomson Gale.

Rue, Nancy N. The Accused. 1998. (Christian Heritage Ser.). (Illus.). 224p. (J). (gr. 3-7). pap. 5.99 (978-1-56179-398-3(1)) Bethany Hse. Pubs.

—Samaritan. 1998. (gr. 3-6). lib. bdg. 14.15 (978-0-613-88494-5(9)) Tandem Library Bks.

—The Secret. 1998. (Christian Heritage Ser.). 192p. (Orig.). (J). (gr. 3-7). pap. (978-1-56179-443-0(0)) Focus on the Family Publishing.

Speare, Elizabeth George. The Witch of Blackbird Pond. 2002. (Illus.). (J). 14.47 (978-0-7587-0227-2(2)) Book Wholesalers, Inc.

—The Witch of Blackbird Pond. Moser, Barry, illus. 2001. (Illustrated American Classics Ser.). 224p. (YA). (gr. 7-9). tchr. ed. 22.00 (978-0-395-91367-3(5)) Houghton Mifflin Co. Trade & Reference Div.

—The Witch of Blackbird Pond. 2004. 223p. (J). (gr. 4-7). pap., tchr.'s planning gde. ed. 38.00 incl. audio (978-0-8072-0862-5(0) , Listening Library) Random Hse. Audio Publishing Group.

Vernon, Louise A. Peter & the Pilgrims. Eitzen, Allan, illus. 2nd ed. 2002. 128p. (YA). (gr. 4-9). 7.99 (978-0-8361-9226-1(5)) Herald Pr.

PUZZLES

see also Bible Games and Puzzles; Kakuro; Sudoku

Adams, Colleen. Tangram Puzzles: Describing & Comparing Attributes of Plane Geometric Shapes. 2004. (PowerMath Ser.). (Illus.). 24p. (J). (978-0-8239-7449-8(9)); lib. bdg. 21.25 (978-0-8239-8976-8(3)) Rosen Publishing Group, Inc., The. (PowerKids Pr.).

Advantage Publishers Group & DePrisco, Dorothea. A Swim in the Ocean. 2007. (Illus.). 14p. (J). bds. 12.95 (*978-1-59223-475-2(5) , Silver Dolphin Bks.) Advantage Pubs. Group.

African American Heritage Pictures, Puzzles, & Word Games. 2004. (YA). per. 16.00 (978-0-9758586-0-8(2)) Jenkins-Simmons, Glenda.

Aigner-Clark, Julie. Baby Einstein: Puzzling Shapes, Spanish-Language Edition. Zaidi, Nadeem, illus. 2005. (Baby Einstein: Libros de Carton Ser.). (SPA.). 12p. (J). bds. 6.95 (978-970-718-303-2(9) , Silver Dolphin en Español) Advanced Marketing, S. de R. L. de C. V. MEX. *Dist:* Perseus Distribution.

Akaishi, Shinobu & Sarris, Eno, eds. My Book of Easy Mazes. 2006. (J). per. 6.95 (978-1-933241-24-1(1)) Kumon Publishing North America, Inc.

—My Book of Mazes: Animals. 2006. (Illus.). 80p. (J). per. 6.95 (978-1-933241-25-8(X)) Kumon Publishing North America, Inc.

—My Book of Mazes: Things That Go! 2006. (Illus.). 80p. (J). per. 6.95 (978-1-933241-31-9(4)) Kumon Publishing North America, Inc.

—My Book of Pasting: Jigsaw Puzzles. 2006. (Illus.). 80p. (J). per. 6.95 (978-1-933241-29-6(2)) Kumon Publishing North America, Inc.

All about Me. 2002. (Holiday Fun Bks.). 32p. (J). per. 2.99 (978-0-88724-925-9(6) , CD-0193) Carson-Dellosa Publishing Co., Inc.

All about Me. 2002. (First Words & Pictures Book Ser.). 14p. (J). bds. 7.95 (978-0-7525-7977-1(0)) Parragon, Inc.

All about Me. (Poster Projects Ser.). (gr. 3-6). 9.99 (978-0-7424-0694-0(6) , IF22451) School Specialty Publishing.

All Sorts of Sports Puzzles. 2000. 48p. (J). (gr. 2-8). pap. 2.99 (978-1-886749-90-0(6)) Sports Illustrated For Kids.

All Through the Year (Gr. 1-2) 2003. (J). (978-1-58232-055-7(1)) Bryan Hse. Pubs., Inc.

All Through the Year (Gr. 1-3) 2003. (J). (978-1-58232-065-6(9)) Bryan Hse. Pubs., Inc.

All Through the Year (Gr. 2-4) 2003. (J). (978-1-58232-056-4(X)) Bryan Hse. Pubs., Inc.

Allen, Robert. Mensa Mighty Mindbusters for Kids. 2003. 256p. (J). (gr. 4-7). per. 12.95 (978-1-84222-897-5(8)) Carlton Bks., Ltd. GBR. *Dist:* Ingram Pub. Services.

—Mensa Presents Secret Codes for Kids. 2003. (Illus.). 128p. (J). pap. 7.95 (978-1-84222-767-1(X)) Carlton Bks., Ltd. GBR. *Dist:* Ingram Pub. Services.

—Mind Mazes for Kids. 2000. (gr. 3-6). lib. bdg. 12.40 (978-0-613-89573-6(8)) Tandem Library Bks.

—Number Puzzles for Kids. 2000. (Mensa Ser.). (Illus.). 224p. (J). (gr. 4). pap. 4.50 (978-0-439-10841-6(1)) Scholastic, Inc.

—Secret Codes for Kids. 2000. (Mensa Ser.). (Illus.). 224p. (J). (gr. 4). pap. 4.50 (978-0-439-10842-3(X)) Scholastic, Inc.

—Secret Codes for Kids. 2000. (gr. 3-6). lib. bdg. 12.40 (978-0-613-87579-0(6)) Tandem Library Bks.

Allman, Barbara. Language Arts Puzzles & Games. 1999. (Gifted & Talented Ser.). (Illus.). 64p. (J). (ps-1). pap. 4.95 (978-0-7373-0206-6(2)) Lowell Hse.

Alphabet Puzzle Pairs. 2004. (J). pap. (978-1-59461-051-6(7)) eeBoo Corp.

Amazing Adventures on the Cowboy Trail. 2001. 32p. (J). pap. 4.95 (978-0-9662738-2-3(6)) Monjeu Pr., Inc.

American Girl Editorial Staff. Pencil Play. 2005. (American Girls Collection). (Illus.). 64p. (J). pap. 5.95 (978-1-59369-007-6(X) , American Girl) American Girl Publishing, Inc.

American Girl Editorial Staff, ed. AG Collection Mystery Puzzle. 2005. (American Girls Collection). (Illus.). 16p. (J). pap. 16.95 (978-1-58485-964-2(4) , American Girl) American Girl Publishing, Inc.

—The American Girls Mini Puzzles. 2002. (American Girls Collection Ser.). (Illus.). (J). 9.95 (978-1-58485-514-9(2)) American Girl Publishing, Inc.

American Heritage Dictionary Editors, ed. What Am I Playing? Zagarenski, Pamela, illus. 2004. (Good Beginnings Ser.). 4p. (J). (ps-k). bds. 3.95 (978-0-618-43169-4(1)) Houghton Mifflin Co. Trade & Reference Div.

Amery, H. Bible Stories Jigsaw Book. 2004. 20p. (J). 14.95 (978-0-7945-0558-5(9)) EDC Publishing.

—Navidad en la Granja Libro Con Paginas Puzzle. 2004. Orig. Title: Christmas Jigsaw Book. (SPA.). 6p. (J). 8.95 (978-0-7460-5092-7(5)) EDC Publishing.

—The Steam Train Jigsaw Book. 2004. 14p. (J). 8.95 (978-0-7945-0296-6(2)) EDC Publishing.

Amery, H. & Cartwright, S. ABC Jigsaw Book. rev. ed. 2004. 18p. (J). 14.95 (978-0-7945-0619-3(4)) EDC Publishing.

—Christmas Jigsaw Book. 2004. (Farmyard Tales Ser.). 14p. (J). 8.95 (978-0-7945-0219-5(9) , Usborne) EDC Publishing.

—Farm Animal Jigsaw Book. 2004. (Jigsaw Bks.). (Illus.). 14p. (J). 8.95 (978-0-7945-0162-4(1) , Usborne) EDC Publishing.

Amery, Heather. Christmas Story Jigsaw Book. 2004. (Jigsaw Bks.). (Illus.). 14p. (J). 8.95 (978-0-7945-0223-2(7) , Usborne) EDC Publishing.

—Greek Myths Jigsaw Book. Edwards, Linda, illus. 2006. 14p. (J). bds. 14.99 (978-0-7945-1183-8(X) , Usborne) EDC Publishing.

Analogy Challenges Level A. 2004. (J). pap. 12.95 (978-1-892069-77-1(6)) MindWare Holdings, Inc.

Analogy Challenges Level B. 2004. (J). pap. 12.95 (978-1-892069-78-8(4)) MindWare Holdings, Inc.

Andersen, Scoular. Space Pirates & the Monster of the Malswamp Cave. 2007. (Illus.). 32p. (J). (gr. k-3). 16.95 (***978-1-84507-480-7(7)***) Lincoln, Frances Ltd. GBR. *Dist:* Perseus Distribution.

Anderson, Scoular. Space Pirates: A Map-Reading Adventure. Anderson, Scoular, illus. 2004. (Illus.). 32p. (J). (gr. 1-4). act. bk. ed. 19.95 (978-1-55037-881-8(3)); pap., act. bk. ed. 8.95 (978-1-55037-880-1(5)) Annick Pr., Ltd. CAN. *Dist:* Firefly Bks., Ltd.

Andrews McMeel Publishing Staff, et al. Puzzle Pack for Kids: Over 100 Mensa Puzzles, Games, & Exercises Especially. 2000. 72p. (J). (gr. 4-7). pap. 19.95 (978-1-85613-387-6(7)) Carlton Bks., Ltd. GBR. *Dist:* Ingram Pub. Services, Simon & Schuster, Inc.

Anholt, Catherine & Anholt, Laurence. Can You Guess? A Lift-the-Flap Birthday Party Book. 2003. (Illus.). 16p. pap. 7.95 (978-0-7112-2214-4(2)) Lincoln, Frances Ltd. GBR. *Dist:* Transition Vendor.

Animal Clues: 6 Small Books. (gr. k-1). 35.00 (978-0-7635-6226-7(2)) Rigby Education.

Animals Puzzle Tower. 2003. pap. 9.99 (978-0-7424-1522-5(8)) School Specialty Publishing.

Arensen, Shel. The First Christmas: Nativity Puzzle Book with 6 Play Pieces. 2003. (Illus.). 16p. (J). 10.99 (978-0-8254-5509-4(X)) Kregel Pubns.

Artell, Mike. Backyard Bloodsuckers: Questions, Facts & Tongue Twisters about Creepy Crawlers. 2004. (Illus.). 80p. pap. (978-0-673-59248-4(0)) Good Year Bks.

Artell, Mike & Rosenbloom, Joseph. The Little Giant Book of Tongue Twisters. 1999. (Little Giant Bks.). (Illus.). 352p. (J). (gr. 4-7). pap. 6.95 (978-0-8069-0951-6(X)) Sterling Publishing Co., Inc.

AZ Hidden Pictures/Alphabet. 2004. (Activity Zone Workbook Ser.). 32p. (J). pap. 2.49 (978-1-58947-395-9(7) , 02197) School Zone Publishing Co.

Baifang. More Chinese Brain Twisters: 60 Fast, Fun Puzzles That Help Children Develop Quick Minds. 1999. (Illus.). 128p. pap. 14.95 (978-0-471-24613-8(1) , Wiley-Interscience) Wiley, John & Sons, Inc.

Bailey, Todd, ed. The Clue Searcher's Discovery Guide To: A Clue Search Puzzles Book: the 50 States, 1. 2004. (Illus.). 60p. spiral bd. 14.99 (978-0-9753879-0-0(1)) ClueSearchPuzzles.com.

Bak, Jenny. Transformers Activity Book & Gel Pen. 2007. (Transformers Ser.). 32p. (J). pap. 4.99 (***978-0-06-088827-5(X)*** , Harper Entertainment) HarperCollins Pubs.

Ball, Liz. ABC - What Job Do You See? 2001. (Hidden Treasures Ser.). (Illus.). 56p. (J). pap. 4.95 (978-0-9678159-2-3(4)) Hidden Pictures.

—Hidden Picture Puzzles Vol. 4: Merry Christmas Hidden Treasures. 2002. (Illus.). 56p. (J). pap. 4.95 (978-0-9678159-3-0(2)) Hidden Pictures.

—Hidden Treasures: Hidden Picture Puzzles. 1999. (Illus.). 56p. (J). 4.50 (978-0-9678159-0-9(8)) Hidden Pictures.

—Holiday Hidden Treasures: Hidden Picture Puzzles, 2 vols. 2000. (Illus.). 56p. (J). act. bk. ed. 4.50 (978-0-9678159-1-6(6)) Hidden Pictures.

Ball, Liz, illus. Bible Stories: Find-the-Picture Puzzles. 2004. (Find-the-Picture Puzzle Ser.: 1). 24p. (J). pap. 2.95 (978-0-8198-1163-9(7) , 332-026) Pauline Bks. & Media.

—Miracles & Parables of Jesus: Find-the-Picture Puzzles. 2004. (Find-the-Picture Puzzle Ser.: 2). 24p. (J). pap. 2.95 (978-0-8198-4830-7(1) , 332-221) Pauline Bks. & Media.

Balloon Books. Dot to Dot Count to 10. 2003. 64p. (J). pap. 4.95 (978-1-4027-0630-1(8) , Balloon Bks.) Sterling Publishing Co., Inc.

Balloon Books Staff. Dot to Dot Count to 25. 2007. (Illus.). 64p. (J). pap. 4.95 (978-1-4027-4626-0(1)) Sterling Publishing Co., Inc.

—Great Brain Workout. 2003. 48p. pap. 3.95 (978-1-4027-0499-4(2) , Balloon Bks.) Sterling Publishing Co., Inc.

—Tricky Brain Puzzles. 2003. 48p. pap. 3.95 (978-1-4027-0500-7(X) , Balloon Bks.) Sterling Publishing Co., Inc.

—Wacky Brainteasers. 2002. (Illus.). 48p. (gr. 3-7). pap. 3.95 (978-1-4027-0100-9(4) , Balloon Bks.) Sterling Publishing Co., Inc.

Balloon Books Staff, ed. Click & Stick: Sticker Book with CD Rom. 2001. (Balloon Ser.). (Illus.). 8p. (J). (ps-k). pap., pap., stu. ed. 8.95 incl. cd-rom (978-0-8069-2262-1(1) , Balloon Bks.) Sterling Publishing Co., Inc.

—Sticker Puzzles: Stick & Learn 4 Years. 2001. (Stick & Learn Bks.). (Illus.). 12p. (J). pap. 3.95 (978-0-8069-8063-8(X)) Sterling Publishing Co., Inc.

—Tricky Detective Puzzles. 2002. (Illus.). 48p. (gr. 3-7). pap. 3.95 (978-1-4027-0181-8(0) , Balloon Bks.) Sterling Publishing Co., Inc.

Bamberger, Honi. Logic Posters, Problems & Puzzles Grades 3-6: 4 Big Posters & Dozens of Brain Boosting Reproducibles. 1999. 64p. (J). pap., tchr. ed. 12.95 (978-0-590-64273-6(1)) Scholastic, Inc.

Banjo - Tooie. 2000. (J). 6.50 (978-0-7615-3146-3(7) , Prima Lifestyles) Crown Publishing Group.

Barbaresi, Nina. Animal Search-a-Word Puzzles. 2003. (Dover Little Activity Bks.). (Illus.). 64p. (J). pap. 1.50 (978-0-486-42767-6(6)) Dover Pubns., Inc.

—Horses. 2005. (Illus.). 64p. (J). pap., act. bk. ed. 1.50 (978-0-486-44195-5(4)) Dover Pubns., Inc.

Barber, Patti. First Number Book. Stanley, Mandy, illus. 2001. (First Bks.). 48p. (J). (gr. k-ps). tchr. ed. 12.95 (978-0-7534-5338-4(X) , Kingfisher) Houghton Mifflin Co. Trade & Reference Div.

Barber, Shirley. Fairytale Jigsaw Book: With Seven 48-Piece Jigsaws. 2001. (Illus.). 14p. (J). (978-1-86503-496-6(7)) Five Mile Pr. Pty Ltd. The.

Barberi, Marco, et al, trs. Sabelotodo: 1000 Desafíos para Tu Inteligencia. Bertran, Nuria, illus. 2003. (SPA.). 384p. 35.00 (978-84-494-2372-7(4) , GML07104-192209) Oceano Grupo Editoria, S.A. ESP. *Dist:* Thomson Gale.

Baron, Celia. Brain Sizzlers. 2004. (Illus.). 48p. (gr. 4-7). pap. (978-0-673-59962-9(0)) Good Year Bks.

Baron, Celia. Brain Sizzlers: Puzzles for Critical Thinkers. 2nd ed. 2007. 88p. (J). pap. 7.95 (***978-1-59647-232-7(4)***) Good Year Bks.

Bates, Michelle. Christmas Puzzles. 2004. (Young Puzzles Sticker Bks.). (Illus.). 24p. (J). (gr. k up). pap., act. bk. ed. 6.95 (978-0-7945-0045-0(5) , Usborne) EDC Publishing.

Baumgart, Susan. Extinct Creatures Dot-to-Dot. Salvucci, Richard J., illus. 2005. 80p. (J). (gr. 1-4). pap. 5.95 (978-1-4027-0931-9(5)) Sterling Publishing Co., Inc.

Beaton, Clare. Two-in-One Animal Puzzle. (J). 9.99 (978-0-7353-0597-7(8)) Galison.

Beatty, Sarah. On the Farm (Full-Color) (Prek-K) 2006. pap. 16.99 (978-1-4206-8144-4(3)) Teacher Created Resources, Inc.

Beaulieu, Jeannine. Caillou, 4 vols. 3rd rev. ed. 2006. (Caillou Activity Bks.). (Illus.). 24p. (J). pap. 3.95 (***978-2-89450-573-1(6)***) Chouette Publishing CAN. *Dist:* Independent Pubs. Group.

Becker, Karen Jessie, et al, contrib. by. Bible Puzzles for Kids: Ages 6-8. 2005. (Illus.). 144p. (J). (ps-3). pap. 14.99 (978-0-7847-1787-5(7) , 02260) Standard Publishing.

Beech, Linda Ward. Fun Phonics Puzzles & Games. 1999. 48p. (J). pap. 7.95 (978-0-439-04760-9(9)) Scholastic, Inc.

Begin Bible My Favorite Puzzle. 2004. 1.59 (978-0-7696-0216-5(9)) School Specialty Publishing.

Ben, Tausig. Mad Tausig vs the Interplaneta. 2007. 80p. pap. 7.95 (***978-0-9741319-4-8(6)***) 4N Publishing LLC.

Bergen, Lara. Pretty Puzzles & Sweet Stories. 2004. (Illus.). 16p. (J). (ps-2). 17.99 (978-0-7868-3489-1(7) , Disney Editions) Disney Pr.

—Puzzle Time. 2006. 16p. (ps-2). 17.99 (978-0-7868-3809-7(4)) Disney Pr.

Berthel, Alice H. Power Puzzles: John. 2007. (J). per. 12.95 (978-1-59352-193-6(6)) Christian Services Publishing.

—Power Puzzles: Luke. 2007. (J). per. 12.95 (978-1-59352-192-9(8)) Christian Services Publishing.

—Power Puzzles: Matthew. 2006. (J). per. 12.95 (978-1-59352-174-5(X)) Christian Services Publishing.

Best Travel Activity Book Ever! (Backseat Bks.). (Illus.). 256p. (J). pap. 3.95 (978-0-528-96542-5(5)) Rand McNally.

Beyblade Giant Coloring & Activity Books. 2004. (J). act. bk. ed. (978-0-7666-1257-0(0) , 49285); act. bk. ed. (978-0-7666-1258-7(9) , 49285) Modern Publishing.

Beylon, Cathy. Easy Beauty & the Beast Sticker Picture Puzzle. 2006. 4p. (J). (ps-2). pap. 1.50 (978-0-486-44473-4(2)) Dover Pubns., Inc.

—Easy Firehouse Sticker Picture Puzzle. 2005. (Illus.). 4p. (J). pap. 1.50 (978-0-486-43850-4(3)) Dover Pubns., Inc.

—Easy Nativity Scene Sticker Picture Puzzle. 2006. 4p. (J). 1.50 (978-0-486-44824-4(X)) Dover Pubns., Inc.

—Easy Noah's Ark Sticker Picture Puzzle. 2004. (Illus.). 4p. (J). 1.50 (978-0-486-43864-1(3)) Dover Pubns., Inc.

Bible Brain Teasers. 2006. 144p. (YA). (gr. 8-12). 15.99 (978-1-4206-7063-9(8)) Teacher Created Resources, Inc.

Bible Brain Teasers: Fun Little Activities That Teach Big Bible Messages. 2004. (Christian Bks.). (Illus.). 144p. (J). 14.99 (978-0-7439-7100-3(0)) Teacher Created Materials, Inc.

Bible Story Puzzles Grade 1-3. 2002. (Christian Product Ser.). (J). per. 3.99 (978-0-88724-866-5(7) , CD-2023) Carson-Dellosa Publishing Co., Inc.

Bible Story Puzzles Grade 4-6. 2002. (Christian Product Ser.). (J). per. 3.99 (978-0-88724-867-2(5) , CD-2024) Carson-Dellosa Publishing Co., Inc.

The Big Book of Kindergarten Puzzles. (Big Book Ser.). 216p. pap. 19.99 (978-0-8307-2757-5(4)); Vol. 2. pap. 19.99 (978-0-8307-2884-8(8)) Gospel Light Pubns. (Gospel Light).

Big Book of Puzzles. 12.99 (978-1-58062-902-7(4)) Adams Media Corp.

Billout, Guy. Somethings Not Quite Right. (Illus.). 32p. pap. 14.95 (978-1-56792-266-0(X)) Godine, David R. Pub.

Birthday Puzzles & Games. 2002. (Home Workbooks Ser.). 64p. pap. 2.49 (978-0-88724-698-2(2) , CD-4500) Carson-Dellosa Publishing Co., Inc.

Blair, Beth. The Everything Kids' Hidden Pictures Book. 2004. (Illus.). 144p. (J). 6.95 (978-1-59337-128-9(4)) Adams Media Corp.

Blair, Beth & Ericsson, Jennifer. Everything Kids' Animal Puzzles. 2005. (Illus.). 144p. (J). pap., act. bk. ed. 6.95 (978-1-59337-305-4(8)) Adams Media Corp.

—The Everything Kids' Christmas Puzzle. 2005. (Illus.). 144p. (J). pap., act. bk. ed. 6.95 (978-1-58062-965-2(2)) Adams Media Corp.

—The Everything Kids' Halloween Puzzle. 2005. (Illus.). 144p. (J). pap., act. bk. ed. 6.95 (978-1-58062-959-1(8)) Adams Media Corp.

—The Everything Kids' Pirates Puzzle & Activity Book. 2006. (Illus.). 144p. pap. 7.95 (978-1-59337-607-9(3)) Adams Media Corp.

Blair, Beth L. Jumbo Animal Puzzle & Activity Book: Enter the Wild Kingdom of Mind-Bending Fun! 2006. 384p. pap. 8.95 (978-1-59869-046-0(9)) Adams Media Corp.

—Jumbo Puzzle Book: Word Searches, Hidden Pictures, & Wild, Wacky Puzzles! 2006. 384p. pap. 8.95 (978-1-59869-048-4(5)) Adams Media Corp.

—Kids' Everything Mazes: Twist, Squirm & Wind Your Way Through Subways, Museums, Monster Lairs & Tombs! 2001. (Everything Kids Ser.). (Illus.). 144p. (J). (gr. 3-7). 6.95 (978-1-58062-558-6(4)) Adams Media Corp.

Blair, Beth L. & Ericsson, Jennifer A. The Everything Kids' Gross Puzzle: Hours of Disgusting Fun. 2005. (Illus.). 144p. (J). (ps-3). pap., act. bk. ed. 6.95 (978-1-59337-447-1(X)) Adams Media Corp.

Blincoe, Neale. How to Dazzle at Maths Crosswords. 2004. 48p. (J). pap. 30.00 (978-1-903853-38-2(9)) Brilliant Pubns. GBR. *Dist:* Parkwest Pubns., Inc.

Block, Cheryl. Think Analogies Level B Book 1: Learning to Connect Words & Relationships. 2002. (J). pap. 13.99 (978-0-89455-792-7(0)) Critical Thinking Bks. & Software.

Blundell, Kim & Tyler, Jenny. Big book of Mazes. rev. ed. 2005. 72p. (J). pap. 10.95 (978-0-7945-0697-1(6) , Usborne) EDC Publishing.

Book Company Staff. Busy Bugs. 2003. (Puzzles Ser.). (Illus.). (J). bds. 10.95 (978-1-74047-335-4(3)) Book Co. Publishing Pty, Ltd., The AUS. *Dist:* Penton Overseas, Inc.

—Fun with Friends & a Day at the Zoo. 2002. (Puzzles Ser.). 20p. (J). 12.95 (978-1-74047-171-8(7)) Book Co. Publishing Pty, Ltd., The AUS. *Dist:* Penton Overseas, Inc.

—Ocean Friends. Lassen, Christian R., illus. 2003. (Puzzles Ser.). (J). bds. 14.95 (978-1-74047-381-1(7)) Book Co. Publishing Pty, Ltd., The AUS. *Dist:* Penton Overseas, Inc.

—Toy Party & Busy Wheels. 2002. (Puzzles Ser.). 20p. (J). 12.95 (978-1-74047-167-1(9)) Book Co. Publishing Pty, Ltd., The AUS. *Dist:* Penton Overseas, Inc.

Booth, Karon. Aslan Is on the Move: Romp in Narnia with Study Helps, Art & Play. 2003. (Illus.). 196p. (J). per. (978-0-941367-13-4(4)) Peach Blossom Pubns.

Boyds Mills Press Staff. Hidden Pictures 2002, Vol. 2. 2001. (Hidden Pictures Ser.). (Illus.). 48p. (J). (gr. k-4). pap. 4.95 (978-1-56397-809-8(1)) Boyds Mills Pr.

Brain Teasers. 2002. 96p. (J). pap. 2.98 (978-0-7525-7517-9(1)) Parragon, Inc.

Brain Teasers from the World Almanac(R) for Kids, Book 1. 2003. pap. 12.99 (978-0-7439-3782-5(1)); pap. 12.99 (978-0-7439-3788-7(0)); pap. 12.99 (978-0-7439-3785-6(6)) Teacher Created Materials, Inc.

Brain Teasers from the World Almanac(R) for Kids, Book 2. 2003. pap. 12.99 (978-0-7439-3783-2(X)); pap. 12.99 (978-0-7439-3789-4(9)); pap. 12.99 (978-0-7439-3786-3(4)) Teacher Created Materials, Inc.

Brain Teasers from the World Almanac(R) for Kids, Book 3. 2003. pap. 12.99 (978-0-7439-3784-9(8)); pap. 12.99 (978-0-7439-3790-0(2)); pap. 12.99 (978-0-7439-3787-0(2)) Teacher Created Materials, Inc.

Brainteasers 2-3. 2004. 48p. (J). per. 6.99 (978-0-88724-184-0(0) , CD-104005) Carson-Dellosa Publishing Co., Inc.

Brainteasers 4-5. 2004. 48p. (J). per. 6.99 (978-0-88724-185-7(9)) Carson-Dellosa Publishing Co., Inc.

Brainteasers 6-8. 2004. (J). per. 6.99 (978-0-88724-186-4(7) , CD-104007) Carson-Dellosa Publishing Co., Inc.

Brandreth, Gyles. Biggest Book of Kids Fun Ever. 2002. (Illus.). 576p. (J). pap. 9.99 (978-0-233-05061-4(2)) Andre Deutsch GBR. *Dist:* Independent Pubs. Group.

—Madcap Book of Brain Teasers. Axworthy, Anni & Miller, Mike, illus. 288p. (J). pap. 6.95 (978-0-233-99568-7(4)) Andre Deutsch GBR. *Dist:* Trafalgar Square Publishing.

Brandreth, Gyles & Joyce, Katherine. Optical Illusion Flip Book: Astounding Optical Illusions Amazing Optical Tricks. 2001. (Illus.). 144p. (J). (gr. 2-7). pap. 6.95 (978-0-8069-6689-2(0)) Sterling Publishing Co., Inc.

Brian, Sarah Jane. Brainiac's Mindbenders: Fun Activities for Geniuses of All Ages. 2005. (Activity Journal Ser.). (Illus.). 128p. (J). act. bk. ed. 12.99 (978-0-88088-591-1(2)) Peter Pauper Pr. Inc.

—Brainiac's Secret Agent: Fun Activities for Spies of All Ages. 2005. (Activity Journal Ser.). 128p. act. bk. ed. 12.99 (978-0-88088-446-4(0)) Peter Pauper Pr. Inc.

Brighter Vision Publishing Staff. Look & Find Activity Book. 2000. (Illus.). 32p. (J). (ps). pap. 1.39 (978-1-55254-149-4(5)) Brighter Vision Pubns.

—Word Games & Puzzles. 2000. (Illus.). 32p. (J). (gr. 1). pap. 1.39 (978-1-55254-152-4(5)) Brighter Vision Pubns.

Bronniche, Richard. Dr. Funster's Visual Mind Benders Level A Book 1: Creative Problem-Solving Fun. 2003. (J). pap 7.99 (978 0 89455-823-8(4)) Critical Thinking Bks. & Software.

—Dr. Funster's Visual Mind Benders Level B Book 1: Creative Problem-Solving Fun. 2003. (J). pap. 7.99 (978-0-89455-824-5(2)) Critical Thinking Bks. & Software.

—Dr. Funster's Visual Mind Benders Level C Book 1: Creative Problem-Solving Fun. 2003. (J). pap. 7.99 (978-0-89455-825-2(0)) Critical Thinking Bks. & Software.

Brooks, Felicity. Big Red Tractor Chunky Jigsaw Book. 2006. 10p. (J). bds. 7.99 (978-0-7945-1130-2(9) , Usborne) EDC Publishing.

—Como Te Has Puesto. 2006. 10p. (J). bds. 8.99 (978-0-7460-7401-5(8) , Usborne) EDC Publishing.

—Emergency! Chunky Jigsaw Book. 2005. (Chunky Jigsaw Books Ser.). 14p. (J). 7.95 (978-0-7945-0860-9(X) , Usborne) EDC Publishing.

—Juega con Gabi. 2006. 10p. (J). bds. 8.99 (978-0-7460-7387-2(9) , Usborne) EDC Publishing.

—Naughty Woolly Chunky Jigsaw Book. 2006. 10p. (J). bds. 7.99 (978-0-7945-1128-9(7) , Usborne) EDC Publishing.

—Rusty's Friends Chunky Jigsaw Book. 2006. 10p. (J). bds. 7.99 (978-0-7945-1127-2(9) , Usborne) EDC Publishing.

—Tractors Chunky Jigsaw Book. 2005. (Chunky Jigsaw Books Ser.). 14p. (J). 7.95 (978-0-7945-0861-6(8) , Usborne) EDC Publishing.

—Trains Chunky Jigsaw Book. 2005. (Chunky Jigsaw Books Ser.). 14p. (J). 7.95 (978-0-7945-0859-3(6) , Usborne) EDC Publishing.

Brooks, Felicity & Tyler, Jenny. The Usborne 1, 2, 3 Jigsaw Book. Cartwright, Stephen, illus. 2005. 12p. (J). bds. 15.95 (978-0-7945-1168-5(6) , Usborne) EDC Publishing.

Brown, Ian. Along the Puzzle Trail. 2001. 98p. pap. 9.99 (978-1-84030-112-0(0)) Emerald Hse. Group, Inc.

Brown, Jeff. Amazing Washington! A Collection of Puzzlers, Mazes, & Fun! 2005. (Illus.). 48p. (J). (ps-7). pap. 6.00 (978-0-87842-508-2(X) , 345) Mountain Pr. Publishing Co., Inc.

Bruzzone, Catherine. French Fun. 2004. (Illus.). 20p. 12.95 (978-0-07-142825-5(9) , 9780071428255) McGraw-Hill Cos., The.

—Spanish Fun. 3rd ed. 2004. (Illus.). 20p. 12.95 (978-0-07-142816-3(X) , 9780071428163) McGraw-Hill Cos., The.

Bryant-Mole, Karen. Dot-to-Dot Animals. rev. ed. 2004. (Dot to Dot Ser.). (Illus.). 24p. (J). pap. 3.99 (978-0-7945-0497-7(3)) EDC Publishing.

—Dot-to-Dot in Space. 2004. (Dot to Dot Ser.). (Illus.). 24p. (J). pap. 3.95 (978-0-7945-0495-3(7)) EDC Publishing.

—Dot-to-Dot Machines. Round, Graham, illus. rev. ed. 2003. 24p. (J). pap. 3.99 (978-0-7945-1495-2(2) , Usborne) EDC Publishing.

—Dot-to-Dot Nature. 2004. (Dot to Dot Ser.). (Illus.). 24p. (J). 3.99 (978-0-7945-0493-9(0)) EDC Publishing.

—Mortimer Plays I-Spy. Mukhida, Zul, illus. 2000. (Mortimer's Fun with Words Ser.). 24p. (J). (ps up). lib. bdg. 22.00 (978-0-8368-2749-1(X)) Stevens, Gareth Inc.

Buehner, Caralyn. It's a Spoon Not a Shovel. Buehner, Mark, illus. 1998. 40p. (J). (ps-3). pap. 6.99 (978-0-14-056427-3(6) , Puffin) Penguin Group (USA) Inc.

Bugs' Vocabulary Skills Challenger. 1999. (McGraw-Hill Junior Academic Ser.). (Illus.). 32p. (J). (gr. k-2). pap. 2.49 (978-1-57768-236-3(X)) School Specialty Publishing.

Buller, Laura. On the Farm Dot-to-Dot. 2005. (Illus.). 80p. (J). pap. 5.95 (978-1-4027-1185-5(9)) Sterling Publishing Co., Inc.

Bullimore, Tom. Baker Street Whodunits: Puzzles of Deduction. Anderson, Ian, illus. 2001. 96p. (gr. 5-9). pap. 6.95 (978-0-8069-4763-1(2)) Sterling Publishing Co., Inc.

—Sherlock Holmes Whodunits. 2002. (gr. 5-8). lib. bdg. 15.25 (978-0-613-75663-1(0)) Tandem Library Bks.

Bumper Puzzle Fun. 2002. 576p. (J). pap. 6.98 (978-0-7525-8924-4(5)) Parragon, Inc.

The Bunty Annual 2004. annual 2004. 128p. (J). 9.95 (978-0-85116-882-1(5)) Thomson, D.C. & Co., Ltd. GBR. *Dist:* APG Sales and Fulfillment.

Burgess, Mark. Mutiny at Crossbones Bay. Burgess, Mark, illus. 2006. (Illus.). 48p. (J). pap. 4.99 (978-0-7945-1407-5(3) , Usborne) EDC Publishing.

Burgess, Thornton W. & Stewart, Pat. Peter Cottontail Mazes. 1999. (Dover Little Activity Bks.). (Illus.). 64p. (J). pap. 1.50 (978-0-486-40968-9(6)) Dover Pubns., Inc.

Butterfield, Moira. Switches, Doors, Knobs & Drawers. Lewis, Jan, illus. 1998. (Can You Find? Ser.). (J). (978-0-382-39991-6(9)); pap. (978-0-382-39990-9(0)) Silver Pr. Co.

Campbell, Rod. On the Move. 2003. (Illus.). 10p. (J). 5.99 (978-1-85292-190-3(0) , Campbell Bks.) Pan Macmillan GBR. *Dist:* Trafalgar Square Publishing.

Carlton Books Staff & Allen, Robert. Mensa Mighty Mystery Puzzles for Kids. 2003. (Illus.). 256p. pap. 12.95 (978-1-84222-925-5(7)) Carlton Bks., Ltd. GBR. *Dist:* Ingram Pub. Services, Simon & Schuster, Inc.

Carmona, Lisa. Games & Puzzles. 2002. (Activity Zone Workbooks Ser.). (Illus.). 64p. (J). pap., wbk. ed. 3.79 (978-1-58947-055-2(9) , 02349) School Zone Publishing Co.

Carson, Karen. Horseplay: 50 Puzzles & Games for Horse Lovers. 2004. 68p. (J). pap. 9.95 (978-1-57779-068-6(5)) Alpine Pubns., Inc.

Cartoon Network Staff, contrib. by. Brain Strain: Puzzle Book. 2000. (Illus.). 48p. (J). (ps-3). pap. 3.99 (978-0-307-10776-3(0) , Golden Bks.) Random Hse. Children's Bks.

Cartwright, S. Fairy Jigsaw Puzzle. gif. ed. 2004. (Fairy Jigsaw in A Box Ser.) (Illus.). (J). 11.95 (978-0-7945-0592-9(9)) EDC Publishing.

Cartwright, Stephen. Abc Floor. Cartwright, Stephen, illus. 2006. 16p. (J). bds. 15.99 (978-0-7945-1367-2(0) , Usborne) EDC Publishing.

Casey, Kathy & Bunnell, Deb T. Spanish Search-a-Word Picture Puzzles. 2001. (SPA., Illus.). 32p. (J). pap. 3.95 (978-0-486-41552-9(X)) Dover Pubns., Inc.

Challenging Puzzles & Games. 2004. (Gel Pen Activity Bks.). (Illus.). 24p. (J). (gr. 2-5). act. bk. ed. (978-0-7666-0598-5(1) , 66000) Modern Publishing.

Champagne, Ruth. Friendly Math Shape & Pattern Puzzles. Champagne, Ronald, illus. 1999. 108p. (Orig.). (J). (gr. k up). pap. (978-1-929245-00-0(9)) Friendly Math.

Cheney, Martha C. Reading Puzzles & Games. 1998. (Gifted & Talented Ser.). (Illus.). 64p. (J). (gr. 2). pap., wbk. ed. 4.95 (978-1-56565-837-0(X) , 08379W) Lowell Hse. Juvenile.

Cherician, David. Traba Lenguas. 2000. (SPA., Illus.). 24p. (J). (978-84-95040-58-9(1)) Serres, Ediciones, S. L. ESP. *Dist:* Lectorum Pubns., Inc.

Children of the World (Gr. 2-4) 2003. (J). (978-1-58232-057-1(8)) Bryan Hse. Pubs., Inc.

Children's Puzzle Book. 2003. (J). per. (978-1-884907-26-5(1)); per. (978-1-884907-27-2(X)) Paradise Pr., Inc.

Chouette & Beaulieu, Jeannine. Caillou, 4 vols. 4th rev. ed. 2006. (Caillou Activity Bks.). (Illus.). 24p. (J). pap. 3.95 (***978-2-89450-574-8(4)***) Chouette Publishing CAN. *Dist:* Independent Pubs. Group.

Christian, Judith A. Celebration Puzzle Pieces. 2000. (Illus.). 64p. (J). (gr. 2-5). 8.99 (978-0-570-07058-0(9)) Concordia Publishing Hse.

Christmas Dot to Dot ¿ Santa¿s Big Dot to Dot. 2004. (J). per. 6.95 (978-1-885920-89-8(X)) Pyramid Publishing, Inc.

Chronicle Books Staff. Nick Jr. Puzzle Block Book: Counting. 2006. (Illus.). 12p. (J). 12.95 (978-0-8118-5147-3(8)) Chronicle Bks. LLC.

—Nick Jr. Puzzle Block Book: Shapes. 2006. 12p. (J). 12.95 (978-0-8118-5149-7(4)) Chronicle Bks. LLC.

Chronicle Books Staff, creator. Genius Deck: Secret Codes for Kids. 2005. (gr. 2-6). 9.95 (978-0-8118-5192-3(3)) Chronicle Bks. LLC.

—75 Brain Bafflers: Brain Bafflers for Kids. 2005. (Illus.). 75p. (gr. 2-6). 9.95 (978-0-8118-5189-3(3)) Chronicle Bks. LLC.

—75 Color Puzzles. 2005. 13.95 (978-0-8118-5194-7(X)) Chronicle Bks. LLC.

—75 Logic Puzzles. 2005. 13.95 (978-0-8118-5173-2(7)) Chronicle Bks. LLC.

—75 More Word Puzzles. 2005. 13.95 (978-0-8118-5197-8(4)) Chronicle Bks. LLC.

—75 Puzzle Challenges. 2005. 13.95 (978-0-8118-5198-5(2)) Chronicle Bks. LLC.

El Circo: Un Acercamiento al Arte a Traves del Juego. (Arte en Puzzle Ser.). (CAT., Illus.). 14p. (J). 12.95 (978-84-8488-027-1(3)) Serres, Ediciones, S. L. ESP. *Dist:* Lectorum Pubns., Inc.

Clark, Diane C. & Chernick, Miriam. A Kid's Guide to Washington, D.C. Brown, Richard E., illus. 2008. (J). pap. (***978-0-15-206125-8(8)***) Harcourt Trade Pubs.

Clarke, Catriona. Pirates (Level 2) - Internet Referenced. 2006. (Illus.). 32p. (J). 4.99 (978-0-7945-1332-0(8) , Usborne) EDC Publishing.

Clarke, Phillip & Rogers, Kirsteen. Unicorns Jigsaw Bk. 2007. 14p. (J). bds. 14.99 (978-0-7945-1467-9(7) , Usborne) EDC Publishing.

Cleveland, Alexandra, et al. On Track to First Grade. Koeller, Carol, illus. 2002. 128p. (Orig.). (J). pap. 14.95 (978-0-943452-34-0(1)) Building Blocks, LLC.

Cloutier, Toni Lynn. World Search Puzzles. 2005. (Illus.). 112p. (gr. k-9). pap., pap., spiral bd. 6.95 (978-1-4027-1414-6(9)) Sterling Publishing Co., Inc.

Cohen, Gilles & Editions POLE Staff. 50 Mathematical Puzzles & Problems: Orange Collection. 2000. (Illus.). 96p. (YA). (gr. 9-12). pap. 14.95 (978-1-55953-499-4(0) , 1559534990) Key Curriculum Pr.

Coin Clue Puzzles Book. 2000. (J). pap. 12.95 (978-1-56911-085-0(9)) Learning Resources, Inc.

Conley, Erin, ed. Madcap Mazes. 2005. (Made You Laugh for Kids). (Illus.). 96p. pap. (978-1-57528-931-1(8)) University Games.

Conrad, Hy. Kids' Whodunits: Catch the Clues. Blanchard, Sue, illus. 2007. 96p. (J). pap. 6.95 (***978-1-4027-3966-8(4)***) Sterling Publishing Co., Inc.

Conrad, Hy, et al. Mensa Whodunits. 2004. (Official Mensa Puzzle Book Ser.). (Illus.). 286p. (J). pap. (978-1-4027-1643-0(5) , Sterling/Main St.) Sterling Publishing Co., Inc.

Corr, Christopher. Map of the World Play Scene. 2005. (J). 9.99 (978-0-7353-0898-5(5)) Galison.

Counting Puzzles. Date not set. (Illus.). 96p. (J). 2.98 (978-0-7525-7519-3(8)) Parragon, Inc.

Cox, Emily, et al. The Big Book of Crossword Puzzles: 288 Puzzles for the Crossword Fanatic. 2002. (Illus.). 384p. (J). pap. 14.95 (978-1-4027-0161-0(6)) Sterling Publishing Co., Inc.

Crawford, Chris. Tangram Puzzles: 500 Tricky Shapes to Confound & Astound. 2002. (Illus.). 96p. 14.95 (978-0-8069-7589-4(X)) Sterling Publishing Co., Inc.

Crerand, John J. & Crerand, Teresa. The Adventures of Christopher Otter: Stories for Storytellers, Color Activity Book. Dannerfelter, Bea, illus. 2002. 40p. (J). (gr. k-6). pap. 4.50 (978-0-9719724-1-4(9) , CO-1A) TACCO.

Critical Thinking Co. Dr. Funster's Think-A-Minutes Level A Book 1: Quick, Fun Thinking Activities for Better Grades & Higher Test Scores. 2003. (J). (gr. 2-3). pap. 5.99 (978-0-89455-806-1(4)) Critical Thinking Bks. & Software.

Critical Thinking Co. Dr. Funster's Think-A-Minutes Level A Book 2: Quick, Fun Thinking Activities for Better Grades & Higher Test Scores. 2004. (J). (gr. 2-3). pap. 5.99 (978-0-89455-807-8(2)) Critical Thinking Bks. & Software.

—Dr. Funster's Think-A-Minutes Level B Book 1: Quick, Fun Thinking Activities for Better Grades & Higher Test Scores. 2004. (J). (gr. 4-6). pap. 5.99 (978-0-89455-808-5(0)) Critical Thinking Bks. & Software.

—Dr. Funster's Think-A-Minutes Level B Book 2: Quick, Fun Thinking Activities for Better Grades & Higher Test Scores. 2004. (J). (gr. 4-6). pap. 5.99 (978-0-89455-809-2(9)) Critical Thinking Bks. & Software.

—Dr. Funster's Think-A-Minutes Level C Book 1: Quick, Fun Thinking Activities for Better Grades & Higher Test Scores. 2005. (YA). (gr. 7-8). pap. 5.99 (978-0-89455-810-8(2)) Critical Thinking Bks. & Software.

—Dr. Funster's Think-A-Minutes Level C Book 2: Quick, Fun Thinking Activities for Better Grades & Higher Test Scores. 2004. (YA). (gr. 7-8). 5.99 (978-0-89455-811-5(0)) Critical Thinking Bks. & Software.

Critical Thinking-What's Wrong with This Picture? (Gr. 1-3) 2003. (J). (978-1-58232-066-3(7)) Bryan Hse. Pubs., Inc.

Crompton, Richmal. Just William's Puzzles. 2003. 64p. (J). pap. 3.95 (978-0-333-62680-1(X)) Macmillan Publishers Ltd. GBR. *Dist:* Trafalgar Square Publishing.

Curious Critters. 1998. (High Q Book Ser.). (Illus.). 48p. (J). (gr. k-3). pap. 3.99 (978-0-7681-0023-5(2) , McClanahan Bk.) Learning Horizons, Inc.

Curry, Don, ed. Bee Movie Mix & Match Jigsaw Puzzle Book. 2007. 10p. (J). bds. 9.99 (***978-0-696-23479-8(3)***) Meredith Bks.

—It's A Big Big World Mix & Match Jigsaw Puzzle Book. 2007. 10p. (J). 9.99 (***978-0-696-23544-3(7)***) Meredith Bks.

Curry, Don, ed. Kong Jigsaw Book: With Stickers & Activities. 2005. (Illus.). 10p. (J). (ps-3). bds. 9.95 (978-0-696-22814-8(9)) Meredith Bks.

Curtis, Dolores. Rhyming Pretzels. 2003. pap. 21.00 (978-0-8059-5907-9(6)) Dorrance Publishing Co., Inc.

D C Thomson Staff, ed. Animals & You Annual 2004. 2003. (Illus.). 128p. (J). 9.95 (978-0-85116-840-1(X)) Thomson, D.C. & Co., Ltd. GBR. *Dist:* APG Sales and Fulfillment.

—Bunty Annual for Girls 2004. 2003. (Illus.). 128p. (J). (ps-4). (978-0-85116-825-8(6)) Thomson, D.C. & Co., Ltd. GBR. *Dist:* APG Sales and Fulfillment.

Dadey, Debbie & Jones, Marcia Thornton. Ogres Don't Hunt Easter Eggs. 2004. (Adventures of the Bailey School Kids Ser.). 96p. (J). pap. 3.99 (978-0-439-40834-9(2) , Scholastic Paperbacks) Scholastic, Inc.

Dahl, Michael. Downhill Fun: A Counting Book about Winter. Ouren, Todd, illus. 2004. (Know Your Numbers Ser.). 24p. (C). (gr. k-3). 22.60 (978-1-4048-0579-8(6)) Picture Window Bks.

—If You Were a Palindrome. Gray, Sara, illus. 2006. 24p. (J). (***978-1-4048-3162-9(2)***) Picture Window Bks.

—One Big Building: A Counting Book about Construction. Ouren, Todd, illus. 2004. (Know Your Numbers Ser.). 24p. (C). (gr. k-3). 22.60 (978-1-4048-0580-4(X) , 1229521) Picture Window Bks.

—One Checkered Flag: A Counting Book about Racing. Aldermand, Derrick & Shea, Denise, illus. 2004. (Know Your Numbers Ser.). 24p. (J). (gr. k-3). 22.60 (978-1-4048-0576-7(1) , 1229522) Picture Window Bks.

Daily Problems & Weekly Puzzlers Mind Stretching Math Problems. 64p. (gr. 1 up). 7.99 (978-1-56451-257-4(6) , ID7418); (gr. 2 up). 7.99 (978-1-56451-258-1(4) , ID7419); (gr. 3 up). 7.99 (978-1-56451-195-9(2) , ID7420) School Specialty Publishing.

Daily Problems & Weekly Puzzlers-Science. 64p. (gr. 1 up). 7.99 (978-1-56451-290-1(8) , ID5941); (gr. 2 up). 7.99 (978-1-56451-291-8(6) , ID5942); (gr. 3 up). 7.99 (978-1-56451-272-7(X) , ID5943); (gr. 4 up). 7.99 (978-1-56451-273-4(8) , ID5944); (gr. 5 up). 7.99 (978-1-56451-274-1(6) , ID5945); (gr. 6 up). 7.99 (978-1-56451-275-8(4) , ID5946) School Specialty Publishing.

Dalmatian Press Staff. Cartoon Network Puzzles & Games! 2004. (Cartoon Network Ser.). 64p. (J). pap. 2.99 (978-1-4037-0767-3(7)) Dalmatian Pr.

—Pencil Me In: Cartoon Network Puzzles & Games! (Cartoon Network Ser.). 96p. (J). pap. 2.99 (978-1-4037-0765-9(0)) Dalmatian Pr.

Dalmatian Press Staff, ed. Go-o-o Games! Cartoon Network Puzzles & Games! (Cartoon Network Ser.). 96p. (J). pap. 2.99 (978-1-4037-0766-6(9)) Dalmatian Pr.

Daly, Gayle H. Scissors, Glue & Phonological Processes, Too! 1999. (Scissors, Glue Ser.). (Illus.). 174p. (J). (ps-4). stu. ed., spiral bd. 37.95 (978-0-7606-0303-1(0) , 6-0303-0A1) LinguiSystems, Inc.

D'Amico, Fran Newman. Animal Dot to Dot. 2000. (Illus.). 32p. (J). pap. 2.95 (978-0-486-41312-9(8)) Dover Pubns., Inc.

Danna, Mark. Amazing Word Search Puzzles for Kids. 2008. (Mensa Ser.). 96p. (J). pap. 5.95 (***978-1-4027-4676-5(8)***) Sterling Publishing Co., Inc.

—Awesome Word Search Puzzles for Kids. 2003. (Mensa Ser.). (Illus.). 96p. (J). pap. 5.95 (978-1-4027-0436-9(4)) Sterling Publishing Co., Inc.

—Baffling Word Search Puzzles for Kids. 2005. (Mensa Ser.). 96p. pap. 5.95 (978-1-4027-1041-4(0)) Sterling Publishing Co., Inc.

—Fantastic Word Search Puzzles for Kids. 2004. (Mensa Ser.). (Illus.). 96p. pap. 5.95 (978-1-4027-1042-1(9)) Sterling Publishing Co., Inc.

—Great Word Search Puzzles for Kids. 1999. (Official Mensa Puzzle Book Ser.). (Illus.). 96p. (J). (gr. 3-7). pap. 5.95 (978-0-8069-2469-4(1)) Sterling Publishing Co., Inc.

—Totally Cool Word Search Puzzles. 2002. (Illus.). 96p. (J). pap. 5.95 (978-0-8069-8069-0(9)) Sterling Publishing Co., Inc.

—Word Search Puzzles for Kids. 1999. (Official Mensa Puzzle Book Ser.). (Illus.). 96p. (J). (gr. 4-7). pap. 5.95 (978-0-8069-6557-4(6)) Sterling Publishing Co., Inc.

—Word Search Puzzles for Word-Crazy Kids. 2005. (Mensa Ser.). (Illus.). 96p. (J). (gr. 2-5). pap. 5.95 (978-1-4027-2165-6(X)) Sterling Publishing Co., Inc.

—The 21-Foot-Long Word Search Puzzle Book: Fold-Out Fun for More Than One! 2007. 64p. (J). 9.95 (978-1-4027-4553-9(2) , Sterling Innovation) Sterling Publishing Co., Inc.

Danna, Mark, et al. Mensa Word Puzzles. 2004. (Official Mensa Puzzle Book Ser.). 287p. (J). (978-1-4027-1640-9(0) , Sterling/Main St.) Sterling Publishing Co., Inc.

Daste, Larry. Hidden Pictures. 2001. (Illus.). 32p. (gr. 4-7). pap., pap. 3.95 (978-0-486-41576-5(7)) Dover Pubns., Inc.

Detective Club: Mysteries for Young Thinkers. 2001. (J). per. 11.95 (978-0-88305-531-1(7)) Dandy Lion Pubns.

Detective Shadow. Lateral Mindtrap Puzzles: Challenge the Way You Think & See. 2000. (gr. 5-8). lib. bdg. 15.25 (978-0-613-75534-4(0)) Tandem Library Bks.

Detective, Shadow, as told by & reader. Tricky Mindtrap Puzzles: Challenge the Way You Think & See. Detective, Shadow, reader. 2000. (gr. 5-8). lib. bdg. 15.25 (978-0-613-75531-3(6)) Tandem Library Bks.

Detective Shadow Staff. Tricky Mindtrap Puzzles: Challenge the Way You Think & See. 2000. (Mindtrap Puzzles Ser.). (Illus.). 96p. (gr. 5-9). pap. 6.95 (978-0-8069-4488-3(9) , GAM005000) Sterling Publishing Co., Inc.

Dewin, Howie. Monopoly Junior Number Puzzles. 2002. (Hasbro Ser.). 64p. (J). pap. 4.50 (978-0-439-27568-2(7)) Scholastic, Inc.

—Wacky World of Words Puzzle Book. 2002. (Hasbro Ser.). 64p. (J). pap. 4.50 (978-0-439-27569-9(5)) Scholastic, Inc.

D'Harcourt, Claire. Art up Close. 6th ed. 2006. 64p. (J). 22.95 (978-0-8118-5464-1(7)) Chronicle Bks. LLC.

Diagram. Mazes. 2004. (Kids' Bathroom Bks.). (Illus.). 96p. (J). pap. 4.95 (978-1-4027-1712-3(1)) Sterling Publishing Co., Inc.

Diagram Group. The Little Giant Book of Amazing Mazes. 2001. (Little Giant Bks.). (Illus.). 360p. (J). (gr. 3-7). pap. 6.95 (978-0-8069-3676-5(2)) Sterling Publishing Co., Inc.

Diagram Staff. Weird Facts. 2004. (Kids' Bathroom Bks.). (Illus.). 96p. (J). pap. 4.95 (978-1-4027-1713-0(X)) Sterling Publishing Co., Inc.

Diagram Visual Staff & Bounford, Trevor. Super Little Giant Book of Picture Puzzles. 2006. (Illus.). 288p. (J). pap. 6.95 (978-1-4027-2594-4(9)) Sterling Publishing Co., Inc.

Diaz, Jamie, Studios Staff, illus. Batman. l.t. ed. 1998. (Look & Find Ser.: Vol. 19). 24p. (J). (gr. k-6). lib. bdg. 14.95 (978-1-56674-230-6(7) , HTS Bks.) Forest Hse. Publishing Co., Inc.

Dingwall, Cindy. Library Celebrations. 1999. (Illus.). 96p. (J). (gr. k-5). pap. 16.95 (978-1-57950-027-6(7) , Upstart Bks.) Highsmith Inc.

DiSpezio, Michael Anthony. Challenging Critical Thinking Puzzles. Date not set. (J). (978-0-8069-3848-6(X)) Sterling Publishing Co., Inc.

Dixon, Andy. Star Quest. rev. ed. 2006. 32p. (J). pap. 7.99 (978-0-7945-1099-2(X) , Usborne) EDC Publishing.

DK Publishing Staff. Word: My First Activity Box. 2007. (My First Bks.). (J). (ps-1). 19.99 (978-0-7566-3022-5(3)) Dorling Kindersley Publishing, Inc.

Doherty, Gillian. Fairyland Jigsaw Bk. Gower, Teri, illus. 2007. 14p. (J). bds. 14.99 (978-0-7945-1430-3(8) , Usborne) EDC Publishing.

—1001 Cosas Que Buscar en el Mundo de las Hadas. 2007. 32p. (J). 9.99 (***978-0-7460-8346-8(7)***, Usborne) EDC Publishing.

Doherty, Gillian. 1001 Things to Spot in Fairyland. 2006. 32p. (J). 9.99 (978-0-7945-1220-0(8) , Usborne) EDC Publishing.

Dolby, Karen & Fischel, Emma. Chocolate Island. 2004. (Young Puzzle Adventures Ser.). (Illus.). 32p. (J). (gr. 2 up). pap. 4.95 (978-0-7945-0231-7(8) , Usborne); lib. bdg. 12.95 (978-1-58086-458-9(9)) EDC Publishing.

—Molly's Magic Carpet. 2004. (Young Puzzle Adventures Ser.). (Illus.). 32p. (J). (gr. 2 up). pap. 4.99 (978-0-7945-0233-1(4) , Usborne); lib. bdg. 12.99 (978-1-58086-459-6(7)) EDC Publishing.

—Spooks' Surprise. 2004. (Young Puzzle Adventures Ser.). (Illus.). 32p. (J). (gr. 2 up). pap. 4.95 (978-0-7945-0234-8(2) , Usborne) EDC Publishing.

—Usborne Young Puzzle Adventure Stories. Bates, Michelle, ed. (Young Puzzle Adventures Ser.). (Illus.). 96p. (J). pap. 11.95 (978-0-7460-3454-5(7)) EDC Publishing.

Doolittle, John. Dr. Funster's Creative Thinking Puzzlers Level A Book 1: Creative Problem Solving Fun. 2003. (J). pap. 5.99 (978-0-89455-826-9(9)) Critical Thinking Bks. & Software.

—Dr. Funster's Creative Thinking Puzzlers Level B Book 1: Creative Problem Solving Fun. 2003. (YA). pap. 5.99 (978-0-89455-827-6(7)) Critical Thinking Bks. & Software.

—Dr. Funster's Creative Thinking Puzzlers Level C Book 1: Creative Problem Solving Fun. 2003. (YA). pap. 5.99 (978-0-89455-828-3(5)) Critical Thinking Bks. & Software.

Dorling Kindersley Publishing Staff. Animal Hide & Seek. 2006. (Dk Readers Ser.). (Illus.). 32p. (J). 14.99 (978-0-7566-1962-6(9)); (gr. 5). pap. 3.99 (978-0-7566-1961-9(0)) Dorling Kindersley Publishing, Inc.

Dorling Kindersley Publishing Staff, ed. Bulldozer. 2004. (Ultimate Sticker Bks.). 16p. (J). pap. 6.99 (978-0-7566-0563-6(6)) Dorling Kindersley Publishing, Inc.

Dorling Kindersley Publishing Staff & King, Dave. Counting Book. 1998. (Illus.). 32p. (J). (ps-2). 12.99 (978-0-7894-3448-7(2)) Dorling Kindersley Publishing, Inc.

Dot-to-Dot Activity Zone. 2004. (Activity Zone Workbook Ser.). 32p. (J). pap. 2.49 (978-1-58947-385-0(X) , 02190) School Zone Publishing Co.

Douglas, Vincent & School Specialty Publishing Staff. Alphabet Puzzles. 2003. (Homework Helpers Ser.). (Illus.). 32p. (J). (gr. k-1). pap. 2.99 (978-0-7696-2948-3(2) , American Education Publishing) School Specialty Publishing.

—Dinosaur Dot-to-Dot. 2003. (Homework Helpers Ser.). (Illus.). 32p. (J). (gr. k-1). pap. 2.99 (978-0-7696-2913-1(X) , American Education Publishing) School Specialty Publishing.

—Dot-to-Dots, Puzzles, & Games. 2003. (Homework Helpers Ser.). (Illus.). 32p. (J). (gr. k-1). pap. 2.99 (978-0-7696-2914-8(8) , American Education Publishing) School Specialty Publishing.

—Hidden Pictures & Mazes. 2004. (My Little Heavenly Helpers Ser.). (Illus.). 32p. (J). (ps-k). pap. 3.99 (978-0-7696-3659-7(4) , Brighter Child) School Specialty Publishing.

—Kids' Puzzle Book. (Kid#39;s Puzzle Book Ser.). 128p. (J). No. 17. 2004. (Illus.). pap. 2.99 (978-0-7696-3146-2(0) , American Education Publishing); No. 18. 2004. (Illus.). pap. 2.99 (978-0-7696-3147-9(9) , American Education Publishing); No. 19. 2004. (Illus.). pap. 2.99 (978-0-7696-3148-6(7) , American Education Publishing); No. 20. 2004. (Illus.). pap. 2.99 (978-0-7696-3149-3(5) , American Education Publishing); No. 21. 2005. pap. 2.99 (978-0-7696-3952-9(6) , Brighter Child); No. 22. 2005. pap. 2.99 (978-0-7696-3953-6(4) , Brighter Child); No. 23. 2005. pap. 2.99 (978-0-7696-3954-3(2) , Brighter Child); No. 24. 2005. pap. 2.99 (978-0-7696-3955-0(0) , Brighter Child) School Specialty Publishing.

—Number Puzzles. 2003. (Brighter Child Homework Helpers Ser.). (Illus.). 32p. (J). (gr. k-1). pap., wbk. ed. 2.99 (978-0-7696-2923-0(7) , Brighter Child) School Specialty Publishing.

—Smart 2 the Max Learning Activities, Preschool. 2004. (Smart 2 the Max Ser.). (Illus.). 416p. (J). (ps-1). pap. 12.99 (978-0-7696-3369-5(2) , American Education Publishing) School Specialty Publishing.

—Word Puzzles. 2003. (Homework Helpers Ser.). (Illus.). 32p. (J). (gr. k-1). pap. 2.99 (978-0-7696-2927-8(X) , American Education Publishing) School Specialty Publishing.

Dover. Hidden Picture Mania. 2006. (Boxed Sets/Bindups Ser.). (Illus.). 96p. pap. 7.95 (***978-0-486-45911-0(X)***) Dover Pubns., Inc.

Dowley, Tim. Giant Jigsaw Book. 2004. (Illus.). 14p. 11.99 (978-0-8254-7295-4(4)) Kregel Pubns.

Dworkin, Brooke. Phonics Puzzles. Snider, Jackie & Harpster, Steve, illus. 2006. (First Word Search Ser.). 64p. (J). pap. 3.95 (978-1-4027-3590-5(1)) Sterling Publishing Co., Inc.

Easley, Maryann. Hidden Pictures 2005, Vol. 4. 2004. (Illus.). 48p. (J). (gr. 6-9). pap., act. bk. ed. 5.95 (978-1-59078-297-2(6)) Boyds Mills Pr.

Eck, Kristin. Hide-and-Seek Animals. 2004. (Hide-And-Seek Books). (Illus.). (J). lib. bdg. 7.95 (978-1-4042-2702-6(4) , PowerKids Pr.) Rosen Publishing Group, Inc., The.

—Hide-and-Seek Clothes. 2004. (Hide-And-Seek Books). (Illus.). (J). lib. bdg. 7.95 (978-1-4042-2705-7(9) , PowerKids Pr.) Rosen Publishing Group, Inc., The.

—Hide-and-Seek Food. 2004. (Hide-And-Seek Books). (Illus.). 16p. (J). lib. bdg. 7.95 (978-1-4042-2703-3(2) , PowerKids Pr.) Rosen Publishing Group, Inc., The.

—Hide-and-Seek Toys. 2004. (Hide-And-Seek Books). (Illus.). (J). lib. bdg. 7.95 (978-1-4042-2704-0(0) , PowerKids Pr.) Rosen Publishing Group, Inc., The.

Edmiston, Margaret C., et al. Mensa Logic. 2004. (Official Mensa Puzzle Book Ser.). (Illus.). 286p. (J). pap. (978-1-4027-1637-9(0) , Sterling/Main St.) Sterling Publishing Co., Inc.

Edmunds, Tracy. In the Ocean (Full-Color) (Prek-K) 2006. pap. 16.99 (978-1-4206-8145-1(1)) Teacher Created Resources, Inc.

Eid, Klaus. Mind-Boggling Mazes & Loopy Labyrinths. 2004. (Adventures in Art Ser.). (Illus.). 30p. (J). 14.95 (978-3-7913-3062-4(4)) Prestel Publishing.

Elite Find-a-Word Puzzles. 2003. per. (978-1-884907-16-6(4)) Paradise Pr., Inc.

Engelbreit, Mary. Fun & Games with Ann Estelle. 2007. 104p. pap. 6.99 (***978-0-7407-7058-6(6)***) Andrews McMeel Publishing.

Equipo Staff. Las Estaciones: Un Acercamiento al Arte a Traves del Juego. (Arte en Puzzle Ser.). (SPA., Illus.). 12p. (J). 12.95 (978-84-8488-024-0(9)) Serres, Ediciones, S. L. ESP. *Dist:* Lectorum Pubns., Inc.

Ericsson, Jennifer A. & Blair, Beth L. The Everything Kids' Puzzle Book: Mazes, Word Games, Puzzles & More! Hours of Fun! 2000. (Everything Kids Ser.). (Illus.). 144p. (J). (gr. 4-7). 6.95 (978-1-58062-687-3(4)) Adams Media Corp.

Eskeland, N. Lucia. Fun with Gene. 2001. 48p. (YA). (gr. 5-8). stu. ed., wbk. ed. 10.95 (978-0-9673811-3-8(4)) Science2Discover, Inc.

Esparza, Thomas, Jr., prod. Esther's Playhouse, Disk D. 2004. (Illus.). (J). cd-rom (978-1-879817-45-6(4) , Children) Star Light Pr.

Las Estaciones: Un Acercamiento al Arte a Traves del Juego. (Arte en Puzzle Ser.). (CAT., Illus.). 14p. (J). 12.95 (978-84-8488-025-7(7)) Serres, Ediciones, S. L. ESP. *Dist:* Lectorum Pubns., Inc.

Evans, Larry & Evans, Barry. Maze Book. 1998. (Illus.). 48p. (J). (gr. 3-7). stu. ed., spiral bd. 12.95 (978-1-57054-253-4(8)) Klutz.

Fair Ideal Instructional Staff. What Matches with Sammy Spider. 1999. (Lost-N-Found Book Ser.). (Illus.). (J). 7.95 (978-1-56451-294-9(0) , Ideal School Supply) Schaffer, Frank Pubns.

—What's Different with Freddy Frog, Vol. 1. 1999. (Lost-N-Found Book Ser.). (Illus.). (J). 7.95 (978-1-56451-293-2(2) , Ideal School Supply) Schaffer, Frank Pubns.

Famous People Puzzles: Exercises in Inference & Research. 2001. (J). pap. 11.95 (978-1-883055-48-6(2)) Dandy Lion Pubns.

Farmer Fred's Activity Book: Dot-to-Dot. 2002. 64p. pap. 2.98 (978-0-7525-8340-2(9)) Parragon, Inc.

Farmyard Tales Christmas Jigsaw Book. 2002. (Farmyard Tales Jigsaw). 14p. (J). bds. (978-0-7945-0057-3(9) , Usborne) EDC Publishing.

Felix the Cat/el Gato Felix: A Fun Surprise. 2005. 32p. (J). pap. (978-0-9762071-1-5(7)) Big City Publishing.

Fililpowich, Bob & Ikids. My Easter Basket. 2004. (Soft Shapestm Ser.). (Illus.). 6p. (J). (ps-ps). 9.99 (978-1-58476-220-1(9)) Innovative Kids.

Finch, Spencer. 25 Map Crossword Puzzles That Teach Map & Geography Skills. 1999. (Illus.). 64p. (J). 12.95 (978-0-590-76992-1(8)) Scholastic, Inc.

Fink, Jeri & Paltrowitz, Donna. Gizmo's Tail Twisters. 2004. (Illus.). 36p. (J). per. 8.95 (978-0-9716567-4-1(6)) Book Web Publishing, Ltd.

First Puzzles: Baby Animals. 2003. (Illus.). pap. 9.99 (978-0-7424-1549-2(X)) School Specialty Publishing.

Fisher, Ann Richmond. Primary Puzzlers. 2001. 144p. (gr. 1-4). tchr. ed. 15.99 (978-0-86653-720-9(1) , GA1438) School Specialty Publishing.

FlashKids Editors. My First Book of Tracing. 2004. (Illus.). 80p. (J). 6.95 (978-4-7743-0707-7(6)) Kumon Publishing North America, Inc.

Fleming, Sarah. Pictures in the Stars: American English Edition. 2000. (Cambridge Reading Ser.). (Illus.). pap. 5.00 (978-0-521-79884-6(1)) Cambridge Univ. Pr.

Ford, Barbara E. Tangrams: The Magnificent Seven Piece Puzzle. 2003. (Illus.). 64p. (J). bds. 19.95 (978-0-9627337-7-2(6)) Tandora's Box Pr.

Francia, Giada. Alex & Penny in the Wild West Jigsaw Book. 2007. (Illus.). 14p. (J). (gr. 1-3). pap. 14.95 (*978-88-544-0285-0(0)*, White Star) Rizzoli International Pubns., Inc.

Franco, Betsy. Guess-Me Poems & Puzzles: Alphabet. 2003. (Guess-me Poems & Puzzles Ser.). (Illus.). 64p. pap. 11.95 (978-0-439-38529-9(6) , Teaching Resources) Scholastic, Inc.

Free Spirit Publishing. How to be Bully Free: Word Searches, Mazes, What-Ifs, & Other Fun Activities for Kids. 2006. (Illus.). 32p. (gr. 3-5). pap., wbk. ed. 5.95 (978-1-57542-215-2(8)) Free Spirit Publishing, Inc.

Fremont, Victoria & Marshall, David. All about the First Ladies Search-a-Word Puzzles. 2001. (Illus.). 64p. (gr. 3). pap. 1.50 (978-0-486-41577-2(5)) Dover Pubns., Inc.

Frey, Daniel J., illus. Jacy's Coloring & Activity Book. 2006. 32p. (J). 3.00 (978-0-9755314-2-6(5)) Majestic Publishing, LLC.

Fujimoto, Makoto. Spot 7: Christmas. 2006. (Illus.). 38p. (J). 12.95 (978-0-8118-5323-1(3)) Chronicle Bks. LLC.

Fujimoto, Mokoto & Kidslabel Staff. Spot 7 School. 2006. (Illus.). 38p. (J). (gr. k-4). 12.95 (978-0-8118-5324-8(1)) Chronicle Bks. LLC.

Fun, Games, & Mind-Bogglers! 2004. (Gel Pen Activity Bks.). (Illus.). 24p. (J). (gr. 2-5). act. bk. ed. (978-0-7666-0595-4(7) , 66000) Modern Publishing.

Gall, Steve J. Professor Gall's Explorer Ball. 2002. (J). cd-rom 12.00 (978-1-931457-13-2(1)) Stargate Electronic Library, Inc.

Galvin, Jennifer. My Catholic Pray & Play. 2002. (Illus.). 32p. act. bk. ed. 6.95 (978-0-8091-6701-2(8) , 6701-8) Paulist Pr.

Game Time! A Super-Cool Collection of Sports Puzzles, Crosswords, Quizzes & More! 2000. (Illus.). 48p. (J). (gr. 3-9). pap. 2.99 (978-1-930623-18-7(6)) Sports Illustrated For Kids.

Gardner, Martin. Classic Brainteasers. Sinclair, Jeff, illus. 2003. 96p. (gr. 4-7). pap. 6.95 (978-0-8069-1261-5(8)) Sterling Publishing Co., Inc.

Garland, Michael. Mystery Mansion: A Look Again Book. Garland, Michael, illus. 2001. (Illus.). 32p. (J). 15.99 (978-0-525-46675-8(4) , Dutton Juvenile) Penguin Group (USA) Inc.

Gaydos, Nora. The Big Race, Level 2. Becker, Paula, illus. 2006. (innovativeKids readers ser.: level 2). 24p. (J). (gr. k-2). pap. 6.99 (978-1-58476-477-9(5) , IKIDS) Innovative Kids.

Geisert, Arthur. Pigs from 1 to 10. 2002. (Illus.). 32p. (J). (gr. k-3). pap. 6.95 (978-0-618-21611-6(1) , Walter Lorraine) Houghton Mifflin Co. Trade & Reference Div.

Geyer, Beth & Geyer, Frank. Teaching Early Concepts with Photos of Kids: Easy Activities Using Snapshots of Students to Build Early Skills, Self-Esteem & Classroom Community. 2005. (Illus.). 48p. (J). pap. 10.99 (978-0-439-51770-6(2) , Teaching Resources) Scholastic, Inc.

Gifford, Clive. Murder Map Mystery. 1998. (Puzzle Adventure Kit Ser.). (J). (gr. 4-7). pap. 8.95 (978-0-7460-2830-8(X)) EDC Publishing.

Gikow, Louise. What Do You See? Ulrich, George, illus. 2005. (My First Reader Ser.). 32p. (J). (gr. k-1). 18.50 (978-0-516-25177-6(5) , Children's Pr.) Scholastic Library Publishing.

Gikow, Louise A. What Do You See? Ulrich, George, illus. 2005. (My First Reader Ser.). 31p. (J). (gr. k-1). pap. 3.95 (978-0-516-25278-0(X) , Children's Pr.) Scholastic Library Publishing.

Giles, Geoff. Match the Views: Cut & Fold Puzzles to Imagine & Solve. 2004. (Illus.). 32p. 10.00 (978-1-899618-55-2(4)) Tarquin Pubns. GBR. *Dist:* Parkwest Pubns., Inc.

Gilliland, Lucille. What's All This? Gilliland, Lucille, illus. 2001. (Illus.). 24p. (J). (ps-6). pap. 8.95 (978-0-9716539-0-0(9)) LG Fun Learning Pubns.

Golden Books Staff. Air Power! 2007. (Color Plus Tattoos Ser.). (Illus.). 32p. (J). (gr. k-4). pap. 3.99 (978-0-375-84142-2(3) , Golden Bks.) Random Hse. Children's Bks.

—Friends to Find. Hall, Susan T., illus. 2003. 32p. (J). (ps-2). pap. 3.99 (978-0-307-10492-2(3) , Golden Bks.) Random Hse. Children's Bks.

—Mummy's Tomb Maze Book. 2000. (Scooby-Doo Ser.). (Illus.). 8p. (J). (ps-3). 9.99 (978-0-307-11127-2(X) , 11127, Golden Bks.) Random Hse. Children's Bks.

—Mystery Mazes & Puzzles. 2000. (Scooby-Doo Ser.). (Illus.). 32p. (J). (ps-3). pap. 3.99 (978-0-307-10479-3(6) , 10479, Golden Bks.) Random Hse. Children's Bks.

—The New Master. 2007. (Deluxe Coloring Book Ser.). (Illus.). 96p. (J). (gr. k-4). pap. 3.99 (978-0-375-84143-9(1) , Golden Bks.) Random Hse. Children's Bks.

—Puzzles for a Princess. 2007. (Color Plus Puzzles to Color Ser.). (Illus.). 32p. (J). (ps-2). pap. 6.99 (*978-0-375-84190-3(3)* , Golden/Disney) Random Hse. Children's Bks.

Golden Books Staff. Welcome to the Team! Baker, Darrell, illus. 2006. (Stickerific Ser.). 32p. (J). (ps-2). pap. 2.99 (978-0-375-83483-7(4) , Golden Bks.) Random Hse. Children's Bks.

Gospel Light Publications Staff. Big Book of Bible Puzzles. 2000. (Big Book Ser.). (Illus.). 216p. pap. 17.99 (978-0-8307-2542-7(3) , Gospel Light) Gospel Light Pubns.

Goss, Lynn & Donaldson, Helen. New Spellaway. 1999. (Illus.). 31p. (J). (gr. 2-6). Bk. 1. pap. 20.00 (978-0-7217-0768-6(8)); Bk. 2. pap. 20.00 (978-0-7217-0769-3(6)); Bk. 3. pap. 20.00 (978-0-7217-0770-9(X)); Bk. 4. pap. 20.00 (978-0-7217-0771-6(8)) Schofield & Sims Ltd. GBR. *Dist:* State Mutual Bk. & Periodical Service, Ltd.

Green, Rod. Where's Mr. Bean? 2002. (Illus.). 32p. (J). pap. 18.00 (978-1-84222-662-9(2)) Carlton Bks., Ltd. GBR. *Dist:* Independent Pubs. Group.

Group/McGraw-Hill, Wright. And the Winner Is: Level N, 6 vols. 128p. (gr. 3-6). 36.95 (978-0-322-05885-9(6)) Wright Group, The.

—Bats about Bats! Level M, 6 vols. 128p. (gr. 3-6). 36.95 (978-0-322-06724-0(3)) Wright Group, The.

—Cat Culture: Level O, 6 vols. 128p. (gr. 5 up). 36.95 (978-0-322-06735-6(9)) Wright Group, The.

—Cheetah Conservation: Level P, 6 vols. 128p. (gr. 5 up). 36.95 (978-0-322-06736-3(7)) Wright Group, The.

—Groovy Gran & the Karaoko Kid: Level S, 6 vols. 128p. (gr. 5 up). 36.95 (978-0-322-05906-1(2)) Wright Group, The.

—How not to Catch the Moon: Level L, 6 vols. 128p. (gr. 3-6). 36.95 (978-0-322-05886-6(4)) Wright Group, The.

—The Magic Shoes: Level N, 6 vols. 128p. (gr. 3-6). 36.95 (978-0-322-05884-2(8)) Wright Group, The.

—Samantha's Sea: Level Q, 6 vols. 128p. (gr. 5 up). 36.95 (978-0-322-05907-8(0)) Wright Group, The.

—Survival in Cyberspace: Level T, 6 vols. 128p. (gr. 5 up). 36.95 (978-0-322-05904-7(6)) Wright Group, The.

—Wolf Master: Level R, 6 vols. 128p. (gr. 5 up). 36.95 (978-0-322-05900-9(3)) Wright Group, The.

Halverson, Jim. Punctuation Puzzles & Mazes. 2001. (Joyful Learning Ser.). 64p. pap., tchr. ed. 10.95 (978-0-439-40808-0(3) , Teaching Resources) Scholastic, Inc.

Hamilton, Inga. Illusions. 2004. (Brainbusters Ser.). (Illus.). 16p. (J). (gr. 3-6). pap. 5.95 (978-1-58728-680-3(7) , Two Can Publishing) T&N Children's Publishing.

Hamilton, Tisha. Old Mcdonald's Noisy Farm. 2006. 10p. (J). bds. 9.99 (978-0-7944-0759-9(5)) Reader's Digest Assn., Inc., The.

Handford, Martin. Where's Waldo? With Free Magnifying Lens. Handford, Martin, illus. 2002. (Where's Waldo? Ser.). (Illus.). 32p. (J). (gr. 1-5). 5.99 (978-0-7636-1920-6(5)) Candlewick Pr.

—Where's Waldo Now? Handford, Martin, illus. 2002. (Where's Waldo? Ser.). (Illus.). 32p. (J). (gr. 1-5). 5.99 (978-0-7636-1921-3(3)) Candlewick Pr.

Hands on Crafts for Kids Staff. Find the Words on the Farm. 2002. (Balloon Ser.). (Illus.). 10p. (J). bds. 4.95 (978-1-4027-0175-7(6) , Balloon Bks.) Sterling Publishing Co., Inc.

Harcourt School Publishers Staff. A Peanut, an Apple & Toast: Library Book. 1999. (Collections Ser.). (Illus.). pap. 14.90 (978-0-15-313399-2(6)) Harcourt Schl. Pubs.

—Use Your Noodle Tales Advanced Level. 3rd ed. 2002. (Trophies Reading Program Ser.). (Illus.). pap. 5.10 (978-0-15-323300-5(1)) Harcourt Schl. Pubs.

Harpster, Steve, illus. Easy First Words. 2005. (First Word Search Ser.). 64p. pap. 3.95 (978-1-4027-2298-1(2)) Sterling Publishing Co., Inc.

—Easy Reader Phonics. 2005. (First Word Search Ser.). 64p. pap. 3.95 (978-1-4027-2297-4(4)) Sterling Publishing Co., Inc.

Harris, Jerald D. Dino Finder Dot-to-Dot. 2002. (Connect the Dots & Color Ser.). (Illus.). 80p. (J). (gr. 1-4). pap. 5.95 (978-0-8069-9093-4(7)) Sterling Publishing Co., Inc.

Harrison, Erica, illus. Box of Fairies. 2005. 6p. (J). 11.95 (978-0-7945-1125-8(2) , Usborne) EDC Publishing.

Harte, May. Hide-and-Seek Kids. 2004. (Hide-And-Seek Books). (Illus.). (J). lib. bdg. 15.95 (978-1-4042-2816-0(0) , PowerKids Pr.) Rosen Publishing Group, Inc., The.

—Hide-and-Seek Pets. 2004. (Hide-And-Seek Books). (J). lib. bdg. 15.95 (978-1-4042-2815-3(2) , PowerKids Pr.) Rosen Publishing Group, Inc., The.

Hawkins, Colin & Hawkins, Jacqui. Whose House? 1998. (Illus.). 16p. (J). (ps-1). 8.95 (978-0-7641-5144-6(4)) Barron's Educational Series, Inc.

Head, Honor. Opposites. Stower, Adam, illus. 1998. (Ed Mouse Finds Out about Ser.). 32 p. (J). (ps-2). 19.98 (978-0-8172-5202-1(9)) Raintree.

—Size & Shape. Stower, Adam, illus. 1998. (Ed Mouse Finds Out about Ser.). 32p. (J). (ps-2). 19.98 (978-0-8172-5201-4(0)) Raintree.

Heimann, Rolf. Rolf's Flummoxing Flabbergasters: Featuring Fickle & Fetch. Heimann, Rolf, illus. 2007. (Illus.). 64p. (J). (gr. 2-4). pap. 7.95 (*978-1-921049-10-1(3)*) Little Hare Bks. AUS. *Dist:* Independent Pubs. Group.

Hellen, Nancy. Jigsaw Books, 6 vols. Hellen, Nancy, illus. 2000. 6p. (J). 8.95 (978-1-902413-40-2(7)) Van der Meer, a Div. of PHPC GBR. *Dist:* Abbeville Pr., Inc.

Hendra, Sue. In the Air. 2000. (Puzzle Play Ser.). (Illus.). 10p. (J). (ps-k). bds. 10.95 (978-1-57145-422-5(5) , Silver Dolphin Bks.) Advantage Pubs. Group.

—On Safari. 2000. (Puzzle Play Ser.). (Illus.). 10p. (J). (ps-k). bds. 10.95 (978-1-57145-421-8(7) , Silver Dolphin Bks.) Advantage Pubs. Group.

—On the Farm. 2000. (Puzzle Play Ser.). (Illus.). 10p. (J). (ps-k). bds. 10.95 (978-1-57145-420-1(9) , Silver Dolphin Bks.) Advantage Pubs. Group.

—Under the Sea. 2000. (Puzzle Play Ser.). (Illus.). 10p. (J). (ps-k). bds. 10.95 (978-1-57145-423-2(3) , Silver Dolphin Bks.) Advantage Pubs. Group.

Hergé, illus. Tintin & Snowy: Album 1. 2006. 68p. (J). pap. 9.99 (978-0-86719-668-9(8)) Last Gasp of San Francisco.

Herzog, Brad. Heads Up! Puzzles for Sports Brains. 1999. (Sports Illustrated for Kids Bks.). 64p. (J). (gr. 4-6). pap. 3.99 (978-1-886749-62-7(0)) Sports Illustrated For Kids.

Herzog, Brad & Lerner, Andy. All-Star Sports Puzzle Book. Goehner, Amy Lennard, ed. Staake, Bob, illus. 2000. 48p. (J). (gr. 2-8). pap. 2.99 (978-1-886749-93-1(0)) Sports Illustrated For Kids.

Herzog, Brad & Sports Illustrated for Kids Editors. MVP Sports Puzzles. Gramling, Scott, ed. rev. ed. 1999. (Sports Illustrated for Kids Bks.). 64p. (J). (gr. 4-6). pap. 3.99 (978-1-886749-60-3(4)) Sports Illustrated For Kids.

Heywood, Rosie. Great Balloon Race. 2004. (Picture Puzzles Ser.). (Illus.). 32p. (J). (gr. k-3). pap. 6.95 (978-0-7460-3388-3(5)) EDC Publishing.

—Puzzle Car Race. Haw, Brenda, illus. 2004. (Young Puzzles Ser.). 32p. (J). pap. 6.95 (978-0-7945-0689-6(5) , Usborne) EDC Publishing.

Heywood, Rosie, ed. Travel Puzzles Sticker Book. Haw, Brenda, illus. rev. ed. (Travel Puzzles Sticker Book Ser.). 24p. (J). 6.95 (978-0-7945-0729-9(8) , Usborne) EDC Publishing.

Hidden Pictures 1-20 (Gr. K-2) 2003. (J). (978-1-58232-063-2(2)) Bryan Hse. Pubs., Inc.

Highlights for Children Editorial Staff. Mathmania. (Illus.). 48p. (YA). Vol. 1. 2003. pap. 5.95 (978-0-87534-931-2(5)); Vol. 2. 2003. pap. 5.95 (978-0-87534-932-9(3)); Vol. 3. 2003. pap. 5.95 (978-0-87534-933-6(1)); Vol. 4. 2003. pap. 5.95 (978-0-87534-934-3(X)); Vol. 13. 2004. (gr. 4-7). pap., act. bk. ed. 5.95 (978-0-87534-945-9(5)); Vol. 14. 2004. (gr. 4-7). pap., act. bk. ed. 5.95 (978-0-87534-946-6(3)); Vol. 15. 2004. (gr. 4-7). pap., act. bk. ed. 5.95 (978-0-87534-969-5(2)); Vol. 16. 2004. (gr. 4-7). pap., act. bk. ed. 5.95 (978-0-87534-970-1(6)) Highlights for Children.

—Puzzlemania. 2003. (Illus.). 48p. (YA): Bk. 1. (gr. 1-7). pap. 5.95 (978-0-87534-701-1(0)); Vol. 2. pap. 5.95 (978-0-87534-702-8(9)); Vol. 3. pap. 5.95 (978-0-87534-703-5(7)); Vol. 4. pap. 5.95 (978-0-87534-704-2(5)); Vol. 5. pap. 5.95 (978-0-87534-705-9(3)); Vol. 6. pap. 5.95 (978-0-87534-706-6(1)); Vol. 7. pap. 5.95 (978-0-87534-707-3(X)); Vol. 8. pap. 5.95 (978-0-87534-708-0(8)) Highlights for Children.

—Puzzlemania Superchallenge, Vol. 4. O'Hare, Jeff, ed. 2003. (Illus.). 48p. (YA). (gr. 5 up). pap. 6.95 (978-1-56397-792-3(3)) Boyds Mills Pr.

Highlights for Children Editorial Staff, compiled by. The Fourth Jumbo Book of Hidden PicturesTM, Vol. 4. 2003. (Illus.). 96p. (J). (gr. 6-9). pap. 6.95 (978-1-59078-097-8(3)) Boyds Mills Pr.

—Mathmania. 2003. (Illus.). 48p. (YA). Vol. 5. pap. 5.95 (978-0-87534-935-0(8)); Vol. 6. pap. 5.95 (978-0-87534-936-7(6)); Vol. 7. pap. 5.95 (978-0-87534-937-4(4)); Vol. 8. pap. 5.95 (978-0-87534-938-1(2)) Highlights for Children.

—Rebus Treasury: Forty-Four Stories Kids Can Read by Following the Pictures. 2003. (Illus.). 48p. (J). (ps up). pap., act. bk. ed. 4.95 (978-1-56397-777-0(X)) Boyds Mills Pr.

—The Super Colossal Book of Hidden Pictures, Vol. 3. 2003. (Illus.). 192p. (J). (gr. 6-9). pap. 9.95 (978-1-56397-952-1(7)) Boyds Mills Pr.

Highlights for Children Editorial Staff, contrib. by. Puzzlemania. 2003. (Illus.). 48p. (YA). Vol. 9. pap. 5.95 (978-0-87534-721-9(5)); Vol. 10. pap. 5.95 (978-0-87534-722-6(3)); Vol. 11. pap. 5.95 (978-0-87534-723-3(1)); Vol. 12. pap. 5.95 (978-0-87534-724-0(X)) Highlights for Children.

Highlights for Children Editorial Staff, ed. Mathmania. 2004. (Illus.). 48p. (YA). Vol. 17. pap. 5.95 (978-0-87534-949-7(8)); Vol. 18. pap. 5.95 (978-0-87534-950-3(1)) Highlights for Children.

—Puzzlemania. 2004. (Illus.). 48p. (YA). Vol. 17. pap. 5.95 (978-0-87534-719-6(3)); Vol. 18. pap. 5.95 (978-0-87534-720-2(7)) Highlights for Children.

—The Super Colossal Book of Hidden Pictures, Vol. 2. 2003. (Illus.). 192p. (J). (gr. 6-9). pap. 9.95 (978-1-56397-951-4(9)) Boyds Mills Pr.

Highlights USA for Children Staff. Puzzlemania. (Illus.). 48p. (J). pap. 5.95 (978-0-87534-710-3(X)); (J). pap. 5.95 (978-0-87534-711-0(8)); (J). pap. 5.95 (978-0-87534-712-7(6)); (J). pap. 5.95 (978-0-87534-709-7(6)); Vol. 13. 2004. (YA). pap., act. bk. ed. 5.95 (978-0-87534-713-4(4)); Vol. 14. 2004. (YA). pap., act. bk. ed. 5.95 (978-0-87534-714-1(2)); Vol. 15. 2004. (YA). pap., act. bk. ed. 5.95 (978-0-87534-729-5(0)); Vol. 16. 2004. (YA). pap., act. bk. ed. 5.95 (978-0-87534-730-1(4)) Highlights for Children.

Hill, Sandi. Playground Problem Solvers, Vol. 4413. Kupperstein, Joel, ed. Dunne, Kathleen, illus. 1998. (Learn to Read Social Studies). 16p. (J). (ps-2). pap. 2.75 (978-1-57471-336-7(1) , 4413) Creative Teaching Pr., Inc.

Hockett, M. A. Punctuation Puzzler: Run-Ons Level C1. 2005. (YA). pap. 9.99 (978-0-89455-819-1(6)) Critical Thinking Bks. & Software.

Hoehn, Robert G. Science Puzzlers! 150 Ready-to-Use Activities to Make Learning Fun. 2002. 272p. (gr. 4-8). pap. 27.95 (978-0-7879-6660-7(6) , Jossey-Bass) Wiley, John & Sons, Inc.

Holt, Rinehart and Winston Staff. Holt Science & Technology: Earth: Science Puzzles, Twisters & Teasers. 2000. pap. 11.33 (978-0-03-054391-3(6)) Holt, Rinehart & Winston.

—Holt Science & Technology: Life: Science Puzzles, Twisters & Teasers. 2000. pap. 11.33 (978-0-03-054381-4(9)) Holt, Rinehart & Winston.

—Holt Science & Technology: Physics: Science Puzzles, Twisters & Teasers. 2000. pap. 11.33 (978-0-03-054401-9(7)) Holt, Rinehart & Winston.

—Science Puzzlers, Twisters & Teasers. 5th ed. 2004. (Illus.). pap. 26.46 (978-0-03-035192-1(8)) Holt, Rinehart & Winston.

Holzhuher, Cynthia. U. S. Olympic Brain Teasers. Teacher Created Materials Staff, ed. 2000. (U. S. Olympic Committee's Activity Book Ser.). (Illus.). 32p. (J). pap., tchr. ed. 4.99 (978-1-58000-057-4(6) , TCM 2220) Griffin Publishing Group.

Hop, L. L. C. Hooked on First Grade: Puzzles & Mazes. 2006. 64p. 3.79 (978-1-931020-71-8(X)) HOP, LLC.

—Hooked on Kindergarten Super Workbook. 2006. 320p. 12.99 (978-1-931020-73-2(6)) HOP, LLC.

HOP, LLC. Hooked on Learning Puzzles & Mazes. 2006. 64p. 3.79 (978-1-933863-90-0(0)) HOP, LLC.

Horn, Randy. Would You Rather... 2008. 416p. pap. 9.95 (978-0-7611-4364-2(5)) Workman Publishing Co., Inc.

Hot Wheels Giant Coloring. 2004. (J). act. bk. ed. (978-0-7666-0675-3(9) , 49540) Modern Publishing.

Hot Wheels Giant Coloring & Activity Books. 2004. (J). act. bk. ed. (978-0-7666-0676-0(7) , 49540) Modern Publishing.

Houssin, Frédéric & Ramadier, Cédric. The Big Book of Car Games. 2003. (Illus.). 120p. spiral bd. 12.95 (978-1-57912-276-8(0) , 81276) Black Dog & Leventhal Pubs., Inc.

Hovanec, Helene. Christmas Puzzles. 2006. 80p. (J). pap. 3.95 (978-1-4027-3821-0(8)) Sterling Publishing Co., Inc.

—Crisscross Puzzles for Kids. 2005. (Mensa Ser.). 96p. (J). pap. 5.95 (978-1-4027-2137-3(4)) Sterling Publishing Co., Inc.

—Easy First Puzzles. Shems, Ed, illus. 2005. (My First Puzzles Ser.). 64p. (ps-ps). pap. 3.95 (978-1-4027-2322-3(9)) Sterling Publishing Co., Inc.

—Funny Animal Puzzles. Leary, Catherine, illus. 2002. 80p. (gr. 2-4). pap. 5.95 (978-0-8069-7374-6(9)) Sterling Publishing Co., Inc.

—Halloween Puzzles. 2006. 80p. (J). pap. 3.95 (978-1-4027-3820-3(X)) Sterling Publishing Co., Inc.

—I Can Read Puzzles. Shems, Ed, illus. 2005. (My First Puzzles Ser.). 64p. (ps). pap. 3.95 (978-1-4027-2323-0(7)) Sterling Publishing Co., Inc.

—My First Puzzles: Fun with Words. Shems, Ed, illus. 2006. (My First Puzzles Ser.). 64p. (J). pap. 3.95 (978-1-4027-3640-7(1)) Sterling Publishing Co., Inc.

—My First Puzzles: Letter Games. Conger, Holli, illus. 2007. (My First Puzzles Ser.). 64p. (J). pap. 3.95 (978-1-4027-4263-7(0)) Sterling Publishing Co., Inc.

—My First Puzzles: Reading Fun. Conger, Holli, illus. 2007. (My First Puzzles Ser.). 64p. (J). pap. 3.95 (978-1-4027-4264-4(9)) Sterling Publishing Co., Inc.

—Sit & Solve Crisscross Puzzles. 2003. (Sit & Solve Ser.). 96p. (J). pap. 4.95 (978-1-4027-0381-2(3)) Sterling Publishing Co., Inc.

—Word Search Puzzles for Young Einsteins. 2001. (Illus.). 96p. (J). (gr. 2-7). pap. 6.95 (978-0-8069-5849-1(9)) Sterling Publishing Co., Inc.

—The 21-Foot-Long Brainteaser Book: Fold-Out Fun for More Than One. 2007. 64p. (J). 9.95 (978-1-4027-4211-8(8) , Sterling Innovation) Sterling Publishing Co., Inc.

Hovanec, Helene & Merrell, Patrick. Country Fun Games & Puzzles. 2007. 144p. (J). pap. 9.95 (978-1-58017-679-8(8)) Storey Publishing, LLC.

Humbert, Ellen, et al, contrib. by. Bible Puzzles for Kids: Ages 8-10. 2005. (Illus.). 143p. (J). (gr. 4-7). pap. 14.99 (978-0-7847-1788-2(5) , 02267) Standard Publishing.

I Spy Funhouse. 2003. (J). 129.50 (978-0-590-66383-0(6)) Scholastic, Inc.

I Spy Mystery. 2006. cd-rom 29.99 (*978-0-439-90057-7(3)* , Scholastic) Scholastic, Inc.

I Spy Mystery: A Book of Picture Riddles. 2002. (I Spy Ser.). (Illus.). (J). 21.45 (978-0-7587-4106-6(5)) Book Wholesalers, Inc.

Jacobs, Lana. Surf's Up: Coloring & Activity Book & Tattoos. Merkel, Joe F., illus. 2007. (Surf's Up Ser.). 32p. (J). pap. 3.99 (*978-0-06-115336-5(2)* , Harper Entertainment) HarperCollins Pubs.

—Transformers Coloring & Activity Book & Stickers. 2007. (Transformers Ser.). 32p. (J). pap. 3.99 (*978-0-06-088826-8(1)* , Harper Entertainment) HarperCollins Pubs.

Jacobs, Lana & Raymond, N. T. Surf's up: Coloring & Activity Book 3-in-1. Morgan, Tom & Sazaklis, John, illus. 2007. (Surf's Up Ser.). 96p. (J). pap. 2.99 (*978-0-06-115338-9(9)* , Harper Entertainment) HarperCollins Pubs.

James, Diane. Baa, Baa, Black Sheep. 2004. (Jigsaw Nursery Rhymes Ser.). (Illus.). 12p. (J). (ps-k). bds. 9.95 (978-1-58728-625-4(4) , Two Can Publishing) T&N Children's Publishing.

—Here We Go. 2004. (Jigsaw Rhymes Ser.). (Illus.). 12p. (J). (ps-k). bds. 9.95 (978-1-58728-024-5(8) , Two Can Publishing) T&N Children's Publishing.

—Lavender Blue. 2004. (Jigsaw Nursery Rhymes Ser.). (Illus.). 12p. (J). (ps-k). bds. 9.95 (978-1-58728-624-7(6) , Two Can Publishing) T&N Children's Publishing.

—Pat-a-Cake. 2004. (Jigsaw Nursery Rhymes Ser.). (Illus.). 12p. (J). (ps-k). bds. 9.95 (978-1-58728-623-0(8) , Two Can Publishing) T&N Children's Publishing.

—Splish Splash. 2004. (Jigsaw Rhymes Ser.). (Illus.). 12p. (J). (ps-k). bds. 9.95 (978-1-58728-022-1(1) , Two Can Publishing) T&N Children's Publishing.

—Spots & Stripes. 2004. (Jigsaw Rhymes Ser.). (Illus.). 12p. (J). (ps-k). bds. 9.95 (978-1-58728-021-4(3) , Two Can Publishing) T&N Children's Publishing.

—Three Blind Mice. 2004. (Jigsaw Nursery Rhymes Ser.). (Illus.). 12p. (J). (ps-k). bds. 9.95 (978-1-58728-626-1(2) , Two Can Publishing) T&N Children's Publishing.

Janeczko, Paul B., ed. Top Secret: A Handbook of Codes, Ciphers & Secret Writing. Lareau, Jenna, illus. 2006. 144p. (J). (gr. 4). pap. 7.99 (978-0-7636-2972-4(3)) Candlewick Pr.

Jay Jay the Jet Plane Coloring & Activity Books. 2004. (J). act. bk. ed. (978-0-7666-0877-1(8) , 99680); act. bk. ed. (978-0-7666-0878-8(6) , 99680); act. bk. ed. (978-0-7666-0879-5(4) , 99680); act. bk. ed. (978-0-7666-0880-1(8) , 99680) Modern Publishing.

Jay Jay the Jet Plane Fun Activity Box Set. 2004. (J). act. bk. ed. (978-0-7666-0900-6(6) , 64050) Modern Publishing.

Jenkins, Gerald & Bear, Magdalen. Tarquin Number Challenges: A Collection of 50 Puzzles to Test Your Mathematical Skills. 2004. (Illus.). 56p. 10.00 (978-1-899618-49-1(X)) Tarquin Pubns. GBR. *Dist:* Parkwest Pubns., Inc.

P Q R

Jesus' Life Hidden Pictures. 1998. 48p. (J). (gr. 4-6). pap. 5.95 (978-0-7647-0428-4(1) , SS4863, In Celebration) Schaffer, Frank Pubns.

Joachim, Jean. Construction Vehicles Dot-to-Dot. 2006. 80p. (J). pap. 5.95 (978-1-4027-1276-0(6)) Sterling Publishing Co., Inc.

Jones, David. Little Box O'Luck. 2007. 48p. pap. 6.95 (978-0-7624-2938-7(0) , Running Pr. Minature Editions) Running Pr. Bk. Pubs.

Jones, Evelyn. World's Wackiest Riddle Book. 2004. (Illus.). 96p. (J). pap. 4.95 (978-1-4027-0924-1(2)) Sterling Publishing Co., Inc.

Jones, Rob Lloyd. 1001 Pirate Things to Spot. 2007. 32p. (J). 9.99 (978-0-7945-1513-3(4) , Usborne) EDC Publishing.

Jones, Victoria. Ancient Greece Dot-to-Dot. Salvucci, Richard J., illus. 2005. 80p. (J). (gr. 1-5). pap. 5.95 (978-1-4027-2432-9(2)) Sterling Publishing Co., Inc.

Jugran, Feb & Jugran, Jan. Puzzles to Go: 3 Little Ducks. Vagnozzi, Barbara, illus. 2007. 8p. (J). (ps-17). 9.99 (978-1-58476-635-3(2)) Innovative Kids.

Jugran, Jan. Puzzles to Go: I Love You Teddy. Logan, Laura, illus. 2007. 8p. (J). (ps-17). 9.99 (978-1-58476-548-6(8)) Innovative Kids.

Jumbo Puzzle Book. 2004. (J). per. (978-1-57657-006-7(1)) Paradise Pr., Inc.

Junior Puzzles. 2004. 112p. (J). 4.99 (978-1-85997-389-9(2)) Byeway Bks.

Kalvitis, David. The Greatest Dot-to-Dot Book in the World. 48p. (YA). Vol. 1. 2000. (Illus.). 6.95 (978-0-9700437-0-2(8)); Vol. 2. 2001. 6.95 (978-0-9700437-1-9(6)); Vol. 3. 2002. 6.95 (978-0-9700437-2-6(4)); Vol. 4. 2003. 6.95 (978-0-9700437-3-3(2)) Monkeying Around.

Katz, Alan. Stinky Thinking No. 2: Another Big Book of Gross Games & Brainteasers. Kalis, Jennifer, illus. 2007. 112p. (J). pap. 7.99 (978-1-4169-2546-0(5) , Aladdin) Simon & Schuster Children's Publishing.

Kay, Keith. The Who, What & Where Book of Brain Bafflers. 2002. (Illus.). 96p. (J). (978-1-4027-0682-0(0)) Sterling Publishing Co., Inc.

Kelleher, Pat & Twist, Clint. Puzzle Quest Around the World. Tomblin, Gill & Bonson, Richard, illus. 2006. (Puzzle Quest Ser.). 22p. (J). bds. 22.95 (978-0-7696-4875-4(4) , Brighter Child) School Specialty Publishing.

—Puzzle Quest Through Space. Pastor, Terry, illus. 2006. (Puzzle Quest Ser.). 22p. (J). bds. 22.95 (978-0-7696-4877-4(0) , Brighter Child) School Specialty Publishing.

Keller, Charles. Super Silly Riddles. Winter, Dave, illus. 2002. 96p. (J). (gr. 1-4). pap. 4.95 (978-0-8069-7723-2(X)) Sterling Publishing Co., Inc.

Kellogg's Coloring & Activity Books. 2004. (J). act. bk. ed. (978-0-7666-1004-0(7) , 99350); act. bk. ed. (978-0-7666-1005-7(5) , 99350); act. bk. ed. (978-0-7666-1006-4(3) , 99350); act. bk. ed. (978-0-7666-1007-1(1) , 99350) Modern Publishing.

Kellogg's Fun Activity Box Set. 2004. (J). act. bk. ed. (978-0-7666-1120-7(5) , 64019) Modern Publishing.

Kellogg's Giant Coloring & Activity Books. 2004. (J). act. bk. ed. (978-0-7666-1008-8(X) , 49435); act. bk. ed. (978-0-7666-1009-5(8) , 49435) Modern Publishing.

Khanduri, Kamini. Great History Search. Hancock, David, illus. rev. ed. 2005. 48p. (J). pap. 8.95 (978-0-7945-1029-9(9) , Usborne) EDC Publishing.

Khanduri, Kamini & Heywood, Rosie. Big Book of Picture Puzzles (Combined Volume) 2005. 176p. (J). 18.99 (978-0-7945-1165-4(1) , Usborne) EDC Publishing.

Kidslabel Staff. Spot 7 Spooky. 2007. (Illus.). 40p. (J). (gr. 1-6). 12.95 (978-0-8118-5723-9(9)) Chronicle Bks. LLC.

Kim, Jeannie. Body & Mind: A Guide to Life. 2003. (gr. 3-6). lib. bdg. 12.40 (978-0-613-72134-9(9)) Tandem Library Bks.

Kimble, Evan & Kimble, Lael. African Animals Dot-to-Dot. Harrison, Nancy, illus. 2005. 80p. (J). (gr. 1-4). pap. 5.95 (978-1-4027-2343-8(1)) Sterling Publishing Co., Inc.

—Farm Animals Dot-to-Dot. 2004. (Illus.). 80p. pap. 5.95 (978-1-4027-0993-7(5)) Sterling Publishing Co., Inc.

—Ice Age Creatures Dot-to-Dot. 2004. (Illus.). 80p. pap. 5.95 (978-1-4027-0994-4(3)) Sterling Publishing Co., Inc.

—Wizard's World Dot-to-Dot. 2004. (Illus.). 80p. pap. 5.95 (978-1-4027-0995-1(1)) Sterling Publishing Co., Inc.

Kimpton, Diana. Pony Puzzles: Test Your Pony Knowledge. 2000. (Illus.). 120p. (J). (gr. 2-7). mass mkt. (978-0-330-33640-6(1) , Pan) Pan Macmillan.

King, Colin. Puzzle Del Mundo. 2005. (Titles in Spanish Ser.). (SPA.). 14p. (J). 14.95 (978-0-7460-6395-8(4) , Usborne) EDC Publishing.

Klutz Press Staff & Green, Marilyn, eds. Made You Look: A Book of Puzzling Pictures. 2007. 60p. pap. 16.95 ***978-1-57054-894-9(3))** Klutz.

Kohart, Georgia. A Heritage of the Heart Teaching Companion. 2003. (Illus.). ring bd. 24.95 (978-0-9706348-1-8(1)) Heritage Heart Farm.

Krings, Antoon. Droles de Petites Betes. (FRE.). pap. 18.95 (978-2-07-058437-6(2)) Gallimard, Editions FRA. *Dist:* Distribooks, Inc.

Krulik, Nancy E. Puzzlers. 1999. (My Very First Winnie the Pooh Ser.). (Illus.). 64p. (J). (ps-1). pap. 4.99 (978-0-7868-4344-2(6)) Disney Pr.

LaBarge, R. L. Fitting the Pieces Together. unabr. ed. 2000. (Illus.). 500p. (YA). pap. 65.00 (978-0-9617796-1-0(6)) Allfit.

LaFosse, Michael. Making Origami Puzzles Step by Step. 2004. (Kid's Guide to Origami Ser.). (Illus.). 24p. (J). lib. bdg. 21.25 (978-0-8239-6704-9(2) , PowerKids Pr.) Rosen Publishing Group, Inc., The.

Lagonegro, Melissa. G'Day, Friends! an Outback Puzzle Book. 2004. (Illus.). 12p. (J). (ps-2). bds. 9.99 (978-0-375-82956-7(3) , Golden Bks.) Random Hse. Children's Bks.

Langton, Mandy & Pilgrim, Anne. The Pony Puzzle Book, Bk. 2. 2001. (Illus.). 92p. pap. 11.99 (978-0-85131-850-9(9) , Allen, J. A. & Company, Limited) Hale, Robert Ltd. GBR. *Dist:* Independent Pubs. Group.

Larochelle, David. Detective Dave's Mad Mysteries. 2006. 304p. (J). (gr. 3). pap. 4.99 (978-0-8431-2126-1(2) , Price Stern Sloan) Penguin Group (USA) Inc.

LaRochelle, David. Picture That! Christmas Puzzles. LaRochelle, David, illus. 2002. (Illus.). 48p. (J). 4.99 (978-0-8431-4883-1(7) , Price Stern Sloan) Penguin Group (USA) Inc.

Lassen, Christian Riese. Sea Creatures: A Read & Play Carry Puzzle Book. 2001. (Illus.). 10p. (J). (ps-3). 12.95 (978-0-7407-1800-7(2)) Andrews McMeel Publishing.

Lawless, Laura & Blair, Beth. The Everything Kids' First Spanish Puzzle: Make Practicing Español Fun & Facil! 2006. (SPA & ENG., Illus.). 144p. (J). pap. 7.95 (978-1-59337-717-5(7)) Adams Media Corp.

Learn to Juggle. 2004. (How 2 Kits Ser.). (Illus.). 48p. (J). (978-1-84229-929-6(8)) Top That! Publishing PLC.

Learning Horizons, ed. Games & Puzzles: Grade 2. 2004. (Learn on the GOTM Workbooks Ser.). (Illus.). 64p. (gr. 2 up). pap. 2.95 (978-1-58610-708-6(9) , 61056) Learning Horizons, Inc.

LeCompte, David & Padrick, Kendell. Eugene Stillwell Wants to Know!, Pt. 2. 2007. 96p. (J). pap. 4.95 ***(978-1-929945-74-0(4))** Big Guy Bks., Inc.

Lee, Helen, ed. PowerGuide Logbook 2: Fun-Filled, Grace-Growing Activities. 2002. 96p. (YA). pap. 3.99 (978-0-8280-1592-9(9)) Review & Herald Publishing Assn.

Leichter, Albert. Staunton Treasures Past & Present Connect the Dots. 2005. (J). act. bk. ed. 3.95 (978-0-9704280-6-6(5)) ClockTower Pubns.

Leigh, S. Puzzle Dungeon. 2004. (Young Puzzles Ser.). (Illus.). 32p. (J). pap. 6.95 (978-0-7945-0511-0(2) , Usborne); lib. bdg. 14.95 (978-1-58086-599-9(2)) EDC Publishing.

—Puzzle Farm. 2004. (Young Puzzles Ser.). 32p. (J). lib. bdg. 14.95 (978-1-58086-627-9(1) , Usborne); (Illus.). pap. 6.95 (978-0-7945-0625-4(9)) EDC Publishing.

—Puzzle Jungle. 2004. (Young Puzzles Ser.). (Illus.). 32p. (J). pap. 6.95 (978-0-7945-0435-9(3)); lib. bdg. 14.95 (978-1-58086-534-0(8)) EDC Publishing.

—Puzzle Ocean. 2004. (Young Puzzles Ser.). (Illus.). 32p. (J). pap. 6.95 (978-0-7945-0436-6(1)); lib. bdg. 14.95 (978-1-58086-535-7(6)) EDC Publishing.

—Puzzle Planet. 2004. (Young Puzzles Ser.). (Illus.). 32p. (J). lib. bdg. 14.95 (978-1-58086-536-4(4)); pap. 6.95 (978-0-7945-0437-3(X) , Usborne) EDC Publishing.

—Puzzle School. 2004. (Young Puzzles Ser.). (Illus.). 32p. (J). pap. 6.95 (978-0-7945-0512-7(0)); lib. bdg. 14.95 (978-1-58086-600-2(X)) EDC Publishing.

—Puzzle Town. 2004. (Young Puzzles Ser.). 32p. (J). lib. bdg. 14.95 (978-1-58086-537-1(2) , Usborne); (Illus.). pap. 6.95 (978-0-7945-0438-0(8)) EDC Publishing.

—Puzzle Train. 2004. (Young Puzzles Ser.). 32p. (J). lib. bdg. 14.95 (978-1-58086-633-0(6) , Usborne) EDC Publishing.

Leigh, S. & Haw, B. Puzzle Island. 32p. (J). lib. bdg. 14.95 (978-1-58086-675-0(1) , Usborne) EDC Publishing.

Leigh, Susannah. Ciudad Enigma: Lumen Puzzles Infantiles. (SPA., Illus.). (J). pap. (978-950-724-182-6(5)) Lumen.

—L' Ile Fantastique: Fantastic Island. Gemmell, Kathy & Irving, Nicole, eds. Haw, Brenda, illus. (FRE.). 25p. (J). (gr. 2-3). reprint ed. 17.00 (978-0-7881-9300-2(7)) DIANE Publishing Co.

—Isla Enigma: Lumen Puzzles Infantiles. (SPA., Illus.). (J). pap. (978-950-724-183-3(3)) Lumen.

—Pirates. 2006. 32p. (J). pap. 6.99 (978-0-7945-1359-7(X) , Usborne) EDC Publishing.

—Puzzle Castle. Waters, Gaby, ed. Haw, Brenda, illus. rev. ed. 2004. (Young Puzzles Ser.). 32p. (J). pap. 6.95 (978-0-7945-0433-5(7) , Usborne) EDC Publishing.

—Puzzle Dinosaurs. 2007. (Young Puzzles Ser.). 32p. (J). pap. 6.99 ***(978-0-7945-1778-6(1)** , Usborne) EDC Publishing.

—Puzzle Palace. Tyler, Jenny, ed. Haw, Brenda, illus. 2005. 32p. (J). (ps-7). pap. 6.95 (978-0-7945-1120-3(1) , Usborne) EDC Publishing.

—Puzzle Pyramid. Haw, Brenda, illus. 2004. 32p. (J). pap. 6.95 (978-0-7945-0791-6(3) , Usborne) EDC Publishing.

—Puzzle Train. Waters, Gaby, ed. Haw, Brenda, illus. 2003. (Young Puzzles Ser.). 32p. (J). pap. 6.95 (978-0-7945-0683-4(6) , Usborne) EDC Publishing.

—Puzzle Train. 1998. (Young Puzzles Ser.). (Illus.). 32p. (YA). (gr. k-3). lib. bdg. 13.95 (978-0-88110-798-2(0)) EDC Publishing.

—Puzzle World: Combined Volume. Waters, Gaby, ed. Haw, Brenda, illus. 2004. (Young Puzzles Ser.). 96p. (J). pap. 13.95 (978-0-7945-0688-9(7) , Usborne) EDC Publishing.

Leighton, Robert, et al. The Brainiest Insaniest Puzzle Book. 2006. (Illus.). 160p. (J). (gr. 2-8). pap. 10.95 (978-0-7611-4386-4(6)) Workman Publishing Co., Inc.

Levin, David H. Bridge Puzzles for Children Vol. 1: Simple Card Play Problems to Introduce Them to This Wonderful Game. 2004. (Illus.). 128p. (J). pap. 14.95 (978-0-9638001-2-1(4)) Syllogism Pr.

Levy, Barbara Soloff. Little Farm Follow-the-Dots. 2005. (Illus.). 64p. (J). pap. 1.50 (978-0-486-44050-7(8)) Dover Pubns., Inc.

—Little Zoo Animal Mazes. 2006. 64p. (J). (ps-3). pap. 1.50 (978-0-486-44440-6(6)) Dover Pubns., Inc.

—Pets Follow the Dots. 2006. 64p. (J). pap. 1.50 (978-0-486-44890-9(8)) Dover Pubns., Inc.

Levy, Barbara Soloff. Who's Who in the Zoo? Dot-to-Dot Fun. 2007. (Pictorial Archive Ser.). (Illus.). 30p. (J). (ps-3). per. 3.95 ***(978-0-486-46181-6(5))** Dover Pubns., Inc.

Lewis, Peter. Famous Cities: Search-a-Word Puzzles. 2001. (Illus.). 80p. (gr. 3). pap. 1.50 (978-0-486-41370-9(5)) Dover Pubns., Inc.

Life Magazine Editors. Life: The Original Picture Puzzle. 2007. 176p. (YA). pap. 10.99 ***(978-1-933821-96-2(5))** Time, Inc. Home Entertainment.

Litchfield, Jo. Socorro! Litchfield, Jo, illus. 2005. (SPA.). 14p. (J). 7.95 (978-0-7460-6641-6(4) , Usborne) EDC Publishing.

—Tractores. Litchfield, Jo, illus. 2005. (SPA.). 14p. (J). 7.95 (978-0-7460-6642-3(2) , Usborne) EDC Publishing.

Litchfield, Jo, illus. Box of Trucks. 2004. (Boxed Jigsaws Ser.). 10p. (J). 11.99 (978-0-7945-0916-3(9) , Usborne) EDC Publishing.

Little Tikes Coloring & Activity Books. 2004. (J). act. bk. ed. (978-0-7666-0910-5(3) , 99310); act. bk. ed. (978-0-7666-0911-2(1) , 99310); act. bk. ed. (978-0-7666-0912-9(X) , 99310); act. bk. ed. (978-0-7666-0913-6(8) , 99310) Modern Publishing.

Little Tikes Fun Activity Box Set. 2004. (J). act. bk. ed. (978-0-7666-1022-4(5) , 64017) Modern Publishing.

Little Tikes Giant Coloring & Activity Books. 2004. (J). act. bk. ed. (978-0-7666-0963-1(4) , 49280); act. bk. ed. (978-0-7666-0964-8(2) , 49280) Modern Publishing.

Littlefield, Cindy A. Sea Life Games & Puzzles. 2006. (Illus.). 144p. (J). pap. 9.95 (978-1-58017-624-8(0)) Storey Publishing, LLC.

Littlefield, Cindy A. & Littlefield. Horse Games & Puzzles for Kids: 102 Brainteasers, Word Games, Jokes & Riddles, Picture Puzzlers, Matches & Logic Tests for Horse-Loving Kids. 2004. (Illus.). 144p. (J). pap. 9.95 (978-1-58017-538-8(4) , 67538, Storey Kids) Storey Publishing, LLC.

Long, Cathryn J. Famous Places. 2001. (Crossword America Ser.). (Illus.). 64p. (J). (gr. 3-7). pap. 5.95 (978-0-7373-0582-1(7)) Lowell Hse. Juvenile.

Long, Laurie. Valuable Bible Characters - New Testament Math Puzzle Grade 1-2. Jackson, Cindy, illus. l.t. ed. 1999. 20p. (J). (gr. 1-2). pap. 4.50 (978-1-878669-75-9(3) , 3513) Creative Teaching Assocs.

—Valuable Bible Characters - New Testament Math Puzzles Grade 3-4. Jackson, Cindy, illus. l.t. ed. 1999. 20p. (J). (gr. 3-4). pap. 4.50 (978-1-878669-76-6(1) , 3514) Creative Teaching Assocs.

—Valuable Bible Characters - Old Testament Math Puzzles Grades 3-4. Jackson, Cindy, illus. l.t. ed. 1999. 20p. (J). (gr. 3-4). pap. 4.50 (978-1-878669-73-5(7) , 3511) Creative Teaching Assocs.

Look & Find Ser., 19 bks. (Illus.). (J). lib. bdg. 284.05 (978-1-56674-907-7(7)) Forest Hse. Publishing Co., Inc.

Lucas, Vivien. A Puzzle a Day: A Collection of Mathematical Problems for Every Day of the Year. 2004. (Illus.). 96p. 14.00 (978-1-899618-52-1(X)) Tarquin Pubns. GBR. *Dist:* Parkwest Pubns., Inc.

Lupton, Hugh. Riddle Me This! Riddles & Stories to Challenge Your Mind. Fatus, Sophie, illus. 2003. 64p. (J). 19.99 (978-1-84148-169-2(6)) Barefoot Bks., Inc.

MacHale, Des & Sloane, Paul. Sit & Solve Lateral Thinking Puzzles. 2003. (Sit & Solve Ser.). (Illus.). 96p. pap. 4.95 (978-0-8069-5705-0(0)) Sterling Publishing Co., Inc.

Mackenzie, Carine. In the Lord's Army. 2nd ed. Date not set. (Illus.). 32p. (J). pap. 2.50 (978-1-871676-65-5(7) , Christian Focus) Christian Focus Pubns. GBR. *Dist:* Riverside, Spring Arbor Distributors, Inc.

—Talking to You. 96p. (J). mass mkt. 4.99 (978-1-871676-45-7(2) , Christian Focus) Christian Focus Pubns. GBR. *Dist:* Riverside, Spring Arbor Distributors, Inc.

Magruder, Trula. What a Girl Loves: Puzzle Book. 2004. (American Girl Library(R) Ser.). (Illus.). 128p. (J). 7.95 (978-1-58485-909-3(1)) American Girl Publishing, Inc.

Maizels, Jennie. Party in Jigsaw Forest. 2000. (Jigsaw Bks.). (Illus.). 14p. (J). (ps-k). bds. 10.95 (978-1-86233-153-2(7)) David & Charles Children's Bks. GBR. *Dist:* Sterling Publishing Co., Inc.

—Rocket to Jigsaw Planet: A Book & Jigsaw in One! 2000. (Jigsaw Bks.). (Illus.). 14p. (J). (ps-k). bds. 10.95 (978-1-86233-148-8(0)) David & Charles Children's Bks. GBR. *Dist:* Sterling Publishing Co., Inc.

Maring, Therese, ed. Top-Secret Code Book: Tricky, Fun Codes for You & Your Friends. Lukatz, Casey, illus. 2005. (American Girl Today Ser.). 32p. (J). (gr. 4-7). pap. 5.95 (978-1-59369-018-2(5) , American Girl) American Girl Publishing, Inc.

Marsh, Carole. The Big Alabama Reproducible Activity Book! 2001. (Illus.). 96p. (J). (gr. 2-6). pap., act. bk. ed. 9.95 (978-0-7933-9934-5(3)) Gallopade International.

Marsh, T. J. & Ward, Jennifer. Way Out in the Desert. Spengler, Kenneth J., illus. 2002. 20p. (J). bds. 6.95 (978-0-87358-802-7(9)); 1999. 32p. 15.95 (978-0-87358-687-0(5)) Northland Publishing. (Rising Moon Bks. for Young Readers).

Marzollo, Jean. Extreme Challenger! A Book of Picture Riddles. Wick, Walter, illus. 2005. (I Spy Ser.). 20p. (J). pap. 18.95 (978-0-439-68421-7(8)) Scholastic, Inc.

—Extreme Challenger! A Book of Picture Riddles. Wick, Walter, photos by. 2000. (I Spy Bks.). (Illus.). 40p. (J). (ps-3). pap. 13.95 (978-0-439-19900-1(X)) Scholastic, Inc.

—I Spy: A Book of Picture Riddles. Wick, Walter, illus. 10th ed. 2001. (I Spy Bks.). 40p. (J). (ps-3). pap. 13.95 (978-0-590-45087-4(5) , Cartwheel Bks.) Scholastic, Inc.

—I Spy a Balloon. Wick, Walter, illus. 2006. (Scholastic Reader Level 1 Ser.). 32p. (J). pap. 3.99 (978-0-439-73864-4(4) , Cartwheel Bks.) Scholastic, Inc.

—I Spy a Candy Cane. Wick, Walter, illus. Wick, Walter, photos by. 2004. (Scholastic Reader Ser.). 32p. (J). (ps-3). pap. 3.99 (978-0-439-52474-2(1) , Cartwheel Bks.) Scholastic, Inc.

—I Spy a Penguin. Wick, Walter, illus. 2005. (Scholastic Reader Ser.). 32p. (J). (ps-3). pap. 3.99 (978-0-439-73862-0(8) , Cartwheel Bks.) Scholastic, Inc.

—I Spy a Scary Monster. Wick, Walter, illus. Wick, Walter, photos by. 2005. (Scholastic Reader Ser.). 32p. (J). pap. 3.99 (978-0-439-68054-7(9) , Cartwheel Bks.) Scholastic, Inc.

—I Spy a Scary Monster. Wick, Walter, photos by. 2005. (Illus.). 28p. (J). (ps-3). lib. bdg. 11.19 (978-0-606-33831-8(4)) Tandem Library Bks.

—I Spy a School Bus. Wick, Walter, illus. 2003. (Scholastic Reader Ser.). 32p. (J). pap. 3.99 (978-0-439-52473-5(3) , Cartwheel Bks.) Scholastic, Inc.

—I Spy Christmas: A Book of Picture Riddles. Wick, Walter, photos by. 2002. (I Spy Ser.). (Illus.). (J). 21.45 (978-0-7587-4104-2(9)) Book Wholesalers, Inc.

—I Spy Christmas: A Book of Picture Riddles. Wick, Walter, illus. 2005. (I Spy Ser.). 20p. (J). pap. 18.95 (978-0-439-68420-0(X)) Scholastic, Inc.

—I Spy Fantasy. Wick, Walter, photos by. (I Spy Bks.). (FRE., Illus.). (J). (ps-3). pap. 16.99 (978-0-590-24340-7(3)) Scholastic, Inc.

—I Spy Funny Teeth. Wick, Walter, photos by. 2003. (Scholastic Reader Ser.). (Illus.). 32p. (J). 3.99 (978-0-439-52472-8(5) , Cartwheel Bks.) Scholastic, Inc.

—I Spy Gold Challenger! Wick, Walter, illus. 2005. (I Spy Ser.). 20p. (J). pap. 18.95 (978-0-439-68426-2(9)) Scholastic, Inc.

—I Spy Lightning in the Sky. Wick, Walter, illus. 2005. 26p. (J). (ps-ps). lib. bdg. 10.79 (978-0-606-33288-0(X)) Tandem Library Bks.

—I Spy Little Animals. Wick, Walter, photos by. 1998. (I Spy Bks.). (Illus.). 26p. (J). (ps). bds. 6.99 (978-0-590-11711-1(4) , Cartwheel Bks.) Scholastic, Inc.

—I Spy Little Bunnies. Wick, Walter, illus. 2006. (J). bds. 6.99 (978-0-439-78535-8(9) , Cartwheel Bks.) Scholastic, Inc.

—I Spy Little Wheels. Wick, Walter, illus. 1998. (I Spy Bks.). 26p. (J). (ps). bds. 6.99 (978-0-590-04706-7(X) , Cartwheel Bks.) Scholastic, Inc.

—I Spy Merry Christmas. 2007. (Scholastic Reader Level 1 Ser.). 64p. (J). pap. 5.99 ***(978-0-545-03945-1(2)** , Cartwheel Bks.) Scholastic, Inc.

—I Spy Mystery: A Book of Picture Riddles. Wick, Walter, photos by. (I Spy Bks.). (FRE., Illus.). (J). (ps-3). pap. 16.99 (978-0-590-24317-9(9)) Scholastic, Inc.

—I Spy Mystery: A Book of Picture Riddles. Wick, Walter, illus. 2005. (I Spy Ser.). (J). (ps). 40p. 9.95 (978-0-439-78731-4(9) , Cartwheel Bks.); 20p. pap. 18.95 (978-0-439-68427-9(7)) Scholastic, Inc.

—I Spy Nature: A Book of Picture Riddles. Wick, Walter, photos by. 2006. (J). (978-0-439-80732-6(8)) Scholastic, Inc.

—I Spy Santa Claus. Wick, Walter, illus. Wick, Walter, photos by. 2006. (Scholastic Reader Ser.). 32p. (J). pap. 3.99 (978-0-439-78414-6(X)) Scholastic, Inc.

—I Spy Spooky Night. Wick, Walter, illus. 2005. (I Spy Ser.). 20p. (J). pap. 18.95 (978-0-439-68429-3(3)) Scholastic, Inc.

—I Spy Super Challenger! A Book of Picture Riddles. Wick, Walter, illus. 2005. (I Spy Ser.). 20p. (J). pap. 18.95 (978-0-439-68430-9(7)) Scholastic, Inc.

—I Spy Year-Round Challenger! A Book of Picture Riddles. Wick, Walter, illus. 2005. (I Spy Ser.). 20p. (J). pap. 18.95 (978-0-439-68433-0(1)) Scholastic, Inc.

—School Days: A Book of Picture Riddles. Wick, Walter, illus. (J). 2007. 40p. 9.95 ***(978-0-545-02933-9(3));** 2005. 20p. pap. 18.95 (978-0-439-68428-6(5)) Scholastic, Inc.

—Treasure Hunt. Wick, Walter, illus. (J). 2007. 40p. pap. 13.99 ***(978-0-439-02674-1(1));** 2005. 20p. pap. 18.95 (978-0-439-68431-6(5)); 1999. 233.10 (978-0-439-11749-6(X)) Scholastic, Inc.

—Treasure Hunt. Wick, Walter, photos by. 1999. (I Spy Bks.). (Illus.). 40p. (J). (ps-3). pap. 13.95 (978-0-439-04244-4(5) , Cartwheel Bks.) Scholastic, Inc.

—Ultimate Challenger! A Book of Picture Riddles. Wick, Walter, illus. (I Spy Ser.). 40p. (J). 2005. pap. 18.95 (978-0-439-68432-3(3)); 2003. (gr. 1-5). pap. 13.95 (978-0-439-45401-8(8) , Cartwheel Bks.) Scholastic, Inc.

Marzollo, Jean & Wick, Walter. I Spy a Butterfly. 2007. (Scholastic Reader Level 1 Ser.). 32p. (J). pap. 3.99 (978-0-439-73865-1(2) , Cartwheel Bks.) Scholastic, Inc.

—I Spy Funny Teeth. 2003. (ps-2). lib. bdg. 11.80 (978-0-613-72245-2(0)) Tandem Library Bks.

—I Spy Gold Challenger! 1998. (I Spy Bks.). (Illus.). 40p. (J). (ps-3). pap. 13.95 (978-0-590-04296-3(3) , Cartwheel Bks.) Scholastic, Inc.

Maschke, Ruby. Bible Puzzles for Children: 130 Fun Games to Help Children Learn about God & Jesus. 2004. 208p. (J). pap. 5.99 (978-0-517-22341-3(4) , Testament) Random Hse. Value Publishing.

Math Puzzles & Games. 2002. (Home Workbooks Ser.). 64p. pap. 2.49 (978-0-88724-735-4(0) , CD-4537); pap. 2.49 (978-0-88724-728-6(8) , CD-4530); pap. 2.49 (978-0-88724-741-5(5) , CD-4543) Carson-Dellosa Publishing Co., Inc.

Matlock, Mark. Truth Puzzlers. 1998. (Wise Guides Ser.). 48p. (YA). pap. 5.95 (978-1-888237-22-1(8)) Baxter Pr.

Matthies, Don-Oliver & Arena Verlag Staff. Explorer Mazes. 2004. (Illus.). 40p. (J). pap. 3.95 (978-1-4027-1757-4(1)) Sterling Publishing Co., Inc.

—Magical Forest Mazes. 2004. (Maze Craze Book Ser.). (Illus.). 40p. (J). pap. 3.95 (978-1-4027-1758-1(X)) Sterling Publishing Co., Inc.

Matthies, Don-Oliver & Hall, Jody. The Gigantic Book of Mazes. 2004. 254p. (978-1-4027-1539-6(0) , Sterling/ Main St.) Sterling Publishing Co., Inc.

McGraw-Hill Staff & School Specialty Publishing Staff. Challenge Puzzles & Mazes. 2001. (Homework Helpers Activity Bks.). (Illus.). 56p. (J). (gr. 3-3). pap., act. bk. ed. 2.99 (978-0-7682-0718-7(5) , FS109047, Schaffer, Frank) Schaffer, Frank Pubns.

—Dot-to-Dot: Puzzles & Games. 2001. (Homework Helpers Activity Bks.). (Illus.). 56p. (J). (gr. k-1). pap., act. bk. ed. 2.99 (978-0-7682-0689-0(8) , FS109018, Schaffer, Frank) Schaffer, Frank Pubns.

Mckell, Teresa Kane. Algebra Puzzlers. 2001. 112p. (YA). (gr. 9-12). pap. 14.99 (978-0-7682-0101-7(2) , GA1687) School Specialty Publishing.

Medabots Coloring & Activity Books. 2004. (J). act. bk. ed. (978-0-7666-0965-5(0) , 99340); act. bk. ed. (978-0-7666-0966-2(9) , 99340); act. bk. ed. (978-0-7666-0967-9(7) , 99340); act. bk. ed. (978-0-7666-0968-6(5) , 99340) Modern Publishing.

Medabots Giant Coloring & Activity Books. 2004. (J). act. bk. ed. (978-0-7666-0969-3(3) , 49270); act. bk. ed. (978-0-7666-0970-9(7) , 49270) Modern Publishing.

Mega Puzzle Fun. Date not set. 576p. (J). 6.98 (978-0-7525-9824-6(4)) Parragon, Inc.

Mega Travel Fun. Date not set. 576p. (J). 6.98 (978-0-7525-9825-3(2)) Parragon, Inc.

Menotti, Andrea. How to Tackle Puzzles, Unravel Riddles, Crack Codes, & Other Ways to Bend Your Brain. 2004. (Illus.). 80p. (J). (978-0-439-57905-6(8)) Scholastic, Inc.

Mental Aerobics: 442 Thinking Workouts. 96p. (gr. 5-8). 9.99 (978-1-56822-958-4(5) , IF19312) School Specialty Publishing.

Meredith Books Staff & Curry, Don, eds. Superman Returns Jigsaw Book. movie tie-in ed. 2006. 10p. (J). bds. 9.95 (978-0-696-22898-8(X)) Meredith Bks.

Merrell, Patrick. Everything Kids' Racecars Puzzle & Activity Book: Put the pedal to the metal for laps & laps of Fun! 2008. 144p. pap. 7.95 (*978-1-59869-243-3(7)) Adams Media Corp.

Merrell, Patrick. Mind-Melting Mazes. 2004. (Maze Madness Ser.). (Illus.). 64p. (J). pap. 5.95 (978-1-4027-1024-7(0)) Sterling Publishing Co., Inc.

Merrell, Patrick, illus. Maze Halloween. 2002. 32p. (J). (978-0-439-42972-6(2)) Scholastic, Inc.

Messenger, Norman. Imagine. Messenger, Norman, illus. 2005. (Illus.). 32p. (J). (gr. 1 up). 17.99 (978-0-7636-2757-7(7)) Candlewick Pr.

Mignon, Philippe. Labyrinths: Can You Escape from the 26 Letters of the Alphabet? 2002. (Illus.). 60p. (J). (gr. 5). 14.95 (978-1-55297-559-6(2)); pap. 9.95 (978-1-55297-579-4(7)) Firefly Bks., Ltd.

Milbourne, A. Baby Animals Jigsaw Book. 2004. (SPA.). 14p. (J). 8.95 (978-0-7945-0448-9(5)) EDC Publishing.

Milbourne, Anna. Familias de Animales Libro Con Paginas Puzzle. Butler, John, illus. 2004. (Titles in Spanish Ser.). (SPA.). 8p. (J). 8.95 (978-0-7460-6108-4(0) , Usborne) EDC Publishing.

Milito, John. Basketball Puzzles. 2001. (Champion Sport Word Game Ser.). 120p. (J). pap. (978-1-894622-05-9(7)) Warwick Publishing.

—Football Puzzles. 2001. (Champion Sport Word Game Ser.). 120p. (J). pap. (978-1-894622-04-2(9)) Warwick Publishing.

Millhauser, Cathy. Humorous Crosswords. 2003. 96p. pap. 7.95 (978-0-8069-8951-8(3)) Sterling Publishing Co., Inc.

Miss O, Harlie, Justine, and Isabella, with Devra Newberger Speregen, Juliette. Miss O & Friends Book of Fabulous Fun: Cool Stuff to make, recipes, quizzes, & More! 2006. (Miss O & Friends Ser.). (Illus.). 96p. (J). pap. 9.95 (978-0-8230-2943-3(3)) Watson-Guptill Pubns., Inc.

Mitchell, Melanie. Mommy & Baby: Safari. 2006. (Illus.). 10p. (J). bds., bds. 6.95 (978-0-8027-8064-5(4)) Walker & Co.

Mitton, Tony. Amazing Machines Jigsaw Book. Parker, Ant, illus. 2004. 12p. (J). (gr. k-ps). bds. 8.95 (978-0-7534-5741-2(5) , Kingfisher) Houghton Mifflin Co. Trade & Reference Div.

Monica, Carol & Moroney, Christopher. Sesame Street Let's Match. 2007. 12p. (J). bds. 12.99 (978-0-7944-1212-8(2)) Reader's Digest Assn., Inc., The.

Monkey Business: Level K, 6 vols. 128p. (gr. 2-3). 40.50 (978-0-7699-0994-3(9)) Shortland Pubns. (U. S. A.) Inc.

Monro, Roxie. Amazement Park: 14 Wild Mazes. 2005. (Illus.). 40p. (J). 16.95 (978-0-8118-4581-6(8)) Chronicle Bks. LLC.

Moog, Bob. Do I Bug You? The San Francisco School Staff, The, illus. 2006. 32p. bds. (978-1-57528-898-7(2)) University Games.

—I-Ballers: Little Books for Big Minds. 2005. 60p. (J). pap. (978-1-57528-937-3(7)) University Games.

—i-Ballers: Picture Puzzles. 2004. 48p. pap. (978-1-57528-951-9(2)) University Games.

—Spinner Books: the Grateful Dead. 2006. 240p. pap. (978-1-57528-897-0(4)) University Games.

Moore, Eva. Penguin Puzzle. 2001. (978-0-606-22230-3(8)) Tandem Library Bks.

Moore, Gareth. The Kids' Book of Hanjie! Catlow, Nikalas, illus. 2006. 224p. (J). mass mkt. 5.99 (978-1-4169-4029-6(4) , Simon Scribbles) Simon & Schuster Children's Publishing.

—The Kids' Book of Number Puzzles. Catlow, Nikalas, illus. 2006. 256p. (J). mass mkt. 5.99 (978-1-4169-2733-4(6) , Simon Scribbles) Simon & Schuster Children's Publishing.

Moran, Colette. Disney's the Lion King. 1999. (Illus.). (J). (978-0-7853-4148-2(X)) Publications International, Ltd.

More Brain Puzzlers. 2002. 304p. (J). (gr. 3-7). 20.99 (978-0-7439-3355-1(9) , 3355) Teacher Created Materials, Inc.

More Time for Bible Puzzles & Games. (Illus.). 32p. (YA). (gr. 5 up). pap. 2.25 (978-0-87162-664-6(0) , E9706) Warner Pr. Pubs.

More Word Winks: Over 300 Visual Verbal Puzzles. 2004. (J). pap. 12.95 (978-1-892069-76-4(8)) MindWare Holdings, Inc.

Moreau, Roger. History Mystery Mazes: An A-Maze-Ing Colorful Journey Back in Time. 2004. (Illus.). 80p. (J). pap. 7.95 (978-1-4027-1171-8(9)) Sterling Publishing Co., Inc.

Morris, Michael, illus. Puzzle Cards Letters. gif. ed. 2005. 16p. (J). 9.99 (978-1-57791-188-3(1)) Brighter Minds Children's Publishing.

—Puzzle Cards Numbers. gif. ed. 2005. 16p. (J). 9.99 (978-1-57791-187-6(3)) Brighter Minds Children's Publishing.

Moscovich, Ivan. The Network Games. Brion, David, illus. 2001. 24p. (J). (gr. 3-7). 6.95 (978-0-7611-2019-3(X) , 12019) Workman Publishing Co., Inc.

Mouse Works Staff. A Bugs Life: Can You Find the Difference? 1998. (Seek & See Book Ser.). (Illus.). 24p. (J). (gr. k-3). 3.99 (978-1-57082-937-6(3)) Mouse Works.

—Scary Seek & See. 1998. (Illus.). (J). 3.98 (978-1-57082-240-7(9)) Mouse Works.

Mudpuppy Press Staff. Alligator Alphabet Floor Puzzle. 2005. (J). 17.99 (978-0-7353-1224-1(9)) Galison.

—Baby Animal Block Puzzle. 2005. (J). 12.99 (978-0-7353-0174-0(3)) Galison.

—Dinosaur Block Puzzle. 2005. (J). 12.99 (978-0-7353-0903-6(5)) Galison.

—Magic Horses 100-piece Puzzle. 2005. (J). 12.99 (978-0-7353-0512-0(9)) Galison.

Munro, Roxie. Ranch. 2004. (Illus.). 36p. (J). 16.95 (978-1-931721-37-0(8)) Bright Sky Pr.

—The Wild West Trail Ride Maze. 2006. (Illus.). 40p. (J). 16.95 (978-1-931721-67-7(X)) Bright Sky Pr.

My Book of Mazes: Around the World. 2007. (J). per. 6.95 (*978-1-933241-40-1(3)) Kumon Publishing North America, Inc.

My First Book of Mazes. 2004. (Illus.). 80p. (J). per. 6.95 (978-4-7743-0709-1(2)) Kumon Publishing North America, Inc.

My First Hidden Pictures (Gr. K-1) 2003. (J). (978-1-58232-061-8(6)) Bryan Hse. Pubs., Inc.

My Little Pony Surprize Ink! Clipboard I. 2004. 24p. (J). 9.99 (978-1-932125-92-4(2)) Giddy Up, LLC.

N. E. Thing Enterprises Staff. Garfield's Magic Eye. (FRE., Illus.). 32p. (J). pap. 9.99 (978-0-590-16004-9(4)) Scholastic, Inc.

—Magic Eye III.Tr. of Oeil Magique III. (FRE., Illus.). (J). pap. 7.99 (978-0-590-24610-1(0)) Scholastic, Inc.

Nathan, Cheryl. Animal Hidden Pictures. 2002. (Illus.), 32p. (J). pap. 3.50 (978-0-486-42073-8(6)) Dover Pubns., Inc.

Needham, Kate. Great Undersea Search. Jackson, Ian, illus. rev. ed. 2005. 32p. (J). pap. 7.99 (978-0-7945-1228-6(3) , Usborne) EDC Publishing.

New Testament Hidden Pictures. 1998. (Illus.). 48p. (J). (gr. 1-3). pap. 5.95 (978-0-7647-0436-9(2) , SS4871, In Celebration) Schaffer, Frank Pubns.

Newman-D'Amico, Fran. Animal Spot-the-Differences. 2007. 64p. (J). pap. 1.50 (*978-0-486-45649-2(8)) Dover Pubns., Inc.

—Bugs Activity & Coloring Book. 2007. 32p. (J). pap. 3.95 (*978-0-486-46199-1(8)) Dover Pubns., Inc.

—Bugs Mazes. 2002. (Dover Little Activity Bks.). (Illus.). 64p. (J). (ps-2). pap. 1.50 (978-0-486-42173-5(2)) Dover Pubns., Inc.

—Farm Animal Mazes. 2006. 32p. (J). pap. 2.95 (978-0-486-45184-8(4)) Dover Pubns., Inc.

—Halloween Fun. 2005. 32p. (J). (ps-2). pap. 2.95 (978-0-486-44699-8(9)) Dover Pubns., Inc.

—Little Gardener's. 2005. (Illus.). 32p. (J). pap., act. bk. ed. 2.95 (978-0-486-43990-7(9)) Dover Pubns., Inc.

—My First Book of Puzzle Fun. 2005. (Illus.). 64p. (J). (ps-ps). pap. 4.95 (978-0-486-44075-0(3)) Dover Pubns., Inc.

—Spot-the-Differences Puzzle Fun. 2004. 64p. (J). pap. 1.50 (978-0-486-43841-2(4)) Dover Pubns., Inc.

Newmarket Press, ed. Kidoku. 2006. (Illus.). 224p. (YA). pap. 6.95 (978-1-55704-720-5(0)) Newmarket Pr.

Nicholas, Mother Andrea, compiled by. My Little Orthodox Christian Feast Days Activity Book. 2005. (J). spiral bd. 6.95 (978-0-9773579-0-1(2)) St. Nicholas Monastery.

Niederman, Derrick. Mind-Stretching Math Puzzles. 2005. (Illus.). 112p. (J). (978-1-4156-0492-2(4)) Sterling Publishing Co., Inc.

Niederman, Derrick, et al. The Secret Clubhouse Game Book. 2004. (Illus.). 128p. (J). pap. 4.95 (978-1-4027-1107-7(7)) Sterling Publishing Co., Inc.

—Whodunits. Sterling Publishing Company Staff, ed. 2000. (Pocket Puzzlers Ser.). (Illus.). 96p. (gr. 5-9). pap. 2.95 (978-0-8069-4991-8(0)) Sterling Publishing Co., Inc.

Nilsen, Anna. Art Auction Mystery: Find the Fakes, Save the Sale! 2005. (Illus.). 48p. (J). (gr. 5-9). 17.95 (978-0-7534-5842-6(X) , Kingfisher) Houghton Mifflin Co. Trade & Reference Div.

—The Great Art Scandal: Solve the Crime, Save the Show! 2003. (Illus.). 48p. (J). (gr. 5-9). tchr. ed. 16.95 (978-0-7534-5587-6(0) , Kingfisher) Houghton Mifflin Co. Trade & Reference Div.

Noble, Marty. Fairyland Sticker Picture Puzzle. 2004. 4p. (J). pap. 1.50 (978-0-486-43849-8(X)) Dover Pubns., Inc.

Noodlers: Elusive Illusions. 2004. (J). pap. 12.95 (978-1-892069-80-1(6)) MindWare Holdings, Inc.

Noodlers: Eye-Bending Icon. 2004. (J). pap. 12.95 (978-1-892069-79-5(2)) MindWare Holdings, Inc.

Norman, D. Dinosaurs Sticker & Puzzle Kid Kit (Bag) 2007. (Kid Kits Ser.). 24p. (J). pap. 14.99 (*978-1-60130-054-6(9)) EDC Publishing.

Number Puzzles. 2002. (Wipe It Off Ser.). 24p. (J). spiral bd. 4.98 (978-0-7525-8356-3(5)) Parragon, Inc.

O'Brien, Joan. Nutcracker Sticker Picture Puzzle. 2004. 4p. (J). (ps-5). 1.50 (978-0-486-43848-1(1)) Dover Pubns., Inc.

Oburkova, Eva. Toby's Travels Through Time: Puzzle Adventures in Dinosaur Days. 2006. (J). lib. bdg. (*978-0-8368-7497-6(8)) Stevens, Gareth Inc.

O'Hare, Jeff. Big Book of Fun: An Amazing Collection of Jokes, Riddles, Puzzles, & More. 2002. (gr. k-3). lib. bdg. 18.75 (978-0-613-79873-0(2)) Tandem Library Bks.

—Bogus Beasts: In Search of Imaginary Animals. Hadel, Marc, illus. 2003. 32p. (YA). (gr. 2-7). pap. 7.95 (978-1-56397-812-8(1)) Boyds Mills Pr.

—Mighty Champions. Scholastic, Inc. Staff & Swendsen, Silje, eds. 2004. (Yu-gi-oh Ser.). 32p. (J). pap. 3.99 (978-0-439-67191-0(4)) Scholastic, Inc.

O'Hare, Jeff, ed. Puzzlemania Superchallenge. 2003. (Puzzlemania Superchallenge Ser.: Vol. 1). (Illus.). 48p. (YA). Bk. 1. (gr. 5-9). pap. 6.95 (978-1-56397-789-3(3)); Vol. 2. (gr. 4-7). pap. 6.95 (978-1-56397-790-9(7)); Vol. 3. (gr. 4-7). pap. 6.95 (978-1-56397-791-6(5)) Boyds Mills Pr.

O'Hare, Jeffrey A. The Best of Puzzlemania Mazes, Vol. 4. 2003. (Illus.). 48p. (YA). (gr. 1-7). pap. 6.95 (978-1-56397-957-6(8)) Boyds Mills Pr.

—The Big Book of Puzzle Fun: Over 500 Puzzles, Quizzes & Brain Teasers. 2003. (Illus.). 144p. (YA). (gr. 3-7). pap. 8.95 (978-1-56397-879-1(2)) Boyds Mills Pr.

O'Hare, Jeffrey A., ed. The Best of Puzzlemania Mazes. 2003. (Illus.). 48p. (YA). (gr. 1-7). Vol. 1. pap. 6.95 (978-1-56397-954-5(3)); Vol. 2. pap. 6.95 (978-1-56397-955-2(1)); Vol. 3. pap. 6.95 (978-1-56397-956-9(X)) Boyds Mills Pr.

—The Big Book of Mazes. 2003. (Illus.). 72p. (YA). (gr. k-7). pap. 8.95 (978-1-56397-990-3(X)) Boyds Mills Pr.

—The Big Book of Winter Fun: Puzzles, Mazes, Jokes, & Games to Last the Entire Season. 2002. (Illus.). 64p. (YA). (gr. 2-5). pap. 7.95 (978-1-59078-001-5(9)) Boyds Mills Pr.

—The Highlights Big Book of Fun: An Amazing Collection of Jokes, Riddles, Puzzles, & More! 2003. (Illus.). 96p. (YA). (gr. k-7). pap., act. bk. ed. 9.95 (978-1-59078-006-0(X)) Boyds Mills Pr.

O'Keefe, M. Timothy. If I Were a Manatee: A Coloring & Activity Book. l.t. ed. 2002. 48p. (J). (ps-7). 4.95 (978-0-936513-50-8(0)) Larsen's Outdoor Publishing.

Olefsky, Jake. The Everything Brain Strain Book. 2005. (Everything Ser.). (Illus.). 213p. pap. 9.95 (978-1-59337-315-3(5)) Adams Media Corp.

Olenych, Bob. Ready-to-Go Reproducibles: Math Practice Puzzles. 2002. 48p. (J). 9.95 (978-0-439-28850-7(9)) Scholastic, Inc.

—40 Fun-Tabulous Puzzles for Multiplication, Division, Decimals, Fraction: Riveting Reproducible Puzzles That Reinforce Essential Computation Skills & Engage Kids to the Nth Degree. 2000. 48p. pap. 9.95 (978-0-439-19941-4(7)) Scholastic, Inc.

Orr, Julie. Hidden Pictures. 2002. (Activity Zone Workbooks Ser.). 64p. (J). pap., wbk. ed. 3.79 (978-1-58947-054-5(0) , 02348) School Zone Publishing Co.

Packard, Mary. When I Grow Up: Learning about Animals. Tagel, Peggy, illus. 1999. (Fisher-Price Puzzle Playbooks Ser.: Vol. 1). 12p. (J). (gr. k-3). bds. 7.99 (978-1-57584-272-1(6) , Reader's Digest Children's Bks.) Reader's Digest Children's Publishing, Inc.

Parri, Celia. Cyfoeth Cudd y Capten: Llyfr Stori a Phosau. 2005. (WEL., Illus.). 28p. (978-0-86381-397-9(6)) Gwasg Carreg Gwalch.

Paterson, Katherine. The Puzzling Book. Date not set. 96p. (J). pap., act. bk. ed. 3.99 (978-0-906731-81-9(X) , Christian Focus) Christian Focus Pubns. GBR. *Dist:* Riverside, Spring Arbor Distributors, Inc.

Patilla, Peter. Fun with Sizes. McDonald, Brigitte, illus. 1998. (Fun with... Ser.). 32p. (ps-2). lib. bdg. 23.90 (978-0-7613-0959-8(4) , Millbrook Pr.) Lerner Publishing Group.

Pattern Animals: Puzzles for Pattern Blocks. 2000. (J). pap. 9.95 (978-1-56911-086-7(7)) Learning Resources, Inc.

Payne, Trip. Great Crosswords for Kids: An Official American Mensa Puzzle Book. 2002. (Mensa Ser.). (Illus.). 96p. (gr. 3-7). pap. 5.95 (978-0-8069-9289-1(1)) Sterling Publishing Co., Inc.

Pearcey, Alice. Castle Jigsaw Book. Groebner, Dominic, illus. 2006. 14p. (J). bds. 14.95 (978-0-7945-1137-1(6) , Usborne) EDC Publishing.

Pelizzari, Nora. Transformers Coloring & Activity Book & Crayons. 2007. (Transformers Ser.). 32p. (J). pap. 4.99 (*978-0-06-088825-1(3) , Harper Entertainment) HarperCollins Pubs.

Penton, ed. A Happy Bugs. 2003. (J). 12.95 (978-1-74047-216-6(0)) Penton Overseas, Inc.

Penton Overseas, Inc. Staff. U. S. Presidents. 2002. (Smart Kids Flippers Ser.). (Illus.). (J). pap. 7.95 (978-1-59125-165-1(6)) Penton Overseas, Inc.

Perplexing Logic Puzzles Using Venn Diagrams. 2001. 12.95 (978-0-9714997-0-6(5)) Amazing Minds.

Perplexing Placement Puzzles. 2001. 12.95 (978-0-9714997-1-3(3)) Amazing Minds.

Perrin, James W., Jr. Back to School Puzzlers: An Awesome Array of Puzzles & Fun! 2004. (Illus.). 58p. (gr. 4-7). pap. (978-0-673-59963-6(9)) Good Year Bks.

—Holiday Puzzlers. 2005. 64p. pap. (978-1-59647-063-7(1)) Good Year Bks.

—Spring Puzzlers. 2004. 58p. pap. (978-0-673-61733-0(5)) Good Year Bks.

—Winter Puzzlers. 2001. (Illus.). 58p. (gr. 4-7). pap. (978-0-673-59961-2(2)) Good Year Bks.

Petruccio, Steven James. Battling Knights Sticker Picture Puzzle. 2004. 4p. (J). pap. 1.50 (978-0-486-43637-1(3)) Dover Pubns., Inc.

—Construction Site Sticker Picture Puzzle. 2005. (Illus.). 4p. (J). pap. 1.50 (978-0-486-44156-6(3)) Dover Pubns., Inc.

Phillips, Dave. Animal Mazes. 1998. (Illus.). 48p. (J). (gr. 2-8). pap. 3.95 (978-0-486-26707-4(5)) Dover Pubns., Inc.

Phillips, Dave. Haunted Pirates Mazes. 2008. 48p. (J). pap. 4.95 (*978-0-486-46216-5(1)) Dover Pubns., Inc.

Picture Puzzles. 2002. (Home Workbooks Ser.). 64p. pap. 2.49 (978-0-88724-716-3(4) , CD-4518) Carson-Dellosa Publishing Co., Inc.

Picture Puzzles with Cuisenaire Rods. 2000. (J). pap. (978-1-56911-092-8(1)) Learning Resources, Inc.

Picture Puzzles Workbook. 2002. (J). pap. 8.95 (978-1-56911-048-5(4)) Learning Resources, Inc.

Pierce, Martin, illus. Seek & Find Bible Mazes. 2001. 24p. (J). (gr. k up). Bk. 1. 2.99 (978-0-8254-7206-0(7)); Vol. 2. pap. 2.99 (978-0-8254-7207-7(5)) Kregel Pubns.

Pomaska, Anna. ABC Picture Puzzle: With 26 Reusable Peel-and-Apply Stickers. 1999. (Illus.). (J). pap. 4.95 (978-0-486-40819-4(1)) Dover Pubns., Inc.

—Animal Alphabet Follow the Dots. 2002. (Dover Little Activity Bks.). (Illus.). 64p. (J). pap. 1.50 (978-0-486-42101-8(5)) Dover Pubns., Inc.

—Anna Pomaska's Big Book of Puzzle Fun. 2002. (Dover Super Value Editions Ser.). (Illus.). 144p. (J). pap. 7.95 (978-0-486-42790-4(0)) Dover Pubns., Inc.

—Dot-to-Dot. 2005. 32p. (J). pap. 2.95 (978-0-486-44700-1(6)) Dover Pubns., Inc.

—Easy Same & Different Puzzles. 2003. (Dover Little Activity Bks.). (Illus.). 64p. (J). pap. 1.50 (978-0-486-42997-7(0)) Dover Pubns., Inc.

—Easy Wizards Sticker Picture Puzzle. 2004. (Illus.). 4p. (J). 1.50 (978-0-486-43845-0(7)) Dover Pubns., Inc.

Poskitt, Kjartan & Mepham, Michael. Sodoku: 100 Fun Number Puzzles. 2005. 144p. (J). pap. 4.99 (978-0-439-84570-0(X)) Scholastic, Inc.

Potter, Beatrix. Jigsaw Book. 2003. (Illus.). 18p. (J). (ps-ps). pap. 9.99 (978-0-7232-4866-8(4) , Warne) Penguin Group (USA) Inc.

Preschool Bible Puzzlers Grade. 2004. pap. 9.95 (978-0-7647-0499-4(0)) School Specialty Publishing.

Priddy, Roger. My Giant Sticker Puzzle Book 2 (with CD) 2nd ed. 2007. (J). pap. 12.95 (*978-0-312-50094-8(7) , Priddy Bks.) St. Martin's Pr.

Priddy, Roger. Wipe Clean Activity Puzzle Fun. 2007. 42p. (J). bds. 14.95 (978-0-312-49737-8(7) , Priddy Bks.) St. Martin's Pr.

Pullman, Philip, ed. Whodunit? Utterly Baffling Detective Stories. 2007. 272p. (J). (gr. 4-7). pap. 6.95 (*978-0-7534-6142-6(0) , Kingfisher) Houghton Mifflin Co. Trade & Reference Div.

The Puzzle: Individual Title-Six Packs. (Chiquilibros Ser.). (gr. k-1). 23.00 (978-0-7635-0440-3(8)) Rigby Education.

Puzzle Fun. 2002. 192p. (J). pap. 3.98 (978-0-7525-7917-7(7)) Parragon, Inc.

Puzzle House Staff. Puzzles. Teviotdale, Stuart, illus. 2001. (File-Online.Com). 128p. (J). (gr. 3-8). pap. 7.95 (978-0-439-22007-1(6)) Scholastic, Inc.

The Puzzle Machine. 2002. (Illus.). (J). (gr. 4-6). pap. (978-1-876367-80-0(6)) Wizard Bks.

Puzzler's Guide to the Grand Canyon. 2002. (National Parks series). 48p. (J). 4.95 (978-0-9714226-0-5(5)) Puzzler's Guides.

Puzzles & Dot-to-Dot. (My First Homework Booklets Ser.). 80p. 2.99 (978-1-56822-763-4(9) , IF0313) School Specialty Publishing.

Puzzles & Games. 2002. (Home Workbooks Ser.). 64p. pap. 2.49 (978-0-88724-734-7(2) , CD-4536); pap. 2.49 (978-0-88724-722-4(9) , CD-4524) Carson-Dellosa Publishing Co., Inc.

Puzzles for Pals - Grade 3. 2001. (Wipe-Off Activity Bks.). 16p. 3.79 (978-1-58792-021-9(2)) Trend Enterprises, Inc.

Quarto Children's Books Staff, contrib. by. Buildings: Pocket Tangrams. 2001. (Illus.). (J). (978-0-439-27310-7(2)) Scholastic, Inc.

Quinlan, Heather. Myths & Legends Word Search. 2005. (Illus.). 80p. (J). (gr. 1-4). pap. 5.95 (978-1-4027-2750-4(X)) Sterling Publishing Co., Inc.

—Sports & Hobbies Word Search. 2005. (Illus.). 80p. (J). (gr. 1-4). pap. 5.95 (978-1-4027-2751-1(8)) Sterling Publishing Co., Inc.

Radtke, Becky. Christmas Puzzle Fun. 2005. (Illus.). 32p. (J). (ps-ps). pap. 2.95 (978-0-486-44076-7(1)) Dover Pubns., Inc.

—Christmas Puzzles. 1998. (Illus.). 32p. (J). (ps-5). pap. 2.95 (978-0-486-40556-8(7)) Dover Pubns., Inc.

—Little Animals Hidden Pictures. 2006. (Dover Little Activity Bks.). 64p. (J). pap. 1.50 (978-0-486-44899-2(1)) Dover Pubns., Inc.

—Little Wizards Activity Book. 2002. (Dover Little Activity Bks.). (Illus.). 64p. (J). pap. 1.50 (978-0-486-42336-4(0)) Dover Pubns., Inc.

Radtke, Becky. Trains Activity Book. 2007. 64p. (J). pap. 1.50 (*978-0-486-45683-6(8)) Dover Pubns., Inc.

Random House Disney Staff. Puzzle Magic. 2005. (Disney Princess Ser.). (Illus.). 32p. (J). (ps-2). 4.99 (978-0-375-83088-4(X) , Golden/Disney) Random Hse. Children's Bks.

Random House Staff, ed. Babe's Busy Day. 1999. (Illus.). (J). 7.99 (978-0-375-80083-2(2) , Random Hse. Bks. for Young Readers) Random Hse. Children's Bks.

P
Q
R

Rao, Lisa. Surf's Up: Coloring & Activity Book & Crayons. Merkel, Joe F., illus. 2007. (Surf's Up Ser.). 32p. (J). pap. 4.99 (***978-0-06-115335-8(4)***, Harper Entertainment) HarperCollins Pubs.

Rath, Robert. Go Wild for Puzzles: Great Smoky Mountains NP. 2007. 32p. pap. 5.95 (***978-1-56037-406-0(3)***) Farcountry Pr.

Reading Puzzles. 2001. (Wipe-Off Activity Bks.). 16p. (J). (gr. 2). 3.79 (978-1-58792-017-2(4)) Trend Enterprises, Inc.

Red, White & Blue: The Search for Liberty. 2004. (J). cd-rom 19.95 (978-1-931203-11-1(3)) Inspired Idea.

Reguigne, Christine. Animals: 50 Mind-Bending Photographic Puzzles. 2004. (Spot the Difference Ser.). (Illus.). 80p. (J). pap. 6.95 (978-1-4027-1203-6(0), 1233010) Sterling Publishing Co., Inc.

—Spot the Differences: 50 Mind-Bending Photographic Puzzles. 2003. (gr. 5-8). lib. bdg. 15.25 (978-0-613-78035-3(3)) Tandem Library Bks.

—Vehicles: 50 Mind-Bending Photographic Puzzles. 2004. (Spot the Difference Ser.). (Illus.). 80p. (J). pap. 6.95 (978-1-4027-1202-9(2)) Sterling Publishing Co., Inc.

Reid, Struan. Ancient Egypt Jigsaw Bk. Allen, Peter, illus. 2006. 14p. (J). bds. 14.99 (978-0-7945-1236-1(4), Usborne) EDC Publishing.

—Ancient Romans Jigsaw Book. 2007. 14p. (J). bds. 14.99 (***978-0-7945-1591-1(6)***, Usborne) EDC Publishing.

Reid, Struan. Pirate Jigsaw Bk. Allen, Peter, illus. 2007. 14p. (J). bds. 14.99 (978-0-7945-1432-7(4), Usborne) EDC Publishing.

Richards, Karen C. Mulan Puzzlers. 1998. (Illus.). 176p. (J). (gr. 3-7). pap. 9.95 (978-0-7868-4224-7(5)) Little Brown & Co.

Riedler, Isabella. Tricky Puzzles for Clever Kids. 2001. (Illus.). 128p. pap. 5.95 (978-0-8069-6753-0(6)) Sterling Publishing Co., Inc.

Rigby. Spelling Puzzlers. (Illus.). (J). 2002. (gr. 3). pap. (978-0-7578-2419-7(6)); 2001. (gr. 1). pap. (978-0-7635-7343-0(4)); 2001. (gr. 2). pap. (978-0-7635-7753-7(7)) Steck-Vaughn.

Rios, Michael. Sit & Solve Cross Sums. 2003. (Sit & Solve Ser.). (Illus.). 96p. (J). pap. 4.95 (978-0-8069-4413-5(7)) Sterling Publishing Co., Inc.

Risby, Bonnie. Analogies for the 21st Century, 1 vols. 2nd ed. 2001. 33p. (J). pap., wbk. ed. 8.95 net. (978-1-883055-41-7(5)) Dandy Lion Pubns.

Risco, Elle D. Cars - Get into Gear: Sliding Puzzle Book. Disney Storybook Artists Staff, illus. 2006. 32p. (ps-17). 12.99 (978-0-7868-3595-9(8)) Disney Pr.

Ritchie, Scot. Everything Kids' Spies Puzzle & Activity Book: Discover the secrets, tricks, & tools of Spies. 2008. 184p. pap. 7.95 (***978-1-59869-409-3(X)***) Adams Media Corp.

Ritchie, Scot. Up, up & Away: A Round-the-World Puzzle Adventure. Ritchie, Scot, illus. 2006. (Illus.). 32p. (J). 16.95 (978-1-897066-59-1(7)) Maple Tree Pr. CAN. *Dist:* Perseus Distribution.

—Up, up & Away: A Round-the-World Puzzle Adventure. 2006. (Illus.). 32p. (J). pap. 6.95 (978-1-897066-60-7(0)) Maple Tree Pr. CAN. *Dist:* Perseus Distribution.

Robert Merry, compiled by. Merry's Puzzle Book C1850. 2002. cd-rom 19.95 (978-1-59090-061-1(8)) Golden Age Publishing, LLC.

Rogers, Kirsteen. Under the Sea Jigsaw Bk. Scott, Peter, illus. 2007. 14p. (J). bds. 14.99 (978-0-7945-1330-6(1), Usborne) EDC Publishing.

Rose, J. R. Christmas Fun with Pup. 2000. (Illus.). 64p. (J). (gr. k-3). pap. 5.95 (978-1-56554-713-1(6)) Pelican Publishing Co., Inc.

Ross, Jesse. All-Star Sports Puzzles: Basketball: Games, Trivia, Puzzles & More! 2007. 64p. pap. 7.95 (***978-1-55192-822-7(1)***) Raincoast Bk. Distribution CAN. *Dist:* Perseus Distribution.

—All-Star Sports Puzzles: Hockey: Games, Trivia, Puzzles & More! 2007. 64p. pap. 7.95 (***978-1-55192-810-4(8)***) Raincoast Bk. Distribution CAN. *Dist:* Perseus Distribution.

Ross, Suzanne. Aquarium Activity Book. 2000. (Illus.). 64p. (J). pap. 1.50 (978-0-486-41255-9(5)) Dover Pubns., Inc.

Rossell, Judith. Inspector Rockfort & the Missing Jewels: Search * Solve * Seek. 2007. (Illus.). 32p. (J). pap. 4.95 (978-1-60059-051-1(9)) Lark Bks.

—Inspector Rockfort & the Missing Treasure: Search * Solve * Seek. 2007. (Illus.). 32p. (J). pap. 4.95 (978-1-60059-050-4(0)) Lark Bks.

Roxbee-Cox, Phil. Find the Kitten. Cartwright, Stephen, illus. rev. ed. 2004. (Treasury of Farmyard Tales Ser.). 10p. (J). bds. 3.99 (978-0-7460-3822-2(4)) EDC Publishing.

Roxbee-Cox, Phil, et al. El Reino de los Juguetes. 2004. Tr. of Magic Toyshop. (SPA., Illus.). 32p. (J). (ps-3). lib. bdg. 14.95 (978-1-58086-215-8(2), EU1202) EDC Publishing.

Rudisill, J. J., et al, illus. Horace's Hidden Pictures. 1999. (Wimzie's House Bks.). 32p. (J). pap. 2.99 (978-0-88724-483-4(1), CD-4851) Carson-Dellosa Publishing Co., Inc.

—Jonas's Puzzles & Games. 1999. 32p. (J). pap. 2.99 (978-0-88724-484-1(X), CD-4852) Carson-Dellosa Publishing Co., Inc.

—Wimzie's Birthday Fun & Games. 1999. (Wimzie's House Bks.). 32p. (J). pap. 2.99 (978-0-88724-514-5(5), CD-4855) Carson-Dellosa Publishing Co., Inc.

Russell, Ken & Carter, Philip. Bumper Quiz Book for Kids. (Illus.). 160p. (J). 17.95 (978-1-85479-300-3(4)) O'Mara, Michael Bks., Ltd. GBR. *Dist:* Trans-Atlantic Pubns., Inc.

Russo, M. Great Book of Dot to Dot: Omnibus Edition. Date not set. (J). 19.95 (978-0-8069-6140-8(6)) Sterling Publishing Co., Inc.

Russo, Monica. Giant Book of Dot-to-Dot. 2003. (Illus.). 256p. (J). pap. 12.95 (978-0-8069-3681-9(9)) Sterling Publishing Co., Inc.

—Mythical Animals Dot-to-Dot. 2003. (Illus.). 64p. (J). (gr. 5-7). pap. 5.95 (978-0-8069-9716-2(8)) Sterling Publishing Co., Inc.

—Reptiles & Amphibians Dot-to-Dot. 2005. (Illus.). 64p. (J). (gr. 1-4). pap. 5.95 (978-1-4027-1204-3(9)) Sterling Publishing Co., Inc.

Ryan, Steve. Clever Lunchbox Puzzles: Fun Tear-Outs to Pack with Your Sandwiches. Ottinger, Jon, illus. 2005. 128p. (J). (gr. 2-4). pap. 6.95 (978-1-4027-1386-6(X)) Sterling Publishing Co., Inc.

—Sit & Solve Pencil Puzzles. 2003. (Sit & Solve Ser.). 96p. (J). pap. 4.95 (978-1-4027-0712-4(6)) Sterling Publishing Co., Inc.

Santa's House Activity Fun. Date not set. (Christmas Activity Bks.). (Illus.). 128p. (J). 3.98 (978-0-7525-6498-2(6)) Parragon, Inc.

Schimmel, Schim. Furry Friends: An Illustrated Anthology of Nature Poetry. 2002. (Illus.). 24p. (J). 15.95 (978-1-74047-199-2(7)) Book Co. Publishing Pty, Ltd., The AUS. *Dist:* Penton Overseas, Inc.

Schimmel, Schim, illus. Mother Nature Jigsaw Puzzle Book. 2002. (J). 12.95 (978-1-74047-196-1(2)) Book Co. Publishing Pty, Ltd., The AUS. *Dist:* Penton Overseas, Inc.

Scholastic, Inc. Staff. I (Heart) Puzzles. 2007. (Littlest Pet Shop Ser.). 96p. (J). pap. 4.99 (***978-0-439-91903-6(7)***) Scholastic, Inc.

—Scholastic Success with Numbers & Concepts. 2004. (Scholastic Success With Ser.). 48p. pap. 4.99 (978-0-439-55369-8(5)) Scholastic, Inc.

—100 Palabras En Ingles Que Los Ninos Deben Leer En: 2nd Grado. Salas, Macarena, ed. 2004. (101 Words Kids Need to Read Ser.). (SPA.). 32p. (J). (gr. 2-5). pap. 2.99 (978-0-439-56024-5(1), Scholastic en Espanol) Scholastic, Inc.

—100 Words Kids Need to Read 1st Grade: Spanish. Salas, Macarena, ed. 2004. (100 Words Kids Need to Read Ser.). (SPA.). 32p. (J). (ps-3). pap. 2.99 (978-0-439-54845-8(4), Scholastic en Espanol) Scholastic, Inc.

—100 Words Kids Need to Read 3rd Grade: Spanish. Salas, Macarena, ed. 2004. (102 Words Kids Need to Read Ser.). (SPA.). 32p. (J). (gr. 2-5). pap. 2.99 (978-0-439-66356-4(3), Scholastic en Espanol) Scholastic, Inc.

School Specialty Publishing. Daily Warmups - Math Problems & Puzzles. 2003. (100+ Seriestm Ser.). 128p. (J). (gr. 1-1). pap. 12.99 (978-0-7424-1791-5(3), IFG99039); (J). (gr. 2-2). pap. 12.99 (978-0-7424-1792-2(1), IFG99040); (J). (gr. 5-5). pap. 12.99 (978-0-7424-1795-3(6), IFG99043); (J). (gr. 3-3). pap. 12.99 (978-0-7424-1793-9(X), IFG99041); (J). (gr. 4-4). pap. 12.99 (978-0-7424-1794-6(8), IFG99042); (J). (gr. 6-6). pap. 12.99 (978-0-7424-1796-0(4), IFG99044); (YA). (gr. 7-7). pap. 12.99 (978-0-7424-1797-7(2), IFG99045); (YA). (gr. 8-8). pap. 12.99 (978-0-7424-1798-4(0), IFG99046) School Specialty Publishing.

—Dot-to-Dots, Mazes & More: Creepy Crawlies. 2002. (Homework Booklets Ser.). 80p. (J). (gr. k-1). pap. 2.99 (978-0-7424-0258-4(4), IF0414) School Specialty Publishing.

School Zone Publishing Company Staff. Readiness Fun. 2000. (Flash Cards 4-Pack Ser.). (J). 12.99 (978-0-88743-816-5(4), 04033) School Zone Publishing Co.

—Reading Fun. 2000. (Flash Cards 4-Pack Ser.). (J). 12.99 (978-0-88743-814-1(8), 04031) School Zone Publishing Co.

—Vocabulary Puzzles 2. (Illus.). (J). 19.99 incl. audio compact disk (978-0-88743-968-1(3)) School Zone Publishing Co.

School Zone Staff. Puzzle Cards - Match & Mix. 55p. 2.89 (978-0-88743-275-0(1)) School Zone Publishing Co.

School Zone Staff, ed. AZ Dot-to-Dot. 2004. (Activity Zone Workbook Ser.). 32p. (J). pap. 2.49 (978-1-58947-393-5(0), 02195) School Zone Publishing Co.

—Hidden Pictures Activity Zone. 2004. (Activity Zone Workbook Ser.). 32p. (J). pap. 2.49 (978-1-58947-387-4(6), 02192) School Zone Publishing Co.

Schujer, Silvia. Palabras para Jugar. 2002. (SPA.). 96p. (J). pap. 12.95 (978-1-4000-0054-8(8)) Random Hse., Inc.

—350 Adivinanzas para Jugar. 2002. (SPA.). 104p. (J). pap. 13.95 (978-1-4000-0055-5(6)) Random Hse., Inc.

Schwartz, David M. Among the Flowers. Kuhn, Dwight, photos by. 1999. (Springboards into Science Ser.). (Illus.). 24p. (J). (gr. 1 up). lib. bdg. 19.93 (978-0-8368-2241-0(2)) Stevens, Gareth Inc.

—At the Pond. Kuhn, Dwight, photos by. 1999. (Springboards into Science Ser.). (Illus.). 24p. (J). (gr. 1 up). lib. bdg. 19.93 (978-0-8368-2244-1(7)) Stevens, Gareth Inc.

—In a Tree. Kuhn, Dwight, photos by. 1999. (Springboards into Science Ser.). (Illus.). 24p. (J). (gr. 1 up). lib. bdg. 20.67 (978-0-8368-2245-8(5)) Stevens, Gareth Inc.

—In the Garden. Kuhn, Dwight, photos by. 1999. (Springboards into Science Ser.). (Illus.). 24p. (J). (gr. 1 up). lib. bdg. 19.93 (978-0-8368-2242-7(0)) Stevens, Gareth Inc.

—In the Park. Kuhn, Dwight, photos by. (Habitats Ser.). (Illus.). 16p. (J). (gr. 1-3). pap. 2.99 (978-1-57471-214-8(4), 3006) Creative Teaching Pr., Inc.

—In the Park. Kuhn, Dwight, photos by. 1999. (Springboards into Science Ser.). (Illus.). 24p. (J). (gr. 1 up). lib. bdg. 20.67 (978-0-8368-2243-4(9)) Stevens, Gareth Inc.

—Underfoot. Kuhn, Dwight, photos by. 1999. (Springboards into Science Ser.). (Illus.). 24p. (J). (gr. 1 up). lib. bdg. 20.67 (978-0-8368-2246-5(3)) Stevens, Gareth Inc.

Schwartz, Linda. Language Critical Thinking, Grades 2-4: Creative Puzzles to Challenge the Brain. Armstrong, Bev & Grayson, Rick, illus. 2005. 64p. (J). pap. 11.99 (978-0-88160-384-2(8), LW423, Learning Works, The) Creative Teaching Pr., Inc.

Scott, Peter, illus. Box of Dinosaurs. 2004. (Boxed Jigsaws Ser.). 10p. (J). 11.95 (978-0-7945-0915-6(0), Usborne) EDC Publishing.

Scott, Peter & Justine, Torode, illus. Box of Bugs. 2005. 6p. (J). 11.95 (978-0-7945-1023-7(X), Usborne) EDC Publishing.

Seeley, Laura. Shadowbox Hunt: A Search & Find Odyssey. Guevara, Linda L., ed. Seeley, Laura, illus. 2004. (Illus.). 32p. (J). (gr. 3 up). 17.95 (978-0-9700863-8-9(5)) All About Kids Publishing.

Sember, Brette. The Quiz Book 3: Three Times the Fun! Scheuer, Lauren, illus. 2003. (American Girl Library). 80p. (J). spiral bd. 7.95 (978-1-58485-746-4(3)) American Girl Publishing, Inc.

Shadow, Detective. Lateral Mindtrap Puzzles: Challenge the Way You Think & See. 2000. (Mindtrap Puzzles Ser.). (Illus.). 96p. (gr. 5-9). pap. 6.95 (978-0-8069-7135-3(5)) Sterling Publishing Co., Inc.

Shaloum, Alli. Boggle Jr. Word Search Puzzles. 2007. (Illus.). 64p. (J). pap. 4.95 (***978-1-4027-5150-9(8)***) Sterling Publishing Co., Inc.

Shauers, Margaret. Puzzles & Prayers. 2000. (Illus.). 64p. (gr. 3-6). 5.99 (978-0-570-07032-0(5)) Concordia Publishing Hse.

Shears, William. My Little Pony. Utopia, illus. 2005. (Look & Find Ser.). 18p. (J). (ps-ps). per. 7.98 (978-1-4127-3316-8(2), 7241700) Publications International, Ltd.

Simpson, Fraser. Beat-the-Clock Puzzles. 2005. (Illus.). 96p. pap. 6.95 (978-1-4027-1783-3(0)) Sterling Publishing Co., Inc.

—Sit & Solve IQ Tests. 2003. (Sit & Solve Ser.). (Illus.). 96p. pap. 4.95 (978-1-4027-0410-9(0)) Sterling Publishing Co., Inc.

Simpson, Fraser & Hovanec, Helene. Stopwatch Puzzles. 2004. (Illus.). 96p. 14.95 (978-1-4027-0580-9(8)) Sterling Publishing Co., Inc.

Sims, L. Puzzle Journey Around the World. 2004. (Puzzle Journey Ser.). 32p. (J). pap. 6.95 (978-0-7945-0510-3(4)) EDC Publishing.

—Puzzle Journey into Space. 2004. (Puzzle Journey Ser.). 32p. (J). pap. 6.95 (978-0-7945-0439-7(6)) EDC Publishing.

—Puzzle Journey under the Sea. 2004. (Puzzle Journey Ser.). 32p. (J). pap. 6.95 (978-0-7945-0481-6(7)) EDC Publishing.

Sims, Lesley. Puzzle Journey Around the World. Stitt, Sue, illus. 1998. (Usborne Young Puzzle Adventures Ser.). 32p. (YA). (gr. 3 up). pap. 6.95 (978-0-7460-2682-3(X)); lib. bdg. 14.95 (978-0-88110-975-7(4)) EDC Publishing.

Sims, Lesley, ed. Puzzle Journey under the Sea. 1999. (Usborne Young Puzzle Adventures Ser.). (Illus.). 32p. (YA). pap. 6.95 (978-0-7460-2685-4(4)); (gr. 3 up). lib. bdg. 14.95 (978-1-58086-133-5(4)) EDC Publishing.

Sloane, Paul. Super Lateral Thinking Puzzles. 2000. (gr. 5-8). lib. bdg. 15.25 (978-0-613-75556-6(1)) Tandem Library Bks.

Sloane, Paul & MacHale, Des. Super Lateral Thinking Puzzles. Miller, Myron, illus. 2000. 96p. (gr. 5-9). pap. 6.95 (978-0-8069-4470-8(6), GAM005000) Sterling Publishing Co., Inc.

—Tricky Lateral Thinking Puzzles. Miller, Myron, illus. 1999. 96p. (gr. 5-9). pap. 6.95 (978-0-8069-1248-6(0)) Sterling Publishing Co., Inc.

Sloane, Paul, et al. The Mind-Challenge Puzzle Book. 2002. (Illus.). 320p. (J). pap. 14.95 (978-1-4027-0477-2(1)) Sterling Publishing Co., Inc.

—The Who, What & Where Book of Brain Bafflers: 50 Whodunits & Puzzles for the Junior Detective. 2003. (Illus.). 96p. (J). 4.95 (978-1-4027-0681-3(2), Sterling/Main St.) Sterling Publishing Co., Inc.

Smith, Stan. Five-Minute Crimebusters: Clever Mini-Mysteries. O'Malley, Kathleen, illus. 1999. 96p. (gr. 5-9). pap. 6.95 (978-0-8069-1827-3(6)) Sterling Publishing Co., Inc.

Smith, Stan, et al. Giant Book of Puzzles for Young Einsteins/Giant Book of Whodunit Puzzles: Flip Book. 2002. (Illus.). 512p. pap. 9.98 (978-1-4027-0468-0(2)) Sterling Publishing Co., Inc.

Smolik, Jane. The Great Massachusetts Puzzle Book: Over 75 Puzzles about Life in the Bay State. rev. ed. 2006. (Illus.). 96p. (J). per. 11.95 (978-0-9664095-5-0(8)) MidRun Pr.

—The Great State of Maine Activity Book: Over 75 Puzzles about Life in Maine. rev. ed. 2006. (J). per. 11.95 (978-0-9664095-6-7(6)) MidRun Pr.

Soffer, Ruth. Butterfly Garden Sticker Picture Puzzle. 2005. 4p. (J). (gr. 2). pap. 1.50 (978-0-486-44469-7(4)) Dover Pubns., Inc.

Somper, Justin. Pyramid Plot. Wingham, Peter, illus. 2004. (Puzzle Adventures Ser.). 48p. (J). pap. 4.95 (978-0-7945-0139-6(7), Usborne) EDC Publishing.

Sovak, Jan. Dinosaur Sticker Picture Puzzle. 2004. (Illus.). 4p. (J). pap. 1.50 (978-0-486-43857-3(0)) Dover Pubns., Inc.

—T-Rex Sticker Picture Puzzle. 2006. 4p. (J). pap. 1.50 (978-0-486-44825-1(8)) Dover Pubns., Inc.

Spelling Is Fun. 2004. (Play & Learn Pads Ser.). 48p. (J). 3.99 (978-1-85997-721-7(9)) Byeway Bks.

Sports Illustrated for Kids Editors, ed. Laugh Locker Joke & Puzzle Book. 2000. (Illus.). (J). (gr. 2-8). pap. (978-1-930623-10-1(0)) Sports Illustrated For Kids.

Stanley, Stephen. Hidden Picture Challenge. 2000. (Illus.). 32p. (gr. 4-7). pap. 3.95 (978-0-486-41141-5(9)) Dover Pubns., Inc.

Stark, Katherine. El Reino de los Juguetes. 2004. (Young Puzzles Ser.). (SPA., Illus.). 32p. (J). (ps-3). pap. 6.95 (978-0-7460-3646-4(9)) EDC Publishing.

Stearns, Velda. Crossnumber Puzzles Grade 3: Extended Skills. Rogers, Kathy, ed. 2001. 32p. (J). pap. 3.99 (978-1-56472-251-5(1)) Edupress, Inc.

—Crossnumber Puzzles Grade 3 Operations. Rogers, Kathy, ed. 2001. 32p. (J). pap. 3.99 (978-1-56472-250-8(3)) Edupress, Inc.

—Crossnumber Puzzles Grade 4: Extended Skills. Rogers, Kathy, ed. 2001. 32p. (J). pap. 3.99 (978-1-56472-253-9(8)) Edupress, Inc.

—Crossnumber Puzzles Grade 4 Operations. Rogers, Kathy, ed. 2001. 32p. (J). pap. 3.99 (978-1-56472-252-2(X)) Edupress, Inc.

—Crossnumber Puzzles Grade 5: Extended Skills. Rogers, Kathy, ed. 2001. 64p. (J). pap. 3.99 (978-1-56472-255-3(4)) Edupress, Inc.

—Crossnumber Puzzles Grade 5 Operations. Rogers, Kathy, ed. 2001. 32p. (J). pap. 3.99 (978-1-56472-254-6(6)) Edupress, Inc.

—Crossnumber Puzzles Grade 6: Extended Skills. Rogers, Kathy, ed. 2001. 32p. (J). pap. 3.99 (978-1-56472-257-7(0)) Edupress, Inc.

—Crossnumber Puzzles Grade 6 Operations. Rogers, Kathy, ed. 2001. 32p. (J). pap. 3.99 (978-1-56472-256-0(2)) Edupress, Inc.

—Crossnumber Puzzles Grade 7: Extended Skills. Rogers, Kathy, ed. 2001. 32p. (J). pap. 3.99 (978-1-56472-259-1(7)) Edupress, Inc.

—Crossnumber Puzzles Grade 7 Operations. Rogers, Kathy, ed. 2001. 64p. (J). pap. 3.99 (978-1-56472-258-4(9)) Edupress, Inc.

—Crossnumber Puzzles Grade 8: Extended Skills. Rogers, Kathy, ed. 2001. 32p. pap. 3.99 (978-1-56472-261-4(9)) Edupress, Inc.

—Crossnumber Puzzles Grade 8 Operations. Rogers, Kathy, ed. 2001. 32p. pap. 3.99 (978-1-56472-260-7(0)) Edupress, Inc.

Steinbacher, Philip A. Quotation Quizzlers: Puzzling Your Way Through Famous Quotations. 2003. (J). per. 11.95 (978-1-883055-60-8(1), 151) Dandy Lion Pubns.

Steiner, Joan. Look-Alikes. 2000. (Illus.). (J). (ps-3). 12.95 (978-0-316-89077-9(4)) Little Brown & Co.

—Look-Alikes: The More You Look, the More You See! Steiner, Joan, illus. Lindley, Thomas, photos by. 2003. (Illus.). 32p. (J). (ps-17). 13.99 (978-0-316-71348-1(1)) Little Brown & Co.

—Look-Alikes Around the World. rev. ed. 2007. (Illus.). 40p. (J). (ps-1). 15.99 (***978-0-316-81172-9(6)***) Little, Brown Bks. for Young Readers.

—Look-Alikes Christmas: The More You Look, the More You See! Steiner, Joan, illus. 2003. (Illus.). 32p. (J). (ps-17). 14.95 (978-0-316-81187-3(4), 51394553) Little Brown & Co.

—Look-Alikes Jr. 2000. (Illus.). (J). (ps-3). 13.95 (978-0-316-89073-1(1)) Little Brown & Co.

—Look-Alikes Jr. The More You Look, the More You See! Steiner, Joan, illus. 2003. (Illus.). 32p. (J). (ps-17). 13.95 (978-0-316-71347-4(3)) Little Brown & Co.

Sterling Publishing Co., Inc., ed. Giant Book of Pencil Puzzles/Giant Book of Optical Puzzles: Flip Book. 512p. pap. 9.98 (978-1-4027-0049-1(0)) Sterling Publishing Co., Inc.

Sterling Publishing Company Staff. Whodunits. 2003. (Kids' Bathroom Bks.). (Illus.). 96p. (J). (gr. 2-7). pap. 4.95 (978-1-4027-0719-3(3)) Sterling Publishing Co., Inc.

Sterling Publishing Company Staff & Ward, Adam. The Little Giant Book of Brain Twisters. 2001. (Little Giant Bks.). (Illus.). 360p. (gr. 3-7). pap. 6.95 (978-0-8069-9711-7(7)) Sterling Publishing Co., Inc.

Stevens, Bette A. The Tangram Zoo & Word Puzzles Too!, Vol. 1000. 1998. (J). (gr. 1-3). pap. 4.50 (978-1-883650-47-6(X)) Windswept Hse. Pubs.

Stevenson, Joan. Search & Solve Bible Puzzlers: 48 Pages Reproducible Patterns. 1999. (Illus.). 48p. (gr. 3-5). 9.99 (978-0-570-05367-5(6)) Concordia Publishing Hse.

Stickels, Terry & Belotto, Sam. Puzzles & Gel Pen. 2007. (Spider-Man Ser.). 32p. (J). pap. 4.99 (978-0-06-083731-0(4), Harper Entertainment) HarperCollins Pubs.

Stillerman, Robbie. Easy Old MacDonald's Farm Sticker Picture Puzzle. 2004. (Illus.). 4p. (J). pap. 1.50 (978-0-486-43840-5(6)) Dover Pubns., Inc.

—Easy Seashore Sticker Picture Puzzle. 2006. 4p. (J). (gr. k-2). pap. 1.50 (978-0-486-44446-8(5)) Dover Pubns., Inc.

Stillson, Alan. Middle School Word Puzzles. Oliver, Jeff, illus. 2002. 114p. (YA). (gr. 5-8). pap. 11.00 (978-0-9723009-0-2(2)) Stillsonworks.

Strang Communications Company Staff, ed. Grades 1-2 Activities: Spring 2002. 2002. (J). (gr. 1-2). pap., act. bk. ed. 3.29 (978-1-57405-934-2(3)) CharismaLife Pubs.

—Grades 1-2 Activities: Summer 2002. 2002. (J). (gr. 1-2). pap., act. bk. ed. 3.29 (978-1-57405-972-4(6)) CharismaLife Pubs.

Sukach, Jim. Challenging Whodunit Puzzles: Dr. Quicksolve's Mini-Mysteries. Corvino, Lucy, illus. 1998. (Dr. Quicksolve Mini-Mysteries Ser.). 96p. (gr. 4-7). pap. 6.95 (978-0-8069-9619-6(6)) Sterling Publishing Co., Inc.

Sullivan, Scott. The Amazing 50 State Maze Book. Sullivan, Scott, illus. 2001. (Illus.). 64p. (J). (gr. 4-7). pap. 5.99 (978-0-8431-7656-8(3), Price Stern Sloan) Penguin Group (USA) Inc.

Summers, George J. The Great Book of Mind Teasers & Mind Puzzlers. 2003. (Illus.). 256p. (gr. 4-7). pap. 8.95 (978-0-8069-6320-4(4)) Sterling Publishing Co., Inc.

Super Activity Pad. Date not set. 384p. (J). 7.98 (978-0-7525-9573-3(3)) Parragon, Inc.

Super Brain Builders. 2005. (Illus.). 548p. per. (978-0-7853-8684-1(X), 3468600) Publications International, Ltd.

Super Puzzle Pad. Date not set. (Illus.). 384p. (J). 7.98 (978-0-7525-9575-7(X)) Parragon, Inc.

Super Puzzles. 2004. 112p. (J). 4.99 (978-1-85997-388-2(4)) Byeway Bks.

Super Travel Pad. Date not set. 384p. (J). 7.98 (978-0-7525-9576-4(8)) Parragon, Inc.

Sweeney, Alyse. All about Me Write & Read Books: 15 Fun-Shaped Book Patterns with Motivating Prompts to Get Kids Excited about Writing. 2000. 64p. pap. 10.95 (978-0-439-55752-8(6) , Teaching Resources) Scholastic, Inc.

Tallarico, Tony. The Big Book of Search & Find. 2002. (Illus.). (J). (978-1-58865-048-1(0)) Kidsbooks, Inc.

—Dinosaurs. 2003. (Ultimate Hidden Pictures Ser.). (Illus.). 48p. (J). (ps-4). pap. 3.99 (978-0-8431-0602-2(6) , Price Stern Sloan) Penguin Group (USA) Inc.

—Where Are They? More Than 1,000 Fun Things to Search & Find. 2001. (Illus.). (J). (978-1-56156-916-8(X)) Kidsbooks, Inc.

Tallarico, Tony & Tallarigo, Tony. License Plates Across the States: Travel Puzzles & Games. Eagle, Cameron, illus. 2005. (Ultimate Sticker Puzzles). 24p. (J). (gr. 1-7). mass mkt. 4.99 (978-0-8431-7737-4(3) , Price Stern Sloan) Penguin Group (USA) Inc.

Tatchell, Judy. Jigsaw book of Dragons. 2005. (Illus.). 20p. (J). 14.95 (978-0-7945-1117-3(1) , Usborne) EDC Publishing.

Taylor, Jody. Hidden Pictures 2008, Vol. 4. 2007. 48p. pap. 5.95 ***978-1-59078-542-3(8));** pap. 5.95 **(*978-1-59078-544-7(4))** Boyds Mills Pr.

—Hidden Pictures 2008 Vol 1. 2007. 48p. pap. 5.95 **(*978-1-59078-541-6(X))** Boyds Mills Pr.

—Hidden Pictures 2008 Vol 3. 2007. 48p. pap. 5.95 **(*978-1-59078-543-0(6))** Boyds Mills Pr.

Taylor, Jody, selected by. Hidden Pictures 1999: With Picture & Word Clues. 1998. (Hidden Pictures Ser.: Vol. 1). (Illus.). 48p. (J). (gr. k-4). pap. 4.95 (978-1-56397-750-3(8)) Boyds Mills Pr.

—Hidden Pictures 2002. 2001. (Hidden Pictures Ser.). (Illus.). 48p. (J). (gr. k-4). Vol. 1. pap. 4.95 (978-1-56397-807-4(5)); Vol. 3. pap. 4.95 (978-1-56397-975-0(6)); Vol. 4. pap. 4.95 (978-1-56397-865-4(2)) Boyds Mills Pr.

Teacher Created Materials Staff, ed. U. S. Olympic Crossword Puzzles & Word Searches: Primary. 2000. (U. S. Olympic Committee's Activity Book Ser.). (Illus.). 16p. (J). (gr. 1-5). pap. 3.95 (978-1-58000-059-8(2)) Griffin Publishing Group.

Teenage Mutant Ninja Turtles Activity Books. 2004. (J). act. bk. ed. (978-0-7666-1293-8(7) , 99180); act. bk. ed. (978-0-7666-1294-5(5) , 99180); act. bk. ed. 1.49 (978-0-7666-1295-2(3) , 99180); act. bk. ed. (978-0-7666-1296-9(1) , 99180) Modern Publishing.

Teenage Mutant Ninja Turtles Fun Activity Box Set. 2004. (J). act. bk. ed. (978-0-7666-1362-1(3) , 64024) Modern Publishing.

Teenage Mutant Ninja Turtles Giant Activity Books. 2004. (J). act. bk. ed. (978-0-7666-1297-6(X) , 49210); act. bk. ed. (978-0-7666-1298-3(8) , 49210) Modern Publishing.

Tenah, Ann. Brainiac's Bug Book: Creepy Crawly Activities. McGuinness, Tracy, illus. 2005. (Activity Journals Ser.). 128p. 12.99 (978-0-88088-362-7(6)) Peter Pauper Pr. Inc.

Teora, ed. Amazing Animal Puzzle Stickers BK 1. 2004. (Illus.). 8p. pap. 5.99 (978-1-59496-063-5(1)) Teora USA LLC.

—Amazing Animal Puzzle Stickers BK 2, Vol. 2. 2004. (Illus.). 8p. pap. 5.99 (978-1-59496-064-2(X)) Teora USA LLC.

—Amazing Animal Puzzle Stickers BK 3, Vol. 3. 2004. (Illus.). 8p. pap. 5.99 (978-1-59496-065-9(8)) Teora USA LLC.

Theisen, Michael. Ready-to-Go Game Shows (That Teach Serious Stuff) Bible Edition. 2003. (Illus.). 128p. (YA). pap. 24.95 (978-0-88489-689-0(7)) St. Mary's Pr.

Thomas, Lyn. Ha! Ha! Ha! 1,000+ Jokes, Riddles, Facts, & More. Eastman, Dianne, illus. 2004. 128p. (J). pap. 9.95 (978-1-897066-12-6(0)) Maple Tree Pr. CAN. *Dist:* Perseus Distribution.

Through the Bible Puzzles. 2006. (Illus.). 192p. (YA). (gr. 3-7). 14.99 (978-0-7847-1171-2(2) , 02726) Standard Publishing.

Time for Bible Puzzles & Games. (Illus.). 32p. (YA). (gr. 5 up). pap. 2.25 (978-0-87162-662-2(4) , E9705) Warner Pr. Pubs.

Timmerman, Charles. The Everything Kids' Cars & Trucks Puzzle: Race Your Way Through Miles of Turbo-Charged Fun! 2006. (Illus.). 144p. pap. 7.95 (978-1-59337-703-8(7)) Adams Media Corp.

Timmerman, Charles & Timmerman, Calla. Everything Kids' Fairies Puzzle & Activity Book: Enter the make-believe world of these magical Creatures. 2007. 144p. pap. 7.95 **(*978-1-59869-394-2(8))** Adams Media Corp.

Timmerman, Charles & Timmerman, Calla. The Everything Kids' Princess Puzzle & Activity Book: Play, search, & solve happily ever After! 2006. (Illus.). 144p. pap. 7.95 (978-1-59337-704-5(5)) Adams Media Corp.

Tonka Giant Coloring & Activity Books. 2004. (J). act. bk. ed. (978-0-7666-0951-8(0) , 49260); act. bk. ed. (978-0-7666-0952-5(9) , 49260) Modern Publishing.

Tonka Sticker Activity Books. 2004. (J). act. bk. ed. 2.99 (978-0-7666-1142-9(6) , 69685); act. bk. ed. 2.99 (978-0-7666-1143-6(4) , 69685) Modern Publishing.

Top That Publishing Staff, ed. Brain Workout. 2004. (Illus.). 96p. pap. (978-1-84510-211-1(8)); Vol. 2. pap. (978-1-84510-210-4(X)); Vol. 3. pap. (978-1-84510-209-8(6)); Vol. 4. pap. (978-1-84510-208-1(8)); Vol. 5. pap. (978-1-84510-309-5(2)); Vol. 6. pap. (978-1-84510-310-1(6)) Top That! Publishing PLC.

—101 Brainbender Puzzles. 2005. (Illus.). 48p. pap. (978-1-84510-202-9(9)) Top That! Publishing PLC.

—101 Picture Puzzles. 2005. (Illus.). 48p. pap. (978-1-84510-201-2(0)) Top That! Publishing PLC.

Townsend, Charles B. The World's Biggest Puzzle Book. 2002. (Illus.). 704p. pap. 12.95 (978-1-4027-0246-4(9)) Sterling Publishing Co., Inc.

Toys. 2002. (Little Pups Board Bks.). (Illus.). 11p. (J). (ps). bds. 2.99 (978-1-57759-997-5(7)) Dalmatian Pr.

Travis, Falcon. Great Book of Whodunit Puzzles: Mini-Mysteries for You to Solve. 2003. (Mini-Mysteries for You to Solve Ser.). (Illus.). 128p. (gr. 4-7). pap. 6.95 (978-0-8069-0348-4(1)) Sterling Publishing Co., Inc.

Trek Puzzles. 2001. (Wipe-Off Activity Bks.). 16p. (J). (gr. 3). 3.79 (978-1-58792-020-2(4)) Trend Enterprises, Inc.

Tribune Media Services Staff. Jumble Brain Busters for Kids: Because Learning Can Be Fun! 2001. 192p. (J). pap. 9.95 (978-1-892049-29-2(5) , Benchmark Pr.) Triumph Bks.

Tuller, Dave. Super Tough Word Search Puzzles. 2002. (Illus.). 96p. (YA). (gr. 7 up). pap. 7.95 (978-0-8069-8525-1(9)) Sterling Publishing Co., Inc.

Turnbull, S. Dinosaur Jigsaw Book. 2004. (SPA.). 14p. (J). 8.99 (978-0-7945-0525-7(2)) EDC Publishing.

Turnbull, Stephanie. Los Dinosaurios Con Cuatro Puzzles Sencillos. Scott, Peter, illus. 2004. (Titles in Spanish Ser.). (SPA.). 6p. (J). 8.95 (978-0-7460-6109-1(9) , Usborne) EDC Publishing.

Twist, Clint. An Amazing Magic Mazes: Jungle Mazes:An Amazon Adventure. Aldous, Kate, illus. 2004. (Magic Color Bks.). 12p. (J). 9.95 (978-1-4027-1594-5(3) , Sterling/Pinwheel) Sterling Publishing Co., Inc.

—Haunted Castle Mazes: A Spooky Adventure. Aldous, Kate, illus. 2004. (Magic Color Bks.). 12p. (J). 9.95 (978-1-4027-1595-2(1) , Sterling/Pinwheel) Sterling Publishing Co., Inc.

Twist, Clint & Kelleher, Pat. Puzzle Quest Through Prehistoric Times. Mendez, Simon, illus. 2006. (Puzzle Quest Ser.). 22p. (J). bds., bds. 22.95 (978-0-7696-4878-1(9) , Brighter Child) School Specialty Publishing.

Two by Two a Puzzle Book. 2004. bds. 10.99 (978-0-8254-5510-0(3)) Kregel Pubns.

Tyler, Jenny. Dot-to-Dot on the Farm. rev. ed. 2004. (Dot to Dot Ser.). (Illus.). 24p. (J). pap. 3.99 (978-0-7945-0492-2(2)) EDC Publishing.

Tyler, Jenny & Blundell, Kim. Animal Mazes. rev. ed. 2004. (Maze Fun Ser.). 24p. (J). pap. 5.95 (978-0-7945-0538-7(4)) EDC Publishing.

—Monster Mazes. rev. ed. 2004. (Maze Fun Ser.). 24p. (J). pap. 5.95 (978-0-7945-0536-3(8)) EDC Publishing.

Tyler, Judy. Picture Puzzles. 1999. (Brain Benders Ser.). (Illus.). 321p. (J). (gr. 3 up). lib. bdg. 12.95 (978-0-88110-049-5(8)) EDC Publishing.

Tyo, Courtney. Holiday Puzzles. 2004. 47p. (J). (978-0-439-68016-5(6)) Scholastic, Inc.

U. S. Kids Editorial Staff. The Best Adventure of the Puzzle Squad. (Illus.). 48p. (J). (gr. k-6). stu. ed. 6.95 (978-1-885453-75-4(2)) Children's Better Health Institute.

The Ultimate Alphabet Games & Puzzles Workbook. 2002. (Illus.). 158p. (J). (gr. k-1). wbk. ed. 4.97 (978-1-57759-125-2(9)) Dalmatian Pr.

Unite the World & Unite the States: Interactive Geographical Jigsaw Puzzles with 3 Inflatable Globes (5 Computer License) 2001. cd-rom (978-0-9708398-2-4(0)) Orbigo.

Unite the World & Unite the States: Interactive Geographical Jigsaw Puzzles with 5 Inflatable Globes (10 Computer License) 2001. cd-rom (978-0-9708398-1-7(2)) Orbigo.

University Games Staff. Made You Laugh for Kids! Books So Fun You'll Pee Your Pants! 2005. (Illus.). 224p. (J). (ps-3). pap. 14.95 (978-1-57528-995-3(4)) University Games.

University Games Staff, compiled by. I-Ballers: Little Books for Big Minds. 2005. 60p. (J). pap. (978-1-57528-936-6(9)) University Games.

—Spinner Books Kids: Dinomite. 2005. (Illus.). 160p. (J). pap. (978-1-57528-948-9(2)) University Games.

Usborne Books Staff. 1001 Cosas Que Buscar en la Granja. 1999. (SPA.). (gr. k-3). lib. bdg. 15.25 (978-0-613-74444-7(6)) Tandem Library Bks.

Vidro, Kenn. Square Pears. 2003. (Illus.). 112p. (J). spiral bd. 7.95 (978-0-9745308-0-2(8)) Gilbert Square Bks.

Volke, Gordon. Big World Activity Sticker Book, Vol. 2. 2004. (Illus.). 16p. 7.25 (978-1-84161-130-3(1)) Ravette Publishing, Ltd. GBR. *Dist:* Parkwest Pubns., Inc.

Volke, Gordon, et al, illus. Panda Patrol Big Activity Book. 2004. 24p. 6.00 (978-1-84161-111-2(5)) Ravette Publishing, Ltd. GBR. *Dist:* Parkwest Pubns., Inc.

Walton, Rick. Brain Waves Puzzle Book. Osiecki, Lori, illus. 2002. (American Girl Library). 128p. (J). (gr. 3 up). spiral bd. 7.95 (978-1-58485-504-0(5)) American Girl Publishing, Inc.

—Puzzle Book: Games, Riddles, Mazes, & More! 2003. (Coconut Ser.). (Illus.). 64p. (J). 5.95 (978-1-58485-799-0(4)) American Girl Publishing, Inc.

—Puzzle Crazy. Stace, Peterson, illus. 2005. (American Girl Library). 112p. (J). pap. 7.95 (978-1-58485-981-9(4) , American Girl) American Girl Publishing, Inc.

Ward, Gail. Animals along the Lewis & Clark Trail. 2002. 32p. (978-1-886609-32-7(2)) Tamarack Bks., Inc.

Ward, Mike. Hangman, No. 4. 2007. (Scratch & Solve Ser.). 96p. pap. 5.95 (978-1-4027-4370-2(X)) Sterling Publishing Co., Inc.

—Scratch & Solve Hangman #3, Vol. 3. 2006. (Sit & Solve Ser.). 96p. pap. 5.95 (978-1-4027-2582-1(5)) Sterling Publishing Co., Inc.

—Scratch & Solve Hangman #5. 2007. (Scratch & Solve Ser.). 96p. (J). pap. 5.95 **(*978-1-4027-4513-3(3))** Sterling Publishing Co., Inc.

—Scratch & Solve Tough Hangman, No. 4. 2007. (Scratch & Solve Ser.). 96p. pap. 5.95 (978-1-4027-4371-9(8)) Sterling Publishing Co., Inc.

—Scratch & Solve Tough Hangman #3. 2006. (Sit & Solve Ser.). 96p. pap. 5.95 (978-1-4027-2581-4(7)) Sterling Publishing Co., Inc.

Watt, F. & Wells, R. Farm Animals. 2004. 14p. (J). 9.95 (978-0-7945-0561-5(9)) EDC Publishing.

—Pets. 2004. 14p. (J). 9.95 (978-0-7945-0621-6(6)) EDC Publishing.

—Things That Go. 2004. 14p. (J). 9.95 (978-0-7945-0622-3(4)) EDC Publishing.

Watt, Fiona. Animales de la Granja. Wells, Rachel, illus. 2004. (SPA.). 14p. (J). 9.95 (978-0-7460-6113-8(7) , Usborne) EDC Publishing.

—Animals Baby Jigsaw Book. Wells, Rachel, illus. 2006. 10p. (J). bds. 9.99 (978-0-7945-1227-9(5) , Usborne) EDC Publishing.

—Christmas Baby. 2005. 10p. (J). 8.95 (978-0-7945-1185-2(6) , Usborne) EDC Publishing.

—Fairies Jigsaw Book. Cartwright, Stephen, illus. 2005. 12p. (J). bds. 14.95 (978-0-7945-1131-9(7) , Usborne) EDC Publishing.

—Mascotas. Wells, Rachel, illus. 2004. (Titles in Spanish Ser.). (SPA.). 14p. (J). 9.95 (978-0-7460-6112-1(9) , Usborne) EDC Publishing.

—Mermaids Jigsaw Book. Cartwright, Stephen, illus. 2006. 12p. (J). bds. 14.99 (978-0-7945-1189-0(9) , Usborne) EDC Publishing.

Watt, Fiona & Wells, Rachel. Anifeiliaid y Fferm. 2005. (WEL., Illus.). 8p. (978-1-84512-000-9(0)) Cymdeithas Lyfrau Ceredigion.

Weber, Ken. More Five-Minute Mysteries. 2005. (Illus.). 224p. (YA). (gr. 7-17). pap. 8.95 (978-0-7624-2438-2(9) , Running Pr. Kids) Running Pr. Bk. Pubs.

—5 Minute Mysteries. 2005. (Illus.). 198p. (YA). (gr. 7-12). pap. 8.95 (978-0-7624-2437-5(0) , Running Pr. Kids) Running Pr. Bk. Pubs.

Weddle, Jodie. Texas Brain Twisters. Taylor, Michael, illus. 2000. 40p. (J). pap. 10.95 (978-1-885777-28-7(0)) Hendrick-Long Publishing Co.

Weintraub, Aileen. The Everything Kids' Knock Knock Book. 2004. (Illus.). 144p. (J). 6.95 (978-1-59337-127-2(6)) Adams Media Corp.

West, Tracey & Nolls, Katherine. Pokemon Challenge. 2003. (Illus.). 59p. (J). (978-0-439-53052-1(0)) Scholastic, Inc.

What's Going On? 1998. (High Q Book Ser.). (Illus.). 48p. (J). (gr. k-2). pap. 3.99 (978-0-7681-0021-1(6) , McClanahan Bk.) Learning Horizons, Inc.

What's Wrong with This Picture? 2005. (Illus.). 16p. act. bk. ed. (978-0-7853-8908-8(3) , 7182901) Publications International, Ltd.

White, Graham. Secrets of the Pyramids: National Geographic Maze Adventures. 2002. (Illus.). 32p. (J). (gr. 3-7). pap. 8.95 (978-0-7922-6938-0(1) , National Geographic Children's Bks.) National Geographic Society.

—Secrets of the Pyramids: National Geographic Maze Adventures. 2002. (gr. 3-6). lib. bdg. 17.60 (978-0-613-84045-3(3)) Tandem Library Bks.

—Storming A Castle: National Geographic Maze Adventures. 2002. (Illus.). 32p. (J). (gr. 3-7). pap. 8.95 (978-0-7922-6940-3(3) , National Geographic Children's Bks.) National Geographic Society.

Wick, Walter. Can You See What I See? Dream Machine. Wick, Walter, illus. 2003. (Illus.). 40p. (J). 13.95 (978-0-439-39950-0(5) , Cartwheel Bks.) Scholastic, Inc.

—Can You See What I See? Games Read-and-Seek. 2007. (Scholastic Reader Level 1 Ser.). 32p. (J). pap. 3.99 **(*978-0-439-86229-5(9))** Scholastic, Inc.

—Can You See What I See? Nature Read-and-Seek. 2008. (Scholastic Reader Level 1 Ser.). 32p. (J). pap. 3.99 **(*978-0-439-86226-4(4))** Scholastic, Inc.

—Can You See What I See? Picture Puzzles to Search & Solve. Wick, Walter, illus. 2002. (Illus.). 40p. (J). (gr. 3-6). pap. 13.95 (978-0-439-16391-0(9) , Cartwheel Bks.) Scholastic, Inc.

—Can You See What I See? Seymour & the Juice Box Boat. Wick, Walter, illus. 2004. (Seymour Ser.). (Illus.). 40p. (J). pap. 8.99 (978-0-439-61778-9(2) , Cartwheel Bks.) Scholastic, Inc.

—Can You See What I See? Animals. Animals Read-and-Seek. 2007. (Scholastic Reader Level 1 Ser.). 32p. (J). pap. 3.99 **(*978-0-439-86227-1(2))** Scholastic, Inc.

—Can You See What I See? Cool Collections. Wick, Walter, illus. 2004. (Illus.). 40p. (J). (ps up). pap. 13.95 (978-0-439-61772-7(3) , Cartwheel Bks.) Scholastic, Inc.

—Night Before Christmas. Wick, Walter, illus. 2005. (Can You See What I See?). (Illus.). 40p. (J). pap. 13.99 (978-0-439-76927-3(2) , Cartwheel Bks.) Scholastic, Inc.

—Seymour Makes New Friends. Wick, Walter, illus. 2006. (Can You See What I See Ser.). (Illus.). 32p. (J). (ps-k). pap. 8.99 (978-0-439-61780-2(4)) Scholastic, Inc.

Wick, Walter, photos by. I Spy: Interactive Sound Book of Picture Riddles. 2003. (Illus.). 30p. (J). 15.98 (978-0-7853-8424-3(3)) Publications International, Ltd.

The Wiggles Coloring & Activity Books. 2004. (J). act. bk. ed. (978-0-7666-1046-0(2) , 99530); act. bk. ed. 0.99 (978-0-7666-1047-7(0) , 99530); act. bk. ed. 0.99 (978-0-7666-1048-4(9) , 99530); act. bk. ed. 0.99 (978-0-7666-1049-1(7) , 99530) Modern Publishing.

The Wiggles Giant Coloring & Activity Books. 2004. (J). act. bk. ed. 1.99 (978-0-7666-1050-7(0) , 49220); act. bk. ed. 1.99 (978-0-7666-1051-4(9) , 49220) Modern Publishing.

Williams, Carla. Big Puzzles for Little Hands: Children of the Bible. 2004. (Illus.). 96p. (J). (ps-2). pap. 11.95 (978-1-885358-49-3(0)) Rainbow Pubs. & Legacy Pr.

—Big Puzzles for Little Hands: Jesus' Life & Lessons. 2004. (Illus.). 96p. (J). (ps-2). pap. 11.95 (978-1-885358-79-0(2)) Rainbow Pubs. & Legacy Pr.

—Big Puzzles for Little Hands: People Who Obeyed God. 2004. (Illus.). 96p. (J). (ps-2). pap. 11.95 (978-1-885358-48-6(2)) Rainbow Pubs. & Legacy Pr.

—Big Puzzles for Little Hands: The Bible Tells Me So. 2004. (Illus.). 96p. (J). (ps-2). pap. 11.95 (978-1-885358-80-6(6)) Rainbow Pubs. & Legacy Pr.

Williams, Susan. Second Grade Math Puzzles & Games: Boosting Your Way to Success in School. 1998. (Grade Boosters Ser.). (Illus.). 64p. (J). (gr. 1-3). pap. 4.95 (978-1-56565-754-0(3) , 07543W) Lowell Hse.

Wood, A. J. Errata: A Book of Historical Errors. Alles, Hamesh, illus. 1999. 32p. (J). (gr. 5-8). pap. 17.00 (978-0-7881-6206-0(3)) DIANE Publishing Co.

Woodworth, Viki. Farm Animal Mazes. 2004. (Illus.). 64p. (J). pap. 1.50 (978-0-486-43842-9(2)) Dover Pubns., Inc.

Word Puzzles. 2003. (Basic Skill Ser.). (Illus.). 48p. (gr. 7-8). 5.99 (978-1-56822-046-8(4) , IF5057) School Specialty Publishing.

Word Puzzles & Games. 2002. (Home Workbooks Ser.). 64p. pap. 2.49 (978-0-88724-736-1(9) , CD-4538) Carson-Dellosa Publishing Co., Inc.

Word Puzzles & Games: CD-4525. 2002. (Learning Fun for Little Ones Ser.). 64p. pap. 2.49 (978-0-88724-723-1(7)) Carson-Dellosa Publishing Co., Inc.

Word Winks: Over 300 Visual Verbal Puzzles. 2004. (J). pap. 12.95 (978-1-892069-75-7(X)) MindWare Holdings, Inc.

Workman Publishing Company Staff. Brain Quest Bathtime: 175 Stories, Poems, Questions & Answers—Even Jokes & Riddles—to Read Together with a Little Duck Named Gus, Set. 2002. (Illus.). 52p. (J). 10.95 (978-0-7611-2819-9(0) , 12819) Workman Publishing Co., Inc.

—Brain Quest Bedtime: 175 Stories, Poems, & Jokes to Read Together with Questions & Answers, Set. 2002. (Illus.). 52p. (J). 10.95 (978-0-7611-2641-6(4) , 12641) Workman Publishing Co., Inc.

World Book, Inc. Staff. Mind Benders, 5 vols., Set. 2001. 32p. (J). (gr. 2-6). 23.00 (978-0-7166-4111-7(9) , 20107) World Bk., Inc.

—World Book's Mind Benders. 1999. (Illus.). 224p. (J). (gr. 3-6). pap. (978-0-7166-4110-0(0)) World Bk., Inc.

Wynne, Patricia J. Easy Dinosaur Mazes. 2006. 48p. (J). pap. 3.95 (978-0-486-45363-7(4)) Dover Pubns., Inc.

Young, Caroline. Big Bug Search. Jackson, Ian, illus. rev. ed. 2005. 32p. (J). pap. 7.95 (978-0-7945-1045-9(0) , Usborne) EDC Publishing.

Young, Caroline & Needham, Kate. Great Wildlife Search: Big Bug Search, Great Animal Search & Great Undersea Search. Jackson, Ian, illus. 2004. (Great Searches Ser.). 112p. (J). pap. 15.99 (978-0-7945-0892-0(8) , Usborne) EDC Publishing.

Young, Jay, creator. Secret Ziga Zaga. 2003. (Ziga Zaga Ser.). 192p. (YA). (978-1-84347-034-2(9)) Chrysalis Children's Bks.

Youngs, Dave & Pauls, Michelle. Puzzle Play. Pauls, Michelle & Cordel, Betty, eds. Schlotterback, Dave, illus. 2001. 211p. (J). pap. 18.95 (978-1-881431-95-4(9) , 1722) AIMS Education Foundation.

Yoyo Books. An Exciting Day Trip: Princess Charlotte's Picture Puzzles. 2005. 32p. 9.95 (978-90-5843-456-2(7)) YoYo Bks. BEL. *Dist:* National Bk. Network.

—A Magic Gift: Princess Charlotte's Picture Puzzles. 2005. 32p. 9.95 (978-90-5843-457-9(5)) YoYo Bks. BEL. *Dist:* National Bk. Network.

Yoyo Books Staff. Animals Around Me: Animal Jigsaw Fun. 2004. 12p. bds. 9.95 (978-90-5843-550-7(4)) YoYo Bks. BEL. *Dist:* National Bk. Network.

—Baby Animals: Animal Jigsaw Fun. 2004. 12p. bds. 9.95 (978-90-5843-551-4(2)) YoYo Bks. BEL. *Dist:* National Bk. Network.

—Farm Animals: Animal Jigsaw Fun. 2004. 12p. bds. 9.95 (978-90-5843-549-1(0)) YoYo Bks. BEL. *Dist:* National Bk. Network.

—Wild Animals: Animal Jigsaw Fun. 2004. 12p. bds. 9.95 (978-90-5843-552-1(0)) YoYo Bks. BEL. *Dist:* National Bk. Network.

Zimmerman, Jerry. Around the World in 80 Mazes. 1999. (Around-the-World Bks.). (Illus.). 80p. (J). (gr. 3-7). pap. 6.95 (978-0-7373-0171-7(6) , 01716W) McGraw-Hill/Contemporary.

Zourelias, Diana. Fairy Tale Search-a-Word. 2006. 64p. (J). pap. 1.50 (978-0-486-45206-7(9)) Dover Pubns., Inc.

—Fairyland Hidden Pictures. 2006. 32p. (J). pap. 3.95 (978-0-486-45187-9(9)) Dover Pubns., Inc.

3D Circus Puzzle Book. 12p. (J). (978-2-89393-867-7(1)) Phidal Publishing, Inc./Editions Phidal, Inc.

PYLE, ERNIE, 1900-1945

Boomhower, Ray E. The Soldier's Friend: A Life of Ernie Pyle. 2006. (Illus.). 134p. 17.95 (978-0-87195-200-4(9)) Indiana Historical Society.

PYRAMIDS

Anastasio, Dina. Pyramids. 2003. (Early Connections Ser.). (J). pap. 33.00 (978-1-4108-1067-0(4)) Benchmark Education Co.

Bingham, Caroline & Dorling Kindersley Publishing Staff. Pyramid. 2004. (Eye Wonder Ser.). (Illus.). 48p. (J). 9.99 (978-0-7566-0287-1(4)); lib. bdg. 17.99 (978-0-7566-0286-4(6)) Dorling Kindersley Publishing, Inc.

Bodden, Valerie. Pyramids. 2008. (J). **(*978-1-58341-563-4(7)** , Creative Education) Creative Co., The.

Chapman, Lynne F. Egyptian Pyramids. 1999. (Designing the Future Ser.). (Illus.). 32p. (YA). (gr. 4-7). lib. bdg. (978-0-88682-717-5(5) , Creative Education) Creative Co., The.

Chrisp, Peter. Pyramid. 2006. (Experience Ser.). (Illus.). 64p. (J). (gr. 4-8). 15.99 (978-0-7566-1410-2(4)) Dorling Kindersley Publishing, Inc.

Cooper, Terry, ed. Pyramids & Mummies. 2001. (Instant Internet Activities Folder Ser.). 6p. pap. 3.95 (978-0-439-30956-1(5)) Scholastic, Inc.

Dorling Kindersley Publishing Staff. Piramide. 2004. (Dk Eyewitness Books Ser.). (SPA.). 72p. (J). 15.99 (978-0-7566-0633-6(0)) Dorling Kindersley Publishing, Inc.

—Pyramide. 2004. (Eyewitness Books). 72p. (J). lib. bdg. 19.99 (978-0-7566-0796-8(5)) Dorling Kindersley Publishing, Inc.

Dorling Kindersley Publishing Staff, ed. Pyramid. 2004. (Dk Eyewitness Books Ser.). (Illus.). 72p. (J). 15.99 (978-0-7566-0717-3(5)) Dorling Kindersley Publishing, Inc.

Filer, Joyce. Pyramids. 2nd ed. 2005. (Illus.). 48p. (YA). 16.95 (978-0-19-530521-0(3)); 18.95 (978-0-19-530525-8(6)) Oxford Univ. Pr., Inc.

Great Pyramids & the Sphinx. (Butterfly Bks.). (ARA., Illus.). 46p. (YA). (gr. 5-8). 9.95 (978-0-86685-400-9(2)) International Bk. Ctr., Inc.

Harris, Nicholas. Pyramid. Dennis, Peter, illus. 2006. 31p. (J). ***(978-0-7607-7526-4(5))*** backpackbook.

Herbst, Judith. Lands of Mystery. (Unexplained Ser.). (Illus.). 48p. (J). 2005. lib. bdg. 26.60 (978-0-8225-1630-9(6)); 2004. pap. 7.95 (978-0-8225-2407-6(4)) Lerner Publishing Group.

Hooper, Meredith. Who Built the Pyramid? Heighway-Bury, Robin, illus. 2006. 40p. (J). (gr. 2-5). pap. 6.99 (978-0-7636-3046-1(2)) Candlewick Pr.

Hyman, Teresa L. Pyramids. 2004. (J). (gr. 4-7). 26.20 (978-0-7377-2055-6(7) , Greenhaven Pr., Inc.) Thomson Gale.

—The Pyramids of Giza. 2005. (Great Structures in History Ser.). (Illus.). 48p. (J). (gr. 4-8). 26.20 (978-0-7377-1560-6(X) , Greenhaven Pr., Inc.) Thomson Gale.

Hynson, Colin. The Building of the Great Pyramid. 2006. (Stories from History Ser.). 48p. (J). 14.95 (978-0-7696-4708-1(1)); pap. 6.95 (978-0-7696-4692-3(1)) School Specialty Publishing.

Kallen, Stuart A. Pyramids. 2002. (Mystery Library). (Illus.). 112p. (YA). (gr. 4-12). 29.95 (978-1-56006-773-3(X) , Lucent Bks.) Thomson Gale.

Keyes, Anna. Faraones, piramides y momias & Pharaohs, Pyramids & Mummies. 2005. spiral bd. 88.00 ***(978-1-4108-5732-3(8))*** Benchmark Education Co.

Leardi, Jeanette. The Great Pyramid: Egypt's Tomb for All Time. 2007. (Castles, Palaces, & Tombs Ser.). (Illus.). 32p. (J). lib. bdg. 25.27 (978-1-59716-266-1(3)) Bearport Publishing Co., Inc.

MacDonald, Fiona. Pyramids. 2001. (Topic Bks.). (Illus.). 32p. (J). (gr. 2-5). 23.50 (978-0-531-14552-4(2) , Watts, Franklin) Scholastic Library Publishing.

—Pyramids. 2000. (gr. 3-6). lib. bdg. 15.25 (978-0-613-34424-1(3)); (Illus.). (J). (978-0-606-20869-7(0)) Tandem Library Bks.

Mann, Elizabeth. The Great Pyramid: The Story of the Farmers, the God-King & the Most Astonding Structure Ever Built. Turco, Laura Lo, illus. 2006. (Wonders of the World Book Ser.). 48p. (J). (gr. 4-8). pap. 9.95 (978-1-931414-11-1(4)) Mikaya Pr.

—The Great Pyramid: The Story of the Farmers, the God-King & the Most Astounding Structure Ever Built. Turco, Laura, illus. 2003. (Wonders of the World Ser.). 48p. (J). (ps-7). 22.95 (978-0-9650493-1-3(0)) Mikaya Pr.

Matthews, Sheelagh. Pyramids of Giza. 2007. (J). ***(978-1-59036-725-4(1)); (978-1-59036-726-1(X))*** Weigl Pubs., Inc.

McCall, Henrietta. Pyramid. 1999. (Fast Forward Ser.). (Illus.). 32p. (J). (gr. 4-8). 29.00 (978-0-531-14584-5(0) , Watts, Franklin) Scholastic Library Publishing.

—Pyramid. 1999. (gr. 3-6). lib. bdg. 18.75 (978-0-613-37518-4(1)) Tandem Library Bks.

—Pyramids. 1999. (Fast Forward Ser.).Tr. of Pyramide. (Illus.). 32p. (J). (gr. 4-8). pap. 9.95 (978-0-531-15435-9(1) , Watts, Franklin) Scholastic Library Publishing.

McNeil, Niki, et al. HOCPP 1071 Pyramids of Egypt. 2006. spiral bd. 12.00 ***(978-1-60308-071-2(6))*** In the Hands of a Child.

Mellett, Peter. Pyramids. 2000. (Fantastic Facts Ser.). (Illus.). 64p. (gr. 3-7). pap. 6.95 (978-1-84215-323-9(4) , Southwater) Anness Publishing GBR. *Dist:* National Bk. Network.

—Pyramids. 1999. (Young Scientist Concepts & Projects Ser.). (Illus.). 68p. (J). (gr. 4 up). lib. bdg. 27.33 (978-0-8368-2267-0(6)) Stevens, Gareth Inc.

Millard, Anne. Misterios de las Piramides. (Coleccion Misterios De). (SPA., Illus.). 48p. (YA). (gr. 5-8). 19.95 (978-84-348-5690-5(5) , SM6076) SM Ediciones ESP. *Dist:* AIMS International Bks., Inc., Lectorum Pubns., Inc.

—Pyramids. 2007. (Hallmarks of History Ser.). (Illus.). 32p. (J). ***(978-1-59604-122-6(6))*** Stargazer Bks.

Millard, Anne. The World of Pyramids. 2004. (World Of Ser.). (Illus.). 64p. (J). (gr. 4-6). pap. 8.95 (978-0-7534-5787-0(3) , Kingfisher) Houghton Mifflin Co. Trade & Reference Div.

Naden, Corinne J. & Blue, Rose. Ancient Egyptians & the Pyramids. 2003. (J). (978-1-58417-310-6(6)); pap. (978-1-58417-311-3(4)) Lake Street Pubs.

Nardo, Don. Pyramids of Egypt. 2002. (Watts Library). (Illus.). (J). (gr. 5-7). 63p. pap. 8.95 (978-0-531-16226-2(5)); 64p. 25.50 (978-0-531-20359-0(X)) Scholastic Library Publishing. (Watts, Franklin).

—Pyramids of Egypt. 2002. (gr. 3-6). lib. bdg. 17.60 (978-0-613-53855-8(2)) Tandem Library Bks.

O'Donnell, Kerri. The Pyramids of Egypt. 2002. (Places Around the World Ser.). (Illus.). 24p. (J). lib. bdg. 18.75 (978-0-8239-3739-4(9)) Rosen Publishing Group, Inc., The.

Orr, Joel N. Structure Is Destiny: The Dandelion Paradox. 2004. (ALB.). (YA). per. 19.95 (978-0-9634168-9-6(8)) ZEM Pr.

Osborne, Mary Pope & Osborne, Will. Mummies & Pyramids: A Nonfiction Companion to Mummies in the Morning. Murdocca, Sal, illus. 2001. (Magic Tree House Research Guide Ser.: No. 3). 128p. (J). (gr. k-3). lib. bdg. 11.99 (978-0-375-90298-7(8) , Random Hse. Bks. for Young Readers) Random Hse. Children's Bks.

Osborne, Will & Osborne, Mary Pope. Mummies & Pyramids: A Nonfiction Companion to Mummies in the Morning. Murdocca, Sal, illus. 2001. (Magic Tree House Research Guide Ser.: No. 3). 128p. (J). (gr. k-3). pap. 4.99 (978-0-375-80298-0(3) , Random Hse. Bks. for Young Readers) Random Hse. Children's Bks.

—Mummies & Pyramids: A Nonfiction Companion to Mummies in the Morning. Murdocca, Salvatore, illus. 2001. (Magic Tree House Research Guide Ser.: No. 3). 119p. (J). (gr. k-3). per. 13.00 (978-0-613-33837-0(5)) Tandem Library Bks.

Pace, Mildred M. Pyramids: Tombs for Eternity. Vero, Radu & Zisu, Mirela, illus. 1998. 192p. (J). (gr. 7-12). pap. 10.95 (978-0-87226-548-6(X) , 6548XB, Bedrick, Peter Bks.) School Specialty Publishing.

Peterson, Sheryl. Egyptian Pyramids. 2005. (Ancient Wonders of the World Ser.). (Illus.). 32p. (gr. 4-7). 18.95 (978-1-58341-359-3(6) , Creative Education) Creative Co., The.

Las Piramides Fueron Construidas. 2003. (Enciclopedia Me Pregunto Por Que). (SPA., Illus.). 32p. (J). (gr. 3-5). 12.99 (978-84-241-2171-6(6) , EV2033) Everest de Ediciones y Distribucion, S.L. ESP. *Dist:* Lectorum Pubns., Inc.

Pratchett, Terry. Pyramids. 2001. (gr. 5-8). lib. bdg. 15.30 (978-0-613-57264-4(5)) Tandem Library Bks.

Putnam, James & Dorling Kindersley Publishing Staff. Pyramid. Brightling, Geoff & Hayman, Peter, photos by. 2004. (Eyewitness Books). (Illus.). 72p. (J). lib. bdg. 19.99 (978-0-7566-0716-6(7)) Dorling Kindersley Publishing, Inc.

Rau, Dana Meachen. Bookworms: The Inside Story, 6 bks., Set. Incl. Castle. 32p. lib. bdg. 22.79 (978-0-7614-2272-3(2)); Igloo. 24p. lib. bdg. 22.79 (978-0-7614-2273-0(0)); Log Cabin. 24p. lib. bdg. 22.79 ***(978-0-7614-2274-7(9));*** Pyramid. 32p. lib. bdg. 22.79 ***(978-0-7614-2275-4(7));*** Skyscraper. 32p. lib. bdg. 22.79 (978-0-7614-2276-1(5)); Tepee. 32p. lib. bdg. 22.79 (978-0-7614-2277-8(3)); (Illus.). (J). (gr. k-2). 2006. 2006. Set lib. bdg. 136.71 ***(978-0-7614-2271-6(4)*** , Benchmark Bks.) Cavendish, Marshall Corp.

—Pyramid. 2006. (Bookworms Ser.). (Illus.). 32p. (J). (gr. k-2). lib. bdg. 22.79 ***(978-0-7614-2275-4(7)*** , Benchmark Bks.) Cavendish, Marshall Corp.

Reid, S. & Chisholm, J. Who Built the Pyramids? 2004. (Starting Point History Ser.). 32p. (J). lib. bdg. 12.95 (978-1-58086-629-3(8) , Usborne) EDC Publishing.

Scholastic, Inc. Staff, ed. Pyramids Discovery Box. 1999. (Scholastic Discovery Box Ser.). (Illus.). 32p. (J). (gr. 3-5). 12.95 (978-0-590-92688-1(8)) Scholastic, Inc.

Shuter, Jane. The Pyramids. 2003. (Visiting the Past Ser.). (Illus.). 32p. (J). pap. 7.50 (978-1-4034-0622-4(7)); (gr. 5-7). lib. bdg. 25.64 (978-1-58810-706-0(X)) Heinemann Library.

Simon, Seymour. Pyramids & Mummies. 2004. (See More Readers). (Illus.). 40p. (J). 14.50 (978-1-58717-240-3(2)); Vol. 3. pap. 3.95 (978-1-58717-241-0(0)) Chronicle Bks. LLC. (SeaStar Bks.).

—Seemore Pyramids & Mummies. 2006. 40p. (J). pap. 3.95 (978-0-8118-5497-9(3)) Chronicle Bks. LLC.

Steele, Philip. Pyramids Were Built: And Other Questions about Ancient Egypt. 2006. (I Wonder Why Ser.). 32p. (J). (gr. k-3). pap. 6.95 (978-0-7534-5963-8(9) , Kingfisher) Houghton Mifflin Co. Trade & Reference Div.

Strom, Laura Layton. The Egyptian Science Gazette. 2007. (Shockwave: Science in Practice Ser.). (Illus.). 36p. (J). (gr. 4-6). lib. bdg. 25.00 ***(978-0-531-17582-8(0)*** , Children's Pr.) Scholastic Library Publishing.

Taplin, Sam. Mummies & Pyramids. 2004. (Discovery Program Ser.). (Illus.). 48p. (J). pap. 8.95 (978-0-7945-0317-8(9) , Usborne); lib. bdg. 16.95 (978-1-58086-479-4(1)) EDC Publishing.

White, Graham. Secrets of the Pyramids: National Geographic Maze Adventures. 2002. (Illus.). 32p. (J). (gr. 3-7). pap. 8.95 (978-0-7922-6938-0(1) , National Geographic Children's Bks.) National Geographic Society.

—Secrets of the Pyramids: National Geographic Maze Adventures. 2002. (gr. 3-6). lib. bdg. 17.60 (978-0-613-80045-3(3)) Tandem Library Bks.

Williams, Brenda & Williams, Brian. Reach for the Stars: Ancient Egyptian Pyramids. 2007. (J). ***(978-1-4109-2888-7(8));*** pap. ***(978-1-4109-2895-5(0))*** Steck-Vaughn.

Wood, Tim. Maravillas de la Antig Edad. Colella, Elida Marta, tr. Adams, Jonathan, illus. 2002. (SPA.). 48p. (J). 24.95 (978-950-11-1566-6(6)) Sigmar ARG. *Dist:* Lectorum Pubns., Inc.

Zuravicky, Orli. Exploring Pyramids Around the World: Making Models of Geometric Solids. 2004. (PowerMath Ser.). (Illus.). 32p. (J). lib. bdg. 22.50 (978-0-8239-8992-8(5) , PowerKids Pr.) Rosen Publishing Group, Inc., The.

PYTHAGOREAN PROPOSITION

Ellis, Julie. What's Your Angle, Pythagoras? A Math Adventure. Hornung, Phyllis, illus. 2004. (Math Adventures Ser.). 32p. (J). pap. 6.95 (978-1-57091-150-7(9)); 16.95 (978-1-57091-197-2(5)) Charlesbridge Publishing, Inc.

Harkins, Susan and William. The Life & Times of Pythagoras. 2007. (Biography from Ancient Civilizations Ser.). (Illus.). 48p. (J). lib. bdg. 29.95 ***(978-1-58415-545-4(0))*** Mitchell Lane Pubs., Inc.

Q

QUACKS AND QUACKERY—FICTION

Hiebert, Elfrieda H. & Juel, Connie. The Quack. (Little Book Practice Reader Ser.). (J). (978-0-8136-0778-8(7)) Modern Curriculum Pr.

QUAILS

Packard, Janet & McKellar, Carol. The Quails' Quest. 2002. (Illus.). 32p. (J). (gr. k-2). pap. 9.92 (978-0-9709717-1-5(0)) Janella Pr.

World Book, Inc. Staff, contrib. by. Quail & Other Galliforms. 2005. (World Book's Animals of the World Ser.). (Illus.). 64p. (J). (978-0-7166-1266-7(6)) World Bk., Inc.

QUAILS—FICTION

Clark, Irene M. Feathery Tales: Benny Penguin, Huffer & Puffer California Quail, Paco Pelican. Clark, Cynthia D., illus. unabr. ed. 2001. 147p. (J). (ps-3). 12.95 incl. cd-rom (978-0-9709843-0-2(8)) Creekside Stories.

Erickson, John R. The Case of the Missing Bird Dog. 2002. (Hank the Cowdog Ser.: No. 40). (gr. 3-6). lib. bdg. 13.00 (978-0-613-50279-5(5)) Tandem Library Bks.

Newth, Rebecca. Antonia Quail (Antonia la Codorniz) Horton, James F. & Fernandez, Ines, trs. Ruleman, Anne, illus. 2000. (ENG & SPA.). 32p. (J). (gr. k-3). (978-0-9630310-3-7(1)) Will Hall Bks.

Sargent, Dave. Bob White the Quail. Lenoir, Jane, illus. 2000. (J). lib. bdg. 19.95 (978-1-56763-481-5(8)); pap. 6.95 (978-1-56763-482-2(6)) Ozark Publishing.

QUAKERS

see also Society of Friends

Baczynski, Bernadette L. William Penn: Founder of the Pennsylvania Colony. 2004. (Let Freedom Ring Ser.). (Illus.). 48p. (J). 17.95 (978-0-7368-2459-0(6) , Bridgestone Bks.) Capstone Pr., Inc.

Bodie, Idella. Quaker Commander. 2001. (Illus.). 89p. (J). 6.95 (978-0-87844-160-0(3)) Sandlapper Publishing Co., Inc.

Boothroyd, Jennifer. William Penn: A Life of Tolerance. 2007. (Pull Ahead Books). (Illus.). 32p. (J). 22.60 (978-0-8225-6387-7(8) , Lerner Pubns.) Lerner Publishing Group.

De Angelis, Gina. Lucretia Mott: Woman Suffragist. 2000. (Women of Achievement Ser.). (Illus.). 112p. (J). (gr. 4-7). 30.00 (978-0-7910-5295-2(8) , Chelsea Hse.) Facts On File, Inc.

Friends General Conference (U.S.), Religious Education Committee Staff, contrib. by. Lives That Speak: Stories of Twentieth-Century Quakers. 2004. (Illus.). viii, 168p. (J). (978-1-888305-32-6(0)) Quaker Press of Friends General Conference.

Gillis, Jennifer Blizin. William Penn. 2004. (Illus.). 32p. (J). pap. 7.50 (978-1-4034-5971-8(1)); lib. bdg. 25.64 (978-1-4034-5963-3(0)) Heinemann Library.

Jacobson, Ryan. William Penn. Stiles, Tim, illus. 2007. (Graphic Library). 32p. (J). 25.26 (978-0-7368-6501-2(2)) Capstone Pr., Inc.

Lilly, Melinda. Quakers in Early America. 2003. (Rourke Discovery Library). (Illus.). 24p. (gr. 1-4). 14.95 (978-1-58952-370-8(9)) Rourke Publishing, LLC.

Lucas, Eileen. Prudence Crandall. Smith, Kimanne, illus. 2001. (On My Own Biographies Ser.). 48p. (J). (gr. 1-3). lib. bdg. (978-1-57505-480-3(9) , Carolrhoda Bks.) Lerner Publishing Group.

Lutz, Norma Jean. William Penn: Founder of Democracy. 2000. (gr. 5-8). lib. bdg. 17.60 (978-0-613-43400-3(5)) Tandem Library Bks.

Mierka, Gregg A. Nathanael Greene: The General Who Saved the Revolution. 2006. (J). pap. (978-1-59556-017-9(3)); (Illus.). 88p. (gr. 5-11). lib. bdg. 23.95 (978-1-59556-012-4(2)) OTTN Publishing.

Rand, Carol. Lydia Darragh: Quaker Patriot. Marshall, Dan, illus. (J). 15.95 (978-0-945912-33-0(1)) Pippin Pr.

Somervill, Barbara A. William Penn: Founder of Pennsylvania. 2006. (Signature Lives Ser.). (Illus.). 112p. (J). (gr. 5-7). 30.60 (978-0-7565-1598-0(X)) Compass Point Bks.

Swain, Gwenyth. Freedom Seeker: A Story about William Penn. Harvey, Lisa, illus. 2003. 64p. (J). pap. 6.95 (978-0-87614-931-7(X) , Carolrhoda Bks.) Lerner Publishing Group.

Walsh, Kieran. William Penn. 2005. (Discover the Life of a Colonial American Ser.). (Illus.). 24p. (gr. 2-5). 14.95 (978-1-59515-139-1(7)) Rourke Publishing, LLC.

Yolen, Jane. Friend: The Story of George Fox & the Quakers. 2nd ed. 2005. (Illus.). xii, 179p. (J). (978-1-888305-41-8(X)) Quaker Press of Friends General Conference.

QUALITATIVE ANALYSIS

see Chemistry, Analytic

QUANTITATIVE ANALYSIS

see Chemistry, Analytic

QUANTUM THEORY

see also Chemistry; Force and Energy; Radiation; Relativity (Physics); Thermodynamics

Fleisher, Paul. Relativity & Quantum Mechanics: Principles of Modern Physics. 2005. (Secrets of the Universe Ser.). (Illus.). 80p. (gr. 6-12). 25.26 (978-0-8225-2989-7(0)) Lerner Publishing Group.

Topp, Patricia. This Strange Quantum World & You. 2006. 69p. (YA). per. 10.95 ***(978-1-60002-195-4(6)*** , 2844, Airleaf Publishing) Airleaf Publishing & Bookselling.

Willett, Edward. The Basics of Quantum Physics: Understanding the Photoelectric Effect & Line Spectra. 2004. (Library of Physics). (Illus.). 48p. (YA). lib. bdg. 25.25 (978-1-4042-0334-1(6)) Rosen Publishing Group, Inc., The.

QUARANTINE

see Communicable Diseases

QUARTER HORSE

Dell, Pamela. American Quarter Horses. 2007. (Majestic Horses Ser.). 32p. (J). (gr. k-4). 27.07 (978-1-59296-779-7(5)) Child's World, Inc.

Gentle, Victor & Perry, Janet. Quarter Horses. 1998. (Illus.). 24p. (J). (gr. 1 up). lib. bdg. 19.93 (978-0-8368-2134-5(3)) Stevens, Gareth Inc.

Parise-Peterson, Amanda. The American Quarter Horse. 2005. (Horses Ser.). (Illus.). 32p. (J). 22.60 (978-0-7368-3764-4(7)) Capstone Pr., Inc.

Price, Steven D. Kids' Book of the American Quarter Horse. 1999. (gr. 3-6). lib. bdg. 30.35 (978-0-613-90263-2(7)) Tandem Library Bks.

—The Kids' Book of the American Quarter Horse: Two Bits' Guide to Owning, Riding & Caring for Your Horse. 1999. (American Quarter Horse Association Bks.). (Illus.). 200p. (gr. 4-7). pap. 19.95 (978-1-55821-975-5(7) , Lyons Pr.) Globe Pequot Pr., The.

Stone, Lynn M. American Quarter Horses. 2008. (J). ***(978-1-60044-579-8(9))*** Rourke Publishing, LLC.

QUASIMODO (FICTITIOUS CHARACTER)—FICTION

Friedman, Michael Jan. Hunchdog of Notre Dame. l.t. ed. 1999. (Adventures of Wishbone Ser.: No. 5). (Illus.). 139p. (J). (gr. 4 up). lib. bdg. 22.60 (978-0-8368-2301-1(X)) Stevens, Gareth Inc.

Hugo, Victor. The Hunchback of Notre- Dame. Famig, Jon L., illus. 1998. (Illustrated Classic Book Ser.). 61p. (J). (gr. 3 up). pap. 4.95 (978-1-56767-247-3(7)) Educational Insights, Inc.

—The Hunchback of Notre- Dame. unabr. ed. 1998. (Wordsworth Classics Ser.). (YA). (gr. 6-12). 5.27 (978-0-89061-068-8(1) , R0681WW) Jamestown.

—The Hunchback of Notre- Dame. (Young Collector's Illustrated Classics Ser.). (Illus.). 192p. (J). (gr. 3-7). 9.95 (978-1-56156-458-3(3)) Kidsbooks, Inc.

—Hunchback of Notre Dame. 2002. (Great Illustrated Classics Ser.). (Illus.). 240p. (J). (gr. 3-8). 21.35 (978-1-57765-813-9(2) , ABDO & Daughters) ABDO Publishing Co.

The Hunchback of Notre Dame. (Read-Along Ser.). (J). 7.99 incl. audio (978-1-55723-992-1(4)) Walt Disney Records.

QUEBEC (PROVINCE)

Hamilton, J. Quebec. 1999. (Hello Canada Ser.). (J). pap. (978-1-55041-275-8(2)) Fitzhenry & Whiteside, Ltd.

Hamilton, Janice. Quebec. 2nd rev. ed. (Hello Canada Ser.). 72p. (J). pap. (978-1-55041-764-7(9)) Fitzhenry & Whiteside, Ltd.

—Quebec. 1998. (Hello Canada Ser.). (Illus.). (J). (gr. 3-6). pap. 6.95 (978-0-8225-9810-7(8)) Lerner Publishing Group.

Kizilos, Peter. Quebec: Province Divided. 1999. (World in Conflict Ser.). (Illus.). 104p. (YA). (gr. 7-12). lib. bdg. 25.26 (978-0-8225-3562-1(9) , Lerner Pubns.) Lerner Publishing Group.

LeVert, Suzanne. Quebec. 2000. (Canada in the Twenty First Century Ser.). (Illus.). (J). (gr. 8-12). 18.95 (978-0-7910-6070-4(5) , Chelsea Hse.) Facts On File, Inc.

QUEBEC (PROVINCE)—FICTION

Autio, Karen. Second Watch. 2006. (Illus.). 208p. (J). pap. 8.95 (978-1-55039-151-0(8)) Sono Nis Pr. CAN. *Dist:* Orca Bk. Pubs. USA.

Bruchac, Joseph. The Winter People. 2004. (Illus.). 176p. (J). (gr. 5). pap. 5.99 (978-0-14-240229-0(X) , Puffin) Penguin Group (USA) Inc.

—The Winter People. Bernardin, James, illus. 2002. 176p. (J). 16.99 (978-0-8037-2694-9(5) , Dial) Penguin Group (USA) Inc.

Carrier, Roch. The Longest Home Run. Fischman, Sheila, tr. from FRE. Cohen, Sheldon, illus. 2001. Orig. Title: Le Plus Long Circuit. 24p. (J). (gr. 3). pap. 7.95 (978-0-88776-312-0(X)) Tundra Bks., Inc./Livres Toundra, Inc. CAN. *Dist:* Random Hse., Inc.

Downie, Mary Alice & Downie, John. Danger in Disguise. 2001. (On Time's Wing Ser.). (Illus.). 178p. (J). (gr. 4-7). pap. (978-1-896184-72-2(3)) Roussan Pubs., Inc./Roussan Editeur, Inc.

Dubois, Muriel L. Abenaki Captive. 16.00 (978-0-9723410-0-4(5)) Apprentice Shop Bks., LLC.

Fitch, Sheree. One More Step. 2006. (Orca Soundings Ser.). 112p. (YA). lib. bdg. 14.95 (978-1-55143-554-1(3)) Orca Bk. Pubs. USA.

Grant, Robert. Jack in the Bush or A Summer on a Salmon River. 2005. pap. 33.95 (978-1-4179-5573-2(2)) Kessinger Publishing, LLC.

Noel, Michel. Good for Nothing. Tanaka, Shelley, tr. from FRE. 2004. (J). 18.95 (978-0-88899-478-3(8)) Groundwood Bks. CAN. *Dist:* Transition Vendor.

Noel, Michel & Tanaka, Shelley. Good for Nothing. 2006. 256p. (J). pap. 9.95 (978-0-88899-616-9(0) , Libros Tigrillo) Groundwood Bks. CAN. *Dist:* Perseus Distribution.

Stoddart, Heidi Jardine. Return to the Sea. Stoddart, Heidi Jardine, illus. 2007. (Illus.). 32p. (J). (ps-3). pap. ***(978-1-55109-606-3(4))*** Nimbus Publishing, Ltd.

Wallace, Karen. Raspberries on the Yangtze. 2002. 160p. (YA). pap. 8.99 (978-0-689-83699-2(6)) Simon & Schuster, Ltd. GBR. *Dist:* Independent Pubs. Group.

Warner, Gertrude Chandler. The Mystery of the Screech Owl, Vol. 16. 2004. (Boxcar Children Special Ser.: No. 16). (Illus.). 144p. (J). (gr. 2-5). 14.95 (978-0-8075-5481-4(2)); pap. 3.95 (978-0-8075-5482-1(0)) Whitman, Albert & Co.

QUEBEC (QUEBEC)—FICTION

Henty, G. A. With Wolfe in Canada: The Winning of a Continent. 2006. per. 8.95 (978-1-57646-980-4(8)) Quiet Vision Publishing.

Murray, Susan. Panic in Puerto Vallarta: Quebec's Intelligentsia & the Fascist Temptation, 19. 1998. (gr. 7-12). lib. bdg. 15.30 (978-0-613-78576-1(2)) Tandem Library Bks.

Page, Katherine Hall. Bon Voyage, Christie & Company. (Christie & Company Ser.). (YA). (gr. 6-8). 1999. (Illus.). 10p. pap. 3.99 (978-0-380-78035-8(6)); 1998. 288p. 14.00 (978-0-380-97398-9(7)) HarperCollins Pubs.

QUEENS

see also Kings, Queens, Rulers, etc.

also names of countries with the subdivision Kings and Rulers; and names of queens.

Adams, Michelle Medlock. The Life & Times of Cleopatra. 2005. (Biography from Ancient Civilizations Ser.). (Illus.). 48p. (J). (gr. 4-8). lib. bdg. 29.95 (978-1-58415-335-1(0)) Mitchell Lane Pubs., Inc.

Ashworth, Leon. Queen Elizabeth I. 2002. (Illus.). 32p. (J). (gr. 4-6). (978-1-84234-071-4(9) , Evans Brothers, Limited) Evans Publishing Group.

—Queen Victoria. 1999. (British History Makers Ser.). (Illus.). 32p. pap. 11.99 (978-0-7540-9014-4(0) , Cherrytree Books) Evans Publishing Group GBR. *Dist:* Independent Pubs. Group.

Barnes-Murphy, Rowan. Kings & Queens of Britain. 2003. (Illus.). 40p. (YA). (978-1-84365-027-0(4)) Chrysalis Children's Bks.

Blackburn, Mark. Hula Heaven: The Queen's Album. 2001. (Illus.). 96p. (J). pap. 19.95 (978-0-7643-1333-2(9)) Schiffer Publishing, Ltd.

Buchanan, Jane. Mary Tudor: Courageous Queen or Bloody Mary? 2007. (Wicked Historytrade; Ser.). 128p. (J). spiral bd. 30.00 (***978-0-531-12595-3(5)** , Children's Pr.) Scholastic Library Publishing.

Fowke, Bob. The Secret Life of Elizabeth I. 2005. (Illus.). (YA). pap. 9.99 (978-0-340-88422-5(3) , Hodder & Stoughton) Hodder General Publishing Division GBR. *Dist:* Trafalgar Square Publishing.

—The Secret Life of Queen Victoria. 2005. (Illus.). (YA). pap. 9.99 (978-0-340-88423-2(1) , Hodder & Stoughton) Hodder General Publishing Division GBR. *Dist:* Trafalgar Square Publishing.

Geras, Adèle. Cleopatra. 2009. (Illus.). 64p. (J). (gr. 1-5). 16.95 (***978-0-7534-6025-2(4)** , Kingfisher) Houghton Mifflin Co. Trade & Reference Div.

Gibson, Karen Bush. The Life & Times of Catherine the Great. 2005. (Biography from Ancient Civilizations Ser.). (Illus.). 48p. (J). (gr. 4-7). lib. bdg. 29.95 (978-1-58415-347-4(4)) Mitchell Lane Pubs., Inc.

Hilliam, David. Eleanor of Aquitaine: The Richest Queen in Medieval Europe. 2004. (Leaders of the Middle Ages Ser.). (Illus.). 112p. (J). lib. bdg. 31.95 (978-1-4042-0162-0(9)) Rosen Publishing Group, Inc., The.

Holub, Joan. Cleopatra & the King's Enemies: Based on a True Story of Cleopatra in Egypt. Aleshina, Nonna, illus. 2007. (Young Princesses Around the World Ser.). 48p. (J). (gr. 1-3). pap. 3.99 (978-0-689-87194-8(5)); lib. bdg. 13.89 (978-0-689-87196-2(1)) Simon & Schuster Children's Publishing. (Aladdin).

Jeffrey, Gary & Ganeri, Anita. Cleopatra: The Life of an Egyptian Queen. 2005. (Graphic Nonfiction Ser.). (Illus.). 48p. (J). lib. bdg. 26.50 (978-1-4042-0242-9(0)) Rosen Publishing Group, Inc., The.

Koestler-Grack, Rachel A. Eleanor of Aquitaine: Heroine of the Middle Ages. 2005. (Makers of the Middle Ages & Renaissance Ser.). (Illus.). 158p. (J). (gr. 4-8). lib. bdg. 30.00 (978-0-7910-8633-9(X) , Chelsea Hse.) Facts On File, Inc.

Lace, William W. Elizabeth I & Her Court. 2002. (Lucent Library of Historical Eras. Elizabethan England Library). (Illus.). 112p. (J). 28.70 (978-1-59018-098-3(4) , Lucent Bks.) Thomson Gale.

MacDonald, Fiona. Cleopatra. 2006. (DK Discoveries Ser.). 48p. (J). pap. 6.99 (978-0-7566-1964-0(5)) Dorling Kindersley Publishing, Inc.

Meltzer, Milton. Ten Queens: Portraits of Women of Power. Andersen, Bethanne, illus. 2003. 144p. (J). (gr. 7-12). reprint ed. pap. 14.99 (978-0-525-47158-5(8) , Dutton Juvenile) Penguin Group (USA) Inc.

—Ten Queens: Portraits of Women of Power. 2004. (gr. 7-12). lib. bdg. 24.60 (978-0-613-72581-1(6)) Tandem Library Bks.

Plain, Nancy. Eleanor of Aquitaine & the High Middle Ages. 2005. (Rulers & Their Times Ser.). (Illus.). 96p. (J). (gr. 3-7). lib. bdg. 29.93 (978-0-7614-1834-4(2) , Benchmark Bks.) Cavendish, Marshall Corp.

Sapet, Kerrily. Eleanor of Aquitaine: Medieval Queen. 2006. (European Queens Ser.). (Illus.). 176p. (J). (gr. 6-12). 26.95 (978-1-931798-90-7(7)) Reynolds, Morgan Inc.

Shone, Rob & Ganeri, Anita. Elizabeth I: The Life of England's Renaissance Queen. 2005. (Graphic Nonfiction Ser.). (Illus.). 48p. lib. bdg. 26.50 (978-1-4042-0246-7(3)) Rosen Publishing Group, Inc., The.

Tait, Leia. Queen Rania Al-Abdullah. 2007. (J). (***978-1-59036-645-5(X)**); (***978-1-59036-646-2(8)**) Weigl Pubs., Inc.

Vennema, Peter & Stanley, Diane. Good Queen Bess: The Story of Elizabeth I of England. Stanley, Diane, illus. 2001. (Illus.). 40p. (J). (gr. 2 up). 16.99 (978-0-688-17961-8(4)) HarperCollins Pubs.

Weatherly, Myra. Elizabeth I: Queen of Tudor England. 2005. (Signature Lives Ser.). (Illus.). 112p. (J). (gr. 5-7). (978-0-7565-0988-0(2)) Compass Point Bks.

Wood, Richard & Barton-Wood, Sara. The Queen Mother: Grandmother of a Nation. 2000. (Famous Lives Ser.). (Illus.). 48p. (J). (gr. 3-7). lib. bdg. 27.12 (978-0-8172-5715-6(2)) Raintree.

Worth, Richard. Cleopatra: Queen of Ancient Egypt. 2006. (Rulers of the Ancient World Ser.). (Illus.). 160p. (J). lib. bdg. 27.93 (978-0-7660-2559-2(4)) Enslow Pubs., Inc.

QUERIES

see Questions and Answers

QUESTIONS AND ANSWERS

Abitz, Diana. Know-the-Facts Review Game: 100 Must-Know Facts in a Q&A Game Format to Help Kids Really Remember Standards-Based Social Studies Information. 2005. (American History Ser.). 48p. pap. 14.99 (978-0-439-37434-7(0)); (Illus.). pap. 14.99 (978-0-439-37431-6(6)) Scholastic, Inc. (Teaching Resources).

Abitz, Diana & LaRoy, Susan. Know-the-Facts Review Game: 100 Must-Know Facts in a Q&A Game Format to Help Kids Really Remember Standards-Based Social Studies Information. 2005. (U. S. & World Geography Ser.). 48p. pap. 14.99 (978-0-439-37433-0(2)); pap. 14.99 (978-0-439-37432-3(4)) Scholastic, Inc. (Teaching Resources).

Amazing Questions & Answers. 2003. 512p. 9.98 (978-1-4054-0738-0(7)) Parragon, Inc.

Ambrose, Ann & Wells, Dolores J. Computer Concepts BASICS. 3rd rev. ed. 2006. 480p. (C). spiral bd. 59.95 (978-1-4188-6503-0(6)) Thomson Course Technology, Inc.

American Girl Editorial Staff. Coconut Quiz Book: Tear & Share Quizzes for You & a Friend. 2004. (Illus.). 80p. (J). 7.95 (978-1-58485-912-3(1)) American Girl Publishing, Inc.

Amerikaner, Susan, et al. Questions & Answers. 2000. (Questions & Answers Ser.). (Illus.). 184p. (J). (gr. 1-3). pap. 9.95 (978-0-7373-0512-8(6)) Lowell Hse. Juvenile.

Anello, Marc. The Totally Righteous, Awesomely Cool, Simply Outrageous List Book. Barbas, Kerren, illus. 2005. (Journal Ser.). 128p. 12.99 (978-0-88088-777-9(X)) Peter Pauper Pr. Inc.

Anthony, Erin. I-Ballers: Little Books for Big Minds. 2005. 60p. (J). pap. (978-1-57528-938-0(5)) University Games.

Ashbe, Jeanne. What's Inside? Ashbe, Jeanne, illus. 2001. (Illus.). 12p. (J). (ps). 9.95 (978-0-916291-97-6(9)) Kane/Miller Bk. Pubs., Inc.

Baifang. More Chinese Brain Twisters: 60 Fast, Fun Puzzles That Help Children Develop Quick Minds. 1999. (Illus.). 128p. pap. 14.95 (978-0-471-24613-8(1) , Wiley-Interscience) Wiley, John & Sons, Inc.

Bailey, Jacqui. Amazing Animal Facts: A Visual Guide to the World's Most Incredible Creatures. 2003. (Illus.). 64p. (J). pap. 12.99 (978-0-7894-9870-0(7)) Dorling Kindersley Publishing, Inc.

Beecroft, Simon. A Queen's Diary. 2007. (DK Readers: Level 2 (Paperback) Ser.). (Illus.). 32p. (J). (gr. 1-3). per. 3.99 (***978-0-7566-3269-4(2)**) Dorling Kindersley Publishing, Inc.

—Star Wars: A Queen's Diary. 2007. (DK Readers: Level 2 (Hardcover) Ser.). (Illus.). 32p. (J). (gr. 1-3). 14.99 (***978-0-7566-3268-7(4)**) Dorling Kindersley Publishing, Inc.

Behr, Alexandra. Where Did They Go? 2005. (Illus.). 32p. (J). 18.50 (978-0-7910-8774-9(3) , Chelsea Hse.) Facts On File, Inc.

Bell, Alison. Your Body, Yourself Q & A: Questions & Answers about Your Changing Body. 1999. (Teen Body Book Ser.). (Illus.). 191p. (J). (gr. 4-8). pap. 9.95 (978-0-7373-0190-8(2) , 01902W) McGraw-Hill/ Contemporary.

Beres, Samantha. Questions & Answers. 1999. (Grade Boosters Ser.: Vol. 2). (Illus.). 64p. (J). pap. 5.95 (978-0-7373-0200-4(3) , 02003w) McGraw-Hill/ Contemporary.

Bergen, Lara Rice. Ultimate Rugrats Trivia Sticker Book. 1999. (Rugrats Ser.). (J). pap. 5.99 (978-0-689-82892-8(6) , Little Simon) Simon & Schuster Children's Publishing.

Berger, Gilda & Berger, Melvin. Se Puede Escuchar un Grito en el Espacio. 2007. Tr. of Can You Hear a Shout in Space?. (SPA., Illus.). 48p. (J). (gr. 3-5). pap. 5.99 (978-0-439-76538-1(2) , SO33881, Scholastic en Espanol) Scholastic, Inc.

—Why Don't Haircuts Hurt? Questions & Answers about the Human Body. Barnes, Karen, illus. 1999. (Scholastic Question & Answer Ser.). 48p. (J). (gr. 2-4). pap. 6.99 (978-0-439-08569-4(1) , Scholastic Reference) Scholastic, Inc.

Berger, Melvin. Can It Rain Cats & Dogs? 1999. (gr. 3-6). lib. bdg. 14.10 (978-0-613-16903-5(4)) Tandem Library Bks.

—Can You Hear a Shout in Space? 2000. (gr. 3-6). lib. bdg. 14.10 (978-0-613-32367-3(X)) Tandem Library Bks.

—Did Dinosaurs Live in Your Backyard? 1999. (Question & Answer Ser.). (J). 12.75 (978-0-606-20053-0(3)) Tandem Library Bks.

—Do All Spiders Spin Webs? 2000. (gr. 3-6). lib. bdg. 14.10 (978-0-613-24865-5(1)) Tandem Library Bks.

—Do Penguins Get Frostbite? 2001. 12.75 (978-0-606-22177-1(8)) Tandem Library Bks.

—Do Spiders Spin Webs? 2000. (Question & Answer Ser.). (J). 12.75 (978-0-606-19553-9(X)) Tandem Library Bks.

—Do Stars Have Points? 1999. (Question & Answer Ser.). (J). 12.75 (978-0-606-20054-7(1)) Tandem Library Bks.

—Do Tarantulas Have Teeth? 2000. (Question & Answer Ser.). (J). 12.75 (978-0-606-19554-6(8)) Tandem Library Bks.

—Do Tornadoes Really Twist? 2000. (gr. 3-6). lib. bdg. 14.10 (978-0-613-32476-2(5)) Tandem Library Bks.

—Do Whales Have Belly Buttons? Questions & Answers about Whales & Dolphins. 1999. (Question & Answer Ser.). (J). 12.75 (978-0-606-20055-4(X)) Tandem Library Bks.

—How Do Flies Walk Upside Down? Questions & Answers about Insects. 1999. (Question & Answer Ser.). (J). 12.75 (978-0-606-20062-2(2)) Tandem Library Bks.

—What Do Sharks Eat for Dinner? 2000. (gr. 3-6). lib. bdg. 14.10 (978-0-613-35801-9(5)) Tandem Library Bks.

—Why Do Volcanoes Blow Their Tops? Questions & Answers about Volcanoes & Earthquakes. 2000. (Question & Answer Ser.). (J). (978-0-606-19623-9(4)) Tandem Library Bks.

—Why Don't Haircuts Hurt? Questions & Answers about Your Body. 1999. (Question & Answer Ser.). (J). (978-0-606-20067-7(3)) Tandem Library Bks.

Berger, Melvin & Berger, Gilda. Can Snakes Crawl Backward? Questions & Answers about Reptiles. Male, Alan, illus. 2002. (Question & Answer Ser.). 48p. (J). (gr. 2-4). pap. 5.95 (978-0-439-19381-8(8) , Scholastic Reference) Scholastic, Inc.

—Did Dinosaurs Live in Your Backyard? Male, Alan, illus. 1999. (Scholastic Question & Answer Ser.). 48p. (J). (gr. 2-4). pap. 12.95 (978-0-590-13078-3(1) , Scholastic Reference) Scholastic, Inc.

—Did Dinosaurs Live in Your Backyard? Questions & Answers about Dinosaurs. Male, Alan, illus. 1999. (Scholastic Question & Answer Ser.). 48p. (J). (gr. 2-4). 5.95 (978-0-439-08568-7(3) , Scholastic Reference) Scholastic, Inc.

—Do All Spiders Spin Webs? Questions & Answers about Spiders. Osti, Roberto, illus. 2000. (Question & Answer Ser.). 48p. (J). (gr. 2-4). pap. 5.95 (978-0-439-14881-8(2) , Scholastic Reference); pap. 14.95 (978-0-439-09586-0(7)) Scholastic, Inc.

—Do Bears Sleep All Winter? Questions & Answers about Bears. Osti, Roberto, illus. 2002. (Question & Answer Ser.). 48p. (J). pap. 5.95 (978-0-439-26671-0(8) , Scholastic Reference) Scholastic, Inc.

—Do Stars Have Points? Questions & Answers about Stars & Planets. Di Fate, Vincent, illus. 1999. (Scholastic Question & Answer Ser.). 48p. (J). (gr. 2-4). pap. 12.95 (978-0-590-13080-6(3) , Scholastic Reference) Scholastic, Inc.

—Do Tarantulas Have Teeth? Questions & Answers about Poisonous Creatures. Effler, Jim, illus. 2000. (Question & Answer Ser.). 48p. (J). (gr. 2-4). pap. 5.95 (978-0-439-14877-1(4) , Scholastic Reference); (gr. 4-7). pap. 14.95 (978-0-439-09578-5(6)) Scholastic, Inc.

—Do Tarantulas Have Teeth? Questions & Answers about Poisonous Creatures. Effler, Jim, illus. 2000. 48p. (J). (ps-7). lib. bdg. 14.10 (978-0-613-24866-2(X)) Tandem Library Bks.

—Do Tornadoes Really Twist? Questions & Answers about Tornadoes & Hurricanes. Bond, Barbara Higgins, illus. 2000. (Question & Answer Ser.). 48p. (J). (gr. 2-5). pap. 14.95 (978-0-439-09584-6(0)) Scholastic, Inc.

—Do Tornadoes Really Twist? Questions & Answers about Tornadoes & Hurricanes. 2000. (Scholastic Question & Answer Ser.). (J). 10.01 (978-0-439-09585-3(9)) Scholastic, Inc.

—Do Whales Have Belly Buttons? Questions & Answers about Whales & Dolphins. Bond, Higgins, illus. 1999. (Scholastic Question & Answer Ser.). 48p. (J). (gr. 2-4). 5.95 (978-0-439-08571-7(3)); pap. 12.95 (978-0-590-13081-3(1)) Scholastic, Inc. (Scholastic Reference).

—Does It Always Rain in the Rain Forest? Questions & Answers about Rain Forests. Rothman, Michael, illus. 2001. (J). (978-0-439-19382-5(6) , Scholastic Reference) Scholastic, Inc.

—How Do Flies Walk Upside Down? Questions & Answers about Insects. Effler, Jim, illus. 1999. (Scholastic Question & Answer Ser.). 48p. (J). (gr. 2-4). pap. 12.95 (978-0-590-13082-0(X) , Scholastic Reference) Scholastic, Inc.

—Hurricanes Have Eyes but Can't See: And Other Amazing Facts about Wild Weather. 2003. (Illus.). 48p. (J). (978-0-439-54980-6(9)) Scholastic, Inc.

—Why Do Volcanoes Blow Their Tops? Questions & Answers about Volcanoes & Earthquakes. Bond, Barbara Higgins, illus. 2000. (Question & Answer Ser.). 48p. (J). (gr. 2-5). pap. 14.95 (978-0-439-09580-8(8)) Scholastic, Inc.

—Why Do Wolves Howl? Questions & Answers about Wolves. Osti, Roberto, illus. 2001. (Question & Answer Ser.). 48p. (J). (gr. 2-4). 12.95 (978-0-439-19378-8(8) , Scholastic Reference) Scholastic, Inc.

—Why Don't Haircuts Hurt? Questions & Answers about Your Body. Barnes, Karen, illus. 1999. (Scholastic Question & Answer Ser.). 48p. (J). (gr. 2-4). pap. 12.95 (978-0-590-13079-0(X) , Scholastic Reference) Scholastic, Inc.

Berger, Melvin, et al. Do All Spiders Spin Webs? Questions & Answers about Spiders. 2000. (Question & Answer Ser.). (Illus.). 48p. (J). pap. (978-0-439-09587-7(5)) Scholastic, Inc.

—Do Tarantulas Have Teeth? Questions & Answers about Poisonous Creatures. 1999. (Question & Answer Ser.). (J). 4.99 (978-0-439-09579-2(4)) Scholastic, Inc.

—Why Do Volcanoes Blow Their Tops? Questions & Answers about Volcanoes & Earthquakes. 1999. (Question & Answer Ser.). (J). (978-0-439-09581-5(6)) Scholastic, Inc.

—Why Do Wolves Howl? Questions & Answers about Wolves. Osti, Roberto, illus. 2002. (Question & Answer Ser.). 48p. (J). (gr. 2-4). pap. 5.95 (978-0-439-19379-5(6) , Scholastic Reference) Scholastic, Inc.

Berry, Joy Wilt. Death: Good Answers to Tough Questions. Bartholomew, illus. rev. ed. 2000. (Good Answers to Tough Questions Ser.: Vol. 16). 48p. (J). (gr. 4-7). pap. 4.95 (978-1-58634-226-5(6) , 01-0901-16) Goldstar Publishing, Inc.

—Eating Disorders: Good Answers to Tough Questions. Bartholomew, illus. rev. ed. 2000. (Good Answers to Tough Questions Ser.: Vol. 7). 48p. (J). (gr. 4-7). pap. 4.95 (978-1-58634-217-3(7) , 01-0901-07) Goldstar Publishing, Inc.

—Substance Abuse: Good Answers to Tough Questions. Bartholomew, illus. rev. ed. 2000. (Good Answers to Tough Questions Ser.: Vol. 8). 48p. (J). (gr. 4-7). pap. 4.95 (978-1-58634-218-0(5) , 01-0901-08) Goldstar Publishing, Inc.

The Big Book of Bible Questions. 2008. 14.00 (***978-0-687-65088-0(7)**) Abingdon Pr.

Biggest Ever Book of Questions & Answers. 2003. 256p. (J). 12.98 (978-1-4054-1710-5(2)) Parragon, Inc.

Borgenicht, David. Sesame Street Unpaved: Scripts, Stories, Secrets & Songs. 1998. (Illus.). 193p. (YA). (gr. 5 up). 24.95 (978-0-7868-6460-7(5)) Hyperion Pr.

Bowman, Amy. Sports. 2001. (It's All about! Ser.). (Illus.). 32p. (J). (gr. 2-5). lib. bdg. 25.27 (978-1-58952-161-2(7)) Rourke Publishing, LLC.

Bracken, Mary S. Bindla Stiff's How Comes. Hepting, Jonah, illus. 2000. 56p. (J). (ps-6). pap. 14.95 (978-0-9704487-2-9(4)) Dandle Pr.

Brain Teasers. 2002. 96p. (J). pap. 2.98 (978-0-7525-7517-9(1)) Parragon, Inc.

Brewster, Hugh. 882 1/2 Amazing Answers to Your Questions about the Titanic. Marschall, Ken, illus. 1999. 96p. (J). (gr. 3-7). pap. 9.99 (978-0-439-04296-3(8)) Scholastic, Inc.

Brian, Sarah Jane. The Quiz Book 2: More Secrets Revealed. Tilley, Debbie, illus. 2001. (American Girl Library). 80p. (gr. 3 up). spiral bd. 7.95 (978-1-58485-285-8(2)) American Girl Publishing, Inc.

Brooks, Philip. Exploration & Discovery. 2002. (Questions & Answers about... Ser.). (Illus.). 40p. (J). (gr. 4-8). pap. 7.95 (978-0-7534-5492-3(0) , Kingfisher) Houghton Mifflin Co. Trade & Reference Div.

—How Things Work. 2002. (Questions & Answers about... Ser.). (Illus.). 40p. (J). (gr. 4-8). pap. 7.95 (978-0-7534-5490-9(4) , Kingfisher) Houghton Mifflin Co. Trade & Reference Div.

—Knights & Castles. Kingfisher Editors, ed. 2001. (Questions & Answers about... Ser.). 40p. (J). (gr. 4-6). pap. 7.95 (978-0-7534-5371-1(1) , Kingfisher) Houghton Mifflin Co. Trade & Reference Div.

—Transportation. Kingfisher Editors, ed. 2001. (Questions & Answers about... Ser.). 40p. (J). (gr. 4-6). pap. 7.95 (978-0-7534-5373-5(8) , Kingfisher) Houghton Mifflin Co. Trade & Reference Div.

Bruce, Jim. Creepy Crawlies. Kingfisher Editors, ed. 2001. (Question Time Ser.). (Illus.). 32p. (J). pap. 6.95 (978-0-7534-5413-8(0)); tchr. ed. 11.95 (978-0-7534-5342-1(8)) Houghton Mifflin Co. Trade & Reference Div. (Kingfisher).

—Mammals: Explore & Discover Mammals. 2001. (Question Time Ser.). (Illus.). 32p. (J). (gr. k-3). tchr. ed. 11.95 (978-0-7534-5340-7(1) , Kingfisher) Houghton Mifflin Co. Trade & Reference Div.

Brynie, Faith Hickman. 101 Questions..., 6 vols. Holm, Sharon Lane, illus. Incl. 101 Questions about Blood & Circulation with Answers Straight from the Heart. 2001. lib. bdg. 27.90 (978-0-7613-1455-4(5)); 101 Questions about Food & Digestion That Have Been Eating at You until Now. 2002. lib. bdg. 27.90 (978-0-7613-2309-9(0)); 101 Questions about Your Immune System You Felt Defenseless to Answer until Now. 2000. lib. bdg. (978-0-7613-1569-8(1)); 101 Questions about Your Skin That Got under Your Skin . . . until Now. 1999. lib. bdg. 27.90 (978-0-7613-1259-8(5)); 101 Questions Your Brain Has Asked about Itself but Couldn't Answer... until Now. 1998. lib. bdg. 27.90 (978-0-7613-0400-5(2)); 176p. (gr. 7 up). (Illus.). 2004. 139.50 (978-0-7613-3139-1(5) , Twenty-First Century Bks.) Lerner Publishing Group.

—101 Questions about Sex & Sexuality: With Answers for the Curious, Cautious, & Confused. 2003. (Single Titles Ser.). (Illus.). 176p. (gr. 7 up). lib. bdg. 27.90 (978-0-7613-2310-5(4) , Twenty-First Century Bks.) Lerner Publishing Group.

—101 Questions about Your Immune System You Felt Defenseless to Answer until Now. Holm, Sharon Lane, illus. 2000. (One Hundred One Questions... Ser.). 176p. (gr. 7 up). lib. bdg. (978-0-7613-1569-8(1) , Twenty-First Century Bks.) Lerner Publishing Group.

—101 Questions about Your Skin That Got under Your Skin . . . until Now. Holm, Sharon Lane, illus. 1999. (One Hundred One Questions... Ser.). 176p. (gr. 7 up). lib. bdg. 27.90 (978-0-7613-1259-8(5) , Twenty-First Century Bks.) Lerner Publishing Group.

—101 Questions Your Brain Has Asked about Itself but Couldn't Answer... until Now. Holm, Sharon Lane, illus. 1998. (One Hundred One Questions... Ser.). 176p. (gr. 7 up). lib. bdg. 27.90 (978-0-7613-0400-5(2) , Twenty-First Century Bks.) Lerner Publishing Group.

Buehner, Caralyn. It's a Spoon Not a Shovel. Buehner, Mark, illus. 1998. 40p. (J). (ps-3). pap. 6.99 (978-0-14-056427-3(6) , Puffin) Penguin Group (USA) Inc.

Bussolati, Emanuela. If You Put . . . Pagnoni, Roberta, illus. 2001. (Open the Little Windows Ser.). 22p. (J). (ps-k). bds. 4.95 (978-0-7641-5339-6(0)) Barron's Educational Series, Inc.

Callella, Trisha. I Have, Who Has? Language Arts Grades 1-2. Taylor, Jennifer, ed. Peterson, Barbara, illus. 2007. (J). per. 19.99 (***978-1-59198-429-0(7)**) Creative Teaching Pr., Inc.

Campbell, John P. Campbell's 177 Lightning Rounds. 2000. 181p. (YA). (gr. 6-8). per. 15.95 (978-0-944322-30-7(1) , 440) Patrick's Pr.

—Campbell's 214 Lightning Rounds. 2000. 217p. (YA). (gr. 9-12). per. 15.95 (978-0-944322-31-4(X) , 449) Patrick's Pr.

P Q R

—Campbell's 2501 Quiz Questions. Brewbaker, Rinda, ed. 1999. 250p. (J). (gr. 5-6). per. 15.95 (978-0-944322-26-0(3) , 435) Patrick's Pr.

Campbell's Comstant Quiz Companion: The Middle/High School Book of Lists, Terms, & Questions. 2004. (YA). per. 24.95 (978-0-944322-39-0(5)) Patrick's Pr.

Card, Michael. Tell Me Why: Eternal Answers to Children's Timeless Questions. 2004. (Tell Me Ser.). (Illus.). 48p. (ps-3). 17.99 (978-1-58134-031-0(1)) Crossway Bks.

Carle, Eric. From Head to Toe. 1999. lib. bdg. 15.30 (978-0-613-22852-7(9)) Tandem Library Bks.

—From Head to Toe Big Book. Carle, Eric, illus. 2007. 32p. (J). pap. 24.99 ***978-0-06-111972-9(5)** , Harper Festival) HarperCollins Pubs.

Carle, Eric. From Head to Toe (Spanish Edition) De la cabeza a los Pies. Carle, Eric, illus. 2007. (SPA.). 32p. (J). pap. 6.99 (978-0-06-051313-9(6) , Rayo) HarperCollins Pubs.

Chadow, Alysa. US States. 2003. pap. 14.00 (978-0-8059-6054-9(6)) Dorrance Publishing Co., Inc.

Charman, Andrew. Dodo Is Dead & other questions about extinct & endangered Animals. 2007. (I Wonder Why Ser.). (Illus.). 32p. (J). pap. 6.95 (***978-0-7534-6095-5(5)** , Kingfisher) Houghton Mifflin Co. Trade & Reference Div.

Charman, Andrew. I Wonder Why Trees Have Leaves: And Other Questions about Plants. 2003. (I Wonder Why Ser.). 32p. (J). (gr. k-3). pap. 6.95 (978-0-7534-5663-7(X) , Kingfisher) Houghton Mifflin Co. Trade & Reference Div.

—I Wonder Why Trees Have Leaves: And Other Questions about Plants. 2003. (gr. k-3). lib. bdg. 14.10 (978-0-613-90898-6(8)) Tandem Library Bks.

A Child's First Library of Learning, 30 bks. Incl. Animal Friends. Time-Life Staff. (Illus.). 88p. (ps-4). 1999. 14.95 (978-0-8094-4849-1(1)); Animals in Action. (Illus.). 88p. (ps-2). 1999. 14.95 (978-0-8094-4869-2(6)); Dangerous Animals. Time-Life Books Editors. Kinney, Karin, ed. (Illus.). 88p. (ps-3). 1996. 16.00 (978-0-8094-9480-4(9)); Everyday Life. Cfl. (Illus.). 88p. (ps-4). 1999. 14.95 (978-0-8094-4865-4(3)); Explorers & Adventurers. Time-Life Books Editors. Fallow, Allan, ed. (Illus.). 88p. (ps-3). 1996. lib. bdg. (978-0-8094-9482-8(5)); Famous Places. Gakken Co. Ltd. Editors. Time-Life Books Editors, tr. (Illus.). 88p. (gr. 1-4). 1999. 14.95 (978-0-8094-4893-7(9)); Feelings & Manners. Time-Life Books Editors. Fallow, Allan, ed. (Illus.). 88p. (ps-3). 1997. 14.95 (978-0-8094-9483-5(3)); Flowers & Trees. Time-Life Staff. (Illus.). 88p. (gr. 1-4). 1999. 14.95 (978-0-8094-4857-9(2)); Health & Safety. Time-Life Books Editors. 1996. (978-0-8094-9479-8(5)); How Things Work in Your Home. Time-Life Books Editors. (Illus.). 88p. (gr. 1-4). 1999. 14.95 (978-0-8094-4873-9(4)); Insect World. Time-Life Books Editors. (Illus.). 88p. (ps-3). 1999. 14.95 (978-0-8094-4841-8(6)); Science Starter. Time-Life Books Editors. (Illus.). 88p. (gr. 1-4). 1999. 14.95 (978-0-8094-4881-4(5)); Sky & Earth. Time-Life Books Editors. (Illus.). 88p. (gr. 1-4). 1999. 14.95 (978-0-8094-4837-1(8)); Things Around Us. Time-Life Staff. (Illus.). 88p. (ps-2). 1999. 14.95 (978-0-8094-4845-6(9)); Things to Do. Gakken Co. Ltd. Editors & Time-Life Books Editors. (Illus.). 88p. (gr. 1-4). 1999. 14.95 (978-0-8094-4897-5(1)); Wheels & Wings. Gakken Co. Ltd. Editors. Time-Life Books Editors, tr. (Illus.). 88p. (gr. 1-4). 1999. 14.95 (978-0-8094-4861-6(0)); Where Things Come From. Time-Life Books Editors. Fallow, Allan, ed. (Illus.). 88p. (ps-3). 1997. (978-0-8094-9484-2(1)); Wind & Weather. Gakken Co. Ltd. Editors. Time-Life Books Editors, tr. (Illus.). 88p. (gr. 1-4). 1999. 14.95 (978-0-8094-4829-6(7)); World We Live In. Gakken Co. Ltd. Editors. Time-Life Books Editors, tr. (Illus.). 88p. (gr. 1-4). 1999. 14.95 (978-0-8094-4885-2(8)); (J). 403.88 (978-0-8094-9499-6(X)) Time-Life, Inc.

Christie, Les. Have You Ever.... ? 450 Intriguing Questions Guaranteed to Get Teenagers Talking. 1998. (Quick Questions Ser.). (Illus.). 136p. pap. 10.99 (978-0-310-22439-6(X)) Zondervan.

Ciencias. (Enciclopedias Everest Internacional Ser.). (SPA., Illus.). (YA). (gr. 5-8). 41.95 (978-84-241-9405-5(5) , EV7495) Everest de Ediciones y Distribucion, S.L. ESP. *Dist:* Lectorum Pubns., Inc.

Collins, Fergus & Garner, Braum A. Birds. 2001. (Questions & Answers about... Ser.). (Illus.). 40p. (J). (gr. 4-6). pap. 7.95 (978-0-7534-5370-4(3) , Kingfisher) Houghton Mifflin Co. Trade & Reference Div.

Cosgrove, Stephen & Higgins, Kitty. Trivia Pursuit. ed. 2004. (Reader's Theater Ser.). (J). pap. 22.00 (978-1-4108-1140-0(9)) Benchmark Education Co.

CosmoGIRL! Editors. All about Guys. Cosmopolitan Editors, ed. 2004. (CosmoGIRL Quiz Book Ser.). (Illus.). 128p. pap. 5.95 (978-1-58816-382-0(2)) Hearst Bks.

—All about You. Cosmopolitan Editors, ed. 2004. (CosmoGIRL Quiz Book Ser.). (Illus.). 128p. pap. 5.95 (978-1-58816-381-3(4)) Hearst Bks.

Creepy & Crawly. 2002. (Questions & Answers Ser.). 12p. (J). pap. 3.98 (978-0-7525-7898-9(7)) Parragon, Inc.

Crompton, Samuel Willard. 100 Families Who Shaped World History. 2000. (100 Ser.). (Illus.). (J). (978-0-606-20522-1(5)) Tandem Library Bks.

—100 Relationships That Shaped World History. 2000. 112p. 7.95 (978-0-912517-40-7(9)) Bluewood Bks.

—100 Relationships That Shaped World History. 2000. (100 Ser.). (Illus.). (J). (978-0-606-20526-9(8)) Tandem Library Bks.

Cron, Mary Herd. Dreams: Mind Movies of the Night. Ning, Amy, illus. 2000. 6. 64p. (gr. 4-6). lib. bdg. (978-0-7613-1512-4(8) , Millbrook Pr.) Lerner Publishing Group.

D C Thomson Staff, ed. Bunty Annual for Girls 2004. 2003. (Illus.). 128p. (J). (ps-4). (978-0-85116-825-8(6)) Thomson, D.C. & Co., Ltd. GBR. *Dist:* APG Sales and Fulfillment.

Daniels, Kathryn. A Bluestocking Guide - Justice: Companion Workbook to Richard J. Maybury's Book Whatever Happened to Justice? Williams, Jane A., ed. 2004. (Bluestocking Guide Ser.). (YA). pap. 15.95 (978-0-942617-45-0(2)) Bluestocking Pr.

—A Bluestocking Guide - the Money Mystery: Based on Richard J. Maybury's book the Money Mystery. Williams, Jane A., ed. 2004. (Bluestocking Guide Ser.). 31p. (YA). pap. 8.95 (978-0-942617-49-8(5)) Bluestocking Pr.

Davis, Katie. Who Hoots? 2004. (Illus.). 36p. (J). pap. 7.00 (978-0-15-205027-6(2) , Voyager Bks./Libros Viajeros) Harcourt Children's Bks.

Davis, Kenneth C. Don't Know Much about Abraham Lincoln Abraham Lincoln, Vol. 4. Shepperson, Rob, illus. 2004. (Don't Know Much About Ser.). 144p. (J). (gr. 2-5). 15.89 (978-0-06-028820-4(5)) HarperCollins Pubs.

—Don't Know Much about American History. 2004. (Don't Know Much about(R) Ser.). 224p. (J). (gr. 4-7). pap. 40.00 incl. audio (978-0-8072-2092-4(2) , Listening Library) Random Hse. Audio Publishing Group.

—Don't Know Much about American History. 2003. (gr. 3-6). lib. bdg. 30.40 (978-0-613-59234-5(4)) Tandem Library Bks.

—Don't Know Much about' American History. Faulkner, Matt, illus. 2003. (Don't Know Much About Ser.). 224p. (J). pap. 6.99 (978-0-06-440836-3(1) , Harper Trophy) HarperCollins Pubs.

—Don't Know Much about Planet Earth. Bloom, Tom, illus. 2001. (Don't Know Much About Ser.). (J). (gr. 2-6). 144p. pap. 7.99 (978-0-06-440834-9(5) , Harper Trophy); 160p. 19.89 (978-0-06-028600-2(8)) HarperCollins Pubs.

—Don't Know Much about Planet Earth. unabr. ed. 2004. (Don't Know Much about Ser.). 144p. (J). (gr. 4-7). pap. 29.00 incl. audio (978-0-8072-0660-7(1) , Listening Library) Random Hse. Audio Publishing Group.

—Don't Know Much about Planet Earth. 2001. (J). 13.60 (978-0-606-22303-4(7)) Tandem Library Bks.

—Don't Know Much about Sitting Bull Sitting Bull, Vol. 2. 2003. (Don't Know Much About Ser.). (Illus.). 144p. (J). (gr. 3-7). 16.89 (978-0-06-028818-1(3)) HarperCollins Pubs.

—Don't Know Much about Space. Ruzzier, Sergio, illus. 2001. (Don't Know Much About Ser.). 144p. (J). (gr. 2 up). pap. 6.99 (978-0-06-440835-6(3) , Harper Trophy); 19.89 (978-0-06-028602-6(4)) HarperCollins Pubs.

—Don't Know Much about Space. unabr. ed. 2004. (Don't Know Much about(R) Ser.). 144p. (J). (gr. 4-7). pap. 29.00 incl. audio (978-0-8072-0661-4(X) , Listening Library) Random Hse. Audio Publishing Group.

—Don't Know Much about Space. 2001. 13.64 (978-0-606-22305-8(3)) Tandem Library Bks.

—Don't Know Much about the 50 States. Andriani, Renee, illus. 2004. (Don't Know Much About Ser.). 64p. (J). (gr. 1-4). pap. 7.99 (978-0-06-446227-3(7)) HarperCollins Pubs.

Deadly & Dangerous. 2002. (Questions & Answers Ser.). 12p. (J). pap. 3.98 (978-0-7525-7897-2(9)) Parragon, Inc.

Diagram Group. Funky, Freaky Facts Most People Don't Know. 1998. (gr. 3-6). lib. bdg. 16.40 (978-0-613-75495-8(6)) Tandem Library Bks.

Douglas, Vincent. The Complete Book of Questions & Answers. 2001. (Complete Book Ser.). (Illus.). 352p. (J). (gr. 4-8). pap. 14.95 (978-1-56189-107-8(X) , 90001, American Education Publishing) School Specialty Publishing.

Dowley, Tim & Wyart, Peter. The Shepherd's Tale. Pierce, Martin, illus. 2002. 14p. (J). (gr. k-3). 5.99 (978-0-8254-7257-2(1)) Kregel Pubns.

—The Wise Men's Tale. Pierce, Martin, illus. 2002. 14p. (J). (gr. k-3). 5.99 (978-0-8254-7256-5(3)) Kregel Pubns.

Draper, Dar & Helser, Sarah Dawn. What is Love? Questions a Child Asks. 2004. (Illus.). 32p. 14.95 (978-0-9740880-4-4(8)) Lifebridge Bks.

Drohan, Michele Ingber & Levchuck, Caroline M. Environment. 2001. (It's All about! Ser.). (Illus.). 32p. (J). (gr. 2-5). lib. bdg. 25.27 (978-1-58952-160-5(9)) Rourke Publishing, LLC.

Dumont, Virginie. Preguntas Al Amor: 5-8 Años. García, Mabel, tr. 2nd ed. 2002. (Preguntas Al Amor Ser.). (SPA., Illus.). 32p. (978-84-89804-18-0(4)) Loguez Ediciones ESP. *Dist:* Lectorum Pubns., Inc.

Dumont, Virginie & Montagnat, Serge. Preguntas Al Amor: 11-14 Años. 2nd ed. 2002. (Preguntas Al Amor Ser.). (SPA., Illus.). 74p. (978-84-89804-20-3(6)) Loguez Ediciones ESP. *Dist:* Lectorum Pubns., Inc.

—Preguntas Al Amor: 8-11 Años. García, Mabel, tr. 2nd ed. 2002. (SPA., Illus.). 46p. (978-84-89804-19-7(2)) Loguez Ediciones ESP. *Dist:* Lectorum Pubns., Inc.

Edwards, Shawn, et al. Name Your Favorite: 700 Rapid-Fire Ice Breakers to Get Teenagers Talking. 2002. (Quick Questions Ser.). (Illus.). 160p. pap. 10.99 (978-0-310-24197-3(9)) Zondervan.

Ehrlich, Robert. What If? Mind-Boggling Science Questions for Kids. 1998. (Illus.). 192p. (gr. 3-7). pap. 13.95 (978-0-471-17608-4(7) , Jossey-Bass) Wiley, John & Sons, Inc.

Ellis, Barbara C. & Feder, Chris Welles. Brain Quest Black History. rev. ed. 2005. (Illus.). 148p. (J). 10.95 (978-0-7611-3996-6(6) , 13996) Workman Publishing Co., Inc.

Equipo Staff. Una Pregunta para Cada Dia. 2001. Tr. of Question for Each Day. (SPA.). 304p. (978-84-305-2257-6(3)) Lectorum Pubns., Inc.

—1000 Preguntas y Respuestas. (SPA., Illus.). 96p. (J). (gr. 3-5). (978-84-305-8671-4(7) , SU2565) Susaeta Ediciones, S.A. ESP. *Dist:* Lectorum Pubns., Inc.

Evans, Lesli. Open-Ended Questions, Grade 3. 2005. (Test Connection Ser.). (Illus.). 80p. (J). pap. 10.99 (978-0-7682-3083-3(7) , Schaffer, Frank) Schaffer, Frank Pubns.

—Open-Ended Questions, Grade 4. 2005. (Test Connection Ser.). (Illus.). 80p. (J). pap. 10.99 (978-0-7682-3084-0(5) , Schaffer, Frank) Schaffer, Frank Pubns.

—Open-Ended Questions, Grade 5. 2005. (Test Connection Ser.). (Illus.). 80p. (J). pap. 10.99 (978-0-7682-3085-7(3) , Schaffer, Frank) Schaffer, Frank Pubns.

Far from the Madding Crowd: Teaching Unit. 2003. 92p. (YA). ring bd. (978-1-58049-471-7(4) , TU4714) Prestwick Hse., Inc.

Feder, Chris, ed. Brain Quest Grade 3. 3rd ed. 2005. (Illus.). 148p. (J). (gr. 3 up). 10.95 (978-0-7611-3764-1(5) , 13764) Workman Publishing Co., Inc.

Feder, Chris Welles. Brain Quest for Threes. 3rd ed. 2005. (Illus.). 148p. (J). (ps-ps). 10.95 (978-0-7611-3774-0(2) , 13774) Workman Publishing Co., Inc.

—Brain Quest Grade 1. 3rd ed. 2005. (Illus.). 148p. (J). (gr. 1 up). 10.95 (978-0-7611-3762-7(9) , 13762) Workman Publishing Co., Inc.

—Brain Quest Grade 2. 3rd ed. 2005. (Illus.). 148p. (J). (gr. 2 up). 10.95 (978-0-7611-3763-4(7) , 13763) Workman Publishing Co., Inc.

—Brain Quest Grade 4. 3rd ed. 2005. (Illus.). 148p. (J). (gr. 4 up). 10.95 (978-0-7611-3765-8(3) , 13765) Workman Publishing Co., Inc.

—Brain Quest Grade 5. 3rd ed. 2005. (Illus.). 148p. (J). (ps-7). 10.95 (978-0-7611-3766-5(1) , 13766) Workman Publishing Co., Inc.

—Brain Quest Grade 6. 3rd ed. 2005. (Illus.). 148p. (J). (ps-7). 10.95 (978-0-7611-3767-2(X) , 13767) Workman Publishing Co., Inc.

—Brain Quest Grade 7. 3rd ed. 2005. (Illus.). 148p. (J). (gr. 7 up). 10.95 (978-0-7611-3768-9(8) , 13768) Workman Publishing Co., Inc.

—Brain Quest Hispanic America. 2005. (Illus.). (J). 10.95 (978-0-7611-3997-3(4) , 13997) Workman Publishing Co., Inc.

—Brain Quest Kindergarten. 3rd ed. 2005. (Illus.). 148p. (J). (ps-ps). 10.95 (978-0-7611-3771-9(8) , 13771) Workman Publishing Co., Inc.

—Brain Quest Preschool. 3rd ed. 2005. (Illus.). 148p. (J). (ps-7). 10.95 (978-0-7611-3770-2(X) , 13770) Workman Publishing Co., Inc.

—Brain Quest Presidents. 2005. (Illus.). 148p. (J). 10.95 (978-0-7611-3998-0(2) , 13998) Workman Publishing Co., Inc.

—My First Brain Quest. 3rd ed. 2005. (Illus.). 148p. (J). (ps). 10.95 (978-0-7611-3773-3(4) , 13773) Workman Publishing Co., Inc.

Ferguson, Sinclair B. Big Book of Questions & Answers: A Family Guide to the Christian Faith. 2003. (gr. k-3). lib. bdg. 21.10 (978-0-613-80048-8(6)) Tandem Library Bks.

Feyh, Janelle. Does God Have a Remote Control? Feyh, Alexa & Deghand, Tim, illus. l.t. ed. 2003. 66p. (J). per. 11.95 (978-1-932344-26-4(8)) Thornton Publishing.

Fierce & Furious. 2002. (Questions & Answers Ser.). 12p. (J). pap. 3.98 (978-0-7525-7896-5(0)) Parragon, Inc.

Finding the Answers. 1998. (Captain Kangaroo Fun-to-Learn Activity Bks.: Vol. 1). (J). pap. (978-0-7666-0215-1(X) , Honey Bear Bks.) Modern Publishing.

Fischer, David. Do Curveballs Really Curve? 1999. (Avon Camelot Bks.). 96p. (J). (gr. 3-7). pap. 4.95 (978-0-380-80362-0(3)) HarperCollins Pubs.

Fisher-Price Question & Answer Books. 2004. (J). (978-0-7666-0315-8(6) , 49325); (978-0-7666-0316-5(4) , 49325); (978-0-7666-0317-2(2) , 49325); (978-0-7666-0318-9(0) , 49325) Modern Publishing.

Flip Quiz: 2nd-4th Grade. 2002. (Flip Quiz Ser.). (Illus.). 114p. (J). (gr. 2-4). spiral bd. 12.95 (978-1-57145-808-7(5) , Silver Dolphin Bks.) Advantage Pubs. Group.

Flip Quiz: 4th-5th Grade. 2002. (Flip Quiz Ser.). (Illus.). 114p. (J). (gr. 4-5). spiral bd. 12.95 (978-1-57145-809-4(3) , Silver Dolphin Bks.) Advantage Pubs. Group.

Flip Quiz: 5th-6th Grade. 2002. (Flip Quiz Ser.). (Illus.). 114p. (J). (gr. 5-6). spiral bd. 12.95 (978-1-57145-810-0(7) , Silver Dolphin Bks.) Advantage Pubs. Group.

Flip Quiz: 6th-7th Grade. 2002. (Flip Quiz Ser.). (Illus.). 114p. (YA). (gr. 6-7). spiral bd. 12.95 (978-1-57145-811-7(5) , Silver Dolphin Bks.) Advantage Pubs. Group.

Foul Facts: Our World the Awful Truth! 2002. 176p. (J). 9.98 (978-0-7525-5308-5(9)) Parragon, Inc.

Freeman, Cathy, et al. Middle Ages. 2000. (Students' Active Interdisciplinary Learning Ser.). (YA). (gr. 1 up). pap. 20.00 (978-1-893413-07-8(1)) Univ. Schl. at the Univ. of Tulsa.

French, Jackie. The Little Book of Big Questions. Newbigging, Martha, illus. 2000. 128p. (J). (gr. 3-7). 19.95 (978-1-55037-655-5(1)); pap. 9.95 (978-1-55037-654-8(3)) Annick Pr., Ltd. CAN. *Dist:* Firefly Bks., Ltd.

—Little Book of Big Questions. 2000. (gr. 3-6). lib. bdg. 18.75 (978-0-613-78405-4(7)) Tandem Library Bks.

Furry & Feathery. 2002. (Questions & Answers Ser.). 12p. (J). pap. 3.98 (978-0-7525-7901-6(0)) Parragon, Inc.

Gaff, Jackie. Fish Grew Legs: And Other Questions about Prehistoric Life. 2004. (I Wonder Why Ser.). 32p. (J). (gr. k-3). pap. 6.95 (978-0-7534-5762-7(8) , Kingfisher) Houghton Mifflin Co. Trade & Reference Div.

—I Wonder Why Mountains Have Snow on Top: And Other Questions about Mountains. Gaff, Jackie, illus. 2001. (I Wonder Why Ser.). (Illus.). 32p. (J). (gr. k-3). tchr. ed. 12.95 (978-0-7534-5344-5(4) , Kingfisher) Houghton Mifflin Co. Trade & Reference Div.

—I Wonder Why the Sahara Is Cold at Night & Other Questions about Deserts. 2004. (I Wonder Why Ser.). (Illus.). 32p. (J). (gr. k-3). pap. 6.95 (978-0-7534-5764-1(4) , Kingfisher) Houghton Mifflin Co. Trade & Reference Div.

—Stalactites Hang down & Other Questions about Caves. 2003. (I Wonder Why Ser.). (Illus.). 32p. (J). (gr. k-3). 11.95 (978-0-7534-5573-9(0) , Kingfisher) Houghton Mifflin Co. Trade & Reference Div.

Gallivan, Susan. Mr. Jeffries Magic Supermarket. 2006. pap. 10.49 (***978-1-4259-5425-3(1)**) AuthorHouse.

Ganeri, Anita. Animal Families. 2004. (Nature Files Ser.). (Illus.). 32p. (J). (gr. 4-8). 28.00 (978-0-7910-8215-7(6) , Chelsea Hse.) Facts On File, Inc.

—I Wonder Why Camels Have Humps: And Other Questions about Animals. 2003. (I Wonder Why Ser.). (Illus.). 32p. (J). (gr. k-3). pap. 6.95 (978-0-7534-5660-6(5) , Kingfisher) Houghton Mifflin Co. Trade & Reference Div.

—I Wonder Why Camels Have Humps: And Other Questions about Animals. 2003. (gr. k-3). lib. bdg. 14.10 (978-0-613-90576-3(8)) Tandem Library Bks.

—I Wonder Why the Sea Is Salty: And Other Questions about the Oceans. 2003. (I Wonder Why Ser.). 32p. (J). (gr. k-3). pap. 6.95 (978-0-7534-5611-8(7) , Kingfisher) Houghton Mifflin Co. Trade & Reference Div.

—I Wonder Why the Sea Is Salty: And Other Questions about the Oceans. 2003. (gr. k-3). lib. bdg. 14.10 (978-0-613-63165-5(X)) Tandem Library Bks.

Gifford, Clive. So You Think You Know Alex Rider. 2006. 144p. pap. 8.95 (978-0-340-91713-8(X)) Hodder General Publishing Division GBR. *Dist:* Trafalgar Square Publishing.

—So You Think You Know Harry Potter: Over 1000 Wizard Quiz Questions. 2003. (Illus.). 160p. (J). mass mkt. (978-0-340-87337-3(X) , Hodder & Stoughton) Hodder General Publishing Division.

—So You Think You Know His Dark Materials? 2006. (Orig.). (YA). (gr. 2-3). pap. 8.95 (978-0-340-91186-0(7)) Hodder General Publishing Division GBR. *Dist:* Independent Pubs. Group.

Gifford, Clive, et al. Quiz Quest 2. 2007. (Quiz Quest Ser.). (Illus.). 160p. (J). (gr. 3-5). pap. 11.95 (***978-0-7534-6078-8(5)** , Kingfisher) Houghton Mifflin Co. Trade & Reference Div.

Glaser, Linda. Fabulous Frogs. 1999. (Linda Glaser's Classic Creatures Ser.). (Illus.). 32p. (ps-3). lib. bdg. 22.90 (978-0-7613-0424-1(X) , Millbrook Pr.) Lerner Publishing Group.

—Fabulous Frogs. 1999. (gr. k-3). lib. bdg. 17.60 (978-0-613-25111-2(3)); (Illus.). (J). (978-0-606-18289-8(6)) Tandem Library Bks.

Godwin, Parke. Are You Betty or Veronica? A Quiz Book. 2005. 80p. (gr. 3-7). pap. 3.99 (978-0-7868-5571-1(1) , Volo) Hyperion Bks. for Children.

Gold, Sharon. Brain Quest for the Car. Feder, Chris, ed. 3rd rev. ed. 2005. (Illus.). 148p. (J). 10.95 (978-0-7611-3776-4(9) , 13776) Workman Publishing Co., Inc.

Graham, Buck. My First Big Book of Questions & Answers: Things That Go. 2005. (Illus.). 10p. bds. 9.98 (978-0-7853-7227-1(X) , 7171500) Publications International, Ltd.

Graham, Monty Dr. My First Big Book of Questions & Answers: Under the Sea. 2005. (Illus.). 10p. bds. 9.98 (978-0-7853-7228-8(8) , 7171400) Publications International, Ltd.

Grambo, Rebecca L. The Kids' Fun-Filled Nature Question & Answer Book. Tallarico, Tony, illus. 2000. 93p. (J). (978-1-56156-839-0(2)) Kidsbooks, Inc.

—Technology. 2001. (It's All about! Ser.). (Illus.). 32p. (J). (gr. 2-5). lib. bdg. 25.27 (978-1-58952-162-9(5)) Rourke Publishing, LLC.

Great Americans. (Biographies Ser.). (Illus.). (978-0-7613-3307-4(X) , Twenty-First Century Bks.) Lerner Publishing Group.

Great Americans. (Mini Question & Answers America Ser.). 32p. Date not set. (J). 3.98 (978-0-7525-9872-7(4)); 2000. (YA). 7.50 (978-0-7525-4644-5(9)) Parragon, Inc.

Great Historic Debates & Speeches, 6 Bks, Set. 2004. (J). 175.50 (978-1-4042-0350-1(8)) Rosen Publishing Group, Inc., The.

Great Scientific Questions & the Scientists Who Answered Them. 2005. (Illus.). 112p. (gr. 7-12). lib. bdg. 319.20 (978-1-4042-0356-3(7)) Rosen Publishing Group, Inc., The.

Greenwood, Rosie. I Wonder Why Volcanoes Blow Their Tops & Other Questions about Natural Disasters. 2004. (I Wonder Why Ser.). (Illus.). 32p. (J). (gr. k-3). 11.95 (978-0-7534-5751-1(2) , Kingfisher) Houghton Mifflin Co. Trade & Reference Div.

Grimshaw, Caroline. Buildings. 2000. (Connections Ser.). (Illus.). 32p. (J). (gr. 3-6). 9.95 (978-1-58728-314-7(X)); pap. 5.95 (978-1-58728-320-8(4)) T&N Children's Publishing. (Two Can Publishing).

—Energy. 2000. (Invisible Journeys Ser.). (Illus.). 32p. (J). (gr. 3-6). 10.95 (978-1-58728-331-4(X)); pap. 5.95 (978-1-58728-327-7(1)) T&N Children's Publishing. (Two Can Publishing).

—Sound: A Journey That Changes Silence to Sound. 2000. (Invisible Journeys Ser.). (Illus.). 32p. (J). (gr. 3-6). 10.95 (978-1-58728-335-2(2) , Two Can Publishing) T&N Children's Publishing.

—Sun: Follow the Journey of a Sunbeam. 2000. (Invisible Journeys Ser.). (Illus.). 32p. (J). (gr. 3-6). 10.95 (978-1-58728-332-1(8)); pap. 5.95 (978-1-58728-329-1(8)) T&N Children's Publishing. (Two Can Publishing).

Grossblatt, Ben. SmartLab Weird & Gross Challenge. 2006. (Illus.). 144p. (gr. 3 up). 19.99 (978-1-932855-48-7(3)) becker&mayer! books.

Gutman, Dan. Landslide! 2000. 128p. (J). (gr. 4-7). pap. 3.99 (978-0-689-83591-9(4) , Aladdin) Simon & Schuster Children's Publishing.

Hamilton, John. Behind the Terror. 2002. (War on Terrorism Ser.). (Illus.). 24p. (J). (gr. 4-8). lib. bdg. 25.65 (978-1-57765-659-3(8) , ABDO & Daughters) ABDO Publishing Co.

Hanna, Madonna B. Mommy Why Are My Eyes So Big?, No.1. Hushimoto, Christina, illus. 1999. 16p. (J). (gr. 3-12). pap. 15.00 (978-0-9650634-1-8(0)) Hanna Publishing.

Harcourt School Publishers Staff. Accelerated Reader Quiz Disk: Teaching Collection: Macintosh Edition. 2002. (J). (gr. 1). stu. ed. 68.50 incl. cd-rom (978-0-15-325855-8(1)) Harcourt Schl. Pubs.

—Guess Who? Library Book. 3rd ed. 2002. (Trophies Reading Program Ser.). (Illus.). pap. 14.00 (978-0-15-326533-4(7)) Harcourt Schl. Pubs.

Harrald-Pilz, Marilee, illus. Kids Ask Who? 2006. 32p. (J). ***978-1-4127-1362-7(5))** Publications International, Ltd.

Harris, Nicholas. Questions & Answers. 2002. (Blackbirch Visual Encyclopedia Ser.). 64p. (J). 24.94 (978-1-56711-524-6(1) , Blackbirch Pr., Inc.) Thomson Gale.

Hart-Davis, Adam. Why Does a Ball Bounce? 101 Questions You Never Thought of Asking. 2005. (Illus.). 224p. 19.95 (978-1-55407-113-5(5)) Firefly Bks., Ltd.

Haynes, A. K., Sr. Love Conquers All: Devotionals with Soul Searching Questions to Ask Yourself Daily. AGB S Writers' Guild, ed. 2002. 144p. per. 12.95 (978-1-930908-20-8(2) , LCA, Great Beginning-AGB, A) AGB Publishing.

Hazan, Maurice, creator. Dime quien Es: Spanish Dialogues Level 1. 2000. (SPA.). (J). 99.00 (978-1-932770-43-8(7) , SG4) Symtalk, Inc.

—Dime quien Es: Spanish Dialogues Level 2. 2000. (SPA.). (J). 99.00 (978-1-932770-45-2(3) , SG6) Symtalk, Inc.

—Dime quien Es: Spanish Dialogues Level 3. 2000. (SPA.). (YA). 199.00 (978-1-932770-55-1(0) , SG16) Symtalk, Inc.

Heinemann, Sue & New York Public Library Staff. Amazing Women in American History: A Book of Answers for Kids. 1998. (New York Public Library Books for Kids Ser.: Vol. 6). (Illus.). 192p. (gr. 5-9). pap. 12.95 (978-0-471-19216-9(3) , Wiley-Interscience) Wiley, John & Sons, Inc.

Hewitt, Sally. Fly Like a Superhero? 2001. (Why Can't I Ser.). (Illus.). 30p. (J). lib. bdg. 24.25 (978-1-930643-03-1(9)) Chrysalis Education.

—Live Underwater with the Fish? 2001. (Why Can't I Ser.). (Illus.). 30p. (J). lib. bdg. 24.25 (978-1-930643-00-0(4)) Chrysalis Education.

Hill, Sandi. Did You Know?, Vol. 4412. Kupperstein, Joel, ed. Newsome, Andy, illus. 1998. (Learn to Read Social Studies: Vol. 4412). 16p. (J). (ps-2). pap. 2.75 (978-1-57471-335-0(3) , 4412) Creative Teaching Pr., Inc.

Hirsch, Jennifer, ed. The American Girls Quiz Book. Andreasen, Dan & Backes, Nick, illus. 2005. (American Girls Collection). 69p. (J). (gr. 3). pap. 5.95 (978-1-59369-019-9(3) , American Girl) American Girl Publishing, Inc.

Holt, Rinehart and Winston Staff. Call to Freedom: Beginning-1914: Daily Quizzes with Answer Key. 1998. pap. 45.60 (978-0-03-054502-3(1)) Holt, Rinehart & Winston.

Holub, Joan. Why Do Birds Sing? Divito, Anna, illus. 2004. (Easy-to-Read, Puffin Ser.). 48p. (J). (gr. k-2). pap. 3.99 (978-0-14-240106-4(4) , Puffin) Penguin Group (USA) Inc.

—Why Do Cats Meow? 2001. (Easy-to-Read Ser.). (Illus.). 48p. (J). (ps-3). 13.99 (978-0-8037-2503-4(5) , Dial) Penguin Group (USA) Inc.

—Why Do Snakes Hiss? And Other Questions about Snakes, Lizards & Turtles. Divito, Anna, illus. 2004. (Easy-to-Read, Puffin Ser.). 48p. (J). (gr. k-2). pap. 3.99 (978-0-14-240105-7(6) , Puffin) Penguin Group (USA) Inc.

—Why Do Snakes Hiss? And Other Questions about Snakes, Lizards, & Turtles. 2004. (Easy-to-Read, Dial Ser.). (Illus.). 48p. (J). (gr. k). 14.99 (978-0-8037-3000-7(4) , Dial) Penguin Group (USA) Inc.

—Why Do Snakes Hiss? And Other Questions about Snakes, Lizards, & Turtles. DiVito, Anna, illus. 2004. 48p. (J). (ps-ps). lib. bdg. 11.19 (978-0-606-32712-1(6)) Tandem Library Bks.

Horn, Randy. You Gotta be Kidding! 2006. (Illus.). 416p. (J). pap. 8.95 (978-0-7611-4365-9(3)) Workman Publishing Co., Inc.

Horne, Richard & Turner, Tracey. 101 Things You Need to Know... & Some You Don't! 2007. (Illus.). 224p. (YA). (gr. 7 up). pap. 9.95 ***978-0-8027-9674-5(5))** Walker & Co.

Hort, Lenny. Did Dinosaurs Eat Pizza? Mysteries Science Hasn't Solved. O'Brian, John, illus. rev. ed. 2006. 32p. (J). 15.95 (978-0-8050-6757-6(4) , Holt, Henry & Co. Bks. For Young Readers) Holt, Henry & Co.

How the West Was Won. 2000. 32p. (YA). 7.49 (978-0-7525-4642-1(2)) Parragon, Inc.

Humberstone, E. C. The Usborne First Book of Knowledge. 2004. (Explainers Ser.). 248p. (J). 16.95 (978-0-7460-1963-4(7) , Usborne) EDC Publishing.

Humphrey, Melanie Friedersdorf. Where Do Falling Stars Go? 3rd ed. 1999. (Illus.). 48p. (J). (ps-1). pap. 14.95 (978-0-9658061-6-9(2)) Peaceful Village Publishing.

Instructional Fair Staff & Fisk, Sally. Big Book of Everything. 1999. (Illus.). 320p. (J). (gr. k-2). pap. 21.99 (978-1-56822-206-6(8) , IF8654) School Specialty Publishing.

Instructional Fair Staff & Miller Molengraft, Lisa. Big Book of Everything. 1999. 320p. (J). (gr. k-1). pap. 21.99 (978-1-56822-205-9(X) , IF8653) School Specialty Publishing.

Is That Your Final Answer? 2000. 192p. (YA). (gr. 5 up). Vol. 1. pap. (978-0-7666-0600-5(7)); Vol. 2. pap. (978-0-7666-0601-2(5)) Modern Publishing.

Isaacs, Ronald H. Ask the Rabbi: The Book of Answers to Jewish Kids' Questions. 2001. (J). (978-0-7657-6165-1(3) , Aronson, Jason) Rowman & Littlefield Pubs., Inc.

Itty Bitty Activity Book of Trivia, Vol. 2. 2005. (J). pap. 1.29 (978-1-59317-071-4(8)) Warner Pr. Pubs.

Jacobs, Marian B. Why Can Airplanes Fly? 1999. (Library of Why). (Illus.). 24p. (J). (gr. k-4). lib. bdg. 18.75 (978-0-8239-5274-8(6) , PowerKids Pr.) Rosen Publishing Group, Inc., The.

—Why Did the Dinosaurs Become Extinct? 1999. (Library of Why). (Illus.). 24p. (J). (gr. k-4). lib. bdg. 18.75 (978-0-8239-5276-2(2) , PowerKids Pr.) Rosen Publishing Group, Inc., The.

—Why Do Leaves Change Color? 1999. (Library of Why). (Illus.). 24p. (J). (gr. k-4). lib. bdg. 18.75 (978-0-8239-5275-5(4) , PowerKids Pr.) Rosen Publishing Group, Inc., The.

—Why Does It Rain? 1999. (Library of Why). (Illus.). 24p. (J). (gr. k-4). lib. bdg. 18.75 (978-0-8239-5273-1(8) , PowerKids Pr.) Rosen Publishing Group, Inc., The.

—Why Is the Sky Blue? 1999. (Library of Why). (Illus.). 24p. (J). (gr. k-4). lib. bdg. 18.75 (978-0-8239-5271-7(1) , PowerKids Pr.) Rosen Publishing Group, Inc., The.

Jacobson, Jennifer. SmartLab: 4th Grade Challenge. Bradrick, Jim, illus. 2007. 144p. (gr. 3 up). 19.99 ***978-1-932855-70-8(X))** becker&mayer! books.

January, Brendan. New York Public Library Amazing Explorers: A Book of Answers for Kids. 2001. (gr. 5-8). lib. bdg. 22.20 (978-0-613-85110-7(2)) Tandem Library Bks.

—New York Public Library Amazing Mythology: A Book of Answers for Kids. 2000. (gr. 5-8). lib. bdg. 22.20 (978-0-613-26380-1(4)) Tandem Library Bks.

January, Brendan, et al. The New York Public Library Amazing Mythology: A Book of Answers for Kids. 2000. (New York Public Library Books for Kids Ser.: Vol. 9). (Illus.). 176p. (gr. 5-9). pap. 13.95 (978-0-471-33205-3(4) , Capstone) Wiley, John & Sons, Inc.

Jenkins, Steve & Page, Robin. What Do You Do with a Tail Like This? 2003. (Illus.). 32p. (J). (gr. k-3). 15.00 (978-0-618-25628-0(8)) Houghton Mifflin Co. Trade & Reference Div.

Johnson, John L. 500 Questions & Answers on the Black Presenc in the Bible. 2002. (YA). per. 10.95 (978-0-9709715-6-2(7)) Johnson Bks., Inc.

Kain, Kathleen. All about Holidays: With Inspector McQ. Mahan, Ben, illus. 2004. (Early Literacy Library). 32p. (gr. 2-5). 219.00 (978-0-7166-1647-4(5)) World Bk., Inc.

—All about Pets. Miyake, Yoshi, illus. 2004. (Treasure Tree Ser.). 32p. (J). (978-0-7166-1626-9(2)) World Bk., Inc.

Kamma, Anne. If You Were at the First Thanksgiving. 2001. (gr. k-3). lib. bdg. 14.15 (978-0-613-89056-4(6)); 12.79 (978-0-606-22213-6(8)) Tandem Library Bks.

Katz, Alan. That's Right, That's Wrong: Level 4, Set 1. Day, Bruce, illus. 2007. (That's Our School Ser.). 100p. (J). 9.99 (978-1-4169-0674-2(6) , Little Simon) Simon & Schuster Children's Publishing.

—That's Right, That's Wrong!: Level Four, Set Two. Day, Bruce, illus. 2007. (That's Right, That's Wrong! Ser.). 100p. (J). 9.99 ***978-1-4169-0678-0(9)** , Little Simon) Simon & Schuster Children's Publishing.

—That's Right, That's Wrong!: Level One, Set Two. Gary Swift Studios Staff, illus. 2007. (That's Right, That's Wrong! Ser.). 100p. (J). 9.99 ***978-1-4169-0675-9(4)** , Little Simon) Simon & Schuster Children's Publishing.

—That's Right, That's Wrong!: Level Three, Set Two. McDonnell, Luke, illus. 2007. (That's Right, That's Wrong! Ser.). 100p. (J). 9.99 ***978-1-4169-0677-3(0)** , Little Simon) Simon & Schuster Children's Publishing.

—That's Right, That's Wrong!: Level Two, Set Two. Lloyd, Mary Anne, illus. 2007. (That's Right, That's Wrong! Ser.). 100p. (J). 9.99 ***978-1-4169-0676-6(2)** , Little Simon) Simon & Schuster Children's Publishing.

Katz, Karen A., et al. What Does Being Jewish Mean? Read-Aloud Responses to Questions Jewish Children Ask about History, Culture, & Religion. 2003. 160p. pap. 11.00 (978-0-7432-5413-7(9) , Fireside) Simon & Schuster.

Kennedy, Anne, illus. Kids Ask Where? 2006. 31p. (J). ***978-1-4127-1361-0(7))** Publications International, Ltd.

Kennedy, Bailey & Howell, Louise. First Grade Questions & Answers: Boosting Your Way to Success in School. Dubin, Jill, illus. 1998. (Grade Boosters Ser.). 64p. (J). (gr. 1). pap. 5.95 (978-1-56565-756-4(X) , 0756XW) Lowell Hse.

Kerrod, Robin. 1000 Questions & Answers. 2002. (Illus.). 320p. (J). (978-0-7534-0763-9(9) , Kingfisher) Houghton Mifflin Co. Trade & Reference Div.

Ketchum, Ron, illus. Rochestrivia: 2,000 Amazing questions & answers all about Rochester NY, it's people & surrounding Towns. l.t. ed. 2005. 250p. per. 19.95 (978-0-930249-01-4(1)) Big Kids Productions (Publishing).

Khidekel, Marina. The Quiz Life. 2008. 224p. (J). lib. bdg. ***978-0-375-94063-7(4));** (YA). (gr. 5). pap. 6.99 ***978-0-375-84263-4(2))** Dell Publishing. (Delacorte Pr.).

Kiefer, Jeanne. Jobs for Kids: A Smart Kid's Q & A Guide. Green, Anne Canevari, illus. 2003. (Single Titles Ser.). 112p. (gr. 5-8). lib. bdg. 25.90 (978-0-7613-2611-3(1) , Millbrook Pr.) Lerner Publishing Group.

Kieran, Viola. High School Musical: High School Musical Trivia/Quiz. 2007. 96p. (gr. 2-7). pap. 7.99 ***978-1-4231-0828-3(0))** Disney Pr.

Kinney, Donald. Q & A for Young Readers. 2000. 103p. (J). (gr. 3-9). per. (978-0-9702889-2-9(1)) Kinney Brothers Publishing.

Klutz Press Staff, ed. Road Trip Trivia: A Big Book of Backseat Brainteasers. 2004. (Illus.). 120p. (YA). 12.95 (978-1-57054-825-3(0)) Klutz.

Kramer, Ann, et al. The Big Book of Questions & Answers. 1999. (J). 50.85 (978-0-7894-4383-0(X)) Dorling Kindersley Publishing, Inc.

Laffon, Martine & Chabaneix, Hortense De. The Book of Why. Azam, Jacques, illus. 2006. 96p. (J). (ps-1). 16.95 (978-0-8109-5987-3(9)) Abrams, Harry N. , Inc.

Laffon, Martine & De Chabaneix, Hortense. The Book of How. Azam, Jacques, illus. 2007. 90p. (J). (gr. 4-6). 16.95 (978-0-8109-0716-4(X) , Abrams Bks. for Young Readers) Abrams, Harry N. , Inc.

Landau, Elaine. Date Violence. (Life Balance Ser.). 80p. (J). 2005. (Illus.). (gr. 5-8). pap. 6.95 (978-0-531-16613-0(9)); 2004. 19.50 (978-0-531-12214-3(X)) Scholastic Library Publishing. (Watts, Franklin).

Larousse, el Gran Libro de Preguntas y Respuestas (Larousse, the Big Book of Questions & Answers) 1999. (ENG & SPA.). 318p. (J). (gr. 5-7). (978-970-607-928-2(9)) Larousse.

Larousse Kingfisher Chambers Staff. 1000 Questions & Answers. Kingfisher Editors, ed. 2002. (Illus.). 320p. (J). (gr. 5-9). tchr. ed. 19.95 (978-0-7534-5541-8(2) , Kingfisher) Houghton Mifflin Co. Trade & Reference Div.

Lawrence, Paul R. Question Quest HSPA Math Geometry Companion. 2003. (Illus.). (YA). pap. 8.95 (978-1-931104-16-6(6)) L L Teach.

Le Compte, David & Rolland, Carol. Eugene Stillwell Wants to Know! 2007. (Illus.). 96p. (J). pap. 4.95 (978-1-929945-71-9(X)) Big Guy Bks., Inc.

LeCompte, David & Padrick, Kendell. Eugene Stillwell Wants to Know!, Pt. 2. 2007. 96p. (J). pap. 4.95 ***978-1-929945-74-0(4))** Big Guy Bks., Inc.

Leipe, Ulla. Lo Que los Ninos Quieren Saber. Limmer, Hannes, illus. (SPA.). 180p. (YA). 11.95 (978-84-241-5501-8(7) , EV867) Everest de Ediciones y Distribucion, S.L. ESP. *Dist:* Continental Bk. Co., Inc.

Leslie, Amanda. Are Chickens Stripey? Leslie, Amanda, illus. 2000. (Illus.). 12p. (J). 5.99 (978-1-58048-088-8(8)) Sandvik Publishing.

Levine, Annalee. Love & Romance Teen Quiz Book. 2001. (gr. 7-12). lib. bdg. 18.75 (978-0-613-87260-7(6)) Tandem Library Bks.

Levine, Annalee, et al. The Teen Quiz Book. 1998. 320p. (YA). pap. 9.95 (978-0-8362-5415-0(5)) Andrews McMeel Publishing.

Llewellyn, Claire. How Things Work. 2000. (978-0-606-18599-8(2)) Tandem Library Bks.

Llull, Maria. I-Ballers: Little Books for Big Minds. 2005. (Illus.). 60p. (J). pap. (978-1-57528-939-7(3)) University Games.

Loewen, Nancy. No Fair! Kids Talk about Fairness. Wesley, Omarr, illus. 2004. (Kids Talk Ser.). 32p. (C). (gr. 2-5). 23.93 (978-1-4048-0033-5(6)) Picture Window Bks.

Long Ago. 2002. (First Book of History Questions & Answers Ser.). 32p. (J). 9.95 (978-0-7525-7579-7(1)) Parragon, Inc.

Luke, Deanna. What Good Is... Woytek, Joann A., illus. 2000. 32p. (J). (gr. k-2). 15.95 (978-1-928777-00-7(7) , BOW Bks.) Blessing Our World, Inc.

Lyon, Tammie, illus. Kids Ask: Why? 2005. 32p. (J). (978-1-4127-1130-2(4) , 5550700) Publications International, Ltd.

MacDonald, Fiona. I Wonder Why Greeks Built Temples & Other Questions about Ancient Greece. 2006. (I Wonder Why Ser.). 32p. (J). (gr. k-3). pap. 6.95 (978-0-7534-5961-4(2) , Kingfisher) Houghton Mifflin Co. Trade & Reference Div.

Mackenzie, Carine. Talking to You. 96p. (J). mass mkt. 4.99 (978-1-871676-45-7(2) , Christian Focus) Christian Focus Pubns. GBR. *Dist:* Riverside, Spring Arbor Distributors, Inc.

Macleod, E. Everything but the Kitchen Sink: Weird Stuff You. 2008. (Everything but the Kitchen Sink Ser.). 128p. (J). pap. 7.99 ***978-0-545-00398-8(9)** , Scholastic Reference) Scholastic, Inc.

Macmillan United Kingdom Staff, ed. Who Wants to be a Millionaire: Junior UK Edition. 2001. 295p. (978-0-7522-1964-6(2) , Boxtree) Pan Macmillan.

Madgwick, Wendy. Inventions. 2000. (gr. 3-6). lib. bdg. 16.40 (978-0-613-90909-9(7)) Tandem Library Bks.

—Questions & Answers: Inventions. 2000. (J). (978-0-606-20872-7(0)) Tandem Library Bks.

Male, Alan. Can Snakes Crawl Backwards? 2001. (gr. 3-6). lib. bdg. 14.10 (978-0-613-45359-2(X)) Tandem Library Bks.

Manning, Mick. Que Hay Debajo de la Cama? Cortes, Eunice, tr. Granstrom, Brita, illus. 2003. (Descubriendo Mi Mundo Ser.). (SPA.). 32p. (J). (978-970-690-588-8(X)) Planeta Mexicana Editorial S. A. de C. V.

Marsh, Carole. Alabama Millionaire. 2001. (GameBook Ser.). 32p. (J). (gr. 3-8). pap., act. bk. ed. 9.95 (978-0-635-00018-7(0)) Gallopade International.

—Alabama Survivor: Game Book. 2001. (Carole Marsh Alabama Bks.). 32p. (J). (gr. 3-8). pap., act. bk. ed. 9.95 (978-0-635-00522-9(0)) Gallopade International.

—Alaska Millionaire: Game Book. 2001. (Carole Marsh Alaska Bks.). (Illus.). 32p. (J). (gr. 3-8). pap., act. bk. ed. 9.95 (978-0-635-00020-0(2)) Gallopade International.

—Alaska Survivor: Game Book. 2001. (Carole Marsh Alaska Bks.). (Illus.). 32p. (J). (gr. 3-8). pap. 9.95 (978-0-635-00523-6(9)) Gallopade International.

—Arizona Millionaire: Game Book. 2001. (Carole Marsh Arizona Bks.). (Illus.). 32p. (J). (gr. 3-8). pap., act. bk. ed. 9.95 (978-0-635-00022-4(9)) Gallopade International.

—Arizona Survivor: Game Book. 2001. (Carole Marsh Arizona Bks.). (Illus.). 32p. (J). (gr. 3-8). pap., act. bk. ed. 9.95 (978-0-635-00524-3(7)) Gallopade International.

—The Big Canada Reproducible Activity Book! 2001. (Canada Experience! Ser.). (Illus.). 96p. (J). (gr. 2-6). pap., act. bk. ed. 9.95 (978-0-635-00513-7(1)) Gallopade International.

—California Millionaire: Game Book. 2001. (Carole Marsh California Bks.). (Illus.). 32p. (J). (gr. 3-8). pap., act. bk. ed. 9.95 (978-0-635-00026-2(1)) Gallopade International.

—California Survivor: Game Book. 2001. (Carole Marsh California Bks.). (Illus.). 32p. (J). (gr. 3-8). pap., act. bk. ed. 9.95 (978-0-635-00526-7(3)) Gallopade International.

—Canada Jeopardy! 2001. (Canada Experience! Ser.). (Illus.). 32p. (J). (gr. 3-8). pap., act. bk. ed. 7.95 (978-0-635-00520-5(4)) Gallopade International.

—Canada Millionaire. 2001. (GameBook Ser.). (Illus.). 32p. (J). (gr. 3-8). pap., act. bk. ed. 9.95 (978-0-635-00702-5(9)) Gallopade International.

—Canada Wheel of Fortune. 2001. (GameBook Ser.). (Illus.). 32p. (J). (gr. 3-8). pap., act. bk. ed. 9.95 (978-0-635-00700-1(2)) Gallopade International.

—Colorado Millionaire: Game Book. 2001. (Illus.). 32p. (J). (gr. 3-8). pap., act. bk. ed. 9.95 (978-0-635-00028-6(8)) Gallopade International.

—Colorado Survivor: Game Book. 2001. (Carole Marsh Colorado Bks.). (Illus.). 32p. (J). (gr. 3-8). pap., act. bk. ed. 9.95 (978-0-635-00527-4(1)) Gallopade International.

—Delaware Millionaire: Game Book. 2001. (Carole Marsh Delaware Bks.). (Illus.). 32p. (J). (gr. 3-8). pap., act. bk. ed. 9.95 (978-0-635-00032-3(6)) Gallopade International.

—Delaware Survivor: Game Book. 2001. (Carole Marsh Delaware Bks.). (Illus.). 32p. (J). (gr. 3-8). pap., act. bk. ed. 9.95 (978-0-635-00529-8(8)) Gallopade International.

—Florida Millionaire: Game Book. 2001. (Carole Marsh Florida Bks.). (Illus.). 32p. (J). (gr. 3-8). pap., act. bk. ed. 9.95 (978-0-635-00034-7(2)) Gallopade International.

—Florida Survivor: Game Book. 2001. (Carole Marsh Florida Bks.). (Illus.). 32p. (J). (gr. 3-8). pap., act. bk. ed. 9.95 (978-0-635-00530-4(1) , Marsh, Carole Bks.) Gallopade International.

—Georgia Millionaire: Game Book. 2001. (Carole Marsh Georgia Bks.). (Illus.). 32p. (J). (gr. 3-8). pap., act. bk. ed. 9.95 (978-0-635-00036-1(9)) Gallopade International.

—Gigantic Titanic Trivia for Kids! 1998. (Titanic for Kids! Ser.). (Illus.). pap. 19.95 (978-0-7933-8988-9(7) , Marsh, Carole Family CD-Rom) Gallopade International.

—Hawaii Millionaire: Game Book. 2001. (Carole Marsh Hawaii Bks.). (Illus.). 32p. (J). (gr. 3-8). pap., act. bk. ed. 9.95 (978-0-635-00038-5(5)) Gallopade International.

—Hawaii Survivor: Game Book. 2001. (Carole Marsh Hawaii Bks.). (Illus.). 32p. (J). (gr. 3-8). pap., act. bk. ed. 9.95 (978-0-635-00532-8(8)) Gallopade International.

—Idaho Millionaire: Game Book. 2001. (Carole Marsh Idaho Bks.). (Illus.). 32p. (J). (gr. 3-8). pap., act. bk. ed. 9.95 (978-0-635-00040-8(7)) Gallopade International.

—Illinois Millionaire: Game Book. 2001. (Carole Marsh Illinois Bks.). (Illus.). 32p. (J). (gr. 3-8). pap., act. bk. ed. 9.95 (978-0-635-00042-2(3)) Gallopade International.

—Indiana Survivor: Game Book. 2001. (Carole Marsh Indiana Bks.). (Illus.). 32p. (J). (gr. 3-8). pap., act. bk. ed. 9.95 (978-0-635-00535-9(2)) Gallopade International.

—Iowa Millionaire: Game Book. 2001. (Carole Marsh Iowa Bks.). (Illus.). 32p. (J). (gr. 3-8). pap., act. bk. ed. 9.95 (978-0-635-00046-0(6)) Gallopade International.

—Iowa Survivor: Game Book. 2001. (Carole Marsh Iowa Bks.). (Illus.). 32p. (J). (gr. 3-8). pap., act. bk. ed. 9.95 (978-0-635-00536-6(0)) Gallopade International.

—Jeopardy: Answers & Questions about Our State! 2001. (Nebraska Experience Ser.). 32p. (J). (gr. 3-8). pap. 7.95 (978-0-7933-9803-4(7)) Gallopade International.

—Kansas Millionaire: Game Book. 2001. (Carole Marsh Kansas Bks.). (Illus.). 32p. (J). (gr. 3-8). pap., act. bk. ed. 9.95 (978-0-635-00048-4(2)) Gallopade International.

—Kentucky Millionaire: Game Book. 2001. (Carole Marsh Kentucky Bks.). (Illus.). 32p. (J). (gr. 3-8). pap., act. bk. ed. 9.95 (978-0-635-00050-7(4)) Gallopade International.

—Louisiana Millionaire: Game Book. 2001. (Carole Marsh Louisiana Bks.). (Illus.). 32p. (J). (gr. 3-8). pap., act. bk. ed. 9.95 (978-0-635-00052-1(0)) Gallopade International.

—Maine Millionaire: Game Book. 2001. (Carole Marsh Maine Bks.). (Illus.). 32p. (J). (gr. 3-8). pap., act. bk. ed. 9.95 (978-0-635-00054-5(7)) Gallopade International.

—Maine Survivor: Game Book. 2001. (Carole Marsh Maine Bks.). (Illus.). 32p. (J). (gr. 3-8). pap., act. bk. ed. 9.95 (978-0-635-00540-3(9)) Gallopade International.

—Massachusetts Survivor: Game Book. 2001. (Carole Marsh Massachusetts Bks.). (Illus.). 32p. (J). (gr. 3-8). pap., act. bk. ed. 9.95 (978-0-635-00542-7(5)) Gallopade International.

—Michigan Millionaire: Game Book. 2001. (Carole Marsh Michigan Bks.). (Illus.). 32p. (J). (gr. 3-8). pap., act. bk. ed. 9.95 (978-0-635-00060-6(1)) Gallopade International.

—Michigan Survivor: Game Book. 2001. (Carole Marsh Michigan Bks.). (Illus.). 32p. (J). (gr. 3-8). pap., act. bk. ed. 9.95 (978-0-635-00543-4(3)) Gallopade International.

—Minnesota Millionaire: Game Book. 2001. (Carole Marsh Minnesota Bks.). (Illus.). 32p. (J). (gr. 3-8). pap., act. bk. ed. 9.95 (978-0-635-00062-0(8)) Gallopade International.

—Mississippi Millionaire: Game Book. 2001. (Carole Marsh Mississippi Bks.). (Illus.). 32p. (J). (gr. 3-8). pap., act. bk. ed. 9.95 (978-0-635-00064-4(4)) Gallopade International.

—Missouri Millionaire: Game Book. 2001. (Carole Marsh Missouri Bks.). (Illus.). 32p. (J). (gr. 3-8). pap., act. bk. ed. 9.95 (978-0-635-00066-8(0)) Gallopade International.

—The Missouri Survivor: A Class Challenge. 2001. (Carole Marsh Missouri Bks.). (J). lib. bdg. 29.95 (978-0-635-00671-4(5)) Gallopade International.

—Montana Millionaire. 2001. (GameBook Ser.). 32p. (J). (gr. 3-8). pap., act. bk. ed. 9.95 (978-0-635-00068-2(7)) Gallopade International.

—Montana Survivor. 2001. (GameBook Ser.). 32p. (J). (gr. 3-8). pap., act. bk. ed. 9.95 (978-0-635-00547-2(6)) Gallopade International.

—The Montana Survivor: A Class Challenge. 2001. (Carole Marsh Montana Bks.). (J). lib. bdg. 29.95 (978-0-635-00672-1(3)) Gallopade International.

—Montana Wheel of Fortune. 2001. (GameBook Ser.). 32p. (J). (gr. 3-8). pap., act. bk. ed. 9.95 (978-0-7933-9668-9(9)) Gallopade International.

—Nebraska Millionaire. 2001. (GameBook Ser.). 32p. (J). (gr. 3-8). pap., act. bk. ed. 9.95 (978-0-635-00070-5(9)) Gallopade International.

—Nebraska Survivor. 2001. (GameBook Ser.). 32p. (J). (gr. 3-8). pap., act. bk. ed. 9.95 (978-0-635-00548-9(4)) Gallopade International.

—The Nebraska Survivor: A Class Challenge. 2001. (Carole Marsh Nebraska Bks.). (J). lib. bdg. 29.95 (978-0-635-00673-8(1)) Gallopade International.

—Nebraska Wheel of Fortune. 2001. (GameBook Ser.). 32p. (J). (gr. 3-8). pap., act. bk. ed. 9.95 (978-0-7933-9670-2(0)) Gallopade International.

—Nevada Millionaire. 2001. (GameBook Ser.). 32p. (J). (gr. 3-8). pap., act. bk. ed. 9.95 (978-0-635-00072-9(5)) Gallopade International.

—Nevada Survivor. 2001. (GameBook Ser.). 32p. (J). (gr. 3-8). pap., act. bk. ed. 9.95 (978-0-635-00549-6(2)) Gallopade International.

—Nevada Wheel of Fortune. 2001. 32p. (J). (gr. 3-8). pap., act. bk. ed. 9.95 (978-0-7933-9672-6(7)) Gallopade International.

—New Hampshire Millionaire. 2001. (GameBook Ser.). 32p. (J). (gr. 3-8). pap., act. bk. ed. 9.95 (978-0-635-00074-3(1)) Gallopade International.

—New Hampshire Survivor. 2001. (GameBook Ser.). 32p. (J). (gr. 3-8). pap., act. bk. ed. 9.95 (978-0-635-00550-2(6)) Gallopade International.

—The New Hampshire Survivor: A Class Challenge. 2001. (J). lib. bdg. 29.95 (978-0-635-00675-2(8)) Gallopade International.

—New Hampshire Wheel of Fortune. 2001. (GameBook Ser.). 32p. (J). (gr. 3-8). pap., act. bk. ed. 9.95 (978-0-7933-9674-0(3)) Gallopade International.

—New Jersey Millionaire. 2001. (GameBook Ser.). 32p. (J). (gr. 3-8). pap., act. bk. ed. 9.95 (978-0-635-00076-7(8)) Gallopade International.

—New Jersey Survivor. 2001. (GameBook Ser.). 32p. (J). (gr. 3-8). pap., act. bk. ed. 9.95 (978-0-635-00551-9(4)) Gallopade International.

—The New Jersey Survivor: A Classroom Challenge! 2001. (Carole Marsh New Jersey Bks.). lib. bdg. 29.95 (978-0-635-00676-9(6)) Gallopade International.

—New Jersey Wheel of Fortune. 2001. (GameBook Ser.). 32p. (J). (gr. 3-8). pap., act. bk. ed. 9.95 (978-0-7933-9676-4(X)) Gallopade International.

—New Mexico Millionaire. 2001. (GameBook Ser.). 32p. (J). (gr. 3-8). pap., act. bk. ed. 9.95 (978-0-635-00078-1(4)) Gallopade International.

—New Mexico Survivor. 2001. (GameBook Ser.). 32p. (J). (gr. 3-8). pap., act. bk. ed. 9.95 (978-0-635-00552-6(2)) Gallopade International.

—The New Mexico Survivor: A Class Challenge. 2001. (Carole Marsh New Mexico Bks.). (J). lib. bdg. 29.95 (978-0-635-00677-6(4)) Gallopade International.

—New Mexico Wheel of Fortune. 2001. (GameBook Ser.). 32p. (J). (gr. 3-8). pap., act. bk. ed. 9.95 (978-0-7933-9678-8(6)) Gallopade International.

—New York Millionaire. 2001. (GameBook Ser.). 32p. (J). (gr. 3-8). pap., act. bk. ed. 9.95 (978-0-635-00080-4(6)) Gallopade International.

—The New York Survivor: A Class Challenge. 2001. (Carole Marsh New York Bks.). (J). lib. bdg. 29.95 (978-0-635-00678-3(2)) Gallopade International.

—New York Wheel of Fortune. 2001. (GameBook Ser.). 32p. (J). (gr. 3-8). pap., act. bk. ed. 9.95 (978-0-7933-9680-1(8)) Gallopade International.

—North Carolina Millionaire. 2001. (GameBook Ser.). 32p. (J). (gr. 3-8). pap., act. bk. ed. 9.95 (978-0-635-00082-8(2)) Gallopade International.

—North Carolina Survivor. 2001. (GameBook Ser.). 32p. (J). (gr. 3-8). pap., act. bk. ed. 9.95 (978-0-635-00554-0(9)) Gallopade International.

—The North Carolina Survivor: A Class Challenge. 2001. (Carole Marsh North Carolina Bks.). lib. bdg. 29.95 (978-0-635-00679-0(0)); (J). lib. bdg. 29.95 (978-0-635-00680-6(4)) Gallopade International.

—North Carolina Wheel of Fortune. 2001. (GameBook Ser.). 32p. (J). (gr. 3-8). pap., act. bk. ed. 9.95 (978-0-7933-9682-5(4)) Gallopade International.

—North Dakota Millionaire. 2001. (GameBook Ser.). 32p. (J). (gr. 3-8). pap., act. bk. ed. 9.95 (978-0-635-00084-2(9)) Gallopade International.

—North Dakota Survivor. 2001. (GameBook Ser.). 32p. (J). (gr. 3-8). pap., act. bk. ed. 9.95 (978-0-635-00555-7(7)) Gallopade International.

—North Dakota Wheel of Fortune. 2001. (GameBook Ser.). 32p. (J). (gr. 3-8). pap., act. bk. ed. 9.95 (978-0-7933-9684-9(0)) Gallopade International.

—Ohio Millionaire. 2001. (GameBook Ser.). 32p. (J). (gr. 3-8). pap., act. bk. ed. 9.95 (978-0-635-00086-6(5)) Gallopade International.

—Ohio Survivor. 2001. (GameBook Ser.). 32p. (J). (gr. 3-8). pap., act. bk. ed. 9.95 (978-0-635-00556-4(5)) Gallopade International.

—The Ohio Survivor: A Class Challenge. 2001. (Carole Marsh Ohio Bks.). (J). lib. bdg. 29.95 (978-0-635-00681-3(2)) Gallopade International.

—Ohio Wheel of Fortune. 2001. (GameBook Ser.). 32p. (J). (gr. 3-8). pap., act. bk. ed. 9.95 (978-0-7933-9686-3(7)) Gallopade International.

—Oklahoma Millionaire. 2001. (GameBook Ser.). 32p. (J). (gr. 3-8). pap., act. bk. ed. 9.95 (978-0-635-00088-0(1)) Gallopade International.

—Oklahoma Survivor. 2001. (GameBook Ser.). 32p. (J). (gr. 3-8). pap., act. bk. ed. 9.95 (978-0-635-00557-1(3)) Gallopade International.

—The Oklahoma Survivor: A Class Challenge. 2001. (Carole Marsh Oklahoma Bks.). (J). lib. bdg. 29.95 (978-0-635-00682-0(0)) Gallopade International.

—Oklahoma Wheel of Fortune. 2001. (GameBook Ser.). 32p. (J). (gr. 3-8). pap., act. bk. ed. 9.95 (978-0-7933-9688-7(3)) Gallopade International.

—Oregon Millionaire. 2001. (GameBook Ser.). 32p. (J). (gr. 3-8). pap., act. bk. ed. 9.95 (978-0-635-00090-3(3)) Gallopade International.

—Oregon Survivor. 2001. (GameBook Ser.). 32p. (J). (gr. 3-8). pap., act. bk. ed. 9.95 (978-0-635-00558-8(1)) Gallopade International.

—Oregon Wheel of Fortune. 2001. (GameBook Ser.). 32p. (J). (gr. 3-8). pap., act. bk. ed. 9.95 (978-0-7933-9690-0(5)) Gallopade International.

—Pennsylvania Millionaire. 2001. (GameBook Ser.). 32p. (J). (gr. 3-8). pap., act. bk. ed. 9.95 (978-0-635-00092-7(X)) Gallopade International.

—Pennsylvania Survivor. 2001. (GameBook Ser.). 32p. (J). (gr. 3-8). pap., act. bk. ed. 9.95 (978-0-635-00559-5(X)) Gallopade International.

—Pennsylvania Wheel of Fortune. 2001. (GameBook Ser.). 32p. (J). (gr. 3-8). pap., act. bk. ed. 9.95 (978-0-7933-9692-4(1)) Gallopade International.

—Rhode Island Millionaire. 2001. (GameBook Ser.). 32p. (J). (gr. 3-8). pap., act. bk. ed. 9.95 (978-0-635-00094-1(6)) Gallopade International.

—Rhode Island Survivor. 2001. (GameBook Ser.). 32p. (J). (gr. 3-8). pap., act. bk. ed. 9.95 (978-0-635-00560-1(3)) Gallopade International.

—Rhode Island Wheel of Fortune. 2001. (GameBook Ser.). 32p. (J). (gr. 3-8). pap., act. bk. ed. 9.95 (978-0-7933-9694-8(8)) Gallopade International.

—South Carolina Millionaire. 2001. (GameBook Ser.). 32p. (J). (gr. 3-8). pap., act. bk. ed. 9.95 (978-0-635-00096-5(2)) Gallopade International.

—South Carolina Survivor. 2001. (GameBook Ser.). 32p. (J). (gr. 3-8). pap., act. bk. ed. 9.95 (978-0-635-00561-8(1)) Gallopade International.

—South Carolina Wheel of Fortune. 2001. (GameBook Ser.). 32p. (J). (gr. 3-8). pap., act. bk. ed. 9.95 (978-0-7933-9696-2(4)) Gallopade International.

—South Dakota Millionaire. 2001. (GameBook Ser.). 32p. (J). (gr. 3-8). pap., act. bk. ed. 9.95 (978-0-635-00098-9(9)) Gallopade International.

—South Dakota Survivor. 2001. (GameBook Ser.). 32p. (J). (gr. 3-8). pap., act. bk. ed. 9.95 (978-0-635-00562-5(X)) Gallopade International.

—South Dakota Wheel of Fortune. 2001. (GameBook Ser.). 32p. (J). (gr. 3-8). pap., act. bk. ed. 9.95 (978-0-7933-9698-6(0)) Gallopade International.

—The Survivor: A Class Challenge. 2001. (Carole Marsh Arkansas Bks.). lib. bdg. 29.95 (978-0-635-00650-9(2)); lib. bdg. 29.95 (978-0-635-00651-6(0)); lib. bdg. 29.95 (978-0-635-00691-2(X)); lib. bdg. 29.95 (978-0-635-00670-7(7)); lib. bdg. 29.95 (978-0-635-00669-1(3)); lib. bdg. 29.95 (978-0-635-00668-4(5)); lib. bdg. 29.95 (978-0-635-00667-7(7)); lib. bdg. 29.95 (978-0-635-00690-5(1)); lib. bdg. 29.95 (978-0-635-00692-9(8)); lib. bdg. 29.95 (978-0-635-00693-6(6)); lib. bdg. 29.95 (978-0-635-00694-3(4)); lib. bdg. 29.95 (978-0-635-00695-0(2)); lib. bdg. 29.95 (978-0-635-00696-7(0)); lib. bdg. 29.95 (978-0-635-00647-9(2)); lib. bdg. 29.95 (978-0-635-00648-6(0)); lib. bdg. 29.95 (978-0-635-00649-3(9)); lib. bdg. 29.95 (978-0-635-00652-3(9)); lib. bdg. 29.95 (978-0-635-00653-0(7)); lib. bdg. 29.95 (978-0-635-00655-4(3)); lib. bdg. 29.95 (978-0-635-00658-5(8)); lib. bdg. 29.95 (978-0-635-00661-5(8)); lib. bdg. 29.95 (978-0-635-00662-2(6) , Marsh, Carole Bks.); lib. bdg. 29.95 (978-0-635-00663-9(4)); lib. bdg. 29.95 (978-0-635-00664-6(2)); lib. bdg. 29.95 (978-0-635-00665-3(0)); lib. bdg. 29.95 (978-0-635-00666-0(9)); (J). lib. bdg. 29.95 (978-0-635-00684-4(7)); (J). lib. bdg. 29.95 (978-0-635-00683-7(9)); (J). lib. bdg. 29.95 (978-0-635-00689-9(8)); (J). lib. bdg. 29.95 (978-0-635-00688-2(X)); (J). lib. bdg. 29.95 (978-0-635-00687-5(1)); (J). lib. bdg. 29.95 (978-0-635-00686-8(3)); (J). lib. bdg. 29.95 (978-0-635-00685-1(5)) Gallopade International.

—Tennessee Millionaire. 2001. (GameBook Ser.). 32p. (J). (gr. 3-8). pap., act. bk. ed. 9.95 (978-0-635-00100-9(4)) Gallopade International.

—Tennessee Survivor. 2001. (GameBook Ser.). 32p. (J). (gr. 3-8). pap., act. bk. ed. 9.95 (978-0-635-00563-2(8)) Gallopade International.

—Tennessee Wheel of Fortune. 2001. (GameBook Ser.). 32p. (J). (gr. 3-8). pap., act. bk. ed. 9.95 (978-0-635-00000-2(8)) Gallopade International.

—Texas Millionaire. 2001. (GameBook Ser.). 32p. (J). (gr. 3-8). pap., act. bk. ed. 9.95 (978-0-635-00102-3(0)) Gallopade International.

—Texas Survivor. 2001. (GameBook Ser.). 32p. (J). (gr. 3-8). pap., act. bk. ed. 9.95 (978-0-635-00564-9(6)) Gallopade International.

—Texas Wheel of Fortune. 2001. (GameBook Ser.). 32p. (J). (gr. 3-8). pap., act. bk. ed. 9.95 (978-0-635-00002-6(4)) Gallopade International.

—Utah Millionaire. 2001. (GameBook Ser.). 32p. (J). (gr. 3-8). pap., act. bk. ed. 9.95 (978-0-635-00104-7(7)) Gallopade International.

—Utah Survivor. 2001. (GameBook Ser.). 32p. (J). (gr. 3-8). pap., act. bk. ed. 9.95 (978-0-635-00565-6(4)) Gallopade International.

—Utah Wheel of Fortune. 2001. (GameBook Ser.). 32p. (J). (gr. 3-8). pap., act. bk. ed. 9.95 (978-0-635-00004-0(0)) Gallopade International.

—Vermont Millionaire. 2001. (GameBook Ser.). 32p. (J). (gr. 3-8). pap., act. bk. ed. 9.95 (978-0-635-00106-1(3)) Gallopade International.

—Vermont Survivor. 2001. (GameBook Ser.). 32p. (J). (gr. 3-8). pap., act. bk. ed. 9.95 (978-0-635-00566-3(2)) Gallopade International.

—Vermont Wheel of Fortune. 2001. (GameBook Ser.). 32p. (J). (gr. 3-8). pap., act. bk. ed. 9.95 (978-0-635-00006-4(7)) Gallopade International.

—Virginia Millionaire. 2001. (GameBook Ser.). 32p. (J). (gr. 3-8). pap., act. bk. ed. 9.95 (978-0-635-00108-5(X)) Gallopade International.

—Virginia Survivor. 2001. (GameBook Ser.). 32p. (J). (gr. 3-8). pap., act. bk. ed. 9.95 (978-0-635-00567-0(0)) Gallopade International.

—Virginia Wheel of Fortune. 2001. (Carole Marsh Virginia Bks.). lib. bdg. 29.95 (978-0-635-00009-5(1) , Marsh, Carole Bks.); 32p. (J). (gr. 3-8). pap., act. bk. ed. 9.95 (978-0-635-00008-8(3)) Gallopade International.

—Washington Millionaire. 2001. (GameBook Ser.). (Illus.). 32p. (J). (gr. 3-8). pap., act. bk. ed. 9.95 (978-0-635-00110-8(1)) Gallopade International.

—Washington Wheel of Fortune. 2001. (GameBook Ser.). (Illus.). 32p. (J). (gr. 3-8). pap., act. bk. ed. 9.95 (978-0-635-00010-1(5)) Gallopade International.

—West Virginia Millionaire. 2001. (GameBook Ser.). (Illus.). 32p. (J). (gr. 3-8). pap., act. bk. ed. 9.95 (978-0-635-00112-2(8)) Gallopade International.

—West Virginia Survivor. 2001. (GameBook Ser.). (Illus.). 32p. (J). (gr. 3-8). pap., act. bk. ed. 9.95 (978-0-635-00569-4(7)) Gallopade International.

—West Virginia Wheel of Fortune. 2001. (GameBook Ser.). (Illus.). 32p. (J). (gr. 3-8). pap., act. bk. ed. 9.95 (978-0-635-00012-5(1)) Gallopade International.

—Wheel of Fortune. 2001. (Carole Marsh West Virginia Bks.). lib. bdg. 29.95 (978-0-635-00013-2(X) , Marsh, Carole Bks.); lib. bdg. 29.95 (978-0-635-00699-8(5)); (J). lib. bdg. 29.95 (978-0-7933-9673-3(5)); (J). lib. bdg. 29.95 (978-0-635-00001-9(6)); (J). lib. bdg. 29.95 (978-0-7933-9667-2(0)); (J). lib. bdg. 29.95 (978-0-7933-9675-7(1)); (J). lib. bdg. 29.95 (978-0-7933-9677-1(8)); (J). lib. bdg. 29.95 (978-0-7933-9679-5(4)); (J). lib. bdg. 29.95 (978-0-7933-9681-8(6)); (J). lib. bdg. 29.95 (978-0-7933-9683-2(2)); (J). lib. bdg. 29.95 (978-0-7933-9671-9(9)); (J). lib. bdg. 29.95 (978-0-7933-9691-7(3)); (J). lib. bdg. 29.95 (978-0-7933-9693-1(X)); (J). lib. bdg. 29.95 (978-0-7933-9695-5(6)); (J). lib. bdg. 29.95 (978-0-7933-9697-9(2)); (J). lib. bdg. 29.95 (978-0-7933-9699-3(9)); (J). lib. bdg. 29.95 (978-0-635-00003-3(2)); (J). lib. bdg. 29.95 (978-0-635-00005-7(9)); (J). lib. bdg. 29.95 (978-0-635-00007-1(5)); (J). lib. bdg. 29.95 (978-0-7933-9687-0(5)); (J). lib. bdg. 29.95 (978-0-7933-9669-6(7)) Gallopade International.

—Who Wants to Be a Colorado Millionaire? 2001. (Carole Marsh Colorado Bks.). lib. bdg. 29.95 (978-0-635-00029-3(6)) Gallopade International.

—Who Wants to Be a Connecticut Millionaire? 2001. (Carole Marsh Connecticut Bks.). lib. bdg. 29.95 (978-0-635-00031-6(8)) Gallopade International.

—Who Wants to Be a Delaware Millionaire? 2001. (Carole Marsh Delaware Bks.). lib. bdg. 29.95 (978-0-635-00033-0(4)) Gallopade International.

—Who Wants to Be a Millionaire? 2001. lib. bdg. 29.95 (978-0-635-00701-8(0)); lib. bdg. 29.95 (978-0-635-00069-9(5)); lib. bdg. 29.95 (978-0-635-00111-5(X)); lib. bdg. 29.95 (978-0-635-00065-1(2)); lib. bdg. 29.95 (978-0-635-00063-7(6)); lib. bdg. 29.95 (978-0-635-00059-0(8)); lib. bdg. 29.95 (978-0-635-00057-6(1)); lib. bdg. 29.95 (978-0-635-00055-2(5)); lib. bdg. 29.95 (978-0-635-00053-8(9)); lib. bdg. 29.95 (978-0-635-00051-4(2)); lib. bdg. 29.95 (978-0-635-00049-1(0)); lib. bdg. 29.95 (978-0-635-00047-7(4)); lib. bdg. 29.95 (978-0-635-00045-3(8)); lib. bdg. 29.95 (978-0-635-00113-9(6)); lib. bdg. 29.95 (978-0-635-00115-3(2)); lib. bdg. 29.95 (978-0-635-00117-7(9)); lib. bdg. 29.95 (978-0-635-00109-2(8)); lib. bdg. 29.95 (978-0-635-00039-2(3)); lib. bdg. 29.95 (978-0-635-00043-9(1)); (J). lib. bdg. 29.95 (978-0-635-00095-8(4)); (J). lib. bdg. 29.95 (978-0-635-00097-2(0)); (J). lib. bdg. 29.95 (978-0-635-00099-6(7)); (J). lib. bdg. 29.95 (978-0-635-00101-6(2)); (J). lib. bdg. 29.95 (978-0-635-00103-0(9)); (J). lib. bdg. 29.95 (978-0-635-00105-4(5)); (J). lib. bdg. 29.95 (978-0-635-00093-4(8)); (J). lib. bdg. 29.95 (978-0-635-00091-0(1)); (J). lib. bdg. 29.95 (978-0-635-00089-7(X)); (J). lib. bdg. 29.95 (978-0-635-00071-2(7)); (J). lib. bdg. 29.95 (978-0-635-00087-3(3)); (J). lib. bdg. 29.95 (978-0-635-00085-9(7)); (J). lib. bdg. 29.95 (978-0-635-00083-5(0)); (J). lib. bdg. 29.95 (978-0-635-00081-1(4)); (J). lib. bdg. 29.95 (978-0-635-00077-4(6)); (J). lib. bdg. 29.95 (978-0-635-00075-0(X)); (J). lib. bdg. 29.95 (978-0-635-00073-6(3)); (J). lib. bdg. 29.95 (978-0-635-00107-8(1)); (J). lib. bdg. 29.95 (978-0-635-00067-5(9)) Gallopade International.

—Who Wants to Be an Alabama Millionaire? 2001. (Carole Marsh Alabama Bks.). lib. bdg. 29.95 (978-0-635-00019-4(9)) Gallopade International.

—Who Wants to Be an Alaska Millionaire? 2001. (Carole Marsh Alaska Bks.). lib. bdg. 29.95 (978-0-635-00021-7(0)) Gallopade International.

—Who Wants to Be an Arkansas Millionaire? 2001. (Carole Marsh Arkansas Bks.). lib. bdg. 29.95 (978-0-635-00025-5(3)) Gallopade International.

—Wisconsin Survivor. 2001. (GameBook Ser.). (Illus.). 32p. (J). (gr. 3-8). pap., act. bk. ed. 9.95 (978-0-635-00570-0(0)) Gallopade International.

—Wisconsin Wheel of Fortune. 2001. (GameBook Ser.). (Illus.). 32p. (J). (gr. 3-8). pap., act. bk. ed. 9.95 (978-0-635-00014-9(8)) Gallopade International.

—Wyoming Millionaire. 2001. (GameBook Ser.). (Illus.). 32p. (J). (gr. 3-8). pap., act. bk. ed. 9.95 (978-0-635-00116-0(0)) Gallopade International.

—Wyoming Wheel of Fortune. 2001. (Carole Marsh Wyoming Bks.). lib. bdg. 29.95 (978-0-635-00017-0(2)) Gallopade International.

Martin, Mary-Jane. Let Me Put It This Way. 2004. (Illus.). 32p. 11.95 (978-0-9730583-1-4(5)) Lion & Mouse Tales, Inc. CAN. *Dist:* Hushion Hse. Publishing, Ltd.

Marx, David F. What Is up When You Are Down? Miller, Susan, illus. 2000. (Rookie Reader Espanol Ser.). 24p. (J). (gr. k-2). pap. 4.95 (978-0-516-27044-9(3)); 19.50 (978-0-516-22007-9(1)) Scholastic Library Publishing. (Children's Pr.).

—What Is up When You Are Down? 2000. (gr. k-3). lib. bdg. 12.95 (978-0-613-54774-1(8)) Tandem Library Bks.

Maurice, creator. The Spanish Question Game. 2000. (SPA.). (YA). 99.00 (978-1-932770-48-3(8) , SG9) Symtalk, Inc.

Maynard, Christopher. I Wonder Why Planes Have Wings: And Other Questions about Transportation. 2003. (gr. k-3). lib. bdg. 14.10 (978-0-613-90897-9(X)) Tandem Library Bks.

Mehling, Carl. Dinosaurs. 2001. (It's All about! Ser.). (Illus.). 32p. (J). (gr. 2-5). lib. bdg. 25.27 (978-1-58952-159-9(5)) Rourke Publishing, LLC.

Miles Kelly Staff. Animals. 2003. (Info Bank Ser.). (Illus.). 96p. (J). 7.95 (978-1-84236-153-5(8)) Miles Kelly Publishing, Ltd. GBR. *Dist:* Independent Pubs. Group.

—Geography. 2003. (Info Bank Ser.). (Illus.). 96p. (J). 7.95 (978-1-84236-055-2(8)) Miles Kelly Publishing, Ltd. GBR. *Dist:* Independent Pubs. Group.

—History. 2003. (Info Bank Ser.). (Illus.). 96p. (J). 7.95 (978-1-84236-056-9(6)) Miles Kelly Publishing, Ltd. GBR. *Dist:* Independent Pubs. Group.

—How Things Work. 2003. (Ask Me a Question Ser.). (Illus.). 20p. spiral bd. 7.95 (978-1-84236-127-6(9)) Miles Kelly Publishing, Ltd. GBR. *Dist:* Independent Pubs. Group.

—Nature. 2003. (Ask Me a Question Ser.). (Illus.). 20p. spiral bd. 7.95 (978-1-84236-125-2(2)) Miles Kelly Publishing, Ltd. GBR. *Dist:* Independent Pubs. Group.

—Our Planet. 2003. (Ask Me a Question Ser.). (Illus.). 20p. (J). spiral bd. 7.95 (978-1-84236-128-3(7)) Miles Kelly Publishing, Ltd. GBR. *Dist:* Independent Pubs. Group.

—People & Places. 2003. (Ask Me a Question Ser.). (Illus.). 20p. spiral bd. 7.95 (978-1-84236-126-9(0)) Miles Kelly Publishing, Ltd. GBR. *Dist:* Independent Pubs. Group.

—Science. 2003. (Info Bank Ser.). (Illus.). 96p. (J). 7.95 (978-1-84236-152-8(X)) Miles Kelly Publishing, Ltd. GBR. *Dist:* Independent Pubs. Group.

Mission City Press Inc. Staff. Dear Elsie. 2001. (Elsie Dinsmore). 208p. (YA). (gr. 5-9). 12.99 (978-1-928749-55-4(0)) Zonderkidz.

Moran, Paul, illus. World's Greatest Who What Where When Quiz Book for Kids. 2003. 112p. (J). pap. 3.99 (978-0-603-56100-9(4)) Egmont Bks., Ltd. GBR. *Dist:* Trafalgar Square Publishing.

Mosatche, Harriet S. & Lawner, Elizabeth K. Getting to Know the Real You: 50 Fun Quizzes Just for Girls. 2002. (Illus.). 240p. pap. 12.95 (978-0-7615-2954-5(3) , Three Rivers Pr.) Crown Publishing Group.

The Moves Make the Man: Teaching Unit. 2003. 73p. (YA). ring bd. (978-1-58049-433-5(1) , TU4331) Prestwick Hse., Inc.

Munrriz, Mercedes. Por Qué? Martinez, Rocio, illus. 2003. (SPA.). 16p. (J). (978-84-667-2627-6(6)) Grupo Anaya, S.A. ESP. *Dist:* Lectorum Pubns., Inc.

—Qué Es? Martinez, Rocio, illus. 2003. (SPA.). 16p. (J). (978-84-667-2626-9(8)) Grupo Anaya, S.A. ESP. *Dist:* Lectorum Pubns., Inc.

My Big Book of Questions & Answers. 2003. 512p. (J). 9.98 (978-1-4054-0758-8(1)) Parragon, Inc.

My First Bible Sticker Questions & Answers. 2000. 48p. (J). (ps-3). pap. 4.99 (978-0-570-05579-2(2)) Concordia Publishing Hse.

My First Book of Questions & Answers about Science & Nature. 2001. 128p. (J). 15.95 (978-0-7525-5846-2(3)) Parragon, Inc.

My First Book of Questions & Answers about Wings & Wheels. 2001. 128p. (J). 15.95 (978-0-7525-5848-6(X)) Parragon, Inc.

Nathan, Emma. What Do You Call a Group of Butterflies? And Other Insect Groups. 2000. (What Do You Call a Group of... Ser.). (Illus.). 24p. (J). (gr. 3-6). 21.20 (978-1-56711-359-4(1) , Blackbirch Pr., Inc.) Thomson Gale.

National Geographic Society Staff. Eyewitness to the 20th Century. 1998. (National Geographic Destinations Ser.). (Illus.). 400p. (J). (gr. 5-8). 40.00 (978-0-7922-7049-2(5) , National Geographic) National Geographic Society.

National Parents Council - Primary Staff, ed. The Whiz Quiz Book: For Children & Grown-Up Children. 2006. 96p. pap. 9.95 (978-1-903464-98-4(6)) Collins Pr., The IRL. *Dist:* Dufour Editions, Inc.

The Natural: Teaching Unit. 2002. 49p. (J). ring bd. (978-1-58049-421-2(8) , TU202) Prestwick Hse., Inc.

Natural World. 2002. 256p. (J). 25.95 (978-0-7525-4350-5(4)) Parragon, Inc.

Natural World, 14 bks., Set. Incl. Chimpanzee : Habitats, Life Cycles, Food Chains, Threats. Banks, Martin. (gr. 3-7). 2000. lib. bdg. 27.12 (978-0-7398-1062-0(6)); Crocodile : Habitats, Life Cycles, Food Chains, Threats. Pope, Joyce. (gr. 4-7). 2000. lib. bdg. 27.12 (978-0-7398-2764-2(2)); Dolphin : Habitats, Life Cycles, Food Chains, Threats. Davies, Nicola. (gr. 3-7). 2000. lib. bdg. 27.12 (978-0-7398-2766-6(9)); Elephant : Habitats, Life Cycles, Food Chains, Threats. Travers, Will. (gr. 3-7). 1999. lib. bdg. 27.12 (978-0-7398-1056-9(1)); Giant Panda : Habitats, Life Cycles, Food Chains, Threats. Penny, Malcolm. (gr. 4-7). 2000. lib. bdg. 27.12 (978-0-7398-1063-7(4)); Great White Shark : Habitats, Life Cycles, Food Chains, Threats. Westwood, Brett. (gr. 3-7). 2000. lib. bdg. 27.12 (978-0-7398-1061-3(8)); Grizzly Bear : Habitats, Life Cycles, Food Chains, Threats. Leach, Michael. (gr. 3-7). 2001. lib. bdg. 27.12 (978-0-7398-2768-0(5)); Hippopotamus : Habitats, Life Cycles, Food Chains, Threats. Leach, Michael. (gr. 3-7). 2001. lib. bdg. 27.12 (978-0-7398-2769-7(3)); Killer Whale : Habitats, Life Cycles, Food Chains, Threats. Carwardine, Mark. (gr. 3-7). 1999. lib. bdg. 27.12 (978-0-7398-1058-3(8)); Lion : Habitats, Life Cycles, Food Chains, Threats. Jordan, Bill. (gr. 3-7). 1999. lib. bdg. 27.12 (978-0-7398-1057-6(X)); Orangutan : Habitats, Life Cycles, Food Chains, Threats. Brend, Stephen. (gr. 4-7). 2000. lib. bdg. 27.12 (978-0-7398-2765-9(0)); Penguin : Habitats, Life Cycles, Food Chains, Threats. Reid, Keith. (gr. 4-7). 2000. lib. bdg. 27.12 (978-0-7398-2767-3(7)); Polar Bear : Habitats, Life Cycles, Food Chains, Threats. Penny, Malcolm. (gr. 4-7). 2000. lib. bdg. 27.12 (978-0-7398-1060-6(X)); Tiger : Habitats, Life Cycles, Food Chains, Threats. Thapar, Valmik. (gr. 3-7). 1999. lib. bdg. 27.12 (978-0-7398-1055-2(3)); 48p. (J). (Illus.). 1999. 265.72 (978-0-7398-2770-3(7)) Raintree.

New York Public Library Staff & January, Brendan. The New York Public Library Amazing Explorers: A Book of Answers for Kids. 2001. (New York Public Library Books for Kids: Vol. 11). (Illus.). 176p. (gr. 3-7). pap. 13.95 (978-0-471-39291-0(X) , Wiley) Wiley, John & Sons, Inc.

New York Public Library Staff & Sutcliffe, Andrea. The New York Public Library Amazing U. S. Geography: A Book of Answers for Kids. 2002. (New York Public Library Books for Kids: Vol. 12). (Illus.). 176p. pap. 12.95 (978-0-471-39294-1(4) , Wiley) Wiley, John & Sons, Inc.

Newman, Stanley. 10,000 Answers: The Ultimate Trivia Encyclopedia. 2001. (gr. 3-6). lib. bdg. 36.15 (978-0-613-50072-2(5)) Tandem Library Bks.

Nicholaus, Bret & Lowrie, Paul. Christmas Kidchat: Holiday Questions for Kids (and Kids-at-heart) Luken, Scott, illus. 2002. 128p. (J). per. 8.95 (978-0-9634251-7-1(X)) Questmarc Publishing.

—Kidchat: 222 Creative Questions to Spark Conversations. Luken, Scott, illus. 2001. 128p. (J). pap. 8.95 (978-0-9634251-6-4(1)) Questmarc Publishing.

—Kidchat: 222 Creative Questions to Spark Conversations. 2nd rev. ed. 2004. (Illus.). 128p. (J). pap. 9.95 (978-0-9755801-0-3(8) , KCR) Questmarc Publishing.

—Kidchat: 222 Creative Questions to Spark Conversations. 2007. (KidChat Ser.). (Illus.). 128p. (J). pap. 6.99 ***(978-1-59643-314-4(0))*** Roaring Brook Pr.

—KidChat Gone Wild! 202 Creative Questions to Unleash the Imagination. 2007. (KidChat Ser.). (Illus.). 128p. (J). (gr. 3 up). pap. 6.99 ***(978-1-59643-316-8(7))*** Roaring Brook Pr.

—KidChat Oh, the Places to Go! 204 Creative Questions to Let the Imagination Travel. 2007. (KidChat Ser.). (Illus.). 128p. (J). (gr. 3 up). pap. 6.99 ***(978-1-59643-317-5(5))*** Roaring Brook Pr.

Nicholaus, Bret & Lowrie, Paul. KidChat Too! All-New Questions to Fuel Young Minds & Mouths. 2004. (Illus.). 128p. (J). pap. 9.95 (978-0-9755801-1-0(6) , KCT) Questmarc Publishing.

—KidChat Too! All-New Questions to Fuel Young Minds & Mouths. 2nd rev. ed. 2007. (KidChat Ser.). (Illus.). 128p. (J). (gr. 3 up). pap. 6.99 ***(978-1-59643-315-1(9))*** Roaring Brook Pr.

No Fair! (Kids Talk Ser.). 32p. (J). 8.95 (978-1-4048-0366-4(1)) Picture Window Bks.

Noble, David G. 101 Questions about Ancient Indians of the Southwest. 1998. (Illus.). 32p. (J). (gr. 1-6). pap. 9.95 (978-1-877856-87-7(8)) Western National Parks Assn.

Ochoa, George & New York Public Library Staff. The New York Public Library Amazing Hispanic American History: A Book of Answers for Kids. 1998. (New York Public Library Books for Kids: Vol. 7). (Illus.). 192p. (gr. 5-9). pap. 12.95 (978-0-471-19204-6(X) , Wiley-Interscience) Wiley, John & Sons, Inc.

Otfinoski, Steven. Hedgehogs & Other Insectivores, Vol. 4. World Book, Inc. Staff, ed. 2002. (World Book's Animals of the World Ser.: Set 1). 64p. (J). (978-0-7166-1241-4(0)) World Bk., Inc.

Page, Don, illus. How Big Was Noah's Ark? And Other Questions Kids Ask about the Bible. 1998. 48p. (J). (gr. 4-7). pap. 7.99 (978-0-88486-221-5(6) , Arrowood Pr.) BBS Publishing Corp.

Pear, Nancy & Galens, Judy. The Handy Answer Book for Kids (And Parents) 2001. (Handy Answer Book Ser.). (Illus.). 400p. pap. 19.95 (978-1-57859-110-7(4)) Visible Ink Pr.

Pearce, Querida L. The Land Before Time Dinosaur Q & A. Baugh, Bryan, illus. 1999. (Roxbury Park Bks.). 63p. (J). (gr. 1-3). pap. 7.95 (978-0-7373-0281-3(X) , 0281XW, Roxbury Park) Lowell Hse.

Pilgrims. 2000. 32p. (YA). 7.49 (978-0-7525-4647-6(3)) Parragon, Inc.

Pilgrims. 96p. (gr. 4-8). 13.99 (978-0-7682-0628-9(6) , GA13085) School Specialty Publishing.

Potts, Kimberly. Boost Your Guy-Q: Quizzes to Test Your Guy Smarts. 2007. 160p. pap. 8.95 ***(978-1-59869-230-3(5))*** Adams Media Corp.

Preszler, June. Haiti: A Question & Answer Book. 2007. (Fact Finders Ser.). (Illus.). 32p. (J). ***(978-0-7368-6770-2(8)*** , 1264916) Capstone Pr., Inc.

Q&A of the U. S. A. 2002. 256p. (J). 25.95 (978-0-7525-8725-7(0)) Parragon, Inc.

Question & Answer Encyclopedia: The Natural World. 2002. 256p. (J). 15.98 (978-0-7525-3843-3(8)) Parragon, Inc.

Question & Answer Library, 8 vols., Set. 2000. 256p. (J). 59.95 (978-0-7525-4640-7(6)) Parragon, Inc.

Questions & Answers: Countries. 2005. (Fact Finders Ser.). (Illus.). (J). (gr. 3-4). lib. bdg. 813.60 (978-0-7368-4425-3(2)) Capstone Pr., Inc.

Questions & Answers of the Natural World. 2003. (Illus.). 256p. (J). 12.98 (978-1-4054-1682-5(3)) Parragon, Inc.

Radabaugh, Melinda Beth. Going to a Restaurant. 2003. (ps-2). lib. bdg. 13.30 (978-0-613-60879-4(8)) Tandem Library Bks.

—Going to School. 2003. (ps-2). lib. bdg. 13.30 (978-0-613-60880-0(1)) Tandem Library Bks.

—Going to the Library. 2003. (ps-2). lib. bdg. 13.30 (978-0-613-60881-7(X)) Tandem Library Bks.

Raintree Steck-Vaughn Staff. Country Books: Arkansas Edition, 39 bks., Set. 2003. (Illus.). 1058.46 (978-1-4109-0165-1(3)) Raintree.

Realtime Associates and Mazer Corporation Staff & LeapFrog Staff, compiled by. Support an Answer. 2002. (J). (gr. 3). 66.75 (978-1-58605-365-9(5)); (gr. 4). 66.75 (978-1-58605-421-2(X)) LeapFrog Enterprises, Inc. (LeapFrog Schl. Hse.).

Rey, H. A. & Rey, Margaret. Curious George's Big Book of Curiosity. Paprocki, Greg, illus. 2005. 48p. (J). (ps-k). 11.99 (978-0-618-58338-6(6)) Houghton Mifflin Co. Trade & Reference Div.

Rissinger, Matt & Yates, Philip. Kids' Quickest Comebacks. Collinet, Rob, illus. 2004. 96p. (J). pap. 4.95 (978-1-4027-0987-6(0)) Sterling Publishing Co., Inc.

Ristuccia, Christine & Ristuccia, James. The Entire World of WH? Questions. 2004. (J). 39.99 (978-0-9723457-9-8(5)) Say It Right.

—The Entire World of WH? Questions Flip Book. 2004. (Illus.). 9p. (J). spiral bd. 14.99 (978-0-9723457-8-1(7)) Say It Right.

Ross, Edward S. Ants. 2003. (Naturebooks: Creepy Crawlers Ser.). (Illus.). 32p. (J). (gr. 1-5). 25.64 (978-1-56766-398-3(2)) Child's World, Inc.

Ruditis, Paul. Roswell Pop Quiz. 2000. (gr. 7-12). lib. bdg. 13.00 (978-0-613-74173-6(0)) Tandem Library Bks.

Russell, Ken & Carter, Philip. Bumper Quiz Book for Kids. (Illus.). 160p. (J). 17.95 (978-1-85479-300-3(4)) O'Mara, Michael Bks., Ltd. GBR. *Dist:* Trans-Atlantic Pubns., Inc.

Saari, Peggy, ed. U X L History Fact Finder, 3 vols. 2001. (Illus.). xxxi, 620p. (J). (978-0-7876-4844-2(2) , UXL) Thomson Gale.

—U-X-L History Fact Finder, 3 vols., Set. 2001. (Illus.). xxxi, 620p. (J). lib. bdg. 181.00 (978-0-7876-4843-5(4) , GML00602-114887, UXL) Thomson Gale.

Saffer, Barbara. Science Questions & Answers: The Human Body. 1998. (Gifted & Talented Ser.). (Illus.). 64p. (J). (gr. 1-3). pap. 5.95 (978-1-56565-910-0(4) , 09104W) Lowell Hse. Juvenile.

Salzmann, Mary Elizabeth. Do You Wonder?, , Set. l.t. ed. Incl. How? lib. bdg. 19.93 (978-1-57765-174-1(X)); What? lib. bdg. 19.93 (978-1-57765-170-3(7)); When? lib. bdg. 19.93 (978-1-57765-171-0(5)); Where? lib. bdg. 19.93 (978-1-57765-172-7(3)); Who? lib. bdg. 19.93 (978-1-57765-169-7(3)); Why? lib. bdg. 19.93 (978-1-57765-173-4(1)); 24p. (J). (ps-3). 2000. (Illus.). 2000. Set lib. bdg. 119.58 (978-1-57765-281-6(9) , SandCastle) ABDO Publishing Co.

—How? l.t. ed. 2000. (Do You Wonder? Ser.). (Illus.). 24p. (J). (ps-3). lib. bdg. 19.93 (978-1-57765-174-1(X) , SandCastle) ABDO Publishing Co.

—What? l.t. ed. 2000. (Do You Wonder? Ser.). (Illus.). 24p. (J). (ps-3). lib. bdg. 19.93 (978-1-57765 170-3(7) , SandCastle) ABDO Publishing Co.

—When? l.t. ed. 2000. (Do You Wonder? Ser.). (Illus.). 24p. (J). (ps-3). lib. bdg. 19.93 (978-1-57765-171-0(5) , SandCastle) ABDO Publishing Co.

—Where? l.t. ed. 2000. (Do You Wonder? Ser.). (Illus.). 24p. (J). (ps-3). lib. bdg. 19.93 (978-1-57765-172-7(3) , SandCastle) ABDO Publishing Co.

—Who? l.t. ed. 2000. (Do You Wonder? Ser.). (Illus.). 24p. (J). (ps-3). lib. bdg. 19.93 (978-1-57765-169-7(3) , SandCastle) ABDO Publishing Co.

—Why? l.t. ed. 2000. (Do You Wonder? Ser.). (Illus.). 24p. (J). (ps-3). lib. bdg. 19.93 (978-1-57765-173-4(1) , SandCastle) ABDO Publishing Co.

Schnidman, Ellen. African American Answer Book, 6 bks. 1999. (Illus.). 64p. (J). (gr. 5-12). pap. 29.70 (978-0-7910-3765-2(7) , Chelsea Hse.) Facts On File, Inc.

Scholastic, Inc. Staff. World of Info Wheel Pack. 1998. (Wheel Ser.). (J). (gr. 4-7). 3.95 (978-0-590-02729-8(8) , Scholastic Reference) Scholastic, Inc.

Scholastic, Inc. Staff & Entin, Carli. Pokemon Pop Quiz! 2000. (Pokemon Ser.). (Illus.). 64p. (J). (gr. 2-7). pap. 3.99 (978-0-439-15406-2(5)) Scholastic, Inc.

Scott, James. Watership Down: Reproducible Teaching Unit. 2002. 86p. (J). ring bd. (978-1-58049-413-7(7)) Prestwick Hse., Inc.

—Young Goodman Brown: Reproducible Teaching Unit. 2002. 88p. (J). ring bd. (978-1-58049-416-8(1) , TU199) Prestwick Hse., Inc.

Seip, Shannon Payette. The Pop Quiz Book: Tons of Trivia! Sheuer, Lauren, illus. 2005. (American Girl Library). 77p. (J). (gr. 3-7). spiral bd. 7.95 (978-1-58485-844-7(3) , American Girl) American Girl Publishing, Inc.

Seuss, Dr. The Cat's Quizzer. Seuss, Dr., illus. 2002. (Illus.). (J). 16.70 (978-0-7587-1059-8(3)) Book Wholesalers, Inc.

Shellenberger, Susie. Girlz Want to Know: Answers to Real Life Questions. 2001. (Ywof Library). (Illus.). 128p. (J). (gr. 3-7). pap. 7.99 (978-0-310-70045-6(0)) Zonderkidz.

Slimy & Scaly. 2002. (Questions & Answers Ser.). 12p. (J). pap. 3.98 (978-0-7525-7900-9(2)) Parragon, Inc.

Sloan, Peter. What If? 1999. (gr. k-3). lib. bdg. 11.55 (978-0-613-30862-5(X)) Tandem Library Bks.

Solomon, Barbara, ed. Haves & Have Nots. 1999. (gr. 7-12). lib. bdg. 14.10 (978-0-613-21684-5(9)) Tandem Library Bks.

Solomon, Iris L. & Solomon, Ron. Friendz Pakz: Friends. 2003. (YA). (gr. 3 up). 4.99 (978-1-930680-04-3(X) , SSP-08FR) Swingset Pr., LLC.

—Friendz Pakz: Future. 2003. (YA). (gr. 3 up). 4.99 (978-1-930680-05-0(8) , SSP-08FT) Swingset Pr., LLC.

—Friendz Pakz: Love. 2003. (YA). (gr. 3 up). 4.99 (978-1-930680-07-4(4) , SSP-08LV) Swingset Pr., LLC.

Sonneborn, Elizabeth. New York Public Library Amazing Native American History. 1999. (gr. 5-8). lib. bdg. 22.20 (978-0-613-26381-8(2)) Tandem Library Bks.

Sonneborn, Liz & New York Public Library Staff. The New York Public Library Amazing Native American History: A Book of Answers for Kids. 1999. (New York Public Library Books for Kids Ser.: Vol. 8). (Illus.). 176p. (gr. 5-9). pap. 16.95 (978-0-471-33204-6(6) , Wiley) Wiley, John & Sons, Inc.

Spengler, Kremena. The United States: A Question & Answer Book. 2007. 32p. (J). ***(978-0-7368-6774-0(0))*** Capstone Pr., Inc.

Sporting Heroes. 2000. 32p. (YA). 7.49 (978-0-7525-4645-2(7)) Parragon, Inc.

Steele, Philip. I Wonder Why Castles Had Moats & Other Questions about Long Ago. 2004. (I Wonder Why Ser.). (Illus.). 32p. (J). (gr. k-3). pap. 6.95 (978-0-7534-5809-9(8) , Kingfisher) Houghton Mifflin Co. Trade & Reference Div.

Stewart, Arlene Hamilton, et al. The Love & Romance Teen Quiz Book. 2001. 240p. pap. 9.95 (978-0-7407-1988-2(2)) Andrews McMeel Publishing.

Stewart, Wayne, et al. The Big Book of Baseball Brainteasers. 2004. 288p. 6.98 (978-1-4027-1337-8(1) , Sterling/Main St.) Sterling Publishing Co., Inc.

Stock, Gregory. The Kids' Book of Questions: Revised for the New Century. 2nd rev. expurg. ed. 2004. (Illus.). 208p. (J). pap. 7.95 (978-0-7611-3595-1(2) , 13595) Workman Publishing Co., Inc.

Stott, Carole. I Wonder Why Stars Twinkle: And Other Questions about Space. 2003. (J). lib. bdg. 14.10 (978-0-613-63164-8(1)) Tandem Library Bks.

Sutcliffe, Andrea. The New York Public Library Amazing World Geography: A Book of Answers for Kids. 2002. (gr. 5-8). lib. bdg. 22.20 (978-0-613-82482-8(2)) Tandem Library Bks.

Svancara, Theresa. Sea Stars & Other Echinoderms, Vol. 7. World Book, Inc. Staff, ed. 2002. (World Book's Animals of the World Ser.: Set 3). (Illus.). 64p. (J). (978-0-7166-1230-8(5)) World Bk., Inc.

Sytsma, Mary & Vogel, Jane. Questions Worth Asking: A Study of the Heidelberg Catechism, Year 1. 2001. (Reformed Faith Ser.). 272p. (gr. 9-10). tchr. ed. 20.95 (978-1-56212-781-7(0) , 130155, Faith Alive Christian Resources) CRC Pubns.

Take a Guess. 2002. (Illus.). (J). pap. (978-0-7398-5942-1(0)) Steck-Vaughn.

Tallarico, Tony, tr. & illus. The Big Book of Questions & Answers. Tallarico, Tony, illus. 2002. 381p. (J). (978-1-58865-049-8(9)) Kidsbooks, Inc.

Taylor, Barbara. I Wonder Why Zippers Have Teeth: And Other Questions about Inventions. 2003. (I Wonder Why Ser.). 32p. (J). (gr. k-3). pap. 6.95 (978-0-7534-5665-1(6) , Kingfisher) Houghton Mifflin Co. Trade & Reference Div.

—Oceans & Rivers. 2002. (Questions & Answers about... Ser.). (Illus.). 40p. (J). (gr. 4-8). pap. 7.95 (978-0-7534-5491-6(2) , Kingfisher) Houghton Mifflin Co. Trade & Reference Div.

—Why Don't Elephants Live in the City? 2002. (Animal Puzzlers Ser.). (Illus.). 32p. (J). 12.95 (978-1-57768-948-5(8) , Waterbird Bks.) School Specialty Publishing.

—Why Don't Gorillas Lay Eggs? 2004. (Animal Puzzlers Ser.). (Illus.). 32p. (J). 12.95 (978-1-57768-949-2(6) , Waterbird Bks.) School Specialty Publishing.

—Why Don't Polar Bears Have Stripes? 2004. (Animal Puzzlers Ser.). (Illus.). 32p. (J). 12.95 (978-1-57768-946-1(1) , Waterbird Bks.) School Specialty Publishing.

—Why Don't Tigers Eat Bananas? 2004. (Animal Puzzlers Ser.). (Illus.). 32p. (J). 12.95 (978-1-57768-947-8(X) , Waterbird Bks.) School Specialty Publishing.

Tears of a Tiger: Teaching Unit. 2003. 88p. (YA). ring bd. (978-1-58049-429-8(3) , TU4293) Prestwick Hse., Inc.

Theodorou, Rod. Dinosaurs. 2002. (Curious Kids Guides). (Illus.). 32p. (J). tchr. ed. 6.95 (978-0-7534-5474-9(2) , Kingfisher) Houghton Mifflin Co. Trade & Reference Div.

—I Wonder Why Triceratops Had Horns: And Other Questions about Dinosaurs. 2003. (I Wonder Why Ser.). (Illus.). 32p. (J). (gr. k-3). pap. 6.95 (978-0-7534-5615-6(X) , Kingfisher) Houghton Mifflin Co. Trade & Reference Div.

—I Wonder Why Triceratops Had Horns: And Other Questions about Dinosaurs. 2003. (gr. k-3). lib. bdg. 14.10 (978-0-613-63166-2(8)) Tandem Library Bks.

The Things They Carried: Reproducible Teaching Unit. 2002. 65p. (J). ring bd. (978-1-58049-450-2(1) , TU206) Prestwick Hse., Inc.

Thomson, Ruth. Eat Just Sweets? And Other Questions about My Body. 2001. (Why Can't I Ser.). (Illus.). 30p. (J). lib. bdg. 24.25 (978-1-930643-01-7(2)) Chrysalis Education.

—Take My Plant for a Walk? 2001. (Why Can't I Ser.). (Illus.). 30p. (J). lib. bdg. 24.25 (978-1-930643-02-4(0)) Chrysalis Education.

Tiede, Karen. Carve Smart. 2004. 189p. (YA). pap. 19.95 (978-0-7414-2093-0(7)) Infinity Publishing.

Time for Kids Editors. Time for Kids: Almanac 2008. rev. ed. 2007. (Illus.). 256p. (J). (gr. 2-8). pap. 12.99 ***(978-1-933821-84-9(1))*** Time, Inc. Home Entertainment.

The Time-Life Library of First Questions & Answers, 18 bks. Incl. Are There Diamonds in My Backyard? First Questions & Answers about the Earth. Time-Life for Children Staff. Mark, Sara, ed. 1995. 14.95 (978-0-7835-0902-0(2)); Did Triceratops Have Polka Dots? First Questions & Answers about Dinosaurs. Time-Life Books Editors. Fallow, Allan, ed. 1995. 14.95 (978-0-7835-0903-7(0)); Do Bears Give Bear Hugs? First Questions & Answers about Animals. Time-Life Books Editors. Fallow, Allan, ed. 1994. 14.95 (978-0-7835-0870-2(0)); Do Buildings Have Bones? First Questions & Answers about Buildings. Time-Life Books Editors. Mark, Sara, ed. 1995. 14.95 (978-0-7835-0900-6(6)); Do Fish Drink? First Questions & Answers about Water. Time-Life Books Editors. Kagan, Neil, ed. 1993. 14.95 (978-0-7835-0850-4(6)); Do Mommies Have Mommies? First Questions & Answers about Families. Time-Life Books Editors. Fallow, Allan, ed. 1994. 14.95 (978-0-7835-0874-0(3)); Do Skyscrapers Touch the Sky? First Questions & Answers about Cities. Time-Life Books Editors. Fallow, Allan, ed. 1994. 14.95 (978-0-7835-0886-3(7)); How Big Is the Ocean? First Questions & Answers about the Beach. Time-Life Books Editors. Fallow, Allan, ed. 1994. 14.95 (978-0-7835-0897-9(2)); How Far Can a Butterfly Fly? First Questions & Answers about Bugs. Time-Life Books Editors. Lesk, Sara M., ed. 1994. 14.95 (978-0-7835-0882-5(4)); What Makes Popcorn Pop? First Questions & Answers about Food. Ward, Elizabeth, ed. 1994. 14.95 (978-0-7835-0862-7(X)); Where Does the Sun Sleep? First Questions & Answers about Bedtime. Time-Life Books Editors. Kagan, Neil, ed. 1993. 14.95 (978-0-7835-0866-5(2)); Who Named My Street Magnolia? First Questions & Answers about Neighborhoods. Time-Life Books Editors. Mark, Sara, ed. 1995. 14.95 (978-0-7835-0898-6(0)); Why Are Wagons Red? First Questions & Answers about Transportation. Time-Life Books Editors. Lesk, Sara M., ed. 1994. 14.95 (978-0-7835-0878-8(6)); Why Do Balls Bounce? First Questions & Answers about How Things Work. Time-Life Books Editors. Fallow, Allan, ed. 1995. 14.95 (978-0-7835-0901-3(4)); Why Do Roosters Crow? First Questions & Answers about Farms. Time-Life Books Editors. Fallow, Allan, ed. Kavanagh, Peter & Kavanagh, Jim, illus. 1995. 14.95 (978-0-7835-0899-3(9)); Why Is the Grass Green? First Questions & Answers about Nature. Time-Life Books Editors. Kagan, Neil, ed. 1993. 14.95 (978-0-7835-0858-0(1)); (Illus.). 48p. (J). (gr. k-2). (978-0-7835-0894-8(8)) Time-Life, Inc.

Todo Sobre Nuestro Mundo. (Coleccion Todo Sobre...). (SPA.). (J). (gr. k-1). (978-84-243-2966-2(X) , FH5249) Publicaciones Fher, S.A.

Trotter, Pamela D., III. Lantern on a Hitching Post: African-American Heritage Quiz Book, 2003. 114p. (YA). per. 12.00 (978-0-9754540-0-8(5)) Arrinton Pubns.

Ueda, Reed & Stotsky, Sandra, eds. African-American Answer Book. 1999. (Ethnic Answer Book Ser.). (Illus.). 136p. (YA). (gr. 5 up). pap. 9.95 (978-0-7910-4913-6(2)); lib. bdg. 19.75 (978-0-7910-4912-9(4)) Facts On File, Inc. (Chelsea Hse.).

—Irish-American Answer Book. 1999. (Ethnic Answer Book Ser.). (Illus.). 136p. (YA). (gr. 5 up). pap. 9.95 (978-0-7910-4796-5(2)); lib. bdg. 19.75 (978-0-7910-4795-8(4)) Facts On File, Inc. (Chelsea Hse.).

—Jewish-American Answer Book. 1999. (Ethnic Answer Book Ser.). (Illus.). 136p. (gr. 5 up). (J). lib. bdg. 19.75 (978-0-7910-4799-6(7)); (YA). pap. 9.95 (978-0-7910-4800-9(4)) Facts On File, Inc. (Chelsea Hse.).

University Games Staff. More 30 Second Mysteries for Kids. 2007. 160p. (J). pap. ***(978-1-57528-839-0(7))*** University Games.

VanCleave, Janice Pratt. Janice VanCleave's Play & Find Out about Bugs: Easy Experiments for Young Children. 1999. (Play & Find Out Ser.: Vol. 9). (Illus.). 122p. (ps-2). pap. 12.95 (978-0-471-17663-3(X) , Wiley) Wiley, John & Sons, Inc.

—Janice VanCleave's Play & Find Out about the Human Body: Easy Experiments for Young Children. 1998. (Play & Find Out Ser.: Vol. 7). (Illus.). 128p. (ps-2). 32.50 (978-0-471-12934-9(8) , Wiley) Wiley, John & Sons, Inc.

Vogel, Carole Garbuny. Breast Cancer: Questions & Answers for Young Women. 2001. (Single Titles Ser.). (Illus.). 176p. (gr. 7 up). lib. bdg. 25.90 (978-0-7613-1855-2(0) , Twenty-First Century Bks.) Lerner Publishing Group.

Waddell, Nancy. SmartLab: Science & Nature Challenge. 2006. 144p. 19.99 (978-1-932855-47-0(5)) becker&mayer! books.

Wagner, Kathi & Wagner, Aubrey. The Everything Kids' Bible Trivia Book: Stump Your Friends & Family with Your Bible Knowledge! 2004. (Illus.). 138p. (J). 6.95 (978-1-59337-031-2(8)) Adams Media Corp.

Warner. Ask Quinney. Date not set. 160p. (J). (gr. 3-7). pap. 4.99 (978-0-06-440762-5(4)) HarperCollins Pubs.

Warner, Sally. Totally Confidential. 2000. (Illus.). 208p. (J). (gr. 3-7). 15.95 (978-0-06-028261-5(4)) HarperCollins Pubs.

Watson, Robert W. A Student's Companion to the Tragedy of Julius Caesar. 1999. stu. ed. 6.96 (978-1-929579-52-5(7) , SG6003) Smarr Pubs.

P Q R

Watson, Yolanda. Which Holiday Is It? 2003. (Compass Point Phonics Readers Ser.). (Illus.). 16p. (J). (gr. 1 up). 13.26 (978-0-7565-0533-2(X)) Compass Point Bks.

Webber, Sharon G. Ask & Answer "WH" Fun Sheets. DeShong, Molly et al, eds. 2000. (Illus.). 218p. (J). (ps). spiral bd. 33.95 (978-1-58650-155-6(0) , BK-285) Super Duper Pubns.

Wet & Wild. 2002. (Questions & Answers Ser.). 12p. (J). pap. 3.98 (978-0-7525-7899-6(5)) Parragon, Inc.

White, Trudy. Could You? Would You? White, Trudy, illus. 2007. (Illus.). 96p. (Orig.). (J). (gr. k up). pap. 12.95 (***978-1-933605-45-6(6)***) Kane/Miller Bk. Pubs., Inc.

Wilkes, Angela. Birds. 2002. (Question Time Ser.). (Illus.). 32p. (J). (gr. k-3). tchr. ed. 11.95 (978-0-7534-5450-3(5)); pap. 6.95 (978-0-7534-5462-6(9)) Houghton Mifflin Co. Trade & Reference Div. (Kingfisher).

—Question Time: Birds. 2002. (gr. k-3). lib. bdg. 15.25 (978-0-613-88141-8(9)) Tandem Library Bks.

—Rainforest. 2002. (Question Time Ser.). (Illus.). 32p. (J). (gr. k-3). tchr. ed. 11.95 (978-0-7534-5438-1(6) , Kingfisher) Houghton Mifflin Co. Trade & Reference Div.

—Reptiles. 2002. (Question Time Ser.). (Illus.). 32p. (J). (gr. k-3). tchr. ed. 11.95 (978-0-7534-5451-0(3) , Kingfisher) Houghton Mifflin Co. Trade & Reference Div.

—The Seashore. 2001. (Question Time Ser.). (Illus.). 32p. (J). (gr. k-3). tchr. ed. 11.95 (978-0-7534-5339-1(8) , Kingfisher) Houghton Mifflin Co. Trade & Reference Div.

Williams, Jane A. A Bluestocking Guide - Building a Personal Model for Success: Companion Workbook to Richard J. Maybury's Uncle Eric Talks about Personal, Career, & Financial Security. Daniels, Kathryn, ed. 2004. (Bluestocking Guide Ser.). 47p. (YA). pap. 10.95 (978-0-942617-39-9(8)) Bluestocking Pr.

—A Bluestocking Guide - Political Philosophies: Companion Workbook to Richard J. Maybury's Are You Liberal? Conservative? or Confused? Daniels, Kathryn, ed. 2004. (Bluestocking Guide Ser.). 63p. (YA). pap. 12.95 (978-0-942617-47-4(9)) Bluestocking Pr.

Williams, Jane A. & Daniels, Kathryn, eds. Economics - A Free Market Reader. 2004. 127p. (YA). pap. 12.95 (978-0-942617-44-3(4)) Bluestocking Pr.

Williams, S. J. Grade Boosters: Second Grade Questions & Answers. 1998. (Grade Boosters Ser.). (Illus.). 64p. (J). (ps-3). pap. 5.95 (978-1-56565-674-1(1) , 06741W) Lowell Hse. Juvenile.

Windeatt, Mary Fabyan & Ignatz, Marie. Vocabulary Quiz Workbook: Based on 6 Great Saints' Lives by Mary Fabyan Windeatt. Lester, Mary Frances, ed. 2003. (J). pap., wbk. ed. 21.00 (978-0-89555-743-8(6) , 1841) TAN Bks. and Pubs., Inc.

Witherspoon Press Staff, contrib. by. Belonging to God: A First Catechism. 2003. (J). (978-1-57153-036-3(3) , Witherspoon Pr.) Curriculum Publishing, Presbyterian Church (U. S. A.).

Wollard, Kathy. How Come? Planet Earth. 1999. (gr. 3-6). lib. bdg. 22.20 (978-0-613-88984-1(3)) Tandem Library Bks.

Wollard, Kathy. How Come: Backyard Mysteries. Solomon, Debra, illus. 2007. 304p. (J). pap. 12.95 (***978-0-7611-4429-8(3)***) Workman Publishing Co., Inc.

Wood, Jenny. I Wonder Why Kangaroos Have Pouches: And Other Questions about Baby Animals. 2003. (I Wonder Why Ser.). (Illus.). 32p. (J). (gr. k-3). pap. 6.95 (978-0-7534-5661-3(3) , Kingfisher) Houghton Mifflin Co. Trade & Reference Div.

World Almanac Editors. Yo! I Know: Brain-Building Quizzes. Kashner, Zoe, ed. 2006. (World Almanac for Kids Ser.). (Illus.). 112p. pap. 9.99 (978-0-88687-948-8(5)) World Almanac Bks.

Young, Jay. Magic World of Learning. Tucker, Sian, illus. 2003. 32p. (978-1-903174-42-5(2)) Chrysalis Children's Bks.

Young, Jay, creator. Ziga Zaga. 2003. (Illus.). 144p. (978-1-903174-64-7(3)) Chrysalis Children's Bks.

The 5 W's (Gr. 1-3) 2003. (J). (978-1-58232-075-5(6)) Bryan Hse. Pubs., Inc.

50 States. 2000. 32p. (YA). 7.50 (978-0-7525-4641-4(4)) Parragon, Inc.

1001 Questions & Answers for Kids. 2005. (Illus.). 548p. per. (978-0-7853-9601-7(2) , 3482200) Publications International, Ltd.

QUI-GON JINN (FICTITIOUS CHARACTER)—FICTION

Watson, Jude. The Captive Temple. 2000. (Star Wars Ser.: Bk. 7). (J). (gr. 4-7). 11.64 (978-0-606-19619-2(6)) Tandem Library Bks.

—The Fight for Truth. 2000. (Star Wars Ser.: Bk. 9). (J). (gr. 4-7). 11.64 (978-0-606-19621-5(8)) Tandem Library Bks.

—The Hidden Past. 1999. (Star Wars Ser.: Bk. 3). (J). (gr. 4-7). 11.64 (978-0-606-17040-6(5)) Tandem Library Bks.

—The Mark of the Crown. 1999. (Star Wars Ser.: Bk. 4). 144p. (J). (gr. 4-7). pap. 4.99 (978-0-590-51934-2(4)) Scholastic, Inc.

—The Mark of the Crown. 1999. (Star Wars Ser.: Bk. 4). (J). (gr. 4-7). (978-0-606-19617-8(X)) Tandem Library Bks.

—The Shattered Peace. Nielsen, Cliff, illus. 2000. (Star Wars Ser.: Bk. 10). 144p. (J). (gr. 3-7). pap. 4.99 (978-0-590-52084-3(9)) Scholastic, Inc.

—The Shattered Peace. 2000. (Star Wars Ser.: Bk. 10). (J). (gr. 4-7). (978-0-606-19615-4(3)) Tandem Library Bks.

—The Uncertain Path. 2000. (Star Wars Ser.: Bk. 6). (Illus.). 144p. (J). (gr. 4-7). pap. 5.99 (978-0-590-51969-4(7)) Scholastic, Inc.

—The Uncertain Path. 2000. (Star Wars Ser.: Bk. 6). (J). (gr. 4-7). (978-0-606-19618-5(8)) Tandem Library Bks.

Wolverton, Dave. The Rising Force. 1999. (Star Wars Ser.: Bk. 1). (J). (gr. 4-7). (978-0-606-16649-2(1)) Tandem Library Bks.

QUILTS

Anderson, Alex. Kids Start Quilting with Alex Anderson: 7 Fun & Easy Projects, Quilts for Kids by Kids, Tips for Quilting with Children. 2002. (Best Crafts for Kids Ser.). (Illus.). 48p. pap. 14.95 (978-1-57120-141-6(6) , 10275) C&T Publishing.

Cardon, Jenny Wilding. The Little Box of Baby Quilts. 2007. 20p. pap. 22.95 (978-1-56477-699-0(9) , That Patchwork Place) Martingale & Co.

Cool Stuff Teach Me to Quilt. 2005. 52p. 10.95 (978-1-57486-635-3(4)) Leisure Arts, Inc.

Harcourt School Publishers Staff. Freedom Quilts. 3rd ed. 2002. (Horizons Ser.). (Illus.). (J). pap. 7.30 (978-0-15-333579-2(3)) Harcourt Schl. Pubs.

Heavenly Patchwork: Quilt Stories Stitched with Love. 2005. bds. 9.95 (978-0-9762375-0-1(4)) Dorcas Publishing.

Hicks, Kyra E. Martha Ann's Quilt for Queen Victoria. 2006. (J). 16.95 (978-1-933285-59-7(1)) Brown Bks. Publishing Group.

Higgins, Julie. Keepsake Quilts for Baby: 7 Precious Baby Quilts. 2006. (Illus.). 32p. (***978-1-59217-118-7(4)***) House of White Birches, Inc.

Hilton, Nanette. Design a Quilt. 2001. (Illus.). pap. 1.50 (978-0-486-41274-0(1)) Dover Pubns., Inc.

Jim Henson Company Staff & Children's Television Workshop Staff. Quilting with the Muppets: 15 Fun & Creative Patterns. 2000. (Illus.). 112p. 25.95 (978-1-57120-101-0(7) , 10224) C&T Publishing.

Kinsey-Warnock, Natalie. Canada Geese Quilt. Bowman, Leslie, illus. 2000. (Chapters Ser.). 64p. (J). (gr. 2-5). pap. 4.99 (978-0-14-130462-5(6) , Puffin) Penguin Group (USA) Inc.

Lakeshore Learning Materials Staff, contrib. by. Quilt Patterns Kit. 2000. (J). pap. 29.95 (978-1-929255-56-6(X)) Lakeshore Learning Materials.

Lowell, Susan. The Wagon Quilt. 2008. (Illus.). 40p. (J). 16.95 (978-0-374-38223-0(9) , Farrar, Straus & Giroux (BYR)) Farrar, Straus & Giroux.

My New Quilt: Individual Title Six-Packs. (Rigby Focus Ser.). 16p. (gr. 1 up). 28.00 (978-0-7578-5322-7(6)); 30.00 (978-0-7578-5554-2(7)) Rigby Education.

Paul, Ann Whitford. The Seasons Sewn: A Year in Patchwork. 2000. (978-0-606-18189-1(X)) Tandem Library Bks.

—Seasons Sewn: A Year in Patchwork. 2000. (gr. 3-6). lib. bdg. 15.30 (978-0-613-28634-3(0)) Tandem Library Bks.

Stapleton, Dorothy. Kids Can Quilt: Fun & Easy Projects for Your Small Quilter. 2004. (Illus.). 128p. (J). pap. 16.95 (978-0-7641-2770-0(5)) Barron's Educational Series, Inc.

Storms, Biz. All-American Quilts. Bradford, June, illus. 2004. (Kids Can Do It Ser.). 40p. (J). (gr. 4-6). (978-1-55337-539-5(4)); (978-1-55337-538-8(6)) Kids Can Pr., Ltd.

—Quilting. Bradford, June, illus. 2004. (Kids Can Do It Ser.). 40p. (J). (gr. 4-6). (978-1-55074-805-5(X)); (978-1-55074-967-0(6)) Kids Can Pr., Ltd.

—Quilting. Bradford, June, illus. 2003. 40p. (J). (ps-7). lib. bdg. 14.10 (978-0-613-50827-8(0)) Tandem Library Bks.

Sturgill, Ruthy. Christmas Tree Advent Calendar: A Country Quilted & Appliquéd Project. 2006. 96p. pap. 24.95 (978-1-59800-539-4(1)) Outskirts Press, Inc.

Tenorio-Coscarelli, Jane. The Ants. Coscarelli, Nicole, tr. l.t. ed. 1998. Tr. of Hormigas. (SPA & ENG.). 32p. (J). (gr. k-4). pap. 11.95 (978-0-9653422-2-3(0)) Quarter-Inch Publishing.

Thibault, Terri. Kids' Easy Quilting Projects. 2001. (gr. 3-6). lib. bdg. 16.40 (978-0-613-57608-6(X)) Tandem Library Bks.

Thibault, Terri & Hoffman, Beth. Kids' Easy Quilting Projects. Barberie, Heather, illus. 2000. (Quick Starts for Kids! Ser.). 64p. (J). (gr. 3 up). pap. 8.95 (978-1-885593-49-8(X) , Williamson Bks.) Ideals Pubns.

Waldvogel, Merikay. Childhood Treasures: Doll Quilts By & For Children. 2008. 180p. pap. 24.95 (***978-1-56148-599-4(3)***) Good Bks.

Weaver, Janice. The Quilt of Belonging: Stitching Together the Stories of a Nation. 2006. (Illus.). 64p. (J). 24.95 (978-1-897066-49-2(X)); pap. 14.95 (978-1-897066-50-8(3)) Maple Tree Pr. CAN. *Dist:* Perseus Distribution.

QUILTS—FICTION

Bourgeois, Paulette. Oma's Quilt. ed. 2004. (Illus.). (J). (gr. k-3). spiral bd. (978-0-616-11099-7(5)); spiral bd. (978-0-616-11100-0(2)) Canadian National Institute for the Blind/Institut National Canadien pour les Aveugles.

—Oma's Quilt. Jorisch, Stephane, illus. 32p. (J). (gr. k-3). 2003. (978-1-55337-625-5(0)); 2001. (978-1-55074-777-5(0)) Kids Can Pr., Ltd.

Bowman, Andy. The Quilt. Travis, Stephanie, illus. 25p. (J). (gr. 1-6). pap. 6.95 (978-1-931650-04-5(7)); lib. bdg. 14.95 (978-1-931650-05-2(5)) Coastal Publishing Carolina, Inc.

Cates, Karin. The Far-Fetched Story Quilt. Carpenter, Nancy, illus. 2002. 32p. (J). 15.95 (978-0-688-15938-2(9)) HarperCollins Pubs.

Coerr, Eleanor. The Josefina Story Quilt: Josefina y la colcha de Retazos. Degen, Bruce, illus. 2006. (I Can Read Bks.). (SPA.). 64p. (J). pap. 3.99 (978-0-06-088713-1(3)) HarperCollins Pubs.

Dallas, Sandra. Alice's Tulips. 2000. (gr. 7-12). lib. bdg. 22.20 (978-0-613-42657-2(6)) Tandem Library Bks.

Dwyer, Mindy. Quilt of Dreams. 2000. (Illus.). 32p. (J). (gr. 2-4). 15.95 (978-0-88240-522-3(5)); pap. 8.95 (978-0-88240-521-6(7)) Graphic Arts Ctr. Publishing Co. (Alaska Northwest Bks.).

—Quilt of Dreams. 2000. (978-0-606-22817-6(9)); (gr. 3-6). lib. bdg. 17.60 (978-0-613-49764-0(3)) Tandem Library Bks.

Fitzgerald, Gyleen Xavier. The Dream: A Magical Journey in Colourful Stitches. 2006. (Illus.). 96p. (J). 29.95 (978-0-9768215-1-9(6)) FPI Publishing.

Franco, Betsy. Grandpa's Quilt. Bild, Linda, illus. 1999. (Rookie Readers Ser.). 32p. (J). (gr. 1-2). 19.50 (978-0-516-21604-1(X) , Children's Pr.) Scholastic Library Publishing.

—Grandpa's Quilt. 1999. (gr. k-3). lib. bdg. 12.95 (978-0-613-54523-5(0)) Tandem Library Bks.

Franco, Betsy & Bild, Linda A. Grandpa's Quilt. 2000. (Rookie Reader Skill Set Ser.). (Illus.). 32p. (J). (gr. k-2). pap. 4.95 (978-0-516-26551-3(2) , Children's Pr.) Scholastic Library Publishing.

Geras, Adele. Apricots at Midnight: And Other Stories from a Patchwork Quilt. 2005. (Illus.). 189p. (J). (ps-17). pap. 5.95 (978-1-903015-29-2(4)) Barn Owl Bks, London GBR. *Dist:* Independent Pubs. Group.

Griffith, Michelle & Conder, Jen. Rosie's Quilt. 2006. (Illus.). (J). 4.99 (978-0-9789969-4-9(1)) Michelle's Designs.

Harcourt School Publishers Staff. My Family Quilt: Below Level. 3rd ed. 2002. (Trophies Reading Program Ser.). (Illus.). (J). pap. 3.20 (978-0-15-322953-4(5)) Harcourt Schl. Pubs.

—Trofeos Below Level: La Colcha. 3rd ed. 2002. (SPA., Illus.). (J). pap. 3.50 (978-0-15-323864-2(X)) Harcourt Schl. Pubs.

Hopkinson, Deborah. Sweet Clara & the Freedom Quilt. Ransome, James E., illus. 2003. 40p. (J). (gr. k-5). 15.95 (978-0-679-82311-7(5) , Knopf Bks. for Young Readers) Random Hse. Children's Bks.

Johnston, Tony. That Summer. Moser, Barry, illus. 2007. 32p. (J). (gr. 1-4). pap. 6.00 (978-0-15-205856-2(7) , Voyager Bks./Libros Viajeros) Harcourt Children's Bks.

Jonas, Ann. The Quilt. Jonas, Ann, illus. 2002. (Illus.). (J). 13.19 (978-0-7587-3478-5(6)) Book Wholesalers, Inc.

Kennedy, Pamela. Granny's Cozy Quilt of Memories. Wummer, Amy, illus. 2006. 32p. (J). (gr. 4-6). 8.95 (978-0-8249-5538-0(2) , Guideposts) Ideals Pubns.

Kenrick, Angela. The Quilt That Wouldn't Be Built. Hunt, Devin, illus. 2001. (J). (978-1-57102-177-9(9) , Ideals Children's Bks.) Ideals Pubns.

Kinsey-Warnock, Natalie. Canada Geese Quilt. 2000. 11.79 (978-0-606-20354-8(0)) Tandem Library Bks.

Kirby. Ida Lou's Story. 2000. (American Quilts Ser.: Vol. 4). (J). 11.64 (978-0-606-20082-0(7)) Tandem Library Bks.

Kirby, Susan E. Ellen's Story. 2000. (gr. 3-6). lib. bdg. 13.00 (978-0-613-31156-4(6)) Tandem Library Bks.

—Hattie's Story. 2000. (American Quilts Ser.: Vol. 2). (J). 11.64 (978-0-606-20080-6(0)) Tandem Library Bks.

Leppard, Lois Gladys. Mandie & the Quilt Mystery, Vol. 35. 2002. (Mandie Bks.). 160p. (J). mass mkt. 5.99 (978-1-55661-676-1(7)) Bethany Hse. Pubs.

—Mandie & the Quilt Mystery. 2002. (gr. 3-6). lib. bdg. 13.00 (978-0-613-67464-5(2)) Tandem Library Bks.

Lewis, Kim. Quilt for Baby. Lewis, Kim, illus. 2002. (Illus.). 32p. (J). (gr. k-k). 15.99 (978-0-7636-1925-1(6)) Candlewick Pr.

London, Victoria. Lucy & the Liberty Quilt. collector's ed. 2001. (Gifted Girls Ser.: Bk. 1). 64p. (J). (gr. 2-7). per. 7.95 (978-0-9714776-0-5(4)) Sparklesoup Studios, Inc.

Lowell, Susan. The Wagon Quilt. 2008. (Illus.). 40p. (J). 16.95 (978-0-374-38223-0(9) , Farrar, Straus & Giroux (BYR)) Farrar, Straus & Giroux.

McKissack, Pat. Stitchin' & Pullin' A Gee's Bend Quilt. Cabrera, Cozbi S., illus. 2007. (J). (***978-0-375-83163-8(0)***); lib. bdg. (***978-0-375-93163-5(5)***) Random Hse., Inc.

Morningforest, Chris & Raymond, Rebecca. Read along Ranch & Little Lacy Ladybug. 2006. 36p. (J). pap. 15.43 (978-1-4116-9804-8(5)) Lulu.com.

Orem Werner, Teresa. A Quilt of Wishes. Tremlin, Nathan, illus. l.t. ed. 2005. 22p. 16.95 (978-1-59879-147-1(8)) Lifevest Publishing, Inc.

Parrish, Shelley Berlin. Sharing Grandma's Gift. Petosa-Sigel, Kristi, illus. 2000. 40p. (J). 18.00 (978-0-89716-936-3(0)) Peanut Butter Publishing.

Polacco, Patricia. The Keeping Quilt. Polacco, Patricia, illus. 2002. (Illus.). (J). 26.17 (978-0-7587-2927-9(8)) Book Wholesalers, Inc.

—The Keeping Quilt. 2001. (J). (gr. k-3). 26.95 incl. audio (978-0-8045-6842-5(1) , 6842) Spoken Arts, Inc.

—The Keeping Quilt. 2001. (J). (978-0-606-20749-2(X)) Tandem Library Bks.

—Keeping Quilt. 2001. (gr. k-3). lib. bdg. 15.30 (978-0-613-37155-1(0)) Tandem Library Bks.

Polacco, Patricia, illus. The Keeping Quilt. 2001. 32p. (J). (ps-3). pap. 6.99 (978-0-689-84447-8(6) , Aladdin) Simon & Schuster Children's Publishing.

Ransom, Candice F. The Promise Quilt. Beier, Ellen, illus. 2002. 32p. (J). (gr. k-3). pap. 7.95 (978-0-8027-7648-8(5)) Walker & Co.

Root, Phyllis. The Name Quilt. Apple, Margot, illus. 2003. 32p. (J). (gr. k-3). 16.00 (978-0-374-35484-8(7) , Farrar, Straus & Giroux (BYR)) Farrar, Straus & Giroux.

Rumford, James. When Silver Needles Swam: The Story of Tutu's Quilt. 1998. (ENG & HAW., Illus.). 30p. (J). (gr. 1-6). 10.95 (978-1-891839-00-9(4)) Manoa Pr.

Rylant, Cynthia. Poppleton Has Fun. Teague, Mark, illus. 2002. (Poppleton Ser.). (J). 11.91 (978-0-7587-6242-9(9)) Book Wholesalers, Inc.

—Poppleton Has Fun. Teague, Mark, illus. 2000. (Poppleton Ser.). 56p. (J). (gr. k-3). pap. 15.95 (978-0-590-84839-8(9)) Scholastic, Inc.

Stroud, Bettye. The Patchwork Path: A Quilt Map to Freedom. Bennett, Erin Susanne, illus. 32p. (J). (gr. k-3). 2007. pap. 7.99 (***978-0-7636-3519-0(7)***); 2005. 16.99 (978-0-7636-2423-1(3)) Candlewick Pr.

Tenorio-Coscarelli, Jane. The Tamale Quilt. Coscarelli, Nichole, tr. 1998. (Illus.). 48p. (J). (gr. k-6). pap. 11.95 (978-0-9653422-4-7(7)) Quarter-Inch Publishing.

Tenorio-Coscarelli, Jane & Coscarelli, Nicole. The Tamale Quilt. l.t. ed. 1998. (Illus.). 48p. (J). (gr. k-6). 15.95 (978-0-9653422-3-0(9)) Quarter-Inch Publishing.

Van Leeuwen, Jean. Papa & the Pioneer Quilt. Bond, Rebecca, illus. 2007. (J). (gr. k-3). 32p. 16.99 (978-0-8037-3028-1(4)); (***978-1-4287-3972-7(6)***) Penguin Group (USA) Inc. (Dial).

Vaughan, Marcia. The Secret to Freedom. Johnson, Larry, illus. 32p. (J). 2001. (gr. 1-4). 16.95 (978-1-58430-021-2(3)); 2nd ed. 2005. (ps-ps). pap. 7.95 (978-1-58430-251-3(8)) Lee & Low Bks., Inc.

von Olfers, Sibylle. Mother Earth & Her Children: A Quilted Fairy Tale. Zipes, Jack, tr. from GER. Schoen-Smith, Sieglinde, illus. 2007. 32p. (J). (ps-2). 17.95 (***978-1-933308-18-0(4)***) Breckling Pr.

Webb, Kimberly. The Christmas Memory Quilt. Gaskin, Jennifer, illus. 2007. 32p. (J). 17.95 (***978-1-934393-00-0(2)***) Silverleaf Pr.

Weber, Jane. The Riches of Rangoberra/Las riquezas de Rangoberra. de la Vega, Eida, tr. Saari, Rijalynne, illus. 2002. Tr. of Las riquezas de Rangoberra. (SPA & ENG.). 32p. (J). (gr. 4-6). 16.95 (978-0-9720192-1-7(9) , 626999) Raven Tree Pr.

Woodson, Jacqueline. Show Way. Talbott, Hudson, illus. 2005. 48p. (J). (ps). 16.99 (978-0-399-23749-2(6) , Putnam Juvenile) Penguin Group (USA) Inc.

QUIMBY, RAMONA (FICTITIOUS CHARACTER)—FICTION

Cleary, Beverly. Beezus & Ramona. Dockray, Tracy, illus. 2006. 183p. (J). lib. bdg. 20.00 (***978-1-4242-0409-0(7)***) Fitzgerald Bks.

—Beezus & Ramona. (Ramona Quimby Ser.). 142p. (J). (gr. 3-5). pap. 4.99 (978-0-8072-1441-1(8) , Listening Library) Random Hse. Audio Publishing Group.

—Ramona & Her Family. (J). Dell Publishing.

—Ramona & Her Father. 2002. (Illus.). (J). 13.83 (978-0-7587-5636-7(4)) Book Wholesalers, Inc.

—Ramona & Her Father. (Ramona Quimby Ser.). 186p. (J). (gr. 3-5). pap. 4.99 (978-0-8072-1439-8(6) , Listening Library) Random Hse. Audio Publishing Group.

—Ramona & Her Mother. (Ramona Quimby Ser.). 208p. (J). (gr. 3-5). pap. 4.99 (978-0-8072-1435-0(3) , Listening Library) Random Hse. Audio Publishing Group.

—The Ramona Collection, 4 vols., Vol. 1. Dockray, Tracy, illus. 1999. (Ramona Quimby Ser.). (J). (gr. 3-7). pap. 23.96 (978-0-380-81468-8(4)) HarperCollins Pubs.

—The Ramona Collection: Ramona & Her Father; Ramona & Her Mother; Ramona Forever; Ramona's World, Vol. 2. Tiegreen, Alan, illus. 2002. (Cleary Reissue Ser.). (J). pap. 23.96 (978-0-06-441006-9(4) , Harper Trophy) HarperCollins Pubs.

—Ramona Forever. 2001. (Ramona Ser.). (J). (gr. 3-5). pap., wbk. ed. (978-1-58130-690-3(3)); pap., wbk. ed. (978-1-58130-691-0(1)) Novel Units, Inc.

—Ramona Forever. (Ramona Quimby Ser.). 182p. (J). (gr. 3-5). pap. 4.99 (978-0-8072-1437-4(X) , Listening Library) Random Hse. Audio Publishing Group.

—Ramona la Valiente. 2003. (SPA., Illus.). 124p. (J). pap. 15.95 (978-84-239-7099-5(X) , AV2133) Espasa Calpe, S.A. ESP. *Dist:* Distribooks, Inc., Libros Sin Fronteras.

—Ramona Quimby, Age 8. (Ramona Ser.). (J). (gr. 3-5). Dell Publishing.

—Ramona Quimby, Age 8. (Ramona Ser.). (J). (gr. 3-5). 1999. 9.95 (978-1-56137-448-9(2)); 1998. 44p. 11.95 (978-1-56137-708-4(2) , NU7082SP) Novel Units, Inc.

—Ramona Quimby, Age 8. (Ramona Quimby Ser.). 190p. (J). (gr. 3-5). pap. 4.99 (978-0-8072-1436-7(1) , Listening Library) Random Hse. Audio Publishing Group.

—Ramona the Brave. 2000. (Ramona Ser.). (J). (gr. 3-5). 9.95 (978-1-56137-444-1(X)) Novel Units, Inc.

—Ramona the Brave. (Ramona Quimby Ser.). 190p. (J). (gr. 3-5). pap. 4.99 (978-0-8072-1440-4(X) , Listening Library) Random Hse. Audio Publishing Group.

—Ramona the Pest. (Ramona Ser.). (J). (gr. 3-5). Dell Publishing.

—Ramona the Pest. (Ramona Quimby Ser.). 192p. (J). (gr. 3-5). pap. 4.99 (978-0-8072-1438-1(8) , Listening Library) Random Hse. Audio Publishing Group.

—Ramona y Su Padre. 10th ed. 2003. (SPA., Illus.). 136p. (J). (gr. 3-5). 15.95 (978-84-239-9020-7(6) , EC1443) Espasa Calpe, S.A. ESP. *Dist:* Distribooks, Inc., Lectorum Pubns., Inc., Planeta Publishing Corp.

—Ramona's World. Tiegreen, Alan & Dockray, Tracy, illus. 2001. (Ramona Quimby Ser.). 240p. (J). (gr. 3-5). 16.99 (978-0-688-16816-2(7)) HarperCollins Pubs.

—Ramona's World. Tiegreen, Alan, illus. 1999. (Ramona Quimby Ser.). 208p. (gr. 3-5). pap. 5.99 (978-0-380-73272-2(6)) HarperCollins Pubs.

—Ramona's World. unabr. ed. 2004. (Ramona Quimby Ser.). 194p. (J). (gr. 3-7). pap. 29.00 incl. audio (978-0-8072-8169-7(7) , Listening Library) Random Hse. Audio Publishing Group.

QUIZ BOOKS

see Questions and Answers

QUOTATIONS

see also Proverbs

Bell, Janet Cheatham. Stretch Your Wings: Famous Black Quotations for Teens. 1999. (978-0-606-17507-4(5)) Tandem Library Bks.

Bender, Robert. Lima Beans Would Be Illegal: Children's Ideas of a Perfect World. Bender, Robert, illus. 2000. (Illus.). 48p. (J). (gr. 2-5). 12.00 (978-0-8037-2532-4(9) , Dial) Penguin Group (USA) Inc.

Betz, Adrienne. Scholastic Treasury of Quotations for Children. 1998. 256p. (YA). (gr. 4-7). pap. 16.95 (978-0-590-27146-2(6) , Scholastic Reference) Scholastic, Inc.

Brooks, Walter R. The Wit & Wisdom of Freddy & His Friends. Wiese, Kurt, illus. 1999. (Freddy the Pig Bks.). 272p. (J). (gr. 3-7). 23.95 (978-0-87951-725-0(5)) Overlook Pr., The.

Carlson, Dale. Who Said What? Philosophy Quotes for Teens. Nicklaus, Carol, illus. 2003. 256p. (gr. 7-12). 14.95 (978-1-884158-28-5(5)) Bick Publishing Hse.

Celebrate Freedom: Songs, Symbols, & Sayings of the United States. 2003. (Illus.). 32p. (gr. k-2). (978-0-328-03672-1(2)); 48p. (gr. 3-6). (978-0-328-03674-5(9)) Addison-Wesley Educational Pubs., Inc. (Scott Foresman).

Dee, Catherine. Girls' Book of Wisdom. 1999. (gr. 7-12). lib. bdg. 18.50 (978-0-613-21601-2(6)) Tandem Library Bks.

—The Girls' Book of Wisdom: Empowering, Inspirational Quotes from over 400 Fabulous Females. Douglass, Ali, ed. Pollack, Lou M., illus. 1999. 208p. (J). (gr. 7-17). pap. 9.99 (978-0-316-17956-0(6)) Little, Brown Bks. for Young Readers.

Eitel, Charles R. 84 Quotes, One. 1999. 93p. (YA). pap. (978-0-9700219-0-8(9)) Eitel, Charles R.

Farina von Buchwald, Martin & Prado Farina, Gabriela. The Joy of Giving. Avendano, Dolores, illus. Testino, Mario et al, photos by. 2005. 89p. (J). 18.00 (978-0-9777266-0-8(6)) von Buchwald, Martin Farina.

Friedman, Margo R., ed. In Hope Freedom Rings. Mullett, Glenn C., illus. 2002. 96p. (J). per. 5.95 (978-0-9659488-4-5(6)) In Hope Freedom Rings, Inc.

Hess, Jared & Hess, Jerusha. Napoleon Dynamite: The Complete Quote Book. 2005. (Illus.). 96p. (YA). pap. 7.95 (978-1-4169-1391-7(2) , Simon Spotlight Entertainment) Simon & Schuster.

Hudson, Katura J. Afro-Bets Quotes for Kids: Words for Kids to Live By. Simpson, Howard, illus. 2004. 64p. (J). (gr. k-4). pap. 5.95 (978-0-940975-89-7(0) , Sankofa Bks.) Just Us Bks., Inc.

I Love Babies. 2004. per. 9.95 (978-0-9754779-1-5(9)) Chosen Word Publishing.

Kuchler, Bonnie Louise, compiled by. Just Kids: Pictures, Poems & Other Silly Animal Stuff Just for Kids! 2003. (Illus.). 32p. tchr. ed. 12.95 (978-1-57223-598-4(5) , 5985) Willow Creek Pr., Inc.

Meyer, Lisa. Quotes for Kids: Today's Interpretations of Timeless Quotes Designed to Nurture the Young Spirit. Holt, Dan, illus. 1998. 160p. (YA). (gr. 5 up). 13.95 (978-0-9660148-0-8(4)) Reach Pr.

Nava, Yolanda. It's All in the Frijoles: 100 Famous Latinos Share Real-Life Stories, Time-Tested Dichos, Favorite Folk Tales & Inspiring Words of Wisdom. 2000. (Illus.). (J). 21.65 (978-0-606-18894-4(0)) Tandem Library Bks.

Penn, Shirah Skop. Gramma Shirah Says MORE Words of Wisdom. Guerra, Khary Olivares, illus. 2005. 52p. (J). 11.00 (***978-0-9753382-3-0(4)***) Joysong Creations.

Petrie, H. D., photos by. All God's Creatures; Jesus Loves Me. ed. 2005. 32p. (J). spiral bd. (978-0-9774115-0-4(8)) AGC Outreach Ministry.

Quotes from the Masters. 2001. 17p. pap. (978-0-9623694-3-8(8)) JR Pubs.

Seduction by Shakespeare: Advice, Observations & Quotes on Love, Lust, Beauty & Desire. 2004. 128p. (YA). (gr. 11 up). per. 11.95 (978-0-9674898-6-5(5)) TCB-Cafe Publishing.

Senn, J. A. Quotations for Kids. 1999. up. (Illus.). 256p. (gr. 3-7). 24.95 (978-0-7613-1296-3(X) , Millbrook Pr.) Lerner Publishing Group.

—Quotations for Kids. Pica, Steve, illus. 1999. 256p. (gr. 3 up). lib. bdg. 39.90 (978-0-7613-0267-4(0) , Millbrook Pr.) Lerner Publishing Group.

Senn, J. A., ed. Quotations for Kids. Pica, Steve, illus. 2006. 256p. (J). (gr. 4-8). reprint ed. pap. 25.00 (978-1-4223-5244-1(7)) DIANE Publishing Co.

Snicket, Lemony, pseud. Horseradish: Bitter Truths You Can't Avoid. Tucker, Mark, illus. 2007. 176p. (J). (gr. 5 up). 12.99 (***978-0-06-124006-5(0)***) HarperCollins Pubs.

R

RABBIS

Simon, Solomon & Bial, Morrison D. The Rabbi's Bible Vol. 1: Torah. (J). (gr. 5-6). pap., stu. ed. 3.95 (978-0-87441-319-9(2)); Wkbk. 2. pap., stu. ed. 3.95 (978-0-87441-320-5(6)) Behrman Hse., Inc.

RABBITS

Alderton, David. Rabbit: Looking After My Pet. 2002. (Illus.). 24p. 7.99 (978-0-7548-1097-1(6) , Lorenz Bks.) Anness Publishing GBR. *Dist:* National Bk. Network.

Baker, Alan. Little Rabbits' First Number Book. 2001. (ps-2). lib. bdg. 14.10 (978-0-613-90587-9(3)) Tandem Library Bks.

Barbé-Julien, Colette. Little Rabbits. 2007. (Born to Be Wild Ser.). (Illus.). 23p. (J). lib. bdg. (***978-0-8368-6699-5(1)***) Stevens, Gareth Inc.

Barnes, Julia. Pet Rabbits. 2006. (Pet Pals Ser.). (Illus.). 32p. (J). (gr. 2-5). lib. bdg. 23.93 (978-0-8368-6781-7(5)) Stevens, Gareth Inc.

Barnes, Julia, et al. 101 Facts about Rabbits. 2001. (One Hundred One Facts about Pets Ser.). (Illus.). 32p. (J). (gr. 3 up). lib. bdg. 23.33 (978-0-8368-2891-7(7)) Stevens, Gareth Inc.

Bekkering, Annalise. Rabbits. 2007. (J). (***978-1-59036-679-0(4)); (*978-1-59036-680-6(8))*** Weigl Pubs., Inc.

Bjorklund, Ruth. Rabbits. 2007. (Great Pets Ser.). 48p. (J). lib. bdg. 28.50 (***978-0-7614-2708-7(2)*** , Benchmark Bks.) Cavendish, Marshall Corp.

Blackaby, Susan. A Rabbit for You: Caring for Your Rabbit. DeLage, Charlene, illus. 2004. (Pet Care Ser.). 24p. (C). (gr. k-3). 22.60 (978-1-4048-0118-9(9)) Picture Window Bks.

Bodden, Valerie. Rabbits. 2006. (Illus.). 24p. (J). 15.95 (978-1-58341-460-6(6) , Creative Education) Creative Co., The.

Book Company Staff. Rabbit's Happy Day. 2004. (Pond Sparkle Bks.). (Illus.). 10p. (J). (gr. 4-7). bds. 4.95 (978-1-74047-495-5(3)) Book Co. Publishing Pty, Ltd., The AUS. *Dist:* Penton Overseas, Inc.

Boring, Mel. Rabbits, Squirrels & Chipmunks. Garrow, Linda, illus. 1999. (Young Naturalist Field Guides Ser.). 40p. (J). (gr. 3 up). lib. bdg. 24.67 (978-0-8368-2146-8(7)) Stevens, Gareth Inc.

Bunnies. 2003. (Three Minute Tales Ser.). 32p. (J). 5.98 (978-0-7525-8914-5(8)); 7.95 (978-0-7525-4758-9(5)) Parragon, Inc.

Butterfield, Moira. Rabbit. (Illus.). 32p. lib. bdg. 24.25 (978-1-930643-93-2(4)) Chrysalis Education.

Coppendale, Jean. Rabbit. 2004. (QEB You & Your Pet Ser.). (Illus.). 32p. (J). lib. bdg. 18.95 (978-1-59566-053-4(4)) QEB Publishing Inc.

Dalmatian Press Staff. Caring for Your Rabbit. rev. ed. 2005. (Illus.). 64p. (J). pap. 5.99 (978-1-4037-0887-8(8)) Dalmatian Pr.

—Disney Bunnies Big Best Book to Color with Stickers. 2007. 96p. pap. 2.99 (***978-1-4037-3009-1(1)***) Dalmatian Pr.

—Disney Bunnies Big Crayon Book to Color. 2007. 48p. pap. 3.99 (***978-1-4037-3010-7(5)***) Dalmatian Pr.

—Disney Bunnies Sticker Book to Color. 2007. 48p. pap. 2.99 (***978-1-4037-3021-3(0)***) Dalmatian Pr.

D'Andrea, Deborah. Picture Me As a Bunny. Ayers, Michael B., illus. rev. ed. 2000. (Picture Me Ser.). 10p. (J). (ps-1). bds. 4.99 (978-1-57151-577-3(1)) Playhouse Publishing.

DK Publishing Staff. Bunny. 2007. (See How They Grow Ser.). 24p. (J). pap. 3.99 (***978-0-7566-3264-9(1)***) Dorling Kindersley Publishing, Inc.

Doudna, Kelly. Bunnies. l.t. ed. 1999. (Baby Animals Ser.). (Illus.). 24p. (J). (ps-3). lib. bdg. 19.93 (978-1-57765-184-0(7) , SandCastle) ABDO Publishing Co.

Doudna, Kelly. Rascally Rabbits. Nobens, C. A., illus. 2007. (Perfect Pets Ser.). 24p. (J). (gr. k-3). lib. bdg. 19.93 (***978-1-59928-753-9(6)*** , SandCastle) ABDO Publishing Co.

Endres, Hollie. Rabbits. 2007. (Illus.). 24p. (J). lib. bdg. 19.95 (978-1-60014-085-3(8)) Bellwether Media.

Evans, Mark. Rabbit. 2001. (ASPCA Pet Care Guides for Kids). (Illus.). (J). (978-0-606-21392-9(9)) Tandem Library Bks.

Fiona, Patchett. Rabbits - internet Linked. rev. ed. 2005. 32p. (J). (gr. 1 up). pap. 5.95 (978-0-7945-0797-8(2) , Usborne) EDC Publishing.

Foran, Jill. Caring for Your Rabbit. Marshall, Diana & Nault, Jennifer, eds. 2003. (Caring for Your Pet Ser.). (Illus.). 32p. (J). pap. 7.95 (978-1-59036-064-4(8)) Weigl Pubs., Inc.

—Caring for Your Rabbit. 2002. (Caring for Your Pet Ser.). (Illus.). 32p. (J). lib. bdg. 18.20 (978-1-59036-034-7(6)) Weigl Pubs., Inc.

Frost, Helen. Arctic Hares. 2006. (Polar Animals Ser.). (Illus.). 24p. (J). (978-0-7368-4243-3(8)) Capstone Pr., Inc.

—Rabbits. 2000. (All about Pets Ser.). (Illus.). 24p. (J). (gr. k-1). lib. bdg. 15.93 (978-0-7368-0659-6(8) , Pebble Bks.) Capstone Pr., Inc.

Gallagher, Kristin Ellerbusch. Cottontail Rabbits. 2000. (gr. k-3). lib. bdg. 15.25 (978-0-613-81869-8(5)) Tandem Library Bks.

Ganeri, Anita. A Pet's Life: Rabbits. 2003. (Heinemann First Library). (Illus.). 32p. (J). lib. bdg. 22.79 (978-1-4034-3995-6(8)) Heinemann Library.

—Rabbits. 2003. (Heinemann First Library). (Illus.). 32p. (J). pap. (978-1-4034-4274-1(6)) Heinemann Library.

—Rabbits. 2003. (gr. k-3). lib. bdg. 15.25 (978-0-613-86559-3(6)) Tandem Library Bks.

Gibbons, Gail. Rabbits, Rabbits & More Rabbits! Gibbons, Gail, illus. (Illus.). (J). (ps-ps). 2001. 32p. pap. 6.95 (978-0-8234-1660-8(7)); 2000. 36p. tchr. ed. 16.95 (978-0-8234-1486-4(8)) Holiday Hse., Inc.

Glover, David & Glover, Penny. Rabbit. 2006. (Owning a Pet Ser.). (J). (978-1-59771-055-8(5)) Sea-To-Sea Pubns.

Goldish, Meish. Cottontails & Their Relatives, Vol. 3. World Book, Inc. Staff, ed. 2001. (World Book's Animals of the World Ser.: Set 2). (Illus.). 64p. (J). (978-0-7166-1214-8(3)) World Bk., Inc.

Hall, Kirsten. Bunny, Bunny. Wilburn, Kathy, illus. 2003. (My First Reader Ser.). 32p. (J). 18.50 (978-0-516-22923-2(0) , Children's Pr.) Scholastic Library Publishing.

Head, Honor. Rabbit. Burton, Jane, photos by. 2000. (My Pet Ser.). (Illus.). 32p. (J). (gr. 3-5). lib. bdg. 25.69 (978-0-7398-2887-8(8)) Raintree.

—Rabbit. 2000. (My Pet Ser.). (Illus.). 32p. (J). (gr. 3-5). pap. 8.95 (978-0-7398-3013-0(9)) Steck-Vaughn.

—Rabbit. 2000. (gr. 3-6). lib. bdg. 18.60 (978-0-613-74046-3(7)) Tandem Library Bks.

Helfrich, Rebecca. Baby Bunny is Out to Lunch! Helfrich, Rebecca, illus. 2000. (J). (ps-k). mass mkt. 4.95 (978-1-888537-09-3(4)) Publisher Plus.

Hinds, Kathryn. Rabbits. 1999. (Perfect Pets Ser.). (Illus.). 32p. (J). (gr. 3-5). lib. bdg. 25.64 (978-0-7614-0793-5(6) , Benchmark Bks.) Cavendish, Marshall Corp.

Holub, Joan. Why Do Rabbits Hop? A & Other Questions about Rabbits, Guinea Pigs, Hamsters. 2003. (gr. k-3). lib. bdg. 11.80 (978-0-613-61671-3(5)) Tandem Library Bks.

—Why Do Rabbits Hop? And Other Questions about Rabbits, Guinea Pigs, Hamsters & Gerbils. DiVito, Anna, illus. 2003. (Easy-to-Read Ser.). 48p. (J). (gr. 1-3). pap. 3.99 (978-0-14-230120-3(5) , Puffin) Penguin Group (USA) Inc.

Hooper, Meredith. Tom's Rabbit: A Surprise on the Way to Antarctica. Kitchen, Bert, illus. 2002. 27p. reprint ed. 16.00 (978-0-7567-5620-8(0)) DIANE Publishing Co.

Jacobs, Lee. Rabbit. 2002. (Illus.). 24p. (J). 24.94 (978-1-56711-645-8(0) , Blackbirch Pr., Inc.) Thomson Gale.

Kitchen, Bert & Tagholm, Sally. The Rabbit. 2000. (Animal Lives Ser.). (Illus.). 32p. (J). (gr. k-3). tchr. ed. 9.95 (978-0-7534-5214-1(6) , Kingfisher) Houghton Mifflin Co. Trade & Reference Div.

Lapin. 1999. (Pocket Pals Ser.). (FRE.). (J). (ps-1). pap. 1.99 (978-0-85953-733-9(1)) Child's Play International Ltd. GBR. *Dist:* Child's Play-International.

Leach, Michael. Hare. 2003. (Animal Neighbours Ser.). (Illus.). 32p. (978-0-7502-4170-0(5) , Hodder Wayland) Hodder Children's Division.

Lewis, David, contrib. by. Rabbit. 1999. (Junior Pet Care Ser.). (Illus.). 48p. (gr. 4-7). 18.65 (978-0-7910-4904-4(3) , Chelsea Hse.) Facts On File, Inc.

Los Conejos: Individual Title Six-Packs. (Literatura 2000 Ser.). (SPA.). (gr. 2-3). 33.00 (978-0-7635-1259-0(1)) Rigby Education.

Loves, June. Guinea Pigs & Rabbits. 2003. (Pets Ser.). (Illus.). 32p. (gr. 2-4). 23.00 (978-0-7910-7552-4(4) , Chelsea Hse.) Facts On File, Inc.

MacAulay, Kelley & Kalman, Bobbie. Rabbits. Crabtree, Marc, illus. Crabtree, Marc, photos by. 2004. (Pet Care Ser.). 32p. (J). (978-0-7787-1756-0(9)); pap. (978-0-7787-1788-1(7)) Crabtree Publishing Co.

Macken, JoAnn Early. Jackrabbits. 2005. (J). pap. (978-0-8368-4835-9(7)); (Illus.). 24p. lib. bdg. 19.33 (978-0-8368-4828-1(4)) Stevens, Gareth Inc.

—Jackrabbits: Liebres Americanas. 2005. (ENG & SPA., Illus.). 24p. (J). pap. (978-0-8368-4849-6(7)); lib. bdg. 19.33 (978-0-8368-4842-7(X)) Stevens, Gareth Inc.

—Rabbits. 2003. (Let's Read about Pets Ser.). (Illus.). 24p. (J). (ps up). lib. bdg. 19.33 (978-0-8368-3802-2(5)); pap. 7.93 (978-0-8368-3849-7(1)) Stevens, Gareth Inc. (Weekly Reader Early Learning Library).

Magloff, Lisa & Dorling Kindersley Publishing Staff. Rabbit. 2004. (Watch Me Grow Ser.). 24p. (J). 7.99 (978-0-7566-0262-8(9)) Dorling Kindersley Publishing, Inc.

McBratney, Sam. Colors Everywhere. Jeram, Anita, illus. 2007. (Guess How Much I Love You Ser.). 24p. (J). (gr. k-ps). bds. 7.99 (***978-0-7636-3545-9(6)***) Candlewick Pr.

Miller, M. Rabbits. 2002. (Pets Ser.). (Illus.). 24p. (J). (gr. k-3). pap. 6.50 (978-1-57572-482-9(0) , 90471) Heinemann Library.

Miller, Michaela. Rabbits. 2007. (QEB Everybody Feels Ser.). (Illus.). 32p. (J). lib. bdg. 19.95 (978-1-59566-220-0(0)) QEB Publishing Inc.

Miller, Sara Swan. Rabbits, Pikas, & Hares. Gonzales, Jose & Savage, Stephen, illus. 2002. (Animals in Order Ser.). 48p. (J). (gr. 4-6). 26.50 (978-0-531-11634-0(4) , Watts, Franklin) Scholastic Library Publishing.

Mitchell, Melanie S. Rabbits. (First Step Nonfiction Ser.). (Illus.). (gr. k-2). 2005. 24p. lib. bdg. 17.27 (978-0-8225-4604-7(3)); 2003. 23p. (J). pap. 5.95 (978-0-8225-4605-4(1) , Lerner Pubns.) Lerner Publishing Group.

Moday, Jane, illus. Little Bunny's Easter Day. 1999. (Bend-N-Snuggle Bks.). 18p. (gr. k-ps). 10.99 (978-0-7847-0971-9(8) , 03541, Bean Sprouts) Standard Publishing.

Morley, Christine & Orbell, Carole. Mon Lapin. 2000. (Me & My Pet Ser.). (FRE., Illus.). 32p. (J). (gr. 2-5). pap. 4.95 (978-1-58728-198-3(8) , Two Can Publishing) T&N Children's Publishing.

Morris, Ting. Rabbit. Rosewarne, Graham, illus. 2005. 32p. (J). (gr. 3-7). lib. bdg. 27.10 (978-1-58340-521-5(6)) Smart Apple Media.

Orbell, Carole. Rabbit. Morley, Choshre, illus. rev. ed. 2004. (Me & My Pet Ser.). 32p. (J). (ps-1). pap. 4.95 (978-1-58728-203-4(8) , Two Can Publishing) T&N Children's Publishing.

Petty, Kate. Rabbit. 2005. (Illus.). 24p. (J). (gr. 2-5). lib. bdg. 22.80 (978-1-59604-027-4(0)) Stargazer Bks.

Pickett, Robert & Pickett, Justine, illus. Rabbit. Pickett, Robert & Pickett, Justine, photos by. 2004. 32p. (J). lib. bdg. (978-1-58340-432-4(5)) Smart Apple Media.

Powell, R. This Little Bunny. Curry, Peter, illus. 2004. (Mini Movers Ser.). 14p. (J). bds. 3.50 (978-0-7641-5739-4(6)) Barron's Educational Series, Inc.

A Rabbit for You. (Pet Care Ser.). 24p. (J). 7.95 (978-1-4048-0395-4(5)) Picture Window Bks.

Rabbits, 6 vols. (gr. k-2). 28.95 (978-0-7368-9239-1(7)) Red Brick Learning.

Rabbits & Their Burrows. (Animal Homes Ser.). 24p. (J). 6.95 (978-0-7368-5124-4(0)) Capstone Pr., Inc.

Rabbits Have Bunnies. (Animals & Their Young Ser.). 24p. (J). 7.95 (978-0-7565-1246-0(8)) Compass Point Bks.

Rabbit's Nap. (Acorn Wood Lift-the-Flap Bks.). (YA). bds. 3.50 net. (978-1-56021-380-2(9)) W.J. Fantasy, Inc.

Randolph, Joanne. Rabbits. 2007. (Classroom Pets Ser.). (Illus.). 24p. (J). (gr. k-5). lib. bdg. 21.25 (***978-1-4042-3680-6(5)*** , PowerKids Pr.) Rosen Publishing Group, Inc., The.

Rau, Dana Meachen. The Rabbit in the Garden. 2006. (Nature Ser.). 24p. (J). lib. bdg. 22.79 (***978-0-7614-2308-9(7)*** , Benchmark Bks.) Cavendish, Marshall Corp.

Rayner, Matthew & BVetMed MRCVS Staff. Rabbit. Burton, Jane & Greenaway, Frank, photos by. 2004. (I Am Your Pet Ser.). (Illus.). 32p. (J). (gr. 2 up). lib. bdg. 23.33 (978-0-8368-4105-3(0)) Stevens, Gareth Inc.

Ross, Veronica. Rabbit. 2002. (My First Ser.). (Illus.). 32p. (J). lib. bdg. 24.25 (978-1-930643-73-4(X)) Chrysalis Education.

Royston, Angela. Rabbit. 2004. (J). lib. bdg. 27.10 (978-1-59389-160-2(1)) Chrysalis Education.

Schuh, Mari C. Rabbits on the Farm. 2003. (On the Farm Ser.). (Illus.). 24p. (J). (gr. k-1). lib. bdg. 15.93 (978-0-7368-1663-2(1) , Pebble Bks.) Capstone Pr., Inc.

—Rabbits on the Farm. (On the Farm Ser.). 24p. (J). pap. 5.95 (978-0-7368-3425-4(7)) Capstone Pr., Inc.

Spilsbury, Louise & Spilsbury, Richard. Rabbits. 2006. (Keeping Pets Ser.). (Illus.). 48p. (J). (978-1-4034-7705-7(1)) Heinemann Library.

Stewart, Melissa. Rabbits. 2007. (Animals Animals Ser.). (Illus.). 48p. (J). (gr. 4-7). lib. bdg. 28.50 (978-0-7614-2528-1(4)) Cavendish, Marshall Corp.

Stone, Lynn M. Rabbits Have Bunnies. 2000. (Animals & Their Young Ser.). (Illus.). 24p. (J). (gr. 1 up). lib. bdg. 18.60 (978-0-7565-0005-4(2)) Compass Point Bks.

Swanson, Diane. Rabbits & Hares. 2002. (Welcome to the World of Animals Ser.). (Illus.). 32p. (J). (gr. 3 up). lib. bdg. 23.33 (978-0-8368-3316-4(3)) Stevens, Gareth Inc.

—Rabbits & Hares. 2000. (gr. k-3). lib. bdg. 14.10 (978-0-613-78564-8(9)) Tandem Library Bks.

—Welcome to the World of Rabbits & Hares. 2000. (Welcome to the World Ser.). (Illus.). 32p. (J). (ps-2). pap. 5.95 (978-1-55285-024-4(2)) Whitecap Bks., Ltd. CAN. *Dist:* Firefly Bks., Ltd.

Tagholm, Sally. The Rabbit. Kitchen, Bert, illus. 2003. (Animal Lives Ser.). 32p. (J). (gr. k-3). 4.95 (978-0-7534-5607-1(9) , Kingfisher) Houghton Mifflin Co. Trade & Reference Div.

—Rabbit. 2003. (gr. k-3). lib. bdg. 12.95 (978-0-613-90775-0(2)) Tandem Library Bks.

Tagliaferro, Linda. Rabbits & Their Burrows. 2004. (Pebble Plus, Animal Homes Ser.). (Illus.). 24p. (J). 13.95 (978-0-7368-2384-5(0)) Capstone Pr., Inc.

There's a Rabbit in God's Garden! 1999. (Peek-In Board Book Ser.). (Illus.). 10p. (J). (ps-k). bds. 4.99 (978-0-7847-1083-8(X) , 04289, Bean Sprouts) Standard Publishing.

Townsend, Emily Rose. Jackrabbits. Saunders-Smith, Gail, ed. 2003. (Desert Animals Ser.). (Illus.). 24p. (J). (gr. k-1). lib. bdg. 15.93 (978-0-7368-2076-9(0) , Pebble Bks.) Capstone Pr., Inc.

Treselt, Alvin & Ewing, Carolyn. The Rabbit Story.Tr. of Histoire de Lapins. (FRE.). (J). pap. 6.99 (978-0-590-74143-9(8)) Scholastic, Inc.

Trumbauer, Lisa. The Life Cycle of a Rabbit. 2003. (Life Cycles Ser.). (Illus.). 24p. (J). (gr. k-1). lib. bdg. 15.93 (978-0-7368-2091-2(4) , Pebble Bks.) Capstone Pr., Inc.

Vannatta, T. R. Between a Wink & a Dream. Telford, Laura, illus. 1998. 32p. (J). (gr. k-3). 18.95 (978-1-891992-01-8(5)) Owl's Hse. Pr.

Viner, Bradley. Rabbit. 1999. (All about Your Pet Ser.). (Illus.). 32p. pap. 4.99 (978-0-7641-1015-3(2)) Barron's Educational Series, Inc.

Whitehouse, Patricia. Rabbits. 2003. (Heinemann Read & Learn Ser.). (Illus.). 24p. (J). pap. 5.25 (978-1-4034-4330-4(0)); lib. bdg. 18.50 (978-1-4034-4321-2(1)) Heinemann Library.

Why Rabbits Have Long Ears: Individual Title Six-Packs. (Literatura 2000 Ser.). (gr. 2-3). 33.00 (978-0-7635-0270-6(7)) Rigby Education.

Why the Rabbit Has Such Long Ears: Lap Book. (Pebble Soup Explorations Ser.). (SPA.). 16p. (ps up). 21.00 (978-0-7578-1667-3(3)) Rigby Education.

Why the Rabbit Has Such Long Ears: Small Book. (Pebble Soup Explorations Ser.). (SPA.). 16p. (ps up). 5.00 (978-0-7578-1707-6(6)) Rigby Education.

Wild Rabbits: Individual Title Six-Packs. (Sails Literacy Ser.). (gr. 1-2). 36.00 (978-0-7578-4030-2(2)) Rigby Education.

World Book, Inc Staff, contrib. by. Holland Lops & Other Rabbits. 2007. (World Book's Animals of the World Ser.). (Illus.). 64p. (J). (978-0-7166-1330-5(1)) World Bk., Inc.

RABBITS—FICTION

Ada, Alma Flor. A Surprise for Mother Rabbit. (Stories the Year 'Round Ser.). (J). (gr. k-3). (Illus.). 28p. pap. 8.95 (978-1-58105-214-5(6)); 1998. pap. 7.95 (978-1-56014-280-5(4)) Santillana USA Publishing Co., Inc.

—A Surprise for Mother Rabbit. 2000. (gr. k-3). lib. bdg. 17.60 (978-0-613-79391-9(9)) Tandem Library Bks.

Adams, Adrienne. The Easter Egg Artists. Adams, Adrienne, illus. 2002. (Illus.). (J). 14.47 (978-0-7587-2429-8(2)) Book Wholesalers, Inc.

Adams, Jeanette. Tales from Within the Rabbitry. Adams, Jeanette, illus. 1999. (Camelot Rabbitry Ser.: Vol. 1). (Illus.). 110p. (J). (gr. 2-7). per. 9.95 (978-0-9672375-0-3(5)) Camelot Tales.

Adams, Richard. Watership Down. 2001. (Perennial Classics Ser.). (Illus.). 512p. pap. 13.00 (978-0-06-093545-0(6)) HarperCollins Pubs.

—Watership Down: A Novel. 2005. (Illus.). 496p. pap. 15.00 (978-0-7432-7770-9(8) , Scribner) Simon & Schuster.

Adams, Richard & Adams, Richard. Tales from Watership Down. 1998. 335p. (gr. 7-12). per. 15.30 (978-0-613-37671-6(4)) Tandem Library Bks.

Aesop. The Hare & the Tortoise. 2006. 132p. (J). 12.95 (978-1-59764-186-9(3)) New Line Bks.

—Hare & the Tortoise. 2006. (Illus.). 32p. (J). (ENG & SPA.). 14.95 (978-0-8118-5057-5(9)); pap. 6.95 (978-0-8118-5058-2(7)) Chronicle Bks. LLC.

Aesop & Miles, Betty. The Tortoise & the Hare. Meisel, Paul, illus. 1998. (Starting to Read Ser.). (J). (978-0-606-13858-1(7)) Tandem Library Bks.

Afetian, "Uncle Ted". The Adventures of Midas & the Little Red Airplane. 2005. (Illus.). 32p. (J). 16.95 (978-0-9752749-0-3(2)) Snyder-Winston Pr.

Agard, John & Paul, Korky. Brer Rabbit & the Great Tug-O-War. 1998. (Illus.). 32p. (J). (ps-2). 13.95 (978-0-7641-5077-7(4)) Barron's Educational Series, Inc.

Akmon, Nancy C. Peter Rabbit Celebrates Christmas. Akmon, Roni, ed. 1999. (Illus.). 48p. (J). 8.95 (978-1-884807-45-9(3) , EC745) Blushing Rose Publishing.

Albee, Sarah. The Bunny Hop. Swanson, Maggie, illus. 2004. 24p. (J). (gr. k-ps). bds. 4.99 (978-0-375-82693-1(9) , Random Hse. Bks. for Young Readers) Random Hse. Children's Bks.

Alex Toys. Bunny's Easter Basket. Silver-Thompson, Pattie, illus. rev. ed. 2008. 10p. (J). (ps-1). 5.99 (***978-0-316-15404-8(0)***) Little, Brown Bks. for Young Readers.

Allan, Nicholas. More & More Rabbits. 2007. (Illus.). 32p. (J). pap. 9.95 (***978-0-09-947758-7(0)*** , Red Fox) Random Hse. Children's Bks. GBR. *Dist:* Independent Pubs. Group.

Anderson, Dee, retold by. Otter Gets Tricked! A Cherokee Trickster Story. l.t. ed. 2004. (Illus.). 32p. (J). pap. 6.00 (978-0-9755934-1-7(2)) Colonel Davenport Historical Foundation.

Anderson, Derek. How the Easter Bunny Saved Christmas. Anderson, Derek, illus. 2006. (Illus.). 40p. (J). 15.95 (978-0-689-87634-9(3) , Simon & Schuster Children's Publishing) Simon & Schuster Children's Publishing.

Animal Friends Squeaky- Bunny. 2005. (J). bds. (978-1-4194-0091-9(6)) Paradise Pr., Inc.

Araki, Mie. Perfect Tail. 2004. (Illus.). 32p. (J). 14.95 (978-0-8118-4266-2(5)) Chronicle Bks. LLC.

Arnold, Marsha Diane & Pelzel, Vernise Elaine. Hugs on the Wind. Warnick, Elsa, illus. 2006. 32p. (J). (ps-1). 15.95 (978-0-8109-5968-2(2)) Abrams, Harry N. , Inc.

Arnold, Robyn. Branli Says Bye-Bye to Binky. 2007. 32p. 16.50 (***978-0-615-15292-9(9)***) Robyn Z Moon Publishing.

Arnosky, Jim. Rabbits & Raindrops. Arnosky, Jim, illus. 2001. (Illus.). 32p. (J). (ps-k). pap. 5.99 (978-0-698-11815-7(4) , Putnam Juvenile) Penguin Group (USA) Inc.

—Rabbits & Raindrops. 2000. (gr. k-3). lib. bdg. 14.15 (978-0-613-36004-3(4)) Tandem Library Bks.

Ashby, Dolores. Baby Bunny's Promise. 2006. 17.00 (978-0-8059-9929-7(9)) Dorrance Publishing Co., Inc.

Asher, Sandy. Too Many Frogs! Graves, Keith, illus. 2005. 32p. (J). (ps-1). 15.99 (978-0-399-23978-6(2) , Philomel) Penguin Group (USA) Inc.

—Why Rabbit's Nose Twitches. 2003. (Illus.). 14.95 (978-1-59319-019-4(0)) LeapFrog Enterprises, Inc.

Ashworth, Camilla. La Cama de Horacio. (Picture Books Collection). (SPA., Illus.). 32p. (J). (gr. k-3). pap. 10.95 (978-1-56014-581-3(1)) Santillana USA Publishing Co., Inc.

Atkinson, Juliette. I'm Sorry. Atkinson, John, illus. 2008. 32p. (J). (ps-k). 16.99 (***978-0-698-40079-5(8)*** , Minedition) Penguin Group (USA) Inc.

Avery, Terry. Moon Rabbit Builds a Fine House. l.t. ed. 2000. (Illus.). 32p. (J). (ps-3). 17.95 (978-1-929115-00-6(8)) Azro Pr., Inc.

Baglio, Ben M. Bunnies in the Bathroom. McNicholas, Shelagh, illus. 2000. (Animal Ark Ser.: No. 15). 144p. (J). (gr. 3-5). 3.99 (978-0-439-09700-0(2)) Scholastic, Inc.

—Bunny Bonanza. Howard, Paul, illus. 2001. (Animal Ark Pets Ser.: Vol. 15). 128p. (J). (gr. 2-5). pap. 3.99 (978-0-439-23024-7(1)) Scholastic, Inc.

—Bunny in a Basket. Baum, Ann, illus. 2005. 142p. (J). (978-0-439-68761-4(6)) Scholastic, Inc.

Baglio, Ben M. Runaway Rascal. 2006. (Illus.). 157p. (J). (***978-0-439-79250-9(9)***) Scholastic, Inc.

Baguley, Elizabeth. The Little Lost Robin. Macnaughton, Tina, illus. 2007. 28p. (J). (ps-2). 16.95 (***978-1-56148-590-1(X)***) Good Bks.

Bailey, Arthur Scott. The Tale of Peter Mink. 2005. pap. 20.95 (978-0-7661-9699-5(2)) Kessinger Publishing, LLC.

Bailey, Carolyn S. The Little Rabbit Who Wanted Red Wings. Rogers, Jacqueline, illus. 2001. (Reading Railroad Bks.). 32p. (J). (ps-3). pap. 3.49 (978-0-448-19089-1(3) , Grosset & Dunlap) Penguin Group (USA) Inc.

Bailey, Rosemary. Benjamin Bunny A Childrens Story. 2004. 12p. (J). pap. 10.33 (978-1-4116-1043-9(1)) Lulu.com.

Bain, Sherry. Benjamin Gets Saved. 1998. (Illus.). 100p. (J). pap. 9.95 (978-1-889448-23-7(0)) Great House Publishers Grp., Inc., The.

Baker, Alan. Black & White Rabbit's ABC. Baker, Alan, illus. 2002. (Illus.). (J). 11.87 (978-0-7587-4101-1(4)) Book Wholesalers, Inc.

—Black & White Rabbit's ABC. 1999. (Little Rabbit Bks.). (Illus.). 24p. (J). (gr. k-ps). 4.95 (978-0-7534-5253-0(7) , Kingfisher) Houghton Mifflin Co. Trade & Reference Div.

—Brown Rabbit's Day. 1999. (Little Rabbit Bks.). (Illus.). 24p. (J). (gr. k-ps). pap. 3.95 (978-0-7534-5256-1(1) , Kingfisher) Houghton Mifflin Co. Trade & Reference Div.

—Brown Rabbit's Day. 1999. (gr. k-3). lib. bdg. 11.80 (978-0-613-88046-6(3)) Tandem Library Bks.

—Gray Rabbit's 1, 2, 3. 1999. (Little Rabbit Bks.). (Illus.). 24p. (J). (gr. k-ps). 4.95 (978-0-7534-5252-3(9) , Kingfisher) Houghton Mifflin Co. Trade & Reference Div.

—Gray Rabbit's 1, 2, 3. 1999. (ps-2). lib. bdg. 11.80 (978-0-613-88047-3(1)) Tandem Library Bks.

—Gray Rabbit's Odd One Out. 1999. (Little Rabbit Bks.). (Illus.). 24p. (J). (gr. k-ps). pap. 4.95 (978-0-7534-5257-8(X) , Kingfisher) Houghton Mifflin Co. Trade & Reference Div.

—Gray Rabbit's Odd One Out. 1999. (gr. k-3). lib. bdg. 11.80 (978-0-613-88048-0(X)) Tandem Library Bks.

—Little Rabbit's Bedtime. 1998. (Little Rabbit Bks.). (Illus.). 24p. (J). (gr. k-ps). tchr. ed. 10.95 (978-0-7534-5143-4(3) , Kingfisher) Houghton Mifflin Co. Trade & Reference Div.

—Little Rabbits First Farm Book. 2001. (Little Rabbit Bks.). (Illus.). 32p. (J). (ps-k). tchr. ed. 11.95 (978-0-7534-5352-0(5) , Kingfisher) Houghton Mifflin Co. Trade & Reference Div.

—Little Rabbits' First Farm Book. 2003. (Little Rabbit Bks.). 32p. (J). (ps up). pap. 5.95 (978-0-7534-5594-4(3) , Kingfisher) Houghton Mifflin Co. Trade & Reference Div.

—Little Rabbits' First Time Book. 1999. (Little Rabbit Bks.). (Illus.). 16p. (J). (ps-k). tchr. ed. 11.95 (978-0-7534-5220-2(0) , Kingfisher) Houghton Mifflin Co. Trade & Reference Div.

—Little Rabbit's Snacktime. 1998. (Little Rabbit Bks.). (Illus.). 24p. (J). (gr. k-ps). tchr. ed. 10.95 (978-0-7534-5144-1(1) , Kingfisher) Houghton Mifflin Co. Trade & Reference Div.

—White Rabbit's Color Book. 1999. (Little Rabbit Bks.). (Illus.). 24p. (J). (gr. k-ps). pap. 4.95 (978-0-7534-5254-7(5) , Kingfisher) Houghton Mifflin Co. Trade & Reference Div.

Balian, Lorna. Humbug Rabbit. 2004. (Illus.). 40p. (J). 15.95 (978-1-932065-40-4(7)) Star Bright Bks., Inc.

Banks, Steven. Show Me the Bunny! Greenblatt, C. H. & Reiss, William, illus. ed. 2005. 32p. (J). lib. bdg. 15.00 (978-1-59054-985-8(6)) Fitzgerald Bks.

Bate, Lucy. Little Rabbit's Loose Tooth. De Groat, Diane, illus. 2006. 32p. (J). (ps-3). reprint ed. 9.95 (978-0-375-83277-2(7) , Crown Books For Young Readers) Random Hse. Children's Bks.

Bauer, Marion Dane. One Brown Bunny. Bates, Ivan, illus. 2008. (J). (***978-0-439-68010-3(7)*** , Orchard Bks.) Scholastic, Inc.

Baumbach, Rudolph. Summer Legends. 2004. reprint ed. pap. 21.95 (978-1-4191-4993-1(8)); pap. 1.99 (978-1-4192-4993-8(2)) Kessinger Publishing, LLC.

Becker, John E. Seven Little Rabbits. Cooney, Barbara, illus. 2007. 32p. (J). 8.85 (978-0-8027-9635-6(4)); 7.95 (978-0-8027-9634-9(6)) Walker & Co.

Bedtime for Bunny. 2001. (J). (978-1-931312-00-4(1)) Soft-Play, Inc.

Bentley, Dawn. Hoppy Goes to School Micro Bk And. Huerta, Catherine, illus. 2006. 32p. 9.95 (978-1-59249-559-7(1)) Soundprints.

Benton, Jim. The Good, the Bad, & the Bunny. 2006. (It's Happy Bunny Ser.: No. 4). (Illus.). 72p. (J). pap. 7.99 (978-0-439-70593-6(2) , Scholastic Paperbacks) Scholastic, Inc.

—Guess What? It's Still All about Me. 2006. (It's Happy Bunny Ser.). 32p. (J). bds. 7.99 (978-0-439-84775-9(3) , Scholastic) Scholastic, Inc.

—Life Get One. 2nd ed. 2005. (It's Happy Bunny Ser.: No. 2). (Illus.). 72p. (J). 7.99 (978-0-439-69346-2(2)) Scholastic, Inc.

Berenstain, Jan. The Berenstain Bears' Baby Easter Bunny. Berenstain, Jan, illus. 2008. (Berenstain Bears Ser.). 16p. (J). 6.99 (***978-0-06-057420-8(8)*** , Harper Festival) HarperCollins Pubs.

Bergen, Lara. Diego's Springtime Fiesta. Oesch, Brian, illus. 2008. (Go, Diego, Go! Ser.). 24p. (J). pap. 3.99 (***978-1-4169-4800-1(7)*** , Simon Spotlight/Nickelodeon) Simon & Schuster Children's Publishing.

Berger, Barbara Helen. Thunder Bunny. Berger, Barbara Helen, illus. 2007. (Illus.). 32p. (J). (ps-3). 16.99 (978-0-399-22035-7(6) , Philomel) Penguin Group (USA) Inc.

Bernstein, Dan. The Tortoise & the Hare Race Again. Glass, Andrew, illus. (J). (ps-3). 36p. 6.95 (***978-0-8234-2070-4(1)***); 32p. 16.95 (978-0-8234-1867-1(7)) Holiday Hse., Inc.

Berry, Eileen M. Buttercup Hill. Harrald-Pilz, Marilee, illus. 2006. 39p. (J). (978-1-59166-667-7(8)) Jones, Bob Univ. Pr.

Betz, Adrienne. A Deal Is a Deal. Andriani, Vincent, illus. 1999. (Scholastic At-Home Phonics Reading Program Ser.: Vol. 33). 24p. (J). pap. (978-0-590-68782-9(4)) Scholastic, Inc.

Billings, David Joseph. Road Trip with Rabbit & Squash. Billings, David Joseph, illus. 2006. (Illus.). 48p. (J). per. (978-0-9789036-0-2(9)) Billings, David J.

Billy Bunny's Shopping List. 2002. (My First Tab Story Ser.). (J). bds. 3.98 (978-0-7525-8953-4(9)) Parragon, Inc.

Binkow, Howard. Howard B. Wigglebottom Learns to Listen. Cornelison, Susan F., illus. 2006. 32p. (J). (ps-2). 15.00 (978-0-9715390-1-3(4)) Thunderbolt Publishing.

Birchall, Mark. Rabbit's Birthday Surprise. Birchall, Mark, illus. 2003. (Illus.). 32p. (J). (ps-3). 15.95 (978-0-87614-910-2(7) , Carolrhoda Bks.) Lerner Publishing Group.

—Rabbit's Wooly Sweater. Birchall, Mark, illus. 2003. (Picture Bks.). (Illus.). 32p. (J). (ps-3). 15.95 (978-1-57505-465-0(5) , Carolrhoda Bks.) Lerner Publishing Group.

Bishop, Gavin. Conejito y el Mar. 2000. (SPA., Illus.). (J). (978-0-606-18317-8(5)) Tandem Library Bks.

—Little Rabbit & the Sea. 2000. (Illus.). 32p. (J). (ps-1). pap. 6.95 (978-0-7358-1312-0(4)) North-South Bks., Inc.

—Little Rabbit & the Sea. 2000. (gr. k-3). lib. bdg. 15.25 (978-0-613-28558-2(1)); (Illus.). (J). (978-0-606-18322-2(1)) Tandem Library Bks.

Bloss, Janet A. Ballet Bunny. Bloss, Janet A., illus. 1998. (Illus.). 24p. (J). (gr. k-3). reprint ed. pap. 1.99 (978-0-87406-374-5(4) , Willowisp Pr.) Darby Creek Publishing.

Blumberg, Margie. Sunny Bunnies. Goulding, June, illus. 2008. 32p. (J). 15.00 (***978-0-9624166-4-4(9)***) MB Publishing, LLC.

Blyton, Enid. Binkle & Flip Misbehave. 1999. (Enid Blyton's Happy Days Ser.). (Illus.). 95p. (J). (gr. 1-4). pap. 7.99 (978-0-7475-4350-3(X)) Bloomsbury Publishing Plc GBR. *Dist:* Trafalgar Square Publishing.

Boelts, Maribeth. You're a Brother, Little Bunny! Parkinson, Kathy, illus. 2001. 32p. (J). (ps-k). 15.95 (978-0-8075-9446-9(6)) Whitman, Albert & Co.

Bolam, Emily. Bunny. 2003. (Chunky Pet Bks.). (Illus.). 14p. (J). bds. 4.95 (978-0-7641-5607-6(1)) Barron's Educational Series, Inc.

Bolam, Emily, illus. Father's Day Is Coming. 2007. (I'm Going to Read Ser.: No. 2). 32p. (J). pap. 3.95 (978-1-4027-4247-7(9)) Sterling Publishing Co., Inc.

Boniface, William. Easter Bunnies Everywhere. Rooney, Ronnie, illus. 2003. 12p. (J). (ps-2). bds. 9.99 (978-0-8431-0257-4(8) , Price Stern Sloan) Penguin Group (USA) Inc.

—Fleecy Bunny. Jennings, Patti & Adams, Lynn, illus. 2003. (Fleecy Friends Ser.). 10p. (J). (ps). 9.99 (978-0-8431-7786-2(1) , Price Stern Sloan) Penguin Group (USA) Inc.

Book Buddy: Rabbit with Story Book. Orig. Title: Child's Play. (Illus.). 10p. (J). (ps-3). reprint ed. (978-1-881469-47-6(6)) Safari, Ltd.

Book Company Staff. Who Am I: Rabbit. 2003. (Board Bks.). (Illus.). (J). bds. 10.95 (978-1-74047-308-8(6)) Book Co. Publishing Pty, Ltd., The AUS. *Dist:* Penton Overseas, Inc.

Borgo, Deborah Colvin, illus. Baby Bunny. 1999. (J). (978-0-7853-3353-1(3)) Publications International, Ltd.

Bornstein, Ruth. Brave Bunny. Bornstein, Ruth, illus. 2003. (Illus.). 32p. (J). 9.95 (978-1-58685-282-5(5)) Gibbs Smith, Publisher.

Boujon, Claude. Que Aproveche, Senor Conejo! (SPA.). 32p. (978-84-8470-009-8(7)) Corimbo, Editorial S.L.

Bourély, Antoinette & Caviezel, Giovanni. Lullabies under the Moon. Pledger, M., illus. 2006. 12p. (J). 6.99 (978-1-4169-1359-7(9) , Little Simon) Simon & Schuster Children's Publishing.

Bradman, Tony. Nicky & the Twins' Lost Rabbit. 1999. (Illus.). 32p. (J). pap. 9.99 (978-0-00-664511-5(9)) HarperCollins Pubs. Ltd. GBR. *Dist:* Independent Pubs. Group.

Brandt-Taylor, Diane. The Bunny, the Bear, the Bug & the Bee. Brandt, Michael, illus. 2005. (J). cd-rom 9.88 (978-0-9773236-0-9(9)) TaySysCo Publishing.

Brenner, Barbara, et al. Bunny Tails. Munsinger, Lynn, illus. 2005. 32p. 15.95 (978-1-59687-177-9(6)); 15.95 (978-0-689-03925-6(5)) ibooks, Inc. (Milk & Cookies).

Bridwell, Norman. The Runaway Rabbit. Bridwell, Norman, illus. 2002. (Big Red Readers Ser.). (Illus.). (J). 11.91 (978-0-7587-5219-2(9)) Book Wholesalers, Inc.

Broder, Lynn. The Long Winding Road. 2006. (ENG.). 37p. per. 15.95 (***978-1-59526-366-7(7)***) Media Creations, Inc.

Brookes, C. Avery. Sea Breezes, Salt Air. 1999. (Illus.). 53 p. (J). 6.95 (978-0-9666246-0-1(2) , Bunny Express Pr.) Brookes, C. Avery Ltd.

Broster, Marie. Binky Bunny's Day Out & Poems for Children. 2006. (Illus.). 60p. pap. (***978-1-84401-793-5(1)***) Athena Pr.

Brown, Janet Allison. Bunny Backpack. O'Neill, Rachael, illus. 2007. 10p. (J). bds. 12.95 (978-1-4027-4479-2(X)) Sterling Publishing Co., Inc.

Brown, Marc. Arthur Loses a Friend. 2006. (Illus.). 24p. (J). (gr. 1-3). pap. 3.99 (978-0-375-82974-1(0)); lib. bdg. 11.99 (978-0-375-92974-8(6)) Random Hse. Children's Bks. (Random Hse. Bks. for Young Readers).

—Buster & the Dance Contest. 2005. (Postcards from Buster Ser.). (Illus.). 32p. (J). (gr. 1-4). 14.99 (978-0-316-15889-3(5)); pap., pap. 3.99 (978-0-316-00118-2(X)) Little, Brown Bks. for Young Readers.

—Buster & the Giant Pumpkin. 2005. (Postcards from Buster Ser.). (Illus.). 32p. (J). (gr. 1-4). 14.99 (978-0-316-15887-9(9)) Little Brown & Co.

—Buster & the Giant Pumpkin. 2005. (Postcards from Buster Ser.). (Illus.). 32p. (J). (gr. 1-4). pap., pap. 3.99 (978-0-316-00111-3(2)) Little, Brown Bks. for Young Readers.

—Buster & the Great Swamp. 8th ed. 2005. (Postcards from Buster Ser.). (Illus.). 32p. (J). (gr. 1-4). pap. 14.99 (978-0-316-15912-8(3)); pap. 3.99 (978-0-316-00125-0(2)) Little Brown & Co.

—Buster Catches a Wave. 7th ed. 2005. (Postcards from Buster Ser.). (Illus.). 32p. (J). (gr. 1-4). pap. 3.99 (978-0-316-00122-9(8)) Little Brown & Co.

—Buster Changes His Luck. 2006. (Postcards from Buster Ser.). (Illus.). 48p. (J). (gr. 1-4). 14.99 (978-0-316-15916-6(6)); 12th ed. pap. 3.99 (978-0-316-00129-8(5)) Little Brown & Co.

—Buster Climbs the Walls. 9th ed. 2005. (Postcards from Buster Ser.). (Illus.). 48p. (J). (gr. 1-4). pap. 14.99 (978-0-316-15913-5(1)); pap. 3.99 (978-0-316-00126-7(0)) Little Brown & Co.

—Buster Hits the Trail. 2005. (Postcards from Buster Ser.). (Illus.). 48p. (J). (gr. 1-4). 14.99 (978-0-316-15900-5(X)); pap., pap. 3.99 (978-0-316-00121-2(X)) Little, Brown Bks. for Young Readers.

—Buster Hunts for Dinosaurs. 2006. (Postcards from Buster Ser.). 32p. (J). (gr. 1-4). 14.99 (978-0-316-15914-2(X)); 10th ed. (Illus.). pap. 3.99 (978-0-316-00127-4(9)) Little Brown & Co.

—Buster on the Farm. 2005. (Postcards from Buster Ser.). (Illus.). 32p. (J). (gr. 1-4). 14.99 (978-0-316-15884-8(4)); pap. 3.99 (978-0-316-00108-3(2)) Little, Brown Bks. for Young Readers.

—Buster on the Town. 2005. (Postcards from Buster Ser.). (Illus.). 32p. (J). (gr. 1-4). 14.99 (978-0-316-15882-4(8)); pap. 3.99 (978-0-316-00107-6(4)) Little, Brown Bks. for Young Readers.

—Buster Plays Along. 2005. (Postcards from Buster Ser.). (Illus.). (J). (gr. 1-4). 48p. 14.99 (978-0-316-15886-2(0)); 32p. pap. 3.99 (978-0-316-00109-0(0)) Little, Brown Bks. for Young Readers.

—Buster's Sugartime. 2006. (Postcards from Buster Ser.). 32p. (J). (gr. 1-4). 14.99 (978-0-316-15915-9(8)); 11th ed. (Illus.). pap. 3.99 (978-0-316-00128-1(7)) Little Brown & Co.

Brown, Margaret. Over the Moon: A Collection of First Books: Goodnight Moon, the Runaway Bunny, & My World. Hurd, Clement, illus. 2006. 108p. (J). 19.99 (978-0-06-076162-2(8)) HarperCollins Pubs.

Brown, Margaret Wise. Boa Noite Lua. pap. 19.95 (978-85-336-0713-2(X)) Livraria Martins Editora BRA. *Dist:* Distribooks, Inc.

—Bonsoir Lune.Tr. of Goodnight Moon. (FRE.). (J). pap. 21.95 (***978-2-211-01028-3(8)***) Archimede Editions FRA. *Dist:* Distribooks, Inc.

—Buenas Noches, Luna. Hurd, Clement, illus. 2002. (SPA.). 34p. (J). (ps up). bds. 8.99 (978-0-694-01651-8(9) , HC8997) HarperCollins Pubs.

—Bunny's Noisy Book. McCue, Lisa, illus. 2002. 32p. (J). (ps-k). bds. 6.99 (978-0-7868-0744-4(X)) Hyperion Bks. for Children.

—El Conejito Andarin. Hurd, Clement, illus. (SPA.). (J). 2006. 48p. pap. 6.99 (978-0-06-077694-7(3) , Rayo); 2002. 34p. 7.99 (978-0-694-01650-1(0)) HarperCollins Pubs.

—The Golden Egg Book. Weisgard, Leonard, illus. 2004. (Big Little Golden Book Ser.). 32p. (J). (gr. k-k). 8.99 (978-0-375-82717-4(X) , Golden Bks.) Random Hse. Children's Bks.

—Goodnight Bunny. 2006. (J). 11p. 12.99 (978-1-4037-2549-3(7)); 24p. 12.99 (978-1-4037-2703-9(1)); 12p. 5.99 (978-1-4037-2705-3(8)) Dalmatian Pr.

—Goodnight Moon. Hurd, Clement, illus. (J). 2005. 32p. lib. bdg. 17.89 (978-0-06-077586-5(6)); 2001. 34p. 12.99 (978-0-694-01675-4(6) , Harper Festival); 2001. 16p. 15.99 (978-0-694-01638-9(1) , Harper Festival); 60th anniv. ed. 2005. 32p. 16.99 (978-0-06-077585-8(8)) HarperCollins Pubs.

—Goodnight Moon. Hurd, Clement, illus. (J). pap. 32.75 incl. audio. 24.95 incl. audio. 2004. pap. 14.95 incl. audio (978-0-89719-775-5(5) , PRA298) Weston Woods Studios, Inc.

—Goodnight Moon: Board Book & Baby Socks. Hurd, Clement, illus. 2002. 34p. (J). (ps up). 12.99 (978-0-06-009427-0(3) , Harper Festival) HarperCollins Pubs.

—Goodnight Moon 123: A Counting Book. Hurd, Clement, illus. 2007. 32p. (J). lib. bdg. 17.89 (978-0-06-112594-2(6)); 16.99 (978-0-06-112593-5(8)) HarperCollins Pubs.

—Goodnight Moon 123/Buenas Noches, Luna 123: A Counting Book/Un Libro para Contar. Hurd, Clement, illus. 2007. (ENG & SPA.). 32p. (J). (ps-k). 16.99 (***978-0-06-117325-7(8)*** , Rayo) HarperCollins Pubs.

—Goodnight Moon Big Book. Hurd, Clement, illus. 2007. 32p. (J). pap. 24.99 (***978-0-06-111977-4(6)*** , Harper Festival) HarperCollins Pubs.

—Goodnight Moon Board Book & Bunny. Hurd, Clement, illus. 2005. 34p. (J). (ps up). bds. 14.99 (978-0-06-076027-4(3) , Harper Festival) HarperCollins Pubs.

—Goodnight Moon Board Book & Nightlight. Hurd, Clement, illus. 2003. 34p. (J). (ps up). 12.99 (978-0-06-054179-8(2) , Harper Festival) HarperCollins Pubs.

—Home for a Bunny. Williams, Garth, illus. 2003. (Big Little Golden Bks.). 32p. (J). (gr. k-k). reprint ed. 8.99 (978-0-307-10546-2(6) , Golden Bks.) Random Hse. Children's Bks.

—Home for a Bunny. 1999. (978-0-606-22796-4(2)) Tandem Library Bks.

—Mon Petit Monde (French edition of My World) 2004. 40p. 29.95 (978-0-320-06689-4(4)) French & European Pubns., Inc.

—My World: A Companion to Goodnight Moon. Hurd, Clement, illus. (J). (ps up). 2004. 40p. pap. 5.99 (978-0-694-01660-0(8) , Harper Trophy); 2003. 36p. bds. 7.99 (978-0-694-00862-9(1) , Harper Festival); 2001. 32p. 15.95 (978-0-06-024798-0(3) , Harper Festival) HarperCollins Pubs.

—My World: A Companion to Goodnight Moon. 2004. (ps-2). lib. bdg. 14.15 (978-0-613-83488-9(7)) Tandem Library Bks.

—The Runaway Bunny. Hurd, Clement, illus. (J). (ps up). 2005. 48p. 16.99 (978-0-06-077582-7(3)); 2005. 48p. lib. bdg. 17.89 (978-0-06-077583-4(1)); 2001. 36p. bds. 12.99 (978-0-694-01671-6(3)); 2007. 36p. 9.99 (978-0-06-114271-0(9) , Harper Festival); 1998. 16p. 9.99 (978-0-694-70095-0(9)) HarperCollins Pubs.

—The Runaway Bunny. Hurd, Clement, illus. 2000. 40p. (J). (ps-3). pap. 6.95 (978-0-9629298-8-5(3) , MHC-8-3) Minnesota Humanities Commission.

Brown, Margaret Wise. The Runaway Bunny Big Book. Hurd, Clement, illus. 2008. 48p. (J). pap. 24.99 (***978-0-06-111976-7(8)*** , Harper Festival) HarperCollins Pubs.

Brown, Margaret Wise & Hurd, Clement. Goodnight Moon. unabr. ed. 2000. (J). pap. 7.98 incl. audio Random Hse. Audio Publishing Group.

Brown, Margaret Wise & Kahn, Si. Goodnight Moon. Hurd, Clement, illus. unabr. abr. ed. 1998. (Share a Story Ser.). (J). (ps up). 9.95 (978-0-694-70094-3(0)) HarperCollins Pubs.

Brown, Margaret Wise & Wiggins, Beth Foster. Buenas noches Conejito. 2006. 24p. (J). 12.95 (978-1-882077-63-2(6)) Sweetwater Pr.

Brown, Margaret Wise, et al. The Runaway Bunny: Board Book & Doll. Hurd, Clement, illus. 1999. 18p. (J). (ps up). 14.99 (978-0-694-01214-5(9) , Harper Festival) HarperCollins Pubs.

Bruna, Dick. Hide & See. 2004. (Illus.). 12p. 6.99 (978-1-59226-042-3(X)) Big Tent Entertainment, Inc.

—Let's Learn: Animals. 2004. (Illus.). 24p. pap. 4.99 (978-1-59226-167-3(1)) Big Tent Entertainment, Inc.

—Let's Learn: Boris in the Forest. 2004. (Illus.). 24p. pap. 4.99 (978-1-59226-174-1(4)) Big Tent Entertainment, Inc.

—Let's Learn: Miffy Looks Around. 2004. (Illus.). 24p. pap. 4.99 (978-1-59226-173-4(6)) Big Tent Entertainment, Inc.

—Let's Learn: Miffy's Adventure. 2004. (Illus.). 24p. pap. 4.99 (978-1-59226-171-0(X)) Big Tent Entertainment, Inc.

—Let's Learn: Miffy's Day. 2004. (Illus.). 24p. pap. 4.99 (978-1-59226-170-3(1)) Big Tent Entertainment, Inc.

—Let's Learn: School Time. 2004. (Illus.). 24p. pap. 4.99 (978-1-59226-172-7(8)) Big Tent Entertainment, Inc.

—Let's Learn: Seasons of the Year. 2004. (Illus.). 24p. pap. 4.99 (978-1-59226-168-0(X)) Big Tent Entertainment, Inc.

—Let's Learn: The Great Outdoors. 2004. (Illus.). 24p. pap. 4.99 (978-1-59226-169-7(8)) Big Tent Entertainment, Inc.

—Miffy. 2004. (Illus.). 24p. (J). 7.99 (978-1-59226-022-5(5)) Big Tent Entertainment, Inc.

—Miffy & Friends: Blue-Green Coloring Book. 2004. (Illus.). 48p. pap. 5.99 (978-1-59226-096-6(9)) Big Tent Entertainment, Inc.

—Miffy & Friends: Yellow-Red Coloring Book. 2004. (Illus.). 48p. pap. 5.99 (978-1-59226-098-0(5)) Big Tent Entertainment, Inc.

—Miffy Dances. 2004. 24p. 7.99 (978-1-59226-024-9(1)); (Illus.). pap. 4.99 (978-1-59226-010-2(1)) Big Tent Entertainment, Inc.

—Miffy in the Tent. 1998. (Miffy Ser.). (Illus.). 28p. (J). (ps-k). pap. 4.95 (978-1-56836-218-2(8)) Kodansha America, Inc.

—Miffy Loves New York City! 2004. 32p. (ps-3). 9.99 (978-1-59226-179-6(5)) Big Tent Entertainment, Inc.

—Miffy Says, I Love You! 2004. (Illus.). 12p. bds. 5.99 (978-1-59226-187-1(6)) Big Tent Entertainment, Inc.

—Miffy the Ghost. 2004. (Illus.). 24p. (ps-k). 7.99 (978-1-59226-063-8(2)) Big Tent Entertainment, Inc.

—Miffy's Counting Book. 2004. (Illus.). 20p. bds. 7.99 (978-1-59226-034-8(9)) Big Tent Entertainment, Inc.

—Miffy's House. 2004. 24p. 7.99 (978-1-59226-023-2(3)); (Illus.). pap. 4.99 (978-1-59226-008-9(X)) Big Tent Entertainment, Inc.

—Miffy's Magnifying Glass. 2004. (Illus.). 16p. bds. 5.99 (978-1-59226-031-7(4)) Big Tent Entertainment, Inc.

—My Miffy. 2000. (Illus.). (J). (ps-k). pap. 10.95 (978-1-56836-307-3(9)) Kodansha America, Inc.

—Places to Go. 2004. (Illus.). 12p. 6.99 (978-1-59226-043-0(8)) Big Tent Entertainment, Inc.

—What Will I Do Today? Miffy's Big Flap Book. 2004. 10p. 9.99 (978-1-59226-178-9(7)) Big Tent Entertainment, Inc.

—What's at the Zoo, Miffy? 2004. 16p. bds. 5.99 (978-1-59226-033-1(0)) Big Tent Entertainment, Inc.

Bryan, Sean. A Boy & His Bunny. Murphy, Tom, illus. rev. ed. 2005. 32p. (J). (ps-1). pap. 14.99 (978-1-55970-725-1(9)) Arcade Publishing, Inc.

Bugsilocks & the Three Bears. 1999. (McGraw-Hill Junior Academic Ser.). (Illus.). 16p. (J). (gr. k-2). pap. 3.99 (978-1-57768-215-8(7)) School Specialty Publishing.

Bunnicula. 2005. (J). (978-1-59564-838-9(0)) Steps To Literacy, LLC.

Bunny's House. Date not set. (Illus.). (J). bds. 4.98 (978-1-4054-0785-4(9)) Parragon, Inc.

Burgess, Thornton W. The Adventures of Old Mr. Toad. 1998. (Illus.). 80p. (J). (gr. 3-6). pap. 1.50 (978-0-486-40385-4(8)) Dover Pubns., Inc.

—Big Book of Animal Stories. 2001. (Illus.). 208p. (J). (gr. 4-7). pap. 7.95 (978-0-486-41980-0(0)) Dover Pubns., Inc.

—Mrs. Peter Rabbit. (J). 18.95 (978-0-8488-0390-2(6)) Amereon LTD.

—Mrs. Peter Rabbit. 2004. reprint ed. pap. 15.95 (978-1-4191-3581-1(3)); pap. 1.99 (978-1-4192-3581-8(8)) Kessinger Publishing, LLC.

Burgess, W. Thornton. Mrs. Peter Rabbit. 2006. pap. 55.99 (***978-1-4280-1040-6(8)***) IndyPublish.com.

Burningham, John. Aldo. 2000. (Illus.). 32p. (J). pap. 8.99 (978-0-09-918501 7(6) , Red Fox) Random Hse. Children's Bks. GBR. *Dist:* Trafalgar Square Publishing.

Butler, Dori. The Tortoise & the Hare: An Aesop's Fable. 2006. 42.00 (***978-1-4108-6167-2(8)***) Benchmark Education Co.

Butler, M. Christina. Snow Friends. Macnaughton, Tina, illus. 2005. 28p. (J). (ps-2). 16.00 (978-1-56148-485-0(7)) Good Bks.

Cain, Sheridan. Goodnight, Little Hare. Percy, Sally, illus. 1998. 14p. (J). pap. 16.98 (978-1-58048-044-4(6)) Sandvik Publishing.

—Why So Sad, Brown Rabbit? 2001. (Illus.). (J). (978-0-606-20990-8(5)) Tandem Library Bks.

Campbell-Ernst, Lisa. Good Morning, Sun! 2006. (Illus.). 5p. (J). bds. 6.95 (978-1-59354-154-5(6)) Blue Apple Bks.

—Learn to Turn: Breakfast Time! 2006. (Illus.). 5p. (J). bds. 6.95 (978-1-59354-155-2(4)) Blue Apple Bks.

Candlewick Press Staff. Ghmily Ams Ed. 2002. (J). bds. 12.99 (978-0-7636-1820-9(9)) Candlewick Pr.

Carlson, Amanda. Sultenfuss Moose's Lost Slipper. 2006. 26p. 18.03 (978-1-4116-7729-6(3)) Lulu.com.

Carlson, Nancy. Get up & Go! 2008. 32p. (J). (ps). pap. 5.99 (***978-0-14-241064-6(0)*** , Puffin) Penguin Group (USA) Inc.

—Harriet & George's Christmas Treat. Carlson, Nancy, illus. 2005. (Picture Bks.). (Illus.). 32p. (J). (gr. k-2). 15.95 (978-1-57505-506-0(6)) Lerner Publishing Group.

—Harriet & George's Christmas Treat. 2003. (Illus.). 32p. (J). (gr. k-2). pap. (978-1-57505-639-5(9)) Lerner Publishing Group.

—Harriet & George's Christmas Treat. 2001. (gr. k-3). lib. bdg. 15.25 (978-0-613-68088-2(X)) Tandem Library Bks.

—Harriet & the Roller Coaster. 20th anniv. ed. (Nancy Carlson's Neighborhood Ser.). (Illus.). 32p. (J). (gr. k-2). 2005. 15.95 (978-1-57505-053-9(6)); 2003. (J). (978-1-57505-202-1(4)) Lerner Publishing Group.

—Harriet & the Roller Coaster. 2003. (gr. k-3). lib. bdg. 15.25 (978-0-613-68089-9(8)) Tandem Library Bks.

—Loudmouth George & the Big Race. rev. ed. (Carolrhoda Picture Books Ser.). (Illus.). 32p. (J). (gr. k-2). 2005. 15.95 (978-1-57505-673-9(9)); 2004. pap. 6.95 (978-1-57505-724-8(7)) Lerner Publishing Group.

—Loudmouth George & the Cornet. rev. ed. 2004. (Carolrhoda Picture Books Ser.). (Illus.). 32p. (J). (gr. k-2). pap. 6.95 (978-1-57505-725-5(5)) Lerner Publishing Group.

—Loudmouth George & the Fishing Trip. 2nd rev. ed. 2005. (Illus.). 32p. (J). (gr. k-3). pap. 6.95 (978-1-57505-733-0(6) , First Avenue Editions) Lerner Publishing Group.

—Loudmouth George & the Sixth Grade Bully. 20th anniv. ed. (Nancy Carlson's Neighborhood Ser.). (Illus.). 32p. (gr. k-2). 2005. 15.95 (978-1-57505-218-2(0)); 2003. (J). pap. 23.95 (978-1-57505-549-7(X)) Lerner Publishing Group.

—Loudmouth George & the Sixth Grade Bully. 2003. (gr. k-3). lib. bdg. 15.25 (978-0-613-58927-7(0)) Tandem Library Bks.

Carlson, Nancy L. Loudmouth George Earns His Allowance. 2007. (Illus.). 32p. (J). (gr. k-3). spiral bd. 15.95 (978-0-8225-6560-4(9) , Carolrhoda Bks.) Lerner Publishing Group.

Carrigan, Nancy J., et al. Rabbinia Hopinska's Magic Music. Carrigan, Nancy J., illus. 1998. 32p. (J). (gr. 2-5). pap. 6.95 (978-1-890156-01-5(9)) Arbor Hill Pr.

Carroll, Lewis, pseud. Alice's Adventures in Wonderland. 1998. (Classics Ser.). (ENG., Illus.). 288p. pap. (978-1-85326-002-5(9) , 0029WW) Wordsworth Editions, Ltd.

Carrotblanca. Date not set. (J). 7.98 incl. audio (978-1-57042-320-8(2)) Warner Brothers Records.

Cate, Annette LeBlanc. The Magic Rabbit. Cate, Annette LeBlanc, illus. 2007. (Illus.). 32p. (J). (ps-3). 15.99 (***978-0-7636-2672-3(4)***) Candlewick Pr.

Caviezel, Giovanni. Bunny's Egg Hunt. Pagnoni, Roberta, illus. 2003. 12p. (J). bds. 4.99 (978-0-689-85246-6(0) , Little Simon) Simon & Schuster Children's Publishing.

Chandler, Pauline. Mr. Rabbit the Farmer. Smith, Eric, illus. 2005. 24p. (J). lib. bdg. 22.65 (***978-1-59646-736-1(3)***) Dingles & Co.

Charlotte Latin School Staff. Ann & the Bunny. Sher, illus. 2001. 32p. (J). per. 4.95 (978-0-9707920-3-7(4)) Charlotte's Storybooks.

Chen, Zhiyuan, illus. Artie & Julie. 2007. (J). (***978-0-9787550-3-4(0)***) Heryin Publishing Corp.

Ciminera, Siiobhan & Ostby, Kristin. Paas: The Great Egg Show! 2006. 32p. (J). (ps-1). act. bk. ed. 2.99 (978-0-448-44136-8(5)) Penguin Group (USA) Inc.

Ciminera, Siobhan. The Funniest Bunny Ever. Petrosino, Tamara, illus. 2007. 16p. (J). pap. 4.99 (978-0-8431-2175-9(0) , Price Stern Sloan) Penguin Group (USA) Inc.

Circle of Friends: The Camelot Rabbitry Serires - Volume Three. 2006. (Camelot Rabbitry Ser.: 3). (Illus.). 98p. (J). per. 9.95 (978-0-9672375-3-4(X)) Camelot Tales.

Clements, Andrew. Riff's Be Bop Book. 2000. (J). 3.99 (978-0-689-81304-7(X) , Simon Spotlight/Nickelodeon) Simon & Schuster Children's Publishing.

Clifton, Lisa. The Bunny Who Could Fly. Begley, Melinda, ed. Clifton, Paul, illus. l.t. ed. 1999. 36p. (J). (gr. k-6). 10.00 (978-1-886623-07-1(4)) Canal Side Pubs.

Cloke, Rene. My Big Book of Brer Stories. 2006. (Illus.). 80p. (J). 7.99 (978-0-517-22871-5(8) , Gramercy) Random Hse. Value Publishing.

Coe, Frances. Who's That Bouncing? With Miniature Blanket. Elgar, Rebecca, illus. 1999. (Little Blanket Bks.). 10p. (J). (ps). bds. 3.95 (978-0-7641-5177-4(0)) Barron's Educational Series, Inc.

Coleman, Michael. One, Two, Three, Oops! Williamson, Gwyneth, illus. 1999. 32p. (J). (ps-2). 14.95 (978-1-888444-45-2(2)) Little Tiger Pr.

Conejito Azul: Es un Valiente Socorrista.Tr. of Little Blue Bunny: Fairy Tale Story of Bunny Rabbit to the Rescue. (SPA.). (J). 2.98 (978-970-22-0018-5(0)) Larousse, Ediciones, S. A. de C. V. MEX. *Dist:* Continental Bk. Co., Inc.

Conejito Azul: Salva a los Peces.Tr. of Bunny Rabbit Saves the Fish. (SPA.). (J). 2.98 (978-970-22-0021-5(0)) Larousse, Ediciones, S. A. de C. V. MEX. *Dist:* Continental Bk. Co., Inc.

Conejito Azul: Y la Aventura de Pap Conejo.Tr. of Bunny Rabbit-Father's Adventure. (SPA.). (J). 2.98 (978-970-22-0019-2(9)) Larousse, Ediciones, S. A. de C. V. MEX. *Dist:* Continental Bk. Co., Inc.

Conlon, Mara. One Hungry Bunny. Wittwer, Hala, illus. 2003. (Reading Railroad Bks.). 14p. (J). (ps-1). bds. 5.99 (978-0-448-43121-5(1) , Grosset & Dunlap) Penguin Group (USA) Inc.

Conly, Jane Leslie. While No One Was Watching. 2000. 233p. (J). (gr. 3-7). per. 14.15 (978-0-613-28699-2(5)) Tandem Library Bks.

Connor, Joynce. Micheal & Mr. B. 2006. 48p. (J). (gr. k-3). 19.95 (978-0-9765469-1-7(4)) Diamond Cutter Pr., LLC.

Cook, Sherry & Johnson, Terri. Ronnie Rock, 26. Kuhn, Jesse, illus. l.t. ed. 2006. (Quirkles—Exploring Phonics through Science Ser.: 18). 32p. (J). 7.99 (978-1-933815-17-6(5) , Quirkles, The) Creative 3, LLC.

—Vinnie Volcano, 26. Kuhn, Jesse, illus. l.t. ed. 2006. (Quirkles—Exploring Phonics through Science Ser.: 22). 32p. (J). 7.99 (978-1-933815-21-3(3) , Quirkles, The) Creative 3, LLC.

Cooke, Tahnee. The Adventures of Rupert the Rabbit. 2004. 91p. pap. 14.95 (978-1-4137-2297-0(0)) PublishAmerica, Inc.

Cooper, Helen. Ella & the Rabbit. 1999. (Illus.). 32p. (J). (ps-k). pap. 6.99 (978-0-7112-0635-9(X)) Lincoln, Frances Ltd. GBR. *Dist:* Antique Collectors' Club.

—Tatty Ratty. Cooper, Helen, illus. 2002. (Illus.). 32p. (J). (ps-3). 16.00 (978-0-374-37386-3(8) , Farrar, Straus & Giroux (BYR)) Farrar, Straus & Giroux.

—Tatty-Ratty. Cooper, Helen, illus. 2004. (Illus.). 28p. (J). (gr. k-3). reprint ed. 19.00 (978-0-7567-7214-7(1)) DIANE Publishing Co.

Copeland, Eric, illus. Brer Rabbit & Friends. 2006. 64p. (J). (gr. 8). pap. 6.99 (978-0-7566-1813-1(4)) Dorling Kindersley Publishing, Inc.

Coronado, Jinky. Banzai Girl: Manga TPB. 2006. (YA). 9.95 (978-0-9763095-2-9(1)) Arcana Studio, Inc.

Cory, David. Little Jack Rabbit & Mr. Wicked Wolf. 2005. pap. 20.95 (978-1-4179-0098-5(9)) Kessinger Publishing, LLC.

Cosgrove, Stephen. Buttermilk. James, Robin, illus. ed. 2003. (Serendipity Ser.). 32p. (J). (gr. k-3). pap. 4.99 (978-0-8431-0487-5(2) , Price Stern Sloan) Penguin Group (USA) Inc.

—Buttermilk. 2003. (gr. k-3). lib. bdg. 13.00 (978-0-613-89165-3(1)) Tandem Library Bks.

—Leo the Lop: Tail One. 2002. (gr. k-3). lib. bdg. 13.00 (978-0-613-81290-0(5)) Tandem Library Bks.

Costello, Emily. Rabbit Rescue, No. 15. 2000. (Animal Emergency Ser.: No. 5). 128p. (J). (gr. 3-7). pap. 3.99 (978-0-380-81110-6(3)) HarperCollins Pubs.

Cote, Genevieve. With You Always, Little Monday. 2007. (Illus.). 32p. (J). (ps-2). 16.00 (978-0-15-205997-2(0)) Harcourt Children's Bks.

Cottontail's Dance. 2002. (Backyard Mini Bks.). (Illus.). 32p. (J). (978-1-59069-015-4(X) , H2004) Studio Mouse LLC.

Cousins, Lucy. Go, Maisy, Go! Cousins, Lucy, illus. 2003. (Maisy Ser.). (Illus.). 10p. (J). (gr. k-k). bds. 8.99 (978-0-7636-2118-6(8)) Candlewick Pr.

Coutu, Raymond & Jones, Dawn L. Babette & the Apple Bandit. Graef, Renee, illus. 2001. (J). (978-0-9712840-8-1(3)) Boyds Collection Ltd., The.

Cowell, Cressida. That Rabbit Belongs to Emily Brown. Layton, Neal, illus. 2007. 40p. (ps-2). 16.99 (978-1-4231-0645-6(8)) Hyperion Bks. for Children.

Cox, Judy. Rabbit Pirates: A Tale of the Spinach Main. McCully, Emily Arnold, illus. 1999. 32p. (J). (ps-3). 16.00 (978-0-15-201832-0(8)) Harcourt Children's Bks.

Crabtree, Sally. Animal Snuggles: Easter Bunny. Chambers, Sally, illus. 2005. 8p. (J). bds. 7.95 (978-1-4027-2052-9(1) , Sterling/Pinwheel) Sterling Publishing Co., Inc.

Craner, Kathy. Nibbles the Rabbit Has a Good Habit. 1998. (Illus.). (J). (ps-2). pap. 12.95 (978-0-7880-1404-8(8) , Fairway Pr.) CSS Publishing Co.

Creamer, Joan Klatil. The Magic Sceptre & Reginald the Rabbit. ed. 2007. (Illus.). 32p. (J). 16.95 (***978-0-9778476-5-5(9)***) Silver Snowflake Publishing.

Crimi, Carolyn. Henry & the Buccaneer Bunnies. Manders, John, illus. 2005. 40p. (J). (ps-3). 15.99 (978-0-7636-2449-1(7)) Candlewick Pr.

Crownover, Ashley, ed. The Velveteen Rabbit. Thompson, Pat, illus. 2002. 24p. (J). (gr. k-5). pap. 2.99 (978-1-57759-375-1(8)) Dalmatian Pr.

Crummel, Susan Stevens. Tumbleweed Stew. Stevens, Janet, illus. 2003. (Green Light Readers Level 2 Ser.). 32p. (J). 11.95 (978-0-15-204870-9(7)); pap. 3.95 (978-0-15-204830-3(8)) Harcourt Children's Bks. (Green Light Readers).

—Tumbleweed Stew. 2000. (Green Light Readers Ser.). (978-0-606-20335-7(4)); (J). (978-0-606-20173-5(4)); lib. bdg. 11.80 (978-0-613-64607-9(X)) Tandem Library Bks.

Cuyler, Margery. Road Signs: A Harey Race with a Tortoise. Haskamp, Steven, illus. 2000. 40p. (J). (ps-1). 15.95 (978-1-890817-23-7(6)) Winslow Pr.

Cuyler, Margery. Roadsigns. Haskamp, Steve, illus. 2008. (J). (***978-0-7614-5306-2(7)***) Cavendish, Marshall Corp.

Dalmatian Press Staff. Bunny Tale: Soft Spot Board Book. 2002. (Soft Spot Bks.). (Illus.). 10p. (J). bds. 3.99 (978-1-57759-626-4(9)) Dalmatian Pr.

—Disney Alice in Wonderland. 2006. 72p. (J). 9.99 (978-1-4037-2185-3(8)) Dalmatian Pr.

—Little Bunny: Little Pups. 2002. (Little Pups Board Bks.). (Illus.). 20p. (J). bds. 2.99 (978-1-57759-631-8(5)) Dalmatian Pr.

—The Velveteen Rabbit. 2004. (Illus.). 14p. (J). (ps-1). bds. 5.99 (978-1-57759-611-0(0)) Dalmatian Pr.

—The Velveteen Rabbit: Happy Tale. 2005. (Illus.). 24p. (J). 2.99 (978-1-4037-1270-7(0)) Dalmatian Pr.

DALP, ed. The Veleveteen Rabbit: Board Book with Plush Toy. 2007. 12p. 12.99 (***978-1-4037-2552-3(7)***) Dalmatian Pr.

Davis, Caroline. Bunny Book. 2001. (Illus.). 12p. (J). 5.95 (978-0-7641-5419-5(2)) Barron's Educational Series, Inc.

de Beer, Hans. Little Polar Bear & the Brave Little Hare. 2000. (Illus.). 32p. (J). (gr. k-3). pap. 6.95 (978-0-7358-1332-8(9)) North-South Bks., Inc.

—Little Polar Bear & the Brave Little Hare. de Beer, Hans, illus. 1998. (Illus.). 32p. (J). (gr. k-3). 15.95 (978-0-7358-1011-2(7)) North-South Bks., Inc.

—El Osito Polar y el Conejito Valiente. 2000. (SPA.). (gr. k-3). lib. bdg. 15.25 (978-0-613-32923-1(6)) Tandem Library Bks.

Denim, Sue & Pilkey, Dav. The Dumb Bunnies. 2005. (Bookshelf Ser.). (Illus.). 32p. (J). pap. 5.99 (978-0-439-66944-3(8)) Scholastic, Inc.

—The Dumb Bunnies' Easter. Pilkey, Dav, illus. 1998. (Dumb Bunnies Ser.). (Illus.). 32p. (J). (ps-3). pap. 4.99 (978-0-590-20242-8(1)) Scholastic, Inc.

DeRosier, Cher. The Plight of the Jelly Bean. Contreras, Gilbert, illus. 2005. (J). (978-1-891685-50-7(3)) Dearborn Publishing.

Dewan, Ted. Bing: Bed Time. 2004. 24p. (J). (gr. k-ps). 5.99 (978-0-385-75045-5(5) , Fickling, David Bks.) Random Hse. Children's Bks.

—Bing: Get Dressed. 2004. (Illus.). 24p. (J). (gr. k-ps). 5.95 (978-0-385-75020-2(X) , Fickling, David Bks.) Random Hse. Children's Bks.

—Bing: Go Picnic. 2005. (Illus.). 24p. (J). (gr. k-ps). 5.99 (978-0-385-75056-1(0) , Fickling, David Bks.) Random Hse. Children's Bks.

—Bing: Make Music. 2005. (Illus.). 24p. (J). (gr. k-ps). 5.99 (978-0-385-75057-8(9) , Fickling, David Bks.) Random Hse. Children's Bks.

—Bing: Something for Daddy. 2004. (Illus.). 24p. (J). (gr. k-ps). 5.99 (978-0-385-75046-2(3) , Fickling, David Bks.) Random Hse. Children's Bks.

Dewdney, Anna. Bad Bunnies. Dewdney, Anna, illus. 2008. 32p. (J). (ps). 12.99 (***978-0-670-06288-1(X)*** , Viking Juvenile) Penguin Group (USA) Inc.

DiCamillo, Kate. The Miraculous Journey of Edward Tulane. Ibatoulline, Bagram, illus. 2006. 228p. (J). (gr. 2). 18.99 (978-0-7636-2589-4(2)) Candlewick Pr.

Dijkstra, Lida. Cute. Tolman, Marije, illus. 2007. 28p. (J). (ps-1). 16.95 (***978-1-59078-505-8(3)*** , Lemniscaat) Boyds Mills Pr.

Dillard, Sarah, illus. Follow the Bunny. 2006. 10p. (J). (ps-1). bds. 5.99 (978-0-8431-1813-1(X) , Price Stern Sloan) Penguin Group (USA) Inc.

Dining with Prunella. 1998. (Books to Go). (J). pap. (978-0-8136-7877-1(3)) Modern Curriculum Pr.

Disney, Bunnies. Thumper Makes a Splash. rev. ed. 2008. 12p. pap. 6.99 (***978-1-4231-0431-5(5)***) Disney Pr.

Disney, Bunnies & Driscoll, Laura. Surprise for Thumper. rev. ed. 2008. 16p. 5.99 (***978-1-4231-0439-1(0)***) Disney Pr.

Disney Press Staff. Easter Bear? 2003. (gr. k-3). lib. bdg. 10.95 (978-0-613-73671-8(0)) Tandem Library Bks.

Disney Press Staff & Driscoll, Laura. I Love You, My Bunnies. Disney Storybook Artists Staff et al, illus. 2007. 32p. (J). (ps-1). 9.99 (978-1-4231-0078-2(6)) Disney Pr.

Disney Press Staff & Richards, Kitty. Goodnight, Thumper! Disney Storybook Artists Staff & Tyminski, Lori, illus. 2007. 16p. (J). (ps-k). 5.99 (978-1-4231-0077-5(8)) Disney Pr.

DK Publishing. Hop A Long Bunny: Fiberoptic Light. 2007. 16p. (J). pap. 4.99 (***978-0-7566-3447-6(4)***) Dorling Kindersley Publishing, Inc.

Dockray, Tracy. My Life Story. Dockray, Tracy, illus. 2003. (Illus.). 40p. (J). lib. bdg. 15.95 (978-1-58717-218-2(6) , SeaStar Bks.) Chronicle Bks. LLC.

Doctor Bunny: New Heroes Backpack Story. 2002. (J). (978-1-931312-57-8(5)) SoftPlay, Inc.

Donaki & Rosenberry, Donald. Spectacular Journey. Rosenberry, Akiko & Rosenberry, Susan, illus. 2006. (J). per. 20.00 (***978-0-9771482-6-4(2)*** , Ithaca Pr.) Authors & Artists Publishers of New York, Inc.

Donohue, Dorothy. Veggie Soup. 40p. (J). (ps-1). 2002. pap. 6.95 (978-1-58837-020-4(8)); 2000. (Illus.). 16.95 (978-1-890817-21-3(X)) Winslow Pr.

Dorling Kindersley Publishing Staff. Bunny. Deschamps, Nicola, ed. 2002. (Jumbo Shaped Board Bks.). (Illus.). 12p. (J). (ps-k). bds. 6.95 (978-0-7894-7855-9(2)) Dorling Kindersley Publishing, Inc.

Doudna, Kelly. Rabbit Ears. 2006. (Fact & Fiction Ser.). (Illus.). 24p. (J). 21.35 (978-1-59679-961-5(7) , SandCastle) ABDO Publishing Co.

—Rabbit Ears. Nobens, C. A., illus. 2006. (Fact & Fiction Ser.). 24p. (J). pap. (***978-1-59679-962-2(5)***) ABDO Publishing Co.

Dougherty, Mary. Life Adventures with Fossy. 2004. 7p. (J). pap. 10.58 (978-1-4116-1497-0(6)) Lulu.com.

Doyle, Charlotte. Where's Bunny's Mommy? Brown, Rick, illus. 1999. 29p. (J). (ps-k). reprint ed. 14.00 (978-0-7881-6653-2(0)) DIANE Publishing Co.

Doyle, Tara. Little Bunny's Easter Surprise. McQueen, Lucinda, illus. 2005 8p (J) bds. 1.99 (978 0 439 69682-1(8) , Cartwheel Bks.) Scholastic, Inc.

Driscoll, Laura. Thumper Finds a Friend. Disney Storybook Artists Staff & Tyminski, Lori, illus. 2008. 32p. (J). (ps-1). 9.99 (***978-1-4231-0437-7(4)***) Disney Pr.

Droop, Constanza, illus. Felix's Cookbook. 2001. 72p. (J). pap. 24.95 (978-0-7892-0750-0(8) , Abbeville Kids) Abbeville Pr., Inc.

Dub-u-el. Zoom-Zoom & Slo-Poke. 2005. (J). pap. 15.00 (978-0-8059-6808-8(3)) Dorrance Publishing Co., Inc.

Dubois, Liz Goulet. What Kind of Rabbit Are You? Dubois, Liz Goulet, illus. 2008. (Preschool Pop-Ups Ser.). 14p. (J). bds. 7.99 (***978-1-4169-4914-5(3)*** , Little Simon) Simon & Schuster Children's Publishing.

Dunbar. Tell Me What Its Like to Be Big. 2001. (Illus.). (J). 16.00 (978-0-15-204741-2(7)) Harcourt Trade Pubs.

Dunbar, Joyce. Tell Me Something Happy Before I Go to Sleep. Gliori, Debi, illus. 32p. (J). (ps-3). 1998. 17.00 (978-0-15-201795-8(X)); Set. 2003. 16.95 (978-0-15-204756-6(5) , Red Wagon Bks.) Harcourt Children's Bks.

—Tell Me What It's Like to Be Big. Gliori, Debi, illus. 32p. (J). (ps-2). 2001. 16.00 (978-0-15-202564-9(2)); 2005. reprint ed. pap. 6.00 (978-0-15-205247-8(X) , Voyager Bks./Libros Viajeros) Harcourt Children's Bks.

Duvall, Deborah L. Rabbit Goes to Kansas. 2007. (Illus.). 32p. (J). (gr. 1 up). 16.95 (***978-0-8263-4181-5(0)***) Univ. of New Mexico Pr.

Duvall, Deborah L., text. How Rabbit Lost His Tail: A Traditional Cherokee Legend. 2004. (Grandmother Stories Ser.: Vol. 3). (Illus.). 32p. (J). 14.95 (978-0-8263-3010-9(X)) Univ. of New Mexico Pr.

East, Jacqueline, illus. Bunny. 2007. (Wiggle-Waggles Ser.). 8p. (J). (ps). bds. 4.99 (***978-0-7641-6071-4(0)***) Barron's Educational Series, Inc.

Edvall, Lilian. The Rabbit Who Couldn't Find His Daddy. Dyssegaard, Elisabeth Kallick, tr. from SWE. Gimbergsson, Sara, illus. 2006. 32p. (J). 15.00 (978-91-29-66429-4(2)) R & S Bks. SWE. *Dist:* Macmillan.

Eggleton, Jill. Rabbit & Rooster's Ride: 3-in-1 Package. Taylor, Clive, illus. (Sails Literacy Ser.). 24p. (gr. k up). 57.00 (978-0-7578-8617-1(5)) Rigby Education.

—Rabbit & Rooster's Ride: 6 Small Books. Taylor, Clive, illus. (Sails Literacy Ser.). 24p. (gr. k up). 25.00 (978-0-7578-7727-8(3)) Rigby Education.

—Rabbit & Rooster's Ride: Big Book Only. Taylor, Clive, illus. (Sails Literacy Ser.). 24p. (gr. k up). 27.00 (978-0-7578-6200-7(4)) Rigby Education.

—The Rock Boss: Early Level Satellite Individual Title Six-Packs. (Sails Literacy Ser.). 16p. (gr. 1-2). 27.00 (978-0-7578-2934-5(1)) Rigby Education.

Emerson, Carl. Opie the Opossum Wakes Up. Trover, Zachary, illus. 2007. (Animal Underdogs Ser.). 32p. (J). (ps-4). lib. bdg. 27.07 (***978-1-60270-017-8(6)*** , Looking Glass Library) Magic Wagon.

Equipo Staff. El Conejo. 2000. (SPA., Illus.). 12p. (J). (ps-k). 7.95 (978-84-488-0890-7(8)) Beascoa, Ediciones S.A. ESP. *Dist:* Distribooks, Inc., Lectorum Pubns., Inc.

—Este No es Mi Conejito. 2004. Tr. of That's Not My Bunny. (SPA., Illus.). 12p. (J). (ps). 7.95 (978-0-7460-4512-1(3)) EDC Publishing.

Erickson, Betty. The Little Rabbit Who Wanted Red Wings. Durney, Ryan, illus. (J). (gr. k-2). pap. 3.75 (978-1-58323-035-0(1) , Seedling Pubns.) Continental Pr., Inc.

Evans, Lezlie. The Bunnies' Picnic. Chorao, Kay, illus. 2007. 32p. (ps-1). 16.99 (978-0-7868-1612-5(0)) Hyperion Pr.

Evans, Lezlie. The Bunnies' Trip. Chorao, Kay, illus. 2008. 32p. 16.99 (***978-0-7868-1898-3(0)***) Hyperion Bks. for Children.

Fanger, Rolf. Benjamin Bunny Learns to Fly. 2004. (Just in Time for Easter Fun! Ser.). (Illus.). 32p. (J). 10.99 (978-1-59384-042-6(X)) Parklane Publishing.

Faulkner, Keith. Bedtime, Bunny! 2004. (Illus.). 14p. (J). (ps-1). bds. 4.99 (978-0-8431-0636-7(0) , Price Stern Sloan) Penguin Group (USA) Inc.

Faye, Charlet. The Feather-Dusted Easter. Letterman, Kimberlee, illus. 1999. 48p. (J). (gr. k-3). 16.95 (978-0-9655222-0-5(2)) FayeHouse. Pr. International.

Feely, Jenny. Looking for Fang. 1999. (ps-2). lib. bdg. 11.80 (978-0-613-30566-2(3)) Tandem Library Bks.

Felton, Carol. Where's Harley? 2003. (gr. k-3). lib. bdg. 12.95 (978-0-613-79280-6(7)) Tandem Library Bks.

Felton, Carol & Felton, Amanda. Where's Harley? O'Rourke, Page Eastburn, illus. 2003. (Math Matters Ser.). 32p. (J). 4.99 (978-1-57565-132-3(7)) Kane Pr., The.

Ferri, Francesca, illus. Little Rabbit. 2003. 8p. (J). pap. 12.95 (978-0-7641-2597-3(4)) Barron's Educational Series, Inc.

First Bunny Stories. (J). Date not set. (Illus.). bds. 9.98 (978-0-7525-9170-4(3)); 2002. 47p. bds. 9.95 (978-0-7525-7038-9(2)) Parragon, Inc.

Fisher, Aileen. Do Rabbits Have Christmas, YOU. 2007. (Illus.). 32p. (J). (ps up). 16.95 (978-0-8050-7491-8(0) , Holt, Henry & Co. Bks. For Young Readers) Holt, Henry & Co.

Fleming, Candace. Muncha! Muncha! Muncha! Karas, G. Brian, illus. pap. 16.95 incl. audio (978-1-59112-463-4(8)); pap. incl. audio (978-1-59112-465-8(4)); pap. 18.95 incl. audio compact disk (978-1-59112-923-3(0)); pap. incl. audio compact disk (978-1-59112-925-7(7)) Live Oak Media.

—Muncha! Muncha! Muncha! 2004. (Illus.). (J). 25.95 incl. audio (978-1-59112-464-1(6)); 28.95 incl. audio compact disk (978-1-59112-924-0(9)) Live Oak Media.

—Muncha! Muncha! Muncha! Karas, G. Brian, illus. 2002. 32p. (J). (ps-2). 17.99 (978-0-689-83152-2(8) , Atheneum/Anne Schwartz Bks.) Simon & Schuster Children's Publishing.

—Tippy-Tippy-Tippy, Hide! Karas, G. Brian, illus. 2007. 40p. (J). (ps-3). 16.99 (978-0-689-87479-6(0) , Atheneum) Simon & Schuster Children's Publishing.

Fleming, Maria. Hippity Skippity Easter. Bratun, Katy, illus. 2004. 32p. (J). pap. 3.50 (978-0-439-56417-5(4) , Cartwheel Bks.) Scholastic, Inc.

Floppy's Friends. 2004. (J). (ALB & ENG.). (978-1-84444-647-6(6)); (ARA & ENG.). (978-1-84444-648-3(4)); (BEN & ENG.). (978-1-84444-649-0(2)); (CHI & ENG.). (978-1-84444-650-6(6)); (CHI & ENG.). (978-1-84444-651-3(4)); (CRO & ENG.). (978-1-84444-652-0(2)); (ENG & PER.). (978-1-84444-653-7(0)); (ENG & FRE.). (978-1-84444-654-4(9)); (ENG & GUJ.). (978-1-84444-655-1(7)); (ENG & HIN.). (978-1-84444-656-8(5)); (ENG & LAO.). (978-1-84444-657-5(3)); (ENG & PAN.). (978-1-84444-658-2(1)); (ENG & POL.). (978-1-84444-659-9(X)); (ENG & POR.). (978-1-84444-660-5(3)); (ENG & SOM.). (978-1-84444-661-2(1)); (ENG & SPA.). (978-1-84444-662-9(X)); (ENG & TAM.). (978-1-84444-663-6(8)); (ENG & TUR.). (978-1-84444-664-3(6)); (ENG & URD.). (978-1-84444-665-0(4)); (ENG & VIE.). (978-1-84444-666-7(2)) Mantra Publishing, Ltd.

Fontes, Justine. Clean up, Grumpy Bunny. 2006. (Illus.). (***978-0-439-68779-9(9)***) Scholastic, Inc.

Ford, Bernette. No More Bottles for Bunny! Williams, Sam, illus. 2007. 32p. (J). (ps). 12.95 (978-1-905417-34-6(9)) Boxer Bks., Ltd. GBR. *Dist:* Sterling Publishing Co., Inc.

Ford, Bernette G. First Snow. Braun, Sebastien, illus. 2005. 32p. (J). (***978-0-9547373-3-7(4)***) Boxer Bks., Ltd.

—First Snow. Braun, Sebastien, illus. 2005. 32p. (J). (ps-ps). 16.95 (978-0-8234-1937-1(1)) Holiday Hse., Inc.

Freedman, Claire. Follow That Bear If You Dare! Edgson, Alison, illus. 2008. (J). (***978-1-56148-588-8(8)***) Good Bks.

—Hushabye Lily. Bendall-Brunello, John, illus. 2003. 32p. (J). (ps-1). pap. 15.95 (978-0-439-47106-0(0) , Orchard Bks.) Scholastic, Inc.

—Oops-a-Daisy! Hansen, Gaby, illus. 32p. (J). 2004. tchr. ed. 15.95 (978-1-58925-037-6(0)); 2006. reprint ed. 6.95 (978-1-58925-398-8(1)) ME Media LLC. (tiger tales).

French, Vivian & Ayliffe, Alex. Not Again Anna! (Illus.). (J). 1999. 32p. pap. 6.95 (978-1-86233-077-1(8)); 1998. 24p. 14.95 (978-1-899607-96-9(X)) Sterling Publishing Co., Inc.

Friedrich, Priscilla & Friedrich, Otto. The Easter Bunny That Overslept. Saaf, Donald, illus. 2002. 32p. (J). (ps-3). 16.99 (978-0-06-029645-2(3)); lib. bdg. 17.89 (978-0-06-029646-9(1)) HarperCollins Pubs.

Fry, Sonali. Bang! Clang! 2005. (Ready-to-Read Ser.). (J). pap. 3.99 (978-0-689-87419-2(7) , Simon Spotlight) Simon & Schuster Children's Publishing.

Fuerst, Jeff. Lion & Rabbit: A Fable from India. 2006. spiral bd. 23.00 (***978-1-4108-7156-5(8)***) Benchmark Education Co.

Fuller, Suzy. Andrew Discovers A Cottontail. 2005. (Illus.). 30p. (J). per. 9.99 (978-1-932338-77-5(2)) Lifevest Publishing, Inc.

Galbraith, Kathryn Osebold. One Shy Bunny, One Dark Night. Mack, Jeff, illus. 2008. (J). (***978-0-15-216246-7(1)***) Harcourt Trade Pubs.

Gallagher, Kristin Ellerbusch. Cottontail Rabbits. (Pull Ahead Bks.). (Illus.). 32p. (gr. k-3). 2005. lib. bdg. 22.60 (978-0-8225-3617-8(X)); 2003. (J). pap. 5.95 (978-0-8225-3623-9(4)) Lerner Publishing Group.

Gantschev, Ivan. The Rabbit & the Bear: A Christmas Tale. Gantschev, Ivan, illus. 2007. (Illus.). 32p. (J). (ps). 16.95 (***978-0-7358-2145-3(3)***) North-South Bks., Inc.

Garis, Howard Roger. Johnnie & Billie Bushytail. 2006. (ENG.). 248p. per. 17.95 (978-1-59462-365-3(1) , 401, Book Jungle) Standard Pubns., Inc.

—Johnnie & Billie Bushytail - 1910. 2006. (ENG.). 248p. per. 17.95 (978-1-59462-366-0(X) , 402, Book Jungle) Standard Pubns., Inc.

—Listen & Read Uncle Wiggily Stories. 1998. (Illus.). 66p. (gr. 3-6). pap. 7.95 (978-0-486-40102-7(2)) Dover Pubns., Inc.

—Uncle Wiggily in the Woods. 2006. 41.99 (***978-1-4280-1466-4(7)***); pap. 34.99 (***978-1-4280-1462-6(4)***) IndyPublish.com.

—Uncle Wiggilys Adventures. 2006. 77.99 (***978-1-4280-3867-7(1)***); pap. 71.99 (***978-1-4280-3852-3(3)***) IndyPublish.com.

—Uncle Wiggily's Travels. 2006. pap. 26.99 (***978-1-4280-4239-1(3)***) IndyPublish.com.

Garrido, Felipe. El Coyote Tonto. Gonzalez, Francisco, illus. 2003. (Infantil Alfaguara Ser.). (SPA.). 60p. (J). (gr. 3-5). pap. 10.95 (978-968-19-0277-3(7)) Santillana USA Publishing Co., Inc.

Gay, Marie-Louise. Rabbit Blue. 2005. (Illus.). 32p. (J). (ps-ps). pap. 7.95 (978-1-55005-083-7(4)) Fitzhenry & Whiteside, Ltd.

Genechten, Guido van. Flop-Ear. 2002. (Illus.). (J). (978-0-7641-5543-7(1)) Barron's Educational Series, Inc.

—Floppy. 2004. (Illus.). (J). (TAM, VIE, GUJ, WEL & URD.). 28p. (978-1-85269-516-3(1)); (TAM, VIE, GUJ, WEL & URD., 28p. (978-1-85269-517-0(X)); (TAM, VIE, GUJ, WEL & URD., 28p. (978-1-85269-523-1(4)); (TAM, VIE, GUJ, WEL & URD., 28p. (978-1-85269-524-8(2)); (TAM, VIE, GUJ, WEL & URD., 28p. (978-1-85269-525-5(0)); (TAM, VIE, GUJ, WEL & URD., 28p. (978-1-85269-526-2(9)); (TAM, VIE, GUJ, WEL & URD., 28p. (978-1-85269-527-9(7)); (TAM, VIE, GUJ, WEL & URD., 28p. (978-1-85269-529-3(3)); (TAM, VIE, GUJ, WEL & URD., 28p. (978-1-85269-530-9(7)); (POR, TAM, VIE, CHI & ARA., 26p. (978-1-85269-518-7(8)); (POR, TAM, VIE, ARA & CHI., 26p. (978-1-85269-519-4(6)); (TAM, VIE, GUJ, WEL & URD., 25p. (978-1-85269-520-0(X)); (TAM, VIE, GUJ, WEL & URD., 25p. (978-1-85269-522-4(6)) Mantra Publishing, Ltd.

—Robbie. 2004. (TAM, VIE, GUJ, WEL & URD., Illus.). 25p. (J). (978-1-85269-528-6(5)) Mantra Publishing, Ltd.

Genechten, Guido van, tr. from DUT. Floppy in the Dark: Floppy Dans le Noir. 2004. (TAM, CZE, VIE, SPA & GUJ., Illus.). 25p. (J). (978-1-85269-242-1(1)) Mantra Publishing, Ltd.

George, Lindsay B. My Bunny & Me. 2001. (Illus.). 32p. (J). (ps up). 15.89 (978-0-688-16075-3(1)) HarperCollins Pubs.

Ghana National Association Of Teachers Staff. The Lazy Little Rabbit. 1999. pap. (978-9964-72-165-7(X)) Sedco Publishing, Ltd.

Gill, Janie S. Why Rabbits Ears Are Long Today. Reese, Robert, illus. 1999. 23p. (J). 5.95 (978-0-89868-477-3(3)); pap. 3.95 (978-0-89868-476-6(5)); lib. bdg. 10.95 (978-0-89868-475-9(7)) ARO Publishing Co.

Glaser, Shirley. The Big Race. Glaser, Milton & Glaser, Shirley, illus. 2005. 32p. (ps-2). 16.99 (978-0-7868-1821-1(2)) Hyperion Bks. for Children.

Gliori, Debi. Flora's Blanket. Gliori, Debi, illus. 2001. (Illus.). 32p. (J). (ps-1). pap. 15.95 (978-0-531-30305-4(5) , Orchard Bks.) Scholastic, Inc.

—Flora's Surprise! 2003. (Illus.). 32p. (J). (ps-1). pap. 15.95 (978-0-439-45590-9(1) , Orchard Bks.) Scholastic, Inc.

Gobo Books Staff. Up Goes the Bunny. 2006. 10p. (J). 9.95 (978-1-932915-11-2(7)) Sandvik Innovations, LLC.

Golden Books Staff. Grandpa Bunny. 2007. (Little Golden Book Ser.). (Illus.). 24p. (J). (gr. k-k). 2.99 (978-0-375-83930-6(5) , Golden/Disney) Random Hse. Children's Bks.

—Here Comes Peter Cottontail. Karl, Linda & Nowell, Christopher, illus. 2004. 24p. (J). (ps-2). pap. 3.99 (978-0-375-82725-9(0) , Golden Bks.) Random Hse. Children's Bks.

—Pat the Bunny Alphabet Book. LV Studio Staff, illus. 2006. (Pat the Bunny Ser.). 30p. (J). (gr. k-ps). 10.95 (978-0-375-83550-6(4) , Golden Bks.) Random Hse. Children's Bks.

—Peter Cottontail: A Colorful Easter. 2001. 32p. (J). (ps-2). pap. 3.99 (978-0-307-09225-0(9) , Golden Bks.) Random Hse. Children's Bks.

—Sleepy Bunny. 2003. (Cloth Book Ser.). (Illus.). 8p. (J). (gr. k-k). 12.95 (978-0-375-82531-6(2) , Golden Bks.) Random Hse. Children's Bks.

—Tawny Scrawny Lion. 2001. (Little Golden Bks.). (Illus.). 24p. (J). (gr. k-k). 2.99 (978-0-307-02168-7(8) , 98093, Golden Bks.) Random Hse. Children's Bks.

Goodnight Moon. 2004. (J). 24.95 incl. audio (978-0-89719-774-8(7)); pap. 32.75 incl. audio (978-1-55592-233-7(3)); pap. 32.75 incl. audio (978-1-55592-234-4(1)) Weston Woods Studios, Inc.

Gorbachev, Valeri. Christopher Counting. Gorbachev, Valeri, illus. 2008. 32p. (J). (ps). 15.99 (***978-0-399-24629-6(0)*** , Philomel) Penguin Group (USA) Inc.

Gorbachev, Valeri. Nico Y Los Lobos Feroces. 2000. (SPA.). (gr. k-3). lib. bdg. 15.25 (978-0-613-32887-6(6)) Tandem Library Bks.

Gore, Leonid. Danny's First Snow. Gore, Leonid, illus. 2007. 40p. (J). (ps-2). 16.99 (978-1-4169-1330-6(0)) Simon & Schuster Children's Publishing.

Got, Yves. Sweet Dreams, Sam. 2000. (Illus.). 14p. (J). (ps). 9.95 (978-0-8118-2985-4(5)) Chronicle Bks. LLC.

Gravett, Emily. Wolves. Gravett, Emily, illus. 2006. (Illus.). 40p. (J). (gr. k-3). 16.99 (978-1-4169-1491-4(9) , Simon & Schuster Children's Publishing) Simon & Schuster Children's Publishing.

Gray, Kes. Our Twitchy. McQuillan, Mary, illus. rev. ed. 2003. 32p. (J). 15.95 (978-0-8050-7454-3(6) , Holt, Henry & Co. Bks. For Young Readers) Holt, Henry & Co.

Gretz, Susanna. Rabbit Food. Gretz, Susanna, illus. 2001. (Illus.). 32p. (J). (ps-2). pap. 6.99 (978-0-7636-1293-1(6)) Candlewick Pr.

Grindley, Sally, et al. Pam Mae'r Awyr Yn Las? Stori Gan Sally Grindley. 2005. (WEL., Illus.). 25p. (978-1-85596-265-1(9)) Dref Wen.

Grist, Paul. Rabbit Hunt. (Kane Ser.: Vol. 2). 144p. (YA). pap. 12.95 (978-1-58240-355-7(4)) Image Comics.

Gruetzke, Mary, ed. Bunny Book & Purse. McDonald, Jill, illus. 2006. 8p. (J). bds. 5.99 (978-0-439-73022-8(8) , Cartwheel Bks.) Scholastic, Inc.

Guarnieri, Rossana. Fiabe della Buonanotte. pap. 26.95 (978-88-09-02216-4(5)) Giunti, Gruppo Editoriale ITA. *Dist:* Distribooks, Inc.

Guest, C. Z. Tiny Green Thumbs. Krupinski, Loretta, illus. 2000. 32p. (ps-2). 15.99 (978-0-7868-0516-7(1)) Hyperion Bks. for Children.

Hagen, Oddmund. Campo Abierto (Open Field) Santos, Nuria G., tr. from NOR. Dezakin, Akin, illus. 2003. (Rosa y Manzana Ser.). (SPA.). 32p. 16.95 (978-84-89804-42-5(7)) Loguez Ediciones ESP. *Dist:* Baker & Taylor Bks., Lectorum Pubns., Inc.

Hague. Tale of Peter Rabbit. 2005. (Illus.). 32p. (J). pap. 6.95 (978-0-8118-4906-7(6)) Chronicle Bks. LLC.

Hall, Kirsten. Bunny, Bunny. 2004. (My First Reader Ser.). (J). (gr. k-1). pap. 3.95 (978-0-516-24625-3(9) , Children's Pr.) Scholastic Library Publishing.

Hamilton, Elizabeth L. Jeremy Rabbit's Honesty Pie. 2003. (Character Critters Ser.: No. 2). (Illus.). 32p. (J). (ps-3). per. 5.95 (978-0-9713749-5-9(3) , Character-in-Action) Quiet Impact, Inc.

Hamilton, Martha & Weiss, Mitch. Tricky Rabbit. Paris, Pat, illus. 2005. 12p. (J). pap. 5.00 (978-1-57274-716-6(1) , 2786, Bks. for Young Learners) Owen, Richard C. Pubs., Inc.

Hample, Stoo. I Will Kiss You (Lots & Lots & Lots!) 2006. (Illus.). 32p. (J). (ps up). 15.99 (978-0-7636-2787-4(9)) Candlewick Pr.

Haneberg, Janet. Eggie Rabbit. 2006. 37p. (J). pap. 15.23 (978-1-4116-4157-0(4)) Lulu.com.

Harcourt School Publishers Staff. The Best Home: Take-Home Book. rev. ed. 2001. (Collections Ser.: Bk. 10). (Illus.). (J). pap. 1.90 (978-0-15-319068-1(X)) Harcourt Schl. Pubs.

—Bunny Cakes: Library Book. 1999. (Collections Ser.). (Illus.). pap. 14.90 (978-0-15-313403-6(8)) Harcourt Schl. Pubs.

—The Enormous Carrot: Library Book. 1999. (Collections Ser.). (Illus.). pap. 13.60 (978-0-15-313400-5(3)) Harcourt Schl. Pubs.

—Help! Take-Home Book. 1999. (Collections Ser.). (Illus.). (J). pap. 1.90 (978-0-15-317224-3(X)) Harcourt Schl. Pubs.

—Help! Below Level. 3rd ed. 2002. (Trophies Reading Program Ser.). (Illus.). pap. 5.10 (978-0-15-323047-9(9)) Harcourt Schl. Pubs.

—In the Desert: Take-Home Book. rev. ed. 2001. (Collections Ser.: Bk. 17). (Illus.). (J). pap. 1.90 (978-0-15-319075-9(2)) Harcourt Schl. Pubs.

—No, No Rabbit: Take-Home Book. 1999. (Signatures Ser.). (Illus.). (J). pap. 1.70 (978-0-15-314556-8(0)) Harcourt Schl. Pubs.

—The Polar Bear & the Brave Hare: Library Edition. 1999. (Collections Ser.). (Illus.). (J). 4.70 (978-0-15-314306-9(1)) Harcourt Schl. Pubs.

—Rabbit Has Some Fun: Take-Home Book. 1999. (Signatures Ser.). (Illus.). (J). pap. 1.90 (978-0-15-313892-8(0)) Harcourt Schl. Pubs.

—Rella Rabbit: Take-Home Book. 1999. (Signatures Ser.). (Illus.). (J). pap. 1.70 (978-0-15-313842-3(4)) Harcourt Schl. Pubs.

—Sister Rabbit: Take-Home Book. 1999. (Collections Ser.). (Illus.). (J). pap. 1.90 (978-0-15-317204-5(5)) Harcourt Schl. Pubs.

The Hare & the Tortoise: Individual Title Six-Packs. 32p. (gr. 2 up). 37.00 (978-0-7635-9219-6(6)) Rigby Education.

Harry, Rebecca, illus. Little Bunny. 2006. (Noisy Farm Babies Ser.). 8p. (J). bds. 5.99 (978-0-7641-5934-3(8)) Barron's Educational Series, Inc.

Hartzell, Andy. Fox Bunny Funny. 2007. 104p. pap. 10.00 (***978-1-891830-97-6(X)***) Top Shelf Productions.

Harwood, Beth. The Easter Basket. Ronchi, Susanna, illus. 2007. 10p. (J). (ps). 15.99 (978-0-525-47846-1(9) , Dutton Juvenile) Penguin Group (USA) Inc.

Hayes, Geoffrey. A Night-Light for Bunny. Date not set. 32p. (J). (ps-3). pap. 5.99 (978-0-06-443728-8(0)) HarperCollins Pubs.

—A Night-Light for Bunny. Hayes, Geoffrey, illus. 2004. (Illus.). 32p. (J). (ps-3). 14.99 (978-0-06-029163-1(X)) HarperCollins Pubs.

Heap, Sue. Four Friends in the Garden. Heap, Sue, illus. 2004. (Illus.). 32p. (J). (gr. k-ps). 15.99 (978-0-7636-2371-5(7)) Candlewick Pr.

Henderson, Malcolm. Katie & Her Friends. Moss, P. Buckley, illus. 1998. 32p. (J). (ps-3). 15.95 (978-0-9665198-0-8(9) , 0998001000) Moss Portfolio, The.

Henkes, Kevin. So Happy! Lobel, Anita, illus. 2005. 32p. (J). 15.99 (978-0-06-056483-4(0)); lib. bdg. 16.89 (978-0-06-056484-1(9)) HarperCollins Pubs.

Henry, Rohan. The Perfect Gift. 2007. (Illus.). 32p. 8.95 (***978-1-58479-658-9(8)***) Abrams, Harry N. , Inc.

Henson, Heather, et al. The Vampire Bunny. Mack, Jeff, tr. Mack, Jeff, illus. 2004. (Bunnicula & Friends Ser.: Vol. 1). 48p. (J). 14.95 (978-0-689-85724-9(1) , Atheneum) Simon & Schuster Children's Publishing.

Here Comes Easter Bunny. 1999. (Easter Mini Storybooks Ser.: Vol. 2). (Illus.). 32p. (J). (978-0-7666-0248-9(6) , Honey Bear Bks.) Modern Publishing.

Hermes, Patricia. Hoppy Easter. 1998. (Little Apple Ser.). (J). (gr. 1-4). pap. 3.50 (978-0-590-38365-3(5) , Scholastic Paperbacks) Scholastic, Inc.

Hesel, Alma (Trish). Billy Bunny's First Day Out. 2005. pap. 7.95 (978-0-533-14998-8(3)) Vantage Pr., Inc.

Hiebert, Elfrieda H. & Juel, Connie. Where Does the Rabbit Hop? (Little Book Practice Reader Ser.). (J). (978-0-8136-0794-8(9)) Modern Curriculum Pr.

Higginson, Sheila Sweeny. Thumper's Fluffy Tail. rev. ed. 2008. 12p. 6.99 (***978-1-4231-0443-8(9)***) Disney Pr.

Hill, Karen. Grandmother's Book of Promises. Clar, David Austin, illus. 2000. 48p. (J). (ps-2). 9.99 (978-1-57856-221-3(X) , WaterBrook Pr.) WaterBrook Pr.

Hillert, Margaret. The Baby Bunny. 2002. (Illus.). (J). 15.00 (978-0-7587-9495-6(9)) Book Wholesalers, Inc.

—Baby Bunny. (Illus.). (J). 4.95 (978-0-87895-653-1(0)) Modern Curriculum Pr.

Hinkle, Clark Thomas. Doctor Rabbit & Brushtail the Fox. 2006. pap. 33.99 (***978-1-4280-4109-7(5)***) IndyPublish.com.

Hodgson, Mona Gansberg. Jumping Jokers. 1999. (Desert Critter Friends Ser.: Vol. 7). (Illus.). 48p. (J). (ps-2). 4.99 (978-0-570-05481-8(8)) Concordia Publishing Hse.

—Jumping Jokers. 1999. (ps-2). lib. bdg. 13.00 (978-0-613-72657-3(X)) Tandem Library Bks.

—Sour Snacks. Sharp, Chris, illus. 1998. (Desert Critter Friends Ser.: Vol. 3). 48p. (J). (ps-2). 4.99 (978-0-570-05070-4(7) , 56-1894) Concordia Publishing Hse.

—Sour Snacks. 1998. (ps-2). lib. bdg. 13.00 (978-0-613-72806-5(8)) Tandem Library Bks.

Hollar, Cheryl Faye. Billy the Bunny Goes to the State Fair. 2005. (J). pap. 7.97 (978-0-9763826-0-7(1)) Hollar, Cheryl Public Relations.

Holmes, Melody Moore. Buenos Dias, Carlitos! Garvin, Elaine, illus. 1999. Tr. of Good Day, Carlitos. (SPA.). 32p. (J). (ps-1). pap. 6.49 (978-1-57924-230-5(8) , 115022) Jones, Bob Univ. Pr.

Honigsberg, Peter Jan. Pillow of Dreams. Morse, Tony, illus. 2004. 32p. (gr. k-4). 17.95 (978-1-57143-076-2(8)) RDR Bks.

Hop-along Bunny. 2004. (J). per. (978-1-57657-515-4(2)) Paradise Pr., Inc.

Hope, Laura Lee. The Story of a Candy Rabbit. 2006. pap. 87.99 (***978-1-4280-0272-2(3)***) IndyPublish.com.

Horse, Harry. Little Rabbit Lost. 2005. (Illus.). 32p. (J). (ps). per. 9.95 (978-1-56145-345-0(5) , Peachtree Junior) Peachtree Pubs., Ltd.

—Little Rabbit Lost. Horse, Harry, illus. 2002. (Illus.). 30p. (J). (ps-1). 15.95 (978-1-56145-273-6(4)) Peachtree Pubs., Ltd.

Horse, Harry, illus. Little Rabbit Goes to School. 2004. 32p. (J). 15.95 (978-1-56145-320-7(X)) Peachtree Pubs., Ltd.

—Little Rabbit Runaway. 2005. 30p. (J). 15.95 (978-1-56145-343-6(9)) Peachtree Pubs., Ltd.

Horse, Harry, illus. Little Rabbit's Christmas. 2007. 32p. (J). (ps-1). 15.95 (***978-1-56145-419-8(2)*** , Peachtree Junior) Peachtree Pubs., Ltd.

Houston, Julie. Too Many Bunnies. 1998. (Illus.). 24p. (J). (gr. k-3). reprint ed. pap. 3.99 (978-0-87406-906-8(8) , Willowisp Pr.) Darby Creek Publishing.

How Rabbit Caught the Sun: Individual Title Six-Packs. (Story Steps Ser.). (gr. k-2). 32.00 (978-0-7635-9811-2(9)) Rigby Education.

Howard, Katherine. Little Bunny Follows His Nose. Miller, J. P., illus. 2004. (Scratch & Sniff Bks.). 32p. (J). (gr. k-k). 8.99 (978-0-375-82644-3(0) , Golden Bks.) Random Hse. Children's Bks.

Howe, Deborah & Howe, James. A Rabbit-Tale of Mystery. unabr. ed. 2004. (Bunnicula Ser.). 98p. (J). (gr. 3-7). pap. 29.00 incl. audio (978-0-8072-8204-5(9) , YYA139SP, Listening Library) Random Hse. Audio Publishing Group.

—A Rabbit-Tale of Mystery. Daniel, Alan, illus. 2006. 128p. (J). pap. 4.99 (978-1-4169-2817-1(0) , Aladdin) Simon & Schuster Children's Publishing.

Howe, James. Bonicula: Una Historia de Misterio Conejil. 2000. Tr. of Bunnicula. (SPA.). (gr. 3-6). lib. bdg. 14.15 (978-0-613-85443-6(8)) Tandem Library Bks.

—Bunnicula & Friends: Hot Fudge. Mack, Jeff, illus. 2004. 42p. (J). lib. bdg. 15.00 (*978-1-4242-1149-4(2)) Fitzgerald Bks.

—Bunnicula-in-a-Box: Bunnicula, the Celery Stalks at Midnight, Howliday Inn. 2006. 496p. (J). pap. 14.99 (978-1-4169-3498-1(7) , Aladdin) Simon & Schuster Children's Publishing.

—Bunnicula Strikes Again! 2004. (Bunnicula Ser.). 116p. (J). (gr. 3-7). pap. 29.00 incl. audio (978-0-8072-8213-7(8) , Listening Library) Random Hse. Audio Publishing Group.

—Bunnicula Strikes Again! Daniel, Alan, illus. (Bunnicula Ser.). (J). 2007. 144p. pap. 5.99 (*978-1-4169-3968-9(7) , Aladdin); 1999. 128p. (gr. 3-5). 16.00 (978-0-689-81463-1(1) , Atheneum) Simon & Schuster Children's Publishing.

—Bunnicula Strikes Again! 2001. (Bunnicula Ser.). (gr. 3-6). lib. bdg. 13.00 (978-0-613-49480-9(6)) Tandem Library Bks.

—The Celery Stalks at Midnight. unabr. ed. 2004. (Bunnicula Ser.). 111p. (J). (gr. 3-7). pap. 29.00 incl. audio (978-0-8072-8357-8(6) , YA173SP, Listening Library) Random Hse. Audio Publishing Group.

—The Celery Stalks at Midnight. Morrill, Leslie H., illus. 2006. (Bunnicula Ser.). 144p. (J). pap. 4.99 (978-1-4169-2814-0(6) , Aladdin) Simon & Schuster Children's Publishing.

—The Celery Stalks at Midnight. 2002. (Bunnicula Ser.). (gr. 3-6). lib. bdg. 13.00 (978-0-613-50190-3(X)) Tandem Library Bks.

—Creepy-Crawly Birthday. Morrill, Leslie H., illus. 1999. (Bunnicula & Friends Ser.). 48p. (J). (gr. k-3). pap. 5.95 (978-0-688-16700-4(4)) HarperCollins Pubs.

—The Fright Before Christmas. 1999. (Bunnicula & Friends Ser.). (J). (gr. k-3). (978-0-606-17244-8(0)) Tandem Library Bks.

—Harold & Chester Stories. Date not set. (Bunnicula & Friends Ser.). (J). (gr. k-3). (978-0-688-10298-2(0)); lib. bdg. (978-0-688-10299-9(9)) HarperCollins Pubs.

—Hot Fudge. Mack, Jeff, tr. Mack, Jeff, illus. 2004. (Bunnicula & Friends Ser.). 48p. (J). 14.95 (978-0-689-85725-6(X) , Atheneum) Simon & Schuster Children's Publishing.

—Hot Fudge. 1999. (Bunnicula & Friends Ser.). (J). (gr. k-3). (978-0-606-17394-0(3)) Tandem Library Bks.

—Howliday Inn. unabr. ed. 2004. (Bunnicula Ser.). 195p. (J). (gr. 3-7). pap. 29.00 incl. audio (978-0-8072-8382-0(7) , YA179SP, Listening Library) Random Hse. Audio Publishing Group.

—Rabbit-Cadabra! Daniel, Alan, illus. 1999. (Bunnicula & Friends Ser.). 48p. (J). (gr. k-3). pap. 5.95 (978-0-688-16699-1(7)) HarperCollins Pubs.

—Rabbit-Cadabra! Mack, Jeff, illus. 2006. (Bunnicula & Friends Ser.: Vol. 4). 48p. (J). 14.95 (978-0-689-85727-0(6) , Atheneum) Simon & Schuster Children's Publishing.

—Rabbit-cadabra! Mack, Jeff, illus. 2007. (Bunnicula & Friends Ser.). 48p. (J). pap. 3.99 (*978-0-689-85752-2(7) , Aladdin) Simon & Schuster Children's Publishing.

—Scared Silly. Morrill, Leslie H., illus. 1998. (Bunnicula & Friends Ser.). 48p. (J). (gr. k-3). pap. 4.95 (978-0-688-16322-8(X)) HarperCollins Pubs.

—Scared Silly. Mack, Jeff, illus. (Bunnicula & Friends Ser.). (J). 2006. 40p. pap. 3.99 (978-0-689-85751-5(9) , Aladdin); 2005. 48p. 14.95 (978-0-689-85726-3(8) , Atheneum) Simon & Schuster Children's Publishing.

—The Vampire Bunny. Mack, Jeff, illus. 2005. (Bunnicula & Friends Ser.). 48p. (J). pap. 3.99 (978-0-689-85749-2(7) , Aladdin) Simon & Schuster Children's Publishing.

Hubbell, Patricia. Rabbit Moon: A Book of Holidays & Celebrations. Watson, Wendy, illus. 2002. 32p. (J). (ps-3). 15.95 (978-0-7614-5103-7(X) , Cavendish Children's Bks.) Cavendish, Marshall Corp.

The Hungry Baby Bunny. (J). (gr. k-3). 30.00 (978-0-8431-4169-6(7) , Price Stern Sloan) Penguin Group (USA) Inc.

Ichikawa, Satomi. La-La Rose. Ichikawa, Satomi, illus. 2004. (Illus.). 40p. (J). (ps). 15.99 (978-0-399-24029-4(2) , Philomel) Penguin Group (USA) Inc.

Isbrecht, Lucky. Rooster's Rescue. 2004. (Illus.). 23p. (J). (ps-7). per. 4.95 (978-1-59453-262-7(1) , 2690) Airleaf Publishing & Bookselling.

Ives, Penny. Rabbit Pie. 2006. (Illus.). 32p. (J). (ps-1). 15.99 (978-0-670-05951-5(X) , Viking Adult) Penguin Group (USA) Inc.

Jacques, Brian. The Long Patrol. Curless, Allan, illus. 2004. (Redwall Ser.). 368p. (YA). pap. 8.99 (978-0-14-240245-0(1) , Puffin) Penguin Group (USA) Inc.

James, Brian. Easter Bunny's on His Way! 2005. pap. (*978-0-439-74530-7(6)) Scholastic, Inc.

James, Catherine. Bobby Cottontail's Gift. Collier, Kevin Scott, illus. 2006. 32p. (J). E-Book 9.95 incl. cd-rom (978-1-933090-24-5(3)) Guardian Angel Publishing, Inc.

Jammes, Francis. Romance of the Rabbit. 2006. 77.99 (*978-1-4280-0048-3(8)); pap. 70.99 (*978-1-4280-0047-6(X)) IndyPublish.com.

Jarrell, Randall. The Gingerbread Rabbit. Williams, Garth, illus. 64p. (J). 2004. pap. 6.95 (978-0-06-053302-1(1) , Harper Trophy); 2003. 16.95 (978-0-06-052768-6(4)) HarperCollins Pubs.

—Gingerbread Rabbit. 2004. (gr. k-3). lib. bdg. 15.30 (978-0-613-70970-5(5)) Tandem Library Bks.

Jay, Alison, illus. The Race. 2006. 32p. (J). reprint ed. pap. 6.95 (978-0-8118-5226-5(1)) Chronicle Bks. LLC.

Jennings, Richard W. Orwell's Luck. 2006. 160p. (J). (gr. 5-9). pap. 5.95 (978-0-618-69335-1(1)) Houghton Mifflin Co.

—Orwell's Luck. 2000. (Illus.). 160p. (J). (gr. 5-9). tchr. ed. 15.00 (978-0-618-03628-8(8) , Walter Lorraine) Houghton Mifflin Co. Trade & Reference Div.

Jeram, Anita. All Together Now. Jeram, Anita, illus. 2005. (Illus.). 40p. (J). (gr. k-k). reprint ed. pap. 5.99 (978-0-7636-2690-7(2)) Candlewick Pr.

—Bunny, My Honey. Jeram, Anita, illus. 2001. (Illus.). 40p. (J). (gr. k-ps). bds. 6.99 (978-0-7636-1201-6(4)) Candlewick Pr.

—Bunny My Honey. Jeram, Anita, illus. 2006. (Illus.). 32p. (J). (ps). reprint ed. pap. 4.99 (978-0-7636-3217-5(1)) Candlewick Pr.

—I Love My Little Storybook. Jeram, Anita, illus. 2002. (Illus.). 32p. (J). (gr. k-k). 12.99 (978-0-7636-1698-4(3)) Candlewick Pr.

—Me Gusta Mi Libro de Cuentos. Mlawer, Teresa, tr. (SPA.). (J). (ps-k). 14.95 (978-1-930332-29-4(7) , LC5087) Lectorum Pubns., Inc.

JJ Rabbit & the Monster: Level K, 6 vols. 128p. (gr. 2-3). 49.95 (978-0-7699-0981-3(7)) Shortland Pubns. (U. S. A.) Inc.

Johannes, Avril & Branham, Jan. Bunny an Alaskan Hare. 2006. 32p. 7.95 (978-0-9749360-3-1(0)) Icilcle Falls Publishing Co.

Johnson, Jane. Are You Ready for Bed? Hansen, Gaby, illus. 2004. 32p. (J). tchr. ed. 14.95 (978-1-58925-017-8(6) , tiger tales) ME Media LLC.

—Little Bunny's Bathtime! 2004. (Illus.). 32p. (J). tchr. ed. 15.95 (978-1-58925-043-7(5) , tiger tales) ME Media LLC.

—Little Bunny's Bedtime. Hansen, Gaby, illus. 2006. Orig. Title: Are You Ready for Bed?. 16p. (J). bds. 6.95 (978-1-58925-773-3(1) , tiger tales) ME Media LLC.

Johnson, Kimberly P. The Adventures of the Itty Bitty Bunny. 2004. (Illus.). 24p. (gr. k-2). 14.95 (978-1-57197-155-5(6)) Pentland Pr., Inc.

Johnson, Paul Brett, tr. & illus. Little Bunny Foo Foo: Told & Sung by the Good Fairy. Johnson, Paul Brett, illus. 2004. 32p. (J). pap. 15.95 (978-0-439-37301-2(8)) Scholastic, Inc.

Johnson, Regan. Little Bunny Kung Fu. Johnson, Regan, illus. 2005. (Illus.). 32p. (J). 16.95 (978-0-9769417-8-1(3)) Blooming Tree Pr.

Johnston, Tony. The Tale of Rabbit & Coyote. DePaola, Tomie, illus. 1998. 32p. (J). (ps-ps). pap. 6.99 (978-0-698-11630-6(5) , Putnam Juvenile) Penguin Group (USA) Inc.

—The Tale of Rabbit & Coyote. de Paola, Tomie, illus. 1998. (978-0-606-13834-5(X)) Tandem Library Bks.

Jones, E. Payson, 3rd. The Penny Tree Stories: Bumble Bunny & the Enchanted Forest. 2002. ring bd. 20.00 (978-0-9729194-0-1(6)) Jones, E. Payson.

Jones, Nancy. The Grandpaws. 2005. 57p. pap. 12.95 (978-1-4137-4778-2(7)) PublishAmerica, Inc.

Journey of Egg & Rabbit by Lee Grass Whitefeather. 2004. (YA). cd-rom (978-0-9767413-5-0(0)) Wakinglion Studio.

Julian, Alison. Brave as a Bunny Can Be. Julian, Alison, illus. 2001. (Illus.). 40p. (J). (gr. 2 up). 15.95 (978-0-931674-46-4(8)) Waldman Hse. Pr., Inc.

Just Bunny & Me: Big Book. (Pebble Soup Explorations Ser.). (SPA.). 16p. (ps up). 31.00 (978-0-7578-1666-6(5)) Rigby Education.

Just Bunny & Me: Small Book. (Pebble Soup Explorations Ser.). (SPA.). 16p. (ps up). 5.00 (978-0-7578-1706-9(8)) Rigby Education.

Kaminsky, Jeff & Atwater, Martha. Bunny. 2002. (Stickamajigs Ser.: Vol. 4). (Illus.). 8p. (ps-1). 5.99 (978-0-7868-0713-0(X)) Hyperion Bks. for Children.

Karon, Jan. Jeremy: The Tale of an Honest Bunny. Weidner, Teri, illus. 80p. 2003. 8.99 (978-0-14-250004-0(6) , Puffin); 2000. (J). (gr. 4-7). 15.99 (978-0-670-88104-8(X) , Viking Juvenile) Penguin Group (USA) Inc.

Keilbart, L. S. One. Benson, Barbara, illus. 2007. 76p. (J). pap. 10.95 (*978-1-85756-610-9(6)) Janus Publishing Co. GBR. *Dist:* Independent Pubs. Group.

Keller, Holly. What a Hat! Keller, Holly, illus. 2003. (Illus.). 24p. (J). 15.99 (978-0-06-051479-2(5)) HarperCollins Pubs.

Keller, Laurie. Do unto Otters: A Book about Manners. 2007. (Illus.). 40p. (J). (gr. k-3). 16.95 (*978-0-8050-7996-8(3)) Holt, Henry & Co.

Kerr, Judith. Cuando Hitler Robo el Conejo Rosa. (SPA.). 272p. (J). 9.95 (978-84-204-4791-9(9)) Alfaguara, Ediciones, S.A.- Grupo Santillana ESP. *Dist:* Santillana USA Publishing Co., Inc.

—Cuando Hitler Robo el Conejo Rosa. 2003. (SPA.). (YA). (gr. 5-8). pap. (978-84-345-8586-7(3) , AF0202) Salvat Editores, S.A. ESP. *Dist:* Lectorum Pubns., Inc.

Kibuishi, Kazu. Amulet: Book 1. 2008. 192p. (J). pap. 9.99 (*978-0-439-84681-3(1) , Graphix) Scholastic, Inc.

Kirk, David. Little Bunny, Biddle Bunny. 2002. (Illus.). 32p. (J). (ps). pap. 9.95 (978-0-439-33819-6(0) , Scholastic Pr.) Scholastic, Inc.

Kiser, Dolores White. The Marriage of White Rabbit. 2005. (J). 10.00 net. (978-0-9766648-3-3(6)) White Kiser, Dolores.

Kisseloff, Jeff & Wells, Rosemary. Ruby's Tea for Two. 2003. (Max & Ruby Ser.). 12p. (J). bds. 5.99 (978-0-670-03652-3(8) , Puffin) Penguin Group (USA) Inc.

Kline, Trish. Jackrabbit's Tale. Smith, Fred, illus. (Read-and-Discover - Great Plains Ser.). 48p. (J). (ps-1). 2005. pap. 3.95 (978-1-56899-910-4(0) , S2016); 2002. 7.95 (978-1-56899-909-8(7) , B2016) Soundprints.

—Jackrabbit's Tale. 2002. (gr. k-3). lib. bdg. 11.80 (978-0-613-70877-7(6)) Tandem Library Bks.

Kline, Trish & Donev, Mary. A Scary Day in the Forest: KA Reader 5. 2007. (Illus.). 32p. (J). per. 20.00 (*978-0-9717234-8-1(6)) Ghost Hunter Productions.

Klise, Kate. Shall I Knit You A Hat? A Christmas Yarn. Klise, M. Sarah, illus. 2007. 32p. (J). pap. 6.99 (*978-0-312-37139-5(X)) Square Fish.

Klise, Kate. Why Do You Cry? Not a Sob Story. Klise, M. Sarah, illus. rev. ed. 2006. 32p. (J). 16.95 (978-0-8050-7319-5(1) , Holt, Henry & Co. Bks. For Young Readers) Holt, Henry & Co.

Klise, Kate & Klise, M. Sarah. Imagine Harry. Klise, Kate & Klise, M. Sarah, illus. 2007. (Illus.). 32p. (J). (ps-1). 16.00 (978-0-15-205704-6(8)) Harcourt Trade Pubs.

Klise, Kate & Klise, M. Sarah, illus. Little Rabbit & the Nightmare. 2008. (J). (*978-0-15-205717-6(X)) Harcourt Trade Pubs.

Knox, Mark. Tunny MacBunny & the Time Machine. unabr. ed. 2001. (J). lib. bdg. 15.00 (978-0-9713187-0-0(0)) Knox, Mark M.

Knutson, Barbara. Sungura & Leopard: A Swahili Trickster Tale. 2007. (Illus.). 32p. (J). (gr. k-5). pap. 6.95 (978-0-8225-6801-8(2) , First Avenue Editions) Lerner Publishing Group.

Korman Fontes, Justine. Clean up, Grumpy Bunny! 2007. (Scholastic Reader Level 1 Ser.). 32p. (J). pap. 3.99 (978-0-439-87381-9(9) , Cartwheel Bks.) Scholastic, Inc.

Korman, Justine. The Grumpy Easter Bunny. McQueen, Lucinda, illus. 2004. 32p. (J). 3.50 (978-0-439-63595-0(0)) Scholastic, Inc.

—Merry Christmas, Grumpy Bunny. 1999. (gr. k-3). lib. bdg. 11.25 (978-0-613-30602-7(3)) Tandem Library Bks.

Korman, Justine. Spring Is Here, Grumpy Bunny! 2008. (Clifford's Bedtime Ser.). 64p. (J). pap. 4.99 (*978-0-545-03402-9(7) , Cartwheel Bks.) Scholastic, Inc.

Kortepeter, Paul. Oliver's Red Toboggan. Wheeler, Susan, illus. 2006. 28p. (J). (ps). 15.99 (978-0-525-47752-5(7) , Dutton Juvenile) Penguin Group (USA) Inc.

Kramer, Alan & Kramer, Candice. Brer Rabbit Hears a Big Noise in the Woods: An African /American Folktale. 2006. spiral bd. 42.00 (*978-1-4108-7163-3(0)) Benchmark Education Co.

Krensky, Stephen. Milo the Really Big Bunny. Suber, Melissa, illus. 2006. 32p. (J). (ps-1). 14.95 (978-0-689-87345-4(X)) Simon & Schuster Children's Publishing.

Kroll, Virginia L. Really Rabbits. O'Neill, Philomena, illus. 2006. (Math Adventures Ser.). 32p. (J). 16.95 (978-1-57091-897-1(X)); pap. 6.95 (978-1-57091-898-8(8)) Charlesbridge Publishing, Inc.

Kunhardt, Dorothy. Pat the Bunny. Kunhardt, Dorothy, illus. 2001. (Touch & Feel Bks.). (Illus.). 20p. (J). (gr. k-ps). pap. 16.99 (978-0-307-16327-1(X) , 16327); pap. 9.99 (978-0-307-12000-7(7)) Random Hse. Children's Bks. (Golden Bks.).

—Pat the Bunny. 2000. (Touch & Feel Bks.). (Illus.). 20p. (J). (ps-k). bds. 17.95 (978-0-307-16209-0(5) , 16209, Golden Bks.) Random Hse. Children's Bks.

Kunhardt, Edith. Pat the Christmas Bunny Gift Set, Set. gif. ed. 2005. (Illus.). 18p. (J). (gr. k-ps). 12.95 (978-0-375-83405-9(2) , Golden Bks.) Random Hse. Children's Bks.

Lacey, Lois. Rockie & the Baby Bunnies. 1999. (Illus.). 24p. (J). (gr. k-3). pap. 11.00 (978-0-9667395-3-4(1)) Escapr Pr.

Lade, Linda. Peter Bunny: Adventures in the Kudzu Pat. 2006. 82p. pap. 14.95 (978-1-4241-3818-0(3)) PublishAmerica, Inc.

Lamm, C. Drew & Sherrow, Victoria. Smithsonain Backyard Cottontail & Chipmunk Box. Davis, Allen, illus. 2002. (Smithsonian Soundprints Ser.). 64p. (J). 19.95 (978-1-931465-54-0(1) , Silver Dolphin Bks.) Advantage Pubs. Group.

—Smithsonian Backyard Cottontail & Chipmunk Box, 4 bks., Set. Davis, Allen, illus. 2002. (Smithsonian Soundprints Mini Book & Plush Ser.). 32p. (J). (ps-2). bds. (978-1-931465-56-4(8)) Soundprints.

Lamm, Drew C. Cottontail at Clover Crescent. Davis, Allen, illus. 2005. (Smithsonian's Backyard Ser.). 32p. (J). (ps-2). pap. 6.95 (978-1-59249-112 4(X) , S5005) Soundprints.

—Cottontail at Clover Crescent. 2005. (Smithsonian's Backyard Ser.). (Illus.). 32p. (J). (ps-2). 8.95 incl. audio (978-1-59249-225-1(8) , SC5005) Soundprints.

Lane, Barry. The Tortoise & the Hare Continued. Bodimeade, Miles, illus. 2001. (J). (gr. 1-6). 16.00 (978-1-931492-01-0(8)) Discover Writing Pr.

Langen, Annette. Felix & the Flying Suitcase Adventure. Droop, Constanza, illus. 2003. 47p. (J). 14.99 (978-1-59384-035-8(7)) Parklane Publishing.

—Felix Explores Planet Earth. Droop, Constanza, illus. 2004. (Perfect for Earth Day Promotions! Ser.). 47p. (J). 14.99 (978-1-59384-030-3(6)) Parklane Publishing.

—Felix's Christmas Around the World. Droop, Constanza, illus. 2003. 40p. (J). 14.99 (978-1-59384-036-5(5)) Parklane Publishing.

—Letters from Felix: A Little Rabbit on a World Tour. Droop, Constanza, illus. 2003. 47p. (J). 14.99 (978-1-59384-034-1(9)) Parklane Publishing.

LaReau, Kara. Rabbit & Squirrel. Magoon, Scott, illus. 2008. (J). (*978-0-15-206307-8(2)) Harcourt Trade Pubs.

Larsen, Andrew. Bella & the Bunny. Endle, Kate, illus. 2007. 32p. (J). (ps-k). (*978-1-55337-970-6(5)) Kids Can Pr., Ltd.

Lasky, Kathryn. Lunch Bunnies. Hafner, Marylin, illus. 1999. 32p. (J). (ps-3). pap. 6.99 (978-0-316-51586-3(8)) Little Brown & Co.

—Show & Tell Bunnies. Hafner, Marylin, illus. 2001. 32p. (J). (ps-3). pap. 5.99 (978-0-7636-1050-0(X)) Candlewick Pr.

—Show & Tell Bunnies. 2001. (ps-2). lib. bdg. 14.15 (978-0-613-44257-2(1)) Tandem Library Bks.

—Tumble Bunnies. Hafner, Marylin, illus. 2005. 32p. (J). (gr. k-3). 15.99 (978-0-7636-2265-7(6)) Candlewick Pr.

Law, Felicia. Rumble Meets Randy Rabbit. Pak, Yoon Mi, illus. 2006. (Read-It! Readers Ser.). 32p. (J). (gr. 2-4). 18.60 (978-1-4048-1337-3(3)) Picture Window Bks.

Lawhead, Stephen R. Brown-Ears: The Adventures of a Lost-and-Found Rabbit. 2002. (Illus.). 96p. pap. 5.99 (978-0-7459-4776-1(X) , Lion) Lion Hudson plc GBR. *Dist:* Trafalgar Square Publishing.

—Brown-Ears at Sea: More Adventures of a Lost-and-Found Rabbit. 2002. (Illus.). 112p. pap. 5.99 (978-0-7459-4777-8(8) , Lion) Lion Hudson plc GBR. *Dist:* Trafalgar Square Publishing.

Lawson, Robert. Rabbit Hill. 2002. (Illus.). (J). 12.34 (978-0-7587-0208-1(6)) Book Wholesalers, Inc.

—Rabbit Hill. l.t. ed. (J). (gr. 4-6). reprint ed. 10.00 (978-0-89064-076-0(9)) National Assn. for Visually Handicapped.

LeapFrog Staff, compiled by. Pooh Gets Stuck. 2001. (SPA.). (J). (ps-2). spiral bd. 14.99 (978-1-58605-133-4(4)) LeapFrog Enterprises, Inc.

—Squire Hare & Sir Turtle. 2001. (J). (ps-2). spiral bd. 14.95 (978-1-58605-065-8(6)) LeapFrog Enterprises, Inc.

Learning Wrap-Ups: The Grasshopper & the Ants, The Turtle & the Rabbit. 2006. 66p. (J). 12.99 (978-1-59204-203-6(1)) Learning Wrap-Ups.

Lee, Ho Baek. While We Were Out. Lee, Ho Baek, illus. 2003. (Illus.). 32p. (J). (ps-1). 15.95 (978-1-929132-44-7(1)) Kane/Miller Bk. Pubs., Inc.

Legere, James. The Hare of the Hollow. 1998. (Illus.). 42p. (J). (ps-7). pap. 16.95 (978-0-9677090-0-0(8)) We Believe Publishing.

El leon y el Conejo: Individual Title Six-Packs. (Coleccion Pm Ser.).Tr. of Lion & the Rabbit. (SPA.). 16p. (gr. 1 up). 26.00 (978-0-7578-3007-5(2)) Rigby Education.

LeSieg, Theo. The Eye Book. Mathieu, Joe, illus. 1999. (Bright & Early Bks.). 36p. (J). (gr. k-1). lib. bdg. 11.99 (978-0-375-90033-4(0) , Random Hse. Bks. for Young Readers) Random Hse. Children's Bks.

LeSieg, Theo., ed. & illus. The Eye Book. LeSieg, Theo., illus. Mathieu, Joe, illus. (J). (gr. k-ps). 2001. 24p. bds. 4.99 (978-0-375-81240-8(7)); 1999. 36p. 8.99 (978-0-375-80033-7(6)) Random Hse. Children's Bks. (Random Hse. Bks. for Young Readers).

Leslie, Amanda, illus. Hopping Rabbit. 2001. 14p. (J). (ps-k). bds. 5.95 (978-1-58925-656-9(5) , tiger tales) ME Media LLC.

Lester, Julius. The Tales of Uncle Remus: The Adventures of Brer Rabbit. Pinkney, Jerry, illus. 1999. 143p. (J). (ps-7). lib. bdg. 17.60 (978-0-613-17870-9(X)) Tandem Library Bks.

Levy, Elizabeth. A Hare-Raising Tale: A Fletcher Mystery. Gorstein, Mordicai, illus. unabr. ed. 2006. (First Chapter Bks.). (J). (gr. 2-4). pap. 17.95 incl. audio (*978-1-59519-704-7(4)); pap. 20.95 incl. audio compact disk (*978-1-59519-705-4(2)) Live Oak Media.

Levy, Elizabeth & Coville, Bruce. The Dragon of Doom. Gerstein, Mordicai & Coville, Katherine, illus. ed. 2005. 71p. (J). lib. bdg. 15.00 (978-1-59054-903-2(1)) Fitzgerald Bks.

Levy, Elizabeth & Gerstein, Mordicai. A Hare-Raising Tail. 2002. (Fletcher Mystery Ser.: No. 1). (Illus.). 80p. (J). (gr. 2-5). pap. 3.99 (978-0-689-84626-7(6) , Aladdin) Simon & Schuster Children's Publishing.

Lewandowski, Frrich. The First Easter Bunny. 1999. (Illus.). 24p. (J). (ps-3). 9.50 (978-0-9646439-2-5(8)) Ambassador Bks., Inc.

Lewison, Wendy Cheyette. Easter Bunny's Amazing Egg Machine. 2002. (ps-2). lib. bdg. 10.95 (978-0-613-83538-1(7)) Tandem Library Bks.

Lionni, Leo. Let's Make Rabbits: A Board Book Edition. Lionni, Leo, illus. 2002. (Illus.). 30p. (J). (gr. k-ps). bds. 6.99 (978-0-375-81564-5(3) , Knopf Bks. for Young Readers) Random Hse. Children's Bks.

Lispector, Clari. Misterio do Cuelho Pensante. pap. 19.95 (978-85-325-1061-7(2)) Rocco, Editora, Ltda BRA. *Dist:* Distribooks, Inc.

Little Bunny. 2003. (Goodnight Mr. Moon Ser.). (Illus.). (J). bds. 2.98 (978-0-7525-4741-1(0)) Parragon, Inc.

Livingston, Irene. Finklehopper Frog. Lies, Brian, illus. 2004. 30p. (J). (ps-2). 14.95 (978-1-58246-075-8(2) , Tricycle Pr.) Ten Speed Pr.

—Finklehopper Frog Cheers. Lies, Brian, illus. 2005. 32p. (J). 14.95 (978-1-58246-138-0(4) , Tricycle Pr.) Ten Speed Pr.

Llewellyn, Claire. The Best Ears in the World: A First Look at Sound & Hearing. 2002. (Little Bees Ser.). (Illus.). 31p. (J). lib. bdg. 24.25 (978-1-58340-250-4(0)) Smart Apple Media.

Lobel, Gillian. Little Bear's Special Wish. Hansen, Gaby, illus. 2004. 32p. (J). tchr. ed. 16.95 (978-1-58925-034-5(6) , tiger tales) ME Media LLC.

Loomis, Christine. Astro Bunnies. Loomis, Christine & Eitan, Ora, illus. 2001. 1p. (J). (ps-3). 15.99 (978-0-399-23175-9(7) , Putnam Juvenile) Penguin Group (USA) Inc.

—Cowboy Bunnies. Eitan, Ora, illus. 2000. (J). (978-0-606-18397-0(3)) Tandem Library Bks.

—Cowboy Bunnies. Eitan, Ora, illus. 2004. 26p. (J). (ps-1). 6.99 (978-0-399-24182-6(5) , Putnam Juvenile) Penguin Group (USA) Inc.

Louvier, Randy. The Many Misadventures of Randy Rabbit. 2005. 71p. pap. 14.95 (978-1-4137-3776-9(5)) PublishAmerica, Inc.

Lowell, Susan. The Tortoise & the Jackrabbit. Harris, Jim, illus. 2004. (New Bilingual Picture Book Ser.). (ENG & SPA.). 32p. (J). 7.95 incl. 5.25 hd (978-0-87358-869-0(X) , Rising Moon Bks. for Young Readers) Northland Publishing.

Lyons, Anna. The Bunny Meets Ann Peacock. 1998. (Illus.). 16p. (J). (gr. k-3). pap. 6.00 (978-0-8059-4362-7(5)) Dorrance Publishing Co., Inc.

Maccarone, Grace. Peter Rabbit's Happy Easter. 2008. 11p. bds. 5.99 (***978-0-545-03784-6(0)*** , Cartwheel Bks.) Scholastic, Inc.

—Peter Rabbit's Happy Easter. McPhail, David, illus. 2006. 32p. (J). pap. 5.99 (978-0-439-79139-7(1)) Scholastic, Inc.

MacDonald, Margaret Read. Pickin' Peas. Cummings, Pat, illus. 1998. 32p. (J). (ps-3). 16.99 (978-0-06-027235-7(X)); 15.89 (978-0-06-027970-7(2)) HarperCollins Pubs.

MacDonald, Maryann. Rabbit's Birthday Kite. Munsinger, Lynn, illus. 1999. (Bank Street Reader Collection). 48p. (J). (gr. 1-3). lib. bdg. 22.60 (978-0-8368-1779-9(6)) Stevens, Gareth Inc.

MacHado, Ana Maria. Nina Bonita. Iribarren, Elena, tr. Faria, Rosana, illus. 2001. 24p. (J). (gr. k-4). reprint ed. 7.95 (978-1-929132-11-9(5)) Kane/Miller Bk. Pubs., Inc.

—Nina Bonita. 2001. (J). (978-0-606-20824-6(0)) Tandem Library Bks.

Machle, Rick. Ester's Easter Tale: How the Easter Bunny Came to Be. Nervig, Sandy, illus. 1999. 36p. (J). pap. 7.99 (978-0-9670375-0-9(6)) Growing Ideas, L.L.C.

Mackinnon, Mairi. Hare & the Tortoise. Howarth, Daniel, illus. 2007. (First Reading Level 4 Ser.). 48p. (J). 8.99 (***978-0-7945-1612-3(2)*** , Usborne) EDC Publishing.

Mallat, Kathy. Oh, Brother. Mallat, Kathy, illus. 2004. (Illus.). 32p. (J). 15.95 (978-0-8027-8875-7(0)) Walker & Co.

Man-Kong, Mary. Eggstra-Special Easter! Nowell, Christopher, illus. 2007. 12p. (J). (ps-1). pap. 6.99 (978-0-375-84012-8(5) , Golden Bks.) Random Hse. Children's Bks.

Marcus, Leonard S. & Schwartz, Amy. Oscar: The Big Adventure of a Little Sock Monkey. Schwartz, Amy, illus. 2006. (Illus.). 32p. (J). 16.99 (978-0-06-072622-5(9) , Tegen, Katherine Bks); lib. bdg. 17.89 (978-0-06-072623-2(7)) HarperCollins Pubs.

Margulies, Teddy. El Conejo Fugitivo. Bracken, Carolyn et al, illus. 2002. (Clifford Big Red Readers Ser.). (SPA.). 32p. (J). (ps-3). pap. 3.99 (978-0-439-25039-9(0) , SO0080) Scholastic, Inc.

Margulies, Teddy Slater. The Runaway Rabbit. Studio Orlando Staff, illus. 2001. (J). 10.79 (978-0-606-19915-5(2)) Tandem Library Bks.

Margulies, Teddy Slater & Bridwell, Norman. Clifford & the Runaway Rabbit. Studio Orlando Staff, illus. 2001. (Clifford, the Big Red Dog Ser.). 32p. (J). (gr. k-2). pap. 3.99 (978-0-439-21361-5(4)) Scholastic, Inc.

Marsden, John & Tan, Shaun. The Rabbits. 2003. (Illus.). 32p. 16.95 (978-0-9688768-8-6(9)) Simply Read Bks. CAN. *Dist:* Perseus Distribution.

Martin, W. Lyon. An Ordinary Girl, a Magical Child. 2005. (Illus.). (J). per. 16.95 (978-1-59405-515-7(7)) New Age World Publishing.

Marzot, Janet. Las Liebres Blancas. (SPA.). 32p. (J). 13.95 (978-84-261-1459-4(8)) Juventud, Editorial ESP. *Dist:* AIMS International Bks., Inc., Lectorum Pubns., Inc.

Masino, Brian. Easter Bunny's on His Way. 2007. 24p. (J). pap. 3.99 (978-0-439-87389-5(4) , Cartwheel Bks.) Scholastic, Inc.

Mastrangelo, Judy. What Do Bunnies Do All Day? Mastrangelo, Judy, illus. (Illus.). 32p. (J). pap. 4.95 (978-0-8249-5370-6(3) , Ideals) Ideals Pubns.

—What Do Bunnies Do All Day? 2001. (ps-2). lib. bdg. 12.95 (978-0-613-90549-7(0)) Tandem Library Bks.

Mastrangelo, Judy, illus. What Do Bunnies Do All Day? 2003. 24p. (J). bds. 6.95 (978-0-8249-6520-4(5)) Ideals Pubns.

Mastrongelo, Judy. What Do Bunnies Do All Day. 2006. 24p. pap. 3.95 (978-0-8249-5532-8(3) , Ideals Children's Bks.) Ideals Pubns.

Masurel, Claire. Emily & Her Daddy. Calitri, Susan, illus. 2003. (Lift-the-Flap Ser.). 16p. (J). (gr. k-1). pap. 6.99 (978-0-14-250080-4(1) , Puffin) Penguin Group (USA) Inc.

—Emily Is a Flower Girl. Calitri, Susan, illus. 2003. (Reading Railroad Bks.). 48p. (J). (ps-4). pap. 3.99 (978-0-448-43127-7(0) , Grosset & Dunlap) Penguin Group (USA) Inc.

—Emily Is a Flower Girl. 2003. (gr. k-3). lib. bdg. 11.25 (978-0-613-72541-5(7)) Tandem Library Bks.

—Emily's First Sleepover. 2003. (gr. k-3). lib. bdg. 11.25 (978-0-613-72542-2(5)) Tandem Library Bks.

—Happy Halloween Emily! Calitri, Susan, illus. 2002. (Reading Railroad Bks.). 32p. (J). pap. 3.99 (978-0-448-42691-4(9) , Grosset & Dunlap) Penguin Group (USA) Inc.

—Happy Halloween, Emily! 2002. (gr. k-3). lib. bdg. 11.25 (978-0-613-72492-0(5)) Tandem Library Bks.

—Merry Christmas, Emily! Calitri, Susan, illus. 2002. (Lift-the-Flap Book Ser.). 16p. (J). pap. 6.99 (978-0-14-230198-2(1) , Puffin) Penguin Group (USA) Inc.

McAllister, Angela. The Little Blue Rabbit. Cockcroft, Jason, illus. 2003. 32p. (J). (gr. k-3). 16.95 (978-1-58234-834-6(0) , Bloomsbury Children) Bloomsbury Publishing.

McBratney, Sam. Advina Cuanto Te Quero. 2001. Tr. of Guess How Much I Love You. (J). 13.75 (978-0-606-21016-4(4)) Tandem Library Bks.

—Devine Combien Je T'aime. 1998. (FRE., Illus.). (J). (ps-3). pap. 14.95 (978-2-211-03745-7(3)) Distribooks, Inc.

—Guess How Much I Love You. 2002. (Illus.). (J). 23.40 (978-0-7587-2668-1(6)) Book Wholesalers, Inc.

—Guess How Much I Love You. Jeram, Anita, illus. 2005. 34p. (J). bds. 19.95 (978-0-9769313-1-7(1)) BrailleInk.

—Guess How Much I Love You. 10th anniv. ed. 2003. (Illus.). 32p. (J). 19.99 (978-0-7636-2106-3(4)) Candlewick Pr.

—Guess How Much I Love You. Jeram, Anita, illus. 10th gif. anniv. ed. 2003. 32p. (J). 12.00 (978-0-7636-2240-4(0)) Candlewick Pr.

—Guess How Much I Love You. Jeram, Anita, illus. 1999. 24p. (J). (ps). bds. 6.99 (978-0-8499-5971-4(3)) Nelson, Thomas Inc.

—Guess How Much I Love You: My Baby Book. Jeram, Anita, illus. 10th anniv. ed. 2002. 48p. (J). (gr. k-12). 18.00 (978-0-7636-1909-1(4)) Candlewick Pr.

—Guess How Much I Love You & Story Time DVD. Jeram, Anita, illus. 2006. 32p. (J). (ps-3). 15.99 incl. DVD (978-0-7636-3503-9(0)) Candlewick Pr.

McBratney, Sam. When I'm Big. Jeram, Anita, illus. 2007. (Guess How Much I Love You Ser.). 24p. (J). (gr. k-ps). bds. 7.99 (***978-0-7636-3546-6(4)***) Candlewick Pr.

McCallum, Ann. Rabbits, Rabbits Everywhere: A Fibonacci Tale. Kendall, Gideon, illus. 2008. (J). (978-1-57091-895-7(3)); pap. (978-1-57091-896-4(1)) Charlesbridge Publishing, Inc.

McCarty, Peter. Little Bunny on the Move. McCarty, Peter, illus. rev. ed. 2003. (Illus.). 32p. (J). pap. 5.95 (978-0-8050-7259-4(4) , Holt, Henry & Co. Bks. For Young Readers) Holt, Henry & Co.

—Little Bunny on the Move. 2003. (gr. k-3). lib. bdg. 14.10 (978-0-613-90147-5(9)) Tandem Library Bks.

McCoy, Ellen R. The Bunny Run. 2nd l.t. ed. 2002. (Illus.). 144p. (J). per. 14.95 (978-0-9726065-0-9(5)) Paper Tale Pr.

McCue, Dick. Bunny's Numbers. McCue, Lisa, illus. 2000. 14p. (J). (ps-3). bds. 4.99 (978-0-689-83086-0(6) , Little Simon) Simon & Schuster Children's Publishing.

McCue, Lisa & Falken, L. C. Snuggle Bunnies. McCue, Lisa, illus. 2003. (Illus.). 11p. (J). bds. 6.99 (978-0-7944-0040-8(X)) Reader's Digest Assn., Inc., The.

McCullough, Sharon Pierce. Bunbun at the Fair. 2002. (Bunbun Ser.). (Illus.). 24p. (J). (gr. k-2). 14.99 (978-1-84148-900-1(X)) Barefoot Bks., Inc.

—Bunbun, the Middle One. McCullough, Sharon Pierce, illus. 2002. (Bunbun Ser.). (Illus.). 24p. (J). (gr. k-2). bds. 6.99 (978-1-84148-377-1(X)) Barefoot Bks., Inc.

—Bunbun, the Middle One. 2001. (Illus.). 24p. (J). (ps-k). 14.99 (978-1-84148-325-2(7)) Barefoot Bks., Inc.

McKee, David. Four Red Apples. 2007. (Illus.). 32p. (J). (ps-k). 15.99 (***978-1-84270-544-5(X)***) Andersen GBR. *Dist:* Independent Pubs. Group.

McLean, Janet. Josh & Thumper. McLean, Andrew, illus. 2000. (Josh Ser.). 32p. (J). (ps-k). mass mkt. 4.95 (978-1-86448-491-5(8)) Allen & Unwin AUS. *Dist:* Independent Pubs. Group.

McMullan, Kate. Pearl & Wagner: Three Secrets. Alley, R. W., illus. 2004. (Easy-to-Read, Dial Ser.). 48p. (J). (gr. 2). 14.99 (978-0-8037-2574-4(4) , Dial) Penguin Group (USA) Inc.

MCP Staff. Little Bunny's Lunch: Short u; Consonants b, h; Blends br, cr; Digraphs ch, sh, th. (J). (gr. 1-2). 38.50 (978-0-8136-1116-7(4)) Modern Curriculum Pr.

McPhail, David. Rick Is Sick. McPhail, David, illus. 2004. (Illus.). 24p. (J). lib. bdg. 10.00 (***978-1-4242-0183-9(7)***) Fitzgerald Bks.

McPhail, David M. The Blue Door. O'Connor, John, illus. 2004. 32p. (978-1-55041-917-7(X)) Fitzhenry & Whiteside, Ltd.

—Rick Is Sick. 2004. (Green Light Readers Level 1 Ser.). (Illus.). 24p. (J). 12.95 (978-0-15-205091-7(4)); pap. 3.95 (978-0-15-205092-4(2)) Harcourt Children's Bks. (Green Light Readers).

—The Sled & other Fox & Rabbit Stories. O'Connor, John, illus. 1999. (First Flight Ser.). 32p. (J). lib. bdg. (978-1-55041-515-5(8)) Fitzhenry & Whiteside, Ltd.

McPhail, David M. & O'Connor. The Sled: Fox & Rabbit Stories. 1999. (First Flight Ser.). (Illus.). 32p. (J). (ps-k). pap. (978-1-55041-517-9(4)) Fitzhenry & Whiteside, Ltd.

McPhail, David M. & O'Connor, John. The Blue Door. 2001. (Illus.). 32p. (J). (ps-k). (978-1-55041-647-3(2)) Fitzhenry & Whiteside, Ltd.

McQueen, Lucinda & Shaw, Gina. Little Bunny's Easter Surprise. 1999. (Illus.). 10p. (J). (ps-1). pap. 3.50 (978-0-590-65029-8(7)) Scholastic, Inc.

Medearis, Deanna. Bunny's Easter Hunt. Bratun, Katy, illus. 2006. (Cuddle & Read Ser.). 24p. (J). (ps-ps). 6.95 (978-1-4027-2019-2(X)) Sterling Publishing Co., Inc.

Miles, Gloria. Red Rabbit. 2005. pap. 7.95 (978-0-533-14598-0(8)) Vantage Pr., Inc.

Miller, Jayna. Too Much Trick or Treat. Thatch, Nancy, ed. Miller, Jayna, illus. 2005. (Illus.). 29p. (J). per. 19.95 (978-0-933849-83-9(4)) Landmark Editions, Inc.

Minich, Eric. Digger & the Search for Home. 2006. 48p. pap. 12.95 (978-1-4241-0321-8(5)) PublishAmerica, Inc.

Modesitt, Jeanne. Little Bunny's Easter Surprise. Spowart, Robin, illus. 2002. 32p. (J). pap. 5.99 (978-0-689-84895-7(1) , Aladdin) Simon & Schuster Children's Publishing.

Monsen, Annie. Rusty Raccoon Meets Ricky Rabbit. Saint, Crystal, illus. 2006. 36p. (J). per. (978-1-59453-996-1(0) , Airleaf Publishing) Airleaf Publishing & Bookselling.

Montanari, Eva. A Very Full Morning. 2006. (Illus.). 32p. (J). (gr. k-3). 16.00 (978-0-618-56318-0(0)) Houghton Mifflin Co. Trade & Reference Div.

Moon, Nicola. J. J. Rabbit & the Monster. Parker, Ant, illus. 2005. (I Am Reading Ser.). 48p. (J). (gr. k-3). pap., pap. 3.95 (978-0-7534-5855-6(1) , Kingfisher) Houghton Mifflin Co. Trade & Reference Div.

Mora, Jo. Budgee Budgee Cottontail. Mora, Jo, illus. 2004. (Jo Mora Titles Ser.). (Illus.). 60p. (gr. 2 up). 15.00 (978-0-922029-23-5(7) , BK-30004) Stoecklein Publishing.

Morgan, Michaela. Bunny Wishes. 2007. 32p. (J). (ps-k). pap. 16.99 (***978-0-439-91812-1(X)*** , Chicken Hse., The) Scholastic, Inc.

Morgan, Michaela. Dear Bunny. 2007. 32p. (J). pap. 5.99 (978-0-439-74834-6(8) , Scholastic Paperbacks) Scholastic, Inc.

—Dear Bunny. Jayne Church, Caroline, illus. 2006. 32p. (J). pap. 15.99 (978-0-439-74833-9(X) , Chicken Hse., The) Scholastic, Inc.

Morgan, Ruth. The Funny Easter Bunny. 2003. (Illus.). 22p. per. 1.95 (978-1-932338-10-2(1)) Lifevest Publishing, Inc.

Morton, Christine. Run Rabbit Run. Taylor, Eleanor, illus. 2002. 32p. pap. 10.99 (978-0-7475-5607-7(5)) Bloomsbury Publishing Plc GBR. *Dist:* Trafalgar Square Publishing.

Moss, Miriam. Bad Hare Day. Chapman, Lynne, illus. 2003. 32p. (J). (gr. k-3). 15.95 (978-1-58234-785-1(9) , Bloomsbury Children) Bloomsbury Publishing.

—Don't Forget I Love You. Currey, Anna, illus. 2005. 32p. (J). pap. 5.99 (978-0-14-240548-2(5) , Puffin) Penguin Group (USA) Inc.

Mowry, Jess. Crusader Rabbit & Other Stories. 2007. 280p. (YA). pap. 14.99 (978-1-59092-231-6(X) , Blue Works) Windstorm Creative.

Murphy. Rabbit's Pajama Party. 1999. pap., tchr. ed. 2.00 (978-0-7398-2527-3(5)) Steck-Vaughn.

Murphy, Stuart J. Rabbit's Pajama Party. Remkiewicz, Frank, illus. 1999. (MathStart Ser.). 40p. (ps up). (J). pap. 5.99 (978-0-06-446722-3(8) , Harper Trophy); (YA). 15.89 (978-0-06-027617-1(7)) HarperCollins Pubs.

—Rabbit's Pajama Party. 1999. (Math Start Ser.). (978-0-606-18713-8(8)); lib. bdg. 13.00 (978-0-613-22235-8(0)) Tandem Library Bks.

Mussenbrock, Anne. Easter Notes. 2004. 12p. (J). (ps-k). 5.99 (978-1-59384-037-2(3)) Parklane Publishing.

Nass, Marcia Shoshana. The Rabbit Who Lost His Hop: A Story about Self-Control. Gilgannon-Collins, Denise, illus. 2004. (Early Prevention Ser.: 5). (J). per. 19.95 (978-1-58815-061-5(5) , 66525) Childswork/Childsplay.

Nelson, Steve & Rollins, Jack. Here Comes Peter Cottontail. Levy, Pamela R., illus. 2007. 26p. bds. 12.99 (***978-0-8249-6690-4(2)*** , Candy Cane Pr.) Ideals Pubns.

—Here Comes Peter Cottontail. Rasmussen, Wendy, illus. 2005. 20p. (J). bds. 9.95 (978-0-8249-6573-0(6)) Ideals Pubns.

—Here Comes Peter Cottontail, Set. Levy, Pamela R., illus. 2007. 26p. pap. 16.99 (***978-0-8249-6689-8(9)*** , Candy Cane Pr.) Ideals Pubns.

Newberry. Marshmallow. 2008. 32p. (J). 17.89 (***978-0-06-072487-0(0)***) HarperCollins Pubs.

Newberry, Clare Turlay. Marshmallow. Newberry, Clare Turlay, illus. 2008. 32p. (J). 16.99 (***978-0-06-072486-3(2)***) HarperCollins Pubs.

Nicely, Adam. Naptime for Thaddeus. 2005. (Illus.). 32p. (J). 16.95 (978-1-894965-28-6(0)) Simply Read Bks. CAN. *Dist:* Perseus Distribution.

Nishimura, Kae. Bunny Lune. Nishimura, Kae, illus. 2007. (Illus.). 32p. (J). (gr. k-3). 15.00 (978-0-618-71606-7(8) , Clarion Bks.) Houghton Mifflin Co. Trade & Reference Div.

Nolan, Allia Zobel. I Love You the World. Mitchell, Susan, illus. 2006. 20p. (J). (ps-1). bds. 10.99 (978-0-7944-1218-0(1)) Reader's Digest Assn., Inc., The.

Noll, Katherine, et al. I've Got Bunny Business! 2004. (Full House Ser.: No. 4). (Illus.). 96p. (J). mass mkt. 4.99 (978-0-06-054086-9(9) , Harper Entertainment) HarperCollins Pubs.

Noonan, Julia. Friends Forever: Hare & Rabbit. Noonan, Julia, illus. 2000. (Hello Reader! Ser.: Level 3). (Illus.). 40p. (J). (gr. 1-2). pap. 3.99 (978-0-439-08753-7(8)) Scholastic, Inc.

—Hare & Rabbit: Friends Forever. 2004. 40p. (J). lib. bdg. 15.00 (978-1-59054-493-8(5)) Fitzgerald Bks.

—Hare & Rabbit: Friends Forever. 2000. (gr. k-3). lib. bdg. 11.80 (978-0-613-21678-4(4)); (Illus.). (J). 10.79 (978-0-606-18556-1(9)) Tandem Library Bks.

Novak, Matt. Too Many Bunnies. Novak, Matt, illus. rev. ed. 2005. (Illus.). 16p. (J). 7.95 (978-1-59643-038-9(9)) Roaring Brook Pr.

O'Keefe, Susan Heyboer. Love Me, Love You. Spowart, Robin, illus. 2003. 32p. (J). (ps up). 15.95 (978-1-56397-837-1(7)) Boyds Mills Pr.

Oliver, Oliver J. Hare & Tortoise Race to the Moon. Oliver, Oliver J., illus. 2002. (Illus.). 40p. (J). (ps-3). 14.95 (978-0-8109-0566-5(3)) Abrams, Harry N. , Inc.

Oller, Erika. The Cabbage Soup Solution. Oller, Erika, illus. 2004. (Illus.). 32p. (J). (ps-1). 15.99 (978-0-525-47005-2(0) , Dutton Juvenile) Penguin Group (USA) Inc.

Oppenheim, Shulamith Levey. I Love You, Bunny Rabbit. Moore, Cyd, illus. 2005. 32p. (J). pap. 7.95 (978-1-59078-337-5(9)) Boyds Mills Pr.

Oramas, Rafael. El Hojarasquerito del Monte. 2001. Tr. of Leaf Pile of the Mountain. (SPA., Illus.). 24p. (J). pap. 2.95 (978-980-257-011-9(7)) Ekare, Ediciones VEN. *Dist:* AIMS International Bks., Inc.

Otterman, Lynn. Fluffy Bunny. Fletcher, Rusty, illus. 2002. (Animal Snuggles Ser.). 8p. (J). bds. 7.95 (978-0-8069-8403-2(1)) Sterling Publishing Co., Inc.

The Package: KinderConcepts Individual Title Six-Packs. (Kinderstarters Ser.). 8p. (ps-1). 21.00 (978-0-7635-8737-6(0)) Rigby Education.

Packard, Mary. Don't Make a Sound. Yerkes, Lane, illus. 2004. 16p. (J). (gr. 1 up). lib. bdg. 19.33 (978-0-8368-4099-5(2)) Stevens, Gareth Inc.

Page, Josephine. Always Friends: Honey Bunny. Beasley, Roberta, illus. 2006. 6p. (J). 5.99 (978-0-439-77246-4(X) , Cartwheel Bks.) Scholastic, Inc.

Park, Barbara. Junie B., First Grader: Dumb Bunny. Brunkus, Denise, illus. 2007. (Junie B. Jones Ser.: No. 27). 128p. (J). (gr. k-3). lib. bdg. 14.99 (978-0-375-93809-2(5) , Random Hse. Bks. for Young Readers) Random Hse. Children's Bks.

Park, Linda Sue. What Does Bunny See? A Book of Colors & Flowers. Smith, Maggie, illus. 2005. 32p. (J). (ps-k). 15.00 (978-0-618-23485-1(3) , Clarion Bks.) Houghton Mifflin Co. Trade & Reference Div.

Paul, Ann Whitford. Fiesta Fiasco. Long, Ethan, illus. 2007. 32p. (J). (ps-3). 16.95 (978-0-8234-2037-7(X)) Holiday Hse., Inc.

—Hop! Hop! Hop! Gerardi, Jan, illus. 2005. 32p. (J). (ps-1). pap. 3.99 (978-0-375-82857-7(5) , Random Hse. Bks. for Young Readers) Random Hse. Children's Bks.

Paxton, Tom. Jennifer's Rabbit. Miles, Elizabeth, illus. 2001. 32p. (J). (ps-3). 15.89 (978-0-06-029216-4(4)); 15.95 (978-0-688-15262-8(7)) HarperCollins Pubs.

PC Treasures, prod. Peter Rabbit. 2007. (J). (***978-1-60072-021-5(8)***) PC Treasures, Inc.

Perkins, Larry B. Jasper Rabbit. 2005. 33p. per. 8.95 (978-1-4116-1936-4(6)) Lulu.com.

Peter Rabbit. (Story Reader Ser.). 26p. (J). spiral bd. (978-1-4127-0121-1(X) , 7213800) Publications International, Ltd.

Peter Rabbit Books 800845, 3. 2005. (J). (978-1-59794-046-7(1)) Environments, Inc.

Peters, Lisa Westberg. We're Rabbits! Mack, Jeff, illus. 2004. 32p. (J). 16.00 (978-0-15-204671-2(2)) Harcourt Children's Bks.

Pfister, Marcus. Henri Egg Artiste. Pfister, Marcus, illus. 2008. 32p. (J). (ps). 15.95 (***978-0-7358-2130-9(5)***) North-South Bks., Inc.

Piggy Toes Press Staff. Baby Bugs' Toys. 2000. (Lovable Huggable Baby Looney Tunes Cloth Bks.). (Illus.). 6p. (J). (ps up). 14.95 (978-1-58117-078-8(5) , Intervisual/ Piggy Toes) Dalmatian Pr.

Pilkey, Dav. The Dumb Bunnies. 2007. 32p. (J). pap. 10.99 (***978-0-545-03938-3(X)*** , Levine, Arthur A. Bks.) Scholastic, Inc.

—The Dumb Bunnies. 2005. (Illus.). 30p. (J). (ps-ps). lib. bdg. 12.79 (978-0-606-33285-9(5)) Tandem Library Bks.

—Dumb Bunnies Collection. 2007. (J). pap. 12.99 (***978-0-439-75666-2(9)*** , Blue Sky Pr., The) Scholastic, Inc.

—Dumb Bunnies' Easter (Bkshelf) 2008. 32p. pap. 6.99 (***978-0-545-00880-8(8)*** , Scholastic Paperbacks) Scholastic, Inc.

—Dumb Bunnies Go to the Zoo, The. 2007. 32p. pap. 5.99 (***978-0-439-93049-9(9)***) Scholastic, Inc.

—Make Way for Dumb Bunnies. 2007. 32p. (J). pap. 10.99 (***978-0-545-03939-0(8)*** , Levine, Arthur A. Bks.) Scholastic, Inc.

Pilkey, Dav, illus. The Dumb Bunnies Go to the Zoo. 2002. (Dumb Bunnies Ser.). (J). 22.91 (978-0-7587-2424-3(1)) Book Wholesalers, Inc.

—Make Way for Dumb Bunnies. 2002. (Dumb Bunnies Ser.). (J). 20.49 (978-0-7587-3078-7(0)) Book Wholesalers, Inc.

Pinkwater, Daniel M. Bad Bears & a Bunny. Pinkwater, Jill, illus. 2005. (Irving & Muktuk Story Ser.). 32p. (J). (gr. k-3). 16.00 (978-0-618-33926-6(4)) Houghton Mifflin Co. Trade & Reference Div.

Piper, Sophie. Little Bunnys Easter. 2008. (Illus.). 32p. (J). pap. 10.95 (***978-0-7459-4961-1(4)***) Lion Hudson plc GBR. *Dist:* Independent Pubs. Group.

Pockets Learning Staff. Bunny House. 1998. (Illus.). (ps up). 35.00 (978-1-888074-94-9(9)) Pockets of Learning.

Ponti, Claude. En El Coche. 2003. (SPA.). 32p. 15.95 (978-84-95150-08-0(5)) Corimbo, Editorial S.L. ESP. *Dist:* Distribooks, Inc.

Por que el conejo tiene las orejas tan Largas? Lap Book. (Pebble Soup Exploraciones Ser.). (SPA.). 16p. (ps up). 21.00 (978-0-7578-1691-8(6)) Rigby Education.

Por que el conejo tiene las orejas tan Largas? Small Book. (Pebble Soup Exploraciones Ser.). (SPA.). 16p. (ps up). 5.00 (978-0-7578-1731-1(9)) Rigby Education.

Por que los conejos tienen las orejas Largas: Individual Title Six-Packs. (Literatura 2000 Ser.). (SPA.). (gr. 2-3). 33.00 (978-0-7635-1271-2(0)) Rigby Education.

Portis, Antoinette. Not a Box. Portis, Antoinette, illus. 2006. (Illus.). 32p. (J). (ps-1). 12.99 (978-0-06-112322-1(6)); lib. bdg. 14.89 (978-0-06-112323-8(4)) HarperCollins Pubs.

Posey, Lee. Night Rabbits. Montgomery, Michael, illus. 2007. 32p. pap. 7.95 (***978-1-56145-397-9(8)*** , Peachtree Junior) Peachtree Pubs., Ltd.

—Night Rabbits. Montgomery, Michael G., illus. 1999. 32p. (J). (ps-3). 15.95 (978-1-56145-164-7(9) , 51649) Peachtree Pubs., Ltd.

Potter, Beatrix. A Beatrix Potter Treasury. 2007. 192p. (J). (ps). 19.99 (***978-0-7232-5957-2(7)*** , Warne) Penguin Group (USA) Inc.

—Complete Tales of Peter Rabbit. 2008. 56p. (J). 7.98 (***978-0-7624-3161-8(X)*** , Courage Bks.) Running Pr. Bk. Pubs.

—Cuento - Perico el Conejo. Orig. Title: Tale of Peter Rabbit. (SPA.). 60p. (J). 8.95 (978-84-7444-725-5(9)) Debate, Editorial ESP. *Dist:* AIMS International Bks., Inc.

—El Gato Tomas. 2003. (Coleccion el Mundo de Peter Rabbit). (SPA., Illus.). (J). (gr. k-2). pap. (978-950-07-1722-9(0) , SA30685) Editorial Sudamericana S.A. ARG. *Dist:* Lectorum Pubns., Inc.

—Jeremias el Pescador. 2003. (Coleccion el Mundo de Peter Rabbit). (SPA., Illus.). (J). (gr. k-2). pap. (978-950-07-1721-2(2) , SA30686) Editorial Sudamericana S.A. ARG. *Dist:* Lectorum Pubns., Inc.

—La Oca Carlota. 2003. (Coleccion el Mundo de Peter Rabbit). (SPA., Illus.). (J). (gr. k-2). pap. (978-950-07-1723-6(9) , SA30687) Editorial Sudamericana S.A. ARG. *Dist:* Lectorum Pubns., Inc.

—Peter Rabbit. 2006. (Illus.). 32p. pap. 3.95 (978-0-8249-5533-5(1) , Ideals Children's Bks.) Ideals Pubns.

—Peter Rabbit. Britt, Stephanie McFetridge, illus. 2001. 26p. (J). (ps-k). bds. 6.95 (978-0-8249-4108-6(X)) Ideals Pubns.

—Peter Rabbit: A Lucky Escape. 2008. (J). (gr. k). 16p. 17.99 (*978-0-7232-5988-6(7)); (Illus.). 18p. 17.99 (*978-0-7232-5927-5(5)) Penguin Group (USA) Inc. (Warne).

—The Peter Rabbit & Friends Treasury. Potter, Beatrix, illus. 2006. (Illus.). 240p. (J). (gr. k-4). reprint ed. 20.00 (978-1-4223-5452-0(0)) DIANE Publishing Co.

—Peter Rabbit Lift-the-flap Shapes, Opposites & Sizes. 2007. (Potter Ser.). 12p. (J). (ps). 14.99 (*978-0-7232-5961-9(5) , Warne) Penguin Group (USA) Inc.

—Peter Rabbit Lift-the-Flap Words, Colors, Numbers (R/I) 2007. 12p. (J). 14.99 (978-0-7232-5828-5(7) , Warne) Penguin Group (USA) Inc.

—Peter Rabbit's Five Fluffy Bunnies: A Touch & Feel Counting Book. 2005. (Potter Shaped Board Book Ser.). (Illus.). 14p. (J). (ps). bds. 6.99 (978-0-7232-5354-9(4) , Warne) Penguin Group (USA) Inc.

—Peter Rabbit's Giant Storybook. 2000. (Illus.). 192p. (J). (ps-3). 15.99 (978-0-7232-4583-4(5) , Warne) Penguin Group (USA) Inc.

—Quack Quack with Peter Rabbit. 2006. (Potter Ser.). 10p. (J). 6.99 (978-0-7232-5718-9(3) , Warne) Penguin Group (USA) Inc.

—The Story of a Fierce Bad Rabbit. 2002. (Illus.). 40p. (J). 6.99 (978-0-7232-4789-0(7) , Warne) Penguin Group (USA) Inc.

—The Story of Miss Moppet. Potter, Beatrix, illus. 2002. (Illus.). (J). 14.79 (978-1-4046-2495-5(3)) Book Wholesalers, Inc.

—The Story of Miss Moppet. 2002. (Illus.). 40p. (J). 6.99 (978-0-7232-4790-6(0) , Warne) Penguin Group (USA) Inc.

—The Story of Peter Rabbit. McCue, Lisa, illus. 2005. 20p. (J). bds. 10.99 (978-0-7944-0527-4(4)) Reader's Digest Assn., Inc., The.

—The Tale of Benjamin Bunny. Potter, Beatrix, illus. 2002. (Illus.). (J). 15.23 (978-0-7587-4499-9(4)) Book Wholesalers, Inc.

—The Tale of Benjamin Bunny. 2002. (Illus.). 57p. (J). 6.99 (978-0-7232-4773-9(0) , Warne) Penguin Group (USA) Inc.

—The Tale of Benjamin Bunny: A Sticker Story Book. 2008. (Potter Ser.). 24p. (J). (ps). 5.99 (*978-0-7232-6287-9(X) , Warne) Penguin Group (USA) Inc.

—The Tale of Benjamin Bunny: Adapted from the Original. 2003. (Illus.). 32p. (J). 3.99 (978-0-7232-4718-0(8) , Warne) Penguin Group (USA) Inc.

—The Tale of Flopsy Bunnies, Vol. 10. 2002. (Illus.). 64p. (J). 6.99 (978-0-7232-4779-1(X) , Warne) Penguin Group (USA) Inc.

—The Tale of Ginger & Pickles. Potter, Beatrix, illus. 2002. (Illus.). 15.23 (978-1-4046-2494-8(5)) Book Wholesalers, Inc.

—The Tale of Ginger & Pickles, Vol. 18. 2002. (Illus.). 64p. (J). 6.99 (978-0-7232-4787-6(0) , Warne) Penguin Group (USA) Inc.

—The Tale of Johnny Town-Mouse. Potter, Beatrix, illus. 2002. (Illus.). (J). 15.23 (978-0-7587-4501-9(X)) Book Wholesalers, Inc.

—The Tale of Johnny Town-Mouse, Vol. 13. 2002. (Illus.). 64p. (J). 6.99 (978-0-7232-4782-1(X) , Warne) Penguin Group (USA) Inc.

—The Tale of Little Pig Robinson. 2002. (Illus.). 128p. (J). 6.99 (978-0-7232-4788-3(9) , Warne) Penguin Group (USA) Inc.

—The Tale of Peter Rabbit. Jorgensen, David, illus. 2007. (J). 25.65 (978-1-59961-313-0(1)) ABDO Publishing Co.

—The Tale of Peter Rabbit. Potter, Beatrix, illus. 2004. (Wee Books for Wee Folks). (Illus.). 64p. (J). (ps-3). reprint ed. 6.95 (978-1-55709-412-4(8)) Applewood Bks.

—The Tale of Peter Rabbit. Hague, Michael, illus. 2003. 29p. (J). (gr. 2-5). reprint ed. 16.00 (978-0-7567-6968-0(X)) DIANE Publishing Co.

—The Tale of Peter Rabbit. 1999. (Illus.). 12p. (J). (ps-k). bds. 6.99 (978-0-7232-4432-5(4) , Warne) Penguin Group (USA) Inc.

—The Tale of Peter Rabbit. (Illus.). 12p. 4.95 (978-1-58989-271-2(2)) Thurman Hse., LLC.

—The Tale of Peter Rabbit & Benjamin Bunny Book & DVD. Potter, Beatrix, illus. 2007. 80p. (J). (ps). 14.99 (*978-0-7232-5965-7(8) , Warne) Penguin Group (USA) Inc.

—The Tale of Peter Rabbit Sticker Storybook R/I. 2007. (Potter Ser.). 24p. (J). pap. 5.99 (*978-0-7232-5876-6(7) , Warne) Penguin Group (USA) Inc.

—The Tale of Samuel Whiskers or the Roly-Poly Pudding, Vol. 16. 2002. (Illus.). 88p. (J). (ps). 6.99 (978-0-7232-4785-2(4) , Warne) Penguin Group (USA) Inc.

—The Tale of the Flopsy Bunnies. Potter, Beatrix, illus. 2002. (Illus.). (J). 15.23 (978-0-7587-3754-0(8)) Book Wholesalers, Inc.

—The Tale of the Pie & the Patty-Pan. 2002. (Illus.). 64p. (J). 6.99 (978-0-7232-4786-9(2) , Warne) Penguin Group (USA) Inc.

Potter, Beatrix, text. Peter Rabbit. 2003. (Play-A-Sound Ser.). (Illus.). (J). (978-0-7853-7972-0(X)); (978-0-7853-7971-3(1)) Publications International, Ltd.

Potter, Beatrix, et al. The Tale of Peter Rabbit. Andersen, Alan, illus. 2001. (Little Golden Bks.). 24p. (gr. k-k). 2.99 (978-0-307-03071-9(7) , 98039, Golden Bks.) Random Hse. Children's Bks.

Powell, Richard. Becky Bunny. Rhodes, Katie, illus. 2004. (Fuzzy Friends Ser.). 10p. (J). 7.95 (978-1-58925-723-8(5) , tiger tales) ME Media LLC.

—Bunny's Tail. Davis, Caroline, illus. 2002. (Animal Tails Ser.). 8p. (J). 3.95 (978-1-58925-676-7(X) , tiger tales) ME Media LLC.

—Formula Bunny. Holt, Emma, illus. 2003. (Whizzy Wheels Bks.). 20p. (J). bds. 4.95 (978-0-7641-5590-1(3)) Barron's Educational Series, Inc.

Powers, Paul. Tales of the Swamp Creatures. 2003. 71p. pap. 11.95 (978-1-4137-0160-9(4)) PublishAmerica, Inc.

Poydar, Nancy. Bunny Business. 2003. (Illus.). 32p. (J). (gr. k-3). tchr. ed. 16.95 (978-0-8234-1771-1(9)) Holiday Hse., Inc.

Preble Mike. Why the Owl Has Big Ears. McCann Shawn, illus. 2005. 32p. 8.75 (978-0-9771466-0-4(X)) Goulasche Pr.

Price, Mathew. Polo y Los Conejos. (SPA.). pap. 7.95 (978-950-07-1978-0(9)) Editorial Sudamericana S.A. ARG. *Dist:* Distribooks, Inc.

Quadrillion Media Staff. Sniffer, the Rabbit & Friends. 1999. 5.95 (978-1-58185-218-9(5)) Quadrillion Media LLC.

Rabbit Ears-A Classic Tale. 2005. (Rabbit Ears-A Classic Tale Ser.). (J). (gr. k-5). 359.10 (978-1-59197-745-2(2)) Spotlight.

Rabey, Katharine. Hare & the Big Green Lawn. MacDougall, Larry, illus. 2006. 32p. 15.95 (978-0-87358-889-8(4) , Rising Moon Bks. for Young Readers) Northland Publishing.

Rain, Rain, Go Away. 2000. (ps-2). lib. bdg. 11.80 (978-0-613-26708-3(7)) Tandem Library Bks.

Ralph the Rabbit. 2003. (Chunky Animal Shaped Boards Ser.). (J). 10p. bds. 9.95 (978-0-7525-7855-2(3)); (Illus.). bds. 1.98 (978-0-7525-7776-0(X)) Parragon, Inc.

Random House Disney Staff. Bambi's Hide & Seek. 2002. (ps-2). lib. bdg. 11.80 (978-0-613-73649-7(4)) Tandem Library Bks.

Raschka, Chris. Five for a Little One. Raschka, Chris, illus. 2006. (Illus.). 48p. (J). (ps-k). 16.95 (978-0-689-84599-4(5) , Atheneum/Richard Jackson Bks.) Simon & Schuster Children's Publishing.

Ratoff, Michael. Silent Noisy Spring, 3 vols. Painter, Laurie, illus. l.t. ed. 2001. (Every Thing in an Empty Box Ser.). 56p. (J). (ps-3). lib. bdg. 9.95 (978-0-9627986-4-1(9)) Rebel Butterfly Pr.

—Silver & Shiny, 3 vols. Painter, Laurie, illus. 2nd l.t. ed. 2001. (Every Thing in an Empty Box Ser.). 56p. (J). (ps-3). lib. bdg. 9.95 (978-0-9627986-2-7(2)) Rebel Butterfly Pr.

Rawlinson, Julia & Warnes, Tim. A Surprise for Rosie. 2005. (Illus.). 32p. (J). 15.95 (978-1-58925-046-8(X) , tiger tales) ME Media LLC.

Ray, Mary Lyn. All Aboard! Hirao, Amiko & Goodwin-Sturges, illus. 2002. 32p. (J). (ps-3). 14.95 (978-0-316-73507-0(8)) Little, Brown Bks. for Young Readers.

Reeves, Jeni, illus. Lion & Rabbit. 2008. (On My Own Folklore Ser.). (J). lib. bdg. (*978-0-8225-7546-7(9) , Millbrook Pr.) Lerner Publishing Group.

Reitze, Glenn Logan. Ernie the Easter Hippopotamus: A Comic Adventure for Anytime. Reitze, Glenn Logan, illus. 2007. (Illus.). 50p. (J). lib. bdg. 19.95 (*978-0-88265-040-1(8) , Fine Art Editions) North American International.

Reitze, Glenn Logan, illus. & text. Ernie the Easter Hippotamus: A Comic Adventure for Anytime. Reitze, Glenn Logan, text. 2007. (J). pap. (*978-0-88265-041-8(6)) North American International.

Renick, Sam X. The Adventures of Sammy the Saver: It's a Habit, Sammy Rabbit! Alvarado, Juan Carlos, illus. 2001. iv, 24p. (J). pap. 8.95 (978-0-9713664-0-4(3)) It's A Habit! Co., The.

Rettore, A. S. Lucky Ladybug. 2004. 4p. (J). 7.99 (978-0-439-62770-2(2) , Cartwheel Bks.) Scholastic, Inc.

Rex, Michael. Where Can Bunny Paint? Rex, Michael, illus. 2003. (Word-by-Word First Reader Ser.). (Illus.). 32p. (J). (ps-k). pap. 3.99 (978-0-439-36605-2(4) , Cartwheel Bks.) Scholastic, Inc.

Rey, Margret & Rey, H. A. Curious George & the Bunny. 1998. (Curious George Ser.). (Illus.). 12p. (J). (gr. k-ps). bds. 5.95 (978-0-395-89922-9(2)) Houghton Mifflin Co. Trade & Reference Div.

Rhae, Sympne. My Name Is Johnson? l.t. ed. 2006. (Illus.). 53p. (J). per. 13.75 (978-0-9770043-9-3(2)) New Global Publishing.

Rhodes, C. J. The Rabbit, the Skunk & the Cuckoo. Spears-Stewart, Reta, ed. Secca, Phillip, illus. 1998. 36p. (J). pap. 12.00 (978-0-9638648-5-7(8)) Nottinghill Bks.

Richards, Kitty. Bunnies: Thumper Counts to Ten. Disney Storybook Artists Staff et al, illus. 2007. 16p. (J). (ps-k). 5.99 (978-1-4231-0076-8(X)) Disney Pr.

Rigby Education Staff. Baby Kangaroo. (Sails Literacy Ser.). (Illus.). 16p. (gr. k-1). 27.00 (978-0-7635-9879-2(8) , 698798C99) Rigby Education.

—A Class Pet. (Illus.). 8p. (J). bds. 6.95 (978-0-7635-6439-1(7) , 764397C99) Rigby Education.

—Look Out, Fox! (Sails Literacy Ser.). (Illus.). 16p. (gr. k-1). 27.00 (978-0-7635-9874-7(7) , 698747C99) Rigby Education.

Riordan, James. Little Bunny Bobkin. Warnes, Tim, illus. 1999. 32p. (J). (ps-2). 14.95 (978-1-888444-38-4(X)) Little Tiger Pr.

Risom, Ole. I Am a Bunny. Scarry, Richard, illus. 2004. 26p. (J). (gr. k-k). bds. 5.99 (978-0-375-82778-5(1) , Golden Bks.) Random Hse. Children's Bks.

Ritchie, Joseph R. Peter Cottontail's Busy Day. Halverson, Lydia, illus. 2005. 16p. (J). bds. 9.95 (978-0-8249-6571-6(X)) Ideals Pubns.

—Peter Cottontail's Easter Egg Hunt. Thornburgh, Rebecca McKillip, illus. 2004. 12p. (J). (ps-k). bds. 9.95 (978-0-8249-6522-8(1)) Ideals Pubns.

—Peter Cottontail's Easter Surprise. Rasmussen, Wendy, illus. 2006. 18p. (J). bds. 9.95 (978-0-8249-6627-0(9) , Candy Cane Pr.) Ideals Pubns.

Robbins, Beth. Tom, Ally & the Babysitter. Stuart, Jon, illus. 2001. (It's OK! Ser.). 24p. (J). (ps-k). pap. 3.95 (978-0-7894-7426-1(3) , D K Ink) Dorling Kindersley Publishing, Inc.

Robbins, Terrie C. Bushtail Is Our Cousin. Mezza, J. Di, illus. 2002. 32p. (J). (gr. 3-6). pap. 7.99 (978-0-9711577-0-5(7)) Possibilities Unlimited.

Robertson, Susan, illus. Little Bunny. 2005. (Bedtime Babies Ser.). 8p. (J). (ps). per. 6.99 (978-1-57755-503-2(1)) Allied Publishing.

Rockwell, Anne F. Chip & the Karate Kick. Meisel, Paul, illus. 2004. (Good Sports Ser.). 40p. (J). (ps-1). lib. bdg. 15.89 (978-0-06-028446-6(3)) HarperCollins Pubs.

Rohmann, Eric. My Friend Rabbit. Rohmann, Eric, illus. rev. ed. 2002. (Illus.). 32p. (J). (ps-3). 16.95 (978-0-7613-1535-3(7)) Roaring Brook Pr.

—My Friend Rabbit. Rohmann, Eric, illus. 2007. (Illus.). 32p. (J). pap. 6.95 (*978-0-312-36752-7(X)) Square Fish.

Root, Phyllis. Hop! Meade, Holly, illus. 2005. (Board Books). 16p. (J). (gr. k-ps). bds. 6.99 (978-0-7636-1794-3(6)) Candlewick Pr.

Rosie Rabbit's Radish. 2001. (ps-2). lib. bdg. 9.80 (978-0-613-33000-8(5)) Tandem Library Bks.

Ross, Katharine. The Wide-Awake Bunnies. 1999. (J). 1.99 (978-0-679-89209-0(5) , Random Hse. Bks. for Young Readers) Random Hse. Children's Bks.

Roth, Carol. Little Bunny's Sleepless Night. Gorbachev, Valeri, illus. 32p. (J). (ps-2). 2002. pap. 6.95 (978-0-7358-1804-0(5)); 1999. 15.95 (978-0-7358-1069-3(9)); 1999. 16.50 (978-0-7358-1070-9(2)) North-South Bks., Inc.

Running Press Staff & Studio Books Staff. Easter Bunny's Egg Hunt. 2006. (Illus.). 8p. (J). 4.95 (978-0-7624-2633-1(0) , Running Pr. Kids) Running Pr. Bk. Pubs.

Russo, Marisabina. The Bunnies Are Not in Their Beds. Russo, Marisabina, illus. 2007. 40p. (J). (ps-2). lib. bdg. 17.99 (978-0-375-93961-7(X)); (Illus.). 15.99 (978-0-375-83961-0(5)) Random Hse. Children's Bks. (Schwartz & Wade Bks.).

Rylant, Cynthia. Annie & Snowball & the Dress-Up Birthday. Stevenson, Sucie, illus. 2007. (Annie & Snowball Ser.). 40p. (J). (gr. k-3). 14.99 (978-1-4169-0938-5(9) , Simon & Schuster Children's Publishing) Simon & Schuster Children's Publishing.

—Annie & Snowball & the Tea Cup Club. Stevenson, Sucie, illus. 2008. (Annie & Snowball Ser.). 32p. (J). 15.99 (*978-1-4169-0940-8(0) , Simon & Schuster Children's Publishing) Simon & Schuster Children's Publishing.

—Bunny Bungalow. Hayashi, Nancy, illus. 2002. 32p. (J). (ps-k). pap. 6.00 (978-0-15-216316-7(6) , Voyager Bks./Libros Viajeros) Harcourt Children's Bks.

—Bunny Bungalow. Hayashi, Nancy, illus. 2002. (J). (ps-3). lib. bdg. 14.15 (978-0-613-53798-8(X)) Tandem Library Bks.

—The Case of the Climbing Cat. Karas, G. Brian, illus. 2003. (High-Rise Private Eyes Ser.: No. 2). (J). (gr. k-3). pap. 16.95 incl. audio (978-1-59112-189-3(2)); pap. 18.95 incl. audio compact disk (978-1-59112-610-2(X)); 25.96 incl. audio (978-1-59112-190-9(6)); pap. 29.95 incl. audio (978-1-59112-191-6(4)) Live Oak Media.

—The Case of the Climbing Cat. 2001. (High-Rise Private Eyes Ser.: No. 2). (J). (gr. k-3). lib. bdg. 11.80 (978-0-613-44193-3(1)) Tandem Library Bks.

—The Case of the Puzzling Possum. Karas, G. Brian, illus. (High-Rise Private Eyes Ser.: No. 3). (J). (ps-2). 2004. 48p. pap. 18.95 incl. audio compact disk (978-1-59112-618-8(5)); 2003. pap. 29.95 incl. audio (978-1-59112-199-2(X)); 2003. pap. 16.95 incl. audio (978-1-59112-197-8(3)); 2003. 25.95 incl. audio (978-1-59112-198-5(1)) Live Oak Media.

—The Case of the Puzzling Possum. 2002. (High-Rise Private Eyes Ser.: No. 3). (J). (gr. k-3). lib. bdg. 11.80 (978-0-613-44514-6(7)) Tandem Library Bks.

—Henry & Mudge & Annie's Perfect Pet. Stevenson, Sucie, illus. 2002. (Henry & Mudge Ser.). (J). 11.91 (978-0-7587-5054-9(4)) Book Wholesalers, Inc.

—Henry & Mudge & Annie's Perfect Pet. 2000. (Henry & Mudge Ser.). lib. bdg. 11.80 (978-0-613-33701-4(8)) Tandem Library Bks.

Sadler, Marilyn. Honey Bunny's Honey Bear. Bollen, Roger, illus. 2008. (Step into Reading Ser.). (J). (978-0-375-84326-6(4)); lib. bdg. 11.99 (978-0-375-94326-3(9)) Random Hse. Children's Bks.

—P. J. Funnybunny's Bag of Tricks. Bollen, Roger, illus. 2004. (Step into Reading Ser.). 32p. (J). (ps-2). pap. 3.99 (978-0-375-82444-9(8) , Random Hse. Bks. for Young Readers) Random Hse. Children's Bks.

—P J Funnybunny's Bag of Tricks. 2004. (ps-2). lib. bdg. 11.80 (978-0-613-83535-0(2)) Tandem Library Bks.

Sadler, Marilyn & Bollen, Roger. Money, Money, Honey Bunny! 2006. (Bright & Early Bks.). (Illus.). 36p. (J). 8.99 (978-0-375-83370-0(6)); lib. bdg. 12.99 (978-0-375-93370-7(0)) Random Hse. Children's Bks. (Random Hse. Bks. for Young Readers).

Sakai, Stan. Usagi Yojimbo Vol. 3: Al Filo de la Vida y la Muerte. 2007. (SPA., Illus.). 200p. reprint ed. pap. 15.95 (*978-1-59497-319-2(9)) Public Square Bks.

—Usagi Yojimbo Vol. 4: Estaciones. 2007. (SPA., Illus.). 200p. reprint ed. pap. 15.95 (*978-1-59497-320-8(2)) Public Square Bks.

—Usagi Yojimbo Vol. 5: Segadora. 2007. (SPA., Illus.). 256p. reprint ed. pap. 17.95 (*978-1-59497-321-5(0)) Public Square Bks.

—Usagi Yojimbo Vol. 6: Primeras Andanzas. 2007. (SPA., Illus.). 128p. reprint ed. pap. 12.95 (*978-1-59497-322-2(9)) Public Square Bks.

—Usagi Yojimbo Vol. 7: Samurai (en Español) 2007. (SPA., Illus.). 144p. reprint ed. pap. 14.95 (*978-1-59497-323-9(7)) Public Square Bks.

Sakairi, Masao. Vietnamese Tales of Rabbits & Watermelons. Kojima, Shoko, illus. 2006. (Asian Folktales Retold Ser.). 32p. (J). 16.95 (978-0-89346-948-1(3)) Heian International Publishing, Inc.

Saltzberg, Barney. Hi, Blueberry! 2007. (Illus.). 14p. (J). bds. 8.95 (978-0-15-205984-2(9) , Red Wagon Bks.) Harcourt Children's Bks.

Saltzberg, Barney. Peekaboo, Blueberry! 2008. (Illus.). 14p. (J). bds. 8.95 (*978-0-15-206062-6(6) , Red Wagon Bks.) Harcourt Children's Bks.

San Souci, Daniel. Rabbit & the Dragon King. 2006. 32p. pap. 9.95 (978-1-59078-418-1(9)) Boyds Mills Pr.

Sargent, Dave & Sargent, Pat. Cammie Camel: Endurance, 56 bks, Vol. 42. Lenoir, Jane, illus. 2000. (Animal Pride Ser.). 36p. (J). lib. bdg. 19.95 (978-1-56763-525-6(3)) Ozark Publishing.

—Chrissy Cottontail: Mind Your Mama, 15 bks, 7. Huff, Jeane, illus. 2nd rev. ed. 2003. (Animal Pride Ser.: 7). 42p. (J). pap. 6.95 (978-1-56763-772-4(8)); lib. bdg. 19.95 (978-1-56763-771-7(X)) Ozark Publishing.

—Fuzzy Bunny, 10, 19. Robinson, Laura, illus. 2004. (Learn to Read Ser.: 10). 18p. (J). lib. bdg. 19.95 (978-1-56763-833-2(3)); lib. bdg. 9.95 (978-1-56763-834-9(1)) Ozark Publishing.

—Fuzzy Bunny/el conejito Velloso, 10, 19. Robinson, Laura, illus. 2004. (Learn to Read Ser.: 10). (ENG & SPA.). 18p. (J). pap. 9.95 (978-1-56763-998-8(4)); lib. bdg. 19.95 (978-1-56763-997-1(6)) Ozark Publishing.

—Young Chrissy: Mind Your Mama!, 7. Woodword, Elaine, illus. 2005. (Young Animal Pride Ser.). 24p. (J). pap. 6.95 (978-1-56763-876-9(7)) Ozark Publishing.

—Young Dawn: Friends Care!, 8. Woodword, Elaine, illus. 2005. (Young Animal Pride Ser.: 8). 24p. (J). pap. 6.95 (978-1-56763-878-3(3)); lib. bdg. 19.95 (978-1-56763-877-6(5)) Ozark Publishing.

—Young Dike: Teamwork!, 5. Woodward, Elaine, illus. 2003. (Young Animal Pride Ser.: 5). 24p. (J). pap. 6.95 (978-1-56763-872-1(4)); lib. bdg. 19.95 (978-1-56763-871-4(6)) Ozark Publishing.

—Young Sammy: I'm a Little Stinker, 9. Woodword, Elaine, illus. 2005. (Young Animal Pride Ser.). 24p. (J). lib. bdg. 19.95 (978-1-56763-879-0(1)) Ozark Publishing.

—Young Sammy: I'm a Little Stinker!, 9. Woodword, Elaine, illus. 2005. (Young Animal Pride Ser.). 24p. (J). pap. 6.95 (978-1-56763-880-6(5)) Ozark Publishing.

—Young White Thunder: I'm a Leader!, 6. Woodword, Elaine, illus. 2005. (Young Animal Pride Ser.). 24p. (J). pap. 6.95 (978-1-56763-874-5(0)); lib. bdg. 19.95 (978-1-56763-873-8(2)) Ozark Publishing.

Sargent, Dave, et al. Cammie Camel: Endurance, 17, 42. 2000. (Animal Pride Ser.: 42). (Illus.). (J). pap. 6.95 (978-1-56763-526-3(1)) Ozark Publishing.

—Young Chrissy: Mind Your Mama!, 7. 2005. (Young Animal Pride Ser.). (Illus.). 24p. (J). lib. bdg. 19.95 (978-1-56763-875-2(9)) Ozark Publishing.

Scaglione, Dapos & Maria. A Unique Bunny. 2005. 65p. pap. 12.95 (978-1-4137-9530-1(7)) PublishAmerica, Inc.

Scarry, Patricia M. The Bunny Book. Scarry, Richard, illus. 2005. (Little Golden Book Classic Ser.). 24p. (J). (gr. k-k). 2.99 (978-0-375-83224-6(6) , Golden Bks.) Random Hse. Children's Bks.

Schneider, Cheryl & Olson, Carole. Bunnaby Bunny (L) Toddler Reader. Schneider, Cheryl, illus. deluxe ed. 2006. (Illus.). 20p. (J). bds. 10.00 (978-0-9712816-5-3(3)) Third Week Bks.

Scholastic, Inc. Staff. Fluffy Bunny. Harper, Piers, illus. 2004. 32p. (J). 15.95 (978-0-439-57825-7(6) , Cartwheel Bks.) Scholastic, Inc.

Scholastic, Inc. Staff & Rettore, A. S. Hop-A-Long Bunny: A Pull-the-Tab Cloth Book. 2004. 8p. (J). 7.99 (978-0-439-62659-0(5) , Cartwheel Bks.) Scholastic, Inc.

Schotter, Roni. Missing Rabbit. Moore, Cyd, illus. 2002. 32p. (J). (gr. k-ps). 15.00 (978-0-618-03432-1(3) , Clarion Bks.) Houghton Mifflin Co. Trade & Reference Div.

Schulman, Janet. A Bunny for All Seasons. So, Meilo, illus. 2003. 32p. (J). (gr. k-1). 9.95 (978-0-375-82256-8(9) , Knopf Bks. for Young Readers) Random Hse. Children's Bks.

Schwartz, Betty Ann. What Makes a Rainbow? A Magic Ribbon Book. Turner, Dona, illus. 2000. (Novelty Book Ser.). (J). (ps-k). 14p. 8.95 (978-1-58117-076-4(9)); 12p. 10.95 (978-1-58117-115-0(3)) Dalmatian Pr. (Intervisual/Piggy Toes).

Scott, Michael, photos by. Bunny Day. 2004. (Illus.). 12p. (ps-ps). 5.99 (978-0-7868-1921-8(9) , Disney Editions) Disney Pr.

Segal, John. Carrot Soup. Segal, John, illus. 2006. (Illus.). 32p. (J). (ps-1). 12.95 (978-0-689-87702-5(1) , McElderry, Margaret K.) Simon & Schuster Children's Publishing.

Selby. Beach Bunny. 1999. (J). pap. 6.00 (978-0-15-201961-7(8)) Harcourt Trade Pubs.

Serwacki, Kevin, illus. Doorknob the Rabbit & the Carnival of Bugs. 2003. 32p. (J). 14.95 (978-1-58246-143-4(0) , Tricycle Pr.) Ten Speed Pr.

Shannon, George & Dronzek, Laura. Rabbit's Gift. 2007. (Illus.). 32p. (J). (ps-2). 16.00 (978-0-15-206073-2(1)) Harcourt Trade Pubs.

Sherwood, Barbara B. Jan & Ann & the Pet Rabbit. Campbell, Nancy T., illus. 1998. 16p. (J). (ps). pap. 5.95 (978-1-891846-03-8(5)) Business Word, The.

Shoelace, CM. Thumper: The Story of a Curious Little Bunny. 2002. 108p. (J). pap. 9.95 (978-0-595-21234-7(4)) iUniverse, Inc.

Shulman, Mark. Storytime Stickers: Easter Bunny. Swanson, Maggie, illus. 2007. (Storytime Stickers Ser.). 16p. (J). pap. 4.95 (978-1-4027-3363-5(1)) Sterling Publishing Co., Inc.

Siegel, Bernie S. Smudge Bunny. Bryant, Laura J., illus. 2004. 32p. 15.95 (978-1-932073-03-4(5)) Kramer, H.J. Inc.

Sims, Janet. Mark's Big Surprise. 2007. (J). pap. 8.00 (*978-0-8059-7355-6(9)) Dorrance Publishing Co., Inc.

Slater, Jean M. The Adventures of Hopper. Slater, Jean M., illus. 2003. (Illus.). 8p. (J). bds. 16.00 (978-0-9743149-3-8(5)) Slater Software. Inc.

P
Q
R

Slater, Teddy. The Bunny Hop. Di Fiori, Larry, illus. 2004. 32p. (J). lib. bdg. 15.00 (978-1-59054-342-9(4)) Fitzgerald Bks.

Slaughter, Hope. Buckley & Wilberta, Forever Friends. Torrence, Susan, illus. l.t. ed. 1998. 64p. (J). (gr. 1-3). lib. bdg. 14.95 (978-0-931093-16-6(3)) Red Hen Pr.

Smath, Jerry. The Best Easter Egg Ever! Smath, Jerry, illus. 2003. (Illus.). 32p. (J). (ps-3). 3.50 (978-0-439-44321-0(0) , Cartwheel Bks.) Scholastic, Inc.

—Best Easter Eggs Ever! 2003. (gr. k-3). lib. bdg. 11.25 (978-0-613-66616-9(X)) Tandem Library Bks.

Smith, Kathryn & Scott, Karen. King Murray's Royal Tail: The True Story of an Easter Bunny. 2004. 59p. pap. 8.95 (978-0-595-31090-6(7)) iUniverse, Inc.

Smith, Maggie Caldwell. Tommy Wilson, Junior Veterinarian: The Case of the Wounded Jack Rabbit. McHose, Jean, illus. 2005. 104p. (J). (gr. 3-6). pap. 7.95 (978-1-889159-14-0(X)) Magpie Pr., Pine Mtn Club, CA.

Smith, Simon. Stumpy Stomps Off: A Retelling of the Parable of the Prodigal Son. 2004. (Clay Pot Parables Ser.). (Illus.). 32p. (J). 9.99 (978-0-310-70660-1(2)) Zonderkidz.

Smith, Stephanie. Snowshoe Hare. Hynes, Robert, illus. 2002. (J). bds. (978-1-59069-256-1(X) , HS3002) Studio Mouse LLC.

—Snowshoe Hare's Family. Hynes, Robert, illus. 2nd ed. 2005. (Soundprints' Read-And-Discover Ser.). (J). (gr. 1-3). 48p. 7.95 (978-1-931465-16-8(9) , B2003); 32p. pap. 3.95 (978-1-931465-15-1(0) , S2003) Soundprints.

—Snowshoe Hare's Family. 2002. (gr. k-3). lib. bdg. 16.40 (978-0-613-70884-5(9)) Tandem Library Bks.

Smith, Suzanne C. Peter Cottontail & the Easter Bunny Imposter. Brittingham, Geoffrey, illus. 24p. (J). pap. 3.25 (978-0-8249-5372-0(X) , Ideals) Ideals Pubns.

Snowshoe Hare's Coat. 2002. (Wild Heritage Collection Mini Bks.). (Illus.). 32p. (J). (978-1-59069-161-8(X) , H3005) Studio Mouse LLC.

Snyder, Bethany. Herbie's Easter Bunny. Campbell, Jenny, illus. 2001. 24p. (J). (ps-3). 7.95 (978-1-57102-145-8(0)) Warehousing & Fulfillment Specialists, LLC (WFS, LLC).

Sontag, Mary G. The Move of Eb & Flo. 2006. (ENG.). 44p. per. 18.49 (***978-1-4259-7832-7(0)***) AuthorHouse.

Spowart, Robin. Ten Little Bunnies. Spowart, Robin, illus. 2001. (Illus.). 24p. (J). (ps). pap. 7.95 (978-0-439-20863-5(7)) Scholastic, Inc.

Sprick, Marilyn & Lemieux, Aurora, adapted by. The Race: Read Well Level K Unit 13 Storybook. 2003. (Read Well Level K Ser.). (Illus.). 20p. (J). (978-1-57035-684-1(X) , 55538) Sopris West Educational Services.

Sprunger, Reed, photos by. The Velveteen Rabbit. 1998. (Illus.). 32p. (J). (ps-1). 12.99 (978-1-929174-01-0(2)) Oshkosh B'Gosh, Inc.

Stanley, Mandy. Lettice: The Flower Girl. Stanley, Mandy, illus. 2006. (Illus.). 32p. (J). (ps-3). 9.95 (978-1-4169-1157-9(X)) Simon & Schuster Children's Publishing.

—Lettice the Dancing Rabbit. Stanley, Mandy, illus. 2005. (Illus.). 32p. (J). 6.99 (978-0-689-87608-0(4) , Aladdin) Simon & Schuster Children's Publishing.

Steig, William. Which Would You Rather Be? Bliss, Harry, illus. 32p. (J). (ps-3). 2002. 17.99 (978-0-06-029653-7(4) , Cotler, Joanna Books); 2005. reprint ed. pap. 6.99 (978-0-06-443792-9(2) , Harper Trophy) HarperCollins Pubs.

Steiner, Jorg. The Bear Who Wanted to Be a Bear. Mueller, Jorg, illus. 2nd ed. 2007. 44p. (J). 16.95 (978-0-9762056-0-9(2)) Heryin Publishing Corp.

Stevens, Terry. The Battle at Longshore Causeway. 2006. 64p. pap. (***978-1-84401-751-5(6)***) Athena Pr.

Stewart, Amber. I'm Big Enough. Marlow, Layn, illus. 2007. 32p. (J). 12.99 (978-0-439-90666-1(0) , Orchard Bks.) Scholastic, Inc.

—Rabbit Ears. Rankin, Laura, illus. 2006. 32p. (J). 16.95 (978-1-58234-959-6(2) , Bloomsbury Children) Bloomsbury Publishing.

Stewart, Paul. A Little Bit of Winter. Riddell, Chris, illus. 1999. 32p. (J). (ps-2). 14.95 (978-0-06-028278-3(9)) HarperCollins Pubs.

—Un Poquito de Invierno. Riddell, Chris, illus. 2003. (SPA.). 30p. (J). (gr. k-2). (978-84-348-6839-7(3) , SM30933) SM Ediciones ESP. *Dist:* Lectorum Pubns., Inc.

—Rabbit's Wish. Riddell, Chris, illus. 2001. 32p. (J). (ps-2). 12.95 (978-0-06-029518-9(X)) HarperCollins Pubs.

—Un Regalo de Cumpleanos. Riddell, Chris, illus. (SPA.). 30p. (J). (gr. k-2). (978-84-348-6840-3(7) , SM30935) SM Ediciones ESP. *Dist:* Lectorum Pubns., Inc.

Stroschin, Jane H. Atsa & Ga: A Story from the High Desert. Stich, Carolyn R., illus. 2005. 32p. (J). (gr. k-6). (978-1-883960-29-2(0)) Henry Quill Pr.

Sullivan, William J. Taylor Rabbit & the Seeds of Success. 2001. 32p. (J). pap. 4.95 (978-0-9708066-1-1(2)) Painted Horse Pubns., Inc.

Sutherland, David. Samantha Cardigan & the Genie's Revenge. Roberts, David, illus. 2005. (Red Bananas Ser.). 48p. (J). (978-0-7787-1070-7(X)) Crabtree Publishing Co.

—Samantha Cardigan & the Genie's Revenge. 2005. (Red Bananas Ser.). (Illus.). 48p. (J). (ps). pap. (978-0-7787-1086-8(6)) Crabtree Publishing Co.

—Samantha Cardigan & the Ghastly Twirling Sickness. Roberts, David, illus. 2005. (Red Bananas Ser.). 48p. (J). (978-0-7787-1069-1(6)) Crabtree Publishing Co.

—Samantha Cardigan & the Ghastly Twirling Sickness. 2005. (Red Bananas Ser.). (Illus.). 48p. (J). (ps). pap. (978-0-7787-1085-1(8)) Crabtree Publishing Co.

Sweeney, Jacqueline. Just Call Me J. P. Hart, G. K. & Empey, Mark, illus. 2000. (We Can Read! Ser.). 32p. (J). (gr. 1-2). lib. bdg. 21.36 (978-0-7614-0922-9(X) , Benchmark Bks.) Cavendish, Marshall Corp.

Symes, Ruth Louise. Floppy Ears. Kenyon, Tony, illus. 2005. (J). 14.99 (978-1-84255-264-3(3)) Orion Children's Bks. GBR. *Dist:* Trafalgar Square Publishing.

Szekeres, Cyndy. I Can Count 100 Bunnies: And So Can You! 1999. (Illus.). 48p. (J). (ps-2). pap. 12.95 (978-0-590-38361-5(2)) Scholastic, Inc.

—Wilbur Bunny's Funny Friends A to Z. Szekeres, Cyndy, illus. 2000. (Illus.). 15p. (J). (ps). bds. 6.99 (978-0-439-17327-8(2)) Scholastic, Inc.

Tafuri, Nancy. Where Did Bunny Go? A Bunny & Bird Story. 2001. (Illus.). (J). pap. (978-0-439-16960-8(7)) Scholastic, Inc.

—Where Did Bunny Go? A Bunny & Bird Story. Tafuri, Nancy, illus. 2001. (Illus.). 32p. (J). (ps-2). pap. 15.95 (978-0-439-16959-2(3) , Levine, Arthur A. Bks.) Scholastic, Inc.

—Will You Be My Friend? A Bunny & Bird Story. 2000. (Illus.). (J). (978-0-439-05943-5(7)) Scholastic, Inc.

Tagg, Christine. A Very Special Valentine. Kneen, Maggie, illus. 2003. (J). 15.95 (978-0-8118-4073-6(5)) Chronicle Bks. LLC.

Tales from the Carrot Patch, 5 vols. 2001. (J). (978-1-58805-122-6(6)) DS-Max USA, Inc.

Tales from the Carrot Patch Vol. 1: A Tale Told Twice, 5 vols. 2001. (J). (978-1-58805-123-3(4)) DS-Max USA, Inc.

Tales from the Carrot Patch Vol. 2: The First Prize Carrot; 5 vols. 2001. (J). (978-1-58805-124-0(2)) DS-Max USA, Inc.

Tales from the Carrot Patch Vol. 3: Bunny Magic, 5 vols. 2001. (J). (978-1-58805-125-7(0)) DS-Max USA, Inc.

Tales from the Carrot Patch Vol. 4: Upside Down Ears, 5 vols. 2001. (J). (978-1-58805-126-4(9)) DS-Max USA, Inc.

Talley, Linda. Toad in Town. Maeno, Itoko, illus. 2001. (Key Concepts in Personal Development Ser.). (gr. k-4). 30p. (J). 89.95 incl. VHS (978-1-55942-165-2(7)); 32p. pap., tchr. ed. 89.95 incl. VHS (978-1-55942-168-3(1) , 9387K3) Marsh Media.

Tanaka, Usa. Give Me That! 2007. 32p. 15.95 (***978-0-9741319-0-0(3)***) 4N Publishing LLC.

Taylor, Chet. Last, but Not Least. Taylor, Chet, illus. l.t. ed. 2004. (Illus.). 20p. (J). 17.99 (978-0-9755888-6-4(9)); lib. bdg. 22.99 (978-0-9755888-1-9(8)) Dragonfly Publishing, Inc.

Taylor, Shirley A. The Cross in the Egg. Hall, Wendell E., illus. 1999. 32p. (J). (ps-2). 15.95 (978-0-87483-549-6(6)) August Hse. Pubs., Inc.

Tegen, Katherine. The Story of the Easter Bunny. Lambert, Sally Anne, illus. 40p. (J). 2007. pap. 6.99 (978-0-06-058781-9(4) , Harper Trophy); 2005. 12.99 (978-0-06-050711-4(X)); 2005. lib. bdg. 14.89 (978-0-06-050712-1(8)) HarperCollins Pubs.

Thomson, Emma. Dandelion's Day. 2007. (Dandelion Ser.). (Illus.). 32p. (J). (ps-k). 9.95 (***978-0-340-88404-1(5)***) Hodder Children's Division GBR. *Dist:* Independent Pubs. Group.

Thoughts Staff. Bugsy Rabbit: Furry Tales, No. 1. 2005. 13p. 8.99 (978-1-4116-3331-5(8)) Lulu.com.

Tiger Tales Staff. Little Bunny. Finn, Rebecca, illus. 2005. (Cuddly Cuffs Ser.). 6p. (J). 6.95 (978-1-58925-763-4(4) , tiger tales) ME Media LLC.

Tinder, Jeremy. Cry Yourself to Sleep. 2006. (Illus.). 88p. (YA). pap. 7.00 (978-1-891830-81-5(3)) Top Shelf Productions.

Toad in Town - Teaching Guide. 2000. 17.95 (978-1-55942-167-6(3)) Marsh Media.

Todd, Burt Kerr. Bun Bun & Other Tales. 2006. pap. 10.00 (***978-1-4257-1857-2(4)***) Xlibris Corp.

Todd, Diana. Carrotsville. 2004. 42p. per. 12.95 (978-1-932344-61-5(6)) Thornton Publishing.

Torrel, Wendy. Guardian of Dreams: A Bedtime Story, Klingbeil, Kendall, illus. l.t. ed. 2004. 32p. (J). 14.95 (978-0-9746890-0-5(9)); pap. 10.95 (978-0-9746890-1-2(7)) White Tulip Publishing.

Trondheim, Lewis. McConey Vol. 2: The Hoodoodad. 1998. (Fantagraphics Ser.). (Illus.). 48p. (gr. 10 up). pap. 10.95 (978-1-56097-338-6(2)) Fantagraphics Bks.

Trondhein, Lewis. Harum Scarum: The Spiffy Adventures of McConey, Vol. 1. (Illus.). 48p. (gr. 10 up). pap. 10.95 (978-1-56097-288-4(2)) Fantagraphics Bks.

Umansky, Kaye. Sophie & the Mother's Day Card. Currey, Anna, illus. 2005. 30p. (J). 3.95 (978-1-56148-481-2(4)); 9.95 (978-1-56148-479-9(2)) Good Bks.

—Sophie in Charge. Currey, Anna, illus. 2005. 30p. (J). 3.95 (978-1-56148-480-5(6)); 9.95 (978-1-56148-478-2(4)) Good Bks.

Umansky, Kaye & Currey, Anna, illus. Sophie & Abigail. 2004. 30p. (J). 3.95 (978-1-56148-444-7(X)); 9.95 (978-1-56148-434-8(2)) Good Bks.

Vallee, Art. Rainbow Rabbit. 2004. pap. 17.32 (***978-1-4134-0193-6(7)***) Xlibris Corp.

van Ommen, Sylvia. Jellybeans. 2006. (Illus.). 56p. (J). pap. 8.95 (978-1-55643-632-1(7)) North Atlantic Bks.

Van Oss, Laura. Indigo's Gift: Does Indigo Have a Secret Gift? Wolf, Claudia, illus. 2006. 24p. (J). per. 2.99 (978-1-59958-003-6(9)) Journey Stone Creations, LLC.

Varley, Susan & Grindley, Sally. Why Is the Sky Blue? 2007. (Illus.). 32p. (J). pap. 9.95 (***978-1-84270-589-6(X)***) Andersen GBR. *Dist:* Independent Pubs. Group.

Vaughan, Christina. The Girl Who Lived with Rabbits. 2000. (Laura Lapin Stories Ser.). 32p. (J). (gr. 1-4). spiral bd. 18.95 (978-0-9641697-7-7(0) , You-Draw-It Bks.) Castlebrook Pubns.

Velthuijs, Max. Frog & Hare. (Illus.). 16p. (J). 6.99 (978-0-86264-995-1(1)) Andersen GBR. *Dist:* Trafalgar Square Publishing.

The Velveteen Rabbit. 2002. (Puppy Tales Ser.). (Illus.). 24p. (J). (gr. k-3). 1.49 (978-1-57759-257-0(3)) Dalmatian Pr.

The Velveteen Rabbit. 2003. (J). 9.99 (978-0-9740847-3-2(5)) GiGi Bks.

Voorheis, Tracy. Nibbles... a strawberry Tale. Voorheis, Tracy, illus. 2007. (Illus.). 60p. (J). per. 19.00 (***978-0-9787113-0-6(0)*** , Ithaca Pr.) Authors & Artists Publishers of New York, Inc.

Waddell, Martin. Tom Rabbit. Firth, Barbara, illus. 2006. 32p. (J). (ps-1). pap. 6.99 (978-0-7636-2879-6(4)) Candlewick Pr.

Wahl, Jan. Rabbits on Mars. Schamber, Kimberly, illus. 2005. 32p. (gr. k-2). 15.25 (978-1-57505-511-4(2)) Lerner Publishing Group.

Wakeman, Daniel. Ben's Bunny Trouble. Van Stralen, Dirk, illus. 2007. 32p. (J). (ps-3). (***978-1-55143-611-1(6)***) Orca Bk. Pubs.

Wallace, Ivy. Pookie. (Illus.). 32p. 2002. pap. 9.99 (978-0-00-664731-7(6)); 2001. (J). 19.99 (978-0-00-198377-9(6)) HarperCollins Pubs. Ltd. GBR. *Dist:* Trafalgar Square Publishing.

—Pookie Believes in Santa Claus. 2001. (Illus.). 32p. (J). (gr. k-4). 19.99 (978-0-00-198380-9(6)) HarperCollins Pubs. Ltd. GBR. *Dist:* Trafalgar Square Publishing.

Wallace, John. Tiny Rabbit Goes to a Birthday Party. Wallace, John, illus. 2000. (Illus.). 32p. (J). (gr. k-3). 16.95 (978-0-8234-1489-5(2)) Holiday Hse., Inc.

Wallace, Nancy Elizabeth. Count down to Clean Up! 2001. (Illus.). 32p. (J). (gr. k-3). tchr. ed. 14.00 (978-0-618-10130-6(6)) Houghton Mifflin Co. Trade & Reference Div.

—El Dia del Bebe. 2003. (SPA & ENG., Illus.). 32p. (J). (gr. k-ps). tchr. ed. 9.95 (978-0-618-38795-3(1)) Houghton Mifflin Co. Trade & Reference Div.

—Pumpkin Day! 2002. (Illus.). 32p. (J). (ps-2). 16.95 (978-0-7614-5128-0(5)) Cavendish, Marshall Corp.

—Pumpkin Day. Wallace, Nancy Elizabeth, illus. 2006. (Illus.). 32p. 5.99 (978-0-7614-5327-7(X)) Cavendish, Marshall Corp.

—Rabbit's Bedtime. Wallace, Nancy Elizabeth, illus. 1999. (Illus.). 32p. (J). (gr. k-ps). tchr. ed. 9.95 (978-0-395-98266-2(9)) Houghton Mifflin Co. Trade & Reference Div.

—Recycle Every Day! (Illus.). 32p. (J). 2006. 5.95 (978-0-7614-5290-4(7)); 2003. 16.95 (978-0-7614-5149-5(8)) Cavendish, Marshall Corp.

—A Taste of Honey. Wallace, Nancy Elizabeth, illus. 2000. (Illus.). 40p. (J). (ps-3). 15.95 (978-1-890817-19-0(8)) Winslow Pr.

Wallace, Nancy Elizabeth. Tell-a-Bunny. 2007. 32p. (J). pap. 5.99 (***978-0-7614-5369-7(5)***) Cavendish, Marshall Corp.

—Tell-a-Bunny. Wallace, Nancy Elizabeth, illus. 2000. (Illus.). 40p. (J). (ps-2). 15.95 (978-1-890817-29-9(5)) Winslow Pr.

Wallace, Nancy Elizabeth, illus. Pumpkins, Pumpkins, Pumpkins. 2002. (J). (978-1-58837-029-7(1)) Winslow Hse. Bks.

—Recycle Every Day! 2002. 40p. (J). 15.95 (978-1-58837-018-1(6)) Winslow Pr.

—Snow. 2007. 24p. (J). (ps-3). bds. 6.99 (***978-0-7614-5362-8(8)***) Cavendish, Marshall Corp.

Wallace, Nancy Elizabeth, illus. The Valentine Express. 2004. 32p. (J). 16.95 (978-0-7614-5183-9(8)) Cavendish, Marshall Corp.

Wallen, Ila. The Not Me Monster. Sauber, Robert, illus. 2002. 16.95 (978-0-9710627-1-9(4)) Bent Willow Publishing.

Walsh, Ellen Stoll. Hop Jump. Walsh, Ellen Stoll, illus. 2002. (Illus.). (J). 13.19 (978-0-7587-2747-3(X)) Book Wholesalers, Inc.

Walsh, Ethelbert Geo. Bumper, the White Rabbit. 2006. pap. 34.99 (***978-1-4280-4105-9(2)***) IndyPublish.com.

Walsh, Vivian & Seibold, J. Otto. Gluey: A Snail Tale. 2002. (Illus.). 48p. (J). 15.00 (978-0-15-216620-5(3)) Harcourt Children's Bks.

Walton, Rick. Bunnies on the Go: Getting from Place to Place. Miglio, Paige, illus. 2003. 32p. (J). 16.99 (978-0-06-029185-3(0)) HarperCollins Pubs.

—Bunny Christmas: A Family Celebration. Miglio, Paige, illus. 2004. 32p. (J). 15.99 (978-0-06-008415-8(4)); lib. bdg. 16.89 (978-0-06-008416-5(2)) HarperCollins Pubs.

—Bunny Day: Telling Time from Breakfast to Bedtime. Miglio, Paige, illus. 2002. 32p. (J). (gr. 2 up). 16.99 (978-0-06-029183-9(4)) HarperCollins Pubs.

—Bunny School: A Learning Fun-for-All. Miglio, Paige, illus. 2005. 32p. (J). 15.99 (978-0-06-057508-3(5)); lib. bdg. 16.89 (978-0-06-057509-0(3)) HarperCollins Pubs.

—One More Bunny: Adding from One to Ten. 2000. (Illus.). 24p. (J). (ps-3). 15.89 (978-0-688-16848-3(5)) HarperCollins Pubs.

—So Many Bunnies: A Bedtime ABC & Counting Book. Miglio, Paige, illus. 32p. (J). (ps-3). 2002. pap. 5.95 (978-0-06-443751-6(5) , Harper Trophy); 2000. 6.99 (978-0-688-17364-7(0) , Harper Festival) HarperCollins Pubs.

—So Many Bunnies: A Bedtime ABC & Counting Book. 1998. (Illus.). 32p. (J). (ps-1). 15.89 (978-0-688-13657-4(5)) HarperCollins Pubs.

—So Many Bunnies: A Bedtime ABC & Counting Book. Miglio, Paige, illus. 1998. 32p. (J). (ps-3). 17.99 (978-0-688-13656-7(7)) HarperCollins Pubs.

—What Do We Do with the Baby? Miglio, Paige, illus. 2008. 32p. (J). 16.99 (978-0-06-008419-6(7)) HarperCollins Pubs.

Ward, Helen. The Hare & the Tortoise: A Fable from Aesop. 1999. (Illus.). 40p. (J). (gr. k up). 16.95 (978-0-7613-0988-8(8) , First Avenue Editions) Lerner Publishing Group.

—Hare & Tortoise. 2005. (ENG & ALB., Illus.). 32p. (J). pap. 12.95 (978-1-84444-779-4(0)) Mantra Lingua GBR. *Dist:* Mantra Publishing, Ltd.

Ward, Helen & Aesop. Hare & Tortoise. 2005. (ENG & CHI., Illus.). 32p. (J). pap. 12.95 (978-1-84444-784-8(7)) Mantra Lingua GBR. *Dist:* Mantra Publishing, Ltd.

Washington, LaVonne and LaShawn. The Rabbit & the Resurrection Story. 2005. 37p. 11.95 (978-1-4116-2541-9(2)) Lulu.com.

Watase, Yuu. Alice 19th Vol. 1: Lotis Master. Watase, Yuu, illus. 2003. (Alice 19th Ser.). (Illus.). 192p. (YA). pap. 9.95 (978-1-59116-215-5(7)) Viz Media.

Watson, Richard Jesse. The Magic Rabbit. Watson, Richard Jesse, illus. 2005. (Illus.). 40p. (J). pap. 15.95 (978-0-590-47964-6(4) , Blue Sky Pr., The) Scholastic, Inc.

Watt, Fiona. Hide-And-Seek Bunnies. Danson, Lesley, illus. 2007. (Touchy-Feely Flap Bks). 10p. (J). bds. 16.99 (***978-0-7945-1566-9(5)*** , Usborne) EDC Publishing.

Watt, Fiona. That's Not My Bunny. Wells, Rachel, illus. 2004. (Touchy-Feely Board Bks.). (SPA.). 10p. (J). (ps up). bds. 7.99 (978-0-7460-4179-6(9)) EDC Publishing.

Watts, Bernadette. Harvey Hare, Postman Extraordinaire. 1999. (J). (978-0-606-17020-8(0)) Tandem Library Bks.

Weaver, Alexis Rae. Hunter Bunny Saves Easter. Kohnke, Jennifer M., illus. 2002. (Hunter Bunny: Vol. 1). 42p. (J). (ps-2). per. (978-0-9712473-6-9(6)) Golden Bunny Publishing.

Weber, Lou, ed. Tale of Peter Rabbit & Benjamin Bunny. 2004. 24p. (J). 15.98 (978-1-4127-3123-2(2) , 7231600) Publications International, Ltd.

Wedge, Chris. Bunny: A Picture Book Adapted from the Animated Film. Wedge, Chris, illus. 2004. (Illus.). 30p. (J). (gr. k-4). reprint ed. 19.00 (978-0-7567-7460-8(8)) DIANE Publishing Co.

Weeks, Sarah. Bunny Fun. Williams, Sam, illus. 2008. 40p. (J). (ps-k). 14.00 (978-0-15-205838-8(9)) Harcourt Trade Pubs.

Wehr, Paul. The Animated Bunny's Tail. wehr, Julian, illus. 2005. 20p. (J). 18.95 (978-0-9748093-1-1(4)) Wehr Animations.

Weiss, Ellen. Winter Spring Summer Fall: A Touch & Feel Seasons Book. Bennett, Andy, illus. 2006. (PBS Kids(R) Ser.). 10p. (J). 6.95 (***978-1-57791-312-2(4)***) Brighter Minds Children's Publishing.

Welch, Willy. Grumbly Bunnies. Lyon, Tammie, illus. 2004. 28p. (J). bds. 6.95 (978-1-58089-088-5(1)) Charlesbridge Publishing, Inc.

—Grumbly Bunnies. Lyon, Tammie Speer, illus. 2004. 32p. (J). 15.95 (978-1-58089-086-1(5)); pap. 6.95 (978-1-58089-087-8(3)) Charlesbridge Publishing, Inc.

—Grumpy Bunnies. Lyon, Tammie Speer, illus. 2000. 32p. (J). (ps-2). 16.95 (978-1-58089-053-3(9)) Charlesbridge Publishing, Inc.

Welling, Peter J. Justin Potemkin & the 500-Mile Race. Welling, Peter J., illus. 2004. (Illus.). 32p. (J). pap. 15.95 (978-1-58980-149-3(0)) Pelican Publishing Co., Inc.

Wells, Rosemary. Bingo Display. 1999. (Bruno & Boots Book Ser.). (J). 79.20 (978-0-439-06287-9(X)) Scholastic, Inc.

—Bunny Cakes. Wells, Rosemary, illus. 2002. (Max the Bunny Ser.). (Illus.). (J). 13.19 (978-0-7587-5445-5(0)) Book Wholesalers, Inc.

—Bunny Cakes. 1999. (Max & Ruby Ser.). (Illus.). 32p. (J). (gr. k-2). 15.99 (978-0-670-88686-9(6) , Viking Juvenile) Penguin Group (USA) Inc.

—Bunny Mail. 2004. (Max & Ruby Ser.). (Illus.). 32p. (J). (ps-3). 15.99 (978-0-670-03630-1(7) , Viking Juvenile) Penguin Group (USA) Inc.

—Bunny Money. 2000. (gr. k-3). lib. bdg. 14.15 (978-0-613-33681-9(X)) Tandem Library Bks.

—Bunny Party. 2003. (Max & Ruby Ser.). (Illus.). 24p. (J). (ps-k). pap. 5.99 (978-0-14-250162-7(X) , Puffin) Penguin Group (USA) Inc.

—Bunny Party. Wells, Rosemary, illus. 2001. (Max & Ruby Ser.). (Illus.). 32p. (J). (gr. k-2). 15.99 (978-0-670-03501-4(7) , Viking Juvenile) Penguin Group (USA) Inc.

—Carry Me! 2006. (Illus.). 40p. (ps-ps). 15.99 (978-0-7868-0396-5(7)) Hyperion Bks. for Children.

—Christmas Stocking. 2003. (Max & Ruby Ser.). (Illus.). 16p. (J). (ps-ps). pap. 5.99 (978-0-670-03667-7(6) , Viking Juvenile) Penguin Group (USA) Inc.

—Emily's First 100 Days of School. 2000. (Illus.). 64p. (J). (ps-1). 16.99 (978-0-7868-0507-5(2)) Hyperion Bks. for Children.

—Emily's First 100 Days of School. 2000. (Illus.). 64p. (ps-1). pap. 5.99 (978-0-7868-1354-4(7)) Hyperion Paperbacks for Children.

—Emily's First 100 Days of School. 2006. (Illus.). (J). (ps-4). 29.95 incl. audio compact disk (978-0-439-84900-5(4) , WHCD654); 24.95 incl. audio (978-0-439-84898-5(9) , WHRA654); pap. 14.95 incl. audio (978-0-439-84902-9(0) , WPRA654); pap. 18.95 incl. audio compact disk (978-0-439-84903-6(9) , WPCD654) Weston Woods Studios, Inc.

—Leale a Su Conejito. 2000. (SPA.). (gr. k-3). lib. bdg. 10.65 (978-0-613-25929-3(7)); (Illus.). (J). (978-0-606-18879-1(7)) Tandem Library Bks.

—Max & Ruby Play School. 2003. (ps-2). lib. bdg. 11.80 (978-0-613-64064-0(0)) Tandem Library Bks.

—Max & Ruby's Busy Week. Wells, Rosemary, illus. 2002. (Sticker Stories Ser.). (Illus.). 16p. (J). (ps-1). pap. 4.99 (978-0-448-42853-6(9) , Grosset & Dunlap) Penguin Group (USA) Inc.

—Max & Ruby's Christmas Tree. 2007. (Max & Ruby Ser.). 12p. (J). (ps-k). bds. 7.99 (***978-0-448-44685-1(5)*** , Grosset & Dunlap) Penguin Group (USA) Inc.

—Max & Ruby's Midas: Another Greek Myth. 2003. (Max & Ruby Ser.). (Illus.). 32p. (J). (gr. k-2). pap. 5.99 (978-0-14-250066-8(6) , Puffin) Penguin Group (USA) Inc.

—Max & Ruby's Snowy Day. 2004. (Max & Ruby Ser.). 10p. (J). (ps). bds. 6.99 (978-0-448-43567-1(5) , Grosset & Dunlap) Penguin Group (USA) Inc.

—Max & Ruby's Winter Adventure. 2007. (Max & Ruby Ser.). 16p. (J). (ps-k). pap. 5.99 (***978-0-448-44684-4(7)*** , Grosset & Dunlap) Penguin Group (USA) Inc.

—Max Cleans Up. Wells, Rosemary, illus. 2002. (Max the Bunny Ser.). (Illus.). 13.19 (978-1-4046-0741-5(2)) Book Wholesalers, Inc.

—Max Cleans Up. (Max & Ruby Ser.). (Illus.). 32p. (J). 2002. pap. 5.99 (978-0-14-230133-3(7) , Puffin); 2000. 15.99 (978-0-670-89218-1(1) , Viking Juvenile) Penguin Group (USA) Inc.

—Max et la Poule en Chocolat. 1999. (FRE.). (J). (ps-3). pap. 12.95 (978-2-211-02083-1(6)) Distribooks, Inc.

—Max's Breakfast. 2004. 12p. (J). 5.99 (978-0-670-88712-5(9) , Viking Juvenile) Penguin Group (USA) Inc.

—Max's Chocolate Chicken. Wells, Rosemary, illus. 2002. (Max the Bunny Ser.). (Illus.). (J). 13.19 (978-0-7587-3110-4(8)) Book Wholesalers, Inc.

—Max's Chocolate Chicken. Wells, Rosemary, illus. 2000. (Max & Ruby Ser.). (Illus.). 32p. (J). (gr. k-2). pap. 5.99 (978-0-14-056672-7(4) , Puffin) Penguin Group (USA) Inc.

—Max's Chocolate Chicken. 1999. (Max & Ruby Ser.). (Illus.). 32p. (J). (gr. k-2). 16.99 (978-0-670-88713-2(7) , Viking Juvenile) Penguin Group (USA) Inc.

—Max's Chocolate Chicken. 2000. (Max & Ruby Ser.). (J). (gr. k-2). (978-0-606-18431-1(7)) Tandem Library Bks.

—Max's Christmas. 2000. (Max & Ruby Ser.). (J). (gr. k-2). (978-0-606-20244-2(7)) Tandem Library Bks.

—Max's First Word. 2004. 12p. (J). bds. 5.99 (978-0-670-88717-0(X) , Viking Juvenile) Penguin Group (USA) Inc.

—Max's Ride. 2003. 12p. (J). pap. 6.99 (978-0-670-88719-4(6) , Viking Juvenile) Penguin Group (USA) Inc.

—Max's Valentine. 2003. (Illus.). 32p. (J). (ps-ps). 5.99 (978-0-670-03668-4(4) , Viking Juvenile) Penguin Group (USA) Inc.

—Morris's Disappearing Bag. 2001. (ps-ps). (Illus.). (J). lib. bdg. 15.30 (978-0-613-44236-7(9)); (978-0-606-22499-4(8)) Tandem Library Bks.

—Play with Max & Ruby. Wells, Rosemary, illus. 2002. (All Aboard Reading Ser.). (Illus.). 32p. (J). (ps-1). pap. 3.99 (978-0-448-42854-3(7) , Grosset & Dunlap) Penguin Group (USA) Inc.

—Play with Max & Ruby. 2002. (ps-2). lib. bdg. 11.80 (978-0-613-64094-7(2)) Tandem Library Bks.

—Read to Your Bunny. Wells, Rosemary, illus. (Illus.). (J). 2003. 12p. bds. 7.99 (978-0-439-54337-8(1) , Cartwheel Bks.); 1999. 32p. pap. 3.99 (978-0-439-08717-9(1)) Scholastic, Inc.

—Read to Your Bunny. 1998. (Bruno & Boots Book Ser.). (Illus.). 32p. (J). (ps). bds. 7.95 (978-0-590-30284-5(1)) Scholastic, Inc.

—Read to Your Bunny. 1999. (978-0-606-17056-7(1)); lib. bdg. 10.65 (978-0-613-16996-7(4)) Tandem Library Bks.

—Read to Your Bunny Very First Library Gift Set. 2006. 64p. (J). pap. 19.99 (978-0-439-87190-7(5) , Scholastic Pr.) Scholastic, Inc.

—Ruby's Beauty Shop. Wells, Rosemary, illus. (Max & Ruby Ser.). 32p. (J). (gr. k-3). 2004. pap. 6.99 (978-0-14-240194-1(3) , Puffin); 2002. (Illus.). 15.99 (978-0-670-03553-3(X) , Viking Juvenile) Penguin Group (USA) Inc.

—Ruby's Falling Leaves. 2007. (Max & Ruby Ser.). 24p. (J). (ps-k). 3.99 (***978-0-448-44686-8(3)*** , Grosset & Dunlap) Penguin Group (USA) Inc.

—Ruby's Rainy Day. Wells, Rosemary, illus. 2004. (Max & Ruby Ser.). (Illus.). 10p. (J). (ps). pap. 6.99 (978-0-448-43184-0(X) , Grosset & Dunlap) Penguin Group (USA) Inc.

Wells, Rosemary. Voyage to the Bunny Planet. 2008. 88p. (J). (ps). 17.99 (***978-0-670-01103-2(7)*** , Viking Juvenile) Penguin Group (USA) Inc.

Weninger, Brigitte. Dany, Mira lo Que Has Hecho! 1999. (gr. k 3). (SPA.). lib. bdg. 15.25 (978-0-613-81373-0(1)); 13.75 (978-0-606-17631-6(4)) Tandem Library Bks.

—Davy's Christmas Gift. Tharlet, Eve, illus. 2003. 16p. (J). bds. 6.95 (978-0-7358-1754-8(5)) North-South Bks., Inc.

—Donde Estas Dany? 1999. Tr. of Where Is Davy?. (Illus.). (978-0-606-17639-2(X)) Tandem Library Bks.

—Don't Fight, Davy. Tharlet, Eve, illus. 2003. 16p. (J). bds. 6.95 (978-0-7358-1753-1(7)) North-South Bks., Inc.

—Stay in Bed Davy. Tharlet, Eve, illus. 2007. 0032p. pap. 6.95 (***978-0-7358-2154-5(2)***) North-South Bks., Inc.

—Stay in Bed Davy. 2006. (Illus.). 32p. (J). 15.95 (978-0-7358-2048-7(1)) North-South Bks., Inc.

—What Have You Done, Davy? 1999. (gr. k-3). lib. bdg. 15.25 (978-0-613-37172-8(0)) Tandem Library Bks.

—Why Are You Fighting, Davy? Lanning, Rosemary, tr. from GER. Tharlet, Eve, illus. 2002. 32p. (J). pap. 6.95 (978-0-7358-1601-5(8)) North-South Bks., Inc.

—Why Are You Fighting, Davy? 2002. (gr. k-3). lib. bdg. 15.25 (978-0-613-87277-5(0)) Tandem Library Bks.

West, C. Helicopter Hare. (Illus.). 61p. (J). pap. 7.95 (978-0-340-66095-9(3) , Hodder & Stoughton) Hodder General Publishing Division GBR. *Dist:* Trafalgar Square Publishing.

Westenbroek, K. John. Blessly the Redemption Rabbit Easter Book & Coloring Book Attached. Escobar, Rudt & Nauta, Paul, illus. l.t. ed. 2002. 43p. (J). 14.99 (978-0-9771623-8-5(4)) Hope Harvest Publishing.

White, Carolyn. The Adventure of Louey & Frank. Dronzek, Laura, illus. 2001. 24p. (J). (ps). 14.95 (978-0-688-16503-1(6)) HarperCollins Pubs.

White, Kathryn. Snowshoe the Hare. Rivers, Ruth, illus. 2005. (Red Go Bananas Ser.). 48p. (J). pap. (978-0-7787-2699-9(1) , 1253648) Crabtree Publishing Co.

White, Mark. La Liebre y la Tortuga: Version de la Fabula de Esopo. Rojo, Sara, illus. 2006. (Read-It! Readers en Espanol Ser.).Tr. of Tortoise & the Hare: A Retelling of Aesop's Fable. (SPA.). 32p. (J). (ps-3). 19.95 (978-1-4048-1624-4(0)) Picture Window Bks.

Whybrow, Ian. Bella Gets Her Skates On. Reeve, Rosie, illus. 2007. 32p. (J). (ps-3). 15.95 (***978-0-8109-9416-4(X)***) Abrams, Harry N. , Inc.

—Parcel for Stanley. Hobson, Sally, illus. 1998. 32p. (J). (ps-3). 14.95 (978-1-899607-53-2(6)) Sterling Publishing Co., Inc.

—Parcel for Stanley. Hobson, Sally, illus. 1999. (J). (ps-ps). lib. bdg. 15.25 (978-0-613-22155-9(9)) Tandem Library Bks.

—A Parcel for Stanley. Hobson, Sally, illus. 1999. 32p. (J). pap. 6.95 (978-1-86233-082-5(4)) Sterling Publishing Co., Inc.

Wild, Margaret & Shaw, Peter. Hop, Little Hare! 2008. (Illus.). 0024p. pap. 10.95 (***978-1-921049-68-2(5)***) Little Hare Bks. AUS. *Dist:* Independent Pubs. Group.

Wilhelm, Hans. Bunny Trouble. rev. ed. 2001. (Illus.). 32p. (J). (gr. k-3). pap. 4.99 (978-0-439-25982-8(7)) Scholastic, Inc.

—Bunny Trouble. 2001. (gr. k-3). lib. bdg. 13.00 (978-0-613-71982-7(4)) Tandem Library Bks.

Willems, Mo. Knuffle Bunny: A Cautionary Tale. 2004. (Illus.). 36p. (J). (ps-1). 15.99 (978-0-7868-1870-9(0)) Hyperion Bks. for Children.

Willever, Lisa Funari & Funari, Lorraine. The Easter Chicken. Overman, Emma, illus. 2001. 32p. (ps-3). 9.95 (978-0-9679227-6-8(3) , 329-002) Franklin Mason Pr.

Williams, Larry. The League of Clique. Williams, Larry, illus. 2007. (ENG., Illus.). 80p. per. 19.95 (***978-1-4241-5976-5(8)***) PublishAmerica, Inc.

Williams, Margery. The Velveteen Rabbit. Felix, Monique, illus. 2005. 40p. pap. 8.95 (978-0-89812-383-8(6)) Creative Co., The.

—The Velveteen Rabbit. Nicholson, William, illus. 1999. 40p. (J). (ps-3). reprint ed. pap. 3.99 (978-0-380-00255-9(8)) HarperCollins Pubs.

—The Velveteen Rabbit, Set. Nicholson, William, illus. gif. ed. 2005. 96p. (J). 16.95 (978-0-7573-0355-5(2)) Health Communications, Inc.

—The Velveteen Rabbit. (J). 2006. 32p. pap. 3.95 (978-0-8249-5530-4(7) , Ideals Children's Bks.); 2000. (Illus.). bds. 6.95 (978-0-8249-4173-4(X)) Ideals Pubns.

—The Velveteen Rabbit. Daily, Don, illus. 2007. 28p. (J). pap. 5.95 (978-0-7624-2935-6(6) , Running Pr. Kids) Running Pr. Bk. Pubs.

—The Velveteen Rabbit. 2007. (J). 18.95 (***978-0-545-00512-8(4)***) Scholastic, Inc.

—The Velveteen Rabbit. Jorgensen, David, illus. 2006. (J). (gr. 2-6). 25.65 (978-1-59197-757-5(6)) Spotlight.

—The Velveteen Rabbit. Hague, Michael, illus. 2008. 48p. (J). pap. 7.99 (***978-0-312-37750-2(9)***) Square Fish.

—The Velveteen Rabbit. 1999. (gr. k-3). lib. bdg. 15.25 (978-0-613-16871-7(2)) Tandem Library Bks.

—The Velveteen Rabbit & Other Stories Book & Charm. 2008. 128p. (J). pap. 6.99 (***978-0-06-145942-9(9)*** , Harper Festival) HarperCollins Pubs.

Williams, Margery. The Velveteen Rabbit Book & Charm. Nicholson, William, illus. 2006. 40p. (J). (ps-3). pap. 4.99 (978-0-06-076067-0(2) , Harper Festival) HarperCollins Pubs.

Williams, Margery, adapted by. The Velveteen Rabbit. 2006. (Illus.). 20p. (J). bds. 10.99 (978-0-7944-0948-7(2)) Reader's Digest Assn., Inc., The.

Williams, Margery, ed. The Velveteen Rabbit: Or, How Toys Become Real. Nicholson, William, illus. 2005. 96p. (J). (ps-1). 9.95 (978-0-7573-0333-3(1)) Health Communications, Inc.

Williams, Margery & Daily, Don. The Classic Tale of the Velveteen Rabbit. 2007. 56p. 9.98 (***978-0-7624-3023-9(0)*** , Courage Bks.) Running Pr. Bk. Pubs.

Williams, Margery & Green, Michael. The Velveteen Rabbit: Or, How Toys Become Real. deluxe ed. 2001. (Running Press Kids Ser.). (Illus.). 48p. (ps-3). 9.95 (978-0-89471-153-4(9) , Running Pr. Kids) Running Pr. Bk. Pubs.

Williams, Sam. School Bus, Bunny Bus. Trotter, Stuart, illus. 2006. 10p. (J). 12.95 (978-1-905417-17-9(9)) Boxer Bks., Ltd. GBR. *Dist:* Sterling Publishing Co., Inc.

Williams, Ted. Curly Hare Gets It Straight. 2001. (Kiss a Me Teacher Creature Stories Ser.). (Illus.). (J). (978-1-890343-35-4(8)) Kiss A Me Productions, Inc.

Willson, Sarah. La Canasta Pascual de Dora. Hall, Susan T., illus. 2004. (Dora the Explorer Ser.).Tr. of Dora's Easter Basket. (SPA.). 32p. (J). 5.99 (978-0-689-86649-4(6) , Libros Para Ninos) Simon & Schuster Children's Publishing.

Winget, Susan. Tucker's Apple Dandy Day. Winget, Susan, illus. 2006. (Illus.). 40p. (J). lib. bdg. 13.89 (978-0-06-054647-2(6)) HarperCollins Pubs.

—Tucker's Apple-Dandy Day. Winget, Susan, illus. 2006. (Illus.). 40p. (J). 12.99 (978-0-06-054646-5(8)) HarperCollins Pubs.

—Tucker's Four-Carrot School Day. Winget, Susan, illus. 2005. (Illus.). 40p. (J). (ps-k). 12.99 (978-0-06-054642-7(5)); lib. bdg. 13.89 (978-0-06-054643-4(3)) HarperCollins Pubs.

Witt, Rici. God, Santa & the Easter Bunny. 2006. 32p. (J). pap. 12.95 (978-1-4116-8014-2(6)) Lulu.com.

Wolif, T. Hal & His Pal Al: The Easter Bunny's Helpers. 2007. (Illus.). 36p. per. 12.97 (***978-1-932344-93-6(4)***) Thornton Publishing.

Wood, Christine. Runaway Rabbit. 2000. (gr. 3-6). lib. bdg. 14.15 (978-0-613-89222-3(4)) Tandem Library Bks.

Wood, David & Fowler, Richard. Funny Bunny's Magic Show: A Pop-in-the-Slot. 2002. (Illus.). 16p. (J). 11.99 (978-0-385-60021-7(6) , Doubleday) Transworld Publishers Ltd. GBR. *Dist:* Trafalgar Square Publishing.

Wormell, Christopher. The Big Ugly Monster & the Little Stone Rabbit. 2004. (Illus.). 32p. (J). (gr. k-3). 15.95 (978-0-375-82891-1(5) , Knopf Bks. for Young Readers) Random Hse. Children's Bks.

Yang, Huan. Artie & Julie. Chen, Zhiyuan & Huang, Hsiao-Yen, illus. 2007. 32p. (J). 15.95 (978-0-9787550-0-3(6)) Heryin Publishing Corp.

Young, James. My Bunny. 1999. (Read with Me Paperback Ser.). (Illus.). 32p. (J). (ps-1). pap. 3.25 (978-0-590-18375-8(3)) Scholastic, Inc.

Zarins, Kimberly. Playful Bunny. Pons, Bernadette, illus. 2006. (Cartwheel Books). 32p. (J). pap. 5.99 (978-0-439-72538-5(0) , Cartwheel Bks.) Scholastic, Inc.

Ziefert, Harriet. It's Valentine's Day! A Rosie Rabbit Book. Rader, Laura, illus. 2005. 12p. (J). (ps-ps). bds., bds. 7.95 (978-1-4027-2395-7(4)) Sterling Publishing Co., Inc.

—Ready for Easter: A Rosie Rabbit Book. Rader, Laura, illus. 2005. 14p. (J). bds. 7.95 (978-1-4027-2296-7(6)) Sterling Publishing Co., Inc.

Zolotow, Charlotte. The Bunny Who Found Easter. Craig, Helen, illus. 32p. (J). (gr. k-3). 2001. pap. 5.95 (978-0-618-11127-5(1)); 1998. tchr. ed. 16.00 (978-0-395-86265-0(5)) Houghton Mifflin Co. Trade & Reference Div.

—The Bunny Who Found Easter. Craig, Helen, illus. 2001. (J). (ps-3). lib. bdg. 14.10 (978-0-613-35493-6(1)) Tandem Library Bks.

—The Bunny Who Found Easter. 2001. (Illus.). (J). 12.75 (978-0-606-21091-1(1)) Tandem Library Bks.

—Mr. Rabbit & the Lovely Present. Sendak, Maurice, illus. 2000. (J). pap. 19.97 incl. audio (978-0-7366-9195-6(2)) Books on Tape, Inc.

—El Senor Conejo y el Hermoso Regalo. Sendak, Maurice, illus. 2006. (SPA.). 40p. (J). pap. 6.99 (978-0-06-088704-9(4) , Rayo) HarperCollins Pubs.

Zuckerman, Linda. A taste for Rabbit. 2007. 320p. (J). (gr. 7 up). pap. 16.99 (***978-0-439-86977-5(3)*** , Levine, Arthur A. Bks.) Scholastic, Inc.

—A Taste for Rabbit. 2007. (J). (***978-0-439-86978-2(1)*** , Levine, Arthur A. Bks.) Scholastic, Inc.

RACCOONS

Baicker, Karen. Raccoons. 2007. (J). (***978-1-59939-125-0(2)*** , Reader's Digest Young Families, Inc.) Reader's Digest Children's Publishing, Inc.

Crossingham, John, et al. Les Ratons Laveurs. 2005. (FRE., Illus.). 32p. (J). pap. (978-2-89579-048-8(5)) Crabtree Publishing Co.

Hancock, Lyn. Tabasco the Saucy Raccoon. Kemp, Loraine, illus. 2006. 168p. (J). pap. 10.95 (978-1-55039-156-5(9)) Sono Nis Pr. CAN. *Dist:* Orca Bk. Pubs. USA.

Hurtig, Jennifer. Raccoons. 2007. (J). (***978-1-59036-669-1(7)***); (***978-1-59036-670-7(0)***) Weigl Pubs., Inc.

Kalman, Bobbie & Crossingham, John. The Life Cycle of a Raccoon. Bedell, Barbara, illus. 2003. (Life Cycle Ser.). 32p. (J). (gr. 3-4). (978-0-7787-0661-8(3)); pap. (978-0-7787-0691-5(5)) Crabtree Publishing Co.

—The Life Cycle of a Raccoon. Bedell, Barbara, illus. 2003. 32p. (J). (gr. 4-7). lib. bdg. 15.25 (978-0-613-59129-4(1)) Tandem Library Bks.

Kite, L. Patricia. Raccoons. Boucher, Jerry, illus. Boucher, Jerry, photos by. 2004. (Early Bird Nature Bks.). 47p. (J). 25.26 (978-0-8225-3049-7(X) , Lerner Pubns.) Lerner Publishing Group.

Landau, Elaine. Raccoons: Scavengers of the Night. 2007. (Animals after Dark Ser.). (Illus.). 32p. (J). (gr. 2-4). lib. bdg. 22.60 (978-0-7660-2767-1(8) , Enslow Elementary) Enslow Pubs., Inc.

Mattern, Joanne. Raccoons Are Night Animals. 2006. (Illus.). 24p. (J). pap. (***978-0-8368-7856-1(6)***); lib. bdg. (***978-0-8368-7849-3(3)***) Stevens, Gareth Inc. (Weekly Reader Early Learning Library).

—Raccoons Are Night Animals: Los Mapaches Son Animales Nocturnos. 2006. (SPA & ENG., Illus.). 24p. (J). pap. (***978-0-8368-8053-3(6)***); lib. bdg. (***978-0-8368-8046-5(3)***) Stevens, Gareth Inc. (Weekly Reader Early Learning Library).

MCP Staff. A Small Baby Raccoon, 6 bks., set, Level 12, Bk. 42. 2003. (J). (ps-3). 33.50 (978-0-8136-2079-4(1)) Modern Curriculum Pr.

Merrick, Patrick. Raccoons. 2006. (New Naturebooks). (Illus.). 32p. (J). (gr. 1-5). 27.07 (978-1-59296-647-9(0)) Child's World, Inc.

Nelson, Kristin L. Clever Raccoons. (Pull Ahead Bks.). (Illus.). 32p. (gr. k-3). 2005. lib. bdg. 22.60 (978-0-8225-3763-2(X)); 2003. (J). pap. 5.95 (978-0-8225-3644-4(7)) Lerner Publishing Group.

—Clever Raccoons. 2001. (gr. k-3). lib. bdg. 14.10 (978-0-613-58827-0(4)) Tandem Library Bks.

North, Sterling. Rascal. 2004. (Illus.). 240p. (J). pap. 5.99 (978-0-14-240252-8(4) , Puffin) Penguin Group (USA) Inc.

—Rascal. unabr. ed. 1998. 189p. (J). (gr. 4-7). pap. 36.00 incl. audio (978-0-8072-7897-0(1) , 1124-AB, Listening Library) Random Hse. Audio Publishing Group.

—Rascal. unabr. ed. 1998. (YA). Class Set. 100.70 incl. audio (978-0-7887-2541-8(6) , 46711); Homework Set. (gr. 7). 43.24 incl. audio (978-0-7887-2236-3(0) , 40720) Recorded Bks., LLC.

—Rascal. 2001. (SPA.). (J). (978-0-606-20879-6(8)) Tandem Library Bks.

Raccoons: Individual Title Six-Packs. 16p. (gr. 2 up). 36.00 (978-0-7635-9394-0(X)) Rigby Education.

Ripple, William John. Raccoons. 2006. (Woodland Animals Ser.). (Illus.). 24p. (J). (978-0-7368-4250-1(0) , Pebble Bks.) Capstone Pr., Inc.

Sullivan, Pat Harvey. Raccoons & Their Relatives, Vol. 5. World Book, Inc. Staff, ed. 2002. (World Book's Animals of the World Ser.: Set 3). (Illus.). 64p. (J). (978-0-7166-1228-5(3)) World Bk., Inc.

Swanson, Diane. Raccoons. 1998. (gr. k-3). lib. bdg. 14.10 (978-0-613-78493-1(6)) Tandem Library Bks.

—Welcome to the World of Raccoons. 1998. (Welcome to the World Ser.). (Illus.). 32p. (J). (ps-2). pap. 5.95 (978-1-55110-782-0(1)) Whitecap Bks., Ltd. CAN. *Dist:* Firefly Bks., Ltd.

Whitehouse, Patricia. El Mapache. 2003. (Que Esta Despierto? (What's Awake?) Ser.).Tr. of Racoons. (SPA.). 24p. (ps-1). (J). lib. bdg. 17.08 (978-1-4034-0396-4(1)); (Illus.). pap. 5.25 (978-1-4034-0637-8(5)) Heinemann Library.

—Raccoons. 2003. (What's Awake? Ser.). (Illus.). 24p. pap. 5.25 (978-1-4034-0628-6(6)) Heinemann Library.

—Racoons. 2003. (What's Awake? Ser.). (Illus.). 24p. (J). (ps-1). lib. bdg. 17.08 (978-1-58810-882-1(1)) Heinemann Library.

Willis, Nancy Carol. Raccoon Moon. Willis, Nancy Carol, illus. 2002. (Accelerated Reader Program Ser.). (Illus.). 32p. (J). (ps). pap. 6.95 (978-0-9662761-3-8(2)); 15.95 (978-0-9662761-2-1(4)) Birdsong Bks.

—Raccoon Moon. 2002. (gr. k-3). lib. bdg. 15.25 (978-0-613-62643-9(5)) Tandem Library Bks.

RACCOONS—FICTION

The Adventures of Ricky Raccoon & Jodi the Cat. 2001. 28p. (J). 7.95 (978-0-9709408-0-3(7)) Pinetree Pubns.

The Adventures of Rowdy Raccoon. 2006. (J). per. 16.95 incl. audio compact disk (***978-0-9766823-8-7(9)***) Sable Creek Pr. LLC.

Arnosky, Jim. Raccoon on His Own. Arnosky, Jim, illus. 2003. (Illus.). 32p. (J). (gr. k-1). pap. 6.99 (978-0-14-250071-2(2) , Puffin) Penguin Group (USA) Inc.

—Raccoon on His Own. 2003. (gr. k-3). lib. bdg. 15.30 (978-0-613-67471-3(5)) Tandem Library Bks.

Auerbach, Annie. The Cookie Heist. 2006. (Over the Hedge Ser.: No. 1). (Illus.). 24p. (J). pap. 3.99 (978-0-439-80144-7(3)) Scholastic, Inc.

Bentley, Nancy. The Case of the Garden Monster. Borlasca, Hector, illus. 2003. 32p. (J). (978-0-439-47470-2(1)) Scholastic, Inc.

Bloom, Becky. Leo & Lester. Biet, Pascal, illus. 2003. (J). 32p. 15.95 (978-1-59034-582-5(7)); 33p. pap. (978-1-59034-583-2(5)) Mondo Publishing.

Bluedorn, Johannah. The Story of Mr. Pippin. Bluedorn, Johannah, illus. 2004. (Illus.). 32p. (J). 12.00 (978-0-9743616-8-0(2)) Trivium Pursuit.

Brightwood, Laura, illus. King Zargon Rules. Brightwood, Laura, . 2006. (J). (978-0-9789871-0-7(1)) 3-C Institute for Social Development.

Brightwood, Laura, illus. Look What You've Done. Brightwood, Laura, . 2007. (J). DVD (***978-1-934409-03-9(0)***) 3-C Institute for Social Development.

Brown, Margaret Wise. Wait till the Moon Is Full. 2002. (Illus.). (J). 15.53 (978-0-7587-3911-7(7)) Book Wholesalers, Inc.

Burgess, Thornton. The Adventures of Bobby Coon. 2006. pap. 10.95 (***978-1-59605-767-8(X)*** , Cosimo Classics) Cosimo, Inc.

Burgess, Thornton W. The Adventures of Bobby Coon. (J). 18.95 (978-0-8488-0383-4(3)) Amereon LTD.

Chowen, Ewan, illus. Eseban the Rascally Raccoon. 2001. (J). lib. bdg. 12.50 (978-0-9716405-1-3(3)) Unique Consulting.

Dexter, Anthony. The Adventures of Manny the Manatee. 2004. 45p. pap. 19.95 (978-1-4137-2751-7(4)) PublishAmerica, Inc.

Duchesne. Edmund the Terrible Raccoon, Edmund Series. 2000. (Illus.). 32p. (J). (ps-3). pap. (978-1-894363-31-0(0)) Dominique & Friends.

Duchesne, Christiane, et al. Edmund, the Raccoon Prince. 2000. (Illus.). 29p. (J). (ps-3). pap. (978-1-894363-47-1(7)) Dominique & Friends.

Elliott, Laura. Hunter & Stripe & the Soccer Showdown. Munsinger, Lynn, illus. 2005. 32p. (J). (ps-2). lib. bdg. 16.89 (978-0-06-052760-0(9)) HarperCollins Pubs.

—Hunter's Annoying Big Sister. Munsinger, Lynn, illus. 2007. 32p. (J). (ps-2). 16.99 (978-0-06-000233-6(6)) HarperCollins Pubs.

Elliott, Laura Malone. Hunter & Stripe & the Soccer Showdown. Munsinger, Lynn, illus. 2005. 32p. (J). (ps-2). 15.99 (978-0-06-052759-4(5)) HarperCollins Pubs.

—Hunter's Best Friend at School. Munsinger, Lynn, illus. 2002. 32p. (J). (ps-2). 16.99 (978-0-06-000230-5(1)); 17.89 (978-0-06-000231-2(X)) HarperCollins Pubs.

Erickson, John R. Moonlight Madness. Holmes, Gerald L., illus. 1998. (Hank the Cowdog Ser.: No. 23). 144p. (J). (gr. 2-5). 15.99 (978-0-670-88430-8(8) , Viking Juvenile); Vol. 23. pap. 4.99 (978-0-14-130399-4(9) , Puffin) Penguin Group (USA) Inc.

—The Secret Laundry Monster Files, Vol. 39. Holmes, Gerald L., illus. 2002. (Hank the Cowdog Ser.: No. 39). 144p. (J). pap. 4.99 (978-0-14-230076-3(4) , Puffin) Penguin Group (USA) Inc.

Fontenot, Mary Alice. Clovis Crawfish & Raoul Raccoon. Landry, Cat, illus. 1999. (Clovis Crawfish Ser.). 32p. (J). (gr. k-3). 15.95 (978-1-56554-369-0(6)) Pelican Publishing Co., Inc.

—Clovis Ecrevisse et Charles Chatoui. Landry, Julie Fontenot, tr. Landry, Cat, illus. 2001. (FRE.). 32p. (J). (gr. k-3). 16.95 (978-1-56554-699-8(7)) Pelican Publishing Co., Inc.

Friend, Catherine. Eddie the Raccoon. Yee, Wong Herbert, illus. 2004. (Brand New Readers Ser.). 32p. (J). (ps-2). pap. 5.99 (978-0-7636-2334-0(2)) Candlewick Pr.

Good Night Adam: First Adam Raccoon, No. 4. 1999. 12p. (J). pap. 10.99 (978-0-7814-0259-0(X)) Cook, David C. Publishing Co.

Hallagin, Janet. The Way of Courage. 2006. 30.99 (***978-1-4257-1249-5(5)***); pap. 20.99 (***978-1-4257-1248-8(7)***) Xlibris Corp.

P
Q
R

Hamilton, Elizabeth L. Ricky Raccoon's Trustworthiness Tree. l.t. ed. 2005. (Character Critters Ser.: No. 11). (Illus.). 32p. (J). per. 5.95 (978-0-9754629-8-0(9) , Character-in-Action) Quiet Impact, Inc.

Harcourt School Publishers Staff. Help! Take-Home Book. 1999. (Collections Ser.). (Illus.). (J). pap. 1.90 (978-0-15-317224-3(X)) Harcourt Schl. Pubs.

—Help! Below Level. 3rd ed. 2002. (Trophies Reading Program Ser.). (Illus.). pap. 5.10 (978-0-15-323047-9(9)) Harcourt Schl. Pubs.

Haverfield, Mary. Harriett the Homeless Raccoon. Haverfield, Mary, illus. 2005. (Illus.). 32p. (J). (ps-3). 17.95 (978-1-931721-60-8(2)) Bright Sky Pr.

Hill, Susan. Ruby Bakes a Cake. Moore, Margie, illus. (I Can Read Bks.). 32p. (J). (gr. k-3). 2005. pap. 3.99 (978-0-06-008977-1(6) , Harper Trophy); 2004. 15.99 (978-0-06-008975-7(X)); 2004. lib. bdg. 16.89 (978-0-06-008976-4(8)) HarperCollins Pubs.

—Ruby Bakes a Cake. Moore, Margie, illus. 2004. 32p. (J). lib. bdg. 13.85 ***(978-1-4242-0476-2(3))*** Fitzgerald Bks.

Hill, Susan. Ruby Paints a Picture. Moore, Margie, illus. 2005. (I Can Read Bks.). 32p. (J). (ps-ps). 15.99 (978-0-06-008978-8(4)) HarperCollins Pubs.

Hubery, Julia. A Friend for All Seasons. Matsuoka, Mei, illus. 2007. 32p. (J). (ps-2). 15.99 ***(978-1-4169-2685-6(2))*** Simon & Schuster Children's Publishing.

Jackson, Bobby L. Boon the Raccoon & Easel the Weasel. Rodriguez, Christina, illus. 2004. 32p. (J). pap. 11.95 (978-1-884242-03-8(0) , BREW2NED); 19.95 (978-1-884242-02-1(2) , BREW2NED) Multicultural Pubns.

Jones, Esther B. The Raccoon Who Lost His Mask. 2006. pap. 7.95 (978-0-533-15304-6(2)) Vantage Pr., Inc.

Keffer, Lois & Haidle, Helen. Ripples Raccoon Shares His Balloon. Spengler, Ken, illus. 1999. (Read-To-Me Puppet Buddies Ser.: Vol. 9). 24p. (J). (ps-1). 9.99 (978-1-57673-438-4(2) , Multnomah) WaterBrook Pr.

Lyle-Soffe, Shari. The Misadventures of Rooter & Snuffle. Collier, Kevin Scott, illus. 2006. 28p. (J). E-Book 5.00 incl. cd-rom ***(978-1-933090-43-6(X))*** Guardian Angel Publishing, Inc.

McCorkle, Barbara. Bandit Raccoon. Taylor, David, illus. l.t. ed. 2006. 39p. (J). 19.95 ***(978-1-59879-170-9(2));*** per. 13.99 ***(978-1-59879-123-5(0))*** Lifevest Publishing, Inc.

McPhail, David. The Searcher & Old Tree. 2008. (J). ***(978-1-58089-223-0(X))*** Charlesbridge Publishing, Inc.

Monsen, Annie. Rusty Raccoon Meets Ricky Rabbit. Saint, Crystal, illus. 2006. 36p. (J). per. (978-1-59453-996-1(0) , Airleaf Publishing) Airleaf Publishing & Bookselling.

Murray, Betty Jean. The Little Raccoon: A True Story. Douthit, Karen, illus. 2005. (J). pap. 10.95 (978-1-933916-63-7(X) , Ferne Pr.) Nelson Publishing & Marketing.

Neugebauer, Charise. Real Winner. Nascimbeni, Barbara, illus. 2000. 32p. (J). (gr. k-3). 16.50 (978-0-7358-1253-6(5) , Michael Neugebauer Bks.) North-South Bks., Inc.

Otto, Carolyn B. Raccoon at Clear Creek Road. Trachok, Cathy, illus. 2005. (Smithsonian's Backyard Ser.). (J). (ps-2). 32p. pap. 8.95 incl. audio (978-1-59249-490-3(0) , SC5008); 31p. per. 6.95 (978-1-59249-481-1(1) , S5008) Soundprints.

Otto, Carolyn B., et al. Big Box of Backyard Animals, 4 bks., Set. Sherrow, Victoria et al, illus. 2002. (Big Box of Board Bks.). 10p. (J). (ps-k). bds. (978-1-59069-177-9(6)) Studio Mouse LLC.

Penn, Audrey. Un Beso en Mi Mano. 2006. (SPA.). 32p. 16.95 (978-1-933718-01-9(3)) Tanglewood Pr.

—The Kissing Hand. 2007. 32p. (ps-3). 28.95 ***(978-1-933718-07-1(2))*** Tanglewood Pr.

—The Kissing Hand. Harper, Ruth E. & Leak, Nancy M., illus. 2006. 32p. 16.95 (978-1-933718-00-2(5)) Tanglewood Pr.

—The Kissing Hand. unabr. ed. 2007. 32p. (J). (ps-3). pap. 9.95 incl. audio compact disk ***(978-1-933718-10-1(2))*** Tanglewood Pr.

Penn, Audrey. A Pocket Full of Kisses. Gibson, Barbara Leonard, illus. 2004. (New Child & Family Press Titles Ser.). (ps-1). 16.95 (978-0-87868-894-4(3) , 8943, Child & Family Pr.) Child Welfare League of America, Inc.

—A Pocket Full of Kisses. Gibson, Barbara, illus. 2006. 32p. 16.95 (978-1-933718-02-6(1)) Tanglewood Pr.

Raye, Rebekah. The Very Best Bed. Raye, Rebekah, illus. 2006. (Illus.). 32p. (J). (ps-3). 16.95 (978-0-88448-284-0(7)) Tilbury Hse. Pubs.

Recheis, Kathe. Little Raccoon Always Knows Best. Kunstreich, Pieter, illus. 2002. Tr. of Kleiner Waschbar Weiss Alles Besser. 24p. (J). 14.95 (978-0-7940-0009-7(6)); lib. bdg. 15.95 (978-0-7940-0010-3(X)) Munchweiler Pr.

Ring, Elizabeth. The Little Raccoon. 2001. (Illus.). (J). (978-0-606-21302-8(3)) Tandem Library Bks.

Rylant, Cynthia. The Case of the Climbing Cat. Karas, G. Brian, illus. 2003. (High-Rise Private Eyes Ser.: No. 2). (J). (gr. k-3). pap. 16.95 incl. audio (978-1-59112-189-3(2)); pap. 18.95 incl. audio compact disk (978-1-59112-610-2(X)); 25.96 incl. audio (978-1-59112-190-9(6)); pap. 29.95 incl. audio (978-1-59112-191-6(4)) Live Oak Media.

—The Case of the Climbing Cat. 2001. (High-Rise Private Eyes Ser.: No. 2). (J). (gr. k-3). lib. bdg. 11.80 (978-0-613-44193-3(1)) Tandem Library Bks.

—The Case of the Puzzling Possum. Karas, G. Brian, illus. (High-Rise Private Eyes Ser.: No. 3). (J). (ps-2). 2004. 48p. pap. 18.95 incl. audio compact disk (978-1-59112-618-8(5)); 2003. pap. 29.95 incl. audio (978-1-59112-199-2(X)); 2003. pap. 16.95 incl. audio (978-1-59112-197-8(3)); 2003. 25.95 incl. audio (978-1-59112-198-5(1)) Live Oak Media.

—The Case of the Puzzling Possum. 2002. (High-Rise Private Eyes Ser.: No. 3). (J). (gr. k-3). lib. bdg. 11.80 (978-0-613-44514-6(7)) Tandem Library Bks.

Sargent, Dave & Sargent, David, Jr. Hoot Owl: Mind Your Mamma, 19, 9. Lenoir, Jane, illus. 2003. (Feather Tales Ser.: 9). 42p. (J). pap. 6.95 (978-1-56763-736-6(1)) Ozark Publishing.

Sargent, Dave & Sargent, David M., Jr. Hoot Owl: Mind Your Mamma, 20, 9. Lenoir, Jane, illus. 2nd ed. 2003. (Feather Tales Ser.: 9). 42p. (J). lib. bdg. (978-1-56763-735-9(3)) Ozark Publishing.

Sargent, Dave & Sargent, Pat. Roy Raccoon: I Love Adventure, 15 vols., vol. 1. Huff, Jeane, illus. 2nd rev. ed. 2003. (Animal Pride Ser.: 1). 42p. (J). pap. 6.95 (978-1-56763-760-1(4)); lib. bdg. 19.95 (978-1-56763-759-5(0)) Ozark Publishing.

Schlein, Miriam. Little Raccoon's Big Question. Schoenherr, Ian, illus. 2004. 32p. (J). 15.99 (978-0-06-052116-5(3)); lib. bdg. 16.89 (978-0-06-052117-2(1)) HarperCollins Pubs.

Shaw, Nancy. Raccoon Tune. Fine, Howard, illus. rev. ed. 2003. 32p. (J). (ps-2). 16.95 (978-0-8050-6544-2(X) , Holt, Henry & Co. Bks. For Young Readers) Holt, Henry & Co.

Simpson, Fiona. We Are Family: Animal Antics. 2006. (Over the Hedge Ser.: No. 2). (Illus.). 17p. (J). pap. 3.99 (978-0-439-80146-1(X)) Scholastic, Inc.

Thomas, Jerry D. The Midnight Raccoon Alarm. 1999. (Great Stories for Kids Ser.: Vol. 3). (J). 14.99 (978-0-8163-1697-7(X)) Pacific Pr. Publishing Assn.

Wallace, Karen. Albert's Raccoon. Percy, Graham, illus. (I Am Reading Ser.). (J). (gr. k-3). 2004. 48p. pap. 3.95 (978-0-7534-5717-7(2)); 2001. (978-0-7534-5354-4(1)) Houghton Mifflin Co. Trade & Reference Div. (Kingfisher).

—Albert's Raccoon. Percy, Graham, illus. 2004. 48p. (J). (ps-ps). lib. bdg. 10.75 (978-0-606-32861-6(0)) Tandem Library Bks.

Wegman, Marcia. Lula Belle. 2007. (ENG.). 32p. per. 16.95 ***(978-1-4327-0146-8(0))*** Outskirts Press, Inc.

Wells, Rosemary. Timothy Goes to School. 2000. (Illus.). 32p. (J). (ps-3). pap. 5.99 (978-0-14-056742-7(9) , Puffin) Penguin Group (USA) Inc.

—Timothy Goes to School. 2000. (978-0-606-18457-1(0)); lib. bdg. 14.15 (978-0-8085-3410-5(6)) Tandem Library Bks.

Westen, Betty. A Boat Ride for Two Raccoons. Thompson, Lisa Ann, illus. 2001. 93p. 14.95 (978-0-9718177-0-8(7) , W7770001) Westen Integrity Bk. Pubs.

Wheeler, Kathryn. Finders Keepers! A Tale in Which Robby Stops Stealing & Starts Giving. Sharp, Dan, illus. 2000. (Stories to Grow By Ser.). 19p. (J). (978-0-7424-0011-5(5) , Instructional Fair) Schaffer, Frank Pubns.

Woods, Shirley. Kit: The Adventures of a Raccoon. Godkin, Celia, illus. 2001. 96p. (J). (gr. 3-7). pap. 6.95 (978-0-88899-376-2(5)) Groundwood Bks. CAN. *Dist:* Perseus Distribution.

Woodworth, Chris. When Ratboy Lived Next Door. 2005. (Illus.). 192p. (J). 16.00 (978-0-374-34677-5(1) , Farrar, Straus & Giroux (BYR)) Farrar, Straus & Giroux.

RACE

All about Us Interactive Packages: Here I Am. (Pebble Soup Explorations Ser.). (ps up). 52.00 (978-0-7578-5227-5(0)) Rigby Education.

All about Us Interactive Packages: Making Friends. (Pebble Soup Explorations Ser.). (ps up). 52.00 (978-0-7578-5228-2(9)) Rigby Education.

The Amazing Race, 6 vols., Pack. (Chiquilibros Ser.). (gr. k-1). 23.00 (978-0-7635-0437-3(8)) Rigby Education.

An Approach to Race (20 pack) 2001. (StudyLaB: Vol. 1). (J). (gr. 3 up). 32.00 (978-1-930281-13-4(7)) FINK, Inc.

Barber, Phil. Bill Elliott: The Fastest Man Alive. 2003. (World of Nascar Ser.). (Illus.). 32p. (J). (gr. 2-6). 25.64 (978-1-59187-037-1(2)) Child's World, Inc.

La Carrera: Individual Title Six-Packs. (Coleccion Pm Ser.).Tr. of Cross-country Race. (SPA.). 16p. (gr. 1 up). 26.00 (978-0-7578-3052-5(8)) Rigby Education.

La carrera Increible: Individual Title-Six Packs. (Chiquilibros Ser.). (SPA.). (gr. k-1). 23.00 (978-0-7635-8603-4(X)) Rigby Education.

Green, Jen. Racism. 2007. (J). ***(978-1-59604-153-0(6))*** Stargazer Bks.

Kelley, K. C. NASCAR Authorized Handbook. rev. ed. 2005. 48p. pap. 5.99 (978-0-7944-0679-0(3)) Reader's Digest Assn., Inc., The.

RACE DISCRIMINATION

see also Race Relations

Altman, Linda Jacobs. Racism & Ethnic Bias: Everybody's Problem. 2001. (Teen Issues Ser.). (Illus.). 64p. (J). (gr. 6-12). lib. bdg. 22.60 (978-0-7660-1578-4(5)) Enslow Pubs., Inc.

Cooper. Racism. 2003. (Face the Facts Ser.). (Illus.). 56p. (J). pap. 8.50 (978-1-4109-0047-0(9)) Raintree.

Cooper, Adrian. Racism. 2003. (Face the Facts Ser.). (Illus.). 56p. (J). lib. bdg. 28.56 (978-0-7398-6434-0(3)) Raintree.

Cushman, Clare & Urofsky, Melvin I., eds. Black, White, & Brown: The Landmark School Desegregation Case in Retrospect. 2004. (Illus.). 352p. (gr. 9 up). 45.00 (978-1-56802-911-5(X)) CQ Pr.

Gray, Valerie A. The Court-Martial Trial of West Point Cadet Johnson Whittaker: A Headline Court Case. 2001. (Headline Court Cases Ser.). (Illus.). 104p. (J). (gr. 6-12). lib. bdg. 26.60 (978-0-7660-1485-5(1)) Enslow Pubs., Inc.

Green, Jen. Racism. 2007. (J). ***(978-1-59604-153-0(6))*** Stargazer Bks.

Holt, Rinehart and Winston Staff. Bat 6. 2nd ed. 2002. (J). pap., stu. ed. 13.20 (978-0-03-066281-2(8)) Holt, Rinehart & Winston.

—Bat 6: With Connections. 2nd ed. 2002. (J). 14.64 (978-0-03-066279-9(6)) Holt, Rinehart & Winston.

Lishak, Antony. Racism. 2007. (J). ***(978-1-59920-038-5(4))*** Smart Apple Media.

Sanders, Bruce. Racism. 2005. (Let's Talk about Ser.). (Illus.). 32p. (J). (gr. 3-7). lib. bdg. 27.10 (978-1-59604-046-5(7)) Stargazer Bks.

Steele, Shelby. Dream Deferred: The Second Betrayal of Black Freedom in America. 1999. (gr. 7-12). lib. bdg. 23.45 (978-0-613-49555-4(1)) Tandem Library Bks.

Thomas, Pat. The Skin I'm In: A First Look at Racism. Harker, Lesley, illus. 2003. (First Look at Bks.). 32p. (J). pap. 6.95 (978-0-7641-2459-4(5)) Barron's Educational Series, Inc.

Tubbs, Janet. Racism. 2000. (Spud Packs Ser.). (Illus.). 16p. (J). (ps-4). pap. 19.95 (978-1-881185-18-5(4)) Arcadia Pr.

Watson, Marilyn Myrick. Raul Castro: Arizona's First Hispanic Governor. 2007. (J). ***(978-0-9790826-5-8(X)); (978-0-9790826-6-5(8))*** Acacia Publishing, Inc.

RACE PROBLEMS

see Race Relations

RACE RELATIONS

see also Discrimination; Emigration and Immigration; Multicultural Education

also names of countries, cities, etc. with the subdivision Race Relations, e.g. U. S.—Race Relations

Aikins, Anne Marie. Racism: Before It Gets under Your Skin. Murray, Steven, illus. 2004. (Deal with It Ser.). 32p. (J). (gr. 4-8). 12.95 (978-1-55028-844-5(X)) Lorimer, James & Co., Ltd., Pubs. CAN. *Dist:* Casemate Pubs. & Bk. Distributors, LLC.

Altman, Linda Jacobs. Hate & Racist Groups. 2001. (Hot Issues Ser.). (Illus.). 64p. (J). (gr. 6-12). lib. bdg. 27.93 (978-0-7660-1371-1(5)) Enslow Pubs., Inc.

Armitage, Ronda. Violence in Society. 2004. (21st Century Debates Ser.). lib. bdg. 28.56 (978-0-7398-6469-2(6)) Raintree.

Aronson, Marc. Race: A History Beyond Black & White. 2007. 336p. (YA). (gr. 7 up). 18.99 ***(978-0-689-86554-1(6)*** , Ginne Seo Bks) Simon & Schuster Children's Publishing.

Bridges, Ruby. Through My Eyes. 1999. (Illus.). 64p. (J). (gr. 3-7). pap. 16.95 (978-0-590-18923-1(9)) Scholastic, Inc.

Cole, Michael D. The L. A. Riots: Rage in the City of Angels. 1999. (American Disasters Ser.). (Illus.). 48p. (YA). (gr. 4-10). lib. bdg. 23.93 (978-0-7660-1219-6(0)) Enslow Pubs., Inc.

Cooper, John. Season of Rage: Hugh Burnett & the Struggle for Civil Rights. 2005. (Illus.). 80p. (J). (gr. 5-12). pap. 9.95 (978-0-88776-700-5(1)) Tundra Bks., Inc./Livres Toundra, Inc. CAN. *Dist:* Random Hse., Inc.

Edward, Davis. I'm Black What's Wrong. 2001. 36p. (J). per. 12.95 (978-0-7414-0625-5(X)) Infinity Publishing.

Edwards, Nicola. Racism. (Illus.). 32p. (YA). (gr. 1 up). lib. bdg. 27.10 (978-1-932333-06-0(1)) Chrysalis Education.

Fiorelli, June Estep. Fannie Lou Hamer: A Voice for Freedom. 2004. (Avisson Young Adult Ser.). (Illus.). 117p. (J). pap. 19.95 (978-1-888105-62-9(3)) Avisson Pr., Inc.

Ford, Carin T. African-American Soldiers in the Civil War: Fighting for Freedom. 2004. (Civil War Library Ser.). (Illus.). 48p. (J). lib. bdg. 23.93 (978-0-7660-2254-6(4)) Enslow Pubs., Inc.

Gandara & Hewitt. Racism. 1998. (Life Files Ser.). (Illus.). 64p. 24.99 (978-0-237-51512-6(1) , Evans Brothers, Limited) Evans Publishing Group GBR. *Dist:* Independent Pubs. Group.

Gay, Kathlyn. Cultural Diversity: Conflicts & Challenges: The Ultimate Teen Guide. 2003. (It Happened to Me Ser.: No. 6). (Illus.). 144p. pap. 30.95 (978-0-8108-4805-4(8)) Scarecrow Pr., Inc.

Gifford, Clive. Racism. (Illus.). 64p. (YA). (gr. 5 up). lib. bdg. 29.95 (978-1-931983-83-9(6)) Chrysalis Education.

—Racism. 2006. (Global Issues Ser.). (Illus.). 64p. (J). (gr. 4-12). pap. 12.95 (978-1-55285-745-8(X) , Walrus Bks.) Whitecap Bks., Ltd. CAN. *Dist:* Firefly Bks., Ltd.

Hanes, Richard Clay, et al. Prejudice in the Modern World. 2007. (J). ***(978-1-4144-0205-5(8)); (978-1-4144-0206-2(6))*** Thomson Gale.

Heberlein, Regine I. White Supremacists. 2002. (Contemporary Issues Companion Ser.). 155p. (J). 36.20 (978-0-7377-0847-9(6) , Greenhaven Pr., Inc.) Thomson Gale.

Jelloun, Tahar. Racisme Explique a Ma Fille. pap. 19.95 (978-88-7754-206-9(3)) Cideb ITA. *Dist:* Distribooks, Inc.

Kallen, Stuart A. Striving into 2000. 2001. (Black History Ser.). (Illus.). 48p. (J). (gr. 3-8). lib. bdg. 25.65 (978-1-57765-467-4(6) , ABDO & Daughters) ABDO Publishing Co.

Landau, Elaine. The Civil Rights Movement in America. 2007. (Cornerstones of Freedomtrade;, Second Ser.). 48p. (J). pap. 5.95 ***(978-0-531-18765-4(9)*** , Children's Pr.) Scholastic Library Publishing.

Lester, Julius. Let's Talk about Race. Date not set. 32p. (J). 6.99 (978-0-06-446226-6(9)) HarperCollins Pubs.

—Let's Talk about Race. Barbour, Karen, illus. 2005. (Amistad Ser.). 32p. (J). (gr. 1-5). 16.99 (978-0-06-028596-8(6)); lib. bdg. 16.89 (978-0-06-028598-2(2)) HarperCollins Pubs. (Amistad).

Levine, Ellen. Freedom's Children: Young Civil Rights Activists Tell Their Own Stories. 2000. 14.64 (978-0-606-20359-3(1)); (gr. 7-12). lib. bdg. 15.30 (978-0-613-33699-4(2)) Tandem Library Bks.

Marcovitz, Hal. Teens & Race. 2004. (Gallup Youth Survey, Major Issues & Trends Ser.). (Illus.). 112,128p. (J). (gr. 7-9). lib. bdg. 22.95 (978-1-59084-721-3(0)) Mason Crest Pubs.

Matthews, Sherrie Voss, ed. Free at Last: The Struggle for Civil Rights. 2000. (Literature & Thought Ser.). (Illus.). 144p. (J). (978-0-7807-9633-1(0)); (978-0-7891-5213-8(4)); pap. (978-0-7891-5212-1(6)) Perfection Learning Corp.

Miller, Jake. The Montgomery Bus Boycott: Integrating Public Buses. 2004. (Library of the Civil Rights Movement Ser.). (Illus.). 24p. (J). lib. bdg. 19.95 (978-0-8239-6251-8(2) , PowerKids Pr.) Rosen Publishing Group, Inc., The.

Morrison, John. Cornel West. 2003. (African American Leaders Ser.). (Illus.). 112p. (J). (gr. 6-12). 30.00 (978-0-7910-7686-6(5) , Chelsea Hse.) Facts On File, Inc.

Polakow, Amy. Daisy Bates: Civil Rights Crusader. 2002. (Illus.). 128p. (J). 25.00 (978-0-208-02513-5(8) , Linnet Bks.) Shoe String Pr., Inc.

Rappaport, Doreen. The School Is Not White! A True Story of the Civil Rights Movement. James, Curtis, illus. 2005. 32p. (gr. 2-7). 16.99 (978-0-7868-1838-9(7) , Jump at the Sun) Hyperion Bks. for Children.

Schramm, Linda Anette. Don't Let the Ziglers into the Zoo! 2004. 31p. pap. 17.95 (978-1-4137-1541-5(9)) PublishAmerica, Inc.

Sinnott, Susan. Welcome to Addy's World, 1864: Growing up During America's Civil War. 1999. (American Girls Collection). (Illus.). 64p. (J). (gr. 2 up). 16.95 (978-1-56247-771-4(4)) American Girl Publishing, Inc.

St. Lawrence, Genevieve. Medgar Evers. 2003. (gr. 3-6). lib. bdg. 18.20 (978-0-613-78291-3(7)) Tandem Library Bks.

Supples, Kevin. Speaking Out: The Civil Rights Movement 1950-1964. 2005. (Crossroads America Ser.). (Illus.). 40p. (J). (gr. k-3). 12.95 (978-0-7922-8279-2(5)); 21.90 (978-0-7922-8359-1(7)) National Geographic Society. (National Geographic Children's Bks.).

Sutherland, Jonathan & Canwell, Diane. African Americans in the Vietnam War. 2005. (American Experience in Vietnam Ser.). (Illus.). 48p. (J). pap. (978-0-8368-5779-5(8)); lib. bdg. 30.00 (978-0-8368-5772-6(0)) Stevens, Gareth Inc. (World Almanac Library).

Tackach, James. The Civil Rights Movement. 2001. (Opposing Viewpoints Digests Ser.). (Illus.). 112p. (J). 21.20 (978-0-7377-0355-9(5) , Greenhaven Pr., Inc.) Thomson Gale.

Thomson Gale Staff. Prejudice in the Modern World: Almanac, 2 vols. Hanes, Richard C. et al, eds. rev. ed. 2007. (Prejudice Throughout History Reference Library). 462p. (YA). 120.00 (978-1-4144-0204-8(X) , UXL) Thomson Gale.

—Prejudice in the Modern World: Biographies. Hanes, Richard C. & Rudd, Kelly, eds. rev. ed. 2007. (Prejudice Throughout History Reference Library). 920p. (YA). 67.00 (978-1-4144-0207-9(4) , UXL) Thomson Gale.

—Prejudice in the Modern World: Cumulative Index. Hermsen, Sarah, ed. rev. ed. 2007. (Prejudice Throughout History Reference Library). 34p. (YA). 5.00 (978-1-4144-0209-3(0) , UXL) Thomson Gale.

—Prejudice in the Modern World: Primary Sources. Hanes, Sharon M., ed. rev. ed. 2007. (Prejudice Throughout History Reference Library). 214p. (YA). 67.00 (978-1-4144-0208-6(2) , UXL) Thomson Gale.

Turck, Mary. Civil Rights Movement for Kids: A History with 21 Activities. 2000. (For Kids Ser.). (Illus.). 208p. (J). (gr. 4-8). pap. 14.95 (978-1-55652-370-0(X)) Chicago Review Pr., Inc.

Uschan, Michael V. Life on the Front Lines: The Fight for Civil Rights. 2004. (Illus.). 112p. (J). 32.45 (978-1-59018-387-8(8) , Lucent Bks.) Thomson Gale.

Vaughn, Wally G. & Davis, Mattie Campbell, eds. The Selma Campaign, 1963-1965: The Decisive Battle of the Civil Rights Movement. 2006. 261p. pap. 19.95 (978-0-912469-44-7(7)) Majority Pr., Inc., The.

Where Did the Races Come from? 2003. (BUL.). (YA). 0.75 (978-1-893345-13-3(0)) Answers in Genesis Ministries.

Williams, Mary E. The White Separatist Movement. 2002. (American Social Movements Ser.). (Illus.). 240p. (J). 36.20 (978-0-7377-1054-0(3) , Greenhaven Pr., Inc.) Thomson Gale.

Worth, Richard. Slave Life on the Plantation: Prisons Beneath the Sun. 2004. (Slavery in American History Ser.). (Illus.). 128p. (J). lib. bdg. 26.60 (978-0-7660-2152-5(1)) Enslow Pubs., Inc.

Wright, John D. Hate Crimes. 2002. (Crime & Detection Ser.). (Illus.). 96p. (J). (gr. 7 up). lib. bdg. (978-1-59084-379-6(7)) Mason Crest Pubs.

RACE RELATIONS—FICTION

Armistead, John. The Return of Gabriel. Gregory, Fran, illus. 2002. 240p. (J). (gr. 3-8). 17.95 (978-1-57131-637-0(X)); pap. 6.95 (978-1-57131-638-7(8)) Milkweed Editions.

—The $66 Summer. 2000. (978-0-606-21752-1(5)) Tandem Library Bks.

—The $66 Summer: A Novel of the Segregated South. 2nd ed. 2006. (Milkweed Prize for Children's Literature Ser.). 240p. (J). reprint ed. pap. 6.95 (978-1-57131-663-9(9)) Milkweed Editions.

Barron, Marietta. Two Worlds. 1999. 94p. (J). (gr. 3-6). 9.99 (978-0-88092-120-6(X) , 120-X) Royal Fireworks Publishing Co.

Bell, Helen. Idjhil. Bell, Helen, illus. 2003. (Illus.). 40p. (J). pap. 15.25 (978-1-876268-90-9(5)) Univ. of Western Australia Pr. AUS. *Dist:* International Specialized Bk. Services.

Blackman, Malorie. Black & White. 2007. 512p. (YA). (gr. 9 up). pap. 7.99 (978-1-4169-0017-7(9) , Simon Pulse) Simon & Schuster Children's Publishing.

—Knife Edge. 2007. 368p. (YA). (gr. 9 up). 16.99 (978-1-4169-0018-4(7) , Simon & Schuster Children's Publishing) Simon & Schuster Children's Publishing.

—Naughts & Crosses. 2005. (Illus.). 400p. (YA). (gr. 9 up). 15.95 (978-1-4169-0016-0(0)) Simon & Schuster Children's Publishing.

Blakeslee, Ann R. Summer Battles. 2000. (Illus.). 128p. (YA). (gr. 5-9). 14.95 (978-0-7614-5064-1(5) , Cavendish Children's Bks.) Cavendish, Marshall Corp.

Blume, Judy. Iggie's House. 2002. 128p. (J). (gr. 4-6). 17.99 (978-0-689-84291-7(0) , Atheneum/Richard Jackson Bks.) Simon & Schuster Children's Publishing.

Bond, Katherine Grace & Tate, Don, II. The Legend of the Valentine: An Inspirational Story of Love & Reconciliation. 2002. (Illus.). 32p. (J). 15.99 (978-0-310-70039-5(6)) Zonderkidz.

Brooks, Bruce. The Moves Make the Man. (J). pap., stu. ed. (978-0-13-017518-2(8)); 3rd ed. pap. 3.95 (978-0-13-800079-0(4)) Prentice Hall (Schl. Div.).

Carbone, Elisa. Storm Warriors. 2002. (gr. 5-8). lib. bdg. 13.55 (978-0-613-61730-7(4)) Tandem Library Bks.

Carter, Dorothy. Grandma's General Store - The Ark. Allen, Thomas B., illus. 2005. 144p. (J). 16.00 (978-0-374-32766-8(1) , Farrar, Straus & Giroux (BYR)) Farrar, Straus & Giroux.

Catran, Wendy. Not Raining Today. 2002. (Takeaways Ser.). (Illus.). 160p. (YA). pap. (978-0-7344-0260-8(0) , Lothian Bks.) Hachette Livre Australia.

Chass, Vikentia. The Visiting Angels. 1999. 16p. (J). (gr. k-6). pap. 8.00 (978-0-8059-4713-7(2)) Dorrance Publishing Co., Inc.

Cherie, J. Speed. 2003. (gr. 7-12). lib. bdg. 14.15 (978-0-613-61675-1(8)) Tandem Library Bks.

Choldenko, Gennifer. If a Tree Falls at Lunch Period. 2007. (Illus.). 224p. (J). (gr. 5 up). 17.00 (***978-0-15-205753-4(6))*** Harcourt Trade Pubs.

Christopher, Matt. Cool as Ice. 2001. 160p. (J). (gr. 3-7). pap. 4.99 (978-0-316-13520-7(8)) Little Brown & Co.

—Cool as Ice. 2001. (J). 11.15 (978-0-606-21121-5(7)); (gr. 3-6). lib. bdg. 12.40 (978-0-613-35635-0(7)) Tandem Library Bks.

Christopher, Matt & Mantell, Paul. Cool as Ice. 2001. 160p. (J). (gr. 4-7). 15.95 (978-0-316-13489-7(9)) Little Brown & Co.

Clements, Andrew. The Jacket. 2002. (gr. 3-6). lib. bdg. 13.00 (978-0-613-66513-1(9)) Tandem Library Bks.

Coleman, Evelyn. Freedom Train. Riley, David, illus. 2008. 160p. (J). 15.99 (***978-0-689-84716-5(5)*** , McElderry, Margaret K.) Simon & Schuster Children's Publishing.

Coleman, Evelyn. White Socks Only. Geter, Tyrone, illus. 2004. (Prairie Paperback Bks.). 32p. (J). (gr. k-4). pap. 6.95 (978-0-8075-8956-4(X)) Whitman, Albert & Co.

Coles, William E., Jr. Another Kind of Monday. 1999. 246p. per. 14.64 (978-0-606-16357-6(3)) Tandem Library Bks.

Collier, Kristi. Jericho Walls. 2007. 224p. (YA). pap. 7.95 (***978-0-8050-8184-8(4)*** , Holt, Henry & Co. Bks. For Young Readers) Holt, Henry & Co.

Cooney, Caroline B. Burning Up. 2001. (gr. 7-12). lib. bdg. 13.55 (978-0-613-33682-6(8)) Tandem Library Bks.

Crawford, Ann Fears. Keechee: The Witch of the Woods. 2005. (J). (978-1-931823-21-0(9)) Halcyon Pr.

Crowe, Chris. The Mississippi Trial, 1955. 2003. 240p. (YA). pap. 5.99 (978-0-14-250192-4(1) , Puffin) Penguin Group (USA) Inc.

—The Mississippi Trial, 1955. 2003. (gr. 7-12). lib. bdg. 14.15 (978-0-613-86522-7(7)) Tandem Library Bks.

de La Pena, Matt. Ball Don't Lie. 2005. 288p. (YA). (gr. 8-12). lib. bdg. 18.99 (978-0-385-90258-8(1)); (gr. 9-12). 16.95 (978-0-385-73232-1(5)) Random Hse. Children's Bks. (Delacorte Bks. for Young Readers).

de la Pena, Matt. Ball Don't Lie. 2007. 288p. (YA). (gr. 9). pap. 7.99 (978-0-385-73425-7(5) , Delacorte Bks. for Young Readers) Random Hse. Children's Bks.

Devoto, Pat Cunningham. My Last Days As Roy Rogers. 2000. (gr. 7-12). lib. bdg. 23.40 (978-0-613-27988-8(3)) Tandem Library Bks.

Down, Heather. A Deadly Distance. 2005. (Illus.). 128p. (YA). pap. (978-0-88878-455-1(4) , Sandcastle Bks.) Dundurn Group, The.

Draper, Sharon. Fire from the Rock. 2007. 240p. (YA). (gr. 7). 16.99 (***978-0-525-47720-4(9)*** , Dutton Juvenile) Penguin Group (USA) Inc.

Draper, Sharon M. Copper Sun. 2006. 320p. (YA). (gr. 8 up). 16.95 (978-0-689-82181-3(6) , Atheneum) Simon & Schuster Children's Publishing.

Ehrenberg, Pamela. Ethan, Suspended. 2007. 336 Pagesp. 16.00 (***978-0-8028-5317-2(X));*** vi, 266p. (J). (gr. 6 up). 16.00 (***978-0-8028-5324-0(2)*** , Eerdmans Bks For Young Readers) Eerdmans, William B. Publishing Co.

Elkins, Stephen. Ebony & Ivory: Discovering 10 Keys to Racial Harmony. Reisch, Jessie, illus. 2003. 32p. (J). (gr. k up). 14.99 incl. audio compact disk (978-0-8054-2674-8(4)) B&H Publishing Grp.

Ellis, Deborah & Walters, Eric. Bifocal. 2007. 240p. (YA). (gr. 7 up). (***978-1-55455-036-4(X))*** Fitzhenry & Whiteside, Ltd.

English, Karen. Francie. 2002. (Illus.). (J). 25.45 (978-0-7587-0355-2(4)) Book Wholesalers, Inc.

—Francie. 2002. 208p. (J). pap. 5.95 (978-0-374-42459-6(4) , Sunburst) Farrar, Straus & Giroux.

—Francie. 2007. 224p. (J). pap. 6.99 (***978-0-312-37383-2(X))*** Square Fish.

—Francie. 2002. (gr. 5-8). lib. bdg. 14.10 (978-0-613-54223-4(1)) Tandem Library Bks.

—Francie. l.t. ed. 2002. 220p. (J). 21.95 (978-0-7862-3717-3(1)) Thomson Gale.

Ferreira, Anton. Zulu Dog. 2002. (Illus.). 208p. (J). (gr. 5 up). 16.00 (978-0-374-39223-9(4) , Farrar, Straus & Giroux (BYR)) Farrar, Straus & Giroux.

Fuqua, Jonathan Scott. Darby. 2002. 256p. (J). (gr. 5 up). 16.99 (978-0-7636-1417-1(3)) Candlewick Pr.

Fuqua, Jonathon Scott. Darby. 2006. 256p. (J). (gr. 5). 5.99 (978-0-7636-2290-9(7)) Candlewick Pr.

Garlington, William R. The Great Divide: Coloring & Activity Book. 2004. (Illus.). (J). 5.95 (978-0-9708395-4-1(5)) Legacy Publishing Services, Inc.

—The Great Divide: The Adventures of Billy Bean & Bobby Nut. 2004. (Illus.). 127p. (J). pap. 12.95 (978-0-9708395-2-7(9)) Legacy Publishing Services, Inc.

Gibbons, Alan. Caught in the Crossfire. 2006. 304p. (J). pap. 11.99 (***978-1-84255-096-0(9))*** Orion Publishing Group, Ltd. GBR. *Dist:* Independent Pubs. Group.

Gillan, Maria. Growing up Ethnic in America: Contemporary Fiction about Learning to Be American. 1999. (gr. 7-12). lib. bdg. 26.85 (978-0-613-21652-4(0)) Tandem Library Bks.

Going, K. L. The Liberation of Gabriel King. 2007. 160p. (J). (gr. 3 up). pap. 6.99 (978-0-14-240766-0(6) , Puffin) Penguin Group (USA) Inc.

Gonzalez, Tomas. El Cayo. 2000. (SPA., Illus.). (J). (978-0-606-18242-3(X)) Tandem Library Bks.

Graham, Lorenz. Return to South Town. Graham, Lorenz, illus. 2003. (Illus.). 240p. (YA). (gr. 6-9). 16.95 (978-1-59078-164-7(3)) Boyds Mills Pr.

—South Town. Graham, Lorenz, illus. 2003. (Illus.). 188p. (YA). (gr. 6-9). 16.95 (978-1-59078-161-6(9)) Boyds Mills Pr.

—Whose Town? Graham, Lorenz, illus. 2003. (Illus.). 204p. (YA). (gr. 6-9). 16.95 (978-1-59078-163-0(5)) Boyds Mills Pr.

Gray, Libba Moore. Dear Willie Rudd. 2000. (gr. k-3). lib. bdg. 15.30 (978-0-613-22980-7(0)) Tandem Library Bks.

Gutman, Dan. Jackie & Me. 2005. (Baseball Card Adventures Ser.). (Illus.). 145p. (YA). (gr. 4-8). reprint ed. 20.00 (978-0-7567-9569-6(9)) DIANE Publishing Co.

—Jackie & Me. 2000. (Baseball Card Adventures Ser.). (gr. 5-8). lib. bdg. 14.15 (978-0-613-27912-3(3)) Tandem Library Bks.

Halpin, Brendan. How Ya Like Me Now. 2007. 208p. (YA). (gr. 7 up). 16.00 (978-0-374-33495-6(1)) Farrar, Straus & Giroux.

Hamilton, Virginia. A White Romance. 1998. (Point Signature Ser.). 450p. (YA). (gr. 8-12). pap. 4.50 (978-0-590-13005-9(6)) Scholastic, Inc.

Harrington, Janice N. & Lagarrigue, Jerome. Going North. 2004. (Illus.). 40p. (J). 16.00 (978-0-374-32681-4(9) , Farrar, Straus & Giroux (BYR)) Farrar, Straus & Giroux.

Harris, E. Lynn. Diaries of a Light Skinned Colored Boy, No. 1. 2020. (Illus.). 160p. (J). (gr. 7-17). 15.99 (978-0-7868-0632-4(X) , Jump at the Sun) Hyperion Bks. for Children.

Harrison, Marie Joseph. Mosanna & Me. 2003. 160p. pap. 12.95 (978-0-916251-62-8(4)) Sunbelt Pubns., Inc.

—Mosanna & Me. 2003. (gr. 7-12). lib. bdg. 22.20 (978-0-613-89684-9(X)) Tandem Library Bks.

Haugaard, Kay. The Day the Dragon Danced. Barritt, Carolyn Reed, illus. 2006. (J). (gr. 2-4). 16.95 (978-1-885008-30-5(9)) Shen's Bks.

Henderson, Alicia Terry, 1st. Call Me Black Call Me Beautiful, 1. Kindert, Jennifer, illus. 2002. 28p. (J). (gr. k-3). lib. bdg. 9.95 (978-0-9719490-1-0(8)) Royal Regal Bks.

Hewett, Lorri. Lives of Our Own. 2000. (J). (978-0-606-19695-6(1)) Tandem Library Bks.

Hirsch, Odo. Have Courage, Hazel Green! 2006. 262p. (J). 15.95 (978-1-58234-659-5(3) , Bloomsbury Children) Bloomsbury Publishing.

Johnson-Simpson, Gwendolyn. Difference. 1998. (Illus.). 32p. (J). pap. 8.00 (978-0-8059-4409-9(5)) Dorrance Publishing Co., Inc.

Johnston, Tony. Bone by Bone by Bone. 2007. 192p. (YA). (gr. 7 up). 17.95 (***978-1-59643-113-3(X))*** Roaring Brook Pr.

Jordan, Rosa. Lost Goat Lane. 2004. 192p. (J). 14.95 (978-1-56145-325-2(0)) Peachtree Pubs., Ltd.

Justus, Adalu. The Storyteller House. Justus, Adalu, illus. 1999. 180p. (YA). (gr. 5-12). per. (978-0-937109-11-3(8)) Ike, J. Bks.

Klass, David. Danger Zone. 1998. (J). 11.64 (978-0-606-13080-6(2)) Tandem Library Bks.

Koertge, Ronald. The Heart of the City. 1998. 128p. (J). (gr. 3-7). 16.99 (978-0-531-33078-4(8) , Orchard Bks.) Scholastic, Inc.

Krech, Bob. Rebound. 2006. 272p. (J). (gr. 9 up). 16.99 (978-0-7614-5319-2(9)) Cavendish, Marshall Corp.

Kytle, Calvin. Like a Tree. 2007. 430p. 28.95 (***978-1-58838-220-7(6)*** , NewSouth Bks.) NewSouth, Inc.

Les Becquets, Diane. The Stones of Mourning Creek. 2005. 306p. (YA). (gr. 7). reprint ed. pap. 6.95 (978-0-7614-5238-6(9)) Cavendish, Marshall Corp.

—The Stones of Mourning Creek. 2001. (Illus.). 320p. (J). (gr. 7 up). 16.95 (978-1-58837-004-4(6)) Winslow Pr.

Littlesugar, Amy. Freedom School, Yes! Cooper, Floyd, illus. 2001. 1p. (J). (ps-3). 16.99 (978-0-399-23006-6(8) , Philomel) Penguin Group (USA) Inc.

Lorbiecki, Marybeth. Jackie's Bat. Pinkney, Brian, illus. 2006. 40p. (J). (gr. k-3). 15.95 (978-0-689-84102-6(7)) Simon & Schuster Children's Publishing.

Lucashenko, Melissa. Killing D'arcy. 1998. 240p. (YA). (gr. 8-12). pap. 16.95 (978-0-7022-3041-7(3)) Univ. of Queensland Pr. AUS. *Dist:* International Specialized Bk. Services.

Lynch, Chris. Gold Dust. 2002. 208p. (J). (gr. 5 up). pap. 7.99 (978-0-06-447201-2(9)) HarperCollins Pubs.

—Gold Dust. 2002. (gr. 5-8). lib. bdg. 14.10 (978-0-613-67089-0(2)) Tandem Library Bks.

Lyon, George Ella. Sonny's House of Spies. 2004. (Illus.). 304p. (J). 16.95 (978-0-689-85168-1(5) , Atheneum/Richard Jackson Bks.) Simon & Schuster Children's Publishing.

Manns, Nick. Dead Negative. 2003. mass mkt. (978-0-340-85566-9(5) , Hodder Children's Books) Hodder Children's Division.

Martin, Ann M. Amalia: Diary Three. 2000. (California Diaries: Bk. 14). (Illus.). 144p. (YA). (gr. 6-8). pap. 4.99 (978-0-439-09548-8(4)) Scholastic, Inc.

—Amalia: Diary Three. 1999. (California Diaries: Bk. 14). (Illus.). (YA). (gr. 6-8). (978-0-606-18525-7(9)) Tandem Library Bks.

Masson, Sophie. Sooner or Later. 115p. pap. 11.95 (978-0-7022-2336-5(0)) Univ. of Queensland Pr. AUS. *Dist:* International Specialized Bk. Services.

Mazellan, Ron, illus. We Will Walk. 2005. 16p. (J). pap. (***978-0-7367-2919-2(4))*** Zaner-Bloser, Inc.

McDonald, Joyce. Devil on My Heels. 272p. (YA). (gr. 7 up). 2005. pap. 6.50 (978-0-440-23829-4(3) , Laurel Leaf); 2004. 15.95 (978-0-385-73107-2(8) , Delacorte Bks. for Young Readers) Random Hse. Children's Bks.

McGuigan, Mary Ann. Morning in a Different Place. 2008. (J). (***978-1-59078-551-5(7)*** , Front Street) Boyds Mills Pr.

McKissack, Patricia C. Abby Takes a Stand. James, Gordon C., illus. 2005. (Scraps of Time Ser.). 112p. (J). (gr. 3). 14.99 (978-0-670-06011-5(9) , Viking Juvenile) Penguin Group (USA) Inc.

McKissack, Patricia C. & Pinkney, Jerry. Goin' Someplace Special. 2001. (Illus.). 40p. (J). (ps-3). 16.99 (978-0-689-81885-1(8) , Atheneum/Anne Schwartz Bks.) Simon & Schuster Children's Publishing.

McMullan, Margaret. When I Crossed No-Bob. 2007. 224p. (J). (gr. 5-9). 16.00 (***978-0-618-71715-6(3))*** Houghton Mifflin Co. Trade & Reference Div.

Medearis, Angela Shelf. Singing for Dr. King. Wright and Hu, Cornelius Van and Ying-Hwa, illus. 2004. 32p. (J). lib. bdg. 15.00 (***978-1-4242-0237-9(X))*** Fitzgerald Bks.

Meyer, Carolyn. White Lilacs. 2007. (Illus.). 256p. (YA). pap. 6.95 (978-0-15-205851-7(6) , Harcourt Paperbacks) Harcourt Children's Bks.

Mickles Sr., Robert T. S. Blood Kin, a Savannah Story. 2007. 108p. per. 9.95 (***978-0-595-45129-6(2))*** iUniverse, Inc.

Miller, William. The Bus Ride. Ward, John, illus. 1998. 32p. (YA). (gr. k up). 15.95 (978-1-880000-60-1(1)) Lee & Low Bks., Inc.

—The Bus Ride. 2001. (J). 13.75 (978-0-606-21094-2(6)) Tandem Library Bks.

Moses, Shelia P. The Legend of Buddy Bush. unabr. ed. 2005. (J). (gr. 3-7). 55.70 incl. audio (978-1-4193-3575-4(8) , 42043) Recorded Bks., LLC.

—The Legend of Buddy Bush. (Illus.). 224p. 2005. (YA). pap. 5.99 (978-1-4169-0716-9(5) , Simon Pulse); 2003. (J). 15.95 (978-0-689-85839-0(6) , McElderry, Margaret K.) Simon & Schuster Children's Publishing.

—The Legend of Buddy Bush. l.t. ed. 2005. 179p. 22.95 (978-0-7862-7311-9(9)) Thorndike Pr.

Moses, Shelia P. The Return of Buddy Bush. 2008. 176p. (YA). pap. 5.99 (***978-1-4169-3925-2(3)*** , Simon Pulse); 2005. (Illus.). 160p. (J). 15.95 (978-0-689-87431-4(6) , McElderry, Margaret K.) Simon & Schuster Children's Publishing.

Murphy, Rita. Black Angels. 2002. 176p. (J). (gr. 4). pap. 4.99 (978-0-440-22934-6(0) , Yearling) Random Hse. Children's Bks.

—Black Angels. 2002. (gr. 3-6). lib. bdg. 13.00 (978-0-613-57701-4(9)) Tandem Library Bks.

Myers, Anna. Tulsa Burning. 2004. 184p. (J). pap. 7.95 (978-0-8027-7696-9(5)); (Illus.). (gr. 3-7). 16.95 (978-0-8027-8829-0(7)) Walker & Co.

Naidoo, Beverley. Out of Bounds: Seven Stories of Conflict & Hope. 2003. (Illus.). 192p. (J). (gr. 5 up). 16.99 (978-0-06-050799-2(3)); lib. bdg. 17.89 (978-0-06-050800-5(0)) HarperCollins Pubs.

Nelson, Vaunda Micheaux. Beyond Mayfield. 1999. 1p. (J). (gr. 5-9). 15.99 (978-0-399-23355-5(5) , Putnam Juvenile) Penguin Group (USA) Inc.

—Mayfield Crossing. 2002. (gr. 3-6). lib. bdg. 14.15 (978-0-613-43634-2(2)) Tandem Library Bks.

Nolan, Han. A Summer of Kings. 2006. (Illus.). 352p. (YA). 17.00 (978-0-15-205108-2(2)) Harcourt Children's Bks.

—A Summer of Kings. 2006. 334p. (J). (978-1-4156-7340-9(3)) Harcourt Trade Pubs.

Nye, Naomi Shihab. Habibi. unabr. ed. 2000. (YA). pap. 49.24 incl. audio (978-0-7887-3642-1(6) , 41008X4) Recorded Bks., LLC.

—Habibi. 1999. 272p. (YA). (gr. 5 up). pap. 5.99 (978-0-689-82523-1(4) , Simon Pulse) Simon & Schuster Children's Publishing.

Owens, Tom. Free to Learn. Pollema-Cahill, Phyllis, illus. 2000. (Cover-to-Cover Bks.). (J). 55p. pap. (978-0-7891-5164-3(2)); 56p. (gr. 1-4). lib. bdg. 16.95 (978-0-7807-9314-9(5)) Perfection Learning Corp.

Parkhurst, Liz S. Under One Flag: A Year at Rohwer. Clifton, Tom, illus. 2005. 32p. (J). 16.95 (978-0-87483-759-9(6) , 1241971) August Hse. Pubs., Inc.

Pearsall, Shelley. Trouble Don't Last. 256p. (gr. 4-8). 2002. (Illus.). 14.95 (978-0-375-81490-7(6) , Knopf Bks. for Young Readers); 2002. (Illus.). lib. bdg. 16.99 (978-0-375-91490-4(0) , Knopf Bks. for Young Readers); 2003. (J). reprint ed. pap. 5.99 (978-0-440-41811-5(9) , Yearling) Random Hse. Children's Bks.

—Trouble Don't Last. 2003. (gr. 3-6). lib. bdg. 13.55 (978-0-613-85706-2(2)) Tandem Library Bks.

Peck, Richard. The River Between Us. 176p. (J). 2003. (gr. 7). 16.99 (978-0-8037-2735-9(6) , Dial); 2005. (gr. 5-7). reprint ed. pap. 6.99 (978-0-14-240310-5(5) , Puffin) Penguin Group (USA) Inc.

—The River Between Us. 2005. 164p. (J). (ps-7). lib. bdg. 12.64 (978-0-606-33120-3(4)) Tandem Library Bks.

Perez, L. King. Remember As You Pass Me By. 2007. 224p. (J). (gr. 4-8). 16.95 (***978-1-57131-677-6(9))*** Milkweed Editions.

—Remember as You Pass Me By. 2007. 184p. (J). (gr. 2-7). per. 6.95 (***978-1-57131-678-3(7))*** Milkweed Editions.

Perkyns, Dorothy. Last Days in Africville. 2005. (Illus.). 144p. (YA). pap., tchr. ed. (978-0-88878-446-9(5) , Sandcastle Bks.) Dundurn Group, The.

—Last Days in Africville. 2006. 120p. (J). pap. 10.99 (***978-1-55002-630-6(5)*** , Dundurn Pr.) Dundurn Group, The CAN. *Dist:* Univ. of Toronto Pr.

Peterseil, Tehila. Unjust Cause. 1998. (gr. 3-6). lib. bdg. 18.75 (978-0-613-89954-3(7)) Tandem Library Bks.

Pinkney, Andrea Davis. Boycott Blues. 2008. (J). (***978-0-06-082118-0(3)); (978-0-06-082119-7(1))*** HarperCollins Pubs. (Greenwillow Bks.).

Pinkney, Andrea Davis. Fishing Day. Evans, Shane W., illus. 2003. 32p. (gr. k-4). 15.99 (978-0-7868-0766-6(0)); 16.49 (978-0-7868-2614-8(2) , Jump at the Sun) Hyperion Bks. for Children.

Powers, J. L. The Confessional. 2007. 304p. (gr. 9). (J). 16.99 (***978-0-375-83872-9(4));*** (YA). lib. bdg. 19.99 (***978-0-375-93872-6(9))*** Random Hse. Children's Bks. (Knopf Bks. for Young Readers).

Raschka, Chris. Yo ! Yes. 2004. (J). (ps-5). 24.95 incl. audio (978-1-55592-066-1(7)); pap. 14.95 incl. audio (978-1-55592-067-8(5) , QPRA566) Weston Woods Studios, Inc.

—Yo! Yes? 2007. 32p. (J). pap. 6.99 (978-0-439-92185-5(6)) Scholastic, Inc.

Reitano, John. What If the Zebra Lost Their Stripes? Haines, William, illus. 1998. 32p. (ps-3). 16.95 (978-0-8091-6649-7(6) , 6649-6) Paulist Pr.

Rinaldi, Ann. The Education of Mary: A Little Miss of Color, 1832. 2000. 256p. (gr. 5-9). 15.99 (978-0-7868-0532-7(3) , Jump at the Sun) Hyperion Bks. for Children.

—The Education of Mary: A Little Miss of Color, 1832. 2005. 176p. (J). pap. (978-0-7868-1377-3(6)) Hyperion Pr.

Robinet, Harriette Gillem. Walking to the Bus-Rider Blues. 2002. (gr. 3-6). lib. bdg. 13.00 (978-0-613-57932-2(1)) Tandem Library Bks.

Robles, Tony. Joey Gonzales, Real American. 2007. (J). 12.95 (***978-0-9767269-3-7(9))*** World Ahead Media.

Rodman, Mary Ann. Yankee Girl. 2004. (Illus.). 224p. (J). 17.00 (978-0-374-38661-0(7) , Farrar, Straus & Giroux (BYR)) Farrar, Straus & Giroux.

Rogers, Kenny. Christmas in Canaan. 2002. (gr. 7-12). lib. bdg. 15.30 (978-0-613-68413-2(3)) Tandem Library Bks.

Rogers, Kenny & Davenport, Donald. Christmas in Canaan. 2002. 336p. (J). (gr. 6-9). 15.99 (978-0-06-000746-1(X)) HarperCollins Pubs.

Rue, Nancy N. Do I Have to Paint You a Picture. 1998. (gr. 7-12). lib. bdg. 15.25 (978-0-613-88736-6(0)) Tandem Library Bks.

—The Stunt. 1999. (Christian Heritage Ser.). 208p. (J). (gr. 3-7). pap. 5.99 (978-1-56179-833-9(9)) Bethany Hse. Pubs.

Russell, Barbara Timberlake. Maggie's Amerikay. Burke, Jim, illus. 2006. 40p. (J). 17.00 (978-0-374-34722-2(0) , Farrar, Straus & Giroux (BYR)) Farrar, Straus & Giroux.

Salcedo, Betsy. Together we Can. 2006. 9.00 (978-0-8059-9155-0(7)) Dorrance Publishing Co., Inc.

Schmidt, Gary D. Lizzie Bright & the Buckminster Boy. (gr. 5). 2008. 240p. (YA). mass mkt. 6.99 (***978-0-375-84169-9(5)*** , Laurel Leaf); 2006. 224p. (J). reprint ed. pap. 6.50 (978-0-553-49495-2(3) , Yearling) Random Hse. Children's Bks.

Scholastic, Inc. Staff & Medearis, Angela Shelf. Singing for Dr. King. Van Wright, Cornelius & Hu, Ying-Hwa, illus. 2004. (Just for You! Ser.). 32p. (gr. k-3). pap. 3.99 (978-0-439-56855-5(2) , Teaching Resources) Scholastic, Inc.

Schraff, Anne. Freedom Knows No Color. 2000. 118p. (J). pap. (978-0-7891-5136-0(7)); (gr. 5-12). lib. bdg. 13.95 (978-0-7807-9270-8(X)) Perfection Learning Corp.

Schunk, Laurel. Black & Secret Midnight. 1998. 238p. (gr. 6-8). 24.99 (978-0-9661879-0-8(3) , SKP98-41) St Kitts Pr.

Schwartz, Ellen. Stealing Home. 2006. 224p. (J). (gr. 4-7). pap. 8.95 (978-0-88776-765-4(6)) Tundra Bks., Inc./Livres Toundra, Inc. CAN. *Dist:* Random Hse., Inc.

Sharenow, Robert. My Mother the Cheerleader. 2007. 304p. (gr. 7 up). (J). lib. bdg. 17.89 (978-0-06-114897-2(0)); (YA). 16.99 (978-0-06-114896-5(2)) HarperCollins Pubs. (Geringer, Laura Book).

Shaw, Marilyn Bishop. Solomon. 2006. 203p. (J). 14.95 (978-1-56164-349-3(1)) Pineapple Pr., Inc.

Smadja, Brigitte. Tarte aux Escargots. pap. 17.95 (978-2-211-03633-7(3)) Archimede Editions FRA. *Dist:* Distribooks, Inc.

Smothers, Ethel Footman. Moriah's Pond. 2004. 96p. (J). pap. 7.00 (978-0-8028-5249-6(1)) Eerdmans, William B. Publishing Co.

—Moriah's Pond. 2003. (gr. 3-6). lib. bdg. 15.30 (978-0-613-67247-4(X)) Tandem Library Bks.

Stephenson, Lynda. Dancing with Elvis. 2006. 331p. (YA). pap. 8.00 (978-0-8028-5300-4(5) , Eerdmans Bks For Young Readers) Eerdmans, William B. Publishing Co.

Taylor, Mildred D. The Friendship. Ginsberg, Max, illus. 1998. 56p. (gr. 2-6). pap. 4.99 (978-0-14-038964-7(4) , Puffin) Penguin Group (USA) Inc.

—The Friendship. 1998. 11.79 (978-0-606-12938-1(3)) Tandem Library Bks.

—The Gold Cadillac. Hays, Michael & Ginsberg, Max, illus. 1998. 48p. (YA). (gr. 2-6). pap. 4.99 (978-0-14-038963-0(6) , Puffin) Penguin Group (USA) Inc.

—The Gold Cadillac. 1998. 11.79 (978-0-606-13433-0(6)) Tandem Library Bks.

—The Land. 2003. 400p. (YA). pap. 6.99 (978-0-14-250146-7(8) , Puffin) Penguin Group (USA) Inc.

—The Land. Ginsburg, Max, illus. 2001. 392p. (J). (gr. 7 up). 17.99 (978-0-8037-1950-7(7) , Dial) Penguin Group (USA) Inc.

—Mississippi Bridge. 2002. (J). 12.87 (978-0-7587-9586-1(6)) Book Wholesalers, Inc.

—Mississippi Bridge. Ginsburg, Max, illus. 2000. 64p. (J). (gr. 4-7). pap. 4.99 (978-0-14-130817-3(6) , Puffin) Penguin Group (USA) Inc.

—Mississippi Bridge. 2002. (J). (gr. 2-6). 21.00 (978-0-8446-7213-7(0)) Smith, Peter Pub., Inc.

—Mississippi Bridge. Ginsburg, Max, illus. 2000. 62p. (J). (ps-7). lib. bdg. 13.00 (978-0-8335-9262-0(9)) Tandem Library Bks.

—Mississippi Bridge. 2000. (978-0-606-18434-2(1)) Tandem Library Bks.

—Roll of Thunder, Hear My Cry. l.t. ed. 2000. (LRS Large Print Cornerstone Ser.). 348p. (YA). (gr. 5-12). lib. bdg. 32.95 (978-1-58118-057-2(8) , 23471) LRS.

—Roll of Thunder, Hear My Cry. 1998. (J). (gr. 5). pap. 3.95 (978-0-439-04476-9(6)) Scholastic, Inc.

Tocher, Timothy. Chief Sunrise, John McGraw, & Me. 2004. 168p. (J). 16.95 (978-0-8126-2711-4(3)) Cricket Bks.

Turner, Ann. Sitting Bull Remembers. 2007. 32p. (J). (ps-4). lib. bdg. 17.89 (978-0-06-051400-6(0)) HarperCollins Pubs.

—Sitting Bull Remembers. Minor, Wendell, illus. 2007. 32p. (J). (gr. 1-4). 16.99 (978-0-06-051399-3(3)) HarperCollins Pubs.

Twain, Mark. The Adventures of Huckleberry Finn. 2007. (Children's Classics Ser.). (Illus.). 256p. (J). 6.99 (978-0-517-22999-6(4) , Gramercy) Random Hse. Value Publishing.

Twain, Mark & Olmos. The Adventures of Huckleberry Finn. 2004. (SPA.). 360p. pap. 17.95 (***978-84-263-5252-1(9)***) Vives, Luis Editorial (Edelvives) ESP. *Dist:* Lectorum Pubns., Inc.

Vander Zee, Ruth. Mississippi Morning. Cooper, Floyd, illus. 2004. 32p. (J). 16.00 (978-0-8028-5211-3(4)) Eerdmans, William B. Publishing Co.

Volponi, Paul. Black & White. 2005. 192p. (YA). (gr. 7). 15.99 (978-0-670-06006-1(2) , Viking Adult) Penguin Group (USA) Inc.

—Rooftop. (gr. 7). 2007. 224p. (J). pap. 6.99 (978-0-14-240844-5(1) , Puffin); 2006. 208p. (YA). 15.99 (978-0-670-06069-6(0) , Viking Adult) Penguin Group (USA) Inc.

Walsh, Ann. Shabash! 2006. 120p. (J). (gr. 3-8). pap., tchr. ed. 5.95 (978-0-88878-355-4(8) , Sandcastle Bks.) Dundurn Group, The CAN. *Dist:* Univ. of Toronto Pr.

Walvoord, Linda. Rosetta, Rosetts, Sit by Me! Velasquez, Eric, illus. 2004. 80p. (J). 14.95 (978-0-7614-5171-6(4)) Cavendish, Marshall Corp.

Watlington, Calvin. Zoe. 2002. (Illus.). (J). 9.95 (978-0-9724284-0-8(2)) Ebonylaw Publishing.

Weatherford, Carole Boston. Freedom on the Menu: The Greensboro Sit-Ins. Lagarrigue, Jerome Lagarrigue, illus. 2007. 32p. (J). (ps). pap. 5.99 (***978-0-14-240894-0(8)*** , Puffin) Penguin Group (USA) Inc.

—Freedom on the Menu: The Greensboro Sit-Ins. Lagarrigue, Jerome, illus. 2004. 32p. (J). (gr. 1). 16.99 (978-0-8037-2860-8(3) , Dial) Penguin Group (USA) Inc.

Wiles, Deborah. The Aurora County All-Stars. 2007. (Illus.). 256p. (J). (gr. 5 up). 16.00 (***978-0-15-206068-8(5)***) Harcourt Children's Bks.

Woodson, Jacqueline. Feathers. 2007. 128p. (J). (gr. 3-7). 15.99 (978-0-399-23989-2(8) , Putnam Juvenile) Penguin Group (USA) Inc.

—I Hadn't Meant to Tell You This. 2006. (YA). 176p. (gr. 4). 17.99 (978-0-399-24499-5(9) , Putnam Juvenile); 128p. (gr. 7). pap. 5.99 (978-0-14-240555-0(8) , Puffin) Penguin Group (USA) Inc.

—If You Come Softly. (gr. 5). 2006. 192p. (YA). pap. 5.99 (978-0-14-240601-4(5) , Puffin); 1998. 1p. (J). 16.99 (978-0-399-23112-4(9) , Putnam Juvenile) Penguin Group (USA) Inc.

—If You Come Softly. 2000. 12.64 (978-0-606-17863-1(5)) Tandem Library Bks.

—The Other Side. Lewis, Earl, illus. 2001. 1p. (J). (gr. k up). 16.99 (978-0-399-23116-2(1) , Putnam Juvenile) Penguin Group (USA) Inc.

Wright, Sue. Blind Man's Bluff. 2005. (Davey & Goliath Ser.). (Illus.). 32p. (J). (ps-ps). pap. 3.50 (978-0-439-75830-7(0) , Scholastic Paperbacks) Scholastic, Inc.

Yee, Paul. What Happened This Summer. 2006. 128p. (YA). 15.95 (978-1-896580-88-3(2)) Tradewind Bks. CAN. *Dist:* Orca Bk. Pubs. USA.

RACES OF MAN

see Ethnology

RACIAL BALANCE IN SCHOOLS

see Segregation in Education

RACIALLY MIXED PEOPLE

Armentrout, David & Armentrout, Patricia, trs. Tiger Woods. 2003. (Discover the Life of a Sports Star Ser.). (Illus.). 24p. (J). 20.64 (978-1-58952-656-3(2)) Rourke Publishing, LLC.

Bankston, John. Alicia Keys. l.t. ed. 2002. (Real Life Reader Biography Ser.). (Illus.). 32p. (gr. 3-8). lib. bdg. 15.95 (978-1-58415-133-3(1)) Mitchell Lane Pubs., Inc.

Brewster, Hugh. The Other Mozart: The Life of the Famous Chevalier de Saint-George. Velasquez, Eric, illus. 2006. 48p. (J). (gr. k-5). 18.95 (978-0-8109-5720-6(5) , Abrams Bks. for Young Readers) Abrams, Harry N. , Inc.

Brill, Marlene Targ. Barack Obama. 2006. (J). pap. 6.95 (978-0-8225-6056-2(9) , First Avenue Editions) Lerner Publishing Group.

—Barack Obama: Working to Make a Difference. 2006. (Gateway Biographies Ser.). (Illus.). 48p. (J). 23.93 (978-0-8225-3417-4(7)) Lerner Publishing Group.

Brown, Jonatha A. & Raatma, Lucia. Tiger Woods. 2004. (Illus.). 24p. (J). pap. (978-0-8368-4320-0(7)); (YA). lib. bdg. 19.33 (978-0-8368-4313-2(4)) Stevens, Gareth Inc.

Christopher, Matt. En el Campo de Juego con Derek Jeter. 2005. (Illus.). 138p. (J). (ps-7). per. 11.64 (978-0-606-33452-5(1)) Tandem Library Bks.

—On the Course with... Tiger Woods. rev. ed. 1998. (Matt Christopher Sports Biographies Ser.). (Illus.). 144p. (J). (gr. 3-7). pap. 4.99 (978-0-316-13445-3(7)) Little, Brown Bks. for Young Readers.

—On the Course with... Tiger Woods. 1998. (978-0-606-13676-1(2)) Tandem Library Bks.

—On the Field with... Derek Jeter. 2000. (J). (978-0-606-19840-0(7)); (gr. 3-6). lib. bdg. 13.00 (978-0-613-30646-1(5)) Tandem Library Bks.

Collins, David R. Tiger Woods: Golf Superstar. Nolte, Larry, illus. 1998. 32p. (J). (gr. k-3). pap. 15.95 (978-1-56554-321-8(1)) Pelican Publishing Co., Inc.

—Tiger Woods: Golfing Champion. Nolte, Larry, illus. 1999. 104p. (J). (gr. 3-7). 14.95 (978-1-56554-322-5(X)) Pelican Publishing Co., Inc.

Covert, Kim. Derek Jeter. 2001. (Sports Heroes Ser.). (Illus.). 48p. (J). (gr. 3-4). lib. bdg. 21.26 (978-0-7368-0777-7(2) , Capstone High-Interest Bks.) Capstone Pr., Inc.

Davis, William Michael. Barack Obama: The Politics of Hope. 2007. (Illus.). 168p. (YA). (gr. 10 up). lib. bdg. 25.95 (***978-1-59556-024-7(6)***) OTTN Publishing.

Devaney, Sherri. Barack Obama. 2006. (Illus.). 112p. (J). (gr. 7-10). 32.45 (978-1-59018-937-5(X) , Lucent Bks.) Thomson Gale.

Doeden, Matt. Tiger Woods. 2005. (Sports Heroes & Legends Ser.). (Illus.). 106p. (J). (gr. 3-7). 27.93 (978-0-8225-3082-4(1) , Lerner Pubns.) Lerner Publishing Group.

Donovan, Sandy. Derek Jeter. 2004. (Illus.). 32p. (J). (ps-7). lib. bdg. 12.75 (978-0-606-30542-6(4)) Tandem Library Bks.

Dougherty, Terri. Tiger Woods. 1999. (Jam Session Ser.). (Illus.). 32p. (J). (gr. 3-8). lib. bdg. 24.21 (978-1-57765-041-6(7) , ABDO & Daughters) ABDO Publishing Co.

Durbin, William. Tiger Woods: Golf Star. 1999. (Golf Legends Ser.). (Illus.). (YA). 64p. (gr. 4-7). 18.65 (978-0-7910-4563-3(3)); 144p. (gr. 5 up). pap. 30.00 (978-0-7910-4687-6(7)) Facts On File, Inc. (Chelsea Hse.).

Edwards, Nicholas. Tiger Woods: An American Master. rev. ed. 2001. (J). (978-0-606-22872-5(1)) Tandem Library Bks.

Edwards, Roberta. Barack Obama: An American Story. Call, Ken, illus. 2007. (All Aboard Reading Ser.). 48p. (J). (gr. 1-3). pap. 3.99 (***978-0-448-44799-5(1)*** , Grosset & Dunlap) Penguin Group (USA) Inc.

Frisch, Aaron. Derek Jeter. 2003. (Ovations Ser.). (Illus.). 32p. (J). pap. (978-1-58341-247-3(6) , Creative Education) Creative Co., The.

Fuyo Gaskins, Pearl, ed. What Are You? Voices of Mixed-Race Young People. rev. ed. 1999. (Illus.). 288p. (YA). (gr. 7-12). 18.95 (978-0-8050-5968-7(7) , Holt, Henry & Co. Bks. For Young Readers) Holt, Henry & Co.

Goodman, Michael E. Tiger Woods. 2003. (Ovations Ser.). (Illus.). 32p. (J). (978-1-58341-246-6(8) , Creative Education) Creative Co., The.

Gutelle, Andrew. Tiger Woods. Gutelle, Andrew, illus. 2002. (All Aboard Reading Ser.). (Illus.). 48p. (J). pap. 3.99 (978-0-448-42663-1(3) , Grosset & Dunlap) Penguin Group (USA) Inc.

—Tiger Woods. 2002. (gr. k-3). lib. bdg. 11.80 (978-0-613-43647-2(4)) Tandem Library Bks.

Hughes, Libby. Tiger Woods: A Biography for Kids. 2000. (Illus.). 70p. (J). pap. 5.95 (978-1-58571-003-4(2)) Kensington Publishing Corp.

—Tiger Woods: A Biography for Kids. 2000. (gr. 3-6). lib. bdg. 14.10 (978-0-613-88468-6(X)) Tandem Library Bks.

Knapp, Ron. Sports Great Derek Jeter. 2001. (Sports Great Bks.). (Illus.). 64p. (YA). (gr. 4-10). lib. bdg. 22.60 (978-0-7660-1470-1(3)) Enslow Pubs., Inc.

Kramer, Sydelle A. Tiger Woods: Golf's Young Master. 1998. (Step into Reading Step 4 Bks.). (J). (gr. 2-4). (978-0-606-13970-0(2)) Tandem Library Bks.

Lace, William W. Tiger Woods: Star Golfer. 1999. (Sports Reports). (Illus.). 104p. (YA). (gr. 4-10). lib. bdg. 20.95 (978-0-7660-1081-9(3)) Enslow Pubs., Inc.

Lanier, Shannon & Feldman, Jane. Jefferson's Children: The Story of One American Family. 2004. (Illus.). 144p. (J). (gr. 4-8). reprint ed. 20.00 (978-0-7567-7418-9(7)) DIANE Publishing Co.

—Jefferson's Children: The Story of One American Family. Feldman, Jane, photos by. 2002. 160p. (gr. 5). pap. 16.95 (978-0-375-82168-4(6) , Random Hse. Bks. for Young Readers) Random Hse. Children's Bks.

—Jefferson's Children: The Story of One American Family. Feldman, Jane, photos by. 2002. (Illus.). 160p. (J). (ps-7). lib. bdg. 24.55 (978-0-613-57230-9(0)) Tandem Library Bks.

Macnow, Glen. Sports Great Tiger Woods. 2001. (Sports Great Bks.). (Illus.). 64p. (YA). (gr. 4-10). lib. bdg. 22.60 (978-0-7660-1468-8(1)) Enslow Pubs., Inc.

Naden, Corinne J. Halle Berry. 2001. (gr. 3-6). lib. bdg. 18.75 (978-0-613-86157-1(4)) Tandem Library Bks.

O'Connell, Jack. Derek Jeter: The Yankee Kid. Rains, Rob, ed. 2003. (Super Star Ser.). 96p. (J). pap. 4.95 (978-1-58261-043-6(6)) Sports Publishing, LLC.

Raatma, Lucia. Tiger Woods. 2001. (Trailblazers of the Modern World Ser.). (Illus.). 48p. (J). (gr. 5 up). pap. 14.95 (978-0-8368-5226-4(5)); lib. bdg. 30.00 (978-0-8368-5066-6(1)) Stevens, Gareth Inc. (World Almanac Library).

Rapoport, Ken. Jason Kidd: Leader on the Court. 2004. (Sports Leaders Ser.). (Illus.). 104p. (J). lib. bdg. 26.60 (978-0-7660-2214-0(5)) Enslow Pubs., Inc.

Rappoport, Ken. Super Sports Star Derek Jeter. 2004. (Super Sports Star Ser.). (Illus.). 48p. (J). lib. bdg. 23.93 (978-0-7660-2139-6(4)) Enslow Pubs., Inc.

Roberts, Jeremy. Tiger Woods. 2002. (Illus.). 112p. (J). (gr. 6-12). lib. bdg. 16.40 (978-0-613-46178-8(9)) Tandem Library Bks.

—Tiger Woods: Biography A&E Series. 2001. (Biography Ser.). (Illus.). 112p. (YA). (gr. 6-12). 27.93 (978-0-8225-0030-8(2) , Lerner Pubns.) Lerner Publishing Group.

Sapet, Kerrily. Barack Obama. 2007. (Political Profiles Ser.). (Illus.). 128p. (YA). (gr. 5 up). lib. bdg. 27.95 (***978-1-59935-045-5(9)***) Reynolds, Morgan Inc.

Savage, Jeff. Tiger Woods. 2005. (Amazing Athletes Ser.). (Illus.). 32p. (gr. 3-4). lib. bdg. 22.60 (978-0-8225-1337-7(4)) Lerner Publishing Group.

Schuman, Michael. Barack Obama: We Are One People. 2008. (African-American Biography Library). (Illus.). 128p. (J). (gr. 6 up). lib. bdg. 31.93 (***978-0-7660-2891-3(7)***) Enslow Pubs., Inc.

Sirimarco, Elizabeth. Tiger Woods. 2000. (Sports Heroes Ser.). (Illus.). 48p. (J). (gr. 3-4). lib. bdg. 21.26 (978-0-7368-0581-0(8) , Capstone High-Interest Bks.) Capstone Pr., Inc.

Stewart, Mark. Derek Jeter: Substance & Style. 1999. (New Wave Ser.). (Illus.). 48p. (gr. 4 up). lib. bdg. 22.90 (978-0-7613-1516-2(0) , Millbrook Pr.) Lerner Publishing Group.

—Tiger Woods: Drive to Greatness. 2001. (Inspiring People Ser.). (Illus.). 64p. (gr. 4 up). lib. bdg. 24.90 (978-0-7613-1966-5(2) , Millbrook Pr.) Lerner Publishing Group.

Stewart, Mark Alan. Tiger Woods: Drive to Greatness. 2001. (Illus.). 64p. (J). (gr. 4-12). pap. 7.95 (978-0-7613-1477-6(6) , Millbrook Pr.) Lerner Publishing Group.

Thornley, Stew. Derek Jeter: Daring to Dream. 2004. (Sports Leaders Ser.). (Illus.). 104p. (J). lib. bdg. 26.60 (978-0-7660-2035-1(5)) Enslow Pubs., Inc.

—Super Sports Star Jason Kidd. 2002. (Super Sports Star Ser.). (Illus.). 48p. (J). (gr. 1-4). lib. bdg. 23.93 (978-0-7660-1806-8(7)) Enslow Pubs., Inc.

Tiger Woods (Revised Edition) 2007. (J). pap. 5.95 (***978-0-8225-6890-2(X)*** , First Avenue Editions) Lerner Publishing Group.

Torres, John Albert. Tiger Woods. 2001. (Real-Life Reader Biography Ser.). (Illus.). 32p. (J). (gr. 3-8). lib. bdg. 15.95 (978-1-58415-067-1(X)) Mitchell Lane Pubs., Inc.

Uschan, Michael V. Tiger Woods. 2002. (Stars of Sports Ser.). (Illus.). 48p. (J). 26.20 (978-0-7377-1397-8(6) , Greenhaven Pr., Inc.) Thomson Gale.

RACIALLY MIXED PEOPLE—FICTION

Andrews, V. C. Eye of the Storm. 2000. (gr. 7-12). lib. bdg. 16.45 (978-0-613-33585-0(6)) Tandem Library Bks.

Barkow, Henriette. That's My Mum. Brazell, Derek, illus. 2004. (J). (CZE, VIE, SPA, GUJ & PER.). 24p. (978-1-85269-597-2(8)); (CZE, VIE, SPA, GUJ & PER.). 24p. (978-1-85269-598-9(6)); (CZE, VIE, SPA, GUJ & PER.). 24p. (978-1-85269-599-6(4)); (CZE, VIE, SPA, GUJ & PER.). 24p. (978-1-85269-601-6(X)); (CZE, VIE, SPA, GUJ & PER.). 24p. (978-1-85269-602-3(8)); (CZE, VIE, SPA, GUJ & PER.). 24p. (978-1-85269-603-0(6)); (CZE, VIE, SPA, GUJ & PER.). 24p. (978-1-85269-604-7(4)); (CZE, VIE, SPA, GUJ & PER.). 24p. (978-1-85269-605-4(2)); (CZE, VIE, SPA, GUJ & PER.). 24p. (978-1-85269-606-1(0)); (CZE, VIE, SPA, GUJ & PER.). 24p. (978-1-85269-608-5(7)); (CZE, VIE, SPA, GUJ & PER.). 24p. (978-1-85269-609-2(5)); (CZE, VIE, SPA, GUJ & PER.). 24p. (978-1-85269-628-3(1)); (CZE, SPA, VIE, GUJ & PER.). 24p. (978-1-85269-802-7(0)); (CZE, VIE, SPA, GUJ & PER.). 24p. (978-1-85269-803-4(9)); (CZE, VIE, SPA, GUJ & PER.). 24p. (978-1-85269-804-1(7)); (ALB & ENG.). 24p. (978-1-85269-595-8(1)); (ENG & YOR.). (978-1-84444-381-9(7)) Mantra Publishing, Ltd.

Barkow, Henriette & Brazell, Derek. That's My Mum: Ajo Eshte Nena Ime. 2004. (CZE, VIE, SPA, GUJ & PER., Illus.). 24p. (J). (978-1-85269-596-5(X)) Mantra Publishing, Ltd.

—That's My Mum: Voici Ma Mere. 2004. (CZE, VIE, SPA, GUJ & PER., Illus.). 23p. (J). (978-1-85269-600-9(1)) Mantra Publishing, Ltd.

Bell, William. Zack. l.t. ed. 2000. (LRS Large Print Cornerstone Ser.). 256p. (YA). (gr. 5-12). lib. bdg. 28.95 (978-1-58118-072-5(1) , 23656) LRS.

—Zack. 2000. (J). (978-0-606-20095-0(9)) Tandem Library Bks.

Benedict, Helen. Opposite of Love. 2007. 256p. (J). (gr. 6 up). 16.99 (***978-0-670-06135-8(2)*** , Viking Juvenile) Penguin Group (USA) Inc.

Cheng, Andrea. Grandfather Counts. Zhang, Ange, illus. 32p. (J). 2003. (978-1-58430-158-5(9)); 2000. 15.95 (978-1-58430-010-6(8)) Lee & Low Bks., Inc.

—Grandfather Counts. 2000. (gr. k-3). lib. bdg. 15.25 (978-0-613-65692-4(X)) Tandem Library Bks.

—Shanghai Messenger. Young, Ed, illus. 2005. 40p. (J). (ps-7). 17.95 (978-1-58430-238-4(0)) Lee & Low Bks., Inc.

Crutcher, Chris. Whale Talk. 2001. 224p. (J). (gr. 7 up). 16.99 (978-0-688-18019-5(1)) HarperCollins Pubs.

—Whale Talk. 2004. 224p. (J). (gr. 7 up). pap. 38.00 incl. audio (978-0-8072-2289-8(5) , Listening Library) Random Hse. Audio Publishing Group.

—Whale Talk. 2002. 224p. (YA). (gr. 7). pap. 6.99 (978-0-440-22938-4(3) , Laurel Leaf) Random Hse. Children's Bks.

—Whale Talk. 2002. (gr. 5-8). lib. bdg. 13.55 (978-0-613-61739-0(8)) Tandem Library Bks.

Cruz, Maria Colleen. Border Crossing. 128p. (YA). pap. 9.95 (978-1-55885-405-5(3) , Piñata Books) Arte Publico Pr.

—Border Crossing. 2003. (gr. 7-12). lib. bdg. 18.75 (978-0-613-90255-7(6)) Tandem Library Bks.

Curry, Jane Louise. The Black Canary. 2005. (Illus.). 288p. (J). (gr. 5 up). 17.99 (978-0-689-86478-0(7) , McElderry, Margaret K.) Simon & Schuster Children's Publishing.

Dell, Pamela. Half-Breed: A Story of Two Boys During the Klondike Gold Rush. 2003. (Scrapbooks of America Ser.). (Illus.). 48p. (J). (gr. 2-6). 28.50 (978-1-59187-044-9(5)) Child's World, Inc.

Easton, Kelly. Hiroshima Dreams. 2007. 192p. (YA). (gr. 7). 16.99 (***978-0-525-47821-8(3)*** , Dutton Juvenile) Penguin Group (USA) Inc.

Edmonds, Lyra. An African Princess. Wilson, Anne, illus. 2004. 32p. (J). (ps-2). 15.99 (978-0-7636-2595-5(7)) Candlewick Pr.

Ernst, Kathleen. Trouble at Fort la Pointe. 2000. (American Girl Collection). (Illus.). (J). (978-0-606-20956-4(5)) Tandem Library Bks.

Flood, Pansie Hart. It's Test Day, Tiger Turcotte. Wummer, Amy, tr. Wummer, Amy, illus. 2004. (Young Reader Fiction Ser.). 72p. (J). (gr. 1-4). pap. 6.95 (978-1-57505-670-8(4)); lib. bdg. 19.93 (978-1-57505-056-0(0) , Carolrhoda Bks.) Lerner Publishing Group.

—Tiger's Trouble with Donut Head. Wummer, Amy, illus. 2005. 71p. (J). lib. bdg. 19.93 (978-1-57505-814-6(6) , Carolrhoda Bks.) Lerner Publishing Group.

Frazier, Sundee Tucker. Brendan Buckley's Universe & Everything in It. 2007. 208p. (J). (gr. 4-7). 14.99 (***978-0-385-73439-4(5));*** lib. bdg. 17.99 (***978-0-385-90445-2(2))*** Random Hse. Children's Bks. (Delacorte Bks. for Young Readers).

García, Cristina. I Wanna Be Your Shoebox. 2008. 208p. (J). (***978-1-4169-3928-3(8)*** , Simon & Schuster Children's Publishing) Simon & Schuster Children's Publishing.

Garland, Sherry. Valley of the Moon: The Diary of Maria Rosalia de Milagros, Sonoma Valley, Alta California, 1846. 2001. (Dear America Ser.). (Illus.). 208p. (J). (gr. 4-9). pap. 10.95 (978-0-439-08820-6(8)) Scholastic, Inc.

Graham, Bob. Oscar's Half Birthday. Graham, Bob, illus. 2005. (Illus.). 32p. (J). (gr. k-1). 16.99 (978-0-7636-2699-0(6)) Candlewick Pr.

Hamilton, Virginia. Plain City. (Barco de Vapor). (SPA.). 176p. (YA). (gr. 5-8). 6.95 (978-84-348-4686-9(1) , LEC6861) SM Ediciones ESP. *Dist:* Continental Bk. Co., Inc.

—Plain City. 2003. 208p. (J). (gr. 4-7). pap. 5.99 (978-0-590-47365-1(4) , Scholastic Paperbacks) Scholastic, Inc.

Haslam, Gerald W. & Haslam, Janice E. Manuel & the Madman. 2000. viii, 206p. (J). pap. 9.95 (978-0-915685-11-0(6)) Devil Mountain Bks.

Headley, Justina Chen. Nothing but the Truth (And a Few White Lies) 2006. 256p. (J). (gr. 5-9). 16.99 (978-0-316-01128-0(2)) Little Brown & Co.

—Nothing but the Truth (And a Few White Lies) 2007. 256p. (J). (gr. 7 up). pap. 7.99 (***978-0-316-01131-0(2))*** Little, Brown Bks. for Young Readers.

Hesse, Karen. Aleutian Sparrow. Zerbetz, Evon, illus. 2003. 160p. (J). (gr. 5-9). 16.95 (978-0-689-86189-5(3) , McElderry, Margaret K.) Simon & Schuster Children's Publishing.

—Aleutian Sparrow. McGillivray, Kim & Zerbetz, Evon, illus. 2005. 160p. (J). reprint ed. pap. 5.99 (978-1-4169-0327-7(5) , Aladdin) Simon & Schuster Children's Publishing.

Igus, Toyomi. Two Mrs Gibsons. 2001. (gr. k-3). lib. bdg. 16.40 (978-0-613-65372-5(6)) Tandem Library Bks.

Jaffe, Michele. Bad Kitty. 2006. (Illus.). 288p. (J). 16.99 (978-0-06-078108-8(4)); lib. bdg. 17.89 (978-0-06-078109-5(2)) HarperCollins Pubs.

Kallok, Emma & Bower, Joel. Gem. 2004. (Illus.). 32p. (J). (gr. k-2). 14.95 (978-1-58246-027-7(2) , Tricycle Pr.) Ten Speed Pr.

Katz, Karen. Colors of Us. 2007. (Illus.). 32p. (J). 22.95 (***978-0-8050-8118-3(6)*** , Holt, Henry & Co. Bks. For Young Readers) Holt, Henry & Co.

Katz, Karen. The Colors of Us. rev. ed. (Illus.). 32p. (J). (ps-3). 2002. pap. 7.95 (978-0-8050-7163-4(6)); 1999. 17.00 (978-0-8050-5864-2(8)) Holt, Henry & Co. (Holt, Henry & Co. Bks. For Young Readers).

Lewis, Richard. The Demon Queen. 2008. 252p. (J). (***978-1-4169-3589-6(4)*** , Simon & Schuster Children's Publishing) Simon & Schuster Children's Publishing.

Little, Kimberley Griffiths. Enchanted Runner. 1999. (Avon Camelot Bks.). 149p. (J). (gr. 5-7). 15.00 (978-0-380-97623-2(4)) HarperCollins Pubs.

—The Last Snake Runner. 2004. 208p. (YA). (gr. 7). pap. 5.99 (978-0-440-23782-2(3) , Laurel Leaf) Random Hse. Children's Bks.

Little, Kimberley Griffiths. The Last Snake Runner: A Novel. 2006. 201p. (YA). (gr. 7-10). reprint ed. 16.00 (***978-1-4223-5838-2(0))*** DIANE Publishing Co.

McCaffrey, Tony. Emmanuel McClue & The Mystery of the Shroud. 2002. 155p. (J). (gr. 5-9). pap. 11.95 (978-1-929039-08-1(5)) Ambassador Bks., Inc.

McDonald, Janet. Off-Color. 2007. 176p. (YA). (gr. 7 up). 16.00 (***978-0-374-37196-8(2))*** Farrar, Straus & Giroux.

Meyer, Carolyn. Jubilee Journey. 2007. (Illus.). 288p. (YA). pap. 6.95 (978-0-15-205845-6(1) , Harcourt Paperbacks) Harcourt Children's Bks.

Monk, Isabell. Hope. Porter, Janice Lee, illus. (Carolrhoda Picture Books Ser.). 32p. (J). (ps-3). 2004. pap. 6.95 (978-1-57505-792-7(1)); 1998. 15.95 (978-1-57505-230-4(X)) Lerner Publishing Group.

Murphy, Rita. Black Angels. 2002. 176p. (J). (gr. 4). pap. 4.99 (978-0-440-22934-6(0) , Yearling) Random Hse. Children's Bks.

—Black Angels. 2002. (gr. 3-6). lib. bdg. 13.00 (978-0-613-57701-4(9)) Tandem Library Bks.

Namioka, Lensey. Half & Half. 2004. 144p. (gr. 3-7). pap. 5.50 (978-0-440-41890-0(9) , Yearling) Random Hse. Children's Bks.

Olivas, Daniel. Benjamin & Word Benjamin Y la Palabra. (SPA & ENG., Illus.). 32p. 15.95 (978-1-55885-413-0(4) , Piñata Books) Arte Publico Pr.

Osborne, Mary Pope. Adaline Falling Star. unabr. ed. 2004. (Middle Grade Cassette Librariestm Ser.). 176p. (J). (gr. 3-7). pap. 29.00 incl. audio (978-0-8072-1195-3(8) , S YA 319 SP, Listening Library) Random Hse. Audio Publishing Group.

Ostow, Micol. Emily Goldberg Learns to Salsa. 2007. 288p. (J). (gr. 7). pap. 7.99 (***978-1-59514-144-6(8)*** , Razorbill) Penguin Group (USA) Inc.

Peck, Richard. The River Between Us. 176p. (J). 2003. (gr. 7). 16.99 (978-0-8037-2735-9(6) , Dial); 2005. (gr. 5-7). reprint ed. pap. 6.99 (978-0-14-240310-5(5) , Puffin) Penguin Group (USA) Inc.

—The River Between Us. 2005. 164p. (J). (ps-7). lib. bdg. 12.64 (978-0-606-33120-3(4)) Tandem Library Bks.

Raffa, Edwina & Rigsby, Annelle. Escape to the Everglades. 2006. pap., tchr. ed., act. bk. ed. 6.00 (978-1-56164-362-2(9)); (Illus.). 100p. (J). 12.95 (978-1-56164-351-6(3)) Pineapple Pr., Inc.

Resau, Laura. What the Moon Saw. l.t. rev. ed. 2007. 300p. (YA). 22.95 (***978-0-7862-9278-3(4)***) Thorndike Pr.

Reynolds, Marilyn. If You Loved Me. 1999. (True-to-Life Series from Hamilton High: Vol. 7). 32p. (J). pap., tchr. ed. 2.50 (978-1-885356-59-8(5)) Morning Glory Pr., Inc.

—If You Loved Me: True-to-Life Stories from Hamilton High. 1999. (True-to-Life Series from Hamilton High: Vol. 7). 224p. (J). (gr. 7-12). pap. 8.95 (978-1-885356-55-0(2)) Morning Glory Pr., Inc.

Rinaldi, Ann. The Education of Mary: A Little Miss of Color, 1832. 2000. 256p. (gr. 5-9). 15.99 (978-0-7868-0532-7(3) , Jump at the Sun) Hyperion Bks. for Children.

—The Education of Mary: A Little Miss of Color, 1832. 2005. 176p. (J). pap. (978-0-7868-1377-3(6)) Hyperion Pr.

—Mutiny's Daughter. 2005. 224p. (J). (ps-7). pap. 5.99 (978-0-06-441010-6(2) , Harper Trophy) HarperCollins Pubs.

Rodowsky, Colby F. That Fernhill Summer. 2006. 176p. (J). 16.00 (978-0-374-37442-6(2)) Farrar, Straus & Giroux.

Rosten, Carrie. Chloe Leiberman (Sometimes Wong) 2007. 224p. (YA). (gr. 7). pap. 8.99 (978-0-385-73248-2(1) , Delacorte Bks. for Young Readers) Random Hse. Children's Bks.

Saksena, Kate. Hang on in There, Shelley. 2003. 219p. (J). 16.95 (978-1-58234-822-3(7) , Bloomsbury Children) Bloomsbury Publishing.

Shin, Sun Yung. Cooper's Lesson. Cogan, Kim & Paek, Min, trs. from ENG. Cogan, Kim, illus. 2004. (ENG & KOR.). 32p. (J). 16.95 (978-0-89239-193-6(6)) Children's Bk. Pr.

Shusterman, Neal. Red Rider's Hood. 2006. (Dark Fusion Ser.). 192p. (YA). (gr. 7). pap. 6.99 (978-0-14-240678-6(3) , Puffin) Penguin Group (USA) Inc.

Skurzynski, Gloria. Escape from Fear. 2002. (gr. 3-6). lib. bdg. 14.10 (978-0-613-62746-7(6)) Tandem Library Bks.

Skurzynski, Gloria & Ferguson, Alane. Escape from Fear. 2002. (Mysteries in Our National Parks Ser.: Vol. 9). 160p. (J). (gr. 3-7). 15.95 (978-0-7922-6780-5(X)); No. 9. pap. 5.95 (978-0-7922-6782-9(6)) National Geographic Society. (National Geographic Children's Bks.).

Smith, Sherri L. Hot, Sour, Salty, Sweet. 2008. 176p. (J). (***978-0-385-73417-2(4));*** lib. bdg. (***978-0-385-90431-5(2)***) Dell Publishing. (Delacorte Pr.).

Sweeney, Joyce. Waiting for June. 2006. 160p. 5.99 (978-0-7614-5329-1(6)); 2003. 144p. (YA). 15.95 (978-0-7614-5138-9(2)) Cavendish, Marshall Corp.

Taylor, Mildred D. The Land. 2003. 400p. (YA). pap. 6.99 (978-0-14-250146-7(8) , Puffin) Penguin Group (USA) Inc.

—The Land. Ginsburg, Max, illus. 2001. 392p. (J). (gr. 7 up). 17.99 (978-0-8037-1950-7(7) , Dial) Penguin Group (USA) Inc.

Tucker, Zekita. Don't Call Me N!gga. 2007. per. 0.01 net. (***978-1-60402-249-0(3)***) Independent Pub.

Uff, Caroline. Hello, Lulu. 2004. (Illus.). 14p. (J). bds. 5.95 (978-0-8027-8928-0(5)) Walker & Co.

—Lulu's Busy Day. Uff, Caroline, illus. 2004. (Illus.). 14p. (J). bds. 5.95 (978-0-8027-8929-7(3)) Walker & Co.

Vigil-Pion, Evangelina. Marina's Muumuu/ el muumuu de Marina. Torrecilla, Pablo, illus. 2001. Tr. of Muumuu de Marina. (ENG & SPA.). 32p. (J). (ps-3). 14.95 (978-1-55885-350-8(2) , Piñata Books) Arte Publico Pr.

Voorhees, Coert. Los Torres. 2008. 320p. 16.99 (***978-1-4231-0304-2(1)***) Hyperion Pr.

Willis, Meredith Sue. Billie of Fish House Lane. 2006. (J). pap. 12.95 (978-1-932727-02-9(7)) Montemayor Pr.

Wilson, Barbara. A Clear Spring. 2002. (Girls First! Ser.: Vol. 1). 112p. 12.50 (978-1-55861-277-8(7)) Feminist Pr. at The City Univ. of New York.

Wilson, Diane Lee. Black Storm Comin' (J). 2006. 240p. pap. 5.99 (978-0-689-87138-2(4) , Aladdin); 2005. 304p. (gr. 5-9). 17.99 (978-0-689-87137-5(6) , McElderry, Margaret K.) Simon & Schuster Children's Publishing.

Woodson, Jacqueline. The House You Pass on the Way. 2003. 112p. (YA). reprint ed. pap. 5.99 (978-0-14-250191-7(3) , Puffin); (gr. 5). 16.99 (978-0-399-23969-4(3) , Putnam Juvenile) Penguin Group (USA) Inc.

—The House You Pass on the Way. 1999. (J). (978-0-606-16085-8(X)) Tandem Library Bks.

—The House You Pass on the Way. l.t. ed. 2004. 109p. (J). 22.95 (978-0-7862-6428-5(4)) Thorndike Pr.

—Miracle's Boys. (gr. 5). 2006. 144p. (J). pap. 5.99 (978-0-14-240602-1(3) , Puffin); 2000. 1p. (YA). 15.99 (978-0-399-23113-1(7) , Putnam Juvenile) Penguin Group (USA) Inc.

Wyeth, Sharon Dennis. Orphea Proud. 2006. 208p. (YA). (gr. 9). pap. 5.99 (978-0-440-22706-9(2) , Laurel Leaf) Random Hse. Children's Bks.

—The World of Daughter McGuire. 2001. 176p. (gr. 3-7). pap. 12.00 (978-0-375-89502-9(7) , Delacorte Bks. for Young Readers) Random Hse. Children's Bks.

Yep, Laurence. Angelfish. 2001. 1p. (J). (gr. 5 up). 16.99 (978-0-399-23041-7(6) , Putnam Juvenile) Penguin Group (USA) Inc.

RACKET GAMES

see also Badminton; Tennis

Everitt, Robert T. Racket Sports Collectibles. 2002. (Schiffer Book for Collectors Ser.). (Illus.). 288p. (gr. 10-13). 69.95 (978-0-7643-1647-0(8)) Schiffer Publishing, Ltd.

RACKETEERING

Black, J. Anderson. Organized Crime. 2002. (Crime & Detection Ser.). (Illus.). 96p. (J). (gr. 7 up). lib. bdg. (978-1-59084-367-3(3)) Mason Crest Pubs.

MacDonald, Alan. Al Capone & His Gang. Reeve, Philip, illus. 2000. (Famous Dead People Ser.). 192p. (J). (gr. 3-7). pap. 4.50 (978-0-439-21124-6(7)) Scholastic, Inc.

Torr, James D., ed. Organized Crime. 1998. (Contemporary Issues Companion Ser.). 192p. (YA). (gr. 9-12). lib. bdg. 36.20 (978-1-56510-891-2(4) , Greenhaven Pr., Inc.) Thomson Gale.

Trespacz, Karen L. The Trial of Gangster Al Capone: A Headline Court Case. 2001. (Headline Court Cases Ser.). (Illus.). 112p. (J). (gr. 6-12). lib. bdg. 26.60 (978-0-7660-1482-4(7)) Enslow Pubs., Inc.

Wilker, Josh. Organized Crime. 1999. (Crime, Justice & Punishment Ser.). (Illus.). 80p. (YA). (gr. 7-12). 30.00 (978-0-7910-4271-7(5) , Chelsea Hse.) Facts On File, Inc.

RACKETEERING—FICTION

Lee, Sun-Hee, creator. Neck & Neck, Vol. 5. 5th rev. ed. 2006. (Illus.). 192p. (YA). pap. 9.99 (978-1-59816-099-4(0) , Tokyopop Kids) TOKYOPOP, Inc.

Whyman, Matt. Boy Kills Man. 2006. 160p. (J). pap. 6.99 (978-0-06-074665-0(3) , HarperTeen) HarperCollins Pubs.

RADIATION

see also Light; Quantum Theory; Radioactivity; Radium; Sound; X-Rays

Pettigrew, Mark. Radiation. 2004. (J). lib. bdg. (978-1-932799-21-7(4)) Stargazer Bks.

Salway, Andrew. Waves, Vibration & Radiation. 2007. (J). lib. bdg. (***978-1-4042-3746-9(1)*** , Rosen Central) Rosen Publishing Group, Inc., The.

Woodford, Chris. Light & Radiation. 2004. (Routes of Science Ser.). (Illus.). 40p. (J). pap. 11.20 (978-1-4103-0296-0(2)); (gr. 4-7). 24.95 (978-1-4103-0297-7(0)) Thomson Gale. (Blackbirch Pr., Inc.).

RADIATION, SOLAR

see Solar Radiation

RADIATION CHEMISTRY

see Radiochemistry

RADICALS

see also Reformers; Revolutions; Right and Left (Political Science)

Grabowski, John F. The Ruby Ridge Scandal. 2005. (American Secrets & Scandals Ser.). (J). (978-1-59018-485-1(8) , Lucent Bks.) Thomson Gale.

Robinson, C. L. MATH1on1 Radicals Foundation. 2006. (YA). per. 9.99 (978-0-9786767-8-0(5)) Robinson, Consuelo.

RADIO

Goldsmith, Mike. Guglielmo Marconi. 2002. (Scientists Who Made History Ser.). (Illus.). 48p. (J). lib. bdg. 27.12 (978-0-7398-5227-9(2)) Raintree.

Inventing the Radio. 2007. (Illus.). 32p. (J). (gr. 3-9). (***978-0-7787-2817-7(X)***); pap. (***978-0-7787-2839-9(0)***) Crabtree Publishing Co.

Lafferty, Peter. Radio & Television. Antram, David, illus. 1998. (Worldwise Ser.: Vol. 17). 40p. (J). (gr. 4-7). pap. 7.00 (978-0-531-15317-8(7) , Watts, Franklin) Scholastic Library Publishing.

Mattern, Joanne. The History of Radio. 2002. (Transportation & Communication Ser.). (Illus.). 48p. (J). (gr. 1-4). lib. bdg. 23.93 (978-0-7660-2027-6(4)) Enslow Pubs., Inc.

—The Radio: The World Tunes In. 2003. (Reading Power Ser.). (Illus.). 24p. (J). lib. bdg. 17.25 (978-0-8239-6491-8(4) , PowerKids Pr.) Rosen Publishing Group, Inc., The.

O'Shei, Tim. Marconi & Tesla: Pioneers of Radio Communication. 2008. (Inventors Who Changed the World Ser.). (Illus.). 128p. (J). (gr. 6 up). lib. bdg. 33.27 (***978-1-59845-076-7(X)*** , MyReportLinks.com Bks.) Enslow Pubs., Inc.

Oxlade, Chris. Radio. 2001. (In Touch Ser.). (Illus.). 32p. (J). (gr. 1-3). lib. bdg. 22.79 (978-1-58810-066-5(9)) Heinemann Library.

The Radio: The World Tunes In, 6 Packs. (On Deck Ser.: Vol. 2). 24p. (gr. 4-5). 35.00 (978-0-7578-5861-1(9)) Rigby Education.

Radios, Phones & Telecommunications. 2005. (Inventions Ser.). (Illus.). 30p. (J). pap. 15.95 incl. audio (978-0-9724983-4-0(6)) Jazwares Distribution, Inc.

Sherrow, Victoria. Guglielmo Marconi: Inventor of Radio & Wireless Communication. 2004. (Nobel Prize-Winning Scientists Ser.). (Illus.). 112p. (J). lib. bdg. 26.60 (978-0-7660-2280-5(3)) Enslow Pubs., Inc.

Slade, Suzanne. My Adventure Inventing the Radio. 2007. 44p. (J). 8.99 (978-1-59092-440-2(1) , Orchard Academy Pr.) Windstorm Creative.

Stille, Darlene R. Radio. 2001. (Communications Ser.). (Illus.). 24p. (J). (gr. 1 up). lib. bdg. 18.60 (978-0-7565-0136-5(9)) Compass Point Bks.

Teitelbaum, Michael. Radio & Television. 2005. (Great Inventions Ser.). (Illus.). 48p. (YA). lib. bdg. 30.00 (978-0-8368-5802-0(6) , World Almanac Library) Stevens, Gareth Inc.

Worland, Gayle. The Radio. 2003. (Fact Finders Ser.). (Illus.). 32p. (J). lib. bdg. 22.60 (978-0-7368-2217-6(8)) Capstone Pr., Inc.

—The Radio, 6 vols. (gr. 2-5). 36.95 (978-0-7368-4616-5(6)) Red Brick Learning.

Zannos, Susan. Guglielmo Marconi & Radio Waves. 2004. (Uncharted, Unexplored, & Unexplained Ser.). (Illus.). 48p. (J). (gr. 4-8). lib. bdg. 29.95 (978-1-58415-265-1(6)) Mitchell Lane Pubs., Inc.

RADIO—BROADCASTING

see Radio Broadcasting

RADIO—VOCATIONAL GUIDANCE

Weigsant, Chris. Careers as a Disc Jockey. rev. ed. 1999. (Careers). (Illus.). 192p. (YA). (gr. 7-12). lib. bdg. 26.50 (978-0-8239-3043-2(2) , CADIJO) Rosen Publishing Group, Inc., The.

RADIO ASTRONOMY

see also names of celestial radio sources, e.g. Quasars

Firestone, Mary. SETI Science. 2005. (Weird Careers in Science Ser.). (Illus.). 81p. (J). (gr. 4-8). lib. bdg. 25.00 (978-0-7910-8701-5(8) , Chelsea Hse.) Facts On File, Inc.

Gibson, Diane. Nuclear Power. 2001. (Sources of Energy Ser.). (Illus.). 24p. (J). (gr. 2-7). lib. bdg. 21.30 (978-1-887068-80-2(5)) Smart Apple Media.

Richardson, Adele D. Radio Astronomy. 1999. (Above & Beyond Ser.). (Illus.). 32p. (J). (gr. 4 up). lib. bdg. 16.95 (978-1-58340-051-7(6)) Smart Apple Media.

RADIO BROADCASTING

see also Television Broadcasting

Chambers, Catherine. Radio. 2001. (Behind Media Ser.). (Illus.). 48p. (YA). (gr. 6-8). lib. bdg. 24.22 (978-1-58810-034-4(0)) Heinemann Library.

Facts on File, Inc. Staff. Careers in Focus. 2nd ed. 2004. (Careers in Focus Ser.). (Illus.). 192p. (YA). (gr. 6-12). 22.95 (978-0-8160-5551-7(3) , Ferguson Publishing Co.) Facts On File, Inc.

Facts on File, Inc. Staff, ed. Aviation. 4th ed. 2004. (Careers in Focus Ser.). (Illus.). 192p. (J). (gr. 6-12). 22.95 (978-0-8160-5552-4(1) , Ferguson Publishing Co.) Facts On File, Inc.

Ferguson. Careers in Focus. 2nd ed. 2002. (Careers in Focus Ser.). 192p. (YA). (gr. 6-12). 22.95 (978-0-89434-440-4(4) , Ferguson Publishing Co.) Facts On File, Inc.

Finkelstein, Norman H. Sounds in the Air: The Golden Age of Radio. 2000. (gr. 7-12). lib. bdg. 18.75 (978-0-613-84092-7(5)) Tandem Library Bks.

—Sounds in the Air: The Golden Age of Radio. 2000. (Illus.). 144p. (gr. 7-12). pap. 9.95 (978-0-595-13190-7(5) , Backinprint.com) iUniverse, Inc.

J. G. Ferguson Publishing Company Staff, contrib. by. Careers in Focus. 2nd ed. 2004. (Careers in Focus Ser.). (Illus.). 192p. (J). (gr. 6-12). 22.95 (978-0-8160-5549-4(1) , Ferguson Publishing Co.) Facts On File, Inc.

J. G. Ferguson Publishing Company Staff, ed. Careers in Focus, 12 vols., Set 3. 2001. 2304p. (YA). 186.00 (978-0-89434-423-7(4) , Ferguson Publishing Co.) Facts On File, Inc.

McCarthy, Meghan. Aliens Are Coming! The True Account of the 1938 War of the Worlds Radio Broadcast. 2006. (Illus.). 40p. (J). (ps-3). 16.95 (978-0-375-83518-6(0)); lib. bdg. 18.99 (978-0-375-93518-3(5)) Random Hse. Children's Bks. (Knopf Bks. for Young Readers).

Oxlade, Chris. Radio. 2001. (In Touch Ser.). (Illus.). 32p. (J). (gr. 1-3). lib. bdg. 22.79 (978-1-58810-066-5(9)) Heinemann Library.

Pelusey, Michael & Pelusey, Jane. Radio (Media) 2005. (Media Ser.). (Illus.). 32p. (J). (ps-8). lib. bdg. 21.95 (978-0-7910-8801-2(4) , Chelsea Hse.) Facts On File, Inc.

Snow, Panky. Radio Announcers. 2001. (Community Helpers Ser.). (Illus.). 24p. (J). (gr. 1-2). lib. bdg. 18.60 (978-0-7368-0958-0(9) , Bridgestone Bks.) Capstone Pr., Inc.

RADIO CHEMISTRY

see Radiochemistry

RADIO JOURNALISM

see Journalism; Radio Broadcasting

RADIO OPERATORS—FICTION

Wall, Cynthia. A Spark to the Past. 1998. 184p. (J). (gr. 5-8). pap. 6.95 (978-0-931625-34-3(3)) DIMI Pr.

Williamson, Barbara. Sparino de Birdarack. 2006. (Illus.). 24p. (J). per. 12.95 (978-1-59453-774-5(7) , Airleaf Publishing) Airleaf Publishing & Bookselling.

RADIOACTIVE SUBSTANCES

see Radioactivity

RADIOACTIVE WASTES

Capstone Press Editors. Nuclear Waste. 2002. (Our Planet in Peril Ser.). (Illus.). 48p. (J). (gr. 3-4). lib. bdg. 22.60 (978-0-7368-1362-4(4) , Bridgestone Bks.) Capstone Pr., Inc.

—Our Planet in Peril, 4 bks. Incl. Acid Rain. lib. bdg. 22.60 (978-0-7368-1360-0(8)); Global Warming. lib. bdg. 22.60 (978-0-7368-1361-7(6)); Nuclear Waste. lib. bdg. 22.60 (978-0-7368-1362-4(4)); Oil Spills. lib. bdg. 22.60 (978-0-7368-1363-1(2)); 48p. (J). (gr. 3-4). 2002. (Illus.). 2002. Set lib. bdg. 90.40 (978-0-7368-1364-8(0) , Bridgestone Bks.) Capstone Pr., Inc.

RADIOACTIVITY

see also Nuclear Physics; Radiochemistry; Radium; Uranium; X-Rays

Cheney, Glenn A. Nuclear Proliferation: The Problems & Possibilities. 1999. (Impact Bks.). (Illus.). 144p. (YA). (gr. 8-12). 22.00 (978-0-531-11431-5(7) , Watts, Franklin) Scholastic Library Publishing.

Graham, Ian. Curie & the Science of Radioactivity. Antram, David, illus. 2006. (Explosion Zone Ser.). 32p. (J). 12.99 (978-0-7641-5973-2(9)); pap. 6.99 (978-0-7641-3489-0(2)) Barron's Educational Series, Inc.

Jackson, Tom. Radioactive Elements. 2005. (Elements Ser.). (Illus.). 32p. (J). (gr. 3-7). lib. bdg. (978-0-7614-1923-5(3) , Benchmark Bks.) Cavendish, Marshall Corp.

Jerome, Kate Boehm. Atomic Universe: The Quest to Discover Radioactivity. 2006. (Science Quest Ser.). (Illus.). 64p. (J). (gr. 5-9). 17.95 (978-0-7922-5543-7(7) , National Geographic Children's Bks.) National Geographic Society.

Miller, Connie Colwell. Marie Curie & Radioactivity. Larson, Scott & Heike, Mark, illus. 2007. (Graphic Library). 32p. (J). 25.26 (978-0-7368-6486-2(5)); pap. (***978-0-7368-7521-9(2)***) Capstone Pr., Inc.

Nardo, Don. Atoms. 2001. (Kidhaven Science Library). (Illus.). 48p. (J). (gr. 3-5). 23.70 (978-0-7377-0942-1(1) , LML00102-178579, Kidhaven) Thomson Gale.

Tracy, Kathleen. Pierre & Marie Curie & the Discovery of Radium. 2004. (Uncharted, Unexplored, & Unexplained Ser.). (Illus.). 48p. (J). (gr. 4-8). lib. bdg. 29.95 (978-1-58415-310-8(5)) Mitchell Lane Pubs., Inc.

RADIOCHEMISTRY

Jackson, Tom. Radioactive Elements. 2005. (Elements Ser.). (Illus.). 32p. (J). (gr. 3-7). lib. bdg. (978-0-7614-1923-5(3) , Benchmark Bks.) Cavendish, Marshall Corp.

RADIOGRAPHY

see X-Rays

RADISSON, PIERRE ESPRIT, CA. 1636-1710

Bailey, Katie. Radisson & Groseilliers: Fur Traders of the North. 2006. (In the Footsteps of Explorers Ser.). (Illus.). 32p. (J). (gr. 3-14). pap. (978-0-7787-2458-2(1) , 1253444); (978-0-7787-2422-3(0) , 1253444) Crabtree Publishing Co.

RADIUM

see also Radioactivity

Miller, Connie Colwell. Marie Curie & Radioactivity. Larson, Scott & Heike, Mark, illus. 2007. (Graphic Library). 32p. (J). 25.26 (978-0-7368-6486-2(5)); pap. (***978-0-7368-7521-9(2)***) Capstone Pr., Inc.

RAILROAD CONSTRUCTION

see Railroad Engineering

RAILROAD ENGINEERING

Ambrose, Stephen E. Nothing Like It in the World: The Men Who Built the Transcontinental Railroad 1863-1869. 2001. (gr. 7-12). lib. bdg. 25.75 (978-0-613-50134-7(9)) Tandem Library Bks.

RAILROADS

see also Freight and Freightage; Railroad Engineering; Subways

Armentrout, David & Armentrout, Patricia, trs. Trains. 2003. (Transportation Ser.). (Illus.). 24p. (J). 20.64 (978-1-58952-672-3(4)) Rourke Publishing, LLC.

Balkwill, Richard. The Best Book of Trains. 1999. (Best Book of... Ser.). (Illus.). 32p. (J). (gr. k-3). tchr. ed. 12.95 (978-0-7534-5200-4(6) , Kingfisher) Houghton Mifflin Co. Trade & Reference Div.

Bender, Lionel. Trains & Trams. 2006. (On the Move Ser.). (978-1-59389-269-2(1)) Chrysalis Education.

Biello, David. Bullet Trains: Inside & Out. 2005. (Technology Ser.). (Illus.). 48p. (YA). (gr. 4-8). lib. bdg. 26.50 (978-0-8239-6113-9(3)) Rosen Publishing Group, Inc., The.

Book Studio Staff. Cool Trains. 2006. (Cool Kits Ser.). 1p. (J). 7.99 (978-0-7566-2431-6(2)) Dorling Kindersley Publishing, Inc.

Bridges, Sarah. I Drive a Freight Train. Muehlenhardt, Amy Bailey, illus. 2006. (Working Wheels Ser.). 24p. (J). (ps-2). 22.60 (978-1-4048-1607-7(0)) Picture Window Bks.

Brooks, Felicity. Trains lift & Look. Litchfield, Jo, illus. 2005. 12p. (J). 9.99 (978-0-7945-0935-4(5) , Usborne) EDC Publishing.

Burch, Lynda S. Wicky Wacky Things that Go! Trains 1. Burch, Lynda S., photos by. 2004. (Illus.). 16p. (J). E-Book 9.95 incl. cd-rom (978-1-933090-02-3(2)) Guardian Angel Publishing, Inc.

Cefrey, Holly. The Inventions of Granville Woods: The Railroad Telegraph System & the "Third Rail" 2003. (19th Century American Inventors Ser.). (Illus.). 24p. (J). lib. bdg. 17.25 (978-0-8239-6442-0(6) , PowerKids Pr.) Rosen Publishing Group, Inc., The.

Chiu, David. Government Regulation of the Railroads: Fighting Unfair Trade Practices in America. (Progressive Movement, 1900-1920—Efforts to Reform America's New Industrial Society Ser.). (Illus.). 32p. (J). 2006. (978-1-4042-0849-0(6)); 2004. lib. bdg. (978-1-4042-0190-3(4)) Rosen Publishing Group, Inc., The.

Chronicle Books LLC Staff. Look at Me! My Photo Book of Trains. Stephens, Moniqu, ed. 2005. (Illus.). 20p. (J). 6.95 (978-0-8118-4752-0(7)) Chronicle Bks. LLC.

Collicutt, Paul. This Train. Collicutt, Paul, illus. 2001. (Illus.). 32p. (J). pap. 5.95 (978-0-374-47518-5(0) , Sunburst) Farrar, Straus & Giroux.

—This Train. 2001. (ps-2). lib. bdg. 14.10 (978-0-613-84584-7(6)); (J). (978-0-606-22632-5(X)) Tandem Library Bks.

Davies, Gill. Trains, Boats & Planes. Guile, Gill, illus. 2005. 20p. (J). (gr. k-4). reprint ed. 20.00 (978-0-7567-8703-5(3)) DIANE Publishing Co.

Draw 50 Boats, Ships, Trucks & Trains. 2002. (Draw 50 Ser.). (Illus.). (J). 17.60 (978-0-7587-6968-8(7)) Book Wholesalers, Inc.

Dubowski, Mark. Superfast Trains. 2005. (Ultimate Speed Ser.). (Illus.). 32p. (J). lib. bdg. 25.27 (978-1-59716-084-1(9)) Bearport Publishing Co., Inc.

Emberley, Ed. Ed Emberley's Drawing Book of Trucks & Trains. Emberley, Ed, illus. 2005. (Illus.). 32p. (J). (gr. 2-17). pap. 6.99 (978-0-316-78967-7(4)) Little, Brown Bks. for Young Readers.

Gibbons, Gail. Trains. Gibbons, Gail, illus. 2002. (Illus.). (J). 15.49 (978-0-7587-4306-0(8)) Book Wholesalers, Inc.

Gintzler, A. S. Rough & Ready Railroaders. Brigman, Chris, illus. 1998. (Rough & Ready Ser.). 46p. (J). lib. bdg. 16.95 (978-1-887238-12-0(3)) Fitzgerald Bks.

Goodman, Steve. The Train They Call New Orleans. McCurdy, Michael, illus. pap. 16.95 incl. audio (978-1-59112-899-1(4)); pap. incl. audio (978-1-59112-901-1(X)); pap. 18.95 incl. audio compact disk (978-1-59112-903-5(6)); pap. incl. audio compact disk (978-1-59112-905-9(2)) Live Oak Media.

Graham, Ian. On the Rails: Machines at Work. 2007. (J). lib. bdg. 19.95 (978-1-59566-316-0(9)) QEB Publishing Inc.

—You Wouldn't Want to Work on the Railroad! 2001. (gr. 3-6). lib. bdg. 18.75 (978-0-613-44281-7(4)) Tandem Library Bks.

—You Wouldn't Want to Work on the Railroad! A Track You'd Rather Not Go Down. Antram, David, illus. 2001. (You Wouldn't Want to Be Ser.). 32p. (J). (gr. 2-5). 28.50 (978-0-531-14603-3(0)); pap. 9.95 (978-0-531-16208-8(7)) Scholastic Library Publishing. (Watts, Franklin).

Griffiths, Rose. First Step Math, 2 bks. Millard, Peter, photos by. Incl. Boxes. lib. bdg. 21.26 (978-0-8368-1179-7(8)); Printing. lib. bdg. 21.26 (978-0-8368-1181-0(X)); 32p. (J). (gr. 1 up). 1995. (Illus.). Set lib. bdg. 42.53 (978-0-8368-1183-4(6)) Stevens, Gareth Inc.

Hanson, Anders. Let's Go by Cable Car. 2007. (Let's Go! Ser.). (ENG., Illus.). 24p. (J). (ps-3). lib. bdg. 19.93 (***978-1-59928-896-3(6)***, SandCastle) ABDO Publishing Co.

Harris, Michael. All about Trains. 2004. (Illus.). 64p. pap. 8.99 (978-1-84215-976-7(3) , Southwater) Anness Publishing GBR. *Dist:* National Bk. Network.

Jackson, Melanie. Shadows on the Train: A Dinah Galloway Mystery. 2007. 208p. (J). (gr. 3-7). pap. (***978-1-55143-660-9(4)***) Orca Bk. Pubs.

Johnson, Mary Ellen, ed. Journeys of Hope: Orphan Train Riders Tell Their Own Stories. 1999. (Illus.). 360p. (J). (gr. 10-12). pap. 17.50 (978-0-9635902-5-1(1)) Orphan Train Heritage Society of America, Inc. (OTHSA).

Kraft, Eric. The Transcontinental Railroad. 2004. (Navigators Ser.). (J). pap. 42.00 (978-1-4108-0436-5(4)) Benchmark Education Co.

Lindeen, Mary. Trains. 2007. (Blastoff! Readers Ser.). (Illus.). 24p. (J). (gr. k-3). lib. bdg. 16.95 (978-1-60014-062-4(9)) Bellwether Media.

Lusted, Marcia Amidon. The Chunnel. 2005. (Building History Ser.). (Illus.). 112p. (YA). (gr. 7-10). lib. bdg. 32.45 (978-1-59018-545-2(5) , Lucent Bks.) Thomson Gale.

Matthews, John. Railroad. 2006. 80p. (YA). (gr. 5-8). pap. 9.95 (978-0-531-16745-8(3) , Watts, Franklin) Scholastic Library Publishing.

Matthews, John R. The Railroad. 2005. (Inventions That Shaped the World Ser.). (Illus.). 80p. (J). 30.50 (978-0-531-12372-0(3) , Watts, Franklin) Scholastic Library Publishing.

O'Brien, Patrick. Steam, Smoke, & Steel: Back in Time with Trains. O'Brien, Patrick, illus. 2000. (Illus.). 32p. (J). (ps-3). pap. 16.95 (978-0-88106-969-3(8)) Charlesbridge Publishing, Inc.

—Steam, Smoke, & Steel: Back in Time with Trains. 2000. (J). (978-0-606-19333-7(2)) Tandem Library Bks.

Parker, Lewis K. Cornelius Vanderbilt & the Railroad Industry. 2003. (Reading Power Ser.). (Illus.). 24p. (J). lib. bdg. 17.25 (978-0-8239-6450-5(7) , PowerKids Pr.) Rosen Publishing Group, Inc., The.

Perry, Phyllis J. Trains. 2001. (Transportation & Communication Ser.). (Illus.). 46p. (J). (gr. 1-4). lib. bdg. 23.93 (978-0-7660-1645-3(5)) Enslow Pubs., Inc.

Priddy Books Staff & Priddy, Roger. Happy Baby: Things That Go. 2004. (Illus.). 28p. (J). bds. 8.95 (978-0-312-49198-7(0) , Priddy Bks.) St. Martin's Pr.

Priddy, Roger. My Big Train Book. rev. ed. 2003. (Priddy Books Big Ideas for Little People). (Illus.). 12p. (J). bds. 5.95 (978-0-312-49186-4(7) , Priddy Bks.) St. Martin's Pr.

Schaefer, Lola M. Trains. 2003. (Wheels, Wings, & Water Ser.). (Illus.). 24p. (J). lib. bdg. 18.50 (978-1-4034-0885-3(8)); pap. (978-1-4034-3624-5(X)) Heinemann Library.

—Trenes. 2003. (Ruedas, Alas y Agua Ser.). (SPA & ENG., 24p. (J). (ps-1). Illus.). lib. bdg. 18.50 (978-1-4034-0922-5(6)); pap. 5.25 (978-1-4034-3536-1(7)) Heinemann Library.

Schlesinger, Arthur M., Jr. & Israel, Fred L., eds. Touring America Seventy-Five Years Ago. 1999. (Cultural & Geographical Exploration Ser.). (Illus.). x, 122p. (J). (gr. 4-7). lib. bdg. 21.95 (978-0-7910-5098-9(X) , Chelsea Hse.) Facts On File, Inc.

Serensits, Jaime F. M. Children's Railroad Learning & Activity Book. Serensits, Jaime F. M., illus. 2000. 64p. (J). pap. 5.95 (978-0-9657709-5-8(8)) Railroad Pr., The.

—Railroads in the 50 States. 2002. 56p. (J). pap. 5.00 (978-1-931477-05-5(1)) Railroad Pr., The.

Simon, Seymour. Seymour Simon's Book of Trains. (Illus.). 40p. (J). (ps-1). 2002. 16.99 (978-0-06-028475-6(7)); 2002. lib. bdg. 18.89 (978-0-06-028476-3(5)); 2004. reprint ed. pap. 6.99 (978-0-06-446223-5(4)) HarperCollins Pubs.

Sloan, Peter. Old & New Trains. 1999. (gr. k-3). lib. bdg. 11.80 (978-0-613-30642-3(2)) Tandem Library Bks.

—Trains. 1999. (gr. k-3). lib. bdg. 11.80 (978-0-613-30807-6(7)) Tandem Library Bks.

Smith, A. G. Train Station Sticker Activity Book. 1998. (Dover Little Activity Bks.). (Illus.). 4p. (J). (ps-3). 1.50 (978-0-486-40512-4(5)) Dover Pubns., Inc.

Smithyman, Kathryn & Kalman, Bobbie. Trains on the Tracks. 2007. (Vehicles on the Move Ser.). (Illus.). 32p. (J). (gr. 1-5). (***978-0-7787-3045-3(X)***) Crabtree Publishing Co.

Snyder, Margaret. Trains. 1999. (Storyshapes Ser.). (Illus.). 24p. (J). (ps-1). pap. 2.25 (978-0-7681-0135-5(2) , 57046, McClanahan Bk.) Learning Horizons, Inc.

St. Louis Union Station: A City Within a City. 2003. 19.95 (978-0-9748109-0-4(8)) Market 1 Group Inc.

Stickland, Paul. Trains. Stickland, Paul, illus. 1998. (On the Move Ser.). (Illus.). 16p. (J). (ps up). lib. bdg. 19.93 (978-0-8368-2154-3(8)) Stevens, Gareth Inc.

Tieck, Sarah. Trains. 2005. (Buddy Book Ser.). (Illus.). 24p. (J). (gr. k-4). lib. bdg. 21.35 (978-1-59197-830-5(0)) ABDO Publishing Co.

Tiner, John Hudson. Trains. (Illus.). 32p. 2004. pap. 8.95 (978-0-89812-391-3(7) , Creative Paperbacks); 2003. (J). lib. bdg. 18.95 (978-1-58341-260-2(3) , Creative Education) Creative Co., The.

Tlock, Andrew. The Train, 4 vols. 1999. (Little Library). (Illus.). (J). (ps-k). bds. 5.95 (978-1-57717-118-8(7)) New Line Bks.

Trains. (Color & Learn Ser.). 36p. (J). (gr. 1-5). pap. (978-1-882210-11-4(5)) Action Publishing, Inc.

Trains of the Past, 6 Packs. (On Deck Ser.). 24p. (gr. 4-5). 35.00 (978-0-7578-1051-0(9)) Rigby Education.

Trenes Bala: Individual Title, 6 packs. (On Deck en Espanol Ser.).Tr. of Bullet Trains. (SPA.). 24p. (gr. 4-5). 35.00 (978-0-7578-6429-2(5)) Rigby Education.

Turnbull, S. Trains. 2004. (Discovery Program Ser.). (SPA., Illus.). 48p. (J). (gr. 3 up). pap. 8.95 (978-0-7945-0174-7(5) , Usborne) EDC Publishing.

—Los Trenes. 2004. Orig. Title: Trains. (SPA.). (J). lib. bdg. 16.95 (978-1-58086-500-5(3) , Usborne) EDC Publishing.

Walker, Pam. Train Rides. 2000. (Welcome Bks.). (Illus.). 24p. (J). (ps-2). 17.00 (978-0-516-23104-4(9) , Children's Pr.) Scholastic Library Publishing.

—Train Rides. 2000. (gr. k-3). lib. bdg. 12.95 (978-0-613-52204-5(4)) Tandem Library Bks.

Wetterer, Margaret K. Kate Shelley y el Tren de Medianoche. Ritz, Karen, illus. 2005. (Yo Solo - Historia (on My Own - History) Ser.).Tr. of Kate Shelley & the Midnight Express. (SPA.). 48p. (J). (gr. 3-7). lib. bdg. 25.26 (978-0-8225-3096-1(1) , Ediciones Lerner); (gr. 2-5). pap. 5.95 (978-0-8225-3193-7(3)) Lerner Publishing Group.

Zimmerman, Brooke. Trains: Lift-A-Flap Fun. Wieland, Don & Lovell, Mike, trs. Wieland, Don, illus. 2002. (Active Minds Ser.). 12p. (J). bds. 12.98 (978-0-7853-6303-3(3) , 7158300) Publications International, Ltd.

Zimmerman, Karl. All Aboard. 2006. (Illus.). 48p. (J). 19.95 (978-1-59078-325-2(5)) Boyds Mills Pr.

RAILROADS—FICTION

Alger, Horatio. The Erie Train Boy. reprint ed. pap. 79.00 (978-1-4047-3565-1(8)) Classic Textbooks.

Allcroft, Britt. A Better View for Gordon: And Other Thomas the Tank Engine Stories. 2001. (Pictureback Ser.). (Illus.). 24p. (J). (gr. k-ps). pap. 3.99 (978-0-375-81157-9(5) , Random Hse. Bks. for Young Readers) Random Hse. Children's Bks.

—Better View for Gordon: And Other Thomas the Tank Engine Stories. 2001. (ps-2). lib. bdg. 10.95 (978-0-613-83540-4(9)) Tandem Library Bks.

—Diesel 10 Means Trouble. Courtney, Richard, illus. 2000. (Thomas & the Magic Railroad Ser.). 24p. (J). (ps-1). pap. 3.25 (978-0-375-80552-3(4) , Random Hse. Bks. for Young Readers) Random Hse. Children's Bks.

—Diesel 10 Means Trouble. 2000. (gr. k-3). lib. bdg. 10.95 (978-0-613-24830-3(9)) Tandem Library Bks.

—Little Engines Can Do Big Things. Coatimundi Studios, illus. 2000. (Thomas & the Magic Railroad Ser.). 24p. (J). (ps-1). pap. 3.25 (978-0-375-80553-0(2) , Random Hse. Bks. for Young Readers) Random Hse. Children's Bks.

—Little Engines Can Do Big Things. 2000. (gr. k-3). lib. bdg. 10.95 (978-0-613-26025-1(2)) Tandem Library Bks.

Allcroft, Britt & Random House Staff. Thomas & the Magic Railroad. Stubbs, Tommy, illus. movie tie-in ed. 2000. (Thomas & the Magic Railroad Ser.). 32p. (J). (gr. k-1). 10.99 (978-0-375-80551-6(6) , Random Hse. Bks. for Young Readers) Random Hse. Children's Bks.

Amaral, Gayla. Barney's Color Train Readalong. Hernandez, Joseph, illus. 2000. 24p. (J). (ps-2). 6.95 (978-1-57064-713-0(5) , 97964) Scholastic, Inc.

Amery, Heather. Old Steam Train. rev. ed. 2007. 16p. (J). pap. 5.99 (***978-0-7945-0804-3(9)***, Usborne) EDC Publishing.

—Old Steam Train. Tyler, Jenny, ed. Cartwright, Stephen, illus. rev. ed. 1999. 15p. (J). (ps-ps). pap. 4.95 (978-0-7945-0648-3(8) , Usborne) EDC Publishing.

Amery, Heather. Rusty's Train Ride. rev. ed. 2007. 16p. (J). pap. 5.99 (***978-0-7945-0802-9(2)***, Usborne) EDC Publishing.

Anna, Jennifer. Maxwell Dreams of Trains. Blue, Buster, illus. 2007. 88p. (J). 10.99 (978-1-883573-05-8(X) , Little Blue Works) Windstorm Creative.

Appleton, Victor. Tom Swift & His Electric Locomotive or. 2006. pap. (***978-1-4065-0899-4(3)***) Dodo Pr.

Awdry, Christopher, ed. Thomas the Really Useful Engine. Stubbs, Tommy, illus. 1999. (Thomas the Tank Engine & Friends Ser.). 48p. (J). (gr. k-3). 11.99 (978-0-375-80242-3(8) , Random Hse. Bks. for Young Readers) Random Hse. Children's Bks.

Awdry, W. Thomas & Friends: Lift-the-Flap Freight. Courtney, Richard, illus. 2008. (Thomas & Friends Ser.). 10p. (J). (gr. k-k). bds. 6.99 (***978-0-375-84301-3(9)***, Random Hse. Bks. for Young Readers) Random Hse. Children's Bks.

Awdry, Wilbert V. Blue Train, Green Train. Stubbs, Tommy, illus. 2006. 36p. (J). (gr. k-1). 8.99 (978-0-375-83463-9(X) , Random Hse. Bks. for Young Readers) Random Hse. Children's Bks.

—Blue Train, Green Train. Stubbs, Tommy, illus. (J). (gr. k-ps). 2007. 24p. bds. 4.99 (***978-0-375-83984-9(4));*** 2006. 36p. lib. bdg. 12.99 (978-0-375-93463-6(4)) Random Hse. Children's Bks. (Random Hse. Bks. for Young Readers).

—Calling All Engines! Courtney, Richard, illus. 2005. (Thomas & Friends Ser.). (J). (***978-1-4156-2388-6(0)***) Random Hse. Children's Bks.

—The Cranky Day & Other Thomas the Tank Engine Stories. 2000. (Random House Picturebacks Ser.). (Illus.). 24p. (J). (gr. k-3). pap. 3.25 (978-0-375-80246-1(0) , Random Hse. Bks. for Young Readers) Random Hse. Children's Bks.

—Down at the Docks. Courtney, Richard, illus. 2003. (Thomas & Friends Ser.). 24p. (J). (ps-2). pap. 3.25 (978-0-375-82592-7(4) , Random Hse. Bks. for Young Readers) Random Hse. Children's Bks.

—Edward the Blue Engine. Dalby, C. Reginald, illus. 2003. 64p. (J). (ps-4). 6.99 (978-0-375-82407-4(3) , Random Hse. Bks. for Young Readers) Random Hse. Children's Bks.

—Go, Train, Go! Stubbs, Tommy, illus. 2006. 24p. (J). (gr. k-ps). bds. 4.99 (978-0-375-83461-5(3) , Random Hse. Bks. for Young Readers) Random Hse. Children's Bks.

—Gordon the Big Engine. 2002. (Illus.). 64p. (J). (ps-2). 6.99 (978-0-375-81550-8(3) , Random Hse. Bks. for Young Readers) Random Hse. Children's Bks.

—Happy Birthday, Thomas. Bell, Owain, illus. 2003. (Step into Reading Ser.). 32p. (J). (ps-2). 11.99 (978-0-679-90809-8(9) , Random Hse. Bks. for Young Readers) Random Hse. Children's Bks.

—Henry's Bad Day. Courtney, Richard, illus. 2006. (Step into Reading Ser.). 32p. (J). (ps-1). pap. 3.99 (978-0-375-83464-6(8) , Random Hse. Bks. for Young Readers) Random Hse. Children's Bks.

—Hooray for Thomas! Book & CD. 2006. (Illus.). 24p. (J). (ps-2). 9.95 (978-0-375-83506-3(7) , Random Hse. Bks. for Young Readers) Random Hse. Children's Bks.

—James & the Red Balloon & Other Thomas the Tank Engine Stories. 2004. (Thomas & Friends Ser.). (Illus.). 24p. (J). (ps-2). pap. 3.99 (978-0-375-82753-2(6) , Random Hse. Bks. for Young Readers) Random Hse. Children's Bks.

—Thomas & Friends: Gordon's New View. Courtney, Richard, illus. 2007. (Step into Reading Ser.). 32p. (J). (ps-1). pap. 3.99 (***978-0-375-83978-8(X));*** lib. bdg. 11.99 (***978-0-375-93978-5(4)***) Random Hse. Children's Bks. (Random Hse. Bks. for Young Readers).

—Thomas & Friends: James & the Red Balloon & Other Thomas the Tank Enginestor. 2004. (ps-2). lib. bdg. 11.80 (978-0-613-86695-8(9)) Tandem Library Bks.

—Thomas & Friends: May the Best Engine Win. Stubbs, Tommy, illus. 2006. (Thomas & Friends Ser.). 32p. (J). (ps-2). lib. bdg. 14.99 (978-0-375-93842-9(7) , Random Hse. Bks. for Young Readers) Random Hse. Children's Bks.

—Thomas & Percy & the Dragon. 2003. (ps-2). lib. bdg. 11.80 (978-0-613-89791-4(9)) Tandem Library Bks.

—Thomas & the Castle. Stubbs, Tommy, illus. 2004. (Thomas & Friends Ser.). 32p. (J). (ps-2). 11.99 (978-0-375-81393-1(4) , Random Hse. Bks. for Young Readers) Random Hse. Children's Bks.

—Thomas & the Naughty Diesel. Yee, Josie, illus. 1999. (Random House Picturebacks Ser.). 24p. (gr. k-3). pap. 3.99 (978-0-375-80079-5(4) , Random Hse. Bks. for Young Readers) Random Hse. Children's Bks.

—Thomas & the Naughty Diesel. 1999. (gr. k-3). lib. bdg. 10.95 (978-0-613-82500-9(4)) Tandem Library Bks.

—Thomas & the School Trip. Bell, Owain, illus. 2003. (Step into Reading Step 1 Bks.). 32p. (J). (ps-1). 11.99 (978-0-679-94365-5(X) , Random Hse. Bks. for Young Readers) Random Hse. Children's Bks.

—Thomas & the School Trip. 1999. (Illus.). (J). (ps-2). lib. bdg. 11.80 (978-0-7857-2522-0(9)) Tandem Library Bks.

—Thomas Gets Stuck. 2006. (Illus.). 10p. (J). (gr. k-k). bds. 5.99 (978-0-375-83639-8(X) , Random Hse. Bks. for Young Readers) Random Hse. Children's Bks.

—Thomas Goes Fishing. Courtney, Richard, illus. 2005. 32p. (J). (ps-1). lib. bdg. 11.99 (978-0-375-93118-5(X) , Random Hse. Bks. for Young Readers) Random Hse. Children's Bks.

—Thomas the Tank Engine: Cranky Bugs & Other Stories. 2000. (gr. k-3). lib. bdg. 10.95 (978-0-613-27235-3(8)) Tandem Library Bks.

—Thomas the Tank Engine's Hidden Surprises. Yee, Josie, illus. 1999. (Let's Go Lift & Peek Bks.). 14p. (J). (gr. k-ps). bds. 4.99 (978-0-679-89482-7(9) , Random Hse. Bks. for Young Readers) Random Hse. Children's Bks.

—Thomas's Christmas Delivery. Stubbs, Tommy, illus. 2004. (Thomas & Friends Ser.). 32p. (J). (ps-2). 8.99 (978-0-375-82877-5(X) , Random Hse. Bks. for Young Readers) Random Hse. Children's Bks.

—The Three Railway Engines. Dalby, C. Reginald, illus. 2003. (Railway Ser.). 64p. (J). (ps-4). 6.99 (978-0-375-82408-1(1) , Random Hse. Bks. for Young Readers) Random Hse. Children's Bks.

—Track Stars! Three Thomas & Friends Stories. 2007. (Thomas & Friends Ser.). (Illus.). 24p. (J). (ps-2). 9.99 incl. audio compact disk (978-0-375-83924-5(0) , Random Hse. Bks. for Young Readers) Random Hse. Children's Bks.

Awdry, Wilbert V. Track Stars! Three Thomas & Friends Stories. Permane, Terry, illus. Palone, Terry & Permane, Terry, photos by. 2006. (Thomas & Friends Ser.). (J). (***978-1-4156-5364-7(X)***) Random Hse. Children's Bks.

Awdry, Wilbert V. & Gerver, Jane E. A Crack in the Track: A Thomas the Tank Engine Story. Stubbs, Tommy & Nelson, Mary Beth, illus. 2001. (Beginner Bks.). 48p. (J). (gr. k-3). 8.99 (978-0-375-81246-0(6) , Random Hse. Bks. for Young Readers) Random Hse. Children's Bks.

Awdry, Wilbert V. & Random House Staff. Thomas & the Shooting Star. Stubbs, Tommy, illus. 2002. (Thomas & Friends Ser.). 32p. (J). (ps-2). 8.99 (978-0-375-81523-2(6) , Random Hse. Bks. for Young Readers) Random Hse. Children's Bks.

Ayres, Katherine. North by Night: A Story of the Underground Railroad. 2000. (Illus.). 192p. (J). (gr. 5 up). pap. 5.99 (978-0-440-22747-2(X) , Yearling) Random Hse. Children's Bks.

—North by Night: A Story of the Underground Railroad. 2000. (978-0-606-18786-2(3)) Tandem Library Bks.

Bailer, Darice. Railroad! A Story of the Transcontinental Railroad. Farnsworth, Bill, illus. 3rd ed. 2005. (Soundprints' Read-and-Discover Ser.). 48p. (J). (gr. 2-4). pap. 3.95 (978-1-59249-017-2(4) , S2007) Soundprints.

Barton, Byron. Trains Lap Edition. Barton, Byron, illus. 2006. 34p. (J). 12.99 (978-0-06-115018-0(5) , Harper Festival) HarperCollins Pubs.

Bee, William. And the Train Goes... Bee, William, illus. 2007. (Illus.). 32p. (J). (ps-1). 15.99 (978-0-7636-3248-9(1)) Candlewick Pr.

Bentley, Dawn. All Aboard: Trains, Trains, Trains. Greisen, Robert, illus. gif. ed. 2000. 16p. (J). (ps-3). act. bk. ed. 19.95 (978-1-58117-117-4(X) , Intervisual/Piggy Toes) Dalmatian Pr.

Bingham, Jane. The Story of Trains. King, Colin, illus. 2004. (Young Reading Series Two Ser.). 64p. (J). (gr. 2 up). pap. 5.95 (978-0-7945-0737-4(9) , Usborne) EDC Publishing.

Blathwayt, Benedict. Faster, Faster, Little Red Train. 2000. (Illus.). 25p. (J). pap. 9.99 (978-0-09-926499-6(4)) Random Hse. GBR. *Dist:* Independent Pubs. Group.

Brooks, Felicity. Trenes. 2006. (Illus.). 12p. (J). bds. 9.99 (978-0-7460-7402-2(6) , Usborne) EDC Publishing.

Brown, Margaret Wise. Two Little Trains. Dillon, Leo & Dillon, Diane, illus. 32p. (J). (ps-1). 2003. pap. 6.99 (978-0-06-443568-0(7)); 2001. 16.99 (978-0-06-028376-6(9)) HarperCollins Pubs.

—Two Little Trains. 2001. (gr. 3-6). lib. bdg. 15.25 (978-0-613-49533-2(0)) Tandem Library Bks.

Bryant, Megan E. The Little Engine That Could (TM) Choo Choo Charlie Saves the Carnival. Ong, Cristina, tr. Ong, Cristina, illus. 2004. (Reading Railroad Bks.). 32p. (J). (ps-4). pap. 3.99 (978-0-448-43513-8(6) , Grosset & Dunlap) Penguin Group (USA) Inc.

Bryant, Raymond. On the Tracks. 2004. (Funtime Rhymes Ser.). 10p. (J). bds. 4.95 (978-0-7641-5718-9(3)) Barron's Educational Series, Inc.

Burleigh, Robert. It's Funny Where Ben's Train Takes Him. Yardley, Joanna, illus. 1999. 32p. (J). (ps-2). pap. 15.95 (978-0-531-30106-7(0) , Orchard Bks.) Scholastic, Inc.

Busy Green Train. 2002. (Vehicle Lights Ser.). (J). (ps-k). 6.98 (978-0-7525-8888-9(5)) Parragon, Inc.

Capeci, Anne. Ghost Train, Vol. 3. Casale, Paul, illus. 2004. (Cascade Moutain Railroad Mystery Ser.: 3). 144p. (J). (gr. 2-5). 12.95 (978-1-56145-324-5(2)) Peachtree Pubs., Ltd.

—Missing! Casale, Paul, illus. 2005. 144p. (J). 12.95 (978-1-56145-334-4(X)) Peachtree Pubs., Ltd.

Casad, Mary Brooke. Bluebonnet at the Marshall Train Depot. Vincent, Benjamin, illus. 1999. 32p. (J). (gr. k-3). 15.95 (978-1-56554-311-9(4)) Pelican Publishing Co., Inc.

Chin, Oliver Clyde. Timmy & Tammy's Train of Thought. McPherson, Heath, illus. 2007. (ENG.). 36p. (J). 15.95 (978-1-59702-008-4(7)) Immedium.

Choo Choo. (Dora the Explorer). (Illus.). 10p. (J). bds. 9.98 (978-0-7853-8278-2(X) , 7182700) Publications International, Ltd.

Courtney, Richard, illus. James Goes Buzz, Buzz. 2004. (Step into Reading Ser.). 32p. (J). (ps-2). pap. 3.99 (978-0-375-82860-7(5) , Random Hse. Bks. for Young Readers) Random Hse. Children's Bks.

—The Monster under the Shed. 2001. (Pictureback Bk.). 24p. (J). (ps-3). pap. 3.25 (978-0-375-81371-9(3) , Random Hse. Bks. for Young Readers) Random Hse. Children's Bks.

—The Special Delivery. 2002. (Jellybean Bks.). 24p. (J). (gr. k-k). pap. 3.25 (978-0-375-81494-5(9) , Random Hse. Bks. for Young Readers) Random Hse. Children's Bks.

—Thomas Gets a Snowplow. 2004. 24p. (J). (ps-2). 3.99 (978-0-375-82783-9(8) , Random Hse. Bks. for Young Readers) Random Hse. Children's Bks.

Cowley, Joy. The Bedtime Train. Odone, Jamison, illus. 2008. (J). (***978-1-59078-493-8(6)***, Front Street) Boyds Mills Pr.

Crabtree, Sally. Magic Train Ride. Esplugas, Sonia, illus. 2006. 0032p. (J). 16.99 (978-1-905236-52-7(2)) Barefoot Bks., Inc.

Crebbin, June. Train Ride. Lambert, Stephen, illus. 1999. (Read & Share Ser.). 24p. (J). (ps). pap. 3.99 (978-0-7636-0866-8(1)) Candlewick Pr.

—El Viaje en Tren. Rubio, Esther, tr. Lambert, Stephen, illus. 2004. (SPA.). (J). 7.95 (978-1-930332-76-8(9)) Lectorum Pubns., Inc.

Crews, Donald. Freight Train. Crews, Donald, illus. 2003. (SPA & ENG., Illus.). 24p. (J). lib. bdg. bds. 16.89 (978-0-06-056203-8(X)) HarperCollins Pubs.

—Freight Train/Tren de Carga. Crews, Donald, illus. 24p. (J). 2008. pap. 7.99 (***978-0-06-056204-5(8));*** 2003. (SPA., Illus.). 16.99 (978-0-06-056202-1(1)) HarperCollins Pubs. (Rayo).

Crews, Donald. Inside Freight Train. Crews, Donald, illus. 2001. (Illus.). 12p. (J). (ps-3). 9.99 (978-0-688-17087-5(0) , Harper Festival) HarperCollins Pubs.

Crunk, Tony. Railroad John & the Red Rock Run. Austin, Michael, illus. 2006. 32p. (J). 16.95 (978-1-56145-363-4(3)) Peachtree Pubs., Ltd.

Dawes, Claiborne. Daniel on the Run: Louisa, Will, & the Underground Railroad. 2001. (Illus.). 40p. (J). pap. 7.95 (978-1-57960-078-5(6)) History Compass, LLC.

Day, Roselie. Ruby, the Little Girl Who Loved Trains, 10 chapters. 2004. (Illus.). 170p. (J). (ps-7). per. 12.95 (978-0-9749826-0-1(1)) Next Page Pr., The.

Delittle, Cathy. Sleepytime Train. Delittle, Cathy, illus. 1998. (Illus.). 12p. (J). (ps-1). spiral bd. 7.95 (978-1-892633-04-0(3) , OOCD204) Delittle Storyteller Co.

Demers, David & Demers, Lee Ann. My Grandpa Loves Trains: A Picture Storybook for Preschoolers. Demers, David, photos by. l.t. ed. 2005. (Illus.). 76p. (J). 27.95 (978-0-922993-36-9(X)) Marquette Bks., LLC.

—My Grandpa Loves Trains: A Storybook for Preschoolers. Demers, David, photos by. l.t. ed. 2005. (Illus.). 76p. (J). per. 19.95 (978-0-922993-23-9(8)) Marquette Bks., LLC.

Dorfman, Craig. I Knew You Could! A Book for All the Stops in Your Life. Ong, Cristina, illus. 2003. (Little Engine That Could Ser.). 32p. (J). (gr. 1-2). 11.99 (978-0-448-43148-2(3) , Grosset & Dunlap) Penguin Group (USA) Inc.

Dorfman, Craig. I Knew You Could! Celebrate All the Stops in Your Life. Ong, Cristina, illus. 2008. (Little Engine That Could Ser.). 32p. (J). (ps). 12.99 ***978-0-448-44813-8(0)*** , Grosset & Dunlap) Penguin Group (USA) Inc.

Down the Track, 6 Packs. (Story Steps Ser.). (gr. k-2). 32.00 (978-0-7635-9804-4(6)) Rigby Education.

Doyle, Bill. Nabbed! The 1925 Journal of G. Codd Fitzmorgan. 2nd ed. 2006. (Crime Through Time Ser.: No. 2). (Illus.). 128p. (J). (gr. 3-7). pap. 5.99 (978-0-316-05737-0(1)) Little Brown & Co.

—Silenced! The 1969 Journal of Malcolm Moorie. 3rd ed. 2006. (Crime Through Time Ser.: No. 3). (Illus.). 144p. (J). (gr. 3-7). pap. 5.99 (978-0-316-05738-7(X)) Little Brown & Co.

—Swindled! The 1906 Journal of Fitz Morgan. Dow, Brian, illus. 2006. 138p. (J). lib. bdg. 18.46 ***(*978-1-4242-1737-3(7))*** Fitzgerald Bks.

—Swindled! The 1906 Journal of Fitz Morgan. 2006. (Crime Through Time Ser.: No. 1). (Illus.). 144p. (J). (gr. 3-7). pap. 5.99 (978-0-316-05736-3(3)) Little Brown & Co.

Duey, Kathleen & Bale, Karen. Trainwreck: Kansas, 1892. 1999. (Survival! Ser.: No. 8). (J). (gr. 4-7). (978-0-606-16279-1(8)) Tandem Library Bks.

Dunn, Opal. Little Train. Paterson, Bettina, illus. rev. ed. 2000. (Track-Me-Back Board Bks.). 12p. (J). (ps-k). 5.95 (978-0-8050-6419-3(2) , Holt, Henry & Co. Bks. For Young Readers) Holt, Henry & Co.

Dunnavant, Michelle. Josh & Jennie & George's Velocipede. Reed, Mike, illus. 1998. (Rail Rales Ser.: Vol. 4). 20p. (J). (ps up). mass mkt. 5.00 (978-1-892136-03-9(1)) Lionel L.L.C.

Fedewa, Lanna C. Reid Rides the Railroad. Batson, Mary, illus. 2002. 18p. (J). (gr. k-3). pap. 9.95 (978-0-9702880-5-9(0)) Sun R.A.Y.S., LLC.

Fry, Sonali, adapted by. All Aboard! ed. 2005. (Rubbadubbers Ser.: 2). (Illus.). 24p. (J). lib. bdg. 15.00 (978-1-59054-820-2(5)) Fitzgerald Bks.

Gerald, Tom. Traveling by Train: Read Well Level K Unit 19 Storybook. Weber, Philip A., Jr., illus. 2003. (Read Well Level K Ser.). 20p. (J). (978-1-57035-690-2(4) , 55597) Sopris West Educational Services.

Gerver, Jane E. A Crack in the Track: A Thomas the Tank Engine Story. Stubbs, Tommy, illus. 2001. (Beginner Bks. Ser.). 48p. (J). (ps-3). lib. bdg. 11.99 (978-0-375-91246-7(0) , Random Hse. Bks. for Young Readers) Random Hse. Children's Bks.

Golden Books Staff. Count along with Thomas. 2000. (Thomas the Tank Engine Ser.). (J). (ps-3). bds. 12.99 (978-0-307-71308-7(3) , Golden Bks.) Random Hse., Inc.

Golden Books Staff. Friends from Sodor. 2008. (Deluxe Paint Box Book Ser.). (Illus.). 128p. (J). (ps-2). pap. 7.99 ***(*978-0-375-84292-4(6)*** , Golden Bks.) Random Hse., Inc.

Golden Books Staff & Crampton, Gertrude. Tootle. 2001. (Little Golden Bks.). (Illus.). 24p. (J). (gr. k-k). 2.99 (978-0-307-02097-0(5) , 98097, Golden Bks.) Random Hse. Children's Bks.

Goodman, Steve. The Train They Call the City of New Orleans. McCurdy, Michael, illus. 2005. (J). pap. 28.95 incl. audio compact disk (978-1-59112-904-2(4)) Live Oak Media.

Grace, Will. Red Train. Vere, Ed, illus. 2006. 18p. (J). bds. 3.99 (978-0-439-81439-3(1) , Cartwheel Bks.) Scholastic, Inc.

Grandpa's Trains. 2001. (978-1-58453-158-6(4)) Pioneer Valley Educational Pr., Inc.

Greenburg, Dan. When Bad Snakes Attack Good Children. Fischer, Scott M., illus. 2007. (Secrets of Dripping Fang Ser.: Bk. 8). 144p. (J). 9.95 (978-0-15-206056-5(1)) Harcourt Children's Bks.

Griffiths, Robert. Adventures of Clive. 2005. 45p. (J). pap. 10.01 (978-1-4116-5332-0(7)) Lulu.com.

Guthrie, Woody. New Baby Train. Frazee, Marla, illus. 2004. 32p. (J). 15.99 (978-0-316-07020-1(3) , Tingley, Megan Bks.) Little, Brown Bks. for Young Readers.

Haddon, Mark. Ocean Star Express. 2002. (Illus.). 29p. (J). pap. 11.00 (978-0-00-664600-6(X)) HarperCollins Pubs. Ltd. GBR. *Dist:* Independent Pubs. Group.

Happy Birthday, Thomas. 2002. (Thomas the Tank Engine Ser.). (Illus.). (J). 11.91 (978-0-7587-1242-4(1)) Book Wholesalers, Inc.

Harris, Christine. Danger. 2006. (Undercover Girl Ser.: No. 4). 176p. (J). pap. 4.99 (978-0-439-76128-4(X) , Scholastic Paperbacks) Scholastic, Inc.

Hautman, Pete. Invisible. Hautman, Pete, illus. 160p. (YA). 2005. (gr. 7 up). 16.99 (978-0-689-86800-9(6) , Simon & Schuster Children's Publishing); 2006. reprint ed. pap. 7.99 (978-0-689-86903-7(7) , Simon Pulse) Simon & Schuster Children's Publishing.

—Invisible. l.t. ed. 2005. 192p. (YA). 20.95 (978-0-7862-7909-8(5) , Large Print Pr.) Thorndike Pr.

Hillenbrand, Will. Down by the Station. (Illus.). 40p. (J). (gr. k-2). 2002. pap. 6.00 (978-0-15-216790-5(0) , Voyager Bks./Libros Viajeros); 1999. 16.00 (978-0-15-201804-7(2) , Gulliver Bks.) Harcourt Children's Bks.

—Down by the Station. 2002. (gr. k-3). lib. bdg. 14.15 (978-0-613-56325-3(5)) Tandem Library Bks.

Hope, Laura Lee. Freddie & Flossie & the Train Ride. Pyle, Chuck, illus. 2005. (Ready-To-Read Ser.). 32p. (J). (ps-ps). pap. 3.99 (978-1-4169-0269-0(4) , Aladdin) Simon & Schuster Children's Publishing.

—Freddie & Flossie & the Train Ride. 2006. (Ready-To-Read Ser.). (J). (ps-2). 21.35 (978-1-59961-097-9(3)) Spotlight.

Horsbrugh, Wilma. The Train to Glasgow. Cox, Paul, illus. 2004. 32p. (J). (gr. k-3). 16.00 (978-0-618-38143-2(0) , Clarion Bks.) Houghton Mifflin Co. Trade & Reference Div.

Howard, Elizabeth Fitzgerald. The Train to Lulu's. 1998. (J). pap. 4.95 (978-0-87628-336-3(9)) Simon & Schuster.

Hubbell, Patricia. Trains: Steaming! Pulling! Huffing! Halsey, Megan & Addy, Sean, illus. 2005. 32p. (J). (ps-3). per. 14.95 (978-0-7614-5194-5(3)) Cavendish, Marshall Corp.

James, Susan. Shiny Dinah: Sing, Dance & Read with Me. 2000. 12p. (J). (ps-3). pap. 9.95 incl. audio (978-1-931127-49-3(2) , 986-007); pap. 14.95 incl. audio (978-1-931127-48-6(4) , 986-008) Kindermusik International.

—Shiny Dinah: Sing, Dance & Read with Me, Read-Along with Big Book. 2000. 12p. (J). (ps-3). pap. 29.95 incl. audio compact disk (978-1-931127-50-9(6) , 986-009) Kindermusik International.

Johnson, Angela & Long, Loren. I Dream of Trains. 2003. (Illus.). 32p. (J). (gr. k-2). 17.99 (978-0-689-82609-2(5)) Simon & Schuster Children's Publishing.

Kalman, Maira. Next Stop, Grand Central. 2001. (J). (978-0-606-21348-6(1)) Tandem Library Bks.

Kalz, Jill. Boy Who Loved Trains. Erkocak, Sahin, illus. 2007. (Read-It! Readers Ser.). (J). 19.93 (978-1-4048-2401-6(4)) Picture Window Bks.

Kay, Verla. Iron Horses. McCurdy, Michael, illus. 1999. 32p. (J). (ps-3). 16.99 (978-0-399-23119-3(6) , Putnam Juvenile) Penguin Group (USA) Inc.

Kehret, Peg. The Hideout. 2002. (gr. 3-6). lib. bdg. 13.00 (978-0-613-63944-6(8)) Tandem Library Bks.

Kelly, John & Simkins, Kate. Wagon Train Adventure. Inklink, illus. 2008. 48p. (J). (gr. 3-4). 14.99 ***(*978-0-7566-3852-8(6));*** pap. 3.99 ***(*978-0-7566-3851-1(8))*** Dorling Kindersley Publishing, Inc.

Kimmel, Eric A. Stormy's Hat. U'Ren, Andrea, illus. 2008. 32p. (J). 16.95 (978-0-374-37262-0(4)) Farrar, Straus & Giroux.

Kivel, Lee. The Lonely Train. Tucci, Al, illus. 2005. 36p. (J). per. 14.95 (978-0-9774999-0-8(1)) Kivel, Lee.

Latta, Richard. The Old Train. Taylor, Stephen, illus. 1998. (Books for Young Learners). 12p. (J). (gr. k-2). pap. 5.00 (978-1-57274-133-1(3) , A2487) Owen, Richard C. Pubs., Inc.

—El Viejo Tren. Romo, Alberto, tr. Taylor, Stephen, illus. 1999. (Books for Young Learners).Tr. of Old Train. (SPA.). 12p. (J). (gr. k-2). pap. 5.00 (978-1-57274-295-6(X)) Owen, Richard C. Pubs., Inc.

Lawson, Julie. Bear on the train. Deines, Brian, illus. 2001. 32p. (J). (gr. k-3). (978-1-55337-068-0(6)) Kids Can Pr., Ltd.

—Emma & the Silk Train. Mombourquette, Paul, illus. 32p. (J). (gr. k-3). 2002. (978-1-55074-651-8(0)); 1998. (978-1-55074-388-3(0)) Kids Can Pr., Ltd.

—Emma & the Silk Train. 2002. (gr. k-3). lib. bdg. 14.10 (978-0-613-83948-8(X)) Tandem Library Bks.

—White Jade Tiger. rev. ed. 2005. 168p. (YA). (gr. 3-8). reprint ed. pap., tchr. ed. 6.95 (978-0-88878-332-5(9)) Beach Holme Pubs., Ltd. CAN. *Dist:* Literary Pr. Group of Canada.

Le Guin, Ursula K. Tom Mouse. ed. 2004. (Illus.). (J). (gr. k-3). spiral bd. (978-0-616-14584-5(5)) Canadian National Institute for the Blind/Institut National Canadien pour les Aveugles.

—Tom Mouse & Ms. Howe. Downing, Julie, illus. 1999. (J). (978-0-7894-2554-6(8)) Dorling Kindersley Publishing, Inc.

Lehman, Barbara. Train Stop. 2008. 32p. (J). (ps-k). 16.00 ***(*978-0-618-75640-7(X))*** Houghton Mifflin Co.

Lenski, Lois. The Little Train. 2002. (Lois Lenski Bks.). (Illus.). 32p. (J). (gr. k-ps). bds. 6.99 (978-0-375-82264-3(X) , Random Hse. Bks. for Young Readers) Random Hse. Children's Bks.

—The Little Train. Kilgras, Heidi, ed. Lenski, Lois, illus. 2000. (Lois Lenski Bks.). (Illus.). 56p. (J). (gr. k-3). 13.95 (978-0-375-81071-8(4) , Random Hse. Bks. for Young Readers) Random Hse. Children's Bks.

Lewis, Kevin. Chugga Chugga Choo Choo. Kirk, Daniel, illus. 1999. 32p. (ps-k). 12.99 (978-0-7868-0429-0(7)) Disney Pr.

—Chugga Chugga Choo-Choo Big Book. Kirk, Daniel, illus. 2001. 32p. (ps-k). 6.99 (978-0-7868-0760-4(1)) Hyperion Bks. for Children.

Lukas, Catherine & Artifact Group. Trouble on the Train. 2007. (Backyardigans Ser.). (Illus.). 24p. (J). pap. 3.99 (978-1-4169-2818-8(9) , Simon Spotlight/Nickelodeon) Simon & Schuster Children's Publishing.

Lund, Deborah. All Aboard the Dinotrain. Fine, Howard, illus. 2006. 40p. (J). 16.00 (978-0-15-205237-9(2)) Harcourt Trade Pubs.

Lytle, Robert A. A Pitch in Time. Williams, Bill, illus. 2002. 368p. (YA). pap. 12.95 (978-0-9712692-5-5(4)) EDCO Publishing, Inc.

Mackall, Dandi Daley. Rudy Rides the Rails: A Depression Era Story. Ellison, Chris, illus. rev. ed. 2007. (Tales of Young Americans Ser.). 40p. (J). (gr. 3-6). 17.95 ***(*978-1-58536-286-8(7))*** Sleeping Bear Pr.

Mallat, Kathy. Trouble on the Tracks. 2001. (Illus.). 24p. (J). (ps-2). lib. bdg. 16.85 (978-0-8027-8773-6(8)) Walker & Co.

—Trouble on the Tracks. Mallat, Kathy, illus. 2001. (Illus.). 24p. (J). (ps-2). 15.95 (978-0-8027-8771-2(1)) Walker & Co.

McCaughrean, Geraldine. Stop the Train! (J). (gr. 5 up). 2003. 304p. 16.99 (978-0-06-050749-7(7)); 2005. 384p. reprint ed. pap. 6.99 (978-0-06-050751-0(9) , Harper Trophy) HarperCollins Pubs.

McNamara, Margaret. The Whistle on the Train. rev. ed. 2007. 16p. (J). (ps-1). 18.99 ***(*978-0-7868-4890-4(1))*** Hyperion Pr.

Metzger, Steve. The Little Red Caboose. Dubin, Jill, illus. 1998. (My First Hello Reader! Ser.). 32p. (J). (ps-1). pap. 3.99 (978-0-590-63598-1(0)) Scholastic, Inc.

Miller, Edward. Trains. 1998. (Sticker Stories Ser.). (Illus.). 16p. (J). (ps-1). pap. 4.99 (978-0-448-41826-1(6) , Grosset & Dunlap) Penguin Group (USA) Inc.

Mills, Claudia. Gus & Grandpa Ride the Train. Stock, Catherine, illus. 2000. (Gus & Grandpa Ser.). 48p. (J). (ps-3). pap. 5.95 (978-0-374-42813-6(1) , Sunburst) Farrar, Straus & Giroux.

—Gus & Grandpa Ride the Train. 2000. (Illus.). (J). 11.75 (978-0-606-18133-4(4)) Tandem Library Bks.

Mitton, David, et al, photos by. Percy's Chocolate Crunch & Other Thomas the Tank Engine Stories. 2003. (Random House Pictureback Book Ser.). (Illus.). 32p. (J). (ps-2). pap. 3.25 (978-0-375-81392-4(6) , Random Hse. Bks. for Young Readers) Random Hse. Children's Bks.

Murray, Regina Waldron. The Very Exciting Train Ride: An Adventure. 2006. (J). per. 15.95 ***(*978-0-9664042-1-0(1))*** Murray, Regina Waldron.

Murrell, Diane. Tobin Learns to Make Friends. 2001. (Illus.). (J). (ps-3). per. 16.95 (978-1-885477-79-8(1)) Future Horizons, Inc.

Neitzel, Shirley. I'm Taking a Trip on My Train. Parker, Nancy Winslow, illus. 1999. 40p. (J). (ps-3). 14.89 (978-0-688-15834-7(X)) HarperCollins Pubs.

Nesbit, E. The Railway Children. Dryhurst, Dinah, illus. 2000. 224p. (J). pap. 8.99 (978-1-86205-235-2(2) , Pavilion Bks., Ltd.) Anova Bks. GBR. *Dist:* Trafalgar Square Publishing.

—The Railway Children. Dryhurst, Dinah, tr. Dryhurst, Dinah, illus. 2004. 184p. 18.95 (978-1-56792-261-5(9)) Godine, David R. Pub.

—The Railway Children. 2002. (gr. 3-6). lib. bdg. 23.40 (978-0-613-86551-7(0)) Tandem Library Bks.

—The Railway Children. 1998. (Children's Classics). (ENG., Illus.). 208p. (J). (gr. 4-7). pap. (978-1-85326-107-7(6) , 1076WW) Wordsworth Editions, Ltd.

—Railway Children. Brock, C. E., illus. (YA). 14.95 (978-0-8118-4933-3(3)) Chronicle Bks. LLC.

—Railway Children. 2000. (Dover Juvenile Classics Ser.). (Illus.). 208p. (J). (gr. 4-7). pap. 2.50 (978-0-486-41022-7(6)) Dover Pubns., Inc.

—Railway Children. 2006. pap. ***(*978-1-4068-3505-2(6))*** Echo Library.

—Railway Children. (J). (978-0-340-71497-3(2) , Hodder & Stoughton) Hodder General Publishing Division.

—Railway Children. 2004. (ENG.). 580p. ***(*978-0-9548401-2-9(7))*** Shoes & Ships & Sealing Wax Ltd.

—The Railway Children. Brock, C. E., illus. 100th ed. 2005. 240p. (J). (ps-7). 14.95 (978-1-58717-279-3(8)) ; pap. 9.95 (978-1-58717-280-9(1)) Chronicle Bks. LLC. (Sea-Star Bks.).

—The Railway Children. unabr. ed. 2004. (Chrysalis Children's Classics Ser.). (Illus.). 190p. (YA). pap. (978-1-84365 050 8(9)) Chrysalis Children's Bks.

—The Railway Children. 2004. reprint ed. pap. 22.95 (978-1-4191-7972-3(1)); pap. 1.99 (978-1-4192-7972-0(6)) Kessinger Publishing, LLC.

—The Railway Children. l.t. ed. 2006. (Large Print Ser.). lib. bdg. 26.00 ***(*978-1-58287-890-4(0))*** North Bks.

—The Railway Children, Level 3. 2nd ed. 2000. (Bookworms Ser.). (Illus.). 74p. 6.50 (978-0-19-423013-1(9)) Oxford Univ. Pr., Inc.

—The Railway Children, Level 2. 2000. (Illus.). 48p. (C). pap. 9.00 (978-0-582-41790-8(2)) Pearson ESL.

Newman, Patricia. Jingle the Brass. Chesworth, Michael, illus. 2004. 32p. (J). 16.50 (978-0-374-33679-0(2) , Farrar, Straus & Giroux (BYR)) Farrar, Straus & Giroux.

Nichols, Paul. Thomas' Railway Word Book. 2000. (gr. k-3). lib. bdg. 10.95 (978-0-613-33140-1(0)) Tandem Library Bks.

O'Flatharta, Antoine. The Prairie Train. Rohmann, Eric, illus. 2004. 40p. (J). (ps-3). reprint ed. pap. 6.99 (978-0-553-11334-1(8) , Dragonfly Bks.) Random Hse. Children's Bks.

Ogilvy, Ian. Measle & the Wrathmonk. 2004. 224p. (J). (gr. 4-6). 15.99 (978-0-06-058685-0(0)); lib. bdg. 16.89 (978-0-06-058686-7(9)) HarperCollins Pubs.

Oliver, Lin. Beezy's Big Boy. Dodge, Bill, illus. l.t. ed. 2000. 32p. (J). pap. 14.99 incl. audio (978-1-890647-61-2(6)); 14.95 (978-1-890647-60-5(8)) RC2 Corp.

—Journey of the Jupiter. Dodge, Bill, illus. l.t. ed. 2000. 32p. (J). pap. 14.99 incl. audio (978-1-890647-59-9(4)); 14.95 (978-1-890647-58-2(6)) RC2 Corp.

—The Mighty Mogul. Lindberg, Jeffrey, illus. 1999. (Great Railway Adventures Ser.: Vol. 2;1). 32p. (J). (gr. k-4). 14.95 (978-1-890647-56-8(X)); pap. 14.99 incl. audio (978-1-890647-57-5(8)) RC2 Corp.

—The President Express. 1999. (Lionel Great Railway Adventures Ser.). (Illus.). 72p. (J). (gr. 4-7). 14.95 (978-1-56799-867-2(4)) Friedman, Michael Publishing Group, Inc.

—Torpedo Run. 1999. (Illus.). 32p. (J). 14.95 (978-1-56799-868-9(2)) Friedman, Michael Publishing Group, Inc.

Ong, Cristina, illus. The Little Engine That Could Storybook Treasury. 2003. (Little Engine That Could Ser.). 176p. (J). (ps-2). 10.99 (978-0-448-43114-7(9) , Grosset & Dunlap) Penguin Group (USA) Inc.

Pallotta, Jerry. The Big Engine: Counting on the Big Engine. Butler, Paul, illus. l.t. ed. 2000. (Big Engine Ser.: No. 1). 12p. (J). (ps-k). 7.99 (978-0-9700383-0-2(5)) Great Train Stores, The.

Panahi, H. L. The Bebop Express. Johnson, Steve & Fancher, Lou, illus. 2005. 32p. (J). (ps-3). 15.99 (978-0-06-057190-0(X)); lib. bdg. 16.89 (978-0-06-057191-7(8)) HarperCollins Pubs. (Geringer, Laura Book).

Papp, Robert, illus. The Mystery of the Orphan Train, 105. 2005. (Boxcar Children Mysteries Ser.: No. 105). 120p. (J). (gr. 2-7). lib. bdg. 14.95 (978-0-8075-5558-3(4)) Whitman, Albert & Co.

Parker, Marjorie Blain. Hello, Freight Train! Kolar, Bob, illus. 2005. (Scholastic Reader Ser.). (J). ***(*978-1-4155-7966-4(0))*** Scholastic, Inc.

—Hello, Freight Train! Kolar, Bob, illus. 2005. 28p. (J). (ps-ps). lib. bdg. 10.79 (978-0-606-33279-8(0)) Tandem Library Bks.

Pillaha, Randell Lane. Tommy T the Railroad Bear. 2003. pap. 6.95 (978-0-533-14307-8(1)) Vantage Pr., Inc.

Piper, Watty. The Little Engine That Could. Hauman, George, illus. 2002. 14.38 (978-1-4046-1064-4(2)) Book Wholesalers, Inc.

—The Little Engine That Could. 2002. (Illus.). (J). 5.99 (978-0-448-43151-2(3) , Grosset & Dunlap) Penguin Group (USA) Inc.

—The Little Engine That Could. Ong, Cristina, illus. 2001. (All Aboard Reading Ser.). 32p. (J). (ps-2). mass mkt. 3.99 (978-0-448-42482-8(7) , Grosset & Dunlap) Penguin Group (USA) Inc.

—The Little Engine That Could. Long, Loren, illus. 4th ltd. ed. 2006. 32p. (J). (ps). 85.00 (978-0-399-24710-1(6) , Philomel) Penguin Group (USA) Inc.

—The Little Engine That Could: A Storybook & Wind-up Train/Dutton Motorbook. Bernal, Richard, illus. 1998. 8p. (J). (ps-2). pap. 21.99 (978-0-525-46029-9(2) , Dutton Juvenile) Penguin Group (USA) Inc.

—Little Engine That Could Gets a Checkup. 2003. (gr. k-3). lib. bdg. 11.25 (978-0-613-67562-8(2)) Tandem Library Bks.

—The Little Engine That Could Goes on a Class Trip. Cardona, Jose Maria & Cardona, Joseph, illus. 2003. (Reading Railroad Bks.). 32p. (J). (ps-4). pap. 3.49 (978-0-448-43180-2(7) , Grosset & Dunlap) Penguin Group (USA) Inc.

—The Little Engine That Could Saves the Thanksgiving Day Parade. Ong, Cristina, illus. 2002. (Reading Railroad Bks.). 32p. (J). pap. 3.49 (978-0-448-42861-1(X) , Grosset & Dunlap) Penguin Group (USA) Inc.

—Meet the Little Engine That Could. 2001. lib. bdg. 11.80 (978-0-613-64068-8(3)); (Illus.). (J). (978-0-606-21324-0(4)) Tandem Library Bks.

Potter, Marian. The Little Red Caboose. Wilburn, Kathy, illus. 2000. (Little Golden Bks.). 24p. (J). (gr. k-k). 2.99 (978-0-307-02152-6(1) , 98098, Golden Bks.) Random Hse. Children's Bks.

Powell, Richard. Puff & the Long Train. Hawksley, Gerald, illus. 2004. (Softy Wheels Ser.). 18p. (J). bds. 8.95 (978-0-7641-7790-3(7)) Barron's Educational Series, Inc.

Prince, Joshua. I Saw an Ant on the Railroad Track. Pamintuan, Macky, illus. 2006. 24p. (J). 14.95 (978-1-4027-2183-0(8) , 1252268) Sterling Publishing Co., Inc.

Pugliano-Martin, Carol. John Henry: An AMER Tall Tale. 2006. 42.00 ***(*978-1-4108-6170-2(8))*** Benchmark Education Co.

Puzzle Track Staff, ed. Great Train Ride. 2007. (Puzzle Track Ser.). 20p. (J). bds. 18.95 ***(*978-0-7696-5599-4(8))*** School Specialty Publishing.

Pyle, Charles S., illus. The Daylight Limited: Lionel American Legend. l.t. ed. 1998. (Great Railway Adventures Ser.: Vol. 1). 30p. (J). 14.95 (978-1-890647-50-6(0)) RC2 Corp.

Quadrillion Media Staff. Show Me the Train! 1999. bds. 3.95 (978-1-58185-213-4(4)) Quadrillion Media LLC.

Random House Staff. Feliz Cumpleanos, Tomas! Marquez, Desiree, tr. Bell, Owain, illus. 2002. (SPA.). 32p. (J). (ps-1). pap. 3.99 (978-0-375-82339-8(5)); lib. bdg. 11.99 (978-0-375-92339-5(X)) Random Hse. Children's Bks. (RH Para Ninos).

—Thomas & Friends. Milliron, Kerry, ed. Yee, Josie, illus. 2000. (Baby Fingers Ser.). 14p. (J). (gr. k-ps). bds. 4.99 (978-0-375-80344-4(0) , Random Hse. Bks. for Young Readers) Random Hse. Children's Bks.

—Thomas & Friends: All Around the Island. Courtney, Rick F., illus. 2002. (Great Big Board Book Ser.). 12p. (J). (ps-2). bds. 11.99 (978-0-375-82212-4(7) , Random Hse. Bks. for Young Readers) Random Hse. Children's Bks.

—Thomas & the Rumors: And Other Thomas the Tank Engine Stories. 2002. (Please Read to Me Ser.). (Illus.). 24p. (J). (gr. k-3). pap. 3.25 (978-0-375-81372-6(1) , Random Hse. Bks. for Young Readers) Random Hse. Children's Bks.

Random House Staff. Thomas' Milkshake Muddle Book & CD. 2008. (Book & CD Ser.). (Illus.). 24p. (J). (ps-2). 9.99 ***(*978-0-375-84227-6(6)*** , Random Hse. Bks. for Young Readers) Random Hse. Children's Bks.

Ray, Mary Lyn. All Aboard! Hirao, Amiko & Goodwin-Sturges, illus. 2002. 32p. (J). (ps-3). 14.95 (978-0-316-73507-0(8)) Little, Brown Bks. for Young Readers.

Rex, Michael. My Freight Train. rev. ed. 2002. (Illus.). 32p. (J). (ps-2). 15.95 (978-0-8050-6682-1(9) , Holt, Henry & Co. Bks. For Young Readers) Holt, Henry & Co.

Richards, Kitty. The Journey Begins: An Early Reader. movie tie-in ed. 2004. (Polar Express Ser.). (Illus.). 32p. (J). (gr. k-3). pap. 3.99 (978-0-618-47795-1(0)) Houghton Mifflin Co. Trade & Reference Div.

Rizzo, Kay D. Bells & Whistles. 2003. 96p. (J). (978-0-8163-1984-8(7)) Pacific Pr. Publishing Assn.

Roche, Denis & London, Jonathan. Train Goes Clickety-clack. 2007. (Illus.). 32p. (J). (ps-k). 15.95 (*978-0-8050-7972-2(6)) Holt, Henry & Co.

Rockwell, Anne F., tr. & illus. At the Train Station. Rockwell, Anne F., illus. 2005. (J). 15.99 (978-0-06-056227-4(7)); 16.89 (978-0-06-056228-1(5)) HarperCollins Pubs.

Ross, Diane. The Little Red Engine & the Rocket. Wood, Leslie, illus. 2005. (Little Red Engine Ser.). 32p. (J). pap. 8.99 (978-0-233-00146-3(8)) Andre Deutsch GBR. *Dist:* Independent Pubs. Group.

—The Little Red Engine Goes to Town. Wood, Leslie, illus. 2005. (Little Red Engine Ser.). 32p. (J). pap. 8.99 (978-0-233-00151-7(4)) Andre Deutsch GBR. *Dist:* Independent Pubs. Group.

—The Story of the Little Red Engine. Wood, Leslie, illus. 2006. 32p. (J). pap. 8.99 (978-0-233-00147-0(6)) Andre Deutsch GBR. *Dist:* Trafalgar Square Publishing.

Ruggiero, Carol K. Rudy the steam Engine. 2006. pap. 7.95 (978-0-533-15494-4(4)) Vantage Pr., Inc.

The Runaway Engine & Other Stories: Individual Title Six-Pack. (Story Steps Ser.). (gr. k-2). 48.00 (978-0-7635-9803-7(8)) Rigby Education.

Rylant, Cynthia. Mr. Putter & Tabby Take the Train. Howard, Arthur, illus. 1998. (Mr. Putter & Tabby Ser.). 44p. (J). (gr. 1-5). 14.00 (978-0-15-201786-6(0)) Harcourt Children's Bks.

Santillo, LuAnn. The Tracks. Santillo, LuAnn, ed. 2003. (Half-Pint Kids Readers Ser.). (Illus.). 7p. (J). (ps-1). pap. (978-1-59256-080-6(6)) Half-Pint Kids, Inc.

Santnach, Celestino, illus. Fun All Year. 2002. (Thomas the Tank Engine & Friends Ser.). 80p. (J). (ps-2). pap. 2.99 (978-0-375-81495-2(7) , Golden Bks.) Random Hse. Children's Bks.

Schiller, Pam. This Little Train. Janes, Joshua, illus. 2006. (Noodlebug Ser.). (J). 12.95 (978-0-7696-4278-9(0)) School Specialty Publishing.

Sebag-Montefiore, Mary. Railway Children. Marks, Alan, illus. 2007. (Young Reading Series 2 Gift Bks). 64p. (J). 8.99 (*978-0-7945-1615-4(7) , Usborne) EDC Publishing.

Selznick, Brian. The Invention of Hugo Cabret. Selznick, Brian, illus. 2007. (Illus.). 544p. (J). (gr. 4-7). pap. 22.99 (978-0-439-81378-5(6) , Scholastic Pr.) Scholastic, Inc.

Sharmat, Marjorie Weinman & Sharmat, Mitchell. Nate the Great on the Owl Express. Weston, Martha, illus. 2003. (Nate the Great Ser.). 48p. (gr. 1-4). (J). 14.95 (978-0-385-73078-5(0)); lib. bdg. 16.99 (978-0-385-90102-4(X)) Random Hse. Children's Bks. (Delacorte Bks. for Young Readers).

Siebert, Diane. Train Song. Wimmer, Michael, illus. 2002. (J). 16.60 (978-0-7587-3855-4(2)) Book Wholesalers, Inc.

Skinner, Daphne. All Aboard! Smath, Jerry, illus. 2007. 32p. (J). (gr. 1-3). pap. 4.95 (*978-1-57565-239-9(0)) Kane Pr., The.

Skudera, George. The Adventures of Freddie the Little Fir. 2006. pap. 10.49 (*978-1-4259-5950-0(4)) AuthorHouse.

Snelling, Lauraine. The Long Way Home. 2001. (gr. 5-8). lib. bdg. 21.10 (978-0-613-55627-9(5)) Tandem Library Bks.

Sobel, June. The Goodnight Train. Huliska-Beith, Laura, illus. 2006. 32p. (J). 16.00 (978-0-15-205436-6(7)) Harcourt Trade Pubs.

Sommer, Carl. The Little Red Train. 2003. (Another Sommer-Time Story Ser.). (Illus.). 48p. (J). (gr. k-4). lib. bdg. 23.95 incl. audio (978-1-57537-764-3(0)); (gr. k-4). lib. bdg. 23.95 incl. audio compact disk (978-1-57537-714-8(4)); (gr. 1-4). 16.95 incl. audio (978-1-57537-563-2(X)); (gr. 1-4). 16.95 incl. audio compact disk (978-1-57537-514-4(1)) Advance Publishing, Inc.

—The Little Red Train. James, Kennon, illus. (Another Sommer-Time Story Ser.). 48p. (J). (gr. k-3). 2000. lib. bdg. 16.95 (978-1-57537-061-3(1)); 1999. 9.95 (978-1-57537-014-9(X)) Advance Publishing, Inc.

Spanyol, Jessica. Come on, Bugs! Let's Have Some Fun! Spanyol, Jessica, illus. 2006. (Illus.). 32p. (J). (gr. k-k). 15.99 (978-0-7636-3055-3(1)) Candlewick Pr.

Spence, Rob & Spence, Amy. Clickety Clack. Spengler, Margaret, illus. 1999. 32p. (J). (ps-3). 15.99 (978-0-670-87946-5(0) , Viking Juvenile) Penguin Group (USA) Inc.

Stickland, Henrietta. The Christmas Express: A Pop-Up Village, Toy Train, Light & Sound! Stickland, Paul, illus. 1999. (J). (ps up). 16.95 (978-1-58117-048-1(3) , Intervisual/Piggy Toes) Dalmatian Pr.

Stock, Catherine, illus. Gus & Grandpa Ride the Train. 2002. (Gus & Grandpa Ser.). (J). 13.36 (978-0-7587-0576-1(X)) Book Wholesalers, Inc.

Stockham, Jessica. Runaway Train. 2004. (Illus.). 24p. (J). 9.99 (978-0-85953-144-3(9)) Child's Play-International.

Stockham, Jessica, illus. Down by the Station. 2002. 16p. (J). bds. 5.99 (978-0-85953-140-5(6)) Child's Play-International.

Stockham, Jessica, tr. & illus. Down by the Station. Stockham, Jessica, illus. 2003. (Classic Books with Holes). (J). 6.99 (978-0-85953-132-0(5)) Child's Play-International.

Strickland, Brad, et al. Disoriented Express. l.t. ed. 2000. (Wishbone Mysteries Ser.: No. 14). 167p. (J). (gr. 4 up). lib. bdg. 23.33 (978-0-8368-2697-5(3)) Stevens, Gareth Inc.

Stubbs, Tommy, illus. A Crack in the Track: A Thomas the Tank Engine Story. 2004. (Bright & Early Board Bks.). 24p. (J). (gr. k-ps). bds. 4.99 (978-0-375-82755-6(2) , Random Hse. for Young Readers) Random Hse. Children's Bks.

Stubbs, Tommy & Awdry, Wilbert V. Thomas & Friends: May the Best Engine Win. 2006. (Thomas & Friends Ser.). (Illus.). 32p. (J). (ps-2). 12.95 (978-0-375-83842-2(2) , Golden Bks.) Random Hse. Children's Bks.

Sturges, Philemon. I Love Trains! Halpern, Shari, illus. (J). 2006. 28p. 6.99 (978-0-06-083774-7(8) , Harper Festival); 2003. 32p. pap. 6.99 (978-0-06-443667-0(5)); 2001. 32p. 14.99 (978-0-06-028900-3(7)) HarperCollins Pubs.

—I Love Trains! Halpern, Shari, illus. 2003. (ps-ps). lib. bdg. 14.15 (978-0-613-65696-2(2)) Tandem Library Bks.

Suen, Anastasia. Window Music. 2000. (978-0-606-20382-1(6)); (J). (978-0-606-20305-0(2)) Tandem Library Bks.

Sweet, Melissa, illus. Tupelo Rides the Rails. 2008. (J). (*978-0-618-71714-9(5)) Houghton Mifflin Co.

Terhune, Albert Payson. Caleb Conover: Railroader. (J). 13.95 (978-0-8488-1484-7(3)) Amereon LTD.

—Lad: A Dog. (J). 24.95 (978-0-8488-1485-4(1)) Amereon LTD.

Thompson, B. B. Strangetales: A Book of Beginning. Cuce, Thomas A. & Sutphin, Eric, illus. 2002. (Strangetales Ser.). 172p. pap. 4.95 (978-0-9725614-0-2(4)) Tricorner Publishing.

Tunnell, Michael. Mailing May. 2000. (gr. k-3). lib. bdg. 15.30 (978-0-613-30016-2(5)) Tandem Library Bks.

Tunnell, Michael O. Mailing May. Rand, Ted, illus. 2000. 32p. (J). (ps-3). pap. 6.99 (978-0-06-443724-0(8) , Harper Trophy) HarperCollins Pubs.

—Mailing May. Rand, Ted, illus. 2000. (J). (978-0-606-19983-4(7)) Tandem Library Bks.

Vanoosting, James. Walking Mary. 2005. 144p. (J). (gr. 7 up). lib. bdg. 16.89 (978-0-06-028472-5(2)) HarperCollins Pubs.

Warner, Gertrude Chandler. The Mystery of the Orphan Train, 105. Papp, Robert, illus. 2005. (Boxcar Children Mysteries Ser.: No. 105). 120p. (J). (gr. 2-7). pap. 4.50 (978-0-8075-5559-0(2)) Whitman, Albert & Co.

Warren, Bertie. Sammie's Journey to Freedom. 2006. (ENG.). 52p. per. 12.95 (*978-1-4241-5142-4(2)) PublishAmerica, Inc.

Watty, Piper. Little Engine That Could Goes on a Class Trip. 2003. (gr. k-3). lib. bdg. 11.25 (978-0-613-67563-5(0)) Tandem Library Bks.

Weiss, Ellen, et al. Trip to the North Pole: A Junior Novel. movie tie-in ed. 2004. (Polar Express Ser.). (Illus.). 128p. (J). (gr. 5-6). pap. 4.99 (978-0-618-47790-6(X)) Houghton Mifflin Co. Trade & Reference Div.

Weston, Martha. Curious George Takes a Train. 2002. (ps-2). lib. bdg. 11.80 (978-0-613-50553-6(0)) Tandem Library Bks.

Weston, Martha, illus. Curious George Takes a Train. 2002. 24p. (J). (gr. k-3). pap. 3.95 (978-0-618-06567-7(9)); tchr. ed. 12.00 (978-0-618-06566-0(0)) Houghton Mifflin Co. Trade & Reference Div.

Whipple, Wayne. Radio Boys Cronies. 2004. reprint ed. pap. 15.95 (978-1-4191-4378-6(6)) Kessinger Publishing, LLC.

Wickberg, Susan. Hey Mr. Choo-Choo, Where Are You Going? Heo, Yumi, illus. 2008. 32p. (J). (ps). 16.99 (*978-0-399-23993-9(6) , Putnam Juvenile) Penguin Group (USA) Inc.

Wilcoxen, Chuck. Niccolini's Song. Buehner, Mark, illus. 2006. 40p. (J). (ps). pap. 6.99 (978-0-14-240710-3(0) , Puffin) Penguin Group (USA) Inc.

Wilson, Linda Miller. A Few Days Journey. 1998. 124p. (YA). (gr. 4-8). 9.99 (978-0-88092-402-3(0) , 4020) Royal Fireworks Publishing Co.

Yee, Paul. Ghost Train. Chan, Harvey, illus. 2004. 29p. (J). (gr. k-4). reprint ed. 16.00 (978-0-7567-9083-7(2)) DIANE Publishing Co.

Yee, Wong Herbert. Here Come Train Mice! 2000. (Illus.). 9p. (J). (gr. k-ps). bds. 4.95 (978-0-395-98401-7(7)) Houghton Mifflin Co. Trade & Reference Div.

Yin. Coolies. Soentpiet, Chris, illus. 2003. 40p. (J). (gr. k-3). pap. 7.99 (978-0-14-250055-2(0) , Puffin) Penguin Group (USA) Inc.

—Coolies. Soentpiet, Chris K., illus. 2001. 1p. (J). (ps-3). 16.99 (978-0-399-23227-5(3) , Philomel) Penguin Group (USA) Inc.

—Coolies. 2003. (gr. 3-6). lib. bdg. 16.45 (978-0-613-62936-2(1)) Tandem Library Bks.

Ziefert, Harriet & Saaf, Donald. Train Song. 2000. (Illus.). 32p. (J). pap. 14.95 (978-0-531-30204-0(0) , Orchard Bks.) Scholastic, Inc.

RAILROADS—FREIGHT

see Freight and Freightage

RAILROADS—HISTORY

Ashley, Susan. Por Tren. Coffey, Colleen & Carrillo, Consuelo, trs. 2003. (Weekly Reader Early Learning Library). (SPA., Illus.). 24p. (J). (gr. 2 up). lib. bdg. 19.33 (978-0-8368-3737-7(1)) Stevens, Gareth Inc.

—Por Tren. 2003. (Weekly Reader Early Learning Library). (SPA., Illus.). 24p. (J). (gr. 2 up). pap. (978-0-8368-3842-8(4) , Weekly Reader Early Learning Library) Stevens, Gareth Inc.

Barron's Educational Editorial Staff. Railways. 1998. (History Ser.). (Illus.). 32p. (J). (gr. 5). pap. 5.95 (978-0-7641-0538-8(8)) Barron's Educational Series, Inc.

Barter, James E. A Worker on the Transcontinental Railroad. 2002. (Working Life Ser.). (Illus.). 112p. (J). 29.95 (978-1-59018-247-5(2) , Lucent Bks.) Thomson Gale.

Burgan, Michael. The Pullman Strike of 1894. 2007. (J). lib. bdg. (*978-0-7565-3348-9(1)) Compass Point Bks.

Burger, James P. The Transcontinental Railroad. 2002. (Library of the Westward Expansion). (Illus.). 24p. (J). (gr. 3). lib. bdg. 19.95 (978-0-8239-5852-8(3) , PowerKids Pr.) Rosen Publishing Group, Inc., The.

Chant, Christopher. Early Pioneers. Moore, John, ed. 2000. (World's Railroads Ser.). (Illus.). 64p. (YA). (gr. 5 up). 27.50 (978-0-7910-5559-5(0) , Chelsea Hse.) Facts On File, Inc.

Coleman, Wim & Perrin, Pat. The Transcontinental Railroad & the Great Race to Connect the Nation. 2006. (Wild History of the American West Ser.). (Illus.). 128p. (J). lib. bdg. 33.27 (978-1-59845-014-9(X) , MyReportLinks.com Bks.) Enslow Pubs., Inc.

Dolan, Edward F., Jr. The Transcontinental Railroad. 2002. (Kaleidoscope - American History Ser.). (Illus.). 48p. (J). 25.64 (978-0-7614-1455-1(X) , Benchmark Bks.) Cavendish, Marshall Corp.

Evans, Clark J. The Central Pacific Railroad. (Cornerstones of Freedomtrade;, Second Ser.). 48p. (J). 2007. pap. 5.95 (*978-0-531-18764-7(0)); 2003. (Illus.). (gr. 4-6). 26.00 (978-0-516-22677-4(0)) Scholastic Library Publishing. (Children's Pr.).

Gove, Bill. Sky Route to the Quarries: History of the Barre Railroad. 2003. 98p. per. 21.95 (978-1-931271-12-7(7)) Bondcliff Bks.

Halpern, Monica. Railroad Fever: Building the Transcontinental Railroad 1830-1870. 2004. (Crossroads America Ser.). (Illus.). 40p. (J). (gr. 5-9). 21.90 (978-0-7922-6993-9(4)); 12.95 (978-0-7922-6767-6(2)) National Geographic Society. (National Geographic Children's Bks.).

Hansen, Holly T. & Johnson, Jennifer Hunt. Memories of the Railroad, 14 vols. 2003. (Illus.). 21p. 9.95 (978-0-9741172-3-2(4) , CMB10) Tapis & Assocs., Inc.

Hanson-Harding, Alexandra. Transcontinental Railroad. 2002. (Instant Social Studies Activities Folders Ser.). (Illus.). 6p. (gr. 4-8). 3.95 (978-0-439-37087-5(6)) Scholastic, Inc.

Hodge, Deborah. The Kids Book of Canada's Railway: And How the CPR Was Built. Mantha, John, illus. 2000. 544p. (YA). (gr. 3 up). (978-1-55074-526-9(3)) Kids Can Pr., Ltd.

Hynson, Colin. A History of Railroads. 2006. (From Past to Present Ser.). (Illus.). 36p. (J). lib. bdg. 24.67 (978-0-8368-6287-4(2)) Stevens, Gareth Inc.

Isaacs, Sally Senzell. The First Railroads. 2004. (Illus.). 32p. (J). pap. 7.50 (978-1-4034-4791-3(8)); lib. bdg. (978-1-4034-2506-5(X)) Heinemann Library.

Jarnow, Jesse. Oil, Steel, & Railroads: America's Big Businesses in the Late 1800s. 2003. (America's Industrial Society in the Nineteenth Century Ser.). (Illus.). 32p. (J). pap. (978-0-8239-4276-3(7)) Rosen Publishing Group, Inc., The.

Kalman, Bobbie. Railroad. 1999. (978-0-606-16432-0(4)); (gr. 3-6). lib. bdg. 16.40 (978-0-613-12014-2(0)) Tandem Library Bks.

Laughlin, Rosemary. The Pullman Strike of 1894. 2006. (American Workers Ser.). (Illus.). 144p. (J). (gr. 4 up). lib. bdg. 26.95 (978-1-931798-89-1(3)) Reynolds, Morgan Inc.

Magram, Hannah Straus. Railroads of the West. 2002. (History of the Old West Ser.). (Illus.). 64p. (YA). (gr. 5 up). lib. bdg. (978-1-59084-073-3(9)) Mason Crest Pubs.

Meltzer, Milton. Hear That Train Whistle Blow! How the Railroad Changed the World. 2005. (Landmark Books Ser.). (Illus.). 176p. (J). (gr. 6-7). pap. 8.95 (978-0-375-82922-2(9) , Random Hse. Bks. for Young Readers) Random Hse. Children's Bks.

—Hear That Train Whistle Blow! How the Railroad Changed the World. 2004. (Landmark Books Ser.). (Illus.). 176p. (J). (gr. 5). 18.95 (978-0-375-81563-8(5) , Random Hse. Bks. for Young Readers) Random Hse. Children's Bks.

Morris, Neil. Trains. (Past & Present Ser.). (Illus.). 32p. lib. bdg. 24.25 (978-1-931983-37-2(2)) Chrysalis Education.

Murdico, Suzanne J. Railroads & Steamships: Important Developments in American Transportation. 2003. (America's Industrial Society in the Nineteenth Century Ser.). (Illus.). 32p. (J). (978-0-8239-4278-7(3)) Rosen Publishing Group, Inc., The.

Murphy, Jim. Across America on an Emigrant Train. 2003. (Illus.). 168p. (J). (gr. 4-6). pap. 10.95 (978-0-395-76483-1(1) , Clarion Bks.) Houghton Mifflin Co. Trade & Reference Div.

—Across America on an Emigrant Train. unabr. ed. 1998. (YA). (gr. 7 up). Class Set. 198.80 incl. audio (978-0-7887-2559-3(9) , 46729); Homework Set. 44.95 incl. audio (978-0-7887-2272-1(7) , 40739) Recorded Bks., LLC.

O'Brien, Patrick. Steam, Smoke, & Steel: Back in Time with Trains. O'Brien, Patrick, illus. 2000. (Illus.). 32p. (J). (ps-3). pap. 16.95 (978-0-88106-969-3(8)); pap. 6.95 (978-0-88106-972-3(8)) Charlesbridge Publishing, Inc.

—Steam, Smoke, & Steel: Back in Time with Trains. 2000. (J). (978-0-606-19333-7(2)) Tandem Library Bks.

Parker, Lewis K. Cornelius Vanderbilt & the Railroad Industry: Individual Title Six-Packs. (On Deck Ser.: Vol. 2). 24p. (gr. 4-5). 35.00 (978-0-7578-5848-2(1)) Rigby Education.

Perrin, Pat, intro. The Underground Railroad: Life on the Road to Freedom. 1999. (Perspectives on History Ser.). (Illus.). 66p. (YA). (gr. 5-12). pap. 6.95 (978-1-57960-051-8(4)) History Compass, LLC.

Pierce, Alan. The Transcontinental Railroad. 2005. (American Moments Ser.). (Illus.). 48p. (J). lib. bdg. 25.65 (978-1-59197-941-8(2)) ABDO Publishing Co.

Rach, Julie. The Transcontinental Railroad. 2002. (History of the Old West Ser.). (Illus.). 64p. (J). (gr. 5 up). lib. bdg. (978-1-59084-063-4(1)) Mason Crest Pubs.

Renehan, Edward J. The Transcontinental Railroad: The Gateway to the West. 2007. (Milestones in American History Ser.). 128p. (J). (gr. 6-12). 35.00 (*978-0-7910-9351-1(4) , Chelsea Hse.) Facts On File, Inc.

Richter, Bernd & Richter, Susan. All Aboard the White Pass & Yukon Route Railroad. 2003. 48p. 9.95 (978-1-931353-11-3(5)) Saddle Pal Creations, Inc.

Sandler, Martin W. Riding the Rails in the USA: Trains in American Life. 2003. (Transportation in America Ser.). (Illus.). 64p. (YA). 21.95 (978-0-19-513228-1(9)) Oxford Univ. Pr., Inc.

Shea, Therese. The Transcontinental Railroad: Using Proportions to Solve Problems. 2006. (Math for the Real World Ser.). (Illus.). 32p. (J). pap. (978-1-4042-6075-7(7)); (gr. 4-8). lib. bdg. 23.95 (978-1-4042-3361-4(X)) Rosen Publishing Group, Inc., The.

Shuter. Riding the Rails. 2004. (Technology Through Time Ser.). (Illus.). pap. 7.50 (978-1-4109-0983-1(2)) Raintree.

Shuter, Jane. Riding the Rails: Travel by Rail. 2004. (Technology Through Time Ser.). (Illus.). 32p. (J). lib. bdg. 25.70 (978-1-4109-0584-0(5)) Raintree.

Sis, Peter. The Train of States. Sis, Peter, illus. 2004. (Illus.). 64p. (J). (gr. 1 up). 17.99 (978-0-06-057838-1(6)) HarperCollins Pubs.

Spangenburg, Ray & Moser, Diane. The Story of America's Railroads. 1999. (Illus.). 96p. (YA). (gr. 6-9). lib. bdg. 23.95 (978-0-7351-0197-5(3)) Replica Bks.

Stein, R. Conrad. The Pullman Strike & the Labor Movement in American History. 2001. (In American History Ser.). (Illus.). 128p. (YA). (gr. 5-12). lib. bdg. 26.60 (978-0-7660-1300-1(6)) Enslow Pubs., Inc.

Stunkard, Geoff. Rail Mail: A Century of American Railroading on Picture Postcards. 2004. (Illus.). 128p. pap. 17.95 (978-0-9748216-0-3(8) , QMP608) Quarter Milestones Publishing.

Trenes del Pasado: Individual Title, 6 packs. (On Deck en Espanol Ser.).Tr. of Trains of the Past. (SPA.). 24p. (gr. 4-5). 35.00 (978-0-7578-6426-1(0)) Rigby Education.

Uschan, Michael V. The Transcontinental Railroad. (Events That Shaped America Ser.). (Illus.). (J). 2004. 32p. (gr. 3 up). lib. bdg. 24.67 (978-0-8368-3401-7(1)); 2003. 48p. (gr. 5 up). pap. 14.95 (978-0-8368-5410-7(1) , World Almanac Library); 2003. 48p. (gr. 5 up). lib. bdg. 30.00 (978-0-8368-5382-7(2) , World Almanac Library) Stevens, Gareth Inc.

Wetterer, Margaret K. Kate Shelley & the Midnight Express. 2005. (On My Own History Ser.). (Illus.). (J). pap. 18.95 incl. audio compact disk (978-1-59112-663-8(0)) Live Oak Media.

Williams, Harriet. Road & Rail Transportation. 2004. (History of Invention Ser.). (Illus.). 96p. (YA). (gr. 6-12). 35.00 (978-0-8160-5437-4(1)) Facts On File, Inc.

The World's Railroads. 2005. 64p. pap. 192.50 (978-0-7910-5558-8(2) , Chelsea Hse.) Facts On File, Inc.

Zimmermann, Karl. Steam Locomotives: Whistling, Chugging, Smoking Iron Horses of the Past. 2004. (Illus.). 48p. (YA). (gr. 4-6). pap. 19.95 (978-1-59078-165-4(1)) Boyds Mills Pr.

Zollitsch, Mike. Buffalo, Rochester, & Pittsburgh Railway: In Color. 2004. (Illus.). (978-1-58248-092-3(3)) Morning Sun Bks., Inc.

RAILROADS—ROLLING STOCK

see Locomotives

RAILROADS—TRAINS

Amato, William. Bullet Trains. 2002. (Reading Power Ser.). (Illus.). 24p. (J). (gr. 2). lib. bdg. 17.25 (978-0-8239-6008-8(0) , PowerKids Pr.) Rosen Publishing Group, Inc., The.

—Trenes Bala. 2004. (Vehiculos de Alta Tecnologia Ser.). (SPA & ENG., Illus.). 24p. (J). (gr. 3-6). lib. bdg. 17.25 (978-0-8239-6881-7(2) , Buenas Letra) Rosen Publishing Group, Inc., The.

Armentrout, David & Armentrout, Patricia, trs. Trains. 2003. (Transportation Ser.). (Illus.). 24p. (J). 20.64 (978-1-58952-672-3(4)) Rourke Publishing, LLC.

Ashley, Susan. Going by Train. 2003. (Going Places Ser.). (Illus.). 24p. (gr. 2 up). (YA). lib. bdg. 19.33 (978-0-8368-3732-2(0)); (J). pap. 5.95 (978-0-8368-3837-4(8)) Stevens, Gareth Inc. (Weekly Reader Early Learning Library).

Awdry, Wilbert V. Thomas & Friends ABC Wipe-Off Sound Activity Book. 2002. (Illus.). 16p. (J). spiral bd., bds. 12.98 (978-0-7853-6397-2(1) , 7160400) Publications International, Ltd.

Barish, Wendy & Jeunesse, Gallimard. Trains. Miller, Heather, tr. from ENG. Prunier, James, illus. 1998. (First Discovery Book Ser.). 24p. (J). (ps-2). 12.95 (978-0-590-38156-7(3)) Scholastic, Inc.

Barton, Byron. Trains. Barton, Byron, illus. 1998. (Illus.). 17p. (J). (ps up). bds. 6.99 (978-0-694-01167-4(3) , Harper Festival) HarperCollins Pubs.

Beyer, Mark. Trains of the Past. 2002. (Reading Power Ser.). (Illus.). 24p. (J). (gr. 1). lib. bdg. 17.25 (978-0-8239-5986-0(4) , PowerKids Pr.) Rosen Publishing Group, Inc., The.

—Trenes del Pasado. 2004. (Transporte Ayer y Hoy Ser.). (SPA & ENG., Illus.). 24p. (J). (gr. 3-6). lib. bdg. 17.25 (978-0-8239-6852-7(9) , Buenas Letra) Rosen Publishing Group, Inc., The.

Bullet Trains, 6, Pack. (On Deck Ser.). 24p. (gr. 4-5). 35.00 (978-0-7578-1054-1(3)) Rigby Education.

Candlewick Books Staff, Books. Train Ride. 2003. (gr. k-3). lib. bdg. 11.80 (978-0-613-74747-9(X)) Tandem Library Bks.

Cefrey, Holly. High Speed Trains. 2001. (High Interest Bks.). (Illus.). 48p. (J). (gr. 7-12). pap. 6.95 (978-0-516-23260-7(6) , Children's Pr.) Scholastic Library Publishing.

—High Speed Trains. 2001. (gr. 7-12). lib. bdg. 15.25 (978-0-613-52080-5(7)) Tandem Library Bks.

Chant, Christopher. Famous Trains of the 20th Century. Moore, John, ed. 2000. (World's Railroads Ser.). (Illus.). 64p. (J). (gr. 5 up). 27.50 (978-0-7910-5563-2(9) , Chelsea Hse.) Facts On File, Inc.

—High Speed Trains. Moore, John, ed. 2000. (World's Railroads Ser.). (Illus.). 64p. (J). (gr. 5 up). 27.50 (978-0-7910-5565-6(5) , Chelsea Hse.) Facts On File, Inc.

—Passenger Trains. Moore, John, ed. 2000. (World's Railroads Ser.). (Illus.). 64p. (J). (gr. 5 up). 27.50 (978-0-7910-5561-8(2) , Chelsea Hse.) Facts On File, Inc.

—Railway Locomotives. Moore, John, ed. 2000. (World's Railroads Ser.). (Illus.). 64p. (J). (gr. 5 up). 27.50 (978-0-7910-5560-1(4) , Chelsea Hse.) Facts On File, Inc.

—Rapid Transit Systems. Moore, John, ed. 2000. (World's Railroads Ser.). (Illus.). 64p. (J). (gr. 5 up). 27.50 (978-0-7910-5564-9(7) , Chelsea Hse.) Facts On File, Inc.

Coiley, John. Train. 2000. (Eyewitness Bks.). (Illus.). 64p. (J). (gr. 4-7). 15.99 (978-0-7894-5756-1(3)) Dorling Kindersley Publishing, Inc.

Coiley, John & Dorling Kindersley Publishing Staff. Train. 2000. (Eyewitness Bks.). (Illus.). 64p. (J). (gr. 4-7). lib. bdg. 19.99 (978-0-7894-6588-7(4)) Dorling Kindersley Publishing, Inc.

Crowther, Robert. Trains: A Pop-Up Railroad Book. Crowther, Robert, illus. 2006. (Illus.). 10p. (J). (gr. 1). 17.99 (978-0-7636-3082-9(9)) Candlewick Pr.

D'Amelio, Dennis P. All Aboard the Alphabet Train. D'Amelio, Dennis P., illus. 1998. (Right Track Bks.: Vol. 3). (Illus.). (J). (ps). pap. (978-1-891528-61-3(0)) Telescopic Pr.

—Shape Train Coming. D'Amelio, Dennis P., illus. 1998. (Right Track Bks.: Vol. 2). (Illus.). (J). (ps). pap. (978-1-891528-55-2(6)) Telescopic Pr.

David West. Train. 2006. (Illus.). 32p. (J). pap. (978-1-4109-2564-0(1)) Steck-Vaughn.

DK Publishing Staff. Little Choo Choo Box Set. 2007. 20p. (J). (ps-2). 19.99 ***(978-0-7566-3091-1(6))*** Dorling Kindersley Publishing, Inc.

Doeden, Matt. Trains. 2007. (Mighty Machines Ser.). 24p. (J). (978-0-7368-6722-1(8) , Pebble Bks.) Capstone Pr., Inc.

Dorling Kindersley Publishing Staff. The Big Book of Trains. 1998. (Illus.). 32p. (J). (gr. k-3). 14.99 (978-0-7894-3436-4(9)) Dorling Kindersley Publishing, Inc.

—Train. (Ultimate sticker Bks.). 16p. (J). 2005. pap. 6.99 (978-0-7566-1460-7(0)); 2004. pap. 3.99 (978-0-7566-0249-9(1)) Dorling Kindersley Publishing, Inc.

Gaff, Jackie & Harris, Michael. Trains: All Aboard for a Journey into the History & Science of Travel by Rail. 2002. (Investigations Ser.). (Illus.). 64p. (gr. 3-7). 14.95 (978-0-7548-0837-4(8) , Lorenz Bks.) Anness Publishing, Inc.

Gerver, Jane E. A Crack in the Track: A Thomas the Tank Engine Story. Stubbs, Tommy, illus. 2001. (Beginner Bks. Ser.). 48p. (J). (ps-3). lib. bdg. 11.99 (978-0-375-91246-7(0) , Random Hse. Bks. for Young Readers) Random Hse. Children's Bks.

Golden Books Staff. Thomas' New Route. 2005. (Illus.). 32p. (J). (ps-2). pap. 4.99 (978-0-375-83085-3(5) , Golden Bks.) Random Hse. Children's Bks.

Hanson, Anders. Let's Go by Train. 2007. (Let's Go! Ser.). (ENG., Illus.). 24p. (J). (ps-3). lib. bdg. 19.93 ***(978-1-59928-903-8(2)*** , SandCastle) ABDO Publishing Co.

Harrison, Peter, et al. Car & Road, Train & Track: Discover How Modern Land-Based Vehicles Changed Our World, How They Have Evolved & How They Work. 2004. (Illus.). 128p. pap. 17.99 (978-1-84476-004-6(9) , Southwater) Anness Publishing GBR. *Dist:* National Bk. Network.

Hill, Lee Sullivan. Trains. 2003. (gr. k-3). lib. bdg. 14.10 (978-0-613-52517-6(5)) Tandem Library Bks.

Hofer, Charles. Bullet Trains. 2008. (J) lib. bdg. ***(978-1-4042-4174-9(4)*** , PowerKids Pr.) Rosen Publishing Group, Inc., The.

Isaacs, Sally Senzell. The First Railroads. 2004. (Illus.). 32p. (J). pap. 7.50 (978-1-4034-4791-3(8)); lib. bdg. (978-1-4034-2506-5(X)) Heinemann Library.

Johnstone, Michael, et al. Trains. (Illus.). 32p. (J). mass mkt. 8.99 (978-0-590-24654-5(2)) Scholastic, Inc.

Kate Shelley & the Midnight Express. 9.95 (978-1-59112-169-5(8)) Live Oak Media.

Kirk, Ellen. My Train Book. 2007. (Illus.). 16p. (J). 5.99 ***(978-0-06-089970-7(0))*** HarperCollins Pubs.

Kraft, Earle R. The Mightiest of Them All: The Pennsylvania Railroad. 2002. 94p. per. 22.00 (978-1-893108-70-7(8)) Neighborhood Pr. Publishing.

LaFontaine, Bruce. Train Stickers. 1998. (Illus.). 4p. (J). (ps-5). 1.50 (978-0-486-40310-6(6)) Dover Pubns., Inc.

Litchfield, Jo & Brooks, F. Trains. 2004. (Chunky Board Bks.). (Illus.). 10p. (J). 4.95 (978-0-7945-0348-2(9) , Usborne) EDC Publishing.

Loves, June. Trains. 2001. (Database Transportation Ser.). (Illus.). 32p. (J). (gr. 4 up). 22.95 (978-0-7910-6586-0(3) , 010506, Chelsea Hse.) Facts On File, Inc.

Maggard, John & LaFever, Greg, illus. Name That Train. 1998. 10p. (J). (ps-3). 7.95 (978-1-929174-07-2(1)) Oshkosh B'Gosh, Inc.

Mayer, Cassie. By Train. 2006. (Illus.). 24p. (J). (978-1-4034-8392-8(2)); pap. (978-1-4034-8399-7(X)) Heinemann Library.

Maynard, Christopher. High-Speed Trains. 2003. (Need for Speed Ser.). (Illus.). 32p. (J). (gr. 3-6). pap. 7.95 (978-0-8225-0390-3(5)) Lerner Publishing Group.

—Trains. 2005. (Need for Speed Ser.). (Illus.). 32p. (gr. 3-5). lib. bdg. 23.93 (978-0-8225-0387-3(5)) Lerner Publishing Group.

Mitton, Tony. Terrific Trains. Parker, Ant, illus. 2000. (Amazing Machines Ser.). 24p. (J). (ps-k). 3.95 (978-0-7534-5306-3(1) , Kingfisher) Houghton Mifflin Co. Trade & Reference Div.

—Terrific Trains. 2000. (ps-2). lib. bdg. 11.80 (978-0-613-90365-3(X)) Tandem Library Bks.

O'Brien, Patrick. Steam, Smoke & Steel: Back in Time with Trains. 2000. (gr. k-3). lib. bdg. 15.25 (978-0-613-35240-6(8)) Tandem Library Bks.

Oxlade, Chris. Train. 2002. (Take It Apart Ser.). (Illus.). 32p. (J). lib. bdg. 24.25 (978-1-930643-96-3(9)) Chrysalis Education.

—Train. Grey, Mike, illus. 1999. (Take It Apart Ser.). (J). 22.00 (978-0-382-42075-7(6)) Silver, Burdett & Ginn, Inc.

—Trains. (Transportation Around the World Ser.). 32p. pap. 6.95 (978-1-4034-4135-5(9)); 2001. (Illus.). (J). lib. bdg. 21.36 (978-1-57572-307-5(7)) Heinemann Library.

—Trains. 2006. (Mighty Machines Ser.). (978-1-58340-922-0(X)) Smart Apple Media.

Parker, Marjorie. Hello, Freight Train Level 1. Kolar, Bob, illus. 2005. (Scholastic Reader Ser.). 32p. (J). pap. 3.99 (978-0-439-59891-0(5)) Scholastic, Inc.

Parker, Steve. The Inside & Out Guide to Speed Machines. 2006. (Illus.). 32p. (J). (978-1-4034-9089-6(9)); pap. (978-1-4034-9096-4(1)) Heinemann Library.

Perry, Phyllis J. Trains. 2001. (Transportation & Communication Ser.). (Illus.). 46p. (J). (gr. 1-4). lib. bdg. 23.93 (978-0-7660-1645-3(5)) Enslow Pubs., Inc.

Pipe, Jim. Trains. 2007. (J). ***(978-1-59604-165-3(X))*** Stargazer Bks.

Priddy, Roger. 3 in 1: My Big Truck, Train, Rescue. 2005. (J). bds. 16.95 (978-0-312-49561-9(7) , Priddy Bks.) St. Martin's Pr.

Radtke, Becky. Trains Activity Book. 2007. 64p. (J). pap. 1.50 ***(978-0-486-45683-6(8))*** Dover Pubns., Inc.

Ray, Mary Lyn. All Aboard! Hirao, Amiko & Goodwin-Sturges, illus. 2002. 32p. (J). (ps-3). 14.95 (978-0-316-73507-0(8)) Little, Brown Bks. for Young Readers.

Richardson, Adele D. Freight Trains. 2000. (Transportation Library). (Illus.). 24p. (J). (gr. 1-2). lib. bdg. 18.60 (978-0-7368-0607-7(5) , Bridgestone Bks.) Capstone Pr., Inc.

Riggs, Kate. Trains. 2007. (J). (978-1-58341-529-0(7) , Creative Education) Creative Co., The.

Rockwell, Anne F. Trains. Rockwell, Anne F., illus. 2002. (Illus.). (J). 13.19 (978-0-7587-4353-4(X)) Book Wholesalers, Inc.

Rogers, Hal. Trains. 2008. (Machines at Work Ser.). 24p. (J). 22.79 ***(978-1-59296-960-9(7))*** Child's World, Inc.

Roza, Greg. The Incredible Story of Trains. 2004. (Kid's Guide to Incredible Technology Ser.). (Illus.). 24p. (J). lib. bdg. 19.95 (978-0-8239-6712-4(3) , PowerKids Pr.) Rosen Publishing Group, Inc., The.

Scholastic Editorial Staff. Learn with Lego: Trains. 2007. (Lego Ser.). 24p. (J). pap. 4.99 ***(978-0-439-91546-5(5))*** Scholastic, Inc.

Sheffield, Sarah. A Train on the Track: Learning the TR Sound. 2002. (PowerPhonics Ser.). (Illus.). 24p. (J). (gr. 1). lib. bdg. 18.50 (978-0-8239-5937-2(6) , PowerKids Pr.) Rosen Publishing Group, Inc., The.

Shuter, Jane. Riding the Rails: Travel by Rail. 2004. (Technology Through Time Ser.). (Illus.). 32p. (J). lib. bdg. 25.70 (978-1-4109-0584-0(5)) Raintree.

Sievert, Terri. The World's Fastest Trains. 2002. (Built for Speed Ser.). (Illus.). 48p. (J). (gr. 3-4). lib. bdg. 21.26 (978-0-7368-1061-6(7) , Capstone High-Interest Bks.) Capstone Pr., Inc.

Smithyman, Kathryn & Kalman, Bobbie. Trains on the Tracks. rev. ed. 2007. (Vehicles on the Move Ser.). (Illus.). 32p. (J). (gr. 1-5). pap. ***(978-0-7787-3059-0(X))*** Crabtree Publishing Co.

Stickland, Paul. Trains. 2004. (By Air, Sea, & Land Ser.). (Illus.). 24p. (J). pap. 3.99 (978-0-7696-3378-7(1) , Waterbird Bks.) School Specialty Publishing.

—Trains. Stickland, Paul, illus. 1998. (On the Move Ser.). (Illus.). 16p. (J). (ps up). lib. bdg. 19.93 (978-0-8368-2154-3(8)) Stevens, Gareth Inc.

Stille, Darlene R. Freight Trains. 2001. (Illus.). 32p. (J). (gr. 1 up). lib. bdg. 19.93 (978-0-7565-0148-8(2)) Compass Point Bks.

Stone, Lynn M. Freight Trains. 1999. (Trains Discovery Library). (Illus.). 24p. (J). (gr. 1-4). lib. bdg. 19.27 (978-0-86593-517-4(3)) Rourke Publishing, LLC.

—Freight Yards. 1999. (Trains Discovery Library). (Illus.). 24p. (J). (gr. 1-4). lib. bdg. 19.27 (978-0-86593-522-8(X)) Rourke Publishing, LLC.

—Passenger Trains. 1999. (Trains Discovery Library). (Illus.). 24p. (J). (gr. 1-4). lib. bdg. 19.27 (978-0-86593-518-1(1)) Rourke Publishing, LLC.

Todd, Traci. C Is for Caboose: Riding the Rails from A to Z. 2007. (Illus.). 40p. (J). (ps-3). 14.95 (978-0-8118-5643-0(7)) Chronicle Bks. LLC.

Trombello, William. How a Real Locomotive Works. 2006. (Illus.). 33p. (J). per. 18.95 (978-1-933449-21-0(7)) Nightengale Pr.

Weitzman, David L. The John Bull: A British Locomotive Comes to America. Weitzman, David L., illus. 2004. (Illus.). 40p. (J). 16.00 (978-0-374-38037-3(6) , Farrar, Straus & Giroux (BYR)) Farrar, Straus & Giroux.

West, David. Train. 2006. (Why Things Don't Work Ser.). (Illus.). 32p. (J). (gr. 4-6). lib. bdg. 29.29 (978-1-4109-2557-2(9)) Raintree.

Whiteside, Sandra M. A Train Named McSwain. Stancil, Mary H., ed. Ritter, Donna C., illus. 1998. 40p. (J). (gr. k-2). pap. 5.95 (978-1-892212-03-0(X)) Love Publishing Co.

Zimmerman, Brooke. Trains: Lift-A-Flap Fun. Wieland, Don & Lovell, Mike, trs. Wieland, Don, illus. 2002. (Active Minds Ser.). 12p. (J). bds. 12.98 (978-0-7853-6303-3(3) , 7158300) Publications International, Ltd.

RAILROADS, UNDERGROUND

see Subways

RAILWAYS

see Railroads

RAIN AND RAINFALL

see also Floods; Meteorology; Snow; Storms

Ada, Alma Flor. How the Rainbow Came to Be. (Stories the Year 'Round Ser.). (Illus.). 16p. (J). (gr. k-3). pap. 8.95 (978-1-58105-220-6(0)) Santillana USA Publishing Co., Inc.

Barry, Frances. Duckie's Rainbow. Barry, Frances, illus. 2004. (Illus.). 14p. (J). (gr. k-ps). 7.99 (978-0-7636-2066-0(1)) Candlewick Pr.

Bauer, Marion Dane & Wallace, John. Rain. 2004. (Ready-to-Reads Ser.). (Illus.). 32p. (J). pap. 3.99 (978-0-689-85439-2(0) , Aladdin) Simon & Schuster Children's Publishing.

Berger, Melvin & Berger, Gilda. A Rainy Day. 2003. (Scholastic Readers Ser.). (Illus.). (J). pap. (978-0-439-56694-0(0)) Scholastic, Inc.

Boerger, Kristin & Boyett, Suzi. Let's Read about Rain. 2006. (J). lib. bdg. ***(978-0-8368-7805-9(1));*** (Illus.). 12p. pap. ***(978-0-8368-7810-3(8))*** Stevens, Gareth Inc. (Weekly Reader Early Learning Library).

—Llueve. 2006. (ENG & SPA.). (J). pap. ***(978-0-8368-8118-9(4));*** lib. bdg. ***(978-0-8368-8113-4(3))*** Stevens, Gareth Inc. (Weekly Reader Early Learning Library).

Brimner, Larry Dane. Raindrops. Brooks, David J., illus. 1999. (Rookie Reader Skill Set Ser.). 32p. (J). (gr. k-2). pap. 4.95 (978-0-516-26477-6(X) , Children's Pr.) Scholastic Library Publishing.

—Raindrops. Brooks, David J., illus. 1999. (J). (gr. k-3). lib. bdg. 12.95 (978-0-613-37520-7(3)) Tandem Library Bks.

Bundey, Nikki. Rain & People. 2005. (Science of Weather Ser.). (Illus.). 32p. (gr. 4-6). lib. bdg. 21.27 (978-1-57505-494-0(9)) Lerner Publishing Group.

—Rain & the Earth. 2005. (Science of Weather Ser.). (Illus.). 32p. (gr. 4-6). lib. bdg. 21.27 (978-1-57505-469-8(8)) Lerner Publishing Group.

Burke, Jennifer S. Rainy Days. 2000. (Illus.). 24p. (J). (gr. 4-7). lib. bdg. 12.95 (978-0-613-50492-8(5)) Tandem Library Bks.

Capstone Press, contrib. by. Rain. 2005. (Our Seasons & Weather Ser.). 24p. (YA). (gr. k-3). pap. (978-1-56065-841-2(X) , Pebble Bks.) Capstone Pr., Inc.

Cary Brown. Rain. 2006. 267p. 25.95 (978-1-59414-424-0(9) , Five Star Trade) Thomson Gale.

D'Aubuisson, Elisabeth. Rainy Days. 2007. (What's the Weather? Ser.). (Illus.). 24p. (J). (gr. k-3). lib. bdg. 21.25 (978-1-4042-3682-0(1) , PowerKids Pr.) Rosen Publishing Group, Inc., The.

Un día lluvioso (A Rainy Day) 2006. (J). 18.60 (978-0-8225-6211-5(1) , Ediciones Lerner) Lerner Publishing Group.

Un Día lluvioso (A Rainy Day) 2007. (J). pap. 4.25 (978-0-8225-6550-5(1) , Ediciones Lerner) Lerner Publishing Group.

Doherty, Gillian. Rainy Day. 2005. (First Discovery Ser.). 24p. (J). 9.99 (978-0-7945-0867-8(7) , Usborne) EDC Publishing.

Donnelly, Karen J. Droughts of the Past & the Future. 2003. (Earths Changing Weather & Climate Ser.). (Illus.). 24p. (J). lib. bdg. 18.75 (978-0-8239-6217-4(2) , PowerKids Pr.) Rosen Publishing Group, Inc., The.

Dorling Kindersley Publishing Staff, contrib. by. Rainbow Colors. 2004. (Baby Love Ser.). (Illus.). 16p. (J). bds. 4.99 (978-0-7566-0212-3(2)) Dorling Kindersley Publishing, Inc.

Doubleday Entertainment USA - Weather Watch: Rain. 2006. (J). per. 7.95 (978-1-59566-230-9(8)); per. 7.95 (978-1-59566-231-6(6)) QEB Publishing Inc.

Doudna, Kelly. It Is Raining. 2003. (Weather Ser.). (Illus.). 23p. (J). (ps-3). lib. bdg. 19.93 (978-1-57765-774-3(8)) ABDO Publishing Co.

Firely, G. M. The Raindrop. Holmes, Joshua D., illus. 2004. 21p. pap. 14.95 (978-1-4137-3388-4(3)) PublishAmerica, Inc.

Flanagan, Alice K. Rain. 2003. (Wonder Books Level 1: Weather Ser.). (Illus.). 24p. (J). (ps-2). 22.79 (978-1-56766-452-2(0)) Child's World, Inc.

Galiano, Dean. Clouds, Rain & Snow. rev. ed. 2005. (Weather Watcher's Library). (Illus.). 48p. (gr. 5-8). lib. bdg. 23.95 (978-0-8239-3771-4(2)) Rosen Publishing Group, Inc., The.

Ganeri, Anita. Rain. 2004. (Illus.). 24p. (J). pap. (978-0-8368-4304-0(5)); lib. bdg. 19.33 (978-0-8368-4299-9(5)) Stevens, Gareth Inc.

Harcourt School Publishers Staff. Welcome to the Rain: Take-Home Book. 1999. (Signatures Ser.). (Illus.). (J). pap. 1.90 (978-0-15-313911-6(0)) Harcourt Schl. Pubs.

Harvey, Roger. Caillou & the Rain. rev. ed. 2006. (Abracadabra Ser.). (Illus.). 24p. (J). pap. 4.95 ***(978-2-89450-595-3(7))*** Chouette Publishing CAN. *Dist:* Independent Pubs. Group.

Head, Honor. Rain. 2006. (QEB Weather Watch Ser.). (Illus.). 24p. (J). lib. bdg. 16.95 (978-1-59566-185-2(9)) QEB Publishing Inc.

Herriges, Ann. Rain. 2006. (Blastoff! Readers Ser.). (Illus.). 24p. (J). lib. bdg. 16.95 (978-1-60014-027-3(0)) Bellwether Media.

I Feel Cold: Individual Title Six-Packs. (ps-2). 23.00 (978-0-7635-9015-4(0)) Rigby Education.

Jacobs, Marian B. Why Does It Rain? 1999. (Library of Why). (Illus.). 24p. (J). (gr. k-4). lib. bdg. 18.75 (978-0-8239-5273-1(8) , PowerKids Pr.) Rosen Publishing Group, Inc., The.

Jango-Cohen, Judith. Why Does It Rain? Feltes, Tess, illus. 2006. (On My Own Science Ser.). (J). 48p. pap. 5.95 (978-1-57505-854-2(5)); 47p. (gr. 2-4). lib. bdg. 25.26 (978-1-57505-762-0(X)) Lerner Publishing Group. (Millbrook Pr.).

Jennings, Terry J. The Weather: Rain. 2004. (J). lib. bdg. 27.10 (978-1-59389-143-5(1)) Chrysalis Education.

Kerr, Kimberly. The Raindrops Adventure: From Raindrops to Rainbows. Kerr, Kimberly, illus. 1999. (Illus.). 48p. (ps-6). pap. 14.95 (978-0-9672073-0-8(4)) Kerr, Kimberly Pr.

Lazo, Caroline Evensen. Frank Gehry. 2006. (First Step Nonfiction Ser.). (Illus.). 112p. (J). (ps-7). 29.27 (978-0-8225-2649-0(2) , Lerner Pubns.) Lerner Publishing Group.

Lynn, Sara. Rain & Shine: A First Look at Seasons. James, Diane, illus. rev. ed. 2000. (Play & Discover Ser.). (J). (ps-2). 9.95 (978-1-58728-042-9(6) , Two Can Publishing) T&N Children's Publishing.

Maas, K. C. Rain. 2000. 245p. (YA). (gr. 9 up). pap. 24.95 (978-1-930002-23-4(8)) I & L Publishing.

Mann, Rachel. Sun & Rain. 2003. (Compass Point Phonics Readers Ser.). (Illus.). 16p. (J). (gr. 1 up). 13.26 (978-0-7565-0525-7(9)) Compass Point Bks.

Mayer, Cassie. Lluvia. 2006. (ENG & SPA., Illus.). 24p. (J). ***(978-1-4034-8655-4(7))*** Heinemann Library.

—Lluvia (Rain) 2006. (ENG & SPA., Illus.). 24p. (J). pap. ***(978-1-4034-8663-9(8))*** Heinemann Library.

Mayer, Cassie. Rain. 2006. (Illus.). 24p. (J). (978-1-4034-8414-7(7)); pap. 5.99 (978-1-4034-8422-2(8)) Heinemann Library.

McKinney, Barbara Shaw. A Drop Around the World. Maydak, Michael S., illus. 1998. 32p. (YA). (gr. k-7). 16.95 (978-1-883220-71-6(8)); pap. 7.95 (978-1-883220-72-3(6)) Dawn Pubns.

Merk, A. Rain, Snow & Ice. 2003. (Weather Report Discovery Library). (Illus.). 24p. (gr. 1-4). 14.95 (978-1-58952-571-9(X)) Rourke Publishing, LLC.

Milbourne, Anna. Un Dia de Lluvia. Gill, Sarah, illus. 2005. (SPA.). 24p. (J). (ps-ps). 9.99 (978-0-7460-6636-2(8) , Usborne) EDC Publishing.

Nelson, Robin. Rainy. 2004. (First Step Nonfiction Ser.). (J). pap. (978-0-8225-5365-6(1) , Lerner Pubns.) Lerner Publishing Group.

—A Rainy Day. (First Step Nonfiction Ser.). (Illus.). 24p. (gr. k-2). 2005. lib. bdg. 17.27 (978-0-8225-0173-2(2)); 2003. (J). pap. 4.25 (978-0-8225-1962-1(3)) Lerner Publishing Group.

—The Water Cycle. 2003. (First Step Nonfiction Ser.). (Illus.). 24p. (J). (gr. k-2). lib. bdg. 18.60 (978-0-8225-4596-5(9)) Lerner Publishing Group.

Owen, Andy & Ashwell, Miranda. Rain. (What Is Weather? Ser.). (Illus.). 32p. (J). (gr. k-2). 2002. pap. 6.95 (978-1-4034-0062-8(8) , 91506); 1999. lib. bdg. 21.36 (978-1-57572-789-9(7)) Heinemann Library.

Picture Window Books, contrib. by. Flakes & Flurries. (Amazing Science Ser.). 24p. (J). pap. 7.95 (978-1-4048-0342-8(4)) Picture Window Bks.

—Splish! Splash! (Amazing Science Ser.). 24p. (J). pap. 7.95 (978-1-4048-0339-8(4)) Picture Window Bks.

Posner, Renee & Quinton, Sasha. Suzy Season Loves Fall. D'Argo, Laura, illus. 2003. (Be Mine Bears Ser.). (J). bds. 4.99 (978-1-58209-352-9(0)) Books Are Fun, Ltd.

Powell, Jillian. Rain & Us. 1998. (Weather Ser.). (Illus.). 32p. (J). (gr. 1-5). lib. bdg. 16.95 (978-1-887068-38-3(4)) Smart Apple Media.

Rain, 6 vols. (gr. k-2). 28.95 (978-0-7368-8009-1(7)) Red Brick Learning.

Rain, Snow, & Hail: Individual Title Six-Packs. (Discovery World Ser.). 16p. (gr. 1-2). 28.00 (978-0-7635-8466-5(5)) Rigby Education.

Rain Weather. 2006. (Illus.). 24p. (J). (gr. k-2). 18.50 ***(978-0-531-17879-9(X))*** Scholastic Library Publishing.

Raintree Steck-Vaughn Staff. Esta Lloviendo. 2000. (Coleccion en Parejas). (SPA.). (J). pap., stu. ed. 20.45 (978-0-7398-0829-0(X)) Steck-Vaughn.

—Rainy Day. 2000. (Read All about It Ser.). (Illus.). (J). pap. 4.95 (978-0-8114-3749-3(3)) Steck-Vaughn.

A Rainy Day, Vol. 2. 2005. (Our Seasons & Weather Ser.). (YA). (gr. k-3). (978-0-7368-8622-2(2) , Pebble Bks.) Capstone Pr., Inc.

A Rainy Day, 6 vols. (gr. k-2). 28.95 (978-0-7368-8628-4(1)) Red Brick Learning.

Richards, Julie. It's Raining! 2004. (J). lib. bdg. 27.10 (978-1-58340-536-9(4)) Smart Apple Media.

Rogers, Alan. Sol y Lluvia. 2004. (Pequenos Gigantes Ser.).Tr. of Bright & Breezy. (SPA., Illus.). 16p. (ps-k). 5.95 (978-1-58728-298-0(4) , Two Can Publishing) T&N Children's Publishing.

Rosenberg, Pam. Rainy Weather Days. 2006. (Scholastic News Nonfiction Readers Ser.). 24p. (J). 19.00 (978-0-531-16769-4(0) , Children's Pr.) Scholastic Library Publishing.

Rustad, Martha E. H. Today Is Rainy. 2006. (Illus.). 24p. (J). 19.93 (978-0-7368-5344-6(8)) Capstone Pr., Inc.

Sanchez, Juan J. Where Does the Rainbow Live? (Donde Vive el Arco Iris?) Xu, Paul, illus. 1998. (Tales in Two Languages Ser.). (ENG & SPA.). 16p. (J). (ps-3). pap. 6.95 (978-1-56492-253-3(7)) Laredo Publishing Co., Inc.

Saunders-Smith, Gail. Las Nubes/Clouds. 2003. (Weather Bilingual Ser.). (ENG & SPA., Illus.). 24p. (J). lib. bdg. 15.93 (978-0-7368-2307-4(7)) Capstone Pr., Inc.

—Rain. 1998. (Weather Ser.). (Illus.). 24p. (J). (ps-2). pap. 13.25 (978-0-516-21331-6(8) , Children's Pr.) Scholastic Library Publishing.

Schaefer, Lola M. A Rainy Day. Saunders-Smith, Gail, ed. 1999. (What Kind of Day is It? Ser.). (Illus.). 24p. (J). (gr. k-1). lib. bdg. 15.93 (978-0-7368-0404-2(8) , Pebble Bks.) Capstone Pr., Inc.

PQR

—A Rainy Day. 1999. pap. 13.25 (978-0-516-21929-5(4) , Children's Pr.) Scholastic Library Publishing.

Scholastic, Inc. Staff. Follow a Raindrop: The Water Cycle. 2000. (Super Science Readers Ser.). (Illus.). 16p. (J). 10.95 (978-0-439-18622-3(6)) Scholastic, Inc.

Sherman, Joseph. Splish! Splash! A Book about Rain. Wesley, Omarr, illus. 2004. (Amazing Science Ser.). 24p. (C). (gr. k-3). 22.60 (978-1-4048-0095-3(6)) Picture Window Bks.

Sievert, Terri. Precipitation. 2005. (Weather Update Ser.). (Illus.). 24p. (J). 21.26 (978-0-7368-3737-8(X)) Capstone Pr., Inc.

Sloan, Peter. Rain. 1999. (gr. k-3). lib. bdg. 11.80 (978-0-613-30691-1(0)) Tandem Library Bks.

Solanet & Bergandi. ¿Que Hace Llover? (Coleccion Primeros Pasos en la Ciencia). (SPA., Illus.). 176p. (J). (gr. 1-3). (978-950-724-017-1(9) , LMA8215) Lumen ARG. *Dist:* Lectorum Pubns., Inc.

Staunton, Ted & Clark, Brenda. L' Homme De Boue, Mini Bk. (FRE.). (J). pap. 3.99 (978-0-590-74821-6(1)) Scholastic, Inc.

Stein, Meg. Rain. 1999. (ps-2). lib. bdg. 11.80 (978-0-613-30690-4(2)) Tandem Library Bks.

Stojic, Manya. Rain. Stojic, Manya, illus. 2000. (Illus.). 32p. (J). (gr. k-3). 15.95 (978-0-517-80085-0(3) , Crown Books For Young Readers) Random Hse. Children's Bks.

Thomas, Meredith. Rainbows of the Sea. Thomas, Meredith, illus. 1998. (Illus.). 32p. (J). (gr. k-3). 15.95 (978-1-57255-432-0(0)) Mondo Publishing.

Thompson, C. E. Where Does Rain Come From? 1998. (Junior Scientist Ser.). (J). pap. 9.95 (978-0-8362-5328-3(0)) Andrews McMeel Publishing.

Vastola, Pam. Rain: Learning the AI Sound. (PowerPhonics Ser.). (Illus.). (J). 2002. 24p. (gr. 1). lib. bdg. 18.50 (978-0-8239-5943-3(0)); 2001. 23p. pap. 26.40 (978-0-8239-8288-2(2)) Rosen Publishing Group, Inc., The. (PowerKids Pr.).

Waiakea High Writer's Group. Hot Lava, Cool Rain. 2001. (gr. 7-12). lib. bdg. 25.20 (978-0-613-74532-1(9)) Tandem Library Bks.

Watts, Claire. Heat Hazard: Droughts. 2004. (Turbulent Planet Ser.). (Illus.). 48p. (J). 28.56 (978-1-4109-1098-1(9)) Harcourt Schl. Pubs.

—Heat Hazards: Droughts. 2004. (Turbulent Planet Ser.). (Illus.). 48p. (J). pap. 8.50 (978-1-4109-1209-1(4)) Harcourt Schl. Pubs.

We Need Rain. 2002. (Benchmark Bks.). (J). pap. 3.74 (978-0-7398-5839-4(4)) Steck-Vaughn.

Wilkes, Angela. Lluvia y Sol. 2004. (Ladders Ser.).Tr. of Rain & Sunshine. (SPA., Illus.). 32p. (J). (ps-3). pap. 6.95 (978-1-58728-408-3(1) , Two Can Publishing) T&N Children's Publishing.

Williams, Judith. Why Is It Raining? 2005. (I Like Weather! Ser.). (Illus.). 24p. (J). lib. bdg. 21.26 (978-0-7660-2318-5(4) , Enslow Elementary) Enslow Pubs., Inc.

Willis, Shirley. Dime Por Que Es Mojada la Lluvia. 2000. (SPA.). (gr. k-3). lib. bdg. 14.10 (978-0-613-72671-9(5)) Tandem Library Bks.

—Tell Me Why Rain Is Wet. 2000. (Whiz Kids Ser.). (Illus.). 32p. (J). (gr. 1-3). pap. 5.95 (978-0-531-15982-8(5) , Watts, Franklin) Scholastic Library Publishing.

RAIN AND RAINFALL—FICTION

Aigner-Clark, Julie. What Does Violet See? Raindrops & Puddles. Zaidi, Nadeem, illus. 2002. (Baby Einstein Ser.). 16p. (ps-ps). 5.99 (978-0-7868-0871-7(3)) Disney Pr.

Alumenda, Stephen. Toko & the Lost Kittens. 2004. (Illus.). 19p. 13.95 (978-9966-25-170-1(7)) Heinemann Kenya, Limited (East African Educational Publishers Ltd E.A.E.P.) KEN. *Dist:* Michigan State Univ. Pr.

Amick, Wanda Codper & Jharpe, Sandra Codper. The Mystery of the Rainbow & the Showdown Between Two Angels. Hardy, Lea, ed. 1999. 104p. (J). pap. 7.95 (978-0-9675187-0-1(9)) Rainbow Angel Pubns.

Appelt, Kathi. Rain Dance. Chollat, Emilie, illus. 2001. (Growing Tree Ser.). 24p. (J). (ps up). 9.95 (978-0-694-01291-6(2) , Harper Festival) HarperCollins Pubs.

Arnosky, Jim. Rabbits & Raindrops. Arnosky, Jim, illus. 2001. (Illus.). 32p. (J). (ps-k). pap. 5.99 (978-0-698-11815-7(4) , Putnam Juvenile) Penguin Group (USA) Inc.

—Rabbits & Raindrops. 2000. (gr. k-3). lib. bdg. 14.15 (978-0-613-36004-3(4)) Tandem Library Bks.

Azordegan, Kambiz. Mr. Rain: The Grate Rain. Sajem, Johnny, illus. abr. l.t. ed. 1998. (Tootee's Magical Stories Ser.: Vol. 4). 40p. (J). 9.95 (978-1-890571-28-3(8)) Positive Children's Programming Corp.

Balok, Becki. Bouncer & the Stream of Life. Thomas, Richard F., illus. 1999. 64p. (J). (gr. 3-12). pap. 9.95 (978-0-9662759-1-9(8) , BCP-0999) Becalm Publishing.

Base, Graeme. The Water Hole. Base, Graeme, illus. 2001. (Illus.). 32p. (J). (gr. 2-7). 18.95 (978-0-8109-4568-5(1)) Abrams, Harry N. , Inc.

Batson, Mary. Head in the Clouds. 2000. 9p. (J). (gr. 1-3). (978-0-9702880-4-2(2)) Sun R.A.Y.S., LLC.

Bauer, Marion. Rain. Wallace, John, illus. 2005. (Ready-to-Read Ser. Level 1). 32p. (J). lib. bdg. 15.00 (978-1-59054-933-9(3)) Fitzgerald Bks.

The Big Rain. 2003. (Illus.). 32p. (J). mass mkt. (978-0-9740599-2-1(7) , 3) Omnibus Publishing.

Boswell, Addie K. The Rain Stomper. Velasquez, Eric, illus. 2008. (J). ***(978-0-7614-5393-2(8))*** Cavendish, Marshall Corp.

Brafman, Bonnie. Treasure in Marci's House. 2007. (J). pap. 8.00 ***(978-0-8059-7418-8(0))*** Dorrance Publishing Co., Inc.

Bridges, Margaret Park & Davenier, Christine. I Love the Rain. 2005. (Illus.). 32p. (J). 15.95 (978-1-58717-208-3(9) , SeaStar Bks.) Chronicle Bks. LLC.

Bronzaft, Arline L. Listen to the Raindrops. Parton, Steven, illus. unabr. ed. 2000. 26p. (J). (gr. 1-5). pap. 9.95 (978-0-9677843-1-1(X)) League for The Hard of Hearing.

Brooks, Kevin. Kissing the Rain. (J). 2004. 336p. pap. 16.95 (978-0-439-57742-7(X) , Chicken Hse., The); 2005. 352p. reprint ed. pap. 7.99 (978-0-439-57743-4(8) , PUSH) Scholastic, Inc.

Brouillard, Anne. The Bathtub Prima Donna. Brouillard, Anne, illus. 2004. (Illus.). 24p. (J). (gr. k-4). reprint ed. 13.00 (978-0-7567-7755-5(0)) DIANE Publishing Co.

Canela, Montserrat. Yoshi y la Lluvia. Max, illus. 2001. (SPA.). 48p. (J). (gr. 3-5). (978-84-246-3904-4(9)) La Galera, S.A. Editorial ESP. *Dist:* Lectorum Pubns., Inc.

Carle, Eric. Let's Paint a Rainbow. Carle, Eric, illus. 1998. (Play-and-Read Book Ser.). (Illus.). 12p. (J). (ps). bds. 6.95 (978-0-590-32844-9(1) , Cartwheel Bks.) Scholastic, Inc.

Carroll, John. The Adventures of Robbie the Raindrop. 2006. 32p. (J). 19.99 ***(978-1-59886-991-0(4));*** per. 21.99 ***(978-1-59886-706-0(7))*** Tate Publishing & Enterprises, L.L.C.

Carter, Joey. Lost in a Submarine! A Cantor Kids! Book. 2006. 56p. pap. 9.95 (978-1-59800-312-3(7)) Outskirts Press, Inc.

Chess, Victoria. The Costume Party. Chess, Victoria, illus. 2005. (Illus.). 32p. (J). (ps-ps). 15.95 (978-1-929132-87-4(5)) Kane/Miller Bk. Pubs., Inc.

Choi, Yangsook. Peach Heaven. 2005. (Illus.). 32p. (J). 16.00 (978-0-374-35761-0(7) , Farrar, Straus & Giroux (BYR)) Farrar, Straus & Giroux.

Come on Rain. 2004. (J). pap. 14.95 incl. audio (978-0-7882-0513-2(7)) Weston Woods Studios, Inc.

Cotten, Cynthia S. & Steptoe, Javaka. Rain Play. Steptoe, Javaka, illus. rev. ed. 2008. (Illus.). 32p. (J). 16.95 (978-0-8050-6795-8(7) , Holt, Henry & Co. Bks. For Young Readers) Holt, Henry & Co.

Courtin, Thierry. T'choupi Aime Bien la Pluie. 2000. (FRE.). (J). 13.95 (978-2-09-202027-2(7)) Nathan, Fernand FRA. *Dist:* Distribooks, Inc.

Daly, Niki & Turkington, Nola. Dancer. 2004. (Illus.). 36p. (J). pap. 7.95 (978-1-84507-181-3(6)) Lincoln, Frances Ltd. GBR. *Dist:* Perseus Distribution.

Davoll, Barbara. Rainy Day Rescue. Hockerman, Dennis, illus. 1999. (Christopher Churchmouse Classics Ser.). 24p. (J). (ps-3). 7.99 (978-0-8024-4933-7(6)) Moody Pubs.

Denega, Danielle. Dick & Jane Reader: Dick & Jane Picture Readers. 2005. (Dick & Jane Ser.). 32p. (J). (ps-1). pap. 3.99 (978-0-448-43985-3(9) , Grosset & Dunlap) Penguin Group (USA) Inc.

DePalma, Johnny. The Raindrop Keeper. Crabapple, Molly, illus. 2006. (J). per. 8.50 ***(978-0-9791127-1-3(0))*** Umbrelly Bks.

—The Raindrop Keeper: (Limited Edition Hardcover) Crabapple, Molly, illus. 2006. 50p. (J). 16.50 ***(978-0-9791127-8-2(8))*** Umbrelly Bks.

Dharmarajan, Geeta. The Magic Raindrop. Bist, Vandana, illus. 2002. 32p. (J). (978-81-87649-60-1(7)) Katha.

Dodd, Emma. Amazing Baby: Rain or Shine! Jolley, Mike, illus. 2007. (Amazing Baby Ser.). 10p. (J). bds. 6.95 ***(978-1-59223-801-9(7)***, Silver Dolphin Bks.) Advantage Pubs. Group.

Douglas, Vincent & School Specialty Publishing Staff. Rainy Day Fun Kit. 2005. (Book Notes Ser.). (Illus.). 64p. (J). pap. 17.95 (978-0-7696-3878-2(3) , American Education Publishing) School Specialty Publishing.

Eagle, Kin. It's Raining, It's Pouring. Eagle, Kin, illus. 1998. (Nursery Rhyme Ser.). (Illus.). 26p. (J). (ps-k). bds. 6.95 (978-1-58089-017-5(2)) Charlesbridge Publishing, Inc.

Eaton, Deborah. The Rainy Day Grump. Handelman, Dorothy, photos by. 1998. (Real Kids Readers Ser.). (Illus.). 32p. (gr. k-2). (J). pap. 4.99 (978-0-7613-2043-2(1)); lib. bdg. 18.90 (978-0-7613-2018-0(0)) Lerner Publishing Group. (Millbrook Pr.).

Eding, June. Easter Showers. Chauhan, Manhar, illus. 2007. (Puppy Scooby-Doo Ser.). 32p. (J). pap. 3.99 (978-0-448-44485-7(2) , Grosset & Dunlap) Penguin Group (USA) Inc.

Fleischman, Sid. McBroom the Rainmaker. 1999. (J). (978-0-606-19074-9(0)) Tandem Library Bks.

Fournier, Mark Edward. Rain: Attitude Is Everything. Kyle, Patricia Lynn, illus. 2nd l.t. ed. 2002. 50p. spiral bd. 17.99 (978-0-9725243-1-5(2)) Fournier Media.

Gabriel, Nat. Day with May. 2000. (ps-2). lib. bdg. 11.80 (978-0-613-24786-3(8)) Tandem Library Bks.

Garelick, May. Where Does the Butterfly Go When It Rains? Wilton, Nicholas, illus. 2001. (J). (gr. 1-6). pap. 6.00 (978-1-57255-162-6(3)) Mondo Publishing.

—Where Does the Butterfly Go When It Rains? 2001. (978-0-606-22653-0(2)) Tandem Library Bks.

Gay, Marie-Louise. Rainy Day Magic. 30p. mass mkt. 6.95 (978-0-7736-7366-3(0)) Stoddart Kids CAN. *Dist:* Fitzhenry & Whiteside, Ltd.

Germein, Katrina. Big Rain Coming. Bancroft, Bronwyn, illus. 2000. 32p. (J). (gr. k-3). tchr. ed. 16.00 (978-0-618-08344-2(8) , Clarion Bks.) Houghton Mifflin Co. Trade & Reference Div.

Ginsburg, Mirra. Mushroom in the Rain. 2002. (Illus.). (J). 15.53 (978-0-7587-6377-8(8)) Book Wholesalers, Inc.

Gorbachev, Valeri. Un Dia de lluvia. Puerta, Cristina, tr. 2003. (SPA.). 40p. (J). 8.95 (978-958-04-7074-8(X)) Norma S.A. COL. *Dist:* Distribuidora Norma, Inc., Lectorum Pubns., Inc.

Haas, Jessie. Scamper & the Horse Show. Apple, Margot, illus. 2004. 32p. (J). 15.99 (978-0-06-001338-7(9)) HarperCollins Pubs.

Harcourt School Publishers Staff. Go out in the Rain: Take-Home Book. 1999. (Collections Ser.). (Illus.). (J). pap. 1.90 (978-0-15-317212-0(6)) Harcourt Schl. Pubs.

—If Rain Were Donuts: Take-Home Book. 1999. (Collections Ser.). (Illus.). (J). (gr. 3). pap. 1.90 (978-0-15-317307-3(6)) Harcourt Schl. Pubs.

—Very Cool Rain On Level. 3rd ed. 2002. (Trophies Reading Program Ser.). (Illus.). pap. 5.10 (978-0-15-323089-9(4)) Harcourt Schl. Pubs.

—When the Rains Came Below Level. 3rd ed. 2002. (Trophies Reading Program Ser.). (Illus.). pap. 5.10 (978-0-15-323151-3(3)) Harcourt Schl. Pubs.

HarperEntertainment Staff. Li'l Pet Hospital No.3: The Very Rainy Day. 2003. (gr. k-3). lib. bdg. 11.80 (978-0-613-86273-8(2)) Tandem Library Bks.

Hergenroeder, Ernie, illus. Little Drop of Water. 2007. 24p. (J). 15.00 ***(978-0-9724272-4-1(4))*** Katydid Publishing LLC.

Herman, Gail. Splish! Splash! Basso, Bill, illus. 2003. (Hello Reader Ser.). (J). (978-0-439-44164-3(1)) Scholastic, Inc.

Hesse, Karen. Come on, Rain! 1999. (J). (ps up). (978-0-439-06015-8(X)) Scholastic, Inc.

—Come on, Rain! 2004. (J). 24.95 incl. audio (978-1-55592-177-4(9)); 29.95 incl. cd-rom (978-1-55592-500-0(6)) Weston Woods Studios, Inc.

—Come on, Rain. Muth, Jon J., illus. 1999. 32p. (J). (ps-2). pap. 16.95 (978-0-590-33125-8(6)) Scholastic, Inc.

Hill, Elizabeth Starr. Chang & the Bamboo Flute. Liu, Lesley, illus. 2002. 64p. (J). (gr. 3 up). 15.00 (978-0-374-31238-1(9) , Farrar, Straus & Giroux (BYR)) Farrar, Straus & Giroux.

Hobbie, Nathaniel. Priscilla & the Splish-Splash Surprise. Hobbie, Jocelyn, illus. 2006. 32p. (J). (ps-1). 15.99 (978-0-316-01046-7(4)) Little Brown & Co.

Hodson, Debbie. A Mountain Rainbow. 2004. (Illus.). 31p. (J). per. 10.95 (978-0-9755771-0-3(7)) Ivystone Pr.

Hojel, Barbara & Guy, Ginger F. Rainy Day Picnic. 1999. Bk. 8. (Illus.). 16p. (C). pap. 7.66 (978-0-201-35139-2(0)) Longman Publishing Group.

Hope, Laura Lee. Bunny Brown & His Sister Sue Keeping Store. 2006. 142p. pap. 10.99 ***(978-1-4264-5200-0(4));*** 160p. pap. 14.99 ***(978-1-4264-5501-8(1))*** BiblioBazaar.

Hull, Maureen. Rainy Days with Bear. Franson, Leanne, illus. 2005. 32p. pap. (978-1-897073-34-6(8)) Lobster Pr.

Hurd, Clement, illus. Johnny Lion's Rubber Boots. 2002. (Johnny Lion Ser.). (J). 12.34 (978-0-7587-5040-2(4)) Book Wholesalers, Inc.

Hurd, Edith Thacher. Johnny Lion's Rubber Boots. Hurd, Clement, illus. 2000. (I Can Read Bks.). 64p. (J). (gr. k-3). 14.95 (978-0-06-029337-6(3)) HarperCollins Pubs.

—Johnny Lion's Rubber Boots. Hurd, Clement, illus. 2001. (I Can Read Bks.). (J). (978-0-606-20746-1(5)) Tandem Library Bks.

Husted, Ursula. Making Rain. 2004. 56p. (J). per. 9.95 (978-0-9753225-0-5(8)) Atomic Fruit Pr.

Hyde, Judith Jensen. Rainy-Day Music. Abbott, Jason, illus. 2006. (Rookie Reader Skill Set Ser.). 32p. (J). (gr. k-2). 19.50 (978-0-516-24983-4(5) , Children's Pr.) Scholastic Library Publishing.

Hyde, Judith Jensen & Abbott, Jason. Rainy-day Music. 2006. (Illus.). 32p. (YA). pap. 4.95 (978-0-516-24998-8(3) , Children's Pr.) Scholastic Library Publishing.

Inkpen, Mick. Splosh. 1999. (978-0-606-22347-8(9)) Tandem Library Bks.

Jackson, Alison. Rainmaker. 2004. (Illus.). 200p. (J). 16.95 (978-1-59078-309-2(3)) Boyds Mills Pr.

James, Betsy. Mud Family. 1998. (gr. k-3). lib. bdg. 19.90 (978-0-613-70810-4(5)) Tandem Library Bks.

Kelleher, Victor. Dogboy. 2006. (YA). (gr. 9 up). 16.95 (978-1-932425-76-5(4) , Lemniscaat) Boyds Mills Pr.

Kerlikowske, Elizabeth. Before the Rain. 2003. 72p. per. 15.00 (978-1-882983-90-2(4)) March Street Pr.

Knutson, Kimberley. Jungle Jamboree. 1998. (Accelerated Reader Bks.). (Illus.). 32p. (J). (ps-3). 15.95 (978-0-7614-5032-0(7) , Cavendish Children's Bks.) Cavendish, Marshall Corp.

Kolodny, Cynthia. We Like Puddles. Sagasti, Miriam, illus. 2004. 12p. (J). (gr. k-2). pap. 4.95 (978-1-57874-040-6(1)) Kaeden Corp.

Krupp, Edwin C. Rainbow & You. Krupp, Robin Rector, illus. 2000. 32p. (J). (ps-3). 16.99 (978-0-688-15601-5(0)) HarperCollins Pubs.

Kurtz, Jane. Rain Romp: Stomping Away a Grouchy Day. Wolcott, Dyanna, illus. 2002. 32p. (J). (ps up). 16.99 (978-0-06-029805-0(7)) HarperCollins Pubs.

Ladd, Debbie. Puddles. Morejon, Tom, illus. 2006. 32p. (J). pap. 8.95 (978-0-9727615-4-3(3)) Deb on Air Bks.

Lakin, Patricia. Rainy Day! Nash, Scott, illus. 2007. 40p. (J). (ps-1). 16.99 (978-0-8037-3092-2(6) , Dial) Penguin Group (USA) Inc.

Latty, Jasmin. Oh, My Boring Toes! 2005. (J). pap. 12.00 (978-0-8059-6668-8(4)) Dorrance Publishing Co., Inc.

Law, Felicia. Joey's Day at Rumble's Cave Hotel. Pak, Yoon Mi, illus. 2006. (Read-It! Readers Ser.). 32p. (J). (gr. 2-4). 18.60 (978-1-4048-1339-7(X)) Picture Window Bks.

—The Rainy Day. Evans, Nicola, illus. 2005. (Bamboo & Friends Ser.). 24p. (J). (ps-3). lib. bdg. 22.60 (978-1-4048-1280-2(6)) Picture Window Bks.

Leonard, Marcia. Splish, Splash! Handelman, Dorothy, photos by. 2000. (Hanna Bks.). (Illus.). 24p. (J). (ps up). 7.95 (978-0-694-01365-4(X)) HarperCollins Pubs.

Levy, Pamela R. Otto's Rainy Day. Yim, Natasha, illus. 2000. 32p. (J). (ps-3). 15.95 (978-1-57091-400-3(1)) Charlesbridge Publishing, Inc.

Lewison, Wendy Cheyette. Raindrop, Plop! Paparone, Pamela, tr. Paparone, Pamela, illus. 2004. 32p. (J). (ps-3). 15.99 (978-0-670-03620-2(X) , Viking Juvenile) Penguin Group (USA) Inc.

Liu, Jae Soo. Yellow Umbrella. Liu, Jae Soo, illus. 2002. (Illus.). 32p. (J). (gr. k-3). 19.95 incl. audio compact disk (978-1-929132-36-2(0)) Kane/Miller Bk. Pubs., Inc.

London, Jonathan. Puddles. Karas, G. Brian, illus. 1999. 32p. (J). (ps-1). pap. 5.99 (978-0-14-056175-3(7) , Puffin) Penguin Group (USA) Inc.

Lucas, David. Whale. 2007. 32p. (J). (gr. k-3). 16.99 (978-0-375-84338-9(8)); lib. bdg. 19.99 (978-0-375-94338-6(2)) Random Hse. Children's Bks. (Knopf Bks. for Young Readers).

Magee, Kanika. Rain, Rain, Come Today. Crosson, Cierra, illus. 2004. (J). (978-0-9748834-2-7(5)) Ebenezer A.M.E. Church.

Mase, Naokata. The Rainy Trip Surprise. 2006. (Illus.). 24p. (J). 19.95 (978-1-74126-436-4(7)) R.I.C. Pubns. AUS. *Dist:* SCB Distributors.

Masterson, Carla Jo. What's on the Other Side of the Rainbow? The Secret of the Golden Mirror. Fochtman, Omra Jo, illus. 2006. 40p. (J). 24.95 (978-1-59975-228-0(X)) Father & Son Publishing.

McPhail, David M. Big Brown Bear Goes to Town. O'Connor, John, illus. 2006. 40p. (J). 16.00 (978-0-15-205317-8(4)) Harcourt Trade Pubs.

—Puddle. 2000. (978-0-606-17841-9(4)); lib. bdg. 12.95 (978-0-613-30099-5(8)) Tandem Library Bks.

Medearis, Angela Shelf. We Play on a Rainy Day. Walker, Sylvia, illus. 2004. 32p. (J). lib. bdg. 15.00 (978-1-59054-671-0(7)) Fitzgerald Bks.

Melmed, Laura Krauss. The Rainbabies. LaMarche, Jim, illus. 2004. 32p. (J). (ps-3). pap. 6.99 (978-0-688-15113-3(2)) HarperCollins Pubs.

Metzger, Steve. Rain! Rain! Go Away! Wilhelm, Hans, illus. 2002. (J). pap. 3.25 (978-0-439-29572-7(6)) Scholastic, Inc.

Mitra, Annie. Chloe the Cat Rainy Day. 1998. (Chloe Weather Board Bks.). (Illus.). 16p. pap. 5.95 (978-1-86233-041-2(7)) Sterling Publishing Co., Inc.

Morgan, Michaela. Dear Bunny. 2007. 32p. (J). pap. 5.99 (978-0-439-74834-6(8) , Scholastic Paperbacks) Scholastic, Inc.

—Dear Bunny. Jayne Church, Caroline, illus. 2006. 32p. (J). pap. 15.99 (978-0-439-74833-9(X) , Chicken Hse., The) Scholastic, Inc.

Moss, Lucille. The Gift Within. Uhouse, Debra, illus. l.t. ed. 2005. 19p. (J). 14.95 (978-1-59879-063-4(3)) Lifevest Publishing, Inc.

Muhammad, Renay. Daddy Why Do We Have Rain. 2004. (Illus.). (J). cd-rom (978-0-9754024-1-2(2)) Sharif, Mboya.

Notrog, Bryna. It's Raining Whisper. Schwarz, Terri, illus. 1998. 48p. (J). lib. bdg. 17.95 (978-0-9652479-1-7(0)) Zipper Pr., Inc.

O'Day, Joseph E. I Like Rain! Foster, Ron, illus. 2007. (J). ***(978-1-929039-39-5(5))*** Ambassador Bks., Inc.

Pachela, Czes, illus. The Rainy Day Adventure. 2001. 24p. (J). pap. 3.50 (978-1-58925-362-9(0) , tiger tales) ME Media LLC.

Padilla, Felix M. Smiling at the Rain. Padilla, Eren Star, illus. 32p. (J). (gr. 3 up). 16.00 (978-0-9710860-4-3(4)) Libros, Encouraging Cultural Literacy.

Rain, Rain, Go Away. 2001. (Take-Home Bks.). (YA). (ps-k). 15.00 (978-0-8215-6985-6(6)) Sadlier, William H. Inc.

A Rainbow in our Yard. 2005. (J). bds. (978-0-9761228-1-4(2)) World of Imagination.

Raintree Steck-Vaughn Staff. Me Gusta la Lluvia! 2000. (Coleccion en Parejas). (SPA.). (J). pap., stu. ed. 20.45 (978-0-7398-0828-3(1)) Steck-Vaughn.

The Rainy Day: Individual Title Two-Packs. (Chiquilibros Ser.). (ps-1). 12.00 (978-0-7635-8532-7(7)) Rigby Education.

The Rainy Day Adventure: Third Grade Guided Reading Level O. (On Our Way to English Ser.). (gr. 3 up). 34.50 (978-0-7578-7140-5(2)) Rigby Education.

Ray, Mary Lyn. Red Rubber Boot Day. Stringer, Lauren, illus. 32p. (J). (ps-ps). 2005. pap., pap. 6.00 (978-0-15-205398-7(0) , Voyager Bks./Libros Viajeros); 2000. 16.00 (978-0-15-213756-4(4)) Harcourt Children's Bks.

Reber, Deborah. Blue un día de lluvia. Cardinali, Kevin, illus. 2005. (Blue's Clues Ser.).Tr. of Blue's Best Rainy Day. (SPA.). 24p. (J). pap. 3.99 (978-1-4169-0068-9(3) , Libros Para Ninos) Simon & Schuster Children's Publishing.

Roche, Hannah. Pete's Puddles. 1998. (My First Weather Bks.). (Illus.). 24p. (J). (ps-3). (978-1-84089-031-0(2) , Zero to Ten, Limited) Evans Publishing Group.

Root, Phyllis. Mouse Goes Out. Croft, James, illus. 2002. (Brand New Readers Ser.). (J). (ps-2). 48p. 12.99 (978-0-7636-1351-8(7)); 32p. pap. 5.99 (978-0-7636-1352-5(5)) Candlewick Pr.

Schaefer, Lola M. This Is the Rain. Wattenberg, Jane, illus. 2001. 40p. (J). 16.99 (978-0-688-17039-4(0)); 16.89 (978-0-688-17040-0(4)) HarperCollins Pubs.

Schwartz, Roslyn. The Mole Sisters & the Rainy Day. Schwartz, Roslyn, illus. 2001. (Mole Sisters Ser.). (Illus.). 32p. (J). (ps-k). pap. 4.95 (978-1-55037-610-4(1)); lib. bdg. 14.95 (978-1-55037-611-1(X)) Annick Pr., Ltd. CAN. *Dist:* Firefly Bks., Ltd.

Scott, Janine. Fun in the Sun. Forss, Ian, illus. 2006. (Farmer Claude & Farmer Maude Ser.). 32p. (J). (gr. k-2). 22.60 (978-1-4048-1697-8(6) , 1253180) Picture Window Bks.

—Rain on the Roof. Forss, Ian, illus. 2006. 32p. (J). (gr. k-2). 22.60 (978-1-4048-1698-5(4)) Picture Window Bks.

Scott, Jeanne Ann. Raining Worms. 2005. 160p. (J). pap. 6.99 net. (978-1-59975-218-1(2)) Independent Pub.

Sendak, Jack. The Happy Rain. Sendak, Maurice, illus. 2004. (Sendak Reissues Ser.). 48p. reprint ed. 13.95 (978-0-06-028785-6(3)) HarperCollins Pubs.

Sheldon, Sidney & Sheldon, Mary. The Adventures of Drippy the Runaway Raindrop. Sheldon, Alexandra, illus. 2003. 64p. (J). (ps-3). 14.95 (978-1-893224-81-0(3)) New Millennium Entertainment.

Shollar, Leah Pearl. Shadow Play: A True Story of Tefillah. Gerber, Pesach, illus. 2006. 32p. (J). 11.95 (978-1-929628-21-6(8)) Hachai Publishing.

Silverman, Erica. Cowgirl Kate & Cocoa: Rain or Shine. Lewin, Betsy, illus. 2008. 44p. (J). 15.00 ***978-0-15-205384-0(0))*** Harcourt Trade Pubs.

Singer, Marilyn. The Company of Crows: A Book of Poems. Saport, Linda, illus. 2002. 48p. (J). (gr. k-3). tchr. ed. 16.00 (978-0-618-08340-4(5) , Clarion Bks.) Houghton Mifflin Co. Trade & Reference Div.

Sonriendole a la Lluvia. (SPA.). (J). (978-0-9710860-5-0(2)) Libros, Encouraging Cultural Literacy.

Spalding, Andrea. It's Raining, It's Pouring. Watts, Leslie Elizabeth, illus. 2001. 32p. (J). (ps-2). 15.95 (978-1-55143-186-4(6)) Orca Bk. Pubs. USA.

—It's Raining It's Pouring. Watts, Leslie Elizabeth, illus. 2002. 32p. (J). (ps-2). 7.95 (978-1-55143-229-8(3)) Orca Bk. Pubs. USA.

—Sarah May & the New Red Dress. 2000. (ps-2). lib. bdg. 15.25 (978-0-613-83716-3(9)) Tandem Library Bks.

Staunton, Ted. The Puddleman. Clark, Brenda, illus. 2004. 32p. (J). (ps-4). pap. 6.95 (978-0-88995-190-7(X)) Red Deer Pr. CAN. *Dist:* Fitzhenry & Whiteside, Ltd.

Stewart, Paul. Rabbit's Wish. Riddell, Chris, illus. 2001. 32p. (J). (ps-2). 12.95 (978-0-06-029518-9(X)) HarperCollins Pubs.

Stock, Catherine. Gugu's House. 2001. (Illus.). 32p. (J). (gr. k-3). tchr. ed. 16.00 (978-0-618-00389-1(4) , Clarion Bks.) Houghton Mifflin Co. Trade & Reference Div.

Swope, Sam. The Krazees. Brace, Eric, illus. 2003. 32p. (J). pap. 6.95 (978-0-374-44090-9(5) , Sunburst) Farrar, Straus & Giroux.

Sykes, Julie. Rainy Day Adventure. 2001. (gr. k-3). lib. bdg. 11.25 (978-0-613-53545-8(6)) Tandem Library Bks.

—Smudge. Chapman, Jane, illus. 2001. 32p. (J). (ps-k). 5.95 (978-1-58925-355-1(8) , tiger tales) ME Media LLC.

—Smudge. 2001. (gr. k-3). lib. bdg. 14.10 (978-0-613-42439-4(5)) Tandem Library Bks.

Todd, Barbara. The Rainmaker. Roge, illus. 2003. 32p. (J). (ps-2). lib. bdg. 18.95 (978-1-55037-775-0(2)) Annick Pr., Ltd. CAN. *Dist:* Firefly Bks., Ltd.

Tuzee, John, text. Puffy: La Nube Que No Podia Llover. 2005. (SPA.). (J). 8.95 (978-0-9755348-1-6(5)) Kids Life Pr.

Urmston, Kathleen & Urmston, Grant. A Rainy Day for Sammy. Gedeon, Gloria, illus. 2004. 22p. (J). (gr. k-3). pap. 4.95 (978-1-57874-078-9(9)) Kaeden Corp.

Vail, Rachel. Mama Rex & T: Lose a Waffle. Bjorkman, Steve, illus. 2000. (Mama Rex & T Ser.). (J). (978-0-439-19918-6(2)) Scholastic, Inc.

Van Straaten, Harmen. TIM & the FLYING MACHINE. 2008. 28p. 12.95 ***978-1-60136-003-8(7))*** Mars Media Pubs.

Weaver, Griz. A Day in the Rain. 2005. 35p. (J). 12.28 (978-1-4116-0565-7(9)) Lulu.com.

Weeks, Sarah. Drip Drop. 2002. (gr. k-3). lib. bdg. 11.80 (978-0-613-44518-4(X)) Tandem Library Bks.

Wenger, Brahm & Green, Alan. Dewey Doo-It Builds a House: A Children's Story about Habitat for Humanity. 2006. (Illus.). 32p. 17.95 (978-0-9745143-2-1(2)) RandallFraser Publishing.

Winter, Jeanette. Elsina's Clouds. 2004. (Illus.). 40p. (J). 16.00 (978-0-374-32118-5(3) , Farrar, Straus & Giroux (BYR)) Farrar, Straus & Giroux.

Yashima, Taro. Umbrella. 2000. (J). pap. 19.97 incl. audio (978-0-7366-9216-8(9)) Books on Tape, Inc.

Yee, Wong Herbert. Who Likes Rain? 2007. (Illus.). (J). ***(*978-1-4287-3979-6(3));*** 32p. 14.95 (978-0-8050-7734-6(0)) Holt, Henry & Co.

RAIN AND RAINFALL—POETRY

Plourde, Lynn. Pigs in the Mud in the Middle of the Rud. Schoenherr, John, illus. ed. 2006. 32p. 15.95 (978-0-89272-719-3(5)) Down East Bks.

RAIN FOREST ECOLOGY

Allaby, Michael. Tropical Forests. 2006. (Biomes of the Earth Ser.). (Illus.). 288p. (J). (gr. 6-12). 39.50 (978-0-8160-5322-3(7)) Facts On File, Inc.

Aloian, Molly. Un Habitat de Bosque Tropical. 2007. (SPA.). 32p. (J). (gr. 1-2). ***(*978-0-7787-8333-6(2))*** Crabtree Publishing Co.

Aloian, Molly. A Rainforest Habitat. 2006. (Illus.). 32p. (J). (gr. 2). pap. (978-0-7787-2986-0(9)) Crabtree Publishing Co.

Aloian, Molly & Kalman, Bobbie. Un Habitat de Bosque Tropical. rev. ed. 2007. (SPA.). 32p. (J). (gr. 1-2). pap. ***(*978-0-7787-8357-2(X))*** Crabtree Publishing Co.

—Rainforest Food Chains. 2006. (Food Chains Ser.). (Illus.). 32p. (J). (978-0-7787-1951-9(0)); (gr. 2-3). pap. (978-0-7787-1997-7(9)) Crabtree Publishing Co.

—A Rainforest Habitat. 2006. (Illus.). 32p. (J). (978-0-7787-2958-7(3)) Crabtree Publishing Co.

Animals of the Rain Forest, 30 bks. 2002. (978-0-7398-5376-4(7)) Raintree.

Animals of the Rainforest, 6 bks. 2003. 145.68 (978-1-4109-0026-5(6)); 874.08 (978-1-4109-0152-1(1)) Raintree.

Aspen-Baxter, Linda. Rainforests. 2006. (J). (978-1-59036-447-5(3)); (Illus.). 32p. (gr. 4-6). lib. bdg. 26.00 (978-1-59036-446-8(5)) Weigl Pubs., Inc.

Baker, Lucy. Life in the Rain Forests. 2001. (World Book Ecology Ser.). (Illus.). 32p. (J). (978-0-7166-5224-3(2)) World Bk., Inc.

—Life in the Rain Forests: Animals, People, Plants. 2000. (gr. 3-6). lib. bdg. 15.25 (978-0-613-43347-1(5)) Tandem Library Bks.

Baldwin, Carol. Living in a Rain Forest. 2003. (Living Habitats Ser.). (Illus.). 32p. (J). pap. 6.95 (978-1-4034-3234-6(1)); lib. bdg. 24.22 (978-1-4034-2992-6(8)) Heinemann Library.

Ballard, Carol. The Search for Cures from the Rainforest. 2005. (Science Quest Ser.). (Illus.). 32p. (J). lib. bdg. 24.67 (978-0-8368-4554-9(4)) Stevens, Gareth Inc.

Barnes, Julia. 101 Facts about Tropical Rain Forests. 2003. (One Hundred One Facts about Our World Ser.). (Illus.). 32p. (J). (gr. 3 up). lib. bdg. 23.33 (978-0-8368-3710-0(X)) Stevens, Gareth Inc.

Behler, Deborah A., ed. The Rain Forest of the Pacific Northwest. 2001. (Ecosystems of North America Ser.). (Illus.). 64p. (J). (gr. 6 up). lib. bdg. 27.07 (978-0-7614-0926-7(2) , Benchmark Bks.) Cavendish, Marshall Corp.

Berger, Melvin & Berger, Gilda. Life in the Rainforest: Plants, Animals, & People. Brittingham, Geoffrey H., illus. 1999. (Discovery Readers Ser.). 48p. (YA). (ps up). lib. bdg. 15.95 (978-0-7910-5068-2(8) , Chelsea Hse.) Facts On File, Inc.

Bodden, Valerie. Rainforests. 2006. (Illus.). 24p. (J). 16.95 (978-1-58341-465-1(7) , Creative Education) Creative Co., The.

Braun, Eric & Donovan, Sandy. Bats. 2001. (Animals of the Rain Forest Ser.). (Illus.). 32p. (YA). lib. bdg. 22.83 (978-0-7398-4679-7(5)) Raintree.

—Butterflies. 2001. (Animals of the Rain Forest Ser.). (Illus.). 32p. (YA). lib. bdg. 22.83 (978-0-7398-4680-3(9)) Raintree.

Carole Telford and Rod Theodorou. Up a Rainforest Tree. 2nd ed. 2006. (Illus.). 32p. (J). pap. ***(*978-1-4034-8800-8(2))*** Heinemann Library.

Castaldo, Nancy F. Rainforests: An Activity Guide for Ages 6-9. 2003. (Illus.). 144p. (J). pap. 14.95 (978-1-55652-476-9(5)) Chicago Review Pr., Inc.

—Rainforests: An Activity Guide for Ages 6-9. 2003. (gr. k-3). lib. bdg. 24.55 (978-0-613-89931-4(8)) Tandem Library Bks.

Castner, James L. Layers of Life: Deep in the Amazon. 2001. (Deep in the Amazon Ser.). (Illus.). 32p. (J). (gr. 5 up). lib. bdg. 28.50 (978-0-7614-1130-7(5) , Benchmark Bks.) Cavendish, Marshall Corp.

—Partners & Rivals: Deep in the Amazon. 2001. (Deep in the Amazon Ser.). (Illus.). 32p. (J). (gr. 5 up). lib. bdg. 28.50 (978-0-7614-1131-4(3) , Benchmark Bks.) Cavendish, Marshall Corp.

Champion, Neil. Rainforests. 2005. (Caring for the Planet Ser.). (Illus.). 48p. (J). (978-1-58340-508-6(9)) Smart Apple Media.

Cheshire, Gerald. Nature Unfolds the Tropical Rainforest. 2001. (Nature Unfolds Ser.). (Illus.). 40p. (J). (gr. 4). lib. bdg. (978-0-7787-0308-2(8)); pap. (978-0-7787-0320-4(7)) Crabtree Publishing Co.

Chinery, Michael. Plants & Planteaters. 2000. (Secrets of the Rainforest Ser.). (Illus.). 32p. (J). (gr. 3-4). lib. bdg. (978-0-7787-0218-4(9)) Crabtree Publishing Co.

—Plants & Planteaters. 2000. (gr. 3-6). lib. bdg. 16.40 (978-0-613-28023-5(7)) Tandem Library Bks.

Cole, Melissa S. Rain Forests. 2003. (Wild America Habitats Ser.). (Illus.). 24p. (J). 21.20 (978-1-56711-808-7(9) , Blackbirch Pr., Inc.) Thomson Gale.

Collard, Sneed B., III. In the Rain Forest Canopy. 2005. (Science Adventures Ser.). (Illus.). 44p. (J). (gr. 3-7). lib. bdg. 25.64 (978-0-7614-1954-9(3) , Benchmark Bks.) Cavendish, Marshall Corp.

Davis, Rebecca Fjelland. More or Less: A Rain Forest Counting Book. 2007. (Illus.). 32p. (J). 23.93 (978-0-7368-6376-6(1)) Capstone Pr., Inc.

Dunphy, Madeleine. Here Is the Tropical Rain Forest. Rothman, Michael, illus. 2006. (Web of Life Ser.). 32p. (J). 16.95 (978-0-9773795-1-4(5)) Web of Life Children's Bks.

Frost, Helen. Chimpanzees. Saunders-Smith, Gail, ed. 2002. (Rain Forest Animals Ser.). (Illus.). 24p. (J). (gr. k-1). lib. bdg. 15.93 (978-0-7368-1455-3(8) , Pebble Bks.) Capstone Pr., Inc.

—Leaf-Cutting Ants. Saunders-Smith, Gail, ed. 2002. (Rain Forest Animals Ser.). (Illus.). 24p. (J). (gr. k-1). lib. bdg. 15.93 (978-0-7368-1457-7(4) , Pebble Bks.) Capstone Pr., Inc.

—Lemurs. Saunders-Smith, Gail, ed. 2002. (Rain Forest Animals Ser.). (Illus.). 24p. (J). (gr. k-1). lib. bdg. 15.93 (978-0-7368-1456-0(6) , Pebble Bks.) Capstone Pr., Inc.

—Rain Forest Animals, 6 bks. Saunders-Smith, Gail, ed. Incl. Boa Constrictors. lib. bdg. 15.93 (978-0-7368-1191-0(5)); Chimpanzees. lib. bdg. 15.93 (978-0-7368-1455-3(8)); Gorillas. lib. bdg. 15.93 (978-0-7368-1192-7(3)); Jaguars. lib. bdg. 15.93 (978-0-7368-1193-4(1)); Leaf-Cutting Ants. lib. bdg. 15.93 (978-0-7368-1457-7(4)); Lemurs. lib. bdg. 15.93 (978-0-7368-1456-0(6)); Parrots. lib. bdg. 15.93 (978-0-7368-1194-1(X)); Tarantulas. lib. bdg. 15.93 (978-0-7368-1195-8(8)); Tigers. lib. bdg. 15.93 (978-0-7368-1458-4(2)); Tree Frogs. lib. bdg. 15.93 (978-0-7368-1196-5(6)); 24p. (J). (gr. k-1). 2002. (Illus.). 2001. Set lib. bdg. 159.30 (978-0-7368-1459-1(0) , Pebble Bks.) Capstone Pr., Inc.

—Tigers. Saunders-Smith, Gail, ed. 2002. (Rain Forest Animals Ser.). (Illus.). 24p. (J). (gr. k-1). lib. bdg. 15.93 (978-0-7368-1458-4(2) , Pebble Bks.) Capstone Pr., Inc.

Gray, Shirley W. Rain Forests. 2000. (First Reports). (Illus.). 48p. (J). (gr. 3 up). lib. bdg. 21.26 (978-0-7565-0023-8(0)) Compass Point Bks.

Greeley, August. Fading Forests: The Destruction of Our Rainforests. 2003. (Reading Power Ser.). (Illus.). 24p. (J). lib. bdg. 17.25 (978-0-8239-6486-4(8) , PowerKids Pr.) Rosen Publishing Group, Inc., The.

Greenaway, Theresa & Dorling Kindersley Publishing Staff. Jungle. Dann, Geoff, photos by. 2004. (Eyewitness Books). (Illus.). 72p. (J). lib. bdg. 19.99 (978-0-7566-0693-0(4)) Dorling Kindersley Publishing, Inc.

Greenwood, Elinor. Rain Forest. 2001. (Eye Wonder Ser.). (Illus.). 48p. (J). (gr. k-3). 9.99 (978-0-7894-7853-5(6)) Dorling Kindersley Publishing, Inc.

Guiberson, Brenda Z. Rain, Rain, Rain Forest. Jenkins, Steve, tr. Jenkins, Steve, illus. rev. ed. 2004. 32p. (J). 16.95 (978-0-8050-6582-4(2) , Holt, Henry & Co. Bks. For Young Readers) Holt, Henry & Co.

Hantula, Richard. Rocks & Fossils. 2006. (Vital Science Earth Science Ser.). (Illus.). 48p. (YA). (gr. 6-8). lib. bdg. 26.60 ***(*978-0-8368-7765-6(9)*** , World Almanac Library) Stevens, Gareth Inc.

Jackson, Tom. Tropical Forests. 2003. (Biomes Atlases Ser.). (Illus.). 64p. (J). lib. bdg. 31.42 (978-0-7398-5250-7(7)) Raintree.

—Tropical Forests. 2003. (gr. 5-8). lib. bdg. 18.20 (978-0-613-78190-9(2)) Tandem Library Bks.

Johansson, Philip. The Tropical Rain Forest: A Web of Life. 2004. (World of Biomes Ser.). (Illus.). 48p. (J). lib. bdg. 23.93 (978-0-7660-2199-0(8)) Enslow Pubs., Inc.

Kite, Lorien. A Rain Forest Tree. 1999. (Illus.). 32p. (J). (ps-7). lib. bdg. 17.60 (978-0-613-19529-4(9)) Tandem Library Bks.

—Rain Forest Tree. 1999. (978-0-606-18065-8(6)) Tandem Library Bks.

Knight, Tim. Journey into the Rainforest. Knight, Tim & Moreiras, Juan Pablo, photos by. 2001. (Illus.). 48p. (YA). (gr. 4-7). 19.95 (978-0-19-521751-3(9)) Oxford Univ. Pr., Inc.

Lewington, Anna & Parker, Edward. People of the Rain Forests. 1998. (Wide World Ser.). (Illus.). 48p. (J). (gr. 3-7). 18.98 (978-0-8172-5061-4(1)) Raintree.

Lindeen, Carol. Life in a Rain Forest. 2003. (Pebble Plus: Living in a Biome Ser.). (Illus.). 24p. (J). lib. bdg. 17.26 (978-0-7368-2102-5(3)) Capstone Pr., Inc.

Lynch, Emma. Rainforest Food Chains. 2004. (Food Webs Ser.). (Illus.). 32p. (J). pap. 7.50 (978-1-4034-5865-0(0)); lib. bdg. 24.22 (978-1-4034-5858-2(8)) Heinemann Library.

Mayer, Cassie. Rain Forest. 2007. (J). ***(*978-1-4034-9427-6(4)); pap. (*978-1-4034-9433-7(9))*** Heinemann Library.

McCormick, Rosie. Rain Forest Worlds. 2004. (Discovery Guides Ser.). (SPA., Illus.). 32p. (gr. 2-5). (J). pap. 6.95 (978-1-58728-216-4(X)); 11.95 (978-1-58728-222-5(4)) T&N Children's Publishing. (Two Can Publishing).

—Rain Forest Worlds. 2001. (gr. 7-12). lib. bdg. 15.25 (978-0-613-43497-3(8)); (Illus.). (J). (978-0-606-20874-1(7)) Tandem Library Bks.

McKissack, Fredrick, Jr. & McKissack, Lisa Beringer. Counting in the Rain Forest. 2008. (J). ***(*978-0-7660-2992-7(1))*** Enslow Pubs., Inc.

McLeish, Ewan. Rain Forest Destruction. 2006. (Illus.). 48p. (J). pap. ***(*978-0-8368-8158-5(3));*** lib. bdg. ***(*978-0-8368-7758-8(6))*** Stevens, Gareth Inc. (World Almanac Library).

McLeish, Ewan. Rain Forests: Our Impact on the Planet. 2001. (Twenty-First Century Debates Ser.). (Illus.). 64p. (YA). (gr. 6-8). lib. bdg. 27.12 (978-0-7398-3179-3(8)) Raintree.

McNeil, Niki, et al. HOCPP 1095 Rainforest Habitats. 2006. spiral bd. 22.50 ***(*978-1-60308-095-8(3))*** In the Hands of a Child.

Morey, Allan. Rain Forest Food Chains. 2003. (What Eats What? Ser.). (J). pap. (978-1-58417-225-3(8)); lib. bdg. (978-1-58417-224-6(X)) Lake Street Pubs.

Morgan, Sally. A Giant Tree in the Rainforest. 2000. (Life in... Ser.). (Illus.). 32p. (J). (gr. 2-6). lib. bdg. 16.95 (978-1-929298-85-3(4)) Chrysalis Education.

Mullican, Judy. What's in the Rain Forest? Metzger, Jeanne, illus. 2000. (Big Bks.). 8p. (J). (ps). pap. 10.95 (978-1-57332-185-3(0)); pap. 10.95 (978-1-57332-186-0(9)) HighReach Learning, Inc.

Nicholson, Sue. Rainforest Explorer. 2002. 48p. (J). pap. 6.95 (978-0-439-31689-7(8)) Scholastic, Inc.

O'Hare, Ted. People of the Rain Forest. (Rain Forest Today Discovery Library Ser.). 24p. 2005. (Illus.). (gr. 1-4). 14.95 (978-1-59515-153-7(2)); 2004. pap. 4.95 (978-1-59515-301-2(2)) Rourke Publishing, LLC.

—Plants of the Rain Forest. (Rain Forest Today Discovery Library Ser.). 24p. 2005. (Illus.). (gr. 1-4). 14.95 (978-1-59515-154-4(0)); 2004. pap. 4.95 (978-1-59515-302-9(0)) Rourke Publishing, LLC.

—Rain Forest at Night. 2005. (Rain Forest Today Discovery Library). 24p. (gr. 1-4). 5.45 (978-1-59515-303-6(9)); (Illus.). 14.95 (978-1-59515-155-1(9)) Rourke Publishing, LLC.

—Vanishing Rain Forests. 2005. (Rain Forest Today Discovery Library Ser.). (Illus.). 24p. (gr. 1-4). 14.95 (978-1-59515-156-8(7)) Rourke Publishing, LLC.

Osborne, Mary Pope & Osborne, Will. Rain Forests. Murdocca, Sal, illus. 2001. (Magic Tree House Research Guide Ser.: No. 5). 128p. (J). (gr. k-3). 4.99 (978-0-375-81355-9(1) , Random Hse. Bks. for Young Readers) Random Hse. Children's Bks.

—Rain Forests: A Nonfiction Companion to Afternoon on the Amazon. Murdocca, Sal, illus. 2001. (Magic Tree House Research Guide Ser.: No. 5). 128p. (J). (gr. k-3). lib. bdg. 11.99 (978-0-375-91355-6(6) , Random Hse. Bks. for Young Readers) Random Hse. Children's Bks.

Osborne, Will & Osborne, Mary Pope. Rain Forests: A Nonfiction Companion to Afternoon on the Amazon. 2001. (Magic Tree House Research Guide Ser.: No. 5). (J). (gr. k-3). (978-0-606-22388-1(6)) Tandem Library Bks.

Parker, Edward, photos by. People. 2002. (Rain Forest Pilot Ser.). (Illus.). 48p. (J). lib. bdg. 27.12 (978-0-7398-5242-2(6)) Raintree.

—Trees & Plants. 2002. (Rain Forest Pilot Ser.). (Illus.). 48p. (J). lib. bdg. 27.12 (978-0-7398-5244-6(2)) Raintree.

Pascoe, Gwen. Deep in a Rainforest. Jefferis, Veronica, illus. 1999. 32p. (J). (gr. k up). lib. bdg. 23.33 (978-0-8368-2149-9(1)) Stevens, Gareth Inc.

Patent, Dorothy Hinshaw. Garden of the Spirit Bear: Life in the Great Northern Rainforest. Milton, Deborah Jane, illus. 2004. 40p. (J). (gr. 3-5). tchr. ed. 16.00 (978-0-618-21259-0(0) , Clarion Bks.) Houghton Mifflin Co. Trade & Reference Div.

Pirotta, Saviour. Deep in the Rain Forest Collection, 4 vols. 2001. (Illus.). (J). pap. (978-0-7398-4947-7(6)) Steck-Vaughn.

—Trees & Plants in the Rain Forest. 1999. (Deep in the Rain Forest Ser.). (Illus.). 32p. (J). (978-0-7502-2198-6(4)) Steck-Vaughn.

Pratt-Serafini, Kristin Joy. A Walk in the Rainforest. Pratt-Serafini, Kristin Joy, illus. 2007. (Illus.). 26p. (J). (ps-ps). bds. 7.95 ***(*978-1-58469-088-7(7))*** Dawn Pubns.

Pyers, Greg. Rain Forest Explorer. 2004. (Habitat Explorer Ser.). (Illus.). 32p. (J). (ps-ps). lib. bdg. 25.70 (978-1-4109-0511-6(X)) Raintree.

The Rain Forest, 6 Packs. (Action Packs Ser.). 128p. (gr. 3-5). 44.00 (978-0-7635-3311-3(4)) Rigby Education.

The Rain Forest: Fourth Grade Newcomer Books. (On Our Way to English Ser.). (gr. 4 up). 34.50 (978-0-7578-7262-4(X)) Rigby Education.

Rain Forest Secrets. 1998. (J). pap. 3.95 (978-0-439-04455-4(3)) Scholastic, Inc.

Reid, Greg. Rain Forests. 2004. (Ecosystems Ser.). (Illus.). 32p. (J). (gr. 3-5). 23.00 (978-0-7910-7941-6(4) , Chelsea Hse.) Facts On File, Inc.

Richardson, Adele D. Rain Forests. 2001. (Bridgestone Science Library). (Illus.). 24p. (J). (gr. 2-3). lib. bdg. 18.60 (978-0-7368-0839-2(6) , Bridgestone Bks.) Capstone Pr., Inc.

Riley, Peter D. Rain Forest. 2004. (Survivor's Science Ser.). (J). 28.56 (978-1-4109-0227-6(7)) Harcourt Schl. Pubs.

Sayre, April Pulley. Tropical Rainforest. 2003. (Scholastic Science Readers Ser.). (Illus.). 48p. (J). (978-0-439-26994-0(6)) Scholastic, Inc.

Senior, Kathryn. Life in a Rain Forest. 2005. (What on Earth? Ser.). (Illus.). 32p. (J). 25.50 (978-0-516-25315-2(8) , Children's Pr.) Scholastic Library Publishing.

—Rain Forest. 1999. (Fast Forward Ser.). (Illus.). 32p. (J). (gr. 4-8). 29.00 (978-0-531-14572-2(7) , Watts, Franklin) Scholastic Library Publishing.

—Rain Forest. 1999. (gr. k-3). lib. bdg. 18.75 (978-0-613-31624-8(X)) Tandem Library Bks.

Serrano, Marta. Rain Forests. 2002. (Living Planet Ser.). (Illus.). 32p. (J). 23.70 (978-1-56711-670-0(1) , Blackbirch Pr., Inc.) Thomson Gale.

Smith, Kathie Billingslea. Rainforest Animals. Bonforte, Lisa, illus. 2005. 12p. (J). (gr. k-3). 6.99 (978-1-57755-509-4(0)) Allied Publishing.

Snedden, Robert. Tropical Rain Forests. 2003. (Illus.). 32p. (J). lib. bdg. (978-1-58340-382-2(5)) Smart Apple Media.

—Who Eats Who in the Rainforest? 2006. (Food Chains in Action Ser.). (Illus.). 32p. (J). (978-1-58340-961-9(0)) Smart Apple Media.

Steck-Vaughn Staff. Animals of the Rainforest, Set 1. 2001. pap., tchr. ed. (978-0-7398-3362-9(6)) Steck-Vaughn.

Stille, Darlene R. Tropical Rain Forest. 1999. (True Bks.). (Illus.). 48p. (J). (gr. 3-5). 25.00 (978-0-516-21511-2(6) , Children's Pr.) Scholastic Library Publishing.

—Tropical Rain Forests. 2000. (True Bks.). (Illus.). 48p. (J). (gr. 3-5). pap. 6.95 (978-0-516-26774-6(4) , Children's Pr.) Scholastic Library Publishing.

—Tropical Rain Forests. 2000. (Illus.). 47p. (J). (gr. 3-5). lib. bdg. 15.25 (978-0-613-37568-9(8)) Tandem Library Bks.

Stradling, Jan. Rain Forest Life: Level I, 6 vols., Vol. 2. (First Explorers Ser.). 24p. (gr. 1-2). 29.95 (978-0-7699-1463-3(2)) Shortland Pubns. (U. S. A.) Inc.

Tagliaferro, Linda. Explore the Tropical Rain Forest. 2006. (Fact Finders Ser.). (Illus.). 32p. (J). 22.60 (978-0-7368-6407-7(5) , Fact Finders) Capstone Pr., Inc.

Tarbox, A. D. The Rainforest. 2008. (J). ***(*978-1-58341-601-3(3)*** , Creative Education) Creative Co., The.

Taylor, Barbara. In the Rainforest. 1999. (Natural World Ser.). (Illus.). 29p. (J). (gr. 5-9). pap. 5.95 (978-0-7641-0642-2(2)) Barron's Educational Series, Inc.

Taylor-Butler, Christine. A Home in the Rain Forest. 2006. (Scholastic News Nonfiction Readers Ser.). 24p. (J). 19.00 (978-0-516-25347-3(6) , Children's Pr.) Scholastic Library Publishing.

Telford & Theodorou, Rod. Up a Rainforest Tree. 2002. (Amazing Journeys Ser.). (Illus.). 32p. (J). (gr. 2-6). pap. 7.50 (978-1-58810-304-8(8) , 91074) Heinemann Library.

Telford, Carole & Theodorou, Rod. Up a Rainforest Tree. (Illus.). 32p. (J). 2006. ***(*978-1-4034-8793-3(6));*** 1998. (gr. 2-4). lib. bdg. 22.79 (978-1-57572-156-9(2)) Heinemann Library.

Welsbacher, Anne. Life in a Rain Forest. 2003. (Ecosystems in Action Ser.). (Illus.). 72p. (J). (gr. 6-12). lib. bdg. 26.60 (978-0-8225-4685-6(X)) Lerner Publishing Group.

Wiley, G. D. Tropical Rain Forests. 2003. (Biomes Around the World Ser.). (J). pap. (978-1-58417-301-4(7)); lib. bdg. (978-1-58417-300-7(9)) Lake Street Pubs.

Wilkes, Angela. Rainforest. 2002. (Question Time Ser.). (Illus.). 32p. (J). (gr. k-3). tchr. ed. 11.95 (978-0-7534-5438-1(6) , Kingfisher) Houghton Mifflin Co. Trade & Reference Div.

Wilkes, Angela, et al. Rain Forest Animals. Holmes, Steve, illus. rev. ed. 2004. (Ladders Ser.). 32p. (J). (ps-3). 12.95 (978-1-58728-606-3(8) , Two Can Publishing) T&N Children's Publishing.

Woods, Mae. People of the Rain Forest. 1999. (Rain Forest Ser.). (Illus.). 24p. (J). (gr. k-6). lib. bdg. 21.35 (978-1-57765-020-1(4) , Checkerboard Library) ABDO Publishing Co.

—Plants of the Rain Forest. 1999. (Rain Forest Ser.). (Illus.). 24p. (J). (gr. k-6). lib. bdg. 21.35 (978-1-57765-018-8(2) , Checkerboard Library) ABDO Publishing Co.

—Protecting the Rain Forest. 1999. (Rain Forest Ser.). (Illus.). 24p. (J). (gr. k-6). lib. bdg. 21.35 (978-1-57765-022-5(0) , Checkerboard Library) ABDO Publishing Co.

—The Remarkable Rain Forest. 1999. (Rain Forest Ser.). (Illus.). 24p. (J). (gr. k-6). lib. bdg. 21.35 (978-1-57765-021-8(2) , Checkerboard Library) ABDO Publishing Co.

Worth, Bonnie. If I Ran the Rainforest. Ruiz, Aristides, illus. 2003. (Cat in the Hat's Learning Library). 48p. (J). (gr. k-3). 8.99 (978-0-375-81097-8(8) , Random Hse. Bks. for Young Readers) Random Hse. Children's Bks.

—If I Ran the Rainforest: All about Tropical Rain Forests. Ruiz, Aristides, illus. 2003. (Cat in the Hat's Learning Library Ser.). 48p. (J). (gr. k-3). lib. bdg. 12.99 (978-0-375-91097-5(2) , Random Hse. Bks. for Young Readers) Random Hse. Children's Bks.

Wright-Frierson, Virginia. A North American Rain Forest Scrapbook. Wright-Frierson, Virginia, illus. 2003. (Illus.). 40p. (J). (gr. 1-5). pap. 8.95 (978-0-8027-7651-8(5)) Walker & Co.

RAIN FORESTS

Allan, Tony. Rainforests. 2003. (Illus.). lib. bdg. 28.50 (978-1-59389-124-4(5)) Chrysalis Education.

Aloian, Molly & Kalman, Bobbie. Rainforest Food Chains. 2006. (Food Chains Ser.). (Illus.). 32p. (J). (978-0-7787-1951-9(0)) Crabtree Publishing Co.

Amazon Rain Forest. 2001. (J). cd-rom 69.95 (978-1-56791-299-9(0)) Environmental Media Corp.

Anastasio, Dina. In the Rain Forest. 2002. 16p. (J). (978-0-439-35148-5(0)) Scholastic, Inc.

Animals of the Rain Forest. 2000. (Illus.). (J). (978-0-7398-4167-9(X)) Raintree.

Animals of the Rain Forest, 12 bks., Set. Incl. Anacondas. Steele, Christy. 2000. lib. bdg. 22.83 (978-0-7398-3099-4(6)); Anteaters. Dollar, Sam. Sloan, Frank, ed. 2001. lib. bdg. 22.83 (978-0-7398-3552-4(1)); Ants. Steele, Christy. 2000. lib. bdg. 22.83 (978-0-7398-3098-7(8)); Boa Constrictors. Dollar, Sam. Sloan, Frank, ed. 2001. lib. bdg. 22.83 (978-0-7398-3553-1(X)); Caimans. Dollar, Sam. 2000. lib. bdg. 22.83 (978-0-7398-3097-0(X)); Jaguars. Lalley, Pat. 2000. lib. bdg. 22.83 (978-0-7398-3102-1(X)); Ocelots. Dollar, Sam. Sloan, Frank, ed. 2001. lib. bdg. 22.83 (978-0-7398-3554-8(8)); Orangutans. Steele, Christy. Sloan, Frank, ed. 2001. lib. bdg. 22.83 (978-0-7398-3555-5(6)); Piranhas. Dollar, Sam. 2000. lib. bdg. 22.83 (978-0-7398-3101-4(1)); Tarantulas. Steele, Christy. Sloan, Frank, ed. 2001. lib. bdg. 22.83 (978-0-7398-3556-2(4)); Toucans. Dollar, Sam. 2000. lib. bdg. 22.83 (978-0-7398-3100-7(3)); Tree Frogs. Deiters, Erika & Deiters, Jim. Sloan, Frank, ed. 2001. lib. bdg. 22.83 (978-0-7398-3557-9(2)); (Illus.). 32p. (J). (gr. 4-7). 2001. Set lib. bdg. 273.96 (978-0-7398-3559-3(9)) Raintree.

Animals of the Rain Forest: Includes: Anteaters, Boa Constrictors, Ocelots, Orangutans, Tarantulas, Tree Frogs, 6 bks., Set. 2001. (Illus.). (J). (gr. 4-7). lib. bdg. 136.98 (978-0-7398-3558-6(0)) Raintree.

Animals of the Rain Forest Collection 3. 2002. (Illus.). (J). pap. (978-0-7398-6027-4(5)) Steck-Vaughn.

Animals of the Rain Forest Series, 30 bks., Set. 2003. (Illus.). (gr. 4 up). lib. bdg. 728.40 (978-0-7398-5374-0(0)) Raintree.

Animals of the Rain Forest Set: Includes: Anacondas, Ants, Caimans, Jaguars, Piranhas, Toucans, 6 bks., Set. 2001. (Illus.). (J). (gr. 4-7). lib. bdg. 136.98 (978-0-7398-3103-8(8)) Raintree.

Animals of the Rainforest. 2001. (Illus.). (J). Set 1. pap. (978-0-7398-3363-6(4)); Set 2. pap. (978-0-7398-4670-4(1)); Set 3. pap. (978-0-7398-4932-3(8)) Steck-Vaughn.

Baker, Lucy. Life in the Rain Forests. 2001. (World Book Ecology Ser.). (Illus.). 32p. (J). (978-0-7166-5224-3(2)) World Bk., Inc.

—Rain Forests. (Illus.). 2004. (Interfact Ser.). (SPA.). 48p. (J). (gr. 3-6). pap. 14.95 incl. cd-rom (978-1-58728-461-8(8)); 2004. (Life In... Ser.). (SPA., 32p. (J). (gr. 3-6). pap. 6.95 (978-1-58728-573-8(8)); 2004. (Life In Ser.). (SPA., 31p. (gr. 3-6). 12.95 (978-1-58728-558-5(4)); 2000. (Collectafact Ser.: Vol. 1). 48p. (J). (gr. 1-5). 4.95 (978-1-58728-755-8(2)) T&N Children's Publishing. (Two Can Publishing).

Baldwin, Carol. Living in a Rain Forest. 2003. (Living Habitats Ser.). (Illus.). 32p. (J). pap. 6.95 (978-1-4034-3234-6(1)); lib. bdg. 24.22 (978-1-4034-2992-6(8)) Heinemann Library.

Banner, Horace. Rain Forest Adventures. (Illus.). 96p. (J). pap. 5.99 (978-1-85792-627-9(7) , Christian Focus) Christian Focus Pubns. GBR. *Dist:* Riverside.

Barnett, Michelle Noble, et al. Theme Pockets - June: Amazon Rainforest; Artists; Farmers Feed Us. Evans, Marilyn, ed. Larsen, Jo, illus. 1999. (Making Books with Pockets). 96p. (J). pap., tchr. ed. 12.99 (978-1-55799-703-6(9) , EMC 589) Evan-Moor Educational Pubs.

Bartholomew, Linda & Bartholomew, Al. Adventures in the Tropics. Bartholomew, Linda & Bartholomew, Al, photos by. 2005. 76p. (J). 15.00 (978-0-9764802-1-1(2)) Solutions for Human Services, LLC.

—The Rain Forest Book for Kids. Bartholomew, Linda & Bartholomew, Al, photos by. 2005. 32p. (J). 9.00 (978-0-9764802-0-4(4)) Solutions for Human Services, LLC.

Bedford, Kate. Rainforests. 2005. (Illus.). 32p. (J). (gr. 3-7). lib. bdg. 27.10 (978-1-59604-040-3(8)) Stargazer Bks.

Benchmark Education Staff. Tropical Rain Forests. 2005. 2.00 (***978-1-4108-4649-5(0)***) Benchmark Education Co.

Benduhn, Tea. Living in Tropical Rain Forests. 2007. (J). pap. (***978-0-8368-8349-7(7));*** 24p. (gr. 2-4). lib. bdg. 19.93 (***978-0-8368-8344-2(6))*** Stevens, Gareth Inc. (Weekly Reader Early Learning Library).

Berger, Gilda. Rain Forest. Date not set. (Smart Science Ser.). (Illus.). 16p. (J). (gr. 2-5). pap. 5.95 (978-1-58273-510-8(7)) Sundance/Newbridge Educational Publishing.

Berger, Melvin & Berger, Gilda. Does It Always Rain in the Rain Forest? Questions & Answers about Rain Forests. Rothman, Michael, illus. 2001. (J). (978-0-439-19382-5(6) , Scholastic Reference) Scholastic, Inc.

—Life in the Rainforest: Plants, Animals, & People. Brittingham, Geoffrey H., illus. 1999. (Discovery Readers Ser.). 48p. (YA). (ps up). lib. bdg. 15.95 (978-0-7910-5068-2(8) , Chelsea Hse.) Facts On File, Inc.

Beylon, Cathy. My Rain Forest Sticker Activity Book. 1998. (Illus.). 4p. (J). pap. 1.50 (978-0-486-40509-4(5)) Dover Pubns., Inc.

Bodden, Valerie. Rainforests. 2006. (Illus.). 24p. (J). 16.95 (978-1-58341-465-1(7) , Creative Education) Creative Co., The.

Brannon, Barbara. Discover Tropical Rain Forests. 2005. 39.00 (***978-1-4108-5130-7(3))*** Benchmark Education Co.

Braun, Eric & Donovan, Sandy. Tamarins. 2001. (Animals of the Rain Forest Ser.). (Illus.). 32p. (YA). lib. bdg. 22.83 (978-0-7398-4684-1(1)) Raintree.

Brighter Vision Publishing Staff. Rain Forest. 1999. (Learning Adventures Preschool Ser.). (Illus.). (J). (ps-k). pap. 2.25 (978-1-55254-057-2(X) , BV12006) Brighter Vision Pubns.

Brim, Warren & Eglitis, Anna. Creatures of the Rainforest: Two Artists Explore Djabugay Country. Brim, Warren & Eglitis, Anna, illus. 2005. (Illus.). 60p. (J). 24.50 (978-1-875641-99-4(8)) Magabala Bks. AUS. *Dist:* International Specialized Bk. Services.

Butterfield, Moira. Protecting Rain Forests. 2005. (Protecting Habitats Ser.). (Illus.). 32p. (J). lib. bdg. 24.67 (978-0-8368-4994-3(9)) Stevens, Gareth Inc.

—Rainforest. 1999. (Where Am I? Ser.). (Illus.). 32p. (J). (gr. 2-6). lib. bdg. 16.95 (978-1-929298-37-2(4)) Chrysalis Education.

Castaldo, Nancy F. Rainforests: An Activity Guide for Ages 6-9. 2003. (Illus.). 144p. (J). pap. 14.95 (978-1-55652-476-9(5)) Chicago Review Pr., Inc.

—Rainforests: An Activity Guide for Ages 6-9. 2003. (gr. k-3). lib. bdg. 24.55 (978-0-613-89931-4(8)) Tandem Library Bks.

Castner, James L. Rainforest Researchers: Deep in the Amazon. 2001. (Deep in the Amazon Ser.). (Illus.). 32p. (J). (gr. 5 up). lib. bdg. 27.07 (978-0-7614-1129-1(1) , Benchmark Bks.) Cavendish, Marshall Corp.

Chapman, Simon. Explorers Wanted! In the Jungle. 2005. (Illus.). 128p. (J). (gr. 5-8). pap. 5.99 (978-0-316-15539-7(X)) Little Brown & Co.

Chapman, Simon. In the Jungle. Chapman, Simon, illus. 2005. (Illus.). 116p. (J). lib. bdg. 20.00 (***978-1-4242-0630-8(8))*** Fitzgerald Bks.

Cheshire, Gerard. Tropical Rainforest. 2001. (gr. 5-8). lib. bdg. 18.75 (978-0-613-89191-2(0)) Tandem Library Bks.

Chinery, Michael. Partners & Parents. 2000. (Secrets of the Rainforest Ser.). (Illus.). 32p. (J). (gr. 3-4). pap. (978-0-7787-0226-9(X)); lib. bdg. (978-0-7787-0216-0(2)) Crabtree Publishing Co.

—Partners & Parents. 2000. (gr. 3-6). lib. bdg. 16.40 (978-0-613-28012-9(1)) Tandem Library Bks.

—People & Places. 2000. (Secrets of the Rainforest Ser.). (Illus.). 32p. (J). (gr. 3-4). pap. (978-0-7787-0230-6(8)); lib. bdg. (978-0-7787-0220-7(0)) Crabtree Publishing Co.

—People & Places. 2001. (gr. 3-6). lib. bdg. 16.40 (978-0-613-32935-4(X)); (Illus.). (J). (978-0-606-20851-2(8)) Tandem Library Bks.

—Poisoners & Pretenders. 2000. (Secrets of the Rainforest Ser.). (Illus.). (J). (978-0-606-20859-8(3)) Tandem Library Bks.

—Resources & Conservation. 2000. (Secrets of the Rainforest Ser.). (Illus.). 32p. (J). (gr. 3-4). pap. (978-0-7787-0231-3(6)); lib. bdg. (978-0-7787-0221-4(9)) Crabtree Publishing Co.

—Resources & Conservation. 2001. (gr. 3-6). lib. bdg. 16.40 (978-0-613-32995-8(3)); (Illus.). (J) (978-0-606-20881-9(X)) Tandem Library Bks.

—Secrets of the Rainforest, 6 bks. Incl. Partners & Parents. lib. bdg. (978-0-7787-0216-0(2)); People & Places. lib. bdg. (978-0-7787-0220-7(0)); Plants & Planteaters. lib. bdg. (978-0-7787-0218-4(9)); Poisoners & Pretenders. lib. bdg. (978-0-7787-0219-1(7)); Predators & Prey. lib. bdg. (978-0-7787-0217-7(0)); Resources & Conservation. lib. bdg. (978-0-7787-0221-4(9)); 32p. (J). (gr. 3-4). 2000. (Illus.). 2001. (978-0-7787-0215-3(4)); Set pap. (978-0-7787-0225-2(1)) Crabtree Publishing Co.

—Las Selvas.Tr. of Rain Forests. (SPA.). 40p. (J). (gr. 3-5). 12.76 (978-84-241-2052-8(3)) Everest de Ediciones y Distribucion, S.L. ESP. *Dist:* Lectorum Pubns., Inc.

Clarke, Penny. Scary Creatures of the Rain Forest! (Scary Creatures Ser.). 32p. (J). 2008. pap. 8.95 (***978-0-531-21010-9(3)*** , Watts, Franklin); 2007. spiral bd. 26.00 (***978-0-531-20544-0(4)*** , Children's Pr.) Scholastic Library Publishing.

Cole, Melissa S. Rain Forests. 2003. (Wild America Habitats Ser.). (Illus.). 24p. (J). 21.20 (978-1-56711-808-7(9) , Blackbirch Pr., Inc.) Thomson Gale.

Cory, Christopher. The Rain Forest. Curry, Don, ed. 1998. (Early Science Ser.). 16p. (J). (ps-2). pap., stu. ed. 3.33 (978-1-56784-380-4(8)); (Illus.). pap. 16.95 (978-1-56784-379-8(4)) Sundance/Newbridge Educational Publishing.

Costain, Meredith. Rainforests. 2000. (gr. k-3). lib. bdg. 11.80 (978-0-613-30693-5(7)) Tandem Library Bks.

Cowcher, Helen. Rainforest. (Illus.). 40p. (CHI, ENG, URD, TUR & VIE.). (J). 16.95 (978-1-84059-017-3(3)); (VIE, ENG, URD, TUR & CHI., (J). 16.95 (978-1-84059-022-7(X)); 2001. (GRE, ENG, URD, TUR & VIE., (YA). 16.95 (978-1-84059-018-0(1)); 2001. (GUJ, ENG, URD, TUR & VIE., (YA). 16.95 (978-1-84059-019-7(X)); 2001. (TUR, ENG, URD, VIE & CHI., (YA). 16.95 (978-1-84059-020-3(3)); 2001. (BEN, ENG, URD, TUR & VIE., (YA). 16.95 (978-1-84059-016-6(5)) Milet Publishing.

Cowley, Joy. The Red-Eyed Tree Frog. Bishop, Nic, illus. 1999. (J). pap. (978-0-590-87176-1(5)); 32p. pap. 16.95 (978-0-590-87175-4(7)) Scholastic, Inc.

Datta, Aparajita & Manjrekar, Nima. Walk the Rainforest with Niwupah. Ramaswamy, Maya, illus. 2004. (J). (978-81-89020-15-6(3)) Katha.

Davis, Rebecca Fjelland. More or Less: A Rain Forest Counting Book. 2007. (Illus.). 32p. (J). 23.93 (978-0-7368-6376-6(1)) Capstone Pr., Inc.

Dawson, Paul. Rain Forest. 2003. (gr. k-3). lib. bdg. 14.10 (978-0-613-83249-6(3)) Tandem Library Bks.

Declus, Jennifer. What Might I Find in a Rainforest. Kalasea, illus. 2004. (ENG.). (J). (978-0-9743690-1-3(2)) Britt Allcroft Productions.

Deiters, Erika & Deiters, Jim. Tree Frogs. Sloan, Frank, ed. 2001. (Animals of the Rain Forest Ser.). (Illus.). 32p. (J). (gr. 4-7). lib. bdg. 22.83 (978-0-7398-3557-9(2)) Raintree.

Doering, Amanda. Rain Forest ABC: An Alphabet Book. 2004. (A+ Alphabet Books). (Illus.). 32p. (J). 22.60 (978-0-7368-2611-2(4) , Aplus Bks.) Capstone Pr., Inc.

Donovan, Sandy. Beetles. 2002. (Animals of the Rain Forest Ser.). (Illus.). 32p. (YA). lib. bdg. 22.83 (978-0-7398-5368-9(6)) Raintree.

—Chimpanzees. 2002. (Animals of the Rain Forest Ser.). (Illus.). 32p. (YA). lib. bdg. 22.83 (978-0-7398-5370-2(8)) Raintree.

—Iguanas. 2002. (Animals of the Rain Forest Ser.). (Illus.). 32p. (YA). lib. bdg. 22.83 (978-0-7398-5372-6(4)) Raintree.

—Quetzals. 2002. (Animals of the Rain Forest Ser.). (Illus.). 32p. (YA). (gr. 4 up). lib. bdg. 22.83 (978-0-7398-5530-0(1)) Raintree.

Doris, Ellen. Life at the Top: Discoveries in a Tropical Forest Canopy. 1999. (Rain Forest Pilot Ser.). (Illus.). 48p. (J). (gr. 3-7). 18.98 (978-0-7398-2220-3(9)) Raintree.

—Life at the Top: Discoveries in a Tropical Forest Canopy. 2000. (Turnstone Rain Forest Pilot Book Ser.). (Illus.). 48p. (J). (gr. 4-6). pap. 7.95 (978-0-7398-2229-6(2)) Steck-Vaughn.

—Life at the Top: Discoveries in a Tropical Forest Canopy. 2000. (gr. 3-6). lib. bdg. 17.85 (978-0-613-74072-2(6)) Tandem Library Bks.

Dorling Kindersley Publishing Staff. Rain Forest. 2006. (Dk 24 Hours Ser.). (Illus.). 48p. (J). 12.99 (978-0-7566-1985-5(8)) Dorling Kindersley Publishing, Inc.

Dunphy, Madeleine. Here Is the Tropical Rain Forest. Rothman, Michael, illus. 2006. (Web of Life Ser.). 32p. (J). 16.95 (978-0-9773795-1-4(5)); pap. 9.95 (978-0-9773795-0-7(7)) Web of Life Children's Bks.

Fabiny, Sarah. Rainforest Animal Adventure. Kees, Chantal & Shields, Chris, illus. 2003. (Magic Color Bks.). 12p. (J). (gr. k-2). 9.95 (978-1-4027-0823-7(8)) Sterling Publishing Co., Inc.

Fading Forests: the Destruction of Our Rainforests: Individual Title Six-Packs. (On Deck Ser.: Vol. 2). 24p. (gr. 4-5). 35.00 (978-0-7578-5830-7(9)) Rigby Education.

Fitzgerald, Stephanie. Remote Jungles. 2007. (J). (***978-1-4329-0109-7(5));*** pap. (***978-1-4329-0115-8(X))*** Heinemann Library.

Forsyth, Adrian. How Monkeys Make Chocolate: Unlocking the Mysteries of the Rain Forest. 2nd ed. 2006. (Illus.). 48p. pap. 9.95 (978-1-897066-78-2(3)) Maple Tree Pr. CAN. *Dist:* Perseus Distribution.

—How Monkeys Make Chocolate: Unlocking the Mysteries of the Rainforest. 2nd ed. 2006. (Illus.). 48p. 19.95 (978-1-897066-77-5(5)) Maple Tree Pr. CAN. *Dist:* Perseus Distribution.

Fowler, Allan. Living in a Rain Forest. 2000. (Rookie Read-About Geography Ser.). (Illus.). 32p. (J). (gr. 1-2). pap. 5.95 (978-0-516-27050-0(8) , Children's Pr.) Scholastic Library Publishing.

—Living in a Rain Forest. 2000. (gr. k-3). lib. bdg. 14.10 (978-0-613-54732-1(2)) Tandem Library Bks.

Fraggalosch, Audrey. Great Grizzy Wilderness: A Story of the Pacific Rain Forest. Eberhart, Donald G., illus. 2000. (Habitat Ser.). (J). (gr. 1-4). 32p. 15.95 (978-1-56899-838-1(4)); 36p. 26.95 (978-1-56899-842-8(2)) Soundprints.

Framingham Community Charter School Grade Students. Rainforest Exhibits: How We Learned about Designing & Creating an Authentic Biome. 2003. 73p. pap. 6.25 (978-1-4116-0071-3(1)) Lulu.com.

Galko, Francine. Rain Forest Animals. 2003. (Animals in Their Habitats Ser.). (Illus.). 32p. (J). (gr. k-2). lib. bdg. 21.36 (978-1-4034-0182-3(9)) Heinemann Library.

—Rain Forest Animals. 2003. (gr. k-3). lib. bdg. 14.75 (978-0-613-45815-3(X)) Tandem Library Bks.

—Rainforest Animals. 2003. (Animals in Their Habitats Ser.). (Illus.). 32p. (J). pap. 6.95 (978-1-4034-0439-8(9)) Heinemann Library.

Ganeri, Anita. Living in the Amazon Rainforest. 2007. (J). pap. (***978-1-4109-2826-9(8));*** lib. bdg. (***978-1-4109-2817-7(9))*** Steck-Vaughn.

George, Michael. Rainforests: Endangered Jewels. 2003. (LifeViews Ser.). (Illus.). 32p. (J). lib. bdg. (978-1-58341-252-7(2) , Creative Education) Creative Co., The.

Gidwitz, Tim. Story in the Stone: The Formation of a Tropical Land Bridge. 1999. (Rain Forest Pilot Ser.). (Illus.). 48p. (J). (gr. 4-6). 18.98 (978-0-7398-2217-3(9)) Raintree.

—Story in the Stone: The Formation of a Tropical Land Bridge. 2000. (Turnstone Rain Forest Pilot Book Ser.). (Illus.). 48p. (J). (gr. 4-6). pap. 7.95 (978-0-7398-2226-5(8)) Steck-Vaughn.

Gill, Shelley R. The Last American Rainforest: Tongass. Cartwright, Shannon, illus. 2002. 32p. (J). (gr. 1-12). pap. (978-0-934007-33-7(0)) Paws IV Publishing.

Gray, Shirley W. Rain Forests. 2000. (First Reports). (Illus.). 48p. (J). (gr. 3 up). lib. bdg. 21.26 (978-0-7565-0023-8(0)) Compass Point Bks.

Greeley, August. Fading Forests: The Destruction of Our Rainforests. 2003. (Reading Power Ser.). (Illus.). 24p. (J). lib. bdg. 17.25 (978-0-8239-6486-4(8) , PowerKids Pr.) Rosen Publishing Group, Inc., The.

Green, Jen. Rainforests. 2001. (Fantastic Facts Ser.). (Illus.). 64p. pap. 6.95 (978-1-84215-372-7(2) , Southwater) Anness Publishing GBR. *Dist:* National Bk. Network.

—Rainforests at Risk. 2006. (Illus.). 32p. (YA). (gr. 4 up). lib. bdg. 27.10 (978-1-59389-116-9(4)) Chrysalis Education.

Green, Jen & Dorling Kindersley Publishing Staff. Rainforest. 2004. (Dk Revealed Ser.). 40p. (J). 12.99 (978-0-7566-0538-4(5)) Dorling Kindersley Publishing, Inc.

Greenaway, Theresa & Dorling Kindersley Publishing Staff. Jungle. Dann, Geoff, photos by. 2004. (Eyewitness Books). (Illus.). 72p. (J). lib. bdg. 19.99 (978-0-7566-0693-0(4)) Dorling Kindersley Publishing, Inc.

Greenwood, Elinor. Rain Forest. 2001. (Eye Wonder Ser.). (Illus.). 48p. (J). (gr. k-3). 9.99 (978-0-7894-7853-5(6)) Dorling Kindersley Publishing, Inc.

Group/McGraw-Hill, Wright. In the Rain Forest, 6 vols. (Wildcats Ser.). 32p. (gr. 2-8). (978-0-322-00599-0(X)) Wright Group, The.

—Tropical Treasure: The Rain Forest, 6 vols. (Book2WebTM Ser.). (gr. 4-8). 36.50 (978-0-322-04432-6(4)) Wright Group, The.

—La Vida en la Selva Tropical, 6 vols., Vol. 2. (First Explorers. Primeros Exploradores Nonfiction Sets Ser.). (SPA.). (gr. 1-2). 29.95 (978-0-7699-1487-9(X)) Shortland Pubns. (U. S. A.) Inc.

Habitats & Rain Forests Theme Package. 1999. (Illus.). (J). 188.30 (978-0-7398-1676-9(4)) Raintree.

Hamilton, Jean. The Secrets of Tropical Rainforests: Hot & Humid & Teeming with Life. Leon, Vicki, ed. 2nd ed. 2005. (Jean-Michel Cousteau Presents Ser.). Orig. Title: Tropical Rainforests. (Illus.). 48p. (J). pap. 7.95 (978-0-9666490-5-5(2)) London Town Pr.

Hammerslough, Jane. Into the Rainforest. 2003. (Animal Planet Ser.). (Illus.). 88p. (J). pap. 3.99 (978-0-439-43565-9(X)) Scholastic, Inc.

Harcourt School Publishers Staff. Plants of the Rain Forest Advanced Level. 3rd ed. 2002. (Trophies Reading Program Ser.). (Illus.). pap. 5.10 (978-0-15-323309-8(5)) Harcourt Schl. Pubs.

—The Rain Forest. 3rd ed. 2002. (Horizons Ser.). (Illus.). (J). pap. 3.70 (978-0-15-333119-0(4)) Harcourt Schl. Pubs.

—Rainforest Plants Advanced Level. 3rd ed. 2002. (Trophies Reading Program Ser.). (Illus.). pap. 5.10 (978-0-15-323112-4(2)) Harcourt Schl. Pubs.

Hardy. Who Lives in the Rain Forest? 1998. (J). pap. 2.95 (978-0-87628-185-7(4)) Ctr. for Applied Research in Education, The.

In the Rain Forest: Level F. 16p. 31.50 (978-0-322-00376-7(8)) Wright Group, The.

Jackson. Tropical Forests. 2003. (Biomes Atlas Ser.). (Illus.). 64p. pap. 9.50 (978-1-4109-0018-0(5)); pap. 48.30 (978-1-4109-0253-5(6)) Raintree.

Jackson, Kay. Rain Forests. 2007. (Our Environment Ser.). 48p. (J). (gr. 4-8). 26.20 (***978-0-7377-3624-3(0)*** , Kidhaven) Thomson Gale.

Johnson, Jinny & Nadkarni, Naklini. Rain Forest. 2006. (Kingfisher Voyages Ser.). (Illus.). 60p. (J). (gr. 4-6). 15.95 (978-0-7534-5904-1(3) , Kingfisher) Houghton Mifflin Co. Trade & Reference Div.

Johnson, Linda Carlson. Rain Forests: A Pro/Con Issue. 1999. (Hot Pro/Con Issues Ser.). (Illus.). 64p. (YA). (gr. 6-12). lib. bdg. 21.95 (978-0-7660-1202-8(6)) Enslow Pubs., Inc.

Johnson, Rebecca L. A Walk in the Rain Forest. Saroff, Phyllis V., illus. Braasch, Gary, photos by. 2005. (Biomes of North America Ser.). 48p. (gr. 3-6). 23.93 (978-1-57505-154-3(0)) Lerner Publishing Group.

Kallen, Stuart A. Life in the Amazon Rain Forest. 1999. (Way People Live Ser.). (Illus.). 96p. (YA). (gr. 7-10). 27.45 (978-1-56006-387-2(4) , LML00902-177770, Lucent Bks.) Thomson Gale.

Kalman, Bobbie. Rainforest Birds. 1998. (Birds Up Close Ser.). (Illus.). 32p. (J). (gr. 3-4). pap. (978-0-86505-767-8(2)); lib. bdg. (978-0-86505-753-1(2)) Crabtree Publishing Co.

Kite, Lorien. A Rain Forest Tree. 1999. (Illus.). 32p. (J). (ps-7). lib. bdg. 17.60 (978-0-613-19529-4(9)) Tandem Library Bks.

—Rain Forest Tree. 1999. (978-0-606-18065-8(6)) Tandem Library Bks.

Knight, Tim. Journey into the Rainforest. Knight, Tim & Moreiras, Juan Pablo, photos by. 2001. (Illus.). 48p. (YA). (gr. 4-7). 19.95 (978-0-19-521751-3(9)) Oxford Univ. Pr., Inc.

Kovacs. Noises in the Night. 1999. (Illus.). (J). pap. (978-0-7398-2472-6(4)) Steck-Vaughn.

Kratter, Paul. The Living Rain Forest: An Animal Alphabet. Kratter, Paul, illus. 2004. (Illus.). 64p. (J). 17.95 (978-1-57091-603-8(9)) Charlesbridge Publishing, Inc.

Leber, Nancy. Rain Forest Animals. 2003. (Compass Point Phonics Readers Ser.). (Illus.). 16p. (J). (gr. 1 up). 13.26 (978-0-7565-0523-3(2)) Compass Point Bks.

Lee, Justin. How to Draw Animals of the Rain Forest. 2002. (Kid's Guide to Drawing Ser.). (Illus.). 24p. (J). lib. bdg. 21.25 (978-0-8239-5793-4(4) , PowerKids Pr.) Rosen Publishing Group, Inc., The.

Levinson, Nancy Smiler. Rain Forests. Hearn, Diane Dawson, illus. 2006. (J). (978-0-8234-1899-2(5)) Holiday Hse., Inc.

Levy, Janey. Discovering Rain Forests. 2007. (J). lib. bdg. ***(*978-1-4042-3782-7(8)*** , PowerKids Pr.) Rosen Publishing Group, Inc., The.

Lewington, Anna & Parker, Edward. People of the Rain Forests. 1998. (Wide World Ser.). (Illus.). 48p. (J). (gr. 3-7). 18.98 (978-0-8172-5061-4(1)) Raintree.

Lindeen, Carol. Life in a Rain Forest. 2003. (Pebble Plus: Living in a Biome Ser.). (Illus.). 24p. (J). lib. bdg. 17.26 (978-0-7368-2102-5(3)) Capstone Pr., Inc.

Lindeen, Carol K. Life in a Rain Forest, Vol. 3. 2005. (Earth & Outer Space Ser.). 24p. (YA). (gr. k-3). pap. (978-0-7368-3403-2(6) , Pebble Bks.) Capstone Pr., Inc.

Lindeen, Mary. Rain Forests. 2007. (Illus.). 24p. (J). lib. bdg. 19.95 (978-1-60014-115-7(3)) Bellwether Media.

Llewellyn, Claire. Deserts & Rainforests. 1998. (Illus.). 24p. (J). (gr. 1-6). (978-1-57572-196-5(1)) Heinemann Library.

Longnecker, Theresa. Who Grows Up in the Rain Forest? A Book about Rain Forest Animals & Their Offspring. Carpenter, Melissa, illus. 2004. (Who Grows Up Here? Ser.). 24p. (C). (gr. k-4). 21.26 (978-1-4048-0027-4(1)) Picture Window Bks.

MacDonald, Fiona. Rain Forest. 2000. (Topic Bks.). (Illus.). 32p. (J). (gr. 2-5). pap. 6.95 (978-0-531-15425-0(4) , Watts, Franklin) Scholastic Library Publishing.

Macken, JoAnn Early. Rain Forest Animals. Hess, Paul, illus. 2002. (Animal Worlds Ser.). 24p. (J). (ps up). lib. bdg. 20.67 (978-0-8368-3041-5(5)) Stevens, Gareth Inc.

Mattern, Joanne. Animals of the Tropical Rain Forest. 2006. (Rosen Publishing Group's Reading Room Collection). (Illus.). 16p. (J). lib. bdg. (978-1-4042-3341-6(5) , PowerKids Pr.) Rosen Publishing Group, Inc., The.

Mayer, Cassie. Rain Forest. 2007. (J). ***(*978-1-4034-9427-6(4));*** pap. ***(*978-1-4034-9433-7(9))*** Heinemann Library.

McCormick, Rosie. La Selva Tropical. Sanz, Maria Teresa, tr. 2004. (Discovery Guides Ser.). (SPA., Illus.). 32p. (gr. 2-5). (J). pap. 11.95 (978-1-58728-702-2(1)); 11.95 (978-1-58728-645-2(9)) T&N Children's Publishing. (Two Can Publishing).

McKay, Sindy. We Both Read-about the Rain Forest. 2000. (We Both Read Ser.). (Illus.). 44p. (J). (gr. 1-2). pap. 3.99 (978-1-891327-24-7(0)) Treasure Bay, Inc.

McKissack, Fredrick, Jr. & McKissack, Lisa Beringer. Counting in the Rain Forest. 2008. (J). ***(*978-0-7660-2992-7(1))*** Enslow Pubs., Inc.

McLeish, Ewan. Rain Forest Destruction. 2006. (Illus.). 48p. (J). pap. ***(*978-0-8368-8158-5(3)*** , World Almanac Library) Stevens, Gareth Inc.

McLeish, Ewan. Rain Forests: Our Impact on the Planet. 2001. (Twenty-First Century Debates Ser.). (Illus.). 64p. (YA). (gr. 6-8). lib. bdg. 27.12 (978-0-7398-3179-3(8)) Raintree.

McMorrow, Annalisa. Rain Forest: A Science Discovery Book. Barr, Marilynn G., illus. 1999. 48p. (J). (gr. 3-6). pap. 7.95 (978-1-57612-079-8(1) , MM2093) Monday Morning Bks., Inc.

Miranda, Anne. Rain Forest. 2002. (Illus.). 16p. (J). (978-0-439-35095-2(6)) Scholastic, Inc.

Moore, Eva. The Magic School Bus in the Rain Forest. Spiers, John, illus. 2001. (Magic School Bus Ser.). 32p. (J). (gr. k-2). pap. 5.99 (978-0-439-23960-8(5)) Scholastic, Inc.

Morey, Allan. Rain Forest Food Chains. 2003. (What Eats What? Ser.). (J). pap. (978-1-58417-225-3(8)); lib. bdg. (978-1-58417-224-6(X)) Lake Street Pubs.

Morgan, Sally. Saving the Rainforests. 2007. (Illus.). 32p. (J). ***(*978-1-59771-065-7(2))*** Sea-To-Sea Pubns.

Morris, Ting & Morris, Neil. Rainforest. Hulse, Gillian, illus. 2006. 32p. (J). (978-1-59771-028-2(8)) Sea-To-Sea Pubns.

Mullican, Judy. What's in the Rain Forest? Metzger, Jeanne, illus. 2000. (Big Bks.). 8p. (J). (ps). pap. 10.95 (978-1-57332-185-3(0)); pap. 10.95 (978-1-57332-186-0(9)) HighReach Learning, Inc.

Mulroney, Merryl. Treasures of the Rainforest: An Introduction to the Endangered Forest Birds of Hawaii. 1999. (Illus.). 42p. (J). (gr. 3-6). pap. 8.95 (978-0-9669569-0-0(7)) Peregrine Fund, The.

National Geographic Society Staff. Destination Rain Forest. 2000. (J). 14.95 incl. VHS (978-0-7922-2701-4(8) , 51667) National Geographic Society.

Nichols, Catherine. In the Rain Forest. 2002. (We Can Read about Nature! Ser.). (Illus.). 32p. (J). 21.36 (978-0-7614-1432-2(0) , Benchmark Bks.) Cavendish, Marshall Corp.

O'Hare, Ted. Amazing Rain Forest. (Rain Forest Today Discovery Library Ser.). 24p. 2005. (Illus.). (gr. 1-4). 14.95 (978-1-59515-151-3(6)); 2004. pap. 4.95 (978-1-59515-299-2(7)) Rourke Publishing, LLC.

—Animals of the Rain Forest. 2004. (Rain Forest Today Discovery Library). 24p. pap. 4.95 (978-1-59515-300-5(4)) Rourke Publishing, LLC.

—People of the Rain Forest. (Rain Forest Today Discovery Library Ser.). 24p. 2005. (Illus.). (gr. 1-4). 14.95 (978-1-59515-153-7(2)); 2004. pap. 4.95 (978-1-59515-301-2(2)) Rourke Publishing, LLC.

—Vanishing Rain Forest. 2004. (Rain Forest Today Discovery Library). 24p. pap. 4.95 (978-1-59515-304-3(7)) Rourke Publishing, LLC.

—Vanishing Rain Forests. 2005. (Rain Forest Today Discovery Library Ser.). (Illus.). 24p. (gr. 1-4). 14.95 (978-1-59515-156-8(7)) Rourke Publishing, LLC.

O'Neil, Sarah. Rainforest Plants. 1999. (gr. k-3). lib. bdg. 11.80 (978-0-613-19435-8(7)) Tandem Library Bks.

Osborne, Will. Rain Forests: A Nonfiction Companion to Afternoon on the Amazon. 2001. (Magic Tree House Research Guide Ser.: No. 5). (J). (gr. k-3). lib. bdg. 13.00 (978-0-613-36865-0(7)) Tandem Library Bks.

Parker, Edward, photos by. Insects & Spiders. 2002. (Rain Forest Pilot Ser.). (Illus.). 48p. (J). lib. bdg. 27.12 (978-0-7398-5240-8(X)) Raintree.

—Mammals. 2002. (Rain Forest Pilot Ser.). (Illus.). 48p. (J). lib. bdg. 27.12 (978-0-7398-5241-5(8)) Raintree.

Pascoe, Gwen. Deep in a Rainforest. Jefferis, Veronica, illus. 1999. 32p. (J). (gr. k up). lib. bdg. 23.33 (978-0-8368-2149-9(1)) Stevens, Gareth Inc.

Patent, Dorothy Hinshaw. Fabulous Fluttering Tropical Butterflies. Jubb, Kendahl Jan, illus. 2003. 32p. (J). (gr. 1-5). 17.85 (978-0-8027-8839-9(4)); 16.95 (978-0-8027-8838-2(6)) Walker & Co.

—Garden of the Spirit Bear: Life in the Great Northern Rainforest. Milton, Deborah Jane, illus. 2004. 40p. (J). (gr. 3-5). tchr. ed. 16.00 (978-0-618-21259-0(0) , Clarion Bks.) Houghton Mifflin Co. Trade & Reference Div.

Pinkham, Julia. The Rainforest Encyclopedia Coloring Book. Pinkham, Julia, illus. 1998. (Naturencyclopedia Ser.). (Illus.). 48p. (J). (gr. 3-6). pap. 6.95 (978-0-88045-142-0(4)) Stemmer Hse. Pubs., Inc.

Pirotta, Saviour. Deep in the Rain Forest, 4 bks., Set. (Illus.). (J). 2000. (978-0-7398-4184-6(X)); 1998. (gr. 2-5). 102.76 (978-0-8172-5136-9(7)) Raintree.

—Deep in the Rain Forest Collection, 4 vols. 2001. (Illus.). (J). pap. (978-0-7398-4947-7(6)) Steck-Vaughn.

—People in the Rain Forest. 1999. (Deep in the Rain Forest Ser.). (Illus.). 32p. (J). (gr. 2-5). 25.69 (978-0-8172-5137-6(5)) Raintree.

—People in the Rain Forest. 1999. (Deep in the Rain Forest Ser.). (Illus.). 32p. (gr. 2-5). pap. 7.95 (978-0-8172-8111-3(8)); (978-0-7502-2197-9(6)) Steck-Vaughn.

—Trees & Plants in the Rain Forest. 1999. (Deep in the Rain Forest Ser.). (Illus.). 32p. (J). (978-0-7502-2198-6(4)) Steck-Vaughn.

Powzyk, Joyce A. In Search of Lemurs: My Days & Nights in a Madagascar Rain Forest. 1998. (Illus.). 48p. (J). (gr. 3-7). 17.95 (978-0-7922-7072-0(X) , T07072C, National Geographic Children's Bks.) National Geographic Society.

Prebeg, Rick. Into the Jungle. Prebeg, Rick, photos by. 2005. (J). (978-1-933248-05-9(X)) World Quest Learning.

Pyers. Rain Forest Explorer. 2004. (Illus.). (J). pap. 7.50 (978-1-4109-0840-7(2)); 6 Pack. lib. bdg. 40.50 (978-1-4109-0846-9(1)) Raintree.

Quadrillion Media Staff. Rain Forests, Vol. 6. 1998. (Start Me Up Ser.: Vol. 6). 48p. (J). (gr. 3-8). mass mkt. 12.95 (978-1-58185-006-2(9) , Tessloff Publishing) Quadrillion Media LLC.

A Rain Forest, 6 Packs. (Rigby Focus Ser.). 16p. (gr. k up). 26.00 (978-0-7578-5283-1(1)) Rigby Education.

A Rain Forest: Individual Title Six-Packs. (Rigby Focus Ser.). 16p. (gr. k up). 28.00 (978-0-7578-5517-7(2)) Rigby Education.

Rain Forest Color & Discover Pack. 1998. (Color & Discover Packs Ser.). (Illus.). 28p. (J). reprint ed. pap. (978-1-881469-34-6(4)) Safari, Ltd.

Rain Forest Pilot, 4 bks., Set. Incl. Life at the Top : Discoveries in a Tropical Forest Canopy. Doris, Ellen. (gr. 3-7). 18.98 (978-0-7398-2220-3(9)); Noises in the Night : The Habits of Bats. Kovacs, Deborah. (gr. 4-6). 18.98 (978-0-7398-2218-0(7)); Story in the Stone : The Formation of a Tropical Land Bridge. Gidwitz, Tim. (gr. 4-6). 18.98 (978-0-7398-2217-3(9)); What's the Buzz : The Secret Lives of Bees. Facklam, Margery. (gr. 4-6). 18.98 (978-0-7398-2219-7(5)); (Illus.). 48p. (J). 1999. 75.92 (978-0-7398-2221-0(7)) Raintree.

Rain Forest Secrets. 1998. (J). pap. 3.95 (978-0-439-04455-4(3)) Scholastic, Inc.

Rain Forests. (Ecosystems Ser.). 24p. (J). 6.95 (978-0-7368-9165-3(X)) Capstone Pr., Inc.

Rain Forests, 6 vols. (gr. 2-5). 36.95 (978-0-7368-9266-7(4)) Red Brick Learning.

Rainforest. 2003. (J). per. (978-1-57657-884-1(4)) Paradise Pr., Inc.

The Rainforest with Book & Puzzle. 2000. (Illus.). (J). (ps-3). 9.95 (978-1-878427-81-6(4)) Cimino Publishing Group.

Raintree Steck-Vaughn Staff. Animals of the Rainforest, Set 4. 2002. pap., tchr. ed. (978-0-7398-5818-9(1)) Steck-Vaughn.

Reid, Greg. Rain Forests. 2004. (Ecosystems Ser.). (Illus.). 32p. (J). (gr. 3-5). 23.00 (978-0-7910-7941-6(4) , Chelsea Hse.) Facts On File, Inc.

Richardson, Adele D. Rain Forests. 2001. (Bridgestone Science Library). (Illus.). 24p. (J). (gr. 2-3). lib. bdg. 18.60 (978-0-7368-0839-2(6) , Bridgestone Bks.) Capstone Pr., Inc.

Riley, Peter D. & Gerstein, Sherry. Nightwatch: Nightlife in the Tropical Rain Forest. Croucher, Barry & Edwards, Brin, illus. Coleman, Bruce & Natural History Photographs Agency Staff, photos by. 1999. (Windows on Science Ser.). 16p. (YA). (gr. 3-7). 12.99 (978-1-57584-251-6(3) , Reader's Digest Children's Bks.) Reader's Digest Children's Publishing, Inc.

Romero, Libby. Tropical Rain Forests. 2005. 39.00 ***(*978-1-4108-4601-3(6))*** Benchmark Education Co.

Salas, Laura Purdie. Rain Forests. 2007. (Amazing Science Ser.). (Illus.). 24p. (J). ***(*978-1-4048-3472-9(9)*** , 1265694) Picture Window Bks.

Salas, Laura Purdie & Yesh, Jeff. Rain Forests: Gardens of Green. 2006. (Amazing Science Ser.). (Illus.). 24p. (J). (978-1-4048-3098-1(7) , 1265694) Picture Window Bks.

Sandler, Michael. Rain Forests: Surviving in the Amazon. 2005. (X-treme Places Ser.). (Illus.). 32p. (J). (gr. 3-7). lib. bdg. 25.27 (978-1-59716-089-6(X)) Bearport Publishing Co., Inc.

Sasman, Irene D. H. Rain Forests of the World Children's Library, Set. 1999. (Illus.). (J). (ps-5). pap. 99.95 (978-1-56831-060-2(9)) Learning Connection, The.

Sayre, April Pulley. Tropical Rainforest. 2003. (Scholastic Science Readers Ser.). (Illus.). 48p. (J). (978-0-439-26994-0(6)) Scholastic, Inc.

Schofield, Jennifer. Animal Babies in Rain Forests. 2004. (Animal Babies Ser.). (Illus.). 32p. (J). (ps-k). 7.95 (978-0-7534-5788-7(1) , Kingfisher) Houghton Mifflin Co. Trade & Reference Div.

Scholastic, Inc. Staff. Rain Forest. 2008. (Littlest Pet Shop Ser.). 24p. (J). pap. 5.99 ***(*978-0-545-00142-7(0)*** , Scholastic Reference) Scholastic, Inc.

Scholastic, Inc. Staff & Andrews, Julia. Rain Forest Ride: Colorful & Engaging Books on Favorite Thematic Topics for Guided & Independent Reading. 2000. (Super Science Readers Ser.). (Illus.). 16p. pap. 10.95 (978-0-439-16774-1(4)) Scholastic, Inc.

Scholastic, Inc. Staff & Dawson, Paul. Rain Forests. Wasserman, Robin, ed. 2003. (Extraordinary Ser.). 32p. (J). pap. 5.95 (978-0-439-28601-5(8) , Scholastic Paperbacks) Scholastic, Inc.

Scott, Janine. Jungle Life. 2002. (Spyglass Books). (Illus.). 24p. (J). (gr. 1 up). lib. bdg. 18.60 (978-0-7565-0235-5(7)) Compass Point Bks.

Selvas Tropicales. (SPA.). (YA). (gr. 5-8). (978-84-236-3191-9(5) , ED5686) Edebé ESP. *Dist:* Lectorum Pubns., Inc.

Senior, Kathryn. Rain Forest. 1999. (Fast Forward Ser.). (Illus.). 32p. (J). (gr. 4-8). 29.00 (978-0-531-14572-2(7) , Watts, Franklin) Scholastic Library Publishing.

—Rain Forest. 1999. (gr. k-3). lib. bdg. 18.75 (978-0-613-31624-8(X)) Tandem Library Bks.

Serrano, Marta. Rain Forests. 2002. (Living Planet Ser.). (Illus.). 32p. (J). 23.70 (978-1-56711-670-0(1) , Blackbirch Pr., Inc.) Thomson Gale.

Silver, Donald. Tropical Rain Forest. 1999. (gr. 3-6). lib. bdg. 16.40 (978-0-613-09199-2(X)) Tandem Library Bks.

Silver, Donald M. Tropical Rain Forest. Wynne, Patricia J., illus. 1998. (One Small Square Ser.). 48p. (C). (gr. 1-4). pap. 7.95 (978-0-07-058051-0(0) , 9780070580510) McGraw-Hill Cos., The.

Slater, Patrick. Australian Rainforest Animals. 2002. (Nature Kids Ser.). (Illus.). 52p. (J). (gr. 3 up). lib. bdg. (978-1-59084-213-3(8)) Mason Crest Pubs.

Smith, Kathie Billingslea. Rainforest Animals. Bonforte, Lisa, illus. 2005. 12p. (J). (gr. k-3). 6.99 (978-1-57755-509-4(0)) Allied Publishing.

Snedden, Robert. Tropical Rain Forests. 2003. (Illus.). 32p. (J). lib. bdg. (978-1-58340-382-2(5)) Smart Apple Media.

Steck-Vaughn Staff. Animals of the Rainforest. 2001. (Illus.). Set 2. (J). pap., tchr. ed. (978-0-7398-4143-3(2)); Set 3. pap., tchr. ed. (978-0-7398-4931-6(X)) Steck-Vaughn.

Stille, Darlene R. Tropical Rain Forest. 1999. (True Bks.). (Illus.). 48p. (J). (gr. 3-5). 25.00 (978-0-516-21511-2(6) , Children's Pr.) Scholastic Library Publishing.

—Tropical Rain Forests. 2000. (True Bks.). (Illus.). 48p. (J). (gr. 3-5). pap. 6.95 (978-0-516-26774-6(4) , Children's Pr.) Scholastic Library Publishing.

—Tropical Rain Forests. 2000. (Illus.). 47p. (J). (gr. 3-5). lib. bdg. 15.25 (978-0-613-37568-9(8)) Tandem Library Bks.

Taylor, Barbara. Tropical Rain Forest Habitats. 2006. (Exploring Habitats Ser.). 36p. (J), lib. bdg. (978-0-8368-7258-3(4)) Stevens, Gareth Inc.

Telford, Carole & Theodorou, Rod. Up a Rainforest Tree. 1998. (Amazing Journeys Ser.). (Illus.). 32p. (J). (gr. 2-4). lib. bdg. 22.79 (978-1-57572-156-9(2)) Heinemann Library.

Thompson, Gare. Amazon Journey: Cruising the Rainforest. 2006. (National Geographic Science Chapters Ser.). (Illus.). 48p. (J). (gr. 1-4). 17.90 (978-0-7922-5951-0(3) , National Geographic Children's Bks.) National Geographic Society.

Trumbauer, Lisa. Discover the Rain Forest. 2005. (Yellow Umbrella Ser.). (Illus.). 17p. (J). (978-0-7368-5258-6(1)), (978-0-7368-5294-4(8)) Capstone Pr., Inc.

Watson, Galadriel Findlay. The Amazon Rain Forest: The Largest Rain Forest in the World. 2004. (Illus.). 32p. (J). lib. bdg. 18.20 (978-1-59036-270-9(5)) Weigl Pubs., Inc.

Whitehouse, Patricia. Hiding in a Rain Forest. 2003. (Illus.). 32p. pap. 6.50 (978-1-4034-3188-2(4)); (J). lib. bdg. 22.79 (978-1-4034-0799-3(1)) Heinemann Library.

—Living in a Rainforest. 2007. (Illus.). 24p. (J). (978-1-60044-186-8(6)) Rourke Publishing, LLC.

Who Grows up in the Rain Forest? (Who Grows up Here? Ser.). 24p. (J). 7.95 (978-1-4048-0209-4(6)) Picture Window Bks.

Wilkes, Angela. Rain Forest. 2002. (Question Time Ser.). (Illus.). 32p. (J). (gr. k-3). pap. 6.95 (978-0-7534-5442-8(4) , Kingfisher) Houghton Mifflin Co. Trade & Reference Div.

—Rain Forest. 2002. (gr. k-3). lib. bdg. 15.25 (978-0-613-87035-1(2)) Tandem Library Bks.

—Rain Forest Animals. 2000. (ps-2). lib. bdg. 15.25 (978-0-613-43496-6(X)) Tandem Library Bks.

Wilkes, Angela & Webster, Belinda. Rain Forest Animals. Holmes, Steve, illus. rev. ed. 2004. (Ladders Ser.). 32p. (J). (ps-3). pap. 6.95 (978-1-58728-618-6(1) , Two Can Publishing) T&N Children's Publishing.

Williams, Judith. Exploring the Rain Forest Treetops with a Scientist. 2004. (I Like Science! Ser.). (Illus.). 24p. (J). lib. bdg. 21.26 (978-0-7660-2294-2(3)) Enslow Pubs., Inc.

Winne, Joanne. Living in a Rain Forest. 2000. (Welcome Bks.). (Illus.). 24p. (J). (ps-2). 17.00 (978-0-516-23301-7(7) , Children's Pr.) Scholastic Library Publishing.

—Living in a Rain Forest. 2000. (ps-2). lib. bdg. 12.95 (978-0-613-90483-4(4)) Tandem Library Bks.

Woods, Mae. Animals of the Rain Forest. 1999. (Rain Forest Ser.). 24p. (J). (gr. k-6). lib. bdg. 21.35 (978-1-57765-019-5(0) , Checkerboard Library) ABDO Publishing Co.

—People of the Rain Forest. 1999. (Rain Forest Ser.). (Illus.). 24p. (J). (gr. k-6). lib. bdg. 21.35 (978-1-57765-020-1(4) , Checkerboard Library) ABDO Publishing Co.

—Plants of the Rain Forest. 1999. (Rain Forest Ser.). (Illus.). 24p. (J). (gr. k-6). lib. bdg. 21.35 (978-1-57765-018-8(2) , Checkerboard Library) ABDO Publishing Co.

—Protecting the Rain Forest. 1999. (Rain Forest Ser.). (Illus.). 24p. (J). (gr. k-6). lib. bdg. 21.35 (978-1-57765-022-5(0) , Checkerboard Library) ABDO Publishing Co.

—The Rain Forest, Set. Incl. Animals of the Rain Forest. lib. bdg. 21.35 (978-1-57765-019-5(0)); Insects of the Rain Forest. lib. bdg. 21.35 (978-1-57765-023-2(9)); People of the Rain Forest. lib. bdg. 21.35 (978-1-57765-020-1(4)); Plants of the Rain Forest. lib. bdg. 21.35 (978-1-57765-018-8(2)); Protecting the Rain Forest. lib. bdg. 21.35 (978-1-57765-022-5(0)); Remarkable Rain Forest. lib. bdg. 21.35 (978-1-57765-021-8(2)); 24p. (J). (gr. k-6). 1999. (Illus.). 1999. Set lib. bdg. 128.10 (978-1-57765-267-0(3) , Checkerboard Library) ABDO Publishing Co.

—The Remarkable Rain Forest. 1999. (Rain Forest Ser.). (Illus.). 24p. (J). (gr. k-6). lib. bdg. 21.35 (978-1-57765-021-8(2) , Checkerboard Library) ABDO Publishing Co.

World Book, Inc Staff, contrib. by. Rain Forest Animals. 2007. (J). ***(*978-0-7166-7729-1(6))*** World Bk., Inc.

Worth, Bonnie. If I Ran the Rainforest: All about Tropical Rain Forests. Ruiz, Aristides, illus. 2003. (Cat in the Hat's Learning Library Ser.). 48p. (J). (gr. k-3). lib. bdg. 12.99 (978-0-375-91097-5(2) , Random Hse. Bks. for Young Readers) Random Hse. Children's Bks.

Wright-Frierson, Virginia. A North American Rain Forest Scrapbook. Wright-Frierson, Virginia, illus. 2003. (Illus.). 40p. (J). (gr. 1-5). pap. 8.95 (978-0-8027-7651-8(5)) Walker & Co.

—North American Rain Forest Scrapbook. 2003. (gr. 3-6). lib. bdg. 17.60 (978-0-613-75344-9(5)) Tandem Library Bks.

RAIN FORESTS—FICTION

Aigner-Clark, Julie. Baby Einstein: Rain-forest Discoveries, Spanish-Language Edition. Zaidi, Nadeem, illus. 2005. (Baby Einstein: Libros de Carton Ser.). (SPA.). 10p. (J). bds. 9.95 (978-970-718-306-3(3) , Silver Dolphin en Español) Advanced Marketing, S. de R. L. de C. V. MEX. *Dist:* Perseus Distribution.

Albert, Toni Diana. Saving the Rain Forest with Cammie & Cooper. Bowles, Carol, illus. l.t. ed. 32p. (J). 2003. pap. 7.95 (978-1-929432-02-8(X) , 800-353-2791); 2002. 16.95 (978-1-929432-03-5(8) , 800-353-2791) Trickle Creek Bks.

Allen, Nancy Kelly. On the Banks of the Amazon/en las orillas del Amazonas. de la Vega, Eida, tr. Driessen, Elizabeth, illus. 2004. Tr. of En las orillas del Amazonas. (SPA & ENG.). 32p. (J). (gr. 4-6). 16.95 (978-0-9720192-7-9(8) , 626999) Raven Tree Pr.

Ballantyne, R. M. The Lighthouse. 2006. pap. ***(*978-1-4065-0531-3(5))*** Dodo Pr.

Banks, Joan. Song of La Selva: A Story of a Costa Rican Rain Forest. Bond, Higgins, illus. 1998. (Habitat Ser.: No. 9). 36p. (J). (gr. 1-4). 15.95 (978-1-56899-586-1(5) , B7009); 19.95 incl. audio (978-1-56899-588-5(1) , BC7009); pap. 6.95 (978-1-56899-587-8(3)); pap. 10.95 incl. audio (978-1-56899-589-2(X)) Soundprints.

—Song of la Selva: A Story of a Costa Rican Rain Forest. 2005. (Soundprints' Wild Habitats Ser.). (Illus.). 36p. (J). (gr. 1-4). 8.95 incl. audio (978-1-59249-097-4(2)) Soundprints.

—Song of La Selva: A Story of a Costa Rican Rain Forest, Incl. toy. Higgins-Bond, illus. 1998. (Habitat Ser.: Vol. 9). 36p. (J). (gr. 1-4). 26.95 (978-1-56899-590-8(3)) Soundprints.

—Song of La Selva. A Story of a Costa Rican Rain Forest, Incl. toy. Bond, Higgins, illus. 1998. (Habitat Ser.: Vol. 9). 36p. (J). (gr. 1-4). 31.95 incl. audio (978-1-56899-592-2(X)) Soundprints.

—Song of La Selva: A Story of a Costa Rican Rain Forest, Incl. toy. Bond, Higgins & Kaye, Randye, illus. 1998. (Habitat Ser.: Vol. 9). 36p. (J). (gr. 1-4). pap. 19.95 incl. audio (978-1-56899-593-9(8)) Soundprints.

Bromden, David. A Gathering in the Mist. 2006. 280p. (YA). pap. 14.99 (978-1-59092-341-2(3)) Windstorm Creative.

Bunton, M. Catherine. The Little Maestro. 2000. 108p. pap. 9.95 (978-0-595-13855-5(1)) iUniverse, Inc.

Burns, Ian. Possum & Python. 2005. 23p. 8.00 (978-1-4116-5490-7(0)) Lulu.com.

Carle, Eric. "Slowly, Slowly, Slowly," Said the Sloth. Carle, Eric, illus. 2002. (Illus.). 32p. (J). (ps-1). 16.99 (978-0-399-23954-0(5) , Philomel) Penguin Group (USA) Inc.

Cherry, Lynne. Great Kapok Tree. 2000. (gr. k-3). lib. bdg. 15.30 (978-0-613-28507-0(7)) Tandem Library Bks.

—Great Kapok Tree: A Tale of the Amazon Rain Forest. 2000. (Illus.). 33p. lib. bdg. 13.80 (978-0-606-17843-3(0)) Tandem Library Bks.

Cherry, Lynne & Plotkin, Mark J. The Shaman's Apprentice: A Tale of the Amazon Rain Forest. Cherry, Lynne, illus. 2001. (Illus.). 36p. (J). (gr. 1-4). pap. 7.00 (978-0-15-202486-4(7) , Harcourt Paperbacks) Harcourt Children's Bks.

Dalmatian Press Staff. Rainforest Friends. 2002. (Illus.). 24p. (J). (gr. k-5). pap. 2.99 (978-1-57759-278-5(6)) Dalmatian Pr.

Fallon, Karla. Rainforest Moon. 2005. 102p. pap. 9.98 (978-1-4116-3776-4(3)) Lulu.com.

Faye, Charlet. The Chilling Adventures of Marshall McCaw. 2004. (Illus.). 60p. (J). 18.95 (978-0-9655222-1-2(0)) FayeHouse. Pr. International.

Giancamilli, Vanessa. Gecko Gathering. Kest, Kristin, illus. 2005. (Amazing Animal Adventures Ser.). 32p. (J). (ps-2). 2.95 (978-1-59249-289-3(4) , S7157); 15.95 (978-1-59249-288-6(6) , B7107); 9.95 (978-1-59249-323-4(8) , PS7157); pap. 6.95 (978-1-59249-290-9(8) , S7107) Soundprints.

Greenburg, J. C. In the Jungle. Gerardi, Jan, illus. 2007. (Andrew Lost Ser.: Bk. 15). 96p. (J). (gr. 2-4). 3.99 (978-0-375-83564-3(4)); lib. bdg. 11.99 (978-0-375-93564-0(9)) Random Hse. Children's Bks. (Random Hse. Bks. for Young Readers).

Grote, Rich. Megan & the Borealis Butterfly. 1999. (Magic Attic Club Ser.). (J). lib. bdg. (978-0-606-16953-0(9)) Tandem Library Bks.

Hammond, Jo. Home Before Dark. 2005. 144p. (YA). (gr. 7-12). pap. 7.95 (978-1-55143-340-0(0)) Orca Bk. Pubs. USA.

Harman, Chuck. Lost City. 2000. (Adventures of Artie the Airplane & His Friends Ser.). (Illus.). 40p. (J). (ps-6). pap. 6.95 (978-1-891736-10-0(8)) Studio Five/Fourteen.

Harvey, M. A. Attack of the Jaguar: Dare to Take the Test. 2004. (Illus.). 128p. (J). pap. (978-1-84458-051-4(2)) Chrysalis Children's Bks.

Hoch, Jeff. Guess Who Saves the Rain Forest? Hoch, Jeff, ed. Kiedrowski, Steve, illus. Date not set. 39p. (J). (gr. k-5). pap. 7.00 (978-0-9650629-3-0(7)) Coulee Region Pubns., Inc.

Keister, Douglas. Fernando's Gift/el Regalo de Fernando. Keister, Douglas, photos by. 2001. (SPA., Illus.). 32p. (J). (ps-3). pap. 7.95 (978-0-87156-927-1(2)) Sierra Club Bks. for Children.

—El Regalo de Fernando. 1998. (Sierra Club Bks.).Tr. of Fernando's Gift. (J). 13.75 (978-0-606-13382-1(8)) Tandem Library Bks.

Law, Felicia. The Bookseller Bird. Evans, Nicola, illus. 2005. (Bamboo & Friends Ser.). 24p. (J). (ps-7). lib. bdg. 22.60 (978-1-4048-1283-3(0)) Picture Window Bks.

—The Creeping Vine. Evans, Nicola, illus. 2005. (Bamboo & Friends Ser.). 24p. (J). (ps-3). lib. bdg. 22.60 (978-1-4048-1284-0(9)) Picture Window Bks.

—The Dragonfly. Philpott, Claire, illus. 2005. (Bamboo & Friends Ser.). 24p. (J). (ps-3). lib. bdg. 22.60 (978-1-4048-1302-1(0)) Picture Window Bks.

—The Feathers. Philpott, Claire & Radford, Karen, illus. 2006. (J). (978-1-4048-2596-3(7)) Picture Window Bks.

—The Flower's Busy Day. Evans, Nicola, illus. 2005. (Bamboo & Friends Ser.). 24p. (J). (ps-3). lib. bdg. 22.60 (978-1-4048-1281-9(4)) Picture Window Bks.

—The Furry Caterpillar. Philpott, Claire & Radford, Karen, illus. 2006. (J). (978-1-4048-2599-4(1)) Picture Window Bks.

—Marvelous Meals. Evans, Nicola, illus. 2005. (Bamboo & Friends Ser.). 24p. (J). (ps-3). lib. bdg. 22.60 (978-1-4048-1285-7(7)) Picture Window Bks.

—The Moon. Evans, Nicola, illus. 2005. (Bamboo & Friends Ser.). 24p. (J). (ps-3). lib. bdg. 22.60 (978-1-4048-1282-6(2)) Picture Window Bks.

—The Mushroom Ring. Philpott, Claire & Radford, Karen, illus. 2007. (J). 23.93 (978-1-4048-2595-6(9)) Picture Window Bks.

—The Rainbow. Philpott, Claire & Radford, Karen, illus. 2007. (J). (978-1-4048-2598-7(3)) Picture Window Bks.

—The Rainy Day. Evans, Nicola, illus. 2005. (Bamboo & Friends Ser.). 24p. (J). (ps-3). lib. bdg. 22.60 (978-1-4048-1280-2(6)) Picture Window Bks.

—The Snowflakes. Philpott, Claire & Radford, Karen, illus. 2007. (J). (978-1-4048-2597-0(5)) Picture Window Bks.

—The Tree. Philpott, Claire, illus. 2005. (Bamboo & Friends Ser.). 24p. (J). (ps-3). lib. bdg. 22.60 (978-1-4048-1301-4(2)) Picture Window Bks.

—The Walk. Philpott, Claire & Radford, Karen, illus. 2007. (J). (978-1-4048-2594-9(0)) Picture Window Bks.

Lumry, Amanda & Hurwitz, Laura. Operation Orangutan. 2007. 36p. 15.95 (978-0-9748411-4-4(5)) Eaglemont Pr.

Marsh, Carole. The Mystery in the Amazon Rainforest. 2007. 144p. (gr. 3-5). 14.95 (***978-0-635-06212-3(7)***) Gallopade International.

—The Mystery in the Amazon Rainforest: South America. 2007. (Around the World in 80 Mysteries (Paperback) Ser.). (Illus.), 131p. (J). (gr. 3-5). per. 5.95 (***978-0-635-06208-6(9)***) Gallopade International.

Mitchell, Susan K. The Rainforest Grew All Around. 2007. (Illus.). 32p. (J). (ps-2). 15.95 (978-0-9768823-6-7(1)) Sylvan Dell Pubng.

—The Rainforest Grew All Around. McLennan, Connie, illus. 2007. 1p. (J). (ps-2). 8.95 (***978-0-9777423-8-7(5)***) Sylvan Dell Pubng.

Peebles, Vince and Emily. Cam Goes to the Rain Forest. 2006. (ENG.). 40p. per. 16.99 (***978-1-4259-8033-7(3)***) AuthorHouse.

Pelizzari, Nora. Who Lives in the Rainforest? 2008. (Fisher-Price Ser.). 16p. (J). 6.99 (***978-0-06-144770-9(6)*** , Harper Festival) HarperCollins Pubs.

Platt, Richard. The Vanishing Rainforest. van Wyk, Rupert, illus. 32p. 2004. (J). pap. 7.95 (978-1-84507-321-3(5)); 2003. (YA). 14.99 (978-0-7112-1960-1(5)) Lincoln, Frances Ltd. GBR. *Dist:* Perseus Distribution, Antique Collectors' Club.

Plotkin, Mark. The Shaman's Apprentice: A Tale of the Amazon Rain Forest. 2001. (J). (978-0-606-21429-2(1)) Tandem Library Bks.

Rigby Education Staff. Animals of the Rainforest. (Sails Literacy Ser.). (Illus.). 16p. (gr. k-1). 27.00 (978-0-7635-9867-9(4) , 698674C99) Rigby Education.

Sarago-Kendrick, Delphine. Nana's Land. Sarago-Kendrick, Delphine, illus. 2004. (Illus.). 35p. (J). pap. 17.00 (978-1-875641-90-1(4)) Magabala Bks. AUS. *Dist:* International Specialized Bk. Services.

Smith, Dale. What the Orangutan Told Alice: A Rain Forest Adventure. Smith, Dale & Russon, Anne E., photos by. 2003. (Illus.). 192p. (gr. 6-12). pap. 15.95 (978-0-9651452-8-2(X)) Deer Creek Publishing.

Smith, Roland. Jaguar. 1999. 256p. (gr. 4-7). pap. 5.95 (978-0-7868-1312-4(1)) Disney Pr.

Tennyson, Michael. Morpha: A Rain Forest Story. Yoswa, Jennifer H., illus. 2002. (CMC Wilderness Kids Ser.). 40p. 14.95 (978-0-9671466-8-3(2)) Colorado Mountain Club Pr., The.

Thomas, Rob. Green Thumb. unabr. ed. 2000. (YA). pap. 59.00 incl. audio (978-0-7887-3641-4(8) , 41007) Recorded Bks., LLC.

—Green Thumb. 2000. (978-0-606-20048-6(7)) Tandem Library Bks.

Thornhill, Jan. A Tree in the Forest. 1999. 40p. (Orig.). (J). (gr. 3). pap. 10.11 (978-0-382-24374-5(9)) Silver, Burdett & Ginn, Inc.

Vanderdoes, Amanda & Ratcliffe, T. J., Jr. The Adventures of Makui. 1999. (J). (gr. 2-5). pap. 12.95 incl. audio compact disk (978-1-928632-17-7(3)); (Illus.). (gr. k-5). pap. 8.95 incl. audio (978-1-928632-18-4(1)) Writers Marketplace:Consulting, Critiquing & Publishing.

—The Adventures of Makui. Vanderdoes, Amanda & Ratcliffe, T. J., Jr., illus. l.t. ed. 1999. (Illus.). 40p. (J). (gr. k-5). pap. 5.95 (978-1-928632-16-0(5)) Writers Marketplace:Consulting, Critiquing & Publishing.

What's in the Rainforest. 2003. (J). per. (978-1-57657-933-6(6)) Paradise Pr., Inc.

Wilson, Eric G. Spirit in the Rainforest. 2001. (Tom & Liz Austen Mystery Ser.). (Illus.). 144p. (J). (gr. 3-7). pap. 4.99 (978-1-55143-224-3(2)) Orca Bk. Pubs. USA.

Witte, Anna. The Parrot Tico Tango. Witte, Anna, illus. (Illus.). 24p. (J). (gr. k-3). 2005. 15.99 (978-1-84148-243-9(9)); 2004. pap. 6.99 (978-1-905236-11-4(5)) Barefoot Bks., Inc.

Wolfe, Corey & Mawhinney, Art, illus. The Rainforest Race. 2006. (Ready-To-Read Ser.). 24p. (J). pap. 3.99 (978-1-4169-1756-4(X) , Simon Spotlight/Nickelodeon) Simon & Schuster Children's Publishing.

Worth, Bonnie. If I Ran the Rainforest. Ruiz, Aristides, illus. 2003. (Cat in the Hat's Learning Library). 48p. (J). (gr. k-3). 8.99 (978-0-375-81097-8(8) , Random Hse. Bks. for Young Readers) Random Hse. Children's Bks.

Wundrow, Deanna. Jungle Drum. Swan, Susan E., illus. 1999. (Our World Ser.). 24p. (gr. k-2). lib. bdg. 22.90 (978-0-7613-1270-3(6) , Millbrook Pr.) Lerner Publishing Group.

Zoehfeld, Kathleen Weidner. Amazon Fever. Bogan, Paulette, illus. 2006. (Road to Reading Ser.). 48p. (J). (gr. 1-4). 11.99 (978-0-307-46407-1(5)); pap. 3.99 (978-0-307-26407-7(6)) Random Hse. Children's Bks. (Random Hse. Bks. for Young Readers).

RAINFALL

see Rain and Rainfall

RAINFORESTS

see Rain Forests

RALEIGH, WALTER, SIR, 1552?-1618

Aronson, Marc. Sir Walter Ralegh & the Quest for El Dorado. 2000. (Illus.). 240p. (YA). (gr. 7-12). tchr. ed. 20.00 (978-0-395-84827-2(X) , Clarion Bks.) Houghton Mifflin Co. Trade & Reference Div.

Bedesky, Baron. Sir Walter Raleigh: Founding the Virginia Colony. 2006. (In the Footsteps of Explorers Ser.). (Illus.). 32p. (J). (gr. 3-9). pap. (978-0-7787-2460-5(3) , 1253445); (978-0-7787-2424-7(7) , 1253445) Crabtree Publishing Co.

Chippendale, Neil. Sir Walter Raleigh & the Search for El Dorado. 2001. (Explorers of New Worlds Ser.). (Illus.). 63p. (J). 31.00 (978-0-7910-6434-4(4) , Chelsea Hse.) Facts On File, Inc.

Korman, Susan. Sir Walter Raleigh: English Explorer & Author. 2000. (Colonial Leaders Ser.). (Illus.). 80p. (J). (gr. 4-7). pap. 27.50 (978-0-7910-6126-8(4)); (gr. 8-12). 27.50 (978-0-7910-5969-2(3)) Facts On File, Inc. (Chelsea Hse.).

Larkin, Tanya. Sir Walter Raleigh. 2001. (Famous Explorers Ser.). (Illus.). 24p. (J). (gr. 3). lib. bdg. 18.75 (978-0-8239-5558-9(3) , PowerKids Pr.) Rosen Publishing Group, Inc., The.

McCarthy, Sharon. Sir Walter Raleigh. 2002. (Groundbreakers Ser.). 48p. (J). (gr. 5-7). pap. 8.50 (978-1-58810-987-3(9) , 91602) Heinemann Library.

McCarthy, Shaun. Sir Walter Raleigh. 2002. (Groundbreakers Ser.). (Illus.). 48p. (J). (gr. 5-7). lib. bdg. 27.07 (978-1-58810-599-8(7)) Heinemann Library.

—Sir Walter Raleigh. 2002. (gr. 5-8). lib. bdg. 16.40 (978-0-613-45831-3(1)) Tandem Library Bks.

McPherson, Stephanie Sammartino. Sir Walter Raleigh. 2006. (History Maker Bios Ser.). (Illus.). 48p. (J). (gr. 3-7). 26.60 (978-0-8225-2945-3(9) , Lerner Pubns.) Lerner Publishing Group.

Petrie, Kristin. Sir Walter Raleigh. 2007. (Illus.). 32p. (J). 22.78 (978-1-59679-748-2(7)) ABDO Publishing Co.

Rice Jr., Earle. Sir Walter Raleigh. 2006. (Profiles in American History Ser.). (Illus.). 48p. (J). (gr. 4-8). lib. bdg. 20.95 (978-1-58415-452-5(7)) Mitchell Lane Pubs., Inc.

RAMS

see Sheep

RANCH LIFE

see also Cowboys

Ancona, George. Mi Casa: My House. (Somos Latinos (We Are Latinos) Ser.). (Illus.). 32p. (J). 2005. (SPA & ENG.). (gr. 1-3). pap. 8.95 (978-0-516-25065-6(5)); 2004. (ENG & SPA., 20.00 (978-0-516-23688-9(1)) Scholastic Library Publishing. (Children's Pr.).

Colley, Betty Bailey & Monday, Jane Clements. Tales of the Wild Horse Desert. 2001. (Jack & Doris Smothers Series in Texas History, Life, & Culture: Vol.4). (Illus.). 138p. (J). pap. 19.95 (978-0-292-71241-6(3)) Univ. of Texas Pr.

Craats, Rennay. Ranching. 2003. (Real Life Stories Ser.). (Illus.). 24p. (J). lib. bdg. 15.95 (978-1-59036-081-1(8)) Weigl Pubs., Inc.

Drinkard, Lawson. Riding on a Range: Western Activities for Kids. Lee, Fran, illus. 2003. 64p. (YA). pap. 8.95 (978-1-58685-036-4(9)) Gibbs Smith, Publisher.

Freedman, Russell. In the Days of the Vaqueros: America's First True Cowboys. 2001. (Illus.). 80p. (J). (gr. 7-7). tchr. ed. 18.00 (978-0-395-96788-1(0) , Clarion Bks.) Houghton Mifflin Co. Trade & Reference Div.

Get Inside Series. Incl. Baseball. Almonte, Paul. 80p. 14.95 (978-1-881889-55-7(6)); Ranch. Morgenroth, Barbara. 64p. 14.95 (978-1-881889-56-4(4)); (Illus.). (J). 1994. 29.90 (978-1-881889-79-3(3)) Silver Moon Pr.

Gilkerson, Patricia. My Adventure on a Ranch. 2006. 44p. (J). 8.99 (978-1-59092-282-8(4) , Orchard Academy Pr.) Windstorm Creative.

Gordon, Sharon. At Home on the Ranch. 2005. (Bookworms Ser.). (ENG & SPA., Illus.). 32p. (J). (gr. 3-7). lib. bdg. (978-0-7614-1962-4(4) , Benchmark Bks.) Cavendish, Marshall Corp.

—At Home on the Ranch (Mi Casa en el Rancho) 2006. (Bookworms Ser.). (ENG & SPA., Illus.). 32sp. (J). lib. bdg. 22.79 (978-0-7614-2458-1(X)) Cavendish, Marshall Corp.

—Mi Casa en el Rancho. 2006. (Bookworms Ser.). (SPA & ENG., Illus.). 32p. (J). lib. bdg. 22.79 (978-0-7614-2378-2(8)) Cavendish, Marshall Corp.

Holling, Holling C. The Book of Cowboys. 2000. (YA). 20.95 (978-0-8488-2969-8(7)) Amereon LTD.

Isaacs, Sally Senzell. Cattle Trails & Cowboys. 2004. (Illus.). 32p. (J). (978-1-4034-2502-7(7)); pap. 7.50 (978-1-4034-4773-9(X)) Heinemann Library.

James, Will. The Will James Cowboy Book, Vol. 1. rev. ed. (Illus.). 128p. (J). (gr. 4). 18.00 (978-0-87842-469-6(5) , 816) Mountain Pr. Publishing Co., Inc.

Kalman, Bobbie. Life on the Ranch. 1998. (Life in the Old West Ser.). (Illus.). 32p. (J). (gr. 3-4). pap. (978-0-7787-0103-3(4)) Crabtree Publishing Co.

—Life on the Ranch. 1999. (Life in the Old West Ser.). (J). (978-0-606-16429-0(4)) Tandem Library Bks.

—Life on the Trail. 1998. (Life in the Old West Ser.). (Illus.). 32p. (J). (gr. 3-4). lib. bdg. (978-0-7787-0072-2(0)) Crabtree Publishing Co.

—Life on the Trail. 1999. (gr. 3-6). lib. bdg. 16.40 (978-0-613-11779-1(4)) Tandem Library Bks.

LeapFrog Staff, compiled by. Life on the Ranch. 2001. (J). (ps-2). spiral bd. 14.95 (978-1-58605-055-9(9)) LeapFrog Enterprises, Inc.

Letters of a Woman Homesteader. 2003. (Our American Heritage Ser.). (J). pap. 62.00 incl. audio compact disk (978-1-58472-527-5(3) , In Audio) Sound Room Pubs., Inc.

Munro, Roxie. Ranch. 2004. (Illus.). 36p. (J). 16.95 (978-1-931721-37-0(8)) Bright Sky Pr.

Page, Deb, illus. Darby-the Cow Dog, 9 vols. l.t. ed. 2005. (ZC Horses: 9). 76p. (J). pap. 5.00 net. (978-0-9721496-8-6(6)) ZC Horses Series of Children's Bks.

Peterson, Cris. Amazing Grazing. Upitis, Alvis, photos by. 2003. (Illus.). 32p. (J). (gr. k-2). 16.95 (978-1-56397-942-2(X)) Boyds Mills Pr.

Reinstedt, Randall A. Tales & Treasures of California's Ranchos. Bergéz, John, ed. Greco, Ed, illus. 1999. (History & Happenings of California Ser.). 127p. (J). (gr. 3-6). 14.95 (978-0-933818-29-3(7)) Ghost Town Pubns.

Rosinsky, Natalie M. California Ranchos. 2006. (We the People Ser.). (Illus.). 48p. (J). (gr. 4-6). 23.93 (978-0-7565-1633-8(1)) Compass Point Bks.

Savage, Candace. Born to Be a Cowgirl. 2001. (gr. 3-6). lib. bdg. 18.75 (978-0-613-49287-4(0)) Tandem Library Bks.

Savage, Candace C. Born to Be a Cowgirl: A Spirited Ride Through the Old West. 2004. (Illus.). (978-1-55054-838-9(7) , Greystone Bks.) Douglas & McIntyre, Ltd. CAN. *Dist:* Transition Vendor.

—Born to Be a Cowgirl: A Spirited Ride Through the Old West. 2001. 16.75 (978-0-606-22827-5(6)) Tandem Library Bks.

—Born to Be a Cowgirl: A Spirited Ride Through the Old West. 2004. (Illus.). 64p. (J). pap. 10.95 (978-1-58246-020-8(5)); (gr. 4-8). 15.95 (978-1-58246-019-2(1)) Ten Speed Pr. (Tricycle Pr.).

Steck-Vaughn Staff. On the Ranch. 2003. pap. 4.10 (978-0-7398-7641-1(4)) Steck-Vaughn.

Sundling, Charles W. Cowboys of the Frontier. 2000. (Frontier Land Ser.). (Illus.). 32p. (J). (gr. 3-8). lib. bdg. 24.21 (978-1-57765-045-4(X) , ABDO & Daughters) ABDO Publishing Co.

Thompson, Gare. Missions & Ranchos: Early California Life. 2004. (National Geographic Reading Expeditions Ser.). (Illus.). 40p. (J). pap. (978-0-7922-4548-3(2)) National Geographic Society.

—When the Mission Padre Came to the Rancho: The Early California Adventures of Rosalinda & Simon Delgado. 2004. (I Am American Ser.). (Illus.). 40p. (J). (gr. 3-7). pap. 6.99 (978-0-7922-6945-8(4) , National Geographic Children's Bks.) National Geographic Society.

Urbigkit, Cat. Cattle Kids: A Year on the Western Range. 2007. 32p. (J). (gr. 2-4). 16.95 (***978-1-59078-508-9(8)***) Boyds Mills Pr.

Whitney, Gleaves & Whitney, Louise. B Is for Buckaroo: A Cowboy Alphabet. Guy, Sue, illus. rev. ed. 2003. 40p. (J). 17.95 (978-1-58536-139-7(9)) Sleeping Bear Pr.

RANCH LIFE—FICTION

Bell, Mary Reeves. Sagebrush Rebellion. 1999. (Passport to Danger Ser.: Vol. 2). 208p. (YA). (gr. 7-12). pap. 5.99 (978-1-55661-550-4(7)) Bethany Hse. Pubs.

—Sagebrush Rebellion. 1999. (J). (978-0-606-18973-6(4)) Tandem Library Bks.

Bograd, Larry & Hubbard, Coleen. Colorado Summer. Rabinowitz, Sandy & Keiffer, Christa, illus. l.t. ed. 1999. (Treasured Horses Collection). 128p. (J). (gr. 4 up). lib. bdg. 23.33 (978-0-8368-2277-9(3)) Stevens, Gareth Inc.

Brammer, Ethriam Cash. The Rowdy, Rowdy Ranch / Alla en el Rancho Grande. Cruz, D. Nina, illus. (ENG & SPA.). 32p. 15.95 (978-1-55885-409-3(6) , Piñata Books) Arte Publico Pr.

Brooke, Lauren. Darkest Hour. 2003. (Heartland Ser.). 160p. mass mkt. 4.99 (978-0-439-42508-7(5) , Scholastic Paperbacks) Scholastic, Inc.

—Darkest Hour. 2003. (gr. 3-6). lib. bdg. 12.40 (978-0-613-72128-8(4)) Tandem Library Bks.

Brouwer, Sigmund. Blazer Drive. 2007. (Orca Sports Ser.). 176p. (YA). (gr. 5 up). pap. (***978-1-55143-717-0(1)***) Orca Bk. Pubs.

Carr, Annie Roe. Nan Sherwood at Rose Ranch or the Old Me. 2007. pap. (***978-1-4065-1295-3(8)***) Dodo Pr.

Carr, Roe Annie. Nan Sherwood at Rose Ranch or the Old Me. 2006. 63.99 (***978-1-4219-9653-0(7)***); pap. 57.99 (***978-1-4219-9654-7(5)***) IndyPublish.com.

Cheek, Roland. Lincoln County Crucible, 6 vols. 2003. 288p. pap. 14.95 (978-0-918981-10-3(7) , 3) Skyline Publishing.

Christian, Diana. The Lucky Seven. 2005. 71p. pap. 14.95 (978-1-4137-5471-1(6)) PublishAmerica, Inc.

Cowboys on a Ranch: Second Grade Guided Reading Level G. (On Our Way to English Ser.). (gr. 2 up). 34.50 (978-0-7578-7079-8(1)) Rigby Education.

Creel, Ann Howard. Nowhere, Now Here. 2000. (J). (978-0-606-21789-7(4)); (gr. 5-8). lib. bdg. 14.10 (978-0-613-31532-6(4)) Tandem Library Bks.

Davis, Susan Page. Sarah's Long Ride. 2007. 173p. (J). (***978-1-59166-737-7(2)***) Jones, Bob Univ. Pr.

Drake, Jane & Love, Ann. Farming. Cupples, Pat, illus. 2002. (America at Work Ser.). 32p. (J). (gr. k-3). (978-1-55074-451-4(8)) Kids Can Pr., Ltd.

Edge, Laura Bufano. Wild West Dreams. 2006. (J). pap. (978-0-88092-623-2(6)); lib. bdg. (978-0-88092-622-5(8)) Royal Fireworks Publishing Co.

Ehrlich, Gretel. A Blizzard Year. Kiesler, Kate A., illus. 2001. 128p. (gr. 4-8). pap. 5.99 (978-0-7868-1245-5(1)) Hyperion Bks. for Children.

—A Blizzard Year. 2001. (J). (gr. 4-8). 12.64 (978-0-606-22572-4(2)) Tandem Library Bks.

Erickson, John R. The Case of the Black-Hooded Hangmans. Holmes, Gerald L., illus. 1998. (Hank the Cowdog Ser.: No. 24). 144p. (J). (gr. 2-5). 15.99 (978-0-670-88431-5(6) , Viking Juvenile); Vol. 24. pap. 4.99 (978-0-14-130400-7(6) , Puffin) Penguin Group (USA) Inc.

—The Case of the Black-Hooded Hangmans. 1999. (Hank the Cowdog Ser.: No. 24). (gr. 3-6). lib. bdg. 13.00 (978-0-7857-6345-1(7)) Tandem Library Bks.

—The Case of the Blazing Sky #51. Holmes, Gerald L., illus. 2008. (Hank the Cowdog Ser.). 144p. (J). (gr. 3). 15.99 (***978-0-670-06260-7(X)*** , Viking Juvenile) Penguin Group (USA) Inc.

—The Case of the Burrowing Robot, Vol. 42. Holmes, Gerald L., illus. 2003. (Hank the Cowdog Ser.: No. 42). 144p. (J). (gr. 3). 15.99 (978-0-670-03632-5(3) , Viking Juvenile); (gr. 4-6). pap. 4.99 (978-0-14-250063-7(1) , Puffin) Penguin Group (USA) Inc.

—The Case of the Burrowing Robot. 2003. (Hank the Cowdog Ser.: No. 42). (gr. 3-6). lib. bdg. 13.00 (978-0-613-66353-5(3)) Tandem Library Bks.

—The Case of the Car-Barkaholic Dog. Holmes, Gerald L., illus. 1998. (Hank the Cowdog Ser.: No. 17). 144p. (J). (gr. 2-5). pap. 4.99 (978-0-14-130393-2(X) , Puffin) Penguin Group (USA) Inc.

—The Case of the Deadly Ha-Ha Game. 2001. (Hank the Cowdog Ser.: No. 37). (gr. 3-6). lib. bdg. 13.00 (978-0-613-33649-9(6)) Tandem Library Bks.

—The Case of the Double Bumblebee Sting. Holmes, Gerald L., illus. 1998. (Hank the Cowdog Ser.: No. 22). 144p. (J). (gr. 2-5). 14.99 (978-0-670-88429-2(4) , Viking Juvenile); Vol. 22. pap. 4.99 (978-0-14-130398-7(0) , Puffin) Penguin Group (USA) Inc.

—The Case of the Falling Sky. Holmes, Gerald L., illus. 2005. (Hank the Cowdog Ser.: No. 45). 129p. (J). lib. bdg. 17.00 (***978-1-4242-1602-4(8)***) Fitzgerald Bks.

—The Case of the Garbage Monster from Outer Space. Holmes, Gerald L., illus. 1999. (Hank the Cowdog Ser.: No. 32). 144p. (J). (gr. 2-5). 13.99 (978-0-670-88488-9(X) , Viking Juvenile) Penguin Group (USA) Inc.

—The Case of the Haystack Kitties. Holmes, Gerald L., illus. 1998. (Hank the Cowdog Ser.: No. 30). 144p. (J). (gr. 2-5). 14.99 (978-0-670-88437-7(5) , Viking Juvenile); Vol. 30. pap. 4.99 (978-0-14-130406-9(5) , Puffin) Penguin Group (USA) Inc.

—The Case of the Haystack Kitties. 1999. (Hank the Cowdog Ser.: No. 30). (gr. 3-6). lib. bdg. 13.00 (978-0-613-07442-1(4)) Tandem Library Bks.

—The Case of the Hooking Bull, Vol. 18. Holmes, Gerald L., illus. 1998. (Hank the Cowdog Ser.: No. 18). 144p. (J). (gr. 2-5). pap. 4.99 (978-0-14-130394-9(8) , Puffin) Penguin Group (USA) Inc.

—The Case of the Kidnapped Collie. Holmes, Gerald L., illus. 1998. (Hank the Cowdog Ser.: No. 26). 144p. (J). (gr. 2-5). 14.99 (978-0-670-88433-9(2) , Viking Juvenile); Vol. 26. pap. 4.99 (978-0-14-130402-1(2) , Puffin) Penguin Group (USA) Inc.

—The Case of the Kidnapped Collie. 1999. (Hank the Cowdog Ser.: No. 26). (gr. 3-6). lib. bdg. 13.00 (978-0-7857-9075-4(6)) Tandem Library Bks.

RAPHAEL, 1483-1520

Klein, Adam G. & Raphael. Raphael. 2007. (Illus.). 32p. (J). 22.78 (978-1-59679-734-5(7)) ABDO Publishing Co.

Venezia, Mike. Raphael. Venezia, Mike, illus. 2001. (Getting to Know the World's Greatest Artists Ser.). (Illus.). 32p. (J). (gr. 3-4). pap. 6.95 (978-0-516-27285-6(3)); 27.00 (978-0-516-22028-4(4)) Scholastic Library Publishing. (Children's Pr.).

—Raphael. 2001. (gr. 3-6). lib. bdg. 15.25 (978-0-613-49592-9(6)) Tandem Library Bks.

RATS

Burt, Jonathan. Rat. 2006. (Animal Ser.). (Illus.). 192p. pap. 19.95 (978-1-86189-224-9(1)) Reaktion Bks., Ltd. GBR. *Dist:* Chicago Distribution Ctr.

Conniff, Richard. Rats! The Good, the Bad, & the Ugly. 2002. (Illus.). 40p. (gr. 3-7). lib. bdg. 17.99 (978-0-375-91207-8(X) , Crown Books For Young Readers) Random Hse. Children's Bks.

Coppendale, Jean. Rats. 2004. (QEB You & Your Pet Ser.). (Illus.). 32p. (J). lib. bdg. 18.95 (978-1-59566-054-1(2)) QEB Publishing Inc.

Doudna, Kelly. Running Rats. Nobens, C. A., illus. 2007. (Perfect Pets Ser.). 24p. (J). (gr. k-3). lib. bdg. 19.93 (***978-1-59928-754-6(4)*** , SandCastle) ABDO Publishing Co.

Grolier Educational Staff, contrib. by. Rats. 2001. (Nature's Children Ser.). (Illus.). 48p. (J). (978-0-7172-5544-3(1) , Grolier) Scholastic Library Publishing.

Head, Honor. Rats & Mice. Burton, Jane, photos by. 2000. (My Pet Ser.). (Illus.). 32p. (J). (gr. 3-5). lib. bdg. 25.69 (978-0-7398-2889-2(4)) Raintree.

—Rats & Mice. 2000. (My Pet Ser.). (Illus.). 32p. (J). (gr. 3-5). pap. 8.95 (978-0-7398-3014-7(7)) Steck-Vaughn.

Laslo, Cynthia. Rat Attacks. 2000. (High Interest Bks.). (Illus.). 48p. (J). (gr. 7-12). pap. 6.95 (978-0-516-23517-2(6) , Children's Pr.) Scholastic Library Publishing.

Legg, Gerald. Rats. Bergin, Mark, illus. 2002. (Scary Creatures Ser.). (J). (gr. 2-4). pap. 6.95 (978-0-531-14852-5(1)); 32p. pap. 22.50 (978-0-531-14671-2(5)) Scholastic Library Publishing. (Watts, Franklin).

—Rats. 2003. (gr. 3-6). lib. bdg. 15.25 (978-0-613-54318-7(1)) Tandem Library Bks.

Loves, June. Mice & Rats. 2003. (Pets Ser.). (Illus.). 32p. (gr. 2-4). 23.00 (978-0-7910-7551-7(6) , Chelsea Hse.) Facts On File, Inc.

Marrin, Albert. Oh, Rats! The Story of Rats & People. Mordan, C. B., illus. 2006. 48p. (J). (gr. 3-6). 16.99 (978-0-525-47762-4(4) , Dutton Juvenile) Penguin Group (USA) Inc.

McNicholas, June. Rats. 2003. (Keeping Unusual Pets Ser.). (Illus.). 48p. (J). (gr. 3-5). lib. bdg. 25.64 (978-1-4034-0283-7(3)) Heinemann Library.

Rayner, Matthew. Rat. 2007. (I Am Your Pet Ser.). 32p. (J). (gr. 2-4). lib. bdg. 23.93 (***978-0-8368-8386-2(1)***) Stevens, Gareth Inc.

Simon, Elizabeth. Caring for Your Rat. 2004. (Caring for Your Pet Ser.). (Illus.). (J). pap. (978-1-59036-217-4(9)); 32p. lib. bdg. 16.95 (978-1-59036-197-9(0)) Weigl Pubs., Inc.

Steck-Vaughn Staff. Early Reader Program Level C: The Rat Princess, 6 Pack. 2004. (Illus.). pap. 33.00 (978-0-7398-8317-4(8)) Steck-Vaughn.

University Of Portsmouth, prod. The Rat: A Functional Anatomy. (Multimedia Dissection Library). (YA). cd-rom 149.95 (978-0-7365-3857-2(7)) Films Media Group.

Vidner, Bradley. All about Your... Rat. 1998. (All about Your...Ser.). (Illus.). 64p. 2.95 (978-1-86054-062-2(7)) Ringpress Bks., Ltd. GBR. *Dist:* 7 Hills Bk. Distributors.

Waters, Jo. The Wild Side of Mice & Rats. 2004. (Raintree Perspectives Ser.). (Illus.). 32p. (J). pap. (978-1-4109-1412-5(7)) Harcourt Schl. Pubs.

—The Wild Side of Pet Mice & Rats. 2005. (Raintree Perspectives Ser.). (Illus.). 32p. (J). (ps-ps). lib. bdg. 27.50 (978-1-4109-1406-4(2)) Harcourt Schl. Pubs.

Whitehouse, Patricia. La Rata. 2003. (Que Esta Despierto? (What's Awake?) Ser.).Tr. of Rats. (ENG & SPA.). 24p. (J). (ps-1). lib. bdg. 17.08 (978-1-4034-0397-1(X)) Heinemann.

—La Rata. 2003. (¿Qué esta despierto? Ser.).Tr. of Rats. (SPA., Illus.). 24p. pap. 5.25 (978-1-4034-0638-5(3)) Heinemann Library.

—Rats. 2003. (What's Awake? Ser.). (Illus.). 24p. (ps-1). (J). lib. bdg. 17.08 (978-1-58810-881-4(3)); pap. 5.25 (978-1-4034-0629-3(4)) Heinemann Library.

The Wild Side of Mice & Rats. 2004. pap. (978-1-4109-1418-7(6)) Harcourt Schl. Pubs.

RATS—FICTION

AaronG, Driftin'. Claude Henry, the Iditarod Mouse: The Adventures Begin. 2007. 108p. (J). per. 9.95 (***978-0-595-44990-3(5)***) iUniverse, Inc.

Adeney, Anne, retold by. The Pied Piper of Hamelin. 2007. (First Fairy Tales Ser.). (Illus.). 30p. (J). (***978-1-59771-072-5(5)***) Sea-To-Sea Pubns.

Atwood, Margaret. Rude Ramsay & the Roaring Radishes. Petricic, Dusan, illus. 2004. 32p. (J). 16.95 (978-1-58234-950-3(9) , Bloomsbury Children) Bloomsbury Publishing.

Avi. The Christmas Rat. 2002. 144p. (J). pap. 4.99 (978-0-689-83843-9(3) , Aladdin) Simon & Schuster Children's Publishing.

—The Christmas Rat. 2002. (gr. 3-6). lib. bdg. 13.00 (978-0-613-88162-3(1)) Tandem Library Bks.

—The Mayor of Central Park. Floca, Brian, illus. 2003. 208p. (J). (gr. 3-6). 15.99 (978-0-06-000682-2(X)); lib. bdg. 16.89 (978-0-06-051556-0(2)) HarperCollins Pubs.

Bang-Campbell, Monika. Little Rat Makes Music. Bang, Molly, illus. 2007. (Little Rat Ser.). 48p. (J). (gr. 1-4). 15.00 (978-0-15-205305-5(0)) Harcourt Trade Pubs.

—Little Rat Rides. Bang, Molly, illus. 2006. (Little Rat Ser.). 48p. (J). pap. 5.95 (978-0-15-205598-1(3) , Harcourt Paperbacks) Harcourt Children's Bks.

—Little Rat Rides. Bang, Molly Garrett, tr. Bang, Molly Garrett, illus. 2004. (Little Rat Ser.). 48p. (J). 15.00 (978-0-15-204667-5(4)) Harcourt Children's Bks.

—Little Rat Sets Sail. Bang, Molly Garrett, illus. (Little Rat Ser.). 48p. (J). 2003. pap. 5.95 (978-0-15-204769-6(7) , Harcourt Paperbacks); 2002. (gr. 1-3). 14.00 (978-0-15-216297-9(6)) Harcourt Children's Bks.

—Little Rat Sets Sail. 2003. (gr. k-3). lib. bdg. 14.10 (978-0-613-70519-6(X)) Tandem Library Bks.

Barkow, Henriette. The Pied Piper. Dry, Roland, illus. 2004. 32p. (J). (TAM, CZE, VIE, SPA & GUJ.). (978-1-85269-901-7(9)); (CZE, TAM, VIE, SPA & GUJ.). (978-1-85269-906-2(X)); (TAM, CZE, VIE, SPA & GUJ.). (978-1-85269-911-6(6)); (TAM, CZE, VIE, SPA & GUJ.). (978-1-85269-915-4(9)); (TAM, CZE, VIE, SPA & GUJ.). (978-1-85269-916-1(7)); (TAM, CZE, VIE, SPA & GUJ.). (978-1-85269-920-8(5)); (TAM, CZE, SPA, VIE & GUJ.). (978-1-85269-921-5(3)); (TAM, CZE, VIE, SPA & GUJ.). (978-1-85269-925-3(6)); (TAM, CZE, VIE, SPA & GUJ.). (978-1-85269-930-7(2)); (TAM, CZE, VIE, SPA & GUJ.). (978-1-85269-935-2(3)); (TAM, CZE, VIE, SPA & GUJ.). (978-1-85269-940-6(X)); (TAM, CZE, VIE, SPA & GUJ.). (978-1-85269-945-1(0)); (TAM, CZE, VIE, SPA & GUJ.). (978-1-85269-950-5(7)); (TAM, CZE, VIE, SPA & GUJ.). (978-1-85269-955-0(8)); (TAM, CZE, VIE, SPA & GUJ.). (978-1-85269-960-4(4)); (TAM, CZE, VIE, SPA & GUJ.). (978-1-85269-965-9(5)); (TAM, CZE, VIE, SPA & GUJ.). (978-1-85269-970-3(1)); (TAM, CZE, VIE, SPA & GUJ.). (978-1-85269-975-8(2)); (TAM, CZE, VIE, SPA & GUJ.). (978-1-85269-980-2(9)); (TAM, CZE, VIE, SPA & GUJ.). (978-1-85269-985-7(X)); (TAM, CZE, VIE, SPA & GUJ.). (978-1-85269-990-1(6)); (TAM, CZE, VIE, SPA & GUJ.). (978-1-85269-995-6(7)) Mantra Publishing, Ltd.

Blacker, Terence. Ms. Wiz Smells a Rat. 2003. (Illus.). 64p. (J). pap. (978-0-330-37466-8(4) , Pan) Pan Macmillan.

Bondoux, Anne-Laure. Vasco, Leader of the Tribe. Maudet, Y., tr. from FRE. 2007. (J). (gr. 3-7). 352p. 15.99 (***978-0-385-73363-2(1)***); 256p. lib. bdg. 18.99 (***978-0-385-90378-3(2)***) Random Hse. Children's Bks. (Delacorte Bks. for Young Readers).

Brooke, Samantha. Portraits from the Pipes. Simpson, Fiona, ed. 2006. (Flushed Away Ser.). 32p. (J). pap. 3.99 (978-0-439-90080-5(8)) Scholastic, Inc.

Brown, Alan. Incredible Journey of Walter Rat. (Illus.). 63p. (J). pap. (978-0-340-72750-8(0) , Hodder & Stoughton) Hodder General Publishing Division.

Brown, Tony. Water's Edge. 2006. 180p. per. (***978-1-84685-163-6(7)*** , Exposure Publishing) Meadow Bks.

Buchanan, Paul. The Rat That Ate Poodles. 1998. (Heebie Jeebies Ser.: Vol. 1). 144p. (J). (gr. 1-6). pap. 5.99 (978-0-8054-0170-7(9)) B&H Publishing Grp.

Caple, Kathy. Duck & Company. 2007. (Illus.). 32p. (J). (gr. k-3). 14.95 (978-0-8234-1993-7(2)); pap. 4.95 (***978-0-8234-2125-1(2)***) Holiday Hse., Inc.

Carballeira, Paula. Paco. Barrio, Blanca, illus. 2003. 32p. (J). 14.95 (978-84-95730-38-1(3)) Kalandraka Catalunya, Edicions, S.L. ESP. *Dist:* Independent Pubs. Group.

Cat & Rat Fall Out: Individual Title Six-Pack Pouch - Level K. (Lighthouse Ser.). 16p. (gr. 2 up). 28.00 (978-0-7578-0870-8(0)) Rigby Education.

Child, Lauren. Que Lata de Rata. 2002. (Illus.). (J). (SPA.). 32p. 17.95 (978-84-8488-058-5(3)); (CAT & SPA., 26p. (978-84-8488-059-2(1)) Serres, Ediciones, S. L. ESP. *Dist:* Lectorum Pubns., Inc.

Chin, Oliver Clyde. The Year of the Rat: Tales from the Chinese Zodiac. Alcorn, Miah, illus. 2008. (Tales from the Chinese Zodiac Ser.). 36p. (J). 15.95 (***978-1-59702-011-4(7)***) Immedium.

Clairmont, Patsy. Spud. 2006. (Tails from the Pantry Ser.). (Illus.). 32p. (J). 9.99 (978-1-4003-0802-6(X)) Nelson, Thomas Inc.

Claycomb, Patty. Love Me Said the Rat. Chapin, Patrick, illus. 2002. (Two Can Read Ser.). 16p. (J). 2.99 (978-1-56472-651-3(7)) Edupress, Inc.

Combel Editorial Staff. El Leon y el Raton. 2004. (Caballo alado clasicos-Al Galope Ser.). (SPA., Illus.). 24p. 6.95 (978-84-7864-784-2(8)) Combel Editorial, S.A. ESP. *Dist:* Independent Pubs. Group.

Comino, Sandra. Morning Glory. Amado, Elisa, tr. Max, illus. 2006. 64p. (J). 14.95 (978-0-88899-642-8(X)) Groundwood Bks. CAN. *Dist:* Perseus Distribution.

Cousineau, Craig S. Skippy & Oaf: The Battle Against Oxygen Radicals. 2007. (Illus.). 48p. (J). pap. 8.95 (978-1-933255-27-9(7)) DNA Pr.

Cousins, Lucy. Maisy Goes to School. Cousins, Lucy, illus. 2005. (Maisy Ser.). (Illus.). 16p. (J). (gr. k-k). 4.99 (978-0-7636-2898-7(0)) Candlewick Pr.

—Pina Piace Giocare. pap. 18.95 (978-88-04-48797-5(6)) Mondadori ITA. *Dist:* Distribooks, Inc.

Cox, Judy. The Mystery of the Burmese Bandicoot. Rayyan, Omar, illus. 2007. (Tails of frederick & Ishbu Ser.). 256p. (YA). (gr. 5 up). 16.99 (***978-0-7614-5376-5(8)***) Cavendish, Marshall Corp.

Crimi, Carolyn. No Necesito Amigos. 2004. (SPA.). 32p. (978-84-7720-798-6(4)) Obelisco, Ediciones S.A.

Crocker, Carter & Snyder, Carrie A. The Tale of the Swamp Rat. 2005. 176p. (J). (gr. 4). reprint ed. pap. 6.99 (978-0-14-240314-3(8) , Puffin) Penguin Group (USA) Inc.

Crompton, Paul. Remarkable for Short. 2005. 113p. pap. 16.95 (978-1-4241-0287-7(1)) PublishAmerica, Inc.

Crow, Kristyn. Cool Daddy Rat. Lester, Mike, illus. 2008. 32p. (J). (ps). 16.99 (***978-0-399-24375-2(5)*** , Putnam Juvenile) Penguin Group (USA) Inc.

Cutler, Jane. Rats! Pearson, Tracey Campbell, illus. 1998. 128p. (J). (ps-k). pap. 5.95 (978-0-374-46203-1(8) , Sunburst) Farrar, Straus & Giroux.

Daley, Michael J. Space Station Rat. 2005. 144p. (J). 15.95 (978-0-8234-1866-4(9)) Holiday Hse., Inc.

David, Erica. Plumbing Problems. Simpson, Fiona, ed. 2006. (Flushed Away Ser.). 32p. (J). pap. 3.99 (978-0-439-90077-5(8)) Scholastic, Inc.

Derrick, Patricia. Rathbone the Rat. 2007. 32p. 18.95 (978-1-933818-17-7(4)) Animalations.

DK Publishing Staff. Ratatouille: The Guide to Remy's World. 2007. 48p. (J). (gr. 1-4). 12.99 (978-0-7566-2991-5(8)) Dorling Kindersley Publishing, Inc.

Dodson, Emma. Very Important Idea The. 2007. (Illus.). 32p. 19.95 (***978-0-340-87808-8(8)***); pap. 9.95 (***978-0-340-87809-5(6)***) Hodder Children's Division GBR. *Dist:* Independent Pubs. Group.

Doudna, Kelly. Pack Rat. 2006. (Fact & Fiction Ser.). (Illus.). 24p. (J). 21.35 (978-1-59679-955-4(2) , Sand-Castle) ABDO Publishing Co.

—Pack Rat. Chawla, Neena, illus. 2006. (Fact & Fiction Ser.). 24p. (J). pap. (978-1-59679-956-1(0)) ABDO Publishing Co.

Durkee, Sarah. Movie Storybook. Simpson, Fiona, ed. 2006. (Flushed Away Ser.). 48p. (J). pap. 6.99 (978-0-439-90079-9(4)) Scholastic, Inc.

Egielski, Richard. Slim & Jim. Egielski, Richard, illus. 2005. (Illus.). 37p. (J). (gr. k-4). reprint ed. 16.00 (978-0-7567-8936-7(2)) DIANE Publishing Co.

Escott, Jamison. The Clockmaker of Mullen. Escott, Esther, illus. 2004. 24p. (J). pap. 8.95 (978-1-57733-127-8(3) , Papillon Publishing) Blue Dolphin Publishing, Inc.

Ewers, Joe, illus. The Pied Piper: A Tale about Promises. 2006. (J). 6.99 (978-1-59939-004-8(3)) Reader's Digest Young Families, Inc.

Fourteen Rats & a Rat-Catcher. 2004. (J). 24.95 incl. audio (978-1-56008-200-2(3)) Weston Woods Studios, Inc.

France, Anthony. From Me to You. Beeke, Tiphanie, illus. 2003. 32p. (J). (ps-2). 15.99 (978-0-7636-2255-8(9)) Candlewick Pr.

Fraser, Mary Ann. I. Q. Goes to School. Fraser, Mary Ann, illus. 2004. (Illus.). 32p. (J). (ps-3). pap. 6.95 (978-0-8027-7698-3(1)) Walker & Co.

Frederick, Heather Vogel. For Your Paws Only. Comport, Sally Wern, illus. 2006. (Spy Mice Ser.). 272p. (J). pap. 5.99 (978-1-4169-4025-8(1) , Aladdin) Simon & Schuster Children's Publishing.

—Goldwhiskers. Comport, Sally Wern, illus. 2007. (Spy Mice Ser.). 256p. (J). pap. 5.99 (978-1-4169-1442-6(0) , Simon & Schuster Children's Publishing) Simon & Schuster Children's Publishing.

Gardner, Sally. Countess's Calamity. 2003. (gr. 3-6). lib. bdg. 15.25 (978-0-613-63271-3(0)) Tandem Library Bks.

Geshell, Carmen. The Surf Rats of Waikiki Beach. Pagay, Jeff, illus. 2004. 24p. 10.95 (978-1-57306-226-8(X)) Bess Pr., Inc.

Golden Books Staff. Rat Pack. 2007. (Color Plus Chunky Crayons Ser.). (Illus.). 48p. (J). (ps-2). pap. 3.99 (978-0-7364-2446-2(6) , Golden/Disney) Random Hse. Children's Bks.

Grahame, Kenneth. Open Road Bk. 2. Iosa, Ann, illus. 2006. (Easy Reader Classics Ser.). 32p. (J). pap. 3.95 (978-1-4027-3294-2(5)) Sterling Publishing Co., Inc.

—The Wind in the Willows Bk. 1: The Riverbank. Iosa, Ann, illus. 2006. (Easy Reader Classics Ser.). 32p. (J). pap. 3.95 (978-1-4027-3293-5(7)) Sterling Publishing Co., Inc.

Guy, Geoffrey. Hannibal's Rat. 2003. (Illus.). mass mkt. (978-0-340-85485-3(5) , Hodder Children's Books) Hodder Children's Division.

Hanson, Mary Elizabeth. How to Save Your Tail: If You Are a Rat Nabbed by Cats Who Really Like Stories about Magic Spoons, Wolves with Snout-Warts, Big Hairy Chimney Trolls—And Cookies Too. Hendrix, John, illus. 2007. 112p. (J). (gr. 1-5). 15.99 (978-0-375-83755-5(8) , Schwartz & Wade Bks.) Random Hse. Children's Bks.

—How to Save Your Tail: If You Are a Rat Nabbed by Cats Who Really Like Stories about Magic Spoons, Wolves with Snout-Warts, Big Hairy Chimney Trolls—and Cookies Too. 2007. (Illus.). 112p. (J). (gr. 1-5). lib. bdg. 18.99 (978-0-375-93755-2(2) , Schwartz & Wade Bks.) Random Hse. Children's Bks.

Harris, Marian. Tuesday in Arizona. Harris, Jim, illus. 1998. 32p. (J). (ps-3). 15.95 (978-1-56554-233-4(9)) Pelican Publishing Co., Inc.

Hedrick, Georgia. Different Is Cool! A Skater Mouse Saga. Hedrick, Georgia, illus. l.t. ed. 2002. (Illus.). 34p. (J). cd-rom 11.95 (978-0-9706612-9-6(0)) JetKor.

Heinz, Brian J. The Barnyard Cat. Blair, June H., illus. 2000. 32p. (J). (gr. k-4). 14.95 (978-0-936335-04-9(1)) Ballyhoo BookWorks, Inc.

—The Barnyard Cat. l.t. ed. 2003. (Illus.). 32p. (J). pap. 6.96 (978-0-936335-07-0(6)) Ballyhoo BookWorks, Inc.

Herbert, James. The Rats. 2003. 197p. (J). 32.50 (978-0-333-76118-2(9)) Macmillan Publishers Ltd. GBR. *Dist:* Trafalgar Square Publishing.

—The Rats. (Illus.). 197p. (J). pap. 13.99 (978-0-330-37614-3(4) , Pan) Pan Macmillan GBR. *Dist:* Trafalgar Square Publishing.

Hofmeister, Alan, et al. The Bat Rat. (Reading for All Learners Ser.). (Illus.). (J). pap. (978-1-56861-119-8(6)) Swift Learning Resources.

—Mat. (Reading for All Learners Ser.). (Illus.). (J). pap. (978-1-56861-077-1(7)) Swift Learning Resources.

—Mat & the Nut. (Reading for All Learners Ser.). (Illus.). (J). pap. (978-1-56861-109-9(9)) Swift Learning Resources.

—Mat at Bat. (Reading for All Learners Ser.). (Illus.). (J). pap. (978-1-56861-118-1(8)) Swift Learning Resources.

—Mat Did It. (Reading for All Learners Ser.). (Illus.). (J). pap. (978-1-56861-102-0(1)) Swift Learning Resources.

—Mat Is Wet. (Reading for All Learners Ser.). (Illus.). (J). pap. (978-1-56861-120-4(X)) Swift Learning Resources.

—Mat the Rat. (Reading for All Learners Ser.). (Illus.). (J). pap. (978-1-56861-111-2(0)) Swift Learning Resources.

—Nat. (Reading for All Learners Ser.). (Illus.). (J). pap. (978-1-56861-093-1(9)) Swift Learning Resources.

Hooper. Pole-Seekers. 2000. (Illus.). 165p. pap. 8.99 (978-0-340-75734-5(5) , Hodder & Stoughton) Hodder General Publishing Division GBR. *Dist:* Trafalgar Square Publishing.

Hurd, Thacher. Mystery on the Docks. Hurd, Thacher, illus. 2001. (Illus.). pap. 39.95 incl. audio compact disk (978-1-59112-529-7(4)) Live Oak Media.

Jarvis, Robin. The Crystal Prison. (Deptford Mice Ser.: Bk. 2). (Illus.). 256p. (YA). 2002. pap. 6.95 (978-1-58717-161-1(9)); 2001. (gr. 5 up). 17.95 (978-1-58717-107-9(4)) Chronicle Bks. LLC. (SeaStar Bks.).

—Crystal Prison. 2002. (gr. 5-8). lib. bdg. 15.25 (978-0-613-56295-9(X)) Tandem Library Bks.

—Dark Portal. 2000. (gr. 5-8). lib. bdg. 15.25 (978-0-613-44356-2(X)) Tandem Library Bks.

Kasza, Keiko. The Rat & the Tiger. 2007. 32p. (J). (ps). pap. 6.99 (***978-0-14-240900-8(6)*** , Puffin) Penguin Group (USA) Inc.

Kasza, Keiko. El Tigre y el Raton. (SPA.). (J). pap. 7.16 (978-958-04-2583-0(3)) Norma S.A. COL. *Dist:* Lectorum Pubns., Inc.

Kilaka, John. True Friends: A Tale from Tanzania. 2006. (Illus.). 32p. (J). 16.95 (978-0-88899-698-5(5)) Groundwood Bks. CAN. *Dist:* Perseus Distribution.

Kim, Wu-kyung. Su-il vs. Su-il. Park, Jung-eun, tr. from KOR. Kwon, Sawoo, illus. 2005. 164p. (J). pap. 20.00 (978-0-89581-839-3(6)) Jain Publishing Company, Inc.

Kirlin, Deborah S. A Rat Like Me. Faust, Angela & Buckwalter, Betsy, illus. 1998. (J). (ps-4). pap. 4.95 (978-0-9668263-0-2(2)) Salty DeSK Pubns.

Krensky, Stephen. Snack Attack. Curtis, Stacy, illus. 2008. (Ready-to-Reads Ser.). 32p. (J). pap. 3.99 (***978-1-4169-0238-6(4)***); lib. bdg. 13.89 (***978-1-4169-0239-3(2)***) Simon & Schuster Children's Publishing. (Aladdin).

Lamson, Sharon & Wacky World Staff. Batter up, Squiggz! A Story about Making Big Things Happen. Barry, Bruce, illus. 2006. 28p. (J). 4.99 (978-0-310-71308-1(0)) Zonderkidz.

Liberto, Lorenzo. Matt the Rat & His Magic Cloud / Raton Mateo y Su Nube Magica: A Day at School / un Dia de Escuela. Gomez, Rocio, ed. Torres, Irving, illus. 2003. (Matt the Rat Ser. / La Serie de Raton Mateo). (ENG & SPA.). 32p. (J). lib. bdg. 20.00 (978-0-9743668-0-7(3)) Harvest Sun Pr., LLC.

—Matt the Rat & His Sister Maggie (Raton Mateo y Su Hermana Maggie) When I Grow Up (Cuando Yo Crezca) Gomez, Rocio, ed. Torres, Irving, illus. 2003. (Matt the Rat Ser. / La Serie de Raton Mateo). (SPA & ENG.). 40p. (J). lib. bdg. 20.00 (978-0-9743668-1-4(1)) Harvest Sun Pr., LLC.

—Matt the Rat Fights Back / Raton Mateo se Defiende. Gomez, Rocio, tr. from ENG. Torres, Irving, illus. 2005. (Matt the Rat Ser. / La Serie de Raton Mateo). (ENG & SPA.). 32p. (J). lib. bdg. 20.00 (978-0-9743668-4-5(6)) Harvest Sun Pr., LLC.

—Save the Planet / Salva el Planeta. Gomez, Rocio, tr. Torres, Irving, illus. 2005. (Matt the Rat Ser. / La Serie de Raton Mateo). (ENG & SPA.). 32p. (J). lib. bdg. 20.00 (978-0-9743668-5-2(4)) Harvest Sun Pr., LLC.

Liberto, Lorenzo, et al. Matt the Rat's Incredible Creations / Las Creaciones Increíbles de Raton Mateo. Torres, Irving, illus. 2004. (ENG & SPA.). 32p. (J). lib. bdg. 20.00 (978-0-9743668-3-8(8)) Harvest Sun Pr., LLC.

—Practice Makes Perfect / la Practica Hace al Maestro. Torres, Irving, illus. 2004. (ENG & SPA.). 32p. (J). lib. bdg. 20.00 (978-0-9743668-2-1(X)) Harvest Sun Pr., LLC.

Luke, Deanna. Marky & the Rat. Chambers, Lynne, illus. (Marky Ser.: Vol. 3). (J). 2001. cd-rom 3.95 (978-1-928777-16-8(3)); 2000. 40p. (gr. 2-6). 8.95 (978-1-928777-07-6(4)) Blessing Our World, Inc. (BOW Bks.).

Marciano, John Bemelmans. Harold's Tail. 2003. (Illus.). 144p. (J). (gr. 3-7). 15.99 (978-0-670-03660-8(9) , Viking Juvenile) Penguin Group (USA) Inc.

Masters, Anthony. Doughnut Danger. Fisher, Chris, illus. 2004. (I Am Reading Ser.). 48p. (J). (gr. k-3). pap. 3.95 (978-0-7534-5821-1(7) , Kingfisher) Houghton Mifflin Co. Trade & Reference Div.

—Ricky's Rat Gang. Fisher, Chris, illus. 2004. (I Am Reading Ser.). 48p. (J). (gr. 1-3). pap. 3.95 (978-0-7534-5800-6(4) , Kingfisher) Houghton Mifflin Co. Trade & Reference Div.

McFarlane, Brian. Coaching the River Rats. 10th ed. 2008. 198p. pap. 6.95 (***978-1-55168-302-7(4)***) Key Porter Bks. CAN. *Dist:* Perseus Distribution.

McPhail, David. Big Brown Bear's Birthday Surprise. O'Connor, John, illus. 2007. (Big Brown Bear Ser.). 32p. (J). (ps-2). 16.00 (978-0-15-206098-5(7)) Harcourt Trade Pubs.

—Big Brown Bear's up & down Day. 2006. (Illus.). 48p. (J). pap. 6.00 (978-0-15-205684-1(X) , Voyager Bks./Libros Viajeros) Harcourt Children's Bks.

McPhail, David M. Big Brown Bear Goes to Town. O'Connor, John, illus. 2006. 40p. (J). 16.00 (978-0-15-205317-8(4)) Harcourt Trade Pubs.

—Big Brown Bear's up & down Day. McPhail, David M., illus. 2005. (Illus.). 42p. (J). (ps-3). reprint ed. 16.00 (978-0-7567-8542-0(1)) DIANE Publishing Co.

—Big Brown Bear's up & down Day. McPhail, David M., illus. 2003. (Illus.). 48p. (J). 16.00 (978-0-15-216407-2(3)) Harcourt Trade Pubs.

Meddaugh, Susan. Cinderella's Rat. Meddaugh, Susan, illus. 2002. (Illus.). 32p. (J). (gr. k-3). pap. 5.95 (978-0-618-12540-1(X) , Walter Lorraine) Houghton Mifflin Co. Trade & Reference Div.

—Cinderella's Rat. 2002. (gr. k-3). lib. bdg. 14.10 (978-0-613-72920-8(X)) Tandem Library Bks.

O'Brien, Robert C. Mrs. Frisby & the Rats of Nimh. Bernstein, Zena, illus. 2002. (J). 13.94 (978-0-7587-0205-0(1)) Book Wholesalers, Inc.

—Mrs. Frisby & the Rats of Nimh. Bernstein, Zena, illus. l.t. ed. 2000. (Rats of NIMH Ser.). 300p. (J). (gr. 4-7). lib. bdg. 29.95 (978-1-58118-056-5(X) , 23470) LRS.

O'Brien, Robert C. & Pryne, Jane. Mrs. Frisby & the Rats of Nimh. 1998. (Literature Unit Ser.). (Illus.). 48p. pap., tchr. ed. 7.99 (978-1-55734-523-3(6) , TCA0523) Teacher Created Materials, Inc.

Parsons, Tom. Pinky the Rat at the Brussels Sprout Museum. 2007. 194p. 27.76 (***978-1-4303-1538-4(5)***) Lulu.com.

Pearce, Jacqueline. The Truth about Rats (and Dogs) 2006. 176p. (J). pap. 7.95 (978-1-55143-473-5(3)) Orca Bk. Pubs. USA.

Pratchett, Terry. The Amazing Maurice & His Educated Rodents. 2003. 368p. (YA). (gr. 7 up). pap. 6.99 (978-0-06-001235-9(8)) HarperCollins Pubs.

—The Amazing Maurice & His Educated Rodents. 2003. (gr. 5-8). lib. bdg. 15.30 (978-0-613-65757-0(8)) Tandem Library Bks.

Priest, Nancy. Where Can Bebe Be: The Tale of Bebe's Great Adventures. 2004. (Illus.). 16p. (J). pap. 14.95 (978-1-932373-62-2(4) , Cedar Hill Pr.) Cedar Hill Publishing.

Pullman, Philip. Yo Era una Rata. Azaola, Miguel, tr. Bailey, Peter, illus. 2001. (Barco de Vapor: No. 22). Orig. Title: I Was a Rat!. (SPA.). 178p. 9.95 (978-84-348-7811-2(9)) SM Ediciones ESP. *Dist:* AIMS International Bks., Inc.

Random House Disney Staff. The Big Cheese. 2007. (Step into Reading Ser.). (Illus.). 32p. (J). (ps-2). pap. 3.99 (978-0-7364-2430-1(X)); lib. bdg. 11.99 (978-0-7364-8053-6(6)) Random Hse. Children's Bks. (RH/Disney).

—Bon Appetit! 2007. (Illus.). 12p. (J). (ps-3). pap. 6.99 (978-0-7364-2437-0(7) , RH/Disney) Random Hse. Children's Bks.

—I Smell a Rat. Disney Storybook Artists Staff, illus. 2007. (Scented Storybook Ser.). 24p. (J). (ps-2). 9.99 (978-0-7364-2467-7(9) , RH/Disney) Random Hse. Children's Bks.

—Ratatouille. 2007. (J). (Illus.). 24p. 2.99 (***978-0-7364-2421-9(0)*** , Golden/Disney); 72p. (ps-3). 8.99 (978-0-7364-2440-0(7) , RH/Disney); (Illus.). 24p. (gr. k-k). 2.99 (978-0-7364-2423-3(7) , RH/Disney); (Illus.). 128p. (gr. 3-7). pap. 4.99 (978-0-7364-2439-4(3) , RH/Disney) Random Hse. Children's Bks.

—Recipe for Disaster. 2007. (Illus.). 80p. (J). (gr. 2-5). pap. 3.99 (978-0-7364-2449-3(0) , RH/Disney) Random Hse. Children's Bks.

—Run, Remy, Run! 2007. (Step into Reading Ser.). (Illus.). 32p. (J). (ps-1). pap. 3.99 (978-0-7364-2476-9(8)); lib. bdg. 11.99 (978-0-7364-8054-3(4)) Random Hse. Children's Bks. (RH/Disney).

Rigby Education Staff. Look Out, Fox! (Sails Literacy Ser.). (Illus.). 16p. (gr. k-1). 27.00 (978-0-7635-9874-7(7) , 698747C99) Rigby Education.

Riva, Renee. Guido's Gondola. Bjorkman, Steve, illus. 2005. 40p. (J). 9.99 (978-1-4000-7060-2(0) , WaterBrook Pr.) WaterBrook Pr.

Rosie & Roger. 2002. (Illus.). 32p. (J). 16.95 (978-1-931290-09-8(1)) Tallfellow Pr.

Salas, Macarena, ed. La Ratita Presumida / the Conceited Little Rat. 2006. (Bilingual Tales Ser.). 24p. (J). pap. 3.50 (978-0-439-77379-9(2) , Scholastic en Espanol) Scholastic, Inc.

Sargent, Dave & Sargent, Pat. Pansy Packrat: But I Want It!, 56 vols., 33. Huff, Jean Lirley, illus. 2001. (Animal Pride Ser.: Vol. 33). 36p. (J). lib. bdg. 19.95 (978-1-56763-382-5(X)) Ozark Publishing.

Satterfield, Barbara. Tomias the Cat. 2000. (Illus.). 30p. (J). (gr. 2-6). pap. 9.99 (978-0-9725941-0-3(8)) Milligan Bks., Inc.

Schade, Susan. Cat on Ice. 2001. (Road to Reading Ser.). (Illus.). (J). 10.79 (978-0-606-20596-2(9)) Tandem Library Bks.

Schietinger-Cachina, Daryl A. Pat & Pat the Cat & Rat. Schietinger-Cachina, Daryl A., illus. 1999. (Illus.). 8p. (J). (ps-5). pap. 5.00 (978-1-928641-00-1(8)) Daryl Ann Pubns.

Schwabauer, Daniel. Runt the Brave. 2004. (Illus.). 224p. 16.99 (978-0-9742972-1-7(6)) Clear Water Pr.

Seidler, Tor. A Rat's Tale. Marcellino, Fred, illus. 1999. 192p. (J). (gr. 5 up). pap. 5.99 (978-0-06-440779-3(9) , Harper Trophy) HarperCollins Pubs.

—A Rat's Tale. 186p. (J). (gr. 3-5). pap. 6.95 (978-0-8072-1514-2(7) , Listening Library) Random Hse. Audio Publishing Group.

—Rat's Tale. 1999. (978-0-606-16698-0(X)); (gr. 3-6). lib. bdg. 15.25 (978-0-613-12367-9(0)) Tandem Library Bks.

—A Rat's Tale. unabr. ed. 1998. 186p. (J). (gr. 3-5). pap. 35.00 incl. audio (978-0-8072-7951-9(X) , YA947SP, Listening Library) Random Hse. Audio Publishing Group.

—The Revenge of Randal Reese-Rat. Helquist, Brett, illus. 2004. 240p. (J). reprint ed. pap. 5.99 (978-0-06-050867-8(1) , Harper Trophy) HarperCollins Pubs.

Simpson, Fiona. Heroes, Henchrats & Hooligans. 2006. (Flushed Away Ser.). 24p. (J). pap. 3.99 (978-0-439-90076-8(X)) Scholastic, Inc.

Smiley, Mark. A Journey Far Away. 2005. pap. 13.95 (***978-1-59526-494-7(9)***) Media Creations, Inc.

Staunton, Ted. Morgan's Pet Plot. Slavin, Bill, illus. 2003. (First Novel Ser.). 64p. (J). (gr. 1-5). 4.95 (978-0-88780-587-5(6)); (***978-0-88780-588-2(4)***) Formac Publishing Co., Ltd. CAN. *Dist:* Casemate Pubs. & Bk. Distributors, LLC.

Stierle, Cynthia. Ratatouille Movie Theater Storybook & Movie Projector. Disney, Reader's Digest, Pixar, illus. 2007. (RD Innovative Book & Player Format Ser.). 48p. (J). (ps-4). bds. 24.99 (***978-0-7944-1284-5(X)***) Reader's Digest Assn., Inc., The.

Stilton, Geronimo. A Cheese-Colored Camper. 2005. (Geronimo Stilton Ser.: No. 16). (Illus.). 128p. (J). pap. 6.99 (978-0-439-69139-0(7) , Scholastic Paperbacks) Scholastic, Inc.

—Watch Your Whiskers, Stilton! 17th ed. 2005. (Geronimo Stilton Ser.: No. 17). (Illus.). 128p. (J). pap. 5.99 (978-0-439-69140-6(0) , Scholastic Paperbacks) Scholastic, Inc.

Stimson, Joan, ed. Oscar's Starry Night. 1999. (J). 12.95 (978-0-7641-1136-5(1)) Barron's Educational Series, Inc.

Stone, David Lee. The Ratastrophe Catastrophe. 2006. (Illmore Chronicles: Bk. 1). 288p. (gr. 5-9). reprint ed. pap. 6.99 (978-0-7868-5129-4(5)) Hyperion Pr.

Storad, Conrad J. Desert Night Shift: A Pack Rat Story. Jensen, Nathaniel P., illus. 2006. (J). lib. bdg. 15.95 (978-1-891795-16-9(3)) RGU Group, The.

Thompson, Colin. The Short & Incredibly Happy Life of Riley. Lissiat, Amy, illus. 2006. 32p. (J). (***978-0-7344-0806-8(4)*** , Lothian Bks.) Hachette Livre Australia.

—The Short & Incredibly Happy Life of Riley. Lissiat, Amy, illus. 2007. 32p. (J). 15.95 (***978-1-933605-50-0(2)***) Kane/Miller Bk. Pubs., Inc.

Tremblay, Carole. Romeo, le Rat Romantique. ed. 2004. (FRE., Illus.). (J). (ps-3). spiral bd. (978-0-616-07266-0(X)) Canadian National Institute for the Blind/Institut National Canadien pour les Aveugles.

Tremblay, Carole, et al. Romeo the Romantic Rat. 2000. (Illus.). 30p. (ps-3). pap. (978-1-894363-26-6(4)) Dominique & Friends.

Umansky, Kaye. Three Rapping Rats: Making Music with Traditional Stories. 1998. (gr. 3-6). lib. bdg. 23.40 (978-0-613-90604-3(7)) Tandem Library Bks.

Vecchione, Glen & Worms, Penny. Movie Novel. 2006. (Flushed Away Ser.). (Illus.). 128p. (J). pap. 4.99 (978-0-439-90078-2(6)) Scholastic, Inc.

Velthuijs, Max. Frog & Rat. 2000. (Illus.). 16p. (J). 7.50 (978-0-86264-996-8(X)) Andersen GBR. *Dist:* Independent Pubs. Group.

—Frog & the Stranger. ed. 2006. (Illus.). 32p. (J). 8.99 (***978-1-84270-466-0(4)***) Andersen GBR. *Dist:* Independent Pubs. Group.

—Frog & the Stranger. Iqbal, Gulshan, tr. 2005. (Frog Ser.). (URD, ENG, VIE, CHI & BEN., Illus.). 32p. (J). 13.50 (978-1-84059-190-3(0)) Milet Publishing.

—Frog & the Stranger. 2000. (Frog Ser.). (Illus.). 32p. (J). (BEN, ENG, VIE, CHI & URD.). 13.50 (978-1-84059-187-3(0)); (VIE, ENG, CHI, BEN & URD., 13.50 (978-1-84059-191-0(9)); (ALB & ENG., 13.50 (978-1-84059-186-6(2)); (VIE, CHI, BEN, ENG & URD., 13.50 (978-1-84059-189-7(7)) Milet Publishing.

Walton, Rick. Just Me & 6,000 Rats: A Tale of Conjunctions. Gordon, Mike & Gordon, Carl, illus. 2007. 32p. (J). (ps-3). 15.95 (***978-1-4236-0219-4(6)***) Gibbs Smith, Publisher.

Walton, Rick. The Remarkable Friendship of Mr. Cat & Mr. Rat. McCue, Lisa, illus. 2006. 32p. (J). (ps-3). 14.99 (978-0-399-23899-4(9) , Putnam Juvenile) Penguin Group (USA) Inc.

Wersba, Barbara. Walter: The Story of a Rat. Diamond, Donna, illus. 2005. 64p. (J). (gr. 4-8). 16.95 (978-1-932425-41-3(1) , Lemniscaat) Boyds Mills Pr.

White, E. B. Kleine Stuart. 2000. Tr. of Stuart Little. (GER.). (J). pap. 22.95 (978-3-257-23147-2(4)) Diogenes Verlag AG CHE. *Dist:* Distribooks, Inc.

The Wild, Wild West. 2005. (Illus.). 106p. (J). (978-1-4156-0684-1(6)) Scholastic, Inc.

Willis, Jeanne. Never Too Little to Love. Fearnley, Jan, illus. 2004. 32p. (J). (ps up). 10.99 (978-0-7636-2267-1(2)) Candlewick Pr.

Winthrop, Elizabeth. Red-Hot Rattoons. Lewin, Betsy, illus. 2006. 224p. (J). pap. 6.95 (978-0-8050-7986-9(6)) Holt, Henry & Co.

—The Red-Hot Rattoons. Lewin, Betsy, illus. rev. ed. 2003. 224p. (J). 15.95 (978-0-8050-7229-7(2) , Holt, Henry & Co. Bks. For Young Readers) Holt, Henry & Co.

Zindel, Paul. Rats. 2000. (Untitled Zindel #2 Ser.: Vol. 2). 176p. (gr. 5-9). pap. 4.99 (978-0-7868-1225-7(7)) Disney Pr.

—Rats. unabr. ed. 2000. (YA). pap., stu. ed. 59.99 incl. audio (978-0-7887-4346-7(5) , 41140) Recorded Bks., LLC.

—Rats. 2000. (gr. 5-8). lib. bdg. 13.00 (978-0-613-30103-9(X)) Tandem Library Bks.

RAVENS

Bradley, James V. Ravens & Crows. 2006. (Nature Walk Ser.). (Illus.). 64p. (J). 28.00 (978-0-7910-9115-9(5) , Chelsea Hse.) Facts On File, Inc.

Dewey, Jennifer Owings. Clem: The Story of a Raven. Dewey, Jennifer Owings, illus. 2003. (Illus.). 128p. pap. 10.95 (978-0-8263-3023-9(1)) Univ. of New Mexico Pr.

RAVENS—FICTION

Aiken, Joan. Arabel & Mortimer. Blake, Quentin, illus. 2007. 192p. (J). pap. 5.95 (***978-0-15-206082-4(0)*** , Odyssey Classics) Harcourt Children's Bks.

—Arabel's Raven. Blake, Quentin, illus. 2007. 160p. (J). pap. 5.95 (***978-0-15-206094-7(4)*** , Odyssey Classics) Harcourt Children's Bks.

Alfonsi, Alice. Superstar: Junior Novel. 16th rev. ed. 2006. (That's So Raven Ser.: Vol. 16). (Illus.). 144p. (gr. 3-7). pap. 4.99 (978-0-7868-3836-3(1)) Disney Pr.

Anacker, John. The Raven's Ring Pin. Hill, Connie, ed. 2004. (Illus.). 336p. pap. 12.95 (978-0-7387-0433-3(4)) Llewellyn Pubns.

Anastasio, Dina. How Raven Became Black & Owl Got Its Spots. 2003. (Early Connections Ser.). (J). pap. 33.00 (978-1-4108-1093-9(3)) Benchmark Education Co.

Blaikie, Lynn. Beyond the Northern Lights. 2006. (Illus.). 24p. (J). (ps-k). (***978-1-55005-123-0(7)***) Fitzhenry & Whiteside, Ltd.

Bradman, Tony. Elvis the Squirrel. Finlay, Lizzie, illus. 2006. (Read-It! Chapter Books). 48p. (J). (***978-1-4048-3119-3(3)*** , 1265806) Picture Window Bks.

Brouillet, Chrystine. Le Corbeau. 2003. (Roman Jeunesse Ser.). (FRE.). 96p. (YA). (gr. 4-7). pap. (978-2-89021-132-2(0)) Diffusion du livre Mirabel.

Cotes, Gilles. OGM et Chant de Mais. Begin, Jean-Guy, illus. 2004. (FRE.). 112p. (J). (978-2-89599-002-4(6)) Editions de la Paix CAN. *Dist:* World of Reading, Ltd.

Disney Press Staff & Morris, Kimberly. Dueling Divas. 8th rev. ed. 2005. (That's So Raven Ser.: Vol. 8). (Illus.). 144p. (J). (gr. 3-7). pap. 4.99 (978-0-7868-4685-6(2)) Disney Pr.

Galera Staff. Cuervo y la Raposa (Raven & the Fox) (SPA.). 24p. (J). 9.95 (978-84-246-1601-4(4)) La Galera, S.A. Editorial ESP. *Dist:* AIMS International Bks., Inc.

George, Jean Craighead. Charlie's Raven. 2006. 208p. (YA). (gr. 4). reprint ed. pap. 5.99 (978-0-14-240547-5(7) , Puffin) Penguin Group (USA) Inc.

Hall, Margaret & Jones, Dawn L. Sebastian at the Tower of London. Wenzel, David, illus. 2001. (Suitcase Bear Adventures Ser.). (J). (978-0-9713174-1-3(0) , Bear & Co.) Bear & Co.

Hammerschlag, Carl A. Sika & the Raven. Havill, Juanita, ed. Whitethorne, Baje, Sr., illus. 1999. 32p. (J). (gr. k-5). 16.95 (978-1-889166-23-0(5) , Dr. H Bks.) Turtle Island Pr., Inc.

Kusugak, Michael Arvaarluk. Arctic Stories. Krykorka, Vladyana Langer, illus. 1998. 40p. (J). (gr. k-4). pap. 7.95 (978-1-55037-452-0(4)) Annick Pr., Ltd. CAN. *Dist:* Firefly Bks., Ltd.

—Arctic Stories. 1999. (J). (978-0-606-16482-5(0)) Tandem Library Bks.

Larson, Helen C. Kia Kayanguqau? Larson, Helen C. & Shantz, Joy, illus. 1998. Tr. of Whose Egg is This?. (ESK.). 8p. (J). (gr. k-3). pap. 6.00 (978-1-58084-040-8(X)) Lower Kuskokwim Schl. District.

Osborne, Mary Pope. Haunted Castle on Hallows Eve. Murdocca, Sal, illus. 2003. (Magic Tree House Ser.: No. 30). 128p. (J). (gr. k-3). 11.95 (978-0-375-82521-7(5)); lib. bdg. 13.99 (978-0-375-92521-4(X)) Random Hse. Children's Bks. (Random Hse. Bks. for Young Readers).

Oz School (Santa Fe, N.M.) Staff, contrib. by. Raven's Tale: One Story about Many Ravens. 2002. (Illus.). 24p. (J). (ps-2). 14.95 (978-1-929115-06-8(7)) Azro Pr., Inc.

Stewart, Sharon. Raven Quest. 2005. 320p. (J). (gr. 3-7). per. 15.95 (978-1-57505-894-8(4) , Carolrhoda Bks.) Lerner Publishing Group.

Torres, J. Teen Titans: Raven's Secret. MacKenzie, Kevin, illus. 2005. (Teen Titans Chapter Bks.: No. 4). 64p. (J). 3.99 (978-0-439-69636-4(4)) Scholastic, Inc.

Warbelow, Willy Lou & Warbelow-Tack, Cyndie, illus. The Guffinys Too. 1999. 104p. (J). (gr. 2-6). 19.95 (978-0-9618314-4-8(8)) Warbelow, Willy Lou.

Wolfe, Anne & Hill, Liz. Raven's Blood/Web of Death: Twin Spins #5. 2001. (Twin Spins Ser.: 5). 293p. (YA). pap. 12.95 (978-0-7599-1004-1(9)) Hard Shell Word Factory.

Woodruff, Elvira. Escape from the Tower of London. 2005. 240p. (J). pap. 4.99 (978-0-439-28134-8(2) , Scholastic Paperbacks) Scholastic, Inc.

—The Ravenmaster's Secret. 2003. (Illus.). 240p. (J). pap. 15.95 (978-0-439-28133-1(4)) Scholastic, Inc.

RAYS, ROENTGEN

see X-Rays

RCMP

see Royal Canadian Mounted Police

REACTORS (NUCLEAR PHYSICS)

see Nuclear Reactors

READERS

Here are entered school readers in English. For readers in other languages, use the name of the language with the subdivision Readers, e.g. French Language—Readers.

see also Primers

Level 3, 6 vols. (Fluency Strand Ser.). (YA). 45.00 (978-1-4045-1217-7(9)) Wright Group, The.

Level I, 6 vols. (Wonder WorldTM Ser.). 16p. 29.95 (978-0-7802-1035-6(2)) Wright Group, The.

Aarons, Louis. English Say Hello. 2000. (WordMate Ser.). iv, 194p. (YA). pap., wbk. ed. 49.95 incl. audio (978-1-887447-04-1(0)) WordMate.

Above the Chalkboard: Cursive. 1999. (gr. 2-4). 10.95 (978-0-673-36158-5(6)); (SPA., Illus.). 10.95 (978-0-673-36384-8(8)) Addison-Wesley Educational Pubs., Inc. (Scott Foresman).

Abraham, Philip. Reading Comprehension. 2004. 48p. pap. 6.95 (978-1-4042-8521-7(0)) Rosen Publishing Group, Inc., The.

Abrams, Patricia W. & Myers, Darcy, trs. Ms. V's Vacation. Myers, Darcy, illus. 2002. (Read-To-Me Ser.). (Illus.). 24p. (J). (978-0-7665-1222-1(3)) Abrams, Harry N. , Inc.

Accelerated Reader. 2005. cd-rom (978-1-59455-200-7(2)) Renaissance Learning, Inc.

Accelerated Reader RP Complete Subscription Package. 2004. cd-rom (978-1-59455-165-9(0)) Renaissance Learning, Inc.

Accelerated Reader RP Economy Package. 2004. cd-rom 1299.00 (978-1-59455-161-1(8)) Renaissance Learning, Inc.

Accelerated Reader RP Set Up. 2004. cd-rom 299.00 (978-1-59455-163-5(4)) Renaissance Learning, Inc.

Accelerated Reader RP Starter Package. 2004. cd-rom 499.00 (978-1-59455-162-8(6)) Renaissance Learning, Inc.

Accelerated Reader RP Student Subscription. 2004. cd-rom (978-1-59455-164-2(2)) Renaissance Learning, Inc.

Accelerated Reader RP Student Subscription Renewal. 2004. cd-rom (978-1-59455-166-6(9)) Renaissance Learning, Inc.

Accelerated Reader RP Super Package. 2004. cd-rom 2599.00 (978-1-59455-160-4(X)) Renaissance Learning, Inc.

Accelerated Writer Rating Practice Forms. 2004. pap. 25.00 (978-1-59455-123-9(5)) Renaissance Learning, Inc.

Achieve Now Institute Staff. AIT Band One Anthology. 2004. Vol. 1. pap. 122.85 (978-1-4190-0411-7(5)); Vol. 2. pap. 111.65 (978-1-4190-0412-4(3)) Steck-Vaughn.

—AIT Band Two Anthology. 2004. Vol. 1. pap. 87.15 (978-1-4190-0413-1(1)); Vol. 2. pap. 65.45 (978-1-4190-0414-8(X)) Steck-Vaughn.

—ESR Anthology. 2004. Band 1-2. pap. 48.72 (978-0-7398-9887-1(6)); Band 1-2. pap. 52.36 (978-0-7398-9888-8(4)); Band 3-5. pap. 24.08 (978-0-7398-9889-5(2)); Band 3-5. pap. 21.84 (978-0-7398-9890-1(6)) Steck-Vaughn.

—ESR Student Resource Book. 2004. pap. 8.96 (978-0-7398-9882-6(5)); pap. 7.84 (978-0-7398-9883-3(3)); pap. 9.24 (978-0-7398-9884-0(1)); pap. 9.24 (978-0-7398-9885-7(X)) Steck-Vaughn.

Act It Out with Readers¿ Theater. 2005. 112p. (J). per. 10.99 (978-1-59441-180-9(8) , CD-104096); per. 10.99 (978-1-59441-181-6(6) , CD-104097) Carson-Dellosa Publishing Co., Inc.

ACT Reading Victory Student Textbook. 2nd ed. 2005. per. (978-1-58894-033-9(0)) Cambridge Educational Services, Inc.

Action Defense: MainSails Individual Title Six-Packs. (Sails Literacy Ser.). (gr. 5 up). 37.00 (978-0-7578-8048-3(7)) Rigby Education.

Action Packs: Complete Action Packs Add-to Pack. 492.00 (978-0-7578-8404-7(0)) Rigby Education.

Action Words Board Books 800670, 5. 2005. (J). bds. (978-1-59794-011-5(9)) Environments, Inc.

Activity Worksheets. 2004. (J). spiral bd. 29.95 (978-1-886441-64-4(2)) Zoo-phonics, Inc.

Ada, Alma Flor. Stories for the Telling, Classroom Kit. Escriva, Viví, illus. 2001. (J). (gr. k-3). act. bk. ed., tchr.'s training gde. ed. 615.00 (978-1-58105-149-0(2)) Santillana USA Publishing Co., Inc.

—Stories the Year 'Round: Classroom Kit, Grades K-3. Escriva, Viví, illus. 2001. (J). act. bk. ed., tchr.'s training gde. ed. 1155.95 (978-1-58105-381-4(9)) Santillana USA Publishing Co., Inc.

Ada, Alma Flor & Campoy, F. Isabel. Colecciones de Libros Avanzados. 3rd ed. 2002. (Trofeos Ser.). (SPA.). (gr. 5 up). pap. 1009.20 (978-0-15-334035-2(5)) Harcourt Schl. Pubs.

Ada, Alma Flor & Compoy, F. Isabel. Colecciones de Libros Decodificables: Libro Decodificable. 3rd ed. 2002. (Trofeos Ser.). (SPA.). (gr. 1 up). pap. 28.80 (978-0-15-331774-3(4)); (gr. 1 up). pap. 28.80 (978-0-15-331775-0(2)); (gr. 1 up). pap. 28.80 (978-0-15-331950-1(X)); (gr. 1 up). pap. 28.80 (978-0-15-331951-8(8)); (gr. 1 up). pap. 28.80 (978-0-15-331952-5(6)); (gr. 1 up). pap. 28.80 (978-0-15-331979-2(8)); (gr. 1 up). pap. 28.80 (978-0-15-331980-8(1)); (gr. 1 up). pap. 28.80 (978-0-15-331981-5(X)); (gr. 1 up). pap. 28.80 (978-0-15-331982-2(8)); (gr. 1 up). pap. 28.80 (978-0-15-331983-9(6)); (gr. 1 up). pap. 28.80 (978-0-15-331984-6(4)); (gr. 1 up). pap. 28.80 (978-0-15-331985-3(2)); (gr. 1 up). pap. 28.80 (978-0-15-331986-0(0)); (gr. 1 up). pap. 28.80 (978-0-15-331987-7(9)); (gr. 1 up). pap. 28.80 (978-0-15-331988-4(7)); (gr. 1 up). pap. 28.80 (978-0-15-331989-1(5)); (gr. 1 up). pap. 28.80 (978-0-15-332003-3(6)); (gr. 1 up). pap. 28.80 (978-0-15-332004-0(4)); (gr. 1 up). pap. 28.80 (978-0-15-332008-8(7)); (gr. 1 up). pap. 28.80 (978-0-15-332009-5(5)); (gr. 1 up). pap. 28.80 (978-0-15-332013-2(3)); (gr. 1 up). pap. 28.80 (978-0-15-332014-9(1)); (gr. 1 up). pap. 28.80 (978-0-15-332018-7(4)); (gr. 1 up). pap. 28.80 (978-0-15-332019-4(2)); (gr. 1 up). pap. 28.80 (978-0-15-332023-1(0)); (gr. 1 up). pap. 28.80 (978-0-15-332024-8(9)); (gr. 1 up). pap. 28.80 (978-0-15-332028-6(1)); (gr. 1 up). pap. 28.80 (978-0-15-332029-3(X)); (gr. 1 up). pap. 28.80 (978-0-15-332030-9(3)); (gr. 1 up). pap. 28.80 (978-0-15-332031-6(1)); (gr. 1 up). pap. 28.80 (978-0-15-332032-3(X)); (gr. 1 up). pap. 28.80 (978-0-15-332033-0(8)); (gr. 1 up). pap. 28.80 (978-0-15-332034-7(6)); (gr. 1 up). pap. 28.80 (978-0-15-332038-5(9)); (gr. 2 up). pap. 40.90 (978-0-15-332398-0(1)); (gr. 2 up). pap. 40.90 (978-0-15-332399-7(X)); (gr. 2 up). pap. 40.90 (978-0-15-332401-7(5)); (gr. 2 up). pap. 40.90 (978-0-15-332402-4(3)); (gr. 2 up). pap. 40.90 (978-0-15-332403-1(1)); (gr. 2 up). pap. 40.90 (978-0-15-332404-8(X)); (gr. 2 up). pap. 40.90 (978-0-15-332407-9(4)); (gr. 2 up). pap. 40.90 (978-0-15-332408-6(2)); (gr. 2 up). pap. 40.90 (978-0-15-332409-3(0)); (gr. 2 up). pap. 40.90 (978-0-15-332412-3(0)); (gr. 2 up). pap. 40.90 (978-0-15-332413-0(9)); (gr. 2 up). pap. 40.90 (978-0-15-332414-7(7)); (gr. 2 up). pap. 40.90 (978-0-15-332418-5(X)); (gr. 2 up). pap. 40.90 (978-0-15-332419-2(8)); (gr. 2 up). pap. 40.90 (978-0-15-332421-5(X)); (gr. 2 up). pap. 40.90 (978-0-15-332422-2(8)); (gr. 2 up). pap. 40.90 (978-0-15-332423-9(6)); (gr. 2 up). pap. 40.90 (978-0-15-332424-6(4)); (gr. 2 up). pap. 40.90 (978-0-15-332426-0(0)); (gr. 2 up). pap. 40.90 (978-0-15-332427-7(9)); (gr. 2 up). pap. 40.90 (978-0-15-332521-2(6)); (gr. 2 up). pap. 40.90 (978-0-15-332522-9(4)); (gr. 2 up). pap. 40.90 (978-0-15-332523-6(2)) Harcourt Schl. Pubs.

Adams, Pam, illus. Old Macdonald Storysack. (J). 65.00 (978-0-85953-083-5(3)) Child's Play-International.

—There Was an Old Lady Storysack. (J). 65.00 (978-0-85953-835-0(4)) Child's Play-International.

Add-on Components. (Alphachant Phonics Ser.). (ps-k). 7.85 (978-0-7362-2007-1(0)) Hampton-Brown Bks.

Add-On Literature Set, 5 vols. 2002. (Into English! Ser.). (gr. 4 up). 45.45 (978-1-56334-899-0(3)) Hampton-Brown Bks.

Adding Arctic Animals Math, 6 vols. (gr. k-2). 28.95 (978-0-7368-2990-8(3) , Yellow Umbrella Bks.) Capstone Pr., Inc.

Addison-Wesley Publishing Staff. Et Level 2: The Extraterrestrial. 2002. (Illus.). 48p. (C). pap. 9.00 (978-0-582-51747-9(8)) Pearson ESL.

Adler, David A. Helen Keller. Wallner, John, illus. 32p. (J). 4.95 (978-0-8234-2042-1(6)) Holiday Hse., Inc.

The Alamo Journals. 2003. (Illus.). pap. 7.60 (978-0-7398-7523-0(X)) Steck-Vaughn.

Albom, Mitch. The Five People You Meet in Heaven. 2004. (YA). (gr. 9-12). stu. ed. (978-1-58130-854-9(X)) Novel Units, Inc.

Aldecoa, Josefina. El Enigma. 2005. (SPA., Illus.). 264p. pap. 22.95 (978-84-204-4346-1(8) , Alfaguara) Santillana USA Publishing Co., Inc.

Alexander, Linda. As-Easy-As-ABC-123. 50th ed. 2003. (Illus.). (J). cd-rom (978-0-9714299-2-5(8)) I Save A Tree.

—As-Easy-As-ABC-123 Bilingual. 2003. (SPA., Illus.). (J). cd-rom (978-0-9714299-3-2(6)) I Save A Tree.

Alexander's Enrichment Activties. 2006. (J). pap. 5.95 ***(*978-0-9742806-6-0(6))*** Heart to Heart Publishing.

The Alien, 6 vols., Pack. (gr. 1-2). 25.00 (978-0-7635-9192-2(0)) Rigby Education.

All Across America. (Guided Reading Levels Ser.). 28.56 (978-0-7362-1060-7(1)) Hampton-Brown Bks.

All from a Bottle. (Early Intervention Levels Ser.). 31.86 (978-0-7362-0662-4(0)) Hampton-Brown Bks.

All From a Bottle (28), Vol. 28. (Early Intervention Levels Ser.). 5.31 (978-0-7362-0650-1(7)) Hampton-Brown Bks.

All in the Family. 2005. (Little Celebrations Thematic Packages Ser.). (J). (gr. k-3). 133.50 (978-0-673-75386-1(7)) Celebration Pr.

All Kinds of Babies: Kindergarten Guided Reading Level B. (On Our Way to English Ser.). (gr. k up). 27.75 (978-0-7578-7013-2(9)) Rigby Education.

All Sorts of Things. 2005. (Illus.). (C). (gr. k-1). 90.40 (978-1-4048-1065-5(X)) Picture Window Bks.

Allen, Margaret. Jingle Jangles Vol 2256: Fun, Interactive Reading Selections for Fluency Practice. Walter, LaDawn, ed. Rojas, Mary & Vangsgard, Amy, illus. 2004. 128p. (J). (gr. k-2). pap. 14.99 (978-1-59198-048-3(8) , 2256) Creative Teaching Pr., Inc.

—Pom-Pom's Big Win. 1999. (978-0-606-22755-1(5)) Tandem Library Bks.

Alley, R. W., illus. The Prince's Tooth Is Loose! 2005. (I'm Going to Read Ser.). 28p. (J). (ps-k). pap., pap. 3.95 (978-1-4027-2721-4(6)) Sterling Publishing Co., Inc.

Almy, Judy. My Name Is Ick: A Rhyming Story of an Alaska Caribou. 2005. 9.95 (978-1-59433-009-4(3)) Publication Consultants.

Alvarez, Lourdes M. Things. Brooks, David, illus. 2005. (My First Book Ser.). 9p. (J). (ps-ps). bds. 3.95 (978-1-933050-10-2(1)) Sweetwater Pr.

Amelia Bedilia Book Set 800916, 3 vols. 2005. (J). pap. (978-1-59794-081-8(X)) Environments, Inc.

Amer Ed Pub, ed. More SkillBuilding Act Gr1. 2007. (Skill Building Learning Activities Ser.). 416p. (J). pap. 15.95 ***(*978-0-7696-8441-3(6)*** , American Education Publishing) School Specialty Publishing.

—More SkillBuilding Act GrK. 2007. (Skill Building Learning Activities Ser.). 416p. (J). pap. 15.95 ***(*978-0-7696-8440-6(8)*** , American Education Publishing) School Specialty Publishing.

—More SkillBuilding Act PreK. 2007. (Skill Building Learning Activities Ser.). 416p. (J). pap. 15.95 ***(*978-0-7696-8439-0(4)*** , American Education Publishing) School Specialty Publishing.

—SkillBuilding Activities Gr1. 2007. (Skill Building Learning Activities Ser.). 416p. (J). pap. 15.95 ***(*978-0-7696-8431 4(9)*** , American Education Publishing) School Specialty Publishing.

—SkillBuilding Activities GrK. 2007. (Skill Building Learning Activities Ser.). 416p. (J). pap. 15.95 ***(*978-0-7696-8430-7(0)*** , American Education Publishing) School Specialty Publishing.

—SkillBuilding Activities PreK. 2007. (Skill Building Learning Activities Ser.). 416p. (J). pap. 15.95 ***(*978-0-7696-8429-1(7)*** , American Education Publishing) School Specialty Publishing.

American Heritage Dictionary Editors. What Day Is It? Zagarenski, Pamela, illus. 2005. (Good Beginnings Ser.). 4p. (J). (ps-k). bds. 3.95 (978-0-618-45714-4(3)) Houghton Mifflin Co. Trade & Reference Div.

—Where Am I Hiding? Zagarenski, Pamela, illus. 2005. (Good Beginnings Ser.). 4p. (J). (ps-k). bds. 3.95 (978-0-618-45715-1(1)) Houghton Mifflin Co. Trade & Reference Div.

American Heritage Dictionary Editors, ed. Where Am I Hiding? / ?Donde Me Escondo? Zagarenski, Pamela, illus. 2005. (Good Beginnings/Un Buen Comienzo Ser.). (ENG & SPA.). 4p. (J). (ps-k). bds. 3.95 (978-0-618-51176-1(8)) Houghton Mifflin Co. Trade & Reference Div.

American Heroes Set C, 6 vols. (Phonics Readers Ser.). (gr. k-2). 17.50 (978-0-7368-3205-2(X)) Red Brick Learning.

American Indian Crafts. 2005. (Book Treks Ser.). (J). (gr. 3 up). stu. ed. 34.95 (978-0-673-62838-1(8)) Celebration Pr.

American Journeys: Fourth Grade Class Collection Books. (On Our Way to English Ser.). (gr. 4 up). 29.95 (978-0-7578-4337-2(9)) Rigby Education.

American Journeys: Small Versions of Class Collection Books. (On Our Way to English Ser.). (gr. 4 up). 34.50 (978-0-7578-7265-5(4)) Rigby Education.

American Lives Low Intermediate Student Book. 2005. per. (978-1-56420-435-6(9)) New Readers Pr.

American Symbols, 6 bks. Incl. American Flag. Yanuck, Debbie L. lib. bdg. 18.60 (978-0-7368-1628-1(3)); Bald Eagle. Yanuck, Debbie L. lib. bdg. 23.93 (978-0-7368-1629-8(1)); Liberty Bell. Yanuck, Debbie L. lib. bdg. 18.60 (978-0-7368-1630-4(5)); Pledge of Allegiance. Nobleman, Marc Tyler. lib. bdg. 18.60 (978-0-7368-1631-1(3)); Statue of Liberty. Nobleman, Marc Tyler. lib. bdg. 18.60 (978-0-7368-1632-8(1)); White House. Yanuck, Debbie L. lib. bdg. 18.60 (978-0-7368-1633-5(X)); 24p. (J). (gr. 1-2). (Illus.). 2003. lib. bdg. (978-0-7368-1639-7(9) , Bridgestone Bks.) Capstone Pr., Inc.

The American Tradition: The EMC Write-in Reader. 2nd ed. (Literature & the Language Arts Ser.). (YA). (gr. 11 up). wbk. ed. 17.95 (978-0-8219-2918-6(6)) EMC/Paradigm Publishing.

America's Secret Weapon: The Navajo Code Talkers of World War II. 2005. (Book Treks Ser.). (J). 37.95 (978-0-7652-3246-5(4)) Celebration Pr.

Amery, Heather. Dolly & the Train. Cartwright, Stephen, illus. rev. ed. 1999. 16p. (J). pap. 4.95 (978-0-7945-0649-0(6) , Usborne) EDC Publishing.

—Grumpy Goat. Cartwright, Stephen, illus. 2004. 16p. (J). pap. 5.95 (978-0-7945-0788-6(3) , Usborne) EDC Publishing.

—Market Day. Cartwright, Stephen, illus. 2004. 16p. (J). pap. 5.95 (978-0-7945-0783-1(2) , Usborne) EDC Publishing.

—Runaway Tractor. Cartwright, Stephen, illus. 2004. 16p. (J). pap. 5.95 (978-0-7945-0748-0(4) , Usborne) EDC Publishing.

Amos Fortune Free Man Student Packet, Gr. 5-6. 2004. (J). (978-1-58130-506-7(0)) Novel Units, Inc.

Anastasio, Dina, et al. Apollo 13. 2002. (Illus.). 48p. (C). pap. 9.00 (978-0-582-45184-1(0)) Pearson ESL.

Andersen, Hans Christian & Davidson, Susanna. Princess & Pea. 2004. 48p. (J). (gr. 2 up). 8.99 (978-0-7945-0812-8(X) , Usborne) EDC Publishing.

Andersen, Hans Christian & Sims, Lesley. Snow Queen. 2004. 64p. (J). (gr. 2 up). 8.99 (978-0-7945-0717-6(4) , Usborne) EDC Publishing.

Anderson, Al. Pegasus: Adventures with Bingo Borden. Kurzyca, Krystyna Emilia, illus. 2006. 77p. (J). per. 19.50 ***(*978-1-887250-46-7(8))*** Agora Pubns., Inc.

Anderson, Dianne & Anderson, Ian. Cambridge Checkpoints VCE English 2005. 2004. (Cambridge Checkpoints Ser.). 192p. pap., stu. ed. 11.85 (978-0-521-60841-1(4)) Cambridge Univ. Pr.

Anderson, Neil J. Active Skills for Reading Book 3. 2002. pap. 25.95 (978-0-8384-2611-1(5)) Thomson Heinle.

Anderson, Wendy & Anderson, W. M. Livewire Real Lives Steve Irwin. 2003. (Livewires Ser.). (Illus.). 32p. pap. 4.50 (978-0-521-53839-8(4)) Cambridge Univ. Pr.

Andrews, Becky, ed. Increasing Comprehension. 2005. 80p. 12.95 (978-1-56234-651-5(2) , Mailbox Bks., The) Education Ctr., Inc.

—Literacy for Little Learners Stories & Language Skills. 2004. (Literacy for Little Learners Ser.). (Illus.). 80p. 12.95 (978-1-56234-619-5(9) , Mailbox Bks., The) Education Ctr., Inc.

Animal Parade Books 800790, 4. 2005. (J). bds. (978-1-59794-021-4(6)) Environments, Inc.

Animal Story Board Books 800556, 5. 2005. (J). bds. (978-1-59794-005-4(4)) Environments, Inc.

Animal Tricks. 2004. (J). (978-1-58453-278-1(5)) Pioneer Valley Educational Pr., Inc.

Animal Walk. 2005. (J). (978-1-58453-300-9(5)) Pioneer Valley Educational Pr., Inc.

Animals at School. 2001. (J). (978-1-58453-135-7(5)) Pioneer Valley Educational Pr., Inc.

Animals Live Everywhere. (Early Intervention Levels Ser.). 28.38 (978-0-7362-0412-5(1)) Hampton-Brown Bks.

Animals Live Everywhere (16), Vol. 16. (Early Intervention Levels Ser.). 4.73 (978-0-7362-0237-4(4)) Hampton-Brown Bks.

Ankers, Angela M. Summerbook Readers: Short a & i words, 3. l.t. ed. 2004. (Illus.). 40p. (J). 5.95 (978-1-933055-00-8(6)) Summerbook Co.

Anthony, Ross. Please Don't Step on the Ants. Anthony, Ross, illus. 2006. (ENG, CHI, SPA & JPN.). (J). per. ***(*978-0-9727894-4-8(8))*** Arizona Blueberry Studios.

Antologia: Para leer en voz Alta: Student & Teacher Support Resources. 2003. (MacMillan/McGraw-Hill. Estudios Sociales Ser.). (ENG & SPA.). (gr. 1 up). (978-0-02-149464-4(9)); (gr. 2 up). (978-0-02-149465-1(7)); (gr. 3 up). (978-0-02-149466-8(5)) Macmillan/McGraw-Hill Schl. Div.

The Apple Tree Dilemma: MainSails Individual Title Six-Packs. (Sails Literacy Ser.). (gr. 5 up). 37.00 (978-0-7578-8050-6(9)) Rigby Education.

Apte, Sunita, text. Moving Home. 2005. (Illus.). 16p. ***(*978-0-7367-2954-3(2))*** Zaner-Bloser, Inc.

La arana y el elefante Travieso 21: Leveled Books. 2001. (McGraw-Hill. Lectura Ser.). (ENG & SPA.). (gr. 2 up). (978-0-02-188022-5(0)) Macmillan/McGraw-Hill Schl. Div.

Archer, Anita L., et al. REWARDS Plus: Reading Excellence: Reading Strategies Applied to Science Passages. 2004. (Illus.). 200p. per. (978-1-59318-286-1(4)) Sopris West Educational Services.

La ardilla, el grillo y la Polilla 17: Leveled Books. 2001. (McGraw-Hill. Lectura Ser.). (ENG & SPA.). (gr. 1 up). (978-0-02-187946-5(X)) Macmillan/McGraw-Hill Schl. Div.

Are We There Yet? Second Grade Big Books. (On Our Way to English Ser.). (gr. 2 up). 29.95 (978-0-7578-1415-0(8)) Rigby Education.

Are We There Yet? Small Versions of Big Books. (On Our Way to English Ser.). (gr. 2 up). 29.00 (978-0-7578-7233-4(6)) Rigby Education.

Arengo, Sue. Classic Tales: Classic Tales Activity Books : The Shoemaker & the Elves. 2002. (Illus.). (J). 2.95 (978-0-19-422081-1(8)) Oxford Univ. Pr., Inc.

—Classic Tales: Beginner 1: 100 Headwords: Rumplestiltskin Activity Book. 2005. 16p. pap. 2.95 (978-0-19-422089-7(3)) Oxford Univ. Pr., Inc.

—Classic Tales: Beginner 1: 100 Headwords: the Little Red Hen Activity Book. 2005. (Illus.). 16p. 2.95 (978-0-19-422088-0(5)) Oxford Univ. Pr., Inc.

—The Enormous Turnip. Mumford, Clare & Rees, Gary, illus. 2001. 18p. (978-0-19-422056-9(7)) Oxford Univ. Pr.

—The Gingerbread Man. Gower, Terry & Rees, Gary, illus. 2001. 18p. (J). act. bk. ed. 2.95 (978-0-19-422062-0(1)) Oxford Univ. Pr., Inc.

—Little Red Riding Hood. Kenyon, Tony, illus. 2001. 18p. (J). act. bk. ed. 2.95 (978-0-19-422065-1(6)) Oxford Univ. Pr., Inc.

—Sleeping Beauty Activity Book. Nesbitt, Jan & Rees, Gary, illus. 2001. 18p. (J). 2.95 (978-0-19-422059-0(1)) Oxford Univ. Pr., Inc.

—Snow White & the Seven Dwarfs Activity Book. Rowe, Susan & Rees, Gary, illus. 2001. 18p. (J). 2.95 (978-0-19-422066-8(4)) Oxford Univ. Pr., Inc.

—Three Billy-Goats. Anstey, Caroline & Rees, Gary, illus. 2001. 18p. (J). act. bk. ed. 2.95 (978-0-19-422061-3(3)) Oxford Univ. Pr., Inc.

—The Town Mouse & the County Mouse Activity Book. 2001. (Illus.). (J). 2.95 (978-0-19-422063-7(X)) Oxford Univ. Pr., Inc.

Arengo, Sue, et al. Classic Tales: Classic Tales Activity Books : The Fisherman & his Wife Activity Book. 2003. (Illus.). 2.95 (978-0-19-422082-8(6)) Oxford Univ. Pr., Inc.

—Classic Tales: Classic Tales Activity Books The Ugly Duckling. 2003. (Illus.). 2.95 (978-0-19-422083-5(4)) Oxford Univ. Pr., Inc.

Arnold, Eric. Race into Space. Torrisi, Gary, illus. 2004. (Step into Reading Ser.: Vol. 4). 48p. (J). (gr. 2-4). pap. 3.99 (978-0-375-80195-2(2) , Random Hse. Bks. for Young Readers) Random Hse. Children's Bks.

Arnold Lobel Book Set 800917, 3 vols. 2005. (J). pap. (978-1-59794-082-5(8)) Environments, Inc.

Around the Sun: Fifth Grade Newcomer Books. (On Our Way to English Ser.). (gr. 5 up). 34.50 (978-0-7578-7279-2(4)) Rigby Education.

Arrigan, Mary & Paul, Korky. Pa Jinglebob & the Grabble Gang. 2006. (Red Bananas Ser.). (Illus.). 47p. (J). (978-0-7787-1074-5(2)) Crabtree Publishing Co.

Art Pen Pal. 2003. 31.95 (978-0-673-75796-8(X)) Celebration Pr.

As a Child Grows Revision. 2005. per. 12.00 (978-1-56420-398-4(0)) New Readers Pr.

As Time Goes By: Third Grade Guided Reading Level O. (On Our Way to English Ser.). (gr. 3 up). 34.50 (978-0-7578-7142-9(9)) Rigby Education.

Ashe, Susan & Lawrie, Robin. Cuda of the Celts. 2005. (Yellow Go Bananas Ser.). (Illus.). 48p. (J). pap. (978-0-7787-2742-2(4)) Crabtree Publishing Co.

Askew, Gordon, et al. I-Read Year 1 Anthology: Hometime. 2007. (I-read Ser.). (Illus.). 40p. pap. ***(*978-0-521-70475-5(8))*** Cambridge Univ. Pr.

Assortment. 2003. (Notebook Reference Ser.). 128p. pap. 118.80 (978-1-57768-395-7(1)); (Illus.). 32p. pap. 191.52 (978-1-57768-319-3(6)) School Specialty Publishing.

The Asteroid: Individual Title Six-Packs. 16p. (gr. 2 up). 35.00 (978-0-7635-9388-9(5)) Rigby Education.

Asthma in Action. 2005. (Book Treks Ser.). (J). (gr. 3 up). stu. ed. 34.95 (978-0-673-62843-5(4)) Celebration Pr.

Astronaut Adventure. (Early Intervention Levels Ser.). 21.30 (978-0-7362-0378-4(8)) Hampton-Brown Bks.

At My House: First Grade Guided Reading Level A. (On Our Way to English Ser.). (gr. 1 up). 27.75 (978-0-7578-7028-6(7)) Rigby Education.

At School. 2005. (Look, Listen, & Speak Ser.). 80p. (gr. k-3). cd-rom 29.99 (978-1-55799-926-9(0) , EMC 2739) Evan-Moor Educational Pubs.

At School. (Early Intervention Levels Ser.). 3.85 (978-1-56334-952-2(3)); 23.10 (978-0-7362-0000-4(2)) Hampton-Brown Bks.

At School Set 1. 2004. (J). (978-1-58453-262-0(9)) Pioneer Valley Educational Pr., Inc.

At the Coal Mine. (Rigby Focus Ser.). 24p. (gr. 2 up). 6 Pcks. 28.00 (978-0-7578-5348-7(X)); 6 Pcks. 30.00 (978-0-7578-5578-8(4)) Rigby Education.

At the Fair. (Early Intervention Levels Ser.). 23.10 (978-0-7362-0013-4(4)); Vol. 2. 3.85 (978-1-56334-963-8(9)) Hampton-Brown Bks.

At the Museum. (J). (978-0-8136-5375-4(4)) Modern Curriculum Pr.

At the Ocean. 2000. (J). (978-1-58453-091-6(X)) Pioneer Valley Educational Pr., Inc.

At the Toyshop: Individual Title Six-Packs. (ps-2). 23.00 (978-0-7635-9005-5(3)) Rigby Education.

Atkins, Jill. Toad Swims for his Life! Mostyn, David, illus. 2004. 24p. (J). lib. bdg. 22.65 ***(*978-1-59646-712-5(6))*** Dingles & Co.

ATV Racing, 6 vols. (gr. 4 up). 39.95 (978-0-7368-8963-6(9)) Red Brick Learning.

Auch, Allison. Women Who Dared. 2004. (Navigators Ser.). (J). pap. 42.00 (978-1-4108-0427-3(5)) Benchmark Education Co.

Aunts, 6 vols. (gr. k-2). 28.95 (978-0-7368-8263-7(4)) Red Brick Learning.

Aunty Mo's Kids, 6 Pcks. (Sails Literacy Ser.). (gr. 1-2). 36.00 (978-0-7578-4009-8(4)) Rigby Education.

Authentic Reading Practice. 2001. 288p. (J). Pts. 1-4. (gr. 4-6). pap. 24.99 (978-1-55799-831-6(0) , EMC 3301); Pts. 1-5. (gr. 1-3). pap. 24.99 (978-1-55799-830-9(2) , EMC 3300) Evan-Moor Educational Pubs.

Author's Purpose. 2003. (Test Connection Ser.). 48p. (J). (gr. 2 up). pap. 6.99 (978-0-7424-1862-2(6) , FS99187); (gr. 5 up). pap. 6.99 (978-0-7424-1865-3(0) , FS99190); (gr. 6 up). pap. 6.99 (978-0-7424-1866-0(9) , FS99191) School Specialty Publishing.

Avenues Language & Literacy Tests: Level C Posttest Booklet (10-Pack) 30.00 (978-0-7362-2514-4(5)) Hampton-Brown Bks.

Avenues Language & Literacy Tests: Level D Posttest Booklet (10-Pack) 30.00 (978-0-7362-2516-8(1)) Hampton-Brown Bks.

Avenues Language & Literacy Tests: Level E Posttest Booklet (10-Pack) 30.00 (978-0-7362-2518-2(8)) Hampton-Brown Bks.

Avenues Language & Literacy Tests: Level F Posttest Booklet (10-Pack) 30.00 (978-0-7362-2520-5(X)) Hampton-Brown Bks.

A Avenues Level. (gr. k up). 1185.93 (978-0-7362-2541-0(2)) Hampton-Brown Bks.

A Avenues Level: Little Language Book Set (11 Titles) (Avenues Ser.). (gr. k up). 41.53 (978-0-7362-1790-3(8)) Hampton-Brown Bks.

A Avenues Level: Practice Book. (Avenues Ser.). (gr. k up). 7.60 (978-0-7362-1786-6(X)) Hampton-Brown Bks.

A Avenues Level: Teacher Support Pack. (Avenues Ser.). (gr. k up). 716.47 (978-0-7362-2200-6(6)) Hampton-Brown Bks.

A Avenues Level: Theme Library (10 Titles), 10 vols. (Avenues Ser.). (gr. k up). 143.98 (978-0-7362-2108-5(5)) Hampton-Brown Bks.

Avenues Level B. (gr. 1 up). 921.20 (978-0-7362-2542-7(0)) Hampton-Brown Bks.

Avenues Level B: Leveled Books & ETools. (gr. 1 up). 377.86 (978-0-7362-2535-9(8)) Hampton-Brown Bks.

Avenues Level B: Literature Anthology Set, 2 vols. (Avenues Ser.). (gr. 1 up). 41.20 (978-0-7362-2022-4(4)) Hampton-Brown Bks.

Avenues Level B: Practice Book. (Avenues Ser.). (gr. 1 up). 7.60 (978-0-7362-1835-1(1)) Hampton-Brown Bks.

Avenues Level B: Teacher Support Pack. (Avenues Ser.). (gr. 1 up). 517.25 (978-0-7362-2202-0(2)) Hampton-Brown Bks.

Avenues Level B: Theme Library, 12 vols. (Avenues Ser.). (gr. 1 up). 109.16 (978-0-7362-1842-9(4)) Hampton-Brown Bks.

Avenues Level C: Leveled Books & ETools. (gr. 2 up). 447.46 (978-0-7362-2536-6(6)) Hampton-Brown Bks.

Avenues Level C: Literature Anthology. (Avenues Ser.). (gr. 2 up). 38.77 (978-0-7362-1876-4(9)) Hampton-Brown Bks.

Avenues Level C: Practice Book. (Avenues Ser.). (gr. 2 up). 6.16 (978-0-7362-1884-9(X)) Hampton-Brown Bks.

Avenues Level C: Teacher Support Pack. (Avenues Ser.). (gr. 2 up). 405.33 (978-0-7362-2204-4(9)) Hampton-Brown Bks.

Avenues Level C: Theme Library (12 Titles), 12 vols. (Avenues Ser.). (gr. 2 up). 182.78 (978-0-7362-1891-7(2)) Hampton-Brown Bks.

Avenues Level D. (gr. 3 up). 415.57 (978-0-7362-2544-1(7)) Hampton-Brown Bks.

Avenues Level D: Leveled Books & ETools. (gr. 3 up). 553.30 (978-0-7362-2537-3(4)) Hampton-Brown Bks.

Avenues Level D: Literature Anthology. (Avenues Ser.). (gr. 3 up). 38.77 (978-0-7362-1673-9(1)) Hampton-Brown Bks.

Avenues Level D: Practice Book. (Avenues Ser.). (gr. 3 up). 6.16 (978-0-7362-1678-4(2)) Hampton-Brown Bks.

Avenues Level D: Theme Library (16 Titles), 16 vols. (Avenues Ser.). (gr. 3 up). 231.85 (978-0-7362-1684-5(7)) Hampton-Brown Bks.

Avenues Level E. (gr. 4 up). 415.57 (978-0-7362-2545-8(5)) Hampton-Brown Bks.

Avenues Level E: Leveled Books & ETools. (gr. 4 up). 527.49 (978-0-7362-2538-0(2)) Hampton-Brown Bks.

Avenues Level E: Literature Anthology. (Avenues Ser.). (gr. 4 up). 38.77 (978-0-7362-1709-5(6)) Hampton-Brown Bks.

Avenues Level E: Practice Book. (Avenues Ser.). (gr. 4 up). 6.16 (978-0-7362-1714-9(2)) Hampton-Brown Bks.

Avenues Level E: Theme Library (16 Titles), 16 vols. (Avenues Ser.). (gr. 4 up). 186.23 (978-0-7362-1720-0(7)) Hampton-Brown Bks.

Avenues Level F. (gr. 5 up). 415.57 (978-0-7362-2546-5(3)) Hampton-Brown Bks.

Avenues Level F: Leveled Books & ETools. (gr. 5 up). 574.52 (978-0-7362-2539-7(0)) Hampton-Brown Bks.

Avenues Level F: Literature Anthology. (Avenues Ser.). (gr. 5 up). 38.77 (978-0-7362-1745-3(2)) Hampton-Brown Bks.

Avenues Level F: Practice Book. (Avenues Ser.). (gr. 5 up). 6.16 (978-0-7362-1750-7(9)) Hampton-Brown Bks.

Avenues Level F: Theme Library (16 Titles), 16 vols. (Avenues Ser.). (gr. 5 up). 220.14 (978-0-7362-1756-9(8)) Hampton-Brown Bks.

Avenues PreK Level. 388.57 (978-0-7362-2469-7(6)) Hampton-Brown Bks.

Avenues Unit Progress Tests: Level A Progress Test Booklets (10-Pack) (gr. k up). 40.00 (978-0-7362-2227-3(8)) Hampton-Brown Bks.

Avenues Unit Progress Tests: Level B Progress Test Booklets (10-Pack) (gr. 1 up). 60.00 (978-0-7362-2230-3(8)) Hampton-Brown Bks.

Avenues Unit Progress Tests: Level C Progress Test Booklets - Advanced (10-Pack) (gr. 2 up). 80.00 (978-0-7362-2241-9(3)) Hampton-Brown Bks.

P Q R

Avenues Unit Progress Tests: Level C Progress Test Booklets - Beginning (10-Pack) (gr. 2 up). 80.00 (978-0-7362-2235-8(9)) Hampton-Brown Bks.

Avenues Unit Progress Tests: Level C Progress Test Booklets - Intermediate (10-Pack) (gr. 2 up). 80.00 (978-0-7362-2238-9(3)) Hampton-Brown Bks.

Avenues Unit Progress Tests: Level D Progress Test Booklets - Advanced (10-Pack) (gr. 3 up). 80.00 (978-0-7362-2252-5(9)) Hampton-Brown Bks.

Avenues Unit Progress Tests: Level D Progress Test Booklets - Beginning (10-Pack) (gr. 3 up). 80.00 (978-0-7362-2246-4(4)) Hampton-Brown Bks.

Avenues Unit Progress Tests: Level D Progress Test Booklets - Intermediate (10-Pack) (gr. 3 up). 80.00 (978-0-7362-2249-5(9)) Hampton-Brown Bks.

Avenues Unit Progress Tests: Level E Progress Test Booklets - Advanced (10-Pack) (gr. 4 up). 80.00 (978-0-7362-2263-1(4)) Hampton-Brown Bks.

Avenues Unit Progress Tests: Level E Progress Test Booklets - Beginning (10-Pack) (gr. 4 up). 80.00 (978-0-7362-2257-0(X)) Hampton-Brown Bks.

Avenues Unit Progress Tests: Level E Progress Test Booklets - Intermediate (10-Pack) (gr. 4 up). 80.00 (978-0-7362-2260-0(X)) Hampton-Brown Bks.

Avenues Unit Progress Tests: Level F Progress Test Booklets - Advanced (10-Pack) (gr. 5 up). 80.00 (978-0-7362-2284-6(7)) Hampton-Brown Bks.

Avenues Unit Progress Tests: Level F Progress Test Booklets - Beginning (10-Pack) (gr. 5 up). 80.00 (978-0-7362-2278-5(2)) Hampton-Brown Bks.

Avenues Unit Progress Tests: Level F Progress Test Booklets - Intermediate (10-Pack) (gr. 5 up). 80.00 (978-0-7362-2281-5(2)) Hampton-Brown Bks.

Avi Author Reading Tape. 2000. (J). pap. (978-0-380-29960-7(7) , Harper Trophy) HarperCollins Pubs.

Away from Home: Fourth Grade Guided Comprehension Level M. (On Our Way to English Ser.). (gr. 4 up). 34.50 (978-0-7578-7155-9(0)) Rigby Education.

Ayu & the Perfect Moon. (Lexile Levels Ser.). 7.98 (978-1-56334-691-0(5)); 47.88 (978-0-7362-2166-5(2)) Hampton-Brown Bks.

Babies: Kindergarten Newcomer Books. (On Our Way to English Ser.). (gr. k up). 23.50 (978-0-7578-7197-9(6)) Rigby Education.

Baby Animals Board Books 800849, 4 vols. 2005. (J). bds. (978-1-59794-050-4(X)) Environments, Inc.

A Baby Animals Set, 6 vols. (Phonics Readers Ser.). (gr. k-2). 17.50 (978-0-7368-3188-8(6)) Red Brick Learning.

Baby Bear's Toys, Vol. 2. (Early Intervention Levels Ser.). 3.55 (978-0-7362-0082-0(7)) Hampton-Brown Bks.

Baby Faces Board Books 800669, 5. 2005. (J). bds. (978-1-59794-010-8(0)) Environments, Inc.

Baby Love Board Book Set 800703, 4. 2005. (J). bds. (978-1-59794-012-2(7)) Environments, Inc.

Baby Play Board Book Set 800807, 2. 2005. (J). bds. (978-1-59794-044-3(5)) Environments, Inc.

Baby's Birthday: Individual Title Six-Packs. (Literatura 2000 Ser.). (gr. k-1). 28.00 (978-0-7635-0021-4(6)) Rigby Education.

Baby's World Board Books 800848, 4. 2005. (J). bds. (978-1-59794-049-8(6)) Environments, Inc.

Back & Forth, 6 vols. (gr. k-2). 28.95 (978-0-7368-8613-0(3)) Red Brick Learning.

The Bake Sale Battle: Fourth Grade Guided Comprehension Level Q. (On Our Way to English Ser.). (gr. 4 up). 34.50 (978-0-7578-7176-4(3)) Rigby Education.

Baker, Sandy. Reading DoodleLoops. 2007. (DoodleLoops Ser.). 48p. (C). pap. 7.99 (*978-0-7682-3349-0(6) , Schaffer, Frank) Schaffer, Frank Pubns.

—Word Family DoodleLoops. 2007. (DoodleLoops Ser.). 48p. (C). pap. 7.99 (*978-0-7682-3369-8(0) , Schaffer, Frank) Schaffer, Frank Pubns.

—Writing DoodleLoops. 2007. (DoodleLoops Ser.). 48p. pap. 7.99 (*978-0-7682-3359-9(3) , Schaffer, Frank) Schaffer, Frank Pubns.

Balderstone, Rachel. What Am I? Big Book. 2000. (Cambridge Reading Ser.). (Illus.). 8p. pap. 20.00 (978-0-521-80574-2(0)) Cambridge Univ. Pr.

Baldwin, James. Old Greek Stories. 2005. 192p. pap. 11.95 (978-1-4218-0155-1(8) , 1st World Library - Literary Society) 1st World Publishing, Inc.

—Old Greek Stories. 2004. reprint ed. pap. 19.95 (978-1-4191-3803-4(0)); pap. 1.99 (978-1-4192-3803-1(5)) Kessinger Publishing, LLC.

Baldwin, James. Old Greek Stories (Illustrated Edition) 2006. pap. (*978-1-4065-0511-5(0)) Dodo Pr.

La ballena de Lucia 16: Leveled Books. 2001. (McGraw-Hill. Lectura Ser.). (ENG & SPA.). (gr. 3 up). (978-0-02-188113-0(8)) Macmillan/McGraw-Hill Schl. Div.

Ballooning Adventures, 6 vols. (gr. 4 up). 39.95 (978-0-7368-9028-1(9)) Red Brick Learning.

Bananas on My Table: Kindergarten Guided Reading Level B. (On Our Way to English Ser.). (gr. k up). 27.75 (978-0-7578-7015-6(5)) Rigby Education.

Bantick, Christopher. The Inheritors. 2002. (Wizard Study Guides Ser.). 48p. pap., stu. ed. 6.00 (978-1-875739-13-4(0)) Cambridge Univ. Pr.

Barber, Antonia. The Cape of Rushes. 2005. (Cambridge Storybooks Ser.). 32p. pap. 7.00 (978-0-521-67486-7(7)) Cambridge Univ. Pr.

Barbour Publishing, compiled by. What's an Alpha-Beta-Soupa? An Indispensable Guide to College. 2005. 192p. pap. 4.97 (978-1-59310-664-5(5)) Barbour Publishing, Inc.

Barclay Family Adventures Resource Guide. 2003. (Barclay Family Adventure Ser.). 48p. (YA). tchr. ed., per. 9.95 (978-1-56254-560-4(4) , SP 5604) Saddleback Educational Publishing.

Barge Cat: Second Grade Big Books. (On Our Way to English Ser.). (gr. 2 up). 29.95 (978-0-7578-1423-5(9)) Rigby Education.

Barge Cat: Small Versions of Big Books. (On Our Way to English Ser.). (gr. 2 up). 29.00 (978-0-7578-7234-1(4)) Rigby Education.

Barnyard Board Book Set 800784, 5. 2005. (J). bds. (978-1-59794-019-1(4)) Environments, Inc.

Barr, Linda. Captured. 2004. 64p. (YA). per. 3.95 (978-1-56254-816-2(6) , SP8166) Saddleback Educational Publishing.

—Long Road to Freedom: Journey of the Hmong, 6 vols. (gr. 4 up). 49.95 (978-0-7368-3870-2(8) , High Five) Red Brick Learning.

Barrett. Lethal Delivery, Postage Prepaid. (Thumbprint Mysteries Ser.). 32.86 (978-0-8092-0425-0(8)) McGraw-Hill/Contemporary.

Baruffi, Andrea, illus. If I Had a Robot Dog. 2005. (I'm Going to Read Ser.). 32p. (J). (ps-ps). 11.95 (978-1-4027-3026-9(8)) Sterling Publishing Co., Inc.

Basic Book Set 800082, 20 vols. 2005. (J). bds. (978-1-59794-000-9(3)) Environments, Inc.

Bassett, Jennifer. One-Way Ticket Level 1: Short Stories. 2nd ed. 2000. (Bookworms Ser.). (Illus.). 64p. 6.50 (978-0-19-422950-0(5)) Oxford Univ. Pr., Inc.

Bates, Dianne. Pobblebonk Reading 4. 4 Blowflies & Glow Worms. 2008. pap. (*978-0-521-71067-1(7)) Cambridge Univ. Pr.

—Pobblebonk Reading 4. 8 Your Teeth. 2008. pap. (*978-0-521-71068-8(5)) Cambridge Univ. Pr.

—Pobblebonk Reading 5. 5 Whales. 2008. pap. (*978-0-521-71069-5(3)) Cambridge Univ. Pr.

—Pobblebonk Reading 5. 9 Skin & Bones. 2008. pap. (*978-0-521-71070-1(7)) Cambridge Univ. Pr.

—Pobblebonk Reading 6. 8 Zoo Animals. 2008. pap. (*978-0-521-71071-8(5)) Cambridge Univ. Pr.

Bathroom Readers' Institute Staff. Uncle John's under the Slimy Sea Bathroom Reader for Kids Only. 2007. (Illus.). 144p. pap. 8.95 (*978-1-59223-711-1(8) , Portable Pr.) Advantage Pubs. Group.

Bat's Band, Vol. 4. (Early Intervention Levels Ser.). 3.55 (978-0-7362-0163-6(7)) Hampton-Brown Bks.

Bauer, Andrea. De las Cenizas del Antiguo Siglo Esta Naciendo un Mundo Mejor. 2001. (Red Banner Reader Ser.).Tr. of From the Ashes of the Old Century, a Better World's in Birth. (SPA.). 68p. 4.00 (978-0-932323-10-1(3)) Red Letter Pr.

Bauer, Marion. Rain. Wallace, John, illus. 2005. (Ready-to-Read Ser. Level 1). 32p. (J). lib. bdg. 15.00 (978-1-59054-933-9(3)) Fitzgerald Bks.

BBB Bats Song. (Song Box(R) Ser.). (gr. 1-2). 8.50 incl. audio (978-0-322-00247-0(8)); Set. 68.95 (978-0-322-00273-9(7)) Wright Group, The.

BBB Bats Song Big Book. (Song Box(R) Ser.). (gr. 1-2). 31.50 (978-0-322-00264-7(8)) Wright Group, The.

BBB Bats Song Small Books Pack of 6, 6 vols. (Song Box(R) Ser.). (gr. 1-2). 29.50 (978-0-322-00269-2(9)) Wright Group, The.

Beake, Lesley. One Dark, Dark Night. Dube, Grace, tr. 1999. (Cambridge African Language Library Ser.). (NDE., Illus.). 16p. pap. 3.70 (978-0-521-65807-2(1)) Cambridge Univ. Pr.

—One Dark, Dark Night: Lunda Version. 1998. (Cambridge African Language Library). (Illus.). 16p. pap. 3.70 (978-0-521-63840-1(2)) Cambridge Univ. Pr.

—One Dark, Dark Night: Silozi Version. Silumesii, Penelope, tr. 1998. (Cambridge African Language Library Ser.). (Illus.). 16p. pap. 3.70 (978-0-521-63810-4(0)) Cambridge Univ. Pr.

Beake, Lesley, et al. One Dark, Dark Night: Luganda Version. Lubega, Bonnie, tr. 1998. (Cambridge African Language Library Ser.). (LUG., Illus.). 16p. pap. 3.65 (978-0-521-63793-0(7)) Cambridge Univ. Pr.

—One Dark, Dark Night: Shona Version. Chateuka, Keresia, tr. 1999. (Cambridge African Language Library). (SHO., Illus.). 16p. pap. 3.70 (978-0-521-65814-0(4)) Cambridge Univ. Pr.

Beals, Jane & Beals, Graeme. Final Consonant Sounds Vol. 3: Phonics in Action Series, 4 vols. 2001. 56p. pap. 6.95 (978-1-58324-096-0(9) , World Teachers Pr.) Didax Educational Resources, Inc.

Bear Story Board Books 800655, 5. 2005. (J). bds. (978-1-59794-007-8(0)) Environments, Inc.

A Bear's Year Set C, 6 vols. (Phonics Readers Ser.). (gr. k-2). 17.50 (978-0-7368-3200-7(9)) Red Brick Learning.

Because I'm Little, 6 Packs. (ps-2). 23.00 (978-0-7635-8798-7(2)) Rigby Education.

Beck, Isabel L., et al. Decodable Books Collections. (Trophies Ser.). 2003. (gr. 1 up). 15.60 (978-0-15-326715-4(1)); 2003. (gr. 1 up). 15.60 (978-0-15-326716-1(X)); 2003. (gr. 1 up). 15.60 (978-0-15-326717-8(8)); 2003. (gr. 1 up). 15.60 (978-0-15-326718-5(6)); 2003. (gr. 1 up). 15.60 (978-0-15-326719-2(4)); 2003. (gr. 1 up). 15.60 (978-0-15-326720-8(8)); 2003. (gr. 1 up). 15.60 (978-0-15-326721-5(6)); 2003. (gr. 1 up). 15.60 (978-0-15-326722-2(4)); 2003. (gr. 1 up). 15.60 (978-0-15-326723-9(2)); 2003. (gr. 1 up). 15.60 (978-0-15-326724-6(0)); 2003. (gr. 1 up). 15.60 (978-0-15-326726-0(7)); 2003. (gr. 1 up). 15.60 (978-0-15-326728-4(3)); 2003. (gr. 1 up). 15.60 (978-0-15-326731-4(3)); 2003. (gr. 1 up). 15.60 (978-0-15-326734-5(8)); 2003. (gr. 1 up). 15.60 (978-0-15-326735-2(6)); 2003. (gr. 1 up). 15.60 (978-0-15-326736-9(4)); 2003. (gr. 1 up). 15.60 (978-0-15-326737-6(2)); 2003. (gr. 1 up). 15.60 (978-0-15-327353-7(4)); 2003. (gr. 1 up). 15.60 (978-0-15-326740-6(2)); 2003. (gr. 1 up). 15.60 (978-0-15-326742-0(9)); 2003. (gr. 1 up). 15.60 (978-0-15-326743-7(7)); 2003. (gr. 1 up). 15.60 (978-0-15-326745-1(3)); 2003. (gr. 1 up). 15.60 (978-0-15-326746-8(1)); 2003. (gr. 1 up). 15.60 (978-0-15-326747-5(X)); 2003. (gr. 2 up). 18.40 (978-0-15-326773-4(9)); 2003. (gr. 2 up). 18.40 (978-0-15-326774-1(7)); 2003. (gr. 2 up). 18.40 (978-0-15-326778-9(X)); 3rd ed. 2002. (gr. 1 up). pap. 31.90 (978-0-15-326725-3(9)); 3rd ed. 2002. (gr. 1 up). pap. 31.90 (978-0-15-326727-7(5)); 3rd ed. 2002. (gr. 1 up). pap. 31.90 (978-0-15-326729-1(1)); 3rd ed. 2002. (gr. 1 up). pap. 41.30 (978-0-15-326730-7(5)); 3rd ed. 2002. (gr. 1 up). pap. 31.90 (978-0-15-326732-1(1)); 3rd ed. 2002. (gr. 1 up). pap. 41.30 (978-0-15-326733-8(X)); 3rd ed. 2002. (gr. 1 up). pap. 31.90 (978-0-15-326738-3(0)); 3rd ed. 2002. (gr. 1 up). pap. 31.90 (978-0-15-326739-0(9)); 3rd ed. 2002. (gr. 1 up). pap. 31.90 (978-0-15-326741-3(0)); 3rd ed. 2002. (gr. 1 up). pap. 31.90 (978-0-15-326744-4(5)); 3rd ed. 2002. (gr. 2 up). pap. 34.90 (978-0-15-326769-7(0)); 3rd ed. 2002. (gr. 2 up). pap. 34.90 (978-0-15-326770-3(4)); 3rd ed. 2002. (gr. 2 up). pap. 34.90 (978-0-15-326771-0(2)); 3rd ed. 2002. (gr. 2 up). pap. 34.90 (978-0-15-326772-7(0)); 3rd ed. 2002. (gr. 2 up). pap. 46.20 (978-0-15-326775-8(5)); 3rd ed. 2002. (gr. 2 up). pap. 34.90 (978-0-15-326776-5(3)); 3rd ed. 2002. (gr. 2 up). pap. 46.20 (978-0-15-326777-2(1)); 3rd ed. 2002. (gr. 2 up). pap. 46.20 (978-0-15-326779-6(8)); 3rd ed. 2002. (gr. 2 up). pap. 34.90 (978-0-15-326780-2(1)); 3rd ed. 2002. (gr. 2 up). pap. 34.90 (978-0-15-326781-9(X)); 3rd ed. 2002. (gr. 2 up). pap. 34.90 (978-0-15-326782-6(8)); 3rd ed. 2002. (gr. 2 up). pap. 34.90 (978-0-15-326783-3(6)); 3rd ed. 2002. (gr. 2 up). pap. 34.90 (978-0-15-326784-0(4)); 3rd ed. 2002. (gr. 2 up). pap. 34.90 (978-0-15-326785-7(2)); 3rd ed. 2002. (gr. 2 up). pap. 34.90 (978-0-15-326786-4(0)); 3rd ed. 2002. (gr. 2 up). pap. 34.90 (978-0-15-326787-1(9)); 3rd ed. 2002. (gr. 2 up). pap. 34.90 (978-0-15-326788-8(7)) Harcourt Schl. Pubs.

—Decodable Books Collections: Take-Home Versions, 2 vols. 3rd ed. 2002. (Trophies Ser.). (gr. 1 up). pap. 103.80 (978-0-15-326714-7(3)); (gr. 2 up). pap. 103.80 (978-0-15-326768-0(2)) Harcourt Schl. Pubs.

Beckerman, Menucha. Welcome Home. (My Little World Ser.: Vol. 6). (Illus.). 34p. (J). (gr. k-5). 4.95 (978-1-931681-11-7(2)) Israel Bk. Shop.

Beckwith, Carrie, et al. Reading Detective' Beginning: Using Higher-Order Thinking to Improve Reading Comprehension. 2005. (J). (gr. 3-4). pap. 23.99 (978-0-89455-769-9(6)) Critical Thinking Bks. & Software.

Becky, Andrews, ed. Increasing Comprehension. 2005. 80p. 12.95 (978-1-56234-652-2(0) , Mailbox Bks., The) Education Ctr., Inc.

Bednarz, Robert, et al. TIME for Kids Readers: Across the Wide Oceans. 3rd ed. 2002. (Harcourt Horizons Ser.). (gr. k-7). pap. 38.10 (978-0-15-335277-5(9)) Harcourt Schl. Pubs.

—TIME for Kids Readers: Atlanta. 3rd ed. 2002. (Harcourt Horizons Ser.). (gr. k-7). pap. 38.10 (978-0-15-335268-3(X)) Harcourt Schl. Pubs.

—TIME for Kids Readers: Carrie Chapman Catt. 3rd ed. 2002. (Harcourt Horizons Ser.). (gr. k-7). pap. 38.10 (978-0-15-335264-5(7)) Harcourt Schl. Pubs.

—TIME for Kids Readers: Charles Town, Charleston. 3rd ed. 2002. (Harcourt Horizons Ser.). (gr. k-7). pap. 38.10 (978-0-15-335274-4(4)) Harcourt Schl. Pubs.

—TIME for Kids Readers: Eleanor Roosevelt. 3rd ed. 2002. (Harcourt Horizons Ser.). (gr. k-7). pap. 38.10 (978-0-15-335293-5(0)) Harcourt Schl. Pubs.

—TIME for Kids Readers: From Silents to Talkies. 3rd ed. 2002. (Harcourt Horizons Ser.). (gr. k-7). pap. 38.10 (978-0-15-335296-6(5)) Harcourt Schl. Pubs.

—TIME for Kids Readers: Malcolm X. 3rd ed. 2002. (Harcourt Horizons Ser.). (gr. k-7). pap. 38.10 (978-0-15-335307-9(4)) Harcourt Schl. Pubs.

—TIME for Kids Readers: Omaha Beach, Normandy. 3rd ed. 2002. (Harcourt Horizons Ser.). (gr. k-7). pap. 38.10 (978-0-15-335303-1(1)) Harcourt Schl. Pubs.

—TIME for Kids Readers: On the Home Front. 3rd ed. 2002. (Harcourt Horizons Ser.). (gr. k-7). pap. 38.10 (978-0-15-335301-7(5)) Harcourt Schl. Pubs.

—TIME for Kids Readers: Robert E. Lee. 3rd ed. 2002. (Harcourt Horizons Ser.). (gr. k-7). pap. 38.10 (978-0-15-335279-9(5)) Harcourt Schl. Pubs.

—TIME for Kids Readers: Talking in Code. 3rd ed. 2002. (Harcourt Horizons Ser.). (gr. k-7). pap. 38.10 (978-0-15-335305-5(8)) Harcourt Schl. Pubs.

—TIME for Kids Readers: The Big Crash. 3rd ed. 2002. (Harcourt Horizons Ser.). (gr. k-7). pap. 38.10 (978-0-15-335298-0(1)) Harcourt Schl. Pubs.

—TIME for Kids Readers: The Genius of Menlo Park. 3rd ed. 2002. (Harcourt Horizons Ser.). (gr. k-7). pap. 38.10 (978-0-15-335283-6(3)) Harcourt Schl. Pubs.

—TIME for Kids Readers: The Last Voyage of the Lusitania. 3rd ed. 2002. (Harcourt Horizons Ser.). (gr. k-7). pap. 38.10 (978-0-15-335288-1(4)) Harcourt Schl. Pubs.

—TIME for Kids Readers: The Long Road to Statehood. 3rd ed. 2002. (Harcourt Horizons Ser.). (gr. k-7). pap. 38.10 (978-0-15-335291-1(4)) Harcourt Schl. Pubs.

—TIME for Kids Readers: U. S. Highways. 3rd ed. 2002. (Harcourt Horizons Ser.). (gr. k-7). pap. 38.10 (978-0-15-335309-3(0)) Harcourt Schl. Pubs.

—TIME for Kids Readers: Walter Reed. 3rd ed. 2002. (Harcourt Horizons Ser.). (gr. k-7). pap. 38.10 (978-0-15-335286-7(8)) Harcourt Schl. Pubs.

—TIME for Kids Readers: Welcome to the Space Age. 3rd ed. 2002. (Harcourt Horizons Ser.). (gr. k-7). pap. 38.10 (978-0-15-335313-0(9)) Harcourt Schl. Pubs.

—TIME for Kids Readers: What Happened at Little Bighorn? 3rd ed. 2002. (Harcourt Horizons Ser.). (gr. k-7). pap. 38.10 (978-0-15-335281-2(7)) Harcourt Schl. Pubs.

—TIME for Kids Readers: World Landmarks. 3rd ed. 2002. (Harcourt Horizons Ser.). (gr. 2 up). pap. 19.40 (978-0-15-333215-9(8)) Harcourt Schl. Pubs.

Beebe, Katherine & Kingsley, Nellie F. The First Year Nature Reader. 2004. reprint ed. pap. 21.95 (978-1-4191-3072-4(2)) Kessinger Publishing, LLC.

Beech, Linda Ward. Compare & Contrast. 2005. (Reading Passages That Build Comprehension Ser.). 48p. pap. 10.99 (978-0-439-55427-5(6) , Teaching Resources) Scholastic, Inc.

—Context Clues. 2005. (Reading Passages That Build Comprehension Ser.). 48p. pap. 10.99 (978-0-439-55426-8(8) , Teaching Resources) Scholastic, Inc.

—Fact & Opinion. 2005. (Reading Passages That Build Comprehension Ser.). 48p. pap. 10.99 (978-0-439-55422-0(5) , Teaching Resources) Scholastic, Inc.

—Inference. 2005. (Reading Passages That Build Comprehensio Ser.). 48p. pap. 10.99 (978-0-439-55424-4(1) , Teaching Resources) Scholastic, Inc.

—Main Idea & Details. 2005. (Reading Passages That Build Comprehension Ser.). 48p. pap. 10.99 (978-0-439-55425-1(X) , Teaching Resources) Scholastic, Inc.

—Predicting. 2005. (Reading Passages That Build Comprehensio Ser.). 48p. pap. 10.99 (978-0-439-55423-7(3) , Teaching Resources) Scholastic, Inc.

—Short Passages/Graphic Organizers/Comprehension. 2001. (Illus.). 48p. pap. 8.95 (978-0-439-16358-3(7) , Teaching Resources) Scholastic, Inc.

Being Kind to Naomi: Social/Emotional Lap Book. (Pebble Soup Explorations Ser.). (ps up). 16.00 (978-0-7635-7567-0(4)) Rigby Education.

Belcher, Angie. Storyteller Chapter Books: Fluency - 1 Each of 1 Title: Level T. 6.50 (978-0-7699-1070-3(X)) Shortland Pubns. (U. S. A.) Inc.

Belgue, Nancy. Casey Little: Yo-Yo Queen. 2005. (Orca Young Readers Ser.). (Illus.). 144p. (J). (gr. 3-6). pap. 5.95 (978-1-55143-357-8(5)) Orca Bk. Pubs. USA.

Bell, Mary. The Long Ride. 2000. 250p. otabind 10.95 (978-0-9653572-2-7(8)) Dry Store Publishing Co., The.

Bella & Rosie Chapter Set 1. 2005. (J). (978-1-932570-48-9(9)) Literacy Footprints Inc.

Bella & Rosie Play Hide & Seek. 2003. (J). (978-1-932570-11-3(X)) Literacy Footprints Inc.

Bella & Rosie Set 1. 2003. (J). (978-1-932570-08-3(X)) Literacy Footprints Inc.

Bella Is a Bad Dog. 2003. (J). (978-1-932570-14-4(4)) Literacy Footprints Inc.

Bella's Birthday. 2003. (J). (978-1-932570-09-0(8)) Literacy Footprints Inc.

Ben Franklin: Third Grade Guided Reading Level N. (On Our Way to English Ser.). (gr. 3 up). 34.50 (978-0-7578-7139-9(9)) Rigby Education.

Ben Nighthorse Campbell, Senador Y Artista. 2003. (Notas Biograficas Ser.). pap. 48.95 (978-0-8136-5913-8(2)) Modern Curriculum Pr.

Benchmark Education Staff. Spanish/English Emergent Supplement. 2005. 260.00 (*978-1-4108-5616-6(X)); (J). spiral bd. 1685.00 (*978-1-4108-5614-2(3)) Benchmark Education Co.

Benchmark Education Staff, compiled by. Fluency Kits for Independent Practice. 2005. spiral bd. 3345.00 (*978-1-4108-5380-6(2)); spiral bd. 4150.00 (*978-1-4108-6219-8(4)) Benchmark Education Co.

—Reading First Bookroom COLL. 2005. spiral bd. 11275.00 (*978-1-4108-4157-5(X)) Benchmark Education Co.

—Spanish/English Early/Fluent Supplement. 2005. spiral bd. 2650.00 (*978-1-4108-5662-3(3)) Benchmark Education Co.

Benita's Plan: Fourth Grade Guided Comprehension Level M. (On Our Way to English Ser.). (gr. 4 up). 34.50 (978-0-7578-7159-7(3)) Rigby Education.

Benjamin, Ruth. My Little Pony: Very Lucky Ponies. Fletcher, Lyn, illus. 2008. (I Can Read Bks.). 24p. (J). pap. 3.99 (*978-0-06-122836-0(2) , Harper Trophy) HarperCollins Pubs.

—A Secret Gift. Middleton, Gayle, illus. 2006. (I Can Read Bks.). 24p. (J). pap. 3.99 (978-0-06-079474-3(7) , Harper Trophy) HarperCollins Pubs.

—Sleepover Surprise. Yee, Josie, illus. 2006. (I Can Read Bks.). 24p. (J). pap. 3.99 (978-0-06-079469-9(0) , Harper Trophy) HarperCollins Pubs.

Benkamoun, Sophie & McRoberts, Richard. The Shipping News. 2002. (Wizard Study Guides Ser.). 64p. pap., stu. ed. 6.00 (978-1-875739-57-8(2)) Cambridge Univ. Pr.

Bennet, Elizabeth. Ballet: A Dancer's Diary. 2007. 32p. (J). (gr. 1). pap. 6.99 (*978-1-58476-631-5(X) , IKIDS) Innovative Kids.

Bennett, Leonie. Locket Out. Adams, Arlene, illus. 2004. 24p. (J). lib. bdg. 22.65 (*978-1-59646-688-3(X)) Dingles & Co.

—No Problem! Brown, Judy, illus. 2004. 16p. (J). lib. bdg. 22.65 (*978-1-59646-680-7(4)) Dingles & Co.

Ben's Bike, 6 Packs. (Sails Literacy Ser.). (gr. 1-2). 36.00 (978-0-7578-4007-4(8)) Rigby Education.

Berger, Melvin. Discovery Readers, 13 vols. 1999. (Illus.). (ps-12). 191.40 (978-0-7910-5075-0(0) , Chelsea Hse.) Facts On File, Inc.

Bergeron Bijak Staff. Skill Review Practice & Evaluation. 5th ed. 1999. (C). (978-0-8359-5399-3(8)) Globe Fearon Educational Publishing.

Berres, et al. Sea Hunt. Date not set. (J). (978-0-89064-249-8(4)) National Assn. for Visually Handicapped.

Best-Loved Stories. (Illus.). 40p. (J). bds. 7.98 (978-0-7853-4867-2(0) , 7130900) Publications International, Ltd.

Betsy Ross. (Lexile Levels Ser.). 9.09 (978-1-56334-735-1(0)) Hampton-Brown Bks.

Betsy Ross, 6 vols. (gr. 2-5). 39.95 (978-0-7368-4587-8(9)) Red Brick Learning.

Bevan, Claire & Glasspoole, Louise. I-Read Year 1 Anthology: The Magic Castle. 2007. (I-read Ser.). (Illus.). 40p. pap. (*978-0-521-70482-3(0)) Cambridge Univ. Pr.

Bevan, Clare. The Creature in Wide-Mouth Cave, 8 vols. 2005. (QEB Readers). (Illus.). 24p. (J). (ps-3). lib. bdg. 15.95 (978-1-59566-065-7(8)) QEB Publishing Inc.

—The Jolly Rascal. 2004. (QEB Start Reading Ser.). (Illus.). 24p. (J). lib. bdg. 15.95 (978-1-59566-013-8(5)) QEB Publishing Inc.

—Said Mouse to Mole. 2004. (QEB Start Reading Ser.). (Illus.). 24p. (J). lib. bdg. 15.95 (978-1-59566-014-5(3)) QEB Publishing Inc.

—The Wobbly Wand, 8 vols. 2005. (QEB Readers). (Illus.). 24p. (J). (ps-3). lib. bdg. 15.95 (978-1-59566-073-2(9)) QEB Publishing Inc.

Beyond Our Planet: Large-Format Books. (Rigby Infoquest Ser.). (gr. 4 up). 30.00 (978-0-7578-3904-7(5)) Rigby Education.

Big Bend Treasure Hunt: Fifth Grade Guided Comprehension Level R. (On Our Way to English Ser.). (gr. 5 up). 34.50 (978-0-7578-6621-0(2)) Rigby Education.

Big Book Grade Level Package, 18 bks., Set. 2000. (SPA.). (gr. k up). 698.55 (978-0-673-64027-7(2)); (gr. 3 up). 232.85 (978-0-673-64030-7(2)) Addison-Wesley Educational Pubs., Inc.

Big Book of R Carry-over Stories. 2004. per. 34.99 (978-0-9760490-4-3(X)) Say It Right.

Big Book Package, 6 bks., Set. 2004. (gr. 3 up). 218.30 (978-0-673-61079-9(9)); 2000. (SPA.). (gr. 2 up). 232.85 (978-0-673-64029-1(9)) Addison-Wesley Educational Pubs., Inc.

Big Book Package 1.1. 2000. (SPA.). (gr. 1 up). 116.40 (978-0-673-60734-8(8)) Addison-Wesley Educational Pubs., Inc.

Big Book Package 1.2. 2000. (SPA.). (gr. 1 up). 232.85 (978-0-673-64028-4(0)) Addison-Wesley Educational Pubs., Inc.

Big Book Package 1.3-1.6. 2000. (SPA.). (gr. 1 up). 116.50 (978-0-673-62869-5(8)) Addison-Wesley Educational Pubs., Inc.

Big Book Tote Bag. (ps-12). 18.13 (978-0-7362-1101-7(2)) Hampton-Brown Bks.

Big Books, 22 bks. 2004. (gr. k up). 654.90 (978-0-328-02950-1(5)) Addison-Wesley Educational Pubs., Inc.

Big Books. (Rosen Real Readers Big Bookstm Ser.). (J). 8p. (gr. k-1). 167.70 (978-1-4042-6291-1(1)); 12p. (gr. 1-2). 191.70 (978-1-4042-6292-8(X)); 16p. (gr. 2-3). 232.50 (978-1-4042-6293-5(8)) Rosen Publishing Group, Inc., The.

Big Books Package 1.1, 3 bks., Set. 2004. (gr. 1 up). 109.15 (978-0-328-02951-8(3)) Addison-Wesley Educational Pubs., Inc.

Big City Port. (Lexile Levels Ser.). 7.98 (978-1-56334-693-4(1)) Hampton-Brown Bks.

Big Hungry Bear Storysack. (J). 50.00 (978-0-85953-684-4(X)) Child's Play-International.

A Big Mess: Third Grade Guided Reading Level J. (On Our Way to English Ser.). (gr. 3 up). 34.50 (978-0-7578-7105-4(4)) Rigby Education.

Big or Small? Math, 6 vols. (gr. k-2). 28.95 (978-0-7368-1728-8(X) , Yellow Umbrella Bks.) Capstone Pr., Inc.

Bila, Fred Vonani. Boy-Fish: Lunda Version. Kambangaji, Thomson, tr. 1998. (Cambridge African Language Library Ser.). (Illus.). 8p. pap. 3.75 (978-0-521-64715-1(0)) Cambridge Univ. Pr.

Billings, Henry & Billings, Melissa. Climbing the World's Highest Mountains. 1999. (Livewire Investigates Ser.). (Illus.). 32p. pap. (978-0-340-74777-3(3) , Hodder Arnold) Hodder Education.

—Stunt Flying: Livewire Investigates. 1999. (Livewires Ser.). (Illus.). 32p. pap. (978-0-340-74780-3(3) , Hodder Arnold) Hodder Education.

Biographies Classroom Library. (gr. k-2). lib. bdg. 90.95 (978-0-7368-9457-9(8)) Red Brick Learning.

Biographies Complete Unit. (gr. k-2). 520.95 (978-0-7368-9458-6(6)) Red Brick Learning.

Bird Talk. 2005. (Book Treks Ser.). (J). (gr. 3 up). stu. ed. 34.95 (978-0-673-62846-6(9)) Celebration Pr.

The Bird Who Ate Too Much: Small Versions of Big Books. (On Our Way to English Ser.). (gr. 3 up). 35.50 (978-0-7578-7246-4(8)) Rigby Education.

The Bird Who Ate Too Much: Third Grade Big Books. (On Our Way to English Ser.). (gr. 3 up). 29.95 (978-0-7578-4208-5(9)) Rigby Education.

The Birth of an Island. (Guided Reading Levels Ser.). 4.73 (978-0-7362-1760-6(6)); 28.38 (978-0-7362-2167-2(0)) Hampton-Brown Bks.

The Birthday: First Wave Satellite Individual Title Six-Packs. (Sails Literacy Ser.). 16p. (gr. k up). 27.00 (978-0-7578-6849-8(5)) Rigby Education.

Birthday in the Bathtub. 1999. (Books to Go Ser.). (J). pap. (978-0-8136-7865-8(X)) Modern Curriculum Pr.

The Birthday Party. (Early Intervention Levels Ser.). 3.85 (978-1-56334-953-9(1)) Hampton-Brown Bks.

A Birthday Present for Spaceboy. 2003. (J). (978-1-932570-03-8(9)) Literacy Footprints Inc.

A Birthday Surprise. 2000. (J). (978-1-58453-130-2(4)) Pioneer Valley Educational Pr., Inc.

The Birthday Surprise: Second Grade Guided Reading Level H. (On Our Way to English Ser.). (gr. 2 up). 34.50 (978-0-7578-7080-4(5)) Rigby Education.

BJU Staff. Reading Student Text Grd 2 If. 2004. 21.00 (978-1-57924-170-4(0)) Jones, Bob Univ. Pr.

—Reading Student Text Grd 2 Whe. 2004. 21.00 (978-1-57924-171-1(9)) Jones, Bob Univ. Pr.

—A Reading Student Text Grd 3. 2004. 21.00 (978-1-57924-172-8(7)) Jones, Bob Univ. Pr.

—Reading Student Text Grd 3 B. 2004. 21.00 (978-1-57924-173-5(5)) Jones, Bob Univ. Pr.

—Reading Student Text Grd 4. 2004. 32.00 (978-1-57924-348-7(7)) Jones, Bob Univ. Pr.

—Reading Student Text Grd 5. 2004. 32.00 (978-1-57924-371-5(1)) Jones, Bob Univ. Pr.

—Reading Student Text Grd 6. 2004. 32.00 (978-1-57924-542-9(0)) Jones, Bob Univ. Pr.

—Reading Worktext Student Grd 2. 2004. pap. 16.50 (978-1-57924-174-2(3)) Jones, Bob Univ. Pr.

—Reading Worktext Student Grd 3. 2004. pap. 16.50 (978-1-57924-175-9(1)) Jones, Bob Univ. Pr.

—Reading Worktext Student Grd 4. 2004. pap. 16.50 (978-1-57924-458-3(0)) Jones, Bob Univ. Pr.

—Reading Worktext Student Grd 5. 2004. pap. 16.50 (978-1-57924-443-9(2)) Jones, Bob Univ. Pr.

—Reading Worktext Student Grd 6. 2004. pap. 16.50 (978-1-57924-543-6(9)) Jones, Bob Univ. Pr.

Blachowicz, Camille L. Z. Reading Fluency: Level A. 2004. pap. 15.96 (978-0-07-861709-6(X) , 9780078617096) Jamestown.

—Reading Fluency: Reader's Record A. 2004. pap. 10.64 (978-0-07-861712-6(X) , 9780078617126) Jamestown.

Black. StarGate, Level 3. 2000. (Illus.). 48p. (C). pap. 9.00 (978-0-582-41691-8(4)) Longman Publishing Group.

Black Beauty Student Packet, Gr. 5-6. 2004. (J). (978-1-58130-852-5(3)) Novel Units, Inc.

Black, Jessica L. The New Toys. Ruminski, Jeff, illus. 2003. 8p. (J). (ps-1). bds. 10.95 (978-1-57332-243-0(1)) High-Reach Learning, Inc.

Blackaby, Susan. Read-It! Readers Classroom Tales, 6 bks. Muehlenhardt, Amy Bailey, illus. Incl. Classroom Cookout. 18.60 (978-1-4048-0583-5(4)); Fire Drill with Mr. Dill. 18.60 (978-1-4048-0584-2(2)); Hatching Chicks. 18.60 (978-1-4048-0585-9(0)); Pup Shows Up. 18.60 (978-1-4048-0586-6(9)); Sunny Bumps the Drums. 18.60 (978-1-4048-0587-3(7)); Word of the Day. 18.60 (978-1-4048-0588-0(5)); 32p. (C). (gr. k-3). (Illus.). 2004. 111.60 (978-1-4048-0640-5(7)) Picture Window Bks.

Blackledge, Annabel. Let's Go Riding. 2005. (Dk Readers Ser.). (Illus.). 32p. (J). pap. 3.99 (978-0-7566-1694-6(8)) Dorling Kindersley Publishing, Inc.

Blair's Deer (24), Vol. 24. (Early Intervention Levels Ser.). 5.31 (978-0-7362-0612-9(4)) Hampton-Brown Bks.

Blank Tabletop Pocket Chart Cards. 2004. (J). 4.95 (978-1-56911-200-7(2)) Learning Resources, Inc.

Blasser-Riley, Gail. Nonfiction Reading Comprehension. 2002. (100+ Seriestm Ser.). 128p. (J). (gr. 3-4). pap. 12.99 (978-0-7424-0219-5(3) , IF87027) School Specialty Publishing.

Blast Zone: The Eruption & Recovery of Mount St. Helens. 2005. (Book Treks Ser.). (J). 37.95 (978-0-7652-3245-8(0)) Celebration Pr.

Blastoff! Readers, 50 bks., Set. 2006. (Illus.). (J). (gr. k-2). 925.00 (***978-0-531-17934-5(6)***) Scholastic Library Publishing.

Blaxland, Wendy. Pobblebonk Reading 4. 5 Trick the Trolls. 2008. pap. (***978-0-521-71072-5(3)***) Cambridge Univ. Pr.

—Pobblebonk Reading 4. 9 the Sun & the Wind. 2008. pap. (***978-0-521-71073-2(1)***) Cambridge Univ. Pr.

—Pobblebonk Reading 5. 4 Kiwi. 2008. pap. (***978-0-521-71074-9(X)***) Cambridge Univ. Pr.

—Pobblebonk Reading 5. 8 Pirates. 2008. pap. (***978-0-521-71075-6(8)***) Cambridge Univ. Pr.

—Pobblebonk Reading 6. 1 Grandpa's Farm. 2008. pap. (***978-0-521-71076-3(6)***) Cambridge Univ. Pr.

—Pobblebonk Reading 6. 10 Exercise Is Cool. 2008. pap. (***978-0-521-71078-7(2)***) Cambridge Univ. Pr.

—Pobblebonk Reading 6. 7 the Magic Paintbrush. 2008. pap. (***978-0-521-71077-0(4)***) Cambridge Univ. Pr.

Blends & Digraphs Set: Level D. (Sing-along Songs Ser.). (ps-2). 48.46 incl. audio compact disk (978-0-7362-0422-4(9)) Hampton-Brown Bks.

Blevins, Wiley. Parts of a Plant, 6 vols., Set C. (Phonics Readers Ser.). (gr. k-2). 17.50 (978-0-7368-3219-9(X)) Red Brick Learning.

—Phonics from A to Z. 2nd ed. 2006. 240p. pap. 19.99 (978-0-439-84511-3(4) , Teaching Resources) Scholastic, Inc.

Blevins, Wiley, ed. Grade PreK. 2006. (SmartSquares Ser.). 16p. spiral bd. 14.99 (978-0-439-83829-0(0) , Teaching Resources) Scholastic, Inc.

Block, Cheryl, et al. Reading Detective Rx: Using Higher-Order Thinking to Improve Reading Comprehension. 2003. (YA). pap. 23.99 (978-0-89455-801-6(3)) Critical Thinking Bks. & Software.

Blood, Danielle, ed. Read-Aloud Passages & Strategies to Model Fluency: Grades 1-2: More Than 20 Teacher Read-Alouds with Discussion Questions, Think-Alouds, & Tips That Support Students' Fluency Development & Comprehension. 2007. 96p. pap. 13.99 (***978-0-439-53127-6(6)*** , Teaching Resources) Scholastic, Inc.

—Read-Aloud Passages & Strategies to Model Fluency: Grades 3-4: More Than 20 Teacher Read-Alouds with Discussion Questions, Think-Alouds, & Tips That Support Students' Fluency Development & Comprehension. 2007. 96p. pap. 13.99 (***978-0-439-53130-6(6)*** , Teaching Resources) Scholastic, Inc.

—Read-Aloud Passages & Strategies to Model Fluency: Grades 5-6: More Than 20 Teacher Read-Alouds with Discussion Questions, Think-Alouds, & Tips That Support Students' Fluency Development & Comprehension. 2007. 96p. pap. 13.99 (***978-0-439-53132-0(2)*** , Teaching Resources) Scholastic, Inc.

Bloom, Harold. Bloom's Guides, 32 Vols., Set. 2006. 960.00 (978-0-7910-9329-0(8) , Chelsea Hse.) Facts On File, Inc.

Bloom, Val & Willmott, Alison. Bella. 2007. (I-read Ser.). (Illus.). 48p. pap. (***978-0-521-70486-1(3)***) Cambridge Univ. Pr.

Bloques. 2000. (J). (978-1-58453-106-7(1)) Pioneer Valley Educational Pr., Inc.

Blue & Green Levels Certificate Only. (gr. k-5). 89.00 (978-0-7578-6540-4(2)) Rigby Education.

Blue, Green, Orange, Turquoise, Purple & Gold Levels Certificate Only. (gr. k-5). 89.00 (978-0-7578-6538-1(0)) Rigby Education.

Blumenfeld, Samuel L. Blumenfeld's Alpha-Phonics: A Primer for Beginning Readers. 2006. spiral bd. 29.95 (978-0-9776024-0-7(0)) Blumont Company, The.

BMX Billy, 6 pack. (Literatura 2000 Ser.). (gr. 1-2). 28.00 (978-0-7635-0083-2(6)) Rigby Education.

Board Book Classics Set, 8. 2005. (J). bds. (978-1-59794-009-2(7)) Environments, Inc.

Board Books & Tapes 800865, 4 vols. 2005. (J). (978-1-59794-051-1(8)) Environments, Inc.

Bob & Billy, 6 pack. (Sails Literacy Ser.). (gr. 1-2). 36.00 (978-0-7578-4017-3(5)) Rigby Education.

La boda de Bharati 5: Leveled Books. 2001. (McGraw-Hill. Lectura Ser.). (ENG & SPA.). (gr. 5 up). (978-0-02-188253-3(3)) Macmillan/McGraw-Hill Schl. Div.

Body Numbers, 6 pack. (Discovery World Ser.). 16p. (gr. 1-2). 28.00 (978-0-7635-8467-2(3)) Rigby Education.

Body, Wendy. Zeebo's Numbers, 4 vols. 2005. (QEB Readers). (Illus.). 24p. (J). (ps-3). lib. bdg. 15.95 (978-1-59566-103-6(4)) QEB Publishing Inc.

—Zia's Colors, 4 vols. 2005. (QEB Readers). (Illus.). 24p. (J). (ps-3). lib. bdg. 15.95 (978-1-59566-105-0(0)) QEB Publishing Inc.

Body Works. (Guided Reading Levels Ser.). 32.22 (978-0-7362-1053-9(9)) Hampton-Brown Bks.

Bolam, Emily, illus. Can You Play? 2005. (J). (ps-k). lib. bdg. 11.15 (978-0-606-33865-3(9)) Tandem Library Bks.

Bonnell, Kris. The Big Hungry Cat. 2006. (J). 3.95 (***978-1-933727-33-2(0)***) Reading Reading Bks., LLC.

—Down in the Sea. 2006. (J). 3.95 (***978-1-933727-38-7(1)***) Reading Reading Bks., LLC.

—Frog Fun. 2006. (J). 3.95 (***978-1-933727-39-4(X)***) Reading Reading Bks., LLC.

—The Happy Moon. 2006. (J). 3.95 (***978-1-933727-30-1(6)***) Reading Reading Bks., LLC.

—Lemonade. 2006. (J). 3.95 (***978-1-933727-31-8(4)***) Reading Reading Bks., LLC.

—The Little Boat. 2006. (J). 3.95 (***978-1-933727-34-9(9)***) Reading Reading Bks., LLC.

—The Little Sprout. 2007. (J). 3.95 (***978-1-933727-54-7(3)***) Reading Reading Bks., LLC.

—Look Up! 2007. (J). 3.95 (***978-1-933727-48-6(9)***) Reading Reading Bks., LLC.

—Mother Animals. 2007. (J). 3.95 (***978-1-933727-49-3(7)***) Reading Reading Bks., LLC.

—The Mudskipper. 2006. (J). 3.75 (***978-1-933727-24-0(1)***) Reading Reading Bks., LLC.

—Mudskipper & the Water. 2006. (J). 3.95 (***978-1-933727-21-9(7)***) Reading Reading Bks., LLC.

—Pets for Us. 2007. (J). 3.95 (***978-1-933727-50-9(0)***) Reading Reading Bks., LLC.

—Picking a Pumpkin. 2007. (J). 3.95 (***978-1-933727-51-6(9)***) Reading Reading Bks., LLC.

—Pizza for Carl. 2006. (J). 3.95 (***978-1-933727-27-1(6)***) Reading Reading Bks., LLC.

—Presents for Mom. 2007. (J). 3.95 (***978-1-933727-61-5(6)***) Reading Reading Bks., LLC.

—Red Apples for Me. 2007. (J). 3.95 (***978-1-933727-52-3(7)***) Reading Reading Bks., LLC.

—Robins in the Spring. 2007. (J). 3.95 (***978-1-933727-53-0(5)***) Reading Reading Bks., LLC.

—Spring Is Coming! 2007. (J). 3.95 (***978-1-933727-64-6(0)***) Reading Reading Bks., LLC.

—Too Big to Play. 2006. (J). 3.95 (***978-1-933727-35-6(7)***) Reading Reading Bks., LLC.

—We Like the Beach. 2007. (J). 3.95 (***978-1-933727-55-4(1)***) Reading Reading Bks., LLC.

—We Love Pets. 2007. (J). 3.95 (***978-1-933727-56-1(X)***) Reading Reading Bks., LLC.

—What Tigers Do. 2006. (J). 3.95 (***978-1-933727-41-7(1)***) Reading Reading Bks., LLC.

—Where Can Louis Sleep? 2007. (J). 3.95 (***978-1-933727-57-8(8)***) Reading Reading Bks., LLC.

—Where Is a Bear? 2007. (J). 3.95 (***978-1-933727-63-9(2)***) Reading Reading Bks., LLC.

—Where Is the Big Cat? 2007. (J). 3.95 (***978-1-933727-62-2(4)***) Reading Reading Bks., LLC.

—The White, White Snow. 2007. (J). 3.95 (***978-1-933727-44-8(6)***) Reading Reading Bks., LLC.

—Who Can Wiggle? 2006. (J). 3.95 (***978-1-933727-42-4(X)***) Reading Reading Bks., LLC.

—Who Has a Hump? 2007. (J). 3.95 (***978-1-933727-58-5(6)***) Reading Reading Bks., LLC.

—The Worm Book. 2006. (J). 3.75 (***978-1-933727-25-7(X)***) Reading Reading Bks., LLC.

—Yellow Flowers. 2006. (J). 3.95 (***978-1-933727-36-3(5)***) Reading Reading Bks., LLC.

Bonnie Pearson Education staff. Spin! Level D. 2003. 112p. (C). pap., stu. ed. 20.00 (978-0-13-041994-1(X)) Pearson ESL.

—Spin! Level E. 2003. 112p. (C). pap., stu. ed. 20.00 (978-0-13-041999-6(0)) Pearson ESL.

Bonsall, Crosby N. The Case of the Cat's Meow. Bonsall, Crosby N., illus. 2002. (Illus.). (J). 12.30 (978-0-7587-6045-6(0)) Book Wholesalers, Inc.

Book Builder. 2004. (gr. k up). cd-rom 29.97 (978-0-673-64103-8(1)); (gr. 1 up). cd-rom 29.97 (978-0-673-64104-5(X)); (gr. 2 up). cd-rom 29.97 (978-0-673-64105-2(8)); (gr. 3 up). cd-rom 29.97 (978-0-673-64106-9(6)) Addison-Wesley Educational Pubs., Inc.

Books, 6 Pack. (Chiquilibros Ser.). (gr. k-1). 23.00 (978-0-7635-0423-6(8)) Rigby Education.

Bookweb 3 & 4 Certificate Only. (Bookweb Ser.). (gr. 4 up). 89.00 (978-0-7578-6525-1(9)) Rigby Education.

Bookweb 4 Blackline Masters Book, Vol. 4. (Bookweb Ser.). (gr. 4 up). 52.00 (978-0-7635-5937-3(7)) Rigby Education.

Bookweb 5 & 6 Certificate Only. (Bookweb Ser.). (gr. 6 up). 89.00 (978-0-7578-6526-8(7)) Rigby Education.

Bookweb 5 Blackline Masters Book, Vol. 5. (Bookweb Ser.). (gr. 5 up). 52.00 (978-0-7635-5926-7(1)) Rigby Education.

Bookweb 6 Blackline Masters Book, Vol. 6. (Bookweb Ser.). (gr. 6 up). 52.00 (978-0-7578-1653-6(3)) Rigby Education.

The Bookweb Science Dog's Guide to Humans. 2001. (Bookweb Ser.). 32p. (J). (gr. 3). 38.95 (978-0-7635-3937-5(6)) Rigby Education.

Boom-Boom-Bey! (Early Intervention Levels Ser.). 28.38 (978-0-7362-0396-8(6)) Hampton-Brown Bks.

Boom-Boom-Bey! (8), Vol. 8. (Early Intervention Levels Ser.). 4.73 (978-0-7362-0221-3(8)) Hampton-Brown Bks.

Boomerangs, 6 Pack. (Story Steps Ser.). (gr. k-2). 32.00 (978-0-7635-9805-1(4)) Rigby Education.

Booth, Jack. The 10 Deadliest Sea Creatures. 2008. (Tentrade; Ser.). 48p. (J). pap. 14.99 (***978-1-55448-482-9(0)*** , Watts, Franklin) Scholastic Library Publishing.

Bot's Bits: Set A Individual Title Six-Packs. (gr. k-3). 29.00 (978-0-7635-0534-9(X)) Rigby Education.

Bottino, Marlane. Pup Tales Stories for Beginning Readers, 9 vols. Bottino, Marlane, illus. 2001. (Pup Tales Ser.). (Illus.). (J). (gr. k-2). Set 1. pap. 7.00 (978-1-893615-03-8(0)); Set 2. pap. 7.00 (978-1-893615-04-5(9)) Creative Enterprises.

Boundaries Washed Away: Fifth Grade Guided Comprehension Level P. (On Our Way to English Ser.). (gr. 5 up). 34.50 (978-0-7578-6608-1(5)) Rigby Education.

Bowers, Linda. Spotlight on Reading Comprehension Makin Inferences & Drawing Conclusions. 2005. (Illus.). (J). per. 11.95 (978-0-7606-0585-1(8)) LinguiSystems, Inc.

Bowers, Linda, et al. Spotlight on Reading Comprehension Characters & Actions. 2005. (J). per. 11.95 (978-0-7606-0583-7(1)) LinguiSystems, Inc.

—Spotlight on Reading Comprehension Comparing & Contrasting. 2005. (Illus.). (J). per. 11.95 (978-0-7606-0581-3(5)) LinguiSystems, Inc.

—Spotlight on Reading Comprehension Figurative Language & Exclusion. 2005. (Illus.). (J). per. 11.95 (978-0-7606-0582-0(3)) LinguiSystems, Inc.

—Spotlight on Reading Comprehension Paraphrasing & Summarizing. 2005. (J). per. 11.95 (978-0-7606-0584-4(X)) LinguiSystems, Inc.

—Spotlight on Reading Comprehension Sequencing & Problem Solving. 2005. (Illus.). (J). 11.95 (978-0-7606-0580-6(7)) LinguiSystems, Inc.

Bowler, Bill. Wrong Trousers. 2005. (Dominoes Ser.). (Illus.). 48p. 6.50 (978-0-19-424396-4(6)) Oxford Univ. Pr., Inc.

The Boy Who Cried Wolf: Individual Title Six-Packs. 32p. (gr. 2 up). 37.00 (978-0-7635-9218-9(8)) Rigby Education.

Boyd, Anne. Summer Storm: Australian Edition. 1998. (Cambridge Reading Australia Ser.). (Illus.). 32p. (ps-1). pap. 5.00 (978-0-521-64579-9(4)) Cambridge Univ. Pr.

—Sunshine Lamb: Australian Edition. 1998. (Cambridge Reading Australia Ser.). (Illus.). 32p. (ps-1). pap. 5.00 (978-0-521-64581-2(6)) Cambridge Univ. Pr.

—Windy Night: Australian Edition. 1998. (Cambridge Reading Australia Ser.). (Illus.). 32p. (ps-1). pap. 5.00 (978-0-521-64578-2(6)) Cambridge Univ. Pr.

Boyd, David. Marco Polo & the Roc. Ng, Drew, illus. 2007. 48p. (J). lib. bdg. 23.08 (***978-1-4242-1621-5(4)***) Fitzgerald Bks.

Boynton, Alice & Blevins, Wiley. Nonfiction Passages with Graphic Organizers for Independent Practice: Selections with Graphic Organizers, Assessments, & Writing Activities That Help Students Understand the Structures & Features of Nonfiction. 2005. 128p. pap. 17.99 (978-0-439-59018-1(3) , Teaching Strategies) Scholastic, Inc.

Bracken, Carolyn. Gets Crabby. Earhart, Kristin, ed. 2006. (Msb Science Reader Ser.). (Illus.). 32p. (J). pap. 3.99 (978-0-439-68403-3(X) , Scholastic) Scholastic, Inc.

Bradman, Tony. Let's Pretend Big Book. Harker, Lesley, illus. 1999. (Cambridge Reading Ser.). 14p. pap. 16.95 (978-0-521-66699-2(6)) Cambridge Univ. Pr.

Bradman, Tony & Chatterton, Martin. The Mummy Family Finds Fame. 2006. (Illus.). 46p. (J). (978-0-7787-1076-9(9)) Crabtree Publishing Co.

Bradshaw, Georgine & Wrighton, Charlene. Basic Kit - Kindergarten. Clark, Irene, illus. 2005. Orig. Title: Basic Kit II. (J). 249.95 (978-1-886441-31-6(6)) Zoo-phonics, Inc.

—Kindergarten Zoo-per Kit. Clark, Irene, illus. 2005. (J). 499.95 (978-1-886441-34-7(0) , ZOP4219) Zoo-phonics, Inc.

—Preschool Zoo-per Kit. Clark, Irene, illus. 2005. (J). 449.95 (978-1-886441-32-3(4) , ZOP4218) Zoo-phonics, Inc.

Bremer, Paula. High Interest Reading. 1999. (100+ Seriestm Ser.). 128p. (J). (gr. 3-5). pap. 12.99 (978-0-88012-813-1(5) , IF8713); (gr. 6-8). pap. 12.99 (978-0-88012-814-8(3) , IF8714) School Specialty Publishing.

Brenner, Barbara. The Plant That Kept on Growing. Sweet, Melissa, illus. 1999. (Bank Street Reader Collection). 48p. (J). (ps-2). lib. bdg. (978-0-8368-1776-8(1)) Stevens, Gareth Inc.

Brett Favre, 6 vols. (gr. 4 up). 39.95 (978-0-7368-9270-4(2)) Red Brick Learning.

Bridges, Sarah. Working Wheels, 6 bks. Alderman, Derrick & Shea, Denise, illus. Incl. I Drive a Bulldozer. (C). 22.60 (978-1-4048-0613-9(X)); I Drive a Dump Truck. (C). 22.60 (978-1-4048-0614-6(8)); I Drive a Garbage Truck. (J). 22.60 (978-1-4048-0615-3(6)); I Drive a Semitruck. (C). 22.60 (978-1-4048-0616-0(4)); I Drive a Snowplow. (J). 22.60 (978-1-4048-0617-7(2)); I Drive an Ambulance. (C). 22.60 (978-1-4048-0618-4(0)); 24p. (gr. k-2). (Illus.). 2004. 135.60 (978-1-4048-0634-4(2)) Picture Window Bks.

Bridgestone Reading Add-on Set. (gr. 2-5). 368.95 (978-0-7368-1812-4(X) , Bridgestone Bks.) Capstone Pr., Inc.

Bridgestone Reading, Set 1. (gr. 2-5). 664.95 (978-0-7368-1802-5(2) , Bridgestone Bks.) Capstone Pr., Inc.

Bridgestone Reading, Set 1 Add-on Set. (gr. 2-5). 122.95 (978-0-7368-1803-2(0) , Bridgestone Bks.) Capstone Pr., Inc.

Bridgestone Reading, Set 2. (gr. 2-5). 664.95 (978-0-7368-1805-6(7) , Bridgestone Bks.) Capstone Pr., Inc.

Bridgestone Reading, Set 2 Add-on Set. (gr. 2-5). 122.95 (978-0-7368-1806-3(5) , Bridgestone Bks.) Capstone Pr., Inc.

Bridgestone Reading, Set 3. (gr. 2-5). 664.95 (978-0-7368-1808-7(1) , Bridgestone Bks.) Capstone Pr., Inc.

Bridgestone Reading, Set 3 Add-on Set. (gr. 2-5). 122.95 (978-0-7368-1809-4(X) , Bridgestone Bks.) Capstone Pr., Inc.

Brimax, S. My First Word Book. 1998. (Illus.). 48p. (J). pap. 40.00 (978-81-86982-65-5(5)) Business Pubns. Inc. IND. *Dist:* State Mutual Bk. & Periodical Service, Ltd.

Brimner, Larry Dane. Elwood's Bath. Weidner, Teri, illus. 2005. (Magic Door to Reading Ser.). 24p. (J). (ps-3). 21.36 (978-1-59296-521-2(0)) Child's World, Inc.

—In the Fall. Alley, R. W., illus. 2005. (Magic Door to Reading Ser.). 24p. (J). (ps-3). 21.36 (978-1-59296-517-5(2)) Child's World, Inc.

—Loud Larry. Adinolfi, JoAnn, illus. 2005. (Magic Door to Reading Ser.). 24p. (J). (ps-3). 21.36 (978-1-59296-530-4(X)) Child's World, Inc.

—Max's Math Machine. Squier, Robert, illus. 2005. (Magic Door to Reading Ser.). 24p. (J). (ps-3). 21.36 (978-1-59296-522-9(9)) Child's World, Inc.

—One Summery Day. Alley, R. W., illus. 2005. (Magic Door to Reading Ser.). 24p. (J). (ps-3). 21.36 (978-1-59296-518-2(0)) Child's World, Inc.

—Rumble Bus. Rooney, Ronnie, illus. 2005. (Magic Door to Reading Ser.). 24p. (J). (ps-3). 21.36 (978-1-59296-524-3(5)) Child's World, Inc.

—A Shake & a Shiver. Adinolfi, JoAnn, illus. 2005. (Magic Door to Reading Ser.). 24p. (J). (ps-3). 21.36 (978-1-59296-531-1(8)) Child's World, Inc.

—Spring Sail. Alley, R. W., illus. 2005. (Magic Door to Reading Ser.). 24p. (J). (ps-3). 21.36 (978-1-59296-519-9(9)) Child's World, Inc.

—Twelve Plump Cookies. Holm, Sharon, illus. 2005. (Magic Door to Reading Ser.). 24p. (J). (ps-3). 21.36 (978-1-59296-523-6(7)) Child's World, Inc.

—Winter Blanket. Alley, R. W., illus. 2005. (Magic Door to Reading Ser.). 24p. (J). (ps-3). 21.36 (978-1-59296-520-5(2)) Child's World, Inc.

Bring Me Your Horses. (Early Intervention Levels Ser.). 28.38 (978-0-7362-0410-1(5)) Hampton-Brown Bks.

Bring Me Your Horses (16), Vol. 16. (Early Intervention Levels Ser.). 4.73 (978-0-7362-0235-0(8)) Hampton-Brown Bks.

Brinton, Margaret. 100 Little Reading Comprehension Lessons: Fun-to-Read Stories with Skill-Building Exercises. Mitchell, Judy, ed. Shalansky, Len, illus. 2004. 112p. (J). pap. 11.95 (978-1-57310-425-8(6)) Teaching & Learning Co.

Briscoe, Diana C. King Tut: Tales from the Tomb, 6 vols. (gr. 4 up). 49.95 (978-0-7368-9542-2(6) , High Five) Red Brick Learning.

The British Tradition: The EMC Write-in Reader. 2nd ed. (Literature & the Language Arts Ser.). (YA). (gr. 12 up). wbk. ed. 17.95 (978-0-8219-2920-9(8)) EMC/Paradigm Publishing.

Brocklehurst, Ruth. Princess Things to Make & Do. 2005. (Illus.). 32p. (J). pap. 6.95 (978-0-7945-0908-8(8) , Usborne) EDC Publishing.

Brooks, David, illus. The First Noel. 2005. (Soft Shapes Ser.). 8p. (J). (ps). 8.99 (978-1-58476-363-5(9)) Innovative Kids.

Brooks, Felicity. School Look & Say. Litchfield, Jo, illus. 2005. 10p. (J). 7.95 (978-0-7945-1015-2(9) , Usborne) EDC Publishing.

Brothers Grimm Staff & Daynes, Katie. Hansel & Gretel. 2005. 48p. (J). (gr. 2 up). 8.95 (978-0-7945-1053-4(1) , Usborne) EDC Publishing.

Brown Bear Figures It Out. (Early Intervention Levels Ser.). 31.86 (978-0-7362-0667-9(1)) Hampton-Brown Bks.

Brown Bear Figures It Out (20), Vol. 20. (Early Intervention Levels Ser.). 5.31 (978-0-7362-0655-6(8)) Hampton-Brown Bks.

Brown, Karen. Quotes & Proverbs That Build Character. Rogers, Kathy, ed. 2001. 64p. (J). per. 8.95 (978-1-56472-340-6(2)) Edupress, Inc.

Brown, Marc. Buster & the Dance Contest. 2005. (Postcards from Buster Ser.). (Illus.). 32p. (J). (gr. 1-4). 14.99 (978-0-316-15889-3(5)); pap., pap. 3.99 (978-0-316-00118-2(X)) Little, Brown Bks. for Young Readers.

—Buster & the Giant Pumpkin. 2005. (Postcards from Buster Ser.). (Illus.). 32p. (J). (gr. 1-4). pap., pap. 3.99 (978-0-316-00111-3(2)) Little, Brown Bks. for Young Readers.

—Buster Hits the Trail. 2005. (Postcards from Buster Ser.). (Illus.). 48p. (J). (gr. 1-4). 14.99 (978-0-316-15900-5(X)) Little, Brown Bks. for Young Readers.

—Buster on the Farm. 2005. (Postcards from Buster Ser.). (Illus.). 32p. (J). (gr. 1-4). 14.99 (978-0-316-15884-8(4)) Little, Brown Bks. for Young Readers.

—Buster on the Town. 2005. (Postcards from Buster Ser.). (Illus.). 32p. (J). (gr. 1-4). 14.99 (978-0-316-15882-4(8)); pap. 3.99 (978-0-316-00107-6(4)) Little, Brown Bks. for Young Readers.

—Buster Plays Along. 2005. (Postcards from Buster Ser.). (Illus.). (J). (gr. 1-4). 48p. 14.99 (978-0-316-15886-2(0)); 32p. pap. 3.99 (978-0-316-00109-0(0)) Little, Brown Bks. for Young Readers.

Brown, Richard. All by Myself. 1998. (Cambridge Reading Ser.). (Illus.). 18p. (ps-1). pap. 20.00 (978-0-521-63467-0(9)) Cambridge Univ. Pr.

—Snow in the Kitchen. 2005. (Cambridge Storybooks Ser.). 32p. pap. 7.00 (978-0-521-67480-5(8)) Cambridge Univ. Pr.

—A Welsh Lamb. 2005. (Cambridge Storybooks Ser.). 32p. pap. 7.00 (978-0-521-67482-9(4)) Cambridge Univ. Pr.

Brown, Richard, illus. Wait for Us! 2005. (I'm Going to Read Ser.). 28p. (J). (ps-k). pap., pap. 3.95 (978-1-4027-2506-7(X)); 11.95 (978-1-4027-2507-4(8)) Sterling Publishing Co., Inc.

Brown, Richard & O'Neill, Judith. Heroes & Villains, 8 vols. 2000. (Cambridge Reading Ser.). (Illus.). 96p. pap. 54.00 (978-0-521-78631-7(2)) Cambridge Univ. Pr.

Brown, Richard & Ruttle, Kate. Nonsense! Big Book. 1998. (Cambridge Reading Ser.). (Illus.). 25p. (ps-1). pap. 30.00 (978-0-521-63473-1(3)) Cambridge Univ. Pr.

—Walking in the Jungle: American English Edition. 2000. (Cambridge Reading Ser.). (Illus.). 8p. pap. 5.00 (978-0-521-79519-7(2)) Cambridge Univ. Pr.

—Walking in the Jungle American English Edition, 6, Pack. 2000. (Cambridge Reading Ser.). (Illus.). pap. 28.00 (978-0-521-79517-3(6)) Cambridge Univ. Pr.

—Walking in the Jungle Big Book: American English Edition. 2000. (Cambridge Reading Ser.). (Illus.). 8p. pap. 20.00 (978-0-521-79518-0(4)) Cambridge Univ. Pr.

Browne, Eileen. Handa's Surprise: Read & Share. Browne, Eileen, illus. 1999. (Reading Together Ser.). (Illus.). 32p. (J). (gr. k). pap. 3.99 (978-0-7636-0863-7(7)) Candlewick Pr.

—Handa's Surprise: Read & Share. 2004. (Illus.). 28p. (J). (TAM, SPA, GUJ, PER & URD.). (978-1-85269-473-9(4)); (TAM, SPA, GUJ, PER & URD., (978-1-85269-474-6(2)); (TAM, SPA, GUJ, PER & URD., (978-1-85269-475-3(0)); (TAM, SPA, GUJ, PER & URD., (978-1-85269-477-7(7)); (TAM, SPA, GUJ, PER & URD., (978-1-85269-478-4(5)); (TAM, SPA, GUJ, PER & URD., (978-1-85269-472-2(6)); (TAM, SPA, GUJ, PER & URD., (978-1-85269-508-8(0)); (TAM, SPA, GUJ, PER & URD., (978-1-85269-509-5(9)); (TAM, SPA, GUJ, PER & URD., (978-1-85269-512-5(9)); (TAM, SPA, GUJ, PER & URD., (978-1-85269-513-2(7)); (TAM, SPA, GUJ, PER & URD., (978-1-85269-515-6(3)); (POR, TAM, TWI, SPA & CHI., (978-1-85269-476-0(9)); (TAM, SPA, GUJ, PER & URD., (978-1-85269-514-9(5)) Mantra Publishing, Ltd.

—Handa's Surprise: Read & Share. 2004. (TAM, SPA, GUJ, PER & URD., Illus.). 28p. (J). 13.50 (978-1-85269-511-8(0)); 13.50 (978-1-85269-507-1(2)) Mantra Publishing, Ltd. GBR. *Dist:* AIMS International Bks., Inc.

—Wait for Me!, 8 bks. 2005. (QEB Readers). (Illus.). 24p. (J). (ps-3). lib. bdg. 15.95 (978-1-59566-075-6(5)) QEB Publishing Inc.

Browne, Eileen & Habashi, Azza. Handa's Surprise: Read & Share. 2004. (TAM, SPA, GUJ, PER & URD., Illus.). 28p. (J). 13.50 (978-1-85269-471-5(8)) Mantra Publishing, Ltd. GBR. *Dist:* AIMS International Bks., Inc.

Bruzzone, Catherine. Lucy the Cat at the Party/La Gatita Lucia en la Fiesta. Beaton, Claire, illus. 2006. (Bilingual Picture Strip Bks.). (SPA & ENG.). 24p. (J). pap. 4.99 (978-0-7641-3408-1(6)) Barron's Educational Series, Inc.

Buchanan, Fannie R. Magic Music Story Interpretations. 2006. (Illus.). pap. 21.95 (***978-1-4286-5945-2(5)***) Kessinger Publishing, LLC.

Buckley, James. A Bat Boy's Day. 2005. (Dk Readers Ser.). (Illus.). 32p. (J). 14.99 (978-0-7566-1206-1(3)); (gr. 2-3). pap. 3.99 (978-0-7566-1207-8(1)) Dorling Kindersley Publishing, Inc.

—Let's Go to the Ballpark. 2005. (Dk Readers Ser.). (Illus.). 32p. (J). (gr. 2-3). pap. 3.99 (978-0-7566-1209-2(8)) Dorling Kindersley Publishing, Inc.

Buckton, Chris & Hammond, Andrew. I-read Year 2 Anthology: Puppet Parade: Volume 0, Part 0. 2007. (I-read Ser.). (Illus.). 40p. pap. (***978-0-521-70484-7(7)***) Cambridge Univ. Pr.

Budgell, Gill. My Vacation Week American English Edition. 2000. (Cambridge Reading Ser.). (Illus.). 12p. pap. 5.00 (978-0-521-79900-3(7)) Cambridge Univ. Pr.

Buena Pata 12: Leveled Books. 2001. (McGraw-Hill. Lectura Ser.). (ENG & SPA.). (gr. 4 up). (978-0-02-188157-4(X)) Macmillan/McGraw-Hill Schl. Div.

Buenas Letras Reading Room Series, Set. 2003. (Buenas Letras Reading Room Ser.). (SPA & ENG., Illus.). (J). lib. bdg. 112.50 (978-0-8239-7278-4(X) , Buenas Letra) Rosen Publishing Group, Inc., The.

Buenas Noches! 22: Leveled Books. 2001. (McGraw-Hill. Lectura Ser.). (ENG & SPA.). (gr. 1 up). (978-0-02-187975-5(3)) Macmillan/McGraw-Hill Schl. Div.

Bugs! (18), Vol. 18. (Early Intervention Levels Ser.). 5.31 (978-0-7362-0614-3(0)) Hampton-Brown Bks.

Bugs, Beware! Fifth Grade Guided Comprehension Level T. (On Our Way to English Ser.). (gr. 5 up). 34.50 (978-0-7578-6631-9(X)) Rigby Education.

Building a Doghouse: Fourth Grade Guided Comprehension Level M. (On Our Way to English Ser.). (gr. 4 up). 34.50 (978-0-7578-7157-3(7)) Rigby Education.

Building a House: Second Grade Newcomer Books. (On Our Way to English Ser.). (gr. 2 up). 29.50 (978-0-7578-7215-0(8)) Rigby Education.

Building Reading Skills: Book B. 2nd ed. 2001. (Building Reading Skills). 96p. (YA). pap., wbk. ed. (978-1-892437-34-8(8)) Brigance Publishing.

Built for Speed Complete Unit. (gr. 4 up). 142.95 (978-0-7368-8950-6(7)) Red Brick Learning.

Built to Last: Individual Title Six-Packs. (Rigby Infoquest Ser.). (gr. 6 up). 37.00 (978-0-7578-7996-8(9)) Rigby Education.

Bully Cat: Individual Title Six-Packs. (Sails Literacy Ser.). (gr. 1-2). 36.00 (978-0-7578-6718-7(9)) Rigby Education.

Bully Cat & Fat Cat: Individual Title Six-Packs. (Sails Literacy Ser.). (gr. 1-2). 36.00 (978-0-7578-4004-3(3)) Rigby Education.

The Bumper Cars: First Wave Satellite Individual Title, 6 pack. (Sails Literacy Ser.). 16p. (gr. k up). 27.00 (978-0-7578-6870-2(3)) Rigby Education.

Bunting, Eve. My Box. Banta, Susan, illus. 2000. (Books for Young Learners). 12p. (J). pap. 5.00 (978-1-57274-397-7(2)) Owen, Richard C. Pubs., Inc.

Burch, Regina G. Character Builders Set 1: Doing Right & Trying Hard, 6 bks. 2002. (Illus.). (J). (ps-3). 15.99 (978-1-57471-990-1(4)) Creative Teaching Pr., Inc.

—Character Builders Set 2: Sharing & Caring, 6 bks. 2002. (Illus.). (J). (ps-3). 15.99 (978-1-57471-991-8(2)) Creative Teaching Pr., Inc.

Burchett, J. & Vogler, S. Tower Block Blowdown. Sharpe, Caroline, illus. 1998. (Cambridge Reading Ser.). 32p. (gr. 2-6). pap. 9.00 (978-0-521-63746-6(5)) Cambridge Univ. Pr.

Burgess, Chris. Study Reading Modules: (B) Bear. 1999. (Illus.). 24p. (J). pap. 19.95 (978-0-7217-0505-7(7)) Schofield & Sims Ltd. GBR. *Dist:* State Mutual Bk. & Periodical Service, Ltd.

—Study Reading Modules: (C) Crocodile. 1999. (Illus.). 24p. (J). pap. 19.95 (978-0-7217-0506-4(5)) Schofield & Sims Ltd. GBR. *Dist:* State Mutual Bk. & Periodical Service, Ltd.

—Study Reading Modules: (D) Dolphin. 1999. (Illus.). 24p. (J). pap. 19.95 (978-0-7217-0507-1(3)) Schofield & Sims Ltd. GBR. *Dist:* State Mutual Bk. & Periodical Service, Ltd.

—Study Reading Modules: (F) Frog. 1999. (Illus.). 24p. (J). pap. 19.95 (978-0-7217-0509-5(X)) Schofield & Sims Ltd. GBR. *Dist:* State Mutual Bk. & Periodical Service, Ltd.

—Study Reading Modules: (G) Goldfinch. 1999. (Illus.). 24p. (J). pap. 19.95 (978-0-7217-0510-1(3)) Schofield & Sims Ltd. GBR. *Dist:* State Mutual Bk. & Periodical Service, Ltd.

—Study Reading Modules: (H) Horse. 1999. (Illus.). 24p. (J). pap. 19.95 (978-0-7217-0511-8(1)) Schofield & Sims Ltd. GBR. *Dist:* State Mutual Bk. & Periodical Service, Ltd.

—Study Reading Modules: (I) Ibis. 1999. (Illus.). 24p. (J). pap. 19.95 (978-0-7217-0512-5(X)) Schofield & Sims Ltd. GBR. *Dist:* State Mutual Bk. & Periodical Service, Ltd.

—Study Reading Modules: (J) Jaguar. 1999. (Illus.). 24p. (J). pap. 19.95 (978-0-7217-0513-2(8)) Schofield & Sims Ltd. GBR. *Dist:* State Mutual Bk. & Periodical Service, Ltd.

—Study Reading Modules: (L) Lion. 1999. (Illus.). 24p. (J). pap. 19.95 (978-0-7217-0498-2(0)) Schofield & Sims Ltd. GBR. *Dist:* State Mutual Bk. & Periodical Service, Ltd.

—Study Reading Modules: (M) Mole. 1999. (Illus.). 24p. (J). pap. 19.95 (978-0-7217-0499-9(9)) Schofield & Sims Ltd. GBR. *Dist:* State Mutual Bk. & Periodical Service, Ltd.

—Study Reading Modules: (N) Nightingale. 1999. (Illus.). 24p. (J). pap. 19.95 (978-0-7217-0500-2(6)) Schofield & Sims Ltd. GBR. *Dist:* State Mutual Bk. & Periodical Service, Ltd.

Burke. Whos Hiding There. 1999. pap. (978-0-7398-2398-9(1)) Steck-Vaughn.

Burke, David, adapted by. GOLDILOCKS (English to Chinese - Level 2) Learn MANDARIN CHINESE Through Fairy Tales. 2007. (Learn Chinese Through Fairy Tales Ser.). (ENG & CHI., Illus.). (J). per. 14.95 incl. audio compact disk (***978-1-891888-85-4(4)***) Slangman Publishing.

Burke, Sandra & Flebotte, Morrigan. The Crusading Communicator. Flebotte, Morrigan, ed. 2004. (Illus.). 2p. (J). per. (978-0-9735303-8-4(3)) Black Castle Industries, Inc.

—Hercules Novel Study. Flebotte, Morrigan, ed. 2004. (Illus.). (J). per. (978-0-9735303-1-5(6)) Black Castle Industries, Inc.

Burkett, Beverley. Yawning Is Catching. Moyo, Sihambile, tr. 1999. (Cambridge African Language Library). (NBL & NDE., Illus.). 16p. pap. 3.70 (978-0-521-65809-6(8)) Cambridge Univ. Pr.

—Yawning Is Catching. Tadjo, Veronique, tr. from ENG. 1998. (Cambridge African Language Library). (FRE., Illus.). 16p. pap. 3.75 (978-0-521-64788-5(6)) Cambridge Univ. Pr.

—Yawning Is Catching: Lunda Version. Kambangaji, Thomson, tr. 1998. (Cambridge African Language Library Ser.). (Illus.). 16p. pap. 3.75 (978-0-521-63836-4(4)) Cambridge Univ. Pr.

—Yawning Is Catching: Shona Version. Chirikure, Chirulure, tr. 1999. (Cambridge African Language Library Ser.). (SHO., Illus.). 16p. pap. 3.70 (978-0-521-65816-4(0)) Cambridge Univ. Pr.

Burns, Laura J. & Metz, Melinda. Escape from Skull Island. 2005. (King Kong Ser.). (Illus.). 64p. (J). pap. 4.99 (978-0-06-077301-4(4)) HarperCollins Pubs.

Burton, Margie, et al. Let's Go. Evento, Susan, ed. 1998. (Early Connections Ser.). 16p. (J). (gr. k-2). pap. 4.25 (978-1-892393-45-6(X)) Benchmark Education Co.

—Long Ago. Evento, Susan, ed. 1998. (Early Connections Ser.). 16p. (J). (gr. k-2). pap. 4.25 (978-1-892393-50-0(6)) Benchmark Education Co.

—What Are My Chances? Adams, Alison, ed. 1999. (Early Connections Ser.). 16p. (J). (gr. k-2). pap. 4.50 (978-1-58344-077-3(1)) Benchmark Education Co.

Buskermolen, Sunniva. The 10 Most Fascinating Phenomena. 2008. (Tentrade; Ser.). 48p. (J). pap. 14.99 (***978-1-55448-471-3(5)*** , Watts, Franklin) Scholastic Library Publishing.

Bustard, Ned. Red Hood. Bustard, Ned, illus. 2000. per. 3.00 (978-1-930710-39-9(9)) Veritas Pr., Inc.

Buster MCluster: Level G. (Wonder Worldtm Ser.). 16p. 29.95 (978-0-7802-1033-2(6)) Wright Group, The.

Buster MCluster has Chicken Pox: Level G, 6 vols. (Wonder Worldtm Ser.). 16p. 29.95 (978-0-7802-4563-1(6)) Wright Group, The.

Busy Animals Book Set 800896, 6 vols. 2005. (J). pap. (978-1-59794-071-9(2)) Environments, Inc.

Busy Bear Book Set 800938, 4 vols. 2005. (J). bds. (978-1-59794-097-9(6)) Environments, Inc.

Busy Bees: Cassette. (Song Box(R) Ser.). (gr. 1-2). 8.50 incl. audio (978-0-7802-2269-4(5)) Wright Group, The.

Busy Children Book Set 800897, 6 vols. 2005. (J). pap. (978-1-59794-072-6(0)) Environments, Inc.

But I Want It! Second Grade Guided Reading Level K. (On Our Way to English Ser.). (gr. 2 up). 34.50 (978-0-7578-7099-6(6)) Rigby Education.

By the People: Fifth Grade Class Collection Books. (On Our Way to English Ser.). (gr. 5 up). 29.95 (978-0-7578-4468-3(5)) Rigby Education.

By the People: Small Versions of Class Collection Books. (On Our Way to English Ser.). (gr. 5 up). 34.50 (978-0-7578-7282-2(4)) Rigby Education.

By the Tree. (Little Book Practice Reader Ser.). (J). (978-0-8136-0737-5(X)) Modern Curriculum Pr.

The Cake: Individual Title Six-Packs. (Story Steps Ser.). (gr. k-2). 29.00 (978-0-7635-9601-9(9)) Rigby Education.

Callaghan, Paul & Burrell, Emma. Highways to a War. 2002. (Wizard Study Guides Ser.). 64p. pap., stu. ed. 6.00 (978-1-876367-14-5(8)) Cambridge Univ. Pr.

Called to a Cause. 2003. (Illus.). pap. 5.60 (978-0-7398-7516-2(7)) Steck-Vaughn.

Callella, Trisha. Developing Reading Fluency, Grade 2: Using Modeled Reading, Phrasing, & Repeated Oral Reading. Fisch, Teri L., ed. Iosa, Ann W., illus. 2003. (Developing Reading Fluency Ser.). 96p. (J). (gr. 2-3). pap. 11.99 (978-1-57471-995-6(5) , 2248) Creative Teaching Pr., Inc.

—Developing Reading Fluency, Grade 3: Using Modeled Reading, Phrasing, & Repeated Oral Reading. Fisch, Teri L., ed. Yamada, Jane, illus. 2003. (Developing Reading Fluency Ser.). 96p. (J). (gr. 3-4). pap. 11.99 (978-1-57471-996-3(3) , 2240) Creative Teaching Pr., Inc.

—Developing Reading Fluency, Grade 4: Using Modeled Reading, Phrasing, & Repeated Oral Reading. Fisch, Teri L., ed. Iosa, Ann W., illus. 2003. (Developing Reading Fluency Ser.). 96p. (J). (gr. 4-5). pap. 11.99 (978-1-57471-997-0(1) , 2250) Creative Teaching Pr., Inc.

Calvert, Pam & Torrey, Richard. Clue School: Mysetery at the Ballpark. 2007. 32p. (J). (gr. 1). pap. 6.99 (***978-1-58476-609-4(3)*** , IKIDS) Innovative Kids.

Cam in the Cave: Individual Title, 6 vols. (Sails Literacy Ser.). (gr. 1-2). 36.00 (978-0-7578-3999-3(1)) Rigby Education.

La cama de Mama 1: Leveled Books. 2001. (McGraw-Hill. Lectura Ser.). (ENG & SPA.). (gr. 1 up). (978-0-02-187978-6(8)) Macmillan/McGraw-Hill Schl. Div.

Cambridge University Press Staff. Joey's Quiet War & Other Stories. (J). pap. 8.50 (978-0-13-177460-5(3)) Globe Fearon Educational Publishing.

Camden, Greg & Migliaccio, Eric. Wold Almanac for Kids Scavengar Hunts Grades 3-5. 2005. 112p. pap. 14.99 (978-1-4206-3852-3(1)) Teacher Created Resources, Inc.

—World Almanac for Kids Scavenger Hunts. 2005. 112p. pap. 14.99 (978-1-4206-3853-0(X)) Teacher Created Resources, Inc.

Camouflage, 6 Packs. (Rigby Focus Ser.). 16p. (gr. 1 up). 28.00 (978-0-7578-5323-4(4)); 30.00 (978-0-7578-5555-9(5)) Rigby Education.

Campbell, Dorthina A. Step Forward Strategies for Struggling Readers: Student Resource Guide. 2005. 59p. (J). stu. ed., per. 8.99 (978-0-9768208-0-2(3)) Edutech Learning Resource Ctr.

Camping in the Woods: MainSails Individual Title Six-Packs. (Sails Literacy Ser.). (gr. 5 up). 37.00 (978-0-7578-8053-7(3)) Rigby Education.

Camping Out, 6 vols. (Multicultural Programs Ser.). 16p. (gr. 1-3). 24.95 (978-0-7802-9203-1(0)) Wright Group, The.

Can-Do Cat. (Early Intervention Levels Ser.). 21.30 (978-0-7362-0384-5(2)) Hampton-Brown Bks.

Can You Help Me Find My Puppy? Kindergarten Big Books. (On Our Way to English Ser.). (gr. k up). 29.95 (978-0-7578-1618-5(5)) Rigby Education.

Can You Help Me Find My Puppy? Small Versions of Big Books. (On Our Way to English Ser.). (gr. k up). 29.00 (978-0-7578-7217-4(4)) Rigby Education.

Can You See? First Wave Satellite Individual Title Six-Packs. (Sails Literacy Ser.). 16p. (gr. k up). 27.00 (978-0-7578-6851-1(7)) Rigby Education.

A Can You See It?, 6 vols., Set. (Phonics Readers Ser.). (gr. k-2). 17.50 (978-0-7368-3191-8(6)) Red Brick Learning.

Can You See the Wagon? Kindergarten Guided Reading Level A. (On Our Way to English Ser.). (gr. k up). 27.75 (978-0-7578-7003-3(1)) Rigby Education.

Candlewick Books Staff, Books. One, Two, Flea! 2003. (gr. k-3). lib. bdg. 11.80 (978-0-613-74741-7(0)) Tandem Library Bks.

Canfield, Jack L. Sopa de Polo Para el Alma Del Adolescente. 1999. (SPA.). (gr. 7-12). lib. bdg. 22.20 (978-0-613-27001-4(0)) Tandem Library Bks.

Capucilli, Alyssa Satin. Biscuit & the Baby. Schories, Pat, illus. 2005. (My First I Can Read Bks.). 32p. (J). (ps up). pap. 3.99 (978-0-06-009461-4(3) , Harper Trophy) HarperCollins Pubs.

Capucilli, Alyssa Satin. Biscuit's Day at the Farm. Schories, Pat, illus. 2008. (My First I Can Read Bks.). 32p. (J). pap. 3.99 (***978-0-06-074169-3(4)*** , Harper Trophy) HarperCollins Pubs.

Carey Molter. Ate As in Skate. 2003. (Word Families Ser.: Vol. 8). (Illus.). 23p. (J). (ps-3). lib. bdg. 19.93 (978-1-59197-271-6(X) , SandCastle) ABDO Publishing Co.

Carla's Bookcase: First Grade Guided Reading Level F. (On Our Way to English Ser.). (gr. 1 up). 27.75 (978-0-7578-7051-4(1)) Rigby Education.

Carlos Comes to Lakeside School. 2002. (gr. 6-12). 285.36 (978-0-7362-1291-5(4)); stu. ed. 5.65 (978-0-7362-1293-9(0)); stu. ed. 4.34 (978-0-7362-1294-6(9)) Hampton-Brown Bks.

Carlson, Lavelle. Can a Toucan Hoot Too? A Phonemic Awareness Tale, 10 vols. Adams, Lucas, illus. 2003. 32p. (J). (ps-1). per. 16.95 (978-0-9725803-0-4(1)) Children's Publishing.

Carmen's Star Party. (Early Intervention Levels Ser.). 31.86 (978-0-7362-0622-8(1)) Hampton-Brown Bks.

Carmen's Star Party (20), Vol. 20. (Early Intervention Levels Ser.). 5.31 (978-0-7362-0610-5(8)) Hampton-Brown Bks.

Carole, Jane. Get Ready for First Grade! 1,107 Interactive & Educational Exercises for Curriculum-Based Learning That's Fun! 2005. (Illus.). 320p. spiral bd., spiral bd. 17.95 (978-1-57912-461-8(5) , 81461) Black Dog & Leventhal Pubs., Inc.

Carpas, Jackie. Learning Through Literature. 2004. (Illus.). 128p. (J). per. 11.99 (978-0-88724-260-1(X) , CD-0584) Carson-Dellosa Publishing Co., Inc.

Carr, Roger. Present for Dad. 2001. (gr. k-3). lib. bdg. 11.65 (978-0-613-33414-3(0)) Tandem Library Bks.

Carson, Jana. We Both Read-Stop Teasing Taylor! Treatner, Meryl, illus. 2005. (We Both Read Ser.). 44p. (J). (gr. 1-2). 7.99 (978-1-891327-61-2(5)); pap. 3.99 (978-1-891327-62-9(3)) Treasure Bay, Inc.

Carus, Andre W. Flint Holds Fire, Level D. Incl. Great Beginnings. 1982. pap., wbk. ed. (978-0-89688-292-8(6) , 88-292); Headway Level D Real Phonics Workbook A. (978-0-89688-294-2(2) , 88-294); Level D. tchr.'s training gde. ed. (978-0-89688-456-4(2) , 88-456); Level D. pap., wbk. ed. (978-0-89688-462-5(7) , 88-462); Level D. suppl. ed. (978-0-89688-468-7(6) , 88-468); Level D. suppl. ed. (J). (gr. 2-6). (978-0-89688-451-9(1) , 88-451) Open Court Publishing Co.

The Case of the Furry Thing. (Little Book Practice Reader Ser.). (J). (978-0-8136-0849-5(X)) Modern Curriculum Pr.

The Case of the Missing Planet. 2005. (Book Treks Ser.). (J). (gr. 3 up). stu. ed. 34.95 (978-0-673-62845-9(0)) Celebration Pr.

Casey & the Nest. 2005. (J). (978-1-932570-47-2(0)) Literacy Footprints Inc.

The Cat-Flap Trap: Individual Title Six-Packs. (Story Steps Ser.). (gr. k-2). 32.00 (978-0-7635-9824-2(0)) Rigby Education.

Catchpole, Barbara. Spirals Stories: Nick! Jackson, Anita, ed. 1998. 32p. 22.00 (978-0-7487-3653-9(0)) Nelson Thornes Ltd. GBR. *Dist:* Trans-Atlantic Pubns., Inc.

Caulson, Kathleen. Power Reading: Games. Caulson, Kathleen, illus. 2005. (Illus.). (J). 76p. (gr. 2-4). 29.95 (978-1-883186-98-2(6) , PPMXG2-3); 88p. (gr. 4-5). 79.95 (978-1-883186-99-9(4) , PPMXG45) National Reading Styles Institute, Inc.

—Power Reading: Games/Mixed P1. 2005. (Illus.). 76p. (J). (gr. k-2). 29.95 (978-1-883186-97-5(8) , PPMXGP1) National Reading Styles Institute, Inc.

Causley, Charles & Hammond, Andrew. I-Read Year 2 Anthology: Down on the Farm. 2007. (I-read Ser.). (Illus.). 40p. pap. (***978-0-521-70470-0(7)***) Cambridge Univ. Pr.

Cave. The Big Box. 1998. (Illus.). (J). pap. 3.90 (978-0-8172-5636-4(9)) Steck-Vaughn.

Caving Adventures, 6 vols. (gr. 4 up). 39.95 (978-0-7368-9284-1(2)) Red Brick Learning.

CD & the Giant Cat: Individual Title Six-Packs. (Action Packs Ser.). 120p. (gr. 3-5). 44.00 (978-0-7635-8426-9(6)) Rigby Education.

Cecil the Caterpillar: Individual Title Six-Pack Pouch - Level E. (Lighthouse Ser.). 12p. (gr. 1 up). 26.00 (978-0-7578-0836-4(0)) Rigby Education.

Celebrating Children Set 800827, 7. 2005. (J). (978-1-59794-024-5(0)) Environments, Inc.

Celebrations Grade Level Libraries: I Like Me! 2005. (Little Celebrations Ser.). (J). (gr. k-3). 74.50 (978-0-673-77743-0(X)) Celebration Pr.

Celebrations Grade Level Libraries: Jamberry. 2005. (Little Celebrations Ser.). (J). (gr. k-3). 82.95 (978-0-673-75782-1(X)) Celebration Pr.

Celebrations Grade Level Libraries: The Best Bug Parade. 2005. (Little Celebrations Ser.). (J). (gr. k-3). 82.95 (978-0-673-77590-0(9)) Celebration Pr.

Cell City: Individual Title Six-Packs. (Rigby Infoquest Ser.). (gr. 5 up). 37.00 (978-0-7578-6490-2(2)) Rigby Education.

Certificate Only. (gr. k-5). 89.00 (978-0-7578-6542-8(9)); (gr. 3-5). 89.00 (978-0-7578-6524-4(0)); (gr. 3-5). 89.00 (978-0-7578-6523-7(2)); (gr. 4-5). 89.00 (978-0-7578-6535-0(6)); (gr. 4-5). 89.00 (978-0-7578-6536-7(4)) Rigby Education.

Cesar Chavez: Second Grade Guided Reading Level L. (On Our Way to English Ser.). (gr. 2 up). 34.50 (978-0-7578-7104-7(6)) Rigby Education.

Chamberlain, Judith A. Perlitas. Brammer, Erin McGonigle, illus. 2000. (Books for Young Learners). 12p. (J). pap. 5.00 (978-1-57274-143-0(0)) Owen, Richard C. Pubs., Inc.

Chancellor, Deborah & Waddell, Martin. Dinosaurs. 2007. (I-read Ser.). (Illus.). 48p. pap. (***978-0-521-70488-5(X)***) Cambridge Univ. Pr.

Chandler. Con Destinos. 1998. (J). pap., tchr. ed. 53.32 (978-0-07-027513-3(0)) McGraw-Hill Cos., The.

Chandler, Pauline. Mr. Rabbit the Farmer. Smith, Eric, illus. 2005. 24p. (J). lib. bdg. 22.65 (***978-1-59646-736-1(3)***) Dingles & Co.

A Change in Plans: Fourth Grade Guided Comprehension Level M. (On Our Way to English Ser.). (gr. 4 up). 34.50 (978-0-7578-7156-6(9)) Rigby Education.

Changing & Growing: Individual Title Six-Packs. (Sails Literacy Ser.). (gr. 1-2). 36.00 (978-0-7578-6730-9(8)) Rigby Education.

The Changing Face of... Series, 28 vols., Set. 2004. 838.04 (978-1-4109-1369-2(4)) Harcourt Schl. Pubs.

Character Education Classroom Library. (gr. 2-5). lib. bdg. 45.95 (978-0-7368-9260-5(5)) Red Brick Learning.

Character Education Complete Unit. (gr. 2-5). 265.95 (978-0-7368-9261-2(3)) Red Brick Learning.

Charlesworth, Liza. My First Bilingual Little Readers. 2007. 64p. Level C. pap. 11.99 (***978-0-439-02425-9(0));*** Level B. pap. 11.99 (***978-0-439-02424-2(2))*** Scholastic, Inc.

—My First Little Readers: 25 Reproducible Mini-Books That Give Kids a Great Start in Reading. 2005. 64p. pap. 11.99 (978-0-439-51760-7(5) , Teaching Resources) Scholastic, Inc.

—My First Little Readers Level B: 25 Reproducible Mini-Books That Give Kids a Great Start in Reading. 2005. (My First Little Readers Ser.). 64p. pap. 11.99 (978-0-439-51758-4(3) , Teaching Resources) Scholastic, Inc.

Charlie & Champ. 2nd ed. 2004. (J). 4.95 (978-0-943864-57-0(7)) Davenport, May Pubs.

Charlie's PE Gear: Individual Title Six-Pack Pouch - Level E. (Lighthouse Ser.). 12p. (gr. 1 up). 26.00 (978-0-7578-0838-8(7)) Rigby Education.

Charlotte's Web Page: Individual Title Six-Packs. (Action Packs Ser.). 104p. (gr. 3-5). 44.00 (978-0-7635-2987-1(7)) Rigby Education.

Chatterjee, Debjani, et al. Tiger Time. 2007. (I-read Ser.). (Illus.). 40p. pap. (***978-0-521-70478-6(2))*** Cambridge Univ. Pr.

Chefs: Individual Title Six-Packs. (On Deck Ser.). 24p. (gr. 4-5). 35.00 (978-0-7578-1031-2(4)) Rigby Education.

Cheney, Glen. Shot Down! 2004. 64p. (YA). per. 3.95 (978-1-56254-826-1(3) , SP8263) Saddleback Educational Publishing.

Chewy Books 800779, 2. 2005. (J). (978-1-59794-040-5(2)) Environments, Inc.

Chicken Food: 3-in-1 Package. (Sails Literacy Ser.). 24p. (gr. 2 up). 57.00 (978-0-7578-3213-0(X)) Rigby Education.

Chicken Food: 6 Small Books. (Sails Literacy Ser.). 24p. (gr. 2 up). 25.00 (978-0-7578-3189-8(3)) Rigby Education.

Chicken Food: Big Book Only. (Sails Literacy Ser.). 24p. (gr. 2 up). 27.00 (978-0-7635-6999-0(2)) Rigby Education.

Chico: Kindergarten Guided Reading Level C. (On Our Way to English Ser.). (gr. k up). 27.75 (978-0-7578-7017-0(1)) Rigby Education.

Childers, Erskine. Riddle of the Sands. 2004. (Oxford Bookworms Ser.). (Illus.). 104p. 6.50 (978-0-19-423072-8(4)) Oxford Univ. Pr., Inc.

Children & Families Books 800716, 10. 2005. (J). (978-1-59794-014-6(3)) Environments, Inc.

Children of Ancient Greece. (Rosen Real Readers Big Bookstm Ser.). 16p. (J). (gr. 2-3). 38.75 (978-1-4042-6223-2(7)) Rosen Publishing Group, Inc., The.

Children's Feelings Books 800829, 14. 2005. (J). (978-1-59794-026-9(7)) Environments, Inc.

Childrens Press Staff, ed. A Rookie Reader, Set. 2005. (Rookie Reader Ser.). 96p. (J). (ps-2). pap. 9.95 (978-0-516-25326-8(3) , Children's Pr.) Scholastic Library Publishing.

—A Rookie Reader - Level A, Set. 2005. (Rookie Reader Ser.). 72p. (J). (ps-2). pap. 9.95 (978-0-516-25325-1(5) , Children's Pr.) Scholastic Library Publishing.

—A Rookie Reader - Level C, Set. 2005. (Rookie Reader Ser.). 96p. (J). (ps-2). pap. 9.95 (978-0-516-25327-5(1) , Children's Pr.) Scholastic Library Publishing.

Children's World Books 800828, 10. 2005. (J). (978-1-59794-025-2(9)) Environments, Inc.

Child's Play Staff. Hyd A Lled. 1999. (WEL., Illus.). 14p. (J). (978-0-85953-482-6(0)) Child's Play International Ltd. GBR. *Dist:* Child's Play-International.

—Mae'n Braf Allan. 1999. (WEL., Illus.). 24p. (J). pap. (978-0-85953-652-3(1)) Child's Play International Ltd. GBR. *Dist:* Child's Play-International.

—Pawb Yn Coginio! 1999. (WEL., Illus.). 24p. (J). pap. (978-0-85953-651-6(3)) Child's Play International Ltd. GBR. *Dist:* Child's Play-International.

—Seirff Y Swltan. 1999. (WEL., Illus.). 21p. (J). pap. (978-0-85953-690-5(4)) Child's Play International Ltd. GBR. *Dist:* Child's Play-International.

Child's World Tapes Book Set 800912, 3 vols. 2005. (J). pap. (978-1-59794-077-1(1)) Environments, Inc.

Chile Fever. (Lexile Levels Ser.). 9.09 (978-1-56334-733-7(4)) Hampton-Brown Bks.

Chile Peppers: Second Grade Guided Reading Level E. (On Our Way to English Ser.). (gr. 2 up). 34.50 (978-0-7578-7069-9(4)) Rigby Education.

Chinery, Michael. Animales Salvajes. (Enciclopedias Everest Internacional Ser.). (SPA., Illus.). 320p. (J). (gr. 3-5). (978-84-241-9399-7(7) , EV1502) Everest de Ediciones y Distribucion, S.L. ESP. *Dist:* Lectorum Pubns., Inc.

—Enciclopedia de los Animales Salvajes, 8 vols.Tr. of Wild World of Animals. (SPA.). 346p. (J). (gr. 3-5). 100.00 (978-84-241-2059-7(0)) Everest de Ediciones y Distribucion, S.L. ESP. *Dist:* Lectorum Pubns., Inc.

Chin's Lunch: First Grade Guided Reading Level G. (On Our Way to English Ser.). (gr. 1 up). 27.75 (978-0-7578-7056-9(2)) Rigby Education.

Chiquilibros: Add-to Packs. (Smart Start Ser.). (gr. k-1). 37.00 (978-0-7635-4062-3(5)); 37.00 (978-0-7635-4064-7(1)); 37.00 (978-0-7635-4066-1(8)); 76.00 (978-0-7635-4068-5(4)) Rigby Education.

Chiquilibros: Chiquicuentos Complete Package. (ps-1). 250.00 (978-0-7635-8570-9(X)) Rigby Education.

Chiquilibros: Chiquicuentos Grupo A Add-to Pack. (ps-1). 125.00 (978-0-7635-8566-2(1)) Rigby Education.

Chiquilibros: Chiquicuentos Grupo B Add-to Pack. (ps-1). 125.00 (978-0-7635-8567-9(X)) Rigby Education.

Chiquilibros: Cuentos listos Complete Packages. (gr. k-1). 151.00 (978-0-7635-4061-6(7)); 151.00 (978-0-7635-4063-0(3)); 151.00 (978-0-7635-4065-4(X)); 250.00 (978-0-7635-4067-8(6)) Rigby Education.

Chopsticks: Second Grade Guided Reading Level H. (On Our Way to English Ser.). (gr. 2 up). 34.50 (978-0-7578-7081-1(3)) Rigby Education.

Ciencias. (Enciclopedias Everest Internacional Ser.). (SPA., Illus.). (YA). (gr. 5-8). 41.95 (978-84-241-9405-5(5) , EV7495) Everest de Ediciones y Distribucion, S.L. ESP. *Dist:* Lectorum Pubns., Inc.

Cimochowski, Anna. FOL Intermediate Level, 80 bks., Set. 2001. (J). pap. 91.19 (978-0-7398-5721-2(5)) Steck-Vaughn.

—FOL Introductory Level, 80 bks., Set. 2001. (J). pap. (978-0-7398-5720-5(7)) Steck-Vaughn.

—FOL Preparatory Level, 80 bks., Set. 2001. (J). pap. (978-0-7398-5719-9(3)) Steck-Vaughn.

Circles Everywhere: Kindergarten Guided Reading Level A. (On Our Way to English Ser.). (gr. k up). 27.75 (978-0-7578-7002-6(3)) Rigby Education.

Citra, Becky. Jeremy & the Golden Fleece. Milne, Jessica, illus. 2007. (Orca Echoes Ser.). 64p. (J). (gr. 2-4). pap. (***978-1-55143-657-9(4))*** Orca Bk. Pubs.

Citra, Becky. Strawberry Moon, Vol. 5. 2005. (Orca Young Readers Ser.: Book #5). (Illus.). 96p. (J). (gr. 3-6). pap. 5.95 (978-1-55143-367-7(2)) Orca Bk. Pubs. USA.

A City Divided. 2003. (Illus.). pap. 7.60 (978-0-7398-7526-1(4)) Steck-Vaughn.

City Life. (Rosen Real Readers Big Bookstm Ser.). 8p. (J). (gr. k-1). 27.95 (978-1-4042-6210-2(5)) Rosen Publishing Group, Inc., The.

City Sights. (Early Intervention Levels Ser.). 28.38 (978-0-7362-0404-0(0)) Hampton-Brown Bks.

City Sights (12), Vol. 12. (Early Intervention Levels Ser.). 4.73 (978-0-7362-0229-9(3)) Hampton-Brown Bks.

Civardi, Anne. The Complete Book of First Experiences. Cartwright, Stephen, illus. 2005. 144p. (J). 19.95 (978-0-7945-1012-1(4) , Usborne) EDC Publishing.

Claire, Elizabeth. Where Is Taro? Rosenthal, Marilyn, ed. Lustig, Loretta, illus. 2000. (J). pap., act. bk. ed., instr.'s gde. ed. 15.00 (978-0-937630-10-5(1)) Eardley Pubns.

Clap for the Show. (Early Intervention Levels Ser.). 28.38 (978-0-7362-0407-1(5)) Hampton-Brown Bks.

Clap for the Show (12), Vol. 12. (Early Intervention Levels Ser.). 4.73 (978-0-7362-0232-9(3)) Hampton-Brown Bks.

Clarke, Jane. I'm Not Wearing That! Mostyn, David, illus. 2005. 24p. (J). lib. bdg. 22.65 (***978-1-59646-716-3(9))*** Dingles & Co.

—Prince Albert's Birthday. Chatterton, Martin, illus. 2005. 24p. (J). lib. bdg. 22.65 (***978-1-59646-748-4(7))*** Dingles & Co.

La clase de Equitacion 5: Leveled Books. 2001. (McGraw-Hill. Lectura Ser.). (ENG & SPA.). (gr. 5 up). (978-0-02-188277-9(0)) Macmillan/McGraw-Hill Schl. Div.

La clase Vale por 2 junta Fondos 5: Leveled Books. 2001. (McGraw-Hill. Lectura Ser.). (ENG & SPA.). (gr. 2 up). (978-0-02-188054-6(9)) Macmillan/McGraw-Hill Schl. Div.

Class Collection: Fifth Grade, (On Our Way to English Ser.). (gr. 5 up). cd-rom 29.95 (978-0-7578-4498-0(7)) Rigby Education.

Class Collection: Fourth Grade. (On Our Way to English Ser.). (gr. 4 up). cd-rom 29.95 (978-0-7578-4368-6(9)) Rigby Education.

Classic Storytapes Book Set 800911, 3 vols. 2005. (J). pap. (978-1-59794-076-4(3)) Environments, Inc.

Classification (Gr. 1-2) 2003. (J). (978-1-58232-040-3(3)) Bryan Hse. Pubs., Inc.

Classroom Rules: First Grade Guided Reading Level F. (On Our Way to English Ser.). (gr. 1 up). 27.75 (978-0-7578-7054-5(6)) Rigby Education.

Claycomb, Patty. Lost in the Dark Woods. Chapin, Patrick, illus. 2002. (Two Can Read Ser.). 16p. (J). 2.99 (978-1-56472-655-1(X)) Edupress, Inc.

Cleaning up the Park: Individual Title Six-Packs. (ps-2). 23.00 (978-0-7635-8817-5(2)) Rigby Education.

Climbing: Individual Title Six-Packs. (Literatura 2000 Ser.). (gr. k-1). 28.00 (978-0-7635-0047-4(X)) Rigby Education.

Clish, Marian L. Fish Don't Swim in a Tree. Clish, Lori, illus. (J). (gr. k-3). pap. 7.95 (978-1-928632-12-2(2)); 1999. pap. 10.95 incl. audio (978-1-928632-13-9(0)); 1999. pap. 14.95 incl. audio compact disk (978-1-928632-14-6(9)) Writers Marketplace:Consulting, Critiquing & Publishing.

Close up on Careers: Individual Title Six-Packs. (Rigby Infoquest Ser.). (gr. 6 up). 37.00 (978-0-7578-7984-5(5)) Rigby Education.

Cloudcatcher, 6 Packs. (Action Packs Ser.). 104p. (gr. 3-5). 44.00 (978-0-7635-8412-2(6)) Rigby Education.

Cloze Encounters Vol. 3: Space, 3 vols. 2000. 48p. pap. 6.95 (978-1-58324-046-5(2) , World Teachers Pr.) Didax Educational Resources, Inc.

Coaching for Comprehension 1-2. 2004. (Basic Skills Ser.). 48p. (J). pap. 6.99 (978-0-88724-164-2(6) , CD-4715) Carson-Dellosa Publishing Co., Inc.

Coaching for Comprehension 2-3. 2004. (Basic Skills Ser.). 48p. (J). pap. 6.99 (978-0-88724-165-9(4) , CD-4716) Carson-Dellosa Publishing Co., Inc.

Coaching for Comprehension 3-4. 2004. (Basic Skills Ser.). 48p. (J). pap. 6.99 (978-0-88724-166-6(2) , CD-4717) Carson-Dellosa Publishing Co., Inc.

Coaching for Comprehension 4-5. 2004. (Basic Skills Ser.). 48p. (J). pap. 6.99 (978-0-88724-167-3(0) , CD-4718) Carson-Dellosa Publishing Co., Inc.

Coaching for Comprehension 5-6. 2004. (Basic Skills Ser.). 48p. (J). pap. 6.99 (978-0-88724-173-4(5) , CD-4719) Carson-Dellosa Publishing Co., Inc.

Cogs in the Wheel: Individual Title Six-Packs. (Rigby Infoquest Ser.). (gr. 6 up). 37.00 (978-0-7578-7995-1(0)) Rigby Education.

Cohen, Santiago, illus. Go Away, Crows! 2005. (J). (gr. 1-2). lib. bdg. 11.15 (978-0-606-33877-6(2)) Tandem Library Bks.

A Cold Day, 6 vols. (gr. k-2). 28.95 (978-0-7368-8626-0(5)) Red Brick Learning.

Cold Day, Hot Chocolate: First Grade Guided Reading Level D. (On Our Way to English Ser.). (gr. 1 up). 27.75 (978-0-7578-7040-8(6)) Rigby Education.

Cole, Bob. Power Reading: Chapter Books/Wizard of OZ. Sirrell, Terri, illus. 2004. 94p. (J). (gr. 3-4). vinyl bd. 39.95 (978-1-883186-64-7(1) , PPCL1) National Reading Styles Institute, Inc.

—Power Reading: Chapter/Sci-Fi/Dr. Little. Sirrell, Terri, illus. 2004. 25p. (J). (gr. 3-4). vinyl bd. 39.95 (978-1-883186-63-0(3) , PPSF1) National Reading Styles Institute, Inc.

—Power Reading: Chapter/Sci-Fi/Dr. Little 2. Ford, David, illus. 2005. 25p. (J). (gr. 3-4). vinyl bd. 39.95 (978-1-883186-76-0(5) , PPSF4) National Reading Styles Institute, Inc.

—Power Reading: Chapter/Sci-Fi/Superhero. Ford, David, illus. 2004. 25p. (J). (gr. 3-4). vinyl bd. 39.95 (978-1-883186-62-3(5) , PPSF2) National Reading Styles Institute, Inc.

—Power Reading: Chapter/Sci-Fi/Time Warp. Ford, David, illus. 2004. 25p. (J). (gr. 4 up). vinyl bd. 39.95 (978-1-883186-60-9(9) , PPSF3) National Reading Styles Institute, Inc.

—Power Reading: Chapter/Sci-Fi/Time Warp 2. Ford, David, illus. 2005. 52p. (J). (gr. 4 up). vinyl bd. 39.95 (978-1-883186-75-3(7) , PPSF5) National Reading Styles Institute, Inc.

—Power Reading: Classics/Jungle Book. Connor, Robin, illus. 2004. 94p. (J). (gr. 4 up). vinyl bd. 39.95 (978-1-883186-61-6(7) , PPCL2) National Reading Styles Institute, Inc.

—Power Reading: Classics/Treasure Island. Lee, Joe, illus. 2004. 94p. (J). (gr. 5-6). vinyl bd. 39.95 (978-1-883186-59-3(5) , PPCL3) National Reading Styles Institute, Inc.

—Power Reading: Comic Book/Dr. Little. Sirrell, Terri, illus. 2005. 36p. (J). (gr. 2-4). vinyl bd. (978-1-883186-77-7(3) , PPSFC1) National Reading Styles Institute, Inc.

—Power Reading: Comic Book/Jungle Book. Connor, Robin, illus. 2005. 62p. (J). (gr. 3 up). vinyl bd. 39.95 (978-1-883186-74-6(9) , PPCLC2) National Reading Styles Institute, Inc.

—Power Reading: Comic Book/Time Warp. Ford, David, illus. 2005. 36p. (J). (gr. 3 up). vinyl bd. 29.95 (978-1-883186-69-2(2) , PPSFC3) National Reading Styles Institute, Inc.

—Power Reading: Comic Book/Time Warp 2. Ford, David, illus. 2005. 36p. (J). (gr. 3-4). vinyl bd. 29.95 (978-1-933533-01-8(3) , PPSFC3A) National Reading Styles Institute, Inc.

—Power Reading: Comic Book/Wizard of OZ. Sirrell, Terri, illus. 2005. 60p. (J). (gr. 3-4). vinyl bd. 39.95 (978-1-883186-80-7(3) , PPCLC1) National Reading Styles Institute, Inc.

—Power Reading: Nail-Biters! 2. Morton, Vivian, illus. 2005. 94p. (J). (gr. 6 up). vinyl bd. 89.95 (978-1-883186-25-8(0) , PPNB2) National Reading Styles Institute, Inc.

Cole, Bob & Sirrell, Terri. Power Reading: Comic Book/Dr. Little 2. 2005. (Illus.). 36p. (J). (gr. 2-4). vinyl bd. 29.95 (978-1-933533-00-1(5) , PPSFC1A) National Reading Styles Institute, Inc.

Collection for Readers Bookshelf Collection. 2004. (gr. 5 up). 180.00 (978-0-328-03137-5(2)); Set. (gr. 3 up). 180.00 (978-0-328-03135-1(6)); Set. (gr. 6 up). 180.00 (978-0-328-03138-2(0)); Units 1-6. (gr. 4 up). 180.00 (978-0-328-03136-8(4)) Addison-Wesley Educational Pubs., Inc.

Collection for Readers Take-Home. 2004. (gr. 3 up). 48.00 (978-0-328-02302-8(7)); (gr. 4 up). 48.00 (978-0-328-02684-5(0)); (gr. 5 up). 48.00 (978-0-328-02685-2(9)); (gr. 6 up). 48.00 (978-0-328-02686-9(7)) Addison-Wesley Educational Pubs., Inc.

Color It My Way: Individual Title Six-Packs. (Story Steps Ser.). (gr. k-2). 32.00 (978-0-7635-9611-8(6)) Rigby Education.

The Color Purple Student Packet, Gr. 9-12. 2004. (YA). (978-1-58130-508-1(7)) Novel Units, Inc.

Come & Have Fun: KinderWords Individual Title Six-Packs. (Kinderstarters Ser.). 8p. (ps-1). 21.00 (978-0-7635-8701-7(X)) Rigby Education.

Come on Up: KinderWords Individual Title Six-Packs. (Kinderstarters Ser.). 8p. (ps-1). 21.00 (978-0-7635-8698-0(6)) Rigby Education.

Come to My House. (Greetings Ser.: Vol. 3). 24p. (gr. 2-3). 31.00 (978-0-7635-5702-7(1)) Rigby Education.

Comic Book Facts. 2003. (Illus.). pap. 5.60 (978-0-7398-7514-8(0)) Steck-Vaughn.

Communicating with Animals. 2005. (Book Treks Ser.). (J). 37.95 (978-0-7652-3247-2(2)) Celebration Pr.

Como buenos Amigos: Social/Emotional Lap Book. (Pebble Soup Exploraciones Ser.). (ps up). 16.00 (978-0-7578-1782-3(3)) Rigby Education.

Complete Add-on. 2005. (Book Treks Ser.). (J). (gr. 3 up). 152.95 (978-0-7652-6134-2(0)); (gr. 4 up). 157.50 (978-0-7652-6135-9(9)); (gr. 5 up). 157.50 (978-0-7652-6136-6(7)) Celebration Pr.

Complete Bridgestone Reading Program. (gr. 2-5). 1772.95 (978-0-7368-1811-7(1) , Bridgestone Bks.) Capstone Pr., Inc.

Complete DRA Pack. (Dra Levels Ser.). 752.54 (978-0-7362-2576-2(5)) Hampton-Brown Bks.

Complete Early Intervention Pack. (Early Intervention Levels Ser.). 610.07 (978-0-7362-2557-1(9)) Hampton-Brown Bks.

Complete Guided Reading Pack. (Guided Reading Levels Ser.). 752.54 (978-0-7362-2565-6(X)) Hampton-Brown Bks.

Complete High Five USA Reading Program I. (gr. 4 up). 667.95 incl. audio (978-0-7368-9580-4(9) , High Five) Red Brick Learning.

Complete High Five USA Reading Program I, Books Only. (gr. 4 up). 599.95 (978-0-7368-9581-1(7) , High Five) Red Brick Learning.

Complete High Five USA Reading Program II. (gr. 4 up). 667.95 incl. audio (978-0-7368-3859-7(7) , High Five) Red Brick Learning.

Complete High Five USA Reading Program II, Books Only. (gr. 4 up). 599.95 (978-0-7368-3861-0(9) , High Five) Red Brick Learning.

Complete Letter Books Program. (gr. k-2). 409.95 (978-0-7368-4127-6(X)) Red Brick Learning.

Complete Lexile Pack. (Lexile Levels Ser.). 967.73 (978-0-7362-2577-9(3)) Hampton-Brown Bks.

Complete Pebble Reading Program. (gr. k-2). 2836.95 (978-0-7368-1489-8(2) , Pebble Bks.) Capstone Pr., Inc.

Complete Yellow Umbrella Program. (gr. k-2). 1810.95 (978-0-7368-1778-3(6) , Yellow Umbrella Bks.) Capstone Pr., Inc.

Complete Yellow Umbrella Spanish & English Program. (ENG & SPA.). (gr. k-2). 3395.95 (978-0-7368-3178-9(9) , Yellow Umbrella Bks.) Capstone Pr., Inc.

Complete Yellow Umbrella Spanish Program. (SPA.). (gr. k-2). 1810.95 (978-0-7368-1779-0(4) , Yellow Umbrella Bks.) Capstone Pr., Inc.

Comprehension Power Readers: Add-on Pack (Reading Level 1-2) 2005. (Comprehension Power Readers Ser.). (J). (gr. 1 up). 166.95 (978-0-7652-4339-3(3)); (gr. 2 up). 166.95 (978-0-7652-4340-9(7)) Modern Curriculum Pr.

Comprehension Power Readers: Add-on Pack (Reading Level 3-4) 2005. (Comprehension Power Readers Ser.). (J). (gr. 3 up). 194.50 (978-0-7652-4341-6(5)); (gr. 4 up). 194.50 (978-0-7652-4342-3(3)) Modern Curriculum Pr.

Comprehension Power Readers: Add-on Pack (Reading Level 5-6) 2005. (Comprehension Power Readers Ser.). (J). (gr. 5 up). 219.95 (978-0-7652-4343-0(1)); (gr. 6 up). 219.95 (978-0-7652-4344-7(X)) Modern Curriculum Pr.

Comprehension Power Readers: Library (Reading Level 1-2) 2005. (Comprehension Power Readers Ser.). (J). (gr. 1 up). 1026.50 (978-0-7652-4333-1(4)); (gr. 2 up). 1026.50 (978-0-7652-4334-8(2)) Modern Curriculum Pr.

Comprehension Power Readers: Library (Reading Level 3-4) 2005. (Comprehension Power Readers Ser.). (J). (gr. 3 up). 1193.50 (978-0-7652-4335-5(0)); (gr. 4 up). 1193.50 (978-0-7652-4336-2(9)) Modern Curriculum Pr.

Comprehension Power Readers: Library (Reading Level 5-6) 2005. (Comprehension Power Readers Ser.). (J). (gr. 5 up). 1334.95 (978-0-7652-4337-9(7)); (gr. 6 up). 1334.95 (978-0-7652-4338-6(5)) Modern Curriculum Pr.

La confederacion de las hermanas Bronte 12: Leveled Books. 2001. (McGraw-Hill. Lectura Ser.). (ENG & SPA.). (gr. 4 up). (978-0-02-188212-0(6)) Macmillan/McGraw-Hill Schl. Div.

Connolly, Debbie & Danley, Laurie. Passport to Genre: A Literature Enrichment Guide. Mitchell, Judy, ed. Hillam, Corbin, illus. 2006. 64p. (J). pap. 9.95 (978-1-57310-488-3(4)) Teaching & Learning Co.

Contemporary Biography, 7 Bks, Set. (Robbie Reader Ser.). (Illus.). (gr. 1-4). lib. bdg. (978-1-58415-350-4(4)) Mitchell Lane Pubs., Inc.

Content Connect! (gr. 3-5). 1081.53 (978-0-7362-2579-3(X)) Hampton-Brown Bks.

Content Connect! Picture It! Big Book with Pen & Teacher's Guide. (gr. 4-8). tchr. ed. 54.98 (978-0-7362-2436-9(X)) Hampton-Brown Bks.

Context Clues (Gr. 1-3) 2003. (J). (978-1-58232-080-9(2)) Bryan Hse. Pubs., Inc.

Cooke, Andy. Wheels on the Bus. Cooke, Andy, illus. 1999. (Read & Share Ser.). (Illus.). 24p. (J). (ps). pap. 3.99 (978-0-7636-0877-4(7)) Candlewick Pr.

Cookson, Paul & Johnson, Vicki. I-Read Year 2 Anthology: Days Out. 2007. (I-read Ser.). (Illus.). 40p. pap. (*978-0-521-70473-1(1)) Cambridge Univ. Pr.

The Coolest Rock (28), Vol. 28. (Early Intervention Levels Ser.). 5.31 (978-0-7362-0656-3(6)) Hampton-Brown Bks.

Cooper, Arin. Boots & Shoes. 2004. 12p. (J). pap. 4.95 (978-1-57874-044-4(4)) Kaeden Corp.

Cooper, Terry, ed. Reading & Math Jumbo Workbook Grade 3. 2005. 320p. pap. 14.99 (978-0-439-78602-7(9) , Teaching Resources) Scholastic, Inc.

—Reading & Math Jumbo Workbook: Grade K. 2005. 320p. pap. 14.99 (978-0-439-78599-0(5) , Teaching Resources) Scholastic, Inc.

—Schol Success Reading & Math Gr4. 2005. 320p. pap. 14.99 (978-0-439-78603-4(7) , Teaching Resources) Scholastic, Inc.

—1st Grade Reading Practice. 2006. 48p. pap. 5.99 (978-0-439-81900-8(8) , Teaching Resources) Scholastic, Inc.

—2nd Grade Reading Practice. 2006. 48p. pap. 5.99 (978-0-439-81901-5(6) , Teaching Resources) Scholastic, Inc.

—3rd Grade Reading Practice. 2006. 48p. pap. 5.99 (978-0-439-81902-2(4) , Teaching Resources) Scholastic, Inc.

—4th Grade Reading Practice. 2006. 48p. pap. 5.99 (978-0-439-81903-9(2) , Teaching Resources) Scholastic, Inc.

Corbett, Pie. I-read Year 3. 2005. (Illus.). 16p. cd-rom 600.00 (978-1-84565-102-2(2)) Cambridge Univ. Pr.

—I-Read Year 4. 2005. cd-rom 600.00 (978-1-84565-103-9(0)) Cambridge Univ. Pr.

—I-read Year 5. 2006. cd-rom 600.00 (978-1-84565-104-6(9)) Cambridge Univ. Pr.

—I-read Year 6. 2006. cd-rom 600.00 (978-1-84565-105-3(7)) Cambridge Univ. Pr.

Corn Bread for Everyone! Second Grade Guided Reading Level J. (On Our Way to English Ser.). (gr. 2 up). 34.50 (978-0-7578-7092-7(9)) Rigby Education.

Corner Store. (J). 21.95 (978-0-8136-4337-3(6)); pap. 13.15 (978-0-8136-4336-6(8)) Modern Curriculum Pr.

Cosgrove, Stephen. Across a Stream. ed. 2004. (Reader's Theater Ser.). (J). pap. 22.00 (978-1-4108-1142-4(5)) Benchmark Education Co.

—Columbus Meets Isabella & Ferdinand. ed. 2004. (Reader's Theater Ser.). (J). pap. 22.00 (978-1-4108-1138-7(7)) Benchmark Education Co.

—Storybook Readers, 5 bks. Steelhammer, Illona, illus. (J). lib. bdg. 73.75 (978-1-56674-921-3(2)) Forest Hse. Publishing Co., Inc.

Cosgrove, Stephen & Higgins, Kathy. Under Siege. ed. 2004. (Reader's Theater Ser.). (J). pap. 22.00 (978-1-4108-1143-1(3)) Benchmark Education Co.

Cosgrove, Stephen & Higgins, Kitty. The Golden Spike. ed. 2004. (Reader's Theater Ser.). (J). pap. 22.00 (978-1-4108-1141-7(7)) Benchmark Education Co.

Cottringer, Anne. Hot Dog. Walker, Katherine, illus. 2005. 24p. (J). lib. bdg. 22.65 (*978-1-59646-738-5(X)) Dingles & Co.

Cousineau-Peiffer, Trisha. Have You Ever Heard of a Rainbow Farm. Everett-Hawkes, Bonnie, illus. 2006. 32p. (J). 12.95 (*978-0-9792084-1-6(6)) Dream Ridge Pr.

—Have You Ever Heard of a Rainbow Farm: The Missing Color Kittens. Everett-Hawkes, Bonnie, illus. 2007. 48p. (J). per. 15.95 (*978-0-9792084-2-3(4)) Dream Ridge Pr.

Covey, Stephen R. I Can Read, Bk. 2. 2000. (Step Ahead Workbooks Ser.). (Illus.). 32p. (J). (gr. k-1). pap. 2.99 (978-0-307-03588-2(3) , 03588, Golden Bks.) Random Hse. Children's Bks.

Coville, Bruce. In the Land of Always October. 2005. (Illus.). (J). 16.00 (978-0-15-202369-0(0)) Harcourt Trade Pubs.

Cowley, Joy. Mrs. Wishy-Washy's Tub. (Story Box(R) Ser.). 8p. 20.95 (978-0-7802-9365-6(7)) Wright Group, The.

—Mud Walk. (Story Box(R) Ser.). 16p. 31.50 (978-0-322-02463-2(3)) Wright Group, The.

The Craft Stick Project: Fourth Grade Guided Comprehension Level L. (On Our Way to English Ser.). (gr. 4 up). 34.50 (978-0-7578-7152-8(6)) Rigby Education.

Cranium Inc. Staff. Cranium: the Word Worm Book of Outrageous Fun! Write it, Read it, Say It! Baseman, illus. 2006. 38p. (J). (gr. 2-17). 14.99 (978-0-316-05762-2(2)) Little, Brown Bks. for Young Readers.

The Creature of Cassidy's Creek: Individual Chapter Book Title Six-Packs. Vol. 26. 32p. (gr. 3-4). 44.00 (978-0-7635-4481-2(7)) Rigby Education.

Crebbin, June. A Cat for Tom. 2005. (Cambridge Storybooks Ser.). 32p. pap. 7.00 (978-0-521-67471-3(9)) Cambridge Univ. Pr.

—The Dog Show. 2005. (Cambridge Storybooks Ser.). 32p. pap. 7.00 (978-0-521-67474-4(3)) Cambridge Univ. Pr.

—Please Sit Still ELT Edition. 2004. (Cambridge Storybooks Ser.). (Illus.). 24p. pap. 6.00 (978-0-521-75235-0(3)) Cambridge Univ. Pr.

Crebbin, June, et al. Spike & the Concert. 2005. (Cambridge Reading Ser.). pap. (978-5-7107-6036-9(6)) Cambridge Univ. Pr.

Crittenden, Alex. Reading for Real. 2007. 384p. (C). pap. 52.00 (*978-0-13-150034-1(1) , Prentice Hall) Prentice Hall PTR.

Crocodile Tears. (Sails Literacy Ser.). 24p. (gr. k up). 8.00 (978-0-7635-7034-7(6)) Rigby Education.

Crocodile's Bag: Level J, 6 vols. 128p. (gr. 2-3). 41.95 (978-0-7699-0992-9(2)) Shortland Pubns. (U. S. A.) Inc.

Croft, Andy. David Beckham. 3rd rev. ed. 2005. (Illus.). 32p. pap. (978-0-340-90072-7(5)) Cambridge Univ. Pr.

Croft, Andy & Basic Skills Agency Staff. Michael Schumacher. 2005. 32p. pap. 8.50 (978-0-340-84882-1(0)) Cambridge Univ. Pr.

Crops. (Guided Reading Levels Ser.). 28.56 (978-0-7362-1061-4(X)) Hampton-Brown Bks.

Cross, Gillian. Sam Sorts It Out. Mier, Colin, illus. 2005. 24p. (J). lib. bdg. 22.65 (*978-1-59646-702-6(9)) Dingles & Co.

Crowther, Terence G., contrib. by. Up & Away in English. 1999. (Illus.). (J). (978-0-19-434990-1(X)) Oxford Univ. Pr., Inc.

Crum, Anna-Maria. Trackers of Dynamic Earth. 2004. (Navigators Ser.). (J). pap. 42.00 (978-1-4108-0441-9(0)) Benchmark Education Co.

The Crystal Unicorn: Individual Chapter Book Title Six-Packs. Vol. 26. 32p. (gr. 3-4). 44.00 (978-0-7635-4479-9(5)) Rigby Education.

Cullimore, Stan. Alien Swap. Schon, Nick, illus. 2005. 24p. (J). lib. bdg. 22.65 (*978-1-59646-744-6(4)) Dingles & Co.

Cunningham, Patricia. Making Names. 2004. 240p. (J). pap. 24.99 (978-0-88724-212-0(X) , CD-2429) Carson-Dellosa Publishing Co., Inc.

Cunningham, Patricia & Hall, Dorothy P. Making More Big Words. 2001. (Making More Big Words Ser.). 208p. (J). (gr. 3-6). pap. 18.99 (978-1-56417-899-2(4) , GA1589) Schaffer, Frank Pubns.

Custureri, Mary. Happy Anderson & Connie Clam. 2006. (Illus.). 36p. (J). spiral bd. 24.95 (978-1-933190-00-6(0)) HighPoint Publishing, Inc.

Cutting, Robert. Falling Star. Ng, Drew, illus. 2007. 48p. (J). lib. bdg. 23.08 (*978-1-4242-1625-3(7)) Fitzgerald Bks.

—Mars Colony. Jeevan, Dhamindra, illus. 2007. 48p. (J). lib. bdg. 23.08 (*978-1-4242-1630-7(3)) Fitzgerald Bks.

Cuxart, Bernardette, illus. Cuentame un Cuento, No. 4. (SPA.). 96p. (J). (gr. k-3). (978-84-480-1602-9(5) , TM8095) Timun Mas, Editorial S.A. ESP. *Dist:* Lectorum Pubns., Inc.

Czajkowski, Bernice & McRoberts, Richard. Going Home. 2002. (Wizard Study Guides Ser.). 48p. pap., stu. ed. 6.00 (978-1-876367-74-9(1)) Cambridge Univ. Pr.

Dad & I, Vol. 3. (Early Intervention Levels Ser.). 3.85 (978-1-56334-977-5(9)) Hampton-Brown Bks.

Dad & Wag. (Early Intervention Levels Ser.). 21.30 (978-0-7362-0385-2(0)) Hampton-Brown Bks.

Dale, Penny. Ten in the Bed: Level One, Red. Dale, Penny, illus. 1999. (Reading Together Ser.). (Illus.). 32p. (J). pap. (978-0-7636-0868-2(8)) Candlewick Pr.

Dallas Shapes Up! Fourth Grade Guided Comprehension Level R. (On Our Way to English Ser.). (gr. 4 up). 34.50 (978-0-7578-7182-5(8)) Rigby Education.

Dalton, Annie. Lilac Peabody, No. 4. 2005. (Illus.). 96p. (J). pap. 7.95 (*978-0-00-713774-9(5)) HarperCollins Pubs. Ltd. GBR. *Dist:* Independent Pubs. Group.

Danforth, Audrey & Kennedy, Jane. Good Night Sky. Terry, Christy, illus. 1999. 8p. (J). (gr. k-2). pap. 3.75 (978-1-58323-005-3(X) , Seedling Pubns.) Continental Pr., Inc.

Dangerous Adventures Complete Unit. (gr. 4 up). 142.95 (978-0-7368-9025-0(4)) Red Brick Learning.

Daniel. The Early Birds Alarm Clock. 1999. pap. 5.60 (978-0-7398-2400-9(7)) Steck-Vaughn.

Daniel, Becky. The "UnWorkbook" Creative Reading, Grade 1. 2005. (Illus.). 96p. (J). (gr. 1-1). pap. 12.99 (978-0-7682-3121-2(3) , Schaffer, Frank) Schaffer, Frank Pubns.

—The "UnWorkbook" Creative Reading, Grade 2. 2005. (Illus.). 96p. (J). (gr. 2-2). pap. 12.99 (978-0-7682-3122-9(1) , Schaffer, Frank) Schaffer, Frank Pubns.

Dann, Geoff. At Home. 1999. (Baby's World Ser.). (Illus.). 10p. (J). (ps). (978-0-7112-1123-0(X)) Lincoln, Frances Ltd.

—Outdoors. 1999. (Baby's World Ser.). (Illus.). 10p. (J). (ps). (978-0-7112-1124-7(8)) Lincoln, Frances Ltd.

Daronco, Mickey. A Good Cook. 2003. (BuildUp Ser.). (J). pap. 22.00 (978-1-4108-0771-7(1)) Benchmark Education Co.

—I Know! 2003. (BuildUp Ser.). (J). pap. 22.00 (978-1-4108-0775-5(4)) Benchmark Education Co.

—Meet Us All. 2003. (BuildUp Ser.). (J). pap. 22.00 (978-1-4108-0770-0(3)) Benchmark Education Co.

Daronco, Mickey & Ohanesian, Diane. Am I in It? 2nd rev. ed. 2003. (BuildUp Ser.). (J). pap. 22.00 (978-1-4108-0736-6(3)) Benchmark Education Co.

—The Big Band. 2nd rev. ed. 2004. (BuildUp Ser.). (J). pap. 22.00 (978-1-4108-1525-5(0)) Benchmark Education Co.

—I See! I Hear! rev. ed. 2003. (BuildUp Ser.). Orig. Title: Looking Up. (J). pap. 22.00 (978-1-4108-0767-0(3)) Benchmark Education Co.

—I Will Try. 2003. (BuildUp Ser.). (J). pap. 22.00 (978-1-4108-0763-2(0)) Benchmark Education Co.

—Look at Me Now! 2nd rev. ed. 2004. (BuildUp Ser.). (J). pap. 22.00 (978-1-4108-1528-6(5)) Benchmark Education Co.

—A Lot to Sell. 2nd rev. ed. 2004. (BuildUp Ser.). (J). pap. 22.00 (978-1-4108-1524-8(2)) Benchmark Education Co.

—My Big Day. 2nd rev. ed. 2004. (BuildUp Ser.). (J). pap. 22.00 (978-1-4108-1532-3(3)) Benchmark Education Co.

—On a Cold Day. 2nd rev. ed. 2004. (BuildUp Ser.). (J). pap. 22.00 (978-1-4108-1529-3(3)) Benchmark Education Co.

—Play this Game with Me. 2nd rev. ed. 2003. (BuildUp Ser.). (J). pap. 22.00 (978-1-4108-0759-5(2)) Benchmark Education Co.

—Show Me! 2nd rev. ed. 2003. (BuildUp Ser.). Orig. Title: We Can. (J). pap. 22.00 (978-1-4108-0760-1(6)) Benchmark Education Co.

—What Might I Spy? 2nd rev. ed. 2004. (BuildUp Ser.). (J). pap. 22.00 (978-1-4108-1536-1(6)) Benchmark Education Co.

—Will It Eat? 2003. (BuildUp Ser.). (J). pap. 22.00 (978-1-4108-0761-8(4)) Benchmark Education Co.

—Will It Float? 2nd rev. ed. 2004. (BuildUp Ser.). (J). pap. 22.00 (978-1-4108-1531-6(5)) Benchmark Education Co.

Davidson, Susanna. Little Princess. 2005. (Illus.). 48p. (J). (gr. 2 up). 8.95 (978-0-7945-1123-4(6) , Usborne) EDC Publishing.

Davidson, Susanna. The Story of Hanukkah. 2007. (Young Reading Series 1 Gift Bks). 48p. (J). 8.99 (*978-0-7945-1781-6(1) , Usborne) EDC Publishing.

Davies, Caroline & Martin, Sharon. Y Frech Goch. 2005. (WEL., Illus.). 12p. (978-1-86101-079-7(6)) Acen Limited.

Davies, Gill & Freeman, Tina. Friend for Flash. 2004. (Tales from Yellow Barn Farm Ser.). (Illus.). 24p. (J). 3.99 (978-1-85854-324-6(X)) Brimax Books Ltd. GBR. *Dist:* Byeway Bks.

Davis. Book Reports Plus. 1999. (Illus.). (J). pap. (978-0-7398-1218-1(1)) Steck-Vaughn.

—Preschool Ages 3-4. 1999. (J). (ps). pap. (978-0-7398-1221-1(1)) Steck-Vaughn.

—Preschool Ages 4-5. 1999. (J). (ps). pap. (978-0-7398-1222-8(X)) Steck-Vaughn.

Davis, Anita. Cinde' Reader: In the Town of Reading Land. l.t. ed. 2004. (Illus.). 100p. per. 15.00 (978-1-59453-177-4(3) , 1901) Airleaf Publishing & Bookselling.

Davis, Jim. Garfield y el Deporte. (SPA.). 96p. (J). 9.95 (978-84-7419-470-8(9) , AU003) Grijalbo Mondadori, S.A.-Junior ESP. *Dist:* Continental Bk. Co., Inc.

Day. Simons Big Challenge. 1999. pap. (978-0-7398-0878-8(8)) Steck-Vaughn.

The Day: Individual Title Six-Packs. (Sails Literacy Ser.). 16p. (gr. k up). 27.00 (978-0-7635-4390-7(X)) Rigby Education.

Day & Night. (J). pap. 13.15 (978-0-8136-4306-9(6)) Modern Curriculum Pr.

A Day in the Life of a Computer: Third Grade Guided Reading Level J. (On Our Way to English Ser.). (gr. 3 up). 34.50 (978-0-7578-7119-1(4)) Rigby Education.

The Day of the Dead, 6 packs. (Greetings Ser.: Vol. 1). Tr. of El Dia La Noche. 24p. (gr. 2-3). 31.00 (978-0-7635-9411-4(3)) Rigby Education.

The Day the Sky Fell Down: Individual Title Six-Pack Pouch - Level I. (Lighthouse Ser.). 16p. (gr. 1 up). 26.00 (978-0-7578-0857-9(3)) Rigby Education.

Daynes, Katie. Chocolate. Larkum, Adam, illus. 2004. 48p. (J). (gr. 2 up). pap. 5.95 (978-0-7945-0759-6(X) , Usborne) EDC Publishing.

Days In... Set 1, 4 vols. 2004. (Illus.). 74.24 (978-1-4109-0740-0(6)); pap. 19.80 (978-1-4109-0745-5(7)) Raintree.

Dean, Jan. Harry & the Megabyte Brain, 6 vols., Pack. 2000. (Cambridge Reading Ser.). (Illus.). 40p. pap. 44.75 (978-0-521-78629-4(0)) Cambridge Univ. Pr.

Dean, Michael. Extreme Sports, Level 2. 2003. (Illus.). 32p. (C). pap. 9.00 (978-0-582-46168-0(5)) Pearson ESL.

Dear Bess, Vol. 6. (Early Intervention Levels Ser.). 3.55 (978-0-7362-0172-8(6)) Hampton-Brown Bks.

DeBoer, Rondi & Tangvald, Christine. Daniel & the Lions. Conger, Holli, illus. 2007. (J). 5.99 (*978-0-7847-1948-0(9)) Standard Publishing.

—David & Goliath. Conger, Holli, illus. 2007. (J). 5.99 (*978-0-7847-1950-3(0)) Standard Publishing.

The Deer Report. 2005. (J). (978-1-58453-311-5(0)) Pioneer Valley Educational Pr., Inc.

Deighton, Jo, adapted by. Ali Baba & the Forty Thieves: Traditional Stories:Cinderella: The Elves & the Shoemaker. (Scheherezade Presents Ser.: No. 11). (Illus.). 48p. (J). pap. (978-1-85964-101-9(6) , Ithaca Pr.) Garnet Publishing, Ltd.

—Bacbouc the Lazy Tailor: Traditional Stories:Beauty & the Beast: The Red Shoes. (Scheherezade Presents Ser.: No. 12). (Illus.). 48p. (J). pap. (978-1-85964-102-6(4) , Ithaca Pr.) Garnet Publishing, Ltd.

—Codadad & His Brothers: Traditional Stories:The Grocer, the Student & the Elf: The Ugly Duckling. (Scheherezade Presents Ser.: No. 13). (Illus.). 48p. (J). pap. (978-1-85964-103-3(2) , Ithaca Pr.) Garnet Publishing, Ltd.

—The Fisherman & the Wicked Genie: Traditional Stories-:The Shepherdess & the Chimney Sweep: Seven with One Blow. (Scheherezade Presents Ser.: No. 14). (Illus.). 48p. (J). pap. (978-1-85964-104-0(0) , Ithaca Pr.) Garnet Publishing, Ltd.

Denstaedt, Linda. I Love Reading, Level 8. Rozines Roy, Jennifer, illus. 1999. (Homework Booklets Ser.). 80p. (YA). (gr. 7-9). pap. 2.99 (978-1-56822-833-4(3) , IF0328, Instructional Fair) Schaffer, Frank Pubns.

The Dentist, 2 Packs. (Chiquilibros Ser.). (ps-1). 12.00 (978-0-7635-8545-7(9)) Rigby Education.

Denton, Kady MacDonald. Watch Out, William. 2006. (I Am Reading Ser.). (Illus.). 48p. (J). (gr. k-3). pap. 3.95 (978-0-7534-5960-7(4) , Kingfisher) Houghton Mifflin Co. Trade & Reference Div.

Depree, Helen. Foundations: Upper Emergent - Upper Emergent - Complete Kit, Vol. 2. 2nd ed. (gr. 1 up). 423.95 (978-0-322-04291-9(7)) Wright Group, The.

Derico, Laura. All God¿s Bugs. Smith, Matt, illus. 2007. (Happy Day Bks.). (J). 1.99 (*978-0-7847-1933-6(0)) Standard Publishing.

—Easter Surprises. Harris, Phyllis, illus. 2007. (Happy Day Bks.). (J). 1.99 (*978-0-7847-2085-1(1)) Standard Publishing.

deRubertis, Barbara. Let's Read Together Set 5: Vowel Team Books. 1998. (Illus.). 32p. (J). (ps-3). pap. 24.75 (978-1-57565-079-1(7)) Kane Pr., The.

—Let's Read Together Set 6: Vowel Team Book & Tape Packages. 1998. (Illus.). 32p. (J). (ps-3). pap. 44.75 incl. audio (978-1-57565-080-7(0)) Kane Pr., The.

Designed for Living: Individual Title Six-Packs. (Rigby Infoquest Ser.). 32p. (gr. 4 up). 37.00 (978-0-7578-5724-9(8)) Rigby Education.

Developing Set 2. 2002. (J). (978-1-58453-127-2(4)) Pioneer Valley Educational Pr., Inc.

Developing Set 4. 2005. (J). (978-1-58453-289-7(0)) Pioneer Valley Educational Pr., Inc.

Dhami, Narinder. Monster under the Stairs. Spoor, Mike, illus. 2005. 24p. (J). lib. bdg. 22.65 (*978-1-59646-718-7(5)) Dingles & Co.

—Samosa Thief. Blundell, Tony, illus. 2005. 24p. (J). lib. bdg. 22.65 (*978-1-59646-708-8(8)) Dingles & Co.

Dibels. 2003. (gr. k up). (978-0-328-07800-4(X)); (gr. k up). (978-0-328-07796-0(8)); (gr. 1 up). (978-0-328-07801-1(8)); (gr. 1 up). (978-0-328-07797-7(6)); (gr. 2 up). (978-0-328-07798-4(4)); (gr. 3 up). (978-0-328-07799-1(2)) Addison-Wesley Educational Pubs., Inc. (Scott Foresman).

Dickson, Sue. Sing, Spell, Read & Write: All Aboard. rev. ed. 2005. (J). (gr. k-3). stu. ed. 12.95 (978-0-7652-3211-3(1)) Modern Curriculum Pr.

—Sing, Spell, Read & Write: On Track. rev. ed. 2005. (J). (gr. k-3). stu. ed. 8.50 (978-0-7652-3210-6(3)) Modern Curriculum Pr.

A Dictionary of Space: Second Grade Guided Reading Level F. (On Our Way to English Ser.). (gr. 2 up). 34.50 (978-0-7578-7073-6(2)) Rigby Education.

Did You Hear? Fourth Grade Guided Comprehension Level N. (On Our Way to English Ser.). (gr. 4 up). 34.50 (978-0-7578-7160-3(7)) Rigby Education.

Diego Saves the Planet! Small Versions of Big Books. (On Our Way to English Ser.). (gr. 3 up). 35.50 (978-0-7578-7241-9(7)) Rigby Education.

Diego Saves the Planet! Third Grade Big Books. (On Our Way to English Ser.). (gr. 3 up). 29.95 (978-0-7578-4212-2(7)) Rigby Education.

Diego's Moving Day: Second Grade Guided Reading Level F. (On Our Way to English Ser.). (gr. 2 up). 34.50 (978-0-7578-7070-5(8)) Rigby Education.

Different Places, Different Faces: Individual Title Six-Packs. (Rigby Infoquest Ser.). 24p. (gr. 3 up). 34.00 (978-0-7578-5765-2(5)) Rigby Education.

Digging for History: Individual Title Six-Packs. (Rigby Infoquest Ser.). (gr. 6 up). 37.00 (978-0-7578-7998-2(5)) Rigby Education.

Digraph. 2001. pap. 3.25 (978-0-7398-4560-8(8)) Steck-Vaughn.

Dijs, Carla. Truck One: On Safari in Africa, Europe A, Australia, The Poles, 4. 1999. (Illus.). 12p. (J). (ps-3). 12.99 (978-0-85953-830-5(3)) Child's Play-International.

Dill, Bonnie. Brain Quest Grade 1 Reading. 2nd rev. ed. 2007. 148p. (J). 10.95 (978-0-7611-4139-6(1)) Workman Publishing Co., Inc.

—Brain Quest Grade 2 Reading. 2nd rev. ed. 2007. (Illus.). 148p. (J). 10.95 (978-0-7611-4140-2(5)) Workman Publishing Co., Inc.

Ding-a-lings & Flutterbys. (Sails Literacy Ser.). 24p. (gr. k up). 8.00 (978-0-7635-7033-0(8)) Rigby Education.

Dining with Prunella. (J). pap. 13.75 (978-0-8136-4640-4(5)) Modern Curriculum Pr.

Dinner Time. 2005. (J). (978-1-58453-298-9(X)) Pioneer Valley Educational Pr., Inc.

Dinner Time: Kindergarten Newcomer Books. (On Our Way to English Ser.). (gr. k up). 23.50 (978-0-7578-7188-7(7)) Rigby Education.

Dinosaur Detective: 6 Each of 1 Anthology, 6 vols. (Wildcats Ser.). 32p. (gr. 2-8). (978-0-322-00586-0(8)) Wright Group, The.

The dinosaur Hunt: Individual Title, 6 packs. (gr. 1-2). 22.00 (978-0-7635-9185-4(8)) Rigby Education.

Dippold, Jane, illus. Alphabet Activities: Sticker Fun. 2003. (Sticker Fun Ser.). 16p. (J). spiral bd. 10.98 (978-0-7853-7825-9(1) , PIL Kids) Publications International, Ltd.

A Disaster Is Coming! Second Grade Newcomer Books. (On Our Way to English Ser.). (gr. 2 up). 29.50 (978-0-7578-7214-3(X)) Rigby Education.

Discover America State by State, 51 vols., Set. 2005. (Illus.). (J). (gr. k-5). 895.00 (978-1-58536-294-3(8)) Sleeping Bear Pr.

Discovering Literature: The EMC Write-in Reader. 2nd ed. (Literature & the Language Arts Ser.). (J). (gr. 6 up). wbk. ed. 15.95 (978-0-8219-2908-7(9)) EMC/Paradigm Publishing.

Disney Publishing Staff. Where Is Your Home?, 15 vols. 2003. (It's Fun to Learn Ser.). (Illus.). 32p. (J). (ps-3). 3.99 (978-1-57973-133-5(3)) Advance Pubs. LLC.

Disney Staff. Everyone Is Special. 2000. (Lessons from the Hundred-Acre Woods: Vol. 2). (Illus.). 32p. (J). (ps-4). pap. 3.49 (978-1-57973-088-8(4)) Advance Pubs. LLC.

Disney's World of English. 2005. 899.00 incl. VHS (978-1-59172-098-0(2)); 899.00 incl. DVD (978-1-59172-090-4(7)) Lexicon Marketing Corp.

Dixon, Dougal. Dinosaur Explorer, 8 vols. 2005. (QEB Readers). (Illus.). 24p. (J). (ps-3). lib. bdg. 15.95 (978-1-59566-070-1(4)) QEB Publishing Inc.

DK Publishing. All about Me! 2008. (Baby Fun Ser.). 14p. (J). 4.99 (***978-0-7566-3438-4(5)***) Dorling Kindersley Publishing, Inc.

—Nature Detectives. 2007. 48p. (J). (gr. 5-12). 3.99 (***978-0-7566-3512-1(8)***) Dorling Kindersley Publishing, Inc.

Do-It-Yourself D'Nealian. 1999. (gr. k up). 85.55 (978-0-673-30125-3(7)); (gr. k up). 85.55 (978-0-673-30047-8(1)); (gr. 1 up). 85.55 (978-0-673-30126-0(5)); (gr. 1 up). 85.55 (978-0-673-30048-5(X)); (gr. 2 up). 85.55 (978-0-673-30127-7(3)); (gr. 2 up). 85.55 (978-0-673-30049-2(8)); (gr. 3 up). 85.55 (978-0-673-30128-4(1)); (gr. 3 up). 85.55 (978-0-673-30050-8(1)); (gr. 4 up). 85.55 (978-0-673-59280-4(4)); (gr. 4 up). 85.55 (978-0-673-59278-1(2)); (gr. 5 up). 85.55 (978-0-673-59281-1(2)); (gr. 5 up). 85.55 (978-0-673-59279-8(0)) Addison-Wesley Educational Pubs., Inc.

Do That, Do This! Set B, 6 Pack. (gr. k-3). 29.00 (978-0-7635-0540-0(4)) Rigby Education.

Do You Like My Pet? (Early Intervention Levels Ser.). 21.30 (978-0-7362-0369-2(9)); Vol. 2. 3.55 (978-0-7362-0090-5(8)) Hampton-Brown Bks.

Dobson, Josh, illus. Come in the Grass: First Wave Satellite Individual Title Six-Packs. (Sails Literacy Ser.). 16p. (gr. k up). 27.00 (978-0-7578-6872-6(X)) Rigby Education.

The Doctor, 2 Pack. (Chiquilibros Ser.). (ps-1). 12.00 (978-0-7635-8544-0(0)) Rigby Education.

The Dog & the Bone, Set 2. l.t. ed. 1999. (Illus.). 19p. (J). (gr. k-6). reprint ed. pap. 2.50 (978-1-893688-02-5(X)) Carroll Schl., The.

The Dog & the Wolf, Set 1. l.t. ed. 1999. (Illus.). 25p. (J). (gr. k-6). reprint ed. pap. 2.50 (978-1-893688-04-9(6)) Carroll Schl., The.

The Dog from Outer Space: Individual Title Six-Pack Pouch - Level J. (Lighthouse Ser.). 16p. (gr. 2 up). 28.00 (978-0-7578-0864-7(6)) Rigby Education.

Doherty, Ellen. Williiam's Journal. ed. 2003. (Early Connections Ser.). (J). pap. 35.00 (978-1-4108-1558-3(7)) Benchmark Education Co.

Dolan, Penny. Moo! Sharp, Melanie, illus. 2004. (Read-It! Readers Ser.). 32p. (C). (gr. k-3). 18.60 (978-1-4048-0643-6(1)) Picture Window Bks.

The Dolphin Caller: Chapter Book, 6 Packs. Vol. 30. 32p. (gr. 5 up). 44.00 (978-0-7578-0983-5(9)) Rigby Education.

The Dolphin on the Wall: Individual Title Six-Packs. (gr. 3 up). 35.00 (978-0-7635-9662-0(0)) Rigby Education.

The Dolphins, 6 Packs. 16p. (gr. 2 up). 35.00 (978-0-7635-9384-1(2)) Rigby Education.

The Dome. 2003. (Illus.). pap. 7.60 (978-0-7398-7525-4(6)) Steck-Vaughn.

Domnauer, Teresa. The First to Finish, Level 3. 2007. (Extreme Readers Ser.). 32p. (J). (gr. 1-2). pap. 3.95 (***978-0-7696-6391-3(5)***) School Specialty Publishing.

Donaghey, Sean. The 10 Funniest People. 2008. (Tentrade; Ser.). 48p. (J). pap. 14.99 (***978-1-55448-474-4(X)*** , Watts, Franklin) Scholastic Library Publishing.

Donaldson, Julia. Spirals Plays: Books & Crooks. Jackson, Anita, ed. 1998. 48p. 22.00 (978-0-7487-3656-0(5)) Nelson Thornes Ltd. GBR. *Dist:* Trans-Atlantic Pubns., Inc.

Donaldson, Julia & Richards, Lucy. The Quick Brown Fox Club. 2006. (Red Bananas Ser.). (Illus.). 48p. (J). (978-0-7787-1080-6(7)) Crabtree Publishing Co.

Donkin, Andrew. Transformers Armada: The Unicron Battles. 2004. (Dk Readers Ser.). (Illus.). 48p. (J). pap. 3.99 (978-0-7566-0312-0(9)) Dorling Kindersley Publishing, Inc.

Donkin, Andrew & Dorling Kindersley Publishing Staff. Transformers Armada: The Unicron Battles. 2004. (Dk Readers Ser.). (Illus.). 48p. (J). 12.99 (978-0-7566-0313-7(7)) Dorling Kindersley Publishing, Inc.

—Transformers Armada: The Uprising. 2004. (Dk Readers Ser.). (Illus.). 48p. (J). 12.99 (978-0-7566-0311-3(0)) Dorling Kindersley Publishing, Inc.

—Transformers Armada: The Uprising, Level 4. 2004. (Dk Readers Ser.). (Illus.). 48p. (J). pap. 3.99 (978-0-7566-0310-6(2)) Dorling Kindersley Publishing, Inc.

Don't Get Lost. 2004. (J). (978-1-58453-214-9(9)) Pioneer Valley Educational Pr., Inc.

Don't Interrupt! Individual Title Six-Packs. (gr. 1-2). 25.00 (978-0-7635-9193-9(9)) Rigby Education.

Don't Splash Me!, 6 Packs. (gr. 1-2). 22.00 (978-0-7635-9160-1(2)) Rigby Education.

Don't Touch: Early Level Satellite Individual Title Six-Packs. (Sails Literacy Ser.). 16p. (gr. 1-2). 27.00 (978-0-7578-6515-2(1)) Rigby Education.

Doodt, Melissa. Where's the Baby? 1999. (ps-2). lib. bdg. 11.80 (978-0-613-30874-8(3)) Tandem Library Bks.

Dooley, Virginia. School Success Reading & Math Prek. Cooper, Terry, ed. 2005. 320p. pap., wbk. ed. 14.99 (978-0-439-78598-3(7) , Teaching Resources) Scholastic, Inc.

Dora's Decision: Fifth Grade Guided Comprehension Level N. (On Our Way to English Ser.). (gr. 5 up). 34.50 (978-0-7578-6599-2(2)) Rigby Education.

Dora's Soapbox Car: Second Grade Guided Reading Level K. (On Our Way to English Ser.). (gr. 2 up). 34.50 (978-0-7578-7096-5(1)) Rigby Education.

Dora's Time to Shine: Fifth Grade Guided Comprehension Level Q. (On Our Way to English Ser.). (gr. 5 up). 34.50 (978-0-7578-6614-2(X)) Rigby Education.

Doudna, Kelly. Any Day but Today! 2004. (Sight Words Ser.). (Illus.). 23p. (J). (ps-3). lib. bdg. 19.93 (978-1-59197-464-2(X)) ABDO Publishing Co.

—Cc: See It Say It Hear It. l.t. ed. 2000. (Alphabet Ser.). (Illus.). 24p. (J). (ps-3). lib. bdg. 19.93 (978-1-57765-396-7(3) , SandCastle) ABDO Publishing Co.

—Dd: See It Say It Hear It. l.t. ed. 2000. (Alphabet Ser.). (Illus.). 24p. (J). (ps-3). lib. bdg. 19.93 (978-1-57765-397-4(1) , SandCastle) ABDO Publishing Co.

—Et As in Jet. 2003. (Word Families Ser.). 23p. (J). (ps-3). lib. bdg. 19.93 (978-1-59197-230-3(2) , SandCastle) ABDO Publishing Co.

—Give It a Try! 2004. (Sight Words Ser.). (Illus.). 23p. (J). (ps-3). lib. bdg. 19.93 (978-1-59197-469-7(0)) ABDO Publishing Co.

—Id As in Squid. 2003. (Word Families Ser.). (Illus.). 23p. (J). (ps-3). lib. bdg. 19.93 (978-1-59197-235-8(3) , SandCastle) ABDO Publishing Co.

—Ig As in Pig. Marx, Monica, ed. 2003. (Word Families Ser.). (Illus.). 23p. (J). (ps-3). lib. bdg. 19.93 (978-1-59197-236-5(1)) ABDO Publishing Co.

—Ii: See It Say It Hear It. l.t. ed. 2000. (Alphabet Ser.). (Illus.). 24p. (J). (ps-3). lib. bdg. 19.93 (978-1-57765-402-5(1) , SandCastle) ABDO Publishing Co.

—Ill As in Grill. 2003. (Word Families Ser.). (Illus.). 23p. (J). (ps-3). lib. bdg. 19.93 (978-1-59197-237-2(X) , SandCastle) ABDO Publishing Co.

—In As in Twin. 2003. (Word Families Ser.). (Illus.). 23p. (J). (ps-3). lib. bdg. 19.93 (978-1-59197-238-9(8) , SandCastle) ABDO Publishing Co.

—Ip As in Ship. 2003. (Word Families Ser.). (Illus.). 23p. (J). (ps-3). lib. bdg. 19.93 (978-1-59197-239-6(6) , SandCastle) ABDO Publishing Co.

—It As in Sit. 2003. (See It, Say It, Hear It Ser.). (Illus.). 23p. (J). (ps-3). lib. bdg. 19.93 (978-1-59197-240-2(X) , SandCastle) ABDO Publishing Co.

—Just Make Some Art! 2004. (Sight Words Ser.). (Illus.). 23p. (J). (ps-3). lib. bdg. 19.93 (978-1-59197-481-9(X)) ABDO Publishing Co.

—Long & Short. l.t. ed. 2000. (Opposites Ser.). (Illus.). 24p. (J). (ps-3). lib. bdg. 19.93 (978-1-57765-146-8(4) , SandCastle) ABDO Publishing Co.

—Near & Far. l.t. ed. 2000. (Opposites Ser.). (Illus.). 24p. (J). (ps-3). lib. bdg. 19.93 (978-1-57765-147-5(2) , SandCastle) ABDO Publishing Co.

—Oo: See It Say It Hear It. l.t. ed. 2001. (Alphabet Ser.). (Illus.). 24p. (J). (ps-3). lib. bdg. 19.93 (978-1-57765-435-3(8) , SandCastle) ABDO Publishing Co.

—Ow As in Crow. 2003. (Word Families Ser.). (Illus.). 23p. (J). (ps-3). lib. bdg. 19.93 (978-1-59197-265-5(5) , SandCastle) ABDO Publishing Co.

—Pp: See It Say It Hear It. l.t. ed. 2001. (Alphabet Ser.). (Illus.). 24p. (J). (ps-3). lib. bdg. 19.93 (978-1-57765-436-0(6) , SandCastle) ABDO Publishing Co.

—Rr: See It Say It Hear It. l.t. ed. 2001. (Alphabet Ser.). (Illus.). 24p. (J). (ps-3). lib. bdg. 19.93 (978-1-57765-438-4(2) , SandCastle) ABDO Publishing Co.

—Ss: See It Say It Hear It. l.t. ed. 2001. (Alphabet Ser.). (Illus.). 24p. (J). (ps-3). lib. bdg. 19.93 (978-1-57765-439-1(0) , SandCastle) ABDO Publishing Co.

—There Are Ants down There! 2004. (Sight Words Ser.). (Illus.). 23p. (J). (ps-3). lib. bdg. 19.93 (978-1-59197-473-4(9)) ABDO Publishing Co.

—Tt: See It Say It Hear It. l.t. ed. 2001. (Alphabet Ser.). (Illus.). 24p. (J). (ps-3). lib. bdg. 19.93 (978-1-57765-440-7(4) , SandCastle) ABDO Publishing Co.

—Uu: See It Say It Hear It. l.t. ed. 2001. (Alphabet Ser.). (Illus.). 24p. (J). (ps-3). lib. bdg. 19.93 (978-1-57765-441-4(2) , SandCastle) ABDO Publishing Co.

—Vv: See It Say It Hear It. l.t. ed. 2001. (Alphabet Ser.). (Illus.). 24p. (J). (ps-3). lib. bdg. 19.93 (978-1-57765-442-1(0) , SandCastle) ABDO Publishing Co.

—Was That Fun? 2004. (Sight Words Ser.). (Illus.). 23p. (J). (ps-3). lib. bdg. 19.93 (978-1-59197-475-8(5)) ABDO Publishing Co.

—Wet & Dry. l.t. ed. 2000. (Opposites Ser.). (Illus.). 24p. (J). (ps-3). lib. bdg. 19.93 (978-1-57765-149-9(9) , SandCastle) ABDO Publishing Co.

—When Can You Play Again? 2004. (Sight Words Ser.). (Illus.). 23p. (J). (ps-3). lib. bdg. 19.93 (978-1-59197-478-9(X)) ABDO Publishing Co.

—Ww: See It Say It Hear It. l.t. ed. 2001. (Alphabet Ser.). (Illus.). 24p. (J). (ps-3). lib. bdg. 19.93 (978-1-57765-443-8(9) , SandCastle) ABDO Publishing Co.

—Xx: See It Say It Hear It. l.t. ed. 2001. (Alphabet Ser.). (Illus.). 24p. (J). (ps-3). lib. bdg. 19.93 (978-1-57765-444-5(7) , SandCastle) ABDO Publishing Co.

—Yy: See It Say It Hear It. l.t. ed. 2001. (Alphabet Ser.). (Illus.). 24p. (J). (ps-3). lib. bdg. 19.93 (978-1-57765-445-2(5) , SandCastle) ABDO Publishing Co.

—Zz: See It Say It Hear It. l.t. ed. 2001. (Alphabet Ser.). (Illus.). 24p. (J). (ps-3). lib. bdg. 19.93 (978-1-57765-446-9(3) , SandCastle) ABDO Publishing Co.

Douglas, Vincent. The Lion King - Not So Fast. 2001. (Disney Parent & Child Read Together Ser.). 40p. (ps-k). 4.99 (978-1-57768-738-2(8)) School Specialty Publishing.

—The Little Mermaid - The Big Baby. 2001. (Disney Parent & Child Read Together Ser.). 40p. (ps-k). 4.99 (978-1-57768-739-9(6)) School Specialty Publishing.

—101 Dalmations. 2002. (Disney Parent & Child Read Together Ser.). 40p. (ps-k). 4.99 (978-1-57768-737-5(X)) School Specialty Publishing.

—101 Dalmations - Puppy Parade. 2001. (Disney Parent & Child Read Together Ser.). 40p. (ps-k). 4.99 (978-1-57768-736-8(1)) School Specialty Publishing.

Douglas, Vincent & School Specialty Publishing Staff. Early Learning Kit. 2005. (Book Notes Ser.). (Illus.). 64p. (J). pap. 17.95 (978-0-7696-3877-5(5) , American Education Publishing) School Specialty Publishing.

—More Everything for Early Learning, Preschool, Vol. 2. 2005. (Everything for Early Learning Ser.). (Illus.). 320p. (J). pap. 7.95 (978-0-7696-4099-0(0) , American Education Publishing) School Specialty Publishing.

—Total Reading, Grade 1. 2005. (Total Reading Ser.). (Illus.). 352p. (J). (gr. 1-1). pap., pap. 14.95 (978-0-7696-3881-2(3) , American Education Publishing) School Specialty Publishing.

—Total Reading, Grade 2. 2005. (Total Reading Ser.). (Illus.). 352p. (J). (gr. 2-2). pap. 14.95 (978-0-7696-3882-9(1) , American Education Publishing) School Specialty Publishing.

—Total Reading, Grade 3. 2005. (Total Reading Ser.). (Illus.). 352p. (J). (gr. 3-3). pap. 14.95 (978-0-7696-3883-6(X) , American Education Publishing) School Specialty Publishing.

—Total Reading, Grade 4. 2005. (Total Reading Ser.). (Illus.). 352p. (J). (gr. 4-4). pap., pap. 14.95 (978-0-7696-3884-3(8) , American Education Publishing) School Specialty Publishing.

—Total Reading, Grade 5. 2005. (Total Reading Ser.). (Illus.). 352p. (J). (gr. 5-5). pap., pap. 14.95 (978-0-7696-3885-0(6) , American Education Publishing) School Specialty Publishing.

—Total Reading, Grade 6. 2005. (Total Reading Ser.). (Illus.). 352p. (J). (gr. 6-6). pap., pap. 14.95 (978-0-7696-3886-7(4) , American Education Publishing) School Specialty Publishing.

—Total Reading, Kindergarten. 2005. (Total Reading Ser.). (Illus.). 352p. (J). (gr. k-k). pap., pap. 14.95 (978-0-7696-3880-5(5) , American Education Publishing) School Specialty Publishing.

—Total Reading, Preschool. 2005. (Total Reading Ser.). (Illus.). 352p. (J). (gr. k-k). pap. 14.95 (978-0-7696-3879-9(1) , American Education Publishing) School Specialty Publishing.

—Word Searches. 2003. (Homework Helpers Ser.). (Illus.). 32p. (J). (gr. 3-3). pap. 2.99 (978-0-7696-2928-5(8) , American Education Publishing) School Specialty Publishing.

Down on the Farm. 2005. (Little Celebrations Thematic Packages Ser.). (J). (gr. k-3). 133.50 (978-0-673-75377-9(8)) Celebration Pr.

Down the Hill: KinderReaders Individual Title Six-Packs. (Kinderstarters Ser.). 8p. (ps-1). 21.00 (978-0-7635-8654-6(4)) Rigby Education.

Downey, Glen. Escape from East Berlin. Lingas, Leo, illus. 2007. 48p. (J). lib. bdg. 23.08 (***978-1-4242-1635-2(4)***) Fitzgerald Bks.

Doyle, Malachy. Hair Scare. Allen, Jonathan, illus. 2005. 24p. (J). lib. bdg. 22.65 (***978-1-59646-724-8(X)***) Dingles & Co.

—King Donal's Secret. Watson, Richard, illus. 2005. 24p. (J). lib. bdg. 22.65 (***978-1-59646-740-8(1)***) Dingles & Co.

—Rory's Lost His Voice. Semple, David, illus. 2005. 24p. (J). lib. bdg. 22.65 (***978-1-59646-714-9(2)***) Dingles & Co.

Dr. Seuss Book Set 800481, 4. 2005. (J). (978-1-59794-033-7(X)) Environments, Inc.

Dr. Seuss Book Set 800877, 6 vols. 2005. (J). bds. (978-1-59794-055-9(0)) Environments, Inc.

Dr. Seuss Books & Tapes Book Set 800910, 3 vols. 2005. (J). pap. (978-1-59794-075-7(5)) Environments, Inc.

The Dragon Compass: Individual Title Six-Packs. (Bookweb Ser.). 32p. (gr. 6 up). 34.00 (978-0-7578-0898-2(0)) Rigby Education.

The Dragon Inside. 2003. (Illus.). pap. 5.60 (978-0-7398-7517-9(5)) Steck-Vaughn.

Drawing Conclusions & Inferences (Gr. 1-3) 2003. (J). (978-1-58232-079-3(9)) Bryan Hse. Pubs., Inc.

A Dream Come True: Third Grade Guided Reading Level L. (On Our Way to English Ser.). (gr. 3 up). 34.50 (978-0-7578-7128-3(3)) Rigby Education.

The Dream Team: Individual Title Six-Pack Pouch - Level J. (Lighthouse Ser.). 16p. (gr. 2 up). 28.00 (978-0-7578-0865-4(4)) Rigby Education.

The Dreamer Behind the Dome: Judge Roy Hofheinz: Fifth Grade Guided Comprehension Level O. (On Our Way to English Ser.). (gr. 5 up). 34.50 (978-0-7578-6605-0(0)) Rigby Education.

Dreaming of Great Ideas Set E, 6 vols. (Phonics Readers Ser.). (gr. k-2). 28.95 (978-0-7368-4064-4(8)) Red Brick Learning.

DuFalla, Anita, illus. Sumac & the Magic Lake: Levels F-M (9-28) ed. 2004. (Reader's Theater Ser.). 16p. (J). pap. 22.00 (978-1-4108-2291-8(5) , A22915) Benchmark Education Co.

Dunham, Anne M. & O'Neal, Debbie M. Monopoly Junior Kindergarten Early Reading. 2002. 32p. (J). 3.99 (978-1-58792-023-3(9)) Trend Enterprises, Inc.

—Monopoly Language Grades 1-2. 2002. 32p. (YA). 3.99 (978-1-58792-027-1(1)) Trend Enterprises, Inc.

—Monopoly Reading Grades 1-2. 2002. 32p. (J). 3.99 (978-1-58792-026-4(3)) Trend Enterprises, Inc.

Dunmore, Helen. Clyde's Leopard. 1998. (Cambridge Reading Ser.). (Illus.). 32p. (gr. 2-6). pap. 9.00 (978-0-521-63743-5(0)) Cambridge Univ. Pr.

Dupasquier, Philippe. La Obra. (Coleccion Aqui Se Trabaja). (SPA., Illus.). 22p. (J). 10.95 (978-84-207-3799-7(2) , ANY762) Grupo Anaya, S.A. ESP. *Dist:* Continental Bk. Co., Inc.

Durno, James. Eddie Ndlovu: Ateso Version. Ejalu, Ateker & Omare-Okurut, Augustine, trs. 1998. (Cambridge African Language Library Ser.). (Illus.). 16p. pap. 3.65 (978-0-521-63785-5(6)) Cambridge Univ. Pr.

—Eddie Ndlovu: Chilomwe Version. Nkhoma, Wilson, tr. 1999. (Cambridge Reading Routes Ser.). (Illus.). 16p. pap. 3.70 (978-0-521-66850-7(6)) Cambridge Univ. Pr.

—Eddie Ndlovu: Chinyanja Version. Iphani, Max, tr. 1999. (Cambridge Reading Routes Ser.). (Illus.). 16p. pap. 3.70 (978-0-521-66882-8(4)) Cambridge Univ. Pr.

—Eddie Ndlovu: Chitonga Version. Hamoonga, Lazarous, tr. 1998. (Cambridge African Language Library Ser.). (Illus.). 16p. pap. 3.75 (978-0-521-63861-6(5)) Cambridge Univ. Pr.

—Eddie Ndlovu: Chitumbuka Version. Chirambo, Reuben, tr. 1999. (Cambridge Reading Routes Ser.). (Illus.). 16p. pap. 3.70 (978-0-521-66871-2(9)) Cambridge Univ. Pr.

—Eddie Ndlovu: Chiyao Version. Mjaya, Ahmmardouh, tr. 1999. (Cambridge Reading Routes Ser.). (Illus.). 16p. pap. 3.70 (978-0-521-66861-3(1)) Cambridge Univ. Pr.

—Eddie Ndlovu: Cinyanja Version. Mwale, Brian, tr. 1998. (Cambridge African Language Library Ser.). (Illus.). 16p. pap. 3.75 (978-0-521-63851-7(8)) Cambridge Univ. Pr.

—Eddie Ndlovu: Icibemba Version. Mwansa, Bupe, tr. 1998. (Cambridge African Language Library). (Illus.). 16p. pap. 3.75 (978-0-521-63811-1(9)) Cambridge Univ. Pr.

—Eddie Ndlovu: Kiikaonde Version. Muyebaa, Kyangubabi, tr. 1998. (Cambridge African Language Library). (Illus.). 16p. pap. 3.75 (978-0-521-63841-8(0)) Cambridge Univ. Pr.

—Eddie Ndlovu: Luganda Version. Lubega, Bonnie, tr. 1998. (Cambridge African Language Library). (LUG., Illus.). 16p. pap. 3.75 (978-0-521-63798 5(8)) Cambridge Univ. Pr.

—Eddie Ndlovu: Lunda Version. Kambangaji, Thomson, tr. 1998. (Cambridge African Language Library). (Illus.). 16p. pap. 3.75 (978-0-521-63831-9(3)) Cambridge Univ. Pr.

—Eddie Ndlovu: Luvale Version. Kaleyi, Kakoma, tr. 1998. (Cambridge African Language Library). (Illus.). 16p. pap. 3.75 (978-0-521-63821-0(6)) Cambridge Univ. Pr.

—Eddie Ndlovu: Runyankore-Rukiga Version. Bahemuka, Gaetano & Kagoro, Stephen, trs. 1998. (Cambridge African Language Library). (Illus.). 16p. pap. 3.65 (978-0-521-63779-4(1)) Cambridge Univ. Pr.

—Eddie Ndlovu: Silozi Version. Silumesii, Penelope, tr. 1998. (Cambridge African Language Library Ser.). (Illus.). 16p. pap. 3.70 (978-0-521-63801-2(1)) Cambridge Univ. Pr.

—Eddie Ndlovu: South African Edition. 1998. (Illus.). 16p. pap. 22.75 (978-0-521-64449-5(6)) Cambridge Univ. Pr.

—Eddie Ndlovu Lugbara Version: Ewa Odulu. Draville, Ben & Mawa, Robert, trs. 2001. 16p. pap. 1.40 (978-0-521-00616-3(3)) Cambridge Univ. Pr.

Dyer, Dorothy & Lloyd, Glynis. Reading Matters Grade 8. 2006. 120p. pap. 11.00 (978-0-521-69513-8(9)) Cambridge Univ. Pr.

—Reading Matters Grade 9. 2006. pap. (978-0-521-69514-5(7)) Cambridge Univ. Pr.

Dyer, Dorothy, et al. Radio Days & Other Stories: Icibemba Version. Mulilo, tr. 2001. (Illus.). 48p. pap. 0.45 (978-0-521-01484-7(0)) Cambridge Univ. Pr.

Dynamic Dance: Individual Title Six-Packs. (Rigby Infoquest Ser.). (gr. 5 up). 37.00 (978-0-7578-6492-6(9)) Rigby Education.

DynaNotes Grade 9 Reading Review Guide. 2006. (YA). pap. (978-1-933854-29-8(4)) DynaStudy, Inc.

DynaNotes Grade 9 Reading Review Guide Transparency Set. 2006. (YA). trans. (978-1-933854-33-5(2)) Dyna-Study, Inc.

e-Educators. Full-Color Standards-Based Language Arts: Activities & Games. 2007. 176p. pap. 21.99 ***(978-1-4206-8717-0(4))*** Teacher Created Resources, Inc.

Eagles: Lions of the Sky. (Lexile Levels Ser.). 9.09 (978-1-56334-722-1(9)) Hampton-Brown Bks.

The Early Americas: Fourth Grade Class Collection Books. (On Our Way to English Ser.). (gr. 4 up). 29.95 (978-0-7578-4341-9(7)) Rigby Education.

The Early Americas: Small Versions of Class Collection Books. (On Our Way to English Ser.). (gr. 4 up). 34.50 (978-0-7578-7269-3(7)) Rigby Education.

Early Elementary Level: Practice Book. (English at Your Command! Ser.). (gr. 2-3). 5.89 (978-0-7362-1648-7(0)) Hampton-Brown Bks.

Early Elementary Level: Student Handbook. (English at Your Command! Ser.). (gr. 2-3). stu. ed. 19.17 (978-0-7362-1646-3(4)); stu. ed. 22.87 (978-0-7362-1645-6(6)) Hampton-Brown Bks.

Early Emergent Guided Reading, Vol. 1. (gr. k up). 372.95 (978-0-7802-2770-5(0)) Wright Group, The.

Early Emergent Set 3. 2000. (J). (978-1-58453-095-4(2)) Pioneer Valley Educational Pr., Inc.

Early Emergent Set 4. 2000. (J). (978-1-58453-096-1(0)) Pioneer Valley Educational Pr., Inc.

Early in the Morning. (Early Intervention Levels Ser.). 23.10 (978-0-7362-0039-4(8)); Vol. 4. 3.85 (978-1-56334-986-7(8)) Hampton-Brown Bks.

Early Learning: My First Library. (J). bds. 10.98 (978-0-7853-7919-5(3) , 7179500) Publications International, Ltd.

Early Level Spanish & English. (ENG & SPA.). (gr. k-2). 1923.95 (978-0-7368-3182-6(7) , Yellow Umbrella Bks.) Capstone Pr., Inc.

Early Level Spanish & English Add-on Set. (ENG & SPA.). (gr. k-2). 346.95 (978-0-7368-3183-3(5) , Yellow Umbrella Bks.) Capstone Pr., Inc.

Early Reading Comprehension. 2004. (gr. 2-4). pap. 8.65 (978-0-8388-0621-0(X)) Educators Publishing Service, Inc.

Early Transitional Set 1. 2001. (J). (978-1-58453-134-0(7)) Pioneer Valley Educational Pr., Inc.

Early Transitional Set 2. 2001. (J). (978-1-58453-142-5(8)) Pioneer Valley Educational Pr., Inc.

Earth, Moon, & Sun: Fifth Grade Class Collection Books. (On Our Way to English Ser.). (gr. 5 up). 29.95 (978-0-7578-4473-7(1)) Rigby Education.

Earth, Moon, & Sun: Small Versions of Class Collection Books. (On Our Way to English Ser.). (gr. 5 up). 34.50 (978-0-7578-7283-9(2)) Rigby Education.

Eclipse: Individual Title, 6 pack. (Story Steps Ser.). (gr. k-2). 32.00 (978-0-7635-9810-5(0)) Rigby Education.

Edgar Allan Poe Collection of Stories Student Packet, Gr. 9-12. 2004. (YA). (978-1-58130-510-4(9)) Novel Units, Inc.

Educational Solutions Staff & Gattegno, Caleb. Primary 3. (J). 84.00 (978-0-87825-170-4(7)); tchr. ed. 6.85 (978-0-87825-205-3(3)) Educational Solutions, Inc.

EduTax, Vol. 1. Date not set. (978-1-888042-02-3(8)); (978-1-888042-03-0(6)) Good Reading Bks.

Edwards, Ann & Goldberg, Karen. Bumpy Books. 2006. (J). spiral bd. (978-0-9778736-0-9(9)) Bumpy Bks Inc.

Edwards, Nicola. Leaves. 2005. (Illus.). 24p. (YA). (gr. 1 up). lib. bdg. 22.80 (978-1-59389-211-1(X)) Chrysalis Education.

Eggleton, Jill. Bertha & the Beeman. (Sails Literacy Ser.). 24p. (gr. 1 up). 27.00 (978-0-7578-6201-4(2)) Rigby Education.

—Bertha & the Beeman: 3-in-1 Package. (Sails Literacy Ser.). 24p. (gr. 1 up). 57.00 (978-0-7578-8618-8(3)) Rigby Education.

—Bertha & the Beeman: 6 Small Books. (Sails Literacy Ser.). 24p. (gr. 1 up). 25.00 (978-0-7578-7733-9(8)) Rigby Education.

—Billy Mcbrown. Pye, Trevor, illus. (Sails Literacy Ser.). 24p. (gr. 1 up). 27.00 (978-0-7578-6202-1(0)); Pack. 57.00 (978-0-7578-8620-1(5)) Rigby Education.

—Billy Mcbrown: 6 Small Books. Pye, Trevor, illus. (Sails Literacy Ser.). 24p. (gr. 1 up). 25.00 (978-0-7578-7730-8(3)) Rigby Education.

—Bubble Trouble: 3-in-1 Package. Webb, Philip, illus. (Sails Literacy Ser.). 24p. (gr. k up). 57.00 (978-0-7578-8614-0(0)) Rigby Education.

—Bubble Trouble: 6 Small Books. Webb, Philip, illus. (Sails Literacy Ser.). 24p. (gr. k up). 25.00 (978-0-7578-7726-1(5)) Rigby Education.

—Bubble Trouble: Big Book Only. Webb, Philip, illus. (Sails Literacy Ser.). 24p. (gr. k up). 27.00 (978-0-7578-6197-0(0)) Rigby Education.

—The Dream Catcher. (Sails Literacy Ser.). 24p. (gr. 1 up). 8.00 (978-0-7635-6983-9(6)) Rigby Education.

—Fearless Phil: 3-in-1 Package. McGrath, Raymond, illus. (Sails Literacy Ser.). 24p. (gr. 3 up). 57.00 (978-0-7578-6996-9(3)) Rigby Education.

—Fearless Phil: 6 Small Books. McGrath, Raymond, illus. (Sails Literacy Ser.). 24p. (gr. 3 up). 25.00 (978-0-7578-6988-4(2)) Rigby Education.

—Fearless Phil: Big Book Only. McGrath, Raymond, illus. (Sails Literacy Ser.). 24p. (gr. 3 up). 27.00 (978-0-7578-6980-8(7)) Rigby Education.

—Going Fast: Early Level Satellite Individual Title Six-Packs. (Sails Literacy Ser.). 16p. (gr. 1-2). 27.00 (978-0-7578-6510-7(0)) Rigby Education.

—Granny Groggin: 3-in-1 Package. (Sails Literacy Ser.). 24p. (gr. 3 up). 57.00 (978-0-7578-6997-6(1)) Rigby Education.

—The Hat: Emergent Level Satellite Individual Title Six-Packs. (Sails Literacy Ser.). (gr. k-1). 27.00 (978-0-7578-7920-3(9)) Rigby Education.

—Help for Eyes: Early Level Satellite Individual Title Six-Packs. (Sails Literacy Ser.). 16p. (gr. 1-2). 27.00 (978-0-7578-6514-5(3)) Rigby Education.

—The Hole in the Garden: Early Level Satellite Individual Title Six-Packs. (Sails Literacy Ser.). 16p. (gr. 1-2). 27.00 (978-0-7578-2932-1(5)) Rigby Education.

—Mickey Maloney-Spy: Individual Title Six-Packs. Pye, Trevor, illus. (Sails Literacy Ser.). 20p. (gr. 2-3). 27.00 (978-0-7578-0722-0(4)) Rigby Education.

—The Mystery of Missing Big Wig, 3 vols., Pack. (Sails Literacy Ser.). 24p. (gr. 3 up). 57.00 (978-0-7578-6998-3(X)) Rigby Education.

—On the Menu: Individual Title Six-Packs. (Sails Literacy Ser.). 16p. (gr. 2-3). 27.00 (978-0-7578-0699-5(6)) Rigby Education.

—Police Files, 6 Packs. Webb, Philip, illus. (Sails Literacy Ser.). 16p. (gr. 2-3). 27.00 (978-0-7578-0700-8(3)) Rigby Education.

—Police Work: Individual Title Six-Packs. Storey, Jim, illus. (Sails Literacy Ser.). 20p. (gr. 4 up). 27.00 (978-0-7578-0788-6(7)) Rigby Education.

—Rain, Rain, Rain: Emergent Level Satellite Individual Title Six-Packs. Webb, Philip, illus. (Sails Literacy Ser.). (gr. k-1). 27.00 (978-0-7578-7914-2(4)) Rigby Education.

—Silly Clown: Emergent Level Satellite Individual Title Six-Packs. (Sails Literacy Ser.). (gr. k-1). 27.00 (978-0-7578-7912-8(8)) Rigby Education.

—The Sky Bridge. (Sails Literacy Ser.). 24p. (gr. 1 up). 8.00 (978-0-7635-6982-2(8)) Rigby Education.

—What a Wedding! Individual Title Six-Packs. Williamson, Fraser, illus. (Sails Literacy Ser.). 20p. (gr. 4 up). 27.00 (978-0-7578-0790-9(9)) Rigby Education.

—Who Did It? Individual Title Six-Packs. Storey, Jim, illus. (Sails Literacy Ser.). 20p. (gr. 2-3). 27.00 (978-0-7578-0720-6(8)) Rigby Education.

Elephant Walk: Level K, 6 vols. 128p. (gr. 2-3). 40.50 (978-0-7699-0993-6(0)) Shortland Pubns. (U. S. A.) Inc.

Elson, H. William. Elson Grammer School Literature, Book Fo. 2006. 31.99 ***(978-1-4219-7647-1(1));*** pap. 25.99 ***(978-1-4219-7635-8(8))*** IndyPublish.com.

—Elson Readers Book 5. 2006. 67.99 ***(978-1-4280-3525-6(7));*** pap. 61.99 ***(978-1-4280-3522-5(2))*** IndyPublish.com.

Elson, William H. The Elson Readers, Bk. 5. l.t. ed. 2006. 436p. pap. 21.99 (978-1-4264-3446-4(4)) BiblioBazaar.

—The Elson Readers, Vol. 5. 2004. reprint ed. pap. 1.99 (978-1-4192-6079-7(0)) Kessinger Publishing, LLC.

—The Elson Readers, Book 5. 2006. 372p. pap. 15.99 (978-1-4264-3396-2(4)) BiblioBazaar.

Ely, Jennifer W. Mommy Teach Me to Read: Pre-Reader Series 1. 2006. (J). 16.99 (978-0-9777150-0-8(0)) Growing Little Readers.

Emerald, Ruby & Sapphire Levels Certificate Only. (gr. k-5). 89.00 (978-0-7578-6537-4(2)) Rigby Education.

Emergent: 1 Each of 8 Big Books, Vol. 3. (Sunshinetm Science Ser.). (gr. 1-2). 250.50 (978-0-7802-0571-0(5)) Wright Group, The.

Emergent Level Spanish & English. (ENG & SPA.). (gr. k-2). 1923.95 (978-0-7368-3180-2(0) , Yellow Umbrella Bks.) Capstone Pr., Inc.

Emergent Level Spanish & English Add-on Set. (ENG & SPA.). (gr. k-2). 346.95 (978-0-7368-3181-9(9) , Yellow Umbrella Bks.) Capstone Pr., Inc.

Emergent Set 4. 2004. (J). (978-1-58453-213-2(0)) Pioneer Valley Educational Pr., Inc.

Emergent Vol. 3: 1 Each of 8 Student Books. (Sunshinetm Science Ser.). (gr. 1-2). 48.95 (978-0-7802-0572-7(3)) Wright Group, The.

En el Colegio. (Coleccion Pequeno Simon). (SPA., Illus.). 32p. (J). 7.95 (978-84-7189-170-9(0) , ORT327) Ortells, Alfredo Editorial S.L. ESP. *Dist:* Continental Bk. Co., Inc.

En Japon. (Coleccion Pequeno Simon). (SPA., Illus.). 32p. (J). 7.95 (978-84-7189-176-1(X) , ORT331) Ortells, Alfredo Editorial S.L. ESP. *Dist:* Continental Bk. Co., Inc.

En la Montana. (Coleccion Pequeno Simon). (SPA., Illus.). 32p. (J). 7.95 (978-84-7189-167-9(0) , ORT343) Ortells, Alfredo Editorial S.L. ESP. *Dist:* Continental Bk. Co., Inc.

Ende, Michael. El Largo Camino Hacia Santa Cruz. Kehn, Regina, illus. (SPA.). 64p. (J). (gr. 3-5). 6.95 (978-84-241-3354-2(4) , EV3073) Everest de Ediciones y Distribucion, S.L. ESP. *Dist:* Lectorum Pubns., Inc.

Ender's Game Student Packet, Gr. 7-8. 2004. (YA). (978-1-58130-512-8(5)) Novel Units, Inc.

Energy Every Day Set F, 6 vols. (Phonics Readers Ser.). (gr. k-2). 28.95 (978-0-7368-4086-6(9)) Red Brick Learning.

Engelmann, Siegfried & Engelmann, Owen. Funnix Beginning Reading Program. 2001. (J). cd-rom 129.00 (978-0-9714798-0-7(1)) Royal Limited Partnership.

—Funnix Teacher's Guide. 2002. (J). instr.'s gde. ed. (978-0-9714798-5-4(4)) Royal Limited Partnership.

Engelmann, Siegfried, et al. Funnix 2. 2002. (J). cd-rom 99.00 (978-0-9714798-2-1(8)) Royal Limited Partnership.

—Funnix 2 Reader. 2002. (J). 20.00 (978-0-9714798-3-8(6)) Royal Limited Partnership.

—Funnix Beginning Reading Workbook. 2001. (J). 12.00 (978-0-9714798-1-4(X)) Royal Limited Partnership.

English in a Flash. 2004. cd-rom (978-1-59455-194-9(4)) Renaissance Learning, Inc.

English in a Flash Library 1 (BICS/Tier 1) 2004. cd-rom 699.00 (978-1-59455-193-2(6)) Renaissance Learning, Inc.

English in a Flash/Fluent Reader RP Student Subscription Renewal. 2004. cd-rom (978-1-59455-192-5(8)) Renaissance Learning, Inc.

English in My Pocket: Add-to Pack of Little Books. 34.00 (978-0-7635-2931-4(1)) Rigby Education.

English in My Pocket: Add-to Pack of Manipulatives. 42.00 (978-0-7635-2932-1(X)) Rigby Education.

English in My Pocket: Complete Program. 425.00 (978-0-7635-2929-1(X)) Rigby Education.

English-Language Arts Skills & Strategies Level 7. 2005. 144p. (YA). per. 17.95 (978-1-56254-841-4(7) , SP8417) Saddleback Educational Publishing.

English-Language Arts Skills & Strategies Level 8. 2005. 144p. (YA). per. 17.95 (978-1-56254-842-1(5) , SP8425) Saddleback Educational Publishing.

English-Spanish Book Set 800937, 4 vols. 2005. (J). bds. (978-1-59794-096-2(8)) Environments, Inc.

English to a Beat! (gr. 2-8). 763.19 (978-0-7362-2508-3(0)) Hampton-Brown Bks.

English to a Beat! Folk Tales Single-Copy Set. (gr. 2-8). 95.84 (978-0-7362-2507-6(2)) Hampton-Brown Bks.

English to a Beat! Practice Book. (gr. 2-8). 4.83 (978-0-7362-2498-7(X)) Hampton-Brown Bks.

Enrichment Reading: Animaniacs. 1999. (McGraw-Hill Junior Academic Ser.). (Illus.). 80p. (J). (gr. 2). pap., wbk. ed. 2.99 (978-1-57768-292-9(0)) School Specialty Publishing.

The Entire World of SH & CH Book of Stories. 2004. per. 34.99 (978-0-9760490-2-9(3)) Say It Right.

Eric Carle Board Book Set 800489, 3. 2005. (J). bds. (978-1-59794-003-0(8)) Environments, Inc.

Erickson, Amy, ed. Listen, Make, & Learn at Storytime. 2002. 192p. 24.95 (978-1-56234-489-4(7) , Mailbox Bks., The) Education Ctr., Inc.

Escape! Individual Title, 6 pack. (Rigby Infoquest Ser.). (gr. 6 up). 37.00 (978-0-7578-7988-3(8)) Rigby Education.

Escott, John & Hedge, Tricia. Dead Man's Island, Level 2. 2nd ed. 2000. (Bookworms Ser.). (Illus.). 64p. 6.50 (978-0-19-422968-5(8)) Oxford Univ. Pr., Inc.

Escott, John, et al. A Pretty Face. Damerum, KanakoILL-Takasaki, illus. 2003. (Dominoes Ser.). 48p. 6.50 (978-0-19-424339-1(7)) Oxford Univ. Pr., Inc.

La escuela de Modales 6: Leveled Books. 2001. (McGraw-Hill. Lectura Ser.). (ENG & SPA.). (gr. 3 up). (978-0-02-188079-9(4)) Macmillan/McGraw-Hill Schl. Div.

Essential Words Reading & Language Arts Activity Book (Elementary) Elementary. 2006. (J). 8.95 (978-1-933655-01-7(1)) New Leaf Educ., Inc.

Estice, Rose Mary & Fried, Mary. Emergent Reader 1: Playing; Boo-Boos!; Zoo Animals; Building a House; the Swimming Pool; Scrub-a-dub-dub!; Getting Dressed; My Cat. Simon, Sue A. et al, illus. 1999. 8p. (J). pap. (978-1-893986-20-6(9)) Keep Bks.

Eubanks, Holly L. Through the Eye of the Needle. (J). stu. ed. 18.95 (978-1-56270-047-8(2)) Dominie Pr., Inc.

—Through the Eye of the Needle: Answer Key. (J). 395.00 (978-1-56270-049-2(9)) Dominie Pr., Inc.

Eva's Lost & Found Report: Fourth Grade Guided Comprehension Level L. (On Our Way to English Ser.). (gr. 4 up). 34.50 (978-0-7578-7150-4(X)) Rigby Education.

The Everett Eyes. 2001. (YA). (gr. 6-12). pap. incl. audio (978-0-8224-3299-9(4)) Globe Fearon Educational Publishing.

Every Body Tells a Story: Level Q, 6 vols., Vol. 3. (Explorers Ser.). 32p. (gr. 3-6). 44.95 (978-0-7699-0621-8(4)) Shortland Pubns. (U. S. A.) Inc.

Every Landmark Has a Story. (Rigby Infoquest Ser.). (gr. 3 up). 30.00 (978-0-7578-3901-6(0)) Rigby Education.

Every Morning: Lap Book. (Pebble Soup Explorations Ser.). 16p. (ps up). 21.00 (978-0-7578-1656-7(8)) Rigby Education.

Every Morning: Small Book. (Pebble Soup Explorations Ser.). 16p. (ps up). 5.00 (978-0-7578-1696-3(7)) Rigby Education.

Everyday Assessment with Reading Rods. 2004. (J). lib. bdg. 24.95 (978-1-56911-176-5(6)) Learning Resources, Inc.

Everyone Is Coming: Kindergarten Newcomer Books. (On Our Way to English Ser.). (gr. k up). 23.50 (978-0-7578-7191-7(7)) Rigby Education.

Excuse Me, Sir. (J). 26.20 (978-0-8136-8396-6(3)); 59.50 (978-0-8136-7912-9(5)); 1998. pap. (978-0-8136-8291-4(6)) Modern Curriculum Pr.

Excuses, Excuses: 6 Small Books. (gr. k-3). 24.00 (978-0-7635-6236-6(X)) Rigby Education.

Explore! (Early Intervention Levels Ser.). 21.42 (978-0-7362-1051-5(2)); (Illus.). 3.57 (978-0-7362-0958-8(1)) Hampton-Brown Bks.

The Explorer: Individual Title Six-Packs. (ps-2). 27.00 (978-0-7635-9448-0(2)) Rigby Education.

Explorers: Fluency - Student Book Set - 1 Each of 12 Titles. (Explorers. Exploradores Nonfiction Sets Ser.). (gr. 3-6). 89.95 (978-0-7699-0815-1(2)) Shortland Pubns. (U. S. A.) Inc.

Exploring Literature: The EMC Write-in Reader. 2nd ed. (Literature & the Language Arts Ser.). (YA). (gr. 7 up). wbk. ed. 15.95 (978-0-8219-2910-0(0)) EMC/Paradigm Publishing.

Exploring the World: Fifth Grade Guided Comprehension Level M. (On Our Way to English Ser.). (gr. 5 up). 34.50 (978-0-7578-6597-8(6)) Rigby Education.

Extensions Through the Library TAKS Reading Preparation Grades 3-5: Curriculum Connected Resources. 2004. (Region IV ESC Resources for Librarian Ser.). spiral bd. (978-1-933049-05-2(7)) Region IV Education Service Ctr.

Extensions Through the Library TAKS Reading Preparation Grades 6-8. 2005. spiral bd. (978-1-933049-46-5(4)) Region IV Education Service Ctr.

Eye on the Ball: Individual Title, 6 pack. (Rigby Infoquest Ser.). (gr. 5 up). 37.00 (978-0-7578-6486-5(4)) Rigby Education.

Fabregat, Antonio-Manuel. Los Cuentos de Mi Escuela. (SPA.). 64p. (J). (gr. 4). (978-84-216-1593-5(9) , BU4751) Bruño, Editorial ESP. *Dist:* Lectorum Pubns., Inc.

La Fabrica. (Coleccion Aqui Se Trabaja). (SPA., Illus.). (J). 10.95 (978-84-207-3624-2(4) , ANY765) Grupo Anaya, S.A. ESP. *Dist:* Continental Bk. Co., Inc.

Fabricio aprende a jugar al Baloncesto 22: Leveled Books. 2001. (McGraw-Hill. Lectura Ser.). (ENG & SPA.). (gr. 1 up). (978-0-02-187999-1(0)) Macmillan/McGraw-Hill Schl. Div.

The Fabulous Fish from Lake Wiggawalla. 1999. (Books to Go Ser.). (J). pap. (978-0-8136-7882-5(X)) Modern Curriculum Pr.

Fabulous PH Riddles Blends/Dig. (J). pap. 18.16 (978-0-8136-0864-8(3)) Modern Curriculum Pr.

Fact & Fiction. 2006. 512.40 (978-1-59679-923-3(4) , Sand-Castle) ABDO Publishing Co.

Fact & Opinion (Gr. 1-3) 2003. (J). (978-1-58232-078-6(0)) Bryan Hse. Pubs., Inc.

A Fair Swap: Individual Title, 6 pack. (gr. 3 up). 35.00 (978-0-7635-9658-3(2)) Rigby Education.

Fair Weather Student Packet, Gr. 5-6. 2004. (J). (978-1-58130-514-2(1)) Novel Units, Inc.

Fall 2004 Complete Freestyle. 2004. 568.70 (978-1-4109-1379-1(1)) Raintree.

Fall Fun Set. (gr. k-2). 114.95 (978-0-7368-9057-1(2)) Red Brick Learning.

Falletta, Bernadette. We Love to Read Stories Coloring Book & Word Search Puzzles. 2005. 23p. (J). 10.95 (978-1-4116-6291-9(1)) Lulu.com.

Falletta, Bernadette & Lewis, Marla. We Love to Read Stories & Songs. 2005. 27p. (J). 14.95 (978-1-4116-4734-3(3)) Lulu.com.

La familia de Andres era muy Normal 23: Leveled Books. 2001. (McGraw-Hill. Lectura Ser.). (ENG & SPA.). (gr. 3 up). (978-0-02-188096-6(4)) Macmillan/McGraw-Hill Schl. Div.

Families Set. (gr. k-2). 288.95 (978-0-7368-9064-9(5)) Red Brick Learning.

The Family: Individual Title, 6 pack. (Sails Literacy Ser.). 16p. (gr. k up). 27.00 (978-0-7635-4409-6(4)) Rigby Education.

Family Counts. (Early Intervention Levels Ser.). 23.10 (978-0-7362-0001-1(0)) Hampton-Brown Bks.

Family Living Board Book Set 800646, 4. 2005. (J). bds. (978-1-59794-038-2(0)) Environments, Inc.

Family Stories: Individual Packs Pack A. (gr. k-2). 15.40 (978-0-7362-0491-0(1)) Hampton-Brown Bks.

Family Stories: Individual Packs Pack B. (gr. k-2). 15.40 (978-0-7362-0493-4(8)) Hampton-Brown Bks.

Family Stories: Jumbo Packs. (gr. k-2). 157.08 (978-0-7362-0051-6(7)) Hampton-Brown Bks.

Famous Faces: Individual Title Six-Packs. (Rigby Infoquest Ser.). (gr. 6 up). 37.00 (978-0-7578-7991-3(8)) Rigby Education.

Far Away. (Early Intervention Levels Ser.). 3.85 (978-0-7362-1865-8(3)) Hampton-Brown Bks.

Farm Tools over Time Set F, 6 vols. (Phonics Readers Ser.). (gr. k-2). 28.95 (978-0-7368-4084-2(2)) Red Brick Learning.

Farmer's Market. (Early Intervention Levels Ser.). 3.55 (978-0-7362-1898-6(X)); 21.30 (978-0-7362-2126-9(3)) Hampton-Brown Bks.

Farming. (Early Intervention Levels Ser.). 8.48 (978-0-7362-1900-6(5)); 50.88 (978-0-7362-2127-6(1)) Hampton-Brown Bks.

Farr. Power Up Level 1. 2003. pap., tchr. ed. (978-0-7398-7537-7(X)) Steck-Vaughn.

—PU Extended Starter Set Level 1. 2003. (Illus.). pap. 100.50 (978-0-7398-8493-5(X)) Steck-Vaughn.

—PU Extended Starter Set Level 2. 2003. (Illus.). pap. 127.00 (978-0-7398-8497-3(2)) Steck-Vaughn.

Fast & Horr. No Power on Earth. 2001. 32p. (YA). (gr. 6-12). pap. (978-0-8224-3776-5(7)) Globe Fearon Educational Publishing.

Fast Forward. 2004. 440.00 (978-0-531-14705-4(3)) Scholastic Library Publishing.

Fast Forward! 2003. (Fast Forward! Ser.). Level C. (J). (gr. 1 up). stu. ed., per. 67.95 (978-1-58830-333-2(0)); Level C. (J). (gr. 1 up). stu. ed., per. 7.95 (978-1-58830-779-8(4)); Level D. (J). (gr. 2 up). stu. ed., per. 67.95 (978-1-58830-334-9(9)); Level D. (J). (gr. 2 up). stu. ed., per. 7.95 (978-1-58830-780-4(8)); Level A. tchr. ed., per., tchr.'s training gde. ed. 39.95 (978-1-58830-783-5(2)); Level A. (J). (gr. 1 up). stu. ed., per. 67.95 (978-1-58830-331-8(4)); Level A. (J). (gr. 1 up). stu. ed., per. 7.95 (978-1-58830-777-4(8)); Level B. tchr. ed., per., tchr.'s training gde. ed. 39.95 (978-1-58830-784-2(0)); Level B. (J). (gr. 1 up). stu. ed., per. 67.95 (978-1-58830-332-5(2)); Level B. (J). (gr. 1 up). stu. ed., per. 7.95 (978-1-58830-778-1(6)); Level E. (J). (gr. 1 up). stu. ed., per. 7.95 (978-1-58830-781-1(6)); Level E. (J). (gr. 2 up). 369.95 (978-1-58830-799-6(9)); Level E. (J). (gr. 2 up). stu. ed., per. 67.95 (978-1-58830-335-6(7)); Level F. (J). (gr. 2 up). 369.95 (978-1-58830-800-9(6)); Level F. (J). (gr. 2 up). stu. ed., per. 67.95 (978-1-58830-336-3(5)); Level F. (J). (gr. 2 up). stu. ed., per. 7.95 (978-1-58830-782-8(4)) Metropolitan Teaching & Learning Co.

Fast/Sports Staff. The Sure Thing. 2001. 32p. (YA). (gr. 6-12). pap. (978-0-8224-6497-6(7)) Globe Fearon Educational Publishing.

Faundez, Anne. A Cloak for Swallow, 4 vols. 2005. (QEB Readers). (Illus.). 24p. (J). (gr. 1-4). lib. bdg. 15.95 (978-1-59566-093-0(3)) QEB Publishing Inc.

—Imaginary Creatures, 4 vols. 2005. (QEB Readers). (Illus.). 24p. (J). (ps-3). lib. bdg. 15.95 (978-1-59566-102-9(6)) QEB Publishing Inc.

—Sing a Song of Sixpence, 8 vols. 2005. (QEB Readers). (Illus.). 24p. (J). (ps-3). lib. bdg. 15.95 (978-1-59566-072-5(0)) QEB Publishing Inc.

From the Lake to Your Faucet: Fourth Grade Guided Comprehension Level L. (On Our Way to English Ser.). (gr. 4 up). 34.50 (978-0-7578-7153-5(4)) Rigby Education.

Fry, Edward B. Reading Drills. 2004. pap., tchr. ed., suppl. ed. (978-0-8092-0358-1(8)) Jamestown.

—Skimming & Scanning. 2004. pap., tchr. ed., suppl. ed. (978-0-8092-0362-8(6)) Jamestown.

—Vocabulary Drills: Introductory. 2002. (gr. 6-12). pap. 16.64 (978-0-07-827367-4(6) , 9780078273674) Jamestown.

Fry, Ron. Como Sacar Provecho de Tu Lectura.Tr. of Improve Your Reading. (SPA.). (YA). pap. 10.95 (978-84-241-2582-0(7) , EV11796) Everest de Ediciones y Distribucion, S.L. ESP. *Dist:* Lectorum Pubns., Inc.

Fuller, Neil & McRoberts, Richard. Remembering Babylon. 2002. (Wizard Study Guides Ser.). 48p. pap., stu. ed. 6.00 (978-1-875739-22-6(X)) Cambridge Univ. Pr.

Fun & Circus. 2000. (Learning Fun for Little Ones Ser.). 64p. (J). (ps-1). pap. 8.99 (978-0-88724-587-9(0)) Carson-Dellosa Publishing Co., Inc.

The Fun Bus: 3-in-1 Package. (Sails Literacy Ser.). 24p. (gr. 1 up). 57.00 (978-0-7578-3207-9(5)) Rigby Education.

The Fun Bus: 6 Small Books. (Sails Literacy Ser.). 24p. (gr. 1 up). 25.00 (978-0-7578-3183-6(4)) Rigby Education.

The Fun Bus: Big Book Only. (Sails Literacy Ser.). 24p. (gr. 1 up). 27.00 (978-0-7635-5931-1(8)) Rigby Education.

Fun Days! Kindergarten Guided Reading Level C. (On Our Way to English Ser.). (gr. k up). 27.75 (978-0-7578-7018-7(X)) Rigby Education.

Fun for Everyone: Fifth Grade Guided Comprehension Level M. (On Our Way to English Ser.). (gr. 5 up). 34.50 (978-0-7578-6593-0(3)) Rigby Education.

Fun in the Snow. 2003. (J). (978-1-932570-13-7(6)) Literacy Footprints Inc.

Fun-to-Learn: All about Me. (ps-1). 2.99 (978-0-7424-0176-1(6) , IF0409) School Specialty Publishing.

Fun-to-Learn: Beginning Reading. (ps-1). 2.99 (978-0-7424-0178-5(2) , IF0411) School Specialty Publishing.

Fun-to-Learn: Ready for Reading. (Homework Booklets Ser.). 80p. (gr. k-1). 2.99 (978-0-7424-0260-7(6) , IF0416) School Specialty Publishing.

Fun with Friends. (Early Intervention Levels Ser.). 23.10 (978-0-7362-0006-6(1)) Hampton-Brown Bks.

Funny Faces & Funny Places. (Little Book Practice Reader Ser.). (J). (978-0-8136-0687-3(X)) Modern Curriculum Pr.

Funny Fish: Early Level Satellite Individual Title Six-Packs. (Sails Literacy Ser.). 16p. (gr. 1-2). 27.00 (978-0-7578-6516-9(X)) Rigby Education.

Furgang, Kathy. Shrimp Joins the Team. ed. 2003. (Early Connections Ser.). (J). pap. 33.00 (978-1-4108-1368-8(1)) Benchmark Education Co.

—Wendy the Water Drop. 2003. (Early Connections Ser.). (J). pap. 33.00 (978-1-4108-1095-3(X)) Benchmark Education Co.

Furman, Simon & Dorling Kindersley Publishing Staff. Transformers: The Ultimate Guide. 2004. (Illus.). 144p. (J). 24.99 (978-0-7566-0314-4(5)) Dorling Kindersley Publishing, Inc.

Future Space Explorers: Small Versions of Big Books. (On Our Way to English Ser.). (gr. 3 up). 35.50 (978-0-7578-7245-7(X)) Rigby Education.

Future Space Explorers: Third Grade Big Books. (On Our Way to English Ser.). (gr. 3 up). 29.95 (978-0-7578-4211-5(9)) Rigby Education.

Gabby Goes up & Down. 2005. (J). (978-1-58453-115-9(0)) Pioneer Valley Educational Pr., Inc.

Gabby Visits Buster. 2000. (J). (978-1-58453-116-6(9)); (978-1-58453-092-3(8)) Pioneer Valley Educational Pr., Inc.

Gabriel. Dragonheart, Level 2. 2000. 48p. (C). pap. 9.00 (978-0-582-36401-1(9)) Longman Publishing Group.

Gabrielle Lyon & the Fossil Hunt: Fifth Grade Guided Comprehension Level O. (On Our Way to English Ser.). (gr. 5 up). 34.50 (978-0-7578-6606-7(9)) Rigby Education.

La Gaceta de Alameda 18: Leveled Books. 2001. (McGraw-Hill. Lectura Ser.). (ENG & SPA.). (gr. 4 up). (978-0-02-188194-9(4)) Macmillan/McGraw-Hill Schl. Div.

Gadgets & Gizmos: Individual Title Six-Packs. (Rigby Infoquest Ser.). 24p. (gr. 3 up). 34.00 (978-0-7578-5767-6(1)) Rigby Education.

Galashan, Kathy. Livewire Investigates Ghosts. 2nd rev. ed. 2004. (Livewires Ser.). (Illus.). 32p. pap. (978-0-340-81126-9(9)) Cambridge Univ. Pr.

—Robots. 2005. (Illus.). 32p. pap. 8.50 (978-0-340-87311-3(6)) Cambridge Univ. Pr.

—Starting a Band. 2nd rev. ed. 2005. (Illus.). 32p. pap. (978-0-340-81125-2(0)) Cambridge Univ. Pr.

—Starting a Band. 2001. (Livewire Ser.). (Illus.). 32p. pap. (978-0-340-80075-1(5) , Hodder Arnold) Hodder Education.

Ganeri, Anita. Jobs People Do, 8 bks. 2005. (QEB Readers). (Illus.). 24p. (J). (ps-3). lib. bdg. 15.95 (978-1-59566-076-3(3)) QEB Publishing Inc.

Ganeri, Anita, et al. I-Read Year 2 Anthology: Celebrate. 2007. (I-read Ser.). (Illus.). 40p. pap. (***978-0-521-70485-4(5)***) Cambridge Univ. Pr.

A Garden: Individual Title Six-Packs. (Sails Literacy Ser.). 16p. (gr. k up). 27.00 (978-0-7635-4384-6(5)) Rigby Education.

Gardner, Lindsey, et al. Pan Fydd Popi a Macs yn Fawr. 2005. (WEL., Illus.). 17p. (978-1-902416-45-8(7)) Cymdeithas Lyfrau Ceredigion.

Garside, Alice H. The Ant & the Duck, Set 2. l.t. ed. 1999. (Illus.). 29p. (Orig.). (J). (gr. k-6). reprint ed. pap. 2.50 (978-1-893688-05-6(4)) Carroll Schl., The.

—The Garside Readers, 6 vols., Set. l.t. ed. Incl. Fox & the Thrush. 15p. pap. 2.50 (978-1-893688-03-2(8)); Set 1. Dog & the Wolf. 25p. pap. 2.50 (978-1-893688-04-9(6)); Set 1. Man, the Fox & the Skunk. 19p. pap. 2.50 (978-1-893688-01-8(1)); Set 2. Ant & the Duck. 29p. pap. 2.50 (978-1-893688-05-6(4)); Set 2. Dog & the Bone. 19p. pap. 2.50 (978-1-893688-02-5(X)); Vol. 2. Fox & the Stork. 43p. pap. 2.50 (978-1-893688-06-3(2)); (J). (gr. k-6). reprint ed. (Illus.). 150p. 1999. reprint ed. Set pap. 15.00 (978-1-893688-00-1(3)) Carroll Schl., The.

—The Man, the Fox & the Skunk, Set 1. l.t. ed. 1999. (Illus.). 19p. (Orig.). (J). (gr. k-6). reprint ed. pap. 2.50 (978-1-893688-01-8(1)) Carroll Schl., The.

Garson, Cindy. Welcome to Kristy's Farm: Book I (Black & White Version) 2007. (ENG.). 56p. per. 21.80 (***978-1-84728-321-4(7)***) Lulu.com.

Garvel, Linda. NoZee in "Where's My Nose Yo?" 2001. (NoZee From Planet Nose). 38p. (J). spiral bd. (978-0-9679979-5-7(X)) Reader's Writes.

—NoZee in "Where's My Nose Yo?" With Sign Language. 2001. (NoZee From Planet Nose). 62p. (J). spiral bd. (978-0-9679979-4-0(1)) Reader's Writes.

—NoZee's Dear Earthling & Writing Tablet. 2001. (NoZee From Planet Nose). 40p. (J). pap. (978-0-9679979-6-4(8)) Reader's Writes.

—NoZee's Flash Book: Sign with NoZee & Feather Nose. 2001. (NoZee From Planet Nose). 50p. (J). spiral bd. (978-0-9679979-3-3(3)) Reader's Writes.

—Signing with NoZee in "Where's My Nose Yo?" 2001. (NoZee From Planet Nose). 113p. (J). pap. (978-0-9679979-2-6(5)); spiral bd. (978-0-9679979-1-9(7)) Reader's Writes.

Gary, Romain. La Vie Devant Soi, Level C. (FRE.). (YA). (gr. 7-12). 8.95 (978-0-8219-0869-3(3) , 40326) EMC/Paradigm Publishing.

Gaskell, Elizabeth. Cranford, Level 3. 2000. (C). pap. 9.00 (978-0-582-41687-1(6)) Longman Publishing Group.

Gates, Susan. Mole Who was Scared of the Dark. Breakespeare, Andrew, illus. 2005. 24p. (J). lib. bdg. 22.65 (***978-1-59646-710-1(X)***) Dingles & Co.

Gaydos, Nora. The Big Race, Level 2. Becker, Paula, illus. 2006. (innovativeKids readers ser.: level 2). 24p. (J). (gr. k-2). pap. 6.99 (978-1-58476-477-9(5) , IKIDS) Innovative Kids.

—Innovative Kids Readers: the Long Ride. Sharp, Chris, illus. 2007. 24p. (J). (gr. k-2). pap. 6.99 (978-1-58476-544-8(5)) Innovative Kids.

—Silly Story Laboratory. Sams, B. B., illus. 2006. (Now I'm Reading! Ser.). 22p. (J). (gr. 1-17). 14.99 (978-1-58476-474-8(0) , IKIDS) Innovative Kids.

—Simply Science Vol. 2: Independent. 2006. (Illus.). 74p. (J). lib. bdg. 16.99 (978-1-58476-247-8(0) , IKIDS) Innovative Kids.

Gaydos, Nora & Girouard, Patrick. The Sleepover. 2007. 24p. (J). (gr. k-17). pap. 6.99 (***978-1-58476-611-7(5)***, IKIDS) Innovative Kids.

Geiger, Beth & Fuerst, Jeffrey B. Return to Earth: Reader's Theater Levels N-U (30-50) Wolk-Stanley, Jessica, illus. ed. 2004. (Reader's Theater Ser.). 16p. (J). pap. 22.00 (978-1-4108-2306-9(7) , A23067) Benchmark Education Co.

Geiser, Traci Ferguson & Boylan, Maureen McCourt. Leap into Literacy Fall. Cernek, Kim, ed. Mason, Mark & Willardson, David, illus. 2003. 160p. (J). (gr. k-2). pap. 17.99 (978-1-57471-960-4(2) , 3376) Creative Teaching Pr., Inc.

—Leap into Literacy Spring. Cernek, Kim, ed. Rojas, Mary & Willardson, David, illus. 2003. 160p. (J). (gr. k-2). pap. 17.99 (978-1-57471-959-8(9) , 3375) Creative Teaching Pr., Inc.

—Leap into Literacy Winter. Cernek, Kim, ed. Valko, Diane & Willardson, David, illus. 2003. 160p. (J). (gr. k-2). pap. 17.99 (978-1-57471-958-1(0) , 3374) Creative Teaching Pr., Inc.

Gemmen, Heather. Learn-to-Read Bible. Wilber, Peggy M., ed. 1999. (Rocket Readers Ser.). (Illus.). 448p. (J). (gr. 1-2). 16.99 (978-0-7814-3975-6(2) , 0781439752) Cook, David C. Publishing Co.

Gentner, Norma L. & Young, Steve. Save a Tree for Me. (Song Box(R) Ser.). (Illus.). 16p. (gr. 1-2). 31.50 (978-0-7802-2264-9(4)) Wright Group, The.

George, Jean Craighead. Goose & Duck. Lamont, Priscilla, illus. 2008. (I Can Read Bks.). 48p. (J). 16.99 (***978-0-06-117076-8(3)***); lib. bdg. 17.89 (***978-0-06-117077-5(1)***) HarperCollins Pubs. (Geringer, Laura Book).

Gerard, Maureen. Reader's Theater: Tall Tales. 2006. 96p. pap. 11.99 (978-1-4206-3066-4(0)) Austin & Company, Inc.

Gerig, Theresa. Nonfiction Reading Comprehension. 2002. (100+ Seriestm Ser.). 128p. (J). (gr. 1-2). pap. 12.99 (978-0-7424-0218-8(5) , IF87026) School Specialty Publishing.

Gerig, Theresa & Robinson-Cobb, Kris. I Love Reading. Rozines Roy, Jennifer, illus. 1999. (Homework Booklets Ser.). 80p. (J). Level 1. (gr. k-2). pap. 2.99 (978-1-56822-826-6(0) , IF0321); Level 2. (gr. 1-3). pap. 2.99 (978-1-56822-827-3(9) , IF0322); Level 3. (gr. 2-4). pap. 2.99 (978-1-56822-828-0(7) , IF0323) Schaffer, Frank Pubns. (Instructional Fair).

Germs Set D, 6 vols. (Phonics Readers Ser.). (gr. k-2). 28.95 (978-0-7368-4055-2(9)) Red Brick Learning.

Gerngross, Gunter & Puchta, Herbert. English with Toby 3. 2000. (Join In Ser.). cd-rom 50.00 (978-0-521-77363-8(6)) Cambridge Univ. Pr.

Gerstein, Mordicai. Leaving the Nest. 2007. (Illus.). 40p. (J). (ps-1). 16.00 (978-0-374-34369-9(1) , Farrar, Straus & Giroux (BYR)) Farrar, Straus & Giroux.

Get Ready! First Grade Newcomer Books. (On Our Way to English Ser.). (gr. 1 up). 23.50 (978-0-7578-7208-2(5)) Rigby Education.

Get Real, 4 vols., Set 1. 2004. (Illus.). (J). 114.24 (978-1-4109-0578-9(0)) Harcourt Schl. Pubs.

Getting Along: Interactive Activities to Encourage Cooperation, Communication, & Respect. 64p. (ps-2). 7.99 (978-0-7424-0110-5(3) , IF19105) School Specialty Publishing.

Getting Along: Social/Emotional Lap Book. (Pebble Soup Explorations Ser.). (ps up). 16.00 (978-0-7635-7563-2(1)) Rigby Education.

Getting Dressed 800638, 3. 2005. (J). bds. (978-1-59794-036-8(4)) Environments, Inc.

Getting Ready: Kindergarten Big Books. (On Our Way to English Ser.). (gr. k up). 29.95 (978-0-7578-1616-1(9)) Rigby Education.

Getting Ready: Small Versions of Big Books. (On Our Way to English Ser.). (gr. k up). 29.00 (978-0-7578-7224-2(7)) Rigby Education.

Getting Ready for Bed: KinderConcepts Individual Title Six-Packs. (Kinderstarters Ser.). 8p. (ps-1). 21.00 (978-0-7635-8729-1(X)) Rigby Education.

Getting Ready for Kindergarten. 2002. (Home Workbooks Ser.). 64p. pap. 2.49 (978-0-88724-717-0(2) , CD-4519) Carson-Dellosa Publishing Co., Inc.

Getting Ready for School: KinderConcepts Individual Title Six-Packs. (Kinderstarters Ser.). 8p. (ps-1). 21.00 (978-0-7635-8730-7(3)) Rigby Education.

Getting the Sequence (Gr. 1-3) 2003. (J). (978-1-58232-076-2(4)) Bryan Hse. Pubs., Inc.

Getting to Know Your Neighbors: Fourth Grade Guided Comprehension Level N. (On Our Way to English Ser.). (gr. 4 up). 34.50 (978-0-7578-7161-0(5)) Rigby Education.

Getting Together: Individual Title Six-Packs. (Rigby Infoquest Ser.). (gr. 5 up). 37.00 (978-0-7578-6493-3(7)) Rigby Education.

Getting Water, 6 Pack. (Sails Literacy Ser.). (gr. 1-2). 36.00 (978-0-7578-6770-5(7)) Rigby Education.

Ghosts! 2003. 31.95 (978-0-673-75801-9(X)) Celebration Pr.

Giant Games. (Early Intervention Levels Ser.). 31.86 (978-0-7362-0665-5(5)) Hampton-Brown Bks.

Giant Games (18), Vol. 18. (Early Intervention Levels Ser.). 5.31 (978-0-7362-0653-2(1)) Hampton-Brown Bks.

The Giant of Ginger Hill: 3-in-1 Package. (Sails Literacy Ser.). 24p. (gr. 2 up). 57.00 (978-0-7578-3216-1(4)) Rigby Education.

The Giant of Ginger Hill: 6 Small Books. (Sails Literacy Ser.). 24p. (gr. 2 up). 25.00 (978-0-7578-3192-8(3)) Rigby Education.

The Giant of Ginger Hill: Big Book Only. (Sails Literacy Ser.). 24p. (gr. 2 up). 27.00 (978-0-7635-6992-1(5)) Rigby Education.

Giants of the Deep: Individual Title Six-Packs. (Rigby Infoquest Ser.). (gr. 6 up). 37.00 (978-0-7578-7985-2(3)) Rigby Education.

Gibson-Hardie, Stephanie Kim. The 10 Boldest Explorers. 2008. (Tentrade; Ser.). 48p. (J). pap. 14.99 (***978-1-55448-456-0(1)*** , Watts, Franklin) Scholastic Library Publishing.

Gifford, Myrna Ross. Silent E: A Read-and-Sing Book. Cooper, Frances, illus. 2005. 12p. (J). 9.95 (978-0-9754618-0-8(X)) Action Factor, Inc.

Gift of Fire. (Guided Reading Levels Ser.). (Illus.). 4.76 (978-0-7362-0985-4(9)) Hampton-Brown Bks.

Gifts from Greece: Individual Title Six-Packs. (Rigby Infoquest Ser.). 24p. (gr. 3 up). 34.00 (978-0-7578-5768-3(X)) Rigby Education.

Gikow, Louise A. I Can Read. Patience, John, illus. 2005. (My First Reader Ser.). 32p. (J). (gr. k-1). pap. 3.95 (978-0-516-25114-1(7) , Children's Pr.) Scholastic Library Publishing.

Gilbert Goes on a Picnic. 2004. (J). (978-1-58453-221-7(1)) Pioneer Valley Educational Pr., Inc.

Gilbert the Pig Set 2. 2004. (J). (978-1-58453-220-0(3)) Pioneer Valley Educational Pr., Inc.

Gilbert the Special Pig. 2004. (J). (978-1-58453-223-1(8)) Pioneer Valley Educational Pr., Inc.

Giles, Jenny & Lowe, Isabel, contrib. by. El Perrito, 6 Packs. (Coleccion Pm Ser.).Tr. of Choosing a puppy. (SPA.). 16p. (gr. 1 up). 26.00 (978-0-7578-2993-2(7)) Rigby Education.

Gill, Jerry. StepbyStep Workbooks, 3 2002. (Illus.). 1000p. (J). cd-rom 16.95 (978-1-889823-17-1(1)) GLB Worldwide.

Gilleland, Rebecca. Little House on the Prairie. 2002. (J). stu. ed., ring bd. 12.99 (978-1-58609-182-8(4)) Progeny Pr.

—Prereader Study Guide: Oscar Otter/Henry & Mudge in Puddle Trouble. 2002. 54p. (J). stu. ed., ring bd. 9.99 (978-1-58609-181-1(6)) Progeny Pr.

Gillen, Lisa P. Spring Time. Gillen, Lisa P., illus. l.t. ed. 2006. (Illus.). 12p. (J). (ps-k). pap. 10.95 (978-1-57332-351-2(9)) HighReach Learning, Inc.

Gillham, Bill. Dirty Dog: Lunda Version. Kambangaji, Thomson, tr. 1998. (Cambridge African Language Library). (Illus.). 8p. pap. 3.75 (978-0-521-64757-1(6)) Cambridge Univ. Pr.

—My Pet: American English Edition. 2000. (Cambridge Reading Ser.). (Illus.). 8p. pap. 20.00 (978-0-521-78412-2(3)) Cambridge Univ. Pr.

—Two Babies: Lunda Version. Kambangaji, Thomson, tr. 1998. (Cambridge African Language Library Ser.). (Illus.). 8p. pap. 3.75 (978-0-521-64764-9(9)) Cambridge Univ. Pr.

—Two Babies American English Edition. 2000. (Cambridge Reading Ser.). (Illus.). 8p. pap. 5.00 (978-0-521-79514-2(1)) Cambridge Univ. Pr.

—Two Babies Big Book American English Edition. Gon, Adriano, illus. 2000. (Cambridge Reading Ser.). 8p. pap. 20.00 (978-0-521-79513-5(3)) Cambridge Univ. Pr.

Gillis, Jennifer B. Two Nice Mice. 2006. (Reader's Clubhouse Set B Ser.). (Illus.). 24p. (J). pap. 3.99 (978-0-7641-3295-7(4)) Barron's Educational Series, Inc.

Gillis, Jennifer B., et al. Reader's Clubhouse Level 1 Short-Vowel Valu-Pak. 2006. (Illus.). 120p. (J). 15.96 (978-0-7641-7967-9(5)) Barron's Educational Series, Inc.

—Reader's Clubhouse Level 2 Long-Vowel Review Valu-Pak. 2006. (Illus.). 96p. (J). pap. 11.97 (978-0-7641-7970-9(5)) Barron's Educational Series, Inc.

The Gingerbread Man: 6 Small Books. (gr. k-1). 30.00 (978-0-7635-6205-2(X)) Rigby Education.

Ginsela, Marion. Aa, Ba, Ca, Da: A Friendly Tool to Help Children to Read. 2002. (J). pap. 13.00 (978-0-8059-5262-9(4)) Dorrance Publishing Co., Inc.

Giraffe's Sad Tale. (Lexile Levels Ser.). 47.88 (978-1-56334-392-6(4)) Hampton-Brown Bks.

Give It a Try. (Rigby Infoquest Ser.). (gr. 3 up). 30.00 (978-0-7578-3902-3(9)) Rigby Education.

Glasspoole, Louise, et al. I-Read Year 2 Anthology: Magical Journeys. 2007. (I-read Ser.). (Illus.). 40p. pap. (***978-0-521-70472-4(3)***) Cambridge Univ. Pr.

Glencoe McGraw-Hill Staff & McGraw-Hill - Jamestown Education Staff. Beyond Belief: The Real World - With a Twist. 2001. (Wild Side Ser.). (gr. 4-12). pap. 15.32 (978-0-8092-9833-4(3)) Jamestown.

—Close Calls: Survival Through Force of Will. 2001. (Wild Side Ser.). (gr. 4-12). pap. 16.64 (978-0-8092-9828-0(7) , 9780809298280) Jamestown.

—Jamestown's Early Civilizations: Chinese Life. 2001. (gr. 5-12). pap. 11.96 (978-0-8092-9490-9(7) , 9780809294909) Jamestown.

—Jamestown's Early Civilizations: Egyptian Life. 2001. (gr. 5-12). pap. 11.96 (978-0-8092-9594-4(6) , 9780809295944) Jamestown.

—Jamestown's Early Civilizations: Inca Life. 2001. (gr. 5-12). pap. 11.96 (978-0-8092-9492-3(3) , 9780809294923) Jamestown.

—Jamestown's Early Civilizations: North American Indian Life. 2001. (gr. 5-12). pap. 11.96 (978-0-8092-9491-6(5) , 9780809294916) Jamestown.

—Jamestown's Early Civilizations: Roman Life. 2001. (gr. 5-12). pap. 11.96 (978-0-8092-9500-5(8) , 9780809295005) Jamestown.

—Jamestown's Early Civilizations: Viking Life. 2001. (gr. 5-12). pap. 11.96 (978-0-8092-9501-2(6) , 9780809295012) Jamestown.

—Six-Way Paragraphs in the Content Areas: Introductory Level. 2000. (gr. 6-12). pap. 17.32 (978-0-8092-0371-0(5) , 9780809203710) Jamestown.

—Six-Way Paragraphs in the Content Areas: Middle Level. 2000. (gr. 6-12). pap. 17.32 (978-0-8092-0372-7(3) , 9780809203727) Jamestown.

—Understanding Literary Forms (Introductory) 3rd ed. 2000. (Comprehension Skills Ser.). (gr. 6-12). pap. 10.64 (978-0-8092-0239-3(5) , 9780809202393) Jamestown.

—Understanding Literary Forms (Middle) 2nd ed. 2000. (Comprehension Skills Ser.). (C). (gr. 6-12). pap. 10.64 (978-0-8092-0152-5(6) , 9780809201525) Jamestown.

—Understanding Organization (Middle) 2nd ed. 2000. (Comprehension Skills Ser.). (C). (gr. 9-12). pap. 10.64 (978-0-8092-0153-2(4) , 9780809201532) Jamestown.

—Understanding Significant Details (Advanced) 2nd ed. 2000. (Comprehension Skills Ser.). (C). (gr. 9-12). pap. 10.64 (978-0-8092-0165-5(8) , 9780809201655) Jamestown.

—Understanding Significant Details (Introductory) 3rd ed. 2000. (Comprehension Skills Ser.). (C). (gr. 6-12). pap. 10.64 (978-0-8092-0241-6(7) , 9780809202416) Jamestown.

—Understanding Significant Details (Middle) 2nd ed. 2000. (Comprehension Skills Ser.). (C). (gr. 6-12). pap. 10.64 (978-0-8092-0154-9(2) , 9780809201549) Jamestown.

—Understanding the Main Idea (Introductory) 3rd ed. 2000. (Comprehension Skills Ser.). (gr. 6-12). pap. 10.64 (978-0-8092-0233-1(6) , 9780809202331) Jamestown.

—Understanding the Main Idea (Middle) 2nd ed. 2000. (Comprehension Skills Ser.). (C). (gr. 6-12). pap. 10.64 (978-0-8092-0244-7(1) , 9780809202447) Jamestown.

—Understanding Vocabulary (Advanced) 3rd ed. 2000. (Comprehension Skills Ser.). (C). (gr. 6-12). pap. 10.64 (978-0-8092-0166-2(6) , 9780809201662) Jamestown.

—Understanding Vocabulary (Introductory) 3rd ed. 2000. (Comprehension Skills Ser.). (gr. 6-12). pap. 10.64 (978-0-8092-0242-3(5) , 9780809202423) Jamestown.

—Understanding Vocabulary (Middle) 2nd ed. 2000. (Comprehension Skills Ser.). (C). (gr. 9-12). pap. 10.64 (978-0-8092-0155-6(0) , 9780809201556) Jamestown.

The Glory Field Student Packet, Gr. 7-8. 2004. (YA). (978-1-58130-516-6(8)) Novel Units, Inc.

Glover, Danny & Glover, Julie, illus. Phonics 1a - Vowel Sounds - School Single. 2002. (ENG & SPA.). 97p. ring bd. incl. cd-rom (978-0-9741687-2-2(6) , 1001s) Help Me 2 Learn Co.

Glover, Danny & Glover, Julie, illus. Letters & Numbers: Single User. 4th ed. 2002. (ENG & SPA.). 100p. ring bd. incl. cd-rom (978-0-9741687-1-5(8) , 1000s) Help Me 2 Learn Co.

A Gnu Named Blue. (Early Intervention Levels Ser.). 31.86 (978-0-7362-0621-1(3)) Hampton-Brown Bks.

A Gnu Named Blue (30), Vol. 30. (Early Intervention Levels Ser.). 5.31 (978-0-7362-0609-9(4)) Hampton-Brown Bks.

Go, Go, Go. 2003. (Read with Dick & Jane Ser.: Vol. 6). (Illus.). 32p. (J). 13.89 (978-0-448-43417-9(2)); pap. 3.99 (978-0-448-43405-6(9)) Penguin Group (USA) Inc. (Grosset & Dunlap).

Go, Go, Go! Kindergarten Guided Reading Level A. (On Our Way to English Ser.). (gr. k up). 27.75 (978-0-7578-7006-4(6)) Rigby Education.

Go, Red Hens! (Early Intervention Levels Ser.). 21.30 (978-0-7362-0393-7(1)); Vol. 6. 3.55 (978-0-7362-0173-5(4)) Hampton-Brown Bks.

Goal! Individual Title Six-Pack Pouch - Level I. (Lighthouse Ser.). 16p. (gr. 1 up). 26.00 (978-0-7578-0856-2(5)) Rigby Education.

Goal: MainSails Individual Title Six-Packs. (Sails Literacy Ser.). (gr. 5 up). 37.00 (978-0-7578-8060-5(6)) Rigby Education.

God Made Funny Bugs. 2000. (978-1-893065-79-6(0) , Family Christian Pr.) Family Christian Stores, Inc.

The Goddess of the Volcano: Six-Pack, 6 packs. (Greetings Ser.: Vol. 1). (gr. 3-5). 31.00 (978-0-7635-1843-1(3)) Rigby Education.

Godfrey. Murder in the Shadows. (Thumbprint Mysteries Ser.). 32.86 (978-0-8092-0418-2(5)) McGraw-Hill/ Contemporary.

Going Fishing. (Little Book Practice Reader). (J). (978-0-8136-5371-6(1)) Modern Curriculum Pr.

Going Home: KinderConcepts Individual Title Six-Packs. (Kinderstarters Ser.). 8p. (ps-1). 21.00 (978-0-7635-8724-6(9)) Rigby Education.

Going to the Park with GranDaDy: Big Book: Level F. (Visionstm Ser.). 8p. 20.95 (978-0-7802-9745-6(8)) Wright Group, The.

Going West: Fifth Grade Newcomer Books. (On Our Way to English Ser.). (gr. 5 up). 34.50 (978-0-7578-7277-8(8)) Rigby Education.

The Golden Dragon: Set D Individual Title Six-Packs. (gr. k-3). 29.00 (978-0-7635-0552-3(8)) Rigby Education.

Golden Opportunities: Fourth Grade Class Collection Books. (On Our Way to English Ser.). (gr. 4 up). 29.95 (978-0-7578-4343-3(3)) Rigby Education.

Golden Opportunities: Small Versions of Class Collection Books. (On Our Way to English Ser.). (gr. 4 up). 34.50 (978-0-7578-7266-2(2)) Rigby Education.

Goldie's Shortcut. 12p. (J). bds. (978-2-7643-0051-0(4)) Phidal Publishing, Inc./Editions Phidal, Inc.

Goldilocks & the Three Bears: Take-Home Book. 2005. (Emergent Library: Vol. 2). (YA). (ps-1). 12.60 (978-0-8215-7260-3(1)) Sadlier, William H. Inc.

Gomboli, Mario. Comer Bien, Saber Comer. (Coleccion Lobo Rojo).Tr. of Eat Well, Know What to Eat. (SPA.). 32p. (J). (gr. k-3). 6.36 (978-84-216-3458-5(5)) Bruño, Editorial ESP. *Dist:* Lectorum Pubns., Inc.

—Lavarse Es Divertido. (SPA.). 32p. (J). (gr. k-3). 6.36 (978-84-216-3459-2(3)) Bruño, Editorial ESP. *Dist:* Lectorum Pubns., Inc.

Good Citizens: Third Grade Newcomer Books. (On Our Way to English Ser.). (gr. 3 up). 29.50 (978-0-7578-7251-8(4)) Rigby Education.

Good News! (Guided Reading Levels Ser.). (Illus.). 3.57 (978-0-7362-0952-6(2)) Hampton-Brown Bks.

Good News: First Grade Big Books. (On Our Way to English Ser.). (gr. 1 up). 29.95 (978-0-7578-1505-8(7)) Rigby Education.

Good News: Small Versions of Big Books. (On Our Way to English Ser.). (gr. 1 up). 29.00 (978-0-7578-7225-9(5)) Rigby Education.

Goodbye Gabby. 2001. (J). (978-1-58453-141-8(X)) Pioneer Valley Educational Pr., Inc.

Goodhart, Pippa. House that Jack Built. Parker, Andy, illus. 2004. 24p. (J). lib. bdg. 22.65 (***978-1-59646-700-2(2)***) Dingles & Co.

Goodman, Burton. Discoveries. 2002. (Goodman's Five-Star Stories Ser.). (gr. 6-12). pap. 17.32 (978-0-07-827355-1(2) , 9780078273551) Jamestown.

Goodnight Board Books Set 800492, 3. 2005. (J). bds. (978-1-59794-004-7(6)) Environments, Inc.

Goodwin, John. Selling Out. 2001. (Livewire Ser.). (Illus.). 32p. pap. (978-0-340-80081-2(X) , Hodder Arnold) Hodder Education.

The Goose Who Acted Like a Cow (18), Vol. 18. (Early Intervention Levels Ser.). 5.31 (978-0-7362-0615-0(9)) Hampton-Brown Bks.

Gordo, Francs. Poema de Mio Cid: Analisis y Estudio Sobre la Obra, el Autor y su Epoca. Gordo, Lydia, ed. 2005. (Compendios Vosgos Ser.). (SPA.). 126p. pap. 8.95 (978-84-95761-15-6(7)) Ediciones Norte, Inc.

Gordo, Lydia & Gordo, Francs, eds. La Celestina: Analisis y Estudio Sobre la Obra, el Autor y su Epoca. 2004. (Compendios Vosgos Ser.). (SPA.). 80p. pap. 8.95 (978-84-95761-08-8(4)) Ediciones Norte, Inc.

—Cien Anos de Soledad: Analisis y Estudios Sobre la Obra, el Autor y su Epoca. 2004. (Compendios Vosgos Ser.). (SPA., Illus.). 118p. pap. 8.95 (978-84-95761-37-8(8)) Ediciones Norte, Inc.

—Lazarillode de Tormes: Analisis y Estudio Sobre la Obra, el Autor y su Epoca. 2005. (Compendios Vosgos Ser.). (SPA.). 86p. pap. 8.95 (978-84-95761-24-8(6)) Ediciones Norte, Inc.

Gordon, Sharon. Bookworms: At Home, 6 bks., Set. Incl. At Home by the Ocean. lib. bdg. (978-0-7614-1959-4(4)); At Home in the City. lib. bdg. (978-0-7614-1960-0(8)); At Home in the Desert. lib. bdg. (978-0-7614-1963-1(2)); At Home on the Farm. lib. bdg. (978-0-7614-1958-7(6)); At Home on the Mountain. lib. bdg. (978-0-7614-1961-7(6)); At Home on the Ranch. lib. bdg. (978-0-7614-1962-4(4)); (Illus.). 32p. (J). (gr. 3-7). 2005. (978-0-7614-1957-0(8) , Benchmark Bks.) Cavendish, Marshall Corp.

—Bookworms: Ready for School, 6 bks., Set. Incl. We Are a Team. lib. bdg. (978-0-7614-1994-5(2)); We Are Kind. lib. bdg. (978-0-7614-1992-1(6)); We Listen. lib. bdg. (978-0-7614-1991-4(8)); We Share. lib. bdg. (978-0-7614-1993-8(4)); We Tell the Truth. lib. bdg. (978-0-7614-1996-9(9)); (Illus.). 24p. (J). (gr. 3-7). 2005. (978-0-7614-1990-7(X) , Benchmark Bks.) Cavendish, Marshall Corp.

—Listos para ir a la Escuela, 6 bks., Set. Incl. Compartimos. (Illus.). lib. bdg. 22.79 (978-0-7614-2360-7(5)); Decimos la Verdad. (Illus.). lib. bdg. 22.79 (978-0-7614-2362-1(1)); Escuchamos. lib. bdg. 22.79 (978-0-7614-2359-1(1)); Respetamos las Reglas. (Illus.). lib. bdg. 22.79 (978-0-7614-2358-4(3)); Somos Amables. (Illus.). lib. bdg. 22.79 (978-0-7614-2356-0(7)); Somos un Equipo. (Illus.). lib. bdg. 22.79 (978-0-7614-2357-7(5)); 24p. (J). 2006. (SPA.). 2007. Set lib. bdg. 136.71 (***978-0-7614-2354-6(0)*** , Benchmark Bks.) Cavendish, Marshall Corp.

—Ready for School (Listos para Ir a la Escuela) Incl. We Are a Team (Somos un Equipo) (Illus.). lib. bdg. 22.79 (978-0-7614-2436-9(9)); We Are Kind (Somos Amables) (Illus.). lib. bdg. 22.79 (978-0-7614-2435-2(0)); We Follow the Rules (Respetamos las Reglas) (Illus.). lib. bdg. 22.79 (978-0-7614-2438-3(5)); We Listen (Esuchamos) lib. bdg. 22.79 (978-0-7614-2439-0(3)); We Share (Compartimos) (Illus.). lib. bdg. 22.79 (978-0-7614-2441-3(5)); We Tell the Truth (Decimos la Verdad) (Illus.). lib. bdg. 22.79 (978-0-7614-2442-0(3)); 24p. (J). 2006. (ENG & SPA.). 2007. Set lib. bdg. 136.71 (***978-0-7614-2434-5(2)***) Cavendish, Marshall Corp.

Gorilla Games. (Early Intervention Levels Ser.). 21.30 (978-0-7362-0363-0(X)); Vol. 2. 3.55 (978-0-7362-0084-4(3)) Hampton-Brown Bks.

Gottlieb, Dale, illus. Are We There Yet?, Level 3. 2005. (I'm Going to Read Ser.). 32p. (J). (gr. 1-2). pap. 3.95 (978-1-4027-2713-9(5)) Sterling Publishing Co., Inc.

Gould, Robert. Dinosaurs. Epstein, Eugene, illus. Gould, Robert, photos by. 2005. (Big Stuff Ser.: 7). 16p. (J). bds. 7.95 (978-1-929945-58-0(2)) Big Guy Bks., Inc.

—Sea Creatures. Epstein, Eugene, illus. Gould, Robert, photos by. 2005. (Big Stuff Ser.: 8). 16p. (J). bds. 7.95 (978-1-929945-59-7(0)) Big Guy Bks., Inc.

Graciela Finds the Fair: Fifth Grade Guided Comprehension Level Q. (On Our Way to English Ser.). (gr. 5 up). 34.50 (978-0-7578-6617-3(4)) Rigby Education.

Gradisher, Martha, illus. A Valentine for Ms. Vanilla. 2005. (I'm Going to Read Ser.). 32p. (J). (ps). pap. 3.95 (978-1-4027-2711-5(9)); 11.95 (978-1-4027-2712-2(7)) Sterling Publishing Co., Inc.

Graham, Elspeth. Sandwich that Jack Made. Mould, Chris, illus. 2004. 24p. (J). lib. bdg. (***978-1-59646-698-2(7)***) Dingles & Co.

Graham, S. Jewels for the Journey. 2004. pap. 8.99 (978-1-58158-043-3(6)) McDougal Publishing Co.

Grahame, Kenneth. The Wind in the Willows. 2004. 224p. pap. 12.95 (978-1-59540-046-8(X) , 1st World Library - Literary Society) 1st World Publishing, Inc.

—The Wind in the Willows, Level 2. 2001. (Illus.). 48p. (C). pap. 9.00 (978-0-582-42660-3(X)) Longman Publishing Group.

Grandfather's Dream. (Lexile Levels Ser.). 9.09 (978-1-56334-707-8(5)) Hampton-Brown Bks.

Grandma Alma's Special Room: First Grade Guided Reading Level H. (On Our Way to English Ser.). (gr. 1 up). 27.75 (978-0-7578-7061-3(9)) Rigby Education.

Grandma's Birthday: First Grade Guided Reading Level F. (On Our Way to English Ser.). (gr. 1 up). 27.75 (978-0-7578-7050-7(3)) Rigby Education.

Grandma's Garden: Individual Title Six-Packs. (Rigby Focus Ser.). 24p. (gr. 2 up). 28.00 (978-0-7578-5345-6(5)) Rigby Education.

Grandma's House. 2004. (J). (978-1-58453-277-4(7)) Pioneer Valley Educational Pr., Inc.

Grandma's Project: Third Grade Guided Reading Level O. (On Our Way to English Ser.). (gr. 3 up). 34.50 (978-0-7578-7141-2(0)) Rigby Education.

Graves, Sue. Jen the Hen. 2007. (Fun with Phonics Ser.). 20p. (J). pap. 4.99 (***978-0-439-02553-9(2)***) Scholastic, Inc.

A Great Day in the City. (Guided Reading Levels Ser.). 4.73 (978-0-7362-1894-8(7)) Hampton-Brown Bks.

A Great Idea: Third Grade Guided Reading Level I. (On Our Way to English Ser.). (gr. 3 up). 34.50 (978-0-7578-7113-9(5)) Rigby Education.

The Great Invention: Individual Title Six-Packs. (ps-2). 27.00 (978-0-7635-9452-7(0)) Rigby Education.

The Greedy King. Individual Title Six-Pack Pouch - Level K. (Lighthouse Ser.). 16p. (gr. 2 up). 28.00 (978-0-7578-0861-6(1)) Rigby Education.

Green. Not a Chance. (Thumbprint Mysteries Ser.). 32.86 (978-0-8092-0422-9(3)) McGraw-Hill/Contemporary.

The Green Dragons: Individual Title Six-Packs. 16p. (gr. 2 up). 35.00 (978-0-7635-9232-5(3)) Rigby Education.

Green Footprints: Individual Title Six-Packs. (Literatura 2000 Ser.). (gr. 1-2). 28.00 (978-0-7635-0053-5(4)) Rigby Education.

Green Light Level 1 Book Set 2 800895, 5 vols. 2005. (J). pap. (978-1-59794-070-2(4)) Environments, Inc.

Green Light Level 1 Book Set 800894, 5 vols. 2005. (J). (978-1-59794-069-6(0)) Environments, Inc.

Green Light Level 2 Book Set 800914, 6 vols. 2005. (J). pap. (978-1-59794-079-5(8)) Environments, Inc.

Green, Rod. Bing & Bong's Tiny Planets Activity Book. 2003. (Tiny Planets Ser.). (Illus.). 24p. (J). pap. 6.99 (978-1-84222-879-1(X)) Carlton Bks., Ltd. GBR. *Dist:* Independent Pubs. Group.

The Green Scene: Individual Title Six-Packs. (Rigby Infoquest Ser.). (gr. 5 up). 37.00 (978-0-7578-6489-6(9)) Rigby Education.

Greene, Janice. The Dark Lady. 2004. (Illus.). 32p. (YA). 2.95 (978-1-56254-741-7(0) , SP7410) Saddleback Educational Publishing.

—Read My Lips. 2004. (Illus.). 32p. (YA). 2.95 (978-1-56254-742-4(9) , SP7429) Saddleback Educational Publishing.

—Tough Girl. 2004. (Illus.). 32p. (YA). 2.95 (978-1-56254-746-2(1) , SP7461) Saddleback Educational Publishing.

Greene, Stephanie. Betsy Ross & the Silver Thimble. Magnuson, Diana, illus. ed. 2005. 32p. (J). lib. bdg. 15.00 (978-1-59054-942-1(2)) Fitzgerald Bks.

Greenfield Educational Center Staff. Anan Is Hungry. 2000. (I Can Read Ser.: Bk. 2). (CHI & ENG., Illus.). 8p. (J). pap. 2.99 (978-962-563-106-6(2)); pap. 24.99 (978-962-563-131-8(3)) Greenfield Enterprises, Ltd. HKG. *Dist:* Cheng & Tsui Co.

—Biamei's Chocolate Peanuts. 2000. (I Can Read Ser.: Bk. 4). (CHI & ENG., Illus.). 8p. (J). pap. 2.99 (978-962-563-097-7(X)) Greenfield Enterprises, Ltd. HKG. *Dist:* Cheng & Tsui Co.

—The Bicycle & the Car. 2000. (I Can Read Ser.: Bk. 12). (CHI & ENG., Illus.). 8p. (J). pap. 2.99 (978-962-563-121-9(6)); pap. 24.99 (978-962-563-133-2(X)) Greenfield Enterprises, Ltd. HKG. *Dist:* Cheng & Tsui Co.

—The Bicycle & the Car: Simplified Edition. 2000. (I Can Read Ser.: Bk. 12). (CHI & ENG., Illus.). 8p. (J). pap. 2.99 (978-962-563-217-9(4)) Greenfield Enterprises, Ltd. HKG. *Dist:* Cheng & Tsui Co.

—Birthday Presents. 2000. (I Can Read Ser.: Bk. 1). (CHI & ENG., Illus.). 8p. (J). pap. 2.99 (978-962-563-078-6(3)); pap. 24.99 (978-962-563-135-6(6)) Greenfield Enterprises, Ltd. HKG. *Dist:* Cheng & Tsui Co.

—Birthday Presents: Simplified Edition. 2000. (I Can Read Ser.: Bk. 1). (CHI & ENG., Illus.). 8p. (J). pap. 2.99 (978-962-563-206-3(9)) Greenfield Enterprises, Ltd. HKG. *Dist:* Cheng & Tsui Co.

—Blue-Green (Qing) 2000. (Rainbow Reading Ser.). (CHI., Illus.). (J). pap. 7.99 (978-962-563-035-9(X)); Bk. 2. pap. 7.99 (978-962-563-086-1(4)); Bk. 3. pap. 7.99 (978-962-563-226-1(3)) Greenfield Enterprises, Ltd. HKG. *Dist:* Cheng & Tsui Co.

—Blue (Lan) 2000. (Rainbow Reading Ser.). (CHI., Illus.). (J). pap. 8.50 (978-962-563-227-8(1)); Bk. 1. pap. 8.50 (978-962-563-036-6(8)); Bk. 2. pap. 8.50 (978-962-563-087-8(2)) Greenfield Enterprises, Ltd. HKG. *Dist:* Cheng & Tsui Co.

—The Cat & the Frog. 2000. (I Can Read Ser.: Bk. 8). (CHI & ENG., Illus.). 8p. (J). pap. 2.99 (978-962-563-118-9(6)); pap. 24.99 (978-962-563-302-2(2)) Greenfield Enterprises, Ltd. HKG. *Dist:* Cheng & Tsui Co.

—The Cat & the Frog: Simplified Edition. 2000. (I Can Read Ser.: Bk. 8). (CHI & ENG., Illus.). 8p. (J). pap. 2.99 (978-962-563-201-8(8)) Greenfield Enterprises, Ltd. HKG. *Dist:* Cheng & Tsui Co.

—Dongdong Has a Party. 2000. (I Can Read Ser.: Bk. 12). (CHI & ENG., Illus.). 8p. (J). pap. 2.99 (978-962-563-113-4(5)); pap. 24.99 (978-962-563-132-5(1)) Greenfield Enterprises, Ltd. HKG. *Dist:* Cheng & Tsui Co.

—The Farm. 2000. (I Can Read Ser.: Bk. 7). (CHI & ENG., Illus.). 8p. (J). pap. 2.99 (978-962-563-100-4(3)) Greenfield Enterprises, Ltd. HKG. *Dist:* Cheng & Tsui Co.

—The First. 2000. (I Can Read Ser.: Bk. 10). (CHI & ENG., Illus.). 8p. (J). pap. 2.99 (978-962-563-052-6(X)); pap. 24.99 (978-962-563-304-6(9)) Greenfield Enterprises, Ltd. HKG. *Dist:* Cheng & Tsui Co.

—The First: Simplified Edition. 2000. (I Can Read Ser.: Bk. 10). (CHI & ENG., Illus.). 8p. (J). pap. 2.99 (978-962-563-203-2(4)) Greenfield Enterprises, Ltd. HKG. *Dist:* Cheng & Tsui Co.

—A Flower. 2000. (I Can Read Ser.: Bk. 9). (CHI & ENG., Illus.). 8p. (J). pap. 2.99 (978-962-563-111-0(9)); pap. 24.99 (978-962-563-289-6(1)) Greenfield Enterprises, Ltd. HKG. *Dist:* Cheng & Tsui Co.

—Flying. 2000. (I Can Read Ser.: Bk. 2). (CHI & ENG., Illus.). 8p. (J). pap. 2.99 (978-962-563-114-1(3)); pap. 24.99 (978-962-563-297-1(2)) Greenfield Enterprises, Ltd. HKG. *Dist:* Cheng & Tsui Co.

—Flying: Simplified Edition. 2000. (I Can Read Ser.: Bk. 2). (CHI & ENG., Illus.). 8p. (J). pap. 2.99 (978-962-563-195-0(X)) Greenfield Enterprises, Ltd. HKG. *Dist:* Cheng & Tsui Co.

—Fruit. 2000. (I Can Read Ser.: Bk. 5). (CHI & ENG., Illus.). 8p. (J). pap. 2.99 (978-962-563-022-9(8)); pap. 24.99 (978-962-563-286-5(7)) Greenfield Enterprises, Ltd. HKG. *Dist:* Cheng & Tsui Co.

—A Fun Vacation. 2000. (I Can Read Ser.: Bk. 12). (CHI & ENG., Illus.). 8p. (J). pap. 2.99 (978-962-563-105-9(4)) Greenfield Enterprises, Ltd. HKG. *Dist:* Cheng & Tsui Co.

—Get Dressed, Younger Brother. 2000. (I Can Read Ser.: Bk. 7). (CHI & ENG., Illus.). 8p. (J). pap. 2.99 (978-962-563-051-9(1)); pap. 24.99 (978-962-563-082-3(1)) Greenfield Enterprises, Ltd. HKG. *Dist:* Cheng & Tsui Co.

—Get Dressed, Younger Brother: Simplified Edition. 2000. (I Can Read Ser.: Bk. 7). (CHI & ENG., Illus.). 8p. (J). pap. 2.99 (978-962-563-200-1(X)) Greenfield Enterprises, Ltd. HKG. *Dist:* Cheng & Tsui Co.

—Going Home. 2000. (I Can Read Ser.: Bk. 5). (CHI & ENG., Illus.). 8p. (J). pap. 2.99 (978-962-563-116-5(X)); pap. 24.99 (978-962-563-300-8(6)) Greenfield Enterprises, Ltd. HKG. *Dist:* Cheng & Tsui Co.

—Going Home: Simplified Edition. 2000. (I Can Read Ser.: Bk. 5). (CHI & ENG., Illus.). 8p. (J). pap. 2.99 (978-962-563-198-1(4)) Greenfield Enterprises, Ltd. HKG. *Dist:* Cheng & Tsui Co.

—Going to the Amusement Park. 2000. (I Can Read Ser.: Bk. 10). (CHI & ENG., Illus.). 8p. (J). pap. 2.99 (978-962-563-103-5(8)) Greenfield Enterprises, Ltd. HKG. *Dist:* Cheng & Tsui Co.

—Going to the Department Store. 2000. (I Can Read Ser.: Bk. 9). (CHI & ENG., Illus.). 8p. (J). pap. 2.99 (978-962-563-102-8(X)) Greenfield Enterprises, Ltd. HKG. *Dist:* Cheng & Tsui Co.

—Green (Lu) 2000. (Rainbow Reading Ser.). (CHI., Illus.). (J). Bk. 1. pap. 7.50 (978-962-563-034-2(1)); Bk. 2. pap. 7.50 (978-962-563-085-4(6)); Bk. 3. pap. 7.50 (978-962-563-225-4(5)) Greenfield Enterprises, Ltd. HKG. *Dist:* Cheng & Tsui Co.

—How Will Santa Get Here? 2000. (I Can Read Ser.: Bk. 9). (CHI & ENG., Illus.). 8p. (J). pap. 2.99 (978-962-563-079-3(1)); pap. 24.99 (978-962-563-137-0(2)) Greenfield Enterprises, Ltd. HKG. *Dist:* Cheng & Tsui Co.

—How Will Santa Get Here? Simplified Edition. 2000. (I Can Read Ser.: Bk. 9). (CHI & ENG., Illus.). 8p. (J). pap. 2.99 (978-962-563-214-8(X)) Greenfield Enterprises, Ltd. HKG. *Dist:* Cheng & Tsui Co.

—I Can Read. 1999. (I Can Read Ser.). (CHI., Illus.). 24p. (J). Level 1. pap., wbk. ed., act. bk. ed. 3.99 (978-962-563-249-0(2)); Level 2. pap., wbk. ed., act. bk. ed. 3.99 (978-962-563-250-6(6)); Level 3. pap., wbk. ed., act. bk. ed. 8.95 (978-962-563-251-3(4)); Level 4. pap., wbk. ed., act. bk. ed. 3.99 (978-962-563-252-0(2)) Greenfield Enterprises, Ltd. HKG. *Dist:* Cheng & Tsui Co.

—I Can Read Series: Level 4, 12 bks., Set. 2000. (CHI & ENG.). (J). pap. 35.00 (978-962-563-143-1(7)) Greenfield Enterprises, Ltd. HKG. *Dist:* Cheng & Tsui Co.

—I Don't Want to Go to Bed. 2000. (I Can Read Ser.: Bk. 4). (CHI & ENG., Illus.). 8p. (J). pap. 2.99 (978-962-563-072-4(4)) Greenfield Enterprises, Ltd. HKG. *Dist:* Cheng & Tsui Co.

—I Don't Want to Go to Bed: Simplified Edition. 2000. (I Can Read Ser.: Bk. 4). (CHI & ENG., Illus.). 8p. (J). pap. 2.99 (978-962-563-209-4(3)) Greenfield Enterprises, Ltd. HKG. *Dist:* Cheng & Tsui Co.

—In a Moment! 2000. (I Can Read Ser.: Bk. 11). (CHI & ENG., Illus.). 8p. (J). pap. 2.99 (978-962-563-120-2(8)); pap. 24.99 (978-962-563-305-3(7)) Greenfield Enterprises, Ltd. HKG. *Dist:* Cheng & Tsui Co.

—In a Moment! Simplified Edition. 2000. (I Can Read Ser.: Bk. 11). (CHI & ENG., Illus.). 8p. (J). pap. 2.99 (978-962-563-204-9(2)) Greenfield Enterprises, Ltd. HKG. *Dist:* Cheng & Tsui Co.

—It's Raining. 2000. (I Can Read Ser.: Bk. 2). (CHI & ENG., Illus.). 8p. (J). pap. 2.99 (978-962-563-071-7(6)); pap. 24.99 (978-962-563-139-4(9)) Greenfield Enterprises, Ltd. HKG. *Dist:* Cheng & Tsui Co.

—It's Raining: Simplified Edition. 2000. (I Can Read Ser.: Bk. 2). (CHI & ENG., Illus.). 8p. (J). pap. 2.99 (978-962-563-207-0(7)) Greenfield Enterprises, Ltd. HKG. *Dist:* Cheng & Tsui Co.

—Last Night. 2000. (I Can Read Ser.: Bk. 9). (CHI & ENG., Illus.). 8p. (J). pap. 2.99 (978-962-563-119-6(4)); pap. 24.99 (978-962-563-303-9(0)) Greenfield Enterprises, Ltd. HKG. *Dist:* Cheng & Tsui Co.

—Last Night: Simplified Edition. 2000. (I Can Read Ser.: Bk. 9). (CHI & ENG., Illus.). 8p. (J). pap. 2.99 (978-962-563-202-5(6)) Greenfield Enterprises, Ltd. HKG. *Dist:* Cheng & Tsui Co.

—The Lazy Sparrow. 2000. (I Can Read Ser.: Bk. 6). (CHI & ENG., Illus.). 8p. (J). pap. 2.99 (978-962-563-101-1(1)) Greenfield Enterprises, Ltd. HKG. *Dist:* Cheng & Tsui Co.

—Letters. 2000. (I Can Read Ser.: Bk. 4). (CHI & ENG., Illus.). 8p. (J). pap. 2.99 (978-962-563-108-0(9)); pap. 24.99 (978-962-563-285-8(9)) Greenfield Enterprises, Ltd. HKG. *Dist:* Cheng & Tsui Co.

—The Lion Is Hungry. 2000. (I Can Read Ser.: Bk. 5). (CHI & ENG., Illus.). 8p. (J). pap. 2.99 (978-962-563-073-1(2)) Greenfield Enterprises, Ltd. HKG. *Dist:* Cheng & Tsui Co.

—The Lion Is Hungry: Simplified Edition. 2000. (I Can Read Ser.: Bk. 5). (CHI & ENG., Illus.). 8p. (J). pap. 2.99 (978-962-563-210-0(7)) Greenfield Enterprises, Ltd. HKG. *Dist:* Cheng & Tsui Co.

—May I Come In? 2000. (I Can Read Ser.: Bk. 5). (CHI & ENG., Illus.). 8p. (J). pap. 2.99 (978-962-563-098-4(8)) Greenfield Enterprises, Ltd. HKG. *Dist:* Cheng & Tsui Co.

—My Dreams. 2000. (I Can Read Ser.: Bk. 10). (CHI & ENG., Illus.). 8p. (J). pap. 2.99 (978-962-563-075-5(9)); pap. 24.99 (978-962-563-130-1(5)) Greenfield Enterprises, Ltd. HKG. *Dist:* Cheng & Tsui Co.

—My Dreams: Simplified Edition. 2000. (I Can Read Ser.: Bk. 10). (CHI & ENG., Illus.). 8p. (J). pap. 2.99 (978-962-563-215-5(8)) Greenfield Enterprises, Ltd. HKG. *Dist:* Cheng & Tsui Co.

—My House. 2000. (I Can Read Ser.: Bk. 1). (CHI & ENG., Illus.). 8p. (J). pap. 2.99 (978-962-563-049-6(X)); pap. 24.99 (978-962-563-296-4(4)) Greenfield Enterprises, Ltd. HKG. *Dist:* Cheng & Tsui Co.

—My House: Simplified Edition. 2000. (I Can Read Ser.: Bk. 1). (CHI & ENG., Illus.). 8p. (J). pap. 2.99 (978-962-563-194-3(1)) Greenfield Enterprises, Ltd. HKG. *Dist:* Cheng & Tsui Co.

—My Wishes. 2000. (I Can Read Ser.: Bk. 6). (CHI & ENG., Illus.). 8p. (J). pap. 2.99 (978-962-563-117-2(8)); pap. 24.99 (978-962-563-301-5(4)) Greenfield Enterprises, Ltd. HKG. *Dist:* Cheng & Tsui Co.

—My Wishes: Simplified Edition. 2000. (I Can Read Ser.: Bk. 6). (CHI & ENG., Illus.). 8p. (J). pap. 2.99 (978-962-563-199-8(2)) Greenfield Enterprises, Ltd. HKG. *Dist:* Cheng & Tsui Co.

—Orange (Cheng) 2000. (Rainbow Reading Ser.). (CHI., (J). Illus.). pap. 6.99 (978-962-563-032-8(5)); Bk. 2. pap. 6.99 (978-962-563-059-5(7)); Bk. 3. (Illus.). pap. 6.99 (978-962-563-223-0(9)) Greenfield Enterprises, Ltd. HKG. *Dist:* Cheng & Tsui Co.

—Purple (Zi) 2000. (Rainbow Reading Ser.). (CHI., Illus.). (J). pap. 8.50 (978-962-563-228-5(X)); Bk. 1. pap. 8.50 (978-962-563-037-3(6)); Bk. 2. pap. 8.50 (978-962-563-088-5(0)) Greenfield Enterprises, Ltd. HKG. *Dist:* Cheng & Tsui Co.

—Red (Hong) 2000. (Rainbow Reading Ser.). (CHI., Illus.). (J). Bk. 1. pap. 6.99 (978-962-563-031-1(7)); Bk. 2. pap. 6.99 (978-962-563-083-0(X)); Bk. 3. pap. 6.99 (978-962-563-222-3(0)) Greenfield Enterprises, Ltd. HKG. *Dist:* Cheng & Tsui Co.

—Red (Hong) Prep Book. 2000. (Rainbow Reading Ser.). (CHI., Illus.). (J). pap. 6.99 (978-962-563-058-8(9)) Greenfield Enterprises, Ltd. HKG. *Dist:* Cheng & Tsui Co.

—Run Fast! 2000. (I Can Read Ser.: Bk. 6). (CHI & ENG., Illus.). 8p. (J). pap. 2.99 (978-962-563-110-3(0)); pap. 24.99 (978-962-563-287-2(5)) Greenfield Enterprises, Ltd. HKG. *Dist:* Cheng & Tsui Co.

—Shoes. 2000. (I Can Read Ser.: Bk. 4). (CHI & ENG., Illus.). 8p. (J). pap. 2.99 (978-962-563-050-2(3)); pap. 24.99 (978-962-563-299-5(9)) Greenfield Enterprises, Ltd. HKG. *Dist:* Cheng & Tsui Co.

—Shoes: Simplified Edition. 2000. (I Can Read Ser.: Bk. 4). (CHI & ENG., Illus.). 8p. (J). pap. 2.99 (978-962-563-197-4(6)) Greenfield Enterprises, Ltd. HKG. *Dist:* Cheng & Tsui Co.

—A Smart Boy. 2000. (I Can Read Ser.: Bk. 11). (CHI & ENG., Illus.). 8p. (J). pap. 2.99 (978-962-563-099-1(6)) Greenfield Enterprises, Ltd. HKG. *Dist:* Cheng & Tsui Co.

—Umbrellas. 2000. (I Can Read Ser.: Bk. 3). (CHI & ENG., Illus.). 8p. (J). pap. 2.99 (978-962-563-023-6(6)); pap. 24.99 (978-962-563-284-1(0)) Greenfield Enterprises, Ltd. HKG. *Dist:* Cheng & Tsui Co.

—Uncle Mianyang. 2000. (I Can Read Ser.: Bk. 11). (CHI & ENG., Illus.). 8p. (J). pap. 2.99 (978-962-563-080-9(5)) Greenfield Enterprises, Ltd. HKG. *Dist:* Cheng & Tsui Co.

—Uncle Mianyang: Simplified Edition. 2000. (I Can Read Ser.: Bk. 11). (CHI & ENG., Illus.). 8p. (J). pap. 2.99 (978-962-563-216-2(6)) Greenfield Enterprises, Ltd. HKG. *Dist:* Cheng & Tsui Co.

—What Happened to My Balloon? 2000. (I Can Read Ser.: Bk. 1). (CHI & ENG., Illus.). 8p. (J). pap. 2.99 (978-962-563-021-2(X)); pap. 24.99 (978-962-563-283-4(2)) Greenfield Enterprises, Ltd. HKG. *Dist:* Cheng & Tsui Co.

—Where Is It? 2000. (I Can Read Ser.: Bk. 8). (CHI & ENG., Illus.). 8p. (J). pap. 2.99 (978-962-563-077-9(5)) Greenfield Enterprises, Ltd. HKG. *Dist:* Cheng & Tsui Co.

—Where Is It? Simplified Edition. 2000. (I Can Read Ser.: Bk. 8). (CHI & ENG.). 8p. (J). pap. 2.99 (978-962-563-213-1(1)) Greenfield Enterprises, Ltd. HKG. *Dist:* Cheng & Tsui Co.

—Where Is the Wind? 2000. (I Can Read Ser.: Bk. 12). (CHI & ENG., Illus.). 8p. (J). pap. 2.99 (978-962-563-069-4(4)); pap. 24.99 (978-962-563-306-0(5)) Greenfield Enterprises, Ltd. HKG. *Dist:* Cheng & Tsui Co.

—Where Is the Wind? Simplified Edition. 2000. (I Can Read Ser.: Bk. 12). (CHI & ENG., Illus.). 8p. (J). pap. 2.99 (978-962-563-205-6(0)) Greenfield Enterprises, Ltd. HKG. *Dist:* Cheng & Tsui Co.

—Who Ate the Pie? 2000. (I Can Read Ser.: Bk. 3). (CHI & ENG., Illus.). 8p. (J). pap. 2.99 (978-962-563-115-8(1)); pap. 24.99 (978-962-563-298-8(0)) Greenfield Enterprises, Ltd. HKG. *Dist:* Cheng & Tsui Co.

—Who Ate the Pie? Simplified Edition. 2000. (I Can Read Ser.: Bk. 3). (CHI & ENG., Illus.). 8p. (Orig.). (J). pap. 2.99 (978-962-563-196-7(8)) Greenfield Enterprises, Ltd. HKG. *Dist:* Cheng & Tsui Co.

—Who Hit Me? 2000. (I Can Read Ser.: Bk. 8). (CHI & ENG., Illus.). 8p. (J). pap. 2.99 (978-962-563-104-2(6)) Greenfield Enterprises, Ltd. HKG. *Dist:* Cheng & Tsui Co.

—Who's Calling? 2000. (I Can Read Ser.: Bk. 7). (CHI & ENG., Illus.). 8p. (Orig.). (J). pap. 2.99 (978-962-563-109-7(7)); pap. 24.99 (978-962-563-288-9(3)) Greenfield Enterprises, Ltd. HKG. *Dist:* Cheng & Tsui Co.

—Who's There? 2000. (I Can Read Ser.: Bk. 6). (CHI & ENG., Illus.). 8p. (J). pap. 2.99 (978-962-563-074-8(0)) Greenfield Enterprises, Ltd. HKG. *Dist:* Cheng & Tsui Co.

—Who's There? Simplified Edition. 2000. (I Can Read Ser.: Bk. 6). (CHI & ENG., Illus.). 8p. (J). pap. 2.99 (978-962-563-211-7(5)) Greenfield Enterprises, Ltd. HKG. *Dist:* Cheng & Tsui Co.

—The Wind Plays with Me. 2000. (I Can Read Ser.: Bk. 10). (CHI & ENG., Illus.). 8p. (J). pap. 2.99 (978-962-563-024-3(4)); pap. 24.99 (978-962-563-290-2(5)) Greenfield Enterprises, Ltd. HKG. *Dist:* Cheng & Tsui Co.

—Xiaoming & His Balloon. 2000. (I Can Read Ser.: Bk. 11). (CHI & ENG., Illus.). 8p. (J). pap. 2.99 (978-962-563-112-7(7)); pap. 24.99 (978-962-563-291-9(3)) Greenfield Enterprises, Ltd. HKG. *Dist:* Cheng & Tsui Co.

—Xigo Hutu. 2000. (I Can Read Ser.: Bk. 2). (CHI & ENG., Illus.). 8p. (J). pap. 2.99 (978-962-563-095-3(3)) Greenfield Enterprises, Ltd. HKG. *Dist:* Cheng & Tsui Co.

—Yellow. 2000. (Rainbow Reading Ser.). (CHI., Illus.). Bk. 1. (J). pap. 7.50 (978-962-563-033-5(3)); Bk. 2. pap. 7.50 (978-962-563-084-7(8)); Bk. 3. (J). pap. 7.50 (978-962-563-224-7(7)) Greenfield Enterprises, Ltd. HKG. *Dist:* Cheng & Tsui Co.

—Yellow Leaves. 2000. (I Can Read Ser.: Bk. 8). (CHI & ENG., Illus.). 8p. (J). pap. 2.99 (978-962-563-107-3(0)); pap. 24.99 (978-962-563-081-6(3)) Greenfield Enterprises, Ltd. HKG. *Dist:* Cheng & Tsui Co.

Greenley, Amanda & Evans, Linda. Sledmere Stories. 2005. (Illus.). 80p. 12.95 (978-1-84312-153-4(0)); 12.95 (978-1-84312-154-1(9)); 12.95 (978-1-84312-152-7(2)) Taylor & Francis, Inc.

Greetings! Add-to Pack. 47.00 (978-0-7635-9407-7(5)) Rigby Education.

Greetings! Cluster Packages. (Saludos Ser.). (gr. 2-3). 135.00 (978-0-7635-9408-4(3)); 135.00 (978-0-7635-9412-1(1)); 135.00 (978-0-7635-9416-9(4)); 135.00 (978-0-7635-9422-0(9)) Rigby Education.

Greetings! The Earth Is Our Home Complete Package. 385.00 (978-0-7635-9420-6(2)) Rigby Education.

Gregorich, Barbara. Same or Different. deluxe ed. 2003. (Deluxe Wkbks.). (Illus.). 64p. (J). pap., wbk. ed. 3.79 (978-1-58947-356-0(6) , 02278) School Zone Publishing Co.

Gregory, the Mean Dragon (16), Vol. 16. (Early Intervention Levels Ser.). 4.73 (978-0-7362-0234-3(X)) Hampton-Brown Bks.

Griffith, Anita. The 10 Most Unforgettable Shipwrecks. 2008. (Tentrade; Ser.). 48p. (J). pap. 14.99 (***978-1-55448-458-4(8)*** , Watts, Franklin) Scholastic Library Publishing.

Grimm, Wilhelm K., et al. Elves & Shoemaker. 2004. 48p. (J). (gr. 2 up). pap. 5.95 (978-0-7945-0758-9(1) , Usborne) EDC Publishing.

Griswell, Kim, ed. Contracts for Independent Readers - Fantasy. 2001. 64p. 11.95 (978-1-56234-405-4(6) , Mailbox Bks., The) Education Ctr., Inc.

—Contracts for Independent Readers - Realistic Fiction. 2001. 64p. 11.95 (978-1-56234-409-2(9) , Mailbox Bks., The) Education Ctr., Inc.

Gro, Wright. Matchword/Prog Set. (Fasttrack Reading Ser.). (gr. k-6). 158.95 incl. cd-rom (978-0-322-03751-9(4)) Wright Group, The.

Grosset & Dunlap. Go Away Spot. 2003. (ps-2). lib. bdg. 11.80 (978-0-613-72505-7(0)) Tandem Library Bks.

—Jump & Run. 2003. (ps-2). lib. bdg. 11.80 (978-0-613-72504-0(2)) Tandem Library Bks.

—Something Funny. 2003. (ps-2). lib. bdg. 11.80 (978-0-613-72503-3(4)) Tandem Library Bks.

—We Look. 2003. (ps-2). lib. bdg. 11.80 (978-0-613-72573-6(5)) Tandem Library Bks.

Grosset & Dunlap Inc. Staff, Inc. Fun with Dick & Jane. 2004. (gr. k-3). lib. bdg. 11.80 (978-0-613-72512-5(3)) Tandem Library Bks.

Grosset and Dunlap Staff. Go Away Spot. 2003. (Read with Dick & Jane Ser.: Vol. 5). 32p. (J). (ps-2). pap. 3.99 (978-0-448-43404-9(0) , Grosset & Dunlap) Penguin Group (USA) Inc.

Group/McGraw-Hill, Wright. Magazine Anthology: Level 2, 6 vols. (Comprehension Strand Ser.). (YA). (gr. 4-8). 54.00 (978-0-322-06028-9(1)) Wright Group, The.

—: Magazine Anthology: Level 3, 6 vols. (Comprehension Strand Ser.). (YA). 54.00 (978-0-322-09849-7(1)) Wright Group, The.

—: Magazine Anthology: Level 5, 6 vols. (Comprehension Strand Ser.). (YA). 54.00 (978-0-322-09857-2(2)) Wright Group, The.

—: Magazine Anthology: Level 6, 6 vols. (Comprehension Strand Ser.). (YA). 54.00 (978-0-322-09858-9(0)) Wright Group, The.

—A Friend in the Wild: Level Q, 6 vols. 128p. (gr. 5 up). 36.95 (978-0-322-05905-4(4)) Wright Group, The.

—Legends of the Wild West: Level O, 6 vols. 128p. (gr. 3-6). 36.95 (978-0-322-06732-5(4)) Wright Group, The.

—Mountain Peaks: Complete Set. 327.95 (978-0-322-07966-3(7)) Wright Group, The.

—Raging Rivers: Classroom Library Set. 81.50 (978-0-322-07970-0(5)) Wright Group, The.

—Raging Rivers: Complete Set. 327.95 (978-0-322-07964-9(0)) Wright Group, The.

—Riverboat Bill: Level H, 6 vols. (Take Twostm Ser.). 16p. 29.95 (978-0-322-08958-7(1)) Wright Group, The.

—Story Box, Leveled Books. 79.95 (978-0-322-02563-9(X)) Wright Group, The.

—Storyteller: Upper Emergent - Upper Emergent-Early Fluency - Complete Kit. (gr. 1 up). 565.50 (978-1-4045-1042-5(7)) Wright Group, The.

—Storyteller Chapter Books: Fluency - 1 Each of 4 Titles: Level S. 24.50 (978-1-4045-0953-5(4)) Wright Group, The.

—Sunshine: Early Fluency - Groups 1-2; 1 each of 17 titles: Level M. 99.50 (978-0-322-04312-1(3)) Wright Group, The.

—Take Twos: Upper Emergent - Level H: 1 Each of 4 Lesson Plans: Level H. 31.50 (978-1-4045-1729-5(4)) Wright Group, The.

A Growing Nation: Fifth Grade Class Collection Books. (On Our Way to English Ser.). (gr. 5 up). 29.95 (978-0-7578-4471-3(5)) Rigby Education.

A Growing Nation: Small Versions of Class Collection Books. (On Our Way to English Ser.). (gr. 5 up). 34.50 (978-0-7578-7281-5(6)) Rigby Education.

Growing Tree Story Time Event Kit. 2000. (J). (978-0-694-01461-3(3) , Harper Festival) HarperCollins Pubs.

Growing up Abenaki: Third Grade Guided Reading Level M. (On Our Way to English Ser.). (gr. 3 up). 34.50 (978-0-7578-7134-4(8)) Rigby Education.

The Grumpy Millionaire: Individual Title Six-Packs. (Bookweb Ser.). 32p. (gr. 5 up). 34.00 (978-0-7635-3777-7(2)) Rigby Education.

Guess What! Individual Title Six-Packs. (Literatura 2000 Ser.). (gr. k-1). 28.00 (978-0-7635-0054-2(2)) Rigby Education.

Guess Who. 2003. (Read with Dick & Jane Ser.: Vol. 4). 32p. (J). (ps-2). pap. 3.99 (978-0-448-43403-2(2) , Grosset & Dunlap) Penguin Group (USA) Inc.

Guess Who? Individual Title Six-Packs. (gr. k-1). 23.00 (978-0-7635-8856-4(3)) Rigby Education.

Guffanti, Stephen & Guffanti, Maureen. Rocket Phonics: The Fast, Fun, Easy Way to Teach Reading! 2005. (J). pap. 98.99 (978-0-89455-871-9(4)) Critical Thinking Bks. & Software.

Guide to Metro Early Reading Program, Levels A-F. 2000. (Metro Reading Ser.). (gr. 12). 10.55 (978-1-58120-232-8(6)) Metropolitan Teaching & Learning Co.

Guided Reading: High School Small-Group Reading Instruction. 2004. spiral bd. 20.00 (978-1-932230-85-7(8)) National Ctr. on Education & The Economy.

Guided Reading: Middle School Small-Group Reading Instruction. 2004. spiral bd. 20.00 (978-1-932230-84-0(X)) National Ctr. on Education & The Economy.

Guided Reading: Middle School Small-Group Reading Instruction. 2003. spiral bd. 20.00 (978-1-932230-56-7(4)) National Ctr. on Education & The Economy.

Guided Reading Levels, 25 bks., Set, Level A. (Guided Reading Levels Ser.). 92.05 (978-0-7362-1186-4(1)) Hampton-Brown Bks.

Gulliver's Travels Study Guide. 2000. (Illus.). 48p. (YA). per. 17.95 (978-1-56254-286-3(9) , SP2869) Saddleback Educational Publishing.

Gunn, Barbara. Old MacDonald's Farm: Read Well Level K Unit 7 Storybook. Marier, Chuck, illus. 2004. (Read Well Level K Ser.). 20p. (J). (978-1-57035-679-7(3)) Sopris West Educational Services.

Gunn, Barbara, et al. Mark & Dan Go West: Read Well Level K Unit 17 Storybook. Weber, Philip A., Jr., illus. 2003. (Read Well Level K Ser.). 20p. (J). (978-1-57035-688-9(2) , 55571) Sopris West Educational Services.

Gunson, Dave, illus. Come: First Wave Satellite Individual Title Six-Packs. (Sails Literacy Ser.). 16p. (gr. k up). 27.00 (978-0-7578-6850-4(9)) Rigby Education.

—Silly Tricks: First Wave Satellite Individual Title Six-Packs. (Sails Literacy Ser.). 16p. (gr. k up). 27.00 (978-0-7578-6855-9(X)) Rigby Education.

Gura, Timothy & Lee, Charlotte. Oral Interpretation. 11th ed. 2004. 544p. (YA). pap. 78.76 (978-0-618-30817-0(2) , 318462) Houghton Mifflin College Div.

Gus the Duck. 2004. (Illus.). (J). (978-1-59577-005-9(4)) Starfall Education.

Gwazube, Fundasile. Crocodile's Sore Tooth Lugbara Version: Eyio Ma Si Azo Ri. Draville, Ben & Mawa, Robert, trs. 2001. 16p. pap. 1.40 (978-0-521-00622-4(8)) Cambridge Univ. Pr.

Gwazube, Fundisile. Crocodile's Sore Tooth: Ateso Version. Ejalu, Ateker & Omare-Okurut, Augustine, trs. 1998. (Cambridge African Language Library Ser.). (Illus.). 16p. pap. 3.65 (978-0-521-63783-1(X)) Cambridge Univ. Pr.

—Crocodile's Sore Tooth: Lunda Version. Kambangaji, Thomson, tr. 1998. (Cambridge African Language Library Ser.). (Illus.). 16p. pap. 3.70 (978-0-521-63832-6(1)) Cambridge Univ. Pr.

Gwent (Wales), Staff Development Unit Staff & Acen Staff, contrib. by. Croeso I Gartref Llew. 2005. (WEL., Illus.). 8p. (978-1-874049-34-0(3)) Acen Limited.

—Nos Da, Arthur. 2005. (WEL., Illus.). 8p. (978-1-874049-31-9(9)) Acen Limited.

Haack, Pamela, reader. Using Guided Reading to Help Your Students Become Better Readers. 2000. (Illus.). (J). (gr. 3-6). pap., wbk. ed. 85.00 incl. audio (978-1-886397-36-1(8)) Bureau of Education & Research.

Hacia arriba cuesta Abajo 6: Leveled Books. 2001. (McGraw-Hill. Lectura Ser.). (ENG & SPA.). (gr. 4 up). (978-0-02-188182-6(0)) Macmillan/McGraw-Hill Schl. Div.

Haley, Amanda, illus. Ready, Alice?, Level 2. 2005. (I'm Going to Read Ser.). 32p. (J). (ps-ps). pap. 3.95 (978-1-4027-2717-7(8)) Sterling Publishing Co., Inc.

Hall, Dorothy & Tillman, Cece. Book Club Groups. Bland, Joey, ed. 2004. (Four-Blocks Ser.). (J). per. 24.99 (978-0-88724-247-2(2) , CD-104000) Carson-Dellosa Publishing Co., Inc.

Hall, Dorothy P. & Loman, Karen. Interactive Charts: Shared Reading for Kindergarten & 1st Grade. 2002. (Illus.). 176p. (J). per. 18.99 (978-0-88724-811-5(X) , CD-2414) Carson-Dellosa Publishing Co., Inc.

Hall, Kirsten. Hide-and-Seek: All about Location. Luedecke, Bev, illus. 2005. (Beastieville Ser.). 32p. (J). (gr. k-1). pap. 3.95 (978-0-516-25519-4(3) , Children's Pr.) Scholastic Library Publishing.

Hamaguchi, Carla, ed. Guided Reading. 2002. (J). (gr. k-3). pap. 9.99 (978-1-57471-909-3(2) , CTP 3495) Creative Teaching Pr., Inc.

Hamlet. 2002. (Illus.). 48p. (YA). stu. ed., per. 17.95 (978-1-56254-601-4(5) , SP6015) Saddleback Educational Publishing.

Hamsters, 6 vols. (gr. k-2). 28.95 (978-0-7368-9238-4(9)) Red Brick Learning.

Handy Handbook: MainSails Individual Title Six-Packs. (Sails Literacy Ser.). (gr. 5 up). 37.00 (978-0-7578-8052-0(5)) Rigby Education.

Hanging Around Bats. 2005. (Book Treks Ser.). (J). (gr. 3 up). stu. ed. 34.95 (978-0-673-62834-3(5)) Celebration Pr.

Hank's Tank, 6 vols. 8p. (gr. k-1). 21.50 (978-0-322-02061-0(1)) Wright Group, The.

Hannam, Joyce & Hedge, Tricia. The Death of Karen Silkwood, Level 2. 2000. (Bookworms Ser.). (Illus.). 64p. 6.50 (978-0-19-422970-8(X)) Oxford Univ. Pr., Inc.

Hanson, Ed. The Floodgates. 2004. 64p. (YA). per. 3.95 (978-1-56254-803-2(4) , SP8034) Saddleback Educational Publishing.

—Ransom. 2004. 64p. (YA). per. 3.95 (978-1-56254-808-7(5) , SP8085) Saddleback Educational Publishing.

Hapka, Catherine. The Search for Kong, No. 2. Bollinger, Peter, illus. 2005. (King Kong Ser.). 24p. (J). pap. 3.99 (978-0-06-077303-8(0)) HarperCollins Pubs.

Hapka, Cathy. Clue School: The Case of the Missing Cat, Level 4. Torrey, Richard, illus. 2006. (innovativeKids readers ser.: level 4). 32p. (J). (gr. 2-17). pap., pap. 6.99 (978-1-58476-479-3(1) , IKIDS) Innovative Kids.

Happy Baby Board Books 800847, 3. 2005. (J). bds. (978-1-59794-048-1(8)) Environments, Inc.

Happy Harriet: Individual Title Six-Packs. (Sails Literacy Ser.). (gr. 1-2). 36.00 (978-0-7578-6716-3(2)) Rigby Education.

Happy Tunes Book Set 800944, 5. 2005. (J). bds. (978-1-59794-031-3(3)) Environments, Inc.

Harcourt School Publishers Staff. Abby's Mark: Take-Home Book. 1999. (Signatures Ser.). (Illus.). (J). pap. 1.90 (978-0-15-313949-9(8)) Harcourt Schl. Pubs.

—Accelerated Reader Quiz Disk Vamos: Windows Intervention Edition. 2002. (SPA.). (J). cd-rom 66.30 (978-0-15-326341-5(5)) Harcourt Schl. Pubs.

—Acercate y Mira. 2000. (SPA., Illus.). pap. 82.60 (978-0-15-315104-0(8)) Harcourt Schl. Pubs.

—Actividades Foneticas. 1999. (Trofeos Ser.). (SPA., Illus.). (gr. k-6). pap., pupil's gde. ed. 13.50 (978-0-15-315910-7(3)) Harcourt Schl. Pubs.

—Adonde Va el Oso Pardo? Superlibros & Coleccion de Superlibros. 1999. (Trofeos Ser.). (SPA., Illus.). (gr. 1 up). pap. 82.60 (978-0-15-315158-3(7)) Harcourt Schl. Pubs.

—Al Norte... Below Level. 3rd ed. 2002. (Trofeos Ser.). (SPA., Illus.). pap. 6.80 (978-0-15-324156-7(X)) Harcourt Schl. Pubs.

—Al Super Mercado: Superlibros & Coleccion de Superlibros. 1999. (Trofeos Ser.). (SPA., Illus.). (gr. 1 up). pap. 82.60 (978-0-15-315163-7(3)) Harcourt Schl. Pubs.

—Alistair & Outer Space: Library Edition. 1999. (Collections Ser.). (Illus.). (J). 5.30 (978-0-15-314308-3(8)) Harcourt Schl. Pubs.

—All My Friends. 1999. (Collections Ser.). (Illus.). 28.20 (978-0-15-314474-5(2)) Harcourt Schl. Pubs.

—Ancient Chinese Secrets On Level. 3rd ed. 2002. (Trophies Reading Program Ser.). (Illus.). pap. 5.10 (978-0-15-323442-2(3)) Harcourt Schl. Pubs.

—Ancient Civilization. 2nd ed. 2003. (Horizons Ser.). (Illus.). (gr. k-7). act. bk. ed. 9.80 (978-0-15-335783-1(5)) Harcourt Schl. Pubs.

—Ancient Civilizations. 2nd ed. 2002. (Horizons Ser.). (gr. k-7). pap., tchr. ed., act. bk. ed. 23.30 (978-0-15-335784-8(3)) Harcourt Schl. Pubs.

—And Now for The... Take-Home Book. 1999. (Signatures Ser.). (Illus.). (J). pap. 1.90 (978-0-15-313868-3(8)) Harcourt Schl. Pubs.

—Another Try for Annie: Take-Home Book. 1999. (Signatures Ser.). (Illus.). (J). pap. 1.90 (978-0-15-313871-3(8)) Harcourt Schl. Pubs.

—The Ant & the Bird: Phonics Practice Reader. 1999. (Collections Ser.). (Illus.). (J). pap. 2.60 (978-0-15-312930-8(1)) Harcourt Schl. Pubs.

—Antologia Para la Lectura en Voz Alta. 1999. (Trofeos Ser.). (SPA., Illus.). (gr. k-6). 35.90 (978-0-15-315107-1(2)) Harcourt Schl. Pubs.

—Ants & People Play: Take-Home Books. 1999. (Collections Ser.). (Illus.). (J). pap. 1.90 (978-0-15-317230-4(4)) Harcourt Schl. Pubs.

—Apples in a Sack: Take-Home Book. 1999. (Collections Ser.). (Illus.). (J). pap. 1.90 (978-0-15-317158-1(8)) Harcourt Schl. Pubs.

—Around the Table: Practice Book: California Edition. 3rd ed. 2002. (Trophies Reading Program Ser.). (Illus.). (J). pap. 2.00 (978-0-15-326625-6(2)) Harcourt Schl. Pubs.

—Around the Table: Theme Book. 1999. (Collections Ser.). (Illus.). (J). pap. 3.00 (978-0-15-314018-1(6)) Harcourt Schl. Pubs.

—Around the Town: Practice Book: California Edition. 3rd ed. 2002. (Trophies Reading Program Ser.). (Illus.). (J). pap. 2.00 (978-0-15-326631-7(7)) Harcourt Schl. Pubs.

—Around the Town: Theme Book. 1999. (Collections Ser.). (Illus.). (J). pap. 3.00 (978-0-15-314025-9(9)) Harcourt Schl. Pubs.

—Arte del Pueble Advanced Level. 3rd ed. 2002. (Trofeos Ser.). (SPA., Illus.). pap. 6.80 (978-0-15-324122-2(5)) Harcourt Schl. Pubs.

—Asambroso Armidillo On Level. 3rd ed. 2002. (Trofeos Ser.). (SPA., Illus.). pap. 6.80 (978-0-15-324100-0(4)) Harcourt Schl. Pubs.

—At Home in the Sea Advanced Level. 3rd ed. 2002. (Trophies Reading Program Ser.). (Illus.). pap. 5.10 (978-0-15-323487-3(3)) Harcourt Schl. Pubs.

—Banner Days Level 2-2. 3rd ed. 2003. (Trophies Ser.). (Illus.). (gr. 2 up). pupil's gde. ed. 42.70 (978-0-15-322475-1(4)) Harcourt Schl. Pubs.

—Basqetbol/Sotano On Level. 3rd ed. 2002. (Trofeos Ser.). (SPA., Illus.). pap. 6.80 (978-0-15-324075-1(X)) Harcourt Schl. Pubs.

—Big Dreams Anthology Level 2. 99th ed. 1999. (Signatures Ser.). (Illus.). (gr. 1). 34.20 (978-0-15-310628-6(X)) Harcourt Schl. Pubs.

—Blue Waters Bk. 4: Standard Anthology. 95th ed. 1998. (Illus.). 44.20 (978-0-15-301250-1(1)) Harcourt Schl. Pubs.

—Bonesy & Isabel: Library Edition. 1999. (Collections Ser.). (Illus.). (J). 5.30 (978-0-15-314347-2(9)) Harcourt Schl. Pubs.

—Burrito y Perrito: Phonics Practice Reader. 1999. (Vamos Ser.). (SPA., Illus.). pap. 5.00 (978-0-15-318988-3(6)) Harcourt Schl. Pubs.

—Carrot Cake: A Reader. 1999. (Collections Ser.). (Illus.). (J). pap. 2.10 (978-0-15-313447-0(X)) Harcourt Schl. Pubs.

—Changes. 3rd ed. 2002. (Trophies Ser.). pap. 5.10 (978-0-15-327890-7(0)) Harcourt Schl. Pubs.

—Coast to Coast Anthology. 99th ed. 1999. (Signatures Ser.). (Illus.). (gr. 5). 74.40 (978-0-15-310111-3(3)) Harcourt Schl. Pubs.

—Collections: Mid-Year/End-of-Year Reading Skills Assessment. 1999. (Illus.). (gr. 1). pap. 42.50 (978-0-15-315206-1(0)); (gr. 2). pap. 42.50 (978-0-15-315207-8(9)); (gr. 3). pap. 42.50 (978-0-15-315208-5(7)); (gr. 4). pap. 37.50 (978-0-15-315209-2(5)) Harcourt Schl. Pubs.

—Collections Level 2. rev. ed. 2000. (Illus.). 30.70 (978-0-15-319079-7(5)) Harcourt Schl. Pubs.

—Collections Level 3. rev. ed. 2000. (Illus.). 31.50 (978-0-15-319080-3(9)) Harcourt Schl. Pubs.

—Collections Level 5: TX Edition. 2000. (Illus.). (gr. 1). 35.50 (978-0-15-319875-5(3)) Harcourt Schl. Pubs.

—A Conversation with Life in the Ocean On Level. 3rd ed. 2002. (Trophies Reading Program Ser.). (Illus.). pap. 5.10 (978-0-15-323457-6(1)) Harcourt Schl. Pubs.

—De la Cabeza a los Pies: Superlibros & Coleccion de Superlibros. 1999. (Trofeos Ser.). (SPA., Illus.). (gr. 1 up). pap. 82.60 (978-0-15-315159-0(5)) Harcourt Schl. Pubs.

—De Visita: Superlibros & Coleccion de Superlibros. 1999. (Trofeos Ser.). (SPA., Illus.). (gr. 1 up). pap. 82.60 (978-0-15-315155-2(2)) Harcourt Schl. Pubs.

—Un Dia de Calor: Superlibros & Coleccion de Superlibros. 1999. (Trofeos Ser.). (SPA., Illus.). (gr. 1 up). pap. 82.60 (978-0-15-315161-3(7)) Harcourt Schl. Pubs.

—A Discovery in Oyster Cove Advanced Level. 3rd ed. 2002. (Trophies Reading Program Ser.). (Illus.). pap. 5.10 (978-0-15-323380-7(X)) Harcourt Schl. Pubs.

—Dolphin Treasure Level D: Reader. 2001. (Collections Ser.). (Illus.). (J). 5.90 (978-0-15-314384-7(3)) Harcourt Schl. Pubs.

—Emergency: Library Edition. 1999. (Collections Ser.). (Illus.). (J). 5.30 (978-0-15-314309-0(6)) Harcourt Schl. Pubs.

—En Busca del Tesoro On Level. 3rd ed. 2002. (Trofeos Ser.). (SPA., Illus.). pap. 6.80 (978-0-15-324186-4(1)) Harcourt Schl. Pubs.

—En Casa de Mi Tia: Take-Home Book. 1999. (Vamos Ser.). (SPA., Illus.). (J). pap. 2.50 (978-0-15-318804-6(9)) Harcourt Schl. Pubs.

—En el Agua. 2000. (SPA., Illus.). pap. 82.60 (978-0-15-315105-7(6)) Harcourt Schl. Pubs.

—En el Circo: Take-Home Book. 1999. (Vamos Ser.). (SPA., Illus.). (J). pap. 2.50 (978-0-15-318813-8(8)) Harcourt Schl. Pubs.

—En el Jardin: Take-Home Book. 1999. (Vamos Ser.). (SPA., Illus.). (J). (gr. 1). pap. 2.50 (978-0-15-318818-3(9)) Harcourt Schl. Pubs.

—En Un Mar Below Level. 3rd ed. 2002. (Trofeos Ser.). (SPA., Illus.). pap. 6.80 (978-0-15-324142-0(X)) Harcourt Schl. Pubs.

—Enganar al Enemigo On Level. 3rd ed. 2002. (Trofeos Ser.). (SPA., Illus.). pap. 6.80 (978-0-15-324189-5(6)) Harcourt Schl. Pubs.

—Es una Emergencia: Take-Home Book. 1999. (Vamos Ser.). (SPA., Illus.). (J). pap. 2.50 (978-0-15-318824-4(3)) Harcourt Schl. Pubs.

—Escapada/Marvin: Big Book. 2000. (SPA., Illus.). pap. 82.60 (978-0-15-315100-2(5)) Harcourt Schl. Pubs.

—Eso Es Mio Below Level. 3rd ed. 2002. (Trofeos Ser.).Tr. of That Is Mine. (SPA., Illus.). pap. 6.80 (978-0-15-324049-2(0)) Harcourt Schl. Pubs.

—Estudiente/Semna On Level. 3rd ed. 2002. (Trofeos Ser.). (SPA., Illus.). pap. 6.80 (978-0-15-324092-8(X)) Harcourt Schl. Pubs.

—Eva y la Zorra: Superlibros & Coleccion de Superlibros. 1999. (Trofeos Ser.). (SPA., Illus.). (gr. 1 up). pap. 82.60 (978-0-15-315162-0(5)) Harcourt Schl. Pubs.

—Excursion a los Everglades On Level. 3rd ed. 2002. (Trofeos Ser.).Tr. of Excursion to the Everglades. (SPA., Illus.). pap. 6.80 (978-0-15-324183-3(7)) Harcourt Schl. Pubs.

—Fantastica Fiesta. 2000. (SPA., Illus.). pap. 82.60 (978-0-15-315092-0(0)) Harcourt Schl. Pubs.

—Farmyard Beds: Take-Home Book. 1999. (Collections Ser.). (Illus.). (J). pap. 1.90 (978-0-15-317213-7(4)) Harcourt Schl. Pubs.

—First Day at School: A Reader. 1999. (Collections Ser.). (Illus.). (J). pap. 2.10 (978-0-15-313434-0(8)) Harcourt Schl. Pubs.

—First Place Reading: Phonics Practice Reader. 2nd ed. 2003. (First-Place Reading Ser.). (gr. 1 up). Bk. 1. 4.10 (978-0-15-334590-6(X)); Bk. 2. (Illus.). 4.10 (978-0-15-334591-3(8)); Bk. 3. (Illus.). 4.10 (978-0-15-334592-0(6)); Bk. 4. (Illus.). 4.10 (978-0-15-334593-7(4)); Bk. 5. (Illus.). 4.10 (978-0-15-334594-4(2)); Bk. 6. (Illus.). 4.10 (978-0-15-334595-1(0)) Harcourt Schl. Pubs.

—El Frijo de Benito: Big Book. 1999. (SPA., Illus.). pap. 82.60 (978-0-15-315103-3(X)) Harcourt Schl. Pubs.

—Frontier Home Level D: Library Edition. 2001. (Collections Ser.). (Illus.). (J). 5.90 (978-0-15-314441-7(6)) Harcourt Schl. Pubs.

—Fun with Clay: Phonics Practice Reader. 1999. (Collections Ser.). (Illus.). (J). pap. 2.60 (978-0-15-312928-5(X)) Harcourt Schl. Pubs.

—La Gente Trabaja. 2000. (SPA., Illus.). pap. 82.60 (978-0-15-315102-6(1)) Harcourt Schl. Pubs.

—Get-Ready: Take-Home Book. 2000. (Collections Ser.). (Illus.). pap. 31.40 (978-0-15-314472-1(6)) Harcourt Schl. Pubs.

—Grandpa Lou: Phonics Practice Reader. 1999. (Collections Ser.). (Illus.). (J). pap. 2.60 (978-0-15-312943-8(3)) Harcourt Schl. Pubs.

—Hands on Reading Act Us. 2nd ed. 2002. pap. 16.00 (978-0-15-336918-6(3)) Harcourt Schl. Pubs.

—Hands on Reading Activities. 2nd ed. 2002. (SPA.). pap. 16.00 (978-0-15-336916-2(7)) Harcourt Schl. Pubs.

—Hands on Reading Activities Us. 2nd ed. 2002. (SPA.). pap. 21.30 (978-0-15-336917-9(5)) Harcourt Schl. Pubs.

—Hay Diez Perros y Tienda: Superlibros & Coleccion de Superlibros. 1999. (Trofeos Ser.). (SPA., Illus.). (gr. 1 up). pap. 82.60 (978-0-15-315156-9(0)) Harcourt Schl. Pubs.

—He Sees Behind Trees Level D: Library Edition. 2001. (Collections Ser.). (Illus.). pap. 12.10 (978-0-15-314404-2(1)) Harcourt Schl. Pubs.

—Hidden Surprises Level 1. 2001. (Collections Ser.). (Illus.). (gr. 3). 48.20 (978-0-15-312046-6(0)) Harcourt Schl. Pubs.

—Horizon Walk in the Wilderness: Time for Kids Reader-s:State & Region 5 Pack. 3rd ed. 2002. (Harcourt Horizons Ser.). (gr. k-7). pap. 28.70 (978-0-15-333389-7(8)) Harcourt Schl. Pubs.

—Horizons: Ancient Civilizations. 2nd ed. 2002. (Harcourt Horizons Ser.). (gr. 4-7). tchr. ed. 196.90 (978-0-15-335782-4(7)); (Illus.). pupil's gde. ed. 75.00 (978-0-15-335781-7(9)) Harcourt Schl. Pubs.

—Horizons: Time for Kids Reader: US History - Civil War to Present. 3rd ed. 2002. (Harcourt Horizons Ser.). (gr. k-7). pap., tchr. ed. 69.40 (978-0-15-334656-9(6)) Harcourt Schl. Pubs.

—Horizons: Time for Kids Readers Grade 3. 3rd ed. 2002. (Harcourt Horizons Ser.). (gr. 3 up). pap., tchr. ed. 56.30 (978-0-15-334648-4(5)) Harcourt Schl. Pubs.

—Horizons: Time for Kids Readers: World Regions. 3rd ed. 2002. (Harcourt Horizons Ser.). (gr. k-7). pap., tchr. ed. 69.40 (978-0-15-334657-6(4)) Harcourt Schl. Pubs.

—Horizons Big Book Collection. 2nd ed. 2003. (Illus.). (gr. 1). pap. 840.00 (978-0-15-337573-6(6)); (gr. 2). pap. 840.00 (978-0-15-337581-1(7)) Harcourt Schl. Pubs.

—Horizons Big Book Collection Unit 1. 2nd ed. 2003. (Illus.). pap. 140.00 (978-0-15-337574-3(4)); pap. 140.00 (978-0-15-337812-6(3)) Harcourt Schl. Pubs.

—Horizons Big Book Collection Unit 2. 2nd ed. 2003. (Illus.). pap. 140.00 (978-0-15-337575-0(2)); pap. 140.00 (978-0-15-337813-3(1)) Harcourt Schl. Pubs.

—Horizons Big Book Collection Unit 3. 2nd ed. 2003. (Illus.). pap. 140.00 (978-0-15-337577-4(9)); pap. 140.00 (978-0-15-337814-0(X)) Harcourt Schl. Pubs.

—Horizons Big Book Collection Unit 4. 2nd ed. 2003. (Illus.). pap. 140.00 (978-0-15-337578-1(7)); pap. 140.00 (978-0-15-337815-7(8)) Harcourt Schl. Pubs.

—Horizons Big Book Collection Unit 5. 2nd ed. 2003. (Illus.). pap. 140.00 (978-0-15-337579-8(5)); (J). pap. 140.00 (978-0-15-337816-4(6)) Harcourt Schl. Pubs.

—Horizons Big Book Collection Unit 6. 2nd ed. 2003. (Illus.). pap. 140.00 (978-0-15-337580-4(9)); pap. 140.00 (978-0-15-337817-1(4)) Harcourt Schl. Pubs.

—Horizons ESL Summary. 4th ed. 2004. (gr. 1). pap. 9.30 (978-0-15-341413-8(8)); (gr. 2). pap. 9.30 (978-0-15-341414-5(6)) Harcourt Schl. Pubs.

—Horizons ESL Summary with Ancient Civilizations. 4th ed. 2004. (gr. 3). pap. 12.40 (978-0-15-341415-2(4)) Harcourt Schl. Pubs.

—Horizons, Grade 2: Time for Kids Readers. 3rd ed. 2003. (Harcourt Horizons Ser.). pap., tchr. ed. 51.20 (978-0-15-334647-7(7)) Harcourt Schl. Pubs.

—Horizontes: States & Regions: Time for Kids Readers. 3rd ed. 2002. (Harcourt Horizontes Ser.). (SPA.). (gr. 3 up). pap., tchr. ed. 65.80 (978-0-15-334663-7(9)) Harcourt Schl. Pubs.

—Horizontes: US History: Time for Kids Readers. 3rd ed. 2002. (Harcourt Horizontes Ser.). (SPA.). (gr. 3 up). pap., tchr. ed. 81.10 (978-0-15-334664-4(7)) Harcourt Schl. Pubs.

—Horizontes, Grade 3: Time for Kids Readers. 3rd ed. 2002. (Harcourt Horizontes Ser.). (SPA.). (gr. 3 up). pap., tchr. ed. 65.80 (978-0-15-334661-3(2)) Harcourt Schl. Pubs.

—How Much Wood: Phonics Practice Reader. 1999. (Collections Ser.). (Illus.). (J). pap. 2.60 (978-0-15-312946-9(8)) Harcourt Schl. Pubs.

—I Have a Friend: A Reader. 1999. (Collections Ser.). (Illus.). (J). pap. 2.10 (978-0-15-313445-6(3)) Harcourt Schl. Pubs.

—I Like Toys: A Reader. 1999. (Collections Ser.). (Illus.). (J). pap. 2.10 (978-0-15-313458-6(5)) Harcourt Schl. Pubs.

—In My Car: A Reader. 1999. (Collections Ser.). (Illus.). (J). pap. 2.10 (978-0-15-313454-8(2)) Harcourt Schl. Pubs.

—In the Garden: A Reader. 1999. (Collections Ser.). (Illus.). (J). pap. 2.10 (978-0-15-313472-2(0)) Harcourt Schl. Pubs.

—Journeys of Wonder: Texas Edition. 1999. (Illus.). (gr. 3). 50.90 (978-0-15-314988-7(4)) Harcourt Schl. Pubs.

—Journeys of Wonder Level 2. 1999. (Collections Ser.). (Illus.). 48.20 (978-0-15-312047-3(9)) Harcourt Schl. Pubs.

—Just in Time Level 2. 2000. (Collections Ser.). (Illus.). 47.50 (978-0-15-312044-2(4)) Harcourt Schl. Pubs.

—Kangaroo Surprise: A Reader. 1999. (Collections Ser.). (Illus.). (J). pap. 2.10 (978-0-15-313459-3(3)) Harcourt Schl. Pubs.

—Kate & the Midnight Express: Reader's Choice Book. 2001. (Collections Ser.). (Illus.). (J). (gr. 4). 5.90 (978-0-15-314356-4(8)) Harcourt Schl. Pubs.

—Knock, Knock: A Reader. 1999. (Collections Ser.). (Illus.). (J). pap. 2.10 (978-0-15-314468-4(8)) Harcourt Schl. Pubs.

—Literature Big Book Collection. 3rd ed. 2003. (gr. 2). pap. 391.20 (978-0-15-338814-9(5)) Harcourt Schl. Pubs.

—Lucita's Home Is in Oaxaca: Reader's Choice Book. 2001. (Collections Ser.). (Illus.). (J). 4.70 (978-0-15-314360-1(6)) Harcourt Schl. Pubs.

—Misery in the Guts Level D: Library Edition. 2001. (Collections Ser.). (Illus.). pap. 12.10 (978-0-15-314409-7(2)) Harcourt Schl. Pubs.

—Moving into English Big Books: Leveled Library Collection. 2nd ed. 2003. (Illus.). (gr. 2). pap. 508.40 (978-0-15-337426-5(8)) Harcourt Schl. Pubs.

—My Pal Paul: Phonics Practice Reader. 1999. (Collections Ser.). (Illus.). (J). pap. 2.60 (978-0-15-312948-3(4)) Harcourt Schl. Pubs.

—Nade Con una Foca: Superlibros & Coleccion de Superlibros. 1999. (Trofeos Ser.). (SPA., Illus.). (gr. 1 up). pap. 82.60 (978-0-15-315164-4(1)) Harcourt Schl. Pubs.

—New Adventures: Intervention Reader. 1999. (Collections Ser.). (Illus.). (gr. 3). pap. 17.00 (978-0-15-312733-5(3)) Harcourt Schl. Pubs.

—On Sam's Boat: A Reader. 1999. (Collections Ser.). (Illus.). (J). pap. 2.10 (978-0-15-314471-4(8)) Harcourt Schl. Pubs.

—On the Farm: A Reader. 1999. (Collections Ser.). (Illus.). (J). pap. 2.10 (978-0-15-313473-9(9)) Harcourt Schl. Pubs.

—Out of the Blue Anthology. 99th ed. 1999. (Signatures Ser.). (Illus.). (gr. 1-2). 51.20 (978-0-15-310106-9(7)) Harcourt Schl. Pubs.

—Out of the Ocean: Library Edition. 1999. (Collections Ser.). (Illus.). (J). 6.90 (978-0-15-314301-4(0)) Harcourt Schl. Pubs.

—Parecia Leche Vertida: Superlibros & Coleccion de Superlibros. 1999. (Trofeos Ser.). (SPA., Illus.). (gr. 1 up). pap. 82.60 (978-0-15-315157-6(9)) Harcourt Schl. Pubs.

—Un Perrito Blanco: Superlibros & Coleccion de Superlibros. 1999. (Trofeos Ser.). (SPA., Illus.). (gr. 1 up). pap. 82.60 (978-0-15-315160-6(9)) Harcourt Schl. Pubs.

—Problem Solving for Reading Strategies Workbook Harcourt. 2nd ed. 2002. pap., wbk. ed. 10.00 (978-0-15-336522-5(6)) Harcourt Schl. Pubs.

—Program Kit: 1st Place Reader. 2nd ed. 2002. (gr. 4). pap. 1428.00 (978-0-15-335178-5(0)); (Illus.). (gr. 1). pap. 1829.80 (978-0-15-335174-7(8)); (Illus.). (gr. 2). pap. 1487.10 (978-0-15-335176-1(4)); (Illus.). (gr. 3). pap. 1487.10 (978-0-15-335177-8(2)); (Illus.). (gr. 5). pap. 1428.00 (978-0-15-335179-2(9)); (Illus.). (gr. 6). pap. 1428.00 (978-0-15-335181-5(0)) Harcourt Schl. Pubs.

—The Rain Forest Is a Home Below Level. 3rd ed. 2002. (Trophies Reading Program Ser.). (Illus.). (gr. 4). pap. 5.10 (978-0-15-323230-5(7)) Harcourt Schl. Pubs.

—Rare Finds Anthology. 99th ed. 1999. (Signatures Ser.). (Illus.). (gr. 4). 74.40 (978-0-15-310110-6(5)) Harcourt Schl. Pubs.

—A Real Winner: Take Home Book. 1999. (Signatures Ser.). (Illus.). (J). pap. 1.90 (978-0-15-313969-7(2)) Harcourt Schl. Pubs.

—A Sack of Trouble: Take-Home Book. 1999. (Signatures Ser.). (Illus.). (J). pap. 1.70 (978-0-15-313841-6(6)) Harcourt Schl. Pubs.

—Set Sail Level 5. 1999. (Collections Ser.). (Illus.). 34.20 (978-0-15-312042-8(8)) Harcourt Schl. Pubs.

—Shh! I'm Writing the Constitution Level D: Reader. 2001. (Collections Ser.). (Illus.). (J). 6.90 (978-0-15-314380-9(0)) Harcourt Schl. Pubs.

—Sid's Surprise. 1999. (Collections Ser.). (Illus.). (gr. 1). 6.40 (978-0-15-314992-4(2)) Harcourt Schl. Pubs.

—Signatures: Antologias Para la Lectura en Voz Alta. 1999. (Trofeos Ser.). (SPA., Illus.). (gr. 1 up). 39.60 (978-0-15-315133-0(1)) Harcourt Schl. Pubs.

—Signatures: Superlibros & Coleccion de Superlibros. 1999. (Trofeos Ser.). (SPA., Illus.). (gr. 1 up). pap. 977.10 (978-0-15-315134-7(X)) Harcourt Schl. Pubs.

—Signatures: Superlibros de Rimas. 1999. (Trofeos Ser.). (SPA., Illus.). (gr. 2 up). pap. 92.00 (978-0-15-315139-2(0)) Harcourt Schl. Pubs.

—Signatures Super Value Pack. 99th ed. 1999. (gr. 1). 7366.10 (978-0-15-312858-5(5)); (gr. 2). 3761.30 (978-0-15-312859-2(3)); (gr. 3). 3964.50 (978-0-15-312860-8(7)); (gr. 4). 2766.50 (978-0-15-312861-5(5)); (gr. 5). 2810.40 (978-0-15-312862-2(3)); (gr. 6). 2860.50 (978-0-15-312863-9(1)) Harcourt Schl. Pubs.

—The Skirt Level D: Reader. 2001. (Collections Ser.). (Illus.). (J). 6.90 (978-0-15-314371-7(1)) Harcourt Schl. Pubs.

—The Sky above & the Earth Below: Take-Home Book. 2001. (Collections Ser.). (Illus.). (J). pap. 1.90 (978-0-15-319667-6(X)) Harcourt Schl. Pubs.

—Something New Level 1. 1999. (Collections Ser.). (Illus.). (gr. 2). 47.50 (978-0-15-312043-5(6)) Harcourt Schl. Pubs.

—A Star in My Yard: Take-Home Book. 1999. (Signatures Ser.). (Illus.). (J). (gr. 2). pap. 1.90 (978-0-15-313874-4(2)) Harcourt Schl. Pubs.

—Superlibro de Rimas y Cantos. 1999. (Trofeos Ser.). (SPA., Illus.). (gr. k-6). pap. 76.40 (978-0-15-315106-4(4)) Harcourt Schl. Pubs.

—Test Best Leap 21/Itbs Reading. 2002. pap. (978-0-7398-7260-4(5)); pap. (978-0-7398-7266-6(4)); pap., tchr. ed. (978-0-7398-7268-0(0)) Steck-Vaughn.

—A Thud on the Porch: Take-Home Book. 1999. (Signatures Ser.). (Illus.). (J). pap. 1.90 (978-0-15-313885-0(8)) Harcourt Schl. Pubs.

—The Tortilla Cat Level D: Library Edition. 2001. (Collections Ser.). (Illus.). (J). (gr. 6). 5.90 (978-0-15-314431-8(9)) Harcourt Schl. Pubs.

—Trofeos: Libros de Intervencion:Sonidos Alegres. 3rd ed. 2002. (Trofeos Ser.). (SPA., Illus.). (gr. 2 up). pap. 21.30 (978-0-15-326477-1(2)) Harcourt Schl. Pubs.

—Trofeos: Una Semana/Pinquinos Little Book. 3rd ed. 2002. (SPA., Illus.). (J). 12.80 (978-0-15-332481-9(3)) Harcourt Schl. Pubs.

—Trofeos Advanced Level: Cultivada en Casa. 3rd ed. 2002. (SPA., Illus.). pap. 6.80 (978-0-15-324199-4(3)) Harcourt Schl. Pubs.

—Trofeos Advanced Level: El Fuego y el Hielo. 3rd ed. 2002. (SPA., Illus.). pap. 6.80 (978-0-15-324198-7(5)) Harcourt Schl. Pubs.

—Trofeos Advanced Level: Eleanor Roosevelt. 3rd ed. 2002. (SPA., Illus.). pap. 6.80 (978-0-15-324195-6(0)) Harcourt Schl. Pubs.

—Trofeos Advanced Level: Mi Radio de Cuarzo. 3rd ed. 2002. (SPA., Illus.). pap. 6.80 (978-0-15-324197-0(7)) Harcourt Schl. Pubs.

—Trofeos Collection, Grade 4. 3rd ed. 2002. (Trofeos Ser.). (SPA.). (gr. 4 up). tchr. ed. 637.70 (978-0-15-335038-2(5)) Harcourt Schl. Pubs.

—Trofeos Collection, Grade 5. 3rd ed. 2002. (Trofeos Ser.). (SPA.). (gr. 5 up). tchr. ed. 637.70 (978-0-15-335075-7(X)) Harcourt Schl. Pubs.

—Trofeos, Grade 3. 3rd ed. 2002. (Trofeos Ser.). (SPA.). Vol. 1, Theme 1. (gr. 1-3). tchr. ed. 99.60 (978-0-15-334837-2(2)); Vol. 1, Theme 2. (gr. 1-3). tchr. ed. 99.60 (978-0-15-334838-9(0)); Vol. 1, Theme 3. (gr. 1-3). tchr. ed. 99.60 (978-0-15-334839-6(9)); Vol. 2, Theme 1. (gr. 2-3). tchr. ed. 99.60 (978-0-15-334861-7(5)); Vol. 2, Theme 2. (gr. 2-3). tchr. ed. 99.60 (978-0-15-334989-8(1)); Vol. 2, Theme 3. (gr. 2-3). tchr. ed. 99.60 (978-0-15-335037-5(7)) Harcourt Schl. Pubs.

—Trofeos, Grade 4. 3rd ed. 2002. (Trofeos Ser.). (SPA.). (gr. 4 up). Theme 1. tchr. ed. 106.30 (978-0-15-335039-9(3)); Theme 2. tchr. ed. 106.30 (978-0-15-335046-7(6)); Theme 3. tchr. ed. 106.30 (978-0-15-335047-4(4)); Theme 4. tchr. ed. 106.30 (978-0-15-335054-2(7)); Theme 5. tchr. ed. 106.30 (978-0-15-335055-9(5)); Theme 6. tchr. ed. 106.30 (978-0-15-335074-0(1)) Harcourt Schl. Pubs.

—Trofeos, Grade 5. 3rd ed. 2002. (Trofeos Ser.). (SPA.). (gr. 5 up). Theme 1. tchr. ed. 106.30 (978-0-15-335076-4(8)); Theme 2. tchr. ed. 106.30 (978-0-15-335077-1(6)); Theme 3. tchr. ed. 106.30 (978-0-15-335078-8(4)); Theme 4. tchr. ed. 106.30 (978-0-15-335079-5(2)); Theme 5. tchr. ed. 106.30 (978-0-15-335080-1(6)); Theme 6. tchr. ed. 106.30 (978-0-15-335081-8(4)) Harcourt Schl. Pubs.

—Trophies: Lead the Way. 3rd ed. 2003. (Illus.). (gr. 4). 65.40 (978-0-15-339787-5(X)) Harcourt Schl. Pubs.

—Trophies: Mr. Putter & Tabby, Set 2. 2004. (Illus.). pap. 17.85 (978-0-15-205375-8(1)) Harcourt Schl. Pubs.

—Trophies: Timeless Treasures. 3rd ed. 2003. (Illus.). (gr. 6). 65.40 (978-0-15-339789-9(6)) Harcourt Schl. Pubs.

—Trophies Level 1-1: Guess Who. 3rd ed. 2003. (Illus.). (gr. 1). 29.90 (978-0-15-339776-9(4)) Harcourt Schl. Pubs.

—Trophies Level 1-2: Catch the Dream. 3rd ed. 2003. (Illus.). 29.90 (978-0-15-339777-6(2)) Harcourt Schl. Pubs.

—Trophies Level 1-3: Here & There. 3rd ed. 2003. (Illus.). 31.40 (978-0-15-339778-3(0)) Harcourt Schl. Pubs.

—Trophies Level 2-2: Banner Days. 3rd ed. 2003. (Illus.). 44.70 (978-0-15-339783-7(7)) Harcourt Schl. Pubs.

—Trophies Level 3-1: Changing Patterns. 3rd ed. 2003. (Illus.). (gr. 3). 47.40 (978-0-15-339784-4(5)) Harcourt Schl. Pubs.

—Trophies Level 3-2: On Your Mark. 3rd ed. 2003. (Illus.). 47.40 (978-0-15-339786-8(1)) Harcourt Schl. Pubs.

—Trophies Big Book: For English-Language Learners. 3rd ed. 2003. (Trophies Ser.). (Illus.). (gr. k-6). 42.00 (978-0-15-329343-6(8)) Harcourt Schl. Pubs.

—Trophies, Grade 1: Intervention Practice Book. 3rd ed. 2002. (Trophies Ser.). (gr. 1 up). pap., tchr. ed. 14.90 (978-0-15-326514-3(0)) Harcourt Schl. Pubs.

—Trophies, Grade 1: Intervention Reader. 3rd ed. 2002. (Trophies Ser.). (gr. 1 up). pap., tchr. ed. 29.20 (978-0-15-326512-9(4)) Harcourt Schl. Pubs.

—Trophies, Grade 5: For English-Language Learners. 3rd ed. 2002. (Trophies Ser.). (gr. 5 up). pap., tchr. ed. 44.80 (978-0-15-329338-2(1)) Harcourt Schl. Pubs.

—Under the Ocean: Practice Book: California Edition. 3rd ed. 2002. (Trophies Reading Program Ser.). (Illus.). (J). pap. 2.00 (978-0-15-326634-8(1)) Harcourt Schl. Pubs.

—Under the Ocean: Practice Book: Florida Edition. 3rd ed. 2002. (Trophies Reading Program Ser.). (Illus.). (J). pap. 2.00 (978-0-15-326607-2(4)) Harcourt Schl. Pubs.

—Vamos de Fiesta: Antologias Para la Lectura en Voz Alta. 1999. (Trofeos Ser.). (Illus.). (SPA.). (gr. 2 up). 37.50 (978-0-15-316136-0(1)); (gr. 3). 37.50 (978-0-15-316143-8(4)) Harcourt Schl. Pubs.

—Vamos de Fiesta: Caliente de Sorpresas Take-Home Book. 2001. (SPA., Illus.). (J). pap. 2.80 (978-0-15-321318-2(3)) Harcourt Schl. Pubs.

—Vamos de Fiesta: Dias de Emigrantes Take-Home Book. 2001. (SPA., Illus.). (J). pap. 2.80 (978-0-15-321307-6(8)) Harcourt Schl. Pubs.

—Vamos de Fiesta: El Elefantes de Raja Take Home Book. 2001. (SPA., Illus.). (J). pap. 2.80 (978-0-15-321301-4(9)) Harcourt Schl. Pubs.

—Vamos de Fiesta: El Loro Excepcional Take-Home Book. 2001. (SPA., Illus.). (J). pap. 2.80 (978-0-15-321311-3(6)) Harcourt Schl. Pubs.

—Vamos de Fiesta: El Mapa de Tosoro Take-Home Book. 2001. (SPA., Illus.). (J). pap. 2.80 (978-0-15-321304-5(3)) Harcourt Schl. Pubs.

—Vamos de Fiesta: El Mejor Canidato Take-Home Book. 2001. (SPA., Illus.). (J). pap. 2.80 (978-0-15-321314-4(0)) Harcourt Schl. Pubs.

—Vamos de Fiesta: El Sueno de una Baterista Take-Home Book. 2001. (SPA., Illus.). (J). pap. 2.80 (978-0-15-321316-8(7)) Harcourt Schl. Pubs.

—Vamos de Fiesta: Epoca de Paz Take-Home Book. 2001. (SPA., Illus.). (J). pap. 2.80 (978-0-15-321309-0(4)) Harcourt Schl. Pubs.

—Vamos de Fiesta: Family Involvement Activities. 1999. (SPA., Illus.). pap. 19.30 (978-0-15-315913-8(8)) Harcourt Schl. Pubs.

—Vamos de Fiesta: Fantasticos los Grandes Take-Home Book. 2001. (SPA., Illus.). (J). pap. 2.80 (978-0-15-321308-3(6)) Harcourt Schl. Pubs.

—Vamos de Fiesta: Get Ready Book Take-Home Version. 2001. (SPA., Illus.). pap. 35.90 (978-0-15-320597-2(0)) Harcourt Schl. Pubs.

—Vamos de Fiesta: Guided Reaading Manual Take-Home Book. 2001. (SPA., Illus.). (gr. 5). pap. 18.80 (978-0-15-319035-3(3)) Harcourt Schl. Pubs.

—Vamos de Fiesta: La Pequina Escuela del Valle Take-Home Book. 2001. (SPA., Illus.). (J). pap. 2.80 (978-0-15-321305-2(1)) Harcourt Schl. Pubs.

—Vamos de Fiesta: La Polizona Take-Home Book. 2001. (SPA., Illus.). (J). pap. 2.80 (978-0-15-321319-9(1)) Harcourt Schl. Pubs.

—Vamos de Fiesta: My Stories Book. 1999. (SPA., Illus.). 10.70 (978-0-15-315082-1(3)) Harcourt Schl. Pubs.

—Vamos de Fiesta: Norte del Rio Grande Take-Home Book. 2001. (SPA., Illus.). (J). pap. 2.80 (978-0-15-321306-9(X)) Harcourt Schl. Pubs.

—Vamos de Fiesta: Norteamericano Take-Home Book. 2001. (SPA., Illus.). (J). pap. 2.80 (978-0-15-321303-8(5)) Harcourt Schl. Pubs.

—Vamos de Fiesta: Nueva Estudiante Take-Home Book. 2001. (SPA., Illus.). (J). (gr. 5). pap. 2.80 (978-0-15-321315-1(9)) Harcourt Schl. Pubs.

—Vamos de Fiesta: Pinatas y Fiestas. 1999. (SPA., Illus.). 37.60 (978-0-15-315081-4(5)) Harcourt Schl. Pubs.

—Vamos de Fiesta: Plantas Carnivora Take-Home Book. 2001. (SPA., Illus.). (J). pap. 2.80 (978-0-15-321310-6(8)) Harcourt Schl. Pubs.

—Vamos de Fiesta: Practice Book. (SPA., Illus.). 1999. (gr. 4). pap. 15.70 (978-0-15-313305-3(8)); 1999. (gr. 5). pap. 15.70 (978-0-15-313306-0(6)); Vol. 1. 1999. (gr. 2). pap. 10.10 (978-0-15-313303-9(1)); Vol. 1. 1999. (gr. 3). pap. 10.10 (978-0-15-313304-6(X)); Vol. 2. 2000. (gr. 2). pap. 10.10 (978-0-15-316243-5(0)); Vol. 2. 1999. (gr. 1). pap. 14.50 (978-0-15-315152-1(8)); Vol. 2. 1999. (gr. 3). pap. 10.10 (978-0-15-316244-2(9)) Harcourt Schl. Pubs.

—Vamos de Fiesta: Tengo Tu Numero Take-Home Book. 2001. (SPA., Illus.). (J). pap. 2.80 (978-0-15-321317-5(5)) Harcourt Schl. Pubs.

—Vamos de Fiesta Level 1: Fiesta Alfabetica. 1999. (SPA., Illus.). 12.10 (978-0-15-315149-1(8)) Harcourt Schl. Pubs.

—Vamos de Fiesta Vol. 1: Practice book. 1999. (SPA., Illus.). (gr. 1). pap. 14.50 (978-0-15-313302-2(3)) Harcourt Schl. Pubs.

—A Veces: Superlibros & Coleccion de Superlibros. 1999. (Trofeos Ser.). (SPA., Illus.). (gr. 1 up). pap. 82.60 (978-0-15-315153-8(6)) Harcourt Schl. Pubs.

—Welcome Home Level 4. 1999. (Collections Ser.). (Illus.). 31.50 (978-0-15-312041-1(X)) Harcourt Schl. Pubs.

—Westward Bound! 3rd ed. 2002. (Trophies English Language Learners Ser.). (Illus.). pap. 5.10 (978-0-15-327838-9(2)) Harcourt Schl. Pubs.

—What a Picnic! A Reader. 1999. (Collections Ser.). (Illus.). (J). pap. 2.10 (978-0-15-313470-8(4)) Harcourt Schl. Pubs.

—What Am I: A Reader. 1999. (Collections Ser.). (Illus.). (J). pap. 2.10 (978-0-15-314469-1(6)) Harcourt Schl. Pubs.

—What Should I Do? 3rd ed. 2002. (Trophies English Language Learners Ser.). (Illus.). pap. 5.10 (978-0-15-327775-7(0)) Harcourt Schl. Pubs.

—Where Is Pig: A Reader. 1999. (Collections Ser.). (Illus.). (J). pap. 2.10 (978-0-15-314470-7(X)) Harcourt Schl. Pubs.

—The Wise Old Woman Level D: Reader. 2001. (Collections Ser.). (Illus.). (J). 4.70 (978-0-15-314370-0(3)) Harcourt Schl. Pubs.

—Yo Opino: Take-Home Book. 2001. (Vamos Ser.). (SPA., Illus.). (J). pap. 2.80 (978-0-15-319949-3(0)) Harcourt Schl. Pubs.

—Yo Soy: Superlibros & Coleccion de Superlibros. 1999. (Trofeos Ser.). (SPA., Illus.). (gr. 1 up). pap. 82.60 (978-0-15-315154-5(4)) Harcourt Schl. Pubs.

—You Better Go: Take-Home Book. rev. ed. 2001. (Collections Ser.: Bk. 8). (Illus.). (J). pap. 1.90 (978-0-15-319066-7(3)) Harcourt Schl. Pubs.

—Young Jose & the Paint Box Below Level. 3rd ed. 2002. (Trophies Reading Program Ser.). (Illus.). pap. 5.10 (978-0-15-323227-5(7)) Harcourt Schl. Pubs.

—Your Health Reader: The Morning. 3rd ed. 2003. (Illus.). pap. 9.40 (978-0-15-338777-7(7)) Harcourt Schl. Pubs.

Hard Workers Set C, 6 vols. (Phonics Readers Ser.). (gr. k-2). 17.50 (978-0-7368-3214-4(9)) Red Brick Learning.

The Hare & the Tortoise: Individual Title Six-Packs. 32p. (gr. 2 up). 37.00 (978-0-7635-9219-6(6)) Rigby Education.

Harold First Readers 800883, 4 vols. 2005. (J). pap. (978-1-59794-058-0(5)) Environments, Inc.

Harper, Kathryn & Mitton, Tony. Animal Antics. 2007. (Illus.). 48p. pap. ***978-0-521-70471-7(5)*** Cambridge Univ. Pr.

Harper, Kathryn, et al. I-Read Year 1 Anthology: Where I Live. 2007. (I-read Ser.). (Illus.). 40p. pap. (***978-0-521-70476-2(6)***) Cambridge Univ. Pr.

Harper, Suzanne. The 10 Most Amazing Bridges. 2008. (Tentrade; Ser.). 48p. (J). pap. 14.99 (***978-1-55448-470-6(7)*** , Watts, Franklin) Scholastic Library Publishing.

Harpster, Steve, illus. Fun First Phonics. 2004. (First Word Search Ser.). 64p. (J). pap. 3.95 (978-1-4027-1321-7(5)) Sterling Publishing Co., Inc.

Hart, Albert Bushnell & Chapman, Annie Bliss. How Our Grandfathers Lived. 1999. (Source-Readers in American History Ser.: No. 3). (Illus.). xiv, 371p. (J). (978-0-89526-297-4(5)) Regnery Publishing, Inc., An Eagle Publishing Co.

Hart, Melissa. Tale of Despereaux Literature Unit. 2005. 48p. pap. 7.99 (978-1-4206-3164-7(0)) Teacher Created Resources, Inc.

Hartley, Susan. The Bib. 2003. (StartUp Ser.). (J). pap. 22.00 (978-1-4108-0703-8(7)) Benchmark Education Co.

—Fit. 2003. (StartUp Ser.). (J). pap. 22.00 (978-1-4108-0698-7(7)) Benchmark Education Co.

—The Ham. 2003. (StartUp Ser.). (J). pap. 22.00 (978-1-4108-0702-1(9)) Benchmark Education Co.

—I Can! 2003. (StartUp Ser.). (J). pap. 22.00 (978-1-4108-0723-6(1)) Benchmark Education Co.

—I Did It! 2nd rev. ed. 2003. (StartUp Ser.). (J). pap. 22.00 (978-1-4108-0719-9(3)) Benchmark Education Co.

—The Job. 2003. (StartUp Ser.). (J). pap. 22.00 (978-1-4108-0711-3(8)) Benchmark Education Co.

—The Nut. 2003. (StartUp Ser.). (J). pap. 22.00 (978-1-4108-0704-5(5)) Benchmark Education Co.

—On Top! 2nd rev. ed. 2003. (StartUp Ser.). (J). pap. 22.00 (978-1-4108-0721-2(5)) Benchmark Education Co.

—Pam Has a Map. 2003. (StartUp Ser.). (J). pap. 22.00 (978-1-4108-0699-4(5)) Benchmark Education Co.

—Pop. 2003. (StartUp Ser.). (J). pap. 22.00 (978-1-4108-0700-7(2)) Benchmark Education Co.

—Pop & Len. 2003. (StartUp Ser.). (J). pap. 22.00 (978-1-4108-0710-6(X)) Benchmark Education Co.

—Quinn. 2003. (StartUp Ser.). (J). pap. 22.00 (978-1-4108-0715-1(0)) Benchmark Education Co.

—The Rat. 2003. (StartUp Ser.). (J). pap. 22.00 (978-1-4108-0705-2(3)) Benchmark Education Co.

—The Red Pen. 2003. (StartUp Ser.). (J). pap. 22.00 (978-1-4108-0708-3(8)) Benchmark Education Co.

—The Sax. 2003. (StartUp Ser.). (J). pap. 22.00 (978-1-4108-0716-8(9)) Benchmark Education Co.

—The Vet. 2003. (StartUp Ser.). (J). pap. 22.00 (978-1-4108-0714-4(2)) Benchmark Education Co.

—Welcome to Our School. ed. 2004. (Shared Connections Ser.). (J). pap. 27.00 (978-1-4108-1626-9(5)) Benchmark Education Co.

—Welcome to Our School (Big Book) ed. 2004. (Shared Connections Ser.). (J). pap., instr.'s gde. ed. 27.00 (978-1-4108-1602-3(8)) Benchmark Education Co.

—The Wig. 2003. (StartUp Ser.). (J). pap. 22.00 (978-1-4108-0709-0(6)) Benchmark Education Co.

—Yip & Yap. 2003. (StartUp Ser.). (J). pap. 22.00 (978-1-4108-0713-7(4) , 6) Benchmark Education Co.

Harvey, Damian. Mr. Fox's Socks. Rescek, Sanja, illus. 2004. 16p. (J). lib. bdg. 22.65 (***978-1-59646-678-4(2)***) Dingles & Co.

Harvey, Ken. The Leftovers. Hermes, Mary Sue, illus. 2003. (Life in the 'Fridge Ser.). (J). 14.95 (978-1-930093-21-8(7)) Brookfield Reader, Inc., The.

Harvey, Paul. Surfer!, Level 1. 2000. (Illus.). 32p. (C). pap. 9.00 (978-0-582-41661-1(2)) Longman Publishing Group.

Harwood, Beth. Amazing Baby Go, Baby, Go! Dodd, Emma, illus. Ellwand, David, photos by. 2006. (Amazing Baby Ser.). 16p. (J). bds. 5.95 (978-1-59223-625-1(1) , Silver Dolphin Bks.) Advantage Pubs. Group.

—Amazing Baby Hello Baby! 2006. (Amazing Baby Ser.). (Illus.). 6p. (J). bds. 5.95 (978-1-59223-701-2(0) , Silver Dolphin Bks.) Advantage Pubs. Group.

—Amazing Baby Peekaboo, Puppy! Dodd, Emma, illus. 2006. (Amazing Baby Ser.). 16p. (J). bds. 5.95 (978-1-59223-587-2(5) , Silver Dolphin Bks.) Advantage Pubs. Group.

—Amazing Baby Slide & Peek! 2006. (Amazing Baby Ser.). (Illus.). 6p. (J). bds. 5.95 (978-1-59223-702-9(9) , Silver Dolphin Bks.) Advantage Pubs. Group.

A Hat for Hippo: Early Level Satellite Individual Title Six-Packs. (Sails Literacy Ser.). 16p. (gr. 1-2). 27.00 (978-0-7578-2909-3(0)) Rigby Education.

Hatched from an Egg. (J). pap. 13.15 (978-0-8136-4261-1(2)) Modern Curriculum Pr.

Hatfield, Kelly & Rob. The "UnWorkbook" Creative Reading, Grade 3. 2005. 96p. (J). (gr. 3-3). pap. 12.99 (***978-0-7682-3123-6(X)*** , Schaffer, Frank) Schaffer, Frank Pubns.

—The "UnWorkbook" Creative Reading, Grade 4. 2005. 96p. (J). (gr. 4-4). pap. 12.99 (***978-0-7682-3124-3(8)*** , Schaffer, Frank) Schaffer, Frank Pubns.

Hautzig, Deborah. Miss Hildy's Missing Cape Capers. 2000. (Step into Reading Ser.). (978-0-606-18858-6(4)) Tandem Library Bks.

Having Fun. 2003. (J). (978-1-58453-111-1(8)) Pioneer Valley Educational Pr., Inc.

Hawaii & Alaska. (Guided Reading Levels Ser.). 4.73 (978-0-7362-1736-1(3)); 28.38 (978-0-7362-2158-0(1)) Hampton-Brown Bks.

Hawes, Alison. School Trip. Mould, Chris, illus. 2004. 24p. (J). lib. bdg. 22.65 (***978-1-59646-694-4(4)***) Dingles & Co.

Hawes, Alison. Stop, Look, & Listen: Individual Title Six-Pack Pouch - Level C. (Lighthouse Ser.). 12p. (gr. k-1). 24.00 (978-0-7578-0826-5(3)) Rigby Education.

The Hawkers' Amazing Machines. (Early Intervention Levels Ser.). 31.86 (978-0-7362-0661-7(2)) Hampton-Brown Bks.

The Hawkers' Amazing Machines (24), Vol. 24. (Early Intervention Levels Ser.). 5.31 (978-0-7362-0649-5(3)) Hampton-Brown Bks.

Hawley, Kelvin, illus. I Can Help: First Wave Satellite Individual Title, 6 Packs. (Sails Literacy Ser.). 16p. (gr. k up). 27.00 (978-0-7578-6865-8(7)) Rigby Education.

Hawthorne, Philip & Tyler, Jenny. Who's Making That Noise? Cartwright, Stephen, illus. 2005. (Flap Books Ser.). 16p. (J). (gr. 1 up). pap. 7.95 (978-0-7945-0432-8(9) , Usborne) EDC Publishing.

Hay, Samantha. Creepy Customers. Warburton, Sarah, illus. 2005. (I Am Reading Ser.). 48p. (J). (gr. k-3). pap., pap. 3.95 (978-0-7534-5857-0(8) , Kingfisher) Houghton Mifflin Co. Trade & Reference Div.

Haye, Lucy. ABCD & an Ant's Story. 2005. 23p. pap. 14.95 (978-1-4137-2537-7(6)) PublishAmerica, Inc.

Hayes, Rosemary. The Amazing Mr Mulch. 2005. (Cambridge Storybooks Ser.). (Illus.). 32p. pap. 7.00 (978-0-521-67479-9(4)) Cambridge Univ. Pr.

—The Big Shrink, 6, Pack. 2000. (Cambridge Reading Ser.). (Illus.). 32p. pap. 38.00 (978-0-521-78625-6(8)) Cambridge Univ. Pr.

—The Magic Sword. 2005. (Cambridge Storybooks Ser.). 32p. pap. 7.00 (978-0-521-67475-1(1)) Cambridge Univ. Pr.

—The Peace Ring. 2005. (Cambridge Storybooks Ser.). 32p. pap. 7.00 (978-0-521-67478-2(6)) Cambridge Univ. Pr.

Hazell, Elsa. And Then There Were None. Bowling, Barbara Hazell, illus. 1999. 182p. 24.95 (978-1-882935-39-0(X)) Westphalia Publishing.

HB. The Perfect Pet. 99th ed. 1999. (gr. 2). pap. 12.00 (978-0-15-314070-9(4)) Harcourt Schl. Pubs.

Headgear: Individual Title, 6 packs. (Sails Literacy Ser.). (gr. 1-2). 36.00 (978-0-7578-6735-4(9)) Rigby Education.

Headphones with Microphone for use with Fluent Reader. 2004. cd-rom 29.95 (978-1-59455-138-3(3)) Renaissance Learning, Inc.

Heads & Tails: Individual Title Six-Packs. (gr. 1-2). 22.00 (978-0-7635-9154-0(8)) Rigby Education.

Heads or Tails? Fourth Grade Guided Comprehension Level Q. (On Our Way to English Ser.). (gr. 4 up). 34.50 (978-0-7578-7177-1(1)) Rigby Education.

Heady, Heather. What's at the Beach? Storch, Ellen N., illus. l.t. ed. 2005. 10p. (J). (ps-k). pap. 10.95 (978-1-57332-355-0(1)) HighReach Learning, Inc.

Health & Safety Book Set 800840, 4. 2005. (J). (978-1-59794-027-6(5)) Environments, Inc.

Health Care Book Set 800842, 6. 2005. (J). (978-1-59794-028-3(3)) Environments, Inc.

Hebrew Reading Homework Book: Lamer Shteigin in Ivri. 2003. Orig. Title: Lamer Shteigin in Ivri. (YID.). 48p. (J). (gr. 2-4). pap. (978-0-9729232-0-0(9)) Kreizel Enterprises, Inc.

Hecho con Desechos 5: Leveled Books. 2001. (McGraw-Hill. Lectura Ser.). (ENG & SPA.). (gr. 4 up). (978-0-02-188150-5(2)) Macmillan/McGraw-Hill Schl. Div.

Heladooooos! 12: Leveled Books. 2001. (McGraw-Hill. Lectura Ser.). (ENG & SPA.). (gr. 1 up). (978-0-02-187941-0(9)) Macmillan/McGraw-Hill Schl. Div.

Helen's Job. (Early Intervention Levels Ser.). 21.30 (978-0-7362-0360-9(5)); Vol. 2. 3.55 (978-0-7362-0081-3(9)) Hampton-Brown Bks.

Hello, Duck! (Early Intervention Levels Ser.). 3.55 (978-0-7362-1861-0(0)) Hampton-Brown Bks.

Helmus, Shirley Sloan, et al. Gudies to Better Reading. 4th ed. 2002. 120p. (YA). stu. ed. 14.00 net. (978-0-9744327-0-0(9)) EverRead Assocs.

Help for Loc: Second Grade Guided Reading Level G. (On Our Way to English Ser.). (gr. 2 up). 34.50 (978-0-7578-7075-0(9)) Rigby Education.

Help for Rosie. 2003. (J). (978-1-932570-10-6(1)) Literacy Footprints Inc.

Help When Needed. 64p. (YA). (gr. 9-12). pap. 9.95 (978-0-8224-7155-4(8) , 7155) Globe Fearon Educational Publishing.

A Helpful Change. (Early Intervention Levels Ser.). 31.86 (978-0-7362-0670-9(1)) Hampton-Brown Bks.

Helping Each Other: First Grade Guided Reading Level C. (On Our Way to English Ser.). (gr. 1 up). 27.75 (978-0-7578-7034-7(1)) Rigby Education.

The Hen, the Rooster, & the Bean. (Lexile Levels Ser.). 47.88 (978-1-56334-393-3(2)) Hampton-Brown Bks.

Henderson, Diane & Snell, Jenepher. Comprehension Today, Grade 2: Getting Meaning from Real-Life Information. 2002. 48p. 6.95 (978-1-58324-142-4(6) , World Teachers Pr.) Didax Educational Resources, Inc.

—Comprehension Today, Grade 3: Getting Meaning from Real-Life Information. 2002. 48p. 6.95 (978-1-58324-143-1(4) , 2-5204, World Teachers Pr.) Didax Educational Resources, Inc.

—Comprehension Today, Grade 4: Getting Meaning from Real-Life Information. 2002. 48p. 6.95 (978-1-58324-144-8(2) , 2-5205, World Teachers Pr.) Didax Educational Resources, Inc.

Henderson, Jason & Salvaggio, Tony. Psy-Comm. 2007. (Kaplan SAT/ACT Score-Raising Manga Ser.). 192p. pap. 9.99 (***978-1-4277-5496-7(9)***) Kaplan Publishing.

Hensley, Sarab M. I Can Be. Teeple, Jackie, illus. l.t. ed. 2006. 12p. (J). (ps-k). pap. 10.95 (978-1-57332-339-0(X)) HighReach Learning, Inc.

Hensley, Sarah M. At the Park. Crowell, Knox, illus. l.t. ed. 2006. 10p. (J). (ps-k). pap. 10.95 (978-1-57332-354-3(3)) HighReach Learning, Inc.

—Water Fun. Crowell, Knox, illus. l.t. ed. 2005. (J). (ps-k). pap. 10.95 (978-1-57332-342-0(X)); pap. 10.95 (978-1-57332-343-7(8)) HighReach Learning, Inc.

Henson, Jim & LeapFrog Staff, compiled by. Tutler's Tiny Trip. 2002. (J). (ps-2). 14.95 (978-1-58605-912-5(2) , LeapFrog Schl. Hse.) LeapFrog Enterprises, Inc.

Her Story. (J). (gr. 4-6). 84.80 (978-0-8136-6024-0(6)) Modern Curriculum Pr.

Herbst, Cheryl. Too Many Nuts. Herbst, John W., photos by. 2000. (Books for Young Learners). 12p. (J). pap. 5.00 (978-1-57274-390-8(5)) Owen, Richard C. Pubs., Inc.

Here It Is! Kindergarten Guided Reading Level B. (On Our Way to English Ser.). (gr. k up). 27.75 (978-0-7578-7009-5(0)) Rigby Education.

Heroes Who Live On. 2002. 103p. (J). per. 6.99 (978-0-9722278-2-7(2)) CE National, Inc.

Herrera, Zanatta. New Parade Puppet: Level 1. 2000. (Illus.). (YA). 7.00 (978-0-13-088762-7(5)) Longman Publishing Group.

Herzog, Joyce. Excursion into Reading Reader: Part of the Little Beginner's Book Series. 2005. (J). spiral bd. 15.00 (***978-1-887225-36-6(6)***) JoyceHerzog.com, Inc.

Heskett, Tracie. Nonfiction Reading Comprehension: Informational Reading. 2007. 144p. pap. 15.99 (***978-1-4206-8861-0(8)***) Teacher Created Resources, Inc.

Hetty Hackett's Farm: 3-in-1 Package. (Sails Literacy Ser.). 24p. (gr. k up). 57.00 (978-0-7578-3197-3(4)) Rigby Education.

Hetty Hackett's Farm: 6 Small Books. (Sails Literacy Ser.). 24p. (gr. k up). 25.00 (978-0-7578-3173-7(7)) Rigby Education.

Hetty Hackett's Farm: Big Book Only. (Sails Literacy Ser.). 24p. (gr. k up). 27.00 (978-0-7635-6985-3(2)) Rigby Education.

Heurtelou, Maude. Mwen Pito Bwokoli. Hippolyte, Johanne & Corbett, Kecia, illus. 2001. Tr. of I Prefer Broccoli. 14p. (J). (gr. k-2). 19.50 (978-1-58432-080-7(X)); (CRP.). pap. 6.50 (978-1-58432-075-3(3)) Educa Vision.

—Mwen Pito Poul. Hippolyte, Johanne & Corbett, Kecia, illus. 2001. (Big Book Ser.).Tr. of I Prefer Poul. (CRP.). 14p. (J). (gr. k-2). 19.50 (978-1-58432-083-8(4)) Educa Vision.

Hewitt, Sally. Going to School, 4 vols. 2005. (QEB Readers). (Illus.). 24p. (J). (gr. 1-4). lib. bdg. 15.95 (978-1-59566-094-7(1)) QEB Publishing Inc.

—Keeping Healthy, 8 vols. 2005. (QEB Readers). (Illus.). 24p. (J). (ps-3). lib. bdg. 15.95 (978-1-59566-071-8(2)) QEB Publishing Inc.

—The Spick-and-Span Fairy, 8 vols. 2005. (QEB Readers). (Illus.). 24p. (J). (ps-3). lib. bdg. 15.95 (978-1-59566-066-4(6)) QEB Publishing Inc.

—Where's My Shirt?, 8 vols. 2005. (QEB Readers). (Illus.). 24p. (J). (ps-3). lib. bdg. 15.95 (978-1-59566-067-1(4)) QEB Publishing Inc.

Hey, Kids! (10-lesson edition All-English version) Book 1 Lesson Plan: English Language Teaching. 2002. 114p. tchr. ed., spiral bd. (978-0-7428-0792-1(4)) CCLS Publishing Hse.

Hey, Kids! (10-lesson edition All-English version) Book 1 Student's Book: English Language Teaching. 2002. (Illus.). 112p. tchr. ed., spiral bd. (978-0-7428-0791-4(6)) CCLS Publishing Hse.

Hey, Kids! (10-lesson edition All-English version) Book 1 Student's Book (with CD) English Language Teaching. 2003. (Illus.). 112p. stu. ed., spiral bd. incl. audio compact disk (978-0-7428-1051-8(8)) CCLS Publishing Hse.

Hey, Kids! (10-lesson edition All-English version) Book 2 Lesson Plan: English Language Teaching. 2003. 120p. tchr. ed., spiral bd. (978-0-7428-0845-4(9)) CCLS Publishing Hse.

Hey, Kids! (10-lesson edition All-English version) Book 2 Student's Book: English Language Teaching. 2002. (Illus.). 112p. stu. ed., spiral bd. (978-0-7428-0793-8(2)) CCLS Publishing Hse.

Hey, Kids! (10-lesson edition All-English version) Book 2 Student's Book (with CD) English Language Teaching. 2003. (Illus.). 112p. stu. ed., spiral bd. incl. audio compact disk (978-0-7428-1052-5(6)) CCLS Publishing Hse.

Hey, Kids! (10-lesson edition All-English version) Book 3 Lesson Plan: English Language Teaching. 2003. 128p. tchr. ed., spiral bd. (978-0-7428-0846-1(7)) CCLS Publishing Hse.

Hey, Kids! (10-lesson edition All-English version) Book 3 Student's Book: English Language Teaching. 2002. (Illus.). 112p. stu. ed., spiral bd. (978-0-7428-0794-5(0)) CCLS Publishing Hse.

Hickle, Victoria. Construction Action. 2007. (Tonka Power Reading Ser.: No. 1). 32p. (J). pap. 3.99 (***978-0-439-88481-5(0)***) Scholastic, Inc.

—Trucks Around Town. 2008. (Tonka Power Reading Ser.: No. 4). 32p. (J). pap. 3.99 (***978-0-439-88480-8(2)***) Scholastic, Inc.

Hicks, Diana & Littlejohn, Andrew. American English Primary Colors 1 Vocabulary Cards. 2004. 96p. 29.95 (978-0-521-60318-8(8)) Cambridge Univ. Pr.

—American English Primary Colors 2. 2003. (Primary Colours Ser.). (Illus.). 68p. pap., stu. ed. 12.00 (978-0-521-53920-3(X)) Cambridge Univ. Pr.

Hide & Seek. (Early Intervention Levels Ser.). 28.38 (978-0-7362-0401-9(6)) Hampton-Brown Bks.

Hide & Seek, 6 Packs. (Chiquilibros Ser.). (gr. k-1). 23.00 (978-0-7635-0439-7(4)) Rigby Education.

Hide & Seek (10), Vol. 10. (Early Intervention Levels Ser.). 4.73 (978-0-7362-0226-8(9)) Hampton-Brown Bks.

Hiebert. Ready Readers Study Guide to the Big Book Collection. (J). (ps-3). Vol. 1. 314.95 (978-0-8136-1697-1(2)); Vol. 2. 2003. 422.95 (978-0-8136-1698-8(0)) Modern Curriculum Pr.

Hiebert, Elfrieda H. The Apple Farm. (Little Book Practice Reader Ser.). (J). (978-0-8136-0805-1(8)) Modern Curriculum Pr.

—Mr. Wink. (Little Book Practice Reader Ser.). (J). (978-0-8136-0782-5(5)) Modern Curriculum Pr.

—Quickreads. 2005. (J). (gr. 2-6). stu. ed. 47.50 (978-0-7652-4420-8(9)); Vol. 2. stu. ed. 47.50 (978-0-7652-4422-2(5)); Vol. 3. stu. ed. 47.50 (978-0-7652-4424-6(1)) Modern Curriculum Pr.

—Quickreads: Level B Macintosh Classroom Package. 2005. (J). (gr. 2 up). 1067.50 (978-0-7652-5115-2(9)) Modern Curriculum Pr.

—Quickreads: Level B Windows Classroom Package. 2005. (J). (gr. 2 up). 1067.50 (978-0-7652-5112-1(4)) Modern Curriculum Pr.

—Quickreads: Level C Macintosh Classroom Package. 2005. (J). (gr. 3 up). 1067.50 (978-0-7652-5116-9(7)) Modern Curriculum Pr.

—Quickreads: Level C Windows Classroom Package. 2005. (J). (gr. 3 up). 1067.50 (978-0-7652-5113-8(2)) Modern Curriculum Pr.

—Quickreads: Level D Macintosh Classroom Package. 2005. (J). (gr. 4 up). 1067.50 (978-0-7652-5117-6(5)) Modern Curriculum Pr.

—Quickreads: Level D Windows Classroom Package. 2005. (J). (gr. 4 up). 1067.50 (978-0-7652-5114-5(0)) Modern Curriculum Pr.

—Quickreads: Level E Complete Program. 2005. (J). (gr. 5 up). 351.95 (978-0-7652-4427-7(6)) Modern Curriculum Pr.

—Quickreads: Macintosh Classroom Program. 2005. (J). (gr. 5 up). 1067.50 (978-0-7652-6157-1(X)) Modern Curriculum Pr.

—Quickreads: Windows Classroom Program. 2005. (J). (gr. 5 up). 1067.50 (978-0-7652-6158-8(8)) Modern Curriculum Pr.

—Shell Shopping. (Little Book Practice Reader Ser.). (J). (978-0-8136-0798-6(1)) Modern Curriculum Pr.

Hiebert, Elfrieda H. & Juel, Connie. At the Track. (J). (978-0-8136-2062-6(7)) Modern Curriculum Pr.

—Ben's New Trick. (Little Book Practice Reader Ser.). (J). (978-0-8136-0831-0(7)) Modern Curriculum Pr.
—The Best Birthday Mole Ever Had. (Little Book Practice Reader Ser.). (J). (978-0-8136-0969-0(0)) Modern Curriculum Pr.
—The Bike That Spike Likes. (Little Book Practice Reader Ser.). (J). (978-0-8136-0963-8(1)) Modern Curriculum Pr.
—Blastoff! (Little Book Practice Reader Ser.). (J). (978-0-8136-0825-9(2)) Modern Curriculum Pr.
—Can a Cow Hop? (Little Book Practice Reader Ser.). (J). (978-0-8136-0796-2(5)) Modern Curriculum Pr.
—Dinner by Five. (Little Book Practice Reader Ser.). (J). (978-0-8136-0961-4(5)) Modern Curriculum Pr.
—Flip's Trick. (J). (978-0-8136-2166-1(6)) Modern Curriculum Pr.
—The Fourth of July. (Little Book Practice Reader Ser.). (J). (978-0-8136-0977-5(1)) Modern Curriculum Pr.
—Good-Bye Summer, Hello Fall. (Little Book Practice Reader Ser.). (J). (978-0-8136-0879-2(1)) Modern Curriculum Pr.
—Haddie's Caps. (Little Book Practice Reader Ser.). (J). (978-0-8136-0786-3(8)) Modern Curriculum Pr.
—I Got a Goldfish. (Little Book Practice Reader). (J). (978-0-8136-2039-8(2)) Modern Curriculum Pr.
—Let's Go Marching. (Little Book Practice Reader Ser.). (J). (978-0-8136-0780-1(9)) Modern Curriculum Pr.
—Let's Move! (Little Book Practice Reader Ser.). (J). (978-0-8136-0685-9(3)) Modern Curriculum Pr.
—Little Frog's Monster Story. (Little Book Practice Reader Ser.). (J). (978-0-8136-0807-5(4)) Modern Curriculum Pr.
—Looking for Angus. (Little Book Practice Reader Ser.). (J). (978-0-8136-0817-4(1)) Modern Curriculum Pr.
—Mrs. Tuck's Little Tune. (Little Book Practice Reader Ser.). (J). (978-0-8136-0965-2(8)) Modern Curriculum Pr.
—My Cat. (Little Book Practice Reader Ser.). (J). (978-0-8136-0680-4(2)) Modern Curriculum Pr.
—My Hamster, Van. (Little Book Practice Reader Ser.). (J). (978-0-8136-0790-0(6)) Modern Curriculum Pr.
—My Monster & Me. (Little Book Practice Reader). (J). (978-0-8136-0677-4(2)) Modern Curriculum Pr.
—My Shadow. (Little Book Practice Reader Ser.). (J). (978-0-8136-0827-3(9)) Modern Curriculum Pr.
—Nanny Goat's Nap. (Little Book Practice Reader Ser.). (J). (978-0-8136-0692-7(6)) Modern Curriculum Pr.
—Night & Day. (Little Book Practice Reader Ser.). (J). (978-0-8136-0813-6(9)) Modern Curriculum Pr.
—Night Animals. (Little Book Practice Reader Ser.). (J). (978-0-8136-0744-3(2)) Modern Curriculum Pr.
—Once upon a Time. (Little Book Practice Reader Ser.). (J). (978-0-8136-0891-4(0)) Modern Curriculum Pr.
—Pat's Perfect Pizza. (Little Book Practice Reader). (J). (978-0-8136-1944-6(0)); Level 3, Bk. 14. 24.50 (978-0-8136-1945-3(9)) Modern Curriculum Pr.
—Pete's Bad Day. (Little Book Practice Reader Ser.). (J). (978-0-8136-0971-3(2)) Modern Curriculum Pr.
—Red & I Visit the Vet. (Little Book Practice Reader Ser.). (J). (978-0-8136-0881-5(3)) Modern Curriculum Pr.
—The River Grows. (Little Book Practice Reader Ser.). (J). (978-0-8136-0815-0(5)) Modern Curriculum Pr.
—Roll Out the Red Rug. (J). (978-0-8136-2060-2(0)) Modern Curriculum Pr.
—Sandy. (Little Book Practice Reader). (J). (978-0-8136-1950-7(5)) Modern Curriculum Pr.
—Save That Trash. (Little Book Practice Reader Ser.). (J). (978-0-8136-0943-0(7)) Modern Curriculum Pr.
—Sea Turtle Night. (Little Book Practice Reader). (J). (978-0-8136-2190-6(9)) Modern Curriculum Pr.
—Six Fine Fish. (Little Book Practice Reader Ser.). (J). (978-0-8136-0877-8(5)) Modern Curriculum Pr.
—Six Go By. (Little Book Practice Reader Ser.). (J). (978-0-8136-0674-3(8)) Modern Curriculum Pr.
—Something to Munch. (Little Book Practice Reader). (J). (978-0-8136-2070-1(8)) Modern Curriculum Pr.
—Sparky's Bone. (Little Book Practice Reader Ser.). (J). (978-0-8136-0839-6(2)) Modern Curriculum Pr.
—Steve's Room. (Little Book Practice Reader Ser.). (J). (978-0-8136-0959-1(3)) Modern Curriculum Pr.
—Stop That! (Little Book Practice Reader Ser.). (J). (978-0-8136-0784-9(1)) Modern Curriculum Pr.
—Too High. (Little Book Practice Reader Ser.). (J). (978-0-8136-0776-4(0)) Modern Curriculum Pr.
—Too Much Ketchup. (Little Book Practice Reader Ser.). (J). (978-0-8136-0748-1(5)) Modern Curriculum Pr.
—The Trip. (Little Book Practice Reader Ser.). (J). (978-0-8136-0792-4(2)) Modern Curriculum Pr.
—We Are Singing. (Little Book Practice Reader Ser.). (J). (978-0-8136-0678-1(0)) Modern Curriculum Pr.
—What Rhymes with Cat? (Little Book Practice Reader). (J). (978-0-8136-1932-3(7)) Modern Curriculum Pr.
—When I Go See Gram. (Little Book Practice Reader Ser.). (J). (978-0-8136-0953-9(4)) Modern Curriculum Pr.
—When We Are Big. (Little Book Practice Reader Ser.). (J). (978-0-8136-0833-4(3)) Modern Curriculum Pr.
—Where Does the Rabbit Hop? (Little Book Practice Reader Ser.). (J). (978-0-8136-0794-8(9)) Modern Curriculum Pr.
—Where Is the Queen? (Little Book Practice Reader Ser.). (J). (978-0-8136-0829-7(5)) Modern Curriculum Pr.
—Who Came Out? (Little Book Practice Reader Ser.). (J). (978-0-8136-0765-8(5)) Modern Curriculum Pr.
—Who Has a Tail? (Little Book Practice Reader Ser.). (J). (978-0-8136-0975-1(5)) Modern Curriculum Pr.
—Who Is Ready? (Little Book Practice Reader Ser.). (J). (978-0-8136-0683-5(7)) Modern Curriculum Pr.
—Who's in the Jungle? (Little Book Practice Reader Ser.). (J). (978-0-8136-0885-3(6)) Modern Curriculum Pr.
—The World's Biggest Baby. (Little Book Practice Reader Ser.). (J). (978-0-8136-0983-6(6)) Modern Curriculum Pr.
Higgins, Maxwell. Hank's Bank. Alley, R. W., illus. 2002. (Word Family Tales Ser.). 16p. (ps-2). pap. 2.95 (978-0-439-26271-2(2)) Scholastic, Inc.
High Five Reading. (High Five Reading Ser.). (Illus.). (J). (gr. 2-5). lib. bdg. 239.30 (978-0-7368-4995-1(5)) Capstone Pr., Inc.
High Five Reading: Blue Level Titles, 10 vols. 2006. (Illus.). (J). lib. bdg. 239.30 (978-0-7368-5730-7(3)) Capstone Pr., Inc.
High Five Reading: Purple Level, 5 bks. Incl. Cameras on the Battlefield : Photos of War. White, Matt. lib. bdg. 22.60 (978-0-7368-4004-0(4)); Endurance : Shipwreck & Survival on a Sea of Ice. White, Matt. lib. bdg. 22.60 (978-0-7368-4000-2(1)); Harlem Globetrotters : The Clown Princes of Basketball. Butler, Robbie. lib. bdg. 22.60 (978-0-7368-4001-9(X)); Michael Jordan : The Best Ever. Houghton, Sarah. lib. bdg. 22.60 (978-0-7368-4002-6(8)); Snakes! Deadly Predators or Harmless Pets? Houghton, Sarah. lib. bdg. 22.60 (978-0-7368-4003-3(6)); 64p. (J). (gr. 4-5). 2001. (Illus.). Set lib. bdg. 113.00 (978-0-7368-4005-7(2) , Capstone High-Interest Bks.) Capstone Pr., Inc.
High Five USA Reading Add-on Set I. (gr. 4 up). 123.95 (978-0-7368-1850-6(2) , High Five) Red Brick Learning.
High Five USA Reading Add-on Set II. (gr. 4 up). 123.95 (978-0-7368-3860-3(0) , High Five) Red Brick Learning.
High Five USA Reading, Green Level I. (gr. 4 up). 250.95 incl. audio (978-0-7368-9570-5(1) , High Five) Red Brick Learning.
High Five USA Reading, Green Level I Add-on Set. (gr. 4 up). 40.95 (978-0-7368-1848-3(0) , High Five) Red Brick Learning.
High Five USA Reading, Green Level II. (gr. 4 up). 250.95 incl. audio (978-0-7368-2860-4(5) , High Five) Red Brick Learning.
High Five USA Reading, Green Level II Add-on Set. (gr. 4 up). 40.95 (978-0-7368-2861-1(3) , High Five) Red Brick Learning.
High Five USA Reading, Purple Level I. (gr. 4 up). 250.95 incl. audio (978-0-7368-9516-3(7) , High Five) Red Brick Learning.
High Five USA Reading, Purple Level I Add-on Set. (gr. 4 up). 40.95 (978-0-7368-1849-0(9) , High Five) Red Brick Learning.
High Five USA Reading, Purple Level II. (gr. 4 up). 250.95 incl. audio (978-0-7368-3863-4(5) , High Five) Red Brick Learning.
High Five USA Reading, Purple Level II Add-on Set. (gr. 4 up). 40.95 (978-0-7368-3864-1(3) , High Five) Red Brick Learning.
High Five USA Reading, Red Level I. (gr. 4 up). 250.95 incl. audio (978-0-7368-9544-6(2) , High Five) Red Brick Learning.
High Five USA Reading, Red Level I Add-on Set. (gr. 4 up). 40.95 (978-0-7368-1847-6(2) , High Five) Red Brick Learning.
High Five USA Reading, Red Level II. (gr. 4 up). 250.95 incl. audio (978-0-7368-2855-0(9) , High Five) Red Brick Learning.
High Five USA Reading, Red Level II Add-on Set. (gr. 4 up). 40.95 (978-0-7368-2856-7(7) , High Five) Red Brick Learning.
High-Interest Reading Comprehension Skills & Strategies Level 3. 2002. (Illus.). 144p. per., act. bk. ed. 16.95 (978-1-56254-030-2(0) , SP 0300) Saddleback Educational Publishing.
High-Interest Reading Comprehension Skills & Strategies Level 4. 2002. (Illus.). 144p. per., act. bk. ed. 16.95 (978-1-56254-031-9(9) , SP 0319) Saddleback Educational Publishing.
High-Interest Reading Comprehension Skills & Strategies Level 5. 2002. (Illus.). 144p. per. 16.95 (978-1-56254-032-6(7) , SP 0327) Saddleback Educational Publishing.
High-Interest Reading Comprehension Skills & Strategies Level 6. 2002. (Illus.). 144p. per. 16.95 (978-1-56254-033-3(5) , SP 0335) Saddleback Educational Publishing.
High-Interest Reading Comprehension Skills & Strategies Level 7. 2002. (Illus.). 144p. per. 16.95 (978-1-56254-034-0(3) , SP 0343) Saddleback Educational Publishing.
High-Interest Reading Comprehension Skills & Strategies Level 8. 2002. (Illus.). 144p. per. 16.95 (978-1-56254-035-7(1) , SP 0351) Saddleback Educational Publishing.
High Point. (High Point Ser.). (gr. 6-12). 57.61 (978-0-7362-0969-4(7)); 7.52 (978-0-7362-0967-0(0)); 7.52 (978-0-7362-0935-9(2)); tchr. ed. 33.37 (978-0-7362-0981-6(6)); tchr. ed. 33.37 (978-0-7362-0949-6(2)); suppl. ed. 57.61 (978-0-7362-0937-3(9)); tchr.'s assessmt. gde. ed. 27.50 (978-0-7362-0950-2(6)); instr.'s hndbk. ed. 27.50 (978-0-7362-0982-3(4)); 2002. tchr. ed. 91.16 (978-0-7362-1224-3(8)); 2002. tchr. ed. 33.37 (978-0-7362-1261-8(2)); 2002. stu. ed. 37.74 (978-0-7362-1223-6(X)); 2002. instr.'s hndbk. ed. 19.96 (978-0-7362-1227-4(2)); 2000. 57.61 (978-0-7362-0905-2(0)); 2000. 7.52 (978-0-7362-0903-8(4)); 2000. tchr. ed. 33.37 (978-0-7362-0917-5(4)); 2000. tchr.'s assessmt. gde. ed. 27.50 (978-0-7362-0918-2(2)); 2000. tchr. ed. 14.19 (978-0-7362-0904-5(2)); tchr. ed. 14.19 (978-0-7362-0936-6(0)); tchr. ed. 14.19 (978-0-7362-0968-7(9)); Level C. stu. ed. 43.80 (978-0-7362-0965-6(4)); Level A. 2000. stu. ed. 43.80 (978-0-7362-0901-4(8)); Level B. stu. ed. 43.80 (978-0-7362-0933-5(6)) Hampton-Brown Bks.
High Point: Decodable Stories Set, 18 vols. (Reading Basics Ser.). (gr. 3-12). 8.31 (978-0-7362-1553-4(0)) Hampton-Brown Bks.
High Point: Reading Basics Package. (gr. 6-12). 160.56 (978-0-7362-1286-1(8)) Hampton-Brown Bks.
High Point: The Basics Bookshelf, 6 vols. (gr. 6-12). 443.72 (978-0-7362-1278-6(7)); 487.59 incl. audio compact disk (978-0-7362-1279-3(5)); 531.44 incl. reel tape (978-0-7362-1280-9(9)) Hampton-Brown Bks.
High Point Diagnosis & Placement Inventory: Test Booklets (10-pack) 19.90 (978-0-7362-2345-4(2)) Hampton-Brown Bks.
A High Point Level: The Basics Bookshelf with Teacher's Guide, 6 vols. (High Point Ser.). (gr. 6-12). tchr. ed. 459.28 (978-0-7362-1281-6(7)) Hampton-Brown Bks.
Hilb, N. Azul. 2004. (SPA.). 32p. 6.95 (978-1-4000-9289-5(2)) Editorial Sudamericana S.A. ARG. *Dist:* Random Hse., Inc.
Hillert, Margaret. Circus Fun. Raphael, Elaine, illus. rev. ed. 2006. (Beginning to Read Ser.). 30p. (J). lib. bdg. 18.60 (978-1-59953-030-7(9)) Norwood Hse. Pr.
—I Can Do It: For the Earliest Reader. 2005. (Illus.). 32p. (J). (978-1-59577-040-0(2)); (978-1-59577-039-4(9)) Starfall Education.
—Not Too Little to Help, 5 bks. (Illus.). 32p. (J). 2005. 6.95 (978-1-59577-026-4(7)); 2004. (978-1-59577-027-1(5)) Starfall Education.
—Penguin, Penguin: For the Earliest Reader, 5 bks. (Illus.). 32p. (J). 2005. 6.95 (978-1-59577-020-2(8)); 2004. (978-1-59577-021-9(6)) Starfall Education.
—Pumpkin, Pumpkin: For the Earliest Reader. 2005. (Illus.). 32p. (J). (978-1-59577-036-3(4)); (978-1-59577-035-6(6)) Starfall Education.
—Three Little Plays, 5 bks. (Illus.). 32p. (J). 2005. 6.95 (978-1-59577-018-9(6)); 2004. (978-1-59577-019-6(4)) Starfall Education.
—Tom Thumb. Hockerman, Dennis, illus. rev. ed. 2006. (Beginning to Read Ser.). 32p. (J). lib. bdg. 18.60 (978-1-59953-028-4(7)) Norwood Hse. Pr.
The History Nook. (Early Intervention Levels Ser.). 31.86 (978-0-7362-0663-1(9)) Hampton-Brown Bks.
The History Nook (30), Vol. 30. (Early Intervention Levels Ser.). 5.31 (978-0-7362-0651-8(5)) Hampton-Brown Bks.
The History of Guitars: Fourth Grade Guided Comprehension Level N. (On Our Way to English Ser.). (gr. 4 up). 34.50 (978-0-7578-7164-1(X)) Rigby Education.
Hobbs, Ruth & Miller, Lester, contrib. by. A Time to Plant. 2005. (Rod & Staff's Readers Ser.). (Illus.). 256p. (gr. 5 up). 10.85 (978-0-7399-0405-3(1) , 11501) Rod & Staff Pubs., Inc.
Hobbs, Ruth K., compiled by. Helping Hands. 1998. (Reading to Learn Ser.). (Illus.). 269p. (J). (gr. 2-3). 7.95 (978-0-87813-933-0(8)) Christian Light Pubns., Inc.
Hoberman, Mary Ann. You Read to Me, I'll Read to You: Very Short Fairy Tales to Read Together. Emberley, Michael, illus. 2004. 32p. (J). (ps-3). 16.99 (978-0-316-14611-1(0)) Little Brown & Co.
The Hobyahs: 6 Small Books. (gr. k-1). 37.00 (978-0-7635-6246-5(7)) Rigby Education.
Hodson, Christopher. Lizo's Song Big Book: South African Edition. 1998. (Illus.). 16p. pap. 13.45 (978-0-521-64450-1(X)) Cambridge Univ. Pr.
—Lizo's Song Lugbara Version: Geria Vele Ongori. Draville, Ben & Mawa, Robert, trs. 2001. 16p. pap. 0.90 (978-0-521-00614-9(7)) Cambridge Univ. Pr.
Hoffman, Mary Ann. Reading Comprehension. 2004. 48p. pap. 6.95 (978-1-4042-8535-4(0)) Rosen Publishing Group, Inc., The.
Hofmeister, Alan. The Creatures of Zoon, 10 vols. 2nd l.t. ed. 2001. (Fluency Builders Ser.: Bk. 4). 48p. (J). pap. (978-0-9709686-3-0(9)) Academic Success for All Learners.
—Found Out of the Past, 10 vols. 2nd ed. 2001. (Fluency Builders Ser.: Bk. 2). 36p. (J). pap. (978-0-9709686-1-6(2)) Academic Success for All Learners.
—Instructor's Resource Manual. 2nd l.t. ed. 2001. (Fluency Builders Ser.: Bk. 10). 26p. (J). pap. (978-0-9709686-7-8(1)) Academic Success for All Learners.
—Plum Comes Home: Fluency Builders Series, 10 vols., 7. 2nd ed. 2001. (Fluency Builders Ser.: Vol. Book 7). 52p. (J). pap. (978-0-9709686-6-1(3)) Academic Success for All Learners.
Hofmeister, Alan, et al. Ann & Nan. (Reading for All Learners Ser.). (Illus.). (J). pap. (978-1-56861-085-6(8)) Swift Learning Resources.
—The Ant & the Bee. (Reading for All Learners Ser.). (Illus.). (J). pap. (978-1-56861-125-9(0)) Swift Learning Resources.
—The Bad Men. (Reading for All Learners Ser.). (Illus.). (J). pap. (978-1-56861-117-4(X)) Swift Learning Resources.
—The Bat Rat. (Reading for All Learners Ser.). (Illus.). (J). pap. (978-1-56861-119-8(6)) Swift Learning Resources.
—The Bee. (Reading for All Learners Ser.). (Illus.). (J). pap. (978-1-56861-124-2(2)) Swift Learning Resources.
—Ben the Ant. (Reading for All Learners Ser.). (Illus.). (J). pap. (978-1-56861-123-5(4)) Swift Learning Resources.
—Bud & the Tree. (Reading for All Learners Ser.). (Illus.). (J). pap. (978-1-56861-135-8(8)) Swift Learning Resources.
—The Bus. (Reading for All Learners Ser.). (Illus.). (J). pap. (978-1-56861-122-8(6)) Swift Learning Resources.
—Cartons & Clouds. (Reading for All Learners Ser.). (Illus.). (J). pap. (978-1-56861-195-2(1)) Swift Learning Resources.
—The Creatures of Loon. (Reading for All Learners Ser.). (Illus.). (J). pap. (978-1-56861-217-1(6)) Swift Learning Resources.
—Freckles & Forests. (Reading for All Learners Ser.). (Illus.). (J). pap. (978-1-56861-201-0(X)) Swift Learning Resources.
—The Fun Fish. (Reading for All Learners Ser.). (Illus.). (J). pap. (978-1-56861-121-1(8)) Swift Learning Resources.
—Fun with the Sheet. (Reading for All Learners Ser.). (Illus.). (J). pap. (978-1-56861-115-0(3)) Swift Learning Resources.
—The Hat. (Reading for All Learners Ser.). (Illus.). (J). pap. (978-1-56861-105-1(6)) Swift Learning Resources.
—I See Sam. (Reading for All Learners Ser.). (Illus.). (J). pap. (978-1-56861-073-3(4)) Swift Learning Resources.
—In a Tub. (Reading for All Learners Ser.). (Illus.). (J). pap. (978-1-56861-128-0(5)) Swift Learning Resources.
—In the Mud. (Reading for All Learners Ser.). (Illus.). (J). pap. (978-1-56861-127-3(7)) Swift Learning Resources.
—In the Tent. (Reading for All Learners Ser.). (Illus.). (J). pap. (978-1-56861-132-7(3)) Swift Learning Resources.
—It Is Ann. (Reading for All Learners Ser.). (Illus.). (J). pap. (978-1-56861-084-9(X)) Swift Learning Resources.
—The Mask. (Reading for All Learners Ser.). (Illus.). (J). pap. (978-1-56861-139-6(0)) Swift Learning Resources.
—Mat. (Reading for All Learners Ser.). (Illus.). (J). pap. (978-1-56861-077-1(7)) Swift Learning Resources.
—Mat & the Nut. (Reading for All Learners Ser.). (Illus.). (J). pap. (978-1-56861-109-9(9)) Swift Learning Resources.
—Mat at Bat. (Reading for All Learners Ser.). (Illus.). (J). pap. (978-1-56861-118-1(8)) Swift Learning Resources.
—Mat Did It. (Reading for All Learners Ser.). (Illus.). (J). pap. (978-1-56861-102-0(1)) Swift Learning Resources.
—Mat in the Hat. (Reading for All Learners Ser.). (Illus.). (J). pap. (978-1-56861-106-8(4)) Swift Learning Resources.
—Mat in the Sun. (Reading for All Learners Ser.). (Illus.). (J). pap. (978-1-56861-094-8(7)) Swift Learning Resources.
—Mat Is Wet. (Reading for All Learners Ser.). (Illus.). (J). pap. (978-1-56861-120-4(X)) Swift Learning Resources.
—Mat the Rat. (Reading for All Learners Ser.). (Illus.). (J). pap. (978-1-56861-111-2(0)) Swift Learning Resources.
—Meet Mit. (Reading for All Learners Ser.). (Illus.). (J). pap. (978-1-56861-079-5(3)) Swift Learning Resources.
—The Men. (Reading for All Learners Ser.). (Illus.). (J). pap. (978-1-56861-116-7(1)) Swift Learning Resources.
—Mit & the Weed. (Reading for All Learners Ser.). (Illus.). (J). pap. (978-1-56861-113-6(7)) Swift Learning Resources.
—Mit Is Wet. (Reading for All Learners Ser.). (Illus.). (J). pap. (978-1-56861-108-2(0)) Swift Learning Resources.
—Nan & the Man. (Reading for All Learners Ser.). (Illus.). (J). pap. (978-1-56861-086-3(6)) Swift Learning Resources.
—Nan Sits. (Reading for All Learners Ser.). (Illus.). (J). pap. (978-1-56861-092-4(0)) Swift Learning Resources.
—Nat. (Reading for All Learners Ser.). (Illus.). (J). pap. (978-1-56861-093-1(9)) Swift Learning Resources.
—Nell & Ed. (Reading for All Learners Ser.). (Illus.). (J). pap. (978-1-56861-097-9(1)) Swift Learning Resources.
—The Pond. (Reading for All Learners Ser.). (Illus.). (J). pap. (978-1-56861-131-0(5)) Swift Learning Resources.
—Ruff. (Reading for All Learners Ser.). (Illus.). (J). pap. (978-1-56861-137-2(4)) Swift Learning Resources.
—Run, Feet, Run. (Reading for All Learners Ser.). (Illus.). (J). pap. (978-1-56861-095-5(5)) Swift Learning Resources.
—Sam. (Reading for All Learners Ser.). (Illus.). (J). pap. (978-1-56861-074-0(2)) Swift Learning Resources.
—Sam Is Mad. (Reading for All Learners Ser.). (Illus.). (J). pap. (978-1-56861-087-0(4)) Swift Learning Resources.
—Sam Sat. (Reading for All Learners Ser.). (Illus.). (J). pap. (978-1-56861-083-2(1)) Swift Learning Resources.
—See It. (Reading for All Learners Ser.). (Illus.). (J). pap. (978-1-56861-080-1(7)) Swift Learning Resources.
—See Mat. (Reading for All Learners Ser.). (Illus.). (J). pap. (978-1-56861-078-8(5)) Swift Learning Resources.
—See Me. (Reading for All Learners Ser.). (Illus.). (J). pap. (978-1-56861-076-4(9)) Swift Learning Resources.
—See Sam. (Reading for All Learners Ser.). (Illus.). (J). pap. (978-1-56861-075-7(0)) Swift Learning Resources.
—See Them. (Reading for All Learners Ser.). (Illus.). (J). pap. (978-1-56861-107-5(2)) Swift Learning Resources.
—The Seed. (Reading for All Learners Ser.). (Illus.). (J). pap. (978-1-56861-112-9(9)) Swift Learning Resources.
—Sell the Shell. (Reading for All Learners Ser.). (Illus.). (J). pap. (978-1-56861-104-4(8)) Swift Learning Resources.
—The Shell. (Reading for All Learners Ser.). (Illus.). (J). pap. (978-1-56861-103-7(X)) Swift Learning Resources.
—The Ship. (Reading for All Learners Ser.). (Illus.). (J). pap. (978-1-56861-133-4(1)) Swift Learning Resources.
—Sid. (Reading for All Learners Ser.). (Illus.). (J). pap. (978-1-56861-088-7(2)) Swift Learning Resources.
—Sid & the Mess. (Reading for All Learners Ser.). (Illus.). (J). pap. (978-1-56861-090-0(4)) Swift Learning Resources.
—Sis. (Reading for All Learners Ser.). (Illus.). (J). pap. (978-1-56861-082-5(3)) Swift Learning Resources.
—Sis in a Mess. (Reading for All Learners Ser.). (Illus.). (J). pap. (978-1-56861-091-7(2)) Swift Learning Resources.
—Sis in the Well. (Reading for All Learners Ser.). (Illus.). (J). pap. (978-1-56861-098-6(X)) Swift Learning Resources.
—Sit on It. (Reading for All Learners Ser.). (Illus.). (J). pap. (978-1-56861-081-8(5)) Swift Learning Resources.
—Smash It. (Reading for All Learners Ser.). (Illus.). (J). pap. (978-1-56861-136-5(6)) Swift Learning Resources.
—Swim with Us. (Reading for All Learners Ser.). (Illus.). (J). pap. (978-1-56861-140-2(4)) Swift Learning Resources.
—To the Den. (Reading for All Learners Ser.). (Illus.). (J). (978-1-56861-138-9(2)) Swift Learning Resources.
—A Trip. (Reading for All Learners Ser.). (Illus.). (J). pap. (978-1-56861-130-3(7)) Swift Learning Resources.
—Up the Path. (Reading for All Learners Ser.). (Illus.). (J). pap. (978-1-56861-134-1(X)) Swift Learning Resources.
—Up We Go. (Reading for All Learners Ser.). (Illus.). (J). pap. (978-1-56861-129-7(3)) Swift Learning Resources.

—Was It Wet? (Reading for All Learners Ser.). (Illus.). (J). pap. (978-1-56861-114-3(5)) Swift Learning Resources.

—We Will Run. (Reading for All Learners Ser.). (Illus.). (J). pap. (978-1-56861-099-3(8)) Swift Learning Resources.

—We Will See. (Reading for All Learners Ser.). (Illus.). (J). pap. (978-1-56861-089-4(0)) Swift Learning Resources.

—Who Am I? (Reading for All Learners Ser.). (Illus.). (J). pap. (978-1-56861-096-2(3)) Swift Learning Resources.

—Will We Win? (Reading for All Learners Ser.). (Illus.). (J). pap. (978-1-56861-110-5(2)) Swift Learning Resources.

Hofmeyr, Dianne. Hic... Hic... Hiccups! Hausa Version. Bello, Gidado, tr. 1998. (Cambridge African Language Library Ser.). (HAU., Illus.). 16p. pap. 6.60 (978-0-521-64796-0(7)) Cambridge Univ. Pr.

—Hic... Hic... Hiccups! Lunda Version. Kambangaji, Thomson, tr. 1998. (Cambridge African Language Library). (Illus.). 16p. pap. 3.70 (978-0-521-63838-8(0)) Cambridge Univ. Pr.

—Hic... Hic... Hiccups! Shona Version. Chirikure, Chirulure, tr. 1999. (Cambridge African Language Library Ser.). (SHO., Illus.). 16p. pap. 3.70 (978-0-521-65815-7(2)) Cambridge Univ. Pr.

—Hic...Hic...Hiccups! Tadjo, Veronique, tr. from ENG. Rankin, Joan, illus. 1998. (Cambridge African Language Library). (FRE.). 16p. pap. 3.75 (978-0-521-64787-8(8)) Cambridge Univ. Pr.

—Mama Mabena's Magic: Shona Version. Chateuka, Keresia, tr. 1999. (Cambridge African Language Library Ser.). (SHO., Illus.). 16p. pap. 3.70 (978-0-521-65813-3(6)) Cambridge Univ. Pr.

Hojel, Barbara & Guy, Ginger F. What Can We Do Today? 1999. (English for Me! Storybooks Ser.: Bk. 7). (Illus.). 16p. (C). pap. 7.66 (978-0-201-35149-1(8)) Pearson ESL.

The Hole: Individual Title Six-Packs. (Sails Literacy Ser.). 16p. (gr. k up). 27.00 (978-0-7635-4418-8(3)) Rigby Education.

The Hole in the Hill: Individual Title Six-Packs. (Action Packs Ser.). 104p. (gr. 3-5). 44.00 (978-0-7635-2993-2(1)) Rigby Education.

A Hole Is a Great Home. (Early Intervention Levels Ser.). 28.38 (978-0-7362-0397-5(4)) Hampton-Brown Bks.

A Hole Is a Great Home (10), Vol. 10. (Early Intervention Levels Ser.). 4.73 (978-0-7362-0222-0(6)) Hampton-Brown Bks.

Holidays & Celebrations Package. 1999. (Illus.). (J). pap. 470.00 (978-0-7398-2801-4(0)) Raintree.

Hollemann, Monika. Chameleon's Clever Trick: Lunda Version. Kambangaji, Thomson, tr. 1998. (Cambridge African Language Library Ser.). (Illus.). 16p. pap. 3.70 (978-0-521-63834-0(8)) Cambridge Univ. Pr.

—Chameleon's Clever Trick: Runyangore-Rukiga Version. Bahemuka, Gaetano & Kagoro, Stephen, trs. 2000. (Cambridge African Language Library Ser.). (Illus.). pap. 3.65 (978-0-521-63772-5(4)) Cambridge Univ. Pr.

Hollemann, Monika & Pooler, Helen. Chameleon's Clever Trick Lugbara Version: Elekendre Ma Lokiri. Draville, Ben & Mawa, Robert, trs. 2001. 16p. pap. 0.90 (978-0-521-00625-5(2)) Cambridge Univ. Pr.

Hollenbeck, Kathleen M. Fluency Practice Mini-Books: 15 Short, Leveled Fiction & Nonfiction Mini-Books with Research-Based Strategies to Help Students Build Word Recognition, Fluency, & Comprehension. 2005. (Best Practices in Action Ser.). 80p. pap. 12.99 (978-0-439-55418-3(7)); pap. 12.99 (978-0-439-55417-6(9)); pap. 12.99 (978-0-439-55416-9(0)) Scholastic, Inc. (Teaching Resources).

Holliday, Patricia. I Look in the Mirror. 2005. 17p. (J). 10.52 (978-1-4116-4656-8(8)) Lulu.com.

Holt, Julia. Beyonce. 2005. 32p. pap. 8.50 (978-0-340-90065-9(2)) Cambridge Univ. Pr.

—Cher. 2001. (Livewire Ser.). (Illus.). 28p. pap. (978-0-340-80093-5(3) , Hodder Arnold) Hodder Education.

—Geri Halliwell. 2001. (Livewire Real Lives Ser.). (Illus.). iv, 28p. pap. (978-0-340-80088-1(7) , Hodder Arnold) Hodder Education.

—Johnny Depp. 2001. (Livewire Ser.). (Illus.). 32p. pap. (978-0-340-80099-7(2) , Hodder Arnold) Hodder Education.

—The Osbournes. 2005. 32p. pap. 8.50 (978-0-340-90062-8(8)) Cambridge Univ. Pr.

—Victoria Beckham. 2001. (Livewire Ser.). (Illus.). iii, 28p. pap. (978-0-340-80089-8(5) , Hodder Arnold) Hodder Education.

Holt, Rinehart and Winston Staff. Apoyo y Practica Elementos: Texas Edition. 2001. pap. 38.66 (978-0-03-064601-0(4)) Holt, Rinehart & Winston.

—Como Disenar tu Escritura Elementos: Grade 6. 2003. (Elementos Del Lenguaje Ser.). (SPA.). 141.80 (978-0-03-064609-6(X)) Holt, Rinehart & Winston.

—CT Strategy & Practice for Reading 2004: Science Spectrum. 2004. pap. 12.80 (978-0-03-074159-3(9)) Holt, Rinehart & Winston.

—Elementos: Evaluacion. 2002. pap. 76.86 (978-0-03-066043-6(2)) Holt, Rinehart & Winston.

—Elementos: Manual/Instrucciones: Texas Edition. 2001. pap. 29.00 (978-0-03-064603-4(0)) Holt, Rinehart & Winston.

—Elementos: Planificador/Lecciones: Texas Edition. 2003. (Elementos Del Lenguaje Ser.). (SPA.). 13.66 (978-0-03-064606-5(5)) Holt, Rinehart & Winston.

—Elementos: Preparacion para TAAS. 2001. pap. 14.53 (978-0-03-064611-9(1)) Holt, Rinehart & Winston.

—Elements of Literature: Adapted Reader. 5th ed. 2003. (Illus.). pap. 13.20 (978-0-03-035459-5(5)); pap. 13.20 (978-0-03-035461-8(7)); pap. 13.20 (978-0-03-035458-8(7)); pap. 13.20 (978-0-03-035454-0(4)) Holt, Rinehart & Winston.

—Elements of Literature: Holt Adapted Reader. 2003. 3rd ed. pap. 12.40 (978-0-03-067864-6(1)); 5th ed. (Illus.). pap. 13.20 (978-0-03-035712-1(8)); 5th ed. pap. 13.20 (978-0-03-035711-4(X)); 5th ed. (Illus.). (J). pap. 13.20 (978-0-03-035709-1(8)) Holt, Rinehart & Winston.

—Elements of Literature: Holt Reader. 2003. (Illus.). 4th ed. (gr. 10). pap. 13.20 (978-0-03-068394-7(7)); 5th ed. (gr. 11). pap. 13.20 (978-0-03-068396-1(3)); 5th ed. (gr. 12). pap. 13.20 (978-0-03-068397-8(1)); 5th ed. (gr. 7). 13.20 (978-0-03-068391-6(2)); 5th ed. (gr. 8). pap. 13.20 (978-0-03-068392-3(0)); 5th ed. (gr. 9). pap. 13.20 (978-0-03-068393-0(9)) Holt, Rinehart & Winston.

—Expresate: Spanish Answer Key for End-of-Chapter Test w/ASM. 2nd ed. 2004. (SPA.). pap. 6.53 (978-0-03-074266-8(8)) Holt, Rinehart & Winston.

—Holt Handbook: With Answer Key - New York State Edition. 2000. pap. 127.73 (978-0-03-053393-8(7)) Holt, Rinehart & Winston.

—Journey to Jo Burg. 2nd ed. 2002. (Illus.). 16.80 (978-0-03-073519-6(X)) Holt, Rinehart & Winston.

—Lecturas Alternativas Elementos: Grde 6. 2003. (Elementos Del Lenguaje Ser.). (SPA.). 12.40 (978-0-03-064596-9(4)) Holt, Rinehart & Winston.

—Medios y Destrezas Elementos: Texas Edition - Grade 6. 2003. (Elementos Del Lenguaje Ser.). (SPA.). 148.73 (978-0-03-064598-3(0)) Holt, Rinehart & Winston.

—MI Strategy & Practice for Reading 2004: Science Spectrum. 2004. pap. 12.80 (978-0-03-074162-3(9)) Holt, Rinehart & Winston.

—Multicultural Connections: Critical Thinking Worksheets. 2001. pap. 10.93 (978-0-03-056551-9(0)) Holt, Rinehart & Winston.

—NJ Strategy & Practice for Reading 2004: Science Spectrum. 2004. pap. 12.80 (978-0-03-074163-0(7)) Holt, Rinehart & Winston.

—NY Strategy & Practice for Reading 2004: Science Spectrum. 4th ed. 2004. pap. 12.80 (978-0-03-074164-7(5)) Holt, Rinehart & Winston.

—OH Strategy & Practice for Reading 2004: Science Spectrum. 2004. pap. 12.80 (978-0-03-074168-5(8)) Holt, Rinehart & Winston.

—Ortografia Integrada Elementos: Grade 6. 2003. (Elementos Del Lenguaje Ser.). (SPA.). 14.33 (978-0-03-064607-2(3)) Holt, Rinehart & Winston.

—Pruebas de Capitulos Elementos: Grade 6. 2003. (Elementos Del Lenguaje Ser.). (SPA.). 14.53 (978-0-03-064591-4(3)) Holt, Rinehart & Winston.

—Pruebas/Estandarizada Elementos: Grade 6. 2003. (Elementos Del Lenguaje Ser.). (SPA.). 13.66 (978-0-03-064592-1(1)) Holt, Rinehart & Winston.

—Transparencias Elementos: Grade 6. 2003. (Elementos Del Lenguaje Ser.). (SPA.). 145.53 (978-0-03-064604-1(9)) Holt, Rinehart & Winston.

—WI Strategy & Practice for Reading 2004: Science Spectrum. 2004. pap. 12.80 (978-0-03-074169-2(6)) Holt, Rinehart & Winston.

Holub, Joan. Elizabeth & the Royal Pony: Based on a True Story of Elizabeth I of England. Aleshina, Nonna, illus. 2007. (Ready-To-Read Ser.). (J). ***978-1-4287-2005-3(7)** , Aladdin) Simon & Schuster Children's Publishing.

A Home: Individual Title Six-Packs. (Sails Literacy Ser.). 16p. (gr. k up). 27.00 (978-0-7635-4387-7(X)) Rigby Education.

A Home for Nellie. 2005. (Book Treks Ser.). (J). (gr. 3 up). stu. ed. 34.95 (978-0-673-62849-7(3)) Celebration Pr.

Homes & Places. 2005. (Little Celebrations Thematic Packages Ser.). (J). (gr. k-3). 133.50 (978-0-673-75385-4(9)) Celebration Pr.

Homework. 2004. (J). (978-1-58453-216-3(5)) Pioneer Valley Educational Pr., Inc.

Honest Abe. (Lexile Levels Ser.). 9.09 (978-1-56334-706-1(7)) Hampton-Brown Bks.

Honey for a Child's Heart. 2001. (978-1-930871-75-5(9) , Family Christian Pr.) Family Christian Stores, Inc.

The Honey Tree, 6 Packs. (Literatura 2000 Ser.). (gr. 2-3). 33.00 (978-0-7635-0262-1(6)) Rigby Education.

Hoop Dancers. (Early Intervention Levels Ser.). 31.86 (978-0-7362-0660-0(4)) Hampton-Brown Bks.

Hoop Dancers (30), Vol. 30. (Early Intervention Levels Ser.). 5.31 (978-0-7362-0648-8(5)) Hampton-Brown Bks.

Hooper, Meredith. The Tomb of Nebamun Big Book. 1999. (Cambridge Reading Ser.). (Illus.). 32p. pap. 36.00 (978-0-521-63475-5(X)) Cambridge Univ. Pr.

Hoops! Third Grade Guided Reading Level L. (On Our Way to English Ser.). (gr. 3 up). 34.50 (978-0-7578-7127-6(5)) Rigby Education.

Hoops with Swoopes. (Guided Reading Levels Ser.). 7.33 (978-0-7362-1763-7(0)); 43.98 (978-0-7362-2169-6(7)) Hampton-Brown Bks.

Hopkins, Lee Bennett. Hanukkah Lights: Holiday Poetry. Hall, Melanie, illus. 2005. (I Can Read Bks.). 32p. (J). pap. 3.99 (978-0-06-008053-2(1) , Harper Trophy) HarperCollins Pubs.

Horner, Teri & Sheldon, Linda, creators. Looking at Print Supplement. 2004. tchr. ed., ring bd. 19.95 (978-1-57874-097-0(5)) Kaeden Corp.

Hoskins, Barbara. Birthday Magic - Baseball Fans, Level 2. 2000. (Let's Go Readers Ser.). (Illus.). 30p. (J). 7.25 (978-0-19-436456-0(9)) Oxford Univ. Pr., Inc.

—The Costume Contest - Carnival Luck, Level 3. 2000. (Let's Go Readers Ser.). (Illus.). 30p. (J). 7.25 (978-0-19-436466-9(6)) Oxford Univ. Pr., Inc.

—The Homestay Friends - Kid Power, Level 6. 2000. (Let's Go Readers Ser.). (Illus.). 32p. (J). 7.25 (978-0-19-436496-6(8)) Oxford Univ. Pr., Inc.

—The Treasure Hunt - The Pet Sitter, Level 5. 2000. (Let's Go Readers Ser.). (Illus.). 32p. (J). 7.25 (978-0-19-436486-7(0)) Oxford Univ. Pr., Inc.

The Hot Shots. 2005. (Book Treks Ser.). (J). 37.95 (978-0-7652-3257-1(X)) Celebration Pr.

Houdini: El Maestro de la Fuga No. 3: Leveled Books. 2001. (McGraw-Hill. Lectura Ser.). (ENG & SPA.). (gr. 3 up). (978-0-02-188124-6(3)) Macmillan/McGraw-Hill Schl. Div.

Houghton Mifflin Company Staff, et al. Horizons: A Reader of Experiences. 2004. 362p. (YA). 50.76 (978-0-618-15569-9(4) , 302990) Houghton Mifflin College Div.

The Hound of the Baskervilles Student Packet, Gr. 9-12. 2004. (YA). (978-1-58130-856-3(6)) Novel Units, Inc.

A House: Individual Title Six-Packs. (Sails Literacy Ser.). 16p. (gr. k up). 27.00 (978-0-7635-4425-6(6)) Rigby Education.

A House for Sergin: Six-Pack. (Greetings Ser.: Vol. 2). 24p. (gr. 2-3). 31.00 (978-0-7635-9427-5(X)) Rigby Education.

A House for the Alien: Early Level Satellite Individual Title Six-Packs. (Sails Literacy Ser.). 16p. (gr. 1-2). 27.00 (978-0-7578-2910-9(4)) Rigby Education.

How Big Is It? Individual Title Six-Pack Pouch - Level J. (Lighthouse Ser.). 16p. (gr. 2 up). 28.00 (978-0-7578-0872-2(7)) Rigby Education.

How Big Is My World? (J). pap. 7.95 (978-0-8136-0082-6(0)) Modern Curriculum Pr.

How Do You Sleep? First Grade Guided Reading Level G. (On Our Way to English Ser.). (gr. 1 up). 27.75 (978-0-7578-7058-3(9)) Rigby Education.

How Many Days to America? (Lexile Levels Ser.). 9.09 (978-1-56334-734-4(2)); 54.54 (978-0-7362-2157-3(3)) Hampton-Brown Bks.

How Many Hats? Kindergarten Guided Reading Level B. (On Our Way to English Ser.). (gr. k up). 27.75 (978-0-7578-7010-1(4)) Rigby Education.

How Many Jelly Beans? (Early Intervention Levels Ser.). 21.30 (978-0-7362-0374-6(5)); Vol. 2. 3.55 (978-0-7362-0095-0(9)) Hampton-Brown Bks.

How Much Does It Weigh? First Grade Guided Reading Level H. (On Our Way to English Ser.). (gr. 1 up). 27.75 (978-0-7578-7062-0(7)) Rigby Education.

How Things Work Interactive Packages: Looking Closer. (Pebble Soup Explorations Ser.). (ps up). 52.00 (978-0-7578-5246-6(7)) Rigby Education.

Howard, Lori. Read All about It. 2000. (Illus.). 16.95 (978-0-19-435224-6(2)) Oxford Univ. Pr., Inc.

Howden, Iris. A Bright Future: Livewire Fiction. 1999. (Livewires Ser.). (Illus.). 48p. pap. (978-0-340-72094-3(8) , Hodder Arnold) Hodder Education.

—Ride to Hell. 2nd rev. ed. 2005. (Illus.). pap. (978-0-340-81684-4(8)) Cambridge Univ. Pr.

Howell, Gill. Selkie Child. Keen, Sophie, illus. 2005. 24p. (J). lib. bdg. 22.65 (***978-1-59646-750-7(9))** Dingles & Co.

—Snow King. Cann, Helen, illus. 2005. 24p. (J). lib. bdg. 22.65 (***978-1-59646-742-2(8))** Dingles & Co.

—Tortoise & the Baboon. Woody, illus. 2004. 16p. (J). lib. bdg. 22.65 (***978-1-59646-686-9(3))** Dingles & Co.

Howlett, Bruce. Means-to-an-End Readers, Bks. 1-4. 2001. (J). (978-0-9704183-7-1(X) , Sound Reading) Sound Reading Solutions.

—Sound Reading Elementary Activity Program. 2000. Orig. Title: Sound Reading Program. per. (978-0-9704183-1-9(0) , Sound Reading) Sound Reading Solutions.

—Sound Reading Emerging Readers Activity Program. 2000. spiral bd. (978-0-9704183-0-2(2) , Sound Reading) Sound Reading Solutions.

Howlett, Bruce & Pitcher, Jeff, creators. Hop, Skip & Jump into Reading Software: For Six Students. 2003. (J). cd-rom (978-0-9742485-1-6(7)) Sound Reading Solutions.

—Hop, Skip & Jump into Reading Software: For Two Students. 2003. (J). cd-rom (978-0-9742485-0-9(9)) Sound Reading Solutions.

—Sound Reading Elementary Software: For Two Students. 2001. (J). cd-rom (978-0-9742485-2-3(5)) Sound Reading Solutions.

—Sound Reading Teen's, 20's & Beyond Software: For Two Students. 2002. (YA). cd-rom (978-0-9742485-5-4(X)) Sound Reading Solutions.

Howlett, Bruce, et al. Hop, Skip & Jump into Reading. Pitcher, Jeff, illus. 2003. (J). Bk. 1. 9.00 (978-0-9704183-4-0(5)); Bk. 2. 9.00 (978-0-9704183-3-3(7) , Sound Reading); Bk. 3. 9.00 (978-0-9704183-8-8(8) , Sound Reading) Sound Reading Solutions.

HSP. First-Place Reading for Title I: A Picture Book of Benjamin Franklin. 2nd ed. 2002. (Harcourt Title I Reading Programs Ser.). (gr. 4 up). pap. 69.60 (978-0-15-338155-3(8)) Harcourt Schl. Pubs.

—First-Place Reading for Title I: All for the Better: a Story of el Barrio. 2nd ed. 2002. (Harcourt Title I Reading Programs Ser.). (gr. 6 up). pap. 52.70 (978-0-15-338164-5(7)) Harcourt Schl. Pubs.

—First-Place Reading for Title I: Amelia's Fantastic Flight. 2nd ed. 2002. (Harcourt Title I Reading Programs Ser.). (gr. 3 up). pap. 69.60 (978-0-15-338151-5(5)) Harcourt Schl. Pubs.

—First-Place Reading for Title I: Anansi the Spider. 2nd ed. 2002. (Harcourt Title I Reading Programs Ser.). (gr. 3 up). pap. 69.60 (978-0-15-338150-8(7)) Harcourt Schl. Pubs.

—First-Place Reading for Title I: Baseball Saved Us. 2nd ed. 2002. (Harcourt Title I Reading Programs Ser.). (gr. 6 up). pap. 69.60 (978-0-15-338167-6(1)) Harcourt Schl. Pubs.

—First-Place Reading for Title I: Christopher Columbus. 2nd ed. 2002. (Harcourt Title I Reading Programs Ser.). (gr. 5 up). pap. 44.00 (978-0-15-338163-8(9)) Harcourt Schl. Pubs.

—First-Place Reading for Title I: Dawn. 2nd ed. 2002. (Harcourt Title I Reading Programs Ser.). (gr. 4 up). pap. 69.60 (978-0-15-338157-7(4)) Harcourt Schl. Pubs.

—First-Place Reading for Title I: Diego Rivera. 2nd ed. 2002. (Harcourt Title I Reading Programs Ser.). (gr. 6 up). pap. 58.40 (978-0-15-338165-2(5)) Harcourt Schl. Pubs.

—First-Place Reading for Title I: Dylan's Day Out. 2nd ed. 2002. (Harcourt Title I Reading Programs Ser.). (gr. 3 up). pap. 69.60 (978-0-15-338147-8(7)) Harcourt Schl. Pubs.

—First-Place Reading for Title I: Five Brave Explorers. 2nd ed. 2002. (Harcourt Title I Reading Programs Ser.). (gr. 5 up). pap. 41.10 (978-0-15-338162-1(0)) Harcourt Schl. Pubs.

—First-Place Reading for Title I: Growing up in Ancient Egypt. 2nd ed. 2002. (Harcourt Title I Reading Programs Ser.). (gr. 6 up). pap. 58.40 (978-0-15-338168-3(X)) Harcourt Schl. Pubs.

—First-Place Reading for Title I: Hill of Fire. 2nd ed. 2002. (Harcourt Title I Reading Programs Ser.). (gr. 6 up). pap. 40.90 (978-0-15-338169-0(8)) Harcourt Schl. Pubs.

—First-Place Reading for Title I: I Hate English! 2nd ed. 2002. (Harcourt Title I Reading Programs Ser.). (gr. 4 up). pap. 46.30 (978-0-15-338156-0(6)) Harcourt Schl. Pubs.

—First-Place Reading for Title I: I Like Music. 2nd ed. 2002. (Harcourt Title I Reading Programs Ser.). (gr. 5 up). pap. 68.80 (978-0-15-338160-7(4)) Harcourt Schl. Pubs.

—First-Place Reading for Title I: Molly's Pilgrim. 2nd ed. 2002. (Harcourt Title I Reading Programs Ser.). (gr. 5 up). pap. 55.20 (978-0-15-338161-4(2)) Harcourt Schl. Pubs.

—First-Place Reading for Title I: Rain Drop Splash. 2nd ed. 2002. (Harcourt Title I Reading Programs Ser.). (gr. 3 up). pap. 46.30 (978-0-15-338149-2(3)) Harcourt Schl. Pubs.

—First-Place Reading for Title I: Sadako & the Thousand Paper Cranes. 2nd ed. 2002. (Harcourt Title I Reading Programs Ser.). (gr. 5 up). pap. 68.80 (978-0-15-338159-1(0)) Harcourt Schl. Pubs.

—First-Place Reading for Title I: The Flower of Sheba. 2nd ed. 2002. (Harcourt Title I Reading Programs Ser.). (gr. 5 up). pap. 41.10 (978-0-15-338158-4(2)) Harcourt Schl. Pubs.

—First-Place Reading for Title I: The Giant Jam Sandwich. 2nd ed. 2002. (Harcourt Title I Reading Programs Ser.). (gr. 3 up). pap. 58.40 (978-0-15-338146-1(9)) Harcourt Schl. Pubs.

—First-Place Reading for Title I: The Little Brown Jay. 2nd ed. 2002. (Harcourt Title I Reading Programs Ser.). (gr. 4 up). pap. 58.40 (978-0-15-338154-6(X)) Harcourt Schl. Pubs.

—First-Place Reading for Title I: The Seven Chinese Brothers. 2nd ed. 2002. (Harcourt Title I Reading Programs Ser.). (gr. 6 up). pap. 46.30 (978-0-15-338166-9(3)) Harcourt Schl. Pubs.

—First-Place Reading for Title I: The Trek. 2nd ed. 2002. (Harcourt Title I Reading Programs Ser.). (gr. 4 up). pap. 46.30 (978-0-15-338152-2(3)) Harcourt Schl. Pubs.

—First-Place Reading for Title I: Wagon Wheels. 2nd ed. 2002. (Harcourt Title I Reading Programs Ser.). (gr. 4 up). pap. 40.90 (978-0-15-338153-9(1)) Harcourt Schl. Pubs.

—First-Place Reading for Title I: When Africa Was Home. 2nd ed. 2002. (Harcourt Title I Reading Programs Ser.). (gr. 3 up). pap. 69.60 (978-0-15-338148-5(5)) Harcourt Schl. Pubs.

Hughes, Monica. Little Mouse Deer & the Crocodile. Moriuchi, Mique, illus. 2004. 24p. (J). lib. bdg. 22.65 (***978-1-59646-684-5(7))** Dingles & Co.

—More Little Mouse Deer Tales. Clementson, John, illus. 2005. 24p. (J). lib. bdg. 22.65 (***978-1-59646-730-9(4))** Dingles & Co.

Hughes, Monica. Up, up & Away: Individual Title Six-Pack Pouch - Level B. (Lighthouse Ser.). 12p. (gr. k-1). 24.00 (978-0-7578-0813-5(1)) Rigby Education.

Hugo & Splot: Individual Title Six-Packs. (Bookweb Ser.). 32p. (gr. 3 up). 34.00 (978-0-7635-3936-8(8)) Rigby Education.

Hulbert, Jan. Oscar Asked Why. 1999. (Metro Reading Program Ser.). (J). (gr. k). 7.98 (978-1-58120-972-3(X)) Metropolitan Teaching & Learning Co.

—Oscar Asked, Why? 1999. (Metro Reading Program Ser.). (J). (gr. k). 29.95 (978-1-58120-115-4(X)); 45.95 (978-1-58830-027-0(7)) Metropolitan Teaching & Learning Co.

The Hummingbirds' Gift. (Lexile Levels Ser.). 9.09 (978-1-56334-720-7(2)) Hampton-Brown Bks.

Humphrey. River Journey. 1998. (Rainbow Big Bks.). (Illus.). 31p. pap. 29.99 (978-0-237-51902-5(X) , Evans Brothers, Limited) Evans Publishing Group GBR. *Dist:* Independent Pubs. Group.

Humphreys, Pauline A. Romance of the Airman. 2005. pap. 43.95 (978-1-4191-0278-3(8)) Kessinger Publishing, LLC.

The Hunchback of Notre Dame Student Packet, Gr. 9-12. 2004. (YA). (978-1-58130-858-7(2)) Novel Units, Inc.

The Hungry Chickens: Individual Title Six-Packs. (Literatura 2000 Ser.). (gr. 1-2). 28.00 (978-0-7635-0136-5(0)) Rigby Education.

Hunting Crocodiles with Steve Irwin. 2005. (Book Treks Ser.). (J). (gr. 3 up). stu. ed. 34.95 (978-0-673-62080-4(8)) Celebration Pr.

Hutchins, Elizabeth. Personal Best: Snowbored, All That Jazz, Thief! 2005. (Triple Play Ser.). (Illus.). 48p. (gr. 4-8). 41.85 (978-0-7910-9075-6(2)) Facts On File, Inc.

I Am Free: Fifth Grade Newcomer Books. (On Our Way to English Ser.). (gr. 5 up). 34.50 (978-0-7578-7273-0(5)) Rigby Education.

I Am Here: First Wave Satellite Individual Title, 6 Packs. (Sails Literacy Ser.). 16p. (gr. k up). 27.00 (978-0-7578-6852-8(5)) Rigby Education.

I Am Six. (Early Intervention Levels Ser.). 10.50 (978-0-7362-0513-9(6)); 63.00 (978-0-7362-2112-2(3)) Hampton-Brown Bks.

I Can Read, Set. 50th anniv. ed. 2007. (I Can Read Bks.). (J). pap. 14.99 (***978-0-06-123469-9(9)*** , Harper Trophy) HarperCollins Pubs.

I Can Read Classroom in a Box Level 1. 2007. (I Can Read Bks.). (J). 460.00 (***978-0-06-137567-5(5)*** , Harper Trophy) HarperCollins Pubs.

I Can Read Classroom in a Box Level 3. 2007. (I Can Read Bks.). (J). 460.00 (***978-0-06-137570-5(5)*** , Harper Trophy) HarperCollins Pubs.

I Can See, 6 Packs. (Rigby Focus Ser.). 16p. (gr. k up). 26.00 (978-0-7578-5282-4(3)) Rigby Education.

I Can See: Individual Title, 6 Packs. (Rigby Focus Ser.). 16p. (gr. k up). 28.00 (978-0-7578-5516-0(4)) Rigby Education.

I Can Swim. (J). 14.15 (978-0-8136-2035-0(X)) Modern Curriculum Pr.

I Have Five Senses: Kindergarten Guided Reading Level C. (On Our Way to English Ser.). (gr. k up). 27.75 (978-0-7578-7020-0(1)) Rigby Education.

I Have Some Money: Second Grade Newcomer Books. (On Our Way to English Ser.). (gr. 2 up). 29.50 (978-0-7578-7216-7(6)) Rigby Education.

I Like to Read. 2003. (J). (978-1-58453-112-8(6)) Pioneer Valley Educational Pr., Inc.

I Love My Grandma, Vol. 6. (Early Intervention Levels Ser.). 3.85 (978-1-56334-970-6(1)) Hampton-Brown Bks.

I Love Reading. 2006. (I Love Reading Ser.). (J). lib. bdg. 216.00 (978-1-59716-199-2(3)) Bearport Publishing Co., Inc.

I Need Something Round: First Grade Guided Reading Level H. (On Our Way to English Ser.). (gr. 1 up). 27.75 (978-0-7578-7060-6(0)) Rigby Education.

I Push, I Pull: Kindergarten Guided Reading Level B. (On Our Way to English Ser.). (gr. k up). 27.75 (978-0-7578-7012-5(0)) Rigby Education.

I See Tails! (Early Intervention Levels Ser.). 23.10 (978-0-7362-0009-7(6)); Vol. 2. 3.85 (978-1-56334-959-1(0)) Hampton-Brown Bks.

I Speak English & Chinese: Second Grade Guided Reading Level E. (On Our Way to English Ser.). (gr. 2 up). 34.50 (978-0-7578-7066-8(X)) Rigby Education.

I Use My Senses: First Grade Newcomer Books. (On Our Way to English Ser.). (gr. 1 up). 23.50 (978-0-7578-7207-5(7)) Rigby Education.

I Wish. (Sunstart Ser.: Series S50). (Illus.). 32p. (J). (ps-5). stu. ed. 1.95 (978-0-7214-8009-1(8) , Dutton Juvenile) Penguin Group (USA) Inc.

Ibis & Jaguar's Dinner: Second Grade Big Books. (On Our Way to English Ser.). (gr. 2 up). 29.95 (978-0-7578-1427-3(1)) Rigby Education.

Ibis & Jaguar's Dinner: Small Versions of Big Books. (On Our Way to English Ser.). (gr. 2 up). 29.00 (978-0-7578-7237-2(9)) Rigby Education.

Ideas of the Modern World, 8 vols., Set. 2003. 205.52 (978-0-7398-6420-3(3)) Steck-Vaughn.

If I Were You. 2003. (Illus.). pap. 5.60 (978-0-7398-7519-3(1)) Steck-Vaughn.

If You Could Be Anything. 2003. (Illus.). pap. 7.60 (978-0-7398-7530-8(2)) Steck-Vaughn.

Iggy Iguana's Trip. (Early Intervention Levels Ser.). 21.30 (978-0-7362-0380-7(X)); Vol. 3. 3.55 (978-0-7362-0101-8(7)) Hampton-Brown Bks.

Ikids & Hapka, Cathy. Innovative Kids Readers: Clue School - the Lost Lunch Mystery. Larranaga, Ana & Torrey, Richard, illus. 2007. 32p. (J). (gr. 2-17). pap. 6.99 (978-1-58476-541-7(0)) Innovative Kids.

Illustrated Classics. 2006. (Illus.). (gr. 5-8). 189.50 (978-0-7910-9111-1(2)) Facts On File, Inc.

I'm Glad I'm Me: Individual Title Six-Packs. (gr. 1-2). 25.00 (978-0-7635-9194-6(7)) Rigby Education.

I'm not, I'm Not: Individual Title Six-Packs. (gr. 1-2). 22.00 (978-0-7635-9155-7(6)) Rigby Education.

IM Pei: a Life in Architecture: Fifth Grade Guided Comprehension Level R. (On Our Way to English Ser.). (gr. 5 up). 34.50 (978-0-7578-6620-3(4)) Rigby Education.

Image Makers, 6 Packs. (Rigby Infoquest Ser.). (gr. 6 up). 37.00 (978-0-7578-8003-2(7)) Rigby Education.

The Imaginer: Individual Title Six-Packs. (Bookweb Ser.). 32p. (gr. 6 up). 34.00 (978-0-7578-0900-2(6)) Rigby Education.

In the Bathroom: Individual Title, 6 Packs. (Chiquilibros Ser.). (gr. k-1). 23.00 (978-0-7635-0452-6(1)) Rigby Education.

In the Box, Vol. 3. (Early Intervention Levels Ser.). 3.55 (978-0-7362-0098-1(3)) Hampton-Brown Bks.

In the City Vol. 4: Step K, Level B. (Early Intervention Levels Ser.). 3.85 (978-1-56334-968-3(X)) Hampton-Brown Bks.

In the Country: Individual Title Six-Packs. (ps-2). 23.00 (978-0-7635-8810-6(5)) Rigby Education.

In the Deep: Fifth Grade Class Collection Books. (On Our Way to English Ser.). (gr. 5 up). 29.95 (978-0-7578-4470-6(7)) Rigby Education.

In the Deep: Small Versions of Class Collection Books. (On Our Way to English Ser.). (gr. 5 up). 34.50 (978-0-7578-7284-6(0)) Rigby Education.

In the Ocean: Fifth Grade Newcomer Books. (On Our Way to English Ser.). (gr. 5 up). 34.50 (978-0-7578-7276-1(X)) Rigby Education.

In the Park: Kindergarten Newcomer Books. (On Our Way to English Ser.). (gr. k up). 23.50 (978-0-7578-7194-8(1)) Rigby Education.

In the Rain. (Little Book Practice Reader). (J). (978-0-8136-5359-4(2)) Modern Curriculum Pr.

In the Rain: First Grade Guided Reading Level D. (On Our Way to English Ser.). (gr. 1 up). 27.75 (978-0-7578-7043-9(0)) Rigby Education.

In the Sun. (Early Intervention Levels Ser.). 21.30 (978-0-7362-0390-6(7)); Vol. 4. 3.55 (978-0-7362-0170-4(X)) Hampton-Brown Bks.

In the Teacup: KinderWords Individual Title, 6 Packs. (Kinderstarters Ser.). 8p. (ps-1). 21.00 (978-0-7635-8695-9(1)) Rigby Education.

In the Woods: First Grade Guided Reading Level B. (On Our Way to English Ser.). (gr. 1 up). 27.75 (978-0-7578-7030-9(9)) Rigby Education.

In the Yard. (Early Intervention Levels Ser.). 5.34 (978-0-7362-1694-4(4)); 32.04 (978-0-7362-2142-9(5)) Hampton-Brown Bks.

Independent Reader Grade Level Package, 36 bks., Set. 2000. (SPA.). (gr. k up). 116.93 (978-0-673-64056-7(6)) Addison-Wesley Educational Pubs., Inc.

Independent Readers Bookshelf Collection, 6 bks., Set. 2004. (gr. 1 up). 99.00 (978-0-328-00408-9(1)); 2000. (SPA.). (gr. k up). 665.28 (978-0-328-00515-4(0)); 2000. (SPA.). (gr. 1 up). 110.88 (978-0-328-00409-6(X)) Addison-Wesley Educational Pubs., Inc.

Independent Readers Grade Level Package, 36 bks. 2004. (gr. k up). 594.00 (978-0-328-02901-3(7)); Set. 2000. (SPA.). (gr. 1 up). 19.49 (978-0-673-64057-4(4)) Addison-Wesley Educational Pubs., Inc.

The Indian Wars: Individual Title Six-Packs. (On Deck Ser.: Vol. 2). 24p. (gr. 4-5). 35.00 (978-0-7578-5809-3(0)) Rigby Education.

Inside a Factory Set D, 6 vols. (Phonics Readers Ser.). (gr. k-2). 28.95 (978-0-7368-4057-6(5)) Red Brick Learning.

Instruc, Shurley. Shurley English 1 Kit H/S Ed. 2004. 70.00 (978-1-58561-048-8(8)) Shurley Instructional Materials, Inc.

—Shurley English 1 Stu Workbook. 2004. pap. 12.00 (978-1-58561-049-5(6)) Shurley Instructional Materials, Inc.

—Shurley English 2 Kit H/S Ed. 2004. pap. 70.00 (978-1-58561-044-0(5)) Shurley Instructional Materials, Inc.

—Shurley English 2 Stu Workbook. 2004. pap. 12.00 (978-1-58561-045-7(3)) Shurley Instructional Materials, Inc.

—Shurley English 3 Kit H/S Ed. 2004. 70.00 (978-1-58561-040-2(2)) Shurley Instructional Materials, Inc.

—Shurley English 3 Stu Workbook. 2004. pap. 12.00 (978-1-58561-041-9(0)) Shurley Instructional Materials, Inc.

—Shurley English 4 Kit H/S Ed. 2004. pap. 70.00 (978-1-58561-036-5(4)) Shurley Instructional Materials, Inc.

—Shurley English 4 Stu Workbook. 2004. pap. 12.00 (978-1-58561-037-2(2)) Shurley Instructional Materials, Inc.

—Shurley English 5 Kit H/S Ed. 2004. pap. 70.00 (978-1-58561-032-7(1)) Shurley Instructional Materials, Inc.

—Shurley English 5 Stu Workbook. 2004. pap. 12.00 (978-1-58561-033-4(X)) Shurley Instructional Materials, Inc.

—Shurley English 6 Stu Workbook. 2004. pap. 12.00 (978-1-58561-029-7(1)) Shurley Instructional Materials, Inc.

Intermediate Level: Practice Book. (English at Your Command! Ser.). (gr. 4-8). 5.89 (978-0-7362-1975-4(7)) Hampton-Brown Bks.

Intermediate Level: Student Handbook. (English at Your Command! Ser.). (gr. 4-8). stu. ed. 25.20 (978-0-7362-1972-3(2)); stu. ed. 28.92 (978-0-7362-1973-0(0)) Hampton-Brown Bks.

Intervention Handbook. 2004. (gr. 3 up). 45.68 (978-0-328-02600-5(X)); (gr. 4 up). 45.68 (978-0-328-02601-2(8)); (gr. 5 up). 45.68 (978-0-328-02602-9(6)); (gr. 6 up). tchr. ed. 45.68 (978-0-328-02603-6(4)) Addison-Wesley Educational Pubs., Inc.

Into English!, 11 vols., Level E. 2002. (Into English! Ser.). (gr. k-6). 97.10 (978-1-56334-903-4(5)); (gr. 4 up). 626.27 (978-1-56334-865-5(9)); (gr. 4 up). stu. ed., act. bk. ed. 5.84 (978-1-56334-732-0(6)); (gr. 4 up). suppl. ed. 648.64 incl. cd-rom (978-1-56334-859-4(4)) Hampton-Brown Bks.

Into English! Portable Packs: Level B. (Into English! Ser.). (gr. 1-5). 286.60 (978-0-7362-1393-6(7)) Hampton-Brown Bks.

Into English! Portable Packs: Level C. (Into English! Ser.). (gr. 1-5). 286.60 (978-0-7362-1394-3(5)) Hampton-Brown Bks.

Into English! Portable Packs: Level D. (Into English! Ser.). (gr. 1-5). 278.51 (978-0-7362-1395-0(3)) Hampton-Brown Bks.

Into English! Portable Packs: Level E. (Into English! Ser.). (gr. 1-5). 278.51 (978-0-7362-1396-7(1)) Hampton-Brown Bks.

Into English! Portable Packs: Level F. (Into English! Ser.). (gr. 1-5). 278.51 (978-0-7362-1397-4(X)) Hampton-Brown Bks.

The Inventions of Alexander Graham Bell: Individual Title Six-Packs. (On Deck Ser.: Vol. 2). 24p. (gr. 4-5). 35.00 (978-0-7578-5853-6(8)) Rigby Education.

The Inventions of Amanda Jones, Pk. 6. (On Deck Ser.: Vol. 2). 24p. (gr. 4-5). 35.00 (978-0-7578-5854-3(6)) Rigby Education.

The Inventions of Eli Whitney: Individual Title, 6 Packs. (On Deck Ser.: Vol. 2). 24p. (gr. 4-5). 35.00 (978-0-7578-5855-0(4)) Rigby Education.

The Inventions of Granville Woods: Individual Title, 6 Packs. (On Deck Ser.: Vol. 2). 24p. (gr. 4-5). 35.00 (978-0-7578-5856-7(2)) Rigby Education.

The Inventions of Martha Coston: Individual Title, 6 Packs. (On Deck Ser.: Vol. 2). 24p. (gr. 4-5). 35.00 (978-0-7578-5857-4(0)) Rigby Education.

The Inventions of Thomas Alva Edison: Individual Title Six-Packs. (On Deck Ser.: Vol. 2). 24p. (gr. 4-5). 35.00 (978-0-7578-5858-1(9)) Rigby Education.

The Invisible World: Individual Title Six-Packs. (Rigby Infoquest Ser.). (gr. 6 up). 37.00 (978-0-7578-7997-5(7)) Rigby Education.

Iopeners: Big Book Collection, 20 vols. 2005. (J). (gr. k up). 525.95 (978-0-7652-4972-2(3)); (gr. 1 up). 587.50 (978-0-7652-4976-0(6)) Modern Curriculum Pr.

Iopeners: Classroom Library. 2005. (J). (gr. k up). 440.50 (978-0-7652-4969-2(3)); (gr. 1 up). 518.50 (978-0-7652-4973-9(1)); (gr. 2 up). 518.50 (978-0-7652-4977-7(4)); (gr. 3 up). 616.50 (978-0-7652-4980-7(4)); (gr. 4 up). 616.50 (978-0-7652-4983-8(9)); (gr. 5 up). 694.50 (978-0-7652-4986-9(3)); (gr. 6 up). 694.50 (978-0-7652-4989-0(8)) Modern Curriculum Pr.

Iopeners: Science Library, 10 vols. 2005. (J). (gr. k up). 220.95 (978-0-7652-4970-8(7)); (gr. 1 up). 259.95 (978-0-7652-4974-6(X)); (gr. 2 up). 259.95 (978-0-7652-4978-4(2)); (gr. 3 up). 308.50 (978-0-7652-4981-4(2)); (gr. 4 up). 308.50 (978-0-7652-4984-5(7)); (gr. 5 up). 347.50 (978-0-7652-4987-6(1)); (gr. 6 up). 347.50 (978-0-7652-4990-6(1)) Modern Curriculum Pr.

Iopeners: Social Studies Library, 10 vols. 2005. (J). (gr. k up). 220.95 (978-0-7652-4971-5(5)); (gr. 1 up). 259.95 (978-0-7652-4975-3(8)); (gr. 2 up). 259.95 (978-0-7652-4979-1(0)); (gr. 3 up). 308.50 (978-0-7652-4982-1(0)); (gr. 4 up). 308.50 (978-0-7652-4985-2(5)); (gr. 5 up). 347.50 (978-0-7652-4988-3(X)); (gr. 6 up). 347.50 (978-0-7652-4991-3(X)) Modern Curriculum Pr.

A Is It Hot? Is It Not? Set, 6 vols. (Phonics Readers Ser.). (gr. k-2). 17.50 (978-0-7368-3186-4(X)) Red Brick Learning.

Is Jim In? Set A Individual Title Six-Packs. (gr. k-3). 29.00 (978-0-7635-0531-8(5)) Rigby Education.

Isabel's Day: First Grade Guided Reading Level C. (On Our Way to English Ser.). (gr. 1 up). 27.75 (978-0-7578-7036-1(8)) Rigby Education.

Iseard, Marian. Night Fishing. 2001. (Livewire Ser.). (Illus.). 32p. pap. (978-0-340-80080-5(1) , Hodder Arnold) Hodder Education.

ISer Amable no Cuesta Nada! Social/Emotional Lap Book. (Pebble Soup Exploraciones Ser.). (SPA.). (ps up). 16.00 (978-0-7578-1783-0(1)) Rigby Education.

It's All Matter Set D, 6 vols. (Phonics Readers Ser.). (gr. k-2). 28.95 (978-0-7368-4060-6(5)) Red Brick Learning.

It's Not Fair: 6 Small Books. (gr. k-3). 24.00 (978-0-7635-6243-4(2)) Rigby Education.

It's Showtime: Individual Title Six-Packs. (Rigby Infoquest Ser.). (gr. 5 up). 37.00 (978-0-7578-6487-2(2)) Rigby Education.

The J-Files: Individual Title, 6 Packs. (Bookweb Ser.). 32p. (gr. 3 up). 34.00 (978-0-7635-3941-2(4)) Rigby Education.

Jack: 6 Small Books. (gr. k-2). 23.00 (978-0-7635-8497-9(5)) Rigby Education.

Jackson, Marjorie. Armadillo. Henry, Marilyn, illus. 2000. (Books for Young Learners). 16p. (J). pap. 5.00 (978-1-57274-243-7(7)) Owen, Richard C. Pubs., Inc.

Jackson, Melanie. The Summer of the Spotted Owl. 2005. (Orca Young Readers Ser.: Book 4). (Illus.). 176p. (J). (gr. 3-7). pap. 6.95 (978-1-55143-412-4(1)) Orca Bk. Pubs. USA.

Jackson, Patrick & Kimura, Rie. Potato Pals 1. 2005. wbk. ed. 6.50 (978-0-19-439191-7(4)); 48p. act. bk. ed. 6.50 (978-0-19-439190-0(6)) Oxford Univ. Pr., Inc.

—Potato Pals 1: User's Guide. 2005. 99p. 8.50 (978-0-19-439193-1(0)) Oxford Univ. Pr., Inc.

The Jade Emperor & the Four Dragons: Individual Title Six-Pack Pouch - Level L. (Lighthouse Ser.). 16p. (gr. 2 up). 28.00 (978-0-7578-0878-4(6)) Rigby Education.

Jake, the Juggler: Individual Title, 6 Packs. (Sails Literacy Ser.). (gr. 1-2). 36.00 (978-0-7578-4014-2(0)) Rigby Education.

James Is Hiding: Individual Title, 6 Packs. (gr. 1-2). 22.00 (978-0-7635-9162-5(9)) Rigby Education.

Jantti, Mariana. Lejos, Cerca. Donde Estan? 2006. (SPA., Illus.). 28p. (J). 14.95 (978-84-933955-6-8(0)) Hardenville SA URY. *Dist:* Independent Pubs. Group.

Jarman, Julia. Molly & the Giant. Sholto, Walker, illus. 2005. 24p. (J). lib. bdg. 22.65 (***978-1-59646-746-0(0)***) Dingles & Co.

Jarrell, Pamela R. A Nice Cool Drink. Teeple, Jackie, illus. l.t. ed. 2005. (J). (ps-k). pap. 10.95 (978-1-57332-340-6(3)); pap. 10.95 (978-1-57332-341-3(1)) HighReach Learning, Inc.

—Planting a Seed. Meler, Kerry L., illus. l.t. ed. 2006. 12p. (J). (ps-k). pap. 10.95 (978-1-57332-350-5(0)) HighReach Learning, Inc.

Jasper & the Kitten. 2004. (J). (978-1-58453-283-5(1)) Pioneer Valley Educational Pr., Inc.

Jasper the Cat Chapter Set 1. 2004. (J). (978-1-58453-287-3(4)) Pioneer Valley Educational Pr., Inc.

Jasper the Cat Set 1. 2004. (J). (978-1-58453-282-8(3)) Pioneer Valley Educational Pr., Inc.

Jasper the Fat Cat. 2004. (J). (978-1-58453-276-7(9)) Pioneer Valley Educational Pr., Inc.

Javernick, Ellen. Fiesta. 2004. 8p. (gr. k-2). pap. 4.95 (978-1-57874-049-9(5)) Kaeden Corp.

Jeffers, Susan, illus. Hansel y Gretel. (SPA.). 32p. (J). (gr. 2-3). 10.36 (978-84-241-3339-9(0) , EV4674) Everest de Ediciones y Distribucion, S.L. ESP. *Dist:* Lectorum Pubns., Inc.

Jennings, Sharon. Franklin's Pond Phantom. McIntyre, Sasha et al, illus. 2005. (Kids Can Read with Help Ser.). 32p. (J). (ps-ps). (978-1-55337-718-4(4)) Kids Can Pr., Ltd.

Jennings, Terry. Bird Watch, 8 bks. 2005. (QEB Readers). (Illus.). 24p. (J). (ps-3). lib. bdg. 15.95 (978-1-59566-078-7(X)) QEB Publishing Inc.

—Bugs & Slugs, 8 vols. 2005. (QEB Readers). (Illus.). 24p. (J). (ps-3). lib. bdg. 15.95 (978-1-59566-069-5(0)) QEB Publishing Inc.

Jespersen, Amanda. The Little Lost Goat: Lunda Version. Kambangaji, Thomson, tr. 1998. (Cambridge African Language Library Ser.). (Illus.). 16p. pap. 3.70 (978-0-521-63835-7(6)) Cambridge Univ. Pr.

A Job for a Day: Third Grade Guided Reading Level M. (On Our Way to English Ser.). (gr. 3 up). 34.50 (978-0-7578-7131-3(3)) Rigby Education.

Johns, Linda & Caputo, Jim. I Can Do It Boxed Set. 2006. pap. 9.95 (978-0-531-16923-0(5) , Children's Pr.) Scholastic Library Publishing.

Johnson, D. C. & Turner, Sandra. Let's Be Friends. Johnson, D. C. & Johnson, Darnell, illus. 2007. (J). per. 9.95 (***978-1-933556-66-6(8)***) Publishers' Graphics, L.L.C.

Johnson, Kristin & Bayrd, Polly. Megawords 1: Multisyllabic Words for Reading, Spelling, & Vocabulary. 2004. 91p. (gr. 4 up). pap. 6.80 (978-0-8388-1825-1(0)) Educators Publishing Service, Inc.

Jolly Readers Level 1Complete Set, Vol. 1. 2005. (J). 22.50 (978-1-84414-075-6(X)) Jolly Learning, Ltd. GBR. *Dist:* American International Distribution Corp.

Jones, Beverly Lyle. Sky Blue. 2000. (Illus.). 16p. (J). pap. 10.00 (978-0-8059-4808-0(2)) Dorrance Publishing Co., Inc.

Jones, Christianne C. Caleb's Race. 2007. (Illus.). 24p. (J). (***978-1-4048-1224-6(5)***) Picture Window Bks.

Jones, Shelley V. & Gunn, Barbara. Read Well Magazine Unit 20: Slanted Text. 2003. (Read Well Level K Ser.). (Illus.). 8p. (J). (978-1-59318-104-8(3)) Sopris West Educational Services.

—Shells on the Shore: Read Well Level K Unit 14 Storybook. Jerde, Susan, illus. 2003. (Read Well Level K Ser.). 20p. (J). (978-1-57035-685-8(8) , 55546) Sopris West Educational Services.

Jordan, B. J. Beginning Literature. 2000. (Logos School Literature Ser.). (J). Bk. 1. 24p. spiral bd. 10.00 (978-1-930443-30-3(7)); Bk. 2. 25p. spiral bd. 10.00 (978-1-930443-31-0(5)) Logos Schl.

Josephson, Lin. Theme-Based Nonfiction Reading Comprehension. 2003. (100+ Seriestm Ser.). 128p. (J). (gr. 6-6). pap. 12.99 (978-0-7424-1906-3(1) , IFG99103) School Specialty Publishing.

Josephson, Lin. The "UnWorkbook" Creative Reading, Grade 5. 2005. 96p. (J). (gr. 5-5). pap. 12.99 (***978-0-7682-3125-0(6)*** , Schaffer, Frank) Schaffer, Frank Pubns.

The Journal: Dear Future II: Individual Title Six-Packs. (Action Packs Ser.). 104p. (gr. 3-5). 44.00 (978-0-7635-8417-7(7)) Rigby Education.

Juel, Connie, et al. Ready Readers: Collection. 2005. (J). (gr. 2 up). 698.50 (978-0-7652-6094-9(8)) Modern Curriculum Pr.

—Ready Readers: Nonfiction Favorites. 2005. (J). (gr. k up). 699.95 (978-0-7652-6089-5(1)); (gr. 1 up). 469.95 (978-0-7652-6093-2(X)) Modern Curriculum Pr.

—Ready Readers: Set 1 Collection. 2005. (J). (gr. k up). 910.50 (978-0-7652-6086-4(7)); (gr. 1 up). 793.50 (978-0-7652-6090-1(5)) Modern Curriculum Pr.

—Ready Readers: Set 2 Collection. 2005. (J). (gr. k up). 979.95 (978-0-7652-6087-1(5)); (gr. 1 up). 1325.95 (978-0-7652-6091-8(3)) Modern Curriculum Pr.

—Ready Readers: Set 3 Collection. 2005. (J). (gr. k up). 793.50 (978-0-7652-6088-8(3)); (gr. 1 up). 1138.50 (978-0-7652-6092-5(1)) Modern Curriculum Pr.

Julius Caesar Study Guide. 2002. (Illus.). 48p. (YA). per. 17.95 (978-1-56254-606-9(6) , SP6066) Saddleback Educational Publishing.

Jump & Run. 2003. (Read with Dick & Jane Ser.: Vol. 3). 32p. (J). (ps-2). pap. 3.99 (978-0-448-43402-5(4)); (Illus.). 13.89 (978-0-448-43414-8(8)) Penguin Group (USA) Inc. (Grosset & Dunlap).

Jump & Thump! Individual Title Six-Packs. (ps-2). 23.00 (978-0-7635-8802-1(4)) Rigby Education.

The Jungle: Individual Title Six-Packs. (Sails Literacy Ser.). 16p. (gr. k up). 27.00 (978-0-7635-4388-4(8)) Rigby Education.

The junk Box 6 Packs. Individual Title. (gr. 1-2). 22.00 (978-0-7635-9170-0(X)) Rigby Education.

The Junk-Food Files. 2003. (Illus.). pap. 5.60 (978-0-7398-7513-1(2)) Steck-Vaughn.

The Junkyard Dog: Individual Chapter Book Title Six-Packs. Vol. 26. 32p. (gr. 3-4). 44.00 (978-0-7635-4478-2(7)) Rigby Education.

Just Ducky Board Book Set 800794, 3. 2005. (J). bds. (978-1-59794-023-8(2)) Environments, Inc.

Just Like Me! First Grade. (On Our Way to English Ser.). (gr. 1 up). 29.95 (978-0-7578-1513-3(8)) Rigby Education.

Just Like Me! Small Versions of Big Books. (On Our Way to English Ser.). (gr. 1 up). 29.00 (978-0-7578-7226-6(3)) Rigby Education.

Just Like My Grandpa, Vol. 4. (Early Intervention Levels Ser.). 3.85 (978-1-56334-981-2(7)) Hampton-Brown Bks.

Just My Luck! 6 Packs. Individual Title. (Literatura 2000 Ser.). (gr. 1-2). 28.00 (978-0-7635-0139-6(5)) Rigby Education.

Just Right: KinderConcepts Individual Title Six-Packs. (Kinderstarters Ser.). 8p. (ps-1). 21.00 (978-0-7635-8738-3(9)) Rigby Education.

Just the Right Word! (gr. k-3). 106.00 (978-0-7362-2594-6(3)); stu. ed. 5.18 (978-0-7362-2533-5(1)) Hampton-Brown Bks.

K Take-Home Readers Blms Set. 2003. (Metro Reading Ser.). (gr. k). (978-1-58120-608-1(9)) Metropolitan Teaching & Learning Co.

Kachur, Matthew. A Miracle Material. 2004. (Navigators Ser.). (J). pap. 42.00 (978-1-4108-0430-3(5)) Benchmark Education Co.

Kalar, Bonnie. At Dawn. Spreen, Kathe, illus. Date not set. 8p. (J). (ps-2). pap. (978-1-891619-24-3(1)) Corona Pr.

—At the Lake. Spreen, Kathe, illus. Date not set. 12p. (J). (ps-2). pap. (978-1-891619-34-2(9)) Corona Pr.

—At the Pond. Spreen, Kathe, illus. Date not set. 8p. (J). (ps-2). pap. (978-1-891619-07-6(1)) Corona Pr.

—At the Zoo. Spreen, Kathe, illus. Date not set. 8p. (J). (ps-2). pap. (978-1-891619-18-2(7)) Corona Pr.

—Beth & Thad. Spreen, Kathe, illus. Date not set. 12p. (J). (ps-2). pap. (978-1-891619-17-5(9)) Corona Pr.

P Q R

—The Bird & the Shirt. Spreen, Kathe, illus. Date not set. 12p. (J). (ps-2). pap. (978-1-891619-30-4(6)) Corona Pr.

—Burt. Spreen, Kathe, illus. Date not set. 8p. (J). (ps-2). pap. (978-1-891619-31-1(4)) Corona Pr.

—Chuck & the Chick. Spreen, Kathe, illus. Date not set. 8p. (J). (ps-2). pap. (978-1-891619-16-8(0)) Corona Pr.

—The Clown. Spreen, Kathe, illus. Date not set. 12p. (J). (ps-2). pap. (978-1-891619-22-9(5)) Corona Pr.

—The Cook & the Crook. Spreen, Kathe, illus. Date not set. 12p. (J). (ps-2). pap. (978-1-891619-29-8(2)) Corona Pr.

—The Crows. Spreen, Kathe, illus. Date not set. 8p. (J). (ps-2). pap. (978-1-891619-28-1(4)) Corona Pr.

—A Dream. Spreen, Kathe, illus. Date not set. 12p. (J). (ps-2). pap. (978-1-891619-23-6(3)) Corona Pr.

—Early Phonetic Readers - Set A, 5 bks., Set. Spreen, Kathe, illus. Incl. Bob. pap. (978-1-891619-01-4(2)); Cat & the Ant. pap. (978-1-891619-02-1(0)); Gus on the Bus. pap. (978-1-891619-03-8(9)); Hen & the Jet. pap. (978-1-891619-05-2(5)); Tim & Kim. pap. (978-1-891619-04-5(7)); (Illus.). 8p. (J). (ps-2). 1998. 8.25 (978-1-891619-00-7(4)) Corona Pr.

—Early Phonetic Readers - Set B, 5 bks., Set. Spreen, Kathe, illus. Incl. At the Pond. pap. (978-1-891619-07-6(1)); Fran & the Doll. pap. (978-1-891619-09-0(8)); Fred. pap. (978-1-891619-10-6(1)); Stan & His Sled. pap. (978-1-891619-08-3(X)); Trip. pap. (978-1-891619-11-3(X)); (Illus.). 8p. (J). (ps-2). 8.25 (978-1-891619-06-9(3)) Corona Pr.

—Early Phonetic Readers - Set C, 20 bks., Set. Spreen, Kathe, illus. Incl. At Dawn. 8p. pap. (978-1-891619-24-3(1)); At the Zoo. 8p. pap. (978-1-891619-18-2(7)); Beth & Thad. 12p. pap. (978-1-891619-17-5(9)); Bird & the Shirt. 12p. pap. (978-1-891619-30-4(6)); Bright Light. 8p. 5.25 hd (978-1-891619-32-8(2)); Burt. 8p. pap. (978-1-891619-31-1(4)); Chuck & the Chick. 8p. pap. (978-1-891619-16-8(0)); Clown. 12p. pap. (978-1-891619-22-9(5)); Cook & the Crook. 12p. pap. (978-1-891619-29-8(2)); Crows. 8p. pap. (978-1-891619-28-1(4)); Dream. 12p. pap. (978-1-891619-23-6(3)); Gail Sails. 12p. pap. (978-1-891619-20-5(9)); Gay & Jay Play. 8p. pap. (978-1-891619-19-9(5)); Jack. 12p. pap. (978-1-891619-13-7(6)); Joan's Coat. 12p. pap. (978-1-891619-21-2(7)); Josh & the Fish. 8p. pap. (978-1-891619-14-4(4)); Lew & His New Cap. 8p. pap. (978-1-891619-27-4(6)); Mark at the Farm. 12p. pap. (978-1-891619-25-0(X)); Scouts. 8p. pap. (978-1-891619-26-7(8)); Sheep & the Bee. 8p. pap. (978-1-891619-15-1(2)); (Illus.). (J). (ps-2). 38.50 (978-1-891619-12-0(8)) Corona Pr.

—Early Phonetic Readers - Set D, 3 bks., Set. Spreen, Kathe, illus. Incl. At the Lake. 12p. pap. (978-1-891619-34-2(9)); Mike. 8p. pap. (978-1-891619-35-9(7)); Rose & the Mole. 12p. pap. (978-1-891619-36-6(5)); (Illus.). (J). (ps-2). 6.25 (978-1-891619-33-5(0)) Corona Pr.

—Fran & the Doll. Spreen, Kathe, illus. Date not set. 8p. (J). (ps-2). pap. (978-1-891619-09-0(8)) Corona Pr.

—Fred. Spreen, Kathe, illus. Date not set. 8p. (J). (ps-2). pap. (978-1-891619-10-6(1)) Corona Pr.

—Gail Sails. Spreen, Kathe, illus. Date not set. 12p. (J). (ps-2). pap. (978-1-891619-20-5(9)) Corona Pr.

—Gay & Jay Play. Spreen, Kathe, illus. Date not set. 8p. (J). (ps-2). pap. (978-1-891619-19-9(5)) Corona Pr.

—Joan's Coat. Spreen, Kathe, illus. Date not set. 12p. (J). (ps-2). pap. (978-1-891619-21-2(7)) Corona Pr.

—Lew & His New Cap. Spreen, Kathe, illus. Date not set. 8p. (J). (ps-2). pap. (978-1-891619-27-4(6)) Corona Pr.

—Mark at the Farm. Spreen, Kathe, illus. Date not set. 12p. (J). (ps-2). pap. (978-1-891619-25-0(X)) Corona Pr.

—Mike. Spreen, Kathe, illus. Date not set. 8p. (J). (ps-2). pap. (978-1-891619-35-9(7)) Corona Pr.

—Rose & the Mole. Spreen, Kathe, illus. Date not set. 12p. (J). (ps-2). pap. (978-1-891619-36-6(5)) Corona Pr.

—The Sheep & the Bee. Spreen, Kathe, illus. Date not set. 8p. (J). (ps-2). pap. (978-1-891619-15-1(2)) Corona Pr.

—Stan & His Sled. Spreen, Kathe, illus. Date not set. 8p. (J). (ps-2). pap. (978-1-891619-08-3(X)) Corona Pr.

—The Trip. Spreen, Kathe, illus. Date not set. 8p. (J). (ps-2). pap. (978-1-891619-11-3(X)) Corona Pr.

Kalwat, Deborah, ed. Cornerstones of Comprehension. 2003. 80p. 12.95 (978-1-56234-501-3(X) , Mailbox Bks., The) Education Ctr., Inc.

Kastner, Erich. Emil & the Detectives, Level 3. 2001. (Illus.). 64p. (C). pap. 9.00 (978-0-582-42699-3(5)) Longman Publishing Group.

Katschke, Judy. Disney First Reader: Howdy. 1999. 32p. (J). pap. 3.99 (978-0-7868-4392-3(6)) Disney Pr.

Katz, Bobbi. Partner Poems for Building Fluency: 25 Original Poems with Research-Based Lessons That Help Students Improve Their Fluency & Comprehension. 2007. 64p. pap. 11.99 (978-0-439-55437-4(3) , Teaching Resources) Scholastic, Inc.

Kaulfersch, Ron & Schwark, Mike. Van Von Hunter. 2007. (Kaplan SAT/ACT Score-Raising Manga Ser.: Vol. 1). 192p. pap. 9.99 (***978-1-4277-5494-3(2)***) Kaplan Publishing.

Keep Books at The Ohio State University Staff. Fact & Fiction 1, Set. 2006. (Illus.). 16p. (J). pap. (978-1-893986-25-1(X)) Keep Bks.

Keeping Track: Large-Format Books. (Rigby Infoquest Ser.). (gr. 4 up). 30.00 (978-0-7578-3905-4(3)) Rigby Education.

Keeping up with Claire: Fifth Grade Guided Comprehension Level R. (On Our Way to English Ser.). (gr. 5 up). 34.50 (978-0-7578-6618-0(2)) Rigby Education.

Keeping Watch. 2005. (J). (978-1-932570-50-2(0)) Literacy Footprints Inc.

Kellaher, Karen. Independent Reading Response Booklets: 15 Reproducible Booklets with Writing Prompts That Motivate Kids to Respond to Any Fiction or Nonfiction Book-And Build Reading Comprehension & Writing Skills. 2004. 64p. pap. 11.99 (978-0-439-39513-7(5) , Teaching Resources) Scholastic, Inc.

Kelly, Matt. Start to Read. Pfeiffer, Judith, illus. 2004. (J). (978-1-4127-3186-7(0)) Publications International, Ltd.

Kelly, Sharon L. C. M. Coco's Vineyard Vacation: Double Fun on Martha's Vineyard. Galbraith, Alison L., illus. 2005. 40p. (J). 16.95 (978-0-9766283-0-9(9)) Secret Garden Bookworks.

Kenah, Katharine. Boxed/Extreme Read, Level 2,Vol. 1. 2006. (Extreme Readers Slipcases Ser.). 128p. (J). pap. 15.95 (978-0-7696-4320-5(5)) School Specialty Publishing.

—Boxed/Extreme Read Level 1, Vol. 1. 2006. (Extreme Readers Slipcases Ser.). 128p. (J). pap. 15.95 (978-0-7696-4319-9(1)) School Specialty Publishing.

—Boxed/Extreme Read Level 3, Vol. 1. 2006. (Extreme Readers Slipcases Ser.). 128p. (J). pap. 15.95 (978-0-7696-4321-2(3)) School Specialty Publishing.

—Extreme Readers Slipcase Levels 1-2 Vol. 1, Levels 1-2: Lectores Curiosos. 2006. (Extreme Readers Slipcases Ser.). (Illus.). 128p. (J). pap. 15.95 (978-0-7696-4479-0(1)) School Specialty Publishing.

Kennedy, Dorothy M., et al. Bedford Reader: High School Reprint. 9th ed. 2005. (C). 54.95 (978-0-312-40400-0(X)) Bedford/Saint Martin's.

Kenrick, Joanna. Tears of a Friend. 2004. (Shades Ser.). 56p. (J). pap. 8.99 (978-0-237-52731-0(6) , Evans Brothers, Limited) Evans Publishing Group GBR. *Dist:* Independent Pubs. Group.

Kerman, S. Rosa Raye, Level 3. 2001. (Illus.). v, 41p. (C). pap. 9.00 (978-0-582-42736-5(3)) Longman Publishing Group.

Kerrin, Jessica Scott. Martin Bridge: On the Lookout! Kelly, Joseph, illus. 2005. 144p. (978-1-55337-773-3(7)) Kids Can Pr., Ltd.

Kerven, Rosalind. Coyote Girl. 2005. (Cambridge Storybooks Ser.). 32p. pap. 7.00 (978-0-521-67483-6(2)); pap. 7.00 (978-0-521-67485-0(9)) Cambridge Univ. Pr.

Kerven, Rosalind. Sparrow, the Crow & the Pearl. Williamson, Melanie, illus. 2005. 24p. (J). lib. bdg. 22.65 (***978-1-59646-754-5(1)***) Dingles & Co.

Ketch, Susan & Scraper, Katherine. Early Readers & Writers. Futrell, Ashley, ed. 2005. 128p. (J). per. 11.99 (978-1-59441-042-0(9) , CD-104042) Carson-Dellosa Publishing Co., Inc.

—Reading First Basics - Comprehension. Futrell, Ashley, ed. 2005. 128p. (J). per. 11.99 (978-1-59441-044-4(5) , CD-104014) Carson-Dellosa Publishing Co., Inc.

The Key: Fifth Grade Guided Comprehension Level M. (On Our Way to English Ser.). (gr. 5 up). 34.50 (978-0-7578-6594-7(1)) Rigby Education.

Key in Car: The Children's Reading Foundation Starter Books. l.t. ed. 2001. 28p. (J). cd-rom (978-0-9705383-0-7(8)) Sun Coast Communications, Inc.

Khan, Sarah. Birds Lift-the-Flap. Scott, Peter, illus. 2004. (Luxury Lift-the-Flap Ser.). 16p. (J). (gr. 1 up). 11.95 (978-0-7945-0714-5(X) , Usborne) EDC Publishing.

Kids Can Be Safe! Kindergarten Guided Reading Level C. (On Our Way to English Ser.). (gr. k up). 27.75 (978-0-7578-7023-1(6)) Rigby Education.

Kids Can Read Staff, ed. Franklin's Pond Phantom. 2005. (Kids Can Read with Help Ser.). (Illus.). 32p. (J). (gr. 1-2). (978-1-55337-719-1(2)) Kids Can Pr., Ltd.

The Kids from Quiller's Bend: Individual Title Six-Packs. (Action Packs Ser.). 120p. (gr. 3-5). 44.00 (978-0-7635-8432-0(0)) Rigby Education.

Kim, Michael. Lincoln-Douglas Debate: An Introductory Guide & Reader. Kim, Michael, illus. abr. ed. 1999. (Illus.). (YA). (gr. 9-12). pap. 22.25 (978-0-9664003-1-3(3)) Kim, Michael.

Kindergarten Book Set 800084, 10. 2005. (J). bds. (978-1-59794-002-3(X)) Environments, Inc.

Kindergarten Ell Picture Book Stories Blms. 2003. (Metro Reading Ser.). (gr. k). 35.99 (978-1-58120-601-2(1)) Metropolitan Teaching & Learning Co.

Kindergarten Ell Practice Picture Cards Blms. 2003. (Metro Reading Ser.). (gr. k). 41.29 (978-1-58120-602-9(X)) Metropolitan Teaching & Learning Co.

Kindergarten Ell Program Lap Book. 2003. (Metro Reading Ser.). (J). (gr. k). spiral bd. 116.55 (978-1-58120-603-6(8)) Metropolitan Teaching & Learning Co.

Kindergarten Ell Program Teacher's Guide. 2003. (Metro Reading Ser.). (gr. k). per. 41.29 (978-1-58120-607-4(0)) Metropolitan Teaching & Learning Co.

Kindergarten Reader: Take-Home Version. 2004. (gr. k up). 48.00 (978-0-328-02300-4(0)) Addison-Wesley Educational Pubs., Inc.

Kindergarten Readers Bookshelf Collection, 36 bks. 2004. (gr. k up). 594.00 (978-0-328-02903-7(3) , Scott Foresman) Addison-Wesley Educational Pubs., Inc.

Kindergarten Review 1.1: Take-Home Version. 2004. (gr. 1 up). stu. ed. 48.00 (978-0-328-02543-5(7)) Addison-Wesley Educational Pubs., Inc.

Kinderstarters: KinderStarters Complete Package. 1840.00 (978-0-7635-8909-7(8)) Rigby Education.

The King's Big Foot: Third Grade Guided Reading Level H. (On Our Way to English Ser.). (gr. 3 up). 34.50 (978-0-7578-7109-2(7)) Rigby Education.

The King's Cake: 3-in-1 Package. (Sails Literacy Ser.). 24p. (gr. k up). 57.00 (978-0-7578-3198-0(2)) Rigby Education.

The King's Cake: 6 Small Books. (Sails Literacy Ser.). 24p. (gr. k up). 25.00 (978-0-7578-3174-4(5)) Rigby Education.

The King's Cake: Big Book Only. (Sails Literacy Ser.). 24p. (gr. k up). 27.00 (978-0-7635-6984-6(4)) Rigby Education.

The King's Ring: KinderReaders Individual Title Six-Packs. (Kinderstarters Ser.). 8p. (ps-1). 21.00 (978-0-7635-8656-0(0)) Rigby Education.

Kinser, Kathy. The Amazon. ed. 2003. (Early Connections Ser.). (J). pap. 35.00 (978-1-4108-1549-1(8)) Benchmark Education Co.

Kipling, Rudyard. The Room in the Tower & Other Stories: Penguin Reading Lab, Level 2. 2001. 48p. pap. 7.66 (978-0-582-41667-3(1)) Longman Publishing Group.

Kirszner, Laurie G. Brief Holt Handbook for UCF. 3rd ed. 2002. pap. 46.95 (978-0-8384-6734-3(2)) Thomson Heinle.

—Casebook: A Good Man Is Hard to Find. pap. 28.95 (978-0-8384-7871-4(9)); pap. 38.95 (978-0-8384-7942-1(1)) Thomson Heinle.

Kites, Vol. 3. (Early Intervention Levels Ser.). 3.55 (978-0-7362-0089-9(4)) Hampton-Brown Bks.

The Kites: First Wave Satellite Individual Title Six-Packs. (Sails Literacy Ser.). 16p. (gr. k up). 27.00 (978-0-7578-6864-1(9)) Rigby Education.

A Kitten for Kate: Second Grade Guided Reading Level E. (On Our Way to English Ser.). (gr. 2 up). 34.50 (978-0-7578-7065-1(1)) Rigby Education.

Kitzmiller, Brenda. Muddy Mud — an Easy to Read Beginning Reader Book. 2005. 24p. 7.85 (978-1-4116-2937-0(X)) Lulu.com.

Klier, Kimberly Wagner. Firefly Friend. Garland, Michael, illus. 2005. (Rookie Reader Skill Set Ser.). 32p. (J). (gr. k-2). pap. 4.95 (978-0-516-26817-0(1) , Children's Pr.) Scholastic Library Publishing.

Kline, Trish & Donev, Mary. Coming Home: KA Reader 8. 2007. (Illus.). 32p. (J). per. 20.00 (***978-1-934307-01-4(7)***) Ghost Hunter Productions.

—Don¿t Frown, Clown! KA Reader 9. 2007. (Illus.). 32p. (J). per. 20.00 (***978-1-934307-02-1(5)***) Ghost Hunter Productions.

—Hoops in the Coop: KA Reader 7. 2007. (Illus.). 32p. (J). per. 20.00 (***978-1-934307-00-7(9)***) Ghost Hunter Productions.

Klingner, Janette K., et al. From Clunk to Click: Collaborative Strategic Reading. 2002. spiral bd. 25.00 (978-1-57035-452-6(9) , 150READ) Sopris West Educational Services.

Kluzek, Stan & Coldwell, Andrew. READ IT Home Reading Middle Level: U.S. Version. 2003. 48p. pap. (978-0-9585742-5-9(1)) Kluwell Pubns.

—READ IT Home Reading Senior Level: U.S. Version. 2003. 48p. pap. (978-0-9585742-6-6(X)) Kluwell Pubns.

Knaak, Richard A. & Kim, Jae-Hwan. Warcraft Vol. 1: Dragon Hunt : SAT/ACT Vocabulary-Building Manga. 2007. (Kaplan SAT/ACT Score-Raising Manga Ser.). 160p. pap. 9.99 (***978-1-4277-5495-0(0)***) Kaplan Publishing.

Knight. Dead Beckoning. (Thumbprint Mysteries Ser.). 32.86 (978-0-8092-0421-2(5)) McGraw-Hill/Contemporary.

—The Monster in the Loch. (Thumbprint Mysteries Ser.). 32.86 (978-0-8092-0411-3(8)) McGraw-Hill/Contemporary.

Knight, Hilary & McClatchy, Lisa. Eloise & the Big Parade. Lyon, Tammie, illus. 2007. (Eloise Ser.). 32p. (J). pap. 3.99 (978-1-4169-3523-0(1) , Aladdin) Simon & Schuster Children's Publishing.

Know Zone Reading. 2004. (gr. k-1). cd-rom 29.97 (978-0-201-68378-3(4)) Addison-Wesley Educational Pubs., Inc.

Koch, Dott Clarke. Jacob's House. Koch, William, ed. 2006. (J). incl. audio compact disk (***978-0-9789043-4-0(6)***); pap. (***978-0-9789043-5-7(4)***) Wildot Pr.

Koh, Frederick. The 10 Most Disastrous Accidents. 2008. (Tentrade; Ser.). 48p. (J). pap. 14.99 (***978-1-55448-479-9(0)*** , Watts, Franklin) Scholastic Library Publishing.

Kohfeldt, Joyce & Collier, Helen. Guess the Covered Word for Fourth Grade. 2000. (Four-Blocks Ser.). 64p. (J). (gr. 3-5). pap. 16.99 incl. trans. (978-0-88724-510-7(2) , CD-2606) Carson-Dellosa Publishing Co., Inc.

Kohfeldt, Joyce, et al. Guess the Covered Word for Second Grade. 2000. (Four-Blocks Ser.). 64p. (gr. 1-3). pap. 16.99 incl. trans. (978-0-88724-508-4(0) , CD-2604) Carson-Dellosa Publishing Co., Inc.

Korky Paul: Biography of an Illustrator: Individual Title Six-Packs. (Discovery World Ser.). 24p. (gr. 1-2). 33.00 (978-0-7635-8471-9(1)) Rigby Education.

Kottke, Jan & Winne, Joanne. Communities, 6 bks., Set. 2004. (Welcome Books Ser.). (Illus.). 24p. (J). (ps-2). 87.00 (978-0-516-23375-8(0) , Children's Pr.) Scholastic Library Publishing.

Kovalski, Maryann. Rain, Rain, Level 2. 2001. (First Flight Ser.). (Illus.). 32p. (J). (ps-2). (978-1-55041-659-6(6)) Fitzhenry & Whiteside, Ltd.

Kramer. Keys to Excellence: Integrated Language Arts - Level B - Grade 2. 1999. pap. 17.27 (978-0-7398-1971-5(2)) Steck-Vaughn.

Kramer, Alan. Path from Extinction. ed. 2004. (Reader's Theater Ser.). (J). pap. 22.00 (978-1-4108-1145-5(X)) Benchmark Education Co.

Kramer, Alan & Romer, Ruth. The Wizard of Wherever. 2004. (Reader's Theater Ser.). (J). pap. 22.00 (978-1-4108-0793-9(2)) Benchmark Education Co.

Kramer, Jennifer E. Good Luck Charlie. Moores, Jeff, illus. 2005. (Rookie Reader Skill Set Ser.). 32p. (J). (gr. k-2). pap. 4.95 (978-0-516-25826-3(5) , Children's Pr.) Scholastic Library Publishing.

Krasinski, Norma. I Am the One That Reads. 2005. (J). per. 16.99 (978-0-9773962-1-4(5)) Marx Group, The.

—I Am Their Reading Hero. 2005. (J). per. 12.99 (978-0-9773962-0-7(7)) Marx Group, The.

—Please, Please, Read to Me. 2005. (J). per. 14.99 (978-0-9773962-2-1(3)) Marx Group, The.

—The Tyler Story. 2005. (J). per. 12.99 (978-0-9773962-3-8(1)) Marx Group, The.

Krasinski, Norma & Marx, Donald. Kids Reading to Kids: The Phenomenon. 2006. per. 29.95 (978-0-9773962-4-5(X)) Marx Group, The.

Krensky, Stephen. Ben Franklin & His First Kite. Dodson, Bert, illus. ed. 2005. (Ready-to-Read Ser. Level 2). 32p. (J). lib. bdg. 15.00 (978-1-59054-941-4(4)) Fitzgerald Bks.

Kruss, Susan. The Kitchen God's Wife. 2002. (Wizard Study Guides Ser.). 56p. pap., stu. ed. 6.00 (978-1-875739-41-7(6)) Cambridge Univ. Pr.

—Lives of Girls & Women. 2002. (Wizard Study Guides Ser.). pap., stu. ed. 6.00 (978-1-875739-27-1(0)) Cambridge Univ. Pr.

—The Longest Memory. 2002. (Wizard Study Guides Ser.). 48p. pap., stu. ed. 6.00 (978-1-875739-63-9(7)) Cambridge Univ. Pr.

—Of Love & Shadows. 2002. (Wizard Study Guides Ser.). 48p. pap., stu. ed. 6.00 (978-1-875739-40-0(8)) Cambridge Univ. Pr.

—Paper Nautilus. 2002. (Wizard Study Guides Ser.). 52p. pap., stu. ed. 6.00 (978-1-875739-17-2(3)) Cambridge Univ. Pr.

—Wild Cat Falling. 2002. (Wizard Study Guides Ser.). (Illus.). 51p. pap., stu. ed. 6.00 (978-1-875739-15-8(7)) Cambridge Univ. Pr.

Kumon Publishing North America, creator. Let's Fold! A Kumon First Steps, 4 vols. 2005. (Illus.). 40p. (J). (ps). per., wbk. ed. 5.95 (978-1-933241-12-8(8)) Kumon Publishing North America, Inc.

—Let's Sticker & Paste! A Kumon First Steps Workbook, 4 vols. 2005. (Illus.). 40p. (J). (ps). per. 5.95 (978-1-933241-13-5(6)) Kumon Publishing North America, Inc.

Labella, Susan. Animal Survivors, 6 bks., Set. Incl. Bats & Other Animals with Amazing Ears. 19.00 (978-0-516-24926-1(6)); Beavers & Other Animals with Amazing Teeth. 19.00 (978-0-516-24930-8(4)); Chameleons & Other Animals with Amazing Skin. 19.00 (978-0-516-24925-4(8)); Octopuses & Other Animals with Amazing Senses. 19.00 (978-0-516-24928-5(2)); Owls & Other Animals with Amazing Eyes. 19.00 (978-0-516-24927-8(4)); Salamanders & Other Animals with Amazing Tails. 19.00 (978-0-516-24929-2(0)); (Illus.). 24p. (J). (gr. 1-2). (Scholastic News Nonfiction Readers Ser.). 2005. 108.00 (978-0-516-25390-9(5) , Children's Pr.) Scholastic Library Publishing.

LaBerge, Margaret M. Sara Safety, Personal Safety: Kid's Activity Book. Lucas, Stacey L. & Lopresti, Sarah H., illus. 2004. 21p. (J). pap. (978-0-9755561-2-2(6)) Reading Resc.

—Sara Safety, School Safety: Kid's Activity Book. Seager, Maryann et al, illus. 2004. (J). pap. (978-0-9755561-1-5(8)) Reading Resc.

LaCoste, Gary, illus. First Word Search: Reading for Beginners. 2007. (First Word Search Ser.). 64p. (J). pap. 3.95 (***978-1-4027-4661-1(X)***) Sterling Publishing Co., Inc.

Ladd, Ann Frances. Scooby Doo Phonics: 12 Book Reading Program, No. 1. 2005. (Scooby Doo Ser.). 240p. (J). 12.99 (978-0-439-66478-3(0)) Scholastic, Inc.

Ladybird. Read & Write. (Key Words Readers Ser.: C Series, No. 641-1c). (Illus.). 56p. (J). (ps-5). 3.50 (978-0-7214-0025-9(6) , Dutton Juvenile) Penguin Group (USA) Inc.

Laird, Elisabeth. Karen & the Artist, Level 1. 2001. 16p. (C). pap. 9.00 (978-0-582-42719-8(3)) Longman Publishing Group.

Laird, Elizabeth & Davidson, Roz. Jungle School. Sim, David, illus. 2006. (Green Bananas Ser.). 48p. (J). (gr. k-2). (978-0-7787-1026-4(2)) Crabtree Publishing Co.

Lakeshore Learning Materials, contrib. by. Read & Learn Nonfiction: Bold Words & Glossaries, Set of 6 Student Books. 2007. (ELX.). (J). pap. 19.95 (***978-1-59746-035-4(4)***) Lakeshore Learning Materials.

—Read & Learn Nonfiction: Bold Words & Glossaries Big Book. 2007. (J). pap. 19.95 (***978-1-59746-032-3(X)***) Lakeshore Learning Materials.

—Read & Learn Nonfiction: Maps, Charts, & Graphs, Set of 6 Student Books. 2007. (J). pap. 19.95 (***978-1-59746-034-7(6)***) Lakeshore Learning Materials.

—Read & Learn Nonfiction: Maps, Charts, & Graphs Big Book. 2007. (J). pap. 19.95 (***978-1-59746-031-6(1)***) Lakeshore Learning Materials.

—Read & Learn Nonfiction: Photos, Captions, & Diagrams, Set of 6 Student Books. 2007. (J). pap. 19.95 (***978-1-59746-033-0(8)***) Lakeshore Learning Materials.

—Read & Learn Nonfiction: Photos, Captions, & Diagrams Big Book. 2007. (J). pap. 19.95 (***978-1-59746-030-9(3)***) Lakeshore Learning Materials.

—Storyteller Complete Library: CD Version. 2007. (J). 99.50 incl. audio compact disk (***978-1-59746-019-4(2)***) Lakeshore Learning Materials.

Lakeshore Learning Materials Staff, contrib. by. If a Tree Could Talk Packet. 2000. (J). pap. 32.95 (978-1-929255-78-8(0)) Lakeshore Learning Materials.

Lakeside Elementary: Add-on Components. (gr. 2-5). stu. ed. 5.02 (978-0-7362-1821-4(1)) Hampton-Brown Bks.

Lambert, Janique. In Country. 2002. (Wizard Study Guides Ser.). 60p. pap., stu. ed. 6.00 (978-0-646-07988-2(3)) Cambridge Univ. Pr.

Lambert, Janique & McRoberts, Richard. Pride & Prejudice. 2002. (Wizard Study Guides Ser.). 72p. (YA). pap., stu. ed. 6.00 (978-1-875739-11-0(4)) Cambridge Univ. Pr.

Lamplighter Staff. The Boys of Grit Who Changed. 2004. 16.00 (978-1-58474-031-5(0)) Cornerstone Family Ministries/Lamplighter Publishing.

—Clean Your Boots Sir? 2004. 14.00 (978-1-58474-015-5(9)) Cornerstone Family Ministries/Lamplighter Publishing.

—Fireside Readings. 2004. 16.00 (978-1-58474-042-1(6)) Cornerstone Family Ministries/Lamplighter Publishing.

—Hidden Hand. 2004. 22.00 (978-1-58474-107-7(4)) Cornerstone Family Ministries/Lamplighter Publishing.

—Highland Chairman. 2004. 12.00 (978-1-58474-037-7(X)) Cornerstone Family Ministries/Lamplighter Publishing.

—Inheritance. 2004. 15.00 (978-1-58474-009-4(4)) Cornerstone Family Ministries/Lamplighter Publishing.

—Me & Nobbles. 2004. 17.00 (978-1-58474-102-2(3)) Cornerstone Family Ministries/Lamplighter Publishing.

—Melody the Story of a Child. 2004. 16.00 (978-1-58474-016-2(7)) Cornerstone Family Ministries/Lamplighter Publishing.

—Nobody Loves Me. 2004. 15.00 (978-1-58474-035-3(3)) Cornerstone Family Ministries/Lamplighter Publishing.

—Probable Sons. 2004. 15.00 (978-1-58474-033-9(7)) Cornerstone Family Ministries/Lamplighter Publishing.

Lanchais, Aurelie, et al. I Have Wheels, What Am I? (Illus.). (ps-1). 2005. (RUS, ENG, TUR, VIE & CHI.). 14p. pap. 9.95 (978-1-84059-239-9(7)); 2000. (GUJ, ENG, VIE, CHI & RUS., 16p. (J). pap. 9.95 (978-1-84059-238-2(9)); 2000. (FRE, ENG, VIE, GUJ & CHI., 16p. (J). pap. 9.95 (978-1-84059-237-5(0)) Milet Publishing.

—I Have Wheels, What Am I? Erdogan, Faith, tr. 2000. (Who Am I? What Am I? Ser.). (TUR, ENG, RUS, VIE & CHI., Illus.). 16p. (J). (ps-1). pap. 9.95 (978-1-84059-240-5(0)) Milet Publishing.

—What Am I? (Illus.). (ps-1). 2005. (ARA, ENG, URD, TUR & CHI.). 14p. 9.95 (978-1-84059-243-6(5)); 2005. (URD, ENG, CHI, ARA & BEN., 14p. 9.95 (978-1-84059-248-1(6)); 2000. (BEN, ENG, URD, CHI & ARA., 16p. (J). pap. 9.95 (978-1-84059-244-3(3)); 2000. (CHI, ENG, URD, TUR & ARA., 16p. (J). pap. 9.95 (978-1-84059-245-0(1)); 2000. (FRE, ENG, URD, CHI & ARA., 16p. (J). pap. 9.95 (978-1-84059-246-7(X)); 2000. (TUR, ENG, URD, CHI & ARA., 16p. (J). pap. 9.95 (978-1-84059-247-4(8)) Milet Publishing.

—Who Am I? (Illus.). (ps-1). 2005. (CHI, ENG, VIE, GUJ & RUS.). 14p. pap. 9.95 (978-1-84059-229-0(X)); 2005. (RUS, ENG, TUR, VIE & CHI., 14p. pap. 9.95 (978-1-84059-232-0(X)); 2000. (FRE, ENG, VIE, GUJ & CHI., 16p. (J). pap. 9.95 (978-1-84059-230-6(3)); 2000. (GUJ, ENG, VIE, CHI & RUS., 16p. (J). pap. 9.95 (978-1-84059-231-3(1)) Milet Publishing.

Lang, Audrey Clifford. Spanish & English Comments for Report Cards & Notes Home. 2004. (ENG & SPA.). 80p. (J). per. 11.99 (978-0-88724-271-7(5) , CD-0868) Carson-Dellosa Publishing Co., Inc.

Lang, Greg. Socks Off! 1999. (gr. k-3). lib. bdg. 11.80 (978-0-613-19458-7(6)) Tandem Library Bks.

—Too Busy. 1999. (ps-2). lib. bdg. 11.55 (978-0-613-30797-0(6)) Tandem Library Bks.

—What's That Noise? 1999. (ps-2). lib. bdg. 11.80 (978-0-613-30868-7(9)) Tandem Library Bks.

Langford, Jane. Hero. Vince, Dawn, illus. 2005. 24p. (J). lib. bdg. 22.65 (***978-1-59646-720-0(7)***) Dingles & Co.

—An Old Red Hat. Axworthy, Anni, illus. 2004. 24p. (J). lib. bdg. 22.65 (***978-1-59646-676-0(6)***) Dingles & Co.

Larousse Mexico Staff, ed. Leer Preescolar Nivel A. 2005. (Yo quiero Saber Ser.). (SPA.). 32p. (ps-k). pap. 3.95 (978-970-22-0911-9(0)) Larousse, Ediciones, S. A. de C. V. MEX. *Dist:* Houghton Mifflin Co. Trade & Reference Div.

—Leer Preescolar Nivel B. 2005. (Yo quiero Saber Ser.). (SPA.). 32p. (ps-k). pap. 3.95 (978-970-22-0914-0(5)) Larousse, Ediciones, S. A. de C. V. MEX. *Dist:* Houghton Mifflin Co. Trade & Reference Div.

—Leer Preescolar Nivel C. 2005. (Yo quiero Saber Ser.). (SPA.). 32p. (ps-k). pap. 3.95 (978-970-22-0917-1(X)) Larousse, Ediciones, S. A. de C. V. MEX. *Dist:* Houghton Mifflin Co. Trade & Reference Div.

The Last Stop. 2001. (YA). (gr. 6-12). pap. incl. audio (978-0-8224-3298-2(6)) Globe Fearon Educational Publishing.

Lavelle, Sheila. Clever Dog, Webster. 2005. (978-1-901358-00-1(3)) CAMFA.

Layton, Meredith. Baby's First Words: A Sign & Say Interactive Language Book. Anderson, Brad & Goodwin, Sharon, illus. David Nester Photography Staff, photos by. 1999. (Sign & Say Interactive Language Ser.). 32p. (J). 16.95 (978-0-9670821-0-3(2)) Peek-A-Boo Publishing.

Leading the Way: Individual Title Six-Packs. (Rigby Infoquest Ser.). 24p. (gr. 3 up). 34.00 (978-0-7578-5770-6(1)) Rigby Education.

Leafcutter Ants: Individual Title Six-Packs. (Sails Literacy Ser.). (gr. 1-2). 36.00 (978-0-7578-4026-5(4)) Rigby Education.

Leaney, Cindy. The Circus. Whitehouse, Patty, ed. King, Sue & Wilks, Peter, illus. 2004. (Friendly Phonics Ser.). 24p. (J). lib. bdg. 14.95 (978-1-59054-114-2(6)) Fitzgerald Bks.

—The Giant's Garden. Whitehouse, Patty, ed. King, Sue & Wilks, Peter, illus. 2004. (Friendly Phonics Ser.). 24p. (J). lib. bdg. 14.95 (978-1-59054-181-4(2)) Fitzgerald Bks.

—Nice News. Whitehouse, Patty, ed. King, Sue & Wilks, Peter, illus. 2004. (Friendly Phonics Ser.). 24p. (J). lib. bdg. 14.95 (978-1-59054-205-7(3)) Fitzgerald Bks.

—Note in a Bottle. Whitehouse, Patty, ed. King, Sue & Wilks, Peter, illus. 2004. (Friendly Phonics Ser.). 24p. (J). lib. bdg. 14.95 (978-1-59054-107-4(3)) Fitzgerald Bks.

—On the Beach. Whitehouse, Patty, ed. King, Sue & Wilks, Peter, illus. 2004. (Friendly Phonics Ser.). 24p. (J). lib. bdg. 14.95 (978-1-59054-108-1(1)) Fitzgerald Bks.

—Oodles of Noodles. Whitehouse, Patty, ed. King, Sue & Wilks, Peter, illus. 2004. (Friendly Phonics Ser.). 24p. (J). lib. bdg. 14.95 (978-1-59054-030-5(1)) Fitzgerald Bks.

—Picnic in the Park. Whitehouse, Patty, ed. King, Sue & Wilks, Peter, illus. 2004. (Friendly Phonics Ser.). 24p. (J). lib. bdg. 14.95 (978-1-59054-217-0(7)) Fitzgerald Bks.

—Rachel the Shy Jellyfish. Whitehouse, Patty, ed. King, Sue & Wilks, Peter, illus. 2004. (Friendly Phonics Ser.). 24p. (J). lib. bdg. 14.95 (978-1-59054-274-3(6)) Fitzgerald Bks.

—Rainy Day Play. Whitehouse, Patty, ed. King, Sue & Wilks, Peter, illus. 2004. (Friendly Phonics Ser.). 24p. (J). lib. bdg. 14.95 (978-1-59054-047-3(6)) Fitzgerald Bks.

—Rescue & Repair. Whitehouse, Patty, ed. King, Sue & Wilks, Peter, illus. 2004. (Friendly Phonics Ser.). 24p. (J). lib. bdg. 14.95 (978-1-59054-225-5(8)) Fitzgerald Bks.

—Station K. I. D. S. Whitehouse, Patty, ed. King, Sue & Wilks, Peter, illus. 2004. (Friendly Phonics Ser.). 24p. (J). lib. bdg. 14.95 (978-1-59054-186-9(3)) Fitzgerald Bks.

—Super Sale. Whitehouse, Patty, ed. King, Sue & Wilks, Peter, illus. 2004. (Friendly Phonics Ser.). 24p. (J). lib. bdg. 14.95 (978-1-59054-231-6(2)) Fitzgerald Bks.

Leap Frog First Grade Reading & Writing Workbook. 2006. (J). spiral bd. 3.95 (***978-1-59545-085-2(8)***) Learning Horizons, Inc.

Leap Frog Kindergarten Reading & Writing Workbook. 2006. (J). spiral bd. 3.95 (***978-1-59545-084-5(X)***) Learning Horizons, Inc.

Leap Frog Pre-K Reading & Writing Workbook. 2006. (J). spiral bd. 3.95 (***978-1-59545-083-8(1)***) Learning Horizons, Inc.

LeapFrog It's a Blast Bindup. 2007. (J). spiral bd. 8.95 (***978-1-59545-168-2(4)***) Learning Horizons, Inc.

LeapFrog Staff, compiled by. Around the Block. 2001. (J). (ps-2). spiral bd. 11.95 (978-1-58605-066-5(4)) LeapFrog Enterprises, Inc.

—At the Lake in June. 2001. (J). (ps-2). spiral bd. 13.95 (978-1-58605-053-5(2)) LeapFrog Enterprises, Inc.

—The Fix-It Kid. 2001. (J). (ps-2). spiral bd. 10.95 (978-1-58605-019-1(2)) LeapFrog Enterprises, Inc.

—Tad Around Town. 2002. (YA). (ps up). lib. bdg. 9.99 (978-1-58605-794-7(4)) LeapFrog Enterprises, Inc.

LeapFrog Staff, compiled by & des. Quantum Pad Smapler - Included Book. LeapFrog Staff, des. 2002. (J). spiral bd. 14.99 (978-1-58605-792-3(8)) LeapFrog Enterprises, Inc.

—Reading Games. LeapFrog Staff, des. 2002. (J). lib. bdg. 9.99 (978-1-58605-796-1(0)) LeapFrog Enterprises, Inc.

A Learn about the Past Set, 6 vols. (Phonics Readers Ser.). (gr. k-2). 17.50 (978-0-7368-3189-5(4)) Red Brick Learning.

Learn to Read, Vol. 2. 2006. (J). per. 10.00 (978-0-9774302-1-5(9)) Braun Pubns.

Learning Through Literature. 2004. 128p. (J). per. 128.00 (978-0-88724-259-5(6) , CD-0583) Carson-Dellosa Publishing Co., Inc.

Learning with Mother Goose PK-K. 2004. 64p. (J). pap. 7.99 (978-0-88724-245-8(6) , CD-0219) Carson-Dellosa Publishing Co., Inc.

Learning Wrap-Ups: The Grasshopper & the Ants, The Turtle & the Rabbit. 2006. 66p. (J). 12.99 (978-1-59204-203-6(1)) Learning Wrap-Ups.

Learning Wrap-Ups: The Sky Is Falling, The City Mouse & The Country Mouse. 2006. 66p. (J). 12.99 (978-1-59204-202-9(3)) Learning Wrap-Ups.

Leaves, 6 vols. (gr. k-2). 28.95 (978-0-7368-8001-5(1)) Red Brick Learning.

Leaving Home: Individual Title Six-Packs. (Rigby Infoquest Ser.). 32p. (gr. 4 up). 37.00 (978-0-7578-5733-1(7)) Rigby Education.

Leber, Nancy Jolson. (K) on the Road to Reading. 2007. (Clear & Simple Ser.). 64p. (J). pap. 4.99 (978-0-448-44435-2(6) , Grosset & Dunlap) Penguin Group (USA) Inc.

—(1) Read with Me. 2007. (Clear & Simple Ser.). 64p. (J). pap. 4.99 (978-0-448-44436-9(4) , Grosset & Dunlap) Penguin Group (USA) Inc.

Lee, Betsy B. A Funny Dolch Word Book # 1: Un Libro Comico # 1 de la Palabra de Dolch. Davis, Pollyanna S., tr. 2006. (ENG & SPA.). pap. 5.95 (978-0-9720267-5-8(4)) Learning Abilities Bks.

Lee, Frances. Worm Rap. 1999. (gr. k-3). lib. bdg. 11.80 (978-0-613-19502-7(7)) Tandem Library Bks.

Lee, Quinlan B. Let's Explore!, Bks. 1-6. 2007. (Dora the Explorer Ser.: Bks. 1-6). 112p. (J). pap. 5.99 (978-0-439-90237-3(1)) Scholastic, Inc.

—On the Go! 2007. (Dora the Explorer Ser.: Bks. 7-12). 112p. (J). pap. 5.99 (978-0-439-90238-0(X)) Scholastic, Inc.

Lee, Quinlan B. Phonics: 12 Book Reading Program, 12 vols. 2006. (Illus.). (***978-0-439-78938-7(9)***); (***978-0-439-78939-4(7)***); (***978-0-439-78940-0(0)***); (***978-0-439-78941-7(9)***); (***978-0-439-78942-4(7)***); (***978-0-439-78943-1(5)***); (***978-0-439-78944-8(3)***); (***978-0-439-78945-5(1)***); (***978-0-439-78946-2(X)***); (***978-0-439-78947-9(8)***); (***978-0-439-78948-6(6)***); (***978-0-439-78949-3(4)***) Scholastic, Inc.

LeFleur, David, illus. Hide & Seek in the Jungle. 2007. 19p. (J). (ps-k). 16.99 (***978-1-58476-623-0(9)*** , IKIDS) Innovative Kids.

The Legend of the Bluebonnet: Fourth Grade Guided Comprehension Level L. (On Our Way to English Ser.). (gr. 4 up). 34.50 (978-0-7578-7151-1(8)) Rigby Education.

Leipe, Ulla. Lo Que los Ninos Quieren Saber. Limmer, Hannes, illus. (SPA.). 180p. (YA). 11.95 (978-84-241-5501-8(7) , EV867) Everest de Ediciones y Distribucion, S.L. ESP. *Dist:* Continental Bk. Co., Inc.

Lemonade for Gilbert. 2004. (J). (978-1-58453-222-4(X)) Pioneer Valley Educational Pr., Inc.

Lemonade on the Double: Second Grade Guided Reading Level G. (On Our Way to English Ser.). (gr. 2 up). 34.50 (978-0-7578-7077-4(5)) Rigby Education.

The Lemonade Stand: Individual Title Six-Packs. (ps-2). 27.00 (978-0-7635-9457-2(1)) Rigby Education.

The Lemonade Stand: Third Grade Newcomer Books. (On Our Way to English Ser.). (gr. 3 up). 29.50 (978-0-7578-7254-9(9)) Rigby Education.

Lend a Hand. (Early Intervention Levels Ser.). 28.38 (978-0-7362-0413-2(X)) Hampton-Brown Bks.

Lend a Hand (18), Vol. 18. (Early Intervention Levels Ser.). 4.73 (978-0-7362-0238-1(2)) Hampton-Brown Bks.

Lesespiele. (Duden-Schuelerhilfen Ser.). (GER.). 96p. (J). (gr. 3-4). (978-3-411-02607-4(3)) Bibliographisches Institut & F. A. Brockhaus AG DEU. *Dist:* International Bk. Import Service, Inc.

Let's Celebrate. (Early Intervention Levels Ser.). 23.10 (978-0-7362-0024-0(X)) Hampton-Brown Bks.

Let's Eat. 2005. (Little Celebrations Thematic Packages Ser.). (J). (gr. k-3). 133.50 (978-0-673-75379-3(4)) Celebration Pr.

Let's Go! Kindergarten Newcomer Books. (On Our Way to English Ser.). (gr. k up). 23.50 (978-0-7578-7190-0(9)) Rigby Education.

Let's Go Shopping! (Early Intervention Levels Ser.). 23.10 (978-0-7362-0027-1(4)); Vol. 4. 3.85 (978-1-56334-975-1(2)) Hampton-Brown Bks.

Let's Hear It for Ears! (Early Intervention Levels Ser.). 5.31 (978-0-7362-1915-0(3)); 31.86 (978-0-7362-2134-4(4)) Hampton-Brown Bks.

Let's Paint!, Vol. 4. (Early Intervention Levels Ser.). 3.85 (978-1-56334-962-1(0)) Hampton-Brown Bks.

Letter Books Add-on Set. (gr. k-2). 75.95 (978-0-7368-4128-3(8)) Red Brick Learning.

Letter Clusters Big Book, 6 vols. 32p. (gr. k-3). 38.50 (978-0-7802-7194-4(7)) Wright Group, The.

The Letter Ee: Things That Are Alike, 6 vols. (gr. k-2). 17.50 (978-0-7368-4104-7(0)) Red Brick Learning.

The Letter Hh: Homes, 6 vols. (gr. k-2). 17.50 (978-0-7368-4107-8(5)) Red Brick Learning.

The Letter Ll: A Trip to the Repair Shop, 6 vols. (gr. k-2). 17.50 (978-0-7368-4111-5(3)) Red Brick Learning.

The Letter Nn: At the Grocery Store, 6 vols. (gr. k-2). 17.50 (978-0-7368-4113-9(X)) Red Brick Learning.

The Letter Xx: Things I Can See, 6 vols. (gr. k-2). 17.50 (978-0-7368-4123-8(7)) Red Brick Learning.

The Letter Yy: All about Me!, 6 vols. (gr. k-2). 17.50 (978-0-7368-4124-5(5)) Red Brick Learning.

Level 1 Reading & Writing Journal - Block Print: Wk201b. 2007. (J). (***978-1-59577-045-5(3)***) Starfall Education.

Level 16 Pack: Set of 17 Titles. (Early Intervention Levels Ser.). 89.99 (978-0-7362-2554-0(4)) Hampton-Brown Bks.

Level 18 Pack: Set of 13 Titles. (Early Intervention Levels Ser.). 71.47 (978-0-7362-2555-7(2)) Hampton-Brown Bks.

Level 2 Book Collection 800920, 6 vols. 2005. (J). (978-1-59794-085-6(2)) Environments, Inc.

Level 2 Pack: Set of 16 Titles. (Dra Levels Ser.). 60.09 (978-0-7362-2566-3(8)) Hampton-Brown Bks.

Level 2 Paperback Book Collection 800921, 6 vols. 2005. (J). pap. (978-1-59794-086-3(0)) Environments, Inc.

Level 3 Books & Tapes Book Set 800927, 6 vols. 2005. (J). pap. (978-1-59794-092-4(5)) Environments, Inc.

Level 3 Pack: Set of 14 Titles. (Dra Levels Ser.). 58.15 (978-0-7362-2567-0(6)) Hampton-Brown Bks.

Level 3 Pack: Set of 18 Titles. (Early Intervention Levels Ser.). 66.90 (978-0-7362-2548-9(X)) Hampton-Brown Bks.

Level 3 Paperback Books Set 800928, 6 vols. 2005. (J). pap. (978-1-59794-093-1(3)) Environments, Inc.

Level 4 Pack: Set of 24 Titles. (Dra Levels Ser.). 89.72 (978-0-7362-2568-7(4)) Hampton-Brown Bks.

Level 5 Pack: Set of 19 Titles. (Early Intervention Levels Ser.). 70.45 (978-0-7362-2549-6(8)) Hampton-Brown Bks.

Level 6 Pack: Set of 11 Titles. (Early Intervention Levels Ser.). 49.29 (978-0-7362-2550-2(1)) Hampton-Brown Bks.

Level 6 Pack: Set of 14 Titles. (Dra Levels Ser.). 51.52 (978-0-7362-2569-4(2)) Hampton-Brown Bks.

Level a Big Book Program. (Phonics & Friends Ser.). (ps-2). 651.23 (978-0-7362-0355-5(9)) Hampton-Brown Bks.

Level A-C Ell Program Lap Book. 2003. (Metro Reading Ser.). (J). (gr. 12). spiral bd. 116.55 (978-1-58120-617-3(8)) Metropolitan Teaching & Learning Co.

Level A-C Ell Program Practice Picture Cards Blms. 2003. (Metro Reading Ser.). (gr. 12). 41.29 (978-1-58120-618-0(6)) Metropolitan Teaching & Learning Co.

Level a Complete Set. (Compass Point Early Readers Ser.). (gr. k-2). 130.20 (978-0-7565-0556-1(9)) Compass Point Bks.

Level A Super Classroom Set. (Into English! Ser.). (gr. k-6). 625.88 (978-1-56334-806-8(3)) Hampton-Brown Bks.

Level B Complete Set. (Compass Point Early Readers Ser.). (gr. k-2). 111.60 (978-0-7565-0557-8(7)) Compass Point Bks.

Level B Pack: Set of 26 Titles. (Guided Reading Levels Ser.). 104.04 (978-0-7362-2558-8(7)) Hampton-Brown Bks.

Level C. (Illus.). 176p. Vol. 4. 2005. pap. 9.99 (978-1-58655-726-3(2) , KGNOV-0539); Vol. 6. 2006. pap. 9.99 (978-1-58655-818-5(8) , KGNOV-0627) Media Blasters, Inc. (Kitty Media).

Level C Complete Set. (Compass Point Early Readers Ser.). (gr. k-2). 93.00 (978-0-7565-0558-5(5)) Compass Point Bks.

Level D Pack: Set of 21 Titles. (Guided Reading Levels Ser.). 101.29 (978-0-7362-2560-1(9)) Hampton-Brown Bks.

Level D Super Classroom Set. (Into English! Ser.). (gr. 3 up). 626.27 (978-1-56334-849-5(7)) Hampton-Brown Bks.

Level E Classroom Set. (Phonics & Friends Ser.). (ps-2). 682.59 (978-0-7362-0601-3(9)) Hampton-Brown Bks.

Level E Let's Read Little Book Set. (Phonics & Friends Ser.). (ps-2). 14.76 (978-0-7362-1068-3(7)) Hampton-Brown Bks.

Level F, 5 vols, Set. 296.29 (978-0-7565-0539-4(9)) Compass Point Bks.

Level F Classroom Set. (Phonics & Friends Ser.). (ps-2). 682.59 (978-0-7362-0644-0(2)) Hampton-Brown Bks.

Level F Let's Read Little Book Set. (Phonics & Friends Ser.). (ps-2). 14.76 (978-0-7362-1069-0(5)) Hampton-Brown Bks.

Level F Super Classroom Set. (Into English! Ser.). (gr. 5 up). 626.27 (978-1-56334-881-5(0)) Hampton-Brown Bks.

Level G-Set Of 21. 414.54 (978-0-7565-0540-0(2)) Compass Point Bks.

Level H-Set Of 15. 298.95 (978-0-7565-0786-2(3)) Compass Point Bks.

Level I-Set Of 21. 418.53 (978-0-7565-0860-9(6)) Compass Point Bks.

Level K-Set Of 4. 79.72 (978-0-7565-0859-3(2)) Compass Point Bks.

Level L-Set Of 6. 126.23 (978-0-7565-0862-3(2)) Compass Point Bks.

Level M-Set Of 8. 162.10 (978-0-7565-0544-8(5)) Compass Point Bks.

Level N-Set Of 6. 127.56 (978-0-7565-0545-5(3)) Compass Point Bks.

Level O-Set Of 7. 148.82 (978-0-7565-0863-0(0)) Compass Point Bks.

Level Q, 10 vols, Set. 226.00 (978-0-7565-0547-9(X)) Compass Point Bks.

Level S, 6 vols, Set. 135.60 (978-0-7565-0548-6(8)) Compass Point Bks.

Leveled Readers A: Easy, Bookshelf Collection, 36 bks., Set. 2004. (gr. 1 up). 495.00 (978-0-328-01865-9(1)); 2004. (gr. 2 up). 495.00 (978-0-328-00411-9(1)); 2004. (gr. 3 up). 495.00 (978-0-328-00412-6(X)); 2004. (gr. 4 up). 495.00 (978-0-328-00413-3(8)); 2004. (gr. 5 up). 495.00 (978-0-328-00414-0(6)); 2004. (gr. 6 up). 495.00 (978-0-328-00415-7(4)); 2000. (SPA.). (gr. 1 up). 557.40 (978-0-328-00416-4(2)); 2000. (SPA.). (gr. 2 up). 554.40 (978-0-328-00417-1(0)); 2000. (SPA.). (gr. 3 up). 554.40 (978-0-328-00418-8(9)); 2000. (SPA.). (gr. 4 up). 554.40 (978-0-328-00419-5(7)); 2000. (SPA.). (gr. 5 up). 554.40 (978-0-328-00420-1(0)) Addison-Wesley Educational Pubs., Inc.

Leveled Readers B: On-Level, Bookshelf Collection, 30 bks., Set. 2004. (gr. 1 up). 495.00 (978-0-328-00422-5(7)); 2004. (gr. 2 up). 495.00 (978-0-328-00423-2(5)); 2004. (gr. 3 up). 495.00 (978-0-328-00424-9(3)); 2004. (gr. 4 up). 495.00 (978-0-328-00425-6(1)); 2004. (gr. 5 up). 495.00 (978-0-328-00426-3(X)); 2004. (gr. 6 up). 495.00 (978-0-328-00427-0(8)); 2000. (SPA.). (gr. 1 up). 554.40 (978-0-328-00428-7(6)); 2000. (SPA.). (gr. 2 up). 554.40 (978-0-328-00429-4(4)); 2000. (SPA.). (gr. 3 up). 554.40 (978-0-328-00430-0(8)); 2000. (SPA.). (gr. 4 up). 554.40 (978-0-328-00431-7(6)); 2000. (SPA.). (gr. 5 up). 554.40 (978-0-328-00432-4(4)) Addison-Wesley Educational Pubs., Inc.

Leveled Readers C: Challenge, Bookshelf Collection, 5 units. 2004. (gr. 1 up). 82.50 (978-0-328-00434-8(0)); Set. 2004. (gr. 2 up). 99.00 (978-0-328-00435-5(9)); Set. 2004. (gr. 3 up). 99.00 (978-0-328-00436-2(7)); Set. 2004. (gr. 4 up). 99.00 (978-0-328-00437-9(5) , Scott Foresman); Set. 2004. (gr. 5 up). 99.00 (978-0-328-00438-6(3)); Set. 2004. (gr. 6 up). 99.00 (978-0-328-00439-3(1)); Set. 2000. (SPA.). (gr. 1 up). 97.50 (978-0-328-00440-9(5)); Set. 2000. (SPA.). (gr. 2 up). 110.88 (978-0-328-00441-6(3)); Set. 2000. (SPA.). (gr. 3 up). 110.88 (978-0-328-00442-3(1)); Set. 2000. (SPA.). (gr. 4 up). 110.88 (978-0-328-00443-0(X)); Set. 2000. (SPA.). (gr. 5 up). 110.88 (978-0-328-00444-7(8)) Addison-Wesley Educational Pubs., Inc.

Levels 10-12 Pack: Set of 9 Titles. (Early Intervention Levels Ser.). 46.43 (978-0-7362-2552-6(8)) Hampton-Brown Bks.

Levels 12-14 Pack: Set of 10 Titles. (Dra Levels Ser.). 85.63 (978-0-7362-2571-7(4)) Hampton-Brown Bks.

Levels 13-15 Pack: Set of 10 Titles. (Early Intervention Levels Ser.). 49.89 (978-0-7362-2553-3(6)) Hampton-Brown Bks.

Levels 16-18 Pack: Set of 22 Titles. (Dra Levels Ser.). 115.82 (978-0-7362-2572-4(2)) Hampton-Brown Bks.

Levels 20-24 Pack: Set of 12 Titles. (Dra Levels Ser.). 63.31 (978-0-7362-2573-1(0)) Hampton-Brown Bks.

Levels 20-24 Pack: Set of 16 Titles. (Early Intervention Levels Ser.). 86.72 (978-0-7362-2556-4(0)) Hampton-Brown Bks.

Levels 28-30 Pack: Set of 18 Titles. (Dra Levels Ser.). 114.42 (978-0-7362-2574-8(9)) Hampton-Brown Bks.

Levels 38-40 Pack: Set of 14 Titles. (Dra Levels Ser.). 88.02 (978-0-7362-2575-5(7)) Hampton-Brown Bks.

Levels 7-8 Pack: Set of 6 Titles. (Early Intervention Levels Ser.). 32.16 (978-0-7362-2551-9(X)) Hampton-Brown Bks.

Levels 8-10 Pack: Set of 15 Titles. (Dra Levels Ser.). 85.63 (978-0-7362-2570-0(6)) Hampton-Brown Bks.

Levels E-F Pack: Set of 20 Titles. (Guided Reading Levels Ser.). 97.02 (978-0-7362-2561-8(7)) Hampton-Brown Bks.

Levels E-F Super Classroom Set. (Phonics & Friends Ser.). (ps-2). 1204.58 (978-0-7362-0596-2(9)) Hampton-Brown Bks.

Levels G-J Pack: Set of 24 Titles. (Guided Reading Levels Ser.). 118.32 (978-0-7362-2562-5(5)) Hampton-Brown Bks.

Levels K-M Pack: Set of 30 Titles. (Guided Reading Levels Ser.). 172.30 (978-0-7362-2563-2(3)) Hampton-Brown Bks.

Levels N-Q Pack: Set of 17 Titles. (Guided Reading Levels Ser.). 106.73 (978-0-7362-2564-9(1)) Hampton-Brown Bks.

Levithan, David. The Mummy, Level 2. 2001. 48p. (C). pap. 9.00 (978-0-582-45193-3(0)) Longman Publishing Group.

Levy, Emily, rev. Strategies for Study Success: Highlighting I. 2004. 12.00 (978-0-9772110-0-5(2)) EBL Coaching.

Lewis, Starin. Reading First Basics - Fluency. Gunzenhauser, Kelly, ed. 2005. 80p. (J). per. 10.99 (978-1-59441-046-8(1) , CD-104016) Carson-Dellosa Publishing Co., Inc.

The Library Set D, 6 vols. (Phonics Readers Ser.). (gr. k-2). 28.95 (978-0-7368-4056-9(7)) Red Brick Learning.

Life Cycles Book Set 800741, 4. 2005. (J). pap. (978-1-59794-039-9(9)) Environments, Inc.

Light. 2000. (Designer Shufa Ser.). 160p. (J). (978-1-55156-167-7(0)); (978-1-55156-185-1(9)) Hartley & Marks Publishers, Inc.

The Light Bulb, 6 vols. (gr. 2-5). 36.95 (978-0-7368-4615-8(8)) Red Brick Learning.

Light, John. Neighbours Are a Nuisance! 2005. (Illus.). 24p. (978-1-897968-22-2(1)) Photon Pr.

Lindeen, Carol K. The Sky at Night Set D, 6 vols. (Phonics Readers Ser.). (gr. k-2). 28.95 (978-0-7368-4062-0(1)) Red Brick Learning.

Lindeen, Mary. The Letter Aa: Things at School, 6 vols. (gr. k-2). 17.50 (978-0-7368-4100-9(8)) Red Brick Learning.

Lindi, Nkululeko. Three Fat Cats. Rankin, Joan, illus. 1999. (Cambridge Reading Ser.). 10p. pap., pap. 19.00 (978-0-521-66705-0(4)) Cambridge Univ. Pr.

Lindsay, Elizabeth, ed. Learning Library-Reading, Spelling & Grammar. 2003. 128p. 19.95 (978-1-56234-532-7(X) , Mailbox Bks., The) Education Ctr., Inc.

Lindsay, Kristine. Basic Reading Series - Binder 3. 2004. (J). ring bd. 49.95 (978-1-58804-371-9(1)) PCI Educational Publishing.

LinkIt Reading Sudent Resource Book, Level 3. 2006. per. (***978-0-9786500-1-8(8)***) Creative Curriculum Initiatives.

Linn, Margot. The Big Red Blanket. Jacobson, David, illus. 2005. (I'm Going to Read Ser.: Level 1). 28p. (J). pap. 3.95 (978-1-4027-2091-8(2)) Sterling Publishing Co., Inc.

—Can You Play?, Bolam, Emily, illus. 2005. (I'm Going to Read Ser.: Level 1). 28p. (J). pap. 3.95 (978-1-4027-2094-9(7)) Sterling Publishing Co., Inc.

—Can You Play? Level 1. Bolam, Emily, illus. 2005. (I'm Going to Read Ser.). 28p. (J). 11.95 (978-1-4027-2072-7(6)) Sterling Publishing Co., Inc.

—A Class Play with Ms. Vanilla. Gradisher, Martha, illus. 2005. (I'm Going to Read Ser.: Level 3). 32p. (J). pap. 3.95 (978-1-4027-2108-3(0)) Sterling Publishing Co., Inc.

—A Class Play with Ms. Vanilla Level 3. Gradisher, Martha, illus. 2005. (I'm Going to Read Ser.). 32p. (J). 11.95 (978-1-4027-2087-1(4)) Sterling Publishing Co., Inc.

—Fish Wish, Kreloff, Elliot, illus. 2005. (I'm Going to Read Ser.). 28p. (J). pap. 3.95 (978-1-4027-2095-6(5)) Sterling Publishing Co., Inc.

—Go Away, Crows! Cohen, Santiago, illus. 2005. (I'm Going to Read Ser.). 32p. (J). 11.95 (978-1-4027-2080-2(7)); pap. 3.95 (978-1-4027-2103-8(X)) Sterling Publishing Co., Inc.

—Good Dog, Rover, Level 2. Hoffman, Sanford, illus. 2005. (I'm Going to Read Ser.). 32p. (J). pap. 3.95 (978-1-4027-2102-1(1)) Sterling Publishing Co., Inc.

—Good Dog, Rover Level 2. Hoffman, Sanford, illus. 2005. (I'm Going to Read Ser.). 32p. (J). 11.95 (978-1-4027-2079-6(3)) Sterling Publishing Co., Inc.

—Good Luck, Bad Luck. Brown, Richard, illus. 2005. (I'm Going to Read Ser.). 32p. (J). 11.95 (978-1-4027-2088-8(2)); Level 3. pap. 3.95 (978-1-4027-2109-0(9)) Sterling Publishing Co., Inc.

—Harry's Bath. Chwast, Seymour, illus. 2005. (I'm Going to Read Ser.: Level 2). 32p. (J). pap. 3.95 (978-1-4027-2100-7(5)) Sterling Publishing Co., Inc.

—Harry's Bath: Level 2. Chwast, Seymour, illus. 2005. (I'm Going to Read Ser.; Level 2). 32p. (J). 11.95 (978-1-4027-2077-2(7)) Sterling Publishing Co., Inc.

—I Won't Go to Bed! Baruffi, Andrea, illus. 2005. (I'm Going to Read Ser.: Level 3). 32p. (J). pap. 3.95 (978-1-4027-2104-5(8)) Sterling Publishing Co., Inc.

—I'm Going to New York to Visit the Lions. Roitman, Tanya, illus. 2005. (I'm Going to Read Ser.). 32p. (J). 11.95 (978-1-4027-2076-5(9)); pap. 3.95 (978-1-4027-2099-4(8)) Sterling Publishing Co., Inc.

—Move Over! Rader, Laura, illus. 2005. (I'm Going to Read Ser.: Level 2). 28p. (J). 11.95 (978-1-4027-2075-8(0)); pap. 3.95 (978-1-4027-2098-7(X)) Sterling Publishing Co., Inc.

—Pizza & Other Stinky Poems. Haley, Amanda, illus. 2005. (I'm Going to Read Ser.). 32p. (J). 11.95 (978-1-4027-2084-0(X) , 1242403); pap. 3.95 (978-1-4027-2110-6(2)) Sterling Publishing Co., Inc.

—The Prince Has a Boo-Boo! Level 1. Alley, R. W., illus. 2005. (I'm Going to Read Ser.). 28p. (J). pap. 3.95 (978-1-4027-2089-5(0)) Sterling Publishing Co., Inc.

—The Prince Has a Boo-Boo! Level 1. Alley, R. W., illus. 2005. (I'm Going to Read Ser.). 28p. (J). 11.95 (978-1-4027-2067-3(X)) Sterling Publishing Co., Inc.

—Silly Pig. Rader, Laura, illus. 2005. (I'm Going to Read Ser.). 32p. (J). pap. 3.95 (978-1-4027-2097-0(1)); 11.95 (978-1-4027-2074-1(2)) Sterling Publishing Co., Inc.

—Sometimes I Share, Level 1. Nicklaus, Carol, illus. 2005. (I'm Going to Read Ser.). 28p. (J). pap. 3.95 (978-1-4027-2090-1(4)) Sterling Publishing Co., Inc.

—Take My Picture. Hoffman, Sanford, illus. 2005. (I'm Going to Read Ser.: Level 2). 28p. (J). 11.95 (978-1-4027-2073-4(4)); pap. 3.95 (978-1-4027-2096-3(3)) Sterling Publishing Co., Inc.

—When Daddy Had the Chicken Pox, Level 3. Kalish, Lionel, illus. 2005. (I'm Going to Read Ser.). 32p. (J). pap. 3.95 (978-1-4027-2105-2(6)) Sterling Publishing Co., Inc.

—When Daddy Had the Chicken Pox Level 3. Kalish, Lionel, illus. 2005. (I'm Going to Read Ser.). 32p. (J). 11.95 (978-1-4027-2083-3(1)) Sterling Publishing Co., Inc.

—Who Spilled the Milk? Gradisher, Martha, illus. 2005. (I'm Going to Read Ser.: Level 1). 28p. (J). 11.95 (978-1-4027-2070-3(X)); Level 1. pap. 3.95 (978-1-4027-2092-5(0)) Sterling Publishing Co., Inc.

Lion King: Simba's Hide & Seek. (My First Read Along Ser.). (J). 7.99 incl. audio (978-1-55723-747-7(6)) Walt Disney Records.

Lippman, Peter. The Ice-Cream Truck. 2006. (Illus.). 20p. (J). bds. 9.95 (978-0-7611-4033-7(6)) Workman Publishing Co., Inc.

Lipson, Greta Barclay. Two Sides to Every Story. Hierstein, Judith, illus. 2004. 128p. (J). pap. 14.95 (978-1-57310-439-5(6)) Teaching & Learning Co.

Litchfield, Jo. First Words Look & Say. Litchfield, Jo, illus. 2005. 18p. (J). 14.99 (978-0-7945-1024-4(8) , Usborne) EDC Publishing.

Literature Guide for the Middle School Classroom. 2006. 48p. (YA). (gr. 6-8). 8.99 (978-1-4206-3078-7(4)) Teacher Created Resources, Inc.

Literature Library Package, 7 bks., Set. 1999. (Literature Libraries Ser.). (SPA.). (gr. 1 up). 74.75 (978-0-201-37242-7(8)) Addison-Wesley Educational Pubs., Inc.

Little Animals Board Books Set 800975, 6. 2005. (J). bds. (978-1-59794-100-6(X)) Environments, Inc.

Little Bear Book Set 2 800890, 6 vols. 2005. (J). pap. (978-1-59794-065-8(8)) Environments, Inc.

Little Bear Book Set 800876, 3 vols. 2005. (J). bds. (978-1-59794-054-2(2)) Environments, Inc.

Little Bear Book Set 800891, 3 vols. 2005. (J). pap. (978-1-59794-066-5(6)) Environments, Inc.

Little Books Collection: Includes 30 Little Books. 2003. 127.95 (978-0-7652-0129-4(1)) Modern Curriculum Pr.

Little, Jean. Forward, Shakespeare! 2005. (Orca Young Readers Ser.). (Illus.). 144p. (J). (gr. 3-6). pap. 5.95 (978-1-55143-339-4(7)) Orca Bk. Pubs. USA.

A Little Seed: Set A Individual Title Six-Packs. (Smart Start Ser.). (gr. k-1). 23.00 (978-0-7635-0411-3(4)) Rigby Education.

Littlefield, Angie & Littlefield, Jennifer. The 10 Grossest Bugs. 2008. (Tentrade; Ser.). 48p. (J). pap. 14.99 (***978-1-55448-462-1(6)*** , Watts, Franklin) Scholastic Library Publishing.

Live Oak Media PB/CD Readalong Collection. pap. 758.00 incl. audio compact disk (978-1-59519-235-6(2)); Vol. 3. pap. 728.00 incl. audio compact disk (978-1-59519-239-4(5)) Live Oak Media.

Live Oak Media Readalong Collection Set. 2004. cd-rom 84.00 (978-0-87499-712-5(7)); cd-rom 84.00 (978-0-87499-713-2(5)); Vol. 2. pap. 610.00 incl. audio (978-1-59519-004-8(X)) Live Oak Media.

Living in Two Worlds: Individual Title Six-Packs. (Rigby Infoquest Ser.). 24p. (gr. 3 up). 34.00 (978-0-7578-5771-3(X)) Rigby Education.

Living Things: Fourth Grade Newcomer Books. (On Our Way to English Ser.). (gr. 4 up). 34.50 (978-0-7578-7264-8(6)) Rigby Education.

Llewellyn, Claire. Asi Nace una Rana. Mendez, Simon, illus. (Coleccion Asi Nace... Ser.). (SPA.). 24p. (J). (gr. k-6). pap. 8.95 (978-1-59437-789-1(8)) Santillana USA Publishing Co., Inc.

—Así Naceun arbol. Mendez, Simon, illus. (SPA.). 24p. (J). (gr. k-6). pap. 8.95 (978-1-59437-449-4(X)) Santillana USA Publishing Co., Inc.

—Así naceun Pato. Mendez, Simon, illus. (SPA.). 24p. (J). (gr. k-6). pap. 8.95 (978-1-59437-448-7(1)) Santillana USA Publishing Co., Inc.

—Going for a Ride, 6, Pack. 2000. (Cambridge Reading Ser.). 8p. pap. 28.00 (978-0-521-78759-8(9)) Cambridge Univ. Pr.

—Going for a Ride Pack: American English Edition, 6. 2000. (Cambridge Reading Ser.). (Illus.). 8p. pap. 28.00 (978-0-521-79909-6(0)) Cambridge Univ. Pr.

—Going for a Ride American English Edition. 2000. (Cambridge Reading Ser.). (Illus.). pap. 5.00 (978-0-521-79908-9(2)) Cambridge Univ. Pr.

—An Owl at School: American English Edition, 6. 2000. (Cambridge Reading Ser.). (Illus.). 12p. pap. 28.00 (978-0-521-79907-2(4)); pap. 5.00 (978-0-521-79906-5(6)) Cambridge Univ. Pr.

—Shadow Play: American English Edition. 2000. (Cambridge Reading Ser.). (Illus.). 12p. pap. 5.00 (978-0-521-79902-7(3)) Cambridge Univ. Pr.

Llorente, Pilar Molina. Aura Gris. (SPA.). 80p. (YA). (gr. 5-8). 7.16 (978-84-216-1636-9(6)) Bruño, Editorial ESP. *Dist:* Lectorum Pubns., Inc.

Lloyd-Jones, Robin. Samurai. 2007. (Young Reading Series 3 Gift Bks). 64p. (J). 8.99 (***978-0-7945-1719-9(6)*** , Usborne) EDC Publishing.

—Story of Spying. 2007. (Young Reading Series 3 Gift Bks). 64p. (J). 8.99 (***978-0-7945-1720-5(X)*** , Usborne) EDC Publishing.

Lloyd, Sue & Wernham, Sara. Finger Phonics Big Books 1-7 (precursive Letters) Vol. 7: Set of 7 Big Books, 7 vols., Set. Stephen, Lib, illus. 2001. (Jolly Phonics Ser.: BIG BOOK SET 1-7). 16p. (J). 97.65 (978-1-870946-94-0(4) , JL944) Jolly Learning, Ltd. GBR. *Dist:* American International Distribution Corp.

—Jolly Phonics Word Book (Precursive Letters) 2001. (Jolly Phonics Ser.). (Illus.). 48p. (J). 3.50 (978-1-870946-79-7(0) , JL790) Jolly Learning, Ltd. GBR. *Dist:* American International Distribution Corp.

Loader, Mandy. The Great Discovery, Level 3. 2001. (Illus.). v, 41p. (C). pap. 9.00 (978-0-582-42730-3(4)) Longman Publishing Group.

Lock, Deborah & Dorling Kindersley Publishing Staff. A Trip to the Doctor. 2005. (Dk Readers Ser.). (Illus.). 32p. (J). 14.99 (978-0-7566-1136-1(9)); pap. 3.99 (978-0-7566-1137-8(7)) Dorling Kindersley Publishing, Inc.

Lockyer, John. Shosun's Mistake, 6 vols., Pack. Eunson, Vanessa, illus. (Sails Literacy Ser.). 20p. (gr. 4 up). 27.00 (978-0-7578-0789-3(5)) Rigby Education.

Lofting, Hugh. La Historia del Doctor Dolittle. (SPA.). 136p. 12.95 (978-84-239-9048-1(6)); (Illus.). 184p. (YA). (gr. 5-8). 11.95 (978-84-239-2733-3(4) , EC2743) Espasa Calpe, S.A. ESP. *Dist:* Planeta Publishing Corp., Continental Bk. Co., Inc., Lectorum Pubns., Inc.

Long Ago Children. (J). pap. 13.15 (978-0-8136-4296-3(5)) Modern Curriculum Pr.

The Long Trail Home: Fifth Grade Guided Comprehension Level T. (On Our Way to English Ser.). (gr. 5 up). 34.50 (978-0-7578-6629-6(8)) Rigby Education.

Longman Group Staff. Rapunzel. 2000. (Illus.). 32p. (J). pap. 6.67 (978-0-582-42871-3(8)) Longman Publishing Group.

The Look-Alike. 2001. (YA). (gr. 6-12). pap. incl. audio (978-0-8224-3289-0(7)) Globe Fearon Educational Publishing.

Look & Learn. (Illus.). (J). (ps-2). lib. bdg. 55.80 (978-1-56674-928-2(X)) Forest Hse. Publishing Co., Inc.

Look at Us: Second Grade Newcomer Books. (On Our Way to English Ser.). (gr. 2 up). 29.50 (978-0-7578-7211-2(5)) Rigby Education.

Look Out for Space Monster. 2003. (J). (978-1-932570-04-5(7)) Literacy Footprints Inc.

Look What I Found! Individual Title Six-Pack Pouch - Level B. (Lighthouse Ser.). 12p. (gr. k-1). 24.00 (978-0-7578-0817-3(4)) Rigby Education.

Looking at Lizards. 2005. (Book Treks Ser.). (J). (gr. 3 up). stu. ed. 34.95 (978-0-673-62835-0(3)) Celebration Pr.

Looking for Eggs: Individual Title Six-Packs. (gr. 1-2). 22.00 (978-0-7635-9179-3(3)) Rigby Education.

Looking for Lewis. (J). pap. 13.75 (978-0-8136-4650-3(2)) Modern Curriculum Pr.

Looking for the Queen. (Early Intervention Levels Ser.). 31.86 (978-0-7362-0628-0(0)) Hampton-Brown Bks.

Looking for the Queen (18), Vol. 18. (Early Intervention Levels Ser.). 5.31 (978-0-7362-0616-7(7)) Hampton-Brown Bks.

Loose Tooth. 2005. (J). (978-1-932570-31-1(4)) Literacy Footprints Inc.

Lorimer, Janet. Time's Reach. (gr. 7-12). lib. bdg. 10.40 (978-0-613-09870-0(6)) Tandem Library Bks.

Loser Student Packet, Gr. 5-6. 2004. (J). (978-1-58130-518-0(4)) Novel Units, Inc.

Lost: Individual Title, 6 Packs. (Story Steps Ser.). (gr. k-2). 23.00 (978-0-7635-9817-4(8)) Rigby Education.

Lost! Individual Title, 6 Packs. (gr. k-1). 23.00 (978-0-7635-9069-7(X)) Rigby Education.

Lost! Set D Individual Title, 6 Packs. (Smart Start Ser.). (gr. k-1). 23.00 (978-0-7635-0450-2(5)) Rigby Education.

Lost in a Cave: Fifth Grade Guided Comprehension Level T. (On Our Way to English Ser.). (gr. 5 up). 34.50 (978-0-7578-6628-9(X)) Rigby Education.

Lost in the Woods. 2003. (J). (978-1-932570-12-0(8)) Literacy Footprints Inc.

Lttle Bear Book Set 800889, 3 vols. 2005. (J). (978-1-59794-064-1(X)) Environments, Inc.

Luckett, Kathy. Does Your Father Snore? 2000. (Illus.). pap. 2.80 (978-0-521-65570-5(6)) Cambridge Univ. Pr.

—Does Your Father Snore? Chitonga Version. Hamoonga, Lazarous, tr. 1998. (Cambridge African Language Library Ser.). (Illus.). 16p. pap. 3.65 (978-0-521-63869-2(0)) Cambridge Univ. Pr.

—Does Your Father Snore? Cinyanja Version. Mwale, Brian, tr. 1998. (Cambridge African Language Library Ser.). (Illus.). 16p. pap. 3.70 (978-0-521-63859-3(3)) Cambridge Univ. Pr.

—Does Your Father Snore? Lunda Version. Kambangaji, Thomson, tr. 1998. (Cambridge African Language Library Ser.). (Illus.). 16p. pap. 3.70 (978-0-521-63839-5(9)) Cambridge Univ. Pr.

Lucky Dip, Vol. A. (Sunstart Ser.: Series S50). (Illus.). 32p. (J). (ps-5). stu. ed. 1.95 (978-0-7214-8007-7(1) , Dutton Juvenile) Penguin Group (USA) Inc.

Lucky Socks: Third Grade Guided Reading Level J. (On Our Way to English Ser.). (gr. 3 up). 34.50 (978-0-7578-7117-7(8)) Rigby Education.

Lucy Meets a Dragon, 6 Packs. (Literatura 2000 Ser.). (gr. 2-3). 33.00 (978-0-7635-0177-8(8)) Rigby Education.

Luke's Adventures: Individual Title Six-Packs. (ps-2). 27.00 (978-0-7635-9460-2(1)) Rigby Education.

Luke's Go-cart: Individual Title Six-Packs. 16p. (gr. 2 up). 35.00 (978-0-7635-9371-1(0)) Rigby Education.

Lunch at the Joy House Cafe. (Early Intervention Levels Ser.). 31.86 (978-0-7362-0666-2(3)) Hampton-Brown Bks.

Lunch at the Joy House Cafe (24), Vol. 24. (Early Intervention Levels Ser.). 5.31 (978-0-7362-0654-9(X)) Hampton-Brown Bks.

Lunch Orders: 6 Small Books. (gr. k-3). 24.00 (978-0-7635-6238-0(6)) Rigby Education.

The Lunchroom: Individual Title Six-Packs. (ps-2). 27.00 (978-0-7635-9461-9(X)) Rigby Education.

Lundy, Kathleen Gould. In a Class of Her Own. Alward, Jeff, illus. 2007. 48p. (J). lib. bdg. 23.08 (***978-1-4242-1629-1(X)***) Fitzgerald Bks.

Lying as Still as I Can: Six-Pack. (Greetings Ser.: Vol. 3). (gr. 2-3). 31.00 (978-0-7635-9433-6(4)) Rigby Education.

Lynne, Rustyna. Another Sign of Chad Maturing Standard & Special Needs. Lynne, Rustyna, illus. 2002. (Illus.). 9p. (YA). (gr. 6-8). spiral bd. 9.95 (978-0-9722829-4-9(7)) Red Carpet Publishing.

—Chad's First Shave. Lynne, Rustyna, illus. 2002. (Illus.). 10p. (YA). (gr. 5-8). spiral bd. 10.95 (978-0-9722829-3-2(9)) Red Carpet Publishing.

Lyons, Scott, ed. Letter of the Week, Vol. 2. 2001. 192p. 19.95 (978-1-56234-473-3(0) , Mailbox Bks., The) Education Ctr., Inc.

Macbeth Study Guide. 2002. (Illus.). 48p. (YA). per. (978-1-56254-611-3(2) , SP6112) Saddleback Educational Publishing.

Maccarone, Grace. Recess Mess. Lewin, Betsy, illus. 2004. 32p. (J). lib. bdg. 15.00 (978-1-59054-665-9(2)) Fitzgerald Bks.

—What Is That? Said the Cat. Scherer, Jeffrey, illus. 2004. 32p. (J). lib. bdg. 15.00 (978-1-59054-662-8(8)) Fitzgerald Bks.

MacDonald, Kimber. The Misfits, Level 3. Swain, Wilson, illus. 2006. (Phonics Comics Ser.). 24p. (J). (gr. 1-17). pap. 3.99 (978-1-58476-421-2(X) , IKIDS) Innovative Kids.

—Time Travelers, Level 3. Sisk, Clay, illus. 2006. (Phonics Comics Ser.). 24p. (J). (gr. 1-17). pap. 3.99 (978-1-58476-472-4(4) , IKIDS) Innovative Kids.

Made in Korea: Six-Pack. (Greetings Ser.: Vol. 3). (gr. 3-5). 31.00 (978-0-7635-1824-0(7)) Rigby Education.

La Madera. (Coleccion Conceptos de Ciencia en Big Books). (SPA., Illus.). (J). (gr. k-3). 21.95 (978-0-8136-7426-1(3) , MD7216) Modern Curriculum Pr.

Madin. Down to a Sunless Sea. 1998. (Illus.). (J). pap. (978-0-7398-0029-4(9)) Steck-Vaughn.

Magazine Level D. 2004. (Reading Central Ser.). (J). (gr. 2 up). 5.95 (978-1-58830-870-2(7)) Metropolitan Teaching & Learning Co.

Magazine Level E. 2004. (Reading Central Ser.). (J). (gr. 2 up). 5.95 (978-1-58830-871-9(5)) Metropolitan Teaching & Learning Co.

Magazine Level F. 2004. (Reading Central Ser.). (J). (gr. 2 up). 5.95 (978-1-58830-872-6(3)) Metropolitan Teaching & Learning Co.

Magee, Wes. Little Dragon. Warburton, Sarah, illus. 2004. 24p. (J). lib. bdg. 22.65 (***978-1-59646-690-6(1)***) Dingles & Co.

Magee, Wes. Who Likes Pancakes?, 4 vols. 2005. (QEB Readers). (Illus.). 24p. (J). (gr. 1-4). lib. bdg. 15.95 (978-1-59566-091-6(7)) QEB Publishing Inc.

Maggart, Kaye Wiley. Shining Star, Introductory Level. 2004. (Illus.). xiv, 289p. 64.67 (978-0-13-111285-8(6)) Pearson ESL.

Magic Food: Individual Title-Six Packs. (Chiquilibros Ser.). (gr. k-1). 23.00 (978-0-7635-0441-0(6)) Rigby Education.

Magic Tricks. 64p. (J). Date not set. (Illus.). 5.98 (978-1-4054-0409-9(4)); 2002. pap. 9.98 (978-0-7525-6290-2(8)) Parragon, Inc.

The Magician's Nephew Student Packet, Gr. 5-6. 2004. (J). (978-1-58130-860-0(4)) Novel Units, Inc.

Mahaffy, Kathy. Reading Comprehension- Prince Caspian. 2001. (Logos School Literature Ser.). 41p. (J). spiral bd. 10.00 (978-1-930443-46-4(3)) Logos Schl.

—Reading Comprehension- The Lion, the Witch, & the Wardrobe. 2001. 27p. (J). spiral bd. 10.00 (978-1-930443-44-0(7)) Logos Schl.

—Reading Comprension- The Magician's Nephew. 2001. (Logos School Literature Ser.). 42p. (J). spiral bd. 10.00 (978-1-930443-45-7(5)) Logos Schl.

The Mail: Individual Title Two-Packs. (Chiquilibros Ser.). (ps-1). 12.00 (978-0-7635-8541-9(6)) Rigby Education.

Maine, Margarita & Rojas. Un Mar Muy Mojado. 2004. (SPA.). 32p. 6.95 (978-1-4000-9290-1(6)) Editorial Sudamericana S.A. ARG. *Dist:* Random Hse., Inc.

Maisy Cloth Books Set 800846, 4. 2005. (J). (978-1-59794-047-4(X)) Environments, Inc.

Make a Tune. (Early Intervention Levels Ser.). 28.38 (978-0-7362-0403-3(2)) Hampton-Brown Bks.

Make a Tune (20), Vol. 20. (Early Intervention Levels Ser.). 4.73 (978-0-7362-0228-2(5)) Hampton-Brown Bks.

Make Believe Ideas. Jonah the Moaner. 2006. (Illus.). 32p. (J). (ps-3). 8.97 (978-1-59145-527-1(8)) Nelson, Thomas Inc.

Make It! (Early Intervention Levels Ser.). 3.55 (978-0-7362-0078-3(9)); 21.30 (978-0-7362-0357-9(5)) Hampton-Brown Bks.

Making a Difference: Small Versions of Big Books. (On Our Way to English Ser.). (gr. 3 up). 35.50 (978-0-7578-7242-6(5)) Rigby Education.

Making a Difference: Third Grade Big Books. (On Our Way to English Ser.). (gr. 3 up). 29.95 (978-0-7578-4213-9(5)) Rigby Education.

Mami, Mami!, Vol. 2. (Spanish Early Intervention Levels Ser.). (SPA.). 3.55 (978-0-7362-0759-1(7)) Hampton-Brown Bks.

Mammoth: MainSails, 6 Packs. (Sails Literacy Ser.). (gr. 5 up). 37.00 (978-0-7578-8047-6(9)) Rigby Education.

Man-Kong, Mary. Barbie: Mariposa. 2008. (Pictureback(R) Ser.). 16p. (J). (ps-1). pap. 3.99 (***978-0-375-84798-1(7)*** , Golden Bks.) Random Hse., Inc.

Man on the Moon. (Guided Reading Levels Ser.). 8.48 (978-0-7362-1692-0(8)); 50.88 (978-0-7362-2141-2(7)) Hampton-Brown Bks.

Mandel Morrow, Lesley & Vacca, Richard T. Sadlier Phonics Reading, Phonics. 2001st ed. 2005. (Sadlier Phonics Reading Program). (YA). (ps-3). 69.00 (978-0-8215-7035-7(8)) Sadlier, William H. Inc.

Mann, Rachol. A Race to a Fire! Set, 6 vols. (Phonics Readers Ser.). (gr. k-2). 17.50 (978-0-7368-3194-9(0)) Red Brick Learning.

Mansfield, Katherine. The Doll's House & Other Stories, Level 4. 2003. 64p. (C). pap. 9.00 (978-0-582-41811-0(9)) Longman Publishing Group.

Mapongwana, Nobantu. Naughty Hare: Lunda Version. Kambangaji, Thomson, tr. 1998. (Cambridge African Language Library Ser.). (Illus.). 8p. pap. 3.75 (978-0-521-64743-4(6)) Cambridge Univ. Pr.

Mapping the World: Individual Title Six-Packs. (Rigby Infoquest Ser.). 32p. (gr. 4 up). 37.00 (978-0-7578-5734-8(5)) Rigby Education.

Marion Nash Jackie Lowe Staff. Spirals Series Activities for Home. 2005. 65.00 (***978-1-84312-412-2(2)***) Fulton, David Pubs. GBR. *Dist:* Taylor & Francis, Inc.

Markowitz-Meredith, Susan. Stump Hill. ed. 2003. (Early Connections Ser.). (J). pap. 35.00 (978-1-4108-1554-5(4)) Benchmark Education Co.

Marks, Melanie. Spooky Sara, Level 3. Ball, Victoria, illus. 2006. (Phonics Comics Ser.). 24p. (J). (gr. 1-17). pap. 3.99 (978-1-58476-473-1(2) , IKIDS) Innovative Kids.

Marland, Michael. Ideas, Insights & Arguments: A Non-Fiction Collection. 2008. (Cambridge Collections). 256p. pap. (***978-0-521-70323-9(9)***) Cambridge Univ. Pr.

Marshall, James. George & Martha: Round & Round Early Reader #3. 2008. 32p. (J). (ps-3). 15.00 (***978-0-618-98505-0(0)***) Houghton Mifflin Co. Trade & Reference Div.

—George & Martha: the Best of Friends Early Reader #4. 2008. 24p. (J). (ps-3). 15.00 (***978-0-618-98451-0(8)***) Houghton Mifflin Co. Trade & Reference Div.

Marshall, Michael J. & Hirsch, E. D., Jr., eds. Realms of Gold: A Core Knowledge Reader. 2000. (YA). (gr. 6-8). Vol. 1. 271p. pap. 19.95 (978-1-890517-22-9(4)); Vol. 2. 328p. pap. 19.95 (978-1-890517-23-6(2)); Vol. 3. 440p. pap. 19.95 (978-1-890517-24-3(0)) Core Knowledge Foundation.

Martin, Bill, et al. I Pledge Allegiance. Raschka, Chris, illus. 2005. 40p. (J). (gr. 1-4). reprint ed. pap. 24.99 (978-0-7636-2815-4(8)) Candlewick Pr.

Martin, John David. A Time to Plant: Tests. 2005. (Rod & Staff's Readers Ser.). 22p. (gr. 5 up). 1.55 (978-0-7399-0404-6(3) , 11511) Rod & Staff Pubs., Inc.

—A Time to Plant: Workbook. 2005. (Rod & Staff's Readers Ser.). 145p. (gr. 5 up). 4.80 (978-0-7399-0402-2(7) , 11521) Rod & Staff Pubs., Inc.

Martin's mighty Hit: Individual Title Six-Packs. (gr. 1-2). 25.00 (978-0-7635-9144-1(0)) Rigby Education.

Maryland Reading Success Grade 1. 2003. (Illus.). 32p. (J). 9.95 (978-0-9722452-0-3(0)) New Leaf Educ., Inc.

Maryland Reading Success Grade 2, 3 vols., Vol. 2. 2003. (Illus.). 32p. (J). 9.95 (978-0-9722452-1-0(9)) New Leaf Educ., Inc.

Maryland Reading Success Grade 3, Vol. 3. 2003. (Illus.). 32p. (J). 9.95 (978-0-9722452-5-8(1)) New Leaf Educ., Inc.

Marzollo, Jean. I Spy a Pumpkin. Wick, Walter, illus. 2006. (Scholastic Reader, Level 1 Ser.). 32p. (J). pap. 3.99 (978-0-439-73863-7(6) , Cartwheel Bks.) Scholastic, Inc.

—I Spy Lightning in the Sky. Wick, Walter, illus. 2005. (Scholastic Reader Ser.). 32p. (J). 3.99 (978-0-439-68052-3(2) , Cartwheel Bks.) Scholastic, Inc.

—Soy el Agua. Moffatt, Judith, illus. 1999. (Coleccion "Hola, Lector" Ser.). (SPA.). 32p. (J). (ps-1). pap. 3.99 (978-0-439-08743-8(0) , SO2913, Scholastic en Espanol) Scholastic, Inc.

—Soy el Agua. 1999. (SPA.). (gr. k-3). lib. bdg. 11.80 (978-0-613-28314-4(7)) Tandem Library Bks.

Masks, 6 vols. (gr. k-2). 28.95 (978-0-7368-8131-9(X)) Red Brick Learning.

Maslen, Bobby L. & Maslen, John R. Bob Books Fun! 2000. (Bob Books: Set 2). 14p. (J). (ps-3). 16.95 (978-0-439-12198-9(1)) Scholastic, Inc.

Maslen, Bobby Lynn & Maslen, John R. Long Vowels! 2006. (Bob Books Ser.: No. 5). 16p. (J). pap. 16.99 (978-0-439-86541-8(7) , Scholastic Paperbacks) Scholastic, Inc.

Maslen, John R. & Maslen, Bobby Lynn. Advancing Beginners. 2006. (Bob Books Set 2 Ser.). (Illus.). 16p. (J). pap. 16.99 (978-0-439-84502-1(5) , Scholastic Paperbacks) Scholastic, Inc.

—Beginning Readers. 2006. (Bob Books Set 1 Ser.). (Illus.). 16p. (J). pap. 16.99 (978-0-439-84500-7(9) , Scholastic Paperbacks) Scholastic, Inc.

—Compound Words. 2006. (Bob Books Set 4 Ser.). (Illus.). 16p. (J). pap. 16.99 (978-0-439-84506-9(8) , Scholastic Paperbacks) Scholastic, Inc.

Masoliver, Juan Antonio. Historias Breves para Leer. (SPA & ENG.). (J). Level 1. 150p. 14.95 (978-84-7143-825-6(9) , SGS8259); Level 2. 128p. 14.95 (978-84-7143-732-7(5) , SGS4393) Sociedad General Espanola de Libreria ESP. *Dist:* Continental Bk. Co., Inc.

Massie, Elizabeth. 1863 - A House Divided: A Novel of the Civil War. 2007. (Young Founders Ser.). 192p. (YA). 5.99 (978-0-7653-5272-9(9) , Tor Bks.) Doherty, Tom Assocs., LLC.

The Masterpiece: Level M, 6 vols. 128p. (gr. 2-3). 41.95 (978-0-7699-1026-0(2)) Shortland Pubns. (U. S. A.) Inc.

The Math Master: Fourth Grade Guided Comprehension Level P. (On Our Way to English Ser.). (gr. 4 up). 34.50 (978-0-7578-7171-9(2)) Rigby Education.

Mathes, Patricia G., et al. First Grade Pals: First Grade Peer-Assisted Literacy Strategies. 2001. 222p. spiral bd. 29.95 (978-1-57035-331-4(X) , 157FIRSTMAN) Sopris West Educational Services.

Matter Splatter: Individual Title Six-Packs. (Rigby Infoquest Ser.). (gr. 5 up). 37.00 (978-0-7578-6481-0(3)) Rigby Education.

Mattern, Joanne. My Little Pony Phonics Fun. Lo Raso, Carlo, illus. 2008. (My First I Can Read Bks.). 12p. (J). pap. 12.99 (***978-0-06-122954-1(7)*** , Harper Trophy) HarperCollins Pubs.

Matthews. Death in the Desert. (Thumbprint Mysteries Ser.). 32.86 (978-0-8092-0416-8(9)) McGraw-Hill/ Contemporary.

Matthews, Cecily. Pobblebonk Reading 4. 1 Playing Shop. 2008. pap. (***978-0-521-71079-4(0)***) Cambridge Univ. Pr.

—Pobblebonk Reading 4. 3 the Wild Wind. 2008. pap. (***978-0-521-71080-0(4)***) Cambridge Univ. Pr.

—Pobblebonk Reading 4. 7 Going to the Snow. 2008. pap. (***978-0-521-71081-7(2)***) Cambridge Univ. Pr.

—Pobblebonk Reading 5. 10 the Plane Crash. 2008. pap. (***978-0-521-71084-8(7)***) Cambridge Univ. Pr.

—Pobblebonk Reading 5. 2 Watch Out! 2008. pap. (***978-0-521-71082-4(0)***) Cambridge Univ. Pr.

—Pobblebonk Reading 5. 6 Race to the Lake. 2008. pap. (***978-0-521-71083-1(9)***) Cambridge Univ. Pr.

—Pobblebonk Reading 6. 3 Leeches & Screeches. 2008. pap. (***978-0-521-71085-5(5)***) Cambridge Univ. Pr.

—Pobblebonk Reading 6. 4 the Spooky Chook. 2008. pap. (***978-0-521-71086-2(3)***) Cambridge Univ. Pr.

—Pobblebonk Reading 6. 9 Go, Go-Cart, Go! 2008. pap. (***978-0-521-71087-9(1)***) Cambridge Univ. Pr.

Matthews, Gill, et al. Pirates Ahoy! 2007. (I-read Ser.). (Illus.). 48p. pap. (***978-0-521-70487-8(1)***) Cambridge Univ. Pr.

Mauer, Julie. Full-Color Reading Games. 2006. 176p. pap. 21.99 (978-1-4206-3120-3(9)); pap. 21.99 (978-1-4206-3121-0(7)) Austin & Company, Inc.

Maule, David. Inventions That Changed the World: Level 4 Book. 2005. (Illus.). 64p. (C). pap. 9.00 (***978-0-582-85489-5(X)***) Pearson ESL.

Maupassant, Guy de. Mon Oncle Jules, Level D. (FRE.). (YA). (gr. 7-12). 8.95 (978-0-88436-044-5(X) , 40281) EMC/Paradigm Publishing.

May I Go Out? (J). 26.20 (978-0-8136-8429-1(3)); 26.20 (978-0-8136-8428-4(5)); 59.50 (978-0-8136-7978-5(8)); 1998. pap. (978-0-8136-8302-7(5)) Modern Curriculum Pr.

May I Stay Home Today? 6 Small Books. (gr. k-3). 24.00 (978-0-7635-6239-7(4)) Rigby Education.

Mayan Writing in Mesoamerica: Individual Title Six-Packs. (On Deck Ser.: Vol. 2). 24p. (gr. 4-5). 35.00 (978-0-7578-5865-9(1)) Rigby Education.

Mayer, Mercer. Little Critter: Snowball Soup. Mayer, Mercer, illus. 2007. (My First I Can Read Bks.). 32p. (J). (ps-k). pap. 3.99 (***978-0-06-083543-9(5)*** , Harper Trophy) HarperCollins Pubs.

—Mercer Mayer's Little Critter First Readers: Skills & Practice, 4 bks., Set 1. Mayer, Mercer, illus. 2001. (Little Critter(R) First Readers Ser.). (Illus.). 96p. (J). Level 1. (ps-k). pap., pap. 15.95 (978-1-57768-823-5(6)); Vol. 2. (gr. k-1). pap., pap. 15.95 (978-1-57768-824-2(4)); Vol. 3. (gr. 1-2). pap. 15.95 (978-1-57768-825-9(2)) School Specialty Publishing.

—Mercer Mayer's Little Critter First Readers: Skills & Practice, Level 1, 4 bks., Set 2. Mayer, Mercer, illus. 2002. (Little Critter(R) First Readers Ser.). (Illus.). 96p. (J). (ps-k). pap. 15.95 (978-1-57768-853-2(8)) School Specialty Publishing.

—Mercer Mayer's Little Critter First Readers: Skills & Practice, Level 2, 4 bks., Set 2, Vol. 2. Mayer, Mercer, illus. 2002. (Little Critter(R) First Readers Ser.). (Illus.). 96p. (J). (gr. k-1). pap. 15.95 (978-1-57768-854-9(6)) School Specialty Publishing.

—Mercer Mayer's Little Critter First Readers: Skills & Practice, Level 3, 4 bks., Set 2, Vol. 3. Mayer, Mercer, illus. 2002. (Little Critter(R) First Readers Ser.). (Illus.). 96p. (J). (gr. 1-2). pap. 15.95 (978-1-57768-855-6(4)) School Specialty Publishing.

—Our Friend Sam. 2002. (Little Critter Ser.). (Illus.). 24p. (J). (ps-2). 10.95 (978-1-57768-458-9(3)) School Specialty Publishing.

—Our Friend Sam. 2002. (gr. k-3). lib. bdg. 11.80 (978-0-613-62430-5(0)) Tandem Library Bks.

—Our Tree House. 2001. (gr. k-3). lib. bdg. 11.80 (978-0-613-67657-1(2)) Tandem Library Bks.

Mayfield, Sue. The Four Franks. Parsons, Garry, illus. 2005. (Blue Go Bananas Ser.). 48p. (J). pap. (978-0-7787-2651-7(7)) Crabtree Publishing Co.

McAllister, Margaret. Emily & the Lamb. Vince, Dawn, illus. 2005. 24p. (J). lib. bdg. 22.65 (***978-1-59646-756-9(8)***) Dingles & Co.

Mcbratney, Sam. Henry Seamouse. 2005. (978-1-901358-13-1(5)) CAMFA.

McCall Crabbs: Standard Test Lessons in Reading, Books A-E. 2001. 400p. 39.95 (978-1-880045-25-1(7)) Back Home Industries.

McCaughtry, Michele. Independent Reading Management Kit: Literary Elements. 2006. 112p. pap. 15.99 (978-0-439-64043-5(1) , Teaching Resources) Scholastic, Inc.

McClenney, Earl H., Jr. Mamma, Is the Maid Goin' Teach? Portraits of Black Women Who Integrated the Public Schools in Richmond, VA. 2005. spiral bd. 10.95 net. (978-0-9618835-5-3(3)) First Associates Publishing.

McEwan, Rebecca. Telling Time Through the Ages. 2004. (Navigators Ser.). (J). pap. 38.00 (978-1-4108-0409-9(7)) Benchmark Education Co.

McGee, Sherry. Apple Jaleel - Pass It On. McDowell, Ryan, illus. 2000. (Applekid's Chapter Bks.). 12p. (J). (gr. k-7). pap. 4.99 (978-0-9673591-3-7(9)) Apple Bk. Ctr.

—Apple Mack - How I Learned to Learn. McDowell, Ryan, illus. 2000. (Applekid's Chapter Bks.). 12p. (J). (gr. k-7). pap. 4.99 (978-0-9673591-5-1(5)) Apple Bk. Ctr.

—Apple Neil - An Apple a Day. McDowell, Ryan, illus. 2000. (Applekid's Chapter Bks.). 12p. (J). (gr. k-7). pap. 4.99 (978-0-9673591-4-4(7)) Apple Bk. Ctr.

McGraw-Hill - Jamestown Education Staff. The Outer Edge: Danger Zone. 2005. pap. 16.64 (978-0-07-872905-8(X) , 9780078729058) Glencoe/McGraw-Hill.

—The Outer Edge: Fateful Journeys. 2005. pap. 16.64 (978-0-07-872906-5(8) , 9780078729065) Glencoe/McGraw-Hill.

—The Outer Edge: Still Unsolved. 2005. pap. 16.64 (978-0-07-869052-5(8) , 9780078690525) Glencoe/McGraw-Hill.

—The Outer Edge: Uncommon Courage. 2005. pap. 16.64 (978-0-07-872904-1(1) , 9780078729041) Glencoe/ McGraw-Hill.

—Timed Readings Plus in Science. 2002. (gr. 6-12). Bk. 1. pap. 16.64 (978-0-07-827370-4(6) , 9780078273704); Bk. 2. pap. 16.64 (978-0-07-827371-1(4) , 9780078273711); Bk. 3. pap. 16.64 (978-0-07-827372-8(2) , 9780078273728); Bk. 4. pap. 16.64 (978-0-07-827373-5(0) , 9780078273735); Bk. 5. pap. 16.64 (978-0-07-827374-2(9) , 9780078273742); Bk. 6. pap. 16.64 (978-0-07-827375-9(7) , 9780078273759); Bk. 7. pap. 16.64 (978-0-07-827376-6(5) , 9780078273766); Bk. 8. pap. 16.64 (978-0-07-827377-3(3) , 9780078273773); Bk. 9. pap. 16.64 (978-0-07-827378-0(1) , 9780078273780); Bk. 10. pap. 16.64 (978-0-07-827379-7(X) , 9780078273797) Jamestown.

McGraw-Hill Staff. The American Vision, Reading Essentials & Study Guide, Student Edition. 2nd ed. 2004. pap. 22.64 (978-0-07-865439-8(4) , 9780078654398) Glencoe/McGraw-Hill.

—The American Vision, StudentWorks Plus CD-ROM. 2nd ed. 2005. 114.64 (978-0-07-865456-5(4) , 9780078654565) Glencoe/McGraw-Hill.

—The Contemporary Reader, Vol. 3. 2002. 74.00 (978-0-07-830496-5(2) , 9780078304965) Jamestown.

—Glencoe Literature, World Literature Interactive Reading. 2002. (C). pap., wbk. ed. 18.00 (978-0-07-825181-8(8) , 9780078251818) Glencoe/McGraw-Hill.

—The Glencoe Reader, Grade 6, Course 1. 2003. 340p. (gr. 6-12). pap., stu. ed. 14.64 (978-0-07-845927-6(3) , 9780078459276) Glencoe/McGraw-Hill.

—The Glencoe Reader, Grade 7, Course 2. 2003. (gr. 6-12). pap., stu. ed. 14.64 (978-0-07-845928-3(1) , 9780078459283) Glencoe/McGraw-Hill.

—Glencoe Reader Grade 7 Georgia Edition. 2003. pap. 12.64 (978-0-07-845948-1(6) , 9780078459481) Glencoe/McGraw-Hill.

—The Glencoe Reader, Grade 9, Course 4. 2003. (C). (gr. 6-12). pap., stu. ed. 14.64 (978-0-07-845930-6(3) , 9780078459306) Glencoe/McGraw-Hill.

—Journey Across Time: Early Ages. 2004. stu. ed. 78.00 (978-0-07-824133-8(2) , 9780078241338) Glencoe/ McGraw-Hill.

—Listen!Listen!Letter Sounds in Rhymes Complt Set. (gr. k-1). 210.95 (978-0-322-02636-0(9)) Wright Group, The.

—Phonics: Grades 2-3. 1999. (J). (gr. 2-3). pap. 19.95 (978-1-57768-037-6(5)) School Specialty Publishing.

—Phonics: Grades K-1. 1999. (J). (gr. k-1). sl. 19.95 (978-1-57768-036-9(7)) School Specialty Publishing.

—Song Box Sets & Resources:Save the Tree for Me Cass. (Song Box(R) Ser.). (gr. 1-2). 8.50 incl. audio (978-0-7802-2265-6(2)) Wright Group, The.

McGraw-Hill Staff & Goodman, Burton. Choices. 2002. (Goodman's Five-Star Stories Ser.). (gr. 6-12). pap. 17.32 (978-0-07-827354-4(4) , 9780078273544) Jamestown.

McGraw-Hill Staff & McGraw-Hill - Jamestown Education Staff. The Contemporary Reader. 2002. (gr. 4-10). Vol. 3, No. 1. stu. ed. 74.00 (978-0-07-828337-6(X) , 9780078283376); Vol. 3, No. 2. stu. ed. 74.00 (978-0-07-828338-3(8) , 9780078283383); Vol. 3, No. 3. stu. ed. 74.00 (978-0-07-828339-0(6) , 9780078283390); Vol. 3, No. 4. stu. ed. 74.00 (978-0-07-828340-6(X) , 9780078283406); Vol. 3, No. 5. stu. ed. 74.00 (978-0-07-828341-3(8) , 9780078283413); Vol. 3, No. 6. stu. ed. 74.00 (978-0-07-828342-0(6) , 9780078283420) Jamestown.

McGuffey, William H. New Mcguffey Fourth Reader. 2006. 204p. pap. 12.99 (978-1-4264-0489-4(1)); pap. 15.99 (978-1-4264-0563-1(4)) BiblioBazaar.

McGuinness, Rik. Cloze Encounters Vol. 1: Animals, 3 vols. 2000. 48p. pap. 6.95 (978-1-58324-044-1(6) , World Teachers Pr.) Didax Educational Resources, Inc.

—Cloze Encounters Vol. 2: The Sea, 3 vols. 2000. 48p. pap. 6.95 (978-1-58324-045-8(4) , World Teachers Pr.) Didax Educational Resources, Inc.

McKay, Sindy. We Both Read-My Car Trip. Johnson, Meredith, illus. 2005. (We Both Read Ser.). 44p. (J). (gr. k up). 7.99 (978-1-891327-63-6(1)); pap. 3.99 (978-1-891327-64-3(X)) Treasure Bay, Inc.

McKeon. Lost. 1998. (Disney First Reader Ser.). 48p. (J). pap. 2.95 (978-0-7868-4294-0(6)) Disney Pr.

McLaughlin, Maureen, et al. Research-Based Reading Lessons for 4-6: Word Study, Fluency, Vocabulary, & Comprehension. 2006. 224p. pap. 25.99 (978-0-439-84381-2(2) , Teaching Resources) Scholastic, Inc.

McNamara, Kilian. Medea. 2002. (Wizard Study Guides Ser.). 64p. pap., stu. ed. 6.00 (978-1-876367-07-7(5)) Cambridge Univ. Pr.

—The Riders. 2002. (Wizard Study Guides Ser.). 48p. pap., stu. ed. 6.00 (978-1-875739-90-5(4)) Cambridge Univ. Pr.

—Sometimes Gladness. 2002. (Wizard Study Guides Ser.). 48p. pap., stu. ed. 6.00 (978-1-875739-43-1(2)) Cambridge Univ. Pr.

McNamara, Margaret. Robin Hill School #19. Gordon, Mike, illus. 2008. (Robin Hill School Ser.). 32p. (J). lib. bdg. 13.89 (***978-1-4169-5536-8(4)*** , Aladdin) Simon & Schuster Children's Publishing.

McNee, I. Knights - Internet Referenced. 2005. (Beginners Ser.). 32p. (J). (gr. 1 up). pap. 4.95 (978-0-7945-0896-8(0) , Usborne) EDC Publishing.

McOmber, Rachel B., ed. McOmber Phonics Storybooks: A Night to Celebrate. rev. ed. (Illus.). (J). (978-0-944991-71-8(8)) Swift Learning Resources.

—McOmber Phonics Storybooks: Fizz in the Pit. rev. ed. (Illus.). (J). (978-0-944991-12-1(2)) Swift Learning Resources.

—McOmber Phonics Storybooks: Fizz Mix. rev. ed. (Illus.). (J). (978-0-944991-11-4(4)) Swift Learning Resources.

—McOmber Phonics Storybooks: Fizz Mud. rev. ed. (Illus.). (J). (978-0-944991-21-3(1)) Swift Learning Resources.

MCP Staff. The Baby Who Got All the Blame. (J). (gr. 1-2). 38.50 (978-0-8136-9136-7(2)); 38.50 (978-0-8136-1071-9(0)) Modern Curriculum Pr.

—The Big Cat, 6 bks., set, Level 4, Bk. 2. 2003. (J). (ps-3). 24.50 (978-0-8136-2373-3(1)) Modern Curriculum Pr.

—By the Tree, Level 4, Bk. 22. (J). (ps-3). 24.50 (978-0-8136-0693-4(4)) Modern Curriculum Pr.

—Can a Cow Hop?, Level 4, Bk. 27. (J). (ps-3). 24.50 (978-0-8136-0795-5(7)) Modern Curriculum Pr.

—Cat's Trip, 6 bks., Set, Level 12, Bk. 50. (J). (ps-3). pap. 33.50 (978-0-8136-2107-4(0)) Modern Curriculum Pr.

—Fast As a Fox, Level 4, Bk. 29. (J). (ps-3). 24.50 (978-0-8136-1961-3(0)) Modern Curriculum Pr.

—Little Bunny's Lunch: Short u; Consonants b, h; Blends br, cr; Digraphs ch, sh, th. (J). (gr. 1-2). 38.50 (978-0-8136-1116-7(4)) Modern Curriculum Pr.

—Lost in the Fog, Level 4, Bk. 25. (J). (ps-3). 24.50 (978-0-8136-1957-6(2)) Modern Curriculum Pr.

—My Cat, Level 4, Bk. 13. 2003. (J). (ps-3). 24.50 (978-0-8136-0679-8(9)) Modern Curriculum Pr.

—The Name Is the Same, 6 bks., set, Level 12, Bk. 43. 2003. (J). (ps-3). 33.50 (978-0-8136-2081-7(3)) Modern Curriculum Pr.

—Nut Pie for Judy, Level 4, Bk. 43. 2003. (J). (ps-3). 24.50 (978-0-8136-1973-6(4)) Modern Curriculum Pr.

—Sandy, Level 3, Bk. 19. (J). (ps-3). 24.50 (978-0-8136-1951-4(3)) Modern Curriculum Pr.

—Six Go By, Level A. 2003. (J). (ps-3). 21.95 (978-0-8136-0672-9(1)) Modern Curriculum Pr.

—Stop That!, Level 3, Bk. 16. (J). (ps-3). 24.50 (978-0-8136-0783-2(3)) Modern Curriculum Pr.

—Terrific Shoes, Level 3, Bk. 8. (J). (ps-3). 24.50 (978-0-8136-1941-5(6)) Modern Curriculum Pr.

—That Pig Can't Do a Anything, 6 bks., set, Level 10, Bk. 37. 2003. (J). (ps-3). 24.50 (978-0-8136-1682-7(4)) Modern Curriculum Pr.

—True or False?, 6 bks., Set, Level 12, Bk. 47. 2003. (J). (ps-3). pap. 33.50 (978-0-8136-2105-0(4)) Modern Curriculum Pr.

—Very Big, Level 4, Bk. 45. 2003. (J). (ps-3). 24.50 (978-0-8136-1447-2(3)) Modern Curriculum Pr.

—We Are Singing, Level 2, Bk. 7. (J). (ps-3). 21.95 (978-0-8136-0673-6(X)) Modern Curriculum Pr.

—When Bob Woke up Late, 6 bks., set, Level 12, Bk. 45. 2003. (J). (ps-3). 33.50 (978-0-8136-2085-5(6)) Modern Curriculum Pr.

—Where Do They Live?, Level 3, Bk. 17. (J). (ps-3). 24.50 (978-0-8136-1949-1(1)) Modern Curriculum Pr.

—Who Made That?, Level 3, Bk. 15. (J). (ps-3). 24.50 (978-0-8136-1947-7(5)) Modern Curriculum Pr.

—Who Said Boo? Long u; Consonants d, m; Blend dr. (J). 38.50 (978-0-8136-1091-7(5)) Modern Curriculum Pr.

—Wilma's Wagon, Level 4, Bk. 32. (J). (ps-3). 24.50 (978-0-8136-1965-1(3)) Modern Curriculum Pr.

McRoberts, Richard. Cambridge Wizard Student Guide A Minimum of Two. 2005. (Cambridge Wizard English Student Guides). 63p. pap. 5.95 (978-0-521-61380-4(9)) Cambridge Univ. Pr.

—The Collector. 2002. (Wizard Study Guides Ser.). 56p. pap., stu. ed. 6.00 (978-1-875739-01-1(7)) Cambridge Univ. Pr.

—The Curious Incident of the Dog in the Night Time. 2005. (Cambridge Wizard English Student Guides). 64p. pap. 5.95 (978-0-521-61379-8(5)) Cambridge Univ. Pr.

—The Great Gatsby. 2002. (Wizard Study Guides Ser.). 48p. (YA). pap., stu. ed. 6.00 (978-1-875739-38-7(6)) Cambridge Univ. Pr.

—Hard Times. 2002. (Wizard Study Guides Ser.). 54p. (YA). pap., stu. ed. 6.00 (978-1-875739-09-7(2)) Cambridge Univ. Pr.

—The Life & Crimes of Harry Lavender. 2002. (Wizard Study Guides Ser.). 48p. pap., stu. ed. 6.00 (978-1-875739-42-4(4)) Cambridge Univ. Pr.

—My Name Is Asher Lev. 2002. (Wizard Study Guides Ser.). (Illus.). 51p. (YA). pap., stu. ed. 6.00 (978-0-646-06746-9(X)) Cambridge Univ. Pr.

—My Place. 2002. (Wizard Study Guides Ser.). (Illus.). 44p. pap., stu. ed. 6.00 (978-0-646-07984-4(0)) Cambridge Univ. Pr.

—Othello. 2002. (Wizard Study Guides Ser.). 64p. pap., stu. ed. 6.00 (978-1-875739-06-6(8)) Cambridge Univ. Pr.

—Scission. 2002. (Wizard Study Guides Ser.). 48p. pap., stu. ed. 6.00 (978-1-875739-47-9(5)) Cambridge Univ. Pr.

—Women of the Sun. 2002. (Wizard Study Guides Ser.). 64p. pap., stu. ed. 6.00 (978-1-875739-26-4(2)) Cambridge Univ. Pr.

McRoberts, Richard & Burrell, Emma. The Blooding. 2002. (Wizard Study Guides Ser.). 48p. pap., stu. ed. 6.00 (978-1-875739-46-2(7)) Cambridge Univ. Pr.

McRoberts, Richard & Pope, Marcia. My Left Foot. 2002. (Wizard Study Guides Ser.). 44p. pap., stu. ed. 6.00 (978-1-875739-10-3(6)) Cambridge Univ. Pr.

—Proof. 2002. (Wizard Study Guides Ser.). 48p. pap., stu. ed. 6.00 (978-1-875739-28-8(9)) Cambridge Univ. Pr.

—Schindler's List. 2002. (Wizard Study Guides Ser.). 48p. pap., stu. ed. 6.00 (978-1-875739-45-5(9)) Cambridge Univ. Pr.

—Strictly Ballroom. 2002. (Wizard Study Guides Ser.). 48p. pap., stu. ed. 6.00 (978-1-875739-23-3(8)) Cambridge Univ. Pr.

McRoberts, Valerie. Tirra Lirra by the River. 2002. (Wizard Study Guides Ser.). 48p. pap., stu. ed. 6.00 (978-1-875739-88-2(2)) Cambridge Univ. Pr.

Medieval Days, 6 vols., Pack. (Rigby Infoquest Ser.). 32p. (gr. 4 up). 37.00 (978-0-7578-5735-5(3)) Rigby Education.

Meet New Friends Reader. 1999. (Metro Reading Ser.). (J). (gr. 12). per. 8.88 (978-1-58120-644-9(5)) Metropolitan Teaching & Learning Co.

Mega Jumbo ABC And 123. 2006. (J). per. 9.95 (978-1-885920-13-3(X)) Pyramid Publishing, Inc.

Megamouths & Hammerheads, 6 vols., Pack. (Sails Literacy Ser.). (gr. 1-2). 36.00 (978-0-7578-4027-2(2)) Rigby Education.

Meg's Mad Magnet, 6 vols., Pack,Set C. (gr. k-3). 29.00 (978-0-7635-0542-4(0)) Rigby Education.

Meissner, David. My Neighborhood. ed. 2003. (Early Connections Ser.). (J). pap. 35.00 (978-1-4108-1540-8(4)) Benchmark Education Co.

Memorial Day, 6 vols. (gr. k-2). 28.95 (978-0-7368-8752-6(0)) Red Brick Learning.

Menon, Esther. In the Mix: A Collection of Writing from Around the World. 2007. (Cambridge Collections). 256p. pap. (*978-0-521-70319-2(0)) Cambridge Univ. Pr.

The Merchant of Venice Study Guide. 2003. (Illus.). 48p. (YA). per. 17.95 (978-1-56254-634-2(1) , SP6341) Saddleback Educational Publishing.

Meredith Books Staff & Curry, Don, eds. Coming Home. movie tie-in ed. 2006. (Superman Returns Ser.). (Illus.). 32p. (J). pap. 3.99 (978-0-696-22961-9(7)) Meredith Bks.

—Superman Returns: Earthquake in Metropolis! 2006. (Superman Returns Ser.). (Illus.). 32p. (J). pap. 3.99 (978-0-696-22909-1(9)) Meredith Bks.

Meredith-Markowitz, Susan. A Seat on the Bus. 2003. (Early Connections Ser.). (J). pap. 33.00 (978-1-4108-1084-7(4)) Benchmark Education Co.

Metzenthen, David. Bay Boys: Big Wave Day, Adrian over the Top, Adrian Goes Out There! 2005. (Triple Play-Yellow Ser.). (Illus.). 48p. (gr. 4-8). 41.85 (978-0-7910-9080-0(9)) Facts On File, Inc.

Mi hermanita Annie. (Pebble Soup Exploraciones Ser.). 16p. (ps up). 31.00 (978-0-7578-1670-3(3)) Rigby Education.

Mi hermanita Annie: Small Book. (Pebble Soup Exploraciones Ser.). 16p. (ps up). 5.00 (978-0-7578-1710-6(6)) Rigby Education.

Michael & the Chicks. 2005. (J). (978-1-58453-295-8(5)) Pioneer Valley Educational Pr., Inc.

Midnight Rescue, 6 vols., Pack. (Action Packs Ser.). 120p. (gr. 3-5). 44.00 (978-0-7635-8391-0(X)) Rigby Education.

The Midnight Ride. (Early Intervention Levels Ser.). 28.38 (978-0-7362-2170-2(0)) Hampton-Brown Bks.

The Midnight Ride of Sybil Ludington: Fifth Grade Guided Comprehension Level N. (On Our Way to English Ser.). (gr. 5 up). 34.50 (978-0-7578-6602-9(6)) Rigby Education.

The Mighty Mississippi: Second Grade Guided Reading Level I. (On Our Way to English Ser.). (gr. 2 up). 34.50 (978-0-7578-7089-7(9)) Rigby Education.

Miles, Betty. Hey! I'm Reading! 2001. (gr. k-3). lib. bdg. 16.45 (978-0-613-71848-6(8)) Tandem Library Bks.

Miles, Lisa. Starting to Read. 2004. (Usborne Farmyard Tales Ser.). (Illus.). 18p. (J). (ps-3). pap. 6.95 (978-0-7460-3408-8(3)) EDC Publishing.

Miles Standish, 6 vols. (gr. 2-5). 39.95 (978-0-7368-4574-8(7)) Red Brick Learning.

The Mill on the Hill, 6 vols., Pack,Set B. (gr. k-3). 29.00 (978-0-7635-0536-3(6)) Rigby Education.

Miller, Austin. All Work, No Play. 2003. (Early Connections Ser.). (J). pap. 33.00 (978-1-4108-1072-4(0)) Benchmark Education Co.

Miller, Michael. Hilde und Gunter Level Two Reader, 2 books. 2003. (GER., Illus.). 53p. 6.00 (978-0-9743522-0-6(9) , 0-9743522-0-9) Miller, Michael.

Milligan, Jean F. Inferences for Young Audiences. Kennedy, Allan, illus. 2004. 96p. (J). (gr. 3-7). 14.95 (978-0-9637825-2-6(5)) Autumn Hse. Publishing.

Milliken, Linda. Triple Writing Treat. 2002. (J). per. 7.99 (978-1-56472-163-1(9)) Edupress, Inc.

Milliken, Linda & Link, Terry. More Fun with Paragraph Writing. 2002. (J). per. 9.99 (978-1-56472-165-5(5)) Edupress, Inc.

Milliken, Linda, et al. More Fun with Paragraph Writing. 2002. (J). (gr. 3-6). per. 9.99 (978-1-56472-164-8(7)) Edupress, Inc.

Mills, Claudia. Trading Places. 2006. 144p. (J). 16.00 (978-0-374-31798-0(4) , Farrar, Straus & Giroux (BYR)) Farrar, Straus & Giroux.

Milne, A. A. Pu Der Bar. 1999. Tr. of Winnie the Pooh. (GER., Illus.). (J). (ps up). pap. 14.95 (978-3-423-70395-6(4)) Deutscher Taschenbuch Verlag GmbH & Co KG DEU. *Dist:* Distribooks, Inc.

Mini Plays & Folktale Plays that Build Reading Skills. 2005. (J). pap. (*978-1-60015-036-4(5)) Steps To Literacy, LLC.

Mis Amigos los Monstruos, 6 vols., Pack. (Literatura 2000 Ser.). (SPA.). (gr. 1-2). 28.00 (978-0-7635-1047-3(5)) Rigby Education.

Mischitelli, Vincent A. Unpopular Animals. 2002. 24.95 (978-0-9721591-0-4(X)) Collaboration for Literacy for All Children.

The Missing Glasses. 2004. (J). (978-1-58453-217-0(3)) Pioneer Valley Educational Pr., Inc.

The Missing Suit. (Early Intervention Levels Ser.). 28.38 (978-0-7362-0405-7(9)) Hampton-Brown Bks.

The Missing Suit (14), Vol. 14. (Early Intervention Levels Ser.). 4.73 (978-0-7362-0230-5(7)) Hampton-Brown Bks.

Mitchell, Pratima. Raju's Ride. Waterhouse, Stephen, illus. 2005. 24p. (J). lib. bdg. 22.65 (*978-1-59646-726-2(6)) Dingles & Co.

Mitchell, Pratima & Askew, Gordon. I-Read Year 1 Anthology: Follow the Fox. 2007. (I-read Ser.). (Illus.). 40p. pap. (*978-0-521-70479-3(0)) Cambridge Univ. Pr.

Mitton, Tony. The Magic Ear. Mosedale, Julian, illus. 2001. (Cambridge Reading Ser.). 16p. pap., stu. ed. 8.00 (978-0-521-01431-1(X)) Cambridge Univ. Pr.

Mitton, Tony & Hammond, Andrew. I-Read Year 1 Anthology: Splish Splash Splosh. 2007. (I-read Ser.). (Illus.). 48p. pap. (*978-0-521-70481-6(2)) Cambridge Univ. Pr.

Mitzo Thompson, Kim & Carder, Ken. Phonics: Songs That Teach Phonics. 2005. (Sing along Activity Books with CDs Ser.). (Illus.). 32p. (J). pap. 4.99 (978-0-7696-4454-7(6)) School Specialty Publishing.

Mix It Up! Individual Title Six-Packs. (Rigby Focus Ser.). 16p. (gr. k up). 26.00 (978-0-7578-5291-6(2)); 28.00 (978-0-7578-5525-2(3)) Rigby Education.

Mixon, Myrtis. Stories from American History. 2001. 96p. (J). tchr. ed. (978-0-8442-0444-4(7)) McGraw-Hill/Contemporary.

Modern Staff. Day at Our Dairy Farm. (J). (gr. k-1). 38.95 (978-0-8136-1358-1(2)) Modern Curriculum Pr.

—Feather for Her Hair Big Book. (J). 22.95 (978-0-8136-4821-7(1)) Modern Curriculum Pr.

—Positively Me!, 8 bks. (J). (gr. k-2). pap. (978-0-8136-4801-9(7)) Modern Curriculum Pr.

—Positively Me! Big Book Collection, 8 bks., No. 1. (J). (gr. k-2). (978-0-8136-4857-6(2)) Modern Curriculum Pr.

Molly & Harry: Individual Title Six-Packs. (Sails Literacy Ser.). (gr. 1-2). 36.00 (978-0-7578-6712-5(X)) Rigby Education.

Molly the Perfect Houseguest. Date not set. (Young Global Reader Ser.: Vol. 1). (J). (978-1-887176-07-1(1)) Global Age Publishing/Global Academy Pr.

Molly's Trampoline: Individual Title Six-Packs. (Sails Literacy Ser.). (gr. 1-2). 36.00 (978-0-7578-4006-7(X)) Rigby Education.

Molter, Carey. -Ain As in Train. 2003. (Word Families Ser.). (Illus.). 23p. (J). (ps-3). lib. bdg. 19.93 (978-1-59197-272-3(8) , SandCastle) ABDO Publishing Co.

—Ake As in Cake. 2003. (Word Families Ser.). (Illus.). 23p. (J). (ps-3). lib. bdg. 19.93 (978-1-59197-270-9(1) , SandCastle) ABDO Publishing Co.

—Eam As in Ice Cream. 2003. (Word Families Ser.). (Illus.). 23p. (J). (ps-3). lib. bdg. 19.93 (978-1-59197-273-0(6) , SandCastle) ABDO Publishing Co.

—En As in Pen. 2003. (Word Families Ser.). (Illus.). 23p. (J). (ps-3). lib. bdg. 19.93 (978-1-59197-229-7(9) , SandCastle) ABDO Publishing Co.

—Ide As in Tide. 2003. (Word Families Ser.). (Illus.). 23p. (J). (ps-3). lib. bdg. 19.93 (978-1-59197-275-4(2) , SandCastle) ABDO Publishing Co.

—One As in Stone. 2003. (Word Families Ser.). (Illus.). 23p. (J). (ps-3). lib. bdg. 19.93 (978-1-59197-274-7(4) , SandCastle) ABDO Publishing Co.

—Oon As in Spoon. 2003. (Word Families Ser.). (Illus.). 23p. (J). (ps-3). lib. bdg. 19.93 (978-1-59197-266-2(3) , SandCastle) ABDO Publishing Co.

—Sh: See It Say It Hear It. l.t. ed. 2000. (Blends Ser.). (Illus.). 24p. (J). (ps-3). lib. bdg. 19.93 (978-1-57765-412-4(9) , SandCastle) ABDO Publishing Co.

Mom & Dad Set 1. 2003. (J). (978-1-58453-250-7(5)) Pioneer Valley Educational Pr., Inc.

Mom's Salsa Garden: Second Grade Guided Reading Level F. (On Our Way to English Ser.). (gr. 2 up). 34.50 (978-0-7578-7071-2(6)) Rigby Education.

Mon Hung & Mon Lung: Second Grade Guided Reading Level I. (On Our Way to English Ser.). (gr. 2 up). 34.50 (978-0-7578-7085-9(6)) Rigby Education.

Monica, Carol. Sesame Street Elmo's Easy As ABC! Kwiat, Ernie, illus. 2005. (Flap Book & DVD Ser.). 10p. (J). bds. 15.99 incl. DVD (978-0-7944-0684-4(X)) Reader's Digest Assn., Inc., The.

The Monkey: Kindergarten Guided Reading Level A. (On Our Way to English Ser.). (gr. k up). 27.75 (978-0-7578-7004-0(X)) Rigby Education.

Monroe, Debra. Little Tikes (r) Let's Play: Pretend Play Book. 2002. (Illus.). 10p. (J). (ps up). bds. 4.99 (978-1-57151-596-4(8)) Playhouse Publishing.

Monster Money Book. (Guided Reading Levels Ser.). 6.84 (978-0-7362-1740-8(1)); 41.04 (978-0-7362-2161-0(1)) Hampton-Brown Bks.

Monster Mop. (J). (978-0-8136-5219-1(7)) Modern Curriculum Pr.

Monuments & Mummies: Individual Title Six-Packs. (Rigby Infoquest Ser.). (gr. 6 up). 37.00 (978-0-7578-7993-7(4)) Rigby Education.

Moore, Clement. The Night Before Christmas. Slocum, Bradley, illus. 2007. 8p. (J). (ps-17). 9.99 (*978-1-58476-549-3(6) , IKIDS) Innovative Kids.

Moore, George. Classical Literature Vol. 1: Comprehension Activities to Develop Interest in Reading, 3 vols. 2000. 48p. (J). (gr. 3-4). pap. 7.95 (978-1-58324-100-4(0) , World Teachers Pr.) Didax Educational Resources, Inc.

—Classical Literature Vol. 2: Comprehension Activities to Develop Interest in Reading, 3 vols. 2000. 48p. (J). (gr. 5-6). pap. 7.95 (978-1-58324-101-1(9) , World Teachers Pr.) Didax Educational Resources, Inc.

Moore, Jo Ellen. Blends & Digraphs Word Machines. Evans, Marilyn, ed. Larsen, Jo, illus. 2000. (Word Machines Ser.). 28p. (J). (gr. 1-3). pap., tchr. ed. 12.95 (978-1-55799-759-3(4) , EMC 782) Evan-Moor Educational Pubs.

—Skill Sharpeners, Reading, Grade Pre-K. 2005. pap. 9.99 (978-1-59673-035-9(8) , emc 4527) Evan-Moor Educational Pubs.

Moore, Monica A. Everyday Heroes. 2006. (ENG.). 52p. per. 12.95 (*978-1-59800-563-9(4)) Outskirts Press, Inc.

Mooser, Stephen. Goofball Malone Ace Detective: All Aboard Mystery Reader Station Stop 3. Biggs, Brian, illus. 2005. (All Aboard Reading Ser.). 48p. (J). 13.99 (978-0-448-43894-8(1)); (gr. 2-4). pap. 3.99 (978-0-448-43893-1(3)) Penguin Group (USA) Inc. (Grosset & Dunlap).

More Easy Stories Plus Student Book. 2005. (978-1-56420-550-6(9)) New Readers Pr.

More Stories Plus Student Book. 2005. (978-1-56420-518-6(5)) New Readers Pr.

More Than a Meal. (Early Intervention Levels Ser.). 28.56 (978-0-7362-1049-2(0)) Hampton-Brown Bks.

Morgan, Michaela. Band of Friends. Price, Nick, illus. 2005. 24p. (J). lib. bdg. 22.65 (*978-1-59646-734-7(7)) Dingles & Co.

—Mouse with No Name. Mikhail, Jess, illus. 2004. 24p. (J). lib. bdg. 22.65 (*978-1-59646-682-1(0)) Dingles & Co.

—Shy Shark. Gomez, Elena, illus. 2005. 24p. (J). lib. bdg. 22.65 (*978-1-59646-722-4(3)) Dingles & Co.

Morgan, Ruth. Big Liam, Little Liam. Archbold, Tim, illus. 2005. 24p. (J). lib. bdg. 22.65 (*978-1-59646-728-6(2)) Dingles & Co.

—Jess & the Bean Root. 2005. (Illus.). 24p. (J). lib. bdg. 22.65 (*978-1-59646-732-3(0)) Dingles & Co.

Morgan, Sally. How Do We Move?, 8 bks. 2005. (QEB Readers). (Illus.). 24p. (J). (ps-3). lib. bdg. 15.95 (978-1-59566-077-0(1)) QEB Publishing Inc.

The Morning: Individual Title, 2 packs. (Chiquilibros Ser.). (ps-1). 12.00 (978-0-7635-8531-0(9)) Rigby Education.

Morris, Deborah. Lost Hiker & Other True Stories. l.t. ed. 2006. 151p. (J). 22.95 (978-0-7862-8034-6(4)) Thorndike Pr.

—Reading Comprehension Grade 5. 2003. (Skill Builders Ser.). 80p. (gr. 5 up). 2.95 (978-1-932210-07-1(5)) Rainbow Bridge Publishing.

Moscovich, Rotem & Lankford, Raye. Curious George Takes a Trip. 2007. (Illus.). 24p. (J). (ps-k). pap. 3.99 (*978-0-618-88403-2(3)) Houghton Mifflin Co.

Moses, Antoinette. The Girl at the Window: Starter/Beginner. 2007. (Cambridge English Readers Ser.). 32p. pap. 5.00 (*978-0-521-70585-1(1)) Cambridge Univ. Pr.

—The Girl at the Window Book: Starter/Beginner. 2007. (Cambridge English Readers Ser.). (Illus.). 32p. pap. 9.00 (*978-0-521-70586-8(X)) Cambridge Univ. Pr.

Moses, Antoinette. John Doe, Level 1. 1999. (Cambridge English Readers Ser.). (Illus.). 32p. pap. 6.00 (978-0-521-65619-1(2)) Cambridge Univ. Pr.

Moses, Brian. Cookie Crumbs, 4 vols. 2005. (QEB Readers). (Illus.). 24p. (J). (ps-3). lib. bdg. 15.95 (978-1-59566-099-2(2)) QEB Publishing Inc.

Moss, Miriam. Can I Have Some? American English Edition. 2000. (Cambridge Reading Ser.). (Illus.). 12p. pap. 5.00 (978-0-521-79526-5(5)) Cambridge Univ. Pr.

Mother Goose Asks Why? A Family Guide Introducing Science Through Great Children's Literature. 2005. (J). spiral bd. (978-0-9753985-6-2(3)) Mother Goose Programs.

A Mouse in the House. 2004. (J). (978-1-58453-281-1(5)) Pioneer Valley Educational Pr., Inc.

Move It! Set F, 6 vols. (Phonics Readers Ser.). (gr. k-2). 28.95 (978-0-7368-4085-9(0)) Red Brick Learning.

Mr. Putter Book Set 800926, 6 vols. 2005. (J). pap. (978-1-59794-091-7(7)) Environments, Inc.

Mr Verdi's New Path: Individual Title Six-Packs. (gr. k-1). 23.00 (978-0-7635-8859-5(8)) Rigby Education.

Mrs Sheep's Garden. (Early Intervention Levels Ser.). 31.86 (978-0-7362-0619-8(1)) Hampton-Brown Bks.

Mud Pie: Individual Title Six-Packs. (Literatura 2000 Ser.). (ps-1). 28.00 (978-0-7635-0034-4(8)) Rigby Education.

Muench-Williams, Heather. I Want a Pet. Teeple, Jackie, illus. l.t. ed. 2006. 12p. (J). (ps-k). pap. 10.95 (978-1-57332-353-6(5)) HighReach Learning, Inc.

Mullican, Jody. What Can It Be? Gray, Stacy A., illus. l.t. ed. 2006. 12p. (J). (ps-k). pap. 10.95 (978-1-57332-352-9(7)) HighReach Learning, Inc.

Mullican, Judy. Mary & Marsha Make Cookies. Storch, Ellen N., illus. l.t. ed. 2005. 18p. (J). (ps-k). pap. 10.95 (978-1-57332-346-8(2)) HighReach Learning, Inc.

—Someone New in the Neighborhood. Storch, Ellen N. & Gillen, Lisa P., illus. l.t. ed. 2005. 20p. (J). (ps-k). pap. 10.95 (978-1-57332-356-7(X)) HighReach Learning, Inc.

Multicultural Book Set 800717, 10. 2005. (J). (978-1-59794-015-3(1)) Environments, Inc.

Multicultural Celebrations II, 6 bks. (J). (gr. 2-4). pap. 34.95 (978-0-8136-2353-5(7)) Modern Curriculum Pr.

Multicultural Nonfiction Photo Books, 6 vols. (Content Collections). (gr. k-2). 180.30 (978-0-7362-2268-6(5)) Hampton-Brown Bks.

Mumbly, Hector. Bagel's Lucky Hat. Cooper, Dave, illus. 2007. 40p. (J). (ps-3). 15.95 (978-0-8118-4875-6(2)) Chronicle Bks. LLC.

Muntean, Michael. Brain Quest Grade 3 Reading. 2nd rev. ed. 2007. 148p. (J). 10.95 (978-0-7611-4141-9(3)) Workman Publishing Co., Inc.

The Mural of Fruit: Six-Packs. (Greetings Ser.: Vol. 1). (gr. 3-5). 31.00 (978-0-7635-1792-2(5)) Rigby Education.

Murray. Boys & Girls. 1999. (Key Words Readers Ser.: B Series, No. 641-3b). (Illus.). 56p. (J). (ps-5). 3.50 (978-0-7214-0015-0(9) , Dutton Juvenile) Penguin Group (USA) Inc.

Murray, W. The Big House. rev. ed. 1999. (Key Words Readers Ser.: B Series, No. 641-8b). (Illus.). 56p. (J). (ps-5). 3.50 (978-0-7214-0544-5(4) , Dutton Juvenile) Penguin Group (USA) Inc.

Murray, W. Key Words Reading Scheme. (Key Words Readers Ser.: C Series, No. 641-4c). (Illus.). 56p. (J). (ps-5). 3.50 (978-0-7214-0028-0(0) , Dutton Juvenile) Penguin Group (USA) Inc.

—Key Words Reading Scheme. Aitchison, Martin, illus. (Key Words Readers Ser.: A Series, No. 641-6a). 56p. (J). (ps-5). 3.50 (978-0-7214-0508-7(8) , Dutton Juvenile) Penguin Group (USA) Inc.

Murray, W. Learning Is Fun. Wingfield, Harry, illus. rev. ed. (Key Words Readers Ser.: C Series, No. 641-10c). 56p. (J). (ps-5). 3.50 (978-0-7214-0628-2(9) , Dutton Juvenile) Penguin Group (USA) Inc.

—More Sounds to Say. (Key Words Readers Ser.: C Series, No. 641-5c). (Illus.). 56p. (J). (ps-5). 3.50 (978-0-7214-0029-7(9) , Dutton Juvenile) Penguin Group (USA) Inc.

—Open Door to Reading. (Key Words Readers Ser.: C Series, No. 641-12c). (Illus.). 56p. (J). (ps-5). 3.50 (978-0-7214-0036-5(1) , Dutton Juvenile) Penguin Group (USA) Inc.

—Sunstart Reading Scheme. (Sunstart Ser.: No. 747-1). (Illus.). 50p. (J). (ps-5). 3.50 (978-0-7214-8000-8(4) , Dutton Juvenile) Penguin Group (USA) Inc.

—We Have Fun. 2nd ed. (Series S705: No. 2). (Illus.). 30p. (J). (ps-5). pap., stu. ed. 1.95 (978-0-7214-3063-8(5) , Dutton Juvenile) Penguin Group (USA) Inc.

—We Like to Help. rev. ed. (Key Words Readers Ser.: B Series, No. 641-6b). (Illus.). 56p. (J). (ps-5). 3.50 (978-0-7214-0542-1(8) , Dutton Juvenile) Penguin Group (USA) Inc.

—Workbook 1: For Use with Books 1a/1b/1c. 2nd ed. (Key Words Readers Ser.: A Series, No. 641-1a). (Illus.). 30p. (J). (ps-5). pap., stu. ed. 1.95 (978-0-7214-3062-1(7) , S705, Dutton Juvenile) Penguin Group (USA) Inc.

—Workbook 3: To Be Used with Books 3a, 3b, 3c. 2nd ed. (Key Words Readers Ser.: A Series, No. 641-3a). (Illus.). 30p. (J). (ps-5). pap., stu. ed. 1.95 (978-0-7214-3064-5(3) , Dutton Juvenile) Penguin Group (USA) Inc.

—Workbook 4: To Be Used with Books 4a, 4b, 4c. 2nd ed. (Key Words Readers Ser.: A Series, No. 641-4a). (Illus.). 30p. (J). (ps-5). pap., stu. ed. 1.95 (978-0-7214-3065-2(1) , Dutton Juvenile) Penguin Group (USA) Inc.

—Workbook 6: To Be Used with Books 6A, 6B, 6C) 2nd ed. (Key Words Readers Ser.: Series S705, No. 6). (Illus.). 30p. (J). (ps-5). pap., stu. ed. 1.95 (978-0-7214-3067-6(8) , Dutton Juvenile) Penguin Group (USA) Inc.

Murray, William. Jump from the Sky. Aitchison, Martin, illus. rev. ed. (Key Words Readers Ser.: B Series, No. 641-9b). 56p. (J). (ps-5). 3.50 (978-0-7214-0545-2(2) , Dutton Juvenile) Penguin Group (USA) Inc.

—Key Words Reading Scheme. Wingfield, W.H., illus. (Key Words Readers Ser.: A Series, No. 641-1a). 56p. (J). (ps-5). 3.50 (978-0-7214-0001-3(9) , Dutton Juvenile) Penguin Group (USA) Inc.

—Key Words Reading Scheme. Wingfield, Harry, illus. (Key Words Readers Ser.: A Series, No. 641-2a). 56p. (J). (ps-5). 3.50 (978-0-7214-0002-0(7) , Dutton Juvenile) Penguin Group (USA) Inc.

—Key Words Reading Scheme. Aitchison, Maria, illus. (Key Words Readers Ser.: C Series, No. 641-2c). 56p. (J). (ps-5). 3.50 (978-0-7214-0479-0(0) , Dutton Juvenile) Penguin Group (USA) Inc.

—Key Words Reading Scheme. Aitchison, Martin, illus. (Key Words Readers Ser.: C Series, No. 641-3c). 56p. (J). (ps-5). 3.50 (978-0-7214-0027-3(2) , Dutton Juvenile) Penguin Group (USA) Inc.

—Key Words Reading Scheme. Wingfield, W.H., illus. 2nd ed. (Key Words Readers Ser.: A Series, No. 641-4a). 56p. (J). (ps-5). 3.50 (978-0-7214-0540-7(1) , Dutton Juvenile) Penguin Group (USA) Inc.

My Big Buddy. (J). 26.20 (978-0-8136-8447-5(1)); 52.45 (978-0-8136-8014-9(X)); 26.20 (978-0-8136-8446-8(3)); 1998. pap. (978-0-8136-8308-9(4)) Modern Curriculum Pr.

My Box: Individual Title-Six Packs. (Chiquilibros Ser.). (gr. k-1). 23.00 (978-0-7635-0435-9(1)) Rigby Education.

My Brother. (Early Intervention Levels Ser.). 23.10 (978-0-7362-0015-8(0)); Vol. 4. 3.85 (978-1-56334-965-2(5)) Hampton-Brown Bks.

My Car: Kindergarten Guided Reading Level A. (On Our Way to English Ser.). (gr. k up). 27.75 (978-0-7578-7001-9(5)) Rigby Education.

My Classroom. 2004. (J). (978-1-58453-266-8(1)) Pioneer Valley Educational Pr., Inc.

My Day. (Early Intervention Levels Ser.).Tr. of Mi dia. 23.10 (978-0-7362-0014-1(2)); Vol. 3. 3.85 (978-1-56334-964-5(7)) Hampton-Brown Bks.

My Family Board Book Set 800645, 6. 2005. (J). bds. (978-1-59794-037-5(2)) Environments, Inc.

My First Reader: Fiction for Beginning Readers That Encourages Independent Reading, 5 Bks., Set. 2005. (Illus.). (J). 87.50 (978-0-516-25204-9(6)) Scholastic Library Publishing.

My Fish. (Early Intervention Levels Ser.). 21.30 (978-0-7362-0359-3(1)) Hampton-Brown Bks.

My Horse Glory. 2004. (Illus.). (J). (978-1-59577-013-4(5)) Starfall Education.

My Little Take-Home Books, Red Set. 2002. (Phonics & Friends Ser.). (gr. k-2). 129.00 (978-0-7362-0578-8(0)) Hampton-Brown Bks.

My Nest, 6 vols. 8p. (gr. k-1). 21.50 (978-0-322-02063-4(8)) Wright Group, The.

My New School: Kindergarten Guided Reading Level A. (On Our Way to English Ser.). (gr. k up). 27.75 (978-0-7578-7007-1(4)) Rigby Education.

My Place: Individual Title Six-Pack. (Story Steps Ser.). (gr. k-2). 20.00 (978-0-7635-9572-2(1)) Rigby Education.

My Planet, 6 Packs. (Chiquilibros Ser.). (gr. k-1). 23.00 (978-0-7635-0446-5(7)) Rigby Education.

My Pony. (Early Intervention Levels Ser.). 23.10 (978-0-7362-0018-9(5)); Vol. 2. 3.85 (978-1-56334-967-6(1)) Hampton-Brown Bks.

My Red Scarf: Individual Title Six-Packs. (Rigby Focus Ser.). 16p. (gr. 1 up). 28.00 (978-0-7578-5308-1(0)); 30.00 (978-0-7578-5540-5(7)) Rigby Education.

My Rooster Speaks Korean: Kindergarten Big Books. (On Our Way to English Ser.). (gr. k up). 29.95 (978-0-7578-1622-2(3)) Rigby Education.

My Rooster Speaks Korean: Small Versions of Big Books. (On Our Way to English Ser.). (gr. k up). 29.00 (978-0-7578-7219-8(0)) Rigby Education.

My School. 2004. (J). (978-1-58453-264-4(5)) Pioneer Valley Educational Pr., Inc.

My Science Project: Fifth Grade Guided Comprehension Level N. (On Our Way to English Ser.). (gr. 5 up). 34.50 (978-0-7578-6601-2(8)) Rigby Education.

My Teacher. 2004. (J). (978-1-58453-263-7(7)) Pioneer Valley Educational Pr., Inc.

My Trip: Individual Title Six-Packs. (Sails Literacy Ser.). 16p. (gr. k up). 27.00 (978-0-7635-4430-0(2)) Rigby Education.

My Two, Very, Special Friends, 1. 2006. (Illus.). 19p. (J). per. 4.00 (978-0-9788386-1-4(0)) Taylor, Y. H.

Myers, R. E. Think & Write. Tunell, Ken, illus. 2002. 48p. (J). per. 7.99 (978-1-56472-199-0(X)) Edupress, Inc.

Myers, Robert. Stories That Build Character. Rogers, Kathy, ed. 2001. 64p. (J). per. 8.95 (978-1-56472-341-3(0)) Edupress, Inc.

The Mysterious Ms Martin: Fourth Grade Guided Comprehension Level R. (On Our Way to English Ser.). (gr. 4 up). 34.50 (978-0-7578-7180-1(1)) Rigby Education.

Mystery Clues. 2005. (YA). ring bd. 49.95 (978-1-58804-403-7(3)) PCI Educational Publishing.

The Mystery of the Missing Book: Fifth Grade Guided Comprehension Level O. (On Our Way to English Ser.). (gr. 5 up). 34.50 (978-0-7578-6603-6(4)) Rigby Education.

A Mystery on Penn Street: Second Grade Guided Reading Level G. (On Our Way to English Ser.). (gr. 2 up). 34.50 (978-0-7578-7076-7(7)) Rigby Education.

Myth or Mystery? Individual Title Six-Packs. (Action Packs Ser.). 104p. (gr. 3-5). 44.00 (978-0-7635-8415-3(0)) Rigby Education.

Naidoo, Beverley. The Great Tug of War. Grobler, Piet, illus. 2006. 96p. (gr. 3). pap. 7.95 (978-1-84507-055-7(0)) Lincoln, Frances Ltd. GBR. *Dist:* Perseus Distribution.

Nap Time, 6 Packs. (Kinderstarters Ser.). 8p. (ps-1). 21.00 (978-0-7635-8647-8(1)) Rigby Education.

Nap Time for Gilbert. 2004. (J). (978-1-58453-224-8(6)) Pioneer Valley Educational Pr., Inc.

Nap Time for Lily. 2004. (J). (978-1-58453-219-4(X)) Pioneer Valley Educational Pr., Inc.

Narvaez, Concha Lopez & Salmeron, Carmelo. Tomas Es Distinto a los Demas.Tr. of Tomas Is Different from the Others. (SPA.). 64p. (J). (gr. 2-4). (978-84-216-3432-5(1)) Bruño, Editorial ESP. *Dist:* Lectorum Pubns., Inc.

A Nation of Immigrants. (Guided Reading Levels Ser.). 4.73 (978-0-7362-1700-2(2)); 28.38 (978-0-7362-2145-0(X)) Hampton-Brown Bks.

Nayer, Judy. 25 Easy Bilingual Nonfiction Mini-Books: Easy-to-Read Reproducible Mini-Books in English & Spanish That Build Vocabulary & Fluency-and Support the Social Studies & Science Topics You Teach. 2005. 64p. pap. 11.99 (978-0-439-70544-8(4) , Teaching Resources) Scholastic, Inc.

—25 Easy Nonfiction Mini-Books: Easy-to-Read Reproducible Mini-Books That Build Vocabulary & Fluency-and Support the Social Studies & Science Topics You Teach. 2005. 64p. pap. 11.99 (978-0-439-46603-5(2) , Teaching Resources) Scholastic, Inc.

Necklaces. (Early Intervention Levels Ser.). 21.30 (978-0-7362-0371-5(0)); Vol. 3. 3.55 (978-0-7362-0092-9(4)) Hampton-Brown Bks.

The Neighborhood Picnic, 6 vols. (Multicultural Programs Ser.). 16p. (gr. 1-3). 24.95 (978-0-7802-9217-8(0)) Wright Group, The.

Neighborhood Soup. (J). 21.95 (978-0-8136-4267-3(1)); (gr. 2). 23.50 (978-0-8136-8830-5(2)) Modern Curriculum Pr.

A Nest of Grass: Individual Title, 6 packs. (Sails Literacy Ser.). (gr. 1-2). 36.00 (978-0-7578-6727-9(8)) Rigby Education.

Never Say Never. (Little Book Practice Reader Ser.). (J). (978-0-8136-0883-9(X)) Modern Curriculum Pr.

The New Class Pet: Second Grade Guided Reading Level K. (On Our Way to English Ser.). (gr. 2 up). 34.50 (978-0-7578-7095-8(3)) Rigby Education.

The New Girl: Third Grade Guided Reading Level H. (On Our Way to English Ser.). (gr. 3 up). 34.50 (978-0-7578-7107-8(0)) Rigby Education.

The New Pen: Third Grade Guided Reading Level M. (On Our Way to English Ser.). (gr. 3 up). 34.50 (978-0-7578-7130-6(5)) Rigby Education.

A New Year Called Tet: Second Grade Guided Reading Level J. (On Our Way to English Ser.). (gr. 2 up). 34.50 (978-0-7578-7094-1(5)) Rigby Education.

Newcomb, Kristene. Molly Q's Trash Travels Through the Water Cycle. Paschall, Patricia, ed. Newcomb, Kristene, illus. 2007. (Illus.). 32p. (J). per. 8.00 (***978-0-9760790-9-5(7)***) Folsom Fallies Pr.

Nice Vine, Quite Fine, Vol. 2. 2005. (Early Library). (YA). (ps-3). 23.94 (978-0-8215-8946-5(6)) Sadlier, William H. Inc.

Nichols, Yuriko. All Around the Farm - Red Readers: Red Book Kit. Mallard, Michelle, illus. 2nd ed. 1998. (Learning Language Arts Through Literature Ser.). 46p. (J). pap. 7.00 (978-1-880892-53-4(7)) Common Sense Pr.

—Forest Fables - Red Readers: Red Book Kit. Mallard, Michelle, illus. 2nd ed. 1998. (Learning Language Arts Through Literature Ser.). 36p. (J). pap. 7.00 (978-1-880892-54-1(5)) Common Sense Pr.

Nicholson, Nancy. Devotional Stories for Little Folks Too. 2007. (J). per. (***978-0-9771236-1-2(8)***) For Little Folks.

Nickelodeon Staff, illus. Dora's Big Book of Stories. 2005. (Dora the Explorer Ser.). 192p. (J). 10.95 (978-1-4169-0708-4(4) , Simon Spotlight/Nickelodeon) Simon & Schuster Children's Publishing.

Nicolson, Cynthia Pratt. Discover Space. Slavin, Bill, illus. 2005. (Kids Can Read Alone Ser.). 32p. (J). (ps-ps). (978-1-55337-823-5(7)) Kids Can Pr., Ltd.

—Discover the Planets. Slavin, Bill, illus. 2005. (Kids Can Read Alone Ser.). 32p. (J). (ps-ps). (978-1-55337-825-9(3)) Kids Can Pr., Ltd.

Night Animals Little Book: Early Reading Fluency, Level A. 2004. pap. 6.00 (978-0-7398-8171-2(X)) Steck-Vaughn.

The Night of the Pumpkins: Second Grade Guided Reading Level K. (On Our Way to English Ser.). (gr. 2 up). 34.50 (978-0-7578-7097-2(X)) Rigby Education.

Nightmare Hill. 2003. (J). (978-1-58453-257-6(2)) Pioneer Valley Educational Pr., Inc.

Niles Likes to Smile, Vol. 2. 2005. (Early Library). (YA). (ps-3). 23.94 (978-0-8215-8956-4(3)) Sadlier, William H. Inc.

Nixon & Brush. Champagne with a Corpse. (Thumbprint Mysteries Ser.). 32.86 (978-0-8092-0420-5(7)) McGraw-Hill/Contemporary.

No Fair! Fifth Grade Guided Comprehension Level S. (On Our Way to English Ser.). (gr. 5 up). 34.50 (978-0-7578-6624-1(7)) Rigby Education.

No Place Like Home. 6.00 (978-0-687-85873-6(9)) Abingdon Pr.

No Place Like Home. (Lexile Levels Ser.). 47.88 (978-1-56334-094-9(1)) Hampton-Brown Bks.

No Queen Today! 3-in-1 Package. (Sails Literacy Ser.). 24p. (gr. 2 up). 57.00 (978-0-7578-3217-8(2)) Rigby Education.

No Queen Today! 6 Small Books. (Sails Literacy Ser.). 24p. (gr. 2 up). 25.00 (978-0-7578-3193-5(1)) Rigby Education.

No Queen Today! Big Book Only. (Sails Literacy Ser.). 24p. (gr. 2 up). 27.00 (978-0-7635-6995-2(X)) Rigby Education.

No Secrets. 64p. (YA). (gr. 6-12). pap. (978-0-8224-2381-2(2)) Globe Fearon Educational Publishing.

No Time to Lose. 2003. (Illus.). pap. 7.60 (978-0-7398-7533-9(7)) Steck-Vaughn.

No TV: Individual Title Six-Packs. (Sails Literacy Ser.). (gr. 1-2). 36.00 (978-0-7578-6708-8(1)) Rigby Education.

Noble, Trinka Hakes. Pennsylvania Reader. Darnell, Kathryn, illus. rev. ed. 2007. (State Readers Ser.). 96p. 12.95 (***978-1-58536-320-9(0)***) Sleeping Bear Pr.

Noises in the Night: Third Grade Guided Reading Level K. (On Our Way to English Ser.). (gr. 3 up). 34.50 (978-0-7578-7121-4(6)) Rigby Education.

Noonan, Diana. On the Move, 6 vols. (Wonder Worldtm Ser.). 16p. 29.95 (978-0-7802-2014-0(5)) Wright Group, The.

Nora's Money: Second Grade Guided Reading Level H. (On Our Way to English Ser.). (gr. 2 up). 34.50 (978-0-7578-7082-8(1)) Rigby Education.

Norris, Jill. Reading, Grade 1 (Skill Sharpeners) 2005. (Sharpeners Ser.). pap. 9.99 (978-1-59673-037-3(4)) Evan-Moor Educational Pubs.

—Skill Sharpeners, Reading, Kindergarten. 2005. pap. 9.99 (978-1-59673-036-6(6) , emc 4528) Evan-Moor Educational Pubs.

Not When It's Hot. (Early Intervention Levels Ser.). 21.30 (978-0-7362-0387-6(7)) Hampton-Brown Bks.

Novelli, Joan. Phonics. 2006. 80p. pap. 12.99 (978-0-439-53796-4(7) , Teaching Resources) Scholastic, Inc.

Now & Long Ago Set C, 6 vols. (Phonics Readers Ser.). (gr. k-2). 17.50 (978-0-7368-3218-2(1)) Red Brick Learning.

Now Hear This! Fifth Grade Class Collection Books. (On Our Way to English Ser.). (gr. 5 up). 29.95 (978-0-7578-4469-0(3)) Rigby Education.

Now Hear This! Small Versions of Class Collection Books. (On Our Way to English Ser.). (gr. 5 up). 34.50 (978-0-7578-7285-3(9)) Rigby Education.

Nutrition Adventures with the Nutri Gang, Race Day, Issue #1: The Nutri Gang. 2007. (J). 2.99 (***978-0-9792383-0-7(7)***) KJ Pubns.

Nuttall, Gina. Is Lion Sick?, 4 vols. 2005. (QEB Readers). (Illus.). 24p. (J). (ps-3). lib. bdg. 15.95 (978-1-59566-100-5(X)) QEB Publishing Inc.

O#39;Connell, Susan R. Real World Math. 2001. 80p. (J). (gr. 4-6). pap. 12.99 (978-0-7682-0100-0(4) , GA1686) School Specialty Publishing.

An Old Family Recipe. (Early Intervention Levels Ser.). 4.73 (978-0-7362-1757-6(6)); 28.38 (978-0-7362-2165-8(4)) Hampton-Brown Bks.

The Old Toad. (Early Intervention Levels Ser.). 28.38 (978-0-7362-0398-2(2)) Hampton-Brown Bks.

The Old Toad (8), Vol. 8. (Early Intervention Levels Ser.). 4.73 (978-0-7362-0223-7(4)) Hampton-Brown Bks.

Oliver Twist Study Guide. 2000. (Illus.). 48p. (YA). per. 17.95 (978-1-56254-296-2(6) , SP2966) Saddleback Educational Publishing.

Olker, Constance. The Punctuation Pals Go to the Baseball Park. 2005. (Illus.). 44p. (J). per. 18.95 (978-1-933449-15-9(2)) Nightengale Pr.

—The Punctuation Pals Go to the Beach. 2005. (Illus.). 36p. (J). per. 18.95 (978-1-933449-12-8(8)) Nightengale Pr.

—The Punctuation Pals Go to the Moon. 2005. (Illus.). 64p. (J). per. 24.95 (978-1-933449-13-5(6)) Nightengale Pr.

—The Punctuation Pals Meet at School. 2005. (Illus.). 40p. (J). per. 18.95 (978-1-933449-07-4(1)) Nightengale Pr.

Olsen, Sylvia. Murphy & Mousetrap. 2005. (Orca Young Readers Ser.). (Illus.). 128p. (J). (gr. 3-6). pap. 5.95 (978-1-55143-344-8(3)) Orca Bk. Pubs. USA.

Omar's Surprise: First Grade Guided Reading Level E. (On Our Way to English Ser.). (gr. 1 up). 27.75 (978-0-7578-7044-6(9)) Rigby Education.

A on a Farm Set, 6 vols. (Phonics Readers Ser.). (gr. k-2). 17.50 (978-0-7368-3187-1(8)) Red Brick Learning.

On a Log: Kindergarten Newcomer Books. (On Our Way to English Ser.). (gr. k up). 23.50 (978-0-7578-7187-0(9)) Rigby Education.

On a Roll: How Communities Build State Parks. 2005. (Book Treks Ser.). (J). 37.95 (978-0-7652-3254-0(5)) Celebration Pr.

On Our Way to English: Complete Package - Grade 1. (gr. 1 up). 2195.00 (978-0-7578-6968-6(8)) Rigby Education.

On Our Way to English: Complete Package - Grade 2. (gr. 2 up). 2195.00 (978-0-7578-6969-3(6)) Rigby Education.

On Our Way to English: Complete Package - Grade 3. (gr. 3 up). 2195.00 (978-0-7578-6970-9(X)) Rigby Education.

On Our Way to English: Complete Package - Grade 4. (gr. 4 up). 2195.00 (978-0-7578-6971-6(8)) Rigby Education.

On Our Way to English: Complete Package - Grade 5. (gr. 5 up). 2195.00 (978-0-7578-6972-3(6)) Rigby Education.

On Our Way to English: Complete Package - Kindergarten. (gr. k up). 1895.00 (978-0-7578-6967-9(X)) Rigby Education.

On the Go. 2005. (Little Celebrations Thematic Packages Ser.). (J). (gr. k-3). 133.50 (978-0-673-75383-0(2)) Celebration Pr.

On the Move, 6 Packs. (Rigby Infoquest Ser.). (gr. 6 up). 37.00 (978-0-7578-7987-6(X)) Rigby Education.

On the Wild Side: Individual Title Six-Packs. (Rigby Infoquest Ser.). 32p. (gr. 4 up). 37.00 (978-0-7578-5743-0(4)) Rigby Education.

On This Earth. (Early Intervention Levels Ser.). 23.10 (978-0-7362-0037-0(1)) Hampton-Brown Bks.

On Your Mark: Grade 1 Reading Fluency Booklet. (gr. 1 up). 57.19 (978-0-7362-2474-1(2)) Hampton-Brown Bks.

On Your Mark: Grade 2 Reading Fluency Booklet. (gr. 2 up). 57.19 (978-0-7362-2475-8(0)) Hampton-Brown Bks.

On Your Mark: Grade 3 Reading Fluency Booklet. (gr. 3 up). 57.19 (978-0-7362-2476-5(9)) Hampton-Brown Bks.

On Your Mark: Grade 4 Reading Fluency Booklet. (gr. 4 up). 57.19 (978-0-7362-2477-2(7)) Hampton-Brown Bks.

On Your Mark: Grade 5 Reading Fluency Booklet. (gr. 5 up). 57.19 (978-0-7362-2478-9(5)) Hampton-Brown Bks.

On Your Mark: Grade 6 Reading Fluency Booklet. (gr. 6 up). 57.19 (978-0-7362-2479-6(3)) Hampton-Brown Bks.

On Your Mark: Grade 7 Reading Fluency Booklet. (gr. 7 up). 57.19 (978-0-7362-2480-2(7)) Hampton-Brown Bks.

On Your Mark: Grade 8 Reading Fluency Booklet. (gr. 8 up). 57.19 (978-0-7362-2481-9(5)) Hampton-Brown Bks.

One Afternoon. (Lexile Levels Ser.). 7.98 (978-1-56334-674-3(5)); 47.88 (978-0-7362-2121-4(2)) Hampton-Brown Bks.

One Land, Many Cultures Set F, 6 vols. (Phonics Readers Ser.). (gr. k-2). 28.95 (978-0-7368-4079-8(6)) Red Brick Learning.

One Piece at a Time. 2003. (Illus.). pap. 5.60 (978-0-7398-7511-7(6)) Steck-Vaughn.

One Piece at a Time 5-Pack. 2003. (Illus.). pap. 28.35 (978-0-7398-7545-2(0)) Steck-Vaughn.

One, Two, Three, Four. (Early Intervention Levels Ser.). 23.10 (978-0-7362-0035-6(5)); Vol. 6. 3.85 (978-1-56334-983-6(3)) Hampton-Brown Bks.

O'Neill, Rachael, illus. My First Library: With Nine Colorful Books. (J). (978-1-85479-804-6(9)) O'Mara, Michael Bks., Ltd.

Open Court Staff. Intermediate Think Storybook: Level 4. (J). pap. (978-0-89688-693-3(X) , 88693) Open Court Publishing Co.

Optometrist: Individual Title Six-Packs. (Bookweb Ser.). 32p. (gr. 3 up). 34.00 (978-0-7635-3946-7(5)) Rigby Education.

Oral Language Flip Chart: Time to Speak & Listen. 2004. (gr. k up). suppl. ed. 109.15 (978-0-328-02214-4(4)) Addison-Wesley Educational Pubs., Inc.

Orange & Red Levels Certificate Only. (Discovery World Ser.). (gr. 1-2). 89.00 (978-0-7578-6527-5(5)) Rigby Education.

O'Reilly, Shelley. One True Thing. 2002. (Wizard Study Guides Ser.). 64p. pap., stu. ed. 6.00 (978-1-876367-73-2(3)) Cambridge Univ. Pr.

Orme, David. Crime. 2008. (Trailblazers Ser.). (Illus.). 36p. pap. 7.95 (***978-1-84167-651-7(9)***) Ransom Publishing Ltd. GBR. *Dist:* International Publishers Marketing.

—Death. 2007. (Trailblazers Ser.). (Illus.). 36p. pap. 7.95 (***978-1-84167-591-6(1)***) Ransom Publishing Ltd. GBR. *Dist:* International Publishers Marketing.

—Don't Try This at Home. 2008. (Trailblazers Ser.). (Illus.). 36p. pap. 7.95 (***978-1-84167-652-4(7)***) Ransom Publishing Ltd. GBR. *Dist:* International Publishers Marketing.

—Extreme Sports. 2007. (Trailblazers Ser.). (Illus.). 36p. pap. 7.95 (***978-1-84167-590-9(3)***) Ransom Publishing Ltd. GBR. *Dist:* International Publishers Marketing.

—Fashion. 2008. (Trailblazers Ser.). (Illus.). 36p. pap. 7.95 (***978-1-84167-650-0(0)***) Ransom Publishing Ltd. GBR. *Dist:* International Publishers Marketing.

—Great Journeys. 2008. (Trailblazers Ser.). (Illus.). 36p. pap. 7.95 (***978-1-84167-653-1(5)***) Ransom Publishing Ltd. GBR. *Dist:* International Publishers Marketing.

—How to Be a Pop Star. 2007. (Trailblazers Ser.). (Illus.). 36p. pap. 7.95 (***978-1-84167-594-7(6)***) Ransom Publishing Ltd. GBR. *Dist:* International Publishers Marketing.

—Manga. 2007. (Trailblazers Ser.). (Illus.). 36p. pap. 7.95 (***978-1-84167-593-0(8)***) Ransom Publishing Ltd. GBR. *Dist:* International Publishers Marketing.

—Plague. 2004. (Shades Ser.). 58p. (J). pap. 7.99 (978-0-237-52729-7(4) , Evans Brothers, Limited) Evans Publishing Group GBR. *Dist:* Independent Pubs. Group.

—Sea Killers. 2007. (Trailblazers Ser.). (ACE., Illus.). 36p. pap. 7.95 (***978-1-84167-592-3(X)***) Ransom Publishing Ltd. GBR. *Dist:* International Publishers Marketing.

—Weird Places. 2007. (Trailblazers Ser.). (Illus.). 36p. pap. 7.95 (***978-1-84167-589-3(X)***) Ransom Publishing Ltd. GBR. *Dist:* International Publishers Marketing.

Orme, Helen. Lost! 2007. (Siti's Sisters Ser.). (Illus.). 36p. pap. 7.95 (***978-1-84167-598-5(9)***) Ransom Publishing Ltd. GBR. *Dist:* International Publishers Marketing.

Ormerod, Jan. I Can Ride. 1998. (Cambridge Reading Ser.). (Illus.). 10p. (ps-1). pap. 3.95 (978-0-521-63630-8(2)) Cambridge Univ. Pr.

—I Can Skate. 1998. (Cambridge Reading Ser.). (Illus.). 10p. (ps-1). pap. 3.95 (978-0-521-63632-2(9)) Cambridge Univ. Pr.

—I Like Playing. 1998. (Cambridge Reading Ser.). (Illus.). 10p. (ps-1). pap. 3.95 (978-0-521-63629-2(9)) Cambridge Univ. Pr.

—In the Pool. 1998. (Cambridge Reading Ser.). (Illus.). 10p. (ps-1). pap. 3.95 (978-0-521-63627-8(2)) Cambridge Univ. Pr.

—Play with Me. 1998. (Cambridge Reading Ser.). (Illus.). 10p. (ps-1). pap. 3.95 (978-0-521-63628-5(0)) Cambridge Univ. Pr.

—Ride with Me. 1998. (Cambridge Reading Ser.). (Illus.). 10p. (ps-1). pap. 3.95 (978-0-521-63631-5(0)) Cambridge Univ. Pr.

—Skate with Me. 1998. (Cambridge Reading Ser.). (Illus.). 10p. (ps-1). pap. 3.95 (978-0-521-63633-9(7)) Cambridge Univ. Pr.

—Splash! 1998. (Cambridge Reading Ser.). (Illus.). 10p. (ps-1). pap. 3.95 (978-0-521-63626-1(4)) Cambridge Univ. Pr.

Orozco, Jose-Luis. Rin, Rin, Rin/Do, Re, Mi. Diaz, David, illus. 2005. 32p. (J). (ps-k). pap. 3.50 (978-0-439-75531-3(X) , Orchard Bks.) Scholastic, Inc.

Ortells, Estela. En Africa. (Coleccion Pequeno Simon). (SPA., Illus.). 32p. (J). 7.95 (978-84-7189-177-8(8) , ORT342) Ortells, Alfredo Editorial S.L. ESP. *Dist:* Continental Bk. Co., Inc.

—En el Aire. (Coleccion Pequeno Simon). (SPA., Illus.). 32p. (J). 7.95 (978-84-7189-173-0(5) , ORT328) Ortells, Alfredo Editorial S.L. ESP. *Dist:* Continental Bk. Co., Inc.

—En el Rio. (Coleccion Pequeno Simon). (SPA., Illus.). 32p. (J). 7.95 (978-84-7189-169-3(7) , ORT346) Ortells, Alfredo Editorial S.L. ESP. *Dist:* Continental Bk. Co., Inc.

—En la India. (Coleccion Pequeno Simon). (SPA., Illus.). 32p. (J). 7.95 (978-84-7189-175-4(1) , ORT330) Ortells, Alfredo Editorial S.L. ESP. *Dist:* Continental Bk. Co., Inc.

—En la Nieve. (Coleccion Pequeno Simon). (SPA., Illus.). 32p. (J). 7.95 (978-84-7189-172-3(7) , ORT344) Ortells, Alfredo Editorial S.L. ESP. *Dist:* Continental Bk. Co., Inc.

—En la Playa. (Coleccion Pequeno Simon). (SPA., Illus.). 32p. (J). 7.95 (978-84-7189-168-6(9) , ORT347) Ortells, Alfredo Editorial S.L. ESP. *Dist:* Continental Bk. Co., Inc.

—Y los Chihuhuas. (Coleccion Pequeno Simon). (SPA., Illus.). 32p. (J). 7.95 (978-84-7189-174-7(3) , ORT345) Ortells, Alfredo Editorial S.L. ESP. *Dist:* Continental Bk. Co., Inc.

Orwell, George. Penguin Reader Level 4: 1984. 2003. (Illus.). 80p. (C). pap. 9.00 (978-0-582-77731-6(3)) Pearson ESL.

Oscar & Tatiana: Individual Title Six-Packs. (Literatura 2000 Ser.). (gr. 2-3). 33.00 (978-0-7635-0267-6(7)) Rigby Education.

Oscar y Tatiana: Individual Title Six-Packs. (Literatura 2000 Ser.). (gr. 2-3). 33.00 (978-0-7635-1268-2(0)) Rigby Education.

Ostby, Kristin. Hide-and-Seek. Ruppert, Larry, illus. 2007. 24p. (J). pap. 3.99 (978-0-448-44467-3(4) , Grosset & Dunlap) Penguin Group (USA) Inc.

Otfinoski, Steve. Coin Collecting for Kids. Graham, Jack, illus. ed. 2007. 12p. (J). (gr. 1-7). bds. 15.99 (***978-1-58476-624-7(7)*** , IKIDS) Innovative Kids.

Otter, Otter. (Early Intervention Levels Ser.). 21.30 (978-0-7362-0381-4(8)); Vol. 4. 3.55 (978-0-7362-0102-5(5)) Hampton-Brown Bks.

Otter, Otter. (J). 26.20 (978-0-8136-8416-1(1)); 59.50 (978-0-8136-7954-9(0)); 1998. pap. (978-0-8136-8298-3(3)) Modern Curriculum Pr.

Ottolenghi, Carol. The Little Red Hen. Holladay, Reggie, illus. 2002. (Brighter Child Keepsake Stories Ser.). 32p. (J). (ps-3). pap. 3.99 (978-1-57768-378-0(1) , Brighter Child) School Specialty Publishing.

Ouch! Fourth Grade Guided Comprehension Level P. (On Our Way to English Ser.). (gr. 4 up). 34.50 (978-0-7578-7173-3(9)) Rigby Education.

Our Adobe House: 6 Small Books. (Greetings Ser.: Vol. 2). 24p. (gr. 2-3). 31.00 (978-0-7635-9428-2(8)) Rigby Education.

Our Adobe House: Big Book. (Greetings Ser.: Vol. 2). 24p. (gr. 2-3). 31.00 (978-0-7635-5860-4(5)) Rigby Education.

Our Flag Set B, 6 vols. (Phonics Readers Ser.). (gr. k-2). 17.50 (978-0-7368-3201-4(7)) Red Brick Learning.

Our Government: Fifth Grade Newcomer Books. (On Our Way to English Ser.). (gr. 5 up). 34.50 (978-0-7578-7274-7(3)) Rigby Education.

Our Inside Story: Individual Title Six-Packs. (Rigby Infoquest Ser.). (gr. 6 up). 37.00 (978-0-7578-7990-6(X)) Rigby Education.

Our Land: Fourth Grade Newcomer Books. (On Our Way to English Ser.). (gr. 4 up). 34.50 (978-0-7578-7258-7(1)) Rigby Education.

Our Natural Resources Set E, 6 vols. (Phonics Readers Ser.). (gr. k-2). 28.95 (978-0-7368-4070-5(2)) Red Brick Learning.

Our New Baby, 6 Packs. (ps-2). 27.00 (978-0-7635-9469-5(5)) Rigby Education.

Our New Baby. 2006. 16p. (J). pap. 1.99 (978-0-7847-1706-6(0) , 04167) Standard Publishing.

Our Place in Space, 6, Pack. (Rigby Infoquest Ser.). 24p. (gr. 3 up). 34.00 (978-0-7578-5775-1(2)) Rigby Education.

Our Red-White-and-Blue Holidays Set D, 6 vols. (Phonics Readers Ser.). (gr. k-2). 28.95 (978-0-7368-4054-5(0)) Red Brick Learning.

Over the Edge: Magazine Anthology: Level 7, 6 vols. (Comprehension Strand Ser.). (gr. 4-8). 54.00 (978-0-322-06043-2(5)) Wright Group, The.

Oxlade, Chris. Mighty Machines, 8bks. 2005. (QEB Readers). (Illus.). 24p. (J). (ps-3). lib. bdg. 15.95 (978-1-59566-079-4(8)) QEB Publishing Inc.

O'Brien, Kathryn. I¿d Be Your Princess. Garland, Michael, illus. 2007. (J). 6.99 (*978-0-7847-1964-0(0)) Standard Publishing.

Pablo's Fiesta: First Grade Guided Reading Level D. (On Our Way to English Ser.). (gr. 1 up). 27.75 (978-0-7578-7039-2(2)) Rigby Education.

Paez, Enrique. Devuelveme el Anillo, Pelo Cepillo. (SPA.). (YA). (gr. 5-8). 112p. (978-84-216-2561-3(6) , BU7584); 12th ed. (Illus.). 144p. (978-84-216-1800-4(8) , BU5113) Bruño, Editorial ESP. *Dist:* Lectorum Pubns., Inc.

Page, Nick & Page, Claire. Read with Me Three Billy Goats Gruff: Sticker Activity Book. Saunders, Katie, illus. 2006. (Read with Me (Make Believe Ideas) Ser.). 12p. (J). (gr. k-2). pap. 4.95 (978-1-84610-181-6(6)) Make Believe Ideas GBR. *Dist:* Ingram Pub. Services.

—Read W/Me 6v. 2006. (Illus.). (J). (ps-3). 23.70 (978-5-558-47727-6(X)) Make Believe Ideas GBR. *Dist:* Ingram Pub. Services.

Page, Nick, et al. Seashore. 2006. (Ready to Read Sticker Ser.). (Illus.). 12p. (J). (ps-3). pap., pap., wbk. ed. 3.95 (978-1-84610-127-4(1)) Make Believe Ideas GBR. *Dist:* Ingram Pub. Services.

Page, Nick & Claire. The Good Samaritan. 2006. (Read with Me (Make Believe Ideas) Ser.). (Illus.). 31p. (J). (gr. k-2). 3.95 (978-1-84610-174-8(3)) Make Believe Ideas GBR. *Dist:* Ingram Pub. Services.

—Jack & the Beanstalk. 2006. (Read with Me (Make Believe Ideas) Ser.). (Illus.). 12p. (J). (gr. k-2). pap. 4.95 (978-1-84610-180-9(8)) Make Believe Ideas GBR. *Dist:* Ingram Pub. Services.

—Jonah the Moaner. 2006. (Read with Me (Make Believe Ideas) Ser.). (Illus.). 12p. (J). (gr. k-2). pap. 4.95 (978-1-84610-183-0(2)) Make Believe Ideas GBR. *Dist:* Ingram Pub. Services.

—Noah & the Ark. 2006. (Read with Me (Make Believe Ideas) Ser.). 32p. (J). (gr. k-2). 3.95 (978-1-84610-168-7(9)) Make Believe Ideas GBR. *Dist:* Ingram Pub. Services.

—Read with Me - Sticker Activity Books: Elves & the Shoemaker. 2006. (Read with Me (Make Believe Ideas) Ser.). (Illus.). 12p. (J). (gr. k-2). pap. 4.95 (978-1-84610-177-9(8)) Make Believe Ideas GBR. *Dist:* Ingram Pub. Services.

—Read with Me Rumpelstiltskin: Sticker Activity Book. 2006. (Read with Me (Make Believe Ideas) Ser.). (Illus.). 12p. (J). (gr. k-2). pap. 4.95 (978-1-84610-182-3(4)) Make Believe Ideas GBR. *Dist:* Ingram Pub. Services.

—The Runaway Son. 2006. (Read with Me Ser.). (Illus.). 31p. (J). (gr. k-2). 3.95 (978-1-84610-176-2(X)) Make Believe Ideas GBR. *Dist:* Ingram Pub. Services.

—Snow White: Sticker Activity Book. Willey, Bee, illus. 2006. (Read with Me (Make Believe Ideas) Ser.). 12p. (J). (gr. k-2). pap. 4.95 (978-1-84610-179-3(4)) Make Believe Ideas GBR. *Dist:* Ingram Pub. Services.

Pan y Canela: Super Classroom Set. (SPA.). (gr. k-2). 1289.61 (978-0-7362-0445-3(8)) Hampton-Brown Bks.

Pandora's Box: Level M, 6 vols. 128p. (gr. 2-3). 41.95 (978-0-7699-1027-7(0)) Shortland Pubns. (U. S. A.) Inc.

Panman, Sandra & Panman, Richard. The Active Reader for Writers. Panman, Sandra, ed. 3rd rev. ed. 2004. 288p. (C). (gr. 9-12). pap. 24.95 (978-0-912813-30-1(X)) Active Learning Corp.

The Paper Trail: Individual Title Six-Packs. (gr. 1-2). 25.00 (978-0-7635-9137-3(8)) Rigby Education.

Paré, Roger. Smart Start, 4 bks. Paré, Roger, illus. Incl. Alphabet. Lantier, Patricia, tr. from FRE. lib. bdg. 22.00 (978-0-8368-2843-6(7)); Colors. lib. bdg. 22.00 (978-0-8368-2844-3(5)); Numbers. Lantier, Patricia, tr. from FRE. lib. bdg. 22.00 (978-0-8368-2845-0(3)); Opposites. lib. bdg. 22.00 (978-0-8368-2846-7(1)); 24p. (J). (ps up). 2001. (Illus.). Set lib. bdg. 88.00 (978-0-8368-2842-9(9)) Stevens, Gareth Inc.

Parker. Days In... 6-Pack (24 Books), Set. 2004. (Illus.). pap. 118.80 (978-1-4109-1250-3(7)) Raintree.

Parker, Don H. & Scannell, Genevieve. My Own Book. 4th ed. 2002. (gr. 1-3). stu. ed. 25.47 (978-0-02-674579-6(8)) SRA/McGraw-Hill.

Parker, Lewis K, J Pierpont Morgan & Wall Street: Individual Title Six-Packs. (On Deck Ser.: Vol. 2). 24p. (gr. 4-5). 35.00 (978-0-7578-5850-5(3)) Rigby Education.

—Why German Immigrants Came to America: Individual Title Six-Packs. (On Deck Ser.: Vol. 2). 24p. (gr. 4-5). 35.00 (978-0-7578-5835-2(X)) Rigby Education.

—Why Irish Immigrants Came to America: Individual Title Six-Packs. (On Deck Ser.: Vol. 2). 24p. (gr. 4-5). 35.00 (978-0-7578-5836-9(8)) Rigby Education.

—Why Italian Immigrants Came to America: Individual Title Six-Packs. (On Deck Ser.: Vol. 2). 24p. (gr. 4-5). 35.00 (978-0-7578-5837-6(6)) Rigby Education.

—Why Japanese Immigrants Came to America: Individual Title Six-Packs. (On Deck Ser.: Vol. 2). 24p. (gr. 4-5). 35.00 (978-0-7578-5838-3(4)) Rigby Education.

—Why Mexican Immigrants Came to America: Individual Title Six-Packs. (On Deck Ser.: Vol. 2). 24p. (gr. 4-5). 35.00 (978-0-7578-5839-0(2)) Rigby Education.

—Why Vietnamese Immigrants Came to America: Individual Title Six-Packs. (On Deck Ser.: Vol. 2). 24p. (gr. 4-5). 35.00 (978-0-7578-5840-6(6)) Rigby Education.

Parkin, Lance & Jones, Mark. Dark Matters: An Unofficial & Unauthorised Guide to Philip Pullman's Dark Materials Trilogy. 2005. 272p. (YA). pap. 7.95 (978-0-7535-1025-4(1)) Virgin Bks. Ltd. GBR. *Dist:* Macmillan.

Parramon, José María. Mi Escuela. Borday, Irene, illus. (Coleccion Estoy En...).Tr. of My School. (SPA.). 32p. (J). (gr. k-3). 6.36 (978-84-342-1004-2(5)) Parramon Ediciones S.A. ESP. *Dist:* Lectorum Pubns., Inc.

Parramon, José María & Bordoy, Irene. Mi Escuela.Tr. of My School. (SPA., Illus.). (J). (ps-1). 6.95 (978-958-04-1276-2(6)) Norma S.A. COL. *Dist:* Distribuidora Norma, Inc.

Partners: Individual Title Six-Packs. (ps-2). 23.00 (978-0-7635-8820-5(2)) Rigby Education.

Partridge, Juliet. That's Me! American English Edition. 2000. (Cambridge Reading Ser.). (Illus.). 8p. pap. 5.00 (978-0-521-78423-8(9)) Cambridge Univ. Pr.

Party Clothes. 2004. (J). (978-1-58453-279-8(3)) Pioneer Valley Educational Pr., Inc.

A Party for the Alley Cats: 3-in-1 Package. (Sails Literacy Ser.). 24p. (gr. 2 up). 57.00 (978-0-7578-6832-0(0)) Rigby Education.

A Party for the Alley Cats: 6 Small Books. (Sails Literacy Ser.). 24p. (gr. 2 up). 25.00 (978-0-7578-6828-3(2)) Rigby Education.

A Party for the Alley Cats: Big Book Only. (Sails Literacy Ser.). 24p. (gr. 2 up). 27.00 (978-0-7578-6820-7(7)) Rigby Education.

Pascal, Francine. Con las Riendas Firmes. Orig. Title: Lucy Takes the Reins. (SPA.). 168p. (J). 6.95 (978-84-272-4645-4(5)) Molino, Editorial ESP. *Dist:* AIMS International Bks., Inc.

El paseo a la Isla: Individual Title Six-Packs. (Coleccion Pm Ser.).Tr. of Island Picnic. (SPA.). 16p. (gr. 1 up). 26.00 (978-0-7578-3038-9(2)) Rigby Education.

El pastel Perfecto: Individual Title Six-Packs. (Literatura 2000 Ser.). (SPA.). (gr. k-1). 28.00 (978-0-7635-1026-8(2)) Rigby Education.

Patchett, Fiona. Puss in Boots. 2005. 48p. (J). (gr. 2 up). 8.95 (978-0-7945-0970-5(3) , Usborne) EDC Publishing.

Patriotic Fun. 2002. (Illus.). 32p. (J). 2.99 (978-0-88724-809-2(8) , CD-0188) Carson-Dellosa Publishing Co., Inc.

Pat's Train: KinderReaders, 6 Packs. (Kinderstarters Ser.). 8p. (ps-1). 21.00 (978-0-7635-8655-3(2)) Rigby Education.

Paul Ahrens-Gray & Ericka Grogan. Fish. 2005. (Illus.). 60p. (J). pap., act. bk. ed. 4.95 (978-1-59867-001-1(8)) Global Learning, Inc.

Paulo the Pilot: Individual Title Six-Packs. (gr. 1-2). 22.00 (978-0-7635-9187-8(4)) Rigby Education.

Paulson, Lucy Hart, et al. Building Early Literacy & Language Skills: A Resource & Activity Guide for Preschool & Kindergarten. 2001. 428p. otabind 35.00 (978-1-57035-360-4(3)) Sopris West Educational Services.

Pavon, Maria del Mar. Selena, Seleeena! 2005. (Caballo alado series-Al Galope Ser.). (SPA., Illus.). 24p. (J). pap. 4.95 (978-84-7864-885-6(2)) Combel Editorial, S.A. ESP. *Dist:* Independent Pubs. Group.

Pearl, Nancy. Book Crush: For Kids & Teens - Recommended Reading for Every Mood, Moment, & Interest. 2007. (Lust Ser.). 304p. pap. 16.95 (*978-1-57061-500-9(4)) Sasquatch Bks.

Pebble Reading, Early Level. (gr. k-2). 1062.95 (978-0-7368-1487-4(6) , Pebble Bks.) Capstone Pr., Inc.

Pebble Reading, Early Level Add-on Set. (gr. k-2). 172.95 (978-0-7368-1814-8(6) , Pebble Bks.) Capstone Pr., Inc.

Pebble Reading, Emergent Level. (gr. k-2). 1062.95 (978-0-7368-1486-7(8) , Pebble Bks.) Capstone Pr., Inc.

Pebble Reading, Emergent Level Add-on Set. (gr. k-2). 172.95 (978-0-7368-1813-1(8) , Pebble Bks.) Capstone Pr., Inc.

Pebble Reading, Fluent Level. (gr. k-2). 1062.95 (978-0-7368-1488-1(4) , Pebble Bks.) Capstone Pr., Inc.

Pebble Reading, Fluent Level Add-on Set. (gr. k-2). 172.95 (978-0-7368-1815-5(4) , Pebble Bks.) Capstone Pr., Inc.

Peg the Hen. 2004. (Illus.). (J). (978-1-59577-002-8(X)) Starfall Education.

Pencils. 1999. suppl. ed. 6.95 (978-0-673-36030-4(X) , Scott Foresman) Addison-Wesley Educational Pubs., Inc.

Penguin Books Staff. Come! Let's Read with Dick & Jane! 12 Book Reading Set. 2005. (Dick & Jane Ser.). 8p. (J). (gr. k-1). 9.99 (978-0-448-43981-5(6) , Grosset & Dunlap) Penguin Group (USA) Inc.

—Pelé Penguin Reader, No. 1. 2001. (Illus.). 16p. (C). pap. 9.00 (978-0-582-45196-4(5)) Longman Publishing Group.

—We Look. 2003. (Read with Dick & Jane Ser.: Vol. 1). 32p. (J). (ps-2). pap. 3.99 (978-0-448-43400-1(8) , Grosset & Dunlap) Penguin Group (USA) Inc.

Penton Overseas, Inc. Staff. Your Baby Can Read! Book 2: Early Language Development System. 2007. (Illus.). 20p. (J). (gr. k-5). pap. 8.95 (*978-1-59125-778-3(6) , Smart Kids) Penton Overseas, Inc.

—Your Baby Can Read! Book 3: Early Language Development System. 2007. (Illus.). 20p. (J). (gr. k-5). pap. 8.95 (*978-1-59125-779-0(4) , Smart Kids) Penton Overseas, Inc.

—Your Baby Can Read! Review Book: Early Language Development System. 2007. (Illus.). 20p. (J). (gr. k-5). pap. 8.95 (*978-1-59125-780-6(8) , Smart Kids) Penton Overseas, Inc.

—Your Baby Can Read! Starter Book: Early Language Development System. 2007. (Illus.). 20p. (J). (gr. k-5). pap. 8.95 (*978-1-59125-776-9(X) , Smart Kids) Penton Overseas, Inc.

Penton Overseas, Inc. Staff & Titzer, Bob. Your Baby Can Read! Book 1: Early Language Development System. 2007. (Illus.). 20p. (J). (gr. k-5). pap. 8.95 (*978-1-59125-777-6(8) , Smart Kids) Penton Overseas, Inc.

People Communities. (J). (gr. 3). (978-0-8374-1457-7(1) , 205) Weekly Reader Corp.

The People, Places & Principles of English Language Skills. 2000. (YA). (gr. 7-12). Vol. 2. stu. ed., spiral bd. (978-1-928629-10-8(5)); Vol. 3. stu. ed., spiral bd. (978-1-928629-11-5(3)); Vol. 4. stu. ed., spiral bd. (978-1-928629-12-2(1)) Paradigm Accelerated Curriculum.

The People, Places & Principles of English Language Skills: Activities, Quizzes & Tests. 2000. (YA). (gr. 7-12). Vol. 1. spiral bd. (978-1-928629-13-9(X)); Vol. 2. spiral bd. (978-1-928629-14-6(8)); Vol. 3. spiral bd. (978-1-928629-15-3(6)); Vol. 4. spiral bd. (978-1-928629-16-0(4)) Paradigm Accelerated Curriculum.

The People, Places & Principles of English Language Skills: Answer Key. 2000. spiral bd. (978-1-928629-17-7(2)) Paradigm Accelerated Curriculum.

The People, Places & Principles of English Language Skills, Chapter 1, Activities. 2003. (978-1-928629-79-5(2)) Paradigm Accelerated Curriculum.

The People, Places & Principles of English Language Skills, Chapter 1, Text. 2003. (978-1-928629-69-6(5)) Paradigm Accelerated Curriculum.

The People, Places & Principles of English Language Skills, Chapter 10, Activities. 2003. (978-1-928629-88-7(1)) Paradigm Accelerated Curriculum.

The People, Places & Principles of English Language Skills, Chapter 10, Text. 2003. (978-1-928629-78-8(4)) Paradigm Accelerated Curriculum.

The People, Places & Principles of English Language Skills, Chapter 2, Activities. 2003. (978-1-928629-80-1(6)) Paradigm Accelerated Curriculum.

The People, Places & Principles of English Language Skills, Chapter 2, Text. 2003. (978-1-928629-70-2(9)) Paradigm Accelerated Curriculum.

The People, Places & Principles of English Language Skills, Chapter 3, Activities. 2003. (978-1-928629-81-8(4)) Paradigm Accelerated Curriculum.

The People, Places & Principles of English Language Skills, Chapter 3, Text. 2003. (978-1-928629-71-9(7)) Paradigm Accelerated Curriculum.

The People, Places & Principles of English Language Skills, Chapter 4, Activities. 2003. (978-1-928629-82-5(2)) Paradigm Accelerated Curriculum.

The People, Places & Principles of English Language Skills, Chapter 4, Text. 2003. (978-1-928629-72-6(5)) Paradigm Accelerated Curriculum.

The People, Places & Principles of English Language Skills, Chapter 5, Activities. 2003. (978-1-928629-83-2(0)) Paradigm Accelerated Curriculum.

The People, Places & Principles of English Language Skills, Chapter 5, Text. 2003. (978-1-928629-73-3(3)) Paradigm Accelerated Curriculum.

The People, Places & Principles of English Language Skills, Chapter 6, Activities. 2003. (978-1-928629-84-9(9)) Paradigm Accelerated Curriculum.

The People, Places & Principles of English Language Skills, Chapter 6, Text. 2003. (978-1-928629-74-0(1)) Paradigm Accelerated Curriculum.

The People, Places & Principles of English Language Skills, Chapter 7, Activities. 2003. (978-1-928629-85-6(7)) Paradigm Accelerated Curriculum.

The People, Places & Principles of English Language Skills, Chapter 7, Text. 2003. (978-1-928629-75-7(X)) Paradigm Accelerated Curriculum.

The People, Places & Principles of English Language Skills, Chapter 8, Activities. 2003. (978-1-928629-86-3(5)) Paradigm Accelerated Curriculum.

The People, Places & Principles of English Language Skills, Chapter 8, Text. 2003. (978-1-928629-76-4(8)) Paradigm Accelerated Curriculum.

The People, Places & Principles of English Language Skills, Chapter 9, Activities. 2003. (978-1-928629-87-0(3)) Paradigm Accelerated Curriculum.

Peppers. (Early Intervention Levels Ser.). 23.10 (978-0-7362-0021-9(5)); Vol. 4. 3.85 (978-1-56334-971-3(X)) Hampton-Brown Bks.

El Pequeno Castor. (Coleccion Pequeno Simon). (SPA., Illus.). 32p. (J). 7.95 (978-84-7189-171-6(9) , ORT329) Ortells, Alfredo Editorial S.L. ESP. *Dist:* Continental Bk. Co., Inc.

Personal Hygiene. 96p. 9.99 (978-0-7424-0200-3(2) , LL80006) School Specialty Publishing.

Pete's Sheep. 2004. (Illus.). (J). (978-1-59577-007-3(0)) Starfall Education.

Petit, Marilyn & Page, Philip. Livewire Shakespeare Much Ado About Nothing. 2005. (Illus.). 64p. pap. (978-0-340-88808-7(3)) Cambridge Univ. Pr.

Petrov, Elena, illus. Grass for Dinner: First Wave Satellite Individual Title Six-Packs. (Sails Literacy Ser.). 16p. (gr. k up). 27.00 (978-0-7578-6867-2(3)) Rigby Education.

Petting Gilbert. 2004. (J). (978-1-58453-225-5(4)) Pioneer Valley Educational Pr., Inc.

Petty, Kate. Don't Wake Stanley, 8 bks. 2005. (QEB Readers). (Illus.). 24p. (J). (ps-3). lib. bdg. 15.95 (978-1-59566-074-9(7)) QEB Publishing Inc.

El pez Voladon: Individual Title, 6 packs. (Coleccion Pm Ser.).Tr. of Flying Fish. (SPA.). 16p. (gr. 1 up). 26.00 (978-0-7578-3047-1(1)) Rigby Education.

Phonemic Awareness Pack. (Phonemic Awareness Pack Ser.). (ps-k). 523.57 incl. audio compact disk (978-0-7362-0899-4(2)) Hampton-Brown Bks.

Phonemic Awareness Pack with Tapes. (Phonemic Awareness Pack Ser.). (ps-k). 538.88 (978-0-7362-0900-7(X)) Hampton-Brown Bks.

Phonics Decodable Reader 1. 2004. (gr. 1 up). suppl. ed. 3.35 (978-0-673-65172-3(X)) Addison-Wesley Educational Pubs., Inc.

Phonics Decodable Reader 2. 2004. (gr. 1 up). suppl. ed. 3.35 (978-0-673-65173-0(8)) Addison-Wesley Educational Pubs., Inc.

Phonics Decodable Reader 3. 2004. (gr. 1 up). suppl. ed. 3.35 (978-0-673-65174-7(6)) Addison-Wesley Educational Pubs., Inc.

Phonics Decodable Reader 33-41. 2004. (gr. 1 up). suppl. ed. 7.75 (978-0-673-65180-8(0)) Addison-Wesley Educational Pubs., Inc.

Phonics Decodable Reader 4. 2004. (gr. 1 up). suppl. ed. 3.35 (978-0-673-65175-4(4)) Addison-Wesley Educational Pubs., Inc.

Phonics Decodable Reader 42-50. 2004. (gr. 1 up). suppl. ed. 7.75 (978-0-673-65181-5(9)) Addison-Wesley Educational Pubs., Inc.

Phonics Decodable Reader 5. 2004. (gr. 1 up). suppl. ed. 3.35 (978-0-673-65176-1(2)) Addison-Wesley Educational Pubs., Inc.

Phonics Fun: Sticker Fun. 2003. (Illus.). 16p. spiral bd. (978-0-7853-7826-6(X) , PIL Kids) Publications International, Ltd.

Phonics Practice Book. 2000. (Phonics Practice Book Ser.). (gr. 1 up). 5.60 (978-0-673-60143-8(9)); (gr. 2 up). 5.60 (978-0-673-60144-5(7)); (gr. 3 up). 5.60 (978-0-673-60145-2(5)) Addison-Wesley Educational Pubs., Inc.

Phonics Practice Book. (De Canciones A Cuentos Ser.). (SPA.). (gr. k up). 9.13 (978-1-56334-580-7(3)); (gr. 1 up). 9.13 (978-1-56334-895-2(0)); (gr. 2 up). 8.36 (978-0-7362-0073-8(8)) Hampton-Brown Bks.

Phonics Readers. (Phonics Readers Ser.). (gr. k-2). Bks. 1-36. 569.95 (978-0-7368-3227-4(0)); Bks. 37-72. 932.95 (978-0-7368-4096-5(6)) Red Brick Learning.

Phonics Readers Add-on Set. (Phonics Readers Ser.). (gr. k-2). 277.95 (978-0-7368-4099-6(0)) Red Brick Learning.

Phonics Readers Big Books. 2005. (J). pap. 95.00 (978-1-58970-687-3(0)) Lakeshore Learning Materials.

Phonics Readers, Books 1-36 Add-on Set. (Phonics Readers Ser.). (gr. k-2). 104.95 (978-0-7368-3228-1(9)) Red Brick Learning.

Phonics Readers, Books 37-72 Add-on Set. (Phonics Readers Ser.). (gr. k-2). 172.95 (978-0-7368-4097-2(4)) Red Brick Learning.

Phonics Readers Bookshelf Collection, 36 bks., Set. 2004. (gr. 1 up). 594.00 (978-0-328-00401-0(4)); 2004. (gr. 2 up). 495.00 (978-0-328-00402-7(2)); 2004. (gr. 3 up). 495.00 (978-0-328-00403-4(0)); 2000. (SPA.). (gr. k up). 665.28 (978-0-328-00404-1(9)); 2000. (SPA.). (gr. 1 up). 665.28 (978-0-328-00405-8(7)); 2000. (SPA.). (gr. 2 up). 554.40 (978-0-328-00406-5(5)); 2000. (SPA.). (gr. 3 up). 554.40 (978-0-328-00407-2(3)) Addison-Wesley Educational Pubs., Inc.

Phonics Readers Student Books. 2005. (J). pap. 29.95 (978-1-58970-685-9(4)) Lakeshore Learning Materials.

Phonics Take-Home Readers. 2004. (gr. 1 up). tchr. ed. 48.00 (978-0-673-61258-8(9)); (gr. 2 up). 48.00 (978-0-673-61259-5(7)); (gr. 3 up). 48.00 (978-0-673-61260-1(0)) Addison-Wesley Educational Pubs., Inc.

Photographic Memory: Individual Chapter Book Title Six-Packs. Vol. 27. 32p. (gr. 4 up). 44.00 (978-0-7635-4492-8(2)) Rigby Education.

Piazza, Linda. Nonfiction Reading Comprehension. 2002. (100+ Seriestm Ser.). 128p. (YA). (gr. 7-8). pap. 12.99 (978-0-7424-0221-8(5) , IF87029) School Specialty Publishing.

Pick a Pet. 2005. (Little Celebrations Thematic Packages Ser.). (J). (gr. k-3). 133.50 (978-0-673-75387-8(5)) Celebration Pr.

Picture Cards: Package of 100 Cards First Grade. (On Our Way to English Ser.). (gr. 1 up). 119.95 (978-0-7578-1598-0(7)) Rigby Education.

Picture Cards: Package of 100 Cards Kindergarten. (On Our Way to English Ser.). (gr. k up). 119.95 (978-0-7578-1611-6(8)) Rigby Education.

Picture Cards: Package of 100 Cards Second Grade. (On Our Way to English Ser.). (gr. 2 up). 119.95 (978-0-7578-1410-5(7)) Rigby Education.

Picture Cards: Package of 100 Cards Third Grade. (On Our Way to English Ser.). (gr. 3 up). 119.95 (978-0-7578-4233-7(X)) Rigby Education.

Picture Perfect Word Book. (ps-2). 206.58 (978-0-7362-2547-2(1)) Hampton-Brown Bks.

Picture Perfect Word Book: My Little Word Books. (ps-2). 4.99 (978-0-7362-2392-8(4)) Hampton-Brown Bks.

The Pie. 2001. (978-1-58453-165-4(7)) Pioneer Valley Educational Pr., Inc.

Pie Day. (Early Intervention Levels Ser.). 28.38 (978-0-7362-0406-4(7)); Vol. 12. 4.73 (978-0-7362-0231-2(5)) Hampton-Brown Bks.

Pin It! Fix It! (Early Intervention Levels Ser.). 21.30 (978-0-7362-0389-0(3)); Vol. 6. 3.55 (978-0-7362-0169-8(6)) Hampton-Brown Bks.

Pioneers: Life as a Homesteader, 6 Packs. (On Deck Ser.: Vol. 2). 24p. (gr. 4-5). 35.00 (978-0-7578-5806-2(6)) Rigby Education.

Pittis, Arthur M. As My Heart Awakes: A Waldorf Reader for Early Third Grade. Mitchell, David S., ed. Peacock, Ausa M., illus. 2005. (J). bds. 10.00 (978-1-888365-62-7(5)) Assn. of Waldorf Schls. of North America Pubns. (AWSNA).

—Fee Fi Fo Fum: A Waldorf Reader for Late Second Grade. Mitchell, David S., ed. Peacock, Ausa M., illus. 2005. (J). bds. 10.00 (978-1-888365-63-4(3)) Assn. of Waldorf Schls. of North America Pubns. (AWSNA).

—Sun So Hot I Froze to Death: A Waldorf Reader for Advanced Fourth Grade. Mitchell, David S., ed. Peacock, Ausa M., illus. 2005. (J). bds. 12.00 (978-1-888365-65-8(X)) Assn. of Waldorf Schls. of North America Pubns. (AWSNA).

—When I Hear My Heart Wonder: A Waldorf Reader for Late Third Grade. Mitchell, David S., ed. Peacock, Ausa M., illus. 2005. (J). bds. 10.00 (978-1-888365-66-5(8)) Assn. of Waldorf Schls. of North America Pubns. (AWSNA).

The Pizza Shop, 2 Packs. (Chiquilibros Ser.). (ps-1). 12.00 (978-0-7635-8535-8(1)) Rigby Education.

Place, Jean & Linington, Vivien. Becoming a Reader: Learner's Workbook Grade 2. 1999. (Cambridge Reading Routes Ser.). (Illus.). 72p. pap. 2.00 (978-0-521-62799-3(0)) Cambridge Univ. Pr.

Place, Jean, et al. Beginning to Read for Grade 1. 1998. (Cambridge Reading Routes Ser.). (Illus.). 132p. pap., tchr. ed. 15.00 (978-0-521-62796-2(6)); 56p. pap., wbk. ed. 2.00 (978-0-521-62798-6(2)) Cambridge Univ. Pr.

Places: KinderFacts Individual Title Six-Packs. (Kinderstarters Ser.). 8p. (ps-1). 21.00 (978-0-7635-8746-8(X)) Rigby Education.

El Planeta de los Cuentos.Tr. of Planet of Storybook Tales. (SPA.). (J). (978-84-7773-630-1(8)) Grafalco, S.A.

Platt, Richard. Extreme Sports. 2001. (Dk Readers Ser.). (Illus.). 48p. (J). (gr. 5-5). pap. 3.99 (978-0-7894-7884-9(6)) Dorling Kindersley Publishing, Inc.

—Extreme Sports. 2001. (gr. k-3). lib. bdg. 11.80 (978-0-613-43930-5(9)) Tandem Library Bks.

Platt, Richard & Dorling Kindersley Publishing Staff. Extreme Sports. 2001. (Dk Readers Ser.). (Illus.). 48p. (J). (gr. 3-5). 12.95 (978-0-7894-7883-2(8)) Dorling Kindersley Publishing, Inc.

Play It Safe! Set B, 6 vols. (Phonics Readers Ser.). (gr. k-2). 17.50 (978-0-7368-3209-0(2)) Red Brick Learning.

Play the Game You Know. 2005. (Book Treks Ser.). (J). 37.95 (978-0-7652-3258-8(8)) Celebration Pr.

Playing at Lily's House: First Grade Guided Reading Level G. (On Our Way to English Ser.). (gr. 1 up). 27.75 (978-0-7578-7057-6(0)) Rigby Education.

Please Read to Me. 2005. (J). (978-1-58453-290-3(4)) Pioneer Valley Educational Pr., Inc.

PM Sapphire Anthology: in Your Dreams: 1 Anthology. (gr. 5 up). 8.00 (978-0-7578-1171-5(X)) Rigby Education.

Pocket Chart. (ps-12). 26.27 (978-0-7362-1100-0(4)) Hampton-Brown Bks.

Pocket Chart Phonics: Advanced Consonants. 2000. (J). pap. 9.95 (978-1-56911-794-1(2)) Learning Resources, Inc.

Pocket Chart Phonics: Advanced Vowels. 2000. (J). pap. 9.95 (978-1-56911-792-7(6)) Learning Resources, Inc.

Pocket Chart Phonics: Beginning Consonants. 2000. (J). pap. 9.95 (978-1-56911-793-4(4)) Learning Resources, Inc.

Pocket Chart Phonics: Blends. 2000. (J). pap. 9.95 (978-1-56911-795-8(0)) Learning Resources, Inc.

Pocket Chart Phonics: Short Vowels. 2002. (J). pap. 9.95 (978-1-56911-791-0(8)) Learning Resources, Inc.

Pocket Chart Reading: Basic Parts of Speech. 2001. (J). pap. 9.95 (978-1-56911-717-0(9)) Learning Resources, Inc.

Pocket Chart Reading: Homophones. 2001. (J). pap. 9.95 (978-1-56911-718-7(7)) Learning Resources, Inc.

Pocket Chart Reading: Opposites. 2000. (J). pap. 9.95 (978-1-56911-797-2(7)) Learning Resources, Inc.

Pocket Chart Reading: Picture ABC's. 2000. (J). pap. 9.95 (978-1-56911-796-5(9)) Learning Resources, Inc.

Pocket Chart Reading: Sequencing. 2000. (J). pap. 9.95 (978-1-56911-798-9(5)) Learning Resources, Inc.

Pocket Chart Reading: Sight Words. 2000. (J). pap. 9.95 (978-1-56911-799-6(3)) Learning Resources, Inc.

A Pocketful of Opossums: Second Grade Big Books. (On Our Way to English Ser.). (gr. 2 up). 29.95 (978-0-7578-1417-4(4)) Rigby Education.

A Pocketful of Opossums: Small Versions of Big Books. (On Our Way to English Ser.). (gr. 2 up). 29.00 (978-0-7578-7238-9(7)) Rigby Education.

Pohrt, Tom. My Brother Bert. Date not set. (J). (978-0-374-39982-5(4) , Farrar, Straus & Giroux (BYR)) Farrar, Straus & Giroux.

Police Work. 2005. (Book Treks Ser.). (J). (gr. 3 up). stu. ed. 34.95 (978-0-673-62839-8(6)) Celebration Pr.

Ponti, James. Santa's Secret. 2006. 32p. (ps-2). pap. 3.99 (978-1-4231-0507-7(9)) Disney Pr.

Pop & Robby: Individual Title Six-Packs. (Sails Literacy Ser.). (gr. 1-2). 36.00 (978-0-7578-6722-4(7)) Rigby Education.

Popcorn: KinderFacts, 6 Packs. (Kinderstarters Ser.). 8p. (ps-1). 21.00 (978-0-7635-8747-5(8)) Rigby Education.

Popper, Lisa. Bunny Bop. 2004. (Illus.). (J). pap. (978-0-9708947-0-0(8)) Northern Speech Services.

—Danny Dragon. 2004. (Illus.). 16p. (J). pap. (978-0-9708947-6-2(7)) Northern Speech Services.

—Hanna Hippo. 2004. (Illus.). 16p. (J). pap. (978-0-9708947-5-5(9)) Northern Speech Services.

—Len & Lil. 2004. (J). pap. (978-0-9761967-2-3(7)) Northern Speech Services.

—Let' Make Music. 2004. (J). pap. (978-0-9761967-1-6(9)) Northern Speech Services.

—My Rad Dad. 2005. (J). pap. (978-0-9765497-2-7(7)) Northern Speech Services.

—Nifty Noodle. 2004. (Illus.). 16p. (J). pap. (978-0-9708947-4-8(0)) Northern Speech Services.

—Patty the Pink Pig. 2004. (J). pap. (978-0-9761967-0-9(0)) Northern Speech Services.

—Rat Rap. 2004. 16p. (J). pap. (978-0-9708947-9-3(1)) Northern Speech Services.

—Sammy. 2004. 16p. (J). pap. (978-0-9708947-8-6(3)) Northern Speech Services.

—Timmy Turtle. 2004. 16p. (J). pap. (978-0-9708947-7-9(5)) Northern Speech Services.

Porell, John. When Things Go Wrong. 2005. (Real Deal-Red Plus Ser.). (Illus.). 32p. (gr. 4-8). 19.00 (978-0-7910-8898-2(7)) Facts On File, Inc.

Positively Me Flying Pigtails. 1999. (J). (978-0-8136-4826-2(2)) Modern Curriculum Pr.

Poteet, Michael. The Strange Case of Dr. Jekll & Mr. Hyde. 2001. 76p. (J). stu. ed., ring bd. 14.99 (978-1-58609-176-7(X)) Progeny Pr.

Powell, Jillian. Tall Tilly. Archbold, Tim, illus. 2005. (Lightning Readers Ser.). 32p. (J). (gr. 1-2). pap. 3.95 (978-0-7696-4051-8(6) , Gingham Dog Pr.) School Specialty Publishing.

—Tina la Alta. Archbold, Tim, illus. 2005. (Lightning Readers Ser.). 32p. (J). (gr. 1-2). pap. 3.95 (978-0-7696-4091-4(5) , Gingham Dog Pr.) School Specialty Publishing.

The Power of the Wind: Third Grade Guided Reading Level K. (On Our Way to English Ser.). (gr. 3 up). 34.50 (978-0-7578-7123-8(2)) Rigby Education.

Power Out. (Early Intervention Levels Ser.). 21.42 (978-0-7362-1056-0(3)) Hampton-Brown Bks.

Power Reading, 26 vols. 2003. (Illus.). (gr. k-9). vinyl bd. incl. audio (978-1-883186-37-1(4) , PPS 25); vinyl bd. incl. audio (978-1-883186-35-7(8) , PPS 25) National Reading Styles Institute, Inc.

Power Reading: Power PAK. 2005. (Illus.). 80p. (J). (gr. 2-4). vinyl bd. 129.95 (978-1-883186-73-9(0) , PPMX2-3); (gr. 4-5). vinyl bd. 129.95 (978-1-883186-72-2(2) , PPMX4-5) National Reading Styles Institute, Inc.

Power Reading: Power PAK 4C. 2005. (Illus.). 80p. (J). (gr. 4-5). vinyl bd. 129.95 (978-1-883186-70-8(6) , PPO4C) National Reading Styles Institute, Inc.

Powling, Chris, et al. School Days. 2007. (I-read Ser.). (Illus.). 38p. pap. (***978-0-521-70483-0(9)*** Cambridge Univ. Pr.

Practice & Review. 1999. (gr. k up). wbk. ed. 6.15 (978-0-673-57640-8(X)); (gr. 1 up). suppl. ed., wbk. ed. 6.15 (978-0-673-57637-8(X)); (gr. 2 up). wbk. ed. 6.15 (978-0-673-57638-5(8)); (gr. 3 up). wbk. ed. 6.15 (978-0-673-57639-2(6)); (gr. 4 up). wbk. ed. 6.15 (978-0-673-59284-2(7)); (Illus.). (gr. 5 up). wbk. ed. 6.15 (978-0-673-59285-9(5)) Addison-Wesley Educational Pubs., Inc. (Scott Foresman).

Practice Makes Perfect: Third Grade Guided Reading Level L. (On Our Way to English Ser.). (gr. 3 up). 34.50 (978-0-7578-7126-9(7)) Rigby Education.

Practice Power Practice Book Division. 2001. (Illus.). 18p. (J). (gr. 2-5). spiral bd., wbk. ed. (978-1-930355-31-6(9)) Greenbrier/Scentex.

Pre-K Literacy Library. 2003. 430.50 (978-0-7652-2478-1(X)) Modern Curriculum Pr.

Preece, Phil. Nightmare Park. 2004. (Shades Ser.). 52p. (J). pap. 7.99 (978-0-237-52730-3(8) , Evans Brothers, Limited) Evans Publishing Group GBR. *Dist:* Independent Pubs. Group.

Prentice-Hall Staff. Bridge to Terabithia. 2nd ed. (J). stu. ed. (978-0-13-717109-5(9)) Prentice Hall (Schl. Div.).

Prereading Activities (K) 2003. (J). (978-1-58232-045-8(4)) Bryan Hse. Pubs., Inc.

Preschool Books 800083, 10. 2005. (J). bds. (978-1-59794-001-6(1)) Environments, Inc.

Price, Mathew. Everyday Collection. 2004. 40p. (J). bds. 19.95 (978-0-7696-3458-6(3)) School Specialty Publishing.

—Tommy Collection. 2004. 40p. (J). bds. 19.95 (978-0-7696-3460-9(5)) School Specialty Publishing.

Price, Susan. Goldilocks & the Three Bears Big Book: American English Edition. Beardshaw, Rosalind, illus. 2000. (Cambridge Reading Ser.). 16p. pap. 29.00 (978-0-521-79523-4(0)) Cambridge Univ. Pr.

Priddy, Roger. First 100 Words. rev. ed. 2005. (Bright Baby Ser.). (Illus.). 16p. (J). bds. 8.95 (978-0-312-49541-1(2) , Priddy Bks.) St. Martin's Pr.

Priddy, Roger. 300 First Words & Pictures. 2006. 42p. (J). bds. 16.95 (***978-0-312-49853-5(5)*** , Priddy Bks.) St. Martin's Pr.

Prince, Sarah. Enjoy! Enjoy! 2000. (gr. k-3). lib. bdg. 11.80 (978-0-613-33363-4(2)) Tandem Library Bks.

—Great Day. 1999. (gr. k-3). lib. bdg. 11.80 (978-0-613-19367-2(9)) Tandem Library Bks.

—Party. 1999. (ps-2). lib. bdg. 11.55 (978-0-613-30664-5(3)) Tandem Library Bks.

—Twins. 1999. (ps-2). lib. bdg. 11.80 (978-0-613-30820-5(4)) Tandem Library Bks.

—What's for Dinner? 1999. (ps-2). lib. bdg. 11.55 (978-0-613-30866-3(2)) Tandem Library Bks.

Prou, Marc . E. Spoken Haitian Creole. 2002. (Illus.). 176p. per. 19.95 (978-1-58432-137-8(7)) Educa Vision.

Prowse, Philip. Help! Level 1. 1999. (Cambridge English Readers Ser.). (Illus.). 32p. pap. 6.00 (978-0-521-65615-3(X)) Cambridge Univ. Pr.

PuffFlashBang! (Lexile Levels Ser.). 9.09 (978-1-56334-703-0(2)) Hampton-Brown Bks.

Pug & Chug: Set C Individual Title Six-Packs. (gr. k-3). 29.00 (978-0-7635-0544-8(7)) Rigby Education.

Pugliano-Martin, Carol. The Day I Followed the Pickle: Reader's Theater Levels I-K (15-20) Beckes, Shirley, illus. ed. 2004. (Reader's Theater Ser.). 16p. (J). pap. 22.00 (978-1-4108-2297-0(4) , A22974) Benchmark Education Co.

—The Earth on Turtle's Back. ed. 2003. (Early Connections Ser.). (J). pap. 35.00 (978-1-4108-1555-2(2)) Benchmark Education Co.

—Why Spiders Have Small Waissts (Big Book) ed. 2004. (Shared Connections Ser.). (J). pap., instr.'s gde, ed. 27.00 (978-1-4108-1621-4(4)) Benchmark Education Co.

—Why Spiders Have Small Waists. ed. 2004. (Shared Connections Ser.). (J). pap. 27.00 (978-1-4108-1645-0(1)) Benchmark Education Co.

Pulse of Life: Fifth Grade Class Collection Books. (On Our Way to English Ser.). (gr. 5 up). 29.95 (978-0-7578-4474-4(X)) Rigby Education.

Pulse of Life: Small Versions of Class Collection Books. (On Our Way to English Ser.). (gr. 5 up). 34.50 (978-0-7578-7286-0(7)) Rigby Education.

The Pumpkin Grows: Kindergarten Newcomer Books. (On Our Way to English Ser.). (gr. k up). 23.50 (978-0-7578-7198-6(4)) Rigby Education.

Purple & Gold Levels Certificate Only. (gr. k-5). 89.00 (978-0-7578-6541-1(0)) Rigby Education.

Push or Pull? Set B, 6 vols. (Phonics Readers Ser.). (gr. k-2). 17.50 (978-0-7368-3212-0(2)) Red Brick Learning.

Pyers. Wasps 6-Pack. 2004. (Minibeasts up Close Ser.). pap. 40.50 (978-1-4109-1547-4(6)) Harcourt Schl. Pubs.

QEB Start Reading & Writing National Book Stores Edition: Little Red Riding Hood. 2006. (J). per. (978-1-59566-267-5(7)) QEB Publishing Inc.

Quality Time Easy Readers, 5 bks. (Illus.). (J). lib. bdg. 64.75 (978-1-56674-925-1(5)) Forest Hse. Publishing Co., Inc.

Queen of the Bean: Individual Title Six-Packs. (Action Packs Ser.). 104p. (gr. 3-5). 44.00 (978-0-7635-2983-3(4)) Rigby Education.

Queen on a Quilt. (J). (978-0-8136-5372-3(X)) Modern Curriculum Pr.

Quick & Quiet. (Early Intervention Levels Ser.). 21.30 (978-0-7362-0376-0(1)); Vol. 3. 3.55 (978-0-7362-0097-4(5)) Hampton-Brown Bks.

Quinlan, Heather. Reading Made Easy. Harpster, Steve, illus. 2005. (First Word Search Ser.). 64p. (ps). pap. 3.95 (978-1-4027-2749-8(6)) Sterling Publishing Co., Inc.

Quinley, Elliott. Practical Reading 1: Reading in Context. 2001. (Illus.). 112p. per., wbk. ed. 8.95 (978-1-56254-189-7(7) , SP 1897) Saddleback Educational Publishing.

—Practical Reading 2: Reading in Context. 2001. (Illus.). 112p. per., wbk. ed. 8.95 (978-1-56254-190-3(0) , SP 1900) Saddleback Educational Publishing.

Rabe, Tish. Harry's Magic Hat. Watson, Richard, illus. 2007. 24p. (J). (ps-1). pap. 6.99 (***978-1-58476-610-0(7)*** , IKIDS) Innovative Kids.

—Innovative Kids Readers: Milly's Silly Suitcase - Level 1. Janovitz, Marilyn, illus. 2006. (J). (ps-1). 6.99 (978-1-58476-493-9(7)) Innovative Kids.

—Innovative Kids Readers: Penguins Perfect Picnic. Ho, Jannie, illus. 2007. 24p. (J). (ps-1). pap. 6.99 (978-1-58476-542-4(9)) Innovative Kids.

—Make a Match: A Preschool Sorting Game. Lloyd, Mary Anne, illus. 2006. 19p. (J). (ps-1). 14.99 (978-1-58476-480-9(5) , IKIDS) Innovative Kids.

—Milly's Silly Suitcase. Janovitz, Marilyn, illus. 2006. (innovativeKids readers ser.: level 1). 24p. (J). (ps-1). pap. 6.99 (978-1-58476-476-2(7) , IKIDS) Innovative Kids.

The Race: Individual Title Six-Packs. (gr. 1-2). 22.00 (978-0-7635-9165-6(3)) Rigby Education.

Radabaugh, Melinda Beth. First Time, 6 bks., Set 1. 2003. (First Time Ser.). 24p. (J). (ps-1). lib. bdg. 92.50 (978-1-4034-0232-5(9)) Heinemann Library.

Radlauer, Edward. More Readers, 3 bks. (Illus.). (J). (ps-4). lib. bdg. 38.85 (978-1-56674-922-0(0)) Forest Hse. Publishing Co., Inc.

Ragbag: Set A Individual Title Six-Packs. (gr. k-3). 29.00 (978-0-7635-0529-5(3)) Rigby Education.

Rainbow Fish Readers 800884, 4 vols. 2005. (J). pap. (978-1-59794-059-7(3)) Environments, Inc.

Raintree IL Staff, ed. Raintree Perspectives Collection, 30 vols., Set. 2004. (Illus.). 501.15 (978-1-4109-1286-2(8)) Raintree.

Raintree Steck-Vaughn Staff. Accelerated Reader Stages 2-3. 1999. (Illus.). (J). pap. 215.60 (978-0-7398-1497-0(4)) Steck-Vaughn.

—Critical Reading Language Arts C. 2002. pap. 5.50 (978-0-7398-5549-2(2)) Harcourt Trade Pubs.

—Los Deportes Son Divertidos. 2000. (Coleccion en Parejas). (SPA.). (J). pap., stu. ed. 20.45 (978-0-7398-0825-2(7)) Steck-Vaughn.

—Hacemos Galletas. 2000. (Coleccion en Parejas). (SPA.). (J). pap., stu. ed. 20.45 (978-0-7398-0833-7(8)) Steck-Vaughn.

—January 2002 New Product Package. 2002. pap. (978-0-7398-6022-9(4)) Steck-Vaughn.

—June 2001 New Product Package. 2001. pap. (978-0-7398-4770-1(8)) Steck-Vaughn.

—June 2002 New Product Package. 2002. pap. (978-0-7398-6352-7(5)) Steck-Vaughn.

—March 2002 New Product Package. 2002. pap. (978-0-7398-6313-8(4)) Steck-Vaughn.

—Power up Workout Books: 30 Pack, Level 1. 2002. pap. (978-0-7398-6676-4(1)) Steck-Vaughn.

—Stolen Bases. 2000. (Illus.). (J). pap. 3.41 (978-0-8114-9300-0(8)) Steck-Vaughn.

—The World's Best Dog-Walker. 1999. (Illus.). (J). pap. 35.60 (978-0-7398-0903-7(2)) Steck-Vaughn.

—Young Library: Arkansas Edition, 40 bks., Set. 2003. (Illus.). 1028.00 (978-1-4109-0140-8(8)) Raintree.

Raintree Steck-Vaughn Staff, contrib. by. Wags & Tags. 1999. (J). (ps-3). pap. 11.20 (978-0-8114-1339-8(X)) Steck-Vaughn.

Ramke, Linda. Theme-Based Nonfiction Reading Comprehension. 2003. (100+ Seriestm Ser.). 128p. (J). (gr. 4-4). pap. 12.99 (978-0-7424-1904-9(5) , IFG99101); (gr. 5-5). pap. 12.99 (978-0-7424-1905-6(3) , IFG99102) School Specialty Publishing.

Ramsey, Kimberly. Stories from Somerville. 2002. Vol. 1. 56p. 12.95 (978-1-881929-17-8(5)); Vol. 2. 64p. 12.95 (978-1-881929-18-5(3)) Oxton Hse., Pubs.

—Stories from Somerville: Comprehension Workbook. 2002. Vol. 1. 32p. 5.00 (978-1-881929-24-6(8)); Vol. 1b. 20p. 5.00 (978-1-881929-25-3(6)); Vol. 2. 52p. 7.00 (978-1-881929-26-0(4)) Oxton Hse., Pubs.

Random House Disney Staff. Love at First Beep. 2008. (Step into Reading Ser.). 32p. (J). (ps-1). pap. 3.99 (***978-0-7364-2514-8(4)*** , RH/Disney) Random Hse. Children's Bks.

Random House Disney Staff. Ride the Wave. 2003. (Illus.). 32p. (J). (ps-3). pap. 3.99 (978-0-7364-2122-5(X) , Golden/Disney) Random Hse. Children's Bks.

Rankin, Joan. Our House: Lunda Version. Sayifwanda, tr. 2001. (Illus.). 8p. pap. 0.45 (978-0-521-01465-6(4)) Cambridge Univ. Pr.

—Our House: Lunda Version. Kambangaji, Thomson, tr. 1998. (Cambridge African Language Library). (Illus.). 8p. pap. 3.75 (978-0-521-64722-9(3)) Cambridge Univ. Pr.

Rasinski, Timothy. Daily Word Ladders Grades 2-3. 2005. (Daily Word Ladders Ser.). (Illus.). 112p. (gr. 2-3). pap. 15.99 (978-0-439-51383-8(9) , Teaching Resources) Scholastic, Inc.

Rau, Dana Meachen. All about Me Boxed Set. 2006. 9.95 (978-0-531-16924-7(3) , Children's Pr.) Scholastic Library Publishing.

Rausch, Kathy. Puppies Came to our House. 2006. (Illus.). 24p. (J). 11.95 (978-1-59598-009-0(1)) Goblin Fern Pr., Inc.

Ravishankar, Anushka. Alphabets Are Amazing Animals. Pieper, Christiane, illus. 2004. 56p. 14.95 (978-81-86211-72-4(1)) Tara Publishing IND. *Dist:* Consortium Bk. Sales & Distribution.

Ray, Blaine. Casi Se Muere: Level 1. 1998. (TPRS First-Year Spanish Novels Ser.). (SPA.). ii, 46p. (YA). (gr. 7-12). pap. 5.95 (978-0-929724-43-0(7) , BR003) Command Performance Language Institute.

Ray, Hannah. The Great Big Friend Hunt. 2004. (QEB Start Reading Ser.). (Illus.). 24p. (J). lib. bdg. 15.95 (978-1-59566-012-1(7)) QEB Publishing Inc.

—Katie's Mom Is a Mermaid, 4 vols. 2005. (QEB Readers). (Illus.). 24p. (J). (ps-3). lib. bdg. 15.95 (978-1-59566-101-2(8)) QEB Publishing Inc.

Ray, Nan. Meet the People. 2004. 66p. (J). per. 8.95 (978-0-9760280-0-0(X)) You're On!, Inc.

Rea-It! Readers: Gus the Hedgehog. 2005. (Illus.). (C). (gr. k-3). 55.80 (978-1-4048-0995-6(3)) Picture Window Bks.

Reaching Higher Additional Resources: English Books (55 Titles) (Reach for Reading Ser.). (gr. 3-5). 260.00 (978-0-7635-3747-0(0)) Rigby Education.

Reaching Higher Additional Workstations: Without Books. (Reach for Reading Ser.). (gr. 3-5). 285.00 (978-0-7578-6847-4(9)) Rigby Education.

Reaching up Additional Resources: English Books (75 Titles) (Reach for Reading Ser.). (gr. 1-3). 205.00 (978-0-7635-3748-7(9)) Rigby Education.

Reaching up Additional Workstations: With Books. (Reach for Reading Ser.). (gr. 1-3). 390.00 (978-0-7635-3698-5(9)) Rigby Education.

Reaching up Additional Workstations: Without Books. (Reach for Reading Ser.). (gr. 1-3). 285.00 (978-0-7578-3536-0(8)) Rigby Education.

Read along with Blue! 2005. (Blue's Clues Ser.). (Illus.). 128p. (J). pap. 7.99 (978-1-4169-0626-1(6) , Simon Spotlight/Nickelodeon) Simon & Schuster Children's Publishing.

Read & Spell with Zoo-phonics. 2004. (J). cd-rom 29.95 (978-1-886441-46-0(4)) Zoo-phonics, Inc.

Read & Spell with Zoo=Phonics Guide for CD-ROM. 2004. (J). 14.95 (978-1-886441-45-3(6)) Zoo-phonics, Inc.

Read & Write. 2005. (J). pap. 3.99 (978-1-933200-18-7(9)) Family Bks. at Home.

Read-at-Home Book, Books 1-36. (Phonics Readers Ser.). (gr. k-2). 29.95 (978-0-7368-3239-7(4)) Red Brick Learning.

Read-at-Home Book, Books 37-72. (Phonics Readers Ser.). (gr. k-2). 29.95 (978-0-7368-4089-7(3)) Red Brick Learning.

Read, Bob. Murder in Mind. 2nd rev. ed. 2004. (Livewires Ser.). 32p. pap. 7.13 (978-0-340-81682-0(1)) Cambridge Univ. Pr.

Read-It! Chapter Books, 6 bks., Set. Incl. Bricks for Breakfast. Donaldson, Julia. Dupasquier, Philippe, illus. 52p. (ps-k). lib. bdg. 19.95 (978-1-4048-1275-8(X)); Duncan & the Pirates. Utton, Peter. Utton, Peter, illus. 52p. (ps-k). lib. bdg. 19.95 (978-1-4048-1277-2(6)); Hetty the Yeti. Shulman, Dee. Shulman, Dee, illus. 52p. (ps-k). lib. bdg. 19.95 (978-1-4048-1276-5(8)); Mean Team from Mars. Anderson, Scoular. Anderson, Scoular, illus. 52p. (ps-k). lib. bdg. 19.95 (978-1-4048-1274-1(1)); Spookball Champions. Anderson, Scoular, illus. 48p. (gr. 2-4). lib. bdg. 19.95 (978-1-4048-1278-9(4)); Toby & His Old Tin Tub. West, Colin. West, Colin, illus. 52p. (ps-k). lib. bdg. 19.95 (978-1-4048-1279-6(2)); (Illus.). (J). 2005. 119.70 (978-1-4048-1529-2(5)) Picture Window Bks.

Read-It! Readers, 41 bks. Incl. At the Beach. Stockland, Patricia M. Muehlenhardt, Amy Bailey, illus. (C). 18.60 (978-1-4048-0651-1(2)); Best Snowman. Nash, Margaret. Saupe, Jorg, illus. (C). 18.60 (978-1-4048-0048-9(4)); Bill's Baggy Pants. Gates, Susan. Axworthy, Anni, illus. (C). 18.60 (978-1-4048-0050-2(6)); Bossy Rooster. Nash, Margaret. Moseng, Elisabeth, illus. (C). 18.60 (978-1-4048-0051-9(4)); Cleo & Leo. Cassidy, Anne. Norman, Philip, illus. (C). 18.60 (978-1-4048-0049-6(2)); Clever Cat. Wallace, Karen. Axworthy, Ann, illus. (C). 18.60 (978-1-4048-0560-6(5)); Crying Princess. Cassidy, Anne. Paine, Colin, illus. (C). 18.60 (978-1-4048-0053-3(0)); Eight Enormous Elephants. Dolan, Penny. Bradley, Leo, illus. (C). 18.60 (978-1-4048-0054-0(9)); Felix on the Move. Friel, Maeve. Blake, Beccy, illus. (C). 18.60 (978-1-4048-0055-7(7)); Flora McQuack. Dolan, Penny. Widdowson, Kay, illus. (C). 18.60 (978-1-4048-0561-3(3)); Flynn Flies High. Robinson, Hilary. Archbold, Tim, illus. (C). 18.60 (978-1-4048-0563-7(X)); Freddie's Fears. Robinson, Hilary.

Collins, Ross, illus. (C). 18.60 (978-1-4048-0056-4(5)); I Am in Charge of Me. Rau, Dana Meachen. Beckes, Shirley, illus. (C). 18.60 (978-1-4048-0646-7(6)); Izzy's Idea. Powell, Jillian. Shearing, Leonie, illus. (C). 18.60 (978-1-4048-0644-3(X)); Jack's Party. Bryant, Ann. Henley, Claire, illus. (C). 18.60 (978-1-4048-0060-1(3)); Jasper & Jess. Cassidy, Anne. Hall, Francois, illus. (C). 18.60 (978-1-4048-0061-8(1)); Lazy Scarecrow. Powell, Jillian. Coughlin, Jayne, illus. (C). 18.60 (978-1-4048-0062-5(X)); Let's Share. Rau, Dana Meachen. Favereau, Beatrice, illus. (C). 18.60 (978-1-4048-0647-4(4)); Little Joe's Big Race. Black, Andy. Archbold, Tim, illus. (C). 18.60 (978-1-4048-0063-2(8)); Little Star. Nash, Deborah. Morgan, Richard, illus. (C). 18.60 (978-1-4048-0065-6(4)); Marvin, the Blue Pig. Wallace, Karen. Williams, Lisa, illus. (C). 18.60 (978-1-4048-0564-4(8)); Mary & the Fairy. Dolan, Penny. Allwright, Deborah, illus. (C). 18.60 (978-1-4048-0066-3(2)); Moo! Dolan, Penny. Sharp, Melanie, illus. (C). 18.60 (978-1-4048-0643-6(1)); Naughty Nancy. Cassidy, Anne. Guicciardini, Desideria, illus. (J). 18.60 (978-1-4048-0558-3(3)); Naughty Puppy. Powell, Jillian. Durantz, Summer, illus. (C). 18.60 (978-1-4048-0067-0(0)); Pippin's Big Jump. Robinson, Hilary. Warburton, Sarah, illus. (C). 18.60 (978-1-4048-0555-2(9)); Playground Snake. Moses, Brian. Mostyn, David, illus. (C). 18.60 (978-1-4048-0556-9(7)); Princess & the Frog. Nash, Margaret. Remphry, Martin, illus. (C). 18.60 (978-1-4048-0562-0(1)); Queen's Dragon. Cassidy, Anne. Williamson, Gwyneth, illus. (C). 18.60 (978-1-4048-0553-8(2)); Recycled! Powell, Jillian. (C). 18.60 (978-1-4048-0068-7(9)); Roly-Poly Rice Ball. Dolan, Penny. Mayo, Diana, illus. (C). 18.60 (978-1-4048-0914-7(7)); Run! Ferraby, Sue. Fiorin, Fabiano, illus. (C). 18.60 (978-1-4048-0552-1(4)); Sassy Monkey. Cassidy, Anne. Smith, Lisa, illus. (C). 18.60 (978-1-4048-0058-8(1)); Sausages! Adeney, Anne. Fereday, Roger, illus. (J). 18.60 (978-1-4048-0645-0(8)); Selfish Sophie. Kelleher, Damian. Birkett, Georgia, illus. (C). 18.60 (978-1-4048-0069-4(7)); Sounds Like Fun. Rau, Dana Meachen. Elizalde, Marcelo, illus. (C). 18.60 (978-1-4048-0649-8(0)); Stickers, Shells, & Snow Globes. Rau, Dana Meachen. Thivierge, Claude, illus. (C). 18.60 (978-1-4048-0648-1(2)); Tired of Waiting. Rau, Dana Meachen. Fitzpatrick, Brad, illus. (C). 18.60 (978-1-4048-0650-4(4)); Truth about Hansel & Gretel. Law, Karina. Counsell, Elke, illus. (C). 18.60 (978-1-4048-0559-0(1)); Whose Birthday Is It? Clark, Sherryl. Smith, Jan, illus. (C). 18.60 (978-1-4048-0554-5(0)); Willie the Whale. Oades, Joy. Vagnozzi, Barbara, illus. (C). 18.60 (978-1-4048-0557-6(5)); 32p. (gr. k-3). 2004. Set lib. bdg. 762.60 (978-1-4048-0652-8(0)) Picture Window Bks.

Read-it! Readers. (C). 1822.80 (978-1-4048-1532-2(5)); (Illus.). (978-1-4048-0996-3(1)) Picture Window Bks.

Read-it! Readers: Blue Level. lib. bdg. 39.86 (978-1-4048-1811-8(1)) Picture Window Bks.

Read-it! Readers: Fairy Tales. (Illus.). (C). (gr. k-3). 483.60 (978-1-4048-0998-7(8)) Picture Window Bks.

Read it! Readers: Folk Tales. 2005. (Illus.). (C). (gr. k-3). 130.20 (978-1-4048-0999-4(6)) Picture Window Bks.

Read-it! Readers: Green Level. lib. bdg. 558.04 (978-1-4048-1812-5(X)) Picture Window Bks.

Read-it! Readers: Gus the Hedgehog. (C). 111.60 (978-1-4048-1526-1(0)) Picture Window Bks.

Read-it! Readers: Purple Level. lib. bdg. 219.23 (978-1-4048-1813-2(8)) Picture Window Bks.

Read-it! Readers: Red Level. lib. bdg. 520.80 (978-1-4048-1905-4(3)); lib. bdg. 119.58 (978-1-4048-1814-9(6)) Picture Window Bks.

Read-it! Readers: Rumbles Cave Hotel. (C). 148.80 (978-1-4048-1527-8(9)) Picture Window Bks.

Read-It! Readers: Tall Tales. 2005. (Illus.). (C). (gr. k-3). 111.60 (978-1-4048-1081-5(1)) Picture Window Bks.

Read-it! Readers: The Life of Max. (C). 111.60 (978-1-4048-1533-9(3)) Picture Window Bks.

Read-it! Readers: Yellow Level. lib. bdg. 259.09 (978-1-4048-1869-9(3)) Picture Window Bks.

Read-It! Readers Fables, 12 bks. Incl. Ant & the Grasshopper : A Retelling of Aesop's Fable. White, Mark. Rojo, Sara, illus. 18.60 (978-1-4048-0217-9(7)); Belling the Cat : A Retelling of Aesop's Fable. Aesop. Silverman, Diane, illus. 18.60 (978-1-4048-0321-3(1)); Boy Who Cried Wolf : A Retelling of Aesop's Fable. Aesop. Silverman, Diane, illus. 18.60 (978-1-4048-0319-0(X)); Country Mouse & the City Mouse : A Retelling of Aesop's Fable. Aesop. Silverman, Diane, illus. 18.60 (978-1-4048-0318-3(1)); Crow & the Pitcher : A Retelling of Aesop's Fable. Aesop. Silverman, Diane, illus. 18.60 (978-1-4048-0322-0(X)); Dog & the Wolf : A Retelling of Aesop's Fable. Aesop. Silverman, Diane, illus. 18.60 (978-1-4048-0323-7(8)); Donkey in the Lion's Skin : A Retelling of Aesop's Fable. Aesop. Silverman, Diane, illus. 18.60 (978-1-4048-0320-6(3)); Fox & the Grapes : A Retelling of Aesop's Fable. White, Mark. Rojo, Sara, illus. 18.60 (978-1-4048-0218-6(5)); Goose That Laid the Golden Egg : A Retelling of Aesop's Fable. White, Mark. Rojo, Sara, illus. 18.60 (978-1-4048-0219-3(3)); Lion & the Mouse : A Retelling of Aesop's Fable. White, Mark. Rojo, Sara, illus. 18.60 (978-1-4048-0216-2(9)); Tortoise & the Hare : A Retelling of Aesop's Fable. White, Mark. Rojo, Sara, illus. 18.60 (978-1-4048-0215-5(0)); Wolf in Sheep's Clothing : A Retelling of Aesop's Fable. White, Mark. Rojo, Sara, illus. 18.60 (978-1-4048-0220-9(7)); 24p. (C). (gr. k-3). 2004. 2003. 223.20 (978-1-4048-0309-1(2)) Picture Window Bks.

Read, Lorna. The Lies They Tell. Date not set. (Sky Bks.). 232p. pap. 54.75 (978-0-582-08109-3(2)) Addison-Wesley Longman, Ltd. GBR. *Dist:* Trans-Atlantic Pubns., Inc.

Read Now Service Package. 2004. cd-rom 299.00 (978-1-59455-129-1(4)) Renaissance Learning, Inc.

Read on Target Grade 4. 2005. (J). stu. ed., per. 10.95 (978-1-59230-127-0(4)) Englefield & Assocs., Inc.

Read on Target Grade 5. 2006. (J). pap., stu. ed. 10.95 (978-1-59230-155-3(X)) Englefield & Assocs., Inc.

Read on Target Grade 6. 2006. (J). stu. ed., per. 10.95 (978-1-59230-153-9(3)) Englefield & Assocs., Inc.

Read, Study, Think. (J). (978-0-8374-0219-2(0) , 270); (978-0-8374-0221-5(2) , 299); (978-0-8374-0233-8(6) , 327); (978-0-8374-0243-7(3) , 329); (978-0-8374-0253-6(0) , 332); (978-0-8374-0263-5(8) , 339) Weekly Reader Corp.

Readers Workshop in Grade 1. 2004. spiral bd. (978-1-58453-288-0(2)) Pioneer Valley Educational Pr., Inc.

Reading Achievement Grade 1: Comprehension Activities to Promote Essential Reading Skills. 2001. (Reading Achievement Ser.). 96p. (J). (gr. 1). pap. 10.99 (978-0-88724-629-6(X) , CD-2200) Carson-Dellosa Publishing Co., Inc.

Reading Achievement Grade 2: Comprehension Activities to Promote Essential Reading Skills. 2001. (Reading Achievement Ser.). 96p. (gr. 2). pap. 10.99 (978-0-88724-630-2(3) , CD-2201) Carson-Dellosa Publishing Co., Inc.

Reading Achievement Grade 3: Comprehension Activities to Promote Essential Reading Skills. 2001. (Reading Achievement Ser.). 96p. (gr. 3). pap. 10.99 (978-0-88724-631-9(1) , CD-2202) Carson-Dellosa Publishing Co., Inc.

Reading Achievement Grade 4: Comprehension Activities to Promote Essential Reading Skills. 2001. (Reading Achievement Ser.). 96p. (gr. 4). pap. 10.99 (978-0-88724-632-6(X) , CD-2203) Carson-Dellosa Publishing Co., Inc.

Reading Achievement Grade 5: Comprehension Activities to Promote Essential Reading Skills. 2001. (Reading Achievement Ser.). 96p. (J). (gr. 5). pap. 10.99 (978-0-88724-633-3(8) , CD-2204) Carson-Dellosa Publishing Co., Inc.

Reading Achievement Grade 6: Comprehension Activities to Promote Essential Reading Skills. 2001. (Reading Achievement Ser.). 96p. (gr. 6). pap. 10.99 (978-0-88724-634-0(6) , CD-2205) Carson-Dellosa Publishing Co., Inc.

Reading Achievement Grade 7: Comprehension Activities to Promote Essential Reading Skills. 2001. (Reading Achievement Ser.). 96p. (YA). (gr. 7). pap. 10.99 (978-0-88724-635-7(4) , CD-2206) Carson-Dellosa Publishing Co., Inc.

Reading Achievement Grade 8: Comprehension Activities to Promote Essential Reading Skills. 2001. (Reading Achievement Ser.). 96p. (gr. 8). pap. 10.99 (978-0-88724-636-4(2) , CD-2207) Carson-Dellosa Publishing Co., Inc.

Reading & Language, Set. 2002. (gr. 6-12). 9.42 (978-0-7362-1228-1(0)); tchr. ed. 22.76 (978-0-7362-1229-8(9)) Hampton-Brown Bks.

Reading at Home: Easy Reading Combo. (gr. k-2). 145.50 (978-1-56334-413-8(0)) Hampton-Brown Bks.

Reading at Home: Jumbo Pack. (gr. k-2). 1235.86 (978-0-7362-1399-8(6)) Hampton-Brown Bks.

Reading at Home: Phonics Grade 1 Combo. (gr. 1 up). 517.92 (978-0-7362-1401-8(1)) Hampton-Brown Bks.

Reading at Home: Sound & Letter Combo. (gr. k-2). 341.12 (978-0-7362-1400-1(3)) Hampton-Brown Bks.

Reading Basics Practice Book. (Reading Basics Ser.). (gr. 3-12). 4.71 (978-0-7362-1236-6(1)) Hampton-Brown Bks.

Reading Buddies. 2005. (J). (978-1-932570-32-8(2)) Literacy Footprints Inc.

Reading Central Level a Kit with 4/C Readers. 2004. (Reading Central Ser.). (J). (gr. 1 up). 299.95 (978-1-58830-855-9(3)) Metropolitan Teaching & Learning Co.

Reading Central Level a Kit with Paperbks. 2004. (Reading Central Ser.). (J). (gr. 1 up). 364.95 (978-1-58830-861-0(8)) Metropolitan Teaching & Learning Co.

Reading Central Level a Sh. 2004. (Reading Central Ser.). (J). (gr. 1 up). per. 67.95 (978-1-58830-168-0(0)) Metropolitan Teaching & Learning Co.

Reading Central Level a Student Handbook. 2004. (Reading Central Ser.). (J). (gr. 1 up). per. 7.95 (978-1-58830-891-7(X)) Metropolitan Teaching & Learning Co.

Reading Central Level B Kit with 4/C Readers. 2004. (Reading Central Ser.). (J). (gr. 1 up). 299.95 (978-1-58830-856-6(1)) Metropolitan Teaching & Learning Co.

Reading Central Level B Kit with Paperbks. 2004. (Reading Central Ser.). (J). (gr. 1 up). 364.95 (978-1-58830-862-7(6)) Metropolitan Teaching & Learning Co.

Reading Central Level B Sh. 2004. (Reading Central Ser.). (J). (gr. 1 up). per. 67.95 (978-1-58830-169-7(9)) Metropolitan Teaching & Learning Co.

Reading Central Level B Student Handbook. 2004. (Reading Central Ser.). (J). (gr. 1 up). per. 7.95 (978-1-58830-892-4(8)) Metropolitan Teaching & Learning Co.

Reading Central Level C Kit with 4/C Readers. 2004. (Reading Central Ser.). (J). (gr. 1 up). 299.95 (978-1-58830-857-3(X)) Metropolitan Teaching & Learning Co.

Reading Central Level C Kit with Paperbks. 2004. (Reading Central Ser.). (J). (gr. 1 up). 364.95 (978-1-58830-863-4(4)) Metropolitan Teaching & Learning Co.

Reading Central Level C Sh. 2004. (Reading Central Ser.). (J). (gr. 1 up). per. 67.95 (978-1-58830-192-5(3)) Metropolitan Teaching & Learning Co.

Reading Central Level C Student Handbook. 2004. (Reading Central Ser.). (J). (gr. 1 up). per. 7.95 (978-1-58830-893-1(6)) Metropolitan Teaching & Learning Co.

Reading Central Level D Kit with 4/C Readers. 2004. (Reading Central Ser.). (J). (gr. 2 up). 299.95 (978-1-58830-858-0(8)) Metropolitan Teaching & Learning Co.

Reading Central Level D Kit with Paperbks. 2004. (Reading Central Ser.). (J). (gr. 2 up). 369.95 (978-1-58830-864-1(2)) Metropolitan Teaching & Learning Co.

Reading Central Level D Sh. 2004. (Reading Central Ser.). (J). (gr. 2 up). per. 67.95 (978-1-58830-193-2(1)) Metropolitan Teaching & Learning Co.

Reading Central Level D Student Handbook. 2004. (Reading Central Ser.). (J). (gr. 2 up). per. 7.95 (978-1-58830-894-8(4)) Metropolitan Teaching & Learning Co.

Reading Central Level E Kit with 4/C Readers. 2004. (Reading Central Ser.). (J). (gr. 2 up). 299.95 (978-1-58830-859-7(6)) Metropolitan Teaching & Learning Co.

Reading Central Level E Kit with Paperbks. 2004. (Reading Central Ser.). (J). (gr. 2 up). 369.95 (978-1-58830-865-8(0)) Metropolitan Teaching & Learning Co.

Reading Central Level E Sh. 2004. (Reading Central Ser.). (J). (gr. 2 up). per. 67.95 (978-1-58830-194-9(X)) Metropolitan Teaching & Learning Co.

Reading Central Level E Student Handbook. 2004. (Reading Central Ser.). (J). (gr. 2 up). per. 7.95 (978-1-58830-895-5(2)) Metropolitan Teaching & Learning Co.

Reading Central Level F Kit with 4/C Readers. 2004. (Reading Central Ser.). (J). (gr. 2 up). 299.95 (978-1-58830-860-3(X)) Metropolitan Teaching & Learning Co.

Reading Central Level F Kit with Paperbks. 2004. (Reading Central Ser.). (J). (gr. 2 up). 369.95 (978-1-58830-866-5(9)) Metropolitan Teaching & Learning Co.

Reading Central Level F Sh. 2004. (Reading Central Ser.). (J). (gr. 2 up). per. 67.95 (978-1-58830-196-3(6)) Metropolitan Teaching & Learning Co.

Reading Central Level F Student Handbook. 2004. (Reading Central Ser.). (J). (gr. 2 up). per. 39.95 (978-1-58830-896-2(0)) Metropolitan Teaching & Learning Co.

Reading Comprehension: Main Idea & Summarizing Grade 1-2. 2005. 48p. (J). per. 6.99 (978-1-59441-102-1(6) , CD-104052) Carson-Dellosa Publishing Co., Inc.

Reading Comprehension & Skills Grade 1. 2000. (Kelley Wingate Ser.). (Illus.). 80p. (J). (ps-2). pap. 9.99 (978-0-88724-604-3(4)) Carson-Dellosa Publishing Co., Inc.

Reading Comprehension & Skills Grade 2. 2000. (Kelley Wingate Ser.). (Illus.). 80p. (J). (gr. 1-3). pap. 9.99 (978-0-88724-605-0(2)) Carson-Dellosa Publishing Co., Inc.

Reading Comprehension & Skills Grade 3. 2000. (Kelley Wingate Ser.). (Illus.). 80p. (J). (gr. 2-4). pap. 9.99 (978-0-88724-606-7(0)) Carson-Dellosa Publishing Co., Inc.

Reading Comprehension & Skills Grade 4. 2000. (Kelley Wingate Ser.). (Illus.). 80p. (J). (gr. 3-5). pap. 9.99 (978-0-88724-607-4(9)) Carson-Dellosa Publishing Co., Inc.

Reading Comprehension & Skills Grade 5. 2000. (Kelley Wingate Ser.). (Illus.). 80p. (J). (gr. 4-6). pap. 9.99 (978-0-88724-608-1(7)) Carson-Dellosa Publishing Co., Inc.

Reading Comprehension & Skills Grade 6. 2000. (Kelley Wingate Ser.). (Illus.). 80p. (J). (gr. 5-7). pap. 9.99 (978-0-88724-609-8(5)) Carson-Dellosa Publishing Co., Inc.

Reading Comprehension & Skills Grade 7. 2000. (Kelley Wingate Ser.). (Illus.). 80p. (YA). (gr. 6-8). pap. 9.99 (978-0-88724-610-4(9)) Carson-Dellosa Publishing Co., Inc.

Reading Comprehension & Skills Grade 8. 2000. (Kelley Wingate Ser.). (Illus.). 80p. (YA). (gr. 7-9). pap. 9.99 (978-0-88724-611-1(7)) Carson-Dellosa Publishing Co., Inc.

Reading First Through Science Grade 4. 2005. (978-0-9766802-6-0(2)) Educational Tools, Inc.

Reading for Detail, Grades 4-5, 2 vols., Vol. 1. 2001. 56p. (J). (gr. 4-5). pap. 7.95 (978-1-58324-116-5(7) , World Teachers Pr.) Didax Educational Resources, Inc.

Reading for Detail, Grades 6-7, 2 vols., Vol. 2. 2001. 56p. (YA). (gr. 6-7). pap. 7.95 (978-1-58324-117-2(5) , World Teachers Pr.) Didax Educational Resources, Inc.

Reading for Understanding (3-4) 2002. 128p. pap. 10.99 (978-0-88724-760-6(1) , CD-4303) Carson-Dellosa Publishing Co., Inc.

Reading Friends Staff. Witches Single. (J). (978-0-8136-3823-2(2)) Modern Curriculum Pr.

Reading Partner. 2004. (J). (978-1-58453-267-5(X)) Pioneer Valley Educational Pr., Inc.

Reading Remedies. 352p. (gr. 1-4). 23.99 (978-0-513-02100-6(0) , TSD21000) Denison, T. S. & Co., Inc.

Reading Rods Beginning Sight Words Double-Sided Activity Cards. 2002. (J). 12.95 (978-1-56911-098-0(0)) Learning Resources, Inc.

Reading Rods Phonemic Awareness: Instruction & Activity Book. 2001. (J). spiral bd. 12.95 (978-1-56911-063-8(8)) Learning Resources, Inc.

Reading Rods Phonemic Awareness Double-Sided Activity Cards. 2001. (J). 12.95 (978-1-56911-070-6(0)) Learning Resources, Inc.

Reading Rods Sentence Building: Instruction & Activity Book. 2001. (J). spiral bd. 12.95 (978-1-56911-066-9(2)) Learning Resources, Inc.

Reading Rods Sentence Building Double-Sided Activity Cards. 2001. (J). 12.95 (978-1-56911-073-7(5)) Learning Resources, Inc.

Reading Rods Sight Words: Instruction & Activity Book. 2001. (J). pap. 12.95 (978-1-56911-096-6(4)) Learning Resources, Inc.

Reading Rods Spelling: Instruction & Activity Book. 2002. (J). pap. 12.95 (978-1-56911-097-3(2)) Learning Resources, Inc.

Reading Rods Spelling Double-Sided Activity Cards. 2002. (J). 12.95 (978-1-56911-099-7(9)) Learning Resources, Inc.

Reading Rods Word Building: Instruction & Activity Book. 2001. (J). spiral bd. 12.95 (978-1-56911-065-2(4)) Learning Resources, Inc.

Reading Rods Word Building Double-Sided Activity Cards. 2001. (J). 12.95 (978-1-56911-072-0(7)) Learning Resources, Inc.

Reading Rods Word Families: Instruction & Activity Book. 2001. (J). spiral bd. 12.95 (978-1-56911-064-5(6)) Learning Resources, Inc.

Reading Skill Sharpeners: First Grade. 2002. (J). pap. 17.95 (978-1-56911-040-9(9)) Learning Resources, Inc.

Reading Skill Sharpeners: Second Grade. 2002. (J). pap. 17.95 (978-1-56911-041-6(7)) Learning Resources, Inc.

Reading Skill Sharpeners: Third Grade. 2002. (J). pap. 17.95 (978-1-56911-042-3(5)) Learning Resources, Inc.

Reading Success 1: A Multisensory Reading Intervention Program. 128p. (gr. 1-4). 13.99 (978-1-56822-933-1(X) , LL80101) School Specialty Publishing.

Reading Success 2: A Multisensory Reading Intervention Program. 176p. (gr. 1-4). 15.99 (978-1-56822-934-8(8) , LL80102) School Specialty Publishing.

Reading Success 3: A Multisensory Reading Intervention Program. 176p. (gr. 1-4). 15.99 (978-1-56822-935-5(6) ; LL80103) School Specialty Publishing.

Reading Test Taking: Grade 1. 2000. (Practice Makes Perfect Ser.). (Illus.). 80p. (J). (gr. 1). pap. 2.99 (978-0-88724-612-8(5) , CD-3622) Carson-Dellosa Publishing Co., Inc.

Reading Test Taking: Grade 2. 2000. (Practice Makes Perfect Ser.). (Illus.). 80p. (J). (gr. 2). pap. 2.99 (978-0-88724-613-5(3) , CD-3623) Carson-Dellosa Publishing Co., Inc.

Reading Test Taking: Grade 3. 2000. (Practice Makes Perfect Ser.). 80p. (J). (gr. 3). pap. 2.99 (978-0-88724-614-2(1) , CD-3624) Carson-Dellosa Publishing Co., Inc.

Reading Test Taking: Grade 4. 2000. (Practice Makes Perfect Ser.). 80p. (J). (gr. 4). pap. 2.99 (978-0-88724-615-9(X) , CD-3625) Carson-Dellosa Publishing Co., Inc.

Reading Test Taking: Grade 5. 2000. (Practice Makes Perfect Ser.). 80p. (J). (gr. 5). pap. 2.99 (978-0-88724-616-6(8) , CD-3626) Carson-Dellosa Publishing Co., Inc.

Reading Test Taking: Grade 6. 2000. (Practice Makes Perfect Ser.). 80p. (J). (gr. 6). pap. 2.99 (978-0-88724-617-3(6) , CD-3627) Carson-Dellosa Publishing Co., Inc.

Reading Test Taking: Grade 7. 2000. (Practice Makes Perfect Ser.). 80p. (YA). (gr. 7). pap. 2.99 (978-0-88724-618-0(4) , CD-3628) Carson-Dellosa Publishing Co., Inc.

Reading Test Taking: Grade 8. 2000. (Practice Makes Perfect Ser.). 80p. (YA). (gr. 8). pap. 2.99 (978-0-88724-619-7(2) , CD-3629) Carson-Dellosa Publishing Co., Inc.

Reading Together Intermediate Phase II&III Tutor's Guide Book. 2004. (J). pap. (978-1-931840-70-5(9)) Learning Together.

Reading Together Tutors Guidebook Phase II&III Grade 3. 2004. (J). pap. (978-1-931840-66-8(0)) Learning Together.

Reading Worktext Grade 1, Book 2. 2004. 10.50 (978-0-89084-472-4(0)) Jones, Bob Univ. Pr.

Ready Reader Staff. Apple Farm, Level 8, Bk. 49. (J). (ps-3). pap. 33.50 (978-0-8136-0799-3(X)) Modern Curriculum Pr.

—The Best Place, 6 bks., set , Level 4, Bk. 4. (J). (ps-3). pap. 24.50 (978-0-8136-2011-4(2)) Modern Curriculum Pr.

Ready Readers: Stage 1: Preschool-Grade 1. (Illus.). 304p. (J). pap. (978-0-7666-0626-5(0) , Honey Bear Bks.) Modern Publishing.

Ready, Set, Pedal! First Grade Guided Reading Level F. (On Our Way to English Ser.). (gr. 1 up). 27.75 (978-0-7578-7049-1(X)) Rigby Education.

Ready, Set, Read 2005, 8. 2005. (Illus.). (J). pap. 37.95 (978-1-57874-303-2(6)) Kaeden Corp.

Ready, Set, Read Fall 2005, 8 books. 2005. (Illus.). (J). pap. 37.95 (978-1-57874-305-6(2)) Kaeden Corp.

Ready, Set, Read (Gr. K-1) 2003. (J). (978-1-58232-033-5(0)) Bryan Hse. Pubs., Inc.

Ready-to-Go Lessons: Reading & Writing, Grade 3. 2006. 144p. 15.99 (978-1-4206-8032-4(3)) Teacher Created Resources, Inc.

Ready-to-Go Lessons: Reading & Writing, Grade 4. 2006. 15.99 (978-1-4206-8033-1(1)) Teacher Created Resources, Inc.

Ready-to-Go Lessons: Reading & Writing, Grade 5. 2006. 15.99 (978-1-4206-8034-8(X)) Teacher Created Resources, Inc.

The Real Deal - Green Plus. 2006. (Illus.). (gr. 4-8). 83.70 (978-0-7910-9068-8(X)) Facts On File, Inc.

The Real Deal - Red Plus. 2006. (Illus.). 32p. (gr. 4-8). 83.70 (978-0-7910-9069-5(8)) Facts On File, Inc.

The Real Deal - Yellow. 2006. (Illus.). (gr. 4-8). 83.70 (978-0-7910-9110-4(4)) Facts On File, Inc.

Realtime Associates and Mazer Corporation Staff & LeapFrog Staff, compiled by. LeapTrack Cards - Reading 3. 2002. (J). (978-1-58605-128-0(8)) LeapFrog Enterprises, Inc.

—LeapTrack Cards - Reading 4. 2002. (J). (978-1-58605-182-2(2)) LeapFrog Enterprises, Inc.

—LeapTrack Cards - Reading 5. 2002. (J). (978-1-58605-185-3(7)) LeapFrog Enterprises, Inc.

Red Egg & Ginger, 6 Pack. (Greetings Ser.: Vol. 1). 24p. (gr. 2-3). 31.00 (978-0-7635-9409-1(1)) Rigby Education.

Red Scarf Girl Student Packet, Gr. 7-8. 2004. (J). (978-1-58130-862-4(0)) Novel Units, Inc.

Red, Yellow, Blue & Green Levels Certificate Only. (Sails Literacy Ser.). (gr. 1-6). 89.00 (978-0-7578-6555-8(0)) Rigby Education.

Redcoats & Petticoats. (Guided Reading Levels Ser.). 8.48 (978-0-7362-1767-5(3)); 50.88 (978-0-7362-2171-9(9)) Hampton-Brown Bks.

Reece, Paula. Settling the West: Adventures in Pioneering & Westward Expansion. 2002. (Skill-Based Reading Anthology Ser.). (Illus.). 124p. (978-0-7891-5582-5(6)) Perfection Learning Corp.

Reid, Carolyn. Busy in the Bushveld: South African Edition. 1998. (Cambridge Reading Routes Ser.). (Illus.). 16p. pap. 5.45 (978-0-521-63680-3(9)) Cambridge Univ. Pr.

Reid, Rob. Storytime Slam! 15 Lesson Plans for Preschool & Primary Story Programs. 2006. (Illus.). 85p. (J). pap. 16.95 (***978-1-932146-52-3(0)*** , Upstart Bks.) Highsmith Inc.

Remarkable Robots. 2005. (Book Treks Ser.). (J). 37.95 (978-0-7652-3243-4(X)) Celebration Pr.

The Renaissance Kids. 2005. (Book Treks Ser.). (J). 37.95 (978-0-7652-3255-7(3)) Celebration Pr.

Responding to Literature: The EMC Write-in Reader. 2nd ed. (Literature & the Language Arts Ser.). (YA). (gr. 8 up). wbk. ed. 15.95 (978-0-8219-2912-4(7)) EMC/Paradigm Publishing.

The Responsible Dr Bones: Social/Emotional Lap Book. (Pebble Soup Explorations Ser.). (ps up). 16.00 (978-0-7635-7566-3(6)) Rigby Education.

Rex Runs Away: First Grade Guided Reading Level G. (On Our Way to English Ser.). (gr. 1 up). 27.75 (978-0-7578-7055-2(4)) Rigby Education.

Rey, H. A. and Margret. Curious George Shapes: CG TV Board Book #5. 2008. 10p. (J). (gr. k-ps). bds. 6.99 (***978-0-618-89198-6(6)***) Houghton Mifflin Co. Trade & Reference Div.

Rhoades, Jacqueline. Rhoades to Reading Level II. 4th ed. 2004. 102p. (YA). spiral bd., wbk. ed. 19.95 (978-1-930006-53-9(5)) Rhoades & Assocs.

—Rhoades to Reading Level III. 4th ed. 2004. 286p. (YA). spiral bd., wbk. ed. 29.95 (978-1-930006-55-3(1)) Rhoades & Assocs.

—Rhoades to Reading Level IV. 4th ed. 2004. 166p. spiral bd., wbk. ed. 19.95 (978-1-930006-57-7(8) , 1008) Rhoades & Assocs.

—Rhoades to Reading Level V. 4th ed. 2004. 80p. (YA). spiral bd., wbk. ed. 14.95 (978-1-930006-59-1(4)) Rhoades & Assocs.

Rhoades, Jacquelline. Rhoades to Reading Level I. 4th ed. 2004. 134p. (YA). spiral bd., wbk. ed. 19.95 (978-1-930006-51-5(9) , 1002) Rhoades & Assocs.

Rhodes, Karen. 7 Sensational Stories. 2005. (J). pap. 1.79 (***978-1-59317-084-4(X)***) Warner Pr. Pubs.

Rhyme Time. 2005. (Little Celebrations Thematic Packages Ser.). (J). (gr. k-3). 133.50 (978-0-673-75380-9(8)) Celebration Pr.

The Ribbon. (Early Intervention Levels Ser.). 23.10 (978-0-7362-0016-5(9)); Vol. 3. 3.85 (978-1-56334-966-9(3)) Hampton-Brown Bks.

Rice All Day: Kindergarten Big Books. (On Our Way to English Ser.). (gr. k up). 29.95 (978-0-7578-1620-8(7)) Rigby Education.

Rice All Day: Small Versions of Big Books. (On Our Way to English Ser.). (gr. k up). 29.00 (978-0-7578-7220-4(4)) Rigby Education.

Richards, Kitty. Meet the Sparkplugs. Simard, Remy, illus. 2006. (Phonics Comics Ser.). 24p. (J). (gr. 1-17). pap. 3.99 (978-1-58476-419-9(8) , IKIDS) Innovative Kids.

—Twisted Tales, Level 3. Juarez, Fernando, illus. 2006. (Phonics Comics Ser.). 24p. (J). (gr. 1-17). pap. 3.99 (978-1-58476-514-1(3) , IKIDS) Innovative Kids.

Richie's Rocket. (Lexile Levels Ser.). 9.09 (978-1-56334-736-8(9)) Hampton-Brown Bks.

Rick & Rosie. (Early Intervention Levels Ser.). 21.30 (978-0-7362-0365-4(6)); Vol. 2. 3.55 (978-0-7362-0086-8(X)) Hampton-Brown Bks.

Rider, Cynthia. Chatterbox Turtle. Petrlik, Andrea, illus. 2004. 24p. (J). lib. bdg. 22.65 (***978-1-59646-696-8(0)***) Dingles & Co.

—The Crocodile's Sky Snack. Clementson, John, illus. 2001. (Cambridge Reading Ser.). 16p. pap. 6.00 (978-0-521-01402-1(6)) Cambridge Univ. Pr.

—The Popcorn Boy. van Vliet, Helen, illus. 2001. (Cambridge Reading Ser.). 16p. pap., stu. ed. 8.00 (978-0-521-01419-9(0)) Cambridge Univ. Pr.

—The Shy Dragon & the White Knight. Vagnozzi, Barbara, illus. 2001. (Cambridge Reading Ser.). 16p. pap., stu. ed. 6.00 (978-0-521-01411-3(5)) Cambridge Univ. Pr.

—The Tricky Troll & the Billy Goats Gruff. Williamson, Melanie, illus. 2001. (Cambridge Reading Ser.). 16p. pap. 6.00 (978-0-521-01399-4(2)) Cambridge Univ. Pr.

—The Wind & the Sun. Stone, Joanne, illus. 2001. (Cambridge Reading Ser.). 16p. pap., stu. ed. 6.00 (978-0-521-01415-1(8)) Cambridge Univ. Pr.

Rider, Cynthia & Lynne, Francis. Beginning to Read: Phonics for Reading 2. 2000. (Cambridge Reading Ser.). (Illus.). 8p. pap. 19.00 (978-0-521-79525-8(7)) Cambridge Univ. Pr.

The Rides 6 Packs. First Wave Satellite. (Sails Literacy Ser.). 16p. (gr. k up). 27.00 (978-0-7578-7505-2(X)) Rigby Education.

Ridgway, Dawn. The Magic Flute: South African Edition: A Traditional Tale from the Bemba & Tonga People of Zimbabwe. Busse, Annette, illus. 1998. (Cambridge Reading Routes Ser.). 16p. pap. 5.45 (978-0-521-63676-6(0)) Cambridge Univ. Pr.

—Takalani & the Elephant: South African Edition. 1998. (Cambridge Reading Routes Ser.). (Illus.). 16p. pap. 5.45 (978-0-521-63675-9(2)) Cambridge Univ. Pr.

Riding: Kindergarten Newcomer Books. (On Our Way to English Ser.). (gr. k up). 23.50 (978-0-7578-7200-6(X)) Rigby Education.

Riding Freedom Student Packet, Gr. 3-4. 2004. (J). (978-1-58130-864-8(7)) Novel Units, Inc.

Riding on Roller Coasters: Fourth Grade Guided Comprehension Level Q. (On Our Way to English Ser.). (gr. 4 up). 34.50 (978-0-7578-7178-8(X)) Rigby Education.

Rigby. Follow That Car. 2002. (Illus.). pap. 41.60 incl. audio compact disk (978-0-7398-6952-9(3)) Steck-Vaughn.

—From the Page to the Stage. 2001. pap. (978-0-7635-7341-6(8)) Steck-Vaughn.

Rigby Education Staff. Activity Guide. (Illus.). (gr. k-1). tchr. ed. 18.00 (978-0-7635-2005-2(5)); tchr. ed. 18.00 (978-0-7635-2006-9(3)); tchr. ed. 18.00 (978-0-7635-2007-6(1)); tchr. ed. 18.00 (978-0-7635-2008-3(X)) Rigby Education.

—A Day on the Farm. (Illus.). 8p. (J). bds. 3.95 (978-0-7635-6463-6(X) , 764639C99) Rigby Education.

—Discovery World Org Where Does. (Discovery World Ser.). (Illus.). 12p. (gr. 1-2). 27.00 (978-0-7635-2698-6(3)) Rigby Education.

—Discovery World Red Biography Ill. (Discovery World Ser.). 12p. (gr. 1-2). 31.00 (978-0-7635-2703-7(3)) Rigby Education.

—Everything Changes Big Book: Little Red Riding Hood. (Pebble Soup Explorations Ser.). 16p. (ps up). 21.00 (978-0-7635-6482-7(6)) Rigby Education.

—Follow the Paw Prints. (Pebble Soup Explorations Ser.). (Illus.). 16p. (ps up). 31.00 (978-0-7635-6446-9(X) , 764469C99) Rigby Education.

—Jack Big Book. (gr. k-2). 21.00 (978-0-7635-2409-8(3)) Rigby Education.

—Jumbled Tumble Little Miss. (gr. k-2). 21.00 (978-0-7635-2415-9(8)) Rigby Education.

—Jumbled Tumble Little Tom. (gr. k-2). 21.00 (978-0-7635-2414-2(X)) Rigby Education.

—Max. (Sails Literacy Ser.). (Illus.). 16p. (gr. 1-2). 27.00 (978-0-7635-9906-5(9) , 699069C99) Rigby Education.

—Roger's Best Friend. (Illus.). 16p. (J). pap. 30.00 (978-0-7635-6434-6(6) , 764346C99) Rigby Education.

—Sails Beginners First Wave. (Sails Literacy Ser.). (gr. k up). tchr.'s planning gde. ed. 24.00 (978-0-7635-7924-1(6)) Rigby Education.

—Sails Emergent Level Magenta. (Sails Literacy Ser.). (Illus.). (gr. k-1). 116.00 (978-0-7635-9856-3(9)) Rigby Education.

—Stage 1 Components. (gr. k-3). 57.00 (978-0-7635-9245-5(5)) Rigby Education.

—Tom Sawyer: Jumbled Tumble. (gr. k-2). 26.00 (978-0-7635-2424-1(7)) Rigby Education.

—Touching the Moon. (Illus.). 16p. (J). pap. 30.00 (978-0-7635-6498-8(2) , 764982C99) Rigby Education.

—Two Eyes That See. (Illus.). 16p. (J). pap. 3.95 (978-0-7635-7037-8(0) , 764265C99) Rigby Education.

—Who Works in Your Neighborhood? (Illus.). (J). suppl. ed. 20.00 (978-0-7635-6453-7(2) , 764532C99) Rigby Education.

—William Tell. (gr. k-2). 21.00 (978-0-7635-2426-5(3)) Rigby Education.

Riley. Casey's Code. 1999. (Illus.). (J). pap. 5.65 (978-0-7398-0876-4(1)) Steck-Vaughn.

Rimes with Ball 6 Packs. KinderRimes. (Kinderstarters Ser.). (ps-1). 21.00 (978-0-7635-8667-6(6)) Rigby Education.

Rimes with Cake 6 Packs. KinderRimes. (Kinderstarters Ser.). (ps-1). 21.00 (978-0-7635-8668-3(4)) Rigby Education.

Rimes with Cap 6 Packs. KinderRimes. (Kinderstarters Ser.). (ps-1). 21.00 (978-0-7635-8669-0(2)) Rigby Education.

Rimes with Cat 6 Packs. KinderRimes. (Kinderstarters Ser.). (ps-1). 21.00 (978-0-7635-8670-6(6)) Rigby Education.

Rimes with Clock 6 Packs. KinderRimes. (Kinderstarters Ser.). (ps-1). 21.00 (978-0-7635-8671-3(4)) Rigby Education.

Rimes with Clown 6 Packs. KinderRimes. (Kinderstarters Ser.). (ps-1). 21.00 (978-0-7635-8672-0(2)) Rigby Education.

Rimes with Drink 6 Packs. KinderRimes. (Kinderstarters Ser.). (ps-1). 21.00 (978-0-7635-8673-7(0)) Rigby Education.

Rimes with Goat 6 Packs. KinderRimes. (Kinderstarters Ser.). (ps-1). 21.00 (978-0-7635-8674-4(9)) Rigby Education.

Rimes with Hay 6 Packs. KinderRimes. (Kinderstarters Ser.). (ps-1). 21.00 (978-0-7635-8675-1(7)) Rigby Education.

Rimes with Hill 6 Packs. KinderRimes. (Kinderstarters Ser.). (ps-1). 21.00 (978-0-7635-8676-8(5)) Rigby Education.

Rimes with Jump 6 Packs. KinderRimes. (Kinderstarters Ser.). (ps-1). 21.00 (978-0-7635-8677-5(3)) Rigby Education.

Rimes with Kick 6 Packs. KinderRimes. (Kinderstarters Ser.). (ps-1). 21.00 (978-0-7635-8678-2(1)) Rigby Education.

Rimes with King 6 Packs. KinderRimes. (Kinderstarters Ser.). (ps-1). 21.00 (978-0-7635-8679-9(X)) Rigby Education.

Rimes with Man 6 Packs. KinderRimes. (Kinderstarters Ser.). (ps-1). 21.00 (978-0-7635-8680-5(3)) Rigby Education.

Rimes with Mice 6 Packs. KinderRimes. (Kinderstarters Ser.). (ps-1). 21.00 (978-0-7635-8681-2(1)) Rigby Education.

Rimes with Net 6 Packs. KinderRimes. (Kinderstarters Ser.). (ps-1). 21.00 (978-0-7635-8682-9(X)) Rigby Education.

Rimes with Pig 6 Packs. KinderRimes. (Kinderstarters Ser.). (ps-1). 21.00 (978-0-7635-8683-6(8)) Rigby Education.

Rimes with Ram 6 Packs. KinderRimes. (Kinderstarters Ser.). (ps-1). 21.00 (978-0-7635-8684-3(6)) Rigby Education.

Rimes with Saw 6 Packs. KinderRimes. (Kinderstarters Ser.). (ps-1). 21.00 (978-0-7635-8685-0(4)) Rigby Education.

Rimes with Ship 6 Packs. KinderRimes. (Kinderstarters Ser.). (ps-1). 21.00 (978-0-7635-8686-7(2)) Rigby Education.

Rimes with Skate 6 Packs. KinderRimes. (Kinderstarters Ser.). (ps-1). 21.00 (978-0-7635-8687-4(0)) Rigby Education.

Rimes with Snail 6 Packs. KinderRimes. (Kinderstarters Ser.). (ps-1). 21.00 (978-0-7635-8688-1(9)) Rigby Education.

Rimes with Track 6 Packs. KinderRimes. (Kinderstarters Ser.). (ps-1). 21.00 (978-0-7635-8689-8(7)) Rigby Education.

Rimes with Train 6 Packs. KinderRimes. (Kinderstarters Ser.). (ps-1). 21.00 (978-0-7635-8690-4(0)) Rigby Education.

Ring, Susan. Dinosaurs: An Adventure Back in Time, Level 3. Wilson, Phil, illus. 2006. (innovativeKids readers ser.: level 3). 32p. (J). (gr. 1-3). pap., pap. 6.99 (978-1-58476-478-6(3) , IKIDS) Innovative Kids.

—Innovative Kids Readers: the Great Barrier Reef - an Undersea Adventure. 2007. 32p. (J). (gr. 1-3). pap. 6.99 (978-1-58476-543-1(7)) Innovative Kids.

Rise & Shine. 2002. (Into English! Ser.). (gr. k-2). 939.12 (978-1-56334-996-6(5)); 500.86 (978-0-7362-0040-0(1)); 500.86 (978-0-7362-0041-7(X)); 154.00 (978-0-7362-0043-1(6)); suppl. ed. 799.44 (978-1-56334-995-9(7)); Collection A. 426.37 (978-1-56334-997-3(3)); Collection A. 77.00 (978-1-56334-911-9(6)); Collection B. 426.37 (978-1-56334-998-0(1)); Collection B. 77.00 (978-1-56334-912-6(4)) Hampton-Brown Bks.

Risk, Mary, et al. Hurry up Molly/English-Spanish: Apurate, Molly. Scriven, Gill, illus. 2000. (I Can Read Bks.).Tr. of Hurry Up, Molly. (SPA, ENG & FRE.). 28p. (J). (ps up). 8.99 (978-0-7641-5286-3(6)) Barron's Educational Series, Inc.

The River. (Pebble Soup Explorations Ser.). 16p. (ps up). 31.00 (978-0-7578-1660-4(6)) Rigby Education.

The River: Small Book. (Pebble Soup Explorations Ser.). 16p. (ps up). 5.00 (978-0-7578-1700-7(9)) Rigby Education.

A River Ran Wild. (Lexile Levels Ser.). 9.09 (978-1-56334-737-5(7)) Hampton-Brown Bks.

Road South. 64p. (YA). (gr. 9-12). pap. 9.50 (978-0-8359-1098-9(9)) Globe Fearon Educational Publishing.

Road to Freedom: Fifth Grade Class Collection Books. (On Our Way to English Ser.). (gr. 5 up). 29.95 (978-0-7578-4467-6(7)) Rigby Education.

Road to Freedom: Small Versions of Class Collection Books. (On Our Way to English Ser.). (gr. 5 up). 34.50 (978-0-7578-7287-7(5)) Rigby Education.

Road to Learning Pack. 2000. (Road to Reading Ser.). (J). 59.99 (978-0-307-19566-1(X) , Golden Bks.) Random Hse. Children's Bks.

Robb, Anina. Graphic Organizers & Strategy Sheets That Scaffold Writing from Paragraphs to Essays: Student Packets with Guided Lessons, Writing Models, Graphic Organizers, & Planning Sheets. 2007. (Teaching Strategies Ser.). 112p. pap. 17.99 (978-0-439-82772-0(8) , Teaching Resources) Scholastic, Inc.

A Robbie Reader Series, 12 Bks, Set. 2004. (Illus.). (gr. 1-4). lib. bdg. 203.40 (978-1-58415-319-1(9)) Mitchell Lane Pubs., Inc.

Roberto Clemente: Fourth Grade Guided Comprehension Level N. (On Our Way to English Ser.). (gr. 4 up). 34.50 (978-0-7578-7162-7(3)) Rigby Education.

Robes, Ruth & Almendro, Herminio. Habia una Vez: Libro Segundo de Lectura. (SPA.). (J). pap. 12.95 (978-84-357-0109-9(3) , CPR30) Ediciones y Distribuciones Codice, S.A. ESP. *Dist:* Continental Bk. Co., Inc.

Robins, Eleanor. Be Fair. 2004. (Illus.). 48p. (YA). per. 3.95 (978-1-56254-768-4(2) , SP7682) Saddleback Educational Publishing.

—Boy of Their Dreams. 2003. (Illus.). 48p. (YA). per. 3.95 (978-1-56254-679-3(1) , SP6791) Saddleback Educational Publishing.

—Time to Move On. 2004. (Illus.). 48p. (YA). per. 3.95 (978-1-56254-778-3(X) , SP778X) Saddleback Educational Publishing.

—The Worst Year Ever. 2004. 48p. (YA). per. 3.95 (978-1-56254-780-6(1) , SP7801) Saddleback Educational Publishing.

—The Wrong Way. 2004. 48p. (YA). per. (978-1-56254-782-0(8) , SP7828) Saddleback Educational Publishing.

Robins, Eleanor, told to. Someone to Count On. 2004. (Illus.). 48p. (YA). per. 3.95 (978-1-56254-776-9(3) , SP7763) Saddleback Educational Publishing.

Robinson. In the Land of the Polar Bear. 1999. (Illus.). (J). pap. 4.93 (978-0-7398-2408-5(2)) Steck-Vaughn.

Robinson, Anthony. Animals in the Jungle: American English Edition. 2000. (Cambridge Reading Ser.). (Illus.). pap. 5.00 (978-0-521-79904-1(X)) Cambridge Univ. Pr.

—Animals in the Jungle Pack of 6 American English Edition. 2000. (Cambridge Reading Ser.). (Illus.). 8p. pap. 28.00 (978-0-521-79905-8(8)) Cambridge Univ. Pr.

Robot & Mr. Mole. 2004. (Illus.). (J). (978-1-59577-009-7(7)) Starfall Education.

Robot Trouble: Fourth Grade Guided Comprehension Level Q. (On Our Way to English Ser.). (gr. 4 up). 34.50 (978-0-7578-7175-7(5)) Rigby Education.

Robshaw, B. The Locked Room. 2nd rev. ed. 2004. (Livewires Ser.). pap. 7.13 (978-0-340-81683-7(X)) Cambridge Univ. Pr.

Robshaw, Brandon & Scholoar, Rochelle. Urban Myths. 2005. (Illus.). 32p. pap. 8.50 (978-0-340-87148-5(2)) Cambridge Univ. Pr.

Rodeo under the Sea: Third Grade Guided Reading Level I. (On Our Way to English Ser.). (gr. 3 up). 34.50 (978-0-7578-7112-2(7)) Rigby Education.

Rodriguez-Nora, Tere. Kikiwi y los desperdicios en el fondo del Mar. Guimaraes, Santi Roman i., illus. 2005. (SPA.). 32p. (J). 10.95 (978-84-96046-36-8(2)) Ediciones Norte, Inc.

Roitman, Tanya, illus. I'm Going to Read (Level 1): I'm Going to Washington to Visit the President. 2006. (I'm Going to Read Ser.). 24p. (J). pap. 3.95 (978-1-4027-3408-3(5)) Sterling Publishing Co., Inc.

Rojas, O. Un Dia Una Abeja. 2004. (SPA.). 32p. 6.95 (978-1-4000-9288-6(4)) Editorial Sudamericana S.A. ARG. *Dist:* Random Hse., Inc.

The Roller Coaster: KinderWords Individual Title Six-Packs. (Kinderstarters Ser.). 8p. (ps-1). 21.00 (978-0-7635-8708-6(7)) Rigby Education.

The Roman Oracle: MainSails Individual Title Six-Packs. (Sails Literacy Ser.). (gr. 5 up). 37.00 (978-0-7578-8051-3(7)) Rigby Education.

Romer, Ruth. Jill Gets Fit. 2004. (Reader's Theater Ser.). (J). pap. 22.00 (978-1-4108-0791-5(6)) Benchmark Education Co.

—Pet Care Kids. ed. 2004. (Reader's Theater Ser.). (J). pap. 22.00 (978-1-4108-1146-2(8)) Benchmark Education Co.

Rondeau, Amanda. Ed As in Bed. 2003. (Word Families Ser.). (Illus.). 23p. (J). (ps-3). lib. bdg. 19.93 (978-1-59197-228-0(0) , SandCastle) ABDO Publishing Co.

—Ob As in Knob. 2003. (Word Families Ser.). (Illus.). 23p. (J). (ps-3). lib. bdg. 19.93 (978-1-59197-249-5(3) , SandCastle) ABDO Publishing Co.

—Ock As in Block. 2003. (Word Families Ser.). (Illus.). 23p. (J). (ps-3). lib. bdg. 19.93 (978-1-59197-250-1(7) , SandCastle) ABDO Publishing Co.

—Og As in Dog. 2003. (Word Families Ser.). (Illus.). 23p. (J). (ps-3). lib. bdg. 19.93 (978-1-59197-251-8(5) , SandCastle) ABDO Publishing Co.

—Op As in Top. 2003. (Word Families Ser.). (Illus.). 23p. (J). (ps-3). lib. bdg. 19.93 (978-1-59197-252-5(3) , SandCastle) ABDO Publishing Co.

—Ore As in Core. 2003. (Word Families Ser.). (Illus.). 23p. (J). (ps-3). lib. bdg. 19.93 (978-1-59197-267-9(1) , SandCastle) ABDO Publishing Co.

—Ot As in Knot. 2003. (Word Families Ser.). (Illus.). 23p. (J). (ps-3). lib. bdg. 19.93 (978-1-59197-253-2(1) , SandCastle) ABDO Publishing Co.

—Ow As in Cow. 2003. (Word Families Ser.). (Illus.). 23p. (J). (ps-3). lib. bdg. 19.93 (978-1-59197-254-9(X) , SandCastle) ABDO Publishing Co.

Rookie Biographies: Biographies Suitable for Emergent Readers, 4 Bks., Set. 2005. (J). 78.00 (978-0-516-25208-7(9)) Scholastic Library Publishing.

A Rookie Reader Espanol: Thes Attractively Illustrated Stories in Spanish Make Learning Fun & Exciting, 10 Bks. , Set. 2005. (J). 170.00 (978-0-516-25213-1(5)) Scholastic Library Publishing.

A Rookie Reader Skill Set: Repetitive Text, 5 bks. Incl. Being Me. Broski, Julie. Vigla, Vincent, illus. 19.50 (978-0-516-24975-9(4)); I Am the Artist! Anderson, Dawn. Cunningham, Kelley, illus. 19.50 (978-0-516-24976-6(2)); So Many Houses. Bass, Hester. Arzoumanian, Alik, illus. 19.50 (978-0-516-24977-3(0)); Who Do I Look Like? Schulte, Mary. Roos, Maryn, illus. 19.50 (978-0-516-24978-0(9)); Who Needs Friends? Taylor-Butler, Christine. Havice, Susan, illus. 19.50 (978-0-516-24979-7(7)); 32p. (J). (gr. k-2). 2006. 2006. 97.50 (978-0-516-25410-4(3) , Children's Pr.) Scholastic Library Publishing.

A Rookie Reader Skill Set: Silent Letters, 4 bks. Incl. Bit Is a Bite. Brimner, Larry Dane. Kono, Erin Eitter, illus. 19.50 (***978-0-531-17547-7(2)***); Kate's Surprise. Burg, Ann. Harris, Phyllis, illus. 19.50 (***978-0-531-17549-1(9)***); Quite Enough Hot Dogs. Mara, Wil. Whitehead, Peter, illus. 19.50 (978-0-531-17548-4(0)); Silent Kay & the Dragon. Brimner, Larry Dane. McMahon, Bob, illus. 19.50 (978-0-531-17546-0(4)); 32p. (J). (gr. k-2). 2007. 2007. 78.00 (***978-0-531-17736-5(X)*** , Children's Pr.) Scholastic Library Publishing.

Rookie Readers Accelerated Readers, 36 bks. 2004. Vol. 1. pap. 700.00 (978-0-516-29920-4(4)); Vol. 2. pap. 684.00 (978-0-516-29921-1(2)) Scholastic Library Publishing. (Children's Pr.).

Rookie Readers & Choices. 2004. 456.00 (978-0-516-27716-5(2)) Scholastic Library Publishing.

Roper, Ann, et al. Readers' Theater: Level 1 - Reading Levels. 2001. 80p. (J). (gr. 2-5). pap. 10.99 (978-0-7424-0165-5(0) , IF19220) School Specialty Publishing.

Rosa's Rebozo: Third Grade Guided Reading Level N. (On Our Way to English Ser.). (gr. 3 up). 34.50 (978-0-7578-7135-1(6)) Rigby Education.

Rosell, J. F. & Deleau, J. La Nube. 2004. (SPA.). 32p. 6.95 (978-1-4000-9292-5(2)) Editorial Sudamericana S.A. ARG. *Dist:* Random Hse., Inc.

Rosen Real Readers Big Books. 855.90 (978-1-4042-6227-0(X)) Rosen Publishing Group, Inc., The.

Roses Sing on New Snow. (Lexile Levels Ser.). 9.09 (978-1-56334-721-4(0)) Hampton-Brown Bks.

Rosita's Robot: Third Grade Big Books. (On Our Way to English Ser.). (gr. 3 up). 29.95 (978-0-7578-4210-8(0)) Rigby Education.

Rosselson, Leon. Tom the Whistling Wonder. Haslam, John, illus. 2005. 24p. (J). lib. bdg. 22.65 (***978-1-59646-758-3(4)***) Dingles & Co.

Rossi, Rich, illus. Pillow Fight. 2005. (I'm Going to Read Ser.). 32p. (J). (gr. k-1). pap. 3.95 (978-1-4027-2719-1(4)) Sterling Publishing Co., Inc.

Rossi, Richard, illus. Pillow Fight. 2005. (I'm Going to Read Ser.). 32p. (J). (ps-ps). 11.95 (978-1-4027-2720-7(8)) Sterling Publishing Co., Inc.

Roth, Philip. El Animal Moribundo. Fibla, Jordi, tr. 2005. (SPA., Illus.). 368p. pap. 22.95 (978-84-204-6506-7(2) , Alfaguara) Santillana USA Publishing Co., Inc.

Round: Individual Title Six-Packs. (gr. 1-2). 22.00 (978-0-7635-9180-9(7)) Rigby Education.

Roy G Biv: Level G. Group 2. (Story Box(R) Ser.). 16p. 31.50 (978-0-322-00333-0(4)) Wright Group, The.

Royston. Young Library: Extreme Survival. 2003. (YA). (978-1-4109-0005-0(3)) Raintree.

Rozines Roy, Jennifer. I Love Reading, Level 5. 1999. (Homework Booklets Ser.). (Illus.). 80p. (J). (gr. 4-6). pap. 2.99 (978-1-56822-830-3(9) , IF0325, Instructional Fair) Schaffer, Frank Pubns.

Rt Sprouts Collections, 29 bks. 2004. pap. 143.55 (978-1-4109-1282-4(5)) Raintree.

Rucco, Alison. I'm Not Scared. 2005. (Cambridge Wizard English Student Guides). 63p. pap., stu. ed. 5.90 (978-0-521-60897-8(X)) Cambridge Univ. Pr.

—The Outsider. 2002. (Wizard Study Guides Ser.). 60p. (YA). pap., stu. ed. 6.00 (978-1-875739-14-1(9)) Cambridge Univ. Pr.

—The Stencil Man. 2002. (Wizard Study Guides Ser.). (Illus.). 47p. pap., stu. ed. 6.00 (978-0-646-07986-8(7)) Cambridge Univ. Pr.

Ruditis, Paul. Ready to Glow. Choi Sung Hwan, Aragon Noel, illus. 2005. (Trollz Ser.). 80p. (J). (gr. 2-5). pap. 5.99 (978-0-439-73386-1(3)) Scholastic, Inc.

Ruffell, Ann. Treachery by Night. 2004. (Shades Ser.). 62p. (J). pap. 7.99 (978-0-237-52728-0(6) , Evans Brothers, Limited) Evans Publishing Group GBR. *Dist:* Independent Pubs. Group.

A Rumble & a Grumble: 3-in-1 Package. (Sails Literacy Ser.). 24p. (gr. 1 up). 57.00 (978-0-7578-3210-9(5)) Rigby Education.

A Rumble & a Grumble: 6 Small Books. (Sails Literacy Ser.). 24p. (gr. 1 up). 25.00 (978-0-7578-3186-7(9)) Rigby Education.

A Rumble & a Grumble: Big Book Only. (Sails Literacy Ser.). 24p. (gr. 1 up). 27.00 (978-0-7635-5934-2(2)) Rigby Education.

Rundstrom, T. S. The Adventures of Tommy Toad. Marshall, Setsu, illus. 2002. 34p. (J). per. 16.00 (978-1-932062-03-8(3)) Hability Solution Services, Inc.

—I Love to Leap! Miller, Bryan & Marshall, H. Keene, illus. 2002. 40p. (J). per. 16.00 (978-1-932062-14-4(9)) Hability Solution Services, Inc.

Rundstrom, T. S. & Waldron, Drue K. Lonely Lion Follows His Lunch. Waldron, Drue K. & Stevens, Amber R., illus. 2002. 32p. (J). per. 16.00 (978-1-932062-16-8(5)) Hability Solution Services, Inc.

Rundstrom, Teressa. Lonely Lion Follows His Lunch. Waldron, Drue, illus. 2002. 35p. (J). per. (978-1-932062-37-3(8)) Hability Solution Services, Inc.

—Sherman the Sheep. Marshall, H. Keene & Miller, Bryan, illus. 2002. 35p. (J). per. (978-1-932062-38-0(6)) Hability Solution Services, Inc.

Ruth, Annie. I Can Read. Ruth, Annie, illus. l.t. ed. 2005. (Illus.). 32p. (J). 9.95 (978-0-9656306-7-2(6)) Ruth, A. Creations.

Ruttle, Kate & Brown, Richard. Itsy Bitsy Spider American English Edtion. 2000. (Cambridge Reading Ser.). 8p. pap. 5.00 (978-0-521-79516-6(8)) Cambridge Univ. Pr.

—Itsy Bitsy Spider Pack of 6 American English Edition. 2000. (Cambridge Reading Ser.). 8p. pap. 28.00 (978-0-521-79515-9(X)) Cambridge Univ. Pr.

Ruttle, Keith. The Lord Mount Dragon. 2005. (Cambridge Storybooks Ser.). (Illus.). 32p. pap. 7.00 (978-0-521-67487-4(5)) Cambridge Univ. Pr.

Ryan. Lost: Big Book: Level Q. Group 1. (Take-Twostm Ser.). 32p. 38.95 (978-0-322-04485-2(5)) Wright Group, The.

S., Philip G. You Are Now Leaving Torporville. 2004. (Illus.). pap. 16.95 (978-0-533-14581-2(3)) Vantage Pr., Inc.

Sacagawea, 6 vols. (gr. 2-5). 36.95 (978-0-7368-4564-9(X)) Red Brick Learning.

Sahara: Individual Title Six-Packs. (On Deck en Espanol Ser.).Tr. of Sahara. (SPA.). 24p. (gr. 4-5). 35.00 (978-0-7578-6451-3(1)) Rigby Education.

Said Mouse to Mole. 2005. (J). per. 8.95 (978-1-59566-139-5(5)) QEB Publishing Inc.

Saint-Exupéry, Antoine de. Le Petit Prince. 2001. Tr. of Little Prince. (FRE.). (J). audio 22.50 (978-0-8442-1383-5(7)) Glencoe/McGraw-Hill.

Salas, Macarena. Peliaro en el Vecindario. 2006. (Over the Hedge Ser.). (SPA., Illus.). 32p. (J). pap. 3.99 (978-0-439-80906-1(1) , Scholastic en Espanol) Scholastic, Inc.

Salas, Macarena, ed. Baby Donald Makes A Snowfriend/beb Donald Hace un Amigo de Nieve: A Book about Shapes/Un Libro Sobre Las Formas. 2005. (SPA.). 10p. (J). bds. 3.99 (978-0-439-66362-5(8) , Scholastic en Espanol) Scholastic, Inc.

—Disney Bil: Follow Your Nose, Baby Pluto/sigue Tu Nariz, Beb Pluto. 2005. (SPA & ENG.). 10p. (J). bds. 3.99 (978-0-439-66365-6(2) , Scholastic en Espanol) Scholastic, Inc.

—Disney Bil: What Will You Do Today/ qu Vas a Hacer Hoy? 2005. (SPA.). 10p. (J). bds. 3.99 (978-0-439-66368-7(7) , Scholastic en Espanol) Scholastic, Inc.

—Dopey's Bedtime/Tontin Se Va la Cama: A Book about Routines/Un Libro Sobre Rutinas. 2005. (SPA.). 6p. (J). bds. 3.99 (978-0-439-66360-1(1) , Scholastic en Espanol) Scholastic, Inc.

—A New Doll for Baby Daisy/Un Mueco para Beb Daisy: A Book about Classifying/Un Libro Sobre Clasificaciones. 2005. (SPA.). 10p. (J). bds. 3.99 (978-0-439-66361-8(X) , Scholastic en Espanol) Scholastic, Inc.

—Pooh's Best Day/El Mejor Dia de Pooh: A Book about Weather/Un Libro sobre el Tiempo. 2005. (Disney Bil Ser.). (SPA & ENG., Illus.). 10p. (J). bds. 3.99 (978-0-439-66364-9(4) , Scholastic en Espanol) Scholastic, Inc.

Salisbury, Kent. A Bear Ate My Pear! Salisbury, Kent, illus. 1998. (Pop into Phonics Ser.). (Illus.). 12p. (J). (ps-2). 6.99 (978-0-7681-0026-6(7) , 67401, McClanahan Bk.) Learning Horizons, Inc.

—There's a Dragon in My Wagon! Salisbury, Kent, illus. 1998. (Pop into Phonics Ser.). (Illus.). 10p. (J). (ps-2). mass mkt. 6.99 (978-0-7681-0025-9(9) , 67404, McClanahan Bk.) Learning Horizons, Inc.

Saltis, Nicki. Sandwiches. 1999. (ps-2). lib. bdg. 11.55 (978-0-613-30706-2(2)) Tandem Library Bks.

Salzmann, Mary Elizabeth. Aa: See It Say It Hear It. l.t. ed. 2000. (Long Vowels Ser.). (Illus.). 24p. (J). (ps-3). lib. bdg. 19.93 (978-1-57765-413-1(7) , SandCastle) ABDO Publishing Co.

—Ad As in Dad. 2003. (Word Families Ser.). (Illus.). 23p. (J). (ps-3). lib. bdg. 19.93 (978-1-59197-226-6(4) , SandCastle) ABDO Publishing Co.

—Ag As in Flag. 2003. (Word Families Ser.). (Illus.). 23p. (J). (ps-3). lib. bdg. 19.93 (978-1-59197-225-9(6) , SandCastle) ABDO Publishing Co.

—Ai: See It Say It Hear It. l.t. ed. 2001. (Vowel Blends Ser.). (Illus.). 24p. (J). (ps-3). lib. bdg. 19.93 (978-1-57765-453-7(6) , SandCastle) ABDO Publishing Co.

—Am As in Ham. 2003. (Word Families Ser.). (Illus.). 23p. (J). (ps-3). lib. bdg. 19.93 (978-1-59197-223-5(X) , SandCastle) ABDO Publishing Co.

—Ap As in Cap. 2003. (Word Families Ser.). (Illus.). 23p. (J). (ps-3). lib. bdg. 19.93 (978-1-59197-224-2(8) , SandCastle) ABDO Publishing Co.

—An As in Fan. 2003. (Word Families Ser.). (Illus.). 23p. (J). (ps-3). lib. bdg. 19.93 (978-1-59197-222-8(1) , SandCastle) ABDO Publishing Co.

—At As in Cat. 2003. (Word Families Ser.). (Illus.). 23p. (J). (ps-3). lib. bdg. 19.93 (978-1-59197-221-1(3) , SandCastle) ABDO Publishing Co.

—Ay As in Clay. 2003. (Word Families Ser.). (Illus.). 23p. (J). (ps-3). lib. bdg. 19.93 (978-1-59197-264-8(7) , SandCastle) ABDO Publishing Co.

—Come Home with Me! 2004. (Sight Words Ser.). (Illus.). 23p. (J). (ps-3). lib. bdg. 19.93 (978-1-59197-465-9(8)) ABDO Publishing Co.

—Did You See One Jump? 2004. (Sight Words Ser.). (Illus.). 23p. (J). (ps-3). lib. bdg. 19.93 (978-1-59197-466-6(6)) ABDO Publishing Co.

—Do You Wonder?, , Set. l.t. ed. Incl. How? lib. bdg. 19.93 (978-1-57765-174-1(X)); What? lib. bdg. 19.93 (978-1-57765-170-3(7)); When? lib. bdg. 19.93 (978-1-57765-171-0(5)); Where? lib. bdg. 19.93 (978-1-57765-172-7(3)); Who? lib. bdg. 19.93 (978-1-57765-169-7(3)); Why? lib. bdg. 19.93 (978-1-57765-173-4(1)); 24p. (J). (ps-3). 2000. (Illus.). 2000. Set lib. bdg. 119.58 (978-1-57765-281-6(9) , SandCastle) ABDO Publishing Co.

—Ea: See It Say It Hear It. l.t. ed. 2001. (Vowel Blends Ser.). (Illus.). 24p. (J). (ps-3). lib. bdg. 19.93 (978-1-57765-454-4(4) , SandCastle) ABDO Publishing Co.

—Ell As in Well. 2003. (Word Families Ser.). (Illus.). 23p. (J). (ps-3). lib. bdg. 19.93 (978-1-59197-231-0(0) , SandCastle) ABDO Publishing Co.

—How? l.t. ed. 2000. (Do You Wonder? Ser.). (Illus.). 24p. (J). (ps-3). lib. bdg. 19.93 (978-1-57765-174-1(X) , SandCastle) ABDO Publishing Co.

—I Had a Great Time! 2004. (Sight Words Ser.). (Illus.). 23p. (J). (ps-3). lib. bdg. 19.93 (978-1-59197-477-2(1)) ABDO Publishing Co.

—II: See It Say It Hear It. l.t. ed. 2000. (Long Vowels Ser.). (Illus.). 24p. (J). (ps-3). lib. bdg. 19.93 (978-1-57765-415-5(3) , SandCastle) ABDO Publishing Co.

—It's Not Good, It's Great! 2003. (Sight Words Ser.). (Illus.). 23p. (J). (ps-3). lib. bdg. 19.93 (978-1-59197-479-6(8)) ABDO Publishing Co.

—No Pigs on the Farm! 2004. (Sight Words Ser.). (Illus.). 23p. (J). (ps-3). lib. bdg. 19.93 (978-1-59197-471-0(2)) ABDO Publishing Co.

—Oo: See It Say It Hear It. (Long Vowels Ser.). (Illus.). 24p. (J). (ps-3). 2000. lib. bdg. 19.93 (978-1-57765-416-2(1)); 2001. lib. bdg. 19.93 (978-1-57765-457-5(9)) ABDO Publishing Co. (SandCastle).

—Out for the Summer! 2004. (Sight Words Ser.). (Illus.). 23p. (J). (ps-3). lib. bdg. 19.93 (978-1-59197-472-7(0)) ABDO Publishing Co.

—Snow & More Snow! 2004. (Sight Words Ser.). (Illus.). 23p. (J). (ps-3). lib. bdg. 19.93 (978-1-59197-470-3(4)) ABDO Publishing Co.

—Sometimes Yy: See It Say It Hear It. l.t. ed. 2000. (Long Vowels Ser.). (Illus.). 24p. (J). (ps-3). lib. bdg. 19.93 (978-1-57765-418-6(8) , SandCastle) ABDO Publishing Co.

—They Are the Best! 2004. (Sight Words Ser.). (Illus.). 23p. (J). (ps-3). lib. bdg. 19.93 (978-1-59197-474-1(7)) ABDO Publishing Co.

—Way to Go! 2004. (Sight Words Ser.). (Illus.). 23p. (J). (ps-3). lib. bdg. 19.93 (978-1-59197-468-0(2)) ABDO Publishing Co.

—We All Like It! 2004. (Sight Words Ser.). (Illus.). 23p. (J). (ps-3). lib. bdg. 19.93 (978-1-59197-467-3(4)) ABDO Publishing Co.

—What? l.t. ed. 2000. (Do You Wonder? Ser.). (Illus.). 24p. (J). (ps-3). lib. bdg. 19.93 (978-1-57765-170-3(7) , SandCastle) ABDO Publishing Co.

—What a Day in the Park! 2004. (Sight Words Ser.). (Illus.). 23p. (J). (ps-3). lib. bdg. 19.93 (978-1-59197-476-5(3)) ABDO Publishing Co.

—When? l.t. ed. 2000. (Do You Wonder? Ser.). (Illus.). 24p. (J). (ps-3). lib. bdg. 19.93 (978-1-57765-171-0(5) , SandCastle) ABDO Publishing Co.

—Where? l.t. ed. 2000. (Do You Wonder? Ser.). (Illus.). 24p. (J). (ps-3). lib. bdg. 19.93 (978-1-57765-172-7(3) , SandCastle) ABDO Publishing Co.

—Who? l.t. ed. 2000. (Do You Wonder? Ser.). (Illus.). 24p. (J). (ps-3). lib. bdg. 19.93 (978-1-57765-169-7(3) , SandCastle) ABDO Publishing Co.

—Who Is This at the Beach? 2004. (Sight Words Ser.). (Illus.). 23p. (J). (ps-3). lib. bdg. 19.93 (978-1-59197-480-2(1)) ABDO Publishing Co.

—Why? l.t. ed. 2000. (Do You Wonder? Ser.). (Illus.). 24p. (J). (ps-3). lib. bdg. 19.93 (978-1-57765-173-4(1) , SandCastle) ABDO Publishing Co.

Sam's big Clean-up: Individual Title Six-Packs. (gr. 1-2). 25.00 (978-0-7635-9145-8(9)) Rigby Education.

Sam's Dad: Level M, 6 vols. 128p. (gr. 2-3). 41.95 (978-0-7699-1029-1(7)) Shortland Pubns. (U. S. A.) Inc.

Samuels. Follow That Fin. 1999. (Illus.). (J). pap. (978-0-7398-0005-8(1)) Steck-Vaughn.

Sanchez, Mireia. Arriba del Arbol. 2002. (Caballo Alado Ser.). (SPA & ENG., Illus.). 24p. 5.95 (978-84-7864-423-0(7)) Combel Editorial, S.A. ESP. *Dist:* Independent Pubs. Group.

—Dentro del Cajon. 2002. (Caballo Alado Ser.). (SPA & ENG., Illus.). 24p. 5.95 (978-84-7864-424-7(5)) Combel Editorial, S.A. ESP. *Dist:* Independent Pubs. Group.

Sand Castles: Level I, 6 vols. (Wonder Worldtm Ser.). 16p. 29.95 (978-0-7802-4597-6(0)) Wright Group, The.

Sandage, Charley. ALL AROUND ARKANSAS Big Book. 2005. (J). pap. (***978-0-9794044-2-9(8)***) Archeological Assessments, Inc.

A Sandwich Person: Level H, 6 vols. (Wonder Worldtm Ser.). 16p. 29.95 (978-0-7802-2028-7(5)) Wright Group, The.

Sanseri, Wanda, des. Primary Learning Log. 2002. (J). 5.00 (978-1-880045-28-2(1)) Back Home Industries.

Santiago Baca, Jimmy. En Suelo Firme: El Nacimiento de un Poeta. Berastegui, Manu, tr. 2005. (SPA., Illus.). 360p. pap. 25.95 (978-84-204-6424-4(4) , Alfaguara) Santillana USA Publishing Co., Inc.

Sargemt, Dave & Sargent, Pat. Batley Needs Glasses, 10, 12. Robinson, Laura, illus. 2004. (Learn to Read Ser.: 10). 18p. (J). lib. bdg. 19.95 (978-1-56763-819-6(8)) Ozark Publishing.

Sargent, Dave & Sargent, Pat. Batley Needs Glasses, 10, 12. Robinson, Laura, illus. 2004. (Learn to Read Ser.: 10). Tr. of Batley Necesita Anteojos. 18p. (J). pap. 9.95 (978-1-56763-820-2(1)) Ozark Publishing.

Sasman, Irene D. H. Lamaze Books & Hands-On ELLIE, Set. 1999. (Illus.). (J). (ps-8). pap. 299.00 (978-1-56831-084-8(6)) Learning Connection, The.

The Saturday Club. (Early Intervention Levels Ser.). 31.86 (978-0-7362-0623-5(X)) Hampton-Brown Bks.

The Saturday Club (18), Vol. 18. (Early Intervention Levels Ser.). 5.31 (978-0-7362-0611-2(6)) Hampton-Brown Bks.

Saving the Zog Level 1, 5 Packs. 2002. (Illus.). pap. 36.75 (978-0-7398-5112-8(8)) Steck-Vaughn.

Say Cheese! Individual Title Six-Packs. (Rigby Focus Ser.). 16p. (gr. 1 up). 28.00 (978-0-7578-5320-3(X)); 30.00 (978-0-7578-5552-8(0)) Rigby Education.

Say Hello! (Early Intervention Levels Ser.). 3.85 (978-1-56334-955-3(8)); 23.10 (978-0-7362-0004-2(5)) Hampton-Brown Bks.

Sayles, Alayne. Alphie & the Alphabets: A Fun Way to Learn to Read. Platt, Greg, illus. 2005. 44p. (J). spiral bd. 79.95 incl. audio compact disk (978-0-9767506-0-4(0)) Reading Studio Pr.

Scaglione/Small. Lifes Little Lessons. 2006. pap. 9.95 (978-1-57886-336-5(8)) Rowman & Littlefield Pubs., Inc.

A Scare in the City. (Early Intervention Levels Ser.). 31.86 (978-0-7362-0625-9(6)) Hampton-Brown Bks.

A Scare in the City (24), Vol. 24. (Early Intervention Levels Ser.). 5.31 (978-0-7362-0613-6(2)) Hampton-Brown Bks.

Schaefer, Lola M. A Hot Day, 6 vols. Saunders-Smith, Gail, ed. (gr. k-2). 28.95 (978-0-7368-8627-7(3)) Red Brick Learning.

Schecter, Deborah. My First Bilingual Little Readers Level A: 25 Reproducible Mini-Books in English & Spanish That Give Kids a Great Start in Reading. 2005. (My First Bilingual Little Readers Ser.). 64p. pap. 11.99 (978-0-439-70069-6(8) , Teaching Resources) Scholastic, Inc.

—Sight Word Manipulatives for Reading Success: Wheels, Pull-Throughs, Puzzles, & Dozens of Other Easy-to-Make Manipulatives That Help Kids Read, Write, & Really Learn High-Frequency Words. 2005. 144p. pap. 17.99 (978-0-439-54259-3(6) , Teaching Resources) Scholastic, Inc.

Scheunemann, Pam. -Ack As in Snack. 2003. (Word Families Ser.). (Illus.). 23p. (J). (ps-3). lib. bdg. 19.93 (978-1-59197-261-7(2) , SandCastle) ABDO Publishing Co.

—Ash As in Trash. 2003. (Word Families Ser.). (Illus.). 23p. (J). (ps-3). lib. bdg. 19.93 (978-1-59197-260-0(4) , SandCastle) ABDO Publishing Co.

—Aw As in Paw. 2003. (Word Families Ser.). (Illus.). 23p. (J). (ps-3). lib. bdg. 19.93 (978-1-59197-263-1(9) , SandCastle) ABDO Publishing Co.

—Ch: See It Say It Hear It. l.t. ed. 2000. (Blends Ser.). (Illus.). 24p. (J). (ps-3). lib. bdg. 19.93 (978-1-57765-409-4(9) , SandCastle) ABDO Publishing Co.

—Dr: See It Say It Hear It. l.t. ed. 2001. (More Blends Ser.). (Illus.). 24p. (J). (ps-3). lib. bdg. 19.93 (978-1-57765-448-3(X)) ABDO Publishing Co.

—Ent As in Cent. 2003. (Word Families Ser.). (Illus.). 23p. (J). (ps-3). lib. bdg. 19.93 (978-1-59197-233-4(7) , SandCastle) ABDO Publishing Co.

—Ght: See It Say It Hear It. l.t. ed. 2001. (More Blends Ser.). (Illus.). 24p. (J). (ps-3). lib. bdg. 19.93 (978-1-57765-449-0(8) , SandCastle) ABDO Publishing Co.

—Ick As in Kick. 2003. (Word Families Ser.). (Illus.). 23p. (J). (ps-3). lib. bdg. 19.93 (978-1-59197-258-7(2) , SandCastle) ABDO Publishing Co.

—Ing As in King. 2003. (Word Families Ser.). (Illus.). 23p. (J). (ps-3). lib. bdg. 19.93 (978-1-59197-256-3(6) , SandCastle) ABDO Publishing Co.

—Ink As in Drink. 2003. (Word Families Ser.). (Illus.). 23p. (J). (ps-3). lib. bdg. 19.93 (978-1-59197-257-0(4) , SandCastle) ABDO Publishing Co.

—Sl: See It Say It Hear It. l.t. ed. 2001. (More Blends Ser.). (Illus.). 24p. (J). (ps-3). lib. bdg. 19.93 (978-1-57765-452-0(8) , SandCastle) ABDO Publishing Co.

—St: See It Say It Hear It. l.t. ed. 2000. (Blends Ser.). (Illus.). 24p. (J). (ps-3). lib. bdg. 19.93 (978-1-57765-407-0(2) , SandCastle) ABDO Publishing Co.

—Th: See It Say It Hear It. l.t. ed. 2000. (Blends Ser.). (Illus.). 24p. (J). (ps-3). lib. bdg. 19.93 (978-1-57765-408-7(0) , SandCastle) ABDO Publishing Co.

—Unk as in Skunk. 2003. (Word Families Ser.). (Illus.). 23p. (J). (ps-3). lib. bdg. 19.93 (978-1-59197-259-4(0) , SandCastle) ABDO Publishing Co.

Schmauss, Judy Kentor, et al. Reader's Clubhouse Level 2 Long-Vowel Valu-Pak. 2006. (Illus.). 120 p. (J). pap. 15.96 (978-0-7641-7969-3(1)) Barron's Educational Series, Inc.

Scholastic, Inc. Staff. Here Comes Diego!, Bks. 7-12. 2007. (Go, Diego, Go! Phonics Reading Program Ser.). 112p. (J). pap. 5.99 (***978-0-439-93228-8(9)***) Scholastic, Inc.

—Let's Go Rescue! 2007. (Go, Diego, Go! Phonics Reading Program Ser.: Bks. 1-6). 112p. (J). pap. 5.99 (***978-0-439-93229-5(7)***) Scholastic, Inc.

Scholastic, Inc. Staff & Barnes, Derrick. Stop, Drop & Chill. Duke, Barbara, illus. 2004. (Just for You! Ser.). 32p. pap. 3.99 (978-0-439-56870-8(6) , Teaching Resources) Scholastic, Inc.

Scholastic, Inc. Staff & Barnes, Derrick D. Low-Down Bad-Day Blues. Boyd, Aaron, illus. 2004. (Just for You! Ser.). 32p. (gr. k-1). pap. 3.99 (978-0-439-56867-8(6) , Teaching Resources) Scholastic, Inc.

Scholastic, Inc. Staff & Bermiss, Aamir Lee. Just for You: I Hate to Be Sick. Wilson-Max, Ken, illus. 2004. (Just for You! Ser.). 32p. (gr. k-3). pap. 3.99 (978-0-439-56877-7(3) , Teaching Resources) Scholastic, Inc.

Scholastic, Inc. Staff & Black, Sonia. Just for You! Jumping the Broom. 2004. (Just for You! Ser.). (Illus.). 32p. pap. 3.99 (978-0-439-56878-4(1) , Teaching Resources) Scholastic, Inc.

Scholastic, Inc. Staff & Ford, Juwanda. Just for You! Sunday Best. Bootman, Colin, illus. 2004. (Just for You! Ser.). 32p. pap. 3.99 (978-0-439-56854-8(4) , Teaching Resources) Scholastic, Inc.

Scholastic, Inc. Staff & Ford, Juwanda G. Shop Talk. Hoston, Jim, illus. 2004. (Just for You! Ser.). 32p. (gr. k-3). pap. 3.99 (978-0-439-56873-9(0) , Teaching Resources) Scholastic, Inc.

Scholastic, Inc. Staff & George, Olivia. Just for You! The Bravest Girls in the World. DuBurke, Randy, illus. 2004. (Just for You! Ser.). 32p. pap. 3.99 (978-0-439-56875-3(7) , Teaching Resources) Scholastic, Inc.

Scholastic, Inc. Staff & Hooks, Gwendolyn. The Mystery of the Missing Dog. Devard, Nancy, illus. 2004. (Just for You! Ser.). 32p. (gr. k-3). pap. 3.99 (978-0-439-56864-7(1) , Teaching Resources) Scholastic, Inc.

—Three's a Crowd. Walker, Sylvia, illus. 2004. (Just for You! Ser.). 32p. (gr. k-3). pap. 3.99 (978-0-439-56865-4(X) , Teaching Resources) Scholastic, Inc.

Scholastic, Inc. Staff & Hudson, Wade. The Two Tyrones. Page, Mark, illus. 2004. (Just for You! Ser.). 32p. (gr. k-3). pap. 3.99 (978-0-439-56866-1(8) , Teaching Resources) Scholastic, Inc.

Scholastic, Inc. Staff & Medearis, Angela Shelf. Singing for Dr. King. Van Wright, Cornelius & Hu, Ying-Hwa, illus. 2004. (Just for You! Ser.). 32p. (gr. k-3). pap. 3.99 (978-0-439-56855-5(2) , Teaching Resources) Scholastic, Inc.

Scholastic, Inc. Staff & Roberson, Karla. My Shoelaces Are Hard to Tie. Holley, Vanessa, illus. 2004. (Just for You! Ser.). 32p. pap. 3.99 (978-0-439-56869-2(2) , Teaching Resources) Scholastic, Inc.

Scholastic, Inc. Staff, et al. Lights Out! Tadgell, Nicole, illus. 2004. (Just for You! Ser.). 32p. (J). (gr. k-1). pap. 3.99 (978-0-439-56868-5(4) , Teaching Resources) Scholastic, Inc.

Scholastic Library Publishing Staff, ed. Rookie Readers, Vol. 5. 2004. 499.00 (978-0-516-24702-1(6)) Scholastic Library Publishing.

—Welcome BooksTM. 2004. 3. 522.00 (978-0-516-22900-3(1)); 7. 348.00 (978-0-516-24701-4(8)); Vol. 6. 348.00 (978-0-516-24700-7(X)) Scholastic Library Publishing.

Scholastic News Nonfiction Readers, 36 bks., Set. Incl. Set. Animal Survivors. 108.00 (978-0-516-25390-9(5)); Set. Biographies. 108.00 (978-0-516-25392-3(1)); Set. Classification. 108.00 (978-0-516-25391-6(3)); Set. Life Cycles. 108.00 (978-0-516-25393-0(X)); Set. Space Science. 216.00 (978-0-516-25394-7(8)); (J). (gr. 1-2). 2005. 648.00 (978-0-516-25370-1(0) , Children's Pr.) Scholastic Library Publishing.

The School Day, 2, Pack. (Chiquilibros Ser.). (ps-1). 12.00 (978-0-7635-8542-6(4)) Rigby Education.

School Lunch. (J). (978-0-8136-5338-9(X)) Modern Curriculum Pr.

School Specialty Publishing. Active Learning Themes from a to Z. 2002. 240p. (J). (ps-1). pap. 16.99 (978-0-7424-0245-4(2) , IF17942) School Specialty Publishing.

—Bilingual Reading Comprehension, Grade 1. 2006. (Bilingual Reading Comprehension Ser.). 160p. (J). (gr. 1-1). pap. 16.99 (978-0-7682-3421-3(2) , Schaffer, Frank) Schaffer, Frank Pubns.

—Bilingual Reading Comprehension, Grade 2. 2006. (Bilingual Reading Comprehension Ser.). 160p. (J). (gr. 2-2). pap. 16.99 (978-0-7682-3422-0(0) , Schaffer, Frank) Schaffer, Frank Pubns.

—Bilingual Reading Comprehension, Grade 3. 2006. (Bilingual Reading Comprehension Ser.). 160p. (J). (gr. 3-3). pap. 16.99 (978-0-7682-3423-7(9) , Schaffer, Frank) Schaffer, Frank Pubns.

—Bilingual Reading Comprehension, Grade 4. 2006. (Bilingual Reading Comprehension Ser.). 160p. (J). (gr. 4-4). pap. 16.99 (978-0-7682-3424-4(7) , Schaffer, Frank) Schaffer, Frank Pubns.

—Bilingual Reading Comprehension, Grade 5. 2006. (Bilingual Reading Comprehension Ser.). 160p. (J). (gr. 5-5). pap. 16.99 (978-0-7682-3425-1(5) , Schaffer, Frank) Schaffer, Frank Pubns.

—Easy Picture Word Opposites. 2001. (Phonics Flash Cards Ser.). 104p. (C). 6.99 (978-0-86734-419-6(9) , Schaffer, Frank) Schaffer, Frank Pubns.

—Easy Sight Words. 2001. (Phonics Flash Cards Ser.). 104p. (C). 6.99 (978-0-86734-403-5(2) , Schaffer, Frank) Schaffer, Frank Pubns.

—Easy Vowels. 2001. (Phonics Flash Cards Ser.). 104p. (C). 6.99 (978-0-86734-410-3(5) , Schaffer, Frank) Schaffer, Frank Pubns.

—Learning about Our World. 2004. (Kindergarten Standards Ser.). 144p. (C). pap. 16.99 (978-0-7682-2840-3(9) , FS99226) Schaffer, Frank Pubns.
—Long Vowels. 2001. (Flip-Flashtm Ser.). 160p. (J). (gr. k up). pap. 7.99 (978-1-56451-382-3(3) , ID2421) School Specialty Publishing.
—Read 4 Today: Grade 2. 2005. (Read 4 Today Ser.). 112p. (C). pap. 13.99 (978-0-7682-3212-7(0) , Schaffer, Frank) Schaffer, Frank Pubns.
—Read 4 Today: Grade 3. 2005. (Read 4 Today Ser.). 112p. (C). pap. 13.99 (978-0-7682-3213-4(9) , Schaffer, Frank) Schaffer, Frank Pubns.
—Read 4 Today: Grade 4. 2005. (Read 4 Today Ser.). 112p. (C). pap. 13.99 (978-0-7682-3214-1(7) , Schaffer, Frank) Schaffer, Frank Pubns.
—Read 4 Today: Grade 5. 2005. (Read 4 Today Ser.). 112p. (C). pap. 13.99 (978-0-7682-3215-8(5) , Schaffer, Frank) Schaffer, Frank Pubns.
—Reading for Meaning, Grades 1-2. 2006. (Frank Schaffer Classic Reproducibles Ser.). 48p. (J). (gr. 1-2). pap. 6.99 (978-0-7682-3461-9(1) , Schaffer, Frank) Schaffer, Frank Pubns.
—Reading for Meaning, Grades 3-4. 2006. (Frank Schaffer Classic Reproducibles Ser.). 48p. (J). (gr. 3-4). pap. 6.99 (978-0-7682-3463-3(8) , Schaffer, Frank) Schaffer, Frank Pubns.
—Reading, Grade 1. 2006. (Skills for Scholars Ser.). 80p. (C). pap. 4.99 (*978-0-7696-8231-0(6) , Schaffer, Frank) Schaffer, Frank Pubns.
—Reading, Grade 2. 2006. (Skills for Scholars Ser.). 80p. (C). pap. 4.99 (*978-0-7696-8232-7(4) , Schaffer, Frank) Schaffer, Frank Pubns.
—Reading, Grade 3. 2006. (Skills for Scholars Ser.). 80p. (C). pap. 4.99 (*978-0-7696-8233-4(2) , Schaffer, Frank) Schaffer, Frank Pubns.
—Reading, Grade 4. 2006. (Skills for Scholars Ser.). 80p. (C). pap. 4.99 (*978-0-7696-8234-1(0) , Schaffer, Frank) Schaffer, Frank Pubns.
—Reading, Kindergarten. 2006. (Skills for Scholars Ser.). 80p. (C). pap. 4.99 (*978-0-7696-8230-3(8) , Schaffer, Frank) Schaffer, Frank Pubns.
—Short Vowels. 2001. (Flip-Flashtm Ser.). 160p. (J). (gr. k up). pap. 7.99 (978-1-56451-381-6(5) , ID2420) School Specialty Publishing.
—Starter Skills Reading Readiness. 2007. (English-Espanol Starter Skills Ser.). 80p. (C). pap. 8.99 (*978-0-7682-3389-6(5) , Schaffer, Frank) Schaffer, Frank Pubns.
—Total English Spanish Learning Kit. 2007. (Total Learning Kits Ser.). 563p. (J). pap. 49.95 (*978-0-7696-5489-8(4)) School Specialty Publishing.
—Total Reading Learning Kit. 2007. (Total Learning Kits Ser.). 868p. (J). pap. 49.95 (*978-0-7696-5509-3(2)) School Specialty Publishing.
—1-2-3 Patterns. 2003. (1-2-3 Ser.). 80p. (J). pap. 10.99 (978-1-57029-469-3(0) , WPH99020, Totline Pubns.) Schaffer, Frank Pubns.
—101 Easy Reading Games, Grade 1. 2006. (101 Easy Reading Games Ser.). 128p. (J). (gr. 1-1). pap. 13.99 (978-0-7682-3411-4(5) , Schaffer, Frank) Schaffer, Frank Pubns.
—101 Easy Reading Games, Grade 3. 2006. (101 Easy Reading Games Ser.). 128p. (J). (gr. 3-3). pap. 13.99 (978-0-7682-3413-8(1) , Schaffer, Frank) Schaffer, Frank Pubns.
—101 Easy Reading Games, Grade 5. 2006. (101 Easy Reading Games Ser.). 128p. (J). (gr. 5-5). pap. 13.99 (978-0-7682-3415-2(8) , Schaffer, Frank) Schaffer, Frank Pubns.
The School Story Student Packet, Gr. 3-4. 2004. (J). (978-1-58130-520-3(6)) Novel Units, Inc.
School-to-Home Book, Early Level. (gr. k-2). 29.95 (978-0-7368-2906-9(7) , Yellow Umbrella Bks.) Capstone Pr., Inc.
School-to-Home Book, Emergent Level. (gr. k-2). 29.95 (978-0-7368-1799-8(9) , Yellow Umbrella Bks.) Capstone Pr., Inc.
School Zone Publishing. Start to Read!, 6 bks. 1998. (Start to Read! 6-Pack Ser.). (Illus.). 96p. (J). (ps-2). Set 2, Level 1. pap. 13.79 (978-0-88743-612-3(9) , 06102); Set 3, Level 2. pap. 13.79 (978-0-88743-613-0(7) , 06103); Set 5, Level 3. pap. 13.79 (978-0-88743-615-4(3) , 06105) School Zone Publishing Co.
School Zone Publishing Company Staff. Beginning Reading. deluxe ed. 2005. 64p. (J). pap., wbk. ed. 3.79 (978-1-58947-337-9(X)) School Zone Publishing Co.
—Jog, Frog, Jog. 1998. (Start to Read! Ser.). (Illus.). (J). (gr. 1-2). ring bd., lab manual ed., tchr.'s training gde. ed. 149.99 incl. audio compact disk (978-0-88743-592-8(0)); ring bd., tchr.'s training gde. ed. 49.99 incl. cd-rom (978-0-88743-591-1(2) , 08504) School Zone Publishing Co.
—Readiness Sticker Workbooks. 1998. (Readiness Sticker Workbooks Ser.: Vol. 2753). (Illus.). 16p. (J). (ps). pap. 3.59 (978-0-88743-121-0(6) , 02753) School Zone Publishing Co.
—Start to Read!, 6 bks. 1998. (Start to Read! 6-Pack Ser.). (Illus.). (J). (ps-2). Set 1, Level 1. pap. 13.79 (978-0-88743-611-6(0) , 06101); Set 4, Level 2. 96p. pap. 13.79 (978-0-88743-614-7(5) , 06104) School Zone Publishing Co.
School Zone Publishing Company Staff & Hoenecke, Karen. The Pea or the Flea? 2000. (Start to Read Board Bks.). (Illus.). 16p. (J). (ps-k). bds. 4.99 (978-0-88743-810-3(5) , 06807) School Zone Publishing Co.
—Poor Polly Pig. 2000. (Start to Read Board Bks.). (Illus.). 10p. (J). (ps-k). bds. 4.99 (978-0-88743-812-7(1) , 06814) School Zone Publishing Co.
School Zone Publishing Company Staff & Hoffman, Joan. Mia's Sun Hat. 2000. (Start to Read Board Bks.). (Illus.). 10p. (J). (ps-k). bds. 4.99 (978-0-88743-811-0(3) , 06813) School Zone Publishing Co.
School Zone Staff. Readiness. 2005. 56p. (J). 2.79 (978-1-58947-479-6(1)) School Zone Publishing Co.
Schorr, Loretta. Attacked. 2004. 64p. (YA). per. 3.95 (978-1-56254-814-8(X) , SP814X) Saddleback Educational Publishing.
Schulz. Buon San Valentino Dolce. pap. 19.95 (978-88-451-2996-4(9)) Fabbri - RCS Libri ITA. *Dist:* Distribooks, Inc.
—Tutti qui Biscotti. pap. 19.95 (978-88-451-2810-3(5)) Fabbri - RCS Libri ITA. *Dist:* Distribooks, Inc.
Schwabacher, Martin. The Fishy Field Trip. Gangloff, Hope, illus. 2004. (Magic School Bus Ser.: Vol. 18). 112p. (J). pap. 4.99 (978-0-439-56052-8(7) , Scholastic Paperbacks) Scholastic, Inc.
Science Fun. 2005. (Little Celebrations Thematic Packages Ser.). (J). (gr. k-3). 133.50 (978-0-673-75382-3(4)) Celebration Pr.
Scott, Caitlin. Condemned. 2004. 64p. (YA). per. 3.95 (978-1-56254-818-6(2) , SP8182) Saddleback Educational Publishing.
Scott Foresman Early Reading Intervention. 2003. (gr. k-1). (978-0-328-03826-8(1) , Scott Foresman) Addison-Wesley Educational Pubs., Inc.
Scott Foresman Family Reading Guide. 2004. (gr. 6 up). 13.50 (978-0-673-63400-9(0)) Addison-Wesley Educational Pubs., Inc.
Scott Foresman Reading. 2004. (gr. 1 up). stu. ed. (978-0-328-04235-7(8)); (gr. 1 up). stu. ed. (978-0-328-03928-9(4)); 2nd ed. (gr. 2 up). stu. ed. (978-0-328-03934-0(9)); 3rd ed. (gr. 3 up). stu. ed. (978-0-328-03936-4(5)) Addison-Wesley Educational Pubs., Inc. (Scott Foresman).
Scott Foresman Reading: Additional Resources. 2004. (gr. 1 up). (978-0-328-04085-8(1)); (gr. 2 up). stu. ed. (978-0-328-04697-3(3)) Addison-Wesley Educational Pubs., Inc. (Scott Foresman).
Scott Foresman Reading: Kindergarten. 2004. (gr. k up). (978-0-328-05065-9(2) , Scott Foresman) Addison-Wesley Educational Pubs., Inc.
Scott Foresman Reading: Links to Reading First. 2004. (gr. k up). (978-0-328-05801-3(7)); (gr. k up). (978-0-328-07612-3(0)); (gr. 1 up). (978-0-328-05802-0(5)); (gr. 1 up). (978-0-328-07613-0(9)); (gr. 2 up). (978-0-328-05803-7(3)); (gr. 2 up). (978-0-328-07614-7(7)); (gr. 3 up). (978-0-328-05804-4(1)); (gr. 3 up). (978-0-328-07615-4(5)) Addison-Wesley Educational Pubs., Inc. (Scott Foresman).
Scott Foresman Reading: Practice. 2004. (gr. k up). (978-0-328-04041-4(X)); (gr. 1 up). (978-0-328-04042-1(8)); (gr. 1 up). (978-0-328-04043-8(6)); (gr. 1 up). (978-0-328-04044-5(4)); (gr. 1 up). (978-0-328-04045-2(2)); (gr. 1 up). (978-0-328-04046-9(0)); (gr. 1 up). (978-0-328-04047-6(9)); (gr. 1 up). (978-0-328-04055-1(X)); (gr. 1 up). (978-0-328-07537-9(X)); (gr. 2 up). (978-0-328-04048-3(7)); (gr. 2 up). (978-0-328-04049-0(5)); (gr. 2 up). (978-0-328-07538-6(8)); (gr. 3 up). (978-0-328-04051-3(7)); (gr. 3 up). (978-0-328-04050-6(9)); (gr. 3 up). (978-0-328-07539-3(6)); (gr. 4 up). (978-0-328-04052-0(5)); (gr. 4 up). (978-0-328-07540-9(X)); (gr. 5 up). (978-0-328-04053-7(3)); (gr. 5 up). (978-0-328-07541-6(8)); (gr. 6 up). (978-0-328-04054-4(1)); (gr. 6 up). (978-0-328-07542-3(6)) Addison-Wesley Educational Pubs., Inc. (Scott Foresman).
Scott Foresman Reading: Pupil Edition. 2004. (gr. 1 up). (978-0-328-03929-6(2)); (gr. 1 up). (978-0-328-03930-2(6)); (gr. 1 up). (978-0-328-03931-9(4)); (gr. 1 up). (978-0-328-03932-6(2)); 2nd ed. (gr. 2 up). (978-0-328-03933-3(0)); 3rd ed. (gr. 3 up). (978-0-328-03935-7(7)) Addison-Wesley Educational Pubs., Inc. (Scott Foresman).
Scott Foresman Reading: School-Home. 2004. (gr. k up). (978-0-328-05806-8(8)); (gr. 1 up). (978-0-328-05644-6(8)) Addison-Wesley Educational Pubs., Inc. (Scott Foresman).
Scott Foresman Reading: Technology. 2004. (gr. 4 up). cd-rom (978-0-328-09376-2(9) , Scott Foresman) Addison-Wesley Educational Pubs., Inc.
Scott, Foresman Reading 2000. 2001. (J). (gr. 2). stu. ed. 79.50 incl. cd-rom (978-0-673-62303-4(3) , Scott Foresman) Addison Wesley Schl.
Scott, Fred & Southworth, Gordon. English for the Thoughtful Child Vol 2, Vol. 2. 2003. (ENG., Illus.). 128p. (J). per. 18.95 (978-1-882514-44-1(0)) Greenleaf Pr.
Scrapbook of ME: Individual Title Six-Packs. (Story Steps Ser.). (gr. k-2). 32.00 (978-0-7635-9814-3(3)) Rigby Education.
Scream Machines: All about Roller Coasters. 2005. (Book Treks Ser.). (J). 37.95 (978-0-7652-3244-1(8)) Celebration Pr.
Sean amables con Naomi: Social/Emotional Lap Book. (Pebble Soup Exploraciones Ser.). (SPA.). (ps up). 16.00 (978-0-7578-1787-8(4)) Rigby Education.
A Second Birthday: 6 Small Books. (Greetings Ser.: Vol. 2). 24p. (gr. 2-3). 31.00 (978-0-7635-9414-5(8)) Rigby Education.
A Second Birthday: Big Book. (Greetings Ser.: Vol. 2). 24p. (gr. 2-3). 31.00 (978-0-7635-5698-3(X)) Rigby Education.
Second Mrs. Gianconda. (J). pap., stu. ed. (978-0-13-017583-0(8)) Prentice Hall (Schl. Div.).
Secret World Of..., 8 bks. 2003. (Illus.). 228.48 (978-0-7398-7026-6(2)) Raintree.
Secrets of the Sky: Individual Title Six-Packs. (Rigby Infoquest Ser.). (gr. 6 up). 37.00 (978-0-7578-7999-9(3)) Rigby Education.
See & Say Vinyl Books 800844, 3. 2005. (J). (978-1-59794-045-0(3)) Environments, Inc.
See Our Show, 6 Packs. (Rigby Focus Ser.). 16p. (gr. k up). 26.00 (978-0-7578-5287-9(4)) Rigby Education.
See Our Show: Individual Title Six-Packs. (Rigby Focus Ser.). 16p. (gr. k up). 28.00 (978-0-7578-5521-4(0)) Rigby Education.
See the Shapes, 6 Packs. (Rigby Focus Ser.). 16p. (gr. k up). 28.00 (978-0-7578-5522-1(9)) Rigby Education.
See the Shapes: Individual Title Six-Packs. (Rigby Focus Ser.). 16p. (gr. k up). 26.00 (978-0-7578-5288-6(2)) Rigby Education.
The Seed: Level A, 6 vols. (Wonder Worldtm Ser.). 16p. 24.95 (978-0-7802-1048-6(4)) Wright Group, The.
Sefchovich, Sara. Vivir la Vida. 2005. Tr. of Living Life. (SPA., Illus.). 243p. pap. 14.95 (978-968-19-0803-4(1)) Aguilar, Altea, Taurus, Alfaguara, S.A. de C.V MEX. *Dist:* Santillana USA Publishing Co., Inc.
Sending Messages: Level B, 6 vols. (Wonder Worldtm Ser.). 16p. 24.95 (978-0-7802-4599-0(7)) Wright Group, The.
Servicio Comunitario: Individual Title Six-Packs. (On Deck en Espanol Ser.).Tr. of Community Service. (SPA.). 24p. (gr. 4-5). 35.00 (978-0-7578-6403-2(1)) Rigby Education.
Sesame Street Early Reading Skills. 2006. (J). spiral bd. 5.99 (*978-1-58610-985-1(5)) Learning Horizons, Inc.
Set a Complete Set. (Compass Point Phonics Readers Ser.). (gr. 1-2). 159.12 (978-0-7565-0559-2(3)) Compass Point Bks.
Set A, Set B & Set C Complete Set. (Compass Point Phonics Readers Ser.). (gr. 1-2). 477.36 (978-0-7565-0498-4(8)) Compass Point Bks.
Set B Complete Set. (Compass Point Phonics Readers Ser.). (gr. 1-2). 159.12 (978-0-7565-0560-8(7)) Compass Point Bks.
Set C Complete Set. (Compass Point Phonics Readers Ser.). (gr. 1-2). 159.12 (978-0-7565-0561-5(5)) Compass Point Bks.
Set of 10 Big Book Favorites 800714, 10. 2005. (J). bds. (978-1-59794-013-9(5)) Environments, Inc.
Set of 17 Titles, Vol. 2. (Early Intervention Levels Ser.). 62.45 (978-0-7362-0998-4(0)) Hampton-Brown Bks.
Set of 5 Titles. (Early Intervention Levels Ser.). 18.95 (978-0-7362-0997-7(2)) Hampton-Brown Bks.
Set of 9 Titles, Vol. 4. (Early Intervention Levels Ser.). 33.15 (978-0-7362-1000-3(8)) Hampton-Brown Bks.
Seuss, Dr. Dr. Seuss's ABC. 2005. (Illus.). 64p. (J). (ps-2). audio compact disk 9.95 (978-0-375-83496-7(6) , Random Hse. Bks. for Young Readers) Random Hse. Children's Bks.
Shadows: Level H, 6 vols. (Wonder Worldtm Ser.). 16p. 29.95 (978-0-7802-1049-3(2)) Wright Group, The.
Shaka: King of the Zulus. (Lexile Levels Ser.). 9.09 (978-1-56334-749-8(0)) Hampton-Brown Bks.
Shake, Rumble, & Roll, 6 Packs. (Rigby Infoquest Ser.). (gr. 5 up). 37.00 (978-0-7578-6479-7(1)) Rigby Education.
Shakespeare, William. A Midsummer Night's Dream. 2005. viii, 53p. (C). pap. 9.00 (*978-0-582-85491-8(1)) Pearson ESL.
Shane & Ned, 6 Packs. (gr. 1-2). 22.00 (978-0-7635-9171-7(8)) Rigby Education.
Shank, Cathy, et al. Collaborations Literacy. pap., stu. ed. 50.95 (978-0-8384-9660-2(1)) Thomson Heinle.
Shapiro, Norma. Dominoes, Level 3. 2003. 6.50 (978-0-19-424411-4(3)) Oxford Univ. Pr., Inc.
Shared Reading with Big Books: Using Building-Blocks & Four-Blocks Strategies. 2002. (Four-Blocks Ser.). (J). per. 18.99 (978-0-88724-868-9(3) , CD-2422) Carson-Dellosa Publishing Co., Inc.
Shark Rescue: Level T, Group 2, 6 vols. (Sunshinetm Ser.). 48p. 44.95 (978-0-7802-4174-9(6)) Wright Group, The.
Shaw, Nancy. Little Leaf Grows Up. McMahon, Kelly, illus. 2002. (Two Can Read Ser.). 16p. (J). 2.99 (978-1-56472-663-6(0)) Edupress, Inc.
She Said. (Little Book Practice Reader). (J). (978-0-8136-5376-1(2)) Modern Curriculum Pr.
Shea, Therese. Reading Comprehension. 2004. 48p. pap. 6.95 (978-1-4042-8541-5(5)) Rosen Publishing Group, Inc., The.
Shehan, L. English Can Be Easy. 2001. pap., tchr. ed. 1.70 (978-0-03-002675-1(X)) Holt, Rinehart & Winston.
Shems, Ed, illus. First Word Search: Reading Is Fun. 2007. (First Word Search Ser.). 64p. (J). pap. 3.95 (978-1-4027-4261-3(4)) Sterling Publishing Co., Inc.
Shepherd Boy & the Giant Color. 2004. pap. 1.50 (978-0-87162-913-5(5)) Warner Pr. Pubs.
Sheryl Swoopes, 6 vols. (gr. 4 up). 39.95 (978-0-7368-9278-0(8)) Red Brick Learning.
Shifflett, Christa. Hands on Reading & Spelling: Grades 3-6. 2002. 16.95 (978-0-9740367-0-0(6)) Shifflett, Christa.
Shifting Perspectives, 6 vols., Pack. (Rigby Infoquest Ser.). (gr. 6 up). 37.00 (978-0-7578-8000-1(2)) Rigby Education.
Shifting Sands, 6 Packs. (Rigby Infoquest Ser.). 32p. (gr. 4 up). 37.00 (978-0-7578-5738-6(8)) Rigby Education.
A Ship Is Coming! Third Grade Guided Reading Level L. (On Our Way to English Ser.). (gr. 3 up). 34.50 (978-0-7578-7125-2(9)) Rigby Education.
Shipton. Beatles, the, Level 3, Penguin Readers. 2002. (Illus.). 48p. (C). pap. 9.00 (978-0-582-51248-1(4)) Pearson ESL.
Shipton, Paul. Clown School. Blake, Beccy, illus. 2005. 24p. (J). lib. bdg. 22.65 (*978-1-59646-752-1(5)) Dingles & Co.
Shoes, Shoes, Shoes. (Lexile Levels Ser.). 7.98 (978-1-56334-670-5(2)) Hampton-Brown Bks.
Shore, Diane Z. A Rosa le Gusta Leer: Rosa Loves to Read. Day, Larry, illus. 2005. (Rookie Reader(R) Espanol Ser.). 32p. (gr. k-2). 19.50 (978-0-516-24440-2(X) , Children's Pr.) Scholastic Library Publishing.
Shores of Freedom: Individual Title Six-Packs. (Rigby Infoquest Ser.). (gr. 5 up). 37.00 (978-0-7578-6482-7(1)) Rigby Education.
Short Vowels Set: Level B. (Sing-along Songs Ser.). (ps-2). 48.46 incl. audio compact disk (978-0-7362-0420-0(2)) Hampton-Brown Bks.
Show Me a Snake Hold (16), Vol. 16. (Early Intervention Levels Ser.). 4.73 (978-0-7362-0241-1(2)) Hampton-Brown Bks.
Show Me a Snake Hole. (Early Intervention Levels Ser.). 28.38 (978-0-7362-0416-3(4)) Hampton-Brown Bks.
Show What You Know on the FCAT 6, Reading Student Workbook. 2006. (J). per. 16.95 (978-1-59230-188-1(6)) Englefield & Assocs., Inc.
Show What You Know on the OAT for Grade 6 Reading Student Workbook. 2007. (J). per. 16.95 (*978-1-59230-279-6(3)) Englefield & Assocs., Inc.
Show What You Know Publishing, ed. Show What You Know on the CSAP 7, Reading/Writing Student Workbook. 2007. (J). per. 13.95 (*978-1-59230-246-8(7)) Englefield & Assocs., Inc.
—Show What You Know on the CSAP for Grade 5, Student Workbook. 2007. (J). per. 13.95 (*978-1-59230-217-8(3)) Englefield & Assocs., Inc.
—Show What You Know on the CSAP for Grade 9 Reading Student Self-Study Workbook. 2007. (YA). per. 18.95 (*978-1-59230-256-7(4)) Englefield & Assocs., Inc.
—Show What You Know on the CSAP Reading & Writing for Grade 6, Student Workbook. 2007. (J). per. 13.95 (*978-1-59230-240-6(8)) Englefield & Assocs., Inc.
—Show What You Know on the OAT for Grade 8 Reading Student Self Study Workbook. 2007. (YA). per. 16.95 (*978-1-59230-282-6(3)) Englefield & Assocs., Inc.
Shurley English 1 H/S/ Ed. 2004. pap. 8.00 (978-1-58561-052-5(6)) Shurley Instructional Materials, Inc.
Shurley English 2 H/S Ed. 2004. pap. 8.00 (978-1-58561-053-2(4)); pap. 30.00 (978-1-58561-059-4(3)) Shurley Instructional Materials, Inc.
Shurley English 3 H/S Ed. 2004. pap. 8.00 (978-1-58561-054-9(2)) Shurley Instructional Materials, Inc.
Si estas Contento, 6 vols., Pack. (Literatura 2000 Ser.). (SPA.). (gr. 1-2). 28.00 (978-0-7635-1078-7(5)) Rigby Education.
Siddiqui, Rifat & Foster, John. I-Read Year 1 Anthology: Rumbling Tums. 2007. (I-read Ser.). (Illus.). 40p. pap. (*978-0-521-70477-9(4)) Cambridge Univ. Pr.
Sideways Stories from Wayside School Student Packet, Gr. 3-4. 2004. (J). (978-1-58130-866-2(3)) Novel Units, Inc.
Siebert, Anne & Clark, Raymond C. All Around America Activities Workbook: The Time Traveler's Talk Show. 2004. 76p. pap. 16.50 (978-0-86647-184-8(7)) Pro Lingua Assocs., Inc.
—All Around America Scripts/Workbook/2 CD's Package: The Time Traveler's Talk Show. 2004. pap. 39.00 (978-0-86647-186-2(3)) Pro Lingua Assocs., Inc.
Sight Word Reproducible Stories. 2005. (J). pap. 9.99 (978-1-58970-702-3(8)) Lakeshore Learning Materials.
Sight Words. 2004. (J). (ps-3). lib. bdg. 358.74 (978-1-59197-463-5(1) , SandCastle) ABDO Publishing Co.
Sight Words with Samson. 2006. (J). cd-rom (*978-0-9766680-2-2(5)) Knowledge Wand, LLC.
Sigue las Huellas: Big Book. (Pebble Soup Exploraciones Ser.). (SPA.). 16p. (ps up). 31.00 (978-0-7578-1675-8(4)) Rigby Education.
Sigue las Huellas: Small Book. (Pebble Soup Exploraciones Ser.). (SPA.). 16p. (ps up). 5.00 (978-0-7578-1715-1(7)) Rigby Education.
Sikic, Jane. What's This? What's That? 1999. (ps-2). lib. bdg. 11.45 (978-0-613-30869-4(7)) Tandem Library Bks.
Silencio! Individual Title-Six Packs. (Chiquilibros Ser.). (SPA.). (gr. k-1). 23.00 (978-0-7635-8609-6(9)) Rigby Education.
Silver, Rhonda Graff. Graphic Organizer Booklets for Reading Response: Grades 2-3: Guided Response Packets for Any Fiction or Nonfiction Book That Boost Students' Comprehension-and Help You Manage Independent Reading. 2007. 64p. pap. 11.99 (978-0-439-65612-2(5) , Teaching Resources) Scholastic, Inc.
—Graphic Organizer Booklets for Reading Response: Grades 4-6: Guided Response Packets for Any Fiction or Nonfiction Book That Boost Students' Comprehension-and Help You Manage Independent Reading. 2007. 64p. pap. 11.99 (978-0-439-66118-8(8) , Teaching Resources) Scholastic, Inc.
Silverstone, Michael. Paramedics to the Rescue: When Every Second Counts, 6 vols. (gr. 4 up). 49.95 (978-0-7368-3867-2(8) , High Five) Red Brick Learning.
Silvia Hops Home: Second Grade Guided Reading Level E. (On Our Way to English Ser.). (gr. 2 up). 34.50 (978-0-7578-7068-2(6)) Rigby Education.
Simms, Rosie. Read, Think, & Write about It - Binder 1. 2004. (YA). ring bd. 59.95 (978-1-58804-356-6(8)) PCI Educational Publishing.
—Read, Think, & Write about It - Binder 2. 2004. (YA). ring bd. 59.95 (978-1-58804-357-3(6)) PCI Educational Publishing.
Simon-Kerr, Julia. Kong's Kingdom. Bollinger, Peter, illus. 2005. (King Kong Ser.). 24p. (J). pap. 3.99 (978-0-06-077302-1(2)) HarperCollins Pubs.
Simon, Mary. Oh Oh. 2004. (SPA.). 32p. (J). 2.75 (978-0-570-05186-2(X)) Concordia Publishing Hse.
Simons, Joseph. Under a Living Sky. 2005. (Orca Young Readers Ser.). (Illus.). 144p. (J). (gr. 3-6). pap. 5.95 (978-1-55143-355-4(9)) Orca Bk. Pubs. USA.
Simple Reading, Handbook for Reading the Alphabet. 2001. 15p. (J). 7.99 (978-0-9713301-1-5(5)) Simple Learning.
Simple Reading, Reading Two Letter Words. 2001. 31p. 12.99 (978-0-9713301-2-2(3)) Simple Learning.
Sims, Lesley. Midsummer Night's Drem. 2005. (Illus.). 48p. (J). (gr. 2 up). 8.95 (978-0-7945-1077-0(9) , Usborne) EDC Publishing.
—Snow white & the seven Dwarfs. 2005. (Illus.). 64p. (J). (gr. 2 up). 8.95 (978-0-7945-1072-5(8) , Usborne) EDC Publishing.

Sing a Song of People. (Early Intervention Levels Ser.). 5.34 (978-0-7362-1895-5(5)); 32.04 (978-0-7362-2125-2(5)) Hampton-Brown Bks.

Sing, Spell, Read & Write Summer School Intervention Kit: Level 1 Student Pack. 2005. (J). (gr. k-2). 32.95 (978-0-7652-3233-5(2)) Modern Curriculum Pr.

Sing, Spell, Read & Write Summer School Intervention Kit: Off We Go. 2005. (J). (gr. k-2). stu. ed. 8.50 (978-0-7652-3173-4(5)) Modern Curriculum Pr.

Sing, Spell, Read & Write Summer School Intervention Kit: Raceway. 2005. (J). (gr. k-2). stu. ed. 12.95 (978-0-7652-3174-1(3)) Modern Curriculum Pr.

Sink or Float? KinderFacts Individual Title Six-Packs. (Kinderstarters Ser.). 8p. (ps-1). 21.00 (978-0-7635-8749-9(4)) Rigby Education.

SIPPS Beginning Hand-held Sound Cards. 2004. (978-1-57621-455-8(9)) Developmental Studies Ctr.

Sishton, Elaine, et al. Readers' Theater: Level 2 - Reading Levels. 2001. 80p. (J). (gr. 3-7). pap. 10.99 (978-0-7424-0166-2(9) , IF19221) School Specialty Publishing.

Six Fish in a Mix. (Early Intervention Levels Ser.). 21.30 (978-0-7362-0388-3(5)) Hampton-Brown Bks.

The Skateboarders' Club: Fifth Grade Guided Comprehension Level P. (On Our Way to English Ser.). (gr. 5 up). 34.50 (978-0-7578-6610-4(7)) Rigby Education.

Skill Sharpeners, Reading, Grade 2. 2005. (J). pap. 9.99 (978-1-59673-038-0(2) , emc 4530) Evan-Moor Educational Pubs.

Skill Sharpeners, Reading, Grade 3. 2005. (J). pap. 9.99 (978-1-59673-039-7(0) , emc 4531) Evan-Moor Educational Pubs.

Skill Sharpeners, Reading, Grade 4. 2005. (J). pap. 9.99 (978-1-59673-040-3(4) , emc 4532) Evan-Moor Educational Pubs.

Skill Sharpeners, Reading, Grade 5. 2005. (J). pap. 9.99 (978-1-59673-041-0(2) , emc 4533) Evan-Moor Educational Pubs.

Skill Sharpeners, Reading, Grade 6. 2005. (J). pap. 9.99 (978-1-59673-042-7(0) , emc 4534) Evan-Moor Educational Pubs.

Skittles & Skullbone, 6 Pack, Set D. (gr. k-3). 29.00 (978-0-7635-0547-9(1)) Rigby Education.

The Sky Is Falling. 2004. (J). (978-1-58453-273-6(4)) Pioneer Valley Educational Pr., Inc.

Sky Ride. 2004. (Illus.). (J). (978-1-59577-008-0(9)) Starfall Education.

Sky Time. (Early Intervention Levels Ser.). 28.38 (978-0-7362-0402-6(4)) Hampton-Brown Bks.

Sky Time (10), Vol. 10. (Early Intervention Levels Ser.). 4.73 (978-0-7362-0227-5(7)) Hampton-Brown Bks.

Sky Watch: Level O, 6 vols. (Explorers Ser.). 32p. (gr. 3-6). mac hd 44.95 (978-0-7699-0595-2(1)) Shortland Pubns. (U. S. A.) Inc.

The Sled Ride: Individual Title Two-Packs. (Chiquilibros Ser.). (ps-1). 12.00 (978-0-7635-8526-6(2)) Rigby Education.

Sleep Tight Spaceboy. 2003. (J). (978-1-932570-02-1(0)) Literacy Footprints Inc.

Slip & Slide (12), Vol. 12. (Early Intervention Levels Ser.). 4.73 (978-0-7362-0233-6(1)) Hampton-Brown Bks.

Sloan, Peter. Build It Big. 1999. (gr. k-3). lib. bdg. 11.65 (978-0-613-30291-3(5)) Tandem Library Bks.

—Sharing Time. 1999. (gr. k-3). lib. bdg. 11.80 (978-0-613-30723-9(2)) Tandem Library Bks.

—Signs Everywhere. 1999. (gr. k-3). lib. bdg. 11.80 (978-0-613-30732-1(1)) Tandem Library Bks.

Small Steps, the Year I Got Polio Student Packet, Gr. 5-6. 2004. (J). (978-1-58130-522-7(2)) Novel Units, Inc.

The Smartest One in Class: Individual Title Six-Packs. (ps-2). 27.00 (978-0-7635-9474-9(1)) Rigby Education.

Smith. The Ring, Level 3. 2001. (Illus.). v, 54p. (C). pap. 9.00 (978-0-582-42737-2(1)) Longman Publishing Group.

Smythe, E. Louise. A Primary Reader: Old Time Stories, Fairy Tales & Myths Retold by Children. 2004. reprint ed. pap. 15.95 (978-1-4191-0287-5(7)); pap. 1.99 (978-1-4192-0287-2(1)) Kessinger Publishing, LLC.

Sneller, Norm. Nonfiction Reading Comprehension. 2002. (100+ Seriestm Ser.). 128p. (J). (gr. 5-6). pap. 12.99 (978-0-7424-0220-1(7) , IF87028) School Specialty Publishing.

Snick Snack Sniffle-Nose: Set C Individual Title Six-Packs. (gr. k-3). 29.00 (978-0-7635-0543-1(9)) Rigby Education.

Snowbound! 2003. (Illus.). pap. 7.60 (978-0-7398-7527-8(2)) Steck-Vaughn.

Snowbound! 5-Pack. 2003. (Illus.). pap. 36.75 (978-0-7398-7561-2(2)) Steck-Vaughn.

Snyder, Inez. Welcome BooksTM: How Things Are Made. 2004. (Illus.). 87.00 (978-0-516-29635-7(3)) Scholastic Library Publishing.

So Many Things to Do, 6 vols., Pack. (ps-2). 23.00 (978-0-7635-9017-8(7)) Rigby Education.

So Much to Do: Third Grade Guided Reading Level H. (On Our Way to English Ser.). (gr. 3 up). 34.50 (978-0-7578-7108-5(9)) Rigby Education.

So, Patty. So Simple Sightwords, 3 vols., 3 discs. 2004. Orig. Title: So Simple Learning: Sightwords. 222p. (J). DVD 189.90 (978-0-9772158-0-5(6)) So Simple Learning.

So Smart! First Words. 2001. VHS, cd-rom 12.95 (978-0-9713747-0-6(8)) So Smart! Productions.

Soap Boat. 2004. (Illus.). (J). (978-1-59577-011-0(9)) Starfall Education.

Socks. (Little Book Practice Reader). (J). (978-0-8136-5346-4(0)) Modern Curriculum Pr.

Socks: Individual Title Six-Packs. (Chiquilibros Ser.). (gr. k-1). 23.00 (978-0-7635-0427-4(0)) Rigby Education.

Soft Cloth Books 800406, 4. 2005. (J). (978-1-59794-032-0(1)) Environments, Inc.

SOft Touch Books 800780, 3. 2005. (J). (978-1-59794-041-2(0)) Environments, Inc.

Solve This! Level J, 6 vols. 128p. (gr. 2-3). 41.95 (978-0-7699-1035-2(1)) Shortland Pubns. (U. S. A.) Inc.

Something Funny. 2003. (Read with Dick & Jane Ser.: Vol. 2). 32p. (J). (ps-2). pap. 3.99 (978-0-448-43401-8(6)); (Illus.). 13.89 (978-0-448-43413-1(X)) Penguin Group (USA) Inc. (Grosset & Dunlap).

Sometimes: Individual Title Six-Packs. (ps-2). 27.00 (978-0-7635-9476-3(8)); 23.00 (978-0-7635-8803-8(2)) Rigby Education.

Sometimes: Kindergarten Newcomer Books. (On Our Way to English Ser.). (gr. k up). 23.50 (978-0-7578-7199-3(2)) Rigby Education.

Sometimes We're Happy, Sometimes We're Sad: Social/Emotional Lap Book. (Pebble Soup Explorations Ser.). (ps up). 16.00 (978-0-7635-7574-8(7)) Rigby Education.

Sorting & Opposites. 2002. (First Steps Reading Ser.). 24p. (J). pap. 3.95 (978-0-7894-8490-1(0)) Dorling Kindersley Publishing, Inc.

Sounds All Around Us Set C, 6 vols. (Phonics Readers Ser.). (gr. k-2). 17.50 (978-0-7368-3217-5(3)) Red Brick Learning.

Sounds & How We Hear Them Set E, 6 vols. (Phonics Readers Ser.). (gr. k-2). 28.95 (978-0-7368-4069-9(9)) Red Brick Learning.

Sows don't Pounce: Decodable Books, 6 vols. (Fasttrack Reading Ser.). 24p. (gr. 4-8). 40.95 (978-0-322-05988-7(7)) Wright Group, The.

Soy Artista: Individual Title Six-Packs. (Literatura 2000 Ser.). (SPA.). (gr. 2-3). 33.00 (978-0-7635-1251-4(6)) Rigby Education.

Soy Chef: Individual Title Six-Packs. (Literatura 2000 Ser.). (SPA.). (gr. 2-3). 33.00 (978-0-7635-1648-2(1)) Rigby Education.

Space Fort. 2005. (J). (978-1-932570-33-5(0)) Literacy Footprints Inc.

Spaceboy Finds a Friend. 2003. (J). (978-1-932570-01-4(2)) Literacy Footprints Inc.

Spaceboy Plays Hide & Seek. 2003. (J). (978-1-932570-05-2(5)) Literacy Footprints Inc.

Spaceboy Set 1. 2003. (J). (978-1-932570-00-7(4)) Literacy Footprints Inc.

Spanish TAKS MASTER Reading, Gr. 5. 2004. (J). (978-1-57022-472-0(2)) ECS Learning Systems, Inc.

Spanish TAKS MASTER Reading, Gr. 6. 2004. (J). (978-1-57022-500-0(1)) ECS Learning Systems, Inc.

The Sparrow's Gift: Second Grade Guided Reading Level L. (On Our Way to English Ser.). (gr. 2 up). 34.50 (978-0-7578-7100-9(3)) Rigby Education.

Speak Your Mind: MainSails, 6 packs. (Sails Literacy Ser.). (gr. 5 up). 37.00 (978-0-7578-8061-2(4)) Rigby Education.

Speaking Out. 2003. (Illus.). pap. 7.60 (978-0-7398-7522-3(1)) Steck-Vaughn.

The Specialist. 2001. (YA). (gr. 6-12). pap. incl. audio (978-0-8224-3287-6(0)) Globe Fearon Educational Publishing.

Speedsters Series. (Illus.). (J). (gr. 2-5). (978-0-525-44950-8(7) , Dutton Juvenile) Penguin Group (USA) Inc.

Spelvin, Justin. My Best Friends. 2006. (Care Bears Ser.). 32p. (J). pap. 3.99 (978-0-439-86232-5(9) , Scholastic) Scholastic, Inc.

Spice It Up!, 6 Packs. (Rigby Infoquest Ser.). (gr. 5 up). 37.00 (978-0-7578-6494-0(5)) Rigby Education.

Spider Night! (16), Vol. 16. (Early Intervention Levels Ser.). 4.73 (978-0-7362-0236-7(6)) Hampton-Brown Bks.

Spinner, Stephanie. The Magic of Merlin. Sokolova, Valerie, illus. 2004. (Road to Reading Ser.). 48p. (J). (gr. k-3). pap. 3.99 (978-0-307-26403-9(3) , Random Hse. Bks. for Young Readers) Random Hse. Children's Bks.

Spirn, Michele Sobel. A Know-Nothing Halloween. Alley, R. W., illus. 2000. (I Can Read Bks.). 48p. (J). (gr. k-3). 14.95 (978-0-06-028185-4(5)) HarperCollins Pubs.

Spon, Rogie A. Truthought Bugs of Doodle Forest Activity Guide: A Companion to the Corrective Thinking Reader. Pendergrass, Mark, illus. 2001. (J). per. (978-0-9653376-5-6(0) , Truthought Pubns.) Truthought Group.

—Truthought Bugs of Doodle Forest Corrective Thinking Reader: Corrective Thinking Reader. Pendergrass, Mark, illus. 2001. (J). per. (978-0-9653376-4-9(2) , Truthought Pubns.) Truthought Group.

Spots, 6 vols., Set C,Pack. (Smart Start Ser.). (gr. k-1). 23.00 (978-0-7635-0436-6(X)) Rigby Education.

Sprick, Jessica. Kangaroos: Read Well Level K Unit 15 Storybook. Crum, Anna-Maria, illus. 2003. (Read Well Level K Ser.). 20p. (J). (978-1-57035-686-5(6) , 55554) Sopris West Educational Services.

Sprick, Marilyn. Monkey Business: Read Well Level K Unit 3 Storybook. Nolte, Larry, illus. 2003. (Read Well Level K Ser.). 20p. (J). (978-1-57035-675-9(0)) Sopris West Educational Services.

Sprick, Marilyn, et al. Man's Best Friend: Read Well Level K Unit 5 Storybook. Zilis, Tom, illus. 2003. (Read Well Level K Ser.). 20p. (J). (978-1-57035-677-3(7)) Sopris West Educational Services.

—Read Well K Magazine Prelude F: Plain Text. 2003. (Read Well Level K Ser.). (Illus.). 12p. (J). (978-1-57035-731-2(5)) Sopris West Educational Services.

—Read Well Magazine Prelude A: Plain Text. 2003. (Read Well Level K Ser.). (Illus.). 12p. (J). (978-1-57035-725-1(0)) Sopris West Educational Services.

—Read Well Magazine Prelude A: Slanted Text. 2003. (Read Well Level K Ser.). (Illus.). 12p. (J). (978-1-57035-776-3(5)) Sopris West Educational Services.

—Read Well Magazine Prelude B: Plain Text. 2003. (Read Well Level K Ser.). (Illus.). 12p. (J). (978-1-57035-727-5(7)) Sopris West Educational Services.

—Read Well Magazine Prelude B: Slanted Text. 2003. (Read Well Level K Ser.). (Illus.). 12p. (J). (978-1-57035-777-0(3)) Sopris West Educational Services.

—Read Well Magazine Prelude C: Plain Text. 2004. (Read Well Level K Ser.). (Illus.). 12p. (J). (978-1-57035-728-2(5)) Sopris West Educational Services.

—Read Well Magazine Prelude C: Slanted Text. 2003. (Read Well Level K Ser.). (Illus.). 12p. (J). (978-1-57035-692-6(0)) Sopris West Educational Services.

—Read Well Magazine Prelude D: Plain Text. 2003. (Read Well Level K Ser.). (Illus.). 12p. (J). (978-1-57035-729-9(3)) Sopris West Educational Services.

—Read Well Magazine Prelude D: Slanted Text. 2003. (Read Well Level K Ser.). (Illus.). 12p. (J). (978-1-57035-693-3(9)) Sopris West Educational Services.

—Read Well Magazine Prelude E: Plain Text. 2003. (Read Well Level K Ser.). (Illus.). 12p. (J). (978-1-57035-730-5(7)) Sopris West Educational Services.

—Read Well Magazine Prelude E: Slanted Text. 2003. (Read Well Level K Ser.). (Illus.). 12p. (J). (978-1-57035-694-0(7)) Sopris West Educational Services.

—Read Well Magazine Preude F: Slanted Text. 2003. (Read Well Level K Ser.). (Illus.). 12p. (J). (978-1-57035-695-7(5)) Sopris West Educational Services.

—Read Well Magazine Unit 1: Plain Text. 2003. (Read Well Level K Ser.). (Illus.). 8p. (J). (978-1-57035-735-0(8)) Sopris West Educational Services.

—Read Well Magazine Unit 1: Slanted Text. 2004. (Read Well Level K Ser.). (Illus.). 8p. (J). (978-1-57035-782-4(X)) Sopris West Educational Services.

—Read Well Magazine Unit 10: Plain Text. 2003. (Read Well Level K Ser.). (Illus.). 8p. (J). (978-1-57035-740-4(4)) Sopris West Educational Services.

—Read Well Magazine Unit 10: Slanted Text. 2003. (Read Well Level K Ser.). (Illus.). 8p. (J). (978-1-57035-791-6(9)) Sopris West Educational Services.

—Read Well Magazine Unit 11: Plain Text. 2003. (Read Well Level K Ser.). (Illus.). 8p. (J). (978-1-57035-741-1(2)) Sopris West Educational Services.

—Read Well Magazine Unit 11: Slanted Text. 2003. (Read Well Level K Ser.). (Illus.). 8p. (J). (978-1-57035-792-3(7)) Sopris West Educational Services.

—Read Well Magazine Unit 12: Plain Text. 2004. (Read Well Level K Ser.). (Illus.). 8p. (J). (978-1-57035-742-8(0)) Sopris West Educational Services.

—Read Well Magazine Unit 12: Slanted Text. 2003. (Read Well Level K Ser.). (Illus.). 8p. (J). (978-1-57035-793-0(5)) Sopris West Educational Services.

—Read Well Magazine Unit 14: Plain Text. 2003. (Read Well Level K Ser.). (Illus.). 8p. (J). (978-1-57035-744-2(7)) Sopris West Educational Services.

—Read Well Magazine Unit 15: Plain Text. 2003. (Read Well Level K Ser.). (Illus.). 8p. (J). (978-1-57035-745-9(5)) Sopris West Educational Services.

—Read Well Magazine Unit 15: Slanted Text. 2003. (Read Well Level K Ser.). (Illus.). 8p. (J). (978-1-59318-099-7(3)) Sopris West Educational Services.

—Read Well Magazine Unit 16. 2003. (Read Well Level K Ser.). (Illus.). 8p. (J). (978-1-59318-100-0(0)) Sopris West Educational Services.

—Read Well Magazine Unit 17: Plain Text. 2003. (Read Well Level K Ser.). (Illus.). 8p. (J). (978-1-57035-747-3(1)) Sopris West Educational Services.

—Read Well Magazine Unit 18: Slanted Text. 2003. (Read Well Level K Ser.). (Illus.). 8p. (J). (978-1-59318-102-4(7)) Sopris West Educational Services.

—Read Well Magazine Unit 19: Plain Text. 2003. (Read Well Level K Ser.). (Illus.). 8p. (J). (978-1-57035-749-7(8)) Sopris West Educational Services.

—Read Well Magazine Unit 19: Slanted Text. 2003. (Read Well Level K Ser.). (Illus.). 8p. (J). (978-1-59318-103-1(5)) Sopris West Educational Services.

—Read Well Magazine Unit 2: Plain Text. 2003. (Read Well Level K Ser.). (Illus.). 8p. (J). (978-1-57035-733-6(1)) Sopris West Educational Services.

—Read Well Magazine Unit 2: Slanted Text. 2003. (Read Well Level K Ser.). (Illus.). 8p. (J). (978-1-57035-783-1(8)) Sopris West Educational Services.

—Read Well Magazine Unit 20: Plain Text. 2003. (Read Well Level K Ser.). (Illus.). 8p. (J). (978-1-57035-775-6(7)) Sopris West Educational Services.

—Read Well Magazine Unit 3: Plain Text. 2003. (Read Well Level K Ser.). (Illus.). 8p. (J). (978-1-57035-734-3(X)) Sopris West Educational Services.

—Read Well Magazine Unit 3: Slanted Text. 2003. (Read Well Level K Ser.). (Illus.). 8p. (J). (978-1-57035-784-8(6)) Sopris West Educational Services.

—Read Well Magazine Unit 4: Plain Text. 2003. (Read Well Level K Ser.). (Illus.). 8p. (J). (978-1-57035-732-9(3)) Sopris West Educational Services.

—Read Well Magazine Unit 4: Slanted Text. 2003. (Read Well Level K Ser.). (Illus.). 8p. (J). (978-1-57035-785-5(4)) Sopris West Educational Services.

—Read Well Magazine Unit 5: Plain Text. 2003. (Read Well Level K Ser.). (Illus.). 8p. (J). (978-1-57035-736-7(6)) Sopris West Educational Services.

—Read Well Magazine Unit 6: Plain Text. 2003. (Read Well Level K Ser.). (Illus.). 8p. (J). (978-1-57035-737-4(4)) Sopris West Educational Services.

—Read Well Magazine Unit 6: Slanted Text. 2003. (Read Well Level K Ser.). (Illus.). 8p. (J). (978-1-57035-787-9(0)) Sopris West Educational Services.

—Read Well Magazine Unit 7: Plain Text. 2003. (Read Well Level K Ser.). (Illus.). 8p. (J). (978-1-57035-738-1(2)) Sopris West Educational Services.

—Read Well Magazine Unit 8: Plain Text. 2003. (Read Well Level K Ser.). (Illus.). 8p. (J). (978-1-57035-726-8(9)) Sopris West Educational Services.

—Read Well Magazine Unit 8: Slanted Text. 2003. (Read Well Level K Ser.). (Illus.). 8p. (J). (978-1-57035-789-3(7)) Sopris West Educational Services.

—Read Well Magazine Unit 9: Plain Text. 2003. (Read Well Level K Ser.). (Illus.). 8p. (J). (978-1-57035-739-8(0)) Sopris West Educational Services.

—Read Well Magazine Unit 9: Slanted Text. 2003. (Read Well Level K Ser.). (Illus.). 8p. (J). (978-1-57035-790-9(0)) Sopris West Educational Services.

—Rescue Workers: Read Well Level K Unit 11 Storybook. Zilis, Tom, illus. 2003. (Read Well Level K Ser.). 20p. (J). (978-1-57035-682-7(3) , 55511) Sopris West Educational Services.

—Spiders: Read Well Level K Unit 1 Storybook. Shupe, Bobbi & Crum, Anna-Maria, illus. 2003. (Read Well Level K Ser.). 20p. (J). (978-1-57035-673-5(4)) Sopris West Educational Services.

—Spiders: Unit 1 Read Well Level K Teacher's Storybook. Shupe, Bobbi & Crum, Anna-Maria, illus. 2003. (Read Well Level K Ser.). 20p. (J). (978-1-57035-696-4(3)) Sopris West Educational Services.

—Student Workbook 1 (Plain Text) Units 1-9 Plus Review Unit. 2003. (Read Well Level K Ser.). (Illus.). 104p. (J). (978-1-59318-166-6(3)) Sopris West Educational Services.

—Student Workbook 1 (Slant Text) Units 1-9 Plus Review Unit. 2003. (Read Well Level K Ser.). (Illus.). 104p. (J). (978-1-59318-169-7(8)) Sopris West Educational Services.

—Student Workbook 2 (Plain Text) Units 10-18 Plus Review Unit. 2003. (Read Well Level K Ser.). (Illus.). 104p. (J). (978-1-59318-167-3(1)) Sopris West Educational Services.

—Student Workbook 2 (Slant Text) Units 10-18 Plus Review Unit. 2003. (Read Well Level K Ser.). (Illus.). 104p. (J). (978-1-59318-170-3(1)) Sopris West Educational Services.

—Student Workbook 3 (Plain Text) Unit 19 through Vowel Review Unit. 2003. (Read Well Level K Ser.). (J). (978-1-59318-168-0(X)) Sopris West Educational Services.

Spring to Success on the PSSA Grade 5: Test Prep & Skills Practice READING. 2004. 112p. (J). per. 8.00 (978-0-9722452-6-5(X)) New Leaf Educ., Inc.

Spring to Success on the PSSA Grade 8: Test Prep & Skills Practice READING. 2004. 112p. (YA). per. 8.00 (978-0-9722452-2-7(7)) New Leaf Educ., Inc.

Sprouts Package, 21 vols. 2003. (Illus.). (978-1-4109-0720-2(1)); pap. (978-1-4109-0815-5(1)) Raintree.

The Spy Meeting. (Sails Literacy Ser.). 24p. (gr. 2 up). 27.00 (978-0-7635-6998-3(4)); Pack. 57.00 (978-0-7578-3218-5(0)) Rigby Education.

The Spy Meeting: 6 Small Books. (Sails Literacy Ser.). 24p. (gr. 2 up). 25.00 (978-0-7578-3194-2(X)) Rigby Education.

Squiggles & Strokes, 6 vols., Pack. (Bookweb Ser.). 32p. (gr. 5 up). 34.00 (978-0-7635-3795-1(0)) Rigby Education.

Stamper Bauer, Judith & Ross Keyes, Joan. Kids' Readers. 2004. (Oxford Picture Dictionary for Kids Ser.). 38.50 (978-0-19-430939-4(8)) Oxford Univ. Pr., Inc.

—Sweet Surprise. 2005. (Oxford Picture Dictionary for Kids Ser.). (Illus.). 16p. 4.50 (978-0-19-430933-2(9)) Oxford Univ. Pr., Inc.

Stamper, Judith Bauer & Blevins, Wiley. The Red Hen. Fritz, Ronald, illus. 1998. (Hello Reader! Science Ser.). 160p. (J). (gr. 1-2). pap. 3.99 (978-0-590-76269-4(9)) Scholastic, Inc.

Stamper, Judith Bauer & Ross Keyes, Joan. Diego's Big Day. 2005. (Oxford Picture Dictionary for Kids Ser.). (Illus.). 16p. 4.50 (978-0-19-430931-8(2)) Oxford Univ. Pr., Inc.

—Fun on the Farm. Springer, Sally, illus. 2005. (Oxford Picture Dictionary for Kids Ser.). 16p. 4.50 (978-0-19-430935-6(5)) Oxford Univ. Pr., Inc.

—Kids' Readers: Hide & Seek. Springer, Sally, illus. 2005. (Oxford Picture Dictionary for Kids Ser.). 15p. 4.50 (978-0-19-430926-4(6)) Oxford Univ. Pr., Inc.

—Kids' Readers: Hop, Hop, Jump! 2005. (Oxford Picture Dictionary for Kids Ser.). (Illus.). 16p. 4.50 (978-0-19-430932-5(0)) Oxford Univ. Pr., Inc.

—Kids' Readers: Out the Window! 2005. (Oxford Picture Dictionary for Kids Ser.). (Illus.). 16p. 4.50 (978-0-19-430927-1(4)) Oxford Univ. Pr., Inc.

—Monster Parade. 2005. (Oxford Picture Dictionary for Kids Ser.). (Illus.). 16p. 4.50 (978-0-19-430929-5(0)) Oxford Univ. Pr., Inc.

—Snow Tracks. 2005. (Oxford Picture Dictionary for Kids Ser.). (Illus.). 16p. 4.50 (978-0-19-430928-8(2)) Oxford Univ. Pr., Inc.

—Trip to Toy Town. 2005. (Oxford Picture Dictionary for Kids Ser.). (Illus.). 16p. 4.50 (978-0-19-430930-1(4)) Oxford Univ. Pr., Inc.

—What's for Breakfast? Springer, Sally, illus. 2005. (Oxford Picture Dictionary for Kids Ser.). 16p. 4.50 (978-0-19-430934-9(7)) Oxford Univ. Pr., Inc.

STAR Early Literacy RP Complete Subscription Package. 2004. cd-rom (978-1-59455-174-1(X)) Renaissance Learning, Inc.

STAR Early Literacy RP Set Up. 2004. cd-rom 299.00 (978-1-59455-177-2(4)) Renaissance Learning, Inc.

STAR Early Literacy RP Student Subscription. 2004. cd-rom (978-1-59455-175-8(8)) Renaissance Learning, Inc.

STAR Early Literacy RP Subscription Renewal. 2004. cd-rom (978-1-59455-176-5(6)) Renaissance Learning, Inc.

STAR Early Literacy RP Subscription Package. 2004. cd-rom 1299.00 (978-1-59455-173-4(1)) Renaissance Learning, Inc.

STAR Reading RP Complete Subscription Package. 2004. cd-rom (978-1-59455-171-0(5)) Renaissance Learning, Inc.

STAR Reading RP Norms Upgrade. 2004. cd-rom 599.00 (978-1-59455-172-7(3)) Renaissance Learning, Inc.

STAR Reading RP Student Subscription. 2004. cd-rom (978-1-59455-169-7(3)) Renaissance Learning, Inc.

STAR Reading RP Student Subscription Renewal. 2004. cd-rom (978-1-59455-170-3(7)) Renaissance Learning, Inc.

STAR Reading RP Subscription Package. 2004. cd-rom 1299.00 (978-1-59455-168-0(5)) Renaissance Learning, Inc.
Stargazers. 2005. (J). (978-1-932570-35-9(7)) Literacy Footprints Inc.
Stark, Barbara. Blue Dinosaur's Friends. l.t. ed. 2006. (Illus.). 24p. (J). E-Book 9.95 incl. cd-rom (978-1-933090-20-7(0)) Guardian Angel Publishing, Inc.
Start It Up! (Early Intervention Levels Ser.). 21.30 (978-0-7362-0391-3(5)); Vol. 6. 3.55 (978-0-7362-0171-1(8)) Hampton-Brown Bks.
Starters Two, Red, & Yellow Levels Certificate Only. (gr. k-5). 89.00 (978-0-7578-6539-8(9)) Rigby Education.
Stckvagn. AC Reading for Today. 2004. pap. (978-0-7398-9859-8(0)) Harcourt Schl. Pubs.
—Erp Lpur Complete Package. 2004. pap. (978-0-7398-9025-7(5)) Harcourt Schl. Pubs.
Steck-Vaughn Staff. After Goldilocks. 1999. (Illus.). pap. (978-0-8172-8707-8(8)) Steck-Vaughn.
—The All-Weather Hat. 2000. pap. (978-0-7398-4488-5(1)) Steck-Vaughn.
—Amazing Whales Level B: Early Reader. 2003. (Illus.). bds. (978-0-7398-8223-8(6)) Steck-Vaughn.
—American Resources on Wheels. 2002. (J). pap. (978-0-7398-6355-8(X)) Steck-Vaughn.
—And Justice for All. 2002. (Illus.). pap. 41.60 incl. audio compact disk (978-0-7398-6980-2(9)) Steck-Vaughn.
—Bilingual Primary Collection, 15 vols. 2000. (J). pap. (978-0-7398-2357-6(4)) Steck-Vaughn.
—Complete Emergent Stage 1 Package. 2000. (Illus.). pap. 870.80 (978-0-7398-3135-9(6)) Steck-Vaughn.
—Content Library: High School. 2002. (Illus.). (YA). pap. 289.00 (978-0-7398-6349-7(5)) Steck-Vaughn.
—Content Library: Middle School. 2002. (Illus.). (J). pap. (978-0-7398-6348-0(7)) Steck-Vaughn.
—Cycles Go Bk. AA: People. 2004. (Illus.). pap. 8.95 (978-0-7398-8967-1(2)) Steck-Vaughn.
—Cycles Go Bk. BA: Windows. 2004. (Illus.). pap. 8.95 (978-0-7398-8968-8(0)) Steck-Vaughn.
—Cycles Go Bk. CA: Images. 2004. (Illus.). pap. 8.95 (978-0-7398-8969-5(9)) Steck-Vaughn.
—Cycles Go Bk. DA: Avenues. 2004. (Illus.). pap. 8.95 (978-0-7398-8970-1(2)) Steck-Vaughn.
—Cycles Go Bk. FA: Quests. 2004. (Illus.). pap. 8.95 (978-0-7398-8972-5(9)) Steck-Vaughn.
—Cycles Go Bk. GA: Choices. 2004. (Illus.). pap. 8.95 (978-0-7398-8973-2(7)) Steck-Vaughn.
—Cycles Go Bk. HA: Visions. 2004. (Illus.). pap. 8.95 (978-0-7398-8974-9(5)) Steck-Vaughn.
—Cycles Go - Reflections. 2004. (Illus.). pap. 8.95 (978-0-7398-8975-6(3)) Steck-Vaughn.
—Dude Ranch Luke/A Huge Smile. 1999. (Take Me Home Ser.). (J). pap. (978-0-7398-2680-5(8)) Steck-Vaughn.
—Early Reader Package Level C: Animal Coats, 6 Pack. 2004. (Illus.). pap. 33.00 (978-0-7398-8312-9(7)) Steck-Vaughn.
—Early Reader Package Level C: Harem Scarem, 6 Pack. 2004. (Illus.). pap. 33.00 (978-0-7398-8311-2(9)) Steck-Vaughn.
—Early Reader Program Level A: A Dog Like Scruff, 6 Pack. 2004. (Illus.). pap. 33.00 (978-0-7398-8250-4(3)) Steck-Vaughn.
—Early Reader Program Level B: Ice Cream Dream, 6 Pack. 2004. (Illus.). pap. 33.00 (978-0-7398-8246-7(5)) Steck-Vaughn.
—Early Reader Program Level B: Lessons from Lester, 6 Pack. 2004. (Illus.). pap. 33.00 (978-0-7398-8249-8(X)) Steck-Vaughn.
—Early Reader Program Level B: Otto's Lunch, 6 Pack. 2004. (Illus.). pap. 33.00 (978-0-7398-8247-4(3)) Steck-Vaughn.
—Early Reader Program Level B: People Love Pasta, 6 Pack. 2004. (Illus.). pap. 33.00 (978-0-7398-8248-1(1)) Steck-Vaughn.
—Early Reader Program Level B: The Lifecycles of Swans, 6 Pack. 2004. (Illus.). pap. 33.00 (978-0-7398-8245-0(7)) Steck-Vaughn.
—Early Reader Program Level B: Then & Now, 6 Pack. 2004. (Illus.). pap. 33.00 (978-0-7398-8244-3(9)) Steck-Vaughn.
—Early Reader Program Level B: Why Bears Have Shoes, 6 Pack. 2004. (Illus.). pap. 33.00 (978-0-7398-8243-6(0)) Steck-Vaughn.
—Early Reader Program Complete Package Level C. 2004. (Illus.). pap. 745.00 (978-0-7398-8283-2(X)) Steck-Vaughn.
—Early Reader Program Complete Package Level A. 2004. (Illus.). pap. 885.00 (978-0-7398-8959-6(1)) Steck-Vaughn.
—Early Reader Program Complete Package Level B. 2004. pap. 885.00 (978-0-7398-8960-2(5)) Steck-Vaughn.
—Early Reader Starter Set Level C. 2003. (Illus.). (J). pap. (978-0-7398-8281-8(3)) Steck-Vaughn.
—Early Reading Program: Feelings Theme, 6 Pack. 2004. (Illus.). pap. 30.00 (978-0-7398-8149-1(3)) Steck-Vaughn.
—Early Reading Program: Once I Was a Baby, 6 Pack. 2004. (Illus.). pap. 30.00 (978-0-7398-8148-4(5)) Steck-Vaughn.
—Early Reading Program: Professional Development. 2004. pap. 45.00 (978-0-7398-9948-9(1)) Harcourt Schl. Pubs.
—Early Reading Program: Purple Big Book Package. 2004. pap. 199.00 (978-0-7398-9422-4(6)) Steck-Vaughn.
—Early Reading Program Level A: Slug Makes a House 6-Pack. 2004. (Illus.). pap. 30.00 (978-0-7398-8150-7(7)) Steck-Vaughn.
—En Parejas Early Emergent Kit - Retail. 2002. (SPA., Illus.). (J). pap. (978-0-7398-6983-3(3)) Steck-Vaughn.
—Exactly the Right Egg. 2003. pap. 4.10 (978-0-7398-7631-2(7)) Steck-Vaughn.
—Fact Family Fun. 2003. pap. 4.10 (978-0-7398-7662-6(7)) Steck-Vaughn.
—The Fight for Right. 2002. (Illus.). pap. 41.60 incl. audio compact disk (978-0-7398-6964-2(7)) Steck-Vaughn.
—First Grade Leveled Reader Package 100. 2002. (Illus.). (J). pap. (978-0-7398-7606-0(6)) Steck-Vaughn.
—First Grade Leveled Reader Package 150. 2002. pap. (978-0-7398-7607-7(4)) Steck-Vaughn.
—First Grade Leveled Reader Package 200. 2002. (Illus.). pap. (978-0-7398-7608-4(2)) Steck-Vaughn.
—Head for Home: Master Kit. 2004. (Illus.). pap. 1293.84 (978-0-7398-9295-4(9)) Steck-Vaughn.
—How the Elephant Got His Trunk Level B: Early Reader. 2003. (Illus.). pap. (978-0-7398-8222-1(8)) Steck-Vaughn.
—Ice Cream Dream Level B: Early Reader. 2003. (Illus.). pap. (978-0-7398-8220-7(1)) Steck-Vaughn.
—January 03 New Product Package. 2003. pap. (978-0-7398-7931-3(6)) Steck-Vaughn.
—Kindergarten Leveled Reader Package 150. 2002. (Illus.). (J). pap. (978-0-7398-7603-9(1)) Steck-Vaughn.
—Kindergarten Leveled Reader Package 200. 2002. (Illus.). pap. (978-0-7398-7604-6(X)) Steck-Vaughn.
—Language Art & Spelling, 8, Pack. 2004. pap. 68.00 (978-0-7398-9933-5(3)) Harcourt Schl. Pubs.
—Language Arts & Spelling. 2004. pap. 8.50 (978-0-7398-9848-2(5)); pap. 68.00 (978-0-7398-9929-8(5)); pap., tchr. ed. 10.00 (978-0-7398-9904-5(X)) Harcourt Schl. Pubs.
—Lessons from Lester Level B: Early Reader. 2003. (Illus.). pap. (978-0-7398-8221-4(X)) Steck-Vaughn.
—A Life in Their Hands. 2002. (Illus.). pap. 41.60 incl. audio compact disk (978-0-7398-6959-8(0)) Steck-Vaughn.
—The Lifecycles of Swans Level B: Early Reader. 2003. (Illus.). pap. (978-0-7398-8219-1(8)) Steck-Vaughn.
—Map Comm Arts F: Soaring Scores. 2002. pap. (978-0-7398-5630-7(8)) Steck-Vaughn.
—National Bookroom Package. 2003. (Illus.). pap. 10000.00 (978-0-7398-8908-4(7)); pap. 5000.00 (978-0-7398-8909-1(5)); pap. 2500.00 (978-0-7398-8910-7(9)) Steck-Vaughn.
—Nonfiction Comprehension. 2005. (gr. 3). pap. 12.99 (978-0-7398-8947-3(8)); (gr. 5). pap. 12.99 (978-0-7398-8948-0(6)) Harcourt Schl. Pubs.
—Nonfiction Comprehension, Middle School. 2005. pap. 12.99 (978-0-7398-8949-7(4)) Harcourt Schl. Pubs.
—Opt Administered Guide Text Insert. 2002. pap. (978-0-7398-5696-3(0)) Steck-Vaughn.
—Other Places: dream Around/Aunt. 1998. (Illus.). (J). pap. (978-0-8172-8641-5(1)) Steck-Vaughn.
—Pair-It Lab Set Stage 3. 1999. (Illus.). (J). pap. (978-0-7398-1593-9(8)) Steck-Vaughn.
—Pair-It Network Set. 2001. cd-rom 1330.80 (978-0-7398-2911-0(4)); cd-rom 1347.00 (978-0-7398-2912-7(2)) Steck-Vaughn.
—Pair-It Stage 1 Network Version. 1999. 828.70 (978-0-7398-1585-4(7)) Steck-Vaughn.
—Pair-It Stage 2 Network Version. 1999. 828.70 (978-0-7398-1586-1(5)) Steck-Vaughn.
—Pair-It Stage 3 Network Version. 1999. 828.70 (978-0-7398-1587-8(3)) Steck-Vaughn.
—Pair-It Stage 4 Network Version. 2001. 1081.20 (978-0-7398-2905-9(X)) Steck-Vaughn.
—Pair-It Stage 5 Network Version. 2001. pap. 1081.20 (978-0-7398-2906-6(8)) Steck-Vaughn.
—Pair It Stages 5-6 Bookroom. 2004. pap. 2460.00 (978-1-4190-0398-1(4)) Steck-Vaughn.
—PU Extended Complete Collection Level 1. 2003. (Illus.). pap. 599.00 (978-0-7398-8913-8(3)) Steck-Vaughn.
—PU Extended Complete Collection Level 2. 2003. (Illus.). pap. 729.00 (978-0-7398-8914-5(1)) Steck-Vaughn.
—Quantum Reading. 2000. (gr. k). pap. 364.00 (978-0-7398-3670-5(6)); Level L. pap. 189.30 (978-0-7398-3660-6(9)); Level L. pap. 189.30 (978-0-7398-3672-9(2)); Level M. pap. 189.30 (978-0-7398-3663-7(3)); Level M. pap. 189.30 (978-0-7398-3675-0(7)); Level J. pap 189.30 (978-0-7398-3654-5(4)); Level J. pap. 189.30 (978-0-7398-3666-8(8)); Level K. pap. 189.30 (978-0-7398-3657-6(9)); Level K. pap. 189.30 (978-0-7398-3669-9(2)) Steck-Vaughn.
—Readers Theatre for Primary Grades. 2004. (Illus.). pap. 16.99 (978-0-7398-9309-8(2)) Steck-Vaughn.
—Reading & Language Arts. 2004. pap. 8.50 (978-0-7398-9845-1(0)) Harcourt Schl. Pubs.
—Reading & Language Arts 8-Pack. 2004. pap. 68.00 (978-0-7398-9926-7(0)) Harcourt Schl. Pubs.
—Reading Comprehension: Building Vocabulary & Measurement. 2003. pap., tchr. ed. 20.70 (978-0-7398-8356-3(9)) Steck-Vaughn.
—Reading Group Packs 1999-2000, 9 Series. 2000. pap. 3199.00 (978-1-58702-545-7(0)) Johnston, Don Inc.
—Reading Intermediate, 8, Pack. 2004. pap. 68.00 (978-0-7398-9928-1(7)) Harcourt Schl. Pubs.
—Reading Introductory, 8, Pack. 2004. pap. 68.00 (978-0-7398-9932-8(5)) Harcourt Schl. Pubs.
—Rise: Ontario MOE Macintosh Version. 1999. (Illus.). pap. 10.00 incl. cd-rom (978-0-7398-1269-3(6)) Raintree.
—Rise: Ontario MOE Windows Version. 1999. (Illus.). (J). pap. 10.00 incl. cd-rom (978-0-7398-1270-9(X)) Raintree.
—Rise: Plus Annual, 25 vols., set. 1998. (Illus.). (J). pap. 569.93 (978-0-8172-4308-1(9)) Raintree.
—The Secret on the Wall. 2002. (Illus.). pap. 41.60 incl. audio compact disk (978-0-7398-6967-3(1)) Steck-Vaughn.
—See What I Can Do. 2000. (Illus.). (J). pap. (978-0-7398-4455-7(5)) Steck-Vaughn.
—Seeing Eye to Eye. 2002. (Illus.). pap. 41.60 incl. audio compact disk (978-0-7398-6974-1(4)) Steck-Vaughn.
—Shifting Ground. 2002. (Illus.). pap. 41.60 incl. audio compact disk (978-0-7398-6971-0(X)) Steck-Vaughn.
—Shutterbug Early Emergent Classroom Set. 2002. (Illus.). pap. 1095.00 (978-0-7398-7809-5(3)) Steck-Vaughn.
—Shutterbug Early Emergent Starter Set. 2002. (Illus.). pap. 260.00 (978-0-7398-7808-8(5)) Steck-Vaughn.
—Shutterbug Emergent Stage Classroom Set. 2002. (Illus.). pap. 1440.00 (978-0-7398-7810-1(7)) Steck-Vaughn.
—Shutterbug Emergent Stage Starter Set. 2002. (Illus.). pap. 315.00 (978-0-7398-7811-8(5)) Steck-Vaughn.
—Single User Packs 1999-2000, 9 Series. 2000. pap. 1399.00 (978-1-58702-546-4(9)) Johnston, Don Inc.
—Siri. 2003. pap. 26.00 (978-0-7398-7947-4(2)) Steck-Vaughn.
—Something Rotten in the Village. 2002. (Illus.). pap. 41.60 incl. audio compact disk (978-0-7398-6975-8(2)) Steck-Vaughn.
—Space Play Single. 2002. (Illus.). pap. 41.60 incl. audio compact disk (978-0-7398-6977-2(9)) Steck-Vaughn.
—Stuck on You. 2003. pap. 4.10 (978-0-7398-7634-3(1)) Steck-Vaughn.
—Summer School Reading Grade. 2001. pap., tchr. ed. 34.13 (978-0-7398-4533-2(0)) Steck-Vaughn.
—Tales from Gull Island. 2002. (Illus.). pap. 41.60 incl. audio compact disk (978-0-7398-6981-9(7)) Steck-Vaughn.
—The Thrill of the Ride. 2002. (Illus.). pap. 41.60 incl. audio compact disk (978-0-7398-6956-7(6)) Steck-Vaughn.
—To Reach the Top. 2002. (Illus.). pap. 41.60 incl. audio compact disk (978-0-7398-6960-4(4)) Steck-Vaughn.
—Totem Story. 2003. pap. 4.10 (978-0-7398-7644-2(9)) Steck-Vaughn.
—Trash with Dash. 2002. (Illus.). pap. 41.60 incl. audio compact disk (978-0-7398-6962-8(0)) Steck-Vaughn.
—Video Dream Givers Reading for Today. 2000. (J). pap. (978-0-7398-2966-0(1)) Steck-Vaughn.
—Video Package Changes All Around Me. 1998. (Illus.). (J). pap. incl. VHS (978-0-8172-3857-5(3)) Steck-Vaughn.
—Weather Wear for Teddy Bear. 2000. (Illus.). (J). pap. (978-0-7398-4450-2(4)) Steck-Vaughn.
—What's the Difference Kit (Lakeshore) 2000. (Illus.). (J). pap. (978-0-7398-2893-9(2)) Steck-Vaughn.
—Who's Hiding in There. 1999. (Take Me Home Ser.). (J). pap. (978-0-7398-2590-7(9)) Steck-Vaughn.
—Who's Hiding There. 1999. (Illus.). (J). bds. (978-0-7398-2447-4(3)) Steck-Vaughn.
—The Will to Survive. 2002. (Illus.). pap. 41.60 incl. audio compact disk (978-0-7398-6972-7(8)) Steck-Vaughn.
—The World's Greatest Showman. 2002. (Illus.). pap. 41.60 incl. audio compact disk (978-0-7398-6958-1(2)) Steck-Vaughn.
Steiner. Murder Takes a Fast Track. (Thumbprint Mysteries Ser.). 32.86 (978-0-8092-0417-5(7)) McGraw-Hill/Contemporary.
Steiner, Rudolf. Fun Days. (J). pap. 2.75 (978-0-87895-956-3(4)) Modern Curriculum Pr.
Stephens, Monique. Fantastic Four: Meet the Fantastic Four. 2005. (Festival Reader Ser.). 32p. (J). 14.99 (978-0-06-082244-6(9)) HarperCollins Pubs.
Stevenson-Spurgon, Barbara J. Have You Ever Made Mud Pies on A Hot Summer Day? Ruffin, Aurzella, illus. 2006. 37p. (J). per. 19.95 ***978-1-60002-234-0(0)**, 4073, Airleaf Publishing) Airleaf Publishing & Bookselling.
A Stomach Full of Stones, 6 vols., Pack. (Sails Literacy Ser.). (gr. 1-2). 36.00 (978-0-7578-6769-9(3)) Rigby Education.
Stontz, Karen & Malone, Kelly. Autism & PDD Concepts How Does Becca Bunny Feel? 2004. (J). spiral bd. (978-0-7606-0594-3(7)) LinguiSystems, Inc.
Stop That Noise! KinderWords Individual Title Six-Packs. (Kinderstarters Ser.). 8p. (ps-1). 21.00 (978-0-7635-8694-2(3)) Rigby Education.
Stop the Car! Individual Title Six-Pack Pouch - Level H. (Lighthouse Ser.). 16p. (gr. 1 up). 26.00 (978-0-7578-0846-3(8)) Rigby Education.
Stop Thief! Level M. (Lighthouse Ser.). 24p. (gr. 2 up). 28.00 (978-0-7578-0881-4(6)) Rigby Education.
Stories & More. 2005. (Little Celebrations Thematic Packages Ser.). (J). (gr. k-3). 133.50 (978-0-673-75376-2(X)) Celebration Pr.
Stories from Many Lands. (J). 3.70 (978-0-8136-2402-0(9)); tchr. ed. 9.30 (978-0-8136-2427-3(4)) Modern Curriculum Pr.
Storm Warning: KinderConcepts Individual Title Six-Packs. (Kinderstarters Ser.). 8p. (ps-1). 21.00 (978-0-7635-8734-5(6)) Rigby Education.
Stormer, Kate. The Rescue of Little Red. Lowes, Tom, illus. 2005. 91p. (J). (gr. 3-5). per. 5.99 (978-0-9765872-0-0(3)) Caseys World Bks.
Story Box. (gr. 2 up). 8.50 (978-0-7802-3064-4(7)) Wright Group, The.
Story Center. 2005. (YA). (ps-3). 19.95 (978-0-8215-7557-4(0)) Sadlier, William H. Inc.
Story Center Guide. 2005. (YA). (ps-3). 6.00 (978-0-8215-7558-1(9)) Sadlier, William H. Inc.
The Story of Dona Chila: Six-Pack. (Greetings Ser.: Vol. 3). (gr. 3-5). 31.00 (978-0-7635-1775-5(5)) Rigby Education.
The Story of Jeans, 6 Pack. (Discovery World Ser.). 24p. (gr. 1-2). 33.00 (978-0-7635-8483-2(5)) Rigby Education.
Story Paper. 1999. (gr. k up). suppl. ed. 6.75 (978-0-673-59153-1(0) , Scott Foresman) Addison-Wesley Educational Pubs., Inc.
Story Starters & Stationary. 2005. 84p. (J). spiral bd. 14.99 (978-1-59441-472-5(6) , K04023) Carson-Dellosa Publishing Co., Inc.
Storytapes Set 800866, 3. 2005. (J). (978-1-59794-029-0(1)) Environments, Inc.
The Streetsweeper, 6 packs. (Bookweb Ser.). 32p. (gr. 3 up). 34.00 (978-0-7635-3943-6(0)) Rigby Education.
Strength in Numbers: Individual Title Six-Packs. (Rigby Infoquest Ser.). 24p. (gr. 3 up). 34.00 (978-0-7578-5778-2(7)) Rigby Education.
Strete, Craig Kee. They Thought They Saw Him. 1999. (Metro Reading Program Ser.). (J). (gr. k). 7.98 (978-1-58120-969-3(X)); 45.95 (978-1-58830-016-4(1)) Metropolitan Teaching & Learning Co.
Strickland, Brenda. Year Round Preschool Reading. 2006. 240p. pap. 24.99 (978-1-4206-3185-2(3)) Austin & Company, Inc.
String Performers: Individual Title Six-Packs. (gr. k-1). 23.00 (978-0-7635-9029-1(0)) Rigby Education.
Strings, Ropes & Cables, 6 Packs. (gr. k-1). 23.00 (978-0-7635-9024-6(X)) Rigby Education.
Strong, Mike. Colin Powell: It Can Be Done!, 6 vols. (gr. 4 up). 49.95 (978-0-7368-9540-8(X) , High Five) Red Brick Learning.
Stuart, Phillip. Stage Fright. 2005. (Young Reading Series 2 Ser.). 64p. (J). (gr. 2 up). pap. 5.95 (978-0-7945-0927-9(4) , Usborne) EDC Publishing.
Stuck in the Mud: Individual Title Six-Pack Pouch - Level E. (Lighthouse Ser.). 12p. (gr. 1 up). 26.00 (978-0-7578-0833-3(6)) Rigby Education.
Suarez, Elizabeth. Reading First Basics - Fluency, Text Comprehension, & Vocabulary. Gunzenhauser, Kelly, ed. 2005. 80p. (J). per. 10.99 (978-1-59441-047-5(X) , CD-104017) Carson-Dellosa Publishing Co., Inc.
Suarez, Elizabeth & Lewis, Starin. Reading First Basics - Comprehension. Gunzenhauser, Kelly, ed. 2005. 80p. (J). per. 10.99 (978-1-59441-045-1(3) , CD-104015) Carson-Dellosa Publishing Co., Inc.
A Sudden Storm, 5 Packs., Level 1. 2002. (Illus.). pap. 36.75 (978-0-7398-5110-4(1)) Steck-Vaughn.
Sugar & Spice & All Things Nice: Level M, 6 vols. 128p. (gr. 2-3). 40.50 (978-0-7699-0998-1(1)) Shortland Pubns. (U. S. A.) Inc.
The Sugar Bush: 6 Small Books. (Greetings Ser.: Vol. 1). 24p. (gr. 2-3). 31.00 (978-0-7635-9424-4(5)) Rigby Education.
The Sugar Bush: Big Book. (Greetings Ser.: Vol. 1). 24p. (gr. 2-3). 31.00 (978-0-7635-5706-5(4)) Rigby Education.
Sulky Simon, 6 Packs. (gr. 1-2). 25.00 (978-0-7635-9146-5(7)) Rigby Education.
The Summer Party: Fourth Grade Guided Comprehension Level P. (On Our Way to English Ser.). (gr. 4 up). 34.50 (978-0-7578-7172-6(0)) Rigby Education.
A Sun & Rain Set, 6 vols. (Phonics Readers Ser.). (gr. k-2). 17.50 (978-0-7368-3192-5(4)) Red Brick Learning.
Sunflower. (Lexile Levels Ser.). 7.98 (978-1-56334-672-9(9)) Hampton-Brown Bks.
The Super Supermarket Plan: Individual Title Six-Packs. (gr. k-1). 23.00 (978-0-7635-8844-1(X)) Rigby Education.
The Supermarket, 6 vols. (gr. k-2). 28.95 (978-0-7368-8007-7(0)) Red Brick Learning.
Surfing 6 Packs. KinderConcepts. (Kinderstarters Ser.). 8p. (ps-1). 21.00 (978-0-7635-8726-0(5)) Rigby Education.
A Surprise for Monica, 6 Packs. (Greetings Ser.: Vol. 2). (gr. 3-5). 31.00 (978-0-7635-1810-3(7)) Rigby Education.
A Surprise for Mrs O'Malley. (Sails Literacy Ser.). 24p. (gr. 2 up). 27.00 (978-0-7578-6821-4(5)) Rigby Education.
A Surprise for Mrs O'Malley: 3-in-1 Package. (Sails Literacy Ser.). 24p. (gr. 2 up). 57.00 (978-0-7578-6833-7(9)) Rigby Education.
A Surprise for Mrs O'Malley: 6 Small Books. (Sails Literacy Ser.). 24p. (gr. 2 up). 25.00 (978-0-7578-6829-0(0)) Rigby Education.
Surprise from the Sky, 6 Packs. (gr. 1-2). 25.00 (978-0-7635-9138-0(6)) Rigby Education.
Survivors: Individual Title Six-Packs. (Rigby Infoquest Ser.). 24p. (gr. 3 up). 34.00 (978-0-7578-5779-9(5)) Rigby Education.
Swain, Cynthia. The Bad Pest. 2003. (BuildUp Ser.). (J). pap. 22.00 (978-1-4108-0748-9(7)) Benchmark Education Co.
—Frank & Brent. 2003. (BuildUp Ser.). (J). pap. 22.00 (978-1-4108-0749-6(5)) Benchmark Education Co.
—In the Sunshine. 2003. (BuildUp Ser.). (J). pap. 22.00 (978-1-4108-0757-1(6)) Benchmark Education Co.
—Scram, Cat! 2003. (BuildUp Ser.). (J). pap. 22.00 (978-1-4108-0751-9(7)) Benchmark Education Co.
Swamp Explorer: Fourth Grade Guided Comprehension Level R. (On Our Way to English Ser.). (gr. 4 up). 34.50 (978-0-7578-7183-2(6)) Rigby Education.
Swan. Five Famous Fairy Tales, Level 2. 2001. (Illus.). 48p. (C). pap. 9.00 (978-0-582-42125-7(X)) Pearson ESL.
—Stories from Shakespeare, Level 3. 2001. (Illus.). 64p. (C). pap. 9.00 (978-0-582-42694-8(4)) Longman Publishing Group.
—Tales from the Arabian Knights, Level 2. 2001. (Illus.). 48p. (C). pap. 9.00 (978-0-582-42658-0(8)) Longman Publishing Group.
SWAT, 8 bks., Set. 2006. (Read It! Chapter Books). (J). (ps-6). 159.60 (978-1-4048-1710-4(7)) Picture Window Bks.
Sweeney, Jacqueline. We Can Read! - Group 2, 4 bks., Set. Hart, G. K. & Empey, Mark, illus. Incl. Critter Day. lib. bdg. 21.36 (978-0-7614-1119-2(4)); Homesick. lib. bdg. 21.36 (978-0-7614-1117-8(8)); Molly's Store. lib. bdg. 21.36 (978-0-7614-1116-1(X)); What about Bettie? lib. bdg. 21.36 (978-0-7614-1118-5(6)); 32p. (J). (gr. 1-2). 2000. (Illus.). 2000. Set lib. bdg. 85.43 (978-0-7614-1115-4(1) , Benchmark Bks.) Cavendish, Marshall Corp.
Swigert, Nancy B. Early Intervention Kit Activities Book. 2004. (J). per. (978-0-7606-0597-4(1)) LinguiSystems, Inc.
Swim, Climb, & Fly: Emergent Level Satellite Individual Title Six-Packs. (Sails Literacy Ser.). (gr. k-1). 27.00 (978-0-7578-7932-6(2)) Rigby Education.
Swimming in the Sand. (J). pap. 13.75 (978-0-8136-3404-3(0)) Modern Curriculum Pr.

Switch It On! Individual Title Six-Packs. (Rigby Infoquest Ser.). 32p. (gr. 4 up). 37.00 (978-0-7578-5739-3(6)) Rigby Education.

Sylvester, H. Charle. Journeys Through Bookland, V2. 2006. 66.99 (***978-1-4219-9727-8(4)*** *);* pap. 60.99 (***978-1-4219-9702-5(9)***) IndyPublish.com.

—Journeys Through Bookland, V3. 2006. 66.99 (***978-1-4219-9733-9(9)*** *);* pap. 59.99 (***978-1-4219-9734-6(7)***) IndyPublish.com.

Tabletop Easel. (ps-12). 81.69 (978-0-7362-0851-2(8)) Hampton-Brown Bks.

Take a Look at My Family. (Early Intervention Levels Ser.). 28.38 (978-0-7362-0395-1(8)) Hampton-Brown Bks.

Take a Look at My Family (8), Vol. 8. (Early Intervention Levels Ser.). 4.73 (978-0-7362-0220-6(X)) Hampton-Brown Bks.

Take-Home Books Collection. 2005. (YA). (ps-3). 225.00 (978-0-8215-7290-0(3)) Sadlier, William H. Inc.

Take-Home Cards, Early Level. (gr. k-2). 69.95 (978-0-7368-1494-2(9) , Pebble Bks.) Capstone Pr., Inc.

Take-Home Cards, Emergent Level. (gr. k-2). 69.95 (978-0-7368-1493-5(0) , Pebble Bks.) Capstone Pr., Inc.

Take-Home Cards, Fluent Level. (gr. k-2). 69.95 (978-0-7368-1495-9(7) , Pebble Bks.) Capstone Pr., Inc.

TAKS MASTER Learning with Graphic Organizers, Gr. 3. 2005. (J). (978-1-57022-550-5(8)) ECS Learning Systems, Inc.

TAKS MASTER Learning with Graphic Organizers, Gr. 4. 2005. (J). (978-1-57022-551-2(6)) ECS Learning Systems, Inc.

TAKS MASTER Learning with Graphic Organizers, Gr. 5. 2005. (J). (978-1-57022-552-9(4)) ECS Learning Systems, Inc.

TAKS MASTER Learning with Graphic Organizers, Gr. 6. 2005. (J). (978-1-57022-553-6(2)) ECS Learning Systems, Inc.

TAKS MASTER Learning with Graphic Organizers, Gr. 7. 2005. (J). (978-1-57022-554-3(0)) ECS Learning Systems, Inc.

TAKS MASTER Learning with Graphic Organizers, Gr. 8. 2005. (YA). (978-1-57022-555-0(9)) ECS Learning Systems, Inc.

TAKS MASTER Power Practice, Reading Gr. 3. 2004. (J). (978-1-57022-541-3(9)) ECS Learning Systems, Inc.

TAKS MASTER Power Practice, Reading Gr. 4. 2004. (J). (978-1-57022-542-0(7)) ECS Learning Systems, Inc.

TAKS MASTER Power Practice, Reading Gr. 5. 2004. (J). (978-1-57022-543-7(5)) ECS Learning Systems, Inc.

TAKS MASTER Power Practice, Reading Gr. 6. 2004. (J). (978-1-57022-544-4(3)) ECS Learning Systems, Inc.

TAKS MASTER Power Practice, Reading Gr. 7. 2004. (J). (978-1-57022-545-1(1)) ECS Learning Systems, Inc.

TAKS MASTER Power Practice, Reading Gr. 8. 2004. (YA). (978-1-57022-546-8(X)) ECS Learning Systems, Inc.

TAKS MASTER Practice Test Reading, Gr. 3. 2004. (J). (978-1-57022-475-1(7)) ECS Learning Systems, Inc.

TAKS MASTER Practice Test Reading, Gr. 4. 2004. (J). (978-1-57022-528-4(1)) ECS Learning Systems, Inc.

TAKS MASTER Practice Test Reading, Gr. 5. 2004. (J). (978-1-57022-529-1(X)) ECS Learning Systems, Inc.

TAKS MASTER Practice Test Reading, Gr. 6. 2004. (J). (978-1-57022-530-7(3)) ECS Learning Systems, Inc.

TAKS MASTER Practice Test Reading, Gr. 7. 2004. (J). (978-1-57022-531-4(1)) ECS Learning Systems, Inc.

TAKS MASTER Practice Test Reading, Gr. 8. 2004. (YA). (978-1-57022-532-1(X)) ECS Learning Systems, Inc.

TAKS Open-Ended Reading Response Guide, Grades 9-11 Exit. 2004. (Region IV ESC Resources for Mathematics, Science, Social Studies & Reading Ser.). spiral bd. (978-1-932797-19-0(X)) Region IV Education Service Ctr.

TAKS Reading Accelerated Curriculum for Grade 5. 2005. (Region IV ESC Resources for Reading Ser.). spiral bd. (978-1-933049-06-9(5)) Region IV Education Service Ctr.

TAKS Reading Accelerated Curriculum Middle School (Volume 1) 2006. spiral bd. (978-1-933049-18-2(9)) Region IV Education Service Ctr.

TAKS Reading Preparation Grade 10 - Student Workbook. 2003. (Region IV ESC Resources for Reading Ser.). stu. ed., per. (978-1-932524-48-2(7)) Region IV Education Service Ctr.

TAKS Reading Preparation Grade 11 Exit. 2003. (Region IV ESC Resources for Reading Ser.). stu. ed., per., wbk. ed. (978-1-932524-49-9(5)) Region IV Education Service Ctr.

TAKS Reading Preparation Grade 4. 2003. (Region IV ESC Resources for Reading Ser.). stu. ed., per., wbk. ed. (978-1-932524-42-0(8)) Region IV Education Service Ctr.

TAKS Reading Preparation Grade 5. 2003. (Region IV ESC Resources for Reading Ser.). stu. ed., per., wbk. ed. (978-1-932524-43-7(6)) Region IV Education Service Ctr.

TAKS Reading Preparation Grade 6. 2003. (Region IV ESC Resources for Reading Ser.). stu. ed., per., wbk. ed. (978-1-932524-44-4(4)) Region IV Education Service Ctr.

TAKS Reading Preparation Grade 8. 2003. (Region IV ESC Resources for Reading Ser.). stu. ed., per., wbk. ed. (978-1-932524-46-8(0)) Region IV Education Service Ctr.

TAKS Reading Preparation Grade 9. 2003. (Region IV ESC Resources for Reading Ser.). stu. ed., per., wbk. ed. (978-1-932524-47-5(9)) Region IV Education Service Ctr.

TAKS Reading Preparaton Grade 7. 2003. (Region IV ESC Resources for Reading Ser.). stu. ed., per., wbk. ed. (978-1-932524-45-1(2)) Region IV Education Service Ctr.

TAKS Readng Preparation Grade 3. 2003. (Region IV ESC Resources for Reading Ser.). stu. ed., per., wbk. ed. (978-1-932524-41-3(X)) Region IV Education Service Ctr.

The Tale of the Golden Goose. (Early Intervention Levels Ser.). 31.86 (978-0-7362-0617-4(5)) Hampton-Brown Bks.

The Tale of the Golden Goose (18), Vol. 18. (Early Intervention Levels Ser.). 5.31 (978-0-7362-0605-1(1)) Hampton-Brown Bks.

Tali Drives His Car. (Pebble Soup Explorations Ser.). 16p. (ps up). 31.00 (978-0-7578-1663-5(0)) Rigby Education.

Tali Drives His Car: Small Book. (Pebble Soup Explorations Ser.). 16p. (ps up). 5.00 (978-0-7578-1703-8(3)) Rigby Education.

Tali Pasea en su Auto. (Pebble Soup Exploraciones Ser.). (SPA.). 16p. (ps up). 31.00 (978-0-7578-1687-1(8)) Rigby Education.

Tali pasea en su Auto: Small Book. (Pebble Soup Exploraciones Ser.). (SPA.). 16p. (ps up). 5.00 (978-0-7578-1727-4(0)) Rigby Education.

Tall Tales: Individual Chapter Book Title Six-Packs. Vol. 25. 32p. (gr. 3-4). 44.00 (978-0-7635-4474-4(4)) Rigby Education.

Tall Talk. (Sails Literacy Ser.). 24p. (gr. 2-3). 8.00 (978-0-7635-7036-1(2)) Rigby Education.

Tan, Lyn. We All Fall Down. 2002. (Wizard Study Guides Ser.). 84p. pap., stu. ed. 6.00 (978-1-876367-86-2(5)) Cambridge Univ. Pr.

Tap into Sap: Individual Title Six-Packs. (Rigby Infoquest Ser.). 24p. (gr. 3 up). 34.00 (978-0-7578-5780-5(9)) Rigby Education.

Tarantulas! Second Grade Guided Reading Level K. (On Our Way to English Ser.). (gr. 2 up). 34.50 (978-0-7578-7098-9(8)) Rigby Education.

Tasmanian Devils: Individual Title Six-Packs. 16p. (gr. 2 up). 36.00 (978-0-7635-9393-3(1)) Rigby Education.

Tatchell, Judy. Bugs & Slugs Lift-the-Flap. 2004. (Luxury Lift-the-Flap Ser.). 16p. (J). (gr. 1 up). 11.95 (978-0-7945-0762-6(X) , Usborne) EDC Publishing.

Tbd. I Am Iron Man. 2008. (I Can Read Bks.). 32p. (J). pap. 3.99 (***978-0-06-082193-7(0)*** , Harper Trophy) HarperCollins Pubs.

Te invito a mi Casa: 6 Small Books. (Saludos Ser.: Vol. 3). (SPA.). 24p. (gr. 2-3). 31.00 (978-0-7635-9529-6(2)) Rigby Education.

Te invito a mi Casa: Big Book. (Saludos Ser.: Vol. 3). (SPA.). 24p. (gr. 2-3). 31.00 (978-0-7635-5727-0(7)) Rigby Education.

Teamwork Saves the Day: Third Grade Guided Reading Level K. (On Our Way to English Ser.). (gr. 3 up). 34.50 (978-0-7578-7120-7(8)) Rigby Education.

Tecnicos en emergencias Medicas: Individual Title Six-Packs. (On Deck en Espanol Ser.).Tr. of Emergency Medical Technicians. (SPA.). 24p. (gr. 4-5). 35.00 (978-0-7578-6405-6(8)) Rigby Education.

Ted's Red Ball: Set B Individual Title, 6 packs. (gr. k-3). 29.00 (978-0-7635-0538-7(2)) Rigby Education.

Tell Me a Story, 6 Packs. (Rigby Infoquest Ser.). 32p. (gr. 4 up). 37.00 (978-0-7578-5740-9(X)) Rigby Education.

Tell Me How You Feel: Big Book. (Pebble Soup Explorations Ser.). 16p. (ps up). 31.00 (978-0-7578-1661-1(4)) Rigby Education.

Tell Me How You Feel: Small Book. (Pebble Soup Explorations Ser.). 16p. (ps up). 5.00 (978-0-7578-1701-4(7)) Rigby Education.

The Tempest Study Guide. 2003. (Illus.). 48p. (YA). per. 17.95 (978-1-56254-639-7(2) , SP6392) Saddleback Educational Publishing.

Tents: Individual Title Six-Packs. (Sails Literacy Ser.). (gr. 1-2). 36.00 (978-0-7578-6742-2(1)) Rigby Education.

The Test of Time: Individual Title Six-Packs. (Rigby Infoquest Ser.). (gr. 5 up). 37.00 (978-0-7578-6484-1(8)) Rigby Education.

Textures: KinderFacts Individual Title Six-Packs. (Kinderstarters Ser.). 8p. (ps-1). 21.00 (978-0-7635-8750-5(8)) Rigby Education.

Thaler, Mike. The Class Trip from the Black Lagoon. D. Lee, Jared, illus. 2004. (Black Lagoon Ser.). 64p. (J). pap. 3.99 (978-0-439-42927-6(7) , Scholastic Paperbacks) Scholastic, Inc.

—The Talent Show from the Black Lagoon. D. Lee, Jared, illus. 2004. (Black Lagoon Ser.). 64p. (J). pap. 3.99 (978-0-439-43894-0(2) , Scholastic Paperbacks) Scholastic, Inc.

That Is Math! First Grade Guided Reading Level D. (On Our Way to English Ser.). (gr. 1 up). 27.75 (978-0-7578-7041-5(4)) Rigby Education.

That Is Symmetry! First Grade Guided Reading Level E. (On Our Way to English Ser.). (gr. 1 up). 27.75 (978-0-7578-7046-0(5)) Rigby Education.

That's about Right: a Book about Estimating: Fifth Grade Guided Comprehension Level S. (On Our Way to English Ser.). (gr. 5 up). 34.50 (978-0-7578-6625-8(5)) Rigby Education.

A Theft in Time: Timedetectors II, 6 Pack. (Action Packs Ser.). 120p. (gr. 3-5). 44.00 (978-0-7635-8425-2(8)) Rigby Education.

Theme Packs for ELL: Complete Set. (gr. k-6). 203.00 (978-0-7635-2865-2(X)) Rigby Education.

Theme Packs for ELL: Early Fluent/Fluent Complete Set. (gr. k-6). 184.00 (978-0-7635-9991-1(3)); 262.00 (978-0-7635-9995-9(6)); 184.00 (978-0-7635-9999-7(9)); 218.00 (978-0-7635-2853-9(6)); 252.00 (978-0-7635-2862-1(5)); 262.00 (978-0-7635-2857-7(9)) Rigby Education.

Theme Packs for ELL: Early Fluent/Fluent Core Set. (gr. k-6). 175.00 (978-0-7635-9987-4(5)); 175.00 (978-0-7635-9994-2(8)); 175.00 (978-0-7635-2852-2(8)); 175.00 (978-0-7635-2861-4(7)); 175.00 (978-0-7635-2856-0(0)); 175.00 (978-0-7635-2868-3(4)) Rigby Education.

Theme Packs for ELL: Early to Fluent Core Set. (gr. k-6). 164.00 (978-0-7635-2864-5(1)) Rigby Education.

Theme Packs for ELL: Emergent to Early Fluent Core Set. (gr. k-6). 153.00 (978-0-7635-2866-9(8)) Rigby Education.

Theme Packs for ELL: Emergent/Early Complete Set. (gr. k-6). 186.00 (978-0-7635-9986-7(7)); 218.00 (978-0-7635-9990-4(5)); 148.00 (978-0-7635-9993-5(X)); 186.00 (978-0-7635-9998-0(0)); 148.00 (978-0-7635-2851-5(X)); 186.00 (978-0-7635-2860-7(9)) Rigby Education.

Theme Packs for ELL: Emergent/Early Core Set. (gr. k-6). 142.00 (978-0-7635-9985-0(9)); 142.00 (978-0-7635-9989-8(1)); 142.00 (978-0-7635-9997-3(2)); 142.00 (978-0-7635-2859-1(5)); 142.00 (978-0-7635-2855-3(2)) Rigby Education.

Theme Packs for ELL: Theme Pack Complete Set. (gr. k-6). 197.00 (978-0-7635-2867-6(6)); 301.00 (978-0-7635-2869-0(2)) Rigby Education.

Theme Packs for ELL: Theme Pack Super Set. (gr. k-6). 344.00 (978-0-7635-9988-1(3)); 383.00 (978-0-7635-9992-8(1)); 383.00 (978-0-7635-9996-6(4)); 349.00 (978-0-7635-2850-8(1)); 349.00 (978-0-7635-2854-6(4)); 415.00 (978-0-7635-2863-8(3)); 383.00 (978-0-7635-2858-4(7)) Rigby Education.

Then & Now, 6 Pack. (Discovery World Ser.). 16p. (gr. 1-2). 28.00 (978-0-7635-8463-4(0)) Rigby Education.

There Are Things I Don't Know: Fifth Grade Guided Comprehension Level R. (On Our Way to English Ser.). (gr. 5 up). 34.50 (978-0-7578-6619-7(0)) Rigby Education.

There Is No Water! Individual Title Six-Packs. (gr. k-1). 23.00 (978-0-7635-8849-6(0)) Rigby Education.

There's a Dinosaur (20), Vol. 20. (Early Intervention Levels Ser.). 4.73 (978-0-7362-0242-8(0)) Hampton-Brown Bks.

There's a Rainbow in the River: Individual Title Six-Packs. (gr. k-1). 23.00 (978-0-7635-8850-2(4)) Rigby Education.

Things I Need: First Grade Newcomer Books. (On Our Way to English Ser.). (gr. 1 up). 23.50 (978-0-7578-7202-0(6)) Rigby Education.

Things to Do. 2005. (Little Celebrations Thematic Packages Ser.). (J). (gr. k-3). 133.50 (978-0-673-75388-5(3)) Celebration Pr.

Think Twice, Be Nice: Social/Emotional Lap Book. (Pebble Soup Explorations Ser.). (ps up). 16.00 (978-0-7635-7570-0(4)) Rigby Education.

This & That, 6 Packs. (ps-2). 23.00 (978-0-7635-8812-0(1)) Rigby Education.

This Is for Me: First Wave Satellite Individual Title Six-Packs. (Sails Literacy Ser.). 16p. (gr. k up). 27.00 (978-0-7578-6857-3(6)) Rigby Education.

This Is My Family: First Grade Guided Reading Level C. (On Our Way to English Ser.). (gr. 1 up). 27.75 (978-0-7578-7035-4(X)) Rigby Education.

Thomas, Christine. Language Development Inquiry Research. 2004. 48p. pap. 6.95 (978-1-4042-8527-9(X)) Rosen Publishing Group, Inc., The.

—Language Development Variety Text. 2004. 48p. pap. 6.95 (978-1-4042-8525-5(3)) Rosen Publishing Group, Inc., The.

Thomas, Marian. Wrack. 2002. (Wizard Study Guides Ser.). 48p. pap., stu. ed. 6.00 (978-1-876367-52-7(0)) Cambridge Univ. Pr.

Thomas, Teri. Bus 99. 2004. (Illus.). 32p. (YA). 2.95 (978-1-56254-740-0(2) , SP7402) Saddleback Educational Publishing.

—Dimes to Dollars. 2004. (Illus.). 32p. (YA). 2.95 (978-1-56254-743-1(7) , SP7437) Saddleback Educational Publishing.

Thomas, Tyren Scott. The Sun. Phillips, Rick, illus. 2005. (ENG.). 28p. (J). (ps-3). per. 20.25 (978-1-4208-5722-1(3)) AuthorHouse.

Thompson, Kim Mitzo. Hello, How Are You? 2006. (Dual Language Readers Ser.). (ENG & SPA.). 32p. (J). pap., pap. 4.99 (978-0-7696-4615-2(8)) School Specialty Publishing.

Thompson, Lisa. On the Trail of the Golden Man. 2005. (Treasure Trackers Ser.). (Illus.). 80p. (gr. 5-9). 19.00 (978-0-7910-8875-3(8)) Facts On File, Inc.

Thomson, Sarah L. Amazing Tigers! 2005. (I Can Read Bks.). (Illus.). 32p. (J). pap. 3.99 (978-0-06-054452-2(X) , Harper Trophy) HarperCollins Pubs.

Those Amazingly Useful Ears. (Early Intervention Levels Ser.). 31.86 (978-0-7362-0669-3(8)) Hampton-Brown Bks.

Those Amazingly Useful Ears (28), Vol. 28. (Early Intervention Levels Ser.). 5.31 (978-0-7362-0657-0(4)) Hampton-Brown Bks.

Three: KinderFacts Individual Title Six-Packs. (Kinderstarters Ser.). 8p. (ps-1). 21.00 (978-0-7635-8751-2(6)) Rigby Education.

The Three Billy Goats Gruff. 2004. (J). (978-1-58453-274-3(2)) Pioneer Valley Educational Pr., Inc.

Three Jars Full, 6 Packs. (Rigby Focus Ser.). 16p. (gr. k up). 28.00 (978-0-7578-5532-0(6)); Pack. 26.00 (978-0-7578-5298-5(X)) Rigby Education.

The Thrill of the Ride 5-Pack. 2002. (Illus.). pap. 28.35 (978-0-7398-5078-7(4)) Steck-Vaughn.

Tides of Change: Individual Title Six-Packs. (Rigby Infoquest Ser.). (gr. 6 up). 37.00 (978-0-7578-7986-9(1)) Rigby Education.

Tiger & Monkey: Early Level Satellite Individual Title Six-Packs. (Sails Literacy Ser.). 16p. (gr. 1-2). 27.00 (978-0-7578-2923-9(6)) Rigby Education.

Tiger Woods, 6 vols. (gr. 4 up). 39.95 (978-0-7368-9279-7(6)) Red Brick Learning.

Time Capsule, 6 Packs. (Bookweb Ser.). 32p. (gr. 5 up). 34.00 (978-0-7635-3780-7(2)) Rigby Education.

Time for Lunch. (J). (978-0-8136-5355-6(X)) Modern Curriculum Pr.

Time for School. 2004. (J). (978-1-58453-265-1(3)) Pioneer Valley Educational Pr., Inc.

Time for Tea. (Early Intervention Levels Ser.). 21.30 (978-0-7362-0366-1(4)); Vol. 2. 3.55 (978-0-7362-0087-5(8)) Hampton-Brown Bks.

The Time Machine Student Packet, Gr. 7-8. 2004. (J). (978-1-58130-526-5(5)) Novel Units, Inc.

Time to Go: Kindergarten Guided Reading Level C. (On Our Way to English Ser.). (gr. k up). 27.75 (978-0-7578-7016-3(3)) Rigby Education.

Time Travelers: Individual Title Six-Packs. 32p. (gr. 5 up). 44.00 (978-0-7578-0989-7(8)) Rigby Education.

Timer for use with Fluent Reader. 2004. cd-rom 9.95 (978-1-59455-139-0(1)) Renaissance Learning, Inc.

Timmy: Individual Title Six-Packs. (Literatura 2000 Ser.). (gr. 1-2). 28.00 (978-0-7635-0067-2(4)) Rigby Education.

Tim's Bedtime: Set D Individual Title Six-Packs. (gr. k-3). 29.00 (978-0-7635-0548-6(X)) Rigby Education.

Tim's Paintings: Individual Title-Six Packs. (Chiquilibros Ser.). (gr. k-1). 23.00 (978-0-7635-0430-4(0)) Rigby Education.

Tim's Pumpkin: Individual Title Six-Packs. (gr. k-1). 23.00 (978-0-7635-9040-6(1)) Rigby Education.

Tin Lizzy: Individual Title Six-Packs. (gr. 1-2). 25.00 (978-0-7635-9147-2(5)) Rigby Education.

Tina Likes Tools: Lap Book. (Pebble Soup Explorations Ser.). 16p. (ps up). 21.00 (978-0-7578-1662-8(2)) Rigby Education.

Tina Likes Tools: Small Book. (Pebble Soup Explorations Ser.). 16p. (ps up). 5.00 (978-0-7578-1702-1(5)) Rigby Education.

TJ's Tree, 6 Packs. (Literatura 2000 Ser.). (gr. 1-2). 28.00 (978-0-7635-0116-7(6)) Rigby Education.

To Begin Again: Six-Pack. (Greetings Ser.: Vol. 3). (gr. 3-5). 31.00 (978-0-7635-2073-1(X)) Rigby Education.

To Market, to Market: Individual Title Six-Packs. (Rigby Infoquest Ser.). 24p. (gr. 3 up). 34.00 (978-0-7578-5782-9(5)) Rigby Education.

To the Other Side: Individual Chapter Book Title Six-Packs. Vol. 30. 32p. (gr. 5 up). 44.00 (978-0-7578-0981-1(2)) Rigby Education.

To the Rescue: Individual Title Six-Packs. (Rigby Infoquest Ser.). 32p. (gr. 4 up). 37.00 (978-0-7578-5741-6(8)) Rigby Education.

To Trade or Not to Trade: Fifth Grade Guided Comprehension Level T. (On Our Way to English Ser.). (gr. 5 up). 34.50 (978-0-7578-6632-6(8)) Rigby Education.

Toby at Stony Bay: Individual Title Six-Packs. 16p. (gr. 2 up). 35.00 (978-0-7635-9242-4(0)) Rigby Education.

Tolerance, 6 vols. (gr. 2-5). 36.95 (978-0-7368-9255-1(9)) Red Brick Learning.

Tom Sawyer: 6 Small Books. (gr. k-2). 23.00 (978-0-7635-8507-5(6)) Rigby Education.

Tomas & the Library Lady. (Guided Reading Levels Ser.). 8.48 (978-0-7362-1776-7(2)); 50.88 (978-0-7362-2175-7(1)) Hampton-Brown Bks.

Tomatoes Everywhere: Second Grade Guided Reading Level H. (On Our Way to English Ser.). (gr. 2 up). 34.50 (978-0-7578-7084-2(8)) Rigby Education.

Tommy's Treasure: Individual Title Six-Packs. (Literatura 2000 Ser.). (gr. 2-3). 33.00 (978-0-7635-0189-1(1)) Rigby Education.

Tommy's Tummy Ache: Individual Title Six-Packs. (Literatura 2000 Ser.). (ps-1). 28.00 (978-0-7635-0015-3(1)) Rigby Education.

Tondreau-Levert, Louise. When Nobody's Looking. St. Aubin, Bruno, illus. 2005. (Read-It! Readers Ser.). 32p. (J). (gr. k-3). 18.60 (978-1-4048-1068-6(4)) Picture Window Bks.

Tongues: Early Level Satellite Individual Title Six-Packs. (Sails Literacy Ser.). 16p. (gr. 1-2). 27.00 (978-0-7578-3161-4(3)) Rigby Education.

Too Many Tickets: Fifth Grade Guided Comprehension Level M. (On Our Way to English Ser.). (gr. 5 up). 34.50 (978-0-7578-6595-4(X)) Rigby Education.

Top Hat Big Bargains, 21 bks. (J). (gr. 1-6). 275.00 (978-0-8136-4013-6(X)); 250.00 (978-0-8136-4014-3(8)); 500.00 incl. cd-rom (978-0-8136-4015-0(6)) Modern Curriculum Pr.

Top That Publishing Staff, ed. What's My Job. 2005. 12p. bds. (978-1-84510-070-4(0)) Top That! Publishing PLC.

The Tortilla Factory. (Lexile Levels Ser.). 7.98 (978-1-56334-687-3(7)) Hampton-Brown Bks.

Touching, 6 vols. (gr. k-2). 28.95 (978-0-7368-8587-4(0)) Red Brick Learning.

Touching Spirit Bear Student Packet, Gr. 7-8. 2004. (J). (978-1-58130-528-9(1)) Novel Units, Inc.

Townsend, John. Clogging & Works. Jackson, Anita, ed. 1998. 48p. 22.00 (978-0-7487-3655-3(7)) Nelson Thornes Ltd. GBR. *Dist:* Trans-Atlantic Pubns., Inc.

—Spirals Stories: Back on the Prowl. Jackson, Anita, ed. 1998. 48p. 22.00 (978-0-7487-3654-6(9)) Nelson Thornes Ltd. GBR. *Dist:* Trans-Atlantic Pubns., Inc.

Toy. 2004. (J). per. (978-1-57657-474-4(1)) Paradise Pr., Inc.

Toyama, Setsuko. English Time. 2003. (Illus.). 48p. (J). (978-0-19-436441-6(0)) Oxford Univ. Pr., Inc.

—English Time Storybook 3: A Day at Storyland. 2002. (Illus.). (J). (978-0-19-436417-1(8)) Oxford Univ. Pr., Inc.

—English Time Storybook 4: A Medal for Ranger Day. 2002. (Illus.). 48p. (J). (978-0-19-436425-6(9)) Oxford Univ. Pr., Inc.

Toyama, Setsuko & Rivers, Susan. English Time Storybook 5: Digger & the Thief. 2003. (Illus.). 48p. (J). (978-0-19-436433-1(X)) Oxford Univ. Pr., Inc.

 For book reviews, descriptive annotations, tables of contents, cover images, author biographies & additional information, updated daily, subscribe to **www.booksinprint.com**

Tracking Wildlife with Frank Craighead. 2005. (Book Treks Ser.). (J). 37.95 (978-0-7652-3252-6(9)) Celebration Pr.

Trade Book Library, 12 bks., Set. 2004. (Trade Book Library). (gr. 6 up). 112.90 (978-0-673-60781-2(X)) Addison-Wesley Educational Pubs., Inc.

Trade Book Library Grade Level Package, 12 bks., Set. 2004. (Trade Book Library). (gr. 1 up). 112.90 (978-0-673-60776-8(3)); (gr. 2 up). 112.90 (978-0-673-60777-5(1)); (gr. 3 up). 112.90 (978-0-673-60778-2(X)); (gr. 4 up). 112.90 (978-0-673-60779-9(8)); (gr. 5 up). 112.90 (978-0-673-60780-5(1)) Addison-Wesley Educational Pubs., Inc.

Trade Book Library Resource Guide. 2004. (Trade Book Library Resource Guide Ser.). (gr. 6 up). 48.00 (978-0-673-63003-2(X)) Addison-Wesley Educational Pubs., Inc.

Traill, Lyn. Pobblebonk Reading 4. 10 the Glowing Ball. 2008. pap. (*978-0-521-71090-9(1)) Cambridge Univ. Pr.

—Pobblebonk Reading 4. 2 It's Fun to Fly. 2008. pap. (*978-0-521-71088-6(X)) Cambridge Univ. Pr.

—Pobblebonk Reading 4. 6 the Wild Child. 2008. pap. (*978-0-521-71089-3(8)) Cambridge Univ. Pr.

—Pobblebonk Reading 5. 1 Out of the Cage. 2008. pap. (*978-0-521-71091-6(X)) Cambridge Univ. Pr.

—Pobblebonk Reading 5. 3 It's Time. 2008. pap. (*978-0-521-71092-3(8)) Cambridge Univ. Pr.

—Pobblebonk Reading 5. 7 Make Believe. 2008. pap. (*978-0-521-71093-0(6)) Cambridge Univ. Pr.

—Pobblebonk Reading 6. 2 Yummy Food. 2008. pap. (*978-0-521-71094-7(4)) Cambridge Univ. Pr.

—Pobblebonk Reading 6. 5 Queen Bee. 2008. pap. (*978-0-521-71095-4(2)) Cambridge Univ. Pr.

Train Time. (Early Intervention Levels Ser.). 31.86 (978-0-7362-0618-1(3)) Hampton-Brown Bks.

Train Time (16), Vol. 16. (Early Intervention Levels Ser.). 5.31 (978-0-7362-0606-8(X)) Hampton-Brown Bks.

Tran & the Beautiful Tree: First Grade Big Books. (On Our Way to English Ser.). (gr. 1 up). 29.95 (978-0-7578-1515-7(4)) Rigby Education.

Tran & the Beautiful Tree: Small Versions of Big Books. (On Our Way to English Ser.). (gr. 1 up). 29.00 (978-0-7578-7231-0(X)) Rigby Education.

Travelers & Traders: Level P, 6 vols., Vol. 2. (Explorers Ser.). 32p. (gr. 3-6). 44.95 (978-0-7699-0611-9(7)) Shortland Pubns. (U. S. A.) Inc.

Traveling in America: Fourth Grade Guided Comprehension Level L. (On Our Way to English Ser.). (gr. 4 up). 34.50 (978-0-7578-7154-2(2)) Rigby Education.

Treasure Hunting: Looking for Lost Riches, 6 vols. (gr. 4 up). 49.95 (978-0-7368-2835-2(4) , High Five) Red Brick Learning.

The Treasure on Fraser Street: Individual Title Six-Packs. (gr. k-1). 23.00 (978-0-7635-9068-0(1)) Rigby Education.

Trimarco, Paola. Gucci, Level 2. 2001. (Illus.). 32p. (C). pap. 9.00 (978-0-582-46159-8(6)) Longman Publishing Group.

Trimmer, Joseph. A&M Kingsville: English Reader. 2002. pap. 33.95 (978-0-8384-7439-6(X)) Thomson Heinle.

—Composition & Literature Reader. 2002. pap. 19.95 (978-0-8384-7387-0(3)) Thomson Heinle.

Trip to Mini Town. (J). pap. 13.15 (978-0-8136-4331-1(7)) Modern Curriculum Pr.

Trouble at Laura's House. 2005. (J). (978-1-58453-291-0(2)) Pioneer Valley Educational Pr., Inc.

Trouble for Jasper. 2004. (ACE.). (J). (978-1-58453-286-6(6)) Pioneer Valley Educational Pr., Inc.

Trouble on the Trail: Fourth Grade Guided Comprehension Level P. (On Our Way to English Ser.). (gr. 4 up). 34.50 (978-0-7578-7170-2(4)) Rigby Education.

Truman, Dennay H. The Happy Endings. 2007. 65p. per. 8.95 (*978-1-59824-435-9(3)) E-BookTime LLC.

Trumbauer, Lisa. Comiendo Bien. Ramos, Gloria, tr. 2005. (SPA., Illus.). 20p. (J). 15.93 (978-0-7368-4159-7(8) , Yellow Umbrella Bks.) Capstone Pr., Inc.

The Truth about Red Allen. 2003. (Illus.). pap. 7.60 (978-0-7398-7521-6(3)) Steck-Vaughn.

Tsunami: MainSails Individual Title Six-Packs. (Sails Literacy Ser.). (gr. 5 up). 37.00 (978-0-7578-8046-9(0)) Rigby Education.

Tuck Everlasting: Student Response Journal. 2002. 28p. (J). (978-1-58049-947-7(3) , RJ72) Prestwick Hse., Inc.

Un Tuffo Nel Mistero. 2000. (ITA., Illus.). 70p. (YA). (gr. 8-10). pap. 11.95 (978-88-8148-334-1(3)) European Language Institute ITA. *Dist:* Distribooks, Inc., Mid-west European Pubns.

Tuminelly, Nancy. -Est As in Nest. 2003. (Word Families Ser.). (Illus.). 23p. (J). (ps-3). lib. bdg. 19.93 (978-1-59197-232-7(9) , SandCastle) ABDO Publishing Co.

—Ook As in Hook. 2003. (Word Families Ser.). (Illus.). 23p. (J). (ps-3). lib. bdg. 19.93 (978-1-59197-268-6(X) , SandCastle) ABDO Publishing Co.

—Ub As in Tub. 2003. (Word Families Ser.). (Illus.). 23p. (J). (ps-3). lib. bdg. 19.93 (978-1-59197-242-6(6) , SandCastle) ABDO Publishing Co.

—Uck As in Duck. 2003. (Word Families Ser.). (Illus.). 23p. (J). (ps-3). lib. bdg. 19.93 (978-1-59197-247-1(7) , SandCastle) ABDO Publishing Co.

—Uff As in Cuff. 2003. (Word Families Ser.). (Illus.). 23p. (J). (ps-3). lib. bdg. 19.93 (978-1-59197-246-4(9) , SandCastle) ABDO Publishing Co.

—Ug As in Bug. 2003. (Word Families Ser.). (Illus.). 23p. (J). (ps-3). lib. bdg. 19.93 (978-1-59197-243-3(4) , SandCastle) ABDO Publishing Co.

—Um As in Drum. Marx, Monica, ed. 2003. (Word Families Ser.). (Illus.). 23p. (J). (ps-3). lib. bdg. 19.93 (978-1-59197-244-0(2)) ABDO Publishing Co.

—Ump As in Jump. 2003. (Word Families Ser.). (Illus.). 23p. (J). (ps-3). lib. bdg. 19.93 (978-1-59197-245-7(0) , SandCastle) ABDO Publishing Co.

The Tune of the Hickory Stick. 2004. (YA). per. 10.92 (978-1-56870-503-3(4)) RonJon Publishing, Inc.

The Tunnel: First Wave Satellite Individual Title Six-Packs. (Sails Literacy Ser.). 16p. (gr. k up). 27.00 (978-0-7578-6860-3(6)) Rigby Education.

Turbulent Planet Series, 9 vols., Set. 2004. (Illus.). pap. 68.85 (978-1-4109-1397-5(X)) Harcourt Schl. Pubs.

The Turkey: First Wave Satellite Individual Title Six-Packs. (Sails Literacy Ser.). 16p. (gr. k up). 27.00 (978-0-7578-6875-7(4)) Rigby Education.

Turquoise, Purple & Gold Levels Certificate Only. (Sails Literacy Ser.). (gr. 1-6). 89.00 (978-0-7578-6556-5(9)) Rigby Education.

Twine, Sheila. Comprehension Lifters Bk. 1: High Interest Skill Builders, 4 vols. 2000. 48p. pap. 6.95 (978-1-58324-047-2(0) , World Teachers Pr.) Didax Educational Resources, Inc.

—Comprehension Lifters Bk. 2: High Interest Skill Builders, 4 vols. 2000. 48p. pap. 6.95 (978-1-58324-048-9(9) , World Teachers Pr.) Didax Educational Resources, Inc.

—Comprehension Lifters Bk. 3: High Interest Skill Builders, 4 vols. 2000. 48p. pap. 6.95 (978-1-58324-049-6(7) , World Teachers Pr.) Didax Educational Resources, Inc.

—Comprehension Lifters Bk. 4: High Interest Skill Builders, 4 vols. 2000. 48p. pap. 6.95 (978-1-58324-050-2(0) , World Teachers Pr.) Didax Educational Resources, Inc.

Twisters & Drenchers: Magazine Anthology: Level 5, 6 vols. (Comprehension Strand Ser.). (gr. 4-8). 54.00 (978-0-322-06038-8(9)) Wright Group, The.

Uhler, Karen. The 10 Worst Natural Disasters. 2008. (Ten-tade; Ser.). 48p. (J). pap. 14.99 (*978-1-55448-469-0(3) , Watts, Franklin) Scholastic Library Publishing.

Unbelievable! (Early Intervention Levels Ser.). 31.86 (978-0-7362-0671-6(X)) Hampton-Brown Bks.

Unbelievable! (28), Vol. 28. (Early Intervention Levels Ser.). 5.31 (978-0-7362-0659-4(0)) Hampton-Brown Bks.

Uncle Jim: Individual Title Six-Packs. (gr. 1-2). 25.00 (978-0-7635-9196-0(3)) Rigby Education.

Uncle Tom's Cabin Student Packet, Gr. 9-12. 2004. (YA). (978-1-58130-870-9(1)) Novel Units, Inc.

Under Lock & Key: Fourth Grade Guided Comprehension Level R. (On Our Way to English Ser.). (gr. 4 up). 34.50 (978-0-7578-7181-8(X)) Rigby Education.

Under the Canopy: Fourth Grade Class Collection Books. (On Our Way to English Ser.). (gr. 4 up). 29.95 (978-0-7578-4342-6(5)) Rigby Education.

Under the Canopy: Small Versions of Class Collection Books. (On Our Way to English Ser.). (gr. 4 up). 34.50 (978-0-7578-7270-9(0)) Rigby Education.

Under the Umbrella. (Early Intervention Levels Ser.). 21.30 (978-0-7362-0382-1(6)); Vol. 4. 3.55 (978-0-7362-0103-2(3)) Hampton-Brown Bks.

Understanding Literature: The EMC Write-in Reader. 2nd ed. (Literature & the Language Arts Ser.). (YA). (gr. 10 up). wbk. ed. 15.95 (978-0-8219-2916-2(X)) EMC/Paradigm Publishing.

Unearthing the Past: Fourth Grade Class Collection Books. (On Our Way to English Ser.). (gr. 4 up). 29.95 (978-0-7578-4340-2(9)) Rigby Education.

Unearthing the Past: Small Versions of Class Collection Books. (On Our Way to English Ser.). (gr. 4 up). 34.50 (978-0-7578-7271-6(9)) Rigby Education.

Unidad 1 Superlibro: Juan y sus Zapatos. 1999. (McGraw-Hill. Lectura Ser.). (ENG & SPA.). (gr. 2 up). (978-0-02-110169-6(8)) Macmillan/McGraw-Hill Schl. Div.

Unidad 1 Superlibro: un sillon para Mama. 1999. (McGraw-Hill. Lectura Ser.). (ENG & SPA.). (gr. 2 up). (978-0-02-110168-9(X)) Macmillan/McGraw-Hill Schl. Div.

Unifix Cubes & Flip Books Set 800913, 2 vols. 2005. (J). pap. (978-1-59794-078-8(X)) Environments, Inc.

Unit Activity Books: 2-Book Set; Consumable First Grade. (On Our Way to English Ser.). (gr. 1 up). 15.00 (978-0-7578-6767-5(7)) Rigby Education.

Unit Activity Books: 2-Book Set; Consumable Kindergarten. (On Our Way to English Ser.). (gr. k up). 15.00 (978-0-7578-6766-8(9)) Rigby Education.

Up & Away: Level P, 6 vols., Vol. 2. (Explorers Ser.). 32p. (gr. 3-6). 44.95 (978-0-7699-0607-2(9)) Shortland Pubns. (U. S. A.) Inc.

Up Cloudy Mountain: MainSails Individual Title Six-Packs. (Sails Literacy Ser.). (gr. 5 up). 37.00 (978-0-7578-8057-5(6)) Rigby Education.

Upper Emergent Guided Reading, Vol. 3. (gr. 1 up). 435.50 (978-0-7802-9342-7(8)) Wright Group, The.

USB Headset & microphone for use with Fluent Reader. 2004. cd-rom 99.95 (978-1-59455-140-6(5)) Renaissance Learning, Inc.

Use Your Head: Social/Emotional Lap Book. (Pebble Soup Explorations Ser.). (ps up). 16.00 (978-0-7635-7571-7(2)) Rigby Education.

Using Technology: Third Grade Newcomer Books. (On Our Way to English Ser.). (gr. 3 up). 29.50 (978-0-7578-7255-6(7)) Rigby Education.

A Vacation Journal: Individual Title Six-Packs. (Discovery World Ser.). 24p. (gr. 1-2). 33.00 (978-0-7635-8469-6(X)) Rigby Education.

Vallejo, Fernando. El Desbarrancadero. 2001. (SPA., Illus.). 224p. 18.95 (978-84-204-4292-1(5)) Alfaguara, Ediciones, S.A.- Grupo Santillana ESP. *Dist:* Bilingual Pubns. Co., The, Santillana USA Publishing Co., Inc.

—El Desbarrancadero. 2005. (SPA.). 197p. pap. 18.95 (978-958-8061-62-7(8) , Alfaguara) Santillana USA Publishing Co., Inc.

The Van. (Early Intervention Levels Ser.). 21.30 (978-0-7362-0372-2(9)); Vol. 4. 3.55 (978-0-7362-0093-6(2)) Hampton-Brown Bks.

Van Heerden, Marjorie. Baobab: Lunda Version. Kambangaji, Thomson, tr. 1998. (Cambridge African Language Library Ser.). 8p. pap. 3.75 (978-0-521-64729-8(0)) Cambridge Univ. Pr.

—Frog: Lunda Version. Kambangaji, Thomson, tr. 1998. (Cambridge African Language Library Ser.). (Illus.). 8p. pap. 3.75 (978-0-521-64750-2(9)) Cambridge Univ. Pr.

VanLeeuwen. Reading Comprehension Grade 4. 2003. (Skill Builders Ser.). 80p. (gr. 4 up). 2.95 (978-1-932210-06-4(7)) Rainbow Bridge Publishing.

—Reading Comprehension Grade 6. 2003. (Skill Builders Ser.). 80p. (gr. 6 up). 2.95 (978-1-932210-08-8(3)) Rainbow Bridge Publishing.

—Reading Connection Grade 4. 2003. (Reading Connection Ser.). 96p. (gr. 4 up). 8.95 (978-1-932210-19-4(9)) Rainbow Bridge Publishing.

—Reading Connection Grade 5. 2003. (Reading Connection Ser.). 96p. (gr. 5 up). 8.95 (978-1-932210-20-0(2)) Rainbow Bridge Publishing.

—Reading Connection Grade 6. 2003. (Reading Connection Ser.). 96p. (gr. 6 up). 8.95 (978-1-932210-21-7(0)) Rainbow Bridge Publishing.

Vargas Llosa, Mario. Historia de Mayta. 2005. (SPA., Illus.). 376p. pap. 19.95 (978-84-204-8415-0(6) , Alfaguara) Santillana USA Publishing Co., Inc.

Varios. El Aprendiz de Brujo. 2001. (SPA.). 146p. (978-970-651-562-9(3) , 1600) Editorial Oceano De Mexico, S.A. DE C.V.

A Vet Set, 6 vols. (Phonics Readers Ser.). (gr. k-2). 17.50 (978-0-7368-3193-2(2)) Red Brick Learning.

Vigne, Elaine W. Jazzgator. 2001. 32p. (J). pap. 8.00 (978-0-8059-4978-0(X)) Dorrance Publishing Co., Inc.

Viljoen, Graeme. Eggs: Lunda Version. Kambangaji, Thomson, tr. 1998. (Cambridge African Language Library Ser.). (Illus.). 8p. pap. 3.75 (978-0-521-64736-6(3)) Cambridge Univ. Pr.

Viljoen, Graeme & Sayifwanda. Eggs: Lunda Version. 2001. (Illus.). 8p. pap. 0.45 (978-0-521-01454-0(9)) Cambridge Univ. Pr.

Villafane-Leon, Ines. A Story for All Seasons: Un Cuento Para Cada Estacion: Immigration of One. 2004. (ENG & SPA.). xiii, 367p. (YA). pap. 22.95 (978-1-882897-78-0(1)) Lost Coast Pr.

Viney, Peter. The Collector. 1998. (Illus.). 24p. (J). 4.95 (978-0-19-421954-9(2)) Oxford Univ. Pr., Inc.

Viva Mexico! 2000. (Metro Reading Ser.). (J). (gr. 12). 5.58 (978-1-58120-839-9(1)) Metropolitan Teaching & Learning Co.

Viverso Lee, Hector. I Had a Hippopotamus-Little Book. 2000. (Metro Reading Ser.). (J). (gr. k). 10.55 (978-1-58120-962-4(2)) Metropolitan Teaching & Learning Co.

The Volcano Awakes! MainSails Individual Title Six-Packs. (Sails Literacy Ser.). (gr. 5 up). 37.00 (978-0-7578-8042-1(8)) Rigby Education.

Volcano Man: Fourth Grade Guided Comprehension Level O. (On Our Way to English Ser.). (gr. 4 up). 34.50 (978-0-7578-7168-9(2)) Rigby Education.

von Bissing, Ronimund. La Tierra del Oro Ardiente. (SPA.). (978-84-216-1631-4(5) , BU4764) Bruño, Editorial ESP. *Dist:* Lectorum Pubns., Inc.

Vonthron, Satanta C. Marsy's Perfect Eyesight. Teeple, Jackie, illus. l.t. ed. 2005. (J). (ps-k). pap. 10.95 (978-1-57332-344-4(6)); pap. 10.95 (978-1-57332-345-1(4)) HighReach Learning, Inc.

La Voz del Feminismo Socialista. 2001. (Red Banner Reader Ser.). (SPA.). 68p. 5.00 (978-0-932323-15-6(4)) Red Letter Pr.

Waddell, Martin. Something So Big. Canty, Charlotte, illus. 2004. 24p. (J). lib. bdg. 22.65 (*978-1-59646-706-4(1)) Dingles & Co.

Waddell, Martin, et al. Crazy Castles. 2007. (I-read Ser.). (Illus.). 40p. pap. (*978-0-521-70474-8(X)) Cambridge Univ. Pr.

Wade, Lee. The Cheerios Animal Play Book. Wade, Lee, illus. 1999. (Illus.). 14p. (J). bds. 7.99 (978-0-689-83014-3(9) , Little Simon) Simon & Schuster Children's Publishing.

Waiting in Line: Individual Title Six-Packs. (ps-2). 27.00 (978-0-7635-9480-0(6)) Rigby Education.

Walbruck, Rita M. Auf Heiber Spur, Erlebnisse in Deutschland: Das Ratsel vom Waldsee, Reader 2. (GER., Illus.). 40p. (J). 3.95 (978-0-88436-851-9(3) , 45255) EMC/Paradigm Publishing.

Walch Staff. Assessment Strategies for Reading. 2003. 86p. 24.99 (978-0-8251-4477-6(9)) Walch Publishing.

A Walk for Jasper. 2004. (J). (978-1-58453-280-4(7)) Pioneer Valley Educational Pr., Inc.

Walker, Colin, et al. Explorando el Espacio. (Coleccion Conceptos de Ciencia en Big Books). (SPA., Illus.). (J). (gr. k-3). 12.00 (978-0-8136-6756-0(9) , MD7215) Modern Curriculum Pr.

—La Tierra Cambia. (Coleccion Conceptos de Ciencia en Big Books). (SPA., Illus.). (J). (gr. k-3). 12.00 (978-0-8136-6729-4(1) , MD7205) Modern Curriculum Pr.

Wallace, Karen. Las Crias del Mundo Animal. 2005. (Dk Readers Ser.). 32p. (J). pap. 3.99 (978-0-7566-1197-2(0)) Dorling Kindersley Publishing, Inc.

Wallaker, Jillayne Prince. Reading for Understanding (5-6) High Interest Activities to Boost Comprehension. 2002. 128p. pap. 10.99 (978-0-88724-761-3(X) , CD-4304) Carson-Dellosa Publishing Co., Inc.

Walter Dragons. (Investigating Ancient Civilizations Ser.). (J). 16.80 (978-0-8136-6342-5(3)) Modern Curriculum Pr.

The War Shirt: Six-Pack. (Greetings Ser.: Vol. 2). 24p. (gr. 2-3). 31.00 (978-0-7635-9413-8(X)) Rigby Education.

War Torn. 2003. (Illus.). pap. 5.60 (978-0-7398-7515-5(9)) Steck-Vaughn.

Ward, Allison, ed. Learning Library-Getting Ready for Reading. 2003. 128p. 19.95 (978-1-56234-540-2(0) , Mailbox Bks., The) Education Ctr., Inc.

Ward, Sally. Dorothy's Visit: Ateso Version. Ejalu, Ateker & Omare-Okurut, Augustine, trs. 1998. (Cambridge African Language Library Ser.). (Illus.). 16p. pap. 3.65 (978-0-521-63790-9(2)) Cambridge Univ. Pr.

—Dorothy's Visit: Lunda Version. Kambangaji, Thomson, tr. 1998. (Cambridge African Language Library Ser.). (Illus.). 16p. pap. 3.70 (978-0-521-63833-3(X)) Cambridge Univ. Pr.

Warren, Celia. Ready for a Picnic. 2004. (QEB Start Reading Ser.). (Illus.). 24p. (J). lib. bdg. 15.95 (978-1-59566-015-2(1)) QEB Publishing Inc.

Watch me Zoom: Individual Title Six-Packs. (gr. 1-2). 22.00 (978-0-7635-9172-4(6)) Rigby Education.

Watcyn-Jones, Peter. Fun Class Activities. 2004. 96p. (C). pap. 32.00 (978-0-582-42785-3(1)) Pearson ESL.

Water: First Grade Guided Reading Level E. (On Our Way to English Ser.). (gr. 1 up). 27.75 (978-0-7578-7047-7(3)) Rigby Education.

Water All Around the Earth: Fifth Grade Guided Comprehension Level P. (On Our Way to English Ser.). (gr. 5 up). 34.50 (978-0-7578-6611-1(5)) Rigby Education.

The Water Caller. 2003. (Illus.). pap. 7.60 (978-0-7398-7529-2(9)) Steck-Vaughn.

Water Detective: Second Grade. (On Our Way to English Ser.). (gr. 2 up). 29.95 (978-0-7578-1421-1(2)) Rigby Education.

Water Detective: Small Versions of Big Books. (On Our Way to English Ser.). (gr. 2 up). 29.00 (978-0-7578-7239-6(5)) Rigby Education.

Water Is Everywhere: Second Grade Newcomer Books. (On Our Way to English Ser.). (gr. 2 up). 29.50 (978-0-7578-7213-6(1)) Rigby Education.

Water Wise, 6 Pack. (Rigby Infoquest Ser.). (gr. 5 up). 37.00 (978-0-7578-6478-0(3)) Rigby Education.

Watermelon. (Early Intervention Levels Ser.). 23.10 (978-0-7362-0038-7(X)); Vol. 6. 3.85 (978-1-56334-985-0(X)) Hampton-Brown Bks.

Watson. The Ghosts of Izieu, Level 3. 2000. (Illus.). v, 41p. (C). pap. 9.00 (978-0-582-42654-2(5)) Longman Publishing Group.

Watt, Fiona. Fairies. Cartwright, Stephen & Bird, Glen, illus. 2004. 10p. (J). (ps-ps). per. 15.95 (978-0-7945-0811-1(1) , Usborne) EDC Publishing.

—That's Not My Fairy. Wells, Rachel, illus. 2004. 10p. (J). 9.99 (978-0-7945-0793-0(X) , Usborne) EDC Publishing.

—That's Not My Monster. Wells, Rachel, illus. 2004. 10p. (J). 7.99 (978-0-7945-0818-0(9) , Usborne) EDC Publishing.

—Ya Se Hacer Lazos. Cartwright, Stephen, illus. 2005. (SPA.). 10p. (J). 7.95 (978-0-7460-6626-3(0) , Usborne) EDC Publishing.

Watt, Suzanna Mayer. Simple Symbol Stories for Beginning Readers, 2 vols., Vol. 2. 2000. 292p. spiral bd. 34.00 (978-1-884135-48-4(X)) Mayer-Johnson LLC.

Wax, Wendy. Phonics Comics: Sugar & Spice. 2007. 24p. (J). (gr. 1). pap. 3.99 (*978-1-58476-614-8(X) , IKIDS) Innovative Kids.

The Way Things Move Set. (gr. k-2). 172.95 (978-0-7368-9054-0(8)) Red Brick Learning.

We Are Working: First Grade Guided Reading Level B. (On Our Way to English Ser.). (gr. 1 up). 27.75 (978-0-7578-7033-0(3)) Rigby Education.

We Can: KinderWords Individual Title Six-Packs. (Kinderstarters Ser.). 8p. (ps-1). 21.00 (978-0-7635-8710-9(9)) Rigby Education.

We Can Be Helpers! First Grade Guided Reading Level G. (On Our Way to English Ser.). (gr. 1 up). 27.75 (978-0-7578-7059-0(7)) Rigby Education.

We Can Do It! Individual Title, 6 packs. (Rigby Focus Ser.). 16p. (gr. k up). 28.00 (978-0-7578-5511-5(3)) Rigby Education.

We Can Do It! Individual Title Six-Packs. (Rigby Focus Ser.). 16p. (gr. k up). 26.00 (978-0-7578-5277-0(7)) Rigby Education.

We Can Measure! Second Grade Guided Reading Level F. (On Our Way to English Ser.). (gr. 2 up). 34.50 (978-0-7578-7072-9(4)) Rigby Education.

We Clean Up! 6 Packs. (ps-2). 23.00 (978-0-7635-8813-7(X)) Rigby Education.

We Come from Everywhere: Second Grade Newcomer Books. (On Our Way to English Ser.). (gr. 2 up). 29.50 (978-0-7578-7210-5(7)) Rigby Education.

We Want Watermelon. (Early Intervention Levels Ser.). 21.30 (978-0-7362-0373-9(7)); Vol. 2. 3.55 (978-0-7362-0094-3(0)) Hampton-Brown Bks.

The Weather: First Grade Newcomer Books. (On Our Way to English Ser.). (gr. 1 up). 23.50 (978-0-7578-7205-1(0)) Rigby Education.

Weather Alert! MainSails Individual Title, 6 packs. (Sails Literacy Ser.). (gr. 5 up). 37.00 (978-0-7578-8044-5(4)) Rigby Education.

The Weather Engine, 6 Packs. (Rigby Infoquest Ser.). (gr. 6 up). 37.00 (978-0-7578-7994-4(2)) Rigby Education.

Weather Words. (Early Intervention Levels Ser.). 8.48 (978-0-7362-1728-6(2)); 50.88 (978-0-7362-2154-2(9)) Hampton-Brown Bks.

Weaver, Kimberley & Murphy, Allyson. Pack Your Bags... Go U. S. A. Holdren, Maria K., illus. 2005. (J). 15.99 (978-0-9767351-0-6(5)) Sorella Bks.

Wee Whopper: Individual Title Six-Packs. (gr. 1-2). 25.00 (978-0-7635-9139-7(4)) Rigby Education.

Wehner, Isabella D. Easy to Read Treasures to Open. 1999. 79p. (J). pap. 10.95 (978-0-7414-0018-5(9)) Infinity Publishing.

Weinberger, Kimberly. Splat. 2000. (Teacher's Pet Ser.: Vol. 1). (J). pap. 4.95 (978-0-439-13244-2(4)) Scholastic, Inc.

—Vibes. 2000. (Teacher's Pet Ser.: Vol. 3). (J). pap. 4.95 (978-0-439-13246-6(0)) Scholastic, Inc.

Weiss, Bobbi. Hiro: Dragon Warrior. Short, Robbie, illus. 2007. 24p. (J). (gr. 1). pap. 3.99 (*978-1-58476-616-2(6) , IKIDS) Innovative Kids.

Welch, Ruth. Our Camping Trip: Level G, 6 Packs. (Lighthouse Ser.). 12p. (gr. 1 up). 26.00 (978-0-7578-0840-1(9)) Rigby Education.

Welcome BooksTM. 2004. 4. 14.50 (978-0-516-27709-7(X)); Vol. 5. 348.00 (978-0-516-27710-3(3)) Scholastic Library Publishing.

Welcome to Our Home. (Early Intervention Levels Ser.). 4.73 (978-0-7362-1724-8(X)); 28.38 (978-0-7362-2152-8(2)) Hampton-Brown Bks.

Welcome to the Zigzag Zoo. (Early Intervention Levels Ser.). 21.30 (978-0-7362-0375-3(3)); Vol. 3. 3.55 (978-0-7362-0096-7(7)) Hampton-Brown Bks.

Wells, H. G. The Island of Dr Moreau. 2007. (Illus.). vii, 54p. (C). pap. 9.00 (***978-1-4058-4999-9(1)***) Pearson ESL.

Wells, James. Stuffy, the Short-Neck Giraffe Who Liked Peanut Butter. 2006. 9.00 (978-0-8059-9174-1(3)) Dorrance Publishing Co., Inc.

Wells, Rosemary. Max's Work of Art: A Coloring & Activity Book. 2008. (Max & Ruby Ser.). 16p. (J). (ps-k). 4.99 (***978-0-448-44785-8(1)*** , Grosset & Dunlap) Penguin Group (USA) Inc.

Wells, Rosemary. Ready to Read: Based on Timothy Goes to School & Other Stories. 2001. (978-0-606-22481-9(5)) Tandem Library Bks.

Welsh Books Staff. Llyfr Lliwio Sali Mali. 2nd ed. 2005. (WEL., Illus.). 22p. (978-1-902416-88-5(0)) Cymdeithas Lyfrau Ceredigion.

Wernham, Sara. Jolly Readers, Vol. 4. 2008. (J). pap. 10.95 (978-1-84414-061-9(X)) Jolly Learning, Ltd. GBR. *Dist:* American International Distribution Corp.

—Jolly Readers Level 1 General Fiction Level 1: 6 Titles in a Pack, 6 vols. 2002. 8p. (J). 8.50 (978-1-903619-60-5(2) , JL602) Jolly Learning, Ltd. GBR. *Dist:* American International Distribution Corp.

—Jolly Readers Level 1 Inky & Friends Level 1: 6 Titles in a Pack, 6 vols. 2002. 8p. (J). 8.50 (978-1-903619-47-6(5) , JL475) Jolly Learning, Ltd. GBR. *Dist:* American International Distribution Corp.

—Jolly Readers Level 1 Nonfiction Level 1: 6 Titles in a Pack, 6 vols. 2002. 8p. (J). 8.50 (978-1-903619-73-5(4) , JL734) Jolly Learning, Ltd. GBR. *Dist:* American International Distribution Corp.

—Jolly Readers Level 3 Inky & Friends, Vol. 3. 2005. (J). 10.95 (978-1-84414-008-4(3)) Jolly Learning, Ltd. GBR. *Dist:* American International Distribution Corp.

Wesson, André. Mrs. Applebee & the Sunshine Band, Book 1: Meet the Class! 2007. 48p. pap. 18.40 (***978-0-615-14849-6(2)***) Se7enth Swan Publishing Group, LLC.

West, Colin. Have You Seen the Crocodile. West, Colin, illus. 2003. (Reading Together Ser.). (Illus.). 32p. (J). (ps). pap. 3.99 (978-0-7636-0862-0(9)) Candlewick Pr.

West, Tracey. Monsters Unleashed: Reader. 2004. (Scooby-Doo Ser.). (Illus.). 32p. (J). pap. 3.99 (978-0-439-56879-1(X) , Scholastic Paperbacks) Scholastic, Inc.

What a Century! Individual Title Six-Packs. (Rigby Infoquest Ser.). (gr. 5 up). 37.00 (978-0-7578-6491-9(0)) Rigby Education.

What a Day! (Early Intervention Levels Ser.). 28.38 (978-0-7362-0418-7(0)) Hampton-Brown Bks.

What a Day! (24), Vol. 24. (Early Intervention Levels Ser.). 4.73 (978-0-7362-0243-5(9)) Hampton-Brown Bks.

What a Load of Garbage: Individual Title Six-Pack Pouch - Level L. (Lighthouse Ser.). 16p. (gr. 2 up). 28.00 (978-0-7578-0874-6(3)) Rigby Education.

What a Mess!, 6, Pack. (Chiquilibros Ser.). (gr. k-1). 23.00 (978-0-7635-0410-6(6)) Rigby Education.

What a Week! (Early Intervention Levels Ser.). 7.16 (978-0-7362-1906-8(4)); 42.96 (978-0-7362-2129-0(8)) Hampton-Brown Bks.

What Am I? Individual Title Six-Packs. (Story Steps Ser.). (gr. k-2). 29.00 (978-0-7635-9593-7(4)) Rigby Education.

What Are the Seasons Like? Kindergarten Big Books. (On Our Way to English Ser.). (gr. k up). 29.95 (978-0-7578-1624-6(X)) Rigby Education.

What Are the Seasons Like? Small Versions of Big Books. (On Our Way to English Ser.). (gr. k up). 29.00 (978-0-7578-7222-8(0)) Rigby Education.

What are We Doing? KinderWords Individual Title Six-Packs. (Kinderstarters Ser.). 8p. (ps-1). 21.00 (978-0-7635-8697-3(8)) Rigby Education.

What Bear Cubs Like to Do. 2005. (Early Library). (YA). (ps-3). 23.94 (978-0-8215-8953-3(9)) Sadlier, William H. Inc.

What Can Change the Land? Fourth Grade Newcomer Books. (On Our Way to English Ser.). (gr. 4 up). 34.50 (978-0-7578-7259-4(X)) Rigby Education.

What Can Float? (Little Book Practice Reader). (J). (978-0-8136-5354-9(1)) Modern Curriculum Pr.

What can Hurt?, 6 Packs. (gr. 1-2). 22.00 (978-0-7635-9088-8(6)) Rigby Education.

What Can I Do?, 6 Packs. (Greetings Ser.: Vol. 1). (gr. 2-3). 31.00 (978-0-7635-9425-1(3)) Rigby Education.

What can Jump?, 6, Pack. (gr. 1-2). 22.00 (978-0-7635-9114-4(9)) Rigby Education.

What Can Swim?, 6, Pack. (gr. 1-2). 22.00 (978-0-7635-9089-5(4)) Rigby Education.

What Can We Smell?, 6, Pack. (gr. 1-2). 22.00 (978-0-7635-9115-1(7)) Rigby Education.

What Can You Do with a Ball of String?, 6, Pack. (gr. k-1). 23.00 (978-0-7635-9027-7(4)) Rigby Education.

What Can You Make? (J). (978-0-8136-5373-0(8)) Modern Curriculum Pr.

What Can You Taste?, 6, Pack. (gr. 1-2). 22.00 (978-0-7635-9116-8(5)) Rigby Education.

What Could It Be? Big Book. (Pebble Soup Explorations Ser.). 16p. (ps up). 31.00 (978-0-7578-1665-9(7)) Rigby Education.

What Could It Be? Small Book. (Pebble Soup Explorations Ser.). 16p. (ps up). 5.00 (978-0-7578-1705-2(X)) Rigby Education.

What Did Ben Want?, 6, Pack. (Chiquilibros Ser.). (gr. k-1). 23.00 (978-0-7635-0444-1(0)) Rigby Education.

What Did I Use?, 6, Pack. (Discovery World Ser.). 12p. (gr. k-1). 28.00 (978-0-7635-8448-1(7)) Rigby Education.

What Did Kim Catch?, 6, Pack. (Literatura 2000 Ser.). (gr. k-1). 28.00 (978-0-7635-0074-0(7)) Rigby Education.

What Did They Want?, 6, Pack. (Chiquilibros Ser.). (gr. k-1). 23.00 (978-0-7635-0445-8(9)) Rigby Education.

What Did You Bring? (J). (978-0-8136-5367-9(3)) Modern Curriculum Pr.

What Do We Have to Get? (Little Book Practice Reader). (J). (978-0-8136-2374-0(X)) Modern Curriculum Pr.

What Do We Need? First Grade Guided Reading Level F. (On Our Way to English Ser.). (gr. 1 up). 27.75 (978-0-7578-7053-8(8)) Rigby Education.

What do you Have? Individual Title Six-Packs. (gr. 1-2). 22.00 (978-0-7635-9173-1(4)) Rigby Education.

What do you Hear? Individual Title Six-Packs. (gr. 1-2). 22.00 (978-0-7635-9117-5(3)) Rigby Education.

What Do You See? (Early Intervention Levels Ser.). 21.30 (978-0-7362-0358-6(3)); Vol. 2. 3.55 (978-0-7362-0079-0(7)) Hampton-Brown Bks.

What do you See? Individual Title Six-Packs. (gr. 1-2). 22.00 (978-0-7635-9100-7(9)) Rigby Education.

What Do You See? Kindergarten Guided Reading Level B. (On Our Way to English Ser.). (gr. k up). 27.75 (978-0-7578-7011-8(2)) Rigby Education.

What Do You See by the Sea? 2005. (Emergent Library: Vol. 2). (YA). (ps-1). 23.94 (978-0-8215-8922-9(9)) Sadlier, William H. Inc.

What Do You See by the Sea? Take-Home Book. 2005. (Emergent Library: Vol. 2). (YA). (ps-1). 12.60 (978-0-8215-7252-8(0)) Sadlier, William H. Inc.

What Do You Think? MainSails Individual Title Six-Packs. (Sails Literacy Ser.). (gr. 5 up). 37.00 (978-0-7578-8054-4(1)) Rigby Education.

What do you Touch? Individual Title Six-Packs. (gr. 1-2). 22.00 (978-0-7635-9118-2(1)) Rigby Education.

What Do You Want That For? Individual Title Six-Pack Pouch - Level E. (Lighthouse Ser.). 12p. (gr. 1 up). 26.00 (978-0-7578-0839-5(5)) Rigby Education.

What Does Lucy Like? 2005. (Emergent Library: Vol. 2). (YA). (ps-1). 23.94 (978-0-8215-8926-7(1)) Sadlier, William H. Inc.

What Does Lucy Like? Take-Home Book. 2005. (Emergent Library: Vol. 2). (YA). (ps-1). 12.60 (978-0-8215-7256-6(3)) Sadlier, William H. Inc.

What Does Sam Sell? 2005. (Emergent Library: Vol. 1). (YA). (ps-1). 23.94 (978-0-8215-8902-1(4)) Sadlier, William H. Inc.

What feels Cold?, 6 Packs. (gr. 1-2). 22.00 (978-0-7635-9101-4(7)) Rigby Education.

What feels Hot?, 6 Packs. (gr. 1-2). 22.00 (978-0-7635-9102-1(5)) Rigby Education.

What feels Sticky?, 6 Packs. (gr. 1-2). 22.00 (978-0-7635-9103-8(3)) Rigby Education.

What Gives You Goose Bumps?, 6 Packs. (gr. k-1). 23.00 (978-0-7635-9044-4(4)) Rigby Education.

What Goes Around & Around?, 6 Packs. (gr. 1-2). 22.00 (978-0-7635-9119-9(X)) Rigby Education.

What Goes in the Bathtub?, 6 Packs. (Literatura 2000 Ser.). (gr. k-1). 28.00 (978-0-7635-0017-7(8)) Rigby Education.

What Goes into a Salad? Individual Title Six-Packs. (ps-2). 23.00 (978-0-7635-8993-6(4)) Rigby Education.

What Goes up & Down?, 6 Packs. (gr. 1-2). 22.00 (978-0-7635-9120-5(3)) Rigby Education.

What Goes up High?, 6 Packs. (gr. 1-2). 22.00 (978-0-7635-9090-1(8)) Rigby Education.

What Grows?, 6 Packs. (Rigby Focus Ser.). 16p. (gr. k up). 28.00 (978-0-7578-5513-9(X)) Rigby Education.

What Grows? Individual Title Six-Packs. (Rigby Focus Ser.). 16p. (gr. k up). 26.00 (978-0-7578-5279-4(3)) Rigby Education.

What Happens When You Recycle? Individual Title Six-Packs. (Discovery World Ser.). 16p. (gr. 1-2). 28.00 (978-0-7635-8464-1(9)) Rigby Education.

What Is a Museum? Set F, 6 vols. (Phonics Readers Ser.). (gr. k-2). 28.95 (978-0-7368-4076-7(1)) Red Brick Learning.

What Is at the Top? (J). (978-0-8136-2018-3(X)) Modern Curriculum Pr.

What Is Enormous?, 6 Packs. (gr. 1-2). 22.00 (978-0-7635-9092-5(4)) Rigby Education.

What Is Fast?, 6 Packs. (gr. 1-2). 22.00 (978-0-7635-9104-5(1)) Rigby Education.

What Is Fierce?, 6 Packs. (gr. 1-2). 22.00 (978-0-7635-9093-2(2)) Rigby Education.

What Is He Looking For? KinderWords Individual Title Six-Packs. (Kinderstarters Ser.). 8p. (ps-1). 21.00 (978-0-7635-8711-6(7)) Rigby Education.

What Is It? (Guided Reading Levels Ser.). 21.42 (978-0-7362-1047-8(4)); (Illus.). 3.57 (978-0-7362-0954-0(9)) Hampton-Brown Bks.

What Is It? 48p. (978-0-86388-511-2(X) , 001-4093) Speechmark Publishing Ltd.

What Is It Like Today? Kindergarten Guided Reading Level C. (On Our Way to English Ser.). (gr. k up). 27.75 (978-0-7578-7022-4(8)) Rigby Education.

What is Little? (Early Intervention Levels Ser.). 3.85 (978-1-56334-954-6(X)) Hampton-Brown Bks.

What Is Little? (Early Intervention Levels Ser.). 23.10 (978-0-7362-0003-5(7)) Hampton-Brown Bks.

What Is Old? Individual Title Six-Packs. (gr. 1-2). 22.00 (978-0-7635-9096-3(7)) Rigby Education.

What Is Slippery?, 6 Packs. (gr. 1-2). 22.00 (978-0-7635-9097-0(5)) Rigby Education.

What Is Slow? Individual Title Six-Packs. (gr. 1-2). 22.00 (978-0-7635-9106-9(8)) Rigby Education.

What Is Soft?, 6 Packs. (gr. 1-2). 22.00 (978-0-7635-9107-6(6)) Rigby Education.

What Is Tall?, 6 Packs. (gr. 1-2). 22.00 (978-0-7635-9108-3(4)) Rigby Education.

What Is This? (Little Book Practice Reader). (J). (978-0-8136-5378-5(9)) Modern Curriculum Pr.

What Is This? KinderWords, 6 Packs. (Kinderstarters Ser.). 8p. (ps-1). 21.00 (978-0-7635-8699-7(4)) Rigby Education.

What Is under the Hat? (J). (978-0-8136-5363-1(0)) Modern Curriculum Pr.

What Is Young?, 6 Packs. (gr. 1-2). 22.00 (978-0-7635-9109-0(2)) Rigby Education.

What Should You Say? What Should You Do? Social/ Emotional Lap Book. (Pebble Soup Explorations Ser.). (ps up). 16.00 (978-0-7635-7569-4(0)) Rigby Education.

What Smells Good? Individual Title Six-Packs. (gr. 1-2). 22.00 (978-0-7635-9121-2(1)) Rigby Education.

What Some People Will Do. 2003. (Illus.). pap. 7.60 (978-0-7398-7535-3(3)) Steck-Vaughn.

What's Around the Corner? Individual Title Six-Packs. (Literatura 2000 Ser.). (gr. 1-2). 28.00 (978-0-7635-0153-2(0)) Rigby Education.

What's Best for Red? (Early Intervention Levels Ser.). 28.38 (978-0-7362-0414-9(8)) Hampton-Brown Bks.

What's Best for Red (16), Vol. 16. (Early Intervention Levels Ser.). 4.73 (978-0-7362-0239-8(0)) Hampton-Brown Bks.

What's for Lunch? (Early Intervention Levels Ser.). 23.10 (978-0-7362-0023-3(1)); Vol. 4. 3.85 (978-1-56334-973-7(6)) Hampton-Brown Bks.

What's for Lunch? (Peek A Boo Pockets Ser.). 12p. (J). bds. (978-2-89393-879-0(5)) Phidal Publishing, Inc./Editions Phidal, Inc.

What's in a Name? Individual Chapter Book Title Six-Packs. Vol. 30. 32p. (gr. 5 up). 44.00 (978-0-7578-0984-2(7)) Rigby Education.

What's in the Castle? (Let's Read about... Ser.). 10p. (J). (978-2-7643-0073-2(5)) Phidal Publishing, Inc./Editions Phidal, Inc.

What's in the Dollhouse? (Let's Read about... Ser.). 10p. (J). (978-2-7643-0195-1(2)) Phidal Publishing, Inc./Editions Phidal, Inc.

What's in the Garage? (Let's Read about... Ser.). 10p. (J). (978-2-7643-0194-4(4)) Phidal Publishing, Inc./Editions Phidal, Inc.

What's It Worth? (Guided Reading Levels Ser.). 4.73 (978-0-7362-1739-2(8)); 28.38 (978-0-7362-2160-3(3)) Hampton-Brown Bks.

What's on My Farm? (Early Intervention Levels Ser.). 23.10 (978-0-7362-0007-3(X)); Vol. 2. 3.85 (978-1-56334-957-7(4)) Hampton-Brown Bks.

What's on the Farm? (Let's Read about Ser.). 10p. (J). (978-2-7643-0163-0(4)) Phidal Publishing, Inc./Editions Phidal, Inc.

What's Underneath? Individual Title Six-Packs. (Discovery World Ser.). 16p. (gr. 1-2). 28.00 (978-0-7635-8465-8(7)) Rigby Education.

What's Wrong? 48p. (978-0-86388-512-9(8) , 001-1725) Speechmark Publishing Ltd.

Wheels Board Book Set 800789, 3. 2005. (J). bds. (978-1-59794-042-9(9)) Environments, Inc.

When I Grow Up. (Early Intervention Levels Ser.). 23.10 (978-0-7362-0025-7(8)); Vol. 3. 3.85 (978-1-56334-491-6(2)) Hampton-Brown Bks.

When I Grow Up: Individual Title Six-Pack Pouch - Level C. (Lighthouse Ser.). 12p. (gr. k-1). 24.00 (978-0-7578-0820-3(4)) Rigby Education.

When I Grow Up: Kindergarten Big Books. (On Our Way to English Ser.). (gr. k up). 29.95 (978-0-7578-1626-0(6)) Rigby Education.

When I Grow Up: Small Versions of Big Books. (On Our Way to English Ser.). (gr. k up). 29.00 (978-0-7578-7223-5(9)) Rigby Education.

When It Snowed: Individual Title, 6 packs. (ps-2). 23.00 (978-0-7635-9018-5(5)) Rigby Education.

When Lana Was Absent: 6 Small Books. (gr. k-3). 24.00 (978-0-7635-6240-3(8)) Rigby Education.

When Mr Quinn Snored. 2005. (Emergent Library: Vol. 2). (YA). (ps-1). 23.94 (978-0-8215-8936-6(9)) Sadlier, William H. Inc.

When Mr Quinn Snored: Take-Home Book. 2005. (Emergent Library: Vol. 2). (YA). (ps-1). 12.60 (978-0-8215-7266-5(0)) Sadlier, William H. Inc.

When My Name Was Keoko Student Packet, Gr. 7-8. 2004. (J). (978-1-58130-872-3(8)) Novel Units, Inc.

When This World Was New. (Guided Reading Levels Ser.). 8.48 (978-0-7362-1701-9(0)); 50.88 (978-0-7362-2146-7(8)) Hampton-Brown Bks.

Where are the car Keys? Individual Title Six-Packs. (gr. 1-2). 22.00 (978-0-7635-9156-4(4)) Rigby Education.

Where are the Chicks? 2004. (J). (978-1-58453-226-2(2)) Pioneer Valley Educational Pr., Inc.

Where Are We Going? (J). 26.20 (978-0-8136-8392-8(0)); 26.20 (978-0-8136-8393-5(9)); 59.50 (978-0-8136-7906-8(0)); 1998. pap. (978-0-8136-8290-7(8)) Modern Curriculum Pr.

Where Are You Going? KinderWords Individual Title Six-Packs. (Kinderstarters Ser.). 8p. (ps-1). 21.00 (978-0-7635-8712-3(5)) Rigby Education.

Where Can I Write. 2000. (J). (978-1-58453-094-7(4)) Pioneer Valley Educational Pr., Inc.

Where Does Breakfast Come From?, 6 Packs. (Discovery World Ser.). 16p. (gr. 1-2). 28.00 (978-0-7635-8454-2(1)) Rigby Education.

Where Is Gabby? 2000. (J). (978-1-58453-117-3(7)) Pioneer Valley Educational Pr., Inc.

Where Is Gabby. 2000. (J). (978-1-58453-099-2(5)) Pioneer Valley Educational Pr., Inc.

Where Is It? (J). (978-0-8136-5347-1(9)) Modern Curriculum Pr.

Where Is Peanut? 2004. (J). (978-1-58453-215-6(7)) Pioneer Valley Educational Pr., Inc.

Where Is the Treasure? KinderConcepts Individual Title Six-Packs. (Kinderstarters Ser.). 8p. (ps-1). 21.00 (978-0-7635-8721-5(4)) Rigby Education.

Where Is Your Home? Set B, 6 vols. (Phonics Readers Ser.). (gr. k-2). 17.50 (978-0-7368-3208-3(4)) Red Brick Learning.

Where We Live Interactive Packages: In My Neighborhood. (Pebble Soup Explorations Ser.). (ps up). 52.00 (978-0-7578-5232-9(7)) Rigby Education.

Where We Live Interactive Packages: What People Do. (Pebble Soup Explorations Ser.). (ps up). 52.00 (978-0-7578-5234-3(3)) Rigby Education.

Where's My Yellow Yo-Yo? (Early Intervention Levels Ser.). 21.30 (978-0-7362-0370-8(2)); Vol. 3. 3.55 (978-0-7362-0091-2(6)) Hampton-Brown Bks.

Which Egg Is Mine? (Early Intervention Levels Ser.). 23.10 (978-0-7362-0034-9(7)); Vol. 6. 3.85 (978-1-56334-982-9(5)) Hampton-Brown Bks.

Which Way, Jack? Individual Title Six-Packs. (Action Packs Ser.). 104p. (gr. 3-5). 44.00 (978-0-7635-8407-8(X)) Rigby Education.

White, Matt. Cameras on the Battlefield: Photos of War, 6 vols. (gr. 4 up). 49.95 (978-0-7368-9514-9(0) , High Five) Red Brick Learning.

—Castles: Towers, Dungeons, Moats, & More, 6 vols. (gr. 4 up). 49.95 (978-0-7368-9538-5(8) , High Five) Red Brick Learning.

—Endurance: Shipwreck & Survival on a Sea of Ice, 6 vols. (gr. 4 up). 49.95 (978-0-7368-9510-1(8) , High Five) Red Brick Learning.

White Paw, Black Paw: KinderReaders Individual Title Six-Packs. (Kinderstarters Ser.). 8p. (ps-1). 21.00 (978-0-7635-8648-5(X)) Rigby Education.

Whiteford, Rhona. Complete English, 3 bks. in 1. (Illus.). 96p. (YA). pap. 15.99 (978-0-340-71582-6(0) , Hodder & Stoughton) Hodder General Publishing Division GBR. *Dist:* Trafalgar Square Publishing.

Whiteford, Rhona & Fitzsimmons, Jim. Complete English, 4 bks. in 1. (Illus.). 96p. (YA). pap. 15.99 (978-0-340-71580-2(4) , Hodder & Stoughton) Hodder General Publishing Division GBR. *Dist:* Trafalgar Square Publishing.

Whitehouse, Patricia. What's Awake?, 9 vols., Set. 2003. (Illus.). (J). (ps-1). lib. bdg. 166.50 (978-1-58810-886-9(4)) Heinemann Library.

Whitling, Matt. The Grammar of Poetry. 2000. (Imitation in Writing Ser.). 87p. (J). spiral bd. 20.00 (978-1-930443-13-6(7)) Logos Schl.

—Reading Comprehension - Charlotte's Web. 2001. (Imitation in Writing Ser.). 29p. (J). spiral bd. 10.00 (978-1-930443-36-5(6)) Logos Schl.

A Who Am I? Set, 6 vols. (Phonics Readers Ser.). (gr. k-2). 17.50 (978-0-7368-3185-7(1)) Red Brick Learning.

Who Are We?, 6 Packs. (ps-2). 23.00 (978-0-7635-8805-2(9)) Rigby Education.

Who Came by Here? (Early Intervention Levels Ser.). 23.10 (978-0-7362-0031-8(2)) Hampton-Brown Bks.

Who Came By Here?, Vol. 4. (Early Intervention Levels Ser.). 3.85 (978-1-56334-979-9(5)) Hampton-Brown Bks.

Who Can Run Fast? 2005. (Early Library). (YA). (ps-3). 23.94 (978-0-8215-8940-3(7)) Sadlier, William H. Inc.

Who Has Four Feet? Big Book. 2005. (Emergent Library: Vol. 1). (YA). (ps-1). 23.94 (978-0-8215-8900-7(8)) Sadlier, William H. Inc.

Who Is My Mom? 2005. (Emergent Library: Vol. 1). (YA). (ps-1). 23.94 (978-0-8215-8901-4(6)) Sadlier, William H. Inc.

Who Likes the Night? (Early Intervention Levels Ser.). 28.38 (978-0-7362-0400-2(8)) Hampton-Brown Bks.

Who Likes the Night? (12), Vol. 12. (Early Intervention Levels Ser.). 4.73 (978-0-7362-0225-1(0)) Hampton-Brown Bks.

Who Lives on a Farm? Individual Title, 6 packs. (Story Steps Ser.). (gr. k-2). 29.00 (978-0-7635-9570-8(5)) Rigby Education.

Who Looks after Our World? Individual Title Six-Packs. (ps-2). 23.00 (978-0-7635-8814-4(8)) Rigby Education.

Who Painted the Porcupine. (J). 23.50 (978-0-8136-3967-3(0)) Modern Curriculum Pr.

Who Took Our Cake? Individual Title, 6 packs. (Rigby Focus Ser.). 16p. (gr. k up). 28.00 (978-0-7578-5533-7(4)) Rigby Education.

Who Took Our Cake? Individual Title Six-Packs. (Rigby Focus Ser.). 16p. (gr. k up). 26.00 (978-0-7578-5299-2(8)) Rigby Education.

Who Will Help Me? Individual Title Six-Packs. (ps-2). 23.00 (978-0-7635-8795-6(8)) Rigby Education.

Who Will Look Out for Danny? Individual Title Six-Packs. (Action Packs Ser.). 120p. (gr. 3-5). 44.00 (978-0-7635-8420-7(7)) Rigby Education.

Who Works Here? 2005. (Emergent/Early (Prek-2) Social Studies Package Ser.). 12p. (YA). (ps-2). 25.20 (978-0-8215-7833-9(2)) Sadlier, William H. Inc.

Whoops! Set D Individual Title, 6 packs. (gr. k-3). 29.00 (978-0-7635-0551-6(X)) Rigby Education.

Who's at the Zoo? (Let's Read about Ser.). 10p. (J). (978-2-7643-0162-3(6)) Phidal Publishing, Inc./Editions Phidal, Inc.

Who's Coming for a Ride? Individual Title, 6 packs. (Literatura 2000 Ser.). (ps-1). 28.00 (978-0-7635-0019-1(4)) Rigby Education.

Who's the Boss. 2004. (J). (978-1-58453-285-9(8)) Pioneer Valley Educational Pr., Inc.

Whose Egg Is This? Individual Title Six-Packs. (Story Steps Ser.). (gr. k-2). 32.00 (978-0-7635-9607-1(8)) Rigby Education.

Whose Footprints? Individual Title Six-Pack Pouch - Level E. (Lighthouse Ser.). 12p. (gr. 1 up). 26.00 (978-0-7578-0835-7(2)) Rigby Education.

Why Coyote Howls at Night. 2005. (Fluent Library). (YA). (ps-3). 29.34 (978-0-8215-8960-1(1)) Sadlier, William H. Inc.

Why I Like Laura. (Early Intervention Levels Ser.). 28.38 (978-0-7362-0399-9(0)) Hampton-Brown Bks.

Why I Like Laura (8), Vol. 8. (Early Intervention Levels Ser.). 4.73 (978-0-7362-0224-4(2)) Hampton-Brown Bks.

Why People Come Here: Fourth Grade Newcomer Books. (On Our Way to English Ser.). (gr. 4 up). 34.50 (978-0-7578-7257-0(3)) Rigby Education.

Why the Moon Is Ivory: Fifth Grade Guided Comprehension Level P. (On Our Way to English Ser.). (gr. 5 up). 34.50 (978-0-7578-6609-8(3)) Rigby Education.

Why the Sea Is Salty: Individual Title Six-Packs. (Literatura 2000 Ser.). (gr. 2-3). 33.00 (978-0-7635-0246-1(4)) Rigby Education.

Whyte, John. Buddy's Adventures in Reading. 2007. pap. 8.95 ***978-0-533-15641-2(6))** Vantage Pr., Inc.

Wight, Albert & Clarke, Roger. What Do You Do with This Book? 2006. (Illus.). 32p. (J). 12.95 (978-0-8048-3645-6(0)) Tuttle Publishing.

Wikki Stix. (ps-12). 5.67 (978-0-7362-1096-6(2)) Hampton-Brown Bks.

Wilbur's Wild Ride & Other Stories: Individual Title Six-Pack. (Story Steps Ser.). (gr. k-2). 42.00 (978-0-7635-9598-2(5)) Rigby Education.

Wilcox. The Hidden Men. (Thumbprint Mysteries Ser.). 32.86 (978-0-8092-0415-1(0)) McGraw-Hill/ Contemporary.

Wild Animal Board Book Set 800785, 5. 2005. (J). bds. (978-1-59794-020-7(8)) Environments, Inc.

Wild Critters. 2005. (Little Celebrations Thematic Packages Ser.). (J). (gr. k-3). 133.50 (978-0-673-75384-7(0)) Celebration Pr.

Wild Easts Wild West: Level K, 6 vols. 128p. (gr. 2-3). 49.95 (978-0-7699-0988-2(4)) Shortland Pubns. (U. S. A.) Inc.

Wild Planet, 6 Packs. (Rigby Infoquest Ser.). (gr. 5 up). 37.00 (978-0-7578-6483-4(X)) Rigby Education.

Wild Rides! Classroom Library. (gr. 4 up). lib. bdg. 49.95 (978-0-7368-9296-4(6)) Red Brick Learning.

Wild Rides! Complete Unit. (gr. 4 up). 286.95 (978-0-7368-9297-1(4)) Red Brick Learning.

Wilde, Oscar. Picture: Penguin Readers Level 4. 1998. (J). pap. 7.00 (978-0-14-081572-6(4)) Penguin Group (USA) Inc.

Wildfire: Large-Format Books. (Rigby Infoquest Ser.). (gr. 4 up). 30.00 (978-0-7578-3907-8(X)) Rigby Education.

Wilhelm, Hans. I Can Help! Wilhelm, Hans, illus. 2005. (Scholastic Reader Level 1 Ser.). (Illus.). 32p. (J). (ps-ps). pap. 3.99 (978-0-439-46621-9(0) , Cartwheel Bks.) Scholastic, Inc.

Wilhelm, Hans, illus. Sing & Read: Bingo. 2005. (Sing & Read Storybook Ser.). 32p. (J). audio compact disk 4.99 (978-0-439-74542-0(X)) Scholastic, Inc.

Will, Rebel. Who Lives/Twgn/C. 8p. 20.95 (978-0-322-00347-7(4)) Wright Group, The.

Will Smith: The Funny, Funky, & Confident Fresh Prince, 6 vols. (gr. 4 up). 49.95 (978-0-7368-2839-0(7) , High Five) Red Brick Learning.

Will You Play with Me? First Grade Guided Reading Level E. (On Our Way to English Ser.). (gr. 1 up). 27.75 (978-0-7578-7045-3(7)) Rigby Education.

William Tell: 6 Small Books. (gr. k-2). 23.00 (978-0-7635-8506-8(8)) Rigby Education.

Williams, Carolea, ed. Ending Consonants Instant Learning Centers, Vol. 2196. 2004. (Illus.). 32p. (J). (gr. k-2). pap. 9.99 (978-1-59198-056-8(9) , CTP 2196) Creative Teaching Pr., Inc.

Williams, Rozanne Lanczak. The Ants & the Grasshopper, Vol. 4262. Adnet, Bernard, illus. 2005. (Reading for Fluency Ser.). 16p. (J). pap. 2.99 (978-1-59198-162-6(X)) Creative Teaching Pr., Inc.

—Are We There Yet? Leary, Catherine, illus. 2005. (Science Mini Units Ser.). 8p. (J). pap. 2.99 (978-1-59198-151-0(4) , 4251) Creative Teaching Pr., Inc.

—The Big Hungry Bear. Hockerman, Dennis, illus. 2005. (Reading for Fluency Ser.). 8p. (J). pap. 1.99 (978-1-59198-146-6(8) , 4246) Creative Teaching Pr., Inc.

—Creepy, Crawly Bugs. Harris, Jennifer Beck, illus. 2005. (Reading for Fluency Ser.). 8p. (J). pap. 1.99 (978-1-59198-149-7(2) , 4249) Creative Teaching Pr., Inc.

—Here Comes Coco. Banta, Susan, illus. 2005. (Reading for Fluency Ser.). 8p. (J). pap. 1.99 (978-1-59198-145-9(X) , 4245) Creative Teaching Pr., Inc.

—Here Is My Cat. Hamaguchi, Carla, ed. Kotomaimoce, Kathy, illus. 2002. (Sight Word Readers Ser.: Vol. 3170). 8p. (J). (gr. k-2). pap. 2.99 (978-1-57471-920-8(3)) Creative Teaching Pr., Inc.

—Hide & Seek Monsters. Dunne, Kathleen, illus. 2005. (Reading for Fluency Ser.). 16p. (J). pap. 2.99 (978-1-59198-154-1(9) , 4254) Creative Teaching Pr., Inc.

—How to Make a Friend. Nobens, Cheryl, illus. 2005. (Reading for Fluency Ser.). 16p. (J). pap. 2.99 (978-1-59198-155-8(7) , 4255) Creative Teaching Pr., Inc.

—I Have Shapes. Hamaguchi, Carla, ed. Thomson, Pam, illus. 2002. (Sight Word Readers Ser.: Vol. 3161). 8p. (J). (gr. k-2). pap. 2.99 (978-1-57471-911-6(4)) Creative Teaching Pr., Inc.

—I Like Colors. Hamaguchi, Carla, ed. Leary, Catherine, illus. 2002. (Sight Word Readers Ser.: Vol. 3160). 8p. (J). (gr. k-2). pap. 2.99 (978-1-57471-910-9(6)) Creative Teaching Pr., Inc.

—I Love Mud! Twinem, Neecy, illus. 2005. (Reading for Fluency Ser.). 8p. (J). pap. 1.99 (978-1-59198-141-1(7) , 4241) Creative Teaching Pr., Inc.

—I See. Hamaguchi, Carla, ed. Catanese, Donna, illus. 2002. (Sight Word Readers Ser.: Vol. 3162). 8p. (J). (gr. k-2). pap. 2.99 (978-1-57471-912-3(2)) Creative Teaching Pr., Inc.

—Kids Like. Hamaguchi, Carla, ed. Burris, Priscilla, illus. 2002. (Sight Word Readers Ser.: Vol. 3165). 8p. (J). (gr. k-2). pap. 2.99 (978-1-57471-915-4(7)) Creative Teaching Pr., Inc.

—Look Closer. Vangsgard, Amy, illus. 2005. (Reading for Fluency Ser.). 8p. (J). pap. 1.99 (978-1-59198-147-3(6) , 4247) Creative Teaching Pr., Inc.

—The Mouse Who Cried Cat, Vol. 4263. Mahan, Benton, illus. 2005. (Reading for Fluency Ser.). 16p. (J). pap. 2.99 (978-1-59198-163-3(8) , 4263) Creative Teaching Pr., Inc.

—My Pink Piggy Bank. Fletcher, Rusty, illus. 2005. (Reading for Fluency Ser.). 8p. (J). pap. 1.99 (978-1-59198-144-2(1) , 4244) Creative Teaching Pr., Inc.

—Pirates Coming Through, 24 vols., Vol. 4257. Pamintuan, Macky, illus. 2005. (Reading for Fluency Ser.). 16p. (J). pap. 2.99 (978-1-59198-157-2(3) , 4257) Creative Teaching Pr., Inc.

—Slow & Steady Wins the Race, Vol. 4260. Edwards, Karl, illus. 2005. (Reading for Fluency Ser.). 16p. (J). pap. 2.99 (978-1-59198-158-9(1) , 4260) Creative Teaching Pr., Inc.

—A Snack for Cat. Christensen, David & Leary, Catherine, illus. 2005. (Reading for Fluency Ser.). 16p. (J). pap. 2.99 (978-1-59198-153-4(0) , 4252) Creative Teaching Pr., Inc.

—Space Trip. Burnett, Lindy, illus. 2005. (Reading for Fluency Ser.). 80p. (J). pap. 1.99 (978-1-59198-142-8(5) , 4242) Creative Teaching Pr., Inc.

—The Swim Lesson. Burris, Priscilla, illus. 2005. (Reading for Fluency Ser.). 8p. (J). pap. 1.99 (978-1-59198-148-0(4) , 4248) Creative Teaching Pr., Inc.

—The Teacher with the Alligator Purse, Vol. 4259. Richard, Ilene, illus. 2005. (Reading for Fluency Ser.). 16p. (J). pap. 2.99 (978-1-59198-159-6(X)) Creative Teaching Pr., Inc.

—Today Is Somebody's Birthday. Mahan, Benton, illus. 2005. (Reading for Fluency Ser.). 8p. (J). pap. 1.99 (978-1-59198-140-4(9) , 4240) Creative Teaching Pr., Inc.

—What Is the Best Pet?, Vol. 4258. Briles, Patty, illus. 2005. 16p. (J). pap. 2.99 (978-1-59198-160-2(3) , 4258) Creative Teaching Pr., Inc.

—What's So Bad about the Big Bad Wolf?, 24 books. Catalano, Dominic, illus. 2005. (Reading for Fluency Ser.). 8p. (J). pap. 1.99 (978-1-59198-143-5(3) , 4243) Creative Teaching Pr., Inc.

—You Can't Catch Me. Edwards, Karl, illus. 2005. (Reading for Fluency Ser.). 8p. (J). pap. 1.99 (978-1-59198-150-3(6) , 4250) Creative Teaching Pr., Inc.

Wilsher, Barry & Wilsher, Jill. Words Alive! Poems to Perform. 1998. (Cambridge Reading Ser.). (Illus.). 80p. pap. 12.00 (978-0-521-48577-7(0)) Cambridge Univ. Pr.

Wilson, Anna. La Tortuga Tonta. Gordon, Mike, illus. 2005. 32p. (J). (ps-ps). lib. bdg. 11.15 (978-0-606-33598-0(6)) Tandem Library Bks.

Wilson, Mike. Adolf Hitler, 6 vols. 1999. (Livewire Real Lives Ser.). (Illus.). 16p. pap. (978-0-340-67983-8(2) , Hodder Arnold) Hodder Education.

—Britney Spears. 2001. (Livewire Ser.). (Illus.). 27p. pap. (978-0-340-80084-3(4) , Hodder Arnold) Hodder Education.

—Eminem. 2005. 32p. pap. 8.50 (978-0-340-90080-2(6)) Cambridge Univ. Pr.

—Lennox Lewis. 2001. (Livewire Ser.). (Illus.). 28p. pap. (978-0-340-80087-4(9) , Hodder Arnold) Hodder Education.

—The Williams Sisters: Venus & Serena. 2005. (Illus.). 32p. pap. 8.50 (978-0-340-84876-0(6)) Cambridge Univ. Pr.

The Wind Eagle. (Guided Reading Levels Ser.). 7.16 (978-0-7362-1695-1(2)); 42.96 (978-0-7362-2143-6(3)) Hampton Brown Bks.

The Wind That Would Not Blow. (Early Intervention Levels Ser.). 31.86 (978-0-7362-0620-4(5)) Hampton-Brown Bks.

The Wind That Would Not Blow (28), Vol. 28. (Early Intervention Levels Ser.). 5.31 (978-0-7362-0608-2(6)) Hampton-Brown Bks.

Windsor, Jo. Big Mouths: Emergent Level Satellite Individual Title Six-Packs. (Sails Literacy Ser.). (gr. k-1). 27.00 (978-0-7578-7930-2(6)) Rigby Education.

—Big Things: Early Level Satellite Individual Title Six-Packs. (Sails Literacy Ser.). 16p. (gr. 1-2). 27.00 (978-0-7578-6497-1(X)) Rigby Education.

—Boot Balancers Wanted, 6 pack. (Sails Literacy Ser.). 16p. (gr. 2-3). 27.00 (978-0-7578-0703-9(8)) Rigby Education.

—Caves: Early Level Satellite Individual Title Six-Packs. (Sails Literacy Ser.). 16p. (gr. 1-2). 27.00 (978-0-7578-6502-2(X)) Rigby Education.

—Climbers: Early Level Satellite Individual Title Six-Packs. (Sails Literacy Ser.). 16p. (gr. 1-2). 27.00 (978-0-7578-6507-7(0)) Rigby Education.

—A Cold Place: Emergent Level Satellite Individual Title Six-Packs. (Sails Literacy Ser.). (gr. k-1). 27.00 (978-0-7578-7929-6(2)) Rigby Education.

—Doors: Early Level Satellite Individual Title Six-Packs. (Sails Literacy Ser.). 16p. (gr. 1-2). 27.00 (978-0-7578-6499-5(6)) Rigby Education.

—Flyers & Swimmers: Emergent Level Satellite Individual Title Six-Packs. (Sails Literacy Ser.). (gr. k-1). 27.00 (978-0-7578-7937-1(3)) Rigby Education.

—For the Feet: Early Level Satellite Individual Title Six-Packs. (Sails Literacy Ser.). 16p. (gr. 1-2). 27.00 (978-0-7578-6508-4(9)) Rigby Education.

—Go Away! Emergent Level Satellite Individual Title Six-Packs. (Sails Literacy Ser.). (gr. k-1). 27.00 (978-0-7578-7933-3(0)) Rigby Education.

—Hiding: Emergent Level Satellite Individual Title Six-Packs. (Sails Literacy Ser.). (gr. k-1). 27.00 (978-0-7578-7934-0(9)) Rigby Education.

—How Many Toes: Emergent Level Satellite Individual Title Six-Packs. (Sails Literacy Ser.). (gr. k-1). 27.00 (978-0-7578-7925-8(X)) Rigby Education.

—In the Air: Emergent Level Satellite Individual Title Six-Packs. (Sails Literacy Ser.). (gr. k-1). 27.00 (978-0-7578-7923-4(3)) Rigby Education.

—Legs: Emergent Level Satellite Individual Title Six-Packs. (Sails Literacy Ser.). (gr. k-1). 27.00 (978-0-7578-7935-7(7)) Rigby Education.

—Long Hair: Emergent Level Satellite Individual Title Six-Packs. (Sails Literacy Ser.). (gr. k-1). 27.00 (978-0-7578-7928-9(4)) Rigby Education.

—A Long Time Ago: Early Level Satellite Individual Title Six-Packs. (Sails Literacy Ser.). 16p. (gr. 1-2). 27.00 (978-0-7578-3163-8(X)) Rigby Education.

—Making Holes: Early Level Satellite Individual Title Six-Packs. (Sails Literacy Ser.). 16p. (gr. 1-2). 27.00 (978-0-7578-6506-0(2)) Rigby Education.

—Moving on Sand & Snow: Early Level Satellite Individual Title Six-Packs. (Sails Literacy Ser.). 16p. (gr. 1-2). 27.00 (978-0-7578-6504-6(6)) Rigby Education.

—My Cheese: Emergent Level Satellite Individual Title Six-Packs. Bennett, John, illus. (Sails Literacy Ser.). (gr. k-1). 27.00 (978-0-7578-7913-5(6)) Rigby Education.

—Nesting Places: Emergent Level Satellite Individual Title Six-Packs. (Sails Literacy Ser.). (gr. k-1). 27.00 (978-0-7578-7936-4(5)) Rigby Education.

—A New Skin 6 Packs. Early Level Satellite. (Sails Literacy Ser.). 16p. (gr. 1-2). 27.00 (978-0-7578-6505-3(4)) Rigby Education.

—Oil on Water, 6 Packs. (Sails Literacy Ser.). 20p. (gr. 2-3). 27.00 (978-0-7578-0715-2(1)) Rigby Education.

—On the List: Individual Title Six-Packs. (Sails Literacy Ser.). 16p. (gr. 2-3). 27.00 (978-0-7578-0698-8(8)) Rigby Education.

—Riding the Bubbly Seas 6 Packs. McGrath, Raymond, illus. (Sails Literacy Ser.). 20p. (gr. 2-3). 27.00 (978-0-7578-0725-1(9)) Rigby Education.

—Slimy Skin: Emergent Level Satellite Individual Title Six-Packs. (Sails Literacy Ser.). (gr. k-1). 27.00 (978-0-7578-7945-6(4)) Rigby Education.

—Tails: Emergent Level Satellite Individual Title Six-Packs. (Sails Literacy Ser.). (gr. k-1). 27.00 (978-0-7578-7950-0(0)) Rigby Education.

—The Tricksters of Fringle: Individual Title Six-Packs. Cochrane, Alan, illus. (Sails Literacy Ser.). 20p. (gr. 4 up). 27.00 (978-0-7578-0795-4(X)) Rigby Education.

—The Water Hole: Emergent Level Satellite, 6 Packs. (Sails Literacy Ser.). (gr. k-1). 27.00 (978-0-7578-7947-0(0)) Rigby Education.

—What a Nose! Early Level Satellite Individual Title Six-Packs. (Sails Literacy Ser.). 16p. (gr. 1-2). 27.00 (978-0-7578-6512-1(7)) Rigby Education.

—What Birds Eat: Emergent Level Satellite, 6 Packs. (Sails Literacy Ser.). (gr. k-1). 27.00 (978-0-7578-7949-4(7)) Rigby Education.

—What Can Jump? Early Level Satellite Individual Title Six-Packs. (Sails Literacy Ser.). 16p. (gr. 1-2). 27.00 (978-0-7578-2918-5(X)) Rigby Education.

—What's for Dinner: Emergent Level Satellite Individual Title Six-Packs. (Sails Literacy Ser.). (gr. k-1). 27.00 (978-0-7578-7905-0(5)) Rigby Education.

—Worm Work: Individual Title Six-Packs. (Sails Literacy Ser.). 20p. (gr. 2-3). 27.00 (978-0-7578-0718-3(6)) Rigby Education.

Wingfield, Ethel. Starting School. 2nd ed. (Talkabouts Ser.: No. 735-9). (Illus.). 48p. (J). (ps). 3.50 (978-0-7214-1086-9(3) , Dutton Juvenile) Penguin Group (USA) Inc.

Wings: KinderWords Individual Title Six-Packs. (Kinderstarters Ser.). 8p. (ps-1). 21.00 (978-0-7635-8691-1(9)) Rigby Education.

Winne, Joanne. Welcome Books, 156 bks., Set. 2001. (Illus.). 24p. (J). (ps-2). 3045.00 (978-0-516-22990-4(7) , Children's Pr.) Scholastic Library Publishing.

Winter, Barbara. Fight for Rights. Kostic, Dimitri, illus. 2007. 48p. (J). lib. bdg. 23.08 ***978-1-4242-1636-9(2))** Fitzgerald Bks.

—The 10 Most Extraordinary Medical Conditions. 2008. (Tentrade; Ser.). 48p. (J). pap. 14.99 ***978-1-55448-481-2(2)** , Watts, Franklin) Scholastic Library Publishing.

Winterdance Student Packet, Gr. 7-8. 2004. (J). (978-1-58130-874-7(4)) Novel Units, Inc.

The Wise Old Woman. (Lexile Levels Ser.). 9.09 (978-1-56334-747-4(4)) Hampton-Brown Bks.

Wishinsky, Frieda. So Long Stinky Queen Level 4: Chapter Book. Hendry, Linda, illus. 2000. (First Flight Ser.). 40p. (J). (gr. 3-7). pap. (978-1-55041-529-2(8)) Fitzhenry & Whiteside, Ltd.

Wohl, Sharon. A Beastly Tale. Byrne, Adam, illus. 1998. 16p. (J). (gr. 1-5). mass mkt. 4.95 (978-0-9665443-0-5(7)) A Better Way of Learning.

—Celia. Schaadt, Celeste, illus. 1998. 16p. (J). (gr. 1-5). mass mkt. 4.95 (978-0-9665443-7-4(4)) A Better Way of Learning.

—Chase & Grace. Bradley, Lisa, illus. 1998. 16p. (J). (gr. 1-5). mass mkt. 4.95 (978-0-9665443-4-3(X)) A Better Way of Learning.

—City in Space. Byrne, Adam, illus. 1998. 16p. (J). (gr. 1-5). mass mkt. 4.95 (978-0-9665443-8-1(2)) A Better Way of Learning.

—A Nose Can Slant. Bradley, Lisa, illus. 1998. 8p. (J). (gr. k-2). mass mkt. 4.95 (978-0-9665443-2-9(3)) A Better Way of Learning.

—Yip Yap Bam Slam. Bradley, Lisa, illus. 1998. 8p. (J). (gr. k-2). mass mkt. 4.95 (978-0-9665443-1-2(5)) A Better Way of Learning.

Wolf, Kathy, ed. Learning Library Phonics, Reading & Spelling. 2002. 128p. 19.95 (978-1-56234-480-1(3)); 19.95 (978-1-56234-481-8(1)); 19.95 (978-1-56234-483-2(8)); 19.95 (978-1-56234-482-5(X)) Education Ctr., Inc. (Mailbox Bks., The).

Women of Courage Set F, 6 vols. (Phonics Readers Ser.). (gr. k-2). 28.95 (978-0-7368-4087-3(7)) Red Brick Learning.

The Wonderful Water Cycle: Second Grade Guided Reading Level L. (On Our Way to English Ser.). (gr. 2 up). 34.50 (978-0-7578-7103-0(8)) Rigby Education.

Wood, Amanda. Amazing Baby Five Fish! 2006. (Amazing Baby Ser.). (Illus.). 18p. (J). bds. 3.95 (978-1-59223-582-7(4) , Silver Dolphin Bks.) Advantage Pubs. Group.

Wood, Audrey. The Princess & the Dragon Storysack. (J). 65.00 (978-0-85953-199-3(6)) Child's Play-International.

Wood, D. K. Nightmare at Indian Cave. 2006. pap. 10.00 ***978-1-4257-1640-0(7))** Xlibris Corp.

Woodcock, Sandra. Tidal Waves. 2001. (Livewire Ser.). (Illus.). 32p. pap. (978-0-340-80063-8(1) , Hodder Arnold) Hodder Education.

Woodcock, Sandra & Basic Skills Agency Staff. Livewire. 2005. (Illus.). 32p. pap. (978-0-340-74716-2(1)) Cambridge Univ. Pr.

Woods, Andrew. Pobblebonk Reading 6. 6 Goose Berry Pie. 2008. pap. ***978-0-521-71096-1(0))** Cambridge Univ. Pr.

Woolly, Woolly: Individual Title Six-Packs. (Literatura 2000 Ser.). (gr. 1-2). 28.00 (978-0-7635-0159-4(X)) Rigby Education.

Word Study Strand: Word Study Song Chart Word Study Word Study Masters Blackline Master Booklet Word Sort Card Masters Blackline Master Booklet Word Study Teacher's Guide. (On Our Way to English Ser.). (gr. 4 up). 295.00 (978-0-7578-7326-3(X)); (gr. 5 up). 295.00 (978-0-7578-7327-0(8)) Rigby Education.

Word Wall Starters: Package of 100 Cards Third Grade. (On Our Way to English Ser.). (gr. 3 up). 24.75 (978-0-7578-4286-3(0)) Rigby Education.

Word Wall Starters: Package of 115 Cards First Grade. (On Our Way to English Ser.). (gr. 1 up). 28.75 (978-0-7578-1474-7(3)) Rigby Education.

Word Wall Starters: Package of 124 Cards Second Grade. (On Our Way to English Ser.). (gr. 2 up). 31.00 (978-0-7578-1386-3(0)) Rigby Education.

Word Wall Starters: Package of 65 Cards Kindergarten. (On Our Way to English Ser.). (gr. k up). 16.25 (978-0-7578-1562-1(6)) Rigby Education.

Wordless Story Book: In My Own Words. 2004. (In My Own Words Reproducible Wordless Story Book Ser.). (ps-k). 29.95 (978-0-673-65205-8(X)) Addison-Wesley Educational Pubs., Inc.

Wordless Story Book Bookshelf Collection, 36 bks. 2004. (gr. k up). 594.00 (978-0-328-02940-2(8)) Addison-Wesley Educational Pubs., Inc.

Wordless Story Books: Take-Home Version. 2004. (gr. k up). 48.00 (978-0-328-02301-1(9)) Addison-Wesley Educational Pubs., Inc.

Work: First Grade Newcomer Books. (On Our Way to English Ser.). (gr. 1 up). 23.50 (978-0-7578-7206-8(9)) Rigby Education.

Workers: KinderWords Individual Title Six-Packs. (Kinderstarters Ser.). 8p. (ps-1). 21.00 (978-0-7635-8714-7(1)) Rigby Education.

Working for the Government: Fifth Grade Guided Comprehension Level P. (On Our Way to English Ser.). (gr. 5 up). 34.50 (978-0-7578-6612-8(3)) Rigby Education.

World of Language Book Set 800930, 5 vols. 2005. (J). pap. (978-1-59794-094-8(1)) Environments, Inc.

A World of Patterns: Third Grade Guided Reading Level I. (On Our Way to English Ser.). (gr. 3 up). 34.50 (978-0-7578-7114-6(3)) Rigby Education.

A World of Treats: Individual Title Six-Packs. (Rigby Infoquest Ser.). 24p. (gr. 3 up). 34.00 (978-0-7578-5764-5(7)) Rigby Education.

World Watch, 6 vols., Set 1. 2003. (World Watch Ser.). (Illus.). (YA). (gr. 6-8). 113.94 (978-0-7398-6618-4(4)) Raintree.

The World's Greatest Showman, 5 Packs. 2002. (Illus.). pap. 28.35 (978-0-7398-5080-0(6)) Steck-Vaughn.

The World's Wildest Roller Coasters, 6 vols. (gr. 4 up). 39.95 (978-0-7368-8947-6(7)) Red Brick Learning.

Worms Eat Our Garbage: Second Grade Guided Reading Level G. (On Our Way to English Ser.). (gr. 2 up). 34.50 (978-0-7578-7078-1(3)) Rigby Education.

Wright Group. Early Emergent Guided Reading. 2nd ed. 2004. (Wright Group Literacy Ser.). (gr. k up). 423.95 (978-0-322-04287-2(9)) Wright Group, The.

—Ssn/Ef/Grk 1/Comp. (gr. 2 up). 524.95 (978-0-322-04213-1(5)) Wright Group, The.

Wright, Holly. Sunflower. 2004. (J). (978-0-9743690-5-1(5)) Britt Allcroft Productions.

Wrighton, Charlene & Bradshaw, Georgine. Basic Kit - Preschool. Clark, Irene, illus. 2005. Orig. Title: Basis Kit I. (J). 249.95 (978-1-886441-30-9(8)) Zoo-phonics, Inc.

Wrighton, Charlene, et al. Zoo-Phonics Reader Level B, Bk. 1. l.t. ed. 1999. (Readers Ser.). (Illus.). 50p. (Orig.). (J). (gr. 1). pap. 8.95 (978-0-9617342-3-7(X)) Zoo-phonics, Inc.

—Zoo-Phonics Reader Level B Bk. 1: Allie, Bubba, Catina. l.t. ed. 1999. (Readers Ser.). (Illus.). 48p. (J). (gr. 1). pap. 8.95 (978-0-9617342-2-0(1)) Zoo-phonics, Inc.

—Zoo-Phonics Reader Level C, Bk. 2. l.t. ed. 1999. (Readers Ser.). (Illus.). 50p. (J). (gr. 1). pap. 8.95 (978-0-9617342-4-4(8)) Zoo-phonics, Inc.

Writing a Research Paper: A Student Guide to Writing a Research Paper. 2005. (YA). (gr. 6-8). stu. ed. 9.45 (978-0-8215-0761-2(3)) Sadlier, William H. Inc.

Wurzburg, Robert. Dogshark Readers: Bue Set. 2005. (Illus.). 96p. 14.95 (978-1-59354-101-9(5)) Blue Apple Bks.

—Dogshark Readers: Red Set. 2005. (Illus.). 96p. (ps-ps). 14.95 (978-1-59354-074-6(4)) Handprint Bks.

Wurzburg, Robert, illus. Where Are the Dogsharks? 2005. (I'm Going to Read Ser.). 28p. (J). (ps-k). pap., pap. 3.95 (978-1-4027-2616-3(3)); 11.95 (978-1-4027-2615-6(5)) Sterling Publishing Co., Inc.

Wyss. The Swiss Family Robinson, Level 3. 2001. (Illus.). 64p. (C). pap. 9.00 (978-0-582-42664-1(2)) Pearson ESL.

A Year Without Rain. (Early Intervention Levels Ser.). 21.42 (978-0-7362-1048-5(2)); (Illus.). 3.57 (978-0-7362-0955-7(7)) Hampton-Brown Bks.

Yellow Overalls: Individual Title Six-Packs. (Literatura 2000 Ser.). (gr. 2-3). 33.00 (978-0-7635-0247-8(2)) Rigby Education.

Yellow Umbrella, Early Level. (gr. k-2). 999.95 (978-0-7368-3056-0(1) , Yellow Umbrella Bks.) Capstone Pr., Inc.

Yellow Umbrella, Early Level Add-on Set. (gr. k-2). 172.95 (978-0-7368-3057-7(X) , Yellow Umbrella Bks.) Capstone Pr., Inc.

Yellow Umbrella, Emergent Level. (gr. k-2). 999.95 (978-0-7368-1794-3(8) , Yellow Umbrella Bks.) Capstone Pr., Inc.

Yellow Umbrella, Emergent Level Add-on Set. (gr. k-2). 172.95 (978-0-7368-1793-6(X) , Yellow Umbrella Bks.) Capstone Pr., Inc.

Yellow Umbrella Spanish Add-on Set. (SPA.). (gr. k-2). 346.95 (978-0-7368-1781-3(6) , Yellow Umbrella Bks.) Capstone Pr., Inc.

Yes I Can. (Little Book Practice Reader Ser.). (J). (978-0-8136-0771-9(X)) Modern Curriculum Pr.

Yes, We Can! First Grade Guided Reading Level B. (On Our Way to English Ser.). (gr. 1 up). 27.75 (978-0-7578-7029-3(5)) Rigby Education.

Yip & Yap: Consonant y: Level A, 6 vols. (Wright Skills Ser.). 12p. (gr. k-3). 17.95 (978-0-322-03120-3(6)) Wright Group, The.

Yo vivo en el Museo 20: Leveled Books. 2001. (McGraw-Hill. Lectura Ser.). (ENG & SPA.). (gr. 2 up). (978-0-02-188021-8(2)) Macmillan/McGraw-Hill Schl. Div.

Yolonda's Genius Student Packet, Gr. 5-6. 2004. (J). (978-1-58130-530-2(3)) Novel Units, Inc.

Yong, Tohmoh J., et al. Tune in CE2 Pupil's Book. 2007. pap., stu. ed. 1.88 (978-0-521-69592-3(9)) Cambridge Univ. Pr.

—Tune in CE2 Pupil's Workbook. 2007. pap., stu. ed. 1.00 (978-0-521-69593-0(7)) Cambridge Univ. Pr.

Yoon, Salina. Count My Blessings 1 Through 10. Yoon, Salina, illus. 2008. 24p. (J). (ps-ps). bds. 6.99 (***978-0-399-25069-9(7)*** , Putnam Juvenile) Penguin Group (USA) Inc.

Yoshizawa. Polly Wants a Cracker Sees the World. 1999. (Illus.). pap. 6.20 (978-0-7398-0886-3(9)) Steck-Vaughn.

You Can Sell: Fourth Grade Newcomer Books. (On Our Way to English Ser.). (gr. 4 up). 34.50 (978-0-7578-7263-1(8)) Rigby Education.

You do ride Well: Individual Title Six-Packs. (gr. 1-2). 25.00 (978-0-7635-9197-7(1)) Rigby Education.

Young, Caroline, et al, des. First Picture Word Book. 2004. (First Picture Word Book Ser.). (Illus.). 16p. (J). 11.95 (978-0-7945-0645-2(3) , Usborne) EDC Publishing.

Young Eagles Take to the Sky. 2005. (Book Treks Ser.). (J). (gr. 3 up). stu. ed. 34.95 (978-0-673-62842-8(6)) Celebration Pr.

Young Explorers in Science. (J). 105.00 (978-0-8136-4363-2(5)) Modern Curriculum Pr.

Young, Ian. The Iditarod: Story of the Last Great Race, 6 vols. (gr. 4 up). 49.95 (978-0-7368-9534-7(5) , High Five) Red Brick Learning.

Young Library Package: Spring 2003, 50 bks. 2003. (Illus.). (J). 1285.00 (978-1-4109-0246-7(3)) Raintree.

Young Reader Series, 9 bks., Set. (Illus.). (J). (gr. 3-6). lib. bdg. 121.05 (978-1-56674-914-5(X)) Forest Hse. Publishing Co., Inc.

Your Great State. (Guided Reading Levels Ser.). 5.34 (978-0-7362-1737-8(1)); 32.04 (978-0-7362-2159-7(X)) Hampton-Brown Bks.

Yoyo. Learning Words. 2005. 40p. bds. 6.95 (978-90-5843-887-4(2)) YoYo Bks. BEL. *Dist:* National Bk. Network.

A Yummy Lunch. 2000. (J). (978-1-58453-097-8(9)) Pioneer Valley Educational Pr., Inc.

A Yummy Snack: Second Grade Guided Reading Level E. (On Our Way to English Ser.). (gr. 2 up). 34.50 (978-0-7578-7067-5(8)) Rigby Education.

Yun's Visit: Fourth Grade Guided Comprehension Level K. (On Our Way to English Ser.). (gr. 4 up). 34.50 (978-0-7578-7146-7(1)) Rigby Education.

Zach & Nate. 2001. (J). (978-1-58453-087-9(1)) Pioneer Valley Educational Pr., Inc.

Zack & Nate. 2001. (J). (978-1-58453-136-4(3)) Pioneer Valley Educational Pr., Inc.

Zack's Spots: Individual Title Six-Packs. (Sails Literacy Ser.). (gr. 1-2). 36.00 (978-0-7578-6717-0(0)) Rigby Education.

Ziefert, Harriet. All Dirty! All Clean! Level 2. Jacobson, David & Brown, Richard, illus. 2005. (I'm Going to Read Ser.). 32p. (J). pap. 3.95 (978-1-4027-2715-3(1)) Sterling Publishing Co., Inc.

—All Dirty! All Clean! (Level 2) Jacobson, David & Brown, Richard, illus. 2005. (I'm Going to Read Ser.). 32p. (J). 11.95 (978-1-4027-2716-0(X)) Sterling Publishing Co., Inc.

—Are We There Yet? Gottleib, Dale, illus. 2005. (I'm Going to Read Ser.). 32p. (J). (ps-ps). 11.95 (978-1-4027-2714-6(3)) Sterling Publishing Co., Inc.

—Class Pets Level 4. Kreloff, Elliot & Gott, Barry, illus. 2005. (I'm Going to Read Ser.). 48p. (J). pap. 3.95 (978-1-4027-2709-2(7)) Sterling Publishing Co., Inc.

—Clown Games. Stevens, Larry, illus. 2005. (I'm Going to Read Ser.: Level 1). 32p. (J). 11.95 (978-1-4027-2724-5(0)) Sterling Publishing Co., Inc.

—I Hate Boots! Rader, Laura, illus. 2005. (I'm Going to Read Ser.: Level 1). 24p. (J). 11.95 (978-1-4027-2071-0(8)) Sterling Publishing Co., Inc.

Ziefert, Harriet. I'm Going to Read Workbook: Rhyming Words. Kido, Yukiko, illus. 2007. (I'm Going to Read Ser.). 64p. (J). pap. 5.95 (***978-1-4027-5059-5(5)***) Sterling Publishing Co., Inc.

Zile, Susan Van. Reading & Writing Graphic Organizers & Mini-Lessons. 2006. 48p. pap. 10.99 (978-0-439-54897-7(7) , Teaching Resources) Scholastic, Inc.

Ziolkowski, Steve. Laughter. 2003. (Oxford Bookworms Factfiles Ser.). (Illus.). 30p. 7.25 (978-0-19-423364-4(2)) Oxford Univ. Pr., Inc.

Zoo Dinners: First Wave Satellite Individual Title Six-Packs. (Sails Literacy Ser.). 16p. (gr. k up). 27.00 (978-0-7578-6868-9(1)) Rigby Education.

Zoo-phonics Quick Tests for the Classroom. 2004. cd-rom (978-1-886441-41-5(3)) Zoo-phonics, Inc.

Zoom In! Level M, 6 vols. 128p. (gr. 2-3). 40.50 (978-0-7699-1032-1(7)) Shortland Pubns. (U. S. A.) Inc.

The Zoomer: KinderWords Individual Title Six-Packs. (Kinderstarters Ser.). 8p. (ps-1). 21.00 (978-0-7635-8709-3(5)) Rigby Education.

Zoqueti-ploc 12: Leveled Books. 2001. (McGraw-Hill. Lectura Ser.). (ENG & SPA.). (gr. 2 up). (978-0-02-188013-3(1)) Macmillan/McGraw-Hill Schl. Div.

1 Potato, 2 Potato: Individual Title Six-Packs. (Literatura 2000 Ser.). (gr. 2-3). 33.00 (978-0-7635-0266-9(9)) Rigby Education.

1st Reading Booster. 2005. (J). per. 1.49 (978-1-59441-339-1(8) , C04015) Carson-Dellosa Publishing Co., Inc.

2nd Reading Booster. 2005. 64p. (J). per. 1.49 (978-1-59441-343-8(6) , C04019) Carson-Dellosa Publishing Co., Inc.

3rd Reading Booster. 2005. 64p. (J). per. 1.49 (978-1-59441-347-6(9) , C04024) Carson-Dellosa Publishing Co., Inc.

4th Reading Booster. 2005. 64p. (J). per. 1.49 (978-1-59441-351-3(7) , C04027) Carson-Dellosa Publishing Co., Inc.

21st Century Debates, 24 bks. 2004. 650.88 (978-0-7398-6472-2(6)) Harcourt Schl. Pubs.

2,4,6,8 Legs: Kindergarten Guided Reading Level C. (On Our Way to English Ser.). (gr. k up). 27.75 (978-0-7578-7019-4(8)) Rigby Education.

READER'S DIGEST

Early Learning Library 800665. 2005. (J). bds. (978-1-59794-008-5(9)) Environments, Inc.

Rucco, Alison. The Lost Salt Gift of Blood. 2002. (Wizard Study Guides Ser.). 48p. pap., stu. ed. 6.00 (978-1-875739-61-5(0)) Cambridge Univ. Pr.

READING

Here are entered books on methods of teaching reading and general books on the art of reading. Works on teaching retarded readers are entered under Reading—Remedial Teaching. books on the cultural aspects of reading and general discussions of books to read are entered under Books and Reading.

see also Books and Reading

Acid Rain: Level M, 6 vols. (Wonder Worldtm Ser.). 16p. 34.95 (978-0-7802-2887-0(1)) Wright Group, The.

Action Adventure. rev. ed. 2004. (High Interest/Low Readability Ser.). 80p. (J). (gr. 5-8). pap. 10.99 (978-0-7696-3392-3(7) , MH1016) School Specialty Publishing.

Action Sports, 12 vols. 2005. (Illus.). 32p. (gr. 4-8). pap. 336.00 (978-0-7910-7532-6(X) , Chelsea Hse.) Facts On File, Inc.

Active Skills for Reading. 2002. pap., tchr. ed. 9.95 (978-0-8384-2608-1(5)) Thomson Heinle.

Actividades diarias de Lenguaje: Resources & Ancillaries. 2001. (McGraw-Hill. Lectura Ser.). (ENG & SPA.). (gr. 1 up). (978-0-02-186574-1(4)); (gr. 2 up). (978-0-02-186575-8(2)); (gr. 3 up). (978-0-02-186576-5(0)); (gr. 4 up). (978-0-02-186577-2(9)); (gr. 5 up). (978-0-02-186578-9(7)); (gr. 6 up). (978-0-02-186579-6(5)) Macmillan/McGraw-Hill Schl. Div.

Ada, Alma Flor, tr. Take-Home Package: Complete Package. 2003. (Dejame Leer Ser.). (J). 124.95 (978-0-673-58720-6(7)) Celebration Pr.

Ada, Alma Flor & Campoy, F. Isabel. Apoyo Adicional Hojas Reproducibles. 3rd ed. 2002. (Trofeos Ser.). (SPA.). (gr. 3 up). pap. 51.40 (978-0-15-323805-5(4)); (gr. 5 up). pap. 51.40 (978-0-15-323814-7(3)); (gr. 6 up). pap. 51.40 (978-0-15-323818-5(6)) Harcourt Schl. Pubs.

—Colecciones de Libros de la Biblioteca: El Coraje de Sarah Noble. 2003. (Trofeos Ser.). (SPA.). (gr. 6 up). 135.90 (978-0-15-322124-8(0)) Harcourt Schl. Pubs.

—Colecciones de Libros de la Biblioteca: El Papalote. 2003. (Trofeos Ser.). (SPA.). (gr. 1 up). 81.60 (978-0-15-319393-4(X)) Harcourt Schl. Pubs.

—Colecciones de Libros de la Biblioteca: Lucita Regresa a Oaxaca. 2003. (Trofeos Ser.). (SPA.). (gr. 3 up). 44.00 (978-0-15-322094-4(5)) Harcourt Schl. Pubs.

—Ediciones del Maestro: Theme 1. 3rd ed. 2002. (Trofeos Ser.). (SPA.). (gr. 6 up). pap., tchr. ed. 110.60 (978-0-15-322701-1(X)) Harcourt Schl. Pubs.

—Ediciones del Maestro: Theme 2. 3rd ed. 2002. (Trofeos Ser.). (SPA.). (gr. 6 up). pap., tchr. ed. 110.60 (978-0-15-322702-8(8)) Harcourt Schl. Pubs.

—Ediciones del Maestro: Theme 3. 3rd ed. 2002. (Trofeos Ser.). (SPA.). (gr. 6 up). pap., tchr. ed. 110.60 (978-0-15-322703-5(6)) Harcourt Schl. Pubs.

—Ediciones del Maestro: Theme 4. 3rd ed. 2002. (Trofeos Ser.). (SPA.). (gr. 6 up). pap., tchr. ed. 110.60 (978-0-15-322704-2(4)) Harcourt Schl. Pubs.

—Ediciones del Maestro: Theme 5. 3rd ed. 2002. (Trofeos Ser.). (SPA.). (gr. 6 up). pap., tchr. ed. 110.60 (978-0-15-322705-9(2)) Harcourt Schl. Pubs.

—Ediciones del Maestro: Theme 6. 3rd ed. 2002. (Trofeos Ser.). (SPA.). (gr. 6 up). pap., tchr. ed. 110.60 (978-0-15-322706-6(0)) Harcourt Schl. Pubs.

—Un Paso Mas Hojas Reproducibles. 3rd ed. 2002. (Trofeos Ser.). (SPA.). (gr. 1 up). pap. 58.60 (978-0-15-323785-0(6)); (gr. 2 up). pap. 58.60 (978-0-15-323802-4(X)); (gr. 3 up). pap. 51.40 (978-0-15-323808-6(9)); (gr. 4 up). pap. 51.40 (978-0-15-323812-3(7)); (gr. 5 up). pap. 51.40 (978-0-15-323816-1(X)); (gr. 6 up). pap. 51.40 (978-0-15-323820-8(8)) Harcourt Schl. Pubs.

Adding English/ESL Support. 2004. (gr. 2 up). 109.15 (978-0-328-03065-1(1)); (gr. 3 up). 109.50 (978-0-328-03066-8(X)); (gr. 4 up). 109.50 (978-0-328-03067-5(8)); (gr. 5 up). 109.50 (978-0-328-03068-2(6)) Addison-Wesley Educational Pubs., Inc.

Adolphs, Robin. The New Neighbours. 2002. (Bright Sparks Ser.). (Illus.). 16p. pap. 2.30 (978-0-521-75412-5(7)) Cambridge Univ. Pr.

—Surfies. 2002. (Bright Sparks Ser.). (Illus.). 16p. pap. 2.30 (978-0-521-75413-2(5)) Cambridge Univ. Pr.

The Adventures of Tutankhamen: Level T. Group 2, 6 vols. (Sunshinetm Ser.). 48p. 44.95 (978-0-7802-4175-6(4)) Wright Group, The.

Afflerbach, Peter. Seeing Is Believing. l.t. ed. 2004. (gr. 4 up). 70.40 (978-0-328-03937-1(3) , Scott Foresman) Addison-Wesley Educational Pubs., Inc.

African American Leaders, 6 vols. 2005. (Illus.). 112p. (gr. 6-12). pap. 180.00 (978-0-7910-7681-1(4) , Chelsea Hse.) Facts On File, Inc.

After the Dinosaurs: Level P, 6 vols. (Wonder Worldtm Ser.). 48p. 39.95 (978-0-7802-7084-8(3)) Wright Group, The.

Against the Odds, 6 vols. (Wildcats Ser.). 32p. (gr. 2-8). (978-0-322-02443-4(9)) Wright Group, The.

Ah-choo! 2005. (Fluent Library). (YA). (ps-3). 29.34 (978-0-8215-8962-5(8)) Sadlier, William H. Inc.

Ahora lo ves, ahora no lo Ves! 10: Leveled Books. 2001. (McGraw-Hill. Lectura Ser.). (ENG & SPA.). (gr. 2 up). (978-0-02-188011-9(5)) Macmillan/McGraw-Hill Schl. Div.

Al habla con los Sordos 2: Leveled Books. 2001. (McGraw-Hill. Lectura Ser.). (ENG & SPA.). (gr. 5 up). (978-0-02-188250-2(9)) Macmillan/McGraw-Hill Schl. Div.

Albee, Jo. American Heroes. 2003. (Compass Point Phonics Readers Ser.). (Illus.). 16p. (J). (gr. 1 up). 13.26 (978-0-7565-0502-8(X)) Compass Point Bks.

Alguien llamado Felix 5: Leveled Books. 2001. (McGraw-Hill. Lectura Ser.). (ENG & SPA.). (gr. 2 up). (978-0-02-188006-5(9)) Macmillan/McGraw-Hill Schl. Div.

Alien Monchers: Level 4, 6 vols. (Fluency Strand Ser.). (gr. 4-8). 45.00 (978-1-4045-1222-1(5)) Wright Group, The.

All about Ants, 6 vols. (Book2WebTM Ser.). (gr. 4-8). 36.50 (978-0-322-02977-4(5)) Wright Group, The.

All about Hair Little Book: Early Reading Fluency, Level C. 2004. pap. 6.00 (978-0-7398-8295-5(3)) Steck-Vaughn.

All about Maps: Level R, 6 vols. (Wonder Worldtm Ser.). 48p. 44.95 (978-0-7802-7074-9(6)) Wright Group, The.

All Kinds of Bears, 6 vols. (Book2WebTM Ser.). (gr. 4-8). 36.50 (978-0-322-02972-9(4)) Wright Group, The.

All Mixed Up. 2005. (Early Library). (YA). (ps-3). 23.94 (978-0-8215-8951-9(2)) Sadlier, William H. Inc.

All Through the Year, 6 vols. (Multicultural Programs Ser.). 16p. (gr. 1-3). 24.95 (978-0-7802-9202-4(2)) Wright Group, The.

Allen, Margaret. Responding to Literature: Activities That Build Confident Readers & Writers. Samoiloff, Sheri, ed. Campbell, Jenny, illus. 2002. 64p. (J). (gr. 1-3). pap. 9.99 (978-1-57471-809-6(6) , CTP 3367) Creative Teaching Pr., Inc.

Alligator Alley, 6 vols., Vol. 3. (Woodland Mysteriestm Ser.). 133p. (gr. 3-7). 42.50 (978-0-322-02372-7(6)) Wright Group, The.

Amaze Us!, 6 vols. (Wildcats Ser.). 32p. (gr. 2-8). (978-0-322-02442-7(0)) Wright Group, The.

Amazing Maps: Level Q, 6 vols. (Wonder Worldtm Ser.). 48p. 39.95 (978-0-7802-2945-7(2)) Wright Group, The.

American Education Publishing, Inc. Staff & Branstetter, Kacy. Reading: Grade 4. 2003. (Brighter Child Workbooks Ser.). (Illus.). 24p. (J). (gr. 4). pap. 2.25 (978-1-56189-125-2(8) , American Education Publishing) School Specialty Publishing.

American Education Publishing Staff. The Complete Book of Reading: Grades 5 - 6. 2001. (Complete Book Ser.). (Illus.). 352p. (J). (gr. 5-6). pap., wbk. ed. 14.95 (978-1-56189-678-3(0) , American Education Publishing) School Specialty Publishing.

American Education Publishing Staff & Douglas, Vincent. Reading for Understanding: Grade 2. 2001. (Together We Learn Ser.). (Illus.). 32p. (C). (gr. 2). pap. 2.99 (978-1-56189-628-8(4) , 31324-628, American Education Publishing) School Specialty Publishing.

American Literature. (gr. 11 up). 2004. cd-rom (978-0-618-30390-8(1) , 2-04295); 2001. cd-rom (978-0-395-97286-1(8) , 2-80756) McDougal Littell Inc.

American Literature: EEdition Plus Online (1 Year License) 2004. (gr. 11 up). (978-0-618-31043-2(6) , 2-04463) McDougal Littell Inc.

American Literature: EEdition Plus Online (2 Year License) 2004. (gr. 11 up). (978-0-618-31256-6(0) , 2-04594) McDougal Littell Inc.

American Literature: EEdition Plus Online (3 Year License) 2004. (gr. 11 up). (978-0-618-31257-3(9) , 2-04595) McDougal Littell Inc.

American Literature: EEdition Plus Online (4 Year License) 2004. (gr. 11 up). (978-0-618-31258-0(7) , 2-04596) McDougal Littell Inc.

American Literature: EEdition Plus Online (5 Year License) 2004. (gr. 11 up). (978-0-618-31259-7(5) , 2-04597) McDougal Littell Inc.

American Literature: EEdition Plus Online (6 Year License) 2004. (gr. 11 up). (978-0-618-30836-1(9) , 2-04342); (978-0-618-31260-3(9) , 2-04598) McDougal Littell Inc.

American Literature: EEdition Plus Online Parent Purchase (1 Year) 2004. (gr. 11 up). (978-0-618-31255-9(2) , 2-04593) McDougal Littell Inc.

American Literature: The InterActive Reader Plus. 2004. (gr. 11 up). (978-0-618-30990-0(X) , 2-04430); (978-0-618-37787-9(5) , 2-10434) McDougal Littell Inc.

American Literature: The InterActive Reader Plus for English Learners. 2004. (gr. 11 up). (978-0-618-31022-7(3) , 2-04444); (978-0-618-37780-0(8) , 2-04397) McDougal Littell Inc.

American Literature: The InterActive Reader Plus with Additional Support. 2004. (gr. 11 up). (978-0-618-31007-4(X) , 2-04437); (978-0-618-37794-7(8) , 2-10441) McDougal Littell Inc.

Amery, Heather. Snow Storm. 1999. (gr. k-3). lib. bdg. 12.95 (978-0-613-91036-1(2)) Tandem Library Bks.

Un amigo Genial 5: Leveled Books. 2001. (McGraw-Hill. Lectura Ser.). (ENG & SPA.). (gr. 2 up). (978-0-02-188030-0(1)) Macmillan/McGraw-Hill Schl. Div.

Amigos en el Mar 14: Leveled Books. 2001. (McGraw-Hill. Lectura Ser.). (ENG & SPA.). (gr. 4 up). (978-0-02-188214-4(2)) Macmillan/McGraw-Hill Schl. Div.

Amigote 4: Leveled Books. 2001. (McGraw-Hill. Lectura Ser.). (ENG & SPA.). (gr. 4 up). (978-0-02-188149-9(9)) Macmillan/McGraw-Hill Schl. Div.

Ana Mazapan y el Empire State 24: Leveled Books. 2001. (McGraw-Hill. Lectura Ser.). (ENG & SPA.). (gr. 3 up). (978-0-02-188121-5(9)) Macmillan/McGraw-Hill Schl. Div.

Anansi y Tortuga Cenan Juntas No. 4: Leveled Books. 2001. (McGraw-Hill. Lectura Ser.). (ENG & SPA.). (gr. 4 up). (978-0-02-188204-5(5)) Macmillan/McGraw-Hill Schl. Div.

And I Mean It, Stanley. 2003. 22.95 (978-0-673-75905-4(9)) Celebration Pr.

Anderson, Neil J. Active Skills for Reading. 2002. pap. 25.95 (978-0-8384-2607-4(7)); Bk. 3. pap. 31.95 (978-0-8384-7048-0(3)) Thomson Heinle.

El angel de las Batallas 4: Leveled Books. 2001. (McGraw-Hill. Lectura Ser.). (ENG & SPA.). (gr. 5 up). (978-0-02-188276-2(2)) Macmillan/McGraw-Hill Schl. Div.

Angela's Ashes: Response Journal. 2003. 40p. (YA). (978-1-58049-991-0(0) , RJ91) Prestwick Hse., Inc.

Animal Coats Little Book: Early Reading Fluency, Level C. 2004. pap. 6.00 (978-0-7398-8294-8(5)) Steck-Vaughn.

Animal Families, 6 vols. 2005. (Animal Families Ser.). (Illus.). 32p. (gr. 2-4). pap. 138.00 (978-0-7910-7539-5(7) , Chelsea Hse.) Facts On File, Inc.

Animal Sounds: Big Book: Level C. (Visionstm Ser.). 8p. 20.95 (978-0-322-00308-8(3)) Wright Group, The.

Animal Tracks: Level C, 6 vols. (Wonder Worldtm Ser.). 16p. 24.95 (978-0-7802-1211-4(8)) Wright Group, The.

Animales maritimos Gigantes 24: Leveled Books. 2001. (McGraw-Hill. Lectura Ser.). (ENG & SPA.). (gr. 2 up). (978-0-02-188073-7(5)) Macmillan/McGraw-Hill Schl. Div.

Los animales no deben actuar como la Gente 2: Leveled Books. 2001. (McGraw-Hill. Lectura Ser.). (ENG & SPA.). (gr. 1 up). (978-0-02-187979-3(6)) Macmillan/McGraw-Hill Schl. Div.

Animales que no pierdan el Tiempo 12: Leveled Books. 2001. (McGraw-Hill. Lectura Ser.). (ENG & SPA.). (gr. 5 up). (978-0-02-188260-1(6)) Macmillan/McGraw-Hill Schl. Div.

Animals Grow: Level J. (Wonder Worldtm Ser.). 16p. 26.50 (978-0-7802-3472-7(3)); 29.95 (978-0-7802-1191-9(X)) Wright Group, The.

Ano nuevo, vida Nueva 7: Leveled Books. 2001. (McGraw-Hill. Lectura Ser.). (ENG & SPA.). (gr. 4 up). (978-0-02-188207-6(X)) Macmillan/McGraw-Hill Schl. Div.

Anteojos para ver Monstruos 8: Leveled Books. 2001. (McGraw-Hill. Lectura Ser.). (ENG & SPA.). (gr. 2 up). (978-0-02-188009-6(3)) Macmillan/McGraw-Hill Schl. Div.

Antologia de Poesia 8: Leveled Books. 2001. (McGraw-Hill. Lectura Ser.). (ENG & SPA.). (gr. 4 up). (978-0-02-188208-3(8)) Macmillan/McGraw-Hill Schl. Div.

Antonio y su caballito de Totora 13: Leveled Books. 2001. (McGraw-Hill. Lectura Ser.). (ENG & SPA.). (gr. 4 up). (978-0-02-188189-5(8)) Macmillan/McGraw-Hill Schl. Div.

The Ants & the Grasshopper: R-Controlled Review: Level C, 6 vols. (Wright Skills Ser.). 16p. (gr. k-3). 26.50 (978-0-322-01501-2(4)) Wright Group, The.

Apgar, Cheryl. Layer It! With Science: Interactive Layer Books that Promote Reading, Writing, & Listening. Samoiloff, Sheri, ed. Tom, Darcy, illus. 2002. 80p. (J). (gr. k-1). pap. 10.99 (978-1-57471-817-1(7) , CTP 3373) Creative Teaching Pr., Inc.

Los Apicultores 18: Leveled Books. 2001. (McGraw-Hill. Lectura Ser.). (ENG & SPA.). (gr. 5 up). (978-0-02-188266-3(5)) Macmillan/McGraw-Hill Schl. Div.

Appleby, Sue. Umoyana the Little Wind: Akwapim Twi Version. Asante, Comfort, tr. 2001. (TWI., Illus.). 16p. pap. 1.40 (978-0-521-79619-4(9)) Cambridge Univ. Pr.

Appointment with Action: 6 Each of 1 Anthology, 6 vols. (Wildcats Ser.). 32p. (gr. 2-8). (978-0-322-00597-6(3)) Wright Group, The.

Archer, Anita L., et al. Rewards. 2000. 78p. (J). pap., stu. ed. 6.00 (978-1-57035-272-0(0) , 136STU) Sopris West Educational Services.

—Rewards: Reading, Excellence, Word Attack & Rate Development Strategies. 2000. 376p. (J). pap., tchr. ed. 45.00 (978-1-57035-271-3(2) , 136MAN) Sopris West Educational Services.

Are they here Yet? Short Vowel e: Level A, 6 vols. (Wright Skills Ser.). 12p. (gr. k-3). 17.95 (978-0-322-03121-0(4)) Wright Group, The.

Are You a Ladybug?, 6 vols. (Sunshinetm Ser.). 16p. (gr. k up). 29.50 (978-0-7802-5430-5(9)) Wright Group, The.

Arnold, Ellen. Magnificent Mind Magnifies Meaning When Reading. Farber, Deborah, illus. 2000. (MI Strategies for Kids Ser.). 32p. (J). (gr. 1-5). pap. 7.00 (978-1-56976-114-4(0) , Zephyr Pr.) Chicago Review Pr., Inc.

Around the World in Eighty Days: Response Journal. 2003. 40p. (YA). (978-1-58049-987-3(2) , RJ87) Prestwick Hse., Inc.

Arroyo de primavera, laguna de Invierno 15: Leveled Books. 2001. (McGraw-Hill. Lectura Ser.). (ENG & SPA.). (gr. 3 up). (978-0-02-188136-9(7)) Macmillan/McGraw-Hill Schl. Div.

Un arte Antiguo 11: Leveled Books. 2001. (McGraw-Hill. Lectura Ser.). (ENG & SPA.). (gr. 3 up). (978-0-02-188084-3(0)) Macmillan/McGraw-Hill Schl. Div.

Ashton, Christine. The Genie of the Bike Lamp: Level P, 6 vols. 128p. (gr. 6 up). 36.95 (978-0-322-05892-7(9)) Wright Group, The.

At Camp with Gramps: Final Blends -mp, -st: Level B, 6 vols. (Wright Skills Ser.). 16p. (gr. k-3). 17.95 (978-0-322-01463-3(8)) Wright Group, The.

Au, Kathryn. Super Qar for Test-Wise Students: Grade 1, 5-Pack, 5 vols. (gr. 1-8). 36.95 (978-0-322-09107-8(1)) Wright Group, The.

—Super Qar for Test-Wise Students: Grade 2 5-Pack, 5 vols. (gr. 1-8). 36.95 (978-0-322-09108-5(X)) Wright Group, The.

—Super Qar for Test-Wise Students: Grade 3 5-Pack, 5 vols. (gr. 1-8). 36.95 (978-0-322-09110-8(1)) Wright Group, The.

—Super Qar for Test-Wise Students: Grade 4 5-Pack, 5 vols. (gr. 1-8). 36.95 (978-0-322-09111-5(X)) Wright Group, The.

—Super Qar for Test-Wise Students: Grade 4 Kit. (gr. 1-8). 264.95 (978-0-322-09189-4(6)) Wright Group, The.

—Super Qar for Test-Wise Students: Grade 5 5-Pack, 5 vols. (gr. 1-8). 36.95 (978-0-322-09112-2(8)) Wright Group, The.

—Super Qar for Test-Wise Students: Grade 5 Kit. (gr. 1-8). 264.95 (978-0-322-09190-0(X)) Wright Group, The.

—Super Qar for Test-Wise Students: Grade 6 5-Pack, 5 vols. (gr. 1-8). 36.95 (978-0-322-09113-9(6)) Wright Group, The.

—Super Qar for Test-Wise Students: Grade 6 Kit. (gr. 1-8). 264.95 (978-0-322-09191-7(8)) Wright Group, The.

—Super Qar for Test-Wise Students: Grade 7 5-Pack, 5 vols. (gr. 1-8). 36.95 (978-0-322-09114-6(4)) Wright Group, The.

—Super Qar for Test-Wise Students: Grade 7 Kit. (gr. 1-8). 264.95 (978-0-322-09212-9(4)) Wright Group, The.

—Super Qar for Test-Wise Students: Grade 8 5-Pack, 5 vols. (gr. 1-8). 36.95 (978-0-322-09115-3(2)) Wright Group, The.

—Super Qar for Test-Wise Students: Grade 8 Kit. (gr. 1-8). 264.95 (978-0-322-09222-8(1)) Wright Group, The.

Auntie Dot's Pot, 6 vols. 8p. (gr. k-1). 21.50 (978-0-322-02082-5(4)) Wright Group, The.

Auntie Jan's Plan, 6 vols. 8p. (gr. k-1). 21.50 (978-0-322-02084-9(0)) Wright Group, The.

The Autobiography of Miss Jane Pittman: SourceBook. 2004. (Literature Connections Ser.). (Illus.). (gr. 6-12). (978-0-395-87490-5(4) , 2-70849) McDougal Littell Inc.

Aventura en la Loma Verde 24: Leveled Books. 2001. (McGraw-Hill. Lectura Ser.). (ENG & SPA.). (gr. 2 up). (978-0-02-188049-2(2)) Macmillan/McGraw-Hill Schl. Div.

Ayudas graficas: Transparencias: Resources & Ancillaries. 2001. (McGraw-Hill. Lectura Ser.). (ENG & SPA.). (gr. 1-6). (978-0-02-186449-2(7)) Macmillan/McGraw-Hill Schl. Div.

Baby Animals at Home: Level F. 16p. 31.50 (978-0-322-00372-9(5)) Wright Group, The.

Backes, Laura. Best Books for Kids Who (Think They) Hate to Read: 125 Books That Will Turn Any Child into a Lifelong Reader. 2001. (Home Learning Library Ser.). (Illus.). 400p. pap. 15.95 (978-0-7615-2755-8(9) , Prima Lifestyles) Crown Publishing Group.

A Bad Job? Consonant b: Level A, 6 vols. (Wright Skills Ser.). 12p. (gr. k-3). 17.95 (978-0-322-03113-5(3)) Wright Group, The.

Bailarines en Danza 7: Leveled Books. 2001. (McGraw-Hill. Lectura Ser.). (ENG & SPA.). (gr. 5 up). (978-0-02-188231-1(2)) Macmillan/McGraw-Hill Schl. Div.

Bailey. Reading Recovery: Complete Pack. 1999. (J). pap. (978-0-7398-1785-8(X)) Steck-Vaughn.

Balderstone, Rachel. What Am I? Icibemba Version. Mulilo, tr. 2001. (Illus.). 8p. pap. 0.45 (978-0-521-01572-1(3)) Cambridge Univ. Pr.

—What Am I? Kiikaonde Version. Muyebaa, tr. 2001. (Illus.). 8p. pap. 0.45 (978-0-521-01573-8(1)) Cambridge Univ. Pr.

—What Am I? Luvale Version. Sakapaji, tr. 2001. (Illus.). 8p. pap. 0.45 (978-0-521-01575-2(8)) Cambridge Univ. Pr.

—What Am I? Silozi Version. Mwendende, tr. 2001. (Illus.). 8p. pap. 0.45 (978-0-521-01576-9(6)) Cambridge Univ. Pr.

Balderstone, Rachel & Chisengele. What Am I? Chitonga Version. 2001. (Illus.). 8p. pap. 0.45 (978-0-521-01569-1(3)) Cambridge Univ. Pr.

—What Am I? Cinyanja Version. 2001. (Illus.). 8p. pap. 0.45 (978-0-521-01570-7(7)) Cambridge Univ. Pr.

Baltas, Joyce Nessel. Easy Mini-Lessons: Reading. 1999. 96p. pap. 12.95 (978-0-439-04092-1(2)) Scholastic, Inc.

Baltasar, la luna, el sol y el Mago 14: Leveled Books. 2001. (McGraw-Hill. Lectura Ser.). (ENG & SPA.). (gr. 5 up). (978-0-02-188238-0(X)) Macmillan/McGraw-Hill Schl. Div.

Bananas Sabrosas! 23: Leveled Books. 2001. (McGraw-Hill. Lectura Ser.). (ENG & SPA.). (gr. 1 up). (978-0-02-187976-2(1)) Macmillan/McGraw-Hill Schl. Div.

Los bandidos del Pedroso 1: Leveled Books. 2001. (McGraw-Hill. Lectura Ser.). (ENG & SPA.). (gr. 4 up). (978-0-02-188146-8(4)) Macmillan/McGraw-Hill Schl. Div.

Barbara va a ser la hermana Mayor 12: Leveled Books. 2001. (McGraw-Hill. Lectura Ser.). (ENG & SPA.). (gr. 3 up). (978-0-02-188133-8(2)) Macmillan/McGraw-Hill Schl. Div.

Barbie Kindergarten Learning Pads: Basic Reading & Writing. 2004. (Illus.). 48p. (J). (978-0-7666-0612-8(0) , 49870) Modern Publishing.

Barker, Cornelius L. & Searchwell, Claudette J. And Yet He Lived? 1999. (Illus.). 100p. (YA). (gr. 7-12). pap. 19.99 (978-0-9678378-0-2(4)) Cordet Bks.

Barney's Horse. 2003. 22.95 (978-0-673-75907-8(5)) Celebration Pr.

The Baseball Heroes, 6 vols. (Woodland Mysteriestm Ser.). 133p. (gr. 3-7). 42.50 (978-0-7802-7931-5(X)) Wright Group, The.

A Basket Full of Surprises. 2005. (Emergent Library: Vol. 2). (YA). (ps-1). 23.94 (978-0-8215-8925-0(3)) Sadlier, William H. Inc.

A Basket Full of Surprises: Take-Home Book. 2005. (Emergent Library: Vol. 2). (J). (ps-1). 12.60 (978-0-8215-7255-9(5)) Sadlier, William H. Inc.

Basketball: Level A, 6 vols. (Wonder Worldtm Ser.). 16p. 24.95 (978-0-7802-1029-5(8)) Wright Group, The.

The Bath. (Little Book Practice Reader). (J). (978-0-8136-5340-2(1)) Modern Curriculum Pr.

Bath Time: Level A, 6 vols. (Wonder Worldtm Ser.). 16p. 24.95 (978-0-7802-1195-7(2)) Wright Group, The.

The Battle of Bowling Street: Level 4, 6 vols. (Fluency Strand Ser.). (gr. 4-8). 45.00 (978-1-4045-1224-5(1)) Wright Group, The.

El baul de Palabras 24: Leveled Books. 2001. (McGraw-Hill. Lectura Ser.). (ENG & SPA.). (gr. 1 up). (978-0-02-187977-9(X)) Macmillan/McGraw-Hill Schl. Div.

Be a Plant Scientist: Level L, 6 vols. (Take-Twostm Ser.). 16p. 36.95 (978-0-322-03403-7(5)) Wright Group, The.

Be Quiet!, 6 Packs. (Chiquilibros Ser.). (gr. k-1). 23.00 (978-0-7635-0429-8(7)) Rigby Education.

Beake, Lesley. One Dark, Dark Night Lugbara Version: O'du Alu Inia-ui. Draville, Ben & Mawa, Robert, trs. 2001. 16p. pap. 1.40 (978-0-521-00628-6(7)) Cambridge Univ. Pr.

—Tendani & the Bad Hippo. Senio, Colette, illus. 1999. (Cambridge Reading Routes Ser.). 24p. pap. 5.50 (978-0-521-77900-5(6)) Cambridge Univ. Pr.

Beake, Lesley & Schouw, Tina. Tina's Song. Andrew, Elizabeth, illus. 1999. (Cambridge Reading Routes Ser.). 24p. pap. 5.50 (978-0-521-77910-4(3)) Cambridge Univ. Pr.

Beake, Lesley, et al. One Dark, Dark Night: Sepedi Version. 2002. (Illus.). 16p. pap. 1.75 (978-0-521-52826-9(7)) Cambridge Univ. Pr.

—One Dark, Dark Night: Sesotho Version. 2002. (Illus.). 16p. pap. 1.75 (978-0-521-52823-8(2)) Cambridge Univ. Pr.

—One Dark, Dark Night: Setswana Version. 2002. (Illus.). 16p. pap. 1.75 (978-0-521-52824-5(0)) Cambridge Univ. Pr.

—One Dark, Dark Night: Xitsonga Version. 2002. (Illus.). 16p. pap. 1.75 (978-0-521-52825-2(9)) Cambridge Univ. Pr.

Beautiful Flowers: Level B, 6 vols. (Wonder Worldtm Ser.). 16p. 24.95 (978-0-7802-1980-9(5)) Wright Group, The.

Beck, Isabel L., et al. Big Book & Big Book Collection: All I Am. 1999. (Trophies Ser.). (gr. 1 up). pap. 56.30 (978-0-15-313367-1(8)) Harcourt Schl. Pubs.

—Big Books & Big Book Collection: From Head to Toe. 1999. (Trophies Ser.). (gr. 1 up). pap. 58.90 (978-0-15-313373-2(2)) Harcourt Schl. Pubs.

—Big Books & Big Book Collection: I Swam with a Seal. 1999. (Trophies Ser.). (gr. 1 up). pap. 61.60 (978-0-15-313378-7(3)) Harcourt Schl. Pubs.

—Big Books & Big Book Collection: Let's Go Visiting. 1999. (Trophies Ser.). (gr. 1 up). pap. 58.90 (978-0-15-313369-5(4)) Harcourt Schl. Pubs.

—Big Books & Big Book Collection: Little White Dog. 1999. (Trophies Ser.). (gr. 1 up). pap. 58.90 (978-0-15-313374-9(0)) Harcourt Schl. Pubs.

—Big Books & Big Book Collection: On a Hot, Hot Day. 1999. (Trophies Ser.). (gr. 1 up). pap. 58.90 (978-0-15-313375-6(9)) Harcourt Schl. Pubs.

—Big Books & Big Book Collection: Sometimes. 99th ed. 1999. (Trophies Ser.). (gr. 1 up). pap. 56.40 (978-0-15-310806-8(1)) Harcourt Schl. Pubs.

—Big Books & Big Book Collection: Ten Dogs in the Window. 1999. (Trophies Ser.). (gr. 1 up). pap. 58.90 (978-0-15-313370-1(8)) Harcourt Schl. Pubs.

—Big Books & Big Book Collection: To Market, to Market. 1999. (Trophies Ser.). (gr. 1 up). pap. 61.60 (978-0-15-313377-0(5)) Harcourt Schl. Pubs.

—Big Books & Big Book Collection: Where Does the Brown Bear Go? 1999. (Trophies Ser.). (gr. 1 up). pap. 58.90 (978-0-15-313372-5(4)) Harcourt Schl. Pubs.

—Decodable Books Collections. 3rd ed. 2002. (Trophies Ser.). Bks. 1-20. (gr. 2 up). pap. 137.30 (978-0-15-323768-3(6)); Bks. 1-34. (gr. 1 up). pap. 148.50 (978-0-15-323767-6(8)) Harcourt Schl. Pubs.

—Julian's Glorious Summer. 2003. (Trophies Ser.). (gr. 3 up). 50.40 (978-0-15-319277-7(1)) Harcourt Schl. Pubs.

The Bee & the Bug, 6 vols. 8p. (gr. k-1). 21.50 (978-0-322-02076-4(X)) Wright Group, The.

The Bee Sting: Digraphs -ck, -ng: Level B, 6 vols. (Wright Skills Ser.). 16p. (gr. k-3). 17.95 (978-0-322-01476-3(X)) Wright Group, The.

Beech. Comprehension Skills: Context - Level B - Special Education. 1999. pap. 11.08 (978-0-7398-2634-8(4)) Steck-Vaughn.

—Comprehension Skills: Facts - Level C - Special Education. 1999. pap. 11.08 (978-0-7398-2635-5(2)) Steck-Vaughn.

—Comprehension Skills: Inference - Level B - Special Education. 1999. pap. 11.08 (978-0-7398-2633-1(6)) Steck-Vaughn.

—Comprehension Skills: Sequence - Level C - Special Education. 1999. pap. 11.08 (978-0-7398-2636-2(0)) Steck-Vaughn.

—Comprehension Skills Main Idea Level C: Main Idea - Level C - Special Education. 1999. pap. 11.08 (978-0-7398-2637-9(9)) Steck-Vaughn.

—Reading for Today Workbook 1. 2000. pap. 9.16 (978-0-7398-2953-0(X)) Steck-Vaughn.

—Reading for Today Workbook 2. 2000. pap. 9.16 (978-0-7398-2954-7(8)) Steck-Vaughn.

—Reading for Today Workbook 3. 2000. pap. 9.16 (978-0-7398-2955-4(6)) Steck-Vaughn.

—Reading for Today Workbook 4. 2000. pap. 9.16 (978-0-7398-2956-1(4)) Steck-Vaughn.

—Reading for Today Workbook 5. 2000. pap. 9.16 (978-0-7398-2957-8(2)) Steck-Vaughn.

—Reading for Today Workbook 6. 2000. pap. 9.16 (978-0-7398-2958-5(0)) Steck-Vaughn.

Beech, Linda Ward. Ready-to-Go Reproducibles: Short Reading Passages & Graphic Organizers to Build Comprehension. 2001. 48p. (gr. 4). pap. 8.95 (978-0-439-16357-6(9)) Scholastic, Inc.

Behind the Rocks: Level E, 6 vols. (Wonder Worldtm Ser.). 16p. 24.95 (978-0-7802-1030-1(1)) Wright Group, The.

Bell, Chris. Fiddly Fingers. Jurevicius, Luke, illus. 2002. (Bright Sparks Ser.). 16p. pap. 2.30 (978-0-521-75424-8(0)) Cambridge Univ. Pr.

—Space Kids' Big Race. Jurevicius, Nathan, illus. 2002. (Bright Sparks Ser.). 16p. pap. 2.30 (978-0-521-75423-1(2)) Cambridge Univ. Pr.

Ben Franklin esta vivo! Conoce a Bill Meikle 19: Leveled Books. 2001. (McGraw-Hill. Lectura Ser.). (ENG & SPA.). (gr. 3 up). (978-0-02-188092-8(1)) Macmillan/McGraw-Hill Schl. Div.

Ben Franklin y sus Cuadernos 19: Leveled Books. 2001. (McGraw-Hill. Lectura Ser.). (ENG & SPA.). (gr. 3 up). (978-0-02-188116-1(2)) Macmillan/McGraw-Hill Schl. Div.

Benton, Celia. How a Frog Grows. 2003. (Compass Point Phonics Readers Ser.). (Illus.). 16p. (J). (gr. 1 up). 13.26 (978-0-7565-0509-7(7)) Compass Point Bks.

—Our Flag. 2003. (Compass Point Phonics Readers Ser.). (Illus.). 16p. (J). (gr. 1 up). 13.26 (978-0-7565-0517-2(8)) Compass Point Bks.

The Best Children in the World: Big Book: Level H. Group 1. (Story Box(R) Ser.). 16p. 31.50 (978-0-322-00324-8(5)) Wright Group, The.

The Best Place. 2005. (Early Library). (YA). (ps-3). 23.94 (978-0-8215-8944-1(X)) Sadlier, William H. Inc.

The Best Ride: Big Book, Vol. 2. 2005. (Emergent Library: Vol. 1). (YA). (ps-1). 23.94 (978-0-8215-8905-2(9)) Sadlier, William H. Inc.

Betty Bline, 6 vols. 8p. (gr. k-1). 21.50 (978-0-322-02069-6(7)) Wright Group, The.

Between the Tides: Level F, 6 vols. (Wonder Worldtm Ser.). 16p. 29.95 (978-0-7802-1982-3(1)) Wright Group, The.

Bevins, Pegi. Language Arts 1. 2002. 100p. ring bd. 29.95 (978-1-56254-508-6(6) , SP 5086) Saddleback Educational Publishing.

—Language Arts 2. 2002. 100p. ring bd. 29.95 (978-1-56254-509-3(4) , SP 5094) Saddleback Educational Publishing.

Beyond the Beyond, 6 vols. (Wildcats Ser.). 32p. (gr. 2-8). (978-0-322-02444-1(7)) Wright Group, The.

Bickel, Karla. The Reading Machine. Bickel, Karla, illus. l.t. ed. 2004. (Illus.). 16p. (J). (ps-6). pap. 5.00 (978-1-891452-15-4(0) , 9) Heart Arbor Bks.

Big & Green: Level A, 6 vols. (Wonder Worldtm Ser.). 16p. 24.95 (978-0-7802-1031-8(X)) Wright Group, The.

Big & Little: Level C. Group 1. (Sunshinetm Ser.). 8p. 20.95 (978-0-7802-5720-7(0)) Wright Group, The.

Big Blank Piece of Paper. (J). (gr. 2). pap. 12.79 (978-0-673-80022-0(9) , Scott Foresman) Addison Wesley Schl.

Big Enough: Level F. (Visionstm Ser.). 8p. 20.95 (978-0-322-00312-5(1)) Wright Group, The.

The Big, Fun Hat: Review of Consonants, Short Vowels, Word Families: Level A, 6 vols. (Wright Skills Ser.). 12p. (gr. k-3). 17.95 (978-0-322-03125-8(7)) Wright Group, The.

The Big Round Up: Big Book: Level I. (Wonder Worldtm Ser.). 16p. 26.50 (978-0-7802-3477-2(4)) Wright Group, The.

The Big Roundup: Level I, 6 vols. (Wonder Worldtm Ser.). 16p. 29.95 (978-0-7802-1245-9(2)) Wright Group, The.

The Big Tan Rat: Short Vowel Word Family Review: Level B, 6 vols. (Wright Skills Ser.). 16p. (gr. k-3). 17.95 (978-0-322-01458-9(1)) Wright Group, The.

Bigger & Bigger: Big Book: Level C. 8p. 20.95 (978-0-322-00355-2(5)) Wright Group, The.

A Bigger Barger: Level I. Group 1. (Story Box(R) Ser.). 16p. 31.50 (978-0-322-02464-9(1)) Wright Group, The.

Bilingual Take-Home Books Collection. 2005. (YA). (ps-1). 113.40 (978-0-8215-1209-8(9)) Sadlier, William H. Inc.

Billy Drake's Cake, 6 vols. 8p. (gr. k-1). 21.50 (978-0-322-02085-6(9)) Wright Group, The.

Bingley, David. Hellions' Hideaway. l.t. ed. 2004. (Linford Western Large Print Ser.). (Illus.). 272p. 20.99 (978-1-84395-471-2(0)) Ulverscroft Large Print Bks. GBR. *Dist:* Ulverscroft Large Print Bks., Ltd.

Bird Beaks: Big Book: Level K. (Wonder Worldtm Ser.). 16p. 26.50 (978-0-7802-3473-4(1)) Wright Group, The.

Bird Beaks: Level K, 6 vols. (Wonder Worldtm Ser.). 16p. 34.95 (978-0-7802-1197-1(9)) Wright Group, The.

Blachowicz, Camille L. Z. Reading Fluency: Reader, Level C. 2003. pap. 15.96 (978-0-07-830908-3(5) , 9780078309083) Jamestown.

—Reading Fluency: Reader, Level D. 2003. pap. 15.96 (978-0-07-830909-0(3) , 9780078309090) Jamestown.

—Reading Fluency: Reader, Level E. 2003. pap. 15.96 (978-0-07-830910-6(7) , 9780078309106) Jamestown.

—Reading Fluency: Reader, Level F. 2003. pap. 15.96 (978-0-07-830911-3(5) , 9780078309113) Jamestown.

—Reading Fluency: Reader, Level G. 2003. pap. 15.96 (978-0-07-830912-0(3) , 9780078309120) Jamestown.

—Reading Fluency: Reader, Level H. 2003. pap. 15.96 (978-0-07-845698-5(3) , 9780078456985) Jamestown.

—Reading Fluency: Reader Level I. 2003. pap. 15.96 (978-0-07-845699-2(1) , 9780078456992) Jamestown.

—Reading Fluency: Reader's Record F. 2003. pap. 10.64 (978-0-07-845703-6(3) , 9780078457036) Jamestown.

—Reading Fluency: Reader's Record I. 2003. pap. 10.64 (978-0-07-845706-7(8) , 9780078457067) Jamestown.

—Reading Fluency: Reader's Record, Level C. 2003. pap. 10.64 (978-0-07-845700-5(9) , 9780078457005) Jamestown.

—Reading Fluency: Reader's Record, Level D. 2003. pap. 10.64 (978-0-07-845701-2(7) , 9780078457012) Jamestown.

—Reading Fluency: Reader's Record, Level E. 2003. pap. 10.64 (978-0-07-845702-9(5) , 9780078457029) Jamestown.

—Reading Fluency: Reader's Record, Level G. 2003. pap. 10.64 (978-0-07-845704-3(1) , 9780078457043) Jamestown.

—Reading Fluency: Reader's Record, Level H. 2003. pap. 10.64 (978-0-07-845705-0(X) , 9780078457050) Jamestown.

Blasser-Riley, Gail. Building Reading Comprehension: High-Interest Selections for Critical Reading Skills. 2000. (100+ Seriestm Ser.). 128p. (J). (gr. 1-2). pap. 12.99 (978-1-56822-912-6(7) , IF8717, Instructional Fair) Schaffer, Frank Pubns.

—Cause & Effect: Using Causes & Effects to Make Connections. 2001. (Basic Skills Ser.). 48p. (J). (gr. 3-4). pap. 6.99 (978-0-7424-0100-6(6) , IF5627) School Specialty Publishing.

Blaxland, Wendy. Granny Paniaris. 2002. (Bright Sparks Ser.). (Illus.). 16p. pap. 2.30 (978-0-521-75380-7(5)) Cambridge Univ. Pr.

—In My Bag. 2002. (Bright Sparks Ser.). (Illus.). 16p. pap. 2.30 (978-0-521-75377-7(5)) Cambridge Univ. Pr.

—In the Garden: Emergent. Martin, Jo, illus. 2002. (Bright Sparks Ser.). 16p. pap. 2.30 (978-0-521-75117-9(9)) Cambridge Univ. Pr.

—My Sandwich: Emergent. Jurevicius, Luke, illus. 2002. (Bright Sparks Ser.). 16p. pap. 2.30 (978-0-521-75118-6(7)) Cambridge Univ. Pr.

—Near the Coral Reef: Emergent. Tilders, Loma, illus. 2002. (Bright Sparks Ser.). 16p. pap. 2.30 (978-0-521-75116-2(0)) Cambridge Univ. Pr.

—New School. 2002. (Bright Sparks Ser.). (Illus.). 16p. pap. 2.30 (978-0-521-75400-2(3)) Cambridge Univ. Pr.

—The Present That Grew. 2002. (Bright Sparks Ser.). (Illus.). 16p. pap. 2.30 (978-0-521-75402-6(X)) Cambridge Univ. Pr.

—Six Big Balloons. 2002. (Bright Sparks Ser.). (Illus.). 16p. pap. 2.30 (978-0-521-75378-4(3)) Cambridge Univ. Pr.

—The Storm. Coutts, Lisa, illus. 2002. (Bright Sparks Ser.). 16p. pap. 2.30 (978-0-521-75401-9(1)) Cambridge Univ. Pr.

—Tides. 2002. (Bright Sparks Ser.). (Illus.). 16p. pap. 2.30 (978-0-521-75379-1(1)) Cambridge Univ. Pr.

—Where's the Cat? Emergent. 2002. (Bright Sparks Ser.). (Illus.). 16p. pap. 2.30 (978-0-521-75115-5(2)) Cambridge Univ. Pr.

Blevins, Wiley. Is It Hot? Is It Hot? 2003. (Compass Point Phonics Readers Ser.). (Illus.). 16p. (J). (gr. 1 up). 13.26 (978-0-7565-0510-3(0)) Compass Point Bks.

—Magnets. 2003. (Compass Point Phonics Readers Ser.). (Illus.). 16p. (J). (gr. 1 up). 13.26 (978-0-7565-0511-0(9)) Compass Point Bks.

—Maps. 2003. (Compass Point Phonics Readers Ser.). (Illus.). 16p. (J). (gr. 1 up). 13.26 (978-0-7565-0512-7(7)) Compass Point Bks.

—Push or Pull? 2003. (Compass Point Phonics Readers Ser.). (Illus.). 16p. (J). (gr. 1 up). 13.26 (978-0-7565-0521-9(6)) Compass Point Bks.

—Who Am I? 2003. (Compass Point Phonics Readers Ser.). (Illus.). 16p. (J). (gr. 1 up). 13.26 (978-0-7565-0534-9(8)) Compass Point Bks.

Blue Bananas, 12 bks. Incl. Big Dog & Little Dog Go Sailing. Young, Selina. Young, Selina, illus. (978-0-7787-0845-2(4)); Big Dog & Little Dog Visit the Moon. Young, Selina. Young, Selina, illus. (978-0-7787-0849-0(7)); Colin & the Curly Claw. Fearnley, Jan. Fearnley, Jan, illus. (978-0-7787-0840-7(3)); Dexter's Journey. D'Lacey, Chris. Roberts, David, illus. (978-0-7787-0846-9(2)); Follow the Swallow. Donaldson, Julia. Ursell, Martin, illus. (978-0-7787-0842-1(X)); "Here I Am!" Said Smedley. Puttock, Simon. Chatterton, Martin & Chatterton, Ann, illus. (978-0-7787-0838-4(1)); Horrible Haircut. Ritchie, Alison. Newsham, Ian, illus. (978-0-7787-0844-5(6)); Magic Lemonade. Dunbar, Joyce. McCafferty, Jan, illus. (978-0-7787-0839-1(X)); Magnificent Mummies. Bradman, Tony. Chatterton, Martin, illus. (978-0-7787-0843-8(8)); Midnight in

P Q R

Memphis. Bradman, Tony. Chatterton, Martin & Chatterton, Ann, illus. (978-0-7787-0848-3(9)); Peg. Stewart, Maddie. Willey, Bee, illus. (978-0-7787-0841-4(1)); Shoot! Mayfield, Sue. Cox, Ken, illus. (978-0-7787-0847-6(0)); 48p. (J). (gr. 1-2). 2001. 2002. (978-0-7787-0837-7(3)); Set pap. (978-0-7787-0883-4(7)) Crabtree Publishing Co.

The Blue Fruit Pie: Digraphs ie, ue: Level B, 6 vols. (Wright Skills Ser.). 16p. (gr. k-3). 17.95 (978-0-322-01481-7(6)) Wright Group, The.

Bobby Fling, 6 vols. 8p. (gr. k-1). 21.50 (978-0-322-02068-9(9)) Wright Group, The.

Boehm, Richard G., et al. Reading Support & Test Preparation: A Child's Place. 2003. (Harcourt Brace Social Studies). (gr. k-7). 27.00 (978-0-15-312374-0(5)) Harcourt Schl. Pubs.

Boggywooga: Level I. Group 1. (Sunshinetm Ser.). 16p. 31.50 (978-0-7802-5754-2(5)) Wright Group, The.

Bogle's Feet: Level L. Group 1, 6 vols. (Sunshinetm Ser.). 16p. 36.50 (978-0-7802-5790-0(1)) Wright Group, The.

Bonnell, Kris. Bedtime for Carl. 2006. (J). 3.75 (***978-1-933727-26-4(8)**) Reading Reading Bks., LLC.

—Clouds Tell the Weather. 2007. (J). 3.95 (***978-1-933727-47-9(0)**) Reading Reading Bks., LLC.

—A Friend for Jellyfish. 2006. (J). 3.95 (***978-1-933727-28-8(4)**) Reading Reading Bks., LLC.

—A Garden Is Fun. 2006. (J). 3.95 (***978-1-933727-37-0(3)**) Reading Reading Bks., LLC.

—A House for Squirrel. 2007. (J). 3.95 (***978-1-933727-46-2(2)**) Reading Reading Bks., LLC.

—A Walk with Dad. 2006. (J). 3.95 (***978-1-933727-43-1(8)**) Reading Reading Bks., LLC.

Book Treks Add-on Pack, Vol. 4. 2005. (Book Treks Ser.). (J). (gr. 4-8). 100.95 (978-0-673-61956-3(7)) Modern Curriculum Pr.

Books Only Package. 2005. (Little Celebrations Picture/Text & Literacy Cards Ser.). (J). (gr. k-3). 510.95 (978-0-673-77194-0(6)); 551.95 (978-0-673-77195-7(4)); 633.50 (978-0-673-77865-9(7)) Celebration Pr.

Boten, Wallace. From Farm to Store. 2003. (Compass Point Phonics Readers Ser.). (Illus.). 16p. (J). (gr. 1 up). 13.26 (978-0-7565-0507-3(0)) Compass Point Bks.

A Bottle Garden: Level F, 6 vols. (Wonder Worldtm Ser.). 16p. 29.95 (978-0-7802-1984-7(8)) Wright Group, The.

Boynton, Bibi. Bats. 2003. (Compass Point Phonics Readers Ser.). (Illus.). 16p. (J). (gr. 1 up). 13.26 (978-0-7565-0505-9(4)) Compass Point Bks.

Bozo: Level I, 6 vols. (Wonder Worldtm Ser.). 16p. 29.95 (978-0-7802-4561-7(X)) Wright Group, The.

Brain, Helen. The Shepherd's Crook. 1999. (Cambridge Reading Routes Ser.). (Illus.). 32p. pap. 6.45 (978-0-521-77905-0(7)) Cambridge Univ. Pr.

Brainteasers & Doodles! 2004. (Gel Pen Activity Bks.). (Illus.). 24p. (J). (gr. 2-5). act. bk. ed. (978-0-7666-0596-1(5) , 66000) Modern Publishing.

Braun, Cheskel. Learn to Read, Vol. 1. 2006. (YID.). (J). per. 12.00 (978-0-9774302-0-8(0)) Braun Pubns.

Bread Sets: 1 Each of 3 Big Books. (Sunshinetm Science Ser.). (gr. 1-2). 111.50 (978-0-7802-2808-5(1)) Wright Group, The.

Bread Sets: 1 Each of 3 Student Books. (Sunshinetm Science Ser.). (gr. 1-2). 20.95 (978-0-7802-2809-2(X)) Wright Group, The.

Breitbart, Mrs, Karen. Theme-Based Reading Comprehension. 2003. (100+ Seriestm Ser.). 128p. (J). (gr. 1-1). pap. 12.99 (978-0-7424-1921-6(5) , IFG99108); (gr. 2-2). pap. 12.99 (978-0-7424-1922-3(3) , IFG99109) School Specialty Publishing.

The Bridge: Level B. Group 2. (Story Box(R) Ser.). 8p. 20.95 (978-0-7802-9364-9(9)) Wright Group, The.

Bridges: 6 Each of 1 Anthology, 6 vols. (Wildcatstm Ser.). 32p. (gr. 2-8). (978-0-322-02425-0(0)) Wright Group, The.

Bridges-Across the Gap: Level O, 6 vols. (Wonder Worldtm Ser.). 48p. 39.95 (978-0-7802-2963-1(0)) Wright Group, The.

Bridges to Literature: Power Words: A Bridge to Reading. 2002. (gr. 6-12). Vol. 2. (978-0-618-36410-7(2) , 2-04684); Vol. 3. (978-0-618-36411-4(0) , 2-04685) McDougal Littell Inc.

Bridging School to Home "B", Set. (J). (ps-1). 32.25 (978-1-57874-069-7(X)) Kaeden Corp.

Bridgman, Beth, rev. Distinguishing Between Fact & Opinion. rev. ed. 1998. (Horizons Ser.). (Illus.). 24p. (J). (gr. 4-9). pap. 5.95 (978-1-58086-042-0(7)); pap. 5.95 (978-1-58086-052-9(4)) EDC Publishing.

—Drawing Conclusions. rev. ed. 1998. (Horizons Ser.). (Illus.). 24p. (J). (gr. 4-9). pap. 5.95 (978-1-58086-043-7(5)); pap. 5.95 (978-1-58086-053-6(2)) EDC Publishing.

—Establishing Sequence. rev. ed. 1998. (Horizons Ser.). (Illus.). 24p. (J). (gr. 4-9). pap. 5.95 (978-1-58086-040-6(0)); pap. 5.95 (978-1-58086-050-5(8)) EDC Publishing.

—Finding the Main Idea. rev. ed. 1998. (Horizons Ser.). (Illus.). 24p. (J). (gr. 4-9). pap. 5.95 (978-1-58086-049-9(4)); Level 1. pap. 5.95 (978-1-58086-039-0(7)) EDC Publishing.

—Following Directions. rev. ed. 1998. (Horizons Ser.). (Illus.). 24p. (J). (gr. 4-9). pap. 5.95 (978-1-58086-041-3(9)); pap. 5.95 (978-1-58086-051-2(6)) EDC Publishing.

—Making Judgments. rev. ed. 1998. (Horizons Ser.). (Illus.). 24p. (J). (gr. 4-9). pap. 5.95 (978-1-58086-047-5(8)); pap. 5.95 (978-1-58086-057-4(5)) EDC Publishing.

—Predicting Outcomes. rev. ed. 1998. (Horizons Ser.). (Illus.). 24p. (J). (gr. 4-9). pap. 5.95 (978-1-58086-045-1(1)); pap. 5.95 (978-1-58086-055-0(9)) EDC Publishing.

—Recalling Details. rev. ed. 1998. (Horizons Ser.). (Illus.). 24p. (J). (gr. 4-9). Level 1. pap. 5.95 (978-1-58086-038-3(9)); Level 2. pap. 5.95 (978-1-58086-048-2(6)) EDC Publishing.

—Recognizing Cause & Effect. rev. ed. 1998. (Horizons Ser.). (Illus.). 24p. (J). (gr. 4-9). pap. 5.95 (978-1-58086-044-4(3)); pap. 5.95 (978-1-58086-054-3(0)) EDC Publishing.

—Recognizing Plot, Character, Mood. rev. ed. 1998. (Horizons Ser.). (Illus.). 24p. (J). (gr. 4-9). pap. 5.95 (978-1-58086-046-8(X)); pap. 5.95 (978-1-58086-056-7(7)) EDC Publishing.

Bright & Beyond - Reading. 2004. (J). (978-0-9726170-8-6(6)) Pal Toys, LLC.

Brighter Vision Publishing Staff. Reading Skills-1: And Language Activities. 1999. (Primary Skills Ser.). (Illus.). 32p. (J). (gr. 1). pap. 2.25 (978-1-55254-117-3(7) , BV13004) Brighter Vision Pubns.

—Reading Skills-2: And Language Activities. 1999. (Primary Skills Ser.). (Illus.). 32p. (J). (gr. 2). pap. 2.25 (978-1-55254-119-7(3) , BV13006) Brighter Vision Pubns.

—Reading Skills-3: And Language Activities. 1999. (Primary Skills Ser.). (Illus.). 32p. (J). (gr. 3). pap. 2.25 (978-1-55254-121-0(5)) Brighter Vision Pubns.

—Reading Skills Grade 1. 1998. (J). (gr. 1). pap. 2.25 (978-1-55254-030-5(8)) Brighter Vision Pubns.

—Reading Skills Grade 2. 1998. (J). (gr. 2). pap. 2.25 (978-1-55254-031-2(6)) Brighter Vision Pubns.

—Reading Skills Grade 3. 1998. (Illus.). 32p. (J). pap. 2.25 (978-1-55254-032-9(4)) Brighter Vision Pubns.

—Reading Skills-K: And Language Activities. 1999. (Primary Skills Ser.). (Illus.). 32p. (J). pap. 2.25 (978-1-55254-115-9(0) , BV13002) Brighter Vision Pubns.

Brocker, Susan. Across the Oregon Trail: Level R, 6 vols. 128p. (gr. 6 up). 36.95 (978-0-322-05890-3(2)) Wright Group, The.

Broken Bones, 6 vols. (Sunshinetm Science Ser.). 24p. (gr. 1-2). 31.50 (978-0-7802-0300-6(3)); 36.95 (978-0-7802-0551-2(0)) Wright Group, The.

Brooks, Bearl. Jumbo Reading Yearbook: Kindergarten. (Jumbo Reading Ser.). 96p. (J). 15.95 (978-0-8209-0011-7(7) , B-JECR-R) ESP, Inc.

Brotherly Love Little Book: Early Reading Fluency, Level A. 2004. pap. 6.00 (978-0-7398-8158-3(2)) Steck-Vaughn.

Brown, Richard & Ruttle, Kate. Beginning to Read Bk. C: Developing Sight Vocabulary American Edition. 2001. (Cambridge Reading Ser.). pap., wbk. ed. 27.00 (978-0-521-00576-0(0)) Cambridge Univ. Pr.

Brown, Richard, et al. Ben's Amazing Birthday: South African Edition. Large, Annabel, illus. 1999. (Cambridge Reading Routes Ser.). 24p. pap. 5.50 (978-0-521-77909-8(X)) Cambridge Univ. Pr.

Brown, Susie. Are We There Yet? Williams, Robbie J., illus. 2002. (Bright Sparks Ser.). 16p. pap. 2.30 (978-0-521-75411-8(9)) Cambridge Univ. Pr.

Brown, Terry. Bible Stories for Bedtime. 2004. (Illus.). 240p. (J). pap. 5.97 (978-1-59310-359-0(X)) Barbour Publishing, Inc.

Brush, Brush, Brush! 2005. (Emergent (Prek-2) Health Package Ser.). 12p. (YA). (ps-2). 25.20 (978-0-8215-7849-0(9)) Sadlier, William H. Inc.

Bryant-Mole, Karen. Picture This! Places, 4 bks., Set. Incl. At the Beach. lib. bdg. 18.50 (978-1-57572-898-8(2)); In the Country. lib. bdg. 18.50 (978-1-57572-899-5(0)); In the Town. lib. bdg. 18.50 (978-1-57572-900-8(8)); On the Farm. lib. bdg. 18.50 (978-1-57572-901-5(6)); 24p. (J). (ps-1). 1999. (Illus.). 1999. Set lib. bdg. 74.00 (978-1-57572-902-2(4)) Heinemann Library.

Bubble Bear. 2001. (ps-2). lib. bdg. 9.80 (978-0-613-32351-2(3)) Tandem Library Bks.

Buchholz, Jeannie. A Tale of Two Cities. 1999. 90p. (YA). (gr. 9-12). stu. ed., ring bd. 14.99 (978-1-58609-168-2(9)) Progeny Pr.

Budgell, Gill. Make Colors American English Edition, 6, Pack. 2000. (Cambridge Reading Ser.). (Illus.). 8p. pap. 28.00 (978-0-521-79891-4(4)) Cambridge Univ. Pr.

Budgell, Gill & Ruttle, Kate. One, Two, Buckle My Shoe. 2001. (Cambridge Reading Ser.). (Illus.). 8p. pap. 5.00 (978-0-521-00201-1(X)) Cambridge Univ. Pr.

—What's the Time, Mr Wolf? 2001. (Cambridge Reading Ser.). (Illus.). 8p. pap. 5.00 (978-0-521-00210-3(9)) Cambridge Univ. Pr.

A Bug in a Rug: Consonants c, l, r; Short Vowel u word families: Level A, 6 vols. (Wright Skills Ser.). 12p. (gr. k-3). 17.95 (978-0-322-01452-7(2)) Wright Group, The.

Bug-Watching: Big Book: Level B, 6 vols. 8p. 20.95 (978-0-7802-9744-9(X)) Wright Group, The.

Building Dreams, Grade 3: American Readers. (J). tchr. ed., wbk. ed. (978-0-669-05019-6(9)); wbk. ed. (978-0-669-05018-9(0)) Houghton Mifflin Co. (Schl. Div.).

Building Dreams Reading Kit: American Readers. (J). (gr. 3). (978-0-669-05026-4(1)) Houghton Mifflin Co. (Schl. Div.).

Building Things, 6 vols. (Sunshinetm Ser.). 16p. (gr. k up). 29.50 (978-0-7802-5420-6(1)) Wright Group, The.

Built for Speed Classroom Library. (gr. 4 up). lib. bdg. 24.95 (978-0-7368-8949-0(3)) Red Brick Learning.

Buller, Laura. Star Wars: Star Pilot. 2005. (Dk Readers Ser.). (Illus.). 48p. (J). (ps-12). pap. 3.99 (978-0-7566-1161-3(X) , 1241628) Dorling Kindersley Publishing, Inc.

Bulloch, Ivan. Sounds Like Smelly! James, Diane, illus. rev. ed. 2004. (My Turn Ser.). 12p. (J). (ps-k). bds. 6.95 (978-1-58728-011-5(6) , Two Can Publishing) T&N Children's Publishing.

Bump! Bump! Bump!, 6 vols. 8p. (gr. k-1). 21.50 (978-0-322-02086-3(7)) Wright Group, The.

Burgess, Chris. Study Reading Modules: (A) Antelope. 1999. (Illus.). 24p. (J). pap. 19.95 (978-0-7217-0504-0(9)) Schofield & Sims Ltd. GBR. *Dist:* State Mutual Bk. & Periodical Service, Ltd.

The Burglars' Ball: Level Q, 6 vols. (Wonder Worldtm Ser.). 48p. 39.95 (978-0-7802-2961-7(4)) Wright Group, The.

Burke. In Hiding: Animals under Cover. 1999. (Illus.). bds. (978-0-7398-2448-1(1)); (J). pap. (978-0-7398-2399-6(X)) Steck-Vaughn.

Burkett, Beverley. Yawning Is Catching: Chilomwe Version. Nkhoma, Wilson, tr. 1999. (Cambridge Reading Routes Ser.). (Illus.). 16p. pap. 3.70 (978-0-521-66849-1(2)) Cambridge Univ. Pr.

—Yawning Is Catching: Chinyanja Version. Iphani, Max, tr. 1999. (Cambridge Reading Routes Ser.). (Illus.). 16p. pap. 3.70 (978-0-521-66883-5(2)) Cambridge Univ. Pr.

—Yawning Is Catching: Chitumbuka Version. Chirambo, Reuben, tr. 1999. (Cambridge Reading Routes Ser.). (Illus.). 16p. pap. 3.70 (978-0-521-66870-5(0)) Cambridge Univ. Pr.

—Yawning Is Catching: Chiyao Version. Mjaya, Ahmmardouh, tr. 1999. (Cambridge Reading Routes Ser.). (Illus.). 16p. pap. 3.70 (978-0-521-66863-7(8)) Cambridge Univ. Pr.

Burroughs, Elizabeth & Partridge, Juliet. Elephant: Chitonga Version. Chisengele, tr. 2001. (Illus.). 16p. pap. 0.45 (978-0-521-01435-9(2)) Cambridge Univ. Pr.

—Elephant: Cinyanja Version. Tembo, tr. 2001. (Illus.). 16p. pap. 0.45 (978-0-521-01437-3(9)) Cambridge Univ. Pr.

—Elephant: Icibemba Version. Mulilo, tr. 2001. (Illus.). 16p. pap. 0.45 (978-0-521-01440-3(9)) Cambridge Univ. Pr.

—Elephant: Kiikaonde Version. Muyebaa, tr. 2001. (Illus.). 16p. pap. 0.45 (978-0-521-01441-0(7)) Cambridge Univ. Pr.

—Elephant: Luvale Version. Sakapaji, tr. 2001. (Illus.). 16p. pap. 0.45 (978-0-521-01445-8(X)) Cambridge Univ. Pr.

—Elephant: Silozi Version. Mwendende, tr. 2001. (Illus.). 16p. pap. 0.45 (978-0-521-01446-5(8)) Cambridge Univ. Pr.

The Bush Telegraph: Level T. Group 2, 6 vols. (Sunshinetm Ser.). 48p. 44.95 (978-0-7802-4178-7(9)) Wright Group, The.

Buster: Level E. 8p. 20.95 (978-0-7802-9742-5(3)) Wright Group, The.

Buster MCluster: Level G. (Wonder Worldtm Ser.). 16p. 26.50 (978-0-7802-2828-3(6)) Wright Group, The.

Busy Bees: 1 Big Book, 6 Each of 1 Student Book, & 1 Cassette. (Song Box(R) Ser.). (gr. 1-2). 68.95 (978-0-7802-3203-7(8)) Wright Group, The.

Busy Bees: 6 Each of 1 Student Book, 6 vols. (Song Box(R) Ser.). (gr. 1-2). 29.50 (978-0-7802-2267-0(9)) Wright Group, The.

Butler, Heather, ed. Reading for Fluency Resource Guide. 2005. (Reading for Fluency Ser.). (Illus.). 64p. (J). pap. (978-1-59198-166-4(2) , 4239) Creative Teaching Pr., Inc.

The Buzz in the Box: Consonant z: Level A, 6 vols. (Wright Skills Ser.). 12p. (gr. k-3). 17.95 (978-0-322-03124-1(9)) Wright Group, The.

Buzzing Files: Level C. Group 1. (Sunshinetm Ser.). 8p. 20.95 (978-0-7802-5721-4(9)) Wright Group, The.

By the Pond: Open Vowel Pattern, Words Ending in y with Long i Sound, Ending in o, Ending in e: Level B, 6 vols. (Wright Skills Ser.). 16p. (gr. k-3). 26.50 (978-0-322-01470-1(0)) Wright Group, The.

El Caballito Troton 18: Leveled Books. 2001. (McGraw-Hill. Lectura Ser.). (ENG & SPA.). (gr. 1 up). (978-0-02-187947-2(8)) Macmillan/McGraw-Hill Schl. Div.

Un Cambio de Impresion 12: Leveled Books. 2001. (McGraw-Hill. Lectura Ser.). (ENG & SPA.). (gr. 4 up). (978-0-02-188188-8(X)) Macmillan/McGraw-Hill Schl. Div.

Cambridge University Press Staff. Clocks, Spots & Dragons Mixed Pack, 6 vols, Pack. 2001. (Cambridge Storybooks Ser.). (Illus.). 8p. pap. 16.00 (978-0-521-00822-8(0)) Cambridge Univ. Pr.

Campbell, Kenneth U. Great Leaps Reading Grades 6-8. 4th ed. 1998. 160p. (YA). (gr. 6-8). reprint ed. 66.00 (978-1-59347-020-3(7) , GL/3) Diarmuid Inc.

—Great Leaps Reading Grades 9-12. 4th ed. 1998. 156p. (YA). reprint ed. 66.00 (978-1-59347-030-2(4) , GL/4) Diarmuid Inc.

Can I have a Cat? Consonant c: Level A, 6 vols. (Wright Skills Ser.). 12p. (gr. k-3). 17.95 (978-0-322-03117-3(6)) Wright Group, The.

Can Kim & Kip Play? Consonant k: Level A, 6 vols. (Wright Skills Ser.). 12p. (gr. k-3). 17.95 (978-0-322-03132-6(X)) Wright Group, The.

Cannon, Shannon. The Seasons. 2003. (Compass Point Phonics Readers Ser.). (Illus.). 16p. (J). (gr. 1 up). 13.26 (978-0-7565-0527-1(5)) Compass Point Bks.

The Canterbury Tales. 2004. (Literature Connections Ser.). (gr. 6-12). (978-0-395-89328-9(3) , 2-70867) McDougal Littell Inc.

Carbo Recorded Books: Primary/Intermediate. 2003. (Illus.). (J). (gr. 2-5). pap. 729.00 incl. audio (978-1-883186-30-2(7) , NPIS9) National Reading Styles Institute, Inc.

Carey Molter. Ate As in Skate. 2003. (Word Families Ser.: Vol. 8). (Illus.). 23p. (J). (ps-3). lib. bdg. 19.93 (978-1-59197-271-6(X) , SandCastle) ABDO Publishing Co.

Carroll, Joyce Armstrong, et al. Writing & Grammar, Grade 9: Communication in Action. 2001. Bronze Level. (YA). (gr. 7). pap. 7.47 (978-0-13-053213-8(4)); Copper Level. (J). (gr. 6). pap. 7.47 (978-0-13-053212-1(6)); Diamond Level. (YA). (gr. 12). pap. 7.47 (978-0-13-053219-0(3)); Gold Level. (YA). (gr. 9). stu. ed. 47.47 (978-0-13-436966-2(1)); Gold Level. (YA). (gr. 9). pap. 7.47 (978-0-13-053216-9(9)); Ruby Level. (YA). (gr. 11). pap. 7.47 (978-0-13-053218-3(5)); Silver Level. (YA). (gr. 8). pap. 7.47 (978-0-13-053214-5(2)) Prentice Hall PTR.

Carson-Dellosa Publishing Staff. Summer Bridge Reading 1-2. 2007. 96p. pap. (***978-1-60022-444-7(X)**) Carson-Dellosa Publishing Co., Inc.

Case, Margaret. The Hanukah Party. Koman, Vasja, illus. 2002. (Bright Sparks Ser.). 16p. pap. 2.30 (978-0-521-75407-1(0)) Cambridge Univ. Pr.

—The Water Festival. 2002. (Bright Sparks Ser.). (Illus.). 16p. pap. 2.30 (978-0-521-75408-8(9)) Cambridge Univ. Pr.

El caso de la profesora Fugada 15: Leveled Books. 2001. (McGraw-Hill. Lectura Ser.). (ENG & SPA.). (gr. 4 up). (978-0-02-188191-8(X)) Macmillan/McGraw-Hill Schl. Div.

Catching Glimpses: American Readers. (J). (gr. 3). (978-0-669-05027-1(X)); (978-0-669-05028-8(8)); wbk. ed. (978-0-669-05032-5(6)) Houghton Mifflin Co. (Schl. Div.).

Catching the Sun: Tales from Asia, 6 vols., Vol. 5. 2005. (Book Treks Ser.). (Illus.). (J). (gr. 4-8). stu. ed. 35.95 (978-0-673-61842-9(0)) Celebration Pr.

Cats: Level F, 6 vols. (Wonder Worldtm Ser.). 16p. 29.95 (978-0-7802-2889-4(8)) Wright Group, The.

A Cat's Day: Level A, 6 vols. 8p. 20.95 (978-0-322-00356-9(3)) Wright Group, The.

Celebrate Reading! (J). pap., stu. ed. 21.29 (978-0-673-80011-4(3)); (J). (gr. 1). pap., stu. ed. 21.29 (978-0-673-80012-1(1)); (J). (gr. 1). pap., stu. ed. 21.29 (978-0-673-80013-8(X)); (J). (gr. 1). pap., stu. ed. 21.29 (978-0-673-80014-5(8)); (J). (gr. 1). pap., stu. ed. 21.29 (978-0-673-80015-2(6)); (J). (gr. 1). pap., stu. ed. 21.29 (978-0-673-80016-9(4)); (J). (gr. 2). pap., stu. ed. 12.79 (978-0-673-80021-3(0)); Bk. C. (J). (gr. 2). pap., stu. ed. 12.79 (978-0-673-80023-7(7)); Bk. C. (J). (gr. 3). pap., stu. ed. 13.73 (978-0-673-80033-6(4)); Bk. C. (J). (gr. 4). pap., stu. ed. 8.98 (978-0-673-80043-5(1)); Bk. C. (J). (gr. 5). pap., stu. ed. 8.98 (978-0-673-80053-4(9)); Bk. C. (J). (gr. 5). pap., stu. ed. 8.98 (978-0-673-80063-3(6)); Bk. C. (YA). (gr. 7). pap., stu. ed. 14.71 (978-0-673-80075-6(X)); Bk. D. (J). (gr. 2). pap., stu. ed. 12.79 (978-0-673-80024-4(5)); Bk. D. (J). (gr. 3). pap., stu. ed. 13.73 (978-0-673-80034-3(2)); Bk. D. (J). (gr. 4). pap., stu. ed. 8.98 (978-0-673-80044-2(X)); Bk. D. (J). (gr. 5). pap., stu. ed. 8.98 (978-0-673-80054-1(7)); Bk. D. (J). (gr. 5). pap., stu. ed. 8.98 (978-0-673-80064-0(4)); Bk. A. (J). (gr. 3). pap., stu. ed. 13.73 (978-0-673-80031-2(8)); Bk. A. (J). (gr. 4). pap., stu. ed. 8.98 (978-0-673-80041-1(5)); Bk. A. (J). (gr. 4). pap., stu. ed. 8.98 (978-0-673-80051-0(2)); Bk. A. (J). (gr. 5). pap., stu. ed. 8.98 (978-0-673-80061-9(X)); Bk. B. (J). (gr. 3). pap., stu. ed. 13.73 (978-0-673-80032-9(6)); Bk. B. (J). (gr. 4). pap., stu. ed. 8.98 (978-0-673-80042-8(3)); Bk. B. (J). (gr. 5). pap., stu. ed. 8.98 (978-0-673-80052-7(0)); Bk. B. (J). (gr. 5). pap., stu. ed. 8.98 (978-0-673-80062-6(8)); Bk. E. (J). (gr. 2). pap., stu. ed. 12.79 (978-0-673-80025-1(3)); Bk. E. (J). (gr. 3). pap., stu. ed. 13.73 (978-0-673-80035-0(0)); Bk. E. (J). (gr. 4). pap., stu. ed. 8.98 (978-0-673-80045-9(8)); Bk. E. (J). (gr. 5). pap., stu. ed. 8.98 (978-0-673-80055-8(5)); Bk. E. (J). (gr. 5). pap., stu. ed. 8.98 (978-0-673-80065-7(2)); Bk. F. (J). (gr. 2). pap., stu. ed. 12.79 (978-0-673-80026-8(1)); Bk. F. (J). (gr. 3). pap., stu. ed. 13.73 (978-0-673-80036-7(9)); Bk. F. (J). (gr. 4). pap., stu. ed. 8.98 (978-0-673-80046-6(6)); Bk. F. (J). (gr. 5). pap., stu. ed. 8.98 (978-0-673-80056-5(3)); Bk. F. (J). (gr. 5). pap., stu. ed. 8.98 (978-0-673-80066-4(0)); Unit 7A, Bk. A. (YA). (gr. 7). pap., stu. ed. 14.71 (978-0-673-80071-8(7)); Unit 7B, Bk. B. (YA). (gr. 7). pap., stu. ed. 14.71 (978-0-673-80072-5(5)); Unit 7D, Bk. D. (YA). (gr. 7). pap., stu. ed. 14.71 (978-0-673-80076-3(8)); Unit 8A, Bk. A. (YA). (gr. 8). pap., stu. ed. 14.71 (978-0-673-80081-7(4)); Unit 8B, Bk. B. (YA). (gr. 8). pap., stu. ed. 14.71 (978-0-673-80083-1(0)); Unit 8C, Bk. C. (YA). (gr. 8). pap., stu. ed. 14.71 (978-0-673-80084-8(9)); Unit 8D, Bk. D. (YA). (gr. 8). pap., stu. ed. 14.71 (978-0-673-80085-5(7)) Addison Wesley Schl. (Scott Foresman).

Cells: Level L, 6 vols. (Wonder Worldtm Ser.). 16p. 34.95 (978-0-7802-2890-0(1)) Wright Group, The.

Center for Learning Network Staff. Reading Strategies: Curriculum Unit. 2001. (English Ser.). 112p. (J). (gr. 4-8). spiral bd. 20.95 (978-1-56077-637-6(4)) Ctr. for Learning, The.

El chacal Ingenioso 7: Leveled Books. 2001. (McGraw-Hill. Lectura Ser.). (ENG & SPA.). (gr. 3 up). (978-0-02-188104-8(9)) Macmillan/McGraw-Hill Schl. Div.

Chad Is the Champ: Digraph ch: Level B, 6 vols. (Wright Skills Ser.). 16p. (gr. k-3). 17.95 (978-0-322-01472-5(7)) Wright Group, The.

Challenges Set. 2005. (Challenges Ser.: Vol. 2). (J). (gr. 3-5). tchr. ed. 198.95 (978-0-7652-2129-2(2)) Modern Curriculum Pr.

Change of Heart: Level 2, 6 vols. (Fluency Strand Ser.). (gr. 4-8). 45.00 (978-1-4045-1214-6(4)) Wright Group, The.

Changing Views: American Readers. (J). (gr. 7). (978-0-669-05084-4(9)); (978-0-669-05086-8(5)); wbk. ed. (978-0-669-05087-5(3)) Houghton Mifflin Co. (Schl. Div.).

Chapman, Cindy. Baby Animals. 2003. (Compass Point Phonics Readers Ser.). (Illus.). 16p. (J). (gr. 1 up). 13.26 (978-0-7565-0504-2(6)) Compass Point Bks.

—On a Farm. 2003. (Compass Point Phonics Readers Ser.). (Illus.). 16p. (J). (gr. 1 up). 13.26 (978-0-7565-0516-5(X)) Compass Point Bks.

—Play It Safe! 2003. (Compass Point Phonics Readers Ser.). (Illus.). 16p. (J). (gr. 1 up). 13.26 (978-0-7565-0520-2(8)) Compass Point Bks.

—What Is in the Sky? 2003. (Compass Point Phonics Readers Ser.). (Illus.). 16p. (J). (gr. 1 up). 13.26 (978-0-7565-0513-4(5)) Compass Point Bks.

—Where Is Your Home? 2003. (Compass Point Phonics Readers Ser.). (Illus.). 16p. (J). (gr. 1 up). 13.26 (978-0-7565-0532-5(1)) Compass Point Bks.

Charlie the Pancake Pirate: Level O, 6 vols. (Wonder Worldtm Ser.). 48p. 39.95 (978-0-7802-2949-5(5)) Wright Group, The.

Chatterjee, Debjani, et al. The Most Beautiful Child: South African Edition. 1999. (Cambridge Reading Routes Ser.). (Illus.). 32p. pap. 6.45 (978-0-521-77896-1(4)) Cambridge Univ. Pr.

The Cheerful King, Vol. 2. 2005. (Fluent Library). (YA). (ps-3). 29.34 (978-0-8215-8967-0(9)) Sadlier, William H. Inc.

Cherrington, Janelle. Where Animals Live. 2003. (Compass Point Phonics Readers Ser.). (Illus.). 16p. (J). (gr. 1 up). 13.26 (978-0-7565-0530-1(5)) Compass Point Bks.

—Who Needs Teeth? 2003. (Compass Point Phonics Readers Ser.). (Illus.). 16p. (J). (gr. 1 up). 13.26 (978-0-7565-0535-6(6)) Compass Point Bks.

Chicchelly, Dana. Preparing for FCAT Reading/ Grade 6. 2007. (J). pap. (***978-1-56765-156-0(9)***, R029W) AMSCO Schl. Pubns., Inc.

Chicko, Joe & Chicko, Terri, illus. The Itsy Bitsy Spider: Getting Ready to Read with Mother Goose. l.t. ed. 2001. (Sadlier Phonics Reading Program). 8p. (YA). (ps-k). 27.00 (978-0-8215-6962-7(7)) Sadlier, William H. Inc.

—The Itsy Bitsy Spider, Little Book: Getting Ready to Read with Mother Goose. 2001. (Sadlier Phonics Reading Program). 8p. (YA). (ps-k). 23.94 (978-0-8215-6977-1(5)) Sadlier, William H. Inc.

The Chocolate War. 2004. (Literature Connections Ser.). (Illus.). (gr. 6-12). (978-0-395-87479-0(3) , 2-70839) McDougal Littell Inc.

Choice-Making Series: High Interest, Low Reading Level, Multicultural Novellas. 2000. 165p. (gr. 3-5). 29.00 (978-1-57861-118-8(0) , IEP RESOURCES) Attainment Co., Inc.

The Chosen. 2004. (Literature Connections Ser.). (gr. 6-12). (978-0-395-88145-3(5) , 2-70858) McDougal Littell Inc.

Chris's Diary: Level 3, 6 vols. (Fluency Strand Ser.). (gr. 4-8). 45.00 (978-1-4045-1216-0(0)) Wright Group, The.

El ciempies sin Pies 20: Leveled Books. 2001. (McGraw-Hill. Lectura Ser.). (ENG & SPA.). (gr. 1 up). (978-0-02-187949-6(4)) Macmillan/McGraw-Hill Schl. Div.

Las ciento y una Noches 12: Leveled Books. 2001. (McGraw-Hill. Lectura Ser.). (ENG & SPA.). (gr. 3 up). (978-0-02-188085-0(9)) Macmillan/McGraw-Hill Schl. Div.

The Circus: Level D, 6 vols. (Wonder Worldtm Ser.). 16p. 24.95 (978-0-7802-1034-9(4)) Wright Group, The.

Claire, Elizabeth. Hi! (Illus.). (J). wbk. ed. (978-0-8056-0122-0(8)) Minerva Bks., Ltd.

Clarke, Jacqueline. Teaching Reading & Writing with Song: Irresistible Pocket Chart Activities, Picture Cards & Props, Read & Write Mini-Books, & More. 2003. 64p. (gr. k-2). pap. 11.99 (978-0-439-39512-0(7) , Teaching Resources) Scholastic, Inc.

Classical Learning Universe. Reading Success: Foundations Student Book: Effective Comprehension Strategies. 2004. (978-0-9763376-0-7(6)) Classical Learning Universe, LLC.

—Reading Success: Student Book: Effective Comprehension Strategies Level C. 2004. (978-0-9721733-7-7(4)) Classical Learning Universe, LLC.

Clausen, Andrew. The Cricket in Times Square. 1998. 60p. (J). stu. ed., ring bd. 12.99 (978-1-58609-134-7(4)) Progeny Pr.

Clearing Paths: American Readers. (J). (gr. 4). (978-0-669-05040-0(7)) Houghton Mifflin Co. (Schl. Div.).

Clearing Paths Reading Kit: American Readers. (J). (gr. 4). (978-0-669-05053-0(9)) Houghton Mifflin Co. (Schl. Div.).

Clearing Paths Workbook: American Readers. (J). (gr. 4). wbk. ed. (978-0-669-05048-6(2)) Houghton Mifflin Co. (Schl. Div.).

Clemens Warrick, Karen. Cause & Effect: Using Causes & Effects to Make Connections. 2001. (Basic Skills Ser.). 48p. (J). (gr. 1-2). pap. 6.99 (978-0-7424-0099-3(9) , IF5626) School Specialty Publishing.

—Story Elements: Learning about the Components of Stories to Deepen Comprehension. 2001. (Basic Skills Ser.). 48p. (J). (gr. 1-2). pap. 6.99 (978-0-7424-0102-0(2) , IF5635) School Specialty Publishing.

Climbing Up: American Readers. (J). (gr. 1). (978-0-669-04965-7(4)) Houghton Mifflin Co. (Schl. Div.).

The Climbing Wall: Level 7, 6 vols. (Fluency Strand Ser.). (gr. 4-8). 45.00 (978-1-4045-1244-3(6)) Wright Group, The.

The Closet in the Hall: Level G, 6 vols. (Wonder Worldtm Ser.). 16p. 29.95 (978-0-7802-1247-3(9)) Wright Group, The.

Clothes: Level N, 6 vols. (Wonder Worldtm Ser.). 48p. 34.95 (978-0-7802-2892-4(8)) Wright Group, The.

El club de las Visitas 7: Leveled Books. 2001. (McGraw-Hill. Lectura Ser.). (ENG & SPA.). (gr. 2 up). (978-0-02-188056-0(5)) Macmillan/McGraw-Hill Schl. Div.

El Club del Universo 8: Leveled Books. 2001. (McGraw-Hill. Lectura Ser.). (ENG & SPA.). (gr. 3 up). (978-0-02-188105-5(7)) Macmillan/McGraw-Hill Schl. Div.

Clubes de ninos al Rescate 7: Leveled Books. 2001. (McGraw-Hill. Lectura Ser.). (ENG & SPA.). (gr. 2 up). (978-0-02-188008-9(5)) Macmillan/McGraw-Hill Schl. Div.

Clyne, Margaret. Kim's Lunch. 2001. (gr. k-3). lib. bdg. 11.95 (978-0-613-33383-2(7)) Tandem Library Bks.

The Coach & the Kid: Level 5, 6 vols. (Fluency Strand Ser.). (gr. 4-8). 45.00 (978-1-4045-1233-7(0)) Wright Group, The.

The Cobsdown Cat Case Little Book: Early Reading Fluency, Level C. 2004. pap. 6.00 (978-0-7398-8303-7(8)) Steck-Vaughn.

Coelho, Elizabeth & Winer, Lise. Jigsaw Plus. 1998. 1422p. (J). pap. 30.00 (978-0-88751-028-1(0)) Pippin Publishing Corp. CAN. *Dist:* Univ. of Toronto Pr.

Cole, Bob. Power Reading. Ford, David, illus. 2002. (J). (gr. 2-5). pap. 129.95 incl. audio (978-1-883186-18-0(8) , PP03C) National Reading Styles Institute, Inc.

Collecting Cones: Level K, 6 vols. (Wonder Worldtm Ser.). 16p. 34.95 (978-0-7802-4565-5(2)) Wright Group, The.

El color de los Animales 21: Leveled Books. 2001. (McGraw-Hill. Lectura Ser.). (ENG & SPA.). (gr. 1 up). (978-0-02-187974-8(5)) Macmillan/McGraw-Hill Schl. Div.

Colors at the Zoo: Take-Home Book. 2005. (Emergent Library: Vol. 2). (YA). (ps-1). 12.60 (978-0-8215-7269-6(5)) Sadlier, William H. Inc.

Come Back, Amelia Bedelia. 2003. 22.95 (978-0-673-75911-5(3)) Celebration Pr.

Come Meet Some Seals, Vol. 2. 2005. (Early Library). (YA). (ps-3). 23.94 (978-0-8215-8959-5(8)) Sadlier, William H. Inc.

Communities: Level F, 6 vols. (Wonder Worldtm Ser.). 16p. 29.95 (978-0-7802-1986-1(4)) Wright Group, The.

Como le salio el colmillo al Narval? 16: Leveled Books. 2001. (McGraw-Hill. Lectura Ser.). (ENG & SPA.). (gr. 3 up). (978-0-02-188089-8(1)) Macmillan/McGraw-Hill Schl. Div.

Companeros 15: Leveled Books. 2001. (McGraw-Hill. Lectura Ser.). (ENG & SPA.). (gr. 5 up). (978-0-02-188239-7(8)) Macmillan/McGraw-Hill Schl. Div.

Companeros de equipo para Siempre 18: Leveled Books. 2001. (McGraw-Hill. Lectura Ser.). (ENG & SPA.). (gr. 2 up). (978-0-02-188067-6(0)) Macmillan/McGraw-Hill Schl. Div.

El concurso de Cerebritos 16: Leveled Books. 2001. (McGraw-Hill. Lectura Ser.). (ENG & SPA.). (gr. 4 up). (978-0-02-188192-5(8)) Macmillan/McGraw-Hill Schl. Div.

El conejo Alejo 13: Leveled Books. 2001. (McGraw-Hill. Lectura Ser.). (ENG & SPA.). (gr. 1 up). (978-0-02-187942-7(7)) Macmillan/McGraw-Hill Schl. Div.

Conlin, Mary. Patterns Plus: A Short Prose Reader with Argumentation. 8th ed. 2004. (Illus.). 337p. (YA). 47.96 (978-0-618-42119-0(X) , 310984) Houghton Mifflin College Div.

Connelly, Mark. Companion to the Thoughtful Reader. 2002. pap. 16.95 (978-0-8384-7466-2(7)) Thomson Heinle.

Conoce tu Mundo 20: Leveled Books. 2001. (McGraw-Hill. Lectura Ser.). (ENG & SPA.). (gr. 2 up). (978-0-02-188045-4(X)) Macmillan/McGraw-Hill Schl. Div.

Content Area Readers Library: Early (K-2) 2005. (YA). (ps-2). 465.00 (978-0-8215-7809-4(X)) Sadlier, William H. Inc.

Content Area Readers Library: Emergent (PreK-1) 2005. (YA). (ps-2). 498.00 (978-0-8215-7885-8(5)) Sadlier, William H. Inc.

Contracorriente 3: Leveled Books. 2001. (McGraw-Hill. Lectura Ser.). (ENG & SPA.). (gr. 4 up). (978-0-02-188203-8(7)) Macmillan/McGraw-Hill Schl. Div.

Corneilse, Janine. The Terrible Graakwa: Kiswahili Version. Lema, Eleishi, tr. 1999. (Cambridge Reading Routes Ser.). (Illus.). 16p. pap. 3.70 (978-0-521-66892-7(1)) Cambridge Univ. Pr.

—The Terrible Graakwa: Oromo Version. Adem, Omer Kedir, tr. 1999. (Cambridge Reading Routes Ser.). (Illus.). 16p. pap. 3.70 (978-0-521-66838-5(7)) Cambridge Univ. Pr.

—The Terrible Graakwa Lugbara Version: Amgbaka Onzi Omba Ru Ri. Draville, Ben & Mawa, Robert, trs. 2001. 16p. pap. 1.40 (978-0-521-00617-0(1)) Cambridge Univ. Pr.

Le Cortan el Pelo a Tristana 17: Leveled Books. 2001. (McGraw-Hill. Lectura Ser.). (ENG & SPA.). (gr. 1 up). (978-0-02-187994-6(X)) Macmillan/McGraw-Hill Schl. Div.

Cosmo the ACountant: Level O, 6 vols. (Wonder Worldtm Ser.). 48p. 39.95 (978-0-7802-2962-4(2)) Wright Group, The.

Count with Me: Take Home Book. 2005. (Emergent Library: Vol. 2). (YA). (ps-1). 12.60 (978-0-8215-7258-0(X)) Sadlier, William H. Inc.

Courtney, Claudia. Blessings: Jesus & the Children. Dorenkamp, Michelle, illus. 2000. (Phonetic Bible Stories Ser.). (ENG.). 16p. (J). (ps-1). 2.99 (978-0-570-07090-0(2)) Concordia Publishing Hse.

—Jesus Is Born: Christmas. 1998. (ps-2). lib. bdg. 10.65 (978-0-613-72654-2(5)) Tandem Library Bks.

—Little Is Big: Jesus Feeds the 5,000 John 6. 1998. (ps-2). lib. bdg. 10.65 (978-0-613-72813-3(0)) Tandem Library Bks.

Cousin. My Friend at School: Big Book: Level C. (Visionstm Ser.). 8p. 20.95 (978-0-7802-9746-3(6)) Wright Group, The.

Cousins, Coleen, et al. Ntsiki's Surprise: Fante Version. Aggrey, Safohen J. E. K., tr. 2001. (Illus.). 16p. pap. 1.40 (978-0-521-79570-8(2)) Cambridge Univ. Pr.

—Ntsiki's Surprise: Sepedi Version. 2002. (Illus.). 16p. pap. 1.75 (978-0-521-52820-7(8)) Cambridge Univ. Pr.

—Ntsiki's Surprise: Sesotho Version. 2002. (Illus.). 16p. pap. 1.75 (978-0-521-52817-7(8)) Cambridge Univ. Pr.

—Ntsiki's Surprise: Setswana Version. 2002. (Illus.). 16p. pap. 1.75 (978-0-521-52818-4(6)) Cambridge Univ. Pr.

—Ntsiki's Surprise: Xitsonga Version. 2002. (Illus.). 16p. pap. 1.75 (978-0-521-52819-1(4)) Cambridge Univ. Pr.

Cox, Phil Roxbee & Cartwright, Stephen. Hen's Pens. 2004. (Phonics Board Bks.). (Illus.). 10p. (J). 4.95 (978-0-7945-0303-1(9) , Usborne) EDC Publishing.

Crackles: Level P, 6 vols. (Wonder Worldtm Ser.). 48p. 39.95 (978-0-7802-7072-5(X)) Wright Group, The.

Crawford, Sheryl Ann & Sanders, Nancy L. Just Right Plays: 25 Science Plays for Emergent Readers. 2001. 64p. pap. 10.95 (978-0-439-11760-9(7)) Scholastic, Inc.

Criaturas Maravillosas 18: Leveled Books. 2001. (McGraw-Hill. Lectura Ser.). (ENG & SPA.). (gr. 1 up). (978-0-02-187971-7(0)) Macmillan/McGraw-Hill Schl. Div.

Cronkite, Walter, frwd. Great American Presidents, 12 vols. 2005. (Great American Presidents Ser.). (Illus.). 112p. (gr. 4-8). pap. 360.00 (978-0-7910-7595-1(8) , Chelsea Hse.) Facts On File, Inc.

The Crook by the Brook: Variant Vowel oo: Level B, 6 vols. (Wright Skills Ser.). 16p. (gr. k-3). 26.50 (978-0-322-01483-1(2)) Wright Group, The.

Crossing Boundaries: American Readers. (J). (978-0-669-05064-6(4)); (gr. 5). (978-0-669-05054-7(7)); (gr. 5). wbk. ed. (978-0-669-05060-8(1)) Houghton Mifflin Co. (Schl. Div.).

Crusius, Timothy & Channell, Carolyn. Aims of Argument: Text & Reader with Student Access to Catalyst. 5th rev. ed. 2005. (C). pap. 63.44 (978-0-07-320196-2(0) , 9780073201962, McGraw-Hill Humanities, Social Sciences & World Languages) McGraw-Hill Higher Education.

The Crypto Files: Level 6, 6 vols. (Fluency Strand Ser.). (gr. 4-8). 45.00 (978-1-4045-1236-8(5)) Wright Group, The.

Cuaderno de Gramatica: Resources & Ancillaries. 2001. (McGraw-Hill. Lectura Ser.). (ENG & SPA.). (gr. 1 up). (978-0-02-186423-2(3)); (gr. 2 up). (978-0-02-186424-9(1)); (gr. 3 up). (978-0-02-186425-6(X)); (gr. 4 up). (978-0-02-186426-3(8)); (gr. 5 up). (978-0-02-186427-0(6)); (gr. 6 up). (978-0-02-186428-7(4)) Macmillan/McGraw-Hill Schl. Div.

Cuaderno de Ortografia: Resources & Ancillaries. 2001. (McGraw-Hill. Lectura Ser.). (ENG & SPA.). (gr. 1 up). (978-0-02-186429-4(2)); (gr. 2 up). (978-0-02-186430-0(6)); (gr. 3 up). (978-0-02-186431-7(4)); (gr. 4 up). (978-0-02-186432-4(2)); (gr. 5 up). (978-0-02-186433-1(0)); (gr. 6 up). (978-0-02-186434-8(9)) Macmillan/McGraw-Hill Schl. Div.

Cuando el senor Rey ronco/When Mr Quinn Snored. 2005. (Libros en Espanol Para Ninos Ser.). (SPA.). (YA). (ps-1). 11.97 (978-0-8215-0997-5(7)); 15.75 (978-0-8215-1207-4(2)) Sadlier, William H. Inc.

Cuantos dias faltan para mi Cumpleanos? 8: Leveled Books. 2001. (McGraw-Hill. Lectura Ser.). (ENG & SPA.). (gr. 1 up). (978-0-02-187985-4(0)) Macmillan/McGraw-Hill Schl. Div.

El cuarto de Virginia Leon 22: Leveled Books. 2001. (McGraw-Hill. Lectura Ser.). (ENG & SPA.). (gr. 2 up). (978-0-02-188023-2(9)) Macmillan/McGraw-Hill Schl. Div.

Las cuevas de Lascaux 3: Leveled Books. 2001. (McGraw-Hill. Lectura Ser.). (ENG & SPA.). (gr. 2 up). (978-0-02-188052-2(2)) Macmillan/McGraw-Hill Schl. Div.

Cuidando a los animales/Keeping Baby Animals Safe. 2005. (Libros en Espanol Para Ninos Ser.). (SPA.). (YA). (ps-1). 11.97 (978-0-8215-0996-8(9)); 15.75 (978-0-8215-1206-7(4)) Sadlier, William H. Inc.

Cummings, Renee. Summarizing: Focusing on Main Ideas & Details & Restating in Concise Form. 2001. (Basic Skills Ser.). 48p. (J). (gr. 1-2). pap. 6.99 (978-0-7424-0105-1(7) , IF5640) School Specialty Publishing.

Cummins & Chamot, Anna Uhl. Scott Foresman ESL - Kindergarten, Bk. 8. 2nd ed. 2000. (J). pap. 41.13 (978-0-13-027512-7(3)) Longman Publishing Group.

—Scott Foresman ESL Little Book - Kindergarten. 2nd ed. 2000. (J). Bk. 1. 24p. pap. 8.80 (978-0-13-027513-4(1)); Bk. 2. pap. 8.80 (978-0-13-027514-1(X)); Bk. 3. (Illus.). 24p. pap. 8.80 (978-0-13-027515-8(8)) Longman Publishing Group.

Cummins, et al. Scott Foresman ESL - Kindergarten. 2nd ed. 2000. (J). Bk. 1. pap. 41.13 (978-0-13-027504-2(2)); Bk. 2. pap. 41.13 (978-0-13-027505-9(0)); Bk. 3. pap. 41.13 (978-0-13-027506-6(9)); Bk. 4. (Illus.). 24p. pap. 41.13 (978-0-13-027507-3(7)); Bk. 5. pap. 41.13 (978-0-13-027509-7(3)); Bk. 6. pap. 41.13 (978-0-13-027500-4(X)); Bk. 7. pap. 41.13 (978-0-13-027511-0(5)) Longman Publishing Group.

—Scott Foresman ESL Little Book - Kindergarten, Bk. 7. 2nd ed. 2000. (Illus.). 24p. (J). pap. 8.80 (978-0-13-027510-3(7)) Longman Publishing Group.

Cummins, Jim P., et al. Scott Foresman ESL. 2nd ed. 2000. (J). (gr. 2). stu. ed. 24.93 (978-0-13-027488-5(7)); (J). (gr. 3). stu. ed. 24.93 (978-0-13-027480-9(1)); (J). (gr. 4). stu. ed. 24.93 (978-0-13-027493-9(3)); (J). (gr. 5). stu. ed. 24.93 (978-0-13-027495-3(X)); (Illus.). iii, 236p. (C). (gr. 8). pap., stu. ed. 30.00 (978-0-13-027501-1(8)) Longman Publishing Group.

—Scott Foresman ESL. 2nd ed. 2000. (Illus.). 236p. (C). (gr. 6). pap., stu. ed. 30.00 (978-0-13-027497-7(6)) Pearson ESL.

A Cup for a Cub: Consonants c, l, r; Short Vowel u word families: Level A, 6 vols. (Wright Skills Ser.). 12p. (gr. k-3). 17.95 (978-0-322-01453-4(0)) Wright Group, The.

El Curioso Periquito Quito 15: Leveled Books. 2001. (McGraw-Hill. Lectura Ser.). (ENG & SPA.). (gr. 2 up). (978-0-02-188016-4(6)) Macmillan/McGraw-Hill Schl. Div.

Custard: Level F, 6 vols. (Wonder Worldtm Ser.). 16p. 29.95 (978-0-7802-2894-8(4)) Wright Group, The.

Cyberspace, 6 vols. (Wildcats Ser.). 32p. (gr. 2-8). (978-0-322-00600-3(7)) Wright Group, The.

Czernecki, Stefan. How a Baby Begins. Date not set. 40p. (YA). (gr. 5-9). 15.99 (978-0-06-025412-4(2)) HarperCollins Pubs.

—Wild Queen. Date not set. 80p. (J). (gr. k-4). 13.99 (978-0-06-026263-1(X)); lib. bdg. 14.89 (978-0-06-026264-8(8)) HarperCollins Pubs.

Dalmatian Press Staff. Precious Moments Reading Readiness. 2000. (Precious Moments Workbooks Ser.). (Illus.). 32p. (J). pap., wbk. ed. 2.99 (978-1-57759-288-4(3)) Dalmatian Pr.

—Reading Readiness. rev. ed. 1999. (Tools Ser.). (Illus.). 32p. (J). (gr. k-1). pap. 2.29 (978-1-57759-146-7(1)) Dalmatian Pr.

Dalmatian Press Staff, creator. Phonics: Flash Cards & Games. 2003. (Home Learning Tools Ser.). 56p. (J). 2.99 (978-1-4037-0217-3(9)) Dalmatian Pr.

Dan Gets Dressed: Level C. Group 2. (Story Box(R) Ser.). 16p. 20.95 (978-0-7802-9366-3(5)) Wright Group, The.

Dance My Dance: Level M, 6 vols. (Take-Twostm Ser.). 32p. 36.95 (978-0-322-03401-3(9)) Wright Group, The.

Dangerous Adventures Classroom Library. (gr. 4 up). lib. bdg. 24.95 (978-0-7368-9024-3(6)) Red Brick Learning.

Dangerous Adventures II Classroom Library. (gr. 4 up). lib. bdg. 24.95 (978-0-7368-9286-5(9)) Red Brick Learning.

Dangerous Adventures II Complete Unit. (gr. 4 up). 142.95 (978-0-7368-9287-2(7)) Red Brick Learning.

Dangerous Jobs: Level T. Group 1, 6 vols. (Sunshinetm Ser.). 48p. 44.95 (978-0-7802-6094-8(5)) Wright Group, The.

Daniel Boone, 6 vols. (gr. 2-5). 39.95 (978-0-7368-4592-2(5)) Red Brick Learning.

Davis. Expressway to Reading. rev. ed. 1999. (Illus.). (J). pap. (978-0-7398-1894-7(5)) Steck-Vaughn.

Davis, Beatrice G. On the Road to Reading: 101 Creative Activities for Beginning Readers. rev. ed. 1999. (Illus.). 96p. pap. (978-0-7398-1893-0(7)) Steck-Vaughn.

Day & Night Little Book: Early Reading Fluency, Level A. 2004. pap. 6.00 (978-0-7398-8170-5(1)) Steck-Vaughn.

Day & Night Little Book, Grade 1: Early Reading Fluency: Teaching Edition, Level A. 2004. pap. 7.50 (978-0-7398-8206-1(6)) Steck-Vaughn.

Day, Eileen. Soy Buena para el Arte. 2003. (SPA.). 24p. pap. 5.25 (978-1-4034-3577-4(4)) Heinemann Library.

—Soy Buena para el Baile. 2003. (SPA.). 24p. pap. 5.25 (978-1-4034-3578-1(2)) Heinemann Library.

De como la rana perdio la Cola 12: Leveled Books. 2001. (McGraw-Hill. Lectura Ser.). (ENG & SPA.). (gr. 2 up). (978-0-02-188061-4(1)) Macmillan/McGraw-Hill Schl. Div.

de Lambana, Martha Lucia Martinez. Grafias 1 1: Escritura Asociativa Script: Afianzamiento. (SPA.). (J). (gr. k-6). 12.00 (978-958-04-5317-8(9)) Norma S.A. COL. *Dist:* Distribuidora Norma, Inc.

—Grafias 2 2: Escritura Asociativa Script: Transicion. (SPA.). (J). (gr. k-6). 12.00 (978-958-04-5327-7(6)) Norma S.A. COL. *Dist:* Distribuidora Norma, Inc.

—Grafias 3 3: Escritura Asociativa Script: Afianzamiento. (SPA.). (J). (gr. k-6). 12.00 (978-958-04-5328-4(4)) Norma S.A. COL. *Dist:* Distribuidora Norma, Inc.

De mar en mar: que aventura Singular! 10: Leveled Books. 2001. (McGraw-Hill. Lectura Ser.). (ENG & SPA.). (gr. 5 up). (978-0-02-188258-8(4)) Macmillan/McGraw-Hill Schl. Div.

De semilla a Secuoya 18: Leveled Books. 2001. (McGraw-Hill. Lectura Ser.). (ENG & SPA.). (gr. 2 up). (978-0-02-188043-0(3)) Macmillan/McGraw-Hill Schl. Div.

Deadbeat: Level O, 6 vols. (Wonder Worldtm Ser.). 48p. 39.95 (978-0-7802-2947-1(9)) Wright Group, The.

Dean, Martin. Look at Me. 2002. (Bright Sparks Ser.). (Illus.). 16p. pap. 2.30 (978-0-521-75393-7(7)) Cambridge Univ. Pr.

—Mike the Magician. 2002. (Bright Sparks Ser.). (Illus.). 16p. pap. 2.30 (978-0-521-75392-0(9)) Cambridge Univ. Pr.

—What a Day! 2002. (Bright Sparks Ser.). (Illus.). 16p. pap. 2.30 (978-0-521-75391-3(0)) Cambridge Univ. Pr.

Dear Pop: Level O, 6 vols. (Wonder Worldtm Ser.). 48p. 39.95 (978-0-7802-2948-8(7)) Wright Group, The.

Dear Tom: Level J, 6 vols. (Wonder Worldtm Ser.). 16p. 29.95 (978-0-7802-4567-9(9)) Wright Group, The.

Decido ser Yo 5: Leveled Books. 2001. (McGraw-Hill. Lectura Ser.). (ENG & SPA.). (gr. 3 up). (978-0-02-188078-2(6)) Macmillan/McGraw-Hill Schl. Div.

Decodable Take-Home Book Set, 450 bks. 2002. (gr. k-2). 270.00 (978-0-7362-0567-2(5)) Hampton-Brown Bks.

El dedito de Lola 6: Leveled Books. 2001. (McGraw-Hill. Lectura Ser.). (ENG & SPA.). (gr. 1 up). (978-0-02-187959-5(1)) Macmillan/McGraw-Hill Schl. Div.

Den of Thieves: Level 6, 6 vols. (Fluency Strand Ser.). (gr. 4-8). 45.00 (978-1-4045-1238-2(1)) Wright Group, The.

Denstaedt, Linda. I Love Reading. Rozines Roy, Jennifer, illus. 1999. (Homework Booklets Ser.). 80p. Level 6. (J). (gr. 5-7). pap. 2.99 (978-1-56822-831-0(7) , IF0326); Level 7, (YA). (gr. 6-8). pap. 2.99 (978-1-56822-832-7(5) , IF0327) Schaffer, Frank Pubns. (Instructional Fair).

Derek Jeter, 6 vols. (gr. 4 up). 39.95 (978-0-7368-9271-1(0)) Red Brick Learning.

Desert Day: Level B. 8p. 20.95 (978-0-322-00358-3(X)); 24.95 (978-0-7802-8916-1(1)) Wright Group, The.

Despues de la Inundacion: Libros Aventuras (Adventure Books) 2000. (MacMillan/McGraw-Hill. Estudios Sociales Ser.). (ENG & SPA.). (gr. 3 up). (978-0-02-148696-0(4)) Macmillan/McGraw-Hill Schl. Div.

Un dia de Nieve 16: Leveled Books. 2001. (McGraw-Hill. Lectura Ser.). (ENG & SPA.). (gr. 1 up). (978-0-02-187993-9(1)) Macmillan/McGraw-Hill Schl. Div.

El dia que el Sol se Detuvo 14: Leveled Books. 2001. (McGraw-Hill. Lectura Ser.). (ENG & SPA.). (gr. 3 up). (978-0-02-188087-4(5)) Macmillan/McGraw-Hill Schl. Div.

Dickey, Laurel. Hard at Work. Weinberg, Richard, photos by. 1999. (Illus.). (J). pap. 3.75 (978-1-58453-029-9(4)) Pioneer Valley Educational Pr., Inc.

—I Love Camping. 1999. (Illus.). (J). pap. 3.75 (978-1-58453-025-1(1)) Pioneer Valley Educational Pr., Inc.

—Where Are We? Dufresne, Michele, photos by. 1999. (Illus.). (J). pap. 3.75 (978-1-58453-026-8(X)) Pioneer Valley Educational Pr., Inc.

Dickey, Laurel & Dufresne, Michele. Early Emergent Set 2: Classroom Collection. Dickey, Laurel et al, photos by. Dufresne, Robert et al, photos by. 1999. (Illus.). (J). pap. 90.00 (978-1-58453-071-8(5)) Pioneer Valley Educational Pr., Inc.

—Early Emergent Set 2, Vol. 2. Dickey, Laurel et al, photos by. Dufresne, Robert et al, photos by. 1999. (Illus.). (J). 16.25 (978-1-58453-030-5(8)) Pioneer Valley Educational Pr., Inc.

Did You Know?, Vol. 2. 2005. (Early Library). (YA). (ps-3). 23.94 (978-0-8215-8947-2(4)) Sadlier, William H. Inc.

Did You Know? Big Book: Level L. Group 1. (Sunshinetm Ser.). 24p. 36.50 (978-0-322-00334-7(2)) Wright Group, The.

Diego en la Invencible 3: Leveled Books. 2001. (McGraw-Hill. Lectura Ser.). (ENG & SPA.). (gr. 5 up). (978-0-02-188227-4(4)) Macmillan/McGraw-Hill Schl. Div.

Dimwood Forest Reading Group Guide. 2000. (J). pap. (978-0-380-29940-9(2) , Harper Trophy) HarperCollins Pubs.

DiSalvo-Ryan, DyAnne. A Dog Like Jack. 2005. (Live Oak Readalong Ser.). (J). pap. 18.95 incl. audio compact disk (978-1-59519-298-1(0)) Live Oak Media.

Discovering Dinosaurs, Vol. 2. 2005. (Fluent Library). (YA). (ps-3). 29.34 (978-0-8215-8966-3(0)) Sadlier, William H. Inc.

Disney Publishing Staff. I Spy Shapes, 15 vols. 2003. (It's Fun to Learn Ser.). (Illus.). 32p. (J). (ps-3). 3.99 (978-1-57973-131-1(7)) Advance Pubs. LLC.

Disney Staff & LeapFrog Staff, compiled by. Pooh Gets Stuck. 2001. (J). (ps-1). spiral bd. 14.99 (978-1-58605-001-6(X)) LeapFrog Enterprises, Inc.

The Divers: Level C, 6 vols. (Wonder Worldtm Ser.). 16p. 24.95 (978-0-7802-1249-7(5)) Wright Group, The.

DK Publishing Staff. My First Phonics Board Book. 2007. 48p. (J). bds. 12.99 (978-0-7566-2590-0(4)) Dorling Kindersley Publishing, Inc.

Do you Like Rice?, 6 vols. 8p. (gr. k-1). 21.50 (978-0-322-02058-0(1)) Wright Group, The.

Do you Remember When?, 6 vols. (Multicultural Programs Ser.). 16p. (gr. 1-3). 24.95 (978-0-7802-9206-2(5)) Wright Group, The.

Do You See a Dozen? Big Book, Vol. 2. 2005. (Emergent Library: Vol. 1). (YA). (ps-1). 23.94 (978-0-8215-8907-6(5)) Sadlier, William H. Inc.

Dobles 16: Leveled Books. 2001. (McGraw-Hill. Lectura Ser.). (ENG & SPA.). (gr. 4 up). (978-0-02-188161-1(8)) Macmillan/McGraw-Hill Schl. Div.

Dogs That Help Us Little Book: Early Reading Fluency, Level A. 2004. pap. 6.00 (978-0-7398-8165-1(5)) Steck-Vaughn.

Dolly Fin & Friends: Level 4, 6 vols. (Fluency Strand Ser.). (gr. 4-8). 45.00 (978-1-4045-1227-6(6)) Wright Group, The.

Dolphin. 2003. 22.95 (978-0-673-75914-6(8)) Celebration Pr.

Donde Esta? 17: Leveled Books. 2001. (McGraw-Hill. Lectura Ser.). (ENG & SPA.). (gr. 1 up). (978-0-02-187970-0(2)) Macmillan/McGraw-Hill Schl. Div.

Don't be Late, 6 vols. 8p. (gr. k-1). 21.50 (978-0-322-02059-7(X)) Wright Group, The.

Don't Tell! 2005. (Early Library). (YA). (ps-3). 23.94 (978-0-8215-8954-0(7)) Sadlier, William H. Inc.

Don't Throw it Away: Level G, 6 vols. (Wonder Worldtm Ser.). 16p. 29.95 (978-0-7802-2896-2(0)) Wright Group, The.

Dora, Dorita, la gran Hormiguita 19: Leveled Books. 2001. (McGraw-Hill. Lectura Ser.). (ENG & SPA.). (gr. 1 up). (978-0-02-187972-4(9)) Macmillan/McGraw-Hill Schl. Div.

Dora y el Sin-club 7: Leveled Books. 2001. (McGraw-Hill. Lectura Ser.). (ENG & SPA.). (gr. 2 up). (978-0-02-188032-4(8)) Macmillan/McGraw-Hill Schl. Div.

Dorling Kindersley Publishing Staff. Star Pilot: Lift Off. 2005. (Dk Readers Ser.). (Illus.). 48p. (J). 14.99 (978-0-7566-1160-6(1) , 1241628) Dorling Kindersley Publishing, Inc.

Dos Pioneras 16: Leveled Books. 2001. (McGraw-Hill. Lectura Ser.). (ENG & SPA.). (gr. 4 up). (978-0-02-188216-8(9)) Macmillan/McGraw-Hill Schl. Div.

Doudna, Kelly. Any Day but Today! 2004. (Sight Words Ser.). (Illus.). 23p. (J). (ps-3). lib. bdg. 19.93 (978-1-59197-464-2(X)) ABDO Publishing Co.

—Et As in Jet. 2003. (Word Families Ser.). 23p. (J). (ps-3). lib. bdg. 19.93 (978-1-59197-230-3(2) , SandCastle) ABDO Publishing Co.

—Give It a Try! 2004. (Sight Words Ser.). (Illus.). 23p. (J). (ps-3). lib. bdg. 19.93 (978-1-59197-469-7(0)) ABDO Publishing Co.

—Id As in Squid. 2003. (Word Families Ser.). (Illus.). 23p. (J). (ps-3). lib. bdg. 19.93 (978-1-59197-235-8(3) , SandCastle) ABDO Publishing Co.

—Ig As in Pig. Marx, Monica, ed. 2003. (Word Families Ser.). (Illus.). 23p. (J). (ps-3). lib. bdg. 19.93 (978-1-59197-236-5(1)) ABDO Publishing Co.

—Ill As in Grill. 2003. (Word Families Ser.). (Illus.). 23p. (J). (ps-3). lib. bdg. 19.93 (978-1-59197-237-2(X) , SandCastle) ABDO Publishing Co.

—In As in Twin. 2003. (Word Families Ser.). (Illus.). 23p. (J). (ps-3). lib. bdg. 19.93 (978-1-59197-238-9(8) , SandCastle) ABDO Publishing Co.

—Ip As in Ship. 2003. (Word Families Ser.). (Illus.). 23p. (J). (ps-3). lib. bdg. 19.93 (978-1-59197-239-6(6) , SandCastle) ABDO Publishing Co.

—It As in Sit. 2003. (See It, Say It, Hear It Ser.). (Illus.). 23p. (J). (ps-3). lib. bdg. 19.93 (978-1-59197-240-2(X) , SandCastle) ABDO Publishing Co.

—Just Make Some Art! 2004. (Sight Words Ser.). (Illus.). 23p. (J). (ps-3). lib. bdg. 19.93 (978-1-59197-481-9(X)) ABDO Publishing Co.

—Ow As in Crow. 2003. (Word Families Ser.). (Illus.). 23p. (J). (ps-3). lib. bdg. 19.93 (978-1-59197-265-5(5) , SandCastle) ABDO Publishing Co.

—There Are Ants down There! 2004. (Sight Words Ser.). (Illus.). 23p. (J). (ps-3). lib. bdg. 19.93 (978-1-59197-473-4(9)) ABDO Publishing Co.

—Was That Fun? 2004. (Sight Words Ser.). (Illus.). 23p. (J). (ps-3). lib. bdg. 19.93 (978-1-59197-475-8(5)) ABDO Publishing Co.

—When Can You Play Again? 2004. (Sight Words Ser.). (Illus.). 23p. (J). (ps-3). lib. bdg. 19.93 (978-1-59197-478-9(X)) ABDO Publishing Co.

Douglas, Vincent & School Specialty Publishing Staff. Everything for Math & Reading, Grade 3. Mcgraw-Hill Editorial Staff, ed. 2004. (Everything for Early Learning Ser.). (Illus.). 320p. (J). (gr. 3-3). pap. 7.95 (978-0-7696-3363-3(3) , American Education Publishing) School Specialty Publishing.

—Everything for Math & Reading, Grade 4. Mcgraw-Hill Editorial Staff, ed. 2004. (Everything for Early Learning Ser.). (Illus.). 320p. (J). (gr. 4-4). pap. 7.95 (978-0-7696-3364-0(1) , American Education Publishing) School Specialty Publishing.

—Math Plus Reading. 2004. (Summer Link Ser.). (Illus.). 320p. (J). (ps-6). pap. 14.95 (978-0-7696-3331-2(5)); pap. 14.95 (978-0-7696-3332-9(3)); pap. 14.95 (978-0-7696-3333-6(1)); pap. 14.95 (978-0-7696-3334-3(X)); pap. 14.95 (978-0-7696-3335-0(8)) School Specialty Publishing. (American Education Publishing).

—Reading Comprehension, Grade 1. 2002. (Fun to Do & Learn Ser.). (Illus.). 32p. (J). pap. 4.99 (978-0-7424-0283-6(5) , In Celebration) Schaffer, Frank Pubns.

—Reading Comprehension, Grade 2. 2002. (Fun to Do & Learn Ser.). (Illus.). 32p. (J). pap. 4.99 (978-0-7424-0284-3(3) , In Celebration) Schaffer, Frank Pubns.

—Reading Comprehension, Grade 3. 2002. (Fun to Do & Learn Ser.). (Illus.). 32p. (J). pap. 4.99 (978-0-7424-0285-0(1) , In Celebration) Schaffer, Frank Pubns.

—Reading Comprehension, Grade 4. 2002. (Fun to Do & Learn Ser.). (Illus.). 32p. (J). pap. 4.99 (978-0-7424-0286-7(X) , In Celebration) Schaffer, Frank Pubns.

—Reading, Grade 2. 2002. (Starburst Spectrum Ser.). (Illus.). 150p. (J). (gr. 2-2). pap. 8.95 (978-1-56189-912-8(7) , American Education Publishing) School Specialty Publishing.

—Reading, Grade 3. 2002. (Starburst Spectrum Workbook Ser.). (Illus.). 150p. (J). (gr. 3-3). pap. 8.95 (978-1-56189-913-5(5) , American Education Publishing) School Specialty Publishing.

—Reading, Grade 4. 2002. (Starburst Spectrum Workbook Ser.). (Illus.). 150p. (J). (gr. 4-4). pap. 8.95 (978-1-56189-914-2(3) , American Education Publishing) School Specialty Publishing.

—Reading, Grade 5. 2002. (Starburst Spectrum Ser.). (Illus.). 150p. (J). (gr. 5-5). pap. 8.95 (978-1-56189-915-9(1) , American Education Publishing) School Specialty Publishing.

—Reading, Kindergarten. 2002. (Starburst Spectrum Workbook Ser.). (Illus.). 150p. (J). (gr. k-k). pap. 8.95 (978-1-56189-910-4(0) , American Education Publishing) School Specialty Publishing.

—Same & Different. 2004. (Kindergarten Bound Ser.). (Illus.). 80p. (J). (ps up). pap. 5.95 (978-0-7696-3439-5(7) , American Education Publishing) School Specialty Publishing.

—Spectrum Enrichment Math & Reading, Grade 4. 2002. (Starburst Spectrum Workbook Ser.). (Illus.). 150p. (J). (gr. 4-4). pap. 8.95 (978-1-57768-504-3(0) , Spectrum) School Specialty Publishing.

—Spectrum Enrichment Math & Reading, Grade 5. 2002. (Starburst Spectrum Workbook Ser.). (Illus.). 150p. (J). (gr. 5-5). pap. 8.95 (978-1-57768-505-0(9) , Spectrum) School Specialty Publishing.

—Spectrum Enrichment Math & Reading, Grade 6. 2002. (Starburst Spectrum Workbook Ser.). (Illus.). 150p. (J). (gr. 6-6). pap. 8.95 (978-1-57768-506-7(7) , Spectrum) School Specialty Publishing.

—Spectrum Reading, Grade 1. 2002. (Starburst Spectrum Workbook Ser.). (Illus.). 150p. (J). (gr. 1-1). pap. 8.95 (978-1-56189-911-1(9) , American Education Publishing) School Specialty Publishing.

—Spectrum Reading, Grade 6. 2002. (Starburst Spectrum Workbook Ser.). (Illus.). 150p. (J). (gr. 6-6). pap. 8.95 (978-1-56189-916-6(X) , American Education Publishing) School Specialty Publishing.

—Summer Link Math plus Reading, Kindergarten-Grade 1. 2004. (Summer Link Ser.). (Illus.). 320p. (J). (ps-6). pap. 14.95 (978-0-7696-3330-5(7) , American Education Publishing) School Specialty Publishing.

—Summer Link Math plus Reading, Preschool-Kindergarten. 2004. (Summer Link Ser.). (Illus.). 320p. (J). (ps-6). pap. 14.95 (978-0-7696-3329-9(3) , American Education Publishing) School Specialty Publishing.

—Summer Link Reading, Grades 1-2. 2004. (Summer Link Ser.). (Illus.). 96p. (J). (ps-6). pap. 6.95 (978-0-7696-3321-3(8) , American Education Publishing) School Specialty Publishing.

—Summer Link Reading, Kindergarten-Grade 1. 2004. (Summer Link Ser.). (Illus.). 96p. (J). (ps-6). pap. 6.95 (978-0-7696-3320-6(X) , American Education Publishing) School Specialty Publishing.

—Summer Link Reading, Preschool-Kindergarten. 2004. (Summer Link Ser.). (Illus.). 96p. (J). (ps-6). pap. 6.95 (978-0-7696-3319-0(6) , American Education Publishing) School Specialty Publishing.

Down by the Pond: Level H. Group 2. (Story Box(R) Ser.). 16p. 31.50 (978-0-322-02458-8(7)) Wright Group, The.

Down to Town: Big Book: Level A. Group 1. (Sunshinetm Ser.). 8p. 20.95 (978-0-7802-5705-4(7)) Wright Group, The.

Dragon! Level F, 6 vols. (Wonder Worldtm Ser.). 16p. 29.95 (978-0-7802-1199-5(5)) Wright Group, The.

The Dragon Who Came to Dinner: Schwa Sound: Level C, 6 vols. (Wright Skills Ser.). 16p. (gr. k-3). 26.50 (978-0-322-01505-0(7)) Wright Group, The.

Dragon with a Cold: Big Book: Level K. Group 1. (Sunshinetm Ser.). 16p. 36.50 (978-0-7802-5792-4(8)) Wright Group, The.

Dragons Galore: 6 Each of 1 Anthology, 6 vols. (Wildcats Ser.). 32p. (gr. 2-8). (978-0-322-00582-2(5)) Wright Group, The.

Ducks: Big Book: Level F. Group 2. (Story Box(R) Ser.). 16p. 20.95 (978-0-7802-9370-0(3)) Wright Group, The.

Duendes en mi Corazon 14: Leveled Books. 2001. (McGraw-Hill. Lectura Ser.). (ENG & SPA.). (gr. 5 up). (978-0-02-188262-5(2)) Macmillan/McGraw-Hill Schl. Div.

Duffy's Reading Rocks Books 1-3: Instructional Activities for Set One, 3 bks. 2002. (Illus.). ring bd. 349.95 (978-0-9754519-0-8(1)) Duffy's Educational Resources, Inc.

Dufresne, Michele. Fruit Salad. Dufresne, Michele, photos by. 1999. (Illus.). (J). pap. 3.75 (978-1-58453-027-5(8)) Pioneer Valley Educational Pr., Inc.

Dulces Suenos 18: Leveled Books. 2001. (McGraw-Hill. Lectura Ser.). (ENG & SPA.). (gr. 4 up). (978-0-02-188163-5(4)) Macmillan/McGraw-Hill Schl. Div.

Durango Street: Student Response Journal. 2002. 32p. (J). (978-1-58049-979-8(1) , RJ79) Prestwick Hse., Inc.

Duro, tio Arturo? 13: Leveled Books. 2001. (McGraw-Hill. Lectura Ser.). (ENG & SPA.). (gr. 5 up). (978-0-02-188261-8(4)) Macmillan/McGraw-Hill Schl. Div.

Dwyer, Judy. Novel Activities. 100p. (J). (gr. 2-6). (978-1-876367-02-2(4)) Wizard Bks.

Dyer, Dorothy & Lenake, Lerato. Radio Days. Menck, Clare, illus. 1999. (Cambridge Reading Routes Ser.). 32p. pap. 6.45 (978-0-521-77902-9(2)) Cambridge Univ. Pr.

Dyer, Dorothy & Lloyd, Glynis. English Matters: Grade 8 Learner's Pack. 2000. (English Matters Ser.). 208p. (gr. 8). pap. 10.60 (978-0-521-78873-1(0)) Cambridge Univ. Pr.

—English Matters Grade 9 Learner's Pack. 2001. (English Matters Ser.). 120p. pap. 9.70 (978-0-521-00244-8(3)) Cambridge Univ. Pr.

Dyer, Dorothy, et al. Radio Days & Other Stories: Chitonga Version. Chisengele, tr. 2001. (Illus.). 48p. pap. 0.45 (978-0-521-01479-3(4)) Cambridge Univ. Pr.

—Radio Days & Other Stories: Kiikaonde Version. Muyebaa, tr. 2001. (Illus.). 48p. pap. 0.45 (978-0-521-01485-4(9)) Cambridge Univ. Pr.

—Radio Days & Other Stories: Luvale Version. Sakapaji, tr. 2001. (Illus.). 48p. pap. 0.45 (978-0-521-01488-5(3)) Cambridge Univ. Pr.

—Radio Days & Other Stories: Silozi Version. Mwendende, tr. 2001. (Illus.). 48p. pap. 0.45 (978-0-521-01489-2(1)) Cambridge Univ. Pr.

Early 1 Package. 2005. (Little Celebrations Emergent & Early Packages Ser.). (J). (gr. k-3). 48.95 (978-0-673-75373-1(5)) Celebration Pr.

Early 2 Package. 2005. (Little Celebrations Emergent & Early Packages Ser.). (J). (gr. k-3). 50.95 (978-0-673-75374-8(3)) Celebration Pr.

Early Emergent: Nonfiction. 2001. (Pair-It Bks.). (J). pap. (978-0-7398-4917-0(4)) Steck-Vaughn.

Early Fluency. (gr. k-3). 26.50 (978-0-322-01620-0(7)) Wright Group, The.

Early Fluency Set 1: 1 Each of 8 Student Books. (Sunshinetm Science Ser.). (gr. 1-2). 55.95 (978-0-7802-1762-1(4)) Wright Group, The.

Early Library. 2005. (YA). (gr. k-2). 756.00 (978-0-8215-8880-2(X)); 239.40 (978-0-8215-8885-7(0)); Vol. 2. 239.40 (978-0-8215-8886-4(9)) Sadlier, William H. Inc.

Early Library Big Book Package. 2005. (YA). (ps-3). 450.00 (978-0-8215-8883-3(4)) Sadlier, William H. Inc.

Early Library Little Book. 2005. (YA). (ps-3). 478.80 (978-0-8215-8882-6(6)) Sadlier, William H. Inc.

Early Library Little Book Package. 2005. (YA). (ps-3). 91.50 (978-0-8215-8881-9(8)) Sadlier, William H. Inc.

Early Stage 2. 2005. (Little Celebrations Picture/Text & Literacy Cards Ser.). (J). (gr. k-3). 128.50 (978-0-673-75273-4(9)) Celebration Pr.

Earthquake! Level F, 6 vols. (Wonder Worldtm Ser.). 16p. 29.95 (978-0-7802-1201-5(0)) Wright Group, The.

The Earthworm: Level I, 6 vols. (Wonder Worldtm Ser.). 16p. 29.95 (978-0-7802-1988-5(0)) Wright Group, The.

Eck, Kristin. Extreme Sports, 6 bks. Incl. Bicycle Stunt Riding : Check It Out. (gr. 1). lib. bdg. 17.25 (978-0-8239-5697-5(0) , PowerKids Pr.); In-Line Skating : Check It Out. (gr. 1). lib. bdg. 17.25 (978-0-8239-5699-9(7) , PKINSK, Rosen Central); Mountain Biking : Check It Out. (gr. 2-4). lib. bdg. 17.25 (978-0-8239-5698-2(9) , PKMOBI, PowerKids Pr.); Skateboarding : Check It Out. (gr. 1). lib. bdg. 17.25 (978-0-8239-5695-1(4) , PKSKBO, PowerKids Pr.); Snowboarding : Check It Out. (gr. 1). lib. bdg. 17.25 (978-0-8239-5694-4(6) , PKSNBO, PowerKids Pr.); Wakeboarding : Check It Out. (gr. 1). lib. bdg. 17.25 (978-0-8239-5696-8(2) , PKWABO, Rosen Central); 24p. (J). (Illus.). 2001. Set lib. bdg. 96.00 (978-0-8239-7076-6(0) , PK-SPOR, PowerKids Pr.) Rosen Publishing Group, Inc., The.

The Education of Little Tree: A Student Response Journal. 2003. 40p. (YA). (978-1-58049-978-1(3) , RJ78) Prestwick Hse., Inc.

Edwards, Fiona. The Lizard's Tail: Chitonga Version. Chisengele, tr. 2001. (Illus.). 8p. pap. 0.45 (978-0-521-01601-8(0)) Cambridge Univ. Pr.

—The Lizard's Tail: Cinyanja Version. Tembo, tr. 2001. (Illus.). 8p. pap. 0.45 (978-0-521-01602-5(9)) Cambridge Univ. Pr.

—The Lizard's Tail: Icibemba Version. Mulilo, tr. 2001. (Illus.). 8p. pap. 0.45 (978-0-521-01604-9(5)) Cambridge Univ. Pr.

—The Lizard's Tail: Kiikaonde Version. Muyebaa, tr. 2001. (Illus.). 8p. pap. 0.45 (978-0-521-01605-6(3)) Cambridge Univ. Pr.

—The Lizard's Tail: Luvale Version. Sakapaji, tr. 2001. (Illus.). 8p. pap. 0.45 (978-0-521-01607-0(X)) Cambridge Univ. Pr.

—The Lizard's Tail: Silozi Version. Mwendende, tr. 2001. (Illus.). 8p. pap. 0.45 (978-0-521-01608-7(8)) Cambridge Univ. Pr.

Electric Eels. 2002. (J). pap. (978-0-7398-5812-7(2)) Steck-Vaughn.

Eller, Jeanie. Fundamentals. 2000. (Illus.). (YA). (gr. 1 up). pap. (978-1-928606-17-8(2)) Action Reading, Inc.

Emergent Library. 2005. (YA). (ps-1). 933.00 (978-0-8215-8860-4(5)); 573.00 (978-0-8215-8861-1(3)); Vol. 2. 933.00 (978-0-8215-8870-3(2)); Vol. 2. 239.40 (978-0-8215-8876-5(1)); Vol. 2. 239.40 (978-0-8215-8877-2(X)); Vol. 2. 239.40 (978-0-8215-8878-9(8)); Vol. 2. 239.40 (978-0-8215-8879-6(6)); Vol. 2. 573.00 (978-0-8215-8871-0(0)) Sadlier, William H. Inc.

Emergent Library I Big Book Package. 2005. (YA). (ps-3). 450.00 (978-0-8215-8864-2(8)) Sadlier, William H. Inc.

Emergent Library I Little Book. 2005. (YA). (ps-1). 478.80 (978-0-8215-8863-5(X)) Sadlier, William H. Inc.

Emergent Library I Little Book Package. 2005. (YA). (ps-3). 91.50 (978-0-8215-8862-8(1)) Sadlier, William H. Inc.

Emergent Library II Big Book Package. 2005. (YA). (ps-3). 450.00 (978-0-8215-8874-1(5)) Sadlier, William H. Inc.

Emergent Library II Little Book, Vol. 2. 2005. (YA). (ps-1). 478.80 (978-0-8215-8873-4(7)) Sadlier, William H. Inc.

Emergent Library II Little Book Package. 2005. (YA). (ps-3). 91.50 (978-0-8215-8872-7(9)) Sadlier, William H. Inc.

Emergent Package. 2005. (Little Celebrations Emergent & Early Packages Ser.). (J). (gr. k-3). 49.95 (978-0-673-75372-4(7)) Celebration Pr.

Emergent Stage 1. 2005. (Little Celebrations Picture/Text & Literacy Cards Ser.). (J). (gr. k-3). 128.50 (978-0-673-75224-6(0)) Celebration Pr.

Emergent Super Big Book Package. 2005. (YA). (ps-3). 900.00 (978-0-8215-8858-1(3)) Sadlier, William H. Inc.

Emergent Super Libraries, 2 vols. 2005. (Emergent Libraries Ser.). (YA). (ps-1). 1749.00 (978-0-8215-8855-0(9)) Sadlier, William H. Inc.

Emergent Super Little Book. 2005. (YA). (ps-3). 957.60 (978-0-8215-8857-4(5)) Sadlier, William H. Inc.

Emergent Super Little Book Package. 2005. (YA). (ps-3). 183.00 (978-0-8215-8856-7(7)) Sadlier, William H. Inc.

En Parejas Early Emergent, Set. 1999. (SPA., Illus.). (J). pap. (978-0-7398-0847-4(8)) Steck-Vaughn.

En Parejas Emergent Big Book Stage 2, Set. 1999. (SPA., Illus.). (J). pap. (978-0-7398-0777-4(3)) Steck-Vaughn.

El enigma de la Esfinge 13: Leveled Books. 2001. (McGraw-Hill. Lectura Ser.). (ENG & SPA.). (gr. 5 up). (978-0-02-188237-3(1)) Macmillan/McGraw-Hill Schl. Div.

Los enormes inventos de Chiquita 9: Leveled Books. 2001. (McGraw-Hill. Lectura Ser.). (ENG & SPA.). (gr. 4 up). (978-0-02-188185-7(5)) Macmillan/McGraw-Hill Schl. Div.

Enrichment Math & Reading: Grade 3. 2002. (Starburst Spectrum Workbook Ser.). (Illus.). 150p. (J). (gr. 3-3). pap. 8.95 (978-1-57768-503-6(2) , Spectrum) School Specialty Publishing.

Entrar es facil pero Salir? 6: Leveled Books. 2001. (McGraw-Hill. Lectura Ser.). (ENG & SPA.). (gr. 3 up). (978-0-02-188103-1(0)) Macmillan/McGraw-Hill Schl. Div.

Eruption: 6 Each of 1 Anthology, 6 vols. (Wildcats Ser.). 32p. (gr. 2-8). (978-0-322-00584-6(1)) Wright Group, The.

Essential Words Reading & Language Arts Activity Book (Intermediate) Intermediate/Middle School. 2005. (Illus.). 50p. (J). 8.95 (978-0-9722452-3-4(5)) New Leaf Educ., Inc.

Essential Words Reading & Language Arts Glossary (Intermediate) Intermediate/Middle School. 2005. (Illus.). 64p. (J). per. 19.95 (978-0-9722452-7-2(8)) New Leaf Educ., Inc.

Evaluacion de las Selecciones: Assessment. 2001. (McGraw-Hill. Lectura Ser.). (ENG & SPA.). (gr. 1 up). (978-0-02-186912-1(X)); (gr. 2 up). (978-0-02-186913-8(8)); (gr. 3 up). (978-0-02-186914-5(6)); (gr. 4 up). (978-0-02-187774-4(2)); (gr. 5 up). (978-0-02-187775-1(0)); (gr. 6 up). (978-0-02-187776-8(9)) Macmillan/McGraw-Hill Schl. Div.

Evaluacion del Desarrollo de la Lectura Leveled Libraries: Extending Stage, Level 40. 2003. (SPA.). tchr. ed. 43.50 (978-0-7652-2389-0(9)) Modern Curriculum Pr.

Las explicaciones de Noche 7: Leveled Books. 2001. (McGraw-Hill. Lectura Ser.). (ENG & SPA.). (gr. 4 up). (978-0-02-188152-9(9)) Macmillan/McGraw-Hill Schl. Div.

Explorers: Fluency - Student Book Set - 1 Each of 12 Titles. (Explorers. Exploradores Nonfiction Sets Ser.). (gr. 3-6). Vol. 2. 89.95 (978-0-7699-0817-5(9)); Vol. 3. 89.95 (978-0-7699-0819-9(5)) Shortland Pubns. (U. S. A.) Inc.

Explorers Exploradores Set 1: English - 1 Each of 12 Student Books, 1 Teacher's Resource Book. (Explorers. Exploradores Nonfiction Sets Ser.). (gr. 3-6). 137.95 (978-0-7699-0576-1(5)) Shortland Pubns. (U. S. A.) Inc.

Explorers Exploradores Set 1: English - 6 Each of 12 Student Books, 1 Teacher's Resource Book. (Explorers. Exploradores Nonfiction Sets Ser.). (gr. 3-6). 558.50 (978-0-7699-0583-9(8)) Shortland Pubns. (U. S. A.) Inc.

Explorers Exploradores Set 1: Spanish - 1 Each of 12 Student Books. (Explorers. Exploradores Nonfiction Sets Ser.). (gr. 3-6). 89.95 (978-0-7699-0816-8(0)) Shortland Pubns. (U. S. A.) Inc.

Explorers Exploradores Set 1: Spanish - 6 Each of 12 Student Books, 1 Teacher's Resource Book. (Explorers. Exploradores Nonfiction Sets Ser.). (ENG & SPA.). (gr. 3-6). 558.50 (978-0-7699-0584-6(6)) Shortland Pubns. (U. S. A.) Inc.

Explorers Exploradores Set 2: English - 1 Each of 12 Student Books, 1 Teacher's Resource Book. (Explorers. Exploradores Nonfiction Sets Ser.). (gr. 3-6). 137.95 (978-0-7699-0578-5(1)) Shortland Pubns. (U. S. A.) Inc.

Explorers Exploradores Set 2: English - 6 Each of 12 Student Books, 1 Teacher's Resource Book. (Explorers. Exploradores Nonfiction Sets Ser.). (gr. 3-6). 558.50 (978-0-7699-0585-3(4)) Shortland Pubns. (U. S. A.) Inc.

Explorers Exploradores Set 2: Spanish - 1 Each of 12 Student Books. (Explorers. Exploradores Nonfiction Sets Ser.). (gr. 3-6). 89.95 (978-0-7699-0818-2(7)) Shortland Pubns. (U. S. A.) Inc.

Explorers Exploradores Set 2: Spanish - 1 Each of 12 Student Books, 1 Teacher's Resource Book. (Explorers. Exploradores Nonfiction Sets Ser.). (gr. 3-6). 137.95 (978-0-7699-0579-2(X)) Shortland Pubns. (U. S. A.) Inc.

Explorers Exploradores Set 2: Spanish - 6 Each of 12 Student Books, 1 Teacher's Resource Book. (Explorers. Exploradores Nonfiction Sets Ser.). (ENG & SPA.). (gr. 3-6). 558.50 (978-0-7699-0586-0(2)) Shortland Pubns. (U. S. A.) Inc.

Explorers Exploradores Set 3: English - 1 Each of 12 Student Books, 1 Teacher's Resource Book. (Explorers. Exploradores Nonfiction Sets Ser.). (gr. 3-6). 137.95 (978-0-7699-0580-8(3)) Shortland Pubns. (U. S. A.) Inc.

Explorers Exploradores Set 3: English - 6 Each of 12 Student Books, 1 Teacher's Resource Book. (Explorers. Exploradores Nonfiction Sets Ser.). (gr. 3-6). 558.50 (978-0-7699-0587-7(0)) Shortland Pubns. (U. S. A.) Inc.

Explorers Exploradores Set 3: Spanish - 1 Each of 12 Student Books. (Explorers. Exploradores Nonfiction Sets Ser.). (gr. 3-6). 89.95 (978-0-7699-0820-5(9)) Shortland Pubns. (U. S. A.) Inc.

Explorers Exploradores Set 3: Spanish - 1 Each of 12 Student Books, 1 Teacher's Resource Book. (Explorers. Exploradores Nonfiction Sets Ser.). (gr. 3-6). 137.95 (978-0-7699-0581-5(1)) Shortland Pubns. (U. S. A.) Inc.

Explorers Exploradores Set 3: Spanish - 6 Each of 12 Student Books, 1 Teacher's Resource Book. (Explorers. Exploradores Nonfiction Sets Ser.). (ENG & SPA.). (gr. 3-6). 558.50 (978-0-7699-0588-4(9)) Shortland Pubns. (U. S. A.) Inc.

Explorers Exploradores Sets 1,3: English - 1 Each of 36 Student Books, 3 Teacher's Resource Books. (Explorers. Exploradores Nonfiction Sets Ser.). (gr. 3-6). 413.95 (978-0-7699-0574-7(9)) Shortland Pubns. (U. S. A.) Inc.

Explorers Exploradores Sets 1,3: English - 6 Each of 36 Student Books, 3 Teacher's Resource Books. (Explorers. Exploradores Nonfiction Sets Ser.). (gr. 3-6). 1587.50 (978-0-7699-0813-7(6)) Shortland Pubns. (U. S. A.) Inc.

Explorers Exploradores Sets 1,3: Spanish - 1 Each of 36 Student Books, 3 Teacher's Resource Books. (Explorers. Exploradores Nonfiction Sets Ser.). (gr. 3-6). 413.95 (978-0-7699-0575-4(7)) Shortland Pubns. (U. S. A.) Inc.

Explorers Exploradores Sets 1,3: Spanish - 6 Each of 36 Student Books, 3 Teacher's Resource Books. (Explorers. Exploradores Nonfiction Sets Ser.). (SPA.). (gr. 3-6). 1587.50 (978-0-7699-0814-4(4)) Shortland Pubns. (U. S. A.) Inc.

The Explosive Trek: Level 6, 6 vols. (Fluency Strand Ser.). (gr. 4-8). 45.00 (978-1-4045-1234-4(9)) Wright Group, The.

Extreme Lives: 6 Each of 1 Anthology, 6 vols. (Wildcatstm Ser.). 32p. (gr. 2-8). (978-0-322-02419-9(6)) Wright Group, The.

Eye Spy: 6 Each of 1 Anthology, 6 vols. (Wildcats Ser.). 32p. (gr. 2-8). (978-0-322-00592-1(2)) Wright Group, The.

Eyes: Level C, 6 vols. (Wonder Worldtm Ser.). 16p. 24.95 (978-0-7802-1992-2(9)) Wright Group, The.

Eyes & Ears Sets: 1 Each of 3 Big Books. (Sunshinetm Science Ser.). (gr. 1-2). 111.50 (978-0-7802-1445-3(5)) Wright Group, The.

Eyes & Ears Sets: 1 Each of 3 Student Books. (Sunshinetm Science Ser.). (gr. 1-2). 20.95 (978-0-7802-1747-8(0)) Wright Group, The.

Face Painting: Level H, 6 vols. (Wonder Worldtm Ser.). 16p. 29.95 (978-0-7802-2897-9(9)) Wright Group, The.

Falletta, Bernadette & Lewis, Marla. We Love to Read: Literature Through Literacy & Music. 1999. (Illus.). 83p. (J). (gr. 1-7). 29.95 (978-0-9675466-1-2(3)); 44.95 incl. cd-rom (978-0-9675466-4-3(8)); 39.95 incl. audio (978-0-9675466-5-0(6)) We Love to Read Productions.

Families, Families: Take-Home Book. 2005. (Lee Bennett Hopkins Worlds of Poetry Classroom Library). (YA). (gr. k-3). 13.50 (978-0-8215-0566-3(1)) Sadlier, William H. Inc.

Families, Families: Teacher's Theme Resource Folder. 2005. (Lee Bennett Hopkins Worlds of Poetry Classroom Library). (YA). (gr. k-3). 12.00 (978-0-8215-0515-1(7)) Sadlier, William H. Inc.

Family Reunion, 6 vols. (Multicultural Programs Ser.). 16p. (gr. 1-3). 24.95 (978-0-7802-9213-0(8)) Wright Group, The.

Fans: Consonant f: Level A, 6 vols. (Wright Skills Ser.). 12p. (gr. k-3). 17.95 (978-0-322-03107-4(9)) Wright Group, The.

Farewell to Manzanar. 2004. (Literature Connections Ser.). (gr. 6-12). (978-0-395-88455-3(1) , 2-70861) McDougal Littell Inc.

The Farm. (Little Book Practice Reader). (J). (978-0-8136-5348-8(7)) Modern Curriculum Pr.

The Farm, 6 vols. (gr. k-2). 28.95 (978-0-7368-8005-3(4)) Red Brick Learning.

The Farm Party: R-Controlled a: Level B, 6 vols. (Wright Skills Ser.). 16p. (gr. k-3). 26.50 (978-0-322-01486-2(7)) Wright Group, The.

Farr. Think Alongs. 1999. (J). pap. incl. VHS (978-0-7398-0095-9(7)) Steck-Vaughn.

—Think-Alongs: Classroom Library Edition. 1999. (J). pap. (978-0-7398-0096-6(5)) Steck-Vaughn.

Faster, Higher, Stronger: The Olympics, 6 vols. (Book2WebTM Ser.). (gr. 4-8). 36.50 (978-0-322-02984-2(8)) Wright Group, The.

Fay & Kay by the Bay: Long a Digraphs: Level B, 6 vols. (Wright Skills Ser.). 16p. (gr. k-3). 26.50 (978-0-322-01478-7(6)) Wright Group, The.

Fearon Staff. The Phantom of the Opera. (YA). (gr. 5-12). pap. 6.50 (978-0-8359-0981-5(6)) Globe Fearon Educational Publishing.

Feellings Little Book: Early Reading Fluency, Level A. 2004. (gr. 1). pap. 6.00 (978-0-7398-8159-0(0)) Steck-Vaughn.

Fehlau, Dagmar, illus. Little Book: Star Light Pack: Getting Ready to Read with Mother Goose, 10 vols. l.t. ed. 2001. (Sadlier Phonics (Pre K-Level C) Ser.). 8p. (YA). (ps-k). 23.94 (978-0-8215-6975-7(9)) Sadlier, William H. Inc.

—Star Light: Getting Ready to Read with Mother Goose. l.t. ed. 2001. (Sadlier Phonics Reading Program). 8p. (YA). (ps-k). 27.00 (978-0-8215-6960-3(0)) Sadlier, William H. Inc.

Feinstein, Stephen. Reading Fiction 1: Reading in Context. 2001. (Illus.). 112p. per., wbk. ed. 8.95 (978-1-56254-193-4(5) , SP 1935) Saddleback Educational Publishing.

—Reading Nonfiction 1: Reading in Context. 2001. (Illus.). 112p. per., wbk. ed. 8.95 (978-1-56254-191-0(9)) Saddleback Educational Publishing.

Feldman, Heather. Superstars of Sports, 6 bks. Incl. Derek Jeter : Baseball's Best. lib. bdg. 17.25 (978-0-8239-5719-4(5) , PKDEJE); Hulk Hogan : Wrestling Pro. lib. bdg. 17.25 (978-0-8239-5720-0(9) , PKHUHO); Marion Jones : World-Class Runner. lib. bdg. 17.25 (978-0-8239-5718-7(7) , PKMAJO); Mia Hamm : Soccer Superstar. lib. bdg. 17.25 (978-0-8239-5716-3(0) , PKHAMM); Venus Williams : Tennis Champion. lib. bdg. 17.25 (978-0-8239-5717-0(9) , PKSUST); Wayne Gretzky : Hockey Star. lib. bdg. 17.25 (978-0-8239-5715-6(2) , PKGRET); 24p. (J). (gr. 1). (Illus.). 2001. Set lib. bdg. 96.00 (978-0-8239-7075-9(2) , PKSUST, PowerKids Pr.) Rosen Publishing Group, Inc., The.

Feldman, Reynold & Rumi, M. Jan. WisingUp: A Youth Guide to Good Living. 2004. 192p. (YA). (978-1-932590-02-9(1)) Wisdom Foundation Publishing.

Felix, the Very Hungry Fish. 2005. (Emergent Library: Vol. 2). (YA). (ps-1). 23.94 (978-0-8215-8920-5(2)) Sadlier, William H. Inc.

Felix, the Very Hungry Fish: Take-Home Bk. 2005. (Emergent Library: Vol. 2). (YA). (ps-1). 12.60 (978-0-8215-7250-4(4)) Sadlier, William H. Inc.

Fences. 2003. 44p. (YA). tchr. ed., ring bd. (978-1-58049-468-7(4) , TU224) Prestwick Hse., Inc.

Fenton, Corinne. A Bit Too Small. 2002. (Bright Sparks Ser.). (Illus.). 16p. pap. 2.30 (978-0-521-75414-9(3)) Cambridge Univ. Pr.

—Mum & the Blowfly. 2002. (Bright Sparks Ser.). (Illus.). 16p. pap. 2.30 (978-0-521-75415-6(1)) Cambridge Univ. Pr.

Ferguson, Walter F. Speed Learning: The Quest for Excellence. 2004. cd-rom 59.95 (978-0-9745333-0-8(0)) Mystique International, Ltd.

Fernandez, Cesar. El bibliobus Magico. Torres, Marina, illus. 2004. 88p. pap. 10.00 (978-84-931888-1-8(6)) Editorial Brief ESP. *Dist:* Independent Pubs. Group.

El ferrocarril Subterraneo 9: Leveled Books. 2001. (McGraw-Hill. Lectura Ser.). (ENG & SPA.). (gr. 4 up). (978-0-02-188209-0(6)) Macmillan/McGraw-Hill Schl. Div.

Festival Fun: 6 Each of 1 Anthology, 6 vols. (Wildcatstm Ser.). 32p. (gr. 2-8). (978-0-322-02424-3(2)) Wright Group, The.

Fetty, Margaret. Theme-Based Reading Comprehension. 2003. (100+ Seriestm Ser.). 128p. (J). (gr. 3-3). pap. 12.99 (978-0-7424-1923-0(1) , IFG99110) School Specialty Publishing.

Fight Deck: Level D, 6 vols. (Wonder Worldtm Ser.). 16p. 24.95 (978-0-7802-1203-9(7)) Wright Group, The.

Find Yourself a Friend, 6 vols. (Multicultural Programs Ser.). 16p. (gr. 1-3). 24.95 (978-0-7802-9210-9(3)) Wright Group, The.

Finding Places, Grade 1: American Readers. (J). (gr. 1). (978-0-669-04936-7(0)); wbk. ed. (978-0-669-04942-8(5)) Houghton Mifflin Co. (Schl. Div.).

Finn, Perdita. Julie of the Wolves: Everything You Need for Sucessful Literature Circles That Get Kids Thinking, Talking, Writing-and Loving Literature. 2001. (Literature Circle Guides Ser.). (Illus.). 32p. (gr. 4-8). pap. 5.95 (978-0-439-16359-0(5)) Scholastic, Inc.

Fire! Fire! 6 Each of 1 Anthology, 6 vols. (Wildcats Ser.). 32p. (gr. 2-8). (978-0-322-00581-5(7)) Wright Group, The.

First Explorers Primeros Exploradores Set. 1: English - 1 Each of 12 Student Books, 1 Each of 12 Lesson Plans. (First Explorers. Primeros Exploradores Nonfiction Sets Ser.). (gr. 1-2). 107.95 (978-0-7699-1360-5(1)) Shortland Pubns. (U. S. A.) Inc.

First Explorers Primeros Exploradores Set 1: English - 6 Each of 12 Student Books, 1 Each of 12 Lesson Plans: Set 1. (First Explorers. Primeros Exploradores Nonfiction Sets Ser.). (gr. 1-2). 407.50 (978-0-7699-1364-3(4)) Shortland Pubns. (U. S. A.) Inc.

First Explorers Primeros Exploradores Set 2: English - 6 Each of 12 Student Books, 1 Each of 12 Lesson Plans, (First Explorers. Primeros Exploradores Nonfiction Sets Ser.). (gr. 1-2). 452.50 (978-0-7699-1365-0(2)) Shortland Pubns. (U. S. A.) Inc.

First Explorers Primeros Exploradores Set. 3: English - 1 Each of 12 Student Books, 1 Each of 12 Lesson Plans. (First Explorers. Primeros Exploradores Nonfiction Sets Ser.). (gr. 1-2). 115.50 (978-0-7699-1361-2(X)) Shortland Pubns. (U. S. A.) Inc.

First Explorers Primeros Exploradores Sets 1-2: English - 1 Each of 24 Student Books, 1 Each of 24 Lesson Plans. (First Explorers. Primeros Exploradores Nonfiction Sets Ser.). (gr. 1-2). 223.50 (978-0-7699-1366-7(0)) Shortland Pubns. (U. S. A.) Inc.

First Explorers Primeros Exploradores Sets 1-2: English - 6 Each of 24 Student Books, 1 Each of 24 Lesson Plans. (First Explorers. Primeros Exploradores Nonfiction Sets Ser.). (gr. 1-2). 816.95 (978-0-7699-1359-9(8)) Shortland Pubns. (U. S. A.) Inc.

First Steps: Sorting & Opposites. 2002. (First Steps Reading Ser.). 32p. (J). pap. 2.95 (978-0-7894-8484-0(6)) Dorling Kindersley Publishing, Inc.

Fish: Level E, 6 vols. (Wonder Worldtm Ser.). 16p. 29.95 (978-0-7802-1994-6(5)); 26.50 (978-0-7802-7004-6(5)) Wright Group, The.

Fishing: Level F, 6 vols. (Wonder Worldtm Ser.). 16p. 29.95 (978-0-7802-1996-0(1)) Wright Group, The.

Fitzgerald, Holly. Reading Skills. 1999. (100+ Seriestm Ser.). 102p. (J). (gr. 3-4). pap. 12.99 (978-0-88012-822-3(4) , IF8711); (Illus.). (gr. 1-2). pap. 12.99 (978-0-88012-821-6(6) , IF8710); (Illus.). (gr. 5-6). pap. 12.99 (978-0-88012-908-4(5) , IF8712) School Specialty Publishing.

The Five Senses: Big Book: Level I. Group 1. (Story Box(R) Ser.). 16p. 31.50 (978-0-322-02459-5(5)) Wright Group, The.

El flamenco Friolento 24: Leveled Books. 2001. (McGraw-Hill. Lectura Ser.). (ENG & SPA.). (gr. 1 up). (978-0-02-187953-3(2)) Macmillan/McGraw-Hill Schl. Div.

Flea Treat Little Book: Early Reading Fluency, Level C. 2004. (gr. 3). pap. 6.00 (978-0-7398-8290-0(2)) Steck-Vaughn.

Fleming, Maria. Poem of the Week: 50 Irresistible Poems with Activities That Teach Key Reading & Writing Skills. 2000. (Illus.). 128p. pap. 14.95 (978-0-439-07751-4(6)) Scholastic, Inc.

Fleming, Sarah. My Dog's Check-Up, 6 vols, Pack. 2000. (Cambridge Reading Ser.). (Illus.). 8p. pap. 28.00 (978-0-521-78768-0(8)) Cambridge Univ. Pr.

Fletcher, Barbara. A Rose on the River: Level U, 6 vols. 128p. (gr. 6 up). 36.95 (978-0-322-05888-0(0)) Wright Group, The.

Flew, Alison. Gone Fishing. 2002. (Bright Sparks Ser.). (Illus.). 16p. pap. 2.30 (978-0-521-75417-0(8)) Cambridge Univ. Pr.

Flip, Flap, & Fluff: Family Blends: Level B, 6 vols. (Wright Skills Ser.). 16p. (gr. k-3). 17.95 (978-0-322-01459-6(X)) Wright Group, The.

The Flood: Level K, 6 vols. (Wonder Worldtm Ser.). 16p. 34.95 (978-0-7802-4571-6(7)) Wright Group, The.

Flores, Debra, et al. Reading Comprehension 1-3: Activities for Understanding. Jennett, Pamela, ed. Grayson, Rick & Iosa, Ann, illus. 2004. 96p. (J). pap. 1.99 (978-1-59198-045-2(3) , 3384) Creative Teaching Pr., Inc.

—Reading Comprehension 4-6: Activities for Understanding. Jennett, Pamela, ed. Grayson, Rick & Iosa, Ann, illus. 2004. 96p. (J). pap. 12.99 (978-1-59198-046-9(1) , 3385) Creative Teaching Pr., Inc.

Flour: Level M, 6 vols. (Wonder Worldtm Ser.). 16p. 34.95 (978-0-7802-1998-4(8)) Wright Group, The.

Fluency Skills Guide. (Sunshine Skills Guides). 25.95 (978-0-7802-9858-3(6)) Wright Group, The.

Fluent Library. 2005. (YA). (gr. 1-3). 459.00 (978-0-8215-8890-1(7)); (ps-3). 119.70 (978-0-8215-8990-8(3)); Vol. 2. (ps-3). 119.70 (978-0-8215-8991-5(1)) Sadlier, William H. Inc.

Fluent Library Big Book Package. 2005. (YA). (ps-3). 315.00 (978-0-8215-8893-2(1)) Sadlier, William H. Inc.

Fluent Library Little Book. 2005. (YA). (ps-3). 293.40 (978-0-8215-8892-5(3)) Sadlier, William H. Inc.

Fluent Library Little Book Package. 2005. (YA). (ps-3). 57.00 (978-0-8215-8891-8(5)) Sadlier, William H. Inc.

Fluent Stage 3. 2005. (Little Celebrations Picture/Text & Literacy Cards Ser.). (J). (gr. k-3). 128.50 (978-0-673-77359-3(0)) Celebration Pr.

Fly Away Home: Level K, 6 vols. (Wonder Worldtm Ser.). 16p. 34.95 (978-0-7802-1205-3(3)) Wright Group, The.

Follow the Map, 6 vols. 8p. (gr. k-1). 21.50 (978-0-322-02067-2(0)) Wright Group, The.

Food Trappers: Level K, 6 vols. (Wonder Worldtm Ser.). 16p. 34.95 (978-0-7802-1209-1(6)) Wright Group, The.

Foods of the World, 6 vols. (Book2WebTM Ser.). (gr. 4-8). 36.50 (978-0-322-02985-9(6)) Wright Group, The.

Ford, Janis. The Hare & the Thorn. Busse, Annette, illus. 1999. (Cambridge Reading Routes Ser.). 32p. pap. 6.45 (978-0-521-77898-5(0)) Cambridge Univ. Pr.

Foster, Kelli C. & Erickson, Gina Clegg. Get Ready... Get Set... Read!, 5 sets (35 bks.) Russell, Kerri G., illus. (J). lib. bdg. 418.25 Set. lib. bdg. 418.25 (978-1-56674-920-6(4)) Forest Hse. Publishing Co., Inc.

Foundations: Early Emergent-Upper Emergent - 1 Each of 25 Student Books: Level E. 124.95 (978-0-322-02722-0(5)) Wright Group, The.

The Four A's: 6 Each of 1 Anthology, 6 vols. (Wildcats Ser.). 32p. (gr. 2-8). (978-0-322-00595-2(7)) Wright Group, The.

The Fox: Consonants q, x, z; -ack, -ick, -ill word families: Level A, 6 vols. (Wright Skills Ser.). 12p. (gr. k-3). 17.95 (978-0-322-01456-5(5)) Wright Group, The.

Fox, Mem. Hattie & the Fox. 99th ed. 1999. (Signatures Ser.). (Illus.). (gr. 1 up). pap. 60.70 (978-0-15-310811-2(8)) Harcourt Schl. Pubs.

Francis, Andre. Cultural Instruments: Big Book: Level R. Group 1. (Take-Twostm Ser.). 32p. 38.95 (978-0-322-04490-6(1)) Wright Group, The.

Francis, Kirsty, et al. Learner's Workbook for Grade 3, Towards Independence. 2000. (Cambridge Reading Routes Ser.). 52p. (gr. 3). pap. 2.30 (978-0-521-77884-8(0)) Cambridge Univ. Pr.

—Teacher's Book for Grade 3, Towards Independence. 2000. (Cambridge Reading Routes Ser.). 136p. (gr. 3). pap., tchr. ed. 17.95 (978-0-521-77883-1(2)) Cambridge Univ. Pr.

Fredericks, Anthony D. & Lynott, Vicky. Write to Comprehend: Using Writing as a Tool to Build Reading Comprehension. 2007. 144p. pap. 19.95 ***(978-1-59647-120-7(4))*** Good Year Bks.

Frog & Toad All Year. 2003. 31.95 (978-0-673-75800-2(1)) Celebration Pr.

Frog on a Log: 1 Big Book, 6 Each of 1 Student Book, & 1 Cassette. (Song Box(R) Ser.). (gr. 1-2). 68.95 (978-0-7802-3204-4(6)) Wright Group, The.

Frog on a Log: 6 Each of 1 Student Book, 6 vols. (Song Box(R) Ser.). (gr. 1-2). 29.50 (978-0-7802-2255-7(5)) Wright Group, The.

Frog on a Log: Big Book. (Song Box(R) Ser.). (gr. 1-2). 31.50 (978-0-7802-2256-4(3)) Wright Group, The.

From Coast to Coast, 6 vols., Set D. (Phonics Readers Ser.). (gr. k-2). 28.95 (978-0-7368-4061-3(3)) Red Brick Learning.

From Farm to Store Set C, 6 vols. (Phonics Readers Ser.). (gr. k-2). 17.50 (978-0-7368-3216-8(5)) Red Brick Learning.

From Rocks to Sand: Level L, 6 vols. (Wonder Worldtm Ser.). 16p. 34.95 (978-0-7802-4575-4(X)) Wright Group, The.

From the Air: Level F, 6 vols. (Wonder Worldtm Ser.). 16p. 29.95 (978-0-7802-2000-3(5)) Wright Group, The.

Fruit Salad: Level D, 6 vols. (Wonder Worldtm Ser.). 16p. 24.95 (978-0-7802-1241-1(X)) Wright Group, The.

Fry, Edward B. Reading Drills: Introductory Level. 1999. (gr. 6-12). pap. 16.64 (978-0-8092-0361-1(8) , 9780809203611) Jamestown.

—Skimming & Scanning: Middle Level. 1999. (gr. 6-12). pap. 16.64 (978-0-8092-0364-2(2) , 9780809203642) Jamestown.

Fue una suerte Perderse! 1: Leveled Books. 2001. (McGraw-Hill. Lectura Ser.). (ENG & SPA.). (gr. 2 up). (978-0-02-188050-8(6)) Macmillan/McGraw-Hill Schl. Div.

Las gallinas nadadoras de Manuela 5: Leveled Books. 2001. (McGraw-Hill. Lectura Ser.). (ENG & SPA.). (gr. 3 up). (978-0-02-188102-4(2)) Macmillan/McGraw-Hill Schl. Div.

Gallinella Rossa. pap. 14.95 (978-88-04-46594-2(8)) Mondadori ITA. *Dist:* Distribooks, Inc.

Gant, Linda G. Readers Are Leaders. Gant, Linda G., illus. Date not set. (Illus.). (J). (ps-3). (978-0-9673625-0-2(4)) Readers Are Leaders.

Gant, Robert, illus. My Big Box of Reading. gif. ed. 2005. 64p. (J). cd-rom 24.95 (978-1-57791-195-1(4)) Brighter Minds Children's Publishing.

Garbage: Big Book: Level D. (Wonder Worldtm Ser.). 16p. 26.50 (978-0-7802-7007-7(X)) Wright Group, The.

Garbage: Level D, 6 vols. (Wonder Worldtm Ser.). 16p. 24.95 (978-0-7802-2026-3(9)) Wright Group, The.

Gates, Phil. Bubbles: South African Edition. 1999. (Cambridge Reading Routes Ser.). (Illus.). 24p. pap. 5.50 (978-0-521-77893-0(X)) Cambridge Univ. Pr.

—Codes & Signals: South African Edition. 1999. (Cambridge Reading Routes Ser.). (Illus.). 24p. pap. 5.50 (978-0-521-77890-9(5)) Cambridge Univ. Pr.

Gates, Phil, et al. Big Book of Bubbles: South African Edition. 2000. (Cambridge Reading Routes Ser.). (Illus.). 24p. pap. 12.40 (978-0-521-77885-5(9)) Cambridge Univ. Pr.

Gatto con gli Stivali. pap. 14.95 (978-88-04-44207-3(7)) Mondadori ITA. *Dist:* Distribooks, Inc.

Gauthier, Gilles. Comment on Fait un Enfant Parfait. Derome, Pierre-Andre, illus. 2001. (Premier Roman Ser.). (FRE.). 64p. (J). (gr. 1-4). pap. (978-2-89021-497-2(4)) Diffusion du livre Mirabel.

Gaydos, Nora. Look Around! Sams, B. B., illus. 2003. (Now I'm Reading! Ser.). 128p. (J). (ps-1). 16.99 (978-1-58476-167-9(9)) Innovative Kids.

—My World. Sams, B. B., illus. 2004. (Now I'm Reading!Tm Beginning Reader Ser.). 128p. (J). (ps-1). 16.99 (978-1-58476-263-8(2)) Innovative Kids.

—Simply Science - Independent. Montgomery, Lee, illus. 2003. (Now I'm Reading! Ser.). 128p. (J). (ps-2). 16.99 (978-1-58476-169-3(5)) Innovative Kids.

Geimer, Allan F. I Can Read, You Can Read: Basic Reading Teaching Guide. 140p. (J). pap. 12.95 (978-1-886358-02-7(8)) Cellular Publishing.

Geiser, Traci Ferguson. Celebrate Reading: Teaching Reading Skills Using Multicultural Celebrations. Dobelmann, Collene, ed. 2005. (Celebrate the Months Ser.). (Illus.). 112p. (J). pap. (978-1-59198-179-4(4) , 4548) Creative Teaching Pr., Inc.

Gemmen, Heather & McNeil, Mary. Escape, Level 3. Argoff, Patti, tr. Argoff, Patti, illus. 1999. (Rocket Readers Ser.). 24p. (J). (gr. 3 up). pap., pap. 8.99 (978-0-7814-3987-6(X) , 0781439876) Cook, David C. Publishing Co.

—How Did That Happen?, Level 4. Foote, Dan, tr. Foote, Dan, illus. 1999. (Rocket Readers Ser.). 32p. (J). (gr. 4 up). pap., pap. 4.99 (978-0-7814-3978-7(7) , 0781439787) Cook, David C. Publishing Co.

—Little Things, Pre-Level 1. Stormer, Karen, illus. 2003. (Rocket Readers Ser.). 40p. (J). (ps-1). pap. 8.99 (978-0-7814-3981-7(7) , 0781439817) Cook, David C. Publishing Co.

—No Fear, Level 3. Graham, Alastair, tr. Graham, Alastair, illus. 1999. (Rocket Readers Ser.). 24p. (J). (gr. 3 up). pap., pap. 8.99 (978-0-7814-3988-6(4) , 0781439884) Cook, David C. Publishing Co.

—Spare Me, Level 3. Mahan, Ben, tr. Mahan, Ben, illus. 1999. (Rocket Readers Ser.). 24p. (J). (gr. 3 up). pap., pap. 8.99 (978-0-7814-3985-5(X) , 078143985X) Cook, David C. Publishing Co.

—What Will You Be?, Level 4. Mones, Isidre, tr. Mones, Isidre, illus. 1999. (Rocket Readers Ser.). 32p. (J). (gr. 4 up). pap., pap. 4.99 (978-0-7814-3977-0(9) , 0781439779) Cook, David C. Publishing Co.

—What Will You Do?, Level 4. Burris, Priscilla, tr. Burris, Priscilla, illus. 1999. (Rocket Readers Ser.). 32p. (J). (gr. 4 up). pap., pap. 4.99 (978-0-7814-3979-4(5) , 0781439795) Cook, David C. Publishing Co.

—Who Cares?, Level 4. Taylor, John, tr. Taylor, John, illus. 1999. (Rocket Readers Ser.). 32p. (J). (gr. 4 up). pap., pap. 4.99 (978-0-7814-3980-0(9) , 0781439809) Cook, David C. Publishing Co.

Geoghegan, Bronwyn. Livewire Real Lives Mick Doohan. 2000. (Livewires Ser.). (gr. 6-9). pap. 6.00 (978-0-521-78992-9(3)) Cambridge Univ. Pr.

Gerber, Carole. Reading: Grade 3. 2003. (Brighter Child Workbooks Ser.). 24p. (J). (gr. 3). pap. 2.25 (978-1-56189-063-7(4) , American Education Publishing) School Specialty Publishing.

—Reading & Phonics: Grade 1. 2003. (Brighter Child Workbooks Ser.). (Illus.). 24p. (J). (gr. 1). pap. 2.25 (978-1-56189-061-3(8) , 31011, American Education Publishing) School Specialty Publishing.

Get Me Out of Here Little Book: Early Reading Fluency, Level C. 2004. pap. 6.00 (978-0-7398-8296-2(1)) Steck-Vaughn.

Get Smart Skills Staff. HSPT Reading: New Jersey High School Proficiency Test. 2004. 192p. (gr. 11 up). pap. 14.95 (978-1-932635-31-7(9)) Webster House Publishing LLC.

—PSSA Reading: Pennsylvania System of School Assessment. 2004. 192p. (gr. 11 up). pap. 14.95 (978-1-932635-28-7(9)) Webster House Publishing LLC.

Getting FIT: Level A, 6 vols. (Wonder Worldtm Ser.). 16p. 24.95 (978-0-7802-1036-3(0)) Wright Group, The.

Getting Glasses: Level I, 6 vols. (Wonder Worldtm Ser.). 16p. 29.95 (978-0-7802-2002-7(1)) Wright Group, The.

Getting the Sequence (Gr. 4-5) 2004. (J). (978-1-58232-131-8(0)) Bryan Hse. Pubs., Inc.

Getting There: Level B, 6 vols. (Wonder Worldtm Ser.). 16p. 24.95 (978-0-7802-1037-0(9)) Wright Group, The.

A Giant-Size Hamburger: Level D, 6 vols. (Wonder Worldtm Ser.). 16p. 24.95 (978-0-7802-1028-8(X)) Wright Group, The.

Giants in the City: Hard & Soft c & g: Level B, 6 vols. (Wright Skills Ser.). 16p. (gr. k-3). 26.50 (978-0-322-01489-3(1)) Wright Group, The.

Giddyoocha! Big Book: Level J. Group 1. (Story Box(R) Ser.). 16p. 31.50 (978-0-322-02468-7(4)) Wright Group, The.

The Gig: Level 4, 6 vols. (Fluency Strand Ser.). (gr. 4-8). 45.00 (978-1-4045-1229-0(2)) Wright Group, The.

Gile, John. What Is That Thing? Whose Stuff Is This? Gruntman, Karen, illus. 2000. (ENG.). (J). 13.95 (978-0-910941-27-3(0)) JGC/United Publishing Corps.

Gillham, Bill. Dirty Dog: Chitonga Version. Chisengele, tr. 2001. (Illus.). 8p. pap. 0.45 (978-0-521-01359-8(3)) Cambridge Univ. Pr.

—Dirty Dog: Chitonga Version. Hamoonga, Lazarous, tr. 1998. (Cambridge African Language Library Ser.). (Illus.). 8p. pap. 3.75 (978-0-521-64761-8(4)) Cambridge Univ. Pr.

—Dirty Dog: Cinyanja Version. Tembo, tr. 2001. (Illus.). 8p. pap. 0.45 (978-0-521-01361-1(5)) Cambridge Univ. Pr.

—Dirty Dog: Cinyanja Version. Mwale, Brian, tr. 1998. (Cambridge African Language Library Ser.). (Illus.). 8p. pap. 3.75 (978-0-521-64760-1(6)) Cambridge Univ. Pr.

—Dirty Dog: Icibemba Version. Mulilo, tr. 2001. (Illus.). 8p. pap. 0.45 (978-0-521-01363-5(1)) Cambridge Univ. Pr.

—Dirty Dog: Icibemba Version. Mwansa, Bupe, tr. 1998. (Cambridge African Language Library Ser.). (Illus.). 8p. pap. 3.75 (978-0-521-64759-5(2)) Cambridge Univ. Pr.

—Dirty Dog: Kiikaonde Version. Muyebaa, tr. 2001. (Illus.). 8p. pap. 0.45 (978-0-521-01365-9(8)) Cambridge Univ. Pr.

—Dirty Dog: Kiikaonde Version. Muyebaa, Kyangubabi, tr. 1998. (Cambridge African Language Library). (Illus.). 8p. pap. 3.75 (978-0-521-64758-8(4)) Cambridge Univ. Pr.

—Dirty Dog: Luvale Version. Sakapaji, tr. 2001. (Illus.). 8p. pap. 0.45 (978-0-521-01367-3(4)) Cambridge Univ. Pr.

—Dirty Dog: Luvale Version. Kaleyi, Kakoma, tr. 1998. (Cambridge African Language Library Ser.). (Illus.). 8p. pap. 3.75 (978-0-521-64756-4(8)) Cambridge Univ. Pr.

—Dirty Dog: Silozi Version. Mwendende, tr. 2001. (Illus.). 8p. pap. 0.45 (978-0-521-01368-0(2)) Cambridge Univ. Pr.

—Dirty Dog: Silozi Version. Silumesii, Penelope, tr. 1998. (Cambridge African Language Library Ser.). (Illus.). 8p. pap. 3.75 (978-0-521-64755-7(X)) Cambridge Univ. Pr.

—Two Babies: Chitonga Version. Chisengele, tr. 2001. (Illus.). 8p. pap. 0.45 (978-0-521-01561-5(8)) Cambridge Univ. Pr.

—Two Babies: Chitonga Version. Hamoonga, Lazarous, tr. 1998. (Cambridge African Language Library Ser.). (Illus.). 8p. pap. 3.75 (978-0-521-64768-7(1)) Cambridge Univ. Pr.

—Two Babies: Cinyanja Version. Tembo, tr. 2001. (Illus.). 8p. pap. 0.45 (978-0-521-01562-2(6)) Cambridge Univ. Pr.

—Two Babies: Cinyanja Version. Mwale, Brian, tr. 1998. (Cambridge African Language Library). (Illus.). 8p. pap. 3.75 (978-0-521-64767-0(3)) Cambridge Univ. Pr.

—Two Babies: Icibemba Version. Mulilo, tr. 2001. (Illus.). 8p. pap. 0.45 (978-0-521-01564-6(2)) Cambridge Univ. Pr.

—Two Babies: Icibemba Version. Mwansa, Bupe, tr. 1998. (Cambridge African Language Library Ser.). (Illus.). 8p. pap. 3.75 (978-0-521-64766-3(5)) Cambridge Univ. Pr.

—Two Babies: Kiikaonde Version. Muyebaa, tr. 2001. (Illus.). 8p. pap. 0.45 (978-0-521-01565-3(0)) Cambridge Univ. Pr.

—Two Babies: Kiikaonde Version. Muyebaa, Kyangubabi, tr. 1998. (Cambridge African Language Library). (Illus.). 8p. pap. 3.75 (978-0-521-64765-6(7)) Cambridge Univ. Pr.

—Two Babies: Luvale Version. Sakapaji, tr. 2001. (Illus.). 8p. pap. 0.45 (978-0-521-01567-7(7)) Cambridge Univ. Pr.

—Two Babies: Luvale Version. Kaleyi, Kakoma, tr. 1998. (Cambridge African Language Library). (Illus.). 8p. pap. 3.75 (978-0-521-64763-2(0)) Cambridge Univ. Pr.

—Two Babies: Silozi Version. Mwendende, tr. 2001. (Illus.). 8p. pap. 0.45 (978-0-521-01568-4(5)) Cambridge Univ. Pr.

—Two Babies: Silozi Version. Silumesii, Penelope, tr. 1998. (Cambridge African Language Library Ser.). (Illus.). 8p. pap. 3.75 (978-0-521-64762-5(2)) Cambridge Univ. Pr.

—What For? American English Edition. 2000. (Cambridge Reading Ser.). (Illus.). 8p. pap. 5.00 (978-0-521-78421-4(2)) Cambridge Univ. Pr.

—What For? Big Book: American English Edition. 2000. (Cambridge Reading Ser.). (Illus.). 8p. pap. 20.00 (978-0-521-78419-1(0)) Cambridge Univ. Pr.

—What's in the Box? Chitonga Version. Chisengele, tr. 2001. (Illus.). 8p. pap. 0.45 (978-0-521-01577-6(4)) Cambridge Univ. Pr.

—What's in the Box? Cinyanja Version. Tembo, tr. 2001. (Illus.). 8p. pap. 0.45 (978-0-521-01578-3(2)) Cambridge Univ. Pr.

—What's in the Box? Icibemba Version. Mulilo, tr. 2001. (Illus.). 8p. pap. 0.45 (978-0-521-01580-6(4)) Cambridge Univ. Pr.

—What's in the Box? Kiikaonde Version. Muyebaa, tr. 2001. (Illus.). 8p. pap. 0.45 (978-0-521-01581-3(2)) Cambridge Univ. Pr.

—What's in the Box? Luvale Version. Sakapaji, tr. 2001. (Illus.). 8p. pap. 0.45 (978-0-521-01583-7(9)) Cambridge Univ. Pr.

—What's in the Box? Silozi Version. Mwendende, tr. 2001. (Illus.). 8p. pap. 0.45 (978-0-521-01584-4(7)) Cambridge Univ. Pr.

—Where's Woolly? American English Edition. 2000. (Cambridge Reading Ser.). (Illus.). 8p. pap. 5.00 (978-0-521-78416-0(6)) Cambridge Univ. Pr.

—Where's Woolly? American English Edition, 6, Pack. 2000. (Cambridge Reading Ser.). (Illus.). 8p. pap. 28.00 (978-0-521-78415-3(8)) Cambridge Univ. Pr.

Gillham, Bill et al. Beginning to Read: Patterned & Natural Language Strand Pack. 1999. (Cambridge Reading Ser.). (Illus.). 8p. pap. 67.00 (978-0-521-78637-9(1)) Cambridge Univ. Pr.

Gilliland, Judith Heide. Strange Birds. 2006. 240p. (J). 17.00 (978-0-374-37275-0(6) , Farrar, Straus & Giroux (BYR)) Farrar, Straus & Giroux.

Ginger's War: Level T. Group 3, 6 vols. (Sunshinetm Ser.). 48p. 44.95 (978-0-322-01939-3(7)) Wright Group, The.

Girard, Sherry. 20 Irresistible Reading-Response Projects Based on Favorite Picture Books. 2002. (Illus.). 80p. (J). (gr. 4-6). 12.95 (978-0-439-20572-6(7)) Scholastic, Inc.

Girl Saves Giant: Level P, 6 vols. (Wonder Worldtm Ser.). 48p. 39.95 (978-0-7802-7070-1(3)) Wright Group, The.

Glencoe McGraw-Hill Staff. Classic Horror Stories. 2001. stu. ed. 32.64 (978-0-8442-8098-1(4) , 9780844280981); stu. ed. 25.32 (978-0-8442-8099-8(2) , 9780844280998) Glencoe/McGraw-Hill.

—Computer Management System Win/Mac Site License. 3rd ed. 2000. (Comprehension Skills Ser.). (gr. 6-12). suppl. ed. 1244.64 (978-0-8092-9885-3(6) , 9780809298853) Jamestown.

—Jamestown Signature Reading: Desktop Resource, Level D. 2000. 60p. (gr. 4-8). spiral bd. 25.32 (978-0-8092-0025-2(2) , 9780809200252) Jamestown.

—Jamestown's Signature Reading, Level H. 2000. (gr. 6-10). pap., stu. ed. 16.64 (978-0-8092-0432-8(0) , 9780809204328) Jamestown.

—Jamestown's Signature Reading: Desktop Resource. 2000. 60p. (C). (gr. 6-10). spiral bd. 25.32 (978-0-8092-0029-0(5) , 9780809200290); (C). (gr. 8-12). pap. 25.32 (978-0-8092-0032-0(5) , 9780809200320); Level E. (C). (gr. 4-8). spiral bd. 25.32 (978-0-8092-0026-9(0) , 9780809200269); Level F. (gr. 6-10). spiral bd. 25.32 (978-0-8092-0027-6(9) , 9780809200276); Level G. (C). (gr. 6-10). spiral bd. 25.32 (978-0-8092-0028-3(7) , 9780809200283) Jamestown.

Glencoe McGraw-Hill Staff & McGraw-Hill - Jamestown Education Staff. Advanced Level Understanding the Main Idea (Advanced) 2nd ed. 2000. (Comprehension Skills Ser.). (C). (gr. 9-12). pap. 10.64 (978-0-8092-0156-3(9) , 9780809201563) Jamestown.

—Drawing Conclusions (Advanced) 2nd ed. 2000. (Comprehension Skills Ser.). (C). (gr. 9-12). pap. 10.64 (978-0-8092-0159-4(3) , 9780809201594) Jamestown.

—Drawing Conclusions (Introductory) 3rd ed. 2000. (Comprehension Skills Ser.). (gr. 6-12). pap. 10.64 (978-0-8092-0236-2(0) , 9780809202362) Jamestown.

—Drawing Conclusions (Middle) 2nd ed. 2000. (Comprehension Skills Ser.). (C). (gr. 6-12). pap. 10.64 (978-0-8092-0248-5(4) , 9780809202485) Jamestown.

—In the Line of Duty: Selfless Acts of Heroism. 2001. (Wild Side Ser.). (gr. 4-12). pap. 16.64 (978-0-8092-9829-7(5) , 9780809298297) Jamestown.

—Jamestown's Signature Reading. 2000. Level I. (C). (gr. 8-12). pap., stu. ed. 16.64 (978-0-8092-0433-5(9) , 9780809204335); Level L. (gr. 8-12). pap., stu. ed. 16.64 (978-0-8092-0436-6(3) , 9780809204366); Level D. (gr. 4-8). pap., stu. ed. 16.64 (978-0-8092-0428-1(2) , 9780809204281); Level E. (gr. 4-8). pap., stu. ed. 16.64 (978-0-8092-0429-8(0) , 9780809204298); Level F. (C). (gr. 6-10). pap., stu. ed. 16.64 (978-0-8092-0430-4(4) , 9780809204304); Level G. (C). (gr. 6-10). pap., stu. ed. 16.64 (978-0-8092-0431-1(2) , 9780809204311); Level J. (C). (gr. 8-12). pap., stu. ed. 16.64 (978-0-8092-0434-2(7) , 9780809204342); Level K. (C). (gr. 8-12). pap., stu. ed. 16.64 (978-0-8092-0435-9(5) , 9780809204359) Jamestown.

—Jamestown's Signature Reading: Desktop Resource, Level L. 2000. 60p. (C). (gr. 8-12). spiral bd. 25.32 (978-0-8092-0033-7(3) , 9780809200337) Jamestown.

—Making Inferences (Advanced) 2nd ed. 2000. (Comprehension Skills Ser.). (C). (gr. 9-12). pap. 10.64 (978-0-8092-0160-0(7) , 9780809201600) Jamestown.

—Making Inferences (Introductory) 3rd ed. 2000. (Comprehension Skills Ser.). (C). (gr. 6-12). pap. 10.64 (978-0-8092-0237-9(9) , 9780809202379) Jamestown.

—Making Inferences (Middle) 2nd ed. 2000. (Comprehension Skills Ser.). (gr. 6-12). pap. 10.64 (978-0-8092-0249-2(2) , 9780809202492) Jamestown.

—Making Judgements (Advanced) 2nd ed. 2000. (Comprehension Skills Ser.). (C). (gr. 9-12). pap. 10.64 (978-0-8092-0157-0(7) , 9780809201570) Jamestown.

—Making Judgements (Introductory) 3rd ed. 2000. (Comprehension Skills Ser.). (C). (gr. 6-12). pap. 10.64 (978-0-8092-0234-8(4) , 9780809202348) Jamestown.

—The Making Judgements (Middle) 2nd ed. 2000. (Comprehension Skills Ser.). (C). (gr. 6-12). pap. 10.64 (978-0-8092-0246-1(8) , 9780809202461) Jamestown.

—Recognizing Tone (Introductory) 3rd ed. 2000. (Comprehension Skills Ser.). (gr. 6-12). pap. 10.64 (978-0-8092-0238-6(7) , 9780809202386) Jamestown.

—Recognizing Tone (Middle) 2nd ed. 2000. (Comprehension Skills Ser.). (C). (gr. 6-12). pap. 10.64 (978-0-8092-0151-8(8) , 9780809201518) Jamestown.

—Understanding Characters (Introductory) 3rd ed. 2000. (Comprehension Skills Ser.). (C). (gr. 6-12). pap. 10.64 (978-0-8092-0235-5(2) , 9780809202355) Jamestown.

—Understanding Characters (Middle) 2nd ed. 2000. (Comprehension Skills Ser.). (C). (gr. 6-12). pap. 10.64 (978-0-8092-0247-8(6) , 9780809202478) Jamestown.

—Understanding Literary Forms (Advanced) 2nd ed. 2000. (Comprehension Skills Ser.). (C). (gr. 9-12). pap. 10.64 (978-0-8092-0162-4(3) , 9780809201624) Jamestown.

—Understanding Organization (Advanced) 2nd ed. 2000. (Comprehension Skills Ser.). (C). (gr. 6-12). pap. 10.64 (978-0-8092-0163-1(1) , 9780809201631) Jamestown.

—Understanding Organization (Introductory) 3rd ed. 2000. (Comprehension Skills Ser.). (C). (gr. 6-12). pap. 10.64 (978-0-8092-0240-9(7) , 9780809202409) Jamestown.

Globe-Fearon Staff. The Sea-Wolf. (YA). (gr. 5-12). pap. 6.50 (978-0-8359-0969-3(7)) Globe Fearon Educational Publishing.

Godwin, Beth. Livewire Investigates: The Sydney Harbour Bridge. 2003. (Livewires Ser.). 32p. pap. 4.95 (978-0-521-53905-0(6)) Cambridge Univ. Pr.

—Livewire Real Lives Kieren Perkins. 2000. (Livewire Real Lives Ser.). pap. 6.00 (978-0-521-00587-6(6)) Cambridge Univ. Pr.

—Livewire Real Lives Michael Jordan. 2000. (Livewires Ser.). pap. 6.00 (978-0-521-00588-3(4)) Cambridge Univ. Pr.

Going Far: American Readers. (J). (gr. 1). (978-0-669-04964-0(6)) Houghton Mifflin Co. (Schl. Div.).

Going on a Field Trip, 6 vols. (Multicultural Programs Ser.). 16p. (gr. 1-3). 24.95 (978-0-7802-9216-1(2)) Wright Group, The.

Goober Peas: 1 Big Book, 6 Each of 1 Student Book, & 1 Cassette. (Song Box(R) Ser.). (gr. 1-2). 68.95 (978-0-7802-0943-5(5)) Wright Group, The.

Good Apple. Beginning Reading for Older Students. 2002. (J). (gr. 4-8). pap. 12.99 (978-0-7682-0661-6(8) , GA13094) School Specialty Publishing.

Good Food. 2005. (Emergent (Prek-2) Health Package Ser.). 12p. (YA). (ps-2). 25.20 (978-0-8215-7847-6(2)) Sadlier, William H. Inc.

Good Girl! (Little Book Practice Reader). (J). (978-0-8136-5351-8(7)) Modern Curriculum Pr.

Good Night, Little Bug. (Little Book Practice Reader). (J). (978-0-8136-1970-5(X)) Modern Curriculum Pr.

Goodman, Burton. Goodman's Five-Star. 2001. (gr. 4-12). Level C. pap., act. bk. ed. 13.96 (978-0-8092-0447-2(9) , 9780809204472); Level A. pap., act. bk. ed. 13.96 (978-0-8092-0445-8(2) , 9780809204458); Level B. pap., act. bk. ed. 13.96 (978-0-8092-0446-5(0) , 9780809204465); Level E. pap., act. bk. ed. 13.96 (978-0-8092-0449-6(5) , 9780809204496) Jamestown.

—Goodman's Five-Star Spelling. 2nd ed. 2002. (gr. 6-12). pap. 16.64 (978-0-07-827356-8(0) , 9780078273568) Jamestown.

Got, Yves. Sam's First Word Book. 2000. (Illus.). 144p. (J). (ps). 12.95 (978-0-8118-2615-0(5)) Chronicle Bks. LLC.

The Gotcha Box: Big Book: Level B. Group 2. (Story Box(R) Ser.). 8p. 20.95 (978-0-322-00328-6(8)) Wright Group, The.

Grabando el Pasado 11: Leveled Books. 2001. (McGraw-Hill. Lectura Ser.). (ENG & SPA.). (gr. 3 up). (978-0-02-188108-6(1)) Macmillan/McGraw-Hill Schl. Div.

Graham, Pamela. A Bone for Grozzle. Jellett, Tom, illus. 2002. (Bright Sparks Ser.). 16p. pap. 2.30 (978-0-521-75409-5(7)) Cambridge Univ. Pr.

—My Magic Box. Curtis, Neil, illus. 2002. (Bright Sparks Ser.). 16p. pap. 2.30 (978-0-521-75410-1(0)) Cambridge Univ. Pr.

Grahame, Kenneth. The Wind in the Willows. 224p. (J). 5.99 (978-1-4037-1436-7(3)) Dalmatian Pr.

Grande y Pequeno 22: Leveled Books. 2001. (McGraw-Hill. Lectura Ser.). (ENG & SPA.). (gr. 3 up). (978-0-02-188143-7(X)) Macmillan/McGraw-Hill Schl. Div.

Grandma's at the Lake. 2003. 22.95 (978-0-673-75917-7(2)) Celebration Pr.

Grandma's Heart: Level J, 6 vols. (Wonder Worldtm Ser.). 16p. 29.95 (978-0-7802-1213-8(4)) Wright Group, The.

Grandpa Knits Hats: Level E. (Wonder Worldtm Ser.). 16p. 29.95 (978-0-7802-1038-7(7)) Wright Group, The.

Grant, Linda. Well Said: Sampling Letter. 2nd ed. 2000. (978-0-8384-2391-2(4)) Thomson Heinle.

Great Art & Artists, 6 vols. (Book2WebTM Ser.). (gr. 4-8). 36.50 (978-0-322-02987-3(2)) Wright Group, The.

Great Battles Through the Ages, 6 vols. 2005. (Great Battles Through the Ages Ser.). (Illus.). 112+p. (gr. 6-12). pap. 180.00 (978-0-7910-7434-3(X) , Chelsea Hse.) Facts On File, Inc.

The Great Monsieur Vertelli: Level R, 6 vols. (Wonder Worldtm Ser.). 48p. 44.95 (978-0-7802-7083-1(5)) Wright Group, The.

Green, Mona & Lofts, Pamela. How the Animals Got Their Tails: South African Edition. 1999. (Cambridge Reading Routes Ser.). (Illus.). 24p. pap. 5.50 (978-0-521-77897-8(2)) Cambridge Univ. Pr.

Greene, Jane Fell & Woods, Judy Fell. J & J Language Readers: Level 1. Ranson, Peggy, illus. 3rd ed. 2000. (J & J Ser.). 508p. (J). 45.00 (978-1-57035-275-1(5) , 59JJ1) Sopris West Educational Services.

—J & J Language Readers: Level 2. Ranson, Peggy, illus. 3rd ed. 2000. (J & J Ser.). 460p. (J). 45.00 (978-1-57035-276-8(3) , 59JJ2) Sopris West Educational Services.

—J & J Language Readers: Level 3. Ranson, Peggy, photos by. 3rd ed. 2000. (J & J Ser.). (Illus.). 380p. (J). 45.00 (978-1-57035-277-5(1) , 59JJ3) Sopris West Educational Services.

Un grillo en mi Cocina 5: Leveled Books. 2001. (McGraw-Hill. Lectura Ser.). (ENG & SPA.). (gr. 1 up). (978-0-02-187982-3(6)) Macmillan/McGraw-Hill Schl. Div.

Grizzly & the Bumble-bee: Big Book: Level K. Group 1. (Sunshinetm Ser.). 16p. 36.50 (978-0-7802-5789-4(8)) Wright Group, The.

Group/McGraw-Hill, Wright. Abraham Lincoln: The Civil War President, 6 vols. (Book2WebTM Ser.). (gr. 4-8). 36.50 (978-0-322-04462-3(6)) Wright Group, The.

—Africa: Rich in Land & History, 6 vols. (Book2WebTM Ser.). (gr. 4-8). 36.50 (978-0-322-04439-5(1)) Wright Group, The.

—African Art: Level E, 6 vols. (Take Twostm Ser.). 16p. 29.95 (978-0-322-08988-4(3)) Wright Group, The.

—Against the Odds: Magazine Anthology: Level 3, 6 vols. (Comprehension Strand Ser.). (gr. 4-8). 54.00 (978-0-322-06031-9(1)) Wright Group, The.

—All's Well that End Well: Level N, 6 vols. (Autumn Leaves Ser.). 128p. (gr. 3-6). 36.95 (978-0-322-06728-8(6)) Wright Group, The.

—Animal Advocates, 6 vols. (Wildcats Ser.). 32p. (gr. 2-8). (978-0-322-05861-3(9)) Wright Group, The.

—Animal Mysteries, 6 vols. (Wildcats Ser.). 32p. (gr. 2-8). (978-0-322-05859-0(7)) Wright Group, The.

—Animals Go Mad: Level 2, 6 vols. (Fluency Strand Ser.). (gr. 4-8). 194.95 (978-1-4045-1292-4(6)) Wright Group, The.

—Art Show, 6 vols. (D-Man Beans Ser.). 47p. (gr. 4-6). 42.50 (978-0-322-06262-7(4)) Wright Group, The.

—Attack! Magazine Anthology: Level 2, 6 vols. (Comprehension Strand Ser.). (gr. 4-8). 54.00 (978-0-322-06029-6(X)) Wright Group, The.

—Autumn Leaves: Classroom Library Set. 81.50 (978-0-322-07969-4(1)) Wright Group, The.

—Autumn Leaves: Complete Set. 327.95 (978-0-322-07967-0(5)) Wright Group, The.

—The Aztec People: Level I, 6 vols. (Take Twostm Ser.). 16p. 29.95 (978-0-322-08995-2(6)) Wright Group, The.

—Bad News Good News: Level N, 6 vols. 128p. (gr. 3-6). 36.95 (978-0-322-06733-2(2)) Wright Group, The.

—Bats about Bats! Level M, 6 vols. 128p. (gr. 3-6). 36.95 (978-0-322-06724-0(3)) Wright Group, The.

—Bears: Magazine Anthology: Level 5, 6 vols. (Comprehension Strand Ser.). (gr. 4-8). 54.00 (978-0-322-09855-8(6)) Wright Group, The.

—Black Tooth the Pirate: Level G, 6 vols. (Take Twostm Ser.). 16p. 29.95 (978-0-322-08969-3(7)) Wright Group, The.

—Blow your Top: Magazine Anthology: Level 6, 6 vols. (Comprehension Strand Ser.). (gr. 4-8). 54.00 (978-0-322-06041-8(9)) Wright Group, The.

—Bobcat Level: Adventure Journal Set. (Wildcats Ser.). (gr. 2-8). 31.95 (978-0-322-05791-3(4)) Wright Group, The.

—Bobcat Level: Lesson Plan Set. (Wildcats Ser.). (gr. 2-8). 96.50 (978-0-322-06676-2(X)) Wright Group, The.

—Bobcat Level: Wildcats Bobcat Complete Kit. (Wildcats Ser.). (gr. 2-8). 599.95 (978-0-322-06484-3(8)) Wright Group, The.

—Brice & the Whale: Decodable Books, 6 vols. (Fasttrack Reading Ser.). 24p. (gr. 4-8). 40.95 (978-0-322-05981-8(X)) Wright Group, The.

—Brice & the Whale Play 4: Decodable Plays, 6 vols. (Fasttrack Reading Ser.). 24p. (gr. 4-8). 40.95 (978-0-322-05994-8(1)) Wright Group, The.

—Building the Railroads, 6 vols. (Book2WebTM Ser.). (gr. 4-8). 36.50 (978-0-322-04448-7(0)) Wright Group, The.

—Burned: Magazine Anthology: Level 7, 6 vols. (Comprehension Strand Ser.). (gr. 4-8). 54.00 (978-0-322-06044-9(3)) Wright Group, The.

—Buttons: Collection 1. (Storyteller Interactive Writing Cards Ser.). (gr. k-3). (978-0-322-09362-1(7)) Wright Group, The.

—Buzz the Beekeeper: Level 6, 6 vols. (Fluency Strand Ser.). (gr. 4-8). 194.95 (978-1-4045-1296-2(9)) Wright Group, The.

—The C & P Pies: Level H, 6 vols. (Take Twostm Ser.). 16p. 29.95 (978-0-322-08973-0(5)) Wright Group, The.

—The Calendar: Level G, 6 vols. (Take Twostm Ser.). 16p. 29.95 (978-0-322-08981-5(6)) Wright Group, The.

—Celebrating the New Year: Level I, 6 vols. (Take Twostm Ser.). 16p. 29.95 (978-0-322-08974-7(3)) Wright Group, The.
—The Chinampa: Level I, 6 vols. (Take Twostm Ser.). 16p. 29.95 (978-0-322-08996-9(4)) Wright Group, The.
—Chocolate: Magazine Anthology: Level 7, 6 vols. (Comprehension Strand Ser.). (gr. 4-8). 54.00 (978-0-322-09861-9(0)) Wright Group, The.
—Complete Level Sets: Level 3 Complete Set. (Fasttrack Reading Ser.). (gr. 4-8). 720.95 (978-1-4045-0396-0(X)) Wright Group, The.
—Complete Level Sets: Level 4 Complete Set. (Fasttrack Reading Ser.). (gr. 4-8). 720.95 (978-1-4045-0397-7(8)) Wright Group, The.
—Complete Level Sets: Level 5 Complete Set. (Fasttrack Reading Ser.). (gr. 4-8). 720.95 (978-1-4045-0398-4(6)) Wright Group, The.
—Complete Level Sets: Level 6 Complete Set. (Fasttrack Reading Ser.). (gr. 4-8). 720.95 (978-1-4045-0399-1(4)) Wright Group, The.
—Complete Level Sets: Level 7 Complete Set. (Fasttrack Reading Ser.). (gr. 4-8). 720.95 (978-1-4045-0400-4(1)) Wright Group, The.
—Complete Level Sets: Levels 1-2 Complete Set. (Fasttrack Reading Ser.). (gr. 4-8). 763.00 (978-1-4045-0395-3(1)) Wright Group, The.
—Complete Program Set. (Fasttrack Reading Ser.). (gr. 4-8). 5435.00 (978-1-4045-0404-2(4)) Wright Group, The.
—Complete Program Set: Comprehension Strand. (Fasttrack Reading Ser.). (gr. 4-8). 2435.00 (978-1-4045-0406-6(0)) Wright Group, The.
—Complete Program Set: Fluency Strand. (Fasttrack Reading Ser.). (gr. 4-8). 1445.00 (978-1-4045-0408-0(7)) Wright Group, The.
—Complete Program Set: Word Work Strand. (Fasttrack Reading Ser.). (gr. 4-8). 1299.00 (978-0-322-07226-8(3)) Wright Group, The.
—Creepers, Crawlers, & Fliers: Magazine Anthology: Level 4, 6 vols. (Comprehension Strand Ser.). (gr. 4-8). 54.00 (978-0-322-06035-7(4)) Wright Group, The.
—Crushed: Magazine Anthology: Level 4, 6 vols. (Comprehension Strand Ser.). (gr. 4-8). 54.00 (978-0-322-09854-1(8)) Wright Group, The.
—A Day to Remember: Level I, 6 vols. (Take Twostm Ser.). 16p. 29.95 (978-0-322-08975-4(1)) Wright Group, The.
—Dinos: Magazine Anthology: Level 2, 6 vols. (Comprehension Strand Ser.). (gr. 4-8). 54.00 (978-0-322-09847-3(5)) Wright Group, The.
—Dog-Sled Racer: Level 5, 6 vols. (Fluency Strand Ser.). (gr. 4-8). 194.95 (978-1-4045-1295-5(0)) Wright Group, The.
—Dom's Dragon: Level E, 6 vols. (Take Twostm Ser.). 16p. 29.95 (978-0-322-08977-8(8)) Wright Group, The.
—Don't Go Out: Level F, 6 vols. (Take Twostm Ser.). 16p. 29.95 (978-0-322-08954-9(9)) Wright Group, The.
—Don't Whistle Around Sprinkle: Decodable Books, 6 vols. (Fasttrack Reading Ser.). 24p. (gr. 4-8). 40.95 (978-0-322-05976-4(3)) Wright Group, The.
—Don't Whistle Around Sprinkle Play 10: Decodable Plays, 6 vols. (Fasttrack Reading Ser.). 24p. (gr. 4-8). 40.95 (978-0-322-05990-0(9)) Wright Group, The.
—Double Dare., 6 vols. (D-Man Beans Ser.). 47p. (gr. 4-6). 42.50 (978-0-322-06265-8(9)) Wright Group, The.
—Drag, Dirt, & Other Racing: Magazine Anthology: Level 4, 6 vols. (Comprehension Strand Ser.). (gr. 4-8). 54.00 (978-0-322-06033-3(8)) Wright Group, The.
—E-search: Level O, 6 vols. 128p. (gr. 3-6). 36.95 (978-0-322-06730-1(8)) Wright Group, The.
—Early Emergent Guided Reading Kit 1: Complete Kit. (gr. k up). 435.96 (978-1-4045-2057-8(0)) Wright Group, The.
—Early Emergent Guided Reading Kit 1: Lesson Plans. (gr. k up). 127.95 (978-1-4045-2071-4(6)) Wright Group, The.
—Early Emergent Guided Reading Kit 1: Student Books. (gr. k up). 71.95 (978-1-4045-2065-3(1)); 66.95 (978-0-322-04214-8(3)) Wright Group, The.
—Early Emergent Guided Reading Kit 4: Student Books, Vol. 4. (gr. k up). 66.95 (978-0-322-03882-0(0)) Wright Group, The.
—Early Fluency-Fluency Writing Kit. 2004. (Wright Group Literacy Ser.). (gr. k-3). 137.50 (978-0-322-07021-9(X)) Wright Group, The.
—Early Fluency Guided Reading Kit 1: Student Books. (gr. 2 up). 93.50 (978-0-322-04217-9(8)) Wright Group, The.
—Early Fluency Guided Reading Kit 5: Student Books, Vol. 5. (gr. 2 up). 93.50 (978-0-322-04750-1(1)) Wright Group, The.
—Early Fluency Kit 1: Complete Kit. (gr. 2 up). 536.95 (978-1-4045-2062-2(7)) Wright Group, The.
—Early Fluency Kit 1: Student Books. (gr. 2 up). 94.95 (978-1-4045-2070-7(8)) Wright Group, The.
—Explorers: Fluency - Complete Kit. (gr. 3-6). 547.95 (978-0-322-09171-9(3)) Wright Group, The.
—Explorers Fluency Complete Kit 2, Vol. 2. (gr. 3-4). 547.95 (978-0-322-09170-2(5)) Wright Group, The.
—Explorers Fluency Complete Kit 3, Vol. 3. (gr. 3-4). 547.95 (978-0-322-09169-6(1)) Wright Group, The.
—Famous Shipwrecks, 6 vols. (Book2WebTM Ser.). (gr. 4-8). 36.50 (978-0-322-04458-6(8)) Wright Group, The.
—FDR & Eleanor: Triumphs & Tragedies, 6 vols. (Book2WebTM Ser.). (gr. 4-8). 36.50 (978-0-322-04463-0(4)) Wright Group, The.
—Fibonacci's Cows: Level O, 6 vols. 128p. (gr. 6 up). 36.95 (978-0-322-06737-0(5)) Wright Group, The.
—Fire at the Museum: Decodable Books, 6 vols. 22nd ed. (Fasttrack Reading Ser.). 24p. (gr. 4-8). 40.95 (978-0-322-05977-1(1)) Wright Group, The.
—Fire at the Museum Play 11: Decodable Plays, 6 vols. (Fasttrack Reading Ser.). 24p. (gr. 4-8). 40.95 (978-0-322-05991-7(7)) Wright Group, The.
—First Explorers: Upper Emergent - Complete Kit. (gr. 1 up). 386.50 (978-0-322-09168-9(3)) Wright Group, The.
—First Explorers: Upper Emergent - Lesson Plan Set - 1 Each of 12 Lesson Plans. (gr. 1 up). 47.95 (978-0-322-08418-6(0)) Wright Group, The.
—First Explorers: Upper Emergent-Early Fluency - Complete Kit. (gr. 1-2). 426.50 (978-0-322-09167-2(5)) Wright Group, The.
—First Explorers: Upper Emergent-Early Fluency - Lesson Plan Set - 1 Each of 12 Lesson Plans. (gr. 1-2). 47.95 (978-0-322-08419-3(9)) Wright Group, The.
—First Explorers: Upper Emergent-Early Fluency - Student Book Set - 1 Each of 12 Titles. (First Explorers. Primeros Exploradores Nonfiction Sets Ser.). (gr. 1-2). 67.50 (978-0-7699-1362-9(8)) Shortland Pubns. (U. S. A.) Inc.
—Fluency Guided Reading Kit 3 Vol. 3: Student Books, (gr. 3-6). 112.50 (978-0-322-04751-8(X)) Wright Group, The.
—Fossils Reveal Clues about Ancient Life, 6 vols. (Book2WebTM Ser.). (gr. 4-8). 36.50 (978-0-322-04431-9(6)) Wright Group, The.
—Found & Lost, 6 vols. (D-Man Beans Ser.). 47p. (gr. 4-6). 42.50 (978-0-322-06268-9(3)) Wright Group, The.
—From Plan to House: Level H, 6 vols. (Take Twostm Ser.). 16p. 29.95 (978-0-322-08999-0(9)) Wright Group, The.
—Fun with Fizz & Frost: Level O, 6 vols. 128p. (gr. 3-6). 36.95 (978-0-322-06725-7(1)) Wright Group, The.
—Gear Up! Early Emergent - 1 Each of 8 Student Books: Level A. 35.95 (978-1-4045-2041-7(4)) Wright Group, The.
—Gear Up! Early Emergent - 1 Each of 8 Student Books: Level B. 35.95 (978-1-4045-2042-4(2)) Wright Group, The.
—Gear Up! Early Emergent - 1 Each of 8 Student Books: Level C. 35.95 (978-1-4045-2043-1(0)) Wright Group, The.
—Gear Up! Early Emergent - 1 Each of 8 Student Books: Level D. 35.95 (978-1-4045-2044-8(9)) Wright Group, The.
—Gear Up! Early Emergent - Complete Kit, Vol. 2. (gr. k-1). 435.95 (978-1-4045-2058-5(9)) Wright Group, The.
—Gear Up! Early Emergent - Student Book Set - 1 Each of 16 Titles, Vol. 2. (gr. k-1). 71.95 (978-1-4045-2066-0(X)) Wright Group, The.
—Gear Up! Early Fluency - Complete Kit, Vol. 2. (gr. 2 up). 536.95 (978-1-4045-2064-6(3)) Wright Group, The.
—Gear Up! Upper Emergent- Student Book Each of 16 Titles. (gr. k-1). 78.95 (978-1-4045-2067-7(8)) Wright Group, The.
—Gear Up! Upper Emergent-Early Fluency - 1 Each of 8 Student Books: Level J. 39.50 (978-1-4045-2051-6(1)) Wright Group, The.
—Gear Up! Upper Emergent-Early Fluency - 1 Each of 8 Student Books: Level K. 47.50 (978-1-4045-2052-3(X)) Wright Group, The.
—Gear Up! Upper Emergent-Early Fluency - 1 Each of 8 Student Books: Level L. 47.50 (978-1-4045-2053-0(8)) Wright Group, The.
—Gear Up! Upper Emergent-Early Fluency - 1 Each of 8 Student Books: Level M. 47.50 (978-1-4045-2054-7(6)) Wright Group, The.
—Gear Up! Upper Emergent-Early Fluency - 1 Each of 8 Student Books: Level N. 47.50 (978-1-4045-2056-1(2)) Wright Group, The.
—Gear Up! Vol. 2: Early Emergent - Gear up! for Guided Reading. (gr. 2 up). 19.50 incl. DVD (978-1-4045-2079-0(1)) Wright Group, The.
—Gear Up! Vol. 2: Early Emergent - Gear up! Guided Reading Overview. (gr. 2 up). 19.50 (978-1-4045-1950-3(5)) Wright Group, The.
—Gear Up! Vol. 2: Early Fluency - Student Book Set - 1 Each of 16 Titles. (gr. 2 up). 71.95 (978-1-4045-2072-1(4)) Wright Group, The.
—Gear Up! Vol. 3: Upper Emergent - Complete Kit. (gr. 1 up). 499.95 (978-1-4045-2061-5(9)) Wright Group, The.
—Gear Up! Vol. 3: Upper Emergent - Student Book Set - 1 Each of 16 Titles. (gr. 1 up). 78.95 (978-1-4045-2069-1(4)) Wright Group, The.
—Ger Up! Upper Emergent - 1 Each of 8 Student Books: Level E. 39.50 (978-1-4045-2045-5(7)) Wright Group, The.
—Ger Up! Upper Emergent - 1 Each of 8 Student Books: Level F. 39.50 (978-1-4045-2046-2(5)) Wright Group, The.
—Ger Up! Upper Emergent - 1 Each of 8 Student Books: Level G. 39.50 (978-1-4045-2048-6(1)) Wright Group, The.
—Ger Up! Upper Emergent - 1 Each of 8 Student Books: Level H. 39.50 (978-1-4045-2049-3(X)) Wright Group, The.
—Ger Up! Upper Emergent - 1 Each of 8 Student Books: Level I. 39.50 (978-1-4045-2050-9(3)) Wright Group, The.
—Going, Going, Gone: Magazine Anthology: Level 3, 6 vols. (Comprehension Strand Ser.). (gr. 4-8). 54.00 (978-0-322-09851-0(3)) Wright Group, The.
—Guided Reading Kits: Upper Emergent Kit 1 (Student Books) (gr. 1 up). 79.95 (978-0-322-04339-8(5)) Wright Group, The.
—Guided Reading Kits: Early Emergent Kit 2 Vol. 2: Student Books. (gr. k up). 66.95 (978-0-322-04350-3(6)) Wright Group, The.
—Guided Reading Kits: Early Emergent Kit 4 Vol. 4: Student Books. (gr. k up). 66.95 (978-0-322-04348-0(4)) Wright Group, The.
—Guided Reading Kits: Upper Emergent Kit 1: Student Books. (gr. 1 up). 79.95 (978-0-322-04347-3(6)) Wright Group, The.
—Guided Reading Kits: Upper Emergent Kit 2 Vol. 2: Student Books. (gr. 1 up). 79.95 (978-0-322-04346-6(8)) Wright Group, The.
—Guided Reading Kits: Upper Emergent Kit 3 Vol. 3: Student Books. (gr. 1 up). 79.95 (978-0-322-04345-9(X)) Wright Group, The.
—Helen Keller: Level 3, 6 vols. (Fluency Strand Ser.). (gr. 4-8). 194.95 (978-1-4045-1293-1(4)) Wright Group, The.
—Hoops & Hardwood: Magazine Anthology: Level 2, 6 vols. (Comprehension Strand Ser.). (gr. 4-8). 54.00 (978-0-322-06027-2(3)) Wright Group, The.
—How Strong Is Strong? Magazine Anthology: Level 2, 6 vols. (Comprehension Strand Ser.). (gr. 4-8). 54.00 (978-0-322-09846-6(7)) Wright Group, The.
—I Want Some Honey: Level E, 6 vols. (Take Twostm Ser.). 16p. 29.95 (978-0-322-08956-3(5)) Wright Group, The.
—In the Rain Forest, 6 vols. (Wildcats Ser.). 32p. (gr. 2-8). (978-0-322-00599-0(X)) Wright Group, The.
—In the Ring: Magazine Anthology: Level 5, 6 vols. (Comprehension Strand Ser.). (gr. 4-8). 54.00 (978-0-322-09856-5(4)) Wright Group, The.
—Jewels: Magazine Anthology: Level 3, 6 vols. (Comprehension Strand Ser.). (gr. 4-8). 54.00 (978-0-322-09848-0(3)) Wright Group, The.
—Jo Tries: Decodable Books, 6 vols. (Fasttrack Reading Ser.). 24p. (gr. 4-8). 40.95 (978-0-322-05983-2(6)) Wright Group, The.
—Jo Tries Play 6: Decodable Plays, 6 vols. (Fasttrack Reading Ser.). 24p. (gr. 4-8). 40.95 (978-0-322-05997-9(6)) Wright Group, The.
—The Lazy Moon: Level G, 6 vols. (Take Twostm Ser.). 16p. 29.95 (978-0-322-08982-2(4)) Wright Group, The.
—Magnificent Masks: 6 Each of 1 Anthology, 6 vols. (Wildcats Ser.). 32p. (gr. 2-8). (978-0-322-05624-4(1)) Wright Group, The.
—Make a Raft: Level E, 6 vols. (Take Twostm Ser.). 16p. 29.95 (978-0-322-08976-1(X)) Wright Group, The.
—Make me Laugh! 6 Each of 1 Anthology, 6 vols. (Wildcats Ser.). 32p. (gr. 2-8). (978-0-322-05628-2(4)) Wright Group, The.
—Maps: Level I, 6 vols. (Take Twostm Ser.). 16p. 29.95 (978-0-322-08966-2(2)) Wright Group, The.
—The Mascot: Decodable Books, 6 vols. (Fasttrack Reading Ser.). 24p. (gr. 4-8). 40.95 (978-0-322-05980-1(1)) Wright Group, The.
—Mira Hacia el Cielo, 6 vols. (First Explorers. Primeros Exploradores Nonfiction Sets Ser.). (SPA.). (gr. 1-2). 29.95 (978-0-7699-1471-8(3)) Shortland Pubns. (U. S. A.) Inc.
—Mischief & Mayhem: Level O, 6 vols. 128p. (gr. 3-6). 36.95 (978-0-322-06727-1(8)) Wright Group, The.
—Mosquito Attack: Level 4, 6 vols. (Fluency Strand Ser.). (gr. 4-8). 194.95 (978-1-4045-1294-8(2)) Wright Group, The.
—Move it & Shake It! 6 Each of 1 Anthology, 6 vols. (Wildcats Ser.). 32p. (gr. 2-8). (978-0-322-05621-3(7)) Wright Group, The.
—Movie Magic, 6 vols. (Wildcats Ser.). 32p. (gr. 2-8). (978-0-322-05630-5(6)) Wright Group, The.
—The Music Scene, 6 vols. (Wildcats Ser.). 32p. (gr. 2-8). (978-0-322-05631-2(4)) Wright Group, The.
—My Word! what a Bird! Collection 4. (Storyteller Interactive Writing Cards Ser.). (gr. k-3). (978-0-322-09325-6(2)) Wright Group, The.
—No Hay Nadie Como Tu, 6 vols. (First Explorers. Primeros Exploradores Nonfiction Sets Ser.). (SPA.). (gr. 1-2). 29.95 (978-0-7699-1478-7(0)) Shortland Pubns. (U. S. A.) Inc.
—No Room, New Rules, 6 vols. (D-Man Beans Ser.). 47p. (gr. 4-6). 42.50 (978-0-322-06263-4(2)) Wright Group, The.
—On the Prowl: 6 Each of 1 Anthology, 6 vols. (Wildcatstm Ser.). 32p. (gr. 2-8). (978-0-322-05852-1(X)) Wright Group, The.
—Outback School: Level E, 6 vols. (Take Twostm Ser.). 16p. 29.95 (978-0-322-08949-5(2)) Wright Group, The.
—Panther Level: Wildcats Panther Complete Kit. (Wildcatstm Ser.). (gr. 2-8). 599.95 (978-0-322-06490-4(2)) Wright Group, The.
—Paper Capers: Level N, 6 vols. 128p. (gr. 3-6). 36.95 (978-0-322-06726-4(X)) Wright Group, The.
—Pat's Picture: Level E, 6 vols. (Take Twostm Ser.). 16p. 29.95 (978-0-322-08989-1(0)) Wright Group, The.
—Phonics & Word Study Complete Kits: Phonics & Word Study: Level B. (gr. k-3). 429.50 (978-0-322-03872-1(3)) Wright Group, The.
—Picture This! 6 Each of 1 Anthology, 6 vols. (Wildcats Ser.). 32p. (gr. 2-8). (978-0-322-05627-5(6)) Wright Group, The.
—Pigeon Princess: Level O, 6 vols. 128p. (gr. 3-6). 36.95 (978-0-322-06729-5(4)) Wright Group, The.
—Pixels & Paint, 6 vols. (Wildcats Ser.). 32p. (gr. 2-8). (978-0-322-05625-1(X)) Wright Group, The.
—Plagues: Magazine Anthology: Level 7, 6 vols. (Comprehension Strand Ser.). (gr. 4-8). 54.00 (978-0-322-09863-3(7)) Wright Group, The.
—The Planet Race: Level F, 6 vols. (Take Twostm Ser.). 16p. 29.95 (978-0-322-08963-1(8)) Wright Group, The.
—The Planets: Level F, 6 vols. (Take Twostm Ser.). 16p. 29.95 (978-0-322-08962-4(X)) Wright Group, The.
—Purl & the Bird Play 5: Decodable Plays, 6 vols. (Fasttrack Reading Ser.). 24p. (gr. 4-8). 40.95 (978-0-322-05996-2(8)) Wright Group, The.
—Reading Recovery Kits: Reading Recovery Complete Set. (Reading Recovery(R) Ser.). (gr. k-6). 2754.50 (978-0-322-04770-9(6)) Wright Group, The.
—The Red Lets Play 1: Decodable Plays, 6 vols. (Fasttrack Reading Ser.). 24p. (gr. 4-8). 40.95 (978-0-322-05992-4(5)) Wright Group, The.
—The Riddle of the Seaplanes: Level S, 6 vols. 128p. (gr. 6 up). 36.95 (978-0-322-06739-4(1)) Wright Group, The.
—River Wild: 6 Each of 1 Anthology, 6 vols. (Wildcats Ser.). 32p. (gr. 2-8). (978-0-322-05857-6(0)) Wright Group, The.
—Rollers & Blades: Level H, 6 vols. (Take Twostm Ser.). 16p. 29.95 (978-0-322-08964-8(6)) Wright Group, The.
—The Salad: Collection 1. (Storyteller Interactive Writing Cards Ser.). (gr. k-3). (978-0-322-09366-9(X)) Wright Group, The.
—The Secret Socer Ball Maker: Level G, 6 vols. (Take Twostm Ser.). 16p. 29.95 (978-0-322-08991-4(3)) Wright Group, The.
—Set 1: Los Alimentos, 6 vols. (First Explorers. Primeros Exploradores Nonfiction Sets Ser.). (SPA.). (gr. 1-2). 29.95 (978-0-7699-1469-5(1)) Shortland Pubns. (U. S. A.) Inc.
—Set 2: Los Dinosaurios, 6 vols., Vol. 2. (First Explorers. Primeros Exploradores Nonfiction Sets Ser.). (SPA.). (gr. 1-2). 34.95 (978-0-7699-1484-8(5)) Shortland Pubns. (U. S. A.) Inc.
—Slimed! 6 Each of 1 Anthology, 6 vols. (Wildcats Ser.). 32p. (gr. 2-8). (978-0-322-05853-8(8)) Wright Group, The.
—So You Want this Job, do You? Magazine Anthology: Level 6, 6 vols. (Comprehension Strand Ser.). (gr. 4-8). 54.00 (978-0-322-06042-5(7)) Wright Group, The.
—Songbirds: Magazine Anthology: Level 4, 6 vols. (Comprehension Strand Ser.). (gr. 4-8). 54.00 (978-0-322-09853-4(X)) Wright Group, The.
—Stories on Stage, 6 vols. (Wildcats Ser.). 32p. (gr. 2-8). (978-0-322-05622-0(5)) Wright Group, The.
—The Story Box: Early Fluency - Student Book Set - 1 Each of 16 Titles. 2nd ed. (gr. 2 up). 98.50 (978-0-322-04052-6(3)) Wright Group, The.
—The Story Box Vol. 3: Early Emergent - Lesson Plan Set - 1 Each of 16 Lesson Plans. (gr. k up). 63.95 (978-0-322-05929-0(1)) Wright Group, The.
—Storyteller: Early Emergent - 1 Each of 16 Student Books: Level D. 78.95 (978-1-4045-1977-0(7)) Wright Group, The.
—Storyteller: Early Emergent - 1 Each of 3 Student Books: Level A. 14.50 (978-1-4045-1954-1(8)) Wright Group, The.
—Storyteller: Early Emergent - 1 Each of 6 Student Books: Level B. 29.50 (978-1-4045-1962-6(9)) Wright Group, The.
—Storyteller: Early Emergent - 1 Each of 7 Student Books: Level C. 34.50 (978-1-4045-1970-1(X)) Wright Group, The.
—Storyteller: Early Emergent - Student Book Set - 1 Each of 16 Fiction & Nonfiction Titles. (gr. k up). 79.95 (978-1-4045-1051-7(6)) Wright Group, The.
—Storyteller: Upper Emergent - 1 Each of 14 Student Books: Level G. 82.95 (978-1-4045-1983-1(1)) Wright Group, The.
—Storyteller: Upper Emergent - 1 Each of 15 Student Books: Level E. 88.95 (978-1-4045-1981-7(5)) Wright Group, The.
—Storyteller: Upper Emergent - 1 Each of 15 Student Books: Level F. 112.95 (978-1-4045-1982-4(3)) Wright Group, The.
—Storyteller: Upper Emergent - 1 Each of 15 Student Books: Level H. 88.95 (978-1-4045-1984-8(X)) Wright Group, The.
—Storyteller: Upper Emergent - Complete Kit, Vol. 5. (gr. 1 up). 549.50 (978-1-4045-1041-8(9)) Wright Group, The.
—Storyteller: Upper Emergent - Lesson Plan Set - 1 Each of 16 Lesson Plans. (gr. 1 up). 127.95 (978-1-4045-1074-6(5)) Wright Group, The.
—Storyteller: Upper Emergent - Student Book Set - 1 Each of 16 Fiction & Nonfiction Titles. (gr. 1 up). 96.50 (978-1-4045-1058-6(3)) Wright Group, The.
—Storyteller: Upper Emergent - Student Book Set -1 Each of 16 Fiction & Nonfiction Titles. (gr. 1 up). 93.50 (978-1-4045-1053-1(2)) Wright Group, The.
—Storyteller: Upper Emergent - Upper Emergent - Complete Kit, Vol. 4. (gr. 1 up). 549.50 (978-1-4045-1040-1(0)) Wright Group, The.
—Storyteller: Upper Emergent-Early Fluency - 1 Each of 14 Student Books: Level I. 82.95 (978-1-4045-1985-5(8)) Wright Group, The.
—Storyteller: Upper Emergent-Early Fluency - 1 Each of 15 Student Books: Level J. 88.95 (978-1-4045-1986-2(6)) Wright Group, The.
—Storyteller: Upper Emergent-Early Fluency - 1 Each of 4 Student Books: Level K. 27.50 (978-1-4045-1987-9(4)) Wright Group, The.
—Storyteller Vol. 2: Early Emergent - Complete Kit. (gr. k up). 485.50 (978-1-4045-1036-4(2)) Wright Group, The.
—Storyteller Vol. 2: Early Emergent - Student Book Set - 1 Each of Fiction & Nonfiction Titles. (gr. k up). 79.95 (978-1-4045-1052-4(4)) Wright Group, The.
—Storyteller Chapter Books: Early Fluency-Fluency - 1 Each of 10 Titles: Level O. 61.50 (978-1-4045-0949-8(6)) Wright Group, The.
—Storyteller Chapter Books: Early Fluency-Fluency - 1 Each of 11 Titles: Level N. 69.50 (978-1-4045-0948-1(8)) Wright Group, The.
—Storyteller Chapter Books: Early Fluency-Fluency - 1 Each of 4 Titles: Level P. 24.50 (978-1-4045-0950-4(X)) Wright Group, The.
—Storyteller Chapter Books: Early Fluency-Fluency - 1 Each of 4 Titles: Level Q. 24.50 (978-1-4045-0951-1(8)) Wright Group, The.
—Storyteller Chapter Books: Fluency - 1 Each of 2 Title: Level U. 11.95 (978-1-4045-0955-9(0)) Wright Group, The.

—Storyteller Chapter Books: Fluency - 1 Each of 2 Titles: Level R. 11.95 (978-1-4045-0952-8(6)) Wright Group, The.

—Storyteller Chapter Books: Upper Emergent-Early Fluency - 1 Each of 18 Titles: Level M. 130.95 (978-1-4045-0947-4(X)) Wright Group, The.

—Storyteller Chapter Books: Upper Emergent-Early Fluency - 1 Each of 4 Titles: Level J. 27.95 (978-1-4045-0944-3(5)) Wright Group, The.

—Storyteller Chapter Books: Upper Emergent-Early Fluency - 1 Each of 8 Titles: Level K. 57.50 (978-1-4045-0945-0(3)) Wright Group, The.

—Storyteller Chapter Books: Upper Emergent-Early Fluency - 1 Each of 8 Titles: Level L. 55.50 (978-1-4045-0946-7(1)) Wright Group, The.

—Storyteller Early Emergent Guided Reading Complete Kit 1. (gr. k up). 485.50 (978-1-4045-1035-7(4)) Wright Group, The.

—Storyteller Upper Emergent Guided Reading Complete Kit 1. (gr. 1 up). 549.50 (978-1-4045-1037-1(0)) Wright Group, The.

—Storyteller Upper Emergent Guided Reading Complete Kit 2, Vol. 2. (gr. 1 up). 549.50 (978-1-4045-1038-8(9)) Wright Group, The.

—Storyteller Upper Emergent Guided Reading Complete Kit 3, Vol. 3. (gr. 1 up). 549.50 (978-1-4045-1039-5(7)) Wright Group, The.

—Storyteller Upper Emergent Guided Reading Kit, Set. (gr. 1 up). 93.50 (978-1-4045-1056-2(7)) Wright Group, The.

—Storyteller Upper Emergent Guided Reading Kit 2, Set. (gr. 1 up). 93.50 (978-1-4045-1054-8(0)) Wright Group, The.

—Storyteller Upper Emergent Guided Reading Kit 3, Set. (gr. 1 up). 93.50 (978-1-4045-1055-5(9)) Wright Group, The.

—Storyteller Upper Emergent Guided Reading Kit 5, Set. (gr. 1 up). 93.50 (978-1-4045-1057-9(5)) Wright Group, The.

—Strange in the Sky: Magazine Anthology: Level 2, 6 vols. (Comprehension Strand Ser.). (gr. 4-8). 54.00 (978-0-322-09845-9(9)) Wright Group, The.

—Stranger Than Fiction: 6 Each of 1 Anthology, 6 vols. (Wildcats Ser.). 32p. (gr. 2-8). (978-0-322-05855-2(4)) Wright Group, The.

—Stunt Doubles: Magazine Anthology: Level 7, 6 vols. (Comprehension Strand Ser.). (gr. 4-8). 54.00 (978-0-322-09862-6(9)) Wright Group, The.

—Summer Skies: Classroom Library Set. 81.50 (978-0-322-07968-7(3)) Wright Group, The.

—Summer Skies: Complete Set. 327.95 (978-0-322-07963-2(2)) Wright Group, The.

—Sunshine: Early Emergent - Complete Kit. (gr. k up). 423.95 (978-0-322-04209-4(7)) Wright Group, The.

—Sunshine: Early Emergent - Group 3: 1 Each of 4 Student Books: Level A. 16.95 (978-0-322-03707-6(7)) Wright Group, The.

—Sunshine: Early Emergent - Group 3: 1 Each of 4 Student Books: Level C. 16.95 (978-0-322-03709-0(3)) Wright Group, The.

—Sunshine: Early Emergent - Group 3: 1 Each of 4 Student Books: Level D. 16.95 (978-0-322-03710-6(7)) Wright Group, The.

—Sunshine: Early Emergent - Group 3:1 Each of 4 Student Books: Level B. 16.95 (978-0-322-03708-3(5)) Wright Group, The.

—Sunshine: Early Emergent-Upper Emergent - Group 2: 1 Each of 8 Student Books: Level E. 39.95 (978-0-322-04317-6(4)) Wright Group, The.

—Sunshine: Early Emergent-Upper Emergent - Group 3: 1 Each of 5 Student Books: Level E. 24.95 (978-0-322-03711-3(5)) Wright Group, The.

—Sunshine: Early Emergent-Upper Emergent - Groups 1-2: 1 Each of 16 Student Books: Level E. 79.95 (978-0-322-04316-9(6)) Wright Group, The.

—Sunshine: Early Fluency - Enrichment Library: 1 each of 12 titles: Level L. 69.95 (978-0-322-04025-0(6)) Wright Group, The.

—Sunshine: Early Fluency - Enrichment Library: 1 each of 5 titles: Level N. 29.50 (978-0-322-04028-1(0)) Wright Group, The.

—Sunshine: Early Fluency - Enrichment Library, Groups 1-2: 1 each of 11 titles: Level K. 69.95 (978-0-322-04024-3(8)) Wright Group, The.

—Sunshine: Early Fluency - Group 1: 1 each of 11 titles: Level K. 64.50 (978-0-322-04308-4(5)) Wright Group, The.

—Sunshine: Early Fluency - Group 1: 1 each of 11 titles: Level L. 64.50 (978-0-322-04311-4(5)) Wright Group, The.

—Sunshine: Early Fluency - Group 1; 1 each of 11 titles: Level M. 64.50 (978-0-322-04313-8(1)) Wright Group, The.

—Sunshine: Early Fluency - Group 3: 1 each of 11 Titles: Level N. 64.50 (978-0-322-05241-3(6)) Wright Group, The.

—Sunshine: Early Fluency - Group 3: 1 each of 8 Titles: Level K. 46.95 (978-0-322-05238-3(6)) Wright Group, The.

—Sunshine: Early Fluency - Groups 1-2: 1 each of 17 titles: Level K. 99.50 (978-0-322-04307-7(7)) Wright Group, The.

—Sunshine: Early Fluency - Groups 1-2: 1 each of 17 titles: Level L. 99.50 (978-0-322-04309-1(3)) Wright Group, The.

—Sunshine: Early Fluency-Enrichment Library; 1 each of 7 titles: Level M. 40.95 (978-0-322-04027-4(2)) Wright Group, The.

—Sunshine: Early Fluency-Group 1; 1 each of 11 titles: Level N. 64.50 (978-0-322-04315-2(8)) Wright Group, The.

—Sunshine: Early Fluency-Group 3: 1 each of 8 Titles: Level L. 46.95 (978-0-322-05239-0(4)) Wright Group, The.

—Sunshine: Early Fluency-Group 3; 1 each of 8 Titles: Level M. 46.95 (978-0-322-05240-6(8)) Wright Group, The.

—Sunshine: Early Fluency-Groups 1-2; 1 each of 17 titles: Level N. 99.50 (978-0-322-04314-5(X)) Wright Group, The.

—Sunshine: Fluency - Group 3: 1 Each of 4 Titles: Level S. 29.95 (978-0-322-05247-5(5)) Wright Group, The.

—Sunshine: Fluency - Group 3: 1 Each of 4 Titles: Level T. 29.95 (978-0-322-05248-2(3)) Wright Group, The.

—Sunshine: Fluency - Group 3: 1 each of 6 Titles: Level O. 39.95 (978-0-322-05242-0(4)) Wright Group, The.

—Sunshine: Fluency - Group 3: 1 Each of 6 Titles: Level R. 44.95 (978-0-322-05246-8(7)) Wright Group, The.

—Sunshine: Fluency-Group 3: 1 each of 6 Titles: Level P. 39.95 (978-0-322-05244-4(0)) Wright Group, The.

—Sunshine: Fluency-Group 3: 1 each of 6 Titles: Level Q. 39.95 (978-0-322-05245-1(9)) Wright Group, The.

—Sunshine: Upper Emergent - Group 1:1 Each of 8 Student Books: Level G. Group 1. 39.95 (978-0-322-04321-3(2)) Wright Group, The.

—Sunshine: Upper Emergent - Group 1:1 Each of 8 Student Books: Level H. Group 1. 39.95 (978-0-322-04324-4(7)) Wright Group, The.

—Sunshine: Upper Emergent - Group 2: 1 Each of 8 Student Books: Level G. Group 1. 39.95 (978-0-322-04322-0(0)) Wright Group, The.

—Sunshine: Upper Emergent - Group 2:1 Each of 7 Student Books: Level F. Group 2. 34.95 (978-0-322-04319-0(0)) Wright Group, The.

—Sunshine: Upper Emergent - Group 2:1 Each of 9 Student Books: Level H. Group 2. 44.95 (978-0-322-04325-1(5)) Wright Group, The.

—Sunshine: Upper Emergent - Group 3:1 Each of 12 Student Books: Level H. 59.95 (978-0-322-03716-8(6)) Wright Group, The.

—Sunshine: Upper Emergent - Group 3:1 Each of 6 Student Books: Level G. 29.95 (978-0-322-03714-4(X)) Wright Group, The.

—Sunshine: Upper Emergent - Group 3:1 Each of 8 Student Books: Level F. Group 3. 24.95 (978-0-322-03713-7(1)) Wright Group, The.

—Sunshine: Upper Emergent - Groups 1-2:1 Each of 15 Student Books: Level F. 74.95 (978-0-322-04318-3(2)) Wright Group, The.

—Sunshine: Upper Emergent - Groups 1-2:1 Each of 16 Student Books: Level G. 79.95 (978-0-322-04320-6(4)) Wright Group, The.

—Sunshine: Upper Emergent - Nonfiction:1 Each of 3 Student Books: Level G. 14.95 (978-0-322-04304-6(2)) Wright Group, The.

—Sunshine: Upper Emergent - Upper Emergent - Complete Kit, Vol. 2. (gr. 1 up). 486.50 (978-0-322-04211-7(9)) Wright Group, The.

—Sunshine: Upper Emergent-Enrichment Library: 1 each of 5 student books: Level J. 24.95 (978-0-322-04023-6(X)) Wright Group, The.

—Sunshine: Upper Emergent-Group 2: 1 each of 5 student books: Level J. 24.95 (978-0-322-03715-1(8)) Wright Group, The.

—Sunshine: Upper Emergent-Group 3: 1 each of 10 student books: Level I. 49.95 (978-0-322-03717-5(4)) Wright Group, The.

—Sunshine: Upper Emergent-Groups 1-2: 1 each of 16 student books: Level I. 79.95 (978-0-322-04326-8(3)) Wright Group, The.

—Sunshine: Upper Emergent-Nonfiction: 1 each of 3 student books: Level H. 14.95 (978-0-322-04305-3(0)) Wright Group, The.

—Sunshine: Upper Emergent-Nonfiction: 1 each of 5 student books: Level I. 24.95 (978-0-322-04306-0(9)) Wright Group, The.

—Sunshine: Upper Emergent-Nonfiction: 1 each of 5 student books: Level J. 24.95 (978-0-322-04329-9(8)) Wright Group, The.

—SUNSHINE Early Emergent Guided Reading Kit 4, Vol. 4. 2004. (Wright Group Literacy Ser.). (gr. k up). 423.95 (978-0-322-03886-8(3)) Wright Group, The.

—SUNSHINE Early Fluency Guided Reading Kit 5, Vol. 5. 2004. (Wright Group Literacy Ser.). (gr. 2 up). 524.95 (978-0-322-04746-4(3)) Wright Group, The.

—SUNSHINE Fluency Guided Reading Kit 3, Vol. 3. 2004. (Wright Group Literacy Ser.). (gr. 3-6). 604.95 (978-0-322-04747-1(1)) Wright Group, The.

—Sunshine Upper Emergent Guided Reading Kit 5, Vol. 5. 2004. (Wright Group Literacy Ser.). (gr. 1 up). 486.50 (978-0-322-03888-2(X)) Wright Group, The.

—Sunshine Upper Emergent Guided Reading Kit 6, Vol. 6. 2004. (Wright Group Literacy Ser.). (gr. 1 up). 486.50 (978-0-322-03889-9(8)) Wright Group, The.

—Take-Twos: Fluency - 1 each of 12 Titles: Level O. 79.95 (978-0-322-04576-7(2)) Wright Group, The.

—Take Twos: Fluency - 1 Each of 4 Titles: Level S. 29.95 (978-1-4045-0737-1(X)) Wright Group, The.

—Take Twos: Fluency - 1 Each of 4Ttitles: Level T. 29.95 (978-1-4045-0738-8(8)) Wright Group, The.

—Take-Twos: Fluency - Group 1; 1 each of 12 Titles: Level P. 79.95 (978-0-322-04577-4(0)) Wright Group, The.

—Take-Twos: Fluency - Group 1; 1 each of 12 Titles: Level Q. 79.95 (978-0-322-04578-1(9)) Wright Group, The.

—Take Twos: Fluency - Group 1: 1 each of 12 Titles: Level R. 89.95 (978-0-322-04579-8(7)) Wright Group, The.

—Take Twos: Fluency - Group 1: 1 each of 6 Lesson Plans: Level R. 47.95 (978-0-322-04573-6(8)) Wright Group, The.

—Take-Twos: Fluency - Group 2; 1 Each of 4 (New) Titles: Level P. 26.95 (978-1-4045-0731-9(0)) Wright Group, The.

—Take-Twos: Fluency - Group 2; 1 Each of 4 (New) Titles: Level Q. 26.95 (978-1-4045-0733-3(7)) Wright Group, The.

—Take Twos: Fluency - Group 2: 1 Each of 8 (New) Titles: Level R. 59.95 (978-1-4045-0735-7(3)) Wright Group, The.

—Take-Twos: Fluency - Groups 1 & 2; 1 Each of 16 Titles: Level P. 106.95 (978-1-4045-0732-6(9)) Wright Group, The.

—Take-Twos: Fluency - Groups 1 & 2; 1 Each of 16 Titles: Level Q. 106.95 (978-1-4045-0734-0(5)) Wright Group, The.

—Take-Twos: Upper Emergent - 1 Each of 10 Titles: Level J. 49.95 (978-1-4045-0744-9(2)) Wright Group, The.

—Take Twos: Upper Emergent - 1 Each of 8 Titles: Level E. 39.95 (978-1-4045-0739-5(6)) Wright Group, The.

—Take Twos: Upper Emergent - 1 Each of 8 Titles: Level F. 39.95 (978-1-4045-0740-1(X)) Wright Group, The.

—Take Twos: Upper Emergent - 1 Each of 8 Titles: Level H. 39.95 (978-1-4045-0742-5(6)) Wright Group, The.

—Take Twos: Upper Emergent - 1 Each of 8 Titles: Level I. 39.95 (978-1-4045-0743-2(4)) Wright Group, The.

—Take-Twos Adventure Vol. 3: Fluency - Complete Kit. (gr. 3-4). 492.50 (978-0-322-09178-8(0)) Wright Group, The.

—Take-Twos Adventure Vol. 3: Fluency - Student Book Set - 1 Each of 12 Titles. (gr. 3-4). 83.50 (978-0-322-09306-5(6)) Wright Group, The.

—Take-Twos Circles & Cycles Vol. 2: Upper Emergent - Student Book Set - 1 Each of 12 Titles. (gr. 1 up). 59.50 (978-0-322-09314-0(7)) Wright Group, The.

—Take-Twos Circles & Cycles Vol. 2: Upper Emergent - Upper Emergent - Complete Kit. (gr. 1 up). 366.95 (978-0-322-09280-8(9)) Wright Group, The.

—Take-Twos Cultures: Upper Emergent - Complete Kit. (gr. 1 up). 366.95 (978-0-322-09279-2(5)) Wright Group, The.

—Take-Twos Cultures: Upper Emergent - Student Book Set - 1 Each of 12 Titles. (gr. 1 up). 59.50 (978-0-322-09312-6(0)) Wright Group, The.

—Take-Twos Earth Links Vol. 3: Upper Emergent - Complete Kit. (gr. 1 up). 366.95 (978-0-322-09282-2(5)) Wright Group, The.

—Take-Twos Earth Links Vol. 3: Upper Emergent - Student Book Set - 1 Each of 12 Titles. (gr. 1 up). 59.50 (978-0-322-09316-4(3)) Wright Group, The.

—Take-Twos Finding Out Vol. 6: Fluency - Complete Kit. (gr. 4-6). 501.50 (978-0-322-09181-8(0)) Wright Group, The.

—Take-Twos Finding Out Vol. 6: Fluency - Student Book Set - 1 Each of 12 Titles. (gr. 4-6). 84.95 (978-0-322-09309-6(0)) Wright Group, The.

—Take-Twos Land & Air: Early Fluency - Complete Kit. (gr. 2 up). 420.50 (978-0-322-09172-6(1)) Wright Group, The.

—Take-Twos Land & Air: Early Fluency - Student Book Set - 1 Each of 12 Titles. (gr. 2 up). 69.95 (978-0-322-09300-3(7)) Wright Group, The.

—Take-Twos Making Things Vol. 3: Early Fluency - Complete Kit. (gr. 2 up). 420.50 (978-0-322-09174-0(8)) Wright Group, The.

—Take-Twos Making Things Vol. 3: Early Fluency - Student Book Set - 1 Each of 12 Titles. (gr. 2 up). 69.95 (978-0-322-09302-7(3)) Wright Group, The.

—Take-Twos Old to New Vol. 4: Fluency - Complete Kit. (gr. 3-4). 492.50 (978-0-322-09179-5(9)) Wright Group, The.

—Take-Twos Old to New Vol. 4: Fluency - Student Book Set - 1 Each of 12 Titles. (gr. 3-4). 83.50 (978-0-322-09307-2(4)) Wright Group, The.

—Take-Twos Play Time Vol. 4: Upper Emergent - Student Book Set - 1 Each of 12 Titles. (gr. 1 up). 59.50 (978-0-322-09318-8(X)) Wright Group, The.

—Take-Twos Play Time Vol. 4: Upper Emergent - Upper Emergent - Complete Kit. (gr. 1 up). 366.95 (978-0-322-09283-9(3)) Wright Group, The.

—Take-Twos Slither, Swim, & Soar: Fluency - Complete Kit. (gr. 3-4). 483.50 (978-0-322-09176-4(4)) Wright Group, The.

—Take-Twos Slither, Swim, & Soar: Fluency - Student Book Set - 1 Each of 12 Titles. (gr. 3-4). 81.95 (978-0-322-09304-1(X)) Wright Group, The.

—Take-Twos Stories & Legends Vol. 5: Fluency - Complete Kit. (gr. 4-6). 519.50 (978-0-322-09180-1(2)) Wright Group, The.

—Take-Twos Stories & Legends Vol. 5: Fluency - Student Book Set - 1 Each of 12 Titles. (gr. 4-6). 88.50 (978-0-322-09308-9(2)) Wright Group, The.

—Teeth: Level G, 6 vols. (Take Twostm Ser.). 16p. 29.95 (978-0-322-08968-6(9)) Wright Group, The.

—Thrill Seekers: Magazine Anthology: Level 5, 6 vols. (Comprehension Strand Ser.). (gr. 4-8). 54.00 (978-0-322-06039-5(7)) Wright Group, The.

—Tiger Level: Adventure Journal Set. (Wildcats Ser.). (gr. 2-8). 31.95 (978-0-322-05790-6(6)) Wright Group, The.

—Tiger Level: Lesson Plan Set. (Wildcats Ser.). (gr. 2-8). 96.50 (978-0-322-06677-9(8)) Wright Group, The.

—Tiger Level: Wildcats Tiger Complete Kit. (Wildcats Ser.). (gr. 2-8). 599.95 (978-0-322-06483-6(X)) Wright Group, The.

—Treacherous Ice: Magazine Anthology: Level 3, 6 vols. (Comprehension Strand Ser.). (gr. 4-8). 54.00 (978-0-322-06032-6(X)) Wright Group, The.

—Tv Times: 6 Each of 1 Anthology, 6 vols. (Wildcats Ser.). 32p. (gr. 2-8). (978-0-322-05629-9(2)) Wright Group, The.

—Twig Books: Early Emergent - 1 each of 16 student books: Level A. 66.95 (978-0-322-04330-5(1)) Wright Group, The.

—Twig Books: Early Emergent - 1 each of 16 student books: Level B. 66.95 (978-0-322-04331-2(X)) Wright Group, The.

—Twig Books: Early Emergent - 1 each of 16 student books: Level C. 66.95 (978-0-322-04332-9(8)) Wright Group, The.

—Twig Books: Early Emergent - Upper Emergent - 1 each of 16 student books: Level D. 66.95 (978-0-322-04333-6(6)) Wright Group, The.

—Twig Books: Early Emergent - Upper Emergent - 1 each of 16 student books: Level E. 79.95 (978-0-322-04334-3(4)) Wright Group, The.

—Twig Books: Student Book Set - 1 Each of 16 Titles. (gr. k up). 66.95 (978-0-322-04351-0(4)) Wright Group, The.

—Twig Books: Upper Emergent - 1 each of 16 student books: Level F. 79.95 (978-0-322-04335-0(2)) Wright Group, The.

—Twig Books: Upper Emergent - 1 each of 16 student books: Level G. 79.95 (978-0-322-04337-4(9)) Wright Group, The.

—Twig Books: Upper Emergent - 1 each of 16 student books: Level H. 77.95 (978-0-322-04338-1(7)) Wright Group, The.

—Twig Books Vol. 3: Early Emergent - Student Book Set - 1 Each of 16 Titles. (gr. k up). 66.95 (978-0-322-04349-7(2)) Wright Group, The.

—Twig Books Vol. 4: Upper Emergent - Student Book Set -1 Each of 16 Titles. (gr. 1 up). 79.95 (978-0-322-04343-5(3)) Wright Group, The.

—Upper Emergent Guided Reading Complete Kit 1. (gr. 1 up). 486.50 (978-0-322-04210-0(0)) Wright Group, The.

—Upper Emergent Guided Reading Kit 1: Student Books. (gr. 1 up). 79.95 (978-0-322-04215-5(1)) Wright Group, The.

—Upper Emergent Guided Reading Kit 2 Vol. 2: Student Books, (gr. 1 up). 79.95 (978-0-322-04216-2(X)) Wright Group, The.

—Upper Emergent Guided Reading Kit 5 Vol. 5: Student Books, (gr. 1 up). 79.95 (978-0-322-03883-7(9)) Wright Group, The.

—Upper Emergent Guided Reading Kit 6 Vol. 6: Student Books, (gr. 1 up). 79.95 (978-0-322-03884-4(7)) Wright Group, The.

—Upper Emergent Kit 1: Complete Kit. (gr. k-1). 499.95 (978-1-4045-2059-2(7)) Wright Group, The.

—Upper Emergent Kit 2 Vol. 2: Complete Kit, (gr. 1 up). 499.95 (978-1-4045-2060-8(0)) Wright Group, The.

—Upper Emergent Kit 2 Vol. 2: Student Books, (gr. 1 up). 78.95 (978-1-4045-2068-4(6)) Wright Group, The.

—Vegetarians: Level H, 6 vols. (Take Twostm Ser.). 16p. 29.95 (978-0-322-08972-3(7)) Wright Group, The.

—Wear your Art: 6 Each of 1 Anthology, 6 vols. (Wildcats Ser.). 32p. (gr. 2-8). (978-0-322-05623-7(3)) Wright Group, The.

—Welcome to the Big Top: 6 Each of 1 Anthology, 6 vols. (Wildcatstm Ser.). 32p. (gr. 2-8). (978-0-322-05626-8(8)) Wright Group, The.

—Whispering Pines: Classroom Library Set. 81.50 (978-0-322-07971-7(3)) Wright Group, The.

—Whispering Pines: Complete Set. 327.95 (978-0-322-07965-6(9)) Wright Group, The.

—Wildcats Strand Kits: Animals & Nature Strand. (Wildcatstm Ser.). (gr. 2-8). 589.95 (978-0-322-06535-2(6)) Wright Group, The.

—Wildcats Strand Kits: Arts & Entertainment Strand. (Wildcatstm Ser.). (gr. 2-8). 589.95 (978-0-322-06534-5(8)) Wright Group, The.

—Wildcats Strand Kits: Myths & Misconceptions Strand. (Wildcatstm Ser.). (gr. 2-8). 589.95 (978-0-322-06532-1(1)) Wright Group, The.

—Wildcats Strand Kits: People & Places Strand. (Wildcatstm Ser.). (gr. 2-8). 589.95 (978-0-322-06528-4(3)) Wright Group, The.

—Wildcats Strand Kits: Science & Technology Strand. (Wildcatstm Ser.). (gr. 2-8). 589.95 (978-0-322-06529-1(1)) Wright Group, The.

—Wildcats Strand Kits: Sports & Action Strand. (Wildcatstm Ser.). (gr. 2-8). 589.95 (978-0-322-06531-4(3)) Wright Group, The.

—Wonder World: Early Emergent - Student Book Set - 1 Each of 16 Titles. (gr. k up). 66.95 (978-0-322-04341-1(7)) Wright Group, The.

—Wonder World: Early Fluency - Student Book Set - 1 Each of 16 Titles. (gr. 1-2). 93.50 (978-0-322-04342-8(5)) Wright Group, The.

—Wonder World: Upper Emergent - Student Book Set - 1 Each of 16 Titles, Vol. 2. (gr. 1 up). 79.95 (978-0-322-04340-4(9)) Wright Group, The.

—Working Like a Dog: 6 Each of 1 Anthology, 6 vols. (Wildcats Ser.). 32p. (gr. 2-8). (978-0-322-05854-5(6)) Wright Group, The.

—The Worm Farm: Level E, 6 vols. (Take Twostm Ser.). 16p. 29.95 (978-0-322-08961-7(1)) Wright Group, The.

—The Wright Skills: Level A Sets - Short Vowels only: 1 Each of 19 Titles. (gr. k-3). 56.95 (978-0-322-06473-7(2)) Wright Group, The.

—The Wright Skills: Level B Sets - 1 Each of 40 Titles (includes long Vowels) (gr. k-3). 143.95 (978-0-322-03878-3(2)) Wright Group, The.

—The Wright Skills: Level B Sets - 6 Each of 40 Titles (includes long Vowels) (gr. k-3). 860.50 (978-0-322-03880-6(4)) Wright Group, The.

—Young & Wild: 6 Each of 1 Anthology, 6 vols. (Wildcatstm Ser.). 32p. (gr. 2-8). (978-0-322-05851-4(1)) Wright Group, The.

—Zoo Tales: 6 Each of 1 Anthology, 6 vols. (Wildcats Ser.). 32p. (gr. 2-8). (978-0-322-05856-9(2)) Wright Group, The.

—The 13th Floor: Level O, 6 vols. 128p. (gr. 3-6). 36.95 (978-0-322-06731-8(6)) Wright Group, The.

Grundon, Holly & Novelli, Joan. Smartpads Rhyming: 40 Fun Games to Help Kids Build Reading Skills. 2005. 48p. pap. 7.99 (978-0-439-72083-0(4) , Teaching Resources) Scholastic, Inc.

Guardians of the Garden: Level 3, 6 vols. (Fluency Strand Ser.). (gr. 4-8). 45.00 (978-1-4045-1218-4(7)) Wright Group, The.

Guess Who - Group 2, 6 Bks, Set. 2004. (J). 128.14 (978-0-7614-1762-0(1)) Cavendish, Marshall Corp.

Guinea Pig, 6 vols. 8p. (gr. k-1). 21.50 (978-0-322-02060-3(3)) Wright Group, The.

Gullane & LeapFrog Staff, compiled by. Thomas the Really Useful Engine. 2002. (J). (ps-2). 14.95 (978-1-58605-923-1(8) , LeapFrog Schl. Hse.) LeapFrog Enterprises, Inc.

Gunn, Barbara. Inuit Tales: Read Well Level K Unit 10 Storybook. Jerde, Susan, illus. 2003. (Read Well Level K Ser.). 20p. (J). (978-1-57035-681-0(5)) Sopris West Educational Services.

Gwazube, Fundisile. Crocodile's Sore Tooth: Chilomwe Version. Nkhoma, Wilson, tr. 1999. (Cambridge Reading Routes Ser.). (Illus.). 16p. pap. 3.70 (978-0-521-66846-0(8)) Cambridge Univ. Pr.

—Crocodile's Sore Tooth: Chinyanja Version. Khomani, Peter J., tr. 1999. (Cambridge Reading Routes Ser.). (AFR., Illus.). 16p. pap. 3.70 (978-0-521-66876-7(X)) Cambridge Univ. Pr.

—Crocodile's Sore Tooth: Chitumbuka Version. Chirambo, Reuben, tr. 1999. (Cambridge Reading Routes Ser.). (Illus.). 16p. pap. 3.70 (978-0-521-66869-9(7)) Cambridge Univ. Pr.

—Crocodile's Sore Tooth: Chiyao Version. Mjaya, Ahmmardouh, tr. 1999. (Cambridge Reading Routes Ser.). (Illus.). 16p. pap. 3.70 (978-0-521-66862-0(X)) Cambridge Univ. Pr.

Haddon, Jean. Words: A Computer Lesson. Vargo, Sharon Hawkins, illus. 2003. (Silly Millies Ser.). 32p. (ps-1). (J). pap. 4.99 (978-0-7613-1797-5(X)); lib. bdg. 17.90 (978-0-7613-2870-4(X)) Lerner Publishing Group. (Millbrook Pr.).

Hairem Scarem Little Books: Early Reading Fluency, Level C. 2004. pap. 6.00 (978-0-7398-8293-1(7)) Steck-Vaughn.

Hall, Katherine Louise. Reading Stories Comprehension Success: Level 1. 2000. (Illus.). (J). wbk. ed. 3.75 (978-0-13-022865-9(6)) Prentice Hall (Schl. Div.).

—Reading Stories for Comprehension Success: Intermediate Level, Grades 4 - 6. 2002. (Illus.). 384p. pap. 29.95 (978-0-7879-6705-5(X) , Jossey-Bass) Wiley, John & Sons, Inc.

Hall, Prentice. Ph Literature: TVTT, Silver Level. 5th ed. 2001. (YA). (gr. 8). stu. ed. 52.97 (978-0-13-435295-4(5)) Prentice Hall PTR.

Hallworth, Grace, et al. Dancing to the River: South African Edition. 1999. (Cambridge Reading Routes Ser.). (Illus.). 24p. pap. 5.50 (978-0-521-77899-2(9)) Cambridge Univ. Pr.

Hamaguchi, Carla, ed. Reading Stickety-Splits. Schamber, Kimberly, illus. 2002. 10p. pap. 6.99 (978-1-57471-890-4(8)) Creative Teaching Pr., Inc.

Hamilton, John. Straight to the Source. 2005. (Straight to the Source Ser.). (J). (gr. k-6). lib. bdg. 136.68 (978-1-59197-542-7(5) , Checkerboard Library) ABDO Publishing Co.

Hand Tools: Level N, 6 vols. (Wonder Worldtm Ser.). 48p. 34.95 (978-0-7802-4577-8(6)) Wright Group, The.

Haney Perez, Jessica. My First 100 Words Book: A Lift-the-Flap, Pull-Tab Learning Book. March, Chloe, illus. 2005. (Learn to Read Ser.). 10p. (J). 10.95 (978-1-58117-210-2(9) , Intervisual/Piggy Toes) Dalmatian Pr.

Hanrahan, Abigail & McSweeny, Catherine. 50 Quick Play Reading Games. 2004. (J). per. 34.95 (978-0-7606-0535-6(1)) LinguiSystems, Inc.

Hansen, Penny. Touch: Chitonga Version. Chisengele, tr. 2001. (Illus.). 16p. pap. 0.45 (978-0-521-01553-0(7)) Cambridge Univ. Pr.

—Touch: Cinyanja Version. Tembo, tr. 2001. (Illus.). 16p. pap. 0.45 (978-0-521-01554-7(5)) Cambridge Univ Pr.

—Touch. Kiikaonde Version. Muyebaa, tr. 2001. (Illus.). 16p. pap. 0.45 (978-0-521-01557-8(X)) Cambridge Univ. Pr.

—Touch: Luvale Version. Sakapaji, tr. 2001. (Illus.). 16p. pap. 0.45 (978-0-521-01559-2(6)) Cambridge Univ. Pr.

—Touch: Silozi Version. Mwendende, tr. 2001. (Illus.). 16p. pap. 0.45 (978-0-521-01560-8(X)) Cambridge Univ. Pr.

—Touch PRP: Icibemba Version. Mulilo, tr. 2001. (Illus.). 16p. pap. 0.45 (978-0-521-01556-1(1)) Cambridge Univ. Pr.

Harcourt School Publishers Staff. Acerquense! Level 1-5. 3rd ed. 2002. (Trofeos Ser.). (SPA., Illus.). (gr. 1 up). pap., pupil's gde. ed. 46.30 (978-0-15-322659-5(5)) Harcourt Schl. Pubs.

—Adivina Quien Level 1-1. 3rd ed. 2002. (Trofeos Ser.). (SPA., Illus.). (gr. 1 up). pupil's gde. ed. 41.50 (978-0-15-322655-7(2)) Harcourt Schl. Pubs.

—After School Kit 1st Place Reading 5 Pack. 2nd ed. 2002. (J). 480.40 (978-0-15-338066-2(7)); (gr. 3). 463.70 (978-0-15-338068-6(3)); (gr. 4). 319.10 (978-0-15-338070-9(5)); (gr. 5). 336.80 (978-0-15-338072-3(1)); (gr. 6). 297.70 (978-0-15-338074-7(8)) Harcourt Schl. Pubs.

—After School Kit 1st Place Reading 5 Pack. 2nd ed. 2002. (J). 901.90 (978-0-15-338049-5(7)) Harcourt Trade Pubs.

—Alcenzia el Sueno Level 1-2. 3rd ed. 2002. (Trofeos Ser.). (SPA., Illus.). (gr. 1 up). pupil's gde. ed. 41.50 (978-0-15-322656-4(0)) Harcourt Schl. Pubs.

—Alerta Roja: Take-Home Book. 1999. (Vamos Ser.). (SPA., Illus.). (J). pap. 2.50 (978-0-15-318854-1(5)) Harcourt Schl. Pubs.

—All Aboard: Intervention Reader. 3rd ed. 2002. (Trophies Reading Program Ser.). (Illus.). (gr. 6 up). pap. 16.70 (978-0-15-325343-0(6)) Harcourt Schl. Pubs.

—All I Am Little Book. 3rd ed. 2002. (Trophies Reading Program Ser.). (Illus.). (J). (gr. 1). pap. 10.20 (978-0-15-329347-4(0)) Harcourt Schl. Pubs.

—All Smiles Anthology. 99th ed. 1999. (Signatures Ser.). (Illus.). (-5). pap. 39.50 (978-0-15-310813-6(4)) Harcourt Schl. Pubs.

—All the Things I Did Today. 3rd ed. 2002. (Trophies English Language Learners Ser.). (Illus.). (J). pap. 4.10 (978-0-15-327584-5(7)) Harcourt Schl. Pubs.

—All the Things I Did Today - 5 Pack - Grade 1. 3rd ed. 2002. (Trophies English Language Learners Ser.). 20.10 (978-0-15-327618-7(5)) Harcourt Schl. Pubs.

—Amelia Bedelia Helps: Library Edition. 1999. (Collections Ser.). (Illus.). (J). 5.30 (978-0-15-314293-2(6)) Harcourt Schl. Pubs.

—Anne Sullivan. 3rd ed. 2002. (Horizons Ser.). (Illus.). (J). (gr. k). pap. 3.70 (978-0-15-333102-2(X)) Harcourt Schl. Pubs.

—Annie's Pictures Advanced Level. 3rd ed. 2002. (Trophies Reading Program Ser.). (Illus.). pap. 5.10 (978-0-15-323103-2(3)) Harcourt Schl. Pubs.

—Antarctica's Challenge Advanced Level. 3rd ed. 2002. (Trophies Reading Program Ser.). (Illus.). (gr. 2). pap. 5.10 (978-0-15-323120-9(3)) Harcourt Schl. Pubs.

—Ants Are Busy: On Level. 3rd ed. 2002. (Trophies Reading Program Ser.). (Illus.). pap. 5.10 (978-0-15-322998-5(5)) Harcourt Schl. Pubs.

—Apple Picking Time Below Level. 3rd ed. 2002. (Trophies Reading Program Ser.). (Illus.). pap. 5.10 (978-0-15-323055-4(X)) Harcourt Schl. Pubs.

—Apples: Below Level. 3rd ed. 2002. (Trophies Reading Program Ser.). (Illus.). (J). pap. 3.20 (978-0-15-322945-9(4)) Harcourt Schl. Pubs.

—Aqui y Alla Level 1-3. 3rd ed. 2002. (Trofeos Ser.). (SPA., Illus.). (gr. 1 up). pap., pupil's gde. ed. 43.80 (978-0-15-322657-1(9)) Harcourt Schl. Pubs.

—El Arbielo/Mistrio Advanced Level. 3rd ed. 2002. (Trofeos Ser.). (SPA., Illus.). pap. 6.80 (978-0-15-324191-8(8)) Harcourt Schl. Pubs.

—Around the Table: Practice Book. 3rd ed. 2001. (Trophies Reading Program Ser.). (Illus.). (J). pap. 1.80 (978-0-15-325083-5(6)) Harcourt Schl. Pubs.

—Around the Table: Practice Book: Florida Edition. 3rd ed. 2002. (Trophies Reading Program Ser.). (Illus.). (J). pap. 2.00 (978-0-15-326598-3(1)) Harcourt Schl. Pubs.

—Around the Town: Practice Book. 3rd ed. 2001. (Trophies Reading Program Ser.). (Illus.). (J). pap. 1.80 (978-0-15-325089-7(5)) Harcourt Schl. Pubs.

—Around the Town: Practice Book: Florida Edition. 3rd ed. 2002. (Trophies Reading Program Ser.). (Illus.). (J). pap. 2.00 (978-0-15-326604-1(X)) Harcourt Schl. Pubs.

—Around the World with Music Below Level. 3rd ed. 2002. (Trophies Reading Program Ser.). (Illus.). pap. 5.10 (978-0-15-323402-6(4)) Harcourt Schl. Pubs.

—Arriba, Sofia: Take-Home Book. 1999. (Vamos Ser.). (SPA., Illus.). (J). pap. 2.50 (978-0-15-318850-3(2)) Harcourt Schl. Pubs.

—Artist at Work: Take-Home Book. 1999. (Signatures Ser.). (Illus.). (J). pap. 1.90 (978-0-15-313876-8(9)) Harcourt Schl. Pubs.

—Asi Cambiamos Level 3-1. 3rd ed. 2002. (Trofeos Ser.). (SPA., Illus.). (gr. 3 up). pap., pupil's gde. ed. 64.00 (978-0-15-322663-2(3)) Harcourt Schl. Pubs.

—Ask Mr. Bear: Library Edition. 1999. (Collections Ser.). (Illus.). (J). 6.90 (978-0-15-314269-7(3)) Harcourt Schl. Pubs.

—Assessment & Information Instruction, Grades K-6: Professional Development in Reading: Participant's Guide. 2nd ed. 2003. pap. 13.70 (978-0-15-338365-6(8)) Harcourt Schl. Pubs.

—Assessment & Information Instructions, Grades K-6: Professional Development for Reading: Guide to Video. 2nd ed. 2003. pap., tchr. ed. 54.90 (978-0-15-337406-7(3)) Harcourt Schl. Pubs.

—At Home: Library Edition. 1999. (Collections Ser.). (Illus.). (J). 4.70 (978-0-15-314277-2(4)) Harcourt Schl. Pubs.

—Baby Chicks: Take-Home Book. 1999. (Collections Ser.). (Illus.). (J). pap. 1.90 (978-0-15-317196-3(0)) Harcourt Schl. Pubs.

—Back to Ancient Times: Take-Home Book. 1999. (Signatures Ser.). (Illus.). (J). pap. 1.90 (978-0-15-313962-8(5)) Harcourt Schl. Pubs.

—Batallon Pon Pon: Take-Home Book. 1999. (Vamos Ser.). (SPA., Illus.). (J). pap. 2.50 (978-0-15-318805-3(7)) Harcourt Schl. Pubs.

—Be Active!, Grade 3-6: Resource Binder Tabs. 4th ed. 2004. 45.60 (978-0-15-341284-4(4)) Harcourt Schl. Pubs.

—Be Active!, Grade K-2: Resource Binder Tabs. 4th ed. 2004. 45.60 (978-0-15-341283-7(6)) Harcourt Schl. Pubs.

—The Bear: Take-Home Book. 1999. (Signatures Ser.). (Illus.). (J). pap. 1.70 (978-0-15-314549-0(8)) Harcourt Schl. Pubs.

—Beauty Surrounds Us: Take Home Book. 1999. (Signatures Ser.). (Illus.). (J). pap. 1.90 (978-0-15-313976-5(5)) Harcourt Schl. Pubs.

—The Best Boat: Independent Reader. 3rd ed. 2002. (Trophies Reading Program Ser.). (Illus.). (J). pap. 2.90 (978-0-15-325547-2(1)) Harcourt Schl. Pubs.

—The Best Food 5-Pack, On Level. 3rd ed. 2002. (Trophies Reading Program Ser.). (Illus.). (gr. 1). pap. 20.10 (978-0-15-326840-3(9)) Harcourt Schl. Pubs.

—The Best Hat: Take-Home Book. 1999. (Signatures Ser.). (Illus.). (J). pap. 1.70 (978-0-15-313835-5(1)) Harcourt Schl. Pubs.

—The Best Machine: Take-Home Book. 1999. (Signatures Ser.). (Illus.). (J). pap. 1.90 (978-0-15-313859-1(9)) Harcourt Schl. Pubs.

—Better Late Than... Take Home Book. 1999. (Signatures Ser.). (Illus.). (J). pap. 1.90 (978-0-15-313977-2(3)) Harcourt Schl. Pubs.

—A Big, Big Van: Decodable Book. 3rd ed. 2002. (Trophies Reading Program Ser.). (Illus.). pap. 2.90 (978-0-15-325426-0(2)) Harcourt Schl. Pubs.

—The Big Brown Bear: Library Edition. 1999. (Collections Ser.). (Illus.). (J). (gr. 1). 4.70 (978-0-15-314265-9(0)) Harcourt Schl. Pubs.

—The Big Brown Bear Big Book Anthology. 99th ed. 1999. (Signatures Ser.). (Illus.). (-2). pap. 60.70 (978-0-15-310808-2(8)) Harcourt Schl. Pubs.

—The Big Carrot: Independent Reader. 3rd ed. 2002. (Trophies Reading Program Ser.). (Illus.). (J). pap. 2.90 (978-0-15-325476-5(9)) Harcourt Schl. Pubs.

—The Big Dipper: Library Edition. 1999. (Collections Ser.). (Illus.). (J). 4.70 (978-0-15-314273-4(1)) Harcourt Schl. Pubs.

—The Big Sneeze: Take-Home Book. 1999. (Signatures Ser.). (Illus.). (J). (gr. 2). pap. 1.90 (978-0-15-313862-1(9)) Harcourt Schl. Pubs.

—The Big Tea Cup: Take-Home Book. 1999. (Signatures Ser.). (Illus.). (J). pap. 1.90 (978-0-15-313925-3(0)) Harcourt Schl. Pubs.

—Biscuit: Library Edition. 1999. (Collections Ser.). (Illus.). (J). 4.70 (978-0-15-314266-6(9)) Harcourt Schl. Pubs.

—Blue Skies: Intervention Reader. 1999. (Collections Ser.). (Illus.). (gr. 2). pap. 17.00 (978-0-15-312731-1(7)) Harcourt Schl. Pubs.

—The Bottom of the Sea: Take-Home Book. 1999. (Collections Ser.). (Illus.). (J). pap. 1.90 (978-0-15-317215-1(0)) Harcourt Schl. Pubs.

—The Box: Take-Home Book. 1999. (Signatures Ser.). (Illus.). (J). pap. 1.70 (978-0-15-313831-7(9)) Harcourt Schl. Pubs.

—Bright Ideas Level 3. 1999. (Collections Ser.). (Illus.). 31.50 (978-0-15-312037-4(1)) Harcourt Schl. Pubs.

—Bright Surprises: Intervention Reader. 3rd ed. 2002. (Trophies Reading Program Ser.). (Illus.). (gr. 3 up). pap. 16.70 (978-0-15-325340-9(1)) Harcourt Schl. Pubs.

—Bright Voice: Intervention Reader & Practice Book. 2001. (Illus.). (gr. 4). pap. 6.00 (978-0-15-324947-1(1)) Harcourt Schl. Pubs.

—Bright Voices: Intervention Reader. 2000. (Collections Ser.). (Illus.). (gr. 4). pap. 16.80 (978-0-15-312734-2(1)) Harcourt Schl. Pubs.

—Brother Moon & Sister Star: Take-Home Book. 1999. (Signatures Ser.). (Illus.). (J). pap. 1.90 (978-0-15-313873-7(4)) Harcourt Schl. Pubs.

—Una Buena Accion: Take-Home Book. 1999. (Vamos Ser.). (SPA., Illus.). (J). pap. 2.50 (978-0-15-318826-8(X)) Harcourt Schl. Pubs.

—The Bug Party: Take-Home Book. 1999. (Signatures Ser.). (J). pap. 1.70 (978-0-15-313836-2(X)) Harcourt Schl. Pubs.

—The Burro's Story: Take-Home Book. 1999. (Collections Ser.). (Illus.). (J). pap. 1.90 (978-0-15-317317-2(3)) Harcourt Schl. Pubs.

—Caminos Abiertos. 3rd ed. 2002. (Trofeos Ser.). (SPA., Illus.). (gr. 4 up). pupil's gde. ed. 85.70 (978-0-15-322665-6(X)) Harcourt Schl. Pubs.

—Cara de Peces: Library Edition. 1999. (SPA., Illus.). pap. 19.10 (978-0-15-315885-8(9)) Harcourt Schl. Pubs.

—The Case of The... Take-Home Book. 1999. (Signatures Ser.). (Illus.). (J). pap. 1.90 (978-0-15-313929-1(3)); (gr. 2). pap. 1.90 (978-0-15-313857-7(2)) Harcourt Schl. Pubs.

—El Caso y Rocas Falsas: Take-Home Book. 2001. (Vamos Ser.). (SPA., Illus.). (J). pap. 2.80 (978-0-15-319958-5(X)) Harcourt Schl. Pubs.

—Catch Me If You Can Big Book Anthology. 99th ed. 1999. (Signatures Ser.). (Illus.). pap. 60.70 (978-0-15-310810-5(X)) Harcourt Schl. Pubs.

—Celebrating a Powwow: Reader's Choice Book. 2001. (Collections Ser.). (Illus.). (J). 5.90 (978-0-15-314367-0(3)) Harcourt Schl. Pubs.

—Centavos/Gustavo: Library Edition. 1999. (SPA., Illus.). pap. 19.10 (978-0-15-315876-6(X)) Harcourt Schl. Pubs.

—Century Club: Take-Home Book. 1999. (Signatures Ser.). (Illus.). (J). pap. 1.90 (978-0-15-313921-5(8)) Harcourt Schl. Pubs.

—Challenge & Change: Take-Home Book. 1999. (Signatures Ser.). (Illus.). (J). pap. 1.90 (978-0-15-313951-2(X)) Harcourt Schl. Pubs.

—Charlie Spots a Fake: Take Home Book. 1999. (Signatures Ser.). (Illus.). (J). pap. 1.90 (978-0-15-313973-4(0)) Harcourt Schl. Pubs.

—Chico y Brighton Beach: Take-Home Book. 2001. (Vamos Ser.). (SPA., Illus.). (J). pap. 2.80 (978-0-15-319929-5(6)) Harcourt Schl. Pubs.

—Cindy's Cellar: On Level. 3rd ed. 2002. (Trophies Reading Program Ser.). pap. 5.10 (978-0-15-322995-4(0)) Harcourt Schl. Pubs.

—The Class Play: Take-Home Book. 1999. (Signatures Ser.). (Illus.). (J). pap. 1.70 (978-0-15-313839-3(4)) Harcourt Schl. Pubs.

—Climbing the Rope: Take-Home Book. 1999. (Signatures Ser.). (Illus.). (J). pap. 1.90 (978-0-15-313937-6(4)) Harcourt Schl. Pubs.

—Cloak for a Dreamer: Reader's Choice Book. 2001. (Collections Ser.). (Illus.). (J). 5.90 (978-0-15-314398-4(3)) Harcourt Schl. Pubs.

—Cloudy..Sunny Day Big Book Anthology Book 2. 99th ed. 1999. (Signatures Ser.). (Illus.). pap. 60.70 (978-0-15-310809-9(6)) Harcourt Schl. Pubs.

—Coast to Coast, Grade 5. 99th ed. 1999. (Signatures Ser.). Vol. 1. tchr. ed. 218.40 (978-0-15-310125-0(3)); Vol. 2. tchr. ed. 218.40 (978-0-15-310126-7(1)) Harcourt Schl. Pubs.

—Collection: Michigan Edition. 2nd ed. 2002. (Trophies Reading Program Ser.). tchr. ed. 501.50 (978-0-15-336464-8(5)); (gr. 5). tchr. ed. 505.50 (978-0-15-336469-3(6)) Harcourt Schl. Pubs.

—Collection, Grade 1: Arizona Edition. 3rd ed. 2002. (Trophies Reading Program Ser.). tchr. ed. 695.50 (978-0-15-334515-9(2)) Harcourt Schl. Pubs.

—Collection, Grade 1: New Jersey Edition. 3rd ed. 2002. (Trophies Reading Program Ser.). tchr. ed. 689.20 (978-0-15-334501-2(2)) Harcourt Schl. Pubs.

—Collection, Grade 1: New York Edition. 3rd ed. 2002. (Trophies Reading Program Ser.). tchr. ed. 686.70 (978-0-15-334445-9(8)) Harcourt Schl. Pubs.

—Collection, Grade 1: Pennsylvania Edition. 3rd ed. 2002. (Trophies Reading Program Ser.). tchr. ed. 695.50 (978-0-15-334459-6(8)) Harcourt Schl. Pubs.

—Collection, Grade 2: Arizona Edition. 3rd ed. 2002. (Trophies Reading Program Ser.). tchr. ed. 472.00 (978-0-15-334517-3(9)) Harcourt Schl. Pubs.

—Collection, Grade 2: Illinois Edition. 3rd ed. 2002. (Trophies Reading Program Ser.). tchr. ed. 472.00 (978-0-15-334475-6(X)) Harcourt Schl. Pubs.

—Collection, Grade 2: New Jersey Edition. 3rd ed. 2002. (Trophies Reading Program Ser.). tchr. ed. 465.70 (978-0-15-334503-6(9)) Harcourt Schl. Pubs.

—Collection, Grade 2: New York Edition. 3rd ed. 2002. (Trophies Reading Program Ser.). tchr. ed. 463.20 (978-0-15-334447-3(4)) Harcourt Schl. Pubs.

—Collection, Grade 2: Pennsylvania Edition. 3rd ed. 2002. tchr. ed. 472.00 (978-0-15-334461-9(X)) Harcourt Schl. Pubs.

—Collection, Grade 3: Arizona Edition. 3rd ed. 2002. (Trophies Reading Program Ser.). tchr. ed. 472.00 (978-0-15-334519-7(5)) Harcourt Schl. Pubs.

—Collection, Grade 3: New Jersey Edition. 3rd ed. 2002. (Trophies Reading Program Ser.). tchr. ed. 465.70 (978-0-15-334505-0(5)) Harcourt Schl. Pubs.

—Collection, Grade 3: New York Edition. 3rd ed. 2002. (Trophies Reading Program Ser.). tchr. ed. 463.20 (978-0-15-334449-7(0)) Harcourt Schl. Pubs.

—Collection, Grade 3: Ohio Edition. 3rd ed. 2002. (Trophies Reading Program Ser.). tchr. ed. 466.10 (978-0-15-334491-6(1)) Harcourt Schl. Pubs.

—Collection, Grade 3: Pennsylvania Edition. 3rd ed. 2002. tchr. ed. 472.00 (978-0-15-334463-3(6)) Harcourt Schl. Pubs.

—Collection, Grade 4: Arizona Edition. 3rd ed. 2002. (Trophies Reading Program Ser.). tchr. ed. 501.00 (978-0-15-334521-0(7)) Harcourt Schl. Pubs.

—Collection, Grade 4: New Jersey Edition. 3rd ed. 2002. (Trophies Reading Program Ser.). tchr. ed. 501.00 (978-0-15-334507-4(1)) Harcourt Schl. Pubs.

—Collection, Grade 4: New York Edition. 3rd ed. 2002. (Trophies Reading Program Ser.). tchr. ed. 501.00 (978-0-15-334451-0(2)) Harcourt Schl. Pubs.

—Collection, Grade 4: Ohio Edition. 3rd ed. 2002. (Trophies Reading Program Ser.). tchr. ed. 495.10 (978-0-15-334493-0(8)) Harcourt Schl. Pubs.

—Collection, Grade 4: Pennsylvania Edition. 3rd ed. 2002. tchr. ed. 501.00 (978-0-15-334465-7(2)) Harcourt Schl. Pubs.

—Collection, Grade 5: Arizona Edition. 3rd ed. 2002. (Trophies Reading Program Ser.). tchr. ed. 501.00 (978-0-15-334523-4(3)) Harcourt Schl. Pubs.

—Collection, Grade 5: New Jersey Edition. 3rd ed. 2002. (Trophies Reading Program Ser.). tchr. ed. 494.80 (978-0-15-334509-8(8)) Harcourt Schl. Pubs.

—Collection, Grade 5: New York Edition. 3rd ed. 2002. (Trophies Reading Program Ser.). tchr. ed. 492.20 (978-0-15-334453-4(9)) Harcourt Schl. Pubs.

—Collection, Grade 6: New Jersey Edition. 3rd ed. 2002. (Trophies Reading Program Ser.). tchr. ed. 519.50 (978-0-15-334511-1(X)) Harcourt Schl. Pubs.

—Collection, Grade 6: New York Edition. 3rd ed. 2002. (Trophies Reading Program Ser.). tchr. ed. 510.70 (978-0-15-334455-8(5)) Harcourt Schl. Pubs.

—Collection, Grade 6: Ohio Edition. 3rd ed. 2002. (Trophies Reading Program Ser.). tchr. ed. 513.60 (978-0-15-334497-8(0)) Harcourt Schl. Pubs.

—Collection, Grade K: Arizona Edition. 3rd ed. 2002. (Trophies Reading Program Ser.). tchr. ed. 492.70 (978-0-15-334513-5(6)) Harcourt Schl. Pubs.

—Collection, Grade K: New Jersey Edition. 3rd ed. 2002. (Trophies Reading Program Ser.). tchr. ed. 480.90 (978-0-15-334499-2(7)) Harcourt Schl. Pubs.

—Collection, Grade K: New York Edition. 3rd ed. 2002. (Trophies Reading Program Ser.). tchr. ed. 480.90 (978-0-15-334443-5(1)) Harcourt Schl. Pubs.

—Collections: Family Involvement Activities. 1999. (Illus.). pap. 14.40 (978-0-15-314886-6(1)) Harcourt Schl. Pubs.

—Collections: Mid-Year/End-of-Year Reading & Language Skills Assessment. rev. ed. 2001. (Illus.). (gr. 1). pap. 40.90 (978-0-15-319457-3(X)) Harcourt Schl. Pubs.

—Collections: Mid-Year/End-of-Year Reading Skills Assessment. 1999. (Illus.). (gr. 5). pap. 37.50 (978-0-15-315210-8(9)); (gr. 6). pap. 37.50 (978-0-15-315211-5(7)) Harcourt Schl. Pubs.

—Collections: My Book: Grade Level Library. 1999. (Illus.). (gr. 1). pap. 13.90 (978-0-15-315200-9(1)) Harcourt Schl. Pubs.

—Collections: Phonics Activity Book. 2003. (First-Place Reading Ser.). (Illus.). (gr. k-6). 6.90 (978-0-15-313423-4(2)) Harcourt Schl. Pubs.

—Collections: Phonics Practice. 1999. (Trophies Ser.). (Illus.). (gr. 1 up). pap. 12.70 (978-0-15-313559-0(X)) Harcourt Schl. Pubs.

—Collections: Phonics Practice Book. 1999. (Trophies Ser.). (Illus.). (gr. 2 up). pap. 12.80 (978-0-15-315212-2(5)) Harcourt Schl. Pubs.
—Collections: Phonics Practice Reader. 1999. (Illus.). Level 1. (gr. 1). pap. 7.00 (978-0-15-314887-3(X)); Level 2. (gr. 1). pap. 7.00 (978-0-15-314888-0(8)); Level 3. (J). pap. 4.40 (978-0-15-314889-7(6)); Level 4. (gr. 1). pap. 7.00 (978-0-15-314890-3(X)); Level 5. (J). pap. 4.20 (978-0-15-314891-0(8)) Harcourt Schl. Pubs.
—Collections: Phonics Practice Readers Collection, 30 vols. 1999. (Harcourt Title I Reading Programs Ser.). (Illus.). (gr. 2 up). pap. 87.20 (978-0-15-313564-4(6)) Harcourt Schl. Pubs.
—Collections: Preparacion Para Pruebas Estandarizadas Lectura y Escritura. 2001. (Trofeos Ser.). (SPA., Illus.). (gr. 1 up). pap. 12.00 (978-0-15-321234-5(9)); (gr. 2 up). pap. 12.00 (978-0-15-321235-2(7)); (gr. 3 up). pap. 12.00 (978-0-15-321236-9(5)); (gr. 4 up). pap. 12.00 (978-0-15-321237-6(3)); (gr. 5 up). pap. 12.00 (978-0-15-321238-3(1)) Harcourt Schl. Pubs.
—Collections: Read-Aloud Anthology. 1999. (Trophies Ser.). (Illus.). (gr. 2 up). pap. 27.20 (978-0-15-314996-2(5)); (gr. 3). 27.20 (978-0-15-314997-9(3)) Harcourt Schl. Pubs.
—Collections: Reading & Language Skills: Standardized Test Preparation. 2003. (Trophies Ser.). (Illus.). (gr. 1 up). 7.50 (978-0-15-321227-7(6)) Harcourt Schl. Pubs.
—Collections: Selection Completion Test. 1999. (Illus.). (gr. 1). pap. 22.10 (978-0-15-312830-1(5)); (gr. 2). pap. 27.60 (978-0-15-312832-5(1)); (gr. 3). pap. 27.60 (978-0-15-312834-9(8)); (gr. 4). pap. 27.60 (978-0-15-312836-3(4)); (gr. 5). pap. 27.60 (978-0-15-312837-0(2)); (gr. 6). pap. 27.60 (978-0-15-312838-7(0)) Harcourt Schl. Pubs.
—Collections: Student Materials Package: Texas Edition. 1999. (Illus.). (gr. 1). 179.30 (978-0-15-315009-8(2)); (gr. 2). 99.70 (978-0-15-315011-1(4)); (gr. 3). 99.70 (978-0-15-315012-8(2)) Harcourt Schl. Pubs.
—Collections: TAAS Preparation Book for Reading & Writing. 2000. (Illus.). (J). (gr. 1). pap. 5.90 (978-0-15-320193-6(2)); (J). (gr. 2). pap. 6.70 (978-0-15-320194-3(0)); (J). (gr. 3). pap. 6.70 (978-0-15-320195-0(9)); (gr. 4). pap. 8.30 (978-0-15-320196-7(7)); (gr. 5). pap. 8.30 (978-0-15-320197-4(5)) Harcourt Schl. Pubs.
—Collections Theme 1: Chicago Edition. 2001. (Illus.). (gr. 4). pap. 18.40 (978-0-15-320654-2(3)) Harcourt Schl. Pubs.
—Collections Theme 2: Chicago Edition. 2001. (Illus.). pap. 18.40 (978-0-15-320655-9(1)) Harcourt Schl. Pubs.
—Collections, Grade 1: Guided Reading Library. 2000. pap., tchr. ed. 15.10 (978-0-15-319196-1(1)) Harcourt Schl. Pubs.
—Collections, Grade 1: Intervention Strategy Manual. 1999. pap. 62.70 (978-0-15-312740-3(6)) Harcourt Schl. Pubs.
—Collections, Grade 1: Lesson Plans: Arizona Edition. 2000. pap. 22.60 (978-0-15-322345-7(6)) Harcourt Schl. Pubs.
—Collections, Grade 1: Phonics Practice. 1999. pap., tchr. ed. 28.30 (978-0-15-313561-3(1)) Harcourt Schl. Pubs.
—Collections, Grade 1: Reading & Language Skills Assessment. 2001. pap., tchr. ed. 62.70 (978-0-15-319458-0(8)); 1999. pap., tchr. ed. 62.70 (978-0-15-312816-5(X)) Harcourt Schl. Pubs.
—Collections, Grade 1: Stanford-9 Test Preparation: Alabama Edition. 2000. pap., tchr. ed. 22.50 (978-0-15-322337-2(5)) Harcourt Schl. Pubs.
—Collections, Grade 1 Level 1: CA Edition. 1999. (Illus.). pap., tchr. ed. 156.70 (978-0-15-318777-3(8)) Harcourt Schl. Pubs.
—Collections, Grade 1 Level 2: CA Edition. 1999. pap., tchr. ed. 156.70 (978-0-15-318778-0(6)) Harcourt Schl. Pubs.
—Collections, Grade 1 Level 3: CA Edition. 1999. pap., tchr. ed. 163.00 (978-0-15-318779-7(4)) Harcourt Schl. Pubs.
—Collections, Grade 1 Level 4: CA Edition. 1999. pap., tchr. ed. 163.00 (978-0-15-318780-3(8)) Harcourt Schl. Pubs.
—Collections, Grade 1 Level B: Phonics Express: Teacher's Guide. 1999. (Trophies Ser.). (gr. 1 up). pap., tchr. ed. 10.70 (978-0-15-314922-1(1)) Harcourt Schl. Pubs.
—Collections, Grade 1, Level 2. rev. ed. 2000. pap., tchr. ed. 133.30 (978-0-15-317802-3(7)) Harcourt Schl. Pubs.
—Collections, Grade 1, Level 3. rev. ed. 2000. pap., tchr. ed. 138.70 (978-0-15-317803-0(5)) Harcourt Schl. Pubs.
—Collections, Grade 1, Level 4. rev. ed. 2000. pap., tchr. ed. 138.70 (978-0-15-317804-7(3)) Harcourt Schl. Pubs.
—Collections, Grade 1, Level 5. rev. ed. 2000. pap., tchr. ed. 144.00 (978-0-15-317806-1(X)) Harcourt Schl. Pubs.
—Collections, Grade 2: Guided Reading Library. 2000. pap., tchr. ed. 12.60 (978-0-15-319197-8(X)) Harcourt Schl. Pubs.
—Collections, Grade 2: Intervention Reading Skills. 1999. pap., tchr. ed. 27.10 (978-0-15-312742-7(2)) Harcourt Schl. Pubs.
—Collections, Grade 2: Practice Book. 1999. Vol. 1. pap., tchr. ed. 16.40 (978-0-15-312721-2(X)); Vol. 2. pap., tchr. ed. 16.40 (978-0-15-312722-9(8)) Harcourt Schl. Pubs.
—Collections, Grade 2: Stanford-9 Test Preparation: Alabama Edition. 2000. pap., tchr. ed. 22.50 (978-0-15-322338-9(3)) Harcourt Schl. Pubs.
—Collections, Grade 2 Level 1: CA Edition. 1999. pap., tchr. ed. 200.60 (978-0-15-318782-7(4)) Harcourt Schl. Pubs.
—Collections, Grade 2 Level 1, Theme 1. 2000. tchr. ed. 76.40 (978-0-15-318916-6(9)) Harcourt Schl. Pubs.
—Collections, Grade 2 Level 1, Theme 2. 2000. tchr. ed. 76.40 (978-0-15-318917-3(7)) Harcourt Schl. Pubs.
—Collections, Grade 2 Level 1, Theme 3. 2000. tchr. ed. 76.40 (978-0-15-318918-0(5)) Harcourt Schl. Pubs.
—Collections, Grade 2 Level 2: CA Edition. 1999. pap., tchr. ed. 200.60 (978-0-15-318783-4(2)) Harcourt Schl. Pubs.
—Collections, Grade 2 Level 2, Theme 1. 2000. tchr. ed. 76.40 (978-0-15-318919-7(3)) Harcourt Schl. Pubs.
—Collections, Grade 2 Level 2, Theme 2. 2000. tchr. ed. 76.40 (978-0-15-318920-3(7)) Harcourt Schl. Pubs.
—Collections, Grade 2 Level C: Phonics Express: Teacher's Guide. 1999. (Trophies Ser.). (gr. 2 up). pap., tchr. ed. 10.70 (978-0-15-314923-8(X)) Harcourt Schl. Pubs.
—Collections, Grade 3: Guided Reading Library. 2000. pap., tchr. ed. 12.60 (978-0-15-319198-5(8)) Harcourt Schl. Pubs.
—Collections, Grade 3: Practice Book. 1999. Vol. 1. pap., tchr. ed. 16.40 (978-0-15-312723-6(6)); Vol. 2. pap., tchr. ed. 16.40 (978-0-15-312724-3(4)) Harcourt Schl. Pubs.
—Collections, Grade 3 Level 1: CA Edition. 1999. pap., tchr. ed. 200.60 (978-0-15-318784-1(0)) Harcourt Schl. Pubs.
—Collections, Grade 3 Level 1, Theme 1. 2000. tchr. ed. 76.40 (978-0-15-318922-7(3)) Harcourt Schl. Pubs.
—Collections, Grade 3 Level 1, Theme 2. 2000. tchr. ed. 76.40 (978-0-15-318923-4(1)) Harcourt Schl. Pubs.
—Collections, Grade 3 Level 1, Theme 3. 2000. tchr. ed. 76.40 (978-0-15-318924-1(X)) Harcourt Schl. Pubs.
—Collections, Grade 3 Level 2: CA Edition. 1999. pap., tchr. ed. 200.60 (978-0-15-318785-8(9)) Harcourt Schl. Pubs.
—Collections, Grade 3 Level 2, Theme 1. 2000. tchr. ed. 76.40 (978-0-15-318925-8(8)) Harcourt Schl. Pubs.
—Collections, Grade 3 Level 2, Theme 2. 2000. tchr. ed. 76.40 (978-0-15-318926-5(6)) Harcourt Schl. Pubs.
—Collections, Grade 3 Level 2, Theme 3. 2000. tchr. ed. 76.40 (978-0-15-318927-2(4)) Harcourt Schl. Pubs.
—Collections, Grade 3 Level D: Phonics Express: Teacher's Guide. 1999. (Trophies Ser.). (gr. 3 up). pap., tchr. ed. 10.70 (978-0-15-314924-5(8)) Harcourt Schl. Pubs.
—Collections, Grade 4: Practice Book. 1999. pap., tchr. ed. 25.10 (978-0-15-312726-7(0)) Harcourt Schl. Pubs.
—Collections, Grade 4: Stanford-9 Test Preparation: Alabama Edition. 2000. pap., tchr. ed. 22.50 (978-0-15-322340-2(5)) Harcourt Schl. Pubs.
—Collections, Grade 4 Theme 1. 2000. tchr. ed. 74.80 (978-0-15-318928-9(2)) Harcourt Schl. Pubs.
—Collections, Grade 4 Theme 2. 2000. tchr. ed. 74.80 (978-0-15-318929-6(0)) Harcourt Schl. Pubs.
—Collections, Grade 4 Theme 3. 2000. tchr. ed. 74.80 (978-0-15-318930-2(4)) Harcourt Schl. Pubs.
—Collections, Grade 4 Theme 4. 2000. tchr. ed. 74.80 (978-0-15-318931-9(2)) Harcourt Schl. Pubs.
—Collections, Grade 4 Theme 5. 2000. tchr. ed. 74.80 (978-0-15-318932-6(0)) Harcourt Schl. Pubs.
—Collections, Grade 4 Theme 6. 2000. tchr. ed. 74.80 (978-0-15-318933-3(9)) Harcourt Schl. Pubs.
—Collections, Grade 5: Practice Book. 1999. pap., tchr. ed. 25.10 (978-0-15-312727-4(9)) Harcourt Schl. Pubs.
—Collections, Grade 5 Theme 2. 2000. tchr. ed. 74.80 (978-0-15-318935-7(5)) Harcourt Schl. Pubs.
—Collections, Grade 5 Theme 3. 2000. tchr. ed. 74.80 (978-0-15-318936-4(3)) Harcourt Schl. Pubs.
—Collections, Grade 5 Theme 4. 2000. tchr. ed. 74.80 (978-0-15-318937-1(1)) Harcourt Schl. Pubs.
—Collections, Grade 5 Theme 5. 2000. tchr. ed. 74.80 (978-0-15-318938-8(X)) Harcourt Schl. Pubs.
—Collections, Grade 5 Theme 6. 2000. tchr. ed. 74.80 (978-0-15-318939-5(8)) Harcourt Schl. Pubs.
—Collections, Grade 6: Practice Book. 1999. pap., tchr. ed. 25.10 (978-0-15-312728-1(7)) Harcourt Schl. Pubs.
—Collections, Grade 6: Reading & Writing Skills: Standardized Test Preparation. 2001. (Trophies Ser.). (gr. 6 up). pap., tchr. ed. 22.50 (978-0-15-321233-8(0)) Harcourt Schl. Pubs.
—Collections, Grade 6: Stanford-9 Test Preparation: Alabama Edition. 2000. pap., tchr. ed. 22.50 (978-0-15-322342-6(1)) Harcourt Schl. Pubs.
—Collections, Grade 6 Theme 1. 2000. tchr. ed. 77.80 (978-0-15-318940-1(1)) Harcourt Schl. Pubs.
—Collections, Grade 6 Theme 2. 2000. tchr. ed. 77.80 (978-0-15-318941-8(X)) Harcourt Schl. Pubs.
—Collections, Grade 6 Theme 3. 2000. tchr. ed. 77.80 (978-0-15-318942-5(8)) Harcourt Schl. Pubs.
—Collections, Grade 6 Theme 4. 2000. pap., tchr. ed. 77.80 (978-0-15-318943-2(6)) Harcourt Schl. Pubs.
—Collections, Grade 6 Theme 6. 2000. tchr. ed. 77.80 (978-0-15-318945-6(2)) Harcourt Schl. Pubs.
—Collections, Grade K Level A: Phonics Express. 1999. (Trophies Ser.). (gr. k up). pap., tchr. ed. 10.70 (978-0-15-314921-4(3)) Harcourt Schl. Pubs.
—Colletions, Grade 1 Level 5: CA Edition. 1999. pap., tchr. ed. 169.30 (978-0-15-318781-0(6)) Harcourt Schl. Pubs.
—Color de la Urraca: Take-Home Book. 1999. (Vamos Ser.). (SPA., Illus.). (J). pap. 2.50 (978-0-15-318834-3(0)) Harcourt Schl. Pubs.
—Come along Daisy! 3rd ed. 2002. (Trophies Reading Program Ser.). (Illus.). pap., lib. bdg. 13.50 (978-0-15-326534-1(5)) Harcourt Schl. Pubs.
—Como Helado de Coco: Take-Home Book. 1999. (Vamos Ser.). (SPA., Illus.). (J). pap. 2.50 (978-0-15-318829-9(4)) Harcourt Schl. Pubs.
—Componer Musica Below Level. 3rd ed. 2002. (Trofeos Ser.). (SPA., Illus.). pap. 6.80 (978-0-15-324067-6(9)) Harcourt Schl. Pubs.
—The Crown of Stars Advanced Level. 3rd ed. 2002. (Trophies Reading Program Ser.). (Illus.). pap. 5.10 (978-0-15-323207-7(2)) Harcourt Schl. Pubs.
—El Cuento de Doris: Take-Home Book. 2001. (Vamos Ser.). (SPA., Illus.). (J). pap. 2.80 (978-0-15-319962-2(8)) Harcourt Schl. Pubs.
—A Day at School: Library Edition. 1999. (Collections Ser.). (Illus.). (J). 4.70 (978-0-15-314276-5(6)) Harcourt Schl. Pubs.
—Decodable Book. 3rd ed. 2002. (Trophies Ser.). Bk. 8. pap. 7.00 (978-0-15-326755-0(0)); Bk. 23. (J). (gr. 1). pap. 3.00 (978-0-15-326703-1(8)) Harcourt Schl. Pubs.
—Decodable Book - Grade 1, Bk. 26. 3rd ed. 2002. (Trophies Reading Program Ser.). pap. 3.30 (978-0-15-327352-0(6)) Harcourt Schl. Pubs.
—Deefer On Level. 3rd ed. 2002. (Trophies Reading Program Ser.). (Illus.). pap. 5.10 (978-0-15-323170-4(X)) Harcourt Schl. Pubs.
—Diamond Cove, Grade 3 Level 2. 99th ed. 1999. (Signatures Ser.). tchr. ed. 205.70 (978-0-15-310122-9(9)) Harcourt Schl. Pubs.
—Dias Maravillosos Level 2-2. 3rd ed. 2002. (Trofeos Ser.). (SPA., Illus.). (gr. 2 up). pap., pupil's gde. ed. 60.50 (978-0-15-322662-5(5)) Harcourt Schl. Pubs.
—Dias/Comercio Advanced Level. 3rd ed. 2002. (Trofeos Ser.). (SPA., Illus.). pap. 6.80 (978-0-15-324125-3(X)) Harcourt Schl. Pubs.
—The Disappearing: Take-Home Book. 1999. (Signatures Ser.). (Illus.). (J). pap. 1.90 (978-0-15-313964-2(1)) Harcourt Schl. Pubs.
—Discovering History on the Staircase Advanced Level. 3rd ed. 2002. (Trophies Reading Program Ser.). (Illus.). pap. 5.10 (978-0-15-323400-2(8)) Harcourt Schl. Pubs.
—Dive In! 3rd ed. 2002. (Trophies Ser.). (gr. 6). pap. 5.10 (978-0-15-327873-0(0)) Harcourt Schl. Pubs.
—Dive in the Ocean: Independent Reader. 3rd ed. 2002. (Trophies Reading Program Ser.). (Illus.). (J). pap. 2.90 (978-0-15-325548-9(X)) Harcourt Schl. Pubs.
—Don Ceno: Phonics Practice Reader. 1999. (Vamos Ser.). (SPA., Illus.). pap. 5.00 (978-0-15-319005-6(1)) Harcourt Schl. Pubs.
—Los Dos Hermanos: Take-Home Book. 1999. (Vamos Ser.). (SPA., Illus.). (J). pap. 2.50 (978-0-15-318833-6(2)) Harcourt Schl. Pubs.
—Down by the Pond: Take-Home Book. 1999. (Signatures Ser.). (Illus.). (J). pap. 1.90 (978-0-15-313895-9(5)) Harcourt Schl. Pubs.
—Dr. Brown at Work 5-Pack, On Level. 3rd ed. 2002. (Trophies Reading Program Ser.). (Illus.). pap. 25.60 (978-0-15-326846-5(8)) Harcourt Schl. Pubs.
—Dreamers & Their Dreams: Take-Home Book. 1999. (Signatures Ser.). (Illus.). (J). pap. 1.90 (978-0-15-313881-2(5)) Harcourt Schl. Pubs.
—Ela/Malvadas Below Level. 3rd ed. 2002. (Trofeos Ser.). (SPA., Illus.). (gr. 3). pap. 6.80 (978-0-15-324060-7(1)) Harcourt Schl. Pubs.
—El Elefantito. 2000. (SPA., Illus.). pap. 82.60 (978-0-15-315099-9(8)) Harcourt Schl. Pubs.
—Empiece la Musica: Take-Home Book. 1999. (Vamos Ser.). (SPA., Illus.). (J). pap. 2.50 (978-0-15-318842-8(1)) Harcourt Schl. Pubs.
—Energia del Agua: Take-Home Book. 2001. (Vamos Ser.). (SPA., Illus.). (J). pap. 2.80 (978-0-15-319957-8(1)) Harcourt Schl. Pubs.
—Erron's Decision: Take-Home Book. 1999. (Signatures Ser.). (Illus.). (J). pap. 1.90 (978-0-15-313939-0(0)) Harcourt Schl. Pubs.
—Es Hora: Big Book. 2000. (SPA., Illus.). pap. 82.60 (978-0-15-315095-1(5)) Harcourt Schl. Pubs.
—Every Animal Has a Home - 5 Pack - Grade 1. 3rd ed. 2002. (Trophies English Language Learners Ser.). 20.10 (978-0-15-327624-8(X)) Harcourt Schl. Pubs.
—Exploring the Surroundings: Practice Book. 3rd ed. 2001. (Trophies Reading Program Ser.). (Illus.). (J). pap. 1.80 (978-0-15-325091-0(7)) Harcourt Schl. Pubs.
—Exploring the Surroundings: Practice Book: Florida Edition. 3rd ed. 2002. (Trophies Reading Program Ser.). (Illus.). (J). pap. 2.00 (978-0-15-326606-5(6)) Harcourt Schl. Pubs.
—Una Fabula Moderna: Take-Home Book. 2001. (Vamos Ser.). (SPA., Illus.). (J). pap. 2.80 (978-0-15-319931-8(8)) Harcourt Schl. Pubs.
—Faeton/Corrazo Below Level. 3rd ed. 2002. (Trofeos Ser.). (SPA., Illus.). pap. 6.80 (978-0-15-324058-4(X)) Harcourt Schl. Pubs.
—Fall: A Reader. 1999. (Collections Ser.). (Illus.). (J). pap. 2.10 (978-0-15-313442-5(9)) Harcourt Schl. Pubs.
—Family & Friends: Theme Book. 1999. (Collections Ser.). (Illus.). (J). pap. 3.00 (978-0-15-314019-8(4)) Harcourt Schl. Pubs.
—Far Away Places: Take-Home Book. 1999. (Signatures Ser.). (Illus.). (J). pap. 1.70 (978-0-15-313852-2(1)) Harcourt Schl. Pubs.
—Farming Naturally: Take-Home Book. 1999. (Signatures Ser.). (Illus.). (J). pap. 1.90 (978-0-15-313944-4(7)) Harcourt Schl. Pubs.
—Favorite Americans On Level. 3rd ed. 2002. (Trophies Reading Program Ser.). (Illus.). pap. 5.10 (978-0-15-323363-0(X)) Harcourt Schl. Pubs.
—Felicia's Audition On Level. 3rd ed. 2002. (Trophies Reading Program Ser.). (Illus.). pap. 5.10 (978-0-15-323432-3(6)) Harcourt Schl. Pubs.
—Finding Your Way. 3rd ed. 2002. (Trophies English Language Learners Ser.). (Illus.). pap. 5.10 (978-0-15-327718-4(1)) Harcourt Schl. Pubs.
—The Fire Bell Rings: Independent Reader. 3rd ed. 2002. (Trophies Reading Program Ser.). (Illus.). (J). pap. 2.90 (978-0-15-325495-6(5)) Harcourt Schl. Pubs.
—Fire Fighters: Library Edition. 1999. (Collections Ser.). (Illus.). (J). 4.70 (978-0-15-314271-0(5)) Harcourt Schl. Pubs.
—The First Artists Below Level. 3rd ed. 2002. (Trophies Reading Program Ser.). (Illus.). pap. 5.10 (978-0-15-323411-8(3)) Harcourt Schl. Pubs.
—First Place Reading. 2nd ed. 2002. (First-Place Reading Ser.). (Illus.). (gr. 2 up). pupil's gde. ed. 9.10 (978-0-15-334556-2(X)); (gr. 3 up). pupil's gde. ed. 9.10 (978-0-15-334557-9(8)); (gr. 4 up). pupil's gde. ed. 9.10 (978-0-15-334558-6(6)); (gr. 5 up). pupil's gde. ed. 9.10 (978-0-15-334559-3(4)); (gr. 6 up). pupil's gde. ed. 9.10 (978-0-15-334560-9(8)) Harcourt Schl. Pubs.
—First Place Reading: Assessment Book. 2nd ed. 2003. (First-Place Reading Ser.). (Illus.). (gr. 1 up). 2.40 (978-0-15-334583-8(7)); (gr. 2 up). 2.90 (978-0-15-334584-5(5)); (gr. 3 up). 2.90 (978-0-15-334585-2(3)); (gr. 4 up). 2.90 (978-0-15-334586-9(1)); (gr. 5 up). 2.90 (978-0-15-334587-6(X)); (gr. 6 up). 2.90 (978-0-15-334588-3(8)) Harcourt Schl. Pubs.
—First Place Reading: Assessment Book/Answer Key. 2nd ed. 2002. (Illus.). (gr. 1). pap. 5.70 (978-0-15-334760-3(0)); (gr. 2). pap. 5.70 (978-0-15-334761-0(9)); (gr. 3). pap. 5.70 (978-0-15-334762-7(7)); (gr. 4). pap. 5.70 (978-0-15-334763-4(5)); (gr. 5). pap. 5.70 (978-0-15-334764-1(3)); (gr. 6). pap. 5.70 (978-0-15-334765-8(1)) Harcourt Schl. Pubs.
—First Place Reading: Practice Book. 2nd ed. 2003. (First-Place Reading Ser.). (Illus.). (gr. 1 up). 4.10 (978-0-15-334569-2(1)); (gr. 2 up). 4.10 (978-0-15-334570-8(5)); (gr. 3 up). 4.10 (978-0-15-334571-5(3)); (gr. 4 up). 4.10 (978-0-15-334572-2(1)); (gr. 5 up). 4.10 (978-0-15-334573-9(X)); (gr. 6 up). 4.10 (978-0-15-334574-6(8)) Harcourt Schl. Pubs.
—First Place Reading: Read-Aloud Collection. 2nd ed. 2002. (Illus.). (gr. 4). 27.80 (978-0-15-328384-0(X)); (gr. 5). 41.30 (978-0-15-328386-4(6)); (gr. 6). 41.90 (978-0-15-328387-1(4)) Harcourt Schl. Pubs.
—First Place Reading, Grade 1. 2nd ed. 2002. pap., tchr. ed. 66.00 (978-0-15-334562-3(4)) Harcourt Schl. Pubs.
—First Place Reading, Grade 1: Practice Book. 2nd ed. 2002. pap., tchr. ed. 15.90 (978-0-15-334576-0(4)) Harcourt Schl. Pubs.
—First Place Reading, Grade 2. 2nd ed. 2002. pap., tchr. ed. 66.00 (978-0-15-334563-0(2)) Harcourt Schl. Pubs.
—First Place Reading, Grade 2: Practice Book. 2nd ed. 2002. pap., tchr. ed. 15.90 (978-0-15-334577-7(2)) Harcourt Schl. Pubs.
—First Place Reading, Grade 3. 2nd ed. 2002. pap., tchr. ed. 102.90 (978-0-15-338001-3(2)); pap., tchr. ed. 69.40 (978-0-15-334564-7(0)) Harcourt Schl. Pubs.
—First Place Reading, Grade 3: Practice Book. 2nd ed. 2002. pap., tchr. ed. 15.90 (978-0-15-334578-4(0)) Harcourt Schl. Pubs.
—First Place Reading, Grade 4. 2nd ed. 2002. pap., tchr. ed. 102.90 (978-0-15-338002-0(0)); pap., tchr. ed. 69.40 (978-0-15-334565-4(9)) Harcourt Schl. Pubs.
—First Place Reading, Grade 4: Practice Book. 2nd ed. 2002. pap., tchr. ed. 15.90 (978-0-15-334579-1(9)) Harcourt Schl. Pubs.
—First Place Reading, Grade 5. 2nd ed. 2002. pap., tchr. ed. 102.90 (978-0-15-338003-7(9)); pap., tchr. ed. 69.40 (978-0-15-334566-1(7)) Harcourt Schl. Pubs.
—First Place Reading, Grade 5: Practice Book. 2nd ed. 2002. pap., tchr. ed. 15.90 (978-0-15-334580-7(2)) Harcourt Schl. Pubs.
—First Place Reading, Grade 6. 2nd ed. 2002. pap., tchr. ed. 102.90 (978-0-15-338004-4(7)); pap., tchr. ed. 69.40 (978-0-15-334567-8(5)) Harcourt Schl. Pubs.
—First Place Reading, Grade 6: Practice Book. 2nd ed. 2002. pap., tchr. ed. 15.90 (978-0-15-334581-4(0)) Harcourt Schl. Pubs.
—First Place Reading, Grade K. 2nd ed. 2002. pap., tchr. ed. 66.00 (978-0-15-334561-6(6)) Harcourt Schl. Pubs.
—Float on the Boat: Independent Reader. 3rd ed. 2002. (Trophies Reading Program Ser.). (Illus.). (J). pap. 2.90 (978-0-15-325499-4(8)) Harcourt Schl. Pubs.
—Flower Garden Lap Book. 3rd ed. 2004. (Trophies Reading Program Ser.). (Illus.). pap. 11.50 (978-0-15-341029-1(9)) Harcourt Schl. Pubs.
—Flowers, Fruits & Seeds: Library Edition. 1999. (Collections Ser.). (Illus.). (J). 5.30 (978-0-15-314294-9(4)) Harcourt Schl. Pubs.
—For Pete's Sake: Library Edition. 1999. (Collections Ser.). (Illus.). (J). (gr. 2). 4.70 (978-0-15-314290-1(1)) Harcourt Schl. Pubs.
—Four Fur Feet: Library Edition. 1999. (Collections Ser.). (Illus.). (J). 4.70 (978-0-15-314282-6(0)) Harcourt Schl. Pubs.
—Fox Goes to the End of the World: Library Edition. 1999. (Collections Ser.). (Illus.). (J). 5.30 (978-0-15-314272-7(3)) Harcourt Schl. Pubs.
—Full Sails Anthology. 99th ed. 1999. (Signatures Ser.). (Illus.). (-4). pap. 36.00 (978-0-15-310812-9(6)) Harcourt Schl. Pubs.
—The Future of Reading: Take-Home Book. 2001. (Collections Ser.). (Illus.). (J). pap. 1.90 (978-0-15-319671-3(8)) Harcourt Schl. Pubs.
—The Game: Take-Home Book. 1999. (Signatures Ser.). (Illus.). (J). pap. 1.70 (978-0-15-313833-1(5)) Harcourt Schl. Pubs.
—Gather Around Level 1-5. 3rd ed. 2002. (Trophies Ser.). (Illus.). (gr. 1 up). pupil's gde. ed. 34.10 (978-0-15-322473-7(8)) Harcourt Schl. Pubs.
—Getting to Know You: Practice Book. 3rd ed. 2001. (Trophies Reading Program Ser.). (Illus.). (J). pap. 1.80 (978-0-15-325081-1(X)) Harcourt Schl. Pubs.
—Getting to Know You: Practice Book: Florida Edition. 3rd ed. 2002. (Trophies Reading Program Ser.). (Illus.). (J). pap. 2.00 (978-0-15-326596-9(5)) Harcourt Schl. Pubs.
—Glouskabi & The... Take-Home Book. 1999. (Signatures Ser.). (Illus.). (J). pap. 1.90 (978-0-15-313923-9(4)) Harcourt Schl. Pubs.
—The Golden Dream: Take-Home Book. 1999. (Signatures Ser.). (Illus.). (J). pap. 1.90 (978-0-15-313917-8(X)) Harcourt Schl. Pubs.
—Good-Bye Country Life On Level. 3rd ed. 2002. (Trophies Reading Program Ser.). (Illus.). pap. 5.10 (978-0-15-323341-8(9)) Harcourt Schl. Pubs.

P Q R

—Trofeos Advanced Level: Vecinos en las Praderas. 3rd ed. 2002. (SPA., Illus.). pap. 6.80 (978-0-15-324203-8(5)) Harcourt Schl. Pubs.

—Trofeos Advanced Level: Viaje en el Tiempo. 3rd ed. 2002. (SPA., Illus.). pap. 6.80 (978-0-15-324389-9(9)) Harcourt Schl. Pubs.

—Trofeos Advanced Level: Vivamos el Dia de la Historia. 3rd ed. 2002. (SPA., Illus.). pap. 6.80 (978-0-15-324308-0(2)) Harcourt Schl. Pubs.

—Trofeos Advanced Level: Voy a Trabajar. 3rd ed. 2002. (SPA., Illus.). pap. 6.80 (978-0-15-323950-2(6)) Harcourt Schl. Pubs.

—Trofeos Advanced Level: Yellowstone: Geologica Dinamica. 3rd ed. 2002. (SPA., Illus.). pap. 6.80 (978-0-15-324293-9(0)) Harcourt Schl. Pubs.

—Trofeos Avanced Level: Por el Gran Canon de Colorado. 3rd ed. 2002. (SPA., Illus.). pap. 6.80 (978-0-15-324218-2(3)) Harcourt Schl. Pubs.

—Trofeos Below Level: A Banda en la Barrio. 3rd ed. 2002. (SPA., Illus.). pap. 6.80 (978-0-15-323974-8(3)) Harcourt Schl. Pubs.

—Trofeos Below Level: A Veces Solo. 3rd ed. 2002. (SPA., Illus.). pap. 6.80 (978-0-15-323955-7(7)) Harcourt Schl. Pubs.

—Trofeos Below Level: Alrededor la Hoqra. 3rd ed. 2002. (SPA., Illus.). pap. 6.80 (978-0-15-323968-7(9)) Harcourt Schl. Pubs.

—Trofeos Below Level: Amigos/Dis/Llvia. 3rd ed. 2002. (SPA., Illus.). pap. 5.50 (978-0-15-323877-2(1)) Harcourt Schl. Pubs.

—Trofeos Below Level: Animales/Crias. 3rd ed. 2002. (SPA., Illus.). pap. 5.50 (978-0-15-323878-9(X)) Harcourt Schl. Pubs.

—Trofeos Below Level: Apollo: A la Luna! 3rd ed. 2002. (SPA., Illus.). pap. 6.80 (978-0-15-324235-9(3)) Harcourt Schl. Pubs.

—Trofeos Below Level: Ben el Sabio. 3rd ed. 2002. (SPA., Illus.). pap. 6.80 (978-0-15-324249-6(3)) Harcourt Schl. Pubs.

—Trofeos Below Level: Bizcochitos. 3rd ed. 2002. (SPA., Illus.). (gr. 2). pap. 6.80 (978-0-15-323960-1(3)) Harcourt Schl. Pubs.

—Trofeos Below Level: Buscar Animales. 3rd ed. 2002. (SPA., Illus.). (gr. 2). pap. 6.80 (978-0-15-323952-6(2)) Harcourt Schl. Pubs.

—Trofeos Below Level: Carrera Al... 3rd ed. 2002. (SPA., Illus.). (gr. 6). pap. 6.80 (978-0-15-324320-2(1)) Harcourt Schl. Pubs.

—Trofeos Below Level: Con las Yemas de los Dedos. 3rd ed. 2002. (SPA., Illus.). (gr. 6). pap. 6.80 (978-0-15-324334-9(1)) Harcourt Schl. Pubs.

—Trofeos Below Level: Daniel y el Dia de Bienvinida. 3rd ed. 2002. (SPA., Illus.). (gr. 6). pap. 6.80 (978-0-15-324312-7(0)) Harcourt Schl. Pubs.

—Trofeos Below Level: Dentro/Ocho. 3rd ed. 2002. (SPA., Illus.). pap. 6.80 (978-0-15-323973-1(5)) Harcourt Schl. Pubs.

—Trofeos Below Level: Dia Inilvidable. 3rd ed. 2002. (SPA., Illus.). pap. 6.80 (978-0-15-324251-9(5)) Harcourt Schl. Pubs.

—Trofeos Below Level: Dibujos/Iluviso. 3rd ed. 2002. (SPA., Illus.). pap. 6.80 (978-0-15-323970-0(0)) Harcourt Schl. Pubs.

—Trofeos Below Level: Domar la Tierra. 3rd ed. 2002. (SPA., Illus.). (gr. 5). pap. 6.80 (978-0-15-324236-6(1)) Harcourt Schl. Pubs.

—Trofeos Below Level: El Agua... 3rd ed. 2002. (SPA., Illus.). pap. 6.80 (978-0-15-324233-5(7)) Harcourt Schl. Pubs.

—Trofeos Below Level: El Camino/Marapasas. 3rd ed. 2002. (SPA., Illus.). pap. 6.80 (978-0-15-323981-6(6)) Harcourt Schl. Pubs.

—Trofeos Below Level: el Campeon De... 3rd ed. 2002. (SPA., Illus.). pap. 6.80 (978-0-15-324315-8(5)) Harcourt Schl. Pubs.

—Trofeos Below Level: El Crater. 3rd ed. 2002. (SPA., Illus.). pap. 6.80 (978-0-15-324327-1(9)) Harcourt Schl. Pubs.

—Trofeos Below Level: El Cuanto De... 3rd ed. 2002. (SPA., Illus.). pap. 6.80 (978-0-15-324238-0(8)) Harcourt Schl. Pubs.

—Trofeos Below Level: El Deseo. 3rd ed. 2002. (SPA., Illus.). pap. 6.80 (978-0-15-323956-4(5)) Harcourt Schl. Pubs.

—Trofeos Below Level: El Domador de Caballos. 3rd ed. 2002. (SPA., Illus.). pap. 6.80 (978-0-15-324336-3(8)) Harcourt Schl. Pubs.

—Trofeos Below Level: El Fantastico... 3rd ed. 2002. (SPA., Illus.). pap. 6.80 (978-0-15-324234-2(5)) Harcourt Schl. Pubs.

—Trofeos Below Level: El Hit Numero Uno. 3rd ed. 2002. (SPA., Illus.). pap. 6.80 (978-0-15-324226-7(4)) Harcourt Schl. Pubs.

—Trofeos Below Level: El Mejor... 3rd ed. 2002. (SPA., Illus.). pap. 6.80 (978-0-15-324241-0(8)) Harcourt Schl. Pubs.

—Trofeos Below Level: El Mundo Bajo Los Pies. 3rd ed. 2002. (SPA., Illus.). pap. 6.80 (978-0-15-323969-4(7)) Harcourt Schl. Pubs.

—Trofeos Below Level: El Poderoso Volcan. 3rd ed. 2002. (SPA., Illus.). pap. 6.80 (978-0-15-324337-0(6)) Harcourt Schl. Pubs.

—Trofeos Below Level: El Sueno y Las... 3rd ed. 2002. (SPA., Illus.). pap. 6.80 (978-0-15-324338-7(4)) Harcourt Schl. Pubs.

—Trofeos Below Level: El Sueno/Botresta. 3rd ed. 2002. (SPA., Illus.). pap. 6.80 (978-0-15-324243-4(4)) Harcourt Schl. Pubs.

—Trofeos Below Level: El Viaje a las Piramides. 3rd ed. 2002. (SPA., Illus.). pap. 6.80 (978-0-15-324324-0(4)) Harcourt Schl. Pubs.

—Trofeos Below Level: En el Sotano. 3rd ed. 2002. (SPA., Illus.). pap. 6.80 (978-0-15-324317-2(1)) Harcourt Schl. Pubs.

—Trofeos Below Level: En la Frontera. 3rd ed. 2002. (SPA., Illus.). pap. 6.80 (978-0-15-323962-5(X)) Harcourt Schl. Pubs.

—Trofeos Below Level: Feliz Ano Nuevo. 3rd ed. 2002. (SPA., Illus.). (gr. 2). pap. 6.80 (978-0-15-323976-2(X)) Harcourt Schl. Pubs.

—Trofeos Below Level: Fiesta de la Manzanas. 3rd ed. 2002. (SPA., Illus.). pap. 6.80 (978-0-15-323966-3(2)) Harcourt Schl. Pubs.

—Trofeos Below Level: Fuego del Hielo. 3rd ed. 2002. (SPA., Illus.). pap. 6.80 (978-0-15-324222-9(1)) Harcourt Schl. Pubs.

—Trofeos Below Level: Huracan! 3rd ed. 2002. (SPA., Illus.). pap. 6.80 (978-0-15-323980-9(8)) Harcourt Schl. Pubs.

—Trofeos Below Level: Ideas Brillantes. 3rd ed. 2002. (SPA., Illus.). pap. 6.80 (978-0-15-324329-5(5)) Harcourt Schl. Pubs.

—Trofeos Below Level: Jil/Gigante. 3rd ed. 2002. (SPA., Illus.). pap. 6.80 (978-0-15-323957-1(3)) Harcourt Schl. Pubs.

—Trofeos Below Level: La Ayuda de un Buen Amigo. 3rd ed. 2002. (SPA., Illus.). pap. 6.80 (978-0-15-324229-8(9)) Harcourt Schl. Pubs.

—Trofeos Below Level: La Carrera... 3rd ed. 2002. (SPA., Illus.). pap. 6.80 (978-0-15-324048-5(2)) Harcourt Schl. Pubs.

—Trofeos Below Level: La Chica... 3rd ed. 2002. (SPA., Illus.). pap. 6.80 (978-0-15-324242-7(6)) Harcourt Schl. Pubs.

—Trofeos Below Level: La Exploracion... 3rd ed. 2002. (SPA., Illus.). pap. 6.80 (978-0-15-324231-1(0)) Harcourt Schl. Pubs.

—Trofeos Below Level: La Fauna Urbana. 3rd ed. 2002. (SPA., Illus.). (gr. 4). pap. 6.80 (978-0-15-324144-4(6)) Harcourt Schl. Pubs.

—Trofeos Below Level: La Foca Que... 3rd ed. 2002. (SPA., Illus.). pap. 6.80 (978-0-15-324069-0(5)) Harcourt Schl. Pubs.

—Trofeos Below Level: La Gran Funcion. 3rd ed. 2002. (SPA., Illus.). pap. 6.80 (978-0-15-324223-6(X)) Harcourt Schl. Pubs.

—Trofeos Below Level: La Jordana. 3rd ed. 2002. (SPA., Illus.). pap. 6.80 (978-0-15-324065-2(2)) Harcourt Schl. Pubs.

—Trofeos Below Level: La Narradora. 3rd ed. 2002. (SPA., Illus.). pap. 6.80 (978-0-15-324059-1(8)) Harcourt Schl. Pubs.

—Trofeos Below Level: La Nina Que... 3rd ed. 2002. (SPA., Illus.). pap. 6.80 (978-0-15-324319-6(8)) Harcourt Schl. Pubs.

—Trofeos Below Level: La Parada de Autobus. 3rd ed. 2002. (SPA., Illus.). pap. 6.80 (978-0-15-324332-5(5)) Harcourt Schl. Pubs.

—Trofeos Below Level: La Pequena... 3rd ed. 2002. (SPA., Illus.). pap. 6.80 (978-0-15-324045-4(8)) Harcourt Schl. Pubs.

—Trofeos Below Level: La Pequena. 3rd ed. 2002. (SPA., Illus.). pap. 6.80 (978-0-15-324155-0(1)) Harcourt Schl. Pubs.

—Trofeos Below Level: La Polizon. 3rd ed. 2002. (SPA., Illus.). pap. 6.80 (978-0-15-324246-5(9)) Harcourt Schl. Pubs.

—Trofeos Below Level: La Selva Tropical. 3rd ed. 2002. (SPA., Illus.). pap. 6.80 (978-0-15-324141-3(1)) Harcourt Schl. Pubs.

—Trofeos Below Level: La Siesta. 3rd ed. 2002. (SPA., Illus.). pap. 5.50 (978-0-15-323882-6(8)) Harcourt Schl. Pubs.

—Trofeos Below Level: La Sorpresa. 3rd ed. 2002. (SPA., Illus.). pap. 6.80 (978-0-15-323963-2(8)) Harcourt Schl. Pubs.

—Trofeos Below Level: La Sorpresa para Sara. 3rd ed. 2002. (SPA., Illus.). pap. 6.80 (978-0-15-324053-9(9)) Harcourt Schl. Pubs.

—Trofeos Below Level: La Tierra/Burrs. 3rd ed. 2002. (SPA., Illus.). pap. 6.80 (978-0-15-324068-3(7)) Harcourt Schl. Pubs.

—Trofeos Below Level: La Verde y Malvada Carnivora. 3rd ed. 2002. (SPA., Illus.). pap. 6.80 (978-0-15-324160-4(8)) Harcourt Schl. Pubs.

—Trofeos Below Level: La Visita. 3rd ed. 2002. (SPA., Illus.). pap. 6.80 (978-0-15-324335-6(X)) Harcourt Schl. Pubs.

—Trofeos Below Level: La Voz de la Fiebre del Oro. 3rd ed. 2002. (SPA., Illus.). (gr. 4). pap. 6.80 (978-0-15-324157-4(8)) Harcourt Schl. Pubs.

—Trofeos Below Level: La Vuelta al Mundo de la Musica. 3rd ed. 2002. (SPA., Illus.). pap. 6.80 (978-0-15-324313-4(9)) Harcourt Schl. Pubs.

—Trofeos Below Level: La Vuelta/Lobo. 3rd ed. 2002. (SPA., Illus.). pap. 6.80 (978-0-15-324146-8(2)) Harcourt Schl. Pubs.

—Trofeos Below Level: Lagrimas de Cocodrilo y Otras Sorpresas. 3rd ed. 2002. (SPA., Illus.). pap. 6.80 (978-0-15-324244-1(2)) Harcourt Schl. Pubs.

—Trofeos Below Level: Las Ardillas. 3rd ed. 2002. (SPA., Illus.). pap. 6.80 (978-0-15-323954-0(9)) Harcourt Schl. Pubs.

—Trofeos Below Level: Las Mujeres y el Beisbol. 3rd ed. 2002. (SPA., Illus.). pap. 6.80 (978-0-15-324314-1(7)) Harcourt Schl. Pubs.

—Trofeos Below Level: Las Tormentas. 3rd ed. 2002. (SPA., Illus.). pap. 5.50 (978-0-15-323880-2(1)) Harcourt Schl. Pubs.

—Trofeos Below Level: Llegar/Abuelo. 3rd ed. 2002. (SPA., Illus.). pap. 6.80 (978-0-15-323978-6(6)) Harcourt Schl. Pubs.

—Trofeos Below Level: Los Comerciantes de Seda China. 3rd ed. 2002. (SPA., Illus.). pap. 6.80 (978-0-15-324323-3(6)) Harcourt Schl. Pubs.

—Trofeos Below Level: Los Efectos Especiales: Los Monstuos Hechos en Casa. 3rd ed. 2002. (SPA., Illus.). pap. 6.80 (978-0-15-324330-1(9)) Harcourt Schl. Pubs.

—Trofeos Below Level: Los Tomates... 3rd ed. 2002. (SPA., Illus.). (gr. 4). pap. 6.80 (978-0-15-324132-1(2)) Harcourt Schl. Pubs.

—Trofeos Below Level: Lose Heroes en las Llamas. 3rd ed. 2002. (SPA., Illus.). pap. 6.80 (978-0-15-324232-8(9)) Harcourt Schl. Pubs.

—Trofeos Below Level: Mantenerse. 3rd ed. 2002. (SPA., Illus.). pap. 6.80 (978-0-15-323971-7(9)) Harcourt Schl. Pubs.

—Trofeos Below Level: Mejores Intenciones. 3rd ed. 2002. (SPA., Illus.). pap. 6.80 (978-0-15-324331-8(7)) Harcourt Schl. Pubs.

—Trofeos Below Level: Mi Amigo Tino. 3rd ed. 2002. (SPA., Illus.). (J). pap. 3.50 (978-0-15-323853-6(4)) Harcourt Schl. Pubs.

—Trofeos Below Level: Mi Mayor Deseo. 3rd ed. 2002. (SPA., Illus.). (gr. 3). pap. 6.80 (978-0-15-324134-5(9)) Harcourt Schl. Pubs.

—Trofeos Below Level: Mil Palabras. 3rd ed. 2002. (SPA., Illus.). (gr. 4). pap. 6.80 (978-0-15-324133-8(0)) Harcourt Schl. Pubs.

—Trofeos Below Level: Mis Nuevos Amigos. 3rd ed. 2002. (SPA., Illus.). (gr. 5). pap. 6.80 (978-0-15-324221-2(3)) Harcourt Schl. Pubs.

—Trofeos Below Level: Naufragio. 3rd ed. 2002. (SPA., Illus.). pap. 6.80 (978-0-15-324230-4(2)) Harcourt Schl. Pubs.

—Trofeos Below Level: No Es Justo! 3rd ed. 2002. (SPA., Illus.). (gr. 6). pap. 6.80 (978-0-15-324316-5(3)) Harcourt Schl. Pubs.

—Trofeos Below Level: Nunca Es... 3rd ed. 2002. (SPA., Illus.). pap. 6.80 (978-0-15-323967-0(0)) Harcourt Schl. Pubs.

—Trofeos Below Level: Oxodo/Kansas. 3rd ed. 2002. (SPA., Illus.). pap. 6.80 (978-0-15-324158-1(6)) Harcourt Schl. Pubs.

—Trofeos Below Level: Parque de Babo. 3rd ed. 2002. (SPA., Illus.). pap. 5.50 (978-0-15-323883-3(6)) Harcourt Schl. Pubs.

—Trofeos Below Level: Paul Bunyan. 3rd ed. 2002. (SPA., Illus.). pap. 6.80 (978-0-15-324061-4(X)) Harcourt Schl. Pubs.

—Trofeos Below Level: Pepe Encuentra. 3rd ed. 2002. (SPA., Illus.). pap. 6.80 (978-0-15-323975-5(1)) Harcourt Schl. Pubs.

—Trofeos Below Level: Pequeno Jose. 3rd ed. 2002. (SPA., Illus.). pap. 6.80 (978-0-15-324138-3(1)) Harcourt Schl. Pubs.

—Trofeos Below Level: Pericles y la Primera Democracia. 3rd ed. 2002. (SPA., Illus.). pap. 6.80 (978-0-15-324326-4(0)) Harcourt Schl. Pubs.

—Trofeos Below Level: Personajes... 3rd ed. 2002. (SPA., Illus.). pap. 6.80 (978-0-15-324227-4(2)) Harcourt Schl. Pubs.

—Trofeos Below Level: Picnic en la Parque. 3rd ed. 2002. (SPA., Illus.). pap. 6.80 (978-0-15-323965-6(4)) Harcourt Schl. Pubs.

—Trofeos Below Level: Planeta H2O. 3rd ed. 2002. (SPA., Illus.). (gr. 6). pap. 6.80 (978-0-15-324341-7(4)) Harcourt Schl. Pubs.

—Trofeos Below Level: Plantar/Jardin. 3rd ed. 2002. (SPA., Illus.). pap. 6.80 (978-0-15-324140-6(3)) Harcourt Schl. Pubs.

—Trofeos Below Level: Pony Express. 3rd ed. 2002. (SPA., Illus.). pap. 6.80 (978-0-15-324063-8(6)) Harcourt Schl. Pubs.

—Trofeos Below Level: Por una Cancion. 3rd ed. 2002. (SPA., Illus.). pap. 6.80 (978-0-15-324328-8(7)) Harcourt Schl. Pubs.

—Trofeos Below Level: Que Es el Dinro. 3rd ed. 2002. (SPA., Illus.). pap. 6.80 (978-0-15-324066-9(0)) Harcourt Schl. Pubs.

—Trofeos Below Level: Que Hora Es? 3rd ed. 2002. (SPA., Illus.). pap. 6.80 (978-0-15-323953-3(0)) Harcourt Schl. Pubs.

—Trofeos Below Level: Que Robots... 3rd ed. 2002. (SPA., Illus.). pap. 6.80 (978-0-15-324245-8(0)) Harcourt Schl. Pubs.

—Trofeos Below Level: Querida Abuela. 3rd ed. 2002. (SPA., Illus.). pap. 6.80 (978-0-15-324224-3(8)) Harcourt Schl. Pubs.

—Trofeos Below Level: Quien Es Necsita. 3rd ed. 2002. (SPA., Illus.). pap. 6.80 (978-0-15-324055-3(5)) Harcourt Schl. Pubs.

—Trofeos Below Level: Quien Ha Sido? 3rd ed. 2002. (SPA., Illus.). pap. 5.50 (978-0-15-323879-6(8)) Harcourt Schl. Pubs.

—Trofeos Below Level: Regreso al Pasado. 3rd ed. 2002. (SPA., Illus.). pap. 6.80 (978-0-15-324325-7(2)) Harcourt Schl. Pubs.

—Trofeos Below Level: Ricts/Tres Osos. 3rd ed. 2002. (SPA., Illus.). pap. 5.50 (978-0-15-323881-9(X)) Harcourt Schl. Pubs.

—Trofeos Below Level: Rosa/Pajarito. 3rd ed. 2002. (SPA., Illus.). pap. 6.80 (978-0-15-323972-4(7)) Harcourt Schl. Pubs.

—Trofeos Below Level: Sera Verdad... 3rd ed. 2002. (SPA., Illus.). pap. 6.80 (978-0-15-324237-3(X)) Harcourt Schl. Pubs.

—Trofeos Below Level: Siempre con Estilo. 3rd ed. 2002. (SPA., Illus.). pap. 6.80 (978-0-15-324239-7(6)) Harcourt Schl. Pubs.

—Trofeos Below Level: Socorro! 3rd ed. 2002. (SPA., Illus.). pap. 6.80 (978-0-15-323958-8(1)) Harcourt Schl. Pubs.

—Trofeos Below Level: Susan B. Anthony. 3rd ed. 2002. (SPA., Illus.). pap. 6.80 (978-0-15-324247-2(7)) Harcourt Schl. Pubs.

—Trofeos Below Level: Tara Lipinski. 3rd ed. 2002. (SPA., Illus.). pap. 6.80 (978-0-15-324046-1(6)) Harcourt Schl. Pubs.

—Trofeos Below Level: Terremoto! 3rd ed. 2002. (SPA., Illus.). pap. 6.80 (978-0-15-324318-9(X)) Harcourt Schl. Pubs.

—Trofeos Below Level: Tesoros de Vietnam. 3rd ed. 2002. (SPA., Illus.). (gr. 6). pap. 6.80 (978-0-15-324333-2(3)) Harcourt Schl. Pubs.

—Trofeos Below Level: Tiempo de Paz. 3rd ed. 2002. (SPA., Illus.). pap. 6.80 (978-0-15-324145-1(4)) Harcourt Schl. Pubs.

—Trofeos Below Level: Tierras Sin Agua. 3rd ed. 2002. (SPA., Illus.). pap. 6.80 (978-0-15-324154-3(3)) Harcourt Schl. Pubs.

—Trofeos Below Level: Tomar la Decision. 3rd ed. 2002. (SPA., Illus.). pap. 6.80 (978-0-15-324054-6(7)) Harcourt Schl. Pubs.

—Trofeos Below Level: Trabajor en el Aeroporto. 3rd ed. 2002. (SPA., Illus.). pap. 6.80 (978-0-15-323977-9(8)) Harcourt Schl. Pubs.

—Trofeos Below Level: Tres Fabulas. 3rd ed. 2002. (SPA., Illus.). (gr. 3). pap. 6.80 (978-0-15-324056-0(3)) Harcourt Schl. Pubs.

—Trofeos Below Level: Tres Orbitas. 3rd ed. 2002. (SPA., Illus.). pap. 6.80 (978-0-15-324339-4(2)) Harcourt Schl. Pubs.

—Trofeos Below Level: Tutora Virtual. 3rd ed. 2002. (SPA., Illus.). pap. 6.80 (978-0-15-324340-0(6)) Harcourt Schl. Pubs.

—Trofeos Below Level: Un Diario/Fibre. 3rd ed. 2002. (SPA., Illus.). pap. 6.80 (978-0-15-324064-5(4)) Harcourt Schl. Pubs.

—Trofeos Below Level: Un Viaje. 3rd ed. 2002. (SPA., Illus.). pap. 6.80 (978-0-15-323979-3(4)) Harcourt Schl. Pubs.

—Trofeos Below Level: Una Aventura. 3rd ed. 2002. (SPA., Illus.). pap. 6.80 (978-0-15-324057-7(1)) Harcourt Schl. Pubs.

—Trofeos Below Level: Una Aventura... 3rd ed. 2002. (SPA., Illus.). pap. 6.80 (978-0-15-324228-1(0)) Harcourt Schl. Pubs.

—Trofeos Below Level: Una Entrevista. 3rd ed. 2002. (SPA., Illus.). pap. 6.80 (978-0-15-324150-5(0)) Harcourt Schl. Pubs.

—Trofeos Below Level: Unas Vaciones... 3rd ed. 2002. (SPA., Illus.). pap. 6.80 (978-0-15-324250-2(7)) Harcourt Schl. Pubs.

—Trofeos Below Level: Visita a San Francisco. 3rd ed. 2002. (SPA., Illus.). pap. 6.80 (978-0-15-324044-7(X)) Harcourt Schl. Pubs.

—Trofeos Below Level: Vuela, Catarita. 3rd ed. 2002. (SPA., Illus.). pap. 6.80 (978-0-15-323959-5(X)) Harcourt Schl. Pubs.

—Trofeos Below Level: Ya Soy Estado... 3rd ed. 2002. (SPA., Illus.). pap. 6.80 (978-0-15-324153-6(5)) Harcourt Schl. Pubs.

—Trofeos Below Level: Yo Deseo... 3rd ed. 2002. (SPA., Illus.). pap. 6.80 (978-0-15-324052-2(0)) Harcourt Schl. Pubs.

—Trofeos Below Level: Zapatillas/Pinata. 3rd ed. 2002. (SPA., Illus.). pap. 6.80 (978-0-15-324240-3(X)) Harcourt Schl. Pubs.

—Trofeos Below Level: Zona de Inundacion. 3rd ed. 2002. (SPA., Illus.). pap. 6.80 (978-0-15-324321-9(X)) Harcourt Schl. Pubs.

—Trofeos Ib Kevek: Fuego en la Pradera. 3rd ed. 2002. (SPA., Illus.). pap. 6.80 (978-0-15-324263-2(9)) Harcourt Schl. Pubs.

—Trofeos On Level: 500 Veses Isabel. 3rd ed. 2002. (SPA., Illus.). pap. 6.80 (978-0-15-323983-0(2)) Harcourt Schl. Pubs.

—Trofeos On Level: A Dormir! 3rd ed. 2002. (SPA., Illus.). pap. 6.80 (978-0-15-323916-8(6)) Harcourt Schl. Pubs.

—Trofeos On Level: A Recolectar. 3rd ed. 2002. (SPA., Illus.). pap. 6.80 (978-0-15-324362-2(7)) Harcourt Schl. Pubs.

—Trofeos On Level: Adios al Campo! Hola a la Ciudad! 3rd ed. 2002. (SPA., Illus.). (gr. 5). pap. 6.80 (978-0-15-324252-6(3)) Harcourt Schl. Pubs.

—Trofeos On Level: Animales Que Nos Socorren. 3rd ed. 2002. (SPA., Illus.). pap. 6.80 (978-0-15-324260-1(4)) Harcourt Schl. Pubs.

—Trofeos On Level: Babo en el Zoo. 3rd ed. 2002. (SPA., Illus.). pap. 6.80 (978-0-15-323917-5(4)) Harcourt Schl. Pubs.

—Trofeos On Level: Bello/Renacuajo. 3rd ed. 2002. (SPA., Illus.). pap. 5.50 (978-0-15-323893-2(3)) Harcourt Schl. Pubs.

—Trofeos On Level: Como Cultivar. 3rd ed. 2002. (SPA., Illus.). pap. 6.80 (978-0-15-323993-9(X)) Harcourt Schl. Pubs.

—Trofeos On Level: Como se Forman las Montanas? 3rd ed. 2002. (SPA., Illus.). (gr. 6). pap. 6.80 (978-0-15-324357-8(0)) Harcourt Schl. Pubs.

—Trofeos On Level: Como Ser Popular. 3rd ed. 2002. (SPA., Illus.). pap. 6.80 (978-0-15-324346-2(5)) Harcourt Schl. Pubs.

—Trofeos On Level: Como/Inventaron. 3rd ed. 2002. (SPA., Illus.). pap. 6.80 (978-0-15-324008-9(3)) Harcourt Schl. Pubs.

—Trofeos On Level: Con Carino... 3rd ed. 2002. (SPA., Illus.). pap. 6.80 (978-0-15-324281-6(7)) Harcourt Schl. Pubs.

—Trofeos On Level: Cuadernos de Practica. 3rd ed. 2002. (Trofeos Ser.). (SPA., Illus.). (gr. 4 up). pap. 15.90 (978-0-15-323809-3(7)); (gr. 5 up). pap. 15.90 (978-0-15-323813-0(5)); (gr. 6 up). pap. 15.90 (978-0-15-

323817-8(8)); Vol. 1. (gr. 1-2). pap. 9.60 (978-0-15-323797-3(X)); Vol. 1. (gr. 1-3). pap. 9.60 (978-0-15-323803-1(8)); Vol. 1. (gr. 1 up). pap. 11.50 (978-0-15-323780-5(5)); Vol. 2. (gr. 1 up). pap. 11.50 (978-0-15-323781-2(3)); Vol. 2. (gr. 2-3). pap. 9.60 (978-0-15-323804-8(6)); Vol. 2. (gr. 2 up). pap. 9.60 (978-0-15-323798-0(8)) Harcourt Schl. Pubs.

—Trofeos On Level: Cuando Baja la Marea. 3rd ed. 2002. (SPA., Illus.). pap. 6.80 (978-0-15-324360-8(0)) Harcourt Schl. Pubs.

—Trofeos On Level: Del Este al Oeste Norteamericano: La Historia de John Wesley Powell. 3rd ed. 2002. (SPA., Illus.). pap. 6.80 (978-0-15-324366-0(X)) Harcourt Schl. Pubs.

—Trofeos On Level: Del Sueno/Hombre. 3rd ed. 2002. (SPA., Illus.). pap. 6.80 (978-0-15-324273-1(6)) Harcourt Schl. Pubs.

—Trofeos On Level: Desvan y Beatriz. 3rd ed. 2002. (SPA., Illus.). pap. 6.80 (978-0-15-323908-3(5)) Harcourt Schl. Pubs.

—Trofeos On Level: Diez Osos. 3rd ed. 2002. (SPA., Illus.). pap. 6.80 (978-0-15-323912-0(3)) Harcourt Schl. Pubs.

—Trofeos On Level: Donde Esta La... 3rd ed. 2002. (SPA., Illus.). pap. 6.80 (978-0-15-323997-7(2)) Harcourt Schl. Pubs.

—Trofeos On Level: Donde Viven de Animales? 3rd ed. 2002. (SPA., Illus.). pap. 5.50 (978-0-15-323904-5(2)) Harcourt Schl. Pubs.

—Trofeos On Level: El Atlas de Oro. 3rd ed. 2002. (SPA., Illus.). pap. 6.80 (978-0-15-324367-7(8)) Harcourt Schl. Pubs.

—Trofeos On Level: El Bote. 3rd ed. 2002. (SPA., Illus.). (J). pap. 3.50 (978-0-15-323887-1(9)) Harcourt Schl. Pubs.

—Trofeos On Level: El Caiman/Justin. 3rd ed. 2002. (SPA., Illus.). (gr. 2). pap. 6.80 (978-0-15-323999-1(9)) Harcourt Schl. Pubs.

—Trofeos On Level: El Camino de Oregon: Diario de Viaje de Lucy Bell. 3rd ed. 2002. (SPA., Illus.). pap. 6.80 (978-0-15-324280-9(9)) Harcourt Schl. Pubs.

—Trofeos On Level: El Caso de Derrick y los Invasores de la Mente. 3rd ed. 2002. (SPA., Illus.). pap. 6.80 (978-0-15-324266-3(3)) Harcourt Schl. Pubs.

—Trofeos On Level: El Caso de Estudiante Perdido. 3rd ed. 2002. (SPA., Illus.). pap. 6.80 (978-0-15-324371-4(6)) Harcourt Schl. Pubs.

—Trofeos On Level: El Cruce de Rio: Un Cuento de Patriotas. 3rd ed. 2002. (SPA., Illus.). (gr. 5). pap. 6.80 (978-0-15-324256-4(6)) Harcourt Schl. Pubs.

—Trofeos On Level: El Diario de Josie. 3rd ed. 2002. (SPA., Illus.). pap. 6.80 (978-0-15-324363-9(5)) Harcourt Schl. Pubs.

—Trofeos On Level: El Equipo... 3rd ed. 2002. (SPA., Illus.). pap. 6.80 (978-0-15-324257-1(4)) Harcourt Schl. Pubs.

—Trofeos On Level: El Gran Debate Sobre Franklin. 3rd ed. 2002. (SPA., Illus.). pap. 6.80 (978-0-15-324279-3(5)) Harcourt Schl. Pubs.

—Trofeos On Level: El Guardian. 3rd ed. 2002. (SPA., Illus.). pap. 6.80 (978-0-15-324347-9(3)) Harcourt Schl. Pubs.

—Trofeos On Level: El Mystrio de Sam. 3rd ed. 2002. (SPA., Illus.). pap. 6.80 (978-0-15-324002-7(4)) Harcourt Schl. Pubs.

—Trofeos On Level: El Perro Es Sombra. 3rd ed. 2002. (SPA., Illus.). pap. 6.80 (978-0-15-323985-4(9)) Harcourt Schl. Pubs.

—Trofeos On Level: El Rey del Feria. 3rd ed. 2002. (SPA., Illus.). pap. 6.80 (978-0-15-323996-0(4)) Harcourt Schl. Pubs.

—Trofeos On Level: El Secreto de la Seda de la Antigua China. 3rd ed. 2002. (SPA., Illus.). pap. 6.80 (978-0-15-324353-0(8)) Harcourt Schl. Pubs.

—Trofeos On Level: El Sombrero Rojo y Azul. 3rd ed. 2002. (SPA., Illus.). (gr. 5). pap. 6.80 (978-0-15-324258-8(2)) Harcourt Schl. Pubs.

—Trofeos On Level: El Sotano. 3rd ed. 2002. (SPA., Illus.). pap. 6.80 (978-0-15-323906-9(9)) Harcourt Schl. Pubs.

—Trofeos On Level: El Trabajo/Chicos. 3rd ed. 2002. (SPA., Illus.). pap. 6.80 (978-0-15-323991-5(3)) Harcourt Schl. Pubs.

—Trofeos On Level: El Trofeo. 3rd ed. 2002. (SPA., Illus.). pap. 6.80 (978-0-15-324344-8(9)) Harcourt Schl. Pubs.

—Trofeos On Level: En las Profundidades: Buceemos Con la Dra. Sylvia Earle. 3rd ed. 2002. (SPA., Illus.). pap. 6.80 (978-0-15-324264-9(7)) Harcourt Schl. Pubs.

—Trofeos On Level: Esperame, Capitan. 3rd ed. 2002. (SPA., Illus.). pap. 6.80 (978-0-15-324010-2(5)) Harcourt Schl. Pubs.

—Trofeos On Level: Estimado Amigo. 3rd ed. 2002. (SPA., Illus.). pap. 6.80 (978-0-15-324003-4(2)) Harcourt Schl. Pubs.

—Trofeos On Level: Felicia Toca el Chelo. 3rd ed. 2002. (SPA., Illus.). pap. 6.80 (978-0-15-324343-1(0)) Harcourt Schl. Pubs.

—Trofeos On Level: Frutas Comicas. 3rd ed. 2002. (SPA., Illus.). pap. 6.80 (978-0-15-323995-3(6)) Harcourt Schl. Pubs.

—Trofeos On Level: Hagamos un Pastel. 3rd ed. 2002. (SPA., Illus.). pap. 6.80 (978-0-15-323988-5(3)) Harcourt Schl. Pubs.

—Trofeos On Level: Hoy Nadare! 3rd ed. 2002. (SPA., Illus.). pap. 5.50 (978-0-15-323894-9(1)) Harcourt Schl. Pubs.

—Trofeos On Level: La Arana Te Vio. 3rd ed. 2002. (SPA., Illus.). pap. 6.80 (978-0-15-324348-6(1)) Harcourt Schl. Pubs.

—Trofeos On Level: La Atleta de Oro. 3rd ed. 2002. (SPA., Illus.). pap. 6.80 (978-0-15-324164-2(0)) Harcourt Schl. Pubs.

—Trofeos On Level: La Bailarina Hace un Trato. 3rd ed. 2002. (SPA., Illus.). (gr. 6). pap. 6.80 (978-0-15-324342-4(2)) Harcourt Schl. Pubs.

—Trofeos On Level: La Camara... 3rd ed. 2002. (SPA., Illus.). pap. 6.80 (978-0-15-324270-0(1)) Harcourt Schl. Pubs.

—Trofeos On Level: La Diversion... 3rd ed. 2002. (SPA., Illus.). pap. 6.80 (978-0-15-324267-0(1)) Harcourt Schl. Pubs.

—Trofeos On Level: La Escuela... 3rd ed. 2002. (SPA., Illus.). (gr. 5). pap. 6.80 (978-0-15-324276-2(0)) Harcourt Schl. Pubs.

—Trofeos On Level: La Panadera y Olga. 3rd ed. 2002. (SPA., Illus.). pap. 6.80 (978-0-15-324185-7(3)) Harcourt Schl. Pubs.

—Trofeos On Level: La Plaza Ghirardelli. 3rd ed. 2002. (SPA., Illus.). pap. 6.80 (978-0-15-324173-4(X)) Harcourt Schl. Pubs.

—Trofeos On Level: La Publicidad en Accion. 3rd ed. 2002. (SPA., Illus.). pap. 6.80 (978-0-15-324272-4(8)) Harcourt Schl. Pubs.

—Trofeos On Level: La Vereda. 3rd ed. 2002. (SPA., Illus.). pap. 5.50 (978-0-15-323891-8(7)) Harcourt Schl. Pubs.

—Trofeos On Level: La Vida de un Carnerotillo. 3rd ed. 2002. (SPA., Illus.). pap. 6.80 (978-0-15-324175-8(6)) Harcourt Schl. Pubs.

—Trofeos On Level: La Vida en el Espacio. 3rd ed. 2002. (SPA., Illus.). pap. 6.80 (978-0-15-324369-1(4)) Harcourt Schl. Pubs.

—Trofeos On Level: La Vida/Vaquero. 3rd ed. 2002. (SPA., Illus.). pap. 6.80 (978-0-15-324005-8(9)) Harcourt Schl. Pubs.

—Trofeos On Level: La Vuelta/Mundo. 3rd ed. 2002. (SPA., Illus.). pap. 6.80 (978-0-15-324007-2(5)) Harcourt Schl. Pubs.

—Trofeos On Level: Las Cuerdas Que Nos Unen. 3rd ed. 2002. (SPA., Illus.). pap. 6.80 (978-0-15-324254-0(X)) Harcourt Schl. Pubs.

—Trofeos On Level: Las Mascotas. 3rd ed. 2002. (SPA., Illus.). pap. 5.50 (978-0-15-323890-1(9)) Harcourt Schl. Pubs.

—Trofeos On Level: Las Pruebas de Resistencia. 3rd ed. 2002. (SPA., Illus.). pap. 6.80 (978-0-15-324358-5(9)) Harcourt Schl. Pubs.

—Trofeos On Level: Lo Que Juegan. 3rd ed. 2002. (SPA., Illus.). (gr. 2). pap. 6.80 (978-0-15-323989-2(1)) Harcourt Schl. Pubs.

—Trofeos On Level: Los Animales del Polo Sur. 3rd ed. 2002. (SPA., Illus.). pap. 6.80 (978-0-15-324350-9(3)) Harcourt Schl. Pubs.

—Trofeos On Level: Los Cocodrilos de Everglades Cove. 3rd ed. 2002. (SPA., Illus.). pap. 6.80 (978-0-15-324262-5(0)) Harcourt Schl. Pubs.

—Trofeos On Level: Los Huevos. 3rd ed. 2002. (SPA., Illus.). pap. 6.80 (978-0-15-324001-0(6)) Harcourt Schl. Pubs.

—Trofeos On Level: Los Ninos. 3rd ed. 2002. (SPA., Illus.). pap. 6.80 (978-0-15-324162-8(4)) Harcourt Schl. Pubs.

—Trofeos On Level: Los Recuerdos de un Perro. 3rd ed. 2002. (SPA., Illus.). pap. 6.80 (978-0-15-324349-3(X)) Harcourt Schl. Pubs.

—Trofeos On Level: Los Viajes/Papa. 3rd ed. 2002. (SPA., Illus.). pap. 6.80 (978-0-15-324009-6(1)) Harcourt Schl. Pubs.

—Trofeos On Level: Luis Flecha y los Diana. 3rd ed. 2002. (SPA., Illus.). pap. 6.80 (978-0-15-324253-3(1)) Harcourt Schl. Pubs.

—Trofeos On Level: Mas Alla/Huerto. 3rd ed. 2002. (SPA., Illus.). pap. 6.80 (978-0-15-323911-3(5)) Harcourt Schl. Pubs.

—Trofeos On Level: Mejor Que el Oro. 3rd ed. 2002. (SPA., Illus.). pap. 6.80 (978-0-15-324078-2(4)) Harcourt Schl. Pubs.

—Trofeos On Level: Mi Nabo Enorme. 3rd ed. 2002. (SPA., Illus.). pap. 6.80 (978-0-15-323987-8(5)) Harcourt Schl. Pubs.

—Trofeos On Level: Mi Viaje a la Edad de Piedra. 3rd ed. 2002. (SPA., Illus.). pap. 6.80 (978-0-15-324352-3(X)) Harcourt Schl. Pubs.

—Trofeos On Level: Mi Vida en un Libra Ilustrado. 3rd ed. 2002. (SPA., Illus.). pap. 6.80 (978-0-15-324269-4(8)) Harcourt Schl. Pubs.

—Trofeos On Level: Mi Visita... 3rd ed. 2002. (SPA., Illus.). pap. 6.80 (978-0-15-324006-5(7)) Harcourt Schl. Pubs.

—Trofeos On Level: Mischa Aprende Ingles. 3rd ed. 2002. (SPA., Illus.). (gr. 3). pap. 6.80 (978-0-15-324073-7(3)) Harcourt Schl. Pubs.

—Trofeos On Level: Momo. 3rd ed. 2002. (SPA., Illus.). (J). (gr. 1). pap. 3.50 (978-0-15-323884-0(4)) Harcourt Schl. Pubs.

—Trofeos On Level: Ninas/Rescates. 3rd ed. 2002. (SPA., Illus.). pap. 6.80 (978-0-15-324359-2(7)) Harcourt Schl. Pubs.

—Trofeos On Level: No Lleva Pilas. 3rd ed. 2002. (SPA., Illus.). pap. 6.80 (978-0-15-324177-2(2)) Harcourt Schl. Pubs.

—Trofeos On Level: No Somos Sucios! 3rd ed. 2002. (SPA., Illus.). pap. 6.80 (978-0-15-323915-1(8)) Harcourt Schl. Pubs.

—Trofeos On Level: Nuestro Escondite Favorito. 3rd ed. 2002. (SPA., Illus.). pap. 6.80 (978-0-15-324345-5(7)) Harcourt Schl. Pubs.

—Trofeos On Level: Operacion Tornado. 3rd ed. 2002. (SPA., Illus.). pap. 6.80 (978-0-15-324361-5(9)) Harcourt Schl. Pubs.

—Trofeos On Level: Pajaro/Abrol. 3rd ed. 2002. (SPA., Illus.). pap. 6.80 (978-0-15-323910-6(7)) Harcourt Schl. Pubs.

—Trofeos On Level: Pajaro/Ciudad. 3rd ed. 2002. (SPA., Illus.). (gr. 1). pap. 5.50 (978-0-15-323903-8(4)) Harcourt Schl. Pubs.

—Trofeos On Level: Palomitas/Maiz. 3rd ed. 2002. (SPA., Illus.). (J). pap. 3.50 (978-0-15-323889-5(5)) Harcourt Schl. Pubs.

—Trofeos On Level: Paul Bunyan. 3rd ed. 2002. (SPA., Illus.). pap. 6.80 (978-0-15-323992-2(1)) Harcourt Schl. Pubs.

—Trofeos On Level: Por Que las Hajas. 3rd ed. 2002. (SPA., Illus.). pap. 6.80 (978-0-15-323984-7(0)) Harcourt Schl. Pubs.

—Trofeos On Level: Por Que Tomas Leche Pasteurizada? Tu Guia de Eponimos. 3rd ed. 2002. (SPA., Illus.). pap. 6.80 (978-0-15-324275-5(2)) Harcourt Schl. Pubs.

—Trofeos On Level: Por Si Acaso. 3rd ed. 2002. (SPA., Illus.). (gr. 2). pap. 6.80 (978-0-15-323982-3(4)) Harcourt Schl. Pubs.

—Trofeos On Level: Principe Eduardo. 3rd ed. 2002. (SPA., Illus.). pap. 6.80 (978-0-15-324365-3(1)) Harcourt Schl. Pubs.

—Trofeos On Level: Proyecto Preferdo. 3rd ed. 2002. (SPA., Illus.). pap. 6.80 (978-0-15-324079-9(2)) Harcourt Schl. Pubs.

—Trofeos On Level: Que Come? 3rd ed. 2002. (SPA., Illus.). (J). pap. 3.50 (978-0-15-323886-4(0)) Harcourt Schl. Pubs.

—Trofeos On Level: Que Es Eso? 3rd ed. 2002. (SPA., Illus.). pap. 5.50 (978-0-15-323892-5(5)) Harcourt Schl. Pubs.

—Trofeos On Level: Que Hay de Comer, Khufu? 3rd ed. 2002. (SPA., Illus.). pap. 6.80 (978-0-15-324354-7(6)) Harcourt Schl. Pubs.

—Trofeos On Level: Que Mimoso! 3rd ed. 2002. (SPA., Illus.). (J). pap. 3.50 (978-0-15-323885-7(2)) Harcourt Schl. Pubs.

—Trofeos On Level: Que Sorpresa! 3rd ed. 2002. (SPA., Illus.). (J). pap. 3.50 (978-0-15-323888-8(7)) Harcourt Schl. Pubs.

—Trofeos On Level: Reconstruir el Pasado. 3rd ed. 2002. (SPA., Illus.). pap. 6.80 (978-0-15-324355-4(4)) Harcourt Schl. Pubs.

—Trofeos On Level: Rescate en Fox Creek. 3rd ed. 2002. (SPA., Illus.). pap. 6.80 (978-0-15-324261-8(2)) Harcourt Schl. Pubs.

—Trofeos On Level: Rios de Baile. 3rd ed. 2002. (SPA., Illus.). pap. 6.80 (978-0-15-324271-7(X)) Harcourt Schl. Pubs.

—Trofeos On Level: Saludos de la Antigua Grecia. 3rd ed. 2002. (SPA., Illus.). pap. 6.80 (978-0-15-324356-1(2)) Harcourt Schl. Pubs.

—Trofeos On Level: Sigue/Repicar. 3rd ed. 2002. (SPA., Illus.). pap. 6.80 (978-0-15-324004-1(0)) Harcourt Schl. Pubs.

—Trofeos On Level: Silencio Detras de Escenario! 3rd ed. 2002. (SPA., Illus.). pap. 6.80 (978-0-15-324268-7(X)) Harcourt Schl. Pubs.

—Trofeos On Level: Somos Detectives. 3rd ed. 2002. (SPA., Illus.). pap. 6.80 (978-0-15-323913-7(1)) Harcourt Schl. Pubs.

—Trofeos On Level: Soy Estadounidense. 3rd ed. 2002. (SPA., Illus.). pap. 6.80 (978-0-15-324182-6(9)) Harcourt Schl. Pubs.

—Trofeos On Level: Sr. Muy Poderoso. 3rd ed. 2002. (SPA., Illus.). pap. 6.80 (978-0-15-324351-6(1)) Harcourt Schl. Pubs.

—Trofeos On Level: Teddy Se Toma. 3rd ed. 2002. (SPA., Illus.). pap. 6.80 (978-0-15-323998-4(0)) Harcourt Schl. Pubs.

—Trofeos On Level: Tisquantum y los Colonos. 3rd ed. 2002. (SPA., Illus.). pap. 6.80 (978-0-15-324277-9(9)) Harcourt Schl. Pubs.

—Trofeos On Level: Todo Saldra Bien. 3rd ed. 2002. (SPA., Illus.). pap. 6.80 (978-0-15-324172-7(1)) Harcourt Schl. Pubs.

—Trofeos On Level: Tortuga en Casa. 3rd ed. 2002. (SPA., Illus.). pap. 6.80 (978-0-15-324077-5(6)) Harcourt Schl. Pubs.

—Trofeos On Level: Tres Historias de Paplotes. 3rd ed. 2002. (SPA., Illus.). pap. 6.80 (978-0-15-324167-3(5)) Harcourt Schl. Pubs.

—Trofeos On Level: Tu Si Pedes, Kerry. 3rd ed. 2002. (SPA., Illus.). pap. 6.80 (978-0-15-323986-1(7)) Harcourt Schl. Pubs.

—Trofeos On Level: Un Arbol/Ano. 3rd ed. 2002. (SPA., Illus.). pap. 6.80 (978-0-15-323994-6(8)) Harcourt Schl. Pubs.

—Trofeos On Level: Un Hogar Digno del President. 3rd ed. 2002. (SPA., Illus.). pap. 6.80 (978-0-15-324278-6(7)) Harcourt Schl. Pubs.

—Trofeos On Level: Un Jardin... 3rd ed. 2002. (SPA., Illus.). (gr. 4). pap. 6.80 (978-0-15-324629-6(4)) Harcourt Schl. Pubs.

—Trofeos On Level: Un Lagarto Como Mascota. 3rd ed. 2002. (SPA., Illus.). (gr. 4). pap. 6.80 (978-0-15-324184-0(5)) Harcourt Schl. Pubs.

—Trofeos On Level: Un Mensaje en el Tiempo Cibernetico. 3rd ed. 2002. (SPA., Illus.). pap. 6.80 (978-0-15-324370-7(8)) Harcourt Schl. Pubs.

—Trofeos On Level: Un Viaje al Observatorio. 3rd ed. 2002. (SPA., Illus.). pap. 6.80 (978-0-15-324265-6(5)) Harcourt Schl. Pubs.

—Trofeos On Level: Un Viaje por Alaska. 3rd ed. 2002. (SPA., Illus.). (gr. 5). pap. 6.80 (978-0-15-324259-5(0)) Harcourt Schl. Pubs.

—Trofeos On Level: Una Adivinanza al Dia. 3rd ed. 2002. (SPA., Illus.). pap. 6.80 (978-0-15-324180-2(2)) Harcourt Schl. Pubs.

—Trofeos On Level: Una Buena Combinacion. 3rd ed. 2002. (SPA., Illus.). pap. 6.80 (978-0-15-324163-5(2)) Harcourt Schl. Pubs.

—Trofeos On Level: Una Carrera en la Oscuridad: Una Obra para Dos Personajes. 3rd ed. 2002. (SPA., Illus.). pap. 6.80 (978-0-15-324364-6(3)) Harcourt Schl. Pubs.

—Trofeos On Level: Una Conversacion. 3rd ed. 2002. (SPA., Illus.). pap. 6.80 (978-0-15-324368-4(6)) Harcourt Schl. Pubs.

—Trofeos On Level: Una Pizca/Acquillo. 3rd ed. 2002. (SPA., Illus.). pap. 6.80 (978-0-15-323990-8(5)) Harcourt Schl. Pubs.

—Trofeos On Level: Y Que Si... 3rd ed. 2002. (SPA., Illus.). pap. 6.80 (978-0-15-324000-3(8)) Harcourt Schl. Pubs.

—Trofeos Collection, Grade 6. 3rd ed. 2002. (SPA.). tchr. ed. 497.00 (978-0-15-335082-5(2)) Harcourt Schl. Pubs.

—Trofeos, Grade 1: Apoyo Adicional Hojas Reproducibles. 3rd ed. 2002. (Trofeos Ser.). (SPA.). (gr. 1 up). pap. 58.60 (978-0-15-323782-9(1)) Harcourt Schl. Pubs.

—Trofeos, Grade 1: Cuadernos de Ortografia. 3rd ed. 2002. (Trofeos Ser.). (SPA.). (gr. 1 up). pap., tchr. ed. 16.90 (978-0-15-323844-4(5)) Harcourt Schl. Pubs.

—Trofeos, Grade 1: Manuales Del Lenguaje. 3rd ed. 2002. (Trofeos Ser.). (SPA.). (gr. 1 up). pap., tchr. ed. 18.60 (978-0-15-323832-1(1)) Harcourt Schl. Pubs.

—Trofeos, Grade 1 On Level: Cuadernos de Practica. 3rd ed. 2002. (Trofeos Ser.). (SPA.). (gr. 1 up). Vol. 1. pap., tchr. ed. 19.20 (978-0-15-323783-6(X)); Vol. 2. pap., tchr. ed. 19.20 (978-0-15-323784-3(8)) Harcourt Schl. Pubs.

—Trofeos, Grade 2: Apoyo Adicional Hojas Reproducibles. 3rd ed. 2002. (Trofeos Ser.). (SPA.). (gr. 2 up). pap. 58.60 (978-0-15-323799-7(6)) Harcourt Schl. Pubs.

—Trofeos, Grade 2: Manuales Del Lenguaje. 3rd ed. 2002. (Trofeos Ser.). (SPA.). (gr. 2 up). pap., tchr. ed. 9.10 (978-0-15-323833-8(X)) Harcourt Schl. Pubs.

—Trofeos, Grade 2 On Level: Cuadernos de Practica. 3rd ed. 2002. (Trofeos Ser.). (SPA., Vol. 1. Illus.). (gr. 1-2). pap., tchr. ed. 17.00 (978-0-15-323800-0(3)); Vol. 2. (gr. 2 up). pap., tchr. ed. 17.00 (978-0-15-323801-7(1)) Harcourt Schl. Pubs.

—Trofeos, Grade 3: Cuadernos de Ortografia. 3rd ed. 2002. (Trofeos Ser.). (SPA.). (gr. 3 up). pap., tchr. ed. 17.90 (978-0-15-323846-8(1)) Harcourt Schl. Pubs.

—Trofeos, Grade 3: Manuales Del Lenguaje. 3rd ed. 2002. (Trofeos Ser.). (SPA.). (gr. 3 up). pap., tchr. ed. 9.10 (978-0-15-323834-5(8)) Harcourt Schl. Pubs.

—Trofeos, Grade 3 On Level: Cuadernos de Practica. 3rd ed. 2002. (Trofeos Ser.). (SPA.). Vol. 1. (gr. 1-3). pap., tchr. ed. 17.00 (978-0-15-323806-2(2)); Vol. 2. (Illus.). (gr. 2-3). pap., tchr. ed. 17.00 (978-0-15-323807-9(0)) Harcourt Schl. Pubs.

—Trofeos, Grade 4: Apoyo Adicional Hojas Reproducibles. 3rd ed. 2002. (Trofeos Ser.). (SPA.). (gr. 4 up). pap. 51.40 (978-0-15-323810-9(0)) Harcourt Schl. Pubs.

—Trofeos, Grade 4: Cuadernos de Ortografia. 3rd ed. 2002. (Trofeos Ser.). (SPA.). (gr. 4 up). pap., tchr. ed. 17.90 (978-0-15-323847-5(X)) Harcourt Schl. Pubs.

—Trofeos, Grade 4: Manuales Del Lenguaje. 3rd ed. 2002. (Trofeos Ser.). (SPA.). (gr. 4 up). pap., tchr. ed. 9.10 (978-0-15-323835-2(6)) Harcourt Schl. Pubs.

—Trofeos, Grade 4 On Level: Cuadernos de Practica. 3rd ed. 2002. (Trofeos Ser.). (SPA.). (gr. 4 up). pap., tchr. ed. 23.00 (978-0-15-323811-6(9)) Harcourt Schl. Pubs.

—Trofeos, Grade 5: Cuadernos de Ortografia. 3rd ed. 2002. (Trofeos Ser.). (SPA.). (gr. 5 up). pap., tchr. ed. 17.90 (978-0-15-323848-2(8)) Harcourt Schl. Pubs.

—Trofeos, Grade 5: Manuales Del Lenguaje. 3rd ed. 2002. (Trofeos Ser.). (SPA.). (gr. 5 up). pap., tchr. ed. 9.10 (978-0-15-323836-9(4)) Harcourt Schl. Pubs.

—Trofeos, Grade 5 On Level: Cuadernos de Practica. 3rd ed. 2002. (Trofeos Ser.). (SPA.). (gr. 5 up). pap., tchr. ed. 23.00 (978-0-15-323815-4(1)) Harcourt Schl. Pubs.

—Trofeos, Grade 6: Cuadernos de Ortografia. 3rd ed. 2002. (Trofeos Ser.). (SPA.). (gr. 6 up). pap., tchr. ed. 17.90 (978-0-15-323849-9(6)) Harcourt Schl. Pubs.

—Trofeos, Grade 6: Manuales Del Lenguaje. 3rd ed. 2002. (Trofeos Ser.). (SPA.). (gr. 6 up). pap., tchr. ed. 9.10 (978-0-15-323837-6(2)) Harcourt Schl. Pubs.

—Trofeos, Grade 6 On Level: Cuadernos de Practica. 3rd ed. 2002. (Trofeos Ser.). (SPA.). (gr. 6 up). pap., tchr. ed. 23.00 (978-0-15-323819-2(4)) Harcourt Schl. Pubs.

—Trofeos, Grade K. 3rd ed. 2002. (SPA.). Vol. 1. 191.60 (978-0-15-334767-2(8)); Vol. 2. tchr. ed. 191.60 (978-0-15-334768-9(6)); Vol. 3. 191.60 (978-0-15-334769-6(4)) Harcourt Schl. Pubs.

—Trofoeos Below Level: A Brillar, Estrella! 3rd ed. 2002. (SPA., Illus.). (gr. 5). pap. 6.80 (978-0-15-324225-0(6)) Harcourt Schl. Pubs.

—Trophies. 3rd ed. 2003. (Trophies Ser.). (gr. 1 up). Grade 1-1. tchr. ed. 115.50 (978-0-15-325022-4(4)); Grade 1-2. tchr. ed. 115.50 (978-0-15-325023-1(2)); Grade 1-3. tchr. ed. 120.20 (978-0-15-325024-8(0)); Grade 1-4. tchr. ed. 120.20 (978-0-15-325025-5(9)); Grade 1-5. tchr. ed. 124.80 (978-0-15-325026-2(7)) Harcourt Schl. Pubs.

—Trophies: Language Handbook. 3rd ed. 2001. (Trophies Ser.). (Illus.). (gr. 1 up). pap. 8.30 (978-0-15-325063-7(1)); (gr. 2 up). pap. 15.00 (978-0-15-325064-4(X)); (gr. 3 up). pap. 19.60 (978-0-15-325065-1(8)); (gr. 4 up). pap. 19.60 (978-0-15-325066-8(6)); (gr. 5 up). pap. 19.60 (978-0-15-325067-5(4)); (gr. 6 up). pap. 19.60 (978-0-15-325068-2(2)) Harcourt Schl. Pubs.

—Trophies Theme 1, Theme 1. 3rd ed. 2003. (Trophies Ser.). (gr. 2 up). tchr. ed. 65.50 (978-0-15-325027-9(5)); (gr. 2 up). tchr. ed. 65.50 (978-0-15-325030-9(5)); (gr. 3 up). tchr. ed. 65.50 (978-0-15-325033-0(X)); (gr. 3 up). tchr. ed. 65.50 (978-0-15-325036-1(4)); (gr. 4 up). tchr. ed. 69.90 (978-0-15-325039-2(9)); (gr. 5 up). tchr. ed. 69.90 (978-0-15-325045-3(3)); (gr. 6 up). tchr. ed. 72.70 (978-0-15-325051-4(8)) Harcourt Schl. Pubs.

—Trophies Theme 2, Theme 2. 3rd ed. 2003. (Trophies Ser.). (gr. 2 up). tchr. ed. 65.50 (978-0-15-325028-6(3)); (gr. 2 up). tchr. ed. 65.50 (978-0-15-325031-6(3)); (gr. 3 up). tchr. ed. 65.50 (978-0-15-325034-7(8)); (gr. 3 up). tchr. ed. 65.50 (978-0-15-325037-8(2)); (gr. 4

up). tchr. ed. 69.90 (978-0-15-325040-8(2)); (gr. 5 up). tchr. ed. 69.90 (978-0-15-325046-0(1)); (gr. 6 up). tchr. ed. 72.70 (978-0-15-325052-1(6)) Harcourt Schl. Pubs.

—Trophies Theme 3, Theme 3. 3rd ed. 2003. (Trophies Ser.). (gr. 2 up). tchr. ed. 65.50 (978-0-15-325029-3(1)); (gr. 2 up). tchr. ed. 65.50 (978-0-15-325032-3(1)); (gr. 3 up). tchr. ed. 65.50 (978-0-15-325035-4(6)); (gr. 3 up). tchr. ed. 65.50 (978-0-15-325038-5(0)); (gr. 4 up). tchr. ed. 69.90 (978-0-15-325041-5(0)); (gr. 5 up). tchr. ed. 69.90 (978-0-15-325047-7(X)); (gr. 6 up). tchr. ed. 72.70 (978-0-15-325053-8(4)) Harcourt Schl. Pubs.

—Trophies Theme 4, Theme 4. 3rd ed. 2003. (Trophies Ser.). (gr. 4 up). tchr. ed. 69.90 (978-0-15-325042-2(9)); (gr. 5 up). tchr. ed. 69.90 (978-0-15-325048-4(8)); (gr. 6 up). tchr. ed. 72.70 (978-0-15-325054-5(2)) Harcourt Schl. Pubs.

—Trophies Theme 5, Theme 5. 3rd ed. 2003. (Trophies Ser.). (gr. 4 up). tchr. ed. 69.90 (978-0-15-325043-9(7)); (gr. 5 up). tchr. ed. 69.90 (978-0-15-325049-1(6)); (gr. 6 up). tchr. ed. 72.70 (978-0-15-325055-2(0)) Harcourt Schl. Pubs.

—Trophies Theme 6, Theme 6. 3rd ed. 2003. (Trophies Ser.). (gr. 4 up). tchr. ed. 69.90 (978-0-15-325044-6(5)); (gr. 5 up). tchr. ed. 69.90 (978-0-15-325050-7(X)); (gr. 6 up). tchr. ed. 72.70 (978-0-15-325056-9(9)) Harcourt Schl. Pubs.

—Trophies Big Book Collection Levels 1-1 & 1-2. 3rd ed. 2002. (Illus.). 344.90 (978-0-15-328371-0(8)) Harcourt Schl. Pubs.

—Trophies Decodable Gratis, 5-Pack. 2nd ed. 2002. (Illus.). (gr. 1). pap. 742.20 (978-0-15-329109-8(5)) Harcourt Schl. Pubs.

—Trophies Decodable Gratis 5-Pack. 2nd ed. 2002. (Illus.). (gr. 2). pap. 686.60 (978-0-15-329110-4(9)) Harcourt Schl. Pubs.

—Trophies, Grade 1: Holistic Assessment. 3rd ed. 2001. (Trophies Ser.). (gr. 1 up). pap., tchr. ed. 61.50 (978-0-15-325159-7(X)) Harcourt Schl. Pubs.

—Trophies, Grade 1: Reading & Language Skills Assessment. 3rd ed. 2001. (Trophies Ser.). (gr. 1 up). pap., tchr. ed. 105.40 (978-0-15-324961-7(7)) Harcourt Schl. Pubs.

—Trophies, Grade 2: Holistic Assessment. 3rd ed. 2001. (Trophies Ser.). (gr. 2 up). pap., tchr. ed. 61.50 (978-0-15-325160-3(3)) Harcourt Schl. Pubs.

—Trophies, Grade 2: Intervention Reader. 3rd ed. 2001. (Trophies Ser.). (gr. 2 up). pap., tchr. ed. 29.20 (978-0-15-325344-7(4)) Harcourt Schl. Pubs.

—Trophies, Grade 2: Reading & Language Skills Assessment. 3rd ed. 2001. (Trophies Ser.). (gr. 2 up). pap., tchr. ed. 105.40 (978-0-15-324962-4(5)) Harcourt Schl. Pubs.

—Trophies, Grade 3: Holistic Assessment. 3rd ed. 2001. (Trophies Ser.). (gr. 3 up). pap., tchr. ed. 61.50 (978-0-15-325161-0(1)) Harcourt Schl. Pubs.

—Trophies, Grade 3: Intervention Reader. 3rd ed. 2002. (Trophies Ser.). (gr. 3 up). pap., tchr. ed. 29.20 (978-0-15-325345-4(2)) Harcourt Schl. Pubs.

—Trophies, Grade 3: Reading & Language Skills Assessment. 3rd ed. 2001. (Trophies Ser.). (gr. 3 up). pap., tchr. ed. 105.40 (978-0-15-324963-1(3)) Harcourt Schl. Pubs.

—Trophies, Grade 3 On Level: Practice Book. 3rd ed. 2002. (Trophies Ser.). Vol. 1. (gr. 1-3). pap., tchr. ed. 14.60 (978-0-15-323519-1(5)); Vol. 2. (gr. 2-3). pap., tchr. ed. 14.60 (978-0-15-323520-7(9)) Harcourt Schl. Pubs.

—Trophies, Grade 4: Holistic Assessment. 3rd ed. 2002. (Trophies Ser.). (gr. 4 up). pap., tchr. ed. 67.70 (978-0-15-325162-7(X)) Harcourt Schl. Pubs.

—Trophies, Grade 4: Intervention Reader. 3rd ed. 2002. (Trophies Ser.). (gr. 4 up). pap., tchr. ed. 29.20 (978-0-15-325346-1(0)) Harcourt Schl. Pubs.

—Trophies, Grade 4: Reading & Language Skills Assessment. 3rd ed. 2001. (Trophies Ser.). (gr. 4 up). pap., tchr. ed. 105.40 (978-0-15-324964-8(1)) Harcourt Schl. Pubs.

—Trophies, Grade 4 On Level: Practice Book. 3rd ed. 2002. (Trophies Ser.). (gr. 4 up). pap., tchr. ed. 21.00 (978-0-15-323524-5(1)) Harcourt Schl. Pubs.

—Trophies, Grade 5: Holistic Assessment. 3rd ed. 2002. (Trophies Ser.). (gr. 5 up). pap., tchr. ed. 67.70 (978-0-15-325163-4(8)) Harcourt Schl. Pubs.

—Trophies, Grade 5: Intervention Reader. 3rd ed. 2002. (Trophies Ser.). (gr. 5 up). pap., tchr. ed. 29.20 (978-0-15-325347-8(9)) Harcourt Schl. Pubs.

—Trophies, Grade 5: Reading & Language Skills Assessment. 3rd ed. 2001. (Trophies Ser.). (gr. 5 up). pap., tchr. ed. 105.40 (978-0-15-324965-5(X)) Harcourt Schl. Pubs.

—Trophies, Grade 5 On Level: Practice Book. 3rd ed. 2002. (Trophies Ser.). (gr. 5 up). pap., tchr. ed. 21.00 (978-0-15-323528-3(4)) Harcourt Schl. Pubs.

—Trophies, Grade 6: For English-Language Learners. 3rd ed. 2002. (Trophies Ser.). (gr. 6 up). pap., tchr. ed. 44.80 (978-0-15-329340-5(3)) Harcourt Schl. Pubs.

—Trophies, Grade 6: Holistic Assessment. 3rd ed. 2002. (Trophies Ser.). (gr. 6 up). pap., tchr. ed. 67.70 (978-0-15-325164-1(6)) Harcourt Schl. Pubs.

—Trophies, Grade 6: Intervention Practice Book. 3rd ed. 2002. (Trophies Ser.). (gr. 6 up). pap., tchr. ed. 14.90 (978-0-15-326154-1(4)) Harcourt Schl. Pubs.

—Trophies, Grade 6: Intervention Reader. 3rd ed. 2002. (Trophies Ser.). (gr. 6 up). pap., tchr. ed. 29.20 (978-0-15-325348-5(7)) Harcourt Schl. Pubs.

—Trophies, Grade 6: Reading & Language Skills Assessment. 3rd ed. 2001. (Trophies Ser.). (gr. 6 up). pap., tchr. ed. 105.40 (978-0-15-324966-2(8)) Harcourt Schl. Pubs.

—Trophies, Grade 6 On Level: Practice Book. 3rd ed. 2002. (Trophies Ser.). (gr. 6 up). pap., tchr. ed. 21.00 (978-0-15-323532-0(2)) Harcourt Schl. Pubs.

—Trophies Practice Book On Level. 3rd ed. 2003. (Trophies Ser.). (Illus.). (gr. 6 up). 11.00 (978-0-15-323530-6(6)); Grade 4. (gr. 4 up). 11.00 (978-0-15-323522-1(5)); Grade 5. (gr. 5 up). 11.00 (978-0-15-323526-9(8)) Harcourt Schl. Pubs.

—Trophies Reading Program, Grade K. 3rd ed. 2003. tchr. ed. 135.30 (978-0-15-339730-1(6)) Harcourt Schl. Pubs.

—Under the Blue Moon: Phonics Practice Reader. 1999. (Collections Ser.). (Illus.). (J). pap. 2.60 (978-0-15-312939-1(5)) Harcourt Schl. Pubs.

—Under the Ocean: Practice Book. 3rd ed. 2001. (Trophies Reading Program Ser.). (Illus.). (J). pap. 1.80 (978-0-15-325092-7(5)) Harcourt Schl. Pubs.

—Under the Old Cherry Tree: Take-Home Book. 1999. (Collections Ser.). (Illus.). (J). pap. 1.90 (978-0-15-317238-0(X)) Harcourt Schl. Pubs.

—Uno, Dos, Tres: Big Book. 1999. (SPA., Illus.). pap. 82.60 (978-0-15-315093-7(9)) Harcourt Schl. Pubs.

—Vale Mana y Fuerza: Take-Home Book. 1999. (Vamos Ser.). (SPA., Illus.). (J). pap. 2.50 (978-0-15-318835-0(9)) Harcourt Schl. Pubs.

—Vamos de Fiesta: Bajo la Luna de Limon: Reader's Choice. 2000. (SPA., Illus.). (gr. 4). pap. 16.30 (978-0-15-319902-8(4)) Harcourt Schl. Pubs.

—Vamos de Fiesta: Big Book Collection. 1999. (SPA., Illus.). pap. 1144.30 (978-0-15-315091-3(2)) Harcourt Schl. Pubs.

—Vamos de Fiesta: El Diario de Pedro: Benchmark. 2000. (SPA., Illus.). pap. 15.10 (978-0-15-322089-0(9)) Harcourt Schl. Pubs.

—Vamos de Fiesta: El Nido mas Bello de Mundo: Benchmark. 2000. (SPA., Illus.). pap. 16.00 (978-0-15-322076-0(7)) Harcourt Schl. Pubs.

—Vamos de Fiesta: El Sabio Ben Take-Home Book. 2001. (SPA., Illus.). (J). pap. 2.80 (978-0-15-321320-5(5)) Harcourt Schl. Pubs.

—Vamos de Fiesta: Emergent Literature Assessment. 1999. (SPA., Illus.). pap. 35.60 (978-0-15-315115-6(3)) Harcourt Schl. Pubs.

—Vamos de Fiesta: Entre Vaqueros Take-Home Book. 2001. (SPA., Illus.). (J). pap. 2.80 (978-0-15-321322-9(1)) Harcourt Schl. Pubs.

—Vamos de Fiesta: Guided Reading Manual Take-Home Book. (SPA., Illus.). 2001. (gr. 4). pap. 18.80 (978-0-15-319034-6(5)); 2000. (gr. 1). pap. 20.70 (978-0-15-316617-4(7)); 2000. (gr. 2). pap. 20.70 (978-0-15-319032-2(9)); 2000. (gr. 3). pap. 20.70 (978-0-15-319033-9(7)) Harcourt Schl. Pubs.

—Vamos de Fiesta: Holistic Reading Assessment. 2001. (SPA., Illus.). (gr. 4). pap. 90.50 (978-0-15-317589-3(3)); (gr. 5). pap. 90.50 (978-0-15-317590-9(7)) Harcourt Schl. Pubs.

—Vamos de Fiesta: Intervention Reader. (SPA., Illus.). 2001. (gr. 4). pap. 29.70 (978-0-15-316615-0(0)); 2001. (gr. 5). pap. 29.70 (978-0-15-316616-7(9)); 2000. (gr. 2). pap. 29.70 (978-0-15-316613-6(4)); 2000. (gr. 3). pap. 29.70 (978-0-15-316614-3(2)) Harcourt Schl. Pubs.

—Vamos de Fiesta: Mai: Benchmark. 2001. (SPA., Illus.). pap. 17.10 (978-0-15-322078-4(3)) Harcourt Schl. Pubs.

—Vamos de Fiesta: Preparadas...Listas...Ya! Reader's Choice. 2001. (SPA., Illus.). pap. 16.30 (978-0-15-319903-5(2)) Harcourt Schl. Pubs.

—Vamos de Fiesta: Reading Inventory. 1999. (SPA., Illus.). (gr. k-1). pap. 70.30 (978-0-15-316350-0(X)); (gr. 2-3). pap. 58.00 (978-0-15-316351-7(8)) Harcourt Schl. Pubs.

—Vamos de Fiesta: Reading Skills Assessment. 2001. (SPA., Illus.). (gr. 4). pap. 86.70 (978-0-15-317578-7(8)); (gr. 5). pap. 86.70 (978-0-15-317579-4(6)) Harcourt Schl. Pubs.

—Vamos de Fiesta: Selection Completion Test with Answer Key. (SPA., Illus.). 2001. (gr. 4). pap. 30.90 (978-0-15-316715-7(7)); 2001. (gr. 5). pap. 30.90 (978-0-15-316716-4(5)); 1999. (gr. 1). pap. 25.00 (978-0-15-316623-5(1)); 1999. (gr. 2). pap. 30.90 (978-0-15-316624-2(X)); 1999. (gr. 3). pap. 30.90 (978-0-15-316625-9(8)) Harcourt Schl. Pubs.

—Vamos de Fiesta: Student Materials Package: Texas Edition. 1999. (SPA., Illus.). (gr. 1). pap. 186.30 (978-0-15-315020-3(3)); (gr. 2). pap. 103.50 (978-0-15-315021-0(1)); (gr. 3). pap. 103.50 (978-0-15-315022-7(X)) Harcourt Schl. Pubs.

—Vamos de Fiesta: Student Materials Package with Translation: Texas Edition. 1999. (SPA & ENG., Illus.). pap. 128.30 (978-0-15-315050-0(5)) Harcourt Schl. Pubs.

—Vamos de Fiesta: Susan B. Anthony Take-Home Book. 2001. (SPA., Illus.). (J). pap. 2.80 (978-0-15-321323-6(X)) Harcourt Schl. Pubs.

—Vamos de Fiesta: TAAS Preparation. (SPA., Illus.). 2001. (gr. 1). pap. 8.00 (978-0-15-320918-5(6)); 2001. (gr. 2). pap. 9.00 (978-0-15-320919-2(4)); 2001. (gr. 3). pap. 9.00 (978-0-15-320920-8(8)); 2000. (gr. 4). pap. 9.10 (978-0-15-320921-5(6)); 2000. (gr. 5). pap. 9.10 (978-0-15-320922-2(4)) Harcourt Schl. Pubs.

—Vamos de Fiesta: Un Grande Dia en Nicodemus Take-Home Book. 2001. (SPA., Illus.). (J). pap. 2.80 (978-0-15-321321-2(3)) Harcourt Schl. Pubs.

—Vamos de Fiesta Below Level: Take-Home Book. 2001. (SPA., Illus.). (gr. 4). pap. 31.60 (978-0-15-317975-4(9)); (gr. 5). pap. 31.60 (978-0-15-317976-1(7)) Harcourt Schl. Pubs.

—Vamos de Fiesta Level D: Asombrosa Graciela. 2001. (SPA., Illus.). pap. 16.90 (978-0-15-319909-7(1)) Harcourt Schl. Pubs.

—Vamos de Fiesta Level D: Babe. 2001. (SPA., Illus.). pap. 18.80 (978-0-15-319908-0(3)) Harcourt Schl. Pubs.

—Vamos de Fiesta Level D: Barriletes. 2001. (SPA., Illus.). pap. 16.00 (978-0-15-319910-3(5)) Harcourt Schl. Pubs.

—Vamos de Fiesta Level D: Beisbol en los Barrios. 2001. (SPA., Illus.). pap. 15.50 (978-0-15-319925-7(3)) Harcourt Schl. Pubs.

—Vamos de Fiesta Level D: Carlos y el Zorrillo. 2001. (SPA., Illus.). pap. 20.90 (978-0-15-319912-7(1)) Harcourt Schl. Pubs.

—Vamos de Fiesta Level D: Chaikovski Descubre America. 2001. (SPA.). pap. 20.70 (978-0-15-319923-3(7)) Harcourt Schl. Pubs.

—Vamos de Fiesta Level D: Doctor De Soto. 2001. (SPA., Illus.). pap. 16.50 (978-0-15-319913-4(X)) Harcourt Schl. Pubs.

—Vamos de Fiesta Level D: El Camino de Amelia. 2000. (SPA., Illus.). (gr. 4). pap. 16.50 (978-0-15-322073-9(2)) Harcourt Schl. Pubs.

—Vamos de Fiesta Level D: La Musica de Chirimia. 2001. (SPA., Illus.). pap. 20.90 (978-0-15-322074-6(0)) Harcourt Schl. Pubs.

—Vamos de Fiesta Level D: Pepita Habla Dos Veces. 2001. (SPA., Illus.). pap. 16.50 (978-0-15-319911-0(3)) Harcourt Schl. Pubs.

—Vamos de Fiesta Level D: Troton Mi Perro. 2000. (SPA., Illus.). pap. 17.50 (978-0-15-322085-2(6)) Harcourt Schl. Pubs.

—Vamos de Fiesta Level D: Volcanes. 2001. (SPA., Illus.). (gr. 5). pap. 22.90 (978-0-15-319922-6(9)) Harcourt Schl. Pubs.

—Vamos de Fiesta Set I: Guided Reading Library. 2001. (SPA., Illus.). (gr. 5). 420.20 (978-0-15-319376-7(X)) Harcourt Schl. Pubs.

—Vamos de Fiesta Set II: Level Library Plus & Good Reading Library. 2000. (SPA., Illus.). (gr. 4). 2089.80 (978-0-15-322924-4(1)); (gr. 5). 2490.90 (978-0-15-322925-1(X)) Harcourt Schl. Pubs.

—Vamos de Fiesta, Grade 2: Guided Reading Library. 2000. (SPA.). pap., tchr. ed. 17.70 (978-0-15-319036-0(1)) Harcourt Schl. Pubs.

—Vamos de Fiesta, Grade 2-3: Phonics Practice Readers. 2000. (SPA.). pap., tchr. ed. 25.10 (978-0-15-316779-9(3)) Harcourt Schl. Pubs.

—Vamos de Fiesta, Grade 3: Guided Reading Library. 2000. (SPA.). pap., tchr. ed. 17.70 (978-0-15-319037-7(X)) Harcourt Schl. Pubs.

—Vamos de Fiesta, Grade 4: Guided Reading Library. 2001. (SPA.). pap., tchr. ed. 17.70 (978-0-15-319038-4(8)) Harcourt Schl. Pubs.

—Vamos de Fiesta, Grade 4: Leveled Library. 2000. (SPA.). pap., tchr. ed. 125.50 (978-0-15-319895-3(8)) Harcourt Schl. Pubs.

—Vamos de Fiesta, Grade 4: TAAS Preparation. 2000. (SPA.). pap., tchr. ed. 12.50 (978-0-15-317979-2(1)) Harcourt Schl. Pubs.

—Vamos de Fiesta, Grade 5: Guided Reading Library. 2001. (SPA.). pap., tchr. ed. 17.70 (978-0-15-319039-1(6)) Harcourt Schl. Pubs.

—Vamos de Fiesta, Grade 5: TAAS Preparation. 2000. (SPA.). pap., tchr. ed. 12.50 (978-0-15-317981-5(3)) Harcourt Schl. Pubs.

—Vamos, Grade 2: Intervention Reader. 2000. pap., tchr. ed. 47.10 (978-0-15-319027-8(2)) Harcourt Schl. Pubs.

—Vamos, Grade 3: Intervention Reader. 2000. pap., tchr. ed. 47.10 (978-0-15-319028-5(0)) Harcourt Schl. Pubs.

—Vamos, Grade 4: Intervention Reader. 2000. pap., tchr. ed. 47.10 (978-0-15-319029-2(9)) Harcourt Schl. Pubs.

—Vamos, Grade 5: Intervention Reader. 2000. pap., tchr. ed. 47.10 (978-0-15-319030-8(2)) Harcourt Schl. Pubs.

—Vamos Take-Home Book Collection: 30 Titles. 2001. (Vamos Ser.). (SPA., Illus.). pap. 105.60 (978-0-15-319944-8(X)) Harcourt Schl. Pubs.

—El Viaje... Advanced Level. 3rd ed. 2002. (Trofeos Ser.). (SPA., Illus.). pap. 6.80 (978-0-15-324026-3(1)) Harcourt Schl. Pubs.

—Viajes Lejanos. 3rd ed. 2002. (Trofeos Ser.). (SPA., Illus.). (gr. 5 up). pupil's gde. ed. 87.50 (978-0-15-322666-3(8)) Harcourt Schl. Pubs.

—Visita en Olvido y Partir: Take-Home Book. 2001. (Vamos Ser.). (SPA., Illus.). (J). pap. 2.80 (978-0-15-319937-0(7)) Harcourt Schl. Pubs.

—Vuelo y Pajaros: Take-Home Book. 1999. (SPA., Illus.). (J). pap. 2.50 (978-0-15-318827-5(8)) Harcourt Schl. Pubs.

—Warm Friends, Grade 1 Level 3. 99th ed. 1999. (Signatures Ser.). tchr. ed. 135.20 (978-0-15-310116-8(4)) Harcourt Schl. Pubs.

—We Are Friends: Library Edition. 1999. (Collections Ser.). (Illus.). pap. 13.90 (978-0-15-314280-2(4)) Harcourt Schl. Pubs.

—Welcome Home, Grades 1-4. 1999. (Collections Ser.). tchr. ed. 152.60 (978-0-15-312080-0(0)) Harcourt Schl. Pubs.

—What a Great Team!, 5 Packs. 3rd ed. 2002. (Trophies English Language Learners Ser.). (gr. 1). 20.10 (978-0-15-327614-9(2)) Harcourt Schl. Pubs.

—What Did I See: Take-Home Book. 1999. (Signatures Ser.). (Illus.). (J). pap. 1.70 (978-0-15-313824-9(6)) Harcourt Schl. Pubs.

—What I See Big Book Anthology. 99th ed. 1999. (Signatures Ser.). (Illus.). (gr. 1). pap. 60.70 (978-0-15-310805-1(3)) Harcourt Schl. Pubs.

—What We Do: Take-Home Book. 1999. (Signatures Ser.). (Illus.). (J). pap. 1.70 (978-0-15-313829-4(7)) Harcourt Schl. Pubs.

—What You Learn, What You Can Do. 3rd ed. 2002. (Trophies English Language Learners Ser.). (Illus.). pap. 5.10 (978-0-15-327813-6(7)) Harcourt Schl. Pubs.

—What's What? Library Book. 3rd ed. 2002. (Trophies Reading Program Ser.). (Illus.). pap. 13.50 (978-0-15-326535-8(3)) Harcourt Schl. Pubs.

—Where Did Sideburns Come From? On Level. 3rd ed. 2002. (Trophies Reading Program Ser.). (Illus.). pap. 5.10 (978-0-15-323364-7(8)) Harcourt Schl. Pubs.

—Where Do I Live? 3rd ed. 2002. (Trophies English Language Learners Ser.). (Illus.). (J). pap. 4.10 (978-0-15-327581-4(2)) Harcourt Schl. Pubs.

—Where Do Pigs Play? Independent Reader. 3rd ed. 2002. (Trophies Reading Program Ser.). (Illus.). (J). pap. 2.90 (978-0-15-325484-0(X)) Harcourt Schl. Pubs.

—Where Is Dolly: Take-Home Book. 1999. (Collections Ser.). (Illus.). (J). (gr. 1). pap. 1.90 (978-0-15-317109-3(X)) Harcourt Schl. Pubs.

—Where There's Smoke There's Fire Below Level. 3rd ed. 2002. (Trophies Reading Program Ser.). (Illus.). pap. 5.10 (978-0-15-323241-1(2)) Harcourt Schl. Pubs.

—Where's My Teddy: A Reader. 1999. (Collections Ser.). (Illus.). (J). pap. 2.10 (978-0-15-313435-7(6)) Harcourt Schl. Pubs.

—Where's My Teddy? Pre-Decodable Book. 3rd ed. 2002. (Trophies Reading Program Ser.). (Illus.). pap. 2.90 (978-0-15-325404-8(1)) Harcourt Schl. Pubs.

—Who Needs a Baby? Below Level. 3rd ed. 2002. (Trophies Reading Program Ser.). (Illus.). pap. 5.10 (978-0-15-323144-5(0)) Harcourt Schl. Pubs.

—Who's Been Eating the Popcorn? 3rd ed. 2002. (Trophies English Language Learners Ser.). (Illus.). pap. 5.10 (978-0-15-327708-5(4)) Harcourt Schl. Pubs.

—Who's New? 3rd ed. 2002. (Trophies English Language Learners Ser.). (Illus.). pap. 5.10 (978-0-15-327691-0(6)) Harcourt Schl. Pubs.

—Windcatcher Level D: Reader. 2001. (Collections Ser.). (Illus.). pap. 12.10 (978-0-15-314377-9(0)) Harcourt Schl. Pubs.

—Wings, Grade 3 Level 1. 99th ed. 1998. (Signatures Ser.). tchr. ed. 205.70 (978-0-15-310121-2(0)) Harcourt Schl. Pubs.

—The Winning: Take Home Book. 1999. (Signatures Ser.). (Illus.). (J). (gr. 6). pap. 1.90 (978-0-15-313966-6(8)) Harcourt Schl. Pubs.

—A World at Your Fingertips. 2001. (Reader's Choice Bks.). (Illus.). (J). pap. 7.20 (978-0-15-314428-8(9)) Harcourt Schl. Pubs.

—Writer's Magazine. 99th ed. 1999. (Signatures Ser.). (Illus.). (gr. 1). pap. 9.30 (978-0-15-310816-7(9)); (gr. 3). pap. 9.30 (978-0-15-310817-4(7)) Harcourt Schl. Pubs.

—Writer's Magazine: Answer Key. 1999. (Signatures Ser.). (Illus.). (J). (gr. 1). pap. 3.00 (978-0-15-310818-1(5)); (gr. 3). pap. 3.00 (978-0-15-310819-8(3)) Harcourt Schl. Pubs.

—Writing Express Espanol, Grade 1. 2nd ed. 2003. (Trofeos Ser.). (SPA.). (gr. 1 up). tchr. ed. 10.10 incl. cd-rom (978-0-15-324608-1(1)) Harcourt Schl. Pubs.

—Ya No Me Atrapas: Take-Home Book. 1999. (Vamos Ser.). (SPA., Illus.). (J). pap. 2.50 (978-0-15-318817-6(0)) Harcourt Schl. Pubs.

—You're Invited Level 2. 1999. (Collections Ser.). (Illus.). (gr. 1). 30.70 (978-0-15-312034-3(7)) Harcourt Schl. Pubs.

—You're Invited, Grades 1 & 2. 1999. (Collections Ser.). tchr. ed. 146.70 (978-0-15-312078-7(9)) Harcourt Schl. Pubs.

—Zapatos Para Zizi: Phonics Practice Reader. 1999. (Vamos Ser.). (SPA., Illus.). pap. 5.00 (978-0-15-318997-5(5)) Harcourt Schl. Pubs.

—1st Place Reading: Title 1 Program Kit. 2nd ed. 2003. (Harcourt Title I Reading Programs Ser.). (gr. 5 up). tchr. ed. 1006.70 (978-0-15-338009-9(8)) Harcourt Schl. Pubs.

Harrison, Vanessa. Colorcards Activities: 101 Ideas for Children & Adults. 128p. pap. (978-0-86388-551-8(9) , 002-5296) Speechmark Publishing Ltd.

Harry's Hat. 2005. (Emergent Library: Vol. 2). (YA). (ps-1). 23.94 (978-0-8215-8924-3(5)) Sadlier, William H. Inc.

Harry's Hat: Take-Home Book. 2005. (Emergent Library: Vol. 2). (YA). (ps-1). 12.60 (978-0-8215-7254-2(7)) Sadlier, William H. Inc.

Harth, Ann. Please Listen. Webb, Melissa, illus. 2002. (Bright Sparks Ser.). 16p. pap. 2.30 (978-0-521-75419-4(4)) Cambridge Univ. Pr.

Hassinger, Mary & School Specialty Publishing Staff. After School Reading Activities Grade 5. 2003. (100+ Seriestm Ser.). 128p. (J). (gr. 5 up). pap. 12.99 (978-0-7424-1775-5(1) , IFG99025, Instructional Fair) Schaffer, Frank Pubns.

Hassinger, Mary, et al. After School Reading Activities, Grade 1. 2003. (100+ Seriestm Ser.). (Illus.). 128p. (J). (gr. 1 up). pap. 12.99 (978-0-7424-1771-7(9) , IFG99021, Instructional Fair) Schaffer, Frank Pubns.

—After School Reading Activities, Grade 2. 2003. (100+ Seriestm Ser.). (Illus.). 128p. (J). (gr. 2 up). pap. 12.99 (978-0-7424-1772-4(7) , IFG99022, Instructional Fair) Schaffer, Frank Pubns.

—After School Reading Activities, Grade 3. 2003. (100+ Seriestm Ser.). (Illus.). 128p. (J). (gr. 3 up). pap. 12.99 (978-0-7424-1773-1(5) , IFG99023, Instructional Fair) Schaffer, Frank Pubns.

—After School Reading Activities, Grade 4. 2003. (100+ Seriestm Ser.). (Illus.). 128p. (J). (gr. 4 up). pap. 12.99 (978-0-7424-1774-8(3) , IFG99024, Instructional Fair) Schaffer, Frank Pubns.

A Hat for Nan: Consonants b, w; Short Vowel i word families: Level A, 6 vols. (Wright Skills Ser.). 12p. (gr. k-3). 17.95 (978-0-322-01451-0(4)) Wright Group, The.

Hats: Big Book: Level B. 8p. 20.95 (978-0-322-00359-0(8)) Wright Group, The.

Hats: Level B. 8p. 24.95 (978-0-7802-8919-2(6)) Wright Group, The.

Hats: Level G, 6 vols. (Wonder Worldtm Ser.). 16p. 29.95 (978-0-7802-4579-2(2)) Wright Group, The.

Haunted, 6 vols. (Ragged Island Mysteriestm Ser.). 161p. (gr. 5-7). 42.50 (978-0-322-01652-1(5)) Wright Group, The.

Hauser, Jill Frankel. Easy Art Fun! Do-It-Yourself Crafts for Beginning Readers. Hauser, Savlan, illus. 2001. (Little Hands Read-and-Do Book Ser.). 112p. (J). (ps-3). pap. 12.95 (978-1-885593-62-7(7) , Williamson Bks.) Ideals Pubns.

—Wow! I'm Reading! 2000. (gr. k-3). lib. bdg. 22.20 (978-0-613-28144-7(6)) Tandem Library Bks.

—Wow! I'm Reading: Fun Activities to Make Reading Happen. Jaskiel, Stan, illus. 2000. (Little Hands Bks.). 144p. (J). (ps-2). pap. 12.95 (978-1-885593-41-2(4) , Williamson Bks.) Ideals Pubns.

Hay Making: Level H, 6 vols. (Wonder Worldtm Ser.). 16p. 29.95 (978-0-7802-1215-2(0)) Wright Group, The.

Hayes, Christine. Fruit Salad: Emergent. 2002. (Bright Sparks Ser.). (Illus.). 16p. pap. 2.95 (978-0-521-75133-9(0)) Cambridge Univ. Pr.

Hayes, Peter. The Farmer: Emergent. Williams, Robbie J., illus. 2002. (Bright Sparks Ser.). 16p. pap. 3.00 (978-0-521-75113-1(6)) Cambridge Univ. Pr.

—The Green & Purple Hat. 2002. (Bright Sparks Ser.). (Illus.). 16p. pap. 2.30 (978-0-521-75387-6(2)) Cambridge Univ. Pr.

—The Hungry Spider. Jurevicius, Luke, illus. 2002. (Bright Sparks Ser.). 16p. pap. 2.30 (978-0-521-75388-3(0)) Cambridge Univ. Pr.

—The Mozzie Bites: Emergent. 2002. (Bright Sparks Ser.). (Illus.). 16p. pap. 2.30 (978-0-521-75114-8(4)) Cambridge Univ. Pr.

Hayes, Rosemary. Big Book of Play a Part. 2000. (Cambridge Reading Routes Ser.). (Illus.). 32p. pap. 14.25 (978-0-521-77886-2(7)) Cambridge Univ. Pr.

—Play a Part. 2000. (Cambridge Reading Routes Ser.). (Illus.). 32p. pap. 6.00 (978-0-521-77906-7(5)) Cambridge Univ. Pr.

HB. First-Place Reading for Title I: Take-Home Books. (Harcourt Title I Reading Programs Ser.). 2001. (gr. 4 up). pap. 22.20 (978-0-15-313364-0(3)); 2001. (gr. 5 up). pap. 22.20 (978-0-15-313365-7(1)); 2001. (gr. 6 up). pap. 22.20 (978-0-15-313366-4(X)); 1999. (gr. 3 up). pap. 20.20 (978-0-15-313363-3(5)) Harcourt Schl. Pubs.

Healy, Jane E. Developing Reading Power, Bk. 1. 1998. (Illus.). 32p. (J). (gr. 1-2). pap., wbk. ed. 3.50 (978-1-56762-089-4(2)) Modern Learning Pr.

Heinrichs, Ann. Prefixes & Suffixes. 2005. (Magic of Language Ser.). (Illus.). 32p. (J). (gr. 1-5). 27.07 (978-1-59296-431-4(1)) Child's World, Inc.

Hello: Big Book: Level D. Group 1. (Story Box(R) Ser.). 16p. 20.95 (978-0-322-00632-4(5)) Wright Group, The.

Hepker, Sue. Baby Monkey's Bananas: Amharic Version. Duguma, Melaku Wakuma, tr. 1999. (Cambridge Reading Routes Ser.). (AMH., Illus.). 16p. pap. 3.70 (978-0-521-66831-6(X)) Cambridge Univ. Pr.

—Baby Monkey's Bananas: Oromo Version. Buse, Abdurahim Adem, tr. 1999. (Cambridge Reading Routes Ser.). (Illus.). 16p. pap. 3.70 (978-0-521-66843-9(3)) Cambridge Univ. Pr.

—Baby Monkey's Bananas: Tigre Version. Kebebew, Amare Hagos, tr. 1999. (Cambridge Reading Routes Ser.). (TIG., Illus.). 16p. pap. 3.70 (978-0-521-66821-7(2)) Cambridge Univ. Pr.

—Baby Monkey's Bananas Lugbara Version: Oyoo-mva Vele A'bua-eka-ri. Draville, Ben & Mawa, Robert, trs. 2001. 16p. pap. 0.90 (978-0-521-00620-0(1)) Cambridge Univ. Pr.

—Cheese! Yummy Cheese! Kiswahili Version. Mulokozi, M. M., tr. 1999. (Cambridge Reading Routes Ser.). (Illus.). 16p. pap. 3.70 (978-0-521-66887-3(5)) Cambridge Univ. Pr.

—Cheese! Yummy Cheese! Oromo Version. Buse, Abdurahim Adem, tr. 1999. (Cambridge Reading Routes Ser.). (Illus.). 16p. pap. 3.70 (978-0-521-66845-3(X)) Cambridge Univ. Pr.

—Cheese! Yummy Cheese! Tigre Version. Kebebew, Amare Hagos, tr. 1999. (Cambridge Reading Routes Ser.). (TIG., Illus.). 16p. pap. (978-0-521-66825-5(5)) Cambridge Univ. Pr.

Hercules & Other Greek Legends: 6 Each of 1 Anthology, 6 vols. (Wildcats Ser.). 32p. (gr. 2-8). (978-0-322-00590-7(6)) Wright Group, The.

Here Comes the Rain! 2005. (Emergent Library: Vol. 2). (YA). (ps-1) 23.94 (978-0-8215-8933-5(4)) Sadlier, William H. Inc.

Here Comes the Rain! Take-Home Book. 2005. (Emergent Library: Vol. 2). (YA). (ps-1). 12.60 (978-0-8215-7263-4(6)) Sadlier, William H. Inc.

Hereford, Jane. Challenge the ISAT: 3rd Grade Reading. 2001. (Illus.). 232p. (J). pap. 12.00 (978-0-89892-222-6(4)) Contemporary Publishing Co. of Raleigh, Inc.

—Challenge the PACT: South Carolina 5th Grade Reading. 1999. (Illus.). 236p. (J). pap. 12.00 (978-0-89892-210-3(0)) Contemporary Publishing Co. of Raleigh, Inc.

—Challenge the PACT: South Carolina 6th Grade Reading. 1999. (Illus.). 228p. (J). pap. 12.00 (978-0-89892-197-7(X)) Contemporary Publishing Co. of Raleigh, Inc.

—Challenge the PACT: South Carolina 8th Grade Reading. 1999. (Illus.). 240p. (J). pap. 12.00 (978-0-89892-195-3(3)) Contemporary Publishing Co. of Raleigh, Inc.

—The Competitive Edge: Passing the EOG in 3rd Grade Reading. 1999. (Illus.). 224p. (J). pap. 12.00 (978-0-89892-187-8(2)) Contemporary Publishing Co. of Raleigh, Inc.

—The Competitive Edge: Passing the EOG in 5th Grade Reading. 1999. (Illus.). 228p. (J). pap. 12.00 (978-0-89892-182-3(1)) Contemporary Publishing Co. of Raleigh, Inc.

Los hermanos Wright aprenden a Volar 23: Leveled Books. 2001. (McGraw-Hill. Lectura Ser.). (ENG & SPA.). (gr. 2 up). (978-0-02-188072-0(7)) Macmillan/McGraw-Hill Schl. Div.

Heroes: 6 Each of 1 Anthology, 6 vols. (Wildcatstm Ser.). 32p. (gr. 2-8). (978-0-322-00579-2(5)) Wright Group, The.

Hetzel, June. Responding to Literature: Activities That Build Confident Readers & Writers. Samoiloff, Sheri, ed. Campbell, Jenny, illus. rev. ed. 2002. 64p. (J). (gr. 3-6). pap. 9.99 (978-1-57471-810-2(X) , CTP 3368) Creative Teaching Pr., Inc.

Hide & Seek: Big Book: Level K. (Wonder Worldtm Ser.). 16p. 26.50 (978-0-7802-3474-1(X)) Wright Group, The.

Hide & Seek: Level K, 6 vols. (Wonder Worldtm Ser.). 16p. 34.95 (978-0-7802-1217-6(7)) Wright Group, The.

Hiebert, Elfrieda H. Eyes Are Everywhere. (Little Book Practice Reader Ser.). (J). (978-0-8136-0811-2(2)) Modern Curriculum Pr.

—Humpback Whales. (Little Book Practice Reader Ser.). (J). (978-0-8136-0809-9(0)) Modern Curriculum Pr.

Hiebert, Elfrieda H. & Juel, Connie. The Best Places. (Little Book Practice Reader). (J). (978-0-8136-2010-7(4)) Modern Curriculum Pr.

—Blue Sue. (Little Book Practice Reader). (J). (978-0-8136-2375-7(8)) Modern Curriculum Pr.

—Dee & Me. (Little Book Practice Reader). (J). (978-0-8136-2112-8(7)) Modern Curriculum Pr.

—The Doctor Has the Flu. (Little Book Practice Reader). (J). (978-0-8136-2158-6(5)) Modern Curriculum Pr.

—Eight Friends in All. (Little Book Practice Reader Ser.). (J). (978-0-8136-0773-3(6)) Modern Curriculum Pr.

—Eve Shops. (Little Book Practice Reader Ser.). (J). (978-0-8136-0957-7(7)) Modern Curriculum Pr.

—A Fun Place to Eat. (Little Book Practice Reader). (J). (978-0-8136-2058-9(9)) Modern Curriculum Pr.

—Goose Chase. (Little Book Practice Reader). (J). (978-0-8136-2068-8(6)) Modern Curriculum Pr.

—The Hiccups Would Not Stop. (Little Book Practice Reader). (J). (978-0-8136-2168-5(2)) Modern Curriculum Pr.

—A Hunt for Clues. (Little Book Practice Reader). (J). (978-0-8136-2148-7(8)) Modern Curriculum Pr.

—Jim's Visit to Kim. (Little Book Practice Reader). (J). (978-0-8136-2108-1(9)) Modern Curriculum Pr.

—Jump Right In. (Little Book Practice Reader Ser.). (J). (978-0-8136-0746-7(9)) Modern Curriculum Pr.

—Just Like Us. (Little Book Practice Reader). (J). (978-0-8136-2022-0(8)) Modern Curriculum Pr.

—Kangaroo in the Kitchen. (Little Book Practice Reader Ser.). (J). 9.90 (978-0-8136-0742-9(6)) Modern Curriculum Pr.

—Lobster Fishing at Dawn. (Little Book Practice Reader). (J). (978-0-8136-2194-4(1)) Modern Curriculum Pr.

—A Mess. (Little Book Practice Reader). (J). (978-0-8136-1934-7(3)) Modern Curriculum Pr.

—Molly's Broccoli. (Little Book Practice Reader). (J). (978-0-8136-2196-8(8)) Modern Curriculum Pr.

—Mr. Fin's Trip. (Little Book Practice Reader). (J). (978-0-8136-2378-8(2)) Modern Curriculum Pr.

—My Clock Is Sick. (Little Book Practice Reader). (J). (978-0-8136-1974-3(2)) Modern Curriculum Pr.

—My Lost Top. (Little Book Practice Reader). (J). (978-0-8136-2047-3(3)) Modern Curriculum Pr.

—The Name Is the Same. (J). (978-0-8136-2080-0(5)) Modern Curriculum Pr.

—A Nut Pie for Jud. (Little Book Practice Reader). (J). (978-0-8136-1972-9(6)) Modern Curriculum Pr.

—Polly's Shop. (Little Book Practice Reader). (J). (978-0-8136-2029-9(5)) Modern Curriculum Pr.

—Pop Pops the Popcorn. (J). (978-0-8136-2008-4(2)) Modern Curriculum Pr.

—Rush, Rush, Rush. (Little Book Practice Reader). (J). (978-0-8136-2074-9(0)) Modern Curriculum Pr.

—Sally's Spaceship. (Little Book Practice Reader). (Illus.). (J). (978-0-8136-2045-9(7)) Modern Curriculum Pr.

—A Sea Star. (Little Book Practice Reader). (J). (978-0-8136-2041-1(4)) Modern Curriculum Pr.

—Ted's Red Sled. (Little Book Practice Reader). (J). (978-0-8136-1968-2(8)) Modern Curriculum Pr.

—Terrific Shoes. (Little Book Practice Reader). (J). (978-0-8136-1940-8(8)) Modern Curriculum Pr.

—That Fly. (Little Book Practice Reader). (J). (978-0-8136-1942-2(4)) Modern Curriculum Pr.

—True Or False? (Little Book Practice Reader). (J). (978-0-8136-2086-2(4)) Modern Curriculum Pr.

—Very Big, Bk. 45. (Little Book Practice Reader). (J). (978-0-8136-1457-1(0)) Modern Curriculum Pr.

—Vultures on Vacation. (Little Book Practice Reader). (J). (978-0-8136-1938-5(6)) Modern Curriculum Pr.

—When Bob Woke Up Late. (Little Book Practice Reader). (J). (978-0-8136-2084-8(8)) Modern Curriculum Pr.

—Where Do They Live? (Little Book Practice Reader). (J). (978-0-8136-1948-4(3)) Modern Curriculum Pr.

—Who Made That? (Little Book Practice Reader). (J). (978-0-8136-1946-0(7)) Modern Curriculum Pr.

—Wilma's Wagon. (J). (978-0-8136-1964-4(5)) Modern Curriculum Pr.

High Five Reading: Green Level, 5 bks. Incl. Colin Powell : It Can Be Done! Strong, Mike. lib. bdg. 22.60 (978-0-7368-9551-4(5)); Iditarod : The Last Great Race. Young, Ian. lib. bdg. 22.60 (978-0-7368-9545-3(0)); Inventions : Great Ideas & Where They Came from. Houghton, Sarah. lib. bdg. 22.60 (978-0-7368-9554-5(X)); King Tut : Tales from the Tomb. Briscoe, Diana. lib. bdg. 22.60 (978-0-7368-9553-8(1)); Smokejumpers : Battling the Forest Flames. Briscoe, Diana. lib. bdg. 22.60 (978-0-7368-9548-4(5)); 48p. (J). (gr. 3-4). 2002. (Illus.). 2002. Set lib. bdg. 113.00 (978-0-7368-9571-2(X) , Capstone High-Interest Bks.) Capstone Pr., Inc.

High Five Reading: Red, Green & Purple Levels, 15 bks. (Illus.). (J). lib. bdg. 339.00 (978-0-7368-9583-5(3) , Capstone High-Interest Bks.) Capstone Pr., Inc.

High Five Reading: Red Level, 5 bks. Incl. Castles : Towers, Dungeons, Moats, & More. White, Matt. lib. bdg. 22.60 (978-0-7368-9549-1(3)); Cesar Chavez : Fighter in the Fields. Matthews, J. L. & Rasinski, Timothy V. lib. bdg. 22.60 (978-0-7368-9550-7(7)); Shark! The Truth Behind the Terror. Strong, Mike. lib. bdg. 22.60 (978-0-7368-9547-7(7)); Storm Chasers : On the Trail of Deadly Tornadoes. White, Matt. lib. bdg. 22.60 (978-0-7368-9552-1(3)); X Games : Action Sports Grab in Spotlight. Young, Ian & Rasinski, Timothy V. lib. bdg. 22.60 (978-0-7368-9546-0(9)); 48p. (J). (gr. 2-3). 2002. (Illus.). 2002. Set lib. bdg. 113.00 (978-0-7368-9555-2(8) , Capstone High-Interest Bks.) Capstone Pr., Inc.

High-Low Reading: Taking Your Camera To..., 18 bks., Set. Incl. Australia. Park, Ted. 2000. lib. bdg. 22.83 (978-0-7398-1810-7(4)); Brazil. Park, Ted. 2000. lib. bdg. 22.83 (978-0-7398-1802-2(3)); Canada. Park, Ted. 1999. lib. bdg. 22.83 (978-0-7398-1803-9(1)); Egypt. Park, Ted. 2000. lib. bdg. 22.83 (978-0-7398-1812-1(0)); France. Sandak, Cass R. 1999. lib. bdg. 22.83 (978-0-7398-1800-8(7)); Israel. Park, Ted. 2000. lib. bdg. 22.83 (978-0-7398-1801-5(5)); Italy. Park, Ted. 2000. lib. bdg. 22.83 (978-0-7398-1807-7(4)); Japan. Park, Ted. 2000. lib. bdg. 22.83 (978-0-7398-1805-3(8)); Mexico. Park, Ted. 1999. lib. bdg. 22.83 (978-0-7398-1804-6(X)); Panama. Park, Ted. 2000. lib. bdg. 22.83 (978-0-7398-1808-4(2)); Russia. Park, Ted. 2000. lib. bdg. 22.83 (978-0-7398-1811-4(2)); Spain. Park, Ted. 2000. lib. bdg. 22.83 (978-0-7398-1809-1(0)); Taking Your Camera to Argentina. Park, Ted. Sloan, Frank, ed. 2001. lib. bdg. 22.83 (978-0-7398-3567-8(X)); Taking Your Camera to China. Park, Ted. Sloan, Frank, ed. 2001. lib. bdg. 22.83 (978-0-7398-3568-5(8)); Taking Your Camera to Germany. Park, Ted. Sloan, Frank, ed. 2001. lib. bdg. 22.83 (978-0-7398-3569-2(6)); Taking Your Camera to India. Park, Ted. Sloan, Frank, ed. 2001. lib. bdg. 22.83 (978-0-7398-3570-8(X)); Taking Your Camera to South Africa. Park, Ted. Sloan, Frank, ed. 2001. lib. bdg. 22.83 (978-0-7398-3571-5(8)); Taking Your Camera to Vietnam. Park, Ted. 2001. lib. bdg. 22.83 (978-0-7398-3572-2(6)); (Illus.). 32p. (J). (gr. 4-7). 2001. Set lib. bdg. 410.94 (978-0-7398-3574-6(2)) Raintree.

High Tide: Level 7, 6 vols. (Fluency Strand Ser.). (gr. 4-8). 45.00 (978-1-4045-1242-9(X)) Wright Group, The.

A Hike in the Trees: Long e Digraphs: Level B, 6 vols. (Wright Skills Ser.). 16p. (gr. k-3). 26.50 (978-0-322-01479-4(4)) Wright Group, The.

Hiking with Dad: Level I, 6 vols. (Wonder Worldtm Ser.). 16p. 29.95 (978-0-7802-2036-2(6)) Wright Group, The.

Hocus Pocus: 6 Each of 1 Anthology, 6 vols. (Wildcatstm Ser.). 32p. (gr. 2-8). (978-0-322-02423-6(4)) Wright Group, The.

Hodson, Christopher. Lizo's Song: Chinyanja Version. Khomani, Peter J., tr. 1999. (Cambridge Reading Routes Ser.). (AFR., Illus.). 16p. pap. 3.70 (978-0-521-66877-4(8)) Cambridge Univ. Pr.

—Lizo's Song: Lunda Version. Kambangaji, Thomson, tr. 1998. (Cambridge African Language Library Ser.). (Illus.). 16p. pap. 3.70 (978-0-521-63837-1(2)) Cambridge Univ. Pr.

—Lizo's Song: Oromo Version. Adem, Omer Kedir, tr. 1999. (Cambridge Reading Routes Ser.). (Illus.). 16p. pap. 3.70 (978-0-521-66836-1(0)) Cambridge Univ. Pr.

Hoffman, Don. A Counting Book with Billy & Abigail. Dakins, Todd, illus. 2004. (Billy & Abigail Ser.). (J). (ps-k). bds. 5.99 (978-1-4037-0543-3(7)) Dalmatian Pr.

Hoffman, Joan. Readiness. 2000. (Whimsy Workbooks Ser.). (Illus.). 32p. (J). pap., wbk. ed. 2.49 (978-0-88743-469-3(X)) School Zone Publishing Co.

—Reading Readiness, Bk. 2. 2001. (Teacher Edition Wkbks.). (Illus.). 32p. (J). (gr. k-1). pap. 3.99 (978-0-88743-864-6(4) , 02842) School Zone Publishing Co.

—Reading Readiness K-1, Bk. 1. 2001. (Teacher Edition Wkbks.). (Illus.). 32p. (J). (gr. k-1). pap., tchr. ed., wbk. ed. 3.99 (978-0-88743-852-3(0) , 02833) School Zone Publishing Co.

Hofmeyr, Dianne. Hic... Hic... Hiccups! Sepedi Version. 2002. (Illus.). 16p. pap. 1.75 (978-0-521-52836-8(4)) Cambridge Univ. Pr.

—Hic... Hic... Hiccups! Sesotho Version. 2002. (Illus.). 16p. pap. 1.75 (978-0-521-52833-7(X)) Cambridge Univ. Pr.

—Hic... Hic... Hiccups! Setswana Version. 2002. (Illus.). 16p. pap. 1.75 (978-0-521-52834-4(8)) Cambridge Univ. Pr.

—Hic... Hic... Hiccups! Xitsonga Version. 2002. (Illus.). 16p. pap. 1.75 (978-0-521-52835-1(6)) Cambridge Univ. Pr.

Hohenthal, K. D., creator. The Reading & Writing Connection Journal with Herman the Crab No. 1: What Is the Story About? 2003. 70p. (J). spiral bd. 15.95 (978-0-9716907-5-2(8) , Ridgewood Publishing) Ridgewood Group, The.

—The Reading & Writing Connection with Herman the Crab No. 2: Story Problem & Solution. 2003. 70p. (J). spiral bd., wbk. ed. 15.95 (978-0-9716907-6-9(6) , Ridgewood Publishing) Ridgewood Group, The.

—The Reading & Writing Connection with Herman the Crab No. 3: Story Beginning, Middle, End. 2003. 70p. (J). spiral bd., wbk. ed. 15.95 (978-0-9716907-8-3(2) , Ridgewood Publishing) Ridgewood Group, The.

—The Reading & Writing Connection with Herman the Crab No. 4: Story Problem, Solution, Beginning, Middle, End. 2003. 70p. (J). spiral bd., wbk. ed. 15.95 (978-0-9716907-9-0(0) , Ridgewood Publishing) Ridgewood Group, The.

Holes. 2000. (Assessment Packs Ser.). (J). pap., tchr.'s training gde. ed. 15.95 (978-1-58303-101-8(4)) Pathways Publishing.

Hollemann, Monika. Chameleon's Clever Trick: Chilomwe Version. Nkhoma, Wilson, tr. 1999. (Cambridge Reading Routes Ser.). (Illus.). 16p. pap. 3.70 (978-0-521-66852-1(2)) Cambridge Univ. Pr.

—Chameleon's Clever Trick: Chitumbuka Version. Chirambo, Reuben, tr. 1999. (Cambridge Reading Routes Ser.). (Illus.). 16p. pap. 3.70 (978-0-521-66866-8(2)) Cambridge Univ. Pr.

—Chameleon's Clever Trick: Chiyao Version. Kaliati, Mailos, tr. 1999. (Cambridge Reading Routes Ser.). (Illus.). 16p. pap. 3.70 (978-0-521-66858-3(1)) Cambridge Univ. Pr.

—Chameleon's Clever Trick: Oromo Version. Buse, Abdurahim Adem, tr. 1999. (Cambridge Reading Routes Ser.). (Illus.). 16p. pap. 3.70 (978-0-521-66841-5(7)) Cambridge Univ. Pr.

—Chameleon's Clever Trick Chinyanja Version. Iphani, Max, tr. 1999. (Cambridge Reading Routes Ser.). (Illus.). 16p. pap. 3.70 (978-0-521-66884-2(0)) Cambridge Univ. Pr.

Holley, Cynthia. Warming up to Big Books. 189p. 26.50 (978-0-7802-2734-7(4)) Wright Group, The.

Holt, Rinehart and Winston Staff. Answers for Directed Reading Worksheets: Holt Science & Technology: Texas Edition. 2nd ed. 2002. (SPA.). (YA). (gr. 7). pap. 11.20 (978-0-03-069206-2(7)); (gr. 8). pap. 11.20 (978-0-03-069207-9(5)) Holt, Rinehart & Winston.

—Bud, Not Buddy: With Connections. 2nd ed. 2002. 14.64 (978-0-03-065483-1(1)); pap., stu. ed. 13.20 (978-0-03-065484-8(X)) Holt, Rinehart & Winston.

—Ciencias y Technologia 2001: Life: Directed Reading Worksheets. 2000. pap. 16.20 (978-0-03-064753-6(3)) Holt, Rinehart & Winston.

—Directed Reading, Grade 7: Texas Edition. 2nd ed. 2002. (Holt Science & Technology Ser.). pap., wbk. ed. 15.00 (978-0-03-067786-1(6)) Holt, Rinehart & Winston.

—Directed Reading, Grade 8: Texas Edition. 2nd ed. 2002. (Holt Science & Technology Ser.). pap., wbk. ed. 15.00 (978-0-03-067787-8(4)) Holt, Rinehart & Winston.

—Directed Reading Worksheets: Holt Science & Technology: Texas Edition. 2nd ed. 2002. (SPA.). (YA). (gr. 7). pap. 15.00 (978-0-03-069198-0(2)); (gr. 8). pap. 15.00 (978-0-03-069199-7(0)) Holt, Rinehart & Winston.

—Elemements of Literature: Holt Reader. 4th ed. Date not set. (Illus.). (J). (gr. 6). pap. 13.20 (978-0-03-068389-3(0)) Holt, Rinehart & Winston.

—Elements of Language: Active Reader's Practice Book - Grade 10. 2000. pap. 13.86 (978-0-03-064578-5(6)) Holt, Rinehart & Winston.

—Elements of Language: Active Reader's Practice Book - Grade 11. 2000. pap. 13.86 (978-0-03-064579-2(4)) Holt, Rinehart & Winston.

—Elements of Language: Active Reader's Practice Book - Grade 12. 2000. pap. 13.86 (978-0-03-064581-5(6)) Holt, Rinehart & Winston.

—Elements of Language: Active Reader's Practice Book - Grade 6. 2000. pap. 13.86 (978-0-03-064574-7(3)) Holt, Rinehart & Winston.

—Elements of Language: Active Reader's Practice Book - Grade 7. 2000. pap. 13.86 (978-0-03-064576-1(X)) Holt, Rinehart & Winston.

—Elements of Language: Active Reader's Practice Book - Grade 8. 2000. pap. 13.86 (978-0-03-064577-8(8)) Holt, Rinehart & Winston.

—Elements of Language: Cross-Curricular Activities. 1999. 29.20 (978-0-03-052367-0(2)); 29.20 (978-0-03-052369-4(9)); 29.20 (978-0-03-052368-7(0)) Holt, Rinehart & Winston.

—Elements of Language: Grammar & Language Links. 1999. 29.20 (978-0-03-052359-5(1)); 29.20 (978-0-03-052364-9(8)); 29.20 (978-0-03-052358-8(3)); 29.20 (978-0-03-052362-5(1)); 29.20 (978-0-03-052363-2(X)) Holt, Rinehart & Winston.

—Elements of Language: Language Handbook Worksheets. 1999. pap. 33.00 (978-0-03-052404-2(0)); pap. 33.00 (978-0-03-052407-3(5)) Holt, Rinehart & Winston.

—Elements of Language: Language Handbook Worksheets Answer Key. 1999. pap. 13.86 (978-0-03-052413-4(X)); pap. 13.86 (978-0-03-052412-7(1)); pap. 13.86 (978-0-03-052409-7(1)); pap. 13.86 (978-0-03-052414-1(8)); pap. 13.86 (978-0-03-052419-6(9)) Holt, Rinehart & Winston.

Elements of Language: Reading Skills & Strategies Handbook - Middle School Edition. 2000. pap. 75.00 (978-0-03-054862-8(4)) Holt, Rinehart & Winston.

—Elements of Language: Spelling & Decoding Worksheets. 1999. pap. 13.86 (978-0-03-052463-9(6)); pap. 13.86 (978-0-03-052464-6(4)) Holt, Rinehart & Winston.

—Elements of Language: Support & Practice - Grade 10. 2000. pap. 37.80 (978-0-03-056399-7(2)) Holt, Rinehart & Winston.

—Elements of Language: Support & Practice - Grade 11. 2000. pap. 37.80 (978-0-03-056401-7(8)) Holt, Rinehart & Winston.

—Elements of Language: Support & Practice - Grade 12. 2000. pap. 37.80 (978-0-03-056402-4(6)) Holt, Rinehart & Winston.

—Elements of Language: Support & Practice - Grade 8. 2000. pap. 37.80 (978-0-03-056397-3(6)) Holt, Rinehart & Winston.

—Elements of Language: Support & Practice - Grade 9. 2000. pap. 37.80 (978-0-03-056398-0(4)) Holt, Rinehart & Winston.

—Elements of Literature: Assessment: Literature, Reading & Vocabulary. 2003. 4th ed. pap. 40.20 (978-0-03-068518-7(4)); 5th ed. pap. 40.20 (978-0-03-068517-0(6)); 5th ed. pap. 40.20 (978-0-03-068519-4(2)) Holt, Rinehart & Winston.

—Holt Ciencias y Technologia 2001: Earth: Directed Reading Worksheets. 2000. pap. 16.20 (978-0-03-064759-8(2)) Holt, Rinehart & Winston.

—Holt Ciencias y Technologia 2001: Physics: Directed Reading Worksheets. 2000. pap. 16.20 (978-0-03-064766-6(5)) Holt, Rinehart & Winston.

—Holt Reading: Interactive Worktext. 3rd ed. 2002. (Illus.). 329.06 incl. cd-rom (978-0-03-073261-4(1)) Holt, Rinehart & Winston.

—Holt Science & Technology: Directed Reading Answer Key. 4th ed. 2004. (Illus.). pap. 11.20 (978-0-03-037018-2(3)); pap. 11.20 (978-0-03-037019-9(1)); pap. 11.20 (978-0-03-037021-2(3)) Holt, Rinehart & Winston.

—Holt Science & Technology: Directed Reading Worksheets. 4th ed. 2004. pap. 15.00 (978-0-03-036992-6(4)); pap. 15.00 (978-0-03-036993-3(2)); pap. 15.00 (978-0-03-036994-0(0)) Holt, Rinehart & Winston.

—Holt Science & Technology: Earth: Directed Reading Worksheets. 2000. pap. 16.06 (978-0-03-054387-6(8)) Holt, Rinehart & Winston.

—Language Art Strategies & Practice for Reading No. 2: Holt Science & Technology. 2002. pap. 13.73 (978-0-03-071221-0(1)) Holt, Rinehart & Winston.

—Pennsylvania Preparation for the PSSA: Reading & Writing Manual. 2001. pap. 12.20 (978-0-03-068468-5(4)) Holt, Rinehart & Winston.

Home Pack Collection. 2005. (Poetry Promotes Literacy Ser.). (YA). (gr. k-3). 48.60 (978-0-8215-0569-4(6)); 48.60 (978-0-8215-0560-1(2)) Sadlier, William H. Inc.

Hooked on Phonics - Learn to Read: Classroom Edition. 1999. (Illus.). 1044p. (J). (ps-3). pap. 594.95 incl. audio (978-1-887942-83-6(1)) HOP, LLC.

Hooked on Phonics - Learn to Read: K-1st Grade. 2000. (Illus.). 266p. (J). (gr. k-1). pap. 49.95 incl. audio (978-1-887942-86-7(6)) HOP, LLC.

Hop, L. L. C. Hooked on First-Grade Super Workbook. 2006. 320p. 12.99 (978-1-931020-74-9(4)) HOP, LLC.

HOP, LLC. Hooked on Phonics Reading Comprehension. 2006. 64p. 3.79 (978-1-933863-94-8(3)) HOP, LLC.

A House for Me: Big Book: Level F. 16p. 31.50 (978-0-322-00375-0(X)) Wright Group, The.

The House on the Hill: Level 5, 6 vols. (Fluency Strand Ser.). (gr. 4-8). 45.00 (978-1-4045-1228-3(4)) Wright Group, The.

Housel, Debra J. Gymnastics: Easy Olympic Sports Reader. 2004. (U. S. Olympic Committee Easy Olympic Sports Readers Ser.). 16p. (J). pap. 2.99 (978-1-58000-112-0(2)) Griffin Publishing Group.

—Soccer: Easy Olympic Sports Reader. 2004. (U. S. Olympic Committee Easy Olympic Sports Readers Ser.). (Illus.). 16p. (J). pap. 2.99 (978-1-58000-113-7(0)) Griffin Publishing Group.

Housel, Debra J. & Migiliaccio, Eric. Cycling: Easy Olympic Sports Reader. 2004. (U. S. Olympic Committee Easy Olympic Sports Readers Ser.). (Illus.). 16p. (J). pap. 2.99 (978-1-58000-111-3(4)) Griffin Publishing Group.

Houses: Big Book: Level D. Group 1. (Story Box(R) Ser.). 16p. 20.95 (978-0-7802-7637-6(X)) Wright Group, The.

Houses: Level M, 6 vols. (Wonder Worldtm Ser.). 16p. 34.95 (978-0-7802-1219-0(3)) Wright Group, The.

How a Volcano Is Formed: Level M, 6 vols. (Wonder Worldtm Ser.). 16p. 34.95 (978-0-7802-2913-6(4)) Wright Group, The.

How Animals Hide: Level G, 6 vols. (Wonder Worldtm Ser.). 16p. 29.95 (978-0-7802-4581-5(4)) Wright Group, The.

How Ants Live, 6 vols. (Sunshinetm Science Ser.). 24p. (gr. 1-2). 31.50 (978-0-7802-0288-7(0)); 36.95 (978-0-7802-0539-0(1)) Wright Group, The.

How Many Are Here? Big Book. 2005. (Emergent Library: Vol. 1). (YA). (ps-1). 23.94 (978-0-8215-8904-5(0)) Sadlier, William H. Inc.

How the Chick Tricked the Fox. (Little Book Practice Reader Ser.). (J). (978-0-8136-0821-1(X)) Modern Curriculum Pr.

How to Make a Hen House. (J). (978-0-8136-5360-0(6)) Modern Curriculum Pr.

A Hug Is Warm: Big Book: Level D. Group 1. (Sunshinetm Ser.). 8p. 20.95 (978-0-7802-5729-0(4)) Wright Group, The.

Huggles Can Jungle: Level A. Group 1. (Sunshinetm Ser.). 8p. 20.95 (978-0-7802-5707-8(3)) Wright Group, The.

Huggles Goes Away: Level A. Group 1. (Sunshinetm Ser.). 8p. 20.95 (978-0-7802-5708-5(1)) Wright Group, The.

Hults, Alaska, ed. American History Reader's Theater Vol. 2244: Develop Reading Fluency & Text Comprehension Skills. Hillam, Corbin & Vangsgard, Amy, illus. 2004. 96p. (J). pap. 12.99 (978-1-59198-039-1(9) , 2244) Creative Teaching Pr., Inc.

—Philosophers to Astronauts Reader's Theater Vol. 2243: Develop Reading Fluency & Text Comprehension Skills. Hillam, Corbin & Vangsgard, Amy, illus. 2004. 96p. (J). pap. 12.99 (978-1-59198-038-4(0) , 2243) Creative Teaching Pr., Inc.

Hunt, Darleen L. Hide & Seek. Komarck, Michael, illus. 1999. 8p. (J). (ps-2). pap. 4.00 (978-1-929591-54-1(3)) Reading Rock, Inc.

Hurst-Nicholson, Janet, et al. Baby Bupe: Chitonga Version. Chisengele, tr. 2001. (Illus.). 32p. pap. 0.45 (978-0-521-01585-1(5)) Cambridge Univ. Pr.

—Baby Bupe: Cinyanja Version. Tembo, tr. 2001. (Illus.). 32p. pap. 0.45 (978-0-521-01586-8(3)) Cambridge Univ. Pr.

—Baby Bupe: Icibemba Version. Mulilo, tr. 2001. (Illus.). 32p. pap. 0.45 (978-0-521-01588-2(X)) Cambridge Univ. Pr.

—Baby Bupe: Kiikaonde Version. Muyebaa, tr. 2001. (Illus.). 32p. pap. 0.45 (978-0-521-01589-9(8)) Cambridge Univ. Pr.

—Baby Bupe: Luvale Version. Sakapaji, tr. 2001. (Illus.). 32p. pap. 0.45 (978-0-521-01591-2(X)) Cambridge Univ. Pr.

—Baby Bupe: Silozi Version. Mwendende, tr. 2001. (Illus.). 32p. pap. 0.45 (978-0-521-01592-9(8)) Cambridge Univ. Pr.

I am a Book Worm: Big Book: Level C. Group 1. (Sunshinetm Ser.). 8p. 20.95 (978-0-7802-5722-1(7)) Wright Group, The.

I am a Twin, 6 vols. 8p. (gr. k-1). 21.50 (978-0-322-02083-2(2)) Wright Group, The.

I Cannot Fit!, 6 vols. 8p. (gr. k-1). 21.50 (978-0-322-02071-9(9)) Wright Group, The.

I Could not Keep Silent: Level T. Group 3, 6 vols. (Sunshinetm Ser.). 48p. 44.95 (978-0-322-04601-6(7)) Wright Group, The.

I Have a Question Vol. 4: Big Book. 2005. (Emergent Library: Vol. 1). (YA). (ps-1). 23.94 (978-0-8215-8916-8(4)) Sadlier, William H. Inc.

I Love My Family: Big Book: Level C. Group 1. (Sunshinetm Ser.). 8p. 20.95 (978-0-7802-5723-8(5)) Wright Group, The.

I Love to Read, Vol. 3. 2005. (Emergent Library: Vol. 1). (YA). (ps-1). 23.94 (978-0-8215-8913-7(X)) Sadlier, William H. Inc.

I See You: Level E. 8p. 20.95 (978-0-322-00342-2(3)) Wright Group, The.

I Wonder, 6 vols. (Sunshinetm Ser.). 16p. (gr. k up). 29.50 (978-0-7802-5423-7(6)) Wright Group, The.

I Wonder Why? Level G, 6 vols. (Wonder Worldtm Ser.). 16p. 29.95 (978-0-7802-2016-4(1)) Wright Group, The.

If I Had a Piece of String. (J). 26.20 (978-0-8136-8426-0(9)); 59.50 (978-0-8136-7972-3(9)); 1998. pap. (978-0-8136-8301-0(7)) Modern Curriculum Pr.

If I Were a Fish. (J). 26.20 (978-0-8136-8443-7(9)); 59.50 (978-0-8136-8008-8(5)) Modern Curriculum Pr.

In January & June, Vol. 4. 2005. (Emergent Library: Vol. 1). (YA). (ps-1). 23.94 (978-0-8215-8915-1(6)) Sadlier, William H. Inc.

In the Graveyard: Decodable Books, 6 vols. (Fasttrack Reading Ser.). 24p. (gr. 4-8). 40.95 (978-0-322-05986-3(0)) Wright Group, The.

In the Graveyard Play 12: Decodable Plays, 6 vols. (Fasttrack Reading Ser.). 24p. (gr. 4-8). 40.95 (978-0-322-06000-5(1)) Wright Group, The.

In the Mirror: Big Book: Level A. Group 1. (Story Box(R) Ser.). 8p. 20.95 (978-0-7802-7625-3(6)) Wright Group, The.

In the News, 6 vols. (Wildcats Ser.). 32p. (gr. 2-8). (978-0-322-02437-3(4)) Wright Group, The.

In the News: Level O, 6 vols. (Wonder Worldtm Ser.). 48p. 39.95 (978-0-7802-2959-4(2)) Wright Group, The.

Incredible Places: 6 Each of 1 Anthology, 6 vols. (Wildcats Ser.). 32p. (gr. 2-8). (978-0-322-00587-7(6)) Wright Group, The.

Los increibles viajes de las Semillas 4: Leveled Books. 2001. (McGraw-Hill. Lectura Ser.). (ENG & SPA.). (gr. 2 up). (978-0-02-188029-4(8)) Macmillan/McGraw-Hill Schl. Div.

Instructional Fair. Story Elements: Learning about the Components of Stories to Deepen Comprehension. 2001. (Basic Skills Ser.). 48p. (J). (gr. 5-6). pap. 6.99 (978-0-7424-0104-4(9) , IF5637) School Specialty Publishing.

Inventions of Ancient Civilization Collection, 4 pkgs., Set. (J). (gr. 3-6). 327.00 (978-0-8136-6355-5(5)) Modern Curriculum Pr.

La invitacion de don Raton 14: Leveled Books. 2001. (McGraw-Hill. Lectura Ser.). (ENG & SPA.). (gr. 1 up). (978-0-02-187967-0(2)) Macmillan/McGraw-Hill Schl. Div.

Iris la Bonga & the Helpful Taxi Driver: Level T. Group 1, 6 vols. (Sunshinetm Ser.). 48p. 44.95 (978-0-7802-5598-2(4)) Wright Group, The.

Las Islas 17: Leveled Books. 2001. (McGraw-Hill. Lectura Ser.). (ENG & SPA.). (gr. 5 up). (978-0-02-188289-2(4)) Macmillan/McGraw-Hill Schl. Div.

Las islas Galapagos: un lugar Maravilloso 11: Leveled Books. 2001. (McGraw-Hill. Lectura Ser.). (ENG & SPA.). (gr. 5 up). (978-0-02-188283-0(5)) Macmillan/McGraw-Hill Schl. Div.

La islita de Palmasiolas 6: Leveled Books. 2001. (McGraw-Hill. Lectura Ser.). (ENG & SPA.). (gr. 2 up). (978-0-02-188007-2(7)) Macmillan/McGraw-Hill Schl. Div.

It Takes Time to Grow, 6 vols. (Sunshinetm Ser.). 16p. (gr. k up). 29.50 (978-0-7802-5434-3(1)) Wright Group, The.

It's Noisy at Night: Level F, 6 vols. (Wonder Worldtm Ser.). 16p. 29.95 (978-0-7802-1039-4(5)) Wright Group, The.

I've Been Working on the Railroad. (Song Box(R) Ser.). (gr. 1-2). 31.50 (978-0-7802-0936-7(2)); 8.50 incl. audio (978-0-7802-0938-1(9)) Wright Group, The.

I've Been Working on the Railroad: 1 Big Book, 6 Each of 1 Student Book, & 1 Cassette. (Song Box(R) Ser.). (gr. 1-2). 68.95 (978-0-7802-0939-8(7)) Wright Group, The.

I've Been Working on the Railroad: 6 Each of 1 Student Book, 6 vols. (Song Box(R) Ser.). (gr. 1-2). 29.50 (978-0-7802-0937-4(0)) Wright Group, The.

Jack de Pert at the Supermarket: Level J, 6 vols. (Wonder Worldtm Ser.). 16p. 29.95 (978-0-7802-1040-0(9)) Wright Group, The.

Jackson, Barbara A. How to Read with Magic Sounds... an Advanced Reading Program Phonics First. 2001. (Illus.). 63p. (J). (ps-6). stu. ed. 10.00 (978-0-9712857-5-0(6)) Educational Innovations, Inc.

—How to Read with Magic Sounds Classic - Continum Collection: Phonics First - Second Guide, 2 vols. 2001. (Illus.). (J). pap. 50.00 (978-0-9712857-0-5(5)) Educational Innovations, Inc.

—How to Read with Magicsounds... a Beginning Reading Program Phonics First, Vol. 2. 2001. (Illus.). 43p. (J). (ps-6). pap., stu. ed. 10.00 (978-0-9712857-4-3(8)) Educational Innovations, Inc.

Jackson, Ian. Livewire Real Lives Pat Rafter. 2000. (Livewires Ser.). (gr. 6-9). pap. 6.00 (978-0-521-79690-3(3)) Cambridge Univ. Pr.

—Livewire Real Lives Silverchair. 2001. (Livewires Ser.). pap. 5.00 (978-0-521-01266-9(X)) Cambridge Univ. Pr.

Jacobs, Heidi. The Literaturea Pocket Anthology. 2001. 72p. suppl. ed. 10.00 (978-0-321-09552-7(9)) Longman Publishing Group.

Jake's Big Day: Long Vowel a, CVCe Pattern: Level B, 6 vols. (Wright Skills Ser.). 16p. (gr. k-3). 17.95 (978-0-322-01465-7(4)) Wright Group, The.

Jan Can Juggle. (Little Book Practice Reader). (J). (978-0-8136-5362-4(2)) Modern Curriculum Pr.

Janet & Donald: Decodable Books, 6 vols. (Fasttrack Reading Ser.). 24p. (gr. 4-8). 40.95 (978-0-322-05984-9(4)) Wright Group, The.

Janet & Donald Play 7: Decodable Plays, 6 vols. (Fasttrack Reading Ser.). 24p. (gr. 4-8). 40.95 (978-0-322-05998-6(4)) Wright Group, The.

Los jardineros de la Sra Mills 6: Leveled Books. 2001. (McGraw-Hill. Lectura Ser.). (ENG & SPA.). (gr. 5 up). (978-0-02-188230-4(4)) Macmillan/McGraw-Hill Schl. Div.

Jean Batter Pioneer of the Sky: Level R, 6 vols. (Wonder Worldtm Ser.). 48p. 44.95 (978-0-7802-7079-4(7)) Wright Group, The.

Jen & the Pets: Consonants k, v, y; Short Vowel e Word Families: Level A, 6 vols. (Wright Skills Ser.). 12p. (gr. k-3). 17.95 (978-0-322-01454-1(9)) Wright Group, The.

Jennett, Pamela. Discoverers & Inventors Reader's Theater Vol. 2245: Develop Reading Fluency & Test Comprehension Skills. Hults, Alaska, ed. Hilliam, Corbin & Vangsgard, Amy, illus. 2004. 96p. (J). pap. 12.99 (978-1-59198-040-7(2) , 2245) Creative Teaching Pr., Inc.

Jespersen, Amanda. The Little Lost Goat: Chilomwe Version. Nkhoma, Wilson, tr. 1999. (Cambridge Reading Routes Ser.). (Illus.). 16p. pap. 3.70 (978-0-521-66848-4(4)) Cambridge Univ. Pr.

—The Little Lost Goat: Chinyanja Version. Iphani, Max, tr. 1999. (Cambridge Reading Routes Ser.). (Illus.). 16p. pap. 3.70 (978-0-521-66879-8(4)) Cambridge Univ. Pr.

—The Little Lost Goat: Chitumbuka Version. Chirambo, Reuben, tr. 1999. (Cambridge Reading Routes Ser.). (Illus.). 16p. pap. 3.70 (978-0-521-66867-5(0)) Cambridge Univ. Pr.

—The Little Lost Goat: Chiyao Version. Kaliati, Mailos, tr. 1999. (Cambridge Reading Routes Ser.). (Illus.). 16p. pap. 3.70 (978-0-521-66857-6(3)) Cambridge Univ. Pr.

Jesperson, Amanda. The Little Lost Goat Lugbara Version: Ndria-mva Avipiri. Draville, Ben & Mawa, Robert, trs. 2001. 16p. pap. 0.90 (978-0-521-00619-4(8)) Cambridge Univ. Pr.

Jim Pig Is Mad: Short Vowel i: Level A, 6 vols. (Wright Skills Ser.). 12p. (gr. k-3). 17.95 (978-0-322-03115-9(X)) Wright Group, The.

Jim's Trumpet: Level K. Group 1. (Sunshinetm Ser.). 16p. 36.50 (978-0-7802-5793-1(6)) Wright Group, The.

Joe's Toe: Long o Digraphs: Level B, 6 vols. (Wright Skills Ser.). 16p. (gr. k-3). 26.50 (978-0-322-01480-0(8)) Wright Group, The.

Joey's Rowboat, Vol. 2. 2005. (Early Library). (YA). (ps-3). 23.94 (978-0-8215-8957-1(1)) Sadlier, William H. Inc.

Jog to the Dam: Consonants g, h, j; Short Vowel o word families: Level A, 6 vols. (Wright Skills Ser.). 12p. (gr. k-3). 17.95 (978-0-322-01448-0(4)) Wright Group, The.

Johnson, Larry C., ed. Securing the Nation: Issues in American National Security Since 9/11, 3 vols. 2005. (Securing the Nation Ser.). (Illus.). 112p. (gr. 9-13). pap. 90.00 (978-0-7910-7750-4(0) , Chelsea Hse.) Facts On File, Inc.

Johnson, Lucille M. Reading Activities: Supplementary Reading with Instructional Games. Johnson, Lucille M., illus. 2002. iv, 42p. (J). (gr. k-3). pap. 8.00 (978-0-9725800-0-7(X)) BOOKLINKS.

Jones, Beau, et al. Insights Reading As Thinking: Strategies for Reading with a Purpose - Purple Level Student Book. 1998. (Illus.). (YA). (gr. 7). pap., stu. ed. 7.00 (978-1-57091-082-1(0)) Charlesbridge Publishing, Inc.

—Insights Reading As Thinking: Strategies for Reading with a Purpose - Silver Level Student Book. 1998. (Illus.). (YA). (gr. 8). pap., stu. ed. 7.00 (978-1-57091-084-5(7)) Charlesbridge Publishing, Inc.

Josephs, Ben. Where Dinosaurs Walked. 2003. (Compass Point Phonics Readers Ser.). (Illus.). 16p. (J). (gr. 1 up). 13.26 (978-0-7565-0531-8(3)) Compass Point Bks.

Joyce, Timothy. Cambridge Checkpoints VCE Accounting Unit 4 2004. 2003. (Cambridge Checkpoints Ser.). pap. 10.55 (978-0-521-54247-0(2)) Cambridge Univ. Pr.

Joyce, William. Santa Calls Stationery Set. Date not set. (J). 11.95 (978-0-694-00806-3(0)) HarperCollins Pubs.

El juego Milenario 2: Leveled Books. 2001. (McGraw-Hill. Lectura Ser.). (ENG & SPA.). (gr. 3 up). (978-0-02-188123-9(5)) Macmillan/McGraw-Hill Schl. Div.

Julio, Susan. 15 Fun & Easy Games for Young Learners: Reading. 2001. 48p. pap. 9.95 (978-0-439-20255-8(8)) Scholastic, Inc.

Kaeden Literature Series: A collection of 48 teacher Favorites!, 48 books. 2006. (Illus.). (J). (ps-1). pap. 215.00 (978-1-57874-005-5(3)) Kaeden Corp.

Kaeden Program: A Collection, 126 books. 2000. (Illus.). (J). (ps-1). pap. 575.00 (978-1-57874-018-5(5)) Kaeden Corp.

Kalaidjian, Walter B. Understanding & Writing about Literature: Used with ... Kalaidjian-Understanding Literature: an Introduction to Reading & Writing, MLA Update. 2003. (YA). 2.76 (978-0-618-45394-8(6) , 328829) Houghton Mifflin College Div.

Kalar, Bonnie. Early Phonetic Readers - Set E, 7 bks., set. Spreen, Kathe, illus. Incl. Ann Paints & Plays. pap. (978-1-891619-40-3(3)); Clair at Home. pap. (978-1-891619-44-1(6)); Good Day. pap. (978-1-891619-41-0(1)); Kirk & the Deer. pap. (978-1-891619-43-4(8)); Miss Lane's Class. pap. (978-1-891619-38-0(1)); Neal Camps Out. pap. (978-1-891619-39-7(X)); Trip to the Beach. pap. (978-1-891619-42-7(X)); 12p. (J). (ps-2). (Illus.). Set pap. 14.50 (978-1-891619-37-3(3)) Corona Pr.

Karwowski, C. Summarizing: Focusing on Main Ideas & Details & Restating in Concise Form. 2001. (Basic Skills Ser.). 48p. (J). (gr. 3-4). pap. 6.99 (978-0-7424-0106-8(5) , IF5641) School Specialty Publishing.

Kauzlarich, David. Sociological Classics: A Prentice Hall Pocket Reader. 2004. 144p. (C). pap. 20.00 (978-0-13-191806-1(0) , Prentice Hall) Prentice Hall PTR.

Keeping Baby Animals Safe. 2005. (Emergent Library: Vol. 2). (YA). (ps-1). 23.94 (978-0-8215-8934-2(2)) Sadlier, William H. Inc.

Keeping Baby Animals Safe: Take-Home Book. 2005. (Emergent Library: Vol. 2). (YA). (ps-1). 12.60 (978-0-8215-7264-1(4)) Sadlier, William H. Inc.

Keller, Ellen. Kids Manage Money. 2002. (Illus.). 32p. (J). pap. (978-0-7922-8694-3(4)) National Geographic Society.

Keys. (J). (978-0-8136-5369-3(X)) Modern Curriculum Pr.

Kids Can Learn Franklin Staff, ed. Early Reading. 2004. 32p. pap. (978-1-55337-604-0(8)) Kids Can Pr., Ltd.

Kids Can Press Staff, Press Can. Alphabet Mazes. 2004. (Kids Can Learn with Franklin Ser.). (Illus.). 32p. (J). (gr. k-3). (978-1-55337-592-0(0)) Kids Can Pr., Ltd.

—Measurement. 2004. (Kids Can Learn with Franklin Ser.). (Illus.). 32p. (J). (gr. k-3). (978-1-55337-595-1(5)) Kids Can Pr., Ltd.

The King Who Could Knit: Initial Silent Consonants: Level C, 6 vols. (Wright Skills Ser.). 16p. (gr. k-3). 26.50 (978-0-322-01502-9(2)) Wright Group, The.

The Kitty: Long Vowels e, y, CVCe & Final y Patterns: Level B, 6 vols. (Wright Skills Ser.). 16p. (gr. k-3). 17.95 (978-0-322-03130-2(3)) Wright Group, The.

Koch, Kamla Devi, et al. Teen Stories: Personal Stories for Students Who Are Beginning to Read. (J). tchr. ed. 8.95 (978-0-916591-20-5(4)); stu. ed. 8.95 (978-0-916591-19-9(0)) Linmore Publishing, Inc.

Kramer. Keys to Excellence: Integrated Language Arts - Level C - Grade 3. 1999. pap. 17.27 (978-0-7398-1972-2(0)) Steck-Vaughn.

—Keys to Excellence: Integrated Language Arts - Level D - Grade 4. 1999. pap. 17.27 (978-0-7398-1973-9(9)) Steck-Vaughn.

—Keys to Excellence: Integrated Language Arts - Level E - Grade 5. 1999. pap. 17.27 (978-0-7398-1974-6(7)) Steck-Vaughn.

—Keys to Excellence: Integrated Language Arts - Level F - Grade 6. 1999. pap. 17.27 (978-0-7398-1975-3(5)) Steck-Vaughn.

—Keys to Excellence: Integrated Language Arts - Level G - Grade 7. 1999. pap. 17.27 (978-0-7398-1976-0(3)) Steck-Vaughn.

—Keys to Excellence: Integrated Language Arts - Level H - Grade 8. 1999. pap. 17.27 (978-0-7398-1977-7(1)) Steck-Vaughn.

Krulik, Nancy E. & Encarnacion, Elizabeth. Rhyme Time. 2005. (Illus.). 20p. (J). pap. 12.95 (978-0-7624-2190-9(8) , Running Pr. Kids) Running Pr. Bk. Pubs.

L Omino di Panpepato. pap. 14.95 (978-88-04-44206-6(9)) Mondadori ITA. *Dist:* Distribooks, Inc.

La Jars, David. Is Anyone Home? rev. ed. 2004. (Talk Together Ser.). (Illus.). 24p. (J). (ps-k). pap. 5.95 (978-1-58728-018-4(3) , Two Can Publishing) T&N Children's Publishing.

A la luz de una Vela 19: Leveled Books. 2001. (McGraw-Hill. Lectura Ser.). (ENG & SPA.). (gr. 2 up). (978-0-02-188068-3(9)) Macmillan/McGraw-Hill Schl. Div.

Lakeshore Learning Materials Staff, contrib. by. Bread & Jam for Frances Packet. 2000. (J). pap. 34.95 (978-1-929255-48-1(9)) Lakeshore Learning Materials.

—Ira Sleeps over Packet. 2000. (J). pap. 19.95 (978-1-929255-44-3(6)) Lakeshore Learning Materials.

—Strega Nona Packet. 2000. (J). pap. 19.95 (978-1-929255-43-6(8)) Lakeshore Learning Materials.

Landry, Deborah. Too Noisy: Emergent. 2002. (Bright Sparks Ser.). (Illus.). 16p. pap. 2.30 (978-0-521-75143-8(8)) Cambridge Univ. Pr.

Landry, Debra. I'm Smart: Emergent. Plant, Andrew, illus. 2002. (Bright Sparks Ser.). 16p. pap. 2.30 (978-0-521-75142-1(X)) Cambridge Univ. Pr.

—Max's Birthday: Emergent. Korcak, Celina, illus. 2002. (Bright Sparks Ser.). 16p. pap. 2.30 (978-0-521-75141-4(1)) Cambridge Univ. Pr.

Lane, Kerri. Sweet Gemma. 2002. (Bright Sparks Ser.). (Illus.). 16p. pap. 2.30 (978-0-521-75405-7(4)) Cambridge Univ. Pr.

The Language of Literature. 2002. (gr. 10 up). stu. ed. (978-0-618-17040-1(5) , 2-71094); (gr. 6 up). stu. ed. (978-0-618-13661-2(4) , 2-04025); (gr. 7 up). stu. ed. (978-0-618-13662-9(2) , 2-04026); (gr. 8 up). stu. ed. (978-0-618-13663-6(0) , 2-04027); (gr. 9 up). stu. ed. (978-0-618-17034-0(0) , 2-71090) McDougal Littell Inc.

Language Works Rhyme Time. 8p. (J). (978-0-8136-3519-4(5)) Modern Curriculum Pr.

Language Works Staff. Message of the Dance. (J). 28.08 (978-0-8136-3504-0(7)) Modern Curriculum Pr.

The Last Draw. 1998. (Comic Book Ser.). (Illus.). (J). (978-0-7652-0300-7(6)) Modern Curriculum Pr.

Last-Minute Rescue Little Book: Early Reading Fluency, Level C. 2004. pap. 6.00 (978-0-7398-8300-6(3)) Steck-Vaughn.

Laura y los zapatos Rojos 23: Leveled Books. 2001. (McGraw-Hill. Lectura Ser.). (ENG & SPA.). (gr. 2 up). (978-0-02-188048-5(4)) Macmillan/McGraw-Hill Schl. Div.

Lazos familiares, Unidad 1: Superlibros (Big Books) 2000. (Aventuras A Traves Del Tiempo Ser.). (ENG & SPA.). (gr. 2 up). (978-0-02-147845-3(7)) Macmillan/McGraw-Hill Schl. Div.

Leaf, Munro. Reading Can Be Fun. 2004. (Illus.). 56p. (J). (gr. 2-7). 14.95 (978-0-7893-1203-7(4)) Universe Publishing.

Leaney, Cindy. What Do You See? Whitehouse, Patty, ed. King, Sue & Wilks, Peter, illus. 2004. (Friendly Phonics Ser.). 24p. (J). lib. bdg. 14.95 (978-1-59054-039-8(5)) Fitzgerald Bks.

LeapFrog Schoolhouse Staff. Read-It-All Books. 2003. (YA). (gr. 3 up). tchr. ed., spiral bd. 19.95 (978-1-59319-017-0(4) , LeapFrog Schl. Hse.) LeapFrog Enterprises, Inc.

LeapFrog Staff, compiled by. The Birthday Surprise. 2002. (J). (ps-2). 14.95 (978-1-58605-905-7(X) , LeapFrog Schl. Hse.) LeapFrog Enterprises, Inc.

LeapFrog Staff & Disney Staff, compiled by. Monsters, Inc. 2002. (J). (gr. k-2). spiral bd. 14.99 (978-1-58605-187-7(3)) LeapFrog Enterprises, Inc.

Learning Co Bks Staff. Best Gift Ever. 2005. (Learn to Read Library). pap. 3.99 (978-0-7630-8030-3(6)) Riverdeep, Inc.

—Lucky for Us! 2005. (Learn to Read Library). pap. 3.99 (978-0-7630-8037-2(3)) Riverdeep, Inc.

—New Friend. 2005. (Learn to Read Library). pap. 3.99 (978-0-7630-8032-7(2)) Riverdeep, Inc.

—Night Noises. 2005. (Learn to Read Library). pap. 3.99 (978-0-7630-8031-0(4)) Riverdeep, Inc.

—Starry, Starry Night. 2005. (Learn to Read Library). pap. 3.99 (978-0-7630-8028-0(4)) Riverdeep, Inc.

Learning Company Books Staff, ed. Reader Rabbit: Reading Comprehension. 2003. (Illus.). 32p. (J). pap., wbk. ed. 3.99 (978-0-7630-7643-6(0)) Learning Co. Bks.

Leber, Nancy. Sounds All Around Us. 2003. (Compass Point Phonics Readers Ser.). (Illus.). 16p. (J). (gr. 1 up). 13.26 (978-0-7565-0524-0(0)) Compass Point Bks.

Lee, Frances. Glasses. 1999. (ps-2). lib. bdg. 11.20 (978-0-613-30435-1(7)) Tandem Library Bks.

Lee tu libro, Lola! 4: Leveled Books. 2001. (McGraw-Hill. Lectura Ser.). (ENG & SPA.). (gr. 1 up). (978-0-02-187933-5(8)) Macmillan/McGraw-Hill Schl. Div.

Legendary Places: 6 Each of 1 Anthology, 6 vols. (Wildcatstm Ser.). 32p. (gr. 2-8). (978-0-322-02427-4(7)) Wright Group, The.

Leggat, Gillian. A Surprise for the Tin Can Gang. Todd, Mel, illus. 1999. (Cambridge Reading Routes Ser.). 24p. pap. 5.50 (978-0-521-77908-1(1)) Cambridge Univ. Pr.

Leggat, Gillian, et al. Stop That Noise! Chitonga Version. Chisengele, tr. 2001. (Illus.). 32p. pap. 0.45 (978-0-521-01609-4(6)) Cambridge Univ. Pr.

—Stop That Noise! Icibemba Version. Mulilo, tr. 2001. (Illus.). 32p. pap. 0.45 (978-0-521-01612-4(6)) Cambridge Univ. Pr.

—Stop That Noise! Kiikaonde Version. Muyebaa, tr. 2001. (Illus.). 32p. pap. 0.45 (978-0-521-01613-1(4)) Cambridge Univ. Pr.

—Stop That Noise! Luvale Version. Sakapaji, tr. 2001. (Illus.). 32p. pap. 0.45 (978-0-521-01615-5(0)) Cambridge Univ. Pr.

—Stop That Noise! Silozi Version. Mwendende, tr. 2001. (Illus.). 32p. pap. 0.45 (978-0-521-01616-2(9)) Cambridge Univ. Pr.

Legler, Caroline. Super Words Early Reading Program, 10 vols. ed. 2005. (Illus.). (J). 16.95 (978-0-9771233-0-8(8)) Legler, Caroline.

Legs: Big Book: Level C. 8p. 20.95 (978-0-322-00343-9(1)) Wright Group, The.

Legs: Level C, 6 vols. 8p. 24.95 (978-0-7802-9120-1(4)) Wright Group, The.

Legs, Legs, Legs: Big Book: Level B. (Wonder Worldtm Ser.). 16p. 26.50 (978-0-7802-2829-0(4)) Wright Group, The.

Legs, Legs, Legs: Level B, 6 vols. (Wonder Worldtm Ser.). 16p. 24.95 (978-0-7802-1087-5(5)) Wright Group, The.

Let's Begin Reading. 1998. (Richard Scarry Bks.). (Illus.). 32p. (J). (gr. k-2). pap. 4.95 (978-0-88724-489-6(0) , CD-5853) Carson-Dellosa Publishing Co., Inc.

Let's Learn First Skills! 1998. (Illus.). 32p. (J). (ps-2). pap. 4.95 (978-0-88724-491-9(2) , CD-5855) Carson-Dellosa Publishing Co., Inc.

Let's Meet Biographies, 6 vols. 2005. (Let's Meet Biographies Ser.). (Illus.). 32p. (gr. 2-4). pap. 138.00 (978-0-7910-7317-9(3) , Chelsea Hse.) Facts On File, Inc.

Letter Cluster Books Reproducibles. 64p. (gr. k-3). 26.50 (978-0-322-01549-4(9)) Wright Group, The.

Letter Clusters Student Book: 6 Each of 1 Student Book. 32p. (gr. k-3). 31.95 (978-0-7802-9033-4(X)) Wright Group, The.

Level C, Vol. 2. (J). 5.99 (978-0-8136-1703-9(0)) Modern Curriculum Pr.

Levin, Amy. A Bear's Year. 2003. (Compass Point Phonics Readers Ser.). (Illus.). 16p. (J). (gr. 1 up). 13.26 (978-0-7565-0500-4(3)) Compass Point Bks.

—Hard Workers. 2003. (Compass Point Phonics Readers Ser.). (Illus.). 16p. (J). (gr. 1 up). 13.26 (978-0-7565-0508-0(9)) Compass Point Bks.

—The Vet. 2003. (Compass Point Phonics Readers Ser.). (Illus.). 16p. (J). (gr. 1 up). 13.26 (978-0-7565-0528-8(3)) Compass Point Bks.

Levinson, Nancy Smiler. Prairie Friends. Schuett, Stacey, illus. 2003. (I Can Read Bks.). 64p. (J). (gr. k-3). 16.89 (978-0-06-028002-4(6)) HarperCollins Pubs.

Libro 1, Libro del Estudiante. 2001. (McGraw-Hill. Lectura Ser.). (ENG & SPA.). (gr. 3 up). stu. ed. (978-0-02-184842-3(4)) Macmillan/McGraw-Hill Schl. Div.

Libro 1, Libro del Estudiante 1: Pupil Edition. 2001. (McGraw-Hill. Lectura Ser.). (ENG & SPA.). (gr. 2 up). (978-0-02-184840-9(8)) Macmillan/McGraw-Hill Schl. Div.

Libro 1, Unidad 1 Guia del Maestro. 2001. (McGraw-Hill. Lectura Ser.). (ENG & SPA.). (gr. 2 up). (978-0-02-184859-1(9)); (gr. 3 up). (978-0-02-184865-2(3)) Macmillan/McGraw-Hill Schl. Div.

Libro 1, Unidad 2 Guia del Maestro, Vol. 2. 2001. (McGraw-Hill. Lectura Ser.). (ENG & SPA.). (gr. 2 up). (978-0-02-184860-7(2)); (gr. 3 up). (978-0-02-184866-9(1)) Macmillan/McGraw-Hill Schl. Div.

Libro 1, Unidad 3 Guia del Maestro, Vol. 3. 2001. (McGraw-Hill. Lectura Ser.). (ENG & SPA.). (gr. 2 up). (978-0-02-184861-4(0)); (gr. 3 up). (978-0-02-184867-6(X)) Macmillan/McGraw-Hill Schl. Div.

Libro 2, Libro del Estudiante. 2001. (McGraw-Hill. Lectura Ser.). (ENG & SPA.). (gr. 2 up). stu. ed. (978-0-02-184841-6(6)); (gr. 3 up). stu. ed. (978-0-02-184843-0(2)) Macmillan/McGraw-Hill Schl. Div.

Libro 2, Unidad 1 Guia del Maestro. 2001. (McGraw-Hill. Lectura Ser.). (ENG & SPA.). (gr. 2 up). (978-0-02-184862-1(9)); (gr. 3 up). (978-0-02-184868-3(8)) Macmillan/McGraw-Hill Schl. Div.

Libro 2, Unidad 2 Guia del Maestro, Vol. 2. 2001. (McGraw-Hill. Lectura Ser.). (ENG & SPA.). (gr. 2 up). (978-0-02-184863-8(7)); (gr. 3 up). (978-0-02-184869-0(6)) Macmillan/McGraw-Hill Schl. Div.

Libro 2, Unidad 3 Guia del Maestro, Vol. 3. 2001. (McGraw-Hill. Lectura Ser.). (ENG & SPA.). (gr. 2 up). (978-0-02-184864-5(5)); (gr. 3 up). (978-0-02-184870-6(X)) Macmillan/McGraw-Hill Schl. Div.

Libro del Estudiante. 2001. (Artes Del Lenguaje Ser.). (ENG & SPA.). (gr. 2 up). (978-0-02-245303-9(2)); (gr. 3 up). (978-0-02-245304-6(0)); (gr. 4 up). (978-0-02-245305-3(9)); (gr. 5 up). (978-0-02-184845-4(9)); (gr. 5 up). (978-0-02-245306-0(7)); (gr. 6 up). (978-0-02-245307-7(5)) Macmillan/McGraw-Hill Schl. Div.

Libro del Estudiante: Pupil Edition. 2001. (McGraw-Hill. Lectura Ser.). (ENG & SPA.). (gr. k up). (978-0-02-186675-5(9)); (gr. 4 up). (978-0-02-184844-7(0)); (gr. 6 up). (978-0-02-184846-1(7)) Macmillan/McGraw-Hill Schl. Div.

Libros de la Biblioteca: Libros de la Biblioteca (Classroom Library) 2000. (Aventuras A Traves Del Tiempo Ser.). (ENG & SPA.). (gr. k up). (978-0-02-148503-1(8)); (gr. 1 up). (978-0-02-148504-8(6)); (gr. 2 up). (978-0-02-148505-5(4)); (gr. 3 up). (978-0-02-148506-2(2)) Macmillan/McGraw-Hill Schl. Div.

Libros para leer en casa y actividades Diarias: Resources & Ancillaries. 2001. (McGraw-Hill. Lectura Ser.). (ENG & SPA.). (gr. 1 up). (978-0-02-186561-1(2)); (gr. 2 up). (978-0-02-186562-8(0)); (gr. 3 up). (978-0-02-186563-5(9)) Macmillan/McGraw-Hill Schl. Div.

Lindi, Nkululeko. Three Fat Cats: Icibemba Version. Mulilo, tr. 2001. (Illus.). 8p. pap. 0.45 (978-0-521-01548-6(0)) Cambridge Univ. Pr.

—Three Fat Cats: Kiikaonde Version. Muyebaa, tr. 2001. (Illus.). 8p. pap. 0.45 (978-0-521-01549-3(9)) Cambridge Univ. Pr.

Lindi, Nkululeko & Chisengele. Three Fat Cats: Chitonga Version. 2001. (Illus.). 8p. pap. 0.45 (978-0-521-01545-5(6)) Cambridge Univ. Pr.

Lindi, Nkululeko & Tembo. Three Fat Cats: Cinyanja Version. 2001. (Illus.). 8p. pap. 0.45 (978-0-521-01546-2(4)) Cambridge Univ. Pr.

Lindstrom, Florence. Adventures in Phonics. (J). Level C. 2000. 91p. pap., tchr. ed. 7.00 (978-1-930092-80-8(6) , CLP29821); Level C. 2000. (Illus.). 212p. (gr. 2). pap., wbk. ed. 8.00 (978-1-930092-79-2(2) , CLP29820); Level B. 2001. (Illus.). 230p. (gr. 1). pap., wbk. ed. 8.00 (978-1-930092-77-8(6) , CLP29815) Christian Liberty Pr.

Listen: Big Book: Level D. (Visionstm Ser.). 8p. 20.95 (978-0-322-00309-5(1)) Wright Group, The.

Literature: Timeless Voices, Timeless Themes, Platinum Level 2001. (gr. 10). pap., tchr.'s training gde. ed. 5.47 (978-0-13-051438-7(1)) Prentice Hall PTR.

Literature Connections English: 1984. 2004. (gr. 6-12). (978-0-395-87471-4(8) , 2-70831) McDougal Littell Inc.

Literature Connections English: A Midsummer Night's Dream. 2004. (gr. 6-12). (978-0-395-77543-1(4) , 2-80112) McDougal Littell Inc.

Literature Connections English: A Place Where the Sea Remembers. 2004. (gr. 6-12). (978-0-395-83361-2(2) , 2-70784) McDougal Littell Inc.

Literature Connections English: Ethan Frome. 2004. (gr. 6-12). (978-0-395-77548-6(5) , 2-80117) McDougal Littell Inc.

Literature Connections English: Fallen Angels. 2004. (gr. 6-12). (978-0-395-83360-5(4) , 2-70783) McDougal Littell Inc.

Literature Connections English: Go Tell It on the Mountain. 2004. (gr. 6-12). (978-0-395-86994-9(3) , 2-70830) McDougal Littell Inc.

Literature Connections English: Jane Eyre. 2004. (gr. 6-12). (978-0-395-77557-8(4) , 2-80126) McDougal Littell Inc.

Literature Connections English: Jubilee. 2004. (gr. 6-12). (978-0-395-83362-9(0) , 2-70785) McDougal Littell Inc.

Literature Connections English: Julius Caesar. 2004. (gr. 6-12). (978-0-395-77542-4(6) , 2-80111) McDougal Littell Inc.

Literature Connections English: Kaffir Boy. 2004. (gr. 6-12). (978-0-395-85804-2(6) , 2-70804) McDougal Littell Inc.

Literature Connections English: Macbeth. 2004. (gr. 6-12). (978-0-395-77553-0(1) , 2-80122) McDougal Littell Inc.

Literature Connections English: My Antonia. 2004. (gr. 6-12). (978-0-395-77539-4(6) , 2-80108) McDougal Littell Inc.

Literature Connections English: Nervous Conditions. 2004. (gr. 6-12). (978-0-395-77560-8(4) , 2-80129) McDougal Littell Inc.

Literature Connections English: Picture Bride. 2004. (gr. 6-12). (978-0-395-77540-0(X) , 2-80109) McDougal Littell Inc.

Literature Connections English: Pride & Prejudice. 2004. (gr. 6-12). (978-0-395-77556-1(6) , 2-80125) McDougal Littell Inc.

Little Bear's Friend. 2003. 31.95 (978-0-673-75802-6(8)) Celebration Pr.

Little Kittens. (Little Book Practice Reader). (J). (978-0-8136-5365-5(7)) Modern Curriculum Pr.

Littlewort, Elizabeth. Thuli's Mattress: Chinyanja Version. Iphani, Max, tr. 1999. (Cambridge Reading Routes Ser.). (Illus.). 16p. pap. 3.70 (978-0-521-66880-4(8)) Cambridge Univ. Pr.

—Thuli's Mattress: Oromo Version. Adem, Omer Kedir, tr. 1999. (Cambridge Reading Routes Ser.). (Illus.). 16p. pap. 3.70 (978-0-521-66837-8(9)) Cambridge Univ. Pr.

—Thuli's Mattress Lugbara Version: Tirua Vele Mufaliso Ri. Draville, Ben & Mawa, Robert, trs. 2001. 16p. pap. 0.90 (978-0-521-00623-1(6)) Cambridge Univ. Pr.

Living in Space: The International Space Station, 6 vols., Vol. 4. 2005. (Book Treks Ser.). (Illus.). (J). (gr. 4-8). stu. ed. 35.95 (978-0-673-61779-8(3)) Celebration Pr.

Lixur la Aventurera 1: Leveled Books. 2001. (McGraw-Hill. Lectura Ser.). (ENG & SPA.). (gr. 5 up). (978-0-02-188249-6(5)) Macmillan/McGraw-Hill Schl. Div.

Lizards: Level N, 6 vols. (Wonder Worldtm Ser.). 48p. 34.95 (978-0-7802-4583-9(0)) Wright Group, The.

Llueve, Truena y Relampaguea, 6 vols. (Explorers. Exploradores Nonfiction Sets Ser.). (SPA.). 32p. (gr. 3-6). 44.95 (978-0-7699-0632-4(X)) Shortland Pubns. (U. S. A.) Inc.

Lobendhan, Deidre. Ants in Red Pants. Webb, Melissa, illus. 2002. (Bright Sparks Ser.). 16p. pap. 2.30 (978-0-521-75383-8(X)) Cambridge Univ. Pr.

—Cats in Pink Hats. 2002. (Bright Sparks Ser.). (Illus.). 16p. pap. 2.30 (978-0-521-75403-3(8)) Cambridge Univ. Pr.

—Flies in Green Ties. Webb, Melissa, illus. 2002. (Bright Sparks Ser.). 16p. pap. 2.30 (978-0-521-75382-1(1)) Cambridge Univ. Pr.

—Goats in Blue Coats. 2002. (Bright Sparks Ser.). (Illus.). 16p. pap. 2.30 (978-0-521-75384-5(8)) Cambridge Univ. Pr.

Log Man: Level 5, 6 vols. (Fluency Strand Ser.). (gr. 4-8). 45.00 (978-1-4045-1232-0(2)) Wright Group, The.

Lolin 4: Leveled Books. 2001. (McGraw-Hill. Lectura Ser.). (ENG & SPA.). (gr. 3 up). (978-0-02-188077-5(8)) Macmillan/McGraw-Hill Schl. Div.

London, S. Keith & Osleeb, Rebecca. Defined Mind Vocabulary Accelerator: Music-Driven Vocabulary & Comprehension Tools for School / Test / SAT Prep, 1. 2004. 416p. (YA). pap. 25.00 (978-0-9763767-0-5(9)) Defined Mind, Inc.

Long Ago & Far Away: 6 Each of 1 Anthology, 6 vols. (Wildcats Ser.). 32p. (gr. 2-8). (978-0-322-00583-9(3)) Wright Group, The.

Look at the Pictures. 2005. (Early Library). (YA). (ps-3). 23.94 (978-0-8215-8941-0(5)) Sadlier, William H. Inc.

Look Closer. (J). (978-0-8136-5364-8(9)) Modern Curriculum Pr.

Look Here! Level D, 6 vols. (Wonder Worldtm Ser.). 16p. 24.95 (978-0-7802-1221-3(5)) Wright Group, The.

Look Out, Dan! Big Book: Level C. Group 2. (Story Box(R) Ser.). 16p. 20.95 (978-0-7802-9367-0(3)) Wright Group, The.

Looking for Crabs: Big Books Packages. 2005. (J). (gr. k-3). 75.95 (978-0-673-77117-9(2)) Celebration Pr.

Looking Out, Climbing up, Going Far Grade 1: American Readers. (J). (gr. 1). wbk. ed. (978-0-669-04968-8(9)) Houghton Mifflin Co. (Schl. Div.).

Lorusso, Cosmo. Pre-HSPA Success Work-a-Text in Language Arts Literacy. 2002. (YA). 215p. pap. (978-1-56749-535-5(4)); 24p. pap., tchr. ed. (978-1-56749-536-2(2)) Instructivision, Inc.

Los aborigenes de la llanura Australiana 10: Leveled Books. 2001. (McGraw-Hill. Lectura Ser.). (ENG & SPA.). (gr. 3 up). (978-0-02-188131-4(6)) Macmillan/McGraw-Hill Schl. Div.

Lovelace, Maud Hart. Betsy-Tacy Mother-Daughter Reading Group Guide. 2000. (J). pap. (978-0-06-449207-2(9) , Harper Trophy) HarperCollins Pubs.

Lowe, Ruby H. David Kalakaua. Burningham, Robin Y., illus. 1998. (Kamehameha Schools Intermediate Reading Program Ser.). 128p. (J). (gr. 3-7). pap. 13.27 (978-0-87336-041-8(9)) Kamehameha Schools Pr.

Luckett, Kathy. Does Your Father Snore? Chinyanja Version. Iphani, Max, tr. 1999. (Cambridge Reading Routes Ser.). (Illus.). 16p. pap. 3.70 (978-0-521-66878-1(6)) Cambridge Univ. Pr.

Lutz, Norma Jean. Mandy the Outsider: Prelude to the Second World War. 2004. 144p. (J). pap. 4.97 (978-1-59310-353-8(0)) Barbour Publishing, Inc.

Lynne, Francis & Rider, Cynthia. Beginning to Read: Phonics for Reading Children's Book, Pack 1. 1999. (Cambridge Reading Ser.). (Illus.). 8p. pap. 19.00 (978-0-521-77550-2(7)); pap. 19.00 (978-0-521-77549-6(3)) Cambridge Univ. Pr.

MacKenzie, Joy & Spangler, Ann. The Growing Reader Book of Prayers. Newton, Jill, illus. 2004. 224p. (J). 12.99 (978-0-8423-8479-7(0)) Tyndale Hse. Pubs.

Madu, Abraham. The Road to take to School Is the Phonics Way: Companion Book for Students. 2003. 98p. pap. 11.95 (978-0-595-27748-3(9)) iUniverse, Inc.

Magic! Big Book: Level C. 8p. 20.95 (978-0-322-00623-2(6)) Wright Group, The.

Magic! Level C, 6 vols. 8p. 24.95 (978-0-7802-9122-5(0)) Wright Group, The.

Mahan, Benton, illus. Rain, Rain, Go Away, Big Book: Getting Ready to Read with Mother Goose. lt. ed. 2001. (Sadlier Phonics Reading Program). 8p. (YA). (ps-k). 27.00 (978-0-8215-6961-0(9)) Sadlier, William H. Inc.

—Rain, Rain, Go Away, Little Book: Getting Ready to Read with Mother Goose. 2001. (Sadlier Phonics Reading Program). 8p. (YA). (ps-k). 23.94 (978-0-8215-6976-4(7)) Sadlier, William H. Inc.

Mai's Big Surprise: Consonant review: Level C, 6 vols. (Wright Skills Ser.). 16p. (gr. k-3). 26.50 (978-0-322-01490-9(5)) Wright Group, The.

Major Jump: Big Book: Level B. Group 1. (Sunshinetm Ser.). 8p. 20.95 (978-0-7802-5713-9(8)) Wright Group, The.

Making a Plate. (Little Book Practice Reader). (J). (978-0-8136-2164-7(X)) Modern Curriculum Pr.

Making a TV Documentary: Level R, 6 vols. (Wonder Worldtm Ser.). 48p. 44.95 (978-0-7802-7082-4(7)) Wright Group, The.

Making Choices: American Readers. (J). (gr. 6). (978-0-669-05069-1(5)); wbk. ed. (978-0-669-05071-4(7)) Houghton Mifflin Co. (Schl. Div.).

Making Music: Level B, 6 vols. (Wonder Worldtm Ser.). 16p. 24.95 (978-0-7802-2008-9(0)) Wright Group, The.

Un mal dia Perfecto 8: Leveled Books. 2001. (McGraw-Hill. Lectura Ser.). (ENG & SPA.). (gr. 4 up). (978-0-02-188184-0(7)) Macmillan/McGraw-Hill Schl. Div.

Mama Goes to School: Big Book: Level D. (Visionstm Ser.). 8p. 20.95 (978-0-322-00310-1(5)) Wright Group, The.

Mama me mima a Mi! 1: Leveled Books. 2001. (McGraw-Hill. Lectura Ser.). (ENG & SPA.). (gr. 1 up). (978-0-02-187930-4(3)) Macmillan/McGraw-Hill Schl. Div.

Los Mamíferos Del Mar, 6 vols. (Explorers. Exploradores Nonfiction Sets Ser.). (SPA.). 32p. (gr. 3-6). 44.95 (978-0-7699-0629-4(X)) Shortland Pubns. (U. S. A.) Inc.

Mammen, Lori. TestSMART for Reading Skills & Comprehension - Grade 3: Help for Basic Reading Skills, State Competency Tests, Achievement Tests. Sullivan, Jennifer, ed. 1999. (Illus.). 128p. (J). (gr. 3). pap., wbk. ed. 16.95 (978-1-57022-198-9(7) , ECS1987) ECS Learning Systems, Inc.

—TestSMART for Reading Skills & Comprehension - Grade 4: Help for Basic Reading Skills, State Competency Tests, Achievement Tests. Sullivan, Jennifer, ed. 1999. (Illus.). 128p. (J). (gr. 4). pap., wbk. ed. 16.95 (978-1-57022-199-6(5) , ECS1995) ECS Learning Systems, Inc.

—TestSMART for Reading Skills & Comprehension - Grade 5: Help for Basic Reading Skills, State Competency Tests, Achievement Tests. Sullivan, Jennifer, ed. 1999. (Illus.). 128p. (J). (gr. 5). pap., wbk. ed. 16.95 (978-1-57022-200-9(2) , ECS2002) ECS Learning Systems, Inc.

—TestSMART for Reading Skills & Comprehension - Grade 6: Help for Basic Reading Skills, State Competency Tests, Achievement Tests. Sullivan, Jennifer, ed. 1999. (Illus.). 128p. (J). (gr. 6). pap., wbk. ed. 16.95 (978-1-57022-201-6(0) , ECS2010) ECS Learning Systems, Inc.

—TestSMART for Reading Skills & Comprehension - Grade 7: Help for Basic Reading Skills, State Competency Tests, Achievement Tests. Sullivan, Jennifer, ed. 1999. (Illus.). 128p. (YA). (gr. 7). pap., wbk. ed. 16.95 (978-1-57022-202-3(9) , ECS2029) ECS Learning Systems, Inc.

—TestSMART for Reading Skills & Comprehension - Grade 8: Help for Basic Reading Skills, State Competency Tests, Achievement Tests. Sullivan, Jennifer, ed. 1999. (Illus.). 128p. (J). (gr. 8). pap., wbk. ed. 16.95 (978-1-57022-203-0(7) , ECS2037) ECS Learning Systems, Inc.

Mann, Rachel. Plants Grow from Seeds. 2003. (Compass Point Phonics Readers Ser.). (Illus.). 16p. (J). (gr. 1 up). 13.26 (978-0-7565-0519-6(4)) Compass Point Bks.

—Race to a Fire! 2003. (Compass Point Phonics Readers Ser.). (Illus.). 16p. (J). (gr. 1 up). 13.26 (978-0-7565-0522-6(4)) Compass Point Bks.

—Sun & Rain. 2003. (Compass Point Phonics Readers Ser.). (Illus.). 16p. (J). (gr. 1 up). 13.26 (978-0-7565-0525-7(9)) Compass Point Bks.

Manualidades Ecologicas 11: Leveled Books. 2001. (McGraw-Hill. Lectura Ser.). (ENG & SPA.). (gr. 2 up). (978-0-02-188036-2(0)) Macmillan/McGraw-Hill Schl. Div.

Los Mapas Del Mundo, 6 vols., Vol. 2. (Explorers. Exploradores Nonfiction Sets Ser.). (SPA.). 32p. (gr. 3-6). 44.95 (978-0-7699-0646-1(X)) Shortland Pubns. (U. S. A.) Inc.

Mapongwana, Nobantu. Naughty Hare: Chitonga Version. Chisengele, tr. 2001. (Illus.). 8p. pap. 0.45 (978-0-521-01469-4(7)) Cambridge Univ. Pr.

—Naughty Hare: Chitonga Version. Hamoonga, Lazarous, tr. 1998. (Cambridge African Language Library Ser.). (Illus.). 8p. pap. 3.75 (978-0-521-64747-2(9)) Cambridge Univ. Pr.

—Naughty Hare: Cinyanja Version. Tembo, tr. 2001. (Illus.). 8p. pap. 0.45 (978-0-521-01470-0(0)) Cambridge Univ. Pr.

—Naughty Hare: Cinyanja Version. Mwale, Brian, tr. 1998. (Cambridge African Language Library Ser.). (Illus.). 8p. pap. 3.75 (978-0-521-64746-5(0)) Cambridge Univ. Pr.

—Naughty Hare: Icibemba Version. Mulilo, tr. 2001. (Illus.). 8p. pap. 0.45 (978-0-521-01473-1(5)) Cambridge Univ. Pr.

—Naughty Hare: Icibemba Version. Mwansa, Bupe, tr. 1998. (Cambridge African Language Library Ser.). (Illus.). 8p. pap. 3.75 (978-0-521-64745-8(2)) Cambridge Univ. Pr.

—Naughty Hare: Kiikaonde Version. Muyebaa, tr. 2001. (Illus.). 8p. pap. 0.45 (978-0-521-01474-8(3)) Cambridge Univ. Pr.

—Naughty Hare: Kiikaonde Version. Muyebaa, Kyangubabi, tr. 1998. (Cambridge African Language Library Ser.). 8p. pap. 3.75 (978-0-521-64744-1(4)) Cambridge Univ. Pr.

—Naughty Hare: Luvale Version. Sakapaji, tr. 2001. (Illus.). 8p. pap. 0.45 (978-0-521-01477-9(8)) Cambridge Univ. Pr.

—Naughty Hare: Luvale Version. Kaleyi, Kakoma, tr. 1998. (Cambridge African Language Library Ser.). (Illus.). 8p. pap. 3.75 (978-0-521-64742-7(8)) Cambridge Univ. Pr.

—Naughty Hare: Silozi Version. Mwendende, tr. 2001. (Illus.). 8p. pap. 0.45 (978-0-521-01478-6(6)) Cambridge Univ. Pr.

—Naughty Hare: Silozi Version. Silumesii, Penelope, tr. 1998. (Cambridge African Language Library). (Illus.). 8p. pap. 3.75 (978-0-521-64741-0(X)) Cambridge Univ. Pr.

La maravilla del Mago Potagio 18: Leveled Books. 2001. (McGraw-Hill. Lectura Ser.). (ENG & SPA.). (gr. 2 up). (978-0-02-188019-5(0)) Macmillan/McGraw-Hill Schl. Div.

La maravillosa Monarca 15: Leveled Books. 2001. (McGraw-Hill. Lectura Ser.). (ENG & SPA.). (gr. 3 up). (978-0-02-188112-3(X)) Macmillan/McGraw-Hill Schl. Div.

Marching Along: American Readers. (J). (gr. 2). (978-0-669-04984-8(0)); wbk. ed. (978-0-669-04991-6(3)) Houghton Mifflin Co. (Schl. Div.).

Maria's Diary: Level R, 6 vols. (Wonder Worldtm Ser.). 48p. 44.95 (978-0-7802-7067-1(3)) Wright Group, The.

Mario Mxwell: Level L, 6 vols. (Take-Twostm Ser.). 16p. 36.95 (978-0-322-03404-4(3)) Wright Group, The.

The Marketplace: Big Book: Level G. (Visionstm Ser.). 16p. 20.95 (978-0-322-00628-7(7)) Wright Group, The.

Martin, Linda, ed. Reading Made Easy Kit. 2002. (Illus.). (J). pap. 60.00 (978-0-7894-8526-7(5)) Dorling Kindersley Publishing, Inc.

Marzollo, Jean & Wick, Walter. I Spy a Dinosaur's Eye. 2003. (ps-2). lib. bdg. 11.80 (978-0-613-72243-8(4)) Tandem Library Bks.

Masks: Level E, 6 vols. (Wonder Worldtm Ser.). 16p. 29.95 (978-0-7802-2010-2(2)) Wright Group, The.

Matross, Vuyokasi. Vusirala the Giant: Amharic Version. Wako, Tegegn Nuresu, tr. 1999. (Cambridge Reading Routes Ser.). (AMH., Illus.). 16p. pap. 3.70 (978-0-521-66834-7(4)) Cambridge Univ. Pr.

—Vusirala the Giant: Chinyanja Version. Iphani, Max, tr. 1999. (Cambridge Reading Routes Ser.). (Illus.). 16p. pap. 3.70 (978-0-521-66885-9(9)) Cambridge Univ. Pr.

—Vusirala the Giant: Kiswahili Version. Lema, Eleishi, tr. 1999. (Cambridge Reading Routes Ser.). (Illus.). 16p. pap. 3.70 (978-0-521-66891-0(3)) Cambridge Univ. Pr.

—Vusirala the Giant: Oromo Version. Adem, Omer Kedir, tr. 1999. (Cambridge Reading Routes Ser.). (Illus.). 16p. pap. 3.70 (978-0-521-66840-8(9)) Cambridge Univ. Pr.

—Vusirala the Giant: Tigre Version. Kebebew, Amare Hagos, tr. 1999. (Cambridge Reading Routes Ser.). (TIG., Illus.). 16p. pap. 3.70 (978-0-521-66824-8(7)) Cambridge Univ. Pr.

Max Is Sick: Consonants q, x, z; -ack, -ick, -ill word families: Level A, 6 vols. (Wright Skills Ser.). 12p. (gr. k-3). 17.95 (978-0-322-01457-2(3)) Wright Group, The.

Mayer, Mercer. Mercer Mayer - Beginning Phonics: Preschool. 2003. (Little Critter Preschool Workbook Ser.). (Illus.). 128p. (J). (ps-2). pap., wbk. ed. 8.95 (978-1-57768-589-0(X) , Spectrum) School Specialty Publishing.

—Mercer Mayer - Reading: Preschool. 2003. (Little Critter Preschool Workbook Ser.). (Illus.). 128p. (J). (ps-2). pap., wbk. ed. 8.95 (978-1-57768-599-9(7) , Spectrum) School Specialty Publishing.

McAndrew, Mark, et al. The Great War & its Aftermath 1914-1921. 2nd rev. ed. 2001. (Cambridge Senior History Ser.). (Illus.). 320p. pap. 24.90 (978-0-521-00090-1(4)) Cambridge Univ. Pr.

McCollum, Betty, intro. Women in the Arts. 2005. (Illus.). 112p. (gr. 6-12). pap. 180.00 (978-0-7910-7454-1(4) , Chelsea Hse.) Facts On File, Inc.

McDonald, Wendy. Susie's Shoelaces. Coutts, Lisa, illus. 2002. (Bright Sparks Ser.). 16p. pap. 2.30 (978-0-521-75421-7(6)) Cambridge Univ. Pr.

McDonnell, Flora. Splash. 2004. (CHI & ENG.). (J). (978-1-85269-549-1(8)) Mantra Publishing, Ltd.

McGraw-Hill - Jamestown Education Staff. Comprehension Skills: Recognizing Tone (Advanced) 2nd ed. 2000. (Comprehension Skills Ser.). (C). (gr. 9-12). pap. 10.64 (978-0-8092-0161-7(5) , 9780809201617) Jamestown.

—Comprehension Skills: Understanding Characters (Advanced) 3rd ed. 2000. (Comprehension Skills Ser.). (C). (gr. 9-12). pap. 10.64 (978-0-8092-0158-7(5) , 9780809201587) Jamestown.

—Timed Readings Plus in Social Studies. 2003. Bk. 1. pap. 16.64 (978-0-07-845799-9(8) , 9780078457999); Vol. 3. pap. 16.64 (978-0-07-845801-9(3) , 9780078458019) Jamestown.

—Timed Readings Plus in Social Studies Bk. 3. 2003. Vol. 2. pap. 16.64 (978-0-07-845800-2(5) , 9780078458002); Vol. 4. pap. 16.64 (978-0-07-845802-6(1) , 9780078458026); Vol. 5. pap. 16.64 (978-0-07-845803-3(X) , 9780078458033); Vol. 6. pap. 16.64 (978-0-07-845804-0(8) , 9780078458040); Vol. 7. pap. 16.64 (978-0-07-845805-7(6) , 9780078458057); Vol. 8. pap. 16.64 (978-0-07-845806-4(4) , 9780078458064); Vol. 9. pap. 16.64 (978-0-07-845807-1(2) , 9780078458071); Vol. 10. pap. 16.64 (978-0-07-845808-8(0) , 9780078458088) Jamestown.

McGraw-Hill Staff. Communication Applications Guided Reading. 2000. pap., wbk. ed., act. bk. ed. 9.32 (978-0-07-821320-5(7) , 9780078213205) Glencoe/McGraw-Hill.

—Glencoe Literature: Florida Edition 2003. 2002. Grade 8. (C). stu. ed. 75.32 (978-0-07-828592-9(5) , 9780078285929); Grade 9. stu. ed. 79.32 (978-0-07-828593-6(3) , 9780078285936) Glencoe/McGraw-Hill.

—Glencoe Literature: Grade 12 Florida Edition 2003. 2002. (C). stu. ed. 80.64 (978-0-07-828596-7(8) , 9780078285967) Glencoe/McGraw-Hill.

—Glencoe Literature: Grade 7 Florida Edition 2003. 2002. (C). stu. ed. 75.32 (978-0-07-828591-2(7) , 9780078285912) Glencoe/McGraw-Hill.

—Glencoe Literature: Interactive Reading, Grade 10. 2002. pap., wbk. ed. 18.00 (978-0-07-825178-8(8) , 9780078251788) Glencoe/McGraw-Hill.

—Glencoe Literature: The Reader's Choice, Course 1, Grade 6. 1999. stu. ed. 90.00 (978-0-02-635367-0(9) , 9780026353670) Glencoe/McGraw-Hill.

—Glencoe Literature: The Reader's Choice, Course 2, Grade 7. 2001. stu. ed. 89.32 (978-0-07-825106-1(0) , 9780078251061) Glencoe/McGraw-Hill.

—Glencoe Literature, Grade 11, Florida. 2002. (C). stu. ed. 80.64 (978-0-07-828595-0(X) , 9780078285950) Glencoe/McGraw-Hill.

—Glencoe Literature, Grade 12, Interactive Reading. 2002. pap., wbk. ed. 18.00 (978-0-07-825180-1(X) , 9780078251801) Glencoe/McGraw-Hill.

—Glencoe Literature Grade 6, Course 1 Interactive Reading Workbook. 2001. pap. 18.00 (978-0-07-825174-0(5) , 9780078251740) Glencoe/McGraw-Hill.

—Glencoe Literature, Grade 6, Florida. 2002. (C). stu. ed. 75.32 (978-0-07-828590-5(9) , 9780078285905) Glencoe/McGraw-Hill.

—Glencoe Literature Interactive Reading American Literature, Grade 11. 2002. (C). pap., wbk. ed. 18.00 (978-0-07-825179-5(6) , 9780078251795) Glencoe/McGraw-Hill.

—Glencoe Literature Interactive Reading Grade 8. 2001. pap., wbk. ed. 18.00 (978-0-07-825176-4(1) , 9780078251764) Glencoe/McGraw-Hill.

—Glencoe Literature Interactive Reading Grade 9. 2001. (C). pap., wbk. ed. 18.00 (978-0-07-825177-1(X) , 9780078251771) Glencoe/McGraw-Hill.

—Glencoe Literature World Literature Florida Edition 2003. 2002. (C). stu. ed. 80.64 (978-0-07-828597-4(6) , 9780078285974) Glencoe/McGraw-Hill.

—The Glencoe Reader, Grade 10, Course 5. 2003. (gr. 6-12). pap., stu. ed. 14.64 (978-0-07-845931-3(1) , 9780078459313) Glencoe/McGraw-Hill.

—The Glencoe Reader, Grade 11, Course 6. 2003. (C). (gr. 6-12). pap., stu. ed. 14.64 (978-0-07-845932-0(X) , 9780078459320) Glencoe/McGraw-Hill.

—The Glencoe Reader, Grade 12, Course 7. 2003. (C). (gr. 6-12). pap., stu. ed. 14.64 (978-0-07-845933-7(8) , 9780078459337) Glencoe/McGraw-Hill.

—The Glencoe Reader World Literature. 2003. (gr. 6-12). pap., stu. ed. 14.64 (978-0-07-845934-4(6) , 9780078459344) Glencoe/McGraw-Hill.

—Windows Single User. 2000. (Comprehension Skills Ser.). (gr. 6-12). suppl. ed. 800.56 (978-0-8092-0035-1(X) , 9780809200351) Jamestown.

—Windows Site License. 2001. (Comprehension Skills Ser.). (gr. 6-12). suppl. ed. 1329.28 (978-0-8092-9681-1(0) , 9780809296811) Jamestown.

McGraw-Hill Staff, ed. The Glencoe Reader, Grade 8, Course 3. 2003. (C). (gr. 6-12). pap., stu. ed. 14.64 (978-0-07-845929-0(X) , 9780078459290) Glencoe/McGraw-Hill.

McKay, Sindy. We Both Read-My Day. Johnson, Meredith, illus. 2002. (We Both Read Ser.). 44p. (J). (gr. k up). 7.99 (978-1-891327-43-8(7)); pap. 3.99 (978-1-891327-44-5(5)) Treasure Bay, Inc.

McLaughlin, Maureen & Fisher, Leslie. Research Based Reading Lessons for K-3. 2005. 224p. pap. 25.99 (978-0-439-75462-0(3) , Teaching Strategies) Scholastic, Inc.

McNeil, Niki, et al. HOCPP 1118 Beginning Reading. 2006. spiral bd. 30.00 (***978-1-60308-118-4(6)***) In the Hands of a Child.

MCP Staff. Jump Right In, Level 4, Bk. 35. 2000. (J). (ps-3). 24.50 (978-0-8136-0745-0(0)) Modern Curriculum Pr.

—My Monster & Me, Level 2, Bk. 6. (J). (ps-3). 24.50 (978-0-8136-0675-0(6)) Modern Curriculum Pr.

—Night Animals, Level 4, Bk. 30. (J). (ps-3). 24.50 (978-0-8136-0743-6(4)) Modern Curriculum Pr.

—One Bee Got on the Bus, Level 3, Bk. 9. (J). (ps-3). 21.95 (978-0-8136-0739-9(6)) Modern Curriculum Pr.

—The Party, Level 4, Bk. 4. (J). (ps-3). 24.50 (978-0-8136-1937-8(8)) Modern Curriculum Pr.

—Shell Shopping, 6 bks., set, Level A. 2003. (J). (ps-3). 33.50 (978-0-8136-0797-9(3)) Modern Curriculum Pr.

—Ted's Red Sled, Level 4, Bk. 40. (J). (ps-3). 24.50 (978-0-8136-1969-9(6)) Modern Curriculum Pr.

—Too High!, Level 4, Bk. 37. 2003. (J). (ps-3). 24.50 (978-0-8136-0774-0(4)) Modern Curriculum Pr.

—Vulture on Vacation, Level 3, Bk. 5. (J). (ps-3). 24.50 (978-0-8136-1939-2(4)) Modern Curriculum Pr.

—What Rhymes with Cat?, Level A, Bk. 2. (J). (978-0-8136-1933-0(5)) Modern Curriculum Pr.

McTrustry, Chris. Is the Spaghetti Ready? Jellett, Tom, illus. 2002. (Bright Sparks Ser.). 16p. pap. 2.30 (978-0-521-75420-0(8)) Cambridge Univ. Pr.

Me llamo Nura 21: Leveled Books. 2001. (McGraw-Hill. Lectura Ser.). (ENG & SPA.). (gr. 2 up). (978-0-02-188070-6(0)) Macmillan/McGraw-Hill Schl. Div.

Meeting Challenges: American Readers. (J). (gr. 8). (978-0-669-05093-6(8)); (978-0-669-05099-8(7)) Houghton Mifflin Co. (Schl. Div.).

Mei Ping y los zapatos de Plata 8: Leveled Books. 2001. (McGraw-Hill. Lectura Ser.). (ENG & SPA.). (gr. 2 up). (978-0-02-188057-7(3)) Macmillan/McGraw-Hill Schl. Div.

Mendoza, Del. Jessie's Daydream. Coutts, Lisa, illus. 2002. (Bright Sparks Ser.). 16p. pap. 2.30 (978-0-521-75398-2(8)) Cambridge Univ. Pr.

—Nick's Treehouse. 2002. (Bright Sparks Ser.). (Illus.). 16p. pap. 2.30 (978-0-521-75397-5(X)) Cambridge Univ. Pr.

—What If... ? 2002. (Bright Sparks Ser.). (Illus.). 16p. pap. 2.30 (978-0-521-75399-9(6)) Cambridge Univ. Pr.

El mensaje de Marybelle 8: Leveled Books. 2001. (McGraw-Hill. Lectura Ser.). (ENG & SPA.). (gr. 5 up). (978-0-02-188280-9(0)) Macmillan/McGraw-Hill Schl. Div.

Mensajes con puntos y Rayas 11: Leveled Books. 2001. (McGraw-Hill. Lectura Ser.). (ENG & SPA.). (gr. 2 up). (978-0-02-188060-7(3)) Macmillan/McGraw-Hill Schl. Div.

Los mensajes del Arbol 4: Leveled Books. 2001. (McGraw-Hill. Lectura Ser.). (ENG & SPA.). (gr. 2 up). (978-0-02-188005-8(0)) Macmillan/McGraw-Hill Schl. Div.

Meow-Meow Gets Out: Diphthongs ou, ow: Level B, 6 vols. (Wright Skills Ser.). 16p. (gr. k-3). 26.50 (978-0-322-01484-8(0)) Wright Group, The.

Mermelstein, Leah. Reading/Writing Connections in the K-2 Classroom: Find the Clarity & Then Blur the Lines. 2005. (Illus.). 240p. (C). pap. 26.99 (978-0-205-41277-8(7)) Allyn & Bacon, Inc.

Metro Early Reading-Cursive Handwriting Blms. 2000. (Metro Reading Ser.). (gr. 12-2). 10.55 (978-1-58120-233-5(4)) Metropolitan Teaching & Learning Co.

Mhlophe, Gcina. Fudukazi's Magic. 1999. (Cambridge Reading Routes Ser.). (Illus.). 32p. pap. 6.45 (978-0-521-77895-4(6)) Cambridge Univ. Pr.

Mi abuela Susana 7: Leveled Books. 2001. (McGraw-Hill. Lectura Ser.). (ENG & SPA.). (gr. 1 up). (978-0-02-187960-1(5)) Macmillan/McGraw-Hill Schl. Div.

Mi Cuate 14: Leveled Books. 2001. (McGraw-Hill. Lectura Ser.). (ENG & SPA.). (gr. 4 up). (978-0-02-188190-1(1)) Macmillan/McGraw-Hill Schl. Div.

Mi gato Paco 3: Leveled Books. 2001. (McGraw-Hill. Lectura Ser.). (ENG & SPA.). (gr. 2 up). (978-0-02-188004-1(2)) Macmillan/McGraw-Hill Schl. Div.

Mi gato se fue a la Luna 14: Leveled Books. 2001. (McGraw-Hill. Lectura Ser.). (ENG & SPA.). (gr. 1 up). (978-0-02-187943-4(5)) Macmillan/McGraw-Hill Schl. Div.

Mi hermanito Roberto 11: Leveled Books. 2001. (McGraw-Hill. Lectura Ser.). (ENG & SPA.). (gr. 1 up). (978-0-02-187964-9(8)) Macmillan/McGraw-Hill Schl. Div.

Mi hermanito y Yo 21: Leveled Books. 2001. (McGraw-Hill. Lectura Ser.). (ENG & SPA.). (gr. 3 up). (978-0-02-188094-2(8)) Macmillan/McGraw-Hill Schl. Div.

Mi Libro 4: Leveled Books. 2001. (McGraw-Hill. Lectura Ser.). (ENG & SPA.). (gr. 1 up). (978-0-02-187957-1(5)) Macmillan/McGraw-Hill Schl. Div.

Mi Lista 9: Leveled Books. 2001. (McGraw-Hill. Lectura Ser.). (ENG & SPA.). (gr. 1 up). (978-0-02-187962-5(1)) Macmillan/McGraw-Hill Schl. Div.

Mi Mama, Memo y Yo 1: Leveled Books. 2001. (McGraw-Hill. Lectura Ser.). (ENG & SPA.). (gr. 1 up). (978-0-02-187954-0(0)) Macmillan/McGraw-Hill Schl. Div.

Mi mundo guia del Maestro: Mi Mundo. 2000. (Aventuras A Traves Del Tiempo Ser.). (ENG & SPA.). (gr. 1 up). (978-0-02-147818-7(X)) Macmillan/McGraw-Hill Schl. Div.

Mi mundo libro del Estudiante: Mi Mundo. 2000. (Aventuras A Traves Del Tiempo Ser.). (ENG & SPA.). (gr. 1 up). (978-0-02-147804-0(X)) Macmillan/McGraw-Hill Schl. Div.

Mi mundo libro del estudiante en Audiocasete: Mi Mundo. 2000. (Aventuras A Traves Del Tiempo Ser.). (ENG & SPA.). (gr. 1 up). (978-0-02-147811-8(2)) Macmillan/McGraw-Hill Schl. Div.

Mi papa es un Puma 2: Leveled Books. 2001. (McGraw-Hill. Lectura Ser.). (ENG & SPA.). (gr. 1 up). (978-0-02-187931-1(1)) Macmillan/McGraw-Hill Schl. Div.

Mi Papalote: Aventuras (Adventure Books) 2000. (Aventuras A Traves Del Tiempo Ser.). (ENG & SPA.). (gr. 1 up). (978-0-02-148671-7(9)) Macmillan/McGraw-Hill Schl. Div.

Mi perro Meloso 5: Leveled Books. 2001. (McGraw-Hill. Lectura Ser.). (ENG & SPA.). (gr. 1 up). (978-0-02-187958-8(3)) Macmillan/McGraw-Hill Schl. Div.

Miau, leyendas de Gatos 3: Leveled Books. 2001. (McGraw-Hill. Lectura Ser.). (ENG & SPA.). (gr. 2 up). (978-0-02-188028-7(X)) Macmillan/McGraw-Hill Schl. Div.

Migliaccio, Eric. Swimming: Easy Olympic Sports Reader. 2004. (U. S. Olympic Committee Easy Olympic Sports Readers Ser.). (Illus.). 16p. (J). pap. 2.99 (978-1-58000-114-4(9)) Griffin Publishing Group.

—Track & Field: Easy Olympic Sports Reader. 2004. (U. S. Olympic Committee Easy Olympic Sports Readers Ser.). (Illus.). 16p. (J). pap. 2.99 (978-1-58000-115-1(7)) Griffin Publishing Group.

Mike & His Bride, 6 vols. 8p. (gr. k-1). 21.50 (978-0-322-02062-7(X)) Wright Group, The.

Milich, Zoran. City signs. Milich, Zoran, illus. 2002. (Illus.). 32p. (J). (ps-k). (978-1-55337-003-1(1)) Kids Can Pr., Ltd.

Milking: Level H, 6 vols. (Wonder Worldtm Ser.). 16p. 29.95 (978-0-7802-1207-7(X)) Wright Group, The.

Milone, Michael. LeapTrack FCAT: Reading 5th Grade. 2001. (J). (gr. k-5). spiral bd. 1.50 (978-1-58605-624-7(7)) LeapFrog Enterprises, Inc.

—LeapTrack Language Arts: 1st Grade Beginning-of-Year. 2001. (J). (gr. k-5). spiral bd. 1.50 (978-1-58605-548-6(8)) LeapFrog Enterprises, Inc.

—LeapTrack Language Arts: 1st Grade End-of-Year. 2001. (J). (gr. k-5). spiral bd. 1.50 (978-1-58605-550-9(X)) LeapFrog Enterprises, Inc.

—LeapTrack Language Arts: 1st Grade Middle-of-Year. 2001. (J). (gr. k-5). spiral bd. 1.50 (978-1-58605-549-3(6)) LeapFrog Enterprises, Inc.

—LeapTrack Language Arts: 2nd Grade Beginning-of-Year. 2001. (J). (gr. k-5). spiral bd. 1.50 (978-1-58605-558-5(5)) LeapFrog Enterprises, Inc.

—LeapTrack Language Arts: 2nd Grade End-of-Year. 2001. (J). (gr. k-5). spiral bd. 1.50 (978-1-58605-560-8(7)) LeapFrog Enterprises, Inc.

—LeapTrack Language Arts: 2nd Grade Middle-of-Year. 2001. (J). (gr. k-5). spiral bd. 1.50 (978-1-58605-559-2(3)) LeapFrog Enterprises, Inc.

—LeapTrack Language Arts: 3rd Grade Beginning-of-Year. 2001. (J). (gr. k-5). spiral bd. 1.50 (978-1-58605-574-5(7)) LeapFrog Enterprises, Inc.

—LeapTrack Language Arts: 3rd Grade End-of-Year. 2001. (J). (gr. k-5). spiral bd. 1.50 (978-1-58605-576-9(3)) LeapFrog Enterprises, Inc.

—LeapTrack Language Arts: 3rd Grade Middle-of-Year. 2001. (J). (gr. k-5). spiral bd. 1.50 (978-1-58605-575-2(5)) LeapFrog Enterprises, Inc.

—LeapTrack Language Arts: 4th Grade Beginning-of-Year. 2001. (J). (gr. k-5). spiral bd. 1.50 (978-1-58605-594-3(1)) LeapFrog Enterprises, Inc.

—LeapTrack Language Arts: 4th Grade End-of-Year. 2001. (J). (gr. k-5). spiral bd. 1.50 (978-1-58605-596-7(8)) LeapFrog Enterprises, Inc.

—LeapTrack Language Arts: 4th Grade Middle-of-Year. 2001. (J). (gr. k-5). spiral bd. 1.50 (978-1-58605-595-0(X)) LeapFrog Enterprises, Inc.

—LeapTrack Language Arts: 5th Grade Beginning-of-Year. 2001. (J). (gr. k-5). spiral bd. 1.50 (978-1-58605-614-8(X)) LeapFrog Enterprises, Inc.

—LeapTrack Language Arts: 5th Grade End-of-Year. 2001. (J). (gr. k-5). spiral bd. 1.50 (978-1-58605-616-2(6)) LeapFrog Enterprises, Inc.

—LeapTrack Language Arts: 5th Grade Middle-of-Year. 2001. (J). (gr. k-5). spiral bd. 1.50 (978-1-58605-615-5(8)) LeapFrog Enterprises, Inc.

—LeapTrack Reading: 1st Grade Beginning-of-Year. 2001. (J). (gr. k-5). spiral bd. 1.50 (978-1-58605-542-4(9)) LeapFrog Enterprises, Inc.

—LeapTrack Reading: 1st Grade End-of-Year. 2001. (J). (gr. k-5). spiral bd. 1.50 (978-1-58605-544-8(5)) LeapFrog Enterprises, Inc.

—LeapTrack Reading: 1st Grade Middle-of-Year. 2001. (J). (gr. k-5). spiral bd. 1.50 (978-1-58605-543-1(7)) LeapFrog Enterprises, Inc.

—LeapTrack Reading: 2nd Grade Beginning-of-Year. 2001. (J). (gr. k-5). spiral bd. 1.50 (978-1-58605-552-3(6)) LeapFrog Enterprises, Inc.

—LeapTrack Reading: 2nd Grade End-of-Year. 2001. (J). (gr. k-5). spiral bd. 1.50 (978-1-58605-554-7(2)) LeapFrog Enterprises, Inc.

—LeapTrack Reading: 2nd Grade Middle-of-Year. 2001. (J). (gr. k-5). spiral bd. 1.50 (978-1-58605-553-0(4)) LeapFrog Enterprises, Inc.

—LeapTrack Reading: 3rd Grade Beginning-of-Year. 2001. (J). (gr. k-5). spiral bd. 1.50 (978-1-58605-568-4(2)) LeapFrog Enterprises, Inc.

—LeapTrack Reading: 3rd Grade End-of-Year. 2001. (J). (gr. k-5). spiral bd. 1.50 (978-1-58605-570-7(4)) LeapFrog Enterprises, Inc.

—LeapTrack Reading: 3rd Grade Middle-of-Year. 2001. (J). (gr. k-5). spiral bd. 1.50 (978-1-58605-569-1(0)) LeapFrog Enterprises, Inc.

—LeapTrack Reading: 4th Grade Beginning-of-Year. 2001. (J). (gr. k-5). spiral bd. 1.50 (978-1-58605-588-2(7)) LeapFrog Enterprises, Inc.

—LeapTrack Reading: 4th Grade End-of-Year. 2001. (J). (gr. k-5). spiral bd. 1.50 (978-1-58605-590-5(9)) LeapFrog Enterprises, Inc.

—LeapTrack Reading: 4th Grade Middle-of-Year. 2001. (J). (gr. k-5). spiral bd. 1.50 (978-1-58605-589-9(5)) LeapFrog Enterprises, Inc.

—LeapTrack Reading: 5th Grade Beginning-of-Year. 2001. (J). (gr. k-5). spiral bd. 1.50 (978-1-58605-608-7(5)) LeapFrog Enterprises, Inc.

—LeapTrack Reading: Kindergarten Beginning-of-Year. 2001. (J). (gr. k-5). spiral bd. 1.50 (978-1-58605-536-3(4)) LeapFrog Enterprises, Inc.

—LeapTrack Reading: Kindergarten End-of-Year. 2001. (J). (gr. k-5). spiral bd. 1.50 (978-1-58605-538-7(0)) LeapFrog Enterprises, Inc.

—LeapTrack Reading: Kindergarten Middle-of-Year. 2001. (J). (gr. k-5). spiral bd. 1.50 (978-1-58605-537-0(2)) LeapFrog Enterprises, Inc.

Milone, Michael, ed. Developing Reading Power. 1998. (Illus.). 64p. (J). Bk. 3. (gr. 3-4). pap., wbk. ed. 3.50 (978-1-56762-091-7(4)); Bk. 4. (gr. 4-5). pap., wbk. ed. 3.50 (978-1-56762-092-4(2)) Modern Learning Pr.

Minden, Cecilia. Celine & Cedric Go to the Circus: The Sound of Soft C. 2004. (Phonics Friends Ser.). 24p. (J). (ps). 21.36 (978-1-59296-291-4(2)) Child's World, Inc.

—Isabel's Favorite Things: The Sound of Short I. 2005. (Phonics Friends Ser.). (Illus.). 24p. (J). (ps). 21.36 (978-1-59296-314-0(5)) Child's World, Inc.

—Olivia by the Ocean: The Sound of Long O. 2005. (Phonics Friends Ser.). (Illus.). 24p. (J). (ps). 21.36 (978-1-59296-320-1(X)) Child's World, Inc.

—Umberto's Summer Day: The Sound of Short U. 2005. (Phonics Friends Ser.). (Illus.). 24p. (J). (ps). 21.36 (978-1-59296-316-4(1)) Child's World, Inc.

—Umeko & the Music Show: The Sound of Long U. 2005. (Phonics Friends Ser.). (Illus.). 24p. (J). (ps). 21.36 (978-1-59296-321-8(8)) Child's World, Inc.

Minden-Cupp, Cecilia. Akiko, Miss Alice, & the Dance Class: The Sound of Short A. 2005. (Phonics Friends Ser.). (Illus.). 24p. (J). (ps). 21.36 (978-1-59296-312-6(9)) Child's World, Inc.

—Amy's Big Race: The Sound of Long A. 2005. (Phonics Friends Ser.). (Illus.). 24p. (J). (ps). 21.36 (978-1-59296-317-1(X)) Child's World, Inc.

—Erin & Her New Pet: The Sound of Short E. 2005. (Phonics Friends Ser.). (Illus.). 24p. (J). (ps). 21.36 (978-1-59296-313-3(7)) Child's World, Inc.

—Eve's Green Garden: The Sound of Long E. 2005. (Phonics Friends Ser.). (Illus.). 24p. (J). (ps). 21.36 (978-1-59296-318-8(8)) Child's World, Inc.

—Fatima & Fay Find a Bird: The Sound of F. 2004. (Phonics Friends Ser.). 24p. (J). (ps). 21.36 (978-1-59296-293-8(9)) Child's World, Inc.

—G—Soft—Title. 2004. (Phonics Friends Ser.). (Illus.). 24p. (J). (ps). 21.36 (978-1-59296-295-2(5)) Child's World, Inc.

—Isaac on the Farm: The Sound of Long I. 2005. (Phonics Friends Ser.). (Illus.). 24p. (J). (ps). 21.36 (978-1-59296-319-5(6)) Child's World, Inc.

—Jamal's Job: The Sound of J. 2004. (Phonics Friends Ser.). 24p. (J). (ps). 21.36 (978-1-59296-297-6(1)) Child's World, Inc.

—K—Title Tk. 2004. (Phonics Friends Ser.). 24p. (J). (ps). 21.36 (978-1-59296-298-3(X)) Child's World, Inc.

—Marcus & the Mail: The Sound of M. 2004. (Phonics Friends Ser.). 24p. (J). (ps). 21.36 (978-1-59296-300-3(5)) Child's World, Inc.

—Nick & Ned: The Sound of N. 2004. (Phonics Friends Ser.). 24p. (J). (ps). 21.36 (978-1-59296-301-0(3)) Child's World, Inc.

—Oliver's Box: The Sound of Short O. 2005. (Phonics Friends Ser.). (Illus.). 24p. (J). (ps). 21.36 (978-1-59296-315-7(3)) Child's World, Inc.

—Quana & Quinn: The Sound of Q. 2004. (Phonics Friends Ser.). (Illus.). 24p. (J). (ps). 21.36 (978-1-59296-303-4(X)) Child's World, Inc.

—R—Title Tk. 2004. (Phonics Friends Ser.). 24p. (J). (ps). 21.36 (978-1-59296-304-1(8)) Child's World, Inc.

—S—Title Tk. 2004. (Phonics Friends Ser.). 24p. (J). (ps). 21.36 (978-1-59296-305-8(6)) Child's World, Inc.

—Zack's Zippers: The Sound of Z. 2004. (Phonics Friends Ser.). 24p. (J). (ps). 21.36 (978-1-59296-311-9(0)) Child's World, Inc.

Minden-Cupp, Cecilia & Meier, Joanne. Gary Gets a Gift: The Sound of Hard G. 2004. (Phonics Friends Ser.). (Illus.). 24p. (J). (ps). 21.36 (978-1-59296-294-5(7)) Child's World, Inc.

—Lilly's Lost Lunch: The Sound of L. 2004. (Phonics Friends Ser.). (Illus.). 24p. (J). (ps). 21.36 (978-1-59296-299-0(8)) Child's World, Inc.

—Pam's Trip to the Park: The Sound of P. 2004. (Phonics Friends Ser.). 24p. (J). (ps). 21.36 (978-1-59296-302-7(1)) Child's World, Inc.

—Yoshi's Yard: The Sound of Y. 2004. (Phonics Friends Ser.). 24p. (J). (ps). 21.36 (978-1-59296-310-2(2)) Child's World, Inc.

Mira como Bateo! 9: Leveled Books. 2001. (McGraw-Hill. Lectura Ser.). (ENG & SPA.). (gr. 1 up). (978-0-02-187938-0(9)) Macmillan/McGraw-Hill Schl. Div.

Mirror, Mirror, 6 vols., Vol. 5. 2005. (Book Treks Ser.). (Illus.). (J). (gr. 4-8). stu. ed. 35.95 (978-0-673-61841-2(2)) Celebration Pr.

Mis cinco Sentidos 7: Leveled Books. 2001. (McGraw-Hill. Lectura Ser.). (ENG & SPA.). (gr. 1 up). (978-0-02-187984-7(2)) Macmillan/McGraw-Hill Schl. Div.

El misterio del Mary Celeste 14: Leveled Books. 2001. (McGraw-Hill. Lectura Ser.). (ENG & SPA.). (gr. 5 up). (978-0-02-188286-1(X)) Macmillan/McGraw-Hill Schl. Div.

Mitchell, Julie. The Walking Leaf. Robertson, Claire, illus. 2002. (Bright Sparks Ser.). 16p. pap. 2.30 (978-0-521-75427-9(5)) Cambridge Univ. Pr.

—You Can Do It, Ella! 2002. (Bright Sparks Ser.). (Illus.). 16p. pap. 2.30 (978-0-521-75426-2(7)) Cambridge Univ. Pr.

Mixed-Up Wishing Well Little Book: Early Reading Fluency, Level C. 2004. pap. 6.00 (978-0-7398-8297-9(X)) Steck-Vaughn.

Moc, Nit y Pon 7: Leveled Books. 2001. (McGraw-Hill. Lectura Ser.). (ENG & SPA.). (gr. 4 up). (978-0-02-188183-3(9)) Macmillan/McGraw-Hill Schl. Div.

Un modelo Especial 10: Leveled Books. 2001. (McGraw-Hill. Lectura Ser.). (ENG & SPA.). (gr. 4 up). (978-0-02-188186-4(3)) Macmillan/McGraw-Hill Schl. Div.

Modern Staff. Discovery Phonics I: Lively Tales Unlock the Mystery of Long & Short Vowels. 2003. (J). 333.95 (978-0-8136-1122-8(9)) Modern Curriculum Pr.

Molter, Carey. -Ain As in Train. 2003. (Word Families Ser.). (Illus.). 23p. (J). (ps-3). lib. bdg. 19.93 (978-1-59197-272-3(8) , SandCastle) ABDO Publishing Co.

—Ake As in Cake. 2003. (Word Families Ser.). (Illus.). 23p. (J). (ps-3). lib. bdg. 19.93 (978-1-59197-270-9(1) , SandCastle) ABDO Publishing Co.

—Eam As in Ice Cream. 2003. (Word Families Ser.). (Illus.). 23p. (J). (ps-3). lib. bdg. 19.93 (978-1-59197-273-0(6) , SandCastle) ABDO Publishing Co.

—En As in Pen. 2003. (Word Families Ser.). (Illus.). 23p. (J). (ps-3). lib. bdg. 19.93 (978-1-59197-229-7(9) , SandCastle) ABDO Publishing Co.

—Ide As in Tide. 2003. (Word Families Ser.). (Illus.). 23p. (J). (ps-3). lib. bdg. 19.93 (978-1-59197-275-4(2) , SandCastle) ABDO Publishing Co.

—One As in Stone. 2003. (Word Families Ser.). (Illus.). 23p. (J). (ps-3). lib. bdg. 19.93 (978-1-59197-274-7(4) , SandCastle) ABDO Publishing Co.

—Oon As in Spoon. 2003. (Word Families Ser.). (Illus.). 23p. (J). (ps-3). lib. bdg. 19.93 (978-1-59197-266-2(3) , SandCastle) ABDO Publishing Co.

Montgomery, Karen & Lloyd, Glynis. English Matters Grade 4 Learner's Pack. 2000. (English Matters Ser.). 200p. (gr. 4). pap. 7.40 (978-0-521-78885-4(4)) Cambridge Univ. Pr.

—English Matters Grade 5 Learner's Pack. 2001. (English Matters Ser.). 192p. pap. 6.90 (978-0-521-00238-7(9)) Cambridge Univ. Pr.

—English Matters Grade 6 Learner's Pack. 2002. (English Matters Ser.). pap. 5.55 (978-0-521-00241-7(9)) Cambridge Univ. Pr.

Montoya, Martha, creator. Huevos o Pollitos: Take-Home. 2005. (Los Kitos Ser.). (SPA.). (YA). (gr. 1-3). 15.00 (978-0-8215-8814-7(1)) Sadlier, William H. Inc.

Moon Stars. 2003. 31.95 (978-0-673-75807-1(9)) Celebration Pr.

Moore, Sheila. Abadaba Alphabet: Learning Letter Sounds. Holsinger, Carol, illus. 2006. (J). *(*978-0-9789473-0-9(4))* Abadaba Reading LLC.

Morgan, Anne. The Crown & Gown. 2002. (Bright Sparks Ser.). (Illus.). 16p. pap. 2.30 (978-0-521-75404-0(6)) Cambridge Univ. Pr.

Morrow, Lesley M. & Gambrell, Linda B. Using Children's Literature in Preschool: Comprehending & Enjoying Books. 2004. (Preschool Literacy Collection). (Illus.). vii, 112p. (ps). pap. 16.95 (978-0-87207-548-1(6)) International Reading Assn.

Moss, Miriam. Can I Have Some? Pack: American English Edition, 6. 2000. (Cambridge Reading Ser.). (Illus.). 12p. pap. 28.00 (978-0-521-79527-2(3)) Cambridge Univ. Pr.

Motorbike Racer: Level P, 6 vols. (Wonder Worldtm Ser.). 48p. 39.95 (978-0-7802-7071-8(1)) Wright Group, The.

Motti, Livia. Chooks Away. 2002. (Bright Sparks Ser.). (Illus.). 16p. pap. 2.30 (978-0-521-75416-3(X)) Cambridge Univ. Pr.

—The Five Cockatoos: Emergent. 2002. (Bright Sparks Ser.). (Illus.). 16p. pap. 2.30 (978-0-521-75127-8(6)) Cambridge Univ. Pr.

Mountain Gorillas: Level N, 6 vols. (Wonder Worldtm Ser.). 48p. 34.95 (978-0-7802-2899-3(5)) Wright Group, The.

Mouse Soup. 2003. 31.95 (978-0-673-75804-0(4)) Celebration Pr.

Mouse Tales. 2003. 31.95 (978-0-673-75805-7(2)) Celebration Pr.

Mouse Train: Big Book: Level C. Group 2. (Story Box(R) Ser.). 16p. 20.95 (978-0-322-00332-3(6)) Wright Group, The.

Move It: Level E, 6 vols. (Wonder Worldtm Ser.). 16p. 29.95 (978-0-7802-1223-7(1)) Wright Group, The.

Moving On: American Readers. (J). (gr. 1). (978-0-669-04950-3(6)); wbk. ed. (978-0-669-04956-5(5)) Houghton Mifflin Co. (Schl. Div.).

Mrs Grindy's Shoes: Level I. Group 1. (Sunshinetm Ser.). 16p. 31.50 (978-0-7802-5756-6(1)) Wright Group, The.

Mundos dentro de nuestro Mundo 22: Leveled Books. 2001. (McGraw-Hill. Lectura Ser.). (ENG & SPA.). (gr. 3 up). (978-0-02-188095-9(6)) Macmillan/McGraw-Hill Schl. Div.

Munton, Gill. How Crayons Are Made American English Edition, 6, Pack. 2000. (Cambridge Reading Ser.). (Illus.). 12p. pap. 28.00 (978-0-521-79895-2(7)) Cambridge Univ. Pr.

—Make a Banana Treat American English Edition, 6, Pack. 2000. (Cambridge Reading Ser.). (Illus.). 8p. pap. 28.00 (978-0-521-79893-8(0)) Cambridge Univ. Pr.

Murphy, G. Let's Read, Bk. 3. 2001. (Illus.). (J). 6.54 (978-0-03-001590-8(1) , Saunders) Elsevier - Health Sciences Division.

My Computer: Level H, 6 vols. (Wonder Worldtm Ser.). 16p. 29.95 (978-0-7802-1225-1(8)) Wright Group, The.

My Dad has Asthma: Level L, 6 vols. (Wonder Worldtm Ser.). 16p. 34.95 (978-0-7802-4587-7(3)) Wright Group, The.

My First Readers: Hooked on Phonics - Learn to Read. 2000. (Illus.). 128p. (J). (ps-1). pap. 14.95 (978-1-887942-85-0(8)) HOP, LLC.

My Friend Jess: Level H, 6 vols. (Wonder Worldtm Ser.). 16p. 29.95 (978-0-7802-1227-5(4)) Wright Group, The.

My Story: Level A, 6 vols. (Wonder Worldtm Ser.). 16p. 24.95 (978-0-7802-2901-3(0)) Wright Group, The.

Mythmakers, 6 vols. (Wildcats Ser.). 32p. (gr. 2-8). (978-0-322-02440-3(4)) Wright Group, The.

Nana la Arana 15: Leveled Books. 2001. (McGraw-Hill. Lectura Ser.). (ENG & SPA.). (gr. 1 up). (978-0-02-187944-1(3)) Macmillan/McGraw-Hill Schl. Div.

Nana's Sweet Potato Pie, 6 vols. (Multicultural Programs Ser.). 16p. (gr. 1-3). 24.95 (978-0-7802-9211-6(1)) Wright Group, The.

A Nap Is not Fun: Short Vowel u: Level A, 6 vols. (Wright Skills Ser.). 12p. (gr. k-3). 17.95 (978-0-322-03131-9(1)) Wright Group, The.

Native Americans: Level O, 6 vols. (Explorers Ser.). 32p. (gr. 3-6). 44.95 (978-0-7699-0600-3(1)) Shortland Pubns. (U. S. A.) Inc.

Naufragios Aterradores 3: Leveled Books. 2001. (McGraw-Hill. Lectura Ser.). (ENG & SPA.). (gr. 5 up). (978-0-02-188275-5(4)) Macmillan/McGraw-Hill Schl. Div.

The Neighborhood Clubhouse, 6 vols. (Multicultural Programs Ser.). 16p. (gr. 1-3). 24.95 (978-0-7802-9212-3(X)) Wright Group, The.

Nell, K. Duke & Bennett-Armistead, V. Susan. Reading & Writing Informational Text in the Primary Grades: Research-Based Practices. 2003. (Illus.). 272p. (gr. k-3). pap. 22.99 (978-0-439-53123-8(3)) Scholastic, Inc.

Nelson. Finding Places: American Readers. (J). (978-0-669-04947-3(6)) Houghton Mifflin Co. (Schl. Div.).

—Looking Out, Climbing Up, Going Far: American Readers. (J). (978-0-669-04973-2(5)) Houghton Mifflin Co. (Schl. Div.).

—Marching Along: American Readers. (J). (978-0-669-04993-0(X)) Houghton Mifflin Co. (Schl. Div.).

—Moving On: American Readers. (J). (978-0-669-04961-9(1)) Houghton Mifflin Co. (Schl. Div.).

—Turning Corners: American Readers. (J). (978-0-669-05008-0(3)) Houghton Mifflin Co. (Schl. Div.).

Nelson, Carol Ann. Red & Red. Costain, illus. unabr. ed. 1998. (Sing along Bks.). 32p. (J). (ps-1). 16.95 (978-1-893886-00-1(X)) How I Learn & Grow.

Nests: Level A, 6 vols. (Wonder Worldtm Ser.). 16p. 24.95 (978-0-7802-1041-7(7)) Wright Group, The.

The New Building, 6 vols. (Sunshinetm Ser.). 16p. (gr. k up). 29.50 (978-0-7802-5424-4(4)) Wright Group, The.

New Shoes: Level C, 6 vols. (Wonder Worldtm Ser.). 16p. 24.95 (978-0-7802-1231-2(2)) Wright Group, The.

Next Chapters Starter Set. 2005. (J). (gr. 3-5). tchr. ed. 119.95 (978-0-7652-2126-1(8)) Modern Curriculum Pr.

Nighttime: Big Book: Level C. Group 1. (Story Box(R) Ser.). 8p. 20.95 (978-0-322-00636-2(8)) Wright Group, The.

No botes esa botella Pontela! 5: Leveled Books. 2001. (McGraw-Hill. Lectura Ser.). (ENG & SPA.). (gr. 4 up). (978-0-02-188181-9(2)) Macmillan/McGraw-Hill Schl. Div.

No lo Creas! 18: Leveled Books. 2001. (McGraw-Hill. Lectura Ser.). (ENG & SPA.). (gr. 3 up). (978-0-02-188139-0(1)) Macmillan/McGraw-Hill Schl. Div.

No Space to Waste: Level L, 6 vols. 128p. (gr. 2-3). 41.95 (978-0-7699-1025-3(4)) Shortland Pubns. (U. S. A.) Inc.

No Sweat! Short e Digraph: Level B, 6 vols. (Wright Skills Ser.). 16p. (gr. k-3). 26.50 (978-0-322-01477-0(8)) Wright Group, The.

Noche de Terror 13: Leveled Books. 2001. (McGraw-Hill. Lectura Ser.). (ENG & SPA.). (gr. 3 up). (978-0-02-188134-5(0)) Macmillan/McGraw-Hill Schl. Div.

Nonfiction. rev. ed. 2004. (High Interest/Low Readability Ser.). 80p. (J). (gr. 5-8). pap. 10.99 (978-0-7696-3396-1(X) , MH1020); Vol. 2. pap. 10.99 (978-0-7696-3397-8(8) , MH1021) School Specialty Publishing.

Not what it Seems, 6 vols. (Wildcats Ser.). 32p. (gr. 2-8). (978-0-322-00602-7(3)) Wright Group, The.

Notorious Nigel: Level Q, 6 vols. (Wonder Worldtm Ser.). 48p. 39.95 (978-0-7802-2960-0(6)) Wright Group, The.

La novena Entrada 6: Leveled Books. 2001. (McGraw-Hill. Lectura Ser.). (ENG & SPA.). (gr. 4 up). (978-0-02-188151-2(0)) Macmillan/McGraw-Hill Schl. Div.

Nuevedades 15: Leveled Books. 2001. (McGraw-Hill. Lectura Ser.). (ENG & SPA.). (gr. 4 up). (978-0-02-188160-4(X)) Macmillan/McGraw-Hill Schl. Div.

Nunca juzgues un libro por su Cubierta 18: Leveled Books. 2001. (McGraw-Hill. Lectura Ser.). (ENG & SPA.). (gr. 1 up). (978-0-02-187995-3(8)) Macmillan/McGraw-Hill Schl. Div.

Oatmeal: Level H, 6 vols. (Wonder Worldtm Ser.). 16p. 29.95 (978-0-7802-1042-4(5)) Wright Group, The.

Oberstar, Lucia. Billy's Adventure. 2002. (Bright Sparks Ser.). (Illus.). 16p. pap. 2.30 (978-0-521-75390-6(2)) Cambridge Univ. Pr.

—Where's Sam? 2002. (Bright Sparks Ser.). (Illus.). 16p. pap. 2.30 (978-0-521-75389-0(9)) Cambridge Univ. Pr.

La obra de Elisabetta Sirani 9: Leveled Books. 2001. (McGraw-Hill. Lectura Ser.). (ENG & SPA.). (gr. 5 up). (978-0-02-188257-1(6)) Macmillan/McGraw-Hill Schl. Div.

Odgers, Sally. Glory Gate: Level Q, 6 vols. 128p. (gr. 6 up). 36.95 (978-0-322-05889-7(9)) Wright Group, The.

Olimpia: los Primeros Juegos Olimpicos 24: Leveled Books. 2001. (McGraw-Hill. Lectura Ser.). (ENG & SPA.). (gr. 3 up). (978-0-02-188097-3(2)) Macmillan/McGraw-Hill Schl. Div.

Olivia Agnew's Wild Imagination: Level O, 6 vols. (Wonder Worldtm Ser.). 48p. 39.95 (978-0-7802-2957-0(6)) Wright Group, The.

On & off the Road: 6 Each of 1 Anthology, 6 vols. (Wildcatstm Ser.). 32p. (gr. 2-8). (978-0-322-02421-2(8)) Wright Group, The.

On My Street, 6 vols. (Multicultural Programs Ser.). 16p. (gr. 1-3). 24.95 (978-0-7802-9205-5(7)) Wright Group, The.

On the Air: Level P, 6 vols. (Wonder Worldtm Ser.). 48p. 39.95 (978-0-7802-7081-7(9)) Wright Group, The.

Once I Was a Baby Little Book: Early Reading Fluency, Level A, Bk. 3. 2004. (gr. 1). pap. 6.00 (978-0-7398-8156-9(6)) Steck-Vaughn.

Ong, Cristina. Little Engine That Could Helps Out. 1999. (ps-2). lib. bdg. 11.80 (978-0-613-64057-2(8)) Tandem Library Bks.

Onish, Liane. Reading Readiness. del Sur, Duendes, illus. 2000. (Jumpstart Ser.). 32p. (J). pap., wbk. ed. 3.99 (978-0-439-16420-7(6)) Scholastic, Inc.

—Reading Skills Card Games: Beginning & Ending Sounds. 2004. (Reading Skills Card Games Ser.). 48p. pap. 10.99 (978-0-439-46598-4(2) , Teaching Resources) Scholastic, Inc.

—Reading Skills Card Games: Long & Short Vowels. 2004. (Reading Skills Card Games Ser.). 48p. pap. 10.99 (978-0-439-46597-7(4) , Teaching Resources) Scholastic, Inc.

—Reading Skills Card Games: Sight Words. 2004. (Reading Skills Card Games Ser.). 48p. pap. 10.99 (978-0-439-46596-0(6) , Teaching Resources) Scholastic, Inc.

Oppenheim, Joanne & Oppenheim, Stephanie. ¡A leer y jugar! con bebés y niños Pequeños. Auclair, Joan, illus. 2006. Tr. of Read It! Play It! with Babies & Toddlers. (SPA.). 102p. pap. 10.00 (978-0-9721050-5-7(0)) Oppenheim Toy Portfolio, Inc.

—Read It! Play It! Auclair, Joan, illus. 2005. 176p. pap. 10.00 (978-0-9721050-1-9(8)) Oppenheim Toy Portfolio, Inc.

—Read It! Play It! with Babies & Toddlers. 2006. (Illus.). pap. 10.00 (978-0-9721050-4-0(2)) Oppenheim Toy Portfolio, Inc.

Orphan Train: Medial Digraphs: Level C, 6 vols. (Wright Skills Ser.). 16p. (gr. k-3). 26.50 (978-0-322-01498-5(0)) Wright Group, The.

Osakawa. Hiking in the Wilds: Level Q. Group 1. (Take-Twostm Ser.). 32p. 38.95 (978-0-322-04488-3(X)) Wright Group, The.

Osborne, Muriel. Jerry the Taxi Driver. Williams, Robbie J., illus. 2002. (Bright Sparks Ser.). 16p. pap. 2.30 (978-0-521-75386-9(4)) Cambridge Univ. Pr.

—The Lollipop Lady: Emergent. Williams, Robbie J., illus. 2002. (Bright Sparks Ser.). 16p. pap. 2.30 (978-0-521-75123-0(3)) Cambridge Univ. Pr.

—Stay Between the Flags! Emergent. 2002. (Bright Sparks Ser.). (Illus.). 16p. pap. 2.30 (978-0-521-75125-4(X)) Cambridge Univ. Pr.

—The Truck Driver. Williams, Robbie J., illus. 2002. (Bright Sparks Ser.). 16p. pap. 2.30 (978-0-521-75124-7(1)) Cambridge Univ. Pr.

Otro caso para Superanuk 10: Leveled Books. 2001. (McGraw-Hill. Lectura Ser.). (ENG & SPA.). (gr. 4 up). (978-0-02-188155-0(3)) Macmillan/McGraw-Hill Schl. Div.

Ottaway, Jacqueline. Riddle of the Seaplanes (Level S), 6 vols. 128p. (gr. 6 up). 36.95 (978-0-322-05891-0(0)) Wright Group, The.

Our Granny: Level B. Group 1. (Sunshinetm Ser.). 8p. 20.95 (978-0-7802-5715-3(4)) Wright Group, The.

Our Letter Chart. 1999. (Metro Reading Ser.). (J). (gr. k). 8.95 (978-1-58120-084-3(6)) Metropolitan Teaching & Learning Co.

Out of Luck!, 6 vols. 8p. (gr. k-1). 21.50 (978-0-322-02081-8(6)) Wright Group, The.

Out of the Computer: Level 6, 6 vols. (Fluency Strand Ser.). (gr. 4-8). 45.00 (978-1-4045-1235-1(7)) Wright Group, The.

Out of the Sunless Land: Level T. Group 2, 6 vols. (Sunshinetm Ser.). 48p. 44.95 (978-0-7802-4186-2(X)) Wright Group, The.

The Ox in the Pit: Consonant x: Level A, 6 vols. (Wright Skills Ser.). 12p. (gr. k-3). 17.95 (978-0-322-03123-4(0)) Wright Group, The.

Pa, Pe, Pi, Po, Pu 2: Leveled Books. 2001. (McGraw-Hill. Lectura Ser.). (ENG & SPA.). (gr. 1 up). (978-0-02-187955-7(9)) Macmillan/McGraw-Hill Schl. Div.

Pacholski, Robert, creator. Aperturas a Lectura. 2003. (SPA., Illus.). (gr. k-3). 78p. stu. ed., wbk. ed. 7.95 (978-0-9745220-1-2(5)); 9p. tchr. ed. 3.95 (978-0-9745220-3-6(1)) Aperturas Foundation.

La paloma en el Nido 6: Leveled Books. 2001. (McGraw-Hill. Lectura Ser.). (ENG & SPA.). (gr. 1 up). (978-0-02-187935-9(4)) Macmillan/McGraw-Hill Schl. Div.

A Pan for Pam: Consonant p: Level A, 6 vols. (Wright Skills Ser.). 12p. (gr. k-3). 17.95 (978-0-322-03108-1(7)) Wright Group, The.

A Pan of Jam: Consonant j: Level A, 6 vols. (Wright Skills Ser.). 12p. (gr. k-3). 17.95 (978-0-322-03109-8(5)) Wright Group, The.

Papalotes 18: Leveled Books. 2001. (McGraw-Hill. Lectura Ser.). (ENG & SPA.). (gr. 5 up). (978-0-02-188290-8(8)) Macmillan/McGraw-Hill Schl. Div.

Papil: Level T. Group 1, 6 vols. (Sunshinetm Ser.). 48p. 44.95 (978-0-7802-5600-2(X)) Wright Group, The.

Para toda la Vida 4: Leveled Books. 2001. (McGraw-Hill. Lectura Ser.). (ENG & SPA.). (gr. 4 up). (978-0-02-188180-2(4)) Macmillan/McGraw-Hill Schl. Div.

Paris, Susan. High Noon: Level P, 6 vols. 128p. (gr. 3-6). 36.95 (978-0-322-05894-1(5)) Wright Group, The.

Partner, Daniel. Bible Devotions for Bedtime. 2004. 256p. (J). pap. 5.97 (978-1-59310-358-3(1)) Barbour Publishing, Inc.

Partridge, Juliet. The Picnic, 6 vols., Pack. 2001. (Cambridge Storybooks Ser.). (Illus.). 8p. pap. 16.00 (978-0-521-00775-7(5)) Cambridge Univ. Pr.

Partridge, Juliet, et al. Beginning to Read: Pattern & Rhyme Strand Pack. 1999. (Cambridge Reading Ser.). 8p. pap. 65.00 (978-0-521-78636-2(3)) Cambridge Univ. Pr.

A Party: Level A. Group 1. (Story Box(R) Ser.). 8p. 20.95 (978-0-322-00634-8(1)) Wright Group, The.

A Party for Nine: Big Book, Vol. 2. 2005. (Emergent Library: Vol. 1). (YA). (ps-1). 23.94 (978-0-8215-8909-0(1)) Sadlier, William H. Inc.

Un paseo en la Selva 8: Leveled Books. 2001. (McGraw-Hill. Lectura Ser.). (ENG & SPA.). (gr. 1 up). (978-0-02-187937-3(0)) Macmillan/McGraw-Hill Schl. Div.

Paso a Paso: Superlibros. 2000. (Aventuras A Traves Del Tiempo Ser.). (ENG & SPA.). (gr. k up). (978-0-02-147856-9(2)) Macmillan/McGraw-Hill Schl. Div.

Un paso Mas: Resources & Ancillaries. 2001. (McGraw-Hill. Lectura Ser.). (ENG & SPA.). (gr. 1 up). (978-0-02-186435-5(7)); (gr. 2 up). (978-0-02-186436-2(5)); (gr. 3 up). (978-0-02-186437-9(3)); (gr. 4 up). (978-0-02-186438-6(1)); (gr. 5 up). (978 0-02-186439-3(X)); (gr. 6 up). (978-0-02-186440-9(3)) Macmillan/McGraw-Hill Schl. Div.

Pedro y el Lobo 17: Leveled Books. 2001. (McGraw-Hill. Lectura Ser.). (ENG & SPA.). (gr. 3 up). (978-0-02-188138-3(3)) Macmillan/McGraw-Hill Schl. Div.

Pember, Brett. Livewire Investigates: The Great Barrier Reef. 2003. (Livewires Ser.). (Illus.). 32p. pap. 4.95 (978-0-521-53835-0(1)) Cambridge Univ. Pr.

People Dance: Level F, 6 vols. (Wonder Worldtm Ser.). 16p. 29.95 (978-0-7802-2018-8(9)) Wright Group, The.

Pepito, patito y Tita, Patita 3: Leveled Books. 2001. (McGraw-Hill. Lectura Ser.). (ENG & SPA.). (gr. 1 up). (978-0-02-187956-4(7)) Macmillan/McGraw-Hill Schl. Div.

Perdido en la Montana 1: Leveled Books. 2001. (McGraw-Hill. Lectura Ser.). (ENG & SPA.). (gr. 4 up). (978-0-02-188201-4(0)) Macmillan/McGraw-Hill Schl. Div.

Perdidos en el Bosque 18: Leveled Books. 2001. (McGraw-Hill. Lectura Ser.). (ENG & SPA.). (gr. 3 up). (978-0-02-188091-1(3)) Macmillan/McGraw-Hill Schl. Div.

Perdidos en el Mar 7: Leveled Books. 2001. (McGraw-Hill. Lectura Ser.). (ENG & SPA.). (gr. 3 up). (978-0-02-188080-5(8)) Macmillan/McGraw-Hill Schl. Div.

Personajes, lugares y celebraciones, Unidad 6: Superlibros (Big Books) 2000. (Aventuras A Traves Del Tiempo Ser.). (ENG & SPA.). (gr. 2 up). (978-0-02-147851-4(1)) Macmillan/McGraw-Hill Schl. Div.

Peter Paper Clip, 6 vols. 8p. (gr. k-1). 21.50 (978-0-322-02065-8(4)) Wright Group, The.

Pets, 6 vols. 2005. (Pets Ser.). (Illus.). 32p. (gr. 2-4). pap. 138.00 (978-0-7910-7546-3(X) , Chelsea Hse.) Facts On File, Inc.

Phonics & Word Study Complete Kits: Phonics & Word Study: Level C. (gr. k-3). 333.95 (978-0-322-01644-6(4)) Wright Group, The.

Phonics & Word Study Core Kits: Phonics & Word Study: Level A. (gr. k-3). 153.50 (978-0-322-01641-5(X)) Wright Group, The.

Phonics & Word Study Core Kits: Phonics & Word Study: Level B. (gr. k-3). 185.50 (978-0-322-01643-9(6)) Wright Group, The.

Phonics & Word Study Core Kits: Phonics & Word Study: Level C. (gr. k-3). 153.50 (978-0-322-01645-3(2)) Wright Group, The.

Phonics Plus Staff. Phonics Plus, Bk. F. 2nd ed. (J). 9.55 (978-0-8136-0396-4(X)) Modern Curriculum Pr.

Photos, Photos: 6 Each of 1 Anthology, 6 vols. (Wildcats Ser.). 32p. (gr. 2-8). (978-0-322-00580-8(9)) Wright Group, The.

Piazza, Linda. Building Reading Comprehension: High-Interest Selections for Critical Reading Skills. 2000. (100+ Seriestm Ser.). 128p. (YA). (gr. 7-8). pap. 12.99 (978-1-56822-915-7(1) , IF8720, Instructional Fair) Schaffer, Frank Pubns.

Picola Mensajera 13: Leveled Books. 2001. (McGraw-Hill. Lectura Ser.). (ENG & SPA.). (gr. 3 up). (978-0-02-188110-9(3)) Macmillan/McGraw-Hill Schl. Div.

Picture & Thematic Dictionary Activity Book. 58p. (gr. k-3). 20.95 (978-0-322-01561-6(8)) Wright Group, The.

La piedra de Rosetta 8: Leveled Books. 2001. (McGraw-Hill. Lectura Ser.). (ENG & SPA.). (gr. 5 up). (978-0-02-188256-4(8)) Macmillan/McGraw-Hill Schl. Div.

Pigs & Dogs Play Ball: Consonants b, w; Short Vowel i word families: Level A, 6 vols. (Wright Skills Ser.). 12p. (gr. k-3). 17.95 (978-0-322-01450-3(6)) Wright Group, The.

The Pink Tent: Final Blends -nd, -nk, -nt: Level B, 6 vols. (Wright Skills Ser.). 16p. (gr. k-3). 17.95 (978-0-322-01462-6(X)) Wright Group, The.

Pinta Ratones 11: Leveled Books. 2001. (McGraw-Hill. Lectura Ser.). (ENG & SPA.). (gr. 1 up). (978-0-02-187988-5(5)) Macmillan/McGraw-Hill Schl. Div.

Place, Jean, et al. Becoming a Reader: Grade 2. 1999. (Cambridge Reading Routes Ser.). (ps). pap., tchr. ed. 21.50 (978-0-521-62797-9(4)) Cambridge Univ. Pr.

Places to Visit, Places to See: Take-Home Book. 2005. (Lee Bennett Hopkins Worlds of Poetry Classroom Library). (YA). (gr. k-3). 13.50 (978-0-8215-0568-7(8)) Sadlier, William H. Inc.

Los Planetas, 6 vols., Vol. 2. (Explorers. Exploradores Nonfiction Sets Ser.). (SPA.). 32p. (gr. 3-6). 44.95 (978-0-7699-0642-3(7)) Shortland Pubns. (U. S. A.) Inc.

Plant, Andrew. The Best Beak. 2002. (Bright Sparks Ser.). (Illus.). 16p. pap. 2.30 (978-0-521-75395-1(3)) Cambridge Univ. Pr.

—Hide & Seek: Emergent. 2002. (Bright Sparks Ser.). (Illus.). 16p. pap. 2.30 (978-0-521-75130-8(6)) Cambridge Univ. Pr.

—I Can Fly. 2002. (Bright Sparks Ser.). (Illus.). 16p. pap. 2.30 (978-0-521-75396-8(1)) Cambridge Univ. Pr.

—Looking for Mum: Emergent. 2002. (Bright Sparks Ser.). (Illus.). 16p. pap. 2.30 (978-0-521-75129-2(2)) Cambridge Univ. Pr.

—Podlet & Spike: Emergent. 2002. (Bright Sparks Ser.). (Illus.). 16p. pap. 2.30 (978-0-521-75131-5(4)) Cambridge Univ. Pr.

—That's My Lunch. 2002. (Bright Sparks Ser.). (Illus.). 16p. pap. 2.30 (978-0-521-75394-4(5)) Cambridge Univ. Pr.

—Watch Out!: Emergent. 2002. (Bright Sparks Ser.). (Illus.). 16p. pap. 2.30 (978-0-521-75132-2(2)) Cambridge Univ. Pr.

—Where's My Shell? 2002. (Bright Sparks Ser.). (Illus.). 16p. pap. 2.30 (978-0-521-75418-7(6)) Cambridge Univ. Pr.

La pluma Presumida 22: Leveled Books. 2001. (McGraw-Hill. Lectura Ser.). (ENG & SPA.). (gr. 1 up). (978-0-02-187951-9(6)) Macmillan/McGraw-Hill Schl. Div.

Poe, Edgar Allan. The Murders in the Rue Morgue & the Purloined Letter. 2nd ed. 2000. (Reading & Training Ser.). 112p. (YA). pap. (978-1-57159-011-4(0)) Los Andes Publishing Co.

Poemario: Big Books. 2001. (McGraw-Hill. Lectura Ser.). (ENG & SPA.). (gr. k up). (978-0-02-186391-4(1)) Macmillan/McGraw-Hill Schl. Div.

Pop, 6 vols. 8p. (gr. k-1). 21.50 (978-0-322-02073-3(5)) Wright Group, The.

Por arte de magia: Trucos sencillos para Ti! 3: Leveled Books. 2001. (McGraw-Hill. Lectura Ser.). (ENG & SPA.). (gr. 3 up). (978-0-02-188100-0(6)) Macmillan/McGraw-Hill Schl. Div.

Por el camino mas Bello 9: Leveled Books. 2001. (McGraw-Hill. Lectura Ser.). (ENG & SPA.). (gr. 4 up). (978-0-02-188154-3(5)) Macmillan/McGraw-Hill Schl. Div.

Por Escrito 8: Leveled Books. 2001. (McGraw-Hill. Lectura Ser.). (ENG & SPA.). (gr. 5 up). (978-0-02-188232-8(0)) Macmillan/McGraw-Hill Schl. Div.

A Porcupine: Big Book: Level C. (Wonder Worldtm Ser.). 16p. 26.50 (978-0-7802-3471-0(5)) Wright Group, The.

A Porcupine: Level C, 6 vols. (Wonder Worldtm Ser.). 16p. 24.95 (978-0-7802-1189-6(8)) Wright Group, The.

Poston, Deborah & Shearin, Grainger. Skill-Building Morning Jumpstarts: Super, Reproducible Practice Pages That Reinforce Skills in Vocabulary, Grammar, Handwriting, Math & More. 2001. 112p. (gr. 2). pap. 14.95 (978-0-439-13116-2(2)) Scholastic, Inc.

PowerPhonics Skill Set I: Includes Animals I, Self I & Growing Things, 18 bks. (Illus.). (J). (gr. 1). lib. bdg. 324.00 (978-0-8239-7204-3(6) , PowerKids Pr.) Rosen Publishing Group, Inc., The.

The Predator. (Song Box(R) Ser.). (gr. 1-2). 8.50 incl. audio (978-0-7802-2261-8(X)) Wright Group, The.

The Predator: 1 Big Book, 6 Each of 1 Student Book, & 1 Cassette. (Song Box(R) Ser.). (gr. 1-2). 68.95 (978-0-7802-3205-1(4)) Wright Group, The.

The Predator: 6 Each of 1 Student Book, 6 vols. (Song Box(R) Ser.). (gr. 1-2). 29.50 (978-0-7802-2259-5(8)) Wright Group, The.

The Predator: Big Book. (Song Box(R) Ser.). (gr. 1-2). 31.50 (978-0-7802-2260-1(1)) Wright Group, The.

Preller, Martie & Williams, Nontsikelelo. Perfectly Me! Chitonga Version. Chisengele, tr. 2001. (Illus.). 32p. pap. 0.45 (978-0-521-01490-8(5)) Cambridge Univ. Pr.

—Perfectly Me! Cinyanja Version. Tembo, tr. 2001. (Illus.). 32p. pap. 0.45 (978-0-521-01492-2(1)) Cambridge Univ. Pr.

—Perfectly Me! Icibemba Version. Mulilo, tr. 2001. (Illus.). 32p. pap. 0.45 (978-0-521-01494-6(8)) Cambridge Univ. Pr.

—Perfectly Me! Kiikaonde Version. Muyebaa, tr. 2001. (Illus.). 32p. pap. 0.45 (978-0-521-01496-0(4)) Cambridge Univ. Pr.

—Perfectly Me! Luvale Version. Sakapaji, tr. 2001. (Illus.). 32p. pap. 0.45 (978-0-521-01498-4(0)) Cambridge Univ. Pr.

—Perfectly Me! Silozi Version. Mwendende, tr. 2001. (Illus.). 32p. pap. 0.45 (978-0-521-01499-1(9)) Cambridge Univ. Pr.

Preparacion para Leer: Resources & Ancillaries. 2001. (McGraw-Hill. Lectura Ser.). (ENG & SPA.). (gr. 1 up). (978-0-02-186052-4(1)) Macmillan/McGraw-Hill Schl. Div.

Preparacion para leer guia del Maestro: Resources & Ancillaries. 2001. (McGraw-Hill. Lectura Ser.). (ENG & SPA.). (gr. 1 up). (978-0-02-186056-2(4)) Macmillan/McGraw-Hill Schl. Div.

Preparados, listos, Ya! 10: Leveled Books. 2001. (McGraw-Hill. Lectura Ser.). (ENG & SPA.). (gr. 2 up). (978-0-02-188035-5(2)) Macmillan/McGraw-Hill Schl. Div.

Pressnall, Debra. Full Color File Folder Games PK-K. 2006. 160p. (J). pap. (978-0-88724-268-7(5) , CD-104047) Carson-Dellosa Publishing Co., Inc.

El primer 4 de Julio de Pop Pop 21: Leveled Books. 2001. (McGraw-Hill. Lectura Ser.). (ENG & SPA.). (gr. 3 up). (978-0-02-188142-0(1)) Macmillan/McGraw-Hill Schl. Div.

The Prince & the Pauper: Response Journal. 2003. 36p. (YA). (978-1-58049-986-6(4) , RJ86) Prestwick Hse., Inc.

Prince Wallaker, Jillayne. Building Reading Comprehension: High-Interest Selections for Critical Reading Skills. 2000. (100+ Seriestm Ser.). 128p. (J). (gr. 3-4). pap. 12.99 (978-1-56822-913-3(5) , IF8718, Instructional Fair) Schaffer, Frank Pubns.

Princeton Review Staff. Roadmap to the AIMS: High School Reading. 2005. (State Test Prep Guides Ser.). 256p. pap. 16.00 (978-0-375-76503-2(4) , Princeton Review) Random Hse. Information Group.

Proof of Magic, 6 vols. (Ragged Island Mysteriestm Ser.). 161p. (gr. 5-7). 42.50 (978-0-322-01649-1(5)) Wright Group, The.

Pruebas de diagnostico y Evaluacion: Resources & Ancillaries. 2001. (McGraw-Hill. Lectura Ser.). (ENG & SPA.). (gr. k-3). (978-0-02-186161-3(7)); (gr. 4-6). (978-0-02-186452-2(7)) Macmillan/McGraw-Hill Schl. Div.

Pruebas de fin de Ano: Assessment. 2001. (McGraw-Hill. Lectura Ser.). (ENG & SPA.). (gr. k up). (978-0-02-186755-4(0)); (gr. 1 up). (978-0-02-186756-1(9)); (gr. 2 up). (978-0-02-186757-8(7)) Macmillan/McGraw-Hill Schl. Div.

Pruebas de fin de ano (End-Year Test Assessment Pupil Edition: Assessment. 2001. (McGraw-Hill. Lectura Ser.). (ENG & SPA.). (gr. 3 up). (978-0-02-186758-5(5)) Macmillan/McGraw-Hill Schl. Div.

Pruebas de la Unidad 1: Assessment. 2001. (McGraw-Hill. Lectura Ser.). (ENG & SPA.). (gr. k up). (978-0-02-186724-0(0)); (gr. 1 up). (978-0-02-186730-1(5)); (gr. 2 up). (978-0-02-186736-3(4)); (gr. 3 up). (978-0-02-186742-4(9)) Macmillan/McGraw-Hill Schl. Div.

Pruebas de la Unidad 2: Assessment. 2001. (McGraw-Hill. Lectura Ser.). (ENG & SPA.). (gr. k up). (978-0-02-186725-7(9)); (gr. 1 up). (978-0-02-186731-8(3)); (gr. 2 up). (978-0-02-186737-0(2)); (gr. 3 up). (978-0-02-186743-1(7)) Macmillan/McGraw-Hill Schl. Div.

Pruebas de la Unidad 3: Assessment. 2001. (McGraw-Hill. Lectura Ser.). (ENG & SPA.). (gr. k up). (978-0-02-186726-4(7)); (gr. 1 up). (978-0-02-186732-5(1)); (gr. 2 up). (978-0-02-186738-7(0)); (gr. 3 up). (978-0-02-186744-8(5)) Macmillan/McGraw-Hill Schl. Div.

Pruebas de la Unidad 4: Assessment. 2001. (McGraw-Hill. Lectura Ser.). (ENG & SPA.). (gr. k up). (978-0-02-186727-1(5)); (gr. 1 up). (978-0-02-186733-2(X)); (gr. 2 up). (978-0-02-186739-4(9)); (gr. 3 up). (978-0-02-186745-5(3)) Macmillan/McGraw-Hill Schl. Div.

Pruebas de la Unidad 5: Assessment. 2001. (McGraw-Hill. Lectura Ser.). (ENG & SPA.). (gr. k up). (978-0-02-186728-8(3)); (gr. 1 up). (978-0-02-186734-9(8)); (gr. 2 up). (978-0-02-186740-0(2)); (gr. 3 up). (978-0-02-186746-2(1)) Macmillan/McGraw-Hill Schl. Div.

Pruebas de la Unidad 6: Assessment. 2001. (McGraw-Hill. Lectura Ser.). (ENG & SPA.). (gr. k up). (978-0-02-186729-5(1)); (gr. 1 up). (978-0-02-186735-6(6)); (gr. 2 up). (978-0-02-186741-7(0)); (gr. 3 up). (978-0-02-186747-9(X)) Macmillan/McGraw-Hill Schl. Div.

Pruebas de mitad de Ano: Assessment. 2001. (McGraw-Hill. Lectura Ser.). (ENG & SPA.). (gr. k up). (978-0-02-187533-7(2)); (gr. 1 up). (978-0-02-186752-3(6)); (gr. 2 up). (978-0-02-186753-0(4)); (gr. 3 up). (978-0-02-186754-7(2)) Macmillan/McGraw-Hill Schl. Div.

Pruebas y Manual del Maestro: Assessment. 2001. (McGraw-Hill. Lectura Ser.). (ENG & SPA.). (gr. k up). (978-0-02-187812-3(9)); (gr. 2 up). (978-0-02-187813-0(7)); (gr. 3 up). (978-0-02-187815-4(3)); (gr. 4 up). (978-0-02-187816-1(1)); (gr. 5 up). (978-0-02-187817-8(X)); (gr. 6 up). (978-0-02-188307-3(6)) Macmillan/McGraw-Hill Schl. Div.

Publ, Griffin. Easy Olympic Sports Reader, 6 Bks, Set. 2004. (U. S. Olympic Committee Easy Olympic Sports Readers Ser.). (Illus.). 16p. (J). pap. 17.95 (978-1-58000-116-8(5)) Griffin Publishing Group.

Pulse- Fun with Reading & Writing. 2006. cd-rom 4.99 ***(*978-1-60245-040-0(4))*** GDL Multimedia, LLC.

Punter, Russell. Ghosts. 2005. (Young Reading Series 1 Ser.). 48p. (J). (gr. 2 up). pap. 5.95 (978-0-7945-0876-0(6) , Usborne) EDC Publishing.

Quack! Quack! Quack!, 6 vols. 8p. (gr. k-1). 21.50 (978-0-322-02074-0(3)) Wright Group, The.

Que Es? 20: Leveled Books. 2001. (McGraw-Hill. Lectura Ser.). (ENG & SPA.). (gr. 1 up). (978-0-02-187973-1(7)) Macmillan/McGraw-Hill Schl. Div.

Que es una mariposa Blanca? 21: Leveled Books. 2001. (McGraw-Hill. Lectura Ser.). (ENG & SPA.). (gr. 1 up). (978-0-02-187950-2(8)) Macmillan/McGraw-Hill Schl. Div.

Que hay en la Bolsa? 19: Leveled Books. 2001. (McGraw-Hill. Lectura Ser.). (ENG & SPA.). (gr. 1 up). (978-0-02-187996-0(6)) Macmillan/McGraw-Hill Schl. Div.

Que hay en las Nubes? 7: Leveled Books. 2001. (McGraw-Hill. Lectura Ser.). (ENG & SPA.). (gr. 1 up). (978-0-02-187936-6(2)) Macmillan/McGraw-Hill Schl. Div.

Que sera, que Sera? 13: Leveled Books. 2001. (McGraw-Hill. Lectura Ser.). (ENG & SPA.). (gr. 2 up). (978-0-02-188014-0(X)) Macmillan/McGraw-Hill Schl. Div.

Que te pasa Julio? 2: Leveled Books. 2001. (McGraw-Hill. Lectura Ser.). (ENG & SPA.). (gr. 2 up). (978-0-02-188003-4(4)) Macmillan/McGraw-Hill Schl. Div.

Que vemos en el mar?/What Do You See by the Sea? 2005. (Libros en Espanol Para Ninos Ser.). (SPA.). (YA). (ps-1). 11.97 (978-0-8215-0992-0(6)); 15.75 (978-0-8215-1202-9(1)) Sadlier, William H. Inc.

Quedense con su Basura! 5: Leveled Books. 2001. (McGraw-Hill. Lectura Ser.). (ENG & SPA.). (gr. 4 up). (978-0-02-188205-2(3)) Macmillan/McGraw-Hill Schl. Div.

Queen Jelly Bean: Vowel Digraph Review: Level C, 6 vols. (Wright Skills Ser.). 16p. (gr. k-3). 26.50 (978-0-322-01499-2(9)) Wright Group, The.

Queen of the Trail: Decodable Books, 6 vols. (Fasttrack Reading Ser.). 24p. (gr. 4-8). 40.95 (978-0-322-05985-6(2)) Wright Group, The.

Querido Diario 15: Leveled Books. 2001. (McGraw-Hill. Lectura Ser.). (ENG & SPA.). (gr. 2 up). (978-0-02-188064-5(6)) Macmillan/McGraw-Hill Schl. Div.

Quien le tiene miedo al Lobo? 17: Leveled Books. 2001. (McGraw-Hill. Lectura Ser.). (ENG & SPA.). (gr. 3 up). (978-0-02-188090-4(5)) Macmillan/McGraw-Hill Schl. Div.

Quien reinara en el Desierto? 1: Leveled Books. 2001. (McGraw-Hill. Lectura Ser.). (ENG & SPA.). (gr. 2 up). (978-0-02-188002-7(6)) Macmillan/McGraw-Hill Schl. Div.

Quiero Escribir 9: Leveled Books. 2001. (McGraw-Hill. Lectura Ser.). (ENG & SPA.). (gr. 3 up). (978-0-02-188082-9(4)) Macmillan/McGraw-Hill Schl. Div.

A Quilt for Kristy: Consonant blend review: Level C, 6 vols. (Wright Skills Ser.). 16p. (gr. k-3). 26.50 (978-0-322-01493-0(X)) Wright Group, The.

Quinley, Elliott. Reading Nonfiction 2: Reading in Context. 2001. (Illus.). 112p. per. 8.95 (978-1-56254-192-7(7) , SP 1927) Saddleback Educational Publishing.

Quit It! Consonant q: Level A, 6 vols. (Wright Skills Ser.). 12p. (gr. k-3). 17.95 (978-0-322-03122-7(2)) Wright Group, The.

Rabo de Gato 12: Leveled Books. 2001. (McGraw-Hill. Lectura Ser.). (ENG & SPA.). (gr. 1 up). (978-0-02-187989-2(3)) Macmillan/McGraw-Hill Schl. Div.

The Race: Level D. Group 1. (Sunshinetm Ser.). 8p. 20.95 (978-0-7802-5733-7(2)) Wright Group, The.

Rader, Laura, illus. Hey Diddle, Diddle, Big Book: Getting Ready to Read with Mother Goose. l.t. ed. 2001. (Sadlier Phonics Reading Program). 8p. (YA). (ps-k). 27.00 (978-0-8215-6963-4(5)) Sadlier, William H. Inc.

—Hey Diddle, Diddle, Pack of 10, Little Book: Getting Ready to Read with Mother Goose. 2001. (Sadlier Phonics Reading Program). 8p. (YA). (ps-k). 23.94 (978-0-8215-6978-8(3)) Sadlier, William H. Inc.

A Rag for Miss Rat: Consonant r: Level A, 6 vols. (Wright Skills Ser.). 12p. (gr. k-3). 17.95 (978-0-322-03128-9(1)) Wright Group, The.

The Rain & the Sun: Level E, 6 vols. (Wonder Worldtm Ser.). 16p. 29.95 (978-0-7802-1046-2(8)) Wright Group, The.

Rainbow Bridge Publishing Staff. Reading Connection First Grade. 2002. (Reading Connection Ser.). (Illus.). 96p. (gr. 1 up). 10.95 (978-1-887923-80-4(2)) Rainbow Bridge Publishing.

—Reading Connection Second Grade: Mastering Basic Skills. 2002. (Reading Connection Ser.). (Illus.). 05/2002p. (gr. 2 up). 10.95 (978-1-887923-81-1(0)) Rainbow Bridge Publishing.

—Reading Connection Third Grade: Mastering Basic Skills. 2002. (Reading Connection Ser.). (Illus.). 96p. (gr. 3 up). 10.95 (978-1-887923-82-8(9)) Rainbow Bridge Publishing.

Raintree Steck-Vaughn Staff. Critical Reading Language Arts E. 2002. pap. (978-0-7398-5553-9(0)) Steck-Vaughn.

—Critical Reading Language Arts G. 2002. pap. (978-0-7398-5557-7(3)) Steck-Vaughn.

—Emergent Stage. 2000. (Illus.). (J). pap. 104.00 (978-0-8172-6595-3(3)) Steck-Vaughn.

Raintree Steck-Vaughn Staff, contrib. by. In Reading: Advanced Level. 2000. (J). pap. 13.12 (978-0-8172-7106-0(6)) Steck-Vaughn.

—Think Alongs: Level A. 1999. (J). (ps-3). pap. 13.26 (978-0-7398-0083-6(3)) Steck-Vaughn.

—Think Alongs: Level B. 1999. (J). (ps-3). pap. 13.26 (978-0-7398-0084-3(1)); pap. 12.10 (978-0-7398-0090-4(6)) Steck-Vaughn.

—Think Alongs: Level C. 1999. (J). (ps-3). pap. 13.26 (978-0-7398-0085-0(X)); pap. 12.10 (978-0-7398-0091-1(4)) Steck-Vaughn.

—Think Alongs: Level D. 1999. (J). (ps-3). pap. 13.26 (978-0-7398-0086-7(8)); pap. 12.10 (978-0-7398-0092-8(2)) Steck-Vaughn.

—Think Alongs: Level E. 1999. (J). (ps-3). pap. 13.26 (978-0-7398-0087-4(6)); pap. 12.10 (978-0-7398-0093-5(0)) Steck-Vaughn.

—Think Alongs: Level F. 1999. (J). (ps-3). pap. 13.26 (978-0-7398-0088-1(4)); pap. 12.10 (978-0-7398-0094-2(9)) Steck-Vaughn.

La rana y el Raton 11: Leveled Books. 2001. (McGraw-Hill. Lectura Ser.). (ENG & SPA.). (gr. 1 up). (978-0-02-187940-3(0)) Macmillan/McGraw-Hill Schl. Div.

Rankin, Joan. Magic Makes the Day. 1999. (Cambridge Reading Routes Ser.). (Illus.). 32p. pap. 6.45 (978-0-521-77903-6(0)) Cambridge Univ. Pr.

—Our House: Chitonga Version. Chisengele, tr. 2001. (Illus.). 8p. pap. 0.45 (978-0-521-01458-8(1)) Cambridge Univ. Pr.

—Our House: Chitonga Version. Hamoonga, Lazarous, tr. 1998. (Cambridge African Language Library Ser.). (Illus.). 8p. pap. 3.75 (978-0-521-64726-7(6)) Cambridge Univ. Pr.

—Our House: Cinyanja Version. Tembo, tr. 2001. (Illus.). 8p. pap. 0.45 (978-0-521-01459-5(X)) Cambridge Univ. Pr.

—Our House: Cinyanja Version. Mwale, Brian, tr. 1998. (Cambridge African Language Library Ser.). (Illus.). 8p. pap. 3.75 (978-0-521-64725-0(8)) Cambridge Univ. Pr.

—Our House: Icibemba Version. Mulilo, tr. 2001. (Illus.). 8p. pap. 0.45 (978-0-521-01462-5(X)) Cambridge Univ. Pr.

—Our House: Icibemba Version. Mwansa, Bupe, tr. 1998. (Cambridge African Language Library Ser.). (Illus.). 8p. pap. 3.75 (978-0-521-64724-3(X)) Cambridge Univ. Pr.

—Our House: Kiikaonde Version. Muyebaa, tr. 2001. (Illus.). 8p. pap. 0.45 (978-0-521-01464-9(6)) Cambridge Univ. Pr.

—Our House: Kiikaonde Version. Muyebaa, Kyangubabi, tr. 1998. (Cambridge African Language Library Ser.). (Illus.). 8p. pap. 3.75 (978-0-521-64723-6(1)) Cambridge Univ. Pr.

—Our House: Luvale Version. Sakapaji, tr. 2001. (Illus.). 8p. pap. 0.45 (978-0-521-01466-3(2)) Cambridge Univ. Pr.

—Our House: Luvale Version. Kaleyi, Kakoma, tr. 1998. (Cambridge African Language Library Ser.). (Illus.). 8p. pap. 3.75 (978-0-521-64721-2(5)) Cambridge Univ. Pr.

—Our House: Silozi Version. Mwendende, tr. 2001. (Illus.). 8p. pap. 0.45 (978-0-521-01468-7(9)) Cambridge Univ. Pr.

—Our House: Silozi Version. Silumesii, Penelope, tr. 1998. (Cambridge African Language Library Ser.). (Illus.). 8p. pap. 3.75 (978-0-521-64720-5(7)) Cambridge Univ. Pr.

Rat Princess Little Book: Early Reading Fluency, Level C. 2004. pap. 6.00 (978-0-7398-8299-3(6)) Steck-Vaughn.

Rawson, C. Giants. 2004. (Young Reading Ser.: Vol. 1). 48p. (J). (gr. 2 up). lib. bdg. 13.95 (978-1-58086-614-9(X) , Usborne) EDC Publishing.

Las razones de Rosamalia 17: Leveled Books. 2001. (McGraw-Hill. Lectura Ser.). (ENG & SPA.). (gr. 2 up). (978-0-02-188018-8(2)) Macmillan/McGraw-Hill Schl. Div.

Reach for Reading: Reaching Higher Self-Training Package. (gr. 3-5). 725.00 (978-0-7578-5931-1(3)) Rigby Education.

Reach for Reading: Reaching up Self-Training Package. (gr. 1-3). 675.00 (978-0-7578-5932-8(1)) Rigby Education.

Reaching Higher Additional Workstations: With Books. (Reach for Reading Ser.). (gr. 3-5). 425.00 (978-0-7635-3700-5(4)) Rigby Education.

Read & Rhyme Memory Match. 2003. (Language Arts Card Games Ser.). (Illus.). (gr. 1-2). 9.99 (978-0-7682-2090-2(4) , J801302) School Specialty Publishing.

Reader's Theater Program Levels (F-U) Set A, 24 vols - 144 Bks. ed. 2004. (J). pap. 375.00 (978-1-4108-1512-5(9)) Benchmark Education Co.

Reading & Writing. 2004. (Help with Homework Ser.). 32p. (J). (gr. k-2). wbk. ed. 3.99 (978-1-904586-24-1(4)); (gr. 1-4). wbk. ed. 3.99 (978-1-904586-20-3(1)) Byeway Bks.

Reading & Writing. 2003. (Full-Color Literacy Activities Ser.). (Illus.). 176p. (J). (ps-1). 19.99 (978-0-7439-3237-0(4)) Teacher Created Materials, Inc.

Reading Comprehension: English in Context. 2000. (Illus.). 112p. per., wbk. ed. 8.95 (978-1-56254-360-0(1) , SP 3601) Saddleback Educational Publishing.

Reading Fluency Grades K-2. 2005. (J). pap. ***(*978-1-60015-039-5(X))*** Steps To Literacy, LLC.

Reading for Information 1. 2002. 100p. ring bd. 29.95 (978-1-56254-222-1(2) , SP 2222) Saddleback Educational Publishing.

Reading for Information 2. 2002. 100p. ring bd. 29.95 (978-1-56254-223-8(0) , SP 2230) Saddleback Educational Publishing.

Reading for Meaning. 2003. (Middle School Mastery Ser.). 64p. (gr. 5-8). 3.99 (978-1-56822-631-6(4) , IF2732) School Specialty Publishing.

Reading Is Everywhere, 6 vols. (Sunshinetm Ser.). 16p. (gr. k up). 29.50 (978-0-7802-5425-1(2)) Wright Group, The.

Reading Quest. 2000. (J). (gr. 3-8). 29.95 (978-1-887942-87-4(4)) HOP, LLC.

Reading Recovery Kits: Reading Recovery Starter Kit. (Reading Recovery(R) Ser.). (gr. k-6). 367.95 (978-0-322-00641-6(4)) Wright Group, The.

Reading Rods Phonemic Awareness Activity Book. 2003. (J). pap. 4.95 (978-1-56911-117-8(0)) Learning Resources, Inc.

Reading Rods Phonemic Awareness Activity Cards, Set 2. 2003. (J). 19.95 (978-1-56911-113-0(8)) Learning Resources, Inc.

Reading Rods Prefixes & Suffixes Activity Cards, Set 2. 2003. (J). pap. 19.95 (978-1-56911-109-3(X)) Learning Resources, Inc.

Reading Rods Readers: Advanced Vowel Mastery Set. 2004. (J). per. 44.95 (978-1-56911-532-9(X)) Learning Resources, Inc.

Reading Rods Readers: Advanced Vowel Mastery Set Classpack. 2004. (J). per. 249.95 (978-1-56911-574-9(5)) Learning Resources, Inc.

Reading Rods Readers: Long Vowel Mastery Set Classpack. 2004. (J). per. 184.95 (978-1-56911-549-7(4)) Learning Resources, Inc.

Reading Rods Readers: Phonics Foundation 1 Classpack. 2003. (J). per. 249.95 (978-1-56911-575-6(3)) Learning Resources, Inc.

Reading Rods Readers: Phonics Foundation 2 Classpack. 2003. (J). per. 249.95 (978-1-56911-576-3(1)) Learning Resources, Inc.

Reading Rods Readers: Phonics Foundation Set 1. 2003. (J). pap. 44.95 (978-1-56911-121-5(9)) Learning Resources, Inc.

Reading Rods Readers: Phonics Foundation Set 2. 2003. (J). pap. 44.95 (978-1-56911-122-2(7)) Learning Resources, Inc.

Reading Rods Readers: Short Vowel Mastery Set Classpack. 2004. (J). per. 184.95 (978-1-56911-548-0(6)) Learning Resources, Inc.

Reading Rods Readers: Word Families Foundation Set. 2004. (J). per. 39.95 (978-1-56911-533-6(8)) Learning Resources, Inc.

Reading Rods Readers: Word Families Foundation Set Classpack. 2004. (J). per. 249.95 (978-1-56911-573-2(7)) Learning Resources, Inc.

Reading Rods Simple Sentences Activity Cards, Set 2. 2003. (J). pap. 19.95 (978-1-56911-112-3(X)) Learning Resources, Inc.

Reading Rods Simple Sentences Instruction & Activity Book. 2003. (J). pap. 12.95 (978-1-56911-110-9(3)) Learning Resources, Inc.

Reading Rods Word Building Activity Book. 2003. (J). pap. 4.95 (978-1-56911-119-2(7)) Learning Resources, Inc.

Reading Rods Word Building Activity Cards, Set 2. 2003. (J). 19.95 (978-1-56911-115-4(4)) Learning Resources, Inc.

Reading Rods Word Families Activity Book. 2003. (J). pap. 4.95 (978-1-56911-118-5(9)) Learning Resources, Inc.

Reading Rods Word Families Activity Cards, Set 2. 2003. (J). 19.95 (978-1-56911-114-7(6)) Learning Resources, Inc.

Reading Skills Mini-Lessons: Grades 4-6. 2003. 96p. (J). tchr. ed. 12.99 (978-0-7439-3288-2(9)) Teacher Created Materials, Inc.

Reading Strategy Cards: Complete Set of 40 Cards (K-5) (On Our Way to English Ser.). (gr. 5 up). 89.95 (978-0-7578-4543-7(6)) Rigby Education.

Reading Success Series A: Guided Reading Program: levels A-F/2-9, 96 books, teacher's guide, 16 instructional cards. 2000. (Illus.). (J). (ps-1). pap. 399.99 (978-1-57874-011-6(8)) Kaeden Corp.

Reading Success Series B: Guided Reading Program: levels F-I/9-16, 72 books, 6 of 12 titles, teacher's guide, 12 ins. 2000. (Illus.). (J). (ps-1). pap. 299.99 (978-1-57874-012-3(6)) Kaeden Corp.

Reading with Emotional Intelligence. 1999. 32p. (J). pap., stu. ed., tchr.'s training gde. ed. 24.95 (978-1-58303-074-5(5)) Pathways Publishing.

Ready, Set, Read Winter 2006: Kaeden's New Titles, 12 vols. 2006. (Illus.). (J). (ps-1). pap. 56.95 (978-1-57874-008-6(8)) Kaeden Corp.

Realtime Associates and Mazer Corporation Staff & LeapFrog Staff, compiled by. Identify Reading Strategies. 2002. (J). (gr. 4). 66.75 (978-1-58605-424-3(4)); (gr. 5). 66.75 (978-1-58605-481-6(3)) LeapFrog Enterprises, Inc. (LeapFrog Schl. Hse.).

—Recognize Cause & Effect. 2002. (J). (gr. 2). 66.75 (978-1-58605-299-7(3)); (gr. 3). 66.75 (978-1-58605-361-1(2)); (gr. 4). 66.75 (978-1-58605-417-5(1)); (gr. 5). 66.75 (978-1-58605-476-2(7)) LeapFrog Enterprises, Inc. (LeapFrog Schl. Hse.).

—Recognize Elements of Plot. 2002. (J). (gr. 2). 66.75 (978-1-58605-303-1(5)); (gr. 3). 66.75 (978-1-58605-367-3(1) , LeapFrog Schl. Hse.); (gr. 4). 66.75 (978-1-58605-425-0(2) , LeapFrog Schl. Hse.); (gr. 5). 66.75 (978-1-58605-485-4(6) , LeapFrog Schl. Hse.) LeapFrog Enterprises, Inc.

—Recognize Genre. 2002. (J). (gr. 3). 66.75 (978-1-58605-369-7(8) , LeapFrog Schl. Hse.); (gr. 4). 66.75 (978-1-58605-427-4(9) , LeapFrog Schl. Hse.); (gr. 5). 66.75 (978-1-58605-490-8(2)) LeapFrog Enterprises, Inc.

—Recognize How Text Is Organized. 2002. 66.75 (978-1-58605-370-3(1)); (J). (gr. 4). 66.75 (978-1-58605-428-1(7)); (J). (gr. 5). 66.75 (978-1-58605-491-5(0)) LeapFrog Enterprises, Inc. (LeapFrog Schl. Hse.).

—Recognize Parts of a Story. 2002. (J). (gr. 2). 66.75 (978-1-58605-290-4(X) , LeapFrog Schl. Hse.) LeapFrog Enterprises, Inc.

—Recognize Point of View. 2002. (J). (gr. 3). 66.75 (978-1-58605-375-8(2)); (gr. 4). 66.75 (978-1-58605-433-5(3)); (gr. 5). 66.75 (978-1-58605-495-3(3)) LeapFrog Enterprises, Inc. (LeapFrog Schl. Hse.).

—Recognize Setting. 2002. (J). (gr. 2). 66.75 (978-1-58605-291-1(8)); (gr. 3). 66.75 (978-1-58605-353-6(1)) LeapFrog Enterprises, Inc. (LeapFrog Schl. Hse.).

—Recognize Story Parts. 2002. (J). (gr. 3). 66.75 (978-1-58605-350-5(7) , LeapFrog Schl. Hse.) LeapFrog Enterprises, Inc.

—Understand Dialogue. 2002. (J). (gr. 2). 66.75 (978-1-58605-294-2(2)); (gr. 3). 66.75 (978-1-58605-356-7(6)); (gr. 4). 66.75 (978-1-58605-412-0(0)); (gr. 5). 66.75 (978-1-58605-472-4(4)) LeapFrog Enterprises, Inc. (LeapFrog Schl. Hse.).

—Understand Events & Actions. 2002. (J). (gr. 3). 66.75 (978-1-58605-351-2(5) , LeapFrog Schl. Hse.) LeapFrog Enterprises, Inc.

—Understand Literary Devices. 2002. (J). (gr. 5). 66.75 (978-1-58605-498-4(8) , LeapFrog Schl. Hse.) LeapFrog Enterprises, Inc.

—Understand Main Idea & Details. 2002. (J). (gr. 2). 66.75 (978-1-58605-293-5(4)); (gr. 3). 66.75 (978-1-58605-354-3(X)); (gr. 4). 66.75 (978-1-58605-410-6(4)) LeapFrog Enterprises, Inc. (LeapFrog Schl. Hse.).

—Understand Mood & Tone. 2002. (J). (gr. 5). 66.75 (978-1-58605-488-5(0) , LeapFrog Schl. Hse.) LeapFrog Enterprises, Inc.

—Understand Story Conflict & Resolution. 2002. (J). (gr. 3). 66.75 (978-1-58605-368-0(X) , LeapFrog Schl. Hse.) LeapFrog Enterprises, Inc.

—Understand the Author's Purpose. 2002. (J). (gr. 2). 66.75 (978-1-58605-307-9(8)); (gr. 3). 66.75 (978-1-58605-376-5(0)); (gr. 4). 66.75 (978-1-58605-434-2(1)); (gr. 5). 66.75 (978-1-58605-496-0(1)) LeapFrog Enterprises, Inc. (LeapFrog Schl. Hse.).

—Understand the Main Idea. 2002. (J). (gr. 5). 66.75 (978-1-58605-470-0(8) , LeapFrog Schl. Hse.) LeapFrog Enterprises, Inc.

—Understand Translations, Reflections, & Rotations. 2002. (J). (gr. 5). 66.75 (978-1-58605-521-9(6) , LeapFrog Schl. Hse.) LeapFrog Enterprises, Inc.

—Understanding Figurative Language. 2002. (J). (gr. 2). 66.75 (978-1-58605-302-4(7) , LeapFrog Schl. Hse.) LeapFrog Enterprises, Inc.

—Understnd a Story's Conflict & Its Resolution. 2002. (J). (gr. 5). 66.75 (978-1-58605-489-2(9) , LeapFrog Schl. Hse.) LeapFrog Enterprises, Inc.

—Use Context to Derive Word Meaning. 2002. (J). (gr. 5). 66.75 (978-1-58605-500-4(3) , LeapFrog Schl. Hse.) LeapFrog Enterprises, Inc.

—Use Context to Determine Word Meaning. 2002. (J). (gr. 3). 66.75 (978-1-58605-379-6(5) , LeapFrog Schl. Hse.) LeapFrog Enterprises, Inc.

—Use Context to Drive Word Meaning. 2002. (J). (gr. 2). 66.75 (978-1-58605-311-6(6)); (gr. 4). 66.75 (978-1-58605-437-3(6)) LeapFrog Enterprises, Inc. (LeapFrog Schl. Hse.).

—Use Story Maps. 2002. (J). (gr. 2). 66.75 (978-1-58605-304-8(3)); (gr. 3). 66.75 (978-1-58605-371-0(X)); (gr. 4). 66.75 (978-1-58605-429-8(5)); (gr. 5). 66.75 (978-1-58605-492-2(9)) LeapFrog Enterprises, Inc. (LeapFrog Schl. Hse.).

Record del Estudiante: Assessment. 2001. (McGraw-Hill. Lectura Ser.). (ENG & SPA.). (gr. k-6). (978-0-02-186567-3(1)) Macmillan/McGraw-Hill Schl. Div.

Red Fox Cub: Review of Consonants, Short Vowels, Word Families: Level A, 6 vols. (Wright Skills Ser.). 12p. (gr. k-3). 17.95 (978-0-322-03126-5(5)) Wright Group, The.

The Red Jets: Decodable Books, 6 vols. (Fasttrack Reading Ser.). 24p. (gr. 4-8). 40.95 (978-0-322-05978-8(X)) Wright Group, The.

Red Or Blue. (Little Book Practice Reader). (J). (978-0-8136-5341-9(X)) Modern Curriculum Pr.

Reece, Colleen L. Rebekah in Danger: Peril at Plymouth Colony. 2004. (Sisters in Time Ser.). 144p. (J). pap. 4.97 (978-1-59310-352-1(2)) Barbour Publishing, Inc.

Reeder. Animals of the Arctic & Antarctic: Level O, 6 vols. (Take-Twostm Ser.). 32p. 38.95 (978-0-322-04489-0(8)) Wright Group, The.

—The Rock Band: Level R. Group 1. (Take-Twostm Ser.). 32p. 38.95 (978-0-322-04487-6(1)) Wright Group, The.

Los reganos de Mama 12: Leveled Books. 2001. (McGraw-Hill. Lectura Ser.). (ENG & SPA.). (gr. 1 up). (978-0-02-187965-6(0)) Macmillan/McGraw-Hill Schl. Div.

Reid, Carolyn & Hepker, Sue. Busy in the Bush: Chitonga Version. Chisengele, tr. 2001. (Illus.). 32p. pap. 0.45 (978-0-521-01370-3(4)) Cambridge Univ. Pr.

—Busy in the Bush: Cinyanja Version. Tembo, tr. 2001. (Illus.). 32p. pap. 0.45 (978-0-521-01371-0(2)) Cambridge Univ. Pr.

—Busy in the Bush: Icibemba Version. Mulilo, tr. 2001. (Illus.). 32p. pap. 0.45 (978-0-521-01374-1(7)) Cambridge Univ. Pr.

—Busy in the Bush: Kiikaonde Version. Muyebaa, tr. 2001. (Illus.). 32p. pap. 0.45 (978-0-521-01375-8(5)) Cambridge Univ. Pr.

—Busy in the Bush: Luvale Version. Sakapaji, tr. 2001. (Illus.). 32p. pap. 0.45 (978-0-521-01378-9(X)) Cambridge Univ. Pr.

—Busy in the Bush: Silozi Version. Sakapaji, tr. 2001. (Illus.). 32p. pap. 0.45 (978-0-521-01379-6(8)) Cambridge Univ. Pr.

Renjilian-Burgy, Joy & Valette, Rebecca. Album - Cuentos Del Mundo Hispanico: Text with in-Text Audio CD. 3rd ed. 2006. (SPA.). 280p. (YA). pap. 64.76 incl. cd-rom (978-0-618-51290-4(X) , 389222) Houghton Mifflin College Div.

Reportajes Sobre el Tiempo 20: Leveled Books. 2001. (McGraw-Hill. Lectura Ser.). (ENG & SPA.). (gr. 3 up). (978-0-02-188141-3(3)) Macmillan/McGraw-Hill Schl. Div.

Rescate de Ballenas! 16: Leveled Books. 2001. (McGraw-Hill. Lectura Ser.). (ENG & SPA.). (gr. 3 up). (978-0-02-188137-6(5)) Macmillan/McGraw-Hill Schl. Div.

Los restos del Naufragio 3: Leveled Books. 2001. (McGraw-Hill. Lectura Ser.). (ENG & SPA.). (gr. 5 up). (978-0-02-188251-9(7)) Macmillan/McGraw-Hill Schl. Div.

La reunion de todos los Animales 1: Leveled Books. 2001. (McGraw-Hill. Lectura Ser.). (ENG & SPA.). (gr. 3 up). (978-0-02-188098-0(0)) Macmillan/McGraw-Hill Schl. Div.

El rey Mocho 14: Leveled Books. 2001. (McGraw-Hill. Lectura Ser.). (ENG & SPA.). (gr. 1 up). (978-0-02-187991-5(5)) Macmillan/McGraw-Hill Schl. Div.

Rhyme Time. 2005. (Rhyme Time Ser.). (J). (ps-3). lib. bdg. 956.64 (978-1-59197-773-5(8) , SandCastle) ABDO Publishing Co.

Rice, Earle, Jr., ed. Great Military Leaders of the 20th Century, 6 vols. 2005. (Illus.). 112p. (gr. 6-12). pap. 180.00 (978-0-7910-7401-5(3) , Chelsea Hse.) Facts On File, Inc.

The Rich & Famous Body & the Empty Checkbook: Level Q, 6 vols. (Wonder Worldtm Ser.). 48p. 39.95 (978-0-7802-2950-1(9)) Wright Group, The.

Richardson, Ellis. Common Short Vowel Syllables Level 9: Brown Sequence. rev. ed. Date not set. (Linguistic Pattern Ser.). (Illus.). 64p. (YA). pap. (978-1-56775-081-2(8)) ISM Teaching Systems, Inc.

—The Sound of Short A Level 4: Green Sequence. rev. ed. Date not set. (Linguistic Pattern Ser.). (Illus.). 64p. (YA). pap. (978-1-56775-079-9(6)) ISM Teaching Systems, Inc.

—The Sound of Short U Level 8: Brown Sequence. rev. ed. Date not set. (Linguistic Pattern Ser.). (Illus.). 64p. (YA). pap. (978-1-56775-080-5(X)) ISM Teaching Systems, Inc.

Rider, Cynthia. The Town Mouse & the Country Mouse. Duffy, Nick, illus. 2001. (Cambridge Reading Ser.). 16p. pap., stu. ed. 8.00 (978-0-521-01421-2(2)) Cambridge Univ. Pr.

—Wisp. Bogie, Dick, illus. 2001. (Cambridge Reading Ser.). 16p. pap. 6.00 (978-0-521-01407-6(7)) Cambridge Univ. Pr.

Ridgway, Dawn. The Clay Boy: Chitonga Version. Chisengele, tr. 2001. (Illus.). 32p. pap. 0.45 (978-0-521-89012-0(8)) Cambridge Univ. Pr.

—The Clay Boy: Cinyanja Version. Tembo, tr. 2001. (Illus.). 32p. pap. 0.45 (978-0-521-89014-4(4)) Cambridge Univ. Pr.

—The Clay Boy: Icibemba Version. Mulilo, tr. 2001. (Illus.). 32p. pap. (978-0-521-89015-1(2)) Cambridge Univ. Pr.

—The Clay Boy: Kiikaonde Version. Muyebaa, tr. 2001. (Illus.). 32p. pap. 0.45 (978-0-521-89016-8(0)) Cambridge Univ. Pr.

—The Clay Boy: Luvale Version. Sakapaji, tr. 2001. (Illus.). 32p. pap. 0.45 (978-0-521-89018-2(7)) Cambridge Univ. Pr.

—The Clay Boy: Silozi Version. Mwendende, tr. 2001. (Illus.). 32p. pap. 0.45 (978-0-521-89019-9(5)) Cambridge Univ. Pr.

Ridgway, Dawn, et al. The Magic Flute & Other Stories: Chitonga Version. Chisengele, tr. 2001. (Illus.). 48p. pap. 0.45 (978-0-521-01529-5(4)) Cambridge Univ. Pr.

—The Magic Flute & Other Stories: Cinyanja Version. Tembo, tr. 2001. (Illus.). 48p. pap. 0.45 (978-0-521-01530-1(8)) Cambridge Univ. Pr.

—The Magic Flute & Other Stories: Icebimba Version. Mulilo, tr. 2001. (Illus.). 48p. pap. 0.45 (978-0-521-01532-5(4)) Cambridge Univ. Pr.

—The Magic Flute & Other Stories: Kiikaonde Version. Muyebaa, tr. 2001. (Illus.). 48p. pap. 0.45 (978-0-521-01533-2(2)) Cambridge Univ. Pr.

—The Magic Flute & Other Stories: Luvale Version. Sakapaji, tr. 2001. (Illus.). 48p. pap. 0.45 (978-0-521-01535-6(9)) Cambridge Univ. Pr.

—The Magic Flute & Other Stories: Silozi Version. Mwendende, tr. 2001. (Illus.). 48p. pap. 0.45 (978-0-521-01536-3(7)) Cambridge Univ. Pr.

Rigby. Extra, Extra, Read All about It. 2001. (Illus.). pap. (978-0-7635-7751-3(0)) Steck-Vaughn.

—Guided Reading in Grades 3-6. 2001. pap. (978-0-7635-7750-6(2)) Steck-Vaughn.

Rigby Education Staff. Where Do People Live? (Illus.). (J). suppl. ed. 20.00 (978-0-7635-6445-2(1) , 764451C99) Rigby Education.

Right or Wrong? 6 Each of 1 Anthology, 6 vols. (Wildcats Ser.). 32p. (gr. 2-8). (978-0-322-00598-3(1)) Wright Group, The.

Ristuccia, Christine & Ristuccia, James. The Entire World of S & Z Instructional Workbook: A Comprehensive Approach to Remediate Frontal & Lateral Lisps. l.t. ed. 2003. (Illus.). 208p. (J). per. 34.99 (978-0-9723457-4-3(4)) Say It Right.

Roberto's Smile: Big Book: Level F. Group 2. (Story Box(R) Ser.). 16p. 20.95 (978-0-322-00318-7(0)) Wright Group, The.

Robinson Crusoe. 2nd ed. 2000. (Reading & Training Ser.). 142p. (YA). pap. (978-1-57159-010-7(2)) Los Andes Publishing Co.

Robledo, Roberto & Howard, Dolores. Read to Succeed, Level 2: Academic Reading Right from the Start. 2004. 229p. (YA). pap. 30.76 (978-0-618-32471-2(2) , 327471) Houghton Mifflin College Div.

Rondeau, Amanda. Ed As in Bed. 2003. (Word Families Ser.). (Illus.). 23p. (J). (ps-3). lib. bdg. 19.93 (978-1-59197-228-0(0) , SandCastle) ABDO Publishing Co.

—Ob As in Knob. 2003. (Word Families Ser.). (Illus.). 23p. (J). (ps-3). lib. bdg. 19.93 (978-1-59197-249-5(3) , SandCastle) ABDO Publishing Co.

—Ock As in Block. 2003. (Word Families Ser.). (Illus.). 23p. (J). (ps-3). lib. bdg. 19.93 (978-1-59197-250-1(7) , SandCastle) ABDO Publishing Co.

—Og As in Dog. 2003. (Word Families Ser.). (Illus.). 23p. (J). (ps-3). lib. bdg. 19.93 (978-1-59197-251-8(5) , SandCastle) ABDO Publishing Co.

—Op As in Top. 2003. (Word Families Ser.). (Illus.). 23p. (J). (ps-3). lib. bdg. 19.93 (978-1-59197-252-5(3) , SandCastle) ABDO Publishing Co.

—Ore As in Core. 2003. (Word Families Ser.). (Illus.). 23p. (J). (ps-3). lib. bdg. 19.93 (978-1-59197-267-9(1) , SandCastle) ABDO Publishing Co.

—Ot As in Knot. 2003. (Word Families Ser.). (Illus.). 23p. (J). (ps-3). lib. bdg. 19.93 (978-1-59197-253-2(1) , SandCastle) ABDO Publishing Co.

—Ow As in Cow. 2003. (Word Families Ser.). (Illus.). 23p. (J). (ps-3). lib. bdg. 19.93 (978-1-59197-254-9(X) , SandCastle) ABDO Publishing Co.

Rooyackers, Paul. 101 Language Games for Children: Fun & Learning with Words, Stories & Poems. Marix Evans, Amina, tr. from DUT. De Groot, Stefan, illus. 2002. (Hunter House Smartfun Book Ser.). 144p. (J). (gr. 4-7). pap. 14.95 (978-0-89793-369-8(9)); (ps up). spiral bd. 19.95 (978-0-89793-370-4(2)) Hunter Hse., Inc.

Rose, Gerald. The Lion & the Mouse, 6, Pack. 2000. (Cambridge Reading Ser.). (Illus.). 24p. pap. 29.00 (978-0-521-78622-5(3)) Cambridge Univ. Pr.

—The Lion & the Mouse: Chitonga Version. Chisengele, tr. 2001. (Illus.). 16p. pap. 0.45 (978-0-521-01513-4(8)) Cambridge Univ. Pr.

—The Lion & the Mouse: Cinyanja Version. Tembo, tr. 2001. (Illus.). 16p. pap. 0.45 (978-0-521-01514-1(6)) Cambridge Univ. Pr.

—The Lion & the Mouse: Icibemba Version. Mulilo, tr. 2001. (Illus.). 16p. pap. 0.45 (978-0-521-01516-5(2)) Cambridge Univ. Pr.

—The Lion & the Mouse: Kiikaonde Version. Muyebaa, tr. 2001. (Illus.). 16p. pap. 0.45 (978-0-521-01517-2(0)) Cambridge Univ. Pr.

—The Lion & the Mouse: Luvale Version. Sakapaji, tr. 2001. (Illus.). 16p. pap. 0.45 (978-0-521-01519-6(7)) Cambridge Univ. Pr.

—The Lion & the Mouse: Silozi Version. Mwendende, tr. 2001. (Illus.). 16p. pap. 0.45 (978-0-521-01520-2(0)) Cambridge Univ. Pr.

—The Little Red Hen, 6, Pack. 2000. (Cambridge Reading Ser.). (Illus.). 24p. pap. 29.00 (978-0-521-78623-2(1)) Cambridge Univ. Pr.

—The Tortoise & the Hare: Chitonga Version. Chisengele, tr. 2001. (Illus.). 16p. pap. 0.45 (978-0-521-01537-0(5)) Cambridge Univ. Pr.

—The Tortoise & the Hare: Cinyanja Version. Tembo, tr. 2001. (Illus.). 16p. pap. 0.45 (978-0-521-01538-7(3)) Cambridge Univ. Pr.

—The Tortoise & the Hare: Icibemba Version. Mulilo, tr. 2001. (Illus.). 16p. pap. 0.45 (978-0-521-01540-0(5)) Cambridge Univ. Pr.

—The Tortoise & the Hare: Kiikaonde Version. Muyebaa, tr. 2001. (Illus.). 16p. pap. 0.45 (978-0-521-01541-7(3)) Cambridge Univ. Pr.

—The Tortoise & the Hare: Luvale Version. Sakapaji, tr. 2001. (Illus.). 16p. pap. 0.45 (978-0-521-01543-1(X)) Cambridge Univ. Pr.

—The Tortoise & the Hare: Silozi Version. Mwendende, tr. 2001. (Illus.). 16p. pap. 0.45 (978-0-521-01544-8(8)) Cambridge Univ. Pr.

Rose, Gerald, et al. The Clever Tortoise: Chitonga Version. Chisengele, tr. 2001. (Illus.). 32p. pap. 0.45 (978-0-521-01503-5(0)) Cambridge Univ. Pr.

—The Clever Tortoise: Cinyanja Version. Chisengele, tr. 2001. (Illus.). 32p. pap. 0.45 (978-0-521-01504-2(9)) Cambridge Univ. Pr.

—The Clever Tortoise: Icibemba Version. Mulilo, tr. 2001. (Illus.). 32p. pap. 0.45 (978-0-521-01506-6(5)) Cambridge Univ. Pr.

—The Clever Tortoise: Kiikaonde Version. Muyebaa, tr. 2001. (Illus.). 32p. pap. 0.45 (978-0-521-01508-0(1)) Cambridge Univ. Pr.

—The Clever Tortoise: Luvale Version. Sakapaji, tr. 2001. (Illus.). 32p. pap. 0.45 (978-0-521-01510-3(3)) Cambridge Univ. Pr.

—The Clever Tortoise: Silozi Version. Mwendende, tr. 2001. (Illus.). 32p. pap. 0.45 (978-0-521-01512-7(X)) Cambridge Univ. Pr.

Rose, Mary. Week-by-Week Homework for Building Reading Comp & Fluency: Grade 2-3. 2004. (Week-by-week Homework for Bldg Reading C Ser.). 96p. (gr. 2-3). pap. 13.99 (978-0-439-51779-9(6) , Teaching Resources) Scholastic, Inc.

—Week-by-Week Homework for Building Reading Comprehension & Fluency: Grade 1. 2004. (Week-by-week Homework for Bldg Reading C Ser.). 96p. (gr. 1). pap. 13.99 (978-0-439-61656-0(5) , Teaching Resources) Scholastic, Inc.

Roso, Calvin. Where the Red Fern Grows. 1998. 58p. (J). (gr. 5-7). stu. ed., ring bd. 12.99 (978-1-58609-151-4(4)) Progeny Pr.

Ross, Val. You Can't Read This: Forbidden Books, Lost Writing, Mistranslations, & Codes. 2006. (Illus.). 152p. (J). (gr. 6). 19.95 (978-0-88776-732-6(X)) Tundra Bks., Inc./Livres Toundra, Inc. CAN. *Dist:* Random Hse., Inc.

A Royal Deal: Diphthongs oi, oy: Level B, 6 vols. (Wright Skills Ser.). 16p. (gr. k-3). 26.50 (978-0-322-01485-5(9)) Wright Group, The.

Rozines Roy, Jennifer. I Love Reading, Level 4. 1999. (Homework Booklets Ser.). (Illus.). 80p. (J). (gr. 3-5). pap. 2.99 (978-1-56822-829-7(5) , IF0324, Instructional Fair) Schaffer, Frank Pubns.

Rude Luke: Long Vowel u, CVCe Pattern: Level B, 6 vols. (Wright Skills Ser.). 16p. (gr. k-3). 17.95 (978-0-322-03103-6(6)) Wright Group, The.

Ruffenach, Jessie E., et al. Learn along with Ashkii: First Grade Level 2. Whitethorne, Bahe, Jr., illus. 2003. (NAV & ENG.). 32p. (J). pap. 7.95 (978-1-893354-42-5(3)) Salina Bookshelf.

—Learn along with Ashkii: Second Grade Level 1. Whitethorne, Bahe, Jr., illus. 2003. (ENG & NAV.). 32p. (J). pap. 7.95 (978-1-893354-43-2(1)) Salina Bookshelf.

—Learn along with Ashkii: Second Grade Level 2. Whitethorne, Bahe, Jr., illus. 2003. (NAV & ENG.). 32p. (J). pap. 7.95 (978-1-893354-44-9(X)) Salina Bookshelf.

—Learn along with Ashkii: Third Grade Level 1. Whitethorne, Bahe, Jr., illus. 2003. (NAV & ENG.). 32p. (J). pap. 7.95 (978-1-893354-45-6(8)) Salina Bookshelf.

Rumblefish: Response Journal. 2003. 32p. (J). (gr. 7-12). (978-1-58049-980-4(5) , RJ80) Prestwick Hse., Inc.

Runaway Hank: Final Blends -ft, -lt: Level C, 6 vols. (Wright Skills Ser.). 16p. (gr. k-3). 26.50 (978-0-322-01495-4(6)) Wright Group, The.

Running, 6 vols. (Multicultural Programs Ser.). 16p. (gr. 1-3). 24.95 (978-0-7802-9215-4(4)) Wright Group, The.

Rushby, Pamela. Last Week in the Creek. Koman, Vasja, illus. 2002. (Bright Sparks Ser.). 16p. pap. 2.30 (978-0-521-75433-0(X)) Cambridge Univ. Pr.

—Nobody Quite Like Me. Webb, Melissa, illus. 2002. (Bright Sparks Ser.). 16p. pap. 2.30 (978-0-521-75432-3(1)) Cambridge Univ. Pr.

Ruttle, Kate. Beginning to Read: Developing Sight Vocabulary American English Edition. 2001. (Cambridge Reading Ser.). 64p. pap., tchr. ed. 7.95 (978-0-521-78407-8(7)) Cambridge Univ. Pr.

Ruttledge, Robert Francis, et al. Becoming a Reader: A Teacher's Resource Book. 1999. (Cambridge Reading Ser.). (Illus.). 80p. pap., tchr. ed. 42.00 (978-0-521-77782-7(8)) Cambridge Univ. Pr.

Sally & the Elephant: Level B, 6 vols. (Wonder Worldtm Ser.). 16p. 24.95 (978-0-7802-1047-9(6)) Wright Group, The.

Salzmann, Mary Elizabeth. -Ad As in Dad. 2003. (Word Families Ser.). (Illus.). 23p. (J). (ps-3). lib. bdg. 19.93 (978-1-59197-226-6(4) , SandCastle) ABDO Publishing Co.

—Ag As in Flag. 2003. (Word Families Ser.). (Illus.). 23p. (J). (ps-3). lib. bdg. 19.93 (978-1-59197-225-9(6) , SandCastle) ABDO Publishing Co.

—Am As in Ham. 2003. (Word Families Ser.). (Illus.). 23p. (J). (ps-3). lib. bdg. 19.93 (978-1-59197-223-5(X) , SandCastle) ABDO Publishing Co.

—Ap As in Cap. 2003. (Word Families Ser.). (Illus.). 23p. (J). (ps-3). lib. bdg. 19.93 (978-1-59197-224-2(8) , SandCastle) ABDO Publishing Co.

—An As in Fan. 2003. (Word Families Ser.). (Illus.). 23p. (J). (ps-3). lib. bdg. 19.93 (978-1-59197-222-8(1) , SandCastle) ABDO Publishing Co.

—At As in Cat. 2003. (Word Families Ser.). (Illus.). 23p. (J). (ps-3). lib. bdg. 19.93 (978-1-59197-221-1(3) , SandCastle) ABDO Publishing Co.

—Ay As in Clay. 2003. (Word Families Ser.). (Illus.). 23p. (J). (ps-3). lib. bdg. 19.93 (978-1-59197-264-8(7) , SandCastle) ABDO Publishing Co.

—Come Home with Me! 2004. (Sight Words Ser.). (Illus.). 23p. (J). (ps-3). lib. bdg. 19.93 (978-1-59197-465-9(8)) ABDO Publishing Co.

—Did You See One Jump? 2004. (Sight Words Ser.). (Illus.). 23p. (J). (ps-3). lib. bdg. 19.93 (978-1-59197-466-6(6)) ABDO Publishing Co.

—Ell As in Well. 2003. (Word Families Ser.). (Illus.). 23p. (J). (ps-3). lib. bdg. 19.93 (978-1-59197-231-0(0) , SandCastle) ABDO Publishing Co.

—It's Not Good, It's Great! 2003. (Sight Words Ser.). (Illus.). 23p. (J). (ps-3). lib. bdg. 19.93 (978-1-59197-479-6(8)) ABDO Publishing Co.

—No Pigs on the Farm! 2004. (Sight Words Ser.). (Illus.). 23p. (J). (ps-3). lib. bdg. 19.93 (978-1-59197-471-0(2)) ABDO Publishing Co.

—Out for the Summer! 2004. (Sight Words Ser.). (Illus.). 23p. (J). (ps-3). lib. bdg. 19.93 (978-1-59197-472-7(0)) ABDO Publishing Co.

—Snow & More Snow! 2004. (Sight Words Ser.). (Illus.). 23p. (J). (ps-3). lib. bdg. 19.93 (978-1-59197-470-3(4)) ABDO Publishing Co.

—They Are the Best! 2004. (Sight Words Ser.). (Illus.). 23p. (J). (ps-3). lib. bdg. 19.93 (978-1-59197-474-1(7)) ABDO Publishing Co.

—Way to Go! 2004. (Sight Words Ser.). (Illus.). 23p. (J). (ps-3). lib. bdg. 19.93 (978-1-59197-468-0(2)) ABDO Publishing Co.

—We All Like It! 2004. (Sight Words Ser.). (Illus.). 23p. (J). (ps-3). lib. bdg. 19.93 (978-1-59197-467-3(4)) ABDO Publishing Co.

—What a Day in the Park! 2004. (Sight Words Ser.). (Illus.). 23p. (J). (ps-3). lib. bdg. 19.93 (978-1-59197-476-5(3)) ABDO Publishing Co.

—Who Is This at the Beach? 2004. (Sight Words Ser.). (Illus.). 23p. (J). (ps-3). lib. bdg. 19.93 (978-1-59197-480-2(1)) ABDO Publishing Co.

Sam & Nan: Consonants d, f, n, p; Short Vowel a word families: Level A, 6 vols. (Wright Skills Ser.). 12p. (gr. k-3). 17.95 (978-0-322-01447-3(6)) Wright Group, The.

Sam & Tat: Consonants m, s, t; Short Vowel a; -am, -at word families: Level A, 6 vols. (Wright Skills Ser.). 12p. (gr. k-3). 17.95 (978-0-322-01444-2(1)) Wright Group, The.

Sam Sat: Consonants m, s, t; Short Vowel a: Level A, 6 vols. (Wright Skills Ser.). 12p. (gr. k-3). 17.95 (978-0-322-03104-3(4)) Wright Group, The.

Sanchez, Mireia. Sobre la Arena. 2002. (Caballo Alado Ser.). (SPA & ENG., Illus.). 24p. 5.95 (978-84-7864-422-3(9)) Combel Editorial, S.A. ESP. *Dist:* Independent Pubs. Group.

Sanders, Lori & Kimble, Linda. Book Projects to Send Home, Grade 3. rev. ed. 2004. (Basic Skills Ser.). (Illus.). 48p. (J). (gr. 3-3). pap. 6.99 (978-0-7424-2733-4(1) , IFG99161, Instructional Fair) Schaffer, Frank Pubns.

Sanders, Nancy I. What I Love Best. Church, Caroline, illus. 2000. (Soft Tabs Bk.). 10p. (J). (978-1-57584-707-8(8)) Reader's Digest Children's Publishing, Inc.

Sanseri, Wanda. Play by the Sea. 2003. (J). 5.00 (978-1-880045-26-8(5)) Back Home Industries.

—SWR Chart Pack. 2003. (J). pap. 9.95 (978-1-880045-30-5(3)) Back Home Industries.

Sanvageau, Juan. Stories, Fables & Poems for You, Vol. 2.Tr. of Cuentos, Fabulas y Poemas Para Ti. (ENG & SPA., Illus.). 89p. (J). (gr. 3-5). pap. 9.95 (978-1-893493-01-8(6)) National Educational Systems, Inc.

Saunders-Smith, Gail. The Farm. 2005. (Transportation Ser.). 24p. (YA). (gr. k-3). pap. (978-1-56065-837-5(1) , Pebble Bks.) Capstone Pr., Inc.

Saving the Florida Panther, 6 vols., Vol. 4. 2005. (Book Treks Ser.). (Illus.). (J). (gr. 4-8). stu. ed. 35.95 (978-0-673-61777-4(7)) Celebration Pr.

Scat! Said the Cat: Big Book: Level D. Group 1. (Sunshinetm Ser.). 8p. 20.95 (978-0-7802-5734-4(0)) Wright Group, The.

Schecter, Deborah. 30 Instant Collaborative Classroom Banners: Easy Patterns for Write-and-Read Banners That Build Literacy & Brighten Your Classroom. 1999. 64p. pap. 10.95 (978-0-439-11103-4(X)) Scholastic, Inc.

Scheunemann, Pam. -Ack As in Snack. 2003. (Word Families Ser.). (Illus.). 23p. (J). (ps-3). lib. bdg. 19.93 (978-1-59197-261-7(2) , SandCastle) ABDO Publishing Co.

—Ape Cape. 2004. (Rhyming Riddles Ser.). (Illus.). 23p. (J). (ps-3). lib. bdg. 19.93 (978-1-59197-457-4(7)) ABDO Publishing Co.

—Ash As in Trash. 2003. (Word Families Ser.). (Illus.). 23p. (J). (ps-3). lib. bdg. 19.93 (978-1-59197-260-0(4) , SandCastle) ABDO Publishing Co.

—Aw As in Paw. 2003. (Word Families Ser.). (Illus.). 23p. (J). (ps-3). lib. bdg. 19.93 (978-1-59197-263-1(9) , SandCastle) ABDO Publishing Co.

—Chipper Flipper. 2004. (Rhyming Riddles Ser.). (Illus.). 23p. (J). (ps-3). lib. bdg. 19.93 (978-1-59197-458-1(5)) ABDO Publishing Co.

—Cooler Ruler. 2004. (Rhyming Riddles Ser.). (Illus.). 23p. (J). (ps-3). lib. bdg. 19.93 (978-1-59197-459-8(3)) ABDO Publishing Co.

—Dill Spill. 2004. (Rhyming Riddles Ser.). (Illus.). 23p. (J). (ps-3). lib. bdg. 19.93 (978-1-59197-460-4(7)) ABDO Publishing Co.

—Ent As in Cent. 2003. (Word Families Ser.). (Illus.). 23p. (J). (ps-3). lib. bdg. 19.93 (978-1-59197-233-4(7) , SandCastle) ABDO Publishing Co.

—Ick As in Kick. 2003. (Word Families Ser.). (Illus.). 23p. (J). (ps-3). lib. bdg. 19.93 (978-1-59197-258-7(2) , SandCastle) ABDO Publishing Co.

—Ing As in King. 2003. (Word Families Ser.). (Illus.). 23p. (J). (ps-3). lib. bdg. 19.93 (978-1-59197-256-3(6) , SandCastle) ABDO Publishing Co.

—Ink As in Drink. 2003. (Word Families Ser.). (Illus.). 23p. (J). (ps-3). lib. bdg. 19.93 (978-1-59197-257-0(4) , SandCastle) ABDO Publishing Co.

—Loud Crowd. 2004. (Rhyming Riddles Ser.). (Illus.). 23p. (J). (ps-3). lib. bdg. 19.93 (978-1-59197-461-1(5)) ABDO Publishing Co.

—Overdue Kangaroo. 2004. (Rhyming Riddles Ser.). (Illus.). 23p. (J). (ps-3). lib. bdg. 19.93 (978-1-59197-462-8(3)) ABDO Publishing Co.

—Unk as in Skunk. 2003. (Word Families Ser.). (Illus.). 23p. (J). (ps-3). lib. bdg. 19.93 (978-1-59197-259-4(0) , SandCastle) ABDO Publishing Co.

Scholastic Clubs US Start Readers Non-Fiction (2 Set) Start Reading. 2006. (J). 27.89 (978-1-59566-326-9(6)) QEB Publishing Inc.

Scholastic, Inc. Staff. Butterflies: The Hands-On Way to Build Reading Skills! Cooper, Terry, ed. 1999. 6p. pap. 7.95 (978-0-439-04311-3(5)) Scholastic, Inc.

—Pumpkins: The Hands-On Way to Build Reading Skills, 2 vols. Cooper, Terry, ed. 1999. pap. 7.95 (978-0-439-05142-2(8)) Scholastic, Inc.

—Seasons. 2000. (Scholastic Interactive Pocket Charts Ser.). (SPA.). 2p. pap. 7.95 (978-0-439-14109-3(5) , Teaching Resources) Scholastic, Inc.

—Teeth: The Hands-On Way to Build Reading Skills, 2 vols. Cooper, Terry, ed. 1999. pap. 7.95 (978-0-439-04303-8(4)) Scholastic, Inc.

—100 Palabras En Ingles Que Los Ninos Deben Leer En: 2nd Grado. Salas, Macarena, ed. 2004. (101 Words Kids Need to Read Ser.). (SPA.). 32p. (J). (gr. 2-5). pap. 2.99 (978-0-439-56024-5(1) , Scholastic en Espanol) Scholastic, Inc.

—100 Words Kids Need to Read 1st Grade: Spanish. Salas, Macarena, ed. 2004. (100 Words Kids Need to Read Ser.). (SPA.). 32p. (J). (ps-3). pap. 2.99 (978-0-439-54845-8(4) , Scholastic en Espanol) Scholastic, Inc.

—100 Words Kids Need to Read 3rd Grade: Spanish. Salas, Macarena, ed. 2004. (102 Words Kids Need to Read Ser.). (SPA.). 32p. (J). (gr. 2-5). pap. 2.99 (978-0-439-66356-4(3) , Scholastic en Espanol) Scholastic, Inc.

Scholastic, Inc. Staff, contrib. by. Entering Pre-K. 2004. (Jumpstart Ser.). (Illus.). 96p. (J). (ps-k). pap. 6.99 (978-0-439-38232-8(7)) Scholastic, Inc.

Scholastic, Inc. Staff, ed. Standardized Test Skill-Builders for Reading. 2000. (Ready-to-Go Reproducibles Ser.). (Illus.). 48p. (J). pap. 8.95 (978-0-439-16230-2(0)) Scholastic, Inc.

School Specialty Publishing. Graphic Organizers. 2003. (Test Connection Ser.). 48p. (J). (gr. 3 up). pap. 6.99 (978-0-7424-1873-8(1) , FS99193); (gr. 4 up). pap. 6.99 (978-0-7424-1874-5(X) , FS99194); (gr. 5 up). pap. 6.99 (978-0-7424-1875-2(8) , FS99195); (gr. 6 up). pap. 6.99 (978-0-7424-1876-9(6) , FS99196) School Specialty Publishing.

—Theme-Based Reading Comprehension. 2003. (100+ Seriestm Ser.). 128p. (J). (gr. 4-4). pap. 12.99 (978-0-7424-1920-9(7) , IFG99111) School Specialty Publishing.

School Zone Publishing. Reading Readiness. 2003. (J). cd-rom 19.99 (978-1-58947-916-6(5)) School Zone Publishing Co.

School Zone Publishing Company Staff. Reading Comprehension 1. (Illus.). (J). 19.99 incl. audio compact disk (978-0-88743-942-1(X)) School Zone Publishing Co.

—Reading Skills-1: And Language Activities. (Illus.). (J). 19.99 incl. audio compact disk (978-0-88743-941-4(1)) School Zone Publishing Co.

Schulz, Charles M. Where Did Woodstock Go? Date not set. (J). 5.95 (978-0-694-00959-6(8)) HarperCollins Pubs.

Schwartz, Sara Jo & Irvin, Barbara Bando. Second Grade Scholar: Grade 2. Speir, Nancy, illus. rev. ed. 2002. (Super-Deluxe Wkbks.). 128p. (J). (gr. k-2). pap. 7.99 (978-1-58947-012-5(5) , 02463) School Zone Publishing Co.

Schwiebert. Reading & Writing from Literature Ap Version. 2002. (YA). (gr. 6-12). stu. ed. 74.36 (978-0-618-21889-9(0) , 349693) Houghton Mifflin College Div.

Scott, Foresman and Company Staff. Away We Go. 2004. (Read with Dick & Jane Ser.). (J). (ps-2). 21.35 (978-1-59197-629-5(4)) Spotlight.

—Fun with Dick & Jane. 2004. (Read with Dick & Jane Ser.). (J). (ps-2). 21.35 (978-1-59197-630-1(8)) Spotlight.

—Go Away, Spot. 2004. (Read with Dick & Jane Ser.). (J). (ps-2). 21.35 (978-1-59197-631-8(6)) Spotlight.

—Go, Go, Go. 2004. (Read with Dick & Jane Ser.). (J). (ps-2). 21.35 (978-1-59197-632-5(4)) Spotlight.

Scott, James. The Crucible: Student Response Journal. 2002. 28p. (J). (978-1-58049-942-2(2) , RJ67) Prestwick Hse., Inc.

—Holes: Student Response Journal. 2002. 38p. (J). (978-1-58049-941-5(4)) Prestwick Hse., Inc.

—The House on Mango Street: A Student Response Journal. 2001. 32p. (YA). (gr. 7-12). wbk. ed. 19.95 (978-1-58049-917-0(1) , RJ26) Prestwick Hse., Inc.

—The Indian in the Cupboard: Response Journal. 2003. 36p. (YA). (978-1-58049-976-7(7) , RJ76) Prestwick Hse., Inc.

—Jane Eyre: A Student Response Journal. 2003. 48p. (YA). (978-1-58049-984-2(8) , RJ84) Prestwick Hse., Inc.

—Silas Marner: Student Response Journal. 2002. 28p. (YA). (gr. 8-12). 19.95 (978-1-58049-972-9(4)) Prestwick Hse., Inc.

—Slam! Student Response Journal. 2002. 32p. (J). (978-1-58049-944-6(9) , RJ69) Prestwick Hse., Inc.

Scott, Janet M. & McCleary, Shelia C. Diagnostic Reading Inventory for Billingual Students. 2000. (SPA & ENG.). 146p. (J). (gr. 1-8). spiral bd. 34.95 (978-0-9636225-1-8(X)) Scott & McCleary Publishing Co.

Se construye un nuevo Establo 10: Leveled Books. 2001. (McGraw-Hill. Lectura Ser.). (ENG & SPA.). (gr. 3 up). (978-0-02-188083-6(2)) Macmillan/McGraw-Hill Schl. Div.

Seddon, Tony. Climbing Mount Everest: South African Edition. Daniel, Gina, illus. 1999. (Cambridge Reading Routes Ser.). 24p. pap. 5.65 (978-0-521-63657-5(4)) Cambridge Univ. Pr.

—Footprints on the Moon: South African Edition. 1999. (Cambridge Reading Routes Ser.). (Illus.). 32p. pap. 6.10 (978-0-521-63656-8(6)) Cambridge Univ. Pr.

Seddon, Tony & Gillham, Bill. Ostrich: Chitonga Version. Chisengele, tr. 2001. (Illus.). 16p. pap. 0.45 (978-0-521-01521-9(9)) Cambridge Univ. Pr.

—Ostrich: Cinyanja Version. Tembo, tr. 2001. (Illus.). 16p. pap. 0.45 (978-0-521-01522-6(7)) Cambridge Univ. Pr.

—Ostrich: Icibemba Version. Mulilo, tr. 2001. (Illus.). 16p. pap. 0.45 (978-0-521-01524-0(3)) Cambridge Univ. Pr.

—Ostrich: Kiikaonde Version. Muyebaa, tr. 2001. (Illus.). 16p. pap. 0.45 (978-0-521-01525-7(1)) Cambridge Univ. Pr.

—Ostrich: Luvale Version. Sakapaji, tr. 2001. (Illus.). 16p. pap. 0.45 (978-0-521-01527-1(8)) Cambridge Univ. Pr.

—Ostrich: Silozi Version. Mwendende, tr. 2001. (Illus.). 16p. pap. 0.45 (978-0-521-01528-8(6)) Cambridge Univ. Pr.

Senisi, Ellen B. Reading Grows. Senisi, Ellen B., photos by. 1999. (Illus.). 32p. (J). (ps-2). 16.95 (978-0-8075-6898-9(8)) Whitman, Albert & Co.

El Senor Calor y el Senor Frio 14: Leveled Books. 2001. (McGraw-Hill. Lectura Ser.). (ENG & SPA.). (gr. 3 up). (978-0-02-188111-6(1)) Macmillan/McGraw-Hill Schl. Div.

El Sentido del Centavo No. 6: Leveled Books. 2001. (McGraw-Hill. Lectura Ser.). (ENG & SPA.). (gr. 5 up). (978-0-02-188278-6(9)) Macmillan/McGraw-Hill Schl. Div.

Sequoyah 19: Leveled Books. 2001. (McGraw-Hill. Lectura Ser.). (ENG & SPA.). (gr. 2 up). (978-0-02-188044-7(1)) Macmillan/McGraw-Hill Schl. Div.

Set 3, 4 bks. Incl. Fishing. Palmer, Kate S. & Yukish, Joseph. 16p. pap. 4.50 (978-1-879835-16-0(9)); Guess What Kind of Ball. Urmston, Kathleen & Evans, Karen. Kaeden Corp. Staff, ed. Gedeon, Gloria, illus. 16p. pap. 4.50 (978-1-879835-15-3(0)); Lunch. Urmston, Kathleen & Evans, Karen. Kaeden Corp. Staff, ed. Gedeon, Gloria, illus. 12p. pap. 4.50 (978-1-879835-14-6(2)); Our Garage. Urmston, Kathleen. Evans, Karen & Kaeden Corp. Staff, eds. Dragony, Barbara, illus. 12p. pap. 4.50 (978-1-879835-17-7(7)); (J). (gr. k-2). 1992. Set pap. 17.50 (978-1-879835-18-4(5)) Kaeden Corp.

Shadows, 6 vols. (Multicultural Programs Ser.). 16p. (gr. 1-3). 24.95 (978-0-7802-9214-7(6)) Wright Group, The.

Shake, Rattle, & Roll: Magazine Anthology: Level 4, 6 vols. (Comprehension Strand Ser.). (gr. 4-8). 54.00 (978-0-322-06034-0(6)) Wright Group, The.

Shane: Student Response Journal. 2002. 28p. (J). (978-1-58049-949-1(X) , RJ74) Prestwick Hse., Inc.

Shapiro, Ellen & Kinney, Judi. Ready, Set, Read! Affordable complete reading Program. 2000. 168p. (gr. k-5). spiral bd. 79.00 (978-1-57861-233-8(0) , IEP RESOURCES) Attainment Co., Inc.

Shay Schumm, Jeanne & Schumm, Gerald E. The Reading Tutor's Handbook: A Commonsense Guide to Helping Students Read & Write. 1998. (Illus.). 152p. (gr. 1-12). pap. 19.95 (978-1-57542-052-3(X)) Free Spirit Publishing, Inc.

Shelly's Shell: Digraph sh: Level B, 6 vols. (Wright Skills Ser.). 16p. (gr. k-3). 17.95 (978-0-322-01471-8(9)) Wright Group, The.

Shoo! Level C. Group 1. (Sunshinetm Ser.). 8p. 20.95 (978-0-7802-5725-2(1)) Wright Group, The.

Shopping: Big Book: Level A. (Sunshinetm Ser.). 8p. 20.95 (978-0-7802-5710-8(3)) Wright Group, The.

Shortland. Busy Bees. (Song Box(R) Ser.). (gr. 1-2). pap. 31.50 (978-0-7802-2268-7(7)) Wright Group, The.

Show & Tell. 2003. (J). per. (978-1-57657-813-1(5)) Paradise Pr., Inc.

Show & Tell. 2005. (Emergent Library: Vol. 2). (YA). (ps-1). 23.94 (978-0-8215-8923-6(7)) Sadlier, William H. Inc.

Show & Tell, 6 vols. 8p. (gr. k-1). 21.50 (978-0-322-02075-7(1)) Wright Group, The.

Show & Tell: Take-Home Book. 2005. (Emergent Library: Vol. 2). (YA). (ps-1). 12.60 (978-0-8215-7253-5(9)) Sadlier, William H. Inc.

Show What You Know on the OAT for Grade 7, Reading/Writing Student Workbook. 2006. (J). per. 16.95 (978-1-59230-172-0(X)) Englefield & Assocs., Inc.

Si yo fuera Rey 15: Leveled Books. 2001. (McGraw-Hill. Lectura Ser.). (ENG & SPA.). (gr. 1 up). (978-0-02-187968-7(0)) Macmillan/McGraw-Hill Schl. Div.

Si yo pudiera Escoger 13: Leveled Books. 2001. (McGraw-Hill. Lectura Ser.). (ENG & SPA.). (gr. 1 up). (978-0-02-187966-3(4)) Macmillan/McGraw-Hill Schl. Div.

Sigmond Slitherforth: Level R, 6 vols. (Wonder Worldtm Ser.). 48p. 44.95 (978-0-7802-7073-2(8)) Wright Group, The.

The Silly Supper: Medial Consonants: Level C, 6 vols. (Wright Skills Ser.). 16p. (gr. k-3). 26.50 (978-0-322-01491-6(3)) Wright Group, The.

Las sirenas Viajeras 3: Leveled Books. 2001. (McGraw-Hill. Lectura Ser.). (ENG & SPA.). (gr. 4 up). (978-0-02-188179-6(0)) Macmillan/McGraw-Hill Schl. Div.

Skin, Skin: Level E, 6 vols. (Wonder Worldtm Ser.). 16p. 29.95 (978-0-7802-1235-0(5)) Wright Group, The.

Skunk in the Trunk, 6 vols. 8p. (gr. k-1). 21.50 (978-0-322-02080-1(8)) Wright Group, The.

The Sky's the Limit, 6 vols. (Wildcats Ser.). 32p. (gr. 2-8). (978-0-322-00603-4(1)) Wright Group, The.

Slater, Jean M. Mixed up Morning. Slater, Jean M., illus. 2003. (Illus.). 13p. (J). bds. 16.00 (978-0-9743149-2-1(7)) Slater Software, Inc.

Sleeping,Dreaming: Level Q, 6 vols. (Wonder Worldtm Ser.). 48p. 39.95 (978-0-7802-2951-8(7)) Wright Group, The.

Sloppy Tiger Bedtime: Big Book: Level M. Group 1. (Sunshinetm Ser.). 24p. 36.50 (978-0-7802-5791-7(X)) Wright Group, The.

Slowpoke, 6 vols. 8p. (gr. k-1). 21.50 (978-0-322-02070-2(0)) Wright Group, The.

Slug Makes a House Little Book: Early Reading Fluency, Level A. 2004. pap. 6.00 (978-0-7398-8160-6(4)) Steck-Vaughn.

Slugs & Snails: Big Book: Level I. (Wonder Worldtm Ser.). 16p. 26.50 (978-0-7802-2831-3(6)) Wright Group, The.

Slugs & Snails: Level I, 6 vols. (Wonder Worldtm Ser.). 16p. 29.95 (978-0-7802-1050-9(6)) Wright Group, The.

The Slumber Party Organizer: Level T. Group 1, 6 vols. (Sunshinetm Ser.). 48p. 44.95 (978-0-7802-6097-9(X)) Wright Group, The.

Smelly Armor: Big Book: Level J. Group 2. (Story Box(R) Ser.). 16p. 31.50 (978-0-322-02470-0(6)) Wright Group, The.

Smiles, 6 vols. (Multicultural Programs Ser.). 16p. (gr. 1-3). 24.95 (978-0-7802-9204-8(9)) Wright Group, The.

Smith & Mare. Concepts for Today: Answer Key. 2000. (978-0-8384-1224-4(6)) Thomson Heinle.

—Issues for Today: Answer Key. 2nd ed. 2000. (978-0-8384-2138-3(5)) Thomson Heinle.

—Themes for Today: Answer Key. 2nd ed. 2000. 5.00 net. (978-0-8384-1973-1(9)) Thomson Heinle.

—Topics for Today: Answer Key. 2nd ed. 2000. (978-0-8384-1208-4(4)) Thomson Heinle.

Snake at the Lake: Long Vowel Review: Level C, 6 vols. (Wright Skills Ser.). 16p. (gr. k-3). 26.50 (978-0-322-01496-1(4)) Wright Group, The.

Snap Happy Little Book: Early Reading Fluency, Level A, Bk. 1. 2004. pap. 6.00 (978-0-7398-8157-6(4)) Steck-Vaughn.

Sneller, Norm. Building Reading Comprehension: High-Interest Selections for Critical Reading Skills. 2000. (100+ Seriestm Ser.). 128p. (J). (gr. 5-6). pap. 12.99 (978-1-56822-914-0(3) , IF8719, Instructional Fair) Schaffer, Frank Pubns.

—Cause & Effect: Using Causes & Effects to Make Connections. 2001. (Basic Skills Ser.). 48p. (J). (gr. 5-6). pap. 6.99 (978-0-7424-0101-3(4) , IF5628) School Specialty Publishing.

—Reading Skills, Grades 7-8. 1999. (100+ Seriestm Ser.). 102p. (YA). (gr. 7-8). pap. 12.99 (978-1-56822-136-6(3) , IF8716) School Specialty Publishing.

—Summarizing: Focusing on Main Ideas & Details & Restating in Concise Form. 2001. (Basic Skills Ser.). 48p. (J). (gr. 5-6). pap. 6.99 (978-0-7424-0107-5(3) , IF5642) School Specialty Publishing.

Snowball Fight: Level B, 6 vols. (Wonder Worldtm Ser.). 16p. 24.95 (978-0-7802-1051-6(4)) Wright Group, The.

Snowman: Level A. Group 2. (Story Box(R) Ser.). 8p. 20.95 (978-0-322-00320-0(2)) Wright Group, The.

La solucion de Tina 6: Leveled Books. 2001. (McGraw-Hill. Lectura Ser.). (ENG & SPA.). (gr. 2 up). (978-0-02-188055-3(7)) Macmillan/McGraw-Hill Schl. Div.

Sometimes: Level A, 6 vols. (Wonder Worldtm Ser.). 16p. 24.95 (978-0-7802-2907-5(X)) Wright Group, The.

Sommer, Carl. Noise! Noise! Noise! Read-along, 2003. (Another Sommer-Time Story Ser.). (Illus.). 48p. (J). lib. bdg. 23.95 incl. audio (978-1-57537-769-8(1)) Advance Publishing, Inc.

Somos Amigos: Aventuras (Adventure Books) 2000. (Aventuras A Traves Del Tiempo Ser.). (ENG & SPA.). (gr. k up). (978-0-02-148651-9(4)) Macmillan/McGraw-Hill Schl. Div.

Soper, Sandra. Reading & Writing, Bk. 3. rev. ed. (Illus.). 32p. (J). pap. 5.99 (978-0-330-32075-7(0) , Pan) Pan Macmillan GBR. *Dist:* Trafalgar Square Publishing.

La sorpresa de cumpleanos del granjero Gomez 19: Leveled Books. 2001. (McGraw-Hill. Lectura Ser.). (ENG & SPA.). (gr. 2 up). (978-0-02-188020-1(4)) Macmillan/McGraw-Hill Schl. Div.

La sorpresa de Nandi 3: Leveled Books. 2001. (McGraw-Hill. Lectura Ser.). (ENG & SPA.). (gr. 1 up). (978-0-02-187980-9(X)) Macmillan/McGraw-Hill Schl. Div.

Soup can Telephone: Level K, 6 vols. (Wonder Worldtm Ser.). 16p. 34.95 (978-0-7802-2912-9(6)) Wright Group, The.

Southwater Staff. Read, Count, Sort & Stick: Activity Play with over 200 Reusable Stickers. 2002. (Superstickers Ser.). (Illus.). 64p. (ps-k). pap. 7.95 (978-1-84215-426-7(5) , Southwater) Anness Publishing GBR. *Dist:* National Bk. Network.

Spanish Little Book, 6 vols., Pack. 2005. (Libros en Espanol Para Ninos Ser.). (SPA.). (YA). (ps-1). 71.82 (978-0-8215-0990-6(X)) Sadlier, William H. Inc.

A Spider Web: Level M, 6 vols. (Wonder Worldtm Ser.). 16p. 34.95 (978-0-7802-4603-4(9)) Wright Group, The.

Spot that Cat! Big Book: Level I. Group 2. (Story Box(R) Ser.). 16p. 31.50 (978-0-322-02460-1(9)) Wright Group, The.

Spreading the Word, 6 vols. (Wildcats Ser.). 32p. (gr. 2-8). (978-0-322-00604-1(X)) Wright Group, The.

Sprick, Marilyn & Sprick, Jessica. Hey Diddle Diddle: Read Well Level K Unit 16 Storybook. Clark, Steve, illus. 2003. (Read Well Level K Ser.). 20p. (J). (978-1-57035-687-2(4) , 55562) Sopris West Educational Services.

Sprick, Marilyn, et al. Read Well Big Book, Units 4-6. 2000. (Read Well Ser.). (Illus.). 48p. (J). (gr. 1-3). pap. 19.50 (978-1-57035-321-5(2) , 93BIG2) Sopris West Educational Services.

—Read Well Homework & Extra Practice Blackline Masters. 1998. (Read Well Ser.). (Illus.). 168p. (J). (gr. 1-3). ring bd. 36.50 (978-1-57035-260-7(7) , 93HWKEX) Sopris West Educational Services.

Spring to Success on the PSSA Grade 3: Test Prep & Skills Practice READING. 2005. (Illus.). 80p. (J). per. 8.00 (978-0-9722452-4-1(3)) New Leaf Educ., Inc.

Stage 1: Nonfiction Set. 2001. (Pair-It Bks.). (J). pap. (978-0-7398-4892-0(5)) Steck-Vaughn.

Stage 2: Nonfiction Set. 2001. (Pair-It Bks.). (J). pap. (978-0-7398-4893-7(3)) Steck-Vaughn.

Stamps: Level H, 6 vols. (Wonder Worldtm Ser.). 16p. 29.95 (978-0-7802-2032-4(3)) Wright Group, The.

Standish, Russell D. & Standish, Ella. Gwanpa & Nanny's Home. 2003. 128p. (J). pap. 14.95 (978-0-923309-89-3(6)) Hartland Pubns.

Stanley Stooks: Super Stuntman: Level 7, 6 vols. (Fluency Strand Ser.). (gr. 4-8). 45.00 (978-1-4045-1245-0(4)) Wright Group, The.

Starting Off: American Readers. (J). (978-0-669-04930-5(1)) Houghton Mifflin Co. (Schl. Div.).

Stauffer, Russell G. & Berg, Jean H. Super Reading: Junior. 295p. (YA). (gr. 10-12). 49.95 incl. audio (978-1-55678-036-3(2) , 1067, Learn, Inc.) Oasis Audio.

Steadwell Reading Collection 2 Level 3. 2002. (Illus.). pap. (978-0-7398-6030-4(5)) Steck-Vaughn.

Steadwell Reading Collection 2 Level 4-6. 2002. (Illus.). pap. (978-0-7398-6031-1(3)) Steck-Vaughn.

Steck-Vaughn Staff. Accelerated Reader Stages 3-4. 1999. (Pair-It Bks.). (J). pap. incl. cd-rom (978-0-7398-0712-5(9)) Steck-Vaughn.

—Accelerated Reader Stages 3-4: Mac Edition. 1999. (Pair-It Bks.). (J). pap. incl. mac hd (978-0-7398-0713-2(7)) Steck-Vaughn.

—Access Reading. 2004. pap., tchr. ed. 5.95 (978-0-7398-8934-3(6)); (Illus.). pap. 14.96 (978-0-7398-8928-2(1)) Steck-Vaughn.

—Answer Key Soaring Score CRCT Reading/Language Arts Level F. 2002. (J). pap. (978-0-7398-5556-0(5)) Steck-Vaughn.

—Answer Key Soaring Score CRCT Reading/Language Arts Level H. 2002. (J). pap. (978-0-7398-5560-7(3)) Steck-Vaughn.

—Answer Key Soaring Score Map Communication Arts Level C. 2002. (J). pap. (978-0-7398-5625-3(1)) Steck-Vaughn.

—Answer Key Soaring Score Map Communication Arts Level G. 2002. (J). pap. (978-0-7398-5633-8(2)) Steck-Vaughn.

—Answer Key Soaring Score Map Communication Arts Level K: High School Edition. 2002. (YA). pap. (978-0-7398-5645-1(6)) Steck-Vaughn.

—Answer Key Soaring Scores & CRCT in Reading: Louisiana Edition: Level D. 2002. pap. (978-0-7398-5552-2(2)) Steck-Vaughn.

—Answer Key Soaring Scores CAHSEE Reading: High School Edition. 2002. pap. (978-0-7398-5543-0(3)) Steck-Vaughn.

—At-Home Workbooks: Reading. 2004. (Illus.). (gr. 1). pap., wbk. ed. (978-0-7398-8524-6(3)); (gr. 2). pap., wbk. ed. (978-0-7398-8525-3(1)); (gr. 4). pap., wbk. ed. 5.99 (978-0-7398-8527-7(8)) Steck-Vaughn.

—Complete Reading Package. 2004. (Illus.). (gr. 3). pap. 399.00 (978-0-7398-8692-2(4)) Steck-Vaughn.

—Comprehension Skills. 1999. pap., tchr. ed. 10.35 (978-0-7398-2659-1(X)) Steck-Vaughn.

—Core Skills Reading Comprehension. 2002. (Illus.). (J). (gr. 1). pap. (978-0-7398-5729-8(0)); (gr. 2). pap. (978-0-7398-5730-4(4)); (gr. 3). pap. (978-0-7398-5731-1(2)); (gr. 4). pap. (978-0-7398-5732-8(0)); (gr. 5). pap. 9.99 (978-0-7398-5733-5(9)); (gr. 6). pap. (978-0-7398-5734-2(7)) Steck-Vaughn.

—CRCT: Answer Key - Reading & Language Arts - Level C. 2002. pap. (978-0-7398-5550-8(6)) Steck-Vaughn.

—CRCT: Answer Key - Reading & Language Arts - Level E. 2002. (Soaring Scores Ser.). pap. (978-0-7398-5554-6(9)) Steck-Vaughn.

—CRCT: Answer Key - Reading & Language Arts - Level G. 2002. (Soaring Scores Ser.). pap. (978-0-7398-5558-4(1)) Steck-Vaughn.

—CRCT Reading/Language C: 10 Pack with Key Soaring Scores. 2002. pap. (978-0-7398-5563-8(8)) Steck-Vaughn.

—CRCT Reading/Language E: 10 Pack with Key Soaring Scores. 2002. pap. (978-0-7398-5565-2(4)) Steck-Vaughn.

—CRCT Reading/Language G: 10 Pack with Key Soaring Scores. 2002. pap. (978-0-7398-5567-6(0)) Steck-Vaughn.

—Danger on Ice Set Level 1. 2002. pap. incl. cd-rom (978-0-7398-6954-3(X)) Steck-Vaughn.

—Early Emergent Level A-D: Shutterbug. 2002. pap., tchr. ed. (978-0-7398-5898-1(X)) Steck-Vaughn.

—Early Reader Program Level C: Alexander Graham Bell, 6 Pack. 2004. (Illus.). pap. 33.00 (978-0-7398-8316-7(X)) Steck-Vaughn.

—Early Reader Program Level C: All about Hair, 6 Pack. 2004. (Illus.). pap. 33.00 (978-0-7398-8313-6(5)) Steck-Vaughn.

—Early Reader Program Level C: Flea Treat, 6 Pack. 2004. (Illus.). pap. 33.00 (978-0-7398-8308-2(9)) Steck-Vaughn.

—Early Reader Program Level C: Get Me Out of Here, 6 Pack. 2004. (Illus.). pap. 33.00 (978-0-7398-8314-3(3)) Steck-Vaughn.

—Early Reader Program Level C: Last-Minute Rescue, 6 Pack. 2004. (Illus.). pap. 33.00 (978-0-7398-8318-1(6)) Steck-Vaughn.

—Early Reader Program Level C: Mysteries of the Past, 6 Pack. 2004. (Illus.). pap. 33.00 (978-0-7398-8322-8(4)) Steck-Vaughn.

—Early Reader Program Level C: The Cobsdown Cat Case, 6 Pack. 2004. (Illus.). pap. 33.00 (978-0-7398-8321-1(6)) Steck-Vaughn.

—Early Reader Program Level C: The Mystery of the Missing Leopard, 6 Pack. 2004. (Illus.). pap. 33.00 (978-0-7398-8320-4(8)) Steck-Vaughn.

—Early Reader Program Level C: The Rat Princess, 6 Pack. 2004. (Illus.). pap. 33.00 (978-0-7398-8317-4(8)) Steck-Vaughn.

—Early Reader Program Level C: Tiny Creatures, 6 Pack. 2004. (Illus.). pap. 33.00 (978-0-7398-8309-9(7)) Steck-Vaughn.

—Early Reader Program Level C: Weird Weather, 6 Pack. 2004. (Illus.). pap. 33.00 (978-0-7398-8319-8(4)) Steck-Vaughn.

—Early Reader Program Level C: Your Body up Close, 6 Pack. 2004. (Illus.). pap. 33.00 (978-0-7398-8310-5(0)) Steck-Vaughn.

—Early Reader Program Level B: Amazing Whales, 6 Pack. 2004. (Illus.). pap. 33.00 (978-0-7398-8256-6(2)) Steck-Vaughn.

—Early Reader Program Level B: Chain of Giving, 6 Pack. 2004. (Illus.). pap. 33.00 (978-0-7398-8252-8(X)) Steck-Vaughn.

—Early Reader Program Level B: How the Elephant Got His Trunk, 6 Pack. 2004. (Illus.). pap. 33.00 (978-0-7398-8253-5(8)) Steck-Vaughn.

—Early Reader Program Level B: King Crab Is Coming, 6 Pack. 2004. (Illus.). pap. 33.00 (978-0-7398-8255-9(4)) Steck-Vaughn.

—Early Reader Program Level B: On Safari, 6 Pack. 2004. (Illus.). pap. 33.00 (978-0-7398-8254-2(6)) Steck-Vaughn.

—Early Reader Program Level B: Sharks, 6 Pack. 2004. (Illus.). pap. 33.00 (978-0-7398-8257-3(0)) Steck-Vaughn.

—English ASAP Level 1. 1998. pap., tchr. ed. 17.60 (978-0-8172-7954-7(7)) Steck-Vaughn.

—FCAT Reading 10 Pack: Key: Soaring Scores. 2002. pap. (978-0-7398-6587-3(0)); pap. (978-0-7398-6588-0(9)); pap. (978-0-7398-6589-7(7)); pap. (978-0-7398-6590-3(0)); pap. (978-0-7398-6591-0(9)); pap. (978-0-7398-6592-7(7)); pap. (978-0-7398-6593-4(5)) Steck-Vaughn.

—GED Exercises: Language Arts - Reading. 2000. pap. 11.67 (978-0-7398-3604-0(8)) Steck-Vaughn.

—HCPS: Answer Key - Reading & Writing - Level C. 2002. (Soaring Scores Ser.). pap. (978-0-7398-6097-7(6)) Steck-Vaughn.

—HCPS: Answer Key - Reading & Writing - Level E. 2002. (Soaring Scores Ser.). pap. (978-0-7398-6101-1(8)) Steck-Vaughn.

—HCPS: Answer Key - Reading & Writing - Level H. 2002. (Soaring Scores Ser.). pap. (978-0-7398-6107-3(7)) Steck-Vaughn.

—High Interest Nonfiction. 1999. (Illus.). (J). (gr. 1). pap. (978-0-7398-1306-5(4)); (gr. 2). pap. (978-0-7398-1307-2(2)); (gr. 3). pap. (978-0-7398-1308-9(0)) Steck-Vaughn.

—Higher Scores in Reading Standardized Tests. 2000. (Illus.). (J). (gr. 2). pap. (978-0-7398-2056-8(7)); (gr. 3). pap. (978-0-7398-2057-5(5)); (gr. 4). pap. (978-0-7398-2058-2(3)); (gr. 5). pap. (978-0-7398-2059-9(1)); (gr. 6). pap. 7.99 (978-0-7398-2060-5(5)) Steck-Vaughn.

—Hop Hop Hop/Lots of Spots. 1999. (Take Me Home Ser.). (Illus.). (J). pap. (978-0-7398-2673-7(5)) Steck-Vaughn.

—Improving Reading Comprehension. 1998. (Illus.). (J). (gr. 2). pap. 10.95 (978-0-8172-5800-9(0)); (gr. 3). pap. (978-0-8172-5801-6(9)); (gr. 4). pap. 11.99 (978-0-8172-5802-3(7)); (gr. 5). pap. 11.99 (978-0-8172-5803-0(5)); (gr. 6). pap. (978-0-8172-5804-7(3)) Steck-Vaughn.

—Keys to Excellence in Reading Comprehension: Level B - Grade 2. 1999. pap. 17.27 (978-0-7398-1978-4(X)) Steck-Vaughn.

—Keys to Excellence in Reading Comprehension: Level C - Grade 3. 1999. pap. 17.27 (978-0-7398-1979-1(8)) Steck-Vaughn.

—Keys to Excellence in Reading Comprehension: Level D - Grade 4. 1999. pap. 17.27 (978-0-7398-1980-7(1)) Steck-Vaughn.

—Keys to Excellence in Reading Comprehension: Level E - Grade 5. 1999. pap. 17.27 (978-0-7398-1981-4(X)) Steck-Vaughn.

—Keys to Excellence in Reading Comprehension: Level F - Grade 6. 1999. pap. 17.27 (978-0-7398-1982-1(8)) Steck-Vaughn.

—Keys to Excellence Reading Comprehension: Level H. 1999. (J). pap. (978-0-7398-1983-8(6)); pap. (978-0-7398-1984-5(4)) Steck-Vaughn.

—Kindergarten Leveled Readers. 2002. (J). pap. (978-0-7398-7601-5(5)) Steck-Vaughn.

—Language Arts Handbook. 1999. (Illus.). (J). (gr. 2). pap. (978-0-8172-3888-9(3)); (gr. 3). pap. (978-0-8172-3889-6(1)); (gr. 4). pap. (978-0-8172-3890-2(5)); (gr. 5). pap. (978-0-8172-3891-9(3)) Steck-Vaughn.

—Leveled Reader Package. 2002. (Illus.). (gr. k). pap. 104.00 (978-0-7398-7602-2(3)); (gr. 1). pap. 52.00 (978-0-7398-7605-3(8)) Steck-Vaughn.

—Middle School Intensive Reading Package. 2000. (Illus.). (J). pap. (978-0-7398-3323-0(5)) Steck-Vaughn.

—National Shared Reading Bookroom Package. 2003. (Illus.). (gr. k-3). pap. 1380.00 (978-0-7398-8911-4(7)) Steck-Vaughn.

—Pair-It: CD-ROM Classroom, Set. 2001. (Illus.). pap. 179.95 incl. cd-rom (978-0-7398-2907-3(6)) Steck-Vaughn.

—Pair-It Books Transition Stage. 1999. pap. 115.00 (978-0-7398-2454-2(6)) Steck-Vaughn.

—Pair-It Classroom Set Stage 1. 1999. (Illus.). (J). pap. (978-0-7398-1588-5(1)) Steck-Vaughn.

—Pair-It Classroom Set Stage 2. 1999. (Illus.). (J). pap. (978-0-7398-1589-2(X)) Steck-Vaughn.

—Pair-It Classroom Set Stage 3. 1999. (Illus.). (J). pap. (978-0-7398-1590-8(3)) Steck-Vaughn.

—Pair-It Classroom Version Stage 1. 1999. (Illus.). (J). pap. (978-0-7398-1705-6(1)) Steck-Vaughn.

—Pair-It Classroom Version Stage 2. 1999. (Illus.). (J). pap. (978-0-7398-1706-3(X)) Steck-Vaughn.

—Pair-It Classroom Version Stage 3. 1999. (Illus.). (J). pap. (978-0-7398-1707-0(8)) Steck-Vaughn.

—Pair-It Classroom Version Stage 4. 2001. (Illus.). (J). pap. (978-0-7398-2895-3(9)) Steck-Vaughn.

—Pair-It Classroom Version Stage 5. 2001. (Illus.). (J). pap. (978-0-7398-2896-0(7)) Steck-Vaughn.

—Pair-It Early Emergent Non-Fiction. 2002. (Illus.). pap. (978-0-7398-7618-3(X)) Steck-Vaughn.

—Pair-It Lab Pack Stage 1. 1999. (Illus.). (J). pap. incl. cd-rom (978-0-7398-1573-1(3)) Steck-Vaughn.

—Pair-It Lab Pack Stage 2. 1999. (Illus.). (J). pap. (978-0-7398-1574-8(1)) Steck-Vaughn.

—Pair-It Lab Pack Stage 3. 1999. (Illus.). (J). pap. (978-0-7398-1575-5(X)) Steck-Vaughn.

—Pair-It Lab Pack Stage 4. 2001. (Illus.). (J). pap. (978-0-7398-2897-7(5)) Steck-Vaughn.

—Pair-It Lab Pack Stage 5. 2001. (Illus.). (J). pap. (978-0-7398-2898-4(3)) Steck-Vaughn.

—Pair-It Lab Set Stage 1. 1999. (Illus.). (J). pap. (978-0-7398-1591-5(1)) Steck-Vaughn.

—Pair-It Lab Set Stage 2. 1999. (Illus.). (J). pap. (978-0-7398-1592-2(X)) Steck-Vaughn.

—Pair-It Non-Fiction Stage 2, Set. 2002. (Illus.). pap. (978-0-7398-7622-0(8)) Steck-Vaughn.

—Pair-It Non-Fiction Transition Stage, Set. 2002. (Illus.). pap. (978-0-7398-7624-4(4)) Steck-Vaughn.

—Pair-It Retail Version: Early Emergent Stage. 2002. (Illus.). (J). pap. 49.90 (978-0-7398-6662-7(1)) Steck-Vaughn.

—Pair-It Retail Version: Emergent Stage. 2002. (Illus.). (J). pap. 49.90 (978-0-7398-6663-4(X)); pap. 49.90 (978-0-7398-6664-1(8)) Steck-Vaughn.

—Pair-It Retail Version: Transition Stage. 2002. (Illus.). (J). pap. 49.90 (978-0-7398-6666-5(4)) Steck-Vaughn.

—Pair-It Stage 3 Non-Fiction. 2002. pap. 100.00 (978-0-7398-7626-8(0)) Steck-Vaughn.

—Pair-It Stage 4 Non-Fiction. 2002. pap. 100.00 (978-0-7398-7628-2(7)) Steck-Vaughn.

—Power Up Multimedia Workout Book Set Level 1. 2002. (Illus.). (J). pap. (978-0-7398-6476-0(9)) Steck-Vaughn.

—Power up Software Package, Levels 1-4. 2002. (Illus.). pap. 3425.00 incl. cd-rom (978-0-7398-6274-2(X)) Steck-Vaughn.

—Quantum Reading Series Version 6.2 Manual. 1998. pap., tchr. ed. (978-0-8172-5859-7(0)) Steck-Vaughn.

—Reading. 2002. (Reading & Math Progress Ser.). (J). (gr. 1). pap., tchr. ed. (978-0-7398-5299-6(X)); (gr. 2). pap., tchr. ed. (978-0-7398-5301-6(5)); (gr. 3). pap., tchr. ed. (978-0-7398-5303-0(1)); (gr. 4). pap., tchr. ed. (978-0-7398-5305-4(8)); (gr. 5). pap., tchr. ed. (978-0-7398-5307-8(4)); (gr. 6). pap., tchr. ed. (978-0-7398-5309-2(0)) Steck-Vaughn.

—Reading & Writing Exercises: High School. 2001. (YA). pap. (978-0-7398-3958-4(6)) Steck-Vaughn.

—Reading & Writing Exercises A. 2001. pap. (978-0-7398-3950-8(0)) Steck-Vaughn.

—Reading & Writing Exercises B. 2001. pap. (978-0-7398-3951-5(9)) Steck-Vaughn.

—Reading & Writing Exercises C. 2001. pap. (978-0-7398-3952-2(7)) Steck-Vaughn.

—Reading & Writing Exercises D. 2001. pap. (978-0-7398-3953-9(5)) Steck-Vaughn.

—Reading & Writing Exercises E. 2001. pap. (978-0-7398-3954-6(3)) Steck-Vaughn.

—Reading & Writing Exercises F. 2001. pap. (978-0-7398-3955-3(1)) Steck-Vaughn.

—Reading Comprehension. 2002. (Illus.). Bk. C. pap. (978-0-7398-5822-6(X)); Bk. D. pap. (978-0-7398-5823-3(8)); Bk. A. (J). pap. (978-0-7398-5820-2(3)); Bk. B. pap. (978-0-7398-5821-9(1)) Steck-Vaughn.

—Reading Level D: Answer Key. 1999. (Strategies for Success Ser.). (J). pap. (978-0-7398-1044-6(8)) Steck-Vaughn.

—Reading Level F: Answer Key. 1999. (Strategies for Success Ser.). (J). pap. (978-0-7398-1046-0(4)) Steck-Vaughn.

—Reading Power Modules Ver 6.2 Manual. 1998. (J). pap. (978-0-8172-5860-3(4)) Steck-Vaughn.

—Reading Recovery: Complete Pack. 2001. (J). pap. (978-0-7398-3607-1(2)) Steck-Vaughn.

—Reading Strategies-Start Smart. 2002. (J). pap. (978-0-7398-6017-5(8)) Steck-Vaughn.

—Scoring Reading Assessment System. 2000. (J). pap. (978-0-7398-3325-4(1)) Steck-Vaughn.

—Second Grade Leveled Reader. 2002. (J). (gr. 2). pap. 150.00 (978-0-7398-7611-4(2)) Steck-Vaughn.

—Shutterbug: Add to Package. 2004. Level A-I. pap. 141.11 (978-0-7398-9431-6(5)); Level E-I. pap. 191.90 (978-0-7398-9432-3(3)); Level H-M. pap. 141.11 (978-0-7398-9433-0(1)); Level J-M. pap. 191.90 (978-0-7398-9434-7(X)) Steck-Vaughn.

—Soaring Scores AIMS Reading - High School: Alaska Edition. 2001. (YA). pap. (978-0-7398-3464-0(9)) Steck-Vaughn.

—Soaring Scores in Reading: Answer Key Open-Ended. 2001. (J). pap. (978-0-7398-3475-6(4)); pap. (978-0-7398-3476-3(2)); pap. (978-0-7398-3477-0(0)); pap. (978-0-7398-3478-7(9)) Steck-Vaughn.

—Soaring Scores in Reading: Answer Key Open/Ended. 2001. (J). pap. (978-0-7398-3472-5(X)); pap. (978-0-7398-3474-9(6)) Steck-Vaughn.

—Soaring Scores in Reading Open-ended: Answer Key Open-Ended. 2001. (J). pap. (978-0-7398-3473-2(8)) Steck-Vaughn.

—Start Smart: Reading Strategies 8-Pack. 2002. (Illus.). pap. 36.90 (978-0-7398-6658-0(3)) Steck-Vaughn.

—Summer School Reading. 2002. (J). (gr. 1). pap., tchr. ed. (978-0-7398-5295-8(7)); (gr. 2). pap., tchr. ed. (978-0-7398-5297-2(3)) Steck-Vaughn.

—Summer School Reading Grade. 2001. pap., tchr. ed. 34.13 (978-0-7398-4529-5(2)); pap., tchr. ed. 34.13 (978-0-7398-4531-8(4)); pap., tchr. ed. 34.13 (978-0-7398-4535-6(7)) Steck-Vaughn.

—Take Me Home: Complete Collection - Stage 5. 1999. (Illus.). (J). pap. 61.90 (978-0-7398-0964-8(4)) Steck-Vaughn.

—Take Me Home: Complete Pack. 1999. (Pair-It Bks.). (J). pap. (978-0-7398-1833-6(3)) Steck-Vaughn.

—Take Me Home Complete Set. 1998. (J). pap. (978-0-8172-8678-1(0)) Steck-Vaughn.

—Take Me Home Complete Transition. 1999. (Take Me Home Ser.). (J). pap. (978-0-7398-2600-3(X)) Steck-Vaughn.

—Take Me Home Primary, Set. 1998. (J). pap. (978-0-8172-8675-0(6)); (gr. 1). pap. (978-0-8172-8676-7(4)); (gr. 2). pap. (978-0-8172-8677-4(2)) Steck-Vaughn.

—A Ten Book Summer. 2002. (Illus.). pap. 41.60 incl. audio compact disk (978-0-7398-6965-9(5)) Steck-Vaughn.

—Ten Cents/What Is under My Bed. 1999. (Take Me Home Ser.). (Illus.). (J). pap. (978-0-7398-2676-8(X)) Steck-Vaughn.

—We Are Friends. 2000. pap. (978-0-7398-4482-3(2)) Steck-Vaughn.

Stevenson, Nancy. Basic Blue Level, B. Gallager, Ann & Stevenson, William, eds. Semple, Janice, illus. 2nd ed. 1998. 92p. (J). (gr. 1-7). wbk. ed. 4.75 (978-0-941112-49-9(7)) Stevenson Learning Skills, Inc.

—Basic Blue Level Reading. Gallager, Ann & Stevenson, William, eds. Semple, Janice, illus. 2nd ed. 1998. (Language Skills Program Ser.). 65p. (J). (gr. 1-7). Bk. 3. pap. 3.95 (978-0-941112-47-5(0)); Vol. 1. 3.95 (978-0-941112-45-1(4)); Vol. 2. pap. 3.95 (978-0-941112-46-8(2)) Stevenson Learning Skills, Inc.

Stingrays: Level L, 6 vols. (Wonder Worldtm Ser.). 16p. 34.95 (978-0-7802-4605-8(5)) Wright Group, The.

Stone Works: Level M, 6 vols. (Wonder Worldtm Ser.). 16p. 34.95 (978-0-7802-2909-9(6)) Wright Group, The.

Stoneman, Sonya. First Aid in Reading. (Illus.). 68p. (J). pap., act. bk. ed. (978-1-876367-37-4(7)) Wizard Bks.

—First Aid in Reading: Program Book. (Illus.). 180p. (J). pap. (978-1-876367-24-4(5)) Wizard Bks.

Stop! Big Book: Level E. Group 1. (Story Box(R) Ser.). 16p. 31.50 (978-0-7802-7638-3(8)) Wright Group, The.

Stop: Level C. (Wonder Worldtm Ser.). 16p. 24.95 (978-0-7802-2910-5(X)) Wright Group, The.

The Story Box: Early Emergent - Group 1:1 Each of 8 Student Books: Level A. 33.50 (978-1-55911-125-6(9)) Wright Group, The.

The Story Box: Early Emergent - Group 1:1 Each of 8 Student Books: Level B. 33.50 (978-1-55911-134-8(8)) Wright Group, The.

The Story Box: Early Emergent - Group 1:1 Each of 8 Student Books: Level C. 33.50 (978-1-55911-143-0(7)) Wright Group, The.

The Story Box: Early Emergent - Group 2:1 Each of 8 Student Books: Level A. 33.50 (978-0-7802-9927-6(2)) Wright Group, The.

The Story Box: Early Emergent - Group 2:1 Each of 8 Student Books: Level B. 33.50 (978-0-7802-9928-3(0)) Wright Group, The.

The Story Box: Early Emergent - Student Book Set - 1 Each of 16 Titles. (gr. k up). 66.95 (978-0-322-03142-5(7)); Vol. 2. 66.95 (978-0-7802-9530-8(7)); Vol. 3. 66.95 (978-0-7802-9531-5(5)) Wright Group, The.

The Story Box: Early Emergent-Upper Emergent - Group 1: 1 Each of 8 Student Books: Level D. 33.50 (978-1-55911-152-2(6)) Wright Group, The.

The Story Box: Early Emergent-Upper Emergent - Group 1: 1 Each of 8 Student Books: Level E. 39.95 (978-1-55911-161-4(5)) Wright Group, The.

The Story Box: Early Emergent-Upper Emergent - Group 2: 1 Each of 8 Student Books: Level C. 33.50 (978-0-7802-9931-3(0)) Wright Group, The.

The Story Box: Early Emergent-Upper Emergent - Group 2: 1 Each of 8 Student Books: Level D. 33.50 (978-0-7802-9932-0(9)) Wright Group, The.

The Story Box: Early Emergent-Upper Emergent - Group 2: 1 Each of 8 Student Books: Level E. 39.95 (978-0-7802-9929-0(9)) Wright Group, The.

The Story Box: Early Fluency - Complete Kit. (gr. 2 up). 537.95 (978-0-7802-2772-9(7)) Wright Group, The.

The Story Box: Upper Emergent - Complete Kit. (gr. 1 up). 435.50 (978-0-7802-2771-2(9)); Vol. 2. 435.50 (978-0-7802-9341-0(X)); Vol. 4. 435.50 (978-0-322-02574-5(5)); Vol. 5. 435.50 (978-0-322-02575-2(3)) Wright Group, The.

The Story Box: Upper Emergent - Group 1: 1 Each of 8 Student Books: Level I. 39.95 (978-0-322-02566-0(4)) Wright Group, The.

The Story Box: Upper Emergent - Group 1: 1 Each of 8 Student Books: Level J. 39.95 (978-0-322-02569-1(9)) Wright Group, The.

The Story Box: Upper Emergent - Group 1-2: 1 Each of 16 Student Books: Level J. 79.95 (978-0-322-02568-4(0)) Wright Group, The.

The Story Box: Upper Emergent - Group 2: 1 Each of 8 Student Books: Level H. 39.95 (978-0-322-02564-6(8)) Wright Group, The.

The Story Box: Upper Emergent - Group 2: 1 Each of 8 Student Books: Level I. 39.95 (978-0-322-02567-7(2)) Wright Group, The.

The Story Box: Upper Emergent - Group 2: 1 Each of 8 Student Books: Level J. 39.95 (978-0-322-02571-4(0)) Wright Group, The.

The Story Box: Upper Emergent - Groups 1: 1 Each of 8 Student Books: Level F. 39.95 (978-1-55911-170-6(4)) Wright Group, The.

The Story Box: Upper Emergent - Groups 1: 1 Each of 8 Student Books: Level G. 39.95 (978-1-55911-179-9(8)) Wright Group, The.

The Story Box: Upper Emergent - Groups 2: 1 Each of 8 Student Books: Level F. 39.95 (978-0-7802-9930-6(2)) Wright Group, The.

The Story Box: Upper Emergent - Groups 2: 1 Each of 8 Student Books: Level G. 39.95 (978-0-7802-9933-7(7)) Wright Group, The.

The Story Box: Upper Emergent - Student Book Set - 1 Each of 16 Titles. (gr. 1 up). 79.95 (978-0-322-03141-8(9)); Vol. 2. 79.95 (978-0-7802-9532-2(3)); Vol. 3. 79.95 (978-0-7802-9533-9(1)); Vol. 4. 79.95 (978-0-322-03139-5(7)); Vol. 5. 79.95 (978-0-322-03140-1(0)) Wright Group, The.

The Story Box Vol. 2: Early Emergent - Early Emergent - Complete Kit. (gr. k up). 372.95 (978-0-7802-9339-7(8)) Wright Group, The.

The Story Box Vol. 3: Early Emergent - Complete Kit. (gr. k up). 372.95 (978-0-7802-9340-3(1)) Wright Group, The.

Story-Huffman, Ru. Caldecott on the Net: Reading & Internet Activities. 2nd rev. ed. 2002. 93p. (J). (gr. k-5). pap. 17.95 (978-1-57950-076-4(5) , Upstart Bks.) Highsmith Inc.

The Story of My Life: Response Journal. 2003. 40p. (YA). (978-1-58049-990-3(2) , RJ90) Prestwick Hse., Inc.

Story Time. (Little Book Practice Reader). (J). (978-0-8136-5358-7(4)) Modern Curriculum Pr.

Story Vine: 1 Each of 12 Student Books. (Story Vinestm Ser.). (gr. 3-6). 88.95 (978-0-7802-9413-4(0)) Wright Group, The.

Story Vine: 6 Each of 12 Student Books. (Story Vinestm Ser.). (gr. 3-6). 434.50 (978-0-7802-9414-1(9)) Wright Group, The.

Stott, Jon C. Gerald Mcdermott & YOU. McDermott, Gerald, illus. 2004. (Author & YOU Ser.). 128p. (C). pap. 35.00 (978-1-59158-175-8(3) , LU1753, Greenwood Pr.) Greenwood Publishing Group, Inc.

Stradling, Jan. Lights On: Level K, 6 vols., Vol. 2. (First Explorers Ser.). 24p. (gr. 1-2). 34.95 (978-0-7699-1461-9(6)) Shortland Pubns. (U. S. A.) Inc.

—Look Up: Level I, 6 vols. (First Explorers Ser.). 24p. (gr. 1-2). 29.95 (978-0-7699-1447-3(0)) Shortland Pubns. (U. S. A.) Inc.

Strange Days: Level 7, 6 vols. (Fluency Strand Ser.). (gr. 4-8). 45.00 (978-1-4045-1241-2(1)) Wright Group, The.

The Stranger from the Sea: Level T. Group 1, 6 vols. (Sunshinetm Ser.). 48p. 44.95 (978-0-7802-5601-9(8)) Wright Group, The.

Strayer, Debbie & Simpson, Susan S. Orange Student Activity Book: Learning Language Arts Through Literature. 2nd rev. ed. 1998. (Learning Language Arts Through Literature Ser.). 253p. (J). pap. 20.00 (978-1-880892-19-0(7)) Common Sense Pr.

—Purple Student Activity Book: Learning Language Arts Through Literature. 2nd rev. ed. 1998. (Learning Language Arts Through Literature Ser.). 312p. (J). pap. 20.00 (978-1-880892-20-6(0)) Common Sense Pr.

Street Action: 6 Each of 1 Anthology, 6 vols. (Wildcats Ser.). 32p. (gr. 2-8). (978-0-322-00577-8(9)) Wright Group, The.

The Strength of Georgia Mills: Level 2, 6 vols. (Fluency Strand Ser.). (gr. 4-8). 45.00 (978-1-4045-1215-3(2)) Wright Group, The.

The Summer Mermaid: R-Controlled e, i, u: Level B, 6 vols. (Wright Skills Ser.). 16p. (gr. k-3). 26.50 (978-0-322-01488-6(3)) Wright Group, The.

Summer Trips, 6 vols. (Multicultural Programs Ser.). 16p. (gr. 1-3). 24.95 (978-0-7802-9219-2(7)) Wright Group, The.

Sunshine: Early Emergent - 1 Each of 32 Big Books: Level A-D. 628.50 (978-0-7802-6775-6(3)) Wright Group, The.

Sunshine: Early Emergent - 1 Each of 4 Big Books: Level A-D. 82.95 (978-0-7802-6772-5(9)) Wright Group, The.

Sunshine: Early Emergent - Group 1: 1 Each of 8 Student Books: Level A. 33.50 (978-0-7802-7118-0(1)) Wright Group, The.

Sunshine: Early Emergent - Group 1: 1 Each of 8 Student Books: Level D. 33.50 (978-0-7802-7124-1(6)) Wright Group, The.

Sunshine: Early Emergent - Group 1:1 Each of 8 Student Books: Level C. 33.50 (978-0-7802-7122-7(X)) Wright Group, The.

Sunshine: Early Emergent - Group 2: 1 Each of 8 Student Books: Level A. 33.50 (978-0-7802-7119-7(X)) Wright Group, The.

Sunshine: Early Emergent - Group 2:1 Each of 8 Student Books: Level B. 33.50 (978-0-7802-7121-0(1)) Wright Group, The.

Sunshine: Early Emergent - Group 2:1 Each of 8 Student Books: Level C. 33.50 (978-0-7802-7123-4(8)) Wright Group, The.

Sunshine: Early Emergent - Nonfiction 1: 1 Each of 4 Student Books: Level A. 16.95 (978-0-7802-3763-6(3)) Wright Group, The.

Sunshine: Early Emergent - Nonfiction: 1 Each of 4 Student Books: Level C. 16.95 (978-0-7802-3781-0(1)) Wright Group, The.

Sunshine: Early Emergent - Nonfiction:1 Each of 4 Student Books: Level A. 16.95 (978-0-7802-3772-8(2)) Wright Group, The.

Sunshine: Early Emergent - Student Book Set - 1 Each of 16 Titles. (gr. k up). Vol. 2. 66.95 (978-0-322-02486-1(2)); Vol. 3. 66.95 (978-0-322-02487-8(0)) Wright Group, The.

Sunshine: Early Emergent: 1 Each of 8 Student Books: Level B. 24.95 (978-0-7802-7120-3(3)) Wright Group, The.

Sunshine: Early Emergent-Upper Emergent - 1 Each of 60 Big Books: Level A-J,A-D. 1345.50 (978-0-7802-6779-4(6)) Wright Group, The.

Sunshine: Early Emergent-Upper Emergent - Group 1: 1 Each of 8 Student Books: Level E. 39.95 (978-0-7802-7126-5(2)) Wright Group, The.

Sunshine: Early Emergent-Upper Emergent - Nonfiction: 1 Each of 4 Student Books: Level D. 16.95 (978-0-7802-3790-2(0)) Wright Group, The.

Sunshine: Early Emergent-Upper Emergent - Nonfiction: 1 Each of 4 Student Books: Level E. 19.95 (978-0-7802-6791-6(5)) Wright Group, The.

Sunshine: Early Fluency - Chapter books, Group 2: 1 each of 2 titles: Level K. 11.95 (978-0-7802-6852-4(0)) Wright Group, The.

Sunshine: Early Fluency - Chapter books, Group 2: 1 each of 2 titles: Level L. 11.95 (978-0-7802-6853-1(9)) Wright Group, The.

Sunshine: Early Fluency - Chapter Books, Group 2; 1 each of 2 titles: Level M. 11.95 (978-0-7802-6854-8(7)) Wright Group, The.

Sunshine: Early Fluency - Fact & Fantasy, Group 1; 1 each of 8 titles: Level L. 46.95 (978-0-7802-8354-1(6)) Wright Group, The.

Sunshine: Early Fluency - Fact & Fantasy, Group 2; 1 each of 2 titles: Level L. 11.95 (978-0-7802-7876-9(3)) Wright Group, The.

Sunshine: Early Fluency - Fact & Fantasy, Groups 1-2; 1 each of 10 titles: Level L. 58.50 (978-0-7802-6849-4(0)) Wright Group, The.

Sunshine: Early Fluency - Group 2: 1 each of 6 titles: Level K. 34.95 (978-0-7802-7138-8(6)) Wright Group, The.

Sunshine: Early Fluency - Group 2; 1 each of 6 titles: Level M. 34.95 (978-0-7802-7140-1(8)) Wright Group, The.

Sunshine: Early Fluency - Nonfiction, Group 1: 1 each of 8 titles: Level K. 46.95 (978-0-7802-8353-4(8)) Wright Group, The.

Sunshine: Early Fluency - Nonfiction, Group 2: 1 each of 2 titles: Level K. 11.95 (978-0-7802-7875-2(5)) Wright Group, The.

Sunshine: Early Fluency - Nonfiction, Groups 1-2: 1 each of 10 titles: Level K. 58.50 (978-0-7802-6848-7(2)) Wright Group, The.

Sunshine: Early Fluency - Student Book Set - 1 Each of 16 Titles. (gr. 2 up). Vol. 2. 93.50 (978-0-322-02491-5(9)); Vol. 3. 93.50 (978-0-322-02492-2(7)); Vol. 4. 93.50 (978-0-322-02493-9(5)) Wright Group, The.

Sunshine: Early Fluency Fiction. 32p. (gr. 1-5). 46.95 (978-0-7802-6856-2(3)) Wright Group, The.

Sunshine: Early Fluency-Nonfiction, Group 1; 1 each of 8 titles: Level M. 46.95 (978-0-7802-8355-8(4)) Wright Group, The.

Sunshine: Early Fluency-Nonfiction, Group 2; 1 each of 2 titles: Level M. 11.95 (978-0-7802-7877-6(1)) Wright Group, The.

Sunshine: Early Fluency-Nonfiction, Groups 1-2; 1 each of 10 titles: Level M. 58.50 (978-0-7802-6850-0(4)) Wright Group, The.

Sunshine: Enrichment Library. 24p. (gr. 1-5). 91.95 (978-0-7802-9382-3(7)) Wright Group, The.

Sunshine: Fact & Fantasy, Group 1: 1 each of 8 titles: Level N. 46.95 (978-0-7802-8356-5(2)) Wright Group, The.

Sunshine: Fact & Fantasy, Group 2: 1 each of 2 titles: Level N. 11.95 (978-0-7802-7878-3(X)) Wright Group, The.

Sunshine: Fact & Fantasy, Groups 1-2: 1 each of 10 titles: Level N. 58.50 (978-0-7802-6851-7(2)) Wright Group, The.

Sunshine: Fluency - Chapter books, Group 2: 1 each of 2 titles: Level O. 13.50 (978-0-7802-6876-0(8)) Wright Group, The.

Sunshine: Fluency - Chapter Books, Group 2: 1 Each of 2 Titles: Level R. 14.95 (978-0-7802-6879-1(2)) Wright Group, The.

Sunshine: Fluency - Chapter Books, Group 2: 1 Each of 2 Titles: Level S. 14.95 (978-0-7802-6880-7(6)) Wright Group, The.

Sunshine: Fluency - Chapter Books, Group 2: 1 Each of 2 Titles: Level T. 14.95 (978-0-7802-6881-4(4)) Wright Group, The.

Sunshine: Fluency - Fact & Fantasy, Group 1: 1 each of 8 titles: Level O. 53.50 (978-0-7802-8357-2(0)) Wright Group, The.

Sunshine: Fluency - Fact & Fantasy, Group 2: 1 each of 2 titles: Level O. 13.50 (978-0-7802-7879-0(8)) Wright Group, The.

Sunshine: Fluency - Fact & Fantasy, Groups 1-2: 1 each of 10 titles: Level O. 66.95 (978-0-7802-6867-8(9)) Wright Group, The.

Sunshine: Fluency - Group 2: 1 each of 6 titles: Level O. 39.95 (978-0-7802-7143-2(2)) Wright Group, The.

Sunshine: Fluency - Group 2: 1 Each of 6 Titles: Level R. 44.95 (978-0-7802-7220-0(X)) Wright Group, The.

Sunshine: Fluency - Group 2: 1 Each of 6 Titles: Level S. 44.95 (978-0-7802-7222-4(6)) Wright Group, The.

Sunshine: Fluency - Group 2: 1 Each of 6 Titles: Level T. 44.95 (978-0-7802-7224-8(2)) Wright Group, The.

Sunshine: Fluency - Nonfiction, Group 1: 1 Each of 8 Titles: Level R. 59.95 (978-0-7802-8360-2(0)) Wright Group, The.

Sunshine: Fluency - Nonfiction, Group 1: 1 Each of 8 Titles: Level T. 59.95 (978-0-7802-8362-6(7)) Wright Group, The.

Sunshine: Fluency - Nonfiction, Group 2: 1 Each of 2 Titles: Level R. 14.95 (978-0-7802-7882-0(8)) Wright Group, The.

Sunshine: Fluency - Nonfiction, Group 2: 1 Each of 2 Titles: Level T. 14.95 (978-0-7802-7884-4(4)) Wright Group, The.

Sunshine: Fluency - Nonfiction, Groups 1-2: 1 Each of 10 Titles: Level R. 74.95 (978-0-7802-6871-5(7)) Wright Group, The.

Sunshine: Fluency - Nonfiction, Groups 1-2: 1 Each of 10 Titles: Level S. 74.95 (978-0-7802-6873-9(3)) Wright Group, The.

Sunshine: Fluency - Nonfiction, Groups 1-2: 1 Each of 10 Titles: Level T. 74.95 (978-0-7802-6874-6(1)) Wright Group, The.

Sunshine: Fluency - Nonfiction, Groups 2: 1 Each of 2 Titles: Level S. 14.95 (978-0-7802-7883-7(6)) Wright Group, The.

Sunshine: Fluency - Student Book Set - 1 Each of 16 Titles. (gr. 3-6). 112.50 (978-0-322-02494-6(3)); Vol. 2. 112.50 (978-0-322-02495-3(1)) Wright Group, The.

Sunshine: Fluency-Chapter books, Group 2: 1 each of 2 titles: Level P. 13.50 (978-0-7802-6877-7(6)) Wright Group, The.

Sunshine: Fluency-Chapter books, Groups 2: 1 each of 2 titles: Level Q. 13.50 (978-0-7802-6878-4(4)) Wright Group, The.

Sunshine: Fluency-Fact & Fantacy, Group 1: 1 each of 8 titles: Level P. 53.50 (978-0-7802-8358-9(9)) Wright Group, The.

Sunshine: Fluency-Fact & Fantasy, Group 2: 1 each of 2 titles: Level P. 13.50 (978-0-7802-7880-6(1)) Wright Group, The.

Sunshine: Fluency-Fact & Fantacy, Groups 1-2: 1 each of 10 titles: Level P. 66.95 (978-0-7802-6868-5(7)) Wright Group, The.

Sunshine: Fluency Fiction. 72p. (gr. 1-5). 84.95 (978-0-7802-6882-1(2)) Wright Group, The.

Sunshine: Fluency-Group 2: 1 each of 6 titles: Level P. 39.95 (978-0-7802-7145-6(9)) Wright Group, The.

Sunshine: Fluency-Group 2: 1 each of 6 titles: Level Q. 39.95 (978-0-7802-7218-7(8)) Wright Group, The.

Sunshine: Fluency-Nonfiction, Group 1: 1 each of 10 titles: Level Q. 66.95 (978-0-7802-6870-8(9)) Wright Group, The.

Sunshine: Fluency-Nonfiction, Group 1: 1 each of 2 titles: Level Q. 13.50 (978-0-7802-7881-3(X)) Wright Group, The.

Sunshine: Fluency-Nonfiction, Group 1: 1 each of 8 titles: Level Q. 53.50 (978-0-7802-8359-6(7)) Wright Group, The.

Sunshine: Upper Emergent - Complete Kit, Vol. 3. (gr. 1 up). 486.50 (978-0-322-02479-3(X)) Wright Group, The.

Sunshine: Upper Emergent - Group 1:1 Each of 8 Student Books: Level F. Group 1. 39.95 (978-0-7802-7128-9(9)) Wright Group, The.

Sunshine: Upper Emergent - Nonfiction:1 Each of 4 Student Books: Level F. Group 1. 19.95 (978-0-7802-6792-3(3)) Wright Group, The.

Sunshine: Upper Emergent - Student Book Set - 1 Each of 16 Titles. (gr. 1 up). Vol. 3. 79.95 (978-0-322-02488-5(9)); Vol. 4. 79.95 (978-0-322-02489-2(7)) Wright Group, The.

Sunshine: Upper Emergent-Group 1: 1 each of 8 student books: Level I. 39.95 (978-0-7802-7134-0(3)) Wright Group, The.

Sunshine: Upper Emergent-Group 1: 1 each of 8 student books: Level J. 39.95 (978-0-7802-7136-4(X)) Wright Group, The.

Sunshine: Upper Emergent-Group 2: 1 each of 8 student books: Level J. 39.95 (978-0-7802-7137-1(8)) Wright Group, The.

SUNSHINE Early Emergent Guided Reading Kit 2, Vol. 2. 2004. (Wright Group Literacy Ser.). (gr. k up). 423.95 (978-0-322-02477-9(3)) Wright Group, The.

SUNSHINE Early Emergent Guided Reading Kit 3, Vol. 3. 2004. (Wright Group Literacy Ser.). (gr. k up). 423.95 (978-0-322-02478-6(1)) Wright Group, The.

SUNSHINE Early Fluency Guided Reading Kit 2, Vol. 2. 2004. (Wright Group Literacy Ser.). (gr. 2 up). 524.95 (978-0-322-02482-3(X)) Wright Group, The.

SUNSHINE Early Fluency Guided Reading Kit 3, Vol. 3. 2004. (Wright Group Literacy Ser.). (gr. 2 up). 524.95 (978-0-322-02483-0(8)) Wright Group, The.

SUNSHINE Early Fluency Guided Reading Kit 4, Vol. 4. 2004. (Wright Group Literacy Ser.). (gr. 2 up). 524.95 (978-0-322-02484-7(6)) Wright Group, The.

Sunshine Fact & Fantasy Sets: Complete Set - 1 Each of 24 students Books. 115.95 (978-0-7802-6785-5(0)) Wright Group, The.

SUNSHINE Fluency Guided Reading Kit 1. 2004. (Wright Group Literacy Ser.). (gr. 3-6). 604.95 (978-0-322-02624-7(5)) Wright Group, The.

SUNSHINE Fluency Guided Reading Kit 2, Vol. 2. 2004. (Wright Group Literacy Ser.). (gr. 3-6). 604.95 (978-0-322-02485-4(4)) Wright Group, The.

Sunshine Language Skills Books: 1 Each of 16 Big Books Set 2. (gr. k-1). 474.95 (978-0-7802-8956-7(0)) Wright Group, The.

Sunshine Language Skills Books: 1 Each of 16 Student Books Set 2. (gr. k-1). 91.95 (978-0-7802-8510-1(7)) Wright Group, The.

Sunshine Language Skills Books: 1 Each of 20 Big Books Sets 1-2. (gr. k-1). 594.50 (978-0-7802-9624-4(9)) Wright Group, The.

Sunshine Language Skills Books: 1 Each of 20 Student Books Set 1. (gr. k-1). 114.50 (978-0-7802-9623-7(0)) Wright Group, The.

Sunshine Language Skills Books: 1 Each of 4 Big Books Set 1. (gr. k-1). 125.50 (978-0-7802-8955-0(2)) Wright Group, The.

Sunshine Language Skills Books: 1 Each of 4 Student Books Set 2. (gr. k-1). 22.95 (978-0-7802-6823-4(7)) Wright Group, The.

Sunshine Language Skills Books: 6 Each of 20 Student Books Sets 1-2. (gr. k-1). 652.50 (978-0-7802-9657-2(5)) Wright Group, The.

Sunshine Street, 6 vols. (Sunshinetm Ser.). 16p. (gr. k up). 29.50 (978-0-7802-5443-5(0)) Wright Group, The.

Sunshine Upper Emergent Guided Reading Kit 4, Vol. 4. 2004. (Wright Group Literacy Ser.). (gr. 1 up). 486.50 (978-0-322-02480-9(3)) Wright Group, The.

Super Qar for Test-Wise Students: Grade 1 Kit. (gr. 1-8). 264.95 (978-0-322-09186-3(1)) Wright Group, The.

Super Qar for Test-Wise Students: Grade 2 Kit. (gr. 1-8). 264.95 (978-0-322-09187-0(X)) Wright Group, The.

Super Qar for Test-Wise Students: Grade 3 Kit. (gr. 1-8). 264.95 (978-0-322-09188-7(8)) Wright Group, The.

Las Supergalletas 18: Leveled Books. 2001. (McGraw-Hill. Lectura Ser.). (ENG & SPA.). (gr. 4 up). (978-0-02-188218-2(5)) Macmillan/McGraw-Hill Schl. Div.

Superlibro 1: un abrigo Crecedero. 2001. (McGraw-Hill. Lectura Ser.). (ENG & SPA.). (gr. k up). (978-0-02-186008-1(4)) Macmillan/McGraw-Hill Schl. Div.

Superlibro 10: Una zanahoria Enorme. 2001. (McGraw-Hill. Lectura Ser.). (ENG & SPA.). (gr. k up). (978-0-02-186018-0(1)) Macmillan/McGraw-Hill Schl. Div.

Superlibro 12: el libro de colores de Conejo Blanco. 2001. (McGraw-Hill. Lectura Ser.). (ENG & SPA.). (gr. k up). (978-0-02-186021-0(1)) Macmillan/McGraw-Hill Schl. Div.

Superlibro 2: Tiempo de Compartir. 2001. (McGraw-Hill. Lectura Ser.). (ENG & SPA.). (gr. k up). (978-0-02-186009-8(2)) Macmillan/McGraw-Hill Schl. Div.

Superlibro 3: Jabalies en la Cocina. 2001. (McGraw-Hill. Lectura Ser.). (ENG & SPA.). (gr. k up). (978-0-02-186011-1(4)) Macmillan/McGraw-Hill Schl. Div.

Superlibro 5: el jardin Florido. 2001. (McGraw-Hill. Lectura Ser.). (ENG & SPA.). (gr. k up). (978-0-02-186013-5(0)) Macmillan/McGraw-Hill Schl. Div.

Superlibro 6: un Papelito. 2001. (McGraw-Hill. Lectura Ser.). (ENG & SPA.). (gr. k up). (978-0-02-186014-2(9)) Macmillan/McGraw-Hill Schl. Div.

Superlibro 7: el arbol de pastel de Manzanas. 2001. (McGraw-Hill. Lectura Ser.). (ENG & SPA.). (gr. k up). (978-0-02-186015-9(7)) Macmillan/McGraw-Hill Schl. Div.

Superlibro 8: Cambios. 2001. (McGraw-Hill. Lectura Ser.). (ENG & SPA.). (gr. k up). (978-0-02-182769-5(9)) Macmillan/McGraw-Hill Schl. Div.

Superlibro de cuentos Descodificables. 2001. (McGraw-Hill. Lectura Ser.). (ENG & SPA.). (gr. k up). (978-0-02-186001-2(7)) Macmillan/McGraw-Hill Schl. Div.

Superlibro de la vida Diaria. 2001. (McGraw-Hill. Lectura Ser.). (ENG & SPA.). (gr. k up). (978-0-02-186030-2(0)) Macmillan/McGraw-Hill Schl. Div.

Los Superzapatos 2: Leveled Books. 2001. (McGraw-Hill. Lectura Ser.). (ENG & SPA.). (gr. 3 up). (978-0-02-188099-7(9)) Macmillan/McGraw-Hill Schl. Div.

Surfing: Level J, 6 vols. (Wonder Worldtm Ser.). 16p. 29.95 (978-0-7802-4609-6(8)) Wright Group, The.

Surfs Up, 6 vols. (Wildcats Ser.). 32p. (gr. 2-8). (978-0-322-00601-0(5)) Wright Group, The.

Survive!, 6 vols. (Wildcats Ser.). 32p. (gr. 2-8). (978-0-322-02439-7(0)) Wright Group, The.

Suter, Joanne. Reading Fiction 2: Reading in Context. 2001. (Illus.). 112p. per., wbk. ed. 8.95 (978-1-56254-194-1(3) , SP 1935) Saddleback Educational Publishing.

Sweeney, Jacqueline. We Can Read! - Group 1, 4 bks., Set. Hart, G. K. & Empey, Mark, illus. Incl. Hester. 1999. lib. bdg. 21.36 (978-0-7614-0923-6(8)); Just Call Me J. P. 2000. lib. bdg. 21.36 (978-0-7614-0922-9(X)); Lou Goes Too! 1999. lib. bdg. 21.36 (978-0-7614-0921-2(1)); Who Said Boo? 2000. lib. bdg. 21.36 (978-0-7614-0924-3(6)); 32p. (J). (gr. 1-2). (We Can Read! Ser.). (Illus.). 2000. Set lib. bdg. 85.43 (978-0-7614-0920-5(3) , Benchmark Bks.) Cavendish, Marshall Corp.

The Swimming Pool: Big Book: Level G. (Visionstm Ser.). 16p. 20.95 (978-0-322-00631-7(7)) Wright Group, The.

Tails: Level C, 6 vols. (Wonder Worldtm Ser.). 16p. 24.95 (978-0-7802-1052-3(2)) Wright Group, The.

Tails & Claws: Level E, 6 vols. (Wonder Worldtm Ser.). 16p. 29.95 (978-0-7802-1243-5(6)); 26.50 (978-0-7802-3478-9(2)) Wright Group, The.

Tails can Tell: Level K, 6 vols. (Wonder Worldtm Ser.). 16p. 34.95 (978-0-7802-2911-2(8)) Wright Group, The.

Take a Look: 6 Each of 1 Anthology, 6 vols. (Wildcatstm Ser.). 32p. (gr. 2-8). (978-0-322-02420-5(X)) Wright Group, The.

Take-Twos: Early Fluency - 1 each of 12 titles: Level K. 69.95 (978-0-322-02642-1(3)) Wright Group, The.

Take-Twos: Early Fluency - 1 each of 12 titles: Level L. 69.95 (978-0-322-02645-2(8)) Wright Group, The.

Take-Twos: Early Fluency - 1 each of 12 titles: Level M. 69.95 (978-0-322-02646-9(6)) Wright Group, The.

Take-Twos: Early Fluency - 1 each of 12 titles: Level N. 69.95 (978-0-322-02644-5(X)) Wright Group, The.

Taking Care of our World, 6 vols. (Multicultural Programs Ser.). 16p. (gr. 1-3). 24.95 (978-0-7802-9220-8(0)) Wright Group, The.

TAKS MASTER Student Practice Book, Reading, Grade 2. 2004. (J). (978-1-57022-468-3(4)) ECS Learning Systems, Inc.

Taylor, Vincent. Rhythmic Reading with Rap. Herron, Tennille, illus. 2000. 36p. (YA). (gr. 2 up). pap., wbk. ed. 12.99 (978-0-9704512-2-4(9)); pap., wbk. ed. 14.99 incl. audio compact disk (978-0-9704512-0-0(2)); pap., wbk. ed. 12.99 incl. audio (978-0-9704512-1-7(0)) TriEclipse, Inc.

Tea: Level M, 6 vols. (Wonder Worldtm Ser.). 16p. 34.95 (978-0-7802-4611-9(X)) Wright Group, The.

Teach Your Child to Read: Reading Tool Kit #1, 5 vols. unabr. ed. 2002. 112p. (J). per. 19.50 (978-0-9720169-1-9(0)) Complete Mastery Learning Systems.

Teamwork Test Practice: Reading. 2005. 48p. (J). per. 5.99 (978-1-59441-145-8(X) , CD-104064); per. 5.99 (978-1-59441-146-5(8) , CD-104065); per. 5.99 (978-1-59441-147-2(6) , CD-104066); per. 5.99 (978-1-59441-148-9(4) , CD-104067); per. 5.99 (978-1-59441-149-6(2) , CD-104068) Carson-Dellosa Publishing Co., Inc.

Teeth: Big Book: Level G. Group 2. (Story Box(R) Ser.). 16p. 20.95 (978-0-322-00321-7(0)) Wright Group, The.

Teeth: Level B, 6 vols. (Wonder Worldtm Ser.). 16p. 24.95 (978-0-7802-1053-0(0)) Wright Group, The.

Teeth: Level R, 6 vols. (Wonder Worldtm Ser.). 48p. 44.95 (978-0-7802-7075-6(4)) Wright Group, The.

Tell Me No Lies, 6 vols. (Ragged Island Mysteriestm Ser.). 161p. (gr. 5-7). 42.50 (978-0-322-01654-5(1)) Wright Group, The.

Telling Stories Through Art: Level L, 6 vols. (Take-Twostm Ser.). 16p. 36.95 (978-0-322-03398-6(5)) Wright Group, The.

Terror Bear Canyon: Level 5, 6 vols. (Fluency Strand Ser.). (gr. 4-8). 45.00 (978-1-4045-1225-2(X)) Wright Group, The.

Tesoros de Lata: 6 Small Books. (Saludos Ser.: Vol. 3). (SPA.). 24p. (gr. 2-3). 31.00 (978-0-7635-9530-2(6)) Rigby Education.

Test Item File. 1999. (J). pap. (978-0-393-97368-6(9)) Norton, W. W. & Co., Inc.

Test-Taking Practice for Reading & Math: With Open-Ended Questions & Scoring Rubrics. 2000. (Illus.). 80p. (gr. 3-5). pap. 10.99 (978-0-88724-564-0(1) , CD-0052) Carson-Dellosa Publishing Co., Inc.

Think, do & Read Mini-Books. 176p. (gr. k-1). 14.99 (978-1-56822-530-2(X) , IF21840) School Specialty Publishing.

This Mouth: Level D, 6 vols. (Wonder Worldtm Ser.). 16p. 24.95 (978-0-7802-2034-8(X)) Wright Group, The.

Thrills at the Fair: 3-letter blends: Level C, 6 vols. (Wright Skills Ser.). 16p. (gr. k-3). 26.50 (978-0-322-01494-7(8)) Wright Group, The.

Through the Looking Glass: Response Journal. 2003. 32p. (YA). (978-1-58049-989-7(9) , RJ89) Prestwick Hse., Inc.

Thud! Thump! Thud! Digraph th: Level B, 6 vols. (Wright Skills Ser.). 16p. (gr. k-3). 17.95 (978-0-322-01473-2(5)) Wright Group, The.

Tick-Tock: Big Book: Level D. Group 2. (Story Box(R) Ser.). 16p. 24.95 (978-0-322-00323-1(7)) Wright Group, The.

Tides: Level L, 6 vols. (Wonder Worldtm Ser.). 16p. 34.95 (978-0-7802-4613-3(6)) Wright Group, The.

Tiempo de Tormenta 20: Leveled Books. 2001. (McGraw-Hill. Lectura Ser.). (ENG & SPA.). (gr. 3 up). (978-0-02-188093-5(X)) Macmillan/McGraw-Hill Schl. Div.

Time Warp: Level T. Group 1, 6 vols. (Sunshinetm Ser.). 48p. 44.95 (978-0-7802-5602-6(6)) Wright Group, The.

Timeless Voices, Timeless Themes: Bronze, Literary Focus & Reading. 2001. (YA). (gr. 7). trans. 109.97 (978-0-13-052359-4(3)) Prentice Hall PTR.

Timeless Voices, Timeless Themes: Bronze, Reading Selection Summaries Practice Book. 2001. (YA). (gr. 7). pap. 6.97 (978-0-13-044103-4(1)) Prentice Hall PTR.

Timeless Voices, Timeless Themes: Bronze, Reading Support Practice Book. 2001. (YA). (gr. 7). pap. 6.97 (978-0-13-052363-1(1)) Prentice Hall PTR.

Timeless Voices, Timeless Themes: Copper, Reading Selection Summaries Practice Book. 2001. (J). (gr. 6). pap. 6.97 (978-0-13-044102-7(3)) Prentice Hall PTR.

Timeless Voices, Timeless Themes: Copper, Reading Support Practice Book. 2001. (J). (gr. 6). pap. 6.97 (978-0-13-052362-4(3)) Prentice Hall PTR.

Timeless Voices, Timeless Themes: Gold, Literary Focus & Reading. 2001. (YA). (gr. 9). trans. 109.97 (978-0-13-051270-3(2)) Prentice Hall PTR.

Timeless Voices, Timeless Themes: Gold, Reading Selection Summaries Practice Book. 2000. (YA). (gr. 9). pap. 6.97 (978-0-13-044105-8(8)) Prentice Hall PTR.

Timeless Voices, Timeless Themes: Gold, Reading Support Practice Book. 2000. (YA). (gr. 9). pap. 6.97 (978-0-13-437564-9(5)) Prentice Hall PTR.

Timeless Voices, Timeless Themes: Platinum, Reading Selection Summaries Practice Book. 2000. (YA). (gr. 10). pap. 6.97 (978-0-13-044106-5(6)) Prentice Hall PTR.

Timeless Voices, Timeless Themes: Platinum, Reading Support Practice Book. 2000. (YA). (gr. 10). pap. 6.97 (978-0-13-437565-6(3)) Prentice Hall PTR.

Timeless Voices, Timeless Themes: Silver, Literary Focus & Reading. 2001. (YA). (gr. 8). trans. 109.97 (978-0-13-052350-1(X)) Prentice Hall PTR.

Timeless Voices, Timeless Themes: Silver, Reading Selection Summaries Practice Book. 2001. (YA). (gr. 8). pap. 6.97 (978-0-13-044104-1(X)) Prentice Hall PTR.

Timeless Voices, Timeless Themes: Silver, Reading Support Practice Book. 2001. (YA). (gr. 8). pap. 6.97 (978-0-13-052364-8(X)) Prentice Hall PTR.

Timeless Voices, Timeless Themes: The American Experience, Literary Focus & Reading. 2000. (YA). (gr. 11). trans. 109.97 (978-0-13-051282-6(6)) Prentice Hall PTR.

Timeless Voices, Timeless Themes: The American Experience, Selection Support, Skills Development Practice Book. 2000. (YA). (gr. 11). pap. 8.47 (978-0-13-436010-2(9)) Prentice Hall PTR.

Timeless Voices, Timeless Themes: The British Tradition, Literary Focus & Reading. 2000. (YA). (gr. 12). trans. 109.97 (978-0-13-051283-3(4)) Prentice Hall PTR.

Timeless Voices, Timeless Themes: The British Tradition, Reading Selection Summaries Practice Book. 2000. (YA). (gr. 12). pap. 6.97 (978-0-13-044109-6(0)) Prentice Hall PTR.

Timeless Voices, Timeless Themes: The British Tradition, Reading Support Practice Book. 2000. (YA). (gr. 11). pap. 6.97 (978-0-13-437566-3(1)); (gr. 12). pap. 6.97 (978-0-13-437568-7(8)) Prentice Hall PTR.

Timeless Voices, Timeless Themes: The British Tradition, Selection Support, Skills Development Practice Book. 2000. (YA). (gr. 12). pap. 8.47 (978-0-13-436011-9(7)) Prentice Hall PTR.

Tiny Creatures Little Book: Early Reading Fluency, Level C. 2004. pap. 6.00 (978-0-7398-8291-7(0)) Steck-Vaughn.

Tio Jaguar y Tio Mono 11: Leveled Books. 2001. (McGraw-Hill. Lectura Ser.). (ENG & SPA.). (gr. 4 up). (978-0-02-188187-1(1)) Macmillan/McGraw-Hill Schl. Div.

To Catch a Thief: Level 3, 6 vols. (Fluency Strand Ser.). (gr. 4-8). 45.00 (978-1-4045-1219-1(5)) Wright Group, The.

To New York: Big Book: Level D. Group 1. (Story Box(R) Ser.). 16p. 20.95 (978-0-322-00637-9(6)) Wright Group, The.

To the Moon & Beyond: Level T. Group 3, 6 vols. (Sunshinetm Ser.). 48p. 44.95 (978-0-322-01835-8(8)) Wright Group, The.

A todo Correr 7: Leveled Books. 2001. (McGraw-Hill. Lectura Ser.). (ENG & SPA.). (gr. 5 up). (978-0-02-188279-3(7)) Macmillan/McGraw-Hill Schl. Div.

Todo el mundo se queja siempre del Tiempo 20: Leveled Books. 2001. (McGraw-Hill. Lectura Ser.). (ENG & SPA.). (gr. 3 up). (978-0-02-188117-8(0)) Macmillan/McGraw-Hill Schl. Div.

Todos Contentos 23: Leveled Books. 2001. (McGraw-Hill. Lectura Ser.). (ENG & SPA.). (gr. 2 up). (978-0-02-188024-9(7)) Macmillan/McGraw-Hill Schl. Div.

Tofte, Mavis. Doogie Dork's Wish. Tofte, Mavis, illus. 2003. (J). per. 5.75 (978-0-9709906-2-4(6)) Creative Quill Publishing, Inc.

Together, 6 vols. (Sunshinetm Ser.). 16p. (gr. k up). 29.50 (978-0-7802-5426-8(0)) Wright Group, The.

Toma un tomate, Teo! 3: Leveled Books. 2001. (McGraw-Hill. Lectura Ser.). (ENG & SPA.). (gr. 1 up). (978-0-02-187932-8(X)) Macmillan/McGraw-Hill Schl. Div.

Tomato: Level 4, 6 vols. (Fluency Strand Ser.). (gr. 4-8). 45.00 (978-1-4045-1223-8(3)) Wright Group, The.

The Tongue Twister Prize. 2005. (Fluent Library). (YA). (ps-3). 29.34 (978-0-8215-8961-8(X)) Sadlier, William H. Inc.

Too Many Graphs: Digraph ph: Level B, 6 vols. (Wright Skills Ser.). 16p. (gr. k-3). 17.95 (978-0-322-01475-6(1)) Wright Group, The.

Too Small Jill, Vol. 2. 2005. (Fluent Library). (YA). (ps-3). 29.34 (978-0-8215-8965-6(2)) Sadlier, William H. Inc.

A Too-Tight Shoes Set, 6 vols. 32p. (gr. 1-3). 26.50 (978-0-7802-8042-7(3)) Wright Group, The.

Tornado! 12: Leveled Books. 2001. (McGraw-Hill. Lectura Ser.). (ENG & SPA.). (gr. 5 up). (978-0-02-188236-6(3)) Macmillan/McGraw-Hill Schl. Div.

Touch: Big Book: Level E. 8p. 20.95 (978-0-322-00369-9(5)) Wright Group, The.

Tovani, Cris. I Read It, but I Don't Get It: Comprehension Strategies for Adolescent Readers. 2000. (gr. 7-12). lib. bdg. 28.65 (978-0-613-64735-9(1)) Tandem Library Bks.

Tracks: Big Book: Level F. 16p. 31.50 (978-0-322-00350-7(4)) Wright Group, The.

Traffic Light Sandwich: Level J, 6 vols. (Wonder Worldtm Ser.). 16p. 29.95 (978-0-7802-4615-7(2)) Wright Group, The.

The Tram Ride, 6 vols. 8p. (gr. k-1). 21.50 (978-0-322-02072-6(7)) Wright Group, The.

Transparencias: Actividades diarias de Lenguaje: Resources & Ancillaries. 2001. (McGraw-Hill. Lectura Ser.). (ENG & SPA.). (gr. 1 up). (978-0-02-186568-0(X)); (gr. 2 up). (978-0-02-186569-7(8)); (gr. 3 up). (978-0-02-186570-3(1)); (gr. 4 up). (978-0-02-186571-0(X)); (gr. 5 up). (978-0-02-186572-7(8)) Macmillan/McGraw-Hill Schl. Div.

Transparencias: Cartelones de Ensenanza: Resources & Ancillaries. 2001. (McGraw-Hill. Lectura Ser.). (ENG & SPA.). (gr. 1 up). (978-0-02-186598-7(1)); (gr. 2 up). (978-0-02-186599-4(X)); (gr. 3 up). (978-0-02-186600-7(7)); (gr. 4 up). (978-0-02-186601-4(5)); (gr. 5 up). (978-0-02-186602-1(3)); (gr. 6 up). (978-0-02-186603-8(1)) Macmillan/McGraw-Hill Schl. Div.

Transparencias: Proceso de Escritura: Resources & Ancillaries. 2001. (McGraw-Hill. Lectura Ser.). (ENG & SPA.). (gr. 1 up). (978-0-02-186580-2(9)); (gr. 2 up). (978-0-02-186581-9(7)); (gr. 3 up). (978-0-02-186582-6(5)); (gr. 4 up). (978-0-02-186583-3(3)); (gr. 5 up). (978-0-02-186584-0(1)); (gr. 6 up). (978-0-02-186585-7(X)) Macmillan/McGraw-Hill Schl. Div.

The Trash Can Band. 2005. (Fluent Library). (YA). (ps-3). 29.34 (978-0-8215-8964-9(4)) Sadlier, William H. Inc.

Travesia Nocturna 15: Leveled Books. 2001. (McGraw-Hill. Lectura Ser.). (ENG & SPA.). (gr. 5 up). (978-0-02-188263-2(0)) Macmillan/McGraw-Hill Schl. Div.

Travesia por el Desierto 3: Leveled Books. 2001. (McGraw-Hill. Lectura Ser.). (ENG & SPA.). (gr. 3 up). (978-0-02-188076-8(X)) Macmillan/McGraw-Hill Schl. Div.

The Tree House: Level B. Group 1. (Story Box(R) Ser.). 8p. 20.95 (978-0-7802-7629-1(9)) Wright Group, The.

Trelease, Jim. Read Aloud Handbook. 5th ed. 2004. 28.25 (978-0-8446-7234-2(3)) Smith, Peter Pub., Inc.

Tristom y el Volcan 17: Leveled Books. 2001. (McGraw-Hill. Lectura Ser.). (ENG & SPA.). (gr. 5 up). (978-0-02-188241-0(X)) Macmillan/McGraw-Hill Schl. Div.

Troughton, Joanna. The Story of Running Water, 6, Pack. 2000. (Cambridge Reading Ser.). (Illus.). 24p. pap. 29.00 (978-0-521-78624-9(X)) Cambridge Univ. Pr.

A Truckload of Chocolate: Level 7, 6 vols. (Fluency Strand Ser.). (gr. 4-8). 45.00 (978-1-4045-1243-6(8)) Wright Group, The.

Tsubakiyama, Margaret. Ninjas. 2004. lib. bdg. (978-0-7613-2153-8(5) , Millbrook Pr.) Lerner Publishing Group.

Tuminelly, Nancy. -Est As in Nest. 2003. (Word Families Ser.). (Illus.). 23p. (J). (ps-3). lib. bdg. 19.93 (978-1-59197-232-7(9) , SandCastle) ABDO Publishing Co.

—Ook As in Hook. 2003. (Word Families Ser.). (Illus.). 23p. (J). (ps-3). lib. bdg. 19.93 (978-1-59197-268-6(X) , SandCastle) ABDO Publishing Co.

—Ub As in Tub. 2003. (Word Families Ser.). (Illus.). 23p. (J). (ps-3). lib. bdg. 19.93 (978-1-59197-242-6(6) , SandCastle) ABDO Publishing Co.

—Uck As in Duck. 2003. (Word Families Ser.). (Illus.). 23p. (J). (ps-3). lib. bdg. 19.93 (978-1-59197-247-1(7) , SandCastle) ABDO Publishing Co.

—Uff As in Cuff. 2003. (Word Families Ser.). (Illus.). 23p. (J). (ps-3). lib. bdg. 19.93 (978-1-59197-246-4(9) , SandCastle) ABDO Publishing Co.

—Ug As in Bug. 2003. (Word Families Ser.). (Illus.). 23p. (J). (ps-3). lib. bdg. 19.93 (978-1-59197-243-3(4) , SandCastle) ABDO Publishing Co.

—Um As in Drum. Marx, Monica, ed. 2003. (Word Families Ser.). (Illus.). 23p. (J). (ps-3). lib. bdg. 19.93 (978-1-59197-244-0(2)) ABDO Publishing Co.

—Ump As in Jump. 2003. (Word Families Ser.). (Illus.). 23p. (J). (ps-3). lib. bdg. 19.93 (978-1-59197-245-7(0) , SandCastle) ABDO Publishing Co.

Tunes for June: Long Vowel u: Level B, 6 vols. (Wright Skills Ser.). 16p. (gr. k-3). 17.95 (978-0-322-01468-8(9)) Wright Group, The.

Turk, Laurel H. & Allen, E. El Espanola al Dia, Bk. 1. 6th ed. (J). (978-0-669-05668-6(5)) Houghton Mifflin Co. (Schl. Div.).

Turkington, Carol & Maack, Molly. Get Ready! for Standardized Tests: Reading Grade 1. 2001. (Get Ready for Standardized Tests Ser.). (Illus.). 168p. (gr. 1). pap. 14.95 (978-0-07-137405-7(1)) McGraw-Hill Cos., The.

Turkington, Nola. The Little Drummer Girl. 1999. (Cambridge Reading Routes Ser.). (Illus.). 32p. pap. 6.45 (978-0-521-77901-2(4)) Cambridge Univ. Pr.

Turning Corners: American Readers. (J). (gr. 2). (978-0-669-04999-2(9)) Houghton Mifflin Co. (Schl. Div.).

Turning Corners: American Readers 2-2. (J). (gr. 2). wbk. ed. (978-0-669-05004-2(0)) Houghton Mifflin Co. (Schl. Div.).

Tuxworth, Nicola & Lorenz Editors. Fruit. 2003. (Illus.). 20p. 5.99 (978-0-7548-1197-8(2)) Anness Publishing GBR. *Dist:* National Bk. Network.

Twig Books: Early Emergent - 1 each of 59 Big Books: Levels A-F Big Books. 1335.95 (978-0-322-00744-4(5)) Wright Group, The.

Twig Books: Early Emergent - Complete Kit. (gr. k up). 319.50 (978-0-7802-9699-2(0)); Vol. 2. 319.50 (978-0-7802-9700-5(8)); Vol. 4. 319.50 (978-0-322-02616-2(4)) Wright Group, The.

Twig Books: Upper Emergent - 1 each of 16 student books: Level I. (gr. 1-2). 79.95 (978-0-322-02653-7(9)) Wright Group, The.

Twig Books: Upper Emergent - 1 each of 16 student books: Level J. (gr. 1-2). 79.95 (978-0-322-02654-4(7)) Wright Group, The.

Twig Books: Upper Emergent - Lesson Plan Set - 1 Each of 16 Lesson Plans, Vol. 6. (gr. 1 up). 127.95 (978-0-322-02814-2(0)) Wright Group, The.

Twig Books: Upper Emergent - Student Book Set - 1 Each of 16 Titles. (gr. 1 up). Vol. 5. 79.95 (978-0-322-02958-3(9)); Vol. 6. 79.95 (978-0-322-02957-6(0)) Wright Group, The.

Twig Books Vol. 3: Early Emergent - Early Emergent - Complete Kit. (gr. k up). 319.50 (978-0-322-02615-5(6)) Wright Group, The.

Twig Books Vol. 5: Upper Emergent Guided Reading Kit 5. 2004. (Wright Group Literacy Ser.). (gr. 1 up). 486.50 (978-0-322-02620-9(2)) Wright Group, The.

Twisters & Other Wind Storms: 6 Each of 1 Anthology, 6 vols. (Wildcats Ser.). 32p. (gr. 2-8). (978-0-322-00591-4(4)) Wright Group, The.

The Two Runaways, 6 vols., Vol. 2. (Woodland Mysteriestm Ser.). 133p. (gr. 3-7). 42.50 (978-0-7802-7941-4(7)) Wright Group, The.

Tyler, Jenny. First Learning Time. 2000. (gr. k-3). lib. bdg. 12.95 (978-0-613-90025-6(1)) Tandem Library Bks.

Tyler, Jenny & Gee, R. Ready for Reading. 2004. (First Learning Ser.). (Illus.). 24p. (J). pap., act. bk. ed. 4.99 (978-0-7460-3519-1(5)) EDC Publishing.

The Ugly Duckling Little Book: Early Reading Fluency, Level A, Bk. 2. 2004. (gr. 1). pap. 6.00 (978-0-7398-8155-2(8)) Steck-Vaughn.

La ultima Adivinanza 13: Leveled Books. 2001. (McGraw-Hill. Lectura Ser.). (ENG & SPA.). (gr. 5 up). (978-0-02-188285-4(1)) Macmillan/McGraw-Hill Schl. Div.

Ultra-Saver Emergent, Early, & Fluent Big Book Package. 2005. (YA). (ps-3). 1665.00 (978-0-8215-8853-6(2)) Sadlier, William H. Inc.

Ultra-Saver Emergent, Early, & Fluent Little Book. 2005. (YA). (ps-3). 1728.00 (978-0-8215-8852-9(4)) Sadlier, William H. Inc.

Ultra-Saver Emergent, Early, & Fluent Little Book Package. 2005. (YA). (ps-3). 330.00 (978-0-8215-8851-2(6)) Sadlier, William H. Inc.

Ultra-Saver Library Emergent, Early, & Fluent. 2005. (YA). (ps-3). 2727.00 (978-0-8215-8850-5(8)) Sadlier, William H. Inc.

Uncle Bill Is Feeling Iii, 6 vols. 8p. (gr. k-1). 21.50 (978-0-322-02078-8(6)) Wright Group, The.

Uncle Mort's: Level T. Group 3, 6 vols. (Sunshinetm Ser.). 48p. 44.95 (978-0-322-04600-9(9)) Wright Group, The.

Under the Clock, 6 vols. 8p. (gr. k-1). 21.50 (978-0-322-02064-1(6)) Wright Group, The.

Underwater Journey, 6 vols. (Sunshinetm Ser.). 16p. (gr. k up). 29.50 (978-0-7802-5437-4(6)) Wright Group, The.

Unidad 1 Guia del Maestro. 2001. (McGraw-Hill. Lectura Ser.). (ENG & SPA.). (gr. k up). (978-0-02-184847-8(5)); (gr. 1 up). (978-0-02-184853-9(X)); (gr. 4 up). (978-0-02-184913-0(7)); (gr. 5 up). (978-0-02-184919-2(6)); (gr. 6 up). (978-0-02-188304-2(1)) Macmillan/McGraw-Hill Schl. Div.

Unidad 1 Libro del Estudiante. 2001. (McGraw-Hill. Lectura Ser.). (ENG & SPA.). (gr. 1 up). stu. ed. (978-0-02-184835-5(1)) Macmillan/McGraw-Hill Schl. Div.

Unidad 1 Superlibro: Comunidades: Vivimos Juntos: Superlibros. 2003. (MacMillan/McGraw-Hill. Estudios Sociales Ser.). (ENG & SPA.). (gr. 2 up). (978-0-02-149441-5(X)) Macmillan/McGraw-Hill Schl. Div.

Unidad 1 Superlibro: Trotelote. 2001. (McGraw-Hill. Lectura Ser.). (ENG & SPA.). (gr. 1 up). (978-0-02-186392-1(X)) Macmillan/McGraw-Hill Schl. Div.

Unidad 2 Guia del Maestro. 2001. (McGraw-Hill. Lectura Ser.). (ENG & SPA.). (gr. k up). (978-0-02-184848-5(3)); (gr. 1 up). (978-0-02-184854-6(8)); (gr. 4 up). (978-0-02-184914-7(5)); (gr. 5 up). (978-0-02-184920-8(X)); (gr. 6 up). (978-0-02-188305-9(X)) Macmillan/McGraw-Hill Schl. Div.

Unidad 2 Libro del Estudiante: Pupil Edition. 2001. (McGraw-Hill. Lectura Ser.). (ENG & SPA.). (gr. 1 up). (978-0-02-184836-2(X)) Macmillan/McGraw-Hill Schl. Div.

Unidad 2 Superlibro: Las vacaciones de Roberta: Big Books. 2001. (McGraw-Hill. Lectura Ser.). (ENG & SPA.). (gr. 1 up). (978-0-02-186393-8(8)) Macmillan/McGraw-Hill Schl. Div.

Unidad 2 Superlibro: Vamos a la feria del ABC. 2001. (McGraw-Hill. Lectura Ser.). (ENG & SPA.). (gr. k up) (978-0-02-186024-1(6)) Macmillan/McGraw-Hill Schl. Div.

Unidad 3 Guia del Maestro. 2001. (McGraw-Hill. Lectura Ser.). (ENG & SPA.). (gr. k up). (978-0-02-184849-2(1)); (gr. 1 up). (978-0-02-184855-3(6)); (gr. 4 up). (978-0-02-184915-4(3)); (gr. 5 up). (978-0-02-184921-5(8)) Macmillan/McGraw-Hill Schl. Div.

Unidad 3 Libro del Estudiante. 2001. (McGraw-Hill. Lectura Ser.). (ENG & SPA.). (gr. 1 up). stu. ed. (978-0-02-184837-9(8)) Macmillan/McGraw-Hill Schl. Div.

Unidad 3 Superlibro: Animalfabeto. 2001. (McGraw-Hill. Lectura Ser.). (ENG & SPA.). (gr. k up). (978-0-02-186025-8(4)) Macmillan/McGraw-Hill Schl. Div.

Unidad 3 Superlibro: el payasos que no hacia Reir. 2001. (McGraw-Hill. Lectura Ser.). (ENG & SPA.). (gr. 2 up). (978-0-02-186400-3(4)) Macmillan/McGraw-Hill Schl. Div.

Unidad 3 Superlibro: Marita no sabe Dibujar. 2001. (McGraw-Hill. Lectura Ser.). (ENG & SPA.). (gr. 3 up). (978-0-02-186406-5(3)) Macmillan/McGraw-Hill Schl. Div.

Unidad 4 Guia del Maestro. 2001. (McGraw-Hill. Lectura Ser.). (ENG & SPA.). (gr. k up). (978-0-02-184850-8(5)); (gr. 1 up). (978-0-02-184856-0(4)); (gr. 4 up). (978-0-02-184916-1(1)); (gr. 5 up). (978-0-02-184922-2(6)) Macmillan/McGraw-Hill Schl. Div.

Unidad 4 Libro del Estudiante. 2001. (McGraw-Hill. Lectura Ser.). (ENG & SPA.). (gr. 1 up). stu. ed. (978-0-02-184838-6(6)) Macmillan/McGraw-Hill Schl. Div.

Unidad 4 Superlibro: Fernando Furioso. 2001. (McGraw-Hill. Lectura Ser.). (ENG & SPA.). (gr. 3 up). (978-0-02-186407-2(1)) Macmillan/McGraw-Hill Schl. Div.

Unidad 4 Superlibro: la senora Reganona. 2001. (McGraw-Hill. Lectura Ser.). (ENG & SPA.). (gr. 1 up). (978-0-02-186395-2(4)) Macmillan/McGraw-Hill Schl. Div.

Unidad 4 Superlibro: Las aventuras de Alba, de la a a la Z. 2001. (McGraw-Hill. Lectura Ser.). (ENG & SPA.). (gr. k up). (978-0-02-186026-5(2)) Macmillan/McGraw-Hill Schl. Div.

Unidad 4 Superlibro: Manuela y el Mar. 2001. (McGraw-Hill. Lectura Ser.). (ENG & SPA.). (gr. 2 up). (978-0-02-186401-0(2)) Macmillan/McGraw-Hill Schl. Div.

Unidad 5 Guia del Maestro. 2001. (McGraw-Hill. Lectura Ser.). (ENG & SPA.). (gr. k up). (978-0-02-184851-5(3)); (gr. 1 up). (978-0-02-184857-7(2)); (gr. 4 up). (978-0-02-184917-8(X)); (gr. 5 up). (978-0-02-184923-9(4)) Macmillan/McGraw-Hill Schl. Div.

Unidad 5 Libro del Estudiante. 2001. (McGraw-Hill. Lectura Ser.). (ENG & SPA.). (gr. 1 up). stu. ed. (978-0-02-184839-3(4)) Macmillan/McGraw-Hill Schl. Div.

Unidad 5 Superlibro: la Sequia. 2001. (McGraw-Hill. Lectura Ser.). (ENG & SPA.). (gr. 3 up). (978-0-02-186408-9(X)) Macmillan/McGraw-Hill Schl. Div.

Unidad 5 Superlibro: No llores, Miguel. 2001. (McGraw-Hill. Lectura Ser.). (ENG & SPA.). (gr. 1 up). (978-0-02-186396-9(2)) Macmillan/McGraw-Hill Schl. Div.

Unidad 5 Superlibro: un dia en el Mar. 2001. (McGraw-Hill. Lectura Ser.). (ENG & SPA.). (gr. k up). (978-0-02-186027-2(0)) Macmillan/McGraw-Hill Schl. Div.

Unidad 6 Guia del Maestro. 2001. (McGraw-Hill. Lectura Ser.). (ENG & SPA.). (gr. k up). (978-0-02-184852-2(1)); (gr. 1 up). (978-0-02-184858-4(0)); (gr. 4 up). (978-0-02-184918-5(8)); (gr. 5 up). (978-0-02-184924-6(2)) Macmillan/McGraw-Hill Schl. Div.

Unidad 6 Superlibro: Una caja, muchas Cosas. 2001. (McGraw-Hill. Lectura Ser.). (ENG & SPA.). (gr. k up). (978-0-02-186028-9(9)) Macmillan/McGraw-Hill Schl. Div.

Unidad 6 Superlibro: Wishi, la Aranita. 2001. (McGraw-Hill. Lectura Ser.). (ENG & SPA.). (gr. 1 up). (978-0-02-186397-6(0)) Macmillan/McGraw-Hill Schl. Div.

Up High in the Mountains: 6 Each of 1 Anthology, 6 vols. (Wildcatstm Ser.). 32p. (gr. 2-8). (978-0-322-02426-7(9)) Wright Group, The.

Up in a Tree: Level D. Group 1. (Sunshinetm Ser.). 8p. 20.95 (978-0-7802-5736-8(7)) Wright Group, The.

Up They Go. (Little Book Practice Reader). (J). (978-0-8136-5361-7(4)) Modern Curriculum Pr.

Upper Emergent Skills Guide. (Sunshine Skills Guides). 25.95 (978-0-7802-9810-1(1)) Wright Group, The.

La Urraca Petra 13: Leveled Books. 2001. (McGraw-Hill. Lectura Ser.). (ENG & SPA.). (gr. 3 up). (978-0-02-188086-7(7)) Macmillan/McGraw-Hill Schl. Div.

Usa la ciencia para jugar al Beisbol 24: Leveled Books. 2001. (McGraw-Hill. Lectura Ser.). (ENG & SPA.). (gr. 3 up). (978-0-02-188145-1(6)) Macmillan/McGraw-Hill Schl. Div.

Usher, Frances. That Rebellious Towne, 8, Pack. Ball, Gerry, illus. 2000. (Cambridge Reading Ser.). 48p. pap. 54.00 (978-0-521-78630-0(4)) Cambridge Univ. Pr.

Using the Library: Level N, 6 vols. (Wonder Worldtm Ser.). 48p. 34.95 (978-0-7802-4617-1(9)) Wright Group, The.

La vaca que decia OINK 10: Leveled Books. 2001. (McGraw-Hill. Lectura Ser.). (ENG & SPA.). (gr. 1 up). (978-0-02-187987-8(7)) Macmillan/McGraw-Hill Schl. Div.

Las Vacaciones 21: Leveled Books. 2001. (McGraw-Hill. Lectura Ser.). (ENG & SPA.). (gr. 3 up). (978-0-02-188118-5(9)) Macmillan/McGraw-Hill Schl. Div.

Valentine's Checkup. 2005. (Emergent Library: Vol. 2). (YA). (ps-1). 23.94 (978-0-8215-8937-3(7)) Sadlier, William H. Inc.

Valentine's Checkup: Take-Home Book. 2005. (Emergent Library: Vol. 2). (YA). (ps-1). 12.60 (978-0-8215-7267-2(9)) Sadlier, William H. Inc.

Valeriapor que No? 1: Leveled Books. 2001. (McGraw-Hill. Lectura Ser.). (ENG & SPA.). (gr. 5 up). (978-0-02-188225-0(8)) Macmillan/McGraw-Hill Schl. Div.

Van Heerden, Marjorie. Frog: Chitonga Version. Chisengele, tr. 2001. (Illus.). 8p. pap. 0.45 (978-0-521-01381-9(X)) Cambridge Univ. Pr.

—Frog: Chitonga Version. Hamoonga, Lazarous, tr. 1998. (Cambridge African Language Library Ser.). (Illus.). 8p. pap. 3.75 (978-0-521-64754-0(1)) Cambridge Univ. Pr.

—Frog: Cinyanja Version. Tembo, tr. 2001. (Illus.). 8p. pap. 0.45 (978-0-521-01382-6(8)) Cambridge Univ. Pr.

—Frog: Cinyanja Version. Mwale, Brian, tr. 1998. (Cambridge African Language Library Ser.). (Illus.). 8p. pap. 3.75 (978-0-521-64753-3(3)) Cambridge Univ. Pr.

—Frog: Icibemba Version. Mulilo, tr. 2001. (Illus.). 8p. pap. 0.45 (978-0-521-01393-2(3)) Cambridge Univ. Pr.

—Frog: Icibemba Version. Mwansa, Bupe, tr. 1998. (Cambridge African Language Library). (Illus.). 8p. pap. 3.75 (978-0-521-64752-6(5)) Cambridge Univ. Pr.

—Frog: Kiikaonde Version. Muyebaa, tr. 2001. (Illus.). 8p. pap. 0.45 (978-0-521-01396-3(8)) Cambridge Univ. Pr.

—Frog: Kiikaonde Version. Muyebaa, Kyangubabi, tr. 1998. (Cambridge African Language Library Ser.). (Illus.). 8p. pap. 3.75 (978-0-521-64751-9(7)) Cambridge Univ. Pr.

—Frog: Luvale Version. Sakapaji, tr. 2001. (Illus.). 8p. pap. 0.45 (978-0-521-01403-8(4)) Cambridge Univ. Pr.

—Frog: Luvale Version. Kaleyi, Kakoma, tr. 1998. (Cambridge African Language Library Ser.). (Illus.). 8p. pap. 3.75 (978-0-521-64749-6(5)) Cambridge Univ. Pr.

—Frog: Silozi Version. Mwendende, tr. 2001. (Illus.). 8p. pap. 0.45 (978-0-521-01434-2(4)) Cambridge Univ. Pr.

—Frog: Silozi Version. Silumesii, Penelope, tr. 1998. (Cambridge African Language Library). (Illus.). 8p. pap. 3.75 (978-0-521-64748-9(7)) Cambridge Univ. Pr.

A Van in the Mud: Consonant v: Level A, 6 vols. (Wright Skills Ser.). 12p. (gr. k-3). 17.95 (978-0-322-03118-0(4)) Wright Group, The.

Vaquita Voladora 15: Leveled Books. 2001. (McGraw-Hill. Lectura Ser.). (ENG & SPA.). (gr. 2 up). (978-0-02-188040-9(9)) Macmillan/McGraw-Hill Schl. Div.

La vasija Irisada 7: Leveled Books. 2001. (McGraw-Hill. Lectura Ser.). (ENG & SPA.). (gr. 5 up). (978-0-02-188255-7(X)) Macmillan/McGraw-Hill Schl. Div.

Vaughan, Marcia. Story Teller Quilts: Level S, 6 vols. 128p. (gr. 3-6). 36.95 (978-0-322-05899-6(6)) Wright Group, The.

Vaya Noche! 15: Leveled Books. 2001. (McGraw-Hill. Lectura Ser.). (ENG & SPA.). (gr. 5 up). (978-0-02-188287-8(8)) Macmillan/McGraw-Hill Schl. Div.

Veo, Veo 8: Leveled Books. 2001. (McGraw-Hill. Lectura Ser.). (ENG & SPA.). (gr. 1 up). (978-0-02-187961-8(3)) Macmillan/McGraw-Hill Schl. Div.

Verdadero Talento 1: Leveled Books. 2001. (McGraw-Hill. Lectura Ser.). (ENG & SPA.). (gr. 5 up). (978-0-02-188273-1(8)) Macmillan/McGraw-Hill Schl. Div.

A Very Fine Time: Long Vowel i, CVCe Pattern: Level B, 6 vols. (Wright Skills Ser.). 16p. (gr. k-3). 17.95 (978-0-322-01467-1(0)) Wright Group, The.

La vida en la Gran Barrera de Coral 8: Leveled Books. 2001. (McGraw-Hill. Lectura Ser.). (ENG & SPA.). (gr. 3 up). (978-0-02-188129-1(4)) Macmillan/McGraw-Hill Schl. Div.

La vida en las rocas: Cuaderno de Evaluacion: Unit 5: la vida en las rocas (Rocky Homes) 2000. (McGraw-Hill Ciencias Ser.). (ENG & SPA.). (gr. 2 up). (978-0-02-278642-7(2)) Macmillan/McGraw-Hill Schl. Div.

La vida en las rocas: Recursos para el maestro con clave de Respuestas: Unit 5: la vida en las rocas (Rocky Homes) 2000. (McGraw-Hill Ciencias Ser.). (ENG & SPA.). (gr. 2 up). (978-0-02-278689-2(9)) Macmillan/McGraw-Hill Schl. Div.

La vieja Escuela 4: Leveled Books. 2001. (McGraw-Hill. Lectura Ser.). (ENG & SPA.). (gr. 3 up). (978-0-02-188101-7(4)) Macmillan/McGraw-Hill Schl. Div.

Viljoen, Graeme. Eggs: Chitonga Version. Chisengele, tr. 2001. (Illus.). 8p. pap. 0.45 (978-0-521-01447-2(6)) Cambridge Univ. Pr.

—Eggs: Chitonga Version. Hamoonga, Lazarous, tr. 1998. (Cambridge African Language Library). (Illus.). 8p. pap. 3.75 (978-0-521-64740-3(1)) Cambridge Univ. Pr.

—Eggs: Cinyanja Version. Tembo, tr. 2001. (Illus.). 8p. pap. 0.45 (978-0-521-01449-6(2)) Cambridge Univ. Pr.

—Eggs: Cinyanja Version. Mwale, Brian, tr. 1998. (Cambridge African Language Library). (Illus.). 8p. pap. 3.75 (978-0-521-64739-7(8)) Cambridge Univ. Pr.

—Eggs: Icibemba Version. Mwansa, Bupe, tr. 1998. (Cambridge African Language Library Ser.). (Illus.). 8p. pap. 3.75 (978-0-521-64738-0(X)) Cambridge Univ. Pr.

—Eggs: Kiikaonde Version. Muyebaa, Kynagubabi, tr. 1998. (Cambridge African Language Library Ser.). (Illus.). 8p. pap. 3.75 (978-0-521-64737-3(1)) Cambridge Univ. Pr.

—Eggs: Luvale Version. Kaleyi, Kakoma, tr. 1998. (Cambridge African Language Library Ser.). (Illus.). 8p. pap. 3.75 (978-0-521-64735-9(5)) Cambridge Univ. Pr.

—Eggs: Silozi Version. Silumesii, Penelope, tr. 1998. (Cambridge African Language Library). (Illus.). 8p. pap. 3.75 (978-0-521-64734-2(7)) Cambridge Univ. Pr.

Viljoen, Graeme & Mulilo. Eggs: Icibemba Version. 2001. (Illus.). 8p. pap. 0.45 (978-0-521-01451-9(4)) Cambridge Univ. Pr.

Viljoen, Graeme & Muyebaa. Eggs: Kiikaonde Version. 2001. (Illus.). 8p. pap. 0.45 (978-0-521-01453-3(0)) Cambridge Univ. Pr.

Viljoen, Graeme & Mwendende. Eggs: Silozi Version. 2001. (Illus.). 8p. pap. 0.45 (978-0-521-01457-1(3)) Cambridge Univ. Pr.

Viljoen, Graeme & Sakapaji. Eggs: Luvale Version. 2001. (Illus.). 8p. pap. 0.45 (978-0-521-01455-7(7)) Cambridge Univ. Pr.

Violets & Vegetables Vol. 4: Big Book. 2005. (Emergent Library: Vol. 1). (YA). (ps-1). 23.94 (978-0-8215-8917-5(2)) Sadlier, William H. Inc.

Visions: Early Emergent - 1 each of 12 Big Books: Levels A-G Big Books. 248.50 (978-0-322-00748-2(8)) Wright Group, The.

Visions: Early Emergent - 1 Each of 12 Student Books: Level A. 49.95 (978 0 7802-9448-6(3)) Wright Group, The.

Visions: Early Emergent - 1 Each of 13 Student Books: Level B. 54.50 (978-0-7802-9449-3(1)) Wright Group, The.

Visions: Early Emergent - 1 Each of 13 Student Books: Level C. 54.50 (978-0-7802-9450-9(5)) Wright Group, The.

Visions: Early Emergent - Complete Kit. (gr. k up). 319.50 (978-0-7802-9397-7(5)) Wright Group, The.

Visions: Early Emergent-Upper Emergent - 1 Each of 12 Student Books: Level D. 49.95 (978-0-7802-9451-6(3)) Wright Group, The.

Visions: Early Emergent-Upper Emergent - 1 Each of 12 Student Books: Level E. 59.95 (978-0-7802-9452-3(1)) Wright Group, The.

Visions: Early Emergent-Upper Emergent - 1 Each of 13 Student Books: Level F. 64.95 (978-0-7802-9453-0(X)) Wright Group, The.

Visions: Upper Emergent - 1 Each of 12 Student Books: Level H. 59.95 (978-0-7802-9454-7(8)) Wright Group, The.

Visions: Upper Emergent - 1 Each of 13 Student Books: Level G. 64.95 (978-0-7802-9455-4(6)) Wright Group, The.

Visions: Upper Emergent - Complete Kit. (gr. 1 up). 383.50 (978-0-7802-9398-4(3)) Wright Group, The.

Visions Enrichment Library: 1 Each of 20 Student Books. (Multicultural Programs Ser.). (gr. 1-3). 83.50 (978-0-7802-9447-9(5)) Wright Group, The.

Voladores de Fondo 3: Leveled Books. 2001. (McGraw-Hill. Lectura Ser.). (ENG & SPA.). (gr. 4 up). (978-0-02-188148-2(0)) Macmillan/McGraw-Hill Schl. Div.

The Voyage of the Clowns: Diphthong Review: Level C, 6 vols. (Wright Skills Ser.). 16p. (gr. k-3). 26.50 (978-0-322-01500-5(6)) Wright Group, The.

La Voz de Saltaire 4: Leveled Books. 2001. (McGraw-Hill. Lectura Ser.). (ENG & SPA.). (gr. 3 up). (978-0-02-188125-3(1)) Macmillan/McGraw-Hill Schl. Div.

La voz del Mar 17: Leveled Books. 2001. (McGraw-Hill. Lectura Ser.). (ENG & SPA.). (gr. 2 up). (978-0-02-188066-9(2)) Macmillan/McGraw-Hill Schl. Div.

El vuelo de los Trompeteros 16: Leveled Books. 2001. (McGraw-Hill. Lectura Ser.). (ENG & SPA.). (gr. 5 up). (978-0-02-188240-3(1)) Macmillan/McGraw-Hill Schl. Div.

Ward, Sally. Dorothy's Visit: Chinyanja Version. Iphani, Max, tr. 1999. (Cambridge Reading Routes Ser.). (Illus.). 16p. pap. 3.70 (978-0-521-66881-1(6)) Cambridge Univ. Pr.

—Dorothy's Visit: Chitumbuka Version. Chirambo, Reuben, tr. 1999. (Cambridge Reading Routes Ser.). (Illus.). 16p. pap. 3.70 (978-0-521-66874-3(3)) Cambridge Univ. Pr.

—Dorothy's Visit: Chiyao Version. Kaliati, Mailos, tr. 1999. (Cambridge Reading Routes Ser.). (Illus.). 16p. pap. 3.70 (978-0-521-66856-9(5)) Cambridge Univ. Pr.

—Dorothy's Visit Lugbara Version: Emu-Taa Ondoru Ni Ri. Draville, Ben & Mawa, Robert, trs. 2001. 16p. pap. 1.40 (978-0-521-00626-2(0)) Cambridge Univ. Pr.

Ward, Sally & Dlhomo, Bongi. Dorothy's Visit: Sepedi Version. 2002. (Illus.). 16p. pap. 1.75 (978-0-521-52831-3(3)) Cambridge Univ. Pr.

—Dorothy's Visit: Sesotho Version. 2002. (Illus.). 16p. pap. 1.75 (978-0-521-52828-3(3)) Cambridge Univ. Pr.

—Dorothy's Visit: Setswana Version. 2002. (Illus.). 16p. pap. 1.75 (978-0-521-52829-0(1)) Cambridge Univ. Pr.

—Dorothy's Visit: Xitsonga Version. 2002. (Illus.). 16p. pap. 1.75 (978-0-521-52830-6(5)) Cambridge Univ. Pr.

Warm & Cool Sets: 1 Each of 3 Big Books. (Sunshinetm Science Ser.). (gr. 1-2). 111.50 (978-0-7802-1450-7(1)) Wright Group, The.

Warming Up: American Readers. (J). (978-0-669-04913-8(1)); (978-0-669-04915-2(8)) Houghton Mifflin Co. (Schl. Div.).

Water: Level J, 6 vols. (Wonder Worldtm Ser.). 16p. 29.95 (978-0-7802-2914-3(2)) Wright Group, The.

Water Worlds Series, 6 bks. Incl. Antarctic. Hook, Cheryl. 28.00 (978-0-7910-6566-2(9) , 010351); Coral Reefs. Hook, Cheryl. 28.00 (978-0-7910-6567-9(7) , 010352); Fresh Water. Ampt, Peter. 28.00 (978-0-7910-6569-3(3) , 010353); Mangroves. Blaxland, Beth. 28.00 (978-0-7910-6565-5(0) , 010354); Oceans. Bell, Mary. 28.00 (978-0-7910-6570-9(7) , 010355); Sea Shores. Blaxland, Beth. 28.00 (978-0-7910-6568-6(5) , 010356); (J). (gr. 4 up). 2001. (Illus.). 32p. 2005. Set pap. 168.00 (978-0-7910-6564-8(2) , 010350S, Chelsea Hse.) Facts On File, Inc.

Watson, Joy. The Birthday Flood: Level O, 6 vols. 128p. (gr. 3-6). 36.95 (978-0-322-05896-5(1)) Wright Group, The.

Watson, Yolanda. Which Holiday Is It? 2003. (Compass Point Phonics Readers Ser.). (Illus.). 16p. (J). (gr. 1 up). 13.26 (978-0-7565-0533-2(X)) Compass Point Bks.

Waves: Level L, 6 vols. (Wonder Worldtm Ser.). 16p. 34.95 (978-0-7802-4619-5(5)) Wright Group, The.

We Care for our School: Level K, 6 vols. (Wonder Worldtm Ser.). 16p. 34.95 (978-0-7802-4621-8(7)); 26.50 (978-0-7802-7009-1(6)) Wright Group, The.

We Look the Same, 6 vols. 8p. (gr. k-1). 21.50 (978-0-322-02079-5(4)) Wright Group, The.

Weather Forecasting: Level R, 6 vols. (Wonder Worldtm Ser.). 48p. 44.95 (978-0-7802-7085-5(1)) Wright Group, The.

Weather Wise, Vol. 3. 2005. (Emergent Library: Vol. 1). (YA). (ps-1). 23.94 (978-0-8215-8911-3(3)) Sadlier, William H. Inc.

The Week That Was: Level 3, 6 vols. (Fluency Strand Ser.). (gr. 4-8). 45.00 (978-1-4045-1221-4(7)) Wright Group, The.

Weeks, Sarah. What Is a Kiss? Date not set. 32p. (J). (ps-2). 15.89 (978-0-06-026256-3(7)) HarperCollins Pubs.

Weird Weather Little Book: Early Reading Fluency, Level C. 2004. pap. 6.00 (978-0-7398-8301-3(1)) Steck-Vaughn.

Welch, Diane & Simpson, Susan S. Green Student Activity Book: Learning Language Arts Through Literature. 2nd rev. ed. 1998. (Learning Language Arts Through Literature Ser.). 314p. (YA). pap. 20.00 (978-1-880892-45-9(6)) Common Sense Pr.

—Tan Student Activity Book: Learning Language Arts Through Literature. 2nd rev. ed. 1998. 348p. (J). pap. 20.00 (978-1-880892-21-3(9)) Common Sense Pr.

Wells, Leanne. School Holidays: Emergent. 2002. (Bright Sparks Ser.). (Illus.). 16p. pap. 2.99 (978-0-521-75145-2(4)) Cambridge Univ. Pr.

Wells, Rosemary. Listos para Leer. Fernandez, Leire Amigo, tr. Koelsch, Michael, illus. 2004. (SPA.). 28p. (J). 13.95 (978-84-241-8712-5(1)) Everest de Ediciones y Distribucion, S.L. ESP. *Dist:* Lectorum Pubns., Inc.

—Ready to Read: Based on Timothy Goes to School & Other Stories. 2001. (ps-2). lib. bdg. 14.15 (978-0-613-43953-4(8)) Tandem Library Bks.

West, Tracey. Botties' Day Off. 2002. (gr. k-3). lib. bdg. 11.80 (978-0-613-72065-6(2)) Tandem Library Bks.

Westmoreland. Good As Any. 2002. (J). pap. (978-0-15-601318-5(5)) Harcourt Schl. Pubs.

Whale Watch. (Little Book Practice Reader). (J). (978-0-8136-5380-8(0)) Modern Curriculum Pr.

What do I See in the Garden: Big Book: Level F. (Wonder Worldtm Ser.). 16p. 29.95 (978-0-7802-2830-6(8)) Wright Group, The.

What do I See in the Garden: Level F, 6 vols. (Wonder Worldtm Ser.). 16p. 29.95 (978-0-7802-1054-7(9)) Wright Group, The.

What Do You Think? 6 Pack. (Wildcats Ser.). 32p. (gr. 2-8). (978-0-322-00578-5(7)) Wright Group, The.

What Else?, 6 vols. (Sunshinetm Ser.). 16p. (gr. k up). 29.50 (978-0-7802-5439-8(2)) Wright Group, The.

What Is It Made From: Early Reading Fluency, Level A. 2004. pap. 6.00 (978-0-7398-8162-0(0)) Steck-Vaughn.

What Season Is This? Level A, 6 vols. (Wonder Worldtm Ser.). 16p. 24.95 (978-0-7802-1055-4(7)) Wright Group, The.

What was This? Level G, 6 vols. (Wonder Worldtm Ser.). 16p. 29.95 (978-0-7802-2038-6(2)) Wright Group, The.

What Will You Pack? (Little Book Practice Reader). (J). (978-0-8136-5357-0(6)) Modern Curriculum Pr.

What's for Dinner? Level T. Group 1, 6 vols. (Sunshinetm Ser.). 48p. 44.95 (978-0-7802-6099-3(6)) Wright Group, The.

What's in the Bag?, 6 vols. (Multicultural Programs Ser.). 16p. (gr. 1-3). 24.95 (978-0-7802-9218-5(9)) Wright Group, The.

What's Inside? Level M, 6 vols. (Wonder Worldtm Ser.). 16p. 34.95 (978-0-7802-2916-7(9)) Wright Group, The.

Wheeler, Kathryn. Story Elements: Learning about the Components of Stories to Deepen Comprehension. 2001. (Basic Skills Ser.). 48p. (J). (gr. 3-4). pap. 6.99 (978-0-7424-0103-7(0) , IF5636) School Specialty Publishing.

When the Sun Goes Down: Level H, 6 vols. (Wonder Worldtm Ser.). 16p. 29.95 (978-0-7802-2040-9(4)) Wright Group, The.

Where Can a Hippo Hide? (Little Book Practice Reader). (J). (978-0-8136-1967-5(X)) Modern Curriculum Pr.

Where do all the Birds Go? Level Q, 6 vols. (Wonder Worldtm Ser.). 48p. 39.95 (978-0-7802-2955-6(X)) Wright Group, The.

Where do I Sleep? Level Q, 6 vols. (Wonder Worldtm Ser.). 48p. 39.95 (978-0-7802-2956-3(8)) Wright Group, The.

Where Do We Go? (Little Book Practice Reader). (J). (978-0-8136-5352-5(5)) Modern Curriculum Pr.

Where Is My Caterpillar? Level J, 6 vols. (Wonder Worldtm Ser.). 16p. 29.95 (978-0-7802-1056-1(5)) Wright Group, The.

Where's Sylvester's Bed? Level G, 6 vols. (Wonder Worldtm Ser.). 16p. 29.95 (978-0-7802-1251-0(7)) Wright Group, The.

Whiskers: Level A, 6 vols. (Wonder Worldtm Ser.). 16p. 24.95 (978-0-7802-2917-4(7)) Wright Group, The.

Whitechurch Reading Group. 2000. (J). pap. (978-0-06-449251-5(6) , Harper Trophy) HarperCollins Pubs.

Whiteford, Rhona. Reading & Writing: Brand New Activities for Key Stage 2. 2003. (Hodder Home Learning Ser.). (Illus.). 32p. (J). pap. 6.99 (978-0-340-79183-7(7) , Hodder & Stoughton) Hodder General Publishing Division GBR. *Dist:* Trafalgar Square Publishing.

Whiting, Sue. The Big Black Blob. Robertson, Claire, illus. 2002. (Bright Sparks Ser.). 16p. pap. 2.30 (978-0-521-75406-4(2)) Cambridge Univ. Pr.

—Pigs Love Mud. Jurevicius, Nathan, illus. 2002. (Bright Sparks Ser.). 16p. pap. 2.30 (978-0-521-75422-4(4)) Cambridge Univ. Pr.

Who Is Quick? Benchmark Assessment for Level A: Level A, 6 vols. (Wright Skills Ser.). 12p. (gr. k-3). 17.95 (978-0-322-03127-2(3)) Wright Group, The.

Why do I Need to Know When?, 6 vols. (Multicultural Programs Ser.). 16p. (gr. 1-3). 24.95 (978-0-7802-9221-5(9)) Wright Group, The.

Wignell, Edel. A Special Dress. Koman, Vasja, illus. 2002. (Bright Sparks Ser.). 16p. pap. 2.30 (978-0-521-75425-5(9)) Cambridge Univ. Pr.

Wilber, Peggy M. & Hering, Marianne. Five Alive: Level 2, 5 vols. Pillo, Cary, illus. 2003. (Rocket Reader Ser.). (J). (gr. 2 up). pap. 8.99 (978-0-7814-3862-9(4) , 0781438624) Cook, David C. Publishing Co.

Wild Cats: Level P, 6 vols. (Wonder Worldtm Ser.). 48p. 39.95 (978-0-7802-7069-5(X)) Wright Group, The.

The Wild Wind: Big Book: Level I. Group 2. (Story Box(R) Ser.). 16p. 31.50 (978-0-322-02467-0(6)) Wright Group, The.

Wildlife Watching: Level R, 6 vols. (Wonder Worldtm Ser.). 48p. 44.95 (978-0-7802-7076-3(2)) Wright Group, The.

Wildman, Chris & Muwela, Mavis. Try & Catch a Tadpole: Chitonga Version. Chisengele, tr. 2001. (Illus.). 16p. pap. 0.45 (978-0-521-01593-6(6)) Cambridge Univ. Pr.

—Try & Catch a Tadpole: Cinyanja Version. Tembo, tr. 2001. (Illus.). 16p. pap. 0.45 (978-0-521-01594-3(4)) Cambridge Univ. Pr.

—Try & Catch a Tadpole: Icibemba Version. Mulilo, tr. 2001. (Illus.). 16p. pap. 0.45 (978-0-521-01596-7(0)) Cambridge Univ. Pr.

—Try & Catch a Tadpole: Kiikaonde Version. Muyebaa, tr. 2001. (Illus.). 16p. pap. 0.45 (978-0-521-01597-4(9)) Cambridge Univ. Pr.

—Try & Catch a Tadpole: Luvale Version. Sakapaji, tr. 2001. (Illus.). 16p. pap. 0.45 (978-0-521-01599-8(5)) Cambridge Univ. Pr.

—Try & Catch a Tadpole: Silozi Version. Mwendende, tr. 2001. (Illus.). 16p. pap. 0.45 (978-0-521-01600-1(2)) Cambridge Univ. Pr.

Wildman, Chris, et al. Grandfather's Hat: Chitonga Version. Chisengele, tr. 2001. (Illus.). 16p. pap. 0.45 (978-0-521-01617-9(7)) Cambridge Univ. Pr.

—Grandfather's Hat: Cinyanja Version. Tembo, tr. 2001. (Illus.). 16p. pap. 0.45 (978-0-521-01618-6(5)) Cambridge Univ. Pr.

—Grandfather's Hat: Icibemba Version. Mulilo, tr. 2001. (Illus.). 16p. pap. 0.45 (978-0-521-01620-9(7)) Cambridge Univ. Pr.

—Grandfather's Hat: Kiikaonde Version. Muyebaa, tr. 2001. (Illus.). 16p. pap. 0.45 (978-0-521-01621-6(5)) Cambridge Univ. Pr.

—Grandfather's Hat: Luvale Version. Sakapaji, tr. 2001. (Illus.). 16p. pap. 0.45 (978-0-521-89002-1(0)) Cambridge Univ. Pr.

—Grandfather's Hat: Silozi Version. Mwendende, tr. 2001. (Illus.). 16p. pap. 0.45 (978-0-521-89003-8(9)) Cambridge Univ. Pr.

Will Eve Win? Long Vowels e, y, CVCe & Final y Patterns: Level B, 6 vols. (Wright Skills Ser.). 16p. (gr. k-3). 17.95 (978-0-322-01469-5(7)) Wright Group, The.

Will it Rain on the Parade? Level J, 6 vols. (Wonder Worldtm Ser.). 16p. 29.95 (978-0-7802-4623-2(3)) Wright Group, The.

Williams, Rozanne Lanczak. Mice Are Nice. Moore, Margie, illus. 2005. (Reading for Fluency Ser.). 16p. (J). pap. 2.99 (978-1-59198-156-5(5) , 4256) Creative Teaching Pr., Inc.

—Old MacDonald's Funny Farm, Vol. 4261. Starr Taylor, Bridget, illus. 2005. (Reading for Fluency Ser.). 16p. (J). pap. 2.99 (978-1-59198-161-9(1) , 4261) Creative Teaching Pr., Inc.

—Super File-Folder Books: Easy How-to's for 10 Interactive Books That Kids Will Love to Make & Read. 2004. 48p. (gr. k-2). pap. 10.99 (978-0-439-39502-1(X)) Scholastic, Inc.

—Super Manipulative Books: Easy How-to's for 10 Interactive Books That Kids Will Love to Make & Read. 2004. 48p. (gr. k-2). pap. 10.99 (978-0-439-39504-5(6)) Scholastic, Inc.

—Super Paper Bag Books: Easy How-to's for 10 Interactive Books That Kids Will Love to Make & Read. 2004. 48p. pap. 10.99 (978-0-439-39503-8(8)) Scholastic, Inc.

The Wind in the Willows. 2001. pap., tchr. ed., wbk. ed. (978-1-56137-208-9(0)) Novel Units, Inc.

Wingate, Lynae, ed. Grade 2 Reading Skillbook. Engblom, Mark, illus. 2000. 32p. (J). (gr. 2-3). pap., wbk. ed. 2.99 (978-1-889319-63-6(5) , KidSparks) Trend Enterprises, Inc.

—Grade 3 Reading Skillbook. Engblom, Mark, illus. 2000. 32p. (J). (gr. 3-4). pap., wbk. ed. 2.99 (978-1-889319-65-0(1) , KidSparks) Trend Enterprises, Inc.

—Grade 4 Reading Skillbook. Engblom, Mark, illus. 2000. 32p. (J). (gr. 4-5). pap., wbk. ed. 2.99 (978-1-889319-67-4(8) , KidSparks) Trend Enterprises, Inc.

—Grade 5 Reading Skillbook. Engblom, Mark, illus. 2000. 32p. (J). (gr. 5-6). pap., wbk. ed. 2.99 (978-1-889319-69-8(4) , KidSparks) Trend Enterprises, Inc.

The Witch of Blackbird Pond: Response Journal. 2003. 36p. (YA). (978-1-58049-993-4(7) , RJ93) Prestwick Hse., Inc.

With Language Development Charts, 12 bks. 2002. (Chorus of Cultures Ser.). (gr. k-6). 270.83 (978-1-56334-408-4(4)); suppl. ed. 184.54 (978-1-56334-407-7(6)) Hampton-Brown Bks.

Wolf Tracks, 6 vols. (Book2WebTM Ser.). (gr. 4-8). 36.50 (978-0-322-02971-2(6)) Wright Group, The.

Wolfe, Patricia & Nevills, Pamela. Building the Reading Brain. 2004. (1-Off Ser.). (Illus.). 200p. (ps-3). 61.95 (978-0-7619-3903-0(2) , B39032C); pap. 27.95 (978-0-7619-3904-7(0) , B39032P) Corwin Pr.

Wonder World: Early Emergent - 1 Each of 10 Student Books: Level A. 41.95 (978-0-7802-8265-0(5)) Wright Group, The.

Wonder World: Early Emergent - 1 Each of 10 Student Books: Level B. 41.95 (978-0-7802-8266-7(3)) Wright Group, The.

Wonder World: Early Emergent - 1 Each of 10 Student Books: Level C. 41.95 (978-0-7802-8267-4(1)) Wright Group, The.

Wonder World: Early Emergent - 1 Each of 10 Student Books: Level D. 41.95 (978-0-7802-8268-1(X)) Wright Group, The.

Wonder World: Early Emergent - 1 Each of 19 Big Books: Levels A-N. 476.95 (978-0-7802-8530-9(1)) Wright Group, The.

Wonder World: Early Emergent - Complete Kit. (gr. k up). 353.50 (978-0-7802-9042-6(9)) Wright Group, The.

Wonder World: Early Fluency - 1 Each of 12 Student Books: Level K. 69.95 (978-0-7802-8275-9(2)) Wright Group, The.

Wonder World: Early Fluency - 1 Each of 12 Student Books: Level L. 69.95 (978-0-7802-8276-6(0)) Wright Group, The.

Wonder World: Early Fluency - 1 Each of 12 Student Books: Level M. 69.95 (978-0-7802-8277-3(9)) Wright Group, The.

Wonder World: Early Fluency - Complete Kit. (gr. 1-2). 540.95 (978-0-7802-9044-0(5)) Wright Group, The.

Wonder World: Fluency-1 Each of 10 Chapter Books: Level O. (gr. 2-3). 66.95 (978-0-7802-8279-7(5)) Wright Group, The.

Wonder World: Fluency-1 Each of 10 Chapter Books: Level P. (gr. 2-3). 66.95 (978-0-7802-8280-3(9)) Wright Group, The.

Wonder World: Fluency-1 Each of 10 Chapter Books: Level Q. (gr. 2-3). 66.95 (978-0-7802-8281-0(7)) Wright Group, The.

Wonder World: Fluency-1 Each of 10 Chapter Books: Level R. (gr. 2-3). 74.95 (978-0-7802-8282-7(5)) Wright Group, The.

Wonder World: Fluency-1 Each of 12 Student Books: Level N. 69.95 (978-0-7802-8278-0(7)) Wright Group, The.

Wonder World: Levels O-R. (gr. 2-3). 275.95 (978-0-7802-8283-4(3)) Wright Group, The.

Wonder World: Upper Emergent - 1 Each of 12 Student Books: Level E. 59.95 (978-0-7802-8269-8(8)) Wright Group, The.

Wonder World: Upper Emergent - 1 Each of 12 Student Books: Level F. 59.95 (978-0-7802-8270-4(1)) Wright Group, The.

Wonder World: Upper Emergent - 1 Each of 12 Student Books: Level G. 59.95 (978-0-7802-8271-1(X)) Wright Group, The.

Wonder World: Upper Emergent - Complete Kit. (gr. 1 up). 396.95 (978-0-7802-9043-3(7)) Wright Group, The.

Wonder World: Upper Emergent - Upper Emergent - Complete Kit, Vol. 2. (gr. 1 up). 396.95 (978-0-7802-9041-9(0)) Wright Group, The.

Wonder World: Upper Emergent-1 Each of 12 Student Books: Level H. 59.95 (978-0-7802-8272-8(8)) Wright Group, The.

Wonder World: Upper Emergent-1 Each of 12 Student Books: Level I. 59.95 (978-0-7802-8273-5(6)) Wright Group, The.

Wonder World: Upper Emergent-1 Each of 12 Student Books: Level J. 59.95 (978-0-7802-8274-2(4)) Wright Group, The.

Woodland Mysteries. (gr. 3-7). Set 1. 424.95 (978-0-7802-7245-3(5)); Set 2. 424.95 (978-0-7802-8002-1(4)); Set 3. 479.95 (978-0-322-02629-2(6)) Wright Group, The.

Woodland Mysteries: Classroom Library Set. (gr. 3-7). 313.95 (978-0-322-02628-5(8)) Wright Group, The.

Woodland Mysteries: Complete Boxed Set. (gr. 3-7). 1238.95 (978-0-322-02625-4(3)) Wright Group, The.

The Woodlanders Begin, 6 vols., Vol. 3. (Woodland Mysteriestm Ser.). 133p. (gr. 3-7). 42.50 (978-0-322-02368-0(8)) Wright Group, The.

Woods, Irons, & Greens: 6 Each of 1 Anthology, 6 vols. (Wildcats Ser.). 32p. (gr. 2-8). (978-0-322-00589-1(2)) Wright Group, The.

Word Work Assessment Guide. (Fasttrack Reading Ser.). (gr. 4-8). 29.50 (978-0-322-05948-1(8)) Wright Group, The.

World of Discovery, Set. (Illus.). (J). (ps-1). pap. 55.80 (978-1-57874-065-9(7)) Kaeden Corp.

A World Worth Keeping: Level T. Group 1, 6 vols. (Sunshinetm Ser.). 48p. 44.95 (978-0-7802-6092-4(9)) Wright Group, The.

The Wrecks: Level T. Group 2, 6 vols. (Sunshinetm Ser.). 48p. 44.95 (978-0-7802-4177-0(0)) Wright Group, The.

Wrestle Mania: Magazine Anthology: Level 5, 6 vols. (Comprehension Strand Ser.). (gr. 4-8). 54.00 (978-0-322-06036-4(2)) Wright Group, The.

Wright Group. Explorers: Early Fluency-Fluency - 1 Each of 11 Titles: Level P. 2002. pap. 121.28 (978-1-4045-0675-6(6)) Wright Group, The.

—Explorers: Early Fluency-Fluency - 1 Each of 14 Titles: Level O. 2002. pap. 154.28 (978-1-4045-0674-9(8)) Wright Group, The.

—Explorers: Early Fluency-Fluency - 1 Each of 3 Titles: Level N. 2002. pap. 33.08 (978-1-4045-0673-2(X)) Wright Group, The.

—Explorers: Early Fluency-Fluency - 1 Each of 8 Titles: Level Q. 2002. pap. 88.00 (978-1-4045-0676-3(4)) Wright Group, The.

—First Explorers: Upper Emergent-Early Fluency - 1 Each of 4 Student Books: Level H. 2002. pap. 29.32 (978-0-322-09961-6(7)) Wright Group, The.

—First Explorers: Upper Emergent-Early Fluency - 1 Each of 4 Student Books: Level J. 2002. pap. 29.32 (978-0-322-09963-0(3)) Wright Group, The.

—First Explorers: Upper Emergent-Early Fluency - 1 Each of 7 Student Books: Level I. 2002. pap. 51.36 (978-0-322-09962-3(5)) Wright Group, The.

—First Explorers: Upper Emergent-Early Fluency - 1 Each of 9 Student Books: Level K. 2002. pap. 77.20 (978-0-322-09964-7(1)) Wright Group, The.

—Wildcats Complete Kit. 2002. (Wildcatstm Ser.). (gr. 2-8). pap. 5015.08 (978-0-322-08422-3(9)) Wright Group, The.

The Wright Skills: Level B Sets - Long vowels only: 1 Each of 6 Titles. (gr. k-3). 17.95 (978-0-322-01934-8(6)) Wright Group, The.

The Wright Skills: Level B Sets - Long vowels only: 6 Each of 6 Titles. (gr. k-3). 109.50 (978-0-322-01935-5(4)) Wright Group, The.

The Wright Skills: Level C Sets - 1 Each of 16 Titles. (gr. k-3). 69.95 (978-0-322-00734-5(8)) Wright Group, The.

The Wright Skills: Level C Sets - 6 Each of 16 Titles. (gr. k-3). 322.95 (978-0-322-00813-7(1)) Wright Group, The.

A Writer's Work: Level N, 6 vols. (Wonder Worldtm Ser.). 48p. 34.95 (978-0-7802-2918-1(5)) Wright Group, The.

Y llego el Jazz! 9: Leveled Books. 2001. (McGraw-Hill. Lectura Ser.). (ENG & SPA.). (gr. 3 up). (978-0-02-188130-7(8)) Macmillan/McGraw-Hill Schl. Div.

Yates, Irene. How to Be a Wizard at Reading. 48p. (J). (gr. 2-6). pap. (978-1-875739-66-0(1)) Wizard Bks.

Yellow Umbrella Books - Science: Animal Ears; Everyone Is a Scientist; Food for Thought; How Things Move; Let's Make Butter; Looking at Ants; Models; Seasons; Stars; The Water Cycle; What Grows from a Tree?; What Hatches?, 12 bks. 2001. (Illus.). (J). (gr. 1). lib. bdg. 175.20 (978-0-7368-0755-5(1) , Pebble Bks.) Capstone Pr., Inc.

Yellow Umbrella Books - Social Studies: About 100 Years Ago; At School; Communities; Earth's Land & Water; Families; On the Go!; Our Favorite Things to Do; People & Places; People Work; Teamwork; What Is a Map?; Who Is a Friend?, 12 bks. 2001. (Illus.). (J). (gr. 1). lib. bdg. 175.20 (978-0-7368-0756-2(X) , Pebble Bks.) Capstone Pr., Inc.

Your Body up Close Little Book: Early Reading Fluency, Level C. 2004. pap. 6.00 (978-0-7398-8292-4(9)) Steck-Vaughn.

Zack Can Fix It! Vol. 4: Big Book. 2005. (Emergent Library: Vol. 1). (YA). (ps-1). 23.94 (978-0-8215-8919-9(9)) Sadlier, William H. Inc.

El zapato del Gorila 19: Leveled Books. 2001. (McGraw-Hill. Lectura Ser.). (ENG & SPA.). (gr. 1 up). (978-0-02-187948-9(6)) Macmillan/McGraw-Hill Schl. Div.

The Zebra's Yellow Van. (Little Book Practice Reader). (J). (978-0-8136-5374-7(6)) Modern Curriculum Pr.

Zeros & Ones, 6 vols. (Wildcats Ser.). 32p. (gr. 2-8). (978-0-322-02438-0(2)) Wright Group, The.

Zone Zoomers: Level 2, 6 vols. (Fluency Strand Ser.). (gr. 4-8). 45.00 (978-1-4045-1213-9(6)) Wright Group, The.

The Zoo: Big Book: Level B. (Wonder Worldtm Ser.). 16p. 26.50 (978-0-7802-2832-0(4)) Wright Group, The.

The Zoo: Level B, 6 vols. (Wonder Worldtm Ser.). 16p. 24.95 (978-0-7802-1058-5(1)) Wright Group, The.

Zumbrock, Kristin. MEville to WEville: Unit 1 ME, 2 books, manual and children's book. 2004. 292p. spiral bd. 75.00 (978-0-9666667-5-5(5)) AbleNet, Inc.

101 Things Every 1st Grader Should Know about Reading. 2005. 128p. (J). (978-1-4127-1146-3(0) , 7260800) Publications International, Ltd.

101 Things Every Kindergartner Should Know about Reading. 2005. 128p. (J). (978-1-4127-1147-0(9) , 7260900) Publications International, Ltd.

365 Reading Activities. 1999. (Homonyms, Phonics & Reading Activities Ser.: Vol. 4). (Illus.). 240p. (J). (gr. k-6). lib. bdg. 24.95 (978-1-56674-271-9(4)) Forest Hse. Publishing Co., Inc.

READING—FICTION

Amelia Bedelia. 2002. (Amelia Bedelia Ser.). (Illus.). (J). 11.91 (978-0-7587-5973-3(8)) Book Wholesalers, Inc.

American Girl Editorial Staff, ed. American Girls Trading Cards. 2002. (American Girls Collection Ser.). (Illus.). (J). 54.00 (978-1-58485-627-6(0) , D110) American Girl Publishing, Inc.

Auch, Mary Jane & Auch, Herm. Souperchicken. 2003. (Illus.). 32p. (J). (gr. k-3). reprint ed. pap. 6.95 (978-0-8234-1829-9(4)) Holiday Hse., Inc.

Baggette, Susan K. Jonathan Goes to the Library. Moriarty, William J., photos by. 1998. (Jonathan Adventures Ser.). (Illus.). 16p. (J). (ps-k). bds. 5.95 (978-0-9660172-3-6(4)) Brookfield Reader, Inc., The.

Baker, Alan. Little Rabbits' First Farm Book. 2003. (ps-2). lib. bdg. 14.10 (978-0-613-88144-9(3)) Tandem Library Bks.

Battersby, Alan R. East 43rd Street: Level 5. 2001. (English Readers Ser.). (Illus.). 96p. pap. 7.00 (978-0-521-78363-7(1)) Cambridge Univ. Pr.

Becky, the Backward Kid: Self Esteem for the Dyslexic Child. 2000. (Illus.). 13p. (J). (ps-3). pap. 8.95 (978-0-9675940-1-9(4)) Angelina-Win Productions.

Bender, Esther. Elisabeth & the Windmill. 2003. (Lemon Tree Ser.). 112p. (J). (gr. 3-7). pap. 6.99 (978-0-8361-9204-9(4)) Herald Pr.

Bertram, Debbie & Bloom, Susan. The Best Place to Read. Garland, Michael, illus. 2003. 32p. (J). (ps-1). 14.95 (978-0-375-82293-3(3) , Random Hse. Bks. for Young Readers) Random Hse. Children's Bks.

—The Best Time to Read. Garland, Michael, illus. 2005. 32p. (J). (ps-2). 14.95 (978-0-375-83025-9(1)); lib. bdg. 16.99 (978-0-375-93025-6(6)) Random Hse. Children's Bks. (Random Hse. Bks. for Young Readers).

Bloom, Susan & Bertram, Debbie. The Best Place to Read. Garland, Michael, illus. 2007. 32p. (J). (ps-3). pap. 6.99 (978-0-375-83757-9(4) , Dragonfly Bks.) Random Hse. Children's Bks.

Bogart, JoEllen. Tomas Aprende a Leer. Fernandez, Laura & Jacobson, Rick, illus. 1998. (SPA.). 40p. (J). (gr. 1-3). 13.56 (978-84-261-3066-2(6)) Juventud, Editorial ESP. *Dist:* Lectorum Pubns., Inc.

Brown, Marc. Arthur & the Race to Read. Brown, Marc, illus. 2001. (Arthur Good Sports Ser.: Bk. 1). (Illus.). 64p. (J). (gr. 2-4). pap. 4.25 (978-0-316-12024-1(3)) Little, Brown Bks. for Young Readers.

Browne, Anthony. I Like Books. Browne, Anthony, illus. 2004. (Super Sturdy Picture Books Ser.). (Illus.). 24p. (J). (gr. k). 8.99 (978-0-7636-2162-9(5)) Candlewick Pr.

Budgell, Gill & Ruttle, Kate. Crows on a Wall. 2001. (Cambridge Reading Ser.). (Illus.). 8p. pap. 5.00 (978-0-521-00218-9(4)) Cambridge Univ. Pr.

—Eight Fat Sausages. 2001. (Cambridge Reading Ser.). (Illus.). 8p. pap. 5.00 (978-0-521-00199-1(4)) Cambridge Univ. Pr.

—Roll Over! 2001. (Cambridge Reading Ser.). (Illus.). 8p. pap. 5.00 (978-0-521-00214-1(1)) Cambridge Univ. Pr.

Chase, Diana. Surf's Up. 1999. 200p. (J). pap. 12.95 (978-1-86368-250-3(3)) Fremantle Pr. AUS. *Dist:* International Specialized Bk. Services.

Citra, Becky. Freezing Moon. 2001. (gr. 3-6). lib. bdg. 13.00 (978-0-613-88905-6(3)) Tandem Library Bks.

Comino, Sandra. La Casita Azul. Zeller, Beatriz, tr. (SPA.). 128p. (J). 2004. pap. 6.95 (978-0-88899-540-7(7)); 2003. (Illus.). 15.95 (978-0-88899-504-9(0)) Groundwood Bks. CAN. *Dist:* Perseus Distribution.

—The Little Blue House. Zeller, Beatriz, tr. from SPA. 2004. 128p. (J). pap. 6.95 (978-0-88899-541-4(5) , Libros Tigrillo) Groundwood Bks. CAN. *Dist:* Perseus Distribution.

—The Little Blue House. Zeller, Beatriz & Wald, Susana, trs. from SPA. 2003. (Illus.). 128p. (J). (gr. 4-7). 15.95 (978-0-88899-503-2(2)) Groundwood Bks. CAN. *Dist:* Perseus Distribution.

Coulton, Mia. Danny & Heather Share. Coulton, Mia, photos by. 2003. (Illus.). 16p. (J). 4.95 (978-0-9720295-8-2(3)) Maryruth Bks., Inc.

Creasy, Mary-Anne. Great Sebastian. 2001. (gr. k-3). lib. bdg. 11.80 (978-0-613-33374-0(8)) Tandem Library Bks.

—Sebastian Tidies Up. 2001. (gr. k-3). lib. bdg. 11.65 (978-0-613-33426-6(4)) Tandem Library Bks.

Cuyler, Margery. Reading Worries. Howard, Arthur, illus. 2008. (J). (***978-0-689-86188-8(5)*** , Simon & Schuster Children's Publishing) Simon & Schuster Children's Publishing.

Dail, Maggie. Getting to First Base - Chris Struggles to Read. 2006. 157p. pap. 13.95 (978-1-4116-8125-5(8)) Lulu.com.

Daly, Niki. Once upon a Time. Daly, Niki, illus. 2003. (Illus.). 32p. (J). (gr. k-3). 16.00 (978-0-374-35633-0(5) , Farrar, Straus & Giroux (BYR)) Farrar, Straus & Giroux.

Damschroder, Scott. Pinky's Rainy Day: Pinky Padooka takes a trip to Imaginationville. Faust, Laurie, illus. 2004. 36p. (J). lib. bdg. 19.95 (978-0-9754728-0-4(1)) MidAmerica Publishing Co.

Danziger, Paula. It's a Fair Day, Amber Brown. Ross, Tony, illus. 2003. (Readalongs for Beginning Readers Ser.). (J). 25.95 incl. audio (978-1-59112-246-3(5)); pap. 16.95 incl. audio (978-1-59112-245-6(7)); pap. 29.95 incl. audio (978-1-59112-247-0(3)); pap. 18.95 incl. audio compact disk (978-1-59112-362-0(3)) Live Oak Media.

Duchesne, Christiane. Kiss for Peter. 2000. (gr. k-3). lib. bdg. 14.10 (978-0-613-25893-7(2)) Tandem Library Bks.

Feely, Jenny. Looking after Their Young. 2001. (gr. k-3). lib. bdg. 11.65 (978-0-613-33389-4(6)) Tandem Library Bks.

Flanagan, Alice K. Blast Off! The Sound of Bl. 2004. (Phonics Readers Ser.). 24p. (J). (ps-3). 21.36 (978-1-59296-154-2(1)) Child's World, Inc.

—Class Clown: The Sound of CL. 2004. (Phonics Readers Ser.). 24p. (J). (ps-3). 21.36 (978-1-59296-155-9(X)) Child's World, Inc.

—I Am Glad: The Sound of Gl. 2004. (Phonics Readers Ser.). 24p. (J). (ps-3). 21.36 (978-1-59296-157-3(6)) Child's World, Inc.

—My Flower Garden: The Sound of FL. 2004. (Phonics Readers Ser.). 24p. (J). (ps-3). 21.36 (978-1-59296-156-6(8)) Child's World, Inc.

—Say Please! The Sound of PL. 2004. (Phonics Readers Ser.). 24p. (J). (ps-3). 21.36 (978-1-59296-158-0(4)) Child's World, Inc.

Gago, Jenny & McKay, Sindy. We Both Read-the Perfect Gift. Harden, Laurie, illus. 2001. (We Both Read Ser.). (ENG & SPA.). 44p. (J). (gr. 1-2). 7.99 (978-1-891327-33-9(X)) Treasure Bay, Inc.

Gaydos, Nora. Playful Pals. Sams, B. B., illus. 2003. (Now I'm Reading!Tm Beginning Reader Ser.). 128p. (J). (ps-2). 16.99 (978-1-58476-203-4(9)); Level 1. 14.99 (978-1-58476-243-0(8)) Innovative Kids.

Giff, Patricia Reilly. Eleven. 2008. 144p. (J). (***978-0-385-73069-3(1)*** , Delacorte Pr.) Dell Publishing.

—Eleven. 2008. 176p. (J). (gr. 3-8). lib. bdg. 18.99 (***978-0-385-90098-0(8)*** , Lamb, Wendy) Random Hse. Children's Bks.

Gikow, Louise. I Can Read. Patience, John, illus. 2004. (My First Reader Ser.). 31p. (J). 18.50 (978-0-516-24678-9(X) , Children's Pr.) Scholastic Library Publishing.

Grosset & Dunlap Inc. Staff, Inc. Away We Go. 2004. (gr. k-3). lib. bdg. 11.80 (978-0-613-72506-4(9)) Tandem Library Bks.

—Who Can Help? 2004. (gr. k-3). lib. bdg. 11.80 (978-0-613-72507-1(7)) Tandem Library Bks.

Gruber, Wilhelm. The Upside-Down Reader. 2000. (Illus.). (978-0-606-18325-3(6)) Tandem Library Bks.

Hall, Fiona. The Birth of Finney. Bundick, Theresa Jane, illus. 2001. 32p. (J). lib. bdg. 12.95 (978-0-9673907-1-0(0) , Kasdan Publishing) Kasdan Communications.

Hall, Patricia. Hooray for Reading! Mitter, Kathryn, illus. 2005. (Ready-to-Read Ser. Level 1). 32p. (J). lib. bdg. 15.00 (978-1-59054-927-8(9)) Fitzgerald Bks.

—Hooray for Reading! Mitter, Kathryn, illus. 2002. (Classic Raggedy Ann & Andy Ser.). 32p. (J). (ps-3). pap. 3.99 (978-0-689-85178-0(2) , Little Simon) Simon & Schuster Children's Publishing.

—Hooray for Reading! 2002. (ps-2). lib. bdg. 11.80 (978-0-613-45064-5(7)) Tandem Library Bks.

Harcourt School Publishers Staff. A Drummer's Dream Below Level. 3rd ed. 2002. (Trophies Reading Program Ser.). (Illus.). pap. 5.10 (978-0-15-323333-3(8)) Harcourt Schl. Pubs.

—A Garden Grows On Level. 3rd ed. 2002. (Trophies Reading Program Ser.). (Illus.). (gr. 4). pap. 5.10 (978-0-15-323251-0(X)) Harcourt Schl. Pubs.

—A Gold Rush Diary Below Level. 3rd ed. 2002. (Trophies Reading Program Ser.). (Illus.). pap. 5.10 (978-0-15-323153-7(X)) Harcourt Schl. Pubs.

—Jake Can Read: Take-Home Book. 1999. (Collections Ser.). (Illus.). (J). (gr. 2). pap. 1.90 (978-0-15-317218-2(5)) Harcourt Schl. Pubs.

—Look at Me! 3rd ed. 2002. (Trophies English Language Learners Ser.). (Illus.). (J). (gr. 1). pap. 3.20 (978-0-15-327562-3(6)) Harcourt Schl. Pubs.

Hardinge, Frances. Fly by Night. 2006. 496p. (J). (gr. 5-9). 16.99 (978-0-06-087627-2(1)) HarperCollins Pubs.

Hoban, Lillian. Arthur's Prize Reader. Hoban, Lillian, illus. 2002. (Arthur the Chimpanzee Ser.). (Illus.). (J). 12.30 (978-0-7587-5554-4(6)) Book Wholesalers, Inc.

I Can Read Classroom in a Box Level 1. 2007. (I Can Read Bks.). (J). 460.00 (***978-0-06-137567-5(5)*** , Harper Trophy) HarperCollins Pubs.

I Can Read Classroom in a Box Level 3. 2007. (I Can Read Bks.). (J). 460.00 (***978-0-06-137570-5(5)*** , Harper Trophy) HarperCollins Pubs.

Jacobson, Jennifer Richard. Winnie at Her Best. Geis, Alissa Imre, illus. 2006. 96p. (J). (gr. 3-5). 15.00 (978-0-618-47277-2(0)) Houghton Mifflin Co.

Klingel, Cynthia Fitterer & Noyed, Robert B. Ezra & the Letter E. 2003. (Alphaphonics Ser.). (Illus.). 24p. (J). (ps-2). 21.36 (978-1-59296-095-8(2)) Child's World, Inc.

LeapFrog Staff, compiled by. Wind in the Willows. (J). 2002. (gr. 3-7). 14.95 (978-1-58605-915-6(7) , LeapFrog Schl. Hse.); 2001. spiral bd. 14.99 (978-1-58605-047-4(8)) LeapFrog Enterprises, Inc.

—Wizard of Oz. 2002. (J). (gr. 3-7). 14.95 (978-1-58605-921-7(1) , LeapFrog Schl. Hse.) LeapFrog Enterprises, Inc.

Lee, Quinlan B. Sail Away. 2005. (Illus.). (J). (***978-0-439-77933-3(2)***) Scholastic, Inc.

Leonard, Marie. Tibili: The Little Boy Who Didn't Want to Go to School. Prigent, Andree, illus. 2002. 36p. (J). (ps-2). 15.95 (978-1-929132-20-1(4)) Kane/Miller Bk. Pubs., Inc.

Mayer, Mercer. Play It Safe. 2004. lib. bdg. 11.80 (978-0-613-88739-7(5)) Tandem Library Bks.

Minden-Cupp, Cecilia. D—Title Tk. 2004. (Phonics Friends Ser.). 24p. (J). (ps). 21.36 (978-1-59296-292-1(0)) Child's World, Inc.

—Erin & Her New Pet: The Sound of Short E. 2005. (Phonics Friends Ser.). (Illus.). 24p. (J). (ps). 21.36 (978-1-59296-313-3(7)) Child's World, Inc.

—Holly & Hank's Snow Holiday: The Sound of H. 2004. (Phonics Friends Ser.). (Illus.). 24p. (J). (ps). 21.36 (978-1-59296-296-9(3)) Child's World, Inc.

Mitton, Tony. Billy Bear & the Pear Tree Fairy. Vagnozzi, Barbara, illus. 2001. (Cambridge Reading Ser.). 16p. pap., stu. ed. 8.00 (978-0-521-01423-6(9)) Cambridge Univ. Pr.

—Charlie Chimpanzee. Chatterton, Martin, illus. 2001. (Cambridge Reading Ser.). 16p. pap., stu. ed. 6.00 (978-0-521-01413-7(1)) Cambridge Univ. Pr.

—The Haunted House. Beer, Tim, illus. 2001. (Cambridge Reading Ser.). 16p. pap., stu. ed. 8.00 (978-0-521-01425-0(5)) Cambridge Univ. Pr.

—The Junk Robot. Williams, Lisa, illus. 2001. (Cambridge Reading Ser.). 16p. pap. 6.00 (978-0-521-01405-2(0)) Cambridge Univ. Pr.

Moncure, Jane Belk. Word Bird's Magic Wand. 2002. (New Word Bird Library). (Illus.). 32p. (J). (ps-3). 22.79 (978-1-56766-630-4(2)) Child's World, Inc.

Nez, John A., illus. One Smart Cookie. 2006. 32p. (J). lib. bdg. 15.95 (978-0-8075-6099-0(5)) Whitman, Albert & Co.

Parsons, Corey. I Can Read. 2005. 29p. (J). 9.98 (978-1-4116-6101-1(X)) Lulu.com.

Paslay, Christopher. The Eisenhower Quarantine. 2002. (gr. 7-12). lib. bdg. 31.55 (978-0-613-77557-1(0)) Tandem Library Bks.

Paterson, Katherine. Marvin One Too Many. Brown, Jane Clark, illus. 2002. (J). 23.98 (978-0-7587-6904-6(0)) Book Wholesalers, Inc.

—Marvin One Too Many. Clark Brown, Jane, illus. 2003. 25.95 incl. audio (978-1-59112-254-8(6)); 28.95 incl. audio compact disk (978-1-59112-635-5(5)); pap. 18.95 incl. audio compact disk (978-1-59112-634-8(7)); pap. 31.95 incl. audio compact disk (978-1-59112-636-2(3)); (J). pap. 29.95 incl. audio (978-1-59112-255-5(4)); (J). pap. 16.95 incl. audio (978-1-59112-253-1(8)) Live Oak Media.

Paul, Sherry. Finn the Foolish Fish: Trouble with Bubbles, Set. Miller, Bob, illus. (See How I Read Ser.). 32p. (Orig.). (J). (ps-2). pap. 14.10 (978-0-675-01084-9(5)) CPI Publishing, Inc.

—Two-B & the Rock 'n' Roll Band, Set. Murphy, Bob, illus. (See How I Read Ser.). 32p. (Orig.). (J). (ps-2). pap. 14.10 (978-0-675-01082-5(9)) CPI Publishing, Inc.

Polacco, Patricia. Gracias, Senor Falker. Mlawer, Teresa, tr. from ENG. 2001. (SPA., Illus.). (J). (gr. 1-3). lib. bdg. 17.00 (978-1-930332-03-4(3) , LC30185) Lectorum Pubns., Inc.

—Thank You, Mr. Falker. 1998. (Illus.). 40p. (J). (gr. k-4). 16.99 (978-0-399-23166-7(8) , Philomel) Penguin Group (USA) Inc.

Rahaman, Vashanti. Read for Me, Mama. McElrath-Eslick, Lori, illus. 2003. 32p. (J). (gr. 2-4). 15.95 (978-1-56397-313-0(8)) Boyds Mills Pr.

Reed, Hannah. Hot Air Balloon. 2001. (gr. k-3). lib. bdg. 11.80 (978-0-613-33378-8(0)) Tandem Library Bks.

Rider, Cynthia. Peacock's New Name. Ellis, Louise, illus. 2001. (Cambridge Reading Ser.). 16p. pap., stu. ed. 8.00 (978-0-521-01433-5(6)) Cambridge Univ. Pr.

—A Star in a Marmalade Jar. Warburton, Sarah, illus. 2001. (Cambridge Reading Ser.). 16p. pap., stu. ed. 8.00 (978-0-521-01417-5(4)) Cambridge Univ. Pr.

Shearer, Cyndy. The Greenleaf Guide to Ancient Literature. 2001. (Orig.). per. 18.95 (978-1-882514-30-4(0)) Greenleaf Pr.

Shore, Diane Z. Rosa Loves to Read. Day, Larry, illus. 2004. (Rookie Reader Skill Set Ser.). 32p. (J). (gr. k-2). pap. 4.95 (978-0-516-25825-6(7) , Children's Pr.) Scholastic Library Publishing.

Sierra, Judy. Born to Read. Brown, Marc, illus. 2008. (J). ***978-0-375-84687-8(5));** lib. bdg. ***978-0-375-94687-5(X))** Knopf, Alfred A. Inc.

Steck-Vaughn Staff. Pair-It Fiction Transition Stage, Set. 2002. (Illus.). pap. (978-0-7398-7623-7(6)) Steck-Vaughn.

—Pair-It Fiction Collection. 2002. (Illus.). (J). (gr. k). pap. (978-0-7398-7803-3(4)); (gr. 1). pap. (978-0-7398-7804-0(2)); (gr. 2). pap. (978-0-7398-7805-7(0)) Steck-Vaughn.

Studio Mouse, ed. Play, Laugh, & Learn All Year Long. 2007. (Illus.). 28p. 16.99 incl. audio compact disk (978-1-59069-503-6(8) , 1P1000) Studio Mouse LLC.

Ten Book Summer. 2002. (Illus.). (J). pap. (978-0-7398-5106-7(3)) Steck-Vaughn.

Toles-Stotts, LaShunda. When I Learned to Read. Stotts, Jasmyn & Jayda, illus. l.t. ed. 2005. 36p. (J). per. 11.99 (978-1-59879-071-9(4)) Lifevest Publishing, Inc.

Various Authors. Boxes, Bears & Bubbles Mixed, 6 vols., Pack. 2001. (Cambridge Storybooks Ser.). (Illus.). 8p. pap. 16.00 (978-0-521-00814-3(X)) Cambridge Univ. Pr.

Vaughan, Marcia. Up the Learning Tree. Blanks, Derek, illus. 2003. 32p. (J). 16.96 (978-1-58430-049-6(3)) Lee & Low Bks., Inc.

Walker, Fred. Lines. 2000. (gr. k-3). lib. bdg. 11.80 (978-0-613-29674-8(5)) Tandem Library Bks.

Walker, Kate. I Hate Books. Cox, David, illus. 2007. 88p. (J). 16.95 (978-0-8126-2745-9(8)) Cricket Bks.

Walter, Mildred Pitts. Alec's Primer. Johnson, Larry, illus. 2005. (Family Heritage Ser.). 36p. (J). 15.95 (978-0-916718-20-6(4)) Vermont Folklife Ctr.

Wang, Adria. My World: My Busy Day. Nicholls, Paul, illus. 2005. 10p. (J). 4.95 (978-1-58117-251-5(6) , Intervisual/Piggy Toes) Dalmatian Pr.

Wells, Rosemary. Read Me a Story. Wheeler, Jody & Nez, John, illus. 2002. (Yoko & Friends School Days Ser.: Bk. 8). 32p. (gr. k-2). pap. 3.99 (978-0-7868-1533-3(7) , Volo) Hyperion Bks. for Children.

—Read Me a Story. 2002. (gr. k-3). lib. bdg. 11.80 (978-0-613-61121-3(7)) Tandem Library Bks.

Williams, Suzanne. Library Lil. Kellogg, Steven, illus. 2001. 32p. (J). (ps-3). pap. 6.99 (978-0-14-056837-0(9) , Puffin) Penguin Group (USA) Inc.

—Library Lil. 2001. (ps-2). lib. bdg. 15.30 (978-0-613-35971-9(2)); (Illus.). (J). (978-0-606-21293-9(0)) Tandem Library Bks.

Wishinsky, Frieda. Give Maggie a Chance. Griffiths, Dean, illus. 2002. 32p. (J). (gr. 1-3). (978-1-55041-682-4(0)) Fitzhenry & Whiteside, Ltd.

READING—REMEDIAL TEACHING

Hooked on Phonics Staff. Hooked on English. 2007. 199.99 ***978-1-60143-752-5(8))** HOP, LLC.

Spilsbury, Louise & Spilsbury, Richard. Super-Flea & Other Animal Champions: Structure of Living Things. 2005. (Illus.). 32p. (J). (978-1-4109-1968-7(4)); lib. bdg. (978-1-4109-1937-3(4)) Steck-Vaughn.

READING—STUDY AND TEACHING

see Reading

READING CLINICS

see Reading—Remedial Teaching

READING INTERESTS

see Books and Reading

READING INTERESTS OF CHILDREN

see Children—Books and Reading

REAGAN, RONALD, 1911-2004

Ashby, Ruth. Ronald & Nancy Reagan. 2004. (Illus.). 48p. (J). pap. 11.95 (978-0-8368-5702-3(X)); lib. bdg. 30.00 (978-0-8368-5696-5(1)) Stevens, Gareth Inc. (World Almanac Library).

Benson, Michael. Ronald Reagan. 2004. (Presidential Leaders Ser.). (Illus.). 112p. (J). 29.27 (978-0-8225-0815-1(X) , Lerner Pubns.) Lerner Publishing Group.

Camardella, Michele L. America in The 1980s. 2005. (Decades of American History Ser.). (Illus.). 128p. (J). (gr. 4-9). per. 35.00 (978-0-8160-5644-6(7)) Facts On File, Inc.

Dohery, Kieran. Ronald Reagan. 2005. (Encyc of Presidents, 2ND Ser.). (Illus.). 112p. (J). (gr. 6-8). 34.00 (978-0-516-22979-9(6) , Watts, Franklin) Scholastic Library Publishing.

Dunham, Montrew. Ronald Reagan: Young Leader. Henderson, Meryl, illus. 1999. (Childhood of Famous Americans Ser.). 192p. (J). (gr. 3-7). pap. 5.99 (978-0-689-83006-8(8) , Aladdin) Simon & Schuster Children's Publishing.

—Ronald Reagan: Young Politician. 1999. (Childhood of Famous Americans Ser.). (978-0-606-17512-8(1)); (gr. 3-6). lib. bdg. 13.00 (978-0-613-22280-8(6)) Tandem Library Bks.

Hinkle, Donald. Ronald Reagan: A MyReportLinks.com Book. 2003. (Presidents Ser.). (Illus.). 48p. (J). (gr. 4-10). lib. bdg. 25.26 (978-0-7660-5112-6(9) , MyReportLinks.com Bks.) Enslow Pubs., Inc.

Johnson, Darv. The Reagan Years. 1999. (World History Ser.). (Illus.). 111p. (YA). (gr. 8-11). 27.45 (978-1-56006-592-0(3) , LML00902-177947, Lucent Bks.) Thomson Gale.

Joseph, Paul. Ronald Reagan. 1999. (United States Presidents Ser.). (Illus.). 32p. (J). (gr. k-6). lib. bdg. 22.78 (978-1-56239-815-6(6) , Checkerboard Library) ABDO Publishing Co.

Klingel, Cynthia Fitterer & Noyed, Robert B. Ronald Reagan: Our Fortieth President. 2001. (Spirit of America: Our Presidents Ser.). (Illus.). 48p. (J). (gr. 2-6). 28.50 (978-1-56766-874-2(7)) Child's World, Inc.

Mara, Wil. Ronald Reagan. 32p. (J). 2006. (gr. 1-2). pap. 4.95 (978-0-516-25482-1(0)); 2005. 20.50 (978-0-516-25271-1(2)) Scholastic Library Publishing. (Children's Pr.).

Margaret, Amy. Ronald Reagan Presidential Library. 2004. (Presidential Libraries Ser.). (Illus.). 24p. (J). lib. bdg. 18.75 (978-0-8239-6272-3(5) , PowerKids Pr.) Rosen Publishing Group, Inc., The.

Marsh, Carole. Ronald Reagan. 2002. (One Thousand Readers Ser.). (Illus.). 12p. (J). (gr. k-4). 2.95 (978-0-635-01555-6(2) , 15552) Gallopade International.

Mattern, Joanne. Nancy Reagan. 2007. (First Ladies Ser.). (Illus.). 32p. (J). (gr. k-6). lib. bdg. 24.21 ***978-1-59928-799-7(4)** , Checkerboard Library) ABDO Publishing Co.

Milton, Joyce. Who Was Ronald Reagan? Wolf, Elizabeth & Harrison, Nancy, illus. 2004. (Who Was... ? Ser.). 112p. (J). pap. 4.99 (978-0-448-43344-8(3) , Grosset & Dunlap) Penguin Group (USA) Inc.

—Who Was Ronald Reagan? Harrison, Nancy & Wolf, Elizabeth, illus. 2004. (Who Was... ? Ser.). 112p. (J). (gr. 3-7). lib. bdg. 13.89 (978-0-448-43345-5(1) , Grosset & Dunlap) Penguin Group (USA) Inc.

—Who Was Ronald Reagan? Wolf, Elizabeth, illus. 2005. 106p. (J). (gr. 2-6). lib. bdg. 12.19 (978-0-606-33099-2(2)) Tandem Library Bks.

Mis, Melody S. How to Draw the Life & Times of Ronald Reagan. 2007. (Kid's Guide to Drawing the Presidents of the United States of America Ser.). (Illus.). 32p. (J). 25.25 (978-1-4042-3016-3(5) , PowerKids Pr.) Rosen Publishing Group, Inc., The.

Orr, Tamra. Ronald Reagan. 2003. (Childhoods of the Presidents Ser.). (Illus.). 48p. (J). (gr. 4 up). lib. bdg. (978-1-59084-280-5(4)) Mason Crest Pubs.

—Ronald Reagan: Portrait of an American Hero. 2003. (Illus.). 96p. (978-0-7853-9734-2(5) , 3126701) Publications International, Ltd.

Patrick, Denise Lewis. Ronald Reagan from Silver Screen to Oval Office. 2006. 44p. (J). lib. bdg. 15.00 ***978-1-4242-0852-4(1))** Fitzgerald Bks.

Pingry, Patricia A. The Story of Ronald Reagan. 2006. (Illus.). 26p. (J). bds. 6.95 (978-0-8249-6621-8(X) , Candy Cane Pr.) Ideals Pubns.

Ronald Reagan. annual Date not set. (Starlog Movie Ser.). (YA). pap. (978-0-934551-04-5(9)) Profile Entertainment, Inc.

Time for Kids Editors. Ronald Reagan: From Silver Screen to Oval Office. 2006. (Time for Kids Ser.). (Illus.). 48p. (J). 14.99 (978-0-06-057627-1(8)); pap. 3.99 (978-0-06-057626-4(X)) HarperCollins Pubs.

Venezia, Mike. Ronald Reagan. (Getting to Know the U. S. Presidents Ser.). 32p. (J). 2008. pap. 7.95 ***978-0-516-26720-3(5));** 2007. 28.00 ***978-0-516-22644-6(4))** Scholastic Library Publishing. (Children's Pr.).

Wagner, Heather Lehr. Ronald Reagan. (Great American Presidents Ser.). (Illus.). (gr. 4-8). 2004. 112p. pap. 30.00 (978-0-7910-7779-5(9)); 2003. 100p. 30.00 (978-0-7910-7604-0(0)) Facts On File, Inc. (Chelsea Hse.).

Williams, Jean Kinney. Ronald W. Reagan. 2003. (Profiles of the Presidents Ser.). (Illus.). 64p. (J). (gr. 4 up). lib. bdg. 23.93 (978-0-7565-0284-3(5)) Compass Point Bks.

Young, Jeff C. Great Communicator: The Story of Ronald Reagan. 2004. (Twentieth Century Leaders Ser.). (Illus.). 128p. (YA). (gr. 6-12). 23.95 (978-1-931798-10-5(9)) Reynolds, Morgan Inc.

REAL ESTATE

see Real Property

REAL ESTATE BUSINESS

Aaseng, Nathan. Business Builders in Real Estate. 2002. (Business Builders Ser.: Vol. 4). (Illus.). 160p. (gr. 5 up). lib. bdg. 22.95 (978-1-881508-79-3(X)) Oliver Pr., Inc.

Clark, Betty. Choosing a Career in Real Estate. 2005. (World of Work Ser.). (Illus.). 64p. (YA). (gr. 7-12). lib. bdg. 25.25 (978-0-8239-3246-7(X) , WWREES) Rosen Publishing Group, Inc., The.

REAL PROPERTY

Here are entered general works on real property in the legal sense i.e., ownership of land and buildings (immovable property) as opposed to personal property. Works limited to the buying and selling of real property are entered under Real Estate Business. General works on land without the ownership aspect are entered under Land Ue.

see also Farms; Real Estate Business

Aaseng, Nathan. Business Builders in Real Estate. 2002. (Business Builders Ser.: Vol. 4). (Illus.). 160p. (gr. 5 up). lib. bdg. 22.95 (978-1-881508-79-3(X)) Oliver Pr., Inc.

Boye, B. D. Our New Home. Boye, B. D., illus. l.t. ed. 2005. (Illus.). 18p. (J). per. 4.99 (978-0-9768078-2-7(3)) Innerchild Publishing, Inc.

Thornton, Jewell. A Kids Journey to Being Rich. 2006. 12p. (J). 15.08 (978-1-4116-8618-2(7)) Lulu.com.

Troisi-Paton, Kimberly. Freedom from Unfair Seizure of Property. 2006. (Illus.). 128p. (gr. 10-12). 33.70 (978-0-7377-3543-7(0) , Greenhaven Pr., Inc.) Thomson Gale.

Wooten, Sara McIntosh. Donald Trump: From Real Estate to Reality TV. 2008. (J). ***978-0-7660-2890-6(9))** Enslow Pubs., Inc.

REALTY

see Real Property

REASONING

see also Intellect; Logic

Activities for Mastering Inferences. 2000. 76p. per. 27.00 (978-1-886143-49-4(8)) Great Ideas for Teaching, Inc.

Beck, Esther. You'll Cause a Stir When You Infer! 2007. (Illus.). 24p. (J). pap. ***978-1-59928-627-3(0))** ABDO Publishing Co.

Berry, Joy Wilt. Saying No. Smith, Maggie, illus. 2001. (J). (978-0-439-34150-9(7)) Scholastic, Inc.

Bowers, Linda, et al. No Glamour Language & Reasoning. 2003. (J). per. 41.95 (978-0-7606-0500-4(9)) LinguiSystems, Inc.

Brown, Robin. Practice Papers: Advanced Non-Verbal Reasoning. 2nd ed. (Illus.). 32p. (YA). pap. 6.99 (978-0-340-72686-0(5) , Hodder & Stoughton) Hodder General Publishing Division GBR. *Dist:* Trafalgar Square Publishing.

Carr, Mary. More One Hour Mysteries. 2005. 64p. 11.95 (978-1-59363-109-3(X)) Prufrock Pr.

Combining Categories, Inferences & Context Clues. 2000. 62p. spiral bd. 26.00 (978-1-886143-50-0(1)) Great Ideas for Teaching, Inc.

Developing Logical Reasoning. 1999. 70p. per. 25.50 (978-1-886143-45-6(5)) Great Ideas for Teaching, Inc.

Doudna, Kelly. You'll Cause a Stir When You Infer. 2007. (Illus.). 24p. (J). 19.93 (978-1-59928-626-6(2) , Sand-Castle) ABDO Publishing Co.

Facione, Peter A. & Blohm, Stephen W. Test of Everyday Reasoning & User's Manual. 2001. 30p. pap. (978-1-891557-75-0(0)) California Academic Pr. LLC, The.

Gillham, Bill, et al. Essential Skills, 4 bks. (Illus.). 128p. (YA). pap. 15.99 (978-0-340-71583-3(9) , Hodder & Stoughton) Hodder General Publishing Division GBR. *Dist:* Trafalgar Square Publishing.

REBUSES

see Riddles

RECLAMATION OF LAND—FICTION

Ward, Helen. The Tin Forest. Anderson, Wayne, illus. 2001. 32p. (J). (gr. 1-5). 15.99 (978-0-525-46787-8(4) , Dutton Juvenile) Penguin Group (USA) Inc.

—The Tin Forest. Anderson, Wayne, illus. 2003. 32p. (J). (gr. k-4). pap. 7.99 (978-0-14-250156-6(5) , Puffin) Penguin Group (USA) Inc.

RECOMMENDED BOOKS

see Best Books

RECONSTRUCTION (U.S. HISTORY, 1865-1877)

Here are entered works dealing with reconstruction in the United States following the Civil War.

Anderson, Dale. The Aftermath of the Civil War. 2004. (World Almanac Library of the Civil War). (Illus.). 48p. (J). (gr. 5 up). pap. 11.95 (978-0-8368-5597-5(3)); lib. bdg. 30.00 (978-0-8368-5588-3(4)) Stevens, Gareth Inc. (World Almanac Library).

—World Almanac Library of the Civil War, 8 bks. Incl. Aftermath of the Civil War. (gr. 5 up). lib. bdg. 30.00 (978-0-8368-5588-3(4)); Causes of the Civil War. (gr. 5 up). lib. bdg. 30.00 (978-0-8368-5581-4(7)); Civil War at Sea. (gr. 5 up). lib. bdg. 30.00 (978-0-8368-5585-2(X)); Civil War in the East (1861-July 1863) (gr. 5 up). lib. bdg. 30.00 (978-0-8368-5582-1(5)); Civil War in the West (1861-July 1863) (gr. 5 up). lib. bdg. 30.00 (978-0-8368-5583-8(3)); Home Fronts in the Civil War. lib. bdg. 30.00 (978-0-8368-5587-6(6)); Soldier's Life in the Civil War. (gr. 5 up). lib. bdg. 30.00 (978-0-8368-5586-9(8)); Union Victory (July 1863-1865) (gr. 5 up). lib. bdg. 30.00 (978-0-8368-5584-5(1)); 48p. (J). (Illus.). 2004. Set lib. bdg. 240.00 (978-0-8368-5580-7(9) , World Almanac Library) Stevens, Gareth Inc.

Barney, William L. The Civil War & Reconstruction: A Student Companion. 2001. (Student Companions to American History Ser.). (Illus.). 368p. (YA). (gr. 7 up). 60.00 (978-0-19-511559-8(7)) Oxford Univ. Pr., Inc.

Burgan, Michael. The Reconstruction Amendments. 2006. (Illus.). 48p. (J). (gr. 4-6). 23.93 (978-0-7565-1636-9(6)) Compass Point Bks.

Center for Learning Network Staff. Civil War & Reconstruction: 1860-1877 — Elementary U. S. History Series — Teacher Guide. 2001. (Social Studies Ser.). 135p. (J). tchr. ed., spiral bd. 29.95 (978-1-56077-680-2(3)) Ctr. for Learning, The.

Collier, Christopher & Collier, James Lincoln. Reconstruction & the Rise of Jim Crow: 1864-1896. 1999. (Drama of American History Ser.). (Illus.). 96p. (YA). (gr. 5-9). lib. bdg. 31.36 (978-0-7614-0819-2(3) , Benchmark Bks.) Cavendish, Marshall Corp.

Cosson, Jody. Civil War & Reconstruction. 2007. (J). ***978-1-59036-743-8(X)); *978-1-59036-744-5(8))** Weigl Pubs., Inc.

Creative Media Applications. Beginning a New Life: African Americans During Reconstruction. 2006. (Slavery in the Americas Ser.). (Illus.). 112p. (J). (gr. 4-9). 35.00 (978-0-8160-6139-6(4)) Facts On File, Inc.

Dudley, William, ed. Reconstruction. 2002. (At Issue in History Ser.). (Illus.). 128p. (YA). (gr. 7-10). pap. 23.70 (978-0-7377-1357-2(7)); lib. bdg. 33.70 (978-0-7377-1356-5(9)) Thomson Gale. (Greenhaven Pr., Inc.).

Flanagan, Timothy. Reconstruction: A Primary Source History of the Struggle to Unite the North & South after the Civil War. 2005. (Illus.). 64p. (J). (gr. 5-8). lib. bdg. 29.25 (978-1-4042-0177-4(7)) Rosen Publishing Group, Inc., The.

Globe Fearon American History Vol. 1: Prehistory Through Reconstruction. 2003. 542p. (YA). (gr. 6-12). 50.95 (978-0-13-024400-0(7)) Globe Fearon Educational Publishing.

Greene, Meg. Into the Land of Freedom: African Americans in Reconstruction. 2004. (People's History Ser.). (Illus.). 96p. (J). lib. bdg. 29.27 (978-0-8225-4690-0(6)) Lerner Publishing Group.

Grumet, Bridget Hall & Baker, Lawrence W. Primary Sources, Reconstruction. 2004. (Illus.). xxv, 228p. (J). lib. bdg. 67.00 (978-0-7876-9219-3(0) , UXL) Thomson Gale.

Hakim, Joy. A History of the US Bk. 7: Reconstructing America, 1865-1890. 3rd rev. ed. 2002. (History of US Ser.). (Illus.). 160p. pap. 15.95 (978-0-19-515332-3(4)) Oxford Univ. Pr., Inc.

—A History of U. S. Vol. 7: Reconstruction & Reform. rev. ed. 2007. (History of US Ser.). 208p. pap. 15.95 ***978-0-19-532721-2(7))** Oxford Univ. Pr., Inc.

—A History of US Bk. 7: Reconstructing America. 3rd rev. ed. 2005. (History of US Ser.). (Illus.). 208p. 19.95 (978-0-19-518900-1(0)) Oxford Univ. Pr., Inc.

—Reconstruction & Reform. 2003. (gr. 5-8). lib. bdg. 23.40 (978-0-613-55187-8(7)) Tandem Library Bks.

Hale, Sarah Elder, ed. Rebuilding a Nation: Picking up the Pieces. 2005. (Cobblestone the Civil War Ser.). (Illus.). 48p. (J). 17.95 (978-0-8126-7909-0(1)) Cobblestone Publishing Co.

Hansen, Joyce. "Bury Me Not in a Land of Slaves" African-Americans in the Time of Reconstruction. 2000. (Single Titles Social Studies Ser.). (Illus.). 160p. (YA). (gr. 8-12). pap. 8.95 (978-0-531-16463-1(2) , Watts, Franklin) Scholastic Library Publishing.

—Bury Me Not in a Land of Slaves: African-Americans in the Time of Reconstruction. 2000. (J). 15.60 (978-0-606-19779-3(6)) Tandem Library Bks.

—Bury Me Not in the Land of Slaves: African-Americans in the Time of Reconstruction. 2000. (Single Titles Ser.). (Illus.). 160p. (YA). (gr. 8-12). 24.00 (978-0-531-11539-8(9) , Watts, Franklin) Scholastic Library Publishing.

Harkrader, Lisa. Reconstruction & Aftermath of the Civil War: A MyReportLinks. com Book. 2004. (American Civil War Ser.). (Illus.). 48p. (J). lib. bdg. 25.26 (978-0-7660-5265-9(6) , MyReportLinks.com Bks.) Enslow Pubs., Inc.

Howes, Kelly King & Baker, Lawrence W. Almanac, Reconstruction Era. 2004. (Reconstruction ERA Reference Library). (Illus.). xxxvii, 228p. (J). lib. bdg. 67.00 (978-0-7876-9217-9(4) , UXL) Thomson Gale.

Kallen, Stuart A. The Civil War & Reconstruction. 2001. (Black History Ser.). (Illus.). 48p. (J). (gr. 3-8). lib. bdg. 25.65 (978-1-57765-469-8(2) , ABDO & Daughters) ABDO Publishing Co.

Matuz, Roger & Baker, Lawrence W. Biography, Reconstruction Era. 2004. (Reconstruction ERA Reference Library). (Illus.). xxiv, 246p. (J). lib. bdg. 67.00 (978-0-7876-9218-6(2) , UXL) Thomson Gale.

McPherson, James M. Into the West: From Reconstruction to the Final Days of the American Frontier. 2006. 96p. (J). (gr. 4-9). 22.95 (978-0-689-86543-5(0) , Atheneum) Simon & Schuster Children's Publishing.

Nelson, Sheila. Americans Divided: The Civil War. 2005. (How America Became America Ser.). (Illus.). 96p. (J). lib. bdg. (978-1-59084-908-8(6)) Mason Crest Pubs.

Peacock, Judith. Reconstruction: Rebuilding after the Civil War. 2002. (Let Freedom Ring Ser.). (Illus.). 48p. (J). (gr. 3-4). lib. bdg. 22.60 (978-0-7368-1341-9(1) , Bridgestone Bks.) Capstone Pr., Inc.

Reconstruction, 6 vols. (gr. 2-5). 39.95 (978-0-7368-4599-1(2)) Red Brick Learning.

Reconstruction: Rebuilding after the Civil War. (Civil War Ser.). 48p. (YA). 7.95 (978-0-7368-4519-9(4)) Capstone Pr., Inc.

Ruggiero, Adriane. Reconstruction. 2006. (American Voices Ser.). (Illus.). 103p. (J). lib. bdg. 37.07 (978-0-7614-2168-9(8) , Benchmark Bks.) Cavendish, Marshall Corp.

Smith, George. The Gentile Nations, or the History & Religion of the Egyptians, Assyrians, Babylonians, Medes, Persians, Greeks, & Romans. 2006. cd-rom (978-1-892824-41-7(8)) AFCHRON.

Stefoff, Rebecca. The Civil War & Reconstruction 1863-1877. 2002. (North American Historical Atlases Ser.). (Illus.). 48p. (J). 27.07 (978-0-7614-1347-9(2) , Benchmark Bks.) Cavendish, Marshall Corp.

Stroud, Bettye & Schomp, Virginia. The Reconstruction ERA. 2006. (Drama of African-American History Ser.). (Illus.). 80p. (J). lib. bdg. 34.21 (978-0-7614-2181-8(5) , Benchmark Bks.) Cavendish, Marshall Corp.

Weber, Michael. Civil War & Reconstruction. 2000. (Making of America Ser.). (Illus.). 96p. (J). (gr. 4-7). lib. bdg. 28.54 (978-0-8172-5707-1(1)) Raintree.

Ziff, Marsha. Reconstruction Following the Civil War in American History. 1999. (In American History Ser.). (Illus.). 128p. (YA). (gr. 5-12). lib. bdg. 26.60 (978-0-7660-1140-3(2)) Enslow Pubs., Inc.

RECONSTRUCTION (U.S. HISTORY, 1865-1877)—FICTION

Asim, Jabari. The Road to Freedom. 2004. 131p. (J). lib. bdg. 16.92 ***(978-1-4242-0765-7(7))*** Fitzgerald Bks.

Asim, Jabari. Road to Freedom: A Story of Reconstruction. 2000. (gr. 5-8). lib. bdg. 14.95 (978-0-613-36867-4(3)) Tandem Library Bks.

Finley, Martha. Elsie's Tender Mercies, Vol. 7. 2006. (Life of Faith': Elsie Dinsmore Ser.). 224p. (J). pap. 7.99 (978-1-928749-86-8(0)) Zonderkidz.

Hansen, Joyce. The Heart Calls Home. 1999. viii, 175p. (J). (gr. 7-12). 16.95 (978-0-8027-8636-4(7)) Walker & Co.

McMullan, Margaret. When I Crossed No-Bob. 2007. 224p. (J). (gr. 5-9). 16.00 ***(978-0-618-71715-6(3))*** Houghton Mifflin Co. Trade & Reference Div.

Osborne, Mary Pope, et al. A Time to Dance Bk. 3: Virginia's Civil War Diary. 2003. (My America Ser.). 112p. (J). pap. 12.95 (978-0-439-44341-8(5)) Scholastic, Inc.

Robinet, Harriette Gillem. Forty Acres & Maybe a Mule. 2000. (YA). (gr. 3 up). pap. 52.00 incl. audio (978-0-7887-4332-0(5) , 41127) Recorded Bks., LLC.

—Forty Acres & Maybe a Mule. Nickens, Bessie, illus. 1998. (Jean Karl Ser.). 144p. (J). (gr. 3-7). 17.99 (978-0-689-82078-6(X) , Atheneum) Simon & Schuster Children's Publishing.

—Forty Acres & Maybe a Mule. 2000. 11.64 (978-0-606-17824-2(4)); (gr. 3-6). lib. bdg. 13.00 (978-0-613-22986-9(X)) Tandem Library Bks.

Robinet, Harriette Gillem & Minor, Wendell. Forty Acres & Maybe a Mule. 2000. (Jean Karl Ser.). 144p. (J). (gr. 3-7). reprint ed. pap. 4.99 (978-0-689-83317-5(2) , Aladdin) Simon & Schuster Children's Publishing.

Shaw, Marilyn Bishop. Solomon. 2006. 203p. (J). 14.95 (978-1-56164-349-3(1)) Pineapple Pr., Inc.

RECORD PLAYERS

see Phonograph

RECREATION

Here are entered works on the psychological and social aspects of recreation and works on organized recreational projects.

see also Amusements; Games; Hobbies; Play; Playgrounds; Sports

Aber, Linda Williams. Fun Family Activities. 2001. (Illus.). 160p. (J). (978-0-7853-4891-7(3)) Publications International, Ltd.

Amery, Heather. What's Happening at the Seaside? Cartwright, Stephen, illus. rev. ed. 2006. 16p. (J). pap. 5.99 (978-0-7945-1290-3(9) , Usborne) EDC Publishing.

Avis, Ed. Come on Dad! 75 Things for Fathers & Sons to Do Together. Despres, Genevieve, illus. 2002. 140p. (J). (ps-3). pap. 9.95 (978-1-894222-72-3(5)) Lobster Pr. CAN. *Dist:* Univ. of Toronto Pr.

Baillie, Marilyn & Ripley, Catherine, eds. The Anti-Boredom Book: 133 Completely Unboring Things to Do! 2000. (Illus.). 128p. (J). (gr. k-4). pap. 12.95 (978-1-895688-99-3(X) , Owl Bks.) Maple Tree Pr. CAN. *Dist:* Firefly Bks., Ltd.

Beak, Nick Huckleberry. Balloon Ideas. 2001. (Illus.). 64p. (gr. 3-7). pap. 6.95 (978-1-84215-479-3(6) , Southwater) Anness Publishing GBR. *Dist:* National Bk. Network.

Beard, Lina & Beard, Adelia B. The American Girl's Handy Book: Making the Most of Outdoor Fun. 2002. 480p. pap. 11.95 (978-1-58667-089-4(1)) Derrydale Pr., The.

Beylon, Cathy. At the Amusement Park. 2004. (Dover Coloring Bks.). 32p. (J). pap. 2.95 (978-0-486-43322-6(6)) Dover Pubns., Inc.

Blakey, Nancy. Go Outside! Over 130 Activities for Outdoor Adventures. 2002. (gr. 3-6). lib. bdg. 23.40 (978-0-613-56912-5(1)) Tandem Library Bks.

—Go Outside! Over 130 Activities for Outdoor Adventures. Doering, Dane Dean, illus. Doering, Dane Dean, photos by. 2004. 144p. (J). (gr. 3-6). 14.95 (978-1-58246-064-2(7) , Tricycle Pr.) Ten Speed Pr.

Boase, Petra. Rainy Day. 2001. (Fun with... Ser.). (Illus.). 96p. 12.95 (978-1-84215-476-2(1) , Southwater) Anness Publishing GBR. *Dist:* National Bk. Network.

Brent, Lynnette R. At Play. 2003. (Times Change Ser.). (Illus.). 32p. (J). (978-1-4034-4538-4(9)) Heinemann Library.

—At Play: Long Ago & Today. 2003. (Times Change Ser.). (Illus.). 32p. (J). lib. bdg. 24.22 (978-1-4034-4532-2(X)) Heinemann Library.

Budd, E. S. Dune Buggies. 2004. (Machines at Work Ser.). 24p. (J). (ps-3). 21.36 (978-1-59296-162-7(2)) Child's World, Inc.

—Jet Watercraft. 2004. (Machines at Work Ser.). 24p. (J). (ps-3). 21.36 (978-1-59296-163-4(0)) Child's World, Inc.

Bull, Jane. The Vacation Activity Book. 2007. 48p. (J). (gr. 1-3). 12.99 (978-0-7566-2942-7(X)) Dorling Kindersley Publishing, Inc.

Byrd, Sandra. Stuff 2 Do: A-to-Z Activities for Girls Like You. 2003. (Girls Like You Ser.). (Illus.). 160p. (J). pap. 8.99 (978-0-7642-2753-0(X)) Bethany Hse. Pubs.

Carter, Stephanie & Lederman, JoAnn. Meditapes Four - Getting a Good Night's Sleep. 1998. (YA). (gr. 7 up). pap. 24.95 incl. audio (978-1-893868-03-8(6)) Meditapes.

Chapman, Cindy. Play It Safe! 2003. (Compass Point Phonics Readers Ser.). (Illus.). 16p. (J). (gr. 1 up). 13.26 (978-0-7565-0520-2(8)) Compass Point Bks.

Cook, Monica Hay. Kickin' up Some Cowboy Fun: 130 Activities for Cowboys & Cowgirls. Cook, Gerard Jude, illus. 1999. 143p. (J). (gr. k-7). pap. 14.95 (978-0-9662738-1-6(8)) Monjeu Pr., Inc.

Copperman, Cara. 60 Super Simple: After School Activities. Abbett, Leo, illus. 2000. 80p. (J). (gr. 2-7). pap. 6.95 (978-0-7373-0485-5(5) , 04855W, Roxbury Park Juvenile) Lowell Hse. Juvenile.

Curtis, Regina. The Little Hands Playtime! Book: 50 Activities to Encourage Cooperation & Sharing. 2000. (Little Hands Bks.). (Illus.). 144p. (J). (ps-3). pap. 12.95 (978-1-885593-42-9(2) , Williamson Bks.) Ideals Pubns.

Dover Staff. Fairies Fun Books, 10 vols. 1998. (J). pap. 10.00 (978-0-486-40252-9(5)) Dover Pubns., Inc.

Espeland, Pamela & Verdick, Elizabeth. Smart Ways to Spend Your Time: The Constructive Use of Time Assets. 2005. (Adding Assets Series for Kids). (Illus.). 80p. (J). (gr. 3-7). pap. 9.95 (978-1-57542-172-8(0) , 912) Free Spirit Publishing, Inc.

Glicksman, Jane. Fun Fingers, Fancy Feet. Olexiewicz, Charlene, illus. Bogart, Ann, photos by. 2000. (Girls Wanna Have Fun! Ser.). 64p. (J). (gr. 3-7). pap. 9.95 (978-0-7373-0330-8(1) , 03301W, Roxbury Park Juvenile) Lowell Hse. Juvenile.

Gorman, Jacqueline Laks. I Like to Visit. 24p. (YA). 115.98 (978-0-8368-4450-4(5)) Stevens, Gareth Inc.

—I Like to Visit/Me gusta visit. 115.98 (978-0-8368-4594-5(3)) Stevens, Gareth Inc.

The Great Outdoors, 10 bks. Incl. Camping. Keller, Kristin Thoennes. 2001. lib. bdg. 21.26 (978-0-7368-0911-5(2)); Canoeing. Salas, Laura Purdie. 2002. lib. bdg. 21.26 (978-0-7368-1055-5(2)); Deer Hunting. Frahm, Randy. 2001. lib. bdg. 21.26 (978-0-7368-0912-2(0)); Duck Hunting. Frahm, Randy. 2001. lib. bdg. 21.26 (978-0-7368-0913-9(9)); Fly Fishing. Hopkins, Ellen. 2001. lib. bdg. 21.26 (978-0-7368-0914-6(7)); Freshwater Fishing. Hopkins, Ellen. 2001. lib. bdg. 21.26 (978-0-7368-0915-3(5)); Hiking. Keller, Kristin Thoennes. 2001. lib. bdg. 21.26 (978-0-7368-0916-0(3)); Ice Fishing. Salas, Laura Purdie. 2002. lib. bdg. 21.26 (978-0-7368-1056-2(0)); Pheasant Hunting. Martin, Michael J. 2002. lib. bdg. 21.26 (978-0-7368-1057-9(9)); Snowmobiling. Salas, Laura Purdie. 2002. lib. bdg. 21.26 (978-0-7368-1058-6(7)); 48p. (J). (gr. 3-4). (Illus.). Set lib. bdg. 212.60 (978-0-7368-1080-7(3) , Capstone High-Interest Bks.) Capstone Pr., Inc.

Hill, Mary. Weekend Fun: Set, 6 Bks. 2004. 87.00 (978-0-516-23744-2(6) , Children's Pr.) Scholastic Library Publishing.

Huckleberry, Bea. Dastardly Detective's Secrets. 2001. (Fun Factory... Ser.). (Illus.). 64p. pap. 6.95 (978-1-84215-483-0(4) , Southwater) Anness Publishing GBR. *Dist:* National Bk. Network.

James, Diane. Fun to Make & Do. 2004. (Crafty Ideas Ser.). (Illus.). 124p. (gr. 3-6). 24.95 (978-1-58728-111-2(2) , Two Can Publishing) T&N Children's Publishing.

Klein, Nancy C. Healing Images for Children: Teaching Relaxation & Guided Imagery to Children Facing Cancer & Other Serious Illnesses. O'Brien, Staci Leigh, ed. Holden, Matthew, illus. 2001. 280p. (J). pap. 24.95 (978-0-9636027-2-5(1)) Inner Coaching.

Love, Ann & Drake, Jane. Kids & Grandparents. Collins, Heather, illus. unabr. ed. 2000. 160p. (J). (gr. k-3). (978-1-55074-492-7(5)); (978-1-55074-784-3(3)) Kids Can Pr., Ltd.

Martin, Sam. The Curious Boy's Book of Adventure: 100 Hijinks & Escapades. 2007. 160p. (J). (gr. 5). pap. 15.00 ***(978-1-59514-206-1(1))*** Penguin Group (USA) Inc.

McLeese, Tex. Lucha con Novillos. Palacios, Argentina, tr. 2002. (Rodeo Ser.).Tr. of Steer Wrestling. (SPA., Illus.). 24p. mass mkt. 5.95 (978-1-58952-256-5(7) , RK31471) Rourke Publishing, LLC.

—Monta de Toro y Toreo. Palacios, Argentina, tr. 2002. (Rodeo Ser.).Tr. of Bull Riding & Bullfighting. (SPA., Illus.). 24p. mass mkt. 5.95 (978-1-58952-257-2(5) , RK31472) Rourke Publishing, LLC.

—Monta en Silla y a Pelo. Palacios, Argentina, tr. 2002. (Rodeo Ser.).Tr. of Bronc & Bareback Riding. (SPA., Illus.). 24p. mass mkt. 5.95 (978-1-58952-258-9(3) , RK31473) Rourke Publishing, LLC.

Mullarkey, Lisa. Splashing by the Shore: Beach Activities for Kids. Dixon, Debra Spina, illus. 2007. 64p. (J). (gr. 1-3). pap. 9.95 (978-1-58685-884-1(X)) Gibbs Smith, Publisher.

Powell, Consie. The First Day of Winter. Powell, Consie, illus. 2005. (Illus.). 32p. (J). (gr. k-4). lib. bdg. 15.95 (978-0-8075-2450-3(6)) Whitman, Albert & Co.

Reagan, Dawn. For Our Baby Scrapbook Kit: Scrapbook Activity Kit for Kids. Takes, Toon, ed. 1999. (Illus.). 29p. (J). (gr. k-6). pap. 15.50 (978-1-929456-04-8(2)) Myrtle-Seal Publishing.

—New Testament Bible Adventure Kit: Bible Storyboard Adventures for Kids. Takes, Toon, ed. Reagan, Dawn, illus. 1999. (Illus.). 16p. (ps-5). pap. 29.95 (978-1-929456-01-7(8)) Myrtle-Seal Publishing.

Salzmann, Mary Elizabeth. Taking Time to Relax. 2004. (Healthy Habits Ser.). (Illus.). 23p. (J). (ps-3). lib. bdg. 19.93 (978-1-59197-555-7(7)) ABDO Publishing Co.

Samuel, Charlie. Entertainment in Colonial America. 2003. (Primary Sources of Everyday Life in Colonial America Ser.). (Illus.). 24p. (J). lib. bdg. 21.25 (978-0-8239-6600-4(3) , PowerKids Pr.) Rosen Publishing Group, Inc., The.

Sklansky, Amy E. Zoom Fun Outside. 2000. (Zoom Ser.). (Illus.). 62p. (J). (gr. 1-7). pap. 7.95 (978-0-316-95278-1(8)) Little Brown & Co.

Stevens, Cara J. After School Stuff, Vol. 1. 1999. (After School Stuff Ser.). (Illus.). 80p. (J). (gr. 3-7). pap. 6.95 (978-0-7373-0239-4(9) , 02399W) McGraw-Hill/ Contemporary.

Takes, Toon, ed. Color 'n' Sticker Scrapbook Kit: Scrapbook Activity Kit for Kids. Reagan, Dawn, illus. 1999. 23p. (J). (ps-5). pap. 15.50 (978-1-929456-03-1(4)) Myrtle-Seal Publishing.

Trumbauer, Lisa. Our Favorite Things to Do. 2000. (Yellow Umbrella Books). (Illus.). 16p. (J). (gr. 1). lib. bdg. 14.60 (978-0-7368-0739-5(X) , Pebble Bks.) Capstone Pr., Inc.

Usilton, Theresa A. Let's Go team: Cheer, Dance, & March, 12 vols., Set. 2003. (Let's Go Team Ser.). (Illus.). 64p. (YA). (gr. 5 up). lib. bdg. (978-1-59084-529-5(3)) Mason Crest Pubs.

Wild Rides!, 8 bks., Set. Incl. BMX Bikes. Deady, Kathleen W. 2001. lib. bdg. 21.26 (978-0-7368-0925-2(2)); Demolition Derby Cars. Savage, Jeff. 2003. lib. bdg. 21.26 (978-0-7368-1516-1(3)); Dirt Bikes. Parr, Danny. 2001. lib. bdg. 21.26 (978-0-7368-0927-6(9)); Dragsters. Deady, Kathleen W. 2001. lib. bdg. 21.26 (978-0-7368-0926-9(0)); Go-Karts. Savage, Jeff. 2003. lib. bdg. 21.26 (978-0-7368-1517-8(1)); Lowriders. Parr, Danny. 2001. lib. bdg. 21.26 (978-0-7368-0928-3(7)); Monster Trucks. Schaefer, A. R. 2001. lib. bdg. 21.26 (978-0-7368-0929-0(5)); Motocross Cycles. Schaefer, A. R. 2001. lib. bdg. 21.26 (978-0-7368-0930-6(9)); Mountain Bikes. Savage, Jeff. 2003. lib. bdg. 21.26 (978-0-7368-1518-5(X)); Pro Stock Cars. Dubois, Muriel L. 2001. lib. bdg. 21.26 (978-0-7368-0931-3(7)); Snowmobiles. Dubois, Muriel L. 2001. lib. bdg. 21.26 (978-0-7368-0932-0(5)); Stunt Planes. Savage, Jeff. 2003. lib. bdg. 21.26 (978-0-7368-1519-2(8)); 32p. (J). (gr. 3-4). (Illus.). Set lib. bdg. 255.12 (978-0-7368-1524-6(4) , Capstone High-Interest Bks.) Capstone Pr., Inc.

Williams, Brett. Xaler & the Dragon: A Relaxation Technique for the Anxious/Fearful Child. 2nd ed. 2001. (Illus.). 15p. (J). per. 11.95 (978-0-9761269-1-(5)) Tapas Pubns.

Winters, Kas. Fall Fun for Families. 2000. (Illus.). 80p. (J). (ps-7). pap. 7.00 (978-1-892225-01-6(8)) Winmark Communications.

Yates, Vicki. Having Fun. 2007. (J). ***(978-1-4034-9832-8(6)); pap. (978-1-4034-9840-3(7))*** Heinemann Library.

RECREATIONAL VEHICLES

see Automobiles—Trailers

RECREATIONS, MATHEMATICAL

see Mathematical Recreations

RECREATIONS, SCIENTIFIC

see Scientific Recreations

RECRUITING AND ENLISTMENT

see United States—Army—Recruiting, Enlistment, etc.

RECTORS

see Clergy

RECYCLING (WASTE, ETC.)

Here are entered works on the processing of waste paper, cans, bottles, etc.

Barraclough, Sue. Reusing Things. 2007. ***(978-1-59771-109-8(8))*** Sea-To-Sea Pubns.

Bedford, Deborah Jackson. Garbage Disposal. 2005. (Action for the Environment Ser.). (Illus.). 32p. (J). (gr. 4-7). lib. bdg. 27.10 (978-1-58340-595-6(X) , 1247278) Smart Apple Media.

Boekhoff, P. M. & Kallen, Stuart A. Recycling. 2004. (Our Environment Ser.). (Illus.). 48p. (J). (gr. 4-7). 26.20 (978-0-7377-1517-0(0) , Kidhaven) Thomson Gale.

Bowden, Rob. Waste, Recycling & Reuse: Our Impact on the Planet. 2001. (Twenty-First Century Debates Ser.). (Illus.). 64p. (YA). (gr. 6-8). lib. bdg. 27.12 (978-0-7398-3180-9(1)) Raintree.

Brend, Dawn. Jazzy Jewelry: Recycle Materials to Make Cool Stuff. 2007. (EcoCrafts Ser.). (Illus.). 48p. (J). pap. 7.95 ***(978-0-7534-5969-0(8)*** , Kingfisher) Houghton Mifflin Co. Trade & Reference Div.

Brend, Dawn & Craig, Rebecca. Jazzy Jewelry: Recycle Materials to Make Cool Stuff. 2007. (EcoCrafts Ser.). 48p. (J). pap. 7.95 ***(978-0-7534-5968-3(X)*** , Kingfisher) Houghton Mifflin Co. Trade & Reference Div.

Chapman, Gillian. Art from Fabric. 2007. (J). lib. bdg. ***(978-1-4042-3722-3(4)*** , PowerKids Pr.) Rosen Publishing Group, Inc., The.

Chapman, Gillian & Robson, Pam. Art from Packaging. 2007. (J). lib. bdg. ***(978-1-4042-3724-7(0)*** , PowerKids Pr.) Rosen Publishing Group, Inc., The.

—Art from Rocks & Shells. 2007. (J). lib. bdg. ***(978-1-4042-3727-8(5)*** , PowerKids Pr.) Rosen Publishing Group, Inc., The.

—Art from Sand & Earth. 2007. (J). lib. bdg. ***(978-1-4042-3723-0(2)*** , PowerKids Pr.) Rosen Publishing Group, Inc., The.

—Art from Wood. 2007. (J). lib. bdg. ***(978-1-4042-3726-1(7)*** , PowerKids Pr.) Rosen Publishing Group, Inc., The.

Clausen-Grace, Nicki. What Can You Make? 2007. (J). (978-1-59515-932-8(0)) Rourke Publishing, LLC.

Costain, Meredith. Garbage Detectives. 2000. (gr. k-3). lib. bdg. 11.80 (978-0-613-30423-8(3)) Tandem Library Bks.

—Old to New. 2000. (gr. k-3). lib. bdg. 11.80 (978-0-613-30643-0(0)) Tandem Library Bks.

—Recycling. 2000. (gr. k-3). lib. bdg. 11.80 (978-0-613-30695-9(3)) Tandem Library Bks.

—Things We Throw Away. 2000. (gr. k-3). lib. bdg. 11.80 (978-0-613-30788-8(7)) Tandem Library Bks.

Cothran, Helen, ed. Garbage & Recycling. 2002. (Opposing Viewpoints Ser.). (Illus.). 200p. (J). (gr. 10-12). pap. 24.95 (978-0-7377-1229-2(5) , Greenhaven Pr., Inc.) Thomson Gale.

Craig, Rebecca. Dream Bedroom: Use Recycled Materials to Make Cool Crafts. 2007. (EcoCrafts Ser.). (Illus.). 48p. (J). (gr. 3-5). pap. 7.95 ***(978-0-7534-5966-9(3)*** , Kingfisher) Houghton Mifflin Co. Trade & Reference Div.

—EcoCrafts. 2007. (Illus.). 48p. (J). ***(978-1-4287-3452-4(X)*** , Kingfisher) Houghton Mifflin Co. Trade & Reference Div.

—Gorgeous Gifts. 2007. (EcoCrafts Ser.). (Illus.). 48p. (J). (gr. 3-5). pap. 7.95 ***(978-0-7534-5967-6(1)*** , Kingfisher) Houghton Mifflin Co. Trade & Reference Div.

Donald, Rhonda Lucas. Recycling. 2001. (True Environment Bks.). (Illus.). 48p. (J). (gr. 3-5). 25.00 (978-0-516-22193-9(0) , Children's Pr.) Scholastic Library Publishing.

—Recycling. 2001. (gr. 3-6). lib. bdg. 15.25 (978-0-613-51668-6(0)) Tandem Library Bks.

Elliot, Marion. Fun with Recycling: 50 Great Things for Kids to Make from Junk. 2001. (Fun with... Ser.). (Illus.). 96p. (gr. 3-7). 12.95 (978-1-84215-408-3(7) , Southwater) Anness Publishing GBR. *Dist:* National Bk. Network.

Emmer, Rae. Community Service. 2002. (Reading Power Ser.). (Illus.). 24p. (J). (gr. 1). lib. bdg. 17.25 (978-0-8239-5967-9(8) , PowerKids Pr.) Rosen Publishing Group, Inc., The.

Filian, Cathie & Piacenza, Steve. Creative Juice (DIY) 50 Re-Crafting Projects to Make with Recycled Stuff. 2007. (Illus.). 128p. pap. 14.95 ***(978-1-60059-148-8(5))*** Lark Bks.

Fix, Alexandra. Energy. 2007. (J). ***(978-1-4034-9715-4(X)); pap. (978-1-4034-9723-9(0))*** Heinemann Library.

—Food. 2007. (J). ***(978-1-4034-9713-0(3)); pap. (978-1-4034-9721-5(4))*** Heinemann Library.

—Glass. 2007. (J). ***(978-1-4034-9718-5(4)); pap. (978-1-4034-9726-0(5))*** Heinemann Library.

—Metal. 2007. (J). ***(978-1-4034-9717-8(6)); pap. (978-1-4034-9725-3(7))*** Heinemann Library.

—Paper. 2007. (J). ***(978-1-4034-9712-3(5)); pap. (978-1-4034-9720-8(6))*** Heinemann Library.

—Plastic. 2007. (J). ***(978-1-4034-9716-1(8)); pap. (978-1-4034-9724-6(9))*** Heinemann Library.

Frank, Marjorie Slavick, et al. Science Instant Readers Bk. 4: Reuse & Recycle. 1999. (Harcourt Science Ser.). (gr. 2 up). pap. 15.50 (978-0-15-316214-5(7)) Harcourt Schl. Pubs.

Galko, Francine. Earth Friends, 4 bks. 2004. (J). (gr. k-2). lib. bdg. 96.86 (978-1-4034-4899-6(X)) Heinemann Library.

—Earth Friends at Home. 2004. (Heinemann First Library). (Illus.). 32p. (J). pap. 7.25 (978-1-4034-4900-9(7)) Heinemann Library.

—Earth Friends at Play. 2004. (Heinemann First Library). (Illus.). 32p. (J). pap. 6.95 (978-1-4034-4901-6(5)) Heinemann Library.

—Earth Friends at School. 2004. (Heinemann First Library). (Illus.). 32p. (J). pap. 6.95 (978-1-4034-4902-3(3)); lib. bdg. 22.79 (978-1-4034-4897-2(3)) Heinemann Library.

—Earth Friends at the Grocery Store. 2004. (Heinemann First Library). (Illus.). 32p. (J). pap. (978-1-4034-4903-0(1)) Heinemann Library.

—Ecology at Home. 2004. (Heinemann First Library). (Illus.). 32p. (J). lib. bdg. 22.79 (978-1-4034-4895-8(7)) Heinemann Library.

—Ecology at the Grocery Store. 2004. (Heinemann First Library). (Illus.). 32p. (J). lib. bdg. 22.79 (978-1-4034-4898-9(1)) Heinemann Library.

—Ecology on the Playground. 2004. (Heinemann First Library). (Illus.). 32p. (J). lib. bdg. 22.79 (978-1-4034-4896-5(5)) Heinemann Library.

Ganeri, Anita. Something Old, Something New: Recycling. 2005. (You Can Save the Planet Ser.). (J). (978-1-4034-6843-7(5)); pap. (978-1-4034-6849-9(4)) Heinemann Library.

Gordon, Jo. Reciclar (Recycling) (SPA., Illus.). 32p. (J). 10.95 (978-84-348-3988-5(1)) SM Ediciones ESP. *Dist:* AIMS International Bks., Inc.

Gould, Roberta. The Kid's Book of Incredibly Fun Crafts. Martin Jourdenais, Norma Jean, illus. 2004. (Williamson's Kids Can! Ser.). 128p. (J). pap. 14.95 (978-1-885593-85-6(6) , Williamson Bks.) Ideals Pubns.

Green, Jen. Recycling. 2005. (Your Environment Ser.). (Illus.). 32p. (J). (gr. 3-7). lib. bdg. 27.10 (978-1-59604-059-5(9)) Stargazer Bks.

—Waste & Recycling. 2004. (J). lib. bdg. 27.10 (978-1-59389-137-4(7)) Chrysalis Education.

—Why Should I Recycle? Gordon, Mike, illus. 2005. (Why Should I? Bks.). 32p. (J). pap. 5.95 (978-0-7641-3155-4(9)) Barron's Educational Series, Inc.

—Why Should I Recycle? Gordon, Mike, illus. 2005. 32p. (J). (ps-ps). lib. bdg. 13.15 (978-0-606-33632-1(X)) Tandem Library Bks.

Harcourt School Publishers Staff. Reuse & Recycle: Science Reader. 1999. (SPA., Illus.). (J). pap. 3.70 (978-0-15-316119-3(1)) Harcourt Schl. Pubs.

Harlow, Rosie. Garbage & Recycling. 2002. (Young Discoverers Ser.). (Illus.). 32p. (J). (gr. k-3). pap. 7.95 (978-0-7534-5503-6(X) , Kingfisher) Houghton Mifflin Co. Trade & Reference Div.

—Garbage & Recycling. 2002. (gr. k-3). lib. bdg. 16.40 (978-0-613-90901-3(1)) Tandem Library Bks.

Inskipp, Carol. Reducing & Recycling Waste. 2005. (Improving Our Environment Ser.). (Illus.). 32p. (J). lib. bdg. 24.67 (978-0-8368-4429-0(7)) Stevens, Gareth Inc.

Irvin, Christine M. Pie Pan Mania. 2002. (Craft Mania Ser.). (Illus.). 32p. (J). (gr. 2-4). pap. 23.50 (978-0-516-22280-6(5) , Children's Pr.) Scholastic Library Publishing.

Kishel, Ann-Marie. Recycle. 2006. (First Step Nonfiction Ser.). (Illus.). 8p. (J). pap. (978-0-8225-5676-3(6) , Lerner Pubns.) Lerner Publishing Group.

—Reduce. 2006. (First Step Nonfiction Ser.). (Illus.). 8p. (J). pap. (978-0-8225-5677-0(4) , Lerner Pubns.) Lerner Publishing Group.

Koontz, Robin Michal. Composting: Nature's Recyclers. Harrad, Matthew, illus. 2007. (J). 23.93 (978-1-4048-2194-1(5)) Picture Window Bks.

Lamerand, Violaine. Crafts from Junk. 2002. (Step by Step Ser.). (Illus.). 32p. (J). (gr. 2-3). lib. bdg. 22.60 (978-0-7368-1479-9(5) , Bridgestone Bks.) Capstone Pr., Inc.

Levete, Sarah. Rot & Decay: Decomposing & Recycling. 2008. (J). (***978-1-60044-602-3(7)***) Rourke Publishing, LLC.

Llewellyn, Claire. Let's Recycle. 2005. (Illus.). 32p. (YA). (gr. 1 up). lib. bdg. 27.10 (978-1-932333-22-0(3)) Chrysalis Education.

Llimos, Anna & Sadurni, Laia. Creating by Recycling. 2000. (Crafts for All Seasons Ser.). (Illus.). 32p. (J). (gr. 3-8). lib. bdg. 23.70 (978-1-56711-436-2(9) , Blackbirch Pr., Inc.) Thomson Gale.

Llimos Plomer, Anna. Easy Earth-Friendly Crafts in 5 Steps. 2008. (Easy Crafts in 5 Steps Ser.). 32p. (J). (gr. 3-4). lib. bdg. 22.60 (***978-0-7660-3086-2(5)***) Enslow Pubs., Inc.

Love, Ann & Drake, Jane. Trash Action: A Fresh Look at Garbage. Thurman, Mark, illus. 2006. 80p. (J). (gr. 3). pap. 14.95 (978-0-88776-721-0(4)) Tundra Bks., Inc./ Livres Toundra, Inc. CAN. *Dist:* Random Hse., Inc.

MacGregor, Cynthia. Recycling a Can. 2002. (Reading Room Collection). (Illus.). 24p. (J). lib. bdg. 18.75 (978-0-8239-3744-8(5)) Rosen Publishing Group, Inc., The.

Mackenzie, Anne L. Let's Recycle! 2007. (Pebble Books). (Illus.). 24p. (J). 15.93 (978-0-7368-6323-0(0)) Capstone Pr., Inc.

Martin, Laura C. Recycled Crafts Box: Sock Puppets, Cardboard Castles, Bottle Bugs & 37 More Earth-Friendly Projects & Activities You Can Create. 2004. (Illus.). 96p. (J). pap. 10.95 (978-1-58017-522-7(8) , 67522); tchr. ed. 19.95 (978-1-58017-523-4(6) , 67523) Storey Publishing, LLC. (Storey Kids).

Miller, Heather. Nifty Thrifty Art Crafts. 2007. (Nifty Thrifty Crafts for Kids Ser.). (Illus.). 32p. (J). (gr. 3-4). lib. bdg. 22.60 (978-0-7660-2780-0(5) , Enslow Elementary) Enslow Pubs., Inc.

Morgan, Sally. Old Clothes. 2007. (***978-1-59920-011-8(2)***) Smart Apple Media.

—Waste & Recycling. 2007. (Sustainable Futures Ser.). (Illus.). 48p. (J). (***978-1-58340-981-7(5)*** , 1262625) Smart Apple Media.

Morgan, Sally. Waste Disposal. 2006. (Earth Watch Ser.). (J). (978-1-59771-069-5(5)) Sea-To-Sea Pubns.

Parramon's Editorial Team Staff. Recyclables. Parramon's Editorial Team Staff, photos by. 2004. (Let's Create! Ser.). (Illus.). 32p. (J). (gr. 2 up). lib. bdg. 23.33 (978-0-8368-4018-6(6)) Stevens, Gareth Inc.

Pohl, Kathleen. What Happens at a Recycling Center? 2006. (Illus.). 24p. (J). pap. (978-0-8368-6895-1(1)); lib. bdg. (978-0-8368-6888-3(9)) Stevens, Gareth Inc.

—What Happens at a Recycling Center? Qué Pasa en un Centro de Reciclaje? 2006. (ENG & SPA., Illus.). 24p. (J). pap. (978-0-8368-7396-2(3)); lib. bdg. (978-0-8368-7389-4(0)) Stevens, Gareth Inc. (Weekly Reader Early Learning Library).

Riley, Karen. Agarranderas Plasticas y Otras Cosas: Plastic Rings & Other Things. 2003. (ENG & SPA., Illus.). 16p. (J). (gr. 2-5). pap. 4.50 (978-0-9708135-2-7(X)) S.C.R.A.P. Gallery.

Roca, Nuria. The Three R's: Reuse, Reduce, Recycle. Curto, Rosa M., illus. 2007. (What Do You Know about? Bks.). 36p. (J). (gr. k-1). pap. 6.99 (978-0-7641-3581-1(3)) Barron's Educational Series, Inc.

Ross, Michael Elsohn. Re-Cycles. Mooore, Gustav, illus. 2003. 32p. (J). (gr. 2-5). pap. 7.95 (978-0-7613-1949-8(2) , First Avenue Editions) Lerner Publishing Group.

Royston, Angela. Recycling. 1999. (Environment Starts Here Ser.). (Illus.). 32p. (J). (gr. 1-4). 17.98 (978-0-8172-5353-0(X)) Raintree.

Sloan, Peter. Garbage Day. 1999. (gr. k-3). lib. bdg. 11.80 (978-0-613-30422-1(5)) Tandem Library Bks.

Thomson, Ruth. Clothes. 2006. (Illus.). 29p. (978-1-58340-939-8(4)) Smart Apple Media.

—Glass. 2006. (Illus.). 29p. (J). (978-1-58340-942-8(4)) Smart Apple Media.

Trash with Dash. 2002. (Illus.). (J). pap. (978-0-7398-5103-6(9)) Steck-Vaughn.

Turnbull, Stephanie. Trash & Recycling (Level 2) - Internet Referenced. 2006. 32p. (J). 4.99 (978-0-7945-1400-6(6) , Usborne) EDC Publishing.

Walker, Kate. Aluminum. 2004. (Recycle, Reduce, Reuse, Rethink Ser.). (J). lib. bdg. 27.10 (978-1-58340-559-8(3)) Smart Apple Media.

—Household Waste. 2004. (Recycle, Reduce, Reuse, Rethink Ser.). (J). lib. bdg. 27.10 (978-1-58340-561-1(5)) Smart Apple Media.

—Plastics. 2004. (Recycle, Reduce, Reuse, Rethink Ser.). (J). lib. bdg. 27.10 (978-1-58340-556-7(9)) Smart Apple Media.

Weber, Rebecca. Waste Not: Time to Recycle. 2002. (Spyglass Books). (Illus.). 24p. (J). (gr. 1 up). lib. bdg. 18.60 (978-0-7565-0387-1(6)) Compass Point Bks.

Wilcox, Charlotte. Recycling & Waste Management. 2007. (Cool Science Ser.). 48p. (J). (gr. 4-8). lib. bdg. 26.60 (***978-0-8225-6768-4(7)***) Lerner Publishing Group.

You Can Recycle! Individual Title Six-Packs. (Rigby Focus Ser.). 24p. (gr. 2 up). 28.00 (978-0-7578-5338-8(2)); 30.00 (978-0-7578-5568-9(7)) Rigby Education.

RECYCLING (WASTE, ETC.)—FICTION

Cohen, Suzanne. The Upside down World. 2007. (J). per. 10.99 (***978-1-59886-684-1(2)***) Tate Publishing & Enterprises, L.L.C.

Cook, Sherry & Johnson, Terri. X. E. Ecology, 26. Kuhn, Jesse, illus. l.t. ed. 2006. (Quirkles—Exploring Phonics through Science Ser.: 24). 32p. (J). 7.99 (978-1-933815-23-7(X) , Quirkles, The) Creative 3, LLC.

Jones, Dorothy Ann. Learn to Recycle with Mary & Goofy Gopher. 2006. 26p. pap. 7.95 (978-0-533-15131-8(7)) Vantage Pr., Inc.

McKay, Sandy. Recycled. 2001. (Illus.). 128p. (J). pap. 13.00 (978-1-877135-49-1(6)) Longacre Pr. NZL. *Dist:* Pacific Island Bks.

Meissner, David. Race to Recycle. ed. 2003. (Early Connections Ser.). (J). pap. 33.00 (978-1-4108-1361-9(4)) Benchmark Education Co.

Powell, Jillian. Recycled! 2004. (Read-It! Readers Ser.). (Illus.). 32p. (C). (gr. k-3). 18.60 (978-1-4048-0068-7(9)) Picture Window Bks.

Sensel, Joni. The Garbage Monster. Bivins, Christopher, illus. 2003. 24p. (J). (ps up). 14.95 (978-0-9701195-2-0(6)) Dream Factory Bks.

Silverman, Toby. The Garbage Grandma. Strapec, Amy, illus. 2005. 23p. (J). 9.50 (***978-0-9793475-0-4(5)***) Silverman, Toby.

Wallace, Nancy Elizabeth. Recycle Every Day! 2006. (Illus.). 32p. (J). 5.95 (978-0-7614-5290-4(7)) Cavendish, Marshall Corp.

Wolf-Sampath, Gita, et al. Elephants Never Forget. 1999. (Illus.). 112p. (978-81-86211-04-5(7)) Tara Publishing.

RED CHINA

see China

RED CLOUD, 1822-1909

McLeese, Don. Red Cloud. 2003. (Native American Legends Ser.). (Illus.). 32p. (J). 28.50 (978-1-58952-727-0(5)) Rourke Publishing, LLC.

Monroe, Judy. Chief Red Cloud 1822-1909. 2004. (American Indian Biographies Ser.). (Illus.). 32p. (J). (gr. 3-4). lib. bdg. 23.93 (978-0-7368-2445-3(6) , Blue Earth Bks.) Capstone Pr., Inc.

RED CROSS

see also American National Red Cross

Bingham, Jane. The Red Cross Movement. 2004. (World Watch Ser.). (Illus.). 48p. (J). (gr. 4-7). lib. bdg. 27.14 (978-0-7398-6613-9(3)) Raintree.

Blashfield, Jean F. Red Cross & Red Crescent. 2003. (International Organizations Ser.). (Illus.). 48p. (J). (gr. 5 up). pap. 11.95 (978-0-8368-5530-2(2)); lib. bdg. 30.00 (978-0-8368-5521-0(3)) Stevens, Gareth Inc. (World Almanac Library).

La Cruz Roja: Individual Title Six-Packs. (On Deck en Espanol Ser.).Tr. of Red Cross. (SPA.). 24p. (gr. 4-5). 35.00 (978-0-7578-6413-1(9)) Rigby Education.

Faulkner, Georgene. Red Cross Stories for Children. 2004. reprint ed. pap. 15.95 (978-1-4179-9875-3(X)) Kessinger Publishing, LLC.

Francis, Dorothy Brenner. Clara Barton: Founder of the American Red Cross. 2002. (Gateway Biography Ser.). (Illus.). 48p. (gr. 2-4). lib. bdg. 23.90 (978-0-7613-2621-2(9) , Millbrook Pr.) Lerner Publishing Group.

Klingel, Cynthia Fitterer & Noyed, Robert B. Clara Barton: Founder of the American Red Cross. 2002. (Spirit of America: Our People Ser.). (Illus.). 32p. (J). (gr. 2-6). 27.07 (978-1-56766-172-9(6)) Child's World, Inc.

Koestler-Grack, Rachel A. The Story of Clara Barton. 2003. (Breakthrough Biographies Ser.). (Illus.). 32p. (gr. 3-5). 23.00 (978-0-7910-7312-4(2) , Chelsea Hse.) Facts On File, Inc.

Mara, Wil. Clara Barton. (Rookie Biographies Ser.). (Illus.). 32p. (J). (gr. 1-2). 2003. pap. 4.95 (978-0-516-27339-6(6)); 2002. 20.50 (978-0-516-22523-4(5)) Scholastic Library Publishing. (Children's Pr.).

—Clara Barton. 2002. (gr. k-3). lib. bdg. 12.95 (978-0-613-59459-2(2)) Tandem Library Bks.

McLuskey, Krista. Red Cross. 2002. (International Organizations Ser.). (Illus.). 32p. (J). lib. bdg. 16.95 (978-1-59036-019-4(2)) Weigl Pubs., Inc.

Parry, Ann. Red Cross. 2005. (Humanitarian Organizations Ser.). (Illus.). 32p. (J). lib. bdg. 22.95 (978-0-7910-8814-2(6) , Chelsea Hse.) Facts On File, Inc.

Perkins, Ralf. International Red Cross. 2001. (World Organizations Ser.). (Illus.). 32p. (J). (gr. 6-8). 24.00 (978-0-531-14623-1(5) , Watts, Franklin) Scholastic Library Publishing.

—International Red Cross. 2001. (gr. 5-8). lib. bdg. 15.25 (978-0-613-54577-8(X)) Tandem Library Bks.

Ransom, Candice F. Clara Barton. 2003. (History Maker Bios Ser.). (Illus.). 48p. (J). (gr. 3-5). lib. bdg. 26.60 (978-0-8225-4677-1(9)) Lerner Publishing Group.

The Red Cross: Individual Title Six-Packs. (On Deck Ser.). 24p. (gr. 4-5). 35.00 (978-0-7578-1034-3(9)) Rigby Education.

Schaefer, Lola M. Clara Barton. Saunders-Smith, Gail, ed. 2002. (First Biographies Ser.). (Illus.). 24p. (J). (gr. k-1). lib. bdg. 15.93 (978-0-7368-1434-8(5) , Pebble Bks.) Capstone Pr., Inc.

Suen, Anastasia. La Cruz Roja. 2004. (Organizaciones de Ayuda Ser.). (SPA & ENG., Illus.). 24p. (J). (gr. 3-6). lib. bdg. 17.25 (978-0-8239-6856-5(1) , Buenas Letra) Rosen Publishing Group, Inc., The.

Wheeler, Jill C. Red Cross Volunteers. 2003. (Everyday Heroes (cb) Ser.). (Illus.). 32p. (J). (gr. k-6). lib. bdg. 22.78 (978-1-57765-857-3(4)) ABDO Publishing Co.

REDUCING

see Weight Control

REDWALL ABBEY (IMAGINARY PLACE)—FICTION

Jacques, Brian. Badgers. Baker, Chris, illus. 2002. (YA). 8.99 (978-0-399-23852-9(2) , Philomel) Penguin Group (USA) Inc.

—Friend & Foe. 2000. (Redwall Ser.). (Illus.). 16p. (J). (gr. 4-7). 8.99 (978-0-399-23589-4(2) , Philomel) Penguin Group (USA) Inc.

—The Great Redwall Feast. Denise, Christopher, illus. 2000. (Redwall Ser.). 64p. (J). (gr. 4-8). pap. 6.99 (978-0-698-11876-8(6) , Putnam Juvenile) Penguin Group (USA) Inc.

—The Great Redwall Feast. Denise, Christopher, illus. 2000. (Redwall Ser.). 64p. (J). (ps-3). lib. bdg. 13.79 (978-0-606-20360-9(5)) Tandem Library Bks.

—The Great Redwall Feast. 2000. (Redwall Ser.). (J). (gr. 4-8). (978-0-606-20236-7(6)) Tandem Library Bks.

—The Legend of Luke. Baker, Chris, illus. (Redwall Ser.). (gr. 4-8). 2000. 384p. (J). 23.99 (978-0-399-23490-3(X) , Philomel); 2001. 368p. reprint ed. mass mkt. 7.99 (978-0-441-00773-8(2) , Ace Bks.) Penguin Group (USA) Inc.

—The Long Patrol. Curless, Allan, illus. 1998. (Redwall Ser.). 352p. (J). (gr. 4-8). 23.99 (978-0-399-23165-0(X) , Philomel) Penguin Group (USA) Inc.

—The Long Patrol. 1999. (Redwall Ser.). (Illus.). 336p. (gr. 4-8). reprint ed. mass mkt. 7.99 (978-0-441-00599-4(3) , Ace Bks.) Penguin Group (USA) Inc.

—The Long Patrol. 1999. (Redwall Ser.). (J). (gr. 4-8). (978-0-606-15882-4(0)) Tandem Library Bks.

—Lord Brocktree. 2000. (Redwall Ser.). (Illus.). 384p. (J). (gr. 4-8). 23.99 (978-0-399-23590-0(6) , Philomel) Penguin Group (USA) Inc.

—Mariel of Redwall. Chalk, Gary, illus. 2003. (Redwall Ser.). 400p. (YA). (gr. 5). pap. 8.99 (978-0-14-230239-2(2) , Puffin) Penguin Group (USA) Inc.

—Mariel of Redwall. 2000. (Redwall Ser.). (Illus.). 384p. (gr. 4-8). mass mkt. 7.99 (978-0-441-00694-6(9) , Ace Bks.) Penguin Group (USA) Inc.

—Marlfox. Baker, Chris, illus. 1998. (Redwall Ser.). 400p. (J). (gr. 4-8). 22.99 (978-0-399-23307-4(5) , Philomel) Penguin Group (USA) Inc.

—Marlfox. (Redwall Ser.). reprint ed. 2005. 400p. (J). (gr. 5). pap. 8.99 (978-0-14-250108-5(5)); 2000. (Illus.). 384p. (gr. 4-8). mass mkt. 7.99 (978-0-441-00693-9(0) , Ace Bks.) Penguin Group (USA) Inc.

—Marlfox. 2000. (Redwall Ser.). (gr. 5-8). lib. bdg. 15.30 (978-0-613-23017-9(5)) Tandem Library Bks.

—Martin the Warrior. Chalk, Gary, illus. 2004. (Redwall Ser.). 376p. (YA). 8.99 (978-0-14-240055-5(6) , Puffin) Penguin Group (USA) Inc.

—Martin the Warrior Bks. 1-3: The Prisoner & the Tyrant; Actors & Searchers; The Battle of Marshank. unabr. ed. 2004. (Redwall Ser.). (J). (gr. 4-7). 10p. pap. 50.00 incl. audio (978-0-8072-8177-2(8) , YA124CX); 376p. pap. 58.00 incl. audio (978-0-8072-8178-9(6) , YA124SP) Random Hse. Audio Publishing Group. (Listening Library).

—Mattimeo. Chalk, Gary, illus. 2003. (Redwall Ser.). 448p. (J). pap. 8.99 (978-0-14-230240-8(6) , Puffin) Penguin Group (USA) Inc.

—Mattimeo. 1999. (Redwall Ser.). (Illus.). 448p. (gr. 4-8). mass mkt. 7.99 (978-0-441-00610-6(8) , Ace Bks.) Penguin Group (USA) Inc.

—Mossflower. 2002. (Redwall Ser.). (Illus.). 432p. pap. 8.99 (978-0-14-230238-5(4) , Puffin) Penguin Group (USA) Inc.

—Mossflower. Elliott, David W., illus. collector's ed. 2004. (Redwall Ser.). 432p. (YA). (gr. 4). 30.00 (978-0-399-24031-7(4) , Philomel) Penguin Group (USA) Inc.

—Mossflower. 1998. (Redwall Ser.). (Illus.). 384p. (gr. 4-8). reprint ed. mass mkt. 7.99 (978-0-441-00576-5(4) , Ace Bks.) Penguin Group (USA) Inc.

—Pearls of Lutra. 1998. (Redwall Ser.). (Illus.). 368p. (gr. 4-8). mass mkt. 7.99 (978-0-441-00508-6(X) , Ace Bks.) Penguin Group (USA) Inc.

—Pearls of Lutra. 1998. (Redwall Ser.). (J). (gr. 4-8). (978-0-606-13015-8(2)) Tandem Library Bks.

—Redwall. 2002. (Redwall Ser.). (Illus.). 352p. (J). pap. 8.99 (978-0-14-230237-8(6) , Puffin) Penguin Group (USA) Inc.

—Redwall. Howell, Troy, illus. 2000. (Redwall Ser.). 352p. (J). (gr. 4-8). pap. 12.99 (978-0-399-23629-7(5) , Philomel) Penguin Group (USA) Inc.

—Redwall. 10th anniv. ed. 1998. (Redwall Ser.). (Illus.). 352p. (gr. 4-8). mass mkt. 7.99 (978-0-441-00548-2(9) , Ace Bks.) Penguin Group (USA) Inc.

—Redwall. 1998. (Redwall Ser.). (J). (gr. 4-8). (978-0-606-13734-8(3)) Tandem Library Bks.

—Redwall Map & Riddle Book: Includes the Redwall Riddler! Baker, Chris & Curless, Allan, illus. 1998. (Redwall Ser.). (J). (gr. 4-8). 9.99 (978-0-399-23248-0(6) , Philomel) Penguin Group (USA) Inc.

—A Redwall Winter's Tale. Denise, Christopher, illus. 2001. (Redwall Ser.). 80p. (J). (gr. 4-8). 18.99 (978-0-399-23346-3(6) , Philomel) Penguin Group (USA) Inc.

—Salamandastron. Chalk, Gary, illus. 2003. (Redwall Ser.). 400p. (YA). pap. 8.99 (978-0-14-250152-8(2) , Puffin) Penguin Group (USA) Inc.

—Salamandastron. 2003. (Redwall Ser.). (gr. 5-8). lib. bdg. 16.45 (978-0-613-71576-8(4)) Tandem Library Bks.

—Seven Strange & Ghostly Tales. 1999. (Illus.). 144p. (J). (gr. 4-7). pap. 5.99 (978-0-698-11808-9(1) , Putnam Juvenile) Penguin Group (USA) Inc.

—Seven Strange & Ghostly Tales. 144p. (J). (gr. 3-5). pap. 5.99 (978-0-8072-1486-2(8) , Listening Library) Random Hse. Audio Publishing Group.

—Seven Strange & Ghostly Tales. 1999. (Illus.). (J). (978-0-606-16802-1(8)) Tandem Library Bks.

—The Taggerung. Standley, Peter, illus. (Redwall Ser.). 448p. 2003. pap. 8.99 (978-0-14-250154-2(9) , Puffin); 2001. (J). (gr. 3-6). 23.99 (978-0-399-23720-1(8) , Philomel) Penguin Group (USA) Inc.

—The Taggerung. 2002. (Redwall Ser.). (Illus.). 416p. reprint ed. mass mkt. 7.99 (978-0-441-00968-8(9) , Ace Bks.) Penguin Group (USA) Inc.

—The Taggerung. 2001. (Redwall Ser.). (Illus.). 384p. (J). (978-0-09-176928-4(0) , Hutchinson) Random Hse.

—The Taggerung. Standley, Peter, illus. l.t. ed. 2002. (Redwall Ser.). 683p. (J). 25.95 (978-0-7862-4014-2(8)) Thomson Gale.

—Triss. Elliot, David, illus. 2002. (Redwall Ser.). 432p. (YA). 23.99 (978-0-399-23723-2(2) , Philomel) Penguin Group (USA) Inc.

REED, HENRY (FICTITIOUS CHARACTER)—FICTION

Robertson, Keith. Henry Reed, Inc. abr. ed. (J). (gr. 4-7). pap. 15.95 incl. audio (978-0-670-36801-3(6)) Live Oak Media.

—Henry Reed, Inc., Set. McCloskey, Robert, illus. abr. ed. (J). (gr. 4-7). 24.95 incl. audio (978-0-670-36800-6(8)) Live Oak Media.

REED, WALTER, 1851-1902

Bednarz, Robert, et al. TIME for Kids Readers: Walter Reed. 3rd ed. 2002. (Harcourt Horizons Ser.). (gr. k-7). pap. 38.10 (978-0-15-335286-7(8)) Harcourt Schl. Pubs.

REFERENCE BOOKS

see also Encyclopedias and Dictionaries

Brown, Liz. Reference Materials. 2007. (J). (***978-1-59036-758-2(8)***); lib. bdg. (***978-1-59036-757-5(X)***) Weigl Pubs., Inc.

Child Horizons, 10 vols, Set. Incl. Bible Story Hour. Johnson, Louisa M. (gr. k-4). 1996. 22.95 (978-0-87392-002-5(3)); Parade of Stories. Neigoff, Anne, ed. (gr. k-4). 1996. 22.95 (978-0-87392-005-6(8)); Plant & Animal Ways. Murphy, Margaret. (gr. 4-6). 1996. 22.95 (978-0-87392-114-5(3)); Questions Children Ask. Bonhivert, Edith & Bonhivert, Ernest. (gr. 2-4). 1997. 22.95 (978-0-87392-010-0(4)); Story Hour. Bjoland, Ester M. (gr. k-4). 1996. 22.95 (978-0-87392-003-2(1)); Words to Know. Bricker, Harry & Beckwith, Yvonne. (gr. k-3). 1997. 22.95 (978-0-87392-011-7(2)); (J). 200.00 (978-0-87392-500-6(9) , Ferguson Publishing Co.) Facts On File, Inc.

Dumont, Thora & Malone, Janet. Nemeth Reference Sheets. 2003. spiral bd. 14.95 (978-0-939173-56-3(5)) National Braille Pr.

Hamilton, John. Libraries & Reference Materials. 2005. (Straight to the Source Ser.). (Illus.). 32p. (J). (gr. k-6). lib. bdg. 22.78 (978-1-59197-545-8(X)) ABDO Publishing Co.

Helbrough, Emma. Book of Knowledge. 2004. 208p. (J). lib. bdg. 27.95 (978-1-58086-612-5(3) , Usborne); (Illus.). 19.99 (978-0-7945-0594-3(5)) EDC Publishing.

Lakeshore Learning Materials Staff, contrib. by. Desktop Reference Library, 10 vols. , Set. 2000. (J). pap. 59.95 (978-1-929255-92-4(6)) Lakeshore Learning Materials.

Lawler, Rick. How to Contact World Leaders 2004 Edition: Write * Phone * Fax * E-mail. 2004. 220p. per. 18.95 (978-1-930322-07-3(0)) MinRef Pr.

Longman. Longman Children's Picture Dictionary. 2002. (Illus.). (C). pap. 19.67 (978-962-00-5233-0(1)) Longman Publishing Group.

Lorenz Books Staff & Charman, Andy. Facts. 2000. (My Big Book of Ser.). (Illus.). 48p. (gr. k-4). pap. 7.95 (978-0-7548-0228-0(0) , Lorenz Bks.) Anness Publishing, Inc.

McGraw-Hill Staff. Children's Factfinder. 2000. (Fact Finders Ser.). (Illus.). 336p. (J). (gr. k-5). pap. 24.95 (978-1-57768-768-9(X)) School Specialty Publishing.

O'Laughlin, Michael C. By Mac & 'O' You'll Always Know, Mac, Mc, & 'O' Names in Ireland, Scotland & America: With Census Records from the 17th to 20th Century. 2003. (Illus.). 60p. spiral bd. 25.00 net. (978-0-940134-60-7(8)) Irish Genealogical Foundation.

Stremme, Robert, et al. Scholastic Book of Lists. 2003. (Illus.). 320p. (J). pap. 8.95 (978-0-439-41905-5(0) , Scholastic Reference) Scholastic, Inc.

Top That Publishing Staff, ed. Survival. 2004. (I-Quest Ser.). (Illus.). 48p. (J). per. (978-1-84510-176-3(6)) Top That! Publishing PLC.

Watson, Carol. My First Book of Facts. (Illus.). (J). pap. 18.95 (978-0-590-74341-9(4)) Scholastic, Inc.

REFORM, SOCIAL

see Social Problems

REFORM OF CRIMINALS

see Crime and Criminals

REFORMATION

see also Europe—History—1492-1789; Protestantism

Booth, Edwin P. Martin Luther: The Great Reformer. 1999. (Heroes of the Faith Ser.). 208p. (J). (ps up). 14.95 (978-0-7910-5037-8(8) , Chelsea Hse.) Facts On File, Inc.

Chibi, Andrew A. The English Reformation: The Effect on a Nation. 2003. (Studymates Ser.). (Illus.). 98p. pap. (978-1-84285-024-4(5)) Studymates Ltd.

—The European Reformation: A Student's Guide to the Key Ideas & the Events They Shaped. 2002. (Illus.). 144p. (YA). pap. 23.50 (978-1-84025-130-2(1)) Studymates Ltd. GBR. *Dist:* Trans-Atlantic Pubns., Inc.

Crompton, Samuel Willard. Martin Luther. 2003. (Spiritual Leaders & Thinkers Ser.). (Illus.). 120p. (gr. 9-13). 30.00 (978-0-7910-7863-1(9) , Chelsea Hse.) Facts On File, Inc.

Davis, Thomas J. John Calvin. 2004. (Spiritual Leaders & Thinkers Ser.). (Illus.). 120p. (J). (gr. 9-13). 30.00 (978-0-7910-8100-6(1) , Chelsea Hse.) Facts On File, Inc.

Hinds, Kathryn. The Church. 2000. (Life in the Middle Ages Ser.). (Illus.). 80p. (J). (gr. 5 up). lib. bdg. 29.93 (978-0-7614-1008-9(2) , Benchmark Bks.) Cavendish, Marshall Corp.

Lockman, Vic. Church History for Young Children with Cartoons: The Reformation, 2 vols. 1998. (Illus.). 45p. (J). (ps-4). 1.75 (978-0-936175-36-2(2)) Lockman, Vic.

MacDonald, Fiona. The Reformation. 2002. (Events & Outcomes Ser.). (Illus.). 80p. (J). lib. bdg. (978-0-7398-5800-4(9)) Raintree.

Meet Martin Luther. 2004. (Exploring Luther's Small Catechism Ser.). (gr. 3-4). 2.99 (978-0-8066-6784-3(2)) Augsburg Fortress, Pubs.

Prum, Deborah M. Rats, Bulls & Flying Machines: A History of the Renaissance & Reformation. Holdren, John, ed. 1999. (Core Chronicles Ser.: Vol. 1). (Illus.). (YA). (gr. 5-10). 106p. 21.95 (978-1-890517-19-9(4)); pap. 11.95 (978-1-890517-18-2(6)) Core Knowledge Foundation.

Reformation: PowerPoint Presentation in World History. 2005. cd-rom 49.95 net. (978-1-56004-216-7(8)) Social Studies Schl. Service.

Reformation DBA. 2003. spiral bd. 16.95 (978-1-56004-167-2(6)) Social Studies Schl. Service.

Rijswijk, Cor van. John Is Not Afraid. 2004. (Illus.). 43p. (J). (978-1-894666-81-7(X)) Inheritance Pubns.

—Martin Shows the Way. 2004. (Illus.). 43p. (J). (978-1-894666-80-0(1)) Inheritance Pubns.

Saari, Peggy, et al, eds. Renaissance & Reformation, 2 vols. 2002. (Illus.). (J). (978-0-7876-5468-9(X)); (978-0-7876-5469-6(8)) Thomson Gale. (UXL).

Saari, Peggy & Saari, Aaron Maurice. Renaissance & Reformation: Biographies, 2 vols. 2002. (Illus.). (J). 400p. 120.00 (978-0-7876-5470-2(1) , GML00502-173752); xxxiv, 386p. (978-0-7876-5472-6(8)); xxxiv, 386p. (978-0-7876-5471-9(X)) Thomson Gale. (UXL).

Somervill, Barbara A. Catherine de Medici: The Power Behind the French Throne. 2006. (Signature Lives Ser.). (Illus.). 112p. (J). (gr. 5-7). 30.60 (978-0-7565-1581-2(5)) Compass Point Bks.

REFORMATION—FICTION

Charles, Elizabeth. From Dark to Dawn: A Tale of Martin Luther & the Reformation. James and Stacy McDonald & Marilyn Rockett, eds. Johannah Bluedorn, illus. 2003. Orig. Title: Chronicles of the Schonburg Cotta Family. xxi, 370p. 19.99 (978-0-9743390-0-9(8)) Books on the Path.

Farenhorst, Christine. Wings like a Dove: The Courage of Queen Jeanne D'Albret. 2006. (Chosen Daughters Ser.). 208p. (J). per. 11.99 (978-0-87552-642-3(X)) P & R Publishing.

Marston, Hope Irvin. Against the Tide: The Valor of Margaret Wilson. 2007. (J). pap. (***978-1-59638-061-5(6)***) P & R Publishing.

Van Heerde, Gerrit. The Man with the Red Beard. Van Bergen, Jantien, illus. 2002. (J). (978-0-9579517-0-9(1)) Inheritance Pubns.

REFORMERS

Allison, Amy. Roger Williams: Founder of Rhode Island. 2000. (Colonial Leaders Ser.). (Illus.). 80p. (J). (gr. 8-12). 27.50 (978-0-7910-5964-7(2) , Chelsea Hse.) Facts On File, Inc.

Bernard, Catherine J. Sojourner Truth: Abolitionist & Women's Rights Activist. 2001. (Historical American Biographies Ser.). (Illus.). 112p. (YA). (gr. 6-12). lib. bdg. 26.60 (978-0-7660-1257-8(3)) Enslow Pubs., Inc.

Butler, Mary G. Sojourner Truth: From Slave to Activist for Freedom. 2005. (Library of American Lives & Times). (Illus.). 112p. (YA). (gr. 4-8). lib. bdg. 31.95 (978-0-8239-5736-1(5)) Rosen Publishing Group, Inc., The.

Collins, Kathleen. Sojourner Truth: Equal Rights Advocate. 2003. (Famous People in American History Ser.). (Illus.). 32p. (J). pap. 6.50 (978-0-8239-4193-3(0)) Rosen Publishing Group, Inc., The.

Cox, Vicki. Margaret Sanger. 2004. (Women in Medicine Ser.). (Illus.). 112p. (gr. 6-12). 30.00 (978-0-7910-8030-6(7) , Chelsea Hse.) Facts On File, Inc.

Crompton, Samuel Willard. Martin Luther. 2003. (Spiritual Leaders & Thinkers Ser.). (Illus.). 120p. (gr. 9-13). 30.00 (978-0-7910-7863-1(9) , Chelsea Hse.) Facts On File, Inc.

Frost, Helen. Sojourner Truth. Saunders-Smith, Gail, ed. 2003. (Famous Americans Ser.). (Illus.). 24p. (J). (gr. k-1). lib. bdg. 15.93 (978-0-7368-1640-3(2) , Pebble Bks.) Capstone Pr., Inc.

Gaustad, Edwin S. Roger Williams: Prophet of Liberty. 2001. (Oxford Portraits Ser.). (Illus.). 144p. (YA). (gr. 9 up). 28.00 (978-0-19-513000-3(6)) Oxford Univ. Pr., Inc.

Gillis, Jennifer Blizin. Sojourner Truth. 2005. (Illus.). 32p. (J). (978-1-4034-6981-6(4)); pap. (978-1-4034-6988-5(1)) Heinemann Library.

Harvey, Bonnie Carman. Carry A. Nation: Saloon Smasher & Prohibitionist. 2002. (Historical American Biographies Ser.). (Illus.). 128p. (YA). (gr. 6-12). lib. bdg. 26.60 (978-0-7660-1907-2(1)) Enslow Pubs., Inc.

Hirsch, E. D., ed. Civil Rights Leaders. 2003. tchr. ed. 9.95 (978-0-7690-5053-9(0)); stu. ed. 49.95 (978-0-7690-2958-0(2)) Pearson Learning.

Jaffe, Elizabeth Dana. Sojourner Truth. 2001. (Compass Point Early Biographies Ser.). (Illus.). 32p. (J). (gr. 2 up). lib. bdg. 21.26 (978-0-7565-0068-9(0)) Compass Point Bks.

Krass, Peter. Sojourner Truth. 2004. (Black Americans of Achievement Ser.). (Illus.). 112p. (J). (gr. 6-12). 30.00 (978-0-7910-8165-5(6) , Chelsea Hse.) Facts On File, Inc.

—Sojourner Truth: Antislavery Activist. 2005. (Black Americans of Achievement Ser.). (Illus.). 112p. (J). (gr. 6-12). pap. 13.25 (978-0-7910-8339-0(X) , Chelsea Hse.) Facts On File, Inc.

Kudlinski, Kathleen. Sojourner Truth. 2003. (gr. 3-6). lib. bdg. 13.00 (978-0-613-61658-4(8)) Tandem Library Bks.

—Sojourner Truth: Voice for Freedom. Wooden, Lenny, illus. 2003. (Childhood of Famous Americans Ser.). 160p. (Orig.). mass mkt. 5.99 (978-0-689-85274-9(6) , Aladdin) Simon & Schuster Children's Publishing.

Leebrick, Kristal. Sojourner Truth. 2002. (Let Freedom Ring Ser.). (Illus.). 48p. (J). (gr. 3-4). lib. bdg. 22.60 (978-0-7368-1090-6(0) , Bridgestone Bks.) Capstone Pr., Inc.

Lutz, Norma Jean. Sojourner Truth. 2001. (gr. 5-8). lib. bdg. 17.60 (978-0-613-33074-9(9)) Tandem Library Bks.

—Sojourner Truth: Abolitionist, Suffragist, & Preacher. (Famous Figures of the Civil War Era Ser.). (Illus.). 80p. (J). (gr. 4-7). 2001. 25.00 (978-0-7910-6007-0(1)); 2000. pap. 25.00 (978-0-7910-6145-9(0)) Facts On File, Inc. (Chelsea Hse.).

Malam, John. Sojourner Truth. 2000. (Tell Me about Ser.). (Illus.). 22p. (J). 16.95 (978-0-237-51972-8(0) , Evans Brothers, Limited) Evans Publishing Group GBR. *Dist:* Independent Pubs. Group.

Marsh, Carole. James Groppi. 2002. (One Thousand Readers Ser.). (Illus.). 12p. (J). (gr. k-4). 2.95 (978-0-635-01543-3(9) , 15439) Gallopade International.

—Jane Addams. 2002. (One Thousand Readers Ser.). (Illus.). 12p. (J). (gr. k-4). 2.95 (978-0-635-01472-6(6) , 14726) Gallopade International.

Mattern, Joanne. Sojourner Truth: Early Abolitionist. 2003. (Reading Power Ser.). (Illus.). 24p. (J). lib. bdg. 17.25 (978-0-8239-6502-1(3) , PowerKids Pr.) Rosen Publishing Group, Inc., The.

McKissack, Patricia C. & McKissack, Fredrick L. Sojourner Truth: A Voice for Freedom. rev. ed. 2002. (Great African Americans Ser.). (Illus.). 32p. (J). (gr. 1-4). lib. bdg. 18.60 (978-0-7660-1693-4(5)) Enslow Pubs., Inc.

Muckenhoupt, Margaret. Dorothea Dix: Advocate for Mental Health Care. 2004. (Oxford Portraits Ser.). (Illus.). 128p. (YA). 28.00 (978-0-19-512921-2(0)) Oxford Univ. Pr., Inc.

Noyed, Robert B. Susan B. Anthony: Reformer. 2002. (Spirit of America: Our People Ser.). (Illus.). 32p. (J). (gr. 2-6). 27.07 (978-1-56766-171-2(8)) Child's World, Inc.

Raum, Elizabeth. Jane Addams. 2004. (American Lives (Heinemann Library (Firm))). (Illus.). 32p. (J). pap. 7.50 (978-1-4034-5707-3(7)); lib. bdg. (978-1-4034-4992-4(9)) Heinemann Library.

—Roger Williams. 2004. (Illus.). 32p. (J). pap. 7.50 (978-1-4034-5969-5(X)); lib. bdg. 25.64 (978-1-4034-5961-9(4)) Heinemann Library.

Rockwell, Anne F. Only Passing Through: The Story of Sojourner Truth. Siscoe, Nancy, ed. Christie, R. Gregory, illus. 2000. 40p. (J). (gr. 2-5). 16.95 (978-0-679-89186-4(2)); lib. bdg. 18.99 (978-0-679-99186-1(7)) Random Hse. Children's Bks. (Knopf Bks. for Young Readers).

Roop, Connie & Roop, Peter. Sojourner Truth. 2003. (In Their Own Words Ser.). (Illus.). 128p. (J). (gr. 2-5). 4.99 (978-0-439-26323-8(9) , Scholastic Nonfiction) Scholastic, Inc.

Roop, Peter. Sojourner Truth. 2002. (gr. 3-6). lib. bdg. 12.40 (978-0-613-66669-5(0)) Tandem Library Bks.

Ruffin, Frances E. "Unsinkable" Molly Brown. 2002. (American Legends Ser.). (Illus.). 24p. (J). (gr. 3). lib. bdg. 18.75 (978-0-8239-5827-6(2) , PowerKids Pr.) Rosen Publishing Group, Inc., The.

Shaw, Maura D. Dorothy Day: A Catholic Life of Action. Marchesi, Stephen, illus. 2004. (Spiritual Biographies for Young Readers Ser.). 32p. (J). 12.99 (978-1-59473-011-5(3)) SkyLight Paths Publishing.

Somervill, Barbara A. Martin Luther: Father of the Reformation. 2006. (Signature Lives Ser.). (Illus.). 112p. (J). (gr. 5-7). 30.60 (978-0-7565-1593-5(9)) Compass Point Bks.

Stuart Kallen. Political Activists of the 1960s. 2004. (History Makers Ser.). (Illus.). 96p. (J). 29.95 (978-1-59018-386-1(X)) Thomson Gale.

Swain, Gwenyth. Sojourner Truth. Archambault, Matthew, illus. 2005. (On My Own Biography Ser.). 48p. (J). (ps-ps). pap. 5.95 (978-1-57505-827-6(8)) Lerner Publishing Group.

—Sojourner Truth. 2005. (On My Own Biography Ser.). (Illus.). 48p. (J). 25.26 (978-1-57505-651-7(8) , Carolrhoda Bks.) Lerner Publishing Group.

Thomas, Paul. Campaigners. 2002. (History Makers Ser.). (Illus.). 48p. (J). lib. bdg. 28.50 (978-1-931983-40-2(2)) Chrysalis Education.

Whalin, W. Terry. Sojourner Truth: American Abolitionist. Landgraf, Ken, illus. 1999. (Young Reader's Christian Library). 222p. (J). (gr. 8-12). pap. 1.39 (978-1-57748-515-5(7)) Barbour Publishing, Inc.

—Sojourner Truth: American Abolitionist. 1999. (Heroes of the Faith Ser.). 208p. (YA). (gr. 4-7). 14.95 (978-0-7910-5034-7(3) , Chelsea Hse.) Facts On File, Inc.

REFRIGERATION AND REFRIGERATING MACHINERY

Ford, Barbara. Keeping Things Cool: Inventions That Changed Our Lives. (J). lib. bdg. 20.90 (978-0-8027-6616-8(1)) Walker & Co.

Plumbing, Heating, Air Conditioning & Refrigeration Student Activity. 2004. (YA). cd-rom (978-1-57078-954-0(1) , CEV60033) C E V Multimedia, Ltd.

El saqueo del Refrigerador. 2000. (McGraw-Hill Ciencias Ser.). (ENG & SPA.). (gr. 3 up). (978-0-02-279632-7(0)) Macmillan/McGraw-Hill Schl. Div.

REFUGEES

Asgedom, Mawi. Of Beetles & Angels: A Boy's Remarkable Journey from A Refugee Camp to Harvard. 2002. (gr. 5-8). lib. bdg. 18.45 (978-0-613-64198-2(1)) Tandem Library Bks.

Barr, Linda. Long Road to Freedom: Journey of the Hmong. (High Five Reading Ser.). (J). (ps-k). 2005. (Illus.). 64p. lib. bdg. 23.93 (978-0-7368-3880-1(5)); 2004. pap. (978-0-7368-3852-8(X)) Capstone Pr., Inc.

Borden, Louise. The Journey That Saved Curious George: The True Wartime Escape of Margret & H. A. Rey. Drummond, Allan, illus. 2005. 80p. (J). (gr. 3-5). 17.00 (978-0-618-33924-2(8)) Houghton Mifflin Co. Trade & Reference Div.

Bryan, Nichol. Haitian Americans. 2004. (One Nation Ser.). (Illus.). 32p. (J). (gr. k-6). lib. bdg. 22.78 (978-1-57765-982-2(1)) ABDO Publishing Co.

—Jewish Americans. 2004. (One Nation Ser.). (Illus.). 32p. (J). (gr. k-6). lib. bdg. 22.78 (978-1-57765-986-0(4)) ABDO Publishing Co.

—Somali Americans. 2004. (One Nation Ser.). (Illus.). 32p. (J). (gr. k-6). lib. bdg. 22.78 (978-1-57765-989-1(9)) ABDO Publishing Co.

Cohen, Sheila. Mai Ya's Long Journey. 2005. (Badger Biographies Ser.). (Illus.). 80p. (J). (gr. 3-8). pap. 12.95 (978-0-87020-365-7(7)) Wisconsin Historical Society.

Coleman, Lori. Vietnamese in America. 2005. (In America Ser.). (Illus.). 80p. (J). (gr. 5-8). lib. bdg. 27.93 (978-0-8225-3951-3(9)) Lerner Publishing Group.

Colson, Mary. The Story Behind Anne Holm's I Am David. 2006. (History in Literature Ser.). (Illus.). 56p. (YA). (gr. 7 up). lib. bdg. 32.86 (978-1-4034-8204-4(7)) Heinemann Library.

Dalton, Dave. Economic Migrants. 2005. (People on the Move Ser.). (Illus.). 56p. (J). pap. (978-1-4034-6964-9(4)); (gr. 6-9). lib. bdg. 31.36 (978-1-4034-6959-5(8)) Heinemann Library.

—Refugees & Asylum Seekers. 2005. (People on the Move Ser.). (Illus.). 56p. (J). pap. (978-1-4034-6966-3(0)); (YA). (gr. 6-9). lib. bdg. 31.36 (978-1-4034-6961-8(X)) Heinemann Library.

Dalton, David. Living in a Refugee Camp: Carbino's Story. 2005. (Illus.). 48p. (J). lib. bdg. 30.00 (978-0-8368-5960-7(X) , World Almanac Library) Stevens, Gareth Inc.

Dolphin, Laurie. Our Journey from Tibet. Johnson, Nancy Jo, photos by. 2006. (Illus.). 40p. (J). (gr. k-4). 16.00 (978-0-7567-9812-3(4)) DIANE Publishing Co.

Downing, David. Persecution & Emigration. 2005. (World Almanac Library of the Holocaust). (Illus.). 48p. (978-0-8368-5951-5(0)); (YA). (gr. 5 up). lib. bdg. 30.00 (978-0-8368-5944-7(8)) Stevens, Gareth Inc. (World Almanac Library).

Fitterer, C. Ann. Vietnamese Americans. 2002. (Spirit of America: Our Cultural Heritage Ser.). (Illus.). 32p. (J). (gr. 2-6). 27.07 (978-1-56766-160-6(2)) Child's World, Inc.

Gay, Kathlyn. Leaving Cuba: From Operation Pedro Pan to Elian. 2000. (Single Titles Ser.: up). (Illus.). 144p. (gr. 7 up). lib. bdg. (978-0-7613-1466-0(0) , Twenty-First Century Bks.) Lerner Publishing Group.

Gifford, Clive. Refugees. 2002. (World Issues Ser.). (Illus.). 57p. (J). lib. bdg. 28.50 (978-1-931983-27-3(5)) Chrysalis Education.

Gottfried, Ted. Displaced Persons: Growing up American after the Holocaust. 2001. (Holocaust Ser.). (Illus.). 112p. (gr. 7 up). lib. bdg. 29.90 (978-0-7613-1924-5(7) , Twenty-First Century Bks.) Lerner Publishing Group.

Howard, Helen, et al. Living As a Refugee in America: Mohammed's Story. 2005. (J). lib. bdg. 30.00 (978-0-8368-5959-1(6) , World Almanac Library) Stevens, Gareth Inc.

Kalman, Bobbie. Refugee Child: My Memories of the 1956 Hungarian Revolution. Bedell, Barbara, illus. 2006. 224p. (J). (gr. 5 up). pap. (978-0-7787-2760-6(2)) Crabtree Publishing Co.

Kalman, Bobbie. Refugee Child Activity Guide. 2006. (Illus.). 32p. (gr. 5-8). (***978-0-7787-2759-0(9)***) Crabtree Publishing Co.

Kaplan, William & Tanaka, Shelley. One More Border: The True Story of One Family's Escape from War-Torn Europe. Taylor, Stephen, illus. 2004. 61p. (J). (gr. 3-6). pap. 9.95 (978-0-88899-638-1(1)) Groundwood Bks. CAN. *Dist:* Perseus Distribution.

Kilbourne, Sarah S. Leaving Vietnam Class set: The True Story of Tuan Ngo. 1999. (J). (gr. 2 up). pap., stu. ed. 22.24 incl. audio (978-0-7887-3176-1(9) , 40911) Recorded Bks., LLC.

Kozol, Jonathan. Rachel & Her Children: Homeless Families in America. 2006. 320p. 13.95 (978-0-307-34589-9(0) , Three Rivers Pr.) Crown Publishing Group.

Leembruggen, Melissa. The Sudan Project: Rebuilding with the People of Darfur: A Young Person's Guide. 2007. pap. 10.00 (***978-0-687-65050-7(X)***) Abingdon Pr.

Levy, Janey. Refugee Workers. 2006. (Extreme Careers Ser.). (Illus.). 64p. (J). (gr. 5-8). lib. bdg. 26.50 (978-1-4042-0960-2(3)) Rosen Publishing Group, Inc., The.

Libal, Autumn. Cuban Americans: Exiles from an Island Home. 2005. (Illus.). 112p. (J). (ps-7). lib. bdg. (978-1-59084-928-6(0)) Mason Crest Pubs.

MacGowan, Shane & O'Callaghan, Deirdre. Hide That Can: A Photographic Diary of the Men of Arlington House. 2002. (Illus.). 192p. 39.95 (978-0-9542079-8-4(X)) Trolley GBR. *Dist:* D.A.P./Distributed Art Pubs.

Maddocks, Steven. Refugees. 2003. (Face the Facts Ser.). (Illus.). 56p. (J). lib. bdg. 28.56 (978-0-7398-6850-8(0)) Raintree.

Marx, Trish. One Boy from Kosovo. 2000. (Illus.). (YA). (gr. 2-5). 24p. 15.95 (978-0-688-17732-4(8)); 32p. 15.89 (978-0-688-17733-1(6)) HarperCollins Pubs.

Miller, Karen, ed. Immigration. 2006. 110p. (YA). (gr. 8 up). lib. bdg. 29.95 (***978-0-7377-2893-4(0)*** , Greenhaven Pr., Inc.) Thomson Gale.

Naidoo, Beverley & Holt, Kate. Making It Home: A Childs Eye of Life As a Refugee. 2004. (Illus.). 144p. (J). (***978-0-14-131867-7(8)*** , Puffin) Penguin Group (USA) Inc.

Price, Sean. Varian Fry: A Hero of the Holocaust. 2007. (J). (***978-1-4109-2696-8(6));*** pap. (***978-1-4109-2707-1(5)***) Steck-Vaughn.

Schwartz, Eric. Central American Immigrants to the United States: Refugees from Unrest. 2005. (Illus.). 112p. (J). (ps-7). lib. bdg. (978-1-59084-929-3(9)) Mason Crest Pubs.

Senker, Cath. Why Are People Refugees? 2004. (Exploring Tough Issues Ser.). (J). 29.93 (978-0-7398-6685-6(0)) Raintree.

Smith, Trevor. Migrants & Refugees. 2004. (Understanding Global Issues Ser.). (Illus.). 56p. (J). (gr. 10-12). (978-1-58340-360-0(4)) Smart Apple Media.

Springstubb, Tricia. The Vietnamese-Americans. 2001. (Immigrants in America Ser.). (Illus.). 104p. (YA). (gr. 4-12). 29.95 (978-1-56006-964-5(3) , LML00902-179007, Lucent Bks.) Thomson Gale.

Staeger, Rob. Asylees. 2003. (Changing Face of North America Ser.). (Illus.). 112p. (J). lib. bdg. (978-1-59084-685-8(0)) Mason Crest Pubs.

Teenage Refugees Speak Out. 2005. (Illus.). (gr. 7-12). lib. bdg. 344.50 (978-0-8239-9331-4(0)) Rosen Publishing Group, Inc., The.

REFUGEES—FICTION

Bat-Ami, Miriam. Two Suns in the Sky. 1999. 208p. (YA). (gr. 7-12). 17.95 (978-0-8126-2900-2(0)) Cricket Bks.

—Two Suns in the Sky. 2001. 208p. (J). pap. 6.99 (978-0-14-230036-7(5) , Puffin) Penguin Group (USA) Inc.

—Two Suns in the Sky. 2001. (gr. 7-12). lib. bdg. 15.30 (978-0-613-44425-5(6)) Tandem Library Bks.

Bradman, Tony. Give Me Shelter. 2007. 127p. (YA). (gr. 4 up). 16.95 (978-1-84507-522-4(6)) Lincoln, Frances Ltd. GBR. *Dist:* Perseus Distribution.

Brown, Jackie. Little Cricket. 2004. (Illus.). 224p. (gr. 4-7). 15.99 (978-0-7868-1852-5(2)) Hyperion Bks. for Children.

Burg, Ann E. Rebekkah's Journey: A World War II Refugee Story. Iskowitz, Joel, illus. 2006. 48p. (J). (gr. 3-5). 17.95 (978-1-58536-275-2(1)) Sleeping Bear Pr.

Burns Knight, Margy, et al. Who Belongs Here? An American Story. 2nd ed. 2004. (Illus.). 40p. (gr. 3-8). 16.95 (978-0-88448-110-2(7)) Tilbury Hse. Pubs.

Casanova, Mary. Klipfish Code. 2007. 240p. (J). (gr. 5-7). 16.00 (***978-0-618-88393-6(2)***) Houghton Mifflin Co. Trade & Reference Div.

Choyce, Lesley. Refuge Cove. 2002. (Orca Soundings Ser.). 96p. (J). (gr. 7-12). pap. 7.95 (978-1-55143-246-5(3)) Orca Bk. Pubs. USA.

—Refuge Cove. 2002. (gr. 7-12). lib. bdg. 16.40 (978-0-613-62990-4(6)) Tandem Library Bks.

Cooney, Caroline B. Diamonds in the Shadow. 2007. (YA). (gr. 7). 240p. lib. bdg. 18.99 (***978-0-385-90278-6(6));*** 228p. 15.99 (***978-0-385-73261-1(9)***) Random Hse. Children's Bks. (Delacorte Bks. for Young Readers).

Cornwell, Nikki. Christophe's Story. Littlewood, Karin, illus. 2007. 96p. (J). (gr. 3 up). 14.95 (***978-1-84507-765-5(2)***) Lincoln, Frances Ltd. GBR. *Dist:* Perseus Distribution.

Dowd, John. Hogsty Reef. 1999. 192p. (YA). (gr. 6-10). pap. 5.95 (978-1-56145-187-6(8) , Q19223) Peachtree Pubs., Ltd.

—Hogsty Reef. 1999. (gr. 7-12). lib. bdg. 14.10 (978-0-613-29258-0(8)) Tandem Library Bks.

Ellis, Deborah. Mud City. (Illus.). 176p. 2004. (J). pap. 5.95 (978-0-88899-542-1(3)); 2003. (gr. 5-9). 15.95 (978-0-88899-518-6(0)) Groundwood Bks. CAN. *Dist:* Perseus Distribution.

Evans, Alwyn. Walk in My Shoes. 2005. 360p. (J). pap. 14.00 (978-0-14-300231-4(7) , Penguin Global) Penguin Group (USA) Inc.

Giff, Patricia Reilly. Lily's Crossing. 2002. (Illus.). (J). 13.94 (978-0-7587-0287-6(6)) Book Wholesalers, Inc.

—Lily's Crossing. 1999. (Yearling Newbery Ser.). 208p. (J). (gr. 5-7). reprint ed. pap. 6.50 (978-0-440-41453-7(9) , Yearling) Random Hse. Children's Bks.

—Lily's Crossing. 1999. (gr. 5-8). lib. bdg. 13.55 (978-0-613-10350-3(5)); (Illus.). (J). (978-0-606-14423-0(4)) Tandem Library Bks.

—Lily's Crossing. l.t. ed. 200p. 2003. pap. 10.95 (978-0-7862-6189-5(7)); 2000. (Illus.). (J). 22.95 (978-0-7862-2771-6(0)) Thorndike Pr.

Goode, Katherine. Jumping to Heaven: Stories about Refugee Children. 2004. 176p. (J). pap. 16.95 (978-1-86254-427-7(1)) Wakefield Pr. Pty, Ltd. AUS. *Dist:* Independent Pubs. Group.

Harris, Christine. The Silver Path. (Illus.). (J). (CHI & ENG.). 32p. (978-1-85430-323-3(6) , 93425); (ENG & VIE., 26p. (978-1-85430-327-1(9) , 93381) Magi Pubns.

Hoffman, Mary. The Color of Home. Littlewood, Karin, illus. 2002. 32p. (J). (gr. k). 17.99 (978-0-8037-2841-7(7) , Dial) Penguin Group (USA) Inc.

Holm, Anne. I Am David. Kingsland, L. W., tr. from DAN. 2004. 256p. (J). pap. 5.95 (978-0-15-205160-0(0) , Harcourt Paperbacks) Harcourt Children's Bks.

Holm, Anne S. I Am David. Kingsland, L. W., tr. from DAN. 2004. (Illus.). 256p. (J). 17.00 (978-0-15-205161-7(9)) Harcourt Children's Bks.

—I Am David. 2004. (gr. 3-6). lib. bdg. 14.10 (978-0-613-71643-7(4)) Tandem Library Bks.

Holt, Rinehart and Winston Staff. Goodbye, Vietnam. 2nd ed. 2002. pap., stu. ed. 13.20 (978-0-03-066514-1(0)) Holt, Rinehart & Winston.

—Goodbye, Vietnam: With Connections. 2nd ed. 2001. 14.64 (978-0-03-066513-4(2)) Holt, Rinehart & Winston.

Khan, Rukhsana. The Roses in My Carpets. Himler, Ronald, illus. 2004. 32p. pap. (978-1-55005-069-1(9)) Fitzhenry & Whiteside, Ltd.

—The Roses in My Carpets. Himler, Ronald, illus. 1998. 32p. (J). (ps-3). 15.95 (978-0-8234-1399-7(3)) Holiday Hse., Inc.

—The Roses in My Carpets. Himler, Ronald, illus. 26p. 16.95 (978-0-7737-3092-2(3)) Stoddart Kids CAN. *Dist:* Fitzhenry & Whiteside, Ltd.

Klar, Elizabeth. Lily's Crossing. Robbins, Dawn Michelle, ed. 2000. (J). 9.95 (978-1-58130-644-6(X)); 11.95 (978-1-58130-645-3(8)) Novel Units, Inc.

Lasenby, Jack. Taur. (Travellers Ser.: No. 2). (Illus.). 160p. (YA). (gr. 8 up). pap. 13.00 (978-1-877135-18-7(6)) Longacre Pr. NZL. *Dist:* Pacific Island Bks.

Lofthouse, Liz. Ziba Came on a Boat. Ingpen, Robert, illus. 2007. 32p. (J). (gr. 1-7). 15.95 (***978-1-933605-52-4(9))*** Kane/Miller Bk. Pubs., Inc.

Lombard, Jenny. Drita, My Homegirl. (J). (gr. 4-6). 2008. 144p. pap. 5.99 (***978-0-14-240905-3(7)*** , Puffin); 2006. 176p. 15.99 (978-0-399-24380-6(1) , Putnam Juvenile) Penguin Group (USA) Inc.

Matas, Carol & Matas, Carol. Greater Than Angels. 1999. 177p. lib. bdg. 11.64 (978-0-606-17196-0(7)) Tandem Library Bks.

Matthews, L. S. Fish. 2004. 192p. (gr. 5). 14.95 (978-0-385-73180-5(9) , Delacorte Bks. for Young Readers) Random Hse. Children's Bks.

Mazer, Norma Fox. Good Night, Maman. Mazer, Norma Fox, illus. 2001. (Harper Trophy Bks.). 192p. (J). (gr. 5 up). pap. 6.99 (978-0-06-440923-0(6) , Harper Trophy) HarperCollins Pubs.

—Good Night, Maman. 2001. (gr. 3-6). lib. bdg. 14.15 (978-0-613-35953-5(4)) Tandem Library Bks.

Mikaelsen, Ben. Tree Girl. 2005. 240p. (J). pap. 7.99 (978-0-06-009006-7(5) , HarperTeen) HarperCollins Pubs.

Morano, John. Makoona. 2nd rev. ed. 2005. (Morano Eco-Adventure Ser.: 2). 280p. (YA). (gr. 8-12). pap. 14.99 (978-1-59092-111-1(9) , Blue Works) Windstorm Creative.

Naidoo, Beverley. The Other Side of Truth. 272p. (J). (gr. 5 up). 2003. pap. 6.99 (978-0-06-441002-1(1)); 2001. 17.99 (978-0-06-029628-5(3)) HarperCollins Pubs.

—The Other Side of Truth. 2000. 240p. (J). pap. (978-0-14-130476-2(6) , Putnam Juvenile) Penguin Group (USA) Inc.

—The Other Side of Truth. 2003. (gr. 5-8). lib. bdg. 14.15 (978-0-613-59158-4(5)) Tandem Library Bks.

Nixon, Joan Lowery. Playing for Keeps. 2003. 208p. (YA). (gr. 7). pap. 5.50 (978-0-440-22867-7(0) , Laurel Leaf) Random Hse. Children's Bks.

—Playing for Keeps. 2003. (gr. 7-12). lib. bdg. 13.55 (978-0-613-64782-3(3)) Tandem Library Bks.

O'Neill, Joan. Daisy Chain Days. 2004. (Daisy Chain War Bks.: Bk. 4). (J). pap. (978-0-340-88178-1(X) , Hodder Children's Books) Hodder Children's Division.

Phan's Diary: Individual Chapter Book Title Six-Packs. Vol. 27. 32p. (gr. 4 up). 44.00 (978-0-7635-4496-6(5)) Rigby Education.

Prins, Piet. The Grim Reaper. 2006. (Illus.). 130p. (J). pap. (978-1-894666-74-9(7)) Inheritance Pubns.

—Hideout in the Swamp. 2006. (Illus.). 136p. (J). pap. (978-1-894666-73-2(9)) Inheritance Pubns.

Sandman, Rochel. Perfect Porridge: A Story about Kindness. Zakashansky-Zverev, Chana, illus. 2000. 32p. (J). (ps-2). 9.95 (978-0-922613-92-2(3)) Hachai Publishing.

Segamu. Sokora Refugees, Vol. 2. DeJesus, Melissa, illus. 2006. (YA). pap. 9.99 (978-1-59816-551-7(8) , Tokyopop Adult) TOKYOPOP, Inc.

Shea, Pegi Deitz. Tangled Threads: A Hmong Girl's Story. 2003. 240p. (J). (gr. 5-9). tchr. ed. 15.00 (978-0-618-24748-6(3) , Clarion Bks.) Houghton Mifflin Co. Trade & Reference Div.

—The Whispering Cloth: A Refugee's Story. Riggio, Anita, illus. 2003. 32p. (J). (gr. k-2). pap. 9.95 (978-1-56397-623-0(4)) Boyds Mills Pr.

Shulevitz, Uri. How I Learned Geography. 2008. 32p. (J). 16.95 (***978-0-374-33499-4(4))*** Farrar, Straus & Giroux.

Staples, Suzanne Fisher. Under the Persimmon Tree. 2008. 304p. (YA). pap. 7.99 (***978-0-312-37776-2(2))*** Square Fish.

Stine, Catherine. Refugees. 288p. (gr. 7). 2006. (YA). pap. 5.99 (978-0-440-23876-8(5) , Laurel Leaf); 2005. (J). 15.95 (978-0-385-73179-9(5) , Delacorte Bks. for Young Readers); 2005. (YA). 17.99 (978-0-385-90216-8(6) , Delacorte Bks. for Young Readers) Random Hse. Children's Bks.

Swindells, Robert. Ruby Tanya. 2006. 256p. (J). (gr. 4-6). pap. 8.99 (978-0-440-86398-4(8) , Corgi) Transworld Publishers Ltd. GBR. *Dist:* Trafalgar Square Publishing.

Weber, Judith Eichler. Seeking Safety. Martin, John F., illus. 2006. (Adventures in America Ser.). (J). (978-1-893110-46-5(X)) Silver Moon Pr.

Williams, Karen Lynn & Mohammed, Khadra. Four Feet, Two Sandals. Chayka, Doug, illus. 2007. 32p. (J). (gr. 2-5). 17.00 (978-0-8028-5296-0(3) , Eerdmans Bks For Young Readers) Eerdmans, William B. Publishing Co.

Williams, Mary. Brothers in Hope: The Story of the Lost Boys of Sudan. Christie, R. Gregory, illus. 2005. (J). 17.95 (978-1-58430-232-2(1)) Lee & Low Bks., Inc.

Wiseman, Eva. Kanada. 2006. (Illus.). 264p. (J). (gr. 5). pap. 9.95 (978-0-88776-729-6(X)) Tundra Bks., Inc./Livres Toundra, Inc. CAN. *Dist:* Random Hse., Inc.

Zephaniah, Benjamin. Refugee Boy. 2004. 296p. (J). (gr. 5-12). reprint ed. pap. 7.95 (978-1-58234-908-4(8) , Bloomsbury Children) Bloomsbury Publishing.

REFUSE AND REFUSE DISPOSAL

see also Hazardous Wastes; Pollution; Sewage Disposal; Waste Products; Water—Pollution

African-Americans in Waste Management Treatment. 2000. (My Ancestors—My Heroes Ser.: Vol. 31). (J). (gr. 3-4). (978-1-893091-30-6(9)) Parker Publishing Co.

Bailey, Jill. Life in a Garbage Dump. 2003. (Microhabitats Ser.). (Illus.). 32p. (J). lib. bdg. 24.28 (978-0-7398-6802-7(0)) Raintree.

—Life in a Garbage Dump. 2003. (gr. k-3). lib. bdg. 15.90 (978-0-613-78242-5(9)) Tandem Library Bks.

Barraclough, Sue. Reducing Garbage. 2007. (J). (***978-1-59771-110-4(1))*** Sea-To-Sea Pubns.

Bedford, Deborah Jackson. Garbage Disposal. 2005. (Action for the Environment Ser.). (Illus.). 32p. (J). (gr. 4-7). lib. bdg. 27.10 (978-1-58340-595-6(X) , 1247278) Smart Apple Media.

Bourgeois, Paulette. Garbage Collectors. LaFave, Kim, illus. 2004. 32p. (J). lib. bdg. 15.38 (***978-1-4242-1190-6(5))*** Fitzgerald Bks.

—Garbage Collectors. LaFave, Kim, illus. (Kids Can Read Ser.). 32p. (J). 2005. (gr. 1-3). (978-1-55337-739-9(7)); 2005. (gr. 1-3). (978-1-55337-573-9(4)); 2000. (gr. k-3). (978-1-55074-826-0(2)) Kids Can Pr., Ltd.

—Garbage Collectors. La Fave, Kim, illus. unabr. ed. 1998. (In My Neighborhood Ser.). 32p. (J). (gr. k-3). (978-1-55074-440-8(2)) Kids Can Pr., Ltd.

—Garbage Collectors. 2000. (Illus.). (J). (978-0-606-18225-6(X)) Tandem Library Bks.

Bowden, Rob. Waste, Recycling & Reuse: Our Impact on the Planet. 2001. (Twenty-First Century Debates Ser.). (Illus.). 64p. (YA). (gr. 6-8). lib. bdg. 27.12 (978-0-7398-3180-9(1)) Raintree.

Bridges, Sarah. I Drive a Garbage Truck. Alderman, Derrick & Shea, Denise, illus. 2004. (Working Wheels Ser.). 24p. (J). (gr. k-2). 22.60 (978-1-4048-0615-3(6)) Picture Window Bks.

Burton, Jane & Taylor, Kim. The Nature & Science of Waste. Burton, Jane & Taylor, Kim, photos by. 1999. (Exploring the Science of Nature Ser.). (Illus.). 32p. (J). (gr. 3 up). lib. bdg. 24.67 (978-0-8368-2186-4(6)) Stevens, Gareth Inc.

Burton, Margie & French, Tammy, Cathy - Jones. Playas limpias & Clean Beaches. 2005. spiral bd. 66.00 (***978-1-4108-5625-8(9))*** Benchmark Education Co.

Burton, Margie, et al. Reduce, Reuse, & Recycle. Adams, Alison, ed. 1999. (Early Connections Ser.). 16p. (J). (gr. k-2). pap. 4.50 (978-1-58344-079-7(8)) Benchmark Education Co.

Center for Mathematics, Science, and Technology, Illinois State University Staff, contrib. by. Integrated Mathematics, Science & Technology: Waste Management. 1999. (Illus.). (YA). (gr. 6-12). stu. ed. 14.99 (978-0-02-647843-4(9)) Glencoe/McGraw-Hill.

Costain, Meredith. Garbage Detectives. 2000. (gr. k-3). lib. bdg. 11.80 (978-0-613-30423-8(3)) Tandem Library Bks.

—Litterbugs. 2000. (gr. k-3). lib. bdg. 11.80 (978-0-613-30557-0(4)) Tandem Library Bks.

Cothran, Helen, ed. Garbage & Recycling. 2002. (Opposing Viewpoints Ser.). (Illus.). 200p. (J). (gr. 10-12). pap. 24.95 (978-0-7377-1229-2(5) , Greenhaven Pr., Inc.) Thomson Gale.

Daynes, Katie. Stinking Story of Garbage. 64p. (J). 2006. pap. 5.99 (978-0-7945-1247-7(X)); 2007. 8.99 (***978-0-7945-1750-2(1))*** EDC Publishing. (Usborne).

Deedrick, Tami. Garbage Collectors. 1998. (Community Helpers Ser.). (Illus.). 24p. (J). (gr. k-3). pap. 14.00 (978-0-516-21259-3(1) , Children's Pr.) Scholastic Library Publishing.

DeGezelle, Terri. Garbage Trucks. 2006. (Pebble Plus Ser.). (Illus.). 24p. (J). (978-0-7368-5356-9(1)) Capstone Pr., Inc.

Dorion, Christiane. Earth's Garbage Crisis. 2006. (Illus.). 48p. (J). pap. (***978-0-8368-8153-0(2));*** lib. bdg. (***978-0-8368-7753-3(5))*** Stevens, Gareth Inc. (World Almanac Library).

Dorling Kindersley Publishing Staff. What's in Your Bin? 2006. 96p. (J). 15.99 (978-0-7566-2217-6(4)) Dorling Kindersley Publishing, Inc.

Emmer, Rae. Community Service. 2002. (Reading Power Ser.). (Illus.). 24p. (J). (gr. 1). lib. bdg. 17.25 (978-0-8239-5967-9(8) , PowerKids Pr.) Rosen Publishing Group, Inc., The.

Furgang, Kathy. ¿Adonde va la basura? & Where Does Your Garbage Go? 2005. spiral bd. 66.00 (***978-1-4108-5635-7(6))*** Benchmark Education Co.

Furgang, Kathy. Where Does Your Garbage Go? 2003. (Early Connections Ser.). (J). pap. 33.00 (978-1-4108-1077-9(1)) Benchmark Education Co.

Gifford, Clive. Waste. 2005. (Planet under Pressure Ser.). (Illus.). 48p. (J). (978-1-4034-7745-3(0)) Heinemann Library.

Green, Jen. Recycling. 2005. (Your Environment Ser.). (Illus.). 32p. (J). (gr. 3-7). lib. bdg. 27.10 (978-1-59604-059-5(9)) Stargazer Bks.

—Waste & Recycling. 2004. (J). lib. bdg. 27.10 (978-1-59389-137-4(7)) Chrysalis Education.

Harlow, Rosie. Garbage & Recycling. 2002. (Young Discoverers Ser.). (Illus.). 32p. (J). (gr. k-3). pap. 7.95 (978-0-7534-5503-6(X) , Kingfisher) Houghton Mifflin Co. Trade & Reference Div.

—Garbage & Recycling. 2002. (gr. k-3). lib. bdg. 16.40 (978-0-613-90901-3(1)) Tandem Library Bks.

—Pollution & Waste: Environmental Facts & Experiments. 2002. (Young Discoverers Ser.). (Illus.). 32p. (J). (gr. k-3). 7.95 (978-0-7534-5505-0(6) , Kingfisher) Houghton Mifflin Co. Trade & Reference Div.

—Pollution & Waste: Environmental Facts & Experiments. 2002. (gr. k-3). lib. bdg. 16.40 (978-0-613-90577-0(6)) Tandem Library Bks.

Harrison, Scott & Ross, Allison J. Choosing a Career in Waste Management. 2005. (World of Work Ser.). (Illus.). 64p. (YA). (gr. 7-12). lib. bdg. 25.25 (978-0-8239-3240-5(0) , WWWAMA) Rosen Publishing Group, Inc., The.

Inskipp, Carol. Reducing & Recycling Waste. 2005. (Improving Our Environment Ser.). (Illus.). 32p. (J). lib. bdg. 24.67 (978-0-8368-4429-0(7)) Stevens, Gareth Inc.

LeBoutillier, Nate. A Day in the Life of a Garbage Collector. 2004. (First Facts Ser.). (Illus.). 24p. (J). lib. bdg. 21.26 (978-0-7368-2629-7(7)) Capstone Pr., Inc.

Leeper, Angela. The Landfill. 2004. (Field Trip! Ser.). (J). pap. 5.25 (978-1-4034-5168-2(0)) Heinemann Library.

—To a Garbage Dump. 2004. (Field Trip! Ser.). (J). lib. bdg. (978-1-4034-5162-0(1)) Heinemann Library.

Lindeen, Mary. Garbage Trucks. 2007. (Illus.). 24p. (J). lib. bdg. 19.95 (978-1-60014-117-1(X)) Bellwether Media.

Lopatka, Michael, compiled by. The Sanitary Landfill. 2002. (YA). (gr. 9-12). cd-rom 24.95 (978-0-9703694-3-7(3)) Awesome Guides, Inc.

Love, Ann & Drake, Jane. Trash Action: A Fresh Look at Garbage. Thurman, Mark, illus. 2006. 80p. (J). (gr. 3). pap. 14.95 (978-0-88776-721-0(4)) Tundra Bks., Inc./ Livres Toundra, Inc. CAN. *Dist:* Random Hse., Inc.

Macken, JoAnn Early. Sanitation Worker/El Recogedor de Basura. Coffey, Colleen & Carrillo, Consuelo, trs. 2003. (Weekly Reader Early Learning Library). (ENG & SPA., Illus.). 24p. (J). (ps up). lib. bdg. 19.33 (978-0-8368-3674-5(X) , Weekly Reader Early Learning Library) Stevens, Gareth Inc.

Macken, JoAnn Early & Gorman, Jacqueline Laks. Sanitation Worker/El Recogedor de Basura. Coffey, Colleen & Carrillo, Consuelo, trs. Andersen, Gregg, photos by. 2003. (Weekly Reader Early Learning Library). (ENG & SPA., Illus.). 24p. (J). (ps up). pap. 5.95 (978-0-8368-3688-2(X) , Weekly Reader Early Learning Library) Stevens, Gareth Inc.

Miller, Heather. Lo que hacen los trabajadores Sanitarios: What Sanitation Workers Do. 2007. (What Does a Community Helper Do? Bilingual Ser.). (ENG & SPA., Illus.). 32p. (J). lib. bdg. 22.60 (978-0-7660-2829-6(1) , Enslow Elementary) Enslow Pubs., Inc.

—What Does a Sanitation Worker Do? 2005. (What Does a Community Helper Do? Ser.). (Illus.). 24p. (J). lib. bdg. 21.26 (978-0-7660-2543-1(8) , Enslow Elementary) Enslow Pubs., Inc.

Morgan, Sally. Waste & Recycling. 2007. (Sustainable Futures Ser.). (Illus.). 48p. (J). (***978-1-58340-981-7(5)*** , 1262625) Smart Apple Media.

Morgan, Sally. Waste Disposal. 2006. (Earth Watch Ser.). (J). (978-1-59771-069-5(5)) Sea-To-Sea Pubns.

Nelson, Sara Elizabeth. Let's Reduce Garbage! 2007. (Pebble Books). (Illus.). 24p. (J). 15.93 (978-0-7368-6324-7(9)) Capstone Pr., Inc.

Nolan, Andrea J. Understanding Garbage & Our Environment. Sarquis, Mickey, ed. 1999. 305p. (J). pap. 23.95 (978-1-883822-35-4(1)) Terrific Science Pr.

Ostopowich, Melanie. The Science of Waste: Refuse, Misuse, & Reuse. 2003. (J). lib. bdg. 27.14 (978-0-7398-6996-3(5)) Raintree.

Peterson, Virginia, ed. Garbage & Other Pollution: How Do We Live with All the Trash. rev. ed. 1999. (Information Plus Compact Ser.). (Illus.). 80p. (YA). pap. 28.00 (978-1-57302-105-0(9) , GML00502-172322) Thomson Gale.

Piehl, Janet. Sanitation Workers. 2006. (Pull Ahead Books). (Illus.). 32p. (J). (ps-3). 22.60 (978-0-8225-2847-0(9) , Lerner Pubns.) Lerner Publishing Group.

Povey, Karen D. Garbage. 2006. (Our Environment Ser.). 48p. (J). (gr. 4-8). 26.20 (978-0-7377-3558-1(9) , Kidhaven) Thomson Gale.

Riley, Karen. Don't Trash My Planet. 2004. (Illus.). 20p. (J). (gr. k-5). pap. 10.00 (978-0-9708135-4-1(6) , "5,000") S.C.R.A.P. Gallery.

Royston, Angela. Recycling. 1999. (Environment Starts Here Ser.). (Illus.). 32p. (J). (gr. 1-4). 17.98 (978-0-8172-5353-0(X)) Raintree.

Sloan, Peter. Garbage Day. 1999. (gr. k-3). lib. bdg. 11.80 (978-0-613-30422-1(5)) Tandem Library Bks.

Souter, Gillian. Odds 'n' Ends Art. Watson, Clare, illus. Martin, Andre, photos by. 2002. (Handy Crafts Ser.). 48p. (J). (gr. 2 up). lib. bdg. 24.67 (978-0-8368-3051-4(2)) Stevens, Gareth Inc.

Torrisi, Cathy. Where Does the Garbage Go? Silver, Pattie, illus. 2002. (Read-to-Me Ser.). 24p. (J). (978-0-7665-1207-8(X)) Letter People, The.

Trumbauer, Lisa. We Need Garbage Collectors. Saunders-Smith, Gail, ed. 2003. (Helpers in Our Community Ser.). (Illus.). 24p. (J). (gr. k-1). lib. bdg. 15.93 (978-0-7368-1650-2(X) , Pebble Bks.) Capstone Pr., Inc.

Turnbull, Stephanie. Trash & Recycling (Level 2) - Internet Referenced. 2006. 32p. (J). 4.99 (978-0-7945-1400-6(6) , Usborne) EDC Publishing.

Walker, Kate. Household Waste. 2004. (Recycle, Reduce, Reuse, Rethink Ser.). (J). lib. bdg. 27.10 (978-1-58340-561-1(5)) Smart Apple Media.

REFUSE AND REFUSE DISPOSAL—FICTION

Brimner, Larry Dane. Messy Lot. 2001. (gr. k-3). lib. bdg. 14.10 (978-0-613-54018-6(2)) Tandem Library Bks.

—Trash Trouble. Tripp, Christine, illus. 2003. (Rookie Choices Ser.). (gr. 1-2). pap. 5.95 (978-0-516-27837-7(1)); 32p. (J). 20.50 (978-0-516-22547-0(2)) Scholastic Library Publishing. (Children's Pr.).

—Trash Trouble. 2003. (gr. k-3). lib. bdg. 14.10 (978-0-613-67676-2(9)) Tandem Library Bks.

Feely, Jenny. Litter. 2001. (gr. k-3). lib. bdg. 11.65 (978-0-613-33387-0(X)) Tandem Library Bks.

Gray, Susan Heinrichs. Living with Cystic Fibrosis. 2002. (Living Well: Chronic Conditions Ser.). (Illus.). 32p. (J). (gr. 2-6). 27.07 (978-1-56766-105-7(X)) Child's World, Inc.

Gutman, Dan. Ms. Hannah Is Bananas! Paillot, Jim, illus. 2005. 84p. (J). (gr. 2-5). lib. bdg. 11.19 (978-0-606-33041-1(0)) Tandem Library Bks.

Mayer, Mercer. Our Park, Vol. 2. 2002. (Little Critter Ser.). (Illus.). 24p. (J). (gr. k-1). pap. 3.95 (978-1-57768-807-5(4)) School Specialty Publishing.

—Our Park. 2000. (gr. k-3). lib. bdg. 11.80 (978-0-613-90231-1(9)) Tandem Library Bks.

McMullan, Kate. I Stink! McMullan, Jim, illus. 40p. (J). (ps-3). 2002. 16.99 (978-0-06-029848-7(0) , Cotler, Joanna Books); 2002. lib. bdg. 16.89 (978-0-06-029849-4(9) , Cotler, Joanna Books); 2006. reprint ed. pap. 6.99 (978-0-06-443836-0(8) , Harper Trophy) HarperCollins Pubs.

McMullan, Kate & McMullan, Jim. I Stink! 2005. (Illus.). 34p. (J). (ps-k). bds. 6.99 (978-0-06-074592-9(4) , Harper Festival) HarperCollins Pubs.

Morris, Garvin. Dump Dog. Morris, Garvin, illus. 2007. 32p. (J). (ps-2). 15.95 (***978-1-60108-012-7(3))*** Red Cygnet Pr.

Odanaka, Barbara. Smash! Mash! Crash! There Goes the Trash! Hillenbrand, Will, illus. 2006. 32p. (J). (ps-3). 15.95 (978-0-689-85160-5(X) , McElderry, Margaret K.) Simon & Schuster Children's Publishing.

Oppenheim, Shulamith Levey. Yanni Rubbish. Chayka, Doug, illus. 32p. (J). 2004. pap. 8.95 (978-1-59078-327-6(1)); 2003. 15.95 (978-1-56397-668-1(4)) Boyds Mills Pr.

Prince, Sarah. Sherman Shrinker. 2001. (gr. k-3). lib. bdg. 11.65 (978-0-613-33429-7(9)) Tandem Library Bks.

Sensel, Joni. The Garbage Monster. Bivins, Christopher, illus. 2003. 24p. (J). (ps up). 14.95 (978-0-9701195-2-0(6)) Dream Factory Bks.

Wallace, Nancy Elizabeth. Recycle Every Day! (Illus.). 32p. (J). 2006. 5.95 (978-0-7614-5290-4(7)); 2003. 16.95 (978-0-7614-5149-5(8)) Cavendish, Marshall Corp.

Wallace, Nancy Elizabeth, illus. Recycle Every Day! 2002. 40p. (J). 15.95 (978-1-58837-018-1(6)) Winslow Pr.

Ward, Helen. The Tin Forest. Anderson, Wayne, illus. 2001. 32p. (J). (gr. 1-5). 15.99 (978-0-525-46787-8(4) , Dutton Juvenile) Penguin Group (USA) Inc.

—The Tin Forest. Anderson, Wayne, illus. 2003. 32p. (J). (gr. k-4). pap. 7.99 (978-0-14-250156-6(5) , Puffin) Penguin Group (USA) Inc.

Zimmerman, Andrea Griffing & Clemesha, David. Trashy Town. Yaccarino, Dan, illus. 1999. 32p. (J). (ps-3). 16.99 (978-0-06-027139-8(6)) HarperCollins Pubs.

REGIONAL PLANNING

see also City Planning

Gish, D. L. Country Music. 2001. (World of Music Ser.). (Illus.). 32p. (J). (gr. 2-7). lib. bdg. 22.60 (978-1-58340-020-3(6)) Smart Apple Media.

REHABILITATION

see also classes of people with subdivision Rehabilitation, e.g. People with Disabilities—Rehabilitation

Youngs, Bettie B. Teen's Guide to Living Drug-Free. 2003. (gr. 7-12). lib. bdg. 22.20 (978-0-613-90161-1(4)) Tandem Library Bks.

REIGN OF TERROR

see France—History—Revolution, 1789-1799

REINDEER

D'Andrea, Deborah. Picture Me As a Reindeer. Ayers, Michael B., illus. 1999. (Picture Me Ser.). 10p. (J). (ps-3). bds. 4.99 (978-1-57151-580-3(1)) Playhouse Publishing.

Miles, Elizabeth. Watching Reindeer in Europe. 2006. (Heinemann First Library). (Illus.). 32p. (J). pap. (978-1-4034-7239-7(4)); lib. bdg. (978-1-4034-7226-7(2)) Heinemann Library.

REINDEER—FICTION

Anderson, Derek. How the Easter Bunny Saved Christmas. Anderson, Derek, illus. 2006. (Illus.). 40p. (J). 15.95 (978-0-689-87634-9(3) , Simon & Schuster Children's Publishing) Simon & Schuster Children's Publishing.

Arkadia, illus. Rudolph the Red-Nosed Reindeer. 2000. (Little Golden Bks.). 24p. (J). (gr. k-k). 2.99 (978-0-307-98829-4(5) , 98829, Golden Bks.) Random Hse. Children's Bks.

Billin-Frye, Paige, illus. This Little Reindeer. 2000. (Playtime Rhymes Ser.). 5p. (J). (ps up). 7.95 (978-0-694-01510-8(5) , Harper Festival) HarperCollins Pubs.

Brett, Jan. The Wild Christmas Reindeer. Brett, Jan, illus. 1998. (Illus.). 32p. (J). (ps-3). reprint ed. pap. 6.99 (978-0-698-11652-8(6) , Putnam Juvenile) Penguin Group (USA) Inc.

—The Wild Christmas Reindeer. 1998. (Illus.). (J). (ps-ps). lib. bdg. 15.30 (978-0-613-10541-5(9)) Tandem Library Bks.

Cereghino, Sandy. Oscar: The Short Legged Reindeer. 2006. (Illus.). 48p. (J). 24.95 (***978-1-59299-248-5(X)***) Inkwater Pr.

Christie, Michael G. Olive the Orphan Reindeer. Lucas, Margeaux, illus. 2000. 46p. (gr. 4-7). pap. 7.95 (978-1-889658-16-2(2)) New Canaan Publishing Co. LLC.

—The Story of Olive. 2000. (Illus.). 46p. (gr. 4-7). 14.95 (978-1-889658-18-6(9)) New Canaan Publishing Co. LLC.

Chronicle Books Staff. Little Reindeer: Finger Puppet Book. 2006. (Illus.). 12p. (J). 6.95 (978-0-8118-5457-3(4)) Chronicle Bks. LLC.

Coffey, Timothy. Christmas at the Top of the World. Coffey, Timothy, illus. 2003. (Illus.). 32p. (J). (ps-1). 16.95 (978-0-8075-5762-4(5)) Whitman, Albert & Co.

Curry, Kenneth. Priscilla & the Reindeer. 2007. (Illus.). 22p. (J). 10.95 (***978-0-9798364-5-9(X)***) Curry Brothers Publishing.

Cuthbert, Ruth. Reindeer. 2005. 32p. (J). per. 12.95 (978-1-56167-908-9(9)) American Literary Pr.

de, Beer Hans. Little Polar Bear & Reindeer. de, Beer Hans, illus. 2007. (Illus.). 0032p. pap. 6.95 (***978-0-7358-2139-2(9)***) North-South Bks., Inc.

Encarnacion, Elizabeth. Rudolph, the Red-Nosed Reindeer. 2007. (Illus.). 128p. 4.95 (***978-0-7624-3098-7(2)*** , Running Pr. Minature Editions) Running Pr. Bk. Pubs.

Eubank, Patricia Reeder. Countdown to Christmas. 2003. (Illus.). 14p. (J). (ps-k). 9.95 (978-0-8249-6505-1(1)) Ideals Pubns.

Fitzgerald, Clyde C. The Year Santa's Reindeer Went. . . on Strike! Cahill, David, illus. 2001. 6.95 (978-0-9715874-0-3(X)) Ira Valley Ideas.

Foreman, Michael. The Little Reindeer. 2007. (Illus.). 32p. (J). (ps-3). per. 9.95 (***978-1-84270-582-7(2)***) Andersen GBR. *Dist:* Independent Pubs. Group.

Golden Books Staff. One Special Christmas Eve. 2001. 32p. (J). (ps-3). pap. 3.99 (978-0-307-29057-1(3) , Golden Bks.) Random Hse. Children's Bks.

—Rudolph, the Red-Nosed Reindeer. Karl, Linda, illus. 2004. (Pictureback(R) Ser.). 24p. (J). (gr. k-k). pap. 3.99 (978-0-375-82530-9(4) , Golden Bks.) Random Hse. Children's Bks.

Green, Rod. Santa's Reindeer. Wright, Carol et al, illus. 2007. 32p. (J). (ps-5). 16.99 (***978-1-4169-5070-7(2)*** , Atheneum) Simon & Schuster Children's Publishing.

Hansen, Brooks. Caesar's Antlers. 2001. (978-0-606-22624-0(9)) Tandem Library Bks.

Hoff, Syd. Where's Prancer? 1999. (Illus.). 32p. (J). (ps-2). pap. 5.95 (978-0-06-443594-9(6) , Harper Trophy) HarperCollins Pubs.

—Where's Prancer? 1999. (978-0-606-17304-9(8)) Tandem Library Bks.

Inger's Promise: Evaluation Guide. 2006. (J). (978-1-55942-409-7(5)) Marsh Media.

Jacobson, Ryan. Santa Claus: Super Spy: The Case of the Florida Freeze. Belkholm, Erica, illus. l.t. ed. 2005. 80p. (J). per. 4.99 (978-0-9774122-0-4(2)) Lake 7 Creative.

Kasen, Marty, ed. The Reindeer Who Didn't Like Christmas. 1998. (Illus.). 24p. (J). (gr. 1-3). 3.98 (978-1-890095-08-6(7)) Nesak International.

Lester, Vivian. Wee-Dolph, the Tiniest Reindeer. Wiggs, Sue, illus. 22p. (J). (ps-3). pap. 4.00 (978-1-929785-01-8(1)) Connexions Unlimited.

May, Robert L. Rudolph Shines Again. Papp, Lisa, illus. 2003. 40p. (J). (ps). 9.99 (978-0-448-43198-7(X) , Grosset & Dunlap) Penguin Group (USA) Inc.

—Rudolph the Red-Nosed Reindeer. Wenzel, David, illus. (J). (ps). 2004. 22p. bds. 5.99 (978-0-448-43642-5(6)); 2001. 40p. 9.99 (978-0-448-42534-4(3)) Penguin Group (USA) Inc. (Grosset & Dunlap).

—Rudolph to the Rescue. Papp, Lisa, illus. 2006. 40p. (J). (ps). pap. 6.99 (978-0-448-44142-9(X) , Grosset & Dunlap) Penguin Group (USA) Inc.

McCaughrean, Geraldine. How the Reindeer Got Their Antlers. Holland, Heather, illus. 2000. 32p. (J). (gr. k-3). 16.95 (978-0-8234-1562-5(7)) Holiday Hse., Inc.

Morningforest, Chris & Raymond, Rebecca. Mooseman Reindeer & Uncle Utley. 2006. 36p. (J). pap. 15.43 (978-1-4116-8390-7(0)) Lulu.com.

Penny, Anne. Scraper. 2006. (Illus.). 56p. pap. (***978-1-84401-921-2(7)***) Athena Pr.

Rader, Laura. Who'll Pull Santa's Sleigh Tonight? Rader, Laura, illus. 2006. 40p. (J). pap. 6.99 (978-0-06-008090-7(6) , Harper Trophy) HarperCollins Pubs.

Rasmussen, Liz, illus. Too Fat to Fly. 2007. 32p. (J). 16.95 (***978-0-9793517-0-9(7)***) Silver Bells Publishing Hse.

Reindeer. 2003. (Shaped Board Books Ser.). 14p. (J). (ps-k). bds. 9.95 (978-0-7525-8850-6(8)) Parragon, Inc.

The Reindeer's Big Night. 2003. (J). per. (978-1-57657-926-8(3)) Paradise Pr., Inc.

Ross, Andrea. Chester Earth Ant Meets Rachel Reindeer. Ross, Andrea, illus. 2000. (Chester Earth Ant Ser.). (Illus.). 26p. (J). (gr. k-3). 7.95 (978-1-887683-31-9(3)) Storybook Pr. & Productions.

Rudolph the Red-Nosed Reindeer. 2004. 4p. (J). 3.95 (978-0-634-09040-0(2)) Leonard, Hal Corp.

Sargent, Dave & Sargent, Pat. Reini Reindeer: Special Events, 17, 56. Lenoir, Jane, illus. 2000. (Animal Pride Ser.: 56). (J). 42p. pap. 6.95 (978-1-56763-554-6(7)); 36p. lib. bdg. 19.95 (978-1-56763-553-9(9)) Ozark Publishing.

Seibold, J. Otto & Walsh, Vivian. Olive, the Other Reindeer. 10th deluxe anniv. ed. 2007. (Illus.). 40p. (J). (ps up). 19.95 (978-0-8118-5719-2(0)) Chronicle Bks. LLC.

Sharp, Rhonda Winchell. The Nine Most Famous Reindeer of All. Vandewater, Rena, illus. 2004. 40p. (J). pap. 15.99 (978-0-9748047-8-1(9)) Hickory Bark Productions.

Shoolbred, Catherine. Santa's Reindeer. Pichon, Liz, illus. 2003. 12p. (J). (gr. k-k). bds. 5.99 (978-0-7636-2143-8(9)) Candlewick Pr.

Stainton, Sue. Christmas Magic. Melhuish, Eva, illus. 2007. 32p. (J). lib. bdg. 16.89 (***978-0-06-078572-7(1)***); 15.99 (***978-0-06-078571-0(3)***) HarperCollins Pubs. (Tegen, Katherine Bks).

Stroschin, Jane H. Emma Lou & the Reindeer Flu. Stroschin, Jane H., illus. 1998. (Illus.). 32p. (J). (ps-6). lib. bdg. 15.00 (978-1-883960-15-5(0)) Henry Quill Pr.

—Emma Lou & the Reindeer Flu. rev. ed. 2001. 32p. (J). (ps-6). lib. bdg. 15.00 (978-1-883960-16-2(9)) Henry Quill Pr.

Tyrell, Melissa. The Little Reindeer. Brooks, Nan, illus. enl. ed. 2005. (Holiday Sparkler Bks.). 10p. (J). (ps-3). 4.95 (978-1-58117-119-8(6) , Intervisual/Piggy Toes) Dalmatian Pr.

Wang, Margaret. Reindeer Waits for Christmas. 2006. 16p. (J). 9.95 (978-1-58117-493-9(4) , Intervisual/Piggy Toes) Dalmatian Pr.

Wilkes, Irene. Elvie, Santa's Ninth Reindeer. Montgomery, Jason, illus. 2006. 28p. (J). 19.95 (***978-1-59299-227-0(7)***) Inkwater Pr.

RELATIVITY (PHYSICS)

see also Quantum Theory

Bankston, John. Albert Einstein & the Theory of Relativity. l.t. ed. 2002. (Unlocking the Secrets of Science Ser.). (Illus.). 56p. (gr. 4-10). lib. bdg. 25.70 (978-1-58415-137-1(4)) Mitchell Lane Pubs., Inc.

Everything you always wanted to know about the Special Theory of Relativity. 2nd ed. 2004. (YA). per. 15.00 (978-0-9749544-1-7(1)) Knight, Kenneth J.

Fleisher, Paul. Relativity & Quantum Mechanics: Principles of Modern Physics. 2005. (Secrets of the Universe Ser.). (Illus.). 80p. (gr. 6-12). 25.26 (978-0-8225-2989-7(0)) Lerner Publishing Group.

Morton, Alan. Einstein's Theories of Relativity. 2005. (Milestones in Modern Science Ser.). (J). pap. (978-0-8368-5860-0(3)); (Illus.). 48p. lib. bdg. 30.00 (978-0-8368-5853-2(0)) Stevens, Gareth Inc. (World Almanac Library).

RELAXATION

see Recreation

RELIGION

see also Belief and Doubt; Faith; God; Indians of North America—Religion and Mythology; Mythology; Religions; Spiritual Life; Superstition; Theology; Worship

Atique, Quazi M. Zahid. The Path of Peace: The Complete Code of Life. 2004. 497p. (YA). pap. 30.00 (978-0-9766702-0-9(8)) Path of Peace Inc., The.

Attinger, Billy, illus. Baby's First Little Book of Prayers. gif. ed. 2003. (Wee Witness Ser.). 32p. 7.99 (978-0-7369-1185-6(5)) Harvest Hse. Pubs.

Aygun, Aysegul. The Brave Elephant. 2002. (Our Dear Prophet in the Words of the Creation Ser.: 1). (Illus.). 24p. (J). pap. 4.99 (978-1-932099-01-0(8)) Light, Inc., The.

Bahr, Ann Marie B., ed. Religions of the World. (Illus.). (gr. 9-13). pap. 83.65 (978-0-7910-8392-5(6)); lib. bdg. 188.65 (978-0-7910-8467-0(1)) Facts On File, Inc. (Chelsea Hse.).

Billups, Don. Taking a Christian Break: Bible Verses, Spiritual Poems, Biblical Puzzles. Taylor, Kendrick, ed. Searle, Helen W., tr. Allen, Mario, illus. 2000. 64p. (YA). pap. 10.00 (978-0-9664709-3-2(1)) Mountain Empire Pubns.

Bishop, Jennie. Crayon Kingdom: Lion Cub Storybooks, Teaches Children about Unity. 1999. (Illus.). 32p. (J). (ps-3). 12.95 (978-0-87162-853-4(8)) Warner Pr. Pubs.

Cavanaugh, Dorothy. Religions of Africa. 2006. (Africa Ser.). 112p. (J). (gr. 7 up). lib. bdg. 24.95 (***978-1-59084-958-3(2)***) Mason Crest Pubs.

Center for Learning Network Staff. Sexuality: Connecting Mind, Body, & Spirit — Minicourse. 2003. (Religion Ser.). 119p. (YA). tchr. ed., spiral bd. 12.95 (978-1-56077-745-8(1)) Ctr. for Learning, The.

The Challenge of Choices. 2003. (YA). tchr. ed. (978-0-9706117-3-4(0)); stu. ed. (978-0-9706117-2-7(2)) Riverstone Group Publishing.

The Challenge of Choices Strategic Planner. 2003. (978-0-9706117-4-1(9)) Riverstone Group Publishing.

Cheng, Fu-Ding. Dream-House. 2000. (Young Spirit Bks.). (Illus.). 48p. (J). (ps-3). 16.95 (978-1-57174-186-8(0)) Hampton Roads Publishing Co., Inc.

Cole, W. Owen & Morgan, Peggy. Six Religions in the Twenty-First Century. 2nd rev. exp. enl. ed. 2000. (Illus.). 352p. (YA). (gr. 9-11). pap. 39.50 (978-0-7487-5167-9(X)) Nelson Thornes Ltd. GBR. *Dist:* Trans-Atlantic Pubns., Inc.

Crosby, Jim. Devotions for the Armchair Quarterback. 2004. 109p. per. 12.95 (978-1-932338-33-1(0)) Lifevest Publishing, Inc.

Damon, Emma. All Kinds of Beliefs. 2004. (J). (ARA & ENG.). (978-1-84444-160-0(1)); (CHI & ENG.). (978-1-84444-162-4(8)); (ENG & SOM.). (978-1-84444-163-1(6)); (ENG & URD.). (978-1-84444-164-8(4)); (BEN & ENG., Illus.). (978-1-84444-161-7(X)) Mantra Publishing, Ltd.

Diner, Hasia. Jews in America. 1998. (Religion in America Ser.). (Illus.). 160p. (YA). (gr. 6 up). 30.00 (978-0-19-510678-7(4)) Oxford Univ. Pr., Inc.

Dobson, Shirley. God's Ten Best Coloring Book 50-Unit Merch. 2004. 16p. 64.50 (978-0-8307-3117-6(2) , Gospel Light) Gospel Light Pubns.

Dolan, Sean. Everything You Need to Know about Cults. 2005. (Need to Know Library). (Illus.). 64p. (YA). (gr. 7-12). 25.25 (978-0-8239-3230-6(3) , NTCLT) Rosen Publishing Group, Inc., The.

Dorling Kindersley Publishing Staff & Wilkinson, Philip. Buddhism. 2003. (Eyewitness Books). 64p. (J). 15.99 (978-0-7894-9833-5(2)) Dorling Kindersley Publishing, Inc.

Downey, Michael. Digging Deep: Fostering the Spirituality of Young Men. 2003. 96p. (YA). per. 24.95 (978-0-88489-803-0(2)) St. Mary's Pr.

Eckersley, Glennyce S. Children & Angels: True Stories of Angelic Help in Times of Trouble. 1999. 176p. pap. 13.99 (978-0-7126-7077-7(7)) Random Hse. GBR. *Dist:* Independent Pubs. Group.

Eisenbise, Debbie. Online with the Holy Spirit. 1999. (Fast Lane Bible Studies Ser.). 49p. (YA). (gr. 7-9). pap. 9.95 (978-0-87303-338-1(8)) Faith & Life Pr.

Eliakopoulos, Angeline. Miracles & More: Exercises for the Church School. 2000. (GRE., Illus.). 136p. (J). (gr. 3-8). pap. 22.90 (978-0-9670030-1-6(6)) Destro Pubs., LLC.

Encyclopaedia Britannica Publishers, Inc. Staff, contrib. by. Religions Around the World. 2003. (Britannica Learning Library). (Illus.). 64p. (J). (gr. 2-5). 14.95 (978-1-59339-007-5(6) , 049908-EN-REF) Encyclopaedia Britannica, Inc.

Farndon, John. Religion, Science, Medicine & Warfare. 2001. (Illustrated Encyclopedia Ser.). (Illus.). 256p. (gr. 3-7). pap. 19.95 (978-1-84215-518-9(0) , Southwater) Anness Publishing GBR. *Dist:* National Bk. Network.

Foce, Natalia, tr. from ENG. El Soñador de Dios: La Historia de José, Apps, Fred, illus. l.t. ed. 2004. (SPA.). 36p. (J). 2.99 (978-1-932789-16-4(2)) Editorial Sendas Antiguas, LLC.

Fruit of the Spirit Poster Pack. 2004. (gr. 1-6). 19.99 (978-0-8307-2581-6(4) , Gospel Light) Gospel Light Pubns.

Gallery, Philip D. & Harlow, Janet L. Can You Find Followers of Jesus? Introducing Your Child to the Disciples. 2003. (Illus.). 40p. (978-2-89507-120-4(9)) Novalis Publishing.

Ganeri, Anita. Religious Articles: Objects Used in Worship. 1999. (What's Sacred to Me Ser.). (Illus.). 32p. (J). (gr. 1-3). lib. bdg. 25.69 (978-0-7398-2759-8(6)) Raintree.

—Religious Articles: Objects Used in Worship. 2000. (What's Sacred to Me Ser.). (Illus.). 32p. (J). (ps-3). pap. 10.34 (978-0-7398-3121-2(6)) Steck-Vaughn.

—Religious Articles: Objects Used in Worship. 2000. (gr. k-3). lib. bdg. 17.60 (978-0-613-74047-0(5)) Tandem Library Bks.

—Religious Books. 1999. (What's Sacred to Me Ser.). (Illus.). 32p. (J). (ps-3). lib. bdg. 25.69 (978-0-7398-2760-4(X)) Raintree.

—Religious Books. 2001. (What's Sacred to Me Ser.). (Illus.). 32p. (J). (ps-3). pap. 10.34 (978-0-7398-3122-9(4)) Steck-Vaughn.

—Religious Books. 2000. (gr. k-3). lib. bdg. 18.60 (978-0-613-74048-7(3)) Tandem Library Bks.

—Religious Buildings. 1999. (What's Sacred to Me Ser.). (Illus.). 32p. (J). (ps-3). lib. bdg. 25.69 (978-0-7398-2761-1(8)) Raintree.

—Religious Buildings. 2000. (What's Sacred to Me Ser.). (Illus.). 32p. (J). (ps-3). pap. 10.34 (978-0-7398-3123-6(2)) Steck-Vaughn.

—Religious Buildings. 2000. (gr. k-3). lib. bdg. 17.60 (978-0-613-74049-4(1)) Tandem Library Bks.

Gospel Light Publications Staff. Celebrate & Worship: 52 Kid's Sermons & Object Talks about Bible Festivals & Holidays. 2000. (Illus.). 112p. pap. 16.99 (978-0-8307-2582-3(2) , Gospel Light) Gospel Light Pubns.

Green, Edna. My Special Thoughts: Designed for African-American Children. 2004. (J). (ps-5). 10.00 (978-0-9743019-1-4(4)) My Special Thoughts.

Hartz, Paula. Zoroastrianism. 2nd rev. ed. 2004. (World Religions Ser.). 128p. (J). (gr. 6-12). 30.00 (978-0-8160-5723-8(0)) Facts On File, Inc.

Haynes, A. K., Sr. Love Conquers All: Devotionals with Soul Searching Questions to Ask Yourself Daily. AGB S Writers' Guild, ed. 2002. 144p. per. 12.95 (978-1-930908-20-8(2) , LCA, Great Beginning-AGB, A) AGB Publishing.

Haywood, John. Gods & Beliefs: Gods, Beliefs & Ceremonies Through the Ages. 2004. (How We Lived Ser.). (Illus.). 64p. pap. 7.99 (978-1-84215-913-2(5) , Southwater) Anness Publishing GBR. *Dist:* National Bk. Network.

Henry, Kim M. Seeds of Heaven. Lard, Mary Anne, illus. 2000. 32p. (ps-1). pap. 9.95 (978-0-8192-1860-5(X)) Morehouse Publishing.

Hossler, Margaret. Spenser Rose Is Born. 2003. 32p. 12.99 (978-0-9650491-4-6(0)) STL Distribution North America.

James, Otto. Religious Extremism. 2007. (Illus.). 48p. (J). (***978-1-58340-987-9(4)***) Smart Apple Media.

Kallen, Stuart A. Voodoo. 2005. (Mystery Library). (Illus.). 112p. (YA). (gr. 7-10). lib. bdg. 29.95 (978-1-59018-630-5(3) , Lucent Bks.) Thomson Gale.

Kaplan, Leslie C. Art & Religion in Ancient Egypt. 2004. (Primary Sources of Ancient Civilizations Ser.). (J). lib. bdg. (978-0-8239-8932-4(1)); (Illus.). 24p. lib. bdg. 19.95 (978-0-8239-6782-7(4)) Rosen Publishing Group, Inc., The. (PowerKids Pr.).

Kendall, Sue. Pilgrimages & Journeys. Sloan, Frank, ed. 2001. (Ceremonies & Celebrations Ser.). (Illus.). 32p. (J). (ps-3). lib. bdg. 25.69 (978-0-7398-3271-4(9)) Raintree.

Klug, Frances Marie. Stories from Heaven, Vol. XVII. l.t. ed. 2000. 371p. (YA). (gr. 7-13). pap. 15.95 (978-1-892957-17-7(5)) City of God, St. Joseph's Hill of Hope.

Kregel Publications Staff. God's an Artist & You're a Masterpiece: The Mind-Boggling Science of an Awesome Creator. 2004. 256p. (J). pap. 11.99 (978-0-8254-3467-9(X)) Kregel Pubns.

Labosh, Kathy. The Child with Autism Learns the Faith: The Sunday School Guide. 2007. per. 14.00 (978-0-9744341-4-8(0)) Labosh Publishing.

Langley, Myrtle & Dorling Kindersley Publishing Staff. Religion. 2005. (Eyewitness Bks.). (Illus.). 72p. (J). (ps-7). 15.99 (978-0-7566-1087-6(7) , 1241924); lib. bdg. 19.99 (978-0-7566-1088-3(5) , 1241924) Dorling Kindersley Publishing, Inc.

Living Religions Series, 6 vols., Set. 2003. 171.36 (978-0-7398-6388-6(6)) Raintree.

Martin, Gardner. Urantia, Revelacion, Divinidad o Negocio Editorial? 2001. Tr. of Urantia, the Great cult Mystery. (SPA.). 478p. (978-84-305-8412-3(9)) Susaeta Ediciones, S.A.

Martin, Oscar, Jr., creator. The Creation Story, l.t. ed. 2003. (Illus.). 25p. (J). E-Book 19.95 incl. cd-rom (978-0-9748416-0-1(9)) Build Your Story.

McNeil, Niki, et al. HOCPP 1126 the Pilgrims. 2006. spiral bd. 16.00 (***978-1-60308-126-9(7)***) In the Hands of a Child.

Meisels, Dovid. Shabbos Secrets: The Mysteries Revealed. 2003. 365p. 25.95 (978-1-931681-43-8(0)) Israel Bk. Shop.

Mills, Ron. A Rock Is My Brother. Padgett, Jim, illus. 1999. 48p. (J). (ps-3). pap. 3.95 (978-0-687-08438-8(5)) Abingdon Pr.

Moehlenpah, Arlo. Creation Versus Evolution: Scientific & Religious Considerations. 2003. 36p. (YA). (978-0-9667054-6-1(7)) Doing Good Ministries.

Nardo, Don. Religion & World Conflict. 2006. (Illus.). 112p. (J). (gr. 7-10). 32.45 (978-1-59018-642-8(7) , Lucent Bks.) Thomson Gale.

Odell, William. What's Special about Being Catholic? Sawyer, Kieran, ed. 2003. (Developing Faith Ser.). (Illus.). 80p. (gr. 9-12). stu. ed. 7.95 (978-0-87793-568-1(8)) Ave Maria Pr.

of Liadi, Rabbi Schneur Zalman. Shulchan Aruch: Hilchot Rosh Hashana thru Lulav -New Edition. 2003. (HEB.). 192p. per. 4.95 (978-0-8266-5189-1(5)) Kehot Pubn. Society.

Ogbonnaya, A. Okechukwu, ed. & contrib. by. Precepts for Living, 2000-2001 Vol. 3: The UMI Annual Sunday School Lesson Commentary. Ogbonnaya, A. Okechukwu, contrib. by. 2000. (Illus.). 521p. (YA). stu. ed., per. 15.45 (978-0-940955-64-6(4) , Catalog # 11-2001) UMI (Urban Ministries, Inc.).

Olsen, Debi W. My Very Own Book about Religious Science. 2004. 32p. (J). 10.95 (978-1-931947-11-4(2)) Ink & Scribe.

Places of Worship, 6 bks. Incl. Buddhist Temple. Wood, Angela. lib. bdg. 23.33 (978-0-8368-2605-0(1)); Christian Church. Wood, Angela. lib. bdg. 23.33 (978-0-8368-2606-7(X)); Hindu Mandir. Wood, Angela. lib. bdg. 23.33 (978-0-8368-2607-4(8)); Jewish Synagogue. Wood, Angela. lib. bdg. 23.33 (978-0-8368-2608-1(6)); Muslim Mosque. Wood, Angela. lib. bdg. 23.33 (978-0-8368-2609-8(4)); Sikh Gurdwara. Kaus-Singh, Kanwaljit. lib. bdg. 23.33 (978-0-8368-2610-4(8)); 32p. (J). (gr. 2 up). (Illus.). 1999. Set lib. bdg. 139.98 (978-0-8368-2604-3(3)) Stevens, Gareth Inc.

Prindle, Twyla D. Can I Have Some Money Please? Hansen, Lorie, illus. 2004. 20p. (J). (gr. k-4). 7.95 (978-0-9759527-2-6(2)) Prindle Hse. Publishing Co.

—Deception: The Devil Hears Your Prayers Too. 2004. 184p. (YA). pap. 14.95 (978-0-9759527-1-9(4)) Prindle Hse. Publishing Co.

—Teacher's Lounge. 2004. 184p. (YA). 19.95 (978-0-9759527-0-2(6)) Prindle Hse. Publishing Co.

Pundit Baraiya, Gopaldasji. Primer of Jain Principles. Gosalia, Kirit, tr. 2004. 210p. pap. 10.00 (978-0-9748681-0-3(8)) Songadh, Jain Swadhyay Mandir.

Religion & Modern Culture: Spiritual Beliefs That Influence North America Today, 13 vols., Set. Incl. Born-Again Believers : Evangelicals & Charismatics. McIntosh, Kenneth & McIntosh, Marsha. (YA). 2005. (978-1-59084-974-3(4)); Color, Culture, & Creed : How Ethnic Background Influences Belief. McIntosh, Kenneth & McIntosh, Marsha. (YA). 2006. lib. bdg. 22.95 (978-1-59084-976-7(0)); Controversial World of Biblical Archaeology : Tomb Raiders, Fakes, & Scholars. McIntosh, Kenneth. (YA). 2006. lib. bdg. 22.95 (978-1-59084-983-5(3)); Grail, the Shroud & Other Religious Relics : Secrets & Ancient Mysteries. McIntosh, Kenneth. (J). 2005. lib. bdg. (978-1-59084-978-1(7) , 1248067); Growth of North American Religious Beliefs : Spiritual Diversity. McIntosh, Kenneth & McIntosh, Jonathan S. (YA). 2006. lib. bdg. 22.95 (978-1-59084-975-0(2)); Issues of Church, State, & Religious Liberties : Whose Freedom, Whose Faith? McIntosh, Kenneth & McIntosh, Marsha. (YA). 2006. lib. bdg. 22.95 (978-1-59084-973-6(6)); Jesus, Fads, & the Media : The Passion & Popular Culture. Evans, Michael. (YA). 2005. lib. bdg. 22.95 (978-1-59084-972-9(8)); Lost Gospels & Hidden Codes : New Concepts of Scripture. McIntosh, Kenneth. (YA). 2006. lib. bdg. 22.95 (978-1-59084-982-8(5)); Popularity of Meditation & Spiritual Practices : Seeking Inner Peace. McIntosh, Kenneth & McIntosh, Marsha. (YA). 2005. (978-1-59084-980-4(9)); Prophecies & End-Time Speculations : The Shape of Things to Come. McIntosh, Kenneth. (J). 2005. (978-1-59084-979-8(5) , 1248068); Touching the Supernatural World : Angels, Miracles, & Demons. McIntosh, Kenneth & McIntosh, Marsha. (YA). 2005. (978-1-59084-981-1(7)); When Religion & Politics Mix : How Matters of Faith Influence Political Policies. McIntosh,

Kenneth & McIntosh, Marsha. (J). 2006. lib. bdg. 22.95 (978-1-59084-971-2(X)); Women & Religion : Reinterpretations Scriptures to Find the Sacred Feminine. McIntosh, Kenneth. (J). 2005. (978-1-59084-977-4(9)); (gr. 7 up). (Illus.). 112p. 2006. Set lib. bdg. 298.35 (978-1-59084-970-5(1) , 1248067) Mason Crest Pubs.

Religions of Humanity, Set. 2005. 32p. pap. 263.40 (978-0-7910-6621-8(5) , Chelsea Hse.) Facts On File, Inc.

Roxburgh, Carole. To Know Him Is to Know His Names: Names & Attributes of God. 2003. 361p. per. 14.50 (978-1-59453-038-8(6) , 1706) Airleaf Publishing & Bookselling.

Rumi, Jalal Al-Din. Rumi for Children Vol. I: Wisdom of the Selfless: Classics from the Mathnawi of Maulana Jalauddin Rumi. rev. ed. 1999. (Illus.). 44p. (YA). (gr. 5-8). 9.00 (978-1-56316-306-7(3)) IQRA International Educational Foundation.

Shaikh, Khalid M. A Study of the Qur'an & Its Teachings. Liddle, Heidi et al, eds. 1999. Tr. of Ulum al-Qur'an. vii, 240p. (YA). (gr. 6-9). pap. 12.00 (978-1-56316-118-6(4)) IQRA International Educational Foundation.

Shaw, Maura D. Ten Amazing People: And How They Changed the World. Marchesi, Stephen, illus. 2002. (SkyLight Lives Ser.). 48p. (J). (gr. 1-5). 17.95 (978-1-893361-47-8(0)) SkyLight Paths Publishing.

Sonnier, Suzanne. Shinto, Spirits, & Shrines: Religion in Japan. 2007. (Lucent Library of Historical Eras:Twentieth-Century Japan Ser.). (Illus.). 128p. (gr. 7-10). 31.20 (***978-1-4205-0029-5(5)*** , Lucent Bks.) Thomson Gale.

Spieler, Cathy M. Dots on the Floor & a Whole Lot More: Scripture References Included. 1999. (Illus.). 64p. (J). (ps-1). pap. 8.99 (978-0-570-05365-1(X)) Concordia Publishing Hse.

Stuart, Jane. I Am a Rastafarian. 1999. (Religions of the World Ser.). 24p. (J). (gr. k-4). lib. bdg. 18.75 (978-0-8239-5260-1(6)) Rosen Publishing Group, Inc., The.

Sullivan, Lawrence Eugene. Nature & Rite in Shinto. 2002. (Religions of Mankind Ser.). (Illus.). 32p. (J). (gr. 5 up). 21.95 (978-0-7910-6631-7(2) , Chelsea Hse.) Facts On File, Inc.

Taylor, Ina. Directions, Bk. 3. 2002. (Illus.). 128p. (J). (gr. 2-4). pap., stu. ed. 24.00 (978-0-7487-6389-4(9)) Nelson Thornes Ltd. GBR. *Dist:* Trans-Atlantic Pubns., Inc.

Video Zoom Box: SWAT Team. 1998. 160p. (J). (gr. 1-6). ring bd. 164.99 incl. audio, sl. (978-1-57405-103-2(2)) CharismaLife Pubs.

Villains: Junior High & Middle School. 1998. (Cross Training Ser.: Vol. 5). 208p. (YA). (gr. 7-9). pap. 99.99 incl. VHS (978-1-57405-084-4(2)) CharismaLife Pubs.

Wall, Phil. I'll Fight: Holiness at War. 1998. 192p. (J). pap. (978-1-85240-223-5(7)) Sovereign World, Ltd.

Williams, Mary E. Education. 2000. (Opposing Viewpoints Ser.). (Illus.). 222p. (YA). (gr. 9-12). lib. bdg. 32.45 (978-0-7377-0125-8(0) , Greenhaven Pr., Inc.) Thomson Gale.

Wolf, Gillian. Religion. 2006. 224p. (gr. 10-12). 29.95 (978-0-7377-2903-0(1) , Greenhaven Pr., Inc.) Thomson Gale.

Wood, Janette, tr. from GER. The Cuckoo. 1999. (Illus.). 55p. (gr. 1-3). 9.45 (978-1-890841-04-1(8) , S606en) Universal Life - The Inner Religion.

Zondervan. Revolution: Devotions & Scriptures for Teen Guys from the NIV Bible. 2004. (Illus.). 160p. 9.99 (978-0-310-80406-2(X)) Inspirio.

RELIGION—PHILOSOPHY

Clarke, Pat. Questions about God. 1999. (Dimensions in Religion Ser.). (Illus.). 194p. (YA). (gr. 11 up). pap. 26.50 (978-0-7487-4340-7(5)) Nelson Thornes Ltd. GBR. *Dist:* Trans-Atlantic Pubns., Inc.

Crispin, Gerald W. God Speaks Through Dreams: But Who's Listening?, No. 1. Crispin, Gerald W. & Crispin, Vera G., eds. unabr. ed. 2003. (Illus.). 160p. (gr. 10 up). reprint ed. pap. 19.95 (978-0-9744015-1-5(X)) Benchmark Book Craft.

Dillon, Sally Pierson & White, Ellen G. Michael Asks Why: Ellen G. White's Classic the Great Controversy Adapted for Children. 2000. (Illus.). 189p. (J). pap. 10.99 (978-0-8163-1759-2(3)) Pacific Pr. Publishing Assn.

RELIGION—STUDY AND TEACHING

see Religious Education

RELIGION AND SCIENCE

see also Creation; Evolution; Human Beings—Origin

Gonzalez, David J. There Are No Space Aliens! 12 Biblical Points Disproving Space Aliens. l.t. ed. 2003. 48p. 9.95 (978-0-9741561-0-1(8)) Gonzalez, David J. Ministries.

Kiyimba, Abasi, et al. Islamic Perspectives on Science. 1998. 132p. (J). pap. 7.95 (978-975-7388-49-4(1) , Fountain, The) Light, Inc., The.

Science & Living in God's World. (J). 10.00 (978-1-931555-49-4(4)); Bk. 1. (J). 10.00 (978-1-931555-50-0(8)); Bk. 2. (J). 20.00 (978-1-931555-51-7(6)); Bk. 3. (J). 22.00 (978-1-931555-52-4(4)); Bk. 4. (J). 16.00 (978-1-931555-53-1(2)); Bk. 5. (YA). 12.00 (978-1-931555-54-8(0)); Bk. 6. (YA). 20.00 (978-1-931555-55-5(9)); Bk. 7. (YA). 20.00 (978-1-931555-56-2(7)); Bk. 8. (YA). 20.00 (978-1-931555-57-9(5)) Our Lady of Victory Schl.

Shermer, Michael. How We Believe: The Search for God in an Age of Science. 2000. (gr. 7-12). lib. bdg. 25.75 (978-0-613-35413-4(3)) Tandem Library Bks.

Strobel, Lee. The Case for a Creator for Kids. 2006. (Illus.). 96p. (J). pap. 7.99 (978-0-310-71148-3(7)) Zonderkidz.

Syed, Ibrahim. Quranic Inspirations. 2007. 688p. (YA). per. 37.95 (***978-0-595-45003-9(2)***) iUniverse, Inc.

RELIGION AND SOCIAL PROBLEMS

see Church and Social Problems

RELIGION AND STATE

see Church and State

RELIGIONS

see also Bahai Faith; Buddhism; Christianity; Confucius and Confucianism; Hinduism; Judaism; Mythology; Religion; Sects

Adams, Simon. World Religions: Discover the Religions That Have Shaped World History. 2000. (Exploring History Ser.). (Illus.). 64p. (gr. 4-7). 14.95 (978-0-7548-0532-8(8)) Anness Publishing GBR. *Dist:* National Bk. Network.

Alexander, Dennis. Mayanisum: A New Look at an Old Religion. Hill, Shadow & Netter, Lisa, eds. Alexander, Fern, photos by. 2001. (Illus.). 151p. (Orig.). (YA). (gr. 10 up). pap. 19.95 (978-1-880534-10-6(X)) Alexander Productions.

Anderson, Dale. Churches & Religion in the Middle Ages. 2005. (World Almanac Library of the Middle Ages). (J). pap. (978-0-8368-5901-0(4)); (Illus.). 48p. (YA). lib. bdg. 30.00 (978-0-8368-5892-1(1)) Stevens, Gareth Inc. (World Almanac Library).

Atkin, Pippa. Flexi-RE Evaluation. (Illus.). 128p. Bk. 1. 2001. (J). (gr. 2-4). pap., stu. ed. 15.95 (978-0-7487-5444-1(X)); Bk. 2. 2002. pap. 13.95 (978-0-7487-6352-8(X)); Bk. 3. 2003. pap., stu. ed. 15.95 (978-0-7487-6354-2(6)) Nelson Thornes Ltd. GBR. *Dist:* Trans-Atlantic Pubns., Inc.

Barnes, Trevor. The Kingfisher Book of Religions: Festivals, Ceremonies & Belief from Around the World. 2001. (Illus.). 160p. (YA). (gr. 6-9). reprint ed. 23.00 (978-0-7881-9708-6(8)) DIANE Publishing Co.

Barnes, Trevor & Kingfisher Editors. Hinduism & Other Eastern Religions: Worship, Festivals, & Ceremonies from Around the World. 2005. (World Faiths Ser.). (Illus.). 40p. (J). (gr. 5-9). pap., pap. 6.95 (978-0-7534-5881-5(0) , Kingfisher) Houghton Mifflin Co. Trade & Reference Div.

Beckwith, Gary L. The Message That Comes from Everywhere: Exploring the Common Core of the World's Religions & Modern Science. 2001. 168p. pap. 14.95 (978-0-9701125-6-9(4)) Harmony Institute, The.

Boraks, Lucius. Religions of the West. 2004. (Illus.). 114p. (Orig.). pap. 8.95 (978-1-55612-141-8(5) , Sheed & Ward) Rowman & Littlefield Pubs., Inc.

Brown, Alan & Langley, Andrew. What I Believe: A Young Person's Guide to the Religions of the World. 2001. 6. (Illus.). 64p. (gr. 3-7). pap. 9.95 (978-0-7613-1448-6(2) , Millbrook Pr.) Lerner Publishing Group.

Center for Learning Network Staff. World Religions: Curriculum Unit. 2002. (Religion Ser.). 200p. (YA). stu. ed., per. 7.95 (978-1-56077-696-3(X)) Ctr. for Learning, The.

Coniaris, Anthony M. Let's Take a Walk Through Our Orthodox Church. Kizilos, Betty, illus. 1998. 100p. (J). (gr. 3-6). pap. 16.95 (978-1-880971-39-0(9)) Light & Life Publishing Co.

Counterfeit Faiths. 1998. (Cross Training Ser.: Vol. 7). 72p. (YA). (gr. 10-12). pap., tchr. ed. 15.00 incl. VHS (978-1-57405-249-7(7)) CharismaLife Pubs.

Davies, Graham, et al. Teacher Resource Book, Bk. 2. 2005. (Illus.). 112p. (C). pap. 24.95 (978-0-7487-9364-8(X)) Nelson Thornes Ltd. GBR. *Dist:* Trans-Atlantic Pubns., Inc.

Dineen, Jacqueline. Hunting, Harvesting, & Home. Wilkinson, Philip, ed. Ingpen, Robert R., illus. 1999. (People & Customs of the World Ser.). 96p. (YA). lib. bdg. 21.95 (978-0-7910-5134-4(X) , Chelsea Hse.) Facts On File, Inc.

—Living with the Gods. Wilkinson, Philip, ed. Ingpen, Robert R., illus. 1999. (People & Customs of the World Ser.). 96p. (YA). lib. bdg. 21.95 (978-0-7910-5135-1(8) , Chelsea Hse.) Facts On File, Inc.

Doudna, Kelly. Religion Around the World. 2004. (Around the World Ser.). (Illus.). 23p. (J). (ps-3). lib. bdg. 19.93 (978-1-59197-568-7(9)) ABDO Publishing Co.

Eastwood, Kay. Places of Worship in the Middle Ages. 2003. (Medieval World Ser.). (Illus.). 32p. (J). (gr. 5). (978-0-7787-1347-0(4)) Crabtree Publishing Co.

Faricy, Robert S. A Pilgrim's Journal. 2004. 60p. (Orig.). pap. 6.95 (978-1-55612-259-0(4) , Sheed & Ward) Rowman & Littlefield Pubs., Inc.

Ganeri, Anita. What's Sacred to Me?, 4 bks., Set. Incl. Religious Articles : Objects Used in Worship. (gr. 1-3). lib. bdg. 25.69 (978-0-7398-2759-8(6)); Religious Books. (ps-3). lib. bdg. 25.69 (978-0-7398-2760-4(X)); Religious Buildings. (ps-3). lib. bdg. 25.69 (978-0-7398-2761-1(8)); Religious Food. (ps-3). lib. bdg. 25.69 (978-0-7398-2762-8(6)); 32p. (J). (Illus.). 1999. Set lib. bdg. 102.76 (978-0-7398-2763-5(4)) Raintree.

Gellman, Marc & Hartman, Thomas. How Do You Spell God? Smith, Jos. A., illus. 1998. 225p. (J). (gr. 5-9). reprint ed. pap. 6.95 (978-0-688-15296-3(1) , Harper Trophy) HarperCollins Pubs.

Glossop, Jennifer. The Kids Book of World Religions. Mantha, John, illus. 2003. 64p. (J). (gr. 4-6). (978-1-55074-959-5(5)) Kids Can Pr., Ltd.

Gunderson, Cory Gideon. Religions of the Middle East. 2004. (World in Conflict-the Middle East Ser.). (Illus.). 48p. (J). (gr. 4-8). lib. bdg. 25.65 (978-1-59197-412-3(7)) ABDO Publishing Co.

Hakowski, Maryann. Vine & Branches, ol. 3. Price, Carolyn, illus. 2003. (Resources for Youth Retreats Ser.: Vol. 3). 176p. (J). (gr. 6-7). pap. 24.95 (978-0-88489-323-3(5)) St. Mary's Pr.

Hill, Linda. Connecting Kids: Exploring Deversity Together. 2001. (Illus.). 192p. pap. (978-0-86571-431-1(2)) New Society Pubs., Ltd.

Holy Places, 6 bks., Set 1. 2003. (Illus.). pap. 35.10 (978-1-4109-0147-7(5)) Raintree.

Kaczynski, Charles R., ed. People of Faith: Parishes & Religious Communities of the Diocese of Cleveland. 1998. (Illus.). 509p. (YA). pap. 14.00 (978-0-9669580-0-3(4)) Diocese of Cleveland.

Lady Eliana. Pagan Children's Workbook. 2006. (Illus.). 68p. (J). per. (***978-1-905524-06-8(4)***) Twin Serpents, Ltd.

Libby, Larry. Someday Heaven. McLoughlin, Wayne, illus. 2001. 40p. (J). 12.99 (978-0-310-70105-7(8)) Zonderkidz.

Marcovitz, Hal. Heroes & Holy Places. 2003. (Introducing Islam Ser.). (Illus.). 112p. (YA). lib. bdg. (978-1-59084-704-6(0)) Mason Crest Pubs.

Mayled, Jon & Ahluwalia, Libby. Philosophy & Ethics for OCR GCSE Religious Studies. 2003. (Illus.). 208p. pap. (978-0-7487-7157-8(3)) Nelson Thornes Ltd.

Meredith, Sue. Usborne Book of World Religions. 2000. (gr. 5-8). lib. bdg. 18.75 (978-0-613-74355-6(5)) Tandem Library Bks.

Meredith, Susan. World Religions. rev. ed. 2006. 64p. (J). pap. 9.99 (978-0-7945-1027-5(2)) EDC Publishing.

Meredith, Susan & Hickman, Clare. Encyclopedia of World Religions - Internet Linked. rev. ed. 2005. 128p. (J). pap. 14.95 (978-0-7945-1059-6(0) , Usborne) EDC Publishing.

Nason, Ruth. Belonging. 2005. (Start up Religion Ser.). (Illus.). 24p. (J). (gr. 1-4). lib. bdg. (978-1-84234-339-5(4) , Cherrytree Books) Evans Publishing Group.

Palmer, Martin, et al. Religions of the World: The Illustrated Guide to Origins, Beliefs, Traditions & Festivals. 2nd rev. ed. (Illustrated Guide to Customs & Beliefs Ser.). (Illus.). 160p. (J). (gr. 6-12). 29.95 (978-0-8160-6258-4(7) , Checkmark Bks.) Facts On File, Inc.

Parker, Victoria. Golden Temple. 2003. (gr. k-3). lib. bdg. 15.25 (978-0-613-78216-6(X)) Tandem Library Bks.

Raushenbush, Paul. Teen Spirit: One World, Many Paths. 2004. (Illus.). 252p. (YA). pap. 11.95 (978-0-7573-0119-3(3)) Health Communications, Inc.

Rogers, Kirsteen & Hickman, Clare. Religiones Del Mundo - Internet Linked. 2005. (Titles in Spanish Ser.). (SPA.). 128p. (J). 19.95 (978-0-7460-5093-4(3) , Usborne) EDC Publishing.

Rotner, Shelley & Kelly, Sheila M. Many Ways: How Families Practice Their Beliefs & Religions. Rotner, Shelley, photos by. 2006. (Shelley Rotner's Early Childhood Library Ser.). (Illus.). 32p. (J). (gr. k-2). 15.95 (978-0-7613-2873-5(4) , Millbrook Pr.) Lerner Publishing Group.

Snodgrass, Mary Ellen. The Encyclopedia of World Scriptures. 2001. (Illus.). 312p. (C). (gr. 10 up). 95.00 (978-0-7864-1005-7(1)) McFarland & Co., Inc. Pubs.

Stack, Peggy Fletcher. A World of Faith: World Celebration Edition. Peterson, Kathleen, illus. 2001. 71p. (J). (gr. 3-5). 24.95 (978-1-56085-162-2(7)) Signature Bks., LLC.

Stockstill, Gloria McQueen. To the Town of Bethlehem. Durrell, Julie, illus. 2004. (ENG.). 20p. (J). bds. 4.99 (978-0-7586-0051-6(8)) Concordia Publishing Hse.

Vivekananda, Swami. Way of the Saint: Swami Vivekananda on Universal Love. 2005. (Illus.). 404p. per. (978-0-9728051-3-1(3)) Temple Universal Publishing.

Wallace, Ann Hamilton. The Messenger: Revelations from an Unlikely Prophet. 2003. (Illus.). 150p. (gr. 9-12). 22.95 (978-0-9724458-0-1(3)) Sonrise Publishing.

What Is Faith? 2006. (J). 16p. pap. 1.99 (978-0-7847-1688-5(9) , 02990); (Illus.). 24p. bds. 6.99 (978-0-7847-1396-9(0) , 04056) Standard Publishing.

Willis, Laurie J. Religions of the World Fact Cards. Tamminga, Jean, illus. 2000. 80p. (YA). (gr. 5-9). ring bd. 36.00 (978-1-884925-76-4(6)) Toucan Valley Pubns., Inc.

Woolf, Alex. Fundamentalism. 2003. (Ideas of the Modern World Ser.). (Illus.). 64p. (J). lib. bdg. 28.56 (978-0-7398-6416-6(5)) Raintree.

World Religions, 14 vols., Set. 2002. 128p. (J). (gr. 4-9). 420.00 (978-0-8160-5016-1(3)) Facts On File, Inc.

World Religions, 6 bks., Set. Incl. Buddhism. Young, Serinity. (YA). lib. bdg. 39.93 (978-0-7614-2114-6(9) , Benchmark Bks.); Hinduism. Young, Serinity. (J). lib. bdg. 39.93 (978-0-7614-2116-0(5) , Benchmark Bks.); Islam. Alkouatli, Claire. (J). lib. bdg. 39.93 (978-0-7614-2120-7(3)); Judaism. Wool, Danny. (YA). lib. bdg. 39.93 (978-0-7614-2118-4(1) , Benchmark Bks.); Protestantism. Eppehimer, Trevor. (YA). lib. bdg. 39.93 (978-0-7614-2117-7(3) , Benchmark Bks.); Roman Catholicism. Otfinoski, Steven. (YA). lib. bdg. 39.93 (978-0-7614-2119-1(X) , Benchmark Bks.); (Illus.). 144p. (gr. 8 up). 2006. 2007. Set lib. bdg. 239.57 (***978-0-7614-2113-9(0)*** , Benchmark Bks.) Cavendish, Marshall Corp.

RELIGIONS—BIOGRAPHY

Here are entered collections of biographies of religious leaders not limited to the Christian religion.

see also Christian Biography

Grant, Myrna. Gladys Aylward, No Mountain too High. 160p. (J). mass mkt. 5.99 (978-1-85792-594-4(7) , Christian Focus) Christian Focus Pubns. GBR. *Dist:* Riverside.

Hamdani, Ibrahim. Karavan Hamara. 2002. (URD., Illus.). (YA). (978-0-9769245-2-4(8)) Islamic Ctr. of Sacramento, The.

Kjelle, Marylou Morano. The Waco Siege. 2002. (Great Disasters, Reforms & Ramifications Ser.). (Illus.). 112p. (J). 30.00 (978-0-7910-6739-0(4) , Chelsea Hse.) Facts On File, Inc.

Marty, Martin E., intro. Spiritual Leaders & Thinkers. (Illus.). (gr. 9-13). lib. bdg. 252.45 (978-0-7910-8413-7(2) , Chelsea Hse.) Facts On File, Inc.

Religionen: Von Alten Naturreligionen bis zu Modernen Sekten, Ursprung und Geschichte aller Religionen. (Duden-Schuelerduden Ser.). (GER., Illus.). 464p. (YA). 27.95 (978-3-411-01369-2(9)) Bibliographisches Institut & F. A. Brockhaus AG DEU. *Dist:* Continental Bk. Co., Inc., International Bk. Import Service, Inc.

RELIGIONS—FICTION

Alberti, Robert. Mitlanyal: The Gods of Change, Vol. 2. 10th ed. 2004. (Illus.). 184p. (YA). pap. 19.95 (978-0-9725880-3-4(5) , mit2) Zottola Publishing, Inc.

Anders, Charlie. Choir Boy. 2005. 280p. (YA). (gr. 8-17). (978-1-932360-81-3(6)) Counterpoint.

Arnold, Edward Ronny. Rashida. 2003. 110p. (YA). pap. 7.99 (978-0-9721216-6-8(8) , 0972121668) Computer Classics (R).

Barricks, Jerim. I Want to Know???, 2003. (Illus.). 26p. (J). 10.00 (978-0-9743512-0-9(2)) Barricks, Jeri Ministry.

Barrie, J. M. The Little Minister. 2002. (Illus.). 385p. (YA). pap. 29.95 (978-1-931839-60-0(3)) Ross & Perry, Inc.

Bell, Keisha. Emerging... free. 2004. 192p. pap. 12.95 (978-0-9754911-0-2(5)) Kei-Vision, Inc.

Bell, Shirley. Boys on the Make. 2007. 54p. 12.95 (***978-1-4241-6575-9(X)***) PublishAmerica, Inc.

Benenfeld, Rikki. I Go Visiting. 2007. (Illus.). 32p. (J). 10.95 (978-1-929628-33-9(1)) Hachai Publishing.

Blume, Judy. Are You There God? It's Me, Margaret. 149p. (J). (gr. 4-6). pap. 3.50 (978-0-8072-1421-3(3)); (YA). (gr. 5 up). pap. 4.99 (978-0-8072-1508-1(2)) Random Hse. Audio Publishing Group. (Listening Library).

—Are You There God Its Me Margaret. 2001. 160p. (J). (gr. 4-6). 17.95 (978-0-689-84158-3(2) , Atheneum/Richard Jackson Bks.) Simon & Schuster Children's Publishing.

Bookworks Staff. Prayertime Bear. 2002. (Baby Blessings Ser.). 6p. 12.99 (978-0-7847-1360-0(X) , 04021) Standard Publishing.

Brindle, Susan A. & Lademan, Miriam A. The Little Creatures' Crusade (La Cruzada de las Criaturitas) A Story of Confirmation (Un Cuentro Acerca de la Confirmacion) Emmanuelli Klosterman, Carmen A., tr. Brindle, Susan A. & Lademan, Miriam A., illus. 1999. (Seven Sacraments Ser.). (ENG & SPA., Illus.). 56p. (gr. k-10). pap. 9.95 (978-1-889733-07-4(5) , 01009) Precious Life Bks., Inc.

Butcher, H. Maxwell. I, Adam. Brookes, Shelley, illus. 2nd l.t. ed. 1999. 160p. (J). pap. (978-1-894303-08-8(3)) Raven Rock Publishing.

Chancellor, Deborah. The Christmas Story. Downing, Julie, illus. 12p. (J). (ps up). bds. 6.95 (978-0-8294-1480-6(0)) Loyola Pr.

Children's Ramayan, Story of Ram. 2003. (J). 2.99 (978-0-9748285-0-3(5)) Anar Bks. LLC.

Cohen, Deborah Bodin. Papa Jethro: A Story of Moses' Interfaith Family. Dippold, Jane, illus. 2007. (Jewish Identity Ser.). (J). (gr. k-3). 17.95 (***978-1-58013-250-3(2));*** pap. 7.95 (***978-1-58013-252-7(9)***) Kar-Ben Publishing.

Connolly, Ed. Summer Dance of the Fireflies. Flynn, Noel, illus. 2003. 44p. (J). per. 10.95 (978-1-888996-64-7(1)) Red Hen Pr.

Cooper, Ilene. Sam I Am. 256p. (J). 2006. pap. 5.99 (978-0-439-43968-8(X)); 2004. (gr. 4-7). pap. 15.95 (978-0-439-43967-1(1) , Scholastic Pr.) Scholastic, Inc.

Dillon, Sally Pierson. Exile of the Chosen: God's Heroes from Solomon to Malachi. 2003. 223p. (J). pap. 10.99 (978-0-8280-1703-9(4) , 58-710) Review & Herald Publishing Assn.

Douglas, Babette. Rosebud. 2004. (J). 9.99 (978-1-890343-12-5(9)) Kiss A Me Productions, Inc.

Finley, Martha. Christmas with Grandma Elsie, Vol. 14. (Elsie Bks.: Vol. 14). 320p. (gr. 4-7). pap. 5.95 (978-1-58182-108-6(5)) Cumberland Hse. Publishing.

—Elsie & the Raymonds, Vol. 15. (Original Elsie Classics Ser.: Vol. 15). 320p. (gr. 4-7). pap. 5.95 (978-1-58182-110-9(7)) Cumberland Hse. Publishing.

—Elsie Yachting with the Raymonds, Vol. 16. (Original Elsie Classics Ser.: Vol. 16). 320p. (gr. 4-7). pap. 5.95 (978-1-58182-111-6(5)) Cumberland Hse. Publishing.

—Elsie's Friends at Woodburn, Vol. 13. (Elsie Bks.: Vol. 13). 320p. (gr. 4-7). pap. 5.95 (978-1-58182-107-9(7)) Cumberland Hse. Publishing.

Ganeri, Anita. Sikh Stories. Phillips, Rachael, illus. 2006. 42p. (J). (gr. 4-6). 23.95 (978-1-4048-1314-4(4)) Picture Window Bks.

Hambrick, Sharon. Stuart's Run to Faith. 1999. 123p. (J). (gr. 4-7). pap. 7.49 (978-1-57924-244-2(8)) Jones, Bob Univ. Pr.

—Stuart's Run to Faith. 1999. (gr. 3-6). lib. bdg. 14.70 (978-0-613-81775-2(3)) Tandem Library Bks.

Hardy, LeAnne. So That's What God Is Like. Wilson, Janet, illus. 2004. 10p. 13.99 (978-0-8254-2782-4(7)) Kregel Pubns.

Hauser, Lisa Kay. 1-2-3, & God Made Me! 2004. (Illus.). 32p. 15.95 (978-1-886864-03-0(9)) Golden Anchor Pr.

—1-2-3, Special Like Me! 2004. (Illus.). 32p. (J). 15.95 (978-1-886864-17-7(9) , 1231325) Golden Anchor Pr.

Hautman, Pete. Godless. 208p. (YA). (gr. 7 up). 2005. pap. 7.99 (978-1-4169-0816-6(1) , Simon Pulse); 2004. (Illus.). 15.95 (978-0-689-86278-6(4)) Simon & Schuster Children's Publishing.

—Godless. l.t. ed. 2004. 219p. (J). 20.95 (978-0-7862-7070-5(5)) Thorndike Pr.

Hawxhurst, Joan C. Bubbe & Gram: My Two Grandmothers. Bynum-Nwulu, Jane, illus. 2003. 32p. (J). (ps-2). 12.95 (978-0-9651284-2-1(3)) Dovetail Publishing.

Holmes, Andy. If You Give a Boy a Bible. 2004. 32p. 11.99 (978-0-8254-5513-1(8)) Kregel Pubns.

Huff, Barb. Backup Singer. 2003. (gr. 7-12). lib. bdg. 11.80 (978-0-613-79646-0(2)) Tandem Library Bks.

Hunermann, Wilhelm. A Crucified Heart: A Novel of St. Herman Joseph. Szanto, Hubert, tr. from GER. 2004. Orig. Title: Der Moench Vom Steinfeld. (Illus.). 176p. (YA). (978-0-9742298-1-2(4)) St. Michael's Abbey.

Isaac, Christine Verney. Faith's Journey. Vaughn, Patrika, ed. Donato, Angela, illus. 2001. 112p. (J). (gr. 2-7). 17.95 (978-0-9706576-3-3(3) , Advocate Hse.) A Cappela Publishing.

Jenkins, Jerry B. & LaHaye, Tim. Death at the Gala: History in the Making. 2003. (Left Behind Ser.: Bk. 25). (gr. 3-6). lib. bdg. 14.15 (978-0-613-63501-1(9)) Tandem Library Bks.

—Left Behind Bks. 31-35, Set: The Kids Collection 6, 5 vols. 2004. (Left Behind Ser.). (J). mass mkt. 27.45 (978-0-8423-8713-2(7)) Tyndale Hse. Pubs.

Jinks, Catherine. Pagan's Vows. De Seve, Peter, illus. 2004. (Pagan Chronicles Ser.: Bk. 3). 336p. (J). (gr. 7 up). 16.99 (978-0-7636-2021-9(1)) Candlewick Pr.

Jungman, Ann. The Most Magnificent Mosque. Fowles, Shelley, illus. 2004. 32p. (J). 15.95 (978-1-84507-012-0(7)) Lincoln, Frances Ltd. GBR. *Dist:* Perseus Distribution.

Lawton, Wendy. Courage to Run: A Story Based on the Life of Harriet Tubman. 2002. (Daughters of the Faith Ser.). 144p. (YA). pap. 6.99 (978-0-8024-4098-3(3)) Moody Pubs.

Layton, Dian. Secret of the Blue Pouch. (J). pap. 4.99 (978-0-9677402-7-0(4)) Mercy Place, Inc.

LeBarre, Matt, illus. NIV Backpack Bible. 2004. 992p. (J). (gr. 3-6). 19.99 (978-0-310-93094-5(4)) Zonderkidz.

Levine, Abby. This Is the Matzah. Billin-Frye, Paige, illus. 2005. 32p. (J). (ps-2). 15.95 (978-0-8075-7885-8(1)) Whitman, Albert & Co.

Levitin, Sonia. Strange Relations. 2007. 304p. (gr. 7). (J). 15.99 (978-0-375-83751-7(5)); (YA). lib. bdg. 18.99 (978-0-375-93751-4(X)) Random Hse. Children's Bks. (Knopf Bks. for Young Readers).

Lewis, Beverly. The Cul-de-Sac Kids Boxed Set: Piggy Party; the Granny Game; Mystery Mutt; Big Bad Beans; the Upside-Down Day; & the Midnight Mystery. 2001. (Cul-de-Sac Kids Ser.: Vols. 19-24). 480p. (J). pap. 23.99 (978-0-7642-8738-1(9)) Bethany Hse. Pubs.

Littman, Sarah. Confessions of a Closet Catholic. 2006. 208p. (J). (gr. 5). reprint ed. pap. 5.99 (978-0-14-240597-0(3) , Puffin) Penguin Group (USA) Inc.

Luedke, Robert James. Eye Witness: A Fictional Tale of Absolute Truth. 2004. (Illus.). 96p. 24.99 (978-0-9758924-1-1(X)); pap. 13.99 (978-0-9758924-0-4(1)) Head Pr. Publishing.

Marcuse, Aida E. Lo Que Cuentan los Incas. 1999. (Cuentamerica Ser.). (SPA.). 64p. (J). (gr. 4-6). pap. (978-950-07-1501-0(5) , SA30063) Editorial Sudamericana S.A. ARG. *Dist:* Lectorum Pubns., Inc.

Martin, W. Lyon. An Ordinary Girl, A Magical Child. Martin, W. Lyon, illus. 2008. (Illus.). 48p. (J). lib. bdg. 16.95 (***978-0-9796834-3-5(2)***) Shades of White.

Max Lucado's Hermie & Friends, creator. The Race of Fear. 2005. (Hermie & Friends Ser.: Vol. 3). (Illus.). 14p. (J). (ps-ps). 9.99 (978-1-4003-0465-3(2)) Nelson, Thomas Inc.

Metaxas, Eric, ed. Khalil & the Big Gulp. 2003. (Illus.). 16p. 6.99 (978-0-310-70471-3(5)) Zondervan.

Mills, Sam. The Viper Within. 2008. 304p. (J). (gr. 7). 16.99 (***978-0-375-84465-2(1)***); lib. bdg. 19.99 (***978-0-375-94465-9(6)***) Random Hse. Children's Bks. (Knopf Bks. for Young Readers).

Myers, Bill. Cards. 2003. (gr. 5-8). lib. bdg. 14.15 (978-0-613-76869-6(8)) Tandem Library Bks.

—Wiccan. 2003. (gr. 5-8). lib. bdg. 14.15 (978-0-613-76870-2(1)) Tandem Library Bks.

Nalbantsky, Danail. Bludnia Sin (the Prodigal Son) Guetov, Dimitar, ed. 2nd unabr. ed. 2004. (BUL.). 228p. per. 9.99 (978-0-9753970-3-9(6)) Capricorn Publishing.

Naughty Krishna. 2003. (J). 2.99 (978-0-9748285-1-0(3)) Anar Bks. LLC.

Oppenheim, Shulamith Levey. I Blis: An Islamic Tale. Young, Ed, illus. 2004. 29p. (J). (gr. k-4). reprint ed. 16.00 (978-0-7567-7575-9(2)) DIANE Publishing Co.

Peretti, Frank E. Escape from the Island of Aquarius. Life Publishers Staff, tr. from ENG. 1998. (Cooper Kids Adventure Ser.: No. 2). (RUS.). 206p. (J). (gr. 4-12). per. (978-0-7361-0038-0(5)) Life Pubs. International.

—The Tombs of Anak, Vol. 3. 2005. (Cooper Kids Adventure Ser.: Vol. 3). 144p. (gr. 3-6). pap. 5.99 (978-1-58134-620-6(4) , Crossway Bibles) Crossway Bks.

Rennie Pattison, Caroline. The Law of Three: A Sarah Martin Mystery. 2007. 200p. (YA). pap. 10.99 (***978-1-55002-733-4(6)*** , Boardwalk Bks.) Dundurn Group, The CAN. *Dist:* Univ. of Toronto Pr.

Rock, Lois. I Wonder Why? Corr, Christopher, illus. 2000. 32p. (J). pap. 9.99 (978-0-7459-4461-6(2) , Lion) Lion Hudson plc GBR. *Dist:* Independent Pubs. Group.

Rose, Robert. Godintoxicated Becoming Paranoid. 2007. 260p. pap. 29.95 (***978-1-4327-0041-6(3)***) Outskirts Press, Inc.

Rue, Nancy N. Lily's Passport to Paris. 2003. (gr. 3-6). lib. bdg. 13.00 (978-0-613-71689-5(2)) Tandem Library Bks.

Sasso, Sandy Eisenberg. God in Between. Sweetland, Sally, illus. 1998. 32p. (J). (ps-3). 16.95 (978-1-879045-86-6(9)) Jewish Lights Publishing.

—Los Matzahs Secretos de Abuelita. Bryer, Diana, illus. 2005. Tr. of Easter Matzahs. (SPA.). 32p. (J). pap. 9.99 (978-1-57860-212-4(2)) Emmis Bks.

Sawyers, Carol. Trapped At 13. 2005. 220p. (YA). pap. 14.00 (978-0-9767778-4-7(3) , 704-724-1683) Alpha & Omega Publishing.

Singer, Marilyn. Brushes with Religion. Date not set. 192p. (YA). (gr. 7 up). mass mkt. 5.99 (978-0-06-440789-2(6)) HarperCollins Pubs.

—I Believe in Water: Twelve Brushes with Religion. 2000. (Illus.). 288p. (YA). (gr. 7 up). lib. bdg. 15.89 (978-0-06-028398-8(X)) HarperCollins Pubs.

Smith, Mark S. Lost World Adventures. 2000. (Illus.). 96p. (J). pap. 10.99 (978-0-89051-277-7(9)) Master Bks.

Spickler, Valerie. God Is for Every Day' - Stories & Songs for Children: Teach-a-Child Companion Book/Compact Disc Set, 2 vols., Vol. 1. 2002. (Illus.). 52p. (J). 24.99 incl. audio compact disk (978-0-9727786-1-9(6) , 978-0-9727786-1-9) JoySoul Corp.

St. John, Patricia. The Victor. 2003. 176p. 6.49 (978-0-86201-139-0(6)) Scripture Union GBR. *Dist:* Gabriel Resources.

Stephenson, Beth Mitchell. The Angel's Song. unabr. ed. 2002. 106p. (Orig.). pap. 7.95 (978-1-930980-93-8(0) , 80930) Granite Publishing & Distribution.

Swindells, Robert. Abomination! 2000. (Yearling Book Ser.). 208p. (J). pap. 9.99 (978-0-440-86362-5(7)) Transworld Publishers Ltd. GBR. *Dist:* Trafalgar Square Publishing.

Taylor, Damon J. Perdona y Olvida: La Historia de Jose. 2003. (Mis Calcetines Ser.).Tr. of Forgive & Forget the Story of Joseph. (SPA., Illus.). 32p. (YA). 6.99 (978-0-8254-0750-5(8) , Editorial Portavoz) Kregel Pubns.

Taylor, Yvonne. Hartlie: The Streak. Taylor, Yvonne, ed. (Hartlie: Vol. 1). (Illus.). 32p. (J). 10.99 (978-0-9709187-0-3(4)) Peaceable Productions.

Thomas, Jerry D. The Missing Manger Mystery. Odell, Lad, illus. 2003. (Detective Zack Ser.). 132p. (J). pap., pap. 6.99 (978-0-7814-3789-9(X) , 078143789X) Cook, David C. Publishing Co.

Thompson, James. The Amarna Experiment. 2003. 128p. (YA). 21.95 (978-0-595-65753-7(2)); pap. 11.95 (978-0-595-28296-8(2)) iUniverse, Inc.

Tika. Baby Love. Standish, Joyce, ed. Burroughs, Derrie, illus. l.t. ed. 2006. 18p. (J). (gr. 1-5). pap. 15.00 (978-0-9716244-1-2(0)) TLS Publishing.

Underwood, Kathie L. Sarah & the Sand Dollar. 2004. (Illus.). 36p. (J). pap. 11.95 (978-0-9672585-7-7(X)) Cy-Press Pubns.

Van Ryk, Laverne. A Garland of Emeralds. 2006. (Illus.). 305p. (***978-1-4122-0156-8(X)***) Trafford Publishing.

Von Schmid. Stolen Child. 2004. 13.00 (978-1-58474-022-3(1)) Cornerstone Family Ministries/Lamplighter Publishing.

Ware, Jim. Crazy Jacob. 2000. (Kidwitness Tales Ser.). (Illus.). 128p. (J). (gr. 3-7). pap. 5.99 (978-1-56179-885-8(1)) Bethany Hse. Pubs.

Weinheimer, Beckie. Converting Kate. 2007. 288p. (YA). (gr. 7 up). 16.99 (978-0-670-06152-5(2) , Viking Juvenile) Penguin Group (USA) Inc.

Wiles, Patricia. My Mom's a Mortician: A Novel. 2004. 249p. (J). (978-1-59156-433-1(6)) Covenant Communications.

Wittlinger, Ellen. Blind Faith. (YA). 2007. 304p. pap. 8.99 (***978-1-4169-4906-0(2)*** , Simon Pulse); 2006. 288p. (gr. 7 up). 16.99 (978-1-4169-0273-7(2) , Simon & Schuster Children's Publishing) Simon & Schuster Children's Publishing.

Woodson, Jacqueline. Feathers. 2007. 128p. (J). (gr. 3-7). 15.99 (978-0-399-23989-2(8) , Putnam Juvenile) Penguin Group (USA) Inc.

Yolen, Jane. Armageddon Summer. 1999. (gr. 7-12). lib. bdg. 14.15 (978-0-613-19505-8(1)) Tandem Library Bks.

Yolen, Jane & Coville, Bruce. Armageddon Summer. 1999. 272p. (YA). (gr. 7-12). pap. 6.95 (978-0-15-202268-6(6) , Harcourt Paperbacks) Harcourt Children's Bks.

—Armageddon Summer. 1999. (YA). (gr. 7 up). pap., stu. ed. 60.24 incl. audio (978-0-7887-3002-3(9) , 40884) Recorded Bks., LLC.

—Armageddon Summer. 1999. 266p. per. 12.64 (978-0-606-17225-7(4)) Tandem Library Bks.

RELIGIOUS ART

see Art, Medieval; Christian Art and Symbolism; Church Architecture

RELIGIOUS BELIEF

see Belief and Doubt; Faith

RELIGIOUS BIOGRAPHY

see Christian Biography; Religions—Biography

RELIGIOUS CEREMONIES

see Rites and Ceremonies

RELIGIOUS DENOMINATIONS

see Sects

RELIGIOUS EDUCATION

see also Bible—Study; Moral Education

Abingdon. By the Waters: Preschool Kit. 2003. (Bible Zone Live Ser.). 79.99 (978-0-687-08127-1(0)) Abingdon Pr.

—By the Waters: Younger Elementary Kit. 2003. (Bible Zone Live Ser.). (gr. 1-3). 79.99 (978-0-687-08137-0(8)) Abingdon Pr.

Amodei, Michael. Send Out Your Spirit: A Confirmation Candidate's Handbook for Faith. 2003. (Send Out Your Spirit Ser.). (Illus.). 256p. (gr. 6-12). 9.95 (978-0-87793-952-8(7)) Ave Maria Pr.

Armor of God Grades 4-6. 2004. pap. 7.99 (978-1-56417-929-6(X)) School Specialty Publishing.

Aron, Tom & Group Publishing Staff. The Ultimate Book of Preteen Games. 2004. (Illus.). 110p. (gr. 5-6). pap. 15.99 (978-0-7644-2291-1(X) , Flagship Church Resources) Group Publishing, Inc.

Arthur, Kay & Domeij, Scoti. Wrong Way, Jonah! Leite, Eleni, tr. 2003. (Discover 4 Yourself Series for Children). (POR., Illus.). 93p. (J). pap. 8.99 (978-1-888655-71-1(2)) Precept Ministries.

The Ascension. (Illus.). (gr. 1-4). 3.00 (978-0-570-05525-9(3) , 54-1035) Concordia Publishing Hse.

Baum, Roberta Osser. Back-to-School Hebrew Reading Refresher. 1999. (ENG & HEB., Illus.). 32p. (J). (978-0-87441-679-4(5)) Behrman Hse., Inc.

Becker, Mary Lee, contrib. by. Living Our Faith Church: A Community of Faith. 2002. (Living Our Faith Ser.). (Illus.). 112p. pap., stu. ed. 8.95 (978-0-15-900500-2(0)) Harcourt Religion Pubs.

Bishop, Jennie. Jesus Must Be Really Special. Wummer, Amy, illus. 2006. (Heritage Builders Ser.). 32p. (J). 14.99 (978-0-7847-1379-2(0) , 04029) Standard Publishing.

Boston, Vicki & Stroh, Debbie. Christ's Kids Create, Vol. 2. 2nd ed. 2006. (ENG., Illus.). 64p. (J). 9.99 (***978-0-7586-1109-3(9)***) Concordia Publishing Hse.

Broslavick, Chris & Pichler, Tony. Totally Lent: A Teen's Journey to Easter 2006. Cannizzo, Karen A., ed. 2005. (Illus.). 64p. (J). 5.95 (978-1-933178-24-0(8) , 3566) Pflaum Publishing Group.

Broyles, Anne. Signs at the Crossroads. 2004. 48p. pap., stu. ed. 6.50 (978-0-687-05860-0(0)) Abingdon Pr.

Bundschuh, Rick. Heartburn: Blazing Hot Worship - A Six-Session Study of the Psalms. Reeves, Dale, ed. 1999. (Illus.). 80p. (YA). pap. 14.99 (978-0-7847-0930-6(0) , 23316) Standard Publishing.

Cannizzo, Karen & Schippe, Cullen, eds. The Church Welcomes Me, 6 books. 2005. (Faith Activities for Catholic Kids Ser.). (Illus.). 32p. (J). 6.95 (978-1-933178-16-5(7) , 2802) Pflaum Publishing Group.

—Jesus Loves Me, 6 books. 2005. (Faith Activities for Catholic Kids Ser.). (Illus.). 32p. (J). 6.95 (978-1-933178-15-8(9) , 2801) Pflaum Publishing Group.

—Learning the Way, 6 books. 2005. (Faith Activities for Catholic Kids Ser.). (Illus.). 55p. (J). (gr. k-6). 6.95 (978-1-933178-17-2(5) , 2803) Pflaum Publishing Group.

Carotta, Michael. Celebrar nuestrafe: Reconciliacion/ Eucaristia, Nivel II. 2001. (Celebrating Our Faith). (SPA.). 208p. pap., tchr.'s training gde. ed. 19.95 (978-0-15-901153-9(1)) Harcourt Religion Pubs.

—Celebrating Our Faith: Reconciliation/Eucharist, Level II. 2001. (Celebrating Our Faith). 208p. pap. 19.95 (978-0-15-901141-6(8)) Harcourt Religion Pubs.

—Reconciliacion/Eucaristia: Nivel 2. 2002. (Celebrating Our Faith). (SPA., Illus.). 144p. pap. 12.95 (978-0-15-901147-8(7)) Harcourt Religion Pubs.

—Reconciliation/Eucharist: Level 2. 2002. (Celebrating Our Faith). (Illus.). 144p. pap. 12.95 (978-0-15-901135-5(3)) Harcourt Religion Pubs.

The Challenge of a Moral Life, 6 booklets. 1998. (Illus.). (YA). (gr. 7-10). stu. ed. 6.95 (978-0-89837-219-9(4)) Pflaum Publishing Group.

Chance, Brenda K. & Smith, Cynthia E. The Cost of Being Jesus' Disciple Vol. 1: The End-Times Childrens Curriculum. 2000. (Illus.). 59p. (J). (gr. k-6). ring bd. 40.00 (978-0-9700603-0-3(0)) End Times Children's Curriculm, The.

A Child's Sacrament Book. 2007. (J). 3.95 (***978-1-933178-67-7(1)***) Pflaum Publishing Group.

Complete 5 Subject Set. 2004. (Switched on Schoolhouse Ser.). (YA). (gr. 8). cd-rom 299.95 (978-0-7403-0591-7(3)) Alpha Omega Pubns., Inc.

Connally, Dale. Games with a Purpose 2. 2001. (Illus.). 128p. (J). (gr. 7-12). 12.95 (978-0-7673-9447-5(X)) LifeWay Christian Resources.

Cook Communications Staff. Toddlerific: Faith Building Activities for Toddlers & Twos. 2004. (Godprints Bible Funstuff Series for Children Ser.). 112p. (J). (gr. 1-2). pap., pap. 16.99 (978-0-7814-4082-0(3) , 0781440823) Cook, David C. Publishing Co.

Cosgrove, Stephen. Zippity Zoom. James, Robin, illus. 2001. (Serendipity Bks.). 32p. (J). (ps-3). pap. 4.99 (978-0-8431-7630-8(X) , Price Stern Sloan) Penguin Group (USA) Inc.

CrossTown. (gr. 1 up). stu. ed. 10.00 (978-0-570-00766-1(6) , 22-2880); (gr. 2 up). stu. ed. 10.00 (978-0-570-00768-5(2) , 22-2882); (gr. 3 up). stu. ed. 10.00 (978-0-570-00770-8(4) , 22-2884) Concordia Publishing Hse.

Day by Day. 2004. (gr. k-12). Vol. 1. 50.00 (978-1-58095-847-9(8) , WB001); Vol. 2. 50.00 (978-1-58095-848-6(6) , WB002); Vol. 3. 50.00 (978-1-58095-849-3(4) , WB003); Vol. 4. 50.00 (978-1-58095-850-9(8) , WB004); Vol. 5. 50.00 (978-1-58095-851-6(6) , WB005) Alpha Omega Pubns., Inc. (Weaver).

Days of Faith: Student Planner & Assignment Book, Intermediate Grades 2006-2007. 2006. (Illus.). 108p. (J). 4.95 (978-1-933178-33-2(7)) Pflaum Publishing Group.

Diagnostic Tests: Student Testing Kit, 5 bks., Set. 2004. (J). (gr. 1-8). suppl. ed. 19.95 (978-0-7403-0096-7(2) , AS9922) Alpha Omega Pubns., Inc.

Dingwall, Cindy. Bible Verse Fun with Kids: 300+ Ideas & Activities to Help Children Learn & Live Scripture. 2004. (Illus.). 192p. pap. 21.00 (978-0-687-04514-3(2)) Abingdon Pr.

Dios Elige a Su Pueblo: Quarter 1, Level 3. (Caminando con Jesus (Walking with Jesus) Series B).Tr. of God Chooses His People. (SPA.). (J). (gr. 3-4). stu. ed. 3.50 (978-0-570-05152-7(5) , 16-3911) Concordia Publishing Hse.

Dios Me Da Su Palabra: Quarter 1, Level 2. (Caminando con Jesus (Walking with Jesus) Series A).Tr. of God Gives Me His Word. (SPA.) (J). (gr. 1-2). stu. ed. 3.50 (978-0-570-05132-9(0) , 16-2811) Concordia Publishing Hse.

Dios Me Dio Relaciones: Quarter 3, Level 1. (Caminando con Jesus (Walking with Jesus) Series B).Tr. of God Gave Me Relationships. (SPA.). (J). (ps-k). stu. ed. 3.50 (978-0-570-05112-1(6) , 16-1913) Concordia Publishing Hse.

Dios Me Dio un Cuerpo: Quarter 2, Level 1. (Caminando con Jesus (Walking with Jesus) Series B).Tr. of God Gave Me a Body. (SPA.). (J). (ps-k). stu. ed. 3.50 (978-0-570-05111-4(8) , 16-1912) Concordia Publishing Hse.

Dios Me Dio un Mundo: Quarter 1, Level 1. (Caminando con Jesus (Walking with Jesus) Series B).Tr. of God Gave Me a World. (SPA.). (J). (ps-k). stu. ed. 3.50 (978-0-570-05110-7(X) , 16-1911) Concordia Publishing Hse.

Dios Prepara a Su Pueblo: Quarter 2, Level 3. (Caminando con Jesus (Walking with Jesus) Series B).Tr. of God Prepares His People. (SPA.). (J). (gr. 3-4). stu. ed. 3.50 (978-0-570-05153-4(3) , 16-3912) Concordia Publishing Hse.

Drury, Keith W, ed. Successful Youth Mentoring Bk. 2: 24 Practical Sessions to Impact Kids' Lives. 1999. 144p. (YA). (gr. 8-12). pap. 16.99 (978-0-7644-2136-5(0)) Group Publishing, Inc.

El Espiritu Santo (The Holy Spirit) Quarter 1, Level 3. (Caminando con Jesus (Walking with Jesus) Series A). (SPA.). (J). (gr. 3-4). stu. ed. 3.50 (978-0-570-05149-7(5) , 16-3811) Concordia Publishing Hse.

Evans, Gwydion, et al. Ar Dîm Duw: Cyfres o Sesiynau Sydd Yn Defnyddio Byd Chwaraeon I Son Am y Ffydd Gristnogol. 2005. (WEL., Illus.). 24p. (978-1-85994-036-5(6)) Cyhoeddiadau'r Gair.

Exploring Questions in RE. 2005. (Illus.). (J). Bk. 1. 96p. pap., stu. ed. 24.95 (978-0-7487-9362-4(3)); Bk. 2. 112p. pap., stu. ed. 24.95 (978-0-7487-9363-1(1)) Nelson Thornes Ltd. GBR. *Dist:* Trans-Atlantic Pubns., Inc.

Fears, Melissa. Thank God It's Sunday. 2004. (J). per. 6.95 (978-0-89315-413-4(X)) Lambert Bk. Hse., Inc.

Fiano, Kim Sullivan. Discovery Lab Crafts for Kids. 2000. (J). 16.99 (978-0-8307-2444-4(3)) Gospel Light Pubns.

Fischer, Carl. Days of Faith: Student Planner & Assignment Book 2004-2005. Connelly, Gwen & Holmberg, Ansgar, illus. 2004. 108p. (J). spiral bd. 3.25 (978-0-89837-199-4(6) , 9805) Pflaum Publishing Group.

Gaited Horse Christian Adventures in Learning Book. 2005. (J). 19.95 (978-1-59649-222-6(8)) Whispering Pine Pr., Inc.

Gaited Horse Hood Christian Educational Curriculum Book. 2005. (J). 19.95 (978-1-59210-371-3(5)) Whispering Pine Pr., Inc.

Gallery, Philip D. Can You Find Saints? Introducing Your Child to Holy Men & Women. Harlow, Janet L., tr. Harlow, Janet L., illus. 2003. (J). 41p. (gr. 2-4). 16.95 (978-0-86716-487-9(5)); 40p. (978-2-89507-437-3(2)) St. Anthony Messenger Pr. & Franciscan Communications.

Ganeri, Anita. What's Sacred to Me, 4 bks., Set. 2000. (Illus.). (J). (978-0-7398-4196-9(3)) Raintree.

God Is All-Knowing. 2.99 (978-0-7847-0864-4(9)) Standard Publishing.

God Is Creator. 2.99 (978-0-7847-0851-4(7)) Standard Publishing.

God Is Eternal. 2.99 (978-0-7847-0854-5(1)) Standard Publishing.

God Is Ever-Present. 2.99 (978-0-7847-0855-2(X)) Standard Publishing.

God's Big Picture: Bible Time Line. 2004. (KidsTime Ser.). (gr. 1-6). 19.99 (978-0-8307-2347-8(1) , Gospel Light) Gospel Light Pubns.

God's People Celebrate: Leader's Guide. 2004. (KidsTime Ser.). (gr. 1-6). 39.99 (978-0-8307-2529-8(6) , Gospel Light) Gospel Light Pubns.

Gold Mine of Crafts for Kids C. 2004. pap. 16.99 (978-0-8307-2626-4(8)) Gospel Light Pubns.

Group Publishing Staff. GroupBuilder Games & Activities for Youth Ministry. 2004. (Illus.). 112p. (gr. 7-12). pap. 15.99 (978-0-7644-2197-6(2) , Flagship Church Resources) Group Publishing, Inc.

—I Can Make It Myself: Bible Story Crafts for Preschoolers. 2004. (Illus.). 95p. pap. 17.99 (978-0-7644-2225-6(1) , Flagship Church Resources) Group Publishing, Inc.

Hakowski, Maryann. Vine & Branches. St. George, Carolyn, illus. 2003. (Resources for Youth Retreats Ser.: Vol. 1). 160p. (YA). (gr. 7-12). spiral bd. 24.95 (978-0-88489-255-7(7)) St. Mary's Pr.

—Vine & Branches, Vol. 2. Stamschror, Robert P., ed. St. George, Carolyn, illus. 2003. (Resources for Youth Retreats Ser.: Vol. 2). 168p. (YA). (gr. 7-12). spiral bd. 24.95 (978-0-88489-278-6(6)) St. Mary's Pr.

Hamby, Joe & Kluever, Karen Trogdon. Gear for the Road. 2003. 48p. pap., stu. ed. 6.50 (978-0-687-02618-0(0)); 80p. pap. 12.00 (978-0-687-02598-5(2)) Abingdon Pr.

Harrison, Mary J. Button. Holy Hogwash: What the Bible Never Said. 2000. (Generation Why Ser.: Vol. 6:2). (Illus.). 41p. (YA). (gr. 9-12). pap. 12.95 (978-0-87303-388-6(4)) Faith & Life Pr.

Holford, Karen. I Miss Grandpa: A Story to Help Your Child Understand Death— & Eternal Life. 2004. (Illus.). 32p. (J). (978-0-8163-2030-1(6)) Pacific Pr. Publishing Assn.

Hood, Karen Jean Matsko. Fun with Foster Kids Christian Educational Curriculum Book. 2004. (J). 19.95 (978-1-59210-441-3(X)) Whispering Pine Pr., Inc.

Hopkins, Paul. Using ICT in RE. 2000. (Illus.). 96p. (YA). (gr. 6-11). pap. 87.50 (978-0-7487-4341-4(3)) Nelson Thornes Ltd. GBR. *Dist:* Trans-Atlantic Pubns., Inc.

Hosch, Jenifer. 50 Bible Activities for Creative Minds. 2004. 64p. (gr. 3-6). 9.99 (978-0-7586-0129-2(8)) Concordia Publishing Hse.

Howie, Vicki. Easy Ways to Bible Fun for the Very Young: Twelve Bible-Based Activities For 3-5s. Taylor, Jane, illus. 2005. 96p. (J). pap. (978-1-84101-135-6(5) , Barnabas) Bible Reading Fellowship.

Hutchens, Paul. Thousand Dollar Fish. 1998. (gr. 3-6). lib. bdg. 13.00 (978-0-613-88120-3(6)) Tandem Library Bks.

I Wonder What Jesus Would Do: Fun to Color & Do. 2001. (978-0-7424-0020-7(4) , Instructional Fair) Schaffer, Frank Pubns.

Icelandic Horse Hood Christian Educational Curriculum Book. 2005. (J). 19.95 (978-1-59210-359-1(6)) Whispering Pine Pr., Inc.

Inspired Idea Staff, creator. One Nation under God: Christian Founders. 2002. cd-rom 29.95 (978-1-931203-06-7(7)) Inspired Idea.

James, Steven. 24 Tandem Bible Hero Story Scripts for Children's Ministry. 2006. (Illus.). 96p. (YA). pap. 10.99 (978-0-7847-1321-1(9), 04312) Standard Publishing.

—24 Tandem Bible Story Scripts for Children's Ministry. 2006. 96p. (YA). pap. 15.99 (978-0-7847-1320-4(0), 42038) Standard Publishing.

Jarrell, Jane & Saathoff, Deborah. Off to Work We Go. 2004. 50p. (ps up). pap., act. bk. ed. 6.99 (978-0-8054-0823-2(1)) B&H Publishing Grp.

Jones, Carolyn. Who Am I, Really? 2000. (Christian Character Development Ser.). (YA). (gr. 8-12). pap. 16.99 (978-0-7644-2132-7(8)) Group Publishing, Inc.

Kadela, Natalie. Our Year with God: A Child's Introduction to Catholic Holy Days & the Liturgical Year. Richards, Virginia Helen & Lane, Helen Rita, illus. 1999. 152p. (J). (gr. 3-7). pap. 14.95 (978-0-8198-5436-0(0), 332-265) Pauline Bks. & Media.

Karyn, Henley. I Learn about God. 2004. pap. 2.99 (978-0-7847-0651-0(4)) Standard Publishing.

Kelly, Mark. Get Real: God & Media. 2000. (Fast Lane Bible Studies Ser.). (Illus.). 64p. (YA). pap. 9.95 (978-0-87303-403-6(1)) Faith & Life Pr.

KidsTime: God's Big Picture Kit. 2004. (gr. 1-6). 139.99 (978-0-8307-2345-4(5), Gospel Light) Gospel Light Pubns.

Kitch. Anglican Kids' Advent Activity Book. 2006. (Illus.). 48p. (J). pap. 7.00 (978-0-8192-2195-7(3)) Morehouse Publishing.

Klug, Frances Marie. Stories from Heaven, Vol. XVII. l.t. ed. 2000. 371p. (YA). (gr. 7-13). pap. 15.95 (978-1-892957-17-7(5)) City of God, St. Joseph's Hill of Hope.

Larkin, Jean K. Days of Faith: Student Planner & Assignment Book, Primary Grades 2006-2007. 2006. (Illus.). 108p. (J). spiral bd. 4.95 (978-1-933178-31-8(0)) Pflaum Publishing Group.

LeFever, Marlene. Flowers from God: Thank-You Notes for Sunday School Teachers. 2002. 64p. pap., pap. 1.99 (978-0-7814-3891-9(8), 0781438918) Cook, David C. Publishing Co.

Lewis, Carole. First Place Group Starter Kit. 2004. 179.99 (978-0-8307-3369-9(8), Gospel Light) Gospel Light Pubns.

Life Together Sunday School Starter Kit: Leader Guide. 2004. (gr. 7 up). (978-0-8066-5091-3(5)); (978-0-8066-5104-0(0)) Augsburg Fortress, Pubs.

Life Together Sunday School Starter Kit: Learner Resources. 2004. (978-0-8066-5069-2(9)); (978-0-8066-5082-1(6)); (978-0-8066-5095-1(8)); (gr. 1-3). (978-0-8066-5072-2(9)); (gr. 1-3). (978-0-8066-5085-2(0)); (gr. 1-3). (978-0-8066-5098-2(2)); (gr. 4-6). (978-0-8066-5075-3(3)); (gr. 4-6). (978-0-8066-5088-3(5)); (gr. 4-6). (978-0-8066-5101-9(6)) Augsburg Fortress, Pubs.

Lingo, Susan L. Collect-n-Tell Bible Stories for Kids: 34 Awesome Bible Stories with Powerful Points from a Few Simple Supplies! Barr, Marilynn G., illus. 2006. 112p. (YA). 15.99 (978-0-7847-1418-8(5), 02456) Standard Publishing.

Little KidsTime: My God & Me. ldr.'s ed. 2004. 464p. 39.99 (978-0-8307-2881-7(3), Gospel Light) Gospel Light Pubns.

Little KidsTime: My Great Big God. ldr.'s ed. 2004. 464p. 39.99 (978-0-8307-2661-5(6), Gospel Light) Gospel Light Pubns.

Little KidsTime 1: Bible Story Pictures. 2004. 104p. 19.99 (978-0-8307-2773-5(6), Gospel Light) Gospel Light Pubns.

Living Our Catholic Faith, 6 booklets. 1998. (Illus.). (YA). (gr. 7-10). pap., stu. ed. 7.95 (978-0-89837-203-8(8)) Pflaum Publishing Group.

Mader, Carol. Crazy Clothesline Characters. 2004. (Illus.). 159p. 16.99 (978-0-7644-2140-2(9), Flagship Church Resources) Group Publishing, Inc.

McNamara, Beth Branigan, et al. Big Book of Ideas for Children's Faith Formation. 2001. (Illus.). 352p. pap. 24.95 (978-0-87973-018-5(8)) Our Sunday Visitor, Publishing Div.

Middler. 2004. (J). (gr. 4 up). stu. ed. 2.69 (978-0-7847-7203-4(7), 09433) Standard Publishing.

Millett, Melanie. Teeny Tiny Talks: Junior Primary: I Will Follow God's Plan for Me, Vol. 1. Millett, Melanie, illus. 2004. (J). per. 12.95 (978-1-55517-778-2(6), Cedar Fort, Inc.) Cedar Fort, Inc./CFI Distribution.

Muggli, Glorianne. Gospel Games: America & the Restored Gospel. 2001. (YA). 7.95 (978-1-57665-076-9(6)) Muggli Graphics.

National Consultants for Education, creator. The Treasure of My Catholic Faith: 2nd Grade. 2004. (Treasure of My Catholic Faith Ser.: No. 2). (Illus.). 240p. pap. 14.95 (978-0-9743661-4-2(5)) Circle Pr.

—The Treasure of My Catholic Faith: 4th Grade. 2004. (Treasure of My Catholic Faith Ser.: No. 4). (Illus.). 272p. pap. 14.95 (978-0-9743661-6-6(1)) Circle Pr.

—The Treasure of My Catholic Faith: 5th Grade. 2004. (Treasure of My Catholic Faith Ser.: No. 5). (Illus.). 295p. pap. 14.95 (978-0-9743661-7-3(X)) Circle Pr.

—The Treasure of My Catholic Faith: 6th Grade. 2004. (Treasure of My Catholic Faith Ser.: No. 6). (Illus.). 295p. pap. 14.95 (978-0-9743661-8-0(8)) Circle Pr.

Neuberger, Anne E. Puppets + Kids + Bible Stories = A Creative Way to Learn. Bundick, Tessie, illus. 2001. 126p. (J). (ps up). 19.95 (978-1-58595-132-1(3)) Twenty-Third Pubns./Bayard.

Niles, Lori, ed. Amazing Science Devotions for Children's Ministry. 1998. (Illus.). 96p. (gr. k-6). pap. 15.99 (978-0-7644-2105-1(0), Flagship Church Resources) Group Publishing, Inc.

Noonan, Joseph. What Is My Vocation? Student Edition. 2005. 7.00 net. (978-0-9774733-0-4(9)) Univ. St. Mary of the Lake, Mundelein Seminary.

Nottingham, Sharon, illus. Sealing Love, Jr. 2002. 182p. (J). pap. 11.95 (978-0-9717734-1-7(6)) Sealing Touch End-Time Memory Fellowship.

Nystrom, Jennifer. Favorite Bible Children: Grades 1 & 2. 2004. (Illus.). 96p. (J). (gr. 1-2). pap. 11.95 (978-1-885358-77-6(6)) Rainbow Pubs. & Legacy Pr.

—Favorite Bible Children: Grades 3 & 4. 2004. (Illus.). 96p. (J). (gr. 3-4). pap. 11.95 (978-1-885358-78-3(4)) Rainbow Pubs. & Legacy Pr.

Olla, Debbie. Confirmation Certificate. 2004. (Illus.). (J). pap. 9.95 (978-0-937997-76-5(5), 504510) Pflaum Publishing Group.

O'Neal, Debbie Trafton. Before & after Easter: Activities & Ideas for Lent to Pentecost. 2nd ed. 2001. (Illus.). 64p. (gr. 3-7). 11.99 (978-0-8066-4157-7(6), Augsburg Bks.) Augsburg Fortress, Pubs.

El Pecado (Sin) Quarter 1, Level 2. (Caminando con Jesus (Walking with Jesus) Series B). (SPA.). (J). (gr. 1-2). stu. ed. 3.50 (978-0-570-05135-0(5), 16-2911) Concordia Publishing Hse.

Plum, Paul & Plum, Joanensor. Ias 3 Year Old Religious Education Program. 2005. (J). bds. 13.95 (978-1-59276-087-9(2)) Our Sunday Visitor, Publishing Div.

Plum, Paul S. & Plum, Joan Ensor. I Am Special Three Year Old Religious Education Program: Activity Book. rev. ed. 2005. (Illus.). (J). per. 9.95 (978-1-59276-085-5(6)) Our Sunday Visitor, Publishing Div.

Power Twins Handbook Volume One. 2006. (J). spiral bd. ***978-0-9742355-1-6(2))** Brda, Tracy.

Primary. 2004. (J). (gr. 2 up). stu. ed. 2.69 (978-0-7847-7202-7(9), 09432) Standard Publishing.

Relating to Self, Others, God, 6 booklets. 1998. (YA). (gr. 7-10). pap., stu. ed. 7.45 (978-0-89837-207-6(0)) Pflaum Publishing Group.

Reuther, Ruth E. For Children of All Ages. Reuther, J. R., photos by. 2000. (Illus.). 34p. (J). pap. (978-0-9622632-2-4(2)) Wee-Chee-Taw Publishing.

Rhydderch, Gwyn, et al. Iesu'r Ffrind: 16 Sesiwn Yn Cyflwyno Bywyd Iesu Ar Gyfer Plant Cynradd Yn Seiliedig Ar Efengyl Luc. 2005. (WEL., Illus.). 63p. (978-1-85994-007-5(2)) Cyhoeddiadau'r Gair.

Rice, Wayne & Yaconelli, Mike. Creative Activities for Small Youth Groups. Youth Specialties Clip Art Staff, illus. 2003. (Creative Resources for Youth Ministry Se Ser.). 104p. (YA). (gr. 7-12). pap. 12.95 (978-0-88489-264-9(6)) St. Mary's Pr.

Roberts, Catrin, et al. Mawredd Mawr Moses! 16 Sesiwn Beiblaidd Ar Gyfer Clwb Plant Neu'r Ysgol Sul. 2005. (WEL., Illus.). 73p. (978-1-85994-034-1(X)) Cyhoeddiadau'r Gair.

Rock, Lois, et al. Beibl y Plant Lleiaf. 2005. (WEL., Illus.). 256p. (978-1-85994-514-8(7)) Cyhoeddiadau'r Gair.

Savitskas, Margaret. Totally Lent! A Kid's Journey to Easter 2006. Larkin, Jean K., ed. 2005. (Illus.). 64p. (J). 5.95 (978-1-933178-25-7(6), 3576) Pflaum Publishing Group.

Savitskas, Margaret & Behe, Mary. Totally Lent! A Child's Journey to Easter 2006. Larkin, Jean K., ed. 2005. (Illus.). 64p. (J). 5.95 (978-1-933178-26-4(4), 3586) Pflaum Publishing Group.

Schippe, Cullen & Cannizzo, Karen, eds. Discovering the Story of God's People, 6 bks. 2005. (Faith Activities for Catholic Kids Ser.). (Illus.). 32p. (J). 6.95 (978-1-933178-20-2(5), 2806) Pflaum Publishing Group.

—Learning How to Live, 6 bks. 2005. (Faith Activities for Catholic Kids Ser.). (Illus.). 32p. (J). 6.95 (978-1-933178-18-9(3), 2804) Pflaum Publishing Group.

—Learning to Celebrate, 6 bks. 2005. (Faith Activities for Catholic Kids Ser.). (Illus.). 32p. (J). 6.95 (978-1-933178-19-6(1), 2805) Pflaum Publishing Group.

School of the Bible for Kids: The Most High God. 2003. (ENG & GER.). 238p. ring bd. 79.95 (978-0-9767647-3-1(3)) Kids in Ministry International.

School Specialty Publishing Staff. Hidden Pictures: Old Testament Heroes: Fun to Color & Do Activity Books. 2003. 32p. pap. (978-0-7424-0279-9(7)) School Specialty Publishing.

Science Discovery Works: Concordia Edition. (J). (gr. 2). stu. ed. 23.00 (978-0-570-02502-3(8), 52-1002); (gr. 3). stu. ed. 33.42 (978-0-570-02504-7(4), 52-1003); (gr. 4). stu. ed. 35.25 (978-0-570-02506-1(0), 52-1004); (gr. 5). stu. ed. 37.98 (978-0-570-02508-5(7), 52-1005); (gr. 6). stu. ed. 37.98 (978-0-570-02510-8(9), 52-1006) Concordia Publishing Hse.

Sonharvest County Fair Starter. 2004. pap. 49.99 (978-0-8307-3008-7(7)) Gospel Light Pubns.

Sonharvest County Fair Super S. 2004. pap. 69.99 (978-0-8307-3005-6(2)) Gospel Light Pubns.

Soul Survivor Guide to Service Projects. 2004. 96p. 19.99 (978-0-8307-3529-7(1), Gospel Light) Gospel Light Pubns.

Soul Survivor Guide to Youth Ministry. 2004. 96p. 19.99 (978-0-8307-3530-3(5), Gospel Light) Gospel Light Pubns.

Soul Survivor Prayer Ministry How to Pray for Others. 2004. 72p. 5.99 (978-0-8307-3527-3(5), Gospel Light) Gospel Light Pubns.

Spieler, Cathy. My More-Than-Coloring Book about God's Creation, Vol. 1. 1999. (My More-Than-Coloring Bks.). 64p. (J). (ps-2). pap. 5.00 (978-0-570-05556-3(3)) Concordia Publishing Hse.

Squint Free Holy Bible for Kids. l.t. ed. 2000. 1952p. (J). (gr. 4-7). lthr. 17.99 (978-0-7852-5676-2(8)) Nelson, Thomas Inc.

Stickler, LeeDell & Newman, Judy. Footprints on the Wall. 2004. (Just Add Kids Ser.). (Illus.). 112p. 14.00 (978-0-687-04850-2(8)) Abingdon Pr.

—The Jailhouse Rocked. 2004. 112p. (gr. 1-6). 14.00 (978-0-687-04860-1(5)) Abingdon Pr.

Stickler, LeeDell, et al. Ring 'Round Jericho. 2004. (Just Add Kids Ser.). (Illus.). 112p. (ps up). 14.00 (978-0-687-04820-5(6)) Abingdon Pr.

Stobaugh, James. Skills for Literary Analysis Student: Encouraging Thoughtful Christians to be World Changers. 2005. (Broadman & Holman Literature Ser.). 272p. stu. ed. 24.99 (978-0-8054-5897-8(2)) B&H Publishing Grp.

Stohs, Anita Reith. Praise God with Paper Cups: 45 Easy Bible Crafts. 2005. (ENG., Illus.). 64p. (J). 9.99 (978-0-7586-0842-0(X)) Concordia Publishing Hse.

Story Cards - Year 1. 2003. (Story Hour Ser.). (Illus.). 5.95 (978-1-56212-346-8(7), 001655, Faith Alive Christian Resources) CRC Pubns.

Story Cards - Year 2. 2003. (Story Hour Ser.). (Illus.). 5.95 (978-1-56212-409-0(9), 001665, Faith Alive Christian Resources) CRC Pubns.

Swain, Sharon J. Calling You. 2nd ed. 1999. (Illus.). 96p. (J). (978-0-304-70613-6(2), Burns & Oates) Continuum International Publishing Group, Ltd.

Tarnor, Pearl, et al. Shalom U-Verakhah: The New Hebrew Primer. 1999. (ENG & HEB., Illus.). 160p. (J). (978-0-87441-654-1(X)); (978-0-87441-677-0(9)) Behrman Hse., Inc.

Teen 2 Teen. 2004. (J). (gr. 7-12). stu. ed. 2.69 (978-0-7847-7185-3(5), 09435) Standard Publishing.

Teen Teacher. 2004. (Illus.). 64p. (J). (ps-k). tchr. ed. 11.99 (978-0-7847-7191-4(X), 09412) Standard Publishing.

Teen Visuals/Learning Resources. 2004. (Illus.). (J). (ps-k). 11.99 (978-0-7847-7197-6(9), 09417) Standard Publishing.

Theisen, Michael. Ready-to-Go Game Shows (That Teach Serious Stuff) Catholic Teachings & Practices Edition. 2003. (Illus.). 144p. (YA). 19.95 (978-0-88489-757-6(5)) St. Mary's Pr.

Thompson, Katie. Step by Step: Take-Home Leaflets for Every Sunday of the Catholic Lectionary. 1999. (Illus.). 376p. (J). (ps-1). pap. 39.95 (978-0-89622-987-7(4)) Twenty-Third Pubns./Bayard.

Thurman, Debbie. Sheer Faith: A Teen's Journey to Godly Growth. 2004. 112p. pap. 10.95 (978-0-9676289-3-6(8)) Cedar Hse. Pubs.

Tokarski, Steve & Mulvey, Kathleen. Making Moral Decisions 6 Booklets: A Guide for Catholic Teens. 1998. (Illus.). (YA). (gr. 9-13). pap., stu. ed. 7.45 (978-0-89837-163-5(5)) Pflaum Publishing Group.

Tokarski, Steve, et al. Making Moral Decisions: A Guide for Catholic Teens. 1998. (Illus.). (J). tchr. ed., spiral bd. 13.95 (978-0-89837-162-8(7)) Pflaum Publishing Group.

Trent, John T. Bedtime Blessings Vol. 2: 100 Bedtime Stories & Activities for Blessing Your Child. 2001. (Heritage Builders Ser.). (Illus.). 224p. (J). (ps-3). 9.99 (978-1-56179-807-0(X)) Focus on the Family Publishing.

The Truth about Sharing Faith. 1998. (Core Belief Bible Study Ser.). (YA). (gr. 7-9). pap. 11.99 (978-0-7644-0873-1(9)) Group Publishing, Inc.

Tyre, Travis. Introduction to Drama: Discovering Theatre in Christian Education. 2001. (Illus.). 256p. (YA). (gr. 7-12). pap. 18.50 (978-1-887710-20-6(5), ArtCan Drama Resources) Promise Productions, Inc.

Vaisey, Gill & Lewis, Sian. William Booth: Cristion Arbennig Iawn. 2005. (WEL., Illus.). 27p. (978-1-85644-620-4(4)) Univ. of Wales, Aberystwyth, Centre for Educational Studies.

Vandermeer, Harriet. Rings, Kings & Butterflies: Lessons on Christian Symbols for Children with CD-ROM. 2006. (Illus.). 160p. (J). pap. 15.99 incl. cd-rom (978-0-8066-4931-3(3), Augsburg Bks.) Augsburg Fortress, Pubs.

Washington, Linda & Dall, Jeanette. Favorite Bible Children: Ages 2 & 3. 2004. (Illus.). 96p. (J). pap. 11.95 (978-1-885358-75-2(X)) Rainbow Pubs. & Legacy Pr.

—Favorite Bible Children: Ages 4 & 5. 2004. (Illus.). 96p. (J). pap. 11.95 (978-1-885358-76-9(8)) Rainbow Pubs. & Legacy Pr.

Webster, Noah. The New-England Primer. 2002. (Illus.). 80p. 9.00 (978-1-929241-25-5(9)) Vision Forum, Inc., The.

—The Orginal Blue Back Speller. 2002. (Illus.). 168p. 12.00 (978-1-929241-16-3(X)) Vision Forum, Inc., The.

Who Am I Inside? (Christian Character Development Ser.). 64p. (YA). (gr. 8-12). pap. 16.99 (978-0-7644-2129-7(8)) Group Publishing, Inc.

Who Am I to God? 2000. (Christian Character Development Ser.). 64p. (YA). (gr. 8-12) pap. 16.99 (978-0-7644-2130-3(1)) Group Publishing, Inc.

Who Am I When Nobody's Looking? (Christian Character Development Ser.). 64p. (YA). (gr. 8-12). pap. 16.99 (978-0-7644-2128-0(X)) Group Publishing, Inc.

Why Evil Matters. 1998. (Core Belief Bible Study Ser.). (YA). (gr. 10-12). pap. 11.99 (978-0-7644-0878-6(X)) Group Publishing, Inc.

Why Our Humanity Matters. 1998. (Core Belief Bible Study Ser.). (YA). (gr. 10-12). pap. 11.99 (978-0-7644-0877-9(1)) Group Publishing, Inc.

Why Sharing Faith Matters. 1998. (Core Belief Bible Study Ser.). (YA). (gr. 10-12). pap. 11.99 (978-0-7644-0897-7(6)) Group Publishing, Inc.

Wonderfully Made: God's Plan for Growing Up. (J). (gr. 2-3). 6.99 (978-1-57153-301-2(X)) Curriculum Publishing, Presbyterian Church (U. S. A.).

RELIGIOUS FESTIVALS

see Fasts and Feasts

RELIGIOUS FREEDOM

see Freedom of Religion

RELIGIOUS HISTORY

see Church History

RELIGIOUS LIBERTY

see Freedom of Religion

RELIGIOUS LITERATURE

see also Bible As Literature; Catholic Literature

Attinger, Billy, illus. Baby's First Little Book of Prayers. gif. ed. 2003. (Wee Witness Ser.). 32p. 7.99 (978-0-7369-1185-6(5)) Harvest Hse. Pubs.

Bawa, Ujagar S. Japuji Sahib, Reharas Sahib, Anand Sahib, Kirtan Sohila: A Part of Sikh Scriptures. 1999. (PAN & ENG.). 416p. (YA). (gr. 8-12). 20.00 (978-0-942245-10-3(5)) Washington Sikh Ctr./Sikh Youth Forum.

Charlesbridge Publication Staff. Xanadu: The Imaginary Place. 1999. (J). (gr. 4-7). pap. 6.95 (978-0-9651722-3-3(6)); (Illus.). 15.95 (978-0-9651722-2-6(8)) Shakti for Children.

Loehe, Wilhelm. Questions & Answers to the Six Parts of Luther's Small Catechism. Horn, Edward T., tr. from GER. 2nd ed. 1998. 198p. (YA). reprint ed. 25.00 (978-1-891469-14-5(2)) Repristination Pr.

McCaughrean, Geraldine, retold by. John Bunyan's The Pilgrim's Progress Retold. l.t. ed. 2005. (Illus.). 176p. (J). pap. (978-0-7540-6174-8(4), CLP 365) BBC Audio.

Orthodox Woodriver District Baptist Association Staff. Treasured Talents in God's Time. Fisher, Suzanne, ed. Wesley, Robert B., illus. l.t. unabr. ed. 1999. (WeWrite Kids! Ser.: Vol. 42). 39p. (YA). (gr. 4-12). pap. 3.95 (978-1-57635-024-9(X)) WeWrite LLC.

Sharma, Bulbul. Ramayan for Children. 2004. (Illus.). 198p. 15.99 (978-0-670-04964-6(6), Penguin Global) Penguin Group (USA) Inc.

Zyromski, Page McKean. Skits from Scripture: 10 Plays from the New Testament. Cannizzo, Karen A., ed. 2001. 36p. (J). pap. 11.95 (978-0-937997-97-0(8)) Pflaum Publishing Group.

RELIGIOUS MUSIC

see Church Music

RELIGIOUS ORDERS

see Monasticism and Religious Orders

RELIGIOUS PAINTING

see Christian Art and Symbolism

RELIGIOUS POETRY

see also Carols; Hymns

Appelt, Kathi. I See the Moon. Jenkins, Debra Reid, illus. 2004. 24p. (J). (ps-2). 15.00 (978-0-8028-5118-5(5)); pap. 8.00 (978-0-8028-5226-7(2)) Eerdmans, William B. Publishing Co.

Benegar, Dawn M. 101 Bouncy Bible Rhyme-Time Games for Childrens Ministry. 2000. (Illus.). (J). (ps-6). pap. 16.99 (978-0-7644-2217-1(0)) Group Publishing, Inc.

Benson, Robert Hugh. Old Testament Rhymes. Pippet, Gabriel, illus. 31p. (J). (ps-7). reprint ed. 15.00 (978-1-930873-11-7(5)) Neumann Pr., The.

Busch, Melinda Kay. The Fiery Furnace. Koehler, Ed, illus. 2004. (Arch Bks.). 16p. (J). (gr. k-4). 1.99 (978-0-7586-0479-8(3)) Concordia Publishing Hse.

Caldwell, Lise. Let's Celebrate God's Blessings on Thanksgiving. Burris, Priscilla, illus. 2006. (Holiday Discovery Ser.). 24p. (J). (ps-3). bds. 6.99 (978-0-7847-1383-9(9), 04048) Standard Publishing.

Cotner, June. House Blessings. 2005. (Illus.). 164p. 15.95 (978-0-9748486-0-0(3)) becker&mayer! books.

Draper, Diane E. Expressions from the Experience: Christian Poetry & Short Inspirations. 2003. 87p. (YA). pap. 9.95 (978-0-7414-1482-3(1)) Infinity Publishing.

Fbs: 1ST & 2ND GRADERS' MEMORY VERSES. (J). (gr. 1-2). (978-0-633-00372-2(7)) LifeWay Christian Resources.

Fulton, Stephen (Abdul-Hakeem). 110 Islamic Poems for Children. 2007. 41p. pap. 8.95 ***978-0-7414-3963-5(8))** Infinity Publishing.

Krug, Christine Suguitan. Favorite Action Bible Verses. 2003. (Illus.). 48p. (ps-k). 9.99 (978-0-7586-0228-2(6)) Concordia Publishing Hse.

McCauley, Marlene. Song of Kateri: Princess of the Eucharist. McCauley, R. Allan, ed. McCauley, Marlene & Children's Art-Friends of Kateri, illus. unabr. ed. 2005. 300p. (YA). (gr. 4-7). per. 14.95 (978-0-9633633-2-9(8)) Grace Hse. Publishing.

Noble, Alfredo D. Poems for All Occasions. Noble, Jean et al, eds. rev. ed. 1998. 72p. (Orig.). (YA). reprint ed. pap. 8.95 (978-1-887653-06-0(6)) Papito Publishing.

Reese, Amy, illus. Illustrated Psalms of Praise: Psalmos de Albanza Ilustrados. 2005. (SPA & ENG.). 64p. (J). 16.95 (978-1-56854-561-5(4)) Liturgy Training Pubns.

Stortz, Diane M. Let's Shine Jesus' Light on Halloween. Fletcher, Rusty, illus. 2006. (Holiday Discovery Ser.). 24p. (J). (ps-3). bds. 6.99 (978-0-7847-1382-2(0), 04047) Standard Publishing.

Tangvald, Christine Harder. Let's Remember Jesus' Birth on Christmas. Nobens, Cheryl A., illus. 2006. (Holiday Discovery Ser.). 24p. (J). (ps-3). bds. 6.99 (978-0-7847-1384-6(7), 04049) Standard Publishing.

Verses from the Quran: Illustrated by Children Around the World. l.t. ed. 2000. (Illus.). 110p. (YA). (gr. 2 up). pap. 12.00 (978-1-879402-79-9(3)) Tahrike Tarsile Quran, Inc.

Ward, Elaine M. Answering Children's Faith Questions: Through Parables, Poetry & Prayer. 1999. 100p. (J). (gr. 1-6). pap. 10.95 (978-1-57438-031-6(1), 5302) Educational Ministries, Inc.

Weisheit, Eldon. 150 Psalms for Teens. 2003. 160p. (YA). 7.99 (978-0-7586-0120-9(4)) Concordia Publishing Hse.

Wilhelm, Hans. Jesus Wants Me for a Sunbeam. 2006. (Illus.). 24p. (J). 5.99 (978-0-439-80003-7(X)) Scholastic, Inc.

RELIGIOUS SYMBOLISM

see Christian Art and Symbolism

REMBRANDT HARMENSZOON VAN RIJN, 1606-1669

David, T. Rembrandt: El Festin del Rey Baltasar. 2002. (Coleccion Joven Arte).Tr. of Rembrandt: The Feast of Belshazzar. (SPA., Illus.). 124p. (YA). 11.96 (978-84-89804-09-8(5)) Loguez Ediciones ESP. *Dist:* Lectorum Pubns., Inc.

de Bie, Ceciel & Leenen, Martijn. Rembrandt. ed. 2001. (See & Do Children's Books Ser.). (Illus.). 64p. (gr. 3-7). 19.95 (978-0-89236-621-7(4)) Oxford Univ. Pr., Inc.

Dunn, Mary. My Adventure with Rembrandt. 2006. 44p. (J). 8.99 (978-1-59092-463-1(0) , Orchard Academy Pr.) Windstorm Creative.

Klein, Adam G. & Rembrandt Harmenszoon van Rijn. Rembrandt. 2007. (Illus.). 32p. (J). 22.78 (978-1-59679-735-2(5)) ABDO Publishing Co.

Mason, Antony & Rembrandt Harmenszoon van Rijn. Rembrandt. 2004. (Lives of the Artists Ser.). (Illus.). 48p. (J). pap. 11.95 (978-0-8368-5656-9(2) , 1233346); lib. bdg. 30.00 (978-0-8368-5651-4(1) , 1233346) Stevens, Gareth Inc. (World Almanac Library).

Mis, Melody S. Rembrandt. 2008. (J). lib. bdg. (***978-1-4042-3840-4(9)*** , PowerKids Pr.) Rosen Publishing Group, Inc., The.

Muhlberger, Richard. What Makes a Rembrandt a Rembrandt? 2002. (Illus.). 48p. (J). 16.99 (978-0-670-03572-4(6) , Viking Juvenile) Penguin Group (USA) Inc.

Niz, Xavier. Rembrandt. 2003. (Masterpieces, Artists & Their Works). (Illus.). 24p. (J). lib. bdg. 19.93 (978-0-7368-2230-5(5) , Bridgestone Bks.) Capstone Pr., Inc.

Pescio, Claudio. Rembrandt. 2008. (YA). lib. bdg. 24.95 net. (***978-1-934545-02-7(3)***) Oliver Pr., Inc.

Pescio, Claudio, et al. Rembrandt & 17th Century Holland. Knight, Simon, tr. from ITA. Sergio, illus. 2nd ed. 2000. (Masters of Art Ser.). 64p. (J). (gr. 3 up). pap. 16.95 (978-0-87226-642-1(7) , Bedrick, Peter Bks.) School Specialty Publishing.

Sturgis, Alexander. Introducing Rembrandt. 2002. (Introducing Painters Ser.). (Illus.). 32p. (J). lib. bdg. 24.25 (978-1-931983-44-0(5)) Chrysalis Education.

Woodhouse, Jayne. Rembrandt Van Rijn. 2002. (Life & Work of. . . Ser.). (Illus.). 32p. (J). (gr. k-2). lib. bdg. 22.79 (978-1-58810-606-3(3)) Heinemann Library.

—Rembrandt Van Rijn. 2002. (gr. k-3). lib. bdg. 14.75 (978-0-613-45817-7(6)) Tandem Library Bks.

REMEDIAL READING

see Reading—Remedial Teaching

REMINGTON, FREDERIC, 1861-1909

Giesecke, Ernestine. Frederic Remington. (Heinemann First Library). (Illus.). 32p. 2006. (J). (***978-1-4034-8490-1(2)***); 2003. pap. 6.50 (978-1-58810-281-2(5)); 1999. (J). lib. bdg. 21.36 (978-1-57572-951-0(2)) Heinemann Library.

—Frederic Remington. 2001. (gr. k-3). lib. bdg. 14.75 (978-0-613-89893-5(1)) Tandem Library Bks.

Mattern, Joanne. Frederic Remington. 2005. (Checkerboard Biography Library). (Illus.). 32p. (J). (gr. k-6). lib. bdg. 22.78 (978-1-59197-848-0(3)) ABDO Publishing Co.

Plain, Nancy. Frederic Remington: Artist of the American West. 2003. (Historical American Biographies Ser.). (Illus.). 160p. (J). (gr. 6-12). lib. bdg. 26.60 (978-0-7660-1975-1(6)) Enslow Pubs., Inc.

Venezia, Mike. Frederic Remington. Venezia, Mike, illus. (Getting to Know the World's Greatest Artists Ser.). (Illus.). 32p. (J). (gr. 3-4). 2003. pap. 6.95 (978-0-516-27812-4(6)); 2002. 27.00 (978-0-516-22497-8(2)) Scholastic Library Publishing. (Children's Pr.).

—Frederic Remington. 2002. (gr. 3-6). lib. bdg. 15.25 (978-0-613-59482-0(7)) Tandem Library Bks.

REMUS, UNCLE (FICTITIOUS CHARACTER)—FICTION

Harris, Joel Chandler. Uncle Remus: His Songs & His Sayings. Date not set. (J). lib. bdg. 24.95 (978-0-8488-0711-5(1)) Amereon LTD.

—Uncle Remus: His Songs & His Sayings. 265p. (J). 18.00 (978-0-9645990-0-0(7)) Historic Pr.-South.

—Uncle Remus: Tales. 1999. (Illus.). 234p. (J). reprint ed. 30.00 (978-0-88322-041-2(5)) Beehive Pr., The.

—Uncle Remus & Brer Rabbit. 1999. (Illus.). 64p. (J). (gr. 4-7). reprint ed. 19.95 (978-1-55709-491-9(8)) Applewood Bks.

Lester, Julius. The Tales of Uncle Remus: The Adventures of Brer Rabbit. Pinkney, Jerry, illus. 1999. 176p. (J). (gr. 3-7). pap. 8.99 (978-0-14-130347-5(6) , Puffin) Penguin Group (USA) Inc.

—The Tales of Uncle Remus: The Adventures of Brer Rabbit. Pinkney, Jerry, illus. 1999. 143p. (J). (ps-7). lib. bdg. 17.60 (978-0-613-17870-9(X)) Tandem Library Bks.

—Uncle Remus: The Complete Tales. Fogelman, Phyllis, ed. Pinkney, Jerry, illus. 1999. 720p. (J). (ps-3). 35.00 (978-0-8037-2451-8(9) , Dial) Penguin Group (USA) Inc.

RENAISSANCE

see also Art, Renaissance; Civilization, Medieval; Humanism; Literature, Medieval; Middle Ages

Benchmark Education Staff, compiled by. The Renaissance. 2006. spiral bd. 125.00 (***978-1-4108-7142-8(8)***) Benchmark Education Co.

Bloom, Harold. The Italian Renaissance. 2004. (Bloom's Period Studies Ser.). (Illus.). 350p. (J). (gr. 9-13). 45.00 (978-0-7910-7895-2(7) , Chelsea Hse.) Facts On File, Inc.

Boekhoff, P. M. & Kallen, Stuart A. The Italian Renaissance. 2003. (History of the World Ser.). (Illus.). 48p. (J). (gr. 3-5). 23.70 (978-0-7377-1036-6(5) , Kidhaven) Thomson Gale.

Brewer, Paul. Warfare in the Renaissance World. 1999. (History of Warfare Ser.). (Illus.). 80p. (YA). (gr. 7-12). lib. bdg. 29.97 (978-0-8172-5444-5(7)) Raintree.

Claybourne, Anna. The Renaissance. 2007. (J). (***978-1-4109-2910-5(8)***); pap. (***978-1-4109-2916-7(7)***) Steck-Vaughn.

Corrick, James A. The Renaissance. 2006. (World History Ser.). 112p. (J). (gr. 7-10). 32.45 (978-1-59018-836-1(5) , Lucent Bks.) Thomson Gale.

Day, Nancy. Your Travel Guide to Renaissance Europe. 2005. (Passport to History Ser.). (Illus.). 96p. (gr. 5-8). lib. bdg. 26.50 (978-0-8225-3080-0(5)) Lerner Publishing Group.

Douglas, Vincent & School Specialty Publishing Staff. Renaissance & Discovery. 2001. (History of the World Ser.). (Illus.). 48p. (J). (gr. 3 up). 18.95 (978-1-57768-953-9(4) , Bedrick, Peter Bks.) School Specialty Publishing.

Grant, Neil, et al. The Atlas of the Renaissance World. Ravaglia, Paola, illus. 2001. (Atlas Ser.). 64p. (J). (gr. 5 up). 19.95 (978-0-87226-692-6(3) , Bedrick, Peter Bks.) School Specialty Publishing.

Greenblatt, Miriam. Lorenzo de Medici & Renaissance Italy. 2002. (Rulers & Their Times Ser.). (Illus.). 80p. (J). (gr. 8-12). lib. bdg. 29.93 (978-0-7614-1490-2(8) , Benchmark Bks.) Cavendish, Marshall Corp.

Grolier Educational Staff, contrib. by. Africa-Bologna, Vol. 1. 2002. (Illus.). (J). (978-0-7172-5663-1(4) , Grolier) Scholastic Library Publishing.

—Books & Libraries-Constantinople, Vol. 2. 2002. (Illus.). (J). (978-0-7172-5664-8(2) , Grolier) Scholastic Library Publishing.

—Copernicus-Exploration, Vol. 3. 2002. (Illus.). (J). (978-0-7172-5665-5(0) , Grolier) Scholastic Library Publishing.

—Eyck-Government, Vol. 4. 2002. (Illus.). (J). (978-0-7172-5666-2(9) , Grolier) Scholastic Library Publishing.

—Guilds & Crafts-Landscape Painting, Vol. 5. 2002. (Illus.). (J). (978-0-7172-5667-9(7) , Grolier) Scholastic Library Publishing.

—Language-Merchants, Vol. 6. 2002. (Illus.). (J). (978-0-7172-5668-6(5) , Grolier) Scholastic Library Publishing.

—Michelangelo-Palaces & Villas, Vol. 7. 2002. (Illus.). (J). (978-0-7172-5669-3(3) , Grolier) Scholastic Library Publishing.

—Palestina-Reformation, Vol. 8. 2002. (Illus.). (J). (978-0-7172-5670-9(7) , Grolier) Scholastic Library Publishing.

—Religious Dissent-Tapestry, Vol. 9. 2002. (Illus.). (J). (978-0-7172-5671-6(5) , Grolier) Scholastic Library Publishing.

—Renaissance, 10 vols. Incl. Vol. 1. Africa-Bologna. (978-0-7172-5663-1(4)); Vol. 2. Books & Libraries-Constantinople. (978-0-7172-5664-8(2)); Vol. 3. Copernicus-Exploration. (978-0-7172-5665-5(0)); Vol. 4. Eyck-Government. (978-0-7172-5666-2(9)); Vol. 5. Guilds & Crafts-Landscape Painting. (978-0-7172-5667-9(7)); Vol. 6. Language-Merchants. (978-0-7172-5668-6(5)); Vol. 7. Michelangelo-Palaces & Villas. (978-0-7172-5669-3(3)); Vol. 8. Palestina-Reformation. (978-0-7172-5670-9(7)); Vol. 9. Religious Dissent-Tapestry. (978-0-7172-5671-6(5)); Vol. 10. Technology-Zwingli. (978-0-7172-5672-3(3)); (J). 2002. (Illus.). 800p. 2002. 345.00 (978-0-7172-5673-0(1) , Grolier) Scholastic Library Publishing.

—Technology-Zwingli, Vol. 10. 2002. (Illus.). (J). (978-0-7172-5672-3(3) , Grolier) Scholastic Library Publishing.

Hancock, Lee. Lorenzo de' Medici: Florence's Great Leader & Patron of the Arts. 2004. (Rulers, Scholars, & Artists of Renaissance Europe Ser.). 112p. (J). lib. bdg. 31.95 (978-1-4042-0315-0(X)) Rosen Publishing Group, Inc., The.

Hay, Jeff. Renaissance. 2001. (gr. 7-12). lib. bdg. 39.05 (978-0-613-73785-2(7)) Tandem Library Bks.

Herold, Vickey. Science During the Renaissance. 2006. pap. 42.00 (***978-1-4108-6464-2(2)***) Benchmark Education Co.

Hinds, Kathryn. The Church. 2000. (Life in the Middle Ages Ser.). (Illus.). 80p. (J). (gr. 5 up). lib. bdg. 29.93 (978-0-7614-1008-9(2) , Benchmark Bks.) Cavendish, Marshall Corp.

—The Countryside. (Illus.). (J). 2004. 72p. 29.93 (978-0-7614-1656-2(0)); 2000. 80p. (gr. 5 up). lib. bdg. 29.93 (978-0-7614-1006-5(6)) Cavendish, Marshall Corp. (Benchmark Bks.).

Hirsch, E. D., ed. The Renaissance, Level 5. 2003. tchr. ed. 9.95 (978-0-7690-5074-4(3)); stu. ed. 49.95 (978-0-7690-2853-8(5)) Pearson Learning.

Hollingsworth, Patricia L., et al. The Renaissance. 1998. (Sails - Students' Active Interdisciplinary Learning Ser.: Vol. 3). (Illus.). (YA). (gr. 3-12). pap. 20.00 (978-1-893413-02-3(0)) Univ. Schl. at the Univ. of Tulsa.

Hotle, Patrick. Renaissance. 1998. (Illus.). 96p. (YA). (gr. 5-8). pap. 10.95 (978-1-58037-072-1(1)) Twain, Mark Media, Inc. Pubs.

Jane Shuter. The Renaissance. 2nd ed. 2007. (Illus.). 32p. (J). pap. (***978-1-4034-8821-3(5)***) Heinemann Library.

Kubesh, Katie & Belletto, Kimm. HOCPP 1056 Renaissance. 2006. spiral bd. 18.50 (***978-1-60308-056-9(2)***) In the Hands of a Child.

Langley, Andrew. Renaissance: An Eyewitness Book. Scott, Carey, ed. Crawford, Andy, photos by. 2004. (Illus.). 60p. (J). (gr. 4-8). reprint ed. 16.00 (978-0-7567-8157-6(4)) DIANE Publishing Co.

Lassieur, Allison. Leonardo da Vinci & the Renaissance in World History. 2000. (In World History Ser.). (Illus.). 128p. (YA). (gr. 5-12). lib. bdg. 26.60 (978-0-7660-1401-5(0)) Enslow Pubs., Inc.

MacDonald, Fiona. You Wouldn't Want to Be a Crusader! A War You'd Rather Not Fight. Bergin, Mark, illus. 2005. (You Wouldn't Want to... Ser.). 32p. (J). (gr. 2-5). 28.50 (978-0-531-12412-3(6)); pap. 9.95 (978-0-531-12392-8(8)) Scholastic Library Publishing. (Watts, Franklin).

Mason, Antony. Everyday Life in Renaissance Times. 2005. (Uncovering History Ser.). (Illus.). 46p. (J). (gr. 6-9). lib. bdg. 29.95 (978-1-58340-710-3(3)) Smart Apple Media.

Merlo, Claudio. Three Masters of the Renaissance: Leonardo, Michelangelo, Raphael. Rosenberg, Marion Lignana, tr. from ITA. Bonini, S. et al, illus. 1999. (Bravo Ser.). 120p. (YA). (gr. 6 up). 8.95 (978-0-7641-0946-1(4)) Barron's Educational Series, Inc.

Prum, Deborah M. Rats, Bulls & Flying Machines: A History of the Renaissance & Reformation. Holdren, John, ed. 1999. (Core Chronicles Ser.: Vol. 1). (Illus.). (YA). (gr. 5-10). 106p. 21.95 (978-1-890517-19-9(4)); pap. 11.95 (978-1-890517-18-2(6)) Core Knowledge Foundation.

Quigley, Mary. The Renaissance. 2003. (Understanding People in the Past Ser.). (Illus.). 64p. (J). (gr. 4-6). pap. 28.50 (978-1-4034-0388-9(0)); pap. 8.95 (978-1-4034-0608-8(1)) Heinemann Library.

The Renaissance, 1300-1600. 2004. (Stories in History Ser.). (Illus.). 190p. (gr. 6-12). 13.32 (978-0-618-14224-8(X) , 2-00244) McDougal Littell Inc.

Saari, Peggy, et al, eds. Renaissance & Reformation, 2 vols. 2002. (Illus.). (J). (978-0-7876-5468-9(X)); (978-0-7876-5469-6(8)) Thomson Gale. (UXL).

Saari, Peggy & Saari, Aaron Maurice. Renaissance & Reformation: Biographies, 2 vols. 2002. (Illus.). (J). 400p. 120.00 (978-0-7876-5470-2(1) , GML00502-173752); xxxiv, 386p. (978-0-7876-5472-6(8)); xxxiv, 386p. (978-0-7876-5471-9(X)) Thomson Gale. (UXL).

Schomp, Virginia. The Italian Renaissance. 2002. (Cultures of the Past Ser.). (Illus.). 80p. (J). (gr. 5). 29.93 (978-0-7614-1492-6(4) , Benchmark Bks.) Cavendish, Marshall Corp.

Shuter, Jane. The Renaissance. 2007. (Illus.). 32p. (J). (***978-1-4034-8814-5(2)***) Heinemann Library.

Story of the Middle Ages, Answer Key. 2002. (J). 4.00 (978-1-930367-78-4(3) , CLP79961) Christian Liberty Pr.

Story of the Middle Ages, Tests. 2002. (J). 3.00 (978-1-930367-79-1(1) , CLP79962) Christian Liberty Pr.

Thompson, Stephen. The Renaissance. 2000. (Turning Points in World History Ser.). (Illus.). 220p. (YA). (gr. 9-12). lib. bdg. 32.45 (978-0-7377-0219-4(2) , Greenhaven Pr., Inc.) Thomson Gale.

Thomson, Melissa & Dean, Ruth. Women of the Renaissance. 2004. (Illus.). 128p. (YA). (gr. 7-10). lib. bdg. 32.45 (978-1-59018-473-8(4) , Lucent Bks.) Thomson Gale.

Wagner, Heather Lehr. Machiavelli: Renaissance Political Analyst & Author. 2005. (Makers of the Middle Ages & Renaissance Ser.). (Illus.). 138p. (J). (gr. 4-8). lib. bdg. 30.00 (978-0-7910-8629-2(1) , Chelsea Hse.) Facts On File, Inc.

Waldman, Nomi J. The Italian Renaissance. 2004. (Daily Life Ser.). (Illus.). 48p. (J). 26.20 (978-0-7377-1398-5(4) , Greenhaven Pr., Inc.) Thomson Gale.

RENAISSANCE—FICTION

Avi. Midnight Magic. 2001. (978-0-606-22158-0(1)); (gr. 5-8). lib. bdg. 13.00 (978-0-613-54286-9(X)) Tandem Library Bks.

Bradford, Emma. Kat & the Missing Notebooks. Sano, Kazuhiko, illus. 1999. (Stardust Classics: No. 4). 119p. (J). (gr. 2-5). 12.95 (978-1-889514-27-7(6)); pap. 5.95 (978-1-889514-28-4(4)) Dolls Corp.

Hawes, Louise. The Vanishing Point: The Story of Lavinia Fontana. 2004. 240p. (YA). (gr. 5-9). 17.00 (978-0-618-43423-7(2)) Houghton Mifflin Co. Trade & Reference Div.

Hoffman, Mary. The Falconer's Knot: A Story of Friars, Flirtation & Foul Play. 2007. (Illus.). 288p. (YA). (gr. 7 up). 16.95 (978-1-59990-056-8(4) , Bloomsbury Children) Bloomsbury Publishing.

RENOIR, AUGUSTE, 1841-1919

Hyde, Margaret E., ed. Renoir for Kids. 2004. (Great Art for Kids Ser.). (Illus.). 10p. (J). pap. 8.95 (978-1-58980-206-3(3)) Pelican Publishing Co., Inc.

Kelley, True. Pierre-Auguste Renoir: Paintings That Smile. 2005. (Smart about Art Ser.). (Illus.). 32p. (J). (gr. k-5). pap. 5.99 (978-0-448-43371-4(0) , Grosset & Dunlap) Penguin Group (USA) Inc.

Klein, Adam G. & Renoir, Auguste. Pierre-Auguste Renoir. 2007. (Illus.). 32p. (J). 22.78 (978-1-59679-736-9(3)) ABDO Publishing Co.

Nichols, Catherine & Renoir, Auguste. Pierre-Auguste Renoir. 2006. (Primary Source Library of Famous Artists). (Illus.). 32p. (J). 21.95 (978-1-4042-2765-1(2) , PowerKids Pr.) Rosen Publishing Group, Inc., The.

Somervill, Barbara. Pierre-Auguste Renoir. 2007. (Art Profiles for Kids Ser.). (Illus.). 48p. (J). lib. bdg. 29.95 (***978-1-58415-566-9(3)***) Mitchell Lane Pubs., Inc.

Spence, David. Renoir. 1998. (Great Artists Ser.). (Illus.). 32p. (J). pap. 5.95 (978-0-7641-0627-9(9)) Barron's Educational Series, Inc.

—Renoir: Color y Naturaleza. (Coleccion Grandes Artistas).Tr. of Renoir: Colot & Nature. (SPA.). (YA). (gr. 5-8). 12.76 (978-84-8211-137-7(X)) Celeste Ediciones, S.A. ESP. *Dist:* Lectorum Pubns., Inc.

REPAIRING

see also Building—Repair and Reconstruction

Van Slyke, Marge. Furniture Refinishing in A Class by Yourself. Lambert, Barbara, ed. Van der Sterre, Johanna, illus. 2004. 91p. per. 9.95 (978-0-9755548-0-7(8)) Log Cabin Bks.

REPORT WRITING

Abraham, Philip. Language Development Writing Process. 2004. 48p. pap. 6.95 (978-1-4042-8520-0(2)) Rosen Publishing Group, Inc., The.

Anderson, Dianne & Anderson, Ian. Cambridge Checkpoints VCE English 2005. 2004. (Cambridge Checkpoints Ser.). 192p. pap., stu. ed. 11.85 (978-0-521-60841-1(4)) Cambridge Univ. Pr.

Becnel, Kim. Bloom's How to Write about F. Scott Fitzgerald. 2007. (Bloom's How to Write about Literature Ser.). 256p. (YA). (gr. 9 up). 45.00 (***978-0-7910-9482-2(0)*** , Chelsea Hse.) Facts On File, Inc.

Bentley, Nancy. Don't Be a Copycat! Write a Great Report Without Plagiarizing. 2008. (Prime Ser.). (Illus.). 64p. (J). (gr. 3-4). lib. bdg. 27.93 (***978-0-7660-2860-9(7)***) Enslow Pubs., Inc.

Burke, Eileen & Putnam, Lillian. Tough Issues, Good Decisions: 20 Reproducible Stories & Writing Prompts That Get Kids Discussing, Writing & Making Good Choices in & Out of School. 2001. 72p. (gr. 4). pap. 11.95 (978-0-439-24117-5(0)) Scholastic, Inc.

Carroll, Joyce Armstrong, et al. Literature: Timeless Voices, Timeless Themes. 2001. (YA). Diamond Level. (gr. 12). trans. 33.47 (978-0-13-043951-2(7)); Diamond Level. (gr. 12). cd-rom 29.97 (978-0-13-437184-9(4)); Platinum Level. (gr. 10). trans. 33.47 (978-0-13-043948-2(7)); Silver Level. (gr. 8). trans. 33.47 (978-0-13-043946-8(0)) Prentice Hall PTR.

—Writing & Grammar: Communicatin in Action, Diamond Level. 2001. (YA). (gr. 12). pap., wbk. ed. 7.47 (978-0-13-043521-7(X)); pap., act. bk. ed. 7.47 (978-0-13-043898-0(7)) Prentice Hall PTR.

—Writing & Grammar, Communication in Action Diamond Level: Writing in the Content Areas & in the Workplace. 2001. (YA). (gr. 12). pap. 6.97 (978-0-13-052662-5(2)); (gr. 8). pap. 6.97 (978-0-13-052658-8(4)) Prentice Hall PTR.

—Writing & Grammar, Communication in Action Gold Level: Basic Skills Intervention Kit. 2001. (YA). (gr. 11). 499.97 (978-0-13-053998-4(8)); (gr. 9). 499.97 incl. audio compact disk (978-0-13-053996-0(1)) Prentice Hall PTR.

—Writing & Grammar, Communication in Action Gold Level: Writing in Content Areas & Workplace. 2001. (YA). (gr. 9). pap. 6.97 (978-0-13-052659-5(2)) Prentice Hall PTR.

—Writing & Grammar, Communication in Action Ruby Level: Writing in the Content Areas & in the Workplace. 2001. (YA). (gr. 11). pap. 6.97 (978-0-13-052661-8(4)) Prentice Hall PTR.

—Writing & Grammar, Grade 9: Communication in Action. 2001. Bronze Level. (YA). (gr. 7). pap., act. bk. ed. 7.47 (978-0-13-043921-5(5)); Copper Level. (J). (gr. 6). act. bk. ed. 7.47 (978-0-13-043891-1(X)); Copper Level. (J). (gr. 6). act. bk. ed. 8.47 (978-0-13-043913-0(4)); Copper Level. (J). (gr. 6). pap. 7.47 (978-0-13-053212-1(6)); Diamond Level. (YA). (gr. 12). 114.47 (978-0-13-052670-0(3)); Diamond Level. (YA). (gr. 12). stu. ed. 50.47 (978-0-13-436971-6(8)); Diamond Level. (YA). (gr. 12). trans. 114.47 (978-0-13-043890-4(1)); Diamond Level. (YA). (gr. 12). trans. 275.47 (978-0-13-043958-1(4)); Gold Level. (YA). (gr. 9). 114.47 (978-0-13-052667-0(3)); Gold Level. (YA). (gr. 9). trans. 114.47 (978-0-13-043887-4(1)); Platinum Level. (YA). (gr. 10). 114.47 (978-0-13-052668-7(1)); Platinum Level. (YA). (gr. 10). pap., act. bk. ed. 7.47 (978-0-13-043896-6(0)); Ruby Level. (YA). (gr. 11). stu. ed. 49.47 (978-0-13-436969-3(6)); Ruby Level. (YA). (gr. 11). pap., wbk. ed. 7.47 (978-0-13-043520-0(1)); Ruby Level. (YA). (gr. 11). pap., act. bk. ed. 7.47 (978-0-13-043897-3(9)); Silver Level. (YA). (gr. 8). 114.47 (978-0-13-052666-3(5)); Silver Level. (YA). (gr. 8). pap., act. bk. ed. 8.47 (978-0-13-043915-4(0)); Silver Level. (YA). (gr. 8). pap., act. bk. ed. 7.47 (978-0-13-043922-2(3)); Silver Level. (YA). (gr. 8). trans. 114.47 (978-0-13-043885-0(5)); Silver Level. (YA). (gr. 8). trans. 275.47 (978-0-13-043954-3(1)) Prentice Hall PTR.

—Writing & Grammar, Grade 9: Communication in Action, Diamond Level. 2001. (YA). (gr. 12). trans. 20.97 (978-0-13-043965-9(7)) Prentice-Hall.

—Writing & Grammer: Communication in Action, Platinum Level. 2001. (YA). (gr. 10). trans. 114.47 (978-0-13-043888-1(X)) Prentice Hall PTR.

Center for Performance Assessment. Write to Know: Nonfiction Writing Prompts for Algebra. 2005. 128p. pap. 9.95 (978-1-933196-07-7(6)) Advanced Learning Pr.

Cranium Inc. Staff. Cranium: the Word Worm Book of Outrageous Fun! Write it, Read it, Say It! Baseman, illus. 2006. 38p. (J). (gr. 2-17). 14.99 (978-0-316-05762-2(2)) Little, Brown Bks. for Young Readers.

Digital Photo Activity Kit Deluxe Vivitar 3700 series Lab-10. 2005. (J). cd-rom 1790.00 (978-1-933229-02-7(0)) APTE, Inc.

Digital Photo Activity Kit Deluxe Vivitar 3700 series Lab-15. 2005. (J). cd-rom 2610.00 (978-1-933229-03-4(9)) APTE, Inc.

Digital Photo Activity Kit Deluxe Vivitar 3700 series Lab-20. 2005. (J). 3260.00 (978-1-933229-04-1(7)) APTE, Inc.

Digital Photo Activity Kit Deluxe Vivitar 3700 series Lab-25. 2005. (J). 3924.00 (978-1-933229-05-8(5)) APTE, Inc.

Digital Photo Activity Kit Deluxe Vivitar 3700 series Lab-30. 2005. (J). 4585.00 (978-1-933229-06-5(3)) APTE, Inc.

Digital Photo Activity Kit Deluxe Vivitar 3700 series Lab-35. 2005. (J). 5239.00 (978-1-933229-07-2(1)) APTE, Inc.

Digital Photo Activity Kit Deluxe Vivitar 3700 series Lab-5. 2005. (J). cd-rom 648.95 (978-1-933229-01-0(2)) APTE, Inc.

Digital Photo Activity Kit Deluxe Vivitar 3700 Series school Version. 2005. (J). cd-rom 133.95 (978-1-933229-00-3(4)) APTE, Inc.

Digital Photo Activity Kit Deluxe Vivitar 5300 series Lab-2005. (J). 1759.95 (978-1-933229-09-6(8)) APTE, Inc.

Digital Photo Activity Kit Deluxe Vivitar 5300 series Lab-10. 2005. (J). 3469.99 (978-1-933229-10-2(1)) APTE, Inc.

Digital Photo Activity Kit Deluxe Vivitar 5300 series Lab-15. 2005. (J). 5129.95 (978-1-933229-11-9(X)) APTE, Inc.

Digital Photo Activity Kit Deluxe Vivitar 5300 series Lab-25. 2005. (J). 8123.90 (978-1-933229-12-6(8)) APTE, Inc.

Digital Photo Activity Kit Deluxe Vivitar 5300 series Lab-30. 2005. (J). 9624.95 (978-1-933229-14-0(4)) APTE, Inc.

Digital Photo Activity Kit Deluxe Vivitar 5300 series Lab-35. 2005. (J). 11119.95 (978-1-933229-15-7(2)) APTE, Inc.

Digital Photo Activity Kit Deluxe Vivitar 5300 series Single. 2005. (J). 359.99 (978-1-933229-08-9(X)) APTE, Inc.

Don't Panic: The Procrastinator's Guide to Writing an Effective Term Paper. 2004. 64p. (YA). per. 9.95 (978-0-9632123-5-1(4)) Crystal Pr.

DynaNotes Grade 4 Writing TAKS Review Guide Transparency Set. 2006. (J). trans. (978-1-933854-42-7(1)) DynaStudy, Inc.

DynaNotes Grade 7 Writing TAKS Review Guide. 2006. (J). pap. (978-1-933854-39-7(1)) DynaStudy, Inc.

DynaNotes Grade 7 Writing TAKS Review Guide Transparency Set. 2006. (J). trans. (978-1-933854-40-3(5)) DynaStudy, Inc.

Easy File Folder Reports. 2004. (J). per. 19.99 (978-1-55799-963-4(5) , EMC 6001) Evan-Moor Educational Pubs.

Elliott, Rebecca S. & Elliott, James. Painless Research Projects. 1998. (Barron's Painless Ser.). (Illus.). 288p. pap. 11.99 (978-0-7641-0297-4(4)) Barron's Educational Series, Inc.

Ellis, Sarah. From Reader to Writer: Teaching Writing Through Classic Children's Books. 2001. (J). (978-0-606-21205-2(1)) Tandem Library Bks.

English Language Arts Core Assignments: Grades 7-8: Report Writing. 1999. 187p. (YA). (gr. 7-8). pap. 40.00 (978-1-889630-22-9(5)) National Ctr. on Education & The Economy.

Evergreen: a Guide to Writing with Readings. 7th ed. 2003. (YA). (gr. 6-12). stu. ed. 3.96 incl. cd-rom (978-0-618-27389-8(1) , 315696) Houghton Mifflin College Div.

Ferguson. Mastering Career Skills: Research & Information Management. 2nd rev. ed. (Mastering Career Skills Ser.). 128p. pap. 12.95 (***978-0-8160-7118-0(7)** , Checkmark Bks.) Facts On File, Inc.

Gleed, Paul. Bloom's How to Write about William Shakespeare. 2007. (Bloom's How to Write about Literature Ser.). 256p. (YA). (gr. 9 up). 45.00 (***978-0-7910-9484-6(7)** , Chelsea Hse.) Facts On File, Inc.

Green, Gordon W. How to Get Straight A's In School & Have Fun at the Same Time. 1999. (Illus.). (YA). 17.60 (978-0-606-18630-8(1)) Tandem Library Bks.

Green, Gordon W., Jr. How to Get Straight A's in School & Have Fun at the Same Time. rev. ed. 1999. 192p. pap. 10.95 (978-0-312-86659-4(3) , Forge Bks.) Doherty, Tom Assocs., LLC.

Grolier Educational Staff. English Matters!, 10 vols., Set. 2000. (Illus.). 960p. (YA). (gr. 5-9). lib. bdg. 349.00 (978-0-7172-9437-4(4) , Grolier) Scholastic Library Publishing.

Hale, Christy. Collaborative Art & Writing Projects for Young Learners: 15 Delightful Projects That Build Early Reading & Writing Skills-and Connect to the Topics You Teach. 2006. 64p. pap. 12.99 (978-0-439-43462-1(9) , Teaching Resources) Scholastic, Inc.

Hamilton, John. Primary & Secondary Sources. 2005. (Straight to the Source Ser.). (J). (gr. k-6). lib. bdg. 22.78 (978-1-59197-548-9(4)) ABDO Publishing Co.

Heiligman, Deborah. The New York Public Library Kid's Guide to Research. 1998. (Illus.). 134p. (YA). (gr. 4-9). pap. 14.95 (978-0-590-30715-4(0) , Scholastic Reference) Scholastic, Inc.

Hereford, Jane. Passing the Georgia High School Graduation Test in Writing. 1999. (Illus.). 224p. (J). pap. 12.00 (978-0-89892-191-5(0)) Contemporary Publishing Co. of Raleigh, Inc.

Holt, Rinehart and Winston Staff. Holt Science: Holt Middle School Handbook Workbook. 95th ed. 1999. (YA). pap. 10.60 (978-0-03-098484-6(X)); pap. 10.60 (978-0-03-098485-3(8)) Holt, Rinehart & Winston.

—Pennsylvania Preparation for the PSSA: Reading & Writing Manual. 2001. pap. 12.20 (978-0-03-068468-5(4)) Holt, Rinehart & Winston.

James, Elizabeth. How to Write a School Report. 1998. (School Survival Guide Ser.). 96p. (gr. 3-7). 15.00 (978-0-688-16132-3(4)) HarperCollins Pubs.

James, Elizabeth & Barkin, Carol. How to Write Super School Reports. 1998. (School Survival Guide Ser.). 90p. 15.00 (978-0-06-881632-4(4) , Harper San Francisco) HarperCollins Pubs.

—How to Write Super School Reports: A School Survival Guide. rev. ed. 1998. 90p. (J). (gr. 5-8). 15.00 (978-0-7567-6461-6(0)) DIANE Publishing Co.

—How to Write Terrific Book Reports. rev. ed. 1998. 80p. (J). (ps-7). lib. bdg. 12.95 (978-0-613-11652-7(6)) Tandem Library Bks.

Janeczko, Paul B., et al. Writing Winning Reports & Essays. 2003. 224p. (J). pap. 7.95 (978-0-439-28718-0(9)) Scholastic, Inc.

Jarnow, Jill. Writing to Describe. 2006. (Write Now Ser.). 24p. (J). 17.25 (978-1-4042-2832-0(2) , PowerKids Pr.) Rosen Publishing Group, Inc., The.

—Writing to Explain. 2006. (Write Now Ser.). (J). 17.25 (978-1-4042-2833-7(0) , PowerKids Pr.) Rosen Publishing Group, Inc., The.

Jensen, Eric. Student Success Secrets. 5th ed. 2003. (Illus.). 256p. pap. 8.99 (978-0-7641-2007-7(7)) Barron's Educational Series, Inc.

Kemmerer, Susan. Research in Increments. 2nd ed. 2004. 9.95 (978-0-9758543-1-0(3)) Schoolhouse Publishing.

Kerr, Christine. Bloom's How to Write about J. D. Salinger. 2007. (Bloom's How to Write about Literature Ser.). 256p. (YA). (gr. 9 up). 45.00 (***978-0-7910-9483-9(9)** , Chelsea Hse.) Facts On File, Inc.

Kordich, Catherine J. Bloom's How to Write about John Steinbeck. 2007. (Bloom's How to Write about Literature Ser.). 256p. (YA). (gr. 9 up). 45.00 (***978-0-7910-9486-0(3)** , Chelsea Hse.) Facts On File, Inc.

The Language of Literature: Writing Research Reports. 2001. (gr. 6-12). (978-0-618-05272-1(0) , 2-22379) McDougal Littell Inc.

Le Patner, Michelle, et al. Nonfiction Writing Prompts for Upper Elementary Science. Whited, Amy M., ed. 2005. (Illus.). 128p. pap. 9.95 (978-1-933196-05-3(X)) Advanced Learning Pr.

—Nonfiction Writing Prompts for Upper Elementary Social Studies. Whited, Amy M., ed. 2005. (Illus.). 128p. pap. 9.95 (978-1-933196-06-0(8)) Advanced Learning Pr.

—Write to Know: Nonfiction Writing Prompts for Kindergarten Math, Science, & Social Studies. Whited, Amy M., ed. 2005. 128p. pap. 9.95 (978-1-933196-00-8(9)) Advanced Learning Pr.

—Write to Know: Nonfiction Writing Prompts for Lower Elementary Science. Whited, Amy M., ed. 2005. 128p. pap. 9.95 (978-1-933196-02-2(5)) Advanced Learning Pr.

—Write to Know: Nonfiction Writing Prompts for Lower Elementary Social Studies. Whited, Amy M., ed. 2005. 128p. pap. 9.95 (978-1-933196-03-9(3)) Advanced Learning Pr.

Levy, Janey. Language Development Writing Process. 2005. 48p. pap. 6.95 (978-1-4042-8569-9(5)) Rosen Publishing Group, Inc., The.

Literature: Timeless Voices, Timeless Themes. 2001. Copper Level (J). (gr. 6). pap. 12.47 (978-0-13-050910-9(8)); Gold Level (YA). (gr. 9). pap., stu. ed. 12.97 (978-0-13-050921-5(3)) Prentice Hall PTR.

Mackall, Joe. Research & Information Management. 2nd ed. 2004. (Career Skills Library). (Illus.). 128p. (YA). (gr. 6-12). 21.95 (978-0-8160-5518-0(1) , Ferguson Publishing Co.) Facts On File, Inc.

Magic Tree House Staff & LeapFrog Staff, compiled by. Knights at Dawn. 2002. (J). (gr. 3-7). 14.95 (978-1-58605-924-8(6) , LeapFrog Schl. Hse.) LeapFrog Enterprises, Inc.

Marlow, Herb. A Student's Guide to Successful Writing. 2005. (J). 24.95 (978-1-893595-53-8(6)) Four Seasons Bks., Inc.

McCarthy, Shaun. Write That Report. 2004. (Illus.). 32p. (J). tchr. ed. (978-0-431-15213-4(6)); pap. (978-0-431-15220-2(9)) Heinemann Library.

Milton, Bess. Language Development Writing Process. 2005. 48p. pap. 6.95 (978-1-4042-8559-0(8)) Rosen Publishing Group, Inc., The.

Morkane, Sue. Original Writing. 2004. (Routledge a Level English Guides Ser.). (Illus.). 112p. 19.95 (978-0-415-31912-6(9)); 71.95 (978-0-415-31911-9(0)) Routledge.

Nash, Kimberley. How to Write Book Reports: A one-year workbook format course for use by students in Grades 4-12. 2006. (ENG., Illus.). 176p. (J). spiral bd., wbk. ed. 25.00 (978-0-9710950-6-9(X) , 13030) Resurrection Resources LLC.

—How to Write Essays & Research Reports - Level A Level A: A Beginner-Intermediate One-Year Workbook Format Course. 2007. (ENG., Illus.). 164p. (J). (gr. 5-7). spiral bd., wbk. ed. 25.00 (978-0-9653723-6-7(7) , #12010) Resurrection Resources LLC.

—How to Write Essays & Research Reports - Level B: An Intermediate-Advanced One-Year Workbook Format Course. 2007. (ENG., Illus.). 168p. spiral bd., wbk. ed. 25.00 (978-0-9710950-2-1(7) , 12020) Resurrection Resources LLC.

O'Conner, Patricia T. Words Fail Me: What Everyone Who Writes Should Know about Writing. 2000. (gr. 7-12). lib. bdg. 21.10 (978-0-613-65854-6(X)) Tandem Library Bks.

Priddy, Anna. Bloom's How to Write about Emily Dickinson. 2007. (Bloom's How to Write about Literature Ser.). 256p. (YA). (gr. 9 up). 45.00 (***978-0-7910-9492-1(8)** , Chelsea Hse.) Facts On File, Inc.

Rasinski, Timothy. Daily Word Ladders Grades 2-3. 2005. (Daily Word Ladders Ser.). (Illus.). 112p. (gr. 2-3). pap. 15.99 (978-0-439-51383-8(9) , Teaching Resources) Scholastic, Inc.

Rigby. Thematic Research Projects. 2002. pap. (978-0-7635-7752-0(9)) Steck-Vaughn.

Rothstein, Evelyn & Gess, Diane. Easy Writer: Level C. 2000. (J). (gr. 1-3). pap. 17.95 (978-0-913935-34-7(4)) Write Track, The.

Roy, Jennifer Rozines. You Can Write a Report. 2003. (You Can Write Ser.). (Illus.). 64p. (J). (gr. 6-12). lib. bdg. 22.60 (978-0-7660-2086-3(X)) Enslow Pubs., Inc.

Ruthven, Rosemary. Write to Know: Nonfiction Writing Prompts for Lower Elementary Math. Whited, Amy M., ed. 2005. 128p. pap. 9.95 (978-1-933196-01-5(7)) Advanced Learning Pr.

—Write to Know: Nonfiction Writing Prompts for Upper Elementary Math. Whited, Amy M., ed. 2005. 128p. pap. 9.95 (978-1-933196-04-6(1)) Advanced Learning Pr.

School Specialty Publishing. Book Reports, Grades 2-3. 2006. (Frank Schaffer Classic Reproducibles Ser.). 48p. (J). (gr. 2-3). pap. 6.99 (978-0-7682-3512-8(X) , Schaffer, Frank) Schaffer, Frank Pubns.

—Note Taking & Outlining. 2003. 48p. (J). (gr. 3-5). pap. 6.99 (978-0-7424-1830-1(8) , FS99157); (gr. 6-8). pap. 6.99 (978-0-7424-1840-0(5) , FS99158) School Specialty Publishing.

Schrecengost, Maity. Researching Events. 1998. (Illus.). (gr. 5-9). 20p. tchr. ed., spiral bd. 7.95 (978-1-57950-022-1(6) , P32-34985); 32p. (J). pap. 8.95 (978-1-57950-018-4(8)) Highsmith Inc. (Upstart Bks.).

Schwartz, Linda. Sizzling State Reports, Grades 4-6: Open-Ended Ideas for Researching & Reporting about Any State! Amerikaner, Kate, ed. Armstrong, Beverly, illus. 2001. 64p. (J). pap., tchr. ed. 13.99 (978-0-88160-298-2(1) , LW-368, Learning Works, The) Creative Teaching Pr., Inc.

Shearer, Cyndy & Washington, George. Handwriting by George 1-27: Rules of Civility & Decent Behaviour in Company & Conversation: Rules 1-27 to Draw & Write, Vol. 1. 2002. (ENG.). 64p. (J). pap. 6.95 (978-1-882514-36-6(X)) Greenleaf Pr.

Shearer, Cynthia & Washington, George. Handwriting by George 28-53: Rules of Civility & Decent Behaviour in Company & Conversation: Rules 28-53 to Draw & Write, Vol. 2. 2007. (ENG.). 64p. (J). pap. 9.95 (978-1-882514-37-3(8)) Greenleaf Pr.

Silate, Jennifer. Language Development Writing Process. 2005. 48p. pap. 6.95 (978-1-4042-8564-4(4)) Rosen Publishing Group, Inc., The.

SIRS Discoverer. 2005. (J). mass mkt. (978-0-89777-566-3(X)) SIRS Publishing, Inc.

SIRS Discoverer: Getting Started Manual Spring 2004. 2003. (YA). cd-rom 1425.00 (978-0-89777-542-7(2)) SIRS Publishing, Inc.

Souter, Gerry, et al. Creating e-Reports & Online Presentations. 2003. (Internet Library). (Illus.). 64p. (J). (gr. 4-12). lib. bdg. 22.60 (978-0-7660-2080-1(0)) Enslow Pubs., Inc.

Spencer, Lauren. A Step-By-Step Guide to Descriptive Writing. 2005. (Illus.). 48p. (J). (gr. 5-8). lib. bdg. 26.50 (978-1-4042-0212-2(9)) Rosen Publishing Group, Inc., The.

Steck-Vaughn Staff. Answer Key Soaring Score Map Communication Arts Level C. 2002. (J). pap. (978-0-7398-5625-3(1)) Steck-Vaughn.

—Answer Key Soaring Score Map Communication Arts Level G. 2002. (J). pap. (978-0-7398-5633-8(2)) Steck-Vaughn.

—Answer Key Soaring Score Map Communication Arts Level K: High School Edition. 2002. (YA). pap. (978-0-7398-5645-1(6)) Steck-Vaughn.

—Reading & Writing Exercises A. 2001. pap. (978-0-7398-3950-8(0)) Steck-Vaughn.

—Reading & Writing Exercises B. 2001. pap. (978-0-7398-3951-5(9)) Steck-Vaughn.

—Reading & Writing Exercises C. 2001. pap. (978-0-7398-3952-2(7)) Steck-Vaughn.

—Reading & Writing Exercises D. 2001. pap. (978-0-7398-3953-9(5)) Steck-Vaughn.

—Reading & Writing Exercises E. 2001. pap. (978-0-7398-3954-6(3)) Steck-Vaughn.

—Reading & Writing Exercises F. 2001. pap. (978-0-7398-3955-3(1)) Steck-Vaughn.

—Report Writing. 2000. (Illus.). (J). (gr. 3). pap. (978-0-7398-2945-5(9)); (gr. 4). pap. (978-0-7398-2946-2(7)); (gr. 5). pap. (978-0-7398-2947-9(5)) Steck-Vaughn.

Sterling, Laurie A. Bloom's How to Write about Nathaniel Hawthorne. 2007. (Bloom's How to Write about Literature Ser.). 256p. (YA). (gr. 9 up). 45.00 (***978-0-7910-9481-5(2)** , Chelsea Hse.) Facts On File, Inc.

Stiles, Mary & Mills, Barbara. A Rookie's Guide to Research. 3rd ed. 2003. 92p. (YA). spiral bd. 10.95 (978-0-9721404-1-6(7)) Union Creek Communications, Inc.

Strausser, Jeffrey. Painless Writing. Gilgannon, Denise, illus. 2001. (Barron's Painless Ser.). 256p. pap. 8.99 (978-0-7641-1810-4(2)) Barron's Educational Series, Inc.

—Painless Writing. 2001. (gr. 5-8). lib. bdg. 17.60 (978-0-613-52781-1(X)) Tandem Library Bks.

Stuart, Samantha L., ed. The Writing Process. 2000. (Illus.). (YA). (gr. 6-9). pap. 4.95 (978-1-55708-668-6(0) , MCR250) McDonald Publishing Co.

Sullivan, Helen. Research Reports: A Guide for Middle & High School Students. 1998. (Single Titles Ser.: up). 128p. (gr. 5-9). pap. 9.95 (978-0-7613-0398-5(7) , Twenty-First Century Bks.) Lerner Publishing Group.

Time for Kids Editors. Writer's Handbook for School & Home, Set. rev. ed. 2006. (Time for Kids Ser.). (Illus.). 112p. (J). (ps-17). pap. 7.99 (978-1-933405-38-4(4)) Time, Inc. Home Entertainment.

Timeless Voices, Timeless Themes, Silver Level. 2001. (YA). (gr. 8). trans. 161.47 (978-0-13-436021-8(4)) Prentice Hall PTR.

Timeless Voices, Timeless Themes: Bronze, Literary Analysis Activity Book. 2001. (YA). (gr. 7). pap. 6.97 (978-0-13-052367-9(4)) Prentice Hall PTR.

Timeless Voices, Timeless Themes: Gold. 2001. (YA). (gr. 9). stu. ed. 52.97 (978-0-13-050287-2(1)) Prentice Hall PTR.

Timeless Voices, Timeless Themes: Platinum, Standardized Test Preparation Notes. 2001. (YA). (gr. 10). trans. 109.97 (978-0-13-052187-3(6)) Prentice Hall PTR.

Tribble. Word for Word. Date not set. (Illus.). 80p. pap. 28.75 (978-0-582-01663-7(0)) Addison-Wesley Longman, Ltd. GBR. *Dist:* Trans-Atlantic Pubns., Inc.

Walters, Jim. 50 Book Report Ideas. 2005. 96p. pap. 13.99 (978-1-4206-3948-3(X)) Teacher Created Materials, Inc.

Whited, Amy. Write to Know: Nonfiction Writing Prompts for Secondary PE. 2006. (Write to Know Ser.). 128p. pap. 9.95 (978-1-933196-21-3(1)) Advanced Learning Pr.

Whited, Amy M., ed. Nonfiction Writing Prompts for Geometry. 2005. (Illus.). 128p. pap. 9.95 (978-1-933196-08-4(4)) Advanced Learning Pr.

—Nonfiction Writing Prompts for Secondary Art. 2005. 128p. pap. 9.95 (978-1-933196-09-1(2)) Advanced Learning Pr.

—Nonfiction Writing Prompts for Secondary Music. 2005. (Illus.). 128p. pap. 9.95 (978-1-933196-10-7(6)) Advanced Learning Pr.

Write on Target for Grade 5. 2006. (J). stu. ed., per., wbk. ed. 16.95 (978-1-59230-159-1(2)) Englefield & Assocs., Inc.

Write on Target Grade 3: Student Workbook. 2005. (J). stu. ed., per. 10.95 (978-1-59230-151-5(7)) Englefield & Assocs., Inc.

Write on Target Grade 4: Student Workbook. 2005. (J). stu. ed., per. 10.95 (978-1-59230-149-2(5)) Englefield & Assocs., Inc.

Write on Target Grade 6: Student Workbook. 2005. (J). pap., stu. ed. 10.95 (978-1-59230-157-6(6)) Englefield & Assocs., Inc.

Zaroulis, Christina. Tackling Your High School Term Paper. 2003. (Students Helping Students Ser.). 80p. (gr. 9-12). pap. 8.95 (978-0-9719392-1-9(7)) Natavi Guides.

REPORTERS AND REPORTING

see also Journalism

Boomhower, Ray E. The Soldier's Friend: A Life of Ernie Pyle. 2006. (Illus.). 134p. 17.95 (978-0-87195-200-4(9)) Indiana Historical Society.

Brandon, Karen & Diani, Stephanie. Nurse. 2005. (How Do I Become a... Ser.). (Illus.). 32p. (J). (gr. 4-7). lib. bdg. 23.70 (978-1-56711-744-8(9) , Blackbirch Pr., Inc.) Thomson Gale.

Colman, Penny. Where the Action Was: Women War Correspondents in World War II. 2002. (Illus.). 128p. (J). (gr. 5 up). lib. bdg. 19.99 (978-0-517-80076-8(4) , Crown Books For Young Readers) Random Hse. Children's Bks.

Gourley, Catherine. War, Women, & the News: How Female Journalists Won the Battle to Cover World War II. 2007. (Illus.). 208p. (J). 21.99 (978-0-689-87752-0(8) , Atheneum) Simon & Schuster Children's Publishing.

Hamilton, John. Real-Time Reporting. 2004. (War in Iraq Ser.). (Illus.). 48p. (J). (gr. 4-8). lib. bdg. 25.65 (978-1-59197-497-0(6)) ABDO Publishing Co.

Harcourt School Publishers Staff. Nellie Bly On Level: Making News. 3rd ed. 2002. (Illus.). pap. 5.10 (978-0-15-323096-7(7)) Harcourt Schl. Pubs.

Hayward, Linda. A Day in the Life of a TV Reporter. 2001. 10.75 (978-0-606-22627-1(3)) Tandem Library Bks.

—Day in the Life of a TV Reporter. 2001. (gr. k-3). lib. bdg. 11.80 (978-0-613-43929-9(5)) Tandem Library Bks.

Hayward, Linda & Dorling Kindersley Publishing Staff. Jobs People Do: A Day in the Life of a Reporter. 2001. (Dk Readers Ser.). (Illus.). 32p. (J). (ps-3). 14.99 (978-0-7894-7956-3(7)); pap. 3.99 (978-0-7894-7957-0(5)) Dorling Kindersley Publishing, Inc.

Johnson, Jennifer Hunt & Hansen, Holly T. Father Remembers, 615 vols., Vol. 6. 2003. (Illus.). 30p. 9.95 (978-0-9729610-5-9(4) , CMB06) Tapis & Assocs., Inc.

—Grandma Remembers, 315 vols., Vol. 3. 2003. (Illus.). 30p. 9.95 (978-0-9729610-2-8(X) , CMB03) Tapis & Assocs., Inc.

—Grandpa Remembers, 415 vols., Vol. 4. 2003. (Illus.). 30p. 9.95 (978-0-9729610-3-5(8) , CMB04) Tapis & Assocs., Inc.

—Mother Remembers, 515 vols., Vol. 5. 2003. (Illus.). 30p. 9.95 (978-0-9729610-4-2(6) , CMB05) Tapis & Assocs., Inc.

—My Memories, 115 vols., Vol. 1. 2003. (Illus.). 29p. 9.95 (978-0-9729610-0-4(3) , CMB01) Tapis & Assocs., Inc.

—Remembering Grandma, 1115 vols., Vol. 11. 2003. (Illus.). 28p. 9.95 (978-0-9729610-6-6(2) , CMB12) Tapis & Assocs., Inc.

—Remembering Grandpa, 1215 vols., Vol. 12. 2003. (Illus.). 28p. 9.95 (978-0-9729610-7-3(0) , CMB12) Tapis & Assocs., Inc.

—Your Memories, 215 vols., Vol. 2. 2003. (Illus.). 29p. 9.95 (978-0-9729610-1-1(1) , CMB02) Tapis & Assocs., Inc.

Minden, Cecilia & Cupp, Dave. Television Reporters. 2006. (Neighborhood Helpers Ser.). (Illus.). 32p. (J). (gr. k-4). 22.79 (978-1-59296-570-0(9)) Child's World, Inc.

Obrist, Hans-Ulrich, contrib. by. Hans Ulrich Obrist: Interviews. 2004. (Illus.). 1000p. (YA). (gr. 13 up). 59.95 (978-88-8158-431-4(X)) Charta ITA. *Dist:* D.A.P./Distributed Art Pubs.

Saenger, Diana. Everyone Wants My Job! The ABCs of Entertainment Writing. Fife, Bruce, ed. unabr. ed. 2003. (Writing & Publishing Ser.). (Illus.). 159p. (YA). (gr. 8-12). pap. 15.00 (978-0-941599-53-5(1)) Piccadilly Bks., Ltd.

Writing to Inform. 2003. 64p. (J). (gr. 3-6). pap. 9.99 (978-0-7424-1838-7(3) , IFG99070) School Specialty Publishing.

REPORTERS AND REPORTING—FICTION

Ace Reporter, 6, Pack. (Bookweb Ser.). 32p. (gr. 3 up). 34.00 (978-0-7635-3940-5(6)) Rigby Education.

Bryant, Bonnie. Hoof Beat. 2008. (Saddle Club(R) Ser.). 144p. (J). (gr. 4-7). lib. bdg. 11.99 (***978-0-385-90536-7(X)** , Yearling) Random Hse. Children's Bks.

Cirrone, Dorian. The Big Scoop. Woodruff, Liza, illus. 2006. (Marshall Cavendish Chapter Book Ser.). 80p. (J). 14.99 (978-0-7614-5323-9(7)) Cavendish, Marshall Corp.

—The Missing Silver Dollar. Woodruff, Liza, illus. 2006. (Lindy Blues Ser.). 80p. (J). 14.95 (978-0-7614-5284-3(2)) Cavendish, Marshall Corp.

Greene, Janice. The Ritual: Set 1. 2002. 32p. (YA). 2.95 (978-1-56254-412-6(8) , SP 4128) Saddleback Educational Publishing.

Harcourt School Publishers Staff. Girasoles On Level. 3rd ed. 2002. (Trofeos Ser.).Tr. of Sunflowers. (SPA., Illus.). pap. 6.80 (978-0-15-324169-7(1)) Harcourt Schl. Pubs.

Hautman, Pete & Logue, Mary. Skullduggery. 2007. (Bloodwater Mysteries Ser.). 176p. (J). (gr. 5-9). 16.99 (978-0-399-24378-3(X) , Putnam Juvenile) Penguin Group (USA) Inc.

—Snatched. 2006. (Bloodwater Ser.: No. 1). 176p. (YA). (gr. 4). 15.99 (978-0-399-24377-6(1) , Putnam Juvenile) Penguin Group (USA) Inc.

Lasky, Kathryn. Alice Rose & Sam. 1999. (J). (978-0-606-17380-3(3)) Tandem Library Bks.

Mercer, Sienna. Fangtastic! 2007. (My Sister the Vampire Ser.: No. 2). 208p. (J). (gr. 3-7). pap. 5.99 (***978-0-06-087115-4(6)** , Harper Trophy) HarperCollins Pubs.

Morrison, Harry Steele. The Adventures of A Boy Reporter. 2004. reprint ed. pap. 20.95 (978-1-4191-5137-8(1)); pap. 1.99 (978-1-4192-5137-5(6)) Kessinger Publishing, LLC.

Steele, Alexander. Case of the Breaking Story. l.t. ed. 2000. (Wishbone Mysteries Ser.: No. 20). (Illus.). 144p. (J). (gr. 4 up). lib. bdg. 23.33 (978-0-8368-2703-3(1)) Stevens, Gareth Inc.

Swallow, Pamela C. Groundhog Gets a Say. Bunkus, Denise, illus. 2007. 40p. (J). (ps). pap. 6.99 (***978-0-14-240896-4(4)*** , Puffin) Penguin Group (USA) Inc.

Wallace, Rich. Curveball, No. 9. 2008. (Winning Season Ser.: No. 9). 128p. (J). (gr. 3). 4.99 (***978-0-14-241092-9(6)*** , Puffin) Penguin Group (USA) Inc.

Zydek, Heather. Basil's Search for Miracles. 2007. 160p. pap. 13.95 (***978-1-888212-86-0(1))*** Conciliar Pr.

REPRODUCTION

see also Cells; Embryology; Pregnancy; Sex

Angliss, Sarah. The Production Line: Reproduction & Growing Up. 1999. (Human Machine Ser.). (Illus.). 32p. (J). lib. bdg. 16.95 (978-1-929298-20-4(X)) Chrysalis Education.

Annunziata, Jane & Nemiroff, Marc A. Sex & Babies: First Facts. Ortakales, Denise & Patrolia, Maureen Tracy, illus. 2003. 48p. (YA). (gr. 3-5). 14.95 (978-1-55798-809-6(9)); pap. 8.95 (978-1-55798-808-9(0)) American Psychological Assn. (Magination Pr.).

Avraham, Regina. Reproductive System. 2000. (Twenty-First Century Health & Wellness Ser.). (Illus.). 128p. (J). (gr. 7-12). 24.95 (978-0-7910-5988-3(X) , Chelsea Hse.) Facts On File, Inc.

Baeuerle, Patrick A. & Landa, Norbert. How the Y Makes the Guy: Microexplorers. 1999. (Microexplorers Ser.: No. 4). (Illus.). 42p. (J). (gr. k up). lib. bdg. 18.95 (978-1-56674-236-8(6)) Forest Hse. Publishing Co., Inc.

Brown, Laurie Krasny. What's the Big Secret? Talking about Sex with Girls & Boys. Brown, Marc, illus. 2000. 32p. (J). (ps-3). pap. 6.99 (978-0-316-10183-7(4)) Little Brown & Co.

—What's the Big Secret? Talking about Sex with Girls & Boys. 2000. (gr. k-3). lib. bdg. 14.95 (978-0-613-28695-4(2)) Tandem Library Bks.

Brynie, Faith Hickman. 101 Questions about Reproduction: Or How 1 + 1 = 3 or 4 or More. 2006. (One Hundred One Questions... Ser.). (Illus.). 176p. (J). (gr. 8-12). 27.93 (978-0-7613-2311-2(2) , Twenty-First Century Bks.) Lerner Publishing Group.

Cassan, Adolfo. Human Reproduction & Development. 2005. (Inside the Human Body Ser.). (Illus.). 32p. (J). (gr. 4-8). 28.00 (978-0-7910-9015-2(9) , Chelsea Clubhouse) Facts On File, Inc.

Chinery, Michael. New Life. 2002. (Wild Animal Planet Ser.). (Illus.). 64p. 14.95 (978-0-7548-1057-5(7) , Lorenz Bks.) Anness Publishing GBR. *Dist:* National Bk. Network.

Claybourne, Anna. Does a Worm Have a Girlfriend? 2005. (Illus.). 32p. (J). (978-1-4109-1935-9(8)) Steck-Vaughn.

—Does a Worm Have a Girlfriend? Reproduction. 2005. (Illus.). 32p. (J). (gr. 3-5). 7.85 (978-1-4109-1966-3(8)) Steck-Vaughn.

Creative Media Applications Staff. The Human Body & Environment: Hormonal & Reproductive Systems, 4 vols., Vol. 4. 2003. (Middle School Reference Ser.). (Illus.). (J). (978-0-313-32562-5(6)) Greenwood Publishing Group, Inc.

Diagram Group. Reproductive System. 2005. (Illus.). 112p. (***978-0-8160-5985-0(3))*** Facts On File, Inc.

The Endocrine System, the Reproductive System, Human Development. 2006. (World Book's Human Body Works). (Illus.). 48p. (J). (978-0-7166-4431-6(2)) World Bk., Inc.

Fullick, Ann. Test Tube Babies: In Vitro Fertilization. (Science at the Edge Ser.). 64p. 8.95 (978-1-4034-4124-9(3)) Heinemann Library.

Green, Jen. Cells & Reproduction. 2005. (Illus.). 32p. (J). (gr. 3-7). lib. bdg. 27.10 (978-1-59604-052-6(1)) Stargazer Bks.

Harcourt School Publishers Staff. Human Growth & Reproduction. 99th ed. 1998. (Your Health Ser.). (Illus.). (gr. 4-6). pap. 33.30 (978-0-15-311355-0(3)) Harcourt Schl. Pubs.

Harris, Robie H. Es Alucinante! Emberley, Michael, illus. 2000. Tr. of It's So Amazing!. (J). (CAT.). 80p. (gr. k-2). pap. 17.95 (978-84-95040-33-6(6)); (SPA.). 84p. (gr. 3-5). 17.95 (978-84-95040-32-9(8) , RR4476) Serres, Ediciones, S. L. ESP. *Dist:* Lectorum Pubns., Inc.

—It's So Amazing! A Book about Eggs, Sperm, Birth, Babies & Families. Emberley, Michael, illus. 1999. 80p. (J). (gr. 2-5). 22.99 (978-0-7636-0051-8(2)) Candlewick Pr.

—It's So Amazing! A Book about Eggs, Sperm, Birth, Babies, & Families. 2002. (gr. k-3). lib. bdg. 19.95 (978-0-613-74790-5(9)) Tandem Library Bks.

—It's So Amazing! A Book about Eggs, Sperm, Birth, Babies & Families. Emberley, Michael, illus. 5th anniv. ed. 2004. 88p. (J). (gr. 2 up). reprint ed. pap. 10.99 (978-0-7636-1321-1(5)) Candlewick Pr.

Heller, Ruth. Chickens Aren't the Only Ones. 1999. (Ruth Heller's World of Nature Ser.). (Illus.). 48p. (J). (ps-3). pap. 7.99 (978-0-698-11778-5(6) , Putnam Juvenile) Penguin Group (USA) Inc.

—Chickens Aren't the Only Ones. 1999. (gr. k-3). lib. bdg. 16.45 (978-0-613-73469-1(6)); (J). 14.79 (978-0-606-16792-5(7)) Tandem Library Bks.

—Chickens Aren't the Only Ones: Big Book. l.t. ed. (FRE., Illus.). (J). bds. 29.95 (978-0-590-73732-6(5)) Scholastic, Inc.

Holt, Rinehart and Winston Staff. Holt Science & Technology Chapter 26: Life Science: Reproduction & Development. 5th ed. 2004. (Illus.). pap. 12.86 (978-0-03-030251-0(X)) Holt, Rinehart & Winston.

Hummel, Ruth. Where Do Babies Come from? 1998. (Learning about Sex Ser.: Vol. 2). (Illus.). 32p. (J). (gr. 1-3). 10.99 (978-0-570-03563-3(5)) Concordia Publishing Hse.

Jones, Stan And Brenna & Jones, Brenna. The Story of Me (Revised) 2007. 48p. pap. 9.99 (978-1-60006-013-7(7)) NavPress Publishing Group.

Kim, Melissa L. The Endocrine & Reproductive Systems. 2003. (Human Body Library Ser.). (Illus.). 48p. (YA). (gr. 4-10). lib. bdg. 23.93 (978-0-7660-2020-7(7)) Enslow Pubs., Inc.

Krohmer, Randolph W. The Reproductive System. 2003. (Your Body, How It Works). (Illus.). 112p. (gr. 9-13). 31.95 (978-0-7910-7629-3(6) , Chelsea Hse.) Facts On File, Inc.

Llamas, Andreu. Digestion & Reproduction. Rizo, Luis, illus. 1998. (Human Body Ser.). 32p. (J). (gr. 5 up). lib. bdg. 24.67 (978-0-8368-2111-6(4)) Stevens, Gareth Inc.

MacDonald, Fiona. The First "Test-Tube Baby" 2004. (Days That Changed the World Ser.). (Illus.). 48p. (J). (gr. 5 up). pap. 11.95 (978-0-8368-5574-6(4)); lib. bdg. 30.00 (978-0-8368-5567-8(1)) Stevens, Gareth Inc. (World Almanac Library).

Mayle, Peter. Where Did I Come From? Robbins, Arthur, illus. 2000. 43p. (gr. 1-4). pap. 9.95 (978-0-8184-0253-1(9) , Stuart, Lyle) Kensington Publishing Corp.

—Where Did I Come From? 2000. (Illus.). 1p. (ps-3). pap. 14.95 (978-0-8184-0608-9(9) , Stuart, Lyle) Kensington Publishing Corp.

McLeod, Beatrice. Growing Up. 2000. (Nature Undercover Ser.). (Illus.). 40p. (J). (gr. 5-8). 23.70 (978-1-56711-501-7(2) , Blackbirch Pr., Inc.) Thomson Gale.

Miller, Michaela. Reproduction & Growth. 2005. (Exploring the Human Body Ser.). (Illus.). 32p. (J). (gr. 4-7). lib. bdg. 24.95 (978-0-7377-3021-0(8) , Greenhaven Pr., Inc.) Thomson Gale.

Morley, Margaret Warner. A Song of Life 1922. Forsyth, Robert, illus. 2004. reprint ed. pap. 21.95 (978-1-4179-7842-7(2)) Kessinger Publishing, LLC.

Naff, Clay Farris. Reproductive Technologies. 2007. (Opposing Viewpoints Ser.). 240p. (J). (gr. 10-12). 36.20 (***978-0-7377-3331-0(4))***; pap. 24.95 (***978-0-7377-3332-7(2))*** Thomson Gale. (Greenhaven Pr., Inc.).

O'Donnell, Kerri. The Reproductive System. 2001. (Insider's Guide to the Body Ser.). (Illus.). 48p. (YA). (gr. 5-8). lib. bdg. 23.95 (978-0-8239-3334-1(2) , Rosen Central) Rosen Publishing Group, Inc., The.

Orr, Tamra. Test Tube Baby. 2003. (Science on the Edge Ser.). (Illus.). 48p. (J). 24.95 (978-1-56711-788-2(0) , Blackbirch Pr., Inc.) Thomson Gale.

Parker, Steve. In Your Genes! Genetics & Reproduction. 2006. (Illus.). 48p. (J). (978-1-4109-1876-5(9)); pap. (978-1-4109-1883-3(1)) Steck-Vaughn.

—Reproduction. 2004. (Our Bodies Ser.). (Illus.). 48p. (J). lib. bdg. 28.56 (978-0-7398-6623-8(0)) Raintree.

—The Reproductive System. (Body Focus Ser.). (Illus.). 48p. (J). 2003. (gr. 6-8). lib. bdg. 27.07 (978-1-4034-0199-1(3)); 2002. pap. 8.50 (978-1-4034-0455-8(0)) Heinemann Library.

Pelham, David & Miller, Jonathan. The Facts of Life. Willock, Harry, illus. 2000. 12p. (YA). (gr. 3 up). 16.95 (978-1-58117-093-1(9) , Intervisual/Piggy Toes) Dalmatian Pr.

Reproducing. 2001. (Animal Marvels Ser.). (Illus.). 32p. (J). (gr. 3 up). lib. bdg. 24.67 (978-0-8368-2932-7(8)) Stevens, Gareth Inc.

Saltz, Gail. Amazing You! Getting Smart about Your Private Parts. Cravath, Lynne Avril, illus. 2008. 32p. (J). (ps). pap. 6.99 (***978-0-14-241058-5(6)*** , Puffin) Penguin Group (USA) Inc.

Solar, Kay. Where Do Babies Come From? Holden, Chanler, illus. Brignac, Candy, photos by. l.t. ed. 1998. 22p. (J). (ps-3). bds. 15.95 (978-0-9666945-0-5(3)) Solar, Kay.

Spilsbury, Louise & Spilsbury, Richard. Life Processes: From Reproduction to Respiration. 2004. (Science Answers Ser.). (Illus.). 32p. (J). pap. 7.50 (978-1-4034-5513-0(9)); lib. bdg. 24.22 (978-1-4034-4767-8(5)) Heinemann Library.

Williams, Kara. Fertility Technology: The Baby Debate. 2003. (Focus on Science & Society Ser.). (Illus.). 64p. (J). lib. bdg. 26.50 (978-0-8239-3762-2(3)); (YA). (gr. 4-6). lib. bdg. 26.50 (978-0-8239-3210-8(9) , FSFETE) Rosen Publishing Group, Inc., The.

Zach, Kim K. Reproductive Technology. 2004. (Great Medical Discoveries Ser.). (Illus.). 112p. (J). 29.95 (978-1-59018-344-1(4) , Lucent Bks.) Thomson Gale.

REPTILES

see also Crocodiles; Lizards; Snakes; Turtles

Amphibians & Reptiles. 2005. (World of Animals Ser.: Vols. 41-50). (J). 499.00 (978-0-7172-5916-8(1)) Scholastic Library Publishing.

Bakker, Robert T. Dactyls! Dragons of the Air. Rey, Luis V., illus. 2005. (Step into Reading Ser.). 48p. (J). (gr. 2-4). lib. bdg. 11.99 (978-0-375-93013-3(2)); pap. 3.99 (978-0-375-83013-6(8)) Random Hse. Children's Bks. (Random Hse. Bks. for Young Readers).

Baquedano, Elizabeth & McCarthy, Colin. Reptiles. 2004. (Dk Eyewitness Books Ser.). (SPA.). 64p. (J). 15.99 (978-0-7566-0412-7(5)) Dorling Kindersley Publishing, Inc.

Barlowe, Sy. Reptiles Stickers. 1998. (Illus.). 4p. (J). 1.50 (978-0-486-40500-1(1)) Dover Pubns., Inc.

Barnes, Julia, et al. 101 Facts about Terrarium Pets. 2002. (One Hundred One Facts about Pets Ser.). (Illus.). 32p. (J). (gr. 3 up). lib. bdg. 23.33 (978-0-8368-3021-7(0)) Stevens, Gareth Inc.

Basic Domestic Reptiles & Amphibians. 2005. 64p. pap. 192.50 (978-0-7910-8062-7(5) , Chelsea Hse.) Facts On File, Inc.

Behler, John L. Reptiles. 1999. (Audubon Society First Field Guide Ser.). (Illus.). 160p. (J). (gr. 3-7). pap. 17.95 (978-0-590-05467-6(8)); pap. 11.95 (978-0-590-05487-4(2)) Scholastic, Inc.

Berger, Melvin & Berger, Gilda. Can Snakes Crawl Backward? Questions & Answers about Reptiles. Male, Alan, illus. 2002. (Question & Answer Ser.). 48p. (J). (gr. 2-4). pap. 5.95 (978-0-439-19381-8(8) , Scholastic Reference) Scholastic, Inc.

Berkowitz, Henry. Amphibians & Reptiles. Lampert, Erv, ed. rev. ed. 1999. (Educational Coloring Bks.). (Illus.). 32p. (J). (gr. 1-4). reprint ed. pap. 3.95 (978-0-932855-49-7(0)) Winner Enterprises.

Birds & Reptiles Action Sticker Book. 2002. 12p. (J). pap. 3.98 (978-0-7525-8034-0(5)) Parragon, Inc.

Bulletpoints Reptiles & Amphibians. 2005. (Illus.). (J). per. 4.99 (978-1-933581-05-7(0)) Byeway Bks.

Bumstead, Pat & Worsley, Norman H. Canadian Skin & Scales. 2003. (Illus.). 168p. (YA). (gr. 5-6). pap. (978-0-9689278-1-6(5)) Simply Wild Pubns., Inc.

Campbell, Jonathan A., et al, trs. The Venomous Reptiles of the Western Hemisphere, 2 vols. 2005. (Comstock Books in Herpetology). (Illus.). 1032p. 149.95 (978-0-8014-4141-7(2)) Cornell Univ. Pr.

Chelsea House Publishing Staff. Reptile & Amphibian, 9 vols., Set. 1998. 161.55 (978-0-7910-5076-7(9) , Chelsea Hse.) Facts On File, Inc.

Cox, Geoffrey & Wiffen, Joan. Dinosaur New Zealand. 2002. (Illus.). 39p. (J). pap. 19.95 (978-1-86950-404-5(6)) HarperCollins Pubs. New Zealand NZL. *Dist:* Antipodes Bks. & Beyond.

Crump, Marty. Amphibians Reptiles & Their Conservation. 2002. (Illus.). 136p. (J). (gr. 8-12). 25.00 (978-0-208-02511-1(1)) Shoe String Pr., Inc.

Dalgleish, Sharon. Reptiles & Amphibians. 2002. (Junior Adventure Ser.). (Illus.). 32p. (J). (gr. 3 up). lib. bdg. (978-1-59084-196-9(4)) Mason Crest Pubs.

—Reptiles & Amphibians. Cavaluzzo, Laura & McEwen, Rebecca, eds. 1999. (Explorers Ser.). (Illus.). 32p. (J). (978-0-7699-0490-0(4)) Shortland Pubns. (U. S. A.) Inc.

—Scaly Things. 1999. (Explorers Ser.). (Illus.). 32p. (J). (978-0-7699-0471-9(8)) Shortland Pubns. (U. S. A.) Inc.

Davies, Valerie. Incredible Reptiles. Tomblin, Gill, illus. 2006. (Wildlife!). 28p. (J). (gr. 3-8). 17.95 (978-0-7696-4823-1(1)) School Specialty Publishing.

Dennard, Deborah. Reptiles: Explore the Fascinating Worlds of Alligators & Crocodiles, Lizards, Snakes, Turtles. Dewey, Jennifer Owings, tr. Dewey, Jennifer Owings, illus. 2004. (Our Wild World Ser.). 192p. (gr. 2-5). 16.95 (978-1-55971-880-6(3) , NorthWord Bks. for Young Readers) T&N Children's Publishing.

DK Publishing. Eye Know Reptile. 2008. (Eye Know Ser.). 24p. (J). (gr. k-3). 8.99 (***978-0-7566-3871-9(2))*** Dorling Kindersley Publishing, Inc.

Donnell, Kerri. Aves: Dinosaurios de Nuestros Dias. Molinero, Leticia, tr. 2002. (Buenas Letras Reading Room Ser.). (SPA., Illus.). 24p. (J). lib. bdg. 18.75 (978-0-8239-6513-7(9) , Buenas Letra) Rosen Publishing Group, Inc., The.

Dorling Kindersley Publishing Staff. Reptile. 2005. (Ultimate sticker Bks.). 16p. (J). pap. 6.99 (978-0-7566-0977-1(1)) Dorling Kindersley Publishing, Inc.

—Reptiles. (Look Closer Ser.). (Illus.). (J). (ps-ps). 2005. 24p. 9.99 (978-0-7566-1434-8(1)); 2nd rev. ed. 2003. 128p. pap. 6.99 (978-0-7894-9595-2(3)) Dorling Kindersley Publishing, Inc.

Einhorn, Kama. My First Book about Reptiles. Moroney, Christopher, illus. 2007. (J). (***978-1-4287-1452-6(9))*** Random Hse., Inc.

Einhorn, Kama. Sesame Subjects: My First Books about Reptiles. Moroney, Christopher, illus. 2007. 24p. (J). (gr. k-k). 7.99 (978-0-375-83685-5(3) , Random Hse. Bks. for Young Readers) Random Hse. Children's Bks.

Fisher, Diana. Reptiles & Amphibians: Step by Step Intsructions for 29 Reptiles & Amphibians. 2006. (Draw & Color Ser.). (Illus.). 40p. (J). pap. 4.95 (978-1-56010-994-5(7)) Foster, Walter Publishing, Inc.

Gareth Stevens Publishing Staff, contrib. by. Reptiles. 2002. (Discovery Channel School Science Ser.). (Illus.). 32p. (J). (gr. 5 up). lib. bdg. 24.67 (978-0-8368-3219-8(1)) Stevens, Gareth Inc.

Gilpin, Daniel. Dwarf Geckos, Rattlesnakes & Other Reptiles. 2005. (Animal Kingdom Classification Ser.). (Illus.). 48p. (J). (gr. 4-6). (978-0-7565-1255-2(7) , 1244058) Compass Point Bks.

Gingold, Janet. My Adventure with Reptiles: Advanced My Adventure. 2007. 44p. (J). pap. 8.99 (978-1-59092-464-8(9) , Orchard Academy Pr.) Windstorm Creative.

Glaser, Jason. Bearded Dragons. 2005. (World of Reptiles Ser.). (Illus.). 24p. (J). (978-0-7368-5419-1(3)) Capstone Pr., Inc.

Grambo, Rebecca L., et al. Animal Kingdom. 2000. (Eyes on Nature Ser.). (Illus.). 109p. (J). (978-1-56156-882-6(1)) Kidsbooks, Inc.

Green. Reptiles. 2003. (Weird Wildlife Ser.). (Illus.). 32p. (J). pap. 7.95 (978-1-4109-0080-7(0)) Raintree.

—Reptiles - Weird Wildlife, 6 bks., Set. 2003. (Illus.). pap. 48.30 (978-1-4109-0299-3(4)) Harcourt Schl. Pubs.

Green, Jen. Reptiles. 2002. (Young Library - Weird Wildlife Ser.). (Illus.). 32p. (J). lib. bdg. 25.69 (978-0-7398-4858-6(5)) Raintree.

Gruber, Beth. Lizard & Reptile Style. 2004. (Pet's Point of View Ser.). 32p. (J). (gr. 4 up). lib. bdg. 22.60 (978-0-7565-0699-5(9)) Compass Point Bks.

Hall, Julie. Reptiles & Amphibians: Grades 2 & 3. (Illus.). (J). pap., wbk. ed. 4.99 (978-0-88743-964-3(0)) School Zone Publishing Co.

Harrison, Paul. Reptiles. 2007. (Up Close Ser.). (Illus.). 24p. (J). (gr. 3-5). lib. bdg. 23.95 (***978-1-4042-3763-6(1)*** , PowerKids Pr.) Rosen Publishing Group, Inc., The.

Harvey, Bev. Reptiles. (Eyes on Nature Ser.). 32p. (J). (gr. 1). pap. (978-1-882210-54-1(9)) Action Publishing, Inc.

—Reptiles. 2002. (Chelsea Clubhouse Science Exploration Ser.). (Illus.). 32p. (gr. k-2). 23.00 (978-0-7910-6984-4(2) , Chelsea Hse.) Facts On File, Inc.

Holland, Simon. Reptiles. Ling, Mary, ed. 2002. (Eye Wonder Ser.). (Illus.). 48p. (J). (gr. k-3). 9.99 (978-0-7894-8554-0(0)) Dorling Kindersley Publishing, Inc.

Holland, Simon & Dorling Kindersley Publishing Staff. Reptiles. 2002. (Eye Wonder Ser.). (Illus.). 48p. (J). (gr. k-3). lib. bdg. 17.99 (978-0-7894-8555-7(9)) Dorling Kindersley Publishing, Inc.

Holt, Rinehart and Winston Staff. Holt Science & Technology Chapter 16: Life Science: Fishes, Amphibians, & Reptiles. 5th ed. 2004. (Illus.). pap. 12.86 (978-0-03-030221-3(8)) Holt, Rinehart & Winston.

Holub, Joan. Why Do Snakes Hiss? And Other Questions about Snakes, Lizards & Turtles. Divito, Anna, illus. 2004. (Easy-to-Read, Puffin Ser.). 48p. (J). (gr. k-2). pap. 3.99 (978-0-14-240105-7(6) , Puffin) Penguin Group (USA) Inc.

—Why Do Snakes Hiss? And Other Questions about Snakes, Lizards, & Turtles. 2004. (Easy-to-Read, Dial Ser.). (Illus.). 48p. (J). (gr. k). 14.99 (978-0-8037-3000-7(4) , Dial) Penguin Group (USA) Inc.

—Why Do Snakes Hiss? And Other Questions about Snakes, Lizards, & Turtles. DiVito, Anna, illus. 2004. 48p. (J). (ps-ps). lib. bdg. 11.19 (978-0-606-32712-1(6)) Tandem Library Bks.

Hudak, Heather C. Reptiles & Amphibians. 2004. (Animal Facts Ser.). (Illus.). 24p. (J). lib. bdg. 24.45 (978-1-59036-204-4(7)) Weigl Pubs., Inc.

Huggins-Cooper, Lynn. Ravenous Reptiles. 2006. (J). (978-1-58340-932-9(7)) Smart Apple Media.

Hughes, Sarah Anne. Reptiles & Amphibians. Hughes, Sarah Anne, illus. 2003. (Peterson Field Guide Coloring Bks.). (Illus.). 64p. pap. 7.95 (978-0-618-30737-1(0)) Houghton Mifflin Co. Trade & Reference Div.

Iguanas & Reptiles. 2007. (Illus.). (J). cd-rom 9.99 (***978-0-9795190-5-5(5))*** Color & Learn.

Insects, Amphibians & Reptiles. 2001. 63p. (YA). 8.65 (978-0-7525-4875-3(1)) Parragon, Inc.

Jango-Cohen, Judith. Desert Iguanas. (Pull Ahead Bks.). (Illus.). 32p. (gr. k-3). 2005. lib. bdg. 22.60 (978-0-8225-3635-2(8)); 2003. (J). pap. 5.95 (978-0-8225-3642-0(0)) Lerner Publishing Group.

—Desert Iguanas. 2001. (gr. k-3). lib. bdg. 14.10 (978-0-613-58830-0(4)) Tandem Library Bks.

Johnson, Jinny. Pteranodon & Other Flying Reptiles. 2007. (***978-1-59920-068-2(6))*** Smart Apple Media.

Kalman, Bobbie. Qué Son los Reptiles? 2005. (Ciencia de los Seres Vivos Ser.). (SPA., Illus.). 32p. (J). (gr. 3-4). pap. (978-0-7787-8808-9(3)) Crabtree Publishing Co.

—Qué Son los Reptiles? 2005. (SPA., Illus.). 32p. (J). (978-0-7787-8762-4(1)) Crabtree Publishing Co.

—Les Reptiles. 2001. (FRE., Illus.). 32p. (J). pap. (978-2-920660-76-2(4)) Crabtree Publishing Co.

—What Is a Reptile? 1999. (Science of Living Things Ser.). (Illus.). 32p. (J). (gr. 2-3). (978-0-86505-881-1(4)); pap. (978-0-86505-893-4(8)) Crabtree Publishing Co.

—What Is a Reptile? 1999. (gr. 3-6). lib. bdg. 14.10 (978-0-613-12262-7(3)) Tandem Library Bks.

Kidd, Nina. Reptiles & Amphibians. Kidd, Nina, illus. 1998. (Draw Science Ser.). (Illus.). 64p. (J). (gr. 3-7). pap. 7.95 (978-1-56565-936-0(8) , 09368W) Lowell Hse. Juvenile.

Landau, Elaine. Pterosaurs. rev. ed. 2006. (True Book Ser.). (Illus.). 47p. (J). (978-0-531-16829-5(8)) Children's Pr., Ltd.

Little & Large Sticker Activity - Reptiles & Amphibians. 2006. (J). 3.99 (978-1-933581-35-4(2)) Byeway Bks.

Llewellyn, Claire. Reptiles. 2002. (Question Time Ser.). (Illus.). 32p. (J). (gr. k-3). pap. 6.95 (978-0-7534-5463-3(7) , Kingfisher) Houghton Mifflin Co. Trade & Reference Div.

—Reptiles. 2002. (gr. k-3). lib. bdg. 15.25 (978-0-613-90172-7(X)) Tandem Library Bks.

MacAulay, Kelley & Kalman, Bobbie. Reptiles de Todo Tipo. 2005. (SPA., Illus.). 32p. (J). (978-0-7787-8835-5(0)) Crabtree Publishing Co.

—Reptiles de Topo Tipo: Reptiles of All Kinds. 2006. (SPA., Illus.). 32p. (978-0-7787-8871-3(7)) Crabtree Publishing Co.

—Reptiles of All Kinds. 2005. (What Kind of Animal Is It? Ser.). (Illus.). 32p. (J). (978-0-7787-2158-1(2)); pap. (978-0-7787-2216-8(3)) Crabtree Publishing Co.

Makowski, Robin. Reptiles Drawing Made Fun. 2005. 32p. pap. 6.45 (978-1-59515-787-4(5)) Rourke Publishing, LLC.

Male, Alan. Can Snakes Crawl Backwards? 2001. (gr. 3-6). lib. bdg. 14.10 (978-0-613-45359-2(X)) Tandem Library Bks.

Matero, Robert. Reptiles. 2001. (Nature's Wild Ser.). (J). lib. bdg. (978-1-58952-203-9(6)) Rourke Publishing, LLC.

Mattern, Joanne. Reptiles & Amphibians. 2002. (Reading Room Collection). (Illus.). 24p. (J). (978-0-8239-8241-7(6)); lib. bdg. 18.75 (978-0-8239-3746-2(1)) Rosen Publishing Group, Inc., The.

—Reptiles y Anfibios. Molinero, Leticia, tr. 2002. (Buenas Letras Reading Room Ser.). (SPA.). 24p. (J). lib. bdg. 18.75 (978-0-8239-6515-1(5) , Buenas Letra) Rosen Publishing Group, Inc., The.

Mattison, Christopher, et al. Reptiles & Amphibians. 2006. (Facts at Your Fingertips Ser.). (Illus.). 64p. (J). (***978-1-933834-04-7(8))*** Brown Bear Books.

Mayer, Cassie. Scales. 2006. (Illus.). 24p. (J). (978-1-4034-8374-4(4)); pap. (978-1-4034-8380-5(9)) Heinemann Library.

McCarthy, Colin. Reptile. 2000. (Eyewitness Bks.). (Illus.). 64p. (J). (gr. 4-7). 15.99 (978-0-7894-5786-8(5)) Dorling Kindersley Publishing, Inc.

—Reptiles. 2004. (Dk Eyewitness Books Ser.). 64p. (J). lib. bdg. 19.99 (978-0-7566-0413-4(3)) Dorling Kindersley Publishing, Inc.

McCarthy, Colin & Dorling Kindersley Publishing Staff. Reptile. 2000. (Eyewitness Bks.). (Illus.). 64p. (J). (gr. 4-7). lib. bdg. 19.99 (978-0-7894-6575-7(2)) Dorling Kindersley Publishing, Inc.

McEvoy, Paul. Reptiles. 2003. (Animal Facts Ser.). (Illus.). 24p. (gr. 2-4). 23.00 (978-0-7910-7283-7(5) , Chelsea Hse.) Facts On File, Inc.

McLaurin, Thad, ed. Investigating Science - Amphibians & Reptiles. 2000. 48p. 9.95 (978-1-56234-365-1(3) , Mailbox Bks., The) Education Ctr., Inc.

McMorrow, Annalisa. Leapin' Lizards & Other Reptiles. 1999. (Illus.). 80p. (J). pap. 9.95 (978-1-57612-110-8(0)) Monday Morning Bks., Inc.

McNab, Chris. Endangered Reptiles. 2006. (Nature's Monsters Ser.). (Illus.). 32p. (J). lib. bdg. 23.33 (978-0-8368-6171-6(X)) Stevens, Gareth Inc.

Mertz, Leslie A., et al. Grzimek's Student Animal Life Resource, 2 vols. 2005. (Illus.). xxxix, 427p. (J). (978-0-7876-9405-0(3)); (978-0-7876-9406-7(1)) Thomson Gale. (UXL).

Miles, Elizabeth. Skin, Scales, & Shells. 2003. (Animal Parts Ser.). (Illus.). 32p. (J). (gr. k-2). lib. bdg. 21.36 (978-1-4034-0021-5(0)); pap. 6.95 (978-1-4034-0430-5(5)) Heinemann Library.

Miller, Jake. The Bearded Dragon. 2003. (Lizard Library). (Illus.). 24p. (J). lib. bdg. 18.75 (978-0-8239-6412-3(4) , PowerKids Pr.) Rosen Publishing Group, Inc., The.

Miller, Ruth. Reptiles. 2004. (Illus.). 64p. (J). 32.79 (978-1-4109-1052-3(0)); pap. 9.50 (978-1-4109-1348-7(1)) Harcourt Schl. Pubs.

Miller, Sara Swan. Radical Reptiles. 2001. (Animals Ser.). (Illus.). 64p. (J). (gr. 5-7). 25.50 (978-0-531-11794-1(4) , Watts, Franklin) Scholastic Library Publishing.

—Radical Reptiles. 2001. (gr. 3-6). lib. bdg. 17.60 (978-0-613-37519-1(X)) Tandem Library Bks.

Miller-Schroeder, Patricia. Scales, Slime & Salamanders: The Science of Reptiles & Amphibians. 1999. (Science @ Work Ser.). (Illus.). 48p. (J). (gr. 4-6). lib. bdg. 27.12 (978-0-7398-0141-3(4)) Raintree.

Murray, Peter. Reptiles. 2004. (Science Around Us Ser.). (Illus.). 32p. (J). (gr. 2-6). 27.07 (978-1-59296-218-1(1)) Child's World, Inc.

Nieves, David M. More Reptiles up Close. Nieves, David M., photos by. l.t. ed. 2002. (Illus.). 56p. (J). per. 11.95 (978-0-9673958-2-1(8)) Reptile Education & Research Publishing.

—Reptiles up Close. Nieves, David M. & Weidner, Tom, photos by. 1999. (Illus.). 56p. (J). (gr. 3-6). pap. 14.95 (978-0-9673958-0-7(1)) Reptile Education & Research Publishing.

Nunn, Daniel. Pterodactyl. 2007. (Illus.). 24p. (J). (***978-1-4034-9446-7(0)*** ; pap. (***978-1-4034-9453-5(3)***) Heinemann Library.

O'Hare, Ted. Reptiles. 2006. (Que es un Animal? Biblioteca del Descubrimiento Ser.). (gr. 1-4). 14.95 (978-1-59515-633-4(X)); (Illus.). 24p. 14.95 (978-1-59515-421-7(3)) Rourke Publishing, LLC.

Ohare, Ted. Reptiles. 2005. 24p. pap. 5.45 (978-1-59515-735-5(2)); (SPA.). pap. 5.45 (978-1-59515-691-4(7)) Rourke Publishing, LLC.

O'Neill, Amanda. I Wonder Why Snakes Shed Their Skin: And Other Questions about Reptiles. 2003. (I Wonder Why Ser.). 32p. (J). (gr. k-3). pap. 6.95 (978-0-7534-5612-5(5) , Kingfisher) Houghton Mifflin Co. Trade & Reference Div.

—I Wonder Why Snakes Shed Their Skins: And Other Questions about Reptiles. 2003. (gr. k-3). lib. bdg. 14.10 (978-0-613-63161-7(7)) Tandem Library Bks.

O'Reilly, Wenda. GO FISH WILDLIFE REPTILES & AMPHIBIANS. 2007. n/ap. pap. 119.40 (***978-1-59960-018-5(8)***) Birdcage Pr.

Parker, Edward. Reptiles & Amphibians. 2002. (Rain Forest Pilot Ser.). (Illus.). 48p. (J). lib. bdg. 27.12 (978-0-7398-5243-9(4)) Raintree.

Parker, Janice. Reptiles. 2007. (J). (***978-1-59036-711-7(1)); (978-1-59036-712-4(X))*** Weigl Pubs., Inc.

Parker, Janice. The Science of Reptiles. 2000. (Living Science Ser.). (Illus.). 32p. (J). (gr. 2 up). lib. bdg. 24.67 (978-0-8368-2681-4(7)) Stevens, Gareth Inc.

Parker, Steve. 50 Things You Should Know about Fierce Creatures. Marshall, Anne, ed. 2004. (50 Things You Should Know Ser.). (Illus.). 112p. (J). 14.99 (978-1-84236-301-0(8)) Miles Kelly Publishing, Ltd. GBR. *Dist:* Independent Pubs. Group.

Parker, Steven. See-Through Reptiles. 2004. 32p. (Illus.). (J). 15.95 (978-0-7624-1989-0(X) , Running Pr. Kids); 15.95 (978-0-7624-2290-6(4)) Running Pr. Bk. Pubs.

Pettifor, Bonnie. Reptiles & Amphibians. 1999. (Gifted & Talented Ser.). (Illus.). 64p. (J). (gr. 1-3). pap. 5.95 (978-0-7373-0208-0(9)) Lowell Hse.

Phelps, Earl R. How to Draw Spectacular Reptiles. Phelps, Earl R., illus. 2002. (Illus.). 112p. (YA). (gr. 4-12). pap. 19.95 (978-1-887627-05-4(7)) Phelps Publishing.

Phillips, Dee. Reptiles & Amphibians. 2006. (Blue Zoo Guides Ser.). (Illus.). 96p. 18.95 (978-1-58728-561-5(4) , Two Can Publishing) T&N Children's Publishing.

Pledger, Maurice. Reptiles. 2005. (Maurice Pledger Nature Trails Ser.). (Illus.). 16p. (J). (ps-ps). 12.95 (978-1-59223-359-5(7) , Silver Dolphin Bks.) Advantage Pubs. Group.

Priddy, Roger. Reptiles - Smart Kids. 2007. 32p. (J). bds. 9.95 (978-0-312-49921-1(3) , Priddy Bks.) St. Martin's Pr.

Pyers, Greg. Why Am I a Reptile? 2005. (Illus.). 32p. (J). (gr. 3-5). lib. bdg. 27.50 (978-1-4109-2017-1(8)); (gr. 5-8). pap. 7.85 (978-1-4109-2024-9(0)) Steck-Vaughn.

Reptiles. Date not set. (Question & Answers of the Natural World Ser.). 32p. 4.98 (978-0-7525-4321-5(0)) Parragon, Inc.

Reptiles & Amphibians. 2003. (Science Card Games Ser.). (gr. 1-3). 9.99 (978-0-7682-1992-0(2) , J53020) School Specialty Publishing.

Reptiles & Amphibians: Level P, 6 vols., Vol. 3. (Explorers Ser.). 32p. (gr. 3-6). 44.95 (978-0-7699-0614-0(1)) Shortland Pubns. (U. S. A.) Inc.

Los Reptiles Y Los Anfibios, 6 vols., Vol. 3. (Explorers. Exploradores Nonfiction Sets Ser.). (SPA.). (gr. 3-6). (978-0-7699-0650-8(8)) Shortland Pubns. (U. S. A.) Inc.

Richardson, Adele D. Reptiles. 2004. (First Facts Ser.). (Illus.). 24p. (J). lib. bdg. 21.26 (978-0-7368-2625-9(4)) Capstone Pr., Inc.

Richardson, Joy. Reptiles. 2005. (Illus.). 32p. (J). lib. bdg. 23.33 (978-0-8368-4508-2(0)) Stevens, Gareth Inc.

Riehecky, Janet. Pteranodonte: Pteranodon. 2007. (ENG & SPA.). (J). (978-0-7368-7640-7(5)) Capstone Pr., Inc.

Ritchey, Richard I. True Adventures of the Reptileman. 2007. 60p. per. 10.95 (***978-0-595-45020-6(2)***) iUniverse, Inc.

Royston, Angela. Reptiles. (Illus.). 32p. (YA). (gr. 2 up). lib. bdg. 27.10 (978-1-932333-38-1(X)) Chrysalis Education.

Rundquist, Eric M. Reptile & Amphibian Parasites. 1999. (Basic Domestic Reptile & Amphibian Library). (Illus.). 64p. (YA). (gr. 4-7). lib. bdg. 19.75 (978-0-7910-5080-4(7) , Chelsea Hse.) Facts On File, Inc.

Salzmann, Mary Elizabeth. What Has a Shell? 2007. (Creature Features Ser.). (ENG., Illus.). 24p. (J). (ps-3). lib. bdg. 24.21 (***978-1-59928-871-0(0)*** , Super SandCastle) ABDO Publishing Co.

—What Has Scales? 2007. (Creature Features Ser.). (ENG., Illus.). 24p. (J). (ps-3). lib. bdg. 24.21 (***978-1-59928-870-3(2)*** , Super SandCastle) ABDO Publishing Co.

Savage, Stephen. Reptiles. 1999. (What's the Difference? Ser.). (Illus.). 32p. (J). (gr. 2-4). lib. bdg. 25.69 (978-0-7398-1358-4(7)) Raintree.

—Reptiles. 2000. (What's the Difference? Ser.). (Illus.). 32p. (J). (ps-3). pap. 9.95 (978-0-7398-2037-7(0)) Steck-Vaughn.

Scaly Things: Level N, 6 vols. (Explorers Ser.). 32p. (gr. 3-6). 44.95 (978-0-7699-0594-5(3)) Shortland Pubns. (U. S. A.) Inc.

Schaefer, Lola M. What Is a Reptile? Saunders-Smith, Gail, ed. 2001. (Animal Kingdom Ser.). (Illus.). 24p. (J). (gr. k-1). lib. bdg. 14.60 (978-0-7368-0868-2(X) , Pebble Bks.) Capstone Pr., Inc.

Scholastic, Inc. Staff. Creepy Crawlies A to Z: Teaching Kit. 2000. (Super Science Readers Ser.). (Illus.). 16p. (J). 10.95 (978-0-439-16766-6(3)) Scholastic, Inc.

School Specialty Publishing. Reptiles. 2004. (On-File Ser.). 4p. (J). (gr. 3-5). ring bd. 4.99 (978-0-7424-2902-4(4) , Instructional Fair) Schaffer, Frank Pubns.

School Zone Publishing Company Staff. Reptiles & Amphibians. (Illus.). (J). 19.99 incl. audio compact disk (978-0-88743-978-0(0)) School Zone Publishing Co.

Schulte, Mary Knudson. Snakes & Other Reptiles. 2005. (Scholastic News Nonfiction Readers Ser.). (Illus.). 24p. (J). (gr. 1-2). 19.00 (978-0-516-24936-0(3) , Children's Pr.) Scholastic Library Publishing.

Sill, Cathryn P. About Reptiles: A Guide for Children. Sill, John, illus. (About...Ser.). 40p. (J). 2003. pap. 7.95 (978-1-56145-233-0(5)); 1999. 15.95 (978-1-56145-183-8(5) , 51835) Peachtree Pubs., Ltd.

—About Reptiles: A Guide for Children. 2003. (gr. k-3). lib. bdg. 16.40 (978-0-613-60381-2(8)) Tandem Library Bks.

Simon, Elizabeth. Caring for Your Iguana. 2004. (Caring for Your Pet Ser.). (Illus.). (J). pap. (978-1-59036-215-0(2)); 32p. lib. bdg. 16.95 (978-1-59036-195-5(4)) Weigl Pubs., Inc.

Simon, Seymour. Crocodiles & Alligators. Simon, Seymour, illus. 1999. (Illus.). 32p. (J). (gr. k-3). 16.89 (978-0-06-027474-0(3)) HarperCollins Pubs.

Slater, Patrick. Australian Frogs & Reptiles. 2002. (Nature Kids Ser.). (Illus.). 52p. (J). (gr. 3 up). lib. bdg. (978-1-59084-216-4(2)) Mason Crest Pubs.

Snakes & Other Reptiles. 2002. (Wild, Wild World Ser.). 32p. (J). 9.95 (978-0-7525-4684-1(8)) Parragon, Inc.

Snedden, Robert. Reptiles. 2007. (J). (***978-1-59920-082-8(1)***) Smart Apple Media.

Solway, Andrew. Deadly Reptiles. 2005. (Illus.). 48p. (J). (978-1-4034-6568-9(1)); pap. (978-1-4034-6574-0(6)) Heinemann Library.

—Snakes & Other Reptiles. 2006. (Illus.). 48p. (J). (978-1-4034-8224-2(1)); pap. (978-1-4034-8231-0(4)) Heinemann Library.

Sovak, Jan. Learning about Reptiles. 2001. (Learning about Ser.). (Illus.). 16p. (J). (ps up). pap. 1.50 (978-0-486-41851-3(0)) Dover Pubns., Inc.

Spilsbury, Louise. Reptiles. 2003. (gr. 3-6). lib. bdg. 15.25 (978-0-613-60924-1(7)) Tandem Library Bks.

Spilsbury, Louise & Spilsbury, Richard. Classifying Reptiles. 2003. (Classifying Living Things Ser.). (Illus.). 32p. (J). (gr. 3-5). lib. bdg. 24.22 (978-1-4034-0848-8(3)); pap. (978-1-4034-3348-0(8)) Heinemann Library.

Spirn, Michele. Ripley's Cold-Blooded Creatures. 2004. (Illus.). 60p. (J). (978-0-439-63362-8(1)) Scholastic, Inc.

Sterling, Mary E. Reptiles Photo Fun Activities. Sedlark, Deneen, ed. Carrozza, John, illus. 1998. (Science Photo Fun Activities Ser.). 8p. (J). pap. 6.95 (978-1-56472-089-4(6)) Edupress, Inc.

Stewart, Melissa. Reptiles. 2001. (True Bks.). (Illus.). 48p. (J). (gr. 3-5). pap. 6.95 (978-0-516-25953-6(9) , Children's Pr.) Scholastic Library Publishing.

—Reptiles. 2001. (gr. 3-6). lib. bdg. 15.25 (978-0-613-54321-7(1)) Tandem Library Bks.

Stone, Tanya Lee. Crocodilians. 2003. (Wild Wild World Ser.). (Illus.). 24p. (J). 22.45 (978-1-4103-0037-9(4) , Blackbirch Pr., Inc.) Thomson Gale.

Taylor, Barbara. Bugs Snakes Spiders & Crocodiles. 2008. (Illus.). 512p. 29.99 (***978-0-7548-1781-9(4)*** , Lorenz Bks.) Anness Publishing GBR. *Dist:* National Bk. Network.

Taylor, Barbara. Dinosaur Legacy. 2005. (Illus.). 128p. pap. 17.99 (978-1-84476-081-7(2) , Southwater) Anness Publishing GBR. *Dist:* National Bk. Network.

Taylor, Barbara & O'Shea, Mark. Reptiles, 10 vols. 2004. (Illus.). 256p. 29.99 (978-0-7548-1503-7(X) , Lorenz Bks.) Anness Publishing GBR. *Dist:* National Bk. Network.

Theodorou, Rod. Reptiles. 2007. (Animal Babies Ser.). (Illus.). 32p. (J). (***978-1-4034-9253-1(0)***) Heinemann Library.

Theodorou, Rod & Fraser, Alan. Reptiles. 2007. (Animal Babies Ser.). (Illus.). 32p. (J). (***978-1-4034-9246-3(8)***) Heinemann Library.

Thomas, Peggy. Reptile Rescue. 2000. (Science of Saving Animals Ser.: 8). (Illus.). 64p. (gr. 5-8). lib. bdg. 25.90 (978-0-7613-3232-9(4) , Twenty-First Century Bks.) Lerner Publishing Group.

Top That Publishing Staff, ed. How to Draw Monster Reptiles. 2005. (Illus.). 48p. pap. (978-1-84510-745-1(4)) Top That! Publishing PLC.

Townsend. Incredible Reptiles, 6 Packs. 2004. (Illus.). (J). pap. 51.30 (978-1-4109-0865-0(8)) Raintree.

Townsend, John. Incredible Reptiles. 2004. (J). pap. 9.50 (978-1-4109-0856-8(9)); (Illus.). 56p. lib. bdg. 31.36 (978-1-4109-0532-1(2)) Harcourt Schl. Pubs.

—Incredible Reptiles. 2005. (J). 56p. (978-1-4109-1722-5(3)); (978-1-4109-1713-3(4)) Steck-Vaughn.

Twist, Clint. Reptiles & Amphibians A-Z. 2005. (A-Z Ser.). (Illus.). 64p. (J). (gr. k-7). per. 26.20 (978-1-4103-0487-2(6) , Blackbirch Pr., Inc.) Thomson Gale.

—Reptiles & Amphibians Dictionary. 2005. (Illus.). 64p. (J). pap. (978-0-439-66828-6(X)) Scholastic, Inc.

Unwin, Mike. The Life Cycle of Reptiles. 2003. (From Egg to Adult Ser.). (J). 24.22 (978-1-4034-0781-8(9)); 32p. pap. 7.50 (978-1-4034-3408-1(5)) Heinemann Library.

Visca, Curt & Visca, Kelley. How to Draw Cartoon Reptiles. 2003. (Kid's Guide to Drawing Ser.). (Illus.). 24p. (J). lib. bdg. 21.25 (978-0-8239-6160-3(5) , PowerKids Pr.) Rosen Publishing Group, Inc., The.

Wallace, Karen. I Am a Quetzalcoatlus. Bostock, Mike, illus. 2005. (J). (ps-ps). (978-0-340-89380-7(X) , Hodder Children's Books) Hodder Children's Division.

Weber, Belinda. Reptiles. 2006. (Kingfisher Young Knowledge Ser.). (Illus.). 48p. (J). (gr. k-3). 9.95 (978-0-7534-5982-9(5) , Kingfisher) Houghton Mifflin Co. Trade & Reference Div.

West, David. Pteranodon: The Toothless Flyer. 2008. (J). lib. bdg. (***978-1-4042-3895-4(6)*** , PowerKids Pr.) Rosen Publishing Group, Inc., The.

What Is a Reptile? 2005. (Animals, Animals, Animals Ser.). (YA). (gr. k-3). (978-0-7368-9097-7(1) , Pebble Bks.) Capstone Pr., Inc.

What Is a Reptile?, 6 vols. (gr. k-2). 28.95 (978-0-7368-9118-9(8)) Red Brick Learning.

Who's Hiding Inside? Reptiles. 2005. (Who's Hiding Inside Ser.). 12p. (J). bds. 7.95 (978-1-58117-307-9(5) , Intervisual/Piggy Toes) Dalmatian Pr.

Wildlife Education, Ltd. Staff, contrib. by. Reptiles, Set. 2002. (All about Animals Ser.). (Illus.). (J). (gr. k-6). 16.95 incl. VHS (978-1-888153-88-0(1)) Wildlife Education, Ltd.

Wilkes, Angela. Reptiles. 2002. (Question Time Ser.). (Illus.). 32p. (J). (gr. k-3). tchr. ed. 11.95 (978-0-7534-5451-0(3) , Kingfisher) Houghton Mifflin Co. Trade & Reference Div.

Wilkes, Sarah. Reptiles. 2006. (J). pap. (978-0-8368-6232-4(5)); (Illus.). 48p. lib. bdg. 30.00 (978-0-8368-6213-3(9)) Stevens, Gareth Inc. (World Almanac Library).

Williams, Sarah, et al. 101 Facts about Iguanas. 2001. (One Hundred One Facts about Pets Ser.). (Illus.). 32p. (J). (gr. 3 up). lib. bdg. 23.33 (978-0-8368-2888-7(7)) Stevens, Gareth Inc.

Wilson, Hannah. Life-Size Reptiles. 2007. (Life-Size Ser.). (Illus.). 28p. (J). (ps-3). 9.95 (978-1-4027-4542-3(7)) Sterling Publishing Co., Inc.

Winner, Cherie. Everything Reptile: What Kids Really Want to Know about Reptiles. 2004. (Kids' FAQs Ser.). (Illus.). 64p. (gr. 2-6). 10.95 (978-1-55971-146-3(9)); (YA). pap. 7.95 (978-1-55971-164-7(7)) T&N Children's Publishing. (NorthWord Bks. for Young Readers).

Wood, Jakki. March of the Dinosaurs. 2004. (Illus.). 30p. (J). pap. 7.95 (978-1-84507-208-7(1)) Lincoln, Frances Ltd. GBR. *Dist:* Perseus Distribution.

World Book, Inc. Staff, contrib. by. Amphibians & Reptiles of the United States & Canada. 2004. (World Book's Science & Nature Guides Ser.). (Illus.). 80p. (J). (978-0-7166-4209-1(3)) World Bk., Inc.

World of Reptiles. 2005. (Illus.). (J). (gr. 2-3). lib. bdg. 212.60 (978-0-7368-4420-8(1)) Capstone Pr., Inc.

Zabludoff, Marc. The Reptile Class. 2005. (Family Trees Ser.). (Illus.). 95p. (J). (gr. 4-7). lib. bdg. 32.79 (978-0-7614-1820-7(2) , Benchmark Bks.) Cavendish, Marshall Corp.

REPTILES—FICTION

Carle, Eric. Al Hirbaa Al Haira: The Mixed-up Chameleon. 2006. 24p. pap. 14.00 (978-977-6171-06-0() , 706-008) Al-Balsam Pubng. Hse. EGY. *Dist:* Bookworld Trade, Inc.

Einhorn, Kama. My First Book about Reptiles. Moroney, Christopher, illus. 2007. (J). (***978-1-4287-1452-6(9)***) Random Hse., Inc.

Eliasen, Lorena. Chameleon & the Dragonfly: A Pop-Up Book. 2004. (Illus.). 12p. (J). pap. 16.95 (978-0-439-52320-2(6) , Orchard Bks.) Scholastic, Inc.

Franco, Betsy. Word Family Tales -Ake: Jake's Cake Mistake. Hervey, Paul, illus. 2002. (Word Family Tales Ser.). 16p. (ps-2). pap. 2.95 (978-0-439-26265-1(8)) Scholastic, Inc.

Hale, Bruce. Farewell, My Lunchbag: A Chet Gecko Mystery. 2002. (Chet Gecko Mystery Ser.: No. 3). (Illus.). 132p. (ps-7). pap. 4.95 (978-0-15-202629-5(0) , Harcourt Paperbacks) Harcourt Children's Bks.

—Farewell, My Lunchbag: A Chet Gecko Mystery. Hale, Bruce, illus. 2001. (Chet Gecko Mystery Ser.: No. 3). (Illus.). 128p. (J). (gr. 3-7). 15.00 (978-0-15-202275-4(9)) Harcourt Children's Bks.

—Farewell, My Lunchbag: A Chet Gecko Mystery. 2002. (Chet Gecko Mystery Ser.: No. 3). (J). (gr. 3-6). lib. bdg. 12.95 (978-0-613-49734-3(1)) Tandem Library Bks.

Hambleton, Laura. Chameleon Races. 2005. (Chameleon Ser.). (Illus.). 16p. (J). bds. 7.95 (978-1-84059-422-5(5)); (ARA & ENG., bds. 8.95 (978-1-84059-423-2(3)); (BEN & ENG., bds. 8.95 (978-1-84059-424-9(1)); (ENG, PER & FAR., bds. 8.95 (978-1-84059-425-6(X)); (ENG & FRE., bds. 8.95 (978-1-84059-426-3(8)); (ENG & ITA., bds. 8.95 (978-1-84059-427-0(6)); (POR & ENG., bds. 8.95 (978-1-84059-428-7(4)); (ENG & JPN., bds. 8.95 (978-1-84059-453-9(5)); (ENG & SOM., bds. 8.95 (978-1-84059-430-0(6)); (ENG & SPA., bds. 8.95 (978-1-84059-431-7(4)); (ENG & TUR., bds. 8.95 (978-1-84059-432-4(2)); (ENG & URD., bds. 8.95 (978-1-84059-433-1(0)); (ENG & VIE., bds. 8.95 (978-1-84059-434-8(9)) Milet Publishing.

—Chameleon Races. Dai, Hongchao, tr. 2005. (Chameleon Ser.). (CHI & ENG., Illus.). 16p. (J). 8.95 (978-1-84059-429-4(2)) Milet Publishing.

—Chameleon Swims. 2005. (Chameleon Ser.). (Illus.). 16p. (J). bds. 7.95 (978-1-84059-435-5(7)); (ARA & ENG., bds. 8.95 (978-1-84059-436-2(5)); (BEN & ENG., bds. 8.95 (978-1-84059-437-9(3)); (ENG, PER & FAR., bds. 8.95 (978-1-84059-438-6(1)); (CHI & ENG., bds. 8.95 (978-1-84059-442-3(X)); (ENG & ITA., bds. 8.95 (978-1-84059-440-9(3)); (ENG & SOM., bds. 8.95 (978-1-84059-443-0(8)); (ENG & SPA., bds. 8.95 (978-1-84059-444-7(6)); (ENG & TUR., bds. 8.95 (978-1-84059-445-4(4)); (ENG & URD., bds. 8.95 (978-1-84059-446-1(2)); (ENG & VIE., bds. 8.95 (978-1-84059-447-8(0)) Milet Publishing.

—Chameleon Swims. Santos, Manolo, tr. 2005. (Chameleon Ser.). (ENG & POR., Illus.). 16p. (J). bds. 8.95 (978-1-84059-441-6(1)) Milet Publishing.

—Chameleon Swims. Sommer, Patricia, tr. 2005. (Chameleon Ser.). (ENG & FRE., Illus.). 16p. (J). bds. 8.95 (978-1-84059-439-3(X)) Milet Publishing.

—Chameleon Swims. Astridge, Nissho, tr. 2005. (Chameleon Ser.). (ENG & JPN., Illus.). 16p. (J). bds. 8.95 (978-1-84059-454-6(3)) Milet Publishing.

Harcourt School Publishers Staff. Como el Camaleion: Take-Home Book. 1999. (Vamos Ser.). (SPA., Illus.). (J). pap. 2.50 (978-0-15-318848-0(0)) Harcourt Schl. Pubs.

—Como Me Veo? Advanced Level. 3rd ed. 2002. (Trofeos Ser.). (SPA., Illus.). (gr. 2). pap. 6.80 (978-0-15-324012-6(1)) Harcourt Schl. Pubs.

—What Do I Look Like? Advanced Level. 3rd ed. 2002. (Trophies Reading Program Ser.). (Illus.). pap. 5.10 (978-0-15-323101-8(7)) Harcourt Schl. Pubs.

Insects, Amphibians & Reptiles. 2001. 63p. (YA). 8.65 (978-0-7525-4875-3(1)) Parragon, Inc.

Krulik, Nancy E. Free the Worms!, No. 28. John and Wendy Staff, illus. 2008. (Katie Kazoo, Switcheroo Ser.: No. 28). 80p. (J). (gr. 2-5). pap. 3.99 (***978-0-448-44675-2(8)*** , Grosset & Dunlap) Penguin Group (USA) Inc.

MacHado, Ana Maria. Tiririca, Jararaca y Perereca. Faria, Rosana, illus. 2003. 28p. pap. (978-980-257-283-0(7)) Ekare, Ediciones.

Peebles, Vince and Emily. Cam Goes to the Rain Forest. 2006. (ENG.). 40p. per. 16.99 (***978-1-4259-8033-7(3)***) AuthorHouse.

San Souci, Daniel. The Dangerous Snake & Reptile Club. 2004. (Illus.). 40p. (J). 15.95 (978-1-58246-131-1(7) , Tricycle Pr.) Ten Speed Pr.

Sanford, Christi. Legare the Lowcountry Lizard & His Sturdy New Tail. 2001. 24p. (J). pap. 11.95 (978-0-9675841-1-9(6)) Lowcountry Literature.

Su Propio Color. 2007. (SPA.). 40p. (J). 12.99 (***978-1-933032-14-6(6)***) Lectorum Pubns., Inc.

Sydor, Colleen. Camilla Chameleon. 2007. 32p. pap. (***978-1-55453-164-6(0)***) Kids Can Pr., Ltd.

Townsend, Wendy. Lizard Love. 2008. (J). (***978-1-932425-34-5(9)*** , Front Street) Boyds Mills Pr.

REPTILES, FOSSIL

see also Dinosaurs

Arnold, Caroline. Giant Sea Reptiles of the Dinosaur Age. Caple, Laurie A., illus. 2007. 40p. (J). (gr. 4-6). 17.00 (978-0-618-50449-7(4) , Clarion Bks.) Houghton Mifflin Co. Trade & Reference Div.

Brown, Charlotte Lewis. Beyond the Dinosaurs: Monsters of the Air & Sea. Wilson, Phil, illus. 2007. (I Can Read Bks.). 32p. (J). (gr. k-3). 15.99 (***978-0-06-053056-3(1)); lib. bdg. 16.89 (978-0-06-053057-0(X))*** HarperCollins Pubs.

Hughes, Monica. Swimming Giants. 2008. (J). lib. bdg. (***978-1-59716-542-6(5)***) Bearport Publishing Co., Inc.

Jay, Michael. Rise of the Reptiles. 2003. (Illus.). 32p. (J). lib. bdg. 25.70 (978-1-4109-0009-8(6)) Raintree.

Kelly, Harold G. How the Dinosaurs Disappeared. 2006. (Rosen Publishing Group's Reading Room Collection). (J). lib. bdg. (978-1-4042-3340-9(7) , PowerKids Pr.) Rosen Publishing Group, Inc., The.

Myers, Tim. If You Give a T-Rex a Bone. Hovemann, Anisa Claire, illus. 2007. 32p. (J). pap. 8.95 (***978-1-58469-098-6(4)***); 16.95 (***978-1-58469-097-9(6)***) Dawn Pubns.

Roberts, Russell. Where Did All the Dinosaurs Go? 2005. (Natural Disasters Ser.). (Illus.). 32p. (J). (gr. 1-4). lib. bdg. (978-1-58415-420-4(9)) Mitchell Lane Pubs., Inc.

RESCUE WORK

see also First Aid

Allberti, Frances C. Finding Rover. Gremillion, Barry, illus. 2006. (J). per. (978-0-9785937-1-1(5)) Open Pages Publishing.

Bingham, Caroline. Rescue-Mania! 2003. (Vehicle-Mania! Ser.). (Illus.). 32p. (J). (gr. 2 up). lib. bdg. 23.33 (978-0-8368-3784-1(3)) Stevens, Gareth Inc.

Bright, J. E. Why We Be Came Rescue Heroes. 2002. (Rescue Heroes Reader Ser.: No. 1). (Illus.). 32p. (J). (ps-3). pap. 3.99 (978-0-439-41909-3(3) , Scholastic Paperbacks) Scholastic, Inc.

Brown, Mike. Rescue Services. 2003. (Twentieth-Century Developments in Fashion & Costume Ser.). (Illus.). 64p. (J). (gr. 7 up). lib. bdg. (978-1-59084-428-1(9)) Mason Crest Pubs.

Bryant, Raymond. To the Rescue. 2004. (Funtime Rhymes Ser.). 10p. (J). bds. 4.95 (978-0-7641-5716-5(7)) Barron's Educational Series, Inc.

Careers in Search & Rescue Operations. 2005. (Illus.). (gr. 5-8). lib. bdg. 159.00 (978-0-8239-4049-3(7)) Rosen Publishing Group, Inc., The.

Clements, Andrew. Tara & Tiree, Fearless Friends: A True Story. 2002. (gr. k-3). lib. bdg. 11.80 (978-0-613-66607-7(0)) Tandem Library Bks.

Collings, Julie & Klutz Editors. Rescue Trucks. 2005. (Illus.). 22p. (J). (ps-3). spiral bd. 12.95 (978-1-59174-089-6(4)) Klutz.

Demarest, Chris L. Mayday! Mayday! A Coast Guard Rescue. Demarest, Chris L., illus. 2004. (Illus.). 40p. (J). 16.95 (978-0-689-85161-2(8) , McElderry, Margaret K.) Simon & Schuster Children's Publishing.

Dewey, Jennifer Owings. Wildlife Rescue: The Work of Kathleen Ramsay. MacCarter, Don, photos by. 1999. (Illus.). 63p. (J). (ps-7). lib. bdg. 18.75 (978-0-613-17889-1(0)) Tandem Library Bks.

Ethan, Eric. Helicopters. Ethan, Eric, photos by. 2002. (Emergency Vehicles Ser.). (Illus.). 24p. (YA). (gr. 1 up). lib. bdg. 20.67 (978-0-8368-3046-0(6)) Stevens, Gareth Inc.

—Rescue Boats. Ethan, Eric, photos by. 2002. (Emergency Vehicles Ser.). (Illus.). 24p. (YA). (gr. 1 up). lib. bdg. 20.67 (978-0-8368-3048-4(2)) Stevens, Gareth Inc.

Fall, Mitchell. Careers in the Fire Department's Search & Rescue Unit. 2005. (Careers in Search & Rescue Operations Ser.). (Illus.). 64p. (YA). (gr. 5-8). lib. bdg. 26.50 (978-0-8239-3833-9(6)) Rosen Publishing Group, Inc., The.

George, Linda & George, Charles. Search & Rescue Dogs. 1998. (Dogs at Work Ser.). 48p. (J). pap. 19.00 (978-0-531-11557-2(7) , Watts, Franklin) Scholastic Library Publishing.

Gonzalez, Lissette. Search & Rescue Specialists. 2008. (J). lib. bdg. (***978-1-4042-3779-7(8)*** , PowerKids Pr.) Rosen Publishing Group, Inc., The.

Green, Michael. Air Rescue Teams. 2000. (Serving Your Country Ser.). (Illus.). 48p. (J). (gr. 3-4). lib. bdg. 21.26 (978-0-7368-0470-7(6) , Capstone High-Interest Bks.) Capstone Pr., Inc.

Greene, Meg. Careers in the National Guards' Search & Rescue Units. 2005. (Careers in Search & Rescue Operations Ser.). (Illus.). 64p. (YA). (gr. 5-8). lib. bdg. 26.50 (978-0-8239-3836-0(0)) Rosen Publishing Group, Inc., The.

Harcourt School Publishers Staff. Saving Ben Advanced Level. 3rd ed. 2002. (Trophies Reading Program Ser.). (Illus.). pap. 5.10 (978-0-15-323118-6(1)) Harcourt Schl. Pubs.

Hickle, Victoria. Fire Trucks in Action. DePew, Bob, illus. 2003. (Tonka Ser.). 4p. (J). (ps-2). bds. 6.99 (978-0-439-43432-4(7)) Scholastic, Inc.

Hoffman, Mary Ann. Hurricane Katrina. 2006. (Nature in the News Ser.). (Illus.). 32p. (J). lib. bdg. (978-1-4042-3537-3(X) , PowerKids Pr.) Rosen Publishing Group, Inc., The.

Hughes, Monica. To the Rescue. 2006. (I Love Reading Ser.). (Illus.). 24p. (J). lib. bdg. 19.96 (978-1-59716-156-5(X)) Bearport Publishing Co., Inc.

Joachim, Jean. Rescue Vehicles Dot-to-Dot. 2005. 80p. (J). pap. 5.95 (978-1-4027-1080-3(1)) Sterling Publishing Co., Inc.

Kalman, Bobbie. Bomberos Al Rescate. 2006. (ENG & SPA., Illus.). 32p. (J). (978-0-7787-8428-9(2)) Crabtree Publishing Co.

—Bomberos al Rescate. 2006. (ENG & SPA., Illus.). 32p. (gr. 1-2). pap. (978-0-7787-8442-5(8)) Crabtree Publishing Co.

—Emergency Workers Are on Their Way! 2004. (My Community & Its Helpers Ser.). (Illus.). (J). 158p. (978-0-7787-2094-2(2)); 32p. pap. (978-0-7787-2122-2(1)) Crabtree Publishing Co.

—Firefighters to the Rescue! 2004. (My Community & Its Helpers Ser.). (Illus.). 32p. (J). (978-0-7787-2096-6(9)); pap. (978-0-7787-2124-6(8)) Crabtree Publishing Co.

Kast, Edie. Heroic Animals. 2005. (Illus.). 24p. (J). (***978-0-328-13606-3(9)*** , Scott Foresman) Addison-Wesley Educational Pubs., Inc.

Katz, Samuel M. Against All Odds: Counterterrorist Hostage Recues. 2005. (Terrorist Dossiers Ser.). (Illus.). 72p. (J). (gr. 6-12). 26.60 (978-0-8225-1567-8(9)) Lerner Publishing Group.

Kyi, Tanya Lloyd. Rescues! 2006. (True Stories from the Edge Ser.). (Illus.). 136p. (J). (gr. 4-12). 18.95 (978-1-55451-034-4(1)); pap. 8.95 (978-1-55451-033-7(3)) Annick Pr., Ltd. CAN. *Dist:* Firefly Bks., Ltd.

Lewis, Brenda Ralph. Hostage Rescue with the FBI. 2002. (Rescue & Prevention Ser.). (Illus.). 96p. (J). (gr. 7 up). lib. bdg. (978-1-59084-403-8(3)) Mason Crest Pubs.

—Wilderness Rescue with the U. S. Search & Rescue Task Force. 2003. (Rescue & Prevention Ser.). (Illus.). 96p. (J). (gr. 7 up). lib. bdg. (978-1-59084-404-5(1)) Mason Crest Pubs.

Lindeen, Carol K. Rescue Boats. (Mighty MacHines Ser.). 24p. (J). pap. 6.95 (978-0-7368-5142-8(9)) Capstone Pr., Inc.

Litchfield, J. & Brooks, F. Rescue Vehicles. 2004. (Illus.). 10p. (J). 4.99 (978-0-7945-0589-9(9)) EDC Publishing.

Locke, Ian. Remarkable Rescue. Rowe, Alan, illus. 2003. 61p. (J). pap. 3.99 (978-0-330-37502-3(4) , Pan) Pan Macmillan GBR. *Dist:* Trafalgar Square Publishing.

Louis, Nancy. Ground Zero. 2002. (War on Terrorism Ser.). (Illus.). 64p. (J). (gr. 4-8). lib. bdg. 25.65 (978-1-57765-657-9(1) , ABDO & Daughters) ABDO Publishing Co.

Lucas, Debra. To the Rescue. 2003. (On the Job Ser.). (Illus.). 32p. (gr. 3-5). 23.00 (978-0-7910-7414-5(5) , Chelsea Hse.) Facts On File, Inc.

Miller, Debra A. Hurricane Katrina: Devastation on the Gulf Coast. 2006. 112p. (J). (gr. 7-10). 29.95 (978-1-59018-936-8(1) , Lucent Bks.) Thomson Gale.

Miller, Mara. Hurricane Katrina Strikes the Gulf Coast: Disaster & Survival. 2006. (Deadly Disasters Ser.). (Illus.). 48p. (J). lib. bdg. 23.93 (978-0-7660-2803-6(8) , 1251895) Enslow Pubs., Inc.

Owen, Ann. Protecting Your Home: A Book about Firefighters. Thomas, Eric, illus. 2004. (Community Workers Ser.). 24p. (C). (gr. k-3). 22.60 (978-1-4048-0088-5(3)) Picture Window Bks.

Parham, Donna. To the Rescue! The SeaWorld/Busch Gardens Animal Rescue & Rehabilitation Program. 2001. (Seaworld Education Ser.). (Illus.). 112p. (gr. 4 up). per. 7.99 (978-1-893698-06-2(8) , B08, SeaWorld Education Dept.) SeaWorld, Inc.

Perry, Phyllis Jean. Sherlock Hounds: Our Heroic Search & Rescue Dogs. 2006. (Illus.). 32p. (J). pap. (978-1-59336-728-2(7)) Mondo Publishing.

Phidal Publishing Staff, ed. Rescue Squad. (Cool Cars Ser.). (J). 16p. (978-2-7643-0132-6(4)); 2004. (Illus.). 10p. (978-2-7643-0209-5(6)) Phidal Publishing, Inc./Editions Phidal, Inc.

Plum, Jennifer. Careers in the Police Department's Search & Rescue Unit. 2005. (Careers in Search & Rescue Operations Ser.). (Illus.). 64p. (YA). (gr. 5-8). lib. bdg. 26.50 (978-0-8239-3834-6(4)) Rosen Publishing Group, Inc., The.

Poolos, Jamie. Hostage Rescuers. 2006. (Extreme Careers Ser.). (Illus.). 64p. (YA). (gr. 5-8). lib. bdg. 26.50 (978-1-4042-0941-1(7)) Rosen Publishing Group, Inc., The.

Presnall, Judith Janda. Rescue Dogs. 2002. (Animals with Jobs Ser.). (Illus.). 48p. (J). (gr. 3-5). 23.70 (978-0-7377-1361-9(5) , Kidhaven) Thomson Gale.

Priddy, Roger. My Big Rescue Book. 2004. (Illus.). (J). 10p. (978-1-84332-215-3(3)); 14p. bds. 5.95 (978-0-312-49327-1(4) , Priddy Bks.) St. Martin's Pr.

Randolph, Joanne. Emergency Helicopters. 2008. (J). lib. bdg. (***978-1-4042-4151-0(5)*** , PowerKids Pr.) Rosen Publishing Group, Inc., The.

Rescue! 6 Each of 1 Anthology, 6 vols. (Wildcats Ser.). 32p. (gr. 2-8). (978-0-322-00585-3(X)) Wright Group, The.

Rettung in Not. (Illus.). 40p. (J). (978-3-411-08181-3(3)) Bibliographisches Institut & F. A. Brockhaus AG DEU. *Dist:* i.b.d., Ltd.

Roleff, Tamara L., ed. The World Trade Center Attack. 2003. (History Firsthand Ser.). (Illus.). 202p. (YA). (gr. 7-10). pap. 21.20 (978-0-7377-1469-2(7)); lib. bdg. 36.20 (978-0-7377-1468-5(9)) Thomson Gale. (Greenhaven Pr., Inc.).

Roza, Greg. Careers in the Coast Guard's Search & Rescue Unit. 2005. (Careers in Search & Rescue Operations Ser.). (Illus.). 64p. (YA). (gr. 5-8). lib. bdg. 26.50 (978-0-8239-3835-3(2)) Rosen Publishing Group, Inc., The.

Schoberle, Cecile. To the Rescue! Mones, Isidre & Mones, Marc, illus. ed. 2005. (Ready-to-Read Ser. Level 1). 31p. (J). lib. bdg. 15.00 (978-1-59054-935-3(X)) Fitzgerald Bks.

—To the Rescue! 2003. (gr. k-3). lib. bdg. 11.80 (978-0-613-66550-6(3)) Tandem Library Bks.

Smith, Roland. Sea Otter Rescue. 1999. (gr. 3-6). lib. bdg. 15.30 (978-0-613-22343-0(8)) Tandem Library Bks.

Somervill, Barbara A. First Response: By Air. 2007. (High Interest Books Ser.). (Illus.). 48p. (J). pap. (978-0-531-18718-0(7)) Children's Pr., Ltd.

—First Response: By Air. 2006. (Natural Disasters Ser.). (Illus.). 48p. (J). (978-0-531-12432-1(0) , Children's Pr.) Scholastic Library Publishing.

Somerville, Louisa. Rescue Vehicles. Jensen, Hans, illus. (J). mass mkt. 8.99 (978-0-590-24557-9(0)) Scholastic, Inc.

Stephens, Rebecca. Everest. 2001. (Eyewitness Books). (Illus.). (J). lib. bdg. (978-0-7566-0001-3(4)) Dorling Kindersley Publishing, Inc.

—Everest. Parsons, Jayne, ed. 2001. (Dorling Kindersley Eyewitness Books). (Illus.). 62p. (J). (978-0-7513-1394-9(7)) Dorling Kindersley Publishing, Inc.

Torres, John Albert. Disaster in the Indian Ocean, Tsunami 2004. 2005. (Monumental Milestones Ser.). (Illus.). 48p. (J). (gr. 5-8). lib. bdg. 29.95 (978-1-58415-344-3(X)) Mitchell Lane Pubs., Inc.

Trew, Delbert. Rescue from the Mesa: A Barbed Wire Story. 1998. (Illus.). 85p. (YA). (gr. 6-12). pap. 8.75 (978-0-9659677-1-6(9)) D.R.M. Publishing Co.

Watts, Claire. Rescue. Parsons, Jayne, ed. 2001. (Eyewitness Bks.: Vol. 115). (Illus.). 64p. (J). (gr. 4-7). 15.99 (978-0-7894-7393-6(3)) Dorling Kindersley Publishing, Inc.

Watts, Claire & Dorling Kindersley Publishing Staff. Rescue. 2001. (Eyewitness Bks.: Vol. 115). (Illus.). 64p. (J). (gr. 4-7). lib. bdg. 19.99 (978-0-7894-7394-3(1)) Dorling Kindersley Publishing, Inc.

Weintraub, Aileen. First Response: By Land. 2007. (Illus.). 48p. (J). pap. (978-0-531-18719-7(5)) Children's Pr., Ltd.

—First Response by Land. 2006. (Natural Disasters Ser.). (Illus.). 48p. (J). (978-0-531-12433-8(9) , Children's Pr.) Scholastic Library Publishing.

—First Response by Sea. 2006. (Natural Disasters Ser.). (Illus.). 48p. (J). (978-0-531-12434-5(7) , Children's Pr.) Scholastic Library Publishing.

Williams, Chris. One Incredible Dog! Kizzy. Friedman, Judith, illus. 2006. 32p. (ps-3). 15.95 (978-0-9766805-5-0(6) , Moo Pr.) Keene Publishing.

RESCUE WORK—FICTION

Abbott, Tony. Chariot of Queen Zara. Merrell, David, illus. 2006. 124p. (J). lib. bdg. 15.38 (***978-1-4242-0308-6(2)***) Fitzgerald Bks.

Abbott, Tony & Gelsey, James. Escape from Jabar-Loo. 2007. (Secrets of Droon Ser.: No. 30). 128p. (J). pap. 3.99 (***978-0-439-90251-9(7)*** , Scholastic Paperbacks) Scholastic, Inc.

Appleton, Victor. Into the Abyss. 2007. (Tom Swift, Young Inventor Ser.). 160p. (J). (gr. 4-7). 27.07 (***978-1-59961-350-5(6)***) Spotlight.

Arctic Airlift. 2005. (Illus.). 36p. (J). 17.00 (978-0-9763119-0-4(9)) Blue Fox Pr.

Artifact Group. Rescue Patrol. 2006. (Backyardigans Ser.). 24p. (J). pap. 3.99 (978-1-4169-1796-0(9) , Simon Spotlight/Nickelodeon) Simon & Schuster Children's Publishing.

Ballantyne, R. M. The Lighthouse. 2006. pap. (***978-1-4065-0531-3(5)***) Dodo Pr.

Ballantyne, R. M. Saved by the Lifeboat. 2004. reprint ed. pap. 1.99 (978-1-4192-4624-1(0)) Kessinger Publishing, LLC.

Barnum, P. T. Dick Broadhead: A Story of Perilous Adve. 2006. pap. 30.95 (***978-1-4286-1959-3(3)***) Kessinger Publishing, LLC.

Bell, Michele Ashman. Rescue: A Jungle Adventure. 2006. 246p. (J). pap. (978-1-59811-093-7(4)) Covenant Communications.

Beresford, Elisabeth. Wombles Tomask to the Rescue. (Illus.). 15p. (J). (gr. k-6). pap. (978-0-340-73581-7(3) , Hodder & Stoughton) Hodder General Publishing Division.

Blazin' Hot: Picture Book (English) 8x8. 2006. (J). (978-1-933934-29-7(8)) Educational Adventures.

Blazin' Hot Picture Book (English) 2005. (Illus.). (J). (978-0-9765953-9-7(7)) Educational Adventures.

Brightwood, Laura, illus. Ka-ulu the Strong. Brightwood, Laura, . 2006. (J). (***978-0-9789871-3-8(6)***) 3-C Institute for Social Development.

Bunting, Eve. Mouse Island. Catalano, Dominic, illus. 2008. (J). (***978-1-59078-447-1(2)***) Boyds Mills Pr.

Butterworth, Nick. The Rescue Party. 2003. (Illus.). 32p. (J). pap. 11.00 (978-0-00-715516-3(6) , HarperSport) HarperCollins Pubs. Ltd. GBR. *Dist:* Independent Pubs. Group.

Carey, Craig Robert. Driving Force: Rescue Action. 2006. (Tonka Ser.: No. 7). (Illus.). 24p. (J). pap. 3.99 (978-0-439-83011-9(7) , Scholastic) Scholastic, Inc.

Carney, Charles. Rescue Heroes. Jankowski, Bill, illus. 2002. (Play-A-Sound Ser.). (J). (978-0-7853-7233-2(4)) Publications International, Ltd.

Carter, Anne Laurel. Under a Prairie Sky. Daniel, Alan & Daniel, Lea, illus. 2004. 32p. (J). (ps-2). 7.95 (978-1-55143-282-3(X)) Orca Bk. Pubs. USA.

Cole, Joanna. Files from the Nest. Bracken, Carolyn, illus. 2005. 32p. (J). (ps-3). lib. bdg. 11.19 (978-0-606-33806-6(3)) Tandem Library Bks.

Collier, Kevin Scott. Journeys of Hope, Pearl of Wisdom. Collier, Kevin Scott, illus. 2006. (Illus.). 28p. (J). E-Book 9.95 incl. cd-rom (978-1-933090-31-3(6)) Guardian Angel Publishing, Inc.

Copeland, Cynthia L. Elin's Island. 2003. (Single Titles Ser.: up). 144p. (gr. 6 up). lib. bdg. 22.90 (978-0-7613-2522-2(0) , Millbrook Pr.) Lerner Publishing Group.

Cynthia DeFelice. Bringing Ezra Back: A Sequel to Weasel. l.t. ed. 2006. (J). 21.95 (978-0-7862-9043-7(9)) Thorndike Pr.

Dahlstrom, Kathryn. Peppy's Rescue. Date not set. (Good News Club Ser.). (J). (gr. 4-11). pap. 4.99 (978-1-55976-826-9(6)) CEF Pr.

DeFelice, Cynthia C. Bringing Ezra Back. 2006. 160p. (J). 16.00 (978-0-374-39939-9(5)) Farrar, Straus & Giroux.

Dezago, Todd. To the Rescue. Mawhinney, Art, illus. 2006. (Firehouse Tales Ser.). 32p. (J). act. bk. ed. 4.99 (978-1-4169-1846-2(9) , Simon Scribbles) Simon & Schuster Children's Publishing.

Dora & Diego's Adventures! 2007. (Dora the Explorer Ser.). 80p. (J). 6.99 (***978-1-4169-3532-2(0)*** , Simon Spotlight/Nickelodeon) Simon & Schuster Children's Publishing.

Edwards, Nicholas. Santa Paws, Come Home. 2000. (Santa Paws Ser.: No. 4). 208p. (J). (gr. 3-7). pap. 4.99 (978-0-590-37990-8(9) , Scholastic Paperbacks) Scholastic, Inc.

Ehlin, Gina. Emma & Friends; Emma Rescues Cali. Ayzenberg, Nina, illus. l.t. ed. 2006. 24p. (J). 17.99 (978-1-59879-113-6(3)); per. 10.99 (978-1-59879-112-9(5)) Lifevest Publishing, Inc.

Fleetwood, Tamela. Nellie Jelly & the Jelly Well, No. 1. 2000. 32p. (J). lib. bdg. 10.95 (978-0-9702128-0-1(1)) Odditeas, Inc.

Free Wheelin' Coloring/Activity Book (English) 2005. (Illus.). (J). (978-0-9770455-7-0(9)) Educational Adventures.

Gleitzman, Morris. Sticky Beak. l.t. ed. 2005. 200p. (J). pap. (978-0-7540-6180-9(9) , CLP 374) BBC Audio.

Gralley, Jean. The Moon Came down on Milk Street. rev. ed. 2004. (Illus.). 32p. (J). 16.95 (978-0-8050-7266-2(7) , Holt, Henry & Co. Bks. For Young Readers) Holt, Henry & Co.

Hall, Marjory. The Gold-Lined Box. 2003. 224p. 11.95 (978-0-9714612-6-0(0)) Green Mansion Pr. LLC.

Harcourt School Publishers Staff. Bird on the Beach: Take-Home Book. 2001. (Collections Ser.). (Illus.). (J). pap. 1.90 (978-0-15-319490-0(1)) Harcourt Schl. Pubs.

—The Bird on the Beach Below Level. 3rd ed. 2002. (Trophies Reading Program Ser.). (Illus.). pap. 5.10 (978-0-15-323228-2(5)) Harcourt Schl. Pubs.

—Cuando Vinron... Below Level. 3rd ed. 2002. (Trofeos Ser.). (SPA., Illus.). pap. 6.80 (978-0-15-324062-1(8)) Harcourt Schl. Pubs.

—The Pony Express. 3rd ed. 2002. (Horizons Ser.). (Illus.). (J). pap. 5.50 (978-0-15-333421-4(5)) Harcourt Schl. Pubs.

—Rescue at Fox Creek On Level. 3rd ed. 2002. (Trophies Reading Program Ser.). (Illus.). pap. 5.10 (978-0-15-323350-0(8)) Harcourt Schl. Pubs.

—Rescue from an Avalanche Advanced Level: A Young Girl's Journal. 3rd ed. 2002. (Trophies Reading Program Ser.). (Illus.). pap. 5.10 (978-0-15-323467-5(9)) Harcourt Schl. Pubs.

Hazen, Lynn E. Buzz Bumble to the Rescue. Newton, Jill, illus. 2005. 32p. (J). 15.95 (978-1-58234-932-9(0) , Bloomsbury Children) Bloomsbury Publishing.

Holsather, Kent /Wilson. Sara's Moon. 2007. (Illus.). 176p. (YA). per. 12.95 (***978-0-9729101-3-2(1)***) Lonejack Mountain Pr.

Hubbard, Coleen. Mountain Dog Rescue. 2000. (Dog Tales Ser.: No. 3). (Illus.). 160p. (J). (gr. 3-7). pap. 4.50 (978-0-590-18977-4(8) , Scholastic Paperbacks) Scholastic, Inc.

—Mountain Dog Rescue. 1999. (978-0-606-18578-3(X)) Tandem Library Bks.

Hulk to the Rescue. 2003. (J). per. (978-1-57657-811-7(9)) Paradise Pr., Inc.

Hutchins, Hazel J. Sidewalk Rescue. 2004. (ps-2). lib. bdg. 15.25 (978-0-613-78420-7(0)) Tandem Library Bks.

John Brown Publishing Ltd. Diego's Rescue Games: Follow the Reader Level I. 2007. (Go, Diego, Go! Ser.). 24p. (J). 24.99 (***978-1-4169-4989-3(5)*** , Simon Scribbles) Simon & Schuster Children's Publishing.

Johns, W. E. Biggles Gets His Men. 2001. 166p. pap. (978-0-7551-0820-6(5)) House of Stratus, Inc.

Johnson, Sandi & Fefie, Flora. Zemo to the Rescue: Dorp 7 Rock Band. l.t. ed. 2003. (Illus.). 15p. (J). (gr. k-5). spiral bd. 4.99 (978-1-929063-25-3(3) , 327) Moons & Stars Publishing For Children.

Kent, Jennifer McGrath. Chocolate River Rescue. 2007. 88p. (J). (gr. 2-5). pap. (***978-1-55109-600-1(5)***) Nimbus Publishing, Ltd.

Kindersley, Dorling. Go Diego Go Essential Gd. 2008. 48p. 8.99 (***978-0-7566-3501-5(2)***) Dorling Kindersley Publishing, Inc.

King, Jamie R. Kodi's Heroic Journey. Lemmon, David, illus. 1999. (Zoooo Stories Ser.). (J). (978-1-893993-01-3(9)) Medias & Co., Inc.

Kita, Suzanne. Three Whales Who Won the Heart of the World. Sundram, Steve, illus. 2000. (ENG & JPN.). (J). 12.99 (978-0-89610-336-8(6)) Island Heritage Publishing.

Lester, Alison. The Snow Pony. 2006. 208p. (J). (gr. 5-9). pap. 5.95 (978-0-618-77125-7(5) , Walter Lorraine) Houghton Mifflin Co. Trade & Reference Div.

Maher, Alex, illus. Diego's Safari Rescue. 2007. (Go, Diego, Go! Ser.). 24p. (J). pap. 3.99 (***978-1-4169-3818-7(4)*** , Simon Spotlight/Nickelodeon) Simon & Schuster Children's Publishing.

—El safari de Diego (Diego's Safari Rescue) 2007. (Go, Diego, Go! Ser.). 24p. (J). pap. 3.99 (***978-1-4169-5998-4(X)*** , Libros Para Ninos) Simon & Schuster Children's Publishing.

Marlow, Herb. Bruno to the Rescue. Rainbolt, Juliette, illus. l.t. ed. 2000. 26p. (J). (gr. k-9). lib. bdg. 14.95 (978-0-9666858-6-2(5)) Four Seasons Bks., Inc.

Martin, Ann M. Mary Anne Saves the Day. 2007. (BSC Graphix Ser.: No. 3). 160p. (J). pap. 8.99 (***978-0-439-88516-4(7)*** , Graphix) Scholastic, Inc.

McKendry, Sam. To the Rescue! 2007. 6p. 9.95 (***978-1-58117-562-2(0)*** , Intervisual/Piggy Toes) Dalmatian Pr.

Morgan, Michaela. Shy Shark. Gomez, Elena, illus. 2005. 24p. (J). lib. bdg. 22.65 (***978-1-59646-722-4(3)***) Dingles & Co.

Moscovich, Rotem & Saric, Lazar. Curious George Snowy Day. 2007. (Illus.). 24p. (J). (gr. k-ps). 3.99 (***978-0-618-80043-8(3)***) Houghton Mifflin Co.

Nimmo, Jenny. Charlie Bone & the Beast. 2007. (Children of the Red King Ser.: Bk. 6). 464p. (J). 10.99 (***978-0-439-84665-3(X)*** , Orchard Bks.) Scholastic, Inc.

Noland, Charles. The Adventures of Drew & Ellie: The Daring Rescue. Moyer, Tom, illus. 2nd ed. 2006. (J). per. 7.95 (***978-0-9789297-2-5(1)***) TMD Enterprises.

O'Donnell, Liam. Duncan, a Brave Rescue. Hynes, Robert, illus. 2005. (Pet Tales Ser.). 32p. (J). (ps-2). 4.95 incl. cd-rom (978-1-59249-291-6(6) , 1B001); 2.95 (978-1-59249-292-3(4) , 1B003) Soundprints.

Offen, Hilda. Rita the Rescuer. (Illus.). 32p. (J). 13.95 (978-0-241-00298-8(2) , Hamilton, Hamish) Penguin Bks., Ltd. GBR. *Dist:* Trafalgar Square Publishing.

Perrow, Angeli. Lighthouse Dog to the Rescue. Harris, Emily, illus. 2000. 30p. pap. 9.95 (978-0-89272-600-4(8)); 32p. (J). 14.95 (978-0-89272-487-1(0)) Down East Bks.

—Lighthouse Dog to the Rescue. 2000. (gr. k-3). lib. bdg. 18.75 (978-0-613-65727-3(6)) Tandem Library Bks.

Peterson Haddix, Margaret. Among the Brave. 2004. (Shadow Children Ser.). 132p. (J). lib. bdg. 20.00 (***978-1-4242-0392-5(9)***) Fitzgerald Bks.

Pippin, Sheila. Katrina: Through Mango's Eyes. 2007. (J). 12.95 (*978-1-56167-956-0(9)*) American Literary Pr.

Q. T. Pie's Rescue Adventure. 2003. (Illus.). 36p. (J). (ps-6). mass mkt. 4.99 (978-0-9670875-3-5(8) , 313-533-7383) SanPaul Group, LLC, The.

Raintree Steck-Vaughn Staff. The Amazing Animal Rescue Team. 1999. (J). pap. 35.60 (978-0-7398-0891-7(5)) Steck-Vaughn.

Ransom, Candice F. Danger at Sand Cave. Schofield, Den, illus. (On My Own History Ser.). 2005. 48p. (gr. 2-5). pap. 23.93 (978-1-57505-454-4(X)); 2000. 47p. (J). (gr. 1-4). lib. bdg. (978-1-57505-379-0(9) , Carolrhoda Bks.) Lerner Publishing Group.

—Danger at Sand Cave. 2000. (gr. k-3). lib. bdg. 14.10 (978-0-613-68228-2(9)) Tandem Library Bks.

Rescue! 6 Packs. Pouch - Level L. (Lighthouse Ser.). 16p. (gr. 2 up). 28.00 (978-0-7578-0880-7(8)) Rigby Education.

Rey, H. A. & Rey, Margret. Curious George to the Rescue: A Slide & Peek Adventure. 2007. (Curious George Ser.). (Illus.). 12p. (J). (ps-k). bds. 8.99 (978-0-618-72401-7(X)) Houghton Mifflin Co. Trade & Reference Div.

Ricci, Christine. Prairie Dog Rescue. Zalme, Ron, illus. 2007. (Go, Diego, Go! Ser.). 24p. (J). pap. 3.99 (*978-1-4169-3363-2(8)* , Simon Spotlight/Nickelodeon) Simon & Schuster Children's Publishing.

Richards, Pat. Bardolph Bedivere Wolf Returns. Richards, Charles, illus. 2007. 42p. (J). (*978-0-9790796-4-1(0)*) PJR Assocs., Ltd.

Richardson, Nigel. The Wrong Hands. 2008. 272p. (YA). (gr. 7). mass mkt. 6.50 (*978-0-553-49500-3(3)* , Laurel Leaf) Random Hse. Children's Bks.

Rigby. Golden Lasso. (gr. k-1). 23.00 (978-0-7635-9021-5(5)) Rigby Education.

Rogers, Wanda Gayle. Miss Bean & the Great Tricycle Rescue: The Great Tricycle Rescue. 2007. (J). 7.95 (*978-1-59872-735-7(4)*) Instantpublisher.com.

Schoberle, Cecile. To the Rescue! Mones, Isidre et al, illus. 2003. (Matchbox Ser.: Vol. 1). 32p. (J). 3.99 (978-0-689-85898-7(1) , Little Simon) Simon & Schuster Children's Publishing.

Scholastic, Inc. Staff. Here Comes Diego!, Bks. 7-12. 2007. (Go, Diego, Go! Phonics Reading Program Ser.). 112p. (J). pap. 5.99 (*978-0-439-93228-8(9)*) Scholastic, Inc.

—Let's Go Rescue! 2007. (Go, Diego, Go! Phonics Reading Program Ser.: Bks. 1-6). 112p. (J). pap. 5.99 (*978-0-439-93229-5(7)*) Scholastic, Inc.

—Meet the Rescue Heroes. 2002. (gr. k-3). lib. bdg. 11.80 (978-0-613-72122-6(5)) Tandem Library Bks.

—Rescue Heroes No. 2: Movie Reader. 2004. (Rescue Heroes Ser.). 32p. (J). pap. 3.99 (978-0-439-62511-1(4)) Scholastic, Inc.

Sheeley, Jill. Rescue on Star Mountain. 2000. (Adventures of Fraser the Yellow Dog Ser.). (Illus.). (J). 15.95 (978-0-9609108-6-1(7)) Courtney Pr.

Smith, Alexander McCall. Akimbo & the Crocodile Man. Pham, LeUyen, illus. 2007. 80p. (J). pap. 4.95 (*978-1-59990-033-9(5)* , Bloomsbury Children) Bloomsbury Publishing.

Smith, Roland. Jack's Run. 2007. 256p. (gr. 5-17). pap. 5.99 (*978-1-4231-0407-0(2)*) Hyperion Pr.

Spiotta-DiMare, Loren. Norman to the Rescue. 1999. (Humane Society of the United States Animal Tales Ser.). (J). (gr. 1-4). pap. 9.95 incl. audio (978-1-58021-055-3(4)) Benefactory, Inc., The.

Stainton, Sue. The Lighthouse Cat. Mortimer, Anne, illus. 2004. 32p. (J). (ps-2). 15.99 (978-0-06-009604-5(7)) HarperCollins Pubs.

Steele, Michael Anthony. Calling All Ham-Hams! 2003. (gr. k-3). lib. bdg. 11.80 (978-0-613-72221-6(3)) Tandem Library Bks.

Szymanski, Lois K. A Pony to the Rescue. 2007. (Charming Ponies Ser.). 96p. (J). (gr. 2-5). pap. 4.99 (*978-0-06-128869-2(1)* , Harper Festival) HarperCollins Pubs.

Thomas, Blair L. The Sabatini Prophecy. 2008. (ENG.). 496p. (YA). 8.99 (*978-0-9760237-4-6(1)*) Axiom Hse.

Varela, Barry. Gizmo. Briant, Ed, illus. 2007. 32p. (J). (ps-3). 16.95 (978-1-59643-115-7(6)) Roaring Brook Pr.

Villalobos, Ligiah. Save the Elephants. Zalme, Ronald, illus. 2007. (Go, Diego, Go! Ser.). 24p. (J). pap. 3.99 (*978-1-4169-3821-7(4)* , Simon Spotlight) Simon & Schuster Children's Publishing.

Wallace, Bill. Skinny-Dipping at Monster Lake. (Illus.). 224p. (J). 2004. pap. 4.99 (978-0-689-85151-3(0) , Aladdin); 2003. 16.95 (978-0-689-85150-6(2)) Simon & Schuster Children's Publishing.

Watson, Jude. Underworld. 2005. (Star Wars Ser.: No. 3). 137p. (J). lib. bdg. 20.00 (*978-1-4242-0776-3(2)*) Fitzgerald Bks.

Wax, Wendy. Diego & Papi to the Rescue. Hom, John, illus. 2007. (Go, Diego, Go! Ser.). 24p. (J). pap. 3.99 (978-1-4169-2781-5(6) , Simon Spotlight/Nickelodeon) Simon & Schuster Children's Publishing.

West, Tracey & Artful Doodlers Limited Staff. Dolphin Rescue. 2006. (Totally Spies! Ser.). (Illus.). 16p. (J). pap. 5.99 (978-1-4169-1560-7(5) , Simon Spotlight) Simon & Schuster Children's Publishing.

Wood, Audrey & Wood, Bruce. Alphabet Rescue. 2006. (Illus.). 40p. (J). pap. 15.99 (978-0-439-85316-3(8) , Blue Sky Pr., The) Scholastic, Inc.

Zocchi, Judy. Paulie & Sasha: The Rescue. Vannozzi, Don, illus. 2001. (Paulie & Sasha Ser.). 32p. (J). lib. bdg. 23.00 (978-1-891997-15-0(7)) Dingles & Co.

RESEARCH

see also Discoveries in Science; Learning and Scholarship also subjects with the subdivision Research, e.g. Agriculture—Research; Medicine—Research

Albee, Michael J. Elements of Research: The Student's Guide to Avoiding Plagiarism in the Information Age. 2003. (Illus.). 140p. per. (978-0-9745405-0-4(1)) Albee, Michael.

Arnone, Marilyn P. Mac, Information Detective, In— the Curious Kids & the Squiggly Question. Stockley, Gerry, illus. 2005. 32p. (J). (*978-1-59158-296-0(2)*) Libraries Unlimited, Inc.

Arnone, Marilyn P. Mac, Information Detective, in the Curious Kids—Digging for Answers: A Storybook Approach to Introducing Research Skills. Stockley, Gerry & Reeves, Andrea, illus. 2006. 71p. (J). 35.00 (978-1-59158-188-8(5)) Libraries Unlimited, Inc.

Arnone, Marilyn P. & Coatney, Sharon. MAC, Information Detective, in the Case Of— Curious Kids & the Squiggly Question: Picture Book. 2005. 32p. (J). 35.00 (978-1-59158-189-5(3)) Libraries Unlimited, Inc.

Arnone, Marilyn P. & Stockley, Gerry, illus. Mac, Information Detective, in the Curious Kids— Digging for Answers: A Storybook Approach to Introducing Research Skills. 2006. 71p. (J). (*978-1-59158-196-3(6)*) Libraries Unlimited, Inc.

Blandford, Elisabeth. How to Write the Best Research Paper Ever. 1998. (Illus.). 112p. (gr. 8-12). pap. 12.95 (978-1-880505-54-0(1) , CLC0201) Pieces of Learning.

Chappell, Rachel M. Solving Science Questions: A Book about the Scientific Process. 2008. (J). (*978-1-60044-542-2(X)*) Rourke Publishing, LLC.

Doris. Life at the Top. 1999. (Illus.). (J). pap. (978-0-7398-2480-1(5)) Steck-Vaughn.

Doudna, Kelly. I'll Use Information for My Explanation! (Illus.). 24p. (J). 2007. 19.93 (978-1-59928-588-7(6)); 2006. (978-1-59928-589-4(4)) ABDO Publishing Co.

Elliott, Rebecca S. & Elliott, James. Painless Research Projects. 1998. (Barron's Painless Ser.). (Illus.). 288p. pap. 11.99 (978-0-7641-0297-4(4)) Barron's Educational Series, Inc.

Gravois, Michael. 35 Ready-to-Go Ways to Publish Students' Research & Writing: Complete How-To's. 1998. (Illus.). 80p. pap. 10.95 (978-0-590-05014-2(1)) Scholastic, Inc.

Hamilton, John. Newspapers. 2005. (Straight to the Source Ser.). (Illus.). 32p. (J). (gr. k-6). lib. bdg. 22.78 (978-1-59197-547-2(6)) ABDO Publishing Co.

—Primary & Secondary Sources. 2005. (Straight to the Source Ser.). (J). (gr. k-6). lib. bdg. 22.78 (978-1-59197-548-9(4)) ABDO Publishing Co.

Heiligman, Deborah. The New York Public Library Kid's Guide to Research. 1998. (Illus.). 134p. (YA). (gr. 4-9). pap. 14.95 (978-0-590-30715-4(0) , Scholastic Reference) Scholastic, Inc.

Hyland, Tony. Scientific & Medical Robots. 2007. (J). (*978-1-59920-118-4(6)*) Smart Apple Media.

Iim: Independent Investigation Method Teacher Manual with Companion CD. 2005. spiral bd. 59.95 incl. audio compact disk (978-1-57652-024-6(2)) Active Learning Systems, LLC.

James, Elizabeth. How to Write a School Report. 1998. (School Survival Guide Ser.). 96p. (gr. 3-7). 15.00 (978-0-688-16132-3(4)) HarperCollins Pubs.

James, Elizabeth & Barkin, Carol. How to Write Super School Reports. 1998. (School Survival Guide Ser.). 90p. 15.00 (978-0-06-881632-4(4) , Harper San Francisco) HarperCollins Pubs.

Mackall, Joe. Research & Information Management. 2nd ed. 2004. (Career Skills Library). (Illus.). 128p. (YA). (gr. 6-12). 21.95 (978-0-8160-5518-0(1) , Ferguson Publishing Co.) Facts On File, Inc.

Markle, Sandra. Super Cool Science: South Pole Stations, Past, Present, & Future. 1998. (Illus.). 32p. (J). (gr. 3-7). 16.95 (978-0-8027-8470-4(4)); lib. bdg. 17.85 (978-0-8027-8471-1(2)) Walker & Co.

Rosenzweig, Charlotte, et al. The Path to Research. 2005. (Illus.). 95p. (YA). (gr. 8 up). pap. 8.95 (978-0-9677925-2-1(5)) Long Beach City Schl. District.

Rt Perspectives Collections, 24 bks. 2004. pap. 162.00 (978-1-4109-1281-7(7)) Raintree.

Schrecengost, Maity. Researching Events. 1998. (Illus.). (gr. 5-9). 20p. tchr. ed., spiral bd. 7.95 (978-1-57950-022-1(6) , P32-34985); 32p. (J). pap. 8.95 (978-1-57950-018-4(8)) Highsmith Inc. (Upstart Bks.).

Schwartz, Linda. Ready to Research, Grades 4-8. Armstrong, Beverly, illus. 1998. 120p. pap., tchr. ed. 12.95 (978-0-88160-321-7(X) , LW-388, Learning Works, The) Creative Teaching Pr., Inc.

Somervill, Barbara A. Collecting Information. 2007. (Scientific Processes Ser.). (Illus.). 24p. (J). pap. (978-1-4042-2193-2(X)); lib. bdg. (978-1-4042-3484-0(5)) Rosen Publishing Group, Inc., The. (PowerKids Pr.).

—Organizing & Evaluating Information. 2007. (Scientific Processes Ser.). (Illus.). 24p. (J). pap. (978-1-4042-2196-3(4) , PowerKids Pr.) Rosen Publishing Group, Inc., The.

Souter, Gerry, et al. Researching on the Internet Using Search Engines, Bulletin Boards, & Listservs. 2003. (Internet Library). (Illus.). 64p. (J). (gr. 4-12). lib. bdg. 22.60 (978-0-7660-2081-8(9)) Enslow Pubs., Inc.

Steck-Vaughn Staff. Noises in the Night: Teacher's Resource Binder. 1999. (J). pap., tchr. ed. (978-0-7398-2475-7(9)) Steck-Vaughn.

Suid, Murray. Research Start-Ups. 1999. (Illus.). 96p. (J). pap. 11.95 (978-1-57612-116-0(X)) Monday Morning Bks., Inc.

Weitzman, David L. Brown Paper School Book: My Backyard History Book. 2006. 128p. (J). pap. 12.99 (978-0-316-05981-7(1)) Little Brown & Co.

Whitley, Peggy, et al. 99 Jumpstarts for Kids: Getting Started in Research. 2003. 240p. (J). pap. 35.00 (978-1-56308-956-5(4) , LU9564) Libraries Unlimited, Inc.

Whitley, Peggy J. & Goodwin, Susan Williams. 99 Jumpstarts for Kids' Science Research. 2005. (Illus.). 264p. pap. 35.00 (978-1-59158-261-8(X) , LU261X) Libraries Unlimited, Inc.

Wiseman, Douglas C. Research Strategies for Education. 1998. (Illus.). 592p. (C). pap. 85.95 (978-0-7668-0013-7(X)) Thomson Wadsworth.

Wishau, Jan. Investigator. 2005. 48p. 9.95 (978-1-59363-083-6(2)) Prufrock Pr.

Wolinsky, Art. Internet Power Research Using the Big6 Approach. 2002. (Internet Library Ser.). (Illus.). 64p. (YA). (gr. 4-12). lib. bdg. 22.60 (978-0-7660-2094-8(0)) Enslow Pubs., Inc.

RESEARCH—VOCATIONAL GUIDANCE

Ferguson. Mastering Career Skills: Research & Information Management. 2nd rev. ed. (Mastering Career Skills Ser.). 128p. pap. 12.95 (*978-0-8160-7118-0(7)* , Checkmark Bks.) Facts On File, Inc.

RESIDENCES

see Architecture, Domestic; Houses

RESOURCES

see Marine Resources

RESPIRATION

Andrews, Barbara. Discover the Respiratory System. 2006. pap. 39.00 (*978-1-4108-6514-4(2)*) Benchmark Education Co.

Aparato Respiratorio Soplo de Vida. (Coleccion Mundo Invisible).Tr. of Respiratory System. (SPA.). (YA). (gr. 5-8). pap. 8.00 (978-958-04-3224-1(4)) Norma S.A. COL. *Dist:* Distribuidora Norma, Inc., Lectorum Pubns., Inc.

Aparato respiratorio soplo de Vida. (SPA.). (J). 10.00 (978-84-342-1909-0(3)) Parramon Ediciones S.A. ESP. *Dist:* Distribuidora Norma, Inc.

Ballard, Carol. Lungs. 2002. (Body Focus Ser.). (Illus.). 48p. (J). pap. (978-1-4034-0454-1(2)) Heinemann Library.

—The Lungs & Breathing. 2005. (Exploring the Human Body Ser.). (Illus.). 32p. (J). (gr. 4-7). lib. bdg. 24.95 (978-0-7377-3020-3(X) , Greenhaven Pr., Inc.) Thomson Gale.

Breathe in, Breathe Out. (Amazing Body Ser.). 24p. (J). 7.95 (978-1-4048-0505-7(2)) Picture Window Bks.

Donavan, Barbar A. Body Systems: Respiratory & Circulatory. 2005. (Navigators Ser.). (J). pap. 42.00 (*978-1-4108-5084-3(6)*) Benchmark Education Co.

Frost, Helen. The Respiratory System. Saunders-Smith, Gail, ed. 2000. (Human Body Systems Ser.). (Illus.). 24p. (J). (gr. k-1). lib. bdg. 15.93 (978-0-7368-0652-7(0) , Pebble Bks.) Capstone Pr., Inc.

Furgang, Kathy. My Lungs. 2001. (My Body Ser.). (Illus.). 24p. (J). lib. bdg. 19.95 (978-0-8239-5575-6(3) , PowerKids Pr.) Rosen Publishing Group, Inc., The.

Ganeri, Anita. Your Lungs. Shott, Steve, photos by. 2003. (How Your Body Works). (Illus.). 32p. (J). (gr. 2 up). lib. bdg. 23.33 (978-0-8368-3634-9(0)) Stevens, Gareth Inc.

Gold, Susan Dudley. The Respiratory System. 2003. (Human Body Library Ser.). (Illus.). 48p. (J). (gr. 4-10). lib. bdg. 23.93 (978-0-7660-2021-4(5)) Enslow Pubs., Inc.

Gray, Susan Heinrichs. The Respiratory System. 2003. (Body Systems Ser.). (Illus.). 32p. (J). (gr. 2-6). 27.07 (978-1-59296-040-8(5)) Child's World, Inc.

Green, Jen. Breathing. 2005. (Illus.). 32p. (J). (gr. 3-7). lib. bdg. 27.10 (978-1-59604-054-0(8)) Stargazer Bks.

Hayhurst, Chris. The Lungs: Learning How We Breathe. 2002. (3-D Library of the Human Body). (Illus.). 48p. (YA). (gr. 5-8). lib. bdg. 26.50 (978-0-8239-3534-5(5) , Rosen Central) Rosen Publishing Group, Inc., The.

Holt, Rinehart and Winston Staff. Holt Science & Technology Chapter 23: Life Science: Circulation & Respiration, 5th ed. 2004. (Illus.). pap. 12.86 (978-0-03-030239-8(0)) Holt, Rinehart & Winston.

Houghton, Gillian. The Respiratory System. 2007. (How Your Body Works). (Illus.). 24p. (J). pap. (978-1-4042-2180-2(8)); lib. bdg. (978-1-4042-3471-0(3)) Rosen Publishing Group, Inc., The. (PowerKids Pr.).

How Does It Breathe?, 6 Packs. (gr. k-1). 23.00 (978-0-7635-9036-9(3)) Rigby Education.

Jakab, Cheryl. The Respiratory System. 2006. (Our Body Ser.). (Illus.). 32p. (J). (gr. 3-5). lib. bdg. 27.10 (978-1-58340-736-3(7)) Smart Apple Media.

Jango-Cohen, Judith. El Aparato Respiratorio. 2006. (Libros Sobre el Cuerpo Humano para Madrugadores Ser.). (ENG & SPA.). 48p. (J). 25.26 (978-0-8225-6256-6(1) , Ediciones Lerner) Lerner Publishing Group.

—The Respiratory System. 2005. (Early Bird Body Systems Ser.). (Illus.). 48p. (J). (gr. 2-4). lib. bdg. 25.26 (978-0-8225-1250-9(5)) Lerner Publishing Group.

Lee, Justin. Everything You Need to Know about Cystic Fibrosis. 2001. (Need to Know Library). (Illus.). 64p. (YA). (gr. 4-6). lib. bdg. 25.25 (978-0-8239-3321-1(0)) Rosen Publishing Group, Inc., The.

LeVert, Suzanne. The Lungs. 2001. (Kaleidoscope Ser.). (Illus.). 48p. (J). (gr. 3 up). lib. bdg. 25.64 (978-0-7614-1307-3(3) , Benchmark Bks.) Cavendish, Marshall Corp.

Lindeen, Carol. The Lungs Inside & Out. 2007. 24p. (J). (978-0-7368-6692-7(2) , Pebble Bks.) Capstone Pr., Inc.

Llamas, Andreu. Respiration & Circulation. Rizo, Luis, illus. 1998. (Human Body Ser.). 32p. (J). (gr. 5 up). lib. bdg. 24.67 (978-0-8368-2110-9(6)) Stevens, Gareth Inc.

Lungs. 2001. (Human Anatomy Ser.). (J). (gr. k-12). vinyl bd. 4.95 (978-1-58845-084-5(8)) School Specialty Publishing.

Parker, Steve. Heart, Lungs, & Blood. 2004. (Our Bodies Ser.). (Illus.). 48p. (J). lib. bdg. 28.56 (978-0-7398-6621-4(4)) Raintree.

—Pump It Up! Respiration & Circulation. 2006. (Illus.). 48p. (J). (978-1-4109-1878-9(5)); pap. (978-1-4109-1885-7(8)) Steck-Vaughn.

Parker, Victoria. Air. 2006. (Illus.). 24p. (J). (978-1-4034-7882-5(1)); pap. (978-1-4034-7888-7(0)) Steck-Vaughn.

Penchina, Sharon R. I Take a Deeep Breath. 2006. (I Am a Lovable Me! Ser.). (Illus.). 32p. 12.95 (978-0-9740684-6-6(2)) 2 Imagine.

Petrie, Kristin. The Respiratory System. 2007. (Checkerboard Science Library). (Illus.). 32p. (J). 22.78 (978-1-59679-713-0(4)) ABDO Publishing Co.

Ramen, Fred. SARS (Serere Acute Respiratory Syndrome) 2005. (Illus.). 64p. (YA). lib. bdg. 26.50 (978-1-4042-0258-0(7)) Rosen Publishing Group, Inc., The.

Reader's Digest Editors, contrib. by. The Lungs & Respiratory System. 2002. (Your Body, Your Health Ser.). (Illus.). 160p. (J). (978-0-7621-0458-1(9)) Reader's Digest Assn., Inc., The.

Roca, Nuria & Serrano, Marta. The Respiratory System. Halton, Frances, ed. (Illus.). 32p. (978-0-7451-5282-0(1) , Cherrytree Books) Evans Publishing Group.

Ross, Veronica. Breathing. 2002. (My Healthy Body Ser.). (Illus.). 32p. (J). lib. bdg. 24.25 (978-1-930643-84-0(5)) Chrysalis Education.

Royston. Breathing. 2004. (My Amazing Body Ser.). (Illus.). pap. 7.50 (978-1-4109-0948-0(4)) Raintree.

—Breathing 6-Pack. 2004. (My Amazing Body Ser.). (Illus.). pap. 40.50 (978-1-4109-0955-8(7)) Raintree.

Royston, Angela. Breathing. 2004. (My Amazing Body Ser.). (Illus.). 32p. 25.70 (978-1-4109-0479-9(2)) Raintree.

—Why Do I Sneeze? 2003. (Body Matters Ser.). (Illus.). 32p. pap. 7.50 (978-1-4034-0460-2(7)) Heinemann Library.

—Why Do I Sneeze? And Other Questions about Breathing. 2003. (Body Matters Ser.). (Illus.). 32p. (J). (gr. 3-5). lib. bdg. 24.22 (978-1-4034-0205-9(1)) Heinemann Library.

—Why Do I Sneeze? And Other Questions about Breathing. 2003. (gr. 3-6). lib. bdg. 15.90 (978-0-613-70687-2(0)) Tandem Library Bks.

Simon, Seymour. Lungs: Your Respiratory System. 2007. (Illus.). 32p. (J). (gr. 3-6). 16.99 (978-0-06-054654-0(9)); lib. bdg. 17.89 (978-0-06-054655-7(7)) HarperCollins Pubs.

Spilsbury, Louise & Spilsbury, Richard. Life Processes: From Reproduction to Respiration. 2004. (Science Answers Ser.). (Illus.). 32p. (J). pap. 7.50 (978-1-4034-5513-0(9)); lib. bdg. 24.22 (978-1-4034-4767-8(5)) Heinemann Library.

Taylor-Butler, Christine. The Respiratory System. 2007. (True Booktrade;: Health & the Human Body Ser.). 48p. (J). spiral bd. 26.00 (*978-0-531-16862-2(X)* , Children's Pr.) Scholastic Library Publishing.

Walker, Pam & Wood, Elaine. The Respiratory System. 2002. (Understanding the Human Body Ser.). (Illus.). 112p. (J). 29.95 (978-1-59018-153-9(0) , Lucent Bks.) Thomson Gale.

Walker, Richard. How We Breathe. 2004. (Body Science Ser.). (J). lib. bdg. 27.10 (978-1-58340-456-0(2)) Smart Apple Media.

Weitzman, Elizabeth. Let's Talk about Having Asthma. 1998. (Conflict Resolution Library). (Illus.). 24p. (J). (gr. k-4). pap. 6.95 (978-1-56838-272-2(3)) Hazelden Publishing & Educational Services.

Whittemore, Susan. The Respiratory System. 2003. (Your Body, How It Works). (Illus.). 112p. (gr. 9-13). 31.95 (978-0-7910-7627-9(X) , Chelsea Hse.) Facts On File, Inc.

Your Lungs. (Your Body Ser.). 24p. (J). 6.95 (978-0-7368-3353-0(6)) Capstone Pr., Inc.

RESTAURANTS

Ancona, George. Let's Eat. 2003. (J). (978-0-7636-1805-6(5)) Candlewick Pr.

Aronson, Virginia. Dave Thomas. 1999. (Overcoming Adversity Ser.). (Illus.). 128p. (YA). pap. 9.95 (978-0-7910-5303-4(2) , Chelsea Hse.) Facts On File, Inc.

Canizares, Susan & Berger, Samantha. Restaurant. 2000. (Placebook Ser.). (Illus.). (J). pap. (978-0-439-15366-9(2)) Scholastic, Inc.

Frisch, Aaron. The Story of McDonald's. 2008. (J). (*978-1-58341-606-8(4)* , Creative Education) Creative Co., The.

Hall, Margaret. Ray Kroc. 2003. (Lives & Times Ser.). (Illus.). (J). 24p. pap. (978-1-4034-4258-1(4)); 32p. lib. bdg. 22.79 (978-1-4034-3251-3(1)) Heinemann Library.

Kishel, Ann-Marie. Server. 2007. (First Step Nonfiction Ser.). (J). pap. (978-0-8225-6847-6(0)) Lerner Publishing Group.

Kuntz, Lynn & Fleming, Jan. American Grub: Eats for Kids from All Fifty States. Hicks, Mark A., illus. 2003. 80p. (YA). pap. 7.95 (978-1-58685-260-3(4)) Gibbs Smith, Publisher.

Minden, Cecilia. Restaurants by the Numbers. 2008. (J). lib. bdg. 25.26 (*978-1-60279-009-4(4)*) Cherry Lake Publishing.

Peacock, Nancy. Dave Thomas. 1999. (Overcoming Adversity Ser.). (Illus.). 128p. (YA). (gr. 5 up). 21.95 (978-0-7910-5302-7(4) , Chelsea Hse.) Facts On File, Inc.

Radabaugh, Melinda Beth. Going to a Restaurant. 2003. (First Time Ser.). (Illus.). 24p. (ps-1). (J). lib. bdg. 18.50 (978-1-4034-0226-4(4)); pap. 5.25 (978-1-4034-0465-7(8)) Heinemann Library.

—Going to a Restaurant. 2003. (ps-2). lib. bdg. 13.30 (978-0-613-60879-4(8)) Tandem Library Bks.

—Voy al restaurante. (La Primera Vez (First Time) Ser.). 24p. pap. 5.25 (978-1-4034-0472-5(0)) Heinemann Library.

Ready Reader Staff. A Fun Place to Eat, 6 bks., set, Level 6, Bk. 27. 2003. (J). (ps-3). pap. 30.95 (978-0-8136-2059-6(7)) Modern Curriculum Pr.

P Q R

Galvan, Nelida. La Revolucion para Ninos. Garcia, Modesto, illus. 2002. (Historia para Ninos Ser.). 123p. (J). pap. 9.95 (978-970-643-514-9(X)) Selector, S.A. de C.V. MEX. *Dist:* Lectorum Pubns., Inc.

Gay, Kathlyn. The Chinese Nationalist Revolution. 2008. (J). lib. bdg. (***978-0-8225-7601-3(5)***) Twenty First Century Bks.

Hughes, Christopher. Cuba. 2003. (Nations in Conflict Ser.). 48p. (J). (Illus.). 24.95 (978-1-4103-0079-9(X)); 26.19 (978-1-56711-511-6(X)) Thomson Gale. (Blackbirch Pr., Inc.).

Maynard, Christopher. Revolution. 2001. (History News Ser.). (Illus.). 32p. (J). (gr. 3 up). lib. bdg. 24.67 (978-0-8368-2878-8(X)) Stevens, Gareth Inc.

—Revolution News. 2001. (History News Ser.). (Illus.). 32p. (J). (gr. 5-9). pap. 6.99 (978-0-7636-1295-5(2)) Candlewick Pr.

—Revolution News. 2001. (J). (978-0-606-22541-0(2)); (gr. 5-8). lib. bdg. 15.30 (978-0-613-44392-0(6)) Tandem Library Bks.

Naden, Corinne J. & Blue, Rose. Lenin. 2003. (Importance of Ser.). (Illus.). 112p. (J). 32.45 (978-1-59018-233-8(2) , Lucent Bks.) Thomson Gale.

Smolinski, Diane. Important People of the Revolutionary War. 2002. (Americans at War Ser.). (Illus.). 32p. (J). (gr. 4-6). pap. 6.95 (978-1-58810-559-2(8) , 91690) Heinemann Library.

REVOLUTIONS—FICTION

Alvarez, Julia. Antes de Ser Libre. Valenzuela, Liliana, tr. 2004. (SPA.). 192p. (YA). (gr. 7). mass mkt. 5.99 (978-0-375-81545-4(7) , Laurel Leaf) Random Hse. Children's Bks.

—Antes de Ser Libre. 2004. (SPA.). (gr. 7-12). lib. bdg. 14.15 (978-0-613-71931-5(X)) Tandem Library Bks.

—Before We Were Free. 2004. 192p. (J). (gr. 7 up). pap. 38.00 incl. audio (978-1-4000-9017-4(2) , Listening Library) Random Hse. Audio Publishing Group.

—Before We Were Free. (gr. 7-10). 2002. (Illus.). 176p. (J). lib. bdg. 17.99 (978-0-375-91544-4(3) , Knopf Bks. for Young Readers); 2002. (Illus.). 176p. (YA). 15.95 (978-0-375-81544-7(9) , Knopf Bks. for Young Readers); 2004. 192p. (YA). reprint ed. mass mkt. 5.99 (978-0-440-23784-6(X) , Laurel Leaf) Random Hse. Children's Bks.

—Before We Were Free. 2004. (gr. 7-12). lib. bdg. 14.15 (978-0-613-72269-8(8)) Tandem Library Bks.

Olasky, Susan. Will Northaway & the Fight for Freedom. 2005. (Young American Patriots Ser.). 96p. (J). pap. 5.99 (978-1-58134-476-9(7) , Crossway Bibles) Crossway Bks.

Peel, John. Revolution. 2000. (Twenty Ninety-Nine Ser.: Bk. 4). (Illus.). 160p. (J). (gr. 3-7). pap. 4.99 (978-0-439-06033-2(8)) Scholastic, Inc.

Rinaldi, Ann. Cast Two Shadows: The American Revolution in the South. 2004. (Great Episodes Ser.). (Illus.). 304p. (YA). pap. 6.95 (978-0-15-205077-1(9) , Gulliver Bks.) Harcourt Children's Bks.

—Cast Two Shadows: The American Revolution in the South. 2000. (Illus.). (J). 12.65 (978-0-606-18805-0(3)) Tandem Library Bks.

Whelan, Gloria. Angel on the Square. 2003. 304p. (J). (gr. k-9). pap. 7.99 (978-0-06-440879-0(5)) HarperCollins Pubs.

—Angel on the Square. 2003. (gr. 3-6). lib. bdg. 15.30 (978-0-613-60651-6(5)) Tandem Library Bks.

RHETORIC

see also Criticism; Debates and Debating; Letter Writing; Punctuation

Abraham, Philip. Language Development Writing Process. 2004. 48p. pap. 6.95 (978-1-4042-8520-0(2)) Rosen Publishing Group, Inc., The.

Accelerated Writer Classmate Rating Forms. 2004. pap. 39.00 (978-1-59455-124-6(3)) Renaissance Learning, Inc.

Accelerated Writer Informative Library Set (10 Qualities) 2004. cd-rom 3499.00 (978-1-59455-125-3(1)) Renaissance Learning, Inc.

Accelerated Writer Narrative Library Set (10 Qualities) 2004. cd-rom 3499.00 (978-1-59455-126-0(X)) Renaissance Learning, Inc.

Accelerated Writer Persuasive Library Set (10 Qualities) 2004. cd-rom 3499.00 (978-1-59455-127-7(8)) Renaissance Learning, Inc.

Accelerated Writer Rating Practice Forms. 2004. pap. 25.00 (978-1-59455-123-9(5)) Renaissance Learning, Inc.

After School Writing Activities. (100+ Seriestm Ser.). 128p. (gr. 5 up). 12.99 (978-0-7424-1785-4(9) , IFG99032) School Specialty Publishing.

Allen, Susan & Lindaman, Jane. Written Anything Good Lately? Enright, Vicky, illus. 2006. 31p. (J). 15.95 (978-0-7613-2426-3(7) , Millbrook Pr.) Lerner Publishing Group.

Atlee, Nancy. The Absolutely Essential Writing Guide. 2004. (J). per. 13.95 (978-1-883055-68-4(7)) Dandy Lion Pubns.

—Beginning Writing Lab. 2005. 64p. 11.95 (978-1-59363-054-6(9)) Prufrock Pr.

Barnard, Roger & Zemach, Dorothy. Writing for the Real World. 2005. (Illus.). 138p. stu. ed., spiral bd. 18.95 (978-0-19-453814-5(1)) Oxford Univ. Pr., Inc.

Beers. Elements of Literature: Enhanced Online Edition. 5th ed. 2004. (J). (gr. k). 19.93 (978-0-03-037277-3(1)); (J). (gr. 2). 19.93 (978-0-03-037279-7(8)); (J). (gr. 3). 19.93 (978-0-03-037281-0(X)); (J). (gr. 4). 19.93 (978-0-03-037282-7(8)); (gr. 5). 19.93 (978-0-03-037283-4(6)); (gr. 6). 19.93 (978-0-03-037284-1(4)) Holt, Rinehart & Winston.

Bevan, Clare. The Wonderful Gift. 2004. (QEB Start Writing Ser.). (Illus.). 24p. (J). lib. bdg. 15.95 (978-1-59566-022-0(4)) QEB Publishing Inc.

BJU Staff. American Republic Activity S 8. 2004. pap. 14.50 (978-1-57924-333-3(9)) Jones, Bob Univ. Pr.

—American Republic Student Grd8. 2004. 32.00 (978-1-57924-312-8(6)) Jones, Bob Univ. Pr.

—Beginnings Write Now Grd K5. 2004. pap. 5.00 (978-1-57924-846-8(2)) Jones, Bob Univ. Pr.

Bolton, Lesley & Wait, Lea. The Only Writing Series You'll Ever Need: Children's Books. 2007. 192p. pap. 9.95 (978-1-59869-088-0(4)) Adams Media Corp.

Bottino, Marlane. My Language Book for Spelling, Writing & Vocabulary: Level F. Bottino, Marlane, illus. 2000. (My Language Books for Spelling, Writing & Vocabulary Ser.: Vol. 6). (Illus.). (J). (gr. k-6). pap. 6.50 (978-1-893615-07-6(3)) Creative Enterprises.

Boynton, Alice & Blevins, Wiley. Nonfic Passages with Graphic Organizers for Independent Practice: Selections with Graphic Organizers, Assessments & Writing Activities That Help Students Understand the Structures & Features of Nonfiction. 2004. 128p. pap. 17.99 (978-0-439-59019-8(1) , Teaching Strategies) Scholastic, Inc.

Bracey, Ronay. Writing ... Take Small Steps: Improve Students' Writing Skills. 2003. spiral bd. (978-1-933570-84-6(9)) Aardvark Global Publishing.

Brown Conroy, Erin. Writing Skillbuilders Bk. 2: A Fun-Filled Activity Book to Build Strong Handwriting Skills. 2004. (J). spiral bd. 14.95 (978-0-9740981-7-3(5)) Celtic Cross Communications.

—Writing Skillbuilders Bk. 3: A Fun-Filled Activity Book for Beautiful Cursive Handwriting. 2004. (J). spiral bd. 14.95 (978-0-9740981-8-0(3)) Celtic Cross Communications.

Bullard, Lisa. You Can Write a Story! A Story-Writing Recipe for Kids. Melmon, Deborah, illus. 2007. 48p. (J). (gr. 1-4). 16.95 (978-1-58728-587-5(8) , Two Can Publishing) T&N Children's Publishing.

Bush, Valerie Chow, et al. Jump Write In! Creative Writing Exercises for Diverse Communities, Grades 6-12, Grd. 6-12. Tannenbaum, Judith, ed. 2005. (Illus.). 176p. pap. 22.95 (978-0-7879-7777-1(2) , Jossey-Bass) Wiley, John & Sons, Inc.

Cannon Hackett, Teresa. Creative Writing: Using Fairy Tales to Enrich Writing Skills. 2005. 42p. 11.95 (978-1-59363-025-6(5)) Prufrock Pr.

Carroll, Joyce Armstrong, et al. Writing & Grammar: Communication in Action, Bronze Level, 3 vols. 2004. 812p. (YA). (gr. 7 up). 406.00 (978-0-13-037492-9(X)) Prentice Hall Pr.

—Writing & Grammar: Communication in Action, Gold Level, 3 vols. 2004. 988p. (YA). (gr. 9 up). 494.00 (978-0-13-037494-3(6)) Prentice Hall Pr.

—Writing & Grammar: Communication in Action, Platinum Level, 3 vols. 2004. 992p. (YA). (gr. 10 up). 496.00 (978-0-13-116634-9(4)) Prentice Hall Pr.

—Writing & Grammar, Communication in Action Gold Level: Writing in Content Areas & Workplace. 2001. (YA). (gr. 9). pap. 6.97 (978-0-13-052659-5(2)) Prentice Hall PTR.

Center for Learning Network Staff. Thinking, Reading, Writing, Speaking: A Synthesis Approach. 2000. (English Ser.). 157p. (YA). (gr. 7-9). spiral bd. 26.95 (978-1-56077-609-3(9)) Ctr. for Learning, The.

Center for Performance Assessment. Write to Know: Nonfiction Writing Prompts for Algebra. 2005. 128p. pap. 9.95 (978-1-933196-07-7(6)) Advanced Learning Pr.

Conflict Resolution: High-Interest Stories That Encourage Critical Thinking, Creative Writing, & Dialogue. 80p. (gr. 5-8). 9.99 (978-0-7424-0180-8(4) , IF19212) School Specialty Publishing.

Contemporaty Handwriting Book. 2006. (J). pap. (***978-1-57332-384-0(5)***) HighReach Learning, Inc.

Cooper, Terry, ed. 1st Grade Manuscript Handwriting Practice. 2006. 48p. pap. 5.99 (978-0-439-81895-7(8) , Teaching Resources) Scholastic, Inc.

—1st Grade Writing Practice. 2006. 48p. pap. 5.99 (978-0-439-81910-7(5) , Teaching Resources) Scholastic, Inc.

—2nd Grade Manuscript Handwriting Practice. 2006. 48p. pap. 5.99 (978-0-439-81896-4(6) , Teaching Resources) Scholastic, Inc.

—2nd Grade Writing Practice. 2006. 48p. pap. 5.99 (978-0-439-81911-4(3) , Teaching Resources) Scholastic, Inc.

—3rd Grade Cursive Handwriting Practice. 2006. 48p. pap. 5.99 (978-0-439-81897-1(4) , Teaching Resources) Scholastic, Inc.

—3rd Grade Writing Practice. 2006. 48p. pap. 5.99 (978-0-439-81912-1(1) , Teaching Resources) Scholastic, Inc.

—4th Grade Writing Practice. 2006. 48p. pap. 5.99 (978-0-439-81913-8(X) , Teaching Resources) Scholastic, Inc.

Cranium Inc. Staff. Cranium: the Word Worm Book of Outrageous Fun! Write it, Read it, Say It! Baseman, illus. 2006. 38p. (J). (gr. 2-17). 14.99 (978-0-316-05762-2(2)) Little, Brown Bks. for Young Readers.

Culham, Ruth. 6+1 Traits of Writing: The Complete Guide for the Primary Grades; Theory & Practice. 2005. (6+1 Traits of Writing Ser.). (Illus.). 304p. pap. 26.99 (978-0-439-57412-9(9) , Teaching Resources) Scholastic, Inc.

Daily Writing Activities. 24p. (gr. 1 up). 5.99 (978-0-7682-0565-7(4) , FS8480); (gr. 1 up). 3.99 (978-0-7682-0819-1(X) , FS194118); (gr. 2 up). 5.99 (978-0-7682-0566-4(2) , FS8481); (gr. 3 up). 5.99 (978-0-7682-0567-1(0) , FS8482) Schaffer, Frank Pubns.

Davidson, Kay. Becoming a Better Writer Using the Simple 6(TM) Grades 3rd - 6th. 2007. pap. 28.95 (***978-1-931334-98-3(6)***) Pieces of Learning.

—The Simple 6(TM) for K-2 Writers. 2007. pap. 28.95 (***978-1-931334-97-6(8)***) Pieces of Learning.

Diamond, Mark. 6 Tricks to Student Story Writing Success: An Easy Guide for Students, Teachers & Parents. l.t. ed. 2005. (Illus.). 96p. per. 14.95 (978-0-9771470-0-7(2)) Anyone Can Write bks.

Digital Photo Activity Kit Deluxe Vivitar 3700 series Lab-10. 2005. (J). cd-rom 1790.00 (978-1-933229-02-7(0)) APTE, Inc.

Digital Photo Activity Kit Deluxe Vivitar 3700 series Lab-15. 2005. (J). cd-rom 2610.00 (978-1-933229-03-4(9)) APTE, Inc.

Digital Photo Activity Kit Deluxe Vivitar 3700 series Lab-20. 2005. (J). 3260.00 (978-1-933229-04-1(7)) APTE, Inc.

Digital Photo Activity Kit Deluxe Vivitar 3700 series Lab-25. 2005. (J). 3924.00 (978-1-933229-05-8(5)) APTE, Inc.

Digital Photo Activity Kit Deluxe Vivitar 3700 series Lab-30. 2005. (J). 4585.00 (978-1-933229-06-5(3)) APTE, Inc.

Digital Photo Activity Kit Deluxe Vivitar 3700 series Lab-35. 2005. (J). 5239.00 (978-1-933229-07-2(1)) APTE, Inc.

Digital Photo Activity Kit Deluxe Vivitar 3700 series Lab-5. 2005. (J). cd-rom 648.95 (978-1-933229-01-0(2)) APTE, Inc.

Digital Photo Activity Kit Deluxe Vivitar 3700 Series school Version. 2005. (J). cd-rom 133.95 (978-1-933229-00-3(4)) APTE, Inc.

Digital Photo Activity Kit Deluxe Vivitar 5300 series Lab-2005. (J). 1759.95 (978-1-933229-09-6(8)) APTE, Inc.

Digital Photo Activity Kit Deluxe Vivitar 5300 series Lab-10. 2005. (J). 3469.99 (978-1-933229-10-2(1)) APTE, Inc.

Digital Photo Activity Kit Deluxe Vivitar 5300 series Lab-15. 2005. (J). 5129.95 (978-1-933229-11-9(X)) APTE, Inc.

Digital Photo Activity Kit Deluxe Vivitar 5300 series Lab-25. 2005. (J). 8123.90 (978-1-933229-12-6(8)) APTE, Inc.

Digital Photo Activity Kit Deluxe Vivitar 5300 series Lab-30. 2005. (J). 9624.95 (978-1-933229-14-0(4)) APTE, Inc.

Digital Photo Activity Kit Deluxe Vivitar 5300 series Lab-35. 2005. (J). 11119.95 (978-1-933229-15-7(2)) APTE, Inc.

Digital Photo Activity Kit Deluxe Vivitar 5300 series Single. 2005. (J). 359.99 (978-1-933229-08-9(X)) APTE, Inc.

Dora the Explorer Prewriting Practice. 2004. (J). pap. 2.95 (***978-1-58610-888-5(3)*** , 74003) Learning Horizons, Inc.

Dot-to-Dot Stories: Creative Activities for Beginning Writers. 64p. (gr. k-3). 9.99 (978-0-7682-0311-0(2) , FE11022, Totline Pubns.) Schaffer, Frank Pubns.

Douglas, Vincent & School Specialty Publishing Staff. Cursive Handwriting. 2002. (Fun to Do & Learn Ser.). (Illus.). 32p. (J). (gr. k-3). pap. 4.99 (978-0-7424-0282-9(7) , In Celebration) Schaffer, Frank Pubns.

—Manuscript Handwriting. 2002. (Fun to Do & Learn Ser.). (Illus.). 32p. (J). (gr. k-3). pap. 4.99 (978-0-7424-0281-2(9) , In Celebration) Schaffer, Frank Pubns.

Dudley, William. Alcohol: An Opposing Viewpoints Guide. 2005. (Writing the Critical Essay Ser.). (Illus.). 96p. (YA). (gr. 10-13). lib. bdg. 29.95 (978-0-7377-3192-7(3) , Greenhaven Pr., Inc.) Thomson Gale.

DynaNotes Grade 4 Writing TAKS Review Guide. 2006. (J). pap. (978-1-933854-41-0(3)) DynaStudy, Inc.

DynaNotes Grade 4 Writing TAKS Review Guide Transparency Set. 2006. (J). trans. (978-1-933854-42-7(1)) DynaStudy, Inc.

DynaNotes Grade 7 Writing TAKS Review Guide. 2006. (J). pap. (978-1-933854-39-7(1)) DynaStudy, Inc.

DynaNotes Grade 7 Writing TAKS Review Guide Transparency Set. 2006. (J). trans. (978-1-933854-40-3(5)) DynaStudy, Inc.

Einhorn, Kama. Cursive Handwriting Lessons: 12 Transparencies, Reproducibles, & Easy, Interactive Lessons for Teaching & Reinforcing Handwriting Skills. 2006. (Overhead Teaching Kit Ser.). 32p. pap. 12.99 (978-0-439-51757-7(5) , Teaching Resources) Scholastic, Inc.

—Manuscript Handwriting Lessons: 12 Transparencies, Reproducibles, & Easy, Interactive Lessons for Teaching & Reinforcing Handwriting Skills. 2006. (Overhead Teaching Kit Ser.). 32p. pap. 12.99 (978-0-439-53125-2(X) , Teaching Resources) Scholastic, Inc.

EMC-Paradigm Publishing Staff. Discovering Literature: Resource. 2002. (J). (gr. 6). Unit 8. pap., tchr. ed. (978-0-8219-2039-8(1)); Unit 9. pap. (978-0-8219-2040-4(5)); Unit 10. pap., tchr. ed. (978-0-8219-2041-1(3)); Unit 11. pap., tchr. ed. (978-0-8219-2042-8(1)); Unit 12. pap. (978-0-8219-2043-5(X)) EMC/Paradigm Publishing.

Evergreen: a Guide to Writing with Readings. 7th ed. 2003. (YA). (gr. 6-12). stu. ed. 3.96 incl. cd-rom (978-0-618-27389-8(1) , 315696) Houghton Mifflin College Div.

F. W. Prep, 4 bks., Set. Incl. Extraordinary Blogs & E-Zines. Rominger, Lynne. 30.50 (978-0-531-16765-6(8)); Extraordinary Debates. Orr, Tamra. Pope, Kevin, illus. 30.50 (978-0-531-16763-2(1)); 128p. (YA). (gr. 8-12). 2006. 2006. 122.00 (978-0-531-16827-1(1) , Watts, Franklin) Scholastic Library Publishing.

Festival Fun: 6 Each of 1 Anthology, 6 vols. (Wildcatstm Ser.). 32p. (gr. 2-8). (978-0-322-02424-3(2)) Wright Group, The.

Fire! Fire! 6 Each of 1 Anthology, 6 vols. (Wildcats Ser.). 32p. (gr. 2-8). (978-0-322-00581-5(7)) Wright Group, The.

Fletcher, Ralph J. Live Writing: Breathing Life into Your Words. 1999. (gr. 3-6). lib. bdg. 14.15 (978-0-613-81411-9(8)) Tandem Library Bks.

Fun-to-Learn: Ready for Writing. (Homework Booklets Ser.). 80p. (gr. k-1). 2.99 (978-0-7424-0261-4(4) , IF0417) School Specialty Publishing.

Giants in the City: Hard & Soft c & g: Level B, 6 vols. (Wright Skills Ser.). 16p. (gr. k-3). 26.50 (978-0-322-01489-3(1)) Wright Group, The.

Gould, Judith S. & Gould, Evan Jay. Four Square: A Companion to the Four Square Writing Method: Writing in the Content Areas for Grades 1-4. Mitchell, Judy, ed. Radtke, Becky J., illus. 2004. 112p. (J). pap. 11.95 (978-1-57310-421-0(3)) Teaching & Learning Co.

—Four Square: A Companion to the Four Square Writing Method: Writing in the Content Areas for Grades 5-9. Mitchell, Judy, ed. Wheeler, Ron, illus. 2004. 112p. (J). pap. 11.95 (978-1-57310-422-7(1)) Teaching & Learning Co.

Grizinski, Yolande. Write on Target Student Workbook: Using Graphic Organizers to Improve Writing Skills. 2002. (J). stu. ed., per., wbk. ed. 10.95 (978-1-884183-94-2(8) , NA1122) Englefield & Assocs., Inc.

Grizinski, Yolande & Holzhauser-Peters, Leslie. Write on Target Parent/Teachers Edition for Grades 1/2: Using Graphic Organizers to Improve Writing Skills. 2002. (gr. 1-2). tchr. ed., per. 16.95 (978-1-884183-93-5(X)) Englefield & Assocs., Inc.

Group/McGraw-Hill, Wright. Early Fluency-Fluency Writing Kit. 2004. (Wright Group Literacy Ser.). (gr. k-3). 132.50 (978-0-322-07021-9(X)) Wright Group, The.

—Emergent Writing Kit. 2004. (Wright Group Literacy Ser.). (gr. k-3). 79.50 (978-0-322-06615-1(8)) Wright Group, The.

—Five Little Frogs: Collection 1. (Storyteller Interactive Writing Cards Ser.). (gr. k-3). (978-0-322-09363-8(5)) Wright Group, The.

—Holly's Birthday Cake: Collection 2. (Storyteller Interactive Writing Cards Ser.). (gr. k-3). (978-0-322-09336-2(8)) Wright Group, The.

—In the Rain Forest, 6 vols. (Wildcats Ser.). 32p. (gr. 2-8). (978-0-322-00599-0(X)) Wright Group, The.

—My Word! what a Bird! Collection 4. (Storyteller Interactive Writing Cards Ser.). (gr. k-3). (978-0-322-09325-6(2)) Wright Group, The.

—Ready, Set, Pop! Collection 3. (Storyteller Interactive Writing Cards Ser.). (gr. k-3). (978-0-322-09348-5(1)) Wright Group, The.

—River Wild: 6 Each of 1 Anthology, 6 vols. (Wildcats Ser.). 32p. (gr. 2-8). (978-0-322-05857-6(0)) Wright Group, The.

—Sand: Collection 3. (Storyteller Interactive Writing Cards Ser.). (gr. k-3). (978-0-322-09349-2(X)) Wright Group, The.

A Guide to Writing: RUMGL A Guide to Writing. 2005. 50p. 17.00 (978-1-932976-98-4(1)) National Ctr. on Education & The Economy.

Hale, Christy. Collaborative Art & Writing Projects for Young Learners: 15 Delightful Projects That Build Early Reading & Writing Skills-and Connect to the Topics You Teach. 2006. 64p. pap. 12.99 (978-0-439-43462-1(9) , Teaching Resources) Scholastic, Inc.

Hall, Dorothy, et al. Writing Mini-Lessons for 2nd Grade: The Four-Blocks Model. 2002. (Four-Blocks Ser.). (Illus.). 80p. per. 17.99 (978-0-88724-814-6(4) , CD-2418) Carson-Dellosa Publishing Co., Inc.

Harcourt School Publishers Staff. Collections: ESL Manual. rev. ed. 2000. (Illus.). pap. 59.30 (978-0-15-317828-3(0)) Harcourt Schl. Pubs.

—Harcourt Language Arts. 2nd ed. 2002. (Harcourt Language Ser.). (Illus.). (gr. k-6). pap., pupil's gde. ed. 21.00 (978-0-15-317998-3(8)); (gr. 2 up). pap., pupil's gde. ed. 47.60 (978-0-15-319094-0(9)); (gr. 4 up). pap., pupil's gde. ed. 58.70 (978-0-15-317834-4(5)); (gr. 5 up). pap., pupil's gde. ed. 63.80 (978-0-15-317836-8(1)) Harcourt Schl. Pubs.

—Harcourt Language Arts: Consumable Edition. 2nd ed. 2002. (Harcourt Language Ser.). (Illus.). (gr. 1 up). pap., pupil's gde. ed. 28.00 (978-0-15-317831-3(0)) Harcourt Schl. Pubs.

—Harcourt Language Arts Big Book. 2nd ed. 2002. (Harcourt Language Ser.). (Illus.). (gr. k-6). pap. 99.70 (978-0-15-319156-5(2)) Harcourt Schl. Pubs.

—Harcourt Language Arts, Grade 1: Language Skills & Writing Assessment. 2nd ed. 2002. (Harcourt Language Ser.). (gr. 1 up). pap., tchr. ed. 57.50 (978-0-15-319123-7(6)) Harcourt Schl. Pubs.

—Lenguaje: Writing Express Network License. 2nd ed. 2002. (SPA.). (gr. 2). cd-rom 154.30 (978-0-15-322319-8(7)) Harcourt Schl. Pubs.

Hennessy, Brendan. Essay to Write? 2nd ed. 2004. 93p. pap. 13.25 (978-1-85703-835-4(5)) How To Books GBR. *Dist:* Parkwest Pubns., Inc.

Hercules & Other Greek Legends: 6 Each of 1 Anthology, 6 vols. (Wildcats Ser.). 32p. (gr. 2-8). (978-0-322-00590-7(6)) Wright Group, The.

Heroes: 6 Each of 1 Anthology, 6 vols. (Wildcatstm Ser.). 32p. (gr. 2-8). (978-0-322-00579-2(5)) Wright Group, The.

Herzog, Joyce. Budding Authors: Adventures in Writing. 2005. (J). spiral bd. 10.00 (***978-1-887225-52-6(8)***) JoyceHerzog.com, Inc.

—Budding Authors: Step into Writing. 2005. (J). spiral bd. 10.00 (***978-1-887225-51-9(X)***) JoyceHerzog.com, Inc.

—Budding Authors: Then & Now. 2005. (J). spiral bd. 10.00 (***978-1-887225-53-3(6)***) JoyceHerzog.com, Inc.

—Budding Authors: Twirling Around. Sinclair, Angie et al, eds. 2005. (J). spiral bd. 10.00 (***978-1-887225-56-4(0)***) JoyceHerzog.com, Inc.

—Budding Authors: Writing U. S. History. 2005. (J). spiral bd. 12.00 (***978-1-887225-55-7(2)***) JoyceHerzog.com, Inc.

—Budding Authors: Zooming Ahead. 2005. (J). spiral bd. 10.00 (***978-1-887225-54-0(4)***) JoyceHerzog.com, Inc.

—Draw & Write 2. 2004. (J). spiral bd. 12.00 (***978-1-887225-32-8(3)***) JoyceHerzog.com, Inc.

—Draw & Write I. 2004. (J). spiral bd. 12.00 (***978-1-887225-31-1(5)***) JoyceHerzog.com, Inc.

Heskett, Tracie. Traits of Good Writing. 2006. 144p. pap. 15.99 (978-1-4206-3584-3(0)); pap. 15.99 (978-1-4206-3587-4(5)) Austin & Company, Inc.

—Traits of Good Writing: Grades 5-6. Fields, Kim et al, eds. Mason, Mark, illus. 2006. (Traits of Good Writing Ser.). 144p. (J). (gr. 5-7). per. 15.99 (978-1-4206-3593-5(X)) Austin & Company, Inc.

Hohlt, Janie. Basic Writing 2. 2005. (J). ring bd. 49.95 (978-1-58804-388-7(6)) PCI Educational Publishing.

—Basic Writing Binder 2. 2005. (J). ring bd. 49.95 (978-1-58804-400-6(9)) PCI Educational Publishing.

Holt, Rinehart and Winston Staff. Elements of Literature: College Test Preparation: Illinois Edition. 2001. (YA). (gr. 11). pap. 4.00 (978-0-03-066948-4(0)) Holt, Rinehart & Winston.

—Elements of Literature: High School HRW Test Practice Booklet: New Jersey Edition. 2002. pap. 13.86 (978-0-03-068274-2(6)) Holt, Rinehart & Winston.

—Elements of Literature: High School PASS Practice Test Workbook: Oklahoma Edition. 2001. pap., wbk. ed. 13.43 (978-0-03-067254-5(6)) Holt, Rinehart & Winston.

—Elements of Literature: Oklaholma Edition. annot. ed. 2001. (gr. 11). tchr. ed. 137.60 (978-0-03-066944-6(8)) Holt, Rinehart & Winston.

—Elements of Literature: Powernotes. 3rd ed. 2004. (gr. 12). 372.93 (978-0-03-067841-7(2)) Holt, Rinehart & Winston.

—Elements of Literature: Standard Test Preparation: Illinois Edition. 2001. pap. 4.00 (978-0-03-066763-3(1)); (YA). (gr. 10). pap. 4.00 (978-0-03-066767-1(4)); (J). (gr. 6). pap. 4.00 (978-0-03-066762-6(3)); (YA). (gr. 8). pap. 4.00 (978-0-03-066764-0(X)); (YA). (gr. 9). pap. 4.00 (978-0-03-066766-4(6)) Holt, Rinehart & Winston.

—Elements of Literature: Standard Test Preparation: Missour Edition. 2001. (YA). (gr. 10). pap. 4.00 (978-0-03-066761-9(5)) Holt, Rinehart & Winston.

—Elements of Literature: Standard Test Preparation: Missouri Edition. 2001. (J). (gr. 6). pap. 4.00 (978-0-03-066756-5(9)); (YA). (gr. 7). pap. 4.00 (978-0-03-066757-2(7)); (YA). (gr. 8). pap. 4.00 (978-0-03-066783-1(6)); (YA). (gr. 9). pap. 4.00 (978-0-03-066759-6(3)) Holt, Rinehart & Winston.

—Elements of Literature, Grade 10: English 1 Practice & Assessment: Maryland Edition. 2001. pap. 13.86 (978-0-03-066773-2(9)) Holt, Rinehart & Winston.

—Elements of Literature, Grade 10: One-Step Lesson Planner & Standard Test Preparation: Indiana Edition. 2001. pap. 271.13 (978-0-03-066782-4(8)) Holt, Rinehart & Winston.

—Elements of Literature, Grade 10: Standard Test Preparation Booklet: Kansas Edition. 2001. pap. 270.45 (978-0-03-066954-5(5)) Holt, Rinehart & Winston.

—Elements of Literature, Grade 10: Standard Test Preparation: Oklahoma Version. 2001. pap. 271.13 (978-0-03-066928-6(6)) Holt, Rinehart & Winston.

—Elements of Literature, Grade 11: College Test Preparation: Missouri Edition. 2001. pap. 4.40 (978-0-03-067119-7(1)) Holt, Rinehart & Winston.

—Elements of Literature, Grade 6: Standard Test Preparation Booklet: Kansas Edition. 2001. pap. 271.13 (978-0-03-066949-1(9)) Holt, Rinehart & Winston.

—Elements of Literature, Grade 7: One-Step Lesson Planner & Test Preparation: Indiana Edition. 2001. pap. 271.13 (978-0-03-066778-7(X)) Holt, Rinehart & Winston.

—Elements of Literature, Grade 7: Standard Test Preparation Booklet: Kansas Edition. 2001. pap. 271.13 (978-0-03-066951-4(0)) Holt, Rinehart & Winston.

—Elements of Literature, Grade 7: Standard Test Preparation: Oklahoma Version. 2001. pap. 248.20 (978-0-03-066924-8(3)) Holt, Rinehart & Winston.

—Elements of Literature, Grade 7: With Correlations to CATS for One-Step Planner: Indiana Edition. 3rd annot. ed. 2001. tchr. ed. 135.46 (978-0-03-066958-3(8)) Holt, Rinehart & Winston.

—Elements of Literature, Grade 8: HRW Test Practice Booklet: New Jersey Edition. 2001. pap. 13.86 (978-0-03-068276-6(2)) Holt, Rinehart & Winston.

—Elements of Literature, Grade 8: One-Step Lesson Planner & Test Preparation: Indiana Edition. 2001. pap. 271.13 (978-0-03-066779-4(8)) Holt, Rinehart & Winston.

—Elements of Literature, Grade 8: Standard Test Preparation Booklet: Kansas Edition. 2001. pap. 271.13 (978-0-03-066952-1(9)) Holt, Rinehart & Winston.

—Elements of Literature, Grade 9: One-Step Lesson Planner & Test Preparation: Indiana Edition. 2001. pap. 271.13 (978-0-03-066781-7(X)) Holt, Rinehart & Winston.

—Elements of Literature, Grade 9: Standard Test Preparation Booklet: Kansas Edition. 2001. pap. 271.13 (978-0-03-066953-8(7)) Holt, Rinehart & Winston.

—TAKS Practice Tests Ansky Elemental Literature/ Language. 2002. (J). pap. 8.00 (978-0-03-072217-2(9)) Holt, Rinehart & Winston of Canada, Ltd. CAN. *Dist:* Harcourt Canada, Ltd.

—TAKS Practice Tests, Grade 1: Elemental Literature & Language. 2002. pap. 14.73 (978-0-03-069186-7(9)) Holt, Rinehart & Winston.

—TAKS Practice Tests, Grade 2: Elemental Literature & Language. 2002. pap. 14.73 (978-0-03-069187-4(7)) Holt, Rinehart & Winston.

—TAKS Practice Tests, Grade 4: Elemental Literature & Language. 2002. pap. 14.73 (978-0-03-069189-8(3)) Holt, Rinehart & Winston.

—TAKS Practice Tests, Grade 5: Elemental Literature & Language. 2002. pap. 14.73 (978-0-03-069191-1(5)) Holt, Rinehart & Winston.

Hop, Jog, & Tap: Consonants g, h, j; Short Vowel o word families: Level A, 6 vols. (Wright Skills Ser.). 12p. (gr. k-3). 17.95 (978-0-322-01449-7(2)) Wright Group, The.

Hutson-Nechkash, Peg. Help Me Write: Frames & Rubrics for Classroom Writing Success. 2003. (Illus.). vii, 295p. (J). (978-1-932054-12-5(X)) Super Duper Pubns.

I Can Print A to Z (Modern) 2000. (Wipe-Off Activity Bks.). (Illus.). 16p. (J). (ps-1). wbk. ed. 3.79 (978-1-889319-79-7(1)) Trend Enterprises, Inc.

Imagine & Write, 5 Bks. (J). (gr. 2-6). (978-0-8374-0229-1(8) , 427); (978-0-8374-0239-0(5) , 428); (978-0-8374-0249-9(2) , 429); (978-0-8374-0259-8(X) , 430); (978-0-8374-0269-7(7) , 431) Weekly Reader Corp.

In the News, 6 vols. (Wildcats Ser.). 32p. (gr. 2-8). (978-0-322-02437-3(4)) Wright Group, The.

Incredible Places: 6 Each of 1 Anthology, 6 vols. (Wildcats Ser.). 32p. (gr. 2-8). (978-0-322-00587-7(6)) Wright Group, The.

Janecko, Paul B. Writing Winning Reports & Essays. 2003. 224p. (J). 18.95 (978-0-439-55495-4(0)) Scholastic, Inc.

Keys for Writers: Electronic Handbook (IBM(r) 3. 5) 1999. (gr. 6-12). (978-0-395-77066-5(1) , 3-45598) McDougal Littell Inc.

Keys for Writers: Electronic Handbook (Macintosh(r)) 1999. (gr. 6-12). (978-0-395-77067-2(X) , 3-45599) McDougal Littell Inc.

Keys for Writers: Instructor's Support Package. 1999. (gr. 6-12). (978-0-395-92644-4(0) , 3-45607) McDougal Littell Inc.

Kieczykowski, Carol. Expanding the Primary Writer's Workshop: 50 Mini-Lessons to Improve Writing. 2001. 144p. (J). (gr. k-2). pap. 15.99 (978-0-7682-0307-3(4) , FE11021, Totline Pubns.) Schaffer, Frank Pubns.

Kinneavy. Elements of Writing. 1998. 74.60 (978-0-03-050867-7(3)); (gr. 3). 74.60 (978-0-03-050864-6(9)); 76.26 (978-0-03-050869-1(X)); 69.86 (978-0-03-050863-9(0)); 67.20 (978-0-03-050858-5(4)) Holt, Rinehart & Winston.

—Elements of Writing: First Course. rev. ed. 1998. (gr. 1). 69.86 (978-0-03-050862-2(2)) Holt, Rinehart & Winston.

—Elements of Writing 5th Course. rev. ed. 2000. (gr. 5). 76.26 (978-0-03-050868-4(1)) Holt, Rinehart & Winston.

Kuligowski, Step. Get up Get Noisy Get Writing. 2007. 80p. pap. 11.99 ***(*978-1-4206-3709-0(6))*** Teacher Created Resources, Inc.

Larsen, Sandy. Igniting Your Writing! 2002. 88p. (J). spiral bd. 16.99 (978-0-9666677-4-5(3)) Merritt Park Pr.

Le Patner, Michelle, et al. Nonfiction Writing Prompts for Upper Elementary Science. Whited, Amy M., ed. 2005. (Illus.). 128p. pap. 9.95 (978-1-933196-05-3(X)) Advanced Learning Pr.

—Nonfiction Writing Prompts for Upper Elementary Social Studies. Whited, Amy M., ed. 2005. (Illus.). 128p. pap. 9.95 (978-1-933196-06-0(8)) Advanced Learning Pr.

—Write to Know: Nonfiction Writing Prompts for Kindergarten Math, Science, & Social Studies. Whited, Amy M., ed. 2005. 128p. pap. 9.95 (978-1-933196-00-8(9)) Advanced Learning Pr.

—Write to Know: Nonfiction Writing Prompts for Lower Elementary Science. Whited, Amy M., ed. 2005. 128p. pap. 9.95 (978-1-933196-02-2(5)) Advanced Learning Pr.

—Write to Know: Nonfiction Writing Prompts for Lower Elementary Social Studies. Whited, Amy M., ed. 2005. 128p. pap. 9.95 (978-1-933196-03-9(3)) Advanced Learning Pr.

Leap Frog First Grade Reading & Writing Workbook. 2006. (J). spiral bd. 3.95 ***(*978-1-59545-085-2(8))*** Learning Horizons, Inc.

Leap Frog Kindergarten Reading & Writing Workbook. 2006. (J). spiral bd. 3.95 ***(*978-1-59545-084-5(X))*** Learning Horizons, Inc.

Leap Frog Pre-K Reading & Writing Workbook. 2006. (J). spiral bd. 3.95 ***(*978-1-59545-083-8(1))*** Learning Horizons, Inc.

LeapFrog It's a Blast Bindup. 2007. (J). spiral bd. 8.95 ***(*978-1-59545-168-2(4))*** Learning Horizons, Inc.

LeapFrog Write Wipe off Book. 2007. (J). 4.99 ***(*978-1-59545-138-5(2))*** Learning Horizons, Inc.

Level 1 Reading & Writing Journal - Block Print: Wk201b. 2007. (J). ***(*978-1-59577-045-5(3))*** Starfall Education.

Levy, Janey. Language Development Writing Process. 2005. 48p. pap. 6.95 (978-1-4042-8569-9(5)) Rosen Publishing Group, Inc., The.

The Library of Writing Skills. 2005. (Illus.). 48p. (gr. 5-8). lib. bdg. 159.00 (978-1-4042-0349-5(4)) Rosen Publishing Group, Inc., The.

Liverman, Debra, ed. Daily Journal Prompts. 2005. 112p. 14.95 (978-1-56234-625-6(3)); 14.95 (978-1-56234-626-3(1)) Education Ctr., Inc. (Mailbox Bks., The).

Lombardi, Kristine. Learning Letters. Garofoli, Vivianna, illus. 2005. (Show & Tell Ser.). 12p. (ps-ps). bds. 12.99 (978-0-7944-0678-3(5)) Reader's Digest Assn., Inc., The.

Mader, Jan. I Love to Write! 2004. 20p. (J). (gr. k-3). pap. 4.95 (978-1-57874-076-5(2)) Kaeden Corp.

Magee, Wes. Pet the Cat. 2004. (QEB Start Writing Ser.). (Illus.). 24p. (J). lib. bdg. 15.95 (978-1-59566-023-7(2)) QEB Publishing Inc.

Marlow, Herb. A Student's Guide to Successful Writing. 2005. (J). 24.95 (978-1-893595-53-8(6)) Four Seasons Bks., Inc.

McCarthy, Tara. Narrative Writing: Mini-Lessons * Strategies * Activities. 1998. (Teaching Writing Ser.). (Illus.). 64p. (gr. 4-8). pap. 9.95 (978-0-590-20937-3(X)) Scholastic, Inc.

McCarty, Diane Bischoff. Copywork for Children: For Grades 1-3. 2004. (Illus.). 63p. (J). (978-0-9712124-1-1(4)) Angel Heart Children's Pr.

McGraw-Hill Staff. Glencoe Language Arts, Grade 6, Grammar & Composition Handbook. 2001. 39.96 (978-0-07-825113-9(3) , 9780078251139) Glencoe/McGraw-Hill.

—Writer's Choice: Florida Edition 2001, Grade 6. 2001. stu. ed. 58.64 incl. cd-rom (978-0-07-827058-1(8) , 9780078270581) Glencoe/McGraw-Hill.

—Writer's Choice: Grade 11 Texas Edition 2001. 2001. (C). stu. ed. 66.64 incl. cd-rom (978-0-07-827083-3(9) , 9780078270833) Glencoe/McGraw-Hill.

—Writer's Choice: Grade 12 Florida Edition 2001. 2001. (C). stu. ed. 66.64 incl. cd-rom (978-0-07-827064-2(2) , 9780078270642) Glencoe/McGraw-Hill.

—Writer's Choice: Grade 6 Texas Edition 2001. 2001. stu. ed. 58.64 incl. cd-rom (978-0-07-827078-9(2) , 9780078270789) Glencoe/McGraw-Hill.

—Writer's Choice: Grade 7 Florida Edition 2001. 2001. stu. ed. 61.32 incl. cd-rom (978-0-07-827059-8(6) , 9780078270598) Glencoe/McGraw-Hill.

—Writer's Choice: Grade 8 Florida Edition 2001. 2001. stu. ed. 61.32 incl. cd-rom (978-0-07-827060-4(X) , 9780078270604) Glencoe/McGraw-Hill.

—Writer's Choice: Grade 9 Texas Edition 2001. 2001. stu. ed. 65.32 incl. cd-rom (978-0-07-827081-9(2) , 9780078270819) Glencoe/McGraw-Hill.

—Writer's Choice: Grammar & Composition, Grade 11, Interactive Student Edition. 2001. (C). stu. ed. 82.64 incl. cd-rom (978-0-07-827070-3(7) , 9780078270703) Glencoe/McGraw-Hill.

—Writer's Choice: Grammar & Composition, Grade 12, Interactive Student Edition. 2001. (C). stu. ed. 82.64 incl. cd-rom (978-0-07-827071-0(5) , 9780078270710) Glencoe/McGraw-Hill.

—Writer's Choice: Grammar & Composition, Grade 7, Interactive Student Edition. 2001. (C). stu. ed. 75.96 incl. cd-rom (978-0-07-827066-6(9) , 9780078270666) Glencoe/McGraw-Hill.

—Writer's Choice: Grammar & Composition, Grade 8, Interactive Student Edition. 2001. (C). stu. ed. 75.96 incl. cd-rom (978-0-07-827067-3(7) , 9780078270673) Glencoe/McGraw-Hill.

—Writer's Choice: Grammar & Composition, Grade 9, Interactive Student Edition. 2001. (C). stu. ed. 80.64 incl. cd-rom (978-0-07-827068-0(5) , 9780078270680) Glencoe/McGraw-Hill.

—Writer's Choice: Texas Edition 2001, Grade 10. 2001. (C). stu. ed. 65.32 incl. cd-rom (978-0-07-827082-6(0) , 9780078270826) Glencoe/McGraw-Hill.

—Writer's Choice Florida Edition 2001, Grade 11. 2001. (C). stu. ed. 66.64 incl. cd-rom (978-0-07-827063-5(4) , 9780078270635) Glencoe/McGraw-Hill.

—Writer's Choice Grammar Practice, Grade 9. 2000. pap., wbk. ed. 17.32 (978-0-07-823355-5(0) , 9780078233555) Glencoe/McGraw-Hill.

—Writer's Choice Grammar Practice Grade 11. 2000. (C). pap., wbk. ed. 17.32 (978-0-07-823357-9(7) , 9780078233579) Glencoe/McGraw-Hill.

—Writer's Choice Interactive: Grade 7 Texas Edition 2001. 2001. (C). stu. ed. 61.32 incl. cd-rom (978-0-07-827079-6(0) , 9780078270796) Glencoe/McGraw-Hill.

—Writer's Choice Interactive: Grade 9 Florida Edition 2001. 2001. (C). stu. ed. 65.32 incl. cd-rom (978-0-07-827061-1(8) , 9780078270611) Glencoe/McGraw-Hill.

—Writer's Choice Interactive Grade 12 Texas Edition 2001. 2001. (C). stu. ed. 66.64 incl. cd-rom (978-0-07-827084-0(7) , 9780078270840) Glencoe/McGraw-Hill.

—Writer's Choice Interactive Grade 8 Texas Edition 2001. 2001. (C). stu. ed. 61.32 incl. cd-rom (978-0-07-827080-2(4) , 9780078270802) Glencoe/McGraw-Hill.

—Writer's Choice Interactive Student Edition Grade 10 Florida Edition 2001. 2001. (C). stu. ed. 65.32 incl. cd-rom (978-0-07-827062-8(6) , 9780078270628) Glencoe/McGraw-Hill.

Mechanech Publications Staff. Writing Better with Every Letter: My Handwriting Practice Book. 2004. (Illus.). (J). 112p. (gr. 1 up). pap. (978-0-9702861-2-3(0)); Vol. 2. 95p. (gr. 2 up). pap. (978-0-9702861-4-7(7)) Mechanech Pubns.

Milton, Bess. Language Development Writing Process. 2005. 48p. pap. 6.95 (978-1-4042-8559-0(8)) Rosen Publishing Group, Inc., The.

Moore, Jo Ellen. How to Teach Nonfiction Writing. Larsen, Jo, illus. 2001. 96p. (J). (gr. 3-6). pap., tchr. ed. 12.99 (978-1-55799-800-2(0) , EMC 719) Evan-Moor Educational Pubs.

Morgenstern, Susie. The Aspiring Writer's Journal. Bronn, Theresa, illus. 2006. 372p. (gr. 8-17). pap. 16.95 (978-0-8109-7058-8(9) , Abrams Bks. for Young Readers) Abrams, Harry N. , Inc.

Morkane, Sue. Original Writing. 2004. (Routledge a Level English Guides Ser.). (Illus.). 112p. 19.95 (978-0-415-31912-6(9)); 71.95 (978-0-415-31911-9(0)) Routledge.

Mythmakers, 6 vols. (Wildcats Ser.). 32p. (gr. 2-8). (978-0-322-02440-3(4)) Wright Group, The.

Nance, Jim. Classical Rhetoric. 2001. (J). cd-rom 200.00 (978-1-930443-47-1(1)) Logos Schl.

Nelson, Linda & Logie, Daniel. Writing Sourcebook: Foundations for Writing. 2004. 6.95 ***(*978-1-931181-38-9(1))*** Universal Publishing.

Olsen, Jan Z. Mat Man Shapes. Delaney, Molly, illus. 2007. 32p. (J). 12.00 ***(*978-1-891627-92-7(9))*** Handwriting Without Tears, Inc.

Orehovec, Barbara & Alley, Marybeth. Revisiting the Writing Workshop. 2007. 160p. pap. 19.99 ***(*978-0-439-92643-0(2))*** Scholastic, Inc.

Orr, Tamra. Extraordinary Essays. 2006. 128p. (YA). (gr. 8-12). pap. 9.95 (978-0-531-17576-7(6) , Watts, Franklin) Scholastic Library Publishing.

Orr, Tamra B. Extraordinary Essays. 2005. (F.W. Prep Ser.). (Illus.). 127p. (YA). (gr. 8-13). 30.50 (978-0-531-16761-8(5) , Watts, Franklin) Scholastic Library Publishing.

Paint A Written Picture - Reading Skill Using Mini Books Grades 2-4. 2000. 64p. (J). pap. 8.94 (978-1-889369-39-6(X)) Teaching Ink, Inc.

Perkins, Sally J. & Stoner, Mark R. Making Sense of Messages: A Critical Apprenticeship in Rhetorical Criticism. 2006. (Illus.). 320p. (YA). pap. 67.56 (978-0-618-14488-4(9) , 351240) Houghton Mifflin College Div.

Persuasive Writing Teacher Notes. 2004. 8p. (YA). 2.95 (978-1-56254-751-6(8) , SP7518) Saddleback Educational Publishing.

Purslow, Frances & Hudak, Heather C. Expository Paragraphs. 2007. (J). ***(*978-1-59036-735-3(9)); (*978-1-59036-736-0(7))*** Weigl Pubs., Inc.

—Narrative Paragraphs: Learning to Write. 2007. (J). ***(*978-1-59036-733-9(2)); (*978-1-59036-734-6(0))*** Weigl Pubs., Inc.

—Persuasive Paragraphs. 2007. (J). ***(*978-1-59036-731-5(6)); (*978-1-59036-732-2(4))*** Weigl Pubs., Inc.

Quinley, Elliott. Persuasive Writing. 2004. 64p. (YA). per. 8.95 (978-1-56254-750-9(X) , SP750X) Saddleback Educational Publishing.

Raintree Steck-Vaughn Staff. Writing Dictionary. 2000. (J). (gr. 4-7). pap. 6.64 (978-0-8114-3050-0(2)) Steck-Vaughn.

Read & Write. 2005. (J). pap. 3.99 (978-1-933200-18-7(9)) Family Bks. at Home.

Ready-to-Go Lessons: Reading & Writing, Grade 3. 2006. 144p. 15.99 (978-1-4206-8032-4(3)) Teacher Created Resources, Inc.

Ready-to-Go Lessons: Reading & Writing, Grade 4. 2006. 15.99 (978-1-4206-8033-1(1)) Teacher Created Resources, Inc.

Ready-to-Go Lessons: Reading & Writing, Grade 5. 2006. 15.99 (978-1-4206-8034-8(X)) Teacher Created Resources, Inc.

Real-World Writing. 2005. (YA). ring bd. 69.95 (978-1-58804-389-4(4)) PCI Educational Publishing.

Reflective Learning Library Set. 2000. (J). 32.95 (978-1-56911-714-9(4)) Learning Resources, Inc.

Right or Wrong? 6 Each of 1 Anthology, 6 vols. (Wildcats Ser.). 32p. (gr. 2-8). (978-0-322-00598-3(1)) Wright Group, The.

Rothstein, Gloria. Real-Life Writing Activities Based on Favorite Picture Books: Super-Fun Activities & Reproducibles That Use Picture Books As Models to Help Kids Practice 11 Kinds of Real-Life Writings. 2002. 80p. pap., tchr. ed. 12.95 (978-0-439-25616-2(X)) Scholastic, Inc.

Ruthven, Rosemary. Write to Know: Nonfiction Writing Prompts for Lower Elementary Math. Whited, Amy M., ed. 2005. 128p. pap. 9.95 (978-1-933196-01-5(7)) Advanced Learning Pr.

—Write to Know: Nonfiction Writing Prompts for Upper Elementary Math. Whited, Amy M., ed. 2005. 128p. pap. 9.95 (978-1-933196-04-6(1)) Advanced Learning Pr.

Scholastic, Inc. Staff. Scholastic Explains Writing Homework: Everything Children (& Parents) Need to Survive 2nd & 3rd Grade. 1998. (Scholastic Explains Ser.). (Illus.). 64p. (J). (gr. 2-4). 14.95 (978-0-590-39756-8(7)) Scholastic, Inc.

School Specialty Publishing. After School Writing Activities. 2003. (100+ Seriestm Ser.). 128p. (J). (gr. 1 up). pap. 12.99 (978-0-7424-1781-6(6) , IFG99028); (gr. 2 up). pap. 12.99 (978-0-7424-1782-3(4) , IFG99029); (gr. 3 up). pap. 12.99 (978-0-7424-1783-0(2) , IFG99030); (gr. 4 up). pap. 12.99 (978-0-7424-1784-7(0) , IFG99031) School Specialty Publishing.

—I Can Write about Me. 2006. (Brighter Child I Can... Ser.). 128p. (J). pap. 3.95 (978-0-7696-4908-5(4) , Brighter Child) School Specialty Publishing.

—Note Taking & Outlining. 2003. 48p. (J). (gr. 3-5). pap. 6.99 (978-0-7424-1830-1(8) , FS99157); (gr. 6-8). pap. 6.99 (978-0-7424-1840-0(5) , FS99158) School Specialty Publishing.

—Write 4 Today, Grade 2. 2005. 112p. (J). (gr. 2-2). pap. 13.99 ***(*978-0-7682-3222-6(8)*** , Schaffer, Frank) Schaffer, Frank Pubns.

—Write 4 Today, Grade 4. 2005. 112p. (J). (gr. 4-4). pap. 13.99 ***(*978-0-7682-3224-0(4)*** , Schaffer, Frank) Schaffer, Frank Pubns.

—Write 4 Today, Grade 5. 2005. 112p. (J). (gr. 5-5). pap. 13.99 ***(*978-0-7682-3225-7(2)*** , Schaffer, Frank) Schaffer, Frank Pubns.

Sesame Street Early Writing Skills. 2006. (J). spiral bd. 5.99 ***(*978-1-58610-983-7(9))*** Learning Horizons, Inc.

Shearer, Cyndy & Washington, George. Handwriting by George 1-27: Rules of Civility & Decent Behaviour in Company & Conversation: Rules 1-27 to Draw & Write, Vol. 1. 2002. (ENG.). 64p. (J). pap. 6.95 (978-1-882514-36-6(X)) Greenleaf Pr.

Shearer, Cynthia & Washington, George. Handwriting by George 28-53: Rules of Civility & Decent Behaviour in Company & Conversation: Rules 28-53 to Draw & Write, Vol. 2. 2007. (ENG.). 64p. (J). pap. 9.95 (978-1-882514-37-3(8)) Greenleaf Pr.

Show What You Know on the FCAT 4, New Writing+ Student Workbook. 2006. (J). per. 8.95 ***(*978-1-59230-231-4(9))*** Englefield & Assocs., Inc.

Show What You Know Publishing, ed. Show What You Know on the CSAP 7, Reading/Writing Student Workbook. 2007. (J). per. 13.95 ***(*978-1-59230-246-8(7))*** Englefield & Assocs., Inc.

—Show What You Know on the CSAP for Grade 5, Student Workbook. 2007. (J). per. 13.95 ***(*978-1-59230-217-8(3))*** Englefield & Assocs., Inc.

—Show What You Know on the CSAP for Grade 9 Writing Student Self-Study Workbook. 2007. (YA). per. 18.95 ***(*978-1-59230-293-2(9))*** Englefield & Assocs., Inc.

—Show What You Know on the CSAP Reading & Writing for Grade 6, Student Workbook. 2007. (J). per. 13.95 ***(*978-1-59230-240-6(8))*** Englefield & Assocs., Inc.

Sigmon, Cheryl M. & Ford, Sylvia M. Just-Right Writing Mini-Lessons: Grades 4-6. 2006. 128p. pap. 17.99 (978-0-439-57410-5(2) , Teaching Resources) Scholastic, Inc.

Silate, Jennifer. Language Development Writing Process. 2005. 48p. pap. 6.95 (978-1-4042-8564-4(4)) Rosen Publishing Group, Inc., The.

Skill Sharpeners, Spell & Write, Grade 1. 2005. (J). pap. 9.99 (978-1-59673-045-8(5) , emc 4537) Evan-Moor Educational Pubs.

Skill Sharpeners, Spell & Write, Grade 2. 2005. (J). pap. 9.99 (978-1-59673-046-5(3) , emc 4538) Evan-Moor Educational Pubs.

Skill Sharpeners, Spell & Write, Grade 3. 2005. (J). pap. 9.99 (978-1-59673-047-2(1) , emc 4539) Evan-Moor Educational Pubs.

Skill Sharpeners, Spell & Write, Grade 4. 2005. (J). pap. 9.99 (978-1-59673-048-9(X) , emc 4540) Evan-Moor Educational Pubs.

Skill Sharpeners, Spell & Write, Grade 5. 2005. (J). pap. 9.99 (978-1-59673-049-6(8) , emc 4542) Evan-Moor Educational Pubs.

Skill Sharpeners, Spell & Write, Grade 6. 2005. (J). pap. 9.99 (978-1-59673-050-2(1) , emc 4542) Evan-Moor Educational Pubs.

Skill Sharpeners, Spell & Write, Grade PreK. 2005. (J). pap. 9.99 (978-1-59673-043-4(9) , emc 4535) Evan-Moor Educational Pubs.

Skills for Young Writers: Helping Students Make Good Stories Great. 48p. (gr. 1 up). 5.99 (978-1-56822-582-1(2) , IF5140); (gr. 2 up). 5.99 (978-1-56822-583-8(0) , IF5141); (gr. 3 up). 5.99 (978-1-56822-584-5(9) , IF5142); (gr. 4 up). 5.99 (978-1-56822-585-2(7) , IF5143); (gr. 5 up). 5.99 (978-1-56822-586-9(5) , IF5144); (gr. 6 up). 5.99 (978-1-56822-587-6(3) , IF5145) School Specialty Publishing.

Soles. Academic Writing Plus Perrin Pocket Guide to Apa Second Edition Plus Trimmer Guide to Mla Document Sixth Edition Plus Vandermey College Writer Handbook Student Exercise Booklet. 2006. (YA). pap., spiral bd. 51.16 (978-0-618-85592-6(0) , 363150) Houghton Mifflin College Div.

Sorenson, Sharon. Student Writing Handbook. 4th rev. ed. 2000. Vol. 4. 600p. pap. 16.99 (978-0-7645-6125-2(1) , Webster's New World) Wiley, John & Sons, Inc.

Spelling & Writing. 2002. (Home Workbooks Ser.). 64p. pap. 2.49 (978-0-88724-732-3(6) , CD-4534) Carson-Dellosa Publishing Co., Inc.

Spencer, Lauren. A Step-By-Step Guide to Descriptive Writing. 2005. (Illus.). 48p. (J). (gr. 5-8). lib. bdg. 26.50 (978-1-4042-0212-2(9)) Rosen Publishing Group, Inc., The.

Steck-Vaughn Staff. GED - The Essay. 2001. pap. 15.67 (978-0-7398-2832-8(0)) Steck-Vaughn.

—Writing Level D: Answer Key. 1999. (Strategies for Success Ser.). (Illus.). (J). pap. (978-0-7398-1048-4(0)) Steck-Vaughn.

—Writing Level F: Answer Key. 1999. (Strategies for Success Ser.). (J). pap., tchr. ed. (978-0-7398-1050-7(2)) Steck-Vaughn.

Stobaugh, James. Skills for Rhetoric: Encouraging Thoughtful Christians to Be World Changers. 2003. (YA). 30.50 (978-0-9725890-4-8(X)) For Such A Time As This Ministries.

—Skills for Rhetoric Student. 2005. (Broadman & Holman Literature Ser.). 272p. stu. ed. 24.99 (978-0-8054-5898-5(0)) B&H Publishing Grp.

Suter, Joanne. Beginning Writing 1. 2001. 100p. ring bd. 29.95 (978-1-56254-147-7(1) , SP 1471) Saddleback Educational Publishing.

—Beginning Writing 2. 2001. 100p. ring bd. 29.95 (978-1-56254-148-4(X) , SP 148X) Saddleback Educational Publishing.

Svitak, Adora & Svitak, Joyce. Flying Fingers: Master the Tools of Learning Through the Joy of Writing. 2005. 290p. pap. 12.95 (978-1-888045-19-2(1)) Action Publishing, LLC.

Take It to Your Seat Writing Centers. 2005. (J). 24.99 (978-1-59673-078-6(1) , EMC 6002); 24.99 (978-1-59673-079-3(X) , EMC 6003); 24.99 (978-1-59673-080-9(3) , EMC 6004); 24.99 (978-1-59673-081-6(1) , EMC 6005); 24.99 (978-1-59673-082-3(X) , EMC 6006) Evan-Moor Educational Pubs.

TAKS MASTER Power Practice, Writing Gr. 4. 2005. (J). per. (978-1-57022-547-5(8)) ECS Learning Systems, Inc.

TAKS MASTER Power Practice, Writing, Gr. 7. 2005. (J). per. (978-1-57022-548-2(6)) ECS Learning Systems, Inc.

TAKS MASTER Practice Test, Writing Gr. 4. 2004. (J). (978-1-57022-533-8(8)) ECS Learning Systems, Inc.

TAKS MASTER Practice Test, Writing Gr. 7. 2004. (J). (978-1-57022-534-5(6)) ECS Learning Systems, Inc.

Thurston, Cheryl Miller. How to Avoid English Teachers' Pet Peeves: Improve Your Writing by Eliminating the Common Errors That English Teachers See Most Often. 2001. 167p. (J). pap. 10.95 (978-1-877673-51-1(X) , PET-BWK03) Cottonwood Pr., Inc.

Time for Kids Editors. Writer's Handbook for School & Home, Set. rev. ed. 2006. (Time for Kids Ser.). (Illus.). 112p. (J). (ps-17). pap. 7.99 (978-1-933405-38-4(4)) Time, Inc. Home Entertainment.

Vargo, Julianna. Ejercicios de Pre-escritura. 2007. (Dora The Explorer Ser.). (SPA & ENG., Illus.). 24p. (J). pap. 2.95 (***978-1-59545-073-9(4)***) Learning Horizons, Inc.

Vinyl Manuscript Mat. 1999. (gr. k-3). suppl. ed. 7.95 (978-0-673-36032-8(6)) Addison-Wesley Educational Pubs., Inc.

Voyages in English: Writing & Grammar. 2004. (gr. 1 up). tchr. ed. (978-0-8294-0980-2(7)); (gr. 1 up). tchr. ed., wbk. ed. (978-0-8294-1383-0(9)); (gr. 1 up). stu. ed. (978-0-8294-0981-9(5)); (gr. 1 up). stu. ed., wbk. ed. (978-0-8294-1382-3(0)); (gr. 2 up). tchr. ed. (978-0-8294-0982-6(3)); (gr. 2 up). tchr. ed., wbk. ed. (978-0-8294-1385-4(5)); (gr. 2 up). stu. ed. (978-0-8294-0983-3(1)); (gr. 2 up). stu. ed., wbk. ed. (978-0-8294-1384-7(7)); (gr. 3 up). (978-0-8294-1303-8(0)); (gr. 3 up). tchr. ed. (978-0-8294-0985-7(8)); (gr. 3 up). tchr. ed., wbk. ed. (978-0-8294-1319-9(7)); (gr. 3 up). stu. ed. (978-0-8294-0986-4(6)); (gr. 3 up). stu. ed., wbk. ed. (978-0-8294-1318-2(9)); (gr. 4 up). tchr. ed., wbk. ed. (978-0-8294-1321-2(9)); (gr. 4 up). stu. ed. (978-0-8294-0988-8(2)) Loyola Pr.

Wach, Martin & Wach, Delia. An Adventure in Writing. Wach, Delia, illus. 2007. (Illus.). 32p. pap. 14.95 (***978-0-929915-54-8(2)***) Headline Bks., Inc.

Wagstaff, Janiel. 20 Tricky Writing Problems-Solved: Surefire Strategies, Mini-Lessons, & Routines That Help You Tackle the Most Common Problems in Writing Classrooms. 2004. 80p. pap. 14.99 (978-0-439-59022-8(1) , Scholastic) Scholastic, Inc.

Wasylyk, Thomas M. Second Edition Handwriting: A Self-Improvement Workbook. 2006. 7.95 (***978-1-931181-66-2(7)*** , Item #139) Universal Publishing.

—Second Edition Handwriting: Beginning Cursive Writing. 2006. (***978-1-931181-62-4(4)*** , Item # 135) Universal Publishing.

—Second Edition Handwriting: Improving Cursive Writing. 2006. 7.95 (***978-1-931181-63-1(2)*** , Item # 136) Universal Publishing.

—Second Edition Handwriting: Introduction to Cursive. 2006. 7.95 (***978-1-931181-61-7(6)*** , Item # 134) Universal Publishing.

—Second Edition Handwriting: Manuscript Review & Enrichment. 2006. 7.95 (***978-1-931181-60-0(8)*** , Item # 133) Universal Publishing.

—Second Edition Handwriting: Manuscript Writing. 2006. 7.95 (***978-1-931181-59-4(4)*** , Item # 132) Universal Publishing.

—Second Edition Handwriting: Reading & Writing Readiness Skills. 2006. 7.95 (***978-1-931181-57-0(8)*** , Item #130) Universal Publishing.

—Second Edition Handwriting: Writing for Learning. 2006. 7.95 (***978-1-931181-65-5(9)*** , Item # 138) Universal Publishing.

—Second Edition Handwriting: Writing in Cursive. 2006. 7.95 (***978-1-931181-64-8(0)*** , Item # 137) Universal Publishing.

—Second Edition Handwriting: Writing the Manuscript Letters. 2nd ed. 2006. (***978-1-931181-58-7(6)*** , Item #131) Universal Publishing.

Watson, Sharon. Jump in, A Workbook for Reluctant Writers: 2-book Set. Wile, Kathleen J., ed. 2006. per. 40.00 (***978-1-932012-76-7(1)***) Apologia Educational Ministries, Inc.

—Jump in, A Workbook for Reluctant Writers: Student Text. Wile, Kathleen J., ed. 2006. per., wbk. ed. 30.00 (***978-1-932012-74-3(5)***) Apologia Educational Ministries, Inc.

A Way with Words: Individual Title Six-Packs. (Rigby Infoquest Ser.). (gr. 5 up). 37.00 (978-0-7578-6485-8(6)) Rigby Education.

Webber, Sharon G. Webber Artic Fun Sheets - Set 1. Webber, Thomas, ed. 2001. (Illus.). (YA). (ps up). spiral bd. 36.95 (978-1-58650-209-6(3)) Super Duper Pubns.

Whited, Amy. Write to Know: Nonfiction Writing Prompts for Secondary PE. 2006. (Write to Know Ser.). 128p. pap. 9.95 (978-1-933196-21-3(1)) Advanced Learning Pr.

Whited, Amy M., ed. Nonfiction Writing Prompts for Geometry. 2005. (Illus.). 128p. pap. 9.95 (978-1-933196-08-4(4)) Advanced Learning Pr.

—Nonfiction Writing Prompts for Secondary Art. 2005. 128p. pap. 9.95 (978-1-933196-09-1(2)) Advanced Learning Pr.

—Nonfiction Writing Prompts for Secondary Music. 2005. (Illus.). 128p. pap. 9.95 (978-1-933196-10-7(6)) Advanced Learning Pr.

Windsor, Jo. Burrows, Tunnels, & Chambers: Individual Title Six-Packs. (Sails Literacy Ser.). 16p. (gr. 2-3). 27.00 (978-0-7578-0711-4(9)) Rigby Education.

Worktext for K5: For Christian Schools. 2004. (Illus.). 392p. pap. 30.00 (978-1-57924-845-1(4)) Jones, Bob Univ. Pr.

Write on Target for Grade 5. 2006. (J). stu. ed., per., wbk. ed. 16.95 (978-1-59230-159-1(2)) Englefield & Assocs., Inc.

Write on Target Grade 3: Student Workbook. 2005. (J). stu. ed., per. 10.95 (978-1-59230-151-5(7)) Englefield & Assocs., Inc.

Write on Target Grade 4: Student Workbook. 2005. (J). stu. ed., per. 10.95 (978-1-59230-149-2(5)) Englefield & Assocs., Inc.

Write on Target Grade 6: Student Workbook. 2005. (J). pap., stu. ed. 10.95 (978-1-59230-157-6(5)) Englefield & Assocs., Inc.

Writing for Results. (J). (gr. 4-12). (978-0-89688-184-6(9) , 88-184) Open Court Publishing Co.

Writing for Standardized Tests: A Student Guide to Writing for Standardized Tests. (YA). (gr. 9-12). stu. ed. (978-0-8215-0763-6(X)) Sadlier, William H. Inc.

Writing Handbook. (J). 15.00 (978-1-931555-02-9(8)) Our Lady of Victory Schl.

Writing Paragraphs (Gr. 3-4) 2003. (J). (978-1-58232-128-8(0)) Bryan Hse. Pubs., Inc.

Writing Resource Book. (J). (gr. 2-9). (978-0-89688-110-5(5) , 88-110) Open Court Publishing Co.

Writing Sentences (Gr. 2-3) 2003. (J). (978-1-58232-127-1(2)) Bryan Hse. Pubs., Inc.

Writing to Explain. 2003. 64p. (J). (gr. 3-6). pap. 9.99 (978-0-7424-1837-0(5) , IFG99069) School Specialty Publishing.

Writing to Persuade. 2003. 64p. (J). (gr. 3-6). pap. 9.99 (978-0-7424-1839-4(1) , IFG99071) School Specialty Publishing.

Writing Works with NC Wordcrafter & Joey: Grade 3+ 2004. 28.00 (***978-0-9790796-0-3(8)***) PJR Assocs., Ltd.

Writing Works with NC Wordcrafter & Joey: Grade 4+ 2004. 28.00 (***978-0-9790796-1-0(6)***) PJR Assocs., Ltd.

Writing Works with NC Wordcrafter & Joey: Grade 5+ 2004. 28.00 (***978-0-9790796-2-7(4)***) PJR Assocs., Ltd.

Zile, Susan Van. Reading & Writing Graphic Organizers & Mini-Lessons. 2006. 48p. pap. 10.99 (978-0-439-54897-7(7) , Teaching Resources) Scholastic, Inc.

RHINE RIVER AND VALLEY

Allan, Tony. The Rhine. 2003. (Great Rivers of the World Ser.). (Illus.). 48p. (gr. 5 up). (J). pap. 14.95 (978-0-8368-5453-4(5)); (YA). lib. bdg. 30.00 (978-0-8368-5446-6(2)) Stevens, Gareth Inc. (World Almanac Library).

Foley, Ronan. The Rhine. 2003. (River Journey Ser.). (Illus.). 48p. (J). lib. bdg. 28.56 (978-0-7398-6073-1(9)) Raintree.

RHINE RIVER AND VALLEY—FICTION

Brabourne, Edward Hugessen Knatchbull-Hugessen. River Legends of the Thames & Rhine. Doré, Gustave, illus. 2005. (J). pap. (978-0-486-44372-0(8)) Dover Pubns., Inc.

RHINOCEROSES

Carson, Mary Kay. Emi & the Rhino Scientist: Saving Species from Extinction. Uhlman, Tom, photos by. 2007. (Illus.). 64p. (J). (gr. 5). 18.00 (***978-0-618-64639-5(6)***) Houghton Mifflin Co.

Ciovacco, Justine. Rhinoceroses. 2007. (J). (***978-1-59939-122-9(8)*** , Reader's Digest Young Families, Inc.) Reader's Digest Children's Publishing, Inc.

Craft, Sarah S. Mother Indian Rhinos & Their Babies. 1999. (Zoo Life Book Ser.). (Illus.). 24p. (J). (gr. k-4). lib. bdg. 18.75 (978-0-8239-5318-9(1) , PowerKids Pr.) Rosen Publishing Group, Inc., The.

Czech, Jan M. The Rhino: A MyReportLinks. com Book. 2005. (Endangered & Threatened Animals Ser.). (Illus.). 48p. (J). lib. bdg. 25.26 (978-0-7660-5062-4(9) , MyReportLinks.com Bks.) Enslow Pubs., Inc.

Goecke, Michael P. Giant Rhino. 2003. (Prehistoric Animals Ser.). (Illus.). 24p. (J). (gr. k-4). lib. bdg. 21.35 (978-1-57765-969-3(4)) ABDO Publishing Co.

—Woolly Rhinoceros. 2004. (Prehistoric Animals Set II Ser.). (Illus.). 24p. (J). (gr. k-4). lib. bdg. 21.35 (978-1-57765-978-5(3)) ABDO Publishing Co.

Hamilton, Garry. Rhino Rescue: Changing the Future for Endangered Wildlife. 2006. (Firefly Animal Rescue Ser.). (Illus.). 64p. (J). (gr. 5-12). pap. 9.95 (978-1-55297-910-5(5)); lib. bdg. 19.95 (978-1-55297-912-9(1)) Firefly Bks., Ltd.

Holmes, Kevin J. Rhinos. 2000. (Animals Ser.). (Illus.). 24p. (J). (gr. 2-3). 18.60 (978-0-7368-0496-7(X) , Bridgestone Bks.) Capstone Pr., Inc.

Jango-Cohen, Judith. Rhinoceroses. 2004. (Animals, Animals Ser.). (J). 25.64 (978-0-7614-1753-8(2) , Benchmark Bks.) Cavendish, Marshall Corp.

Jarrow, Gail. Rhinos. 2003. (Animal Attacks Ser.). (Illus.). 48p. (J). 26.20 (978-0-7377-1543-9(X) , Greenhaven Pr., Inc.) Thomson Gale.

Kalman, Bobbie. Endangered Rhinoceros. 2003. (Earth's Endangered Animals Ser.). (Illus.). 32p. (J). (978-0-7787-1852-9(2)); pap. (978-0-7787-1898-7(0)) Crabtree Publishing Co.

Kendell, Patricia. Rhinos. 2003. (In the Wild Ser.). (Illus.). 32p. (J). lib. bdg. 25.70 (978-0-7398-6638-2(9)) Raintree.

Latta, Jan. Rudy el Rinoceronte. 2006. (SPA.). (J). pap. (***978-0-8368-7977-3(5)***); lib. bdg. (***978-0-8368-7970-4(8)***) Stevens, Gareth Inc.

—Rudy the Rhinoceros. 2006. (Illus.). 24p. (J). pap. (***978-0-8368-7778-6(0)***); lib. bdg. (***978-0-8368-7771-7(3)***) Stevens, Gareth Inc.

McMonigle, Orin. The Complete Guide to Rearing Grant's Rhinoceros Beetles: And Other US Rhinoceros Beetles. 2nd exp. ed. 2001. 37p. (C). 10.00 (978-0-9719129-0-8(4)) Elytra & Antenna.

Murray, Peter. Rhinos. 2005. (World of Mammals Ser.). 40p. (J). (gr. 2-6). 29.93 (978-1-59296-502-1(4)) Child's World, Inc.

Nelson, Kristin L. African Rhinos. 2005. (Pull Ahead Bks.). (Illus.). 32p. (J). 22.60 (978-0-8225-2423-6(6) , Lerner Pubns.); pap. 5.95 (978-0-8225-2442-7(2)) Lerner Publishing Group.

Orme, Helen. Rhinos in Danger. 2007. (Wildlife Survival Ser.). (Illus.). 32p. (J). lib. bdg. 25.27 (978-1-59716-265-4(5)) Bearport Publishing Co., Inc.

Penny, Malcolm. Black Rhino: Habitats, Life Cycle, Food Chains, Threats. 2001. (Illus.). 48p. (J). lib. bdg. 27.12 (978-0-7398-4438-0(5)) Raintree.

Pohl, Kathleen. Rhinos. 2007. (J). pap. (***978-0-8368-8229-2(6)***); 24p. lib. bdg. 19.93 (***978-0-8368-8222-3(9)***) Stevens, Gareth Inc. (Weekly Reader Early Learning Library).

—Rhinos: Rinocerontes. 2007. (SPA & ENG.). (J). pap. (***978-0-8368-8243-8(1)*** , Weekly Reader Early Learning Library) Stevens, Gareth Inc.

—Rhinos/Rinocerontes. 2007. (Animals I See at the Zoo/ Animales que Veo en el Zoologico Ser.). (SPA & ENG.). 24p. (J). (gr. k-2). lib. bdg. 19.93 (***978-0-8368-8236-0(9)*** , Weekly Reader Early Learning Library) Stevens, Gareth Inc.

Riehecky, Janet. Giant Rhinoceros. 2008. (J). (***978-1-4296-0037-8(3)*** , Pebble Bks.) Capstone Pr., Inc.

Schaefer, Lola M. Rhinos: Horn-Faced Chargers. 2001. (Wild World of Animals Ser.). (Illus.). 24p. (J). (gr. 1-2). lib. bdg. 18.60 (978-0-7368-0967-2(8) , Bridgestone Bks.) Capstone Pr., Inc.

Spilsbury, Louise & Spilsbury, Richard. Black Rhino. 2004. (Animals under Threat Ser.). (Illus.). 48p. (J). lib. bdg. 27.07 (978-1-4034-4859-0(0)) Heinemann Library.

—The Black Rhino. 2004. (Animals under Threat Ser.). (Illus.). 48p. (J). pap. 8.50 (978-1-4034-5433-1(7)) Heinemann Library.

—Save the Black Rhino. 2006. (J). 25.36 (978-1-4034-7804-7(X)); 32p. pap. (978-1-4034-7812-2(0)) Heinemann Library.

Stewart, Melissa. Rhinoceroses. 2002. (True Bks.). (Illus.). 48p. (J). (gr. 3-5). pap. 6.95 (978-0-516-26992-4(5)); 25.00 (978-0-516-22201-1(5)) Scholastic Library Publishing. (Children's Pr.).

Stone, Lynn M. Rhinoceros. 2001. (Wildlife in Danger Ser.). (Illus.). 24p. (gr. 1-4). 14.95 (978-1-58952-021-9(1)) Rourke Publishing, LLC.

Stone, Tanya Lee. Rhinos. 2003. (Wild Wild World Ser.). 24p. (YA). 24.94 (978-1-56711-821-6(6) , Blackbirch Pr., Inc.) Thomson Gale.

Suen, Anastasia. A Rhinoceros Grows Up. Denman, Michael L. & Huiett, William J., illus. 2005. (Wild Animals Ser.). 24p. (J). (ps). lib. bdg. 23.93 (978-1-4048-0986-4(4)) Picture Window Bks.

Theodorou, Rod. Black Rhino. (Animals in Danger Ser.). (Illus.). 32p. (J). (gr. k-2). 2002. pap. 6.95 (978-1-58810-442-7(7) , 91150); 2000. lib. bdg. 21.36 (978-1-57572-262-7(3)) Heinemann Library.

Thomas, Isabel. Elephant vs. Rhino. 2006. (Illus.). 32p. (J). (978-1-4109-2393-6(2)); pap. (978-1-4109-2400-1(9)) Steck-Vaughn.

Toon, Ann & Toon, Steve. Rhinos: Natural History & Conservation. 2002. (WorldLife Library Ser.). (Illus.). 72p. pap. 17.95 (978-0-89658-586-7(7)) Voyageur Pr., Inc.

Walker, Sally M. Rhinos. 2007. (Nature Watch Ser.). (Illus.). 48p. (J). 25.26 (978-0-8225-6600-7(1) , Lerner Pubns.) Lerner Publishing Group.

RHINOCEROSES—FICTION

Annunziata, Jane & Nemiroff, Marc A. Why Am I an Only Child? Scott, Margaret, illus. 1998. 36p. (J). (ps-3). 19.95 (978-1-55798-506-4(5) , 441-5065) American Psychological Assn.

Araki, Mie. Perfect Tail. 2004. (Illus.). 32p. (J). 14.95 (978-0-8118-4266-2(5)) Chronicle Bks. LLC.

Blecker, Lisa. The Good in Me from A to Z by Dottie. Blecker, Lisa, illus. 2006. (Illus.). bds. 12.95 (978-1-931492-21-8(2)) Discover Writing Pr.

Bolam, Emily, illus. Chunky Safari Rhino. 2001. (Chunky Farm Ser.). 14p. (J). (ps). bds. 4.95 (978-0-7641-5329-7(3)) Barron's Educational Series, Inc.

Butler, Dori. How the Rhino Got Wrinkly Skin: An Adaptation of a Rudyard Kipling Story. 2006. spiral bd. 23.00 (***978-1-4108-7162-6(2)***) Benchmark Education Co.

Cazet, Denys. Minnie & Moo & the Seven Wonders of the World. Cazet, Denys, illus. 2003. (Illus.). 144p. (J). 16.95 (978-0-689-85330-2(0) , Atheneum/Richard Jackson Bks.) Simon & Schuster Children's Publishing.

Dahl, Michael. Whats Bugging Pamela? Trover, Zachary, illus. 2005. (Read-It! Readers Ser.). 32p. (J). (ps). lib. bdg. 18.60 (978-1-4048-1189-8(3)) Picture Window Bks.

Dana, Martha. No Talk! No Baby! Garamella, Joyce Orchard, illus. 2001. 48p. (J). (ps-3). pap. 11.95 (978-1-880158-31-9(0)) Townsend, J.N. Publishing.

de Brunhoff, Laurent. Babar & the Wully-Wully. 2001. (Illus.). 40p. (J). (ps-3). 16.95 (978-0-8109-4397-1(2)) Abrams, Harry N. , Inc.

—Babar's Battle. 2002. (Babar Ser.). (Illus.). 38p. (J). (ps-3). 16.95 (978-0-8109-5714-5(0)) Abrams, Harry N. , Inc.

—Babar's Little Girl Makes a Friend. 2002. (Babar Ser.). (Illus.). 30p. (J). (ps-3). 9.95 (978-0-8109-0556-6(6)) Abrams, Harry N. , Inc.

Derrick, Patricia. Riley the Rhinoceros. 2007. 32p. 18.95 (978-1-933818-15-3(8)) Animalations.

Ema the Rhinoceros. 2005. (African Wildlife Foundation(R) Kids! Ser.). (Illus.). 32p. (J). (ps-2). 9.95 (978-1-59249-180-3(4) , PS6550) Soundprints.

Ende, Michael. Norberto Nucagorda, Level 5.5. Wittenberg, Stella, illus. 2003. (SPA.). 32p. (J). (gr. 3-5). pap. 8.95 (978-84-204-3719-4(0) , AF1328) Santillana USA Publishing Co., Inc.

Eubank, Patricia Reeder. Do I Belong with You? Eubank, Patricia Reeder, illus. 2002. (Illus.). 32p. (J). (ps-3). 9.95 (978-1-59093-074-8(6) , Eager Minds Pr.) Warehousing & Fulfillment Specialists, LLC (WFS, LLC).

Eubank, Patti Reeder. Just Where You Belong. 2004. 32p. (J). 8.95 (978-0-8249-5481-9(5)) Ideals Pubns.

Gates-Galvin, Laura. Rhinoceros's Bathtime. Cohen, Jessie, photos by. 1999. (Let's Go to the Zoo! Ser.: Vol. 4). (Illus.). 16p. (J). (ps-k). bds. 5.95 (978-1-56899-800-8(7) , B9004) Soundprints.

Hanson, Anders. Rhino Horns. Nobens, C. A., illus. 2006. (Fact & Fiction Ser.). 24p. (J). 21.35 (978-1-59679-963-9(3) , SandCastle); pap. (978-1-59679-964-6(1)) ABDO Publishing Co.

Harrison, Kevin. I Know a Rhino. 2nd rev. ed. 2007. 44p. (J). pap. 10.99 (978-1-59092-223-1(9) , Little Blue Works) Windstorm Creative.

Hughes, Fox Carlton. Rainbow Rhino. Hughes, Fox Carlton, illus. 2007. (Illus.). 36p. 16.95 (***978-0-9790275-3-6(5)***) Ovation Bks.

Justus, Adalu. Bipity Bop: From Grandmomi's Stories. Justus, Adalu, illus. l.t. ed. 1999. (Illus.). 8.50p. (J). (ps-3). spiral bd. 8.50 (978-0-937109-10-6(X) , 500) Ike, J. Bks.

Kennaway, Adrienne. Baby Rhino's Escape. Kennaway, Adrienne, illus. 1999. (Happy Cat Bks.). (Illus.). 32p. (J). (ps-k). pap. 5.95 (978-1-887734-56-1(2)) Star Bright Bks., Inc.

Kessler, Christina. Our Secret, Siri Aang. 2007. 224p. (YA). pap. 6.99 (***978-0-14-240840-7(9)*** , Puffin) Penguin Group (USA) Inc.

Kessler, Cristina. Jubela. Stammen, JoEllen McAllister, illus. 2004. 32p. (J). reprint ed. pap. 6.99 (978-0-689-86690-6(9) , Aladdin) Simon & Schuster Children's Publishing.

—Jubela. 2004. (gr. k-3). lib. bdg. 15.30 (978-0-613-88065-7(X)) Tandem Library Bks.

—Our Secret Siri Aang. 2004. 240p. (YA). (gr. 5). 16.99 (978-0-399-23985-4(5) , Philomel) Penguin Group (USA) Inc.

Kipling, Rudyard. How the Rhinoceros Got His Skin. Raglin, Tim, illus. 2006. (J). (gr. 2-6). 25.65 (978-1-59197-750-6(9)) Spotlight.

Kirkegaard, Ole Lund. Otto Es un Rinoceronte. 2000. (SPA., Illus.). 104p. (J). 15.95 (978-84-204-4774-2(9)) Alfaguara, Ediciones, S.A.- Grupo Santillana ESP. *Dist:* Santillana USA Publishing Co., Inc.

—Otto Es un Rinoceronte. Raul, illus. 2003. (SPA.). 102p. (J). (gr. 3-5). pap. 12.95 (978-958-24-0179-5(6)) Santillana USA Publishing Co., Inc.

Lai, Trevor. Ralphy the Rhino. 1999. (Illus.). (J). pap. 5.99 (978-0-9685903-0-0(6)) Kidmagine Bks. CAN. *Dist:* Milestone Pubns., Ltd.

Louise, T. Paula. Imposibus Rhinoceros, Giraffe & Gnu. Wood, Ashley, illus. 2002. 32p. (J). (gr. 1-5). pap. 7.99 (978-0-9712282-4-5(8)) Idea & Design Works, LLC.

Mammano, Julie. Rhinos Who Play Baseball. Mammano, Julie, illus. 2006. (Illus.). 24p. (J). (gr. k-4). reprint ed. 14.00 (978-0-7567-9995-3(3)) DIANE Publishing Co.

—Rhinos Who Play Soccer. 2001. (Illus.). 32p. (J). (ps-1). 12.95 (978-0-8118-2779-9(8)) Chronicle Bks. LLC.

—Rhinos Who Rescue. 2007. (Illus.). 32p. (J). (ps-2). 13.95 (978-0-8118-5419-1(1)) Chronicle Bks. LLC.

—Rhinos Who Skateboard. 1999. (Illus.). 32p. (J). (ps-3). 12.95 (978-0-8118-2356-2(3)) Chronicle Bks. LLC.

—Rhinos Who Surf. 2006. (Illus.). 32p. (J). pap. 6.95 (978-0-8118-5229-6(6)) Chronicle Bks. LLC.

Nagy, Beth & Nagy, Bridget. Rhino Wings. Nagy, Bridget, photos by. l.t. ed. 1999. (Illus.). 36p. (J). (ps-5). 12.95 (978-0-9679868-0-7(X)) Purple Rhinoceros Publishing Co.

Newman, Jeff. Hippo! No, Rhino! 2006. (Illus.). 36p. (J). (ps-1). 15.99 (978-0-316-15573-1(X)) Little Brown & Co.

Pennington, Beverly. Jonathan's Discovery. 2005. 32p. (J). per. 12.95 (978-1-56167-920-1(8)) American Literary Pr.

Powers, John. Seymour & the Big Red Rhino. Colavecchio, Alan, illus. 2005. 32p. (J). (ps-ps). 14.95 (978-1-929039-21-0(2)) Ambassador Bks., Inc.

Puttock, Simon. Who's the Boss Rhinoceros? Busby, Ailie, illus. 32p. (J). pap. 8.99 (978-0-7497-4354-3(9)) Egmont Bks., Ltd. GBR. *Dist:* Trafalgar Square Publishing.

Rhinoceros Calf. 2002. (Baby Animals Ser.). (Illus.). (J). (978-1-59069-057-4(5) , 1-1004) Studio Mouse LLC.

Rieback, Milton. The Adventures of Webb Ellis, a Tale from the Heart of Africa: The Return of the Protectors. Crowley, Cheryl, illus. 2006. (J). lib. bdg. 19.95 (978-0-9777440-0-8(0)) Inyati Press.

Rodrigues, Ann & Winch, John. What Little Rhino Sees. 2002. (J). 15.99 (978-0-7636-1396-9(7)) Candlewick Pr.

Rogers, Alan. Red Rhino. 2004. (Little Giants Ser.). (Illus.). 16p. (ps-k). (J). pap. 3.95 (978-1-58728-161-7(9)); 5.95 (978-1-58728-154-9(6)) T&N Children's Publishing. (Two Can Publishing).

—Rhino Rouge. 2000. (FRE., Illus.). 16p. (J). (ps-k). 5.95 (978-1-58728-174-7(0) , Two Can Publishing) T&N Children's Publishing.

—El Rinoceronte Rojo. 2004. (Pequenos Gigantes Ser.).Tr. of Red Rhino. (SPA., Illus.). 16p. (ps-k). (J). pap. 3.95 (978-1-58728-958-3(X)); 5.95 (978-1-58728-144-0(9)) T&N Children's Publishing. (Two Can Publishing).

—El Rinoceronte Rojo. Rogers, Alan, illus. 2000. (Pequenos Gigantes Ser.).Tr. of Red Rhino. (Illus.). 15p. (J). (ps-ps). lib. bdg. 10.75 (978-0-606-20885-7(2)) Tandem Library Bks.

Shriver, Chelsea. Ema the Rhinoceros. 2005. (African Wildlife Foundation(R) Kids! Ser.). (Illus.). (J). (ps-2). 36p. 8.95 incl. cd-rom (978-1-59249-202-2(9) , SD6500); 32p. 2.95 incl. cd-rom (978-1-59249-179-7(0) , S6550) Soundprints.

—Ema the Rhinoceros. Leeper, Christopher J., tr. Leeper, Christopher J., illus. 2005. (African Wildlife Foundation(R) Ser.). 36p. (J). (ps-2). 14.95 incl. cd-rom (978-1-59249-177-3(4) , H6500); pap. 6.95 (978-1-59249-178-0(2) , S6500) Soundprints.

Silverstein, Shel. Who Wants a Cheap Rhinoceros? Silverstein, Shel, illus. 2002. (Illus.). 64p. (J). (ps-3). 17.95 (978-0-689-85113-1(8)) Simon & Schuster Children's Publishing.

Sykes, Julie. Great Dinosaur Mystery. 2001. (gr. k-3). lib. bdg. 11.25 (978-0-613-53511-3(1)) Tandem Library Bks.

Terry, Michael. Rhino's Horns. 2001. (Illus.). 32p. (J). (ps up). 19.99 (978-0-7475-5051-8(4)) Bloomsbury Publishing Plc GBR. *Dist:* Independent Pubs. Group.

—Rhinos Horns. 2003. (Illus.). (J). (978-1-58234-796-7(4) , Bloomsbury Children) Bloomsbury Publishing.

—Rhinos Horns. 2002. (Illus.). 32p. (J). pap. 10.99 (978-0-7475-5534-6(6)) Bloomsbury Publishing Plc GBR. *Dist:* Independent Pubs. Group.

Ulick, Michael Ackerman. Romeo the Rhino's Rocky Romance: A Cautionary Tale about Differences. Guy, Will, illus. 32p. (J). 15.95 (978-0-9679813-0-7(1)) Footprints Pr.

Weiss, Ellen, et al. Babar & the Christmas House. 2003. (Illus.). 28p. (J). (ps-1). 9.95 (978-0-8109-4583-8(5) , 53604968) Abrams, Harry N. , Inc.

Willis, Jeanne. The Really Rude Rhino. Ross, Tony, illus. 2007. 32p. (J). pap. 9.95 (978-1-84270-571-1(7)) Andersen GBR. *Dist:* Independent Pubs. Group.

You Should Try That with a Rhino: Individual Title Six-Packs. (ps-2). 23.00 (978-0-7635-8822-9(9)) Rigby Education.

RHODE ISLAND

Allio, Mark R. R Is for Rhode Island Red: A Rhode Island Alphabet. Begin, Mary Jane, illus. 2005. (Discover America State by State Ser.). 40p. (J). (gr. k-5). 17.95 (978-1-58536-149-6(6)) Sleeping Bear Pr.

Deady, Kathleen W. Rhode Island. 2003. (Land of Liberty Ser.). (J). (Illus.). 64p. lib. bdg. 25.26 (978-0-7368-2196-4(1)); (978-0-7368-2342-5(5)) Capstone Pr., Inc.

Doak, Robin S. Rhode Island. 2004. (Life in the Thirteen Colonies Ser.). (Illus.). 124p. (J). 36.00 (978-0-516-24578-2(3) , Children's Pr.) Scholastic Library Publishing.

Feeney, Kathy. Rhode Island Facts & Symbols. (States & Their Symbols Ser.). 24p. (J). 2000. (Illus.). (gr. 2-3). lib. bdg. 18.60 (978-0-7368-0645-9(8) , Bridgestone Bks.); 2003. lib. bdg. 19.93 (978-0-7368-2270-1(4)) Capstone Pr., Inc.

Feinstein, Stephen. Rhode Island: A MyReportLinks.com Book. 2003. (States Ser.). (Illus.). 48p. (J). (gr. 4-10). lib. bdg. 25.26 (978-0-7660-5028-0(9) , MyReportLinks.com Bks.) Enslow Pubs., Inc.

Hallinan, Val. Rhode Island. 2003. (From Sea to Shining Sea Ser.: 2). (Illus.). 80p. (J). 30.50 (978-0-516-22489-3(1) , Children's Pr.) Scholastic Library Publishing.

Heinrichs, Ann. Rhode Island. Kania, Matt, illus. 2005. (Welcome to the USA Ser.). 40p. (J). (gr. 1-5). 27.07 (978-1-59296-481-9(8)) Child's World, Inc.

—Rhode Island. 2003. (This Land Is Your Land Ser.). (Illus.). 48p. (J). (gr. 3 up). lib. bdg. 22.60 (978-0-7565-0358-1(2)) Compass Point Bks.

Klein, T. Rhode Island. 1998. (Celebrate the States Ser.). (Illus.). 144p. (gr. 4-8). lib. bdg. 37.07 (978-0-7614-0417-0(1) , Benchmark Bks.) Cavendish, Marshall Corp.

Klein, Ted. Rhode Island. 2nd ed. 2007. (Celebrate the States Ser.). (J). lib. bdg. 39.93 (***978-0-7614-2560-1(8)*** , Benchmark Bks.) Cavendish, Marshall Corp.

Kummer, Patricia K. Rhode Island. rev. ed. 2002. (One Nation Ser.). (Illus.). 48p. (J). (gr. 3-4). lib. bdg. 22.60 (978-0-7368-1264-1(4) , Bridgestone Bks.) Capstone Pr., Inc.

Labella, Susan. Rhode Island. 2006. (Rookie Read-About Geography Ser.). (Illus.). 32p. (J). (gr. 1-2). 20.50 (***978-0-516-25388-6(3)***) Scholastic Library Publishing.

Marsh, Carole. The BIG Rhode Island Reproducible Activity Book. 2001. (Illus.). 96p. (J). (gr. 2-6). pap. 9.95 (978-0-7933-9954-3(8)) Gallopade International.

—My First Book about Rhode Island. 2001. (Carole Marsh Rhode Island Bks.). (Illus.). 32p. (J). (gr. k-4). pap. 7.95 (978-0-7933-9896-6(7)) Gallopade International.

—Rhode Island Classic Christmas Trivia. 2002. (Carole Marsh Rhode Island Bks.). (Illus.). 32p. pap. 14.95 (978-0-635-01443-6(2) , 14432); lib. bdg. 21.95 (978-0-635-01444-3(0) , 14440) Gallopade International. (Marsh, Carole Bks.).

—Rhode Island Current Events Projects: 30 Cool, Activities, Crafts, Experiments & More for Kids to Do to Learn about Your State! 2003. (Rhode Island Experience Ser.). 32p. (gr. k-8). pap. 5.95 (978-0-635-02058-1(0) , Marsh, Carole Bks.) Gallopade International.

—The Rhode Island Experience Pocket Guide. 2001. (Carole Marsh Rhode Island Bks.). (Illus.). 96p. (J). (gr. 3-8). pap. 6.95 (978-0-7933-9925-3(4)) Gallopade International.

—Rhode Island Geography Projects: 30 Cool, Activities, Crafts, Experiments & More for Kids to Do to Learn about Your State! 2003. (Rhode Island Experience Ser.). 32p. (gr. k-5). pap. 5.95 (978-0-635-01858-8(6) , Marsh, Carole Bks.) Gallopade International.

—Rhode Island Government Projects: 30 Cool, Activities, Crafts, Experiments & More for Kids to Do to Learn about Your State! 2003. (Rhode Island Experience Ser.). 32p. (gr. k-5). pap. 5.95 (978-0-635-01958-5(2) , Marsh, Carole Bks.) Gallopade International.

—Rhode Island History Projects: 30 Cool, Activities, Crafts, Experiments & More for Kids to Do to Learn about Your State! 2003. (Rhode Island Experience Ser.). 32p. (gr. k-5). pap. 5.95 (978-0-635-01808-3(X) , Marsh, Carole Bks.) Gallopade International.

—Rhode Island Jeopardy! Answers & Questions about Our State! 2001. (Carole Marsh Rhode Island Bks.). (Illus.). 32p. (J). (gr. 3-8). pap. 7.95 (978-0-7933-9809-6(6)) Gallopade International.

—Rhode Island "Jography" A Fun Run Thru Our State! 2001. (Carole Marsh Rhode Island Bks.). (Illus.). 32p. (J). (gr. 3-8). pap. 7.95 (978-0-7933-9838-6(X)) Gallopade International.

—Rhode Island People Projects: 30 Cool, Activities, Crafts, Experiments & More for Kids to Do to Learn about Your State! 2003. (Rhode Island Experience Ser.). 32p. (gr. k-5). pap. 5.95 (978-0-635-02008-6(4) , Marsh, Carole Bks.) Gallopade International.

—Rhode Island Symbols & Facts Projects: 30 Cool, Activities, Crafts, Experiments & More for Kids to Do to Learn about Your State! 2003. (Rhode Island Experience Ser.). 32p. (gr. k-5). pap. 5.95 (978-0-635-01908-0(6) , Marsh, Carole Bks.) Gallopade International.

Mattern, Joanne. Rhode Island: The Ocean State. 2003. (World Almanac Library of the States). (Illus.). 48p. (J). (gr. 5 up). pap. 14.95 (978-0-8368-5330-8(X)); lib. bdg. 30.00 (978-0-8368-5159-5(5)) Stevens, Gareth Inc. (World Almanac Library).

Moose, Katie. Uniquely Rhode Island. 2004. (Heinemann State Studies). (Illus.). 48p. (J). 9.00 (978-1-4034-4729-6(2)); lib. bdg. 27.07 (978-1-4034-4660-2(1)) Heinemann Library.

Murray, Julie. Rhode Island. 2006. (Illus.). 32p. (J). (gr. k-4). lib. bdg. 22.78 (978-1-59197-698-1(7) , Buddy Bks.) ABDO Publishing Co.

Petreycik, Ryan. Rhode Island. 2005. (It's My State! Ser.). (Illus.). 80p. (J). 27.07 (978-0-7614-1859-7(8) , Benchmark Bks.) Cavendish, Marshall Corp.

Rhode Island. 2000. (Switched on Schoolhouse Ser.). (Illus.). (YA). (gr. 7-12). pap. 24.95 incl. cd-rom (978-0-7403-0291-6(4) , SOSRI) Alpha Omega Pubns., Inc.

Severin, Carol. Rhode Island. 2006. (Portraits of the States Ser.). (J). pap. (978-0-8368-4724-6(5)); lib. bdg. (978-0-8368-4707-9(5)) Stevens, Gareth Inc.

Warner, J. F. Rhode Island. (Hello U. S. A. Ser.). (Illus.). (J). (gr. 3-6). 2000. 72p. pap. 5.95 (978-0-8225-9792-6(6) , First Avenue Editions); 2nd exp. rev. ed. 2003. 84p. 25.26 (978-0-8225-4108-0(4) , Lerner Pubns.) Lerner Publishing Group.

—Rhode Island. rev. ed. 2003. (gr. 3-6). lib. bdg. 15.25 (978-0-613-52489-6(6)) Tandem Library Bks.

Way, Jennifer. Rhode Island. 2006. (Bilingual Library of the United States of America: Set 2). (ENG & SPA., Illus.). 32p. (J). (gr. 3-6). lib. bdg. 22.50 (978-1-4042-3105-4(6) , Buenas Letra) Rosen Publishing Group, Inc., The.

Whitehurst, Susan. The Colony of Rhode Island. 2000. (Library of the Thirteen Colonies & the Lost Colony). (Illus.). 24p. (J). (gr. 3). lib. bdg. 19.95 (978-0-8239-5476-6(5) , PowerKids Pr.) Rosen Publishing Group, Inc., The.

Wiener, Roberta & Arnold, James R. Rhode Island. 2004. (Illus.). 64p. (J). 28.56 (978-0-7398-6887-4(X)) Harcourt Schl. Pubs.

—The 13 Colonies: Rhode Island. 2004. (Illus.). 64p. (J). 8.95 (978-1-4109-0311-2(7)) Harcourt Schl. Pubs.

Winans, Jay D. A Guide to Rhode Island. 2001. (American States Ser.). (Illus.). 32p. (J). lib. bdg. 16.95 (978-1-930954-84-7(0)) Weigl Pubs., Inc.

RHODE ISLAND—FICTION

Bruchac, Joseph. Whisper in the Dark. Comport, Sally Wern, illus. 2005. 192p. (J). (gr. 5 up). 15.99 (978-0-06-058087-2(9)); lib. bdg. 16.89 (978-0-06-058088-9(7)) HarperCollins Pubs.

Curtis, Alice Turner. A Little Maid of Narragansett Bay. 2004. (Little Maid Ser.). (Illus.). 192p. (J). (gr. 1-6). reprint ed. per. 12.95 (978-1-55709-334-9(2)) Applewood Bks.

—A Little Maid of Virginia. 2004. (Little Maid Ser.). (Illus.). 192p. (J). (gr. 1-3). reprint ed. per. 9.95 (978-1-55709-333-2(4)) Applewood Bks.

Griffin, Adele. Where I Want to Be. 160p. (gr. 7). 2007. (YA). 6.99 (***978-0-14-240948-0(0)*** , Puffin); 2005. (J). 15.99 (978-0-399-23783-6(6) , Putnam Juvenile) Penguin Group (USA) Inc.

Hood, Ann. How I Saved My Father's Life (and Ruined Everything Else) 2008. 224p. (J). pap. 16.99 (***978-0-439-92819-9(2)*** , Scholastic Pr.) Scholastic, Inc.

Johnson, Maureen. Devilish. 2006. 288p. (YA). (gr. 7-12). 16.99 (978-1-59514-060-9(3) , Razorbill) Penguin Group (USA) Inc.

Lisle, Janet Taylor. The Art of Keeping Cool. 2002. 256p. (J). (gr. 5-9). pap. 5.99 (978-0-689-83788-3(7) , Aladdin) Simon & Schuster Children's Publishing.

—The Art of Keeping Cool. Goldstrom, Robert, illus. 2000. 216p. (J). (gr. 5-7). 17.00 (978-0-689-83787-6(9) , Atheneum/Richard Jackson Bks.) Simon & Schuster Children's Publishing.

—The Art of Keeping Cool. 2002. (gr. 5-8). lib. bdg. 13.00 (978-0-613-54109-1(X)) Tandem Library Bks.

—Black Duck. (J). (gr. 5 up). 2007. 256p. 6.99 (***978-0-14-240902-2(2)*** , Puffin); 2006. 240p. 15.99 (978-0-399-23963-2(4) , Philomel) Penguin Group (USA) Inc.

Lisle, Janet Taylor. The Crying Rocks. 2003. (Illus.). 208p. (YA). 16.95 (978-0-689-85319-7(X) , Atheneum/Richard Jackson Bks.) Simon & Schuster Children's Publishing.

—The Crying Rocks. l.t. ed. 2004. (Thorndike Press Large Print Literacy Bridge Ser.). 273p. (J). 22.95 (978-0-7862-6140-6(4)) Thorndike Pr.

Livsey, John. '38: The Great Hurricane in Quonochontaug, Rhode Island. 2004. 288p. (YA). per. 15.49 (978-0-9754979-2-0(8)) Big Wave Bks.

Metz, Melinda. Ravens Point. 2005. pap. (978-0-06-052373-2(5)) HarperCollins Canada, Ltd.

Shea, Pegi Deitz. Tangled Threads: A Hmong Girl's Story. 2003. 240p. (J). (gr. 5-9). tchr. ed. 15.00 (978-0-618-24748 6(3) , Clarion Bks.) Houghton Mifflin Co. Trade & Reference Div.

Wilson, J. M. & Zolkowski, Cathy A. Blue: Adventures of a Gymnast. 2004. 150p. (YA). per. 11.95 (978-0-9667037-5-7(8)) Verona (Bk.) Publishing, Inc.

RHODE ISLAND—HISTORY

Allison, Amy. Roger Williams: Founder of Rhode Island. 2000. (Colonial Leaders Ser.). (Illus.). 80p. (J). (gr. 8-12). 27.50 (978-0-7910-5964-7(2) , Chelsea Hse.) Facts On File, Inc.

Axelrod-Contrada, Joan. A Primary Source History of the Colony of Rhode Island. 2005. (Primary Sources of the Thirteen Colonies & the Lost Colony Ser.). (Illus.). 64p. (J). (gr. 3-7). pap. 14.60 (978-1-4042-0675-5(2)); (YA). (gr. 5-8). lib. bdg. 29.25 (978-1-4042-0434-8(2)) Rosen Publishing Group, Inc., The.

Burgan, Michael. Roger Williams: Founder of Rhode Island. 2006. (Signature Lives Ser.). (Illus.). 112p. (J). (gr. 5-7). 30.60 (978-0-7565-1596-6(3)) Compass Point Bks.

Deady, Kathleen W. The Rhode Island Colony. 2005. (Fact Finders Ser.). (Illus.). 32p. (J). (ps-7). lib. bdg. 22.60 (978-0-7368-2682-2(3)) Capstone Pr., Inc.

Doherty, Craig A. & Doherty, Katherine M. Rhode Island. 2005. (Thirteen Colonies Ser.). (Illus.). 144p. (J). (gr. 4-9). 35.00 (978-0-8160-5415-2(0)) Facts On File, Inc.

Gaustad, Edwin S. Roger Williams: Prophet of Liberty. 2001. (Oxford Portraits Ser.). (Illus.). 144p. (YA). (gr. 9 up). 28.00 (978-0-19-513000-3(6)) Oxford Univ. Pr., Inc.

Gertsacov, Adam G. Rhode Island A to Z: Coloring/Learning Book: A Creative Approach to the History & Natural History of our Nation's Smallest State. Atwood, Donna S., illus. 2001. 64p. pap. 9.95 (978-0-9660293-8-3(0)) Atwood, Donna Design.

Italia, Bob. The Rhode Island Colony. 2001. (Colonies Ser.). (Illus.). 32p. (J). (gr. k-6). lib. bdg. 22.78 (978-1-57765-587-9(7) , Checkerboard Library) ABDO Publishing Co.

Marsh, Carole. My First Pocket Guide Rhode Island. 2000. (Rhode Island Experience! Ser.). (Illus.). 96p. (J). (gr. 3-8). 12.95 (978-0-635-01329-3(0) , 13290) Gallopade International.

—Rhode Island Millionaire. 2001. (GameBook Ser.). 32p. (J). (gr. 3-8). pap., act. bk. ed. 9.95 (978-0-635-00094-1(6)) Gallopade International.

—Rhode Island Survivor. 2001. (GameBook Ser.). 32p. (J). (gr. 3-8). pap., act. bk. ed. 9.95 (978-0-635-00560-1(3)) Gallopade International.

—Rhode Island Wheel of Fortune. 2001. (GameBook Ser.). 32p. (J). (gr. 3-8). pap., act. bk. ed. 9.95 (978-0-7933-9694-8(8)) Gallopade International.

—The Survivor: A Class Challenge. 2001. (Carole Marsh Rhode Island Bks.). (J). lib. bdg. 29.95 (978-0-635-00685-1(5)) Gallopade International.

—Wheel of Fortune. 2001. (Rhode Island Expereince Ser.). (J). lib. bdg. 29.95 (978-0-7933-9695-5(6)) Gallopade International.

—Who Wants to Be a Millionaire? 2001. (Rhode Island Expereince Ser.). (J). lib. bdg. 29.95 (978-0-635-00095-8(4)) Gallopade International.

McDermott, Jesse. Rhode Island 1636-1776. 2006. (Voices from Colonial America Ser.). (Illus.). 112p. (J). (gr. 5-9). 21.95 (978-0-7922-6410-1(X) , National Geographic Children's Bks.) National Geographic Society.

McDermott, Jesse John. Rhode Island 1636-1776. 2006. (Voices from Colonial America Ser.). (Illus.). 112p. (J). (gr. 5-9). 32.90 (978-0-7922-6868-0(7) , National Geographic Children's Bks.) National Geographic Society.

Miller, Jake. The Colony of Rhode Island: A Primary Source History. 2006. (Primary Source Library of the Thirteen Colonies & the Lost Colony). (Illus.). 24p. (J). lib. bdg. (978-1-4042-3032-3(7) , PowerKids Pr.) Rosen Publishing Group, Inc., The.

Raum, Elizabeth. Roger Williams. 2004. (Illus.). 32p. (J). pap. 7.50 (978-1-4034-5969-5(X)); lib. bdg. 25.64 (978-1-4034-5961-9(4)) Heinemann Library.

Schmittroth, Felkins Ryan. Narraganset. 2003. (Tribes of Native America Ser.). (Illus.). 32p. (J). 23.70 (978-1-56711-698-4(1) , Blackbirch Pr., Inc.) Thomson Gale.

Somervill, Barbara A. The Rhode Island Colony. 2003. (Spirit of America). (Illus.). 40p. (J). (gr. 2-6). 28.50 (978-1-56766-685-4(X)) Child's World, Inc.

Walsh, Kieran. Roger Williams. 2005. (Discover the Life of a Colonial American Ser.). (Illus.). 24p. (gr. 2-5). 14.95 (978-1-59515-140-7(0)) Rourke Publishing, LLC.

Weintraub, A. How to Draw Rhode Islands Sights & Symbols. 2002. (Kids Guide to Drawing America Ser.). 32p. (J). lib. bdg. 25.25 (978-0-8239-6096-5(X) , PowerKids Pr.) Rosen Publishing Group, Inc., The.

Wiener. Rhode Island 6-Pack. 2004. (13 Colonies Ser.). (Illus.). 51.30 (978-1-4109-0374-7(5)) Harcourt Schl. Pubs.

Wilson, James, ed. Rhode Island Treasures. 2003. (Illus.). 112p. per. 15.00 (978-0-615-12390-5(2)) Narragansett Graphics.

RHODES (GREECE)—FICTION

Henty, G. A. A Knight of the White Cross: A Tale of the Siege of Rhodes. 2000. (Illus.). 108p. (YA). (gr. 4-7). pap. 15.99 (978-1-887159-25-8(8)) Preston-Speed Pubns.

—A Knight of the White Cross: A Tale of the Siege of Rhodes. 1999. (gr. 3-6). lib. bdg. 26.85 (978-0-613-80289-5(6)) Tandem Library Bks.

Roberts, Katherine. Seven Fabulous Wonders Colossu. 2005. (Seven Fabulous Wonders Ser.). 320p. (J). pap. 11.00 (978-0-00-711283-8(1)) HarperCollins Pubs. Ltd. GBR. *Dist:* Independent Pubs. Group.

RHODESIA, SOUTHERN

see Zimbabwe

RHYMES

see Limericks; Nonsense Verses; Nursery Rhymes; Poetry—Collections

RHYTHM

see also Versification

Feierabend, John M. The Book of Tapping & Clapping. 2000. (First Steps in Music Ser.). (Illus.). 48p. (J). (ps). pap. 7.95 (978-1-57999-054-1(1)) GIA Pubns., Inc.

Handyside, Chris. A History of Soul & R&B. 2006. (Illus.). 48p. (J). (978-1-4034-8153-5(9)) Heinemann Library.

Webb, Steve. Tanka Tanka Skunk! 2004. (Illus.). 32p. (J). 15.95 (978-0-439-57844-8(2) , Orchard Bks.) Scholastic, Inc.

Williams, Charles F. A. The Rhythm of Modern Music. 2001. 321p. (YA). reprint ed. 98.00 (978-0-7222-5808-8(9)) Library Reprints, Inc.

RICE, CONDOLEEZZA, 1954-

Banting, Erinn. Condoleezza Rice. 2007. (J). (***978-1-59036-639-4(5)); (*978-1-59036-640-0(9)***) Weigl Pubs., Inc.

Blakely, Gloria. Condoleezza Rice. 2003. (African American Leaders Ser.). (Illus.). 112p. (gr. 6-12). 30.00 (978-0-7910-7683-5(0) , Chelsea Hse.) Facts On File, Inc.

Ditchfield, Christin. Condoleezza Rice: America's Leading Stateswoman. 2006. (Great Life Stories Ser.). (Illus.). 111p. (J). (gr. 5-8). 30.50 (978-0-531-13874-8(7) , Watts, Franklin) Scholastic Library Publishing.

—Condoleezza Rice: National Security Advisor. 2003. (Great Life Stories: Political Figures Ser.). (Illus.). 112p. (J). 30.50 (978-0-531-12307-2(3) , Watts, Franklin) Scholastic Library Publishing.

Marsh, Carole. Condoleezza Rice. 2003. 12p. (gr. k-4). 2.95 (***978-0-635-02385-8(7)***) Gallopade International.

Naden, Corinne J. & Blue, Rose. Condoleezza Rice. 2004. (African-American Biographies Ser.). (Illus.). 64p. (J). 28.56 (978-1-4109-1039-4(3)) Raintree.

Ryan, Bernard. Condoleeza Rice: National Security Advisor & Musician. 2003. (Ferguson Career Biographies Ser.). (Illus.). 160p. (J). (gr. 6-12). 25.00 (978-0-8160-5480-0(0) , Ferguson Publishing Co.) Facts On File, Inc.

Sharp, Anne Wallace. Condoleezza Rice. 2007. (People in the News Ser.). (Illus.). 128p. (gr. 7-10). 31.20 (***978-1-59018-521-6(8)*** , Lucent Bks.) Thomson Gale.

Wade, Linda R. Condoleeza Rice. l.t. ed. 2002. (Real-Life Reader Biography Ser.). (Illus.). 32p. (gr. 3-8). lib. bdg. 15.95 (978-1-58415-145-6(5)) Mitchell Lane Pubs., Inc.

—Condoleezza Rice. 2004. (Illus.). 32p. (J). lib. bdg. (978-1-58415-332-0(6)) Mitchell Lane Pubs., Inc.

Wade, Mary. Condoleeza Rice: Being the Best. 2003. (gr. 3-6). lib. bdg. 17.60 (978-0-613-58959-8(9)) Tandem Library Bks.

Wade, Mary Dodson. Condoleezza Rice. rev. ed. 2005. (Illus.). 48p. (J). (ps-7). pap. 6.95 (978-0-7613-9549-2(0) , First Avenue Editions) Lerner Publishing Group.

—Condoleezza Rice: Being the Best. 2003. (Gateway Biography Ser.: 4). 48p. lib. bdg. 23.90 (978-0-7613-2619-9(7)); (Illus.). (gr. 2-4). pap. (978-0-7613-1927-6(1)) Lerner Publishing Group. (Millbrook Pr.).

Wheeler, Jill C. Condoleezza Rice. 2004. (Women of the World Ser.). (J). (978-1-59197-616-5(2)) ABDO Publishing Co.

RICE

De Angelis, Therese. The Ojibwa: Wild Rice Gatherers. 2003. (America's First Peoples Ser.). (Illus.). 32p. (J). (gr. 2-3). lib. bdg. 23.93 (978-0-7368-1537-6(6) , Bridgestone Bks.) Capstone Pr., Inc.

Denny, Roz. Rice. 1998. (Food in Focus Ser.). (Illus.). 32p. (J). (978-1-57572-658-8(0)) Heinemann.

Franck, Irene M. & Brownstone, David M. Rice. 2003. (Illus.). 32p. (J). (978-0-7172-5721-8(5) , Grolier) Scholastic Library Publishing.

Gelman, Rita Golden. Rice Is Life. Choi, Yangsook, illus. 2004. 25p. (J). reprint ed. 16.00 (978-0-7567-7202-4(8)) DIANE Publishing Co.

Lilly, Melinda. Rice. 2001. (Around the World with Food & Spices Ser.). (Illus.). 32p. (J). (gr. 3-5). lib. bdg. 26.60 (978-1-58952-047-9(5)) Rourke Publishing, LLC.

Martineau, Susan. Healthy Eating. 2006. (Illus.). 32p. (J). (978-1-58340-894-0(0) , 1262655) Smart Apple Media.

Spilsbury, Louise. El Arroz. 2003. (Alimentos Ser.). (ENG & SPA.). 32p. (J). pap. 6.50 (978-1-4034-3744-0(0)) Heinemann Library.

—El Arroz (Rice) 2003. (Alimentos Ser.). (Illus.). 32p. (J). lib. bdg. 22.79 (978-1-4034-3738-9(6)) Heinemann Library.

—Rice. (Food Ser.). 32p. pap. 6.95 (978-1-4034-4050-1(6)); 2001. (Illus.). (J). lib. bdg. 21.36 (978-1-58810-150-1(9)) Heinemann Library.

Zronik, John Paul. The Biography of Rice. 2005. (How Did That Get Here? Ser.). (Illus.). 32p. (J). (gr. 3-9). (978-0-7787-2482-7(4)); pap. (978-0-7787-2518-3(9)) Crabtree Publishing Co.

RICHARD I, KING OF ENGLAND, 1157-1199

Abbott, Jacob. History of King Richard the First of England. 2003. 336p. 99.00 (978-0-7950-3593-7(4)) New Library Press.Net.

Crompton, Samuel Willard. The Third Crusade: Richard the Lionhearted vs. Saladin. 2003. (Great Battles Through the Ages Ser.). (Illus.). 112p. (J). (gr. 6-12). 30.00 (978-0-7910-7437-4(4) , Chelsea Hse.) Facts On File, Inc.

Doherty, Katherine M. & Doherty, Craig A. King Richard the Lionhearted & the Crusades in World History. 2002. (In World History Ser.). (Illus.). 128p. (YA). (gr. 5-12). lib. bdg. 26.60 (978-0-7660-1459-6(2)) Enslow Pubs., Inc.

Streissguth, Thomas. Richard the Lionheart: Crusader King of England. 2007. (Rulers of the Middle Ages Ser.). (Illus.). 160p. (YA). (gr. 7-9). lib. bdg. 34.60 (978-0-7660-2714-5(7)) Enslow Pubs., Inc.

West, David & Gaff, Jackie. Richard the Lionheart: The Life of a King & Crusade. 2005. (Graphic Nonfiction Ser.). (Illus.). 48p. (J). lib. bdg. 26.50 (978-1-4042-0241-2(2)) Rosen Publishing Group, Inc., The.

RICHARD I, KING OF ENGLAND, 1157-1199—FICTION

Blaisdell, Robert & Scott, Walter, Sr. Ivanhoe. Green, John, illus. 1998. (Dover Children's Thrift Classics Ser.). 76p. (J). pap. 1.00 (978-0-486-40143-0(X)) Dover Pubns., Inc.

Scott, Walter, Sr., et al. Ivanhoe. (Classics Illustrated Ser.). (Illus.). 52p. (YA). pap. 4.95 (978-1-57209-023-1(5)) Classics International Entertainment, Inc.

RICHARD II, KING OF ENGLAND, 1367-1400

Abbott, Jacob. History of King Richard the Second of England. 2003. 347p. 99.00 (978-0-7950-3594-4(2)) New Library Press.Net.

RICHARD III, KING OF ENGLAND, 1452-1485—FICTION

Rose, Simon. The Sorcerer's Letterbox. 2006. 116p. (J). 7.95 (978-1-896580-52-4(1)) Tradewind Bks. CAN. *Dist:* Orca Bk. Pubs. USA.

Stevenson, Robert Louis. The Black Arrow. l.t. ed. 2005. 448p. pap. (978-1-84637-164-6(3)) Echo Library.

RICHTHOFEN, MANFRED ALBRECHT, FREIHERR VON, 1892-1918

Rice, Earle. Manfred Von Richthofen. 2003. (Famous Flyers Ser.). (Illus.). 112p. (gr. 6-12). 30.00 (978-0-7910-7214-1(2) , Chelsea Hse.) Facts On File, Inc.

RICKEY, BRANCH, 1881-1965

Frystak, Timothy D. Jackie Robinson: With Profiles of Satchel Paige & & Branch Rickey. 2006. (Biographical Connections Ser.). (Illus.). 112p. (J). (978-0-7166-1828-7(1)) World Bk., Inc.

RICOTTA, RICKY (FICTITIOUS CHARACTER)—FICTION

Pilkey, Dav. Giant Robot vs. the Mutant Mosquitoes from Mercury. Ontiveros, Martin, illus. 2000. (Ricky Ricotta Ser.: No. 2). 128p. (J). (ps-3). pap. 16.95 (978-0-590-30721-5(5) , Blue Sky Pr., The) Scholastic, Inc.

—Mighty Robot vs. the Jurassic Jackrabbits from Jupiter. Ontiveros, Martin, illus. 2002. (Ricky Ricotta Ser.: No. 5). 128p. (J). (ps-3). pap. 16.95 (978-0-439-37642-6(4) , Blue Sky Pr., The); pap. 3.99 (978-0-439-37643-3(2)) Scholastic, Inc.

—Mighty Robot vs. the Jurassic Jackrabbits from Jupiter. 2002. (Ricky Ricotta Ser.: No. 5). (ps-2). lib. bdg. 11.80 (978-0-613-50493-5(3)) Tandem Library Bks.

—Ricky Ricotta Y el Poderoso Robot Contra Los Mecamonos de Marte. Ontiveros, Martin, illus. 2002. (Ricky Ricotta Ser.: No. 4). 144p. (gr. 2-4). pap. 3.99 (978-0-439-25296-6(2)); (J). (ps-3). pap. 16.95 (978-0-439-25295-9(4)) Scholastic, Inc. (Blue Sky Pr., The).

—Ricky Ricotta Y el Poderoso Robot Contra Los Mecamonos de Marte. 2002. (Ricky Ricotta Ser.: No. 4). (ps-2). lib. bdg. 11.80 (978-0-613-45613-5(0)) Tandem Library Bks.

—Ricky Ricotta's Giant Robot. Ontiveros, Martin, illus. 2000. (Ricky Ricotta Ser.: Bk. 1). (ps-3). 111p. (J). pap. 16.95 (978-0-590-30719-2(3)); 112p. mass mkt. 3.99 (978-0-590-30720-8(7)) Scholastic, Inc. (Blue Sky Pr., The).

—Ricky Ricotta's Giant Robot. Ontiveros, Martin, illus. 2000. (Ricky Ricotta Ser.: Bk. 1). 111p. (J). (ps). lib. bdg. 11.80 (978-0-613-22267-9(9)) Tandem Library Bks.

—Ricky Ricotta's Giant Robot. 2000. (Ricky Ricotta Ser.: No. 1). (J). (ps-3). (978-0-606-18592-9(5)) Tandem Library Bks.

—Ricky Ricotta's Giant Robot vs. the Mutant Mosquitoes from Mercury. Ontiveros, Martin, illus. 2000. (Ricky Ricotta Ser.: No. 2). (J). (ps-3). pap. 47.88 (978-0-439-21522-0(6)) Scholastic, Inc.

—Ricky Ricotta's Giant Robot vs. the Mutant Mosquitoes from Mercury. Ontiveros, Martin, illus. 2000. (Ricky Ricotta Ser.: Bk. 2). 127p. (J). (ps). per. 11.80 (978-0-613-26747-2(8)) Tandem Library Bks.

—Ricky Ricotta's Giant Robot vs. the Mutant Mosquitoes from Mercury. 2000. (Ricky Ricotta Ser.: No. 2). (J). (ps-3). (978-0-606-19604-8(8)) Tandem Library Bks.

—Ricky Ricotta's Giant Robot vs. the Voodoo Vultures from Venus. Ontiveros, Martin, illus. 2001. (Ricky Ricotta Ser.: No. 3). 128p. (J). (ps-3). pap. 16.95 (978-0-439-23624-9(X)) Scholastic, Inc.

—Ricky Ricotta's Giant Robot vs. the Voodoo Vultures from Venus. 2001. (Ricky Ricotta Ser.: No. 3). (gr. 3-6). lib. bdg. 11.80 (978-0-613-32998-9(8)); (J). (ps-3). (978-0-606-20065-3(7)) Tandem Library Bks.

—Ricky Ricotta's Mighty Robot vs. the Mutant Mosquitoes from Mercury. Ontiveros, Martin, illus. 2000. (Ricky Ricotta Ser.: No. 2). 128p. (J). (ps-3). pap. 3.99 (978-0-590-30722-2(3)) Scholastic, Inc.

—Ricky Ricotta's Mighty Robot vs. the Stupid Stinkbugs from Saturn. Ontiveros, Martin, illus. 2003. (Ricky Ricotta Ser.: No. 6). 128p. (J). mass mkt. 3.99 (978-0-439-37645-7(9) , Blue Sky Pr., The) Scholastic, Inc.

—Ricky Ricotta's Mighty Robot vs. the Voodoo Vultures from Venus. Ontiveros, Martin, illus. 2001. (Ricky Ricotta Ser.: No. 3). 128p. (J). (ps-3). pap. 3.99 (978-0-439-23625-6(8)) Scholastic, Inc.

—Y el Poderoso Robot. Ontiveros, Martin, illus. 2003. (Ricky Ricotta Ser.: Bk. 1). (SPA.). 112p. (J). pap. 3.99 (978-0-439-55117-5(X) , Scholastic en Espanol) Scholastic, Inc.

RIDDLES

see also Charades; Puzzles

Agee, Jon. Smart Feller Fart Smeller & Other Spoonerisms. 2006. (Illus.). 64p. (J). (gr. 2-17). 14.95 (978-0-7868-3692-5(X)) Hyperion Bks. for Children.

Alcantara, Ricardo. Adivina, Adivinanza. 2000. Tr. of Take a Guess, Solve the Riddle. (SPA.). (ps-2). lib. bdg. 15.90 (978-0-613-80604-6(2)) Tandem Library Bks.

Anholt, Catherine & Anholt, Laurence. Can You Guess? A Lift-the-Flap Birthday Party Book. 2003. (Illus.). 16p. pap. 7.95 (978-0-7112-2214-4(2)) Lincoln, Frances Ltd. GBR. *Dist:* Transition Vendor.

Aubert, Elena G., illus. Mis 365 Mejores Adivinanzas. 2003. (SPA.). (978-84-7630-904-9(X) , LA30439) Libsa, Editorial S.A. ESP. *Dist:* Lectorum Pubns., Inc.

Barnett, Michelle Noble, et al. Theme Pockets - August: One of a Kind; Ocean Habitats; Insect Riddles. Evans, Marilyn, ed. Larsen, Jo, illus. 1999. (Making Books with Pockets). 96p. (J). pap., tchr. ed. 12.99 (978-1-55799-705-0(5) , EMC 591) Evan-Moor Educational Pubs.

Beach Riddles. 2006. (J). pap. 5.95 (978-0-8225-6471-3(8) , First Avenue Editions) Lerner Publishing Group.

Benny, Mike. Kids' Nuttiest Jokes. Hoffman, Sanford, illus. 2003. 96p. (J). pap. 4.95 (978-1-4027-0624-0(3)) Sterling Publishing Co., Inc.

Benton, Celia. Our Flag. 2003. (Compass Point Phonics Readers Ser.). (Illus.). 16p. (J). (gr. 1 up). 13.26 (978-0-7565-0517-2(8)) Compass Point Bks.

Blair, Beth L. Jumbo Jokes & Riddles Book: Hours of Gut-Busting Fun! 2006. 384p. pap. 8.95 (978-1-59869-049-1(3)) Adams Media Corp.

Blevins, Wiley. Push or Pull? 2003. (Compass Point Phonics Readers Ser.). (Illus.). 16p. (J). (gr. 1 up). 13.26 (978-0-7565-0521-9(6)) Compass Point Bks.

—Who Am I? 2003. (Compass Point Phonics Readers Ser.). (Illus.). 16p. (J). (gr. 1 up). 13.26 (978-0-7565-0534-9(8)) Compass Point Bks.

A Book of Silly Jokes! 2003. (Illus.). (J). (978-0-439-39056-9(7)) Scholastic, Inc.

Buggy Riddles, Vol. 2. 2005. (Fluent Library). (YA). (ps-3). 29.34 (978-0-8215-8969-4(5)) Sadlier, William H. Inc.

Burns, Diane L. Horsing Around: Jokes to Make Ewe Smile. Gable, Brian, illus. 2005. (Make Me Laugh! Ser.). 32p. (J). (gr. k-3). lib. bdg. 19.93 (978-1-57505-662-3(3)) Lerner Publishing Group.

Carlson, Melody. Jammin' with the Fruit Troop Color Book. 1998. (Stories, Songs, & Riddles Ser.). 64p. (J). pap. 9.99 incl. audio (978-1-57673-305-9(X)) Zonderkidz.

Cerf, Bennett. Riddles & More Riddles! Palen, Debbie, illus. 1999. (Beginner Bks.). 48p. (J). (gr. k-3). 8.99 (978-0-679-88970-0(1) , Random Hse. Bks. for Young Readers) Random Hse. Children's Bks.

Cerrillo & Valverde. Adivina Quien Soy. 2004. (SPA., Illus.). 30p. (J). 6.50 (978-84-348-7753-5(8)) SM Ediciones ESP. *Dist:* Lectorum Pubns., Inc.

Chapman, Cindy. Baby Animals. 2003. (Compass Point Phonics Readers Ser.). (Illus.). 16p. (J). (gr. 1 up). 13.26 (978-0-7565-0504-2(6)) Compass Point Bks.

—On a Farm. 2003. (Compass Point Phonics Readers Ser.). (Illus.). 16p. (J). (gr. 1 up). 13.26 (978-0-7565-0516-5(X)) Compass Point Bks.

—Play It Safe! 2003. (Compass Point Phonics Readers Ser.). (Illus.). 16p. (J). (gr. 1 up). 13.26 (978-0-7565-0520-2(8)) Compass Point Bks.

Charney, Steve. Kids' Kookiest Riddles. Collinet, Rob, illus. 96p. (J). 2007. pap. 4.95 (978-1-4027-4058-9(1)); 2005. 14.95 (978-1-4027-2038-3(6)) Sterling Publishing Co., Inc.

Cherrington, Janelle. Where Animals Live. 2003. (Compass Point Phonics Readers Ser.). (Illus.). 16p. (J). (gr. 1 up). 13.26 (978-0-7565-0530-1(5)) Compass Point Bks.

—Who Needs Teeth? 2003. (Compass Point Phonics Readers Ser.). (Illus.). 16p. (J). (gr. 1 up). 13.26 (978-0-7565-0535-6(6)) Compass Point Bks.

Chronicle Books Staff, creator. 75 Riddles & Conundrums. 2005. 13.95 (978-0-8118-5195-4(8)) Chronicle Bks. LLC.

Cidcli. La Quisicosa. 2002. Tr. of Riddles. (SPA.). (J). 14.95 (978-968-494-007-9(6)) Centro de Informacion y Desarrollo de la Comunicacion y la Literatura MEX. *Dist:* AIMS International Bks., Inc.

Cole, Joanna & Calmenson, Stephanie, eds. Tons of Fun: Over 300 Action Rhymes, Old & New Riddles, Tongue Twisters, & Play Rhymes. Tiegren, Alan, illus. 2004. 229p. (J). (gr. k-4). reprint ed. pap. 15.00 (978-0-7567-8222-1(8)) DIANE Publishing Co.

Conley, Erin, ed. Zany Riddles. 2005. (Made You Laugh for Kids). (Illus.). 96p. pap. (978-1-57528-930-4(X)) University Games.

Cornell, Teresa. Math Riddles & Mini-Posters That Build Early Problem-Solving Skills. 2001. 48p. pap. 10.95 (978-0-439-16236-4(X)) Scholastic, Inc.

Corwin, Judith Hoffman. My First Riddles. 1998. (Growing Tree Ser.). (Illus.). 24p. (J). (ps up). 9.95 (978-0-694-01109-4(6) , Harper Festival) HarperCollins Pubs.

Creciendo con la Biblia (Activity & Biblical Riddles), No. 3. (SPA.). (J). (978-0-7899-0550-5(7) , 490536) Editorial Unilit.

Cutrone, Joy Radle. Why Do Cats Purr? Lapham, Sharon Smith, illus. 2002. 24p. per. 9.95 (978-0-9727585-0-5(X) , CatsPurr4-03) Animal Humanity Bks., LLC.

Dahl, Michael. Alphabet Soup: A Book of Riddles about Letters. Reibeling, Brandon, illus. 2004. (Read-It! Joke Books). 24p. (C). (gr. k-3). 18.60 (978-1-4048-0228-5(2)) Picture Window Bks.

—Animal Quack-Ups: Foolish & Funny Jokes about Animals. Yesh, Jeff, illus. 2004. (Read-It! Joke Books Ser.). 24p. (C). (gr. k-3). 18.60 (978-1-4048-0125-7(1)) Picture Window Bks.

—Chewy Chuckles: Deliciously Funny Jokes about Food. Yesh, Jeff, illus. 2004. (Read-It! Joke Books). 24p. (C). (gr. k-3). 18.60 (978-1-4048-0124-0(3)) Picture Window Bks.

—Crazy Criss-Cross: A Book of Mixed-Up Riddles. Reibeling, Brandon, illus. 2004. (Read-It! Joke Books). 24p. (C). (gr. k-3). 18.60 (978-1-4048-0232-2(0)) Picture Window Bks.

—Dino Rib Ticklers: Hugely Funny Jokes about Dinosaurs. Reibeling, Brandon, illus. 2004. (Read-It! Joke Books). 24p. (C). (gr. k-3). 18.60 (978-1-4048-0122-6(7)) Picture Window Bks.

—Family Funnies: A Book of Family Jokes. Haugen, Ryan, illus. 2004. (Read-It! Joke Books). 24p. (C). (gr. k-3). 18.60 (978-1-4048-0304-6(1)) Picture Window Bks.

—Funny Talk: A Book of Chitchat Riddles. Reibeling, Brandon, illus. 2004. (Read-It! Joke Books). 24p. (C). (gr. k-3). 18.60 (978-1-4048-0229-2(0)) Picture Window Bks.

—Laughs on a Leash: A Book of Pet Jokes. Haugen, Ryan, illus. 2004. (Read-It! Joke Books). 24p. (C). (gr. k-3). 18.60 (978-1-4048-0303-9(3)) Picture Window Bks.

—Monster Laughs: Frightfully Funny Jokes about Monsters. Reibeling, Brandon, illus. 2004. (Read-It! Joke Books). 24p. (C). (gr. k-3). 18.60 (978-1-4048-0123-3(5)) Picture Window Bks.

—Rhyme Time: A Book of Rhyming Riddles. Reibeling, Brandon, illus. 2004. (Read-It! Joke Books). 24p. (C). (gr. k-3). 18.60 (978-1-4048-0227-8(4)) Picture Window Bks.

—School Daze: A Book of Riddles about School. Reibeling, Brandon, illus. 2004. (Read-It! Joke Books). 24p. (C). (gr. k-3). 18.60 (978-1-4048-0231-5(2)) Picture Window Bks.

—Teacher Says: A Book of Teacher Jokes. Haugen, Ryan, illus. 2004. (Read-It! Joke Books). 24p. (C). (gr. k-3). 18.60 (978-1-4048-0301-5(7)) Picture Window Bks.

—Three-Alarm Jokes: A Book of Firefighter Jokes. Jensen, Brian, illus. 2004. (Read-It! Joke Books). 24p. (C). (gr. k-3). 18.60 (978-1-4048-0302-2(5)) Picture Window Bks.

—Under Arrest: A Book of Police Jokes. Jensen, Brian, illus. 2004. (Read-It! Joke Books). 24p. (C). (gr. k-3). 18.60 (978-1-4048-0306-0(8)) Picture Window Bks.

—Zoodles: A Book of Riddles about Animals. Reibeling, Brandon, illus. 2004. (Read-It! Joke Books). 24p. (C). (gr. k-3). 18.60 (978-1-4048-0230-8(4)) Picture Window Bks.

Doering, Jennie Spray. Beach Riddles. Pica, Steve, illus. 2006. (Silly Millies Ser.). 32p. (J). 21.27 (978-0-7613-2885-8(8) , Millbrook Pr.) Lerner Publishing Group.

Donahue, Jill L. Artful Antics: A Book of Art, Music, & Theater Jokes. Muehlenhardt, Amy Bailey, illus. 2006. (Read-It! Joke Books—Supercharged!). (J). 19.93 (978-1-4048-2363-1(8)) Picture Window Bks.

—Family Follies: A Book of Family Jokes. Trover, Zachary, illus. 2006. (Read-It! Joke Books—Supercharged!). (J). 19.93 (978-1-4048-2362-4(X)) Picture Window Bks.

—How Do You Get There? A Book of Transportation Jokes. Muehlenhardt, Amy Bailey, illus. 2006. (Read-It! Joke Books—Supercharged!). (J). 19.93 (978-1-4048-2367-9(0)) Picture Window Bks.

—Laughing Letters & Nutty Numerals: A Book of Jokes about ABCs & 123s. Trover, Zachary, illus. 2006. (Read-It! Joke Books—Supercharged!). (J). 19.93 (978-1-4048-2365-5(4)) Picture Window Bks.

—Silly Sports: A Book of Sport Jokes. Muehlenhardt, Amy Bailey, illus. 2006. (Read-It! Joke Books—Supercharged!). (J). 19.93 (978-1-4048-2366-2(2)) Picture Window Bks.

—What's in a Name? A Book of Name Jokes. Trover, Zachary, illus. 2006. (Read-It! Joke Books—Supercharged!). (J). 19.93 (978-1-4048-2364-8(6)) Picture Window Bks.

Doolittle, John H. Dr. DooRiddles Book A2: Associative Reasoning Activities. 2005. (J). pap. 10.99 (978-0-89455-877-1(3)) Critical Thinking Bks. & Software.

—Dr. DooRiddles Book A3: Associative Reasoning Activities. 2005. (J). pap. 10.99 (978-0-89455-878-8(1)) Critical Thinking Bks. & Software.

—Dr. DooRiddles Book B2: Associative Reasoning Activities. 2005. (J). pap. 10.99 (978-0-89455-879-5(X)) Critical Thinking Bks. & Software.

Dotlich, Rebecca Kai. When Riddles Come Rumbling: Poems to Ponder. Dugan, Karen M., illus. 2003. 32p. (YA). (gr. 2-4). 15.95 (978-1-56397-846-3(6)) Boyds Mills Pr.

Downs, Michael. Pig Giggles & Rabbit Rhymes: A Book of Animal Riddles. Sheldon, David, illus. 2002. 32p. (J). (ps-3). 13.95 (978-0-8118-3114-7(0)) Chronicle Bks. LLC.

Dubovoy, Silvia. Alas. 2002. (SPA.). (gr. k-3). lib. bdg. 15.25 (978-0-613-64336-8(4)) Tandem Library Bks.

—Caparazones. 2002. (SPA.). (gr. k-3). lib. bdg. 15.25 (978-0-613-64343-6(7)) Tandem Library Bks.

—Colas. 2002. (SPA.). (gr. k-3). lib. bdg. 15.25 (978-0-613-64345-0(3)) Tandem Library Bks.

—Cuernos. 2002. (SPA.). (gr. k-3). lib. bdg. 15.25 (978-0-613-64346-7(1)) Tandem Library Bks.

—Dientes. 2002. (SPA.). (gr. k-3). lib. bdg. 15.25 (978-0-613-64348-1(8)) Tandem Library Bks.

—Ojos. 2002. (SPA.). (gr. k-3). lib. bdg. 15.25 (978-0-613-64564-5(2)) Tandem Library Bks.

—Patas. 2002. (SPA.). (gr. k-3). lib. bdg. 15.25 (978-0-613-64573-7(1)) Tandem Library Bks.

—Picos. 2002. (SPA.). (gr. k-3). lib. bdg. 15.25 (978-0-613-64576-8(6)) Tandem Library Bks.

Duffey, William, Jr. Riddles & Short Stories & Mini Plays. 2002. 32p. pap. 8.00 (978-0-8059-5927-7(0)) Dorrance Publishing Co., Inc.

Eisenberg, Lisa. Hardy Har Harvest. 2003. (Illus.). (J). 5.99 (978-0-06-008822-4(2)) HarperCollins Pubs.

Eisenberg, Lisa. Silly School Riddles. Smith, Elwood H., illus. 2008. 40p. (J). (gr. 1-3). 14.99 (***978-0-8037-3165-3(5)*** , Dial) Penguin Group (USA) Inc.

Eisenberg, Lisa & Hall, Katy. Ribbit Riddles. 2004. 40p. (J). (gr. 1-3). pap. 3.99 (978-0-14-240056-2(4) , Puffin) Penguin Group (USA) Inc.

En Movimiento, 6 bks., Set. Incl. ¡A Conducir! Rau, Dana Meachen, ed. (Illus.). 2006. lib. bdg. 22.79 (978-0-7614-2422-2(9)); ¡A Flotar! Rau, Dana Meachen. 2007. lib. bdg. 22.79 (***978-0-7614-2420-8(2));*** ¡A Montar! Rau, Dana Meachen. 2007. lib. bdg. 22.79 (***978-0-7614-2423-9(7));*** ¡A Rodar! Rau, Dana Meachen. 2007. lib. bdg. 22.79 (***978-0-7614-2419-2(9));*** ¡A Trepar! Rau, Dana Meachen. 2007. lib. bdg. 22.79 (***978-0-7614-2424-6(5));*** ¡A Volar! Rau, Dana Meachen, ed. (Illus.). 2006. lib. bdg. 22.79 (978-0-7614-2425-3(3)); 24p. (J). (SPA.). 2007. Set lib. bdg. 136.71 (***978-0-7614-2417-8(2)*** , Benchmark Bks.) Cavendish, Marshall Corp.

Engelman Berner, Beth. Finding Fairyland: A Picture Riddle Book. Riggs, Jenna, illus. 2005. 12p. (J). 9.95 (978-1-58117-386-4(5) , Intervisual/Piggy Toes) Dalmatian Pr.

Fabulous PH Riddles Blends/Dig. (J). pap. 18.16 (978-0-8136-0864-8(3)) Modern Curriculum Pr.

Faulkner, Keith. Super Silly Riddles. Spender, Nik, illus. 2001. 16p. (J). (ps-3). pap. 6.00 (978-1-58653-854-5(3)) Mondo Publishing.

Fetty, Maurice A. Money Riddles That Count. 1999. (Illus.). (J). pap. (978-0-7398-2403-0(1)) Steck-Vaughn.

—A Penny Changes the Day. 1999. (Illus.). (J). pap. (978-0-7398-2402-3(3)) Steck-Vaughn.

Fontes, Justine. Cheerios Action Park Adventure. 2005. (Picture Clue Math Reader Ser.). (Illus.). 28p. (J). pap. (***978-0-439-70343-7(3)***) Scholastic, Inc.

Fox, Lori Miller. The Craziest Riddle Book in the World. 2004. 96p. (J). pap. 4.95 (978-1-4027-0898-5(X)) Sterling Publishing Co., Inc.

—Oodles of Riddles. Hoffman, Sandy, illus. 2003. 96p. (J). pap. 4.95 (978-1-4027-0824-4(6)) Sterling Publishing Co., Inc.

—Riddle Riot. Hoffman, Sandy, illus. 2003. 96p. (J). pap. 4.95 (978-1-4027-0825-1(4)) Sterling Publishing Co., Inc.

—2,001 Jokes & Riddles. 2004. (Illus.). 479p. (978-1-4027-1533-4(1) , Sterling/Main St.) Sterling Publishing Co., Inc.

Gallant, Morrie. Awesome Riddle Book. 1998. (Illus.). 96p. (J). (gr. 4-7). 14.95 (978-0-8069-6219-1(4)) Sterling Publishing Co., Inc.

—Funniest Riddle Book in the World. Hoffman, Sanford & Simard, Remy, illus. 2006. 96p. (J). pap. 4.95 (978-1-4027-3434-2(4)) Sterling Publishing Co., Inc.

Garcia, R. Creciendo con la Biblia (Activity & Biblical Riddles), No. 4. 1999. (SPA.). (J). pap. 1.59 (978-0-7899-0551-2(5) , 490537) Editorial Unilit.

Garrett, Ann & Higney, Gene-Michael. Fins & Flippers, Scales & Nippers. 2003. (Illus.). 32p. (J). pap. (978-1-59034-871-0(0)); 15.95 (978-1-59034-869-7(9)) Mondo Publishing.

Goldman, Todd Harris. Boys Are Stupid, Throw Rocks at Them! Goldman, Todd Harris, illus. 2005. (Illus.). 80p. 8.95 (978-0-7611-3593-7(6) , 13593) Workman Publishing Co., Inc.

Grambs, Alison. Crazy Christmas Jokes. Harpster, Steve, illus. 2004. (Giggle Fit Ser.). 48p. (J). 12.95 (978-1-4027-1244-9(8)) Sterling Publishing Co., Inc.

—Nutty Names Knock-Knocks. Harpster, Steve, illus. 2006. (Giggle Fit Ser.). 48p. (J). 12.95 (978-1-4027-3025-2(X)) Sterling Publishing Co., Inc.

Granfield, Linda. What Am I? Herbert, Jennifer, illus. 2007. 32p. (J). (ps-k). 15.95 (*978-0-88776-812-5(1)) Tundra Bks., Inc./Livres Toundra, Inc. CAN. *Dist:* Random Hse., Inc.

Group/McGraw-Hill, Wright. Aunt Victoria's Monster: Level P, 6 vols. 128p. (gr. 5 up). 36.95 (978-0-322-05903-0(8)) Wright Group, The.

Hall, Katy, pseud. Creepy Riddles. 2000. (Easy-to-Read Ser.). (J). 10.79 (978-0-606-20230-5(7)); lib. bdg. 11.80 (978-0-613-31097-0(7)) Tandem Library Bks.

—Dino Riddles. 2003. (gr. k-3). lib. bdg. 11.80 (978-0-613-70800-5(8)) Tandem Library Bks.

—Kitty Riddles. 2002. lib. bdg. 11.80 (978-0-613-55328-5(4)) Tandem Library Bks.

—Mummy Riddles. 1999. (978-0-606-17422-0(2)) Tandem Library Bks.

—Puppy Riddles. 2000. (Puffin Easy-to-Read Ser.). (978-0-606-18448-9(1)) Tandem Library Bks.

—Really, Really, Really Bad Jokes. 1999. (978-0-606-16401-6(4)) Tandem Library Bks.

Hall, Katy, pseud & Eisenberg, Lisa. Creepy Riddles. Schindler, S. D., illus. 2000. (Easy-to-Read Ser.). 32p. (J). (gr. 1-4). pap. 3.99 (978-0-14-130988-0(1) , Puffin) Penguin Group (USA) Inc.

—Dino Riddles. Rubel, Nicole, illus. (J). (gr. k-3). 2003. 48p. pap. 3.99 (978-0-14-250179-5(4) , Puffin); 2002. 40p. 13.99 (978-0-8037-2239-2(7) , Dial) Penguin Group (USA) Inc.

—Easter Yolks Egg-Dyeing Kit. Alley, R. W., illus. 2000. 20p. (J). (gr. k-3). 9.95 (978-0-694-01294-7(7)) HarperCollins Pubs.

—Fishy Riddles. Taback, Simms, illus. unabr. ed. 2000. (J). (gr. 1). pap., stu. ed. 29.95 incl. audio (978-0-941078-71-9(X)); 48p. pap. 16.95 incl. audio (978-0-941078-70-2(1)) Live Oak Media.

—Kitty Riddles. Alley, R. W., illus. 2002. (Easy-to-Read Ser.). 40p. (J). pap. 3.99 (978-0-14-230082-4(9) , Puffin) Penguin Group (USA) Inc.

—Piggy Riddles. Andriani, Renee, illus. 2004. (Easy-to-Read, Dial Ser.). 40p. (J). (gr. 1). 14.99 (978-0-8037-2855-4(7) , Dial) Penguin Group (USA) Inc.

—Ribbit Riddles. Bender, Robert, illus. 2001. (Easy-to-Read Ser.). 40p. (J). (ps-3). 13.99 (978-0-8037-2525-6(6) , Dial) Penguin Group (USA) Inc.

—Stinky Riddles. Andriani, Renee, illus. 2005. (Easy-to-Read, Dial Ser.). 40p. (J). (ps-4). 14.99 (978-0-8037-2928-5(6) , Dial) Penguin Group (USA) Inc.

—Turkey Riddles. Sorra, Kristin, illus. 2005. (Easy-to-Read, Puffin Ser.). 40p. (J). pap. 3.99 (978-0-14-240369-3(5) , Puffin) Penguin Group (USA) Inc.

Harcourt School Publishers Staff. Robots Rush Advanced Level. 3rd ed. 2002. (Trophies Reading Program Ser.). (Illus.). pap. 5.10 (978-0-15-323029-5(0)) Harcourt Schl. Pubs.

HarperCollins Children's Books. Rhymes & Riddles. 2007. (Word Play Ser.). 208p. (J). pap. 5.95 (*978-0-00-724334-1(0)) HarperCollins Pubs. Ltd. GBR. *Dist:* Independent Pubs. Group.

Hawkins, Colin & Hawkins, Jacqui. Whose House? 1998. (Illus.). 16p. (J). (ps-1). 8.95 (978-0-7641-5144-6(4)) Barron's Educational Series, Inc.

Helmer, Marilyn. Critter Riddles. Parker, Eric, illus. 2004. (Kids Can Read Ser.). 32p. (J). (gr. k-3). (978-1-55337-411-4(8)); (978-1-55337-445-9(2)) Kids Can Pr., Ltd.

—Critter Riddles. 2003. (gr. k-3). lib. bdg. 11.80 (978-0-613-84968-5(X)) Tandem Library Bks.

—Funtime Riddles. Kurisu, Jane, illus. 2004. 31p. (J). lib. bdg. 15.38 (*978-1-4242-1184-5(0)) Fitzgerald Bks.

—Recess Riddles. Kurisu, Jane, illus. 2004. 31p. (J). lib. bdg. 15.38 (*978-1-4242-1185-2(9)) Fitzgerald Bks.

—Spooky Riddles. 2003. (gr. k-3). lib. bdg. 11.80 (978-0-613-84413-0(0)) Tandem Library Bks.

—Yucky Riddles. 2003. (gr. k-3). lib. bdg. 11.80 (978-0-613-87149-5(9)) Tandem Library Bks.

—Yummy Riddles. Parker, Eric, illus. 2004. (Kids Can Read Ser.). 32p. (J). (gr. k-3). (978-1-55337-412-1(6)); (978-1-55337-446-6(0)) Kids Can Pr., Ltd.

Helmer, Marilyn & Kurisu, Jane. Funtime Riddles. 2004. (Kids Can Read Ser.). (Illus.). 32p. (J). (gr. k-3). (978-1-55337-580-7(7)); (978-1-55337-579-1(3)) Kids Can Pr., Ltd.

—Recess Riddles. 2004. (Kids Can Read Ser.). (Illus.). 32p. (J). (gr. k-3). (978-1-55337-578-4(5)); (978-1-55337-577-7(7)) Kids Can Pr., Ltd.

Helmer, Marilyn & Parker, Eric. Spooky Riddles. 2004. (Kids Can Read Ser.). (Illus.). 32p. (J). (gr. k-3). (978-1-55337-413-8(4)); (978-1-55337-447-3(9)) Kids Can Pr., Ltd.

—Yucky Riddles. 2004. (Kids Can Read Ser.). (Illus.). 32p. (J). (gr. k-3). (978-1-55337-414-5(2)); (978-1-55337-448-0(7)) Kids Can Pr., Ltd.

Highlights Editors. Riddles: A Summer of Laughs. Highlights Artists Staff, illus. 2007. 32p. 16.99 (978-0-8249-1500-1(3) , Ideals Children's Bks.) Ideals Pubns.

Hoffman, David. Riddles of Middle Earth. 2002. 43p. per. 10.00 (978-0-9718721-0-3(4)) Hoffman Enterprises.

Holub, Joan. Riddle-Iculous Math. Dunnick, Regan, illus. 2003. 32p. (J). (gr. 2-5). 15.95 (978-0-8075-4996-4(7)) Whitman, Albert & Co.

Holub, Joan & Buttler, Elizabeth. Yankee Doodle Riddles: American History Fun. 2003. (Illus.). 32p. (J). (gr. 2-5). 15.95 (978-0-8075-9260-1(9)) Whitman, Albert & Co.

Horsfall, Jacqueline. Funny Riddles. Harpster, Steve, illus. 2006. (Giggle Fit Ser.). 48p. (J). pap. 4.95 (978-1-4027-2770-2(4)) Sterling Publishing Co., Inc.

—Joke & Riddle Ballyhoo. Snider, Jackie, illus. 96p. (J). 2007. pap. 4.95 (978-1-4027-2547-0(7)); 2005. (gr. 4-7). 14.95 (978-1-4027-1953-0(1)) Sterling Publishing Co., Inc.

—Kids' Silliest Riddles. Jones, Buck, illus. 2003. 96p. (J). pap. 4.95 (978-1-4027-0808-4(4)) Sterling Publishing Co., Inc.

—Kids' Silliest Riddles. 2003. (gr. k-3). lib. bdg. 12.95 (978-0-613-77990-6(8)) Tandem Library Bks.

I Spy: A Book of Picture Riddles. 2002. (I Spy Ser.). (Illus.). (J). 21.45 (978-0-7587-4103-5(0)) Book Wholesalers, Inc.

I Spy Extreme Challenger: A Book of Picture Riddles. 2002. (I Spy Ser.). (Illus.). (J). 21.45 (978-0-7587-4099-1(9)) Book Wholesalers, Inc.

I Spy Fantasy: A Book of Picture Riddles. 2002. (Illus.). (J). 21.45 (978-0-7587-4109-7(X)) Book Wholesalers, Inc.

I Spy Funhouse: A Book of Picture Riddles. 2002. (I Spy Ser.). (Illus.). (J). 21.45 (978-0-7587-0022-3(9)) Book Wholesalers, Inc.

I Spy Gold Challenger! A Book of Picture Riddles. 2002. (I Spy Ser.). (Illus.). (J). 21.45 (978-0-7587-4105-9(7)) Book Wholesalers, Inc.

I Spy Spooky Night. 2002. (I Spy Ser.). (Illus.). (J). 21.45 (978-0-7587-2814-2(X)) Book Wholesalers, Inc.

I Spy Super Challenger. 2002. (I Spy Ser.). (Illus.). (J). 21.45 (978-0-7587-4108-0(1)) Book Wholesalers, Inc.

I Spy Treasure Hunt: A Book of Picture Riddles. 2002. (I Spy Ser.). (Illus.). (J). 21.45 (978-0-7587-5114-0(1)) Book Wholesalers, Inc.

I Spy Year-Round Challenger! A Book of Picture Riddles. 2002. (I Spy Ser.). (Illus.). (J). 21.45 (978-1-4046-0026-3(4)) Book Wholesalers, Inc.

Jones, Evelyn. World's Wackiest Riddle Book. 2004. (Illus.). 96p. (J). pap. 4.95 (978-1-4027-0924-1(2)) Sterling Publishing Co., Inc.

Josephs, Ben. Where Dinosaurs Walked. 2003. (Compass Point Phonics Readers Ser.). (Illus.). 16p. (J). (gr. 1 up). 13.26 (978-0-7565-0531-8(3)) Compass Point Bks.

Joyce, Susan. ABC Animal Riddles. DuBosque, Doug, illus. 1998. (ABC Riddles Ser.). 32p. (J). (ps-3). 13.95 (978-0-939217-51-9(1)) Peel Productions, Inc.

—ABC Nature Riddles. DuBosque, Doug, illus. 2004. (ABC Riddles Ser.). 32p. (J). (ps-k). (978-0-939217-53-3(8)) Peel Productions, Inc.

—Alphabet Riddles. DuBosque, Doug, illus. 1998. (ABC Riddles Ser.). 32p. (J). (ps-3). (978-0-939217-50-2(3)) Peel Productions, Inc.

Joyce, Susan, ed. ABC School Riddles. Levin, Freddie, illus. 2000. (ABC Riddles Ser.). 32p. (J). (ps-3). (978-0-939217-54-0(6)) Peel Productions, Inc.

Keller, Charles. Best Riddle Book Ever. 1998. (gr. 3-6). lib. bdg. 12.95 (978-0-613-75642-6(8)) Tandem Library Bks.

—Giggles. 2007. (Illus.). 360p. (J). pap. 6.95 (*978-1-4027-4984-1(8)) Sterling Publishing Co., Inc.

—Little Giant Book of School Jokes. 2000. (gr. 3-6). lib. bdg. 15.25 (978-0-613-75462-0(X)) Tandem Library Bks.

—Riddles. Sterling Publishing Company Staff, ed. 2004. (Kids' Bathroom Bks.). (Illus.). 96p. (J). pap. 4.95 (978-1-4027-1710-9(5)) Sterling Publishing Co., Inc.

Keller, Charles & Sinclair, Jeff. Best Riddle Book Ever. 1998. (Illus.). 96p. (J). (gr. 4-7). pap. 4.95 (978-0-8069-9546-5(7)) Sterling Publishing Co., Inc.

Klutz Press Staff, ed. Carabiners: Weird Facts; Random Riddles; Really Dumb Jokes. 2004. (Illus.). 40p. (J). 3.95 (978-1-59174-295-1(1)) Klutz.

Kowitt, Holly. Funny Bones: Jokes, Riddles, Knock-Knocks, & Loads of Laughs Starring the Fabulous Crazy Bones! 2000. 64p. (J). pap. (978-0-439-18019-1(8)) Scholastic, Inc.

Kresz, Laszlo, et al. Eye-Pleasing, Mind-Teasing 3-D Conundrums. 2003. (Illus.). 96p. pap. 9.95 (978-1-4027-0554-0(9)) Sterling Publishing Co., Inc.

Laffin, Ima. Monster Jokes. 2005. (Jokes Ser.). (Illus.). 24p. (J). (gr. k-4). lib. bdg. 21.35 (978-1-59197-623-3(5) , Buddy Bks.) ABDO Publishing Co.

—More Monster Jokes. 2005. (More Jokes! Ser.). (Illus.). 24p. (gr. k-4). lib. bdg. 21.35 (978-1-59197-874-9(2)) ABDO Publishing Co.

Lanchais, Aurelie, et al. I Can Fly, What Am I? (Illus.). (ps-1). 2005. (ARA, ENG, URD, CHI & BEN.). 14p. 9.95 (978-1-84059-250-4(8)); 2005. (URD, ENG, CHI, ARA & BEN., 14p. pap. 9.95 (978-1-84059-255-9(9)); 2000. (BEN, ENG, URD, TUR & CHI., 16p. (J). pap. 9.95 (978-1-84059-251-1(6)); 2000. (FRE, ENG, URD, TUR & CHI., 16p. (J). pap. 9.95 (978-1-84059-253-5(2)); 2000. (TUR, ENG, URD, CHI & ARA., 16p. (J). pap. 9.95 (978-1-84059-254-2(0)) Milet Publishing.

—I Have Wheels, What Am I? (Illus.). (ps-1). 2005. (RUS, ENG, TUR, VIE & CHI.). 14p. pap. 9.95 (978-1-84059-239-9(7)); 2000. (GUJ, ENG, VIE, CHI & RUS., 16p. (J). pap. 9.95 (978-1-84059-238-2(9)); 2000. (FRE, ENG, VIE, GUJ & CHI., 16p. (J). pap. 9.95 (978-1-84059-237-5(0)) Milet Publishing.

—I Have Wheels, What Am I? Erdogan, Faith, tr. 2000. (Who Am I? What Am I? Ser.). (TUR, ENG, RUS, VIE & CHI., Illus.). 16p. (J). (ps-1). pap. 9.95 (978-1-84059-240-5(0)) Milet Publishing.

—What Am I? (Illus.). (ps-1). 2005. (ARA, ENG, URD, TUR & CHI.). 14p. 9.95 (978-1-84059-243-6(5)); 2005. (URD, ENG, CHI, ARA & BEN., 14p. 9.95 (978-1-84059-248-1(6)); 2000. (BEN, ENG, URD, CHI & ARA., 16p. (J). pap. 9.95 (978-1-84059-244-3(3)); 2000. (CHI, ENG, URD, TUR & ARA., 16p. (J). pap. 9.95 (978-1-84059-245-0(1)); 2000. (FRE, ENG, URD, CHI & ARA., 16p. (J). pap. 9.95 (978-1-84059-246-7(X)); 2000. (TUR, ENG, URD, CHI & ARA., 16p. (J). pap. 9.95 (978-1-84059-247-4(8)) Milet Publishing.

—Who Am I? (Illus.). (ps-1). 2005. (CHI, ENG, VIE, GUJ & RUS.). 14p. pap. 9.95 (978-1-84059-229-0(X)); 2005. (RUS, ENG, TUR, VIE & CHI., 14p. pap. 9.95 (978-1-84059-232-0(X)); 2000. (FRE, ENG, VIE, GUJ & CHI., 16p. (J). pap. 9.95 (978-1-84059-230-6(3)); 2000. (GUJ, ENG, VIE, CHI & RUS., 16p. (J). pap. 9.95 (978-1-84059-231-3(1)) Milet Publishing.

Leber, Nancy J. Ants to Zebras: Silly Animal Jokes & Riddles. Griego, Tony, illus. 2000. (Scholastic At-Home Phonics Reading Program Ser.: Vol. 53). 24p. (J). (978-0-590-68848-2(0)) Scholastic, Inc.

LeCompte, David & Padrick, Kendell. Eugene Stillwell Wants to Know!, Pt. 2. 2007. 96p. (J). pap. 4.95 (*978-1-929945-74-0(4)) Big Guy Bks., Inc.

Lederer, Richard. Pun & Games: Jokes, Riddles, Daffynitions, Tairy Fales, Rhymes, & More Word Play for Kids. Morice, Dave, illus. 2003. 112p. (J). (gr. 5 up). pap. 9.95 (978-1-55652-264-2(9)) Chicago Review Pr., Inc.

Lee, Cyl. More Ridiculous Riddles. 2005. (More Jokes! Ser.). (Illus.). 24p. (gr. k-4). lib. bdg. 21.35 (978-1-59197-876-3(9)) ABDO Publishing Co.

—Really Silly Jokes. 2005. (Jokes Ser.). (Illus.). 24p. (J). (gr. k-4). lib. bdg. 21.35 (978-1-59197-624-0(3) , Buddy Bks.) ABDO Publishing Co.

—Ridiculous Riddles. 2005. (Jokes Ser.). (Illus.). 24p. (J). (gr. k-4). lib. bdg. 21.35 (978-1-59197-625-7(1) , Buddy Bks.) ABDO Publishing Co.

Levin, Amy. The Vet. 2003. (Compass Point Phonics Readers Ser.). (Illus.). 16p. (J). (gr. 1 up). 13.26 (978-0-7565-0528-8(3)) Compass Point Bks.

Lewman, David. More Jokes. 1999. (Rugrats Ser.). (Illus.). 48p. (J). (ps-2). pap. 2.99 (978-0-689-82538-5(2) , Simon Spotlight) Simon & Schuster Children's Publishing.

—More Jokes. 1999. (gr. k-3). lib. bdg. 10.65 (978-0-613-15911-1(X)) Tandem Library Bks.

Libal, Autumn. Folk Proverbs & Riddles. 2003. (North American Folklore Ser.). (Illus.). 112p. (YA). (gr. 7 up). lib. bdg. (978-1-59084-343-7(6)) Mason Crest Pubs.

El Libro de los Acertijos Historicos. (Coleccion Acertijos). (SPA.). (YA). (gr. 5-8). pap. (978-950-724-249-6(X) , LMA8235) Lumen ARG. *Dist:* Lectorum Pubns., Inc.

Lupton, Hugh. Riddle Me This! Riddles & Stories to Challenge Your Mind. Fatus, Sophie, illus. 2003. 64p. (J). 19.99 (978-1-84148-169-2(6)) Barefoot Bks., Inc.

Lupton, Hugh & Fatus, Sophie. Riddle Me This! Riddles & Stories to Challenge Your Mind. 2006. pap. 9.99 (978-1-905236-92-3(1)) Barefoot Bks., Inc.

Lynch, Wayne. Whose Feet Are These? Lynch, Wayne, photos by. 2003. (Name That Animal! Ser.). (Illus.). 32p. (J). (gr. 1 up). lib. bdg. 23.33 (978-0-8368-3640-0(5)) Stevens, Gareth Inc.

—Whose Feet Are These? 1999. (gr. k-3). lib. bdg. 15.25 (978-0-613-78498-6(7)); (978-0-606-18759-6(6)) Tandem Library Bks.

—Whose Feet Are These? 1999. (Whose? Animal Ser.). (Illus.). 32p. (J). (ps-2). pap. 6.95 (978-1-55110-860-5(7)) Whitecap Bks., Ltd. CAN. *Dist:* Firefly Bks., Ltd.

Macari, Mario Duilio, ed. & illus. Funny Riddles for Kids: Squeaky Clean Easy Kid Riddles Drawn As Funny Kid¿s Cartoons in A Cool Comicbook Style. Macari, Mario Duilio, illus. 2007. 104p. (J). per. 10.00 (*978-0-9766755-0-1(1)) Cartoonmario.com.

MacDonald, Margaret Read. Three-Minute Tales: Stories from Around the World to Tell or Read When Time Is Short. 2004. 160p. 24.95 (978-0-87483-728-5(6)); pap. 17.95 (978-0-87483-729-2(4)) August Hse. Pubs., Inc.

Madden, Caolan. Let's Have Fun with Alphabet Riddles. 2007. (Let's Find Out Early Learning Bks.). (Illus.). 32p. (J). (ps-k). 18.00 (*978-0-531-14868-6(8) , Children's Pr.) Scholastic Library Publishing.

Mann, Rachel. Race to a Fire! 2003. (Compass Point Phonics Readers Ser.). (Illus.). 16p. (J). (gr. 1 up). 13.26 (978-0-7565-0522-6(4)) Compass Point Bks.

—Sun & Rain. 2003. (Compass Point Phonics Readers Ser.). (Illus.). 16p. (J). (gr. 1 up). 13.26 (978-0-7565-0525-7(9)) Compass Point Bks.

Martin, Jannelle. ABC Math Riddles. Levin, Freddie, illus. 2003. (ABC Riddles Ser.). 32p. (J). 13.95 (978-0-939217-57-1(0)) Peel Productions, Inc.

Marzollo, Jean. I Spy: A Book of Picture Riddles. Wick, Walter, illus. 2005. (I Spy Ser.). 40p. (J). (ps). 9.95 (978-0-439-78729-1(7) , Cartwheel Bks.) Scholastic, Inc.

—I Spy Fantasy. Wick, Walter, illus. 2005. (I Spy Ser.). 40p. (J). (ps). 9.95 (978-0-439-78732-1(7) , Cartwheel Bks.) Scholastic, Inc.

—I Spy Fun House. Wick, Walter, illus. 2005. (I Spy Ser.).Tr. of C'est Moi l'Espion du Parc d'Attractions. 40p. (J). 9.95 (978-0-439-78730-7(0) , Cartwheel Bks.) Scholastic, Inc.

—Shanna's Animal Riddles. Roos, Maryn, illus. 2004. (J). (ps-ps). lib. bdg. 10.79 (978-0-606-30551-8(3)) Tandem Library Bks.

Marzollo, Jean & Wick, Walter. I Spy a Dinosaur's Eye. 2003. (ps-2). lib. bdg. 11.80 (978-0-613-72243-8(4)) Tandem Library Bks.

—I Spy a School Bus. 2003. (ps-2). lib. bdg. 11.80 (978-0-613-72246-9(9)) Tandem Library Bks.

McIver, Patricia E. Tongue Twisters. 2006. (ENG.). 32p. per. 27.00 (*978-1-4259-4423-0(X)) AuthorHouse.

McKay, Helen & Dudley, Berice. Riotous Riddles. Mannix, Max, illus. 1999. 172p. (J). pap. 8.00 (978-0-86806-664-6(8)) Hale & Iremonger Pty., Ltd. AUS. *Dist:* Empire Publishing Service.

Menotti, Andrea. How to Tackle Puzzles, Unravel Riddles, Crack Codes, & Other Ways to Bend Your Brain. 2004. (Illus.). 80p. (J). (978-0-439-57905-6(8)) Scholastic, Inc.

Mitton, Tony. Riddledy Piggledy. Mounter, Paddy, illus. 2004. 48p. (J). (gr. k-1). 16.95 (978-0-385-75024-0(2) , Fickling, David Bks.) Random Hse. Children's Bks.

Moore, Hugh. Bug Jokes. 2005. (More Jokes! Ser.). (Illus.). 24p. (gr. k-4). lib. bdg. 21.35 (978-1-59197-870-1(X)) ABDO Publishing Co.

—Food Jokes. 2005. (More Jokes! Ser.). (Illus.). 24p. (gr. k-4). lib. bdg. 21.35 (978-1-59197-871-8(8)) ABDO Publishing Co.

Morrison, Lillian. Guess Again! Riddle Poems. Hale, Christy, illus. 2006. 48p. (J). 16.95 (978-0-87483-730-8(8)) August Hse. Pubs., Inc.

Murray, Carol. ABC Art Riddles. Levin, Freddie, illus. 2005. (J). (978-0-939217-58-8(9)) Peel Productions, Inc.

Myers, Janet Nuzum. Spooky Creature Riddles. Ostrom, Bob, illus. 2005. 96p. (J). (ps-ps). pap. 4.95 (978-1-4027-1872-4(1)) Sterling Publishing Co., Inc.

Nelson, Esther & Hirsch, Davida. Riggeldy Jiggeldy Joggeldy Jam: Can You Guess Who I Am? Ellis, Libby, illus. 2003. (J). bds. 5.95 (978-0-7607-3278-6(7)) Barnes & Noble, Inc.

O'Hare, Jeff. Big Book of Fun: An Amazing Collection of Jokes, Riddles, Puzzles, & More. 2002. (gr. k-3). lib. bdg. 18.75 (978-0-613-79873-0(2)) Tandem Library Bks.

O'Hare, Jeffrey A., ed. The Highlights Big Book of Fun: An Amazing Collection of Jokes, Riddles, Puzzles, & More! 2003. (Illus.). 96p. (YA). (gr. k-7). pap., act. bk. ed. 9.95 (978-1-59078-006-0(X)) Boyds Mills Pr.

Packard, Mary & Mitter, Matt. Once upon a Rhyme: Story Rhymes. Banta, Susan & Cushman, Doug, illus. 2004. (Rhyme Time Learning Ser.). 16p. (J). (gr. 1 up). lib. bdg. 20.67 (978-0-8368-4096-4(8)) Stevens, Gareth Inc.

Pellowski, Michael J. Joke & Riddle Jackpot. Reed, Chris, illus. 96p. 2007. (J). pap. 4.95 (*978-1-4027-4056-5(5)); 2005. 14.95 (978-1-4027-1696-6(6)) Sterling Publishing Co., Inc.

Pellowski, Michael J. Wild & Wacky Pet Jokes & Riddles. Snider, Jackie, illus. 2006. 96p. (J). 14.95 (978-1-4027-2431-2(4)) Sterling Publishing Co., Inc.

Peterson, Scott K. Let the Fun Begin: Nifty Knock-Knocks, Playful Puns, & More. Gable, Brian, illus. 2005. (Make Me Laugh! Ser.). 32p. (J). (gr. k-3). lib. bdg. 19.93 (978-1-57505-661-6(5)) Lerner Publishing Group.

Phillips, Bob. All-Time Awesome Collection of Good Clean Jokes for Kids. 2006. (Illus.). 368p. (J). pap. 10.99 (978-0-7369-1777-3(2)) Harvest Hse. Pubs.

Phillips, Louis. Monster Riddles. Dubanevich, Arlene, illus. 1998. (Puffin Easy-to-Read Program Ser.). 32p. (J). (gr. 1-4). pap. 3.99 (978-0-14-038790-2(0) , Puffin) Penguin Group (USA) Inc.

—Monster Riddles. Dubanevich, Arlene, illus. 1998. (J). (ps-ps). lib. bdg. 11.80 (978-0-613-08373-7(3)) Tandem Library Bks.

Phunny, U. R. Animal Jokes. 2005. (Jokes Ser.). (Illus.). 24p. (J). (gr. k-4). lib. bdg. 21.35 (978-1-59197-620-2(0) , Buddy Bks.) ABDO Publishing Co.

—Dinosaur Jokes. 2005. (Jokes Ser.). (Illus.). 24p. (J). (gr. k-4). lib. bdg. 21.35 (978-1-59197-621-9(9) , Buddy Bks.) ABDO Publishing Co.

—More Animal Jokes. 2005. (More Jokes! Ser.). (Illus.). 24p. (gr. k-4). lib. bdg. 21.35 (978-1-59197-872-5(6)) ABDO Publishing Co.

Pierce, Terry. Greatest Goofiest Jokes. 2004. (Illus.). 96p. (J). 14.95 (978-1-4027-0769-8(X)) Sterling Publishing Co., Inc.

Quesada, Maria Fe, illus. Adivina, Adivinanza. (SPA.). (J). pap. 5.56 (978-84-241-8037-9(2)); 6th ed. 2002. 48p. 7.99 (978-84-241-3407-5(9) , EV8795) Everest de Ediciones y Distribucion, S.L. ESP. *Dist:* Lectorum Pubns., Inc.

Raintree Steck-Vaughn Staff. Rebus Puzzles. 2000. (J). pap. (978-0-7398-2942-4(4)); (gr. 1). pap. (978-0-7398-2943-1(2)); (gr. 2). pap. (978-0-7398-2944-8(0)) Steck-Vaughn.

Rau, Dana Meachen. At the Zoo. 2007. (Fun Time Ser.). 24p. (J). lib. bdg. 22.79 (*978-0-7614-2610-3(8) , Benchmark Bks.) Cavendish, Marshall Corp.

—Baker. 2007. (Jobs in Town Ser.). 24p. (J). lib. bdg. 22.79 (*978-0-7614-2623-3(X) , Benchmark Bks.) Cavendish, Marshall Corp.

—Driving. 2006. (On the Move Ser.). (ENG & SPA., Illus.). 24p. (J). lib. bdg. 22.79 (978-0-7614-2316-4(8) , Benchmark Bks.) Cavendish, Marshall Corp.

—Firefighter. 2007. (Jobs in Town Ser.). 24p. (J). lib. bdg. 22.79 (*978-0-7614-2617-2(5) , Benchmark Bks.) Cavendish, Marshall Corp.

—Librarian. 2007. (J). (*978-0-7614-2621-9(3)) Cavendish, Marshall Bks., Ltd.

—On a Farm. 2007. (Fun Time Ser.). 24p. (J). lib. bdg. 22.79 (*978-0-7614-2605-9(1) , Benchmark Bks.) Cavendish, Marshall Corp.

P Q R

Rau, Dana Meachen. Riding. 2006. (On the Move Ser.). (Illus.). 24p. (J). (ps-1). lib. bdg. 22.79 (978-0-7614-2317-1(6)) Cavendish, Marshall Corp.

Reber, Deborah. My Favorite Letters. Craig, Karen, illus. 2001. (Blues Clue's Ready to Read Ser.: Vol. 3). 24p. (J). (ps-1). pap. 3.99 (978-0-689-83797-5(6) , Simon Spotlight/Nickelodeon) Simon & Schuster Children's Publishing.

—My Favorite Letters. 2001. (gr. k-3). lib. bdg. 11.80 (978-0-613-35673-2(X)) Tandem Library Bks.

Riddles with a Reason. 2003. (Illus.). 32p. (gr. 4-8). 6.99 (978-1-56417-978-4(8) , GA1657) Schaffer, Frank Pubns.

Rissinger, Matt & Yates, Philip. Nutty Jokes. Harpster, Steve, illus. 2002. (Giggle Fit Ser.). 48p. (J). (gr. k-2). pap. 4.95 (978-1-4027-0120-7(9)) Sterling Publishing Co., Inc.

Robleda, Margarita. Acertijos y Trabalenguas. Gurovich, Natalia, illus. 2004. (SPA.). 24p. (J). 12.95 (978-970-690-806-3(4)) Planeta Mexicana Editorial S. A. de C. V. MEX. *Dist:* Lectorum Pubns., Inc.

—Quien Soy? Adivinanzas Animales. Gurovich, Natalia, illus. 2003. (SPA.). 32p. (J). 12.95 (978-970-690-805-6(6)) Planeta Mexicana Editorial S. A. de C. V. MEX. *Dist:* Lectorum Pubns., Inc.

Rosenberg, Pam. Dinosaur Jokes. 2004. (Laughing Matters Ser.). 24p. (J). (gr. k-4). 22.79 (978-1-59296-073-6(1)) Child's World, Inc.

—Riddles. 2004. (Laughing Matters Ser.). (Illus.). 24p. (J). (gr. k-4). 22.79 (978-1-59296-076-7(6)) Child's World, Inc.

Rosenbloom, Joseph. Jokes. Hoffman, Sanford, illus. 2007. 360p. (J). pap. 6.95 (***978-1-4027-4973-5(2)***) Sterling Publishing Co., Inc.

—Laughs, Hoots & Giggles. Behr, Joyce & Hoffman, Sanford, illus. 2007. 416p. (J). 9.95 (***978-1-4027-5063-2(3)***) Sterling Publishing Co., Inc.

—The Little Giant Book of Jokes. Hoffman, Sanford, illus. 2003. 352p. (J). (gr. 4-7). pap. 6.95 (978-0-8069-6101-9(5)) Sterling Publishing Co., Inc.

—Riddles. Hoffman, Sanford, illus. 2007. 360p. (J). pap. 6.95 (***978-1-4027-4972-8(4)***) Sterling Publishing Co., Inc.

Rosenbloom, Joseph. 696 Silly School Jokes & Riddles. 2003. (gr. 3-6). lib. bdg. 12.95 (978-0-613-78033-9(7)) Tandem Library Bks.

Rosenbloom, Joseph & Harpster, Steve. Goofy Riddles. 2002. (Giggle Fit Ser.). (Illus.). 48p. (J). (ps-2). pap. 4.95 (978-1-4027-0119-1(5)) Sterling Publishing Co., Inc.

Rossell, Judith. Inspector Rockfort & the Missing Jewels: Search * Solve * Seek. 2007. (Illus.). 32p. (J). pap. 4.95 (978-1-60059-051-1(9)) Lark Bks.

—Inspector Rockfort & the Missing Treasure: Search * Solve * Seek. 2007. (Illus.). 32p. (J). pap. 4.95 (978-1-60059-050-4(0)) Lark Bks.

Roumain, Marika. N ap Tire Kont Tim Tim Bwa Chech. 2001. (CRP., Illus.). 16p. (J). (gr. k-2). pap. 19.50 (978-1-58432-033-3(8)) Educa Vision.

—Tim Tim Bwa Chech N ap Tire Kont. 2001. (Illus.). 16p. (J). (gr. k-2). pap. 6.50 (978-1-58432-035-7(4)) Educa Vision.

Saffer, Barbara. ABC Science Riddles. Johnson, Jennifer, illus. 2004. (ABC Riddles Ser.). 32p. (J). (ps-3). (978-0-939217-55-7(4)) Peel Productions, Inc.

Sawyers, William. What Am I? Book. 2005. 44p. pap. 8.95 (978-1-4116-2899-1(3)) Lulu.com.

—What Am I? Bugs. 2005. 65p. (J). pap. 16.01 (978-1-4116-3402-2(0)) Lulu.com.

Scheunemann, Pam. Ape Cape. 2004. (Rhyming Riddles Ser.). (Illus.). 23p. (J). (ps-3). lib. bdg. 19.93 (978-1-59197-457-4(7)) ABDO Publishing Co.

—Chipper Flipper. 2004. (Rhyming Riddles Ser.). (Illus.). 23p. (J). (ps-3). lib. bdg. 19.93 (978-1-59197-458-1(5)) ABDO Publishing Co.

—Cooler Ruler. 2004. (Rhyming Riddles Ser.). (Illus.). 23p. (J). (ps-3). lib. bdg. 19.93 (978-1-59197-459-8(3)) ABDO Publishing Co.

—Dill Spill. 2004. (Rhyming Riddles Ser.). (Illus.). 23p. (J). (ps-3). lib. bdg. 19.93 (978-1-59197-460-4(7)) ABDO Publishing Co.

—Loud Crowd. 2004. (Rhyming Riddles Ser.). (Illus.). 23p. (J). (ps-3). lib. bdg. 19.93 (978-1-59197-461-1(5)) ABDO Publishing Co.

—Overdue Kangaroo. 2004. (Rhyming Riddles Ser.). (Illus.). 23p. (J). (ps-3). lib. bdg. 19.93 (978-1-59197-462-8(3)) ABDO Publishing Co.

—Rhyming Riddles. 2004. (J). (ps-3). lib. bdg. 119.58 (978-1-59197-456-7(9) , SandCastle) ABDO Publishing Co.

Shannon, George. Red All Over. Date not set. (J). (gr. 3-7). pap. 4.99 (978-0-380-80072-8(1)) HarperCollins Pubs.

Silverman, Erica. Raisel's Riddle. Gaber, Susan, illus. 2003. 40p. (J). pap. 5.95 (978-0-374-46199-7(6) , Sunburst) Farrar, Straus & Giroux.

Smith, Maria. Hidden Riddles: Activity Packet. 1999. 80p. (J). (gr. 2-6). 10.00 (978-0-911943-65-8(X)) Leadership Pub., Inc.

Smith, Shuford. ABC All-American Riddles. 2003. (Illus.). (J). (978-0-939217-56-4(2)) Peel Productions, Inc.

Smith, William Jay. Hey Diddle, a Riddle. 2002. (J). (978-1-58837-009-9(7)) Winslow Pr.

Speirs, John. Best Halloween Hunt Ever. 2000. (gr. k-3). lib. bdg. 10.95 (978-0-613-24343-8(9)) Tandem Library Bks.

Steck-Vaughn Staff. Penny a Day & Money Riddles. 1999. (Take Me Home Ser.). (Illus.). (J). pap. (978-0-7398-2588-4(7)) Steck-Vaughn.

—Riddles & Jokes: Pet Riddles/You'll Roar. 1998. (Illus.). (J). pap. (978-0-8172-8650-7(0)) Steck-Vaughn.

Stemen, Jeffrey, illus. Critter Giggles. 2006. (J). (978-1-58987-035-2(2)) Kindermusik International.

Sterling Publishing Co., Inc. & Rosenbloom, Joseph. The Little Giant Book of Side-Splitters. 2005. (Illus.). 352p. pap. 6.95 (978-1-4027-2062-8(9)) Sterling Publishing Co., Inc.

Super Giggles: Knock-Knocks, Jokes, & Tongue-Twisters. 2005. (Illus.). 176p. pap. (978-0-7607-6782-5(3)) Barnes & Noble, Inc.

Tait, Chris. Ridiculous Riddles. Zahnd, Mark, illus. 2003. 96p. (J). pap. 4.95 (978-1-4027-0608-0(1)) Sterling Publishing Co., Inc.

—Ridiculous Tongue-Twisters. Jones, Buck, illus. 2005. 96p. pap. 4.95 (978-1-4027-2236-3(2)) Sterling Publishing Co., Inc.

Tait, Chris, et al. A Little Giant Book: Super Silliest Riddles. 2007. (Illus.). 360p. (J). pap. 6.95 (***978-1-4027-4992-6(9)***) Sterling Publishing Co., Inc.

Tardieij, Gerard & Tardieij, Marie. Tim tim Bwa Chech N ap Tire 500 Knot Ayisyen. 2001. (CRP.). 78p. (J). (gr. 3-6). pap. 9.50 (978-1-58432-045-6(1)) Educa Vision.

Taylor, Brad. The Family Joke Book: Jokes & Stories for Everyone. Blaustein, Hank, illus. 2000. 64p. (YA). pap. 8.95 (978-0-86534-294-1(6)) Sunstone Pr.

Terban, Marvin. Eight Ate: A Feast of Homonym Riddles. Maestro, Giulio, illus. 2007. 64p. (J). (gr. k-3). pap. 6.95 (978-0-618-76676-5(6) , Clarion Bks.) Houghton Mifflin Co. Trade & Reference Div.

Terban, Marvin. Too Hot to Hoot: Funny Palindrome Riddles. Maestro, Giulio, illus. 2008. 64p. (J). (gr. 2-5). pap. 6.95 (***978-0-618-19165-9(8)*** , Clarion Bks.) Houghton Mifflin Co. Trade & Reference Div.

Thomas, Lyn. Ha! Ha! Ha! 1,000+ Jokes, Riddles, Facts, & More. Eastman, Dianne, illus. 2004. 128p. (J). pap. 9.95 (978-1-897066-12-6(0)) Maple Tree Pr. CAN. *Dist:* Perseus Distribution.

University Games Staff, compiled by. i-Ballers: Riddles. 2004. 48p. pap. (978-1-57528-953-3(9)) University Games.

Varma, Michael. Mental Blocks - at the Movies - Take 2: At the Movies - Take 2, 2 vols. 2002. (Illus.). 114p. per. 6.95 (978-0-9717815-1-1(6)) Magical Concepts.

Vidro, Kenn. Square Pears Three: Hey Diddle Riddle. 2005. (Illus.). (J). spiral bd. 9.95 (978-0-9745308-2-6(4)) Gilbert Square Bks.

—Square Pears Two: The Equal Sequel. Vidro, Kenn, illus. 2004. (J). spiral bd. 9.95 (978-0-9745308-1-9(6)) Gilbert Square Bks.

Vidro, Kenn G. The Fun of Rhyme Square Pears. 2005. (J). 2.50 (978-0-9745308-3-3(2)) Gilbert Square Bks.

Wagner, Kathi & Wagner, Aubrey. The Everything Kid's Riddles & Brain Teasers. 2004. (Illus.). 135p. (J). 6.95 (978-1-59337-036-7(9)) Adams Media Corp.

Walton, Rick & Walton, Ann. Foul Play: Sports Jokes That Won't Strike Out. Gable, Brian, illus. 2005. (Make Me Laugh! Ser.). 32p. (J). (gr. k-3). lib. bdg. 19.93 (978-1-57505-666-1(6)) Lerner Publishing Group.

—Magical Mischief: Jokes That Shock & Amaze. Gable, Brian, illus. 2005. (Make Me Laugh! Ser.). 32p. (J). (gr. k-3). lib. bdg. 19.93 (978-1-57505-664-7(X)) Lerner Publishing Group.

Walton, Rick, et al. Real Classy: Silly School Jokes. Gable, Brian, illus. 2005. (Make Me Laugh! Ser.). 32p. (J). (gr. k-3). lib. bdg. 19.93 (978-1-57505-665-4(8)) Lerner Publishing Group.

Watson, Yolanda. Which Holiday Is It? 2003. (Compass Point Phonics Readers Ser.). (Illus.). 16p. (J). (gr. 1 up). 13.26 (978-0-7565-0533-2(X)) Compass Point Bks.

West, Tracey & Nolls, Katherine. Pokemon Challenge. 2003. (Illus.). 59p. (J). (978-0-439-53052-1(0)) Scholastic, Inc.

Winkler, Lee. Laughter Is the Best Medicine: A Hospital Riddle Book for Kids. 1998. (Illus.). 64p. (J). (gr. k-4). pap. 4.95 (978-1-888237-18-4(X)) Baxter Pr.

Winter, Jeanette. House That Jack Built. 2003. (gr. k-3). lib. bdg. 14.15 (978-0-613-61630-0(8)) Tandem Library Bks.

Yebra, Antonio Gomez & Soler, Eduardo Miguel. Adivina, Adivinanzas. 2003. (SPA.). (978-84-348-7336-0(2) , SM31231) SM Ediciones ESP. *Dist:* Lectorum Pubns., Inc.

Yoe, Craig. The Mighty Big Book of Riddles. 2001. (Illus.). (J). (978-0-606-21329-5(5)) Tandem Library Bks.

—Mighty Big Book of Riddles. 2001. (Library O'Laughs). (Illus.). 288p. (J). (gr. 4-7). mass mkt. 6.99 (978-0-8431-7583-7(4) , Price Stern Sloan) Penguin Group (USA) Inc.

—Thanksgiving Jokes & Riddles. Yoe, Craig, illus. 2003. (Holiday Ha Ha's Ser.). (Illus.). 128p. (J). (gr. 3). pap. 4.99 (978-0-8431-0273-4(X) , Price Stern Sloan) Penguin Group (USA) Inc.

Ziebel, Peter. Where Am I Learning Riddles. 1999. (J). (978-0-590-63599-8(9)) Scholastic Reading Counts.

Ziegler, Mark. Critter Jitters: A Book of Animal Jokes. Haberstroh, Anne, illus. 2005. (Read-It! Readers Ser.). 24p. (C). (gr. 1-3). 18.60 (978-1-4048-0967-3(8)) Picture Window Bks.

—Giggle Bubbles: A Book of Underwater Jokes. Haberstroh, Anne, illus. 2005. (Read-It! Readers Ser.). 24p. (C). (gr. 1-3). 18.60 (978-1-4048-0968-0(6)) Picture Window Bks.

—Goofballs! A Book of Sport Jokes. Haberstroh, Anne, illus. 2005. (Read-It! Readers Ser.). 24p. (C). (gr. 1-3). 18.60 (978-1-4048-0965-9(1)) Picture Window Bks.

—Lunchbox Laughs: A Book of Food Jokes. Haberstroh, Anne, illus. 2005. (Read-It! Readers Ser.). 24p. (C). (gr. 1-3). 18.60 (978-1-4048-0963-5(5)) Picture Window Bks.

—Mind Knots: A Book of Riddles. Haugen, Ryan, illus. 2005. (Read-It! Readers Ser.). 24p. (J). (ps). lib. bdg. 18.60 (978-1-4048-1162-1(1)) Picture Window Bks.

—School Kidders: A Book of School Jokes. Haberstroh, Anne, illus. 2005. (Read-It! Readers Ser.). 24p. (C). (gr. 1-3). 18.60 (978-1-4048-0964-2(3)) Picture Window Bks.

—Wacky Wheelies: A Book of Transportation Jokes. Haberstroh, Anne, illus. 2005. (Read-It! Readers Ser.). 24p. (C). (gr. 1-3). 18.60 (978-1-4048-0966-6(X)) Picture Window Bks.

RIDE, SALLY, 1951-

Mattern, Joanne. Sally Ride: Astronaut & Physicist. 2005. (Ferguson Career Biographies Ser.). (Illus.). 128p. (J). (gr. 6-12). 25.00 (978-0-8160-5892-1(X) , Ferguson Publishing Co.) Facts On File, Inc.

Nettleton, Pamela Hill. Sally Ride. Yesh, Jeff, illus. 2004. (Biographies Ser.). 24p. (C). (gr. k-3). 22.60 (978-1-4048-0189-9(8)) Picture Window Bks.

Nichols, Catherine. Sally Ride. 2005. (Scholastic News Nonfiction Readers Ser.). (Illus.). 24p. (J). (gr. 1-2). 19.00 (978-0-516-24942-1(8) , Children's Pr.) Scholastic Library Publishing.

Raum, Elizabeth. Sally Ride. 2005. (American Lives Ser.). (Illus.). 32p. (J). (978-1-4034-6941-0(5)); pap. (978-1-4034-6948-9(2)) Heinemann Library.

Sally Ride. (Biographies Ser.). 24p. (J). 7.95 (978-1-4048-0462-3(5)) Picture Window Bks.

RIDER, ALEX (FICTITIOUS CHARACTER)—FICTION

Horowitz, Anthony. Ark Angel. (Alex Rider Ser.: Bk. 6). 2007. 336p. (J). 7.99 (978-0-14-240738-7(0) , Puffin); 2006. 326p. (YA). (gr. 5). 17.99 (978-0-399-24152-9(3) , Philomel) Penguin Group (USA) Inc.

—Eagle Strike. (Alex Rider Ser.: Bk. 4). 2006. 352p. (J). (gr. 7). pap. 7.99 (978-0-14-240613-7(9) , Puffin); 2004. (Illus.). 272p. (YA). (gr. 4). 17.99 (978-0-399-23979-3(0) , Philomel) Penguin Group (USA) Inc.

—Eagle Strike. 2003. 352p. (YA). pap. (978-0-7445-9057-9(4)) Walker & Co.

—Gadgets. 2006. (Alex Rider Ser.). (Illus.). 56p. (J). (gr. 5). 15.99 (978-0-399-24486-5(7) , Philomel) Penguin Group (USA) Inc.

—Point Blank. (Alex Rider Ser.: Bk. 2). 2006. 304p. (J). (gr. 7). pap. 7.99 (978-0-14-240612-0(0) , Puffin); 2002. 208p. (YA). (gr. 5 up). 17.99 (978-0-399-23621-1(X) , Philomel) Penguin Group (USA) Inc.

—Scorpia. (Alex Rider Ser.: Bk. 5). (YA). (gr. 5). 2006. 400p. pap. 7.99 (978-0-14-240578-9(7) , Puffin); 2005. 320p. 17.99 (978-0-399-24151-2(5) , Philomel) Penguin Group (USA) Inc.

—Skeleton Key. (Alex Rider Ser.: Bk. 3). 2006. 352p. (J). (gr. 7). pap. 7.99 (978-0-14-240614-4(7) , Puffin); 2003. 240p. (YA). (gr. 5). 17.99 (978-0-399-23777-5(1) , Philomel) Penguin Group (USA) Inc.

—Stormbreaker. (Alex Rider Ser.: Bk. 1). 2006. 256p. (J). (gr. 7). pap. 7.99 (978-0-14-240611-3(2) , Puffin); 2002. (Illus.). (J). (gr. 4-7). 5.99 (978-0-698-11932-1(0) , Puffin); 2001. (Illus.). 1p. (YA). (gr. 5 up). 17.99 (978-0-399-23620-4(1) , Philomel); 2006. 264p. (J). (gr. 5). 7.99 (978-0-14-240656-4(2) , Puffin) Penguin Group (USA) Inc.

—Stormbreaker. 2004. (Alex Rider Ser.: Bk. 1). 208p. (J). (gr. 4-7). pap. 38.00 incl. audio (978-0-8072-2277-5(1) , Listening Library) Random Hse. Audio Publishing Group.

—Stormbreaker: The Graphic Novel. Kanako & Yuzuru, illus. 2006. (Alex Rider Ser.). 144p. (J). (gr. 4). pap. 14.99 (978-0-399-24633-3(9) , Philomel) Penguin Group (USA) Inc.

RIDING

see Horsemanship

RIEL REBELLION, 1885—FICTION

Bayle, B. J. Battle Cry at Batoche. 2008. 160p. (YA). pap. 11.99 (***978-1-55002-717-4(4)*** , Sandcastle Bks.) Dundurn Group, The CAN. *Dist:* Univ. of Toronto Pr.

Scanlan, W. J. Rebellion. 2004. 167p. (J). (gr. 4 up). pap. (978-1-55005-118-6(0)) Fitzhenry & Whiteside, Ltd.

RIFLES

Crompton, Samuel Willard. The Repeating Rifle. 2003. (Transforming Power of Technology Ser.). (Illus.). 112p. (gr. 9-13). 30.00 (978-0-7910-7452-7(8) , Chelsea Hse.) Facts On File, Inc.

Souter, Gerry. Military Rifles: Fierce Firepower. 2006. (Mighty Military Machines Ser.). (Illus.). 48p. (J). (gr. 4-10). lib. bdg. 23.93 (978-0-7660-2662-9(0)) Enslow Pubs., Inc.

RIGHT (POLITICAL SCIENCE)

see Right and Left (Political Science)

RIGHT AND LEFT (POLITICAL SCIENCE)

see also Conservatism

Sonder, Ben. Militia Movement: Fighters of the Far Right. 2000. (Single Titles Social Studies Ser.). (Illus.). 128p. (YA). (gr. 8-12). pap. 8.95 (978-0-531-16466-2(7) , Watts, Franklin) Scholastic Library Publishing.

—The Militia Movement: Fighters of the Far Right. 2000. (Illus.). 128p. (YA). (gr. 8-13). per. 17.60 (978-0-613-31476-3(X)) Tandem Library Bks.

RIGHT OF ASSEMBLY

see Assembly, Right of

RIGHT OF PRIVACY

see Privacy, Right of

RIGHT TO WORK

see Discrimination in Employment

RIGHTS, CIVIL

see Civil Rights

RIIS, JACOB A. (JACOB AUGUST), 1849-1914—FICTION

Kroll, Steven. Sweet America. 2004. 172p. (J). lib. bdg. 16.92 (***978-1-4242-0773-2(8)***) Fitzgerald Bks.

RINGLING BROTHERS

Apps, Jerry. Tents, Tigers, & the Ringling Brothers. 2006. (Badger Biography Ser.). (Illus.). 128p. (J). pap. 12.95 (978-0-87020-374-9(6)) Wisconsin Historical Society.

Marsh, Carole. The Ringling Brothers. 2002. (One Thousand Readers Ser.). (Illus.). 12p. (gr. k-4). 2.95 (978-0-635-01499-3(8) , 14998) Gallopade International.

RIO DE JANEIRO (BRAZIL)

Morrison, Marion. Rio de Janeiro. 2004. (Great Cities of the World Ser.). (Illus.). 48p. (J). (gr. 5 up). pap. 15.93 (978-0-8368-5191-5(9)); lib. bdg. 30.00 (978-0-8368-5031-4(9)) Stevens, Gareth Inc. (World Almanac Library).

Scoones, Simon. Rio de Janeiro. Parker, Edward, photos by. 2006. (Global Cities Ser.). 64p. (YA). (gr. 5-8). 30.00 (978-0-7910-8857-9(X) , Chelsea Hse.) Facts On File, Inc.

RIO GRANDE RIVER AND VALLEY

Fahey, Kathleen. The Rio Grande River. 2003. (Rivers of North America Ser.). (Illus.). 32p. (J). (gr. 3 up). lib. bdg. 24.67 (978-0-8368-3760-5(6)) Stevens, Gareth Inc.

Lourie, Peter. Rio Grande: From the Rocky Mountains to the Gulf of Mexico. 2003. (Illus.). 48p. (YA). (gr. 4-6). 17.95 (978-1-56397-706-0(0)); pap. 9.95 (978-1-56397-896-8(2)) Boyds Mills Pr.

—Rio Grande: From the Rocky Mountains to the Gulf of Mexico. (Illus.). 2000. 46p. (J). (gr. 3-7). lib. bdg. 18.75 (978-0-613-30112-1(9)); 1999. (978-0-606-20101-8(7)) Tandem Library Bks.

McNeese, Tim. The Rio Grande. 2004. (Rivers in World History Ser.). (Illus.). 120p. (J). (gr. 9-13). 30.00 (978-0-7910-8244-7(X) , Chelsea Hse.) Facts On File, Inc.

RIOTS

Alonso, Karen. The Chicago Seven Political Protest Trial: A Headline Court Case. 2002. (Headline Court Cases Ser.). (Illus.). 112p. (J). (gr. 6-12). lib. bdg. 26.60 (978-0-7660-1764-1(8)) Enslow Pubs., Inc.

Arevalo, Luis Paquime. L. A. 's Riots. 2004. (YA). per. 12.99 (978-0-9748598-0-4(X)) L. A. Eng Bks.

Cole, Michael D. The L. A. Riots: Rage in the City of Angels. 1999. (American Disasters Ser.). (Illus.). 48p. (YA). (gr. 4-10). lib. bdg. 23.93 (978-0-7660-1219-6(0)) Enslow Pubs., Inc.

Fireside, Bryna J. The Haymarket Square Riot Trial: A Headline Court Case. 2002. (Headline Court Cases Ser.). (Illus.). 128p. (YA). (gr. 6-12). lib. bdg. 26.60 (978-0-7660-1761-0(3)) Enslow Pubs., Inc.

McGowen, Tom. The 1968 Democratic Convention. 2003. (Cornerstones of Freedom, 2ND Ser.). (Illus.). 48p. (J). 26.00 (978-0-516-24220-0(2) , Children's Pr.) Scholastic Library Publishing.

RIOTS—FICTION

Bunting, Eve. Noche de Humo. Andujar, Gloria de Aragon, tr. Diaz, David, illus. 1999. (SPA.). 36p. (J). (gr. 2-4). pap. 7.00 (978-0-15-201946-4(4) , Voyager Bks./Libros Viajeros) Harcourt Children's Bks.

—Noche de Humo. 1999. (978-0-606-16516-7(9)); (SPA.). lib. bdg. 14.15 (978-0-613-16782-6(1)) Tandem Library Bks.

—Smoky Night. 2002. (Illus.). (J). 13.19 (978-0-7587-0073-5(3)) Book Wholesalers, Inc.

—Smoky Night. Diaz, David, illus. 1999. 36p. (J). (ps-3). pap. 7.00 (978-0-15-201884-9(0) , Harcourt Paperbacks) Harcourt Children's Bks.

—Smoky Night. 1999. (978-0-606-16515-0(0)); lib. bdg. 14.15 (978-0-613-18279-9(0)) Tandem Library Bks.

Casanova, Mary. Riot. 1998. (J). (978-0-606-13743-0(2)) Tandem Library Bks.

Grote, JoAnn A. Danger in the Harbor: Grain Riots Threaten Boston. 1999. (American Adventure Ser.: No. 6). (Illus.). 144p. (J). (gr. 3-7). lib. bdg. 15.95 (978-0-7910-5046-0(7) , Chelsea Hse.) Facts On File, Inc.

Myers, Anna. Tulsa Burning. 2004. 184p. (J). pap. 7.95 (978-0-8027-7696-9(5)); (Illus.). (gr. 3-7). 16.95 (978-0-8027-8829-0(7)) Walker & Co.

RITES AND CEREMONIES

see also Baptism; Fasts and Feasts; Funeral Rites and Ceremonies; Manners and Customs; Marriage Customs and Rites

also classes of people and ethnic groups with the subdivision Rites and Ceremonies, e.g. Jews—Rites and Ceremonies

Behar, Susan. Growing Up. Sloan, Frank, ed. 2001. (Ceremonies & Celebrations Ser.). (Illus.). 32p. (J). (ps-3). lib. bdg. 25.69 (978-0-7398-3269-1(7)) Raintree.

—Growing Up. 2001. (Ceremonies & Celebrations Ser.). (Illus.). 32p. (J). (978-0-7502-2802-2(4)) Steck-Vaughn.

Beker, Jeanne. The Big Night Out. Dion, Nathalie, illus. 2005. 80p. (J). (gr. 4). pap. 15.95 (978-0-88776-719-7(2)) Tundra Bks., Inc./Livres Toundra, Inc. CAN. *Dist:* Random Hse., Inc.

Coon, Nora E. It's Your Rite: Girls' Coming-of-Age Stories. 2002. (gr. 7-12). lib. bdg. 18.75 (978-0-613-67097-5(3)) Tandem Library Bks.

Dineen, Jacqueline. Rites of Passage. Wilkinson, Philip, ed. Ingpen, Robert R., illus. 1999. (People & Customs of the World Ser.). 96p. (YA). lib. bdg. 21.95 (978-0-7910-5133-7(1) , Chelsea Hse.) Facts On File, Inc.

Fearon, Sister Mary. Sacraments: Reproducible Activities. 1999. (God's Gift Ser.). (Illus.). 32p. (J). (gr. 4-8). 9.95 (978-1-893757-00-4(5) , 01) Needer, E.T. Publishing.

Ganeri, Anita. Journey's End: Death & Mourning. 1999. (Life Times Ser.). (Illus.). 30p. (YA). (gr. 2 up). 15.95 (978-0-87226-289-8(8) , 62898B, Bedrick, Peter Bks.) School Specialty Publishing.

—Wedding Days: Celebrations of Marriage. 1999. (Life Times Ser.). (Illus.). 32p. (J). 15.95 (978-0-87226-288-1(X) , 6288XB, Bedrick, Peter Bks.) School Specialty Publishing.

Greene, Jacqueline Dembar. Powwow: A Good Day to Dance. Greene, Jacqueline Dembar, photos by. 1998. (First Bks.). (Illus.). 64p. (J). (gr. 5-7). 22.00 (978-0-531-20337-8(9) , Watts, Franklin) Scholastic Library Publishing.

Harris, Carol & Brown, Mike. Ceremonial Costumes. 2002. (Twentieth-Century Developments in Fashion & Costume Ser.). (Illus.). 64p. (J). (gr. 7 up). lib. bdg. (978-1-59084-424-3(6)) Mason Crest Pubs.

Johnson, Joy & Grollman, Earl, texts. A Child's Book about Burial & Cremation. 2001. (J). (ps-5). 4.95 (978-1-56123-146-1(0) , CABC) Centering Corp.

—A Child's Book about Funerals & Cemeteries. 2001. (J). (ps-5). 4.95 (978-1-56123-148-5(7) , CAFC) Centering Corp.

MacDonald, Fiona, intro. Gods, Beliefs & Ceremonies: Through the Ages. 2001. (Through the Ages Ser.). (Illus.). 64p. (J). (gr. 3-7). 12.95 (978-0-7548-0784-1(3)) Anness Publishing GBR. *Dist:* National Bk. Network.

Mason, Paul. Journeys. 2003. (Rites of Passage Ser.). (Illus.). 32p. (J). pap. (978-1-4034-2513-3(2)); lib. bdg. 24.22 (978-1-4034-3988-8(5)) Heinemann Library.

—Journeys. 2003. (gr. k-3). lib. bdg. 15.90 (978-0-613-89118-9(X)) Tandem Library Bks.

—Weddings. 2003. (Rites of Passage Ser.). (Illus.). 32p. (J). lib. bdg. 24.22 (978-1-4034-3990-1(7)) Heinemann Library.

Myers, Jack & Jack Myers Ministries. Flowing in the Anointing: Understanding the Anointing of God. 2004. 90p. pap. 7.95 (978-0-9720928-1-4(1)) Myers, Jack Ministries, Inc.

Onyefulu, Ifeoma. Welcome Dede! An African Naming Ceremony. 2004. (Illus.). 32p. (J). 14.95 (978-1-84507-267-4(7)) Lincoln, Frances Ltd. GBR. *Dist:* Transition Vendor.

—Welcome Dede! An African Naming Ceremony. 2004. (Illus.). 32p. (J). reprint ed. pap. 7.95 (978-1-84507-311-4(8)) Lincoln, Frances Ltd. GBR. *Dist:* Perseus Distribution.

—Your Name Is Dede: An African Baby's Naming Ceremony. 2003. (Illus.). 32p. (J). 14.95 (978-0-7112-1938-0(9)) Lincoln, Frances Ltd. GBR. *Dist:* Transition Vendor.

Post, John R., compiled by. NPKA Book of Blotar Bk. 1: Catalog of Blots & Rituals of Wotanism. num. ed. 2003. (Illus.). 421p. 35.00 (978-0-9749416-0-8(3)) Himminbjorg Publishing, Inc.

Ross, Mandy. Coming of Age. 2003. (Rites of Passage Ser.). (Illus.). 32p. (J). pap. (978-1-4034-2511-9(6)); lib. bdg. 24.22 (978-1-4034-3986-4(9)) Heinemann Library.

—Coming of Age. 2003. (gr. k-3). lib. bdg. 15.90 (978-0-613-87168-6(5)) Tandem Library Bks.

—Funerals. 2003. (Rites of Passage Ser.). (Illus.). 32p. (J). lib. bdg. 24.22 (978-1-4034-3987-1(7)) Heinemann Library.

—Funerals. 2003. (gr. k-3). lib. bdg. 15.90 (978-0-613-88219-4(9)) Tandem Library Bks.

—Naming Ceremonies. 2003. (Rites of Passage Ser.). (Illus.). 32p. (J). pap. (978-1-4034-4597-1(4)); lib. bdg. 24.22 (978-1-4034-3989-5(3)) Heinemann Library.

—Naming Ceremonies. 2003. (gr. k-3). lib. bdg. 15.90 (978-0-613-88220-0(2)) Tandem Library Bks.

Sita, Lisa. Coming of Age. 1998. (World Celebrations & Ceremonies Ser.). (Illus.). 24p. (J). (gr. 3-5). 21.20 (978-1-56711-276-4(5) , Blackbirch Pr., Inc.) Thomson Gale.

Spirn, Michele Sobel. Birth. 1998. (World Celebrations & Ceremonies Ser.). (Illus.). 24p. (J). (gr. 3-5). 22.45 (978-1-56711-277-1(3) , Blackbirch Pr., Inc.) Thomson Gale.

World Book, Inc. Staff, contrib. by. Birth & Growing up Celebrations. 2002. (World Book's Celebrations & Rituals Around the World Ser.). (Illus.). 44p. (J). (978-0-7166-5010-2(X)) World Bk., Inc.

—Everyday Celebrations & Rituals. 2003. (World Book's Celebrations & Rituals Around the World Ser.). (Illus.). 46p. (J). (978-0-7166-5016-4(9)) World Bk., Inc.

RITUAL

see Rites and Ceremonies

RIVERA, DIEGO, 1886-1957

Bankston, John. Diego Rivera. 2003. (Latinos in American History Ser.). (Illus.). 56p. (gr. 4-8). lib. bdg. 29.95 (978-1-58415-208-8(7)) Mitchell Lane Pubs., Inc.

Foard, Sheila Wood. Diego Rivera. 2003. (Great Hispanic Heritage Ser.). (Illus.). 112p. (gr. 6-12). pap. 30.00 (978-0-7910-7516-6(8) , Chelsea Hse.) Facts On File, Inc.

Foard, Sheila Wood & Rivera, Diego. Diego Rivera. 2003. (Great Hispanic Heritage Ser.). (Illus.). 112p. (gr. 6-12). 30.00 (978-0-7910-7256-1(8) , Chelsea Hse.) Facts On File, Inc.

Guzman, Lila & Guzman, Rick. Diego Rivera: Artist of Mexico. 2006. (Famous Latinos Ser.). (Illus.). 32p. (J). lib. bdg. 22.60 (978-0-7660-2641-4(8) , Enslow Elementary) Enslow Pubs., Inc.

Guzman, Lila & Guzman, Rick. Diego Rivera: Artista de México. 2007. (Latinos Famosos Ser.). (SPA., Illus.). 32p. (J). (gr. 3-4). lib. bdg. 22.60 (***978-0-7660-2676-6(0)*** , Enslow Elementary) Enslow Pubs., Inc.

Hillstrom, Laurie. Diego Rivera. 2007. (Twentieth Century Most Influential Hispanics Ser.). (Illus.). 128p. (gr. 7-10). 31.20 (***978-1-4205-0018-9(X)*** , Lucent Bks.) Thomson Gale.

HSP. First-Place Reading for Title I: Diego Rivera. 2nd ed. 2002. (Harcourt Title I Reading Programs Ser.). (gr. 6 up). pap. 58.40 (978-0-15-338165-2(5)) Harcourt Schl. Pubs.

Kent, Deborah. Diego Rivera: Painting Mexico. 2005. (Proud Heritage: the Hispanic Library Ser.). (Illus.). 40p. (J). (gr. 3-7). 28.50 (978-1-59296-384-3(6)) Child's World, Inc.

Litwin, Laura Baskes. Diego Rivera: Legendary Mexican Painter. 2005. (Latino Biography Library). (Illus.). 128p. (J). (gr. 6-13). lib. bdg. 31.93 (978-0-7660-2486-1(5)) Enslow Pubs., Inc.

Mattern, Joanne. Diego Rivera. 2005. (Checkerboard Biography Library). (Illus.). 32p. (J). (gr. k-6). lib. bdg. 22.78 (978-1-59197-849-7(1)) ABDO Publishing Co.

Sabbeth, Carol. Frida Kahlo & Diego Rivera: Their Lives & Ideas, 24 Activities. 2005. (For Kids Ser.). (Illus.). 160p. (J). pap. 17.95 (978-1-55652-569-8(9) , 1241061) Chicago Review Pr., Inc.

Schaefer, A. R. Diego Rivera. (Life & Work of. . . Ser.). (Illus.). 32p. (J). (gr. k-2). 2003. lib. bdg. 22.79 (978-1-4034-0288-2(4)); 2002. pap. 6.50 (978-1-4034-0494-7(1)) Heinemann Library.

Schoeneberger, Megan & Rivera, Diego. Diego Rivera: Artist & Muralist. 2006. (Fact Finders Ser.). (Illus.). 32p. (J). (978-0-7368-5437-5(1)) Capstone Pr., Inc.

Tieck, Sarah & Rivera, Diego. Diego Rivera. 2007. (Illus.). 32p. (J). 22.78 (978-1-59679-785-7(1)) ABDO Publishing Co.

RIVERS

see also Dams; Floods; Hydraulic Engineering; Inland Navigation; Water—Pollution; Water Power

also names of rivers

Baldwin, Carol. Living by a River. 2003. (Living Habitats Ser.). (Illus.). 32p. (J). lib. bdg. 24.22 (978-1-4034-0842-6(4)); pap. 6.95 (978-1-4034-3226-1(0)) Heinemann Library.

Barnes, Julia. 101 Facts about Rivers. 2003. (One Hundred One Facts about Our World Ser.). (Illus.). 32p. (J). (gr. 3 up). lib. bdg. 23.33 (978-0-8368-3711-7(8)) Stevens, Gareth Inc.

Bedford, Kate. Geography. 2006. (Illus.). 32p. (J). (978-1-59604-100-4(5)) Stargazer Bks.

Bellamy, David. The River. Dow, Jill, illus. 1999. (Our Changing World Ser.). 32p. (J). (gr. 1-5). pap. 7.99 (978-0-7112-1387-6(9)) Lincoln, Frances Ltd. GBR. *Dist:* Transition Vendor.

Bellamy, David & Dow, Jill. Our Changing World: The River. 2004. (Illus.). 32p. (J). pap. 7.95 (978-1-84507-218-6(9)) Lincoln, Frances Ltd. GBR. *Dist:* Transition Vendor.

Blue River Map. 2001. pap. 8.00 (978-0-9715563-4-8(2)) Hidden Lakes Pr.

Braun. Rivers, Lakes & Ponds. 2001. (Biomes Ser.). (Illus.). (J). pap. (978-0-7398-4943-9(3)) Steck-Vaughn.

Braun, Eric & Donovan, Sandy. River, Lakes, & Ponds. 2001. (Illus.). 32p. (J). lib. bdg. 22.83 (978-0-7398-4757-2(0)) Raintree.

—Scientists of Rivers, Lakes, & Ponds. 2001. (Scientists of the Biomes Ser.). (Illus.). 48p. (J). lib. bdg. 24.26 (978-0-7398-4755-8(4)) Raintree.

Bull, Schuyler. Along the Luangwa: A Story of an African Floodplain. Male, Alan, illus. 1999. (Nature Conservancy Habitat Ser.: No. 13). 36p. (J). (gr. 1-4). 15.95 (978-1-56899-776-6(0)); pap. 5.95 (978-1-56899-777-3(9)) Soundprints.

Bulletpoints Oceans & Rivers. 2005. (Illus.). (J). per. 4.99 (978-1-933581-01-9(8)) Byeway Bks.

Burnham & Laurie. Rivers. 2007. (Extreme Earth Ser.). 200p. (gr. 6-12). 35.00 (978-0-8160-5916-4(0)) Facts On File, Inc.

Castaldo, Nancy F. River Wild: An Activity Guide to North American Rivers. 2006. (Illus.). 144p. (J). (gr. 3-5). pap. 14.95 (978-1-55652-585-8(0)) Chicago Review Pr., Inc.

Chambers, Catherine & Lapthorn, Nicholas. Rivers. 2nd ed. 2007. (***978-1-4034-9604-1(8)***); pap. (***978-1-4034-9614-0(5)***) Heinemann.

Champion, Neil. Rivers & Wetlands. 2005. (Caring for the Planet Ser.). (Illus.). 48p. (J). (978-1-58340-510-9(0)) Smart Apple Media.

Cheripko, Jan. Voices of the River: Adventures on the Delaware. 2003. (Illus.). 48p. (YA). (gr. 4-6). pap. 10.95 (978-1-56397-622-3(6)) Boyds Mills Pr.

Cherry, Lynne. A River Ran Wild: An Environmental History. 2002. (Illus.). 40p. (J). (gr. 1-4). pap. 7.00 (978-0-15-216372-3(7) , Voyager Bks./Libros Viajeros) Harcourt Children's Bks.

—A River Ran Wild: An Environmental History. 1998. (978-0-606-13093-6(4)) Tandem Library Bks.

Cherry, Lynne, as told by. A River Ran Wild: An Environmental History. 1998. (J). (gr. 4). pap. 3.95 (978-0-439-04468-4(5)) Scholastic, Inc.

Day, Trevor. Lakes & Rivers. Garratt, Richard, illus. 2006. (Biomes of the Earth Ser.). 272p. (J). (gr. 6-12). 39.50 (978-0-8160-5328-5(6)) Facts On File, Inc.

La Defensa de los Rios y Lagos. (Coleccion Biblioteca Juvenil de Ecología). (SPA., Illus.). (YA). (gr. 5-8). pap. (978-958-04-2672-1(4) , 80426721) Norma S.A. COL. *Dist:* Lectorum Pubns., Inc.

Dorling Kindersley Publishing Staff. Pond & River. 2005. (Eyewitness Books). 72p. (J). 15.99 (978-0-7566-1085-2(0)); lib. bdg. 19.99 (978-0-7566-1086-9(9)) Dorling Kindersley Publishing, Inc.

—Rivers & Lakes. (Eye Wonder Ser.). (Illus.). 48p. (J). (gr. k-3). 2003. 9.99 (978-0-7894-9046-9(3)); 2002. lib. bdg. 17.99 (978-0-7894-9047-6(1)) Dorling Kindersley Publishing, Inc.

Dwyer, Jacqueline. Rivers. 2001. (PowerKids Readers Ser.). (Illus.). 24p. (J). (gr. 1). lib. bdg. 16.00 (978-0-8239-5681-4(4) , PKRIVE, PowerKids Pr.) Rosen Publishing Group, Inc., The.

Edwards, Nicola. Rivers & Streams. 2004. (Geography First Ser.). (J). 23.70 (978-1-4103-0109-3(5) , Blackbirch Pr., Inc.) Thomson Gale.

Fleisher, Paul. Mountain Stream. 1998. (Webs of Life Ser.). (Illus.). 40p. (J). (gr. 2-5). lib. bdg. 22.79 (978-0-7614-0838-3(X) , Benchmark Bks.) Cavendish, Marshall Corp.

Fourment, Tiffany. My Water Comes from the Mountains. Emerling, Dorothy, illus. 2004. 32p. 19.95 (978-1-57098-387-0(9)) Rinehart, Roberts Pubs.

Frahm, Randy. Rivers. 2002. (LifeViews Ser.). (J). (978-0-89812-374-6(7) , Creative Paperbacks) Creative Co., The.

—Rivers: Sculpters of the Land. 2002. (LifeViews Ser.). (Illus.). 32p. (J). lib. bdg. (978-1-58341-124-7(0) , Creative Education) Creative Co., The.

Frisch, Aaron. Rivers. 2008. (J). (***978-1-58341-573-3(4)*** , Creative Education) Creative Co., The.

Galko, Francine. River Animals. 2003. (Animals in Their Habitats Ser.). (Illus.). 32p. (J). (gr. k-2). lib. bdg. 21.36 (978-1-4034-0183-0(7)); pap. 6.95 (978-1-4034-0440-4(2)) Heinemann Library.

—River Animals. 2003. (gr. k-3). lib. bdg. 14.75 (978-0-613-45818-4(4)) Tandem Library Bks.

Geisert, Bonnie & Geisert, Arthur. River Town. 1999. (Small Town U. S. A. Ser.). (Illus.). 32p. (J). (gr. k-3). tchr. ed. 16.00 (978-0-395-90891-4(4) , Walter Lorraine) Houghton Mifflin Co. Trade & Reference Div.

Gilpin, Daniel. The Snake River. 2003. (Rivers of North America Ser.). (Illus.). 32p. (J). (gr. 3 up). lib. bdg. 24.67 (978-0-8368-3761-2(4)) Stevens, Gareth Inc.

Gray, Leon. The Missouri River. 2003. (Rivers of North America Ser.). (Illus.). 32p. (J). (gr. 3 up). lib. bdg. 24.67 (978-0-8368-3758-2(4)) Stevens, Gareth Inc.

Great Rivers, 6 Pack. (Rigby Infoquest Ser.). 32p. (gr. 4 up). 37.00 (978-0-7578-5730-0(2)) Rigby Education.

Great Rivers of the World, 6 bks. Incl. Amazon. Parker, Edward. pap. 14.95 (978-0-8368-5449-7(7)); Ganges. Cumming, David. pap. 14.95 (978-0-8368-5450-3(0)); Mississippi. Walsh, Kieran. pap. 14.95 (978-0-8368-5451-0(9)); Nile. Cumming, David. pap. 14.95 (978-0-8368-5452-7(7)); Rhine. Allan, Tony. pap. 14.95 (978-0-8368-5453-4(5)); Yangtze. Waterlow, Julia. pap. 14.95 (978-0-8368-5454-1(3)); 48p. (J). (gr. 5 up). 2003. (Illus.). 2002. Set pap. 89.70 (978-0-8368-5448-0(9)); Set lib. bdg. 180.00 (978-0-8368-5441-1(1)) Stevens, Gareth Inc. (World Almanac Library).

Green, Emily K. Rivers. 2006. (Blastoff! Readers Ser.). (Illus.). 24p. (J). lib. bdg. 16.95 (978-1-60014-040-2(8)) Bellwether Media.

Green, Mary. Rivers in Action. 2004. (Earth's Changing Landscape Ser.). (Illus.). 46p. (J). lib. bdg. 28.50 (978-1-58340-477-5(5)) Smart Apple Media.

Group/McGraw-Hill, Wright. Rivers: From Beginning to End, 6 vols. (Book2WebTM Ser.). (gr. 4-8). 36.50 (978-0-322-04441-8(3)) Wright Group, The.

—Rivers: Level H, 6 vols. (Take Twostm Ser.). 16p. 29.95 (978-0-322-08957-0(3)) Wright Group, The.

Hamilton, John. The Missouri River. 2003. (Lewis & Clark Expedition Ser.). (Illus.). 32p. (J). (gr. 3-8). lib. bdg. 24.21 (978-1-57765-762-0(4)) ABDO Publishing Co.

Harcourt School Publishers Staff. How Rivers Shape the Land Advanced Level. 3rd ed. 2002. (Trophies Reading Program Ser.). (Illus.). pap. 5.10 (978-0-15-323470-5(9)) Harcourt Schl. Pubs.

—River. 3rd ed. 2002. (Trophies Ser.). pap. 51.00 (978-0-15-327896-9(X)) Harcourt Schl. Pubs.

Harrison, David L. Rivers: Nature's Wondrous Waterways. Nathan, Cheryl, illus. 2003. (Earthworks Ser.). 32p. (J). (gr. k-2). 15.95 (978-1-56397-968-2(3)) Boyds Mills Pr.

Hawkes, Steve. The Tennessee River. 2003. (Rivers of North America Ser.). (Illus.). 32p. (J). (gr. 3 up). lib. bdg. 24.67 (978-0-8368-3763-6(0)) Stevens, Gareth Inc.

Howard, Fran. Rivers & Streams. 2007. (Habitats Ser.). (Illus.). 32p. (J). (gr. k-4). lib. bdg. 22.78 (978-1-59679-782-6(7)) ABDO Publishing Co.

Hughes, Monica. What Is a River? 2004. (Heinemann Read & Learn Ser.). (Illus.). 24p. (J). pap. (978-1-4034-6282-4(8)); lib. bdg. (978-1-4034-6276-3(3)) Steck-Vaughn.

Jackson, Kay. Rivers. 2006. (Earthforms Ser.). (Illus.). 24p. (J). (978-0-7368-5407-8(X) , 1252620) Capstone Pr., Inc.

Jackson, Tom. The Arkansas River. 2003. (Rivers of North America Ser.). (Illus.). 32p. (J). (gr. 3 up). lib. bdg. 24.67 (978-0-8368-3752-0(5)) Stevens, Gareth Inc.

—The Ohio River. 2003. (Rivers of North America Ser.). (Illus.). 32p. (J). (gr. 3 up). lib. bdg. 24.67 (978-0-8368-3759-9(2)) Stevens, Gareth Inc.

Jennings, Terry. Rivers. 2002. (Restless Earth Ser.). (Illus.). 32p. (J). lib. bdg. 24.25 (978-1-931983-20-4(8)) Chrysalis Education.

Johnson, Rebecca L. A Journey into a River. Saroff, Phyllis V., illus. 2004. (Biomes of North America Ser.). (J). pap. 6.95 (978-0-8225-2044-3(3)); 48p. (gr. 3-6). 23.93 (978-1-57505-595-4(3)) Lerner Publishing Group.

Kramme, Michael. Rivers of the U. S. 1999. (Illus.). 80p. (YA). (gr. 5). pap. 9.95 (978-1-58037-108-7(6)) Twain, Mark Media, Inc. Pubs.

Lindeen, Carol. Life in a Stream. 2003. (Pebble Plus: Living in a Biome Ser.). (Illus.). 24p. (J). lib. bdg. 17.26 (978-0-7368-2103-2(1) , Pebble Bks.) Capstone Pr., Inc.

Macken, JoAnn Early. Rios. 2006. (ENG & SPA., Illus.). 24p. (J). pap. (978-0-8368-6554-7(5)); lib. bdg. 19.33 (978-0-8368-6547-9(2)) Stevens, Gareth Inc.

—Rivers. 2005. (Illus.). 24p. (J). pap. (978-0-8368-4893-9(4)); lib. bdg. 19.33 (978-0-8368-4886-1(1)) Stevens, Gareth Inc.

—Rivers: Rios. 2005. (SPA.). (J). (978-0-8368-6038-2(1)) Stevens, Gareth Inc.

—Rivers/Rios. 2005. (ENG & SPA., Illus.). 24p. (J). (ps-17). lib. bdg. 19.33 (978-0-8368-6031-3(4)) Stevens, Gareth Inc.

Martin, Patricia A. Fink. Rivers & Streams. 1999. (Exploring Ecosystems Ser.). (Illus.). 144p. (YA). (gr. 8-12). 24.50 (978-0-531-11523-7(2) , Watts, Franklin) Scholastic Library Publishing.

McNeese, Tim, ed. Rivers in American Life & Times. 2005. (Illus.). 120p. (gr. 9-13). pap. 180.00 (978-0-7910-7722-1(5) , Chelsea Hse.) Facts On File, Inc.

—Rivers in World History. 2005. (Illus.). 120p. (gr. 9-13). pap. 180.00 (978-0-7910-8473-1(6) , Chelsea Hse.) Facts On File, Inc.

Morris, Neil. Earth's Changing Rivers. 2003. (Illus.). (J). 7.50 (978-1-4109-0346-4(X)); 32p. lib. bdg. 25.70 (978-1-4109-0175-0(0)) Raintree.

—Earth's Changing Rivers. 2003. (gr. 3-6). lib. bdg. 15.90 (978-0-613-78240-1(2)) Tandem Library Bks.

—Living by Rivers. 2004. (J). lib. bdg. (978-1-58340-482-9(1)) Smart Apple Media.

—Rivers & Lakes. 1998. (Wonders of Our World Ser.). (Illus.). 32p. (J). (gr. 3-4). (978-0-86505-834-7(2)); pap. (978-0-86505-846-0(6)) Crabtree Publishing Co.

Nadeau, Isaac. Water in Rivers & Lakes. 2003. (Water Cycle Ser.). (Illus.). 24p. (J). lib. bdg. 18.75 (978-0-8239-6266-2(0) , PowerKids Pr.) Rosen Publishing Group, Inc., The.

Nicholson, John. The Mighty Murray. Nicholson, John, illus. 2002. (Illus.). 48p. (Orig.). (J). (978-1-86508-564-7(2)); mass mkt. (978-1-86508-565-4(0)) Allen & Unwin.

Ostopowich, Melanie. Oceans, Rivers, & Lakes. 2005. (Science Matters Ser.). (Illus.). 24p. (J). (ps-7). pap. 6.95 (978-1-59036-310-2(8)); lib. bdg. 24.45 (978-1-59036-304-1(3)) Weigl Pubs., Inc.

Owen, Andy, et al. Rivers. 2003. (Geography Starts Ser.). (Illus.). 32p. pap. 6.95 (978-1-58810-977-4(1)) Heinemann Library.

Oxlade, Chris. Rivers & Lakes. 2003. (Science Files Ser.). (Illus.). 32p. (J). (gr. 3 up). lib. bdg. 24.67 (978-0-8368-3571-7(9)) Stevens, Gareth Inc.

Parker. The Ganges. 2003. (Holy Places Ser.). (Illus.). 32p. (J). pap. 6.95 (978-1-4109-0051-7(7)) Raintree.

Parker, Jane & Parker, Steve. Rivers. 1998. (Take 5 Geography Ser.). (Illus.). 32p. (J). (gr. 3-5). 21.00 (978-0-531-14458-9(5) , Watts, Franklin) Scholastic Library Publishing.

Pollard, Michael. Great Rivers of Britain: The Clyde, Mersey, Severn, Tees, Thames, Trent. (Illus.). 45p. (978-0-237-51829-5(5) , Evans Brothers, Limited) Evans Publishing Group.

—Rivers of Britain & Ireland: The Avon, Yorkshire Ouse, Tyne, Wye, Forth, Liffey, Lagan. (Illus.). 46p. (J). (978-0-237-51805-9(8) , Evans Brothers, Limited) Evans Publishing Group.

Project WET, creator. Big Rivers Kids Activity Booklet. 2000. (J). (978-1-888631-44-9(9)) Watercourse, The.

Puncel, Maria. El Prado del Tio Pedro.Tr. of Uncle Peter's Pasture. (SPA.). 32p. (J). 12.95 (978-84-348-1226-0(6)) SM Ediciones ESP. *Dist:* AIMS International Bks., Inc.

Pyers. The River Explorer 6-Pack. 2004. (Habitat Explorer Ser.). (Illus.). pap. (978-1-4109-0913-8(1)) Raintree.

Raintree Steck-Vaughn Staff. River Journey. 2000. (Read All about It Ser.). (Illus.). (J). pap. 4.95 (978-0-8114-3789-9(2)) Steck-Vaughn.

Rawlins, Carol B. Orinoco River. 1999. (gr. 3-6). lib. bdg. 17.60 (978-0-613-29495-9(5)) Tandem Library Bks.

River Journeys, 6 vols. 2003. (Illus.). (978-0-7398-6075-5(5)) Raintree.

Rivers & Lakes, Set. Incl. Amazon River. Meister, Cari. lib. bdg. 21.35 (978-1-57765-101-7(4)); Lake Superior. Prevost, John F. lib. bdg. 21.35 (978-1-57765-104-8(9)); Lake Victoria. Meister, Cari. lib. bdg. 21.35 (978-1-57765-105-5(7)); Mississippi River. Prevost, John F. lib. bdg. 21.35 (978-1-57765-102-4(2)); Nile River. Meister, Cari. lib. bdg. 21.35 (978-1-57765-098-0(0)); Yangtze River. Meister, Cari. lib. bdg. 21.35 (978-1-57765-103-1(0)); 24p. (J). (gr. k-6). (Illus.). 2002. Set lib. bdg. 128.10 (978 1 57765 526-8(5) , Checkerboard Library) ABDO Publishing Co.

A River's Journey, 6 Packs. (Rigby Focus Ser.). 16p. (gr. 1 up). 30.00 (978-0-7578-5539-9(3)); Pck. 28.00 (978-0-7578-5307-4(2)) Rigby Education.

Rivers Learning about the Earth. 2006. (Illus.). 24p. (J). (gr. k-2). 18.50 (***978-0-531-17892-8(7)***) Scholastic Library Publishing.

Rivers of North America, 12 bks. Incl. Arkansas River. Jackson, Tom. lib. bdg. 24.67 (978-0-8368-3752-0(5)); Colorado River. Gilpin, Daniel. lib. bdg. 24.67 (978-0-8368-3753-7(3)); Columbia River. Jackson, Tom. lib. bdg. 24.67 (978-0-8368-3754-4(1)); Hudson River. Wood, Ian. lib. bdg. 24.67 (978-0-8368-3755-1(X)); Mackenzie River. Harris, Tim. lib. bdg. 24.67 (978-0-8368-3756-8(8)); Mississippi River. Green, Jen. lib. bdg. 24.67 (978-0-8368-3757-5(6)); Missouri River. Gray, Leon. lib. bdg. 24.67 (978-0-8368-3758-2(4)); Ohio River. Jackson, Tom. lib. bdg. 24.67 (978-0-8368-3759-9(2)); Rio Grande River. Fahey, Kathleen. lib. bdg. 24.67 (978-0-8368-3760-5(6)); Snake River. Gilpin, Daniel. lib. bdg. 24.67 (978-0-8368-3761-2(4)); St. Lawrence River. Cooke, Tim. lib. bdg. 24.67 (978-0-8368-3762-9(2)); Tennessee River. Hawkes, Steve. lib. bdg. 24.67 (978-0-8368-3763-6(0)); 32p. (J). (gr. 3 up). (Illus.). 2003. Set lib. bdg. 296.04 (978-0-8368-3751-3(7)) Stevens, Gareth Inc.

Roop, Peter & Roop, Connie. River Roads West: America's First Highways. 2007. 64p. (J). (gr. 3 up). 19.95 (***978-1-59078-430-3(8)***) Boyds Mills Pr.

Ross, Mandy. Rivers. 2004. (Geography Fact Files Ser.). (J). lib. bdg. 28.50 (978-1-58340-429-4(5)) Smart Apple Media.

Royston, Angela. Rivers. 2004. (My World of Geography Ser.). (J). 22.79 (978-1-4034-5594-9(5)) Heinemann Library.

P
Q
R

Ryan, William T. World of Water. 2003. (Science Links Ser.). (Illus.). 32p. (gr. 3-5). 23.00 (978-0-7910-7429-9(3) , Chelsea Hse.) Facts On File, Inc.

Schuh, Mari C. What Are Rivers? Saunders-Smith, Gail, ed. 2002. (Earth Features Ser.). (Illus.). 24p. (J). (gr. k-1). lib. bdg. 15.93 (978-0-7368-1171-2(0) , Pebble Bks.) Capstone Pr., Inc.

Sepheri, Sandy. Major Rivers. 2008. (J). (***978-1-60044-546-0(2)***) Rourke Publishing, LLC.

Stradling, Jan. Ponds & Rivers: Level I, 6 vols. (First Explorers Ser.). 24p. (gr. 1-2). 29.95 (978-0-7699-1451-0(9)) Shortland Pubns. (U. S. A.) Inc.

Taylor, Barbara. Oceans & Rivers. 2002. (Questions & Answers about... Ser.). (Illus.). 40p. (J). (gr. 4-8). pap. 7.95 (978-0-7534-5491-6(2) , Kingfisher) Houghton Mifflin Co. Trade & Reference Div.

—Rivers. 2004. (Make It Work! Geography Ser.). (Illus.). 48p. (J). (gr. 3-6). 12.95 (978-1-58728-256-0(9) , Two Can Publishing) T&N Children's Publishing.

—Rivers. Haslam, Andrew, illus. 2004. (Make It Work! Geography Ser.). 48p. (J). (gr. 3-6). pap. 6.95 (978-1-58728-252-2(6) , Two Can Publishing) T&N Children's Publishing.

—Rivers & Oceans. 2002. (Young Discoverers Ser.). (Illus.). 32p. (J). (gr. k-3). pap. 7.95 (978-0-7534-5508-1(0) , Kingfisher) Houghton Mifflin Co. Trade & Reference Div.

—Rivers & Oceans: Geography Facts & Experiments. 2002. (gr. k-3). lib. bdg. 16.40 (978-0-613-90579-4(2)) Tandem Library Bks.

Telford, Carole & Theodorou, Rod. Down a River. 2006. (Illus.). 32p. (J). (***978-1-4034-8789-6(8)***) Heinemann Library.

—Down a River. 2nd ed. 2006. (Illus.). 32p. (J). pap. (***978-1-4034-8796-4(0)***) Heinemann Library.

Trumbauer, Lisa. Follow the River. Evento, Susan, ed. 1998. (Early Science Ser.). 16p. (J). (ps-2). pap., stu. ed. 3.33 (978-1-56784-378-1(6)); (Illus.). pap. 16.95 (978-1-56784-377-4(8)) Sundance/Newbridge Educational Publishing.

Tull, Mary. Rivers & Lakes. 2004. (National Geographic Reading Expeditions Ser.). (Illus.). 32p. (J). pap. (978-0-7922-4561-2(X)) National Geographic Society.

Van Zandt, Steve. River Song: With the Banana Slug String Band (Includes Music CD) Zecca, Katherine, illus. 2007. 32p. (J). (gr. k-4). 17.95 (***978-1-58469-093-1(3)***); pap. 9.95 (***978-1-58469-094-8(1)***) Dawn Pubns.

Vaughan, Jenny. Rivers & Streams. 1998. (Geography Starts Here Ser.). (Illus.). 32p. (J). (gr. 1-4). 25.69 (978-0-8172-5114-7(6)) Raintree.

Waters, Jo. A Walk by the River. 2006. (Raintree Sprouts Ser.). (Illus.). 24p. (J). (978-1-4109-2292-2(8)); pap. 5.75 (978-1-4109-2297-7(9)) Steck-Vaughn.

What Are Rivers?, 6 vols., Vol. 2. 2005. (Earth & Outer Space Ser.). (gr. k-2). 28.95 (978-0-7368-3279-3(3)) Red Brick Learning.

Whitcraft, Melissa. The Niagara River. 2001. (Watts Library). (Illus.). 64p. (J). (gr. 5-7). pap. 8.95 (978-0-531-13987-5(5)); 25.50 (978-0-531-11903-7(3)) Scholastic Library Publishing. (Watts, Franklin).

Winne, Joanne. Living near a River. 2000. (Welcome Bks.). (Illus.). 24p. (J). (ps-2). 17.00 (978-0-516-23302-4(5) , Children's Pr.) Scholastic Library Publishing.

—Living near a River. 2000. (gr. k-3). lib. bdg. 12.95 (978-0-613-52132-1(3)) Tandem Library Bks.

RIVERS—FICTION

Atwell, Debby. River. 2004. (Illus.). 31p. (J). (ps-ps). lib. bdg. 12.75 (978-0-606-30309-5(X)) Tandem Library Bks.

Boston, Lucy M. River at Green Knowe. 2002. (gr. 3-6). lib. bdg. 14.15 (978-0-613-54444-3(7)) Tandem Library Bks.

—The River at Green Knowe. Boston, Peter, illus. 2002. (Green Knowe Ser.). 176p. (YA). (gr. 4-7). reprint ed. pap. 6.00 (978-0-15-202607-3(X) , Odyssey Classics) Harcourt Children's Bks.

Brown, Don. Our Time on the River. 2003. 144p. (J). (gr. 7-9). tchr. ed. 15.00 (978-0-618-31116-3(5)) Houghton Mifflin Co. Trade & Reference Div.

Byars, Betsy. Trouble River. 158p. (J). (gr. 3-5). pap. 4.99 (978-0-8072-1388-9(8) , Listening Library) Random Hse. Audio Publishing Group.

—Trouble River. 1999. (J). (gr. 5-7). 21.25 (978-0-8446-7024-9(3)) Smith, Peter Pub., Inc.

Cerullo, Jillian. The Danger of the River. 2005. 36p. pap. 14.99 (978-1-4116-6988-6(6)) Lulu.com.

Corentin, Philippe. El Ogro, el Lobo, la Niña y el Pastel. 2004. (SPA.). 202p. (J). 17.99 (978-84-8470-157-6(3)) Corimbo, Editorial S.L. ESP. *Dist:* Lectorum Pubns., Inc.

Corey's Web: Down in the Dumps. 2003. (J). per. (978-0-9716567-9-6(7)) Book Web Publishing, Ltd.

Corwin, Katherine. River of Glass. Jasuna, Aija, illus. 2006. (J). 12.95 (978-1-60131-002-6(1)) Big Tent Bks.

Drawson, Blair. All along the River. Drawson, Blair, illus. 2003. (Illus.). 36p. (J). (ps-2). 16.95 (978-0-88899-546-9(6)) Groundwood Bks. CAN. *Dist:* Perseus Distribution.

Ellsworth, Barry. The Little Stream. Date not set. (Illus.). 48p. (J). 9.95 (978-1-56684-082-8(1)) Evans Bk. Distribution & Pubs., Inc.

Finch, Mary. Los Tres Chivitos Gruff. 2003. (SPA.). (gr. k-3). lib. bdg. 15.30 (978-0-613-67169-9(4)) Tandem Library Bks.

Forney, Melissa. Oonawassee Summer: Something is Lurking Beneath the Surface... Scott, Gregg, illus. 2000. 126p. (J). (gr. 4-8). pap. 14.95 (978-1-928961-04-8(5)) Barker Creek Publishing, Inc.

Frenette, Liza. Dangerous Falls Ahead: An Adirondack Canoeing Adventure. Gillis, Jane, illus. 2001. (J). pap. 11.95 (978-0-925168-79-5(3)) North Country Bks., Inc.

Grahame, Kenneth. The Wind in the Willows Bk. 1: The Riverbank. Iosa, Ann, illus. 2006. (Easy Reader Classics Ser.). 32p. (J). pap. 3.95 (978-1-4027-3293-5(7)) Sterling Publishing Co., Inc.

Harcourt School Publishers Staff. The Big Rivers Level D: Library Edition. 2001. (Collections Ser.). (Illus.). (J). 4.70 (978-0-15-314440-0(8)) Harcourt Schl. Pubs.

Hay, Jerry M. & Pollema-Cahill, Phyllis. A Goose Named Gilligan. 2004. (Illus.). 32p. 15.95 (978-1-932073-09-6(4)) Kramer, H.J. Inc.

Holman, Doris Anne. Come with Me to the Pond. 2004. (Illus.). 26p. (J). (gr. k-5). pap. 11.00 (978-0-9667192-8-4(X)) Holman, Doris Anne.

—Oscar, the River Offer. 2003. (gr. 1-5). pap. 11.00 (978-0-9667192-9-1(8)) Holman, Doris Anne.

Hunter, Erin. Dark River. 2008. (Warriors Ser.: Bk. 2). 352p. (J). lib. bdg. 17.89 (***978-0-06-089206-7(4)***) HarperCollins Pubs.

Johnson, Gwen. The Story of Two-Toed Sam or How the Outer Banks Were Formed. 2006. (J). 8.95 (***978-0-9795860-9-5(7)***) Fish Tales Publishing.

Karwoski, Gail Langer. River Beds: Sleeping in the River. 2007. (Illus.). 32p. (J). 15.95 (978-0-9777423-4-9(2)) Sylvan Dell Pubng.

Klingel, Cynthia Fitterer & Noyed, Robert B. Raquel & the Letter R. 2003. (Alphaphonics Ser.). (Illus.). 24p. (J). (ps-2). 21.36 (978-1-59296-108-5(8)) Child's World, Inc.

LaMarche, Jim. The Raft. LaMarche, Jim, illus. (Illus.). 40p. (J). (gr. 1 up). 2000. 16.99 (978-0-688-13977-3(9)); 2002. reprint ed. pap. 6.99 (978-0-06-443856-8(2) , Harper Trophy) HarperCollins Pubs.

Lancaster, Susan. Hell's Gate. 2004. 200p. pap. 12.95 (978-0-9730350-2-5(1)) Snosrap Publishing CAN. *Dist:* Hushion Hse. Publishing, Ltd.

—Hell's Gate. 2003. (gr. 7-12). lib. bdg. 22.20 (978-0-613-86097-0(7)) Tandem Library Bks.

Magdanz, James. Go Home, River. Widom, Dianne, illus. 2002. 32p. (ps up). 8.95 (978-0-88240-568-1(3)) Graphic Arts Ctr. Publishing Co.

Marshall, James. Taking Care of Carruthers. 2000. (J). (978-0-606-19365-8(0)) Tandem Library Bks.

McCall, Edith. Abe & the Wild River. 1999. 184p. (J). (gr. 5-7). 9.99 (978-0-88092-439-9(X) , 439X) Royal Fireworks Publishing Co.

Mead, Alice & Weber James, Alice. Swimming to America. 2005. 160p. (J). 16.00 (978-0-374-38047-2(3) , Farrar, Straus & Giroux (BYR)) Farrar, Straus & Giroux.

Mullin, Penn. River & the Trace. 1999. (gr. 7-12). lib. bdg. 11.60 (978-0-613-29037-1(2)) Tandem Library Bks.

Oram, Hiawyn & Ross, Tony. Boris: The Beetle Who Wouldn't Stay Down. 2000. (Illus.). 32p. (J). 17.99 (978-0-86264-977-7(3)) Andersen GBR. *Dist:* Independent Pubs. Group.

Papp, Robert, illus. The Ghost of the Chattering Bones, Vol. 102. 2005. (Boxcar Children Mysteries Ser.: 102). 128p. (J). pap. 4.50 (978-0-8075-0874-9(8)) Whitman, Albert & Co.

Paulsen, Gary. The River. 2004. (GLB Reprints Ser.). 144p. (YA). (gr. 5). lib. bdg. 17.99 (978-0-385-90221-2(2) , Delacorte Bks. for Young Readers) Random Hse. Children's Bks.

Perkins, R., illus. Earth Whispers. 32p. (J). (gr. 3 up). 16.00 (978-0-9710860-2-9(8)) Libros, Encouraging Cultural Literacy.

Ricci, Christine. Dora's River Race. Roper, Robert, illus. 2006. (Dora the Explorer Ser.). 16p. (J). pap. 5.99 (978-1-4169-1208-8(8) , Simon Spotlight/Nickelodeon) Simon & Schuster Children's Publishing.

River. 1999. (J). 9.95 (978-1-56137-611-7(6)) Novel Units, Inc.

Rolls, Eric C. River. Yamaguchi, Marianne, illus. 80p. 24.95 (978-0-7022-2574-1(6)) Univ. of Queensland Pr. AUS. *Dist:* International Specialized Bk. Services.

Sage, James. Showboat. 1999. (Illus.). 32p. (J). 16.00 (978-0-15-201398-1(9)) Harcourt Trade Pubs.

Sargent, Dave, et al. On the Banks of the Wallowa River: (Nez Perce) Use Your Talent, 20, 13. Lenoir, Jane, illus. l.t. ed. 2004. (Story Keeper Ser.: 13). 48p. (J). pap. 6.95 (978-1-56763-928-5(3)) Ozark Publishing.

Schaaf, Ron. BearClaw: Finding Courage Within. 2007. (J). (***978-0-9787555-1-5(0)***) Hickory Tales Publishing.

Shinohara, Chie. Red River, Vol. 14. 2006. (Red River Ser.). 208p. (YA). pap. 9.99 (978-1-4215-0556-5(8)) Viz Media.

Sidjanski, Brigitte. The River. Watts, Bernadette, illus. 2008. 32p. (J). (ps). 16.99 (***978-0-698-40077-1(1)*** , Minedition) Penguin Group (USA) Inc.

Southey, Tabatha. The Deep Cold River Story. Savor, Sue, illus. 2000. 28p. (J). 18.95 (978-1-55263-147-8(8)) Key Porter Bks. CAN. *Dist:* Firefly Bks., Ltd.

Susurros de la Tierra. (SPA.). (J). (978-0-9710860-3-6(6)) Libros, Encouraging Cultural Literacy.

Trouble River. 1999. (J). 9.95 (978-1-56137-435-9(0)) Novel Units, Inc.

Turner, John L. Waylon's Wandering Waterdrop. Vrooman, Malia, illus. 1998. 32p. (J). (gr. 3-5). 14.95 (978-0-9628492-5-1(1)) Waterline Bks.

Warren, Adrian. Walking by the Rio. Brown, Craig, illus. 1999. (Books for Young Learners). 16p. (J). (gr. k-2). pap. 5.00 (978-1-57274-153-9(8) , A2780) Owen, Richard C. Pubs., Inc.

Williams, Anita. The Captain's Hat. Banks, Timothy, illus. 2000. 104p. (J). (gr. 1-5). pap. 7.95 (978-1-57924-330-2(4) , 119743) Jones, Bob Univ. Pr.

Williamson, Peggy. Who Was Here First? 2006. (J). per. 12.00 (978-1-59571-155-7(4)) Word Association Pubs.

Wilsdon, Christina. A New York Sailing Adventure. Hockerman, Dennis, illus. 2006. 26p. (J). 7.99 (978-1-59939-014-7(0) , Reader's Digest Young Families, Inc.) Reader's Digest Children's Publishing, Inc.

Woodbury, Mary. Ghost in the Machine. 2003. (gr. 7-12). lib. bdg. 16.40 (978-0-613-78483-2(9)) Tandem Library Bks.

Wright, Holly. River. 2004. (J). (978-0-9743690-8-2(X)) Britt Allcroft Productions.

RIVERS—POLLUTION

see Water—Pollution

RIZAL Y ALONSO, JOSE, 1861-1896

Arruda, Suzanne Middendorf. Freedom's Martyr: The Story of Jose Rizal, National Hero of the Philippines. 2003. (Avisson Young Adult Ser.). (Illus.). 106p. (J). pap. 19.95 (978-1-888105-55-1(0)) Avisson Pr., Inc.

ROAD CONSTRUCTION

see Roads

ROAD SIGNS

see Signs and Signboards

ROADRUNNER

Dewey, Jennifer Owings. Paisano, the Roadrunner. Meinzer, Wyman, photos by. 2002. (Illus.). 48p. (gr. 3-6). lib. bdg. 23.90 (978-0-7613-1250-5(1) , Millbrook Pr.) Lerner Publishing Group.

Macken, JoAnn Early. Roadrunners. 2005. (Illus.). 24p. (J). pap. (978-0-8368-4837-3(3)); lib. bdg. 19.33 (978-0-8368-4830-4(6)) Stevens, Gareth Inc.

—Roadrunners: Correcaminos. 2005. (ENG & SPA., Illus.). 24p. (J). pap. (978-0-8368-4851-9(9)) Stevens, Gareth Inc.

—Roadrunners/ Correcaminos. 2005. (ENG & SPA., Illus.). 24p. (J). (ps-17). lib. bdg. 19.33 (978-0-8368-4844-1(6)) Stevens, Gareth Inc.

Schaefer, Lola M. Roadrunners. 2004. (J). pap. 5.75 (978-1-4034-5736-3(0)); (Illus.). 24p. (gr. 1-3). lib. bdg. (978-1-4034-5048-7(X)) Heinemann Library.

ROADS

see also Streets

Adams, Georgie. Highway Builders. Gregory, Peter, illus. 2nd rev. ed. 2001. 32p. (J). (ps-2). pap. 6.95 (978-1-55037-708-8(6)) Annick Pr., Ltd. CAN. *Dist:* Firefly Bks., Ltd.

Anderson, Mary Elizabeth. Link Across America: A Story of the Historic Lincoln Highway. 2000. (Illus.). 52p. (J). (gr. 1-8). reprint ed. 15.95 (978-1-877810-97-8(5) , LINK) Rayve Productions, Inc.

Bailer, Darice. Roll It! With Road Roller. S. I. International Staff, illus. 2004. (Matchbox Ser.). 16p. (J). bds. 6.99 (978-0-689-86752-1(2) , Little Simon) Simon & Schuster Children's Publishing.

Baxter, Nicola. Roads. 2001. (Topic Bks.). (Illus.). 32p. (J). (gr. 2-5). 23.50 (978-0-531-14550-0(6) , Watts, Franklin) Scholastic Library Publishing.

—Roads. 2000. (gr. 3-6). lib. bdg. 15.25 (978-0-613-34443-2(X)); (Illus.). (J). (978-0-606-20886-4(0)) Tandem Library Bks.

Bednarz, Robert, et al. TIME for Kids Readers: U. S. Highways. 3rd ed. 2002. (Harcourt Horizons Ser.). (gr. k-7). pap. 38.10 (978-0-15-335309-3(0)) Harcourt Schl. Pubs.

Bellamy, David. The Roadside. Dow, Jill, illus. 1999. (Our Changing World Ser.). 32p. (J). (gr. 1-5). pap. 7.99 (978-0-7112-1383-6(6)) Lincoln, Frances Ltd. GBR. *Dist:* Antique Collectors' Club.

Carr, Roger. Roads & Bridges. 1999. (gr. k-3). lib. bdg. 11.80 (978-0-613-19436-5(5)) Tandem Library Bks.

Cooper, Wade. On the Road. 2008. (Scholastic Reader Level 1 Ser.). 32p. (J). pap. 3.99 (***978-0-545-00720-7(8)*** , Cartwheel Bks.) Scholastic, Inc.

Die Geschichte einer Strasse. (GER., Illus.). 32p. (978-3-411-07401-3(9)) Bibliographisches Institut & F. A. Brockhaus AG DEU. *Dist:* i.b.d., Ltd.

Keoke, Emory Dean & Porterfield, Kay Marie. American Indian Contributions to the World. 2005. (American Indian Contributions to the World Ser.). (Illus.). 160p. (gr. 4-9). (J). 35.00 (978-0-8160-5395-7(2)); (YA). 35.00 (978-0-8160-5397-1(9)) Facts On File, Inc.

Mahaney, Ian F. Road Maps. 2007. (Illus.). 24p. (J). pap. (978-1-4042-2212-0(X)); (gr. 3-5). lib. bdg. 21.25 (978-1-4042-3056-9(4)) Rosen Publishing Group, Inc., The.

Mansir, A. Richard. Stagecoach: The Ride of a Century. 1999. (Building America Ser.). (Illus.). 32p. (J). (ps-3). 15.95 (978-1-57091-960-2(7)) Charlesbridge Publishing, Inc.

McCrae, John. Roads. 2001. (Designing the Future Ser.). (Illus.). 32p. (J). (978-1-58341-188-9(7) , Creative Education) Creative Co., The.

Molzahn, Arlene Bourgeois. Highways & Freeways. 2002. (Transportation & Communication Ser.). (Illus.). 48p. (J). (gr. 1-4). lib. bdg. 23.93 (978-0-7660-1891-4(1)) Enslow Pubs., Inc.

Nardo, Don. Roman Roads & Aqueducts. 2000. (Building History Ser.). (Illus.). 96p. (J). (gr. 6-9). 28.70 (978-1-56006-721-4(7) , Lucent Bks.) Thomson Gale.

Pluckrose, Henry Arthur. Building a Road. 1999. (Machines at Work Ser.). (Illus.). 32p. (J). (gr. k-2). pap. 6.95 (978-0-531-15353-6(3) , Watts, Franklin) Scholastic Library Publishing.

Rand McNally Staff. Kids' Road Atlas. (Backseat Bks.). 80p. (J). pap. 3.95 (978-0-528-96544-9(1)) Rand McNally.

Randolph, Joanne. Road Pavers. 2002. (PowerKids Readers Ser.). (Illus.). 24p. (J). (gr. 1). lib. bdg. 16.00 (978-0-8239-6040-8(4) , PowerKids Pr.) Rosen Publishing Group, Inc., The.

—Road Rollers. 2002. (PowerKids Readers Ser.). (Illus.). 24p. (J). (gr. 1). lib. bdg. 16.00 (978-0-8239-6037-8(4) , PowerKids Pr.) Rosen Publishing Group, Inc., The.

—Road Scrapers. 2002. (PowerKids Readers Ser.). (Illus.). 24p. (J). (gr. 1). lib. bdg. 16.00 (978-0-8239-6042-2(0) , PowerKids Pr.) Rosen Publishing Group, Inc., The.

Shuter, Jane. On the Road: Travel by Road. 2004. (Technology Through Time Ser.). (Illus.). 32p. (J). lib. bdg. 25.70 (978-1-4109-0582-6(9)) Raintree.

Sloan, Peter. Making a Road. 2000. (gr. k-3). lib. bdg. 11.80 (978-0-613-30585-3(X)) Tandem Library Bks.

Spangenburg, Ray & Moser, Diane. The Story of America's Roads. 1999. (Illus.). 92p. (J). lib. bdg. 23.95 (978-0-7351-0198-2(1)) Replica Bks.

Stone, Lynn M. Roads & Highways. 2001. (How are They Built? Ser.). (Illus.). 48p. (J). (gr. 4-8). lib. bdg. 29.93 (978-1-58952-138-4(2)) Rourke Publishing, LLC.

Williams, Harriet. Road & Rail Transportation. 2004. (History of Invention Ser.). (Illus.). 96p. (YA). (gr. 6-12). 35.00 (978-0-8160-5437-4(1)) Facts On File, Inc.

ROADS—FICTION

Doyle, Brian. Hey, Dad! 2006. 112p. (J). pap. 6.95 (978-0-88899-708-1(6)) Groundwood Bks. CAN. *Dist:* Perseus Distribution.

Eames, Marion. Baner Beca. 2005. (WEL.). 80p. pap. (978-0-86243-729-9(6)) Y Lolfa.

Educational Adventures, creator. Free Wheelin' Coloring/Activity Book (English) w/ Snipe. 2007. (J). (***978-1-933934-52-5(2)***) Educational Adventures.

—Street Smarts: Coloring/Activity Book (Spanish) w/ Snipe. 2006. (Illus.). (J). (***978-1-933934-19-8(0)***) Educational Adventures.

—Street Smarts: Picture Book (Spanish) 9x9. 2007. (Illus.). (J). per. (***978-1-933934-77-8(8)***) Educational Adventures.

Feiffer, Jules. By the Side of the Road. 2005. (Illus.). 59p. (J). (gr. k-4). reprint ed. 16.00 (978-0-7567-9371-5(8)) DIANE Publishing Co.

Ford, Robert. Adventures of Hit the Road Jack. l.t. ed. 2003. (Illus.). 40p. per. 10.00 (978-1-932338-11-9(X)) Lifevest Publishing, Inc.

Free Wheelin' Picture Book (English) NL 9x9 with Snipe. 2007. (J). (***978-1-933934-48-8(4)***) Educational Adventures.

Gerhardt, Barbara. I Am of Scram. 2007. (Illus.). pap. 12.95 (***978-1-934246-15-3(8)***) Peppertree Pr., The.

Hindley, Judy. Big Red Bus. (J). 12.79 (978-0-606-19311-5(1)) Tandem Library Bks.

Inches, Alison. Wendy Helps Out. 2001. (978-0-606-22131-3(X)); lib. bdg. 11.80 (978-0-613-51329-6(0)) Tandem Library Bks.

Paulsen, Gary. The Cookcamp. 2003. 128p. (J). pap. 4.99 (978-0-439-52357-8(5) , Scholastic Paperbacks) Scholastic, Inc.

Pople, Maureen. Road to Summering. 152p. pap. 11.95 (978-0-7022-2267-2(4)) Univ. of Queensland Pr. AUS. *Dist:* International Specialized Bk. Services.

Price, Doris K. The Bump in the Road. Nance, Alisa, illus. 1998. (978-0-945084-73-0(0)) Stuart, Jesse Foundation, The.

Sargent, Dave & Sargent, David M. Bob White: Use Good Judgement, 20, vol. 3. Lenoir, Jane, illus. 2003. (Feather Tales Ser.: No. 3). 42p. (J). pap. 6.95 (978-1-56763-724-3(8)) Ozark Publishing.

Sargent, David M. Bob White: Use Good Judgement, 20, vol. 3. Lenoir, Jane, illus. 2003. (Feather Tales Ser.: No. 3). 42p. (J). lib. bdg. 19.95 (978-1-56763-723-6(X)) Ozark Publishing.

Skultety, Nancy. From Here to There. Lyon, Tammie, illus. 2004. 32p. (J). 15.95 (978-1-59078-092-3(2)) Boyds Mills Pr.

Steggall, Susan. On the Road. Steggall, Susan, illus. 2005. (Illus.). 32p. (J). 14.95 (978-1-929132-70-6(0)) Kane/Miller Bk. Pubs., Inc.

Street Safe! Life Safety Coloring/Activity Book. 2007. (Illus.). (J). (***978-1-933934-34-1(4)***) Educational Adventures.

Street Smarts: Coloring/Activity Book (English) Incl. Stickers. 2006. (Illus.). (J). (***978-1-933934-18-1(2)***) Educational Adventures.

Street Smarts: Picture Book 9x9 with Snipe. 2006. (Illus.). (J). (***978-1-933934-17-4(4)***) Educational Adventures.

Street Smarts: Picture Book (English) 8x8. 2006. (Illus.). (J). (***978-1-933934-16-7(6)***) Educational Adventures.

ROANOKE ISLAND—HISTORY

Belval, Brian. A Primary Source History of the Lost Colony of Roanoke. 2005. (Primary Sources of the Thirteen Colonies & the Lost Colony Ser.). (J). pap. (978-1-4042-0669-4(8)); (Illus.). 64p. (YA). (gr. 5-8). lib. bdg. 29.25 (978-1-4042-0435-5(0)) Rosen Publishing Group, Inc., The.

Dolan, Edward F., Jr. The Lost Colony of Roanoke. 2001. (Kaleidoscope Ser.). (Illus.). 48p. (J). (gr. 3 up). lib. bdg. 25.64 (978-0-7614-1301-1(4) , Benchmark Bks.) Cavendish, Marshall Corp.

Fritz, Jean. The Lost Colony of Roanoke. Talbott, Hudson, illus. 2004. 64p. (J). (gr. 3-6). 16.99 (978-0-399-24027-0(6) , Putnam Juvenile) Penguin Group (USA) Inc.

Italia, Bob. Roanoke: The Lost Colony. 2001. (Colonies Ser.). (Illus.). 32p. (J). (gr. k-6). lib. bdg. 22.78 (978-1-57765-580-0(X) , Checkerboard Library) ABDO Publishing Co.

Kent, Zachary. The Mysterious Disappearance of Roanoke Colony in American History. 2004. (In American History Ser.). (Illus.). 128p. (J). lib. bdg. 26.60 (978-0-7660-2147-1(5)) Enslow Pubs., Inc.

Miller, Lee. The Mystery of the Lost Colony. 2007. (Roanoke Ser.). (Illus.). 112p. (J). (gr. 4-7). pap. 18.99 (978-0-439-71266-8(1)) Scholastic, Inc.

Simmons, Alex. Mysteries of the Past: A Chapter Book. 48p. (J). 2006. (gr. 2-4). pap. 4.95 (978-0-516-25451-7(0)); 2005. (Illus.). (ps-ps). 22.50 (978-0-516-25184-4(8)) Scholastic Library Publishing. (Children's Pr.).

ROANOKE ISLAND—HISTORY—FICTION

Martin, Faith Ellen. The Lost & Found Colony. 2008. 280p. (YA). pap. 14.99 (978-1-59092-396-2(0) , Blue Works) Windstorm Creative.

Stainer, M. L. The Lyon's Cub. Melvin, James, illus. unabr. ed. 1998. (Book 2 of the Lyon Saga Ser.: Bk. 2). 162p. (YA). (gr. 5-10). pap. 6.95 (978-0-9646904-6-2(2)); lib. bdg. 9.95 (978-0-9646904-5-5(4)) Chicken Soup Pr., Inc.

—The Lyon's Throne. Melvin, James, illus. 1999. (Lyon Saga Ser.: Bk. 4). 153p. (YA). (gr. 5-9). pap. 6.95 (978-1-893337-02-2(2)) Chicken Soup Pr., Inc.

ROBBERS AND OUTLAWS

Bard, Jessica. Lawmen & Outlaws: The Wild, Wild West. 2005. (Trailblazers of the West Ser.). (Illus.). 48p. (J). (ps-7). 24.00 (978-0-516-25130-1(9)); (YA). (gr. 7-12). pap. 6.95 (978-0-516-25085-4(X)) Scholastic Library Publishing. (Children's Pr.).

Blackwood, Gary L. Highwaymen. 2001. (Bad Guys Ser.). (Illus.). 72p. (J). (gr. 5 up). lib. bdg. 29.93 (978-0-7614-1017-1(1) , Benchmark Bks.) Cavendish, Marshall Corp.

—Outlaws. 2001. (Bad Guys Ser.). (Illus.). 72p. (J). (gr. 5 up). lib. bdg. 29.93 (978-0-7614-1015-7(5) , Benchmark Bks.) Cavendish, Marshall Corp.

—Swindlers. 2001. (Bad Guys Ser.). (Illus.). 72p. (J). (gr. 5 up). lib. bdg. 29.93 (978-0-7614-1031-7(7) , Benchmark Bks.) Cavendish, Marshall Corp.

Bruns, Roger A. Billy the Kid: Outlaw of the Wild West. 2000. (Historical American Biographies Ser.). (Illus.). 128p. (YA). (gr. 6-12). lib. bdg. 26.60 (978-0-7660-1091-8(0)) Enslow Pubs., Inc.

Bryant, Jill. John Henry Holliday. 2003. (Folk Heroes Ser.). (Illus.). 24p. (J). lib. bdg. 15.95 (978-1-59036-077-4(X)) Weigl Pubs., Inc.

Deangelis, Gina. The Wild West. 1998. (Costume, Tradition & Culture). (Illus.). 64p. (YA). 19.75 (978-0-7910-5169-6(2) , Chelsea Hse.) Facts On File, Inc.

Elborough, Travis. Highwayman, Outlaws & Bandits of London. 2004. (... of London Ser.). (Illus.). 96p. 8.99 (978-1-904153-13-9(5)) Watling St., Ltd. GBR. *Dist:* Trafalgar Square Publishing.

Farman, John. The Short & Bloody History of Highwaymen. 2005. (Short & Bloody Histories Ser.). (Illus.). 96p. (gr. 6-12). lib. bdg. 19.93 (978-0-8225-0839-7(7)) Lerner Publishing Group.

—Short & Bloody History of Highwaymen. 2002. (gr. 5-8). lib. bdg. 14.10 (978-0-613-52496-4(9)) Tandem Library Bks.

Fenn, George Manvill. Young Robin Hood. 2004. reprint ed. pap. 15.95 (978-1-4191-9534-1(4)) Kessinger Publishing, LLC.

Frisch, Aaron. Jesse James. 2005. (Illus.). 48p. (gr. 5-9). 21.95 (978-1-58341-338-8(3) , Creative Education) Creative Co., The.

Glass, Andrew. Bad Guys: True Stories of Legendary Gunslingers. 2000. (Illus.). (J). (978-0-606-18781-7(2)) Tandem Library Bks.

Harmon, Daniel E. Billy the Kid. 2002. (gr. 5-8). lib. bdg. 17.60 (978-0-613-50869-8(6)) Tandem Library Bks.

Kerr, Daisy. Bandits. 1998. (Worldwise Ser.: Vol. 23). (Illus.). 40p. (J). (gr. 3-5). 24.00 (978-0-531-14463-3(1) , Watts, Franklin) Scholastic Library Publishing.

Landau, Elaine. Billy the Kid: Wild West Outlaw. 2004. (Best of the West Biographies Ser.). (Illus.). 48p. (J). lib. bdg. 23.93 (978-0-7660-2207-2(2)) Enslow Pubs., Inc.

Marvis, B. & Worth, Richard. Great Robberies. 2000. (Crime, Justice & Punishment Ser.). (Illus.). 80p. (J). (gr. 7 up). 30.00 (978-0-7910-4265-6(0) , Chelsea Hse.) Facts On File, Inc.

Miller, Steven G. The Legend of Jessie James. 2001. (History Channel History Guides Ser.). (Illus.). 40p. (J). pap. 9.99 (978-0-86730-845-7(1)) Lebhar-Friedman Bks.

Moody, Ralph. Wells Fargo. Mays, Victor, illus. 2005. 1p. pap. 11.95 (978-0-8032-8303-9(2) , MOOWEX, Bison Bks.) Univ. of Nebraska Pr.

Platt. Outlaws 6-Pack. 2004. (True Crime Ser.). pap. 42.90 (978-1-4109-1179-7(9)) Harcourt Schl. Pubs.

Price, Sean. Crooks, Cowboys, & Characters: The Wild West. 2007. (J). (***978-1-4109-2695-1(8)**); pap. (***978-1-4109-2706-4(7)***) Steck-Vaughn.

Randolph, Ryan P. Wild West Lawmen & Outlaws. 2003. (Library of the Westward Expansion). (Illus.). 24p. (J). lib. bdg. 19.95 (978-0-8239-6293-8(8) , PowerKids Pr.) Rosen Publishing Group, Inc., The.

Raum, Elizabeth. Wild West Legends. 2007. (J). (***978-1-4109-2968-6(X)***); pap. (***978-1-4109-2989-1(2)***) Steck-Vaughn.

Robinson, J. Dennis. Jesse James: Legendary Rebel & Outlaw. 2006. (J). (978-0-7565-1871-4(7)) Compass Point Bks.

Sanford, Carl R. & Sanford, William R. Outlaws & Lawmen of the Wild West, 10 bks., Set. (Illus.). (YA). (gr. 4-10). lib. bdg. 169.50 (978-0-89490-391-5(8)) Enslow Pubs., Inc.

Thomas, Paul. Outlaws. (History Makers Ser.). (Illus.). 48p. (J). lib. bdg. 28.50 (978-1-931983-39-6(9)) Chrysalis Education.

Thrasher, Thomas E. Gunfighters. 1999. (History Makers Ser.). (Illus.). 96p. (YA). (gr. 7-10). 28.70 (978-1-56006-570-8(2) , Lucent Bks.) Thomson Gale.

Townsend, John. Cops & Robbers. 48p. (J). 2006. pap. 8.90 (978-1-4109-1434-7(8)); 2005. lib. bdg. 31.43 (978-1-4109-1428-6(3)) Raintree.

Weil, Ann. Outlaws. 2007. (J). (***978-1-4109-2972-3(8)***); pap. (***978-1-4109-2993-8(0)***) Steck-Vaughn.

—Robberies. 2007. (J). (***978-1-4109-2962-4(0)***); pap. (***978-1-4109-2983-9(3)***) Steck-Vaughn.

ROBBERS AND OUTLAWS—FICTION

Alcock, Deborah. Done & Dared in Old France. 2002. (Huguenot Inheritance Ser.: Vol. 7). (Illus.). 286p. (J). (978-1-894666-03-9(8)) Inheritance Pubns.

Alger, Horatio. Joe's Luck: Or, Always Wide Awake. 2007. 172p. pap. 11.99 (***978-1-4264-6426-3(6)***); 2006. 176p. pap. 13.99 (978-1-4264-0883-0(8)); 2007. 186p. pap. 14.99 (***978-1-4264-6500-0(9)***); 2006. 170p. pap. 16.99 (978-1-4264-0864-9(1)) BiblioBazaar.

—Joe's Luck: Or, Always Wide Awake. 2006. pap. (***978-1-4065-0713-3(X)***) Dodo Pr.

—Struggling Upward: Or, Luke Larkin's Luck. 2006. pap. (***978-1-4065-0723-2(7)***) Dodo Pr.

—Struggling Upward: Or, Luke Larkin's Luck. unabr. ed. 2002. (Polyglot Press Alger Ser.). (Illus.). (J). pap. 17.95 (978-1-4115-0053-2(9)) Polyglot Pr., Inc.

—The Young Book Agent: Or, Frank Hardy's Road to Success. unabr. ed. 2002. (Polyglot Press Alger Ser.). (Illus.). (J). pap. 17.95 (978-1-4115-0074-7(1)) Polyglot Pr., Inc.

Andersen, C. B. The Book of Mormon Sleuth Vol. 3: The Hidden Path. 2003. ix, 214p. (J). pap. (978-1-57008-988-6(4)) Deseret Bk. Co.

Ardagh, Philip. The Green Men of Gressingham. Phillips, Mike, illus. 2006. 72;88p. (J). (gr. 2-3). lib. bdg. (978-1-59889-000-6(X)) Stone Arch Bks.

Arensen, Shel. The Carjackers, Vol. 2. 2003. (Rugendo Rhino Ser.). 128p. pap. 5.99 (978-0-8254-2042-9(3)) Kregel Pubns.

Auer, Chris. The Chinese Puzzle Box. 2005. 128p. (J). pap. 4.99 (978-0-310-70872-8(9)) Zonderkidz.

Ausona, Roberto De. Robin Hood. (SPA., Illus.). 156p. (YA). 11.95 (978-84-7281-110-2(7) , AF1110) Auriga, Ediciones S.A. ESP. *Dist:* Continental Bk. Co., Inc.

Baglio, Ben M. Max Is Missing. 2005. (Pet Finders Club Ser.: Vol. 2). (Illus.). 126p. (J). pap. (***978-0-439-68884-0(1)***) Scholastic, Inc.

Bajoria, Paul. The Printer's Devil. 2007. 400p. (J). (gr. 4-8). pap. 6.99 (978-0-316-10678-8(X)) Little Brown & Co.

Balmes, Kathy. Thunder on the Sierra. Catapano, Vicki, illus. 2001. (Adventures in America Ser.). 96p. (J). (gr. 3-7). lib. bdg. 14.95 (978-1-893110-10-6(9)) Silver Moon Pr.

Barnard, Victoria. Joe on Holiday. Barnard, Victoria & Stephens, Andrew, illus. 2005. 18p. (J). (gr. k-4). reprint ed. 19.00 (978-0-7567-8531-4(0)) DIANE Publishing Co.

Beck, Ian. The Teddy Robber. (Illus.). 32p. (J). (ps). 2005. pap. 9.99 (978-0-552-55319-3(0) , Corgi); 2000. pap. 8.95 (978-0-552-52593-0(6)) Transworld Publishers Ltd. GBR. *Dist:* Independent Pubs. Group, Trafalgar Square Publishing.

Bell, Hilari. Shield of Stars. 2007. (Shield, Sword, & Crown Ser.). (Illus.). 272p. (J). 16.99 (978-1-4169-0594-3(4) , Simon & Schuster Children's Publishing) Simon & Schuster Children's Publishing.

Bessen, Luc. Arthur & the Minimoys. Sowchek, Ellen, tr. from FRE. 2005. 240p. (J). 15.99 (978-0-06-059623-1(6)) HarperCollins Pubs.

Besson, Luc. Arthur & the Invisibles. movie tie-in ed. 2006. 416p. (J). pap. 7.99 (978-0-06-122726-4(9)) HarperCollins Pubs.

—Arthur & the Minimoys. (Illus.). (J). 2006. 256p. pap. 6.99 (978-0-06-059625-5(2) , Harper Trophy); 2005. 240p. lib. bdg. 16.89 (978-0-06-059624-8(4)) HarperCollins Pubs.

Biro, Val, illus. Jack & the Robbers. 1998. 32p. (J). (gr. k-3). pap. 4.99 (978-1-887734-45-5(7)) Star Bright Bks., Inc.

Blackman, Malorie. Thief. 2000. 208p. (J). 16.95 (978-0-385-40504-1(9)) Transworld Publishers Ltd. GBR. *Dist:* Trafalgar Square Publishing.

Bly, Stephen A. Daring Rescue at Sonora Pass. 2005. (Adventures of the American Frontier Ser.). 144p. pap. 6.99 (978-1-58134-471-4(6) , Crossway Bibles) Crossway Bks.

Bondoux, Anne-Laure. The Killer's Tears. Maudet, Y., tr. 176p. (YA). (gr. 7). 2007. pap. 8.99 (978-0-385-73384-7(4)); 2006. (Illus.). 15.95 (978-0-385-73293-2(7)); 2006. (Illus.). lib. bdg. 17.99 (978-0-385-90314-1(6)) Random Hse. Children's Bks. (Delacorte Bks. for Young Readers).

Bossley, Michele Martin. Swiped. 2006. (Orca Currents Ser.). 112p. (J). (gr. 5 up). pap. 8.95 (978-1-55143-646-3(9)) Orca Bk. Pubs. USA.

Brezenoff, Steven. Alley of Shadows. Martin, Cynthia, illus. 2008. (J). pap. (***978-1-59889-922-1(8)***); (YA). (gr. 5-9). lib. bdg. 17.95 (***978-1-59889-856-9(6)***) Stone Arch Bks.

Brouwer, Sigmund. The Volcano of Doom. 2002. (Accidental Detectives). 144p. (J). pap. 5.99 (978-0-7642-2564-2(2)) Bethany Hse. Pubs.

—Volcano of Doom. 2002. (gr. 3-6). lib. bdg. 14.15 (978-0-613-87242-3(8)) Tandem Library Bks.

Buckley-Archer, Linda. Gideon the Cutpurse. 2006. (Gideon Trilogy Ser.). 416p. (J). (gr. 5 up). 17.95 (978-1-4169-1525-6(7)) Simon & Schuster Children's Publishing.

Buckley-Archer, Linda. The Time Thief. 2007. (Gideon Trilogy Ser.). 512p. (J). (gr. 5 up). 17.99 (***978-1-4169-1527-0(3)***) Simon & Schuster Children's Publishing.

Burnett, Frances Hodgson. Editha's Burglar: A Story for Children. Sandham, Henry, illus. 2005. reprint ed. pap. 15.95 (978-1-4179-0135-7(0)) Kessinger Publishing, LLC.

Cadnum, Michael. In a Dark Wood. 1999. 11.64 (978-0-606-17596-8(2)) Tandem Library Bks.

—In a Dark Wood: A Novel. 1998. 246p. (YA). (gr. 7-12). 18.99 (978-0-531-33071-5(0) , Orchard Bks.) Scholastic, Inc.

Capeci, Anne. Ghost Train, Vol. 3. Casale, Paul, illus. 2004. (Cascade Moutain Railroad Mystery Ser.: 3). 144p. (J). (gr. 2-5). 12.95 (978-1-56145-324-5(2)) Peachtree Pubs., Ltd.

—Missing! Casale, Paul, illus. 2005. 144p. (J). 12.95 (978-1-56145-334-4(X)) Peachtree Pubs., Ltd.

Carle, Eric. The Honeybee & the Robber. Carle, Eric, illus. rev. ed. 2001. (Illus.). 1p. (J). (ps-1). 18.99 (978-0-399-23731-7(3) , Philomel) Penguin Group (USA) Inc.

Cazet, Denys. Minnie & Moo: Wanted Dead or Alive. Cazet, Denys, illus. 2007. (I Can Read Bks.). 48p. (J). pap. 3.99 (***978-0-06-073012-3(9)*** , Harper Trophy) HarperCollins Pubs.

Center for Learning Network Staff. Oliver Twist: Curriculum Unit —Novel Series. 2001. (Novel Ser.). 65p. (YA). tchr. ed., spiral bd. 19.95 (978-1-56077-684-0(6)) Ctr. for Learning, The.

Christelow, Eileen. The Robbery at the Diamond Dog Diner. 1999. (Illus.). (J). (ps-2). lib. bdg. 15.25 (978-0-8335-2149-1(7)) Tandem Library Bks.

Cole, Stephen. Thieves Till We Die. 2007. 320p. (YA). 16.95 (***978-1-59990-082-7(3)*** , Bloomsbury Children) Bloomsbury Publishing.

Coren, Alan. Arthur the Kid. 2004. (Illus.). 64p. (978-0-903895-76-7(5) , Robson Bks. Ltd.) Anova Bks.

—Buffalo Arthur. 2004. (Illus.). 64p. (978-0-903895-75-0(7) , Robson Bks. Ltd.) Anova Bks.

—Railroad Arthur. 2004. (Illus.). 64p. (978-0-903895-92-7(7) , Robson Bks. Ltd.) Anova Bks.

Couloumbis, Audrey. Maude March on the Run! 2007. (Illus.). 320p. (J). (gr. 3-7). 15.99 (978-0-375-83246-8(7) , Random Hse. Bks. for Young Readers) Random Hse. Children's Bks.

—Maude March on the Run!, or, Trouble Is Her Middle Name. 2007. (Illus.). 309p. (J). pap. (978-0-375-83248-2(3)) Random Hse., Inc.

—Maude March on the Run!, Or, Trouble Is Her Middle Name. 2007. (Illus.). 320p. (J). (gr. 3-7). lib. bdg. 17.99 (978-0-375-93246-5(1) , Random Hse. Bks. for Young Readers) Random Hse. Children's Bks.

Coutu, Raymond & Jones, Dawn L. Babette & the Apple Bandit. Graef, Renee, illus. 2001. (J). (978-0-9712840-8-1(3)) Boyds Collection Ltd., The.

Croall, Marie P. & Hilinski, Clint. Ali Baba Fooling the Forty Thieves: An Arabian Tale: Story. 2008. (Graphic Myths & Legends Ser.). (J). lib. bdg. 26.60 (***978-0-8225-7525-2(6)*** , Graphic Universe) Lerner Publishing Group.

Davis, Tim. More Tales from Dust River Gulch. 2002. (Tales from Dust River Gulch Ser.). (Illus.). 108p. (J). (gr. 4-7). 7.49 (978-1-57924-855-0(1)) Jones, Bob Univ. Pr.

DeFelice, Cynthia C. Old Granny & the Bean Thief. Smith, Cat Bowman, illus. 2003. 32p. (J). 16.00 (978-0-374-35614-9(9) , Farrar, Straus & Giroux (BYR)) Farrar, Straus & Giroux.

Derby, Sally. Two Fools & a Horse: An Orginal Tale. Rayevsky, Robert, illus. 2003. 32p. (J). (gr. k-3). 16.95 (978-0-7614-5119-8(6)) Cavendish, Marshall Corp.

Deshpande, Shashi. 3 Novels. 2006. 379p. (***978-0-14-333511-5(1)*** , Puffin) Penguin Group (USA) Inc.

Dickens, Charles. Oliver Twist. abr. ed. Date not set. (Nelson Readers Ser.). (J). pap. (978-0-17-557020-1(5)) Addison-Wesley Longman, Inc.

—Oliver Twist. 2002. (Classics for Young Readers Ser.). (SPA.). (YA). 14.95 (978-84-392-0919-5(3) , EV30603) Gaviota Ediciones ESP. *Dist:* Lectorum Pubns., Inc.

—Oliver Twist. abr. ed. (J). 9.95 (978-1-56156-372-2(2)) Kidsbooks, Inc.

—Oliver Twist. 2nd abr. ed. 2000. (Green Apple). 96p. (YA). pap. (978-1-57159-008-4(0)) Los Andes Publishing Co.

—Oliver Twist. 2000. (SPA.). 288p. (YA). (gr. 4-7). pap. 14.95 (978-0-595-13258-4(8)) iUniverse, Inc.

—Oliver Twist: With a Discussion of Honesty. 2003. (Values in Action Illustrated Classics Ser.). (J). (978-1-59203-051-4(3)) Learning Challenge, Inc.

Disney Storybook Artists Staff, illus. Disney's Home on the Range: A Hero of a Horse. 2004. (Step into Reading Ser.). 32p. (J). (ps-1). pap. 3.99 (978-0-7364-2210-9(2) , RH/Disney) Random Hse. Children's Bks.

Dixon, Franklin W. Boardwalk Bust. 2005. 164p. (J). lib. bdg. 16.92 (***978-1-4242-0385-7(6)***) Fitzgerald Bks.

—Disappearing Floor, No. 19. 2006. (Hardy Boys (Hardcover) Ser.). 228p. (J). (ps-3). 17.95 (978-1-55709-287-8(7)) Applewood Bks.

—Hunting for Hidden Gold. Rogers, Walter S., illus. 2004. (Hardy Boys Mystery Stories Ser.: No. 5). 210p. (J). (gr. 4-7). 17.95 (978-1-55709-148-2(X)) Applewood Bks.

Dodd, Lynley. Slinky Malinki. 2005. (Illus.). 32p. (J). reprint ed. 5.95 (978-1-58246-148-9(1) , Tricycle Pr.) Ten Speed Pr.

Durell, Charles Pend. Lights off Shore or Sam & the Outlaws. 2005. pap. 28.95 (978-1-4179-9422-9(3)) Kessinger Publishing, LLC.

Easton, Kelly. Canaries & Criminals: Trouble at Betts Pets. 2003. (Illus.). 128p. (J). (gr. 3-7). 15.99 (978-0-7636-1928-2(0)) Candlewick Pr.

Erickson, John R. The Case of the Monkey Burglar. Holmes, Gerald L., illus. 2006. (Hank the Cowdog Ser.: NMo. 48). 129p. (J). lib. bdg. 17.00 (***978-1-4242-1604-8(4)***) Fitzgerald Bks.

Estrada, Ric, illus. Oliver Twist. 2002. (Great Illustrated Classics Ser.). 240p. (J). (gr. 3-8). 21.35 (978-1-57765-697-5(0) , ABDO & Daughters) ABDO Publishing Co.

Everett, F. The Burglar's Breakfast. (Young Reading Ser.: Vol. 1). 48p. (J). (gr. 2 up). lib. bdg. 13.95 (978-1-58086-786-3(3)); 2004. (Illus.). pap. 5.95 (978-0-7945-0221-8(0)) EDC Publishing. (Usborne).

Fields, Terri. Holdup. 2007. 176p. (YA). (gr. 10 up). 16.95 (978-1-59643-219-2(5)) Roaring Brook Pr.

Funke, Cornelia. The Thief Lord. 2004. 376p. (J). (gr. 5 up). pap. 44.00 incl. audio (978-0-8072-2278-2(X) , Listening Library) Random Hse. Audio Publishing Group.

—The Thief Lord. Burmingham, Christian, illus. 2005. (Thief Lord Ser.). 376p. (ps-7). mass mkt. 2.99 (978-0-439-77132-0(3)) Scholastic, Inc.

—The Thief Lord. Latsch, Oliver, tr. from GER. Burmingham, Christian, illus. (J). 2002. 352p. (gr. 4-7). pap. 16.95 (978-0-439-40437-2(1)); 2003. 376p. (gr. 3-6). reprint ed. 6.99 (978-0-439-42089-1(X)) Scholastic, Inc. (Chicken Hse., The).

—The Thief Lord. 2003. (gr. 3-6). lib. bdg. 15.30 (978-0-613-84572-4(2)) Tandem Library Bks.

—The Thief Lord. l.t. ed. 2005. 483p. (J). (gr. 4-7). pap. 10.95 (978-0-7862-8092-6(1)) Thorndike Pr.

Funke, Cornelia. Thief Lord ('el Senor de Los Ladrones) 2007. 352p. (J). pap. 7.99 (***978-0-545-00517-3(5)*** , Scholastic en Espanol) Scholastic, Inc.

Funke, Cornelia & Latsch, Oliver. The Thief Lord. l.t. ed. 2004. 422p. (J). 23.95 (978-0-7862-7084-2(5)) Thorndike Pr.

Garfield, Leon. Smith. 2000. (J). (978-0-606-21674-6(X)); (gr. 7-12). lib. bdg. 15.25 (978-0-613-30742-0(9)) Tandem Library Bks.

Geisert, Arthur. Nursery Crimes. (Illus.). 32p. (J). (ps-3). 2007. 6.95 (***978-0-618-95671-5(9)***); 2001. tchr. ed. 16.00 (978-0-618-06487-8(7) , Walter Lorraine) Houghton Mifflin Co. Trade & Reference Div.

Goodwin, John. Robin Hood. Date not set. (Nelson Readers Ser.). (Illus.). 36p. (J). pap. (978-0-17-557050-8(7)) Addison-Wesley Longman, Inc.

Graham, Christine. Three Little Robbers. Boase, Susan, illus. 2007. 64p. (J). (gr. 2-5). 16.95 (***978-0-8050-8094-0(5)***) Holt, Henry & Co.

Greene, Janice. No Way to Run: Set 1. 2002. 32p. (YA). 2.95 (978-1-56254-411-9(X) , SP 411X) Saddleback Educational Publishing.

Hahn, Mary Downing. The Gentleman Outlaw & Me: A Story of the Old West. 2007. 224p. (YA). (gr. 7-9). pap. 6.95 (978-0-618-83000-8(6) , Clarion Bks.) Houghton Mifflin Co. Trade & Reference Div.

Hamilton, Richard. Jack Bolt & the Highwaymen's Hideout. Hearn, Sam, illus. 2007. 192p. (J). (gr. 2-5). 15.95 (***978-1-59990-090-2(4)***); pap. 5.95 (***978-1-59990-091-9(2)***) Bloomsbury Publishing.

Hancock, H. Irving. The Young Engineers in Arizona. rev. ed. 2006. 216p. 27.95 (978-1-4218-1751-4(9)); pap. 12.95 (978-1-4218-1851-1(5)) 1st World Publishing, Inc. (1st World Library - Literary Society).

—The Young Engineers in Arizona or Laying. 2004. reprint ed. pap. 21.95 (978-1-4191-8913-5(1)) Kessinger Publishing, LLC.

—The Young Engineers in Colorado. rev. ed. 2006. 212p. 27.95 (978-1-4218-1744-6(6)); pap. 12.95 (978-1-4218-1844-3(2)) 1st World Publishing, Inc. (1st World Library - Literary Society).

—The Young Engineers in Mexico. rev. ed. 2006. 208p. 27.95 (978-1-4218-1738-5(1)); pap. 12.95 (978-1-4218-1838-2(8)) 1st World Publishing, Inc. (1st World Library - Literary Society).

—The Young Engineers in Nevada. rev. ed. 2006. 220p. 27.95 (978-1-4218-1754-5(3)); pap. 12.95 (978-1-4218-1854-2(X)) 1st World Publishing, Inc. (1st World Library - Literary Society).

—The Young Engineers on the Gulf. rev. ed. 2006. 216p. 27.95 (978-1-4218-1752-1(7)); pap. 12.95 (978-1-4218-1852-8(3)) 1st World Publishing, Inc. (1st World Library - Literary Society).

Harris, Peter. Ordinary Audrey. Runert, David, illus. 2001. 32p. (J). tchr. ed. 14.95 (978-1-58925-014-7(1) , tiger tales) ME Media LLC.

Harrison, Charles C. Dick Turpin. 2003. (Historias de Siempre Ser.). (SPA., Illus.). 92p. (J). (gr. 5-8). pap. 12.95 (978-84-204-5701-7(9)) Santillana USA Publishing Co., Inc.

Hendry, Frances. Quest for a Queen: The Jackdaw. 2006. pap. (***978-1-905665-05-1(9)***) Pollinger In Print.

Hillerman, Tony. Buster Mesquite's Cowboy Band (Reprint) 2006. (J). lib. bdg. 14.95 (***978-0-914001-12-6(4)***) Sidewinder Publishing LLC.

Holub, Josef. The Robber & Me. 1999. (J). (gr. 4-7). 19.25 (978-0-8446-7007-2(3)) Smith, Peter Pub., Inc.

—The Robber & Me. 1999. (978-0-606-15909-8(6)) Tandem Library Bks.

Hutchens, Paul. The Watermelon Mystery. 1998. (gr. 3-6). lib. bdg. 13.00 (978-0-613-88823-3(5)) Tandem Library Bks.

Hyde, Ray. The CRIMEBUSTERS Club. 2006. (ENG.). 184p. per. 14.95 (***978-1-59800-970-5(2)***) Outskirts Press, Inc.

Imbernon, Maite & Dickens, Charles. Oliver Twist. 2003. (Timeless Classics Ser.). (SPA., Illus.). 92p. (J). pap. 10.95 (978-84-204-5750-5(7)) Santillana USA Publishing Co., Inc.

Jackson, Melanie. The Man in the Moonstone. 2003. (Dinah Galloway Mystery Ser.). 192p. (J). (gr. 3-7). pap. 6.95 (978-1-55143-264-9(1)) Orca Bk. Pubs. USA.

Jacobson, Rick. The Mona Lisa Caper. Jacobson, Rick & Fernandez, Laura, illus. 2005. 24p. (J). (gr. k-2). 15.95 (978-0-88776-726-5(5)) Tundra Bks., Inc./Livres Toundra, Inc. CAN. *Dist:* Random Hse., Inc.

Jenkins, Jerry B. & Fabry, Chris. Canyon Echoes. 2005. (Tyndale Kids Ser.). 240p. (J). pap. 5.99 (978-1-4143-0147-1(2)) Tyndale Hse. Pubs.

Johnson, Gillian. Thora & the Green Sea-Unicorn: Another Half-Mermaid Tale. Johnson, Gillian, illus. 2007. 288p. (J). (gr. 4-6). 15.99 (***978-0-06-074381-9(6)***); lib. bdg. 16.89 (***978-0-06-074382-6(4)***) HarperCollins Pubs. (Tegen, Katherine Bks).

Jones, Katina, et al. Cowdog Caper: Little Lucy & Friends. Ottinger, Jon, illus. Zaidan, Rick, photos by. 2001. (Little Lucy & Friends Ser.). 24p. (J). (ps-3). 9.99 (978-1-57151-701-2(4)) Playhouse Publishing.

Jones, T. Llew. Storïau Cwm-Pen-Llo. 2005. (WEL., Illus.). 100p. (978-0-86381-750-2(5)) Gwasg Carreg Gwalch.

Kavanagh, Terry. Batman: Tell-A-Riddle Telephone Book. Doescher, Erik et al, illus. 2002. (J). (978-0-7853-6402-3(1)) Publications International, Ltd.

Keene, Carolyn. The Apple Bandit. Jones, Jan Naimo, illus. 2005. 74p. (J). (978-1-4156-2882-9(3) , Aladdin) Simon & Schuster Children's Publishing.

Kinerk, Robert. Slim & Miss Prim. Harris, Jim, illus. (J). pap. 7.95 (978-0-87358-819-5(3) , Rising Moon Bks. for Young Readers) Northland Publishing.

Madonna, Ritchie. Yakov & the Seven Thieves. Madonna, Ritchie, ed. Spirin, Gennady, illus. 2004. 48p. (J). (gr. k-3). 19.95 (978-0-670-05887-7(4)) Callaway Editions, Inc.

Maitland, Barbara. Bookstore Burglar. 2001. (gr. k-3). lib. bdg. 11.80 (978-0-613-35609-1(8)) Tandem Library Bks.

Marsh, Carole. The Mystery at the Ancient Pyramid. 2006. 144p. (gr. 3-5). 14.95 (*978-0-635-03473-1(5))* Gallopade International.

McClintock, Norah. Tell. 2006. 112p. (YA). (gr. 7 up). pap. 8.95 (978-1-55143-511-4(X)); lib. bdg. 14.95 (978-1-55143-672-2(8)) Orca Bk. Pubs. USA.

Miller, Christopher & Miller, Allan. The Legend of Gid the Kid & the Black Bean Bandits: Doing the Right Thing Ain't Always Easy. 2007. (Illus.). 32p. (J). (gr. 1-5). 12.99 (*978-1-59317-202-2(8))* Warner Pr. Pubs.

Mills, Charles. The Bandit of Benson Park. 2003. (Honors Club Story Ser.: Vol. 1). 127p. (J). (978-0-8163-1977-0(4)) Pacific Pr. Pubns.

—The Great Sleepy-Time Stew Rescue. 2004. (Honors Club Story Ser.: Vol. 4). (Illus.). 127p. (J). (978-0-8163-2009-7(8)) Pacific Pr. Publishing Assn.

Morgan, Michaela. Silly Sausage in Trouble. Shulman, Dee, illus. 2006. (Read-It! Chapter Books). (J). 21.26 (978-1-4048-2737-0(4)) Picture Window Bks.

Morgan, Nicola. The Highwayman's Footsteps. 2007. (Illus.). 368p. (YA). (gr. 7). 16.99 (*978-0-7636-3472-8(7))* Candlewick Pr.

Newman, Robert. Lost Treasures Bk. 3: The Teddy Bear Habit. 2001. 184p. (J). 13.49 (978-0-7868-2599-8(5)) Hyperion Pr.

Noyes, Alfred. The Highwayman. Kimber, Murray, illus. 2005. 48p. (gr. 5 up). (978-1-55337-425-1(8)) Kids Can Pr., Ltd.

—The Highwayman. Keeping, Charles, illus. 2nd ed. 1999. 32p. (YA). 12.95 (978-0-19-272370-3(7)) Oxford Univ. Pr., Inc.

Odgers, Darrel & Odgers, Sally. The Sausage Situation: Jack Russell: Dog Detective. Dawson, Janine, illus. 2007. (Jack Russell: Dog Detective Ser.: No. 6). 80p. (J). (gr. 2-6). 4.95 (*978-1-933605-54-8(5))* Kane/Miller Bk. Pubs., Inc.

Osborne, Mary Pope. Pirates Past Noon, Vol. 4. unabr. ed. 2004. (Magic Tree House Ser. : No. 4). 67p. (J). (gr. k-3). pap. 17.00 incl. audio (978-0-8072-0333-0(5) , Listening Library) Random Hse. Audio Publishing Group.

Parish, Peggy. The Cats' Burglar. 1998. (J). (978-0-606-13258-9(9)) Tandem Library Bks.

Peck, Robert Newton. Horse Thief: A Novel. 2003. (Illus.). 288p. (J). (gr. 7 up). pap. 6.99 (978-0-06-441075-5(7)) HarperCollins Pubs.

Petersen, P. J. Rising Water. 2003. (Illus.). 128p. (J). pap. 4.99 (978-0-689-86356-1(X) , Aladdin) Simon & Schuster Children's Publishing.

Petrie, Lettie A. Let Me Tell You About "Minnie the Mule & the Erie Canal" Petrie, Beth L., illus. 2001. (Erie Canal Ser.). (YA). (gr. 5-10). pap. 9.95 (978-0-9711638-0-5(4)) Petrie Pr.

Pinkwater, Daniel M. & Pinkwater, Jill. Mush's Jazz Adventure. 2002. (Ready-for-Chapters Ser.). (Illus.). 48p. (J). pap. 6.99 (978-0-689-84572-7(3) , Aladdin) Simon & Schuster Children's Publishing.

Priestley, Chris. The White Rider. l.t. ed. 2005. 248p. (J). pap. (978-0-7540-7927-9(9) , CLP 481) BBC Audio.

—The White Rider. 2005. (Illus.). 192p. (J). pap. 8.99 (978-0-440-86608-4(1) , Corgi) Transworld Publishers Ltd. GBR. *Dist:* Trafalgar Square Publishing.

Rankin, Laura, illus. The Cowgirl Aunt of Harriet Bean. 2007. 81p. (J). (gr. 2-4). per. 4.95 (*978-1-59990-055-1(6)* , Bloomsbury Children) Bloomsbury Publishing.

Rayes, Michael. Bank Robbery! 2007. (J). per. 13.95 (*978-0-9779628-0-8(6))* Rafka Pr. LLC.

Reece, Colleen L. Thursday Trials. 1998. (Juli Scott, Super Sleuth Ser.: Bk. 4). 176p. (J). (gr. 4-10). pap. 2.97 (978-1-57748-180-5(1)) Barbour Publishing, Inc.

—Thursday Trials. l.t. ed. 2001. (Juli Scott, Super Sleuth Ser.). (Illus.). 204p. (J). 23.95 (978-0-7862-3201-7(3)) Thorndike Pr.

Reynolds, Aaron. The Dung Beetle Bandits. Lervold, Eric, illus. 2007. (J). 40p. (*978-1-59889-317-5(3));* 33p. pap. (*978-1-59889-412-7(9))* Stone Arch Bks.

Richards, Justin. The Invisible Detective: Shadow Beast. 2005. 160p. (YA). (gr. 4). 10.99 (978-0-399-24314-1(3) , Putnam Juvenile) Penguin Group (USA) Inc.

Riordan, Rick. The Lightning Thief. 2005. (Percy Jackson & the Olympians: Bk. 1). 384p. (J). (gr. 5-17). 17.95 (978-0-7868-5629-9(7)) Hyperion Bks. for Children.

The Robber: Individual Title-Six Packs. (Chiquilibros Ser.). (gr. k-1). 23.00 (978-0-7635-0433-5(5)) Rigby Education.

Roberts, Willo Davis. Hostage. 2001. 144p. (J). pap. 5.99 (978-0-689-84446-1(8) , Aladdin) Simon & Schuster Children's Publishing.

—Hostage. 2001. (J). 11.64 (978-0-606-21237-3(X)) Tandem Library Bks.

Robin Hood. (Coleccion Estrella). (SPA., Illus.). 64p. (J). 14.95 (978-950-11-0014-3(6) , SGM014) Sigmar ARG. *Dist:* Continental Bk. Co., Inc.

Roeder, Mark. The Summer of My Discontent: A Better Place II. 2003. 294p. (YA). pap. 18.95 (978-0-595-29806-8(0)) iUniverse, Inc.

Ross, Eileen. Nellie & the Bandit. Kono, Erin Eitter, illus. 2005. 32p. (J). 16.00 (978-0-374-35508-1(8) , Farrar, Straus & Giroux (BYR)) Farrar, Straus & Giroux.

Rowe, W. W. The Robber Chief: A Tale of Vengeance & Compassion. Banigan, Chris, illus. 2003. 48p. (gr. 1 up). 12.95 (978-1-55939-186-3(3)) Snow Lion Pubns., Inc.

Roy, Ron. The Missing Mummy. Gurney, John Steven, illus. 2001. (A to Z Mysteries Ser.: No. 13). 96p. (J). (gr. k-3). 11.99 (978-0-375-90268-0(6)); pap. 3.99 (978-0-375-80268-3(1)) Random Hse. Children's Bks. (Random Hse. Bks. for Young Readers).

—The Ninth Nugget. Gurney, John Steven, illus. 2001. (A to Z Mysteries Ser.: No. 14). 96p. (J). (gr. k-3). 11.99 (978-0-375-90269-7(4)); (gr. 2-5). pap. 3.99 (978-0-375-80269-0(X)) Random Hse. Children's Bks. (Random Hse. Bks. for Young Readers).

—The Ninth Nugget. Gurney, John Steven, illus. 2001. (A to Z Mysteries Ser.: No. 14). (J). (gr. k-3). lib. bdg. 11.80 (978-0-613-33773-1(5)) Tandem Library Bks.

—The Orange Outlaw. Gurney, John Steven, illus. 2001. (A to Z Mysteries Ser.: No. 15). 96p. (J). (gr. 2-5). lib. bdg. 11.99 (978-0-375-90270-3(8) , Random Hse. Bks. for Young Readers) Random Hse. Children's Bks.

—The Quicksand Question. Gurney, John Steven, illus. 2002. (A to Z Mysteries Ser.: No. 17). (J). (gr. k-3). lib. bdg. 11.80 (978-0-613-50491-1(7)) Tandem Library Bks.

—The Talking T. Rex. Gurney, John Steven, illus. 2003. (A to Z Mysteries Ser.: No. 20). 96p. (J). (gr. 2-5). pap. 3.99 (978-0-375-81369-6(1)); lib. bdg. 11.99 (978-0-375-91369-3(6)) Random Hse. Children's Bks. (Random Hse. Bks. for Young Readers).

—The White Wolf. Gurney, John Steven, tr. Gurney, John Steven, illus. 2004. (A to Z Mysteries Ser.: No. 23). 96p. (J). (gr. 1-4). pap. 3.99 (978-0-375-82480-7(4)); lib. bdg. 11.99 (978-0-375-92480-4(9)) Random Hse. Children's Bks. (Random Hse. Bks. for Young Readers).

—The X'ed-Out X-Ray. Gurney, John Steven, illus. 2005. (A to Z Mysteries Ser.: No. 24). 96p. (J). (gr. k-3). pap. 3.99 (978-0-375-82481-4(2)); lib. bdg. 11.99 (978-0-375-92481-1(7)) Random Hse. Children's Bks. (Random Hse. Bks. for Young Readers).

—The X'ed-Out X-Ray. Gurney, John Steven, illus. 2005. (A to Z Mysteries Ser.: No. 25). 85p. (J). (gr. k-3). lib. bdg. 11.19 (978-0-606-33236-1(7)) Tandem Library Bks.

Roy, Ron & Gurney, John Steven. The Orange Outlaw. 2001. (A to Z Mysteries Ser.: No.15). (Illus.). 96p. (J). (gr. 2-5). mass mkt. 3.99 (978-0-375-80270-6(3) , Random Hse. Bks. for Young Readers) Random Hse. Children's Bks.

Rushford, Patricia H. Secrets of Ghost Island. 2007. (J). (*978-88-02-46255-4(0))* Moody Pubs.

Ryan, Margaret. Scratch & Sniff. Reed, Nathan, illus. 2006. 48p. (J). lib. bdg. (*978-1-4048-3130-8(4))* Picture Window Bks.

Santillo, LuAnn. Jim & the Thug. Santillo, LuAnn, ed. 2003. (Half-Pint Kids Readers Ser.). (Illus.). 7p. (J). (ps-1). pap. (978-1-59256-078-3(4)) Half-Pint Kids, Inc.

Sargent, Dave & Sargent, Pat. Ben. Lenoir, Jane, illus. 2001. (Saddle Up Ser.). 36p. (J). pap. 6.95 (978-1-56763-644-4(6)) Ozark Publishing.

—Ben: (Bay Sabino) Help Others, 30. Lenoir, Jane, illus. 2001. (Saddle Up Ser.: 2). 36p. (J). lib. bdg. 22.60 (978-1-56763-643-7(8)) Ozark Publishing.

—Nick: (Linebacked Claybank Dun) Crime Does Not Pay, 30, 42. Lenoir, Jane, illus. 2003. (Saddle Up Ser.: Vol. 42). 42p. (J). pap. 6.95 (978-1-56763-702-1(7)); lib. bdg. 22.60 (978-1-56763-701-4(9)) Ozark Publishing.

—Pal: (Palomino) Be Friendly, 25, 44. Lenoir, Jane, illus. 2001. (Saddle Up Ser.: 44). 36p. (J). pap. 6.95 (978-1-56763-622-2(5)); lib. bdg. 22.60 (978-1-56763-621-5(7)) Ozark Publishing.

—Speck: (Black Patterned Leopard) Good Attitude, 25, 55. Lenoir, Jane, illus. 2001. (Saddle Up Ser.). 36p. (J). pap. 6.95 (978-1-56763-664-2(0)); lib. bdg. 22.60 (978-1-56763-663-5(2)) Ozark Publishing.

—Stinky: (Sorrel) Don't Be Mischievous, 25, 56. Lenoir, Jane, illus. 2001. (Saddle Up Ser.: 56). 36p. (J). pap. (978-1-56763-666-6(7)); lib. bdg. 22.60 (978-1-56763-665-9(9)) Ozark Publishing.

Schnetzler, Pattie L. Fast 'n Snappy. Manning, Jane K., tr. Manning, Jane K., illus. 2004. (Carolrhoda Picture Books Ser.). 32p. (J). (gr. k-3). 16.95 (978-1-57505-539-8(2)) Lerner Publishing Group.

Schultz, Jan Neubert. Horse Sense: The Story of Will Sasse, His Horse Star & the Outlaw Jesse James. (Adventures in Time Ser.). (J). 2005. (Illus.). 180p. (gr. 4-8). 15.95 (978-1-57505-998-3(3)); 2001. lib. bdg. 6.95 (978-1-57505-999-0(1) , Carolrhoda Bks.) Lerner Publishing Group.

Scieszka, Jon. Hey Kid, Want to Buy a Bridge?, Vol. 11. McCauley, Adam, illus. 2004. (Time Warp Trio Ser.: No. 11). 96p. (J). (gr. 2 up). pap. 4.99 (978-0-14-240089-0(0) , Puffin) Penguin Group (USA) Inc.

Scorcia, Yvonne. Joey's Big Adventure. 2001. 56p. (J). pap. 9.00 (978-0-8059-5485-2(6)) Dorrance Publishing Co., Inc.

Shire, Poppy. Magic Pony Carousel #4: Jewel the Midnight Pony. Berg, Ron, illus. 2008. (Magic Pony Carousel Ser.). 96p. (J). pap. 3.99 (*978-0-06-083788-4(8)* , Harper Trophy) HarperCollins Pubs.

Smith, Alexander McCall. The Cowgirl Aunt of Harriet Bean. Rankin, Laura, illus. 2006. (Harriet Bean Ser.). 80p. (J). (gr. 2-4). 9.95 (978-1-58234-977-0(0) , Bloomsbury Children) Bloomsbury Publishing.

Sneed, Brad. Deputy Harvey & the Ant Cow Caper. 2005. (Illus.). 32p. (J). (ps). 16.99 (978-0-8037-3023-6(3) , Dial) Penguin Group (USA) Inc.

Spooner, Michael. Daniel's Walk. rev. ed. 176p. 2004. (J). pap. 7.95 (978-0-8050-7543-4(7)); 2001. (Illus.). (YA). (gr. 7 up). 16.95 (978-0-8050-6750-7(7)) Holt, Henry & Co. (Holt, Henry & Co. Bks. For Young Readers).

Steig, William. The Real Thief. 2007. (Illus.). 64p. (J). pap. 5.99 (*978-0-312-37145-6(4))* Square Fish.

Stellinga, Mark. Buster Boogernose & the Bank Robbers. l.t. ed. 2007. 72p. (J). per. 9.95 (*978-0-9796421-0-4(8))* Stellinga, Mark.

Stengel, Joyce A. Mystery at Kittiwake Bay. 2001. 176p. (J). pap. 9.95 (978-0-689-84595-6(2) , Aladdin) Simon & Schuster Children's Publishing.

Sutton, Rosalind & Rowe, Eric F. Robin Hood. Rowe, Eric F., tr. 4th ed. (Coleccion Clasicos en Accion). (SPA., Illus.). 80p. (YA). (gr. 5-8). 15.95 (978-84-241-5782-1(6) , EV1455) Everest de Ediciones y Distribucion, S.L. ESP. *Dist:* Lectorum Pubns., Inc.

Swift, Carolyn. Robbers in the House. (Illus.). 96p. 2.95 (978-0-900068-59-1(0)) Penguin Group (USA) Inc.

Thoene, Jake & Thoene, Luke. The Giant Rat of Sumatra. 1998. (Baker Street Mysteries Ser.: Vol. 2). 168p. (J). (gr. 4-7). pap. 5.99 (978-0-7852-7079-9(5)) Nelson, Thomas Inc.

—The Giant Rat of Sumatra. 2006. (Tyndale Kids Ser.). 144p. (J). 9.99 (978-1-4143-0367-3(X)) Tyndale Hse. Pubs.

Thomson, Pat. The Badcat Gang. Phillips, Mike, illus. 2006. 48p. (J). lib. bdg. (*978-1-4048-3112-4(6))* Picture Window Bks.

Tromp, Janyre. That Sinking Feeling: Blue Water Mysteries. 2006. 128p. (J). pap. (978-0-8254-3887-5(X)) Kregel Pubns.

Turner, Megan Whalen. The King of Attolia. 2007. 400p. (J). (gr. 5 up). pap. 7.99 (*978-0-06-083579-8(6)* , Eos) HarperCollins Pubs.

Ungerer, Tomi. Three Robbers. 1998. (Illus.). 40p. (J). (ps-1). pap. 6.95 (978-1-57098-206-4(6)) Rinehart, Roberts Pubs.

Updale, Eleanor. Montmorency: Thief, Liar, Gentleman. 2004. (Montmorency Ser.). 240p. (J). pap. 16.95 (978-0-439-58035-9(8) , Orchard Bks.) Scholastic, Inc.

—Montmorency & the Assassins: Master, Criminal, Spy. 2006. 416p. (J). (gr. 4-7). pap. 16.99 (978-0-439-68343-2(2) , Orchard Bks.) Scholastic, Inc.

—Montmorency on the Rocks: Doctor, Aristocrat, Murderer? 2006. 368p. (J). pap. 6.99 (978-0-439-60677-6(2) , Scholastic Paperbacks) Scholastic, Inc.

—Montmorency on the Rocks: Doctor, Aristocrat, Murderer? Hardcastle, Nick, illus. 2005. (Montmorency Ser.). 368p. (J). pap. 16.95 (978-0-439-60676-9(4) , Orchard Bks.) Scholastic, Inc.

—Montmorency's Revenge. 2007. (J). (Montmorency Ser.: Vol. 4). 304p. (gr. 7 up). pap. 16.99 (978-0-439-81373-0(5)); 289p. (*978-1-4287-3312-1(4))* Scholastic, Inc. (Orchard Bks.).

—Thief, Liar, Gentleman? 2005. (Montmorency Ser.). 240p. (J). reprint ed. pap. 6.99 (978-0-439-58036-6(6) , Scholastic Paperbacks) Scholastic, Inc.

—Thief, Liar, Gentleman? l.t. ed. 2006. 261p. 23.95 (978-0-7862-8643-0(1)) Thorndike Pr.

Van Draanen, Wendelin. Sammy Keyes & the Hotel Thief. VanDraanen, Wendelin, illus. 2000. (Sammy Keyes Ser.: Bk. 1). pap. 39.95 incl. audio compact disk (978-0-87499-876-4(X)) Live Oak Media.

—Sammy Keyes & the Hotel Thief. unabr. ed. 2000. (Sammy Keyes Ser.: Bk. 1). (Illus.). (J). (gr. 4-7). 38.95 incl. audio (978-0-87499-694-4(5)); pap. 30.95 incl. audio (978-0-87499-693-7(7)) Live Oak Media.

—Sammy Keyes & the Hotel Thief. 1998. (Sammy Keyes Ser.: Bk. 1). (Illus.). 176p. (J). (gr. 5-8). pap. 5.99 (978-0-679-89264-9(8) , Yearling) Random Hse. Children's Bks.

—Sammy Keyes & the Hotel Thief. 1998. (Sammy Keyes Ser.: Bk. 1). (Illus.). 163p. (J). (gr. k-8). lib. bdg. 13.55 (978-0-613-12062-3(0)) Tandem Library Bks.

Van-Leeuwen, Jan. Lost Treasures Bk. 4: The Great Cheese Conspiracy. 2001. 96p. (J). 13.49 (978-0-7868-2555-4(3)) Hyperion Pr.

Vande Velde, Vivian. Ghost of a Hanged Man. 96p. (J). 2005. pap. 5.95 (978-0-7614-5154-9(4)); 1998. (gr. 3-7). 14.95 (978-0-7614-5015-3(7) , Cavendish Children's Bks.) Cavendish, Marshall Corp.

Vere, Ed. The Getaway. Vere, Ed, illus. 2007. 34p. (J). (gr. k-2). 16.99 (*978-1-4169-4789-9(2)* , McElderry, Margaret K.) Simon & Schuster Children's Publishing.

Wallace, Karen. The Minestrone Mob. Brown, Judy, illus. 2007. (Read-It! Chapter Books). (J). (978-1-4048-2723-3(4)) Picture Window Bks.

Walton, Rick. Bertie Was a Watchdog. Robins, Arthur, illus. 2002. 56p. (J). (ps-2). 12.99 (978-0-7636-1385-3(1)) Candlewick Pr.

Warner, Gertrude Chandler, creator. The Rock 'n' Roll Mystery, Vol. 109. 2006. (Boxcar Children Mysteries Ser.: 109). (Illus.). 128p. (J). (gr. 2-7). 14.95 (978-0-8075-7089-0(3)); lib. bdg. 4.50 (978-0-8075-7090-6(7)) Whitman, Albert & Co.

Watson, Esther Pearl. Trouble at Sugar-Dip Well. 2002. (Illus.). 32p. (J). (gr. k-3). 15.00 (978-0-618-11863-2(2)) Houghton Mifflin Co. Trade & Reference Div.

Wells, Carolyn & E. C. CASWELL. Two Little Women on a Holiday. l.t. ed. 2006. 178p. pap. 14.99 (978-1-4264-2807-4(3)) BiblioBazaar.

Wells, Helen. Cherry Ames, Camp Nurse. 2007. (YA). (*978-0-8261-0417-5(7))* Springer.

—Cherry Ames, Department Store Nurse. 2007. (YA). (*978-0-8261-0415-1(0))* Springer.

Wilson, Bob. Stanley Bagshaw & the Mafeking Square Cheese Robbery. 2006. (Stanley Bagshaw Ser.). (Illus.). 32p. (J). pap. 6.95 (978-1-903015-31-5(6)) Barn Owl Bks, London GBR. *Dist:* Independent Pubs. Group.

Wood, Audrey. Ten Little Monkeys. 2001. (Illus.). 16p. (J). 19.99 (978-0-85953-896-1(6)) Child's Play-International.

—Twenty-Four Robbers. 2005. (Illus.). 32p. (J). (ps). pap. 7.99 (978-1-904550-35-8(5)) Child's Play-International.

Yee, Wong Herbert. Detective Small in the Amazing Banana Caper. 2007. (Illus.). 32p. (J). (gr. k-3). 15.00 (978-0-618-47285-7(1)) Houghton Mifflin Co.

ROBERT I, KING OF SCOTS, 1274-1329

King Robert the Bruce. 2002. 192p. 3.95 (978-1-85534-905-6(1)) Geddes & Grosset, Ltd. GBR. *Dist:* CPG Publishing, Inc.

ROBERT I, KING OF SCOTS, 1274-1329—FICTION

Hunter, Mollie. The King's Swift Rider: A Novel on Robert the Bruce. 1998. 256p. (J). (gr. 7 up). 16.95 (978-0-06-027186-2(8)) HarperCollins Pubs.

—The King's Swift Rider: A Novel on Robert the Bruce. 2000. (Illus.). (J). (978-0-606-18701-5(4)) Tandem Library Bks.

ROBESON, PAUL, 1898-1976

Belton, Sandra. Tallest Tree. 2008. 160p. (J). 16.99 (*978-0-06-052749-5(8)* , Greenwillow Bks.) HarperCollins Pubs.

Ford, Carin T. Paul Robeson: I Want to Make Freedom Ring. 2007. (African-American Biography Library). (Illus.). 128p. (J). (gr. 6 up). lib. bdg. 31.93 (*978-0-7660-2703-9(1))* Enslow Pubs., Inc.

Healy, Nick. Paul Robeson. 2003. (African-American Biographies Ser.). 64p. pap. 8.95 (978-1-4109-0040-1(1)); (Illus.). (J). lib. bdg. 28.56 (978-0-7398-6874-4(8)) Raintree.

McKissack, Patricia C. & McKissack, Fredrick L. Paul Robeson: A Voice to Remember. rev. ed. 2001. (Great African Americans Ser.). (Illus.). 32p. (J). (gr. 1-4). lib. bdg. 18.60 (978-0-7660-1674-3(9)) Enslow Pubs., Inc.

Stewart, Jeffrey C., ed. & intro. Paul Robeson: Artist & Citizen. Stewart, Jeffrey C., intro. 1998. (Illus.). 304p. (C). (gr. 10-12). pap. 22.00 (978-0-8135-2511-2(X)) Rutgers Univ. Pr.

Wright, David K. Paul Robeson: Actor, Singer, Political Activist. 1998. (African-American Biographies Ser.). (Illus.). 128p. (YA). (gr. 6-12). lib. bdg. 26.60 (978-0-89490-944-3(4)) Enslow Pubs., Inc.

ROBIN HOOD (LEGENDARY CHARACTER)

Bull, Angela. Robin Hood. 2000. (gr. k-3). lib. bdg. 11.80 (978-0-613-26766-3(4)) Tandem Library Bks.

Bull, Angela & Dorling Kindersley Publishing Staff. Robin Hood, Vol. 4. 2000. (Classic Readers Ser.). (Illus.). 48p. (J). (gr. 2-4). pap. 3.99 (978-0-7894-5391-4(6)) Dorling Kindersley Publishing, Inc.

Cohen, Barbara. Robin Hood & Little John. 1998. (978-0-606-13744-7(0)) Tandem Library Bks.

Coleman, Diane. Robin Hood Comprehension Guide. Bustard, Ned, illus. 2000. 10.00 (978-1-930710-77-1(1)) Veritas Pr., Inc.

Creswick, Paul & Wyeth, N. C. Robin Hood. 2003. (Scribner Storybook Classic Ser.: Vol. 4). (Illus.). 64p. (J). 18.95 (978-0-689-85467-5(6) , Atheneum) Simon & Schuster Children's Publishing.

Deutsch, Andre. Adventures of Robin Hood. 1999. (Andre Deutsch Classics). (Illus.). 192p. (J). 9.99 (978-0-233-99252-5(9)) Andre Deutsch GBR. *Dist:* Independent Pubs. Group.

Dorling Kindersley Publishing Staff. Robin Hood. 2000. (Classic Readers Ser.). (Illus.). 32p. (J). (gr. 2-4). 14.99 (978-0-7894-5701-1(6)) Dorling Kindersley Publishing, Inc.

Fenn, George Manvill. Young Robin Hood. 2004. reprint ed. pap. 15.95 (978-1-4191-9534-1(4)) Kessinger Publishing, LLC.

Heyer, Carol, illus. & retold by. Robin Hood. Heyer, Carol, retold by. 2002. 32p. (J). (gr. k-5). 9.95 (978-1-59093-027-4(4) , Eager Minds Pr.) Warehousing & Fulfillment Specialists, LLC (WFS, LLC).

Leeson, Robert. The Story of Robin Hood. Lofthouse, Barbara, illus. 2005. (Kingfisher Epics Ser.). 176p. (J). (gr. 4-6). pap. 7.95 (978-0-7534-5817-4(9) , Kingfisher) Houghton Mifflin Co. Trade & Reference Div.

McGovern, Ann. Robin Hood of Sherwood Forest. Sugarman, Tracy, illus. 2001. 128p. (J). pap. 3.99 (978-0-439-23639-3(8)) Scholastic, Inc.

—Robin Hood of Sherwood Forest. 2001. (Scholastic Junior Ser.). (Illus.). (J). (978-0-606-21401-8(1)) Tandem Library Bks.

McKinley, Robin. Outlaws of Sherwood. 2002. (gr. 5-8). lib. bdg. 15.30 (978-0-613-64445-7(X)) Tandem Library Bks.

McSpadden, J. Walker. Robin Hood. 2004. reprint ed. pap. 22.95 (978-1-4191-4516-2(9)); pap. 1.99 (978-1-4192-4516-9(3)) Kessinger Publishing, LLC.

McSpadden, Joseph Walker. Robin Hood. 2000. (Dover Evergreen Classics Ser.). 208p. (J). (gr. 4-7). pap. 3.50 (978-0-486-41021-0(8)) Dover Pubns., Inc.

—Robin Hood & His Merry Outlaws. Marshall, Michael J., ed. abr. ed. 2000. (Core Classics Ser.: Vol. 8). (Illus.). 269p. (J). (gr. 4-6). pap. 7.95 (978-1-890517-16-8(X)) Core Knowledge Foundation.

Miles, Bernard. Robin Hood: His Life & Legend. Ambrus, Victor G., illus. 128p. (J). (gr. 4 up). 12.95 (978-1-56288-412-3(3)) Checkerboard Pr., Inc.

Pyle, Howard. The Merry Adventures of Robin Hood. 2002. (Great Illustrated Classics Ser.). (Illus.). 240p. (J). (gr. 3-8). 21.35 (978-1-57765-694-4(6) , ABDO & Daughters) ABDO Publishing Co.

—The Merry Adventures of Robin Hood. (Young Collector's Illustrated Classics Ser.). (Illus.). 192p. (J). (gr. 3-7). 9.95 (978-1-56156-454-5(0)) Kidsbooks, Inc.

—The Merry Adventures of Robin Hood. (Twelve-Point Ser.). 2002. 321p. lib. bdg. 25.00 (978-1-58287-200-1(7)); 2004. 518p. 26.00 (978-1-58287-684-9(3)) North Bks.

ROBIN HOOD (LEGENDARY CHARACTER)—FICTION

Ausona, Roberto De. Robin Hood. (SPA., Illus.). 156p. (YA). 11.95 (978-84-7281-110-2(7) , AF1110) Auriga, Ediciones S.A. ESP. *Dist:* Continental Bk. Co., Inc.

Bernstein, Nina. Magic by the Book. Kulikov, Boris, illus. 2005. 240p. (J). 17.00 (978-0-374-34718-5(2) , Farrar, Straus & Giroux (BYR)) Farrar, Straus & Giroux.

—Magic by the Book. unabr. ed. 2005. (J). 63.75 incl. audio (978-1-4193-3607-2(X) , 42048) Recorded Bks., LLC.

—Magic by the Book. l.t. ed. 2006. 248p. (J). 22.95 (978-0-7862-8382-8(3)) Thorndike Pr.

Cadnum, Michael. Forbidden Forest: The Story of Little John & the Robin Hood. 2002. 224p. (J). (gr. 7 up). pap. 17.95 (978-0-439-31774-0(6) , Orchard Bks.) Scholastic, Inc.

—In a Dark Wood: A Novel. 1998. 246p. (YA). (gr. 7-12). 18.99 (978-0-531-33071-5(0) , Orchard Bks.) Scholastic, Inc.

Coté, Denis. La Forêt aux Mille et un Périls, Tome 2. Poulin, Stephane, illus. 2004. (Roman Jeunesse Ser.). (FRE.). 96p. (J). (gr. 4-7). pap. (978-2-89021-696-9(9)) Diffusion du livre Mirabel.

Dalmatian Press Staff. Peter Pan/Robin Hood Storybook Treasury. 2006. 64p. pap. 8.99 (978-1-4037-2047-4(9)) Dalmatian Pr.

Dalmatian Press Staff, ed. Peter Pan/Robin Hood. 2006. 64p. pap. 4.99 (978-1-4037-2341-3(9)) Dalmatian Pr.

—Robin Hood. 2006. (J). 3.50 (978-1-4037-2958-3(1)) Dalmatian Pr.

Edwards, Frank B. Robin Hood with Lots of Dogs. Bianchi, John, illus. 1999. (Dog Eared Classics Ser.). 32p. (J). (gr. 3-6). pap. 15.95 (978-1-894323-09-3(2)) Pokeweed Pr. CAN. *Dist:* Fitzhenry & Whiteside, Ltd.

Edwards, Frank B. & Bianchi, John. Robin Hood with Lots of Dogs. 1999. (Dog Eared Classics Ser.). (Illus.). 32p. (J). (gr. 3-6). pap. 5.95 (978-1-894323-08-6(4)) Pokeweed Pr. CAN. *Dist:* Fitzhenry & Whiteside, Ltd.

Goodwin, John. Robin Hood. Date not set. (Nelson Readers Ser.). (Illus.). 36p. (J). pap. (978-0-17-557050-8(7)) Addison-Wesley Longman, Inc.

Larousse Mexico Staff, ed. Robin Hood. 2004. (Encuentro Con la Lectura Ser.). (SPA., Illus.). 48p. (gr. 4-9). pap. 6.50 (978-970-22-0528-9(X)) Larousse, Ediciones, S. A. de C. V. MEX. *Dist:* Houghton Mifflin Co. Trade & Reference Div.

Lasky, Kathryn. Robin Hood: The Boy Who Became a Legend. 1999. (J). (978-0-590-25933-0(4) , Blue Sky Pr., The) Scholastic, Inc.

McSpadden, J. Walker & Hildebrandt, Greg. The Adventures of Robin Hood. gif. ed. 2004. (Illus.). 64p. (J). 9.98 (978-0-7624-2197-8(5) , Courage Bks.) Running Pr. Bk. Pubs.

Neil, Philip. Robin Hood. Harris, Nick, illus. 2005. (READ & LISTEN Bks.). 64p. (J). 9.99 (978-0-7566-1277-1(2)) Dorling Kindersley Publishing, Inc.

Pyle, Howard. The Merry Adventures of Robin Hood. McKowen, Scott, illus. 2004. (Unabridged Classics Ser.). 344p. 9.95 (978-1-4027-1456-6(4)) Sterling Publishing Co., Inc.

Robin Hood. (Coleccion Estrella). (SPA., Illus.). 64p. (J). 14.95 (978-950-11-0014-3(6) , SGM014) Sigmar ARG. *Dist:* Continental Bk. Co., Inc.

Robin Hood & the Silver Trophy: Individual Title Six-Packs. 32p. (gr. 3 up). 37.00 (978-0-7635-9676-7(0)) Rigby Education.

Robin Hood Novel Ties. 18.55 (978-0-613-70537-0(8)) Tandem Library Bks.

Robin Hood Read Along. 1999. (J). (ps-3). pap. 6.98 incl. audio (978-0-7634-0590-8(6)) Walt Disney Records.

Sanderson, Jeanette. Robin Hood Shoots for the Queen: A Legend from England. 2006. spiral bd. 42.00 (***978-1-4108-7167-1(3)***) Benchmark Education Co.

Springer, Nancy. Rowan Hood: Outlaw Girl of Sherwood Forest. 2002. (Tales of Rowan Hood Ser.: No. 1). (gr. 5-8). lib. bdg. 14.15 (978-0-613-53860-2(9)) Tandem Library Bks.

—Rowan Hood Returns: The Final Chapter. (Tales of Rowan Hood Ser.: No. 5). 2006. 176p. (J). (gr. 3). pap. 5.99 (978-0-14-240685-4(6) , Puffin); 2005. 170p. (YA). (gr. 5). 16.99 (978-0-399-24206-9(6) , Philomel) Penguin Group (USA) Inc.

—Wild Boy: A Tale of Rowan Hood. 2004. (Tales of Rowan Hood Ser.: No. 4). 128p. (YA). (gr. 5-7). 16.99 (978-0-399-24015-7(2) , Philomel) Penguin Group (USA) Inc.

Stockton, Sally, retold by. Robin Hood. 2nd ed. 2000. (Green Apple). 92p. (YA). pap. (978-1-57159-009-1(9)) Los Andes Publishing Co.

Storrie, Paul D. Robin Hood: Outlaw of Sherwood Forest. Yeates, Thomas, illus. 2007. (Graphic Myths & Legends Ser.). 48p. (J). (gr. 4-8). 26.60 (978-0-8225-5964-1(1)) Lerner Publishing Group.

Sutton, Rosalind & Rowe, Eric F. Robin Hood. Rowe, Eric F., tr. 4th ed. (Coleccion Clasicos en Accion). (SPA., Illus.). 80p. (YA). (gr. 5-8). 15.95 (978-84-241-5782-1(6) , EV1455) Everest de Ediciones y Distribucion, S.L. ESP. *Dist:* Lectorum Pubns., Inc.

ROBINS

Berger, Melvin & Berger, Gilda. Robins. 2002. (Scholastic Readers Ser.). (Illus.). (J). (978-0-439-44532-0(9)) Scholastic, Inc.

Canizares, Susan & Chessen, Betsey. From Egg to Robin. 1998. (Science Emergent Readers Ser.). 185p. (J). pap. 2.50 (978-0-590-76162-8(5)) Scholastic, Inc.

Holmes, Anita. Where Robins Fly. 2000. (We Can Read about Nature! Ser.). (Illus.). 32p. (J). (gr. 1-2). lib. bdg. 21.36 (978-0-7614-1109-3(7) , Benchmark Bks.) Cavendish, Marshall Corp.

Kalz, Jill. Robins. 2003. (Birds Ser.). (Illus.). 24p. (J). lib. bdg. 21.35 (978-1-58340-131-6(8)) Smart Apple Media.

Meyer, Velma. Robby: The True Story of an Incredible Friendship Between a Robin & his Human Family. 1998. 96p. (Orig.). (J). (ps up). pap. 7.99 (978-0-8280-1291-1(1)) Review & Herald Publishing Assn.

Posada, Mia, tr. & illus. Robins: Songbirds of Spring. Posada, Mia, illus. 2004. (Carolrhoda Picture Books Ser.). 32p. (J). (gr. k-3). 15.95 (978-1-57505-615-9(1)) Lerner Publishing Group.

Rau, Dana Meachen. The Robin in the Tree. 2006. (Nature Ser.). (Illus.). 24p. (J). lib. bdg. 22.79 (***978-0-7614-2304-1(4)*** , Benchmark Bks.) Cavendish, Marshall Corp.

Robinson, Fay. Singing Robins. 2000. (Pull Ahead Bks.). (Illus.). 32p. (J). (gr. k-2). lib. bdg. 22.60 (978-0-8225-3641-3(2) , Lerner Pubns.) Lerner Publishing Group.

Tagliaferro, Linda. Robins & Their Chicks. 2004. (Animal Offspring Ser.). (Illus.). 29p. (J). 13.95 (978-0-7368-2389-0(1) , Pebble Bks.) Capstone Pr., Inc.

Willis, Nancy Carol. The Robins in Your Backyard. Willis, Nancy Carol, illus. 2001. (Accelerated Reader Program Ser.). (Illus.). 32p. (J). (gr. k-3). pap. 6.99 (978-0-9662761-1-4(6)) Birdsong Bks.

—Robins in Your Backyard. 2001. (gr. k-3). lib. bdg. 15.30 (978-0-613-70958-3(6)) Tandem Library Bks.

—The Robins in Your Backyard. Willis, Nancy Carol, illus. 2001. (Accelerated Reader Program Ser.). (Illus.). 32p. (J). (gr. 4-7). reprint ed. 15.95 (978-0-9662761-0-7(8)) Birdsong Bks.

ROBINS—FICTION

Baguley, Elizabeth. The Little Lost Robin. Macnaughton, Tina, illus. 2007. 28p. (J). (ps-2). 16.95 (***978-1-56148-590-1(X)***) Good Bks.

Baran, Robin. Flight of the Robbins. 2006. pap. 7.95 (978-0-533-15430-2(8)) Vantage Pr., Inc.

Bonnell, Kris. Robins in the Spring. 2007. (J). 3.95 (***978-1-933727-53-0(5)***) Reading Reading Bks., LLC.

Brooks, Walter R. Freddy & the Popinjay. Wiese, Kurt, illus. 2001. 244p. (J). (gr. 4-7). 23.95 (978-1-58567-134-2(7)) Overlook Pr., The.

Burgess, Melvin & Brown, Ruth. The Birdman. 2002. (Illus.). 25p. (YA). 17.99 (978-0-86264-976-0(5)) Orion Bks. Ltd. GBR. *Dist:* Trafalgar Square Publishing.

Fearnley, Jan. Little Robin's Christmas. Fearnley, Jan, illus. 2002. 32p. (J). 5.95 (978-1-58925-371-1(X) , tiger tales) ME Media LLC.

Hansle, Chauline. Mr Frog & Kitty Robin. 2006. (ENG., Illus.). 28p. per. 15.49 (***978-1-4259-6920-2(8)***) AuthorHouse.

Jorgensen, Norman. In Flanders Fields. Gray, Peter, ed. 2002. (Illus.). 40p. 22.95 (978-1-86368-369-2(0)) Fremantle Pr. AUS. *Dist:* International Specialized Bk. Services.

—In Flanders Fields. Harrison-Lever, Brian, illus. 2003. 32p. 16.95 (978-1-894965-01-9(9)) Simply Read Bks. CAN. *Dist:* Perseus Distribution.

Jorgensen, Norman & Harrison-Lever, Brian. In Flanders Fields. 2004. (Illus.). 32p. pap. 13.50 (978-1-920731-03-8(2)) Fremantle Pr. AUS. *Dist:* International Specialized Bk. Services.

Powell, Virginia. Sugar Robin. Powell, Wade, illus. 1998. (J). lib. bdg. 17.25 (978-1-56763-304-7(8)) Ozark Publishing.

Salzmann, Mary Elizabeth. Robin Hoods. Haberstroh, Anne, illus. 2007. (Fact & Fiction Ser.). 24p. (J). pap. (978-1-59928-467-5(7)); 21.35 (978-1-59928-466-8(9)) ABDO Publishing Co.

Sawyers, William. The Nest That Could Fly. 2005. 43p. (J). pap. 16.69 (978-1-4116-5446-4(3)) Lulu.com.

Sechelt Nation Staff. How the Robin Got Its Red Breast: A Legend of the Sechelt People. Craigan, Charles J., illus. unabr. ed. 40p. (J). (978-0-88971-158-7(5)) Harbour Publishing Co., Ltd.

Speed, Bryan W. Little Bent Cedar. 2007. 24p. (J). 9.95 (***978-1-933255-38-5(2)***) DNA Pr.

Talbott, Shawn M. Springtime Robins. 2006. (J). lib. bdg. 19.95 (***978-1-933732-05-3(9)*** , Bear Hug Bks.) MidAmerica Publishing Co.

Wolverton, Ray & Livingston, Wayne. The Stories of Zapy Yapy. 1999. (Illus.). 96p. (J). (978-0-9674101-1-1(8)) Wolverton.

ROBINSON, JACKIE, 1919-1972

Abraham, Philip. Jackie Robinson. 2002. (Wel-Real People Ser.). (Illus.). 24p. (J). (ps-2). 18.00 (978-0-516-23950-7(3)); pap. 4.95 (978-0-516-23605-6(9)) Scholastic Library Publishing. (Children's Pr.).

—Jackie Robinson. 2002. (gr. k-3). lib. bdg. 12.95 (978-0-613-58845-4(2)) Tandem Library Bks.

Acosta, Tatiana & Gutierrez, Guillermo, trs. Jackie Robinson. 2004. (Gente Que Hay Que Conocer Ser.). (SPA., Illus.). 24p. (J). lib. bdg. 19.33 (978-0-8368-4353-8(3)) Stevens, Gareth Inc.

Auster, Michael A. They Led the Way. 2005. (Yellow Umbrella Ser.). (J). (978-0-7368-5315-6(4)); (Illus.). 16p. (978-0-7368-5279-1(4)) Capstone Pr., Inc.

Benjamin, Lisa. Jackie Robinson: Changing the Game. 2005. (Voices Reading Ser.). (Illus.). 32p. (J). (978-0-7367-2937-6(2)) Zaner-Bloser, Inc.

Brown, Jonatha A. & Raatma, Lucia. Jackie Robinson. 2004. (Illus.). 24p. (J). pap. (978-0-8368-4318-7(5)); (YA). lib. bdg. 19.33 (978-0-8368-4311-8(8)) Stevens, Gareth Inc.

Burleigh, Robert. Stealing Home: Jackie Robinson: Against the Odds. Wimmer, Mike, illus. 2007. 32p. (J). (gr. 1-4). 16.99 (978-0-689-86276-2(8) , Simon & Schuster Children's Publishing) Simon & Schuster Children's Publishing.

Darraj, Susan Muaddi. Jackie Robinson. 2007. (Baseball Superstars Ser.). 128p. (gr. 6-12). 30.00 (***978-0-7910-9442-6(1)*** , Chelsea Hse.) Facts On File, Inc.

DeAngelis, Gina. Jackie Robinson. 2000. (Overcoming Adversity Ser.). (Illus.). (J). 104p. (gr. 8-12). pap. 30.00 (978-0-7910-5898-5(0)); 112p. (gr. 4-7). 30.00 (978-0-7910-5897-8(2)) Facts On File, Inc. (Chelsea Hse.).

Deangelis, Gina. Jackie Robinson. 2001. (gr. 5-8). lib. bdg. 18.75 (978-0-613-32699-5(7)) Tandem Library Bks.

Dunn, Herb. Jackie Robinson: Young Sports Trailblazer. Henderson, Meryl, illus. 1999. (Childhood of Famous Americans Ser.). 192p. (J). (gr. 3-7). pap. 5.99 (978-0-689-82453-1(X) , Aladdin) Simon & Schuster Children's Publishing.

—Jackie Robinson: Young Sports Trailblazer. 1999. (Childhood of Famous Americans Ser.). (J). 11.64 (978-0-606-16287-6(9)); (gr. 3-6). lib. bdg. 13.00 (978-0-613-15849-7(0)) Tandem Library Bks.

Dunn, Joe. Jackie Robinson. Espinosa, Rod, illus. 2007. (Bio-Graphics Ser.). 32p. (J). (gr. 3-6). lib. bdg. 27.07 (***978-1-60270-068-0(0)*** , Graphic Planet) Magic Wagon.

Elish, Dan. Jackie Robinson. 2005. (Cornerstones of Freedom Ser.). (Illus.). 48p. (J). (ps-6). 26.00 (978-0-516-23635-3(0) , Children's Pr.) Scholastic Library Publishing.

Feinstein, Stephen. Read about Jackie Robinson. 2005. (I Like Biographies! Ser.). (Illus.). 24p. (J). lib. bdg. 21.26 (978-0-7660-2592-9(6) , Enslow Elementary) Enslow Pubs., Inc.

Ford, Carin T. Jackie Robinson: All I Ask Is That You Respect Me as a Human Being. 2005. (African-American Biography Library). (Illus.). 128p. (J). (gr. 6-12). lib. bdg. 31.93 (978-0-7660-2461-8(X)) Enslow Pubs., Inc.

—Jackie Robinson: Hero of Baseball. 2006. (Heroes of American History Ser.). (Illus.). 32p. (J). (ps-3). lib. bdg. 22.60 (978-0-7660-2600-1(0) , Enslow Elementary) Enslow Pubs., Inc.

Frost, Helen. Let's Meet Jackie Robinson. 2003. (Let's Meet Biographies Ser.). (Illus.). 32p. (gr. 2-4). 23.00 (978-0-7910-7321-6(1) , Chelsea Hse.) Facts On File, Inc.

Frystak, Timothy D. Jackie Robinson: With Profiles of Satchel Paige & & Branch Rickey. 2006. (Biographical Connections Ser.). (Illus.). 112p. (J). (978-0-7166-1828-7(1)) World Bk., Inc.

Glaser, Jason. Jackie Robinson: Baseball's Great Pioneer. Lentz, Bob, illus. 2005. (Graphic Library). 32p. (J). (gr. 3-7). lib. bdg. 25.26 (978-0-7368-4633-2(6)) Capstone Pr., Inc.

Glaser, Jason & Lentz, Bob. Jackie Robinson: Gran Pionero Del Béisbol. Lentz, Bob, illus. 2007. (Graphic Library). (ENG & SPA., Illus.). 32p. (J). (978-0-7368-6602-6(7)) Capstone Publishing.

Golenbock, Peter. Teammates. 1998. (Illus.). 32p. (ps-3). 16.98 (978-0-8172-4092-9(6)) Raintree.

Gomez, Rebecca. Jackie Robinson. 2003. (First Biographies Ser.). (Illus.). 32p. (J). (gr. k-4). lib. bdg. 22.78 (978-1-57765-949-5(X)) ABDO Publishing Co.

Gutman, Dan. Jackie Robinson & the Big Game. Garvin, Elaine, illus. 2006. 32p. (J). lib. bdg. 15.00 (***978-1-4242-0957-6(9)***) Fitzgerald Bks.

—Jackie Robinson & the Big Game. Garvin, Elaine, illus. 2006. (Ready-to-Read Cofa Ser.). 32p. (J). pap. 3.99 (978-0-689-86239-7(3) , Aladdin); lib. bdg. 11.89 (978-0-689-86240-3(7) , Aladdin Library) Simon & Schuster Children's Publishing.

Hanft, Joshua E. Jackie Robinson. Marcos, Pablo, illus. 2005. (Heroes of America Ser.). 240p. (J). (gr. 3-8). lib. bdg. 21.35 (978-1-59679-259-3(0)) ABDO Publishing Co.

Jackie Robinson. (Photo Illustrated Biographies Ser.). 24p. (J). 6.95 (978-0-7368-3440-7(0)); Vol. 2. 2005. (YA). (978-0-7368-9412-8(8) , Pebble Bks.) Capstone Pr., Inc.

Jackie Robinson. (Compass Point Early Biographies Ser.). 32p. (J). 7.95 (978-0-7565-1172-2(0)) Compass Point Bks.

Jackie Robinson. 1999. (SmartReader Ser.). (J). Level 1. pap., tchr. ed. 19.95 incl. audio (978-0-7887-1156-5(3) , 79417T3); Level 2. pap., tchr. ed. 19.95 incl. audio (978-0-7887-0280-8(7) , 79320T3) Recorded Bks., LLC.

Jackie Robinson, 6 vols. (gr. k-2). 28.95 (978-0-7368-9413-5(6)) Red Brick Learning.

Jackie Robinson. 2006. (People We Should Know Ser.). (SPA.). (J). (gr. 3-4). 4.76 (978-0-8368-4360-6(6) , GHS33826) Stevens, Gareth Inc.

Jackie Robinson: Libros Aventuras (Adventure Books) 2000. (MacMillan/McGraw-Hill. Estudios Sociales Ser.). (ENG & SPA.). (gr. 2 up). (978-0-02-148677-9(8)) Macmillan/McGraw-Hill Schl. Div.

Klingel, Cynthia Fitterer & Noyed, Robert B. Jackie Robinson. 2001. (Wonder Books Level 2: Biographies Ser.). (Illus.). 24p. (J). (ps-3). 22.79 (978-1-56766-953-4(0)) Child's World, Inc.

Knox, Barbara. Jackie Robinson. 2003. (Photo-Illustrated Biographies Ser.). (Illus.). 24p. (J). lib. bdg. 19.93 (978-0-7368-2224-4(0) , Bridgestone Bks.) Capstone Pr., Inc.

Mara, Wil. Jackie Robinson. 2003. (Rookie Biographies Ser.). (Illus.). 32p. (J). (gr. 1-2). pap. 4.95 (978-0-516-27336-5(1) , Children's Pr.) Scholastic Library Publishing.

—Jackie Robinson. 2003. (Illus.). 31p. (J). (ps-3). lib. bdg. 12.95 (978-0-613-59501-8(7)) Tandem Library Bks.

Marsh, Carole. Jackie Robinson. 2002. (One Thousand Readers Ser.). (Illus.). 12p. (J). (gr. k-4). 2.95 (978-0-635-01529-7(3) , 15293) Gallopade International.

McLeese, Don. Jackie Robinson. 2002. (Illus.). 24p. (J). (ps-3). lib. bdg. 20.64 (978-1-58952-288-6(5)) Rourke Publishing, LLC.

O'Hern, Kerri & Raatma, Lucia. Jackie Robinson. 2006. (Illus.). 31p. (J). pap. (978-0-8368-6250-8(3) , World Almanac Library) Stevens, Gareth Inc.

O'Sullivan, Robyn. Jackie Robinson Plays Ball. 2007. (History Chapters Ser.). 48p. (J). (gr. 1-4). lib. bdg. 17.90 (***978-1-4263-0190-2(1)*** , National Geographic Children's Bks.) National Geographic Society.

Patrick, Denise Lewis. Jackie Robinson Strong Inside & Out. 2005. 44p. (J). lib. bdg. 15.00 (***978-1-4242-0850-0(5)***) Fitzgerald Bks.

Patrick, Denise Lewis & Time for Kids Editors. Jackie Robinson: Strong Inside & Out. 2005. (Time for Kids Ser.). (Illus.). 48p. (J). 15.99 (978-0-06-057601-1(4)); pap. 3.99 (978-0-06-057600-4(6)) HarperCollins Pubs.

Prince, April Jones. Jackie Robinson: He Led the Way. Casilla, Robert, illus. 2007. (All Aboard Reading Ser.). 48p. (J). (gr. 1-3). pap. 3.99 (***978-0-448-44721-6(5)*** , Grosset & Dunlap) Penguin Group (USA) Inc.

Raatma, Kerri & Spay, Anthony, illus. 2006. (Graphic Biographies Ser.). 32p. (J). (gr. 3-5). lib. bdg. 26.00 (978-0-8368-6198-3(1) , World Almanac Library) Stevens, Gareth Inc.

Raatma, Kerri & Raatma, Lucia. Jackie Robinson. Campbell, Alex & Spay, Anthony, illus. 2006. (Graphic Biographies Ser.). 32p. (J). (gr. 3-5). lib. bdg. 26.00 (978-0-8368-6198-3(1) , World Almanac Library) Stevens, Gareth Inc.

Raatma, Lucia. Jackie Robinson. 2000. (Compass Point Early Biographies Ser.). (Illus.). 32p. (J). (gr. 2 up). lib. bdg. 21.26 (978-0-7565-0016-0(8)) Compass Point Bks.

—Jackie Robinson. 2002. (Trailblazers of the Modern World Ser.). (Illus.). 48p. (J). (gr. 5 up). pap. 14.95 (978-0-8368-5232-5(X)); lib. bdg. 30.00 (978-0-8368-5072-7(6)) Stevens, Gareth Inc. (World Almanac Library).

—Jackie Robinson. 2002. (gr. 3-6). lib. bdg. 16.40 (978-0-613-76805-4(1)) Tandem Library Bks.

Robinson, Sharon. Jackie Robinson's Values to Live By: Becoming Your Best Self. 2002. (Jackie's 9 Ser.). 192p. (J). (gr. 4-9). pap. 4.99 (978-0-439-38550-3(4)) Scholastic, Inc.

—Jackie's Nine: Jackie Robinson's Values to Live By. 2002. (gr. 5-8). lib. bdg. 13.00 (978-0-613-50333-4(3)) Tandem Library Bks.

—Promises to Keep: How Jackie Robinson Changed America. 2004. (Illus.). 64p. (YA). pap. 16.95 (978-0-439-42592-6(1)) Scholastic, Inc.

Schaefer, Lola M. Jackie Robinson. Saunders-Smith, Gail, ed. 2002. (First Biographies Ser.). (Illus.). 24p. (J). (gr. k-1). lib. bdg. 15.93 (978-0-7368-1435-5(3) , Pebble Bks.) Capstone Pr., Inc.

Sexton, Colleen. Jackie Robinson: A Life of Determination. 2007. (Illus.). 24p. (J). lib. bdg. 19.95 (978-1-60014-089-1(0)) Bellwether Media.

Stout, Glenn & Christopher, Matt. Jackie Robinson: Legends in Sports. 2006. (Matt Christopher Legends in Sports Ser.). (Illus.). 128p. (J). (gr. 5-8). pap. 4.99 (978-0-316-10826-3(X)) Little Brown & Co.

Walker, Sally M. Jackie Robinson. Pate, Rodney S., illus. 2005. (Yo Solo (On My Own) Ser.). (SPA & ENG.). 48p. (J). (gr. 2-5). lib. bdg. 23.93 (978-0-8225-3126-5(7) , Ediciones Lerner) Lerner Publishing Group.

—Jackie Robinson. Pate, Rodney, illus. 2002. (On My Own Biographies Ser.). 48p. (J). lib. bdg. 23.93 (978-0-87614-599-9(3) , Carolrhoda Bks.) Lerner Publishing Group.

—Jackie Robinson. Pate, Rodney S., illus. 2002. 48p. (J). (ps-3). lib. bdg. 14.10 (978-0-613-52412-4(8)) Tandem Library Bks.

Wheeler, Jill C. Jackie Robinson. 2003. (Breaking Barriers Ser.). (Illus.). 64p. (J). (gr. 3-8). lib. bdg. 25.65 (978-1-57765-739-2(X)) ABDO Publishing Co.

Wilmore, Kathy. Jackie Robinson: With a Discussion of Respect. 2004. (Values in Action Ser.). (J). (978-1-59203-071-2(8)) Learning Challenge, Inc.

Wukovitz, John F. Jackie Robinson & the Integration of Baseball. 2006. (Lucent Library of Black History). 112p. (YA). (gr. 5-8). lib. bdg. 32.45 (978-1-59018-913-9(2) , Lucent Bks.) Thomson Gale.

ROBINSON, JACKIE, 1919-1972—FICTION

Gutman, Dan. Jackie & Me. 2005. (Baseball Card Adventures Ser.). (Illus.). 145p. (YA). (gr. 4-8). reprint ed. 20.00 (978-0-7567-9569-6(9)) DIANE Publishing Co.

—Jackie & Me. (Baseball Card Adventures Ser.). 160p. (J). 2000. (gr. 3-7). pap. 5.99 (978-0-380-80084-1(5)); 1999. (Illus.). (gr. 4-7). 16.99 (978-0-380-97685-0(4)) HarperCollins Pubs.

—Jackie & Me. 2000. (Baseball Card Adventures Ser.). (gr. 5-8). lib. bdg. 14.15 (978-0-613-27912-3(3)); (Illus.). (J). 12.64 (978-0-606-17974-4(7)) Tandem Library Bks.

Isadora, Rachel. Luke Goes to Bat. Isadora, Rachel, illus. 2005. (Illus.). 32p. (J). (ps-3). 15.99 (978-0-399-23604-4(X) , Putnam Juvenile) Penguin Group (USA) Inc.

Lorbiecki, Marybeth. Jackie's Bat. Pinkney, Brian, illus. 2006. 40p. (J). (gr. k-3). 15.95 (978-0-689-84102-6(7)) Simon & Schuster Children's Publishing.

Russell, Nancy L. M. So Long, Jackie Robinson. rev. ed. 2007. 224p. (gr. 7 up). pap. 7.95 (***978-1-55263-863-7(4)***) Key Porter Bks. CAN. *Dist:* Perseus Distribution.

Uhlberg, Myron. Dad, Jackie, & Me. Bootman, Colin, illus. 2005. 32p. (J). (ps-3). 16.95 (978-1-56145-329-0(3)) Peachtree Pubs., Ltd.

ROBINSON, JOHN ROOSEVELT, 1919-1972

see Robinson, Jackie, 1919-1972

ROBOTS

Allman, Toney. From Insect Wings to Flying Robots. 2006. (Imitating Nature Ser.). (Illus.). 32p. (J). (gr. 3-6). 24.95 (978-0-7377-3488-1(4) , Kidhaven) Thomson Gale.

Baker, Christopher W. Robots among Us: The Challenges & Promises of Robotics. 2002. (New Century Technology Ser.: 8). (Illus.). 48p. (gr. 5-8). lib. bdg. 23.90 (978-0-7613-1969-6(7) , Millbrook Pr.) Lerner Publishing Group.

Barnhart, Joseph Karl, prod. Complete Robotics Srs-Hyb Lab. (YA). cd-rom 1958.75 (978-0-7365-6720-6(8)) Films Media Group.

Bergin, Mark. Robots. Bergin, Mark, illus. 2001. (Fast Forward Ser.). (Illus.). 32p. (J). (gr. 4-8). pap. 9.95 (978-0-531-14808-2(4) , Watts, Franklin) Scholastic Library Publishing.

—Robots. 2001. (gr. 3-6). lib. bdg. 18.75 (978-0-613-54327-9(0)) Tandem Library Bks.

Bergin, Mark & Salariya, David. Robots. 2001. (Fast Forward Ser.). (Illus.). 32p. (J). (gr. 4-8). 29.00 (978-0-531-14616-3(2) , Watts, Franklin) Scholastic Library Publishing.

Beyer, Mark. Robotics. 2002. (High Interest Bks.). (Illus.). 48p. (YA). (gr. 7-12). pap. 6.95 (978-0-516-24007-7(2) , Children's Pr.) Scholastic Library Publishing.

—Robotics. 2002. (gr. 7-12). lib. bdg. 15.25 (978-0-613-58727-3(8)) Tandem Library Bks.

Bridgman, Roger & Dorling Kindersley Publishing Staff. Robot. 2004. (Dk Eyewitness Books Ser.). (Illus.). 64p. (J). 15.99 (978-0-7566-0254-3(8)) Dorling Kindersley Publishing, Inc.

Brown, Jordan. Robo World: The Story of Robot Designer Cynthia Breazeal. 2006. (Women's Adventures in Science Ser.). 128p. pap. 9.95 (978-0-309-09556-3(5) , Joseph Henry Pr.) National Academies Pr.

Bryan, Sarah Jane. Robots Everywhere! 2001. (All-Star Readers: Level 3 Ser.). (Illus.). 48p. (J). (gr. 2-3). 3.99 (978-1-57584-726-9(4)) Reader's Digest Children's Publishing, Inc.

Danko, Dan & Mason, Tom. The Official Guide to Battlebots. 2002. (Illus.). 64p. (J). (gr. 4-6). pap. 6.99 (978-0-439-39000-2(1)) Scholastic, Inc.

DK Publishing. Real-Life Robots. 2007. 48p. (J). 12.99 (***978-0-7566-3509-1(8)***); pap. 3.99 (***978-0-7566-3508-4(X)***) Dorling Kindersley Publishing, Inc.

DK Publishing Staff. Transformers Classic. 2003. (Ultimate Sticker Bks.). (Illus.). 16p. (J). pap. 6.99 (978-0-7894-9516-7(3)) Dorling Kindersley Publishing, Inc.

Dorling Kindersley Publishing Staff. Robot. 2004. (Dk Eyewitness Books Ser.). 64p. (J). lib. bdg. 19.99 (978-0-7566-0253-6(X)) Dorling Kindersley Publishing, Inc.

—Transformers Armada Sticker Book. 2003. (Ultimate Sticker Bks.). (Illus.). 16p. (J). pap. 6.99 (978-0-7894-9517-4(1)) Dorling Kindersley Publishing, Inc.

Eckhold, David & Dorling Kindersley Publishing Staff. The Ultimate Robot Kit. Ling, Mary, ed. 2001. (Illus.). 24p. (J). (gr. 3-12). pap. 29.99 (978-0-7894-7945-7(1)) Dorling Kindersley Publishing, Inc.

Eckold, David. Robot Challenge Kit. 2002. (Illus.). 1p. (J). 29.99 (978-0-7894-8888-6(4)) Dorling Kindersley Publishing, Inc.

Fowler, Allan. It Could Still Be a Robot. 1998. (Rookie Read-About Science Ser.). (Illus.). 32p. (J). (gr. k-3). pap. 4.95 (978-0-516-26258-1(0) , Children's Pr.) Scholastic Library Publishing.

Fritz, Sandy. Robotics & Artificial Intelligence. 2003. (Hot Science Ser.). (J). lib. bdg. 28.50 (978-1-58340-364-8(7)) Smart Apple Media.

Galashan, Kathy. Robots. 2005. (Illus.). 32p. pap. 8.50 (978-0-340-87311-3(6)) Cambridge Univ. Pr.

Gifford, Clive. Robots. (Science Kids Ser.). (Illus.). 48p. (J). (gr. k-3). 2007. pap. 6.95 (***978-0-7534-6125-9(0)***); 2003. tchr. ed. 9.95 (978-0-7534-5618-7(4)) Houghton Mifflin Co. Trade & Reference Div. (Kingfisher).

—Robots. 2005. (Technology All Around Us Ser.). (Illus.). 32p. (J). (gr. 4-7). lib. bdg. 27.10 (978-1-58340-752-3(9)) Smart Apple Media.

Gray, Peter C. How to Draw Manga Robots. 2006. (Kid's Guide to Drawing Ser.). (Illus.). 32p. (J). lib. bdg. (978-1-4042-3332-4(6) , PowerKids Pr.) Rosen Publishing Group, Inc., The.

Hamilton, John. Robots & Androids. 2007. (World of Science Fiction Ser.). (Illus.). 32p. (J). 24.21 (978-1-59679-993-6(5)) ABDO Publishing Co.

Harcourt School Publishers Staff. Fun with Robots Below Level. 3rd ed. 2002. (Trophies Reading Program Ser.). (Illus.). pap. 5.10 (978-0-15-323335-7(4)) Harcourt Schl. Pubs.

—Robots Rush Advanced Level. 3rd ed. 2002. (Trophies Reading Program Ser.). (Illus.). pap. 5.10 (978-0-15-323029-5(0)) Harcourt Schl. Pubs.

—Trofeos Advanced Level: Soy un Robot. 3rd ed. 2002. (SPA., Illus.). pap. 6.80 (978-0-15-323940-3(9)) Harcourt Schl. Pubs.

Howard, Ayanna. On the Job with an Engineer. 2003. (Adventures in Science Ser.). (J). pap. (978-1-58417-122-5(7)); lib. bdg. (978-1-58417-059-4(X)) Lake Street Pubs.

Hyland, Tony. Emergency & High-Risk Robots. 2007. (***978-1-59920-119-1(4)***) Smart Apple Media.

—Film & Fiction Robots. 2007. (J). (***978-1-59920-120-7(8)***) Smart Apple Media.

—How Robots Work. 2007. (J). (***978-1-59920-116-0(X)***) Smart Apple Media.

—Robots at Work & Play. 2007. (J). (***978-1-59920-117-7(8)***) Smart Apple Media.

—Space Robots. 2007. (J). (***978-1-59920-121-4(6)***) Smart Apple Media.

Jefferis, David. Robot Brains. 2006. (Robozones Ser.). (Illus.). 32p. (J). (gr. 3-6). pap. (978-0-7787-2900-6(1)); lib. bdg. (978-0-7787-2886-3(2)) Crabtree Publishing Co.

—Robot Voyagers. 2006. (Robozones Ser.). (Illus.). 32p. (J). (gr. 3-6). pap. (978-0-7787-2898-6(6)); lib. bdg. (978-0-7787-2884-9(6)) Crabtree Publishing Co.

—Robot Warriors. 2006. (Illus.). 32p. (J). (***978-0-7787-2887-0(0)***); (gr. 4-5). pap. (978-0-7787-2901-3(X)) Crabtree Publishing Co.

Jefferis, David. Robot Workers. 2006. (Robozones Ser.). (Illus.). 32p. (J). (gr. 3-6). pap. (978-0-7787-2899-3(4)); lib. bdg. (978-0-7787-2885-6(4)) Crabtree Publishing Co.

Jones, David. Mighty Robots: Mechanical Marvels that Fascinate & Frighten. 2005. (Illus.). 144p. (J). (gr. 6-12). 24.95 (978-1-55037-929-7(1)) Annick Pr., Ltd. CAN. *Dist:* Firefly Bks., Ltd.

—Mighty Robots: Mechanical Marvels That Fascinate & Frighten. 2005. (Illus.). 144p. (J). (gr. 6-12). pap. 14.95 (978-1-55037-928-0(3)) Annick Pr., Ltd. CAN. *Dist:* Firefly Bks., Ltd.

Lockman, Darcy. Robots. 2000. (Kaleidoscope Ser.). (Illus.). 48p. (J). (gr. 3 up). lib. bdg. 25.64 (978-0-7614-1047-8(3) , Benchmark Bks.) Cavendish, Marshall Corp.

Malone, Robert. Ultimate Robot. Dorling Kindersley Publishing Staff, ed. 2004. (Illus.). 192p. 30.00 (978-0-7566-0270-3(X)) Dorling Kindersley Publishing, Inc.

Manatt, Kathleen G. Robot Scientist. 2008. (J). lib. bdg. 25.26 (***978-1-60279-051-3(5)***) Cherry Lake Publishing.

McComb, Gordon. Robot Builder's Bonanza. 2001. (gr. 7-12). lib. bdg. 36.15 (978-0-613-59387-8(1)) Tandem Library Bks.

Miller Ron. Robot Explorers. 2007. (Space Innovations Ser.). (Illus.). 112p. (YA). (gr. 6-8). lib. bdg. 31.93 (***978-0-8225-7152-0(8)*** , Twenty-First Century Bks.) Lerner Publishing Group.

Munzer, Stephen. Robotz: An Encyclopedia of Robots in Fact & Fiction. 2002. (gr. 3-6). lib. bdg. 12.40 (978-0-613-67580-2(0)) Tandem Library Bks.

Nardo, Don. Robots. 2007. (Monsters Ser.). (Illus.). 48p. (J). (gr. 4-8). 23.70 (***978-0-7377-3779-0(4)*** , Kidhaven) Thomson Gale.

Parker, Andy. Mekanimals: Robotic Reef, Spanish-Language Edition. 2005. (Mekanimals Ser.). (SPA., Illus.). 8p. (J). bds. 12.95 (978-970-718-321-6(7) , Silver Dolphin en Español) Advanced Marketing, S. de R. L. de C. V. MEX. *Dist:* Perseus Distribution.

Punter, Russell. Robots. Hamilton, Andrew, illus. 2004. 48p. (J). (gr. 2 up). pap. 5.95 (978-0-7945-0760-2(3) , Usborne) EDC Publishing.

Ramsden, Julie & Ramsden, Michael. Robots. 2005. (X-Zone Ser.). (Illus.). 30p. (gr. 4-8). 23.00 (978-0-7910-8987-3(8)) Facts On File, Inc.

Reeve, Tim. Action Robots: A Pop-up Book Showing How They Work. MacLeod, Gavin, illus. 2004. 14p. (YA). (gr. 4-10). reprint ed. 17.00 (978-0-7567-7284-0(2)) DIANE Publishing Co.

Regan, Lisa. Micro Model Battle Bots. 2004. (Illus.). (978-0-439-68926-7(0)) Scholastic, Inc.

Remarkable Robots. 2005. (Book Treks Ser.). (J). 37.95 (978-0-7652-3243-4(X)) Celebration Pr.

Robots: Early Level Satellite Individual Title Six-Packs. (Sails Literacy Ser.). 16p. (gr. 1-2). 27.00 (978-0-7578-6519-0(4)) Rigby Education.

Sautter, Aaron. How to Draw Terrifying Robots. Knudson, Jason, illus. 2008. (J). (***978-1-4296-0080-4(2)***) Capstone Pr., Inc.

Sobey, Edwin J. C. How to Build Your Own Prize-Winning Robot. 2002. (Science Fair Success Ser.). (Illus.). 128p. (YA). (gr. 6-12). lib. bdg. 26.60 (978-0-7660-1627-9(7)) Enslow Pubs., Inc.

Space Robots. (Explore Space! Ser.). 24p. (J). 6.95 (978-0-7368-9169-1(2)) Capstone Pr., Inc.

Space Robots, 6 vols. (gr. 2-5). 36.95 (978-0-7368-9247-6(8)) Red Brick Learning.

Stazzer, James. My TV's Alive! Real Life Robots, Future Computers & Clones. 1999. (Illus.). 128p. (gr. 4-7). pap. 4.95 (978-1-902618-35-7(1)) Element Children's Bks.

Stephens, Jay. Robots! Draw Your Own Androids, Cyborgs & Battle Bots. 2008. (Illus.). 64p. (J). 12.95 (***978-1-57990-937-6(X)***) Lark Bks.

Strom, Laura Layton. From Bugbots to Humanoids: Robotics. (Shockwave: Technology & Manufacturing Ser.). (J). 2008. 32p. pap. 6.95 (***978-0-531-18843-9(4)***); 2007. (Illus.). 36p. (gr. 4-6). lib. bdg. 25.00 (***978-0-531-17585-9(5)***) Scholastic Library Publishing. (Children's Pr.).

White Steve. Military Robots. 2006. (High-Tech Military Weapons Ser.). (Illus.). 48p. (J). (978-0-531-12092-7(9) , Children's Pr.) Scholastic Library Publishing.

White Steve D. Military Robots. 2007. (High-Tech Military Weapons Ser.). (Illus.). 48p. (J). pap. (978-0-531-18708-1(X)) Children's Pr., Ltd.

Wordsworth, William. I Wandered Lonely As a Cloud. Suomalainen, Sami, illus. 2007. 24p. (J). (ps-3). (978-1-897073-25-4(9)) Lobster Pr.

ROBOTS—FICTION

Akira, Shouko & Toriyama, Akira. Dr. Slump. 2005. (Dr. Slump Ser.: Vol. 3). 200p. (YA). pap. 7.99 (978-1-59116-991-8(7)) Viz Media.

All Aboard! Softi's Adventures. 2003. (J). mass mkt. (978-1-932233-36-0(9)) Aurora Libris Corp.

Appleton, Victor. The Robot Olympics. 2006. (Tom Swift, Young Inventor Ser.). 176p. (J). pap. 4.99 (978-1-4169-1361-0(0) , Aladdin) Simon & Schuster Children's Publishing.

—The Robot Olympics. 2007. (Tom Swift, Young Inventor Ser.). 160p. (J). (gr. 4-7). 27.07 (***978-1-59961-351-2(4)***) Spotlight.

—Rocket Racers. 2007. (Tom Swift, Young Inventor Ser.). 160p. (J). (gr. 4-7). 27.07 (***978-1-59961-352-9(2)***) Spotlight.

—The Space Hotel. 2007. (Tom Swift, Young Inventor Ser.). 160p. (J). (gr. 4-7). 27.07 (***978-1-59961-353-6(0)***) Spotlight.

Asimov, Isaac & Asimov, Janet. Norby & the Lost Princess. 128p. (J). lib. bdg. 20.90 (978-0-8027-6593-2(9)) Walker & Co.

Asimov, Janet & Asimov, Isaac. Norby & the Court Jester. l.t. ed. 1999. 168p. 24.95 (978-0-7838-8610-7(1)) Thorndike Pr.

Auerbach, Annie. The Quest for Energon. 2007. (Transformers Ser.). 64p. (J). pap. 4.99 (***978-0-06-088834-3(2)*** , Harper Entertainment) HarperCollins Pubs.

Baruffi, Andrea, illus. If I Had a Robot Dog. 2005. (I'm Going to Read Ser.). 32p. (J). (ps). pap. 3.95 (978-1-4027-3027-6(6)) Sterling Publishing Co., Inc.

Baum, L. Frank. The Wonderful Wizard of Oz. 2005. (Great Classics for Children Ser.). 160p. (J). 5.99 (978-1-4037-1394-0(4)) Dalmatian Pr.

Bear, Carolyn. Sid & Bolter. Cottrill, Peter, illus. 2006. (Read-It! Chapter Books). 64p. (J). lib. bdg. (***978-1-4048-3126-1(6)*** , 1265813) Picture Window Bks.

Bedford, David. Soccer Camp. Brumpton, Keith, illus. 2006. (Team Ser.: 3). 76p. (J). pap. 4.95 (978-1-933605-07-4(3)) Kane/Miller Bk. Pubs., Inc.

Bellairs, John. The Eyes of the Killer Robot. 1998. (Johnny Dixon Mystery Ser.). 12.64 (978-0-606-13371-5(2)) Tandem Library Bks.

Benjamin, A. H. Shamwood. 2006. 140p. pap. 19.95 (978-1-4137-9193-8(X)) PublishAmerica, Inc.

Benton, Jim. The Invisible Fran. Benton, Jim, illus. 2004. (Franny K. Stein, Mad Scientist Ser.: Bk. 3). (Illus.). 112p. (J). (gr. 2-5). 14.95 (978-0-689-86293-9(8)) Simon & Schuster Children's Publishing.

A Bit Haywire. 2006. (YA). per. 11.95 (978-0-9777883-5-4(0)) Viper Comics.

Brooks, Kevin. Being. 2008. 352p. (J). pap. 7.99 (***978-0-439-90342-4(4)*** , PUSH) Scholastic, Inc.

Brouwer, Sigmund. Mission 10: Last Stand. 2002. (Mars Diaries Ser.: Mission 10). 144p. (J). mass mkt. 4.99 (978-0-8423-5634-3(7)) Tyndale Hse. Pubs.

—Mission 9: Manchurian Sector. 2002. (Mars Diaries Ser.: Mission 9). 160p. (J). mass mkt. 4.99 (978-0-8423-5633-6(9)) Tyndale Hse. Pubs.

Bunting, Eve. My Robot. Fehlau, Dagmar, illus. 2006. (Green Light Readers Level 2 Ser.). 24p. (J). 12.95 (978-0-15-205593-6(2) , Green Light Readers) Harcourt Children's Bks.

—My Robot. Fehlau, Dagmar, illus. 2006. (Green Light Reader Ser.). 24p. (J). pap. 3.95 (978-0-15-205617-9(3)) Harcourt Trade Pubs.

Burns, Dal. The Adventures of Phoo. 2006. 148p. pap. 19.95 (978-1-4241-1773-4(9)) PublishAmerica, Inc.

Card, Orson Scott, ed. Future on Ice. rev. ed. 1998. 432p. (YA). (gr. 7 up). 24.95 (978-0-312-86694-5(1) , Tor Bks.) Doherty, Tom Assocs., LLC.

Chesterfield, Sadie. Optimus Prime Versus Megatron. Staples, Val, illus. 2007. (Transformers Ser.). 24p. (J). pap. 3.99 (***978-0-06-088824-4(5)*** , Harper Entertainment) HarperCollins Pubs.

Chiaramonti, Gregory. Probie: the Space Probe, Mission One: the Ocean of Europa. 2007. 32p. (J). 16.72 (***978-0-615-13848-0(9)***) Chiaramonti, Gregory.

Cone, Molly. Mishmash. 2000. (Illus.). 128p. (J). (gr. 4-6). pap. 4.95 (978-0-618-05482-4(0)) Houghton Mifflin Co. Trade & Reference Div.

—Mishmash. 2000. (978-0-606-18213-3(6)) Tandem Library Bks.

Craig, Joe. Jimmy Coates: Assassin? 2005. 224p. (J). (gr. 5 up). 15.99 (978-0-06-077263-5(8)) HarperCollins Pubs.

—Jimmy Coates: Assassin? 2006. 224p. (J). pap. 5.99 (978-0-06-077265-9(4) , Harper Trophy) HarperCollins Pubs.

Crilley, Mark. Akiko: Pieces of Gax. Crilley, Mark, illus. 2006. (Illus.). 224p. (J). (gr. 3). 9.95 (978-0-385-73044-0(6) , Delacorte Bks. for Young Readers) Random Hse. Children's Bks.

Cushman, Doug. Space Cat. Cushman, Doug, illus. (I Can Read Bks.). (Illus.). 32p. (J). 2006. pap. 3.99 (978-0-06-008967-2(9) , Harper Trophy); 2004. 15.99 (978-0-06-008965-8(2)); 2004. lib. bdg. 16.89 (978-0-06-008966-5(0)) HarperCollins Pubs.

Czernecki, Stefan. Lilliput 5357. 2005. (Illus.). 44p. (J). 16.95 (978-1-894965-32-3(9)) Simply Read Bks. CAN. *Dist:* Perseus Distribution.

Dadey, Debbie & Jones, Marcia Thornton. Robots Don't Catch Chicken Pox, No. 42. Gurney, John Steven, illus. 2001. (Adventures of the Bailey School Kids Ser.: No. 42). 80p. (J). (gr. 2-4). 3.99 (978-0-439-21582-4(X)) Scholastic, Inc.

Dark Horse Comics Staff. King Size Big Guy & Rusty the Boy Robot. 1998. (Illus.). 72p. (YA). (gr. 3 up). pap. 29.95 (978-1-56971-191-0(7)) Dark Horse Comics.

Dubowski, Cathy East. Flubber. 2000. (SPA., Illus.). (J). pap. 9.95 (978-84-406-8184-3(4)) Ediciones B ESP. *Dist:* Distribooks, Inc.

Edwards, Pat. Planet X. 1999. (gr. 3-6). lib. bdg. 10.95 (978-0-613-19422-8(5)) Tandem Library Bks.

Egan, Kate. Transformers: The Movie Storybook. Matere, Marcelo, illus. 2007. (Transformers Ser.). 48p. (J). pap. 8.99 (***978-0-06-088836-7(9)*** , Harper Entertainment) HarperCollins Pubs.

Farshtey, Greg. Exo-Force: Attack of the Robots. 2006. (Lego Ser.). 64p. (J). pap. 3.99 (978-0-439-82809-3(0) , Scholastic) Scholastic, Inc.

Fickling, Phillip. Fillmore & Geary Take Off! Shulman, Mark, illus. 2003. 40p. (J). lib. bdg. (978-1-58717-258-8(5) , SeaStar Bks.) Chronicle Bks. LLC.

Figueroa, Acton. Invisible Robot. 2004. (Festival Reader Ser.). (Illus.). 32p. (J). pap. 3.99 (978-0-06-072527-3(3) , Harper Festival) HarperCollins Pubs.

—Rocket Ball. 2004. (Astro Boy Ser.). (Illus.). 24p. (J). pap. 3.50 (978-0-06-072524-2(9) , Harper Festival) HarperCollins Pubs.

Fox, Helen. Eager. 288p. 2006. (gr. 4-7). 5.99 (978-0-553-48795-4(7) , Yearling); 2004. (gr. 3-7). 15.95 (978-0-385-74672-4(5) , Lamb, Wendy) Random Hse. Children's Bks.

—Eager's Nephew. 304p. (gr. 3-7). 2007. 5.99 (***978-0-553-48796-1(5)*** , Yearling); 2006. lib. bdg. 17.99 (978-0-385-90904-4(7) , Lamb, Wendy) Random Hse. Children's Bks.

Fox, Jennifer & Frantz, Jennifer. Meet the Autobots. Guidi, Guido, illus. 2007. (I Can Read Bks.). 32p. (J). pap. 3.99 (***978-0-06-088831-2(8)*** , Harper Trophy) HarperCollins Pubs.

—Transformers: Meet the Decepticons. Guidi, Guido, illus. 2007. (I Can Read Bks.). 32p. (J). pap. 3.99 (***978-0-06-088828-2(8)*** , Harper Trophy) HarperCollins Pubs.

Fullerton, Charlotte. Battle at Ice Palace. 2006. (Sonic X Ser.). (Illus.). 48p. (J). (gr. 1-3). pap. 4.99 (978-0-448-44409-3(7) , Grosset & Dunlap) Penguin Group (USA) Inc.

Gage, Brian. The Saddest Little Robot. Otoshi, Kathryn, tr. Otoshi, Kathryn, illus. 2003. 90p. (J). 12.99 (978-1-932360-05-9(0)) Penguin Group (USA) Inc.

Goodrich, Deborah. Bit-Byte the Robot. 2002. 24p. spiral bd. 13.31 (978-1-4116-2562-4(5)) Lulu.com.

Greenburg, J. C. In the Desert. Gerardi, Jan, illus. 2008. (Andrew Lost: 17). 96p. (J). (***978-0-375-84667-0(0)***) Random Hse., Inc.

Greenburg, J. C. In the Jungle. Gerardi, Jan, illus. 2007. (Andrew Lost Ser.: Bk. 15). 96p. (J). (gr. 2-4). 3.99 (978-0-375-83564-3(4)); lib. bdg. 11.99 (978-0-375-93564-0(9)) Random Hse. Children's Bks. (Random Hse. Bks. for Young Readers).

Hale, Bruce. Murder, My Tweet: A Chet Gecko Mystery. 2004. (Illus.). 117p. (J). (gr. 3-7). per. 12.00 (978-0-606-33413-6(0)) Tandem Library Bks.

Harcourt School Publishers Staff. I Have a Pal: Independent Reader. 3rd ed. 2002. (Trophies Reading Program Ser.). (Illus.). (J). pap. 2.90 (978-0-15-325470-3(X)) Harcourt Schl. Pubs.

—I Have a Robot, 5 Pack, Below Level. 3rd ed. 2002. (Trophies Reading Program Ser.). (Illus.). (gr. 1). pap. 20.10 (978-0-15-326811-3(5)) Harcourt Schl. Pubs.

—The Postcard Robot: Take-Home Book. 1999. (Signatures Ser.). (Illus.). (J). pap. 1.90 (978-0-15-313899-7(8)) Harcourt Schl. Pubs.

—Trofeos Below Level: Tengo un Robot. 3rd ed. 2002. (SPA., Illus.). pap. 5.50 (978-0-15-323872-7(0)) Harcourt Schl. Pubs.

Hebson, Dennis. Robots Everywhere. Hoffman, Todd, tr. Hoffman, Todd, illus. 2004. 32p. (J). 16.85 (978-0-8027-8893-1(9)) Walker & Co.

Hoover, Helen M. Orvis. 2002. (gr. 3-6). lib. bdg. 14.15 (978-0-613-58722-8(7)) Tandem Library Bks.

James, B. J., et al. Supertwins Meet the Dangerous Dino-Robots, No. 3. Demarest, Chris L., illus. 2003. (Scholastic Reader Ser.). 32p. (J). pap. 3.99 (978-0-439-46625-7(3) , Cartwheel Bks.) Scholastic, Inc.

James, Simon. Baby Brains & RoboMom. 2008. (Illus.). 32p. (J). (ps-3). 15.99 (***978-0-7636-3463-6(8)***) Candlewick Pr.

Johnson, Stephen T. My Little Blue Robot. Johnson, Stephen T., illus. 2004. (Illus.). 12p. (J). (gr. k-2). reprint ed. 22.00 (978-0-7567-7612-1(0)) DIANE Publishing Co.

—My Little Blue Robot. 2002. (Illus.). 12p. (J). (ps-3). 21.95 (978-0-15-216524-6(X) , Silver Whistle) Harcourt Trade Pubs.

Jones, Christianne C. Clinks the Robot. Trover, Zachary, illus. 2006. (Read-It! Readers Ser.). 24p. (J). (ps-3). 18.60 (978-1-4048-1579-7(1)) Picture Window Bks.

Joyce, William. Rolie Polie Olie. 2003. 32p. (J). pap. 3.50 (978-0-7868-4533-0(3)); pap. 3.50 (978-0-7868-4534-7(1)); pap. 3.50 (978-0-7868-4535-4(X)) Disney Pr.

—Rolie Polie Olie. Joyce, William, illus. 1999. (Laura Geringer Bks.). (Illus.). 48p. (J). (ps-k). 16.99 (978-0-06-027163-3(9) , Geringer, Laura Book) HarperCollins Pubs.

—Rolie Polie Olie. 1999. (Laura Geringer Bks.). (Illus.). 48p. (J). (ps-3). 15.89 (978-0-06-027164-0(7)) HarperCollins Pubs.

—Rolie Polie Olie. Joyce, William, illus. 2003. (Rolie Polie Olie Ser.). (Illus.). 32p. (J). (ps-k). 6.99 (978-0-06-055716-4(8) , Harper Festival) HarperCollins Pubs.

—Rolie Polie Olie. Joyce, William, illus. 2006. (Rolie Polie Olie Ser.). (Illus.). 48p. (J). reprint ed. pap. 6.99 (978-0-06-053484-4(2) , Harper Trophy) HarperCollins Pubs.

—Sleepy Time Olie. Joyce, William, illus. 2001. (Rolie Polie Olie Ser.). (Illus.). 40p. (J). (ps-3). 15.95 (978-0-06-029613-1(5) , Geringer, Laura Book) HarperCollins Pubs.

—Sleepy Time Olie. 2001. (Rolie Polie Olie Ser.). (Illus.). 40p. (J). (ps-3). 15.89 (978-0-06-029614-8(3) , Geringer, Laura Book) HarperCollins Pubs.

—Sleepy Time Olie. Joyce, William, illus. 2006. (Rolie Polie Olie Ser.). 40p. (J). pap. 6.99 (978-0-06-084222-2(9) , Harper Trophy) HarperCollins Pubs.

—Snowie Rolie. Joyce, William, illus. (Rolie Polie Olie Ser.). (Illus.). 40p. (J). 2005. pap. 5.99 (978-0-06-443742-4(6) , Harper Trophy); 2000. 15.95 (978-0-06-029285-0(7) , Geringer, Laura Book); 2000. 15.89 (978-0-06-029286-7(5) , Geringer, Laura Book) HarperCollins Pubs.

Katschke, Judy. Case of the Weird Science Mystery. 2002. (gr. 3-6). lib. bdg. 12.40 (978-0-613-50431-7(3)) Tandem Library Bks.

Kazenbroot, Nelly. Over the Rainbow with Googol & Googolplex. 2006. (Illus.). 64p. (J). pap. 4.99 (978-1-55143-469-8(5)) Orca Bk. Pubs. USA.

Kazenbroot, Nelly. Under the Sea with Googol & Googolplex. 2005. 63p. (J). lib. bdg. 20.00 (***978-1-4242-1263-7(4)***) Fitzgerald Bks.

—Under the Sea with Googol & Googolplex. 2005. (Orca Echoes Ser.). (Illus.). 64p. (J). (gr. 2-3). pap. 4.99 (978-1-55143-366-0(4)) Orca Bk. Pubs. USA.

Kennedy, Mike. The Language of Chaos. 2003. (Lone Wolf 2100 Ser.: Vol. 2). (Illus.). 120p. (gr. 11 up). pap. 12.95 (978-1-56971-997-8(7)) Dark Horse Comics.

Kirk, David. Nova's Ark: David Kirk's Nova the Robot. 2005. (Nova the Robot Ser.). 40p. pap. 7.99 (978-0-448-43816-0(X)) Penguin Group (USA) Inc.

—Nova's Super-Galactic Pop-up. 2005. (Nova the Robot Ser.). (Illus.). 16p. (J). (ps-3). 22.99 (978-0-448-43993-8(X)) Callaway Editions, Inc.

Lassieur, Allison. Exo-Force. collector's ed. 2007. (Lego Ser.). 80p. (J). pap. 5.99 (978-0-439-82811-6(2)) Scholastic, Inc.

—Exo-force: Race to the Golden City. 2007. (Lego Ser.). 64p. (J). pap. 3.99 ***(*978-0-439-92328-6(X))*** Scholastic, Inc.

—Secret of the Golden Tower. 2007. (Lego Ser.). 48p. (J). pap. 3.99 ***(*978-0-439-92329-3(8))*** Scholastic, Inc.

Lidbert, Paul A. Big Damn Robots. Lidbert, Paul A., illus. 1999. (Illus.). 24p. (J). 5.95 (978-1-929332-06-9(8), CFE0104) Crunchy Frog Enterprises.

Lofficier, Randy & Lofficier, Jean-Marc. Robonocchio. Martiniere, Stephan, illus. 2004. (FRE.). 128p. (YA). per. 14.95 (978-1-932983-04-3(X), Black Coat Pr.) HollywoodComics.com, LLC.

Look at the Robot: Individual Title Six-Packs. (Sails Literacy Ser.). 16p. (gr. k up). 27.00 (978-0-7635-4421-8(3)) Rigby Education.

Marzollo, Dan. Runaway Robot. Mills, Liz, ed. Levin, Jimmy, illus. 2003. (I Spy Ser.: No. 1). 24p. (J). pap. 3.50 (978-0-439-44318-0(0), Cartwheel Bks.) Scholastic, Inc.

Matsuzawa, Mari. Hinaduary Girl, Vol. 2. 2005. (Illus.). 208p. (YA). pap. 9.95 (978-1-59796-007-6(1)) DrMaster Pubns. Inc.

McCall, Bruce. Marveltown Forever. 2008. (J). ***(*978-0-374-39925-2(5))*** Farrar, Straus & Giroux.

McKeever, Sean. Sentinel Vol. 3: Past Imperfect Digest. 2006. (Illus.). 120p. pap. 7.99 (978-0-7851-1914-2(0)) Marvel Enterprises, Inc.

Medina, Rick. Humaliens Vol. 4: Robots Everywhere. 1999. 150p. (J). (gr. 4-7). pap. 4.99 (978-1-892587-03-9(3)) Dualstar, Inc.

Meredith Books Staff, ed. Robo-Monster. 2008. 24p. pap. 3.99 ***(*978-0-696-23957-1(4))*** Meredith Bks.

Milgrim, David. See Pip Point. Milgrim, David, illus. 2004. (Adventures of Otto Ser.). (Illus.). 32p. (J). pap. 3.99 (978-0-689-85140-7(5), Aladdin) Simon & Schuster Children's Publishing.

—See Santa Nap. Milgrim, David, illus. 2004. (Adventures of Otto Ser.). (Illus.). 32p. (J). 14.95 (978-0-689-85928-1(7), Atheneum) Simon & Schuster Children's Publishing.

Mitchell, Richard, illus. Planet X. 1999. (J). (978-0-7608-3202-8(1)) Sundance/Newbridge Educational Publishing.

Mohr, L. C. Krumbuckets. 2008. (Illus.). 144p. (J). per. 8.95 (978-0-9769417-4-5(0)) Blooming Tree Pr.

—Krumbuckets. Musheno, Erica, illus. 2007. 144p. (J). (gr. 2-7). 13.95 (978-0-9769417-6-7(7)) Blooming Tree Pr.

Montgomery, R. A. Your Very Own Robot. 2007. (Choose Your Own Adventure Ser.). (Illus.). 64p. (J). pap. 5.99 ***(*978-1-933390-52-9(2))*** Chooseco LLC.

Olsen, Ashley. Dream Team. 2002. (gr. k-3). lib. bdg. 12.40 (978-0-613-64707-6(6)) Tandem Library Bks.

Peel, John. Beware the Metal Children. 1999. (gr. 3-6). lib. bdg. 11.80 (978-0-613-17111-3(X)) Tandem Library Bks.

Pet Robots. 2007. (J). per. 19.95 (978-0-9789168-2-4(4)) Blue Dream Studios.

Photo Novel. 2007. (Transformers Ser.). 96p. (J). (gr. 2-5). pap. 7.99 ***(*978-0-06-088805-3(9)***, Harper Entertainment) HarperCollins Pubs.

Pilkey, Dav. El Capitan Calzoncillos y el Perverso Plan del Profesor Pipicaca. 2002. (Captain Underpants Ser.: No. 4). (SPA.). (gr. 3-6). lib. bdg. 13.00 (978-0-613-50414-0(3)) Tandem Library Bks.

—Giant Robot vs. the Mutant Mosquitoes from Mercury. Ontiveros, Martin, illus. 2000. (Ricky Ricotta Ser.: No. 2). 128p. (J). (ps-3). pap. 16.95 (978-0-590-30721-5(5), Blue Sky Pr., The) Scholastic, Inc.

—Mighty Robot vs. the Jurassic Jackrabbits from Jupiter. Ontiveros, Martin, illus. 2002. (Ricky Ricotta Ser.: No. 5). 128p. (J). (ps-3). pap. 16.95 (978-0-439-37642-6(4), Blue Sky Pr., The); pap. 3.99 (978-0-439-37643-3(2)) Scholastic, Inc.

—Mighty Robot vs. the Jurassic Jackrabbits from Jupiter. 2002. (Ricky Ricotta Ser.: No. 5). (ps-2). lib. bdg. 11.80 (978-0-613-50493-5(3)) Tandem Library Bks.

—Mighty Robot vs. the Uranium Unicorns from Uranus. Ontiveros, Martin, illus. 2005. (Ricky Ricotta Ser.: Bk. 7). 128p. (J). pap. 16.99 (978-0-439-37646-4(7)); pap. 3.99 (978-0-439-37647-1(5)) Scholastic, Inc. (Blue Sky Pr., The).

—Ricky Ricotta Y el Poderoso Robot Contra Los Mecamonos de Marte. 2007. (Ricky Ricotta Ser.: No. 4). 144p. (J). pap. 3.99 (978-0-439-85105-3(X), Scholastic en Espanol) Scholastic, Inc.

—Ricky Ricotta Y el Poderoso Robot Contra Los Mecamonos de Marte. Ontiveros, Martin, illus. 2002. (Ricky Ricotta Ser.: No. 4). 144p. (gr. 2-4). pap. 3.99 (978-0-439-25296-6(2)); (J). (ps-3). pap. 16.95 (978-0-439-25295-9(4)) Scholastic, Inc. (Blue Sky Pr., The).

—Ricky Ricotta Y el Poderoso Robot Contra Los Mecamonos de Marte. 2002. (Ricky Ricotta Ser.: No. 4). (ps-2). lib. bdg. 11.80 (978-0-613-45613-5(0)) Tandem Library Bks.

—Ricky Ricotta's Giant Robot. Ontiveros, Martin, illus. 2000. (Ricky Ricotta Ser.: Bk. 1). (ps-3). 111p. (J). pap. 16.95 (978-0-590-30719-2(3)); 112p. mass mkt. 3.99 (978-0-590-30720-8(7)) Scholastic, Inc. (Blue Sky Pr., The).

—Ricky Ricotta's Giant Robot. Ontiveros, Martin, illus. 2000. (Ricky Ricotta Ser.: Bk. 1). 111p. (J). (ps). lib. bdg. 11.80 (978-0-613-22267-9(9)) Tandem Library Bks.

—Ricky Ricotta's Giant Robot. 2000. (Ricky Ricotta Ser.: No. 1). (J). (ps-3). (978-0-606-18592-9(5)) Tandem Library Bks.

—Ricky Ricotta's Giant Robot vs. the Mutant Mosquitoes from Mercury. Ontiveros, Martin, illus. 2000. (Ricky Ricotta Ser.: No. 2). (J). (ps-3). pap. 47.88 (978-0-439-21522-0(6)) Scholastic, Inc.

—Ricky Ricotta's Giant Robot vs. the Mutant Mosquitoes from Mercury. Ontiveros, Martin, illus. 2000. (Ricky Ricotta Ser.: Bk. 2). 127p. (J). (ps). per. 11.80 (978-0-613-26747-2(8)) Tandem Library Bks.

—Ricky Ricotta's Giant Robot vs. the Mutant Mosquitoes from Mercury. 2000. (Ricky Ricotta Ser.: No. 2). (J). (ps-3). (978-0-606-19604-8(8)) Tandem Library Bks.

—Ricky Ricotta's Giant Robot vs. the Voodoo Vultures from Venus. Ontiveros, Martin, illus. 2001. (Ricky Ricotta Ser.: No. 3). 128p. (J). (ps-3). pap. 16.95 (978-0-439-23624-9(X)) Scholastic, Inc.

—Ricky Ricotta's Mighty Robot Collection: Ricky Ricotta's Mighty Robot; Ricky Ricotta's Mighty Robot vs. the Mutant Mosquito from Mercury; Ricky Ricotta's Mighty Robot vs. the Voodoo Vultures from Venus; Ricky Ricotta's Mighty Robot vs. the Mechamonkeys from Mars, 4 vols. Ontiveros, Martin, illus. 2002. (Ricky Ricotta Ser.: Bks. 1-4). 128p. (J). 15.96 (978-0-439-43522-2(6), Blue Sky Pr., The) Scholastic, Inc.

—Ricky Ricotta's Mighty Robot vs. the Mutant Mosquitoes from Mercury. Ontiveros, Martin, illus. 2000. (Ricky Ricotta Ser.: No. 2). 128p. (J). (ps-3). pap. 3.99 (978-0-590-30722-2(3)) Scholastic, Inc.

—Ricky Ricotta's Mighty Robot vs. the Stupid Stinkbugs from Saturn. Ontiveros, Martin, illus. 2003. (Ricky Ricotta Ser.: No. 6). 128p. (J). pap. 16.95 (978-0-439-37644-0(0), Blue Sky Pr., The) Scholastic, Inc.

—Y el Poderoso Robot. Ontiveros, Martin, illus. 2003. (Ricky Ricotta Ser.: Bk. 1). (SPA.). 112p. (J). pap. 3.99 (978-0-439-55117-5(X), Scholastic en Espanol) Scholastic, Inc.

Priddy, Roger. Funny Faces Rusty Robot. (J). 2007. 24p. bds. 14.95 ***(*978-0-312-49891-7(8));*** 2006. (Illus.). 10p. bds. 9.95 (978-0-312-49693-7(1)) St. Martin's Pr. (Priddy Bks.).

Random House Disney Staff. Love at First Beep. 2008. (Step into Reading Ser.). 32p. (J). (ps-1). pap. 3.99 ***(*978-0-7364-2514-8(4)***, RH/Disney) Random Hse. Children's Bks.

—Rogue Robots! 2008. 24p. (J). (ps-2). pap. 3.99 ***(*978-0-7364-2519-3(5)***, RH/Disney) Random Hse. Children's Bks.

—Smash Trash! 2008. (Step into Reading Ser.). 32p. (J). (ps-1). pap. 3.99 ***(*978-0-7364-2515-5(2));*** lib. bdg. 11.99 ***(*978-0-7364-8058-1(7))*** Random Hse. Children's Bks. (RH/Disney).

—Space Chase. 2008. (Hologramatic Sticker Book Ser.). 48p. (J). (ps-2). pap. 3.99 ***(*978-0-7364-2522-3(5)***, Golden/Disney) Random Hse. Children's Bks.

—Wall-E. 2008. (Read-Aloud Storybook Ser.). 72p. (J). (ps-3). 8.99 ***(*978-0-7364-2528-5(4)***, RH/Disney) Random Hse. Children's Bks.

Readler, Blaine C. Under the Radar: The Spy Drone Adventure. 2006. 248p. (J). pap. 14.95 (978-1-933255-18-7(8)) DNA Pr.

Richards, Kitty. Meet the Sparkplugs. Simard, Remy, illus. 2006. (Phonics Comics Ser.). 24p. (J). (gr. 1-17). pap. 3.99 (978-1-58476-419-9(8), IKIDS) Innovative Kids.

Rivas, Larissa. Cuentos de Robots Para Ninos. 2000. Tr. of Stories of Robots for Kids. (SPA.). (gr. 3-6). lib. bdg. 15.30 (978-0-613-89816-4(8)) Tandem Library Bks.

The Robot, 6, Pack. (Chiquilibros Ser.). (gr. k-1). 23.00 (978-0-7635 0442-7(4)) Rigby Education.

The Robot: First Wave Satellite Individual Title Six-Packs. (Sails Literacy Ser.). 16p. (gr. k up). 27.00 (978-0-7578-6876-4(2)) Rigby Education.

Robot & Mr. Mole. 2004. (Illus.). (J). (978-1-59577-009-7(7)) Starfall Education.

Rogue Robot: Individual Title Six-Packs. (Bookweb Ser.). 32p. (gr. 4 up). 34.00 (978-0-7635-3735-7(7)) Rigby Education.

Rose, Malcolm. Blood Brother. 2008. (Traces Ser.). 160p. (J). (gr. 4-9). pap. 5.95 ***(*978-0-7534-6170-9(6)***, Kingfisher) Houghton Mifflin Co. Trade & Reference Div.

Rosita's Robot: Small Versions of Big Books. (On Our Way to English Ser.). (gr. 3 up). 35.50 (978-0-7578-7243-3(3)) Rigby Education.

Santillo, LuAnn. Buzz. Santillo, LuAnn, ed. 2003. (Half-Pint Kids Readers Ser.). (Illus.). 7p. (J). (ps-1). pap. (978-1-59256-046-2(6)) Half-Pint Kids, Inc.

Scholastic, Inc. Staff. Zoey 101: Chapter Book: A Quinn in Need. 2007. (Teenick Ser.). 112p. (J). pap. 4.99 ***(*978-0-439-88257-6(5))*** Scholastic, Inc.

Scott, Andrew M. Frank: Can a Mechanical Man Dream of Being Human? Case, Bernie, illus. 2002. 125p. (J). (gr. 4-7). pap. 5.99 (978-1-928556-08-4(6)) Coastal Carolina Pr.

Selznick, Brian. The Invention of Hugo Cabret. Selznick, Brian, illus. 2007. (Illus.). 544p. (J). (gr. 4-7). pap. 22.99 (978-0-439-81378-5(6), Scholastic Pr.) Scholastic, Inc.

Sentinel. 2007. (J). 128.10 ***(*978-1-59961-315-4(8))*** Spotlight.

Sharratt, Nick. Robopop. 2000. (Illus.). 121p. (J). pap. 7.99 (978-0-440-86352-6(X)) Transworld Publishers Ltd. GBR. *Dist:* Trafalgar Square Publishing.

Shepard, Aaron. Timothy Tolliver & the Bully Basher. 2005. 48p. (J). pap. 6.00 (978-0-938497-24-0(3)); lib. bdg. 15.00 (978-0-938497-23-3(5)) Shepard Pubns. (Skyhook Pr.).

Shulman, Mark. Fillmore & Geary Take Off! Fickling, Phillip, illus. 2004. 40p. (J). 14.95 (978-1-58717-256-4(9), SeaStar Bks.) Chronicle Bks. LLC.

—Nutsy the Robot Goes to Bed. Boyce, Katie, illus. 2006. (Nutsy the Robot Ser.). 10p. (J). bds. 15.95 (978-0-7696-4605-3(0), Brighter Child) School Specialty Publishing.

—Nutsy the Robot Goes to School. Boyce, Katie, illus. 2006. (Nutsy the Robot Ser.). 10p. (J). bds. 15.95 (978-0-7696-4606-0(9), Brighter Child) School Specialty Publishing.

Smiley, Mark. A Journey Far Away. 2005. pap. 13.95 ***(*978-1-59526-494-7(9))*** Media Creations, Inc.

Sniegoski, Tom. Billy Hooten. Powell, Eric, illus. 2007. (Owlboy Ser.). 256p. (J). (gr. 4-7). lib. bdg. 9.99 ***(*978-0-385-90402-5(9)***, Yearling) Random Hse. Children's Bks.

—Billy Hooten: Owlboy. Powell, Eric, illus. 2007. (Owlboy Ser.). 256p. (J). (gr. 4-7). 5.99 ***(*978-0-440-42180-1(2)***, Yearling) Random Hse. Children's Bks.

Stanley, George Edward. Swimming with Sharks. Francis, Guy, illus. 2003. (Adam Sharp Ser.: No. 3). 48p. (J). (gr. 2-4). pap. 3.99 (978-0-307-26418-3(1), Random Hse. Bks. for Young Readers) Random Hse. Children's Bks.

Stein, Erin K. Sam's New Car. Staples, Val, illus. 2007. (Transformers Ser.). 24p. (J). pap. 3.99 ***(*978-0-06-088823-7(7)***, Harper Entertainment) HarperCollins Pubs.

Strasser, Dirk. Lost in Space. 2005. (Thrillogy Ser.). (Illus.). 48p. (gr. 4-8). 17.50 (978-0-7910-8868-5(5)) Facts On File, Inc.

Stratford, Ann. Tara Toad Meets Roman the Robot Soldier. 2005. (ENG., Illus.). pap. ***(*978-1-84401-465-1(7))*** Athena Pr.

Tauss, Marc. Superhero. Tauss, Marc, illus. 2005. (Illus.). 40p. (J). (gr. k-3). pap. 16.99 (978-0-439-62734-4(6), Scholastic Pr.) Scholastic, Inc.

Tinder, Jeremy. Cry Yourself to Sleep. 2006. (Illus.). 88p. (YA). pap. 7.00 (978-1-891830-81-5(3)) Top Shelf Productions.

Toriyama, Akira. Dr. Slump, Vol 4. Toriyama, Akira, illus. 2005. (Dr. Slump Ser.). 200p. (YA). pap. 7.99 (978-1-4215-0165-9(1)) Viz Media.

—Dr. Slump. 2006. (Dr. Slump Ser.). 208p. (YA). Vol. 8. pap. 7.99 (978-1-4215-0632-6(7)); Vol. 9. pap. 7.99 (978-1-4215-0633-3(5)) Viz Media.

Torres, J. Birthquake. 2003. (Jason & the Argobots Ser.: Vol. 1). (Illus.). 112p. pap. 11.95 (978-1-929998-55-5(4)) Oni Pr., Inc.

—Machina Ex Deus. 2003. (Jason & the Argobots Ser.: Vol. 2). (Illus.). 88p. pap. 11.95 (978-1-929998-56-2(2)) Oni Pr., Inc.

Trimble, Marcia J. Marsby & the Martian Detectives. Hayden, Jennifer H., illus. 2004. 56p. (J). per. 9.95 (978-1-891577-52-9(2), SAN299-4844) Images Pr.

Weigel, Jeff, illus. Atomic Ace & the Robot Rampage. 2006. 32p. (J). 15.95 (978-0-8075-0484-0(X)); pap. 6.95 (978-0-8075-0485-7(8)) Whitman, Albert & Co.

West, Tracey. Cubix to the Rescue. 2002. (gr. k-3). lib. bdg. 10.65 (978-0-613-72089-2(X)) Tandem Library Bks.

—Dondon for Dinner. 2002. (gr. k-3). lib. bdg. 11.25 (978-0-613-72088-5(1)) Tandem Library Bks.

—Donut Disaster. 2002. (gr. k-3). lib. bdg. 11.80 (978-0-613-72064-9(4)) Tandem Library Bks.

—Me & My Robot: The Show-and-Tell Show Off. Revell, Cindy, illus. 2003. (All Aboard Reading Ser.). 32p. (J). (ps-2). pap. 3.99 (978-0-448-43251-9(X), Grosset & Dunlap) Penguin Group (USA) Inc.

—Me & My Robot: The Show-and-Tell Show-Off. Revell, Cindy, illus. 2003. (All Aboard Math Reader Station Stop 1 Ser.). 48p (J). (ps-2). pap. 3.99 (978-0-448-42895-6(4), Grosset & Dunlap) Penguin Group (USA) Inc.

—Me & My Robot No.2: The Show-and-Tell Show-off. Revell, Cindy, illus. 2003. (All Aboard Reading Ser.). 48p. (J). 13.89 (978-0-448-43282-3(X), Grosset & Dunlap) Penguin Group (USA) Inc.

—Me & My Robot No.2: The Show-and-Tell Show-off. 2003. (ps-2). lib. bdg. 11.80 (978-0-613-72529-3(8)); lib. bdg. 11.80 (978-0-613-64065-7(9)) Tandem Library Bks.

Whybrow, Ian. Sammy & the Robots. Reynolds, Adrian, illus. 2001. 32p. (J). (ps-1). pap. 15.95 (978-0-531-30327-6(6), Orchard Bks.) Scholastic, Inc.

Wilkens, S. G. Transformers: The Junior Novel. 2007. (Transformers Ser.). 144p. (J). pap. 4.99 ***(*978-0-06-088835-0(0)***, Harper Entertainment) HarperCollins Pubs.

ROCK CLIMBING

see Mountaineering

ROCK MUSIC

Anderson, Tom. Top 40 Fun Facts: Rock & Roll. 2003. 64p. pap. 24.95 (978-0-634-06552-1(1)) Leonard, Hal Corp.

Armentrout, David & Armentrout, Patricia. Rock. 1999. (Sounds of Music Ser.). (Illus.). 24p. (J). (gr. 1-4). lib. bdg. 19.27 (978-0-86593-536-5(X)) Rourke Publishing, LLC.

Armstrong, David. The History of Indie Rock. 2007. (Music Library). (Illus.). 128p. (J). (gr. 7-10). 32.45 (978-1-59018-736-4(9), Lucent Bks.) Thomson Gale.

Barnes, Deb. Inside a Rock Band. 2006. (Girls Rock! Ser.). (Illus.). 32p. (J). (gr. 1-5). 24.21 (978-1-59296-745-2(0)) Child's World, Inc.

Beyer, Mark. Stevie Wonder. 2006. (Rock & Roll Hall of Famers Ser.). (Illus.). 112p. (YA). (gr. 5-8). lib. bdg. 29.25 (978-0-8239-3525-3(6)) Rosen Publishing Group, Inc., The.

Bidini, Dave. For Those about to Rock: A Road Map to Being in a Band. 2004. 144p. (J). (gr. 5). pap. 8.95 (978-0-88776-653-4(6)) Tundra Bks., Inc./Livres Toundra, Inc. CAN. *Dist:* Random Hse., Inc.

Black, Peter, photos by. Bush: 8 Frames per Sec. 1999. (Illus.). 104p. (YA). pap. 19.95 (978-0-8256-1781-2(2), BU10000) Omnibus Pr.

Boekhoff, P. M. & Kallen, Stuart A. Famous People - N'SYNC. 2002. (Famous People Ser.). (Illus.). 48p. (J). (gr. 3-5). 26.20 (978-0-7377-1460-9(3), Kidhaven) Thomson Gale.

Boyes, Kate. Paul McCartney. 2003. (Importance of Ser.). (J). 32.45 (978-1-59018-283-3(9), Lucent Bks.) Thomson Gale.

Boynton, Sandra. Dog Train: A Wild Ride on the Rock-and-Roll Side. 2005. (Illus.). 64p. (J). bds. 17.95 (978-0-7611-3966-9(4), 13966) Workman Publishing Co., Inc.

Brasch, Nicolas. Pop & Rock Music. 2004. (J). lib. bdg. 27.10 (978-1-58340-546-8(1)) Smart Apple Media.

Burgan, Michael. Jim Morrison. 2004. (Edge Books, Rock Music Library). (Illus.). 32p. (J). lib. bdg. 22.60 (978-0-7368-2702-7(1)) Capstone Pr., Inc.

Bustard, Anne. Buddy: The Story of Buddy Holly. Cyrus, Kurt, illus. 2005. 32p. (J). 16.95 (978-0-689-86667-8(4), Simon & Schuster Children's Publishing) Simon & Schuster Children's Publishing.

B*Witched: Backstage Pass. 1999. (gr. 3-6). lib. bdg. 14.15 (978-0-613-21275-5(4)) Tandem Library Bks.

Case, Jeremy. Here's Hanson. (Illus.). 96p. (J). 7.95 (978-0-14-130227-0(5)) Penguin Bks., Ltd. GBR. *Dist:* Trafalgar Square Publishing.

Clayton, Marie. Elvis Presley: Unseen Archives. 2003. (Unseen Archives Ser.). (Illus.). 384p. 29.95 (978-0-7525-8335-8(2)) Parragon, Inc.

Derkins, Susie. Bruce Springsteen. 2006. (Rock & Roll Hall of Famers Ser.). (Illus.). 112p. (YA). (gr. 5-8). lib. bdg. 29.25 (978-0-8239-3522-2(1)) Rosen Publishing Group, Inc., The.

Doll, Susan. Elvis Presley: With Profiles of Muddy Waters & Mick Jagger. 2006. (Biographical Connections Ser.). (Illus.). 112p. (J). (978-0-7166-1823-2(0)) World Bk., Inc.

Dorling Kindersley Publishing Staff. Grateful Dead. ltd. ed. 2003. 400p. lthr. 150.00 (978-0-7566-0243-7(2)) Dorling Kindersley Publishing, Inc.

Edgers, Geoff. Who Were the Beatles? Tageau, Jerry, illus. 2006. (Who Was— ? Ser.). 106p. (J). (978-0-448-43907-5(7), Grosset & Dunlap) Penguin Group (USA) Inc.

—Who Were the Beatles? Tugeau, Jeremy, illus. 2006. (Who Was... ? Ser.). 112p. (J). (gr. 2-5). pap. 4.99 (978-0-448-43906-8(9), Grosset & Dunlap) Penguin Group (USA) Inc.

Ewing, Jon. Green Day. 2000. (Illus.). 120p. (YA). reprint ed. pap. 15.00 (978-0-7881-9441-2(0)) DIANE Publishing Co.

Federici & Santelli, Robert. Greetings from E Street. 2006. (Illus.). 98p. 35.00 (978-0-8118-5348-4(9)) Chronicle Bks. LLC.

Forget, Thomas. David Bowie. 2006. (Rock & Roll Hall of Famers Ser.). (Illus.). 112p. (YA). (gr. 5-8). lib. bdg. 29.25 (978-0-8239-3523-9(X)) Rosen Publishing Group, Inc., The.

Franks, Katie. I Want to Be a Rock Star. 2007. (Dream Jobs Ser.). (Illus.). 24p. (J). (gr. 3-5). lib. bdg. 21.25 (978-1-4042-3618-9(X), PowerKids Pr.) Rosen Publishing Group, Inc., The.

Gabriel, Jan. Hanson Forever: Your Tay, Zac & Ike Keepsake Scrapbook. 1998. (Illus.). 48p. (gr. 2-9). pap. 5.99 (978-0-439 01530-8(4)) Scholastic, Inc.

George-Warren, Holly. Shake, Rattle & Roll: The Founders of Rock & Roll. Levine, Laura, illus. 32p. (J). (gr. k-3). 2004. pap. 5.95 (978-0-618-43229-5(9)); 2001. tchr. ed. 16.00 (978-0-618-05540-1(1)) Houghton Mifflin Co. Trade & Reference Div.

Gillie, Brian. A Guide to the Best Vocal Harmonies of Rock 'n' Roll: 1955 - 1985. 2004. 225p. 27.00 (978-0-9760837-1-9(X)); per. 35.00 (978-0-9760837-0-2(1)) Keysquake Music.

Gish, D. L. Rock & Roll. 2001. (World of Music Ser.). (Illus.). 32p. (J). (gr. 2-7). lib. bdg. 15.95 (978-1-58340-060-9(5)) Smart Apple Media.

—Rock 'n' Roll. 2000. (J). (978-1-58341-068-4(6)) Creative Co., The.

Gogerly, Liz. Elvis Presley. 2004. (Illus.). 48p. (J). lib. bdg. 28.56 (978-0-7398-6629-0(X)) Raintree.

—John Lennon: Voice of a Generation. 2002. (Famous Lives Ser.). (Illus.). 48p. (J). lib. bdg. 27.12 (978-0-7398-5522-5(0)) Raintree.

Graves, Karen Marie. Michael Jackson. 2000. (People in the News Ser.). (Illus.). 112p. (J). (gr. 6-9). (978-1-56006-707-8(1), Lucent Bks.) Thomson Gale.

Handyside, Chris. A History of Rock & Roll. 2006. (Illus.). 48p. (J). 31.43 (978-1-4034-8152-8(0)) Heinemann Library.

—A History of Rock & Roll. 2006. (J). (978-1-4109-1815-4(7)) Steck-Vaughn.

Holcomb, Mark. The Beach Boys. 2006. (Rock & Roll Hall of Famers Ser.). (Illus.). 112p. (YA). (gr. 5-8). lib. bdg. 29.25 (978-0-8239-3643-4(0)) Rosen Publishing Group, Inc., The.

Hoppus, Anne. Blink-182: Tales from Beneath Your Mom. 2001. (gr. 7-12). lib. bdg. 24.55 (978-0-613-49285-0(4)) Tandem Library Bks.

Horn, Geoffrey M. Bob Dylan. 2002. (Trailblazers of the Modern World Ser.). (Illus.). 48p. (J). (gr. 5 up). pap. 14.95 (978-0-8368-5236-3(2)); lib. bdg. 30.00 (978-0-8368-5076-5(9)) Stevens, Gareth Inc. (World Almanac Library).

Johns, Michael-Anne. Aaron Carter. 2000. (POP People Ser.). (Illus.). 80p. (J). (gr. 4-7). 4.50 (978-0-439-25417-5(5)) Scholastic, Inc.

—Hanson: 101 Cool Questions. 2000. (Pop People Ser.). (Illus.). 76p. (J). (gr. 4-7). pap. 4.99 (978-0-439-23325-5(9)) Scholastic, Inc.

Joseph, Paul. Hanson. 1999. (Young Profiles Ser.). (Illus.). 32p. (J). (gr. k-6). lib. bdg. 22.78 (978-1-57765-321-9(1) , Checkerboard Library) ABDO Publishing Co.

Juzwiak, Richard. Lifehouse. 2006. (Contemporary Musicians & Their Music Ser.). (Illus.). 48p. (J). lib. bdg. (978-1-4042-0710-3(4)) Rosen Publishing Group, Inc., The.

Kallen, Stuart A. The History of Rock & Roll. 2002. (Illus.). 112p. (J). 32.45 (978-1-59018-126-3(3) , Lucent Bks.) Thomson Gale.

Koopmans, Andy. Madonna. 2002. (People in the News Ser.). (Illus.). 112p. (YA). (gr. 6-9). 32.45 (978-1-59018-138-6(7) , Lucent Bks.) Thomson Gale.

Krull, Kathleen. The Book of Rock Stars: 24 Musical Icons That Shine Through History. Alcorn, Stephen, illus. 2003. 48p. (ps-17). 16.99 (978-0-7868-1950-8(2)) Hyperion Bks. for Children.

Laslo, Cynthia. 'N Sync. 2000. (High Interest Bks.). (Illus.). 48p. (YA). (gr. 7-12). 23.00 (978-0-516-23324-6(6)); pap. 6.95 (978-0-516-23524-0(9)) Scholastic Library Publishing. (Children's Pr.).

Marcovitz, Hal. Rock 'n Roll. 2002. (American Symbols & Their Meanings Ser.). (Illus.). 48p. (YA). (gr. 4 up). lib. bdg. (978-1-59084-036-8(4)) Mason Crest Pubs.

Markel, Rita J. Jimi Hendrix. (Just the Facts Biographies Ser.). (Illus.). 112p. 2006. (J). 27.93 (978-0-8225-3532-4(7) , Lerner Pubns.); 2005. (J). (gr. 6-12). lib. bdg. 27.93 (978-0-8225-4990-1(5)); 2003. (YA). (gr. 6 up). pap. 7.95 (978-0-8225-9697-4(0) , Carolrhoda Bks.) Lerner Publishing Group.

Martin, Michael. Kurt Cobain. 2004. (Edge Books, Rock Music Library). (Illus.). 32p. (J). lib. bdg. 22.60 (978-0-7368-2700-3(5)) Capstone Pr., Inc.

Masar, Brenden. The History of Punk Rock. 2006. (Illus.). 112p. (J). (gr. 7-10). 32.45 (978-1-59018-738-8(5) , Lucent Bks.) Thomson Gale.

Matthews, Jill. Mmmbop to the Top. 1998. mass mkt. (978-0-671-02490-1(6) , Simon Pulse) Simon & Schuster Children's Publishing.

Miles Kelly Staff. Rock & Pop. 2003. (Flip Quiz Ser.). (Illus.). 152p. (J). spiral bd. 12.95 (978-1-84236-145-0(7)) Miles Kelly Publishing, Ltd. GBR. *Dist:* Independent Pubs. Group.

Okun, Milton, ed. Great Rock Ballads. 104p. (YA). pap. 15.95 (978-0-89524-936-4(7) , 02502173) Cherry Lane Music Co.

—Shawn Colvin - Cover Girl. 32p. (Orig.). (YA). pap. 12.95 (978-0-89524-867-1(0) , 02506918) Cherry Lane Music Co.

O'Mahony, John. Elton John. 2003. (World Musicmakers Ser.). (Illus.). 64p. (J). 26.20 (978-1-56711-972-5(7) , Blackbirch Pr., Inc.) Thomson Gale.

Plantz, Connie. Elvis Presley: Music Legend, Movie Star, the King. 2004. (People to Know Ser.). (Illus.). 128p. (J). lib. bdg. 26.60 (978-0-7660-2103-7(3)) Enslow Pubs., Inc.

Powell, Phelan. Hanson. 1999. (Galaxy of Superstars Ser.). (Illus.). 64p. (J). (gr. 3 up). pap. 25.00 (978-0-7910-5325-6(3) , Chelsea Hse.) Facts On File, Inc.

Preszler, June. John Lennon. 2004. (Edge Books, Rock Music Library). (Illus.). 32p. (J). lib. bdg. 22.60 (978-0-7368-2701-0(3)) Capstone Pr., Inc.

Rappaport, Doreen. John's Secret Dreams: The Life of John Lennon. Collier, Bryan, illus. 2004. 48p. (ps-17). 16.99 (978-0-7868-0817-5(9)) Hyperion Bks. for Children.

Remstein, Henna. Carlos Santana. 2001. (Latinos in the Limelight Ser.). (Illus.). 64p. (J). (gr. 4-7). 27.50 (978-0-7910-6473-3(5) , Chelsea Hse.) Facts On File, Inc.

Richardson, Christopher. The Beat Goes On. 2005. (X-Zone Ser.). (Illus.). 30p. (gr. 4-8). 23.00 (978-0-7910-8983-5(5)) Facts On File, Inc.

Riggs, Kate. Rock 'n' Roll Music. 2008. (J). (***978-1-58341-569-6(6)** , Creative Education) Creative Co., The.

Roberts, Jeremy. The Beatles. (Biography Ser.). (Illus.). 112p. (J). (gr. 6-12). 2005. lib. bdg. 27.93 (978-0-8225-4998-7(0)); 2003. pap. 7.95 (978-0-8225-5002-0(4)) Lerner Publishing Group.

—Bob Dylan: Voice of a Generation. 128p. (J). (gr. 6 up). 18.95 (978-1-58013-155-1(7)) Kar-Ben Publishing.

—Bob Dylan: Voice of a Generation. 2005. (Lerner Biographies Ser.). (Illus.). 112p. (J). 27.93 (978-0-8225-1368-1(4) , Lerner Pubns.) Lerner Publishing Group.

Rock & Roll Hall of Famers. 2006. (Illus.). 112p. (gr. 5-8). lib. bdg. 263.40 (978-0-8239-3916-9(2)) Rosen Publishing Group, Inc., The.

Rock & Roll Hall of Famers: Set 1, 6 bks. Incl. Beatles. Wentzel, Jim. lib. bdg. 29.25 (978-0-8239-3526-0(4)); Bruce Springsteen. Derkins, Susie. lib. bdg. 29.25 (978-0-8239-3522-2(1)); David Bowie. Forget, Thomas. lib. bdg. 29.25 (978-0-8239-3523-9(X)); Elvis Presley. Alagna, Magdalena. lib. bdg. 29.25 (978-0-8239-3524-6(8)); Stevie Wonder. Beyer, Mark. lib. bdg. 29.25 (978-0-8239-3525-3(6)); Supremes. Rivera, Ursula. lib. bdg. 29.25 (978-0-8239-3527-7(2)); 112p. (YA). (gr. 5-8). (Illus.). 2006. Set lib. bdg. 175.50 (978-0-8239-9692-6(1)) Rosen Publishing Group, Inc., The.

Rock Music Library. (Illus.). (J). (gr. 3-4). lib. bdg. 180.80 (978-0-7368-2763-8(3)) Capstone Pr., Inc.

Saulmon, Greg. Linkin Park. 2006. (Contemporary Musicians & Their Music Ser.). (Illus.). 48p. (J). (978-1-4042-0713-4(9)) Rosen Publishing Group, Inc., The.

Schaefer, A. R. Booking a First Gig. 2003. (Rock Music Library). (Illus.). 32p. (J). lib. bdg. 22.60 (978-0-7368-2144-5(9) , Capstone High/Low Bks.) Capstone Pr., Inc.

—Equipping a Band. 2003. (Rock Music Library). (Illus.). 32p. (J). lib. bdg. 22.60 (978-0-7368-2145-2(7) , Capstone High/Low Bks.) Capstone Pr., Inc.

—Forming a Band. 2003. (Rock Music Library). (Illus.). 32p. (J). lib. bdg. 22.60 (978-0-7368-2146-9(5) , Capstone High/Low Bks.) Capstone Pr., Inc.

Schaffer, David. Bono. 2003. (Illus.). 112p. (J). 32.45 (978-1-59018-274-1(X) , Lucent Bks.) Thomson Gale.

Schlesinger, Ethan. AC/DC. 2008. (J). (***978-1-4222-0183-1(X))** Mason Crest Pubs.

—Aerosmith. 2008. (J). (***978-1-4222-0184-8(8))** Mason Crest Pubs.

—Led Zeppelin. 2008. (J). (***978-1-4222-0212-8(7))** Mason Crest Pubs.

Scholastic, Inc. Staff. B Witched. 1999. (Illus.). 48p. (J). (gr. 3-7). pap. 5.99 (978-0-439-08227-3(7)) Scholastic, Inc.

Scholastic Teacher Editors. Hanson Forever: Your Tay, Zac & Ike Keepsake Scrapbook. 1998. (J). 149.75 (978-0-439-06586-3(0)) Scholastic, Inc.

Schuman, Michael A. Bob Dylan: The Life & Times of an American Icon. 2003. (People to Know Ser.). (Illus.). 112p. (J). lib. bdg. 26.60 (978-0-7660-2108-2(4)) Enslow Pubs., Inc.

Slavicek, Louise. Carlos Santana. 2006. (Great Hispanic Heritage Ser.). (Illus.). 120p. (J). 30.00 (978-0-7910-8844-9(8) , Chelsea Hse.) Facts On File, Inc.

Small, Doug. The Story of Good Charlotte. 2004. (Illus.). 96p. pap. 12.95 (978-0-8256-2871-9(7) , OP50061) Omnibus Pr.

Sting. Rock Steady: A Story of Noah's Ark. Whyte, Hugh, illus. 2001. 32p. (J). (gr. k-3). 16.95 (978-0-06-029231-7(8)); 16.89 (978-0-06-029232-4(6)) HarperCollins Pubs.

Stockdale, Tom. Jimi Hendrix. 1999. (They Died Too Young Ser.). (Illus.). 48p. (YA). (gr. 5 up). lib. bdg. 18.65 (978-0-7910-4632-6(X) , Chelsea Hse.) Facts On File, Inc.

Tanner, Mike. Flat-Out Rock: Ten Great Bands of The 60s. 2006. (Illus.). 158p. (J). (gr. 7-12). 24.95 (978-1-55451-036-8(8)); pap. 12.95 (978-1-55451-035-1(X)) Annick Pr., Ltd. CAN. *Dist:* Firefly Bks., Ltd.

Thompson, John. Jewel. 2001. (Overcoming Adversity Ser.). 102p. (J). 32.00 (978-0-7910-5895-4(6)); pap. 9.95 (978-0-7910-5896-1(4)) Facts On File, Inc. (Chelsea Hse.).

Torr, James D., ed. Elvis Presley. 2001. (People Who Made History Ser.). (Illus.). 207p. (YA). (gr. 8-8). pap. (978-0-7377-0643-7(0) , LML00501-176910, Greenhaven Pr., Inc.) Thomson Gale.

Tracy, Kathleen. Chris Daughtry. 2007. (Blue Banner Biography Ser.). (Illus.). 32p. (J). (gr. 4-8). lib. bdg. 25.70 (***978-1-58415-629-1(5))** Mitchell Lane Pubs., Inc.

Vance, Vince. The Vince Vance Rock & Roll Reader: Bedtime Stories, Poems, Songs, Jokes, Pictures & Other Real Cool Stuff for Kids of All Ages. Pennington, Carole, ed. Looney, Bill, illus. Rice, Bob, photos by. 2003. 182p. (J). (gr. 3-8). per. (978-0-9652918-0-4(4)) Fullerton Bks., Inc.

Walsh, Kimberly. LFO: Backstage Pass. 1999. (J). (gr. 3-6). lib. bdg. 14.15 (978-0-613-21891-7(4)) Tandem Library Bks.

Weitzman, Elizabeth. Moffats: Backstage Pass. 1999. (gr. 3-6). lib. bdg. 14.15 (978-0-613-22028-6(5)) Tandem Library Bks.

Wentzel, Jim. The Beatles. 2006. (Rock & Roll Hall of Famers Ser.). (Illus.). 112p. (YA). (gr. 5-8). lib. bdg. 29.25 (978-0-8239-3526-0(4)) Rosen Publishing Group, Inc., The.

West, Tracey. Jewel: Music's Hottest Treasure. 1998. (Illus.). (J). (gr. 4-7). pap. 3.99 (978-0-590-51039-4(8)) Scholastic, Inc.

Willett, Edward. Janis Joplin. 2008. (American Rebels Ser.). (Illus.). 152p. (J). (gr. 9-12). lib. bdg. 34.60 (***978-0-7660-2837-1(2))** Enslow Pubs., Inc.

Williams, Tenley. Stevie Wonder. 2001. (Overcoming Adversity Ser.). (Illus.). 112p. (J). 30.00 (978-0-7910-5903-6(0) , Chelsea Hse.) Facts On File, Inc.

Wimmer, Teresa. The Beatles' Sgt. Pepper's Lonely Hearts Club Band. 2008. (J). (***978-1-58341-651-8(X)** , Creative Education) Creative Co., The.

Wyborny, Sheila. Sting. 2004. (World Musicmakers Ser.). (Illus.). 64p. (J). 26.20 (978-1-56711-974-9(3) , Blackbirch Pr., Inc.) Thomson Gale.

Zimmerman, Robert K. Switchfoot. 2006. (Contemporary Musicians & Their Music Ser.). (Illus.). 48p. (J). (978-1-4042-0709-7(0)) Rosen Publishing Group, Inc., The.

ROCK MUSIC—FICTION

Banks, Steve. Battle of the Band. 2003. (ps-2). lib. bdg. 11.25 (978-0-613-58144-8(X)) Tandem Library Bks.

Brown, Marc. Arthur, It's Only Rock 'n' Roll. Brown, Marc, illus. 2002. (Illus.). 32p. (J). (ps-3). 15.95 (978-0-316-11854-5(0)) Little, Brown Bks. for Young Readers.

Carlisle, Kelly. My Mommy Is A Rocker. 2007. (Illus.). 21p. (J). lib. bdg. (***978-0-9795046-2-4(7))** Kwist, Karla.

Chipponeri, Kelli. SpongeBob Rocks! Martinez, Heather, illus. 2006. (SpongeBob SquarePants Ready-To-Read Ser.: Vol. 9). 32p. (J). pap. 3.99 (978-1-4169-1314-6(9) , Simon Spotlight/Nickelodeon) Simon & Schuster Children's Publishing.

Chon, Kye Young. Audition: Volume 1, 10 vols. 2006. (Audition Ser.). (Illus.). 176p. pap. 11.99 (978-1-933809-43-4(4)) DramaQueen, L.L.C.

Cole, Babette. That's Why. 2007. (Illus.). 32p. (J). 17.95 (***978-0-224-07028-7(2))** Transworld Publishers Ltd. GBR. *Dist:* Independent Pubs. Group.

Dent, Grace. LBD: It's a Girl Thing. 2004. 288p. (J). (gr. 7 up). reprint ed. pap. 6.99 (978-0-14-240182-8(X) , Puffin) Penguin Group (USA) Inc.

—LBD: Live & Fabulous! 2006. 288p. (YA). (gr. 5). pap. 6.99 (978-0-14-240662-5(7) , Puffin) Penguin Group (USA) Inc.

Durkee, Sarah. The Fruit Bowl Project. 2006. 160p. (J). (gr. 5-8). 14.95 (978-0-385-73289-5(9)); lib. bdg. 16.99 (978-0-385-90310-3(3)) Random Hse. Children's Bks. (Delacorte Bks. for Young Readers).

Durkee, Sarah. The Fruit Bowl Project: Fifty Ways to Tell a Story. 2007. 160p. (J). (gr. 5). 5.99 (***978-0-385-73385-4(2)** , Yearling) Random Hse. Children's Bks.

Emesse, Tea. Nova & the Charmed Three. 2006. (Star Sisterz Ser.: Bk. 5). 144p. (J). pap. 5.99 (978-0-7869-3991-6(5) , Mirrorstone) Wizards of the Coast.

Epstein, Robin. Rock & Roll: Divas Supreme. 2004. 60p. (J). (978-0-439-65792-1(X)) Scholastic, Inc.

Forman, Gayle. Sisters in Sanity. 2007. 304p. (J). lib. bdg. 17.89 (***978-0-06-088748-3(6)**); (YA). (gr. 7 up). 16.99 (***978-0-06-088747-6(8))** HarperCollins Pubs. (HarperTeen).

G Studios & Crouch, Cheryl. Unplugged. 2007. (Chosen Girls' Ser.). 144p. (J). pap. 6.99 (978-0-310-71269-5(6)) Zonderkidz.

Goetze, Jutta. Luna-C. 2004. 324p. (J). pap. 7.95 (978-1-86508-443-5(3)) Allen & Unwin AUS. *Dist:* Independent Pubs. Group.

Gonzalez, Gabriela & Triana, Gaby. Backstage Pass. 2004. (Illus.). 224p. (J). (gr. 7 up). 15.99 (978-0-06-056017-1(7)); lib. bdg. 16.89 (978-0-06-056018-8(5)) HarperCollins Pubs.

Harwood, Beth. Snappy Sounds Rock & Roll! 2005. (Illus.). 10p. (J). 12.95 (978-1-59223-454-7(2) , Silver Dolphin Bks.) Advantage Pubs. Group.

Hoobler, Dorothy & Hoobler, Thomas. The 1950's: Music. Hoffman, Robin, illus. 2001. (Century Kids Ser.). 160p. (J). (gr. 5-8). lib. bdg. 22.90 (978-0-7613-1605-3(1) , Twenty-First Century Bks.) Lerner Publishing Group.

Huston, Donna. Vincent Rocks. 2006. (Illus.). 30p. (J). spiral bd. 19.99 (978-0-9771192-0-2(3)) Shayne Publishing.

Korman, Gordon. Born to Rock. 2006. 272p. (gr. 7 up). 15.99 (978-0-7868-0920-2(5)) Hyperion Bks. for Children.

Krosoczka, Jarrett. Punk Farm on Tour. 2007. 40p. (J). (gr. k-3). 15.99 (***978-0-375-83343-4(9)**); lib. bdg. 18.99 (***978-0-375-93343-1(3))** Random Hse. Children's Bks. (Knopf Bks. for Young Readers).

Krosoczka, Jarrett J. Punk Farm. 2005. (Illus.). 40p. (J). (gr. k-3). 15.95 (978-0-375-82429-6(4)); lib. bdg. 17.99 (978-0-375-92429-3(9)) Random Hse. Children's Bks. (Knopf Bks. for Young Readers).

Lane, Dakota. Orpheus Obsession. 2005. (Illus.). 288p. (J). 16.99 (978-0-06-074173-0(2) , Tegen, Katherine Bks); lib. bdg. 17.89 (978-0-06-074174-7(0) , HarperTeen) HarperCollins Pubs.

McCann, Jesse Leon. Scooby-Doo & the Rock 'n' Roll Zombie. 2007. (Scooby-doo 8x8 Ser.). 24p. (J). pap. 3.99 (978-0-439-78808-3(0)) Scholastic, Inc.

Moore, B. Clay, et al. Put the Book Back on the Shelf: A Belle & Sebastian Anthology. (Illus.). 144p. (YA). pap. 19.99 (978-1-58240-600-8(6)) Image Comics.

Myers, Bill & Wimbish, David. Mystery of the Melodies from Mars. 2002. (Bloodhounds, Inc. Ser.: No. 11). 128p. (J). pap. 5.99 (978-0-7642-2623-6(1)) Bethany Hse. Pubs.

Nelson, Blake. Rock Star, Superstar. 2004. 224p. (J). (gr. 7). 16.99 (978-0-670-05933-1(1) , Viking Juvenile) Penguin Group (USA) Inc.

—Rock Star Superstar Blake Nelson. 2006. 256p. (YA). (gr. 7). reprint ed. pap. 6.99 (978-0-14-240574-1(4) , Puffin) Penguin Group (USA) Inc.

Petrucha, Stefan & Pendleton, Thomas. Torn. 2007. (Wicked Dead Ser.: No. 2). 224p. (YA). (gr. 7 up). pap. 7.99 (***978-0-06-113850-8(9)** , HarperTeen) HarperCollins Pubs.

Powell. Tribute to Another Dead Rock Star. 2003. (gr. 7-12). lib. bdg. 14.10 (978-0-613-71884-4(4)) Tandem Library Bks.

Powell, Randy. Tribute to Another Dead Rock Star. 224p. (YA). 2003. pap. 5.95 (978-0-374-47968-8(2) , Sunburst); 1999. (gr. 7-12). 17.00 (978-0-374-37748-9(0) , Farrar, Straus & Giroux (BYR)) Farrar, Straus & Giroux.

—Tribute to Another Dead Rock Star. l.t. ed. 2000. 224p. (J). 21.95 (978-0-7862-2191-2(7)) Thorndike Pr.

Reisfeld, Randi, ed. Star Struck. 2006. (Teenick Ser.: Bk. 3). (Illus.). 120p. (J). pap. 4.99 (978-0-439-83157-4(1)) Scholastic, Inc.

Robertson, Barbara. Rosemary Rocks Spain. 2002. (Illus.). 128p. (J). (gr. 4-6). pap. 4.95 (978-1-890817-63-3(5)) Winslow Pr.

Simmons, Michael. Vandal. 2006. 176p. (YA). 16.95 (978-1-59643-070-9(2)) Roaring Brook Pr.

Thiesing, Lisa. The Aliens Are Coming. 2004. (Illus.). 32p. (J). (ps). 13.99 (978-0-525-47277-3(0) , Dutton Juvenile) Penguin Group (USA) Inc.

Trine, Greg. The Grateful Fred. Montijo, Rhode, illus. 3rd rev. ed. 2006. (Melvin Beederman, Superhero Ser.). 144p. (J). 15.95 (978-0-8050-7921-0(1)) Holt, Henry & Co.

—The Grateful Fred. Montijo, Rhode, illus. 3rd rev. ed. 2006. (Melvin Beederman, Superhero Ser.). 144p. (J). pap. 5.99 (978-0-8050-7922-7(X)) Holt, Henry & Co.

Watts, Leander. Beautiful City of the Dead. 2006. 256p. (YA). (gr. 7). 16.00 (978-0-618-59443-6(4)) Houghton Mifflin Co.

Whelan, Gloria. Welcome to Starvation Lake. 2000. (J). (978-0-606-18930-9(0)) Tandem Library Bks.

Yolen, Jane & Stemple, Adam. Pay the Piper: A Rock 'n' Roll Fairy Tale. 2006. 192p. (J). 5.99 (978-0-7653-5041-1(6) , Starscape) Doherty, Tom Assocs., LLC.

ROCKEFELLER, JOHN D. (JOHN DAVISON), 1839-1937

Laughlin, Rosemary. John D. Rockefeller: Oil Baron & Philanthropist. 2004. (American Business Leaders Ser.). (Illus.). 128p. (J). (gr. 5 up). 21.95 (978-1-883846-59-6(5)); (YA). (gr. 6-12). 23.95 (978-1-931798-38-9(9)) Reynolds, Morgan Inc.

Marsh, Carole. John D. Rockefeller: An Ohio Experience Reader. 2001. (J). (gr. k-5). pap. 1.95 (978-0-635-00429-1(1)) Gallopade International.

Parker, Lewis K. John D. Rockefeller & the Oil Industry. 2003. (Reading Power Ser.). (Illus.). 24p. (J). lib. bdg. 17.25 (978-0-8239-6446-8(9) , PowerKids Pr.) Rosen Publishing Group, Inc., The.

—John D Rockefeller & the Oil Industry: Individual Title Six-Packs. (On Deck Ser.: Vol. 2). 24p. (gr. 4-5). 35.00 (978-0-7578-5851-2(1)) Rigby Education.

ROCKET FLIGHT

see Space Flight

ROCKETRY

see also Guided Missiles; Rockets (Aeronautics); Space Vehicles

Asimov, Isaac & Hantula, Richard. Exploring Outer Space. 2005. (Isaac Asimov's 21st Century Library of the Universe). (Illus.). 32p. (J). (gr. 3-7). lib. bdg. 24.67 (978-0-8368-3981-4(1)) Stevens, Gareth Inc.

Dahl, Michael. On the Launch Pad: A Counting Book about Rockets. Aldermand, Derrick & Shea, Denise, illus. 2004. (Know Your Numbers Ser.). 24p. (J). (gr. k-3). 22.60 (978-1-4048-0581-1(8)) Picture Window Bks.

Dartford, Mark. Missiles & Rockets. 2004. (Military Hardware in Action Ser.). (Illus.). 48p. (J). (gr. 4-9). lib. bdg. 25.26 (978-0-8225-4709-9(0)) Lerner Publishing Group.

Feldman, Heather. Sputnik: The First Satellite. 2003. (Space Firsts Ser.). (Illus.). 24p. (J). lib. bdg. 19.95 (978-0-8239-6244-0(X) , PowerKids Pr.) Rosen Publishing Group, Inc., The.

McLeese, Don. Robert Goddard. (Rourke Discovery Library). 2006. (Illus.). 24p. (gr. 2-5). 14.95 (978-1-59515-435-4(3) , 1244322); 2005. (ENG & SPA.). (J). (978-1-59515-675-4(5)) Rourke Publishing, LLC.

Miller, Ron. Rockets. 2007. (Space Innovations Ser.). (Illus.). 112p. (YA). (gr. 6-8). lib. bdg. 31.93 (978-0-8225-7153-7(6) , Lerner Pubns.) Lerner Publishing Group.

On the Launch Pad. (Know Your Numbers Ser.). 24p. (J). 7.95 (978-1-4048-1119-5(2)) Picture Window Bks.

Otfinoski, Steven. Rockets. 2006. (Great Inventions Ser.). (Illus.). 111p. (J). lib. bdg. 39.93 (978-0-7614-2232-7(3) , Benchmark Bks.) Cavendish, Marshall Corp.

Patchett, Kaye. Robert Goddard: Rocket Pioneer. 2005. (Giants of Science Ser.). (Illus.). 64p. (J). (ps-7). lib. bdg. 26.20 (978-1-56711-888-9(7) , Blackbirch Pr., Inc.) Thomson Gale.

Richardson, Hazel. How to Build a Rocket. Anderson, Scoular, illus. 2001. (How to Ser.). 96p. (J). (gr. 5-7). 16.00 (978-0-531-14643-9(X) , Watts, Franklin) Scholastic Library Publishing.

Spangenburg, Ray & Moser, Diane Kit. Wernher Von Braun: Out of the Fire, the Stars. 2nd rev. ed. 2008. (Makers of Modern Science Ser.). 160p. (gr. 6-12). 29.95 (***978-0-8160-6179-2(3)** , Chelsea Hse.) Facts On File, Inc.

Upgrade kit dsm-3 Flight&rocketry. (J). 2004. (978-1-59242-530-3(5)); 2003. (978-1-59242-413-9(9)) Delta Education, LLC.

ROCKETS (AERONAUTICS)

see also Guided Missiles

Collicutt, Paul. This Rocket. 2005. (Illus.). 32p. (J). (ps-ps). 15.00 (978-0-374-37484-6(8)) Farrar, Straus & Giroux.

Dahl, Michael. On the Launch Pad: A Counting Book about Rockets. Aldermand, Derrick & Shea, Denise, illus. 2004. (Know Your Numbers Ser.). 24p. (J). (gr. k-3). 22.60 (978-1-4048-0581-1(8)) Picture Window Bks.

Graham, Ian. The Best Book of Spaceships. 1998. (Best Book of... Ser.). (Illus.). 32p. (J). (gr. k-3). tchr. ed. 12.95 (978-0-7534-5133-5(6) , Kingfisher) Houghton Mifflin Co. Trade & Reference Div.

—Planes, Rockets & Other Flying Machines. 2000. (Fast Forward Ser.). (Illus.). 32p. (J). (gr. 4-8). pap. 9.95 (978-0-531-16444-0(6) , Watts, Franklin) Scholastic Library Publishing.

—Planes, Rockets & Other Flying Machines. 2000. (gr. 3-6). lib. bdg. 18.75 (978-0-613-34898-0(2)) Tandem Library Bks.

—Planes, Rockets, & Other Flying Machines. Hewetson, Nicholas, illus. 2000. (Fast Forward Ser.). 32p. (J). (gr. 4-8). 29.00 (978-0-531-11878-8(9) , Watts, Franklin) Scholastic Library Publishing.

Latham, Donna. Superfast Rockets. 2005. (Ultimate Speed Ser.). (Illus.). 32p. (J). (gr. 3-7). lib. bdg. 25.27 (978-1-59716-083-4(0)) Bearport Publishing Co., Inc.

Miller, Ron. Rockets. 2007. (Space Innovations Ser.). (Illus.). 112p. (YA). (gr. 6-8). lib. bdg. 31.93 (978-0-8225-7153-7(6) , Lerner Pubns.) Lerner Publishing Group.

Mitton, Tony. Roaring Rockets. 2000. (J). (978-0-606-19827-1(X)) Tandem Library Bks.

My Rocket: KinderWords, 6 Packs. (Kinderstarters Ser.). 8p. (ps-1). 21.00 (978-0-7635-8693-5(5)) Rigby Education.

On the Launch Pad. (Know Your Numbers Ser.). 24p. (J). 7.95 (978-1-4048-1119-5(2)) Picture Window Bks.

Otfinoski, Paul. Blasting Off: Rockets Then & Now. 1998. (Here We Go! Ser.). (Illus.). 32p. (J). (gr. 1-12). lib. bdg. 22.79 (978-0-7614-0611-2(5) , Benchmark Bks.) Cavendish, Marshall Corp.

Otfinoski, Steven. Rockets. 2006. (Great Inventions Ser.). (Illus.). 111p. (J). lib. bdg. 39.93 (978-0-7614-2232-7(3) , Benchmark Bks.) Cavendish, Marshall Corp.

Parker, Steve. The M270 Multiple Rocket Launcher. 2008. (J). (***978-1-4296-0096-5(9))** Capstone Pr., Inc.

Raketen und Raumfahrt. (GER.). 40p. (978-3-411-08191-2(0)) Bibliographisches Institut & F. A. Brockhaus AG DEU. *Dist:* i.b.d., Ltd.
Rocket Science. 2004. (Formula Fun Ser.). (Illus.). 48p. (J). (978-1-84229-586-1(1)) Top That! Publishing PLC.
Rockets. (Explore Space! Ser.). 24p. (J). 6.95 (978-0-7368-9168-4(4)) Capstone Pr., Inc.
Rockets, 6 vols. (gr. 2-5). 36.95 (978-0-7368-9246-9(X)) Red Brick Learning.
Rockets: Level O, 6 vols. (Wonder Worldtm Ser.). 48p. 39.95 (978-0-7802-2958-7(4)) Wright Group, The.
Vogt, Gregory L. Rockets. 1999. (Explore Space! Ser.). (Illus.). 24p. (J). (gr. 1-2). lib. bdg. 18.60 (978-0-7368-0198-0(7) , Bridgestone Bks.) Capstone Pr., Inc.

ROCKETS (AERONAUTICS)—FICTION

Anderson, Derek. Romeo & Lou Blast Off. Anderson, Derek, illus. 2007. 32p. (J). (ps-3). 15.99 (*978-1-4169-3784-5(6)* , Simon & Schuster Children's Publishing) Simon & Schuster Children's Publishing.
Anderson, Lynne. Rocket Ship Shapes. 2003. (Early Connections Ser.). (J). pap. 33.00 (978-1-4108-1091-5(7)) Benchmark Education Co.
Banks, Steven. Sandy's Rocket. Bond, Clint, illus. 2001. (SpongeBob SquarePants Chapter Bks.: Vol. 6). 64p. (J). (gr. 2-5). pap. 3.99 (978-0-689-84193-4(0) , Simon Spotlight) Simon & Schuster Children's Publishing.
—Sandy's Rocket. 2001. (gr. 3-6). lib. bdg. 11.80 (978-0-613-43971-8(6)) Tandem Library Bks.
Bergman, Mara. Oliver Who Would Not Sleep! Maland, Nick, illus. 2007. (J). (*978-0-439-92827-4(3)*); 40p. pap. 16.99 (*978-0-439-92826-7(5)*) Scholastic, Inc. (Levine, Arthur A. Bks.).
Hambrick, Sharon. Tommy's Rocket. Manning, Maurie, illus. 2003. (Fig Street Kids Ser.). 83p. (J). (gr. 1-2). 7.49 (978-1-59166-186-3(2)) Jones, Bob Univ. Pr.
Harris, Ann Marie, ed. Krypto the Secret Rocket. 2006. (Scholastic Reader Ser.). (Illus.). 32p. (J). pap. 3.99 (978-0-439-74403-4(2)) Scholastic, Inc.
Inkpen, Mick. Rocket. 2001. (gr. k-3). lib. bdg. 12.95 (978-0-613-53550-2(2)) Tandem Library Bks.
Kirk, Daniel. Moondogs. 1999. (Illus.). 1p. (J). (ps-3). 16.99 (978-0-399-23128-5(5) , Putnam Juvenile) Penguin Group (USA) Inc.
Lee, Ingrid. George Most Wanted. Denis, Stephane, illus. 2005. (Orca Echoes Ser.). 64p. (J). (gr. 2-3). pap. 4.99 (978-1-55143-472-8(5)) Orca Bk. Pubs. USA.
Lia, Simone. Billy Bean's Dream. 2000. (Illus.). 32p. (J). (ps-2). (978-1-86233-260-7(6) , Gullane Children's Bks.) Pinwheel.
Marzollo, Dan, et al. Rocket Ship. Levin, Jimmy, illus. 2004. (I Spy Ser.). 24p. (J). pap. 3.50 (978-0-439-45526-8(X) , Cartwheel Bks.) Scholastic, Inc.
Morrissey, Dean. The Crimson Comet. Morrissey, Dean, illus. 2006. (Illus.). 32p. (J). lib. bdg. 17.89 (978-0-06-008070-9(1)) HarperCollins Pubs.
Morrissey, Dean & Krensky, Stephen. The Crimson Comet. Morrissey, Dean, illus. 2006. (Illus.). 32p. (J). 16.99 (978-0-06-008068-6(X)) HarperCollins Pubs.
Ross, Diana. The Little Red Engine & the Rocket. 1999. (Illus.). 32p. (J). 16.00 (978-0-233-99405-5(X)) Andre Deutsch GBR. *Dist:* Independent Pubs. Group.
Ross, Diane. The Little Red Engine & the Rocket. Wood, Leslie, illus. 2005. (Little Red Engine Ser.). 32p. (J). pap. 8.99 (978-0-233-00146-3(8)) Andre Deutsch GBR. *Dist:* Independent Pubs. Group.
Santillo, LuAnn. Lift-Off. Santillo, LuAnn, ed. 2003. (Half-Pint Kids Readers Ser.). (Illus.). 7p. (J). (ps-1). pap. (978-1-59256-043-1(1)) Half-Pint Kids, Inc.
Sawler, Kimberley. Rocket & the Magical Cosmic Candies. 2007. (YA). 18.95 (*978-1-933285-51-1(6)*) Brown Bks. Publishing Group.
Wilde, Oscar. El Famoso Cohete. Zwerger, Lisbeth, illus. (SPA.). 72p. (J). (978-84-392-8693-6(7)) Gaviota Ediciones ESP. *Dist:* Lectorum Pubns., Inc.
Wilson, Zachary. A Circle in the Sky. Adinolfi, JoAnn, illus. 2007. (Rookie Reader Ser.). 31p. (J). pap. (*978-0-531-12589-2(0)*) Children's Pr., Ltd.
—A Circle in the Sky. 2006. (Rookie Reader Skill Set Ser.). (Illus.). 32p. (J). (gr. k-2). 19.50 (978-0-531-12570-0(X) , Children's Pr.) Scholastic Library Publishing.
Woodward, Kay. Countdown! Level P. Amit, Ofra, illus. 2006. (Lightning Readers Ser.). 32p. (J). pap. 3.95 (978-0-7696-4175-1(X) , Gingham Dog Pr.) School Specialty Publishing.

ROCKETS (AERONAUTICS)—MODELS

Dorling Kindersley Publishing Staff. Ultimate Rocket Kit. 2003. (Illus.). 1p. (J). 29.99 (978-0-7894-9832-8(4)) Dorling Kindersley Publishing, Inc.
Fun Pack Micro Rockets. 2003. (J). 7.99 (978-0-439-43454-6(8)) Scholastic, Inc.

ROCKS

see also Crystallography; Geology; Mineralogy; Stone

Bailey, Jacqui. The Rock Factory: A Story about the Rock Cycle. Lilly, Matthew, illus. 2006. 32p. (J). (gr. 3-6). 23.93 (978-1-4048-1596-4(1)) Picture Window Bks.
Barker, Charles Ferguson. Under Ohio: The Story of Ohio's Rocks & Fossils. 2007. (Illus.). 56p. (J). 17.95 (*978-0-8214-1755-3(X)*) Ohio Univ. Pr.
Barlowe, Sy. Learning about Rocks. 2000. (Learning about Ser.). (Illus.). 16p. (J). (gr. 3-5). pap. 1.50 (978-0-486-41291-7(1)) Dover Pubns., Inc.
Bellamy, David. The Rockpool. Dow, Jill, illus. 1999. (Our Changing World Ser.). 32p. (J). (gr. 1-5). pap. 7.99 (978-0-7112-1386-9(0)) Lincoln, Frances Ltd. GBR. *Dist:* Transition Vendor.
Benchmark Education Staff, compiled by. Rocks & Minerals. 2006. spiral bd. 199.00 (*978-1-4108-7135-0(5)*) Benchmark Education Co.
—Rocky Tales & Earth Systems. 2005. spiral bd. 225.00 (*978-1-4108-5819-1(7)*) Benchmark Education Co.
Bingham, Caroline. Rocks & Minerals. 2003. (Eye Wonder Ser.). (Illus.). 48p. (J). 9.99 (978-0-7894-9760-4(3)) Dorling Kindersley Publishing, Inc.
Bown, Deni & Dorling Kindersley Publishing Staff. Rocks & Minerals. 2003. (Ultimate Sticker Bks.). (Illus.). 16p. (J). (ps-3). pap. 6.99 (978-0-7894-0007-9(3)) Dorling Kindersley Publishing, Inc.
Bramwell, M. Rocks & Fossils. rev. ed. 2007. (Hobby Guides). 32p. (J). pap. 6.99 (*978-0-7945-1526-3(6)* , Usborne) EDC Publishing.
Brinkman, Patricia. Discover Rock Types. 2006. pap. 39.00 (*978-1-4108-6497-0(9)*) Benchmark Education Co.
—Discover the Rock Cycle. 2006. pap. 39.00 (*978-1-4108-6496-3(0)*) Benchmark Education Co.
—The Rock Cycle. 2006. pap. 39.00 (*978-1-4108-6493-2(6)*) Benchmark Education Co.
—Rock Types. 2006. pap. 42.00 (*978-1-4108-6494-9(4)*) Benchmark Education Co.
Burton, Jane & Taylor, Kim. The Nature & Science of Rocks. Bingxin, Wang et al, trs. 2000. (Nature & Science Ser.). (CHI & ENG., Illus.). 32p. (J). 8.95 (978-7-5600-1745-7(2)) Foreign Languages Teaching & Research Pr. CHN. *Dist:* Cheng & Tsui Co.
Burton, Margie, et al. Big Rocks, Little Rocks. Evento, Susan, ed. 1998. (Early Connections Ser.). 16p. (J). (gr. k-2). pap. 4.25 (978-1-892393-66-1(2)) Benchmark Education Co.
Carson, Mary Kay & Stewart, Melissa. Extreme Rocks & Minerals! Q&A. 2007. 48p. (J). (gr. k-4). 16.99 (*978-0-06-089982-0(4)*); (Illus.). pap. 6.99 (*978-0-06-089981-3(6)*) HarperCollins Pubs.
Cefrey, Holly. Igneous Rocks. 2003. (Reading Power Ser.). (Illus.). 24p. (J). lib. bdg. 17.25 (978-0-8239-6464-2(7) , PowerKids Pr.) Rosen Publishing Group, Inc., The.
—Metamorphic Rocks. 2003. (Reading Power Ser.). (Illus.). 24p. (J). lib. bdg. 17.25 (978-0-8239-6466-6(3) , PowerKids Pr.) Rosen Publishing Group, Inc., The.
—Sedimentary Rocks. 2003. (Reading Power Ser.). (Illus.). 24p. (J). lib. bdg. 17.25 (978-0-8239-6465-9(5) , PowerKids Pr.) Rosen Publishing Group, Inc., The.
Challoner, Jack. Rocks & Minerals. 2000. (Illus.). 64p. pap. 6.95 (978-1-84215-309-3(9)) Anness Publishing, Inc.
—Rocks & Minerals. 1999. (Young Scientist Concepts & Projects Ser.). (Illus.). 68p. (J). (gr. 4 up). lib. bdg. 27.33 (978-0-8368-2269-4(2)) Stevens, Gareth Inc.
Chasek, Ruth. Rocks & Minerals. 2000. (High Interest Bks.). (Illus.). 48p. (YA). (gr. 7-12). 24.00 (978-0-516-23333-8(5) , Children's Pr.) Scholastic Library Publishing.
Christian, Peggy. If You Find a Rock. Lember, Barbara Hirsch, photos by. 2000. (Illus.). 32p. (J). (gr. k-4). 16.00 (978-0-15-239339-7(0)) Harcourt Children's Bks.
Christian, Spencer & Felix, Antonia. Is There a Dinosaur in Your Backyard: The World's Most Fascinating Fossils, Rocks, & Minerals. 1998. (Spencer Christians World of Wonders: Vol. 12). (Illus.). 120p. (gr. 4-7). pap. 12.95 (978-0-471-19616-7(9) , Wiley) Wiley, John & Sons, Inc.
Cipriano, Jeri S. Let's Look at Rocks. 2003. (Yellow Umbrella Books for Early Readers). (Illus.). 17p. (J). 15.93 (978-0-7368-2938-0(5)); pap. (978-0-7368-2897-0(4)) Yellow Umbrella Pr.
—Miremos Las Rocas. 2005. (SPA.). (J). 15.93 (978-0-7368-4161-0(X)) Yellow Umbrella Pr.
Clifford, Tim. Geology. 2008. (J). (*978-1-60044-623-8(X)*) Rourke Publishing, LLC.
Complete Pebble Big Books Set. (gr. k-2). 106.95 (978-0-7368-3252-6(1)) Red Brick Learning.
Cooper, Sharon Katz. Using Rocks. 2007. (Illus.). 24p. (J). (*978-1-4034-9320-0(0)*); lib. bdg. 21.36 (*978-1-4034-9312-5(X)*) Heinemann.
Crump, Irving, ed. Investigating Science - Rocks & Minerals. 2000. 48p. 9.95 (978-1-56234-445-0(5) , Mailbox Bks., The) Education Ctr., Inc.
Cryute, Clay. I Was a Prehistoric Sponge: The Rock Cycle. 2005. (Illus.). 32p. (J). lib. bdg. (978-1-4109-1922-9(6)) Steck-Vaughn.
—Tales of a Prehistoric Sponge: The Rock Cycle. 2005. (Illus.). 32p. (J). (gr. 3-5). 7.85 (978 1 4109-1953-3(6)) Steck-Vaughn.
Dayton, Connor. Crystals. 2007. (Rocks & Minerals Ser.). (Illus.). 24p. (J). (gr. 2-5). lib. bdg. 21.25 (*978-1-4042-3687-5(2)* , PowerKids Pr.) Rosen Publishing Group, Inc., The.
—Rocks & Minerals, 6 bks., Set. Incl. Crystals. lib. bdg. 21.25 (*978-1-4042-3687-5(2)*); Fossils. lib. bdg. 21.25 (*978-1-4042-3689-9(9)*); Gemstones. lib. bdg. 21.25 (*978-1-4042-3686-8(4)*); Minerals. lib. bdg. 21.25 (*978-1-4042-3691-2(0)*); Rock Formations. lib. bdg. 21.25 (*978-1-4042-3690-5(2)*); Volcanic Rocks. lib. bdg. 21.25 (*978-1-4042-3688-2(0)*); (Illus.). 24p. (J). (gr. 2-5). 2007. 2007. Set lib. bdg. 127.50 (*978-1-4042-3610-3(4)* , PowerKids Pr.) Rosen Publishing Group, Inc., The.
—Volcanic Rocks. 2007. (Rocks & Minerals Ser.). (Illus.). 24p. (J). (gr. 2-5). lib. bdg. 21.25 (*978-1-4042-3688-2(0)* , PowerKids Pr.) Rosen Publishing Group, Inc., The.
DeWitt, Lockwood. Dig It! Hixson, Bryce, illus. 2003. (J). per. 14.95 (978-1-931801-02-7(9)) Loose In The Lab.
DK Publishing. Rocks & Minerals. 2008. 48p. (J). (gr. 2-8). pap. 9.99 (*978-0-7566-3822-1(4)*) Dorling Kindersley Publishing, Inc.
Dorling Kindersley Publishing Staff. Smithsonian Rock & Fossil Hunter. 2005. (Nature Activities Ser.). (Illus.). 72p. (J). pap. 9.99 (978-0-7566-1127-9(X)) Dorling Kindersley Publishing, Inc.
Dorling Kindersley Publishing Staff & Fuller, Sue. Rocks & Minerals. 2nd rev. ed. 2003. (DK Pockets Ser.). (Illus.). 160p. (J). pap. 6.99 (978-0-7894-9587-7(2)) Dorling Kindersley Publishing, Inc.
Dunlop, Jenna. Minerals. 2004. (Rocks, Minerals, & Resources Ser.). (Illus.). 32p. (J). (978-0-7787-1415-6(2)); pap. (978-0-7787-1447-7(0)) Crabtree Publishing Co.
Dussling, Jennifer. Looking at Rocks. Haggerty, Tim, illus. 2001. (My First Field Guides Ser.). 64p. (J). pap. 6.99 (978-0-448-42516-0(5) , Grosset & Dunlap) Penguin Group (USA) Inc.
Estigarribia, Diana. Learning about Rocks, Weathering, & Erosion with Graphic Organizers. 2005. (Graphic Organizers in Science Ser.). (Illus.). 24p. (J). 19.95 (978-1-4042-2806-1(3)); pap. (978-1-4042-5042-0(5)) Rosen Publishing Group, Inc., The. (PowerKids Pr.).
Evert, Laura. Rocks, Fossils, & Arrowheads. 2002. (gr. 3-6). lib. bdg. 16.40 (978-0-613-55890-7(1)) Tandem Library Bks.
—Rocks, Fossils & Arrowheads. 2002. (Take-Along Guide Ser.). (Illus.). 48p. (gr. 2-5). 10.95 (978-1-55971-805-9(6) , NorthWord Bks. for Young Readers) T&N Children's Publishing.
Farndon, John. Rock & Mineral. 2007. (Dk Online Ser.). 96p. (J). (gr. 3-8). pap. 9.99 (*978-0-7566-3136-9(X)*) Dorling Kindersley Publishing, Inc.
Farndon, John, et al. Rocks & Minerals. 2005. (Google E Guides). (Illus.). 96p. (J). 17.99 (978-0-7566-1140-8(7)) Dorling Kindersley Publishing, Inc.
Farndon, John R. Rock & Crystal Collection Kit: Hold the Treasure of the Earth in the Palm of Your Hand. 1999. (Illus.). 80p. (gr. 4-7). pap. 19.95 (978-0-8069-3147-0(7)) Sterling Publishing Co., Inc.
Faulkner, Rebecca. Crystals. 2007. (J). (*978-1-4109-2751-4(2)*); pap. (*978-1-4109-2759-0(8)*) Steck-Vaughn.
—Igneous Rock. 2007. (J). (*978-1-4109-2747-7(4)*); (*978-1-4109-2755-2(5)*) Steck-Vaughn.
—Metamorphic Rock. 2007. (J). (*978-1-4109-2749-1(0)*); pap. (*978-1-4109-2757-6(1)*) Steck-Vaughn.
—Sedimentary Rock. 2007. (J). (*978-1-4109-2748-4(2)*); (*978-1-4109-2756-9(3)*) Steck-Vaughn.
Firestone, Mary. Rock. 2004. (First Facts Ser.). 24p. (J). lib. bdg. 21.26 (978-0-7368-2651-8(3)) Capstone Pr., Inc.
Flanagan, Alice K. Rocks. 2000. (Simply Science Ser.). (Illus.). 32p. (J). (gr. 3 up). lib. bdg. 19.93 (978-0-7565-0033-7(8)) Compass Point Bks.
Frank, Marjorie Slavick, et al. Science Instant Readers Bk. 5: Rocks. 1999. (Harcourt Science Ser.). (gr. 1 up). pap. 15.50 (978-0-15-316203-9(1)) Harcourt Schl. Pubs.
Fuller, Sue. Backpack Books: 1,001 Facts about Rocks & Minerals. 2003. (gr. 3-6). lib. bdg. 17.60 (978-0-613-55690-3(9)) Tandem Library Bks.
—Rocks & Minerals. 2003. (gr. 3-6). lib. bdg. 15.30 (978-0-613-75184-1(1)) Tandem Library Bks.
Fuller, Sue & Maynard, Christopher. 1,001 Facts about Rocks & Minerals. Grabham, Sue, ed. 2002. (Backpack-Books). (Illus.). 192p. (J). (gr. k-3). pap. 8.99 (978-0-7894-9043-8(9)) Dorling Kindersley Publishing, Inc.
Gallant, Roy A. Rocks. 2000. (Kaleidoscope Ser.). (Illus.). 48p. (J). (gr. 3 up). lib. bdg. 25.64 (978-0-7614-1042-3(2) , Benchmark Bks.) Cavendish, Marshall Corp.
Gardner, Robert. Smashing Science Projects about Earth's Rocks & Minerals. LaBaff, Tom, illus. 2007. (Rockin' Earth Science Experiments Ser.). 48p. (J). (gr. 3-4). lib. bdg. 23.93 (978-0-7660-2731-2(7) , Enslow Elementary) Enslow Pubs., Inc.
Goldman, Phyllis B., ed. Monkeyshines on Rocks & Minerals. (Illus.). 148p. (J). (ps-7). reprint ed. pap. 26.95 (978-1-888325-14-0(3)) Allosaurus Pubs.
Graham, Ian. Rocks: A Resource Our World Depends On. 2004. (J). pap. 7.50 (978-1-4034-5625-0(9)); lib. bdg. 24.22 (978-1-4034-5617-5(8)) Heinemann Library.
Graphic Organizers in Science. (Illus.). (J). (gr. 3-5). 119.70 (978-1-4042-2955-6(8)) Rosen Publishing Group, Inc., The.
Gunzi, Christiane. Coral Reefs. 2001. (Collectafact Ser.: Vol. 11). (Illus.). 48p. (J). (gr. 1-5). 4.95 (978-1-58728-758-9(7) , Two Can Publishing) T&N Children's Publishing.
Halls, Kelly Milner. Rocks & Minerals. 2006. (Illus.). 48p. (J). (978-1-4034-7911-2(9)) Heinemann Library.
Hamilton, John. Landslides. 2006. (Illus.). 32p. (J). (gr. 3-8). lib. bdg. 24.21 (978-1-59679-331-6(7) , ABDO & Daughters) ABDO Publishing Co.
Hantula, Richard. Rocks & Fossils. 2006. (J). pap. (*978-0-8368-7876-9(0)*) Stevens, Gareth Inc.
Harcourt School Publishers Staff. Rocks: Science Reader. 1999. (SPA., Illus.). (J). (gr. 1). pap. 3.70 (978-0-15-316108-7(6)) Harcourt Schl. Pubs.
Harman, Rebecca. Rock Cycles. 2005. (Heinemann Infosearch Ser.). (Illus.). 32p. (J). pap. (978-1-4034-7064-5(2)); lib. bdg. (978-1-4034-7057-7(X)) Heinemann Library.
Hatch Jr., B. J. Butch. Professor Rock Ltd. Chatham, Dennis J., illus. 2003. 32p. (J). 14.95 (978-1-56167-808-2(2)) American Literary Pr.
Hewitt, Sally. Rocks & Soil. 2007. (J). (*978-1-59604-138-7(2)*) Stargazer Bks.
Hil, Mcgraw. Trfpaswak Rocks & Resourc. 2000. (McGraw-Hill Science Ser.). (gr. 3 up). (978-0-02-277633-6(8)) Macmillan/McGraw-Hill Schl. Div.
Hirschmann, Kris. Rocks & Minerals. 2004. (World Discovery Science Readers Ser.). (Illus.). 31p. (J). pap. (978-0-439-56630-8(4)) Scholastic, Inc.
Hiscock, Bruce. The Big Rock, 1vol. Hiscock, Bruce, illus. 1999. (Illus.). 32p. (J). (gr. 2-5). 5.99 (978-0-689-82958-1(2) , Aladdin) Simon & Schuster Children's Publishing.
—The Big Rock. 1999. (J). 12.79 (978-0-606-17197-7(5)) Tandem Library Bks.
—Big Rock. 1999. (gr. 3-6). lib. bdg. 14.15 (978-0-613-22969-2(X)) Tandem Library Bks.
Hodge, Judith. Las riquezas de la tierra & Riches from Earth. 2005. spiral bd. 84.00 (*978-1-4108-5716-3(6)*) Benchmark Education Co.
Holt, Rinehart and Winston Staff. Holt Science & Technology Chptr. 5: Rocks & Fossils: Chapter Resources - Tennessee Edition. 3rd ed. 2003. (J). pap. 11.40 (978-0-03-069111-9(7)) Holt, Rinehart & Winston.
—Holt Science & Technology Chptr. 8: Rocks & Minerals: Chapter Resources - Tennessee Edition. 3rd ed. 2003. (YA). pap. 11.40 (978-0-03-069167-6(2)) Holt, Rinehart & Winston.
—Holt Science & Technology Chptr. 10: Rocks & Fosills: Chapter Resources - Tennessee Edition. 3rd ed. 2003. (YA). pap. 11.40 (978-0-03-069169-0(9)) Holt, Rinehart & Winston.
Hosford, William G. Geo the Geode. Hosford, William G., illus. 2006. (Illus.). 32p. (J). lib. bdg. 19.95 (978-0-9776562-0-2(9) , CN0601) WGH Arts LLC.
Hunter, Rebecca M. Rocks, Minerals & Fossils. 2001. (Discovering Science Ser.). (Illus.). 32p. (J). (gr. 4-7). lib. bdg. 25.69 (978-0-7398-3250-9(6)) Raintree.
Hurst, Carol Otis. Rocks in His Head. Stevenson, James, illus. 2001. 32p. (J). (ps). 16.99 (978-0-06-029403-8(5)); lib. bdg. 17.89 (978-0-06-029404-5(3)) HarperCollins Pubs.
Hynes, Margaret. Rocks & Fossils. 2006. (Kingfisher Knowledge Ser.). (Illus.). 64p. (J). (gr. 5-9). 12.95 (978-0-7534-5974-4(4) , Kingfisher) Houghton Mifflin Co. Trade & Reference Div.
Igneous Rocks: Individual Title, 6 Packs. (On Deck Ser.: Vol. 2). 24p. (gr. 4-5). 35.00 (978-0-7578-5819-2(8)) Rigby Education.
Instructional Fair. Rocks & Minerals. 1999. (Ready Reference Cards Ser.). 12p. (J). (gr. 5-12). ring bd. 11.50 (978-0-7424-0777-0(2) , IF676R) School Specialty Publishing.
Investigating Earth Systems Rocks & Landforms. 2002. stu. ed., bds. (978-1-58591-109-7(7)); 2001. stu. ed. (978-1-58591-079-3(1)) It's About Time, Herff Jones Education Diiv.
Jennings, Terry. Rocas y Suelos (Rocks & Soils) (SPA.). 32p. (J). 6.95 (978-84-348-1912-2(0)) SM Ediciones ESP. *Dist:* AIMS International Bks., Inc.
—Rocks. 1998. (Find Out about Ser.). (Illus.). 24p. (J). (ps-3). (978-0-563-37468-8(3)) BBC Worldwide.
Jones, Robert W. & Discovery Books Staff. Rocks & Minerals. 1999. (Explore Your World Ser.). (Illus.). 192p. (J). pap. 13.95 (978-1-56331-803-0(2)) Discovery Bks.
Kittinger, Jo S. A Look at Rocks: From Coal to Kimberlite. 1998. (First Bks.). (Illus.). 64p. (J). (gr. 5-7). pap. 6.95 (978-0-531-15887-6(X) , Watts, Franklin) Scholastic Library Publishing.
—A Look at Rocks: From Coal to Kimberlite. 1998. (Illus.). 63p. (J). (ps-7). lib. bdg. 15.25 (978-0-613-12846-9(X)) Tandem Library Bks.
Korb, Rena B. Radical Rocks. Reibeling, Brandon, illus. 2007. (Science Rocks Ser.). 32p. (J). (ps-4). lib. bdg. 27.07 (*978-1-60270-040-6(0)* , Looking Glass Library) Magic Wagon.
Kusugak, Michael Arvaarluk. Who Wants Rocks? Krykorka, Vladyana Langer, illus. 1999. 24p. (J). (ps-2). pap. 6.95 (978-1-55037-588-6(1)); lib. bdg. 17.95 (978-1-55037-589-3(X)) Annick Pr., Ltd. CAN. *Dist:* Firefly Bks., Ltd.
—Who Wants Rocks? 1999. (gr. k-3). lib. bdg. 15.25 (978-0-613-27556-9(X)) Tandem Library Bks.
Lands of Rock: Individual Title Six-Packs. (Rigby Infoquest Ser.). (gr. 5 up). 37.00 (978-0-7578-6480-3(5)) Rigby Education.
Lilly, Melinda. Rocks. (Read & Do Science Ser.). (Illus.). (J). 20.64 (978-1-58952-647-1(3)); 2006. 24p. (gr. 1-4). 14.95 (978-1-59515-404-0(3) , 1244275) Rourke Publishing, LLC.
Lindeen, Carol. Rock Basics. 2008. (J). (*978-1-4296-0004-0(7)*) Capstone Pr., Inc.
Lorenz Books Staff, et al. Rocks & Minerals. 2000. (Investigations Ser.). (Illus.). 64p. (gr. 3-7). 12.95 (978-0-7548-0457-4(7) , Lorenz Bks.) Anness Publishing, Inc.
Lunis, Natalie. Rocks & Soil. Ellis, Linette, ed. 1998. (Early Science Ser.). 16p. (J). (ps-2). pap., stu. ed. 3.33 (978-1-56784-384-2(0)); (Illus.). pap. 16.95 (978-1-56784-383-5(2)) Sundance/Newbridge Educational Publishing.
Marzollo, Jean. I Am a Rock, Level 1. Moffatt, Judith, illus. 1998. (Hello Reader! Ser.). (J). pap. 3.99 (978-0-590-37222-0(X)) Scholastic, Inc.
—I Am a Rock. 1998. (Hello Reader! Science Ser.). (978-0-606-13499-6(9)) Tandem Library Bks.
Mattern, Joanne. Igneous Rocks & the Rock Cycle. 2006. (Shaping & Reshaping of Earth's Surface Ser.). (J). lib. bdg. (978-1-4042-3196-2(X) , PowerKids Pr.) Rosen Publishing Group, Inc., The.
—Metamorphic Rocks & the Rock Cycle. 2006. (Shaping & Reshaping of Earth's Surface Ser.). (J). lib. bdg. (978-1-4042-3194-8(3) , PowerKids Pr.) Rosen Publishing Group, Inc., The.
—Minerals & the Rock Cycle. 2006. (J). lib. bdg. (978-1-4042-3199-3(4) , PowerKids Pr.) Rosen Publishing Group, Inc., The.
—Sedimentary Rocks & the Rock Cycle. 2006. (Shaping & Reshaping of Earth's Surface Ser.). (Illus.). 24p. (J). lib. bdg. (978-1-4042-3195-5(1) , PowerKids Pr.) Rosen Publishing Group, Inc., The.
McConnell, William. Rocks & Fossils. 2006. (Rosen Publishing Group's Reading Room Collection). (J). lib. bdg. (978-1-4042-3344-7(X) , PowerKids Pr.) Rosen Publishing Group, Inc., The.
McGraw-Hill Staff. Rocks & Resources. 2000. (McGraw-Hill Science Ser.). (gr. 3 up). (978-0-02-278212-2(5)) Macmillan/McGraw-Hill Schl. Div.
Meierhenry, Mark V. & Volk, David. The Mystery of the Round Rocks. 2007. (J). (*978-0-9777955-3-6(5)* , South Dakota State Historical Society Pr.) South Dakota State Historical Society.

PQR

Metamorphic Rocks: Individual Title Six-Packs. (On Deck Ser.: Vol. 2). 24p. (gr. 4-5). 35.00 (978-0-7578-5820-8(1)) Rigby Education.

Miles, Lisa. Rocas y Minerales. 2004. (Spotter's Guides Sticker Bks.). (SPA., Illus.). 24p. (J). (gr. 2 up). pap. 7.95 (978-0-7460-3642-6(6)) EDC Publishing.

—Rocks & Minerals. 2003. (Usborne Hotshots Ser.). (Illus.). 32p. (YA). (gr. 2 up). pap. 2.95 (978-0-7460-2790-5(7)) EDC Publishing.

—Rocks & Minerals Sticker Book. rev. ed. 2006. 16p. (J). pap. 8.99 (978-0-7945-1413-6(8) , Usborne) EDC Publishing.

Morris, Neil. Rocks & Minerals. 1998. (Wonders of Our World Ser.). (Illus.). 32p. (J). (gr. 3-4). lib. bdg. (978-0-86505-835-4(0)); pap. (978-0-86505-847-7(4)) Crabtree Publishing Co.

—Rocks & Soil. 2002. (Our World Ser.). (Illus.). 32p. (J). lib. bdg. 24.25 (978-1-930643-79-6(9)) Chrysalis Education.

Nelson, Robin. Rocks. 2005. (First Step Nonfiction Ser.). (Illus.). 23p. (J). (ps-ps). 18.60 (978-0-8225-2599-8(2) , Lerner Pubns.) Lerner Publishing Group.

Newson, Lesley & Wadsworth, Pamela. Rhagor Am Greigiau, Pridd a Thywydd. 2005. (WEL., Illus.). 24p. pap. (978-1-85596-238-5(1)) Dref Wen.

O'Donoghue, Michael. Rocks & Minerals of the World. 2004. (World Book's Science & Nature Guides Ser.). (Illus.). 80p. (J). (978-0-7166-4217-6(4)) World Bk., Inc.

Oetting, Judy. Fun Facts & Games: Missouri's Rocks & Minerals. Nolte, Larry, illus. 2000. (Fun Facts & Games Ser.). 64p. (J). (ps-3). pap. 5.95 (978-1-892920-24-9(7)) GHB Publishers, LLC.

—"M" Is for Missouri's Rocks & Minerals. Dorenkamp, Michelle, illus. 2000. (Alpha Flight Bks.). 60p. (J). (ps-3). 17.95 (978-1-892920-29-4(8)) GHB Publishers, LLC.

Ostopowich, Melanie. The Rock Cycle. 2004. (Science Matters Ser.). (Illus.). 24p. (J). lib. bdg. 24.45 (978-1-59036-209-9(8)) Weigl Pubs., Inc.

—Rocks. 2004. (Science Matters Ser.). (Illus.). 24p. (J). lib. bdg. 24.45 (978-1-59036-210-5(1)) Weigl Pubs., Inc.

Oxlade, Chris. How We Use Rock. 2004. (Using Materials Ser.). (Illus.). 32p. (J). lib. bdg. 25.70 (978-1-4109-0597-0(7)) Raintree.

—Rock. 2002. (Materials, Materials, Materials Ser.). (Illus.). 32p. (J). (gr. k-2). lib. bdg. 22.79 (978-1-58810-585-1(7)); pap. 6.95 (978-1-4034-0086-4(5) , 91527) Heinemann Library.

—Rock. 2002. (gr. k-3). lib. bdg. 14.75 (978-0-613-45820-7(6)) Tandem Library Bks.

—Using Materials: How We Use Rock. 2004. (Illus.). pap. 7.50 (978-1-4109-0996-1(4)) Raintree.

El pais de las rocas en pie: una tierra de Sorpresas. 2000. (McGraw-Hill Ciencias Ser.). (ENG & SPA.). (gr. 2 up). (978-0-02-279612-9(6)) Macmillan/McGraw-Hill Schl. Div.

Parker, Steve. Rocks & Minerals. 2002. (Science Files Ser.). (Illus.). 32p. (J). (gr. 3 up). lib. bdg. 24.67 (978-0-8368-3085-9(7)) Stevens, Gareth Inc.

Pellant, Chris. The Best Book of Fossils, Rocks & Minerals. 2007. (Best Book of... Ser.). 32p. (J). (gr. k-3). pap. 6.95 (978-0-7534-6081-8(5) , Kingfisher) Houghton Mifflin Co. Trade & Reference Div.

Pellant, Chris. Rocks & Fossils. (Science Kids Ser.). (Illus.). 48p. (J). (gr. k-3). 2007. pap. 6.95 (***978-0-7534-6126-6(9)***); 2003. tchr. ed. 9.95 (978-0-7534-5619-4(2)) Houghton Mifflin Co. Trade & Reference Div. (Kingfisher).

Pellant, Chris & Pellant, Helen. Granite & Other Igneous Rocks. 2006. (J). lib. bdg. (***978-0-8368-7906-3(6)***) Stevens, Gareth Inc.

—Marble & Other Metamorphic Rocks. 2006. (J). lib. bdg. (***978-0-8368-7907-0(4)***) Stevens, Gareth Inc.

—Sandstone & Other Sedimentary Rocks. 2006. (J). lib. bdg. (***978-0-8368-7909-4(0)***) Stevens, Gareth Inc.

Pellant, Chris & Perrault, Chris. The Best Book of Fossils, Rocks & Minerals. Grinaway, Ray & Forsey, Chris, illus. 2000. (Best Book of... Ser.). 32p. (J). (gr. k-3). tchr. ed. 12.95 (978-0-7534-5274-5(X) , Kingfisher) Houghton Mifflin Co. Trade & Reference Div.

Phelan, Glen. Rocks & Minerals. 2004. (National Geographic Reading Expeditions Ser.). (Illus.). 32p. (J). pap. (978-0-7922-4571-1(7)) National Geographic Society.

The Picture Book of Rock Tools for Children. 2000. 20p. 12.95 (978-0-9673750-1-4(0)) Rock Song Publishing.

Pinet, Michele. Be Your Own Rock & Mineral Expert. Greenbaum, Fay, tr. from FRE. Korkos, Alain, illus. 2003. 40p. (J). (gr. 5-7). 14.95 (978-0-8069-9580-9(7)) Sterling Publishing Co., Inc.

Pluckrose, Henry Arthur. Earth. 2006. (Illus.). 32p. (J). (978-1-59771-036-7(9)) Sea-To-Sea Pubns.

Prokos, Anna. Rocks & Minerals. 2004. (Discovery Channel School Science Ser.). (Illus.). 32p. (J). (gr. 5 up). lib. bdg. 24.67 (978-0-8368-3384-3(8)) Stevens, Gareth Inc.

Red Hot Rocks!, 6 Packs. (Bookweb Ser.). 32p. (gr. 6 up). 34.00 (978-0-7578-0911-8(1)) Rigby Education.

Ricciuti, Edward R. Rocks & Minerals. 2001. (Scholastic Science Readers Ser.). (Illus.). 48p. (J). pap. (978-0-439-26993-3(8)) Scholastic, Inc.

Ricciuti, Edward R., et al. Rocks & Minerals. 1998. (Audubon Society First Field Guide Ser.). (Illus.). 160p. (YA). (gr. 3-7). pap. 17.95 (978-0-590-05463-8(5)) Scholastic, Inc.

Richardson, Adele D. Rocks. 2001. (Bridgestone Science Library). (Illus.). 24p. (J). (gr. 2-3). lib. bdg. 18.60 (978-0-7368-0953-5(8) , Bridgestone Bks.) Capstone Pr., Inc.

Rocks. (Amazing Science Ser.). 24p. (J). 7.95 (978-1-4048-0334-3(3)) Picture Window Bks.

Rocks & Fossils. (Rosen Real Readers Big Bookstm Ser.). 16p. (J). (gr. 2-3). 38.75 (978-1-4042-6221-8(0)) Rosen Publishing Group, Inc., The.

Rocks & Fossils Kid Kit. 32p. (J). 14.99 (978-1-58086-758-0(8) , Usborne) EDC Publishing.

Rocks & Minerals. 2005. 48p. (J). per. 6.99 (978-1-59441-202-8(2) , CD-104110) Carson-Dellosa Publishing Co., Inc.

Rocks & Minerals. 2002. 32p. (J). 7.95 (978-0-7525-7243-7(1)) Parragon, Inc.

Rocks & Minerals. 2002. (Super Science Activities Ser.). 48p. (J). (gr. 2-5). 7.99 (978-0-7439-3666-8(3) , 3666) Teacher Created Materials, Inc.

Rocks & Minerals Set F, 6 vols. (Phonics Readers Ser.). (gr. k-2). 28.95 (978-0-7368-4083-5(4)) Red Brick Learning.

Rocks Fantastic. 2002. (Illus.). (J). pap. 5.43 (978-0-7398-5921-6(8)) Steck-Vaughn.

Rocks from Space, 6, Pack. (Rigby Focus Ser.). 24p. (gr. 2 up). 30.00 (978-0-7578-5581-8(4)) Rigby Education.

Rocks from Space: Individual Title Six-Packs. (Rigby Focus Ser.). 24p. (gr. 2 up). 28.00 (978-0-7578-5351-7(X)) Rigby Education.

Rosinsky, Natalie M. Rocks: Hard, Soft, Smooth, & Rough. John, Matthew, illus. 2004. (Amazing Science Ser.). 24p. (C). (gr. k-4). 22.60 (978-1-4048-0015-1(8)) Picture Window Bks.

Royston, Angela. Rock: Let's Look at a Pebble. 2006. (Illus.). 24p. (J). (978-1-4034-7677-7(2)); pap. (978-1-4034-7686-9(1)) Heinemann Library.

—Rock: Let's Look at a Pebble. 2005. (J). (978-1-4109-1826-0(2)); pap. (978-1-4109-1833-8(5)) Steck-Vaughn.

Rupp, Rebecca. Rocks. 2004. (J). (978-1-58017-540-1(6)); pap. (978-1-58017-539-5(2)) Storey Publishing, LLC.

Schwabacher, Martin. Optical Rocks & Crystals. Nichols, Cathy, ed. Ford, Pam, illus. 2000. 16p. (YA). (978-1-884270-17-8(4)) Hall, Nancy Inc.

Science & Technology for Children BOOKS: Rocks & Minerals Set. 2007. (J). 127.60 (***978-1-933008-44-8(X)***) National Science Resources Ctr.

Sedimentary Rocks, 6 Pcks. (On Deck Ser.: Vol. 2). 24p. (gr. 4-5). 35.00 (978-0-7578-5822-2(8)) Rigby Education.

Sheehan, Thomas F. Blocks of Rocks. 2006. (City Science Ser.). (Illus.). 24p. (gr. k-3). 14.95 (978-1-59515-411-8(6)) Rourke Publishing, LLC.

—Bloques de Piedra. 2005. (Ciencia Citadina Ser.). (SPA.). (978-1-59515-663-1(1)) Rourke Publishing, LLC.

Sheen, Martin, contrib. by. Rocks & Minerals. 2007. 16p. (J). (gr. 3-8). pap. 29.99 (***978-0-7566-3132-1(7)***) Dorling Kindersley Publishing, Inc.

Sian revision rock Origins. 2004. (J). (978-1-59242-063-6(X)) Delta Education, LLC.

Slade, Suzanne. The Rock Cycle. 2007. (Illus.). 24p. (J). (978-1-4042-2392-9(4)); pap. (978-1-4042-2202-1(2)); (gr. 4-6). lib. bdg. 21.25 (978-1-4042-3493-2(4)) Rosen Publishing Group, Inc., The. (PowerKids Pr.).

Spickert, Diane Nelson. Earth Steps: A Rock's Journey Through Time. Wallace, Marianne D., illus. 2004. 32p. (J). (gr. 4-6). 17.95 (978-1-55591-986-3(3)) Fulcrum Publishing.

Squire, Ann O. Rocks & Minerals. 2002. (True Bks.). (Illus.). 48p. (J). (gr. 3-5). pap. 6.95 (978-0-516-26985-6(2) , Children's Pr.) Scholastic Library Publishing.

—Rocks & Minerals. 2002. (gr. 3-6). lib. bdg. 15.25 (978-0-613-54328-6(9)) Tandem Library Bks.

Stamper, Judith Bauer. Rocks & Minerals. Gangloff, Hope, illus. 2004. (Magic School Bus Ser.). 96p. (J). (gr. 3 up). pap. 4.99 (978-0-439-56053-5(5) , Scholastic Paperbacks) Scholastic, Inc.

Steck-Vaughn Staff. One Quiet Afternoon. 1998. (Illus.). pap. (978-0-8172-8694-1(2)) Steck-Vaughn.

—The Strangest Rock on Earth. 2002. pap. (978-0-7398-6147-9(6)) Steck-Vaughn.

Stewart, Melissa. Igneous Rocks. 2002. (Rocks & Minerals Ser.). (Illus.). 32p. (J). (gr. 4-6). lib. bdg. 24.22 (978-1-58810-256-0(4)); pap. 7.50 (978-1-4034-0092-5(X) , 91659) Heinemann Library.

—Metamorphic Rocks. 2002. (Rocks & Minerals Ser.). (Illus.). 32p. (J). (gr. 4-6). lib. bdg. 24.22 (978-1-58810-257-7(2)); pap. 7.50 (978-1-4034-0093-2(8) , 91660) Heinemann Library.

—Sedimentary Rocks. 2002. (Rocks & Minerals Ser.). (Illus.). 32p. (J). (gr. 4-6). lib. bdg. 24.22 (978-1-58810-259-1(9)); pap. 7.50 (978-1-4034-0095-6(4) , 91662) Heinemann Library.

Stones. braille ed. 2001. (gr. 2). spiral bd. (978-0-616-08851-7(5)) Canadian National Institute for the Blind/Institut National Canadien pour les Aveugles.

Storey, Rita. Rocks & Stones. 2007. (J). (***978-1-59920-006-4(6)***) Smart Apple Media.

Summers, Kathy. Petroglyphs. 2005. (J). (978-0-7377-3070-8(6) , Greenhaven Pr., Inc.) Thomson Gale.

Symes, R. F. Rock & Mineral. 2008. (DK Eyewitness Bks.). 72p. (J). (gr. 3-8). 15.99 (***978-0-7566-3777-4(5)***) Dorling Kindersley Publishing, Inc.

Symes, R. F. Rocks & Minerals. 2004. (Dk Eyewitness Books Ser.). (Illus.). 72p. (ps-12). 15.99 (978-0-7566-0719-7(1)) Dorling Kindersley Publishing, Inc.

Symes, R. F., et al. Rocks & Minerals. Keates, Colin & Einsiedel, Andreas, illus. 2004. (Eyewitness Books). 72p. (J). lib. bdg. 19.99 (978-0-7566-0718-0(3)) Dorling Kindersley Publishing, Inc.

Tocci, Salvatore. Experiments with Rocks & Minerals. 2002. (True Bks.). (Illus.). 48p. (J). (gr. 3-5). pap. 6.95 (978-0-516-26995-5(X) , Children's Pr.) Scholastic Library Publishing.

—Experiments with Rocks & Minerals. 2002. (gr. 3-6). lib. bdg. 15.25 (978-0-613-54212-8(6)) Tandem Library Bks.

Trueit, Trudi Strain. Rocks, Gems, & Minerals. 2003. (Watts Library). 64p. (gr. 5-7). pap. 8.95 (978-0-531-16241-5(9)); (Illus.). (J). 25.50 (978-0-531-12195-5(X)) Scholastic Library Publishing. (Watts, Franklin).

—Rocks, Gems, & Minerals. 2003. (gr. 5-8). lib. bdg. 17.60 (978-0-613-67665-6(3)) Tandem Library Bks.

VanCleave, Janice Pratt. Janice VanCleave's Rocks & Minerals: Mind-Boggling Experiments You Can Turn into Science Fair Projects. 2002. (Janice Vancleave Ser.). (Illus.). (J). 19.72 (978-0-7587-4633-7(4)) Book Wholesalers, Inc.

Wadsworth, Pamela. Creigiau, Pridd a Thywydd. 2005. (WEL., Illus.). 24p. pap. (978-1-85596-237-8(3)) Dref Wen.

Wadsworth, Pamela & Tate, Sylvia. Golwg Gyntaf Ar Greigiau, Pridd a Thywydd. 2005. (WEL., Illus.). 24p. pap. (978-1-85596-253-8(5)) Dref Wen.

Walker, Sally M. Rocks. 2007. (Early Bird Earth Science Ser.). (Illus.). 48p. (J). (gr. 2-4). 25.26 (978-0-8225-5947-4(1) , Lerner Pubns.) Lerner Publishing Group.

Walshaw, R. Rocks & Minerals. 2002. (All about Ser.). (Illus.). 64p. (gr. 3-8). pap. 7.95 (978-1-84215-629-2(2) , Southwater) Anness Publishing GBR. *Dist:* National Bk. Network.

Wermund, Jerry. The World According to Rock. Sansevero, Tony, illus. 2005. 48p. (J). pap. (978-0-9726255-1-7(8)) Rockon Publishing.

West, Krista. Hands-On Projects about Rocks, Minerals & Fossils. 2002. (Great Earth Science Projects Ser.). (Illus.). 24p. (J). lib. bdg. 19.95 (978-0-8239-5842-9(6) , PowerKids Pr.) Rosen Publishing Group, Inc., The.

What Happens to Rock? 6 Each of 1 Student Book, 6 vols. (Sunshinetm Science Ser.). 24p. (gr. 1-2). 41.95 (978-0-7802-2720-0(4)) Wright Group, The.

What Happens to Rock? Big Book. (Sunshinetm Science Ser.). 24p. (gr. 1-2). 37.50 (978-0-7802-2794-1(8)) Wright Group, The.

Whyman, Kathryn. Rocks & Minerals & the Environment. 2004. (J). lib. bdg. (978-1-932799-36-1(2)) Stargazer Bks.

Williams, Zella. Experiments on Rocks & the Rock Cycle. 2007. (Do-It-Yourself Science Ser.). (Illus.). 24p. (J). (gr. 2-5). lib. bdg. 23.95 (978-1-4042-3660-8(0)) Rosen Publishing Group, Inc., The.

Woolley, A. Rocks & Minerals. 2004. (Spotter's Guides). (Illus.). 64p. (J). lib. bdg. 13.95 (978-1-58086-309-4(4)) EDC Publishing.

—Rocks & Minerals Spotter's Guide - Internet Referenced. rev. ed. 2007. 64p. (J). pap. 5.99 (978-0-7945-1304-7(2) , Usborne) EDC Publishing.

Zemlicka, Shannon. From Rock to Road. 2004. (Start to Finish Ser.). (J). pap. 4.95 (978-0-8225-2146-4(6)); 18.60 (978-0-8225-1391-9(9) , Lerner Pubns.) Lerner Publishing Group.

Zim, Herbert S. & Shaffer, Paul R. Rocks, Gems & Minerals: A Guide to Familiar Minerals, Gems, Ores & Rocks. Perlman, Raymond, illus. rev. ed. 2001. (Golden Guides Ser.). 160p. pap. 6.95 (978-1-58238-132-9(1) , Golden Guides from Saint Martin's Pr.) St. Martin's Pr.

ROCKS—AGE

see Geology, Stratigraphic

ROCKS—FICTION

Bender, Esther. Thank God for Rocks. Lard, Mary Anne, illus. 2003. 32p. 15.00 (978-0-8192-1902-2(9)) Morehouse Publishing.

Briggs, Molly Anne. Momma's Favorite Rock. 2006. (J). pap. 8.00 (978-0-8059-7070-8(3)) Dorrance Publishing Co., Inc.

Caddy, David. The Reef. 2005. 144p. (Orig.). (J). pap. 13.50 (978-1-920731-29-8(6)) Fremantle Pr. AUS. *Dist:* International Specialized Bk. Services.

Cook, Sherry & Johnson, Terri. Ronnie Rock. 26. Kuhn, Jesse, illus. l.t. ed. 2006. (Quirkles—Exploring Phonics through Science Ser.: 18). 32p. (J). 7.99 (978-1-933815-17-6(5) , Quirkles, The) Creative 3, LLC.

The Coolest Rock. (Early Intervention Levels Ser.). 31.86 (978-0-7362-0668-6(X)) Hampton-Brown Bks.

Dey, Joy Morgan. Agate: What Good Is a Moose? Johnson, Nikki, illus. 2007. (J). 17.95 (***978-0-942235-73-9(8)***) Lake Superior Port Cities, Inc.

Dreyer, Ellen. The Glow Stone. 2006. 186p. (J). 15.95 (978-1-56145-370-2(6) , Peachtree Junior) Peachtree Pubs., Ltd.

Elizabeti's Doll. 2004. 24.95 incl. audio (978-1-55592-053-1(5)); (J). pap. 14.95 incl. audio (978-1-55592-716-5(5)) Weston Woods Studios, Inc.

Fernandez, Laura. La Mejor Coleccion. 2004. Tr. of Best Collection. (SPA., Illus.). (J). pap. 8.50 (978-84-241-8031-7(3)) Everest de Ediciones y Distribucion, S.L. ESP. *Dist:* Lectorum Pubns., Inc.

Fitch, Sheree. Pocket Rocks. Flook, Helen, illus. 2004. 32p. (J). (ps-2). 16.95 (978-1-55143-289-2(7) , 1234125) Orca Bk. Pubs. USA.

Frazier, Sundee Tucker. Brendan Buckley's Universe & Everything in It. 2007. 208p. (J). (gr. 4-7). 14.99 (***978-0-385-73439-4(5)***); lib. bdg. 17.99 (***978-0-385-90445-2(2)***) Random Hse. Children's Bks. (Delacorte Bks. for Young Readers).

Gallup, Tracy. Stone Crazy. Gallup, Tracy, illus. 2007. (Crazy Little Ser.). (Illus.). 40p. (J). (***978-1-934133-13-2(2)***) Mackinac Island Pr., Inc.

Harcourt School Publishers Staff. The Case of the Phony Rocks: Take-Home Book. 2001. (Collections Ser.). (Illus.). (J). pap. 1.90 (978-0-15-319526-6(6)) Harcourt Schl. Pubs.

—Rock Hounds Advanced Level. 3rd ed. 2002. (Trophies Reading Program Ser.). (Illus.). pap. 5.10 (978-0-15-323218-3(8)) Harcourt Schl. Pubs.

—Rock Soup: Below Level. 3rd ed. 2002. (Trophies Reading Program Ser.). (Illus.). (J). pap. 3.20 (978-0-15-322956-5(X)) Harcourt Schl. Pubs.

—Trofeos Below Level: Sopa de Rocas. 3rd ed. 2002. (SPA., Illus.). (J). pap. 3.50 (978-0-15-323867-3(4)) Harcourt Schl. Pubs.

Karwoski, Gail Langer. Julie the Rockhound. Downey, Lisa, illus. 2007. 32p. (J). (gr. k-4). 8.95 (***978-1-934359-21-1(1)***) Sylvan Dell Pubng.

King, Steve. The Stone Dragon. 2005. 80p. pap. 14.95 (978-1-4137-9628-5(1)) PublishAmerica, Inc.

Lewis, Paul Owen. The Jupiter Stone. 2004. (Illus.). 32p. (J). 15.95 (978-1-58246-107-6(4) , Tricycle Pr.) Ten Speed Pr.

Milord, Susan. Pebble. Milord, Susan, illus. 2007. 32p. (J). lib. bdg. 16.89 (978-0-06-085808-7(7) , Julie Andrews Collection) HarperCollins Pubs.

—Pebble. 2007. 32p. (J). (ps-2). 15.99 (978-0-06-085807-0(9) , Julie Andrews Collection) HarperCollins Pubs.

Murray, Andrew. On a Tall, Tall Cliff. Snow, Alan, illus. 2005. 32p. (J). (ps-7). pap. 11.95 (978-0-00-712156-4(3)) HarperCollins Pubs. Ltd. GBR. *Dist:* Trafalgar Square Publishing.

—On a Tall, Tall Cliff. 2005. (Illus.). 32p. (J). 19.99 (978-0-00-712155-7(5)) HarperCollins Pubs. Ltd. GBR. *Dist:* Independent Pubs. Group.

Pair, Regether. The Little Rock Island & a Little Rock Named Sam. 2007. 17.00 (***978-0-8059-8800-0(9)***) Dorrance Publishing Co., Inc.

Perry, Phyllis J. The Secrets of the Rock. Lipking, Ron, illus. 2004. (Fribble Mouse Library Mystery Ser.). 96p. (J). 16.95 (978-1-932146-22-6(9)) Highsmith Inc.

Rosen, Michael L. The Big Bag of Rocks. Morgan, Angelina, illus. 2002. 20p. (J). (978-0-9721044-0-1(2)) Esoteric Ink, LLC.

Stemach, Jerry. Alcatraz, the Rock. Stemach, Jerry et al, eds. Dizick, Phillip, illus. 2000. (Start-to-Finish Books: Vol. 3). (J). (gr. 2-3). 35.00 (978-1-58702-426-9(8)) Johnston, Don Inc.

ROCKY MOUNTAINS

Bauer, Marion Dane. The Rocky Mountains. Wallace, John, illus. 2006. (Wonders of America Ser.). 32p. (J). pap. 3.99 (978-0-689-86948-8(7)); lib. bdg. 11.89 (978-0-689-86949-5(5)) Simon & Schuster Children's Publishing. (Aladdin).

Bograd, Larry. The Rocky Mountains. 2001. (Ecosystems of North America Ser.). (Illus.). 64p. (J). (gr. 6 up). lib. bdg. 27.07 (978-0-7614-0925-0(4) , Benchmark Bks.) Cavendish, Marshall Corp.

Brucken, Kelli M. Bristlecone Pines. 2005. (Wonders of the World Ser.). 48p. (J). (gr. 4-8). 26.20 (978-0-7377-3061-6(7) , Greenhaven Pr., Inc.) Thomson Gale.

Calvert, Patricia. Zebulon Pike: Lost in the Rockies. 2003. (Great Explorations Ser.). (J). (978-0-7614-1740-8(0)); 29.93 (978-0-7614-1612-8(9)) Cavendish, Marshall Corp. (Benchmark Bks.).

Cheshire, Gerard. Nature Unfolds the Rocky Mountains & Deserts. 2002. (gr. 5-8). lib. bdg. 18.75 (978-0-613-81340-2(5)) Tandem Library Bks.

Doak, Robin S. Zebulon Pike: Explorer & Soldier. 2005. (Signature Lives Ser.). (Illus.). 112p. (J). (gr. 5-7). (978-0-7565-0998-9(X)) Compass Point Bks.

Geisert, Bonnie. Mountain Town. Geisert, Arthur, illus. 2000. (Small Town U. S. A. Ser.). 32p. (J). (gr. k-3). tchr. ed. 16.00 (978-0-395-95390-7(1) , Walter Lorraine) Houghton Mifflin Co. Trade & Reference Div.

Hamilton, John. The Mountains. 2003. (Lewis & Clark Expedition Ser.). (Illus.). 32p. (J). (gr. 3-8). lib. bdg. 24.21 (978-1-57765-764-4(0)) ABDO Publishing Co.

Justesen, Kim Williams & Falcon Publishing Staff. Hey Ranger! Kids Ask Questions about Rocky Mountain National Park. Newhouse, Judy, illus. 2005. 48p. (J). pap. 9.95 (978-0-7627-3848-9(0) , Falcon) Globe Pequot Pr., The.

Kathrens, Ginger. Cloud's Legacy: The Wild Stallion Returns. 2004. (Illus.). 200p. 24.95 (978-1-931993-12-8(2)) BowTie Pr.

Loomis, Jennifer A. Wildlife in the Rocky Mountains. Loomis, Jennifer A., photos by. unabr. ed. 2005. (Illus.). 100p. (J). 24.95 (978-0-88045-159-8(9)) Stemmer Hse. Pubs., Inc.

Lynch, Wayne, photos by. Rocky Mountains. 2006. (Illus.). 64p. (gr. 3-7). 16.95 (978-1-55971-948-3(6)); (J). pap. 8.95 (978-1-55971-949-0(4)) T&N Children's Publishing. (NorthWord Bks. for Young Readers).

Mader, Jan. Rocky Mountains. 2004. (Rookie Read-About Geography Ser.). 32p. (J). (gr. 1-2). pap. 5.95 (978-0-516-26832-3(5) , Children's Pr.) Scholastic Library Publishing.

Maynard, Charles W. The Rocky Mountains. 2004. (J). 21.25 (978-0-8239-6698-1(4)); (Illus.). 24p. lib. bdg. 21.25 (978-0-8239-6926-5(6)) Rosen Publishing Group, Inc., The. (PowerKids Pr.).

Mills, Enos A. & Mills, Esther Burnell. Adventures of a Nature Guide. Babcock, Dean, illus. rev. ed. 2001. 180p. 15.95 (978-1-928878-18-6(0)) Temporal Mechanical Pr.

Peluso, Beth. Charcoal Forest. 64p. (J). pap. 12.00 (***978-0-87842-532-7(2)***) Mountain Pr. Publishing Co., Inc.

Uschan, Michael V. A Mountain Man of the American Frontier. 2005. (Working Life Ser.). (Illus.). 111p. (J). (gr. 5-8). lib. bdg. 29.95 (978-1-59018-582-7(X) , Lucent Bks.) Thomson Gale.

ROCKY MOUNTAINS—FICTION

Bender, Carrie. Chestnut Ridge Acres. 2001. 288p. (J). 24.95 (978-0-7862-3416-5(4) , Five Star) Thomson Gale.

Brown, Marc. Buster Climbs the Walls. 9th ed. 2005. (Postcards from Buster Ser.). (Illus.). 48p. (J). (gr. 1-4). pap. 14.99 (978-0-316-15913-5(1)); pap. 3.99 (978-0-316-00126-7(0)) Little Brown & Co.

Bryant, Bonnie. Dude Ranch. 2007. (Saddle Club Ser.: No. 6). 144p. (J). (gr. 4-6). lib. bdg. 11.99 (978-0-385-90422-3(3) , Yearling) Random Hse. Children's Bks.

Burns, Emily. Marked Evidence. 2003. (Rocky Mountain Mysteries Ser.: 3). (J). per. 4.95 (978-0-9723259-2-9(1) , RMM3) Covered Wagon Publishing LLC.

Carole Marsh. The Rocky Mountain Mystery. 2001. 160p. (gr. 2-8). 14.95 (978-0-635-02390-2(3)) Gallopade International.

Carson, James. Saddle Boys of the Rockies or Lost on Th. 2007. pap. (***978-1-4065-1298-4(2)***) Dodo Pr.

—Saddle Boys of the Rockies or Lost on Th. 2007. 41.99 (***978-1-4280-5150-8(3)***); pap. 35.99 (***978-1-4280-5149-2(X)***) IndyPublish.com.

Crum, Anna-Maria & Fielder, John, illus. Maria's Mysterious Mission. Fielder, John, photos by. 2007. (J). 12.95 (***978-1-56579-588-4(1)***) Westcliffe Pubs.

Derrick, Patricia. Beaser the Rocky Mountain Bear. 2007. 18.95 (978-1-933818-09-2(3)) Animalations.

—Rickity & Snickity at the Balloon Fiesta. 2007. 32p. 18.95 (978-1-933818-11-5(5)) Animalations.

Fabry, Chris & Jenkins, Jerry B. Haunted Waters. 2005. (Tyndale Kids Ser.). (Illus.). 224p. (J). (ps-7). pap. 5.99 (978-1-4143-0140-2(5)) Tyndale Hse. Pubs.

Fraggolosch, Audrey. Trails above the Tree Line: A Story of a Rocky Mountain Meadow. 2005. (Soundprints' Wild Habitats Ser.). (Illus.). 32p. (J). (gr. 1-4). 8.95 incl. audio (978-1-59249-109-4(X) , SC7021) Soundprints.

James, Will. Cowboy in the Making. rev. ed. (Illus.). 104p. (gr. 4-6). pap. 15.00 (978-0-87842-439-9(3) , 811) Mountain Pr. Publishing Co., Inc.

Kroll, Virginia L. & Jones, Dawn L. Bluffy's Mighty Mountain. Maydak, Michael S., illus. 2001. (J). (978-0-9712840-3-6(2)) Boyds Collection Ltd., The.

Noland, Monica. Slide. 2006. 116p. pap. 16.95 (***978-1-4241-4966-7(5)***) PublishAmerica, Inc.

Patchin, Gee Frank. The Pony Rider Boys in the Rockies. 2006. 63.99 (***978-1-4280-0930-1(2)***); pap. 57.99 (***978-1-4280-0940-0(X)***) IndyPublish.com.

Richardson, Steve. Alexander Trout's Amazing Adventure. Lowe, Wesley, illus. 2007. 75p. 16.95 (***978-0-9786422-2-8(8)***) Impossible Dreams Publishing Co.

Sargent, Dave & Sargent, Pat. Stinky: (Sorrel) Don't Be Mischievous, 25, 56. Lenoir, Jane, illus. 2001. (Saddle Up Ser.: 56). 36p. (J). pap. (978-1-56763-666-6(7)); lib. bdg. 22.60 (978-1-56763-665-9(9)) Ozark Publishing.

Siamon, Sharon. Brave Horse. 2004. (Mustang Mountain Ser.: Vol. 6). (Illus.). 160p. (J). (gr. 3-7). pap. 6.95 (978-1-55285-528-7(7)) Whitecap Bks., Ltd. CAN. *Dist:* Firefly Bks., Ltd.

Warner, Gertrude Chandler. The Ghost Town Mystery. 1999. (Boxcar Children Ser.: No. 71). (J). (gr. 2-5). 10.75 (978-0-606-18764-0(2)) Tandem Library Bks.

—Ghost Town Mystery. 1999. (gr. 3-6). lib. bdg. 11.80 (978-0-613-16266-1(8)) Tandem Library Bks.

Warner, Gertrude Chandler, creator. The Ghost Town Mystery, Vol. 71. 1999. (Boxcar Children Ser.: No. 71). (Illus.). 128p. (J). (gr. 2-5). 14.95 (978-0-8075-2858-7(7)); pap. 3.95 (978-0-8075-2859-4(5)) Whitman, Albert & Co.

RODENTS

Goldish, Meish. Beavers & Other Rodents, Vol. 2. World Book, Inc. Staff, ed. 2002. (World Book's Animals of the World Ser.). (Illus.). 64p. (J). (978-0-7166-1225-4(9)) World Bk., Inc.

Horton-Bussey, Claire, et al. 101 Facts about Ferrets. 2002. (One Hundred One Facts about Pets Ser.). (Illus.). 32p. (J). (gr. 3 up). lib. bdg. 23.33 (978-0-8368-3016-3(4)) Stevens, Gareth Inc.

Kalman, Bobbie. What Is a Rodent? 2000. (Science of Living Things Ser.). (978-0-606-18073-3(7)); (gr. 3-6). lib. bdg. 14.10 (978-0-613-22605-9(4)) Tandem Library Bks.

Kalman, Bobbie & Langille, Jacqueline. Les Rongeurs. 2003. (FRE., Illus.). 32p. pap. (978-2-89579-005-1(1)) Crabtree Publishing Co.

—What Is a Rodent? 1999. (Science of Living Things Ser.). (Illus.). 32p. (J). (gr. 2-3). (978-0-86505-923-8(3)); pap. (978-0-86505-951-1(9)) Crabtree Publishing Co.

Kalman, Bobbie & Miller, Reagan. Guinea Pigs & Other Rodents. 2005. (What Kind of Animal Is It? Ser.). (Illus.). 32p. (J). (gr. k-6). (978-0-7787-2163-5(9)); pap. (978-0-7787-2221-2(X)) Crabtree Publishing Co.

Manera, Alexandria. Capybaras. 2003. (Animals of the Rain Forest Ser.). (Illus.). 32p. (J). 24.28 (978-0-7398-6835-5(7)) Raintree.

Miller, Sara Swan. Rodents: From Mice to Muskrats. 1998. (Animals in Order Ser.). (Illus.). 48p. (J). (gr. 4-6). 26.50 (978-0-531-11488-9(0) , Watts, Franklin) Scholastic Library Publishing.

Morgan, Sally. Rodents. 2004. (J). lib. bdg. (978-1-59389-177-0(6) , Cherrytree Books) Evans Publishing Group.

Morris, Pat, et al. Rodents 1, 10 vols., Vol. 7. 2003. (Illus.). (J). (978-0-7172-5749-2(5) , Grolier) Scholastic Library Publishing.

Patent, Dorothy Hinshaw. Saving the Prairie Bandit. 2001. (Wildlife Conservation Society Bks.). (Illus.). 48p. (J). (gr. 4-6). 24.50 (978-0-531-11851-1(7) , Watts, Franklin) Scholastic Library Publishing.

Phillips, Meredith. Rodents Rule! 2004. (Pet's Point of View Ser.). (Illus.). 32p. (J). (gr. 4 up). lib. bdg. 22.60 (978-0-7565-0701-5(4)) Compass Point Bks.

Visca, Curt & Visca, Kelley. How to Draw Cartoon Rodents. 2003. (Kid's Guide to Drawing Ser.). (Illus.). 24p. (J). lib. bdg. 21.25 (978-0-8239-6161-0(3) , PowerKids Pr.) Rosen Publishing Group, Inc., The.

RODENTS—FICTION

Howe, James & Walrod, Amy. Horace & Morris but Mostly Delores. 2003. (Illus.). 32p. (J). pap. 7.99 (978-0-689-85675-4(X) , Aladdin) Simon & Schuster Children's Publishing.

Hungry Hedgehog, 6 Packs. (Story Steps Ser.). (gr. k-2). 29.00 (978-0-7635-9583-8(7)) Rigby Education.

Jonell, Lynne. Emmy & the Incredible Shrinking Rat. Bean, Jonathan, illus. 2007. 352p. (J). (gr. 4 up). 17.95 (***978-0-8050-8150-3(X)***) Holt, Henry & Co.

Lopez Parreno, Jose Antonio. La Ratita Presumida. Mestre, Pablo, illus. 2002. (Libros para Soñar Ser.). (SPA.). 32p. (J). (978-84-8464-154-4(6)) Kalandraka Editora, S.L.

Rylant, Cynthia & McDaniels, Preston. The Storm. 2003. (Lighthouse Family Ser.). (Illus.). 80p. (J). pap. 3.99 (978-0-689-84882-7(X) , Aladdin) Simon & Schuster Children's Publishing.

Who Painted the Porcupine. (J). 23.50 (978-0-8136-3967-3(0)) Modern Curriculum Pr.

RODEOS

Andreev, Tania. Rodeo Discovery Library, 6 bks., Set. 2000. (J). (gr. 1-4). lib. bdg. 115.62 (978-1-57103-343-7(2)) Rourke Publishing, LLC.

Dickinson, Malcolm. Bill Pickett's Great Adventures: The Rodeo King's Legend Lives On. 2002. (Illus.). 100p. 10.95 (978-1-57168-737-1(8)) Eakin Pr.

Kupperberg, Paul. Rodeo Clowns. 2005. (World of Rodeo Ser.). (Illus.). 48p. (J). lib. bdg. 26.50 (978-1-4042-0546-8(2)) Rosen Publishing Group, Inc., The.

McLeese, Tex. Bronc & Bareback Riding. 2000. (Illus.). 24p. (J). (gr. 1-4). lib. bdg. 19.27 (978-1-57103-344-4(0)) Rourke Publishing, LLC.

—Bull Riding & Bullfighting. 2000. (Illus.). 24p. (J). (gr. 1-4). lib. bdg. 19.27 (978-1-57103-345-1(9)) Rourke Publishing, LLC.

—Como Hacerse Parte del Rodeo. Palacios, Argentina, tr. 2002. (Rodeo Ser.).Tr. of Joining the Rodeo. (SPA., Illus.). 24p. mass mkt. 5.95 (978-1-58952-254-1(0)) Rourke Publishing, LLC.

—Enlace en el Rodeo. Palacios, Argentina, tr. 2002. (Rodeo Ser.).Tr. of Rodeo Roping. (SPA., Illus.). 24p. mass mkt. 5.95 (978-1-58952-255-8(9) , RK31470) Rourke Publishing, LLC.

—Rodeo Barrel Racing. 2000. (Illus.). 24p. (J). (gr. 1-4). lib. bdg. 19.27 (978-1-57103-347-5(5)) Rourke Publishing, LLC.

Mikkelsen, Glen. Never Holler Whoa. 2001. (Illus.). 210p. (J). (ps-3). pap. (978-1-894454-10-0(3)) Balmur Entertainment, Ltd.

Munro, Roxie. Rodeo. 2007. (J). 15.95 (***978-1-933979-03-8(8)***) Bright Sky Pr.

Murphy, Stuart J. Rodeo Time. Wenzel, David T., illus. 2006. (MathStart Ser.). 40p. (J). 15.99 (978-0-06-055778-2(8)); pap. 5.99 (978-0-06-055779-9(6)) HarperCollins Pubs.

Petruccio, Steven James. Rodeo Coloring Book. 2004. (Dover Coloring Bks.). (Illus.). 32p. (J). pap. 3.95 (978-0-486-43330-1(7)) Dover Pubns., Inc.

Poulsen, David A. Wild Ride. 2001. (Illus.). xv, 183p. (J). (ps-3). pap. (978-1-894454-09-4(X)) Balmur Entertainment, Ltd.

Presnall, Judith Janda. Rodeo Animals. 2003. (Animals with Jobs Ser.). (Illus.). 48p. (J). 26.20 (978-0-7377-2052-5(2) , Greenhaven Pr., Inc.) Thomson Gale.

Rodeo, 6 bks., Set. (SPA.). (J). (gr. 1-4). lib. bdg. 115.62 (978-1-57103-382-6(3)) Rourke Publishing, LLC.

Sherman, Josepha. Bull Riding. (Rodeo Ser.). (Illus.). 32p. (J). (gr. 3-6). 2002. pap. 6.95 (978-1-58810-359-8(5) , 91118); 2000. lib. bdg. 21.36 (978-1-57572-505-5(3)) Heinemann Library.

—Welcome to the Rodeo! 2002. (Rodeo Ser.). (Illus.). 32p. (J). (gr. 3-6). pap. 6.95 (978-1-58810-362-8(5) , 91121) Heinemann Library.

The World of Rodeo, 6 bks., Set. Incl. Barrel Racing. Broyles, Janell. 48p. lib. bdg. 26.50 (978-1-4042-0543-7(8)); Bull Riding. Kubke, Jane & Kubke, Jessica. 48p. lib. bdg. 26.50 (978-1-4042-0544-4(6)); Calf Roping. King, Kimberly. 47p. lib. bdg. 26.50 (978-1-4042-0545-1(4)); Rodeo Clowns. Kupperberg, Paul. 48p. lib. bdg. 26.50 (978-1-4042-0546-8(2)); Team Roping. Ambrosek, Renee. 48p. lib. bdg. 26.50 (978-1-4042-0548-2(9)); (Illus.). (J). 2005. 2006. Set lib. bdg. 159.00 (978-1-4042-0836-0(4)) Rosen Publishing Group, Inc., The.

RODEOS—FICTION

Brett, Jan. Armadillo Rodeo. Brett, Jan, illus. 2002. (Illus.). (J). 23.64 (978-0-7587-1968-3(X)) Book Wholesalers, Inc.

—Armadillo Rodeo. Brett, Jan, illus. 2004. (Illus.). 32p. (J). (ps-1). pap. 6.99 (978-0-14-240125-5(0) , Puffin) Penguin Group (USA) Inc.

Brin, Susannah. Bronco Buster. 2000. (gr. 7-12). lib. bdg. 11.80 (978-0-613-51049-3(6)); (Illus.). (J). 10.75 (978-0-606-20582-5(9)) Tandem Library Bks.

Bryant, Bonnie. Rodeo Rider. 2008. (Saddle Club(R) Ser.). 144p. (J). (gr. 4-7). lib. bdg. 11.99 (***978-0-385-90550-3(5)*** , Yearling) Random Hse. Children's Bks.

Chrismer, Melanie. Phoebe Clappsaddle & The Tumbleweed Gang. Roeder, Virginia M., illus. 2002. 32p. (J). 14.95 (978-1-56554-966-1(X)) Pelican Publishing Co., Inc.

Crowe, Ellie. The Littlest Paniolo. KaMille, Barbara, illus. 2000. (J). 8.99 (978-0-89610-426-6(5)) Island Heritage Publishing.

—The Littlest Paniolo. KaMille, Barbara, illus. 2nd rev. ed. 2000. 42p. (J). per. 12.99 (978-0-9712885-2-2(6)) Regent Music & Bk. Publishing.

Elya, Susan Middleton. Cowboy Jose. Raglin, Tim, illus. 2005. 32p. (J). 15.99 (978-0-399-23570-2(1) , Putnam Juvenile) Penguin Group (USA) Inc.

Gregory, Alison. Rodeo Darcy. Wilson, Mark, illus. 2005. 40p. (J). 24.25 (978-1-876268-95-4(6)) Univ. of Western Australia Pr. AUS. *Dist:* International Specialized Bk. Services.

Halvorson, Marilyn. Bull Rider. 2003. (Orca Soundings Ser.). 96p. (J). (gr. 7-12). pap. 7.95 (978-1-55143-233-5(1)) Orca Bk. Pubs. USA.

Harcourt School Publishers Staff. Bill Pickett Advanced Level. 3rd ed. 2002. (Trophies Reading Program Ser.). (Illus.). pap. 5.10 (978-0-15-323124-7(6)) Harcourt Schl. Pubs.

Harper, Jo. Ollie Jolly, Rodeo Clown. Meissner, Amy, illus. 2002. 32p. (J). (gr. k-3). 15.95 (978-1-55868-552-9(9)); pap. 8.95 (978-1-55868-553-6(7)) Graphic Arts Ctr. Publishing Co. (West Winds Pr.).

—Ollie Jolly, Rodeo Clown. 2002. (gr. k-3). lib. bdg. 17.60 (978-0-613-89457-9(X)) Tandem Library Bks.

Johnston, Tony. Wild, Wild Rodeo! 1998. (Sparky & Eddie Ser.). (978-0-606-13793-5(9)) Tandem Library Bks.

Peck, Robert Newton. Horse Thief: A Novel. 2003. (gr. 7-12). lib. bdg. 14.15 (978-0-613-65695-5(4)) Tandem Library Bks.

Rotenberg, Lisa. Rodeo Pup. 1998. (Illus.). 32p. (J). (gr. k-2). 14.95 (978-1-55209-245-3(3)) Firefly Bks., Ltd.

Santillo, LuAnn. The Best Tricks. Santillo, LuAnn, ed. 2003. (Half-Pint Kids Readers Ser.). (Illus.). 7p. (J). (ps-1). pap. (978-1-59256-082-0(2)) Half-Pint Kids, Inc.

Sargent, Dave & Sargent, Pat. Rusty: (Red Roan) Be Strong & Brave, 30, 52. Lenoir, Jane, illus. 2003. (Saddle Up Ser.: Vol. 52). 42p. (J). pap. 6.95 (978-1-56763-804-2(X)); lib. bdg. 22.60 (978-1-56763-803-5(1)) Ozark Publishing.

Sherman, Josepha. Bronc Riding. (Rodeo Ser.). (Illus.). 32p. (J). (gr. 3-6). 2002. pap. 6.95 (978-1-58810-358-1(7) , 91117); 2000. lib. bdg. 21.36 (978-1-57572-504-8(5)) Heinemann Library.

Siamon, Sharon. Rodeo Horse. 2003. (Mustang Mountain Ser.). (Illus.). 144p. (J). (gr. 3-7). pap. 6.95 (978-1-55285-467-9(1)) Whitecap Bks., Ltd. CAN. *Dist:* Firefly Bks., Ltd.

Speer, Bonnie Stahlman. Miss Little Britches: A Story of Junior Rodeo. 1999. 141p. (J). (gr. 4 up). mass mkt. 11.95 (978-1-889683-12-6(4)) Reliance Pr.

Townsend, Tom. The Ballad of Ol' Hook. 2006. (YA). pap. 9.95 (***978-1-932196-91-7(9)***) WordWright.biz, Inc.

Yorks, Sharon Lene. The Twin Who Wins. 2002. (Cloverleaf Ser.: Bk. 1). (Illus.). 224p. (J). (gr. 6 up). mass mkt. 5.99 (978-0-9720132-0-8(2)) Tumbleweed Publishing.

RODIN, AUGUSTE, 1840-1917

Richard Tames. Auguste Rodin. 2nd ed. 2006. (Heinemann First Library). (Illus.). 32p. (J). pap. (***978-1-4034-8499-4(6)***) Heinemann Library.

Tames, Richard. Auguste Rodin. (Heinemann First Library). 32p. (J). 2006. (Illus.). lib. bdg. (***978-1-4034-8488-8(0)***); 2000. lib. bdg. 21.36 (978-1-57572-342-6(5)); Set 1. 2002. (Illus.). pap. 6.50 (978-1-58810-288-1(2) , 91051) Heinemann Library.

ROENTGEN, WILHELM CONRAD, 1845-1923

Garcia, Kimberly. Wilhelm Roentgen & the Discovery of X-Rays. 2001. (Unlocking the Secrets of Science Ser.). (Illus.). 56p. (gr. 4-10). lib. bdg. 17.95 (978-1-58415-114-2(5)) Mitchell Lane Pubs., Inc.

ROENTGEN RAYS

see X-Rays

ROGERS, ROBERT, 1731-1795

Bruchac, Marge. Malian's Song. Maughan, William, illus. 2006. (Vermont Folklife Center Children's Book Ser.). 36p. 16.95 (978-0-916718-26-8(3)) Univ. Pr. of New England.

Gauch, Patricia Lee. The Impossible Major Rogers. Parker, Robert Andrew, illus. 2008. (J). (978-1-59078-334-4(4)) Boyds Mills Pr.

Quasha, Jennifer. Robert Rogers: Rogers' Rangers & the French & Indian War. 2005. (Library of American Lives & Times). (Illus.). 112p. (J). (gr. 4-8). lib. bdg. 31.95 (978-0-8239-5731-6(4)) Rosen Publishing Group, Inc., The.

ROGERS, WILL, 1879-1935

Donovan, Sandra. Will Rogers: Cowboy, Comedian, & Commentator. 2006. (Signature Lives Ser.). (Illus.). 112p. (J). (gr. 4-8). lib. bdg. 31.93 (978-0-7565-2463-0(6)) Compass Point Bks.

Keating, Frank. Will Rogers: An American Legend. Wimmer, Mike, illus. 2002. 32p. (J). (gr. 1-4). 17.00 (978-0-15-202405-5(0) , Silver Whistle) Harcourt Trade Pubs.

ROLLER-SKATING

see also In-Line Skating; Skateboarding

Group/McGraw-Hill, Wright. Roma Roller Skater: Level H, 6 vols. (Take Twostm Ser.). 16p. 29.95 (978-0-322-08965-5(4)) Wright Group, The.

Mahaney, Ian F. Taig Khris: In-Line Skate Champion. 2005. (Extreme Sports Biographies Ser.). (Illus.). 24p. (J). 19.95 (978-1-4042-2746-0(6) , PowerKids Pr.) Rosen Publishing Group, Inc., The.

Shafran, Michael. Skate! Your Guide to Blading, Aggressive, Vert, Street, Roller Hockey, Speed Skating, Dance, Fitness Training, & More. 2003. (Illus.). 64p. (J). (gr. 4-7). pap. 8.95 (978-0-7922-5107-1(5) , National Geographic Children's Bks.) National Geographic Society.

ROLLER-SKATING—FICTION

Blackaby, Susan. Jake Skates. Olin, Troy, illus. 2007. (Read-It! Readers Ser.). (J). 19.93 (978-1-4048-2412-6(X)) Picture Window Bks.

Hobbie, Nathaniel. Priscilla, Superstar. Hobbie, Jocelyn, illus. 2007. 36p. (J). (ps-1). 16.99 (978-0-316-01386-4(2)) Little Brown & Co.

Johnson, Andi. Rollerskate Kate. 2004. (Illus.). 16p. 9.00 (978-1-84161-115-0(8)) Ravette Publishing, Ltd. GBR. *Dist:* Parkwest Pubns., Inc.

Johnson, Mildred D. Wait, Skates! 1999. (gr. k-3). lib. bdg. 12.95 (978-0-613-54761-1(6)) Tandem Library Bks.

Prince, Sarah. I Can't Find My Roller Skates. 1999. (ps-2). lib. bdg. 11.80 (978-0-613-30487-0(X)) Tandem Library Bks.

Siegel, Phil. Simon the Daredevil Centipede: He Learned to Skate - & Much, Much More. Caiarelli, Alisa, illus. 1998. 28p. (J). pap. 8.95 (978-0-932991-58-4(0) , Different Bks.) Place In The Woods, The.

ROLLING STOCK

see Locomotives

ROMAN ANTIQUITIES

see Classical Antiquities; Rome—Antiquities

ROMAN ART

see Art, Roman

ROMAN CATHOLIC CHURCH

see Catholic Church

ROMAN MYTHOLOGY

see Mythology, Classical

ROMANIA

Itzkowitz, Norman. Vlad the Impaler: The Real Count Dracula. 2007. (Wicked History Ser.). (Illus.). 128p. (YA). (gr. 8-12). lib. bdg. 30.00 (***978-0-531-12599-1(8)*** , Watts, Franklin) Scholastic Library Publishing.

Kerns, Ann. Romania in Pictures. 2007. (Visual Geography Ser.). (Illus.). 80p. (J). 27.93 (978-0-8225-2497-7(X) , Twenty-First Century Bks.) Lerner Publishing Group.

Oprea, Tiberiu. Romania. 2003. (Countries of the World Ser.). (Illus.). 96p. (J). (gr. 6 up). lib. bdg. 30.00 (978-0-8368-2367-7(2)) Stevens, Gareth Inc.

Popescu, Julian. Romania. 1999. (Major World Nations Ser.). (Illus.). 111p. (J). (gr. 4-7). 29.95 (978-0-7910-5396-6(2) , Chelsea Hse.) Facts On File, Inc.

Pundyk, Grace. Welcome to Romania. 2004. (Welcome to My Country Ser.). (Illus.). 48p. (J). lib. bdg. 26.00 (978-0-8368-2567-1(5)) Stevens, Gareth Inc.

Van Cleaf, Kristin. Romania. 2007. (Countries Set VI Ser.). (Illus.). 40p. (J). (gr. k-6). lib. bdg. 24.21 (***978-1-59928-785-0(4)*** , Checkerboard Library) ABDO Publishing Co.

Willis, Terri & Carran, Betty B. Romania. 2001. (Enchantment of the World, Second Ser.). (Illus.). 114p. (J). (gr. 5-9). 36.00 (978-0-516-21635-5(X) , Children's Pr.) Scholastic Library Publishing.

ROMANIA—FICTION

Bush, Suzanne & Takes, Deb. Time Will Tell. 2004. 279p. (YA). lib. bdg. 15.95 (978-0-9747426-0-1(0)) Imagining Possibilities.

Clement-Davies, David. Fell. 2007. 542p. (YA). (gr. 7-17). 19.95 (***978-0-8109-1185-7(X)***) Abrams, Harry N. , Inc.

—Fell. 2007. 432p. (YA). pap. 19.95 (***978-0-8109-9470-6(4)***) Abrams, Harry N. , Inc.

Clement-Davies, David. The Sight. 2002. (gr. 7-12). lib. bdg. 16.45 (978-0-613-68285-5(8)) Tandem Library Bks.

Gundisch, Karin. How I Became an American. Skofield, James, tr. from GER. 2001. (Illus.). 144p. (J). (gr. 3-7). 15.95 (978-0-8126-4875-1(7)) Cricket Bks.

Stoker, Bram. Bram Stoker's Dracula. Needle, Jan, ed. Blythe, Gary, illus. 2004. 336p. (J). (gr. 7 up). 18.99 (978-0-7636-2508-5(6)) Candlewick Pr.

Stoker, Bram, et al. Dracula. Marcos, Pablo, illus. 2005. (Great Illustrated Classics Ser.). 239p. (J). (gr. 3-8). 21.35 (978-1-59679-240-1(X) , ABDO & Daughters) ABDO Publishing Co.

Weber, Lori. Strange Beauty. 2006. (SideStreets Ser.). 144p. (YA). (gr. 7-12). (***978-1-55028-944-2(6)***); 7.95 (***978-1-55028-941-1(1)***) Lorimer, James & Co., Ltd., Pubs. CAN. *Dist:* Casemate Pubs. & Bk. Distributors, LLC.

ROME

Here are entered works about the Roman Empire. Works only on the modern city of Rome are entered under Rome (Italy).

Barghusen, Joan D. Daily Life in Ancient & Modern Rome. Webb, Ray, illus. 1999. (Cities Through Time Ser.). 64p. (gr. 5-12). 25.26 (978-0-8225-3213-2(1)) Lerner Publishing Group.

Beller, Susan Provost. Roman Legions on the March: Soldiering in the Ancient Roman Army. 2007. (Soldiers on the Battlefront Ser.). (Illus.). 112p. (YA). (gr. 6-8). lib. bdg. 33.26 (***978-0-8225-6781-3(4)*** , Twenty-First Century Bks.) Lerner Publishing Group.

Brouillet, Chrystine. La Malediction des Opales. Gagnon, Nathalie, illus. 2002. (Roman Jeunesse Ser.). (FRE.). 96p. (YA). (gr. 4-7). pap. (978-2-89021-280-0(7)) Diffusion du livre Mirabel.

Chrisp, Peter. Ancient Rome. 2007. (Google E Guides). (Illus.). 96p. (J). 17.99 (978-0-7566-1955-8(6)) Dorling Kindersley Publishing, Inc.

—Ancient Rome. 2005. (History in Art Ser.). (Illus.). 48p. (J). lib. bdg. 29.93 (978-1-4109-0520-8(9)) Steck-Vaughn.

—Ancient Rome. 2000. (My World Ser.). (Illus.). (J). 14.75 (978-0-606-21905-1(6)) Tandem Library Bks.

—Romans. 1999. (Interfact Reference Ser.). (Illus.). 48p. (J). (gr. 2-8). 15.00 (978-0-7166-7215-9(4) , 1543) World Bk., Inc.

Crisp, Peter. Romans. (Illus.). 48p. (J). 2004. (Interfact Ser.). (SPA.). (gr. 3-6). pap. 14.95 incl. cd-rom (978-1-58728-462-5(6)); 2000. (Collectafact Ser.: Vol. 6). (gr. 1-5). 4.95 (978-1-58728-753-4(6)) T&N Children's Publishing. (Two Can Publishing).

Dargie, Richard. A Roman Villa. Hook, Adam, illus. 2000. (Look Inside Ser.). 32p. (J). (gr. 4-7). lib. bdg. 25.69 (978-0-7398-2380-4(9)) Raintree.

Di Pasquale, Giovanni & Bardi, Matilde. Ancient Rome. Cantucci, Alessandro, illus. 2002. (Art & Civilization Ser.). 40p. (J). (gr. 3 up). 16.95 (978-0-87226-687-2(7) , Bedrick, Peter Bks.) School Specialty Publishing.

Dorling Kindersley Publishing Staff. Rome. 2006. (Eyewitness Travel Guides Ser.). 448p. pap. 25.00 (978-0-7566-1550-5(X)) Dorling Kindersley Publishing, Inc.

Dorling Kindersley Publishing Staff, ed. Ancient Rome. 2004. (Dk Eyewitness Books Ser.). (Illus.). 72p. (J). 15.99 (978-0-7566-0651-0(9)) Dorling Kindersley Publishing, Inc.

Dubois, Muriel L. Ancient Rome. 2004. (Illus.). 48p. (J). 17.95 (978-0-7368-2469-9(3)) Capstone Pr., Inc.

Ganeri, Anita. Ancient Romans. 2000. (History Starts Here Ser.). (Illus.). 32p. (J). (ps-3). pap. 8.95 (978-0-7398-1822-0(8)) Steck-Vaughn.

Gedacht, Daniel C. Home Life in Ancient Rome. 2004. (Primary Sources of Ancient Civilizations Ser.). (Illus.). 24p. (J). lib. bdg. (978-0-8239-8945-4(3)); lib. bdg. 19.95 (978-0-8239-6778-0(6)) Rosen Publishing Group, Inc., The. (PowerKids Pr.).

—Land & Resources of Ancient Rome. 2004. (Primary Sources of Ancient Civilizations Ser.). (Illus.). 24p. (J). lib. bdg. (978-0-8239-8943-0(7) , PowerKids Pr.) Rosen Publishing Group, Inc., The.

—Politics & Government in Ancient Rome. 2004. (Primary Sources of Ancient Civilizations Ser.). (Illus.). 24p. (J). lib. bdg. (978-0-8239-8948-5(8)); lib. bdg. 19.95 (978-0-8239-6777-3(8)) Rosen Publishing Group, Inc., The. (PowerKids Pr.).

Harris, Jacqueline L. Science in Ancient Rome. 1998. (Illus.). 64p. (J). (ps-6). lib. bdg. 17.60 (978-0-613-19128-9(5)) Tandem Library Bks.

Hart, Avery & Gallagher, Sandra. Ancient Rome! Exploring the Culture, People & Ideas of This Powerful Empire. Kline, Michael P., illus. 2001. (Kaleidoscope Kids Bks.). 96p. (J). (gr. 3-9). pap. 12.95 (978-1-885593-60-3(0) , Williamson Bks.) Ideals Pubns.

Hewitt, Sally. Romans. 1998. (Footsteps in Time Ser.). 24p. (J). (gr. 2-5). pap. 3.95 (978-0-516-26233-8(5) , Children's Pr.) Scholastic Library Publishing.

Hinds, Kathryn. Religion. 2004. (J). 29.93 (978-0-7614-1657-9(9) , Benchmark Bks.) Cavendish, Marshall Corp.

Honan, Linda & Kosmer, Ellen. Spend the Day in Ancient Rome: Projects & Activities that Bring the Past to Life. 1998. (Spend the Day Ser.). (Illus.). 128p. (gr. 3-7). pap. 14.95 (978-0-471-15453-2(9) , Wiley) Wiley, John & Sons, Inc.

Kuntz, Lynn. The Roman Colosseum. 2004. (Great Structures in History Ser.). (Illus.). 48p. (J). (gr. 4-7). 26.20 (978-0-7377-1561-3(8) , Greenhaven Pr., Inc.) Thomson Gale.

Landau, Elaine. Exploring Ancient Rome with Elaine Landau. 2005. (Exploring Ancient Civilizations with Elaine Landau Ser.). (Illus.). 48p. (J). (gr. 3-6). lib. bdg. 23.93 (978-0-7660-2337-6(0) , Enslow Elementary) Enslow Pubs., Inc.

MacDonald, Fiona. Ancient Rome. 2004. (Excavating the Past Ser.). (Illus.). 48p. (J). pap. 8.50 (978-1-4034-5458-4(2)); lib. bdg. (978-1-4034-4838-5(8)) Heinemann Library.

—The Romans. 2003. (Strange Histories Ser.). (Illus.). 32p. (J). lib. bdg. 25.70 (978-0-7398-6442-5(4)) Raintree.

—So You Want to Be a Roman Soldier. Hewetson, Nicholas, illus. 1999. (So You Want to Be... Ser.). 32p. (gr. 3-6). lib. bdg. 21.90 (978-0-7613-1421-9(0) , Twenty-First Century Bks.) Lerner Publishing Group.

Malam, John. Ancient Rome. 2007. (Illus.). 64p. (J). ***(978-1-4109-2734-7(2)); (*978-1-4109-2727-9(X))*** Steck-Vaughn.

Malam, John. Exploring Ancient Rome. 2001. (Remains to Be Seen Ser.). (Illus.). 47p. (gr. 5-8). 22.95 (978-0-237-52003-8(6) , Evans Brothers, Limited) Evans Publishing Group GBR. *Dist:* Independent Pubs. Group.

Mann, Elizabeth. The Roman Colosseum: The Story of the World's Most Famous Stadium & Its Deadly Games. Racz, Michael, illus. 1998. (Wonders of the World Ser.). 48p. (J). (gr. 4-7). 19.95 (978-0-9650493-3-7(7)) Mikaya Pr.

Markel, Rita J. Your Travel Guide to Ancient Rome. 2005. (Passport to History Ser.). (Illus.). 96p. (J). lib. bdg. 26.60 (978-0-8225-3071-8(6)) Lerner Publishing Group.

Mighty Rome! Individual Title Six-Packs. (Rigby Infoquest Ser.). 32p. (gr. 4 up). 37.00 (978-0-7578-5737-9(X)) Rigby Education.

Minnis. Ancient Rome. 2004. (Raintree Perspectives Ser.). (Illus.). 32p. (J). 25.70 (978-1-4109-0618-2(3)) Harcourt Schl. Pubs.

Minnis, Ivan. You Are in Ancient Rome. 2004. (Raintree Perspectives Ser.). (Illus.). 32p. (J). pap. 7.50 (978-1-4109-1010-3(5)) Harcourt Schl. Pubs.

Nardo, Don. The Ancient Romans. 2001. (Lost Civilizations Ser.). (Illus.). 128p. (YA). (gr. 6-9). 29.95 (978-1-56006-706-1(3) , LML00902-178058, Lucent Bks.) Thomson Gale.

—Life in Ancient Rome. 2003. (Life During the Great Civilizations Ser.). (Illus.). 48p. (J). (gr. 3-5). 24.95 (978-1-56711-742-4(2) , Blackbirch Pr., Inc.) Thomson Gale.

—Roman Roads & Aqueducts. 2000. (Building History Ser.). (Illus.). 96p. (J). (gr. 6-9). 28.70 (978-1-56006-721-4(7) , Lucent Bks.) Thomson Gale.

Powell, Anton, et al. Roman News. 1999. (News Ser.). (Illus.). 32p. (J). (gr. 4-9). pap. 6.99 (978-0-7636-0341-0(4)) Candlewick Pr.

Quadrillion Media Staff. Ancient Rome (Das Alte Rom), Vol. 8. 1998. (Start Me Up Ser.: Vol. 8). (Illus.). 48p. (J). (gr. 4-7). pap. 12.95 (978-1-58185-008-6(5) , Tessloff Publishing) Quadrillion Media LLC.

Rees, Rosemary. The Ancient Romans. (Understanding People in the Past Ser.). 64p. (J). (gr. 4-6). 2002. (Illus.). pap. 8.95 (978-1-58810-316-1(1) , 91122); 1999. lib. bdg. 27.07 (978-1-57572-890-2(7)) Heinemann Library.

Shuter, Jane. The Ancient Romans. 1999. (History Opens Windows Ser.). 32p. (J). (gr. 2-4). pap. (978-1-57572-592-5(4)) Heinemann Library.

—Life in a Roman Town. 2004. (Picture the Past Ser.). (Illus.). 32p. (J). 24.22 (978-1-4034-5828-5(6)); pap. 7.50 (978-1-4034-5836-0(7)) Heinemann Library.

Solway, Andrew. Rome: In Spectacular Cross Section. Biesty, Stephen, illus. 2003. (Rome Ser.). 32p. (J). 18.95 (978-0-439-45546-6(4)) Scholastic, Inc.

Steele, Philip. Find Out about the Roman Empire. 2000. (Illus.). 64p. pap. 7.95 (978-1-84215-039-9(1) , Southwater) Anness Publishing GBR. *Dist:* National Bk. Network.

Tames, Richard. Ancient Roman Children. (People in the Past Ser.). (Illus.). 48p. (J). 2003. (gr. 4-6). lib. bdg. 27.07 (978-1-58810-634-6(9)); 2002. pap. 7.95 (978-1-4034-0518-0(2)) Heinemann Library.

Williams, Brenda & Williams, Brian. Staying Alive in Ancient Rome: Life in Ancient Rome. 2007. (J). ***(978-1-4109-2890-0(X)); pap. (*978-1-4109-2897-9(7))*** Steck-Vaughn.

Williams, Brian. Ancient Roman Homes. (People in the Past Ser.). (Illus.). 48p. (J). 2003. (gr. 4-6). lib. bdg. 25.64 (978-1-58810-631-5(4)); 2002. pap. 8.50 (978-1-4034-0519-7(0)) Heinemann Library.

—Ancient Roman Women. (People in the Past Ser.). (Illus.). 48p. (J). 2003. (gr. 4-6). lib. bdg. 27.07 (978-1-58810-632-2(2)); 2002. pap. 8.50 (978-1-4034-0522-7(0)) Heinemann Library.

Wroble, Lisa A. Kids in Ancient Rome. 1999. (Kids Throughout History Ser.). (Illus.). 24p. (J). (gr. 3). lib. bdg. 18.75 (978-0-8239-5253-3(3) , PowerKids Pr.) Rosen Publishing Group, Inc., The.

ROME—ANTIQUITIES

Allen, T. R. Antiquus: The Colosseum of Rome. Allen, T. R. & Kubiak, Mike, photos by. 2002. (Antiquus). cd-rom 12.00 (978-1-931792-19-6(4)) E-Digital Bks., LLC.

Bingham, Jane. Look Around a Roman Villa. 2007. (J). ***(*978-1-84193-723-6(1))*** Smart Apple Media.

Deckker, Zilah Quezado. Ancient Rome: Archaeolology Unlocks the Secrets of Ancient Rome. 2007. (National Geographic Investigates Ser.). (Illus.). 64p. (YA). (gr. 5 up). lib. bdg. 27.90 ***(*978-1-4263-0129-2(4)*** , National Geographic Children's Bks.) National Geographic Society.

MacDonald, Fiona. Ancient Rome. 2004. (Excavating the Past Ser.). (Illus.). 48p. (J). pap. 8.50 (978-1-4034-5458-4(2)); lib. bdg. (978-1-4034-4838-5(8)) Heinemann Library.

Malam, John. The Traveler's Guide to Ancient Rome. Foster, Mike S., illus. 1999. (J). (978-0-590-11763-0(7)) Scholastic, Inc.

Mann, Elizabeth. The Roman Colosseum: The Story of the World's Most Famous Stadium & Its Deadly Games. Racz, Michael, illus. 1998. (Wonders of the World Ser.). 48p. (J). (gr. 4-7). 19.95 (978-0-9650493-3-7(7)) Mikaya Pr.

Nardo, Don. Roman Amphitheaters. 2002. (Watts Library). (Illus.). 64p. (J). (gr. 5-7). pap. 8.95 (978-0-531-16224-8(9)); 25.50 (978-0-531-12036-1(8)) Scholastic Library Publishing. (Watts, Franklin).

—Roman Amphitheaters. 2002. (gr. 3-6). lib. bdg. 17.60 (978-0-613-53859-6(5)) Tandem Library Bks.

—The Roman Colosseum. 2001. (Building History Ser.). (Illus.). 96p. (YA). (gr. 6-9). 27.45 (978-1-56006-429-9(3) , Lucent Bks.) Thomson Gale.

Rees, Rosemary. The Ancient Romans. 2006. (Illus.). 64p. (J). ***(*978-1-4034-8748-3(0))*** Heinemann Library.

Shuter, Jane. Life in a Roman Fort. 2004. (Picture the Past Ser.). (Illus.). 32p. (J). 24.22 (978-1-4034-5829-2(4)) Heinemann Library.

—Life in a Roman Villa. 2004. (Picture the Past Ser.). (Illus.). 32p. (J). 24.22 (978-1-4034-5830-8(8)); pap. (978-1-4034-5838-4(3)) Heinemann Library.

ROME—BIOGRAPHY

Baker, Rosalie F. & Baker, Charles F., III. Ancient Romans: Expanding the Classical Tradition. 1998. (Profiles Ser.). (Illus.). 272p. (YA). (gr. 9 up). reprint ed. 52.95 (978-0-19-510884-2(1)) Oxford Univ. Pr., Inc.

Galford, Ellen. Julius Caesar: The Boy Who Conquered an Empire. 2007. (World History Biographies Ser.). (Illus.). 64p. (J). (gr. 3-7). 17.95 (978-1-4263-0064-6(6)); lib. bdg. 27.90 (978-1-4263-0065-3(4)) National Geographic Society. (National Geographic Children's Bks.).

Haaren, John H. & Poland, A. B. Famous Men of Ancient Rome: Lives of Julius Caesar, Nero, Marcus Aurelius & Others. 2005. 160p. (J). (gr. 3). pap. 7.95 (978-0-486-44361-4(2)) Dover Pubns., Inc.

—Famous Men of Rome (Yesterday's Classics) 2006. (Illus.). 260p. (J). per. 11.95 (978-1-59915-046-8(8)) Yesterday's Classics.

Morgan, Julian. Hadrian: Consolidating the Empire. 2003. (Leaders of Ancient Rome Ser.). (Illus.). 112p. (YA). (gr. 5-8). lib. bdg. 31.95 (978-0-8239-3593-2(0) , Rosen Central) Rosen Publishing Group, Inc., The.

Nardo, Don. Influential Figures of Ancient Rome. 2004. (Lucent Library of Historical Eras). (Illus.). 128p. (J). 27.45 (978-1-59018-285-7(5) , Lucent Bks.) Thomson Gale.

Orr, Tamra. Marcus Brutus. 2006. (J). lib. bdg. (978-1-58415-511-9(6)) Mitchell Lane Pubs., Inc.

White, John S. The Boys' & Girls' Plutarch. 2004. reprint ed. pap. 28.95 (978-1-4191-5511-6(3)); pap. 1.99 (978-1-4192-5511-3(8)) Kessinger Publishing, LLC.

Williams, Rose. The Young Romans. 2007. (LAT & ENG.). pap. ***(*978-0-86516-670-7(6))*** Bolchazy-Carducci Pubs.

ROME—FICTION

Alfonseca, Manuel. El Sello de Eolo (The Aeolus Seal) 2000. (SPA.). 162p. (YA). (gr. 6-8). 9.75 (978-84-236-5515-1(6)) Edebé ESP. *Dist:* Baker & Taylor Bks.

Amery, Heather & Vanagas, Patricia. Rome & Romans. 2005. 32p. (J). pap. 6.95 (978-0-7945-0336-9(5) , Usborne) EDC Publishing.

Banks, Lynne Reid. Tiger, Tiger. 2005. 208p. (gr. 7-12). (J). 15.95 (978-0-385-73240-6(6)); (YA). lib. bdg. 17.99 (978-0-385-90264-9(6)) Random Hse. Children's Bks. (Delacorte Bks. for Young Readers).

Barclay, Katerina & Barclay, Aegea. The Hand of Zeus. Barclay, Katerina, illus. 2004. (J). 24.95 (978-0-9758803-0-2(6) , 206.612.9698); 29.95 (978-0-9758803-1-9(4) , 206 234 2572) Aegean Design.

Downey, Glen. Gladiators. 2007. (Illus.). 48p. (J). lib. bdg. 23.08 ***(*978-1-4242-1627-7(3))*** Fitzgerald Bks.

Goscinny, René & Uderzo, Albert. Asterix Omnibus 1. 2008. (Illus.). 144p. 27.95 ***(*978-0-7528-9154-5(5))*** Orion Bks. Ltd. GBR. *Dist:* Sterling Publishing Co., Inc.

Henty, G. A. The Young Carthaginian: A Tale of the Times of Hannibal. 2004. pap. 8.95 (978-1-57646-874-6(7)) Quiet Vision Publishing.

Jacobson, Jack. No Ordinary Boy. 2003. 188p. (YA). pap. 13.95 (978-1-58736-165-4(5) , Starbound Bks.) Wheatmark.

Lattimore, San Souci. Child of Atlantis. (J). 15.95 (978-0-8118-4089-7(1)) Chronicle Bks. LLC.

Lawrence, Carol & Lawrence, Caroline. The Assassins of Rome. 2003. (Roman Mysteries Ser.: Bk. 4). (Illus.). 176p. (J). (gr. 6-9). 15.95 (978-0-7613-1940-5(9)) Roaring Brook Pr.

Llorente, Pilar Molina. Aura Gris. (SPA.). 192p. (YA). (gr. 5-8). (978-84-216-0993-4(9) , BU3870) Bruño, Editorial ESP. *Dist:* Lectorum Pubns., Inc.

McKee, David. Mr. Benn, Gladiator. 2002. (Illus.). 32p. (J). (ps-3). 17.99 (978-1-84270-024-2(3)) Andersen GBR. *Dist:* Trafalgar Square Publishing.

Oh, Cirro. Greek & Roman Mythology, Vol. 3. Chun, C. S., illus. 2005. 160p. (J). pap. 12.95 (978-981-05-2766-2(7)) Youngjin (Singapore) Pte Ltd. SGP. *Dist:* Independent Pubs. Group.

Riggs, Sandy. Three Ancient Communities. 2005. (Navigators Ser.). (J). pap. 38.00 ***(*978-1-4108-5093-5(5))*** Benchmark Education Co.

Scieszka, Jon. Nos Vemos, Gladiador.Tr. of See you later, gladiator. (SPA.). (J). 7.95 (978-958-04-6484-6(7)) Norma S.A. COL. *Dist:* Distribuidora Norma, Inc.

—See You Later, Gladiator. McCauley, Adam, illus. (Time Warp Trio Ser.: No. 9). 96p. (J). (gr. 2-5). 2000. 14.99 (978-0-670-89340-9(4) , Viking Juvenile); Vol. 9. 2004. pap. 4.99 (978-0-14-240117-0(X) , Puffin) Penguin Group (USA) Inc.

Sienkiewicz, Henryka. Quo Vadis. (SPA., Illus.). 168p. (YA). 11.95 (978-84-7281-132-4(8) , AF1132) Auriga, Ediciones S.A. ESP. *Dist:* Continental Bk. Co., Inc.

Simon, Les. The Secret of the Red Silk Pouch. 1998. 157p. (YA). (gr. 8-12). pap. 9.99 (978-0-88092-362-0(8) , 3628) Royal Fireworks Publishing Co.

Snedeker, Caroline Dale. A Triumph for Flavius. 2004. (Illus.). 87p. (J). per. 13.95 (978-0-9667067-1-0(4)) American Home-School Publishing, LLC.

Strauss, Peggy Guthart. Getting the Boot. 2005. (S. A. S. S. (Students Across the Seven Seas) Ser.). (Illus.). 192p. (YA). (gr. 6). pap. 6.99 (978-0-14-240414-0(4) , Puffin) Penguin Group (USA) Inc.

Vida Publishers Staff, contrib. by. Los Guarda Historias, Bk. 2. 1998. (SPA., Illus.). 64p. (J). (ps-3). pap. 2.49 (978-0-8297-2228-4(9)) Vida Pubs.

Winterfeld, Henry. Detectives in Togas. Winston, Richard & Winston, Clara, trs. from GER. Kleinert, Charlotte, illus. 2002. 272p. (YA). (gr. 3 up). pap. 5.95 (978-0-15-216280-1(1) , Odyssey Classics) Harcourt Children's Bks.

—Detectives in Togas. 2002. (gr. 3-6). lib. bdg. 14.10 (978-0-613-56309-3(3)) Tandem Library Bks.

—Mystery of the Roman Ransom. McCormick, Edith Rockefeller, tr. from GER. Biermann, Fritz, illus. 2002. Tr. of Caius Geht ein Licht Auf. 240p. (YA). (gr. 3 up). pap. 6.95 (978-0-15-216268-9(2) , Odyssey Classics) Harcourt Children's Bks.

—Mystery of the Roman Ransom. 2002. Tr. of Caius Geht ein Licht Auf. (gr. 3-6). lib. bdg. 14.10 (978-0-613-56538-7(X)) Tandem Library Bks.

ROME—HISTORY

Ackroyd, Peter. Ancient Rome. 2007. (Voyages Through Time Ser.). 144p. (J). pap. 9.99 (978-0-7566-2168-1(2)) Dorling Kindersley Publishing, Inc.

Activities Pro Liberis, Vol II: A Collection of Classical Studies Lessons & Activities for the Elementary School. 2000. spiral bd. (978-0-939507-57-3(9) , B35B) American Classical League, The.

Adams, Simon. Life in Ancient Rome. 2005. (Kingfisher Knowledge Ser.). (Illus.). 64p. (J). (gr. 5-9). 12.95 (978-0-7534-5863-1(2) , Kingfisher) Houghton Mifflin Co. Trade & Reference Div.

Ancient Rome, 6 vols. (gr. 2-5). 36.95 (978-0-7368-4621-9(2)) Red Brick Learning.

Ancient Rome. 2003. (Mr. Donn & Maxie's Always Something You Can Use Ser.). spiral bd. 19.95 (978-1-56004-162-7(5)); spiral bd. 16.95 (978-1-56004-154-2(4)) Social Studies Schl. Service.

Ancient Rome Student Book. 2006. (YA). spiral bd. 34.90 ***(*978-0-9773990-8-6(7))*** Mother's Hse. Publishing.

Ardagh, Philip. The Romans. 2001. (History Detectives Ser.). (Illus.). 64p. (J). (gr. 3 up). 16.95 (978-0-87226-631-5(1) , 66311B, Bedrick, Peter Bks.) School Specialty Publishing.

Armentrout, David & Armentrout, Patricia. Rome. 2003. (Illus.). 32p. (J). 28.50 (978-1-58952-723-2(2)) Rourke Publishing, LLC.

Ashworth, Leon. Ancient Rome. 2002. (Illus.). 32p. (J). lib. bdg. 24.25 (978-1-58340-194-1(6)) Smart Apple Media.

Bargallo I Chaves, Eva. Rome. 2005. (Ancient Civilizations Ser.). (Illus.). 32p. (J). (gr. 4-8). lib. bdg. 28.00 (978-0-7910-8602-5(X) , Chelsea Clubhouse) Facts On File, Inc.

Baxter, Nicola. The Romans. (Illus.). 32p. (YA). (gr. 3 up). lib. bdg. 27.10 (978-1-932889-02-4(7)) Sea-To-Sea Pubns.

Benchmark Education Staff. Rome Long Ago. 2005. 2.00 ***(*978-1-4108-4682-2(2))*** Benchmark Education Co.

Benduhn, Tea. Ancient Rome. 2006. (Illus.). 24p. (J). pap. ***(*978-0-8368-7788-5(8));*** (gr. 1-3). lib. bdg. 19.93 ***(*978-0-8368-7783-0(7))*** Stevens, Gareth Inc. (Weekly Reader Early Learning Library).

Bingham, Jane. Ancient Romans. 2006. (Illus.). 48p. pap. (978-0-8368-6243-0(0)); lib. bdg. 30.00 (978-0-8368-6191-4(4)) Stevens, Gareth Inc. (World Almanac Library).

Bingham, Jane. Classical Myth: A Treasury of Greek & Roman Legends, Art, & History. 2007. (World of Mythology Ser.). (Illus.). 96p. (YA). (gr. 6 up). 35.95 ***(*978-0-7656-8104-1(8))*** Sharpe, M.E. Inc.

Bingham, Jane, et al. Encyclopedia of the Roman World. 2004. (History Encyclopedias Ser.). (Illus.). 128p. (J). 19.95 (978-0-7945-0117-4(6) , Usborne); lib. bdg. 27.95 (978-1-58086-386-5(8)) EDC Publishing.

Blacklock, Dyan. The Roman Army: The Legendary Soldiers Who Created an Empire. Kennett, David, tr. Kennett, David, illus. 2004. 48p. (J). 18.85 (978-0-8027-8897-9(1)); 17.95 (978-0-8027-8896-2(3)) Walker & Co.

Book Studio Staff. Blast from the Past: Be an Ancient Egyptian. 2006. (Cool Kits Ser.). 1p. (J). 7.99 (978-0-7566-2432-3(0)) Dorling Kindersley Publishing, Inc.

Brannon, Barbara. Discover Ancient Rome. 2005. 39.00 ***(*978-1-4108-5164-2(8))*** Benchmark Education Co.

Brocklehurst, R. Roman Army. 2004. (Discovery Program Ser.). 48p. (J). lib. bdg. 16.95 (978-1-58086-609-5(3) , Usborne) EDC Publishing.

Burgan, Michael. Roman Empire. 2004. (Great Empires of the Past Ser.). (Illus.). 128p. (J). (gr. 6-12). 35.00 (978-0-8160-5559-3(9)) Facts On File, Inc.

Butterfield, Moira. Going to War in Roman Times. 2001. (Armies of the Past Ser.). (Illus.). 32p. (J). (gr. 3-6). 25.50 (978-0-531-14591-3(3) , Watts, Franklin) Scholastic Library Publishing.

—Going to War in Roman Times. Bergin, Mark, illus. 2001. (Armies of the Past Ser.). 32p. (J). (gr. 3-6). pap. 6.95 (978-0-531-16352-8(0) , Watts, Franklin) Scholastic Library Publishing.

Califf, David J. Battle of Actium. 2003. (Great Battles Through the Ages Ser.). (Illus.). 112p. (gr. 6-12). 30.00 (978-0-7910-7440-4(4) , Chelsea Hse.) Facts On File, Inc.

Carlson, Laurie M. Classical Kids: An Activity Guide to Life in Ancient Greece & Rome. 2003. (Kid's Guide Ser.). (Illus.). 200p. (J). (gr. k-7). pap. 14.95 (978-1-55652-290-1(8)) Chicago Review Pr., Inc.

Charman, Andrew. Life & Times in Ancient Rome. 2007. (Life & Times Ser.). (Illus.). 32p. (J). pap. 9.95 ***(*978-0-7534-6151-8(X)*** , Kingfisher) Houghton Mifflin Co. Trade & Reference Div.

Chrisp, Peter. Ancient Rome: Come & Discover My World. 2002. (gr. 3-6). lib. bdg. 16.40 (978-0-613-43295-5(9)) Tandem Library Bks.

—La Rome Antique. 2000. (Come & Discover My World Ser.). (FRE., Illus.). 32p. (J). (gr. 2-5). pap. 7.95 (978-1-58728-196-9(1) , Two Can Publishing) T&N Children's Publishing.

Corbishley, Mike. Ancient Rome. 2nd rev. ed. 2003. (Cultural Atlas for Young People Ser.). (Illus.). 96p. (J). (gr. 4-9). 35.00 (978-0-8160-5147-2(X)) Facts On File, Inc.

—Everyday Life in Roman Times. 2005. (Clues to the Past Ser.). (Illus.). 32p. (J). (gr. 4-7). lib. bdg. 27.10 (978-1-932889-79-6(5)) Sea-To-Sea Pubns.

Crisp, Peter. Ancient Rome. rev. ed. 2004. (Come & Discover My World Ser.). (Illus.). 32p. (gr. 2-5). (J). pap. 7.95 (978-1-58728-068-9(X)); 14.95 (978-1-58728-062-7(0)) T&N Children's Publishing. (Two Can Publishing).

—Romans. 2000. (Collectafact Ser.: Vol. 6). (Illus.). 48p. (J). (gr. 1-5). 4.95 (978-1-58728-753-4(6) , Two Can Publishing) T&N Children's Publishing.

Dargie, Richard. Ancient Rome. 2004. (Picturing the Past Ser.). (Illus.). 32p. (J). 15.95 (978-1-59270-023-3(3)) Enchanted Lion Bks., LLC.

—Rich & Poor in Ancient Rome. 2005. (Rich & Poor in Ser.). (Illus.). 32p. (J). (gr. 4-7). lib. bdg. 27.10 (978-1-58340-722-6(7)) Smart Apple Media.

Daynes, Katie. Romans. (Beginners Social Studies). 32p. (J). (gr. 1 up). lib. bdg. 12.95 (978-1-58086-688-0(3) , Usborne) EDC Publishing.

—Romans - Internet Referenced. Larkum, Adam, illus. 2004. (Beginners Ser.). 32p. (J). (gr. 1 up). pap. 4.95 (978-0-7945-0719-0(0) , Usborne) EDC Publishing.

—See Inside: Ancient Rome. Hancock, David, illus. 2006. 16p. (J). bds. 12.99 (978-0-7945-1321-4(2) , Usborne) EDC Publishing.

Deckker, Zilah Quezado. Ancient Rome: Archaeolology Unlocks the Secrets of Ancient Rome. 2007. (National Geographic Investigates Ser.). (Illus.). 64p. (YA). (gr. 5 up). 17.95 ***(*978-1-4263-0128-5(6)*** , National Geographic Children's Bks.) National Geographic Society.

Denti, Mario. Imperial Rome. 2001. (Journey to the Past Ser.). (Illus.). 56p. (J). (gr. 6-8). lib. bdg. 27.12 (978-0-7398-1952-4(6)) Raintree.

Dickins, Rosie. Riotous Story of Rome - Internet Referenced. 2006. 64p. (J). pap. 5.99 (978-0-7945-1246-0(1) , Usborne) EDC Publishing.

Dickinson, Rachel. Tools of the Ancient Romans: A Kid's Guide to the History & Science of Life in Ancient Rome. 2006. (Tools of Discovery Ser.). (Illus.). 144p. (J). pap. 16.95 (978-0-9749344-5-7(3)) Nomad Pr.

DK Publishing Staff. Ancient Rome. 2007. (Eyewitness Workbks.). 48p. (J). (gr. 2-8). pap., wbk. ed. 9.99 (978-0-7566-3010-2(X)) Dorling Kindersley Publishing, Inc.

Don Nardo. The Fall of the Roman Empire. 2004. (History's Great Defeats Ser.). (Illus.). 112p. (J). 29.95 (978-1-59018-427-1(0)) Thomson Gale.

Dorling Kindersley Publishing Staff & Ross, Stewart. Ancient Rome. 2005. (Tales of the Dead Ser.). (Illus.). 32p. (J). 14.99 (978-0-7566-1147-7(4)) Dorling Kindersley Publishing, Inc.

Eason, Sarah. Ancient Rome. 2002. (History in Stone Ser.). 64p. (J). (gr. 3-7). 16.95 (978-1-57145-553-6(1) , Silver Dolphin Bks.) Advantage Pubs. Group.

Fall of Rome/Byzantium DBA. 2003. spiral bd. 16.95 (978-1-56004-155-9(2)) Social Studies Schl. Service.

Fix, Alexandra. History & Activities of the Roman Empire. 2006. (Hands-On Ancient History Ser.). (Illus.). 32p. (J). (978-1-4034-7924-2(0)); pap. (978-1-4034-7932-7(1)) Heinemann Library.

Forsyth, Fiona. Augustus: The First Emperor. 2003. (Leaders of Ancient Rome Ser.). (Illus.). 112p. (YA). (gr. 5-8). lib. bdg. 31.95 (978-0-8239-3588-8(4) , Rosen Central) Rosen Publishing Group, Inc., The.

Frankel, Karen. Projects about Ancient Rome. 2006. (Hands-On History Ser.). (Illus.). 48p. (J). lib. bdg. 29.93 (978-0-7614-2260-0(9) , Benchmark Bks.) Cavendish, Marshall Corp.

Galford, Ellen. Julius Caesar: The Boy Who Conquered an Empire. 2007. (World History Biographies Ser.). (Illus.). 64p. (J). (gr. 3-7). 17.95 (978-1-4263-0064-6(6)); lib. bdg. 27.90 (978-1-4263-0065-3(4)) National Geographic Society. (National Geographic Children's Bks.).

Ganeri, Anita. The Ancient Romans. 2005. (Ancient Civilizations Ser.). (Illus.). 32p. (J). (gr. 4-6). 26.60 (978-0-7565-1644-4(7)) Compass Point Bks.

—The Ancient Romans. 1999. (History Starts Here Ser.). (Illus.). 32p. (J). (ps-3). lib. bdg. 25.69 (978-0-7398-1349-2(8)) Raintree.

—Ancient Romans. 2006. (Illus.). 32p. (J). pap. (978-0-7565-1759-5(1)) Compass Point Bks.

—Gladiators & Ancient Rome. 2005. (First Look at History Ser.). (Illus.). 24p. (J). lib. bdg. 22.00 (978-0-8368-4525-9(0)) Stevens, Gareth Inc.

—Legacies from Ancient Rome. 1999. (Legacies Ser.). (Illus.). 32p. (J). (gr. 4-7). lib. bdg. 16.95 (978-1-929298-50-1(1)) Chrysalis Education.

Gedacht, Daniel C. Land & Resources in Ancient Rome. 2004. (Primary Sources of Ancient Civilizations Ser.). (Illus.). 24p. (J). lib. bdg. 19.95 (978-0-8239-6775-9(1) , PowerKids Pr.) Rosen Publishing Group, Inc., The.

Glencoe McGraw-Hill Staff & McGraw-Hill - Jamestown Education Staff. Jamestown's Early Civilizations: Roman Life. 2001. (gr. 5-12). pap. 11.96 (978-0-8092-9500-5(8) , 9780809295005) Jamestown.

Grant, Neil. Every Day Life in Ancient Rome. Cappon, Manuela, tr. Cappon, Manuela, illus. 2003. (Uncovering History Ser.). 46p. (J). lib. bdg. 28.50 (978-1-58340-249-8(7)) Smart Apple Media.

Greenblatt, Miriam. Augustus & Imperial Rome. 1999. (Rulers & Their Times Ser.). (Illus.). 80p. (J). (gr. 6 up). lib. bdg. 29.93 (978-0-7614-0912-0(2) , Benchmark Bks.) Cavendish, Marshall Corp.

—Julius Caesar & the Roman Republic. 2005. (Rulers & Their Times Ser.). (Illus.). 96p. (J). (gr. 3-7). lib. bdg. 29.93 (978-0-7614-1836-8(9) , Benchmark Bks.) Cavendish, Marshall Corp.

Greene, Jacqueline Dembar. Slavery in Ancient Greece & Rome. 2000. (History of Slavery Library). (Illus.). 64p. (J). (gr. 5-7). 25.50 (978-0-531-11693-7(X) , Watts, Franklin) Scholastic Library Publishing.

—Slavery in Ancient Greece & Rome. 2000. (gr. 3-6). lib. bdg. 17.60 (978-0-613-34473-9(1)) Tandem Library Bks.

Guerber, H. A. The Story of the Romans (Yesterday's Classics) 2006. (Illus.). 368p. (J). per. 13.95 (978-1-59915-012-3(5)) Yesterday's Classics.

Haaren, John H. & Poland, A. B. Famous Men of Ancient Rome: Lives of Julius Caesar, Nero, Marcus Aurelius & Others. 2005. 160p. (J). (gr. 3). pap. 7.95 (978-0-486-44361-4(2)) Dover Pubns., Inc.

Hanel, Rachael. Gladiators. 2007. (J). (978-1-58341-535-1(1) , Creative Education) Creative Co., The.

Harding, Alexandra Hanson. Ancient Rome: A Complete Resource Packed with Background Information, Plays, Writing & World Study Activities. 2000. (Illus.). 80p. pap. 12.95 (978-0-439-05920-6(8)) Scholastic, Inc.

Haslam, Andrew. Les Romains. 2000. (Make It Work! History Ser.). (Illus.). 64p. (J). (gr. 3-6). pap. 7.95 (978-1-58728-189-1(9) , Two Can Publishing) T&N Children's Publishing.

—The Roman Empire. 2004. (Make It Work! History Ser.). (Illus.). 64p. (gr. 3-6). (J). pap. 7.95 (978-1-58728-303-1(4)); 14.95 (978-1-58728-309-3(3)) T&N Children's Publishing. (Two Can Publishing).

Hewitt, Sally. The Romans. 2007. (J). ***978-1-59920-046-0(5))** Smart Apple Media.

Hicks, Peter, et al. In the Daily Life of the Ancient Romans. 2002. (Gods & Goddesses Ser.). (Illus.). 48p. (J). (gr. 4 up). 18.95 (978-0-87226-595-0(1) , Bedrick, Peter Bks.) School Specialty Publishing.

Hinds, Kathryn. The City. 2004. (Illus.). 87p. (J). 29.93 (978-0-7614-1655-5(2) , Benchmark Bks.) Cavendish, Marshall Corp.

—The Patricians. 2004. (Illus.). 72p. (J). 29.93 (978-0-7614-1654-8(4) , Benchmark Bks.) Cavendish, Marshall Corp.

Hirsch, E. D., ed. Ancient Rome: Level 3. 2003. tchr. ed. 9.95 (978-0-7690-5057-7(3)) Pearson Learning.

Hunt, Norman Bancroft. Living in Ancient Rome. 2007. (Living in the Ancient World Ser.). 96p. (gr. 6-12). 35.00 (978-0-8160-6340-6(0)) Facts On File, Inc.

Hynson, Colin. Ancient Rome. 2004. (Historic Civilizations Ser.). (Illus.). 32p. (J). lib. bdg. 24.67 (978-0-8368-4200-5(6)) Stevens, Gareth Inc.

James, Simon & Dorling Kindersley Publishing Staff. Ancient Rome. 2004. (Eyewitness Books). (Illus.). 72p. (J). lib. bdg. 19.99 (978-0-7566-0650-3(0)) Dorling Kindersley Publishing, Inc.

Jarvie, Frances. The Romans in Scotland. Philip, Carrie, illus. 1999. (Scottie Bks.). 40p. (J). (gr. 3-7). pap. 6.95 (978-0-11-494277-9(3)) Stationery Office, The GBR. *Dist:* Balogh International, Inc.

Jeffrey, Gary & Petty, Kate. Julius Caesar: The Life of a Roman General. 2005. (Illus.). 48p. (J). lib. bdg. 26.50 (978-1-4042-0239-9(0) , 1241097) Rosen Publishing Group, Inc., The.

Jovinelly, Joann & Netelkos, Jason. The Crafts & Culture of the Romans. 2002. (Crafts of the Ancient World Ser.). (Illus.). 48p. (YA). (gr. 5-8). lib. bdg. 29.25 (978-0-8239-3513-0(2) , Rosen Central) Rosen Publishing Group, Inc., The.

Kent, Zachary. Julius Caesar: Ruler of the Roman World. 2006. (Rulers of the Ancient World Ser.). (Illus.). 160p. (J). lib. bdg. 27.93 (978-0-7660-2563-9(2)) Enslow Pubs., Inc.

Kops, Deborah. Ancient Rome: A MyReportLinks. com Book. 2005. (Civilizations of the Ancient World Ser.). (Illus.). 48p. (J). lib. bdg. 25.26 (978-0-7660-5255-0(9) , MyReportLinks.com Bks.) Enslow Pubs., Inc.

Langley, Andrew. The Roman News. 2000. (History News Ser.). (Illus.). 32p. (J). (gr. 3 up). lib. bdg. 24.67 (978-0-8368-2721-7(X)) Stevens, Gareth Inc.

—Roman News. 1999. (News Ser.). (J). (978-0-606-19320-7(0)) Tandem Library Bks.

Leaders of Ancient Rome, 6 bks. Incl. Augustus : The First Emperor. Forsyth, Fiona. lib. bdg. 31.95 (978-0-8239-3588-8(4)); Cicero : Defender of the Republic. Forsyth, Fiona. lib. bdg. 31.95 (978-0-8239-3590-1(6)); Constantine : Ruler of Christian Rome. Morgan, Julian. lib. bdg. 31.95 (978-0-8239-3592-5(2)); Hadrian : Consolidating the Empire. Morgan, Julian. lib. bdg. 31.95 (978-0-8239-3593-2(0)); Julius Caesar : Conqueror & Dictator. Thorne, James. lib. bdg. 31.95 (978-0-8239-3595-6(7)); Nero : Destroyer of Rome. Morgan, Julian. lib. bdg. 31.95 (978-0-8239-3596-3(5)); 112p. (YA). (gr. 5-8). 2003. (Illus.). 2002. Set lib. bdg. 191.70 (978-0-8239-3887-2(5) , Rosen Central) Rosen Publishing Group, Inc., The.

Levy, Patricia. Ancient Rome. 2001. (People Who Made History Ser.). (Illus.). 48p. (J). (gr. 4-7). lib. bdg. 27.12 (978-0-7398-2749-9(9)) Raintree.

Lin In The Roman Empire Series, 4 Bks, Set. 2004. (J). 119.71 (978-0-7614-1653-1(6)) Cavendish, Marshall Corp.

MacDonald, Fiona. How to Be a Roman Soldier. Hewetson, Nicholas, illus. 2005. (How to Be Ser.). 32p. (J). (gr. 3-7). 21.90 (978-0-7922-3631-3(9) , National Geographic Children's Bks.) National Geographic Society.

—How to Be a Roman Soldier. Heweston, Nicholas, illus. 2005. (How to Be Ser.). 32p. (J). (gr. 3-7). 14.95 (978-0-7922-3616-0(5) , National Geographic Children's Bks.) National Geographic Society.

—The Romans. 2007. (J). lib. bdg. 19.95 ***978-1-59566-353-5(3))** QEB Publishing Inc.

—So You Want to Be a Roman Soldier. Hewetson, Nicholas, illus. 1999. (So You Want to Be... Ser.). 32p. (gr. 3-6). lib. bdg. 21.90 (978-0-7613-1421-9(0) , Twenty-First Century Bks.) Lerner Publishing Group.

—Women in Ancient Rome. 2000. (Other Half of History Ser.). (Illus.). 48p. (J). (gr. 3 up). 17.95 (978-0-87226-570-7(6) , 65706B, Bedrick, Peter Bks.) School Specialty Publishing.

MacDonald, Fiona & Tames, Richard. 100 Things You Should Know about Ancient Rome. 2003. (Illus.). 48p. (J). (gr. 3 up). lib. bdg. (978-1-59084-446-5(7)) Mason Crest Pubs.

Malam, John. Exploring Ancient Rome. 2001. (Remains to Be Seen Ser.). (Illus.). 47p. (gr. 5-8). 22.95 (978-0-237-52003-8(6) , Evans Brothers, Limited) Evans Publishing Group GBR. *Dist:* Independent Pubs. Group.

—The Traveler's Guide to Ancient Rome. Foster, Mike S., illus. 1999. (J). (978-0-590-11763-0(7)) Scholastic, Inc.

—You Wouldn't Want to Be a Roman Gladiator! 2000. (gr. 3-6). lib. bdg. 18.75 (978-0-613-44277-0(6)) Tandem Library Bks.

—You Wouldn't Want to Be a Roman Gladiator! Gory Things You'd Rather Not Know. Antram, David, illus. 2001. (You Wouldn't Want to Ser.). 32p. (J). (gr. 2-5). pap. 9.95 (978-0-531-16204-0(4) , Watts, Franklin) Scholastic Library Publishing.

—You Wouldn't Want to Be a Roman Gladiator! Gory Things You'd Rather Not Know! Antram, David & Salariya, David, illus. 2001. (You Wouldn't Want to Ser.). 32p. (J). (gr. 2-5). 28.50 (978-0-531-14598-2(0) , Watts, Franklin) Scholastic Library Publishing.

Mann, Elizabeth. The Roman Colosseum: The Story of the World's Most Famous Stadium & Its Deadly Games. Racz, Michael, illus. 1998. (Wonders of the World Ser.). 48p. (J). (gr. 4-7). 19.95 (978-0-9650493-3-7(7)) Mikaya Pr.

Manning, Mick & Granstorm, Brita. Roman Fort. 2005. (Illus.). 40p. (J). 15.95 (978-1-84507-050-2(X)) Lincoln, Frances Ltd. GBR. *Dist:* Perseus Distribution.

Martin, Dave, et al. Write Your Own Roman Story. 2001. (Illus.). 64p. pap., stu. ed. 26.00 ***978-0-7195-7717-8(9)** , Hodder Murray) Hodder Education GBR. *Dist:* Trans-Atlantic Pubns., Inc.

Maynard, Charles W. The Technology of Ancient Rome. 2005. (Technology of the Ancient World Ser.). (Illus.). 48p. (J). (978-1-4042-0556-7(X)) Rosen Publishing Group, Inc., The.

Mehta-Jones, Shilpa. Life in Ancient Rome. 2004. (Peoples of the Ancient World Ser.). (Illus.). 32p. (J). (978-0-7787-2034-8(9)) Crabtree Publishing Co.

Minnis. You Are in Ancient Rome 6-Pack. 2004. (Illus.). pap. 40.50 (978-1-4109-1015-8(6)) Harcourt Schl. Pubs.

Moulton, Carroll, ed. Ancient Greece & Rome: An Encyclopedia for Students, 4 vols., Set. 1998. (Illus.). 732p. (YA). (gr. 8 up). 460.00 (978-0-684-80507-8(3) , GML00502-165980, Charles Scribner's Sons) Thomson Gale.

Mulvihill, Margaret. Roman Forts. Wood, Gerlad, illus. 2006. (Hallmarks of History Ser.). 32p. (J). (gr. 4-6). lib. bdg. 27.10 (978-1-59604-121-9(8)) Stargazer Bks.

Murrell, Deborah. The Best Book of Ancient Rome. 2007. (Best Book of... Ser.). 32p. (J). (gr. k-3). pap. 6.95 (978-0-7534-6080-1(7) , Kingfisher) Houghton Mifflin Co. Trade & Reference Div.

Murrell, Deborah Jane. The Best Book of Ancient Rome. 2004. (Best Book of... Ser.). (Illus.). 32p. (J). (gr. k-3). 12.95 (978-0-7534-5756-6(3) , Kingfisher) Houghton Mifflin Co. Trade & Reference Div.

Naden, Corinne J. & Blue, Rose. Ancient Romans & the Colosseum. 2003. (J). (978-1-58417-316-8(5)); pap. (978-1-58417-317-5(3)) Lake Street Pubs.

Nardo, Don. From Founding to Fall: A History of Rome. 2003. (Lucent Library of Historical Eras). (Illus.). 128p. (J). 32.45 (978-1-59018-254-3(5) , Lucent Bks.) Thomson Gale.

—The Greenhaven Encyclopedia of Ancient Rome. 2002. (History of Weapons & Warfare Ser.). (Illus.). 112p. (J). 29.95 (978-1-59018-067-9(4)); 29.95 (978-1-59018-143-0(3)) Thomson Gale. (Lucent Bks.).

—The Roman Army: Instrument of Power. 2003. (Lucent Library of Historical Eras). (Illus.). 112p. (J). 32.45 (978-1-59018-316-8(9) , Lucent Bks.) Thomson Gale.

—Roman Empire. 2005. (World History Ser.). (Illus.). 96-128p. (gr. 7-10). 32.45 (978-1-59018-657-2(5) , Lucent Bks.) Thomson Gale.

—The Roman Republic. 2005. (World History Ser.). (Illus.). 112p. (J). (gr. 6-9). lib. bdg. 32.45 (978-1-59018-658-9(3) , 1244623, Lucent Bks.) Thomson Gale.

—Words of the Ancient Romans: Primary Sources. 2003. (Lucent Library of Historical Eras). (Illus.). 128p. (J). 32.45 (978-1-59018-318-2(5) , Lucent Bks.) Thomson Gale.

Osborne, Mary Pope & Boyce, Natalie Pope. Ancient Rome & Pompeii. Murdocca, Sal, illus. 2006. (Magic Tree House Research Guide Ser.: No. 14). 128p. (J). (gr. k-3). 4.99 (978-0-375-83220-8(3) , Random Hse. Bks. for Young Readers) Random Hse. Children's Bks.

—Ancient Rome & Pompeii: A Nonfiction Companion to Vacation under the Volcano. Murdocca, Sal, illus. 2006. (Magic Tree House Research Guide Ser.: No. 14). 128p. (J). (gr. k-3). lib. bdg. 11.99 (978-0-375-93220-5(8) , Random Hse. Bks. for Young Readers) Random Hse. Children's Bks.

Owens, L. L. Inside Ancient Rome. 2002. (Cover-To-Cover Books). (Illus.). 56p. (J). pap. (978-0-7891-5621-1(0)); (gr. 1-4). lib. bdg. 16.95 (978-0-7569-0457-9(9)) Perfection Learning Corp.

Parker. The Vatican. 2003. (Holy Places Ser.). (Illus.). 32p. (J). pap. 6.95 (978-1-4109-0054-8(1)) Raintree.

Raatma, Lucia. Ancient Rome. 2002. (Let's See Library). (Illus.). 24p. (J). (gr. 1 up). lib. bdg. 19.95 (978-0-7565-0292-8(6)) Compass Point Bks.

Reece, Katherine E. The Romans: Builders of an Empire. 2005. (Ancient Civilizations Ser.). (Illus.). 48p. (gr. 4-8). 20.95 (978-1-59515-507-8(4) , 1244352) Rourke Publishing, LLC.

Rees, Rosemary. The Ancient Romans. 2006. (Illus.). 64p. (J). ***978-1-4034-8748-3(0))** Heinemann Library.

Reference, Brown & Corbishley, Mike. Ancient Rome. 3rd rev. ed. 2007. (Cultural Atlas for Young People Ser.). (Illus.). 96p. (YA). (gr. 5-8). 35.00 ***978-0-8160-6822-7(4)** , Chelsea Hse.) Facts On File, Inc.

Ridgley, Sara & Mole, Gavin. Sing It & Say - Ancient Rome. (Illus.). 140p. (J). 10.95 incl. audio (978-1-85909-390-0(6) , Warner Bros. Pubns.) Alfred Publishing Co., Inc.

Rogora, Bernardo. Los Romanos. (Coleccion Bravo). (SPA., Illus.). 76p. (YA). (gr. 5-8). (978-84-7131-907-4(1) , EDI30259) Editex, Editorial S.A. ESP. *Dist:* Lectorum Pubns., Inc.

The Romans. 2002. (History Makers Ser.). 32p. (J). 9.95 (978-0-7525-7829-3(4)) Parragon, Inc.

Ross, Stewart. Big J. Shields, Sue, illus. 32p. pap. 9.99 (978-0-7502-2852-7(0) , Hodder & Stoughton) Hodder General Publishing Division GBR. *Dist:* Trafalgar Square Publishing.

Roxbee-Cox, Phil. Who Were the Romans? 2002. (gr. 3-6). lib. bdg. 12.95 (978-0-613-88627-7(5)) Tandem Library Bks.

Ryall, Michael. Rome Long Ago. 2005. 42.00 ***978-1-4108-4634-1(2))** Benchmark Education Co.

Sasek, Miroslav. This Is Rome. 2007. (This Is ... Ser.). (Illus.). 64p. (J). (gr. 3-5). 17.95 (978-0-7893-1549-6(1)) Universe Publishing.

Sewell, E. M. The Child's History of Rome. 2005. reprint ed. pap. 26.95 (978-1-4179-6641-7(6)) Kessinger Publishing, LLC.

Sheehan, Sean & Levy, Patricia M. Rome. 1999. (Ancient World Ser.). (Illus.). 63p. (YA). (gr. 5-10). lib. bdg. 27.12 (978-0-8172-5057-7(3)) Raintree.

Shone, Rob & Ganeri, Anita. Spartacus: The Life of a Roman Gladiator. 2005. (Graphic Nonfiction Ser.). (Illus.). 48p. (J). lib. bdg. 26.50 (978-1-4042-0240-5(4) , 1241099) Rosen Publishing Group, Inc., The.

Shoreline Publishing Group Staff. Great Empires of the Past Set 1. 2004. (Great Empires of the Past Ser.). 128-128p. (gr. 9-12). 140.00 (978-0-8160-5575-3(0)) Facts On File, Inc.

Shuter, Jane. The Ancient Romans. 2007. (Illus.). 32p. (J). ***978-1-4034-8812-1(6))** Heinemann Library.

Shuter, Jane. Life in a Roman Fort. 2004. (Picture the Past Ser.). (Illus.). 32p. (J). pap. (978-1-4034-5837-7(5)) Heinemann Library.

Sims, Lesley. Roman Soldier's Handbook. 2006. 96p. (J). 12.99 (978-0-7945-0837-1(5) , Usborne) EDC Publishing.

—Visitor's Guide to Ancient Rome. 2000. (gr. 7-12). lib. bdg. 18.75 (978-0-613-90704-0(3)) Tandem Library Bks.

Steele. Ancient Rome. 2000. (Ancient Civilizations Ser.). (Illus.). (J). pap. (978-0-7398-4149-5(1)) Steck-Vaughn.

Steele, Christy. Rome. Sloan, Frank, ed. 2001. (Ancient Civilizations Ser.). (Illus.). 48p. (J). (gr. 4-7). lib. bdg. 22.83 (978-0-7398-3578-4(5)) Raintree.

Steele, Philip. Clothes & Crafts in Roman Times. 2000. (Clothes & Crafts in History Ser.). (Illus.). 32p. (J). (gr. 4 up). lib. bdg. 24.67 (978-0-8368-2737-8(6)) Stevens, Gareth Inc.

—The Roman Empire. 1998. (Step into Ser.). (Illus.). 64p. (gr. 3-7). 12.95 (978-1-85967-526-7(3) , Lorenz Bks.) Anness Publishing, Inc.

Steele, Philip. Step Into: The Roman Empire. 2007. (Illus.). 64p. pap. 10.99 ***978-1-84476-348-1(X)** , Southwater) Anness Publishing GBR. *Dist:* National Bk. Network.

Stewart, David. Inside Ancient Rome. James, John et al, illus. 2005. (Inside... Ser.). 32p. (J). (gr. 5). 19.95 (978-1-59270-045-5(4)) Enchanted Lion Bks., LLC.

Stimpson, Bea. The Roman World. 2002. (Illus.). 80p. pap., stu. ed. (978-0-7487-6562-1(X)) Nelson Thornes Ltd.

Stroud, Jonathan. Ancient Rome: A Guide to the Glory of Imperial Rome. 2000. (Sightseers Ser.). (Illus.). 32p. (J). (gr. 3-5). tchr. ed. 8.95 (978-0-7534-5235-6(9) , Kingfisher) Houghton Mifflin Co. Trade & Reference Div.

Sullivan, Erin Ash. Ancient Rome. 2005. (Navigators Ser.). (J). pap. 44.00 ***978-1-4108-5115-4(X))** Benchmark Education Co.

Sylvester, Diane. Ancient Rome. Hillam, Corbin & Ciccarelli, Gary, illus. 2006. (Museum Ser.). 64p. pap. 13.99 (978-0-88160-390-3(2) , LW445, Learning Works, The) Creative Teaching Pr., Inc.

Tracy, Kathleen. The Life & Times of Constantine. 2005. (Biography from Ancient Civilizations Ser.). (Illus.). 48p. (J). (gr. 4-8). lib. bdg. 29.95 (978-1-58415-343-6(1)) Mitchell Lane Pubs., Inc.

Trajan's Rome Grades 5-9: The Man, the City, the Empire. (J). tchr. ed., spiral bd. 15.00 (978-0-382-44446-3(9)) Cobblestone Publishing Co.

Van Vleet, Carmella. Explore Ancient Rome! 25 Great Projects, Activities, & Experiments. 2008. (Explore Your World Ser.). 96p. (J). (gr. 1-4). pap. 12.95 ***978-0-9792268-4-7(8))** Nomad Pr.

Warrick, Karen Clemens. Hannibal: Great General of the Ancient World. 2006. (Rulers of the Ancient World Ser.). (Illus.). 160p. (J). lib. bdg. 27.93 (978-0-7660-2564-6(0)) Enslow Pubs., Inc.

Waryncia, Lou, et al. If I Were a Kid in Ancient Rome. 2007. (Children of the Ancient World Ser.). (Illus.). 32p. (J). 17.95 (978-0-8126-7930-4(X)) Cricket Bks.

Watkins, Richard. Gladiator. 2000. (Illus.). 96p. (J). (gr. 4-6). pap. 8.95 (978-0-618-07032-9(X)) Houghton Mifflin Co. Trade & Reference Div.

Weatherill, Steve & Weatherill, Sue. Roman Activity Book. 2006. (Creative Fun Ser.). (Illus.). 24p. (J). pap., act. bk. ed. 5.99 (978-0-7641-3415-9(9)) Barron's Educational Series, Inc.

Whiting, Jim. The Life & Times of Julius Caesar. 2005. (Biography from Ancient Civilizations Ser.). (Illus.). 48p. (J). (ps-7). lib. bdg. 29.95 (978-1-58415-337-5(7)) Mitchell Lane Pubs., Inc.

—The Life & Times of Nero. 2005. (Biography from Ancient Civilizations Ser.). (Illus.). 48p. (J). (gr. 5-8). lib. bdg. 29.95 (978-1-58415-349-8(0)) Mitchell Lane Pubs., Inc.

Wilkinson, Philip. Lift the Lid on Gladiators No. 2: Enter the Roman Colosseum & Prepare Your Gladiator for Combat! 2002. (Illus.). 32p. (J). pap. 21.95 (978-0-7624-1338-6(7) , Running Pr. Kids) Running Pr. Bk. Pubs.

Williams, Brian. Ancient Roman Children. 2002. (gr. 3-6). lib. bdg. 17.05 (978-0-613-85909-7(X)) Tandem Library Bks.

—Ancient Roman War & Weapons. (People in the Past Ser.). (Illus.). 48p. (J). 2003. (gr. 4-6). lib. bdg. 27.07 (978-1-58810-630-8(6)); 2002. pap. 8.50 (978-1-4034-0521-0(2)) Heinemann Library.

Williams, Brian & Tames, Richard. Rome, 5 bks., Set 2. 2003. (People in the Past Ser.). (J). (gr. 4-6). lib. bdg. 135.35 (978-1-58810-578-3(4)) Heinemann Library.

Williams, Jane A. A Bluestocking Guide - Ancient Rome: Companion Workbook for Richard J. Maybury's Ancient Rome: How it Affects You Today. Daniels, Kathryn, ed. 2004. (Bluestocking Guide Ser.). 47p. (YA). pap. 9.95 (978-0-942617-48-1(7)) Bluestocking Pr.

Williams, Rose. The Young Romans. 2007. (LAT & ENG.). pap. ***978-0-86516-670-7(6))** Bolchazy-Carducci Pubs.

ROME—HISTORY—FICTION

Banks, Lynne Reid. Tiger, Tiger. 2007. 208p. (YA). (gr. 7-11). mass mkt. 5.99 (978-0-440-42044-6(X) , Laurel Leaf) Random Hse. Children's Bks.

Birch, Beverley. Julius Caesar. 2007. (Illus.). 80p. 13.95 ***978-0-7502-4962-1(5)** , Hodder Wayland) Hodder Children's Division GBR. *Dist:* Independent Pubs. Group.

Brouwer, Sigmund. The Angel & the Cross. 2005. (Guardian Angel Ser.). 168p. (gr. 3-7). pap. 7.99 (978-0-7369-0296-0(1)) Harvest Hse. Pubs.

—The Angel & the Ring: A Supernatural Adventure. 2005. (Guardian Angel Ser.). 165p. (J). (ps-7). pap. 7.99 (978-0-7369-0294-6(5)) Harvest Hse. Pubs.

Brown, Brian & Melrose, Andrew. The Storykeepers. 2000. (Storykeepers' Ser.). 128p. pap., tchr. ed. 26.99 (978-0-310-23674-0(6)) Zonderkidz.

Denenberg, Barry. Atticus of Rome, 30 B. C. 2004. (Life & Times Ser.). 176p. (J). (gr. 4-7). pap. 10.95 (978-0-439-52453-7(9)) Scholastic, Inc.

Geary, Judith. Getorix: The Eagle & the Bull. 2006. (Illus.). 278p. 24.95 (978-1-932158-74-8(X)) Ingalls Publishing Group, Inc.

Henty, G. A. The Young Carthaginian: A Tale of the Times of Hannibal. 2004. reprint ed. pap. 27.95 (978-1-4191-8911-1(5)); pap. 1.99 (978-1-4192-8911-8(X)) Kessinger Publishing, LLC.

Lawrence, Carol & Lawrence, Caroline. The Dolphins of Laurentum. 2003. (Roman Mysteries Ser.: Bk. 5). 176p. (J). (gr. 6-9). 22.90 (978-0-7613-2606-9(5)) Roaring Brook Pr.

Lawrence, Caroline. The Assassins of Rome, Vol. 4. 2005. (Illus.). 176p. (J). (gr. 3-7). pap. 5.99 (978-0-14-240214-6(1) , Puffin) Penguin Group (USA) Inc.

—The Charioteer of Delphi. 2007. (Roman Mysteries Ser.). (Illus.). 210p. (J). (gr. 6-9). 16.95 (*978-1-59643-085-3(0)) Roaring Brook Pr.

—The Dolphins of Laurentum. 2003. (Roman Mysteries Ser.: Bk. 5). 176p. (J). (gr. 6-9). 15.95 (978-0-7613-2349-5(X)) Roaring Brook Pr.

—The Enemies of Jupiter. 2005. (Roman Mysteries Ser.). (Illus.). 192p. (J). 16.95 (978-1-59643-048-8(6)) Roaring Brook Pr.

—The Fugitive from Corinth. 2006. (Roman Mysteries Ser.). (Illus.). 208p. (J). 16.95 (978-1-59643-083-9(4)) Roaring Brook Pr.

—The Gladiators from Capua. 2005. (Roman Mysteries Ser.). (Illus.). 208p. (J). (gr. 6-9). 16.95 (978-1-59643-074-7(5)) Roaring Brook Pr.

—Pirates of Pompeii, Vol. 3. 2004. (Roman Mysteries Ser.: No. 3). (Illus.). 176p. (J). (gr. 3). pap. 5.99 (978-0-14-240227-6(3) , Puffin) Penguin Group (USA) Inc.

Lawrence, Caroline. The Sirens of Surrentum. 2007. (Roman Mysteries Ser.). (Illus.). 224p. (J). 16.95 (*978-1-59643-084-6(2)) Roaring Brook Pr.

Mitchell, Jack. The Roman Conspiracy. 2005. 172p. (J). (gr. 5-8). pap. 8.95 (978-0-88776-713-5(3)) Tundra Bks., Inc./Livres Toundra, Inc. CAN. *Dist:* Random Hse., Inc.

Moss, Marissa. Galen: My Life in Imperial Rome. Moss, Marissa, illus. 2002. (Ancient World Journals). (Illus.). 48p. (YA). (gr. 3-7). 15.00 (978-0-15-216535-2(5) , Silver Whistle) Harcourt Trade Pubs.

Price, Robin. Catligula, 8 vols. 2006. (Spartapuss Tales Ser.). 192p. (J). pap. 14.95 (978-0-9546576-1-1(6)) Mogzilla GBR. *Dist:* Independent Pubs. Group.

—I Am Spartapuss. 2006. (Spartapuss Tales Ser.). 192p. (J). pap. 14.95 (978-0-9546576-0-4(8)) Mogzilla GBR. *Dist:* Independent Pubs. Group.

Ray, Mary. Beyond the Desert Gate. 2nd ed. 2001. (Young Adult Historical Library). (Illus.). 190p. (YA). (gr. 3-9). 11.95 (978-1-883937-54-6(X) , 54-X) Bethlehem Bks.

Rubalcaba, Jill. The Wadjet Eye. 160p. (J). (gr. 4-6). 2006. pap. 5.95 (978-0-618-68927-9(3)); 2000. (Illus.). tchr. ed. 15.00 (978-0-395-68942-4(2)) Houghton Mifflin Co. Trade & Reference Div. (Clarion Bks.).

Speare, Elizabeth George. The Bronze Bow. 2002. (J). 14.74 (978-0-7587-0173-2(X)) Book Wholesalers, Inc.

—The Bronze Bow. 1999. (J). 9.95 (978-1-56137-726-8(0)) Novel Units, Inc.

Tarr, Judith. Household Gods. 2000. (gr. 7-12). lib. bdg. 16.45 (978-0-613-35147-8(9)) Tandem Library Bks.

Trease, Geoffrey, text. Word to Caesar. 2005. (J). per. 14.95 (978-0-9766386-2-9(2)) Hillside Education.

Vidal, Cesar. Los Tres Dias del Gladiador. 2002. (SPA.). 190p. (978-84-348-8621-6(9)) SM Ediciones ESP. *Dist:* Lectorum Pubns., Inc.

Wallace, Lew. Ben-Hur. (SPA., Illus.). (YA). 11.95 (978-84-7281-099-0(2) , AF1099) Auriga, Ediciones S.A. ESP. *Dist:* Continental Bk. Co., Inc.

Weatherby, W.J. Chariots of Fire. Morris, Margery, ed. abr. ed. Date not set. (Nelson Readers Ser.: 2). (J). pap. (978-0-17-557036-2(1)) Addison-Wesley Longman, Inc.

ROME—HISTORY—REPUBLIC, 510-30 B.C.

Ancient Rome II, Grades 5-9: Theater, Sculpture & Painting, Religion, Daily Life, the Roman at Home, Latin Prefixes in English. (Teaching with Primary Sources Ser.). (Illus.). (J). tchr. ed., ring bd. 28.95 (978-0-382-40865-6(9)) Cobblestone Publishing Co.

Barter, James. Julius Caesar & Ancient Rome in World History. 2001. (In World History Ser.). (Illus.). 128p. (J). (gr. 5-12). lib. bdg. 26.60 (978-0-7660-1461-9(4)) Enslow Pubs., Inc.

Cox, Phil Roxbee. Who Were the Romans? 2004. (Starting Point History Ser.). (Illus.). 32p. (J). pap. 4.95 (978-0-7945-0247-8(4) , Usborne); lib. bdg. 12.95 (978-1-58086-446-6(5)) EDC Publishing.

Crompton, Samuel Willard. Julius Caesar. 2003. (Ancient World Leaders Ser.). (Illus.). 112p. (gr. 6-12). 30.00 (978-0-7910-7220-2(7)); pap. 30.00 (978-0-7910-7494-7(3)) Facts On File, Inc. (Chelsea Hse.).

Curry, Jane Louise & Livy. Brave Cloelia: Retold from the Account in the History of Early Rome by the Roman Historian Titus Livius. Crosby, Jeff, illus. 2004. (Getty Trust Publications: J. Paul Getty Museum Ser.). 34p. 16.95 (978-0-89236-763-4(6)) Getty Pubns.

Firth, Rachel & Parkhouse, Stephen. Julius Caesar. 2007. (Famous Lives Gift Bks). 64p. (J). 8.99 (978-0-7945-1595-9(9) , Usborne) EDC Publishing.

Forsyth, Fiona. Cicero: Defender of the Republic. 2003. (Leaders of Ancient Rome Ser.). (Illus.). 112p. (YA). (gr. 5-8). lib. bdg. 31.95 (978-0-8239-3590-1(6) , Rosen Central) Rosen Publishing Group, Inc., The.

Hollingsworth, Patricia L., et al. Ancient Rome. 1998. (Sails - Students' Active Interdisciplinary Learning Ser.: Vol. 2). (Illus.). (YA). (gr. 3-12). pap. 20.00 (978-1-893413-01-6(2)) Univ. Schl. at the Univ. of Tulsa.

McDougal, Littell Staff, contrib. by. Ancient Rome: 200 B.C.- 350 A.D. 2004. (Stories in History Ser.). (Illus.). 160p. (gr. 6-12). 13.32 (978-0-618-14212-5(6) , 2-00232) McDougal Littell Inc.

Moulton, Carroll, ed. Ancient Greece & Rome: An Encyclopedia for Students, 4 vols., Set. 1998. (Illus.). 732p. (YA). (gr. 8 up). 460.00 (978-0-684-80507-8(3) , GML00502-165980, Charles Scribner's Sons) Thomson Gale.

Murrell, Deborah Jane. The Best Book of Ancient Rome. 2004. (Best Book of... Ser.). (Illus.). 32p. (J). (gr. k-3). 12.95 (978-0-7534-5756-6(3) , Kingfisher) Houghton Mifflin Co. Trade & Reference Div.

Nardo, Don. Life of a Roman Gladiator. 2003. (Way People Live Ser.). (Illus.). 112p. (J). 29.95 (978-1-59018-253-6(7) , Lucent Bks.) Thomson Gale.

—A Roman Senator. 2004. (Working Life Ser.). (Illus.). 112p. (J). (gr. 7-10). 29.95 (978-1-59018-481-3(5) , Lucent Bks.) Thomson Gale.

Reid, Struan. Julius Caesar. 2002. (Historical Biographies Ser.). (Illus.). 32p. (J). (gr. 2-4). lib. bdg. 22.79 (978-1-58810-564-6(4)) Heinemann Library.

Saunders, Nicholas. The Life of Julius Caesar. 2006. (Stories from History Ser.). 48p. (J). 14.95 (978-0-7696-4717-3(0)); pap. 6.95 (978-0-7696-4697-8(2)) School Specialty Publishing.

Sheehan, Sean & Levy, Patricia M. Rome. 1999. (Ancient World Ser.). (Illus.). 63p. (YA). (gr. 5-10). lib. bdg. 27.12 (978-0-8172-5057-7(3)) Raintree.

Thorne, James. Julius Caesar: Conqueror & Dictator. 2003. (Leaders of Ancient Rome Ser.). (Illus.). 112p. (YA). (gr. 5-8). lib. bdg. 31.95 (978-0-8239-3595-6(7) , Rosen Central) Rosen Publishing Group, Inc., The.

Tracy, Kathleen. Cicero. 2006. (Biography from Ancient Civilizations Ser.). (Illus.). 48p. (J). lib. bdg. 20.95 (978-1-58415-510-2(8)) Mitchell Lane Pubs., Inc.

ROME—HISTORY—EMPIRE, 30 B.C.-476 A.D.

Brocklehurst, R. Roman Army. 2004. (Discovery Program Ser.). (Illus.). 48p. (J). pap. 8.95 (978-0-7945-0591-2(0)) EDC Publishing.

Clare, John D. The Roman Empire. 2002. (Illus.). 48p. pap. 23.50 (*978-0-340-84686-5(0) , Hodder Murray) Hodder Education GBR. *Dist:* Trans-Atlantic Pubns., Inc.

Cox, Phil Roxbee. Who Were the Romans? 2004. (Starting Point History Ser.). (Illus.). 32p. (J). pap. 4.95 (978-0-7945-0247-8(4) , Usborne) EDC Publishing.

Honan, Linda & Kosmer, Ellen. Spend the Day in Ancient Rome: Projects & Activities that Bring the Past to Life. 1998. (Spend the Day Ser.). (Illus.). 128p. (gr. 3-7). pap. 14.95 (978-0-471-15453-2(9) , Wiley) Wiley, John & Sons, Inc.

Markel, Rita J. The Fall of the Roman Empire. 2007. (Pivotal Moments in History Ser.). 160p. (YA). (gr. 9-12). lib. bdg. 38.60 (*978-0-8225-5919-1(6) , Twenty-First Century Bks.) Lerner Publishing Group, Inc.

McDougal, Littell Staff, contrib. by. Ancient Rome: 200 B.C.- 350 A.D. 2004. (Stories in History Ser.). (Illus.). 160p. (gr. 6-12). 13.32 (978-0-618-14212-5(6) , 2-00232) McDougal Littell Inc.

Nardo, Don. The Parthenon of Ancient Greece. 1998. (Building History Ser.). (Illus.). 96p. (YA). (gr. 6-9). 27.45 (978-1-56006-431-2(5) , Lucent Bks.) Thomson Gale.

—Rulers of Ancient Rome. 1998. (History Makers Ser.). (Illus.). 128p. (YA). (gr. 7-10). 27.45 (978-1-56006-356-8(4) , Lucent Bks.) Thomson Gale.

Sheehan, Sean & Levy, Patricia M. Rome. 1999. (Ancient World Ser.). (Illus.). 63p. (YA). (gr. 5-10). lib. bdg. 27.12 (978-0-8172-5057-7(3)) Raintree.

Steele, Philip. Find Out about the Roman Empire. 2000. (Illus.). 64p. pap. 7.95 (978-1-84215-039-9(1) , Southwater) Anness Publishing GBR. *Dist:* National Bk. Network.

—Gods & Gladiators: Everyday Life. 2004. (Illus.). 128p. pap. 17.99 (978-1-84476-032-9(4) , Southwater) Anness Publishing GBR. *Dist:* National Bk. Network.

Stewart, David. You Wouldn't Want to Be a Roman Soldier. Antram, David, illus. 2006. 32p. (J). (gr. 2-5). pap. 9.95 (978-0-531-12448-2(7) , Watts, Franklin) Scholastic Library Publishing.

—You Wouldn't Want to Be a Roman Soldier! Barbarians You'd Rather Not Meet. Antram, David, illus. 2006. (You Wouldn't Want To Ser.). 32p. (J). (gr. 2-5). 28.50 (978-0-531-12423-9(1) , Watts, Franklin) Scholastic Library Publishing.

Whiting, Jim. The Life & Times of Augustus Caesar. 2005. (Biography from Ancient Civilizations Ser.). (Illus.). 48p. (J). (ps-7). lib. bdg. 29.95 (978-1-58415-336-8(9)) Mitchell Lane Pubs., Inc.

ROME (ITALY)

Barber, Nicola. Rome. 2000. (World Cities Ser.). (Illus.). 48p. (J). (gr. 2-6). lib. bdg. 16.95 (978-1-929298-32-7(3)) Chrysalis Education.

—Rome. 2004. (Great Cities of the World Ser.). (Illus.). 48p. pap. (978-0-8368-5200-4(1)); (YA). lib. bdg. 30.00 (978-0-8368-5040-6(8)) Stevens, Gareth Inc. (World Almanac Library).

Bloom, Harold, ed. Rome. 2005. (Bloom's Literary Places Ser.). (Illus.). 150p. (gr. 9-13). pap. (978-0-7910-8383-3(7) , Chelsea Hse.) Facts On File, Inc.

DuTemple, Lesley A. The Pantheon. 2003. (Great Building Feats Ser.). (Illus.). 96p. (J). (gr. 5-9). 27.93 (978-0-8225-0376-7(X)) Lerner Publishing Group.

Fay, Martha. City Walks Deck: Rome. 2006. 14.95 (978-0-8118-5127-5(3)) Chronicle Bks. LLC.

Foster, Brett & Marcovitz, Hal. Rome. 2005. (Bloom's Literary Places Ser.). (Illus.). 197p. (YA). (gr. 9-13). per. 40.00 (978-0-7910-7839-6(6) , Chelsea Hse.) Facts On File, Inc.

In the City of Rome: Individual Title Six-Packs. (Literatura 2000 Ser.). (gr. 2-3). 33.00 (978-0-7635-0203-4(0)) Rigby Education.

Mattern, Joanne. Rome. 2006. (J). (978-1-59679-722-2(3)) ABDO Publishing Co.

Ross, Mandy. The Vatican. 2003. (Holy Places Ser.). (Illus.). 32p. (J). lib. bdg. 24.28 (978-0-7398-6081-6(X)) Raintree.

Saunders, Nicholas. Gladiators & the Story of the Colosseum. 2006. (Stories from History Ser.). 48p. (J). 14.95 (*978-0-7696-4704-3(9)); pap. 6.95 (*978-0-7696-4632-9(8)) School Specialty Publishing.

Whittock, Martyn J. The Colosseum & the Roman Forum. 2002. (Visiting the Past Ser.). (Illus.). 32p. (J). pap. 7.95 (978-1-4034-0623-1(5)) Heinemann.

—The Colosseum & the Roman Forum. 2003. (Visiting the Past Ser.). (Illus.). 32p. (J). (gr. 5-7). lib. bdg. 25.64 (978-1-58810-707-7(8)) Heinemann Library.

ROME (ITALY)—FICTION

Getzinger, Donna. Delivering Rome: The Adventures of a Young Roman Courier. unabr. ed. 2002. 30p. (J). pap. 35.00 incl. audio compact disk (978-1-58472-240-3(1) , In Audio) Sound Room Pubs., Inc.

Klass, David. Danger Zone. 1998. (J). 11.64 (978-0-606-13080-6(2)) Tandem Library Bks.

Lawrence, Caroline. The Gladiators from Capua. 2005. (Roman Mysteries Ser.). (Illus.). 208p. (J). (gr. 6-9). 16.95 (978-1-59643-074-7(5)) Roaring Brook Pr.

Marsh, Carole. The Mystery at the Roman Coloseum. 2006. 144p. (gr. 3-5). 14.95 (*978-0-635-06157-7(0)) Gallopade International.

Pedersen, Janet. Pino & the Signora's Pasta. Pedersen, Janet, illus. 2005. (Illus.). 32p. (J). (ps-3). 16.99 (978-0-7636-2396-8(2)) Candlewick Pr.

ROOMING HOUSES

see Hotels, Motels, etc.

ROOSEVELT, ELEANOR, 1884-1962

Adler, David A. A Picture Book of Eleanor Roosevelt. Casilla, Robert, illus. 2004. (J). pap. 18.95 incl. audio compact disk (978-1-59112-753-6(X)) Live Oak Media.

Ashby, Ruth. Franklin & Eleanor Roosevelt. 2005. (Illus.). 48p. (J). pap. (978-0-8368-5764-1(X)); lib. bdg. 30.00 (978-0-8368-5758-0(5)) Stevens, Gareth Inc. (World Almanac Library).

Auch, Allison. Mujeres que se atrevieron & Women Who Dared. 2005. spiral bd. 84.00 (*978-1-4108-5692-0(5)) Benchmark Education Co.

Bednarz, Robert, et al. TIME for Kids Readers: Eleanor Roosevelt. 3rd ed. 2002. (Harcourt Horizons Ser.). (gr. k-7). pap. 38.10 (978-0-15-335293-5(0)) Harcourt Schl. Pubs.

Blevins, Wiley. Eleanor Roosevelt. 2002. (Illus.). 16p. (J). pap. (978-0-439-35193-5(6)) Scholastic, Inc.

Brown, Jonatha A. Eleanor Roosevelt. 2005. (ENG & SPA.). (J). pap. (978-0-8368-4591-4(9)); 2005. (ENG & SPA.). (J). lib. bdg. 19.33 (978-0-8368-4584-6(6)); 2005. (Illus.). 24p. (J). pap. (978-0-8368-4475-7(0)); 2005. (Illus.). 24p. (YA). lib. bdg. 19.33 (978-0-8368-4468-9(8) , Weekly Reader Early Learning Library); 2002. (Illus.). 48p. (J). (gr. 5 up). pap. 14.95 (978-0-8368-5239-4(7) , World Almanac Library); 2002. (Illus.). 48p. (J). (gr. 5 up). lib. bdg. 30.00 (978-0-8368-5079-6(3) , World Almanac Library) Stevens, Gareth Inc.

Cohen, Della. Eleanor Roosevelt: Proud & Tall. 2005. (Illus.). 16p. (J). pap. (*978-0-7367-2879-9(1)) Zaner-Bloser, Inc.

Collier, James Lincoln. The Eleanor Roosevelt You Never Knew. Copeland, Greg, illus. 2004. (You Never Knew Ser.). 80p. (J). 25.50 (978-0-516-24425-9(6) , Children's Pr.) Scholastic Library Publishing.

Compass Point Books, contrib. by. Eleanor Roosevelt. (Compass Point Early Biographies Ser.). 32p. (J). pap. 7.95 (978-0-7565-1167-8(4)) Compass Point Bks.

Cooney, Barbara. Eleanor. Cooney, Barbara, illus. 1999. (Illus.). 32p. (J). (gr. k-3). pap. 6.99 (978-0-14-055583-7(8) , Puffin) Penguin Group (USA) Inc.

—Eleanor. 2000. (YA). pap. 25.24 incl. audio (978-0-7887-4330-6(9) , 41125) Recorded Bks., LLC.

—Eleanor. 1999. (J). 13.79 (978-0-606-17255-4(6)); lib. bdg. 15.30 (978-0-7857-1294-7(1)) Tandem Library Bks.

Donnelly, Shannon. Eleanor Roosevelt. Wolek, Guy, illus. 2005. (Heroes of America Ser.). 240p. (J). (gr. 3-8). lib. bdg. 21.35 (978-1-59679-260-9(4)) ABDO Publishing Co.

Eleanor Roosevelt. (Photo Illustrated Biographies Ser.). 24p. (J). 6.95 (978-0-7368-8420-4(3)) Capstone Pr., Inc.

Eleanor Roosevelt. 2005. 12p. (gr. k-4). 2.95 (*978-0-635-02622-4(8)) Gallopade International.

Eleanor Roosevelt, 6 vols. (gr. 2-5). 36.95 (978-0-7368-8431-0(9)) Red Brick Learning.

Ellwood, Nancy. Learning about Integrity from the Life of Eleanor Roosevelt. 1999. (Character Building Book Ser.). (Illus.). 24p. (J). (gr. 3). lib. bdg. 18.75 (978-0-8239-5345-5(9) , PowerKids Pr.) Rosen Publishing Group, Inc., The.

Feinberg, Barbara Silberdick. Eleanor Roosevelt: Everything She Could Be. 2003. (Gateway Biography Ser.: 4). (Illus.). 48p. lib. bdg. 23.90 (978-0-7613-2623-6(5) , Millbrook Pr.) Lerner Publishing Group.

Fleming, Candace. Our Eleanor: A Scrapbook Look at Eleanor Roosevelt's Remarkable Life. 2005. (Illus.). 192p. (J). (gr. 4-8). 21.99 (978-0-689-86544-2(9) , Atheneum) Simon & Schuster Children's Publishing.

Harcourt School Publishers Staff. Eleanor Roosevelt Advanced Level. 3rd ed. 2002. (Trophies Reading Program Ser.). (Illus.). pap. 5.10 (978-0-15-323285-5(4)) Harcourt Schl. Pubs.

Hoffman, Nancy. Eleanor Roosevelt & the Arthurdale Experiment. 2001. (Illus.). xii, 100p. (J). (gr. 5-9). 22.50 (978-0-208-02504-3(9) , Linnet Bks.) Shoe String Pr., Inc.

Jones, Victoria Garrett. Eleanor Roosevelt: A Courageous Spirit. 2007. (Sterling Biographies Ser.). (Illus.). 128p. (J). 12.95 (978-1-4027-4746-5(2)); pap. 5.95 (978-1-4027-3371-0(2)) Sterling Publishing Co., Inc.

Koestler-Grack, Rachel A. The Story of Eleanor Roosevelt. 2003. (Breakthrough Biographies Ser.). (Illus.). 32p. (gr. 3-5). 23.00 (978-0-7910-7313-1(0) , Chelsea Hse.) Facts On File, Inc.

Kramer, Candice. Eleanor Roosevelt & Marian Anderson. 2005. 40.00 (*978-1-4108-4537-5(0)) Benchmark Education Co.

Kulling, Monica. Eleanor Everywhere: The Life of Eleanor Roosevelt. 1999. (J). (978-0-606-17177-9(0)) Tandem Library Bks.

Lassieur, Allison. Eleanor Roosevelt: Activist for Social Change. 2006. (Great Life Stories Ser.). (Illus.). 111p. (YA). (gr. 5-8). 30.50 (978-0-531-13871-7(2) , Watts, Franklin) Scholastic Library Publishing.

MacLeod, Elizabeth. Eleanor Roosevelt: An Inspiring Life. 2006. (Illus.). 32p. (978-1-55337-811-2(3)); (978-1-55337-778-8(8)) Kids Can Pr., Ltd.

Mattern, Joanne. Eleanor Roosevelt. 2007. (First Ladies Ser.). (Illus.). 32p. (J). (gr. k-6). lib. bdg. 24.21 (*978-1-59928-800-0(1) , Checkerboard Library) ABDO Publishing Co.

—Eleanor Roosevelt: More Than a First Lady. 2003. (Reading Power Ser.). (Illus.). 24p. (J). lib. bdg. 17.25 (978-0-8239-6501-4(5) , PowerKids Pr.) Rosen Publishing Group, Inc., The.

—Eleanor Roosevelt: More Than a First Lady: Individual Title Six-Packs. (On Deck Ser.: Vol. 2). 24p. (gr. 4-5). 35.00 (978-0-7578-5842-0(2)) Rigby Education.

McLeese, Don. Eleanor Roosevelt. 2003. (Discover the Life of an Equal Rights Leader Discovery Library Ser.). (Illus.). 24p. (gr. 2-5). 14.95 (978-1-58952-289-3(3)) Rourke Publishing, LLC.

Merchant, Peter. Eleanor Roosevelt & the Scary Basement. DiVito, Anna, illus. 2006. (Ready-to-read COFA Ser.). 32p. (J). pap. 3.99 (978-0-689-87205-1(4) , Aladdin); lib. bdg. 11.89 (978-0-689-87206-8(2) , Aladdin Library) Simon & Schuster Children's Publishing.

Nabli, Dina E. L. Eleanor Roosevelt First Lady of the World. 2006. 44p. (J). lib. bdg. 15.00 (*978-1-4242-0847-0(5)) Fitzgerald Bks.

Rappaport, Doreen. Eleanor's Big Words. 2006. (J). (978-0-7868-5141-6(4)) Hyperion Bks. for Children.

Rinaldo, Denise. Eleanor Roosevelt: With a Discussion of Respect. 2003. (Values in Action Ser.). (J). (978-1-59203-063-7(7)) Learning Challenge, Inc.

Rosenberg, Pam. Eleanor Roosevelt. 2003. (Compass Point Early Biographies Ser.). (Illus.). 32p. (J). (gr. 2 up). lib. bdg. 21.26 (978-0-7565-0417-5(1)) Compass Point Bks.

—Eleanor Roosevelt: First Lady, Humanitarian, & World Citizen. 2003. (Spirit of America). (Illus.). 32p. (J). (gr. 2-6). 27.07 (978-1-59296-001-9(4)) Child's World, Inc.

Sawyer, Kem Knapp. Eleanor Roosevelt. 2006. (Biography Ser.). (Illus.). 128p. (J). 14.99 (978-0-7566-1495-9(3)); pap. 4.99 (978-0-7566-1496-6(1)) Dorling Kindersley Publishing, Inc.

Somervill, Barbara A. Eleanor Roosevelt: First Lady of the World. 2005. (Signature Lives Ser.). (Illus.). 112p. (J). (gr. 5-7). (978-0-7565-0992-7(0)) Compass Point Bks.

Stone, Amy. Eleanor Roosevelt. 2002. (Beginning Biographies Ser.). (Illus.). 32p. (J). lib. bdg. 25.69 (978-0-7398-5679-6(0)) Raintree.

Thompson, Gare. Who Was Eleanor Roosevelt? Wolf, Elizabeth, tr. Wolf, Elizabeth & Harrison, Nancy, illus. 2004. (Who Was...? Ser.). 112p. (J). (gr. 7-7). pap. 4.99 (978-0-448-43509-1(8) , Grosset & Dunlap) Penguin Group (USA) Inc.

—Who Was Eleanor Roosevelt? 2004. (gr. 3-6). lib. bdg. 13.00 (978-0-613-72563-7(8)) Tandem Library Bks.

Time for Kids Editors. Eleanor Roosevelt: First Lady of the World. 2006. (Time for Kids Ser.). (Illus.). 48p. (J). 14.99 (978-0-06-057614-1(6)); pap. 3.99 (978-0-06-057613-4(8)) HarperCollins Pubs.

Trailblazers of the Modern World: Neil Armstrong; Bob Dylan; Bill Gates; Nelson Mandela; Eleanor Roosevelt; Steven Spielberg, 6 bks. 2002. (Illus.). (J). (gr. 5 up). pap. 87.60 (978-0-8368-5234-9(6) , World Almanac Library) Stevens, Gareth Inc.

Trumbauer, Lisa. Eleanor Roosevelt. (First Biographies Ser.). 24p. (J). pap. 5.95 (978-0-7368-5082-7(1)) Capstone Pr., Inc.

—Eleanor Roosevelt. 2004. (First Biographies Ser.). (Illus.). 24p. (J). lib. bdg. 15.93 (978-0-7368-2080-6(9) , Pebble Bks.) Capstone Pr., Inc.

Westervelt, Virginia. Here Comes Eleanor: A New Life of Eleanor Roosevelt for Young People. 1998. (Illus.). 142 p. (J). (gr. 6-12). pap. 16.00 (978-1-888105-33-9(X)) Avisson Pr., Inc.

Winget, Mary. Eleanor Roosevelt. (Biography Ser.). (Illus.). 2005. 112p. (gr. 6-12). lib. bdg. 27.93 (978-0-8225-4985-7(9)); 2003. 48p. (J). pap. 6.95 (978-0-8225-4801-0(1) , Lerner Pubns.); 2003. 48p. (J). (gr. 3-5). lib. bdg. 26.60 (978-0-8225-4675-7(2)) Lerner Publishing Group.

—Eleanor Roosevelt. 2003. (gr. 3-6). lib. bdg. 15.25 (978-0-613-84031-6(3)) Tandem Library Bks.

Winner, David. Eleanor Roosevelt. (Pacificadores Mundiales Ser.). 64p. (gr. 5-8). 28.70 (978-1-4103-0539-8(2) , Blackbirch Pr., Inc.) Thomson Gale.

ROOSEVELT, ELEANOR, 1884-1962—FICTION

Coleman, Evelyn. Circle of Fire. 2001. (American Girl Collection). (Illus.). (J). 12.60 (978-0-606-21249-6(3)) Tandem Library Bks.

De Young, C. Coco. A Letter to Mrs. Roosevelt. 2000. 112p. (J). (gr. 3-7). pap. 5.50 (978-0-440-41529-9(2) , Yearling) Random Hse. Children's Bks.

de Young, C. Coco. Letter to Mrs. Roosevelt. 2000. 105p. (J). (ps-7). lib. bdg. 12.40 (978-0-613-28551-3(4)) Tandem Library Bks.

Ryan, Pam Muñoz. Amelia & Eleanor Go for a Ride. Selznick, Brian, illus. 1999. 40p. (J). (gr. k-4). pap. 16.95 (978-0-590-96075-5(X)) Scholastic, Inc.

ROOSEVELT, FRANKLIN D. (FRANKLIN DELANO), 1882-1945

Allport, Alan. Franklin Delano Roosevelt. 2003. (Great American Presidents Ser.). (Illus.). 100p. (gr. 4-8). 30.00 (978-0-7910-7598-2(2) , Chelsea Hse.) Facts On File, Inc.

Ashby, Ruth. Franklin & Eleanor Roosevelt. 2005. (Illus.). 48p. (J). pap. (978-0-8368-5764-1(X)); lib. bdg. 30.00 (978-0-8368-5758-0(5)) Stevens, Gareth Inc. (World Almanac Library).

Bardhan-Quallen, Sudipta. Franklin Delano Roosevelt: A National Hero. 2007. (Sterling Biographies Ser.). (Illus.). 128p. (J). 12.95 (978-1-4027-4747-2(0)); pap. 5.95 (978-1-4027-3545-5(6)) Sterling Publishing Co., Inc.

Burgan, Michael. Franklin D. Roosevelt. 2002. (Profiles of the Presidents Ser.). (Illus.). 64p. (J). (gr. 4 up). lib. bdg. 23.93 (978-0-7565-0203-4(9)) Compass Point Bks.

Caplan, Jeremy. Franklin D Roosevelt A Leader in Troubled Times. 2006. 44p. (J). lib. bdg. 15.00 (***978-1-4242-0848-7(3)***) Fitzgerald Bks.

Cronkite, Walter, frwd. Great American Presidents. (Illus.). (gr. 4-8). pap. (978-0-7910-8048-1(X) , Chelsea Hse.) Facts On File, Inc.

DeGezelle, Terri. Franklin D. Roosevelt & the Great Depression. 2007. (J). (***978-1-4034-9670-6(6)***); pap. (***978-1-4034-9678-2(1)***) Heinemann Library.

Doak, Robin S. Franklin D. Roosevelt. 2002. (Trailblazers of the Modern World Ser.). (Illus.). 48p. (J). (gr. 5 up). pap. 14.95 (978-0-8368-5233-2(8)); lib. bdg. 30.00 (978-0-8368-5073-4(4)) Stevens, Gareth Inc. (World Almanac Library).

—Franklin D Roosevelt. 2002. (gr. 3-6). lib. bdg. 16.40 (978-0-613-76723-1(3)) Tandem Library Bks.

Emerson, Judy. Franklin D. Roosevelt. Saunders-Smith, Gail, ed. 2004. (First Biographies Ser.). (Illus.). 24p. (J). (gr. k-1). lib. bdg. 15.93 (978-0-7368-2087-5(6) , Pebble Bks.) Capstone Pr., Inc.

Feinberg, Barbara Silberdick. Franklin D. Roosevelt. 2005. (Encyc of Presidents, 2ND Ser.). (Illus.). 112p. (J). (gr. 6-8). 34.00 (978-0-516-22970-6(2) , Watts, Franklin) Scholastic Library Publishing.

Fitzgerald, Stephanie. The New Deal: FDR's Plan for Recovery. 2006. (J). (978-0-7565-2096-0(7)) Compass Point Bks.

Ford, Carin T. Franklin D. Roosevelt: The 32nd President. 2006. (Heroes of American History Ser.). (Illus.). 32p. (J). lib. bdg. 22.60 (978-0-7660-2603-2(5) , Enslow Elementary) Enslow Pubs., Inc.

Franklin D Roosevelt. (First Biographies Ser.). 24p. (J). 5.95 (978-0-7368-5084-1(8)); 6.95 (978-0-7368-4465-9(1)) Capstone Pr., Inc.

Franklin Delano Roosevelt 2: Leveled Books. 2001. (McGraw-Hill. Lectura Ser.). (ENG & SPA.). (gr. 5 up). (978-0-02-188226-7(6)) Macmillan/McGraw-Hill Schl. Div.

Franklin Roosevelt, 6 vols. (gr. 2-5). 36.95 (978-0-7368-4557-1(7)) Red Brick Learning.

Gilbert, Adrian. Franklin D. Roosevelt. 2003. (Twentieth Century History Makers Ser.). (Illus.). 112p. (J). lib. bdg. 32.85 (978-0-7398-5260-6(4)) Raintree.

Green, Robert. Franklin Delano Roosevelt: U. S. President. 2001. (Career Biographies Ser.). (Illus.). 128p. (J). (gr. 6-12). 25.00 (978-0-89434-373-5(4) , F416, Ferguson Publishing Co.) Facts On File, Inc.

Harcourt School Publishers Staff. From One Man's Dream On Level. 3rd ed. 2002. (Trophies Reading Program Ser.). (Illus.). pap. 5.10 (978-0-15-323362-3(1)) Harcourt Schl. Pubs.

Haugen, Brenda. Franklin Delano Roosevelt: The New Deal President. 2006. (Signature Lives Ser.). (Illus.). 112p. (J). (gr. 5-7). 30.60 (978-0-7565-1586-7(6)) Compass Point Bks.

Isaacs, Sally Senzell. America in the Time of Franklin Delano Roosevelt: The Story of Our Nation from Coast to Coast, from 1929 to 1948. 2002. (Illus.). 48p. (J). (gr. 4-7). pap. 8.50 (978-1-57572-938-1(5)) Heinemann Library.

Joseph, Paul. Franklin D. Roosevelt. 2000. (United States Presidents Ser.). (Illus.). 32p. (J). (gr. k-6). lib. bdg. 22.78 (978-1-56239-813-2(X) , Checkerboard Library) ABDO Publishing Co.

Kent, Deborah. Franklin Delano Roosevelt: Nothing to Fear! 2006. (Defining Moments Ser.). (Illus.). 32p. (J). lib. bdg. 25.27 (978-1-59716-272-2(8)) Bearport Publishing Co., Inc.

Knapp, Ron. Franklin D. Roosevelt: A MyReportLinks.com Book. 2002. (Presidents Ser.). (Illus.). 48p. (J). (gr. 4-10). lib. bdg. 25.26 (978-0-7660-5009-9(2) , MyReportLinks.com Bks.) Enslow Pubs., Inc.

Kudlinski, Kathleen. Franklin Delano Roosevelt: Champion of Freedom. Henderson, Meryl, illus. 2003. (Childhood of Famous Americans Ser.). 192p. (J). pap. 5.99 (978-0-689-85745-4(4) , Aladdin) Simon & Schuster Children's Publishing.

—Franklin Delano Roosevelt: Champion of Freedom. 2003. (gr. 3-6). lib. bdg. 13.00 (978-0-613-91046-0(X)) Tandem Library Bks.

Levine, Michelle & Waxman, Laura Hamilton. Franklin D. Roosevelt. 2005. (History Maker Bios Ser.). (Illus.). 48p. (J). (gr. 3-5). 26.60 (978-0-8225-1545-6(8)) Lerner Publishing Group.

Mara, Wil. Franklin D. Roosevelt. 2004. (Rookie Biographies Ser.). (Illus.). 31p. (J). 20.50 (978-0-516-21844-1(1) , Children's Pr.) Scholastic Library Publishing.

—Franklin D Roosevelt. 2004. (Rookie Biographies Ser.). 32p. (J). (gr. 1-2). pap. 4.95 (978-0-516-25823-2(0) , Children's Pr.) Scholastic Library Publishing.

Margaret, Amy. Franklin D. Roosevelt Library & Museum. 2004. (Presidential Libraries Ser.). (Illus.). 24p. (J). lib. bdg. 18.75 (978-0-8239-6268-6(7) , PowerKids Pr.) Rosen Publishing Group, Inc., The.

Marsh, Carole. Franklin D. Roosevelt. 2002. (One Thousand Readers Ser.). (Illus.). 12p. (J). (gr. k-4). 2.95 (978-0-635-01561-7(7) , 15617) Gallopade International.

Mis, Melody S. How to Draw the Life & Times of Franklin Delano Roosevelt. 2007. (Kid's Guide to Drawing the Presidents of the United States of America Ser.). (Illus.). 32p. (J). 25.25 (978-1-4042-3008-8(4) , PowerKids Pr.) Rosen Publishing Group, Inc., The.

Panchyk, Richard. Franklin Delano Roosevelt for Kids: His Life & Times with 21 Activities. 2007. (For Kids Ser.). 160p. (J). pap. 14.95 (***978-1-55652-657-2(1)***) Chicago Review Pr., Inc.

Roberts, Jeremy. Franklin D. Roosevelt. 2003. (Presidential Leaders Ser.). (Illus.). 112p. (J). (gr. 6-12). lib. bdg. 29.27 (978-0-8225-0095-7(7)) Lerner Publishing Group.

Schaefer, Ted & Schaefer, Lola. The Franklin Delano Roosevelt Memorial. 2005. (Symbols of Freedom Ser.). (Illus.). 32p. (J). (gr. k-2). lib. bdg. 25.36 (978-1-4034-6661-7(0)) Heinemann Library.

Schaefer, Ted & Schaefer, Lola M. The Franklin Delano Roosevelt Memorial. 2005. (Symbols of Freedom Ser.). (Illus.). 32p. (J). pap. (978-1-4034-6670-9(X)) Heinemann Library.

Spies, Karen Bornemann. Franklin D. Roosevelt. 1999. (United States Presidents Ser.). (Illus.). 128p. (J). (gr. 5-12). lib. bdg. 26.60 (978-0-7660-1038-3(4)) Enslow Pubs., Inc.

St. George, Judith. Make Your Mark, Franklin Roosevelt! Spencer, Britt, illus. 2007. 40p. (J). (gr. 2-5). 16.99 (978-0-399-24175-8(2) , Philomel) Penguin Group (USA) Inc.

Sullivan, Anne Marie. Franklin D. Roosevelt. 2003. (Childhood of the Presidents Ser.). (Illus.). 48p. (J). (gr. 4 up). lib. bdg. (978-1-59084-279-9(0)) Mason Crest Pubs.

Taylor, David. Franklin D. Roosevelt. 2003. (Leading Lives Ser.). (Illus.). 64p. pap. 8.95 (978-1-4034-3494-4(8)) Heinemann Library.

—Franklin D Roosevelt. 2003. (gr. 5-8). lib. bdg. 17.60 (978-0-613-88563-8(5)) Tandem Library Bks.

—Franklin Delano Roosevelt. 2001. (Leading Lives Ser.). (Illus.). 64p. (J). (gr. 5-7). lib. bdg. 27.86 (978-1-58810-161-7(4)) Heinemann Library.

Time for Kids Editors. Franklin D. Roosevelt: A Leader in Troubled Times. 2006. (Time for Kids Ser.). (Illus.). 48p. (J). 14.99 (978-0-06-057616-5(2)); pap. 3.99 (978-0-06-057615-8(4)) HarperCollins Pubs.

Uschan, Michael V. Franklin D. Roosevelt. 2002. (Importance of Ser.). (Illus.). 128p. (YA). (gr. 7-10). 32.45 (978-1-56006-967-6(8) , Lucent Bks.) Thomson Gale.

Venezia, Mike. Franklin D. Roosevelt. Venezia, Mike, illus. 2007. (Getting to Know the U. S. Presidents Ser.). 32p. (J). 7.95 (***978-0-531-17945-1(1)***); (Illus.). (gr. 3-4). 27.00 (978-0-516-22636-1(3)) Scholastic Library Publishing. (Children's Pr.).

Waxman, Laura Hamilton. Franklin D. Roosevelt. 2004. (History Maker Bios Ser.). (J). pap. 6.95 (978-0-8225-2539-4(9) , Lerner Pubns.) Lerner Publishing Group.

Wroble, Lisa A. The New Deal & the Great Depression in American History. 2002. (In American History Ser.). (Illus.). 128p. (J). (gr. 5-12). lib. bdg. 26.60 (978-0-7660-1421-3(5)) Enslow Pubs., Inc.

ROOSEVELT, FRANKLIN D. (FRANKLIN DELANO), 1882-1945—FICTION

Winthrop, Elizabeth. Dear Mr. President - Franklin Delano Roosevelt: Letters from a Mill Town Girl. Winthrop, Elizabeth, illus. unabr. ed. 2003. (Illus.). (J). (gr. 4-7). 25.95 incl. audio (978-1-59112-213-5(9)) Live Oak Media.

—Franklin Delano Roosevelt: Letters from a Mill Town Girl. 2001. (Dear Mr. President Ser.). (Illus.). 128p. (J). (gr. 4-6). 9.95 (978-1-890817-61-9(9)) Winslow Pr.

ROOSEVELT, THEODORE, 1858-1919

Benge, Janet & Benge, Geoff. Theodore Roosevelt. 2004. (Illus.). 203p. (J). pap. 8.99 (978-1-932096-10-1(8)) Emerald Bks.

Burke, Rick. Theodore Roosevelt. 2002. (Illus.). 32p. (J). pap. 6.95 (978-1-4034-0415-2(1)) Heinemann Library.

Collins, James. Theodore Roosevelt: With Buffalo Bill & Farley's Raiders. Cox, Brian T., illus. 2006. (Time Traveler's Adventure Ser.). 56p. (J). 13.50 incl. audio compact disk (978-1-932332-60-5(X)) Toy Box Productions.

DeMauro, Lisa & Time for Kids Editors. Theodore Roosevelt: The Adventurous President. 2005. (Time for Kids Ser.). (Illus.). 48p. (J). 14.99 (978-0-06-057606-6(5)); pap. 3.99 (978-0-06-057604-2(9)) HarperCollins Pubs.

Donnelly, Matthew. Theodore Roosevelt: Larger Than Life. 2002. (Illus.). 128p. (J). (gr. 6-12). 27.50 (978-0-208-02510-4(3) , Linnet Bks.) Shoe String Pr., Inc.

Elish, Dan. Theodore Roosevelt. 2007. (Presidents & Their Times Ser.). 96p. (J). lib. bdg. 32.79 (978-0-7614-2429-1(6) , Benchmark Bks.) Cavendish, Marshall Corp.

Emerson, Judy. Theodore Roosevelt. Saunders-Smith, Gail, ed. 2004. (First Biographies Ser.). (Illus.). 24p. (J). (gr. k-1). lib. bdg. 15.93 (978-0-7368-2369-2(7) , Pebble Bks.) Capstone Pr., Inc.

Garraty, John A. Sterling Point Books: Teddy Roosevelt: American Rough Rider. 2007. (Sterling Point Bks.). 176p. (J). 12.95 (978-1-4027-4524-9(9)); pap. 6.95 (978-1-4027-4144-9(8)) Sterling Publishing Co., Inc.

Gayle, Sharon. Teddy Roosevelt the People's President. Dacey, Bob & Bandelin, Debra, illus. ed. 2005. (Ready-to-Read Ser. Level 3). 32p. (J). lib. bdg. 15.00 (978-1-59054-961-2(9)) Fitzgerald Bks.

Gayle, Sharon Shavers. Teddy Roosevelt: The People's President. Dacey, Bob & Bandelin, Debra, trs. Dacey, Bob & Bandelin, Debra, illus. 2003. (Ready-to-Read Stories of Famous Americans Ser.). 32p. (J). pap. 3.99 (978-0-689-85825-3(6) , Aladdin) Simon & Schuster Children's Publishing.

Green, Robert. Theodore Roosevelt. 2003. (Profiles of the Presidents Ser.). (Illus.). 64p. (J). (gr. 4 up). lib. bdg. 23.93 (978-0-7565-0272-0(1)) Compass Point Bks.

Greenhaven Staff. Theodore Roosevelt. 2002. (gr. 7-12). lib. bdg. 33.25 (978-0-613-73893-4(4)) Tandem Library Bks.

Harness, Cheryl. The Remarkable Rough-Riding Life of Theodore Roosevelt & the Rise of Empire America. 2007. (Illus.). 144p. (J). (gr. 3-7). 16.95 (978-1-4263-0008-0(5)); lib. bdg. 25.90 (978-1-4263-0009-7(3)) National Geographic Society. (National Geographic Children's Bks.).

Horn, Geoffrey M. Theodore Roosevelt. 2003. (Trailblazers of the Modern World Ser.). (Illus.). 48p. (J). (gr. 5 up). pap. (978-0-8368-5252-3(4)); lib. bdg. 30.00 (978-0-8368-5092-5(0)) Stevens, Gareth Inc. (World Almanac Library).

Jackson, Ellen, ed. My Tour of Europe: By Teddy Roosevelt, Age 10. Brighton, Catherine, illus. 2003. 40p. 14.95 (978-0-7613-1998-6(0) , Millbrook Pr.) Lerner Publishing Group.

Keating, Frank. Theodore. Wimmer, Mike, illus. 2006. 32p. (J). (gr. 1-4). 16.95 (978-0-689-86532-9(5) , Simon & Schuster/Paula Wiseman Bks.) Simon & Schuster Children's Publishing.

Kelley, Alison. Theodore Roosevelt. 2003. (Great American Presidents Ser.). (Illus.). 100p. (gr. 4-8). 30.00 (978-0-7910-7606-4(7) , Chelsea Hse.) Facts On File, Inc.

Kerley, Barbara. What to Do about Alice?! How Alice Roosevelt Broke the Rules, Charmed the World, & Drove Her Father Teddy Crazy. Fotheringham, Ed, illus. 2008. 48p. (J). pap. 16.99 (***978-0-439-92231-9(3)*** , Scholastic Pr.) Scholastic, Inc.

Kozar, Richard. Theodore Roosevelt & the Exploration of the Amazon Basin. 2000. (Explorers of the New World Ser.). (Illus.). (J). 63p. (gr. 4-7). pap. 25.00 (978-0-7910-6164-0(7)); 64p. 25.00 (978-0-7910-5954-8(5)) Facts On File, Inc. (Chelsea Hse.).

—Theodore Roosevelt & the Exploration of the Amazon Basin. 2001. (gr. 3-6). lib. bdg. 17.60 (978-0-613-33134-0(6)) Tandem Library Bks.

Kraft, Betsy Harvey. Theodore Roosevelt: Champion of the American Spirit. 2003. (Illus.). 192p. (J). (gr. 5-9). tchr. ed. 19.00 (978-0-618-14264-4(9) , Clarion Bks.) Houghton Mifflin Co. Trade & Reference Div.

Mara, Wil. Theodore Roosevelt. 2006. (Illus.). 31p. (J). (978-0-516-29844-3(5)) Children's Pr., Ltd.

Marcovitz, Hal. Theodore Roosevelt. 2003. (Childhood of the Presidents Ser.). (Illus.). 48p. (J). (gr. 4 up). lib. bdg. (978-1-59084-278-2(2)) Mason Crest Pubs.

Marrin, Albert. The Great Adventure: Theodore Roosevelt & the Rise of Modern America. 2007. 256p. (YA). (gr. 7). 30.00 (***978-0-525-47659-7(8)*** , Dutton Juvenile) Penguin Group (USA) Inc.

McCafferty, Jim. Holt & the Teddy Bear. Davis, Florence S., illus. 2001. 40p. (J). pap. 9.95 (978-1-56554-580-9(X)) Pelican Publishing Co., Inc.

McCollum, Sean. Theodore Roosevelt. 2004. (Encyclopedia of Presidents Ser.). (Illus.). 110p. (J). 34.00 (978-0-516-22964-5(8) , Children's Pr.) Scholastic Library Publishing.

McGowen, Tom. The Spanish-American War & Teddy Roosevelt in American History. 2003. (In American History Ser.). (Illus.). 128p. (J). lib. bdg. 26.60 (978-0-7660-1987-4(X)) Enslow Pubs., Inc.

McKay, Sindy. We Both Read-President Theodore Roosevelt. Gampert, John, illus. 2006. (We Both Read Ser.). 48p. (J). 7.99 (978-1-891327-67-4(4)); pap. 3.99 (978-1-891327-68-1(2)) Treasure Bay, Inc.

McPherson, Stephanie Sammartino. Theodore Roosevelt. 2005. (Presidential Leaders Ser.). (Illus.). 112p. (J). 29.27 (978-0-8225-0999-8(7) , Lerner Pubns.) Lerner Publishing Group.

Olson, Nathan. Theodore Roosevelt: Bear of a President. Martin, Cynthia et al, illus. 2007. (Graphic Library). 32p. (J). (gr. 3-5). 25.26 (***978-0-7368-6849-5(6)*** , 1264944); pap. 7.95 (***978-0-7368-7901-9(3)*** , 1264944) Capstone Pr., Inc.

Roosevelt, Theodore. The Boyhood Diary of Theodore Roosevelt, 1869-1870: Early Travels of the 26th U. S. President. Saterern, Shelley Swanson, ed. 2000. (Blue Earth Books). (Illus.). 32p. (J). (gr. 3-4). lib. bdg. 22.60 (978-0-7368-0601-5(6) , Bridgestone Bks.) Capstone Pr., Inc.

—My Tour of Europe: By Teddy Roosevelt. Jackson, Ellen B., ed. Brighton, Catherine, illus. 2003. 40p. lib. bdg. 23.90 (978-0-7613-2516-1(6) , Millbrook Pr.) Lerner Publishing Group.

Ruffin, Frances E. How to Draw the Life & Times of Theodore Roosevelt. 2007. (Kid's Guide to Drawing the Presidents of the United States of America Ser.). (Illus.). 32p. (J). 25.25 (978-1-4042-3002-6(5) , PowerKids Pr.) Rosen Publishing Group, Inc., The.

Santella, Andrew. Roosevelt's Rough Riders. 2005. (We the People Ser.). (Illus.). 48p. (J). (gr. 4-6). 23.93 (978-0-7565-1268-2(9)) Compass Point Bks.

Schueler, Donald G. Theodore Roosevelt: A MyReportLinks.com Book. 2002. (Presidents Ser.). (Illus.). 48p. (J). (gr. 4-10). lib. bdg. 25.26 (978-0-7660-5008-2(4) , MyReportLinks.com Bks.) Enslow Pubs., Inc.

Schwartz, Eric. A World Contender. 2005. (How America Became America Ser.). (Illus.). 96p. (J). lib. bdg. (978-1-59084-911-8(6)) Mason Crest Pubs.

St. George, Judith & Faulkner, Matt. You're on Your Way, Teddy Roosevelt! 2004. (Illus.). 48p. (J). (gr. 3). 16.99 (978-0-399-23888-8(3) , Philomel) Penguin Group (USA) Inc.

Swain, Gwenyth. Theodore Roosevelt. (History Maker Bios Ser.). (J). 2005. (Illus.). 48p. 26.60 (978-0-8225-1548-7(2)); 2004. pap. (978-0-8225-2542-4(9)) Lerner Publishing Group. (Lerner Pubns.).

Theodore Roosevelt. (First Biographies Ser.). 24p. (J). 5.95 (978-0-7368-5089-6(9)); 6.95 (978-0-7368-4473-4(2)) Capstone Pr., Inc.

Theodore Roosevelt, 6 vols. (gr. 2-5). 36.95 (978-0-7368-4565-6(8)) Red Brick Learning.

Trailblazers of the Modern World: Louis Armstrong; Anne Frank; Martin Luther King, Jr.; Theodore Roosevelt; Gloria Steinem; The Wright Brothers, 6 bks. 2003. (Illus.). (J). (gr. 5 up). lib. bdg. 175.60 (978-0-8368-5088-8(2) , World Almanac Library) Stevens, Gareth Inc.

Venezia, Mike, illus. Theodore Roosevelt: Twenty-Sixth President, 1901-1909. 2007. 32p. (J). pap. (***978-0-516-25225-4(9)***) Children's Pr., Ltd.

Welsbacher, Anne. Theodore Roosevelt. 1999. (United States Presidents Ser.). (Illus.). 32p. (J). (gr. k-6). lib. bdg. 22.78 (978-1-56239-742-5(7) , Checkerboard Library) ABDO Publishing Co.

Whitelaw, Nancy. Theodore Roosevelt Takes Charge. 2004. (Illus.). 192p. (J). (gr. 4-8). reprint ed. 20.00 (978-0-7567-7794-4(1)) DIANE Publishing Co.

ROOSEVELT, THEODORE, 1858-1919—FICTION

Armstrong, Jennifer. Theodore Roosevelt: Letters from a Young Coal Miner. 2001. (Dear Mr. President Ser.: Vol. 1). (Illus.). 118p. (J). (gr. 4-7). 8.95 (978-1-890817-27-5(9)) Winslow Pr.

Bradley, Kimberly Brubaker. The President's Daughter. 2004. (Illus.). 176p. (gr. 3-7). 15.95 (978-0-385-73147-8(7) , Delacorte Bks. for Young Readers) Random Hse. Children's Bks.

Lalicki, Tom. Shots at Sea. Cerniglia, Carlyn, illus. 2007. (Houdini & Nate Mysteries Ser.). 208p. (J). (gr. 3-7). 15.95 (***978-0-374-31679-2(1)***) Farrar, Straus & Giroux.

Sargent, Dave & Sargent, Pat. Buckshot: (Blue Eyed Chestnut) Mind Your Manners, 25, 8. Lenoir, Jane, illus. 2001. (Saddle Up Ser.: 8). 36p. (J). pap. 6.95 (978-1-56763-674-1(8)); lib. bdg. 22.60 (978-1-56763-673-4(X)) Ozark Publishing.

Venezia, Mike, illus. Theodore Roosevelt. 2006. 32p. (J). (978-0-516-22630-9(4)) Children's Pr., Ltd.

ROOSEVELT FAMILY

Panchyk, Richard. Franklin Delano Roosevelt for Kids: His Life & Times with 21 Activities. 2007. (For Kids Ser.). 160p. (J). pap. 14.95 (***978-1-55652-657-2(1)***) Chicago Review Pr., Inc.

ROOSEVELT FAMILY—FICTION

Buckley, Anne. The Day Mrs. Roosevelt Came to Town. 2003. 186p. (YA). (gr. 9 up). pap. 9.99 (978-0-88092-458-0(6)) Royal Fireworks Publishing Co.

ROOSTERS

Butterfield, Moira. Rooster. 2000. (Who Am I? Ser.). (Illus.). 32p. (J). (ps-1). lib. bdg. 16.95 (978-1-929298-92-1(7)) Chrysalis Education.

ROOSTERS—FICTION

Auch, Mary Jane. Poultrygeist. Jane, Mary & Auch, Herm, illus. 32p. (J). (gr. k-3). reprint ed. 6.95 (978-0-8234-1876-3(6)) Holiday Hse., Inc.

Baddiel, Ivor & Jubb, Sophie. Cock-A-Doodle Quack Quack. Busby, Ailie, illus. 2007. 40p. (J). (ps-3). 15.99 (978-0-385-75104-9(4)); lib. bdg. 18.99 (978-0-385-75105-6(2)) Random Hse. Children's Bks. (Fickling, David Bks.).

Campoy, F. Isabel. Get up, Rick! Adnet, Bernard, illus. 2007. (Green Light Readers Level 1 Ser.). 24p. (J). (ps-1). 12.95 (***978-0-15-206266-8(1)***); pap. 3.95 (***978-0-15-206272-9(6)***) Harcourt Children's Bks. (Green Light Readers).

Carle, Eric. Rooster's off to See the World. Carle, Eric, illus. 2002. (Illus.). (J). 15.53 (978-0-7587-3530-0(8)) Book Wholesalers, Inc.

—Rooster's off to See the World. Carle, Eric, illus. (Classic Board Bks.). (Illus.). (J). 2002. 26p. bds. 7.99 (978-0-689-84901-5(X) , Little Simon); 1999. 32p. pap. 7.99 (978-0-689-82684-9(2) , 076714005990, Aladdin) Simon & Schuster Children's Publishing.

—Rooster's off to See the World. 1999. (978-0-606-16316-3(6)); lib. bdg. 15.30 (978-0-613-18325-3(8)) Tandem Library Bks.

Cazet, Denys. Elvis the Rooster Almost Goes to Heaven. Cazet, Denys, illus. 2004. (I Can Read Bks.). (Illus.). 48p. (J). (gr. k-3). pap. 3.99 (978-0-06-000502-3(5) , Harper Trophy) HarperCollins Pubs.

—Elvis the Rooster Almost Goes to Heaven. Cazet, Denys, illus. unabr. ed. 2006. (Readalongs for Beginning Readers Ser.). (Illus.). (J). (gr. k-3). 25.95 incl. audio (978-1-59519-686-6(2)); 28.95 incl. audio compact disk (978-1-59519-687-3(0)); pap. 16.95 incl. audio (978-1-59519-682-8(X)); pap. 18.95 incl. audio compact disk (978-1-59519-683-5(8)); Set. pap. 29.95 incl. audio (978-1-59519-684-2(6)); Set. pap. 31.95 incl. audio compact disk (978-1-59519-685-9(4)) Live Oak Media.

Cazet, Denys. Elvis the Rooster & the Magic Words. 2004. (Illus.). 48p. (J). lib. bdg. 13.85 (***978-1-4242-0562-2(X)***) Fitzgerald Bks.

—Elvis the Rooster & the Magic Words. Cazet, Denys, illus. (I Can Read Bks.). 48p. (J). 2005. pap. 3.99 (978-0-06-000511-5(4) , Harper Trophy); 2004. (Illus.). 15.99 (978-0-06-000509-2(2)) HarperCollins Pubs.

—Elvis the Rooster & the Magic Words. unabr. ed. 2006. (Readalongs for Beginning Readers Ser.). (J). 29.95 incl. audio (978-1-59519-694-1(3)); 28.95 incl. audio compact disk (978-1-59519-695-8(1)); pap. 16.95 incl.

audio (978-1-59519-690-3(0)); pap. 18.95 incl. audio compact disk (978-1-59519-691-0(9)); Set. pap. 29.95 incl. audio (978-1-59519-692-7(7)); Set. pap. 31.95 incl. audio compact disk (978-1-59519-693-4(5)) Live Oak Media.

Chanticleer & the Fox. 2004. (J). 24.95 incl. audio (978-1-56008-178-4(3)); pap. 14.95 incl. audio (978-1-56008-179-1(1)) Weston Woods Studios, Inc.

Conrad, Pam. The Rooster's Gift. 1998. (Illus.). 40p. (J). (ps-3). pap. 6.95 (978-0-06-443496-6(6) , Harper Trophy) HarperCollins Pubs.

Crummel, Susan Stevens & Stevens, Janet. Cook-a-Doodle-Doo! 2005. (Illus.). 48p. (J). (ps-ps). reprint ed. pap. 7.00 (978-0-15-205658-2(0) , Voyager Bks./Libros Viajeros) Harcourt Children's Bks.

Davis, Marjorie. Willie the Rooster. 2006. pap. 7.95 (978-0-533-15273-5(9)) Vantage Pr., Inc.

De Anda, Diane. The Immortal Rooster: And Other Stories. 1999. 112p. (YA). (gr. 3-7). pap. 9.95 (978-1-55885-278-5(6) , Piñata Books) Arte Publico Pr.

—Kikirikí / Quiquiriquí. Hernandez, Karina, tr. from ENG. Lechon, Daniel, illus. 2004. (ENG & SPA.). 32p. 14.95 (978-1-55885-382-9(0) , Piñata Books) Arte Publico Pr.

Doudna, Kelly. Rooster Combs. Haberstroh, Anne, illus. 2006. (Fact & Fiction Ser.). 24p. (J). 21.35 (978-1-59679-965-3(X) , SandCastle); pap. (978-1-59679-966-0(8)) ABDO Publishing Co.

Edwards, Pamela Duncan. The Mixed-up Rooster. Lloyd, Megan, illus. 2006. 32p. (J). (ps-1). 15.99 (978-0-06-028999-7(6) , Tegen, Katherine Bks); lib. bdg. 16.89 (978-0-06-029000-9(5)) HarperCollins Pubs.

—The Wrong Way Rooster. Date not set. 32p. (J). (ps-1). pap. 5.99 (978-0-06-443689-2(6)) HarperCollins Pubs.

Eggleton, Jill. Rabbit & Rooster's Ride: 3-in-1 Package. Taylor, Clive, illus. (Sails Literacy Ser.). 24p. (gr. k up). 57.00 (978-0-7578-8617-1(5)) Rigby Education.

—Rabbit & Rooster's Ride: 6 Small Books. Taylor, Clive, illus. (Sails Literacy Ser.). 24p. (gr. k up). 25.00 (978-0-7578-7727-8(3)) Rigby Education.

—Rabbit & Rooster's Ride: Big Book Only. Taylor, Clive, illus. (Sails Literacy Ser.). 24p. (gr. k up). 27.00 (978-0-7578-6200-7(4)) Rigby Education.

French, Vivian & Lewis, Jan. Big Fat Hen & the Hairy Goat. 1999. (Illus.). 24p. (J). pap. 7.95 (978-1-86233-000-9(X)) Sterling Publishing Co., Inc.

—Big Fat Hen & the Red Rooster. 1999. (Illus.). 24p. (J). pap. 7.95 (978-1-86233-005-4(0)) Sterling Publishing Co., Inc.

Gershator, David & Gershator, Phillis. Moon Rooster. Halsey, Megan, illus. 2001. 32p. (J). (gr. k-3). 15.95 (978-0-7614-5092-4(0) , Cavendish Children's Bks.) Cavendish, Marshall Corp.

Giacomucci, Carol. A New Home. 2006. 23p. pap. 10.95 (978-0-7414-3498-2(9)) Infinity Publishing.

Green, Jonathan, illus. Amadeus, the Leghorn Rooster. 2004. (J). 17.95 (978-0-87844-174-7(3)) Sandlapper Publishing Co., Inc.

Hamilton, Martha. Rooster's Night Out. 2007. 32p. pap. 42.95 (***978-0-87483-844-2(4)***) August Hse. Pubs., Inc.

Hayward, Linda. The King's Chorus. Goldfinger, Jennifer P., illus. 2006. 32p. (J). (ps-k). 16.00 (978-0-618-51618-6(2) , Clarion Bks.) Houghton Mifflin Co. Trade & Reference Div.

Hercules's Spring Adventure Pack. 2001. (978-1-883772-01-7(X)) Flying Rhinoceros, Inc.

Hillenbrand, Will. Cock-a-Doodle Christmas! Hillenbrand, Will, illus. 2007. (Illus.). 32p. (J). (ps-2). 16.99 (***978-0-7614-5354-3(7)***) Cavendish, Marshall Corp.

Isbrecht, Lucky. Rooster's Rescue. 2004. (Illus.). 23p. (J). (ps-7). per. 4.95 (978-1-59453-262-7(1) , 2690) Airleaf Publishing & Bookselling.

Jones, Nancy. The Grandpaws. 2005. 57p. pap. 12.95 (978-1-4137-4778-2(7)) PublishAmerica, Inc.

Jungman, Ann. The Prince Who Thought He Was a Rooster. 2008. 96p. (J). 14.95 (***978-1-84507-793-8(8));*** (Illus.). pap. 7.95 (***978-1-84507-794-5(6)***) Lincoln, Frances Ltd. GBR. *Dist:* Perseus Distribution.

Kline, Trish & Donev, Mary. Hoops in the Coop: KA Reader 7. 2007. (Illus.). 32p. (J). per. 20.00 (***978-1-934307-00-7(9)***) Ghost Hunter Productions.

Landstrom, Lena. Four Hens & a Rooster. Sandin, Joan, tr. from SWE. Landstrom, Olof, illus. 2005. 28p. (J). (ps-4). 16.00 (978-91-29-66336-5(9)) R & S Bks. SWE. *Dist:* Macmillan.

Lavette, Lavaille. The Adventures of Roopster Roux: Escape from Vulture's Roost. Mitchell, Louis H., illus. 1998. (Adventures of Roopster Roux Ser.). 32p. (J). (ps-3). pap. 5.95 (978-1-56554-360-7(2)) Pelican Publishing Co., Inc.

—The Adventures of Roopster Roux: Slammin' Slime. Mitchell, Louis H., illus. 1998. (Adventures of Roopster Roux Ser.). 32p. (J). (ps-3). pap. 5.95 (978-1-56554-359-1(9)) Pelican Publishing Co., Inc.

—The Adventures of Roopster Roux: Surfing the Net. Mitchell, Louis H., illus. 1998. (Adventures of Roopster Roux Ser.). 32p. (J). (ps-3). pap. 5.95 (978-1-56554-361-4(0)) Pelican Publishing Co., Inc.

—The Adventures of Roopster Roux: The Monster All-Stars. Mitchell, Louis H., illus. 1998. (Adventures of Roopster Roux Ser.). 32p. (J). (ps-3). pap. 5.95 (978-1-56554-362-1(9)) Pelican Publishing Co., Inc.

—That's Not Punny. Kuon, Vuthy, illus. 2007. (Steve Harvey Presents the Adventures of Roopster Roux Ser.: Vol. 5). 32p. (J). 16.95 (***978-1-58980-483-8(X)***) Pelican Publishing Co., Inc.

—You're So Victor Vain. Kuon, Vuthy, illus. 2007. (Steve Harvey Presents the Adventures of Roopster Roux Ser.). 32p. (J). 15.95 (***978-1-58980-484-5(8)***) Pelican Publishing Co., Inc.

Luke, Deanna. Marky & the Rooster. Chambers, Lynne, illus. 2001. (Marky Ser.: Vol. 5). 48p. (J). (gr. 2-4). 8.95 (978-1-928777-10-6(4) , BOW Bks.) Blessing Our World, Inc.

—Marky & the Rooster: Story Book. 2001. (Marky Ser.: Vol. 5). (J). cd-rom 5.95 (978-1-928777-32-8(5) , BOW Bks.) Blessing Our World, Inc.

Martin, Bill, Jr. Chicken Chuck. Salerno, Steven, illus. 40p. (J). (ps-3). 2001. pap. 7.95 (978-1-58837-017-4(8)); 2000. 16.95 (978-1-890817-31-2(7)) Winslow Pr.

Martin, Bill. Chicken Chuck. Salerno, Steven, illus. 2005. 32p. (J). pap. 5.95 (978-0-7614-5216-4(8)) Cavendish, Marshall Corp.

Martin, Jacqueline Briggs. Chicken Joy on Redbean Road: A Bayou Country Romp. Sweet, Melissa, illus. 2007. 32p. (J). (gr. 3-5). 17.00 (978-0-618-50759-7(0)) Houghton Mifflin Co.

Meadows, Daisy. Weather Fairies: Crystal the Snow Fairy. Ripper, Georgie, illus. 2006. 80p. (J). pap. 4.99 (978-0-439-81387-7(5) , Scholastic Paperbacks) Scholastic, Inc.

Milord, Susan. Three about Thurston. 2005. (Illus.). 32p. (J). (gr. k-3). 15.00 (978-0-618-42850-2(X)) Houghton Mifflin Co. Trade & Reference Div.

Monsen, Annie. Rusty Raccoon Meets Ricky Rabbit. Saint, Crystal, illus. 2006. 36p. (J). per. (978-1-59453-996-1(0) , Airleaf Publishing) Airleaf Publishing & Bookselling.

Nash, Margaret. The Bossy Rooster. Moseng, Elisabeth, illus. 2004. (Read-It! Readers Ser.). 32p. (C). (gr. k-3). 18.60 (978-1-4048-0051-9(4)) Picture Window Bks.

Ocker, Christa Holder. A Rooster Named Lorenz. 2003. (J). per. (978-1-59196-284-7(6)) Instantpublisher.com.

Okereke, Laurence. Barry & Big Joe. 2007. (Illus.). 20p. (J). spiral bd. (***978-0-9795739-0-3(4)***) Dion's Pubn.

Pearson, Tracey Campbell. Bob. Pearson, Tracey Campbell, illus. 2002. (Illus.). 32p. (J). (ps-1). 16.00 (978-0-374-39957-3(3) , Farrar, Straus & Giroux (BYR)) Farrar, Straus & Giroux.

—Bob. Pearson, Tracey Campbell, illus. 2006. (Illus.). 32p. (J). reprint ed. pap. 6.95 (978-0-374-40871-8(8)) Macmillan.

Pilney, Dovie. Charlie, the Cocky Rooster. 2007. (ENG., Illus.). 28p. (J). per. 15.95 (***978-1-4327-0220-5(3)***) Outskirts Press, Inc.

Rascol, Sabina. The Impudent Rooster: A Romanian Folktale. Berry, Holly, illus. 2004. 32p. (J). (ps). 16.99 (978-0-525-47179-0(0) , Dutton Juvenile) Penguin Group (USA) Inc.

Reynolds, Aaron. Buffalo Wings. Bogan, Paulette, illus. 2007. 32p. (J). 17.85 (***978-1-59990-139-8(0));*** 16.95 (***978-1-59990-062-9(9)***) Bloomsbury Publishing.

Rigby Education Staff. The Sick Rooster. (Sails Literacy Ser.). (Illus.). 16p. (gr. 1-2). 27.00 (978-0-7635-9928-7(X) , 699289C99) Rigby Education.

Ross, Tim. Brewster, the Rain-Makin' Rooster. 1999. (Professor Wigglestix & the Weather Ser.). (Illus.). 32p. (ps-3). 7.95 (978-1-57168-357-1(7)) Eakin Pr.

Rostoker-Gruber, Karen. Rooster Can't Cock-a-Doodle-Doo. Ratz de Tagyos, Paul, illus. 32p. (J). (ps). 2006. pap. 5.99 (978-0-14-240646-5(5) , Puffin); 2004. 15.99 (978-0-8037-2877-6(8) , Dial) Penguin Group (USA) Inc.

Ruurs, Margriet. Wake up Henry Rooster. Cassidy, Sean, illus. 2006. 32p. (J). 16.95 (978-1-55041-952-8(8)) Fitzhenry & Whiteside, Ltd. CAN. *Dist:* F & W Pubns., Inc.

Scillian, Devin. Brewster the Rooster. White, Lee, illus. rev. ed. 2007. 32p. (J). (gr. k-2). 16.95 (***978-1-58536-311-7(1)***) Sleeping Bear Pr.

Scott, Janine. The Rowdy Rooster. Forss, Ian, illus. 2006. 32p. (J). (gr. k-2). 22.60 (978-1-4048-1699-2(2)) Picture Window Bks.

Sommer, Carl. Proud Rooster & Little Hen. 2003. (Another Sommer-Time Story Ser.). (Illus.). 48p. (J). (gr. 1-4). 16.95 incl. audio compact disk (978-1-57537-510-6(9)); 16.95 incl. audio (978-1-57537-559-5(1)) Advance Publishing, Inc.

—Proud Rooster & Little Hen. Budwine, Greg, illus. (Another Sommer-Time Story Ser.). 48p. (J). (gr. k-3). 2000. lib. bdg. 16.95 (978-1-57537-060-6(3)); 1999. 9.95 (978-1-57537-010-1(7)) Advance Publishing, Inc.

Stevens, Janet & Crummel, Susan Stevens. Cook-a-Doodle-Doo! Stevens, Janet, illus. 1999. (Illus.). 48p. (J). (ps-3). 17.00 (978-0-15-201924-2(3)) Harcourt Children's Bks.

Stewart, Wilson N. Cock-a-Doodle-Who? 2007. (Illus.). 6p. (J). 15.99 (978-0-7868-0826-7(8)) Hyperion Bks. for Children.

Terry, Will, illus. Little Rooster's Diamond Button. 2007. 32p. (J). (ps-2). 16.95 (978-0-8075-4644-4(5)) Whitman, Albert & Co.

Thomas, Joyce Carol. The Bowlegged Rooster: And Other Tales That Signify. Berry, Holly, illus. 2000. 112p. (J). (gr. k-5). 15.95 (978-0-06-025377-6(0) , Cotler, Joanna Books); 15.89 (978-0-06-025378-3(9)) HarperCollins Pubs.

Toepperwein, Emilie & Toepperwein, Fritz A. Chinto, the Chaparral Cock. (J). (gr. 4-7). 2.95 (978-0-910722-04-9(8)) Highland Pr.

Underwood, Barbara. Brewster Rooster. Grush, Patricia & DeWitt, Robin, illus. 2006. 32p. (J). pap. 5.25 (978-1-57874-108-3(4)) Kaeden Corp.

Ward, Helen, illus. & retold by. The Rooster & the Fox. Ward, Helen, retold by. 2003. 40p. (J). (gr. k-3). 16.95 (978-0-7613-1846-0(1) , First Avenue Editions) Lerner Publishing Group.

Ward, Helen & Ward, Helen. The Rooster & the Fox. 2003. (Single Titles Ser.: Vol. 3). 40p. (gr. k-4). lib. bdg. 24.90 (978-0-7613-2920-6(X) , Millbrook Pr.) Lerner Publishing Group.

Welling, Peter J. Michael le Souffle & the April Fool. Welling, Peter J., illus. 2003. (Illus.). 32p. (J). 15.95 (978-1-58980-105-9(9)) Pelican Publishing Co., Inc.

Wormell, Christopher. Henry & the Fox. 2008. (Illus.). 32p. (J). pap. 9.95 (***978-0-09-948383-0(1)*** , Red Fox) Random Hse. Children's Bks. GBR. *Dist:* Independent Pubs. Group.

—Henry & the Fox. 2008. (Illus.). 32p. (J). 19.95 (***978-0-224-07044-7(4)***) Random Hse. GBR. *Dist:* Independent Pubs. Group.

Wu, Liz. Rosa Farm. Phelan, Matt, illus. 2006. 144p. (J). (gr. 2-7). 15.95 (978-0-375-83681-7(0)); lib. bdg. 17.99 (978-0-375-93681-4(5)) Random Hse. Children's Bks. (Knopf Bks. for Young Readers).

ROOTS (BOTANY)

Blackaby, Susan. Plant Plumbing: A Book about Roots & Stems. DeLage, Charlene, illus. 2004. (Growing Things Ser.). 24p. (C). (gr. k-2). 22.60 (978-1-4048-0109-7(X)) Picture Window Bks.

Bodach, Vijaya. Roots. 2007. (Illus.). 24p. (J). 19.93 (978-0-7368-6345-2(1) , Pebble Bks.) Capstone Pr., Inc.

Farndon, John. Roots. 2005. (Illus.). 24p. (J). (gr. 2-4). 23.70 (978-1-4103-0421-6(3) , Blackbirch Pr., Inc.) Thomson Gale.

Fowler, Allan. Taking Root. 2000. (Rookie Read-About Science Ser.). (Illus.). 32p. (J). (gr. 1-2). pap. 4.95 (978-0-516-27058-6(3) , Children's Pr.) Scholastic Library Publishing.

Kudlinski, Kathleen V. What Do Roots Do? Schuppert, David, illus. 2005. 32p. (J). (gr. k-3). ring bd. 15.95 (978-1-55971-896-7(X) , NorthWord Bks. for Young Readers) T&N Children's Publishing.

Mitchell, Melanie S. Roots. 2003. (First Step Nonfiction Ser.). (Illus.). 8p. (J). pap. 3.95 (978-0-8225-3919-3(5) , Lerner Pubns.) Lerner Publishing Group.

Morgan, Sally. Roots, Stems, & Leaves. 2002. (Looking at Plants Ser.). (Illus.). 32p. (J). lib. bdg. 24.25 (978-1-931983-11-2(9)) Chrysalis Education.

Picture Window Books, contrib. by. Plant Plumbing. (Growing Things Ser.). 24p. (J). pap. 7.95 (978-1-4048-0385-5(8)) Picture Window Bks.

Roots. 2001. (Botany Ser.). (J). (gr. k-12). vinyl bd. 4.95 (978-1-58845-132-3(1)) School Specialty Publishing.

Stone, Lynn M. Roots. 2008. (J). (***978-1-60044-554-5(3)***) Rourke Publishing, LLC.

Whitehouse, Patricia. Las Raíces. (Plantas (Plants) Ser.). (SPA.). 24p. (J). (ps-1). 2003. lib. bdg. 17.08 (978-1-58810-778-7(7)); 2002. (Illus.). pap. 5.25 (978-1-58810-825-8(2) , 91649) Heinemann Library.

—Roots. 2002. (Plants Ser.). (Illus.). 24p. (J). (ps-1). pap. 5.25 (978-1-58810-731-2(0) , 91407); lib. bdg. 17.08 (978-1-58810-524-0(5)) Heinemann Library.

ROPE

King, Kimberly. Calf Roping. 2005. (World of Rodeo Ser.). (Illus.). 47p. (J). lib. bdg. 26.50 (978-1-4042-0545-1(4)) Rosen Publishing Group, Inc., The.

ROSES

Battistoni, Ilse. The Red Rose: Learning the R Sound. (PowerPhonics Ser.). (Illus.). (J). 23p. pap. (978-0-8239-8257-8(2)); 2002. 24p. (gr. 1). lib. bdg. 18.50 (978-0-8239-5912-9(0)) Rosen Publishing Group, Inc., The. (PowerKids Pr.).

Kate, Maggie, ed. Glitter Roses Stickers. 2004. (Glitter Stickers Ser.). (Illus.). 2p. 1.50 (978-0-486-43534-3(2)) Dover Pubns., Inc.

Klose, Liz & Peters, Laura. Roses for Ontario. rev. ed. 2003. (Illus.). 272p. (gr. 4). pap. 18.95 (978-1-55105-263-2(6)) Lone Pine Publishing USA.

Lindley, Nancy & Peters, Laura. Roses for Michigan, Vol. 1. rev. ed. 2004. (Illus.). 272p. (gr. 4). pap. 18.95 (978-1-55105-367-7(5)) Lone Pine Publishing USA.

Peters, Laura & Jalbert, Brad. Roses for British Columbia. rev. ed. 2003. (Illus.). 272p. (J). (gr. 4). pap. 18.95 (978-1-55105-261-8(X)) Lone Pine Publishing USA.

—Roses for Washington & Oregon. rev. ed. 2003. (Illus.). 272p. (J). (gr. 4). pap. 18.95 (978-1-55105-265-6(2)) Lone Pine Publishing USA.

Rosenfeld, Richard & Dorling Kindersley Publishing Staff. Roses. 2004. (Garden Guides Ser.). (Illus.). 320p. pap. 13.00 (978-0-7566-0355-7(2)) Dorling Kindersley Publishing, Inc.

ROSES—FICTION

Brisson, Pat. Wanda's Roses. Cocca-Leffler, Maryann, illus. 2003. 32p. (J). (gr. k-2). pap. 9.95 (978-1-56397-925-5(X)) Boyds Mills Pr.

—Wanda's Roses. 2000. (ps-2). lib. bdg. 16.40 (978-0-613-30181-7(1)) Tandem Library Bks.

De La Ramee, Louise. Bimbi. 2004. reprint ed. pap. 19.95 (978-1-4191-0998-0(7)); pap. 1.99 (978-1-4192-0998-7(1)) Kessinger Publishing, LLC.

Edwards, Pamela Duncan. Rosie's Roses. Cole, Henry, illus. 2003. 32p. (J). (ps-1). 16.99 (978-0-06-028997-3(X)) HarperCollins Pubs.

Erlich, Bev. Pink Roses Everywhere. gif. ed. 2004. (Illus.). 64p. (J). 14.95 (978-0-9743913-0-4(1)) Snojoy Publishing.

Hunt, Angela Elwell. Sleeping Rose. Gillies, Chuck, illus. 1998. 32p. (J). (ps-3). 14.99 (978-0-8499-5847-2(4)) Nelson, Thomas Inc.

Madonna & Madonna. Friends for Life!, No. 1. Fulvimari, Jeffrey, illus. 2007. (English Roses Ser.). 83p. (J). (gr. 3-7). 9.99 (***978-0-14-241114-8(0)*** , Puffin) Penguin Group (USA) Inc.

McKee, Mabel A. The Heart of the Rose. (Illus.). (J). reprint ed. pap. (978-0-9658838-1-8(7)) Young Advent Pilgrim's Bookshelf.

Merriam, Eve. Ten Rosy Roses. Gorton, Julia, illus. 1999. 32p. (J). (ps-2). 14.89 (978-0-06-027888-5(9)) HarperCollins Pubs.

My Roses. 2003. (J). per. (978-1-57657-898-8(4)) Paradise Pr., Inc.

Quattlebaum, Mary. Jackson Jones & the Curse of the Outlaw Rose. 2006. 112p. (J). (gr. 3-7). 14.95 (978-0-385-73349-6(6)); lib. bdg. 16.99 (978-0-385-90365-3(0)) Random Hse. Children's Bks. (Delacorte Bks. for Young Readers).

Reiss-Weimann, Elayne & Friedman, Rita. Real Friends. Yeagle, Barbara, illus. 2002. (Read-To-Me Ser.). 24p. (J). (978-0-7665-1218-4(5)) Abrams, Harry N. , Inc.

Roses for Renee Set B, 6 vols. 32p. (gr. 1-3). 26.50 (978-0-7802-8055-7(5)) Wright Group, The.

Valentina, Marina. Lost in the Roses. Valentina, Marina, illus. 2007. 24p. (J). (ps-1). 14.95 (***978-1-60108-014-1(X)***) Red Cygnet Pr.

Winter, Jeanette. September Roses. 2004. (Illus.). 40p. (J). 14.00 (978-0-374-36736-7(1) , Farrar, Straus & Giroux (BYR)) Farrar, Straus & Giroux.

Yee, Paul. Roses Sing on New Snow: A Delicious Tale. Chan, Harvey, illus. 32p. (J). 16.95 (978-0-88899-144-7(4)); 2003. pap. 5.95 (978-0-88899-217-8(3)) Groundwood Bks. CAN. *Dist:* Transition Vendor, Perseus Distribution.

—Roses Sing on New Snow: A Delicious Tale. 2003. (gr. k-3). lib. bdg. 14.10 (978-0-613-71033-6(9)) Tandem Library Bks.

ROSH HA-SHANAH

Fishman, Cathy Goldberg. On Rosh Hashanah & Yom Kippur. Hall, Melanie W., illus. 2000. 40p. (J). (ps-3). 6.99 (978-0-689-83892-7(1) , Aladdin) Simon & Schuster Children's Publishing.

—On Rosh Hashanah & Yom Kippur. 2000. (J). (978-0-606-19250-7(6)); (gr. 3-6). lib. bdg. 14.15 (978-0-613-31547-0(2)) Tandem Library Bks.

Hashanah, Rosh & Kippur, Yom. Rosh Hashanah & Yom Kippur Coloring Book. 2.99 (978-1-58330-168-5(2)) Feldheim Pubs.

Heinrichs, Ann. Rosh Hashanah. Collier-Morales, Roberta, illus. 2006. (Holidays, Festivals, & Celebrations Ser.). 32p. (J). (gr. k-4). 22.79 (978-1-59296-580-9(6)) Child's World, Inc.

Holub, Joan. Apples & Honey: A Rosh Hashanah Story. Pillo-Lassen, Cary, illus. 2003. (Lift-the-Flap, Puffin Ser.). 16p. (J). (ps-k). pap. 6.99 (978-0-14-250136-8(0) , Puffin) Penguin Group (USA) Inc.

Hughes, Monica. My Rosh Hashanah. 2003. (Festivals Ser.). (Illus.). 24p. (J). pap. 5.50 (978-1-4109-0667-0(1)); lib. bdg. 18.56 (978-1-4109-0641-0(8)) Raintree.

—My Rosh Hashanah. 2003. (ps-2). lib. bdg. 13.55 (978-0-613-78203-6(8)) Tandem Library Bks.

Kropf, Latifa Berry. It's Shofar Time. Cohen, Tod, photos by. 2006. (Illus.). 24p. (J). 12.95 (978-1-58013-158-2(1)) Kar-Ben Publishing.

Marx, David F. Rosh Hashanah & Yom Kippur. 2001. (Rookie Read-About Holidays Ser.). (Illus.). 32p. (J). (gr. 1-2). pap. 5.95 (978-0-516-26313-7(7) , Children's Pr.) Scholastic Library Publishing.

—Rosh Hashanah & Yom Kippur. 2001. (gr. k-3). lib. bdg. 14.10 (978-0-613-54641-6(5)) Tandem Library Bks.

Musleah, Rahel & Jarrett, Judy. Apples & Pomegranates: A Rosh Ha-Shanah Seder. 2004. (ENG & HEB., Illus.). 64p. (J). pap. 7.95 (978-1-58013-123-0(9)) Kar-Ben Publishing.

Rau, Dana Meachen. Rosh Hashanah & Yom Kippur. 2001. (True Holiday Bks.). (Illus.). 48p. (J). (gr. 3-5). 25.00 (978-0-516-22243-1(0) , Children's Pr.) Scholastic Library Publishing.

Zucker, Jonny. Apples & Honey: A Rosh Hashanah Story. 2002. (gr. k-3). lib. bdg. 15.25 (978-0-613-88295-8(4)) Tandem Library Bks.

ROSH HA-SHANAH—FICTION

Gerstein, Mordicai. The White Ram: A Story of Abraham & Isaac. Gerstein, Mordicai, illus. 2006. (Illus.). 32p. (J). (gr. 1-5). 16.95 (978-0-8234-1897-8(9)) Holiday Hse., Inc.

Vander Zee, Ruth & Sneider, Marian. Eli Remembers. Farnsworth, Bill, illus. 2007. 32p. (J). (gr. 3-7). 18.00 (***978-0-8028-5309-7(9)*** , Eerdmans Bks For Young Readers) Eerdmans, William B. Publishing Co.

ROSS, BETSY, 1752-1836

Armentrout, David & Armentrout, Patricia. Betsy Ross. 2004. (Discover the Life of an American Legend Ser.). (Illus.). 24p. (gr. 2-5). 14.95 (978-1-58952-661-7(9)) Rourke Publishing, LLC.

Betsy Ross. (American Revolution Biographies Ser.). 48p. (YA). 7.95 (978-0-7368-4501-4(1)) Capstone Pr., Inc.

Betsy Ross, 6 vols. (gr. 2-5). 39.95 (978-0-7368-4587-8(9)) Red Brick Learning.

Chanko, Pamela. Easy Reader Biographies: Betsy Ross: The Story of Our Flag. 2007. 16p. pap. 2.99 (***978-0-439-77421-5(7)*** , Teaching Resources) Scholastic, Inc.

Cox, Vicki. Betsy Ross: Flag for a New Nation. 2005. (Leaders of the American Revolution Ser.). (Illus.). 148p. (J). (gr. 4-8). lib. bdg. 30.00 (978-0-7910-8618-6(6) , Chelsea Hse.) Facts On File, Inc.

Denega, Danielle. Let's Read About— Betsy Ross. Graeff, Renee, illus. 2004. (Scholastic First Biographies Ser.). (J). pap. (978-0-439-56635-3(5)) Scholastic, Inc.

Devillier, Christy. Betsy Ross. 2004. (First Biographies Set Iv Ser.). (Illus.). 32p. (J). (gr. k-4). lib. bdg. 22.78 (978-1-59197-516-8(6)) ABDO Publishing Co.

Duden, Jane. Betsy Ross. 2000. (Let Freedom Ring Ser.). (Illus.). 48p. (J). (gr. 3-4). lib. bdg. 22.60 (978-0-7368-1036-4(6) , Bridgestone Bks.) Capstone Pr., Inc.

Frost, Helen. Betsy Ross. (Famous Americans Ser.). 24p. (J). pap. 5.95 (978-0-7368-3374-5(9)) Capstone Pr., Inc.

—Betsy Ross. Saunders-Smith, Gail, ed. 2003. (Famous Americans Ser.). (Illus.). 24p. (J). (gr. k-1). lib. bdg. 15.93 (978-0-7368-1641-0(0) , Pebble Bks.) Capstone Pr., Inc.

Greene, Stephanie. Betsy Ross & the Silver Thimble. Magnuson, Diana, illus. 2002. (Ready-to-Read Ser.: Level 2). 32p. (J). (gr. 1-3). pap. 3.99 (978-0-689-84954-1(0), Aladdin); lib. bdg. 11.89 (978-0-689-84967-1(2), Aladdin Library) Simon & Schuster Children's Publishing.

—Betsy Ross & the Silver Thimble. 2002. (gr. k-3). lib. bdg. 11.80 (978-0-613-45012-6(4)) Tandem Library Bks.

Harkins, Susan. Betsy Ross. 2006. (Profiles in American History Ser.). (Illus.). 48p. (J). (gr. 4-8). lib. bdg. 20.95 (978-1-58415-446-4(2)) Mitchell Lane Pubs., Inc.

Mader, Jan. Betsy Ross. 2007. (J). (978-0-7368-6702-3(3), Pebble Bks.) Capstone Pr., Inc.

Manera, Alexandria. Betsy Ross. 2003. (Women of the Revolution Ser.). (J). pap. (978-1-58417-085-3(9)); lib. bdg. (978-1-58417-022-8(0)) Lake Street Pubs.

Mara, Wil. Betsy Ross. (J). 2006. 32p. (gr. 1-2). pap. 4.95 (978-0-516-25369-5(7)); 2005. (Illus.). 31p. (ps-ps). 20.50 (978-0-516-25268-1(2)) Scholastic Library Publishing. (Children's Pr.).

Marsh, Carole. Betsy Ross. 2002. (One Thousand Readers Ser.). (Illus.). 12p. (J). (gr. k-4). 2.95 (978-0-635-01500-6(5), 15005) Gallopade International.

—The Virginia Reader: Betsy Ross. 2001. (Virginia Experience! Ser.). (Illus.). 12p. (J). (gr. k-5). pap. 2.95 (978-0-635-00357-7(0)) Gallopade International.

Miller, Susan Martins. Betsy Ross. 1999. (Revolutionary War Leaders Ser.). (Illus.). 80p. (YA). (gr. 3 up). pap. 27.50 (978-0-7910-5703-2(8), Chelsea Hse.) Facts On File, Inc.

—Betsy Ross: American Patriot. 2000. (Revolutionary War Leaders Ser.). (J). 15.75 (978-0-606-19340-5(5)) Tandem Library Bks.

Olson, Kay Melchisedech. Betsy Ross & the American Flag. Cool, Anna-Maria et al, illus. 2005. (Graphic Library). 32p. (J). (gr. 3-7). lib. bdg. 25.26 (978-0-7368-4962-3(9)) Capstone Pr., Inc.

Randolph, Ryan P. Betsy Ross: The American Flag & Life in Young America. 2005. (Library of American Lives & Times). (Illus.). 112p. (J). (gr. 4-8). lib. bdg. 31.95 (978-0-8239-5730-9(6)) Rosen Publishing Group, Inc., The.

Roop, Peter & Roop, Connie. Sew What, Betsy Ross? 2002. (Before I Made History Ser.). (Illus.). 57p. (J). (978-0-439-43925-1(6)) Scholastic, Inc.

Sargent, Dave & Sargent, Pat. Speck: (Black Patterned Leopard) Good Attitude, 25, 55. Lenoir, Jane, illus. 2001. (Saddle Up Ser.). 36p. (J). pap. 6.95 (978-1-56763-664-2(0)); lib. bdg. 22.60 (978-1-56763-663-5(2)) Ozark Publishing.

Silate, Jennifer. Betsy Ross. 2003. (Famous People in American History Ser.). (Illus.). 32p. (J). pap. (978-0-8239-4176-6(0)) Rosen Publishing Group, Inc., The.

ROSWELL HIGH (N.M. : IMAGINARY PLACE)—FICTION

Mangels, Andy & Martin, Michael A. Pursuit. 2003. (Roswell Ser.). (Illus.). 272p. (YA). pap. 5.99 (978-0-689-85522-1(2), Simon Pulse) Simon & Schuster Children's Publishing.

Metz, Melinda. Stowaway. 2000. (gr. 5-8). lib. bdg. 14.15 (978-0-613-17535-7(2)) Tandem Library Bks.

ROUND TABLE

see Arthur, King

ROUSSEAU, HENRI JULIEN FELIX, 1844-1910

de Duve, Catherine. Hello Rousseau: Get to Know Rousseau through Stories, Games & Draw-It-Yourself Fun. 2007. 132p. pap. 9.95 (978-1-59960-001-7(3)) Birdcage Pr.

Pfleger, Susanne. Henri Rousseau: A Jungle Expedition. 1998. (Adventures in Art Ser.). (Illus.). 30p. (J). (ps-7). 14.95 (978-3-7913-1987-2(6)) Prestel Publishing.

Sommers, Joan. Henri Rousseau Tunnel Book. 2006. (Take a Peek Ser.). (Illus.). 16p. (J). 14.95 (978-0-9754150-1-6(8)) Tunnel Vision.

Stephens, Pam. Dropping in on Rousseau. 2003. (Illus.). (J). (978-1-56290-303-9(9)) Crystal Productions.

Venezia, Mike. Henri Rousseau. 2002. (Getting to Know the World's Greatest Artists Ser.). (Illus.). 32p. (J). (gr. 3-4). pap. 6.95 (978-0-516-26998-6(4), Children's Pr.) Scholastic Library Publishing.

—Henri Rousseau. 2002. (gr. 3-6). lib. bdg. 15.25 (978-0-613-50702-8(9)) Tandem Library Bks.

Venezia, Mike & Rousseau, Henri Julien Felix. Henri Rousseau. 2002. (Getting to Know World Artists Ser.). (Illus.). 32p. (J). (gr. 3-4). 27.00 (978-0-516-22495-4(6), Children's Pr.) Scholastic Library Publishing.

Wenzel, Angela. Henri Rousseau: La Gitana Dormida. 2002. Tr. of Henri Rousseau: The Sleeping Gypsy. (SPA., Illus.). 128p. (YA). 11.96 (978-84-89804-30-2(3)) Loguez Ediciones ESP. *Dist:* Lectorum Pubns., Inc.

ROUTES OF TRADE

see Trade Routes

ROWAN (FICTITIOUS CHARACTER)—FICTION

Rodda, Emily. Rowan & the Ice Creepers. 2003. (Rowan of Rin Ser.). 272p. (J). (gr. 3 up). 15.99 (978-0-06-029780-0(8)) HarperCollins Pubs.

—Rowan & the Keeper of the Crystal. (Rowan of Rin Ser.). 2004. 224p. (gr. 3 up). pap. 5.99 (978-0-06-056073-7(8)); 2002. 208p. (J). (gr. 2 up). pap. 5.99 (978-0-06-441025-0(0)); 2002. 208p. (J). (gr. 2 up). 15.99 (978-0-06-029776-3(X)); 2002. (Illus.). 208p. (J). (gr. 2 up). lib. bdg. 16.89 (978-0-06-029777-0(8)) HarperCollins Pubs.

—Rowan & the Travelers. (Rowan of Rin Ser.). 2004. 192p. (gr. 3 up). pap. 5.99 (978-0-06-056072-0(X)); 2002. 176p. (J). (gr. 2 up). pap. 5.95 (978-0-06-441026-7(9), Harper Trophy) HarperCollins Pubs.

—Rowan & the Zebak. (Rowan of Rin Ser.). (J). 2004. 224p. (gr. 3 up). pap. 5.99 (978-0-06-056074-4(6)); 2003. (Illus.). 208p. (gr. 2 up). pap. 5.99 (978-0-06-441024-3(2), Harper Trophy); 2002. 208p. (gr. 2 up). 15.99 (978-0-06-029778-7(6)) HarperCollins Pubs.

—Rowan of Rin. (Rowan of Rin Ser.). (J). 2004. (Illus.). 176p. (gr. 3 up). pap. 5.99 (978-0-06-056071-3(1)); 2002. (gr. 2 up). pap. 5.95 (978-0-06-441019-9(6), Harper Trophy) HarperCollins Pubs.

ROWING—FICTION

Rau, Dana Meachen. My Red Rowboat, Level A. Sagasti, Miriam, illus. 2002. (Compass Point Early Reader Ser.). 24p. (J). (gr. k up). lib. bdg. 18.60 (978-0-7565-0174-7(1)) Compass Point Bks.

ROWLING, J. K., 1965-

Compson, William. J. K. Rowling. 2003. (Library of Author Biographies). (Illus.). 112p. (YA). (gr. 5-8). lib. bdg. 26.50 (978-0-8239-3774-5(7), Rosen Central) Rosen Publishing Group, Inc., The.

Gaines, Ann Graham. J. K. Rowling. 2001. (Real-Life Reader Biography Ser.). (Illus.). 32p. (J). (gr. 3-8). lib. bdg. 15.95 (978-1-58415-078-7(5)) Mitchell Lane Pubs., Inc.

Harmin, Karen Leigh. J. K. Rowling: Author of Harry Potter. 2006. (People to Know Today Ser.). (Illus.). 128p. (J). lib. bdg. 31.93 (978-0-7660-1850-1(4)) Enslow Pubs., Inc.

Hill, Mary. J K Rowling. 2003. (gr. k-3). lib. bdg. 12.95 (978-0-613-67727-1(7)) Tandem Library Bks.

MacDonald, Joan Vos. J. K. Rowling: Banned, Challenged, & Censored. 2008. (Authors of Banned Books). (Illus.). 160p. (YA). (gr. 9-12). lib. bdg. 34.60 (978-0-7660-2687-2(6)) Enslow Pubs., Inc.

McCarthy, Shaun. All about J. K. Rowling. 2003. (All About Ser.). (Illus.). 32p. (J). pap. 7.50 (978-1-4109-0719-6(8)); lib. bdg. 24.28 (978-1-4109-0718-9(X)) Raintree.

—All about J. K. Rowling. 2003. (gr. 3-6). lib. bdg. 15.90 (978-0-613-78210-4(0)) Tandem Library Bks.

Meister, Cari. J. K. Rowling. 2001. (Children's Authors Ser.). (Illus.). 24p. (J). (gr. k-6). lib. bdg. 21.35 (978-1-57765-482-7(X), Checkerboard Library) ABDO Publishing Co.

Pezzi, Bryan. J. K. Rowling. 2005. (My Favorite Writer Ser.). (Illus.). 32p. (J). (gr. 2-6). pap. 7.95 (978-1-59036-293-8(4)); lib. bdg. 26.00 (978-1-59036-287-7(X)) Weigl Pubs., Inc.

Price, Joan. J.K. Rowling. 2004. (Trailblazers of the Modern World Ser.). (Illus.). 48p. (J). pap. 11.95 (978-0-8368-5268-4(0)); (YA). lib. bdg. 30.00 (978-0-8368-5499-2(3)) Stevens, Gareth Inc. (World Almanac Library).

Sexton, Colleen. J.K. Rowling. 2005. 112p. (J). (gr. 6-12). pap. 7.95 (978-0-8225-3389-4(8)) Lerner Publishing Group.

Sexton, Colleen A. J.K. Rowling. (Biography ' Ser.). (J). 2007. lib. bdg. 30.60 (***978-0-8225-7949-6(9));*** 2006. (Illus.). 112p. 27.93 (978-0-8225-3423-5(1), Lerner Pubns.) Lerner Publishing Group.

Sexton, Colleen A. & Cosgrove, Martha. J.K. Rowling. 2006. (Just the Facts Biographies Ser.). (Illus.). 112p. (J). pap. (***978-0-8225-5995-5(1)***, Lerner Pubns.) Lerner Publishing Group.

Shapiro, Marc. J. K. Rowling: The Wizard Behind Harry Potter. 2007. 288p. pap. 6.99 (***978-0-312-37697-0(9)***, St. Martin's Griffin) St. Martin's Pr.

—J. K. Rowling: The Wizard Behind Harry Potter. 2000. (J). (978-0-606-19640-6(4)) Tandem Library Bks.

—J. K. Rowling: The Wizard Behind Harry Potter. l.t. ed. 2001. (J). (gr. 8-12). 23.95 (978-0-7862-3225-3(0)) Thorndike Pr.

Steffens, Bradley. JK Rowling. 2006. (Illus.). 112p. (J). (gr. 7-10). 32.45 (978-1-59018-963-4(9), Lucent Bks.) Thomson Gale.

ROYAL CANADIAN MOUNTED POLICE

Hamilton-Barry, Joann. Boldly Canadian. Clancy, Tom, illus. 1999. 260p. (J). (gr. 3-7). (978-1-55074-520-7(4)) Kids Can Pr., Ltd.

Newhouse, Maxwell. The RCMP Musical Ride. 2004. (Illus.). 24p. (J). 15.95 (978-0-88776-683-1(8)) Tundra Bks., Inc./Livres Toundra, Inc. CAN. *Dist:* Random Hse., Inc.

ROYAL CANADIAN MOUNTED POLICE—FICTION

Carter, Anne Laurel. Under a Prairie Sky. Daniel, Alan & Daniel, Lea, illus. 2004. 32p. (J). (ps-2). 7.95 (978-1-55143-282-3(X)) Orca Bk. Pubs. USA.

ROYALTY

see Kings, Queens, Rulers, etc.; Queens

RUBBER

Firestone, Mary. Rubber. 2004. (First Facts Ser.). 24p. (J). lib. bdg. 21.26 (978-0-7368-2652-5(1)) Capstone Pr., Inc.

Gleason, Carrie. The Biography of Rubber. 2005. (How Did That Get Here? Ser.). (Illus.). 32p. (J). (gr. 3-9). (978-0-7787-2486-5(7)); pap. (978-0-7787-2522-0(7)) Crabtree Publishing Co.

Llewellyn, Claire. Rubber. 2002. (Material World Ser.). (J). (gr. 2-4). pap. 6.95 (978-0-531-14837-2(8), Watts, Franklin) Scholastic Library Publishing.

—Rubber. 2002. (gr. 3-6). lib. bdg. 15.25 (978-0-613-53642-4(8)) Tandem Library Bks.

Oxlade, Chris. How We Use Rubber. 2004. (Using Materials Ser.). (Illus.). (J). (ps-ps). 32p. lib. bdg. 25.70 (978-1-4109-0604-5(3)); Pack. pap. 40.50 (978-1-4109-0902-2(6)) Harcourt Schl. Pubs.

—Rubber. 2004. (Using Materials Ser.). (J). pap. 7.50 (978-1-4109-0895-7(X)) Harcourt Schl. Pubs.

—Rubber. 2002. (Materials, Materials, Materials Ser.). (Illus.). 32p. (J). (gr. k-2). lib. bdg. 22.79 (978-1-58810-586-8(5)); pap. 6.95 (978-1-4034-0087-1(3), 91528) Heinemann Library.

—Rubber. 2002. (gr. k-3). lib. bdg. 14.75 (978-0-613-45821-4(4)) Tandem Library Bks.

Ridley, Sarah. A Rubber Tire. 2006. (Illus.). 32p. (J). lib. bdg. 23.33 (978-0-8368-6295-9(3)) Stevens, Gareth Inc.

Thomson, Ruth. Rubber. 2006. (978-1-58340-941-1(6)) Smart Apple Media.

RUBBER TIRES

see Tires, Rubber

RUDOLPH, WILMA, 1940-1994

Beck, Isabel L., et al. Wilma Rudolph. 2003. (Trophies Ser.). (gr. 6 up). 88.70 (978-0-15-319349-1(2)) Harcourt Schl. Pubs.

Braun, Eric. Wilma Rudolph. 2005. (Pebble Books). (Illus.). 24p. (J). 15.93 (978-0-7368-4234-1(9), Pebble Bks.) Capstone Pr., Inc.

Conrad, David. Stick to It! The Story of Wilma Rudolph. 2002. (Spyglass Books). (Illus.). 24p. (J). (gr. 1 up). lib. bdg. 18.60 (978-0-7565-0384-0(1)) Compass Point Bks.

Flanagan, Alice K. Wilma Rudolph: Athlete & Educator. 2000. (Career Biographies Ser.). (Illus.). 128p. (YA). (gr. 6-12). 25.00 (978-0-89434-356-8(4), F409, Ferguson Publishing Co.) Facts On File, Inc.

Harcourt School Publishers Staff. The Golden Runner On Level. 3rd ed. 2002. (Trophies Reading Program Ser.). (Illus.). pap. 5.10 (978-0-15-323254-1(4)) Harcourt Schl. Pubs.

Harper, Jo. Wilma Rudolph: Olympic Runner. Henderson, Meryl, illus. 2004. (Childhood of Famous Americans Ser.). 192p. (J). pap. 5.99 (978-0-689-85873-4(6), Aladdin) Simon & Schuster Children's Publishing.

—Wilma Rudolph: Olympic Runner. 2004. (gr. 3-6). lib. bdg. 13.00 (978-0-613-88995-7(9)) Tandem Library Bks.

Krull, Kathleen. Wilma Sin Limites. 2000. Tr. of Wilma Unlimited. (978-0-606-18197-6(0)); (SPA.). (gr. 3-6). lib. bdg. 14.15 (978-0-613-27592-7(6)) Tandem Library Bks.

—Wilma Sin Limites: Como Wilma Rudolph Se Convirtio en la Mujer Mas Rapida del Mundo. Ada, Alma Flor & Campoy, F. Isabel, trs. Diaz, David, illus. 2000. (SPA.). 44p. (J). (gr. 2-4). pap. 7.00 (978-0-15-202360-7(7), HB30426, Voyager Bks./Libros Viajeros) Harcourt Children's Bks.

—Wilma Unlimited. 2000. (978-0-606-18198-3(9)) Tandem Library Bks.

—Wilma Unlimited: How Wilma Rudolph Became the World's Fastest Woman. Diaz, David, illus. 2000. 44p. (J). (gr. 2-7). pap. 7.00 (978-0-15-202098-9(5), Harcourt Paperbacks) Harcourt Children's Bks.

—Wilma Unlimited: How Wilma Rudolph Became the World's Fastest Woman. 2000. (gr. 3-6). lib. bdg. 14.15 (978-0-613-37687-7(0)) Tandem Library Bks.

Naden, Corinne J. Wilma Rudolph. 2003. (gr. 3-6). lib. bdg. 18.20 (978-0-613-78294-4(1)) Tandem Library Bks.

Naden, Corinne J. & Blue, Rose. Wilma Rudolph. 2003. (African-American Biographies Ser.). (Illus.). 64p. (J). pap. 8.95 (978-1-4109-0321-1(4)); lib. bdg. 28.56 (978-0-7398-7033-4(5)) Raintree.

Raintree Steck-Vaughn Staff. Wilma Unlimited. 2000. (Illus.). 40p. (J). (ps-3). 16.98 (978-0-7398-1321-8(8)) Raintree.

Ruth, Amy. Wilma Rudolph. 1999. (Biography Ser.). (Illus.). 112p. (YA). (gr. 6-12). lib. bdg. 27.93 (978-0-8225-4976-5(X), Lerner Pubns.) Lerner Publishing Group.

Schraff, Anne. Wilma Rudolph: The Greatest Woman Sprinter in History. 2004. (African-American Biographies Ser.). (Illus.). 112p. (J). lib. bdg. 26.60 (978-0-7660-2291-1(9)) Enslow Pubs., Inc.

Sherrow, Victoria. Wilma Rudolph. Johnson, Larry, illus. (Yo Solo Biografías Ser.). (J). 2006. (ENG & SPA.). 23.93 (978-0-8225-6260-3(X), Ediciones Lerner); 2000. 56p. (gr. 1-3). lib. bdg. 23.93 (978-1-57505-246-5(6), Carolrhoda Bks.) Lerner Publishing Group.

—Wilma Rudolph. 1999. (Illus.). 48p. (gr. 4-7). pap. 5.95 (978-1-57505-264-9(4)) Lerner Publishing Group.

Streissguth, Thomas. Wilma Rudolph. 2007. (Sports Heroes & Legends Ser.). (J). 27.93 (978-0-8225-5958-0(7), Twenty-First Century Bks.) Lerner Publishing Group.

Wilma Rudolph. 2006. (J). pap. 5.95 (978-0-8225-6623-6(0), Ediciones Lerner) Lerner Publishing Group.

RUG AND CARPET INDUSTRY

Miller, Raymond H. Jhalak Man Tamang: Slave Labor Whistleblower. 2006. (Young Heroes Ser.). (Illus.). 64p. (J). (gr. 4-8). lib. bdg. 27.45 (978-0-7377-3616-8(X), Kidhaven) Thomson Gale.

RUGBY FOOTBALL

De Lacy, Hugh & Fox, Grant. Think & Play Winning Rugby. 2000. 166p. (YA). pap. 29.95 (978-1-86950-338-3(4)) HarperCollins Pubs. New Zealand NZL. *Dist:* Antipodes Bks. & Beyond.

Purslow, Frances. For the Love of Rugby. 2006. (For the Love of Sports Ser.). (J). (978-1-59036-380-5(9)); (978-1-59036-381-2(7)) Weigl Pubs., Inc.

RUGRATS (FICTITIOUS CHARACTERS)—FICTION

Banks, Steven. In Search of Reptar: A Time Travel Adventure. Artful Doodlers Limited Staff, illus. 2002. (Rugrats Files: Bk. 5). 96p. (J). (gr. 3-7). pap. 3.99 (978-0-689-84609-0(6), Simon Spotlight) Simon & Schuster Children's Publishing.

Bergen, Lara Rice. Ultimate Rugrats Trivia Sticker Book. 1999. (Rugrats Ser.). (J). pap. 5.99 (978-0-689-82892-8(6), Little Simon) Simon & Schuster Children's Publishing.

Chevat, Richie. A Pickles Passover. Idea and Design Works Staff, illus. 2003. (Rugrats Ser.). 24p. (J). pap. 3.50 (978-0-689-85232-9(0), Simon Spotlight/Nickelodeon) Simon & Schuster Children's Publishing.

David, Luke. Oh, Brother! 1999. (gr. k-3). lib. bdg. 11.25 (978-0-613-15929-6(2)) Tandem Library Bks.

—Sight for Sore Eyes. Goldberg, Barry, tr. Goldberg, Barry, illus. 1999. (Rugrats Ser.). 32p. (J). (ps-3). per. 3.50 (978-0-671-02866-4(9), Simon & Schuster Children's Publishing) Simon & Schuster Children's Publishing.

—Sight for Sore Eyes. 1999. (gr. k-3). lib. bdg. 11.25 (978-0-613-15977-7(2)) Tandem Library Bks.

—Twin Trouble. 1999. (gr. k-3). lib. bdg. 11.25 (978-0-613-16023-0(1)) Tandem Library Bks.

Dubowski, Cathy East. Rugrats in Paris: The Movie. 2000. (gr. k-3). lib. bdg. 13.00 (978-0-613-31653-8(3)) Tandem Library Bks.

Gold, Becky. Babies in Reptarland. Goldberg, Barry, illus. 2000. (Rugrats Ser.). 32p. (J). (ps-2). 5.99 (978-0-689-83337-3(7), Simon Spotlight/Nickelodeon) Simon & Schuster Children's Publishing.

—Babies in Reptarland. 2000. (gr. k-3). lib. bdg. 14.15 (978-0-613-30972-1(3)) Tandem Library Bks.

—Camp Out. 1999. (Ready-to-Read Ser.). (J). (ps-3). 10.79 (978-0-606-17786-3(8)) Tandem Library Bks.

—Phil & Lil Go to the Doctor. 2001. (gr. k-3). lib. bdg. 11.25 (978-0-613-43948-0(1)) Tandem Library Bks.

—Tommy's Bestest Adventure. 2000. (gr. k-3). lib. bdg. 11.25 (978-0-613-31825-9(0)); (Illus.). (J). (978-0-606-20948-9(4)) Tandem Library Bks.

Gold, Rebecca. Take a Bow, Babies! 2000. (Ready-to-Read Ser.). (Illus.). 32p. (J). (ps-3). pap. (978-0-7434-0854-7(3), Simon & Schuster Children's Publishing) Simon & Schuster Children's Publishing.

Gold, Rebecca & Gold, Becky. Take a Bow, Babies! Lesniewski, Bill & De la Paz, Orlando, illus. 2000. (Ready-to-Read Ser.). 32p. (J). (ps-3). pap. 3.99 (978-0-689-82830-0(6), Simon Spotlight/Nickelodeon) Simon & Schuster Children's Publishing.

Herman, Gail. Pizza Cats. 2000. (Ready-to-Read Ser.). (Illus.). 31p. (J). (ps-3). per. (978-0-671-77316-8(X), Simon & Schuster Children's Publishing) Simon & Schuster Children's Publishing.

—Pizza Cats. 1999. (gr. k-3). lib. bdg. 11.80 (978-0-613-15942-5(X)); (J). (978-0-606-17785-6(X)) Tandem Library Bks.

Herndon, Barbara & Gorey, Jill. No Place Like Home. Giarrano, Vincent, illus. 2000. (Rugrats Ser.). 30p. (J). (ps-3). per. (978-0-7434-0853-0(5), Simon & Schuster Children's Publishing) Simon & Schuster Children's Publishing.

Krulik, Nancy E. Tommy's Last Stand. 1999. (gr. 3-6). lib. bdg. 11.80 (978-0-613-16014-8(2)) Tandem Library Bks.

Lewman, David. Day in the Life of Angelica. 2000. (gr. k-3). lib. bdg. 10.65 (978-0-613-21414-8(5)) Tandem Library Bks.

—A Day in the Life of Tommy. 1999. (Rugrats Ser.). (Illus.). 48p. (J). (ps-2). per. 2.99 (978-0-671-02872-5(3), Simon & Schuster Children's Publishing) Simon & Schuster Children's Publishing.

—More Jokes. 1999. (Rugrats Ser.). (Illus.). 48p. (J). (ps-2). pap. 2.99 (978-0-689-82538-5(2), Simon Spotlight) Simon & Schuster Children's Publishing.

—More Jokes. 1999. (gr. k-3). lib. bdg. 10.65 (978-0-613-15911-1(X)) Tandem Library Bks.

—A Rugrats Night Before Christmas. Cuan, Sergio, illus. 1999. (Rugrats Ser.). 25p. (J). (ps-2). per. 9.99 (978-0-671-03756-7(0), Simon & Schuster Children's Publishing) Simon & Schuster Children's Publishing.

—Twin Talk: Phil & Lil's Guide to Life. 2000. (Rugrats Ser.). (Illus.). 48p. (J). (ps-2). per. (978-0-671-77395-3(X), Simon & Schuster Children's Publishing) Simon & Schuster Children's Publishing.

—Twin Talk: Phil & Lil's Guide to Life. 2000. (gr. k-3). lib. bdg. 10.65 (978-0-613-27352-7(4)) Tandem Library Bks.

Ostrow, Kim. Chuckie's New Mommy. 2002. (gr. k-3). lib. bdg. 11.25 (978-0-613-51297-8(9)) Tandem Library Bks.

—Dil in a Pickle. 2000. (Rugrats Chapter Bks.). (Illus.). (J). 10.79 (978-0-606-20628-0(0)) Tandem Library Bks.

Richards, Kitty. Bowling Twins. 2000. (Rugrats Ser.). (Illus.). 16p. (J). (ps-2). pap. 3.99 (978-0-7434-0801-1(2), Simon & Schuster Children's Publishing) Simon & Schuster Children's Publishing.

—Discovering America. 2000. Orig. Title: Rugrats Discover America. (gr. k-3). lib. bdg. 14.15 (978-0-613-24852-5(X)); (Illus.). (J). 12.79 (978-0-606-20630-3(2)) Tandem Library Bks.

—Ice Cream Fun Day. Goldberg, Barry, illus. 1999. (Rugrats Ser.). 16p. (J). (ps-2). 3.99 (978-0-689-82388-6(6), 076714003996, Simon Spotlight/Nickelodeon) Simon & Schuster Children's Publishing.

—Merry Christmas, Rugrats! Goldberg, Barry, illus. 1999. (Rugrats Ser.). 12p. (J). (ps-2). per. 10.95 (978-0-671-02941-8(X), Simon & Schuster Children's Publishing) Simon & Schuster Children's Publishing.

Rugrats. 2007. (J). 128.10 (***978-1-59961-354-3(9))*** Spotlight.

Rugrats Back to School Riser. 1998. (978-0-689-00701-9(9), Simon & Schuster Children's Publishing) Simon & Schuster Children's Publishing.

Rugrats Rainy Day Advanced. 2001. (Illus.). (J). 15.95 (978-0-7853-4807-8(7)) Publications International, Ltd.

Schoberle, Cecile. Open Wide: A Visit to the Dentist. Goldberg, Barry, illus. 2000. (Rugrats Ser.). 24p. (J). (ps-2). per. (978-0-671-77361-8(5), Simon & Schuster Children's Publishing) Simon & Schuster Children's Publishing.

—Open Wide! a Visit to the Dentist. 2000. (gr. k-3). lib. bdg. 11.25 (978-0-613-22138-2(9)) Tandem Library Bks.

—Reptar's Surprise Visit. Haefele, Steve, illus. 1999. 24p. (J). (gr. k-3). per. 3.50 (978-0-671-02881-7(2), Simon & Schuster Children's Publishing) Simon & Schuster Children's Publishing.

—Reptar's Surprise Visit. 1999. (gr. k-3). lib. bdg. 11.25 (978-0-613-15954-8(3)) Tandem Library Bks.

—Runaway Reptar! Ross, Sharon & Cardona, Jose Maria, illus. 1999. (Rugrats Ser.). 32p. (ps-2). 5.99 (978-0-689-82524-8(2) , 076714005990, Simon Spotlight/ Nickelodeon) Simon & Schuster Children's Publishing.

—Runaway Reptar! 1999. (gr. k-3). lib. bdg. 14.15 (978-0-613-15959-3(4)) Tandem Library Bks.

—Thank You, Angelica: The Rugrats Book of Manners. Resto, Ed, illus. 1999. (Rugrats Ser.). 32p. (J). (ps-2). per. 3.50 (978-0-671-02865-7(0) , Simon & Schuster Children's Publishing) Simon & Schuster Children's Publishing.

St. Pierre, Stephanie. Rugrats Blast Off. 2007. 24p. (J). 21.35 (*978-1-59961-358-1(1)) Spotlight.

Taylor, Donna. Dream Come True. 2000. (gr. k-3). lib. bdg. 11.25 (978-0-613-31140-3(X)) Tandem Library Bks.

—No Place Like Home. 2000. (gr. k-3). lib. bdg. 14.15 (978-0-613-26406-8(1)) Tandem Library Bks.

Thorpe, Kiki. Rugrats in Paris Movie Storybook. 2000. (Rugrats Ser.). (Illus.). 32p. (J). (ps-2). 5.99 (978-0-689-84198-9(1) , Simon Spotlight/Nickelodeon) Simon & Schuster Children's Publishing.

West, Cathy. Kid Cuisine's All Growed Up! Next Stop... the Future. Durk, Jim, illus. 2001. (Rugrats Ser.). 32p. (J). (ps-2). mass mkt. 5.99 (978-0-689-84928-2(1) , Simon Spotlight/Nickelodeon) Simon & Schuster Children's Publishing.

Wigand, Molly. Here Comes Santa! 1999. (gr. k-3). lib. bdg. 11.25 (978-0-613-21698-2(9)) Tandem Library Bks.

Willson, Sarah. Brand-New Daddy. 2001. lib. bdg. 14.15 (978-0-613-43921-3(X)) Tandem Library Bks.

—Chuckie Meets the Beastie Bunny. Talman, Byron et al, illus. 2000. (Rugrats Ser.). 24p. (J). (ps-2). pap. 3.50 (978-0-689-83066-2(1) , Simon Spotlight/Nickelodeon) Simon & Schuster Children's Publishing.

—Just Wanna Have Fun. 2000. (gr. 3-6). lib. bdg. 11.80 (978-0-613-21835-1(3)) Tandem Library Bks.

—The Rugrats & the Zombies. Goldberg, Barry, illus. 1998. (Rugrats Ser.). 24p. (J). (ps-2). pap. 3.50 (978-0-689-82125-7(5) , Simon Spotlight/Nickelodeon) Simon & Schuster Children's Publishing.

—Rugrats in the Ring. 2002. (gr. 3-6). lib. bdg. 11.80 (978-0-613-50542-0(5)) Tandem Library Bks.

—Up & Away, Reptar! Rillo, Cary, illus. (Ready-to-Read Ser.). 32p. (J). (ps-3). 2000. per. 3.99 (978-0-671-77315-1(1) , Simon & Schuster Children's Publishing); 1999. pap. 3.99 (978-0-689-82631-3(1) , 076714003996, Simon Spotlight/Nickelodeon) Simon & Schuster Children's Publishing.

—Up & Away, Reptar! 1999. (gr. k-3). lib. bdg. 11.80 (978-0-613-16029-2(0)) Tandem Library Bks.

Wilson, Sarah. Chuckie Meets the Beastie Bunny. 2000. (Rugrats Chapter Bks.). (Illus.). (J). 10.30 (978-0-606-20604-4(3)) Tandem Library Bks.

RUGS

Taschen Staff. Oriental Carpets. 1998. (Illus.). 532p. (J). 29.99 (978-3-8228-0545-9(9)) TASCHEN DEU. *Dist:* Digital Manga Publishing.

RUINS

see Cities and Towns, Ruined, Extinct, Etc.

RULERS

see Kings, Queens, Rulers, etc.; Queens

RULES OF ORDER

see Parliamentary Practice

RUMANIA

see Romania

RUNAWAYS

Casey, Kevin. The Runaway Game. 2nd ed. 2001. (YA). pap. 18.25 (978-0-943864-24-2(0)) Davenport, May Pubs.

Hyde, Margaret O. Missing & Murdered Children. 1998. (Impact Bks.). (Illus.). 112p. (YA). (gr. 9-12). 25.00 (978-0-531-11384-4(1) , Watts, Franklin) Scholastic Library Publishing.

Krohn, Katherine E. Everything You Need to Know about Living on Your Own. 2005. (Need to Know Library). (Illus.). 64p. (YA). (gr. 7-12). lib. bdg. 25.25 (978-0-8239-3088-3(2) , NTLIOW) Rosen Publishing Group, Inc., The.

Rebman, Renee C. Runaway Teens. 2001. (Hot Issues Ser.). (Illus.). 64p. (YA). (gr. 6-12). lib. bdg. 27.93 (978-0-7660-1640-8(4)) Enslow Pubs., Inc.

Tattersall, Clare. Drugs, Runaways & Teen Prostitution. 1999. (Drug Abuse Prevention Library). (Illus.). 64p. (YA). (gr. 7-12). lib. bdg. 25.25 (978-0-8239-2827-9(6) , DRTEPR) Rosen Publishing Group, Inc., The.

RUNAWAYS—FICTION

Abrams, Teri. When the Mountain Won't Move. 2002. 215p. (YA). per. 14.95 (978-0-9703225-2-4(6)) Blue Swan Bks.

Acampora, Paul. Defining Dulcie. 176p. (gr. 7). 2008. (YA). pap. 6.99 (*978-0-14-241183-4(3)* , Puffin); 2006. (J). 16.99 (978-0-8037-3046-5(2) , Dial) Penguin Group (USA) Inc.

Adams, W. Royce. Jay. 2005. viii, 115p. (YA). pap. (*978-1-58832-120-6(7)*) Unlimited Publishing LLC.

Adler, C. S. The No Place Cat. 2002. 160p. (YA). (gr. 5-9). 15.00 (978-0-618-09644-2(2) , Clarion Bks.) Houghton Mifflin Co. Trade & Reference Div.

Alarcon, Karen Beaumont. Louella Mae, She's Run Away! Litzinger, Rosanne, illus. rev. ed. 2002. 32p. (J). (ps-1). pap. 7.95 (978-0-8050-6830-6(9) , Holt, Henry & Co. Bks. For Young Readers) Holt, Henry & Co.

—Louella Mae, She's Run Away! 2002. (ps-2). lib. bdg. 15.25 (978-0-613-75399-9(2)) Tandem Library Bks.

Alcott, Louisa May. Under the Lilacs. Exams Unlimited, Inc. Staff, ed. 2001. 256p. (C). reprint ed. cd-rom 5.45 (978-1-59132-028-9(3)) Exams Unlimited, Inc.

Alger, Horatio. Driven from Home: Carl Crawford's Experience. reprint ed. pap. 79.00 (978-1-4047-3564-4(X)) Classic Textbooks.

—Driven from Home: Carl Crawford's Experience. 2006. pap. (*978-1-4065-0702-7(4)*) Dodo Pr.

—Phil the Fiddler. 2006. pap. (*978-1-4068-0667-0(6)*) Echo Library.

Alily, Joseph. The Boy & the Wolf. 2007. 9.00 (*978-0-8059-9053-9(4)*) Dorrance Publishing Co., Inc.

Anderson, Max Elliot. Reckless Runaway. 2005. 160p. pap. 10.95 (978-0-9752880-4-7(0)) Baker Trittin Pr.

Armstrong, Rollo. Safe from Harm. White, Jason, illus. 2005. 80p. 17.95 (978-0-283-07031-0(5)) Macmillan Publishers Ltd. GBR. *Dist:* Independent Pubs. Group.

Atkins, Jill. She Had to Leave Home. There Was No Other Way... Lawrie, Robin, illus. 2001. (Go for It! Ser.). 127p. pap. 9.99 (978-0-237-52332-9(9) , Evans Brothers, Limited) Evans Publishing Group GBR. *Dist:* Independent Pubs. Group.

Avi. Encounter at Easton. 2000. (Illus.). (J). 12.64 (978-0-606-17969-0(0)) Tandem Library Bks.

Ayres, Katherine. Silver Dollar Girl. 2002. (Illus.). 208p. (gr. 3-7). pap. 5.50 (978-0-440-41705-7(8) , Yearling) Random Hse. Children's Bks.

—Silver Dollar Girl. 2002. (gr. 3-6). lib. bdg. 13.00 (978-0-613-64685-7(1)) Tandem Library Bks.

Baglio, Ben M. Beagle in a Backpack. Baum, Ann, illus. 2005. 142p. (J). pap. (*978-0-439-77521-2(3)*) Scholastic, Inc.

Bear, Carolyn. Sid & Bolter. Cottrill, Peter, illus. 2006. (Read-It! Chapter Books). 64p. (J). lib. bdg. (*978-1-4048-3126-1(6)* , 1265813) Picture Window Bks.

Bell, William. Death Wind. 2006. 112p. (YA). lib. bdg. 14.95 (978-1-55143-543-5(8)) Orca Bk. Pubs. USA.

Benjamin, David. The Runaway, No. 2. Rawlings, Steve, illus. 2001. (Sixth Sense Ser.: Vol. 2). 164p. (J). (gr. 9). pap. 4.99 (978-0-439-20271-8(X)) Scholastic, Inc.

Black, Holly. Valiant: A Modern Tale of Faerie. 2005. 320p. (YA). (gr. 8 up). 16.95 (978-0-689-86822-1(7)) Simon & Schuster Children's Publishing.

Bodett, Tom, reader. Saving Sweetness. 2005. (Live Oak Readalong Ser.). (Illus.). (J). pap. 16.95 incl. audio (978-0-87499-898-6(0)) BBC Audiobooks America.

—Saving Sweetness. 2002. (Illus.). (J). pap., tchr.'s planning gde. ed. 37.95 incl. audio (978-0-87499-900-6(6)); 25.95 incl. audio (978-0-87499-899-3(9)) Live Oak Media.

Bourgeois, Paulette. Franklin Runs Away. Clark, Brenda, illus. 2001. (Franklin Ser.: Vol. 9). 32p. (J). (gr. 4-7). pap. 4.50 (978-0-439-23821-2(8)) Scholastic, Inc.

—Franklin Runs Away. 2001. 11.30 (978-0-606-22179-5(4)) Tandem Library Bks.

Bradley, Kimberly Brubaker. Halfway to the Sky. 2003. 176p. (J). (gr. 3-7). pap. 5.99 (978-0-440-41830-6(5) , Yearling) Random Hse. Children's Bks.

—Halfway to the Sky. 2003. (gr. 5-8). lib. bdg. 13.00 (978-0-613-62771-9(7)) Tandem Library Bks.

Brown, Margaret Wise. El Conejito Andarin. Hurd, Clement, illus. (SPA.). (J). 2006. 48p. pap. 6.99 (978-0-06-077694-7(3) , Rayo); 2002. 34p. 7.99 (978-0-694-01650-1(0)) HarperCollins Pubs.

—The Runaway Bunny. Hurd, Clement, illus. 2005. 48p. (J). (ps up). 16.99 (978-0-06-077582-7(3)); lib. bdg. 17.89 (978-0-06-077583-4(1)) HarperCollins Pubs.

Bunting, Eve. Hideout. 1999. (J). (gr. 5-8). lib. bdg. 14.15 (978-0-7857-1473-6(1)) Tandem Library Bks.

Burgess, Melvin. Smack. 2003. 384p. pap. 7.99 (978-0-06-052187-5(2)); 1999. 304p. (J). (gr. 7-12). pap. 6.99 (978-0-380-73223-4(8)) HarperCollins Pubs.

—Smack. 1998. 288p. (YA). (gr. 9-13). 17.95 (978-0-8050-5801-7(X) , Holt, Henry & Co. Bks. For Young Readers) Holt, Henry & Co.

—Smack. 2003. (gr. 7-12). lib. bdg. 15.30 (978-0-613-65712-9(8)); 1999. (978-0-606-16355-2(7)) Tandem Library Bks.

Burns, John. Runnerland. 2007. 218p. pap. 9.95 (*978-1-55192-957-6(0)*) Raincoast Bk. Distribution CAN. *Dist:* Perseus Distribution.

Buske, Jody. Wilderness Awakening. 2006. 108p. pap. 16.95 (978-1-4241-2685-9(1)) PublishAmerica, Inc.

Butcher, Kristin. The Runaways. 168p. (YA). (gr. 13 up). 1998. (978-1-55074-413-2(5)); 2002. (Illus.). (978-1-55074-379-1(1)) Kids Can Pr., Ltd.

—Sam Finds a Monster. Sarrazin, Marisol, illus. 2004. (Kids Can Read! Ser.). 32p. (J). (gr. k-3). (978-1-55337-352-0(9)) Kids Can Pr., Ltd.

Callan, Annie. Taf. 2001. 256p. (J). (gr. 9 up). 17.95 (978-0-8126-4933-8(8)) Cricket Bks.

Carroll, Thomas L. The Colony: A Novel for the Young Reader. 2000. 152p. (J). (gr. 4-7). 18.95 (978-0-86534-295-8(4)) Sunstone Pr.

Charles, Norma M. Runaway. 1999. 192p. (J). (gr. 5-9). 5.95 (978-1-55050-143-8(7)) Coteau Bks. CAN. *Dist:* Fitzhenry & Whiteside, Ltd.

Clark, Clara. Willie & the Rattlesnake King. 1999. (gr. 7-12). lib. bdg. 16.40 (978-0-613-16880-9(1)) Tandem Library Bks.

Clark, Sherryl. Take a Hike! 2000. (gr. 7-12). lib. bdg. 12.25 (978-0-613-29088-3(7)) Tandem Library Bks.

Cleary, Beverly. Runaway Ralph. 175p. (J). (gr. 3-5). pap. 4.95 (978-0-8072-1477-0(9)); pap. 4.50 (978-0-8072-1394-0(2)) Random Hse. Audio Publishing Group. (Listening Library).

Cole, Brock. The Goats. 2003. 20.75 (978-0-8446-7238-0(6)) Smith, Peter Pub., Inc.

Collins, Pat L. The Fattening Hut. 2003. 192p. (YA). (gr. 7 up). tchr. ed. 15.00 (978-0-618-30955-9(1)) Houghton Mifflin Co. Trade & Reference Div.

Collins, Pat Lowery. The Fattening Hut. 2005. 192p. (YA). (gr. 7). pap. 7.99 (978-0-618-55209-2(X) , Graphia) Houghton Mifflin Co. Trade & Reference Div.

Colon, Suzan. Runaway. 2003. (gr. 7-12). lib. bdg. 14.15 (978-0-613-71775-5(9)) Tandem Library Bks.

Coville, Bruce. The Mischief Monster. Coville, Katherine, illus. 2007. (Moongobble & Me Ser.). 80p. (J). 15.99 (978-1-4169-0807-4(2) , Simon & Schuster Children's Publishing) Simon & Schuster Children's Publishing.

Crutcher, Chris. Crazy Horse Electric Game. 2003. (gr. 7-12). lib. bdg. 15.30 (978-0-613-66954-2(1)) Tandem Library Bks.

Curtis, Christopher. Bud Not Buddy. l.t. ed. 2003. 278p. pap. 10.95 (978-0-7862-6191-8(9)) Thorndike Pr.

Curtis, Christopher Paul. Bud, Not Buddy. 2002. (Illus.). 14.47 (978-1-4046-1884-8(8)) Book Wholesalers, Inc.

—Bud, Not Buddy. 1999. (Illus.). 256p. (J). (gr. 4-7). 16.95 (978-0-385-32306-2(9) , Delacorte Bks. for Young Readers) Random Hse. Children's Bks.

—Bud, Not Buddy. 2002. (gr. 5-8). lib. bdg. 14.15 (978-0-613-36783-7(9)) Tandem Library Bks.

—Bud, Not Buddy. l.t. ed. 2000. (Illus.). 279p. (J). (gr. 8-12). 22.95 (978-0-7862-2574-3(2)) Thorndike Pr.

Dann, Max. Worst Best Friends. 2004. (Illus.). 144p. pap. 5.99 (978-0-14-330052-6(0) , Penguin Global) Penguin Group (USA) Inc.

Darrow, Sharon. Trash. 2006. 160p. (J). (gr. 7). 16.99 (978-0-7636-2624-2(4)) Candlewick Pr.

De Guzman, Michael. Finding Stinko. 2007. 144p. (J). (gr. 5 up). 16.00 (978-0-374-32305-9(4)) Farrar, Straus & Giroux.

de Harven, Emile. Suivez la Piste. (FRE.). (YA). (gr. 9-12). pap., tchr.'s training gde. ed. 6.95 (978-0-88436-342-2(2) , 40811) EMC/Paradigm Publishing.

De Palma, Toni. Under the Banyan Tree. 2007. 192p. (YA). (gr. 7 up). 16.95 (978-0-8234-1965-4(7)) Holiday Hse., Inc.

DeFelice, Cynthia C. Nowhere to Call Home. 2000. (YA). pap., stu. ed. 60.00 incl. audio (978-0-7887-4179-1(9) , 41113) Recorded Bks., LLC.

—Nowhere to Call Home. 2001. (gr. 5-8). lib. bdg. 14.10 (978-0-613-35992-4(5)) Tandem Library Bks.

Dessen, Sarah. Dreamland. 2000. (Illus.). 256p. (J). (gr. 7-12). 15.99 (978-0-670-89122-1(3) , Viking Juvenile) Penguin Group (USA) Inc.

Dewey, Jennifer Owings. Navajo Summer. 2000. (gr. 3-6). lib. bdg. 18.75 (978-0-8085-8012-6(4)) Tandem Library Bks.

Dufresne, Michele. Gabby Runs Away. Dufresne, Michele, illus. Date not set. (Illus.). (J). pap. 3.75 (978-1-58453-072-5(3)) Pioneer Valley Educational Pr., Inc.

Dunnion, Kristyn. Missing Matthew. 2004. 112p. (J). pap. 7.95 (978-0-88995-278-2(7)) Red Deer Pr. CAN. *Dist:* Fitzhenry & Whiteside, Ltd.

Fleischman, Paul. Breakout. 2005. (Illus.). 137p. (YA). (gr. 7-12). lib. bdg. 15.60 (978-1-4176-6932-5(2)) Tandem Library Bks.

Fletcher, Christine. Tallulah Falls. (YA). 2007. 400p. pap. 7.95 (*978-1-59990-095-7(5)*); 2006. 304p. 16.95 (978-1-58234-662-5(3)) Bloomsbury Publishing. (Bloomsbury Children).

Flinn, Alex. Nothing to Lose. 2004. 288p. (J). 16.99 (978-0-06-051750-2(6)); lib. bdg. 17.89 (978-0-06-051751-9(4)) HarperCollins Pubs. (HarperTeen).

Foard, Sheila Wood. Harvey Girl. 2006. (Illus.). viii, 152p. (J). (978-0-89672-570-6(7)) Texas Tech Univ. Pr.

Foggo, Cheryl. One Thing That's True. unabr. ed. 128p. (YA). (gr. 13 up). 2002. (Illus.). (978-1-55074-377-7(5)); 1998. (978-1-55074-411-8(9)) Kids Can Pr., Ltd.

—Sam Finds a Monster. Sarrazin, Marisol, illus. 2004. (Kids Can Read! Ser.). 32p. (J). (gr. k-3). (978-1-55337-351-3(0)) Kids Can Pr., Ltd.

Funke, Cornelia. The Thief Lord. 2004. 376p. (J). (gr. 5 up). pap. 44.00 incl. audio (978-0-8072-2278-2(X) , Listening Library) Random Hse. Audio Publishing Group.

—The Thief Lord. Burmingham, Christian, illus. 2005. (Thief Lord Ser.). 376p. (ps-7). mass mkt. 2.99 (978-0-439-77132-0(3)) Scholastic, Inc.

—The Thief Lord. Latsch, Oliver, tr. from GER. Burmingham, Christian, illus. (J). 2002. 352p. (gr. 4-7). pap. 16.95 (978-0-439-40437-2(1)); 2003. 376p. (gr. 3-6). reprint ed. 6.99 (978-0-439-42089-1(X)) Scholastic, Inc. (Chicken Hse., The).

—The Thief Lord. 2003. (gr. 3-6). lib. bdg. 15.30 (978-0-613-84572-4(2)) Tandem Library Bks.

—The Thief Lord. l.t. ed. 2005. 483p. (J). (gr. 4-7). pap. 10.95 (978-0-7862-8092-6(1)) Thorndike Pr.

Funke, Cornelia. Thief Lord ('el Senor de Los Ladrones) 2007. 352p. (J). pap. 7.99 (*978-0-545-00517-3(5)* , Scholastic en Espanol) Scholastic, Inc.

Funke, Cornelia & Latsch, Oliver. The Thief Lord. l.t. ed. 2004. 422p. (J). 23.95 (978-0-7862-7084-2(5)) Thorndike Pr.

Gaberman, Judith. Dear Lola: Or How to Build Your Own Family. 2000. 180p. (gr. 4). pap. 11.95 (978-0-595-15795-2(5) , Backinprint.com) iUniverse, Inc.

Gonick, Larry. Attack of the Smart Pies. 2005. (Illus.). 192p. (J). 15.95 (978-0-8126-2740-4(7)) Cricket Bks.

Greenburg, Dan. Claws. 208p. (YA). 2007. (gr. 3-7). 5.99 (978-0-375-83411-0(7) , Yearling); 2006. (gr. 5). 15.95 (978-0-375-83410-3(9) , Random Hse. Bks. for Young Readers); 2006. (gr. 5). lib. bdg. 17.99 (978-0-375-93410-0(3) , Random Hse. Bks. for Young Readers) Random Hse. Children's Bks.

Gregory, Kristiana. The Legend of Jimmy Spoon. 2002. (Great Episodes Ser.). 224p. (YA). pap. 6.00 (978-0-15-216776-9(5) , Gulliver Bks.) Harcourt Children's Bks.

—Orphan Runaways. (J). 2004. 160p. (gr. 4-7). pap. 4.99 (978-0-590-60367-6(1) , Scholastic Paperbacks); 1998. 144p. (gr. 3-7). pap. 15.95 (978-0-590-60366-9(3)) Scholastic, Inc.

Griffin, Adele. Sons of Liberty. 1998. 230p. (gr. 5-17). pap. 4.95 (978-0-7868-1300-1(8)) Disney Pr.

Guest, Jacqueline. At Risk. 2004. (SideStreets Ser.). 192p. (YA). (gr. 7-12). 7.95 (978-1-55028-846-9(6)); (*978-1-55028-847-6(4)*) Lorimer, James & Co., Ltd., Pubs. CAN. *Dist:* Casemate Pubs. & Bk. Distributors, LLC.

Harmon, Michael. Skate. 2008. 256p. (J). (gr. 9). mass mkt. 6.50 (*978-0-553-49510-2(0)* , Laurel Leaf) Random Hse. Children's Bks.

Harrison, Troon. Bushel of Light. 2001. (gr. 5-8). lib. bdg. 16.40 (978-0-613-44633-4(X)) Tandem Library Bks.

Herrick, Steven. The Simple Gift. 2004. 192p. (YA). pap. 6.99 (978-0-689-86867-2(7) , Simon Pulse) Simon & Schuster Children's Publishing.

Hilbtecht, Sharron. The Drummer Boy. 2005. 30p. pap. 6.95 (978-1-889658-35-3(9)) New Canaan Publishing Co. LLC.

Hobbs, Valerie. Charlie's Run. 2000. (Illus.). 176p. (YA). (gr. 4-7). 16.00 (978-0-374-34994-3(0) , Farrar, Straus & Giroux (BYR)) Farrar, Straus & Giroux.

—Charlie's Run. 2002. (gr. 3-6). lib. bdg. 14.15 (978-0-613-85722-2(4)) Tandem Library Bks.

—Charlie's Run. l.t. ed. 2001. (Illus.). 166p. (J). (gr. 4-7). 21.95 (978-0-7862-3104-1(1)) Thorndike Pr.

Hobbs, Will. The Maze. 1999. 248p. (J). (gr. k-9). lib. bdg. 14.15 (978-0-613-19524-9(8)) Tandem Library Bks.

Hobbs, William. The Maze. (J). (gr. 5 up). 1999. (Illus.). 256p. pap. 5.99 (978-0-380-72913-5(X) , Harper Trophy); 1998. 208p. 17.99 (978-0-688-15092-1(6)) HarperCollins Pubs.

—The Maze. unabr. ed. 1999. (YA). pap., stu. ed. 59.00 incl. audio (978-0-7887-3990-3(5) , 41062X4) Recorded Bks., LLC.

—The Maze. 1999. (J). (978-0-606-16369-9(7)) Tandem Library Bks.

Hoffman, Alice. Indigo. 96p. (J). 2003. pap. 5.99 (978-0-439-25636-0(4) , Scholastic Paperbacks); 2002. (Illus.). (gr. 5 up). pap. 16.95 (978-0-439-25635-3(6) , Scholastic Pr.) Scholastic, Inc.

Holcomb, Jerry K. The Chinquapin Tree. 1998. (Accelerated Reader Bks.). 192p. (J). (gr. 3-7). 14.95 (978-0-7614-5028-3(9) , Cavendish Children's Bks.) Cavendish, Marshall Corp.

Hoobler, Dorothy & Hoobler, Thomas. The 1930s: Directions. Hoffman, Robin, illus. 2000. (Century Kids Ser.). 160p. (J). (gr. 5-8). lib. bdg. 22.90 (978-0-7613-1603-9(5) , Twenty-First Century Bks.) Lerner Publishing Group.

Horse, Harry, illus. Little Rabbit Runaway. 2005. 30p. (J). 15.95 (978-1-56145-343-6(9)) Peachtree Pubs., Ltd.

Hubler, Marsha. Teamwork at Camp Tioga. 2005. (Keystone Stables Ser.). (Illus.). 128p. (J). pap. 4.99 (978-0-310-70575-8(4)) Zonderkidz.

—Trouble Times Two. 2005. (Keystone Stables Ser.). (Illus.). 128p. (J). pap. 4.99 (978-0-310-70574-1(6)) Zondervan.

Hutchens, Paul. Runaway Rescue. rev. ed. 1999. (Sugar Creek Gang Ser.: No. 34). 96p. (J). (gr. 4-7). 4.99 (978-0-8024-7038-6(6)) Moody Pubs.

—Runaway Rescue. 1999. (gr. 3-6). lib. bdg. 13.00 (978-0-613-90555-8(5)) Tandem Library Bks.

James, Brian. Tomorrow, Maybe. 2003. 256p. (J). pap. 6.99 (978-0-439-49035-1(9) , PUSH) Scholastic, Inc.

—Tomorrow, Maybe. 2003. (gr. 7-12). lib. bdg. 15.30 (978-0-613-66675-6(5)) Tandem Library Bks.

Jennings, Sharon, et al. Franklin Runs Away. Jeffrey, Sean, illus. 2001. (Franklin TV Storybook Ser.). 32p. (J). (ps-3). (978-1-55074-912-0(9)) Kids Can Pr., Ltd.

Johnson, Angela. Bird. 2004. 144p. (J). (gr. 4). 16.99 (978-0-8037-2847-9(6) , Dial) Penguin Group (USA) Inc.

Kehret, Peg. The Hideout. 2002. (gr. 3-6). lib. bdg. 13.00 (978-0-613-63944-6(8)) Tandem Library Bks.

Keith, Harold. Chico & Dan. Arbuckle, Scott, illus. 1998. 120p. (gr. 4-7). 16.95 (978-1-57168-216-1(3)) Eakin Pr.

Kelly, Tom. Finn's Going. 2007. 288p. (J). (gr. 5-9). 16.99 (*978-0-06-121453-0(1)*); lib. bdg. 17.89 (*978-0-06-121454-7(X)*) HarperCollins Pubs. (Greenwillow Bks.).

Kemp, Kristen. Breakfast at Bloomingdales. 2007. 304p. (J). pap. 16.99 (*978-0-439-80987-0(8)* , Scholastic Pr.) Scholastic, Inc.

Koja, Kathe. The Blue Mirror. 2004. 128p. (YA). 16.00 (978-0-374-30849-0(7) , Farrar, Straus & Giroux (BYR)) Farrar, Straus & Giroux.

—The Blue Mirror. 2006. 128p. (YA). (gr. 8). pap. 6.99 (978-0-14-240693-9(7) , Puffin) Penguin Group (USA) Inc.

—The Blue Mirror. l.t. ed. 2004. 134p. 21.95 (978-0-7862-6960-0(X) , Large Print Pr.) Thorndike Pr.

Konigsburg, E. L. From the Mixed-Up Files of Mrs. Basil E. Frankweiler. 35th anniv. ed. 2002. 208p. (YA). mass mkt. 5.99 (978-0-689-85354-8(8) , Simon Pulse); 1998. (Illus.). 168p. (J). (gr. 3-7). pap. 6.99 (978-0-689-71181-7(6) , Aladdin) Simon & Schuster Children's Publishing.

—From the Mixed-Up Files of Mrs. Basil E. Frankweiler. 35th anniv. ed. 2002. (gr. 5-8). lib. bdg. 14.15 (978-0-613-73358-8(4)) Tandem Library Bks.

—From the Mixed-Up Files of Mrs. Basil E. Frankweiler. l.t. ed. 2005. (Illus.). 205p. (J). 22.95 (978-0-7862-7297-6(X) , Large Print Pr.) Thorndike Pr.

Konigsburg, E. L. & Marcus, Barry David. From the Mixed-Up Files of Mrs. Basil E. Frankweiler. Konigsburg, E. L., illus. 35th anniv. ed. 2002. (Illus.). 176p. (J). (gr. 3-7). 17.99 (978-0-689-85322-7(X) , Atheneum) Simon & Schuster Children's Publishing.

Konnikov, Svetlana. Grapette, the Runaway Who Rolled Away. Smishliaev, Anatoli, illus. 2007. (Grapette's Adventures Ser.). 32p. (J). 15.95 (*978-0-9791758-0-0(1)*) Aurora Pubs., Inc.

Lawrence, Iain. The Convicts. 2005. 208p. (gr. 7-9). (J). lib. bdg. 17.99 (978-0-385-90109-3(7)); (YA). 15.95 (978-0-385-73087-7(X)) Random Hse. Children's Bks. (Delacorte Bks. for Young Readers).

—The Convicts. l.t. ed. 2005. 292p. (YA). 22.95 (978-0-7862-7911-1(7) , Large Print Pr.) Thorndike Pr.

Levin, Betty. Shoddy Cove. 2003. 208p. (J). (gr. 5 up). 15.99 (978-0-06-052271-1(2)) HarperCollins Pubs.

Lobel, Gillian. Does Anybody Love Me? Beardshaw, Rosalind, illus. 2002. 28p. (J). (gr. k-3). 16.00 (978-1-56148-368-6(0)) Good Bks.

Lowry, Brigid. Guitar Highway Rose. 2003. 208p. (J). (gr. 7 up). tchr. ed. 16.95 (978-0-8234-1790-2(5)) Holiday Hse., Inc.

—Guitar Highway Rose. 2006. 208p. (YA). reprint ed. pap. 8.95 (978-0-312-34296-8(9) , St. Martin's Griffin) St. Martin's Pr.

MacCullough, Carolyn. Stealing Henry. rev. ed. 2005. 208p. (YA). 16.95 (978-1-59643-045-7(1)) Roaring Brook Pr.

Madden, Kerry. Jessie's Mountain. 2008. (J). (gr. 3). 16.99 (*978-0-670-06154-9(9) , Viking Juvenile) Penguin Group (USA) Inc.

Marks, Graham. Omega Place. 2007. 256p. (YA). (gr. 7 up). 16.95 (*978-1-59990-127-5(7) , Bloomsbury Children) Bloomsbury Publishing.

Marlow, Susan K. Andrea Carter & the Long Ride Home. 2005. 128p. (J). (ps-7). pap. 7.99 (978-0-8254-3188-3(3)) Kregel Pubns.

Matthews, L. S. A Dog for Life. 2006. 176p. (J). (gr. 5). 16.99 (978-0-385-90381-3(2)); 14.95 (978-0-385-73366-3(6)) Random Hse. Children's Bks. (Delacorte Bks. for Young Readers).

Matthew's Web. 2001. (Books by Teens: Vol. 1). (YA). per. 12.95 (978-0-9716567-0-3(3)) Book Web Publishing, Ltd.

Mazer, Harry. Snow Bound. 144p. (YA). (gr. 7 up). pap. 4.99 (978-0-8072-1367-4(5) , Listening Library) Random Hse. Audio Publishing Group.

—The Wild Kid. 2000. (978-0-606-17946-1(1)) Tandem Library Bks.

Mccann, Clare. Runaway Pickpocket. 2005. 182p. pap. 19.95 (978-1-4137-5908-2(4)) PublishAmerica, Inc.

McKissack, Patricia. Away West. James, Gordon, illus. 2006. (Scraps of Time Ser.). 128p. (J). (gr. 3). pap. 4.99 (978-0-14-240688-5(0) , Puffin) Penguin Group (USA) Inc.

Mills, Charles. Stranger in the Shadows. 1998. (Shadow Creek Ranch Ser.: Vol. 11). 151p. (Orig.). (J). (gr. 4-7). pap. 5.99 (978-0-8280-1316-1(0)) Review & Herald Publishing Assn.

Milyenn, Dorothy A. The Runaway Vol. 2: The Kids from Silvesand Lake. 2001. 82p. (YA). (gr. 7-10). pap. 8.00 (978-0-9679412-6-4(1)) Leapfrog Pr.

Moore, Martha A. Angels on the Roof. 1999. (J). 11.64 (978-0-606-17346-9(3)) Tandem Library Bks.

Moss, Miriam. Smudge's Grumpy Day. Chapman, Lynne, illus. 2002. 24p. (J). (ps-2). (978-1-86233-282-9(7) , Gullane Children's Bks.) Pinwheel.

Murphy, Rita. Looking for Lucy Buick. 176p. (YA). (gr. 7). 2007. mass mkt. 6.50 (*978-0-440-22924-7(3) , Laurel Leaf); 2005. 15.95 (978-0-385-72939-0(1) , Delacorte Bks. for Young Readers); 2005. lib. bdg. 17.99 (978-0-385-90176-5(3) , Delacorte Bks. for Young Readers) Random Hse. Children's Bks.

Napoli, Donna Jo. North. 2004. (Illus.). 352p. (J). (gr. 4 up). 16.99 (978-0-06-057987-6(0)); lib. bdg. 17.89 (978-0-06-057988-3(9)) HarperCollins Pubs.

O'Neill, Joan. Connie 2. 2007. 266p. pap. 10.95 (*978-0-340-91149-5(2)) Hodder Children's Division GBR. *Dist:* Independent Pubs. Group.

Patron, Susan. The Higher Power of Lucky. Phelan, Matt, illus. 2006. 144p. (J). (gr. 4-6). 16.95 (978-1-4169-0194-5(9) , Atheneum/Richard Jackson Bks.) Simon & Schuster Children's Publishing.

Paulsen, Gary. Tasting the Thunder. 144p. (YA). (978-0-330-32705-3(4) , Pan) Pan Macmillan.

Peretti, Frank. Nightmare Academy: The Veritas Project - Volume 2. 2008. 352p. (YA). mass mkt. 7.99 (*978-1-4003-1017-3(2)) Nelson, Thomas Inc.

Peretti, Frank E. Nightmare Academy. 2003. (Veritas Project Ser.). 320p. (YA). pap. 8.99 (978-1-4003-0340-3(0)) Nelson, Thomas Inc.

—Nightmare Academy. 2003. (gr. 3-6). lib. bdg. 17.60 (978-0-613-77930-2(4)) Tandem Library Bks.

Philbrick, Rodman. Max the Mighty. 1998. (J). pap. 47.88 (978-0-590-65859-1(X) , Blue Sky Pr., The) Scholastic, Inc.

Philbrick, Rodman & Philbrick, W. R. Max the Mighty. 1998. 166p. (J). (gr. 7-12). pap. 16.95 (978-0-590-18892-0(5) , Blue Sky Pr., The) Scholastic, Inc.

Posesorski, Sherie. Escape Plans. Pearcey, Dawn, illus. 2005. 272p. (J). (gr. 5). 8.95 (978-1-55050-177-3(1)) Coteau Bks. CAN. *Dist:* Fitzhenry & Whiteside, Ltd.

Poulsen, David A. Last Sam's Cage. rev. ed. 2004. 224p. pap. 9.95 (*978-1-55263-611-4(9)) Key Porter Bks. CAN. *Dist:* Perseus Distribution.

—Last Sam's Cage. 2001. 208p. (YA). pap. 8.95 (978-1-896184-78-4(2)) Roussan Pubs., Inc./Roussan Editeur, Inc. CAN. *Dist:* Orca Bk. Pubs. USA.

Precious, Precious & Juwell, Juwell. Runaway: Platinum Teen Series. 2006. (YA). per. 6.99 (978-0-9729325-6-1(9)) Precioustymes Entertainment, LLC.

Ramadurai, Suchitra. The Runaway Peppercorn. Rajagopalan, Ashok, illus. 2005. 28p. (J). (*978-81-8146-119-3(3)) Tulika Pubs.

Raphael, Maryanne & Wolf, Jenifer. Runaways: America's Lost Youth. 2000. 260p. (YA). pap. 13.95 (978-0-595-14978-0(2)) iUniverse, Inc.

Rosenberry, Vera. Vera Runs Away. Rosenberry, Vera, illus. rev. ed. 2000. (Illus.). 32p. (J). (ps-2). 16.00 (978-0-8050-6267-0(X) , Holt, Henry & Co. Bks. For Young Readers) Holt, Henry & Co.

Rottman, S. L. Shadow of a Doubt. 224p. (YA). 2005. pap. 7.95 (978-1-56145-354-2(4)); 2003. (gr. 6-10). 14.95 (978-1-56145-291-0(2)) Peachtree Pubs., Ltd.

Runaway Ralph. 1999. (J). 9.95 (978-1-56137-174-7(2)) Novel Units, Inc.

Ryan, Pam Muñoz. Riding Freedom. Selznick, Brian, illus. 2007. 144p. (J). (gr. 3-7). mass mkt. 4.99 (978-0-439-08796-4(1) , Scholastic Paperbacks) Scholastic, Inc.

—Riding Freedom. Selznick, Brian, illus. 1999. 138p. per. 11.64 (978-0-606-17445-9(1)) Tandem Library Bks.

Silvey, Diane. Raven's Flight. 2001. (gr. 7-12). lib. bdg. 15.25 (978-0-613-78635-5(1)) Tandem Library Bks.

Skurzynski, Gloria. The Hunted. 2001. 12.60 (978-0-606-22147-4(6)); (gr. 3-6). lib. bdg. 14.10 (978-0-613-62422-0(X)) Tandem Library Bks.

Skurzynski, Gloria & Ferguson, Alane. The Hunted. (National Parks Mysteries Ser.: No. 5). 160p. (J). (gr. 3-7). 2000. (Illus.). 15.95 (978-0-7922-7053-9(3)); 5th ed. 2001. pap. 5.95 (978-0-7922-7665-4(5)) National Geographic Society. (National Geographic Children's Bks.).

Smith, Sherri L. Lucy the Giant. l.t. ed. 2002. 236p. 23.95 (978-0-7862-4751-6(7)) Thorndike Pr.

Snyder, Zilpha Keatley. The Gypsy Game. 1998. 240p. (J). (gr. 5-7). pap. 5.99 (978-0-440-41258-8(7) , Yearling) Random Hse. Children's Bks.

—The Gypsy Game. 1998. (J). 12.64 (978-0-606-13104-9(3)) Tandem Library Bks.

—The Runaways. 2000. (978-0-606-17895-2(3)) Tandem Library Bks.

Sommer, Carl. Miserable Millie. Vignolo, Enrique, illus. (J). 2006. (*978-1-57537-022-4(0)); 2005. (978-1-57537-071-2(9)) Advance Publishing, Inc.

Stine, Catherine. Refugees. 288p. (gr. 7). 2006. (YA). pap. 5.99 (978-0-440-23876-8(5) , Laurel Leaf); 2005. (J). 15.95 (978-0-385-73179-9(5) , Delacorte Bks. for Young Readers); 2005. (YA). 17.99 (978-0-385-90216-8(6) , Delacorte Bks. for Young Readers) Random Hse. Children's Bks.

Stretton, Hesba. Cassy. Hymper, W. & Stacey, W. S., illus. 2006. (Golden Inheritance Ser.: Vol. 9). 117p. (J). pap. (978-0-921100-94-2(9)) Inheritance Pubns.

Tamura, Yumi. Basara, Vol. 15. 2005. (Basara Ser.). (Illus.). 200p. (YA). pap. 9.99 (978-1-4215-0135-2(X)) Viz Media.

Tate, Eleanora E. The Minstrel's Melody. 2001. (American Girl Collection). (Illus.). (J). (978-0-606-21331-8(7)) Tandem Library Bks.

Tocher, Timothy. Chief Sunrise, John McGraw, & Me. 2004. 168p. (J). 16.95 (978-0-8126-2711-4(3)) Cricket Bks.

Upton, Joe. Runaways on the Inside Passage. 2005. (Illus.). 304p. (gr. 5 up). 17.95 (978-0-88240-564-3(0)); pap. 9.95 (978-0-88240-565-0(9)) Graphic Arts Ctr. Publishing Co.

Ure, Jean. Gone Missing. 2007. (Illus.). 192p. (J). pap. 8.99 (*978-0-00-722459-3(1)) HarperCollins Pubs. Ltd. GBR. *Dist:* Independent Pubs. Group.

Van Draanen, Wendelin. Runaway. 256p. 2008. (YA). (gr. 3-7). mass mkt. 6.50 (*978-0-440-42109-2(8) , Laurel Leaf); 2006. (J). (gr. 5). 15.95 (978-0-375-83522-3(9) , Knopf Bks. for Young Readers); 2006. (J). (gr. 5). lib. bdg. 17.99 (978-0-375-93522-0(3) , Knopf Bks. for Young Readers) Random Hse. Children's Bks.

Voigt, Cynthia. Dicey's Song. l.t. ed. 2002. (Tillerman Cycle Ser.: Bk. 2). 370p. (YA). lib. bdg. 35.95 (978-1-58118-106-7(X) , 25790) LRS.

Voss, Dawn. Avenging Aja. 2007. 50p. pap. 15.00 (*978-0-615-15324-7(0)) Voss, Dawn L.

Waddell, Martin. Bee Frog. Firth, Barbara, illus. 2007. 32p. (J). (ps-2). 14.99 (978-0-7636-3310-3(0)) Candlewick Pr.

Walters, Eric. Sketches. 2008. 232p. (YA). (gr. 6). 15.99 (*978-0-670-06294-2(4) , Viking Juvenile) Penguin Group (USA) Inc.

Weninger, Brigitte. Donde Estas Dany? 1999. Tr. of Where Is Davy?. (Illus.). (978-0-606-17639-2(X)) Tandem Library Bks.

Whelan, Gloria. Chu Ju's House. 2004. 240p. (J). (gr. 5 up). 16.99 (978-0-06-050724-4(1)); lib. bdg. 17.89 (978-0-06-050725-1(X)) HarperCollins Pubs.

—Friend on Freedom River. van Frankenhuyzen, Gijsbert, illus. 2004. 48p. (J). 16.95 (978-1-58536-222-6(0)) Sleeping Bear Pr.

Willis, Patricia. The Barn Burner. 2000. 208p. (J). (gr. 5-9). tchr. ed. 15.00 (978-0-395-98409-3(2) , Clarion Bks.) Houghton Mifflin Co. Trade & Reference Div.

Withers, Pam. Camp Wild. 2006. (Orca Currents Ser.). 112p. (J). lib. bdg. 14.95 (978-1-55143-557-2(8)) Orca Bk. Pubs. USA.

Woo, Soo Jung. Legend Volume 3. 2007. (Illus.). 200p. (YA). pap. 10.95 (*978-89-527-4712-9(7)) ICE Kunion KOR. *Dist:* Diamond Bk. Distributors.

—Legend Volume 4. 2007. 200p. (YA). pap. 10.95 (*978-89-527-4871-3(9)) ICE Kunion KOR. *Dist:* Diamond Bk. Distributors.

—Legend Volume 5. 2007. 200p. (YA). pap. 10.95 (*978-89-527-4883-6(2)) ICE Kunion KOR. *Dist:* Diamond Bk. Distributors.

Woodson, Jacqueline. Lena. 2006. 144p. (YA). (gr. 4). 17.99 (978-0-399-24469-8(7) , Putnam Juvenile); (gr. 5). pap. 5.99 (978-0-14-240616-8(3) , Puffin) Penguin Group (USA) Inc.

Wyss, Thelma Hatch. Ten Miles from Winnemucca. 2002. 144p. (J). (gr. 7 up). 15.95 (978-0-06-029783-1(2)) HarperCollins Pubs.

RUNNING

see Track Athletics

RURAL ARCHITECTURE

see Architecture, Domestic

RURAL LIFE

see also Country Life; Outdoor Life

Nicodemus, Laura Konger. Grandma's Scary Mean Gander, 4 vols., Set. Nicodemus, Laura Konger, illus. 2002. (Illus.). 16p. (J). (gr. 1-4). 3.99 (978-0-9722216-0-3(3)) Grandma's Stories, Inc.

RURAL LIFE—FICTION

Asare, Meshack. Meliga's Day. 2000. (Illus.). 31p. pap. (978-9988-550-20-2(0)) Sub-Saharan Pubs. & Traders.

Chambers, Vickie. In the Silence of the Hills. Taylor, LaVonne, ed. (Illus.). (YA). (gr. 9-12). (978-0-9627735-1-8(4)) Excellence Enterprises.

Cummins, Julie. Country Kid, City Kid. Rand, Ted, illus. rev. ed. 2002. 32p. (J). (ps-1). 17.95 (978-0-8050-6467-4(2) , Holt, Henry & Co. Bks. For Young Readers) Holt, Henry & Co.

Graef, Renee, illus. Hard Times on the Prairie. 1998. (Little House Chapter Bks.: No. 8). (J). (gr. 3-6). 11.05 (978-0-606-13458-3(1)) Tandem Library Bks.

McDonald, Joyce. Comfort Creek. 1998. 10.64 (978-0-606-13289-3(9)) Tandem Library Bks.

Morse, Christopher Hill. Ragged Mountain Revelry. l.t. ed. 2000. (Illus.). 74p. (YA). (gr. 1-12). pap. 25.00 (978-0-9678775-0-1(4)) Oculus Pr., The.

Ray, Mary Lyn. The Basket Moon. Cooney, Barbara, illus. 1999. 32p. (J). (ps-3). 16.99 (978-0-316-73521-6(3)) Little Brown & Co.

Sarja, Jennifer. When Watute Wants Some Water. Phan, Henry et al, illus. 2005. 36p. (J). per. 20.00 (978-0-9773451-0-6(6)) Youth Inkwell Publishing.

Trottier, Maxine. Prairie Willow. Fernandez, Laura & Jacobson, Rick, illus. 2000. 22p. (J). (gr. k-5). 7.95 (978-0-7737-6100-1(4)) Stoddart Kids CAN. *Dist:* Fitzhenry & Whiteside, Ltd.

—Prairie Willow. 2000. (J). (978-0-606-19956-8(X)) Tandem Library Bks.

Youmans, Marly. Little Jordan. 1999. 112p. (YA). (gr. 7-12). pap. 6.99 (978-0-380-73136-7(3)) HarperCollins Pubs.

RURAL SOCIOLOGY

see Sociology, Rural

RUSSELL, BILL, 1934-

Hayhurst, Chris. Bill Russell. 2002. (Basketball Hall of Famers Ser.). (Illus.). 112p. (YA). (gr. 5-8). lib. bdg. 29.25 (978-0-8239-3480-5(2) , Rosen Central) Rosen Publishing Group, Inc., The.

Healy, Nick. Bill Russell. 2003. (Illus.). 64p. (J). pap. 9.50 (978-1-4109-0315-0(X)); lib. bdg. 28.56 (978-0-7398-7034-1(3)) Raintree.

—Bill Russell. 2003. (gr. 3-6). lib. bdg. 18.20 (978-0-613-78179-4(1)) Tandem Library Bks.

RUSSIA (FEDERATION)

see also Soviet Union, for works discussing the time period before the dissolution of the former Soviet Union; and Former Soviet Republics, for works discussing collectively the independent countries that emerged from the dissolution of the former Soviet Union.

Auch, Alison. Welcome to Russia. 2002. (Spyglass Books). (Illus.). 24p. (J). (gr. 1 up). lib. bdg. 18.60 (978-0-7565-0371-0(X)) Compass Point Bks.

Beliaev, Edward & Buranbaeva, Oksana. Dagestan: By Edward Beliaev & Oksana Buranbaeva. 2005. (Cultures of the World Ser.). (Illus.). 144p. (J). (978-0-7614-2015-6(0)) Cavendish, Marshall Corp.

Berge, Ann. Russia ABCs: A Book about the People & Places of Russia. Yesh, Jeff, illus. 2004. (Country ABCs Ser.). 32p. (J). (gr. k-5). 23.93 (978-1-4048-0284-1(3)) Picture Window Bks.

Berman, Connie. Anna Kournikova. 2001. (Women Who Win Ser.). (Illus.). 64p. (J). pap. (978-0-7910-6530-3(8)); (gr. 3 up). 25.00 (978-0-7910-6529-7(4)) Facts On File, Inc. (Chelsea Hse.).

Bjornlund, Britta. The Russian Revolution. 2005. (People at the Center of Ser.). (Illus.). 48p. (J). (ps-7). lib. bdg. 24.95 (978-1-56711-923-7(9) , Blackbirch Pr., Inc.) Thomson Gale.

Blomquist, Christopher. Russia, a Primary Source Guide. 2005. (Countries of the World, a Primary Source Journey Ser.). (Illus.). 24p. (J). 19.95 (978-1-4042-2756-9(3) , PowerKids Pr.) Rosen Publishing Group, Inc., The.

Bowden, Rob & Ransome, Galya. Focus on Russia. 2007. (J). pap. (*978-0-8368-6756-5(4)); 64p. (gr. 5-8). lib. bdg. 33.27 (*978-0-8368-6749-7(1)) Stevens, Gareth Inc. (World Almanac Library).

Chanek, Sherilin. Europe & Russia. 2003. (National Geographic Reading Expeditions Ser.). (Illus.). 64p. (978-0-7922-4374-8(9)); (J). (978-0-7922-4375-5(7)) National Geographic Society.

Charting Russia's Future, 2 bks. 9th ed. 2005. 88p. (YA). pap. (978-1-891306-81-5(2)) Choices Education Program, Watson Institute, Brown Univ.

Corona, Laurel. The Russian Federation. 2001. (Former Soviet Republics Ser.). (Illus.). 112p. (J). (gr. 6-9). 29.95 (978-1-56006-675-0(X) , Lucent Bks.) Thomson Gale.

Costain, Meredith & Collins, Paul. Welcome to Russia. 2001. (Countries of the World Ser.). (Illus.). 32p. (J). (gr. 4 up). 28.00 (978-0-7910-6549-5(9) , 010209, Chelsea Hse.) Facts On File, Inc.

Cumming, David. Russia: Modern Industrial. 2000. (Modern Industrial World Ser.). (Illus.). (J). (gr. 5-9). 27.12 (978-0-8172-5525-1(7)) Raintree.

Daley, Patrick. Russia. 2002. (Steadwell Books World Tour). (Illus.). 48p. (J). lib. bdg. 24.26 (978-0-7398-5538-6(7)) Raintree.

Dando, William A. & Pavlovic, Zoran. Russia. 2nd rev. ed. 2007. (Modern World Nations Ser.). (Illus.). 144p. (YA). (gr. 8 up). 30.00 (*978-0-7910-9248-4(8) , Chelsea Hse.) Facts On File, Inc.

Enderlein, Cheryl L. Celebrating Birthdays in Russia. 1998. (Birthdays Around the World Ser.). (Illus.). 24p. (J). (gr. k-3). lib. bdg. 14.00 (978-0-531-11547-3(X) , Watts, Franklin) Scholastic Library Publishing.

Ferro, Jennifer. Russian Foods & Culture. 1999. (Festive Foods & Celebrations Ser.). (Illus.). 48p. (J). (gr. 3-5). lib. bdg. 20.95 (978-1-57103-305-5(X)) Rourke Publishing, LLC.

Fontes, Justine & Fontes, Ron. Russia. (to Z Ser.). (J). 2004. (gr. 2-4). pap. 6.95 (978-0-516-26816-3(3)); 2003. (Illus.). 40p. 24.50 (978-0-516-24558-4(9)) Scholastic Library Publishing. (Children's Pr.).

Frost, Helen. A Look at Russia. Saunders-Smith, Gail, ed. 2001. (Our World Ser.). (Illus.). 24p. (J). (gr. k-1). lib. bdg. 15.93 (978-0-7368-0986-3(4) , Pebble Bks.) Capstone Pr., Inc.

Gordeeva, Ekaterina. Letter for Daria. 1998. 96p. (J). (ps-4). 12.95 (978-0-316-32994-1(0)) Little Brown & Co.

Gray, Susan Heinrichs. Russia. 2001. (First Reports). (Illus.). 48p. (J). (gr. 3 up). lib. bdg. 22.60 (978-0-7565-0130-3(X)) Compass Point Bks.

Greene, Meg. The Russian Kremlin. 2001. (Building History Ser.). (Illus.). 96p. (YA). (gr. 6-9). 32.45 (978-1-56006-840-2(X) , Lucent Bks.) Thomson Gale.

Hintz, Martin. Russia. (True Bks.). (J). 2005. (Illus.). 48p. (gr. 3-5). pap. 6.95 (978-0-516-27929-9(7)); 2004. 25.00 (978-0-516-22814-3(5)) Scholastic Library Publishing. (Children's Pr.).

Hirschmann, Kris. The Deepest Lake. 2002. (Extreme Places Ser.). (Illus.). 48p. (J). (gr. 3-5). 26.20 (978-0-7377-1372-5(0) , Kidhaven) Thomson Gale.

Hite, John, et al. Communist Russia under Lenin & Stalin. 2002. (Illus.). 336p. pap. 54.00 (*978-0-7195-7488-7(9) , Hodder Murray) Hodder Education GBR. *Dist:* Trans-Atlantic Pubns., Inc.

Ilyin, Andrey. A Child's Day in a Russian City. 2001. (Child's Day Ser.). (Illus.). 32p. (J). (gr. k-2). lib. bdg. 25.64 (978-0-7614-1222-9(0) , Benchmark Bks.) Cavendish, Marshall Corp.

Israel, Fred L. Russian People in 1914. 1999. (Cultural & Geographical Exploration Ser.). (Illus.). 144p. (YA). (gr. 7-12). 21.95 (978-0-7910-5446-8(2) , Chelsea Hse.) Facts On File, Inc.

Italia, Bob. Russia. 2000. (Countries Ser.). (Illus.). 40p. (J). (gr. k-6). lib. bdg. 22.78 (978-1-57765-386-8(6) , Checkerboard Library) ABDO Publishing Co.

Jenkins, Ruth. Russia. 2006. (Countries of the World Ser.). 64p. (J). (gr. 6-12). 30.00 (978-0-8160-6011-5(8)) Facts On File, Inc.

A Look at Russia. 2005. (One World, Many Cultures Ser.). (YA). (gr. k-3). (978-0-7368-9424-1(1) , Pebble Bks.) Capstone Pr., Inc.

A Look at Russia, 6 vols. (gr. k-2). 28.95 (978-0-7368-9425-8(X)) Red Brick Learning.

Marquez, Heron. Russia in Pictures. 2nd ed. 2004. (Visual Geography Series, Second Ser.). (Illus.). 80p. (J). (gr. 5-12). 27.93 (978-0-8225-0937-0(7)) Lerner Publishing Group.

Mathur-Kamat, Ambika. Miss Panda in Russia. Crawford, K. Michael, illus. 2001. (Miss Panda Ser.). 40p. (J). pap. 9.99 (978-1-59092-025-1(2) , Little Blue Works) Windstorm Creative.

Maynard, Charles W. The Ural Mountains. 2004. (Great Mountain Ranges of the World Ser.). (Illus.). 24p. (J). lib. bdg. 21.25 (978-0-8239-6699-8(2) , PowerKids Pr.) Rosen Publishing Group, Inc., The.

McGraw-Hill Staff. Exploring Our World, Western Hemisphere with Europe & Russia, Interactive Tutor Self-Assesment CD-ROM. 2007. (C). cd-rom 93.32 (*978-0-07-879088-1(3) , 9780078790881) Glencoe/McGraw-Hill.

—Exploring Our World, Western Hemisphere with Europe & Russia, Reading Essentials & Note-Taking Guide Workbook. 2007. (C). pap. 18.00 (*978-0-07-878170-4(1) , 9780078781704) Glencoe/McGraw-Hill.

—Exploring Our World, Western Hemisphere with Europe & Russia, Spanish Reading Essentials & Note-Taking Guide Workbook. 2007. (C). pap. 18.00 (*978-0-07-878172-8(8) , 9780078781728) Glencoe/McGraw-Hill.

—Exploring Our World, Western Hemisphere with Europe & Russia, Standardized Test Practice Workbook. 2007. (C). pap. 10.00 (*978-0-07-877728-8(3) , 9780078777288) Glencoe/McGraw-Hill.

—Exploring Our World, Western Hemisphere with Europe & Russia, Student Edition. 2nd ed. 2007. 69.32 (*978-0-07-874580-5(2) , 9780078745805) Glencoe/McGraw-Hill.

Morris, Neil. North & East Asia. 2007. (J). (*978-1-4034-9898-4(9)); pap. (*978-1-4034-9907-3(1)) Heinemann Library.

Murdico, Suzanne J. Russia: A Primary Source Cultural Guide. 2005. (Primary Sources of World Cultures Ser.). (Illus.). 128p. (J). (gr. 4-8). lib. bdg. 34.60 (978-1-4042-2913-6(2)) Rosen Publishing Group, Inc., The.

Murrell, Kathleen Berton. Russia. 2000. (Eyewitness Bks.). (Illus.). 64p. (J). (gr. 4-7). 15.99 (978-0-7894-5880-3(2)) Dorling Kindersley Publishing, Inc.

Nickles, Greg. Russia - The Culture. 2000. (Lands, Peoples & Cultures Ser.). (Illus.). 32p. (J). (gr. 4-5). (978-0-86505-240-6(9)); pap. (978-0-86505-320-5(0)) Crabtree Publishing Co.

—Russia - The Land. 2000. (Lands, Peoples & Cultures Ser.). (Illus.). 32p. (J). (gr. 4-5). (978-0-86505-238-3(7)) Crabtree Publishing Co.

—Russia - The People. 2000. (Lands, Peoples & Cultures Ser.). (Illus.). 32p. (J). (gr. 4-5). (978-0-86505-239-0(5)); pap. (978-0-86505-319-9(7)) Crabtree Publishing Co.

—Russia the Culture. 2000. (gr. 3-6). lib. bdg. 16.40 (978-0-613-28048-8(2)) Tandem Library Bks.

—Russia the Land. 2000. (gr. 3-6). lib. bdg. 16.40 (978-0-613-28049-5(0)) Tandem Library Bks.

—Russia the People. 2000. (gr. 3-6). lib. bdg. 16.40 (978-0-613-28050-1(4)) Tandem Library Bks.

Park, Ted. Russia. 2000. (Taking Your Camera to Ser.). (Illus.). 32p. (J). (gr. 4-7). lib. bdg. 22.83 (978-0-7398-1811-4(2)) Raintree.

—Taking Your Camera to Russia. 2001. (Illus.). pap. (978-0-7398-3332-2(4)) Steck-Vaughn.

Powell, Jillian. Descubramos Rusia: By Jillian Powell. 2007. (SPA & ENG.). pap. (***978-0-8368-7959-9(7)***) Stevens, Gareth Inc.

—Looking at Russia. 2007. pap. (***978-0-8368-8180-6(X)***); 32p. (J). (gr. 2-4). lib. bdg. 25.27 (***978-0-8368-8173-8(7)***) Stevens, Gareth Inc.

Powell, Jillian & Pohl, Kathleen. Descubramos Rusia (Looking at Russia) 2007. (Descubramos Países del Mundo (Looking at Countries) Ser.). (SPA.). 32p. (J). (gr. 2-4). lib. bdg. 25.27 (***978-0-8368-8187-5(7)***) Stevens, Gareth Inc.

Ransome, Galya. Russia. 2003. (Changing Face Of... Ser.). (Illus.). 48p. (J). lib. bdg. 28.56 (978-0-7398-6042-7(9)) Raintree.

Rogers, Stillman D. Russia. 2002. (Enchantment of the World, Second Ser.). (Illus.). 144p. (YA). (gr. 5-9). pap. 36.00 (978-0-516-22494-7(8), Children's Pr.) Scholastic Library Publishing.

Rosenberg, Aaron. Vladimir Putin: President of Russia. 2007. (J). (***978-1-4042-1903-8(X)***) Rosen Publishing Group, Inc., The.

Sheen, Barbara. Foods of Russia. 2006. (Taste of Culture Ser.). 64p. (J). (gr. 3-6). 27.45 (978-0-7377-3538-3(4), Greenhaven Pr., Inc.) Thomson Gale.

Shields, Charles J. Vladimir Putin. (Major World Leaders Ser.). (Illus.). (gr. 6-12). 2003. 144p. pap. 30.00 (978-0-7910-7525-8(7)); 2002. 112p. 30.00 (978-0-7910-6945-5(1)) Facts On File, Inc. (Chelsea Hse.).

—Vladimir Putin. 2003. (gr. 5-8). lib. bdg. 18.75 (978-0-613-86155-7(8)) Tandem Library Bks.

Smith, Debbie. Russia: The Culture. 1999. (978-0-606-18066-5(4)) Tandem Library Bks.

Smith, Jessica & Compass Point Books Staff. Teens in Russia. 2006. (Global Connections Ser.). (Illus.). 96p. (J). (gr. 5-7). 31.93 (978-0-7565-2065-6(7)) Compass Point Bks.

Spengler, Kremena. Russia: A Question & Answer Book. 2004. (Fact Finders Ser.). (Illus.). 32p. (J). lib. bdg. 22.60 (978-0-7368-2692-1(0)) Capstone Pr., Inc.

Steinbeck, John. Russian Journal. 1999. (gr. 7-12). lib. bdg. 23.40 (978-0-613-70921-7(7)) Tandem Library Bks.

Streissguth, Thomas. Russia. 2008. (Country Explorers Ser.). (J). lib. bdg. 27.93 (***978-0-8225-8664-7(9)***, Lerner Pubns.) Lerner Publishing Group.

Torchinskii, O. Russia. 2005. (Cultures of the World Ser.). (Illus.). 144p. (J). 37.07 (978-0-7614-1849-8(0)) Cavendish, Marshall Corp.

Zemlicka, Shannon. Colors of Russia. Reeves, Jeni, illus. (Colors of the World Ser.). 24p. (J). 2005. (gr. 3-6). lib. bdg. 19.93 (978-1-57505-513-8(9)); 2003. (gr. 1-4). pap. 5.95 (978-1-57505-564-0(3)) Lerner Publishing Group.

—Colors of Russia. 2001. (gr. k-3). lib. bdg. 14.10 (978-0-613-79239-4(4)) Tandem Library Bks.

RUSSIA (FEDERATION)—COMMUNISM

see Communism—Soviet Union

RUSSIAN AMERICANS

Behnke, Alison. Russians in America. 2006. (In America Ser.). (Illus.). 80p. (J). (ps-7). 27.93 (978-0-8225-3954-4(3), Lerner Pubns.) Lerner Publishing Group.

Bowen, Richard. The Russian-Americans. 2002. (Welcome to America Ser.). (Illus.). 64p. (J). (gr. 5 up). lib. bdg. (978-1-59084-103-7(4)) Mason Crest Pubs.

Bryan, Nichol. Russian Americans. 2004. (One Nation Set Ii Ser.). (Illus.). 32p. (J). (gr. k-6). lib. bdg. 22.78 (978-1-59197-533-5(6)) ABDO Publishing Co.

Fitterer, C. Ann. Russian Americans. 2002. (Spirit of America: Our Cultural Heritage Ser.). (Illus.). 32p. (J). (gr. 2-6). 27.07 (978-1-56766-158-3(0)) Child's World, Inc.

Frost, Helen. Russian Immigrants, 1860-1915. 2002. (Blue Earth Books). (Illus.). 32p. (J). (gr. 4-6). lib. bdg. 22.60 (978-0-7368-1209-2(1), Bridgestone Bks.) Capstone Pr., Inc.

Greene, Meg. The Russian-Americans. 2002. (Immigrants in America Ser.). (Illus.). 104p. (YA). (gr. 4-12). 29.95 (978-1-56006-963-8(5), LML00902-179006, Lucent Bks.) Thomson Gale.

Peterson, Tiffany. Russian Americans. 2003. (We Are America Ser.). 32p. pap. 6.95 (978-1-4034-3138-7(8)); (Illus.). (J). lib. bdg. 24.22 (978-1-4034-0737-5(1)) Heinemann Library.

—Russian Americans. 2003. (gr. 3-6). lib. bdg. 15.25 (978-0-613-67432-4(4)) Tandem Library Bks.

Russian Colonies in the Americas, 6 Packs. (On Deck Ser.: Vol. 2). 24p. (gr. 4-5). 35.00 (978-0-7578-5803-1(1)) Rigby Education.

Trumbauer, Lisa. Russian Immigrants. 2004. (Immigration to the United States Ser.). (Illus.). 96p. (J). (gr. 4-9). 35.00 (978-0-8160-5685-9(4)) Facts On File, Inc.

RUSSIAN AMERICANS—FICTION

Best, Cari. Three Cheers for Catherine the Great! 2003. (gr. k-3). lib. bdg. 15.25 (978-0-613-71883-7(6)) Tandem Library Bks.

—When Catherine the Great & I Were Eight! Potter, Giselle, illus. 2003. 32p. (J). (gr. k-3). 16.00 (978-0-374-39954-2(9), Farrar, Straus & Giroux (BYR)) Farrar, Straus & Giroux.

Best, Cari & Potter, Giselle. Three Cheers for Catherine the Great! 2003. (Illus.). 32p. (J). pap. 6.95 (978-0-374-47551-2(2), Sunburst) Farrar, Straus & Giroux.

Blume, Lesley M. M. The Rising Star of Rusty Nail. 2007. 288p. (J). (gr. 3-7). 15.99 (978-0-375-83524-7(5), Knopf Bks. for Young Readers) Random Hse. Children's Bks.

—The Rising Star of the Rusty Nail. 2007. 288p. (J). (gr. 3-7). lib. bdg. 18.99 (978-0-375-93524-4(X), Knopf Bks. for Young Readers) Random Hse. Children's Bks.

Cohen, Barbara. Molly's Pilgrim. Duffy, Daniel M. & Deraney, Michael J., illus. rev. ed. 1998. 32p. (J). (ps-3). 16.99 (978-0-688-16279-5(7)) HarperCollins Pubs.

—Molly's Pilgrim. Duffy, Daniel Mark & Deraney, Michael J., illus. 97th rev. ed. 1998. 32p. (J). (gr. 1-4). pap. 3.99 (978-0-688-16280-1(0), Harper Trophy) HarperCollins Pubs.

—Molly's Pilgrim. (Literature to Go Ser.). pap., tchr. ed. incl. VHS (978-0-7919-2685-7(0)) Phoenix Films & Video.

Cunningham, Laura Shaine. The Midnight Diary of Zoya Blume. 2006. 176p. (J). pap. 5.99 (978-0-06-072261-6(4), Harper Trophy) HarperCollins Pubs.

Gaberman, Judith. One-Way to Ansonia. 2001. 196p. pap. 12.95 (978-0-595-15830-0(7), Backinprint.com) iUniverse, Inc.

Greenberger, Tehilla. Gifts to Treasure. Toron, Eli, illus. 2007. (Fun to Read Book). 224p. (J). per. 10.95 (***978-1-929628-32-2(3)***) Hachai Publishing.

Hamilton, Morse. Yellow Blue Bus Means I Love You. 2000. 192p. (YA). (gr. 7 up). pap. 6.99 (978-0-380-73301-9(3)) HarperCollins Pubs.

—Yellow Bus Means I Love You. 2000. (978-0-606-17984-3(4)) Tandem Library Bks.

Kalman, Esther. Tchaikovsky Discovers America. Fernandez, Laura & Jacobson, Rick, illus. 2000. 48p. (J). (gr. k-3). pap. 6.95 (978-0-531-07168-7(5), Orchard Bks.) Scholastic, Inc.

Polacco, Patricia. The Trees of the Dancing Goats. Polacco, Patricia, illus. 2002. (Illus.). (J). 25.11 (978-0-7587-3858-5(7)) Book Wholesalers, Inc.

—The Trees of the Dancing Goats. Polacco, Patricia, illus. 2000. (Illus.). 32p. (J). (gr. k-3). 7.99 (978-0-689-83857-6(3), Aladdin) Simon & Schuster Children's Publishing.

—The Trees of the Dancing Goats. 2000. (J). (978-0-606-20094-3(0)) Tandem Library Bks.

—Trees of the Dancing Goats. 2000. (gr. k-3). lib. bdg. 15.30 (978-0-613-30164-0(1)) Tandem Library Bks.

Tarbescu, Edith. Annushka's Voyage. Dabcovich, Lydia & Degen, Bruce, illus. 1998. 32p. (J). (gr. k-3). tchr. ed. 16.00 (978-0-395-64366-2(X), Clarion Bks.) Houghton Mifflin Co. Trade & Reference Div.

RUSSIAN COMMUNISM

see Communism—Soviet Union

RUSSIAN LANGUAGE

Amery, Heather. First Thousand Words in Russian. MacKinnon, Mairi, ed. Cartwright, Stephen, illus. 2005. 63p. (J). 12.99 (978-0-7945-1001-5(9), Usborne) EDC Publishing.

Carole Marsh. False Paw! 2004. (Little Linguist Ser.). 32p. 29.95 (978-0-635-02438-1(1)) Gallopade International.

—From Russia with Love! 2004. (Little Linguist Ser.). 32p. 29.95 (978-0-635-02441-1(1)) Gallopade International.

—From Russia with Love! Russian for Kids. 2004. (Little Linguist Ser.). 32p. (gr. 2-6). pap. 5.95 (978-0-635-02433-6(0)) Gallopade International.

Cartwright, Stephen & Amery, Heather. First Thousand Words in Russian. 2004. (First Thousand Words Ser.). (RUS & ENG., Illus.). 64p. (J). (ps-7). lib. bdg. 20.95 (978-0-88110-574-2(0)) EDC Publishing.

Hippocrene Books Staff. Hippocrene Children's Illustrated Russian Dictionary. 1999. (Children's Illustrated Dictionaries Ser.). (RUS & ENG., Illus.). 96p. (YA). (gr. k-5). 14.95 (978-0-7818-0772-2(7)) Hippocrene Bks., Inc.

—Hippocrene Children's Illustrated Russian Dictionary. 2001. (gr. 3-6). lib. bdg. 21.05 (978-0-613-74954-1(5)) Tandem Library Bks.

Hippocrene Children's Illustrated Russian Dictionary: English-Russian/Russian-English. 2002. (Children's Illustrated Foreign Language Dictionaries Ser.). (ENG & RUS., Illus.). 96p. (gr. k-5). pap. 11.95 (978-0-7818-0892-7(8)) Hippocrene Bks., Inc.

Life Publishers International Staff, tr. from SPA. & prod. My Friends-Student (Russian) Vol. 3, Bk. 1: Russian Sunday School, Life Publishers International Staff, prod. 2000. Orig. Title: Mis Amigos. Alumno. (RUS., Illus.). 48p. (J). (gr. 1-3). stu. ed. (978-0-7361-0163-9(2)) Life Pubs. International.

The Rosetta Stone Language Library: Russian Level 1. 2005. (J). (gr. 1 up). cd-rom 209.00 (978-1-883972-60-8(4)) Fairfield Language Technologies.

The Rosetta Stone Language Library: Russian Level 2. 2005. (J). (gr. 1 up). cd-rom 239.00 (978-1-883972-61-5(2)) Fairfield Language Technologies.

Tcachenco, Natalya. The Best on the East Mystery & Adventures, Vol. 1. 2006th ed. 2005. Orig. Title: The best on the East. (Illus.). (J). 19.99 (978-0-9754433-4-7(8), Language Transformer Bks.) Velichko, Vera.

RUSSIAN LITERATURE

Bloom, Harold, ed. Anton Chekhov. 1999. (Bloom's Modern Critical Views Ser.). 200p. (YA). (gr. 8-12). 45.00 (978-0-7910-4783-5(0), Chelsea Hse.) Facts On File, Inc.

—St. Petersburg. 2005. (Bloom's Literary Places Ser.). (Illus.). 150p. (gr. 9-13). pap. (978-0-7910-8384-0(5), Chelsea Hse.) Facts On File, Inc.

Chapman, Lynne F. Leo Tolstoy. 1999. (Notebooks Ser.). 48p. 17.95 (978-1-56846-156-4(9), Creative Editions) Creative Co., The.

Woodworth, Bradley & Richards, Constance E., eds. St. Petersburg. 2005. (Bloom's Literary Places Ser.). (Illus.). 137p. (YA). (gr. 9-13). lib. bdg. 40.00 (978-0-7910-7837-2(X), Chelsea Hse.) Facts On File, Inc.

RUSSIAN SATELLITES

see Communist Countries

RUSSIANS—ALASKA—FICTION

Hill, Kirkpatrick. Dancing at the Odinochka. 2005. (Illus.). 272p. (J). (ps-1). 15.95 (978-0-689-87388-1(3), McElderry, Margaret K.) Simon & Schuster Children's Publishing.

RUSSIANS—UNITED STATES

Fremon, David K. The Alaska Purchase in American History. 1999. (In American History Ser.). (Illus.). 128p. (YA). (gr. 5-12). lib. bdg. 26.60 (978-0-7660-1138-0(0)) Enslow Pubs., Inc.

Parker, Lewis K. Russian Colonies in the Americas. 2003. (Reading Power Ser.). (Illus.). 24p. (J). lib. bdg. 17.25 (978-0-8239-6470-3(1), PowerKids Pr.) Rosen Publishing Group, Inc., The.

Stotsky, Sandra, ed. The Russian Americans. 1999. (Immigrant Experience Ser.). (Illus.). 128p. (YA). (gr. 5 up). pap. 9.95 (978-0-7910-3389-0(9), Chelsea Hse.) Facts On File, Inc.

RUSSO-TURKISH WAR, 1853-1856

see Crimean War, 1853-1856

RUTH (BIBLICAL CHARACTER)

Adams, Anne Tyra. Beauty in the Fields: The Diary of Ruth's Fellow Harvester, Israel, about 1200 B. C. 2004. (Promised Land Diaries). (Illus.). 192p. (J). 10.99 (978-0-8010-4527-1(4)) Baker Bks.

Baez, Kjersti H. Ruth. 1998. (Young Reader's Christian Library). (Illus.). 224p. (J). (gr. 7 up). per. 1.39 (978-1-55748-173-3(3)) Barbour Publishing, Inc.

Chronicles of Faith - Ruth. 2007. 224p. (J). pap. 4.97 (***978-1-59789-928-4(3)***) Barbour Publishing, Inc.

Connelly, Gwen, illus. The Story of Ruth. 2005. 32p. (J). (gr. 2-4). pap. 6.95 (978-1-58013-130-8(1)) Kar-Ben Publishing.

De Graaf, Anne. Ruth. Montero, Jose Perez, illus. 2001. (Little Children's Bible Bks.). 38p. (J). (ps-1). 5.99 (978-0-8054-2190-3(4)) B&H Publishing Grp.

Dorn, Owen A. Ruth: A Love Story. 2003. (God's People Ser.). (Illus.). pap. 6.99 (978-0-8100-1348-3(7)) Northwestern Publishing Hse.

Frank, Penny. La Nueva Familia de Rut.Tr. of Ruth's New Family. (SPA.). (J). 1.99 (978-1-56063-785-1(4), 490315) Editorial Unilit.

Neely, J. Ruth. 2002. (Daily Bible Study Ser.). 77p. pap. 19.95 (978-1-893968-25-7(1)) Neely, Judy.

Sanders, Karen Nordberg. Ruth & Naomi. Rooney, Ronnie, illus. 2007. 16p. (J). (gr. k-4). 1.99 (***978-0-7586-1283-0(4)***) Concordia Publishing Hse.

Schur, Maxine Rose. The Story of Ruth. Connelly, Gwen, illus. 2005. 32p. (J). (gr. 2-4). lib. bdg. 16.95 (978-1-58013-114-8(X)) Kar-Ben Publishing.

Taylor, Damon. To Cheese or Not to Cheese: The Story of Ruth. 2003. (Child Sockology Ser.). (Illus.). 32p. (J). 10.99 (978-0-8254-3866-0(7)) Kregel Pubns.

RUTH (BIBLICAL CHARACTER)—FICTION

Lundy, Charlotte. Thank You, Ruth & Naomi. Waldrep, Evelyn L., ed. Sagasti, Miriam, illus. 2004. 32p. (gr. k-4). 15.95 (978-0-9741817-0-7(6)) Bay Light Publishing.

Pakulak, Eric. At the Side of Ruth: A Multiple-Ending Bible Adventure. Bulanadi, Danny, illus. 2001. 74p. (J). pap. 6.95 (978-0-8198-0771-7(0)) Pauline Bks. & Media.

RUTH, BABE, 1895-1948

Canter, Len. Babe Ruth. Marcos, Pablo, illus. 2005. (Heroes of America Ser.). 240p. (J). (gr. 3-8). lib. bdg. 21.35 (978-1-59679-261-6(2)) ABDO Publishing Co.

Christopher, Matt. Babe Ruth: Legends in Sports. 2005. (Legends in Sports Ser.). (Illus.). 112p. (J). (gr. 3-7). pap. 4.99 (978-0-316-01113-6(4)) Little Brown & Co.

Harcourt School Publishers Staff. When Willard Met Babe Level D: Library Edition. 2001. (Collections Ser.). (Illus.). pap. 12.10 (978-0-15-314406-6(8)) Harcourt Schl. Pubs.

McLeese, Don. Babe Ruth. 4th ed. 2003. (Rourke Discovery Library). (Illus.). 24p. (gr. 2-5). 14.95 (978-1-58952-304-3(0)) Rourke Publishing, LLC.

Moss, Marissa. Mighty Jackie: The Strike-Out Queen. Payne, C. F., tr. Payne, C. F., illus. 2004. 32p. (J). 16.95 (978-0-689-86329-5(2), Simon & Schuster/Paula Wiseman Bks.) Simon & Schuster Children's Publishing.

Murphy, Frank. Babe Ruth Saves Baseball. Walz, Richard, illus. 2005. (Step into Reading Ser.). 48p. (J). (gr. 1-3). lib. bdg. 11.99 (978-0-375-93048-5(5), Random Hse. Bks. for Young Readers) Random Hse. Children's Bks.

—Babe Ruth Saves Baseball! Walz, Richard, illus. 2005. (Step into Reading Ser.: Vol. 3). 48p. (J). (gr. 1-3). pap. 3.99 (978-0-375-83048-6(0), Random Hse. Bks. for Young Readers) Random Hse. Children's Bks.

Murphy, Frank. Babe Ruth Saves Baseball Book & CD. Walz, Richard, illus. 2008. (Book & CD Ser.). 48p. (J). (gr. 1-3). 9.99 (***978-0-375-84184-2(9)***, Random Hse. Bks. for Young Readers) Random Hse. Children's Bks.

Patrick, Jean L. S. The Girl Who Struck Out Babe Ruth. 2000. (gr. 3-6). lib. bdg. 14.10 (978-0-613-53509-0(X)) Tandem Library Bks.

Patrick Jean L. S. La niña que poncho a Babe Ruth (the Girl Who Struck Out Babe Ruth) Reeves, Jeni, illus. 2007. (Yo solo Historia (on My Own History) Ser.). (J). pap. 6.95 (***978-0-8225-7788-1(7)***, Ediciones Lerner) Lerner Publishing Group.

Patrick, Jean L. S. La Niña Que Poncho a Babe Ruth (The Girl Who Struck Out Babe Ruth) Reeves, Jeni, illus. 2007. (Yo Solo - Historia (on My Own - History) Ser.). (SPA.). 48p. (J). (gr. 2-4). 25.26 (***978-0-8225-7785-0(2)***, Ediciones Lerner) Lerner Publishing Group.

Shaughnessy, Dan. The Legend of the Curse of the Bambino. Payne, C. F., illus. 2005. 32p. (J). 16.95 (978-0-689-87235-8(6), Simon & Schuster Children's Publishing) Simon & Schuster Children's Publishing.

RUTH, GEORGE HERMAN, 1895-1948

see Ruth, Babe, 1895-1948

RUTHERFORD, ERNEST, 1871-1937

Heilbron, J. L. Ernest Rutherford: And the Explosion of Atoms. 2003. (Oxford Portraits in Science Ser.). (Illus.). 144p. (YA). 30.00 (978-0-19-512378-4(6)) Oxford Univ. Pr., Inc.

Pasachoff, Naomi E. Ernest Rutherford: Father of Nuclear Science. 2005. (Great Minds of Science Ser.). (Illus.). 128p. (J). lib. bdg. 26.60 (978-0-7660-2441-0(5)) Enslow Pubs., Inc.

S

SABBATH

Bacchiocchi, Samuele. The Sabbath under Crossfire: A Biblical Analysis of Recent Sabbath/Sunday Developments. 2nd deluxe ed. 1998. (Biblical Perspectives Ser.: Vol. 14). 304p. (YA). pap. 20.00 (978-1-930987-13-5(7)) Biblical Perspectives.

Bagley, Val Chadwick. Sunday Is a Special Day. 2004. 9.95 (978-1-57734-831-3(1)) Covenant Communications, Inc.

Cone, Molly. The Story of Shabbat. Lisker, Emily, illus. 2000. 30p. (J). (gr. 5-7). reprint ed. 15.00 (978-0-7567-5618-5(9)) DIANE Publishing Co.

—The Story of Shabbat. Lisker, Emily, illus. 2000. 40p. (J). (gr. 1-4). 14.95 (978-0-06-027944-8(3)); 14.89 (978-0-06-027945-5(1)) HarperCollins Pubs.

Dorling Kindersley Publishing Staff. Shabbat. 2003. (My First Board Bks.). (Illus.). 36p. (J). bds. 6.99 (978-0-7894-9234-0(2)) Dorling Kindersley Publishing, Inc.

Duncan, Aubrey. Understanding God's Sabbath: A Decision to Make. 2004. per. 12.95 (978-0-9749490-0-0(0), 500) Bridge To Life Ministries, Inc.

Falstein, Mark. Welcoming the Sabbath: Creative Projects, Rituals, & Recipes for Kids. Clark Editorial and Design Staff, ed. Parks, Kathy, illus. 1999. 72p. (J). (gr. 1-7). pap. 9.95 (978-0-88160-323-1(6), LW386) Creative Teaching Pr., Inc.

Ganz, Yaffa & Ari'el, Li'at Binyamini. Shabbos: With Bina, Benny & Chaggai Hayonah. 2000. (ArtScroll Children's Holiday Ser.: Vol. 10). (Illus.). 26p. (J). 9.99 (978-1-57819-499-5(7), YSHA) Mesorah Pubns., Ltd.

Gold, Yeshara. Hurry, Friday's a Short Day: One boy's erev Shabbat in Jerusalem's old City. 2000. 31p. 13.99 (978-1-57819-541-1(1), HURH) Mesorah Pubns., Ltd.

Groner, Judyth Saypol & Wikler, Madeline. Come, Let Us Welcome Shabbat: A Joyful Celebration for Families. Wikler, Madeline, illus. rev. ed. 2000. (HEB., Illus.). 32p. (J). (gr. 5-12). pap. 4.95 (978-1-58013-012-7(7)) Kar-Ben Publishing.

Kropf, Latifa Berry. It's Challah Time! Cohen, Tod, illus. 2002. 24p. (J). (ps-1). 12.95 (978-1-58013-036-3(4)) Kar-Ben Publishing.

Simon, Norma. Every Friday Night. Weiss, Harvey, illus. (Festival Series of Picture Storybooks). (J). (ps). spiral bd. 4.50 (978-0-8381-0708-9(7)) United Synagogue of America Bk. Service.

Sofer, Barbara. Ilan Ramon: Israel's First Astronaut. 2004. (General Jewish Interest Ser.). (J). pap. 6.95 (978-0-929371-49-8(6)) Lerner Publishing Group.

—Shabbat Shalom: Israel's First Astronaut. 2004. (Illus.). 12p. (J). 16.95 (978-0-930494-91-9(1)) Kar-Ben Publishing.

SABBATH—FICTION

Cohen, Deborah Bodin. The Seventh Day. Hall, Melanie, illus. 2005. 24p. (J). (ps-3). pap. 6.95 (978-1-58013-125-4(5)); 16.95 (978-0-929371-24-5(0)) Kar-Ben Publishing.

Emerman, Ellen. Is It Shabbos Yet? Rosenfeld, Dina, ed. Leff, Tova, illus. 2nd ed. 2001. 32p. (J). (ps-k). 9.95 (978-1-929628-02-5(1)) Hachai Publishing.

Garren, Devorah-Leah. Shabbos Is Coming! We're Lost in the Zoo! Katz, Maya S., illus. 1999. 32p. (J). (ps-3). 12.95 (978-1-880582-32-9(5)) Judaica Pr., Inc., The.

Jaffe, Nina & Sutherland, Emily, illus. Tales for the Seventh Day: A Collection of Sabbath Stories. 2000. 73p. (J). pap. (978-0-590-12055-5(7)) Scholastic, Inc.

Rauchwerger, Diane Levin. Dinosaur on Shabbat. Wolff, Jason, illus. 2006. (J). 15.95 (978-1-58013-159-9(X)) Kar-Ben Publishing.

Rouss, Sylvia A. The Littlest Candlesticks. Hannon, Holly, illus. 2005. (Littlest Ser.). 32p. (J). 14.95 (978-1-930143-48-7(6)); pap. 9.95 (978-1-930143-49-4(4)) Pitspopany Pr. (Devora Publishing).

Sigal, Maxine Handelman. Shabbat Angels. Rothenberg, Joani, illus. 2003. (gr. k-3). 13.95 (978-0-8074-0865-0(4), 164051) URJ Pr.

Silberman, Shoshana. A Family Haggadah II, Vol. 2. Kahn, Katherine Janus, illus. l.t. ed. 2003. 64p. (J). pap. 6.95 (978-1-58013-014-1(3)) Kar-Ben Publishing.

Simpson, Lesley. The Shabbat Box. Bosch, Nicole in den, illus. 2001. 32p. (J). (ps-1). pap. 6.95 (978-1-58013-027-1(5)) Kar-Ben Publishing.

Topek, Susan R. Shalom, Shabbat: A Book for Havdalah. Ephraim, Shelly S., illus. 1998. 12p. (J). (ps up). 5.95 (978-1-58013-010-3(0)) Kar-Ben Publishing.

Wasserman, Mira. Too Much of a Good Thing. Carolan, Christine, illus. 2003. 32p. (J). (ps-3). 15.95 (978-1-58013-082-0(8)); pap. 6.95 (978-1-58013-066-0(6)) Kar-Ben Publishing.

—Too Much of a Good Thing. 2003. (gr. k-3). lib. bdg. 15.25 (978-0-613-81210-8(7)) Tandem Library Bks.

SABOTAGE—FICTION

Bossley, Michele Martin. Cracked. 2007. (Orca Currents Ser.). 112p. (YA). (gr. 5 up). pap. (***978-1-55143-700-2(7)***); lib. bdg. (***978-1-55143-702-6(3)***) Orca Bk. Pubs.

Dixon, Franklin W. Running on Fumes. 2005. 150p. (J). lib. bdg. 16.92 (***978-1-4242-0384-0(8)***) Fitzgerald Bks.

—Running on Fumes. 2005. (Illus.). 150p. (J). (***978-1-4156-0714-5(1)*** , Aladdin) Simon & Schuster Children's Publishing.

Keene, Carolyn. Once upon a Crime. 2006. 185p. (J). (978-1-4156-7698-1(4) , Aladdin) Simon & Schuster Children's Publishing.

SABRINA, THE TEENAGE WITCH (FICTITIOUS CHARACTER)—FICTION

Batrae, Margot. Switcheroo. 2000. (Sabrina, the Teenage Witch Ser.: No. 30). (YA). (gr. 5 up). (978-0-606-18380-2(9)) Tandem Library Bks.

—While the Cat's Away. 1999. (gr. 7-12). lib. bdg. 13.00 (978-0-613-73060-0(7)) Tandem Library Bks.

Dubowski, Cathy East. Fortune Cookie Fox. 1999. (gr. 3-6). lib. bdg. 12.40 (978-0-613-21556-5(7)) Tandem Library Bks.

Fiedler, Lisa. Know-It-All. 2002. (gr. 5-8). lib. bdg. 13.00 (978-0-613-74231-3(1)) Tandem Library Bks.

Gallagher, Diana G. Worth a Shot. 2000. (Sabrina, the Teenage Witch: No. 11). 81p. (J). (gr. 2-5). per. (978-0-671-77334-2(8) , Simon & Schuster Children's Publishing) Simon & Schuster Children's Publishing.

Garton, Ray. All That Glitters. 1998. (Sabrina, the Teenage Witch Ser.: No. 12). (Illus.). 176p. (YA). (gr. 5 up). mass mkt. 4.99 (978-0-671-02116-0(8) , Simon Pulse) Simon & Schuster Children's Publishing.

Holder, Nancy. Feline Felon. 1999. (gr. 3-6). lib. bdg. 11.80 (978-0-613-21530-5(3)) Tandem Library Bks.

—Scarabian Nights. 1999. (gr. 7-12). lib. bdg. 12.40 (978-0-613-73075-4(5)) Tandem Library Bks.

—Up, up, & Away. 1999. (gr. 3-6). lib. bdg. 12.40 (978-0-613-22556-4(2)); (Sabrina, the Teenage Witch Ser.: No. 28). (YA). (gr. 5 up). (978-0-606-18381-9(7)) Tandem Library Bks.

Krulik, Nancy E. Rulin' the School. 2000. (Sabrina, the Teenage Witch: No. 12). (Illus.). 85p. (J). (gr. 2-5). per. (978-0-671-77335-9(6) , Simon & Schuster Children's Publishing) Simon & Schuster Children's Publishing.

—Rulin' the School. 2000. (gr. 3-6). lib. bdg. 11.80 (978-0-613-28047-1(4)) Tandem Library Bks.

—The Witch That Launched a Thousand Ships. 2002. (gr. 3-6). lib. bdg. 13.00 (978-0-613-74230-6(3)) Tandem Library Bks.

Odom, Mel. Dream Boat. 2001. (Sabrina, the Teenage Witch Ser.: Bk. 40). 144p. (YA). (gr. 5 up). mass mkt. 4.99 (978-0-7434-1812-6(3) , Simon Pulse) Simon & Schuster Children's Publishing.

—Mummy Dearest. 2000. (Sabrina, the Teenage Witch Ser.: No. 31). 161p. (YA). (gr. 5 up). (978-0-671-77324-3(0) , Simon & Schuster Children's Publishing) Simon & Schuster Children's Publishing.

—Mummy Dearest. 2000. (gr. 3-6). lib. bdg. 12.40 (978-0-613-27985-7(9)) Tandem Library Bks.

Reisfeld, Randi. All You Need Is a Love Spell. 1998. (gr. 7-12). lib. bdg. 13.00 (978-0-613-73088-4(7)) Tandem Library Bks.

Ruditis, Paul. Sabrina the Teenage Witch: The Official Episode Guide. 2002. (Illus.). 192p. (J). pap. (978-0-7522-6493-6(1) , Boxtree) Pan Macmillan.

Simon & Schuster, eds. Millennium Madness. 2000. (gr. 3-6). lib. bdg. 14.15 (978-0-613-22002-6(1)) Tandem Library Bks.

Vornholt, John. Witchopoly. 1999. (gr. 7-12). lib. bdg. 13.00 (978-0-613-73076-1(3)) Tandem Library Bks.

Weiss, Bobbi J. G. Prom Time. 1999. (gr. 7-12). lib. bdg. 13.00 (978-0-613-73077-8(1)) Tandem Library Bks.

Weiss, David Cody. Kitty Cornered. 2000. (Sabrina, the Teenage Witch: No. 13). (Illus.). 64p. (J). (gr. 2-5). per. (978-0-671-77336-6(4) , Simon & Schuster Children's Publishing) Simon & Schuster Children's Publishing.

—Now & Again. 2003. (gr. 5-8). lib. bdg. 13.00 (978-0-613-73348-9(7)) Tandem Library Bks.

SACAGAWEA, 1786-1884

Adler, David A. A Picture Book of Sacagawea. Brown, Dan, illus. 32p. (J). (gr. k-3). 2005. 6.95 (978-0-8234-1665-3(8)); 2000. tchr. ed. 16.95 (978-0-8234-1485-7(X)) Holiday Hse., Inc.

Alter, Judy. Sacagawea: Native American Interpreter. 2002. (Spirit of America: Our People Ser.). (Illus.). 32p. (J). (gr. 2-6). 27.07 (978-1-56766-166-8(1)) Child's World, Inc.

Birchfield, D. L. Sacagawea. 2002. (Raintree Biographies Ser.). (Illus.). 32p. (J). lib. bdg. 25.69 (978-0-7398-5680-2(4)) Raintree.

Bloom Fradin, Judith & Brindell Fradin, Dennis. Who Was Sacagawea? Taylor, Van Paul & Harrison, Nancy, illus. 2002. (Who Was...? Ser.). 112p. (J). pap. 4.99 (978-0-448-42485-9(1) , Grosset & Dunlap) Penguin Group (USA) Inc.

Capstone Press, contrib. by. Sacagawea. (American Indian Biographies Ser.). 48p. (YA). pap. 7.95 (978-0-7368-3291-5(2)) Capstone Pr., Inc.

Collard, Sneed B., III. Sacagawea: Brave Shoshone Girl. 2006. (American Heroes Ser.). (Illus.). 48p. (J). (gr. 3-5). lib. bdg. 28.50 (978-0-7614-2166-5(1) , Benchmark Bks.) Cavendish, Marshall Corp.

Crosby, Michael T. Sacagawea: Lewis & Clark's Pathfinder. 2007. 144p. (J). 25.95 (***978-1-59556-026-1(2)***) OTTN Publishing.

DeKeyser, Stacy. Sacagawea. 2004. (Watts Library). (Illus.). 64p. (J). 25.50 (978-0-531-12290-7(5) , Watts, Franklin) Scholastic Library Publishing.

Erdrich, Lise. Sacagawea. 2005. (Libros Ilustrados (Picture Bks.)). (SPA & ENG., Illus.). 40p. (J). (ps-6). 16.95 (978-0-8225-3191-3(7) , Ediciones Lerner) Lerner Publishing Group.

—Sacagawea. Buffalohead, Julie, illus. 2003. 40p. (J). (gr. 3-6). 16.95 (978-0-87614-646-0(9) , Carolrhoda Bks.) Lerner Publishing Group.

Feinstein, Stephen. Lee sobre Sacagawea/Read about Sacagawea. 2006. (I Like Biographies! Bilingual Ser.). (ENG & SPA., Illus.). 24p. (J). (gr. 1-3). lib. bdg. 21.26 (978-0-7660-2674-2(4) , Enslow Elementary) Enslow Pubs., Inc.

—Read about Sacagawea. 2004. (I Like Biographies Ser.!). (Illus.). 24p. (J). lib. bdg. 21.26 (978-0-7660-2297-3(8)) Enslow Pubs., Inc.

Ford, Carin T. Sacagawea. Meet an American Legend. 2003. (Meeting Famous People Ser.). (Illus.). 32p. (J). lib. bdg. 22.60 (978-0-7660-2004-7(5)) Enslow Pubs., Inc.

Franklin, Virgil. The Story of Sacagawea. 2002. (Reading Room Collection). (Illus.). 24p. (J). pap. (978-0-8239-8162-5(2)); lib. bdg. 18.75 (978-0-8239-3725-7(9)) Rosen Publishing Group, Inc., The.

Frazier, Neta Lohnes. Path to the Pacific: The Story of Sacagawea. 2007. (Sterling Point Bks.). (Illus.). 177p. (J). (***978-1-4287-2899-8(6)***) Sterling Publishing Co., Inc.

Gunderson, Jessica Sarah. Sacagawea: Journey into the West. Martin, Cynthia & Schultz, Barbara, illus. 2007. (Graphic Library). 32p. (J). 25.26 (978-0-7368-6499-2(7)) Capstone Pr., Inc.

Koestler-Grack, Rachel A. Sacagawea. 2004. (Illus.). 32p. (J). pap. 7.50 (978-1-4034-5011-1(0)); lib. bdg. 24.22 (978-1-4034-5004-3(8)) Heinemann Library.

Krensky, Stephen. Sacagawea. Magnuson, Diana, illus. ed. 2005. 32p. (J). lib. bdg. 15.00 (978-1-59054-954-4(6)) Fitzgerald Bks.

Lilly, Melinda. Sacagawea, Lewis, & Clark. 2003. (Rourke Discovery Library). (Illus.). 24p. (J). (gr. 1-4). 14.95 (978-1-58952-362-3(8)) Rourke Publishing, LLC.

Lohof, Arle & Jensen, Joyce. My Story as Told by Sacagawea. Little, Gary, illus. 2006. 32p. (J). (gr. 1-2). 3.95 (978-0-9711667-3-8(0)) Outlook Publishing, Inc.

Lourie, Peter. On the Trail of Sacagawea. (Illus.). 48p. (J). 2004. pap. 11.95 (978-1-59078-266-8(6)); 2003. (gr. 4-6). 18.95 (978-1-56397-840-1(7)) Boyds Mills Pr.

Marcovitz, Hal. Sacagawea: Guide for the Lewis & Clark Expedition. 2007. (Illus.). 63p. (J). pap. 12.00 (***978-1-4223-6712-4(6)***) DIANE Publishing Co.

—Sacagawea: Guide for the Lewis & Clark Expedition. 2000. (Explorers of the New World Ser.). (Illus.). (J). 63p. (gr. 4-7). pap. 25.00 (978-0-7910-6169-5(8)); 64p. (gr. 8-12). 25.00 (978-0-7910-5959-3(6)) Facts On File, Inc. (Chelsea Hse.).

—Sacagawea: Guide for the Lewis & Clark Expedition. 2001. (gr. 3-6). lib. bdg. 17.60 (978-0-613-33014-5(5)) Tandem Library Bks.

McLeese, Don. Sacagawea. 2003. (Native American Legends Ser.). (Illus.). 32p. (J). 28.50 (978-1-58952-729-4(1)) Rourke Publishing, LLC.

Milton, Joyce. Sacajawea. Hehenberger, Shelly, illus. 2001. (All Aboard Reading Ser.). 48p. (J). (gr. 1-3). pap. 3.99 (978-0-448-42539-9(4) , Grosset & Dunlap) Penguin Group (USA) Inc.

Murphy, Claire Rudolf. I Am Sacagawea, I Am York: Our Journey West with Lewis & Clark. Bond, Higgins, illus. 2005. 32p. (J). (gr. 3-5). 17.85 (978-0-8027-8921-1(8)); 16.95 (978-0-8027-8919-8(6)) Walker & Co.

Petrie, Kristin. Sacagawea. 2007. (Illus.). 32p. (J). 22.78 (978-1-59679-749-9(5)) ABDO Publishing Co.

Rausch, Monica. Sacagawea. 2006. (Illus.). 24p. (J). pap. (***978-0-8368-7692-5(X)***); lib. bdg. (***978-0-8368-7685-7(7)***) Stevens, Gareth Inc. (Weekly Reader Early Learning Library).

Sacagawea. (Photo Illustrated Biographies Ser.). 24p. (J). 6.95 (978-0-7368-3437-7(0)) Capstone Pr., Inc.

Tieck, Sarah. Sacagawea. 2007. (Buddy Book Ser.). (Illus.). 32p. (J). 22.78 (978-1-59679-789-5(4)) ABDO Publishing Co.

Wallner, Rosemary. Sacagawea 1788-1812. 2002. (American Indian Biographies Ser.). (Illus.). 32p. (J). (gr. 3-4). lib. bdg. 23.93 (978-0-7368-1213-9(X) , Blue Earth Bks.) Capstone Pr., Inc.

Witteman, Barbara. Sacagawea. 2002. (Photo-Illustrated Biographies Ser.). (Illus.). 24p. (J). (gr. 2-3). lib. bdg. 18.60 (978-0-7368-1112-5(5) , Bridgestone Bks.) Capstone Pr., Inc.

SACCO-VANZETTI CASE

Monroe, Judy. The Sacco & Vanzetti Controversial Murder Trial: A Headline Court Case. 2000. (Headline Court Cases Ser.). (Illus.). 112p. (YA). (gr. 6-12). lib. bdg. 26.60 (978-0-7660-1387-2(1)) Enslow Pubs., Inc.

SACRED ART

see Christian Art and Symbolism

SACRED MUSIC

see Church Music

SAFETY EDUCATION

see also Accidents—Prevention

AAA Staff. Here, There & Everywhere: A Guide to Fun & Safe Travel. 2004. (Illus.). 72p. (J). pap. 4.99 (978-1-56251-373-3(7)) AAA.

Action Safety: Individual Title Six-Packs. (Bookweb Ser.). 32p. (gr. 3 up). 34.00 (978-0-7635-3947-4(3)) Rigby Education.

Adult Guide to Staying Safe. 2003. (YA). (978-0-88441-663-0(1)) Girl Scouts of the USA.

Alimonti, Frederick & Tedesco, Ann. Not Everyone Is Nice: Helping Children Learn Caution with Strangers. DePrince, Erik & Volinski, Jessica, illus. 2003. (Let's Talk Ser.). 48p. (J). pap. 8.95 (978-0-88282-233-4(0)) New Horizon Pr. Pubs., Inc.

American Academy of Pediatrics Staff, contrib. by. Babysitter Lessons & Safety Training. 2nd rev. ed. 2006. (Illus.). 75p. pap. 5.95 (978-0-7637-3516-6(7)) Jones & Bartlett Pubs., Inc.

Baker, Douglas, et al, illus. Now I Know Better, Too: Kids Tell Kids about Safety. 1999. 111p. (J). (gr. k-12). pap. 7.95 (978-0-9676469-0-9(1)) Yale-New Haven Hospital.

Barr, Linda. The Water Patrol: Saving Surfers' Lives in Big Waves. 2005. (High Five Reading Ser.). (Illus.). 64p. (J). (gr. 4-5). lib. bdg. incl. audio (978-0-7368-5759-8(1)) Capstone Pr., Inc.

Barr, Linda & Rasinski, Timothy V. The Water Patrol: Saving Surfers' Lives in Big Waves. 2005. (High Five Reading Ser.). (Illus.). 48p. (J). (978-0-7368-5749-9(4)); (978-0-7368-5739-0(7)) Capstone Pr., Inc.

Barraclough, Sue. Stay Safe. 2007. (J). (***978-1-4034-9856-4(3)***); pap. (***978-1-4034-9863-2(6)***) Heinemann Library.

—Your Own Safety. 2007. (J). (***978-1-4034-9858-8(X)***); pap. (***978-1-4034-9865-6(2)***) Heinemann Library.

Bell, Nasherrall, creator. Child Safety at Home, School & Play, l.t. ed. 2004. (Illus.). 32p. (J). pap. (978-0-9729753-3-9(0)) Really Big Coloring Bks., Inc.

Benchmark Education Staff, compiled by. Safety. 2006. spiral bd. 85.00 (***978-1-4108-7046-9(4)***) Benchmark Education Co.

Berry, Joy Wilt. Being Prepared: A Safety Book About. Bartholomew, illus. rev. ed. 2000. (Living Skills Ser.: Vol. 2). 48p. (J). (gr. 1-7). pap. 4.95 (978-1-58634-099-5(9)) Goldstar Publishing, Inc.

Berry, Joy Wilt. A Book about Being Careless. 2005. (Illus.). (J). (***978-0-7172-8582-2(0)***) Scholastic, Inc.

Beylon, Cathy. Safety First Coloring Book. 2006. 32p. (J). pap. 2.95 (978-0-486-45164-0(X)) Dover Pubns., Inc.

Bowen, Mary & Ruth, Monty. Estar a Salvo Durante un Terremoto y Otras Emergencias. Jepsen, Mark, illus. Reyes, Rico J., photos by. l.t. ed. 2000. (SPA.). 96p. (J). (gr. 4-7). 28.95 (978-0-9702765-1-3(6)) Global Vision, LLC.

Bowen, Mary, et al. To Be Safe During an Earthquake & Other Emergencies: With Lucy & Her Emergency Buddies. Jepsen, Ricki & Jepsen, Mark, illus. Reyes, Rico J., photos by. deluxe l.t. ed. 2000. (To Be Safe Ser.: Vol. 1). 9696p. (J). (ps-3). 28.95 (978-0-9702765-0-6(8)) Global Vision, LLC.

Boyer, Richard G. Oddo Safety Series, 4 vols., Set. (Illus.). (J). (ps-6). lib. bdg. 44.60 (978-0-87783-170-9(X)) Oddo Publishing, Inc.

Brady, Janeen J. Safety Kids Vol. 3: Protect Their Minds. 24p. (J). (gr. k-6). pap. 4.95 (978-0-944803-82-0(2)) Brite Music, Inc.

Burstein, John. Avoiding Injuries. 2006. (Illus.). 32p. (J). lib. bdg. (***978-0-8368-7739-7(X)***) Stevens, Gareth Inc.

—Keeping Safe. 2006. (Illus.). 32p. (J). lib. bdg. (***978-0-8368-7743-4(8)***) Stevens, Gareth Inc.

Burton, Margie, et al. Playing It Safe. Evento, Susan, ed. 1998. (Early Connections Ser.). 16p. (J). (gr. k-2). pap. 4.25 (978-1-892393-72-2(7)) Benchmark Education Co.

Campbell, Maureen & Yoerg, Sharon. Bridges to Safety: A Practical Guide for Adults to Help Teens Teach Conflict Resolution & Character Skills to Children. 2004. (Illus.). 118p. per. 24.94 incl. cd-rom (978-0-9716772-0-3(4)) Six Seconds.

Canatella, Ray, et al. The Save Your Life Anti-Crime Guide for You & Your Family. Bowser, Milton, illus. l.t. ed. 2000. 72p. (YA). 10.00 (978-0-940178-96-0(6) , SYLAC) Sitare, Ltd.

Carter, K. Contra el Crimen. Palacios, Argentina, tr. 2002. (Seguridad (Safety) Ser.).Tr. of From Crime. (SPA., Illus.). 24p. mass mkt. 5.95 (978-1-58952-261-9(3) , RK31475) Rourke Publishing, LLC.

—Cuando Hay Fuego. Palacios, Argentina, tr. 2002. (Seguridad (Safety) Ser.).Tr. of With Fire. (SPA., Illus.). 24p. (J). mass mkt. 5.95 (978-1-58952-262-6(1) , RK31476) Rourke Publishing, LLC.

Caviezel, Giovanni. Fireman's Safety Hints. Mesturini, Cristina, illus. 2004. 10p. (J). bds. 10.99 (978-0-7641-5757-8(4)) Barron's Educational Series, Inc.

—Policeman's Saftey Hints. 2007. (Illus.). 10p. (J). (gr. k-2). bds. 10.99 (978-0-7641-6019-6(2)) Barron's Educational Series, Inc.

—La Seguridad Vial y Tu: Street Safety Hints, Spanish Edition. 2006. (SPA.). 10p. (J). bds. 10.99 (978-0-7641-5915-2(1)) Barron's Educational Series, Inc.

Chaiet, Donna. Safe Zone: A Kid's Guide to Personal Safety. 1998. (Illus.). (J). (978-0-606-15824-4(3)) Tandem Library Bks.

Chaiet, Donna & Russell, Francine. The Safe Zone: A Kid's Guide to Personal Safety. 1998. (Illus.). 160p. (YA). (gr. 6 up). pap. 4.95 (978-0-688-15308-3(9)) HarperCollins Pubs.

Collins, Lori & Koski, Mary B. Impatient Pamela Says: Learn How to Call 9-1-1. Brown, Dan, illus. 2000. (Impatient Pamela Ser.). 16p. (J). (ps-3). pap., wbk. ed. 4.95 (978-0-9663281-1-0(6)) Trellis Publishing, Inc.

Council Guide to Staying Safe. 2003. (YA). (978-0-88441-664-7(X)) Girl Scouts of the USA.

Croft, Jennifer. Everything You Need to Know about Guns in Your Home. 2005. (Need to Know Library). (Illus.). 64p. (YA). (gr. 7-12). lib. bdg. 25.25 (978-0-8239-3162-0(5) , NTGUHO) Rosen Publishing Group, Inc., The.

—Everything You Need to Know about Staying Safe in Cyberspace. rev. ed. 1999. (Need to Know Library). (Illus.). 64p. (YA). (gr. 7-12). lib. bdg. 25.25 (978-0-8239-2957-3(4) , NTCYBE) Rosen Publishing Group, Inc., The.

Dailey, D. C. Use Your Brains Stay Out of Gangs. Boudreau, Dawn, photos by. 1999. (Illus.). 37p. (J). (gr. 1-3). pap. 3.75 (978-1-929662-02-9(5)) Brighter Horizons Publishing.

Deboo, Ana. Safety Around the House. 2007. (J). (***978-1-4034-9739-0(7)***); pap. (***978-1-4034-9744-4(3)***) Heinemann Library.

DeGezelle, Terri. School Crossing Guards. 2001. (Community Helpers Ser.). (Illus.). 24p. (J). (gr. 1-2). lib. bdg. 18.60 (978-0-7368-0959-7(7) , Bridgestone Bks.) Capstone Pr., Inc.

Don't Panic. 2003. (Illus.). pap. 5.60 (978-0-7398-7505-6(1)) Steck-Vaughn.

Don't Talk to Strangers. 2000. (Li'l Learners Club Ser.: Vol. 3). (Illus.). (J). (ps-k). (978-1-930560-74-1(5)) International Masters Pubs., Inc.

Doudna, Kelly. I Feel Safe. l.t. ed. 1999. (How Do You Feel? Ser.). (Illus.). 24p. (J). (ps-3). lib. bdg. 19.93 (978-1-57765-191-8(X) , SandCastle) ABDO Publishing Co.

Egan, Lorraine Hopping. Lightning! Wheeler, Jody, illus. 1999. (Hello Reader! Science Ser.). 48p. (J). (gr. 2-4). pap. 3.99 (978-0-590-52285-4(X)) Scholastic, Inc.

EMP International Inc., Staff. Be Cool - Play It Safe: A Children's Safety Book. 1999. (Illus.). 24p. (J). (ps-4). wbk. ed. 2.50 (978-0-940430-98-3(3)) MEDIC FIRST AID International, Inc.

—Be Cool - Play It Safe: A Children's Safety Video & Accompanying Activity Book. 2nd ed. 1999. (Illus.). 24p. (J). (ps-4). wbk. ed. 19.95 incl. VHS (978-0-940430-99-0(1)) MEDIC FIRST AID International, Inc.

Espeland, Pamela & Verdick, Elizabeth. Helping Out & Staying Safe: The Empowerment Assets. 2004. (Adding Assets Series for Kids: Bk. 2). (Illus.). 80p. (J). (gr. 3-7). pap. 9.95 (978-1-57542-161-2(5)) Free Spirit Publishing, Inc.

Feldman, Heather. My School Bus: A Book about School Bus Safety. 2000. (PowerKids Readers Ser.). (Illus.). 24p. (J). (gr. 1). lib. bdg. 16.00 (978-0-8239-5523-7(0) , PKMYSC, PowerKids Pr.) Rosen Publishing Group, Inc., The.

First Aid & Home Safety. (YA). (gr. 6-12). pap. 10.95 (978-0-8224-4366-7(X)) Globe Fearon Educational Publishing.

Fisher-Price Rescue Heroes Sticker Activity Books. 2004. (J). act. bk. ed. (978-0-7666-0821-4(2) , 69650); act. bk. ed. (978-0-7666-0822-1(0) , 69650) Modern Publishing.

Gordon, Wendy. I'm Safe! at the Mall. Gordon, Paul, illus. 1998. 24p. (J). (ps-3). pap., act. bk. ed. 2.95 (978-1-891596-01-8(2)) Backyard Pub. Co., Inc.

—I'm Safe! in the Car. Gordon, Paul, illus. 2001. (I'm Safe! Ser.). 24p. (J). (ps-2). pap. 6.95 (978-1-891596-14-8(4)) BackYard Bks.

—I'm Safe! In the Car. Gordon, Paul, illus. 2001. (I'm Safe! Ser.). 24p. (J). (ps-2). pap., act. bk. ed. 2.95 (978-1-891596-15-5(2)) BackYard Bks.

Grossblatt, Ben. Keep Out! Door Alarm: Build Your Own Key-Card Security System! 2004. (Illus.). 24p. (J). (978-0-439-66835-4(2)) Scholastic, Inc.

Hardy, Caroline, et al. Busy Places: A Child Safety Book. 2006. (Through the Peephole Ser.). (Illus.). 48p. 9.95 (978-1-84560-015-0(0)) Mercury Bks. Ltd. GBR. *Dist:* International Publishers Marketing.

Holt, Rinehart and Winston Staff. Decisions for Health Blue, Chptr. 13: Preventing Abuse. 4th ed. 2004. pap. 11.20 (978-0-03-068047-2(6)) Holt, Rinehart & Winston.

—Decisions for Health Blue, Chptr. 19: Safety. 4th ed. 2004. pap. 11.20 (978-0-03-068054-0(9)) Holt, Rinehart & Winston.

—Decisions for Health Green Chptr. 15: Health & Safety. 4th ed. 2004. pap. 11.20 (978-0-03-068037-3(9)) Holt, Rinehart & Winston.

—Decisions for Health Red Chptr. 17: Personal Safety. 4th ed. 2004. pap. 11.20 (978-0-03-068044-1(1)) Holt, Rinehart & Winston.

James, Cindy. Ten Easy Tips for Staying Safe. 2002. (Reading Room Collection). (Illus.). 24p. (J). pap. (978-0-8239-8158-8(4)); lib. bdg. 18.75 (978-0-8239-3721-9(6)) Rosen Publishing Group, Inc., The.

Joyce, Julie. What Should You Do? Safety Tips for Kids. 2004. (J). 3.95 (978-0-9656808-4-4(3) , KidBk-1) Dynamic Publishing Co., Inc.

Keep Books at The Ohio State University Staff. Health & Safety 1. ed. 2006. (Illus.). 8p. (J). pap. (978-1-893986-26-8(8)) Keep Bks.

—Health & Safety 2, Set. 2006. (J). pap. (978-1-893986-27-5(6)) Keep Bks.

Krauss, Ronnie. Safety & Direction. 1998. (Captain Kangaroo Ser.). 16p. (J). 0.35 (978-0-06-107143-0(9)) HarperCollins Pubs.

—Safety Rules. 2000. (Captain Kangaroo Ser.). 20p. (J). (gr. k-1). pap. 8.99 (978-0-06-107159-1(5) , Harper Entertainment) HarperCollins Pubs.

Kreiner, Anna. Everything You Need to Know about School Violence. rev. ed. 2000. (Need to Know Library). (Illus.). 64p. (YA). (gr. 4-6). lib. bdg. 25.25 (978-0-8239-3304-4(0) , NTSCVI) Rosen Publishing Group, Inc., The.

LaBerge, Margaret M. Sara Safety, School Safety Pamphlet. Lucas, Stacey L. et al, illus. 2004. (J). pap. (978-0-9755561-0-8(X)) Reading Resc.

Lawler, Jennifer. Cyberdanger & Internet Safety. 2000. (Hot Issues Ser.). (Illus.). 64p. (YA). (gr. 6-12). lib. bdg. 27.93 (978-0-7660-1368-1(5)) Enslow Pubs., Inc.

Leaney, Cindy. Home Sweet Home: Safety at Home. Wilks, Peter, illus. 2003. (Hero Club Safety Ser.). 32p. (J). 28.50 (978-1-58952-740-9(2)) Rourke Publishing, LLC.

—Long Walk to School: Safety Outdoors. Wilks, Peter, illus. 2003. (Hero Club Safety Ser.). 32p. (J). 28.50 (978-1-58952-745-4(3)) Rourke Publishing, LLC.

—Wrong Stop: Safety from Crime. Wilks, Peter, illus. 2003. (Hero Club Safety Ser.). 32p. (J). 28.50 (978-1-58952-742-3(9)) Rourke Publishing, LLC.

S

Leonard, Shirley A. The Safe School Bus. Leonard, Shirley A., illus. l.t. ed. 2004. (Illus.). 30p. (J). (ps-7). pap. 14.95 (978-1-59453-019-7(X) , 1582) Airleaf Publishing & Bookselling.

Levete, Sarah. Keeping Safe. 2006. (Illus.). 32p. (J). (978-1-59604-088-5(2) , 1268913) Stargazer Bks.

Llewelyn, Clair. Stay Safe. 2006. (Illus.). 24p. (J). lib. bdg. 16.95 (978-1-59566-195-1(6)) QEB Publishing Inc.

MacGregor, Cynthia. Listen to Your Instincts. 1999. (Abduction Prevention Library). (Illus.). 24p. (J). (gr. 3). lib. bdg. 18.75 (978-0-8239-5249-6(5) , PowerKids Pr.) Rosen Publishing Group, Inc., The.

—Staying Safe at Home & On-Line. 1999. (Abduction Prevention Library). (Illus.). 24p. (J). (gr. 3). lib. bdg. 18.75 (978-0-8239-5251-9(7) , PowerKids Pr.) Rosen Publishing Group, Inc., The.

—Staying Safe by Saying No. 1999. (Abduction Prevention Library). (Illus.). 24p. (J). (gr. 3). lib. bdg. 18.75 (978-0-8239-5252-6(5) , PowerKids Pr.) Rosen Publishing Group, Inc., The.

—Stranger Danger. 1999. (Abduction Prevention Library). (Illus.). 24p. (J). (gr. 3). lib. bdg. 18.75 (978-0-8239-5247-2(9) , PowerKids Pr.) Rosen Publishing Group, Inc., The.

—Ten Steps to Staying Safe. 1999. (Abduction Prevention Library). (Illus.). 24p. (J). (gr. 3). lib. bdg. 18.75 (978-0-8239-5248-9(7) , PowerKids Pr.) Rosen Publishing Group, Inc., The.

—What to Do If You Get Lost. 1999. (Abduction Prevention Library). (Illus.). 24p. (J). (gr. 3). lib. bdg. 18.75 (978-0-8239-5250-2(9) , PowerKids Pr.) Rosen Publishing Group, Inc., The.

Mattern, Joanne. Safety at Home. 1999. (Safety First Ser.). (Illus.). 24p. (J). (gr. k-6). lib. bdg. 21.35 (978-1-57765-071-3(9) , Checkerboard Library) ABDO Publishing Co.

—Safety at School. 1999. (Safety First Ser.). (Illus.). 24p. (J). (gr. k-6). lib. bdg. 21.35 (978-1-57765-070-6(0) , Checkerboard Library) ABDO Publishing Co.

—Safety in Public Places. 1999. (Safety First Ser.). (Illus.). 24p. (J). (gr. k-6). lib. bdg. 21.35 (978-1-57765-074-4(3) , Checkerboard Library) ABDO Publishing Co.

—Safety on the Go. 1999. (Safety First Ser.). (Illus.). 24p. (J). (gr. k-6). lib. bdg. 21.35 (978-1-57765-075-1(1) , Checkerboard Library) ABDO Publishing Co.

—Safety on Your Bicycle. 1999. (Safety First Ser.). (Illus.). 24p. (J). (gr. k-6). lib. bdg. 21.35 (978-1-57765-073-7(5) , Checkerboard Library) ABDO Publishing Co.

—Staying Safe at Home. 2006. (Illus.). 24p. (J). pap. (*978-0-8368-7798-4(5)); (ENG & SPA., pap. (*978-0-8368-8063-2(3)); lib. bdg. (*978-0-8368-7791-5(8)); (ENG & SPA., lib. bdg. (*978-0-8368-8056-4(0)) Stevens, Gareth Inc. (Weekly Reader Early Learning Library).

—Staying Safe at School. 2006. (J). (ENG & SPA.). pap. (*978-0-8368-8064-9(1)); (ENG & SPA.). lib. bdg. (*978-0-8368-8057-1(9)); (Illus.). 24p. pap. (*978-0-8368-7799-1(3)); (Illus.). 24p. lib. bdg. (*978-0-8368-7792-2(6)) Stevens, Gareth Inc. (Weekly Reader Early Learning Library).

—Staying Safe in the Car. 2006. (J). (ENG & SPA.). pap. (*978-0-8368-8065-6(X)); (ENG & SPA.). lib. bdg. (*978-0-8368-8058-8(7)); (Illus.). 24p. pap. (*978-0-8368-7800-4(0)); (Illus.). 24p. lib. bdg. (*978-0-8368-7793-9(4)) Stevens, Gareth Inc. (Weekly Reader Early Learning Library).

—Staying Safe on My Bike. 2006. (Illus.). 24p. (J). pap. (*978-0-8368-7801-1(9)); lib. bdg. (*978-0-8368-7794-6(2)) Stevens, Gareth Inc. (Weekly Reader Early Learning Library).

—Staying Safe on My Bike: La Seguridad en Mi Bicicleta. 2006. (Illus.). 24p. pap. (*978-0-8368-8066-3(8)); lib. bdg. (*978-0-8368-8059-5(5)) Stevens, Gareth Inc. (Weekly Reader Early Learning Library).

—Staying Safe on the School Bus. 2006. (Illus.). 24p. pap. (*978-0-8368-7802-8(7)); lib. bdg. (*978-0-8368-7795-3(0)) Stevens, Gareth Inc. (Weekly Reader Early Learning Library).

—Staying Safe on the School Bus: La Seguridad en el Autobs Escolar. 2006. (J). pap. (*978-0-8368-8067-0(6)); lib. bdg. (*978-0-8368-8060-1(9)) Stevens, Gareth Inc. (Weekly Reader Early Learning Library).

—Staying Safe on the Street. 2006. (Illus.). 24p. (J). pap. (*978-0-8368-7803-5(5)); (SPA & ENG., pap. (*978-0-8368-8068-7(4)); lib. bdg. (*978-0-8368-7796-0(9)); (SPA & ENG., lib. bdg. (*978-0-8368-8061-8(7)) Stevens, Gareth Inc. (Weekly Reader Early Learning Library).

McCauley, John. Harley Teaches. McCauley, John, illus. 1998. (Illus.). 34p. (J). (gr. k-6). 12.95 (978-0-9664005-7-1(7)) American Health Pr.

McEwen, Rebecca. Safety First. 2004. (Spyglass Books). (Illus.). 24p. (J). (gr. 1 up). lib. bdg. 18.60 (978-0-7565-0626-1(3)) Compass Point Bks.

McKay, Sindy. We Both Read-Being Safe. Photodisc-Getty Staff, Images, photos by. 2003. (We Both Read Ser.). (Illus.). 44p. (J). (gr. 1-2). 7.99 (978-1-891327-51-3(8)); pap. 3.99 (978-1-891327-52-0(6)) Treasure Bay, Inc.

Mehlman, Barbara. Babysitting Safety: Preventing Accidents & Injuries. 2007. (Snap Books). (Illus.). 32p. (J). 25.26 (978-0-7368-6465-7(2)) Capstone Pr., Inc.

Meiners, Cheri J. Be Careful & Stay Safe. 2006. (Learning to Get along(R) Ser.). (Illus.). 40p. (J). pap. 10.95 (978-1-57542-211-4(5)) Free Spirit Publishing, Inc.

Mintzer, Richard. The National Transportation Safety Board. 2002. (Your Government Ser.). (Illus.). 64p. (J). 25.00 (978-0-7910-6794-9(7) , Chelsea Hse.) Facts On File, Inc.

Multimedia Electrical Safety. (Shop Safety Ser.). (YA). cd-rom 69.95 (978-0-7365-9987-0(8)) Films Media Group.

Multimedia Welding Safety. (Shop Safety Ser.). (YA). cd-rom 69.95 (978-0-7365-9986-3(X)); cd-rom 69.95 (978-0-7365-9988-7(6)) Films Media Group.

Naik, Anita. Wise Guides: Personal Safety. 2005. (Illus.). (YA). pap. 12.00 (978-0-340-88436-2(3) , Hodder & Stoughton) Hodder General Publishing Division GBR. *Dist:* Trafalgar Square Publishing.

National Crime Prevention Council Staff. McGruff Wants You to Help Take a Bite Out of Crime. 1999. (Illus.). 16p. (J). (gr. k-12). pap. (978-0-934513-87-6(2)) National Crime Prevention Council.

Nelson, Robin. Staying Safe in Emergencies. 2006. (Pull Ahead Books). (Illus.). 32p. (J). 22.60 (978-0-8225-3391-7(X) , Lerner Pubns.) Lerner Publishing Group.

Newsom, Tony. Student Safety Tips: 40 that Every 1st - 2nd Grader Must Know! 2007. pap. 6.99 (978-0-9787143-1-4(8)); pap. 6.99 (*978-0-9787143-4-5(2)) Carrington Bks.

—Student Safety Tips: 45 that Every 3rd - 5th Grader Must Know! 2007. pap. 6.99 (978-0-9787143-2-1(6)); pap. 6.99 (*978-0-9787143-5-2(0)) Carrington Bks.

No Way! A Book about Staying Safe for Girls Ages 4-6. 2003. (YA). (978-0-88441-660-9(7)) Girl Scouts of the USA.

Obert, Lois. Help! Willie's Choking! 2006. (J). 7.95 (*978-1-57166-370-2(3)) Quixote Pr.

Olson, Karen W. Living Safe, Playing Safe. Hamelin, Marie-Micheline, illus. 2006. 20p. (J). pap. 10.95 (978-1-894778-33-6(2)) Theytus Bks., Ltd. CAN. *Dist:* Orca Bk. Pubs. USA.

O'Neal-Evans, Regina. I Won't Let it Happen to Me! 2001. (Illus.). 48p. (J). (ps-5). pap. 8.95 (978-0-615-11950-2(6)) Child Safety Publishing.

Oregon Center for Applied Science, creator. Bike Smart. 2006. (J). cd-rom 19.95 (*978-1-933898-09-4(7)) Oregon Ctr. for Applied Science, Inc.

—Walk Smart: Children's Pedestrian Safety Program. 2005. (J). cd-rom 19.95 (*978-1-933898-10-0(0)) Oregon Ctr. for Applied Science, Inc.

Pancella, Peggy. Fire Safety. 2004. (Illus.). 32p. (J). pap. 6.95 (978-1-4034-4940-5(6)) Heinemann Library.

—Stranger Danger. 2004. (Illus.). 32p. (J). pap. 6.95 (978-1-4034-4944-3(9)); lib. bdg. (978-1-4034-4935-1(X)) Heinemann Library.

—Your Own Safety. 2004. (Heinemann First Library). (Illus.). 32p. (J). 6.95 (978-1-4034-4938-2(4)); lib. bdg. 22.79 (978-1-4034-4929-0(5)) Heinemann Library.

Parker, Helen. Lift Stick & Learn: Emergency. 2006. (Illus.). 12p. (J). (ps-k). 4.95 (978-1-84610-282-0(0)) Make Believe Ideas GBR. *Dist:* Ingram Pub. Services.

Personal Safety Awareness (AVA) 2001. (YA). pap. 6.00 (978-1-57078-022-6(6) , CEV00022); pap. 8.00 (978-1-57078-023-3(4) , CEV00023) C E V Multimedia, Ltd.

Phillips, Robert. Security Officer's Handbook. 2005. (Illus.). 50p. (J). (ps-ps). per. 10.95 (978-1-56167-900-3(3)) American Literary Pr.

Practice Power Practice Pal Safety for Children. 1999. (Illus.). 24p. (J). (ps-6). spiral bd., wbk. ed. (978-1-930355-11-8(4)) Greenbrier/Scentex.

Raatma, Lucia. Home Safety. 2003. (Living Well). (Illus.). 32p. (J). (gr. 2-6). 27.07 (978-1-59296-088-0(X)) Child's World, Inc.

—Safety Around Strangers. 1998. (Safety First! Ser.). (Illus.). 24p. (J). (gr. 1-2). lib. bdg. 18.60 (978-0-7368-0060-0(3) , Bridgestone Bks.) Capstone Pr., Inc.

—Safety Around Strangers. 2004. (Living Well Ser.). 32p. (J). (gr. 2-6). 27.07 (978-1-59296-244-0(0)) Child's World, Inc.

—Safety at Home. 1998. (Safety First! Ser.). (Illus.). 24p. (J). (gr. 1-2). lib. bdg. 18.60 (978-0-7368-0061-7(1) , Bridgestone Bks.) Capstone Pr., Inc.

—Safety in Public Places. 2004. (Living Well Ser.). 32p. (J). (gr. 2-6). 27.07 (978-1-59296-241-9(6)) Child's World, Inc.

—Safety in Your Neighborhood. 2004. (Living Well Ser.). 32p. (J). (gr. 2-6). 27.07 (978-1-59296-240-2(8)) Child's World, Inc.

—Safety on the Playground. 1998. (Safety First! Ser.). (Illus.). 24p. (J). (gr. 1-2). lib. bdg. 18.60 (978-0-7368-0062-4(X) , Bridgestone Bks.) Capstone Pr., Inc.

—Safety on the Playground & Outdoors. 2004. (Living Well Ser.). 32p. (J). (gr. 2-6). 27.07 (978-1-59296-243-3(2)) Child's World, Inc.

—Safety on the School Bus. 1998. (Safety First! Ser.). (Illus.). 24p. (J). (gr. 1-2). lib. bdg. 18.60 (978-0-7368-0063-1(8) , Bridgestone Bks.) Capstone Pr., Inc.

Raintree Steck-Vaughn Staff. Safety at Home. 2000. (Read All about It Ser.). (Illus.). (J). (ps-3). pap. 4.95 (978-0-8114-3723-3(X)) Steck-Vaughn.

Random House Disney Staff & Angelilli, Chris. Don't Go Bump in the Night! Halloween Safety. Cash, Megan & Emslie, Peter, illus. 2005. 16p. (J). (ps-k). 6.99 (978-0-7364-2232-1(3) , RH/Disney) Random Hse. Children's Bks.

Raymer, Dottie. Staying Home Alone: A Girl's Guide to Staying Safe & Having Fun. Scheuer, Lauren, illus. 2002. (American Girl Library). 72p. (J). pap. 7.95 (978-1-58485-506-4(1)) American Girl Publishing, Inc.

Richardson, Sarah J. What If? The What Ifs of Childhood Safety, 1 bk. 2004. 120p. (J). per. 9.99 (978-0-9752982-0-6(8)) 4 Childrens Sake Pubns.

Riggs, Sandy. Safe Streets. 2006. (Reader's Clubhouse Set B Ser.). (Illus.). 24p. (J). pap. 3.99 (978-0-7641-3300-8(4)) Barron's Educational Series, Inc.

Rivera, Sheila. Emergencies. 2006. (First Step Nonfiction Ser.). (J). pap. (978-0-8225-6824-7(1)) Lerner Publishing Group.

—Home Safety. 2006. (First Step Nonfiction Ser.). (J). pap. (978-0-8225-6823-0(3)) Lerner Publishing Group.

—School Safety. 2006. (First Step Nonfiction Ser.). (J). pap. (978-0-8225-6822-3(5)) Lerner Publishing Group.

Roberts, Robin. Sports Injuries: How to Stay Safe & Keep on Playing. 2001. (Illus.). 48p. (gr. 4-8). lib. bdg. 23.90 (978-0-7613-2116-3(0) , Millbrook Pr.) Lerner Publishing Group.

Rothman, Kevin F. Coping with Dangers on the Internet. 2005. (Coping Ser.). (Illus.). 192p. (YA). (gr. 7-12). lib. bdg. 26.50 (978-0-8239-3201-6(X)) Rosen Publishing Group, Inc., The.

Royston, Angela, contrib. by. Safety First. 2000. (Illus.). 32p. (J). (gr. k-2). lib. bdg. 21.36 (978-1-57572-984-8(9)) Heinemann Library.

Safety: If You Feel Danger. 2002. (J). (gr. k-3). 69.95 (978-1-55942-185-0(1) , 9232V9) Marsh Media.

Safety: Out of the Danger Zone. 2002. (J). (gr. 4-6). 69.95 (978-1-55942-186-7(X) , 9233V9) Marsh Media.

Safety Always Matters (SAM), Vol. II. 12p. (J). (gr. k-3). 29.50 (978-1-883994-05-1(5)); 29.50 (978-1-883994-04-4(7)) Safety Always Matters, Inc.

Savage, Sharon. How to Dial 9-1-1. 2000. (Illus.). 12p. (J). (ps-5). pap. 10.00 incl. cd-rom (978-0-9650312-6-4(8)) Cosmo Starr Bks.

Schulson, Rachel. Guns: What You Should Know. 1999. (Illus.). (J). (978-0-606-18774-9(X)) Tandem Library Bks.

—Guns: What You Should Know. Jones, Mary, illus. 2004. (Concept Book Ser.). 24p. (J). (gr. k-5). pap. 5.95 (978-0-8075-3094-8(8)) Whitman, Albert & Co.

Schulz, Kathy. Always Be Safe. Potter, Katherine, illus. 2003. (Rookie Reader Skill Set Ser.). (J). (gr. k-2). pap. 4.95 (978-0-516-26965-8(3)); 32p. 19.50 (978-0-516-22594-4(4)) Scholastic Library Publishing. (Children's Pr.).

—Always Be Safe. 2003. (gr. k-3). lib. bdg. 12.95 (978-0-613-67595-6(9)) Tandem Library Bks.

La Seguridad. 2006. (Dora The Explorer Ser.). (SPA & ENG., Illus.). 24p. (J). wbk. ed. 4.99 (*978-1-59545-063-0(7)) Learning Horizons, Inc.

Sherman, Joanne. Because It's My Body. Gurney, John Steven, illus. 2002. (Keep 'Em Safe Ser.). 32p. (J). (ps-2). per. 14.95 (978-0-9711735-0-7(8)) S.A.F.E. for Children Publishing, LLC.

Shi, Sharon. Calling 911. Montgomery, Tim, illus. 2000. 24p. (J). (gr. k-3). mass mkt. 4.99 (978-0-9702195-2-7(0) , B013) Tattoo Manufacturing.

Shop Safety. (Shop Safety Ser.). (YA). cd-rom 229.95 (978-0-7365-9985-6(1)); cd-rom 229.95 (978-0-7365-9984-9(3)) Films Media Group.

Silverstein, Alvin. Staying Safe. 2000. (My Health Ser.). (Illus.). (J). (978-0-606-20925-0(5)) Tandem Library Bks.

Simms, Mattie. The "Q" Kids: A Disaster Safety Workbook for Children of All Ages. 1998. 64p. (J). (gr. 1-6). pap. 7.00 (978-0-8059-4307-8(2)) Dorrance Publishing Co., Inc.

Simms, Mattie. The (Q) Kids Help Center. 2006. per. 9.99 (*978-0-9772077-0-1(6)) Kanlearn, Inc.

Smart Kids Publishing Staff. Play It Safe. (Illus.). 14p. (J). bds. 12.95 (978-0-8249-6593-8(0)) Ideals Pubns.

Smith, Kathy. Be Safe on the Bus. 2002. (PowerPhonics Ser.). (Illus.). 23p. (J). lib. bdg. 4.40 (978-0-8239-8245-5(9)) Rosen Publishing Group, Inc., The.

—Be Safe on the Bus: Learning the B Sound. 2002. (Power-Phonics Ser.). (Illus.). 24p. (J). (gr. 1). lib. bdg. 18.50 (978-0-8239-5900-6(7) , PowerKids Pr.) Rosen Publishing Group, Inc., The.

Spikes, James L. Taffey Pop Kids Presents the Adventures of Lemmon Head & Mudd Duck: What to Do if Someone Tries to Grab YOU!!! Spikes, Leon, Jr., illus. 2007. 32p. (J). 14.95 (978-0-9771438-0-1(5)) Taffey Pop Kids Publishing.

Stowell, Jo & Dietzel, Mary. My Very Own Book about Me! Personal Safety Book. Gleason, Barbara Bryan, illus. 1999. 64p. (J). (gr. 3-7). wbk. ed. 15.25 (978-1-930489-00-4(5)) Act For Kids.

Thomas, Pat. I Can Be Safe: A First Look at Safety. Harker, Lesley, illus. 2003. (First Look at Bks.). 32p. (J). pap. 6.95 (978-0-7641-2460-0(9)) Barron's Educational Series, Inc.

Thompson, Gary. What Every Teen Should Know Before Getting Behind the Wheel Alone: A Guide to Increasing Your Child's Safety While Reducing Your Auto Repair Expenses. 2004. 131p. (YA). per. 9.95 (978-0-9749763-1-0(8)) Guiding Horizons.

Unger, Karen. Don't Go There! Staying Safe for Girls Ages 6-8. 2003. (Illus.). 48p. (J). (978-0-88441-661-6(5)) Girl Scouts of the USA.

—I Don't Think So! A Book about Staying Safe for Girls Ages 8-11. 2003. (Illus.). 41p. (J). (978-0-88441-662-3(3)) Girl Scouts of the USA.

Watch out for Banana Peels. 2007. 24p. pap. 3.50 (*978-1-4037-3613-0(8)) Dalmatian Pr.

Weiner, Florence. Little Kid's Safety Center. 1998. (Illus.). 25p. (Orig.). (J). (ps-1). pap. 19.95 (978-1-888241-04-4(7)) Safety Ctr.

Wells, Donna K. & Morris, Bruce C. Live Aware, Not in Fear: The 411 after 9-11, A Book for Teens. 2002. (Illus.). 120p. pap. 9.95 (978-0-7573-0013-4(8)) Health Communications, Inc.

Wood, Ira. How to Stay Safe at Home & On-Line. 2002. (Illus.). 24p. (J). pap. (978-0-8239-8159-5(2)); lib. bdg. 18.75 (978-0-8239-3722-6(4)) Rosen Publishing Group, Inc., The.

SAFETY EDUCATION—FICTION

Bernardini, Robert. Safety First Please & It Won't Make You Sneeze. Donato, Janice, illus. l.t. ed. 2001. 32p. (J). (ps-6). per. 14.95 (978-0-9703269-0-4(4) , 010) P R I Publishing.

Bernstein, Susan H. N. E. Pominonous Epstein Minds His Mind. (E. Pominonous Epstein Ser.). 18p. (J). (ps-3). pap. 8.95 (978-0-9706596-0-6(1)) Bernstein, Susan.

Bike Safe! Life Safety Coloring/Activity Book. 2007. (Illus.). (J). (*978-1-933934-31-0(X)) Educational Adventures.

Blackaby, Susan. Todd's Fire Drill. Greathouse, Justin, illus. 2007. (J). lib. bdg. (*978-1-4048-2332-7(8)) Picture Window Bks.

Blazin' Hot: Coloring/Activity Book (English) 2005. (Illus.). (J). (978-0-9770455-0-1(1)) Educational Adventures.

Blazin' Hot: Coloring/Activity Book (English) Incl. Stickers. 2007. (J). (*978-1-933934-51-8(4)) Educational Adventures.

Blazin' Hot: Picture Book (English) NL 9x9 with Snipe. 2007. (J). (*978-1-933934-46-4(8)) Educational Adventures.

Bourgeois, Paulette & Clark, Brenda. Franklin's Bicycle Helmet. 2000. (Franklin TV StoryBks.). (Illus.). 32p. (J). (gr. k-3). (978-1-55074-730-0(4)); (978-1-55074-728-7(2)) Kids Can Pr., Ltd.

Calmenson, Stephanie. May I Pet Your Dog? The How-To Guide for Kids Meeting Dogs (and Dogs Meeting Kids) Ormerod, Jan, illus. 2007. 32p. (J). (*978-1-4287-3952-9(1) , Clarion Bks.) Houghton Mifflin Co. Trade & Reference Div.

Camping Caper: Coloring/Activity Book (English) incl. Stickers. 2007. (Illus.). (J). (*978-1-933934-65-5(4)) Educational Adventures.

Camping Caper: Picture Book (English) 8x8. 2007. (Illus.). (J). (*978-1-933934-64-8(6)) Educational Adventures.

Christopher, Matt. Into the Danger Zone. Koelsch, Michael, illus. 6th ed. 2004. (Extreme Team Ser.: Vol. 6). 64p. (J). (gr. 2-4). pap. 4.99 (978-0-316-76267-0(9) , Tingley, Megan Bks.) Little, Brown Bks. for Young Readers.

Colgan, Timothy. Rory Stays Safe. Angelo, Michael, photos by. 1999. (Staying Safe Stories Ser.). (Illus.). 35p. (J). pap. 19.95 (978-0-9675587-0-7(0)) TJS Security Services.

Cool by the Pool: Coloring / Activity Book incl Snipe. 2007. (Illus.). (J). (*978-0-9770455-8-7(7)) Educational Adventures.

Cool by the Pool: Picture Book (English) 8x8. 2007. (J). (*978-1-933934-37-2(9)) Educational Adventures.

Cool by the Pool: Picture Book (English) NL 9x9 with Snipe. 2007. (J). (*978-1-933934-47-1(6)) Educational Adventures.

Coulton, Mia. Danny & Bee's Safety Rules. Coulton, Mia, photos by. 2002. (J). (978-0-9720295-1-3(6)) Maryruth Bks., Inc.

Crowley, Kerry. The Smart Thing to Do. 2006. 60p. pap. 7.61 (978-1-4116-7126-3(0)) Lulu.com.

Cuyler, Margery. Please Play Safe! Penguin's Guide to Playground Safety. Hillenbrand, Will, illus. 2006. 32p. (J). pap. 15.99 (978-0-439-52832-0(1) , Scholastic Pr.) Scholastic, Inc.

Danger Alert: Coloring/Activity Book (English) Incl. Stickers. 2007. (J). (*978-1-933934-54-9(9)) Educational Adventures.

Danger Alert: Picture Book (English) 8x8. 2007. (J). (*978-1-933934-39-6(5)) Educational Adventures.

Danger Alert: Picture Book (English) 9x9 with Snipe. 2007. (J). (*978-1-933934-49-5(2)) Educational Adventures.

Danger Ranger Ready! Coloring/Activity Book (English) 2006. (Illus.). (J). (*978-1-933934-22-8(0)) Educational Adventures.

Deem, Saitofi Anne. Myrtle Learns about Dangerous Situations. 1998. (Teachable Moments Ser.). (Illus.). 8p. (J). (ps-3). pap. 7.95 (978-1-930694-03-3(2)) Myrtle Learns.

—Myrtle Learns about Safety. 1998. (Teachable Moments Ser.). (Illus.). 8p. (J). (ps-3). pap. 7.95 (978-1-930694-13-2(X)) Myrtle Learns.

Duracell and the National Center for Missing & Exploited Children (NCMEC), creator. The Great Tomato Adventure: A Story about Smart Safety Choices. 2007. 0.00 (*978-0-9795307-0-8(9)) Duracell & the National Ctr. for Missing & Exploited Children (NCMEC).

Educational Adventures, creator. Cool by the Pool: Coloring/Activity Book (Spanish) w/ Snipe. 2007. (Illus.). (J). per. (*978-1-933934-73-0(5)) Educational Adventures.

—Cool by the Pool: Picture Book (Spanish) 9x9. 2007. (Illus.). (J). per. (*978-1-933934-72-3(7)) Educational Adventures.

—Danger Alert: Coloring/Activity Book (Spanish) w/ Snipe. 2006. (Illus.). (J). (*978-1-933934-06-8(9)) Educational Adventures.

—Danger Alert: Picture Book (Spanish) 9x9. 2006. (Illus.). (J). (*978-1-933934-04-4(2)) Educational Adventures.

—Danger Ranger Ready: Coloring/Activity Book (Spanish) w/ Snipe. 2007. (Illus.). (J). (*978-1-933934-74-7(3)) Educational Adventures.

—Free Wheelin' Coloring/Activity Book (English) w/ Snipe. 2007. (J). (*978-1-933934-52-5(2)) Educational Adventures.

—Free Wheelin' Picture Book (Spanish) w/ Snipe. 2006. (Illus.). (J). (*978-0-9770455-6-3(0)) Educational Adventures.

—It's Smart to be Safe! Coloring/Activity Book (Spanish) w/ Snipe. 2007. (Illus.). (J). (*978-1-933934-76-1(X)) Educational Adventures.

—Poison Patrol: Coloring/Activity Book (Spanish) w/ Snipe. 2006. (Illus.). (J). (*978-1-933934-02-0(6)) Educational Adventures.

—Poison Patrol: Picture Book (Spanish) 9x9. 2006. (Illus.). (J). (*978-1-933934-00-6(X)) Educational Adventures.

—Street Smarts: Coloring/Activity Book (Spanish) w/ Snipe. 2006. (Illus.). (J). (*978-1-933934-19-8(0)) Educational Adventures.

—Street Smarts: Picture Book (Spanish) 9x9. 2007. (Illus.). (J). per. (*978-1-933934-77-8(8)) Educational Adventures.

—That's a Danger Proof Plan! Coloring/Activity Book (Spanish) w/ Snipe. 2007. (Illus.). (J). (*978-1-933934-75-4(1)) Educational Adventures.

—Think Safe! Play Safe! Be Safe! Coloring/Activity Book (Spanish) w/ Snipe. 2006. (Illus.). (J). (*978-1-933934-32-7(8)) Educational Adventures.

Fire Safe! Life Safety Coloring/Activity Book. 2007. (Illus.). (J). ***978-1-933934-23-5(9))** Educational Adventures.

Free Wheelin' Picture Book (English) NL 9x9 with Snipe. 2007. (J). ***978-1-933934-48-8(4))** Educational Adventures.

Gordon, Wendy. I'm Safe! from Monsters. 1999. 24p. (ps-3). pap., act. bk. ed. 2.95 (978-1-891596-03-2(9)) Backyard Pub. Co., Inc.

—I'm Safe! in the Water. 1999. 24p. (J). (ps-3). pap., act. bk. ed. 2.95 (978-1-891596-07-0(1)) Backyard Pub. Co., Inc.

—I'm Safe! on My Bike. 1999. 24p. (J). (ps-3). pap., act. bk. ed. 2.49 (978-1-891596-11-7(X)) Backyard Pub. Co., Inc.

—I'm Safe! with the New Baby. 1999. 24p. (ps-3). pap., act. bk. ed. 2.49 (978-1-891596-05-6(5)) Backyard Pub. Co., Inc.

Hallinan, P. K. Let's Be Safe. 2007. 32p. (J). 8.99 ***978-0-8249-5529-8(3)**, Candy Cane Pr.) Ideals Pubns.

Hassett, John & Hassett, Ann. The Nine Lives of Dudley Dog. 2008. 32p. (J). (gr. k-3). 16.00 ***978-0-618-81153-3(2))** Houghton Mifflin Co.

Hurricane Harbor: Coloring/Activity Book incl Stickers. 2007. (Illus.). (J). ***978-1-933934-69-3(7))** Educational Adventures.

Hurricane Harbor: Picture Book (English) 8x8. 2007. (Illus.). (J). ***978-1-933934-68-6(9))** Educational Adventures.

It's Smart to be Safe! 2006. (Illus.). (J). ***978-1-933934-27-3(1))** Educational Adventures.

Januska, Regina. Deputy Dan Teaches... Stranger Danger. 2000. (Illus.). 32p. (J). (ps-1). pap. 9.95 (978-0-9706975-0-9(3)) Shiny Star Productions.

Kevi, M. Don't Talk to Strangers. JibJab Media Staff, illus. 2003. (Hipkidhop Ser.). 32p. (J). (gr. 1-4). pap. 13.95 (978-0-439-31385-8(6), Cartwheel Bks.) Scholastic, Inc.

Mangal, Roshni. The Stray Bullet. Hammond, Amanda, illus. 1999. 48p. (J). (ps-3). pap. 17.95 (978-0-9644695-3-2(7)) Image Maker Publishing Co., The.

Marcotte, David A. Be Wary of Strangers. 2005. (ENG., Illus.). 36p. per. 14.95 (978-1-932672-47-3(8)) Outskirts Press, Inc.

Mayer, Mercer. Play It Safe, Vol. 2. 2003. (Little Critter Ser.). (Illus.). 24p. (J). (gr. k-1). pap. 3.95 (978-1-57768-586-9(5)) School Specialty Publishing.

Mayo, Margaret. Emergency! Ayliffe, Alex, illus. 2003. 32p. (J). (ps-1). 14.95 (978-0-87614-922-5(0), Carolrhoda Bks.) Lerner Publishing Group.

Metzger, Steve. It's Apple Picking Day! Wilhelm, Hans, illus. 1998. (Dinofours Ser.: No. 8). (J). (ps-1). 3.25 (978-0-590-03549-1(5)) Scholastic, Inc.

Nelson, Tujuana. Billy's Story. 2000. 16p. (J). (gr. 3-11). pap. 5.95 (978-1-56167-484-8(2)) American Literary Pr.

Pendziwol, Jean. Once upon a Dragon: Stranger Safety for Kids (And Dragons) Gourbault, Martine, illus. 2006. 32p. (J). (978-1-55337-722-1(2)) Kids Can Pr., Ltd.

—Once upon a Dragon: Stranger Safety for Kids (And Dragons) Gourbault, Martine, illus. 2006. 32p. 6.95 (978-1-55337-969-0(1)) Kids Can Pr., Ltd. CAN. *Dist:* Wybel Marketing Group.

Poison Patrol: Coloring/Activity (English) Incl. Posters, Stickers. 2007. (J). ***978-1-933934-53-2(0))** Educational Adventures.

Poison Patrol: Picture Book 8x8. 2007. (J). ***978-1-933934-40-2(9))** Educational Adventures.

Poison Patrol: Picture Book (English) 9x9 with Snipe. 2007. (J). ***978-1-933934-50-1(6))** Educational Adventures.

Poison Safe! Life Safety Coloring/Activity Book. 2007. (Illus.). (J). ***978-1-933934-33-4(6))** Educational Adventures.

Rathmann, Peggy. Officer Buckle & Gloria. Rathmann, Peggy, illus. 2002. (Illus.). (J). 23.64 (978-0-7587-0061-2(X)) Book Wholesalers, Inc.

Robbins, Sandra. Ring Around a Rainbow: A Health & Safety Adventure. rev. ed. 2001. 32p. (J). (gr. k-5). pap. 11.95 incl. audio (978-1-882601-31-8(9)); pap. 6.95 (978-1-882601-32-5(7)) See-More's Workshop.

Sargent, Dave. Bob White the Quail. Lenoir, Jane, illus. 2000. (J). lib. bdg. 19.95 (978-1-56763-481-5(8)); pap. 6.95 (978-1-56763-482-2(6)) Ozark Publishing.

Sargent, Dave & Sargent, David M. Bob White: Use Good Judgement, 20, vol. 3. Lenoir, Jane, illus. 2003. (Feather Tales Ser.: No. 3). 42p. (J). pap. 6.95 (978-1-56763-724-3(8)) Ozark Publishing.

Sargent, David M. Bob White: Use Good Judgement, 20, vol. 3. Lenoir, Jane, illus. 2003. (Feather Tales Ser.: No. 3). 42p. (J). lib. bdg. 19.95 (978-1-56763-723-6(X)) Ozark Publishing.

Scoop. 2007. (J). 15.95 ***978-1-934073-00-1(8))** CTC Publishing.

Seidman, David. Safety First! Mawhinney, Art, illus. 2006. (Firehouse Tales Ser.). 48p. (J). act. bk. ed. 3.99 (978-1-4169-1845-5(0), Simon Scribbles) Simon & Schuster Children's Publishing.

Street Safe! Life Safety Coloring/Activity Book. 2007. (Illus.). (J). ***978-1-933934-34-1(4))** Educational Adventures.

Street Smarts: Coloring/Activity Book (English) Incl. Stickers. 2006. (Illus.). (J). ***978-1-933934-18-1(2))** Educational Adventures.

Street Smarts: Picture Book 9x9 with Snipe. 2006. (Illus.). (J). ***978-1-933934-17-4(4))** Educational Adventures.

Street Smarts: Picture Book (English) 8x8. 2006. (Illus.). (J). ***978-1-933934-16-7(6))** Educational Adventures.

That's a Danger Proof Plan! Coloring/Activity Book (English) 2006. (Illus.). (J). ***978-1-933934-28-0(X))** Educational Adventures.

Think Safe! Play Safe! Be Safe! Coloring/Activity Book (English) 2006. (Illus.). (J). ***978-1-933934-26-6(3))** Educational Adventures.

Thomas, Kate. Mother Duck Knows the Way. Larkins, Mona, illus. 2005. 32p. (J). 8.95 (978-1-58374-122-1(4)) Chicago Spectrum Pr.

Water Safe! Life Safety Coloring/Activity Book. 2007. (Illus.). (J). ***978-1-933934-25-9(5))** Educational Adventures.

Willis, Jeanne. Cottonball Colin. Ross, Tony, illus. 2008. (J). ***978-0-8028-5331-8(5)**, Eerdmans Bks For Young Readers) Eerdmans, William B. Publishing Co.

Ziefert, Harriet. Oh No, Nicky! 2003. (Illus.). 14p. 6.95 (978-1-59354-012-8(4)) Blue Apple Bks.

Zoehfeld, Kathleen Weidner. Don't Talk to Strangers, Pooh! 2000. (My Very First Winnie the Pooh Ser.). (Illus.). 32p. (J). (ps-k). pap. 4.99 (978-0-7868-4378-7(0)) Disney Pr.

Zoehfeld, Kathleen Weidner & Milne, A. A. Don't Talk to Strangers, Pooh! Cuddy, Robbin, illus. 1998. (My Very First Winnie the Pooh Ser.). 32p. (J). (ps). pap. 11.95 (978-0-7868-3145-6(6)) Disney Pr.

SAFETY MEASURES

see Accidents—Prevention

also subjects with the subdivision Safety Measures, e.g. Aeronautics—Safety Measures

SAGWA, THE CHINESE SIAMESE CAT (FICTITIOUS CHARACTER)—FICTION

Daugherty, George. Acrobat Cats. Schields, Gretchen, illus. 2002. (Sagwa, the Chinese Siamese Cat Ser.: No. 1). 32p. (J). (ps-3). pap. 3.99 (978-0-439-42873-6(4)) Scholastic, Inc.

Sander, Sonia. Sagwa: Festival of Lanterns. Thompson Brothers Staff, illus. 2003. (Sagwa, the Chinese Siamese Cat Ser.). 32p. (J). (ps-3). pap. 3.99 (978-0-439-45179-6(5)) Scholastic, Inc.

—Sagwa: Sagwa's Lucky Bat. George, Chris, illus. 2003. (Sagwa, the Chinese Siamese Cat Ser.). 64p. (J). (ps-3). 2.99 (978-0-439-45181-9(7)) Scholastic, Inc.

Scholastic, Inc. Staff & Daugherty, George. Princess Sheegwa. Schields, Gretchen, illus. 2002. (Sagwa, the Chinese Siamese Cat Ser.: No. 2). 32p. (J). pap. 3.99 (978-0-439-42880-4(7)) Scholastic, Inc.

Tan, Amy. Sagwa, the Chinese Siamese Cat. Schields, Gretchen, illus. 2001. 40p. (J). 6.99 (978-0-689-84617-5(7), Aladdin) Simon & Schuster Children's Publishing.

—Sagwa, the Chinese Siamese Cat. 2001. (978-0-606-22103-0(4)) Tandem Library Bks.

SAHARA

Barber, Nicola. Living in the Sahara. 2007. (J). ***978-1-4109-2816-0(0)); pap. *978-1-4109-2825-2(X))** Steck-Vaughn.

Chapman, S. I. mon. In the Desert. 2006. (Illus.). 111p. (J). lib. bdg. 20.00 ***978-1-4242-0628-5(6))** Fitzgerald Bks.

Fine, Jil. Sahara. 2004. (Natures Greatest Hits Ser.). (SPA.). 24p. (J). (gr. 3-6). lib. bdg. 17.25 (978-0-8239-6879-4(0), Buenas Letra) Rosen Publishing Group, Inc., The.

Fine, Jill. The Sahara: World's Largest Desert. 2002. (Reading Power Ser.). (Illus.). 24p. (J). (gr. 2). lib. bdg. 17.25 (978-0-8239-6013-2(7), PowerKids Pr.) Rosen Publishing Group, Inc., The.

Harcourt School Publishers Staff. The Sahara Desert. 3rd ed. 2002. (Horizons Ser.). (Illus.). (J). pap. 3.70 (978-0-15-333164-0(X)) Harcourt Schl. Pubs.

Heinrichs, Ann. The Sahara Desert. 2008. (J). ***978-0-7614-2855-8(0))** Cavendish, Marshall Bks., Ltd.

Lappi, Megan. The Sahara Desert. 2005. 32p. pap. (978-1-59036-274-7(8)); 2004. lib. bdg. (978-1-59036-268-6(3)); 2004. lib. bdg. (978-1-59036-452-9(X)) Weigl Pubs., Inc.

Loti, Pierre. The Sahara. 2002. (Kegan Paul Asia Library). 200p. 153.00 (978-0-7103-0817-7(5)) Kegan Paul International, Ltd. GBR. *Dist:* Columbia Univ. Pr.

Pyers. Desert Explorer, 6 Pack. 2004. (Habitat Explorer Ser.). (Illus.). pap. 40.50 (978-1-4109-0911-4(5)) Raintree.

Pyers, Greg. Desert Explorer. 2004. (Habitat Explorer Ser.). (Illus.). 32p. (J). lib. bdg. 25.70 (978-1-4109-0507-9(1)) Raintree.

Reynolds, Jan. Sahara: Vanishing Cultures. 2007. 32p. (J). ***978-1-60060-131-6(6)); *978-1-60060-146-0(4))** Lee & Low Bks., Inc.

The Sahara: Individual Title Six-Packs. (On Deck Ser.). 24p. (gr. 4-5). 35.00 (978-0-7578-1080-0(2)) Rigby Education.

Weintraub, Aileen. The Sahara Desert: The Biggest Desert. 2001. (Great Record Breakers in Nature Ser.). (Illus.). 24p. (J). (gr. 2-5). lib. bdg. 18.75 (978-0-8239-5640-1(7), PowerKids Pr.) Rosen Publishing Group, Inc., The.

Zuravicky, Orli. The Amazon & the Sahara: Using Double Line Graphs & Double Bar Graphs. 2004. (PowerMath Ser.). (Illus.). 32p. (J). lib. bdg. (978-0-8239-8868-6(6)); lib. bdg. 22.50 (978-0-8239-8981-2(X)) Rosen Publishing Group, Inc., The. (PowerKids Pr.).

SAHARA—FICTION

Bellamy, Richard. Saharan Boy. 2002. (gr. 7-12). lib. bdg. 24.00 (978-0-613-78103-9(1)) Tandem Library Bks.

Moss, Miriam. This Is the Oasis. Kennaway, Adrienne, illus. 2005. 32p. (J). 14.95 (978-1-929132-76-8(X)) Kane/Miller Bk. Pubs., Inc.

Okorafor-Mbachu, Nnedi. The Shadow Speaker. rev. ed. 2007. 336p. (gr. 7 up). 16.99 ***978-1-4231-0033-1(6)**, Jump at the Sun) Hyperion Bks. for Children.

Saint-Exupéry, Antoine de. The Little Prince. 1998. (Children's Library). (J). pap. 3.95 Wordsworth Editions, Ltd. GBR. *Dist:* Combined Publishing.

SAILING

see also Boats and Boating; Navigation

Bach, Julie S. Sailing. 2000. (World of Sports Ser.). (Illus.). 32p. (J). (gr. 4 up). lib. bdg. 16.95 (978-1-887068-58-1(9)) Smart Apple Media.

Bayley, Thomas. Sailing Ships: A Lift-the-Flap Discovery. 1998. (Illus.). 18p. (J). (ps up). pap. 16.95 (978-0-531-30065-7(X), Orchard Bks.) Scholastic, Inc.

The Catboat & How to Sail Her. 5th ed. 2000. 36p. 10.00 (978-0-9715041-0-3(5)) Catboat Assn., Inc.

Cefrey, Holly. Steven Callahan: Adrift at Sea. 2003. lib. bdg. 15.25 (978-0-613-67934-3(2)) Tandem Library Bks.

Ensley, Harold. Winds of Chance. 2002. 200p. 29.95 (978-1-58597-131-2(6)) Leathers Publishing.

Long, Ginny, et al. Sailing Smart. Altman, Betsy, ed. 2000. 32p. (YA). (gr. 5-7). pap., act. bk. ed. 5.00 (978-1-882502-90-5(6)) U. S. Sailing Assn.

Mosenthal, Basil. Young Sailor: How to Be a Good Sailor & Have Fun! 2nd ed. 2003. (Illus.). 36p. pap. 12.95 (978-0-7136-6395-2(2)) A & C Black GBR. *Dist:* MBI Distribution Services.

Mosenthal, Basil & Pelling, Sue. Getting Afloat. 2003. (Illus.). 80p. pap. 7.95 (978-0-7136-5278-9(0)) A & C Black GBR. *Dist:* MBI Distribution Services.

Patterson, Kevin. Water in Between: A Journey at Sea. 2001. (gr. 7-12). lib. bdg. 22.25 (978-0-613-36892-6(4)) Tandem Library Bks.

Paulsen, Gary. Caught by the Sea. l.t. ed. 2002. 104p. (J). 22.95 (978-0-7862-4160-6(8)) Thomson Gale.

Ripley, Esther & Dorling Kindersley Publishing Staff. Solo Sailing. 2005. (Dk Readers Ser.). (Illus.). 48p. (J). 12.99 (978-0-7566-0994-8(1)); Level 4. pap. 3.99 (978-0-7566-0993-1(3)) Dorling Kindersley Publishing, Inc.

Sailing Adventures, 6 vols. (gr. 4 up). 39.95 (978-0-7368-9285-8(0)) Red Brick Learning.

Todd, Anne M. Sailing Adventures. 2001. (Dangerous Adventures Ser.). (Illus.). 48p. (J). (gr. 3-4). lib. bdg. 21.26 (978-0-7368-0906-1(6), Capstone High-Interest Bks.) Capstone Pr., Inc.

Veigele, William J. Sea Bag of Memories: Images, Poems, Thoughts, & Crafts of the small Ship Sailors of World War II. 2003. 320p. (YA). (gr. 10 up). 39.95 (978-0-9645867-4-1(6)) Astral Publishing Co.

SAILING—FICTION

Ardizzone, Edward. Little Tim & the Brave Sea Captain. ed. 2006. (Little Tim Ser.). (Illus.). 48p. (J). 15.95 (978-1-84507-456-2(4)) Lincoln, Frances Ltd. GBR. *Dist:* Perseus Distribution.

—Tim & Lucy Go to Sea. ed. 2006. (Little Tim Ser.). (Illus.). 48p. (J). 15.95 (978-1-84507-457-9(2)) Lincoln, Frances Ltd. GBR. *Dist:* Perseus Distribution.

—Tim to the Rescue. ed. 2006. (Little Tim Ser.). (Illus.). 48p. (J). 15.95 (978-1-84507-458-6(0)) Lincoln, Frances Ltd. GBR. *Dist:* Perseus Distribution.

Bang-Campbell, Monika. Little Rat Sets Sail. Bang, Molly Garrett, illus. (Little Rat Ser.). 48p. (J). 2003. pap. 5.95 (978-0-15-204769-6(7), Harcourt Paperbacks); 2002. (gr. 1-3). 14.00 (978-0-15-216297-9(6)) Harcourt Children's Bks.

—Little Rat Sets Sail. 2003. (gr. k-3). lib. bdg. 14.10 (978-0-613-70519-6(X)) Tandem Library Bks.

Barbour, Ralph Henry. The Adventure Club Afloat. 2006. 78.99 ***978-1-4280-1948-5(0))** IndyPublish.com.

Barile, Colleen. A Super Day for Sailing. Van Patter, Bruce, illus. 2002. (Read-To-Me Ser.). 25p. (J). (978-0-7665-1219-1(3)) Abrams, Harry N., Inc.

Beach, John & Lubotsky, Dana, readers. The Wanderer. unabr. ed. 2004. 320p. (J). (gr. 4-7). pap. 36.00 incl. audio (978-0-8072-0864-9(7), LYA 199 SP, Listening Library) Random Hse. Audio Publishing Group.

Beck, Ana. Elliot's Shipwreck. 2000. (gr. 3-6). lib. bdg. 14.10 (978-0-613-36328-0(0)) Tandem Library Bks.

Berger, Barbara Helen. Lot of Otters. 2000. (ps-2). lib. bdg. 15.30 (978-0-613-28563-6(8)) Tandem Library Bks.

Blackstone, Stella. Una Isla Bajo el Sol. 2003. (SPA.). (gr. k-3). lib. bdg. 15.30 (978-0-613-67170-5(8)) Tandem Library Bks.

—Una Isla Bajo el Sol (An Island in the Sun) Ceccoli, Nicoletta, illus. 2003. (SPA.). 24p. (J). pap. 6.99 (978-1-84148-144-9(0)) Barefoot Bks., Inc.

—An Island in the Sun. Ceccoli, Nicoletta, illus. 2005. 24p. (J). pap. 6.99 (978-1-84148-079-4(7)); 15.99 (978-1-84148-193-7(9)) Barefoot Bks., Inc.

Bowler, Tim. Apocalypse. 2005. 352p. (YA). 16.95 (978-1-4169-0370-3(4), McElderry, Margaret K.) Simon & Schuster Children's Publishing.

Brown, Jeff. Stanley, Flat Again! Nash, Scott, illus. (Stanley Lambchop Adventure Ser.). 96p. (J). 2004. pap. 4.99 (978-0-06-442173-7(2), Harper Trophy); 2003. 14.99 (978-0-06-009551-2(2)); 2003. lib. bdg. 15.89 (978-0-06-029826-5(X)) HarperCollins Pubs.

Capsize! Individual Title Six-Packs. (Bookweb Ser.). 32p. (gr. 4 up). 34.00 (978-0-7635-3727-2(6)) Rigby Education.

Carlos the Sailor Visits Atlantic City. 2005. (J). pap. 12.95 (978-0-9766889-0-7(5)) ComteQ Publishing.

Chetkowski, Emily. Mabel Takes a Sail. 2000. (gr. k-3). lib. bdg. 19.35 (978-0-613-85830-4(1)) Tandem Library Bks.

—Mabel Takes a Sail. Peterson, Dawn, illus. 2000. 64p. (J). (ps-3). pap. 10.50 (978-1-880158-26-5(4)) Townsend, J.N. Publishing.

—Mabel Takes the Ferry. Peterson, Dawn, illus. 2001. 40p. (J). pap. 11.95 (978-1-880158-37-1(X)) Townsend, J.N. Publishing.

Creech, Sharon. The Wanderer. Diaz, David, illus. 320p. 2002. (gr. 3-7). pap. 6.99 (978-0-06-441032-8(3)); 2000. (J). (ps-3). 16.99 (978-0-06-027730-7(0), Cotler, Joanna Books); 2000. (J). (ps-3). lib. bdg. 17.89 (978-0-06-027731-4(9), Cotler, Joanna Books) HarperCollins Pubs.

—The Wanderer. 2002. (gr. 3-6). lib. bdg. 14.15 (978-0-613-49702-2(3)) Tandem Library Bks.

—The Wanderer. l.t. ed. 2003. 263p. pap. 10.95 (978-0-7862-6186-4(2)) Thorndike Pr.

—The Wanderer. Diaz, David, illus. l.t. ed. 2002. 263p. (J). 24.95 (978-0-7862-4125-5(X)) Thorndike Pr.

Crews, Donald. Sail Away. Crews, Donald, illus. 2000. (Illus.). 40p. (J). (ps-3). pap. 6.99 (978-0-688-17517-7(1), Harper Trophy) HarperCollins Pubs.

—Sail Away. 2000. (978-0-606-18719-0(7)); lib. bdg. 14.10 (978-0-613-28309-0(0)) Tandem Library Bks.

Daynes, Katie, retold by. Sinbad. 2005. (Young Reading Series 1 Ser.). 48p. (J). (gr. 2 up). pap. 5.95 (978-0-7945-0825-8(1), Usborne) EDC Publishing.

Dowswell, Paul. Prison Ship: Adventures of a Young Sailor. 2006. 300p. (YA). 16.95 (978-1-58234-676-2(3), Bloomsbury Children) Bloomsbury Publishing.

Evans, Michael Robert. 68 Knots: A Novel. 2007. 350p. (gr. 9 up). 15.95 ***978-1-933718-14-9(5))** Tanglewood Pr.

Farias, Juan. Ismael, Que Fue Marinero. (Punto de Encuentro Ser.). (SPA.). 112p. (YA). (gr. 5 up). 9.95 (978-84-241-7906-9(4), EV3284) Everest de Ediciones y Distribucion, S.L. ESP. *Dist:* Lectorum Pubns., Inc.

Fienberg, Anna. Minton Goes Sailing. Gamble, Kim, illus. 2001. (Minton Ser.). 32p. (J). (ps-1). pap. 6.95 (978-1-86448-592-9(2)) Allen & Unwin AUS. *Dist:* Independent Pubs. Group.

Foley, John. Running with the Wind. 2007. 216p. (J). (gr. 7 up). pap. 8.95 ***978-0-7387-1002-0(4)**, Flux) Llewellyn Pubns.

Ford, Sally. Bungee's Voyage. Dudley, Peter, illus. 2002. (J). 14.95 (978-1-931807-04-3(3)) Randall, Peter E. Pub.

Garne, S. T. One White Sail. 1998. (J). 4.95 (978-0-87628-978-5(2)) Ctr. for Applied Research in Education, The.

Geller, Nancy Jewell. Sailor Song. Vitale, Stefano, illus. 1999. 32p. (J). (gr. k-3). tchr. ed. 13.00 (978-0-395-82511-2(3), Clarion Bks.) Houghton Mifflin Co. Trade & Reference Div.

Gershator, Phillis. Someday Cyril. Lucas, Cedric, illus. 2000. (MONDO Chapter Books). 46p. (J). (978-1-57255-748-2(6)) Mondo Publishing.

Graham, Alistair. Full Moon Afloat. Graham, Alistair, illus. 2003. (Full Moon Soup & Full Moon Afloat Ser.). (Illus.). 32p. (YA). pap. (978-1-85602-217-0(X)) Chrysalis Children's Bks.

Gurney, Stella. Marinera Sandra, Level P. Worsley, Belinda, illus. 2006. (Lightning Readers Ser.). 32p. (J). (gr. k-k). pap. 3.95 (978-0-7696-4215-4(2), Gingham Dog Pr.) School Specialty Publishing.

Gurney, Stella. Sailor Sally. Worsley, Belinda, illus. 2006. 32p. (J). lib. bdg. 9.00 ***978-1-4242-0883-8(1))** Fitzgerald Bks.

—Sailor Sally, Level P. Worsley, Belinda, illus. 2006. (Lightning Readers Ser.). 32p. (J). pap. 3.95 (978-0-7696-4185-0(7), Gingham Dog Pr.) School Specialty Publishing.

Hagen, Michael. Sail to Caribee. 1998. 157p. (YA). (gr. 5 up). 9.99 (978-0-88092-410-8(1), 4101) Royal Fireworks Publishing Co.

Harcourt School Publishers Staff. Shipwrecked! Take-Home Book. 2001. (Collections Ser.). (Illus.). (J). pap. 1.90 (978-0-15-319522-8(3)) Harcourt Schl. Pubs.

—Shipwrecked Below Level. 3rd ed. 2002. (Trophies Reading Program Ser.). (Illus.). pap. 5.10 (978-0-15-323320-3(6)) Harcourt Schl. Pubs.

Hopkinson, Deborah. Sailing for Gold. Farnsworth, Bill, illus. ed. 2005. 76p. (J). lib. bdg. 15.00 (978-1-59054-915-5(5)) Fitzgerald Bks.

Kenny, Kathryn & Koelsch, Michael. The Mystery on Cobbett's Island. Frame, Paul, illus. 2005. (Trixie Belden Ser.: Vol. 13). 272p. (J). (gr. 3-7). 6.99 (978-0-375-83053-2(7)); lib. bdg. 9.99 (978-0-375-93053-9(1)) Random Hse. Children's Bks. (Random Hse. Bks. for Young Readers).

Korman, Gordon. The Discovery. 2003. (Dive Ser.: No. 1). (gr. 3-6). lib. bdg. 12.40 (978-0-613-67481-2(2)) Tandem Library Bks.

Kvasnosky, Laura McGee. Frank & Izzy Set Sail. Kvasnosky, Laura McGee, illus. 2004. (Illus.). 32p. (J). (gr. k-4). 15.99 (978-0-7636-2146-9(3)) Candlewick Pr.

LeapFrog Staff, compiled by. Treasure Island. (J). 2002. (gr. 3-7). 14.95 (978-1-58605-920-0(3), LeapFrog Schl. Hse.); 2001. spiral bd. 14.99 (978-1-58605-045-0(1)) LeapFrog Enterprises, Inc.

Lund, Deb. Dinosailors. Fine, Howard, illus. 2003. 40p. (J). (ps-2). 16.00 (978-0-15-204609-5(7)) Harcourt Children's Bks.

McClear, Preston. The Salior & the Sea Witch. Dollak, Micholas, illus. 2002. 32p. (J). (gr. 3-5). 16.95 (978-1-929084-11-1(0)) Malibu Bks. for Children.

McNeil, Florence. Sail Away. McPhail, David M., illus. 2001. (Young Reader Ser.). 32p. (J). (ps-2). 15.95 (978-1-55143-147-5(5)) Orca Bk. Pubs. USA.

Meyer, Louis A. Bloody Jack: Being an Account of the Curious Adventures of Mary Jacky Faber, Ship's Boy. 2004. (Bloody Jack Adventures Ser.). (Illus.). 320p. (YA). reprint ed. pap. 6.95 (978-0-15-205085-6(X), Harcourt Paperbacks) Harcourt Children's Bks.

Mitton, Tony. Once upon a Tide. Young, Selina, illus. 2006. 40p. (J). (gr. k-1). 16.95 (978-0-385-75100-1(1)); lib. bdg. 18.99 (978-0-385-75101-8(X)) Random Hse. Children's Bks. (Fickling, David Bks.).

Neale, Jonathan. Lost at Sea. 112p. (J). (gr. 5-9). 2002. (Illus.). 15.00 (978-0-618-13920-0(6)); 2004. reprint ed. pap. 5.95 (978-0-618-43236-3(1)) Houghton Mifflin Co. Trade & Reference Div.

Nestor, Gregg. All Hands on Deck: Become Part of a Caribbean Sailing Adventure. 2005. (Illus.). 72p. (J). (ps-7). pap. 29.00 (978-1-4208-2407-0(4)) AuthorHouse.

Oppenheim, Shulamith Levey. Rescuing Einstein's Compass. Juhasz, George, illus. 2003. 32p. (J). (gr. k-3). 15.95 (978-1-56656-507-3(3), Interlink Bks.) Interlink Publishing Group, Inc.

S

Patterson, Kevin. The Water in Between: A Journey at Sea. 2001. (J). (978-0-606-21851-1(3)) Tandem Library Bks.

Pendziwol, Jean. Dawn Watch. Debon, Nicolas, illus. 2004. 32p. (J). 15.95 (978-0-88899-512-4(1)) Groundwood Bks. CAN. *Dist:* Perseus Distribution.

Priest, Robert. The Old Pirate of Central Park. Priest, Robert, illus. 1999. (Illus.). 32p. (J). (gr. k-3). tchr. ed. 16.00 (978-0-395-90505-0(2)) Houghton Mifflin Co. Trade & Reference Div.

Prins, Piet. The Sailing Sleuths. Kramer, Jaap, illus. 2006. 137p. (J). pap. (978-1-894666-46-6(1)) Inheritance Pubns.

—Stefan Derksen's Polar Adventure. 2004. (Illus.). 237p. (J). pap. (978-1-894666-67-1(4)) Inheritance Pubns.

Punter, R. Stories of Pirates. 2004. (Young Reading Ser.: Vol. 1). 48p. (J). (gr. 2 up). pap. 5.99 (978-0-7945-0583-7(X)) EDC Publishing.

Ransome, Arthur. Missee Lee. 2002. (Swallows & Amazons Ser.). (Illus.). 352p. (J). pap. 14.95 (978-1-56792-196-0(5)) Godine, David R. Pub.

Rylant, Cynthia. Poppleton Everyday. Teague, Mark, illus. 2002. (Poppleton Ser.). (J). 11.91 (978-0-7587-1586-9(2)) Book Wholesalers, Inc.

—Poppleton Everyday. Teague, Mark, illus. 1998. (Poppleton Ser.). (J). (gr. k-3). 48p. pap. 15.95 (978-0-590-84845-9(3) , Blue Sky Pr., The); 56p. pap. 3.99 (978-0-590-84853-4(4)) Scholastic, Inc.

—Poppleton Everyday. 1998. (Poppleton Ser.). (J). (gr. k-3). (978-0-606-13717-1(3)) Tandem Library Bks.

Sailor Sam & the Captain, 6 Packs. (Sails Literacy Ser.). (gr. 1-2). 36.00 (978-0-7578-6711-8(1)) Rigby Education.

Sailor Sam Gets Lost, 6 Packs. (Sails Literacy Ser.). (gr. 1-2). 36.00 (978-0-7578-4005-0(1)) Rigby Education.

Sailors: Individual Title Six-Packs. (Sails Literacy Ser.). 16p. (gr. k up). 27.00 (978-0-7635-4406-5(X)) Rigby Education.

Schaaf, Ron. Tiger's Quest: Rounding Cape Horn. 2007. (J). ***(978-0-9787555-0-8(2))*** Hickory Tales Publishing.

Thompson, Richard & Spicer, Maggee. We'll All Go Sailing. La Fave, Kim, illus. 32p. (J). (ps-k). 2001. (978-1-55041-662-6(6)); 2000. pap. (978-1-55041-651-0(0)) Fitzhenry & Whiteside, Ltd.

—We'll All Go Sailing: A First Flight Level 1 Reader. La Fave, Kim, illus. 2000. (First Flight Ser.). 32p. (J). (ps-k). lib. bdg. (978-1-55041-650-3(2)) Fitzhenry & Whiteside, Ltd.

Thornton, Duncan. The Star-Glass: The Return of Kalifax & Captain Jenny. Noblet, Yves, illus. 2003. (Kalifax Trilogy Ser.). 432p. (J). (gr. 5-7). pap. 10.95 (978-1-55050-269-5(7)) Coteau Bks. CAN. *Dist:* Fitzhenry & Whiteside, Ltd.

Torrey, Michele. Voyage of Ice. 2005. 208p. (J). (gr. 5 up). pap. 5.99 (978-0-440-41886-3(0) , Yearling) Random Hse. Children's Bks.

The True Confessions of Charlotte Doyle. 2004. (Literature Connections Ser.). (Illus.). (gr. 6-12). (978-0-395-87477-6(7) , 2-70837) McDougal Littell Inc.

Wait, Lea. Seaward Born. (Illus.). 160p. (J). 2004. pap. 5.99 (978-0-689-84860-5(9) , Aladdin); 2003. 16.95 (978-0-689-84719-6(X) , McElderry, Margaret K.) Simon & Schuster Children's Publishing.

Winkler, Henry & Oliver, Lin. The Night I Flunked My Field Trip. Heyer, Carol, illus. 2004. (Hank Zipzer Ser.: No. 5). 176p. (J). (gr. 3-7). 13.99 (978-0-448-43502-2(0) , Grosset & Dunlap) Penguin Group (USA) Inc.

Zeman, Ludmila. Sindbad: Un Conte des Mille et une Nuits. Levesque, Suzanne, tr. Zeman, Ludmila, illus. 1999. (FRE & SPA., Illus.). 32p. (J). (gr. 1-3). 19.95 (978-0-88776-480-6(0) , Livres Toundra) Tundra Bks., Inc./ Livres Toundra, Inc. CAN. *Dist:* Random Hse., Inc.

SAILOR MOON (FICTITIOUS CHARACTER)—FICTION

Takeuchi, Naoko. Sailor Moon, 11 vols. (Illus.). 184p. (gr. 7-12). Vol. 2. 2nd rev. ed. 1998. (Sailor Moon Ser.: Vol. 2). pap. 9.99 (978-1-892213-05-1(2)); Vol. 3. 3rd rev. ed. 1999. pap. 9.99 (978-1-892213-06-8(0)) TOKYOPOP, Inc.

—Sailor Moon Supers, Vol. 3. 3rd rev. ed. 2000. (Illus.). 160p. (gr. 7-12). pap. 9.99 (978-1-892213-26-6(5)) TOKYOPOP, Inc.

SAILORS

see also Naval Biography

also names of countries with the subhead Navy, e.g. United States—Navy, etc.

Anderson, Dale. Soldiers & Sailors in the American Revolution. 2005. (World Almanac Library of the American Revolution). (J). pap. (978-0-8368-5938-6(3)); lib. bdg. 30.00 (978-0-8368-5929-4(4)) Stevens, Gareth Inc. (World Almanac Library).

Brown, Chris. Shiver Me Timbers! A Funbook of Pirates-,Sailors & Other Sea-Farers. 2006. (Illus.). 32p. pap. 8.95 (978-0-7145-3303-2(3)) Consortium Bk. Sales & Distribution.

Duder, Tessa, ed. Down to the Sea Again: True Sea Stories for Young Newzealanders. 2005. 256p. (J). (978-1-86950-476-2(3)) HarperCollins Pubs. New Zealand NZL. *Dist:* HarperCollins Canada, Ltd.

Janveau, Teri-Lynn & Thompson, Allister. Sailing for Glory: The Story of Angus Walters. Thompson, Samantha, illus. 2006. 72p. (J). 16.95 (978-1-894917-09-4(X)) Napoleon Publishing/Rendezvous Pr. CAN. *Dist:* Atlas-Books Distribution.

Marsh, Carole. Christopher Newport. 2002. (One Thousand Readers Ser.). (Illus.). 12p. (J). (gr. k-4). 2.95 (978-0-635-01527-3(7) , 15277) Gallopade International.

SAILORS' LIFE

see Seafaring Life

SAILORS' SONGS

see Sea Songs

SAINT LAWRENCE RIVER

Cooke, Tim. The St. Lawrence River. 2003. (Rivers of North America Ser.). (Illus.). 32p. (J). (gr. 3 up). lib. bdg. 24.67 (978-0-8368-3762-9(2)) Stevens, Gareth Inc.

Lackey, Jennifer D. B. Jacques Cartier: Exploring the St. Lawrence River. 2006. (In the Footsteps of Explorers Ser.). (Illus.). 32p. (J). (gr. 3-9). pap. (978-0-7787-2466-7(2)); lib. bdg. (978-0-7787-2430-8(1)) Crabtree Publishing Co.

SAINT LAWRENCE RIVER VALLEY

Blue, Rose & Naden, Corinne J. Exploring the St. Lawrence River Region. 2003. (Illus.). 64p. (J). pap. 9.50 (978-1-4109-0337-2(0)) Raintree.

—St. Lawrence Explorers. 2003. (Illus.). 64p. (J). lib. bdg. 28.56 (978-0-7398-4955-2(7)) Raintree.

SAINT LAWRENCE SEAWAY

Harcourt School Publishers Staff. Building a Seaway. 3rd ed. 2002. (Horizons Ser.). (Illus.). (J). pap. 7.30 (978-0-15-333606-5(4)) Harcourt Schl. Pubs.

SAINT LOUIS (MO.)

Harris, Phyllis, illus. St. Louis Architecture for Kids. Obata, Gen, photos by. 2005. 32p. 15.95 (978-1-883982-42-3(1)) Missouri Historical Society Pr.

Hintz, Martin. Destination St. Louis. 1998. (Port Cities of North America Ser.). (Illus.). 80p. (YA). (gr. 6-8). lib. bdg. 23.93 (978-0-8225-2794-7(4) , Lerner Pubns.) Lerner Publishing Group.

Murray, Julie. Gateway Arch. 2003. (Buddy Book Ser.). (Illus.). 24p. (J). (gr. k-4). lib. bdg. 21.35 (978-1-57765-671-5(7)) ABDO Publishing Co.

SAINT LOUIS (MO.)—FICTION

Erwin, Vicki B. & Powell, Jennifer, eds. A Midwinter Knight's Dream: A St. Louis Tail. 2000. (Illus.). 64p. (J). (gr. 1-7). 15.99 (978-0-7383-0000-9(4)) Booksource, The.

Hoffman, Allen. Big League Dreams. 1999. (Small Worlds Ser.). 296p. 12.95 (978-0-7892-0583-4(1)) Abbeville Pr., Inc.

Holley, Marietta. Samantha at the St. Louis Exposition. 2007. 188p. pap. 11.99 ***(978-1-4264-6038-8(4))*** BiblioBazaar.

Olswanger, Anna. Shlemiel Crooks. Koz, Paula Goodman, illus. 2005. 36p. (J). (ps-7). 15.95 (978-1-58838-165-1(X)) NewSouth, Inc.

ST. LOUIS CARDINALS (BASEBALL TEAM)

Goodman, Michael E. The History of the St. Louis Cardinals. 1998. (Baseball, the Great American Game Ser.). (Illus.). 32p. (YA). (gr. 3 up). pap. 21.30 (978-0-88682-922-3(4) , Creative Education) Creative Co., The.

—St. Louis Cardinals. 2002. 32p. (J). pap. 5.95 (978-0-89812-355-5(0) , Creative Paperbacks); (Illus.). (978-1-58341-221-3(2)) Creative Co., The.

Mattern, Joanne. Albert Pujols. 2007. (Robbie Reader Ser.). (Illus.). 32p. (J). (gr. 1-4). lib. bdg. 25.70 ***(978-1-58415-596-6(5))*** Mitchell Lane Pubs., Inc.

Murray, Jim, intro. Mark McGwire. 1999. (Baseball Legends Ser.). (Illus.). 64p. (YA). (gr. 3-7). 18.65 (978-0-7910-5155-9(2) , Chelsea Hse.) Facts On File, Inc.

Needham, Tom. Albert Pujols: MVP on & off the Field. 2007. (Sports Stars with Heart Ser.). (Illus.). 128p. (J). (gr. 5). lib. bdg. 31.93 ***(978-0-7660-2866-1(6))*** Enslow Pubs., Inc.

O'Hearn, Michael. The Story of the St. Louis Cardinals. 2007. (J). ***(978-1-58341-551-1(3)*** , Creative Education) Creative Co., The.

Pietrusza, David. The St. Louis Cardinals Baseball Team. 2001. (Great Sports Teams Ser.). (Illus.). 48p. (YA). (gr. 4-10). lib. bdg. 23.93 (978-0-7660-1490-9(8)) Enslow Pubs., Inc.

Rains, Rob. Mark McGwire: "Mac Attack!" 1998. (Superstar Ser.). (Illus.). 100p. (YA). (gr. 7-10). per. 5.95 (978-1-58261-004-7(5)) Sports Publishing, LLC.

—Mark McGwire: Slugger! Sporting News Staff, ed. 1998. (Illus.). 50p. (J). (gr. 1-6). 15.95 (978-1-58261-005-4(3)) Sports Publishing, LLC.

Stewart, Mark. The St. Louis Cardinals. 2007. (Team Spirit Ser.). (Illus.). 48p. (J). lib. bdg. 25.27 ***(978-1-59953-096-3(1))*** Norwood Hse. Pr.

SAINT PATRICK'S DAY

Balian, Lorna. Leprechauns Never Lie. Balian, Lorna, illus. 2004. (Illus.). 40p. (J). 14.95 (978-1-932065-37-4(7)) Star Bright Bks., Inc.

Barnett, Michelle Noble, et al. Theme Pockets - March: St. Patrick's Day; Weather; Our Community. Evans, Marilyn, ed. Larsen, Jo, illus. 1999. (Making Books with Pockets). 96p. (J). pap., tchr. ed. 12.99 (978-1-55799-700-5(4) , EMC 586) Evan-Moor Educational Pubs.

Barth, Edna. Shamrocks, Harps, & Shillelaghs: The Story of the St. Patrick's Day Symbols. Arndt, Ursula, illus. 2001. 96p. (YA). (gr. 4-6). pap. 7.95 (978-0-618-09651-0(5) , Clarion Bks.) Houghton Mifflin Co. Trade & Reference Div.

—Shamrocks, Harps, & Shillelaghs: The Story of the St. Patrick's Day Symbols. 2001. (J). (978-0-606-20909-0(3)); (gr. 3-6). lib. bdg. 16.40 (978-0-613-35567-4(9)) Tandem Library Bks.

Beylon, Cathy. Create Your Own St. Patrick's Day Sticker Card Book. 1998. (Dover Little Activity Bks.). (Illus.). (J). pap. 1.00 (978-0-486-40317-5(3)) Dover Pubns., Inc.

Bredeson, Carmen. St. Patrick's Day. 2003. (Rookie Read-About Holidays Ser.). (Illus.). 31p. (J). (gr. 1-2). pap. 5.95 (978-0-516-27921-3(1) , Children's Pr.) Scholastic Library Publishing.

—St. Patrick's Day. 2003. (gr. k-3). lib. bdg. 14.10 (978-0-613-63655-1(4)) Tandem Library Bks.

Freeman, Dorothy Rhodes. St. Patrick's Day. 2008. (Best Holiday Books Ser.). 48p. (J). (gr. 3-4). lib. bdg. 23.93 ***(978-0-7660-3046-6(6))*** Enslow Pubs., Inc.

Friedman, Pamela. St. Patrick's Day Activities. Cain, Janet, ed. Ponikvar-Frazier, Victoria, illus. 1998. (Holiday Activities Ser.). (Illus.). 32p. (J). pap., tchr. ed. 2.99 (978-1-57690-068-0(1) , TCM2068) Teacher Created Materials, Inc.

Gibbons, Gail. St. Patrick's Day. Gibbons, Gail, illus. 2002. (Illus.). (J). 27.55 (978-0-7587-3691-8(6)) Book Wholesalers, Inc.

—St. Patrick's Day. (Illus.). 32p. (J). (gr. k-3). 6.95 (978-0-8234-1173-3(7)) Holiday Hse., Inc.

—St. Patrick's Day. Gibbons, Gail, illus. (Illus.). 36p. (J). (gr. k-3). tchr. ed. 17.95 (978-0-8234-1119-1(2)) Holiday Hse., Inc.

Gillis, Jennifer Blizin. St. Patrick's Day. 2003. (Holiday Histories Ser.). (Illus.). 32p. (J). pap. 6.50 (978-1-4034-3689-4(4)); lib. bdg. 22.79 (978-1-4034-3504-0(9)) Heinemann Library.

Gnojewski, Carol. St. Patrick's Day Crafts. 2004. (Fun Holiday Crafts Kids Can Do Ser.). (Illus.). 32p. (J). lib. bdg. 22.60 (978-0-7660-2256-0(0)) Enslow Pubs., Inc.

Heinrichs, Ann. Saint Patrick's Day. Snyder, Joel, illus. 2006. (Holidays, Festivals, & Celebrations Ser.). 32p. (J). (gr. k-4). 22.79 (978-1-59296-581-6(4)) Child's World, Inc.

McNeil, Niki, et al. HOCPP 1062 Saint Patrick's Day. 2006. spiral bd. 20.00 ***(978-1-60308-062-0(7))*** In the Hands of a Child.

Miller, Heather. Celebrate St. Patrick's Day. 2006. (Celebrate Holidays Ser.). (Illus.). 104p. (J). lib. bdg. 31.93 (978-0-7660-2581-3(0)) Enslow Pubs., Inc.

Preszler, June. St. Patrick's Day: Day of Irish Pride. 2007. (First Facts Ser.). (Illus.). 24p. (J). 21.26 (978-0-7368-6398-8(2)) Capstone Pr., Inc.

Roop, Peter. Let's Celebrate St Patrick's Day. 2003. (gr. k-3). lib. bdg. 15.25 (978-0-613-58983-3(1)) Tandem Library Bks.

Roop, Peter & Roop, Connie. Let's Celebrate St. Patrick's Day. Connelly, Gwen, illus. 2003. 32p. (J). (gr. 3-6). pap. 6.95 (978-0-7613-1782-1(1)); lib. bdg. 22.90 (978-0-7613-2505-5(0)) Lerner Publishing Group. (Millbrook Pr.).

Rosinsky, Natalie M. St. Patrick's Day. 2002. (Let's See Library). (Illus.). 24p. (J). (gr. 1 up). lib. bdg. 19.93 (978-0-7565-0394-9(9)) Compass Point Bks.

Ross, Kathy. Crafts for St. Patrick's Day. Holm, Sharon Lane, illus. (Holiday Crafts for Kids Ser.). 48p. (gr. k-3). 2000. (J). pap. 7.95 (978-0-7613-0447-0(9)); 1999. lib. bdg. 24.90 (978-0-7613-1306-9(0)) Lerner Publishing Group. (Millbrook Pr.).

Schuh, Mari C. St. Patrick's Day. 2002. (Holidays & Celebrations Ser.). (Illus.). 24p. (J). (gr. k-1). lib. bdg. 15.93 (978-0-7368-1448-5(5) , Pebble Bks.) Capstone Pr., Inc.

Williams, Colleen Madonna Flood. My Adventure on St. Patrick's Day. 2007. 44p. (J). 8.99 (978-1-59092-556-0(4) , Orchard Academy Pr.) Windstorm Creative.

Zocchi, Judy. On Saint Patrick's Day. Wallis, Rebecca, illus. 2005. (Holiday Happenings Ser.). 32p. (J). pap. 9.95 (978-1-59646-232-8(9)); per. 9.95 (978-1-59646-233-5(7)) Dingles & Co.

—On Saint Patrick's Day/el día de San Patricio. Wallis, Rebecca, illus. 2005. (Holiday Happenings Ser.).Tr. of día de San Patricio. (ENG & SPA.). 32p. (J). pap. 9.95 (978-1-59646-234-2(5)); lib. bdg. 20.65 (978-1-891997-40-2(8)); per. 9.95 (978-1-59646-235-9(3)) Dingles & Co.

SAINT PATRICK'S DAY—FICTION

Bodel, Garrett. The St. Patrick's Day Dance. Bodel, Garrett, photos by. 2002. (Doll's Life Story Ser.: Vol. 3). (Illus.). 28p. (J). (gr. 2-3). pap. 7.90 (978-0-9720072-0-7(2)) Doll's Life.

Gomez, Rebecca. It's St. Patrick's Day! Level 1. Morgan, Mary, illus. 2004. (Scholastic Readers Ser.). 32p. (J). pap. 3.99 (978-0-439-44160-5(9) , Cartwheel Bks.) Scholastic, Inc.

—Scholastic Reader Level 1: It's St. Patrick's Day! 2004. (gr. k-3). lib. bdg. 11.80 (978-0-613-72120-2(9)) Tandem Library Bks.

Gorgas, Paula Blais. Little Lost Leprechaun. 2006. (Illus.). 24p. (J). lib. bdg. 24.95 (978-0-9778651-4-7(2)) Dragonfly Publishing, Inc.

Holub, Joan. Good Luck! A St. Patrick's Day Story. Terry, Will, illus. 2007. (Ant Hill Ser.). 24p. (J). pap. 3.99 (978-1-4169-0955-2(9) , Aladdin); lib. bdg. 11.89 (978-1-4169-2560-6(0) , Aladdin Library) Simon & Schuster Children's Publishing.

McNamara, Margaret & Gordon, Mike. The Luck of the Irish. 2007. (Ready-To-Read Ser.). 32p. (J). (SPA.). pap. 3.99 (978-1-4169-1539-3(7) , Aladdin); lib. bdg. 11.89 (978-1-4169-1540-9(0) , Aladdin Library) Simon & Schuster Children's Publishing.

Robertson, Ivan T. Jack & the Leprechaun. 2000. (gr. k-3). lib. bdg. 10.95 (978-0-613-21788-0(8)) Tandem Library Bks.

Schertle, Alice. Jeremy Bean. Slonim, David, illus. 2008. (J). (978-0-8118-5609-6(7)) Chronicle Bks. LLC.

Slater, Teddy. The Luckiest St Patrick's Day Ever. 2008. 32p. pap. 5.99 ***(978-0-545-03943-7(6)*** , Cartwheel Bks.) Scholastic, Inc.

Sypolt, Carl W. Fibber Lygood at Christmas, Easter, & St. Patrick's Day. 2006. 108p. (J). pap. 10.95 (978-0-7414-2982-7(9)) Infinity Publishing.

Yoon, Salina. St. Patrick's Day Countdown. 2006. (Illus.). 10p. (J). (ps-1). bds. 5.99 (978-0-8431-1660-1(9) , Price Stern Sloan) Penguin Group (USA) Inc.

SAINT PETERSBURG (RUSSIA)

Langley, Andrew. St. Petersburg. 2005. (Great Cities of the World Ser.). (Illus.). 48p. (J). pap. (978-0-8368-5214-1(1)); 30.00 (978-0-8368-5054-3(8)) Stevens, Gareth Inc. (World Almanac Library).

SAINT PETERSBURG (RUSSIA)—HISTORY

Bloom, Harold, ed. St. Petersburg. 2005. (Bloom's Literary Places Ser.). (Illus.). 150p. (gr. 9-13). pap. (978-0-7910-8384-0(5) , Chelsea Hse.) Facts On File, Inc.

Woodworth, Bradley & Richards, Constance E., eds. St. Petersburg. 2005. (Bloom's Literary Places Ser.). (Illus.). 137p. (YA). (gr. 9-13). lib. bdg. 40.00 (978-0-7910-7837-2(X) , Chelsea Hse.) Facts On File, Inc.

SAINT VALENTINE'S DAY

see Valentine's Day

SAINTS

see also Legends

Amadeo, Diana M. Holy Friends: Thirty Saints & Blesseds of the Americas. Curreli, Augusta & Lombardo, Irina, illus. 2005. 136p. (J). (ps-7). 19.95 (978-0-8198-3384-6(3)) Pauline Bks. & Media.

Ancell, Carolyn D. Can the Saints Come Out to Play? A Saint Story for Everyday May Saints, Vol. 9. Meehan, Rosario, tr. from SPA. abr. ed. 2000. (Can the Saints Come Out to Play Ser.:). 74p. (J). (gr. k-7). 12.95 (978-1-893757-16-5(1) , 16-1) Needer, E.T. Publishing.

—Can the Saints Come Out to Play: July Saints. Meehan, Rosario, tr. 2000. (Saint for Every Day Ser.: Vol. 11). 74p. (J). (gr. k-7). 12.95 (978-1-893757-18-9(8) , 18-8) Needer, E.T. Publishing.

—Can the Saints Come Out to Play? June Saints: A Saint for Everyday. Meehan, Rosario, tr. from SPA. 2000. (Can the Saints Come Out to Play Ser.: No. 10). 74p. (J). (gr. k-7). 12.95 (978-1-893757-17-2(X) , 17-x) Needer, E.T. Publishing.

—Can the Saints Come Out to Play! - A Saint Story for Every Day Vol. 5: January Saints. Meehan, Rosario, tr. 2000. Tr. of Pueden Salir a Jugar los Santos. (Illus.). 74p. (J). (gr. 1-8). 12.95 (978-1-893757-11-0(0) , 11-0) Needer, E.T. Publishing.

—Can the Saints Come Out to Play - August. Meehan, Rosario, tr. 2000. (Saint for Everyday Ser.: No. 12). 74p. (J). 12.95 (978-1-893757-19-6(6) , 19-6) Needer, E.T. Publishing.

Baudouin-Croix, Marie. Saint Therese of Lisieux: And the "Little Way" of Love. Keefe, Maryellen, tr. from FRE. Bienfait, Andree, illus. 1999. (Along the Paths of the Gospel Ser.). 74p. (J). (gr. 2-5). 6.95 (978-0-8198-7021-6(8) , 332-339) Pauline Bks. & Media.

Benson, Robert Hugh. An Alphabet of Saints. (Illus.). 32p. (J). (ps-7). reprint ed. 16.00 (978-1-930873-12-4(3)) Neumann Pr., The.

Bertanzetti, Eileen Dunn. Saint Pio of Pietrelcina: Rich in Love. Ritz, Karen, illus. 2002. (Encounter the Saints Ser.: Vol. 13). 120p. (J). pap. 5.95 (978-0-8198-7067-4(6) , 332-364) Pauline Bks. & Media.

Betz, Eva K. Blessed Sebastian & the Oxen. 2003. (Illus.). 48p. (J). 16.00 (978-1-930873-82-7(4)) Neumann Pr., The.

—Saint Brigid & the Cows. 2004. (Illus.). 47p. (J). 16.00 (978-1-930873-95-7(6)) Neumann Pr., The.

—Saint Colum & the Crane. 2003. (Illus.). 47p. (J). 16.00 (978-1-930873-84-1(0)) Neumann Pr., The.

—Saint Germaine & the Sheep. 2004. (Illus.). 48p. (J). 16.00 (978-1-930873-96-4(4)) Neumann Pr., The.

—Saint Martin Deporres & the Mice. 2003. (Illus.). 47p. (J). 16.00 (978-1-930873-83-4(2)) Neumann Pr., The.

Billington, Rachel. The Life of Saint Francis. (Illus.). 48p. pap. 11.99 (978-0-340-71427-0(1) , Hodder & Stoughton) Hodder General Publishing Division GBR. *Dist:* Trafalgar Square Publishing.

Bladey, Conrad Jay. The Good Saint Brigid of Kildare: A Guide to the Primary Stories & Instructions for Celebrat. 2000. (Illus.). 20p. pap. 4.00 (978-0-9702386-1-0(4)) Hutman Productions.

Brassey, Richard. George & the Dragon & Other Saintly Stories. 2003. (Illus.). 40p. pap. 11.00 (978-1-84255-082-3(9)) Orion Children's Bks. GBR. *Dist:* Trafalgar Square Publishing.

Brassey, Richard, illus. George & the Dragon & Other Saintly Stories. 2003. 40p. 19.99 (978-1-84255-019-9(5)) Orion Children's Bks. GBR. *Dist:* Trafalgar Square Publishing.

Briere, Euphemia. Victor Constantinus, Maximus Augustus: The Life of Saint Constantine, the First Christian Emperor & His Mother, Saint Helena. 2003. (Illus.). (J). 4.00 (978-0-913026-90-8(5) , VC) St. Nectarios Pr.

Brown, Ann. St. Bakhita: From African Slave to Servant of the Good Master. 2000. (Illus.). 40p. (YA). pap. 3.00 (978-1-892875-11-2(X) , 3020) New Hope Pubns.

Brown, Don. Across a Dark & Wild Sea. ed. 2004. (Illus.). (J). (gr. k-3). spiral bd. (978-0-616-14616-3(7)) Canadian National Institute for the Blind/Institut National Canadien pour les Aveugles.

—Across a Dark & Wild Sea. Brown, Don, illus. rev. ed. 2002. (Illus.). 32p. (J). (gr. 1-4). 22.90 (978-0-7613-2415-7(1)); 15.95 (978-0-7613-1534-6(9)) Roaring Brook Pr.

Buell, Jean. A Beginner's Book of Saints. Larkin, Jean K., ed. 2006. (Illus.). 32p. (J). 3.95 (978-1-933178-30-1(2)) Pflaum Publishing Group.

Canton, William. Childs Book of Saints. 2006. pap. 27.95 ***(978-1-4286-3503-6(3))*** Kessinger Publishing, LLC.

Catholic Book Publishing Company Staff, Co Book Publishing. Book of Saints: XII. 1998. (gr. k-3). lib. bdg. 21.70 (978-0-613-90520-6(2)) Tandem Library Bks.

Contopoulos, Catherine K. The Boy, a Kitchen, & His Cave: The Tale of Saint Euphrosynos the Cook. Greene-Gross, Chrissanth, illus. 2002. 32p. (J). 17.00 (978-0-88141-241-3(4)) St. Vladimir's Seminary Pr.

Cook, Frederick. The Stories of Five Great Saints. (J). reprint ed. 2002. (Illus.). 118p. 13.00 (978-1-930873-49-0(2)); 2001. 17.00 (978-1-930873-29-2(8)) Neumann Pr., The.

S

SAINTS—DICTIONARIES

SAINTS—FICTION

S

Sturt, M. The Canterbury Pilgrims (Being Chaucer's. 2006. 94.99 (***978-1-4280-0313-2(4)***); pap. 88.99 (***978-1-4280-0309-5(6)***) IndyPublish.com.

Thottam, Meena, adapted by. The Sage's Daughter. 2006. (J). 3.95 (***978-0-9776917-2-2(1)***, Curcumin Bks.) Davlaw Press.

Wells, Rosemary. The Miraculous Tale of the Two Maries. Mathers, Petra, illus. 2006. 32p. (J). (gr. 1). 16.99 (978-0-670-05960-7(9), Viking Juvenile) Penguin Group (USA) Inc.

SAINTS—LEGENDS

Alves, Mary E. & Kelley, Patrick, illus. Saint Francis of Assisi: Gentle Revolutionary. rev. ed. 1999. (Encounter the Saints Ser.: No. 4). 120p. (J). (gr. 5-9). pap. 5.95 (978-0-8198-7030-8(7), 332-342) Pauline Bks. & Media.

Bertanzetti, Eileen Dunn. Rich in Love: The Story of Padre Pio of Pietrelcina. 1999. (Weaver Bks.). 72p. (YA). (gr. 6-9). pap. 3.95 (978-0-8198-6470-3(6)) Pauline Bks. & Media.

Grunwell, Jeanne Marie & Goering, Mari, illus. Saint Elizabeth Ann Seton: Daughter of America. 1999. (Encounter the Saints Ser.: No. 3). 132p. (YA). (gr. 5-9). pap. 7.95 (978-0-8198-7022-3(6), 332-340) Pauline Bks. & Media.

Heffernan, Anne Eileen, et al. Saint Bernadette Soubirous: Light in the Grotto. 1999. (Encounter the Saints Ser.: No. 2). Orig. Title: Light in the Grotto. (Illus.). 120p. (YA). (gr. 5-9). pap. 5.95 (978-0-8198-7020-9(X), 332-338) Pauline Bks. & Media.

Jauss, Ann Marie. Legends of Saints & Beasts. 2000. (Illus.). 48p. (J). (gr. 2-6). reprint ed. 19.00 (978-1-930873-18-6(2)) Neumann Pr., The.

Kerry, Margaret Charles, et al. Saint Anthony of Padua: Fire & Light. 1999. (Encounter the Saints Ser.: No. 1). (Illus.). 120p. (YA). (gr. 5-9). pap. 5.95 (978-0-8198-7019-3(6), 332-337) Pauline Bks. & Media.

Rock, Lois. Saintly Tales & Legends. Balit, Christina, illus. 2004. 100p. (J). 15.95 (978-0-8198-7083-4(8), 332-379) Pauline Bks. & Media.

Zarin, Cynthia. Saints among the Animals. Gore, Leonid, illus. 2006. 96p. (J). 17.95 (978-0-689-85031-8(X), Atheneum) Simon & Schuster Children's Publishing.

SALADS

Beck, Isabel L., et al. Trophies Kindergarten: The Salad. 2003. (Trophies Ser.). (gr. k-6). 13.80 (978-0-15-329524-9(4)) Harcourt Schl. Pubs.

La ensalada de Frutas: Individual Title, 6 pack. (Coleccion Pm Ser.: Vol. 2). Tr. of Fruit salad. (SPA.). 16p. (gr. k-1). 26.00 (978-0-7578-0690-2(2)) Rigby Education.

Lee, Frances. Fruit Salad. 1999. (ps-2). lib. bdg. 11.10 (978-0-613-30420-7(9)) Tandem Library Bks.

SALAMANDERS

Bredeson, Carmen. Fun Facts about Salamanders! 2007. (I Like Reptiles & Amphibians! Ser.). (Illus.). 24p. (J). (gr. 1-3). lib. bdg. 21.26 (978-0-7660-2790-9(2), Enslow Elementary) Enslow Pubs., Inc.

Burns, Diane L. Snakes, Salamanders & Lizards. Garrow, Linda, illus. 1998. 47p. (J). (gr. 2-5). lib. bdg. 16.40 (978-0-613-26969-8(1)) Tandem Library Bks.

Dell'Oro, Suzanne Paul. Sneaky Salamanders. 1999. (gr. k-3). lib. bdg. 14.10 (978-0-613-43891-9(4)) Tandem Library Bks.

Dell'Oro, Suzanne Paul & Varela-Paul, Andres. Sneaky Salamanders. Netherton, John, illus. (Pull Ahead Bks.). 32p. (J). (gr. k-2). 1999. lib. bdg. 22.60 (978-0-8225-3612-3(9), Lerner Pubns.); 1998. pap. 5.95 (978-0-8225-3618-5(8)) Lerner Publishing Group.

Do Salamanders Spit? (Animals All Around Ser.). 24p. (J). 7.95 (978-1-4048-0380-0(7)) Picture Window Bks.

Himmelman, John. A Salamander's Life. Stewart, Melissa, ed. Himmelman, John, illus. 1998. (Nature Upclose Ser.). (Illus.). 32p. (J). (gr. k-2). pap. 6.95 (978-0-516-26355-7(2), Children's Pr.) Scholastic Library Publishing.

Maruska, Edward J. Salamanders. 2006. (New Naturebooks). (Illus.). 32p. (J). (gr. 1-5). 27.07 (978-1-59296-648-6(9)) Child's World, Inc.

McNab, Chris. Frogs, Toads & Salamanders. 2006. (Nature's Monsters Ser.). (Illus.). 32p. (J). lib. bdg. 23.33 (978-0-8368-6172-3(8)) Stevens, Gareth Inc.

Miller, Sara Swan. Salamanders: Secret, Silent Lives. (Animals in Order Ser.). (Illus.). 48p. (J). (gr. 4-6). 2000. pap. 6.95 (978-0-531-16402-0(0)); 1999. 26.50 (978-0-531-11568-8(2)) Scholastic Library Publishing. (Watts, Franklin).

—Salamanders: Secret, Silent Lives. 1999. (gr. 3-6). lib. bdg. 15.25 (978-0-613-34925-3(3)) Tandem Library Bks.

Murray, Julie. Salamanders. 2005. (Animal Kingdom Set Ii Ser.). (Illus.). 24p. (J). (gr. k-4). lib. bdg. 21.35 (978-1-59197-334-8(1)) ABDO Publishing Co.

Ogle, Belinda. Cockatiels. 2004. (Keeping Unusual Pets Ser.). (Illus.). 48p. (J). (978-1-4034-0826-6(2)); (978-1-4034-0824-2(6)) Heinemann Library.

Squire, Ann O. Chinese Giant Salamander: The World's Biggest Amphibian. 2007. (SuperSized! Ser.). (Illus.). 24p. (J). (gr. k-2). lib. bdg. 21.28 (978-1-59716-386-6(4), 1265931) Bearport Publishing Co., Inc.

Tomljanovic, Tatiana. Caring for Your Salamander. 2006. (J). (978-1-59036-477-2(5)); lib. bdg. (978-1-59036-476-5(7)) Weigl Pubs., Inc.

SALEM (FICTITIOUS CHARACTER)—FICTION

Gallagher, Diana G. Worth a Shot. 2000. (Sabrina, the Teenage Witch: No. 11). 81p. (J). (gr. 2-5). per. (978-0-671-77334-2(8), Simon & Schuster Children's Publishing) Simon & Schuster Children's Publishing.

—Worth a Shot. 2000. (gr. 3-6). lib. bdg. 11.80 (978-0-613-28143-0(8)) Tandem Library Bks.

Holder, Nancy. Feline Felon. 1999. (gr. 3-6). lib. bdg. 11.80 (978-0-613-21530-5(3)) Tandem Library Bks.

Krulik, Nancy E. Rulin' the School. 2000. (Sabrina, the Teenage Witch: No. 12). (Illus.). 85p. (J). (gr. 2-5). per. (978-0-671-77335-9(6), Simon & Schuster Children's Publishing) Simon & Schuster Children's Publishing.

—Rulin' the School. 2000. (gr. 3-6). lib. bdg. 11.80 (978-0-613-28047-1(4)) Tandem Library Bks.

Weiss, David Cody. Kitty Cornered. 2000. (Sabrina, the Teenage Witch: No. 13). (Illus.). 64p. (J). (gr. 2-5). per. (978-0-671-77336-6(4), Simon & Schuster Children's Publishing) Simon & Schuster Children's Publishing.

SALEM (MASS.)—HISTORY

Asirvatham, Sandy. The Salem Witch Trials. 2001. (Great Disasters, Reforms & Ramifications Ser.). (Illus.). 112p. (J). 30.00 (978-0-7910-6328-6(3), Chelsea Hse.) Facts On File, Inc.

Boraas, Tracey. The Salem Witch Trials. 2004. (Let Freedom Ring Ser.). (Illus.). 48p. (J). lib. bdg. 23.93 (978-0-7368-2464-4(2), Bridgestone Bks.) Capstone Pr., Inc.

Burgan, Michael. The Salem Witch Trials. 2004. (We the People Ser.). (Illus.). 48p. (J). 22.60 (978-0-7565-0845-6(2)) Compass Point Bks.

Crewe, Sabrina & Uschan, Michael V. The Salem Witch Trials. 2004. (Events That Shaped America Ser.). (Illus.). 32p. (J). lib. bdg. 24.67 (978-0-8368-3406-2(2)) Stevens, Gareth Inc.

Dolan, Edward F., Jr. The Salem Witch Trials. 2001. (Kaleidoscope Ser.). (Illus.). 48p. (J). (gr. 3 up). lib. bdg. 25.64 (978-0-7614-1302-8(2), Benchmark Bks.) Cavendish, Marshall Corp.

Fremon, David K. The Salem Witchcraft Trials in American History. 1999. (In American History Ser.). (Illus.). 128p. (YA). (gr. 5-12). lib. bdg. 26.60 (978-0-7660-1125-0(9)) Enslow Pubs., Inc.

Hermes, Patricia. Salem Witch. 2006. (My Side of the Story Ser.). 192p. (J). (gr. 5-9). pap. 7.95 (978-0-7534-5991-1(4), Kingfisher) Houghton Mifflin Co. Trade & Reference Div.

Martin, Michael. The Salem Witch Trials. (Graphic History Ser.). 32p. (YA). pap. 7.95 (978-0-7368-5246-3(8)) Capstone Pr., Inc.

Marvel, Laura, ed. The Salem Witch Trials. 2002. (At Issue in History Ser.). (Illus.). 144p. (J). (gr. 7-10). lib. bdg. 33.70 (978-0-7377-0823-3(9), Greenhaven Pr., Inc.) Thomson Gale.

Nardo, Don. The Salem Witch Trials. 2007. (American History Ser.). 128p. (J). (gr. 7-10). 32.45 (***978-1-59018-950-4(7)***, Lucent Bks.) Thomson Gale.

Orr, Tamra. The Salem Witch Trials. 2003. (People at the Center of Ser.). (Illus.). 48p. (J). 24.95 (978-1-56711-770-7(8), Blackbirch Pr., Inc.) Thomson Gale.

Priestley, Chris. Witch Hunt. 160p. (J). pap. 9.99 (978-0-340-86056-4(1)) Hodder General Publishing Division GBR. *Dist:* Independent Pubs. Group.

Roach, Marilynne K. In the Days of the Salem Witchcraft Trials. 2003. 96p. (J). (gr. 5 up). pap. 5.95 (978-0-618-39196-7(7)) Houghton Mifflin Co. Trade & Reference Div.

—In the Days of the Salem Witchcraft Trials. 2003. (gr. 3-6). lib. bdg. 14.10 (978-0-613-86973-7(7)) Tandem Library Bks.

The Salem Witch Trials, 6 vols. (gr. 2-5). 39.95 (978-0-7368-4570-0(4)) Red Brick Learning.

Salem Witch Trials. (Colonial America Ser.). 48p. (YA). 7.95 (978-0-7368-4481-9(3)) Capstone Pr., Inc.

Uschan, Michael V. The Salem Witch Trials. 2004. (Landmark Events in American History Ser.). (Illus.). 48p. (J). (gr. 5 up). pap. 11.95 (978-0-8368-5415-2(2)); lib. bdg. 30.00 (978-0-8368-5387-2(3)) Stevens, Gareth Inc. (World Almanac Library).

Wallis, Jeffrey. Trials in Salem. 2005. (Houghton Mifflin Social Studies Leveled Readers). (Illus.). 16p. (J). pap. (***978-0-618-56037-0(8)***) Houghton Mifflin Co.

Woods, Geraldine. The Salem Witchcraft Trials: A Headline Court Case. 2000. (Headline Court Cases Ser.). (Illus.). 104p. (YA). (gr. 6-12). lib. bdg. 26.60 (978-0-7660-1383-4(9)) Enslow Pubs., Inc.

SALES PERSONNEL

see also Advertising; Business; Marketing

Adil, Janeen R. Goods & Services. 2006. (First Facts. Learning about Money Ser.). (Illus.). 24p. (J). (978-0-7368-5395-8(2)) Capstone Pr., Inc.

Bailey, Gerry & Law, Felicia. Save, Spend, Share: Using Your Money. Phillips, Mike et al, illus. 2006. (My Money Ser.). 24p. (J). (gr. 4-6). 27.93 (978-0-7565-1672-7(2)) Compass Point Bks.

Ferguson. Careers in Focus: Retail. 3rd rev. ed. 2007. (Careers in Focus Ser.). 192p. (J). (gr. 6-12). 29.95 (***978-0-8160-6593-6(4)***, Ferguson Publishing Co.) Facts On File, Inc.

Sun-Tzu & Gagliardi, Gary. Strategy for Sales Managers: Sun Tzu's the Art of War Plus Book Series. 2005. (Art of War Plus Ser.). (Illus.). 192p. 16.95 (978-1-929194-33-9(1), Art of War Plus Bks.) Clearbridge Publishing.

SALES PERSONNEL—FICTION

Andrews, Jan. Auction. (Illus.). (J). 13.95 (978-0-88899-110-2(X)); pap. 5.95 (978-0-88899-168-3(1)) Groundwood Bks. CAN. *Dist:* Transition Vendor.

Bauer, Joan. Unterwegs Mit Mrs. Gladstone. 2002. (GER.). 224p. pap. 15.00 (978-1-4000-3960-9(6), New Media German Language) Random House Foreign Language Publishing.

London, Jonathan. The Candystore Man. O'Malley, Kevin & Brown, Malcolm, illus. 1998. 24p. (J). (gr. k-3). 16.00 (978-0-688-13241-5(3)); 15.89 (978-0-688-13242-2(1)) HarperCollins Pubs.

McOmber, Rachel B., ed. McOmber Phonics Storybooks: The Lemonade Sale. rev. ed. (Illus.). (J). (978-0-944991-41-1(6)) Swift Learning Resources.

O'Neill, Alexis. Estela's Swap. Sanchez, Enrique O., illus. 2002. 32p. (J). (ps-2). 16.95 (978-1-58430-044-1(2)) Lee & Low Bks., Inc.

Williams-Garcia, Rita. Fast Talk on a Slow Track. 1998. 192p. (J). (gr. 7-12). pap. 6.99 (978-0-14-130231-7(3), Puffin) Penguin Group (USA) Inc.

SALES PERSONNEL—VOCATIONAL GUIDANCE

Bagley, Katie. Cashiers. 2001. (Community Helpers Ser.). (Illus.). 92p. (J). (gr. 1-2). 18.60 (978-0-7368-0806-4(X), Bridgestone Bks.) Capstone Pr., Inc.

Ferguson. Careers in Focus: Retail. 2nd ed. 2002. (Careers in Focus Ser.). 192p. (gr. 6-12). 22.95 (978-0-89434-437-4(4), F516, Ferguson Publishing Co.) Facts On File, Inc.

J. G. Ferguson Publishing Company Staff. Careers in Focus: Retail. 2000. (Careers in Focus Ser.). 188p. (YA). (gr. 7 up). lib. bdg. 98.00 (978-0-89434-357-5(2), F516, Ferguson Publishing Co.) Facts On File, Inc.

SALESMEN

see Sales Personnel

SALINGER, J. D. (JEROME DAVID), 1919-

The Catcher in the Rye. 1998. 44p. (YA). 11.95 (978-1-56137-450-2(4), NU4504SP) Novel Units, Inc.

Kerr, Christine. Bloom's How to Write about J. D. Salinger. 2007. (Bloom's How to Write about Literature Ser.). 256p. (YA). (gr. 9 up). 45.00 (***978-0-7910-9483-9(9)***, Chelsea Hse.) Facts On File, Inc.

SALK, JONAS, 1914-1995

Bankston, John. Jonas Salk & the Polio Vaccine. 2002. (Unlocking the Secrets of Science Ser.). (Illus.). 56p. (gr. 4-10). lib. bdg. 25.70 (978-1-58415-093-0(9)) Mitchell Lane Pubs., Inc.

Barter, James E. Jonas Salk. 2002. (Importance of Ser.). (Illus.). 120p. (J). (gr. 4-12). 32.45 (978-1-56006-968-3(6), Lucent Bks.) Thomson Gale.

Durrett, Deanne. Jonas Salk. 2002. (Inventors & Creators Ser.). (Illus.). 48p. (J). (gr. 3-5). 23.70 (978-0-7377-1277-3(5), LML00902-180219, Kidhaven) Thomson Gale.

Hantula, Richard. Jonas Salk. 2004. (Trailblazers of the Modern World Ser.). (Illus.). 48p. (J). (gr. 5 up). pap. 11.95 (978-0-8368-5260-8(5)); lib. bdg. 30.00 (978-0-8368-5100-7(5)) Stevens, Gareth Inc. (World Almanac Library).

Krohn, Katherine E. Jonas Salk & the Polio Vaccine. Milgrom, A., illus. 2007. (Graphic Library). 32p. (J). 25.26 (978-0-7368-6483-1(0)) Capstone Pr., Inc.

McLeese, Don. Jonas Salk. (Rourke Discovery Library). (Illus.). 24p. 2006. (gr. 2-5). 14.95 (978-1-59515-436-1(1)); 2005. (ENG & SPA., (J). (978-1-59515-676-1(3)) Rourke Publishing, LLC.

McPherson, Stephanie Sammartino. Jonas Salk: Conquering Polio. 128p. (J). (gr. 6 up). 20.95 (978-1-58013-207-7(3)) Kar-Ben Publishing.

—Jonas Salk: Conquering Polio. 2001. (Lerner Biographies Ser.). (Illus.). 128p. (YA). (gr. 6-12). lib. bdg. 27.93 (978-0-8225-4964-2(6), Lerner Pubns.) Lerner Publishing Group.

Naden, Corinne J. & Blue, Rose. Jonas Salk: Polio Pioneer. 2001. (Gateway Biography Ser.). (Illus.). 48p. (J). (gr. 2-4). lib. bdg. 23.90 (978-0-7613-1804-0(6), Millbrook Pr.) Lerner Publishing Group.

Parks, Peggy J. Jonas Salk: Polio Vaccine Pioneer. 2003. (Giants of Science Ser.). (Illus.). 64p. (J). 26.20 (978-1-56711-475-1(X), Blackbirch Pr., Inc.) Thomson Gale.

Reis, Ronald A. Jonas Salk: Microbiologist. 2005. (Ferguson Career Biographies Ser.). (Illus.). 128p. (gr. 6-12). 25.00 (978-0-8160-6186-0(6), Ferguson Publishing Co.) Facts On File, Inc.

Sherrow, Victoria. Jonas Salk: Beyond the Microscope. 2nd rev. ed. 2008. (Makers of Modern Science Ser.). 160p. (J). (gr. 6-12). 29.95 (***978-0-8160-6180-8(7)***, Chelsea Hse.) Facts On File, Inc.

Tocci, Salvatore. Jonas Salk: Creator of the Polio Vaccine. 2003. (Great Minds of Science Ser.). (Illus.). 128p. (J). (gr. 4-10). lib. bdg. 26.60 (978-0-7660-2097-9(5)) Enslow Pubs., Inc.

SALMON

Cooper, Jason. Pacific Salmon. 2003. (Life Cycles Ser.). (Illus.). 24p. (J). (gr. 1-4). 17.95 (978-1-58952-352-4(0)) Rourke Publishing, LLC.

Glimmerveen, Ulco. Leaper: The Amazing Life of the Salmon. (Illus.). 32p. (J). pap. (978-1-86943-042-9(5)) Scholastic New Zealand Ltd.

Goldish, Meish. Salmon & Other Bony Fish, Vol. 6. 2002. (World Book's Animals of the World Ser.: Set 3). (Illus.). 64p. (J). (978-0-7166-1229-2(1)) World Bk., Inc.

Hibbert. Life of a Salmon, 6 Pack. 2004. pap. 40.50 (978-1-4109-0826-1(7)) Harcourt Schl. Pubs.

Hibbert, Clare. The Life of a Salmon. 2004. (Raintree Perspectives Ser.). (Illus.). 32p. (J). pap. (978-1-4109-0819-3(4)) Harcourt Schl. Pubs.

—The Life of a Salmon. 2004. (Life Cycles (Perspectives) Ser.). (Illus.). 32p. (J). (gr. 3-5). lib. bdg. 19.25 (978-1-4109-0543-7(8)) Raintree.

Hodge, Deborah. Salmon. Ogle, Nancy Gray, illus. unabr. ed. 2004. (Kids Can Press Wildlife Ser.). 32p. (J). (gr. k-3). (978-1-55074-963-2(3)); (978-1-55074-961-8(7)) Kids Can Pr., Ltd.

James, Sylvia M. Salmon. Bachem, Paul, illus. 2000. 32p. (J). (gr. 3-5). pap. 4.95 (978-1-57255-805-2(9)) Mondo Publishing.

—Salmon. 2000. (gr. 3-6). lib. bdg. 12.95 (978-0-613-83696-8(0)); (978-0-606-22650-9(8)) Tandem Library Bks.

James, Sylvia M. & Bachem, Paul. Salmon. 2000. (J). (gr. k-5). (978-1-57255-806-9(7)) Mondo Publishing.

Johnson, Guinevere. Wool. 1999. (Let's Investigate Ser.). (Illus.). 32p. (J). (gr. 1-4). lib. bdg. 18.95 (978-0-88682-965-0(8), Creative Education) Creative Co., The.

Kalman, Bobbie & Sjonger, Rebecca. The Life Cycle of a Salmon. 2006. (Life Cycle Ser.). (Illus.). 32p. (J). (gr. 2-3). pap. (978-0-7787-0705-9(9)); lib. bdg. (978-0-7787-0631-1(1)) Crabtree Publishing Co.

The Life Cycle of a Salmon, Vol. 2. 2005. (Animals, Animals, Animals Ser.). (YA). (gr. k-3). (978-0-7368-3397-4(8), Pebble Bks.) Capstone Pr., Inc.

Martin-James, Kathleen. Swimming Salmon. 2002. (Pull Ahead Bks.). (Illus.). 32p. (J). lib. bdg. 22.60 (978-0-8225-0687-4(4)) Lerner Publishing Group.

—Swimming Salmon. 2003. (gr. k-3). lib. bdg. 14.10 (978-0-613-52506-0(X)) Tandem Library Bks.

McMillan, Bruce. Salmon Summer. 1998. (Illus.). 32p. (J). (gr. k-3). tchr. ed. 17.00 (978-0-395-84544-8(0), Walter Lorraine) Houghton Mifflin Co. Trade & Reference Div.

Murray, Julie. Salmon. 2007. (Life Cycles Ser.). 24p. (J). (gr. k-4). lib. bdg. 21.35 (***978-1-59928-710-2(2)***, Buddy Bks.) ABDO Publishing Co.

Reed-Jones, Carol. Salmon Stream. Maydak, Michael S., illus. 2004. (Sharing Nature with Children Book Ser.). 32p. (YA). (gr. 4-7). 16.95 (978-1-58469-014-6(3)); pap. 7.95 (978-1-58469-013-9(5)) Dawn Pubns.

—Salmon Stream. 2001. (978-0-606-22242-6(1)); 2000. lib. bdg. 16.40 (978-0-613-35701-2(9)) Tandem Library Bks.

Royston, Angela. Salmon. 2002. (Life Cycle of a... Ser.). (Illus.). 32p. (J). (gr. k-2). pap. 6.95 (978-1-58810-327-7(7), 91062) Heinemann Library.

—Salmon. 2000. (Illus.). (J). (978-0-606-22018-7(6)) Tandem Library Bks.

Thomson, Ruth. Salmon. 2007. (J). lib. bdg. (***978-1-4042-3712-4(7)***, PowerKids Pr.) Rosen Publishing Group, Inc., The.

Trumbauer, Lisa. The Life Cycle of a Salmon. 2002. (Life Cycles Ser.). (Illus.). 24p. (J). (gr. k-1). lib. bdg. 15.93 (978-0-7368-1453-9(1), Pebble Bks.) Capstone Pr., Inc.

Winkelman, Barbara Gaines. Sockeye's Journey Home: The Story of a Pacific Salmon. Popeo, Joanie, illus. 2005. (Smithsonian Oceanic Collection). 32p. (J). (ps-2). 19.95 incl. reel tape (978-1-56899-831-2(7), BC4019); 15.95 (978-1-56899-829-9(5), B4019) Soundprints.

—Sockeye's Journey Home Micro Edition: The Story of a Pacific Salmon. Popeo, Joanie, illus. 2005. (Smithsonian Oceanic Collection: Vol. 19). 32p. (J). (ps-2). 4.95 (978-1-56899-830-5(9), B4069) Soundprints.

—Sockeye's Journey Home Micro, Included Toy: The Story of a Pacific Salmon. Popeo, Joanie, illus. 2005. (Smithsonian Oceanic Collection: Vol. 19). 32p. (J). (ps-2). 9.95 (978-1-56899-834-3(1), PB4069) Soundprints.

SALOMON, HAYM, 1740-1785

Amler, Jane Frances. Haym Salomon: Patriot Banker of the American Revolution. 2005. (Library of American Lives & Times). (Illus.). 112p. (YA). (gr. 4-8). lib. bdg. 31.95 (978-0-8239-6629-5(1)) Rosen Publishing Group, Inc., The.

Rubin, Susan Goldman. Haym Salomon: American Patriot. Slonim, David, illus. 2007. 40p. (J). (ps-5). 16.95 (978-0-8109-1087-4(X), Abrams Bks. for Young Readers) Abrams, Harry N., Inc.

SALOONS

see Restaurants

SALT

Dunlop, Jenna. Salt. 2004. (Rocks, Minerals, & Resources Ser.). (Illus.). 32p. (J). (978-0-7787-1411-8(X)); pap. (978-0-7787-1443-9(8)) Crabtree Publishing Co.

Franck, Irene M. & Brownstone, David M. Salt. 2003. (Illus.). 32p. (J). (978-0-7172-5722-5(3), Grolier) Scholastic Library Publishing.

Kurlansky, Mark & Schindler, S. D. The Story of Salt. 2006. (Illus.). 48p. (J). (ps-3). 16.99 (978-0-399-23998-4(7), Putnam Juvenile) Penguin Group (USA) Inc.

Lilly, Melinda. Salt. 2001. (Around the World with Food & Spices Ser.). (Illus.). 32p. (J). (gr. 3-5). lib. bdg. 26.60 (978-1-58952-048-6(3)) Rourke Publishing, LLC.

Morris, Neil. Salt. 2005. (Earth's Resources Ser.). (Illus.). 32p. (J). (gr. 4-7). lib. bdg. 27.10 (978-1-58340-633-5(6)) Smart Apple Media.

Nelson, Robin. From Sea to Salt. 2004. (Start to Finish Ser.). (Illus.). 24p. (J). 18.60 (978-0-8225-0946-2(6), Lerner Pubns.) Lerner Publishing Group.

Robinson Masters, Nancy. Salt. 2008. (J). lib. bdg. 25.26 (***978-1-60279-120-6(1)***) Cherry Lake Publishing.

Salt: Individual Title Six-Packs. (Rigby Focus Ser.). 24p. (gr. 2 up). 28.00 (978-0-7578-5334-0(X)); 30.00 (978-0-7578-5564-1(4)) Rigby Education.

Strom, Laura Layton. The Rock We Eat: Salt. 2007. (Shockwave: Economics & Geography Ser.). (Illus.). 36p. (J). (gr. 4-6). lib. bdg. 25.00 (***978-0-531-17799-0(8)***, Children's Pr.) Scholastic Library Publishing.

SALUTATIONS

see Etiquette; Letter Writing

SALVADOR

see El Salvador

SALVAGE

see also Shipwrecks; Skin Diving

Wilcox, Charlotte. Recycling & Waste Management. 2007. (Cool Science Ser.). 48p. (J). (gr. 4-8). lib. bdg. 26.60 (***978-0-8225-6768-4(7)***) Lerner Publishing Group.

SALVATION ARMY

Blackwell, Miriam. Visiting a Salvation Army Citadel. 2000. (gr. 7-12). lib. bdg. 18.80 (978-0-613-89219-3(4)) Tandem Library Bks.

SAMOAN ISLANDS

Puerto Rico y Otras Areas Perifericas. (World Almanac Ser.).Tr. of Puerto Rico & Other Outlying Areas. (SPA.). (J). (gr. 3-5). 30.00 (978-0-8368-5726-9(7), GHS32693) Stevens, Gareth Inc.

SAMOAN ISLANDS—FICTION

Bessey, Sian Ann. Uprising in Samoa: A Novel. 2004. 178p. (J). (978-1-59156-890-2(0)) Covenant Communications.

Hamilton, Bethany & Bundschuh, Rick. Burned. 2007. (Soul Surfer#8482; Ser.). (Illus.). 144p. (J). pap. 6.99 (978-0-310-71223-7(8)) Zonderkidz.

SAMSON (BIBLICAL JUDGE)

Davidson, Alice Joyce. Samson & His Strength. Lyon, Tammie Speer, illus. 1998. (My Bible Friends Board Bks.). 12p. (J). 3.99 (978-0-310-97324-9(4)) Zonderkidz.

Lashbrook, Marilyn. The Weak Strongman: Samson. 1998. (J). (gr. 3-5). pap. 5.95 (978-0-933657-81-6(1)) Standard Publishing.

The Story of Samson. 2002. (Illus.). 24p. (J). bds. 6.95 (978-0-8249-4226-7(4)) Ideals Pubns.

SAMURAI

Collins, Paul. Samurai. 2001. (Illus.). 32p. (J). 28.00 (978-0-7910-6872-4(2) , Chelsea Hse.) Facts On File, Inc.

Dean, Arlan. Samurai: Warlords of Japan. 2005. (Way of the Warrior Ser.). (Illus.). 48p. (J). 24.00 (978-0-516-25119-6(8)); (gr. 7-12). pap. 6.95 (978-0-516-25088-5(4)) Scholastic Library Publishing. (Children's Pr.).

Hall, Eleanor J. Life among the Samurai. 1998. (Way People Live Ser.). (Illus.). 112p. (YA). (gr. 7-10). 28.70 (978-1-56006-390-2(4) , LML00902-177772, Lucent Bks.) Thomson Gale.

Hanel, Rachael. Samurai. 2007. (J). (978-1-58341-538-2(6) , Creative Education) Creative Co., The.

Leavitt, Caroline. Samurai. 2006. (Edge Books, Warriors of History). (Illus.). (J). (gr. 4-7). lib. bdg. 23.93 (***978-0-7368-6433-6(4)*** , Edge Bks.) Capstone Pr., Inc.

MacDonald, Fiona. How to Be a Samurai Warrior. James, John, illus. 2005. (How to Be Ser.). 32p. (J). (gr. 3-7). 21.90 (978-0-7922-3633-7(5) , National Geographic Children's Bks.) National Geographic Society.

MacDonald, Fiona & Donnelly, S. E. How to Be a Samurai Warrior. James, John, illus. 2005. (How to Be Ser.). 32p. (J). (gr. 3-7). 14.95 (978-0-7922-3618-4(1) , National Geographic Children's Bks.) National Geographic Society.

Main Idea & Details Spanish Version, Gr. 1-3. 2005. (J). per. (978-1-58232-147-9(7)) Bryan Hse. Pubs., Inc.

Pickels, Dwayne E. Ancient Warriors. 1998. (Costume, Tradition & Culture). (Illus.). 64p. (YA). 19.75 (978-0-7910-5166-5(8) , Chelsea Hse.) Facts On File, Inc.

Schomp, Virginia. Japan in the Days of the Samurai. 1998. (Cultures of the Past Ser.). (Illus.). 80p. (J). (gr. 5 up). lib. bdg. 29.93 (978-0-7614-0304-3(3) , Benchmark Bks.) Cavendish, Marshall Corp.

SAMURAI—FICTION

Duey, Kathleen. Samurai, 6 vols. 2006. (Time Soldiers Ser.: Bk. 6). (Illus.). 96p. (J). pap. 5.95 (978-1-929945-63-4(9)) Big Guy Bks., Inc.

—Samurai. Epstein, Eugene, illus. Gould, Robert, photos by. l.t. ed. 2006. (Time Soldiers Ser.: Bk. 6). 48p. (J). 15.95 (978-1-929945-62-7(0)) Big Guy Bks., Inc.

—Samurai. 2007. (Illus.). 96p. (J). 24.21 (978-1-59961-229-4(1)) Spotlight.

Gerstein, Mordicai, illus. Three Samurai Cats: A Story from Japan. 2003. 32p. (J). (gr. k-3). 6.95 (978-0-8234-1877-0(4)) Holiday Hse., Inc.

Goto, Scott. The Perfect Sword. 2008. (J). (***978-1-57091-697-7(7)***) Charlesbridge Publishing, Inc.

Gratz, Alan. Samurai Shortstop. 2006. 288p. (J). (gr. 6 up). 17.99 (978-0-8037-3075-5(6) , Dial) Penguin Group (USA) Inc.

Gratz, Alan M. Samurai Shortstop. 2008. 288p. (YA). (gr. 6). pap. 7.99 (***978-0-14-241099-8(3)*** , Puffin) Penguin Group (USA) Inc.

Haugaard, Erik C. The Revenge of the Forty-Seven Samurai. 2005. 240p. (YA). (gr. 5-9). pap. 6.95 (978-0-618-54896-5(3)) Houghton Mifflin Co. Trade & Reference Div.

Haugaard, Erik Christian. The Samurai's Tale. 2005. 256p (YA). (gr. 5-9). pap. 6.95 (978-0-618-61512-4(1)) Houghton Mifflin Co. Trade & Reference Div.

Hightman, Jason. Samurai. 2007. 416p. (J). pap. 6.99 (***978-0-06-054016-6(8)*** , Eos) HarperCollins Pubs.

Hoobler, Dorothy. The Ghost in the Tokaido Inn. 2001. (J). 12.64 (978-0-606-21212-0(4)) Tandem Library Bks.

Hoobler, Dorothy & Hoobler, Thomas. The Demon in the Teahouse. 2005. 192p. (J). (gr. 7). pap. 5.99 (978-0-14-240540-6(X) , Puffin) Penguin Group (USA) Inc.

—The Ghost in the Tokaido Inn. (J). 2005. 240p. (gr. 4). pap. 5.99 (978-0-14-240541-3(8) , Puffin); 1999. 1p. (gr. 5-9). 17.99 (978-0-399-23330-2(X) , Philomel) Penguin Group (USA) Inc.

—In Darkness, Death. 208p. 2005. (J). (gr. 5). pap. 6.99 (978-0-14-240366-2(0) , Puffin); 2004. (YA). (gr. 4). 16.99 (978-0-399-23767-6(4) , Philomel) Penguin Group (USA) Inc.

—A Samurai Never Fears Death. 2007. (Samurai Mystery Ser.). 224p. (YA). (gr. 5-9). 14.99 (978-0-399-24609-8(6) , Philomel) Penguin Group (USA) Inc.

—The Sword That Cut the Burning Grass. (J). (gr. 5). 2006. 224p. pap. 5.99 (978-0-14-240689-2(9) , Puffin); 2005. 212p. 10.99 (978-0-399-24272-4(4) , Philomel) Penguin Group (USA) Inc.

Kimmel, Eric A. Sword of the Samurai. 2000. (gr. 3-6). lib. bdg. 12.10 (978-0-613-33731-1(X)) Tandem Library Bks.

—Sword of the Samurai: Adventure Stories from Japan. Evans, Michael, illus. 2000. (Trophy Chapter Bks.). 112p. (J). (gr. 2-5). pap. 4.99 (978-0-06-442131-7(7) , Harper Trophy) HarperCollins Pubs.

—Sword of the Samurai: Adventure Stories from Japan. 2000. (J). (978-0-606-19999-5(3)) Tandem Library Bks.

Konzak, Burt. Samurai Spirit: Ancient Wisdom for Modern Life. 2002. 144p. (J). (gr. 6 up). pap. 8.95 (978-0-88776-611-4(0)) Tundra Bks., Inc./Livres Toundra, Inc. CAN. *Dist:* Random Hse., Inc.

Namioka, Lensey. Coming of the Bear. 2005. 208p. pap. 7.95 (978-0-8048-3613-5(2)) Tuttle Publishing.

—Island of Ogres. 2005. 1p. pap. 7.95 (978-0-8048-3612-8(4)) Tuttle Publishing.

—Valley of the Broken Cherry Trees. 2005. 256p. pap. 7.95 (978-0-8048-3610-4(8)) Tuttle Publishing.

—Village of the Vampire Cat. 2005. (Zenta & Matsuzo Mystery Ser.). 224p. (J). pap. 7.95 (978-0-8048-3611-1(6)) Tuttle Publishing.

Reed, Gary. Spirit of the Samurai: Of Swords & Rings. Hoberg, Rick, illus. 2006. 107p. (J). 12.95 (978-0-9778809-9-7(0) , Actionopolis) Komikwerks, LLC.

Sakai, Stan. Usagi Yojimbo Vol. 3: Al Filo de la Vida y la Muerte. 2007. (SPA., Illus.). 200p. reprint ed. pap. 15.95 (***978-1-59497-319-2(9)***) Public Square Bks.

—Usagi Yojimbo Vol. 4: Estaciones. 2007. (SPA., Illus.). 200p. reprint ed. pap. 15.95 (***978-1-59497-320-8(2)***) Public Square Bks.

—Usagi Yojimbo Vol. 5: Segadora. 2007. (SPA., Illus.). 256p. reprint ed. pap. 17.95 (***978-1-59497-321-5(0)***) Public Square Bks.

—Usagi Yojimbo Vol. 6: Primeras Andanzas. 2007. (SPA., Illus.). 128p. reprint ed. pap. 12.95 (***978-1-59497-322-2(9)***) Public Square Bks.

—Usagi Yojimbo Vol. 7: Samurai (en Español) 2007. (SPA., Illus.). 144p. reprint ed. pap. 14.95 (***978-1-59497-323-9(7)***) Public Square Bks.

Samurai. (Awesome Adventures Ser.). 16p. (J). (978-2-7643-0167-8(7)) Phidal Publishing, Inc./Editions Phidal, Inc.

Scieszka, Jon. Ay, Samuray!Tr. of Sam Samurai. (SPA.). (J). 7.95 (978-958-04-6867-7(2)) Norma S.A. COL. *Dist:* Distribuidora Norma, Inc.

—Sam Samurai, Vol. 10. McCauley, Adam, illus. (Time Warp Trio Ser.: No. 10). (J). 2004. 112p. (gr. 2-6). pap. 4.99 (978-0-14-240088-3(2) , Puffin); 2001. 80p. (gr. 1-5). 14.99 (978-0-670-89915-9(1) , Viking Juvenile) Penguin Group (USA) Inc.

Teitelbaum, Michael. The Legend Begins. 2002. (Samurai Jack Ser.). (Illus.). 80p. (J). (gr. 3-7). pap. 4.50 (978-0-439-40972-8(1)) Scholastic, Inc.

West, Tracey. Journey to the Impossible Islands. 2003. (gr. 3-6). lib. bdg. 12.40 (978-0-613-72173-8(X)) Tandem Library Bks.

—The Seven Labors of Jack. Rodriguez, Angel, illus. 2003. (Samurai Jack Chapter Bks.: No. 2). 80p. (J). (gr. 3-7). pap. 4.50 (978-0-439-40974-2(8)) Scholastic, Inc.

Whitesel, Cheryl Aylward. Blue Fingers: A Ninja's Tale. 2004. 256p. (YA). (gr. 5-9). tchr. ed. 15.00 (978-0-618-38139-5(2) , Clarion Bks.) Houghton Mifflin Co. Trade & Reference Div.

SAMURAI JACK (FICTITIOUS CHARACTER)—FICTION

Teitelbaum, Michael. Legend Begins. 2002. (gr. 3-6). lib. bdg. 12.40 (978-0-613-50455-3(0)) Tandem Library Bks.

—The Legend Begins. 2002. (Samurai Jack Ser.). (Illus.). 80p. (J). (gr. 3-7). pap. 4.50 (978-0-439-40972-8(1)) Scholastic, Inc.

West, Tracey. Journey to the Impossible Islands. 2003. (gr. 3-6). lib. bdg. 12.40 (978-0-613-72173-8(X)) Tandem Library Bks.

—The Seven Labors of Jack. Rodriguez, Angel, illus. 2003. (Samurai Jack Chapter Bks.: No. 2). 80p. (J). (gr. 3-7). pap. 4.50 (978-0-439-40974-2(8)) Scholastic, Inc.

SAN ANTONIO (TEX.)

Fradin, Dennis B. The Alamo. 2006. (Turning Points in U. S. History Ser.). (Illus.). 48p. (J). (gr. 3-6). lib. bdg. 29.93 (978-0-7614-2127-6(0) , Benchmark Bks.) Cavendish, Marshall Corp.

McReynolds, Stacy. San Antonio Zoo. 2003. (Great Zoos of the United States Ser.). (Illus.). 24p. (J). lib. bdg. 18.75 (978-0-8239-6319-5(5) , PowerKids Pr.) Rosen Publishing Group, Inc., The.

San Antonio: the River City: Third Grade Guided Reading Level O. (On Our Way to English Ser.). (gr. 3 up). 34.50 (978-0-7578-7144-3(5)) Rigby Education.

SAN ANTONIO (TEX.)—FICTION

Brown, Marc. Buster Plays Along. 2005. (Postcards from Buster Ser.). (Illus.). (J). (gr. 1-4). 48p. 14.99 (978-0-316-15886-2(0)); 32p. pap. 3.99 (978-0-316-00109-0(0)) Little, Brown Bks. for Young Readers.

Griffin, Peni R. The Music Thief. rev. ed. 2002. 160p. (YA). (gr. 5-8). 16.95 (978-0-8050-7055-2(9) , Holt, Henry & Co. Bks. For Young Readers) Holt, Henry & Co.

—The Music Thief. l.t. ed. 2003. 190p. (J). 21.95 (978-0-7862-5606-8(0)) Thorndike Pr.

In the City of San Antonio: Lap Book. (Pebble Soup Explorations Ser.). 16p. (ps up). 21.00 (978-0-7578-1659-8(2)) Rigby Education.

In the City of San Antonio: Small Book. (Pebble Soup Explorations Ser.). 16p. (ps up). 5.00 (978-0-7578-1699-4(1)) Rigby Education.

Maruca, Mary. A Kid's Guide to Exploring San Antonio Missions. 2000. (Illus.). 12p. (J). (gr. 3-6). pap. 1.00 (978-1-58369-002-4(6) , E1018) Western National Parks Assn.

Milligan, Bryce. Comanche Captive. 2005. (Illus.). 168p. (YA). (gr. 7). pap. (978-1-57168-849-1(8)) Eakin Pr.

Nye, Naomi Shihab. Going Going. 2005. (Illus.). 240p. (J). 16.99 (978-0-688-16185-9(5)); 232p. (YA). (gr. 7 up). lib. bdg. 16.89 (978-0-06-029366-6(7)) HarperCollins Pubs.

SAN ANTONIO (TEX.)—HISTORY

Collard, Sneed B., III. David Crockett: Fearless Frontiersman. 2006. (American Heroes Ser.). (Illus.). 48p. (J). lib. bdg. 28.50 (978-0-7614-2160-3(2) , Benchmark Bks.) Cavendish, Marshall Corp.

Espinosa, Rod. Battle of the Alamo. Espinosa, Rod, illus. 2007. (Graphic History Ser.). (Illus.). 32p. (J). (gr. 3-6). lib. bdg. 27.07 (***978-1-60270-073-4(7)*** , Graphic Planet) Magic Wagon.

Isaacs, Sally Senzell. Life at the Alamo. 2003. (Picture the Past Ser.). (Illus.). 32p. (J). (gr. 2-4). lib. bdg. (978-1-58810-695-7(0)); pap. 7.50 (978-1-4034-0523-4(9)) Heinemann Library.

Koestler-Grack, Rachel A. Daily Life in a Southwestern Settlement: San Antonio. 2003. (J). (978-1-58417-012-9(3)); pap. (978-1-58417-075-4(1)) Lake Street Pubs.

Riehecky, Janet. The Siege of the Alamo. 2002. (Landmark Events in American History Ser.). (Illus.). 48p. (J). (gr. 5 up). pap. 14.60 (978-0-8368-5356-8(3)); lib. bdg. 30.00 (978-0-8368-5342-1(3)) Stevens, Gareth Inc. (World Almanac Library).

Stout, Mary. San Antonio. 2005. (Great Cities of the World Ser.). (J). pap. (978-0-8368-5213-4(3)); (Illus.). 48p. 30.00 (978-0-8368-5053-6(X)) Stevens, Gareth Inc. (World Almanac Library).

SAN DIEGO CHARGERS (FOOTBALL TEAM)

San Diego Chargers Staff. San Diego Chargers. CWC Sports Inc., ed. 1998. (NFL Team Yearbooks Ser.). (J). (gr. 1-12). pap. 9.99 (978-1-891613-05-0(7)) Everett Sports Publishing & Marketing.

Schmalzbauer, Adam. The History of the San Diego Chargers. 2004. (NFL Today Ser.). (Illus.). 32p. 18.95 (978-1-58341-312-8(X) , Creative Education) Creative Co., The.

SAN DIEGO PADRES (BASEBALL TEAM)

Bloom, Barry. Tony Gwynn: Mr. Padre. Rains, Rob, ed. 1999. (Superstar Ser.). (Illus.). 112p. (J). (gr. 4-7). per. 4.95 (978-1-58261-049-8(5)) Sports Publishing, LLC.

Goodman, Michael E. The History of the San Diego Padres. 1998. (Baseball, the Great American Game Ser.). (Illus.). 32p. (YA). (gr. 3-12). pap. 21.30 (978-0-88682-923-0(2) , Creative Education) Creative Co., The.

—San Diego Padres. 2002. (J). pap. 5.95 (978-0-89812-356-2(9) , Creative Paperbacks); (Illus.). 32p. (978-1-58341-222-0(0) , Creative Education) Creative Co., The.

Hawkes, Brian. The Story of the San Diego Padres. 2007. (J). (***978-1-58341-552-8(1)*** , Creative Education) Creative Co., The.

SAN FRANCISCO (CALIF.)

Ancona, George. Barrio: Jose's Neighborhood. Ancona, George, photos by. 1998. (Illus.). 48p. (J). (gr. 2-7). pap. 10.00 (978-0-15-201048-5(3) , Harcourt Paperbacks) Harcourt Children's Bks.

Brown, Tricia & Junior League of San Francisco Staff. The City by the Bay: A Magical Journey Around San Francisco. Kleven, Elisa, illus. 1998. 32p. (J). (ps-3). pap. 7.95 (978-0-8118-2012-7(2)) Chronicle Bks. LLC.

Chin, Steven A. Dragon Parade: A Chinese New Year Story. 2000. (J). 12.80 (978-0-606-19075-6(9)) Tandem Library Bks.

Cole, David & Trees Cole, Mary Lee. San Francisco. 2001. (Lobster Kids' City Explorers Ser.). (Illus.). 249p. (J). (ps-3). pap. 12.95 (978-1-894222-28-0(8)) Lobster Pr. CAN. *Dist:* Univ. of Toronto Pr.

Dream Soup: Stories from San Francisco Youth, 2 vols. 1999. (J). (Illus.). 176p. spiral bd. (978-0-9646977-5-1(0)); Vol. 2. 196p. spiral bd. 15.00 (978-0-9646977-6-8(9)) Streetside Stories, Inc.

Everything's Different Now: Stories of Change by San Francisco Youth, 2002. (Illus.). 278p. (J). per. 15.00 (978-0-9710606-1-6(4)) Streetside Stories, Inc.

Gamble, Adam. Good Night San Francisco. Cohen, Santiago, illus. 2006. (Good Night Our World Ser.). 22p. (J). bds. 9.95 (978-0-9777979-5-0(3)) Our World of Books.

Hanson, Anders. Let's Go by Cable Car. 2007. (Let's Go! Ser.). (ENG., Illus.). 24p. (J). (ps-3). lib. bdg. 19.93 (***978-1-59928-896-3(6)*** , SandCastle) ABDO Publishing Co.

Hooray! Stories of Celebrations by San Francisco Youth, 2 vols. 2001. (Illus.). (J). 226p. spiral bd. 15.00 (978-0-9646977-9-9(3)); Vol. 2. 238p. spiral bd. 15.00 (978-0-9710606-0-9(6)) Streetside Stories, Inc.

Isaacs, Sally Senzell. Life in San Francisco's Chinatown. 2003. (Picture the Past Ser.). (Illus.). 32p. (J). (gr. 2-4). lib. bdg. 22.79 (978-1-58810-692-6(6)); pap. 7.50 (978-1-4034-0524-1(7)) Heinemann Library.

Luiso, Lisa. What Daddy Sees in San Francisco. 2007. (Illus.). 30p. (J). lib. bdg. 19.95 (***978-1-933732-37-4(7)*** , Bear Hug Bks.) MidAmerica Publishing Co.

—What Mommy Sees in San Francisco. abr. ed. 2007. (J). lib. bdg. 19.95 (***978-1-933732-28-2(8)*** , Bear Hug Bks.) MidAmerica Publishing Co.

Mattern, Joanne. San Francisco. 2006. (Cities Ser.). (J). (978-1-59679-723-9(1)) ABDO Publishing Co.

Raum, Elizabeth. Birth & Death of a City. 2006. (Illus.). 32p. (J). (978-1-4109-2597-8(8)); pap. (978-1-4109-2626-5(5)) Steck-Vaughn.

Sasek, Miroslav. This Is San Francisco. 2003. (This Is ... Ser.). (Illus.). 64p. (J). (gr. k). 17.95 (978-0-7893-0962-4(9)) Universe Publishing.

Turner, Barbara. A Day in San Francisco, Vol. 1. l.t. ed. 2003. (Illus.). 32p. (J). per. 14.95 (978-0-9747019-0-5(4)) Turner, Barbara.

Weintraub, Aileen. Alcatraz Island Light: The West Coast's First Lighthouse. 2003. (Great Lighthouses of North America Ser.). (Illus.). 24p. (J). pap. 18.75 (978-0-8239-6171-9(0) , PowerKids Pr.) Rosen Publishing Group, Inc., The.

White, Tekla N. Missions of the San Francisco Bay Area: Santa Clara de Asis, San Jose, San Francisco de Asis, San Rafael Arcangel, San Francisco Solano. 1999. (California Missions Ser.). (Illus.). 80p. (J). (gr. 4-7). pap. (978-0-8225-9836-7(1) , Lerner Pubns.) Lerner Publishing Group.

Zschock, Martha Day. Journey Around San Francisco. 2003. (Journey Around Ser.). (Illus.). 32p. (J). 17.95 (978-1-889833-49-1(5)) Commonwealth Editions.

SAN FRANCISCO (CALIF.)—BRIDGES

Ashley, Susan. The Golden Gate Bridge. 2004. (Weekly Reader Early Learning Library). (Illus.). 24p. (J). (gr. 2 up). pap. 5.95 (978-0-8368-4147-3(6)); lib. bdg. 19.33 (978-0-8368-4140-4(9)) Stevens, Gareth Inc. (Weekly Reader Early Learning Library).

SAN FRANCISCO (CALIF).—EARTHQUAKE AND FIRE, 1906

see San Francisco Earthquake, Calif., 1906

SAN FRANCISCO (CALIF.)—FICTION

Alef, Daniel. Centennial Stories: A Living History of San Francisco. 2nd ed. 2000. (Illus.). 227p. (J). pap. 15.95 (978-0-9700174-2-0(1)) Maxit Publishing, Inc.

Allison, Jennifer. Gilda Joyce: Psychic Investigator. 2005. 208p. (YA). 12.99 (978-0-525-47375-6(0) , Dutton Juvenile); 2006. 336p. (J). (gr. 5). reprint ed. pap. 6.99 (978-0-14-240698-4(8) , Puffin) Penguin Group (USA) Inc.

Argueta, Jorge. Xochitl & the Flowers / Xochitl, la Nina de Las Flores. Angel, Carl, illus. 2003. Tr. of Xochitl, la Nina de Las Flores. (ENG & SPA.). 32p. (J). 16.95 (978-0-89239-181-3(2)) Children's Bk. Pr.

Brown, Marc. Buster Changes His Luck. 2006. (Postcards from Buster Ser.). (Illus.). 48p. (J). (gr. 1-4). 14.99 (978-0-316-15916-6(6)) Little Brown & Co.

Bunting, Eve. Pop's Bridge. Payne, C. F., illus. 2006. 32p. (J). 17.00 (978-0-15-204773-3(5)) Harcourt Trade Pubs.

Dell, Pamela. The Doctor's Boy: A Story about Valley Forge during the Winter Of 1777-1778. 2003. (Scrapbooks of America Ser.). (Illus.). 48p. (J). (gr. 2-6). 28.50 (978-1-59187-043-2(7)) Child's World, Inc.

—A Song for Sung Li: A Story of the 1906 San Francisco Earthquake. 2002. (Scrapbooks of America Ser.). (Illus.). 48p. (J). (gr. 2-6). 28.50 (978-1-59187-015-9(1)) Child's World, Inc.

Duey, K. & Bale, K. A. Salvados! Terremoto. 2003. (Survival Ser.).Tr. of Survival! Earthquake. (SPA.). (J). pap. 9.95 (978-0-9715256-5-8(X)) Planeta Publishing Corp.

Duey, Kathleen. San Francisco Earthquake, 1906. 1999. (978-0-606-17951-5(8)) Tandem Library Bks.

Emerson, Scott. The Brotherhood of the Moon: From the Notebooks of Edward R. Smithfield, D.V.M. Glasauer, Willi, illus. 2005. (J). 9.95 (978-0-689-87630-1(0) , Simon & Schuster Children's Publishing) Simon & Schuster Children's Publishing.

English, Karen. Speak to Me: And I Will Listen Between the Lines. Bates, Amy June, illus. 2004. 32p. (J). 16.00 (978-0-374-37156-2(3) , Farrar, Straus & Giroux (BYR)) Farrar, Straus & Giroux.

Freeman, Don. Fly High, Fly Low. Freeman, Don, illus. 2004. (Illus.). 32p. (J). (ps-3). reprint ed. 16.99 (978-0-670-03685-1(4) , Viking Juvenile) Penguin Group (USA) Inc.

—Fly High, Fly Low (50th Anniversary Ed.) Freeman, Don, illus. 2007. 64p. (J). (ps). pap. 7.99 (978-0-14-240817-9(4) , Puffin) Penguin Group (USA) Inc.

Freeman, Martha. The Trouble with Babies. Smith, Cat Bowman, illus. 2002. 80p. (J). (gr. 4-6). tchr. ed. 15.95 (978-0-8234-1698-1(4)) Holiday Hse., Inc.

—The Trouble with Cats. Smith, Cat Bowman, illus. 2000. 80p. (J). (gr. 4-6). tchr. ed. 15.95 (978-0-8234-1479-6(5)) Holiday Hse., Inc.

Gonzales, David. Field Trip Trouble. Gonzales, David, illus. 2005. (Miljos Digest Ser.: No. 4). (Illus.). 96p. (J). (gr. 2-5). pap. 4.99 (978-0-439-56803-6(X) , Scholastic Paperbacks) Scholastic, Inc.

Gregory, Kristiana. Earthquake at Dawn. 2003. (gr. 5-8). lib. bdg. 14.10 (978-0-613-64493-8(X)) Tandem Library Bks.

Gregory, Kristiana & Campbell, Mary Exa Atkins. Earthquake at Dawn. 2003. (Great Episodes Ser.). (Illus.). 224p. (J). pap. 5.95 (978-0-15-204681-1(X)) Harcourt Children's Bks.

Harcourt School Publishers Staff. The Autumn of the Earthquake Below Level. 3rd ed. 2002. (Trophies Reading Program Ser.). (Illus.). pap. 5.10 (978-0-15-323407-1(5)) Harcourt Schl. Pubs.

—Hazanas para Gigantes Below Level. 3rd ed. 2002. (Trofeos Ser.). (SPA., Illus.). pap. 6.80 (978-0-15-324159-8(4)) Harcourt Schl. Pubs.

—Two Families On Level. 3rd ed. 2002. (Trophies Reading Program Ser.). (Illus.). pap. 5.10 (978-0-15-323264-0(1)) Harcourt Schl. Pubs.

—Two Julias Advanced Level. 3rd ed. 2002. (Trophies Reading Program Ser.). (Illus.). pap. 5.10 (978-0-15-323193-3(9)) Harcourt Schl. Pubs.

—A Visit to San Francisco Below Level. 3rd ed. 2002. (Trophies Reading Program Ser.). (Illus.). (gr. 3). pap. 5.10 (978-0-15-323133-9(5)) Harcourt Schl. Pubs.

Hinman, Bonnie. San Francisco Earthquake. 32nd ed. 1998. (American Adventure Ser.: No. 32). (Illus.). (J). (gr. 3-7). pap. 3.97 (978-1-57748-393-9(6)) Barbour Publishing, Inc.

Hopkinson, Deborah. Into the Firestorm: A Novel of San Francisco, 1906. 2006. 208p. (J). (gr. 3-7). 15.95 (978-0-375-83652-7(7)); lib. bdg. 17.99 (978-0-375-93652-4(1)) Random Hse. Children's Bks. (Knopf Bks. for Young Readers).

S

Hopkinson, Deborah. Into the Firestorm: A Novel of San Francisco 1906. 2008. 208p. (J). (gr. 4-7). 5.99 (***978-0-440-42129-0(2)*** , Yearling) Random Hse. Children's Bks.

Keene, Carolyn. Trade Wind Danger. 2005. 148p. (J). lib. bdg. 15.00 (***978-1-4242-0243-0(4))*** Fitzgerald Bks.

Lavender, William. Aftershocks. 2006. (Illus.). 352p. (YA). 17.00 (978-0-15-205882-1(6)) Harcourt Children's Bks.

Lee, Milly. Earthquake. Choi, Yangsook, illus. 2006. 32p. (J). reprint ed. pap. 6.95 (978-0-374-41946-2(9)) Macmillan.

—Landed. Choi, Yangsook, illus. 2006. 40p. (J). 16.00 (978-0-374-34314-9(4) , Farrar, Straus & Giroux (BYR)) Farrar, Straus & Giroux.

Levy, Marc. If Only It Were True. 2000. 224p. mass mkt. 6.99 (978-0-7434-1717-4(8) , Pocket) Simon & Schuster.

McDonald, Megan. Julie & the Eagles, Bk. 4. McAliley, Susan, illus. 2007. 88p. (YA). (gr. 3 up). 12.95 (***978-1-59369-351-0(6))*** American Girl Publishing, Inc.

—Julie & the Eagles, Bk. 4. McAliley, Susan & Hunt, Robert, illus. 2007. 88p. (YA). (gr. 3 up). pap. 6.95 (***978-1-59369-350-3(8))*** American Girl Publishing, Inc.

Morris, Paris. I am Having Twins. 2008. (Illus.). 24p. (J). pap. 14.95 (***978-0-9760095-4-2(4))*** New Year Publishing.

—My Twins are Coming Home. 2008. (Illus.). 24p. (J). pap. 14.95 (***978-0-9760095-5-9(2))*** New Year Publishing.

Osborne, Mary Pope. Earthquake in the Early Morning, Vol. 24. unabr. ed. 2004. (Magic Tree House Ser.: No. 24). 71p. (J). (gr. k-3). pap. 17.00 incl. audio (978-0-8072-0933-2(3) , S FTR 256 SP, Listening Library) Random Hse. Audio Publishing Group.

—Earthquake in the Early Morning. Murdocca, Sal, illus. 2001. (Magic Tree House Ser.: No. 24). 96p. (J). (gr. k-3). 11.99 (978-0-679-99070-3(4)); mass mkt. 3.99 (978-0-679-89070-6(X)) Random Hse. Children's Bks. (Random Hse. Bks. for Young Readers).

—Earthquake in the Early Morning. 2001. (Magic Tree House Ser. : No. 24). (J). (gr. k-3). lib. bdg. 11.80 (978-0-613-35684-8(5)); (Illus.). 10.79 (978-0-606-21166-6(7)) Tandem Library Bks.

Partridge, Elizabeth. Oranges on Golden Mountain. Sogabe, Aki, illus. 2003. 36p. (J). pap. 6.99 (978-0-14-250033-0(X) , Puffin) Penguin Group (USA) Inc.

—Oranges on Golden Mountain. 2003. (gr. k-3). lib. bdg. 15.30 (978-0-613-61651-5(0)) Tandem Library Bks.

Pollak, Dale. Velocity. 2008. 144p. pap. 22.95 (***978-0-9760095-7-3(9))*** New Year Publishing.

Reich, Susanna. Penelope Bailey Takes the Stage. 2006. 208p. (J). 16.95 (978-0-7614-5287-4(7)) Cavendish, Marshall Corp.

Reiss, Kathryn. Paperquake: A Puzzle. 2002. (gr. 5-8). lib. bdg. 14.15 (978-0-613-53851-0(X)) Tandem Library Bks.

Robles, Anthony D. Lakas & the Manilatown Fish / Si Lakas at Ang Isdang Manilatown. de Jesus, Eloisa D. & de Guzman, Magdalena, trs. Angel, Carl, illus. 2003. Tr. of Si Lakas at Ang Isdang Manilatown. (ENG & TAG.). 32p. (J). 16.95 (978-0-89239-182-0(0)) Children's Bk. Pr.

Ruckdeschel, Liz & James, Sara. What If... You Broke All the Rules. 2007. (What If... Ser.). 304p. (YA). (gr. 7). 11.99 (***978-0-385-90495-7(9));*** (Illus.). pap. 8.99 (***978-0-385-73501-8(4))*** Random Hse. Children's Bks. (Delacorte Bks. for Young Readers).

Sachs, Marilyn. First Impressions. 2006. 128p. (YA). 16.95 (978-1-59643-117-1(2)) Roaring Brook Pr.

San Francisco Shake-Up, 6 Packs. (Greetings Ser.: Vol. 3). (gr. 3-5). 31.00 (978-0-7635-2075-5(6)) Rigby Education.

Sanders, Evelin. Janine. 1999. 221p. (YA). (gr. 7-17). pap. 9.99 (978-0-88092-444-3(6)) Royal Fireworks Publishing Co.

Sargent, Dave & Sargent, Pat. Hank: (Black Sabino) Be Responsible, 25, 33. Lenoir, Jane, illus. 2001. (Saddle Up Ser.). 36p. (J). pap. 6.95 (978-1-56763-656-7(X)); lib. bdg. 22.60 (978-1-56763-655-0(1)) Ozark Publishing.

Schiller, Gerald A. Two Dogs, an Emperor, & Me. Schiller, Dawn, illus. 2000. 108p. (J). (gr. 4-7). pap. 7.50 (978-1-881164-92-0(6)) Intercontinental Publishing, Inc.

Schomer Wendel, Gretchen & Schomer, Adam Anthony. Becka & the Big Bubble: Becka Goes to San Francisco. 2007. (Illus.). 32p. (J). 11.99 (***978-1-933754-12-3(5))*** Waterside Publishing.

Schulte, Elaine L. Daniel Colton Kidnapped. 2002. (Colton Cousins Adventure Ser.: Bk. 4). (Illus.). 138p. (J). (gr. 4-7). 7.49 (978-1-57924-566-5(8)) Jones, Bob Univ. Pr.

Scott, Michael. The Alchemyst. 2007. (Secrets Imrtl Nicholas Flamel Ser.). (Illus.). 400p. (YA). (gr. 7 up). 16.99 (978-0-385-73357-1(7)); lib. bdg. 19.99 (978-0-385-90372-1(3)) Random Hse. Children's Bks. (Delacorte Bks. for Young Readers).

Snyder, Zilpha Keatley. The Magic Nation Thing. (gr. 3-7). 2007. 192p. 6.50 (***978-0-440-41931-0(X)*** , Yearling); 2005. 176p. (J). 15.95 (978-0-385-73085-3(3) , Delacorte Bks. for Young Readers) Random Hse. Children's Bks.

Stewart, Whitney. Blues Across the Bay. 2001. (Going to Ser.). (Illus.). 151p. (gr. 4-8). pap. 6.95 (978-1-893577-08-4(2)) Four Corners Publishing Co., Inc.

Williams, Carol Lynch. Victoria's Courage. 1998. (Latter-Day Daughters Ser.). (J). 5.95 (978-1-57345-434-6(6)) Deseret Bk. Co.

Wintz, Jack. St. Francis in San Francisco. Baron, Kathy, illus. 2001. 32p. (J). (gr. k-3). 12.95 (978-0-8091-6684-8(4) , 6684-4) Paulist Pr.

Wood, Phyllis. Pass Me a Pine Cone, Please. 2006. pap. 12.50 (***978-1-4259-7445-9(7))*** AuthorHouse.

Yang, Belle. Hannah Is My Name. Yang, Belle, illus. 2004. (Illus.). 40p. (J). (gr. k-4). 16.99 (978-0-7636-2223-7(0)) Candlewick Pr.

Yang, Belle. Hannah Is My Name: A Young Immigrant's Story. Yang, Belle, illus. 2007. (Illus.). 32p. (J). (gr. k-4). pap. 6.99 (***978-0-7636-3521-3(9))*** Candlewick Pr.

Yep, Laurence. Child of the Owl. (J). pap., stu. ed. (978-0-13-053125-4(1)) Prentice Hall (Schl. Div.).

—Child of the Owl. 8.97 (978-0-13-437497-0(5)) Prentice Hall PTR.

—The Earth Dragon Awakes: The San Francisco Earthquake Of 1906. 2006. (Illus.). 128p. (J). (gr. 3-7). 14.99 (978-0-06-027524-2(3)); lib. bdg. 15.89 (978-0-06-027525-9(1)) HarperCollins Pubs.

—The Earth Dragon Awakes: The San Francisco Earthquake Of 1906. 2008. 128p. (J). pap. 5.99 (***978-0-06-000846-8(6)*** , Harper Trophy) HarperCollins Pubs.

—The Imp That Ate My Homework. 2000. 11.75 (978-0-606-17671-2(3)) Tandem Library Bks.

—The Magic Paintbrush. Wang, Suling, illus. 2003. 96p. (J). (gr. 3-7). pap. 4.99 (978-0-06-440852-3(3)) HarperCollins Pubs.

—The Magic Paintbrush. 2003. (gr. 3-6). lib. bdg. 13.00 (978-0-613-65808-9(6)) Tandem Library Bks.

—Sea Glass: Golden Mountain Chronicles. 2002. (gr. 5-8). lib. bdg. 15.25 (978-0-613-89808-9(7)) Tandem Library Bks.

—Tiger Magic. 2006. (Tiger's Apprentice Ser.). 288p. (J). 16.99 (978-0-06-001019-5(3)); lib. bdg. 17.89 (978-0-06-001020-1(7)) HarperCollins Pubs.

—Tiger's Apprentice. 2005. 184p. (J). lib. bdg. 24.62 (***978-1-4242-0449-6(6))*** Fitzgerald Bks.

—Tiger's Apprentice. 2005. 184p. (J). (gr. k-9). per. 12.64 (978-0-606-33327-6(4)) Tandem Library Bks.

—The Tiger's Apprentice. 2005. (Tiger's Apprentice Ser.: Bk. 1). 208p. (J). (gr. 5 up). reprint ed. pap. 5.99 (978-0-06-001015-7(0) , Harper Trophy) HarperCollins Pubs.

—Tiger's Blood. 2005. (Tiger's Apprentice Ser.: Bk. 2). 240p. (J). (gr. 5 up). 15.99 (978-0-06-001016-4(9)); lib. bdg. 16.89 (978-0-06-001017-1(7)) HarperCollins Pubs.

—Tiger's Blood. 2006. (Tiger's Apprentice Ser.: Bk. 2). 240p. (J). pap. 5.99 (978-0-06-001018-8(5) , Harper Trophy) HarperCollins Pubs.

Yep, Laurence & Yep, Laurence. The Case of the Goblin Pearls. 1998. 179p. (J). (ps-7). per. 14.15 (978-0-613-04692-3(7)) Tandem Library Bks.

Yin. Brothers. Soentpiet, Chris, illus. 2006. 32p. (J). (gr. k). 16.99 (978-0-399-23406-4(3) , Philomel) Penguin Group (USA) Inc.

SAN FRANCISCO (CALIF.)—HISTORY

Barter, James. San Francisco in the 1960s. 2003. (Illus.). 96p. (J). 29.95 (978-1-59018-359-5(2) , Lucent Bks.) Thomson Gale.

Burgan, Michael. The Great San Francisco Earthquake & Fire. 2008. (J). (***978-1-4296-0155-9(8))*** Capstone Pr., Inc.

Chippendale, Lisa. San Francisco Earthquake of 1906. 2000. (Great Disasters Ser.). (Illus.). 112p. (J). (gr. 5-9). 30.00 (978-0-7910-5270-9(2) , Chelsea Hse.) Facts On File, Inc.

Cooke, Tim. 1906 San Francisco Earthquake. 2005. (Illus.). 32p. (J). lib. bdg. 24.67 (978-0-8368-4494-8(7)) Stevens, Gareth Inc.

Harcourt School Publishers Staff. Ghirardelli Square On Level. 3rd ed. 2002. (Trophies Reading Program Ser.). (Illus.). pap. 5.10 (978-0-15-323263-3(3)) Harcourt Schl. Pubs.

Herold, Vickey. Discover A Gold Rush Community: San Francisco. 2006. pap. 39.00 (***978-1-4108-6431-4(6))*** Benchmark Education Co.

—A Gold Rush Community: San Francisco. 2006. pap. 42.00 (***978-1-4108-6428-4(6))*** Benchmark Education Co.

Higgins, Christopher. Alcatraz Island. 2004. (American Forts & Their Strategic Importance Ser.). (J). (978-1-59084-710-7(5)) Mason Crest Pubs.

Isaacs, Sally Senzell. Life in San Francisco's Chinatown. 2003. (Picture the Past Ser.). (Illus.). 32p. (J). (gr. 2-4). lib. bdg. 22.79 (978-1-58810-692-6(6)); pap. 7.50 (978-1-4034-0524-1(7)) Heinemann Library.

Mayo, Margaret. Hermano Sol, Hermana Luna: La Historia de San Francisco. Gonzalez Batlle, Jorge, tr. Malone, Peter, illus. 2005. (SPA.). 80p. (J). 14.95 (978-84-95939-31-9(2)) Blume ESP. *Dist:* Independent Pubs. Group.

Meter, Larry Van. Yerba Buena. 2007. (Colonial Settlements in America Ser.). 104p. (J). (gr. 5-8). 30.00 (***978-0-7910-9338-2(7)*** , Chelsea Hse.) Facts On File, Inc.

Nobleman, Marc Tyler. The San Francisco Earthquake of 1906. 2006. 48p. (J). (***978-0-7565-2460-9(1))*** Compass Point Bks.

Tanaka, Shelley. Earthquake! A Day That Changed America. Craig, David, illus. 2006. 48p. (J). (gr. 4-8). reprint ed. 17.00 (978-1-4223-5635-7(3)) DIANE Publishing Co.

White, Tekla N. San Francisco Bay Area Missions. 2007. (Exploring California Missions Ser.). (J). 27.93 (***978-0-8225-0900-4(8)*** , Lerner Pubns.) Lerner Publishing Group.

SAN FRANCISCO EARTHQUAKE, CALIF., 1906

Burgan, Michael. The Great San Francisco Earthquake & Fire. 2008. (J). (***978-1-4296-0155-9(8))*** Capstone Pr., Inc.

Chippendale, Lisa. San Francisco Earthquake of 1906. 2000. (Great Disasters Ser.). (Illus.). 112p. (J). (gr. 5-9). 30.00 (978-0-7910-5270-9(2) , Chelsea Hse.) Facts On File, Inc.

Cooke, Tim. 1906 San Francisco Earthquake. 2005. (Illus.). 32p. (J). lib. bdg. 24.67 (978-0-8368-4494-8(7)) Stevens, Gareth Inc.

Nobleman, Marc Tyler. The San Francisco Earthquake of 1906. 2006. 48p. (J). (***978-0-7565-2460-9(1))*** Compass Point Bks.

Worth, Richard. The San Francisco Earthquake. 2005. (Environmental Disasters Ser.). (Illus.). 112p. (J). (gr. 6-12). 35.00 (978-0-8160-5756-6(7)) Facts On File, Inc.

SAN FRANCISCO GIANTS (BASEBALL TEAM)

Frisch, Aaron. San Francisco Giants. 2002. 32p. (J). pap. 5.95 (978-0-89812-357-9(7) , Creative Paperbacks); (Illus.). (978-1-58341-223-7(9) , Creative Education) Creative Co., The.

Goodman, Michael E. The History of the San Francisco Giants. 1998. (Baseball, the Great American Game Ser.). (Illus.). 32p. (YA). (gr. 3-12). pap. 21.30 (978-0-88682-924-7(0) , Creative Education) Creative Co., The.

Pietrusza, David. The San Francisco Giants Baseball Team. 2000. (Great Sports Teams Ser.). (Illus.). 48p. (YA). (gr. 4-10). lib. bdg. 23.93 (978-0-7660-1284-4(0)) Enslow Pubs., Inc.

Richardson, Adele. The Story of the San Francisco Giants. 2007. (J). (***978-1-58341-499-6(1)*** , Creative Education) Creative Co., The.

SANATORIUMS

see Hospitals

SAND

Edwards, Nicola. Sand. 2005. (Illus.). 24p. (YA). (gr. 1 up). lib. bdg. 22.80 (978-1-59389-214-2(4)) Chrysalis Education.

Gurney, Beth. Sand & Soil. 2004. (Rocks, Minerals, & Resources Ser.). (Illus.). 32p. (J). (978-0-7787-1417-0(9)); pap. (978-0-7787-1449-1(7)) Crabtree Publishing Co.

Miller, Pam. Sand. Stromoski, Rick, illus. 2001. (Rookie Reader Skill Set Ser.). 32p. (J). (gr. k-2). pap. 4.95 (978-0-516-27079-1(6) , Children's Pr.) Scholastic Library Publishing.

Prager, Ellen. Jump into Science: Sand. Woodman, Nancy, illus. 2006. (Jump into Science Ser.). 32p. (J). (ps-3). pap. 6.95 (978-0-7922-5583-3(6) , National Geographic Children's Bks.) National Geographic Society.

Prager, Ellen J. Sand. Woodman, Nancy, illus. 2006. (Jump into Science Ser.). 29p. (J). (***978-1-4156-6952-5(X))*** National Geographic Society.

Snyder, Inez. Sand to Glass. 2005. (How Things Are Made Ser.). (Illus.). 24p. (J). (ps-2). pap. 4.95 (978-0-516-25529-3(0)); 18.00 (978-0-516-25199-8(6)) Scholastic Library Publishing. (Children's Pr.).

Ward, Kristin. Sand. 2000. (PowerKids Readers Ser.). (Illus.). 24p. (J). (gr. 1). lib. bdg. 16.00 (978-0-8239-5530-5(3) , PKNASA, PowerKids Pr.) Rosen Publishing Group, Inc., The.

SAND DUNES

Gallant, Roy A. Sand on the Move: The Story of Dunes. 1998. (First Bks.). (Illus.). 64p. (J). (gr. 5-7). pap. 6.95 (978-0-531-15889-0(6) , Watts, Franklin) Scholastic Library Publishing.

Peggy J. Parks. Sand Dunes. 2004. (Wonders of the World Ser.). (J). 26.20 (978-0-7377-2057-0(3) , Kidhaven) Thomson Gale.

Penny, Malcolm. Life in a Sand Dune. 2003. (Microhabitats Ser.). (Illus.). 32p. (J). pap. (978-1-4109-0350-1(8)); lib. bdg. 24.28 (978-0-7398-6805-8(5)) Raintree.

—Life in a Sand Dune. 2003. (gr. k-3). lib. bdg. 15.90 (978-0-613-78243-2(7)) Tandem Library Bks.

SAND DUNES—FICTION

Baumer, Dawn McVay, creator. Dune Daze: Silver Lake. 2004. (Illus.). (J). (978-0-9754960-0-8(X)) Butters Pr.

SANDBURG, CARL, 1878-1967

Marsh, Carole. Carl Sandburg. 2002. (One Thousand Readers Ser.). (Illus.). 12p. (J). (gr. k-4). 2.95 (978-0-635-01501-3(3) , 15013) Gallopade International.

Murcia, Rebecca Thatcher. Carl Sandburg. 2006. (Poets & Playwrights Ser.). (Illus.). 112p. (YA). (gr. 6-12). lib. bdg. 37.10 (978-1-58415-430-3(6)) Mitchell Lane Pubs., Inc.

Niven, Penelope & Sandburg, Carl. Carl Sandburg: Adventures of a Poet. Nadel, Marc, illus. 2003. 32p. (J). 17.00 (978-0-15-204686-6(0)) Harcourt Children's Bks.

SANDWICHES

Ashley, Susan. I Can Make a Sandwich. 2004. (978-0-8368-4330-9(4)); (Illus.). 24p. (YA). lib. bdg. 19.33 (978-0-8368-4323-1(1)) Stevens, Gareth Inc.

Dunnington, Rose. Super Sandwiches: Wrap 'em, Stack 'em, Stuff 'em. Mann, Steven, photos by. 2006. (Illus.). 112p. (J). (gr. 6 up). 9.95 (978-1-57990-781-5(4) , 1262267) Lark Bks.

Hill, Mary. Let's Make a Sandwich. 2002. (Welcome Bks.). (Illus.). 24p. (J). (ps-2). pap. 4.95 (978-0-516-24017-6(X) , Children's Pr.) Scholastic Library Publishing.

SANGER, MARGARET, 1883-1966

Cox, Vicki. Margaret Sanger. 2004. (Women in Medicine Ser.). (Illus.). 112p. (gr. 6-12). 30.00 (978-0-7910-8030-6(7) , Chelsea Hse.) Facts On File, Inc.

SANITARY AFFAIRS

see Sanitation

SANITATION

see also Cemeteries; Health; Public Health; Refuse and Refuse Disposal; Water—Purification; Water-Supply; World War, 1939-1945—Medical Care

Costain, Meredith. Trash-Free Lunch Day. 2000. (gr. k-3). lib. bdg. 11.80 (978-0-613-30810-6(7)) Tandem Library Bks.

Deedrick, Tami. Garbage Collectors. 1998. (Community Helpers Ser.). (Illus.). 24p. (J). (gr. k-3). pap. 14.00 (978-0-516-21259-3(1) , Children's Pr.) Scholastic Library Publishing.

LeBoutillier, Nate. A Day in the Life of a Garbage Collector. 2004. (First Facts Ser.). (Illus.). 24p. (J). lib. bdg. 21.26 (978-0-7368-2629-7(7)) Capstone Pr., Inc.

Macken, JoAnn Early. Sanitation Worker. 2003. (People in My Community Ser.). (Illus.). 24p. (J). (ps up). lib. bdg. 19.33 (978-0-8368-3592-2(1) , Weekly Reader Early Learning Library) Stevens, Gareth Inc.

—Sanitation Worker/El Recogedor de Basura. Coffey, Colleen & Carrillo, Consuelo, trs. 2003. (Weekly Reader Early Learning Library). (ENG & SPA., Illus.). 24p. (J). (ps up). lib. bdg. 19.33 (978-0-8368-3674-5(X) , Weekly Reader Early Learning Library) Stevens, Gareth Inc.

Macken, JoAnn Early & Gorman, Jacqueline Laks. Sanitation Worker. 2003. (Weekly Reader Early Learning Library). (Illus.). 24p. (J). (ps up). pap. 7.93 (978-0-8368-3599-1(9) , Weekly Reader Early Learning Library) Stevens, Gareth Inc.

—Sanitation Worker/El Recogedor de Basura. Coffey, Colleen & Carrillo, Consuelo, trs. Andersen, Gregg, photos by. 2003. (Weekly Reader Early Learning Library). (ENG & SPA., Illus.). 24p. (J). (ps up). pap. 5.95 (978-0-8368-3688-2(X) , Weekly Reader Early Learning Library) Stevens, Gareth Inc.

Six Rules of Sanitation (AVA) Back to Basics. 2001. (YA). pap. (978-1-57078-005-9(6)) C E V Multimedia, Ltd.

SANTA CLAUS

Adamson, Diane G. I Believe in Santa Claus. 2nd ed. 2000. (Illus.). 48p. (J). (ps-3). 15.95 (978-0-9673571-0-2(1)) Adamson, Diane G.

Allen, Raymond E. From Jesus to Santa Claus. Headings, Wade, photos by. 2000. 16p. (J). (ps-7). pap. 4.95 (978-0-9703697-0-3(0)) True To The Word, LLP.

Atkins, Nancy L. Christmas Through Their Eyes: Letters to Santa. 2001. (Illus.). 48p. (J). (gr. 2-4). pap. 12.95 (978-0-9705747-0-1(3)) EarthSpring Publishing.

Blue Lantern Studio Staff, ed. Truth Abt Santa Claus. 2007. (Illus.). 37p. (J). (ps-3). 19.95 (***978-1-59583-187-3(8)*** , Green Tiger Pr.) Laughing Elephant.

Bonnice, Sherry. Christmas & Santa Claus Folklore. 2003. (North American Folklore Ser.). (Illus.). 112p. (YA). (gr. 7 up). lib. bdg. (978-1-59084-330-7(4)) Mason Crest Pubs.

Church, Francis P. Is There a Santa Claus? A Little Girl's Question Answered. Kaiser, August, illus. 1999. 24p. (ps-3). pap. 8.95 (978-1-883211-23-3(9) , Darling & Co.) Laughing Elephant.

—Yes, Virginia, There Is a Santa Claus. Spector, Joel, illus. 2001. (Courage Children's Ser.). 32p. (gr. 3 up). 9.98 (978-0-7624-1120-7(1) , Courage Bks.) Running Pr. Bk. Pubs.

Church, Francis Pharcellus & O'Hanlon, Virginia. Yes Virginia, There Is a Santa Claus—In Latin! Vere Virginia, Sanctus Nicolaus Est! Kringe, Matthias, illus. 2001. (LAT.). 32p. (J). 12.00 (978-0-86516-506-9(8)) Bolchazy-Carducci Pubs.

Color All About: Santa: A Giant Coloring Book about What Santa Does When It's Not Christmas. 2004. (Illus.). (J). (978-0-9763307-4-5(1)); (SPA & ENG., (978-0-9763307-8-3(4)) Food Marketing Consultants, Inc.

Dalmatian Press Staff. Surprises from Santa Gigantic. 2004. 192p. pap. 2.99 (978-1-4037-0474-0(0)) Dalmatian Pr.

Demi. The Legend of Saint Nicholas. Demi, illus. 2003. (Illus.). 40p. (J). (gr. k-5). 19.95 (978-0-689-84681-6(9) , McElderry, Margaret K.) Simon & Schuster Children's Publishing.

Grafton, Carol Belanger. Santa Claus Stickers. 1998. (Illus.). 4p. 5.95 (978-0-486-40595-7(8)) Dover Pubns., Inc.

Jeffers, H. Paul. Legends of Santa Claus. 2005. (Biography Ser.). (Illus.). 112p. (gr. 6-12). lib. bdg. 27.93 (978-0-8225-4983-3(2)) Lerner Publishing Group.

Kalman, Bobbie. Santa Claus from A to Z. 1999. (AlphaBasiCs Ser.). (Illus.). 32p. (J). (gr. 2-3). pap. (978-0-86505-419-6(3)); lib. bdg. (978-0-86505-389-2(8)) Crabtree Publishing Co.

—Santa Claus from A to Z. 2000. (gr. 3-6). lib. bdg. 16.40 (978-0-613-22328-7(4)) Tandem Library Bks.

Keitz, Roderick K., illus. The North Pole Chronicles, 4 bks., Set. Incl. Christmas Eve Tradition. Thompson, R. W., Jr. 1993. 8.95 (978-0-9636442-1-3(1)); Shopping Trip. Thompson, R. W., Jr. 1995. 8.95 (978-0-9636442-2-0(X)); Star on the Pole. Thompson, R. W. 1996. 8.95 (978-0-9636442-3-7(8)); Wow! I Got to Go to the North Pole. Thompson, R. W., Jr. 1994. 8.95 (978-0-9636442-0-6(3)); (Illus.). 16p. (J). (ps-3). 29.95 (978-0-9636442-8-2(9)) North Pole Chronicles.

Marzollo, Jean. I Spy Santa Claus. Wick, Walter, illus. Wick, Walter, photos by. 2006. (Scholastic Reader Ser.). 32p. (J). pap. 3.99 (978-0-439-78414-6(X)) Scholastic, Inc.

Mayer, Marianna. The Real Santa Claus: Legends of Saint Nicholas. 2001. (Illus.). 32p. (J). (gr. 3 up). 16.99 (978-0-8037-2624-6(4) , Dial) Penguin Group (USA) Inc.

Moritz, Dianne, adapted by. Santa Lives! The Night Before Christmas. 2005. (Charming Petite Ser.). (Illus.). 64p. (J). 4.95 (978-0-88088-467-9(3)) Peter Pauper Pr. Inc.

Ouwendijk, George. Santas of the World. 1999. (Looking Into the Past Ser.). (Illus.). 64p. (YA). (gr. 5 up). 28.00 (978-0-7910-4678-4(8) , Chelsea Hse.) Facts On File, Inc.

Prokop, Paul. The True Story of Santa Claus. 2000. (Illus.). 32p. (J). pap. 5.95 (978-0-8198-7406-1(X) , 332-393) Pauline Bks. & Media.

Santa Visits the Thingumajigs. 2005. (Illus.). 28p. (J). (ps-k). 7.95 (978-0-8249-6619-5(8)) Ideals Pubns.

Santa's Christmas Sparkly Sticker Fun. 2002. 16p. (J). pap. 2.98 (978-0-7525-6502-6(8)) Parragon, Inc.

Schick-Jacobowitz, Jean. A Bit of Applause for Santa Claus. 2005. (Illus.). 64p. 9.95 (978-1-4022-0553-8(8)) Sourcebooks, Inc.

Stanley, Kate. The Santa Map: A Cultural Geography of the World's Most Beloved Man. 2001. pap. 9.95 (978-1-885508-84-3(0) , 612-706-9686) Hedberg Maps, Inc.

Stiegemeyer, Julie. Saint Nicholas: The Real Story of the Christmas Legend. Ellison, Chris, illus. 2003. (ENG.). 32p. (J). 12.99 (978-0-7586-0376-0(2)) Concordia Publishing Hse.

Tonn, Mary Jane. Jolly Old Santa Claus. 2005. (Illus.). 30p. (J). (ps-1). pap. 3.95 (978-0-8249-5513-7(7)) Ideals Pubns.

Walsh, William S. The Story of Santa Klaus: Told for Children of All Ages from Six To. 2007. (ENG.). 216p. per. 24.95 (*978-1-4304-4232-5(8)) Kessinger Publishing, LLC.

Yzermans, Vincent A. Wonderworker: The True Story of How St. Nicholas Became Santa Claus. 2004. 64p. pap. 12.95 (978-0-87946-278-9(7) , 249) ACTA Pubns.

SANTA CLAUS—FICTION

Abbott, Tony. Kringle. Call, Greg, illus. 2005. 304p. (J). (gr. 4-7). pap. 14.99 (978-0-439-74942-8(5) , Scholastic Pr.) Scholastic, Inc.

Aboff, Marcie. Santa's Big Red Helper. Haefele, Steve, illus. 2005. (Clifford Ser.). 80p. (J). (ps-k). pap. 2.99 (978-0-439-79150-2(2)) Scholastic, Inc.

Albertson, Bernard. So You Think There Is No Santa. 2001. 152p. pap. 7.95 (978-0-87714-795-4(7)) Denlingers Pubs., Ltd.

Alsenas, Linas. Mrs. Claus Takes a Vacation. 2006. (Illus.). 32p. (J). pap. 16.99 (978-0-439-77978-4(2) , Scholastic Pr.) Scholastic, Inc.

Anderson, Derek. How the Easter Bunny Saved Christmas. Anderson, Derek, illus. 2006. (Illus.). 40p. (J). 15.95 (978-0-689-87634-9(3) , Simon & Schuster Children's Publishing) Simon & Schuster Children's Publishing.

Andes, Mary Lou. Santa's Prayer. Mattozzi, Patricia, illus. 2007. (J). (ps-k). bds. 11.95 incl. cd-rom (*978-0-8198-7100-8(1)) Pauline Bks. & Media.

Angel, Bruce. I Believe in Santa Claus. 2006. 121p. pap. 17.95 (978-1-4241-1486-3(1)) PublishAmerica, Inc.

Aoki, Hisako. Santa's Favorite Story: Santa Tells the Story of the First Christmas. Gantschev, Ivan, illus. 2007. 28p. (J). (ps-3). 9.99 (*978-1-4169-5029-5(X)) Simon & Schuster Children's Publishing.

Apperley, Dawn, illus. Santa Claus Will Come Tonight. 2002. 24p. (J). (ps-1). pap. 6.95 (978-0-439-40449-5(5) , Cartwheel Bks.) Scholastic, Inc.

Apples for Santa. 2007. (J). (*978-1-932570-73-1(X)) Literacy Footprints Inc.

Arctic Airlift. 2005. (Illus.). 36p. (J). 17.00 (978-0-9763119-0-4(9)) Blue Fox Pr.

Arkadia, illus. Rudolph the Red-Nosed Reindeer. 2000. (Little Golden Bks.). 24p. (J). (gr. k-k). 2.99 (978-0-307-98829-4(5) , 98829, Golden Bks.) Random Hse. Children's Bks.

Augustin, Barbara. Antonella & Her Santa Claus. Lahr, Gerhard, illus. 2001. 40p. (J). (ps-3). 14.95 (978-1-929132-13-3(1)) Kane/Miller Bk. Pubs., Inc.

Autry, Gene & Haldeman, Oakley. Here Comes Santa Claus. Whatley, Bruce, illus. 2002. 32p. (J). (ps up). 18.89 (978-0-06-028269-1(X)) HarperCollins Pubs.

Babcock, Bruce. The Year Santa Got Sick. Babcock, Bruce, illus. unabr. ed. 1998. (Illus.). 32p. (J). (ps-6). pap. 7.95 (978-1-892161-02-4(8)) Babcock Publishing Co.

Balian, Lorna. Bah! Humbug? Balian, Lecia, illus. 2006. 32p. (J). 15.95 (978-1-59572-036-8(7)) Star Bright Bks., Inc.

Baum, L. Frank. The Life & Adventures of Santa Claus. 2005. (Illus.). 192p. (gr. 12). mass mkt. 4.95 (978-0-451-52997-8(9) , Signet Classics) Penguin Group (USA) Inc.

—Life & Adventures of Santa Claus. 2006. 216p. 24.95 (978-1-55709-180-2(3)) Applewood Bks.

—The Life & Adventures of Santa Claus. Hague, Michael, illus. rev. ed. 2003. 192p. (J). 29.95 (978-0-8050-3822-4(1) , Holt, Henry & Co. Bks. For Young Readers) Holt, Henry & Co.

Bedford, David. I've Seen Santa! Warnes, Tim, illus. 2006. 32p. (J). 15.95 (978-1-58925-058-1(3) , tiger tales) ME Media LLC.

Bentley, Dawn. Santa's Surprise: A Pop-Up Story Box. Moerbeek, Kees, illus. 1998. 12p. (YA). (gr. 2 up). (978-1-58117-018-4(1) , Intervisual/Piggy Toes) Dalmatian Pr.

Bolin, Ken & Bolin, Corrine. Santa SP: Santa Clauses of the South Pole. 2003. (J). pap. 9.00 (978-0-8059-6170-4(9)) Dorrance Publishing Co., Inc.

Bonaddio, T. L. Peek-a-Boo Santa. 2008. (Illus.). 8p. (J). pap. 9.95 (*978-0-7624-3011-6(7) , Running Pr. Kids) Running Pr. Bk. Pubs.

—Peek-a-Boo Santa (bag Version) 2008. (Illus.). 8p. (J). pap. 9.95 (*978-0-7624-3163-2(6) , Running Pr. Kids) Running Pr. Bk. Pubs.

Boniface, William. Santa's Sleigh Is Full. Rooney, Ronnie, illus. 2002. (Top This! Ser.). 12p. (J). (ps-2). bds. 9.99 (978-0-8431-4543-4(9) , Price Stern Sloan) Penguin Group (USA) Inc.

Bradbury, Lynne. Santa Claus Has a Busy Night. (Christmas Titles Ser.: No. S808-6). (Illus.). (J). 3.95 (978-0-7214-5077-3(6) , Dutton Juvenile) Penguin Group (USA) Inc.

Bratun, Katy. Gingerbread Mouse. Bratun, Katy, illus. 2003. (Illus.). 32p. (J). (ps-2). lib. bdg. 13.89 (978-0-06-009081-4(2)) HarperCollins Pubs.

Bridgman, C. A. Santa's Hawaiian Vacation. (J). 14.95 (978-0-681-32827-3(4)) Booklines Hawaii, Ltd.

Bridwell, Norman. Clifford's Christmas Treasury. 2005. (Illus.). 96p. (ps-3). pap. 10.99 (978-0-439-79137-3(5)) Scholastic, Inc.

Brooks, Walter R. Freddy Goes to the North Pole. Wiese, Kurt, illus. 2001. 306p. (J). 23.95 (978-1-58567-104-5(5)) Overlook Pr., The.

Brown, Jeff. Stanley's Christmas Adventure. Nash, Scott, illus. 2003. (Stanley Lambchop Adventure Ser.). 80p. (J). pap. 4.99 (978-0-06-442175-1(9) , Harper Trophy) HarperCollins Pubs.

—Stanley's Christmas Adventure. 2003. (gr. k-3). lib. bdg. 13.00 (978-0-613-68466-8(4)) Tandem Library Bks.

Buckner, Arlene. Elphina. Klementz-Harte, Lauren, illus. 1998. 32p. (J). (gr. k-2). 17.95 (978-1-890309-56-5(7)) Tern Bk. Co., Inc., The.

Burgoyne, Tom. Phillie Phanatic's Christmas Wish, Vols. 4. Epstein, Len, illus. 2005. 32p. (J). 5.95 (978-0-9754419-0-9(6)) Middle Atlantic Pr.

Burmingham, John. Harvey Slumfenburger's Christmas Present. 2007. (Illus.). 48p. (J). (ps-3). 8.99 (*978-0-7636-3517-6(0)) Candlewick Pr.

Byrne, Barbara. The Magic Bell On. 2003. 13p. 12.66 (978-1-4116-1078-1(4)) Lulu.com.

Calamari, Barbara. Fright Before Christmas. 2001. (gr. 3-6). lib. bdg. 11.80 (978-0-613-87772-5(1)) Tandem Library Bks.

Campbell, Ellie. The Visiting Elf. 2006. (ENG., Illus.). 32p. per. 25.49 (*978-1-4259-7562-3(3)) AuthorHouse.

Campbell, Rod. Dear Santa. Campbell, Rod, illus. 2004. (Illus.). 16p. (J). bds. 7.99 (978-0-689-87415-4(4) , Little Simon) Simon & Schuster Children's Publishing.

Carey-Thompson, Thelma. I Saw Santa. Carey-Thompson, Thelma, illus. 2004. (Illus.). 32p. pap. 10.00 (978-0-920474-85-3(3) , Natural Heritage Bks.) Natural Heritage/Natural History, Inc. CAN. *Dist:* Three Dimensional Publishing.

Caro, Joe. Santa's Christmas Train. Shih, Lin, illus. 2005. 32p. pap. (978-0-9628078-2-4(6)) Cowboy Collector Pubns.

—Santa's Christmas Train Coloring Book. Shih, Lin, illus. 2005. 32p. pap. (978-0-9628078-5-5(0)) Cowboy Collector Pubns.

Catalano, Dominic. Santa & the Three Bears. Catalano, Dominic, illus. 2001. (Illus.). 32p. (YA). (gr. k-2). 15.95 (978-1-56397-864-7(4)) Boyds Mills Pr.

Charbonnel, Olivier. Santa's Factory. 2000. (Illus.). 12p. (J). pap. 15.95 (978-1-902413-51-8(2)) Van der Meer, a Div. of PHPC GBR. *Dist:* Abbeville Pr., Inc.

Chivus, Mitch. Fartsy Claus. Reed, Mike, illus. 2007. 32p. (J). lib. bdg. 17.89 (*978-0-06-089467-2(9)); 16.99 (*978-0-06-089466-5(0)) HarperCollins Pubs.

Christensen, Lichelle. Santa's Last Delivery. 2005. pap. 8.95 (978-1-933265-81-0(7)) Wasteland Pr.

Christie, Michael G. Olive the Orphan Reindeer. Lucas, Margeaux, illus. 2000. 46p. (gr. 4-7). pap. 7.95 (978-1-889658-16-2(2)) New Canaan Publishing Co. LLC.

—The Story of Olive. 2000. (Illus.). 46p. (gr. 4-7). 14.95 (978-1-889658-18-6(9)) New Canaan Publishing Co. LLC.

Christmas Book - Santa Claus. 2005. (J). bds. (978-1-4194-0074-2(6)) Paradise Pr., Inc.

Christ's Santa. 2004. (YA). 19.95 (978-0-9747815-0-1(9)) Life's Journey of Hope Pubns.

Chronicle Books LLC Staff. Santa Claus: Finger Puppet Book. 2006. (Illus.). 12p. (J). bds. 6.95 (978-0-8118-5458-0(2)) Chronicle Bks. LLC.

Chronicle Books Staff. Little Reindeer: Finger Puppet Book. 2006. (Illus.). 12p. (J). 6.95 (978-0-8118-5457-3(4)) Chronicle Bks. LLC.

Claus, Nancy. Santa's Hat. Ferchaud, Steve, illus. 2006. (J). (*978-0-9746747-6-6(1)) Cypress Bay Publishing.

—Santa's Prize. Ferchaud, Steve, illus. 2006. (J). (*978-0-9746747-5-9(3)) Cypress Bay Publishing.

Claus, Santa. The Santa Legends Present: The Lost Button. 2005. (J). cd-rom 12.00 (978-1-59971-079-2(X)) Aardvark Global Publishing.

—Santa's World: North Pole Series, Volume 1. 2006. (J). bds. 17.95 (978-0-9787129-0-7(0)) Kringle Enterprises Co.

Coffey, Timothy. Christmas at the Top of the World. Coffey, Timothy, illus. 2003. (Illus.). 32p. (J). (ps-1). 16.95 (978-0-8075-5762-4(5)) Whitman, Albert & Co.

Collins, Terry. Rancid Little Christmas. 2000. (gr. 3-6). lib. bdg. 11.80 (978-0-613-31628-6(2)) Tandem Library Bks.

Conrad, Pam. The Tub People's Christmas. Egielski, Richard, illus. 1999. 40p. (J). (ps-3). 15.89 (978-0-06-026029-3(7) , Geringer, Laura Book) HarperCollins Pubs.

Conteh, Gerald. I Still Believe in Santa. 2007. 188p. per. 14.95 (*978-1-60264-014-6(9)) Virtualbookworm.com Publishing, Inc.

Cookies for Santa. 2006. (J). (*978-1-932570-75-5(6)) Literacy Footprints Inc.

Creamer, Joan Klatil. The Magic Sceptre - the Legend of Blue Santa Claus. Creamer, Joan Klatil, illus. ed. 2006. (J). 16.95 (978-0-9778476-3-1(2)) Silver Snowflake Publishing.

Crissey, Brian. The Loneliest Christmas Tree. Crissey, Noah, illus. 2004. 32p. (J). bds. 25.00 (978-1-893183-35-3(1) , 598) Granite Publishing, LLC.

Crissey, Brian L. The Loneliest Christmas Tree. Crissey, Noah, illus. 2004. (J). (978-1-930724-12-9(8)); (978-1-930724-13-6(6)) Granite Publishing, LLC.

Crowson, Andrew. Flip Flap Christmas. Crowson, Andrew, illus. 2003. (Illus.). 12p. (J). bds. (978-1-85602-476-1(8)) Chrysalis Children's Bks.

Cummings, David W. How Biddikins & Buddikins Made Santa Claus Work Fast! 2005. (J). pap. 15.00 (978-0-8059-6814-9(8)) Dorrance Publishing Co., Inc.

Cummings, Priscilla. Santa Claws, the Christmas Crab. Ramsey, Marcy Dunn, illus. 2006. 32p. (J). pap. 10.50 (978-0-87033-576-1(6)) Cornell Maritime Pr., Inc.

Currey, Anna. Truffle's Christmas. 2000. (Illus.). (J). (978-0-531-30289-7(X) , Orchard Bks.) Scholastic, Inc.

Curti, Anna, illus. Santa Claus. 2000. (Portable Holidays Ser.). 10p. (J). (ps). bds. 7.95 (978-0-8109-5653-7(5)) Abrams, Harry N. , Inc.

Daniels, Johanna. What About Claus? 2005. (Illus.). 32p. 15.95 (978-0-9711106-8-7(9)) Mountaintop Pr.

Davies, Margo. Do You Believe in Santa Claus? 2003. (J). 6.00 (978-0-9708959-7-4(6)) Accent Pubns.

Davies, Valentine. Miracle on 34th Street. 2002. 80p. pap. 6.25 (978-0-573-62892-4(0)) French, Samuel Inc.

—Miracle on 34th Street. fac. ed. 2001. 136p. (YA). 13.95 (978-0-15-216377-8(8)) Harcourt Children's Bks.

Davis, Carol. No Cookies for Santa? 2005. 17.00 (978-0-8059-9930-3(2)) Dorrance Publishing Co., Inc.

Davis, Caroline, illus. Trim the Tree! 2004. (Christmas Wood Tops Ser.). 18p. (J). bds. 4.95 (978-0-7641-5755-4(8)) Barron's Educational Series, Inc.

de Brunhoff, Jean. Babar & Father Christmas. Haas, Merle, tr. from FRE. 2001. Tr. of Babar et le Pere Noel. (Illus.). 48p. (J). (ps-2). 15.95 (978-0-375-81444-0(2) , Random Hse. Bks. for Young Readers) Random Hse. Children's Bks.

—Babar und der Weihnachtsmann. Serusclat-Bruett, Francoise, tr. from FRE. 1999. Orig. Title: Babar et le Pere Noel. (GER.). 40p. (J). (978-3-257-00729-9(9)) Diogenes Verlag AG CHE. *Dist:* International Bk. Import Service, Inc.

de Paola, Tomie. Guess Who's Coming to Santa's for Dinner? 2004. (Illus.). 48p. (J). (ps-3). 16.99 (978-0-399-24271-7(6) , Putnam Juvenile) Penguin Group (USA) Inc.

Dear Santa- 2005. (Illus.). 24p. (J). (ps-1). bds. 6.95 (978-0-8249-6618-8(X)) Ideals Pubns.

DePaola, Tomie. Get Dressed, Santa! 2006. (Illus.). 12p. (J). (ps-1). bds. 6.99 (978-0-448-44446-8(1) , Grosset & Dunlap) Penguin Group (USA) Inc.

—Guess Who's Coming to Santa's for Dinner? DePaola, Tomie, illus. 2006. 40p. (J). (ps). pap. 6.99 (978-0-14-240699-1(6) , Puffin) Penguin Group (USA) Inc.

Dewin, Howie. T' Was the Fight Before Christmas. 2003. (gr. k-3). lib. bdg. 11.80 (978-0-613-72149-3(7)) Tandem Library Bks.

Disney Press Staff & Ponti, James. Santa Clause Vol. 3: The Escape Clause. 2006. 128p. (gr. 3-7). pap. 4.99 (978-1-4231-0112-3(X)) Disney Pr.

Dodd, Contance. Santa Meets Mr. Dippleman. 2002. (Illus.). 28p. (J). 10.95 (978-1-886225-76-3(1)) Day of Grace Publishing Services.

Dollin, Laura. Santa Claus. Beardshaw, Rosalind, illus. 2003. 12p. (J). (gr. k-k). bds. 5.99 (978-0-7636-2144-5(7)) Candlewick Pr.

Douglas, Vincent & School Specialty Publishing Staff. Santa's Workshop, 4 bks., Set. Schroeder, Warren L., illus. 2003. (My Block Book Schoolhouse Collection). 88p. (J). (ps up). bds. 12.95 (978-1-58845-523-9(8)) School Specialty Publishing.

Dower, Laura. T' Was the Fight Before Christmas. 2003. (gr. k-3). lib. bdg. 11.25 (978-0-613-72148-6(9)) Tandem Library Bks.

Dunham, Terri Hoover. The Legend of Papa Noël: A Cajun Christmas Story. Knorr, Laura, illus. 2006. 32p. (J). (gr. k-5). 17.95 (978-1-58536-256-1(5)) Sleeping Bear Pr.

Dunrea, Olivier, illus. Merry Christmas, Ollie! 2005. (J). (978-0-618-53242-1(0)) Houghton Mifflin Co.

Dupuis, Ann. Santa's Secret: A Gatecrasher Adventure with "All the Rules You Need to Know" 2nd ed. 1998. (Illus.). 24p. pap. 4.95 (978-1-887154-05-5(1) , GGG3003) Grey Ghost Pr., Inc.

Durant, Alan. Dear Santa Claus. Cabban, Vanessa, illus. 2005. 32p. (J). (ps-2). 14.99 (978-0-7636-2829-1(8)) Candlewick Pr.

Durant, Alan. Dear Santa Claus: Mini Edition. Cabban, Vanessa, illus. 2007. 32p. (J). (ps-2). 6.99 (*978-0-7636-3465-0(4)) Candlewick Pr.

Duval, Kathy. The Three Bears' Christmas. Meisel, Paul, illus. 32p. (J). 6.95 (978-0-8234-2039-1(6)); 16.95 (978-0-8234-1871-8(5)) Holiday Hse., Inc.

Edwards, Gerry. Candy Klaus Trick or Treat. 2004. 56p. per. 10.95 (978-1-59453-394-5(6) , 1074) Airleaf Publishing & Bookselling.

Egan, Kate. What to Do about Frost? 2nd rev. ed. 2006. (Santa Clause Ser.: No. 3). 24p. (ps-2). pap. 3.50 (978-1-4231-0506-0(0)) Disney Pr.

Eldridge, Les. Santa's Cat. Eldridge, Les & Casey, James, illus. 2003. 24p. (J). (978-1-877338-03-8(6)) Steele Roberts Publishing Ltd.

Fearnley, Jan. Little Robin's Christmas. Fearnley, Jan, illus. 2002. 32p. (J). 5.95 (978-1-58925-371-1(X) , tiger tales) ME Media LLC.

Federici, Diane Marie. The Christmas Stocking. 2006. (J). pap. 8.00 (978-0-8059-6874-3(1)) Dorrance Publishing Co., Inc.

Ferguson, Sarah. Little Red's Christmas Story. Williams, Sam, illus. 2004. 40p. (J). 15.95 (978-0-689-85561-0(3)) Simon & Schuster Children's Publishing.

Ferguson, Sarah The Duchess of York. Little Red's Christmas Story. Williams, Sam, illus. 2007. 40p. (J). 6.99 (*978-1-4169-5002-8(8) , Aladdin) Simon & Schuster Children's Publishing.

Fitzgerald, Clyde C. The Year Santa's Reindeer Went. . . on Strike! Cahill, David, illus. 2001. 6.95 (978-0-9715874-0-3(X)) Ira Valley Ideas.

Fitzwater, Ivan W. Cappy the Christmas Woodpecker. Paul Hudgins, illus. 2002. pap. 8.95 (978-0-934955-51-5(4)) Watercress Pr.

Ford, Linda. Santa Claus, Inc. 1998. pap. 3.99 (978-0-590-11504-9(X)) Scholastic, Inc.

—The Santa Season. 2002. 93p. (J). (978-0-439-43532-1(3)) Scholastic, Inc.

Frazee, Marla. Santa Claus: The World's Number One Toy Expert. 2005. (Illus.). 40p. (J). (ps-ps). 16.00 (978-0-15-204970-6(3) , Harcourt Children's Bks) Harcourt Children's Bks.

Funke, Cornelia. When Santa Fell to Earth. Latsch, Oliver, tr. from GER. Howard, Paul, illus. 2006. 192p. (J). pap. 15.99 (978-0-439-78204-3(X) , Chicken Hse., The) Scholastic, Inc.

Garis, Howard Roger. Johnnie & Billie Bushytail. 2004. reprint ed. pap. 15.95 (978-1-4191-2786-1(1)); pap. 1.99 (978-1-4192-2786-8(6)) Kessinger Publishing, LLC.

Gauvey, D. H. Santa's Socks. Fasolino, Peter, illus. 2003. 35p. (J). (ps-7). per. 13.95 (978-1-59453-454-6(3) , 2329) Airleaf Publishing & Bookselling.

Gerver, Jane E. The Santa Snatcher. Spaziante, Patrick, illus. 2004. 32p. (J). lib. bdg. 15.00 (*978-1-4242-0959-0(5)) Fitzgerald Bks.

—The Santa Snatcher. 2004. (Ready-to-Read Ser.). 32p. (J). pap. 3.99 (978-0-689-87018-7(3) , Simon Spotlight) Simon & Schuster Children's Publishing.

Gibbons, Gail. Santa Who? 1999. (Illus.). 32p. (J). (gr. k-3). 15.89 (978-0-688-15529-2(4)) HarperCollins Pubs.

Gifford, Christopher. A Present for Santa! A Lift-the-Flap Book with 45 Flaps! Fruchter, Jason, illus. 2002. (Dora the Explorer Ser.). 12p. (J). bds. 11.95 (978-0-689-84935-0(4) , Simon Spotlight/Nickelodeon) Simon & Schuster Children's Publishing.

Gifford, Myrna. When Santa Got Stuck in the Chimney. Cooper, Frances, illus. 2001. 16p. (J). 5.95 (978-0-9720763-0-2(1) , PB1) Action Factor, Inc.

Gillespie, Haven & Coots, J. Fred. Santa Claus Is Comin' to Town. Kellogg, Steven, illus. 2006. 40p. (J). pap. 6.99 (978-0-06-443865-0(1) , Harper Trophy) HarperCollins Pubs.

Godwin, Laura & Chapman, Jane. Happy Christmas, Honey! 2002. (Happy Honey Ser.). (Illus.). 32p. (J). pap. 3.99 (978-0-689-84764-6(5) , Aladdin) Simon & Schuster Children's Publishing.

Goodrich, Carter & Moore, Clement Clarke. A Creature Was Stirring. Goodrich, Carter, illus. 2006. (Illus.). 40p. (J). 16.95 (978-0-689-86399-8(3) , Simon & Schuster Children's Publishing) Simon & Schuster Children's Publishing.

Graham, Brandon. Perverts of the Unknown. Graham, Brandon, illus. 2003. (Illus.). 56p. 9.95 (978-1-56163-374-6(7) , Amerotica) NBM Publishing Co.

The Great Mix Up. 2005. (Illus.). 40p. (J). lib. bdg. 15.95 (978-0-9772282-0-1(7)) B. T. Brooks.

Green, Rod. Santa Claus. Wright, Carol et al, illus. 2006. 32p. (J). (ps-5). 19.95 (978-1-4169-2758-7(1) , Atheneum) Simon & Schuster Children's Publishing.

Green, Rod. Santa's Reindeer. Wright, Carol et al, illus. 2007. 32p. (J). (ps-5). 16.99 (*978-1-4169-5070-7(2) , Atheneum) Simon & Schuster Children's Publishing.

Greenburg, Dan. Young Santa. Miller, Warren, illus. 2005. 96p. (J). (gr. 2-5). pap. 3.99 (978-0-439-61636-2(0)) Scholastic, Inc.

Greene, Rhonda. Santa's Stuck. Cole, Henry, illus. 2006. 32p. (J). (ps). pap. 5.99 (978-0-14-240686-1(4) , Puffin) Penguin Group (USA) Inc.

Greene, Rhonda Gowler. Santa's Stuck. Cole, Henry, illus. 2004. 32p. (J). (ps). 16.99 (978-0-525-47292-6(4) , Dutton Juvenile) Penguin Group (USA) Inc.

Gregory, Larry. A Christmas Surprise. Woolmer, Nancy, illus. 2004. 24p. pap. 14.95 (978-1-4137-3014-2(0)) PublishAmerica, Inc.

Grimsley-Fambro, Sonja. Santa Spent the Night with Me. Garfinkel, Dana, illus. l.t. ed. 2002. 30p. (J). per. 40.99 (978-1-893108-88-2(0)) Neighborhood Pr. Publishing.

—Santa Spent the Night with Me - Coloring Book. Garfinkel, Dana, illus. l.t. ed. 2002. 16p. (J). 4.99 (978-1-893108-89-9(9)) Neighborhood Pr. Publishing.

Haban, Rita. Who Is Santa? Less, Sally, illus. 2001. 26p. (J). 7.95 net. (978-0-9706654-3-0(1)) Sprite Pr.

Hagen, Carol. Night Henry Ford Met Santa. Faulkner, Matt, illus. 2006. 32p. (J). 17.95 (978-1-58536-132-8(1)) Sleeping Bear Pr.

Harley, Bill. Dear Santa: The Letters of James B. Dobbins. Alley, R. W., illus. 2005. 32p. (J). 15.99 (978-0-06-623778-7(5)); lib. bdg. 16.89 (978-0-06-623779-4(3)) HarperCollins Pubs.

Harper, Stephan J. One Christmas Story. Steuerwald, Joy, illus. 2003. 32p. (J). lib. bdg. 16.95 (978-0-9741800-0-7(9)) Inspire Press, Inc.

Hartelius, Margaret A. Is That You, Santa? 1998. (All Aboard Reading Ser.). (Illus.). 32p. (J). (ps-1). pap. 3.99 (978-0-448-41849-0(5) , Grosset & Dunlap) Penguin Group (USA) Inc.

Hassett, Ann. The Finest Christmas Tree. Hassett, John, illus. 2005. 32p. (J). (gr. k-3). 16.00 (978-0-618-50901-0(1) , Walter Lorraine) Houghton Mifflin Co. Trade & Reference Div.

Haynes, Betsy. Santa's Stowaway: Book Three. 2008. 280p. (YA). pap. 10.99 (978-1-59092-499-0(1) , Blue Works) Windstorm Creative.

Healey, Richard (Dick). Holly the Christmas Dove. 2005. 36p. (J). 13.28 (978-1-4116-5496-9(X)) Lulu.com.

Hegg, Tom. A Silent Night for Peef. Hanson, Warren, illus. 1998. 48p. (J). (ps-3). 15.95 (978-0-931674-35-8(2)) Waldman Hse. Pr., Inc.

Help for Santa. 2006. (J). (*978-1-932570-76-2(4)) Literacy Footprints Inc.

Henkel, Donald G. A Legend of Santa & His Brother Fred. Henkel, Donald B., illus. 2000. 46p. (J). 20.50 (978-0-9673504-0-0(9)) Quillpen.

Herman, Gail. The Secret Santa Mystery. del Sur, Duendes, illus. 2003. (Scooby-Doo! Reader Ser.). 32p. (J). pap. 3.99 (978-0-439-45619-7(3) , Scholastic Paperbacks) Scholastic, Inc.

S

Hoff, Syd. Where's Prancer? 1999. (Illus.). 32p. (J). (ps-2). pap. 5.95 (978-0-06-443594-9(6) , Harper Trophy) HarperCollins Pubs.

Holmquist, Delano. Santasauras. Galey, Chuck, illus. 2002. 32p. (J). (ps-2). 15.95 (978-1-56554-933-3(3)) Pelican Publishing Co., Inc.

Hooper, Ruth. Santa's Factory. Charbonnel, Olivier & Mostyn, David, illus. 2004. 6p. (J). (gr. k-4). reprint ed. 16.00 (978-0-7567-7585-8(X)) DIANE Publishing Co.

Houghton Mifflin Company Staff. The Gift of Christmas: The Movie. 2004. (Illus.). 6p. (J). (ps-k). bds. 4.99 (978-0-618-47791-3(8)) Houghton Mifflin Co. Trade & Reference Div.

Howard, Thomas Lynn. Elf in the Family: An Interview with Santa. 2003. (gr. 3-6). lib. bdg. 24.00 (978-0-613-78074-2(4)) Tandem Library Bks.

Howe, James. The Fright Before Christmas. Mack, Jeff, illus. 2006. (Bunnicula & Friends Ser.). 48p. (J). 14.95 (978-0-689-86939-6(8) , Atheneum) Simon & Schuster Children's Publishing.

Howe, James & Howe, James. The Fright Before Christmas. Mack, Jeff, illus. 2007. (Bunnicula & Friends Ser.). 42p. (J). (gr. 1-3). per. 3.99 (***978-0-689-86941-9(X)*** , Aladdin) Simon & Schuster Children's Publishing.

Hurd, Thacher. Santa Mouse & the Ratdeer. (Illus.). 40p. (J). (ps-1). 2000. pap. 5.95 (978-0-06-443709-7(4) , Harper Trophy); 1998. 14.95 (978-0-06-027694-2(0)) HarperCollins Pubs.

—Santa Mouse & the Ratdeer. 2000. (Illus.). (J). (978-0-606-22063-7(1)) Tandem Library Bks.

It's Santa. 2003. (J). per. (978-1-57657-909-1(3)) Paradise Pr., Inc.

Jacobs, Edwin. The Eve They Hi-Jacked Santa Claus. Simon, Mark & Barker, Aline, illus. l.t. ed. 2001. 47p. (J). 21.95 (978-0-9612948-5-4(X)) Lem Publishing & Production.

Jacobson, Ryan. Santa Claus: Super Spy: The Case of the Florida Freeze. Belkholm, Erica, illus. l.t. ed. 2005. 80p. (J). per. 4.99 (978-0-9774122-0-4(2)) Lake 7 Creative.

James, Sabrina & Scognamiglio, John. Secret Santa. 2007. 368p. (J). (gr. 7 up). pap. 6.99 (***978-0-439-02695-6(4)***) Scholastic, Inc.

Johnston, Patches. Mark's Mixed-up Months. 2004. 33p. pap. 17.95 (978-1-4137-2432-5(9)) PublishAmerica, Inc.

Jones, Brien. The Year the Reindeer Went on Strike. 2003. 72p. (J). per. 9.95 (978-1-59453-071-5(8) , 1669) Airleaf Publishing & Bookselling.

Joyce, Jacqueline. Santa Cookie. Miltenberger, Ami, illus. 1998. 36p. (Orig.). (J). (ps-4). pap. 7.95 (978-0-9652211-6-0(4) , 11133) Bear Path, The.

—Santa Cookie. DelMar Communication International Staff, tr. Miltenberger, Ami, illus. 1998. (SPA.). 36p. (Orig.). (J). (ps-4). pap. 7.95 (978-0-9652211-7-7(2) , 11134) Bear Path, The.

Kelly, Becky. The Night Before Christmas. 2007. 32p. 14.95 (***978-0-7407-6064-8(5)***) Andrews McMeel Publishing.

Kessler, Leonard. That's Not Santa! (Hello Reader! Ser.). (FRE., Illus.). (J). pap. 5.99 (978-0-590-24360-5(8)) Scholastic, Inc.

Kimpton, Diana. Un Osito para Maddie. Roffe, Mercedes, tr. Kiernan, Anna, illus. 2001. (SPA.). 32p. (J). (gr. k-1). pap. 4.00 (978-0-439-31740-5(1) , SO30907, Cartwheel Bks.) Scholastic, Inc.

Klaus, Kenneth. Is There a Christmas Santa. 2004. pap. 4.99 (978-0-570-04952-4(0)) Concordia Publishing Hse.

Knights, Harry B. Luigi & The Lost Wish. 2003. (Nicholas Stories : No. 4). (Illus.). 56p. (J). pap. 16.95 (978-1-58980-162-2(8)) Pelican Publishing Co., Inc.

—The Maiden Voyage of Kris Kringle. 2003. (Nicholas Stories : No. 3). (Illus.). 56p. (J). pap. 16.95 (978-1-58980-161-5(X)) Pelican Publishing Co., Inc.

Koontz, Dean. Robot Santa: The Further Adventures of Santa's Twin. Parks, Phil, illus. 2004. 72p. (J). 20.89 (978-0-06-050944-6(9)) HarperCollins Pubs.

—Santa's Twin. Parks, Phil, illus. 2004. 64p. pap. 12.95 (978-0-06-057223-5(X)) HarperCollins Pubs.

Korman, Justine. Merry Christmas, Grumpy Bunny. 1999. (gr. k-3). lib. bdg. 11.25 (978-0-613-30602-7(3)) Tandem Library Bks.

Kremer, Kevin. Santa's Our Substitute Teacher. 2006. 150p. pap. 5.99 (978-0-9663335-4-1(3) , 703-001) Snow In Sarasota Publishing.

Krensky, Stephen. How Santa Got His Job. Schindler, S. D., illus. 2002. (J). 24.04 (978-0-7587-2770-1(4)) Book Wholesalers, Inc.

—How Santa Got His Job. Schindler, S. D., illus. 2002. 32p. (J). pap. 6.99 (978-0-689-84668-7(1) , Aladdin) Simon & Schuster Children's Publishing.

—How Santa Got His Job. 2002. (gr. k-3). lib. bdg. 15.30 (978-0-613-90196-3(7)) Tandem Library Bks.

—How Santa Lost His Job. Schindler, S. D., illus. 2005. 29p. (J). (gr. k-4). reprint ed. 15.00 (978-0-7567-9405-7(6)) DIANE Publishing Co.

Landolf, Diane Wright. Santa Claus Is Coming to Town. Baker, Darrell, illus. 2004. 24p. (J). (gr. k-k). pap. 3.99 (978-0-375-82932-1(6) , Golden Bks.) Random Hse. Children's Bks.

Lawrence, Michael. Baby Christmas. Robins, Arthur, illus. 2006. 32p. (J). 14.99 (978-0-7641-5998-5(4)) Barron's Educational Series, Inc.

Lee, Kate. Santa's Suit. Eaves, Edward, illus. 2004. 6p. (J). (gr. k-ps). bds. 10.95 (978-0-439-61499-3(6) , Cartwheel Bks.) Scholastic, Inc.

Lee, Stan. Superhero Christmas. Jessell, Tim, illus. 2004. 32p. (J). (ps-2). 16.89 (978-0-06-056560-2(8)) HarperCollins Pubs.

Leitich Smith, Cynthia & Leitich Smith, Greg. Santa Knows. Bjorkman, Steve, illus. 2006. 32p. (J). (ps). 16.99 (978-0-525-47757-0(8) , Dutton Juvenile) Penguin Group (USA) Inc.

Letter to Santa. 2003. (Traditional Christmas Stories Ser.). 32p. (J). 4.98 (978-0-7525-8845-2(1)) Parragon, Inc.

Leuck, Laura. Santa Claws: A Scary Christmas to All. Grimly, Gris, illus. 2006. 32p. (J). 16.95 (978-0-8118-4992-0(9)) Chronicle Bks. LLC.

Lewis, J. Patrick. The Snowflake Sisters. Desimini, Lisa, illus. 2003. 32p. (J). 16.95 (978-0-689-85029-5(8) , Atheneum/Anne Schwartz Bks.) Simon & Schuster Children's Publishing.

Loter, Darlene. Santa's Promise. 2004. 25p. pap. 9.95 (978-1-4137-1238-4(X)) PublishAmerica, Inc.

Lutz, Nancie Anne. Patsy & Freckles Make Christmas Cookies. Lutz, Nancie Anne, illus. 2005. (Illus.). 25p. (J). (978-0-9760064-1-1(3)) Dollworks.

MacLennan, David. Santa's Stormy Christmas Eve. Parkinson, Cheryl, tr. Parkinson, Cheryl, illus. 2004. 32p. 7.95 (978-0-9731960-0-9(9)) Full Satchel Pr. CAN. *Dist:* Wilson & Assocs.

Major, Kevin. The House of Wooden Santas. George, Imelda, illus. Pratt, Ned, photos by. 2004. 96p. (J). 24.95 (978-0-88995-166-2(7)) Red Deer Pr. CAN. *Dist:* Fitzhenry & Whiteside, Ltd.

—The House of Wooden Santas. Pratt, Ned, photos by. gif. ed. 2004. (Illus.). 96p. (J). 34.95 (978-0-88995-249-2(3)) Red Deer Pr. CAN. *Dist:* Fitzhenry & Whiteside, Ltd.

Mammola-Koravos, Beth. Olivia's Magical Christmas. 2006. (J). pap. 16.95 (***978-1-59526-631-6(3)***) Media Creations, Inc.

Marsh, Carole. The Story of Santa Claus. 2003. 12p. (J). (gr. k-4). pap. 2.95 (978-0-635-02151-9(X)) Gallopade International.

Martin, Ann M. On Christmas Eve. 160p. (J). 2007. pap. 5.99 (***978-0-439-74589-5(6)*** , Scholastic Paperbacks); 2006. (Illus.). pap. 15.99 (978-0-439-74588-8(8) , Scholastic) Scholastic, Inc.

Martini, T. J. Christmas Lost & Found. Kiejna, Magdalenea, illus. 2007. (J). per. 15.99 (***978-0-9705018-7-5(0)***) Wings, Inc.

Marunas, Nathaniel. Manga Claus: The Blade of Kringle. Craddock, Erik, illus. 2006. 80p. (J). (gr. 4-12). 12.99 (978-1-59514-134-7(0) , Razorbill) Penguin Group (USA) Inc.

Marzollo, Jean. Ten Little Christmas Presents. 2008. (J). (***978-0-545-02791-5(8)***) Scholastic, Inc.

Matsuura, Richard & Matsuura, Ruth. Gift from Santa. Chao, Linus, illus. (J). 7.95 (978-1-887916-06-6(7)) Orchid Isle Publishing Co.

May, Robert L. Rudolph to the Rescue. Papp, Lisa, illus. 2006. 40p. (J). (ps). pap. 6.99 (978-0-448-44142-9(X) , Grosset & Dunlap) Penguin Group (USA) Inc.

McArdle, Donald. Santa's Newest Friend. 2007. 25p. (J). 21.50 (***978-0-615-14212-8(5)***) McArdle, Donald.

McCann, Jesse Leon. Scooby-Doo! & Santa's Bake Shop. 2000. (gr. 3-6). lib. bdg. 14.15 (978-0-613-54349-1(1)) Tandem Library Bks.

McGauley, Patrick. Santa the King. Wirkklua, Derek, illus. 2004. 40p. (J). 13.95 (978-0-9724209-8-3(3)) McGauley, Patrick.

McGee, Fatty. Santa's Workshop. 2007. 6p. 16.95 (***978-1-58117-599-8(X)*** , Intervisual/Piggy Toes) Dalmatian Pr.

McGuirk, Leslie. Ho, Ho, Ho, Tucker! McGuirk, Leslie, illus. 2007. (Illus.). 30p. (J). (gr. k-k). pap. 4.99 (***978-0-7636-3663-0(0)***) Candlewick Pr.

McGuy, Bruce. Just Ask Santa. 2001. (Santas Ser.: Bk. 4). 56p. pap. 7.95 (978-0-9642311-3-9(1)) Santa's Publishing.

McLendon, Charles H., Jr. Santa's Stories for Children & Adults, Vol. I. collector's ed. 2002. (Illus.). 12p. (J). (ps-6). pap. 19.95 (978-0-9723225-0-8(7)) Christmas City Distribution, Inc.

McMullan, Kate. Fluffy Saves Christmas. Smith, Mavis, illus. 2004. 40p. (J). lib. bdg. 15.00 (978-1-59054-462-4(5)) Fitzgerald Bks.

—Fluffy Saves Christmas, Level 3. Smith, Mavis, illus. 1999. (Hello Reader! Ser.). 40p. (J). (gr. 1-3). pap. 3.99 (978-0-590-52308-0(2) , Cartwheel Bks.) Scholastic, Inc.

Milgrim, David. See Santa Nap. Milgrim, David, illus. 2004. (Adventures of Otto Ser.). (Illus.). 32p. (J). 14.95 (978-0-689-85928-1(7) , Atheneum) Simon & Schuster Children's Publishing.

Miller, Edward. Elf Elementary: A Christmas Story. 2004. (Illus.). 32p. (J). (ps-3). 12.95 (978-0-8109-8721-0(X)) Abrams, Harry N. , Inc.

Moody, Betty G. Magical Wish. 1998. (Illus.). (J). 15.95 (978-0-9663522-1-4(1)) Character Lines Publishing.

Moore, Brian L. The Story Behind Santa Sacks. Mulligan, Todd, illus. 2004. 32p. (978-0-9732651-0-1(8)) Hills-n-Hollows Publishing.

Moore, Clement C. Grumpy Santa. Spiridellis, Gregg & Spiridellis, Evan, illus. 2003. (J). pap. (978-0-439-53039-2(3) , Orchard Bks.) Scholastic, Inc.

Morozumi, Atsuko, et al. Santa's Christmas Countdown. Morozumi, Atsuko, illus. 2003. (Illus.). (J). (gr. k-4). 15.95 (978-0-7696-3189-9(4) , Gingham Dog Pr.) School Specialty Publishing.

Morrissey, Dean. The Christmas Ship. 2000. (Illus.). 40p. (J). (gr. k-4). 16.89 (978-0-06-028576-0(1)) HarperCollins Pubs.

—Christmas Ship. 2000. (gr. k-3). lib. bdg. 14.15 (978-0-613-68414-9(1)) Tandem Library Bks.

Mosley, Keith. A Busy Day for Santa. 2001. 8p. (J). pap. 10.95 (978-1-902413-49-5(0)) Van der Meer, a Div. of PHPC GBR. *Dist:* Abbeville Pr., Inc.

Moulton, Mark. Travelers Gift. Sherwood, Stewart, illus. 2001. 32p. 18.00 (978-0-7412-0867-5(9)) Lang Graphics, Ltd.

Murail, Marie-Aude & Murail, Elvire. Santa's Last Present. Blake, Quentin, illus. 2004. 32p. (J). 12.95 (978-1-56145-319-1(6)) Peachtree Pubs., Ltd.

Myra, Harold. Santa, Are You for Real? Kurisu, Jane, illus. 2005. 18p. (J). (ps-3). bds. 6.99 (978-1-4003-0629-9(9)) Nelson, Thomas Inc.

Nagy, Gloria & Chwast, Seymour. The Wizard Who Wanted to Be Santa. 2000. (Illus.). (J). (ps-3). 16.95 (978-0-9679436-0-2(4)) Sheer Bliss Communications, LLC.

Nguyen, Anthony. Santa with His Reindeer. 2004. pap. 8.00 (978-0-8059-6261-1(1)) Dorrance Publishing Co., Inc.

Nivens, Karen. Benjamin P. Blizzard: Welcome to Christmastown. Grisham, Jason, illus. 2007. 48p. (J). per. (***978-0-9798154-1-6(X)***) Living Waters Publishing Co.

The North Pole Is Sinking! 2005. (J). 9.99 (978-0-9773674-0-5(1)) Blue State Pr.

Nyaradi, J. A. Catching Santa. 2006. 140p. pap. 11.95 (978-0-7414-3462-3(8)) Infinity Publishing.

O'Dea, Kendra. The Stolen Sleigh. McGovern, Sarah, illus. 2006. (J). pap. (978-0-922993-53-6(X)) Marquette Bks., LLC.

Offley, Nancy. The Story of Snickers. 2004. (Illus.). 40p. (J). pap. 9.95 (978-0-9748081-0-9(5)) Classroom Enrichment Assocs.

Oliver Kringle. 2001. 32p. per. 17.00 (978-1-889191-15-7(9)) Clove Pubns.

Olsen, Mary-Kate & Olsen, Ashley. Two of a Kind No. 32: Santa Girls. 2003. (gr. 3-6). lib. bdg. 13.00 (978-0-613-85153-4(6)) Tandem Library Bks.

Ostrow, Kim. A Colorful Christmas. Regan, Dana, illus. 2003. (Magical Color Bks.). 10p. (J). 5.95 (978-1-4027-0991-3(9)) Sterling Publishing Co., Inc.

—Jingle Santa: A Book to Touch & Feel. Durantz, Summer, illus. 2001. (Jingle Ears Ser.). 12p. (J). bds. 4.99 (978-0-689-84281-8(3) , Little Simon) Simon & Schuster Children's Publishing.

Pallotta, Jerry. Who Will Guide My Sleigh Tonight. 2006. (Illus.). 32p. (J). pap. 5.99 (978-0-439-85369-9(9) , Cartwheel Bks.) Scholastic, Inc.

Pallotta, Jerry. Who Will Help Santa This Year? 2007. (Illus.). 32p. (J). (ps-3). pap. 8.99 (***978-0-545-01160-0(4)*** , Cartwheel Bks.) Scholastic, Inc.

Patterson, James. SantaKid. Garland, Michael, illus. 2004. 48p. (J). (gr. k-3). 14.99 (978-0-316-00061-1(2)) Little, Brown Bks. for Young Readers.

Perry, Rex, illus. 'Twas the Night Before Christmas. 2004. 24p. (J). lib. bdg. 8.00 (***978-1-4242-0641-4(3)***) Fitzgerald Bks.

Pingry, Patricia A. Jolly Old Santa Claus: A Christmas Classic. 2000. (Illus.). 24p. (J). (ps-k). bds. 6.95 (978-0-8249-4182-6(9)) Ideals Pubns.

Piper, Watty. The Little Engine That Could & the Snowy, Blowy Christmas. Ong, Cristina, illus. 1998. (All Aboard Bks.). 24p. (J). (ps-4). pap. 3.99 (978-0-448-41850-6(9) , Grosset & Dunlap) Penguin Group (USA) Inc.

—Little Engine That Could & the Snowy, Blowy Christmas. 1998. (gr. k-3). lib. bdg. 11.25 (978-0-613-72413-5(5)) Tandem Library Bks.

Ploog, Michael G. L. Frank Baum's the Life & Adventures of Santa Claus. Ploog, Michael G., illus. 2003. (Illus.). 80p. (YA). (gr. 7-12). reprint ed. 25.00 (978-0-7567-6682-5(6)) DIANE Publishing Co.

Polacco, Patricia. Welcome Comfort. Polacco, Patricia, illus. 2002. 40p. (J). pap. 6.99 (978-0-698-11965-9(7) , Putnam Juvenile) Penguin Group (USA) Inc.

—Welcome Comfort. 1999. (Illus.). 40p. (J). (ps-3). 16.99 (978-0-399-23169-8(2) , Philomel) Penguin Group (USA) Inc.

—Welcome Comfort. 2002. (gr. k-3). lib. bdg. 15.30 (978-0-613-50524-6(7)) Tandem Library Bks.

Ponti, James. Santa's Secret. 2006. 32p. (ps-2). pap. 3.99 (978-1-4231-0507-7(9)) Disney Pr.

—Saving Santa's Workshop. 2006. 32p. (ps-2). pap. 3.99 (978-1-4231-0508-4(7)) Disney Pr.

Powell-Zalewski, Amy. Maybe the Truth about Santa. Mugambi, Nkirote Christina, illus. 2005. (J). 15.00 (978-0-9773608-1-9(4)) Shiny Red Ball Publishing.

Poydar, Nancy. Brave Santa. 2004. (Illus.). 32p. (J). (gr. k-3). tchr. ed. 16.95 (978-0-8234-1821-3(9)) Holiday Hse., Inc.

Preller, James. A Jigsaw Jones Mystery, Vol. 30. Alley, R. W. & Smith, Jamie, illus. 2006. (Jigsaw Jones Super Special Ser.). 112p. (J). pap. 4.99 (978-0-439-79396-4(3)) Scholastic, Inc.

Primavera, Elise. Auntie Claus. 1999. (Illus.). 40p. (J). (ps-3). 16.00 (978-0-15-201909-9(X) , Silver Whistle) Harcourt Trade Pubs.

—Auntie Claus & the Key to Christmas. Primavera, Elise, illus. 2002. (Illus.). 40p. (J). (gr. k-3). 16.00 (978-0-15-202441-3(7) , Silver Whistle) Harcourt Trade Pubs.

Pulver, Robin. Christmas for a Kitten. Johnson, Layne, illus. (Albert Whitman Prairie Bks.). 32p. (J). (gr. k-3). 2005. pap. 6.95 (978-0-8075-1154-1(4)); 2003. 16.95 (978-0-8075-1151-0(X)) Whitman, Albert & Co.

Punter, Russell. Stories of Santa Claus. 2006. 48p. (J). 8.99 (978-0-7945-1476-1(6) , Usborne) EDC Publishing.

Rabe, Tish. Santa's Coming to Town! Sexton, Brenda, illus. 2006. (Nose Knows Ser.). 10p. (J). (ps-17). bds. 9.99 (978-1-58476-484-7(8) , IKIDS) Innovative Kids.

Rader, Laura. Santa's New Suit. Rader, Laura, illus. 2004. (Illus.). 32p. (J). (gr. k-3). reprint ed. 13.00 (978-0-7567-7154-6(4)) DIANE Publishing Co.

—Santa's New Suit. 2000. (Illus.). 40p. (J). (ps-3). 12.95 (978-0-06-028439-8(0)); 12.89 (978-0-06-029284-3(9)) HarperCollins Pubs.

—Who'll Pull Santa's Sleigh Tonight? Rader, Laura, illus. 2006. 40p. (J). pap. 6.99 (978-0-06-008090-7(6) , Harper Trophy) HarperCollins Pubs.

Rae, Jaci. Collista's Search for the True Meaning of Christmas. 2007. (Illus.). 59p. per. 14.95 (***978-0-9746229-1-0(5)***) North Shore Records, Inc.

Ralph, Grampa. How Santa Knows. 2007. 56p. pap. 12.95 (***978-1-4241-2284-4(8)***) PublishAmerica, Inc.

Rasmussen, Liz, illus. Too Fat to Fly. 2007. 32p. (J). 16.95 (***978-0-9793517-0-9(7)***) Silver Bells Publishing Hse.

Rayner, Shoo. Santas Diary. (Illus.). 96p. (J). 5.95 (978-0-14-034429-5(2)) Penguin Bks., Ltd. GBR. *Dist:* Trafalgar Square Publishing.

Reeves, Scott. Billy Barnaby's Twisted Christmas. 2003. 128p. (YA). pap. 11.95 (978-0-595-29570-8(3)) iUniverse, Inc.

Reindeer. 2003. (Shaped Board Books Ser.). 14p. (J). (ps-k). bds. 9.95 (978-0-7525-8850-6(8)) Parragon, Inc.

Reiss, Mike. How Murray Saved Christmas. Catrow, David, illus. 2000. 32p. (J). (ps-3). 10.99 (978-0-8431-7610-0(5) , Price Stern Sloan) Penguin Group (USA) Inc.

—Santa Claustrophobia. Catrow, David, illus. 2002. 32p. (J). (gr. 2-5). 10.99 (978-0-8431-7756-5(X) , Price Stern Sloan) Penguin Group (USA) Inc.

—Santa Claustrophobia. Catrow, David, illus. 2006. 32p. (J). (ps). pap. 5.99 (978-0-14-240376-1(8) , Puffin) Penguin Group (USA) Inc.

Reiss, Mike. Santa's Eleven Months Off. Montgomery, Michael, illus. 2007. 32p. (J). (ps-3). 15.95 (***978-1-56145-421-1(4)*** , Peachtree Junior) Peachtree Pubs., Ltd.

Rice, James. Gaston the Green-Nosed Alligator. Rice, James, illus. 2nd ed. 1998. (Illus.). 32p. (ps up). 15.95 (978-1-56554-285-3(1)) Pelican Publishing Co., Inc.

—Santa's Revenge. Rice, James, illus. 2005. (Illus.). 32p. (J). (ps-3). 15.95 (978-1-58980-250-6(0)) Pelican Publishing Co., Inc.

Richards, Kitty. The Journey Begins: An Early Reader. movie tie-in ed. 2004. (Polar Express Ser.). (Illus.). 32p. (J). (gr. k-3). pap. 3.99 (978-0-618-47795-1(0)) Houghton Mifflin Co. Trade & Reference Div.

Rissman, Angelica. Julius & the Lost Letter to Santa. 2003. (J). 7.99 (978-1-59384-019-8(5)) Parklane Publishing.

Ritchie, Joseph R. Where's Santa? Halverson, Lydia, illus. 2006. 14p. (J). (ps). bds. 7.95 (978-0-8249-6673-7(2) , Candy Cane Pr.) Ideals Pubns.

Robertson, Elysia Hill. Santa the Chimney Sweep / The Candy Cane That Found A Home. Robertson, Elysia Hill, illus. 2005. (Illus.). 37p. (J). per. 6.95 (978-0-9764444-9-7(6)) E. J. Publishing.

Romano, Ralph & Burke, Joe. Elbo Elf: The Package Master of Christmas. l.t. ed. 2000. (Illus.). 29p. (J). (gr. 1-5). 19.95 (978-0-9704125-0-8(9)) Elbo Elf, Inc.

Rumbley, Rose-Mary. Dear Santa: Thanks for the Piano. 2004. (Illus.). 46p. (J). pap. 8.95 (978-1-57168-466-0(2)) Eakin Pr.

Running Press Staff. Santa Claus Is Coming to Town. 2006. (Illus.). 128p. (J). 4.95 (978-0-7624-2826-7(0) , Running Pr.) Running Pr. Bk. Pubs.

Ryan, Brittney. Holly Claus: The Christmas Princess. Long, Laurel & Bedrick, Jeffrey K., illus. 2007. 48p. (J). lib. bdg. 19.89 (***978-0-06-144023-6(X)***); 18.99 (***978-0-06-144022-9(1)***) HarperCollins Pubs. (Julie Andrews Collection).

—The Legend of Holly Claus. Long, Laurel, illus. 2004. 544p. (J). (gr. 4 up). 16.99 (978-0-06-058511-2(0)); lib. bdg. 17.89 (978-0-06-058514-3(5)) HarperCollins Pubs. (Julie Andrews Collection).

—Legend of Holly Claus. Long, Laurel, illus. 2006. 544p. (J). pap. 7.99 (978-0-06-058515-0(3) , Julie Andrews Collection) HarperCollins Pubs.

Rylant, Cynthia. Little Whistle's Christmas. Bowers, Tim, illus. 2003. (Little Whistle Ser.). 32p. (J). 16.00 (978-0-15-204590-6(2)) Harcourt Children's Bks.

—Little Whistle's Christmas. Bowers, Tim, illus. 2007. 32p. (J). 24.21 (***978-1-59961-254-6(2)***) Spotlight.

Sandhaus, Ellen. Santa's Scavenger Hunt (Santa Claus en Busca de Regalos Raros) Blanco, Osvaldo J., tr. unabr. ed. 1999. (SPA & ENG., Illus.). 16p. (J). (gr. k-4). pap. 4.95 (978-1-893266-04-9(4)) Sandhaus, Paul Assocs., Inc.

Santa. 2002. (Little Pups Board Bks.). (Illus.). 11p. (J). (ps). bds. 2.99 (978-1-57759-999-9(3)) Dalmatian Pr.

Santa. 2003. (Shaped Board Books Ser.). 14p. (J). (ps-k). bds. 9.95 (978-0-7525-8851-3(6)) Parragon, Inc.

Santa & the Elves. 2003. (J). per. (978-1-57657-908-4(5)) Paradise Pr., Inc.

Santa Claus & the Kids on the Farm. 2004. (J). per. 15.99 (978-0-9753533-0-1(6)) Golden Eagle Publishing Hse., Inc.

Santa Gets A Haircut. 2005. (J). 5.95 (978-0-9769321-3-0(X)) Steingart, Nathan Publishing.

Santa Gets New Glasses. 2005. (J). 5.95 (978-0-9769321-2-3(1)) Steingart, Nathan Publishing.

Santa Goes to the Dentist. 2005. (J). 5.95 net. (978-0-9769321-5-4(6)) Steingart, Nathan Publishing.

Santa Takes A Vacation. 2005. (J). 5.95 (978-0-9769321-4-7(8)) Steingart, Nathan Publishing.

Santa's Birthday. 2005. (J). 5.95 (978-0-9769321-1-6(3)) Steingart, Nathan Publishing.

Santa's Bodyguard. 2005. (J). (978-0-9771639-0-8(3)) Riverview Foundation.

Santa's Busy Christmas Eve. 2003. (J). 4.99 (978-1-59384-011-2(X)) Parklane Publishing.

Santa's Busy Day. 1998. (Wipe-Off Activity Bks.). (Illus.). 16p. (J). (ps-1). wbk. ed. 3.79 (978-1-889319-26-1(0)) Trend Enterprises, Inc.

Santa's Christmas Cookies. 2003. (J). per. (978-1-57657-708-0(2)) Paradise Pr., Inc.

Santa's Elves Alphabet. 2003. (Illus.). (J). per. (978-1-57657-174-3(2)) Paradise Pr., Inc.

Santa's Hat. 2003. (J). per. (978-1-57657-927-5(1)) Paradise Pr., Inc.

Santa's Jolly Belly. 2003. (J). per. (978-1-57657-923-7(9)) Paradise Pr., Inc.

Santa's Little Helpers. 2003. (J). per. (978-1-57657-809-4(7)); per. (978-1-57657-921-3(2)) Paradise Pr., Inc.

Santa's Suit. 2006. (J). (***978-1-932570-71-7(3)***) Literacy Footprints Inc.

Santa's Thanksgiving. 2005. (J). 5.95 (978-0-9769321-0-9(5)) Steingart, Nathan Publishing.

Santa's Wish List. 2002. (Little Pups Board Bks.). (Illus.). 24p. (J). (gr. k-4). pap. 2.99 (978-1-57759-853-4(9)) Dalmatian Pr.

Saranpa, Rob. The Night Jesus Met Santa Claus. Hicks, John, illus. 2005. 32p. (J). pap. 19.99 incl. audio compact disk (978-1-4141-0554-3(1)) Pleasant Word.

Sargent, Dave & Sargent, Pat. Sweetpea: (Purple Corn Welsh) Be Happy, 30, 58. Lenoir, Jane, illus. 2003. (Saddle Up Ser.: Vol. 58). 42p. (J). pap. 6.95 (978-1-56763-816-5(3)); lib. bdg. 22.60 (978-1-56763-815-8(5)) Ozark Publishing.

Scarry, Richard. Santa Needs Help! 2000. (J). (978-0-606-20036-3(3)) Tandem Library Bks.

Schatzer, Jeffrey L. The Bird in Santa's Beard: How a Christmas Legend Was Forever Changed. 2004. (Illus.). 34p. (J). (978-0-9749554-0-7(X)) Big Belly Bks.

—Bump on Santa's Noggin. 2006. (Illus.). 32p. (J). 18.95 (978-1-58726-289-0(4) , Mitten Pr.) Ann Arbor Media Group, LLC.

Schoberle, Cecile. Santa Claus & the Christmas Fairies. 1999. (ps-2). lib. bdg. 13.00 (978-0-613-88872-1(3)) Tandem Library Bks.

Schonewill, Lisa. Tell Me Mama, Is Santa Claus Real? 2005. (J). pap. 9.00 (978-0-8059-6373-1(1)) Dorrance Publishing Co., Inc.

School Specialty Publishing, et al. Christmas Stories, 2 Pack. Gabriel, Andrea & Riley, R. W., illus. 2006. 36p. (J). bds. 14.98 (978-0-7696-4966-5(1)) School Specialty Publishing.

Schumacher, Claire, illus. Little Mouse Meets Santa. 2005. 16p. (J). (ps-ps). pap. 5.95 (978-1-4027-2848-8(4)) Sterling Publishing Co., Inc.

Schwartz, Betty. Santa's Magic Gifts. Pickering, Jimmy, illus. 2006. 16p. (J). 9.99 (978-0-689-87469-7(3) , Little Simon) Simon & Schuster Children's Publishing.

Scott-Cameron, Nancy. Santa Claus Is on a Diet. Conlan, Craig, illus. 2007. 32p. (J). (ps-k). 19.95 (*978-0-9546576-9-7(1)) Mogzilla GBR. *Dist:* Independent Pubs. Group.

Scott, Christina. All in A Night's Work. 2006. (J). lib. bdg. 19.95 (*978-1-933732-19-0(9) , Bear Hug Bks.) MidAmerica Publishing Co.

—The Chimney. 2006. (J). lib. bdg. 19.95 (*978-1-933732-18-3(0) , Bear Hug Bks.) MidAmerica Publishing Co.

—The North Pole. 2006. (J). lib. bdg. 19.95 (*978-1-933732-17-6(2) , Bear Hug Bks.) MidAmerica Publishing Co.

Scotton, Rob. Russell's Christmas Magic. Scotton, Rob, illus. 2007. 32p. (J). lib. bdg. 17.89 (*978-0-06-059855-6(7)) HarperCollins Pubs.

Seibold, J. Otto & Walsh, Vivian. Olive, the Other Reindeer. 10th deluxe anniv. ed. 2007. (Illus.). 40p. (J). (ps up). 19.95 (978-0-8118-5719-2(0)) Chronicle Bks. LLC.

Seus. Wie der Grinch Weihnachen. pap. 14.95 (978-3-492-23722-2(3)) Piper Verlag GmbH DEU. *Dist:* Distribooks, Inc.

Sharkey, Niamh. Santasaurus. Sharkey, Niamh, illus. 2005. (Illus.). 32p. (J). (ps-1). 15.99 (978-0-7636-2671-6(6)) Candlewick Pr.

Sharp, Rhonda Winchell. The Nine Most Famous Reindeer of All. Vandewater, Rena, illus. 2004. 40p. (J). pap. 15.99 (978-0-9748047-8-1(9)) Hickory Bark Productions.

Sheppard, Dorothy M. & Sheppard, Jack G. Jo Jo the Elf Meets Santa's Enemy. Sheppard, Dorothy M. et al, illus. 65p. (J). (gr. 1-6). pap. 7.95 (978-0-9634300-0-7(9)) D&J Arts Pubs.

Shoolbred, Catherine. Santa's Reindeer. Pichon, Liz, illus. 2003. 12p. (J). (gr. k-k). bds. 5.99 (978-0-7636-2143-8(9)) Candlewick Pr.

Simon, Tom. El Traje Azul de Papa Noel.Tr. of Santa's Blue Suit. (SPA.). 24p. (J). (gr. k-2). 16.95 (978-84-488-0867-9(3) , BS3557) Beascoa, Ediciones S.A. ESP. *Dist:* Lectorum Pubns., Inc.

Skelton, Peter. Mr. Jimmy Chimney Sweep: The Mystery Elf of Christmas. 2000. (Illus.). 29p. (J). (ps-1). per. (978-0-9706099-0-8(6)) Breckenridge Group & Assocs.

—Twinkle Toes: The Magical Elf of Christmas. 2000. 24p. (J). (ps-1). per. (978-0-9706099-1-5(4)) Breckenridge Group & Assocs.

Slangerup, Erik Jon. Santa & Me. Janes, Joshua, illus. 2003. 32p. (J). (gr. k-2). 14.95 (978-1-57768-411-4(7) , Gingham Dog Pr.) School Specialty Publishing.

Smith, John A. A Special Christmas for Oscar. 2004. 31p. pap. 17.95 (978-1-4137-2892-7(8)) PublishAmerica, Inc.

Snow, Alan. How Santa Really Works. Snow, Alan, illus. 48p. (J). 2007. 7.99 (*978-1-4169-5000-4(1) , Aladdin); 2004. (Illus.). 15.95 (978-0-689-85817-8(5) , Atheneum) Simon & Schuster Children's Publishing.

Sobel, Gerrie. Jacob & His Magical Flying Bears: A Christmas Story. Torres, Dottie, illus. 2007. 32p. (J). 12.95 (*978-0-9798244-4-9(3)) TRIAD Publishing Group.

Solheim, James. Santa's Secrets Revealed: All Your Questions Answered about Santa's Super Sleigh, His Flying Reindeer, & Other Wonders. Gott, Barry, illus. 2004. (Carolrhoda Picture Books Ser.). 40p. (J). (gr. k-3). 15.95 (978-1-57505-600-5(3)) Lerner Publishing Group.

Solomon, Aubrey. Twentieth Century-Fox: A Corporate & Financial History. rev. ed. 2002. (Illus.). 300p. pap. 40.95 (978-0-8108-4244-1(0)) Scarecrow Pr., Inc.

Solotareff, Gregoire. The Secret Life of Santa Claus. 2001. (Illus.). 250p. (YA). reprint ed. 18.00 (978-0-7881-9575-4(1)) DIANE Publishing Co.

Sparkie. Jolly Old Santa Claus: Coloring Book. 1998. (Illus.). 48p. (J). pap. 2.49 (978-0-8249-4098-0(9) , Candy Cane Pr.) Ideals Pubns.

Special Delivery from Santa. 2003. (J). per. (978-1-57657-810-0(0)); per. (978-1-57657-922-0(0)) Paradise Pr., Inc.

Spiridellis, Gregg & Spiridellis, Evan. Are You Grumpy, Santa? 2006. 32p. (ps-3). pap. 6.99 (978-0-7868-0997-4(3)) Hyperion Pr.

Stainton, Sue. Christmas Magic. Melhuish, Eva, illus. 2007. 32p. (J). lib. bdg. 16.89 (*978-0-06-078572-7(1)); 15.99 (*978-0-06-078571-0(3)) HarperCollins Pubs. (Tegen, Katherine Bks).

—Santa's Snow Cat. Mortimer, Anne, illus. 32p. (J). 2007. pap. 6.99 (*978-0-06-000540-5(8) , Harper Trophy); 2001. 15.99 (978-0-06-623827-2(7)) HarperCollins Pubs.

—Santa's Snow Kitten. Mortimer, Anne, illus. 2008. (J). (*978-0-06-082714-4(9)); lib. bdg. (*978-0-06-082715-1(7)) HarperCollins Pubs.

Stainton, Sue. Snow Cat: Santa's Littlest Cat. Mortimer, Anne, illus. 2000. (J). (978-0-7868-4437-1(X)) Hyperion Bks. for Children.

Steinhofel, Andreas & Jaffa, Alisa. An Elk Dropped In. Meyer, Kerstin, illus. 80p. (J). 16.95 (978-1-932425-80-2(2) , Lemniscaat) Boyds Mills Pr.

Stoeke, Janet Morgan. A Minerva Louise Christmas. 2007. 24p. (J). (ps). 15.99 (*978-0-525-47857-7(4) , Dutton Juvenile) Penguin Group (USA) Inc.

Sullivan, Ellen. How Santa Got His Elves. Eldredge, Ernie, illus. 1998. (J). (978-1-58173-148-4(5)) Sweetwater Pr.

Sutton, Marvin. Santa & Marvin. 2001. 91p. pap. (978-1-893181-59-5(6) , Lagesse Stevens) Martell Publishing Co.

Sykes, Julie. Bless You, Santa! Warnes, Tim, illus. 2004. 32p. (J). tchr. ed. 15.95 (978-1-58925-041-3(9) , tiger tales) ME Media LLC.

—Careful, Santa! Warnes, Tim, illus. 2002. 32p. (J). (ps-1). tchr. ed. 14.95 (978-1-58925-023-9(0) , tiger tales) ME Media LLC.

—Hurry, Santa! Warnes, Tim, illus. 1998. 32p. (J). (ps-2). 14.95 (978-1-888444-37-7(1)) Little Tiger Pr.

—Shhh! Warnes, Tim, illus. 2006. 18p. (J). bds. 6.95 (978-1-58925-796-2(0) , tiger tales) ME Media LLC.

Sypolt, Carl W. Fibber Lygood at Christmas, Easter, & St. Patrick's Day. 2006. 108p. (J). pap. 10.95 (978-0-7414-2982-7(9)) Infinity Publishing.

Thomas, Garen Eileen. Santa's Kwanzaa. Francis, Guy, illus. 2004. 32p. (ps-2). 15.99 (978-0-7868-5166-9(X)) Hyperion Bks. for Children.

Thomas Nelson Publishing Staff. My Christmas Collection: Three Favorite Stories. 2006. 80p. (J). 14.99 (978-1-4003-0843-9(7)) Nelson, Thomas Inc.

Tiller, Steve. Rudolf the Red Nose Rocket. Cremeans, Robert, illus. 2002. 28p. (J). (gr. k-3). 15.95 (978-0-9704597-9-4(3)) MichaelsMind LLC.

Tolkien, J. R. R. Letters from Father Christmas. Tolkien, Baillie, ed. 2004. (Illus.). 112p. pap. 15.00 (978-0-618-51265-2(9)) Houghton Mifflin Co. Trade & Reference Div.

Trimble, Marcia. Moonbeams for Santa. Bingham, Sid, illus. 2001. 32p. (J). (ps-4). 15.95 (978-1-891577-89-5(1)) Images Pr.

Trondheim, Lewis. Happy Halloween, Li'l Santa. Robin, Thierry, illus. 2003. 48p. 14.95 (978-1-56163-361-6(5)) NBM Publishing Co.

—Li'l Santa. Robin, Thierry, illus. 2003. 48p. 14.95 (978-1-56163-335-7(6)) NBM Publishing Co.

Tryon, Leslie. Albert's Christmas. 2000. (J). (978-0-606-19247-7(6)) Tandem Library Bks.

Turner, Christina. Hello Santa! 2007. (Illus.). 16p. (ps). per., bds. 7.95 (*978-0-9790347-0-1(1)) Mackenzie Smiles.

Turner, Thomas N. Country Music Night Before Christmas. Rice, James, illus. 2003. 32p. (J). pap. 14.95 (978-1-58980-148-6(2)) Pelican Publishing Co., Inc.

Twenstrup, Norm. A Surprise for Santa. DHP, Inc. Staff, ed. (Illus.). 32p. (J). (ps-3). pap. (978-1-885531-12-4(5)) Mess Hall Writers.

Tyrrell, Melissa. Here Comes Santa! A Little Foil Book. 1998. (Merry Little Foil Bks.). (Illus.). 10p. (YA). (ps up). 2.95 (978-1-58117-007-8(6) , Intervisual/Piggy Toes) Dalmatian Pr.

Van Allsburg, Chris. The Polar Express Sam's Edition. 2006. (J). (gr. k-3). 35.00 (978-0-618-83659-8(4)) Houghton Mifflin Co. Trade & Reference Div.

Velde, Henry. The Night I Became... 2007. (J). per. 17.99 (*978-1-933156-18-7(X) , Visikid Bks.) GSVQ Publishing.

Waiting for Santa. 2004. (J). per. (978-1-57657-385-3(0)); per. (978-1-57657-451-5(2)) Paradise Pr., Inc.

Wallace, Carol. The Santa Secret. Bjorkman, Steve, illus. 2007. 40p. (J). (gr. k-3). 15.95 (*978-0-8234-2022-3(1)); pap. 4.95 (*978-0-8234-2126-8(0)) Holiday Hse., Inc.

Wallace, Ivy. Pookie Believes in Santa Claus. 2001. (Illus.). 32p. (J). (gr. k-4). 19.99 (978-0-00-198380-9(6)) HarperCollins Pubs. Ltd. GBR. *Dist:* Trafalgar Square Publishing.

Walters, Eric & Walters, Christina. The True Story of Santa Claus. Gooderham, Andrew, illus. 2005. 38p. (J). 9.95 (978-1-894601-11-5(4)) Chestnut Publishing Group CAN. *Dist:* Hushion Hse. Publishing, Ltd.

Watt, Fiona. Santa Claus. 2004. (Sparkly Touchy-Feely Board Bks.). 10p. (J). 15.95 (978-0-7945-0830-2(8) , Usborne) EDC Publishing.

Weaver, Richard G. & Farrell, John D. Crisis at Santa's Workshop: Using Facilitation to Get More Done in Less Time: Help Others Take Responsibility & Work Together Effectively. 2003. (Illus.). 150p. pap. 17.95 (978-1-57675-279-1(8)) Berrett-Koehler Pubs., Inc.

Weinberg, Larry. The Forgetful Bears Help Santa. Wolff, Jason, illus. 2001. 40p. (J). (gr. k-2). 9.95 (978-0-307-10684-1(5) , Golden Bks.) Random Hse. Children's Bks.

Weiss, Ellen, et al. Trip to the North Pole: A Junior Novel. movie tie-in ed. 2004. (Polar Express Ser.). (Illus.). 128p. (J). (gr. 5-6). pap. 4.99 (978-0-618-47790-6(X)) Houghton Mifflin Co. Trade & Reference Div.

Wells, Rosemary. McDuff's New Friend. 1998. 8.95 (978-0-7868-0493-1(9)) Hyperion Bks. for Children.

—McDuff's New Friend: Includes Stuffed Toy Puppy. 1998. (Illus.). (J). 219.00 (978-0-7868-2825-8(0)) Hyperion Pr.

—McDuff's New Friend with Plush Box Set. 2003. (Illus.). 28p. (J). 14.99 (978-0-7868-1866-2(2) , Disney Editions) Disney Pr.

Wenger, Brahm. Dewey's Magical Sleigh. 2005. 32p. 15.95 (978-0-9745143-5-2(7)) RandallFraser Publishing.

Weninger, Brigitte. Letter to Santa Claus. 2000. (gr. k-3). lib. bdg. 26.35 (978-0-613-81905-3(5)) Tandem Library Bks.

Werkema, Mark A. The Flight Before Christmas. 2004. (YA). pap. 13.95 (978-1-58961-306-5(6)) PageFree Publishing, Inc.

West, Tracey, et al. The Magic Journey. 2004. (Polar Express Ser.). (Illus.). 32p. (J). (gr. k-3). 9.99 (978-0-618-47788-3(8)) Houghton Mifflin Co.

Westcott, Nadine Bernard. Santa's Christmas Eve. Westcott, Nadine Bernard, illus. 2006. (Illus.). 12p. (J). 6.99 (978-0-689-85656-3(3) , Little Simon) Simon & Schuster Children's Publishing.

Wheeler, Lisa. The Christmas Boot. Monroe, Michael Glenn, illus. 2007. 32p. (J). 18.95 (*978-1-58726-327-9(0) , Mitten Pr.) Ann Arbor Media Group, LLC.

Wheeler, Lisa. Where, Oh Where, Is Santa Claus? Bates, Ivan, illus. 2007. 32p. (J). (ps-2). 16.00 (978-0-15-216408-9(1)) Harcourt Trade Pubs.

When Santa Claus Met Sandy Claws: A Cape Cod Christmas Story. 2002. (Illus.). 64p. (978-0-9669240-1-5(0)) Paine Wolf Productions.

Whybrow, Ian. Miss Wire's Christmas Surprise. Clark, E., illus. 2007. 48p. (J). (ps-3). pap. 3.95 (*978-0-7534-6136-5(6) , Kingfisher) Houghton Mifflin Co. Trade & Reference Div.

Wigand, Molly. Here Comes Santa. 2007. 24p. (J). 21.35 (*978-1-59961-357-4(3)) Spotlight.

Wilkes, Irene. Elvie, Santa's Ninth Reindeer. Montgomery, Jason, illus. 2006. 28p. (J). 19.95 (*978-1-59299-227-0(7)) Inkwater Pr.

Willey, Margaret. Clever Beatrice Christmas. Solomon, Heather M., illus. 2006. 40p. (J). 16.95 (978-0-689-87017-0(5) , Atheneum) Simon & Schuster Children's Publishing.

Williams, Jacklyn. Merry Christmas Gus! Cushman, Doug, illus. 2005. (Read-It! Readers Ser.). 32p. (J). (gr. k-3). 18.60 (978-1-4048-0958-1(9)) Picture Window Bks.

Williams, Sam. Santa's Toys. Gill, Tim, illus. 2003. 14p. bds. (978-1-85602-274-3(9)) Chrysalis Children's Bks.

Wilson, Henrike & Stohner, Anu. Santa's Littlest Helper. 2004. (Illus.). 32p. (J). 15.95 (978-1-58234-964-0(9) , Bloomsbury Children) Bloomsbury Publishing.

Witt, Rici. God, Santa & the Easter Bunny. 2006. 32p. (J). pap. 12.95 (978-1-4116-8014-2(6)) Lulu.com.

Wolff, Patricia Rae. A New Improved Santa. Cravath, Lynne W., illus. 2002. 32p. (J). (gr. k-2). pap. 15.95 (978-0-439-35249-9(5) , Orchard Bks.) Scholastic, Inc.

Wood, Douglas & Cushman, Doug. What Santa Can't Do. ed. 2004. 24p. (J). 6.95 (978-0-689-87352-2(2)) Simon & Schuster Children's Publishing.

Yee, Wong Herbert. A Small Christmas. 2004. (Illus.). 32p. (J). (gr. k-3). tchr. ed. 12.95 (978-0-618-32612-9(X)) Houghton Mifflin Co. Trade & Reference Div.

Yee, Wong Herbert. Small Christmas. 2007. (Illus.). 32p. (J). (ps-3). 6.95 (*978-0-618-91534-7(6)) Houghton Mifflin Co. Trade & Reference Div.

Yin & Soentpiet, Chris K. Dear Santa, Please Come to the 19th Floor. Soentpiet, Chris K., illus. 2002. (Illus.). 32p. (J). (gr. k-3). 17.99 (978-0-399-23636-5(8) , Philomel) Penguin Group (USA) Inc.

Yoon, Salina. Santa Claus. 2005. 6p. (J). (ps-1). bds. 3.99 (978-0-8431-1366-2(9) , Price Stern Sloan) Penguin Group (USA) Inc.

Ziefert, Harriet. I Wish Santa Would Come by Helicopter. Haley, Amanda, illus. 2004. 28p. (J). 9.95 (978-1-4027-1708-6(3)) Sterling Publishing Co., Inc.

SANTA CLAUS—POETRY

Blazek, Sarah K., narrated by. Irish Night Before Christmas/ Leprechaun's St. Patrick's Day. 1999. (J). (ps-3). pap. 9.95 (978-1-56554-387-4(4)) Pelican Publishing Co., Inc.

Carabine, Sue. A Dog's Night Before Christmas. Kawasaki, Shauna Mooney, illus. 2001. 60p. 5.95 (978-0-87905-762-6(9)) Gibbs Smith, Publisher.

—A Teacher's Night Before Christmas. Kawasaki, Shauna Mooney, illus. 2000. 60p. 5.95 (978-0-87905-764-0(5)) Gibbs Smith, Publisher.

Dalmatian Press Staff. Santa Claus Picture Book. 2005. (Illus.). 32p. (J). pap. 10.99 (978-1-4037-1605-7(6)) Dalmatian Pr.

Geraty, Virginia Mixson. Gullah Night Before Christmas. Rice, James, illus. 1998. (Night Before Christmas Ser.). 32p. (J). (ps-3). 15.95 (978-1-56554-330-0(0)) Pelican Publishing Co., Inc.

—Gullah Night Before Christmas. 1998. (Night Before Christmas Ser.). (J). (ps-3). pap. 9.95 (978-1-56554-396-6(3)) Pelican Publishing Co., Inc.

Gribnau, Joe. Rocky Mountain Night Before Christmas. Alikhan, Salima, illus. 2007. 32p. (J). (gr. k-3). 15.95 (*978-1-58980-317-6(5)) Pelican Publishing Co., Inc.

Layne, Steven. Preacher's Night Before Christmas. Benioff, Carol, illus. 2006. (Night Before Christmas Ser.). 32p. (J). 15.95 (978-1-58980-321-3(3)) Pelican Publishing Co., Inc.

McWilliams, Amanda & Moore, Clement C. Ozark Night Before Christmas. Rice, James, illus. 2004. 32p. pap. 15.95 (978-1-58980-056-4(7)) Pelican Publishing Co., Inc.

Medina, Tony. Just Us. 2004. (Illus.). 48p. (J). (gr. 4 up). pap. 6.95 (978-0-940975-75-0(0) , Sankofa Bks.) Just Us Bks., Inc.

Mills, Donald. The Night Before Christmas. Moore, Clement C., ed. Moore, Clement C., illus. 2000. 32p. (J). (ps-3). 7.95 (978-0-8249-4186-4(1)) Ideals Pubns.

Moore, Clement C. The Night Before Christmas. Fujikawa, Gyo, illus. 2007. 32p. (J). (ps-2). 9.95 (*978-1-4027-5065-6(X)) Sterling Publishing Co., Inc.

—The Night Before Christmas. abr. ed. 2004. (Wee Books for Wee Folks). (Illus.). 64p. (J). (ps-3). 6.95 (978-1-55709-410-0(1)) Applewood Bks.

—The Night Before Christmas. Spirin, Gennady, illus. ltd. ed. 2006. 32p. (J). 16.99 (978-0-7614-5298-0(2)) Cavendish, Marshall Corp.

—The Night Before Christmas. Whatley, Bruce, illus. (J). (ps up). 2004. 32p. 6.99 (978-0-06-073917-1(7) , Harper Festival); 1999. 40p. 16.99 (978-0-06-026608-0(2)) HarperCollins Pubs.

—The Night Before Christmas. Engelbreit, Mary, illus. rev. ed. 2002. 40p. (J). (gr. k-2). 16.99 (978-0-06-008160-7(0)) HarperCollins Pubs.

—The Night Before Christmas. de Paola, Tomie, illus. abr. ed. 32p. (J). (gr. k-3). 6.95 (978-0-8234-0417-9(X)) Holiday Hse., Inc.

—The Night Before Christmas. Moore, Clement C., ed. Tudor, Tasha, illus. 1999. 32p. (J). (ps-17). 16.99 (978-0-316-85579-2(0)) Little Brown & Co.

—The Night Before Christmas. Moore, Clement C., ed. Tudor, Tasha & Sanderson, Ruth, illus. 2002. 32p. (J). (ps-17). pap. 6.99 (978-0-316-83271-7(5)) Little, Brown Bks. for Young Readers.

S

—The Night Before Christmas. Catusanu, Mircea, illus. 2001. (Little Golden Book Ser.). 24p. (J). (gr. k-k). 2.99 (978-0-307-96003-0(X) , Golden Bks.) Random Hse. Children's Bks.

—The Night Before Christmas. abr. ed. 1998. (Miniature Editionstm Ser.). (Illus.). 112p. (ps up). 4.95 (978-0-7624-0352-3(7) , Running Pr. Minature Editions) Running Pr. Bk. Pubs.

—The Night Before Christmas. Tudor, Tasha, illus. 2000. 64p. (J). (ps up). pap. 7.99 (978-0-689-83932-0(4) , Aladdin) Simon & Schuster Children's Publishing.

—The Night Before Christmas: A Trim-a-Tree Story. l.t. ed. 1999. (Illus.). 16p. (J). (ps-3). 6.99 (978-1-57866-076-6(9) , Galahad Bks.) BBS Publishing Corp.

—The Night Before Christmas: Pull the Tabs! Change the Pictures! 2003. (Magic Windows Ser.). (Illus.). 10p. (gr. k-3). pap. 12.95 (978-0-7624-1573-1(8) , Running Pr. Kids) Running Pr. Bk. Pubs.

—The Night Before Christmas: The Classic Edition. Birmingham, Christian, illus. abr. ed. 2005. (Children's Illustrated Classics Ser.). 48p. (ps-3). 9.98 (978-1-56138-476-1(3) , Running Pr. Kids) Running Pr. Bk. Pubs.

—A Scratch & Sniff Night Before Christmas. Swanson, Maggie, illus. 2007. 24p. (J). (ps-2). 9.95 (*978-1-4027-4215-6(0)) Sterling Publishing Co., Inc.

—The Teddy Bears' Night Before Christmas. 1999. (J). (ps-3). 103.60 (978-0-439-11752-4(6)) Scholastic, Inc.

—'Twas the Night Before Christmas. Smith, Jessie Wilcox, illus. 2005. 32p. (J). (gr. k-3). 5.95 (978-0-618-61510-0(5)) Houghton Mifflin Co. Trade & Reference Div.

—Twas the Night Before Christmas: A Visit from St. Nicholas. Smith, Jessie Willcox, illus. 2005. 32p. (J). (gr. k-3). 14.00 (978-0-618-61682-4(9)) Houghton Mifflin Co. Trade & Reference Div.

—A Visit from St. Nicholas. Nast, Thomas, illus. 2006. 24p. (J). (ps-1). 24.95 (978-1-55709-592-3(2)) Applewood Bks.

Moore, Clement C., ed. & illus. The Night Before Christmas. Moore, Clement C., illus. 1999. 40p. (J). (ps-3). 16.89 (978-0-06-028380-3(7)) HarperCollins Pubs.

—The Night Before Christmas. Moore, Clement C., illus. Porfirio, Guy, illus. 2004. 20p. (J). 9.95 (978-0-8249-6553-2(1)) Ideals Pubns.

—The Night Before Christmas. Moore, Clement C., illus. Finster, Howard, illus. 1998. 26p. reprint ed. 14.95 (978-1-56352-533-9(X)) Longstreet Pr., Inc.

—The Night Before Christmas. Moore, Clement C., illus. Rice, James, illus. 2000. 32p. (J). (ps-3). reprint ed. 15.95 (978-0-88289-755-4(1)) Pelican Publishing Co., Inc.

—The Night Before Christmas. Moore, Clement C., illus. Gorsline, Douglas, illus. 32p. (J). Random Hse. Children's Bks.

—The Night Before Christmas. Moore, Clement C., illus. Lobel, Anita, illus. 2003. 32p. (J). 8.95 (978-0-375-82414-2(6) , Knopf Bks. for Young Readers) Random Hse. Children's Bks.

—The Night Before Christmas. Moore, Clement C., illus. Cartwright, Sharon, illus. 1999. (Jellybean Bks.). 24p. (J). (ps-k). lib. bdg. 7.99 (978-0-375-90147-8(7) , Random Hse. Bks. for Young Readers) Random Hse. Children's Bks.

—The Night Before Christmas. Moore, Clement C., illus. Birmingham, Christian, photos by. 1999. 60p. (J). (ps-1). pap. 12.98 (978-1-58048-065-9(9)) Sandvik Publishing.

—The Night Before Christmas. Moore, Clement C., illus. Brett, Jan, illus. 2001. (J). 27.95 incl. audio (978-0-8045-6859-3(6)) Spoken Arts, Inc.

—The Night Before Christmas. Moore, Clement C., illus. 2000. (gr. 3-6). lib. bdg. 15.30 (978-0-613-31526-5(X)); lib. bdg. 15.30 (978-0-613-32892-0(2)) Tandem Library Bks.

—The Night Before Christmas. Moore, Clement C., illus. Lobel, Anita, illus. 2000. (J). (978-0-606-19773-1(7)) Tandem Library Bks.

Moore, Clement C. & Jaramillo, Raquel. The Night Before Christmas. 2001. (Illus.). 40p. (J). (ps up). 18.95 (978-0-689-84053-1(5) , Atheneum/Anne Schwartz Bks.) Simon & Schuster Children's Publishing.

Moore, Clement C., et al. The Night Before Christmas: A Classic Illustrated Edition. 1998. (Illus.). 44p. (J). (ps up). 16.95 (978-0-8118-1712-7(1)) Chronicle Bks. LLC.

Moore, Clement Clarke. Night Before Christmas. Pinkney, Debbie, illus. 2004. (J). (*978-0-7853-1892-7(5)) Publications International, Ltd.

Running Press Staff, et al. The Night Before Christmas. 2001. (Heirloom Editions Ser.). (Illus.). 48p. 16.95 (978-0-7624-1069-9(8) , Running Pr.) Running Pr. Bk. Pubs.

Sabuda, Robert & Moore, Clement C. The Night Before Christmas. 2002. (Illus.). 12p. (J). 26.99 (978-0-689-83899-6(9) , Little Simon) Simon & Schuster Children's Publishing.

Simmons, Lynne Sheffield. Sugar Lump, the Orphan Calf's Night Before Christmas. Ward, Sue Marshall, illus. 2007. 48p. (J). (gr. k-3). 14.95 (*978-1-58980-439-5(2)) Pelican Publishing Co., Inc.

Tavares, Matt, illus. 'Twas the Night Before Christmas: Or Account of a Visit from St. Nicholas. 2002. 32p. (J). (gr. k up). 16.00 (978-0-7636-1585-7(4)) Candlewick Pr.

Terrill, Beth. The Barnyard Night Before Christmas. Newbold, Greg, illus. 2007. (Picture Book Ser.). 40p. (J). (ps-1). 14.99 (*978-0-375-83682-4(9)); lib. bdg. 17.99 (*978-0-375-93682-1(3)) Random Hse. Children's Bks. (Random Hse. Bks. for Young Readers).

Wick, Walter. Night Before Christmas. Wick, Walter, illus. 2005. (Can You See What I See?). (Illus.). 40p. (J). pap. 13.99 (978-0-439-76927-3(2) , Cartwheel Bks.) Scholastic, Inc.

SANTA FE (N.M.)

Brown, Rachel K. Santa Fe: Daily Life in a Western Trading Center. 2003. (J). pap. (978-1-58417-074-7(3)); lib. bdg. (978-1-58417-011-2(5)) Lake Street Pubs.

Coll, Ivar Da. Maria Juana. (SPA.). (J). bds. (978-958-04-4908-9(2)) Norma S.A. COL. Dist: Lectorum Pubns., Inc.

Dewey, Jennifer Owings. Zozobra: Old Man Gloom. Fleming, Jeanie Puleston, illus. Fleming, Jeanie Puleston, photos by. 2004. (J). (978-0-8263-3278-3(1)) Univ. of New Mexico Pr.

—Zozobra: The Story of Old Man Gloom. Fleming, Jeanie Puleston, illus. Fleming, Jeanie Puleston, photos by. 2004. 32p. (J). (gr. 3 up). pap. 9.95 (978-0-8263-3279-0(X)) Univ. of New Mexico Pr.

Hatch, Lynda. The Santa Fe Trail. 2003. (Crossing America Ser.). 48p. (YA). (gr. 5-8). pap. 5.99 (978-1-56822-655-2(1) , IF6023-E4, Instructional Fair) Schaffer, Frank Pubns.

McNeese, Tim. Santa Fe. 2007. (Colonial Settlements in America Ser.). 120p. (J). (gr. 5-8). 30.00 (*978-0-7910-9332-0(8) , Chelsea Hse.) Facts On File, Inc.

SANTA FE NATIONAL HISTORIC TRAIL

Blashfield, Jean F. The Santa Fe Trail. 2000. (We the People Ser.). (Illus.). 48p. (J). (gr. 4 up). lib. bdg. 22.60 (978-0-7565-0047-4(8)) Compass Point Bks.

Dean, Arlan. The Santa Fe Trail: From Independence, Missouri to Santa Fe, New Mexico. 2003. (Reading Power Ser.). (Illus.). 24p. (J). lib. bdg. 17.25 (978-0-8239-6481-9(7) , PowerKids Pr.) Rosen Publishing Group, Inc., The.

Randolph, Ryan P. The Santa Fe Trail. 2003. (Library of the Westward Expansion). (Illus.). 24p. (J). lib. bdg. 19.95 (978-0-8239-6292-1(X) , PowerKids Pr.) Rosen Publishing Group, Inc., The.

Sanford, William R. The Santa Fe Trail in American History. 2000. (In American History Ser.). (Illus.). 112p. (YA). (gr. 5-12). lib. bdg. 26.60 (978-0-7660-1348-3(0)) Enslow Pubs., Inc.

The Santa Fe Trail, 6 Packs. (On Deck Ser.: Vol. 2). 24p. (gr. 4-5). 35.00 (978-0-7578-5815-4(5)) Rigby Education.

Thompson, Linda. The Santa Fe Trail. (Expansion of America Ser.). 48p. 2005. (Illus.). (gr. 4-8). 20.95 (978-1-59515-226-8(1)); 2004. pap. 7.95 (978-1-59515-325-8(X)) Rourke Publishing, LLC.

Webb, Dave. Santa Fe Trail Adventures: An Activity Book. Buntin, Phillip R., illus. 1999. 88p. (YA). (gr. 3 up). pap. 7.95 (978-1-882404-11-7(4)) Kansas Heritage Ctr.

SANTA FE NATIONAL HISTORIC TRAIL—FICTION

Carson, William C. Peter Becomes a Trail Man: The Story of a Boy's Journey on the Santa Fe Trail. Oliphant, Pat, illus. 2002. 192p. (J). (gr. 6 up). 12.95 (978-0-8263-2895-3(4)) Univ. of New Mexico Pr.

Sargent, Dave & Sargent, Pat. Chub: (Dapple Black) Be Dependable, 30, 17. Lenoir, Jane, illus. 2001. (Saddle Up Ser.: 17). 36p. (J). lib. bdg. 22.60 (978-1-56763-645-1(4)) Ozark Publishing.

—Chub: (Dappled Black) Be Dependable, 25, 17. Lenoir, Jane, illus. 2001. (Saddle Up Ser.: 17). 36p. (J). pap. 6.95 (978-1-56763-646-8(2)) Ozark Publishing.

Sperry, Armstrong. Wagons Westward: The Old Trail to Santa Fe. Sperry, Armstrong, illus. 2005. (Illus.). 200p. (YA). (gr. 6-11). reprint ed. pap. 15.00 (978-0-7567-9693-8(8)) DIANE Publishing Co.

—Wagons Westward: The Old Trail to Santa Fe. 2000. (Illus.). 224p. (J). pap. 14.95 (978-1-56792-128-1(0)) Godine, David R. Pub.

SARATOGA CAMPAIGN, 1777

King, David C. Saratoga. 1998. (Battlefields Across America Ser.: 8). (Illus.). 64p. (gr. 5-8). lib. bdg. 26.90 (978-0-7613-3011-0(9) , Twenty-First Century Bks.) Lerner Publishing Group.

Nardo, Don. The Battle of Saratoga. 2007. (J). lib. bdg. (*978-0-7565-3342-7(2)) Compass Point Bks.

Vierow, Wendy. The Battle of Saratoga. 2003. (Atlas of Famous Battles of the American Revolution Ser.). (Illus.). 24p. (J). lib. bdg. 21.25 (978-0-8239-6332-4(2) , PowerKids Pr.) Rosen Publishing Group, Inc., The.

Worth, Richard. Saratoga. 2002. (Battles That Changed the World Ser.). (Illus.). 112p. (YA). (gr. 7-10). 30.00 (978-0-7910-6682-9(7) , Chelsea Hse.) Facts On File, Inc.

SARGASSO SEA

Heller, Ruth. A Sea within a Sea: Secrets of the Sargasso. Heller, Ruth, illus. 2006. (Illus.). 29p. (J). (gr. 4-8). reprint ed. 17.00 (978-1-4223-5731-6(7)) DIANE Publishing Co.

SASQUATCH

Burgan, Michael. Bigfoot. 2004. (Unexplained Ser.). (Illus.). 32p. (J). lib. bdg. 22.60 (978-0-7368-2715-7(3)) Capstone Pr., Inc.

Cox, Greg. Bigfoot. 2005. (Unsolved Mysteries Ser.). (Illus.). 48p. (YA). (gr. 5-8). lib. bdg. 25.25 (978-0-8239-3561-1(2)) Rosen Publishing Group, Inc., The.

DeMolay, Jack. Bigfoot: A North American Legend. 2007. (Jr. Graphic Mysteries Ser.). (Illus.). 24p. (J). (gr. 2-6). lib. bdg. 21.25 (978-1-4042-3405-5(5)) Rosen Publishing Group, Inc., The.

Gorman, Jacqueline Laks. Bigfoot. 2002. (X Science Ser.). (Illus.). 24p. (YA). (gr. 2 up). lib. bdg. 22.00 (978-0-8368-3197-9(7)) Stevens, Gareth Inc.

Innes, Brian. Giant Humanlike Beasts. 1999. (Unsolved Mysteries Ser.). 48p. (YA). (gr. 3 up). lib. bdg. (978-0-8172-5484-1(6)) Raintree.

—Giant Humanlike Beasts. 1999. (Unsolved Mysteries Ser.). (Illus.). 48p. (J). (gr. 3-7). pap. 8.05 (978-0-8172-5846-7(9)) Steck-Vaughn.

Krensky, Stephen. Bigfoot. 2007. (Monster Chronicles Ser.). (Illus.). 48p. (J). (gr. 4-8). lib. bdg. 26.60 (978-0-8225-5925-2(0) , Lerner Pubns.) Lerner Publishing Group.

Miller, Heather. Bigfoot. 2005. (Monsters Ser.). (Illus.). 48p. (J). (gr. 4-8). 26.20 (978-0-7377-3161-3(3) , Greenhaven Pr., Inc.) Thomson Gale.

Shea, Therese. Bigfoot. 2006. (Tony Stead Nonfiction Independent Reading Collection). (J). pap. (978-1-4042-5675-0(X)) Rosen Publishing Group, Inc., The.

Shone, Rob. Bigfoot & Other Strange Beasts. Spender, Nik, illus. 2005. (Graphic Mysteries Ser.). (J). (978-1-4042-0816-2(X)); 48p. pap. (978-1-4042-0804-9(6)) Rosen Publishing Group, Inc., The.

—Bigfoot & Other Strange Beasts. Spender, Nick, illus. 2005. (Graphic Mysteries Ser.). 48p. (J). (gr. 5-8). lib. bdg. 29.95 (978-1-4042-0793-6(7)) Rosen Publishing Group, Inc., The.

Teitelbaum, Michael. Bigfoot Caught on Film. 2007. (24/7 - Science Behind the Scenes Ser.). 64p. (J). (gr. 8-12). 26.00 (978-0-531-12078-1(3) , Watts, Franklin) Scholastic Library Publishing.

Teitelbaum, Michael. Bigfoot Caught on Film: And Other Monster Sightings! 2008. (24/7: Science Behind the Scenes: Mystery Files Ser.). 64p. (J). pap. 7.95 (*978-0-531-17531-6(6) , Watts, Franklin) Scholastic Library Publishing.

Woog, Adam. Bigfoot. 2006. (Encounters with Ser.). 48p. (J). (gr. 4-8). 26.20 (978-0-7377-3473-7(6) , Greenhaven Pr., Inc.) Thomson Gale.

Yorke, Malcolm & Davis, Lee. Beastly Tales: Big Foot, Yeti & the Loch Ness Monster. 1998. (Eyewitness Readers). (Illus.). 48p. (J). (gr. 2-3). pap. 3.99 (978-0-7894-2962-9(4) , 0-7894-4754-1) Dorling Kindersley Publishing, Inc.

SATAN

see Devil

SATELLITES, ARTIFICIAL

see Artificial Satellites

SATURN (PLANET)

Adamson, Thomas K. Saturn. (J). 2008. (*978-1-4296-0733-9(5)); 2003. (Illus.). 24p. lib. bdg. 17.26 (978-0-7368-2117-9(1) , Pebble Bks.) Capstone Pr., Inc.

Adamson, Thomas K. Saturno: Saturn. 2006. (ENG & SPA., Illus.). 24p. (J). (978-0-7368-5884-7(9)) Capstone Pr., Inc.

Asimov, Isaac & Hantula, Richard. Saturn. rev. ed. 2003. (Isaac Asimov's 21st Century Library of the Universe). (Illus.). 32p. (YA). (gr. 3 up). lib. bdg. 24.67 (978-0-8368-3241-9(8)) Stevens, Gareth Inc.

—Saturn: The Ringed Beauty. 2003. (Isaac Asimov's 21st Century Library of the Universe). (Illus.). 32p. (J). (gr. 3 up). pap. (978-0-8368-3945-6(5) , Weekly Reader Early Learning Library) Stevens, Gareth Inc.

—Saturno: El Planeta de los Anillos. Porras, Carlos & D'Andrea, Patricia, trs. 2003. (Isaac Asimov's Biblioteca del Universo del Siglo XXI). (SPA., Illus.). 32p. (J). (gr. 3 up). lib. bdg. 24.67 (978-0-8368-3860-2(2)); pap. 8.95 (978-0-8368-3873-2(4) , Weekly Reader Early Learning Library) Stevens, Gareth Inc.

Bortolotti, Dan. Exploring Saturn: From Galileo to Cassini. 2003. (Illus.). 64p. (J). (gr. 4-8). 19.95 (978-1-55297-766-8(8)); pap. 9.95 (978-1-55297-765-1(X)) Firefly Bks., Ltd.

—Exploring Saturn: From Galileo to Cassini. 2003. (gr. 3-6). lib. bdg. 11.55 (978-0-613-70568-4(8)) Tandem Library Bks.

Geiger, Beth. The Inside Story of Saturn. 2006. (J). 7.80 (978-1-933798-08-0(4)) Sally Ride Science.

Goldstein, Margaret J. Saturn. 2005. (Pull Ahead Bks.). (Illus.). 32p. (gr. 2-4). lib. bdg. 22.60 (978-0-8225-4653-5(1)) Lerner Publishing Group.

Goss, Tim. Saturn. 2003. (Universe Ser.). (Illus.). 32p. (J). (gr. 3-5). lib. bdg. 22.79 (978-1-58810-915-6(1)); pap. 7.50 (978-1-4034-0616-3(2)) Heinemann Library.

Hofer, Charles. Saturn. 2004. (Library of the Nine Planets). (J). lib. bdg. 26.50 (978-1-4042-0173-6(4)) Rosen Publishing Group, Inc., The.

Howard, Fran. Saturn. 2007. (Planets Ser.). (ENG., Illus.). 32p. (J). (gr. k-4). lib. bdg. 24.21 (*978-1-59928-828-4(1) , Buddy Bks.) ABDO Publishing Co.

Landau, Elaine. Saturn. (True Booktrade;: Space Ser.). 48p. (J). 2008. pap. 6.95 (*978-0-531-14795-5(9)); 2007. (Illus.). (gr. 3-5). lib. bdg. 26.00 (*978-0-531-12567-0(X)) Scholastic Library Publishing. (Children's Pr.).

Miller, Ron. Saturn. 2003. (Worlds Beyond Ser.). (Illus.). 80p. (gr. 7 up). lib. bdg. (978-0-7613-2360-0(0) , Twenty-First Century Bks.) Lerner Publishing Group.

Orme, Helen & Orme, David. Let's Explore Saturn. 2006. (J). pap. (*978-0-8368-8131-8(1)); lib. bdg. (*978-0-8368-7946-9(5)) Stevens, Gareth Inc.

Potts, Steve. Saturn. 2001. (Illus.). 24p. (J). lib. bdg. 21.35 (978-1-58340-098-2(2)) Smart Apple Media.

Rau, Dana Meachen. Saturn. 2002. (Illus.). 32p. (J). (gr. 3 up). lib. bdg. 21.26 (978-0-7565-0298-0(5)) Compass Point Bks.

Richardson, Adele. Saturn. 2008. (J). (*978-1-4296-0728-5(9)) Capstone Pr., Inc.

Richardson, Adele D. Saturn. 2005. (Illus.). 24p. (J). 21.26 (978-0-7368-3694-4(2)) Capstone Pr., Inc.

Ring, Susan. Saturn. (Exploring Planets Ser.). (J). 2004. pap. (978-1-59036-227-3(6)); 2003. (Illus.). 24p. lib. bdg. 15.95 (978-1-59036-100-9(8)) Weigl Pubs., Inc.

Saturn, 6 vols. (gr. 2-5). 36.95 (978-0-7368-8973-5(6)) Red Brick Learning.

Simon, Charnan. Saturn. 2003. (Planets Ser.). (Illus.). 32p. (J). (gr. 2-6). 27.07 (978-1-59296-054-5(5)) Child's World, Inc.

Slade, Suzanne. A Look at Saturn. 2008. (J). lib. bdg. (*978-1-4042-3830-5(1) , PowerKids Pr.) Rosen Publishing Group, Inc., The.

Spangenburg, Ray. Look at Saturn. 2001. (gr. 5-8). lib. bdg. 24.55 (978-0-613-54275-3(4)) Tandem Library Bks.

Sparrow, Giles. Saturn. (Illus.). 39p. (J). (gr. 4-7). 2002. pap. 7.95 (978-1-58810-964-4(X) , 91447); 2001. lib. bdg. 24.22 (978-1-57572-396-9(4)) Heinemann Library.

Taylor-Butler, Christine. Saturn. (Scholastic News Nonfiction Readers: Space Science Ser.). 24p. (J). 2008. pap. 6.95 (*978-0-531-14767-2(3)); 2007. (Illus.). (gr. 1-2). lib. bdg. 20.00 (*978-0-531-14752-8(5)) Scholastic Library Publishing. (Children's Pr.).

Vogt, Gregory L. Jupiter, Saturn, Uranus & Neptune. 2000. (Our Universe Ser.). (Illus.). 48p. (YA). (gr. 5-12). lib. bdg. 22.83 (978-0-7398-3109-0(7)) Raintree.

—Saturn. (Galaxy Ser.). 24p. (J). pap. 6.95 (978-0-7368-8891-2(8)) Capstone Pr., Inc.

Wimmer, Teresa. Saturn. 2007. (J). (978-1-58341-522-1(X) , Creative Education) Creative Co., The.

World Book, contrib. by. Saturn & Uranus. 2nd ed. 2006. (World Book's Solar System & Space Exploration Library). (Illus.). 64p. (J). (*978-0-7166-9519-6(7)) World Bk., Inc.

World Book, Inc. Staff, contrib. by. Saturn & Uranus. 2006. (World Book's Solar System & Space Exploration Library). (Illus.). 63p. (J). (978-0-7166-9506-6(5)) World Bk., Inc.

SAUDI ARABIA

Anderson, Laurie Halse. Saudi Arabia. 2000. (Globe-Trotters Club Ser.). (Illus.). 48p. (J). (gr. 3-5). lib. bdg. 22.60 (978-1-57505-121-5(4) , Carolrhoda Bks.) Lerner Publishing Group.

Anderson, Laurie Halse & Milivojevic, JoAnn. Saudi Arabia. 2005. (Ticket to Ser.). (Illus.). 48p. (gr. 2-4). 22.60 (978-1-57505-147-5(8)) Lerner Publishing Group.

Balcavage, Dynise. Saudi Arabia. 2001. (Countries of the World Ser.). (Illus.). 96p. (J). (gr. 6 up). lib. bdg. 30.00 (978-0-8368-2338-7(9)) Stevens, Gareth Inc.

Broberg, Catherine. Saudi Arabia in Pictures. 2nd rev. ed. 2003. (Visual Geography Ser.). (Illus.). 80p. (J). (gr. 5-12). 27.93 (978-0-8225-1958-4(5)) Lerner Publishing Group.

Cane, Graeme & Balcavage, Dynise. Welcome to Saudi Arabia. 2002. (Welcome to My Country Ser.). (Illus.). 48p. (J). (gr. 2 up). lib. bdg. 26.00 (978-0-8368-2538-1(1)) Stevens, Gareth Inc.

Deady, Kathleen W. Saudi Arabia. 2005. (Fact Finders Ser.). (Illus.). 32p. (J). 22.60 (978-0-7368-3760-6(4)) Capstone Pr., Inc.

Fazio, Wende. Saudi Arabia. 1999. (True Bks.). (Illus.). 48p. (J). (gr. 3-5). pap. 6.95 (978-0-516-26502-5(4) , Children's Pr.) Scholastic Library Publishing.

Ganeri, Anita. Hajj Stories. 2007. (J). (*978-1-84234-434-7(X)) Cherrytree Pubns., Inc.

Goodwin, William. Saudi Arabia. 2000. (Modern Nations of the World Ser.). (Illus.). 112p. (YA). (gr. 7-10). 29.95 (978-1-56006-763-4(2) , Lucent Bks.) Thomson Gale.

Harcourt School Publishers Staff. The Saudi People. 3rd ed. 2002. (Horizons Ser.). (Illus.). (J). pap. 7.30 (978-0-15-333624-9(2)) Harcourt Schl. Pubs.

Harper, Robert Alexander. Saudi Arabia. (Modern World Nations Ser.). (Illus.). (gr. 6-12). 2003. 200p. pap. 30.00 (978-0-7910-7176-2(6)); 2002. 150p. 30.00 (978-0-7910-6935-6(4)) Facts On File, Inc. (Chelsea Hse.).

Heinrichs, Ann. Saudi Arabia. 2002. (Enchantment of the World, Second Ser.). (Illus.). 144p. (YA). (gr. 5-9). pap. 36.00 (978-0-516-22287-5(2) , Children's Pr.) Scholastic Library Publishing.

Husain, Shahrukh. Mecca. 1998. (Holy Cities Ser.). (Illus.). 47p. (J). (gr. 5-8). 15.00 (978-0-7881-5853-7(8)) DIANE Publishing Co.

Ismail, Imam Vehbi. Muhammad, the Last Prophet. 2001. (Illus.). 167p. (J). 9.95 (978-0-915957-58-3(2)) amana pubns.

Italia, Bob. Saudi Arabia. 2003. (Countries Ser.). (Illus.). 40p. (J). (gr. k-6). lib. bdg. 22.78 (978-1-57765-840-5(X)) ABDO Publishing Co.

Keating, Susan Katz. Saudi Arabia. 2003. (Modern Middle East Nations & Their Strategic Place in the World Ser.). (Illus.). 112,128p. (YA). (gr. 7 up). lib. bdg. (978-1-59084-509-7(9)) Mason Crest Pubs.

Khan, Saniyasnain. Tell Me about Hajj: What the Hajj Is, Why It Is So Important, & What It Teaches Me. Ravindran, K.M., illus. 2nd l.t. ed. 2001. (Tell Me about Ser.). 40p. pap. 6.50 (978-81-87570-90-5(3)) Goodword Bks. Pvt. Ltd. IND. Dist: Lodhia Ctr., The.

—Tell Me about Hajj: What the Hajj Is,Why It's So Important & What It Teaches Me. 2nd l.t. ed. 2001. (Tell Me About). (Illus.). 40p. per. 9.75 (978-81-87570-00-4(8)) Goodword Bks. Pvt. Ltd. IND. Dist: Lodhia Ctr., The.

Mulloy, Martin. Saudi Arabia. 1999. (Major World Nations Ser.). (Illus.). 144p. (YA). (gr. 4-7). lib. bdg. 21.95 (978-0-7910-4982-2(5) , Chelsea Hse.) Facts On File, Inc.

O'Shea, Maria. Saudi Arabia. 1999. (Festivals of the World Ser.). (Illus.). 32p. (J). (gr. 3 up). lib. bdg. 24.67 (978-0-8368-2026-3(6)) Stevens, Gareth Inc.

Reed, Jennifer. The Saudi Royal Family. 2nd rev. ed. 2007. (Modern World Leaders Ser.). (Illus.). 120p. (YA). (gr. 6-12). 30.00 (978-0-7910-9218-7(6) , Chelsea Hse.) Facts On File, Inc.

Reed, Jennifer Bond. The Saudi Royal Family. (Major World Leaders Ser.). (Illus.). (gr. 6-12). 2003. 144p. pap. 30.00 (978-0-7910-7187-8(1)); 2002. 112p. 30.00 (978-0-7910-7063-5(8)) Facts On File, Inc. (Chelsea Hse.).

Ross. Mecca. 2003. (Holy Places Ser.). (Illus.). 32p. (J). pap. 6.95 (978-1-4109-0053-1(3)) Raintree.

Ross, Mandy. Mecca. 2003. (Holy Places Ser.). (Illus.). 32p. (J). lib. bdg. 24.28 (978-0-7398-6080-9(1)) Raintree.

Schaffer, David. Saudi Arabia in the News: Past, Present, & Future. 2006. (Middle East Nations in the News Ser.). (Illus.). 128p. (J). lib. bdg. 33.27 (978-1-59845-026-2(3) , MyReportLinks.com Bks.) Enslow Pubs., Inc.

Subanthore, Aswin & Harper, Robert A. Saudi Arabia. 2nd rev. ed. 2007. (Modern World Nations Ser.). 120p. (gr. 6-12). 30.00 (*978-0-7910-9516-4(9) , Chelsea Hse.) Facts On File, Inc.

Temple, Bob. Welcome to Saudi Arabia. 2008. (Welcome to the World Ser.). 32p. (J). (gr. 1-5). 27.07 (*978-1-59296-975-3(5)) Child's World, Inc.

Wagner, Heather Lehr. Gertrude Bell: Explorer of the Middle East. 2004. (Women Explorers Ser.). (Illus.). 120p. 30.00 (978-0-7910-7711-5(X) , Chelsea Hse.) Facts On File, Inc.

—Saudi Arabia. 2002. (Creation of the Modern Middle East Ser.). (Illus.). 125p. (gr. 6-12). 35.00 (978-0-7910-6510-5(3) , Chelsea Hse.) Facts On File, Inc.

Walsh, Kieran. Saudi Arabia. 2003. (Countries in the News Ser.). (Illus.). 24p. (J). 25.64 (978-1-58952-681-5(3)) Rourke Publishing, LLC.

Wynbrandt, James. A Brief History of Saudi Arabia. 2004. (Brief History Ser.). (Illus.). 334p. (YA). (gr. 9-12). per. 45.00 (978-0-8160-5203-5(4)) Facts On File, Inc.

Yackley-Franken, Nicki. Teens in Saudi Arabia. 2007. (Global Connections Ser.). (Illus.). 96p. (J). pap. (*978-0-7565-2074-8(6) , 1265899) Compass Point Bks.

Yackley-Franken, Nicki & Compass Point Books Staff. Teens in Saudi Arabia. 2006. (Global Connections Ser.). (Illus.). 96p. (J). (gr. 5-7). 31.93 (*978-0-7565-2066-3(5) , 1265899) Compass Point Bks.

SAWYER, TOM (FICTITIOUS CHARACTER)—FICTION

The Adventures of Tom Sawyer. 2004. (Classic Retelling Ser.). (gr. 6-12). (978-0-618-12053-6(X) , 2-00218) McDougal Littell Inc.

The Adventures of Tom Sawyer. 1998. 44p. (YA). stu. ed. 11.95 (978-1-56137-528-8(4) , NU5284SP) Novel Units, Inc.

The Adventures of Tom Sawyer. 2004. (Literature Units Ser.). (Illus.). 48p. 7.99 (978-1-57690-637-8(X)) Teacher Created Materials, Inc.

Holt, Rinehart and Winston Staff. The Adventures of Tom Sawyer: With Connections. 1998. pap., stu. ed. 13.20 (978-0-03-054047-9(X)) Holt, Rinehart & Winston.

Rigby Education Staff. Tom Sawyer: Jumbled Tumble. (gr. k-2). 26.00 (978-0-7635-2424-1(7)) Rigby Education.

Tom Sawyer: 6 Small Books. (gr. k-2). 23.00 (978-0-7635-8507-5(6)) Rigby Education.

Twain, Mark. Die Abenteuer von Tom Sawyer. 2000. Tr. of Adventures of Tom Sawyer. (GER.). (J). pap. 14.95 (978-3-596-50166-3(0)) Fischer Taschenbuch Verlag DEU. Dist: Distribooks, Inc.

—The Adv. of Tom Sawyer: #1 A Song for Aunt Polly. 2007. (Easy Reader Classics Ser.). 32p. (J). (ps-3). 21.35 (*978-1-59961-334-5(4)) Spotlight.

—The Adventures of Tom Sawyer. 2005. 264p. 28.95 (978-1-4218-0768-3(8) , 1st World Library - Literary Society) 1st World Publishing, Inc.

—The Adventures of Tom Sawyer. Pablo Marcos Studio Staff, illus. 2002. (Great Illustrated Classics Ser.). 240p. (J). (gr. 3-8). 21.35 (978-1-57765-679-1(2) , ABDO & Daughters) ABDO Publishing Co.

—The Adventures of Tom Sawyer. 1999. (Andre Deutsch Classics). (Illus.). 272p. (J). 9.95 (978-0-233-99242-6(1)) Andre Deutsch GBR. Dist: Trafalgar Square Publishing.

—The Adventures of Tom Sawyer. 2002. 12.17 (978-0-7587-7968-7(2)) Book Wholesalers, Inc.

—The Adventures of Tom Sawyer. (Great Classics for Children Ser.). (J). (Illus.). 192p. 5.99 (978-1-4037-0598-3(4)); 2003. 182p. 4.99 (978-1-57759-556-4(4)) Dalmatian Pr.

—The Adventures of Tom Sawyer. Fletcher, Claire, illus. 2002. (Kingfisher Classics Ser.). 352p. (J). (gr. k-3). tchr. ed. 15.95 (978-0-7534-5478-7(5) , Kingfisher) Houghton Mifflin Co. Trade & Reference Div.

—The Adventures of Tom Sawyer. (Young Collector's Illustrated Classics Ser.). (Illus.). 192p. (J). (gr. 3-7). 9.95 (978-1-56156-453-8(2)) Kidsbooks, Inc.

—The Adventures of Tom Sawyer. 2007. (Oxford Children's Classics). 304p. (YA). 9.95 (*978-0-19-271999-7(8)) Oxford Univ. Pr., Inc.

—The Adventures of Tom Sawyer. (J). (978-0-448-41455-3(4) , Putnam Juvenile); 2006. 272p. (gr. 12). pap. 7.00 (978-0-14-303956-3(3) , Penguin Classics) Penguin Group (USA) Inc.

—The Adventures of Tom Sawyer. 2001. (Paperback Classics Ser.). (Illus.). 304p. pap. 6.95 (978-0-375-75681-8(7) , Modern Library) Random House Publishing Group.

—The Adventures of Tom Sawyer. 2006. (Scholastic Classics Ser.). (Illus.). vi, 219p. (J). (gr. 9-12). 25.00 (978-0-531-16978-0(2) , Watts, Franklin) Scholastic Library Publishing.

—The Adventures of Tom Sawyer. 2001. (Aladdin Classics Ser.). 272p. (J). (gr. 4-7). pap. 4.99 (978-0-689-84224-5(4) , Aladdin) Simon & Schuster Children's Publishing.

—The Adventures of Tom Sawyer. 2001. (gr. 3-6). lib. bdg. 11.80 (978-0-613-63172-3(2)); 1999. (gr. 5-8). lib. bdg. 11.80 (978-0-613-66685-5(2)) Tandem Library Bks.

—The Adventures of Tom Sawyer. 2001. 184p. pap. 9.95 (978-1-57002-169-5(4)) University Publishing Hse., Inc.

—The Adventures of Tom Sawyer. McKowen, Scott, illus. 2004. (Unabridged Classics Ser.). 224p. 9.95 (978-1-4027-1460-3(2)) Sterling Publishing Co., Inc.

—The Adventures of Tom Sawyer. 1999. reprint ed. pap. 28.00 (978-1-4047-1117-4(1)) Classic Textbooks.

—The Adventures of Tom Sawyer. 2004. reprint ed. pap. 1.99 (978-1-4192-5166-5(X)) Kessinger Publishing, LLC.

—The Adventures of Tom Sawyer. l.t. ed. 2006. 510p. 22.95 (978-0-7862-8640-9(7)) Thorndike Pr.

—The Adventures of Tom Sawyer. Williams, True W., illus. 2nd rev. ed. 2002. (Mark Twain Library). 288p. pap. 15.95 (978-0-520-23575-5(4)) Univ. of California Pr.

—The Adventures of Tom Sawyer: Juvenile Classic. 2005. (Illus.). 192p. (J). 5.99 (978-1-4037-1382-7(0)) Dalmatian Pr.

—The Adventures of Tom Sawyer - Literary Touchstone Edition. 2005. 216p. (YA). per. 4.99 (978-1-58049-596-7(6) , PWH5966) Prestwick Hse., Inc.

—The Adventures of Tom Sawyer; Adventures of Huckleberry Finn. 2002. 544p. mass mkt. 5.95 (978-0-451-52864-3(6) , Signet Classics) Penguin Group (USA) Inc.

—The Adventures of Tom Sawyer, Complete. l.t. ed. 2006. 408p. pap. (978-1-84637-320-6(4)) Echo Library.

—Las Aventuras de Tom Sawyer. 2002. (SPA.). (YA). 7.95 (978-956-13-1069-8(4)) Bello, Andres CHL. *Dist:* AIMS International Bks., Inc.

—Las Aventuras de Tom Sawyer. 2000. (SPA., Illus.). 272p. (J). 7.95 (978-84-406-8397-7(9)) Ediciones B ESP. *Dist:* Distribooks, Inc.

—Las Aventuras de Tom Sawyer. (SPA.). (YA). (978-84-7525-151-6(X)) Ediciones Generales Anaya SA.

—Las Aventuras de Tom Sawyer. 2003. (Advanced Reading Ser.). (SPA.). 124p. (J). 11.95 (978-84-239-9045-0(1)) Espasa Calpe, S.A. ESP. *Dist:* Planeta Publishing Corp.

—Las Aventuras de Tom Sawyer. 2002. (Classics for Young Readers Ser.). (SPA.). (YA). 13.99 (978-84-392-0908-9(8) , EV30591) Gaviota Ediciones ESP. *Dist:* Lectorum Pubns., Inc.

—Las Aventuras de Tom Sawyer. (Coleccion Estrella). (SPA., Illus.). 64p. (YA). 14.95 (978-950-11-0012-9(X) , SGM012) Sigmar ARG. *Dist:* Continental Bk. Co., Inc.

—Avventure di Tom Sawyer. pap. 15.95 (978-88-451-2151-7(8)) Fabbri - RCS Libri ITA. *Dist:* Distribooks, Inc.

—The Best Fence Painter. Bates, Amy June, illus. 2006. (Adventures of Tom Sawyer Ser.: Bk. 2). 32p. (J). pap. 3.95 (978-1-4027-3288-1(0)) Sterling Publishing Co., Inc.

—A Song for Aunt Polly. Bates, Amy June, illus. 2006. (Adventures of Tom Sawyer Ser.: Bk. 1). 32p. (J). pap. 3.95 (978-1-4027-3287-4(2)) Sterling Publishing Co., Inc.

—Tom Sawyer. Cruz, E. R., illus. 2nd ed. 1998. (Illustrated Classic Book Ser.). 61p. (J). (gr. 3 up). reprint ed. pap. 4.95 (978-1-56767-263-3(9)) Educational Insights, Inc.

—Tom Sawyer. adapted ed. (YA). (gr. 5-12). pap. 8.50 (978-0-8359-0212-0(9)) Globe Fearon Educational Publishing.

—Tom Sawyer. (Coleccion Clasicos de la Juventud). (SPA., Illus.). 220p. (J). 12.95 (978-84-7189-029-0(1) , ORT310) Ortells, Alfredo Editorial S.L. ESP. *Dist:* Continental Bk. Co., Inc.

—Tom Sawyer. 2003. (Timeless Classics Ser.). (SPA., Illus.). 95p. (J). (gr. 5-8). pap. 12.95 (978-84-372-2235-6(4)) Santillana USA Publishing Co., Inc.

—Tom Sawyer. 1999. (Illus.). 336p. (J). (gr. 4-7). pap. 4.99 (978-0-439-09940-0(4)) Scholastic, Inc.

—Tom Sawyer. unabr. ed. 2002. (YA). pap. incl. audio compact disk (978-1-58472-341-7(6) , In Audio) Sound Room Pubs., Inc.

—Tom Sawyer Abroad. 1999. reprint ed. pap. 28.00 (978-1-4047-1125-9(2)) Classic Textbooks.

—Tom Sawyer Abroad & Tom Sawyer, Detective. l.t. ed. 1999. (Large Print Heritage Ser.). 265p. (YA). (gr. 7-12). lib. bdg. 29.95 (978-1-58118-046-6(2) , 22515) LRS.

—Tom Sawyer & Huckleberry Finn. unabr. ed. 1998. (Wordsworth Classics Ser.). (YA). (gr. 6-12). 5.27 (978-0-89061-011-4(8) , R0118WW) Jamestown.

—Tom Sawyer, Detective. (SPA., Illus.). 160p. (YA). 11.95 (978-84-7281-062-4(3) , AF0623) Auriga, Ediciones S.A. ESP. *Dist:* Continental Bk. Co., Inc.

—Tom Sawyer, Detective. unabr. ed. 2002. (Dover Juvenile Classics Ser.). 80p. (J). (gr. 4-7). pap. 2.00 (978-0-486-42109-4(0)) Dover Pubns., Inc.

—Tom Sawyer, Detective. 2002. (gr. 3-6). lib. bdg. 9.50 (978-0-613-90063-8(4)) Tandem Library Bks.

Twain, Mark & Mucci, Tim. Tom Sawyer. Sechrist, Rad, illus. 2008. (All-Action Classics Ser.). 128p. (J). pap. 6.95 (978-1-4027-3399-4(2)) Sterling Publishing Co., Inc.

SAXONS

see Anglo-Saxons

SAYINGS

see Proverbs; Quotations

SCANDINAVIA

Franklin, Sharon, et al. Scandinavia: Understanding Geography & History Through Art. 1999. (Artisans Around the World Ser.). (Illus.). 48p. (J). (gr. 4-8). lib. bdg. 27.12 (978-0-7398-0122-2(8)) Raintree.

Hatt, Christine. The Viking World. 2004. (Excavating the Past Ser.). (J). pap. 8.50 (978-1-4034-5461-4(2)); lib. bdg. (978-1-4034-4841-5(8)) Heinemann Library.

Hopkins, Andrea. Viking Families & Farms. 2002. (Viking Library). (Illus.). 24p. (J). (gr. 3). lib. bdg. 19.95 (978-0-8239-5815-3(9) , PowerKids Pr.) Rosen Publishing Group, Inc., The.

Nicholson, Sue & Ferris, Julie. Viking World: A Guide to 11th Century Scandinavia. 2000. (Sightseers Ser.). (Illus.). 38p. (J). (gr. 3-5). tchr. ed. 8.95 (978-0-7534-5237-0(5) , Kingfisher) Houghton Mifflin Co. Trade & Reference Div.

Robinson, Deborah B. The Sami of Northern Europe. 2002. (First Peoples Ser.). (Illus.). 48p. (J). (gr. 4-8). lib. bdg. 23.93 (978-0-8225-4175-2(0)) Lerner Publishing Group.

SCARECROWS

Harris, Calvin. Scarecrows. 2008. (J). ***(*978-1-4296-0027-9(6))*** Capstone Pr., Inc.

Schaefer, Lola M. Scarecrows. Saunders-Smith, Gail, ed. 1998. (Fall Fun Ser.). (Illus.). 24p. (J). (gr. k-1). lib. bdg. 15.93 (978-0-7368-0107-2(3) , Pebble Bks.) Capstone Pr., Inc.

—Scarecrows. (Fall Fun Ser.). 24p. (J). pap. 5.95 (978-0-7368-8108-1(5)) Capstone Pr., Inc.

School Zone Publishing Company Staff. Guess Who? A Book of Colors & Shapes. 2000. (Illus.). 16p. (J). bds. 4.99 (978-0-88743-606-2(4) , 06607) School Zone Publishing Co.

SCARECROWS—FICTION

Amery, Heather. Scarecrow's Secret. Tyler, Jenny, ed. Cartwright, Stephen, illus. rev. ed. 2004. (Farmyard Tales Readers Ser.). 16p. (J). pap. 5.95 (978-0-7945-0751-0(4) , Usborne) EDC Publishing.

Balducci, Rita. Scarecrow Mix: Halloween Pigs/Happy Scarecrow. 1999. (Illus.). (J). (ps-3). pap. 4.50 (978-1-55254-089-3(8)) Brighter Vision Pubns.

Brandreth, Gyles. Jack Mouse & the Scarecrow. 2000. (Illus.). 32p. (J). 9.99 (978-0-233-99577-9(3)) Andre Deutsch GBR. *Dist:* Trafalgar Square Publishing.

Brown, Kenneth. The Scarecrow's Hat. 2001. (Illus.). 32p. (J). (ps-1). 15.95 (978-1-56145-240-8(8) , Q25024) Peachtree Pubs., Ltd.

Brown, Margaret Wise. The Little Scarecrow Boy. Diaz, David, illus. 1998. 40p. (J). (ps-2). 16.99 (978-0-06-026284-6(2) , Cotler, Joanna Books) HarperCollins Pubs.

Davis, Lee. Scarecrow: Bear Read Alone. 2001. (Illus.). 24p. (J). (ps-1). pap. 7.95 (978-0-7894-4947-4(1) , D K Ink) Dorling Kindersley Publishing, Inc.

Faulkner, Keith. Surprise on the Farm. Clucas, Philip, illus. 2000. (J). (978-0-439-21059-1(3)) Scholastic, Inc.

Fiorello, Frank. Pumpkin Patch Scarecrows. Fiorello, Frank, illus. 1998. (Illus.). 40p. (J). (ps-1). pap. 7.95 (978-0-9646300-3-1(6)) Pumpkin Patch Publishing.

Hawthorne, Nathaniel & San Souci, Robert D. Feathertop: Based on the Tale by Nathaniel Hawthorne. San Souci, Robert D. & San Souci, Daniel, illus. 2006. (J). reprint ed. pap. 10.95 (978-1-59078-382-5(4)) Boyds Mills Pr.

Holmes, Melody Moore. Buenos Dias, Carlitos! Garvin, Elaine, illus. 1999. Tr. of Good Day, Carlitos. (SPA.). 32p. (J). (ps-1). pap. 6.49 (978-1-57924-230-5(8) , 115022) Jones, Bob Univ. Pr.

McGeorge, Constance W. Waltz of the Scarecrows. 2003. (Illus.). 32p. (J). pap. 6.95 (978-0-8118-4078-1(6)) Chronicle Bks. LLC.

Moulton, Mark Kimball. Scarecrow Pete & His Suitcase of Dreams. Crouch, Karen Hillard, illus. 2005. 36p. (J). (ps-3). 14.95 (978-0-8249-5151-1(4)) Ideals Pubns.

Oblich, Kathleen. Jake & the Scarecrow. 2007. 48p. pap. 12.95 ***(*978-1-4241-3101-3(4))*** PublishAmerica, Inc.

Packard, Mary. The Shy Scarecrow. Huang, Benrei, illus. 2001. (Hello Reader! Ser.). (J). (978-0-439-31704-7(5)) Scholastic, Inc.

Powell, Jillian. The Lazy Scarecrow. Coughlin, Jayne, illus. 2004. (Read-It! Readers Ser.). 32p. (C). (gr. k-3). 18.60 (978-1-4048-0062-5(X)) Picture Window Bks.

Preston, Tim. The Lonely Scarecrow. Kneen, Maggie, illus. 1999. 32p. (J). (ps-3). 14.99 (978-0-525-46080-0(2) , Dutton Juvenile) Penguin Group (USA) Inc.

Pullman, Philip. The Scarecrow & His Servant. Bailey, Peter, illus. 240p. (J). (gr. 3-7). 2007. 6.50 (978-0-440-42130-6(6) , Yearling); 2005. 15.95 (978-0-375-81531-7(7) , Knopf Bks. for Young Readers); 2005. lib. bdg. 17.99 (978-0-375-91531-4(1) , Knopf Bks. for Young Readers) Random Hse. Children's Bks.

Rau, Dana Meachen & Rojas, Mary G. Shoo Crow, Shoo!, Level A. 2001. (Early Reader Ser.). (Illus.). 24p. (J). (gr. k up). lib. bdg. 18.60 (978-0-7565-0072-6(9)) Compass Point Bks.

Rex, Michael. Scarecrow. Rex, Michael, illus. 2003. (Word-by-Word First Reader Ser.). (Illus.). 32p. (J). pap. 3.99 (978-0-439-49311-6(0) , Cartwheel Bks.) Scholastic, Inc.

Rigby Education Staff. Scarecrow's Hair. (Sails Literacy Ser.). (Illus.). 16p. (gr. 1-2). 27.00 (978-0-7635-9892-1(5) , 698925C99) Rigby Education.

Rylant, Cynthia. Scarecrow. Stringer, Lauren, illus. (J). (gr. 1-7). 1998. 40p. 16.00 (978-0-15-201084-3(X)); 2001. 32p. reprint ed. pap. 7.00 (978-0-15-202480-2(8) , Harcourt Paperbacks) Harcourt Children's Bks.

—Scarecrow. 2001. (978-0-606-21411-7(9)); lib. bdg. 14.15 (978-0-613-35564-3(4)) Tandem Library Bks.

School Zone Publishing Company Staff & Hoenecke, Karen. Scarecrow's Friends. 2000. (Start to Read Board Bks.). (Illus.). 10p. (J). (ps-k). bds. 4.99 (978-0-88743-808-0(3) , 06805) School Zone Publishing Co.

Sillifant, Alec. Farmer Ham. 2007. (J). 15.95 ***(*978-0-7358-2134-7(8))*** North-South Bks., Inc.

Smith, Todd Aaron. The Scarecrow & the Spider. 2005. (Illus.). 32p. (J). 9.99 (978-1-4003-0550-6(0)) Nelson, Thomas Inc.

Sweet, J.H. & Sierra, Holly. Spiderwort & the Princess of Haiku: The Fairy Chronicles. 2007. (Fairy Chronicles Ser.). (Illus.). 128p. (J). (gr. 2 up). pap. 6.99 ***(*978-1-4022-1025-9(6)*** , Sourcebooks Jabberwocky) Sourcebooks, Inc.

Thiesing, Lisa. The Scarecrow's New Clothes. Thiesing, Lisa, illus. 2006. (Illus.). 32p. (J). (ps-2). 13.99 (978-0-525-47750-1(0) , Dutton Juvenile) Penguin Group (USA) Inc.

Thompson, Ruth Plumly. The Royal Book of Oz. 2004. reprint ed. pap. 20.95 (978-1-4191-8123-8(8)); pap. 1.99 (978-1-4192-8123-5(2)) Kessinger Publishing, LLC.

Whitlock, Matt. Punk 'n Patch. Whitlock, Matt, illus. 2005. (Illus.). 32p. (ps-ps). 16.95 (978-0-9769057-0-7(1)) Little Hero.

SCENARIOS

see Motion Picture Plays; Television Plays

SCENERY

see Views

SCENERY (STAGE)

see Theaters—Stage Setting and Scenery

SCHLIEMANN, HEINRICH, 1822-1890

Schlitz, Laura Amy. The Hero Schliemann: The Dreamer Who Dug up Troy. Byrd, Robert, illus. 2006. 80p. (J). (gr. 4-8). 17.99 (978-0-7636-2283-1(4)) Candlewick Pr.

SCHOLARSHIP

see Learning and Scholarship

SCHOLARSHIPS

see also Student Loan Funds

Bercik, Mark. America's Complete Sports Scholarship Guide: Giving Back Something to the Game. Wilding, Diane, ed. 2nd rev. ed. 2003. Orig. Title: America's Sports Scholarship Guide. (Illus.). 272p. (YA). (gr. 4-12). per. 19.95 (978-0-9721199-1-7(4)) America Sports Publishing.

Breithaupt, Douglas J. Pacific Northwest Scholarship Guide: Finding Money for College. 7th ed. 1998. 220p. (Orig.). (YA). (gr. 7-12). pap. 29.95 (978-1-880344-09-5(2)) College Planning Network.

Edwards, Christina. Gardner's Guide to Finding Money for School Online. 2004. (Gardner's Guide Ser.). 208p. pap. 19.95 (978-1-58965-012-1(3) , 703 793 8604) Gardner, Garth Co., Inc. (GGC).

Rugg, Frederick E. Financial Aid in Less Than 3000 Words. 7th rev. ed. 2001. 5p. (J). (gr. 11-12). pap. 6.95 (978-1-883062-42-2(X)); 8th rev. ed. 2002. 5p. (YA). (gr. 11-12). pap. 6.95 (978-1-883062-47-7(0)); 9th rev. ed. 2003. 6p. (YA). pap. 6.95 (978-1-883062-51-4(9)); 10th rev. ed. 2004. 6p. (YA). pap. 6.95 (978-1-883062-57-6(8)) Rugg's Recommendations.

SCHOOL ADMINISTRATION

see School Management And Organization

SCHOOL AND HOME

see Home and School

SCHOOL ATTENDANCE

see also Children—Employment; First Day of School

Ada, Alma Flor & Compoy, F. Isabel. Mi Primer Dia de Escuela. 3rd ed. 2002. (Trofeos Ser.). (SPA.). (gr. k-6). pap. 19.70 (978-0-15-329889-9(8)) Harcourt Schl. Pubs.

Barnett, Michelle Noble, et al. Theme Pockets - September: School Days; Africa; Whales. Evans, Marilyn, ed. Larsen, Jo, illus. 1999. (Making Books with Pockets). 96p. (J). (gr. 1-3). pap., tchr. ed. 12.99 (978-1-55799-706-7(3) , EMC 592) Evan-Moor Educational Pubs.

Borden, Sarah & Miller, Sarah. Middle School: How to Deal. Nuts and Bolts Girls Staff, ed. Hatori, Yuki, illus. 2005. 96p. (J). pap. 9.95 (978-0-8118-4497-0(8)) Chronicle Bks. LLC.

Button, Beth & Sussman, Ellen. The Complete Welcome Back-to-School Book. Barr, Marilynn G., illus. 2001. (J). (gr. 1-3). pap. 19.95 (978-1-57310-268-1(7)) Teaching & Learning Co.

Covey, Stephen R. I'm Ready for School. 2000. (Step Ahead Workbooks Ser.). (Illus.). 32p. (J). (ps). pap., wbk. ed. 2.99 (978-0-307-03585-1(9) , 03585, Golden Bks.) Random Hse. Children's Bks.

Cruz, Barbara C. School Shootings & School Violence: A Hot Issue. 2002. (Hot Issues Ser.). (Illus.). 64p. (YA). (gr. 6-12). lib. bdg. 27.93 (978-0-7660-1813-6(X)) Enslow Pubs., Inc.

Davidson, Tish. School Conflict. (Life Balance Ser.). (Illus.). 2004. 79p. (YA). (gr. 5-8). pap. 6.95 (978-0-531-15571-4(4)); 2003. 80p. (J). 20.50 (978-0-531-12251-8(4)) Scholastic Library Publishing. (Watts, Franklin).

Ehrlich, Fred. Does a Panda Go to School? Bolam, Emily, illus. 2003. (Early Experiences Ser.). 32p. 10.95 (978-1-59354-017-3(5)) Blue Apple Bks.

Freed, Shirley Ann & Moon, Louise. School Tools. Morelan, Bill, ed. Harrell, Rob, illus. l.t. ed. 2002. 8p. (J). (ps-k). pap. 3.99 (978-1-58938-003-5(7)) Concerned Communications.

Go Back to School with Jack & Annie! 2003. (978-0-375-88495-5(5)) Random Hse. Children's Bks.

Heydlauff, Lisa. Going to School in India. 2005. 98p. (J). 21.95 (978-1-57091-666-3(7)) Charlesbridge Publishing, Inc.

Hoffman, Joan. First Grade Basics. 2003. (Basics Ser.). 64p. (J). (gr. 1). pap., wbk. ed. 3.79 (978-1-58947-037-8(0)) School Zone Publishing Co.

—Second Grade Basics. 2003. (Basics Ser.). 64p. (J). (gr. k-3). pap., wbk. ed. 3.79 (978-1-58947-038-5(9)) School Zone Publishing Co.

Leatherdale, Mary Beth. My Class & Me: 1st Grade. Ritchie, Scot, illus. 2004. (Memory Scrapbks. for Kids). 32p. (J). (gr. 1 up). (978-1-55337-475-6(4)) Kids Can Pr., Ltd.

—My Class & Me: 2nd Grade. Ritchie, Scot, illus. 2004. (Memory Scrapbks. for Kids). 32p. (J). (gr. 2 up). (978-1-55337-476-3(2)) Kids Can Pr., Ltd.

—My Class & Me: 3rd Grade. Ritchie, Scot, illus. 2004. (Memory Scrapbks. for Kids). 32p. (J). (gr. 3 up). (978-1-55337-477-0(0)) Kids Can Pr., Ltd.

Powling, Chris, et al. School Days. 2007. (I-read Ser.). (Illus.). 38p. pap. ***(*978-0-521-70483-0(9))*** Cambridge Univ. Pr.

Pritchard, M. Ann. Phil the Pill & Friends: Making Positive Choices. 2005. (Illus.). 75p. (J). per. 11.99 (978-0-9772210-0-4(8)) MAMP Creations.

Radabaugh, Melinda Beth. Going to School. 2003. (ps-2). lib. bdg. 13.30 (978-0-613-60880-0(1)) Tandem Library Bks.

Roberts-Davis, Tanya. We Need to Go to School: Voices of the Rugmark Children. 2003. (Illus.). 48p. (J). (gr. 5 up). pap. 7.95 (978-0-88899-426-4(5)) Groundwood Bks. CAN. *Dist:* Perseus Distribution.

Schiller, Melissa. 100th Day of School. 2003. (Rookie Read-about Holidays Ser.). (gr. 1-2). pap. 5.95 (978-0-516-27943-5(2) , Children's Pr.) Scholastic Library Publishing.

—100th Day of School. 2003. (gr. k-3). lib. bdg. 14.10 (978-0-613-63574-5(4)) Tandem Library Bks.

Scholastic, Inc. Staff. Back to School. 2003. (Biggie Patterns Ser.). 48p. pap. 10.99 (978-0-439-46842-8(6)) Scholastic, Inc.

School Zone Interactive Staff. First Grade. 2003. (On-Track Software Ser.). (J). (gr. 1 up). cd-rom 24.99 (978-1-58947-547-2(X)) School Zone Publishing Co.

School Zone Publishing. Third Grade. 2003. (Software Ser.). (J). (gr. 3 up). 24.99 (978-1-58947-538-0(0)) School Zone Publishing Co.

School Zone Publishing Company Staff. School Time Fun. (Illus.). (J). 19.99 incl. audio compact disk (978-0-88743-958-2(6)) School Zone Publishing Co.

Strasser, Todd. Don't Get Caught in the Teachers' Lounge. 2002. (Don't Get Caught Ser.). (Illus.). 144p. (J). (gr. 4-7). pap. 4.50 (978-0-439-21065-2(8) , Scholastic Paperbacks) Scholastic, Inc.

Williams, Julie. A Smart Girl's Guide to Starting Middle School: Everything You Need to Know about Making the Grade, Staying Cool at a New School, & Juggling More Homework, More Teachers, & More Friends! Martini, Angela, illus. 2004. (Americangirl Library(R) Ser.). 96p. (J). 9.95 (978-1-58485-877-5(X)) American Girl Publishing, Inc.

SCHOOL ATTENDANCE—FICTION

Adler, David A. Young Cam Jansen & the New Girl Mystery. Natti, Susanna, illus. 32p. (J). 2005. pap. 3.99 (978-0-14-240353-2(9) , Puffin); Vol. 10. 2004. 13.99 (978-0-670-05915-7(3) , Viking Juvenile) Penguin Group (USA) Inc.

Adoff, Jaime. Names Will Never Hurt Me. 2004. 144p. (J). (gr. 7). 16.99 (978-0-525-47175-2(8) , Dutton Juvenile) Penguin Group (USA) Inc.

Alexie, Sherman. The Absolutely True Diary of a Part-Time Indian. Forney, Ellen, illus. 2007. 240p. (YA). (gr. 7 up). 16.99 ***(*978-0-316-01368-0(4))*** Little, Brown Bks. for Young Readers.

Apostolina, M. Hazing Meri Sugarman. 2005. 272p. (YA). pap. 8.99 (978-1-4169-0610-0(X) , Simon Pulse) Simon & Schuster Children's Publishing.

Arlen, Richard. Girls' Boarding School. 320p. pap. 6.95 (978-0-7472-4039-6(6)) Headline Bk. Publishing GBR. *Dist:* Trafalgar Square Publishing.

Auseon, Andrew. Funny Little Monkey. 2005. 304p. (YA). (gr. 9-12). 17.00 (978-0-15-205334-5(4)) Harcourt Children's Bks.

Azuma, Kiyohiko. Azumanga Daioh, Vol. 3. 2004. (Illus.). 172p. (YA). pap. 9.99 (978-1-4139-0030-9(5)) ADV Manga.

—Azumanga Daioh: The Manga, Vol. 1. 2003. (Illus.). 172p. (YA). pap. 9.99 (978-1-4139-0000-2(3)) A. D. Vision, Inc.

—Azumanga Daioh: The Manga, Vol. 2. 2003. (Illus.). 168p. (YA). pap. (978-1-4139-0023-1(2)) ADV Manga.

Bell, Linda Simmons. Best Friends. 2006. (ENG.). 28p. per. 13.99 ***(*978-1-4259-7559-3(3))*** AuthorHouse.

Bennett, Cherie & Gottesfeld, Jeff. A Heart Divided. 2004. 320p. (YA). (gr. 7). 15.95 (978-0-385-32749-7(8) , Delacorte Bks. for Young Readers) Random Hse. Children's Bks.

Bentley, Dawn. Fuzzy Bear Goes to School. Nagy, Krisztina, illus. 2005. (Fuzzy Bear Ser.). 10p. (J). 10.95 (978-1-58117-124-2(2) , Intervisual/Piggy Toes) Dalmatian Pr.

Blance, Ellen & Cook. Monster Goes to School. Date not set. (Illus.). 24p. pap. 129.15 (978-0-582-18596-8(3)) Addison-Wesley Longman, Ltd. GBR. *Dist:* Trans-Atlantic Pubns., Inc.

Blume, Judy. Tales of a Fourth Grade Nothing. 2002. (Fudge Ser.). (Illus.). (J). 13.40 (978-0-7587-6609-0(2)) Book Wholesalers, Inc.

—Tales of a Fourth Grade Nothing. (Fudge Ser.). (J). 1999. 11.95 (978-1-56137-709-1(0)); 1998. 9.95 (978-1-56137-271-3(4)) Novel Units, Inc.

—Tales of a Fourth Grade Nothing. 2004. (Fudge Ser.). 144p. (gr. 12). mass mkt. 5.99 (978-0-425-19379-2(9), Berkley) Penguin Group (USA) Inc.

Blyton, Enid. The Naughtiest Girl in the School. (Illus.). 160p. (J). 6.95 (978-0-09-945500-4(5)) Random Hse. GBR. *Dist:* Trafalgar Square Publishing.

—The Naughtiest Girl Is a Monitor. (Illus.). 160p. (J). pap. 6.95 (978-0-09-945490-8(4)) Random Hse. GBR. *Dist:* Trafalgar Square Publishing.

Bognomo, Joel Eboueme. Madoulina: A Girl Who Wanted to Go to School. 2003. (Illus.). 32p. (J). (gr. 2-4). 14.95 (978-1-56397-769-5(9)) Boyds Mills Pr.

—Madoulina: A Girl Who Wanted to Go to School. 1999. (978-0-606-17704-7(3)); lib. bdg. 17.60 (978-0-613-23339-2(5)) Tandem Library Bks.

Bradman, Tony. Please, Miss Miller!, 6 vols., Pack. 2001. (Cambridge Storybooks Ser.). (Illus.). 16p. pap. 26.00 (978-0-521-00803-7(4)) Cambridge Univ. Pr.

Bridwell, Norman. Clifford Va a la Escuela de Perros. 2004. (Clifford Ser.). (SPA., Illus.). 32p. (J). 3.50 (978-0-439-54565-5(X)) Scholastic, Inc.

Brimner, Larry Dane. The New Kid. Tripp, Christine, illus. 2003. (Rookie Choices Ser.). (gr. 1-2). pap. 5.95 (978-0-516-27835-3(5) , Children's Pr.) Scholastic Library Publishing.

Brooks, Jillian. The New Girl. 2002. (Wondergirls Ser.: No. 1). (Illus.). 141p. (J). (gr. 3-7). pap. 4.99 (978-0-439-35200-0(2) , Scholastic Paperbacks) Scholastic, Inc.

Brown, Marc. Arthur & the Cootie-Catcher, Vol. 15. unabr. ed. 2004. (Arthur Chapter Bks.: Bk. 15). 60p. (J). (gr. 2-4). pap. 17.00 incl. audio (978-0-8072-0346-0(7) , Listening Library) Random Hse. Audio Publishing Group.

—Arthur & the Cootie-Catcher. 1999. (Arthur Chapter Bks.: Bk. 15). (gr. k-3). lib. bdg. 12.10 (978-0-613-14542-8(9)); (J). (gr. 3-6). 11.05 (978-0-606-17236-3(X)) Tandem Library Bks.

—Arthur & the Recess Rookie. 2001. (Arthur Good Sports Ser.: Bk. 3). (J). pap. 3.95 (978-0-316-12125-5(8)) Little, Brown Bks. for Young Readers.

—Arthur & the School Pet. 2003. (Arthur Ser.). (Illus.). 24p. (J). (gr. k-2). pap. 3.99 (978-0-375-81001-5(3)); lib. bdg. 11.99 (978-0-375-91001-2(8)) Random Hse. Children's Bks. (Random Hse. Bks. for Young Readers).

—Arthur & the School Pet. 2003. (Arthur Ser.). (ps-2). lib. bdg. 11.80 (978-0-613-57492-1(3)) Tandem Library Bks.

—Arthur's Adventures Four Book Set: Arthur's Computer Disaster, Arthur's TV Troubles, Arthur's Teacher Troubles, Arthur's New Puppy. 2002. pap. 23.80 (978-0-316-16961-5(7)) Little Brown & Co.

—Arthur's off to School. 2004. (Arthur's 8 x 8 Bks.). (Illus.). 24p. (J). (ps-1). pap. 3.99 (978-0-316-73378-6(4)) Little, Brown Bks. for Young Readers.

—Arthur's off to School. 2004. (Arthur's 8 x 8 Bks.). (ps-2). lib. bdg. 11.80 (978-0-613-71773-1(2)) Tandem Library Bks.

Bunting, Eve. My Special Day at Third Street School. Bloom, Suzanne, illus. 2004. 32p. (J). (gr. k-2). 15.95 (978-1-59078-075-6(2)) Boyds Mills Pr.

Burke, Morgan. Get It Started. 2005. (Party Room Ser.: No. 1). 272p. (YA). (gr. 11 up). pap. 5.99 (978-0-689-87225-9(9) , Simon Pulse) Simon & Schuster Children's Publishing.

Butcher, A. J. Chaos Rising. 2004. (Spy High Ser.: Vol. 2). (Illus.). 240p. (J). (gr. 5-8). pap. 6.99 (978-0-316-73765-4(8)) Little, Brown Bks. for Young Readers.

—Spy High Mission One. 2004. 224p. (J). (gr. 5-8). pap. 6.99 (978-0-316-73760-9(7)) Little, Brown Bks. for Young Readers.

Capucilli, Alyssa Satin. Biscuit Loves School. Schories, Pat, illus. 2003. 12p. (J). (ps-1). 9.99 (978-0-06-009454-6(0)) HarperCollins Pubs.

Carlson-Mineau, Anita L. Adventures in Yooperland Vol. 4: Golden School Days in War Years. Fudala, Linda, ed. Stillwagon, Mary R., illus. 2000. 125p. (YA). (gr. 7-12). pap. 16.00 (978-0-9662539-4-8(9)) Books By Anita.

Carlson, Nancy. Look Out Kindergarten, Here I Come! 2001. (Illus.). 32p. (J). pap. 6.99 (978-0-14-056838-7(7) , Puffin) Penguin Group (USA) Inc.

Clements, Andrew. Frindle. Selznick, Brian, illus. l.t. ed. 2000. (LRS Large Print Cornerstone Ser.). 116p. (YA). (gr. 4-10). lib. bdg. 24.95 (978-1-58118-062-6(4) , 23476) LRS.

—Frindle. Selznick, Brian, illus. 105p. (J). (gr. 3-5). pap. 4.50 (978-0-8072-1522-7(8) , Listening Library) Random Hse. Audio Publishing Group.

—Frindle. unabr. ed. 2004. (Middle Grade Cassette Librariestm Ser.). 105p. (J). (gr. 3-7). pap. 29.00 incl. audio (978-0-8072-7994-6(3) , S YA 961 SP, Listening Library) Random Hse. Audio Publishing Group.

—Frindle. Selznick, Brian, illus. 1998. 112p. (J). (gr. 3-7). pap. 5.99 (978-0-689-81876-9(9) , Aladdin) Simon & Schuster Children's Publishing.

—Frindle. Selznick, Brian, illus. 1998. (J). 11.64 (978-0-606-12939-8(1)) Tandem Library Bks.

Clements, Andrew & Avendano, Dolores. Class Clown. 2002. (Ready-for-Chapters Ser.: Vol. 4). (Illus.). 80p. (J). (gr. 2-5). 16.95 (978-0-689-83921-4(9)) Simon & Schuster Children's Publishing.

Coplans, Peta. Funny Fred. (Illus.). 32p. (J). 2002. pap. 8.99 (978-1-84270-057-0(X)); 2001. 18.00 (978-1-84270-004-4(9)) Andersen GBR. *Dist:* Independent Pubs. Group.

Couric, Katie. The Brand New Kid. ed. 2004. (Illus.). (J). (ps-3). spiral bd. (978-0-616-07225-7(2)); spiral bd. (978-0-616-07226-4(0)) Canadian National Institute for the Blind/Institut National Canadien pour les Aveugles.

Cozzolino, Ann Yards. The Girl's of St. Mary's. 2001. (Illus.). 116p. (YA). (gr. 6-12). pap. 8.95 (978-0-9603108-2-1(7)) Yards, A.

Dale, Jenny. Puppy Patrol: Teachers Pet. Reid, Mick, illus. l.t. ed. 1999. 184p. (J). pap. (978-0-7540-6086-4(1) , CLP 285) BBC Audio.

Dodd, Christina. Back to School Mom, 18 Copies. 2003. mass mkt. 128.88 (978-0-06-056267-0(6)) HarperCollins Pubs.

Enderle, Judith Ross & Gordon, Stephanie Jacob. School Stinks! 2001. (Illus.). 148p. (J). pap. (978-0-439-32852-4(7)) Scholastic, Inc.

Freeman, Martha. Fourth Grade Weirdo. 2001. 160p. (J). (gr. 4-7). 4.99 (978-0-440-41689-0(2) , Yearling) Random Hse. Children's Bks.

Frost, Helen. Spinning Through the Universe. 2004. (Illus.). 112p. (J). 16.00 (978-0-374-37159-3(8) , Farrar, Straus & Giroux (BYR)) Farrar, Straus & Giroux.

Gerber, Michael. Freshman. 2006. (Illus.). 352p. (gr. 9-17). 16.99 (978-0-7868-3850-9(7)) Hyperion Pr.

Goode, Caroline. Cupidity. 2005. (Romantic Comedies Ser.). 288p. (YA). mass mkt. 3.99 (978-1-4169-1147-0(2) , Simon Pulse) Simon & Schuster Children's Publishing.

Goode, Caroline & Saidens, Amy. Cupidity. 2004. (Romantic Comedies Ser.). 288p. (YA). pap. 6.99 (978-0-689-87228-0(3) , Simon Pulse) Simon & Schuster Children's Publishing.

Goodman, Joan Elizabeth. Bernard Goes to School. Catalano, Dominic, illus. 2003. 32p. (J). (ps up). 15.95 (978-1-56397-958-3(6)) Boyds Mills Pr.

Gowar, Mick. Day We Brightened up the School. (Illus.). 32p. (J). pap. 7.95 (978-0-14-038613-4(0)) Penguin Bks., Ltd. GBR. *Dist:* Trafalgar Square Publishing.

Gutman, Anne. Gaspard & Lisa's Ready-for-School Words. Hallensleben, Georg, illus. 2004. 22p. (J). (gr. k-ps). bds. 6.99 (978-0-375-82890-4(7) , Knopf Bks. for Young Readers) Random Hse. Children's Bks.

Gutman, Dan. Mrs. Roopy Is Loopy! Paillot, Jim, illus. 2004. (My Weird School Ser.: Bk. 3). 96p. (J). lib. bdg. 15.89 (978-0-06-050705-3(5)) HarperCollins Pubs.

Hall, Kirsten. First Day of School: All about Shapes & Sizes. 2004. (Beastieville Ser.). (J). (gr. k-1). pap. 3.95 (978-0-516-24654-3(2) , Children's Pr.) Scholastic Library Publishing.

Harper, Jessica. Lizzy's Ups & Downs: NOT an Ordinary School Day. Dupont, Lindsay Harper, illus. 2004. 32p. (J). (ps-3). 15.99 (978-0-06-052063-2(9)); lib. bdg. 16.89 (978-0-06-052064-9(7)) HarperCollins Pubs.

Harrison, Lisi. Revenge of the Wannabes. 2005. (Clique Ser.: No. 3). 304p. (YA). (gr. 5-8). pap. 9.99 (978-0-316-70133-4(5) , Poppy) Little, Brown Bks. for Young Readers.

Hawkins, Colin. Max & the School Dinners. (Illus.). 28p. (J). pap. 9.95 (978-0-14-055591-2(9)) Penguin Bks., Ltd. GBR. *Dist:* Trafalgar Square Publishing.

Hoban, Lillian. Arthur's Back to School Day. Hoban, Lillian, illus. 64th ed. 1998. (I Can Read Bks.). (Illus.). 48p. (J). (ps-3). pap. 3.99 (978-0-06-444245-9(4) , Harper Trophy) HarperCollins Pubs.

—Arthur's Back to School Day. Hoban, Lillian, illus. 1998. (Illus.). (J). (ps-ps). lib. bdg. 11.80 (978-0-613-11282-6(2)) Tandem Library Bks.

Howe, James. Pinky & Rex & the Spelling Bee. Sweet, Melissa, illus. 1999. (Pinky & Rex Ser.). 48p. (J). (gr. 1-4). reprint ed. pap. 3.99 (978-0-689-82880-5(2) , Aladdin) Simon & Schuster Children's Publishing.

—Pinky & Rex & the Spelling Bee. 1999. (Pinky & Rex Ser.). (J). (gr. 1-4). (978-0-606-17511-1(3)) Tandem Library Bks.

Hubbard, Michelle C. Sour Notes. 1999. (Diamond Head High Ser.: Vol. 3). 144p. (J). (gr. 5-8). 4.95 (978-1-57306-107-0(7)) Bess Pr., Inc.

Hurwitz, Johanna. Fourth-Grade Fuss. Hammond, Andy, illus. 2004. 144p. (J). 15.99 (978-0-06-052343-5(3)); lib. bdg. 16.89 (978-0-06-052344-2(1)) HarperCollins Pubs.

—Spring Break. Dugan, Karen M., illus. 2001. 128p. (J). (gr. 4-7). pap. 5.99 (978-0-380-73257-9(2) , Harper Trophy) HarperCollins Pubs.

—Starting School. 2001. (Illus.). 112p. pap. 3.99 (978-0-439-17215-8(2)) Scholastic, Inc.

Jiménez, Francisco. Breaking Through. 2002. 208p. (J). (gr. 7). pap. 6.95 (978-0-618-34248-8(6)) Houghton Mifflin Co. Trade & Reference Div.

Jocelyn, Marthe. Mable Riley: A Reliable Record of Humdrum, Peril, & Romance. 2004. (Illus.). 288p. (J). (gr. 5 up). 15.99 (978-0-7636-2120-9(X)) Candlewick Pr.

Kalar, Bonnie. Miss Lane's Class. Spreen, Kathe, illus. Date not set. 12p. (J). (ps-2). pap. (978-1-891619-38-0(1)) Corona Pr.

Kikuchi, Hideyuki. Azumanga Daioh Vol. 4: The Manga. 2004. (Illus.). 198p. (YA). pap. (978-1-4139-0048-4(8)) ADV Manga.

Kline, Suzy. Horrible Harry & the Locked Closet. 2004. (Illus.). 80p. (J). (gr. 2). 13.99 (978-0-670-05944-7(7) , Viking Juvenile) Penguin Group (USA) Inc.

—Song Lee & the "I Hate You" Notes. Remkiewicz, Frank, illus. 2001. (Song Lee Ser.). 64p. (J). (gr. 4-7). pap. 3.99 (978-0-14-130303-1(4) , Puffin) Penguin Group (USA) Inc.

Krulik, Nancy E. Rulin' the School. 2000. (Sabrina, the Teenage Witch: No. 12). (Illus.). 85p. (J). (gr. 2-5). per. (978-0-671-77335-9(6) , Simon & Schuster Children's Publishing) Simon & Schuster Children's Publishing.

—Rulin' the School. 2000. (gr. 3-6). lib. bdg. 11.80 (978-0-613-28047-1(4)) Tandem Library Bks.

—Who's Afraid of Fourth Grade? 2004. (Katie Kazoo, Switcheroo Ser.). (Illus.). 160p. (J). (gr. 2-6). mass mkt. 4.99 (978-0-448-43555-8(1) , Grosset & Dunlap) Penguin Group (USA) Inc.

Kwock, Laureen. Kimber's Cowboy. 1999. (Diamond Head High Ser.: Vol. 2). 144p. (J). (gr. 5-8). 4.95 (978-1-57306-106-3(9)) Bess Pr., Inc.

Maccarone, Grace. The Lunch Box Surprise. Lewin, Betsy, illus. 2004. 32p. (J). lib. bdg. 15.00 (978-1-59054-664-2(4)) Fitzgerald Bks.

Mazer, Anne. The Best Is Yet to Come. 2004. (Amazing Days of Abby Hayes Ser.: No. 1). (Illus.). 144p. (J). 5.99 (978-0-439-48282-0(8) , Scholastic Paperbacks) Scholastic, Inc.

—Knowledge Is Power. 2004. (Amazing Days of Abby Hayes Ser.: No. 2). (Illus.). 120p. (J). pap. 5.99 (978-0-439-63775-6(9) , Scholastic Paperbacks) Scholastic, Inc.

—The Pen Is Mightier Than the Sword. Gesue, Monica, illus. 2001. (Amazing Days of Abby Hayes Ser.: No. 6). 128p. (J). (gr. 4-7). pap. 4.99 (978-0-439-17882-2(7)) Scholastic, Inc.

—Some Things Never Change. 2004. (Amazing Days of Abby Hayes Ser.: No. 13). (Illus.). 101p. (J). 4.99 (978-0-439-48281-3(X) , Scholastic Paperbacks) Scholastic, Inc.

McGraw-Hill Staff & Schaffer, Frank. Ready for School. 2001. (Homework Helpers Activity Bks.). (Illus.). 56p. (J). (gr. k-1). pap., act. bk. ed. 2.99 (978-0-7682-0678-4(2) , FS109007, Schaffer, Frank) Schaffer, Frank Pubns.

McNaughton, Colin. Once upon an Ordinary School Day. Kitamura, Satoshi, illus. 2005. 32p. (J). 16.00 (978-0-374-35634-7(3) , Farrar, Straus & Giroux (BYR)) Farrar, Straus & Giroux.

Meddaugh, Susan. Hog-Eye. 1998. (Illus.). 32p. (J). (gr. k-3). 6.95 (978-0-395-93746-4(9) , Walter Lorraine) Houghton Mifflin Co. Trade & Reference Div.

—Hog-Eye. Meddaugh, Susan, illus. 1998. (Illus.). 32p. (J). (ps-ps). lib. bdg. 14.10 (978-0-613-10513-2(3)) Tandem Library Bks.

Miss Nelson Is Back; Miss Nelson Is Missing. 1999. (Miss Nelson Ser.). (J). (ps-3). 9.95 (978-1-56137-032-0(0)) Novel Units, Inc.

Moore, Ishbel. Dolina's Grad. 1998. 144p. (YA). (gr. 8-12). pap. 7.95 (978-1-896184-42-5(1)) Roussan Pubs., Inc./Roussan Editeur, Inc. CAN. *Dist:* Orca Bk. Pubs. USA.

Moran, Maggie A. The Magic in Me. Sasaki, Chie, illus. 2002. 28p. (J). 14.95 (978-1-931642-02-6(8)) New Voices Publishing Co.

Moree, Cody. Her Senior Year: A One-Act Play. 1998. (Illus.). 17p. (YA). (gr. 9-12). pap. 3.50 (978-0-88680-453-4(1) , C4531) Clark, I. E. Pubns.

Moss, Marissa. Amelia's Bully Survival Guide. Moss, Marissa, illus. 2006. (Amelia's Notebooks). (Illus.). 40p. (J). 9.95 (978-1-4169-0907-1(9)) Simon & Schuster Children's Publishing.

Moss, Miriam. Se Me Mueve un Diente. Mockler, Joanna, illus. 2002. (J). (CAT.). 38p. 16.95 (978-84-8488-021-9(4)); (SPA.). 32p. (gr. 1-2). 16.95 (978-84-8488-020-2(6) , RR30960) Serres, Ediciones, S. L. ESP. *Dist:* Lectorum Pubns., Inc.

Naylor, Phyllis Reynolds. A Spy among the Girls. 2002. 144p. (gr. 4-7). 5.50 (978-0-440-41390-5(7) , Yearling) Random Hse. Children's Bks.

Nelson, Vaunda Micheaux. Mayfield Crossing. 2002. 96p. (J). pap. 5.99 (978-0-698-11930-7(4) , Putnam Juvenile) Penguin Group (USA) Inc.

Neri, P. J. In Perfect Harmony. 1999. (Diamond Head High Ser.: Vol. 1). 144p. (gr. 5-8). 4.95 (978-1-57306-105-6(0)) Bess Pr., Inc.

Nickelodeon Staff. Hooray for School: Going to School With Nick. 2007. 4.99 (***978-1-4169-5401-9(5)*** , Simon Spotlight/Nickelodeon) Simon & Schuster Children's Publishing.

Parish, Herman. Amelia Bedelia Goes Back to School. Sweat, Lynn, illus. 2004. 20p. (J). pap. 6.99 (978-0-06-051873-8(1) , Harper Festival) HarperCollins Pubs.

Park, Barbara. Junie B., First Grader: Boss of Lunch. Brunkus, Denise, illus. 2003. (Junie B. Jones Ser.: No. 19). 96p. (J). (gr. k-3). lib. bdg. 11.99 (978-0-375-90294-9(5) , Golden Bks.) Random Hse. Children's Bks.

Pascal, Francine. True Blue. 2000. (Sweet Valley Jr. High Ser.: No. 18). (gr. 3-6). lib. bdg. 12.40 (978-0-613-27335-0(4)) Tandem Library Bks.

Passen, Lisa. The Abominable Snow Teacher. rev. ed. 2004. (Illus.). 32p. (J). 15.95 (978-0-8050-7379-9(5) , Holt, Henry & Co. Bks. For Young Readers) Holt, Henry & Co.

Pike, Christopher, pseud. The Graduation. 1998. (Final Friends Ser.: Vol. 3). (978-0-606-13383-8(6)) Tandem Library Bks.

Poulsen, David A. Wild Thing. 2002. (Lawrence High Yearbook Ser.). 66p. (YA). (gr. 7 up). pap. 3.99 (978-1-55305-009-4(6)) Cygnet Publishing Group, Inc./Coolreading.com CAN. *Dist:* Orca Bk. Pubs. USA.

Powell, Randy. Is Kissing a Girl Who Smokes Like Licking an Ashtray? 2003. 208p. (YA). pap. 5.95 (978-0-374-43628-5(2) , Sunburst) Farrar, Straus & Giroux.

Pulliam, Darlene. Toby: The Terrific Test Taking Toucan. Norcross, Harry, illus. 2001. 32p. (J). (gr. 2-4). pap. 13.95 (978-1-57543-092-8(4)) MAR*CO Products, Inc.

Pulver, Robin & Alley, R. W., illus. Mrs. Toggle's Class Picture Day. 2000. (J). pap. (978-0-590-11741-8(6)) Scholastic, Inc.

Rice, David L. Because Brian Hugged His Mother. 2004. (Sharing Nature with Children Book Ser.). (Illus.). 32p. (YA). (ps-3). 16.95 (978-1-883220-90-7(4)); pap. 7.95 (978-1-883220-89-1(0)) Dawn Pubns.

Rivers, Karen. The Healing Time of Hickeys. 2004. 304p. pap. 6.95 (978-1-55192-600-1(8)) Raincoast Bk. Distribution CAN. *Dist:* Perseus Distribution.

Roberts, Laura Peyton. Get a Life. 1998. (Clearwater Crossing Ser.: No. 1). (YA). (gr. 5-8). (978-0-606-13282-4(1)) Tandem Library Bks.

Robinet, Harriette Gillem. Walking to the Bus-Rider Blues. Colon, Raul, illus. 2002. 160p. (J). pap. 4.99 (978-0-689-83886-6(7) , Aladdin) Simon & Schuster Children's Publishing.

Rockwell, Anne F. Thanksgiving Day. Rockwell, Lizzy, illus. 2002. 40p. (J). (ps-k). pap. 6.99 (978-0-06-443789-9(2)) HarperCollins Pubs.

—Thanksgiving Day. Rockwell, Lizzy, illus. 2002. (J). (ps-ps). lib. bdg. 14.15 (978-0-613-65362-6(9)) Tandem Library Bks.

Rogers, Jacqueline. Tiptoe into Kindergarten. Rogers, Jacqueline, illus. 2003. (Illus.). 40p. (J). (ps-1). pap. 6.99 (978-0-439-48592-0(4) , Cartwheel Bks.) Scholastic, Inc.

—Tiptoe into Kindergarten. 2003. (gr. k-3). lib. bdg. 14.15 (978-0-613-64686-4(X)) Tandem Library Bks.

Rue, Nancy N. Here's Lily. 2003. pap. 2.99 (978-0-310-70590-1(8)) Zondervan.

Sachar, Louis. Sideways Stories from Wayside School. McCauley, Adam, illus. rev. ed. 1998. (Wayside School Ser.). 128p. (J). (gr. 5 up). pap. 5.99 (978-0-380-73148-0(7) , Harper Trophy) HarperCollins Pubs.

—There's a Boy in the Girls' Bathroom. 1999. (J). 9.95 (978-1-56137-410-6(5)) Novel Units, Inc.

Schwabacher, Martin. The Fishy Field Trip. Gangloff, Hope, illus. 2004. (Magic School Bus Ser.: Vol. 18). 112p. (J). pap. 4.99 (978-0-439-56052-8(7) , Scholastic Paperbacks) Scholastic, Inc.

Senderak, Carol Hunt. Mommy in My Pocket. Nakata, Hiroe, illus. 2006. 32p. (ps-1). 12.99 (978-0-7868-5596-4(7)) Hyperion Pr.

Sheldon, Dyan. My Perfect Life. 208p. (YA). (gr. 7). 2004. pap. 5.99 (978-0-7636-2436-1(5)); 2005. reprint ed. pap. 7.99 (978-0-7636-2828-4(X)) Candlewick Pr.

Shepard, Sara. Pretty Little Liars. 2006. (Pretty Little Liars Ser.: Bk. 1). 304p. (J). 16.99 (978-0-06-088730-8(3) , HarperTeen) HarperCollins Pubs.

Shreve, Susan Richards. The Flunking of Joshua T. Bates. 1999. (J). 9.95 (978-1-56137-612-4(4)) Novel Units, Inc.

Simon, Charnan. Show & Tell Sam. Bialke, Gary, illus. 1999. (Rookie Reader Skill Set Ser.). 32p. (J). (gr. k-2). pap. 4.95 (978-0-516-26413-4(3) , Children's Pr.) Scholastic Library Publishing.

Sitomer, Alan Lawrence. Hip-Hop High School. 2006. 384p. (gr. 7-17). 16.99 (978-0-7868-5515-5(0) , Jump at the Sun) Hyperion Bks. for Children.

Sperring, Mark. Wanda's First Day. Pope, Kate & Pope, Liz, illus. 2004. 32p. (J). pap. 15.95 (978-0-439-62773-3(7) , Chicken Hse., The) Scholastic, Inc.

Starting First Grade. (Tami & Moishy Ser.: Vol. 4). (J). bds. 6.95 (978-1-58330-968-1(3)) Feldheim Pubs.

Steck-Vaughn Staff. Lessons from Lester Level B: Early Reader. 2003. (Illus.). pap. (978-0-7398-8221-4(X)) Steck-Vaughn.

Stoeke, Janet Morgan. Minerva Louise at School. Stoeke, Janet Morgan, illus. 2nd ed. 2002. (Illus.). (978-0-525-46876-9(5) , Dutton Juvenile) Penguin Group (USA) Inc.

Stolarz, Laurie Faria. Red Is for Remembrance. 2005. (Blue Is for Nightmares Ser.: Vol. 4). 336p. pap. 8.95 (978-0-7387-0760-0(0)) Llewellyn Pubns.

Switzky, Lynn & Switzky, Alice. Lynn & Alice Going to School. Switzky, Rodger A., ed. 1999. (Illus.). 36p. (J). (ps-4). pap. 7.50 (978-0-9671080-1-0(4)) My Kids' Bk. Co.

Sykes, Julie. Tigrito Va a la Escuela. Warnes, Tim, illus. 2002. (SPA.). 12p. (J). 12.95 (978-84-488-0934-8(3) , BS7979) Beascoa, Ediciones S.A. ESP. *Dist:* Lectorum Pubns., Inc.

Thompson, Lauren. One Riddle, One Answer. Wingerter, Linda S., illus. 2001. (J). pap. (978-0-590-31337-7(1)) Scholastic, Inc.

Turcotte, Elise. La Legon d'Annette. 1999. (La Courte Echelle Premier Roman Ser.). (FRE., Illus.). 64p. (J). (gr. 2-5). pap. (978-2-89021-338-8(2)) Diffusion du livre Mirabel.

Watson, Pat. Slam! Durst, Shirley J., ed. 2000. (YA). 9.95 (978-1-58130-640-8(7)); 11.95 (978-1-58130-641-5(5)) Novel Units, Inc.

Weiss, Bobbi J. G. & Weiss, David Cody. Cootie Wars. LaPadula, Tom, illus. 2003. (Dexter's Laboratory Ser.: No. 1). 24p. (J). pap. 3.50 (978-0-439-44932-8(4)) Scholastic, Inc.

Wiley, Melissa. Down to the Bonny Glen. Graef, Renee, illus. 2001. (Little House Ser.). 336p. (J). (gr. 3-7). pap. 6.99 (978-0-06-440714-4(4) , Harper Trophy) HarperCollins Pubs.

Williams, Suzanne. The Leo School Trio No. 1: Here Comes Hilary. 2003. 112p. (J). (gr. 2-5). pap. 3.99 (978-0-439-32988-0(4)) Scholastic, Inc.

Wolff, Ashley, illus. Miss Bindergarten Stays Home from Kindergarten. 2002. (Miss Bindergarten Ser.). (J). 25.45 (978-0-7587-3144-9(2)) Book Wholesalers, Inc.

Wolff, Patricia Rae. Toll Bridge Troll. 2000. (978-0-606-18906-4(8)) Tandem Library Bks.

SCHOOL ENROLLMENT

see School Attendance

SCHOOL INSPECTION

see School Management And Organization

SCHOOL INTEGRATION

see Segregation in Education

SCHOOL JOURNALISM

see College and School Journalism

SCHOOL LIBRARIES

see also Children's Literature; Libraries

Morris, Ann. That's Our Librarian! 2003. (That's Our School Ser.). 32p. lib. bdg. 22.90 (978-0-7613-2400-3(3) , Millbrook Pr.) Lerner Publishing Group.

SCHOOL LIFE

see Students

SCHOOL MANAGEMENT AND ORGANIZATION

see also Teaching

Boraas, Tracey. School Principals. 1999. (Community Helpers Ser.). (Illus.). 92p. (J). (gr. 1-2). 18.60 (978-0-7368-0074-7(3) , Bridgestone Bks.) Capstone Pr., Inc.

Firestone, Mary. School Secretaries. 2003. (Community Helpers Ser.). (Illus.). 24p. (J). (gr. 1-2). lib. bdg. 19.93 (978-0-7368-1617-5(8) , Bridgestone Bks.) Capstone Pr., Inc.

Klingel, Cynthia Fitterer & Noyed, Robert B. School Cafeteria Workers. 2001. (School Helpers Ser.). (Illus.). 24p. (J). (gr. 1-4). lib. bdg. 19.20 (978-1-57103-327-7(0)) Rourke Publishing, LLC.

—School Custodians. 2001. (School Helpers Ser.). (Illus.). 24p. (J). (gr. 1-4). lib. bdg. 19.27 (978-1-57103-326-0(2)) Rourke Publishing, LLC.

Marx, Jeff. How to Win a High School Election: Advice & Ideas Collected from over 1,000 High School Seniors. 2003. 180p. (gr. 7-12). pap. 14.95 (978-0-9667824-0-0(2)) Marx, Jeff.

Mitchell, Melanie. Principals. (Pull Ahead Bks.). (J). 2005. (Illus.). 32p. lib. bdg. 22.60 (978-0-8225-1694-1(2)); 2004. pap. (978-0-8225-2535-6(6) , Lerner Pubns.) Lerner Publishing Group.

Morris, Ann. That's Our Principal! 2003. (That's Our School Ser.). 32p. lib. bdg. 22.90 (978-0-7613-2374-7(0) , Millbrook Pr.) Lerner Publishing Group.

Thomas, Joyce Carol. Linda Brown, You Are Not Alone: The Brown V. Board of Education Decision. James, Curtis E., illus. 2003. 144p. (gr. 3-7). 15.99 (978-0-7868-0821-2(7) , Disney Editions) Disney Pr.

SCHOOL MUSIC

see Music—Study and Teaching; School Songbooks

SCHOOL NEWSPAPERS

see College and School Journalism

SCHOOL NURSING

Morris, Ann. That's Our Nurse! Linenthal, Peter, illus. 2003. (That's Our School Ser.). 32p. lib. bdg. 22.90 (978-0-7613-2402-7(X) , Millbrook Pr.) Lerner Publishing Group.

Vogel, Elizabeth. Meet the School Nurse. 2002. (PowerKids Readers Ser.). (Illus.). 24p. (J). (gr. 1). lib. bdg. 16.00 (978-0-8239-6034-7(X) , PowerKids Pr.) Rosen Publishing Group, Inc., The.

SCHOOL ORGANIZATION

see School Management And Organization

SCHOOL PLAYGROUNDS

see Playgrounds

SCHOOL PLAYS

see Plays

SCHOOL SONGBOOKS

The Music Connection. 2002. (gr. 7 up). stu. ed. 52.50 (978-0-382-34351-3(4)); 2002. (gr. 8 up). stu. ed. 52.50 (978-0-382-34352-0(2)); 2000. (gr. 7 up). tchr. ed. 83.50 (978-0-382-34360-5(3)); 2000. (gr. 8 up). tchr. ed. 83.50 (978-0-382-34361-2(1)); 1999. (J). (gr. 3). stu. ed. 47.50 (978-0-382-34502-9(9)); 1999. (J). (gr. 5). stu. ed. 50.50 (978-0-382-34504-3(5)); 1999. (J). (gr. 6). stu. ed. 50.50 (978-0-382-34505-0(3)) Silver, Burdett & Ginn, Inc.

Whittaker, William G. Class-Singing. 2001. 136p. (YA). reprint ed. 88.00 (978-0-7222-6099-9(7)) Library Reprints, Inc.

SCHOOL SPORTS

see also Coaching (Athletics)

Gould, Marilyn. Playground Sports: A Book of Ball Games. rev. ed. 1999. (Illus.). 64p. (J). (gr. 2 up). pap. 10.95 (978-0-9632305-2-2(2)) Allied Crafts Pr.

Shivers, Joseph & Shivers, Paul. Harriers: The Making of A Championship Cross Country Team. 2006. 180p. (J). pap. 5.95 (978-1-932802-95-5(9) , Holy Macro! Bks.) MrExcel.com Publishing.

SCHOOL TEACHING

see Teaching

SCHOOLS

see also Boarding Schools; Education; Kindergarten; Public Schools; Universities and Colleges

Adamson, Heather. School in Many Cultures. 2008. (J). ***978-1-4296-0021-7(7))** Capstone Pr., Inc.

Ajmera, Maya. Back to School. 2001. (978-0-606-22636-3(2)); lib. bdg. 15.25 (978-0-613-45461-2(8)) Tandem Library Bks.

Ajmera, Maya & Ivanko, John D. Back to School. 2004. (It's a Kid's World Ser.). (Illus.). 32p. (J). (ps-2). 15.95 (978-1-57091-383-9(8)) Charlesbridge Publishing, Inc.

Ajmera, Maya, et al. Back to School. 2004. (It's a Kid's World Ser.). (Illus.). 32p. (J). (ps-2). pap. 6.95 (978-1-57091-384-6(6)) Charlesbridge Publishing, Inc.

Ambassador-Student (Russian) Vol. 6, Bk. 1: Russian Sunday School, 2001. Orig. Title: El Embajador. Alumno. (RUS.). (YA). stu. ed. (978-0-7361-0202-5(7)) Life Pubs. International.

Ancona, George. Mi Escuela: My School. 2004. (Somos Latino (We Are Latinos) Ser.). 20.00 (978-0-516-23686-5(5) , Watts, Franklin) Scholastic Library Publishing.

Anderson, Sheila. School. 2008. (J). pap. ***(978-0-8225-8838-2(2))** Lerner Publishing Group.

Bauld, Jane Scoggins. Helpers in Our School, 4 bks. Saunders-Smith, Gail, ed. Incl. We Need Custodians. lib. bdg. 15.93 (978-0-7368-0530-8(3)); We Need Librarians. lib. bdg. 15.93 (978-0-7368-0531-5(1)); We Need Principals. lib. bdg. 15.93 (978-0-7368-0532-2(X)); We Need Teachers. lib. bdg. 15.93 (978-0-7368-0533-9(8)); 24p. (J). (gr. k-1). (Illus.). 2000. Set lib. bdg. 63.72 (978-0-7368-0560-5(5) , Pebble Bks.) Capstone Pr., Inc.

Berger, Samantha & Chanko, Pamela. School. 1999. (Social Studies Emergent Readers). (J). 2.50 (978-0-439-04553-7(3)) Scholastic, Inc.

—School. 1999. (ps-2). lib. bdg. 10.10 (978-0-613-22336-2(5)) Tandem Library Bks.

Blackburn, Lynn B. The Class in Room Forty-Four: When a Classmate Dies. Johnson, Joy, ed. Boldt, Ron, illus. rev. ed. 1999. 24p. (J). (gr. 1-6). pap. 6.95 (978-1-56123-025-9(1)) Centering Corp.

Boothroyd, Jennifer. Schools. 2006. (First Step Nonfiction Ser.). (Illus.). 8p. (J). pap. (978-0-8225-5729-6(0) , Lerner Pubns.) Lerner Publishing Group.

Brent, Lynnette R. At School: Long Ago & Today. 2003. (Times Change Ser.). (Illus.). 32p. (J). lib. bdg. 24.22 (978-1-4034-4533-9(8)) Heinemann Library.

Bruce, Lisa. Sizes at School. 2003. (Raintree Sprouts Ser.). (Illus.). 24p. (J). pap. 5.50 (978-1-4109-0659-5(0)); lib. bdg. 18.56 (978-1-4109-0633-5(7)) Raintree.

—Sizes at School. 2003. (ps-2). lib. bdg. 13.55 (978-0-613-78260-9(7)) Tandem Library Bks.

Cassel, Katrina L. The Junior High Survival Manual. 1998. 128p. (YA). (gr. 8-12). 7.99 (978-0-570-05062-9(6)) Concordia Publishing Hse.

Chambers, Catherine E. School Days Around the World. 2007. (Dk Readers Ser.). (Illus.). 48p. (J). 14.99 (978-0-7566-2549-8(1)); pap. 3.99 (978-0-7566-2548-1(3)) Dorling Kindersley Publishing, Inc.

Color All About: A Giant Coloring Book about Fun Things to do at School: Back to School. 2004. (Illus.). 36p. (J). (978-1-59949-005-2(6)) Food Marketing Consultants, Inc.

Cookson, Paul. Crazy Classrooms & Secret Staffrooms. Baines, Nigel, illus. 2001. 96p. (J). pap. 8.99 (978-0-7459-4590-3(2) , Lion) Lion Hudson plc GBR. *Dist:* Independent Pubs. Group.

Cruz, Barbara C. School Dress Codes: A Pro/Con Issue. 2001. (Hot Pro/Con Issues Ser.). (Illus.). 64p. (J). (gr. 6-12). lib. bdg. 27.93 (978-0-7660-1465-7(7)) Enslow Pubs., Inc.

—Separate Sexes, Separate Schools: A Pro/Con Issue. 2000. (Hot Pro/Con Issues Ser.). (Illus.). 64p. (YA). (gr. 6-12). lib. bdg. 27.93 (978-0-7660-1366-7(9)) Enslow Pubs., Inc.

Dahl, Michael. Teacher Says: A Book of Teacher Jokes. Haugen, Ryan, illus. 2004. (Read-It! Joke Books). 24p. (C). (gr. k-3). 18.60 (978-1-4048-0301-5(7)) Picture Window Bks.

Dean, Theresa M. & Lucadamo, Rhonda. School Memories. 2002. (Pocket Full of Memories Collection). (Illus.). 24p. (ps-12). spiral bd. 14.95 (978-1-59093-010-6(X) , Eager Minds Pr.) Warehousing & Fulfillment Specialists, LLC (WFS, LLC).

DeGezelle, Terri. Manners in the Classroom. 2004. (First Facts Ser.). (Illus.). 24p. (J). (gr. k-2). lib. bdg. 21.26 (978-0-7368-2646-4(7) , First Facts) Capstone Pr., Inc.

—School Crossing Guards. 2001. (Community Helpers Ser.). (Illus.). 24p. (J). (gr. 1-2). lib. bdg. 18.60 (978-0-7368-0959-7(7) , Bridgestone Bks.) Capstone Pr., Inc.

DK Publishing Staff & UNICEF Staff. A School Like Mine: A Unique Celebration of Schools Around the World. 2007. 80p. (J). (gr. 1-4). 19.99 (978-0-7566-2913-7(6)) Dorling Kindersley Publishing, Inc.

Doudna, Kelly. School Around the World. 2004. (Around the World Ser.). (Illus.). 23p. (J). (ps-3). lib. bdg. 19.93 (978-1-59197-569-4(7)) ABDO Publishing Co.

Douglas, Vincent & School Specialty Publishing Staff. School Skills. 2004. (My Little Heavenly Helpers Ser.). (Illus.). 64p. (J). (ps-k). pap. 3.99 (978-0-7696-3660-3(8) , Brighter Child) School Specialty Publishing.

Easterling, Lisa. Schools. 2007. (J). pap. ***(978-1-4034-9409-2(6));** (Illus.). 24p. ***(978-1-4034-9400-9(2))** Heinemann Library.

Emberley, Rebecca. My School/Mi Escuela. 2005. (SPA., Illus.). 10p. (J). (ps-ps). bds. 6.99 (978-0-316-00050-5(7)) Little Brown & Co.

Emmer, Rae. Drama Club. 2002. (Reading Power Ser.). (Illus.). 24p. (J). (gr. 1). lib. bdg. 17.25 (978-0-8239-5968-6(6) , PowerKids Pr.) Rosen Publishing Group, Inc., The.

Erlbach, Arlene. The Middle School Survival Guide: How to Survive from the Day Elementary School Ends until the Second High School Begins. Flook, Helen, illus. 2003. 160p. (J). 16.95 (978-0-8027-8852-8(1)); pap. 8.95 (978-0-8027-7657-0(4)) Walker & Co.

Faircloth, Harry W. My First Day at School. Anderson, Billie Ann, illus. 1999. 24p. (J). pap. 12.95 (978-0-9668650-3-5(0)) Maximilian Pr. Pubs.

Feldman, Ruth Tenzer. Don't Whistle in School: The History of America's Public Schools. 2005. (People's History Ser.). (Illus.). 96p. (gr. 6-12). lib. bdg. 26.60 (978-0-8225-1745-0(0)) Lerner Publishing Group.

Godon, Ingrid. El Gran Libro de la Escuela. 2001. (SPA.). 32p. (J). 12.76 (978-84-261-2966-6(8)) Juventud, Editorial ESP. *Dist:* Lectorum Pubns., Inc.

Grapes, Bryan J. Violence. 2001. (Teen Decisions Ser.). (Illus.). 142p. (YA). (gr. 10 up). lib. bdg. 36.20 (978-0-7377-0574-4(4) , Greenhaven Pr., Inc.) Thomson Gale.

Graves, Kerry A. Going to School in Pioneer Times. 2001. (Blue Earth Books). (Illus.). 32p. (J). (gr. 3-4). lib. bdg. 22.60 (978-0-7368-0804-0(3) , Bridgestone Bks.) Capstone Pr., Inc.

Group/McGraw-Hill, Wright. My School, Your School: Level E, 6 vols. (Take Twostm Ser.). 16p. 29.95 (978-0-322-08948-8(4)) Wright Group, The.

Hall, Margaret. Schools. (Around the World Ser.). 32p. pap. 6.95 (978-1-4034-4006-8(9)) Heinemann Library.

Hall, Margaret C. Schools. 2002. (Around the World Ser.). (Illus.). 32p. (J). (gr. k-2). lib. bdg. 22.79 (978-1-58810-477-9(X)) Heinemann Library.

Hallinan, P. K. My First Day of School. 2002. 24p. (J). 7.95 (978-0-8249-5304-1(5) , Ideals) Ideals Pubns.

Harcourt School Publishers Staff. All Kinds of Schools. 3rd ed. 2002. (Horizons Ser.). (Illus.). (J). pap. 3.70 (978-0-15-333140-4(2)) Harcourt Schl. Pubs.

—School in the 50s On Level. 3rd ed. 2002. (Trophies Reading Program Ser.). (Illus.). pap. 5.10 (978-0-15-323365-4(6)) Harcourt Schl. Pubs.

—School Long Ago & Today. 3rd ed. 2002. (Horizons Ser.). (Illus.). (J). pap. 3.70 (978-0-15-333098-8(8)) Harcourt Schl. Pubs.

—We Like School: Independent Reader. 3rd ed. 2002. (Trophies Reading Program Ser.). (Illus.). (J). pap. 2.90 (978-0-15-325469-7(6)) Harcourt Schl. Pubs.

Hayward, Linda & Dorling Kindersley Publishing Staff. Jobs People Do: A Day in the Life of a Teacher. 2001. (Readers Ser.). (Illus.). 32p. (J). (ps-3). 14.99 (978-0-7894-7368-4(2)); pap. 3.99 (978-0-7894-7367-7(4)) Dorling Kindersley Publishing, Inc.

Helpers in Our School Set. (gr. k-2). 114.95 (978-0-7368-9062-5(9)) Red Brick Learning.

Henningfeld, Diane Andrews. Charter Schools. 2007. (At Issue Ser.). (Illus.). 128p. (gr. 10-12). 29.95 ***(978-0-7377-3914-5(2));** pap. 21.20 ***(978-0-7377-3915-2(0))** Thomson Gale. (Greenhaven Pr., Inc.).

Hill, Lee Sullivan. Schools Help Us Learn. 1998. (Building Block Bks.). (Illus.). 32p. (J). (gr. k-3). lib. bdg. (978-1-57505-092-8(7) , Carolrhoda Bks.) Lerner Publishing Group.

Hill, Mary. Signs at School. 2003. (Signs in My World Ser.). (Illus.). 24p. (J). 18.00 (978-0-516-24274-3(1)); pap. 4.95 (978-0-516-24366-5(7)) Scholastic Library Publishing. (Children's Pr.).

—Signs at School. 2003. (gr. k-3). lib. bdg. 12.95 (978-0-613-59719-7(2)) Tandem Library Bks.

Hoena, B. A. Weather ABC: An Alphabet Book. 2005. (A+ Alphabet Books). (Illus.). 32p. (J). 22.60 (978-0-7368-3666-1(7)); 22.60 (978-0-7368-3667-8(5)) Capstone Pr., Inc.

Hughes, Monica. First Day at School. 2003. (Raintree Sprouts Ser.). (Illus.). 24p. (J). pap. 5.50 (978-1-4109-0669-4(8)) Raintree.

—First Day at School. 2003. (ps-2). lib. bdg. 13.55 (978-0-613-78205-0(4)) Tandem Library Bks.

—My First Day at School. 2003. (Raintree Sprouts Ser.). (Illus.). 24p. (J). lib. bdg. 18.56 (978-1-4109-0643-4(4)) Raintree.

In School: Kindergarten Newcomer Books. (On Our Way to English Ser.). (gr. k up). 23.50 (978-0-7578-7195-5(X)) Rigby Education.

The Inside Scoop on American Graduate & Professional Schools. 2004. (C). pap. 4.95 net. (978-1-884169-33-5(3)) International Educational Improvement Ctr. Pr.

Jack's Pack: KinderReaders Individual Title Six-Packs. (Kinderstarters Ser.). 8p. (ps-1). 21.00 (978-0-7635-8660-7(9)) Rigby Education.

Jones, Jeffrey. School Violence. 2001. (Overview Ser.). (Illus.). 112p. (J). (gr. 6-9). lib. bdg. 29.95 (978-1-56006-710-8(1) , LML00902-178062, Lucent Bks.) Thomson Gale.

Kalman, Bobbie. School from A to Z. 1999. (AlphaBasiCs Ser.). (Illus.). 32p. (J). (gr. 1-2). lib. bdg. (978-0-86505-388-5(X)) Crabtree Publishing Co.

—School from A to Z. 1999. (gr. 3-6). lib. bdg. 16.40 (978-0-613-19531-7(0)) Tandem Library Bks.

Keller, Carolyn & Seaman, Jim. Allegheny College College Prowler off the Record. 2005. (College Prowler off the Record Guides: Vol. 1). 160p. (YA). (gr. 12 up). pap., stu. ed. 14.95 (978-1-59658-000-8(3)) College Prowler, Inc.

Kent, Susan. Learning How to Stay Safe at School. 2001. (Violence Prevention Library). (Illus.). 24p. (J). (gr. 3). lib. bdg. 18.75 (978-0-8239-5616-6(4) , PowerKids Pr.) Rosen Publishing Group, Inc., The.

Kreiner, Anna. Everything You Need to Know about School Violence. rev. ed. 2000. (Need to Know Library). (Illus.). 64p. (YA). (gr. 4-6). lib. bdg. 25.25 (978-0-8239-3304-4(0) , NTSCVI) Rosen Publishing Group, Inc., The.

A la Escuela: Individual Title Six-Packs. (Chiquilibros Ser.). (SPA.). (gr. k-1). 23.00 (978-0-7635-8594-5(7)) Rigby Education.

Layne, Deborah Dover & Layne, Stephen L. T Is for Teachers: A School Alphabet. rev. ed. 2005. 52p. 14.95 ***(978-1-58536-266-0(2))** Sleeping Bear Pr.

LeapFrog Staff, compiled by. School: (Blue Book) 2002. (J). (ps-2). 19.95 (978-1-58605-180-8(6)) LeapFrog Enterprises, Inc.

—School: (Green Book) 2002. (J). (ps-2). 19.95 (978-1-58605-178-5(4)) LeapFrog Enterprises, Inc.

—School: (Orange Book) 2002. (J). (ps-2). 19.95 (978-1-58605-179-2(2)) LeapFrog Enterprises, Inc.

—School: (Purple Book) 2002. (J). (ps-2). 19.95 (978-1-58605-177-8(6)) LeapFrog Enterprises, Inc.

—School Days. 2002. (J). (ps-1). 14.95 (978-1-58605-753-4(7)) LeapFrog Enterprises, Inc.

LeBlanc, Terry. Learning to Recycle with Terry the Trashman. 2004. (J). pap. (978-0-9755913-0-7(4)) LeBlanc, Terry Leonard.

Life Publishers, tr. from SPA. Explorer-Student Vol. 2 Bk. 2: Russian Sunday School, 2001. Orig. Title: El Explorador. Alumno. (RUS.). (YA). pupil's gde. ed. (978-0-7361-0033-5(4)) Life Pubs. International.

Macken, JoAnn Early. Crossing Guard/El Guardia de Cruce. Coffey, Colleen & Carrillo, Consuelo, trs. 2003. (Weekly Reader Early Learning Library). (ENG & SPA., Illus.). 24p. (J). (ps up). lib. bdg. 19.33 (978-0-8368-3671-4(5) , Weekly Reader Early Learning Library) Stevens, Gareth Inc.

Macken, JoAnn Early & Gorman, Jacqueline Laks. Crossing Guard/El Guardia de Cruce. Coffey, Colleen & Carrillo, Consuelo, trs. Andersen, Gregg, photos by. 2003. (Weekly Reader Early Learning Library). (SPA & ENG., Illus.). 24p. (J). (ps up). pap. 5.95 (978-0-8368-3685-1(5) , Weekly Reader Early Learning Library) Stevens, Gareth Inc.

—People in My Community, Set II, 6 bks. Incl. Crossing Guard. Andersen, Gregg, photos by. pap. 7.93 (978-0-8368-3596-0(4)); Mail Carrier. Andersen, Gregg, photos by. pap. 7.93 (978-0-8368-3597-7(2)); Nurse. Andersen, Gregg, photos by. pap. 7.93 (978-0-8368-3598-4(0)); Sanitation Worker. pap. 7.93 (978-0-8368-3599-1(9)); Teacher. Andersen, Gregg, photos by. pap. 7.93 (978-0-8368-3600-4(6)); Veterinarian. Andersen, Gregg, photos by. pap. 7.93 (978-0-8368-3601-1(4)); 24p. (J). (ps up). (Illus.). 2003. pap. (978-0-8368-3595-3(6) , Weekly Reader Early Learning Library) Stevens, Gareth Inc.

—People in My Community/La Gente de Mi Comunidad: Set II, 6 bks. Coffey, Colleen & Carrillo, Consuelo, trs. Andersen, Gregg, photos by. Incl. Crossing Guard/El Guardia de Cruce. pap. 5.95 (978-0-8368-3685-1(5) , Weekly Reader Early Learning Library); Mail Carrier/El Cartero. pap. 5.95 (978-0-8368-3686-8(3) , Weekly Reader Early Learning Library); Nurse/El Enfermero. pap. (978-0-8368-3687-5(1) , Weekly Reader Early Learning Library); Sanitation Worker/El Recogedor de Basura. pap. 5.95 (978-0-8368-3688-2(X) , Weekly Reader Early Learning Library); Teacher/El Maestro. pap. 5.95 (978-0-8368-3689-9(8) , Weekly Reader Early Learning Library); Veterinarian/El Veterinario. pap. (978-0-8368-3690-5(1)); 24p. (J). (ps up). (SPA & ENG., Illus.). 2003. pap. (978-0-8368-3684-4(7) , Weekly Reader Early Learning Library) Stevens, Gareth Inc.

Manton, Charlotte. The Community of Lincoln. Stanley, Karen & Bornemeier, Pam, eds. Schellpeper, Kathy, photos by. (Illus.). 116p. (J). (gr. 3-6). pap. 10.50 (978-0-9671920-0-0(5)) Lincoln Public Schls.

Mattern, Joanne. After School. 2006. (Illus.). 24p. (J). pap. (978-0-8368-6790-9(4)); lib. bdg. (978-0-8368-6783-1(1)) Stevens, Gareth Inc.

—Eating Lunch at School. 2006. 24p. (J). pap. (978-0-8368-6791-6(2)); lib. bdg. (978-0-8368-6784-8(X)) Stevens, Gareth Inc.

—Getting Ready for School. 2006. (Illus.). 24p. (J). pap. (978-0-8368-6792-3(0)); lib. bdg. (978-0-8368-6785-5(8)) Stevens, Gareth Inc.

—Going to School. 2006. (Illus.). 24p. (J). pap. (978-0-8368-6793-0(9)); lib. bdg. (978-0-8368-6786-2(6)) Stevens, Gareth Inc.

—In the Classroom. 2006. (Illus.). 24p. (J). pap. (978-0-8368-6794-7(7)); lib. bdg. (978-0-8368-6787-9(4)) Stevens, Gareth Inc.

—In the Classroom: En el Salon de Clases/Joanne Mattern. 2006. (ENG & SPA., Illus.). 24p. (J). pap. (978-0-8368-7368-9(8)); lib. bdg. (978-0-8368-7361-0(0)) Stevens, Gareth Inc. (Weekly Reader Early Learning Library).

—Playing at School. 2006. (Illus.). 24p. (J). pap. (978-0-8368-6795-4(5)); lib. bdg. (978-0-8368-6788-6(2)) Stevens, Gareth Inc.

—Safety at School. 1999. (Safety First Ser.). (Illus.). 24p. (J). (gr. k-6). lib. bdg. 21.35 (978-1-57765-070-6(0) , Checkerboard Library) ABDO Publishing Co.

Mattern, Joanne. Staying Safe at School. 2006. (J). (ENG & SPA.). pap. ***(978-0-8368-8064-9(1));** (ENG & SPA.). lib. bdg. ***(978-0-8368-8057-1(9));** (Illus.). 24p. pap. ***(978-0-8368-7799-1(3));** (Illus.). 24p. lib. bdg. ***(978-0-8368-7792-2(6))** Stevens, Gareth Inc. (Weekly Reader Early Learning Library).

McGowan, Keith. Sexual Harassment. 1998. (Overview Ser.). (Illus.). 112p. (YA). (gr. 6-9). lib. bdg. 29.95 (978-1-56006-507-4(9) , LML00902-177867, Lucent Bks.) Thomson Gale.

Menhard, Francha Roffe. School Violence: Deadly Lessons. 2000. (Teen Issues Ser.). (Illus.). 64p. (YA). (gr. 6-12). lib. bdg. 22.60 (978-0-7660-1358-2(8)) Enslow Pubs., Inc.

Milla Gorilla Goes to School. 2004. pap. 1.50 (978-0-87162-934-0(8)) Warner Pr. Pubs.

Miller, Jake. Who's Who in a School Community. 2005. (Communities at Work Ser.). (Illus.). 24p. (J). 19.95 (978-1-4042-2788-0(1)); pap. (978-1-4042-5030-7(1)) Rosen Publishing Group, Inc., The. (PowerKids Pr.).

Mitchell. Theme Pack: School. 2002. (Pair-It Bks.). (Illus.). (J). pap. (978-0-7398-6375-6(4)) Steck-Vaughn.

Modoc Press Editors. Directory of Distance Learning Opportunities: K-12. 2003. 432p. (gr. k-12). 81.95 (978-1-57356-515-8(6) , OXDLK-12) Greenwood Publishing Group, Inc.

Moss, Marissa. Amelia's School Survival Guide. Moss, Marissa, illus. 2006. (Amelia's Notebooks). (Illus.). 64p. (J). (gr. 2-5). 9.95 (978-1-4169-0915-6(X) , Simon & Schuster Children's Publishing) Simon & Schuster Children's Publishing.

Mundy, Michaelene. Keeping School Cool: A Kid's Guide to Handling School Problems. Mundy, Michaelene & Alley, Robert, illus. 2002. 32p. (J). per. 6.95 (978-0-87029-359-7(1)) Abbey Pr.

Munoz-Furlong, Anne. A Special Day at School. 1999. (J). (gr. k-6). pap. (978-1-882541-08-9(1)) Food Allergy & Anaphylaxis Network.

Murkoff, Heidi. What to Expect at Preschool. Rader, Laura, illus. 2003. (What to Expect Kids Ser.). 24p. (J). (ps-k). pap. 3.99 (978-0-06-052920-8(2)) HarperCollins Pubs.

My First Day of School. 2002. 24p. (J). 5.95 (978-0-8249-5305-8(3)) Ideals Pubns.

Myers, Dean. School. 2006. (978-0-06-052311-4(5)); lib. bdg. (978-0-06-052312-1(3)) HarperCollins Canada, Ltd.

Nelson, Robin. School. 2003. (First Step Nonfiction Ser.). (Illus.). 24p. (J). (gr. k-2). lib. bdg. 18.60 (978-0-8225-4640-5(X)) Lerner Publishing Group.

Nuts and Bolts Girls Staff, et al. Middle School: How to Deal. 2005. (Illus.). 96p. (J). 15.50 (978-0-8118-4845-9(0)) Chronicle Bks. LLC.

Orr, Tamra. Violence in Our Schools: Halls of Hope, Halls of Fear. 2003. (Single Title: Social Studies Ser.). (Illus.). 192p. (YA). 30.50 (978-0-531-12268-6(9) , Watts, Franklin) Scholastic Library Publishing.

Osborne, Judy. My Teacher Said Goodbye Today: Planning for the End of the School Year. Osborne, John, photos by. 2nd ed. 1999. (Illus.). 42p. (J). (ps-2). spiral bd., tchr.'s training gde. ed. 9.95 (978-0-9618303-7-3(9)) Emijo Pubns.

Parker, John. Cool School: Individual Title Six-Packs. Williamson, Fraser, illus. (Sails Literacy Ser.). 16p. (gr. 2-3). 27.00 (978-0-7578-0697-1(X)) Rigby Education.

Parramon, José María. Mi Calle. Borday, Irene, illus. (Coleccion Estoy En...).Tr. of My Street. (SPA.). 32p. (J). (gr. k-3). 6.36 (978-84-342-1003-5(7)) Parramon Ediciones S.A. ESP. *Dist:* Lectorum Pubns., Inc.

—Mi Casa. Borday, Irene, illus. (Coleccion Estoy En...).Tr. of My House. (SPA.). 32p. (J). (gr. k-3). 6.36 (978-84-342-1002-8(9)) Parramon Ediciones S.A. ESP. *Dist:* Lectorum Pubns., Inc.

—Mi Jardin. Borday, Irene, illus. (Coleccion Estoy En...).Tr. of My Garden. (SPA.). 32p. (J). (gr. k-3). 6.36 (978-84-342-1005-9(3)) Parramon Ediciones S.A. ESP. *Dist:* Lectorum Pubns., Inc.

Parramon, José María & Bordoy, Irene. Mi Calle.Tr. of My Street. (SPA., Illus.). (J). (ps-1). 6.95 (978-958-04-1277-9(4)) Norma S.A. COL. *Dist:* Distribuidora Norma, Inc.

Play with me Sesame I Like School. 2007. (J). pap. 2.95 (*978-1-59545-143-9(9)) Learning Horizons, Inc.

Pringle, Laurence P. One Room School. 2003. (Illus.). 32p. (J). (gr. 2-4). 16.95 (978-1-56397-583-7(1)) Boyds Mills Pr.

Procter, Alice. At School: Telling Time by the Half Hour. 2007. (I Can Tell Time Ser.). (Illus.). 24p. (J). (gr. k-2). lib. bdg. 19.93 (*978-0-8368-8390-9(X)) Stevens, Gareth Inc.

Proctor, Alice. At School: Telling Time by the Half Hour. 2007. (Illus.). pap. (*978-0-8368-8395-4(0)) Stevens, Gareth Inc.

Raatma, Lucia. School Safety. 2003. (Living Well). (Illus.). 32p. (J). (gr. 2-6). 27.07 (978-1-59296-089-7(8)) Child's World, Inc.

Radabaugh, Melinda Beth. Going to School. 2003. (First Time Ser.). (Illus.). 24p. (ps-1). (J). lib. bdg. 18.50 (978-1-4034-0227-1(2)); pap. 5.25 (978-1-4034-0466-4(6)) Heinemann Library.

—Voy a la escuela. 24p. pap. 5.25 (978-1-4034-0473-2(9)) Heinemann Library.

Raymer, Dottie. School Smarts Projects. McGuinness, Tracy & McGuinness, Tracey, illus. 2005. (American Girl Library). 96p. (J). (ps-7). pap. 8.95 (978-1-59369-005-2(3) , American Girl) American Girl Publishing, Inc.

Richardson, Adele. Manners in the School Cafeteria. 2006. (First Facts Ser.). (J). (978-0-7368-4296-9(9)) Capstone Pr., Inc.

Rivera, Sheila. School Safety. 2006. (First Step Nonfiction Ser.). (J). pap. (978-0-8225-6822-3(5)) Lerner Publishing Group.

Roop, Peter & Roop, Connie. A School Album. 1999. (Long Ago & Today Ser.). (Illus.). 24p. (J). (gr. 1-3). lib. bdg. 19.92 (978-1-57572-603-8(3)) Heinemann Library.

Rosenberg, Pam. Blecch! Icky, Sticky, Gross Stuff in Your School. 2007. (Icky, Sticky, Gross-Out Bks.). 24p. (J). (gr. 2-6). 22.79 (*978-1-59296-899-2(6)) Child's World, Inc.

Russack, Joy C. Those Wonderful Children. 2000. (Illus.). 32p. (J). pap. 8.00 (978-0-8059-4831-8(7)) Dorrance Publishing Co., Inc.

Sateren, Shelley Swanson. Going to School in Colonial America. 2001. (Blue Earth Books). (Illus.). 32p. (J). (gr. 3-4). lib. bdg. 22.60 (978-0-7368-0803-3(5) , Bridgestone Bks.) Capstone Pr., Inc.

Schaefer, Ted. Ready for School. 2007. (ENG & SPA.). (J). (978-1-59515-952-6(5)) Rourke Publishing, LLC.

Schiller, Melissa. 100th Day of School. 2003. (Rookie Read-About Holidays Ser.). (Illus.). 32p. (J). 20.50 (978-0-516-25856-0(7) , Children's Pr.) Scholastic Library Publishing.

School Matters. ldr.'s ed. 1998. (Cross Training Ser.: Vol. 4). 64p. (YA). (gr. 7-9). pap. 15.00 incl. VHS (978-1-57405-030-1(3)) CharismaLife Pubs.

School Signs: Flip Charts. (J). spiral bd. 15.95 (978-1-930820-35-7(6)) Garlic Pr.

School Specialty Publishing. Learn about Going to School. 2005. (Learn about Coloring Bks.). 32p. (J). (ps-3). pap. 1.99 (978-0-7696-4160-7(1) , Brighter Child) School Specialty Publishing.

Scraper, Katherine. Rules at School. 2006. (Early Explorers Ser.). (J). 30.00 (*978-1-4108-6030-9(2)) Benchmark Education Co.

Senge, Peter. Escuelas que Aprenden. (SPA.). (J). (978-958-04-6511-9(8)) Norma S.A. COL. *Dist:* Distribuidora Norma, Inc.

Sesame Street Hip, Hip, Hooray for School. 2007. (J). pap. 5.95 (*978-1-59545-160-6(9)) Learning Horizons, Inc.

Sharp, Anne Wallace. Separate but Equal: The Desegregation of America's Schools. 2006. (Lucent Library of Black History). 112p. (YA). (gr. 7 up). lib. bdg. 32.45 (978-1-59018-953-5(1) , Lucent Bks.) Thomson Gale.

The Smartest One in Class: Individual Title Six-Packs. (ps-2). 27.00 (978-0-7635-9474-9(1)) Rigby Education.

Snyder, Inez. Home Tools. 2002. (Welcome Bks.). (Illus.). 24p. (J). (ps-2). pap. 4.95 (978-0-516-24038-1(2) , Children's Pr.) Scholastic Library Publishing.

—School Tools. 2002. (Welcome Bks.). (Illus.). 24p. (J). (ps-2). pap. 4.95 (978-0-516-24039-8(0) , Children's Pr.) Scholastic Library Publishing.

Steele, Philip. Going to School. 2000. (Everyday History Ser.). (Illus.). (J). (978-0-606-20676-1(0)) Tandem Library Bks.

Stewart, Faith. Teens & Rural Education: Opportunities & Challenges. 2008. (Youth in Rural North America Ser.). (Illus.). (J). (978-1-4222-0015-5(9)) Mason Crest Pubs.

Thomas, Pat. Do I Have to Go to School? A First Look at Starting School. Harker, Lesley, illus. 2006. (First Look At... Ser.). 32p. (J). pap. 6.99 (978-0-7641-3216-2(4)) Barron's Educational Series, Inc.

Top That Publishing Staff, ed. My School Days Yearbook. 2005. (Illus.). 28p. (978-1-84510-657-7(1)) Top That! Publishing PLC.

Townsend, John. Scary Schools & Horrid Homework. 2006. (Illus.). 48p. (J). (978-1-4109-1871-0(8)) Steck-Vaughn.

Trumbauer, Lisa. At School. 2000. (Yellow Umbrella Books). (Illus.). 16p. (J). (gr. 1). lib. bdg. 14.60 (978-0-7368-0741-8(1) , Pebble Bks.) Capstone Pr., Inc.

Tym, Kate & Worms, Penny. School Survival. 2004. (Illus.). 48p. (J). 29.93 (978-1-4109-0577-2(2)) Harcourt Schl. Pubs.

Vogel, Elizabeth. My School, 6 bks. Incl. Meet My Teacher. lib. bdg. 16.00 (978-0-8239-6032-3(3)); Meet the Cafeteria Workers. lib. bdg. 16.00 (978-0-8239-6035-4(8)); Meet the Librarian. lib. bdg. 16.00 (978-0-8239-6031-6(5)); Meet the Principal. lib. bdg. 16.00 (978-0-8239-6033-0(1)); Meet the School Nurse. lib. bdg. 16.00 (978-0-8239-6034-7(X)); Meet the School Secretary. lib. bdg. 16.00 (978-0-8239-6036-1(6)); 24p. (J). (gr. 1). 2002. (Illus.). Set lib. bdg. 88.50 (978-0-8239-7114-5(7) , PowerKids Pr.) Rosen Publishing Group, Inc., The.

Weber, Valerie & Jenkins, Gloria. School in Grandma's Day. 1999. (In Grandma's Day Ser.). (Illus.). 32p. (J). (ps-3). lib. bdg. 21.27 (978-1-57505-327-1(6) , Carolrhoda Bks.) Lerner Publishing Group.

Weekly Reader Early Learning Library (Firm) Staff, contrib. by. Things at School. 2006. (Things in My World Ser.). (Illus.). 16p. (J). pap. (978-0-8368-6815-9(3)); lib. bdg. (978-0-8368-6808-1(0)) Stevens, Gareth Inc.

—Things at School: Las Cosas de la Escuela. 2006. (Illus.). 16p. (J). pap. (978-0-8368-7227-9(4)); lib. bdg. (978-0-8368-7220-0(7)) Stevens, Gareth Inc. (Weekly Reader Early Learning Library).

Yates, Vicki. Life at School. 2007. (J). (*978-1-4034-9835-9(0)); pap. (*978-1-4034-9843-4(1)) Heinemann Library.

Zannos, Susan. Careers in Education. 2001. (Latinos at Work Ser.). (Illus.). 96p. (gr. 5-12). lib. bdg. 22.95 (978-1-58415-081-7(5)) Mitchell Lane Pubs., Inc.

Ziegler, Mark. School Kidders: A Book of School Jokes. Haberstroh, Anne, illus. 2005. (Read-It! Readers Ser.). 24p. (C). (gr. 1-3). 18.60 (978-1-4048-0964-2(3)) Picture Window Bks.

SCHOOLS—ADMINISTRATION

see School Management And Organization

SCHOOLS, COMMERCIAL

see Business Education

SCHOOLS—FICTION

see also Universities and Colleges—Fiction

A l'Ecole. 2000. (Collection des Mots pour Lire). (FRE.). 28p. (J). 15.95 (978-2-03-653000-3(1)) Librairie Larousse FRA. *Dist:* Distribooks, Inc.

Abbott, Tony. Firegirl. 2006. 160p. (J). (gr. 3-7). 15.99 (978-0-316-01171-6(1)) Little Brown & Co.

—Firegirl. 2007. 144p. (J). (gr. 3-7). 5.99 (*978-0-316-01170-9(3)) Little, Brown Bks. for Young Readers.

Abdel-Fattah, Randa. Does My Head Look Big in This? 2007. 368p. (J). (gr. 7 up). pap. 16.99 (*978-0-439-91947-0(9) , Orchard Bks.) Scholastic, Inc.

Abercrombie, Barbara. The Show-and-Tell Lion. Cravath, Lynne Avril, illus. 2006. 32p. (J). (ps-2). 16.95 (978-0-689-86408-7(6) , McElderry, Margaret K.) Simon & Schuster Children's Publishing.

The Abominable Snowman Doesn't Roast Marshmallows, 6 bks., Pack. 2005. 96p. (J). pap. 3.99 (978-0-439-86573-9(5)) Scholastic, Inc.

Abraham, Susan Gonzales. Cecilia's Year. 2004. (Latino Fiction for Young Adults Ser.). (Illus.). 160p. (J). (gr. 5 up). 16.95 (978-0-938317-87-6(3)) Cinco Puntos Pr.

Abraham, Susan Gonzales & Abraham, Denise Gonzales. Cecilia's Year. 2007. (Latino Fiction for Young Adults Ser.). 210p. (J). pap. 11.95 (978-1-933693-02-6(9)) Cinco Puntos Pr.

—Surprising Cecilia. 2005. (Latino Fiction for Young Adults Ser.). 216p. (YA). 16.95 (978-0-938317-96-8(2)) Cinco Puntos Pr.

Acquaire, M. T. Marty Boggs & the Curse of Kutkara's Tomb. 2006. 328p. (YA). 28.99 (978-1-59507-112-5(1) , ArcheBooks) ArcheBooks Publishing.

Adams, Sherred Willco. Five Little Friends. 2006. pap. 15.95 (*978-1-4304-4149-6(6)) Kessinger Publishing, LLC.

Adler, David A. Andy & Tamika. Hillenbrand, Will, illus. (Andy Russell Ser.). 144p. 2005. (J). pap. 4.95 (978-0-15-205446-5(4)); 1999. (J). (gr. 2-5). 14.00 (978-0-15-201735-4(6)) Harcourt Children's Bks. (Gulliver Bks.).

—Andy Russell, Not Wanted by the Police. Franson, Leanne, illus. (Andy Russell Ser.). 128p. 2005. (J). pap. 4.95 (978-0-15-216719-6(6)); 2001. (YA). (gr. 2-5). 15.00 (978-0-15-216474-4(X) , Gulliver Bks.) Harcourt Children's Bks.

—Andy Russell, Not Wanted by the Police. Franson, Leanne, illus. 2005. (Andy Russell Ser.). 118p. (J). (ps-k). per. 11.60 (978-0-606-33408-2(4)) Tandem Library Bks.

—Bones & the Cupcake Mystery. Newman, Barbara, illus. 2008. (Jeffrey Bones Mystery Ser.: No. 3). 32p. (J). (gr. 1-3). pap. 3.99 (*978-0-14-241147-6(7) , Puffin) Penguin Group (USA) Inc.

—Bones & the Cupcake Mystery. Newman, Barbara Johansen, illus. 2005. (Jeffrey Bones Mystery Ser.: No. 3). 32p. (J). (gr. k-3). 13.99 (978-0-670-05939-3(0) , Viking Juvenile) Penguin Group (USA) Inc.

—Bones & the Math Test Mystery. Newman, Barbara Johansen, illus. 2008. 32p. (J). (gr. k). 13.99 (*978-0-670-06262-1(6) , Viking Adult) Penguin Group (USA) Inc.

—Cam Jansen & the First Day of School Mystery, Vol. 22. Natti, Susanna, illus. 2002. (Cam Jansen Ser.: No. 22). 80p. (J). 13.99 (978-0-670-03575-5(0) , Viking Juvenile) Penguin Group (USA) Inc.

—Cam Jansen & the School Play Mystery. Natti, Susanna, illus. 2001. (Cam Jansen Ser.: No. 21). 64p. (J). (gr. 2-6). 14.99 (978-0-670-89280-8(7) , Viking Juvenile) Penguin Group (USA) Inc.

—Cam Jansen & the Secret Service Mystery. Natti, Susanna, illus. 2006. (Cam Jansen Ser.). 64p. (J). (gr. 2). 13.99 (978-0-670-06092-4(5) , Viking Juvenile) Penguin Group (USA) Inc.

—Don't Talk to Me about the War. 2008. (YA). (gr. 5). 15.99 (*978-0-670-06307-9(X) , Viking Adult) Penguin Group (USA) Inc.

—The First Day of School Mystery. Natti, Susanna, illus. 2005. (Cam Jansen Ser.: No. 22). 64p. (J). (gr. 2-4). pap. 3.99 (978-0-14-240326-6(1) , Puffin) Penguin Group (USA) Inc.

—The School Play Mystery, Vol. 21. Natti, Susanna, illus. 2005. (Cam Jansen Ser.: No. 21). 64p. (J). (gr. 2-4). pap. 3.99 (978-0-14-240355-6(5) , Puffin) Penguin Group (USA) Inc.

—School Trouble for Andy Russell. Hillenbrand, Will, illus. 2005. (Andy Russell Ser.). 128p. (J). pap. 4.95 (978-0-15-205428-1(6) , Gulliver Bks.) Harcourt Children's Bks.

—School Trouble for Andy Russell. Hillenbrand, Will, illus. 1999. (Andy Russell Ser.). 118p. (J). (gr. 2-5). per. 11.60 (978-0-606-19004-6(X)) Tandem Library Bks.

—The Secret Service Mystery. Natti, Susanna, illus. 2008. (Cam Jansen Ser.: No. 26). 64p. (J). (gr. 2). pap. 3.99 (*978-0-14-241074-5(8) , Puffin) Penguin Group (USA) Inc.

—Young Cam Jansen & the Lost Tooth. 1999. (Young Cam Jansen Ser.: No. 3). (gr. k-3). lib. bdg. 11.80 (978-0-613-17895-2(5)) Tandem Library Bks.

—Young Cam Jansen & the Spotted Cat Mystery. (Young Cam Jansen Ser.). 32p. (J). (gr. k-3). 2007. 3.99 (*978-0-14-241012-7(8) , Puffin); 2006. (Illus.). 13.99 (978-0-670-06094-8(1) , Viking Juvenile) Penguin Group (USA) Inc.

—Young Cam Jansen & the Substitute Mystery. Natti, Susanna, illus. 32p. (J). (gr. k). 2006. (Young Cam Jansen Ser.: No. 11). pap. 3.99 (978-0-14-240660-1(0) , Puffin); 2005. (Viking Easy-To-Read Ser.). 13.99 (978-0-670-05988-1(9) , Viking Juvenile) Penguin Group (USA) Inc.

—Young Cam Jansen & the Zoo Note Mystery. Natti, Susanna, illus. (Young Cam Jansen Ser.). 32p. (J). 2004. pap. 3.99 (978-0-14-240204-7(4) , Puffin); 2003. 13.99 (978-0-670-03626-4(9) , Viking Juvenile) Penguin Group (USA) Inc.

Adoff, Jaime. Names Will Never Hurt Me. 2005. 192p. (YA). (gr. 7). pap. 5.99 (978-0-14-240457-7(8) , Puffin) Penguin Group (USA) Inc.

Agnew, Kate. Shout, Show & Tell! Monks, Lydia, illus. 2005. (Green Bananas Ser.). 48p. (J). (ps). pap. (978-0-7787-1040-0(8)) Crabtree Publishing Co.

—Shout, Show, & Tell. Monks, Lydia, illus. 2005. (Green Bananas Ser.). 48p. (J). (978-0-7787-1024-0(6)) Crabtree Publishing Co.

Agnew, Kate, ed. What's Cool about School. Parsons, Garry, illus. 2003. 128p. (J). pap. 7.50 (978-1-4052-0598-6(9)) Egmont Bks., Ltd. GBR. *Dist:* Independent Pubs. Group.

Agnew, Kate, et al. Gweiddi, Dangos a Dweud. 2005. (WEL., Illus.). 47p. (978-1-85596-676-5(X)) Dref Wen.

Ahlberg, Allan. The Cat Who Got Carried Away. McEwen, Katharine, illus. 2003. 96p. (J). (gr. 1-4). 15.99 (978-0-7636-2073-8(4)) Candlewick Pr.

—Starting School. braille ed. 2004. (J). (gr. k-3). spiral bd. (978-0-616-01526-1(7)) Canadian National Institute for the Blind/Institut National Canadien pour les Aveugles.

Ahlberg, Allan & Ahlberg, Janet. Starting School. (Illus.). 32p. (J). pap. 9.95 (978-0-14-050737-9(X)) Penguin Bks., Ltd. GBR. *Dist:* Trafalgar Square Publishing.

Aikawa, Yu. Dark Edge, Vol. 6. 2006. (Illus.). 200p. (YA). pap. 9.95 (978-1-59796-026-7(8)) DrMaster Pubns. Inc.

Al Shaikh, Latifa. I'm Still Waiting for that Chocolate. 2007. 52p. (YA). per. 8.95 (*978-0-595-42982-0(3)) iUniverse, Inc.

Alberto, Daisy. Pete for President! Sims, Blanche, illus. 2004. 32p. (J). lib. bdg. 20.00 (*978-1-4242-1115-9(8)) Fitzgerald Bks.

—Pete for President! Sims, Blanche, illus. 2004. (Social Studies Connects). 32p. (J). (gr. 1-3). pap. 4.99 (978-1-57565-142-2(4)) Kane Pr., The.

Alborough, Jez. Some Dogs Do. Alborough, Jez, illus. 2003. (Illus.). 40p. (J). (ps-2). 15.99 (978-0-7636-2201-5(X)) Candlewick Pr.

Alcantara, Ricardo. Huy, Que Miedo! 13th ed. 2003. (SPA., Illus.). 44p. (978-84-236-2559-8(1) , ED6263) Edebé ESP. *Dist:* Lectorum Pubns., Inc.

Alcott, Louisa May. Hombrecitos.Tr. of Little Men. (SPA., Illus.). 160p. (YA). 11.95 (978-84-7281-168-3(9) , AF1168) Auriga, Ediciones S.A. ESP. *Dist:* Continental Bk. Co., Inc.

—Jo's Boys. 2000. 252p. (J). pap. 9.95 (978-0-594-05147-3(9)) 1873 Pr.

—Jo's Boys. (Dover Juvenile Classics Ser.). (J). 2002. 288p. (gr. 4-7). pap. 3.00 (978-0-486-42226-8(7)); 1999. (Illus.). 80p. pap. 1.00 (978-0-486-40789-0(6)) Dover Pubns., Inc.

—Jo's Boys. l.t. ed. 2005. 424p. pap. (978-1-84637-067-0(1)) Echo Library.

—Kitty's Class Day & Other Stories. 2006. 96.99 (*978-1-4219-7445-3(2)); pap. 90.99 (*978-1-4219-7438-5(X)) IndyPublish.com.

Alcott, Louisa May. Little Men: Life at Plumfield with Jo's Boys. 2001. (Dover Juvenile Classics Ser.). 304p. (J). (gr. 4-7). pap. 3.00 (978-0-486-41808-7(1)) Dover Pubns., Inc.

Aleixandre, Marilar. La Branda Sin Futuro. 2003. (SPA.). 156p. (978-84-348-7193-9(9) , SM30543) SM Ediciones ESP. *Dist:* Lectorum Pubns., Inc.

Alexander, Alma. Spellspam. 2008. (Worldweavers Ser.). 448p. (J). 17.99 (*978-0-06-083958-1(9)); lib. bdg. 18.89 (*978-0-06-083959-8(7)) HarperCollins Pubs. (Eos).

Alfonsi, Alice. Lizzie for President. 2004. 149p. (J). lib. bdg. 16.92 (*978-1-4242-0681-0(2)) Fitzgerald Bks.

Alfonsi, Alice, adapted by. 2 Good 2 Be True, Bk. 6. rev. ed. 2005. (That's So Raven Ser.: Bk. 6). (Illus.). 128p. (J). (gr. 3-7). pap. 4.99 (978-0-7868-4683-2(6)) Disney Pr.

Alger, Horatio. Hector's Inheritance: Or, The Boys of Smith Institute. unabr. ed. 2002. (Polyglot Press Alger Ser.). (Illus.). (J). pap. 17.95 (978-1-4115-0004-4(0)) Polyglot Pr., Inc.

Aliki. Marianthe's Story: Painted Words & Spoken Memories, 2 bks. in 1. Aliki, illus. 1998. (Illus.). 64p. (J). (gr. k-3). lib. bdg. 17.89 (978-0-688-15662-6(2)); 16.99 (978-0-688-15661-9(4)) HarperCollins Pubs.

—Play's the Thing. Aliki, illus. 2005. (Illus.). 32p. (J). 16.99 (978-0-06-074355-0(7)); lib. bdg. 17.89 (978-0-06-074356-7(5)) HarperCollins Pubs.

Allan-Meyer, Kathleen. Little Bear at Big School. Garvin, Elaine, illus. 2000. (Little Bear Adventure Ser.: Vol. 4). 28p. (J). (ps-1). pap. 6.49 (978-1-57924-398-2(3)) Jones, Bob Univ. Pr.

Allan, Nicholas. El Cielo. 2000. Tr. of Heaven. (SPA.). (J). (ps-k). 9.20 (978-980-257-194-9(6)) Ekare, Ediciones VEN. *Dist:* Lectorum Pubns., Inc.

Allard, Harry. Miss Nelson Is Missing. Marshall, James, illus. 2007. 32p. (J). (gr. k-3). pap. 9.95 incl. audio compact disk (*978-0-618-85281-9(6)) Houghton Mifflin Co. Trade & Reference Div.

Allen, C. William. The African Interior Mission. Lee, Xiongpao, illus. 2006. 232p. (J). pap. 20.00 (978-0-9653308-5-5(0)) Africana Homestead Legacy Pubs.

Allen, M. E. Gotta Get Some Bish Bash Bosh. 2005. (Illus.). 208p. (J). 15.99 (978-0-06-073198-4(2) , HarperTeen); lib. bdg. 16.89 (978-0-06-073201-1(6)) HarperCollins Pubs.

Allie, Debora. The Meanest Girl. rev. ed. 2005. 128p. (J). 15.95 (978-1-59643-014-3(1)) Roaring Brook Pr.

Allison, Jennifer. Gilda Joyce & the Ladies of the Lake. 2006. 352p. (J). (gr. 5). 15.99 (978-0-525-47693-1(8) , Dutton Juvenile) Penguin Group (USA) Inc.

Allison, Jennifer. The Ladies of the Lake: Gilda Joyce. 2007. 352p. (J). (gr. 5). 7.99 (*978-0-14-240907-7(3) , Puffin) Penguin Group (USA) Inc.

Allyson, Libby. Scottie Rides the Bus. 2004. 27p. pap. 14.95 (978-1-4137-3298-6(4)) PublishAmerica, Inc.

Alonso, Fernando. Sopaboba. 8th ed. 2003. (SPA., Illus.). 136p. (978-84-239-9025-2(7) , EC1519) Espasa Calpe, S.A. ESP. *Dist:* Lectorum Pubns., Inc.

Alphin, Elaine Marie. The Perfect Shot. 2005. 360p. (YA). (gr. 7-13). per. 16.95 (978-1-57505-862-7(6) , Carolrhoda Bks.) Lerner Publishing Group.

—Picture Perfect. 2003. (Illus.). 252p. (J). (gr. 7 up). 15.95 (978-0-8225-0535-8(5)) Lerner Publishing Group.

—Simon Says. (YA). (gr. 9-12). 2005. 264p. pap. 6.95 (978-0-15-204678-1(X) , Harcourt Paperbacks); 2002. (Illus.). 272p. 17.00 (978-0-15-216355-6(7)) Harcourt Children's Bks.

Alter, Anna. Francine's Day. Alter, Anna, illus. 2003. (Illus.). 32p. (J). lib. bdg. 16.89 (978-0-06-623937-8(0)) HarperCollins Pubs.

Alvarez, Julia. Finding Miracles. (gr. 7). 2006. 288p. (YA). mass mkt. 6.50 (978-0-553-49406-8(6) , Laurel Leaf); 2004. 272p. (J). 15.95 (978-0-375-82760-0(9) , Knopf Bks. for Young Readers) Random Hse. Children's Bks.

Amato, Mary. Drooling & Dangerous: The Riot Brothers Return! Long, Ethan, illus. 2006. 176p. (J). 16.95 (978-0-8234-1986-9(X)) Holiday Hse., Inc.

—Please Write in This Book. Brace, Eric, illus. 2006. 112p. (J). (gr. 2-5). 16.95 (978-0-8234-1932-6(0)) Holiday Hse., Inc.

—Snarf Attack, Underfoodle, & the Secret of Life: The Riot Brothers Tell All. Long, Ethan, illus. 160p. (J). (gr. 1-5). pap. 6.95 (*978-0-8234-2062-9(0)) Holiday Hse., Inc.

—Stinky & Successful: The Riot Brothers Never Stop! Long, Ethan, illus. 2007. 160p. (J). (gr. 1-5). 16.95 (*978-0-8234-2100-8(7)) Holiday Hse., Inc.

Amato, Mary. The Word Eater. 2005. (Illus.). 151p. (YA). (gr. 4-6). tchr. ed. 15.95 (978-0-8234-1468-0(X)) Holiday Hse., Inc.

—The Word Eater. Ryniak, Christopher, illus. 2005. 151p. (J). reprint ed. pap. 6.95 (978-0-8234-1940-1(1)) Holiday Hse., Inc.

Anastasio, Dina. Everyone Clapped for Jason. ed. 2003. (Early Connections Ser.). (J). pap. 33.00 (978-1-4108-1362-6(2)) Benchmark Education Co.

Anderson, Jessica Lee. Trudy. 2005. (Milkweed Prize for Children's Literature Ser.). 192p. (J). (gr. 3-7). 16.95 (978-1-57131-660-8(4)); (gr. 4-7). pap. 6.95 (978-1-57131-659-2(0)) Milkweed Editions.

Anderson, Laurie. Speak. 2006. 23.75 (978-0-8446-7292-2(0)) Smith, Peter Pub., Inc.

Anderson, Laurie Halse. Catalyst. 240p. (YA). 2003. (gr. 6). pap. 7.99 (978-0-14-240001-2(7) , Puffin); 2002. (gr. 7 up). 17.99 (978-0-670-03566-3(1) , Viking Juvenile) Penguin Group (USA) Inc.

—Catalyst. 2003. (gr. 7-12). lib. bdg. 15.30 (978-0-613-70575-2(0)) Tandem Library Bks.

—Habla! (SPA.). (YA). 9.95 (978-958-04-5909-5(6)) Norma S.A. COL. *Dist:* Distribuidora Norma, Inc.

—Speak. 2002. (YA). 14.89 (978-1-4046-1072-9(3)) Book Wholesalers, Inc.

—Speak. 1999. 208p. (YA). (gr. 8-12). 17.00 (978-0-374-37152-4(0) , Farrar, Straus & Giroux (BYR)) Farrar, Straus & Giroux.

—Speak. 2006. 224p. (YA). pap. 10.00 (978-0-14-240732-5(1) , Puffin) Penguin Group (USA) Inc.

—Speak. 2001. (J). (978-0-606-21444-5(5)) Tandem Library Bks.

—Speak. l.t. ed. 2000. 276p. (YA). (gr. 8-12). 20.95 (978-0-7862-2525-5(4)) Thorndike Pr.

—Teacher's Pet. 2003. (Wild at Heart Ser.). (Illus.). 132p. (J). (gr. 4 up). lib. bdg. 23.33 (978-0-8368-3261-7(2)) Stevens, Gareth Inc.

—Teacher's Pet. 2001. (American Girl Wild at Heart Ser.: Bk. 7). (Illus.). (YA). (978-0-606-21529-9(8)) Tandem Library Bks.

Anderson, Lynne. Los campeonatos de Charlie & Charlie's Championships. 2005. spiral bd. 66.00 (***978-1-4108-5655-5(0)***) Benchmark Education Co.

Anderson, Pamela Dell. My New School: Afro Boy. Lee, Hanlim & WU, Stacie, illus. 2003. 24p. (J). 12.95 (978-1-932555-01-1(3)) Watch Me Grow Kids.

—My New School: Afro Girl. Lee, Hanlim & WU, Stacie, illus. 2003. 24p. (J). 12.95 (978-1-932555-00-4(5)) Watch Me Grow Kids.

—My New School: Asian/Latin Boy. Lee, Hanlim & WU, Stacie, illus. 2003. 24p. (J). 12.95 (978-1-932555-03-5(X)) Watch Me Grow Kids.

—My New School: Latin/Asian Girl. Lee, Hanlim & WU, Stacie, illus. 2003. 24p. (J). 12.95 (978-1-932555-02-8(1)) Watch Me Grow Kids.

Andracki, Zenon. Dear Ashley: A Middle Grade Novel. 2006. (ENG.). 84p. per. 14.95 (***978-1-4241-6168-3(1)***) PublishAmerica, Inc.

Andreae, Giles. Captain Flinn & the Pirate Dinosaurs. Ayto, Russell, illus. 2005. 32p. (J). (gr. k-3). 15.95 (978-1-4169-0713-8(0) , McElderry, Margaret K.) Simon & Schuster Children's Publishing.

Andreasen, Dan, illus. Eagle Song. 1999. (Puffin Chapters Ser.). (J). 11.79 (978-0-606-16833-5(8)); (gr. 3-6). lib. bdg. 13.00 (978-0-613-17790-0(8)) Tandem Library Bks.

Anfousse, Ginette. A Terrible Secret. Hutchison, Jennifer, tr. from FRE. 2000. (SideStreets Ser.). (gr. 7-12). 112p. 7.95 (978-1-55028-704-2(4)); 108p. (YA). (***978-1-55028-705-9(2)***) Lorimer, James & Co., Ltd., Pubs. CAN. *Dist:* Casemate Pubs. & Bk. Distributors, LLC.

—Terrible Secret. 2001. (gr. 7-12). lib. bdg. 13.00 (978-0-613-42804-0(8)) Tandem Library Bks.

Angelchild, P. Erotic Memoirs Volume 1. 2007. pap. (***978-1-84747-127-7(7)***) Chipmunkapublishing.

Anholt, Laurence. Billy & the Big New School. 1999. (gr. k-3). lib. bdg. 16.40 (978-0-613-62597-5(8)) Tandem Library Bks.

—Billy & the Big New School. Anholt, Catherine, illus. 2004. (Concept Book Ser.). 32p. (J). (ps-1). pap. 7.95 (978-0-8075-0744-5(X)) Whitman, Albert & Co.

Annie Auerbach & MikeNorton. The Good, the Bad & the Gassy. 2006. (Illus.). 96p. pap. 4.99 (978-1-59816-049-9(4) , Tokyopop Kids) TOKYOPOP, Inc.

Anonymous. Diary of a Senior Year. 2000. (Real Teens Ser.: Vol. 1). (YA). (gr. 7 up). pap. 4.99 (978-0-439-11458-5(X)) Scholastic, Inc.

Anselmo, Robert Louis. We're All Different & yet Still the Same. l.t. ed. 2006. (Illus.). 22p. (J). 14.99 (978-1-59879-107-5(9)); per. 9.99 (978-1-59879-088-7(9)) Lifevest Publishing, Inc.

Anthony, Joseph. Innerworld. 2002. 114p. (YA). pap. 9.95 (978-1-55517-574-0(0) , Bonneville Bks.) Cedar Fort, Inc./CFI Distribution.

—Innerworld. 2002. (gr. 7-12). lib. bdg. 18.75 (978-0-613-89648-1(3)) Tandem Library Bks.

Apelqvist, Eva. Swede Dreams. 2007. (S. A. S. S. (Students Across the Seven Seas) Ser.). (Illus.). (YA). 224p. pap. 6.99 (978-0-14-240746-2(1)); 202p. (***978-1-4287-2702-1(7)***) Penguin Group (USA) Inc. (Puffin).

Applegate, Katherine. Forces of Nature. 2001. (True Love Ser.: No. 5). 224p. (YA). pap. 4.99 (978-1-931497-38-1(9)) 17th Street Productions, An Alloy Online Inc. Co.

Applegate, Katherine. Home of the Brave. 2007. 256p. (J). (gr. 5-9). 16.95 (***978-0-312-36765-7(1)***) Feiwel & Friends.

Arai, Kiyoko. Beauty Pop, Vol. 1. 2006. (Beauty Pop Ser.). (Illus.). 200p. (YA). pap. 8.99 (978-1-4215-0575-6(4)) Viz Media.

Arena, Felice & Kettle, Phil. Rotten School Day. Vane, Mitch, illus. 2004. (J). pap. (978-1-59336-364-2(8)) Mondo Publishing.

Argueta, Jorge & Alvarez, Cecilia Concepcion. Moony Luna. Gomez, Elizabeth, illus. 2005. (ENG & SPA.). 32p. (J). 16.95 (978-0-89239-205-6(3)) Children's Bk. Pr.

Armstrong-Ellis, Carey. Seymour Slug Starts School. 2005. (Illus.). 32p. (J). (ps-3). 14.95 (978-0-8109-5779-4(5) , Abrams Bks. for Young Readers) Abrams, Harry N. , Inc.

Arnold, Louise. Golden & Grey: An Unremarkable Boy & a Rather Remarkable Ghost. 2005. 272p. (J). 15.95 (978-0-689-87473-4(1) , McElderry, Margaret K.) Simon & Schuster Children's Publishing.

—Golden & Grey: (an Unremarkable Boy & a Rather Remarkable Ghost) l.t. ed. 2006. 317p. 22.95 (978-0-7862-8290-6(8)) Thorndike Pr.

—Golden & Grey: The Nightmares That Ghosts Have. 2006. 304p. (J). (gr. 3-7). 16.99 (978-0-689-87586-1(X) , McElderry, Margaret K.) Simon & Schuster Children's Publishing.

—Golden & Grey (an Unremarkable Boy & a Rather Remarkable Ghost) 2006. (Illus.). 272p. (J). reprint ed. pap. 5.99 (978-0-689-87585-4(1) , Aladdin) Simon & Schuster Children's Publishing.

Arnold, Louise. Golden & Grey: the Nightmares That Ghosts Have. 2007. 304p. (J). pap. 5.99 (***978-0-689-87587-8(8)*** , Aladdin) Simon & Schuster Children's Publishing.

Arnold, Tedd. Super Fly Guy. Arnold, Tedd, illus. 2006. (Fly Guy Ser.: No. 2). (Illus.). 32p. (J). pap. 5.99 (978-0-439-63904-0(2) , Cartwheel Bks.) Scholastic, Inc.

Arrington, Aileen. Camp of the Angel. 2003. 154p. (YA). (gr. 5). 16.99 (978-0-399-23882-6(4) , Philomel) Penguin Group (USA) Inc.

—Paper Heart. 2006. 113p. (J). 16.95 (978-1-932425-61-1(6) , Lemniscaat) Boyds Mills Pr.

Arroyo, Madeline. Calie's Gift. Vavak, S. Dean, illus. 2003. 32p. (gr. 2-5). 16.95 (978-0-9740061-0-9(6)) Stairway Pubns.

Arthur M. Winfield (Staff. The Rover Boys at School or the Cadets O. 2006. pap. 27.99 (***978-1-4219-7693-8(5)***) IndyPublish.com.

Aryal, Aimee. Hello Herbie Husker! 2005. (J). 14.95 (978-1-932888-43-0(8)) Mascot Bks., Inc.

Asch, Frank. Battle in a Bottle. Kanzler, John, illus. 2004. (Class Pets Ser.: No. 2). 96p. (J). (gr. 2-6). pap. 3.99 (978-0-689-84654-0(1) , Aladdin) Simon & Schuster Children's Publishing.

Ashcraft, Carolyn. Hamlet Goes to School. 2004. (Illus.). 108p. (J). per. 5.99 net. (978-0-9755232-0-9(1)) Word Seed Publishing.

Asher, Jay. Thirteen Reasons Why. 2007. 256p. (YA). (gr. 7). 16.99 (***978-1-59514-171-2(5)*** , Razorbill) Penguin Group (USA) Inc.

Ashley, Chris. Wasim the Wanderer. 2007. (Illus.). 80p. (J). 15.95 (***978-1-84507-776-1(8)***) Lincoln, Frances Ltd. GBR. *Dist:* Perseus Distribution.

—Wasim the Wanderer. Pankhurst, Kate, illus. 2007. 80p. (J). pap. 7.95 (***978-1-84507-745-7(8)***) Lincoln, Frances Ltd. GBR. *Dist:* Perseus Distribution.

Ashton, Victoria. Confessions of a Teen Nanny. 2006. (Confessions of a Teen Nanny Ser.). 208p. (J). reprint ed. pap. 8.99 (978-0-06-073178-6(8)) HarperCollins Pubs.

—Juicy Secrets. 2006. (Confessions of a Teen Nanny Ser.). 208p. (J). 15.99 (978-0-06-073181-6(8)); lib. bdg. 16.89 (978-0-06-077526-1(2)) HarperCollins Pubs. (HarperTeen).

—Rich Girls. 2006. (Confessions of a Teen Nanny Ser.). 224p. (J). pap. 8.99 (978-0-06-073180-9(X) , Harper-Teen); 15.99 (978-0-06-073179-3(6)) HarperCollins Pubs.

Aston, Dianna Hutts. Not So Tall for Six. Dormer, Frank W., illus. 2008. (J). (***978-1-57091-705-9(1)***) Charlesbridge Publishing, Inc.

Atkins, Catherine. Alt Ed. 2004. 208p. (J). (gr. 8-12). reprint ed. pap. 6.99 (978-0-14-240235-1(4) , Puffin) Penguin Group (USA) Inc.

Atkinson, Beth. From Alice to Zen & Everyone in Between: A Novel. 2008. (Exceptional Reading & Language Arts Titles for Intermediate Grades Ser.). (J). 15.95 (***978-0-8225-7271-8(0)*** , Carolrhoda Bks.) Lerner Publishing Group.

Atkinson, I. J. I Might Just Be a Freshman But. 2002. (gr. 7-12). lib. bdg. 30.35 (978-0-613-86361-2(5)) Tandem Library Bks.

Auch, Mary Jane. I Was a Third Grade Science Project. Auch, Herm, illus. 1999. 112p. (gr. 2-5). 5.50 (978-0-440-41606-7(X) , Yearling) Random Hse. Children's Bks.

—I Was a Third Grade Science Project. 1999. (J). 11.30 (978-0-606-17474-9(5)); (gr. 3-6). lib. bdg. 12.40 (978-0-8085-7157-5(5)) Tandem Library Bks.

—I Was a Third Grade Spy. Auch, Herm, illus. 2001. 96p. (J). (gr. 4-6). tchr. ed. 15.95 (978-0-8234-1576-2(7)) Holiday Hse., Inc.

—I Was a Third Grade Spy. Auch, Herm, illus. 2003. 96p. (J). (gr. 2-5). pap. 5.50 (978-0-440-41871-9(2) , Yearling) Random Hse. Children's Bks.

—I Was a Third Grade Spy. 2003. (gr. 3-6). lib. bdg. 13.00 (978-0-613-60388-1(5)) Tandem Library Bks.

Auer, Chris. Molly & the Good Shepherd. Wummer, Amy, illus. 2005. 40p. (J). 12.99 (978-0-310-70826-1(5)) Zonderkidz.

Auerbach, Annie. Hall Monitor. O'Hare, Mark, illus. 2000. (SpongeBob SquarePants Chapter Bks.: Vol. 3). 64p. (J). (gr. 2-5). pap. 3.99 (978-0-689-84042-5(X) , Simon Spotlight) Simon & Schuster Children's Publishing.

—Hall Monitor. 2000. (gr. 3-6). lib. bdg. 11.80 (978-0-613-31281-3(3)) Tandem Library Bks.

Avi. Don't You Know There's a War On? 2003. 200p. (J). (ps-7). lib. bdg. 14.15 (978-0-613-60338-6(9)) Tandem Library Bks.

—Never Mind! A Twin Novel. 2004. 208p. (J). (gr. 5 up). lib. bdg. 16.89 (978-0-06-054315-0(9)) HarperCollins Pubs.

—The Secret School. (gr. 3-6). 2003. (Illus.). 168p. (J). pap. 5.95 (978-0-15-204699-6(2) , 53582853, Harcourt Paperbacks); 2001. 160p. (YA). 16.00 (978-0-15-216375-4(1)) Harcourt Children's Bks.

Avi & Vail, Rachel. Never Mind! A Twin Novel. 2004. 208p. (J). (gr. 5 up). 15.99 (978-0-06-054314-3(0)) HarperCollins Pubs.

Ayres, Katherine. Macaroni Boy. 2004. 192p. (J). (gr. 3-7). pap. 5.99 (978-0-440-41884-9(4) , Yearling) Random Hse. Children's Bks.

Bader, Bonnie. 100 Monsters in My School, Vol. 2. Hendrix, Bryan, illus. 2002. (All Aboard Math Reader Ser.). 48p. (J). pap. 3.99 (978-0-448-42859-8(8) , Grosset & Dunlap) Penguin Group (USA) Inc.

—100 Monsters in My School. 2002. (gr. k-3). lib. bdg. 11.80 (978-0-613-64089-3(6)) Tandem Library Bks.

Bader, Bonnie & West, Tracey. First Day Fright. Molnar, Albert, illus. 2000. (Spooky School Ser.). 28p. (J). (978-0-439-21553-4(6)) Scholastic, Inc.

—The 100th Day of School. Molnar, Albert, illus. 2001. (Spooky School Ser.). 26p. (J). (978-0-439-21554-1(4)) Scholastic, Inc.

Bagert, Brod. Hormone Jungle: Coming of Age in Middle School. 2006. (Illus.). 121p. (J). (gr. 5-8). 23.95 (978-0-929895-87-1(8)) Maupin Hse. Publishing.

Baglio, Ben M. Puppy Puzzle. 1999. (gr. 3-6). lib. bdg. 11.80 (978-0-613-12010-4(8)) Tandem Library Bks.

—Squirrels in the School. 2000. (gr. 3-6). lib. bdg. 11.80 (978-0-613-27050-2(9)) Tandem Library Bks.

Baker, Barbara. Third Grade Is Terrible. Shepherd, Roni, illus. 1999. (Puffin Chapters Ser.). 112p. (J). (gr. 2-5). reprint ed. pap. 4.99 (978-0-14-130103-7(1) , Puffin) Penguin Group (USA) Inc.

—Third Grade Is Terrible. 1999. (978-0-606-18456-4(2)); (gr. 3-6). lib. bdg. 13.00 (978-0-613-22947-0(9)) Tandem Library Bks.

Baldwin, Rich & Jones, Sandie. The Detective Company. Dawn, Baumer, illus. 2004. 183p. (YA). pap. 9.95 (***978-0-9742920-0-7(1)*** , 2001) Buttonwood Pr.

Baldwin, Richard L. Unity & the Children. 1999. xiv, 160p. (J). (978-0-9660685-3-5(X)) Buttonwood Pr.

Balliett, Blue. The Wright 3. Helquist, Brett, illus. (J). 2007. 352p. (gr. 4-7). pap. 6.99 (***978-0-439-69368-4(3)*** , Scholastic Paperbacks); 2006. 272p. pap. 16.99 (978-0-439-69367-7(5) , Scholastic Pr.) Scholastic, Inc.

—The Wright 3. l.t. ed. 2006. 334p. (YA). 23.95 (978-0-7862-9024-6(2)) Thorndike Pr.

Banerjee, Anjali. Looking for Bapu. 2006. 176p. (J). (gr. 3-6). 15.95 (978-0-385-74657-1(1)); lib. bdg. 17.99 (978-0-385-90894-8(6)) Random Hse. Children's Bks. (Lamb, Wendy).

Banim, Lisa. In the Doghouse. 2005. 124p. (J). lib. bdg. 16.92 (***978-1-4242-0685-8(5)***) Fitzgerald Bks.

Banim, Lisa & Minsky, Terri. The Case of the Kate Haters. 2005. (Illus.). 124p. (J). (***978-1-4156-3927-6(2)***) Disney Pr.

Banks, Jacqueline Turner. A Day for Vincent Chin & Me. 128p. (J). (gr. 5-9). 2005. pap. 5.95 (978-0-618-54879-8(3)); 2001. (Illus.). 15.00 (978-0-618-13199-0(X)) Houghton Mifflin Co. Trade & Reference Div.

—Egg-Drop Blues. 2003. 128p. (J). (gr. 4-6). pap. 4.95 (978-0-618-25080-6(8)); 15.00 (978-0-618-34885-5(9)) Houghton Mifflin Co. Trade & Reference Div.

Banks, Kate. Lenny's Space. 2007. 160p. (J). (gr. 3-7). 16.00 (***978-0-374-34575-4(9)*** , Farrar, Straus & Giroux (BYR)) Farrar, Straus & Giroux.

Banks, Lynne Reid. Alice-by-Accident. 2000. (Avon Camelot Bks.). 144p. (J). (gr. 4-7). 14.95 (978-0-380-97865-6(2)) HarperCollins Pubs.

Banks, Piper. Geek High. 2007. 256p. (gr. 12 up). 9.99 (***978-0-451-22225-1(3)*** , N A L Trade) Penguin Group (USA) Inc.

Banks, Steven. Battle of the Band. Goldberg, Barry, illus. ed. 2005. (Adventures of Jimmy Neutron Ser.: 1). 24p. (J). lib. bdg. 15.00 (978-1-59054-779-3(9)) Fitzgerald Bks.

—Sick Day. 2003. (gr. k-3). lib. bdg. 11.25 (978-0-613-66382-3(9)) Tandem Library Bks.

Banscherus, Jurgen & Baron, Daniel C. After School Ghosthunter. Butschkow, Ralf, illus. 2007. 63p. (J). (***978-1-59889-342-7(4));*** pap. (***978-1-59889-441-7(2)***) Stone Arch Bks.

Banville, Vincent. Hennessy. 180p. pap. 12.95 (978-0-7022-2505-5(3)) Univ. of Queensland Pr. AUS. *Dist:* International Specialized Bk. Services.

Barasch, Lynne. A Country Schoolhouse. 2004. (Illus.). 40p. (J). 16.00 (978-0-374-31577-1(9) , Farrar, Straus & Giroux (BYR)) Farrar, Straus & Giroux.

Baratz-Logsted, Lauren. Angel's Choice. 2006. 256p. (YA). (gr. 9 up). pap. 6.99 (978-1-4169-2524-8(4) , Simon Pulse) Simon & Schuster Children's Publishing.

Barbour, Ralph Henry. The New Boy at Hilltop & Other Stories. 2006. pap. (***978-1-4065-0779-9(2)***) Dodo Pr.

Barlow, Andrew. Jellytoes Misses the Bus. Barlow, Andrew, illus. 2005. (Illus.). 32p. (J). pap. 8.95 (978-0-9764336-0-6(5)) MJS Publishing Group LLC.

Barnes, Derrick D. Stop, Drop, & Chill. Phillips-Duke, Barbara Jean, illus. 2004. 32p. (J). lib. bdg. 15.00 (***978-1-4242-0231-7(0)***) Fitzgerald Bks.

Barnes, Jennifer. Perfect Cover. 2008. (The Squad). 288p. (YA). (gr. 7). mass mkt. 6.99 (***978-0-385-73454-7(9)*** , Delacorte Pr.) Dell Publishing.

—Skin Deep. 2008. (J). (***978-0-385-90477-3(0)*** , Delacorte Pr.) Dell Publishing.

Barnes, Jennifer Lynn. Golden. 2006. 256p. (YA). (gr. 7). pap. 7.95 (978-0-385-73311-3(9)); lib. bdg. 9.99 (978-0-385-90330-1(8)) Random Hse. Children's Bks. (Delacorte Bks. for Young Readers).

Barnes, Joyce Annette. Promise Me the Moon. 1999. (978-0-606-14297-7(5)) Tandem Library Bks.

Barnholdt, Lauren. Reality Chick. 2006. 288p. (YA). pap. 8.99 (978-1-4169-1317-7(3) , Simon Pulse) Simon & Schuster Children's Publishing.

Barrett. Lethal Delivery, Postage Prepaid. (Thumbprint Mysteries Ser.). 32.86 (978-0-8092-0425-0(8)) McGraw-Hill/Contemporary.

Barrett, Anna Pearl. Neecie & the Swarming Germs. Carmical, Phillip, ed. 1998. (Illus.). 50p. (J). (gr. 2-4). pap. 9.95 (978-0-9661330-0-4(5)) Over the Rainbow Productions.

Bartlett, Susan. Seal Island School. Bonnell, J., ed. Tusa, Tricia, illus. 2001. (Chapters Ser.). 80p. (J). (gr. 2-5). pap. 4.99 (978-0-14-131104-3(5) , Puffin) Penguin Group (USA) Inc.

—Seal Island School. Tusa, Tricia, illus. 1999. 80p. (J). (gr. 2-5). 15.99 (978-0-670-88349-3(2) , Viking Juvenile) Penguin Group (USA) Inc.

—Seal Island School. 2001. (gr. 3-6). lib. bdg. 13.00 (978-0-613-63991-0(X)) Tandem Library Bks.

Baskin, Nora Raleigh. In the Company of Crazies. Raleigh, Henry P., illus. 2006. 176p. (J). 15.99 (978-0-06-059607-1(4)); lib. bdg. 16.89 (978-0-06-059608-8(2)) HarperCollins Pubs.

Basye, Dale E. Heck: Where the Bad Kids Go. Dob, Bob, illus. 2008. (J). (***978-0-375-84075-3(3));*** pap. (***978-0-375-84076-0(1));*** lib. bdg. (***978-0-375-94075-0(8)***) Random Hse., Inc.

Bateman, Anya. The Makeover of James Orville Wickenbee. 2007. 262p. (J). pap. (***978-1-59038-707-8(4)***) Deseret Bk. Co.

Bateman, Colin. Bring Me the Head of Oliver Plunkett. 2005. 272p. (gr. 4-7). (J). 15.95 (978-0-385-73245-1(7)); lib. bdg. 17.99 (978-0-385-90269-4(7)) Random Hse. Children's Bks. (Delacorte Bks. for Young Readers).

Bateman, Teresa. The Bully Blockers Club. Urbanovic, Jackie, illus. 32p. (J). (gr. 1-4). 2006. 6.95 (978-0-8075-0919-7(1)); 2004. 15.95 (978-0-8075-0918-0(3)) Whitman, Albert & Co.

Bateson, Catherine. Being Bee. 2007. 136p. (J). (gr. 3-7). 16.95 (***978-0-8234-2104-6(X)***) Holiday Hse., Inc.

Bauer, Joan. Stand Tall. 192p. (YA). 2005. (gr. 5). pap. 7.99 (978-0-14-240427-0(6) , Puffin); 2002. (gr. 6-9). 16.99 (978-0-399-23473-6(X) , Putnam Juvenile) Penguin Group (USA) Inc.

Beale, Fleur. Walking Lightly. Sangl, Michaela, illus. 2006. 72p. (J). 12.95 (978-1-894965-37-8(X)) Simply Read Bks. CAN. *Dist:* Perseus Distribution.

Beam, Matt. Getting to First Base with Danalda Chase. 2007. (Illus.). 192p. (J). (gr. 5-8). 16.99 (978-0-525-47578-1(8) , Dutton Juvenile) Penguin Group (USA) Inc.

Beamer, Cheryl & Beamer, Frank. Yea, It's Hokie Game Day! De Angel, Miguel, illus. 2006. (J). 17.95 (978-1-932888-44-7(6)) Mascot Bks., Inc.

Beamish, Diane. Gentle Jack. 2006. 25p. (J). 10.25 (978-1-4116-5553-9(2)) Lulu.com.

Beanpole Billy: Individual Title Six-Pack Pouch - Level L. (Lighthouse Ser.). 16p. (gr. 2 up). 28.00 (978-0-7578-0885-2(9)) Rigby Education.

Beaty, Andrea. Iggy Peck, Architect. Roberts, David, illus. 2007. 32p. (J). (ps-3). 15.95 (978-0-8109-1106-2(X) , Abrams Bks. for Young Readers) Abrams, Harry N. , Inc.

Beckham, David. Charlie Barker & the Secret of the Deep Dark Woods. 2006. 570p. pap. (***978-1-4120-9264-7(7)***) Trafford Publishing.

Beckwith, Kathy. Critical Mass: I Never Thought It Would Be Like This. . 2003. 192p. (J). pap. 9.95 (978-1-930572-25-6(5)) Educational Media Corp.

Bee, Clair. Pitchers Duel, Vol. 7. 1999. (Chip Hilton Sports Ser.: Vol. 7). (Illus.). x, 213p. (J). reprint ed. pap. 5.99 (978-0-8054-1989-4(6)) B&H Publishing Grp.

BEEBE, Diane. School's Out. 2006. (J). (978-1-4276-0238-1(7)) Aardvark Global Publishing.

Beechen, Adam. Chuckie's Ghost. Artful Doodlers Limited Staff, illus. 2005. (Ready-To-Read Ser.). 32p. (J). (ps-ps). pap. 3.99 (978-0-689-87723-0(4) , Simon Spotlight/ Nickelodeon) Simon & Schuster Children's Publishing.

—What I Did on My Hypergalactic Interstellar Summer Vacation. Hipp, Dan, illus. 2006. 129p. (J). 12.95 (978-0-9742803-6-3(4)) Komikwerks, LLC.

Behrens, Andy. All the Way (Splashproof Edition) 2007. 224p. (YA). (gr. 9). pap. 7.99 (978-0-14-240833-9(6) , Puffin) Penguin Group (USA) Inc.

Belch, Cheryl Renee. The Heroic Adventures of Dizzy Jr. 2007. 20.00 (***978-0-8059-8977-9(3)***) Dorrance Publishing Co., Inc.

Bell, Alison. Zibby Payne & the Drama Trauma. 2007. 96p. (J). (gr. 4-6). pap. (978-1-897073-47-6(X)) Lobster Pr.

Bell-Myers, Darcy, illus. Higgledy-Piggledy: Mabel's World. 2006. 32p. 16.95 (978-0-9716631-1-4(4)) Attitude Pr., Inc.

Bell, Rebecca. Capitano Ricco. Bell, Rebecca, illus. 2005. 36p. (J). per. 9.95 (***978-1-934138-06-9(1)***) Bouncing Ball Bks., Inc.

Benedict, Helen. Opposite of Love. 2007. 256p. (J). (gr. 6 up). 16.99 (***978-0-670-06135-8(2)*** , Viking Juvenile) Penguin Group (USA) Inc.

Benjamin, E. M. Takedown. 1999. 205p. (J). (gr. 7-12). pap. 9.95 (978-1-889199-04-7(4)) Banks Channel Bks.

Bentley, Dawn. Hoppy Goes to School Micro Bk And. Huerta, Catherine, illus. 2006. 32p. 9.95 (978-1-59249-559-7(1)) Soundprints.

Benton, Jim. Attack of the 50-Ft. Cupid. Benton, Jim, illus. 2003. (Franny K. Stein, Mad Scientist Ser.: Bk. 2). (Illus.). 112p. (J). (gr. 2-5). 14.95 (978-0-689-86292-2(X)) Simon & Schuster Children's Publishing.

—The Invisible Fran. Benton, Jim, illus. 2004. (Franny K. Stein, Mad Scientist Ser.: Bk. 3). (Illus.). 112p. (J). (gr. 2-5). 14.95 (978-0-689-86293-9(8)) Simon & Schuster Children's Publishing.

—Let's Pretend This Never Happened. 2007. (Dear Dumb Diary Ser.: Bk. 1). 128p. (J). pap. 2.99 (***978-0-545-01030-6(6)***) Scholastic, Inc.

S

—Lunch Walks among Us. Benton, Jim, illus. (Franny K. Stein, Mad Scientist Ser.: Bk. 2). (Illus.). 112p. (J). 2004. (gr. 2-5). mass mkt. 3.99 (978-0-689-86295-3(4) , Aladdin); 2003. 15.99 (978-0-689-86291-5(1)) Simon & Schuster Children's Publishing.

—Never Do Anything, Ever. Benton, Jim, illus. 2005. (Dear Dumb Diary Ser.: Bk. 4). (Illus.). 144p. (J). (gr. 4-7). pap. 4.99 (978-0-439-62908-9(X) , Scholastic Paperbacks) Scholastic, Inc.

Benton, Jim. Never Underestimate Your Dumb. 2008. (Dear Dumb Diary Ser.: Bk. 7). 160p. (J). pap. 4.99 (*978-0-439-82596-2(2)) Scholastic, Inc.

Bentz, Lindsay. Really Good Friends. 2007. (ENG.). 184p. per. 12.95 (*978-1-59526-720-7(4) , Llumina Pr.) Media Creations, Inc.

Bercaw, Edna Coe. Halmoni's Day. Hunt, Robert, illus. 2004. 29p. (J). reprint ed. 17.00 (978-0-7567-8263-4(5)) DIANE Publishing Co.

Berenstain, Michael, et al. The Berenstain Bears & the Golden Rule. 2008. (J). pap. (*978-0-310-71247-3(5)) Zonderkidz.

Berenstain, Stan & Berenstain, Jan. The Berenstain Bears & No Guns Allowed. 2000. (Berenstain Bears Big Chapter Bks.). (Illus.). (J). (gr. 3-6). 10.79 (978-0-606-18486-1(4)) Tandem Library Bks.

—The Berenstain Bears & the Homework Hassle. Berenstain, Stan & Berenstain, Jan, illus. 2002. (Berenstain Bears First Time Bks.). (Illus.). (J). 11.19 (978-0-7587-0966-0(8)) Book Wholesalers, Inc.

—The Berenstain Bears Go Back to School. Berenstain, Michael, illus. 2005. (Berenstain Bears Ser.). 32p. (J). (ps-3). 9.99 (978-0-06-052673-3(4)); lib. bdg. 14.89 (978-0-06-052674-0(2)) HarperCollins Pubs.

—The Berenstain Bears Lost in Cyberspace. 1999. (Berenstain Bears Big Chapter Bks.). (J). (gr. 2-6). (978-0-606-16839-7(7)) Tandem Library Bks.

Berenzy, Alix. Sammy: The Classroom Guinea Pig. 2008. (Illus.). 32p. (J). pap. 6.99 (*978-0-312-37964-3(1)) Square Fish.

Bergen, Lara. Drama Queen. 2007. (Candy Apple Ser.: No. 5). 176p. (J). pap. 4.99 (*978-0-439-92953-0(9) , Scholastic Paperbacks) Scholastic, Inc.

Bergen, Lara Rice. Stanley: Crying Wolf. 2003. (ps-2). lib. bdg. 11.25 (978-0-613-75009-7(8)) Tandem Library Bks.

Bergeron, Lowell. The New Kid. 2002. 125p. pap. 17.95 (978-1-59286-121-7(0)) PublishAmerica, Inc.

Bernardo, Anilu. Loves Me, Loves Me Not. 1998. 169p. (YA). (gr. 6-12). 16.95 (978-1-55885-258-7(1) , Piñata Books) Arte Publico Pr.

—Loves Me, Loves Me Not. 1999. (gr. 7-12). lib. bdg. 18.75 (978-0-613-23737-6(4)) Tandem Library Bks.

Bernier-Grand, Carmen T. In the Shade of the Nispero Tree. 1999. 192p. (J). (gr. 4-7). 16.99 (978-0-531-33154-5(7)); pap. 15.95 (978-0-531-30154-8(0)) Scholastic, Inc. (Orchard Bks.).

Bernstein, Margery. Stop That Noise! Handelman, Dorothy, photos by. 1999. (Real Kids Readers Ser.). (Illus.). 48p. (gr. 1-3). lib. bdg. 18.90 (978-0-7613-2060-9(1)); 32p. (J). (gr. 2-4). pap. 4.99 (978-0-7613-2085-2(7)) Lerner Publishing Group. (Millbrook Pr.).

—Stop That Noise! 1999. (J). (978-0-606-19174-6(7)); (gr. 3-6). lib. bdg. 11.80 (978-0-613-16851-9(8)) Tandem Library Bks.

Berry, Eileen. Roses on Baker Street. Roberts, John, illus. 1998. 48p. (J). (gr. k-4). pap. 5.49 (978-0-89084-934-7(X) , 106401) Jones, Bob Univ. Pr.

Berry, Eileen M. Haiku on Your Shoes. Regan, Dana, illus. 2005. 56p. (J). (ps-ps). pap. 7.49 (978-1-59166-374-4(1)) Jones, Bob Univ. Pr.

Besser, Kenneth/R. Arnie Carver & the Plague of Demeverde. 2007. (Illus.). x, 338p. (J). (*978-1-934316-02-3(4)) RTMC Organization, LLC.

Best, Cari. Shrinking Violet. Potter, Giselle, illus. 2002. (J). 25.45 (978-0-7587-9811-4(3)) Book Wholesalers, Inc.

—Shrinking Violet. Potter, Giselle, illus. 2000. (J). (978-0-7894-6531-3(0)) Dorling Kindersley Publishing, Inc.

—Shrinking Violet. Potter, Giselle, illus. 2001. 40p. (J). (gr. 9-13). 16.50 (978-0-374-36882-1(1) , Farrar, Straus & Giroux (BYR)) Farrar, Straus & Giroux.

The Best Part: Individual Title, 6 Nos., Pck. (gr. 3 up). 35.00 (978-0-7635-9664-4(7)) Rigby Education.

The Best School Year Ever. 2000. (J). tchr. ed. 9.95 (978-1-58130-646-0(6)); stu. ed. 11.95 (978-1-58130-647-7(4)) Novel Units, Inc.

Betancourt, Jeanne. Fight, Bulldogs, Fight! 1999. (Cheer USA Ser.: Vol. 2). 128p. (J). (gr. 3-7). pap. 4.50 (978-0-590-97808-8(X)) Scholastic, Inc.

—Go, Girl, Go! 1999. (Cheer USA Ser.: Vol. 1). 128p. (J). (gr. 3-7). pap. 4.50 (978-0-590-97806-4(3)) Scholastic, Inc.

—Ready, Shoot, Score, 1 vol., Vol. 4. 1999. (Cheer USA Ser.: Vol. 3). 128p. (J). (gr. 3-7). pap. 4.50 (978-0-590-97809-5(8)) Scholastic, Inc.

—We've Got Spirit! 1999. (Cheer USA Ser.). (J). pap. 36.00 (978-0-439-11748-7(8)); Vol. 4. 128p. (gr. 3-7). pap. 4.50 (978-0-590-97876-7(4)) Scholastic, Inc.

Bial, Raymond. One-Room School. 1999. (Illus.). 48p. (J). (gr. 4-6). tchr. ed. 17.00 (978-0-395-90514-2(1)) Houghton Mifflin Co. Trade & Reference Div.

Bianchi, John. Classic Days at Pokeweed Public School: A Collection of Elementary Tales. 2000. (Public School Ser.). (Illus.). 24p. (J). (gr. 1-5). 17.95 (978-1-894323-24-6(6)) Pokeweed Pr. CAN. *Dist:* Fitzhenry & Whiteside, Ltd.

—Snowed in at Pokeweed Public School. (Illus.). 24p. (J). (gr. 1-5). (978-1-894323-34-5(3)) Pokeweed Pr.

—Snowed in at Pokeweed Public School. 1999. (Illus.). 24p. (J). (gr. 1-5). pap. 4.95 (978-1-894323-12-3(2)) Pokeweed Pr. CAN. *Dist:* Fitzhenry & Whiteside, Ltd.

—Young Author's Day at Pokeweed Public School. 1999. (gr. k-3). lib. bdg. 12.95 (978-0-613-29151-4(4)) Tandem Library Bks.

Bibee, John. The Home School Detectives Series, 8 vols., Set. Incl. Bk. 1. Mystery of the Homeless Treasure. 119p. (gr. 4-7). 1994. pap. 5.00 (978-0-8308-1911-9(8) , 1911); Bk. 3. Mystery of the Mexican Graveyard. 128p. (gr. 3-7). 1995. pap. 5.00 (978-0-8308-1913-3(4) , 1913); Bk. 4. Mystery of the Campus Crook. 123p. (gr. 4-7). 1996. pap. 4.99 (978-0-8308-1914-0(2) , 1914); Bk. 5. Mystery of the Vanishing Cave. (Illus.). 127p. (gr. 4-7). 1996. mass mkt. 5.00 (978-0-8308-1915-7(0) , 1915); Bk. 6. Mystery at the Broken Bridge. 128p. (gr. 5-7). 1997. pap. 5.00 (978-0-8308-1916-4(9) , 1916); (J). 1998. 39.92 (978-0-8308-1910-2(X) , 1910) InterVarsity Pr.

Bienvenido a nuestra escuela - el primer día de escuela de Katy (Teacher Guide) Fiction-to-Fact Big Book Pairs. 2004. (SPA.). instr.'s gde. ed. (978-1-4108-2370-0(9)) Benchmark Education Co.

Bildner, Phil. Busted. 2007. 256p. (YA). (gr. 9 up). 15.99 (*978-1-4169-2424-1(8)) Simon & Schuster Children's Publishing.

Bildner, Phil. Playing the Field. 2006. (Illus.). 192p. (YA). 15.95 (978-1-4169-0284-3(8)) Simon & Schuster Children's Publishing.

Biller, Maxim & Hein, Sybille. Poppy's Biggest Wish. 2006. (Illus.). 32p. (ps). 17.99 (978-0-7475-8236-6(X) , Bloomsbury Children) Bloomsbury Publishing Plc GBR. *Dist:* Independent Pubs. Group.

Billstrom, Diane. You Can't Go to School Naked! Kilpatrick III, Don, illus. 2008. 32p. (J). (ps-k). 16.99 (*978-0-399-24738-5(6) , Putnam Juvenile) Penguin Group (USA) Inc.

Birdseye, Tom. Attack of the Mutant Underwear. 2006. (Illus.). 208p. (J). (gr. 3). pap. 6.99 (978-0-14-240734-9(8) , Puffin) Penguin Group (USA) Inc.

Birney, Betty G. Friendship According to Humphrey. (J). (gr. 2-4). 2006. 176p. pap. 5.99 (978-0-14-240633-5(3) , Puffin); 2005. 160p. 14.99 (978-0-399-24264-9(3) , Putnam Juvenile) Penguin Group (USA) Inc.

—The Princess & the Peabodys. 2007. 256p. (J). lib. bdg. 16.89 (*978-0-06-084721-0(2)); (gr. 5 up). 15.99 (*978-0-06-084720-3(4)) HarperCollins Pubs.

—Surprises According to Humphrey. 2008. 192p. (J). (gr. 3). 14.99 (*978-0-399-24730-9(0) , Putnam Juvenile) Penguin Group (USA) Inc.

—Trouble According to Humphrey. (J). 2008. 192p. (gr. 3-4). 5.99 (*978-0-14-241089-9(6) , Puffin); 2007. 176p. (gr. 2-4). 14.99 (978-0-399-24505-3(7)) Penguin Group (USA) Inc.

Birney, Betty G. The World According to Humphrey. 144p. (J). (gr. 2-4). 2005. pap. 5.99 (978-0-14-240352-5(0) , Puffin); 2004. 14.99 (978-0-399-24198-7(1) , Putnam Juvenile) Penguin Group (USA) Inc.

Blackaby, Susan. The Carnival Committee. Haugen, Ryan, illus. 2007. (J). lib. bdg. (*978-1-4048-2335-8(2)) Picture Window Bks.

—Classroom Cookout. Muehlenhardt, Amy Bailey, illus. 2004. (Read-It! Readers Classroom Tales Ser.). 32p. (C). (gr. k-3). 18.60 (978-1-4048-0583-5(4)) Picture Window Bks.

—A Fire Drill with Mr. Dill. Muehlenhardt, Amy Bailey, illus. 2004. (Read-It! Readers Ser.). 32p. (C). (gr. k-3). 18.60 (978-1-4048-0584-2(2)) Picture Window Bks.

—Hatching Chicks. Muehlenhardt, Amy Bailey, illus. 2004. (Read-It! Readers Classroom Tales Ser.). 32p. (C). (gr. k-3). 18.60 (978-1-4048-0585-9(0)) Picture Window Bks.

—A Pup Shows Up. Muehlenhardt, Amy Bailey, illus. 2004. (Read-It! Readers Classroom Tales Ser.). 32p. (C). (gr. k-3). 18.60 (978-1-4048-0586-6(9)) Picture Window Bks.

—Sunny Bumps the Drums. Muehlenhardt, Amy Bailey, illus. 2004. (Read-It! Readers Classroom Tales Ser.). 32p. (C). (gr. k-3). 18.60 (978-1-4048-0587-3(7)) Picture Window Bks.

—Todd's Fire Drill. Greathouse, Justin, illus. 2007. (J). lib. bdg. (*978-1-4048-2332-7(8)) Picture Window Bks.

—A Trip to the Zoo. Muehlenhardt, Amy Bailey, illus. 2006. (Read-It! Readers Ser.). 24p. (J). (ps-3). 18.60 (978-1-4048-1590-2(2)) Picture Window Bks.

—The Word of the Day. Muehlenhardt, Amy Bailey, illus. 2004. (Read-It! Readers Ser.). 32p. (C). (gr. k-3). 18.60 (978-1-4048-0588-0(5)) Picture Window Bks.

Blacker, Terence. Boy2Girl. 2005. 304p. (J). 16.00 (978-0-374-30926-8(4) , Farrar, Straus & Giroux) Farrar, Straus & Giroux.

—Boy2Girl. 2007. 304p. (YA). pap. 6.99 (*978-0-312-37146-3(2)) Square Fish.

Blacker, Terence. Parent Swap. 2006. 240p. (J). 16.00 (978-0-374-35752-8(8) , Farrar, Straus & Giroux (BYR)) Farrar, Straus & Giroux.

Blahammar, Jern. Blue Valley. 2005. 75p. pap. 14.95 (978-1-4137-6219-8(0)) PublishAmerica, Inc.

Blake, Jon. Dogsbottom School Loses the Plot. (Illus.). 128p. (978-0-19-275395-3(9)) Oxford Univ. Pr., Inc.

Blankenship, Paula. We Both Read-Lulu's Lost Shoes. Reinhart, Larry, illus. 2005. (We Both Read Ser.). 44p. (J). (gr. k-1). 7.99 (978-1-891327-55-1(0)); pap. 3.99 (978-1-891327-56-8(9)) Treasure Bay, Inc.

Blatchford, Claire H. Going with the Flow. 1998. (Illus.). 40p. (J). (gr. 2-4). pap. 7.95 (978-1-57505-284-7(9) , Carolrhoda Bks.) Lerner Publishing Group.

Bleck, Linda. Pepper Goes to School. Bleck, Linda, illus. 2006. (Pepper plays, pulls, & Pops! Ser.). (Illus.). 18p. (J). 8.99 (978-1-4169-0944-6(3) , Little Simon) Simon & Schuster Children's Publishing.

Blomberg, Dianne L. Sam & Gram & the First Day of School. Ulrich, George, illus. 1999. 32p. (J). (ps-1). (978-1-55798-562-0(6) , 441-5626, Magination Pr.) American Psychological Assn.

Bloom, Suzanne. Piggy Monday: A Tale about Manners. Bloom, Suzanne, illus. 2001. (Illus.). 32p. (J). (gr. k-4). 16.95 (978-0-8075-6529-2(6)) Whitman, Albert & Co.

Bloor, Edward. London Calling. 304p. (gr. 5). 2008. (YA). pap. 8.99 (*978-0-375-84363-1(9)); 2006. (J). lib. bdg. 18.99 (978-0-375-93635-7(1)); 2006. (YA). 16.95 (978-0-375-83635-0(7)) Random Hse. Children's Bks. (Knopf Bks. for Young Readers).

Bloor, Edward. Story Time. 2005. (Illus.). 444p. (YA). (gr. 7-12). reprint ed. pap. 7.95 (978-0-15-205222-5(4) , Harcourt Paperbacks) Harcourt Children's Bks.

—Story Time. 2004. (Illus.). 432p. (YA). 17.00 (978-0-15-204670-5(4)) Harcourt Trade Pubs.

—Story Time. 2002. (J). 17.95 (978-0-439-26686-4(6)) Scholastic, Inc.

Blume, Judy. Blubber. l.t. ed. 2005. 166p. 23.95 (978-0-7862-7307-2(0) , Large Print Pr.) Thorndike Pr.

Blume, Judy. Cool Zone with the Pain & the Great One. Stevenson, James, illus. 2008. (J). 12.99 (*978-0-385-73306-9(2)); 16.99 (*978-0-385-90325-7(1)) Dell Publishing. (Delacorte Pr.).

Bo, Ben. Edge. 2002. (gr. 5-8). lib. bdg. 15.25 (978-0-613-76628-9(8)) Tandem Library Bks.

Boelts, Maribeth. When It's the Last Day of School. Wakiyama, Hanako, illus. 2004. 32p. (J). (ps-3). 15.99 (978-0-399-23498-9(5) , Putnam Juvenile) Penguin Group (USA) Inc.

Bogaerts, Jorge. El Dia Que Hizo Mucho Viento. (SPA.). 112p. (J). (978-84-207-3535-1(3)) Grupo Anaya, S.A.

Boggess, Eileen. Mia the Meek. 2006. (Mia Fullerton Ser.: Bk. 1). 155p. (YA). (gr. 6-9). 16.95 (*978-1-890862-46-6(0)) Bancroft Pr.

Bolognese, Don, illus. Abigail Takes the Wheel. 2002. (Avi Ser.). (J). 12.30 (978-0-7587-5967-2(3)) Book Wholesalers, Inc.

Bond, Ruskin. Leopard on the Mountain. 1998. (Cambridge Reading Ser.). (Illus.). 64p. (gr. 2-6). pap. 12.00 (978-0-521-47704-8(2)) Cambridge Univ. Pr.

Bonk, John J. Dustin Grubbs: One Man Show. 2006. 272p. (J). (gr. 3-7). pap. 5.99 (978-0-316-15408-6(3)) Little Brown & Co.

—Dustin Grubbs: Take Two! 2006. 256p. (J). (gr. 3-7). 15.99 (978-0-316-15637-0(X)) Little Brown & Co.

Book Company Staff & Book Company Staff, illus. Little Dinosaur Goes to School. 2002. (Novelty Bks.). (J). 7.95 (978-1-74047-263-0(2)) Book Co. Publishing Pty, Ltd., The AUS. *Dist:* Penton Overseas, Inc.

Borden, Louise. The A+ Custodian. Gustavson, Adam, tr. Gustavson, Adam, illus. 2004. 40p. (J). 15.95 (978-0-689-84995-4(8) , McElderry, Margaret K.) Simon & Schuster Children's Publishing.

—Good Luck, Mrs. K. ! Gustavson, Adam, illus. 2002. 32p. (J). (gr. 1-5). pap. 6.99 (978-0-689-85119-3(7) , Aladdin) Simon & Schuster Children's Publishing.

—The John Hancock Club. Gustavson, Adam, illus. 2007. 48p. (J). (gr. 2-5). 16.99 (978-1-4169-1813-4(2) , McElderry, Margaret K.) Simon & Schuster Children's Publishing.

—The Last Day of School. Gustavson, Adam, illus. 2006. 40p. (J). (gr. 2-5). 15.95 (978-0-689-86869-6(3) , McElderry, Margaret K.) Simon & Schuster Children's Publishing.

—The Lost-And-Found Tooth. 2008. 40p. (J). 16.99 (*978-1-4169-1814-1(0) , McElderry, Margaret K.) Simon & Schuster Children's Publishing.

—Off to First Grade. Schindler, S. D., illus. 2007. 40p. (J). (*978-0-689-87395-9(6) , McElderry, Margaret K.) Simon & Schuster Children's Publishing.

Borden, Louise & Gustavson, Adam. The Day Eddie Met the Author. 2004. (Illus.). 44p. (J). pap. 6.99 (978-0-689-86720-0(4) , Aladdin) Simon & Schuster Children's Publishing.

Bossley, Michele Martin. Swiped. 2006. 112p. (J). lib. bdg. 14.95 (978-1-55143-652-4(3)); (gr. 5 up). pap. 8.95 (978-1-55143-646-3(9)) Orca Bk. Pubs. USA.

Bottner, Barbara. You Have to be Nice to Someone on Their Birthday. Mai-Wyss, Tatjana, illus. 2007. 32p. (J). 15.99 (978-0-399-24295-3(3) , Putnam Juvenile) Penguin Group (USA) Inc.

Bouchard, John L. A Taste of Soda. 2006. 92p. pap. 14.95 (978-1-4241-2482-4(4)) PublishAmerica, Inc.

Bourgeois, Paulette. Franklin Va a la Escuela. Lopez Varela, Alejandra, tr. from ENG. Clark, Brenda, illus. 1998. (Franklin Ser.). (SPA.). 32p. (J). (ps-3). pap. 5.95 (978-1-880507-41-4(2) , LC7792) Lectorum Pubns., Inc.

Bowe, Julie. My Last Best Friend. 2007. (Illus.). 160p. (YA). (gr. 2-5). 16.00 (978-0-15-205777-0(3)) Harcourt Trade Pubs.

Bowen, Anne. The Great Math Tattle Battle. Zollars, Jaime, illus. 2006. 32p. (J). 15.95 (978-0-8075-3163-1(4)) Whitman, Albert & Co.

—What Do Teachers Do? After YOU Leave School. Gott, Barry, illus. 2006. 32p. (J). 15.95 (978-1-57505-922-8(3) , Carolrhoda Bks.) Lerner Publishing Group.

Bowen, Fred. Final Cut. 1999. (gr. 3-6). lib. bdg. 12.95 (978-0-613-23227-2(5)) Tandem Library Bks.

Bowie, Barbara Kay. Ready for School: An Activity & Story Book for Parents & Children Entering Kindergarten. 2004. (J). 7.95 (978-0-9713450-1-0(5)) Educational Expertise, LLC.

Boyne, John. The Boy in the Striped Pajamas. 2007. 240p. (YA). (gr. 7). pap. 8.99 (*978-0-385-75153-7(2) , Fickling, David Bks.) Random Hse. Children's Bks.

Brad el de la Mala Suerte: Bad Luck Brad in Spanish. 2006. (SPA.). 32p. (J). pap. 4.95 (978-1-57565-169-9(6)) Kane Pr., The.

Bradley, Kimberly Brubaker. Leap of Faith. 2007. 192p. (J). (gr. 5 up). 16.99 (978-0-8037-3127-1(2) , Dial) Penguin Group (USA) Inc.

Bradman, Tony. Spooky Teachers, 2 bks. in 1. 2005. (Illus.). 128p. (J). (gr. k-2). pap. (978-0-552-55347-6(6) , Corgi) Transworld Publishers Ltd.

Brady, Bill. A Charm for Jo. Brady, Laurie, illus. l.t. ed. 2005. (Turtle Books). 32p. (J). (gr. 2-5). lib. bdg. 15.95 (978-0-944727-48-5(4)) Jason & Nordic Pubs.

Brady, Bill & Brady, Laurie. A Charm for Jo. Fargo, Todd, illus. l.t. ed. 2005. (Turtle Bks.). (ENG.). 32p. (J). (gr. 2-5). pap. 9.95 (978-0-944727-47-8(6)) Jason & Nordic Pubs.

Braem, Viola Brunette. Woodside: A Novel about the Years from 1930 to 1943. A Fictionalized Autobiography & Funny Events in a One-room School. 2005. (YA). per. 14.95 (978-0-9772315-0-8(X)) Minuteman Pr. of Green Bay.

Brager, Allison. Off-Colored Rainbows. 2005. 64p. pap. 12.95 (978-1-4241-0267-9(7)) PublishAmerica, Inc.

Bramwell, Wendie & Normand, Bridgid. Rhymitis. Kim, Julie J., tr. Kim, Julie J., illus. 2003. 32p. (J). pap. (978-0-9741388-8-6(6)) Committee for Children.

Brande, Robin. Evolution, Me & Other Freaks of Nature. 2007. 272p. (gr. 7). (J). lib. bdg. 18.99 (*978-0-375-94349-2(8)); (YA). 15.99 (*978-0-375-84349-5(3)) Random Hse. Children's Bks. (Knopf Bks. for Young Readers).

Brandon's New School. 2001. (J). (978-1-58453-169-2(X)) Pioneer Valley Educational Pr., Inc.

Braver, Vanita. Madison & the Two-Wheeler. DiRocco, Carl, illus. 2007. 32p. (J). 14.95 (*978-1-59572-109-9(6)) Star Bright Bks., Inc.

Bray, Libba. A Great & Terrible Beauty. (YA). (gr. 7). 2003. 416p. 16.95 (978-0-385-73028-0(4)); 2005. 432p. reprint ed. pap. 8.95 (978-0-385-73231-4(7)) Random Hse. Children's Bks. (Delacorte Bks. for Young Readers).

—A Great & Terrible Beauty. 2005. 403p. (YA). (gr. 8-12). per. 15.60 (978-0-606-33978-0(7)) Tandem Library Bks.

—A Great & Terrible Beauty. l.t. ed. 2005. 512p. (YA). (gr. 8-12). pap. 10.95 (978-1-7862-8082-7(4)); 2004. 507p. 23.95 (978-0-7862-6504-6(3) , Large Print Pr.) Thorndike Pr.

—Rebel Angels. 2005. 560p. (gr. 7). (J). lib. bdg. 18.99 (978-0-385-90257-1(3)); (YA). 16.95 (978-0-385-73029-7(2)) Random Hse. Children's Bks. (Delacorte Bks. for Young Readers).

—Rebel Angels. l.t. ed. 2006. (Thorndike Press Large Print the Literacy Bridge Ser.). 655p. (J). 23.95 (978-0-7862-8087-2(5)) Thorndike Pr.

Brazil, Angela. A Popular Schoolgirl. 2006. 95.99 (*978-1-4280-3666-6(0)); pap. 89.99 (*978-1-4280-3689-5(X)) IndyPublish.com.

Brenner, Emily. On the First Day of Grade School. Whatley, Bruce, illus. 2004. 32p. (J). (ps-1). 15.99 (978-0-06-028013-0(1)); lib. bdg. 16.89 (978-0-06-051041-1(2)) HarperCollins Pubs.

Brent-Dyer, Elinor M. The Chalet School & the Lintons. 2001. (Chalet School Ser.). (Illus.). 300p. pap. 5.95 (978-0-00-690515-8(3)) HarperCollins Pubs. Ltd. GBR. *Dist:* Trafalgar Square Publishing.

—The Chalet School at War. 2001. (Chalet School Ser.). (Illus.). 300p. mass mkt. 5.99 (978-0-00-692944-4(3)) Zondervan.

—Exploits of the Chalet Girls. 2001. (Chalet School Ser.). 300p. (J). pap. 5.99 (978-0-00-692518-7(9)) HarperCollins Pubs. Ltd. GBR. *Dist:* Independent Pubs. Group.

—The Princess of the Chalet School. 2001. (Chalet School Ser.). (Illus.). 300p. pap. 5.99 (978-0-00-690601-8(X)) Zondervan.

—Rivals of the Chalet School. 2001. (Chalet School Ser.). (Illus.). 300p. (J). pap. 5.95 (978-0-00-690723-7(7)) HarperCollins Pubs. Ltd. GBR. *Dist:* Independent Pubs. Group.

—The School at the Chalet. 2001. (Chalet School Ser.). (Illus.). 300p. pap. 5.99 (978-0-00-692517-0(0)) HarperCollins Pubs. Ltd. GBR. *Dist:* Trafalgar Square Publishing.

Breslin, Theresa. New School Blues. 2nd ed. 2002. (Kelpies Ser.). 128p. pap. 10.00 (978-0-86315-409-6(3)) Floris Bks. GBR. *Dist:* SteinerBooks, Inc.

Brewer, Elly. Jerry & the Jannans. 2006. 320p. (J). pap. 11.99 (*978-0-7475-8213-7(0)) Bloomsbury Publishing Plc GBR. *Dist:* Independent Pubs. Group.

Brewer, Heather. The Chronicles of Vladimir Tod: Eighth Grade Bites. 2008. 288p. (J). (gr. 4-6). pap. 7.99 (*978-0-14-241187-2(6) , Puffin) Penguin Group (USA) Inc.

Brian, Kate. Megan Meade's Guide to the McGowan Boys. 2005. (Illus.). 272p. (YA). 15.99 (978-1-4169-0030-6(6)) Simon & Schuster Children's Publishing.

—Megan Meade's Guide to the Mcgowan Boys. 2006. 288p. (YA). pap. 8.99 (978-1-4169-0031-3(4) , Simon Pulse) Simon & Schuster Children's Publishing.

Bridgers, Sue E. Keeping Christina. 1998. 290p. reprint ed. lib. bdg. 29.95 (978-0-7351-0042-8(X)) Replica Bks.

Bridwell, Norman. Clifford Va A la Escuela. Bridwell, Norman, illus. 1999. (Clifford, the Big Red Dog Ser.). (Illus.). 32p. (J). (gr. k-2). 3.50 (978-0-439-08284-6(6) , Cartwheel Bks.) Scholastic, Inc.

—Clifford's Class Trip. Bridwell, Norman, illus. 2003. (Clifford, the Big Red Dog Ser.). (Illus.). 32p. (J). pap. 3.50 (978-0-439-44931-1(6)) Scholastic, Inc.

—Clifford's Class Trip. 2003. (gr. k-3). lib. bdg. 11.25 (978-0-613-70577-6(7)) Tandem Library Bks.

—School Days Treasury. 2007. (Clifford Ser.). 96p. (J). pap. 7.99 (*978-0-439-91568-7(6)) Scholastic, Inc.

Bridwell, Norman. The Show & Tell Surprise. Bridwell, Norman, illus. 2002. (Big Red Readers Ser.). (Illus.). (J). 11.91 (978-0-7587-5217-8(2)) Book Wholesalers, Inc.

Brimner, Larry Dane. The New Kid. Tripp, Christine, illus. 2003. (Rookie Choices Ser.). 32p. (J). 20.50 (978-0-516-22546-3(4) , Children's Pr.) Scholastic Library Publishing.

—New Kid. 2003. (gr. k-3). lib. bdg. 14.10 (978-0-613-67653-3(X)) Tandem Library Bks.

—School Rules. Tripp, Christine, illus. 2002. (Rookie Choices Ser.). 32p. (J). (gr. 1-2). pap. 5.95 (978-0-516-27389-1(2) , Children's Pr.) Scholastic Library Publishing.

—School Rules. 2002. (gr. k-3). lib. bdg. 14.10 (978-0-613-50237-5(X)) Tandem Library Bks.

Brinkerhoff, Shirley. Second Choices. 2000. (Nikki Sheridan Ser.: Vol. 6). (Illus.). 160p. (YA). (gr. 9-13). pap. 5.99 (978-1-56179-880-3(0)) Bethany Hse. Pubs.

—Second Choices. 2000. (gr. 7-12). lib. bdg. 14.15 (978-0-613-82302-9(8)) Tandem Library Bks.

Brisson, Pat. I Remember Miss Perry. Jorisch, Stephane, illus. 2006. 32p. (J). (ps). 16.99 (978-0-8037-2981-0(2) , Dial) Penguin Group (USA) Inc.

Brokaw, Nancy Steele. Leaving Emma. 1999. 144p. (J). (gr. 4-6). tchr. ed. 15.00 (978-0-395-90699-6(7) , Clarion Bks.) Houghton Mifflin Co. Trade & Reference Div.

Brooke, Lauren. Making Strides. 2005. (Chestnut Hill Ser.: No. 2). 224p. (J). (gr. 4-7). pap. 4.99 (978-0-439-73855-2(5) , Scholastic Paperbacks) Scholastic, Inc.

Brooks, Amy. Dorothy Dainty's Gay Times. 2006. 32.99 (***978-1-4280-1766-5(6)***) IndyPublish.com.

Brooks, Amy. Princess Polly's Gay Winter. 2004. reprint ed. pap. 15.95 (978-1-4191-4299-4(2)); pap. 1.99 (978-1-4192-4299-1(7)) Kessinger Publishing, LLC.

Brooks, Jillian. The Makeover. 2003. 157p. (J). (978-0-439-35494-3(3)) Scholastic, Inc.

Brooks, Mel & Reiner, Carl. The 2000 Year Old Man Goes to School. Bennett, James, illus. 2005. 40p. (J). (ps-3). 17.99 (978-0-06-076676-4(X)); lib. bdg. 18.89 (978-0-06-076677-1(8)) HarperCollins Pubs.

Broutin & Stehr. Baldomero Va A la Escuela. (SPA.). 26p. (978-84-95150-47-9(6)) Corimbo, Editorial S.L.

Brown, Amanda. Beach Blonde. 2006. (Legally Elle Woods Ser.: Vol. 1). 240p. (gr. 7-17). pap. 6.99 (978-0-7868-3843-1(4)); 2nd rev. ed. (gr. 3-7). pap. 6.99 (978-0-7868-3844-8(2)) Hyperion Pr.

Brown, Devin. Not Exactly Normal. 2006. 238p. (J). pap. 8.00 (978-0-8028-5287-8(4) , Eerdmans Bks For Young Readers) Eerdmans, William B. Publishing Co.

Brown, Laurie Krasny. Rex & Lilly Schooltime: A Dino Easy Reader. Brown, Marc, illus. 2001. 32p. (J). (ps-1). pap. 4.95 (978-0-316-13535-1(6)) Little, Brown Bks. for Young Readers.

Brown, Marc. Arthur & the Double Dare. 2002. (Arthur Chapter Bks.: Bk. 25). (Illus.). (J). 11.70 (978-0-7587-9423-9(1)) Book Wholesalers, Inc.

—Arthur & the Double Dare. Brown, Marc, illus. 2002. (Arthur Chapter Bks. : Bk. 25). (Illus.). 64p. (J). (gr. 2-4). 13.95 (978-0-316-12264-1(5)); pap. 4.25 (978-0-316-12087-6(1)) Little, Brown Bks. for Young Readers.

—Arthur & the Double Dare. 2002. (Arthur Chapter Bks.: Bk. 25). (gr. k-3). lib. bdg. 12.10 (978-0-613-50586-4(7)) Tandem Library Bks.

—Arthur & the New Kid. 2004. (Arthur Ser.). (Illus.). 24p. (J). (gr. k-3). pap. 3.99 (978-0-375-81381-8(0)); lib. bdg. 11.99 (978-0-375-91381-5(5)) Random Hse. Children's Bks. (Random Hse. Bks. for Young Readers).

—Arthur & the Poetry Contest. Brown, Marc, illus. 18th ed. 1999. (Arthur Chapter Bks. : Bk. 18). (Illus.). 64p. (J). (gr. 2-4). pap. 4.25 (978-0-316-12295-5(5)) Little, Brown Bks. for Young Readers.

—Arthur & the Recess Rookie. 2001. (Arthur Good Sports Ser.: Bk. 3). (Illus.). 64p. (J). (gr. 2-4). 13.95 (978-0-316-11916-0(4)) Little, Brown Bks. for Young Readers.

—Arthur's Classroom Fib. 2007. (Illus.). 24p. (J). (gr. 1-3). pap. 3.99 (978-0-375-82975-8(X)); lib. bdg. 11.99 (978-0-375-92975-5(4)) Random Hse. Children's Bks. (Random Hse. Bks. for Young Readers).

—Arthur's Teacher Moves In. Brown, Marc, illus. 2000. (Arthur Adventure Ser.). (Illus.). 32p. (J). (ps-3). 15.95 (978-0-316-11979-5(2)) Little, Brown Bks. for Young Readers.

—Arthur's Teacher Moves In. 2000. (Arthur Adventure Ser.). (J). (gr. k-3). 15.95 (978-0-316-11856-9(7)) Little, Brown Bks. for Young Readers.

—Arthur's Teacher Trouble. ed. 2004. (Arthur Adventure Ser.). (J). (gr. k-3). spiral bd. (978-0-616-00406-7(0)); spiral bd. (978-0-616-01603-9(4)) Canadian National Institute for the Blind/Institut National Canadien pour les Aveugles.

—Arthur's Underwear: An Arthur Adventure. Brown, Marc, illus. 1999. (Arthur Adventure Ser.). (Illus.). 32p. (J). (ps-3). 15.95 (978-0-316-11012-9(4)) Little, Brown Bks. for Young Readers.

—Arturo y el Dia de Accion de Gracias. 2000. (Arthur Adventure Ser.). (SPA., Illus.). (J). (gr. k-2). pap. 6.95 (978-1-880507-79-7(X) , LC7610) Lectorum Pubns., Inc.

—Arturo y el Dia de Accion de Gracias. 2000. (J). 13.75 (978-0-606-20186-5(6)) Tandem Library Bks.

—Buster Baxter, Cat Saver. 2000. (Arthur Chapter Bks. : Bk. 19). (J). (gr. 3-6). pap. 3.95 (978-0-316-11817-0(6)) Little, Brown Bks. for Young Readers.

—Buster Baxter, Cat Saver. Brown, Marc, illus. 19th ed. 2000. (Arthur Chapter Bks. : Bk. 19). (Illus.). 64p. (J). (gr. 2-4). 13.95 (978-0-316-12111-8(8)); pap. 3.95 (978-0-316-12220-7(3)) Little, Brown Bks. for Young Readers.

—Buster Baxter, Cat Saver. (Arthur Chapter Bks.: Bk. 19). 2000. (gr. k-3). lib. bdg. 11.80 (978-0-613-21268-7(1)); 1999. (Illus.). (J). (gr. 3-6). 10.75 (978-0-606-18250-8(0)) Tandem Library Bks.

—Buster Makes the Grade. ed. 2005. (Arthur Chapter Bks.: No. 16). (Illus.). 55p. (J). lib. bdg. 15.00 (978-1-59054-376-3(3)) Fitzgerald Bks.

—Buster Makes the Grade. Brown, Marc, illus. 16th ed. 1999. (Arthur Chapter Bks. : Bk. 16). (Illus.). 64p. (J). (gr. 2-4). pap. 4.25 (978-0-316-12277-1(7)) Little, Brown Bks. for Young Readers.

—Los Calzoncillos de Arturo. (gr. k-3). 2002. (SPA.). lib. bdg. 15.25 (978-0-613-64538-6(3)); 2001. 13.75 (978-0-606-22643-1(5)) Tandem Library Bks.

—D. W.'s Guide to Preschool. Brown, Marc, illus. 2003. (D. W. Ser.). (Illus.). 32p. (J). (ps-1). 15.95 (978-0-316-12069-2(3)) Little, Brown Bks. for Young Readers.

—Francine, Believe It or Not! ed. 1999. (Arthur Chapter Bks. : Bk. 14). (J). (gr. 3-6). pap. 3.95 (978-0-316-10463-0(9)) Little, Brown Bks. for Young Readers.

—Francine the Superstar. Brown, Marc, illus. 22nd ed. 2000. (Arthur Chapter Bks. : Bk. 22). (Illus.). 64p. (J). (gr. 2-4). 13.95 (978-0-316-12227-6(0)) Little, Brown Bks. for Young Readers.

—Francine the Superstar. Krensky, Stephen, tr. Brown, Marc, illus. 22nd ed. 2000. (Arthur Chapter Bks. : Bk. 22). (Illus.). 64p. (J). (gr. 2-4). pap. 4.25 (978-0-316-12250-4(5)) Little, Brown Bks. for Young Readers.

—Francine the Superstar. 2000. (Arthur Chapter Bks.: Bk. 22). (Illus.). (J). 57p. (ps). lib. bdg. 11.80 (978-0-613-25249-2(7)); (gr. 3-6). 10.75 (978-0-606-18253-9(5)) Tandem Library Bks.

—La Visita del Señor Rataquemada. Sarfatti, Esther, tr. from ENG. 2003. (SPA.). (J). (gr. k-2). pap. 6.95 (978-1-930332-41-6(6)) Lectorum Pubns., Inc.

Brown, Marc, et al. Buster Makes the Grade. Brown, Marc, illus. 16th ed. 1999. (Arthur Chapter Bks. : Bk. 16). (Illus.). 64p. (J). (gr. 2-4). 13.95 (978-0-316-11960-3(1)) Little, Brown Bks. for Young Readers.

Brownlee, Browne. Bad Breath. 2007. 108p. 16.95 (***978-1-4241-5487-6(1)***) PublishAmerica, Inc.

Bruchac, Joseph. Eagle Song. Andreasen, Dan, illus. 1999. 96p. (J). (gr. 2-5). pap. 4.99 (978-0-14-130169-3(4) , Puffin) Penguin Group (USA) Inc.

Bruna, Dick. Let's Learn: School Time. 2004. (Illus.). 24p. pap. 4.99 (978-1-59226-172-7(8)) Big Tent Entertainment, Inc.

Brunstetter, Wanda E. Rachel Yoder: Back to School. 2007. (Rachel yoder Ser.). 160p. (J). pap. 4.97 (***978-1-59789-234-6(3)***) Barbour Publishing, Inc.

Bryant, Jennifer. Pieces of Georgia. 176p. (J). 2007. (gr. 5-9). 5.99 (***978-0-440-42055-2(5)*** , Yearling); 2006. (gr. 6-9). 15.95 (978-0-375-83259-8(9) , Knopf Bks. for Young Readers); 2006. (gr. 6-9). lib. bdg. 17.99 (978-0-375-93259-5(3) , Knopf Bks. for Young Readers) Random Hse. Children's Bks.

Bryant, Megan E. Shape Spotters, Vol. 1. Sweeten, Sami, illus. 2002. (All Aboard Math Reader Ser.). 32p. (J). pap. 3.99 (978-0-448-42858-1(X) , Grosset & Dunlap) Penguin Group (USA) Inc.

—Shape Spotters. 2002. (gr. k-3). lib. bdg. 11.80 (978-0-613-64107-4(8)) Tandem Library Bks.

—Strawberry Shortcake's Show-and-Tell Surprise: All Aboard Reading Station Stop 1. Neely, Scott, illus. 2005. (All Aboard Reading Ser.). 32p. (J). (ps-2). pap. 3.99 (978-0-448-43848-1(8) , Grosset & Dunlap) Penguin Group (USA) Inc.

Bryant, Megan E. Welcome Spring! Nunn, Paul E., illus. 2008. 32p. (J). (gr. 1-4). 6.99 (***978-0-448-44778-0(9)*** , Grosset & Dunlap) Penguin Group (USA) Inc.

Buchanan, Kathy Wierenga & Johnson, Lissa Halls. When Stars Fall, Vol. 11. 2005. (Brio Girls Ser.). 208p. (YA). pap. 7.99 (978-1-58997-090-8(X)) Focus on the Family Publishing.

Buchanan, Paul. Ask Willie. 1999. (gr. 3-6). lib. bdg. 14.15 (978-0-613-72656-6(1)) Tandem Library Bks.

—Friend or Foe. 2000. (gr. 3-6). lib. bdg. 14.15 (978-0-613-72828-7(9)) Tandem Library Bks.

Buchanan, Paul & Randall, Rod. Ask Willie, Vol. 12. 1999. (Misadventures of Willie Plummett Ser.: Bk. 12). 128p. (J). (gr. 3-7). 5.99 (978-0-570-05478-8(8) , 56-1941GJ) Concordia Publishing Hse.

—Face the Music, Vol. 18. 2001. (Misadventures of Willie Plummett Ser.: Vol. 18). (Illus.). 128p. (J). (gr. 3-7). 5.99 (978-0-570-07126-6(7)) Concordia Publishing Hse.

Buchanan, Paul & Randall, Rod, contrib. by. Friend or Foe, Vol. 16. 2000. (Misadventures of Willie Plummett Ser.: Vol. 16). 128p. (J). (gr. 3-7). 5.99 (978-0-570-07005-4(8)) Concordia Publishing Hse.

Buckeridge, Anthony. Jennings' Diary. 2002. 179p. pap. (978-0-7551-0163-4(4)) House of Stratus, Inc.

—Jennings' Little Hut. 2002. 198p. pap. (978-0-7551-1367-5(5)) House of Stratus, Inc.

Buckless, Andrea. Class Picture Day. Goodnow, Patti, illus. 2004. 32p. (J). lib. bdg. 15.00 (978-1-59054-379-5(3)) Fitzgerald Bks.

—Class Picture Day, Level 2. Goodnow, Patti, illus. 1999. (Hello Reader! Ser.: Level 2). 32p. (J). (gr. k-2). pap. 3.99 (978-0-590-37975-5(5) , Cartwheel Bks.) Scholastic, Inc.

Buckley, Michael. The Unusual Suspects. Ferguson, Peter, illus. 2007. (Sisters Grimm Ser.: Bk. 2). 320p. (J). (gr. 2-8). pap. 5.95 (***978-0-8109-9323-5(6)*** , Amulet Bks.) Abrams, Harry N. , Inc.

Budhos, Marina. Ask Me No Questions. 176p. (YA). 2007. pap. 8.99 (***978-1-4169-4920-6(8)*** , Simon Pulse); 2006. (Illus.). (gr. 5-9). 16.95 (978-1-4169-0351-2(8) , Atheneum) Simon & Schuster Children's Publishing.

Bui-Quang, Phuong-Mai. Tea Club. 2006. (YA). per. 10.95 (978-1-59971-581-0(3)) Aardvark Global Publishing.

Bullard, Lisa. My Day: Morning, Noon & Night. Wesley, Omarr, illus. 2004. (All about Me Ser.). 24p. (C). (gr. k-1). 21.26 (978-1-4048-0045-8(X)) Picture Window Bks.

Bunting, Eve. Cheyenne Again. Toddy, Irving, illus. 2002. 32p. (J). (gr. k-3). pap. 5.95 (978-0-618-19465-0(7) , Clarion Bks.) Houghton Mifflin Co. Trade & Reference Div.

—Our Teacher's Having a Baby. deGroat, Diane, illus. 2001. 32p. (J). (gr. k-3). pap. 6.95 (978-0-618-11138-1(7) , Clarion Bks.) Houghton Mifflin Co. Trade & Reference Div.

Burch, Robert. Queenie Peavey. l.t. ed. 2003. (LRS Large Print Cornerstone Ser.). 166p. (J). lib. bdg. 29.95 (978-1-58118-115-9(9)) LRS.

—Queenie Peavy. abr. ed. 1999. (J). (gr. 4-7). pap. 15.95 incl. audio (978-0-670-58427-7(4)) Live Oak Media.

Burchill, Julie. Sugar Rush. 2005. 288p. (J). lib. bdg. 17.89 (978-0-06-077620-6(X) , HarperTeen) HarperCollins Pubs.

Burgess, Melvin. Doing It. 336p. (YA). 2006. reprint ed. pap. 6.95 (978-0-8050-8079-7(1)); 2004. 15.95 (978-0-8050-7565-6(8)) Holt, Henry & Co. (Holt, Henry & Co. Bks. For Young Readers).

Burkholder, Sheila M. Elsie Waits Patiently. 2004. (Illus.). 32p. (ps-5). 2.70 (978-0-7399-2339-9(0) , 2778) Rod & Staff Pubs., Inc.

Burnett, Eric. Gymnastics Jenny Stands on Her Own. 2003. 108p. pap. 9.95 (978-0-595-27919-7(8)) iUniverse, Inc.

Burnett, Frances Hodgson. A Little Princess. Corvino, Lucy, illus. 2005. (Classic Starts Ser.). 160p. 4.95 (978-1-4027-1275-3(8)) Sterling Publishing Co., Inc.

—A Little Princess. Marcos, Pablo, illus. 2005. (Great Illustrated Classics Ser.). 239p. (J). (gr. 3-8). 21.35 (978-1-59679-246-3(9) , ABDO & Daughters) ABDO Publishing Co.

—A Little Princess: The Story of Sara Crewe. unabr. ed. 2000. (Dover Juvenile Classics Ser.). (Illus.). 240p. (J). (gr. 4-7). pap. 2.00 (978-0-486-41446-1(9)) Dover Pubns., Inc.

—A Little Princess: The Story of Sara Crewe. Collier, Mary & McClintock, Barbara, illus. 2000. 32p. (J). (ps-3). 18.99 (978-0-06-027891-5(9)) HarperCollins Pubs.

—A Little Princess: The Story of Sara Crewe. Lindskoog, Kathryn, ed. Chitouras, Barbara, illus. 2002. (Classics for Young Readers Ser.). 208p. (J). pap. 7.99 (978-0-87552-727-7(2)) P & R Publishing.

—A Little Princess: The Story of Sara Crewe. 2006. (Scholastic Classics Ser.). v, 178p. (J). (gr. 9-12). 25.00 (978-0-531-16991-9(X) , Watts, Franklin) Scholastic Library Publishing.

—A Little Princess: The Story of Sara Crewe. (gr. 3-6). 2002. lib. bdg. 16.45 (978-0-613-77102-3(8)); 2001. lib. bdg. 11.80 (978-0-613-63210-2(9)) Tandem Library Bks.

—A Little Princess: The Story of Sara Crewe. l.t. ed. 2003. 342p. (J). 29.95 (978-0-7862-5842-0(X)) Thorndike Pr.

—Sara Crewe. l.t. ed. 2006. 92p. pap. (978-1-84637-263-6(1)) Echo Library.

—Sara Crewe or What Happened at Miss Minc. 2005. pap. 20.95 (978-0-7661-9708-4(5)) Kessinger Publishing, LLC.

Burns, Laura J. & Metz, Melinda. The Case of the Prank That Stank, Vol. 1. 2005. (Wright & Wong Ser.: No. 1). 192p. (J). (gr. 3-7). pap. 5.99 (978-1-59514-014-2(X)) Penguin Group (USA) Inc.

Burt, Steve. Even Odder: More Stories to Chill the Heart. Hagerman, Jessica, illus. 2003. 144p. pap. 14.95 (978-0-9741407-0-4(8)) Burt Creations.

Burton, Rebecca. Leaving Jetty Road. (YA). (gr. 7). 2008. 272p. mass mkt. 6.50 (***978-0-553-49505-8(4)*** , Laurel Leaf); 2006. 256p. 15.95 (978-0-375-83488-2(5) , Knopf Bks. for Young Readers); 2006. 256p. lib. bdg. 17.99 (978-0-375-93488-9(X) , Knopf Bks. for Young Readers) Random Hse. Children's Bks.

Busby, Cylin. The Dance Dilemma: A Choose Your Boyfriend Book. 2007. (Date Him or Dump Him? Ser.). 192p. (J). (gr. 5 up). pap. 6.95 (***978-1-59990-084-1(X)*** , Bloomsbury Children) Bloomsbury Publishing.

Butcher, Kristin. Trouble with Liberty. 2003. (gr. 7-12). lib. bdg. 16.40 (978-0-613-63001-6(7)) Tandem Library Bks.

Butler, Dori. Late Again! 2005. 40.00 (***978-1-4108-4209-1(6)***) Benchmark Education Co.

Butler, Dori Hillestad. Alexandra Hopewell, Labor Coach. 2005. 136p. (J). (gr. 3-6). 15.95 (978-0-8075-0242-6(1)) Whitman, Albert & Co.

—Sliding into Home. Casale, Paul, illus. 2003. (Peachtree Junior Publication Ser.). 192p. (J). 14.95 (978-1-56145-222-4(X)) Peachtree Pubs., Ltd.

—Tank Talbott's Guide to Girls. 2006. (Illus.). 135p. (J). 15.95 (978-0-8075-7761-5(8)) Whitman, Albert & Co.

Byalick, Marcia. Quit It. 2004. 176p. (J). (gr. 3-7). pap. 5.99 (978-0-440-41865-8(8) , Yearling) Random Hse. Children's Bks.

Byars, Betsy. Me Tarzan. Cigliano, Bill, illus. 2000. 96p. (J). (ps-3). lib. bdg. 15.89 (978-0-06-028707-8(1)) HarperCollins Pubs.

—Me Tarzan. 2002. (gr. 3-6). lib. bdg. 13.00 (978-0-613-61917-2(X)) Tandem Library Bks.

Byars, Betsy, et al. The SOS File. Howard, Arthur, illus. rev. ed. 2004. 80p. (J). 16.95 (978-0-8050-6888-7(0) , Holt, Henry & Co. Bks. For Young Readers) Holt, Henry & Co.

Cabot, Meg. All-am. 2008. 256p. (J). pap. 7.99 (***978-0-06-147989-2(6)*** , HarperTeen) HarperTeen) HarperCollins Pubs.

—All American Girl. 2003. 416p. (YA). (gr. 7 up). pap. 6.99 (978-0-06-447277-7(9)) HarperCollins Pubs.

—All American Girl. 2002. (gr. 7-12). lib. bdg. 15.30 (978-0-613-62192-2(1)) Tandem Library Bks.

—All American Girl. l.t. ed. 2003. 354p. (J). 25.95 (978-0-7862-6102-4(1) , Large Print Pr.) Thorndike Pr.

—Avalon High. (J). 2007. 320p. pap. 8.99 (***978-0-06-075588-1(1)*** , HarperTeen); 2006. 304p. 16.99 (978-0-06-075586-7(5)); 2006. 304p. lib. bdg. 17.89 (978-0-06-075587-4(3)) HarperCollins Pubs.

—Avalon High. l.t. ed. 2006. 335p. (YA). 23.95 (978-0-7862-9032-1(3)) Thorndike Pr.

—How to Be Popular. 2008. 320p. (J). pap. 8.99 (***978-0-06-088014-9(7));*** 2006. 304p. (J). lib. bdg. 17.89 (978-0-06-088013-2(9)); 2006. 304p. (YA). 16.99 (978-0-06-088012-5(0)) HarperCollins Pubs. (HarperTeen).

—In Love. 2002. (Princess Diaries: Vol. 3). (YA). (gr. 7 up). 272p. mass mkt. 5.99 (978-0-06-052568-2(1)); 240p. 16.99 (978-0-06-029467-0(1)) HarperCollins Pubs.

—In Love, Vol. 3. 2004. (Princess Diaries: Vol. 3). 288p. (J). (gr. 7 up). pap. 38.00 incl. audio (978-0-8072-2284-3(4) , Listening Library) Random Hse. Audio Publishing Group.

—Jinx. 2007. 272p. (gr. 7 up). (J). 16.99 (***978-0-06-083764-8(0));*** (YA). lib. bdg. 17.89 (***978-0-06-083765-5(9)***) HarperCollins Pubs. (HarperTeen).

—The Merlin Prophecy. Coronado, Jinky, illus. 2007. (Avalon High Coronation Ser.: No. 1). 208p. (J). (gr. 7 up). pap. 7.99 (***978-0-06-117707-1(5))*** TOKYOPOP, Inc.

—Party Princess. 2006. (Princess Diaries: Vol. 7). 304p. (J). 16.99 (978-0-06-072453-5(6)) HarperCollins Pubs.

—Party Princess. l.t. rev. ed. 2007. (Princess Diaries: Vol. 7). 335p. (YA). 23.95 (***978-0-7862-9273-8(3))*** Thorndike Pr.

—The Princess Diaries. movie tie-in ed. 2001. (Princess Diaries: Vol. I). 320p. (YA). (gr. 7 up). pap. 6.99 (978-0-380-81402-2(1) , Harper Trophy) HarperCollins Pubs.

—The Princess Diaries, Volume IX: Princess Mia (international Edition) 2008. (Princess Diaries). 288p. (J). pap. 12.00 (***978-0-06-156819-0(8)*** , HarperTeen) HarperCollins Pubs.

—Princess in Pink. (Princess Diaries: Vol. 5). (J). (gr. 7 up). 2004. 272p. 15.99 (978-0-06-009610-6(1)); 2005. (Illus.). 304p. reprint ed. pap. 6.99 (978-0-06-009612-0(8) , Harper Trophy) HarperCollins Pubs.

—Princess in Pink. l.t. ed. 2004. (Princess Diaries: Vol. 5). 304p. 23.95 (978-0-7862-6735-4(6) , Large Print Pr.) Thorndike Pr.

—Princess in the Spotlight. 2001. (Princess Diaries: Vol. II). 240p. (J). (gr. 7 up). 16.99 (978-0-06-029465-6(5)) HarperCollins Pubs.

—Princess in the Spotlight, unabr. ed. 2004. (Princess Diaries: Vol. II). 272p. (J). (gr. 7 up). pap. 38.00 incl. audio (978-0-8072-1197-7(4) , S YA 332 SP, Listening Library) Random Hse. Audio Publishing Group.

—Princess Mia. 2008. (Princess Diaries: Vol. 9). 288p. (J). lib. bdg. 17.89 (***978-0-06-072462-7(5))*** HarperCollins Pubs.

—Ready or No. 2008. 256p. (J). pap. 7.99 (***978-0-06-147996-0(9)*** , HarperTeen) HarperCollins Pubs.

—Ready or Not. 2nd ed. 2005. 256p. (gr. 7 up). (J). lib. bdg. 16.89 (978-0-06-072451-1(X)); (YA). 16.99 (978-0-06-072450-4(1)) HarperCollins Pubs.

—Ready or Not. l.t. ed. 2006. 322p. (YA). 23.95 (978-0-7862-8282-1(7)) Thorndike Pr.

—Teen Idol. (J). (gr. 7 up). 2004. 304p. 15.99 (978-0-06-009616-8(0)); 2005. (Illus.). 320p. reprint ed. pap. 8.99 (978-0-06-009618-2(7) , Harper Trophy) HarperCollins Pubs.

—Teen Idol. l.t. ed. 2006. 366p. (YA). 23.95 (978-0-7862-7760-5(2)) Thorndike Pr.

—Twilight. 2005. (Mediator Ser.: Bk. 6). 256p. (J). 15.99 (978-0-06-072467-2(6)); (gr. 7 up). lib. bdg. 16.89 (978-0-06-072468-9(4)) HarperCollins Pubs.

Cahall, Maggie. Torn Between Two. 2005. 142p. pap. 19.95 (978-1-4137-7472-6(5)) PublishAmerica, Inc.

Calamari, Barbara. Angela Anaconda the Trouble. 2001. (gr. 3-6). lib. bdg. 11.80 (978-0-613-89752-5(8)) Tandem Library Bks.

—Friends & Foes. Goldberg, Barry, illus. 2001. (Angela Anaconda Ser.: Vol. 4). 64p. (J). pap. 3.99 (978-0-689-84040-1(3) , Simon Spotlight) Simon & Schuster Children's Publishing.

—Friends & Foes. 2001. (gr. 3-6). lib. bdg. 11.80 (978-0-613-87771-8(3)) Tandem Library Bks.

Call Me Nikki. 2000. (YA). per. 8.00 (978-1-57861-106-5(7)) Attainment Co., Inc.

Callahan, Billy. Muckraker. 1999. 224p. (gr. 7-12). pap. 12.75 (978-1-892657-06-0(6)) Town Bk. Pr. The.

Calmenson, Stephanie. The Frog Principal. Brunkus, Denise, illus. 2006. 32p. (J). pap. 5.99 (978-0-439-81217-7(8) , Scholastic Paperbacks) Scholastic, Inc.

Caloggero, Lynne. New Home, New School. Higgins, Don, illus. 2000. 40p. (J). (ps-3). 6.50 (978-0-9700250-0-5(9)) L. Lemon O'Pea Productions.

Calonita, Jen. Secrets of My Hollywood Life. 2006. 256p. (J). (gr. 7-17). 16.99 (978-0-316-15442-0(3)) Little Brown & Co.

—Secrets of My Hollywood Life. 2007. 256p. (J). (gr. 7 up). pap. 7.99 (***978-0-316-15443-7(1)*** , Poppy) Little, Brown Bks. for Young Readers.

Calvert, Pam & Torrey, Richard. Clue School: Mysetery at the Ballpark. 2007. 32p. (J). (gr. 1). pap. 6.99 (***978-1-58476-609-4(3)*** , IKIDS) Innovative Kids.

Cameron, Ann. Gloria Rising. Toft, Lis, illus. 2002. 112p. (J). (gr. 2-5). 15.00 (978-0-374-32675-3(4) , Farrar, Straus & Giroux (BYR)) Farrar, Straus & Giroux.

Campbell, Bebe Moore. I Get So Hungry. Bates, Amy, illus. 2008. 32p. (J). (gr. 1-3). 16.99 (***978-0-399-24311-0(9)*** , Putnam Juvenile) Penguin Group (USA) Inc.

Canales, Viola. The Tequila Worm. 2005. 208p. (YA). (gr. 7 up). 17.99 (978-0-385-90905-1(5) , Lamb, Wendy) Random Hse. Children's Bks.

Capdevila, Juan. Teo en la Escuela (Teo at School) (SPA.). 32p. (J). 12.95 (978-84-7176-311-2(7)) Timun Mas, Editorial S.A. ESP. *Dist:* AIMS International Bks., Inc.

S

Capeci, Anne. Now You See It. 2000. (gr. 3-6). lib. bdg. 12.40 (978-0-613-54061-2(1)) Tandem Library Bks.

Caple, Kathy. The Wimp. 2000. (Illus.). 32p. (J). (gr. k-3). pap. 5.95 (978-0-618-05577-7(0) , Walter Lorraine) Houghton Mifflin Co. Trade & Reference Div.

Cappo, Nan Willard. Cheating Lessons. 2003. 272p. (YA). mass mkt. 5.99 (978-0-689-86018-8(8) , Simon Pulse); 2002. 240p. (J). (gr. 6-10). 16.00 (978-0-689-84378-5(X) , Atheneum) Simon & Schuster Children's Publishing.

—Cheating Lessons. 2003. (gr. 7-12). lib. bdg. 13.00 (978-0-613-64795-3(5)) Tandem Library Bks.

—Cheating Lessons. l.t. ed. 2003. 274p. (J). 24.95 (978-0-7862-5325-8(8)) Thorndike Pr.

Capucilli, Alyssa Satin. Biscuit's 100th Day of School. Young, Mary O'Keefe, illus. 2006. (Biscuit Ser.). 20p. (J). pap. 6.99 (978-0-06-079467-5(4) , Harper Festival) HarperCollins Pubs.

Capucilli, Alyssa Satin. Time for School, Biscuit! Back Lane Studio, illus. 2007. (Biscuit Ser.). 32p. (J). pap. 3.99 (*978-0-06-112834-9(1) , Harper Festival) HarperCollins Pubs.

Cara's Letters: Individual Chapter Book Title Six-Pack. Vol. 29. 32p. (gr. 5 up). 44.00 (978-0-7578-0975-0(8)) Rigby Education.

Carbone, Elisa. The Pack. 2006. 160p. (YA). (gr. 7). pap. 5.99 (978-0-14-240535-2(3) , Puffin) Penguin Group (USA) Inc.

—Starting School with an Enemy. 2005. 110p. (J). per. 10.00 (978-0-9769404-1-8(8) , 0-9769404-1-8) Cloonfad Pr.

—Starting School with an Enemy. 1999. (978-0-606-16568-6(1)) Tandem Library Bks.

Carlson, Melody. Becoming Me. 2000. (Diary of a Teenage Girl Ser.: Bk. 1). (Illus.). 256p. (YA). pap. 12.99 (978-1-57673-735-4(7) , Multnomah) WaterBrook Pr.

—Beyond Reach. 2007. (Secret Life Samantha Mcgregor Ser.). 258p. (YA). pap. 11.99 (978-1-59052-693-4(7) , Multnomah Fiction) WaterBrook Pr.

—Beyond Reach: A Novel. 2007. 250p. (YA). (*978-1-4287-2412-9(5) , Multnomah) WaterBrook Pr.

—Blade Silver: Color Me Scarred. 2005. 197p. (YA). (gr. 8-12). pap. 12.99 (978-1-57683-535-7(9)) NavPress Publishing Group.

—Bright Purple. 2006. 224p. (YA). pap. 12.99 (978-1-57683-950-8(8) , Th1nk Bks.) NavPress Publishing Group.

—Burnt Orange: Color Me Wasted. 2005. 207p. (YA). pap. 12.99 (978-1-57683-533-3(2)) NavPress Publishing Group.

—Dark Blue: Color Me Lonely. 2004. 196p. (J). pap. 12.99 (978-1-57683-529-6(4)) NavPress Publishing Group.

—Moon White. 2007. 224p. (YA). pap. 12.99 (978-1-57683-951-5(6) , Th1nk Bks.) NavPress Publishing Group.

—My Name Is Chloe. 2005. 288p. (YA). mass mkt. 7.99 (978-1-59052-736-8(4) , Multnomah) WaterBrook Pr.

—My Name Is Chloe: Diary of a Teenage Girl. 2003. (gr. 7-12). lib. bdg. 22.25 (978-0-613-87416-8(1)) Tandem Library Bks.

—Who I Am. 2002. (gr. 7-12). lib. bdg. 22.25 (978-0-613-89918-5(0)) Tandem Library Bks.

—Who I Am: Diary Number 3. 2002. (Diary of a Teenage Girl Ser.: Bk. 3). 224p. pap. 12.99 (978-1-57673-890-0(6) , Multnomah Fiction) WaterBrook Pr.

Carlson, Nancy. Henry's 100 Days of Kindergarten. Carlson, Nancy, illus. 32p. (J). 2007. pap. 5.99 (978-0-14-240758-5(5) , Puffin); 2004. (Illus.). 15.99 (978-0-670-05977-5(3) , Viking Juvenile) Penguin Group (USA) Inc.

—Henry's Show & Tell. Carlson, Nancy, illus. 2006. (Illus.). 32p. (J). (ps). reprint ed. pap. 5.99 (978-0-14-240639-7(2) , Puffin) Penguin Group (USA) Inc.

—Hooray for Grandparents' Day! Carlson, Nancy, illus. 2002. (Illus.). (YA). 13.19 (978-1-4046-0774-3(9)) Book Wholesalers, Inc.

—Hooray for Grandparents' Day! 2002. (gr. k-3). lib. bdg. 14.15 (978-0-613-45272-4(0)) Tandem Library Bks.

—Hooray for Grandparents Day! Carlson, Nancy, illus. 2002. (Illus.). 32p. (J). pap. 5.99 (978-0-14-230125-8(6) , Puffin) Penguin Group (USA) Inc.

—Hooray for Grandparent's Day. 2000. (Illus.). 32p. (J). (ps-2). 15.99 (978-0-670-88876-4(1) , Viking Juvenile) Penguin Group (USA) Inc.

—It's Not My Fault! Carlson, Nancy, illus. 2003. (Illus.). 32p. (J). (gr. k-2). 15.95 (978-1-57505-598-5(8)) Lerner Publishing Group.

—Look Out Kindergarten, Here I Come! (Preparante, Kindergarten, Alla Voy!) 2001. (Illus.). (J). (978-0-606-21304-2(X)) Tandem Library Bks.

—Piensa en Grande! 2005. (Libros Ilustrados (Picture Bks.)). (SPA., Illus.). 32p. (J). (ps-ps). lib. bdg. 15.95 (978-0-8225-3192-0(5) , Ediciones Lerner) Lerner Publishing Group.

—Think Big! 2005. (Illus.). 28p. (J). (ps-ps). 15.95 (978-1-57505-622-7(4) , Carolrhoda Bks.) Lerner Publishing Group.

Carlson, Nancy L. First Grade, Here I Come! Carlson, Nancy L., illus. 2006. (Illus.). 32p. (J). (ps-1). 15.99 (978-0-670-06127-3(1) , Viking Adult) Penguin Group (USA) Inc.

—First Grade, Here I Come! 2006. (Illus.). (J). (*978-1-4156-8114-5(7) , Viking Adult) Penguin Group (USA) Inc.

Carney, Jeffrey K. The Adventures of Michael MacInnes. 2006. 256p. (YA). 17.00 (978-0-374-30146-0(8)) Farrar, Straus & Giroux.

Carney, Mary Lou. Tyler Timothy Bradford & the Birthday Surprise. Warren, Shari, illus. 2004. 32p. (J). 14.95 (978-0-7696-3168-4(1)) School Specialty Publishing.

Carr, Annie Roe. Nan Sherwood at Pine Camp or the Old Lum. 2007. pap. (*978-1-4065-1294-6(X)) Dodo Pr.

—Nan Sherwood at Rose Ranch or the Old Me. 2007. pap. (*978-1-4065-1295-3(8)) Dodo Pr.

Carr, Dennis & Carr, Elise. Welcome to Wahoo. 2006. 250p. (YA). 16.95 (978-1-58234-696-0(8) , Bloomsbury Children) Bloomsbury Publishing.

Carr, Elise & Carr, Dennis. Welcome to Wahoo. 2007. 240p. (YA). pap. 6.95 (*978-1-59990-096-4(3) , Bloomsbury Children) Bloomsbury Publishing.

Carr, Pat M. If We Must Die: A Novel. 2004. (Chaparral Book for Young Readers Ser.). 168p. (C). pap. 15.95 (978-0-87565-262-7(X)) Texas Christian Univ. Pr.

Carr, Roe Annie. Nan Sherwood at Pine Camp (the Old Lumbe. 2006. 52.99 (*978-1-4219-7906-9(3)); pap. 45.99 (*978-1-4219-7917-5(9)) IndyPublish.com.

—Nan Sherwood at Rose Ranch or the Old Me. 2006. 63.99 (*978-1-4219-9653-0(7)); pap. 57.99 (*978-1-4219-9654-7(5)) IndyPublish.com.

Carr, Roger. Can-Rolling Race. 2001. (gr. k-3). lib. bdg. 11.65 (978-0-613-33344-3(6)) Tandem Library Bks.

Carrick, Carol. Patrick's Dinosaurs on the Internet. Milgrim, David, illus. 1999. 32p. (J). (gr. k-3). tchr. ed. 16.00 (978-0-395-50949-4(1) , Clarion Bks.) Houghton Mifflin Co. Trade & Reference Div.

Carrier, Roch. The Basketball Player. Fischman, Sheila, tr. from FRE. Cohen, Sheldon, illus. 2001. 24p. (J). (gr. 3). pap. 7.95 (978-0-88776-553-7(X)) Tundra Bks., Inc./Livres Toundra, Inc. CAN. *Dist:* Random Hse., Inc.

Carroll, Jonathan. Meet Julius Carmichael: First Day Blues. Koltun, Amy, illus. 2003. 96p. (J). (gr. 3-6). pap. 6.95 (978-0-9724935-0-5(6)) Striking Presence Pubns.

Carroll, Thomas L. The Colony: A Novel for the Young Reader. 2000. 152p. (J). (gr. 4-7). 18.95 (978-0-86534-295-8(4)) Sunstone Pr.

Carson, Jana. We Both Read-Stop Teasing Taylor! Treatner, Meryl, illus. 2005. (J). (*978-1-4156-3784-5(9)) Book Wholesalers, Inc.

Carter, Alden R. Dustin's Big School Day. Young, Dan & Carter, Carol S., illus. 1999. (Concept Book Ser.). 32p. (J). (gr. k-3). lib. bdg. 14.95 (978-0-8075-1741-3(0)) Whitman, Albert & Co.

—Love, Football, & Other Contact Sports. 2006. 192p. (J). 16.95 (978-0-8234-1975-3(4)) Holiday Hse., Inc.

Carter, Ally. I'd Tell You I Love You, but Then I'd Have to Kill You. 2006. (Gallagher Girls Ser.). 288p. (gr. 7-17). (978-1-4231-0003-4(4)) Hyperion Pr.

Carter, Forrest. The Education of Little Tree. unabr. ed. 1998. (YA). Class Set. 196.30 incl. audio (978-0-7887-2547-0(5) , 46717); Homework Set. 67.20 incl. audio (978-0-7887-2242-4(5) , 40726) Recorded Bks., LLC.

Carvell, Marlene. Who Will Tell My Brother? 2004. 160p. (gr. 7-17). pap. 5.99 (978-0-7868-1657-6(0)) Hyperion Bks. for Children.

Caseley, Judith. The Kissing Diary. 2007. 208p. (J). (gr. 5 up). 16.00 (978-0-374-36346-8(3)) Farrar, Straus & Giroux.

—Mr. Green Peas. 1998. (Illus.). 32p. (J). (ps-3). pap. 4.95 (978-0-688-16092-0(1)) HarperCollins Pubs.

Cash, Rosanne. Penelope Jane: A Fairy's Tale. Karas, G. Brian, illus. 2006. 32p. (J). pap. 6.99 (978-0-06-084230-7(X) , Harper Trophy) HarperCollins Pubs.

Cassidy, Cathy. Indigo Blue. 2006. 240p. (J). (gr. 5). pap. 5.99 (978-0-14-240703-5(8) , Puffin) Penguin Group (USA) Inc.

Castellucci, Cecil. Boy Proof. 208p. (YA). (gr. 9 up). 2005. 15.99 (978-0-7636-2333-3(4)); 2006. reprint ed. pap. 7.99 (978-0-7636-2796-6(8)) Candlewick Pr.

—The Queen of Cool. 2006. 176p. (YA). (gr. 9). 15.99 (978-0-7636-2720-1(8)) Candlewick Pr.

—The Queen of Cool. l.t. rev. ed. 2007. 172p. (YA). 22.95 (*978-0-7862-9551-7(1)) Thorndike Pr.

Catalanotto, Peter. Matthew A. B. C. Catalanotto, Peter, illus. 2002. (Illus.). 32p. (J). (ps-2). 15.95 (978-0-689-84582-6(0) , Atheneum/Richard Jackson Bks.) Simon & Schuster Children's Publishing.

Catalanotto, Peter & Schembri, Pamela. The Secret Lunch Special. 2006. (Illus.). (J). 56p. (*978-1-4156-9204-2(1)); Bk. 1. 64p. 15.95 (978-0-8050-7838-1(X) , Holt, Henry & Co. Bks. For Young Readers) Holt, Henry & Co.

Caudill, Rebecca. Did You Carry the Flag Today, Charley. Grossman, Nancy, illus. 2007. 96p. (J). pap. 7.95 (978-0-8050-8141-1(0) , Holt, Henry & Co. Bks. For Young Readers) Holt, Henry & Co.

—Schoolhouse in the Woods. l.t. ed. 2004. (Fairchild Family Story Ser.: Bk. 2). (Illus.). 130p. (J). pap. 10.95 (978-1-883937-80-5(9)) Bethlehem Bks.

—Schoolroom in the Parlor. l.t. ed. 2005. (Illus.). 150p. (J). pap. 11.95 (978-1-883937-82-9(5)) Bethlehem Bks.

Cavanna, Betty. Going on Sixteen. 1998. 192p. (YA). (gr. 7-12). reprint ed. pap. 5.95 (978-0-688-16324-2(6)) HarperCollins Pubs.

Cazet, Denys. Never Poke a Squid. Cazet, Denys, illus. 2000. (Illus.). 32p. (J). (ps-2). 17.99 (978-0-531-33279-5(9) , Watts, Franklin) Scholastic Library Publishing.

—Never Poke a Squid. Cazet, Denys, illus. 2000. (Illus.). 32p. (J). (ps-2). pap. 16.95 (978-0-531-30279-8(2) , Orchard Bks.) Scholastic, Inc.

Cerasini, Marc. The School of Mandy. Roper, Robert, illus. 2005. (Totally Spies! Ser.). 64p. (J). pap. 4.99 (978-0-689-87725-4(0) , Simon Spotlight) Simon & Schuster Children's Publishing.

Changing Schools: Individual Title Six-Packs. (ps-2). 27.00 (978-0-7635-9440-4(7)) Rigby Education.

Chapra, Mimi. Amelia's Show-and-Tell Fiesta/Amelia y la Fiesta de Muestra y Cuenta. Aviles, Martha, illus. 2004. (ENG & SPA.). 32p. (J). (ps-1). lib. bdg. 17.89 (978-0-06-050256-0(8)) HarperCollins Pubs.

—Amelia's Show-and-Tell Fiesta/Amelia y la Fiesta de "Muestra y Cuenta" Aviles, Martha, illus. 2004. (ENG & SPA.). 32p. (J). (ps-1). 16.99 (978-0-06-050255-3(X)) HarperCollins Pubs.

CHaracter Ed & the Magical Lesson of the Bully. 2004. (J). pap. 15.95 (*978-1-59526-181-6(8)) Media Creations, Inc.

Chardiet, Bernice & Maccarone, Grace. The Snowball War. Karas, G. Brian, illus. 1999. (J). (978-0-439-10803-4(9)) Scholastic, Inc.

Charles, Patricia. High School Is Like Hell. 2001. (gr. 7-12). lib. bdg. 25.70 (978-0-613-82475-0(X)) Tandem Library Bks.

—High School Is Like Hell. 2001. 268p. pap. 15.95 (978-0-595-18936-6(9) , Writers Club Pr.) iUniverse, Inc.

Charlton-Trujillo, E. E. Prizefighter en Mi Casa. (J). (gr. 5-7). 2007. 192p. 5.99 (*978-0-440-42117-7(9) , Yearling); 2006. 224p. 15.95 (978-0-385-73325-0(9) , Delacorte Bks. for Young Readers); 2006. 224p. lib. bdg. 17.99 (978-0-385-90344-8(8) , Delacorte Bks. for Young Readers) Random Hse. Children's Bks.

Chatterton, Martin. Whereit's@ Skool! 2003. (Illus.). 48p. (J). pap., spiral bd. 8.99 (978-1-4052-0750-8(7)) Egmont Bks., Ltd. GBR. *Dist:* Independent Pubs. Group.

—Whereit's@ Spooks! 2003. (Illus.). 48p. (J). pap., spiral bd. 8.99 (978-1-4052-0790-4(6)) Egmont Bks., Ltd. GBR. *Dist:* Independent Pubs. Group.

Chbosky, Stephen. The Perks of Being a Wallflower. 1999. 213p. (gr. 7-12). pap. 14.00 (978-0-671-02734-6(4) , MTV) Simon & Schuster.

—The Perks of Being a Wallflower. 1999. (978-0-606-18378-9(7)) Tandem Library Bks.

Cheat, Sheet & Krulik, Nancy E. Cheat Sheet. 2008. (How I Survived Middle School Ser.). 112p. (J). 4.99 (*978-0-545-01304-8(6) , Scholastic Paperbacks) Scholastic, Inc.

Cheng, Andrea. Where the Steps Were. 2008. (J). (*978-1-932425-88-8(8) , Front Street) Boyds Mills Pr.

Cheshire, Simon. Kissing Vanessa. 2004. 144p. (YA). (gr. 7). 15.95 (978-0-385-73212-3(0) , Delacorte Bks. for Young Readers) Random Hse. Children's Bks.

Child, Lauren. Clarice Bean Spells Trouble. Child, Lauren, illus. 2006. (Clarice Bean Ser.). 192p. (J). (gr. 3-6). pap. 5.99 (978-0-7636-2903-8(0)) Candlewick Pr.

—De Que Planeta Eres, Ana Tarambana? 2002. Tr. of What Planet Are You From, Clarice Bean?. (Illus.). 32p. (J). (SPA.). 17.95 (978-84-8488-036-3(2)); (CAT., 17.95 (978-84-8488-037-0(0)) Serres, Ediciones, S. L. ESP. *Dist:* Lectorum Pubns., Inc.

—I Am Too Absolutely Small for School. Child, Lauren, illus. (Illus.). 32p. (J). (ps-1). 2004. 16.99 (978-0-7636-2403-3(9)); 2005. reprint ed. pap. 6.99 (978-0-7636-2887-1(5)) Candlewick Pr.

—My School Play. Child, Lauren, illus. 2006. (Charlie & Lola Ser.). 16p. (J). (ps-1). 4.99 (978-0-448-44256-3(6) , Grosset & Dunlap) Penguin Group (USA) Inc.

—Utterly Me, Clarice Bean. Child, Lauren, illus. (Illus.). (J). (gr. 3-7). 2003. 192p. 15.99 (978-0-7636-2186-5(2)); 2005. 208p. reprint ed. pap. 5.99 (978-0-7636-2788-1(7)) Candlewick Pr.

—Utterly Me, Clarice Bean. 2002. (Illus.). 160p. (J). 5.99 (978-1-84121-918-9(5) , Orchard Bks.) Scholastic, Inc.

—What Planet Are You from, Clarice Bean? Child, Lauren, illus. 2002. (Illus.). 32p. (J). (gr. 1-5). 16.99 (978-0-7636-1696-0(6)) Candlewick Pr.

Child, Lauren, et al. Fi'n Hollol, Carys Blodyn. 2005. (WEL., Illus.). 192p. pap. (978-1-85596-675-8(1)) Dref Wen.

Choi, Yangsook. The Name Jar. Choi, Yangsook, illus. (Illus.). 40p. (J). (gr. k-3). 2003. pap. 6.99 (978-0-440-41799-6(6) , Dragonfly Bks.); 2001. 16.95 (978-0-375-80613-1(X) , Knopf Bks. for Young Readers); 2001. lib. bdg. 18.99 (978-0-375-90613-8(4) , Knopf Bks. for Young Readers) Random Hse. Children's Bks.

Choldenko, Gennifer. How to Make Friends with a Giant. Walrod, Amy, illus. 2006. 32p. (J). (ps-3). 16.99 (978-0-399-23779-9(8)) Penguin Group (USA) Inc.

Choldenko, Gennifer. If a Tree Falls at Lunch Period. 2007. (Illus.). 224p. (J). (gr. 5 up). 17.00 (*978-0-15-205753-4(6)) Harcourt Trade Pubs.

Choyce, Lesley. Carrie Loses Her Nerve. Thurman, Mark, illus. 2003. (First Novel Ser.). 64p. (J). (gr. 1-5). 4.95 (978-0-88780-591-2(4)); (*978-0-88780-592-9(2)) Formac Publishing Co., Ltd. CAN. *Dist:* Casemate Pubs. & Bk. Distributors, LLC.

—Carrie Loses Her Nerve. 2003. (gr. k-3). lib. bdg. 11.80 (978-0-613-88546-1(5)) Tandem Library Bks.

Choyce, Lesley. The End of the World As We Know It. 2007. 224p. (YA). (gr. 7 up). pap. 9.95 (*978-0-88995-379-6(1)) Red Deer Pr. CAN. *Dist:* Fitzhenry & Whiteside, Ltd.

Christie, Merisue. Oh My Way Home from School Today: The Kitten. 2007. 11.00 (*978-0-8059-9619-7(2)) Dorrance Publishing Co., Inc.

Christopher, Lawrence. The Tickle Fingers: Where Is Pinky? Christopher, Lawrence, illus. 2006. (ENG., Illus.). 24p. (J). (ps up). 9.95 (978-0-9712278-3-5(7)) MF Unlimited.

Christopher, Matt. Soccer Scoop. 2007. (J). lib. bdg. (*978-1-59953-117-5(8)) Norwood Hse. Pr.

Christopher, Matt. Stealing Home. 2004. 144p. (J). (gr. 4-7). pap. 4.99 (978-0-316-60742-1(8)) Hachette Bk. Group.

Christopher, Matt & #1 Sports Writer for Kids Staff. Mountain Bike Mania. 1998. 160p. (J). (gr. 3-7). pap. 4.99 (978-0-316-14292-2(1)) Little Brown & Co.

—Mountain Bike Mania: Is Will Pedaling Out of Control? 1998. 160p. (J). (gr. 3-7). 15.95 (978-0-316-14355-4(3)) Little Brown & Co.

Chung, Helena. Jennifer, the Special One. 2004. (J). pap. 8.00 (978-0-8059-6395-3(2)) Dorrance Publishing Co., Inc.

Cibula, Matt S. What's up with You, Taquandra Fu? Strassburg, Brian J., illus. 1998. 40p. (J). (ps-3). 16.95 (978-1-55933-212-5(3)) Zino Pr. Children's Bks.

Ciocca, Donna. Harley & Homer. 2004. (YA). per. 9.95 (978-0-9747361-2-9(0)) Oak Manor Publishing, Inc.

Ciocca, Donna. Harley & Homer for Hire. 2006. (YA). per. 11.95 (*978-0-9747361-9-8(8)) Oak Manor Publishing, Inc.

Cirrone, Dorian. Dancing in Red Shoes Will Kill You. 2005. 224p. (J). (gr. 7 up). 15.99 (978-0-06-055701-0(X)) HarperCollins Pubs.

Cirrone, Dorian. Prom Kings & Drama Queens. 2008. 208p. (J). 16.99 (*978-0-06-114372-4(3)); lib. bdg. 17.89 (*978-0-06-114373-1(1)) HarperCollins Pubs. (HarperTeen).

Clairday, Robynn. Confessions of a Boyfriend Stealer. 2005. 240p. (YA). (gr. 7-12). pap. 7.95 (978-0-385-73242-0(2) , Delacorte Bks. for Young Readers) Random Hse. Children's Bks.

Clark, Brenda, illus. Franklin Goes to School. 2002. (Franklin Ser.). 12.40 (978-1-4046-0312-7(3)) Book Wholesalers, Inc.

Clark, Catherine. Frozen Rodeo. 2003. 304p. (J). (gr. 8 up). 15.99 (978-0-06-009070-8(7)) HarperCollins Pubs.

—Frozen Rodeo. 2004. lib. bdg. 15.30 (978-0-613-71502-7(0)) Tandem Library Bks.

—Gilmore Girls No. 1: Like Mother, Like Daughter. 2002. 160p. (YA). mass mkt. 5.99 (978-0-06-009212-2(2)) HarperCollins Pubs.

Clark, Eleanor. Victoria Grace: Courageous Patriot. 2007. (Eleanor Jo Ser.). (J). 14.99 (978-0-9753036-8-9(6)) HonorNet.

Clark, Margaret. Lucky Last Luke. 1999. (gr. 3-6). lib. bdg. 12.60 (978-0-613-19389-4(X)) Tandem Library Bks.

Clark, Sherryl. Take a Hike! 2000. (gr. 7-12). lib. bdg. 12.25 (978-0-613-29088-3(7)) Tandem Library Bks.

Clarke, Gus. Eddie & Teddy. 2004. (Illus.). 32p. (J). pap. 8.99 (978-1-84270-373-1(0)) Andersen GBR. *Dist:* Independent Pubs. Group.

—What Would We Do Without Missus Mac. 1999. (Illus.). 24p. (J). 19.99 (978-0-86264-884-8(X)) Andersen GBR. *Dist:* Independent Pubs. Group.

Clarke, Judith. Al Capsella & Watchdogs. 164p. pap. 9.95 (978-0-7022-2294-8(1)) Univ. of Queensland Pr. AUS. *Dist:* International Specialized Bk. Services.

—Kalpana's Dream. 2005. 168p. (J). 16.95 (978-1-932425-22-2(5) , Lemniscaat) Boyds Mills Pr.

Clarke, Judith. Night Train. 2007. (J). pap. 9.95 (*978-1-932425-92-5(6) , Front Street) Boyds Mills Pr.

—Night Train. 2000. 200p. (gr. 7-12). 16.95 (978-0-8050-6151-2(7) , Holt, Henry & Co. Bks. For Young Readers) Holt, Henry & Co.

Clarke, Nicole. London Calling. 2007. (Flirt Ser.: No. 8). 224p. (J). pap. 6.99 (978-0-448-44464-2(X) , Grosset & Dunlap) Penguin Group (USA) Inc.

Clausen, Andrew. In the Year of the Boar & Jackie Robinson. 1999. 66p. (J). (gr. 4-6). stu. ed., ring bd. 12.99 (978-1-58609-135-4(2)) Progeny Pr.

Cleary, Beverly. Dear Mr. Henshaw. 2002. (Illus.). (J). 13.83 (978-0-7587-9140-5(2)) Book Wholesalers, Inc.

—Dear Mr. Henshaw. Zelinsky, Paul O., illus. 2000. (Cleary Reissue Ser.). 160p. (J). (gr. 5 up). pap. 5.99 (978-0-380-70958-8(9) , Harper Trophy) HarperCollins Pubs.

—Henry & Beezus. 2002. (Illus.). (J). 13.83 (978-0-7587-0018-6(0)) Book Wholesalers, Inc.

—The Ramona Collection, 4 vols., Vol. 1. Dockray, Tracy, illus. 1999. (Ramona Quimby Ser.). (J). (gr. 3-7). pap. 23.96 (978-0-380-81468-8(4)) HarperCollins Pubs.

—Ramona Quimby, Age 8. 2002. (Illus.). (J). 13.83 (978-0-7587-5637-4(2)) Book Wholesalers, Inc.

—Ramona Quimby, Age 8. (Ramona Ser.). (J). (gr. 3-5). Dell Publishing.

—Ramona Quimby, Age 8. (Ramona Ser.). (J). (gr. 3-5). 1999. 9.95 (978-1-56137-448-9(2)); 1998. 44p. 11.95 (978-1-56137-708-4(2) , NU7082SP) Novel Units, Inc.

—Ramona Quimby, Age 8. (Ramona Quimby Ser.). 190p. (J). (gr. 3-5). pap. 4.99 (978-0-8072-1436-7(1) , Listening Library) Random Hse. Audio Publishing Group.

—Ramona the Brave. Dockray, Tracy, illus. 2006. 176p. (J). lib. bdg. 20.00 (*978-1-4242-0411-3(9)) Fitzgerald Bks.

—Ramona the Brave. 2000. (Ramona Ser.). (J). (gr. 3-5). 9.95 (978-1-56137-444-1(X)) Novel Units, Inc.

—Ramona the Brave. (Ramona Quimby Ser.). 190p. (J). (gr. 3-5). pap. 4.99 (978-0-8072-1440-4(X) , Listening Library) Random Hse. Audio Publishing Group.

—Ramona the Pest. (Ramona Ser.). (J). (gr. 3-5). Dell Publishing.

—Ramona the Pest. Dockray, Tracy, illus. 2006. 211p. (J). lib. bdg. 20.00 (*978-1-4242-0410-6(0)) Fitzgerald Bks.

—Ramona the Pest. (Ramona Quimby Ser.). 192p. (J). (gr. 3-5). pap. 4.99 (978-0-8072-1438-1(8) , Listening Library) Random Hse. Audio Publishing Group.

Cleary, Beverly. Ramona's World. Dockray, Tracy, illus. 2006. 209p. (J). lib. bdg. 20.00 (*978-1-4242-0407-6(0)) Fitzgerald Bks.

—Ramona's World. Tiegreen, Alan & Dockray, Tracy, illus. 2001. (Ramona Quimby Ser.). 240p. (J). (gr. 3-5). 16.99 (978-0-688-16816-2(7)) HarperCollins Pubs.

—Ramona's World. Tiegreen, Alan, illus. 1999. (Ramona Quimby Ser.). 208p. (gr. 3-5). pap. 5.99 (978-0-380-73272-2(6)) HarperCollins Pubs.

Clement-Moore, Rosemary. Prom Dates from Hell. 2008. 304p. (YA). pap. 8.99 (*978-0-385-73413-4(1) , Delacorte Bks. for Young Readers) Random Hse. Children's Bks.

Clements, Andrew. Back to School: School Story; the Report Card; a Week in the Woods. 2006. 512p. (J). pap. 14.95 (978-1-4169-2681-8(X) , Aladdin) Simon & Schuster Children's Publishing.

—Head of the Class: Frindle; the Landry News; the Janitor's Boy. Selznick, Brian, illus. 2007. 416p. (J). 17.99 (*978-1-4169-4974-9(7) , Aladdin) Simon & Schuster Children's Publishing.

—The Jacket. Henderson, McDavid, illus. 2003. 96p. (J). pap. 5.99 (978-0-689-86010-2(2) , Aladdin) Simon & Schuster Children's Publishing.

—Jake Drake, Bully Buster. Pedersen, Janet, illus. 2007. (Jake Drake Ser.). 80p. (J). pap. 3.99 (*978-1-4169-3933-7(4) , Aladdin) Simon & Schuster Children's Publishing.

—Jake Drake, Bully Buster. 2001. (gr. 3-6). lib. bdg. 11.80 (978-0-613-31375-9(5)); (Illus.). (J). 10.79 (978-0-606-20733-1(3)) Tandem Library Bks.

—Jake Drake, Class Clown. Frazee, Marla & Pedersen, Janet, illus. 2007. (Jake Drake Ser.). 96p. (J). pap. 4.99 (*978-1-4169-4912-1(7) , Aladdin) Simon & Schuster Children's Publishing.

—Jake Drake, Class Clown. Avendano, Dolores, illus. 2002. (Jake Drake Ser.). 80p. (J). 3.99 (978-0-689-85114-8(6) , Aladdin) Simon & Schuster Children's Publishing.

—Jake Drake, Class Clown. 2002. (gr. 3-6). lib. bdg. 11.80 (978-0-613-45071-3(X)) Tandem Library Bks.

—Jake Drake, Know-It-All. Avendano, Dolores, illus. 2001. (Ready-for-Chapters Ser.). 88p. (J). (gr. 4-7). lib. bdg. 10.79 (978-0-606-21259-5(0)) Tandem Library Bks.

—Jake Drake, Know-It-All. 2001. (gr. 3-6). lib. bdg. 11.80 (978-0-613-35670-1(5)) Tandem Library Bks.

—Jake Drake, Know-It-All. l.t. ed. 2002. (Juvenile Ser.). (Illus.). 76p. (J). 21.95 (978-0-7862-4139-2(X)) Thomson Gale.

—Jake Drake, Teacher's Pet. 2001. 10.79 (978-0-606-22090-3(9)) Tandem Library Bks.

—The Janitor's Boy. 2001. 160p. (J). pap. 5.99 (978-0-689-83585-8(X) , Aladdin) Simon & Schuster Children's Publishing.

—The Janitor's Boy. Selznick, Brian, illus. 2000. 144p. (J). (gr. 3-7). 15.95 (978-0-689-81818-9(1)) Simon & Schuster Children's Publishing.

—The Janitor's Boy. 2001. 11.64 (978-0-606-22108-5(5)) Tandem Library Bks.

—The Janitor's Boy. l.t. ed. 2000. 152p. (J). (gr. 4-7). 21.95 (978-0-7862-2903-1(9)) Thorndike Pr.

—Know-It-All. Pedersen, Janet, illus. 2007. (Jake Drake Ser.: No. 2). 112p. (J). pap. 3.99 (*978-1-4169-3931-3(8) , Aladdin) Simon & Schuster Children's Publishing.

—The Landry News. Murdocca, Sal, illus. 2002. (J). 13.40 (978-0-7587-6519-2(3)) Book Wholesalers, Inc.

—The Landry News. Selznick, Brian, illus. 2000. 144p. (J). (gr. 3-7). pap. 5.99 (978-0-689-82868-3(3) , Aladdin) Simon & Schuster Children's Publishing.

—The Landry News. 1999. (J). (978-0-606-19720-5(6)) Tandem Library Bks.

—The Landry News. l.t. ed. 2000. (Juvenile Ser.). (Illus.). 138p. (J). (gr. 4-7). 21.95 (978-0-7862-2707-5(9)) Thorndike Pr.

—The Last Holiday Concert. 2006. 176p. (J). pap. 5.99 (978-0-689-84525-3(1) , Aladdin) Simon & Schuster Children's Publishing.

—The Last Holiday Concert. Selznick, Brian, illus. 2004. 176p. (J). 15.95 (978-0-689-84516-1(2)) Simon & Schuster Children's Publishing.

—Lunch Money. Selznick, Brian, illus. (J). 2007. 240p. (gr. 3-7). pap. 5.99 (*978-0-689-86685-2(2) , Aladdin); 2005. 224p. 16.99 (978-0-689-86683-8(6)) Simon & Schuster Children's Publishing.

—Lunch Money. Selznick, Brian, illus. l.t. ed. 2005. 231p. (J). (gr. 3-7). 21.95 (978-0-7862-8036-0(0) , Large Print Pr.) Thorndike Pr.

—No Talking. Elliott, Mark, illus. 2007. 160p. (J). (gr. 3-7). 15.99 (*978-1-4169-0983-5(4)) Simon & Schuster Children's Publishing.

—El Periodico Landry. Selznick, Brian, illus. 2004. Tr. of Landry News. (SPA.). (YA). pap. 9.99 (978-84-241-7886-4(6)) Everest de Ediciones y Distribucion, S.L. ESP. *Dist:* Lectorum Pubns., Inc.

—The Report Card. (Illus.). (J). 2004. 176p. (gr. 3-7). 15.95 (978-0-689-84515-4(4)); 2005. 192p. reprint ed. pap. 5.99 (978-0-689-84524-6(3) , Aladdin) Simon & Schuster Children's Publishing.

—Room One: A Mystery or Two. Blair, Chris, illus. 2006. 176p. (J). (gr. 3-7). 15.95 (978-0-689-86686-9(0)) Simon & Schuster Children's Publishing.

—Slippers at School. Bynum, Janie, illus. 2005. 32p. (J). (ps-1). 12.99 (978-0-525-47189-9(8) , Dutton Juvenile) Penguin Group (USA) Inc.

Clements, Andrew. Teacher's Pet. Pedersen, Janet, illus. 2007. (Jake Drake Ser.). 96p. (J). pap. 4.99 (*978-1-4169-3932-0(6) , Aladdin) Simon & Schuster Children's Publishing.

Clements, Andrew & Avendano, Dolores. Teacher's Pet. 2001. (Jake Drake Ser.: Bk. 3). (Illus.). 80p. (J). (gr. 2-5). pap. 15.00 (978-0-689-83919-1(7)) Simon & Schuster Children's Publishing.

Clements, Andrew & Murdocca, Salvatore. The Landry News. 1999. (Illus.). 128p. (J). (gr. 3-7). 15.95 (978-0-689-81817-2(3)) Simon & Schuster Children's Publishing.

Clish, Marian L. I Wonder... What Would Happen If I Took an Elephant to School? Anderson, Jan, illus. unabr. ed. 1999. (J). (gr. k-3). 22.95 incl. cd-rom (978-1-928632-37-5(8)); 18.95 incl. audio (978-1-928632-36-8(X)); 15.95 (978-1-928632-35-1(1)); pap. 14.95 incl. cd-rom (978-1-928632-34-4(3)); pap. 7.95 (978-1-928632-32-0(7)); pap. 10.95 incl. audio (978-1-928632-33-7(5)) Writers Marketplace:Consulting, Critiquing & Publishing.

Clugston, Chynna. Queen Bee. 2005. (Illus.). 112p. (J). pap. 16.99 (978-0-439-71572-0(5) , Graphix) Scholastic, Inc.

Cobot, Meg. All-American Girl. 2004. 416p. (J). (gr. 7 up). pap. 44.00 incl. audio (978-0-8072-2281-2(X) , Listening Library) Random Hse. Audio Publishing Group.

Cocca-Leffler, Maryann. Jack's Talent. 2007. (Illus.). 32p. (J). (ps-3). 16.00 (*978-0-374-33681-3(4)) Farrar, Straus & Giroux.

—Mr. Tanen's Ties. 1999. (gr. k-3). lib. bdg. 15.25 (978-0-613-61918-9(8)) Tandem Library Bks.

—Mr. Tanen's Ties. Cocca-Leffler, Maryann, illus. (Illus.). 32p. (J). (gr. k-2). 2004. pap. 6.95 (978-0-8075-5302-2(6)); 1999. 15.95 (978-0-8075-5301-5(8)) Whitman, Albert & Co.

—Mr. Tanen's Ties Rule! Cocca-Leffler, Maryann, illus. 2005. (Illus.). 32p. (J). (gr. k-3). 15.95 (978-0-8075-5308-4(5)) Whitman, Albert & Co.

Cocca-Leffler, Maryann, illus. Mr. Tanen's Tie Trouble. 2003. 32p. (J). (gr. k-3). 15.95 (978-0-8075-5305-3(0)) Whitman, Albert & Co.

Cocca-Leffler, Maryann, illus. Spotlight on Stacey. 2007. (Social Studies Connects). 32p. (J). (*978-1-4287-1948-4(2)); (gr. 2-4). pap. 4.99 (*978-1-57565-236-8(6)) Kane Pr., The.

Codell, Esmé Raji. Sahara Special. (gr. 3-7). 2004. 192p. (J). pap. 5.99 (978-0-7868-1611-8(2)); 2003. (Illus.). 208p. (J). lib. bdg. 16.49 (978-0-7868-2627-8(4)); 2003. (Illus.). 192p. 15.99 (978-0-7868-0793-2(8)) Hyperion Bks. for Children.

—Sahara Special. 2003. (gr. 3-6). lib. bdg. 14.10 (978-0-613-65611-5(3)) Tandem Library Bks.

—Vive la Paris! 2006. 224p. (J). (gr. 3-7). 15.99 (978-0-7868-5124-9(4)) Hyperion Pr.

Cohen, Barbara. Molly's Pilgrim. Duffy, Daniel M. & Deraney, Michael J., illus. rev. ed. 1998. 32p. (J). (ps-3). 16.99 (978-0-688-16279-5(7)) HarperCollins Pubs.

—Molly's Pilgrim. Duffy, Daniel Mark & Deraney, Michael J., illus. 97th rev. ed. 1998. 32p. (J). (gr. 1-4). pap. 3.99 (978-0-688-16280-1(0) , Harper Trophy) HarperCollins Pubs.

—Molly's Pilgrim. (Literature to Go Ser.). pap., tchr. ed. incl. VHS (978-0-7919-2685-7(0)) Phoenix Films & Video.

Cohen, Miriam. Bee My Valentine. Hoban, Lillian, illus. unabr. ed. 2001. (J). (gr. k-3). pap. 16.95 incl. audio Spoken Arts, Inc.

—Eddy's Dream. Cohen, Adam, photos by. l.t. ed. 2000. (Illus.). 32p. (J). (gr. k-2). 16.95 (978-1-887734-57-8(0)) Star Bright Bks., Inc.

—First Grade Takes a Test. Himler, Ronald, illus. 2006. (J). 32p. 15.95 (978-1-59572-054-2(5)); pap. 5.95 (978-1-59572-055-9(3)) Star Bright Bks., Inc.

Cohen, Tish. The Invisible Rules of the Zoe Lama. 2007. 208p. (J). (gr. 4-7). 15.99 (978-0-525-47810-2(8) , Dutton Juvenile) Penguin Group (USA) Inc.

Cohn, Rachel. Shrimp. 288p. (YA). (gr. 7 up). 2005. 15.95 (978-0-689-86612-8(7) , Simon & Schuster Children's Publishing); 2006. reprint ed. pap. 6.99 (978-0-689-86613-5(5) , Simon Pulse) Simon & Schuster Children's Publishing.

Colasanti, Susane. Tara's Triumph. 2006. 320p. (J). (gr. 7). 17.99 (978-0-670-06029-0(1) , Viking Juvenile) Penguin Group (USA) Inc.

Colasanti, Susane & Jeffries, Cindy. Tara's Triumph, Vol. 5. 2007. (Fame School Ser.). 128p. (J). (gr. 7). 5.99 (*978-0-14-240837-7(9)) Penguin Group (USA) Inc.

Colato Lainez, Rene. I Am Rene, the Boy. Graullera Ramirez, Fabiola, illus. Tr. of Yo Soy Rene, el Nino. (ENG & SPA.). 32p. (J). (ps-2). 15.95 (978-1-55885-378-2(2) , Piñata Books) Arte Publico Pr.

Cole, Barbara. Anna & Natalie. Himler, Ronald, illus. 2007. 32p. (J). 16.95 (*978-1-59572-105-1(3)) Star Bright Bks., Inc.

Cole, Grace. The School of Fish. Miller, Lelia, illus. 2002. 12p. (J). 4.95 (978-0-9712923-3-8(7)) Taylor-Dth Publishing.

Cole, Kenneth. Friends & Neighbors: We Love to Learn. Ruebartsch, John, photos by. 2005. (J). pap. 9.95 (978-0-9770816-1-5(3)) SHARP Literacy, Inc.

—Friends & Neighbors: We Love to Learn. Ruebartsch, John, photos by. ed. 2005. (J). 16.95 (978-0-9770816-0-8(5)) SHARP Literacy, Inc.

Cole, Myke. The Wildsidhe Chronicles Bk. 6: Car Trouble. 2003. (J). pap. 7.99 (978-1-890096-18-2(0)) Padwolf Publishing, Inc.

Coleman, Evelyn. Freedom Train. Riley, David, illus. 2008. 160p. (J). 15.99 (*978-0-689-84716-5(5) , McElderry, Margaret K.) Simon & Schuster Children's Publishing.

Coleman, Michael. Weirdo's War. 1998. (Illus.). 192p. (J). (gr. 4-8). pap. 16.95 (978-0-531-30103-6(6) , Orchard Bks.) Scholastic, Inc.

Collard, Sneed B., III. Dog Sense. 2005. 192p. (J). 14.95 (978-1-56145-351-1(X)) Peachtree Pubs., Ltd.

Collicott, Sharleen. Mildred & Sam & Their Babies. Collicott, Sharleen, illus. 2005. (I Can Read Bks.). (Illus.). 48p. (J). (ps-2). 15.99 (978-0-06-058111-4(5)); lib. bdg. 16.89 (978-0-06-058112-1(3)) HarperCollins Pubs. (Geringer, Laura Book).

Collins, Charles. Hover for a Day. Seltzer, Jerry, illus. 2006. (J). 19.95 (978-1-60131-004-0(8)) Big Tent Bks.

Collins, David R. Elsie & Darcy Go to Bible School. Han, George, illus. 1999. 45p. pap. 3.95 (978-0-9657352-1-6(4)) Elsie & Darcy, Inc.

Collins, P. J. Sarah. Sam & Nate. Jin, Katherine, illus. 2005. 60p. (J). lib. bdg. 20.00 (*978-1-4242-1261-3(8)) Fitzgerald Bks.

Condie, Allyson B. Yearbook. 2006. 208p. (YA). pap. 14.95 (978-1-59038-690-3(6)) Deseret Bk. Co.

Condon, Bill. Miss Wolf & the Porkers: These Little Porkers Are in for a Shock! Magerl, Caroline, illus. 2006. (Bites Ser.). 96p. (J). pap. 3.95 (978-0-7624-2649-2(7) , Running Pr. Kids) Running Pr. Bk. Pubs.

Conford, Ellen. Jenny Archer, Author. Palisciano, Diane, illus. 2006. 64p. (J). (gr. 1-4). pap. 3.99 (978-0-316-01487-8(7)) Little Brown & Co.

Conklin, Jennie Maria. Miss Prudence A Story of Two Girls' Lives. 2004. reprint ed. pap. 30.95 (978-1-4191-3464-7(7)); pap. 1.99 (978-1-4192-3464-4(1)) Kessinger Publishing, LLC.

Conway, Celeste. The Melting Season. (YA). (gr. 7). 2008. 224p. mass mkt. 6.50 (*978-0-440-23953-6(2) , Laurel Leaf); 2006. 288p. 15.95 (978-0-385-73339-7(9) , Delacorte Bks. for Young Readers); 2006. 288p. 17.99 (978-0-385-90357-8(X) , Delacorte Bks. for Young Readers) Random Hse. Children's Bks.

A Cool School: Individual Title Six-Packs. (ps-2). 27.00 (978-0-7635-9442-8(3)) Rigby Education.

Coolidge, Susan. What Katy Did at School. 2003. (ENG.). 148p. 23.99 (*978-1-4043-4012-1(2)) IndyPublish.com.

Coolidge, Susan. What Katy Did at School/What Katy Did Next. 2001. (Children's Classics). (ENG.). 352p. (J). pap. (978-1-84022-437-5(1)) Wordsworth Editions, Ltd.

Coombs, Patricia. Dorrie & the Haunted Schoolhouse. Coombs, Patricia, illus. 2001. (Illus.). 32p. (J). (gr. k-3). 5.95 (978-0-618-13053-5(5) , Clarion Bks.) Houghton Mifflin Co. Trade & Reference Div.

—Dorrie & the Haunted Schoolhouse. 2001. (gr. k-3). lib. bdg. 14.10 (978-0-613-44203-9(2)) Tandem Library Bks.

Cooney, Caroline B. Code Orange. 2007. 208p. (YA). (gr. 7). pap. 6.50 (978-0-385-73260-4(0) , Laurel Leaf) Random Hse. Children's Bks.

—Driver's Ed. 2004. 192p. (YA). (gr. 7). lib. bdg. 17.99 (978-0-385-90236-6(0) , Delacorte Bks. for Young Readers) Random Hse. Children's Bks.

Cooney, Doug. I Know Who Likes You. Bernardin, James, illus. 2005. 224p. (J). pap. 4.99 (978-1-4169-0261-4(9) , Aladdin) Simon & Schuster Children's Publishing.

Cooper, Ilene. The Annoying Team. Paine, Colin, illus. 2005. (Stepping Stones Ser.). 80p. (J). (gr. 2-5). pap. 3.99 (978-0-307-26512-8(9) , Random Hse. Bks. for Young Readers) Random Hse. Children's Bks.

Cooper, Ilene. Jake's Best Thumb. Muñoz, Claudio, illus. 2008. 32p. (J). (ps). 16.99 (*978-0-525-47788-4(8) , Dutton Juvenile) Penguin Group (USA) Inc.

Cooper, Wendy. Isaiah's Big Surprise. Mobley, Elizabeth, illus. 2007. (J). per. 11.95 (*978-0-9792074-5-7(2)) Kingdom Publishing Group, Inc.

Copeland, Cynthia L. The 15 Best Things about Being the New Kid. Vargo, Sharon Hawkins, illus. 2006. (Silly Millies Ser.). 32p. (J). 21.27 (978-0-7613-2889-6(0) , Millbrook Pr.) Lerner Publishing Group.

Corbett, Kat. First-String Future. 2000. (gr. 7-12). lib. bdg. 22.20 (978-0-613-83507-7(7)) Tandem Library Bks.

—First-String Future. 2000. 220p. (YA). (gr. 7-12). pap. 12.95 (978-0-595-12738-2(X)) iUniverse, Inc.

Corbett, Sue. 12 Again. 2002. (Illus.). 160p. (J). (gr. 5-9). 16.99 (978-0-525-46899-8(4) , Dutton Juvenile) Penguin Group (USA) Inc.

Corey, Shana. First Graders from Mars. Teague, Mark, illus. 2003. (First Graders from Mars Ser.: No. 4). 32p. (J). pap. 4.99 (978-0-439-45219-9(8) , Scholastic Pr.) Scholastic, Inc.

—Horus's Horrible Day. Teague, Mark, illus. 2001. (First Graders from Mars Ser.: No. 1). 32p. (J). (gr. k-2). pap. 4.99 (978-0-439-31955-3(2) , Levine, Arthur A. Bks.) Scholastic, Inc.

—Horus's Horrible Day. 2001. (gr. k-3). lib. bdg. 12.40 (978-0-613-50324-2(4)); (Illus.). (J). 11.30 (978-0-606-21581-7(6)) Tandem Library Bks.

Corey, Shana & Teague, Mark. Tera, Star Student. 2003. (First Graders from Mars Ser.: No. 4). (Illus.). 32p. (J). pap. 15.95 (978-0-439-26634-5(3) , Scholastic Pr.) Scholastic, Inc.

Cork, Barbara. Sam Starts School. Smee, Nicola, illus. 2002. (First Experiences Ser.). 32p. (J). (gr. k-2). 15.00 (978-1-57768-989-8(5) , Waterbird Bks.) School Specialty Publishing.

Cormier, Robert. The Chocolate War. 2002. (Illus.). (J). 13.94 (978-0-7587-4778-5(0)) Book Wholesalers, Inc.

—The Chocolate War. 191p. (YA). (gr. 7 up). pap. 4.99 (978-0-8072-1428-2(0) , Listening Library) Random Hse. Audio Publishing Group.

—The Chocolate War. 30th ed. 2004. 272p. (YA). (gr. 7-12). pap. 8.95 (978-0-375-82987-1(3) , Knopf Bks. for Young Readers) Random Hse. Children's Bks.

—The Chocolate War. 2000. 12.64 (978-0-606-20038-7(X)) Tandem Library Bks.

Cornwell, Nicki. Christophe's Story. Littlewood, Karin, illus. 2007. 96p. (gr. 3 up). pap. 7.95 (978-1-84507-521-7(8)) Lincoln, Frances Ltd. GBR. *Dist:* Perseus Distribution.

Corrigan, Eireann. Ordinary Ghosts. 2007. 380p. (J). (gr. 7 up). pap. 16.99 (978-0-439-83243-4(8) , Scholastic Pr.) Scholastic, Inc.

Cosgrove, Stephen. Flynn "Flea" Flicker: Sticking to the Truth. Arroyo, Fian, illus. 2004. (J). (978-1-58804-353-5(3)) PCI Educational Publishing.

—Mizz Buggly: Doing Your Best. Arroyo, Fian, illus. 2004. (J). (978-1-58804-380-1(0)) PCI Educational Publishing.

Cottle Street: Individual Title Six-Packs. (Action Packs Ser.). 120p. (gr. 3-5). 44.00 (978-0-7635-8423-8(1)) Rigby Education.

Counsel, June. But Martin! Layton, Neal, illus. 2005. 32p. (J). (ps). pap. 9.99 (978-0-552-55138-0(4) , Corgi) Transworld Publishers Ltd. GBR. *Dist:* Independent Pubs. Group.

Couric, Katie. The Blue Ribbon Day. Priceman, Marjorie, illus. 2004. 32p. (gr. k-2). 15.95 (978-0-385-50142-2(0) , Doubleday) Doubleday Publishing.

—The Brand New Kid. Priceman, Marjorie, illus. 2000. 32p. (J). (gr. 2-3). 15.95 (978-0-385-50030-2(0) , Doubleday) Doubleday Publishing.

CourseCrafters Staff, des. Interactive Storybooks - Let's Go to School! 2003. (J). spiral bd. 14.95 (978-1-58605-961-3(0)) LeapFrog Enterprises, Inc.

—Interactive Storybooks - School Time. 2003. (J). spiral bd. 14.95 (978-1-58605-960-6(2)) LeapFrog Enterprises, Inc.

Courtin, Thierry. T choupi rentre a l Ecole. 13.95 (978-2-09-202041-8(2)) Nathan, Fernand FRA. *Dist:* Distribooks, Inc.

Coville, Bruce. The Monster's Ring. 2002. lib. bdg. 20.00 incl. audio (978-1-932076-10-3(7) , 02009) Full Cast Audio.

—The Monster's Ring. Coville, Katherine, illus. anniv. exp. ed. 2002. (Magic Shop Bks.). 128p. (YA). (gr. 3-7). 16.00 (978-0-15-204618-7(6)) Harcourt Children's Bks.

—The Monster's Ring. 2003. (gr. 3-6). lib. bdg. 13.00 (978-0-613-73386-1(X)) Tandem Library Bks.

—My Teacher Fried My Brains. 2005. (Illus.). 136p. (J). (*978-1-4156-1080-0(0) , Aladdin) Simon & Schuster Children's Publishing.

—My Teacher Fried My Brains. Pierard, John, illus. 2005. 138p. (J). (gr. 3-7). lib. bdg. 12.04 (978-0-606-33890-5(X)) Tandem Library Bks.

—My Teacher Glows in the Dark. 2005. (Illus.). 137p. (J). (*978-1-4156-1081-7(9) , Aladdin) Simon & Schuster Children's Publishing.

—My Teacher Is an Alien. 2005. (Illus.). 123p. (J). (*978-1-4156-1082-4(7) , Aladdin) Simon & Schuster Children's Publishing.

—The Skull of Truth. 1999. (gr. 3-6). lib. bdg. 13.00 (978-0-613-17061-1(X)) Tandem Library Bks.

—The Skull of Truth: A Magic Shop Book. Lippincott, Gary A., illus. 2007. (Magic Shop Book Ser.). 208p. (J). pap. 5.95 (978-0-15-206084-8(7) , Magic Carpet Bks.) Harcourt Children's Bks.

—There's an Alien in My Classroom! l.t. ed. 2000. (Illus.). 184p. (J). pap. 16.95 (978-0-7540-6108-3(6) , Galaxy Children's Large Print) BBC Audiobooks America.

—There's an Alien in My Classroom! (Illus.). 201p. (J). pap. 8.95 (978-0-340-73634-0(8) , Hodder & Stoughton) Hodder General Publishing Division GBR. *Dist:* Trafalgar Square Publishing.

Cowell, Cressida. Super Sue at Super School. Ayto, Russell, illus. 2005. 16p. (J). (ps-k). 8.99 (978-0-7636-2734-8(8)) Candlewick Pr.

Cox, Judy. Butterfly Buddies. Sims, Blanche, illus. 2001. 96p. (J). (gr. 4-6). tchr. ed. 15.95 (978-0-8234-1654-7(2)) Holiday Hse., Inc.

—Cool Cat, School Cat. Sims, Blanche, illus. 2002. 96p. (J). (gr. 4-6). tchr. ed. 15.95 (978-0-8234-1714-8(X)) Holiday Hse., Inc.

—Don't Be Silly, Mrs. Millie! Mathieu, Joe, illus. 2005. 32p. (J). (ps-2). 14.95 (978-0-7614-5166-2(8)) Cavendish, Marshall Corp.

—Mean, Mean Maureen Green. Fisher, Cynthia, illus. 1999. 80p. (J). (gr. 1-5). tchr. ed. 15.95 (978-0-8234-1502-1(3)) Holiday Hse., Inc.

—Mean, Mean Maureen Green. 2001. (Illus.). (J). (978-0-606-21322-6(8)) Tandem Library Bks.

—Mrs. Millie Goes to Philly! Mathieu, Joseph, illus. 2008. (J). (*978-0-7614-5372-7(5)) Cavendish, Marshall Corp.

Cox, Judy. That Crazy Eddie & the Science Project of Doom. Simms, Blanche, illus. 2005. 96p. (J). 15.95 (978-0-8234-1931-9(2)) Holiday Hse., Inc.

Coy, John. Crackback. (J). 2007. 224p. pap. 6.99 (*978-0-439-69734-7(4) , Scholastic Paperbacks); 2005. 208p. (gr. 7 up). pap. 16.99 (978-0-439-69733-0(6) , Scholastic Pr.) Scholastic, Inc.

Creech, Sharon. Absolutely Normal Chaos. 1999. (J). pap. 50.20 incl. audio (978-0-7887-2994-2(2) , 40876); Class Set. pap., wbk. ed. 107.30 incl. audio (978-0-7887-3024-5(X) , 46841) Recorded Bks., LLC.

—Bloomability. 288p. (J). (gr. 3-7). 1999. (Illus.). pap. 6.99 (978-0-06-440823-3(X) , Harper Trophy); 1998. 17.99 (978-0-06-026993-7(6) , Cotler, Joanna Books) HarperCollins Pubs.

—Bloomability. unabr. ed. 2004. 273p. (J). (gr. 4-7). pap. 38.00 incl. audio (978-0-8072-8754-5(7) , YA257SP, Listening Library) Random Hse. Audio Publishing Group.

—Bloomability. 1999. 12.64 (978-0-606-17460-2(5)); (gr. 3-6). lib. bdg. 14.15 (978-0-613-22826-8(X)) Tandem Library Bks.

—A Fine, Fine School. Bliss, Harry, illus. 32p. (J). (ps-3). 2004. pap. 6.99 (978-0-06-000728-7(1) , Harper Trophy); 2001. 16.99 (978-0-06-027736-9(X) , Cotler, Joanna Books); 2001. lib. bdg. 16.89 (978-0-06-027737-6(8) , Cotler, Joanna Books) HarperCollins Pubs.

—A Fine, Fine School. 2003. (Illus.). 25.95 incl. audio (978-1-59112-221-0(X)); (J). pap. 16.95 incl. audio (978-1-59112-220-3(1)) Live Oak Media.

—A Fine, Fine School. Bliss, Harry, illus. 2003. 28.95 incl. audio compact disk (978-1-59112-496-2(4)); pap. 37.95 incl. audio (978-1-59112-222-7(8)); pap. 39.95 incl. audio compact disk (978-1-59112-555-6(3)) Live Oak Media.

—Fine Fine School. 2004. (Live Oak Readalong Ser.). (Illus.). (J). (ps-2). audio compact disk 18.95 (978-1-59112-497-9(2)) Live Oak Media.

—A Fine, Fine School. ed. 2004. (Illus.). (J). (gr. k-3). spiral bd. (978-0-616-11107-9(X)) Canadian National Institute for the Blind/Institut National Canadien pour les Aveugles.

—A Fine, Fine School. Bliss, Harry, illus. ed. 2004. (J). (gr. k-3). spiral bd. (978-0-616-11106-2(1)) Canadian National Institute for the Blind/Institut National Canadien pour les Aveugles.

—Replay. 240p. (J). (gr. 3-7). 2007. pap. 5.99 (978-0-06-054021-0(4) , Harper Trophy); 2005. 15.99 (978-0-06-054019-7(2) , Cotler, Joanna Books); 2005. lib. bdg. 16.89 (978-0-06-054020-3(6) , Cotler, Joanna Books) HarperCollins Pubs.

Crews, Donald. School Bus Board Book. Crews, Donald, illus. 2002. (Illus.). 36p. (J). (ps up). 6.99 (978-0-694-01690-7(X)) HarperCollins Pubs.

S

Cross, Gillian. The Monster from Underground. Priestley, Chris, illus. 2002. (Yellow Bananas Ser.). 48p. (J). (gr. 3-4). pap. (978-0-7787-0981-7(7)); lib. bdg. (978-0-7787-0935-0(3)) Crabtree Publishing Co.

—Monster from Underground. 2002. (gr. 3-6). lib. bdg. 12.95 (978-0-613-52882-5(4)) Tandem Library Bks.

Cross, Vince. The A Club: The Blogs of Abi Goodenough. 2006. 160p. pap. 8.99 (978-0-7459-6019-7(7) , Lion Children's) Lion Hudson plc GBR. *Dist:* Trafalgar Square Publishing.

Croteau, Marie-Danielle. Gabby's School by the Sea. Casson, Sophie, illus. 2005. (Read-It! Readers Ser.). 32p. (J). (gr. k-3). 18.60 (978-1-4048-1072-3(2)) Picture Window Bks.

Crowley, Suzanne Carlisle. The Very Ordered Existence of Merilee Marvelous. 2007. (J). (gr. 5 up). 256p. 16.99 (***978-0-06-123197-1(5)***); 384p. lib. bdg. 17.89 (***978-0-06-123198-8(3)***) HarperCollins Pubs. (Greenwillow Bks.).

Crutcher, Chris. Deadline. 2007. 320p. (gr. 9 up). (J). 16.99 (***978-0-06-085089-0(2)***); (YA). lib. bdg. 17.89 (***978-0-06-085090-6(6)***) HarperCollins Pubs. (Greenwillow Bks.).

—The Sledding Hill. 2005. 240p. (J). (gr. 7 up). 16.99 (978-0-06-050243-0(6)); lib. bdg. 17.89 (978-0-06-050244-7(4)) HarperCollins Pubs.

—Sledding Hill. 2006. 256p. (J). pap. 6.99 (978-0-06-050245-4(2) , HarperTeen) HarperCollins Pubs.

—The Sledding Hill. l.t. ed. 2005. 181p. (YA). 20.95 (978-0-7862-8091-9(3)) Thorndike Pr.

—Staying Fat for Sarah Byrnes. 2003. 304p. (J). (ps-3). pap. 6.99 (978-0-06-009489-8(3)) HarperCollins Pubs.

—Whale Talk. 2001. 224p. (J). (gr. 7 up). 16.99 (978-0-688-18019-5(1)) HarperCollins Pubs.

—Whale Talk. 2004. 224p. (J). (gr. 7 up). pap. 38.00 incl. audio (978-0-8072-2289-8(5) , Listening Library) Random Hse. Audio Publishing Group.

—Whale Talk. 2002. 224p. (YA). (gr. 7). pap. 6.99 (978-0-440-22938-4(3) , Laurel Leaf) Random Hse. Children's Bks.

—Whale Talk. 2002. (gr. 5-8). lib. bdg. 13.55 (978-0-613-61739-0(8)) Tandem Library Bks.

—Whale Talk. l.t. ed. 2005. 323p. 21.95 (978-0-7862-7787-2(4) , Large Print Pr.) Thorndike Pr.

Cuate, Melodie A. Journey to San Jacinto. 2007. (Illus.). 160p. (J). 17.95 (***978-0-89672-602-4(9)***) Texas Tech Univ. Pr.

Cuate, Melodie A. Journey to the Alamo. 2006. 144p. (J). 17.95 (978-0-89672-592-8(8)) Texas Tech Univ. Pr.

Cullen, Lynn. Stink Bomb. 128p. (J). (gr. 3-7). 1999. pap. 3.99 (978-0-380-78507-0(2) , Harper Trophy); 1998. 14.00 (978-0-380-97647-8(1)) HarperCollins Pubs.

Culver, Carol. Manderley Prep: A BFF Novel. 2007. 224p. (gr. 12 up). 9.99 (***978-0-425-21747-4(7)*** , Berkley Trade) Penguin Group (USA) Inc.

—Rich Girl: A BFF Novel. 2008. 240p. pap. 9.99 (***978-0-425-21915-7(1)*** , Berkley Trade) Penguin Group (USA) Inc.

The Culverdale School Tales. 2005. (J). per. (978-1-59872-011-2(2)) Instantpublisher.com.

Cummings, Priscilla. What Mr. Mattero Did. 224p. (J). 2007. (gr. 3). pap. 6.99 (978-0-14-240856-8(5) , Puffin); 2005. (gr. 5-9). 16.99 (978-0-525-47621-4(0) , Dutton Juvenile) Penguin Group (USA) Inc.

Curtis, Mary. Little Stinky Gets Ready for School. 2006. 24p. (J). per. 11.99 (***978-1-59886-586-8(2)***) Tate Publishing & Enterprises, L.L.C.

Cushman, Karen. The Ballad of Lucy Whipple. 1998. 224p. (J). (gr. 5 up). pap. 5.99 (978-0-06-440684-0(9) , Harper Trophy) HarperCollins Pubs.

—The Loud Silence of Francine Green. 2006. 240p. (J). (gr. 5-9). 16.00 (978-0-618-50455-8(9) , Clarion Bks.) Houghton Mifflin Co. Trade & Reference Div.

Cutler, Jane. Spaceman. 1999. (978-0-606-16980-6(6)) Tandem Library Bks.

Cutting, David, illus. The 100th Day of Strawberryland School. 2005. (Strawberry Shortcake Ser.). 16p. (J). (ps-1). pap. 4.99 (978-0-448-43956-3(5) , Grosset & Dunlap) Penguin Group (USA) Inc.

Cuyler, Margery. Invisible in the Third Grade. Gabler, Mirko, illus. 1999. 82p. (J). (gr. 3-4). reprint ed. 15.00 (978-0-7881-6641-9(7)) DIANE Publishing Co.

—Kindness Is Cooler, Mrs. Ruler. Yoshikawa, Sachiko, illus. 2007. 50p. (J). (gr. k-2). 16.99 (978-0-689-87344-7(1) , Simon & Schuster Children's Publishing) Simon & Schuster Children's Publishing.

—Reading Worries. Howard, Arthur, illus. 2008. (J). (***978-0-689-86188-8(5)*** , Simon & Schuster Children's Publishing) Simon & Schuster Children's Publishing.

—That's Good! That's Bad! in Washington, D. C. Garland, Michael, illus. rev. ed. 2007. 32p. (J). (ps-2). 16.95 (***978-0-8050-7727-8(8)***) Holt, Henry & Co.

—100th Day Worries. Howard, Arthur, illus. 2001. (J). (ps-3). 26.90 incl. audio (978-0-8045-6873-9(1)) Spoken Arts, Inc.

—100th Day Worries. Howard, Arthur, illus. 2005. 32p. (J). reprint ed. 6.99 (978-1-4169-0789-3(0) , Aladdin) Simon & Schuster Children's Publishing.

Dabbs, Douglas, illus. The Legend's Granddaughter: Not Quite Super, Book 1. 2007. 281p. (J). pap. (***978-0-9793168-0-7(4)***) NQSBks.

Dad Goes to School. 2003. (J). (978-1-58453-252-1(1)) Pioneer Valley Educational Pr., Inc.

Dadey, Debbie. Swamp Monster in Third Grade. 2003. (Illus.). 96p. (J). (gr. 2-5). pap. 3.99 (978-0-439-42441-7(0) , Scholastic Paperbacks) Scholastic, Inc.

—Swamp Monster in Third Grade 2: Lizards in the Lunch Line. 2004. (Little Apple Ser.). (Illus.). 96p. (J). (gr. 2-5). pap. 3.99 (978-0-439-63161-7(0) , Scholastic Paperbacks) Scholastic, Inc.

Dadey, Debbie & Jones, Marcia Thornton. The Abominable Snowman Doesn't Roast Marshmallows. Gurney, John Steven, illus. 2005. (Little Apple Ser.). 73p. (J). (978-1-4155-8202-2(5)) Scholastic, Inc.

—The Abominable Snowman Doesn't Roast Marshmallows. Gurney, John Steven, illus. 2005. 73p. (J). (ps-k). lib. bdg. 10.79 (978-0-606-33290-3(1)) Tandem Library Bks.

—Beware of the Blabbermouth! 2005. (Ghostville Elementary Ser.: No. 9). (Illus.). 96p. (J). pap. 3.99 (978-0-439-68120-9(0) , Scholastic Paperbacks) Scholastic, Inc.

—The Bride of Frankenstein Doesn't Bake Cookies. 2000. (gr. 3-6). lib. bdg. 11.80 (978-0-613-32344-4(0)) Tandem Library Bks.

—Dragons Don't Throw Snowballs. Gurney, John Steven, illus. 2006. (Little Apple Ser.). 75p. (J). (978-1-4156-4913-8(8)) Scholastic, Inc.

—Ghosts Be Gone! Francis, Guy, illus. 8th ed. 2005. (Ghostville Elementary Ser.). 96p. (J). 3.99 (978-0-439-56004-7(7) , Scholastic Paperbacks) Scholastic, Inc.

—Goblins Don't Play Video Games. 1999. (Bailey School Kids Ser.: No.37). (gr. 3-6). lib. bdg. 11.80 (978-0-613-17914-0(5)) Tandem Library Bks.

—Hercules Doesn't Pull Teeth. Gurney, John Steven, illus. 1998. (Adventures of the Bailey School Kids Ser.: No. 30). 80p. (J). (gr. 2-4). pap. 3.99 (978-0-590-25809-8(5) , Scholastic Paperbacks) Scholastic, Inc.

—Mrs. Jeepers in Outer Space. 1999. (Adventures of the Bailey School Kids Super Special Ser.: No. 4). (J). (gr. 2-4). (978-0-606-19912-4(8)) Tandem Library Bks.

—Mrs. Jeepers' Scariest Halloween Ever. Gurney, John Steven, illus. 2005. 103p. (J). (978-1-4156-2066-3(0)) Scholastic, Inc.

—Sea Monsters Don't Ride Motorcycles. 2000. (Bailey School Kids Ser.: No.40). (gr. 3-6). lib. bdg. 11.80 (978-0-613-26864-6(4)) Tandem Library Bks.

—The Treasure Haunt. Francis, Guy, illus. 2005. (Ghostville Elementary Ser.: No. 11). 96p. (J). (gr. 2-5). pap. 3.99 (978-0-439-67810-0(2) , Scholastic Paperbacks) Scholastic, Inc.

—Wolfmen Don't Hula Dance. 1999. (Bailey School Kids Ser.: No.36). (gr. 3-6). lib. bdg. 11.80 (978-0-613-17044-4(X)) Tandem Library Bks.

Dadey, Debbie, et al. Ghouls Don't Scoop Ice Cream. Gurney, John Steven, illus. 1998. (Adventures of the Bailey School Kids Ser.: No. 31). 80p. (J). (gr. 2-4). 3.99 (978-0-590-25819-7(2) , Scholastic Paperbacks) Scholastic, Inc.

Daffern, Brian. Prince Albert Bk. 2: The Beast School. 2005. 160p. (YA). per. 10.95 (978-0-9709104-6-2(0)) Hickory Tales Publishing.

Dahl, Roald. Matilda. (J). pap. 29.95 incl. audio (978-0-7540-6216-5(3)) BBC Audiobooks America.

—Matilda. (FRE.). (J). pap. 19.95 (978-2-07-051254-6(1)) Gallimard, Editions FRA. *Dist:* Distribooks, Inc.

—Matilda. Blake, Quentin, illus. 240p. 2007. (J). (gr. 2). 6.99 (***978-0-14-241037-0(3)***); 2004. (gr. 3). pap. 6.99 (978-0-14-240253-5(2)) Penguin Group (USA) Inc. (Puffin).

—Matilda. 2000. (GER.). (J). pap. 12.95 (978-3-499-20855-3(5)) Rowohlt Taschenbuch Verlag GmbH DEU. *Dist:* Distribooks, Inc.

Dail, Maggie. Getting to First Base - Chris Struggles to Read. 2006. 157p. pap. 13.95 (978-1-4116-8125-5(8)) Lulu.com.

Dakos, Kalli & Desmarteau, Alicia. Our Principal Promised to Kiss a Pig. DiRocco, Carl, illus. 2004. 32p. (J). (gr. 2-5). 15.95 (978-0-8075-6629-9(2)) Whitman, Albert & Co.

Dale, Mitzi. Sky's the Limit. 2001. (gr. 7-12). lib. bdg. 14.10 (978-0-613-89974-1(1)) Tandem Library Bks.

D'Allance, Mireille. No, No Y No! (SPA.). 88p. (978-84-8470-034-0(8)) Corimbo, Editorial S.L.

D'Allessandro, Alan. Growing Out of Fear. 2005. 62p. pap. 12.95 (978-1-4137-8547-0(6)) PublishAmerica, Inc.

Dalmatian Press Staff. Princess Playset. 2006. 48p. (J). pap. 3.99 (978-1-4037-2559-2(4)) Dalmatian Pr.

Daly, Niki. Once upon a Time. Daly, Niki, illus. 2003. (Illus.). 32p. (J). (gr. k-3). 16.00 (978-0-374-35633-0(5) , Farrar, Straus & Giroux (BYR)) Farrar, Straus & Giroux.

D'Amico, Carmela. Ella Sets the Stage. D'Amico, Steven, illus. 2006. 41p. (J). pap. 16.99 (978-0-439-83153-6(9) , Levine, Arthur A. Bks.) Scholastic, Inc.

D'Amico, Carmela & D'Amica, Steve. Ella the Elegant Elephant. 2005. (J). (gr. k-3). 29.95 incl. audio compact disk (978-0-8045-4128-2(0) , SACD4128) Spoken Arts, Inc.

D'Amico, Carmela & D'Amico, Steven. Ella the Elegant Elephant. 2004. (Illus.). (J). (ps-3). 56p. pap. 16.95 (978-0-439-62792-4(3)); (978-0-439-62793-1(1)) Scholastic, Inc. (Levine, Arthur A. Bks.).

—Ella the Elegant Elephant. 2005. (J). (gr. k-3). 27.95 incl. audio (978-0-8045-6933-0(9) , SAC6933) Spoken Arts, Inc.

Daniel: Individual Title Six-Packs. (Literatura 2000 Ser.). (gr. 1-2). 28.00 (978-0-7635-0129-7(8)) Rigby Education.

Dann, Max. Dead Men Don't Walk. 2004. (Illus.). 132p. pap. 5.99 (978-0-14-330065-6(2) , Penguin Global) Penguin Group (USA) Inc.

Danneberg, Julie. First Year Letters. Love, Judy, illus. 2003. 32p. (J). (gr. k-4). 16.95 (978-1-58089-084-7(9)) Charlesbridge Publishing, Inc.

—First Year Letters. Love, Judith DuFour, illus. 2003. 32p. (J). (gr. k-4). pap. 6.95 (978-1-58089-085-4(7)) Charlesbridge Publishing, Inc.

—Last Day Blues. Love, Judy, illus. 2006. (J). 16.95 (978-1-58089-046-5(6)); 32p. pap. 6.95 (978-1-58089-104-2(7)) Charlesbridge Publishing, Inc.

—Qué nervios! El Primer Dia De Escuela. Mlawer, Teresa, tr. Love, Judy, illus. 2006. 32p. (J). pap. 7.95 (978-1-58089-126-4(8)) Charlesbridge Publishing, Inc.

Danziger, Paula. Amber Brown, Set 1. 2001. (Amber Brown Ser.). (Illus.). (J). (gr. 2-5). pap. 15.96 (978-0-439-26011-4(6)) Scholastic, Inc.

—Amber Brown Goes Fourth. Ross, Tony, illus. 2002. (Amber Brown Ser.: No. 3). (J). (gr. 3-6). 12.17 (978-0-7587-0417-7(8)) Book Wholesalers, Inc.

—Amber Brown Goes Fourth. 2007. (Amber Brown Ser.: No. 3). 112p. (J). (gr. 2-6). 4.99 (***978-0-14-240901-5(4)*** , Puffin) Penguin Group (USA) Inc.

—Amber Brown Goes Fourth. (Amber Brown Ser.: No. 3). 112p. (J). (gr. 3-6). pap. 3.99 (978-0-8072-1291-2(1) , Listening Library) Random Hse. Audio Publishing Group.

—Amber Brown Is Not a Crayon. Ross, Tony, illus. 2006. (Amber Brown Ser.: No. 1). 80p. (J). (gr. 2-6). pap. 4.99 (978-0-14-240619-9(8) , Puffin) Penguin Group (USA) Inc.

—Amber Brown Is Not a Crayon. (Amber Brown Ser.: No. 1). 80p. (J). (gr. 3-6). pap. 3.50 (978-0-8072-1289-9(X) , Listening Library) Random Hse. Audio Publishing Group.

—Amber Brown Sees Red. Ross, Tony, illus. 2002. (Amber Brown Ser.: No. 6). (J). (gr. 3-6). 12.17 (978-0-7587-0420-7(8)) Book Wholesalers, Inc.

—Amber Brown Sees Red. (Amber Brown Ser.: No. 6). 116p. (J). (gr. 3-6). pap. 3.99 (978-0-8072-1294-3(6) , Listening Library) Random Hse. Audio Publishing Group.

—Amber Brown Sees Red. Ross, Tony, illus. 1998. (Amber Brown Ser.: No. 6). 130p. (J). (gr. 3-6). pap. 3.99 (978-0-590-94728-2(1)) Scholastic, Inc.

—Amber Brown Sees Red. 1998. (Amber Brown Ser.: No. 6). (J). (gr. 3-6). 10.64 (978-0-606-12874-2(3)) Tandem Library Bks.

—Amber Brown Wants Extra Credit. Ross, Tony, illus. 2002. (Amber Brown Ser.: No. 4). (J). (gr. 3-6). 12.17 (978-0-7587-0421-4(6)) Book Wholesalers, Inc.

—Amber Brown Wants Extra Credit. Ross, Tony, illus. 2008. (Amber Brown Ser.: No. 4). 128p. (J). (gr. 2-6). 4.99 (***978-0-14-241049-3(7)*** , Puffin) Penguin Group (USA) Inc.

—Amber Brown Wants Extra Credit. (Amber Brown Ser.: No. 4). 120p. (J). (gr. 3-6). pap. 3.99 (978-0-8072-1292-9(X) , Listening Library) Random Hse. Audio Publishing Group.

—The Cat Ate My Gymsuit. 2006. 160p. (J). (gr. 5). pap. 5.99 (978-0-14-240654-0(6) , Puffin) Penguin Group (USA) Inc.

—The Cat Ate My Gymsuit. 1998. (Illus.). 147p. (J). (ps-7). lib. bdg. 14.30 (978-0-88103-336-6(7)) Tandem Library Bks.

—The Cat Ate My Gymsuit. l.t. ed. 2005. 174p. 22.95 (978-0-7862-7310-2(0)) Thorndike Pr.

—Get Ready for Second Grade, Amber Brown. Ross, Tony, illus. (Easy-to-Read Ser.). 48p. (J). (gr. k-2). 2003. pap. 3.99 (978-0-14-250081-1(X) , Puffin); 2002. 13.99 (978-0-399-23607-5(4) , Putnam Juvenile) Penguin Group (USA) Inc.

—Get Ready for Second Grade, Amber Brown. 2003. (gr. k-3). lib. bdg. 11.80 (978-0-613-67547-5(9)) Tandem Library Bks.

—Make Like a Tree & Leave. 1998. (Matthew Martin Ser.: No. 2). 128p. (J). (gr. 4-7). pap. 5.99 (978-0-698-11686-3(0) , Putnam Juvenile) Penguin Group (USA) Inc.

—Make Like a Tree & Leave. 1998. (Matthew Martin Ser.: No. 2). (J). (978-0-606-13593-1(6)) Tandem Library Bks.

—Orange You Glad It's Halloween, Amber Brown. 2007. (Easy-to-Read, Puffin Ser.). 48p. (J). (gr. k-3). pap. 3.99 (978-0-14-240809-4(3) , Puffin) Penguin Group (USA) Inc.

—The Pistachio Prescription. 2006. (J). 160p. (gr. 5). pap. 5.99 (978-0-14-240682-3(1)); 154p. (***978-1-4156-7490-1(6)***) Penguin Group (USA) Inc. (Puffin).

—The Pistachio Prescription. 1999. 154p. (J). (gr. k-9). per. 14.45 (978-0-88103-335-9(9)) Tandem Library Bks.

—Second Grade Rules, Amber Brown. Ross, Tony, tr. Ross, Tony, illus. 2004. 64p. (J). (ps-3). 13.99 (978-0-399-23472-9(1) , Putnam Juvenile) Penguin Group (USA) Inc.

—Second Grade Rules, Amber Brown. Ross, Tony, illus. 2005. 48p. (J). pap. 3.99 (978-0-14-240421-8(7) , Puffin) Penguin Group (USA) Inc.

—Seguiremos Siendo Amigos.Tr. of Amber Brown Is Not a Crayon. (J). (gr. 4-5). 8.95 (978-970-29-0185-3(5) , AF33034) Santillana, S.A. de C.V., Editorial MEX. *Dist:* Santillana USA Publishing Co., Inc.

—¿Seguiremos Siendo Amigos? 97th ed. 2003. (SPA., Illus.). 106p. (gr. 3-5). 24.60 (978-84-204-4857-2(5) , SAN8575) Harcourt Schl. Pubs.

—United Tates of America. 2006. 144p. (J). pap. 5.99 (978-0-439-83883-2(5) , Scholastic Paperbacks) Scholastic, Inc.

—United Tates of America. Danziger, Paula, illus. 2002. (Illus.). 144p. (J). (gr. 3-7). pap. 17.95 (978-0-590-69221-2(6) , Scholastic Pr.) Scholastic, Inc.

—United Tates of America: The Story & the Scrapbook. 2002. (gr. 3-6). lib. bdg. 14.15 (978-0-613-67042-5(6)) Tandem Library Bks.

Danzinger, Paula. Get Ready for Second Grade, Amber Brown. Ross, Tony, illus. 2003. 28.95 incl. audio compact disk (978-1-59112-563-1(4)); pap. 31.95 incl. audio compact disk (978-1-59112-562-4(6)) Live Oak Media.

Daudet, Alphonse. The Siege of Berlin & Other Stories. 2004. reprint ed. pap. 15.95 (978-1-4191-8248-8(X)); pap. 1.99 (978-1-4192-8248-5(4)) Kessinger Publishing, LLC.

David, Lawrence. The Cupcaked Crusader. Gott, Barry, illus. 2002. (Horace Splattly Ser.: Vol. 1). 144p. (J). pap. 4.99 (978-0-14-230021-3(7) , Puffin) Penguin Group (USA) Inc.

—Horace Splattly: The Cupcaked Crusader. (gr. 3-6). 2003. lib. bdg. 13.00 (978-0-613-61708-6(8)); 2002. lib. bdg. 13.00 (978-0-613-45274-8(7)); 2002. lib. bdg. 13.00 (978-0-613-45275-5(5)) Tandem Library Bks.

Davidson, Dana. Jason & Kyra. 2005. 352p. (gr. 7-17). pap. 5.99 (978-0-7868-3653-6(9) , Jump at the Sun) Hyperion Bks. for Children.

Davies, Jacqueline. Where the Ground Meets the Sky. 2002. 224p. (YA). (gr. 5-9). 14.95 (978-0-7614-5105-1(6) , Cavendish Children's Bks.) Cavendish, Marshall Corp.

Davis, Gwendolyn Michelle. Where I Belong. 2004. 114p. pap. 16.95 (978-1-4137-3757-8(9)) PublishAmerica, Inc.

Davis, Heather J. The Friendship Hole. 2006. (ENG.). 28p. per. 13.99 (***978-1-4259-7184-7(9)***) AuthorHouse.

Davis, Lee. PB Bear Goes to School. 1998. (Illus.). 24p. (J). (ps). pap. 12.95 (978-0-7894-1172-3(5) , D K Ink) Dorling Kindersley Publishing, Inc.

Davis, Rebecca. Jake Riley: Irreparably Damaged. 2003. 240p. (J). 16.89 (978-0-06-051838-7(3)) HarperCollins Pubs.

Davis, Terry. If Rock & Roll Were a Machine: A Novel. 2003. 174p. (YA). pap. 15.95 (978-0-910055-86-4(6)) Eastern Washington Univ. Pr.

Dawson, Stephanie Mara. The best recess Ever. 2nd ed. 2004. (J). per. 15.95 (978-0-9748990-0-8(3)) Bk. Nook Productions.

Day, Lauren. Are We There Yet? 1999. (Rockett's World Ser.: No. 3). (Illus.). 128p. (J). (gr. 4-7). pap. 3.99 (978-0-439-08209-9(9)) Scholastic, Inc.

—Are We There Yet? 1999. (Rockett's World Ser.: No. 3). (J). (gr. 4-7). (978-0-606-18593-6(3)) Tandem Library Bks.

—Can You Keep a Secret? 2000. (Rockett's World Ser.: No. 4). (Illus.). 128p. (J). (gr. 4-7). pap. 3.99 (978-0-439-08210-5(2) , Scholastic Paperbacks) Scholastic, Inc.

—Can You Keep a Secret? 2000. (Rockett's World Ser.: No. 4). (J). (gr. 4-7). (978-0-606-18594-3(1)) Tandem Library Bks.

de Alcantara, Pedro. Befiddled. 2007. 192p. (J). (gr. 4-7). 5.99 (***978-0-440-42057-6(1)*** , Yearling) Random Hse. Children's Bks.

De Angeli, Marguerite. Skippack School. De Angeli, Marguerite, illus. 1999. (Illus.). 88p. (J). (ps-3). pap. 15.99 (978-0-8361-9124-0(2)) Herald Pr.

de Brunhoff, Laurent. Babar et ses Amis a L'Ecole. (Babar Ser.). (FRE., Illus.). 48p. (J). (ps-3). 19.95 (978-0-7859-8802-1(5)) French & European Pubns., Inc.

—Babar et ses Amis Font les Courses. (Babar Ser.). (FRE., Illus.). 48p. (J). (ps-3). 19.95 (978-0-7859-8810-6(6)) French & European Pubns., Inc.

de Brunhoff, Laurent & de Brunhoff, Jean. Babar Goes to School. 2003. (Illus.). 32p. (J). (ps-1). 9.95 (978-0-8109-4582-1(7)) Abrams, Harry N. , Inc.

De Campi, Alex. Kat & Mouse Volume 3. 2007. (Illus.). 96p. pap. 5.99 (***978-1-59816-550-0(X)*** , Tokyopop Kids) TOKYOPOP, Inc.

De Groat, Diane. We Gather Together Now Please Get Lost! De Groat, Diane, illus. 2006. (Illus.). 29p. (J). (gr. k-4). reprint ed. 16.00 (978-0-7567-9992-2(9)) DIANE Publishing Co.

De Guzman, Michael. Beekman's Big Deal. 2004. 224p. (J). 16.00 (978-0-374-30672-4(9) , Farrar, Straus & Giroux (BYR)) Farrar, Straus & Giroux.

De Lint, Charles. The Blue Girl. 2006. 384p. (YA). (gr. 7). reprint ed. pap. 7.99 (978-0-14-240545-1(0) , Puffin) Penguin Group (USA) Inc.

de Paola, Tomie. Meet the Barkers. 2003. (Barker Twins Ser.). (Illus.). 32p. (J). (gr. k-1). pap. 5.99 (978-0-14-250083-5(6) , Puffin) Penguin Group (USA) Inc.

—Meet the Barkers: Morgan & Moffat Go to School. 2005. (J). (gr. k-3). pap. 19.95 incl. audio compact disk (978-0-8045-4129-9(9) , SACD4129); pap. 17.95 incl. audio (978-0-8045-6934-7(7) , SAC6934) Spoken Arts, Inc.

—Morgan & Moffat Go to School. 2003. (gr. k-3). lib. bdg. 14.15 (978-0-613-66367-0(5)) Tandem Library Bks.

—Oliver Button Es una Nena. 2003. (SPA.). 48p. (J). 13.99 (978-84-241-8108-6(5)) Everest de Ediciones y Distribucion, S.L. ESP. *Dist:* Lectorum Pubns., Inc.

—Stagestruck. 2005. (Illus.). 32p. (J). (ps-2). 16.99 (978-0-399-24338-7(0) , Putnam Juvenile) Penguin Group (USA) Inc.

—Trouble in the Barkers' Class. de Paola, Tomie, illus. 2003. (Barker Twins Ser.). (Illus.). 32p. (J). (ps-3). 14.99 (978-0-399-24164-2(7) , Putnam Juvenile) Penguin Group (USA) Inc.

De Valera, Sinead. The Magic Gifts: Classic Irish Fairytales. (Illus.). 224p. 16.95 (978-0-86327-822-8(1)) Wolfhound Pr. IRL. *Dist:* Irish Bks. & Media, Inc.

De Young, C. Coco. A Letter to Mrs. Roosevelt. 2000. 112p. (J). (gr. 3-7). pap. 5.50 (978-0-440-41529-9(2) , Yearling) Random Hse. Children's Bks.

de Young, C. Coco. Letter to Mrs. Roosevelt. 2000. 105p. (J). (ps-7). lib. bdg. 12.40 (978-0-613-28551-3(4)) Tandem Library Bks.

Dean, Carolee. Comfort. (J). (gr. 7 up). 2004. 256p. pap. 6.99 (978-0-618-43912-6(9) , Graphia); 2002. 240p. 15.00 (978-0-618-13846-3(3)) Houghton Mifflin Co. Trade & Reference Div.

Dean, Zoey. The A-List: A Novel. 2003. (A-List Ser.: Bk. 1). (YA). lib. bdg. 17.60 (978-0-613-70574-5(2)) Tandem Library Bks.

—Back in Black. 2005. (A-List Ser.: No. 5). 304p. (YA). (gr. 9-17). pap. 9.99 (978-0-316-01092-4(8) , Poppy) Little, Brown Bks. for Young Readers.

—Blonde Ambition. 2004. (A-List Ser.: No. 3). 240p. (YA). (gr. 9-17). pap. 9.99 (978-0-316-73474-5(8) , Poppy) Little, Brown Bks. for Young Readers.

—Blonde Ambition. 2004. (A-List Ser.: No. 3). 233p. (YA). (gr. 8-12). per. 16.64 (978-0-606-33461-7(0)) Tandem Library Bks.

—Girls on Film. 2004. 250p. (YA). (gr. 8-12). per. 16.64 (978-0-606-33460-0(2)) Tandem Library Bks.

—Some Like It Hot. 6th ed. 2006. (A-List Ser.: No. 6). 320p. (J). (gr. 9-17). pap. 9.99 (978-0-316-01093-1(6) , Poppy) Little, Brown Bks. for Young Readers.

—Tall Cool One, No. 4. 2005. (A-List Ser.: No. 4). 304p. (YA). (gr. 9-17). pap. 9.99 (978-0-316-73508-7(6) , Poppy) Little, Brown Bks. for Young Readers.

—Tall Cool One. 2005. (A-List Ser.: No. 4). 295p. (YA). (gr. 7-17). per. 16.64 (978-0-606-33462-4(9)) Tandem Library Bks.

DeAngelo, Jeremy. The Out Crowd. 2006. (J). pap. (978-0-88092-613-3(9)); lib. bdg. (978-0-88092-612-6(0)) Royal Fireworks Publishing Co.

DeClements, Barthe. Liar, Liar. 1998. (Accelerated Reader Bks.). 144p. (J). (gr. 3-7). lib. bdg. 14.95 (978-0-7614-5021-4(1) , Cavendish Children's Bks.) Cavendish, Marshall Corp.

Dee, Barbara. Just Another Day in My Insanely Real Life. 2007. 256p. (J). pap. 5.99 (***978-1-4169-4739-4(6)***) Kaplan Bks.

—Just Another Day in My Insanely Real Life. 2006. (Illus.). 256p. (J). 15.95 (978-1-4169-0861-6(7) , McElderry, Margaret K.) Simon & Schuster Children's Publishing.

DeFelice, Cynthia C. The Ghost & Mrs. Hobbs. 2001. (Ghost Mysteries Ser.). (Illus.). 192p. (J). (gr. 3-7). 16.00 (978-0-374-38046-5(5) , Farrar, Straus & Giroux (BYR)) Farrar, Straus & Giroux.

—The Ghost & Mrs. Hobbs. 2003. 192p. (J). pap. 5.99 (978-0-06-001172-7(6) , Harper Trophy) HarperCollins Pubs.

—The Ghost & Mrs. Hobbs. 2003. (gr. 3-6). lib. bdg. 14.15 (978-0-613-85155-8(2)) Tandem Library Bks.

Defilippis, Nunzio & Weir, Christina. Amazing Agent Luna, Vol. 3. 2006. (Illus.). 192p. (YA). pap. 10.99 (978-1-933164-10-6(7)) Seven Seas Entertainment, LLC.

deGroat, Diane. Annie Pitts, Artichoke. 2001. 10.75 (978-0-606-22330-0(4)) Tandem Library Bks.

—Brand-New Pencils, Brand-New Books. deGroat, Diane, illus. 32p. (J). (ps-3). 2007. pap. 6.99 (***978-0-06-072616-4(4)*** , Harper Trophy); 2005. (Illus.). 15.99 (978-0-06-072613-3(X)); 2005. (Illus.). lib. bdg. 16.89 (978-0-06-072615-7(6)) HarperCollins Pubs.

—Happy Birthday to You, You Belong in a Zoo. deGroat, Diane, illus. 2007. 32p. (J). pap. 6.99 (978-0-06-001029-4(0) , Harper Trophy) HarperCollins Pubs.

—Happy Birthday to You, You Belong in a Zoo. 1999. (Illus.). 32p. (J). (ps-3). 15.00 (978-0-688-16544-4(3)) HarperCollins Pubs.

—Happy Birthday to You, You Belong in a Zoo. deGroat, Diane, illus. 1999. (Illus.). 32p. (J). (ps-3). lib. bdg. 16.89 (978-0-688-16545-1(1)) HarperCollins Pubs.

—Jingle Bells, Homework Smells. deGroat, Diane, illus. 2003. 32p. (J). (ps-3). pap. 6.99 (978-0-688-17545-0(7)) HarperCollins Pubs.

—Jingle Bells, Homework Smells. 2000. (gr. k-3). lib. bdg. 14.15 (978-0-613-68435-4(4)) Tandem Library Bks.

—Liar, Liar, Pants on Fire. deGroat, Diane, illus. 2006. (Illus.). 27p. (J). (gr. k-4). reprint ed. 16.00 (978-0-7567-9987-8(2)) DIANE Publishing Co.

—No More Pencils, No More Books, No More Teacher's Dirty Looks! deGroat, Diane, illus. 2006. (Illus.). 32p. (J). 15.99 (978-0-06-079114-8(4)); lib. bdg. 16.89 (978-0-06-079115-5(2)) HarperCollins Pubs.

—Trick or Treat, Smell My Feet. deGroat, Diane, illus. 1999. (Illus.). 32p. (J). (ps-3). pap. 6.99 (978-0-688-17061-5(7) , Harper Trophy) HarperCollins Pubs.

deGroat, Diane & deGroat, Diane, illus. Trick or Treat, Smell My Feet. 1998. 32p. (J). (ps-3). 14.89 (978-0-688-15767-8(X)) HarperCollins Pubs.

—Trick or Treat, Smell My Feet. 1999. (978-0-606-17241-7(6)) Tandem Library Bks.

DeGross, Monalisa. Donavans Double Trouble. Bates, Amy, illus. 2008. 192p. (J). 15.99 (***978-0-06-077293-2(X)***) HarperCollins Pubs.

—Donavan's Double Trouble. Bates, Amy June, illus. 2008. 192p. (J). lib. bdg. 16.89 (***978-0-06-077294-9(8)*** , Amistad) HarperCollins Pubs.

DeJong, Meindert. The Wheel on the School. (J). 82p. pap. 5.95 (978-0-8072-1539-5(2)); 1999. (gr. 2-7). pap. 35.00 incl. audio (978-0-8072-8110-9(7) , YA104SP) Random Hse. Audio Publishing Group. (Listening Library).

DeLaCroix, Alice F. The Hero of Third Grade. Fisher, Cynthia, illus. 2002. 84p. (J). (gr. 4-6). tchr. ed. 15.95 (978-0-8234-1745-2(X)) Holiday Hse., Inc.

Delaney, Mark. The Protester's Song. 2001. (Misfits, Inc. Ser.: Vol. 5). (Illus.). 224p. (J). (gr. 7-11). pap. 5.95 (978-1-56145-244-6(0)) Peachtree Pubs., Ltd.

—Protester's Song. 2001. (gr. 7-12). lib. bdg. 14.10 (978-0-613-68378-4(1)) Tandem Library Bks.

—The Vanishing Chip. 1998. (Misfits, Inc. Ser.: No. 1). 240p. (J). (gr. 7-11). pap. 5.95 (978-1-56145-176-0(2) , Q21568) Peachtree Pubs., Ltd.

Dellasega, Cheryl. Nugrl90 (Sadie) LaPierre, Karina, illus. 2007. (Bloggrls Ser.). (YA). (gr. 7 up). 200p. 15.99 (***978-0-7614-5375-8(X)***); 190p. per. 6.99 (***978-0-7614-5396-3(2)***) Cavendish, Marshall Corp.

Delval, Marie He. L 'Ecole des Geants. pap. 18.95 (978-2-227-72802-8(7)) Bayard Editions FRA. *Dist:* Distribooks, Inc.

Demas, Corinne. Middle Grade Novel. Date not set. 196p. (J). (gr. 3-7). 15.99 (978-0-06-028725-2(X)); 4.99 (978-0-06-440845-5(0)) HarperCollins Pubs.

Demers, Dominique. Pearl Pennyworth. 1999. (gr. k-3). lib. bdg. 14.10 (978-0-613-26545-4(9)) Tandem Library Bks.

Dempsey, Jody. Images of Me. 2002. (gr. 7-12). lib. bdg. 24.00 (978-0-613-78050-6(7)) Tandem Library Bks.

Denman, K. L. Mirror Image. 2007. (Orca Currents Ser.). 112p. (YA). (gr. 5 up). pap. (***978-1-55143-665-4(5)***); lib. bdg. (***978-1-55143-667-8(1)***) Orca Bk. Pubs.

Dent, Grace. Friends Forever. 2006. 272p. (YA). (gr. 4). 16.99 (978-0-399-24189-5(2) , Putnam Juvenile) Penguin Group (USA) Inc.

—LBD: Friends Forever! Friends Forever! 2007. 272p. (YA). pap. 6.99 (978-0-14-240831-5(X) , Puffin) Penguin Group (USA) Inc.

DePaola, Tomie. Hide-and-Seek All Week. 2001. (Illus.). 32p. (J). (ps-3). lib. bdg. 11.80 (978-0-613-50319-8(8)) Tandem Library Bks.

dePaola, Tomie. Stagestruck. 2007. 32p. (J). (ps). pap. 6.99 (***978-0-14-240899-5(9)*** , Puffin) Penguin Group (USA) Inc.

DePaola, Tomie. Trouble in the Barkers' Class. DePaola, Tomie, illus. 2006. (Barker Twins Ser.). (Illus.). 32p. (J). (ps). reprint ed. pap. 5.99 (978-0-14-240585-7(X) , Puffin) Penguin Group (USA) Inc.

Derby, Kenneth. The Top Ten Ways to Ruin the First Day of 5th Grade. 2004. 176p. (J). (gr. 4-6). tchr. ed. 16.95 (978-0-8234-1851-0(0)) Holiday Hse., Inc.

Derby, Sally. The Wacky Substitute. Herbert, Jennifer, illus. 2005. 32p. (J). (gr. k-3). 14.95 (978-0-7614-5219-5(2)) Cavendish, Marshall Corp.

Deriso, Christine Hurley. Do-Over. 2006. 192p. (J). (gr. 4-7). 15.95 (978-0-385-73333-5(X)); lib. bdg. 17.99 (978-0-385-90350-9(2)) Random Hse. Children's Bks. (Delacorte Bks. for Young Readers).

Deriso, Christine Hurley. Do-over. 2007. 160p. (J). (gr. 4-7). 5.99 (***978-0-440-42119-1(5)*** , Yearling) Random Hse. Children's Bks.

deRubertis, Barbara. Collection for Kate. 1999. (gr. k-3). lib. bdg. 12.95 (978-0-613-17145-8(4)) Tandem Library Bks.

—A Collection for Kate: Math Concept: Addition. Fiammenghi, Gioia, illus. 1999. (Math Matters Ser.). 32p. (J). (gr. k-2). pap. 4.95 (978-1-57565-089-0(4)) Kane Pr., The.

—A Collection for Kate: Math Concept: Addition. 1999. (Math Matters Ser.). (Illus.). (J). 11.75 (978-0-606-18216-4(0)) Tandem Library Bks.

Dessen, Sarah. Just Listen. 384p. (YA). (gr. 7). 2008. pap. 8.99 (***978-0-14-241097-4(7)*** , Puffin); 2006. 17.99 (978-0-670-06105-1(0) , Viking Juvenile) Penguin Group (USA) Inc.

Deuker, Carl. Gym Candy. 2007. 320p. (J). (gr. 7 up). 16.00 (***978-0-618-77713-6(X)***) Houghton Mifflin Co. Trade & Reference Div.

Deuker, Carl. High Heat. 2005. 352p. (J). (gr. 7 up). pap. 6.99 (978-0-06-057248-8(5) , Harper Trophy) HarperCollins Pubs.

—High Heat. 2003. 288p. (J). (gr. 7-9). tchr. ed. 16.00 (978-0-618-31117-0(3)) Houghton Mifflin Co. Trade & Reference Div.

DeVillers, Julia. How My Private, Personal Journal Became a Bestseller. 2004. 224p. (J). (gr. 5). 15.99 (978-0-525-47283-4(5) , Dutton Juvenile) Penguin Group (USA) Inc.

—How My Private Personal Journal Became a Bestseller. 2005. 224p. (J). (gr. 5). pap. 5.99 (978-0-14-240332-7(6) , Puffin) Penguin Group (USA) Inc.

Dhami, Narinder. Bhangra Babes. 192p. (J). 2007. (gr. 4-7). 5.99 (***978-0-440-42106-1(3)*** , Yearling); 2006. (gr. 3-7). 14.95 (978-0-385-73318-2(6) , Delacorte Bks. for Young Readers); 2006. (gr. 3-7). lib. bdg. 16.99 (978-0-385-90337-0(5) , Delacorte Bks. for Young Readers) Random Hse. Children's Bks.

DiGerolamo, Tony. The Wildsidhe Chronicles Bk. 5: The Undercover Dragon. 2003. (J). pap. 7.99 (978-1-890096-17-5(2)) Padwolf Publishing, Inc.

Diggins, Matthew. Andrew & the Secret Gallery. Diggins, Matthew, illus. 2007. 32p. (J). (gr. 1-5). 15.95 (***978-1-60108-016-5(6)***) Red Cygnet Pr.

Dillon, Jana. Lucky O'Leprechaun in School. 2003. (Illus.). 32p. 15.95 (978-1-58980-035-9(4)) Pelican Publishing Co., Inc.

Dilly for President. 2005. (Illus.). 64p. (J). (ps-k). pap. 6.95 (978-0-7613-2442-3(9) , First Avenue Editions) Lerner Publishing Group.

DiOrio, Faith. It's Not Cool to Hug in School. 2004. 21p. pap. 14.95 (978-1-4137-0922-3(2)) PublishAmerica, Inc.

DiSalvo-Ryan, DyAnne. The Sloppy Copy Slipup. 2005. (Illus.). 128p. (J). 16.95 (978-0-8234-1947-0(9)) Holiday Hse., Inc.

Disney Press, ed. Disney High School Musical: Wildcats Box Set. rev. ed. 2007. (gr. 3-7). pap. 15.99 (***978-1-4231-1082-8(X)***) Disney Pr.

Disney Staff. Lilo's Backpack. 2002. (Illus.). 14p. (J). bds. 7.99 (978-0-7364-1340-4(5) , RH/Disney) Random Hse. Children's Bks.

Divine, L. The Fight. 2006. (Drama High Ser.: Vol. 1). 208p. pap. 9.95 (978-0-7582-1633-5(5) , Kensington Bks.) Kensington Publishing Corp.

—Second Chance. 2006. 208p. pap. 9.95 (978-0-7582-1635-9(1) , Kensington Bks.) Kensington Publishing Corp.

Dixon, Franklin W. All Eyes on First Prize. 1999. (Hardy Boys Are: No. 14). (J). (gr. 2-4). (978-0-606-19046-6(5)) Tandem Library Bks.

—The Test Case. l.t. ed. 2002. 169p. (J). 21.95 (978-0-7862-4657-1(X)) Thorndike Pr.

DK Publishing Staff. Let's Go Magic School Bus. 2007. 12p. (J). bds. 14.99 (***978-0-7566-3088-1(6)***) Dorling Kindersley Publishing, Inc.

D'Lacey, Chris. A Break in the Chain. Carey, Joanna, illus. 2002. (Yellow Bananas Ser.). 48p. (J). (gr. 3-4). pap. (978-0-7787-0977-0(9)); lib. bdg. (978-0-7787-0931-2(0)) Crabtree Publishing Co.

—Break in the Chain. 2002. (gr. 3-6). lib. bdg. 12.95 (978-0-613-52812-2(3)) Tandem Library Bks.

Dodds, Dayle Ann. Teacher's Pets. Hafner, Marylin, illus. 2006. 40p. (J). (gr. k-3). 15.99 (978-0-7636-2252-7(4)) Candlewick Pr.

Doherty, Berlie. Coconut Comes to School. Bates, Ivan, illus. 2002. 32p. (J). 18.00 (978-0-00-710433-8(2)) HarperCollins Pubs. Ltd. GBR. *Dist:* Trafalgar Square Publishing.

Dominguez, Carlos. El Hombre de Otra Galaxia. 2001. Tr. of Men from Another Galaxy. (SPA.). 112p. (J). 7.95 (978-84-348-2709-7(3)) SM Ediciones ESP. *Dist:* AIMS International Bks., Inc.

Donahue, Jill L. Last in Line. Previn, Stacey, illus. 2006. (Read-It! Readers Ser.). (J). 19.93 (978-1-4048-2415-7(4)) Picture Window Bks.

Donaldson, Julia. The Wrong Kind of Bark. Parsons, Garry, illus. 2005. (Red Bananas Ser.). 48p. (J). (978-0-7787-1073-8(4)); pap. (978-0-7787-1089-9(0)) Crabtree Publishing Co.

Dong, Haidan. Of Trouble & Trickery. 2004. 58p. pap. 8.95 (978-0-595-31170-5(9)) iUniverse, Inc.

Donofrio, Beverly. Thank You, Lucky Stars. 2008. 240p. (J). 16.99 (***978-0-375-83964-1(X)*** , Schwartz & Wade Bks.) Random Hse. Children's Bks.

Donovan, Gail. 100th Day Fun. Clar, David Austin, illus. 2003. (Rainbow Fish & Friends Ser.). 24p. (J). lib. bdg. 9.95 (978-1-59014-141-0(5)); mass mkt. 3.99 (978-1-59014-140-3(7)) Night Sky Bks.

Doris, Fisher & Dani, Sneed. One Odd Day. Karen, Lee, illus. 2006. 32p. (J). 15.95 (978-0-9768823-3-6(7)) Sylvan Dell Pubng.

Dorros, Arthur. The Fungus That Ate My School. Catrow, David, illus. 32p. (J). (ps-ps). 2005. 5.99 (978-0-439-75539-9(5) , Scholastic Paperbacks); 2000. pap. 15.95 (978-0-590-47704-8(8) , Scholastic Reference) Scholastic, Inc.

Doudna, Kelly. Goat Cheese. Haberstroh, Anne, illus. 2006. (Fact & Fiction Ser.). 24p. (J). 21.35 (978-1-59679-937-0(4) , SandCastle); pap. (978-1-59679-938-7(2)) ABDO Publishing Co.

Dougherty, Terri. Kyle's Recess. Noack, Kristen, illus. 2007. (Read-It! Readers Ser.). (J). 19.93 (978-1-4048-2414-0(6)) Picture Window Bks.

Douglas, Babette. Kiss A Me: Goes to School. 2004. (J). 9.99 (978-1-890343-09-5(9)) Kiss A Me Productions, Inc.

Doust, Jon & Spillman, Ken. Magpie Mischief. Sorensen, Gert, ed. 2002. (Illus.). 72p. pap. 11.95 (978-1-86368-355-5(0)) Fremantle Pr. AUS. *Dist:* International Specialized Bk. Services.

Dowell, Frances O'Roark. Chicken Boy. Krause, George, photos by. 2007. 208p. (J). (gr. 5 up). pap. 5.99 (978-1-4169-3482-0(0) , Aladdin) Simon & Schuster Children's Publishing.

—Chicken Boy. 2005. (Illus.). 208p. (J). 15.95 (978-0-689-85816-1(7) , Atheneum) Simon & Schuster Children's Publishing.

—Chicken Boy. l.t. ed. 2006. 169p. (YA). 22.95 (978-0-7862-8280-7(0)) Thorndike Pr.

—Phineas L. MacGuire ... Erupts! The First Experiment. McDaniels, Preston, illus. 2006. (From the Highly Scientific Notebooks of Phineas L. MacGuire Ser.). 176p. (J). (gr. 3-7). 15.95 (978-1-4169-0195-2(7)) Simon & Schuster Children's Publishing.

—Phineas L. MacGuire ... Erupts! The First Experiment. McDaniels, Preston, illus. 2007. (From the Highly Scientific Notebooks of Phineas L. MacGuire Ser.). 176p. (J). pap. 4.99 (***978-1-4169-4734-9(5)*** , Aladdin) Simon & Schuster Children's Publishing.

—Phineas L. MacGuire... Gets Slimed! The Second Experiment. McDaniels, Preston L., illus. 2007. (From the Highly Scientific Notebooks of Phineas L. MacGuire Ser.). 208p. (J). (gr. 3-7). 16.99 (978-1-4169-0196-9(5)) Simon & Schuster Children's Publishing.

—The Secret Language of Girls. (Illus.). 256p. (J). (gr. 3-7). 2005. pap. 5.99 (978-1-4169-0717-6(3) , Aladdin); 2004. 16.95 (978-0-689-84421-8(2) , Atheneum) Simon & Schuster Children's Publishing.

Dower, Laura. Boy, Oh Boy! 2001. (gr. 3-6). lib. bdg. 13.00 (978-0-613-75038-7(1)) Tandem Library Bks.

—From the Files of Madison Finn: Give & Take. 2002. (gr. 3-6). lib. bdg. 13.00 (978-0-613-75024-0(1)) Tandem Library Bks.

—From the Files of Madison Finn No.15: Off the Wall. 2004. (gr. 3-6). lib. bdg. 13.00 (978-0-613-91008-8(7)) Tandem Library Bks.

—Give & Take. rev. ed. 2002. (From the Files of Madison Finn Ser.: Bk. 10). (Illus.). 176p. (J). (gr. 3-7). pap. 4.99 (978-0-7868-1684-2(8) , Volo) Hyperion Bks. for Children.

—Heart to Heart. rev. ed. 2003. (From the Files of Madison Finn Ser.: Bk. 11). (Illus.). 176p. (J). (gr. 3-7). pap. 4.99 (978-0-7868-1685-9(6) , Volo) Hyperion Bks. for Children.

—Keep It Real. 2005. 171p. (J). (978-1-4156-1057-2(6) , Volo) Hyperion Bks. for Children.

—On the Case. 2004. 170p. (J). lib. bdg. 16.92 (***978-1-4242-0648-3(0)***) Fitzgerald Bks.

Dower, Laura. Paste Makes Waste. 2000. (ps-2). lib. bdg. 11.25 (978-0-613-32931-6(7)) Tandem Library Bks.

Doyle, Dennis M. & Doyle, Patrick J. Rumors at School. 2001. (Illus.). 88p. (J). (gr. 4-9). 7.95 (978-0-8091-6686-2(0) , 6700-x) Paulist Pr.

Doyle, Malachy. Georgie. 2002. 150p. (YA). 13.95 (978-1-58234-753-0(0) , Bloomsbury Children) Bloomsbury Publishing.

—Hero, Toffer & Wallaby. Nesbitt, Jan, illus. 2000. 46p. pap. 11.95 (978-1-85902-845-2(4)) Beekman Bks., Inc.

DPWW, ed. High School Musical Actors' Biography. 2007. (J). (gr. 2-7). pap. 6.99 (***978-1-4231-0827-6(2)***) Disney Pr.

Dragon Slayer's Academy. 2006. (J). (gr. 1-6). 145.26 (978-1-59961-121-1(X)) Spotlight.

Draper, Sharon. Fire from the Rock. 2007. 240p. (YA). (gr. 7). 16.99 (***978-0-525-47720-4(9)*** , Dutton Juvenile) Penguin Group (USA) Inc.

Draper, Sharon M. The Battle of Jericho. 2003. (Illus.). 304p. (YA). 17.95 (978-0-689-84232-0(5) , Atheneum) Simon & Schuster Children's Publishing.

—Darkness Before Dawn. (Hazelwood High Trilogy: Bk. 3). (YA). (gr. 7 up). 2002. 288p. pap. 5.99 (978-0-689-85134-6(0) , Simon Pulse); 2001. 240p. 17.95 (978-0-689-83080-8(7) , Atheneum) Simon & Schuster Children's Publishing.

—Darkness Before Dawn. l.t. ed. 2006. 199p. pap. 10.95 (978-0-7862-8364-4(5)); 2005. 304p. (YA). (gr. 8-12). per. 22.95 (978-0-7862-7416-1(6) , Large Print Pr.) Thorndike Pr.

—Double Dutch. 2003. 192p. (J). pap. 5.99 (978-0-689-84231-3(7) , Aladdin) Simon & Schuster Children's Publishing.

—Double Dutch. Gabbidon, O'Lanso, illus. 2002. 192p. (J). (gr. 7 up). 16.99 (978-0-689-84230-6(9) , Atheneum) Simon & Schuster Children's Publishing.

—November Blues. 2007. 320p. (YA). (gr. 7 up). 16.99 (***978-1-4169-0698-8(3)*** , Atheneum) Simon & Schuster Children's Publishing.

—Romiette & Julio. 2009. 320p. (YA). pap. 8.99 (***978-1-4169-5514-6(3)*** , Simon Pulse) Simon & Schuster Children's Publishing.

—Romiette & Julio. Lowenbein, Adam, illus. (YA). (gr. 7-12). 2001. 336p. mass mkt. 6.99 (978-0-689-84209-2(0) , Simon Pulse); 1999. 240p. 18.99 (978-0-689-82180-6(8) , Atheneum) Simon & Schuster Children's Publishing.

—Tears of a Tiger. l.t. ed. 219p. 2006. pap. 10.95 (978-0-7862-8361-3(0)); 2005. 20.95 (978-0-7862-7418-5(2) , Large Print Pr.) Thorndike Pr.

Draper, Sharon M. & Bascoul, Eric. The Battle of Jericho. 2004. 352p. (YA). mass mkt. 6.99 (978-0-689-84233-7(3) , Simon Pulse) Simon & Schuster Children's Publishing.

Driscoll, Laura. Lila the Fair. Sims, Blanche, illus. 2005. 32p. (J). lib. bdg. 20.00 (***978-1-4242-1106-7(9)***) Fitzgerald Bks.

—Lila the Fair. Sims, Blanche, illus. 2005. (Social Studies Connects). 32p. (J). pap. 4.99 (978-1-57565-148-4(3)) Kane Pr., The.

—Stuart Little Bk. 2: Think Big, Vote Little! 2003. (gr. k-3). lib. bdg. 11.80 (978-0-613-69199-4(7)) Tandem Library Bks.

Driving Mom Crazy 6 Packs: Individual Title. (ps-2). 27.00 (978-0-7635-9446-6(6)) Rigby Education.

Du Jardin, Rosamond. A Man for Marcy. 2003. (YA). pap. 12.95 (978-1-930009-76-9(3) , 800-691-7779) Image Cascade Publishing.

Dubosarsky, Ursula. Rex. Mackintosh, David, illus. 2006. 32p. (J). 16.95 (978-1-59643-186-7(5)) Roaring Brook Pr.

Duey, Kathleen & Bale, Karen. Three of Hearts. 1998. (J). (gr. 3-7). pap. 3.99 (978-0-380-78720-3(2)) HarperCollins Pubs.

Duffey, Betsy. Alien for Rent. 2000. (978-0-606-17889-1(9)) Tandem Library Bks.

—Cody's Secret Admirer. 1998. (Illus.). 80p. (J). (gr. 2-6). 13.99 (978-0-670-87400-2(0) , Viking Juvenile) Penguin Group (USA) Inc.

—Cody's Secret Admirer. 2000. (Illus.). (J). (978-0-606-18396-3(5)) Tandem Library Bks.

—Gadget War. 2000. (gr. 3-6). lib. bdg. 13.00 (978-0-7857-9891-0(9)) Tandem Library Bks.

—How to Be Cool in the Third Grade. Wilson, Janet, illus. 1999. (Chapters Ser.). 80p. (J). (gr. 2-5). pap. 4.99 (978-0-14-130466-3(9) , Puffin) Penguin Group (USA) Inc.

—Spotlight on Cody. Thompson, Ellen, illus. 1998. 96p. (J). (gr. 2-5). 14.99 (978-0-670-88077-5(9) , Viking Juvenile) Penguin Group (USA) Inc.

—Spotlight on Cody. 2000. (978-0-606-20372-2(9)); (gr. 3-6). lib. bdg. 13.00 (978-0-613-30141-1(2)) Tandem Library Bks.

DuJardin, Rosamond. Boy Trouble. 2003. (YA). pap. 12.95 (978-1-930009-70-7(4) , 800-691-7779) Image Cascade Publishing.

—One of the Crowd. 2003. (YA). pap. 12.95 (978-1-930009-73-8(9) , 800-691-7779) Image Cascade Publishing.

—Senior Prom. 2003. (YA). pap. 12.95 (978-1-930009-77-6(1) , 800-691-7779) Image Cascade Publishing.

Dunlevy, Crystal. GOTHAM, Inc. 2005. 108p. pap. 11.95 (978-1-59113-702-3(0)) Booklocker.com, Inc.

Dunlop, Ed. Sherlock Jones: The Assassination Plot. 2004. 116p. (J). (978-1-59166-315-7(6)) Jones, Bob Univ. Pr.

Dunmore, Helen. Amina's Blanket. Dainton, Paul, illus. 2002. (Yellow Bananas Ser.). 48p. (J). (gr. 3-4). pap. (978-0-7787-0984-8(1)); lib. bdg. (978-0-7787-0938-1(8)) Crabtree Publishing Co.

—Amina's Blanket. 2002. (gr. 3-6). lib. bdg. 12.95 (978-0-613-52802-3(6)) Tandem Library Bks.

Dunn, Ben & Mallette, Herb. Ninja High School Pocket Manga, Vol. 8. 2006. 144p. (YA). pap. 9.99 (978-0-9768043-2-1(8)) Antarctic Pr., Inc.

Durkee, Sarah. The Fruit Bowl Project. 2006. 160p. (J). (gr. 5-8). 14.95 (978-0-385-73289-5(9)); lib. bdg. 16.99 (978-0-385-90310-3(3)) Random Hse. Children's Bks. (Delacorte Bks. for Young Readers).

Durkee, Sarah. The Fruit Bowl Project: Fifty Ways to Tell a Story. 2007. 160p. (J). (gr. 5). 5.99 (***978-0-385-73385-4(2)*** , Yearling) Random Hse. Children's Bks.

Durst, Sarah. Into the Wild. 2007. 272p. (J). (gr. 5-7). 15.99 (978-1-59514-156-9(1) , Razorbill) Penguin Group (USA) Inc.

S

S

Dwyer, Cynthia. Four-Eyed Philip. Schuepbach, Lynnette, illus. 2007. (J). 14.95 (***978-0-9793296-0-9(4)***, Thumbprint Pr.) McIntyre, Connie.

Eagle, Rita. Sniffy the Beagle. Rasmussen, Gerry, illus. 2007. (ENG.). 44p. per. 13.95 (***978-1-59800-537-0(5)***) Outskirts Press, Inc.

Easley, Maryann. Warriors Daughter. 2007. 150p. pap. 19.95 (***978-1-4241-4875-2(8)***) PublishAmerica, Inc.

Easton, Kelly. White Magic: Spells to Hold You, A Novel. 2007. 208p. (YA). (gr. 7-11). 15.99 (***978-0-375-83769-2(8)***); lib. bdg. 18.99 (***978-0-375-93769-9(2)***) Random Hse. Children's Bks. (Lamb, Wendy).

Echols, Jennifer. Major Crush. 2006. (Romantic Comedies Ser.). 304p. (YA). pap. 6.99 (978-1-4169-1830-1(2), Simon Pulse) Simon & Schuster Children's Publishing.

Edwards, Julie Andrews & Hamilton, Emma Walton. Dumpy at School. Walton, Tony, illus. 2000. (Dumpy Ser.). 32p. (ps-2). 15.99 (978-0-7868-0610-2(9)) Hyperion Bks. for Children.

Edwards, Michelle. Pa Lia's First Day. 2005. (Jackson Friends Ser.). (Illus.). 64p. (J). (ps-ps). pap., pap. 5.95 (978-0-15-205748-0(X), Harcourt Paperbacks) Harcourt Children's Bks.

—Pa Lia's First Day. 2001. (Jackson Friends Book Ser.). (Illus.). (J). (978-0-606-21377-6(5)) Tandem Library Bks.

Edwards, Michelle. Stinky Stern Forever: A Jackson Friends Book. 2007. (Jackson Friends Ser.). (Illus.). 56p. (J). pap. 5.95 (***978-0-15-206101-2(0)***, Harcourt Paperbacks) Harcourt Children's Bks.

—Stinky Stern Forever: A Jackson Friends Book. 2005. (Jackson Friends Ser.). (Illus.). 56p. (J). (gr. 1-3). 14.00 (978-0-15-216389-1(1)) Harcourt Trade Pubs.

Edwards, Nancy. Mom for Mayor. Chesworth, Michael, illus. 2006. 96p. (J). 16.95 (978-0-8126-2743-5(1)) Cricket Bks.

Edwards, Pamela Duncan. Gigi & Lulu's Gigantic Fight. Cole, Henry, tr. Cole, Henry, illus. 2004. 40p. (J). (ps-2). 14.99 (978-0-06-050752-7(7)); lib. bdg. 15.89 (978-0-06-050753-4(5)) HarperCollins Pubs.

Edwards, Pamela Duncan. Ms. Bitsy Bat's Kindergarten. Cole, Henry, illus. 2005. (J). (***978-1-4156-2782-2(7)***) Hyperion Bks. for Children.

Edwards, Pat & Edwards, LaVell. Hello, Cosmo! De Angel, Miguel, illus. 2006. (J). 17.95 (978-1-932888-45-4(4)) Mascot Bks., Inc.

Ehrenberg, Pamela. Ethan, Suspended. 2007. 336 Pagesp. 16.00 (***978-0-8028-5317-2(X)***); vi, 266p. (J). (gr. 6 up). 16.00 (***978-0-8028-5324-0(2)***, Eerdmans Bks For Young Readers) Eerdmans, William B. Publishing Co.

Ehrenhaft, Daniel. Drawing a Blank: Or How I Tried to Solve a Mystery, End a Feud, & Land the Girl of My Dreams. Ristow, Trevor, illus. 2006. 336p. (J). 16.99 (978-0-06-075252-1(1)); lib. bdg. 16.89 (978-0-06-075253-8(X)) HarperCollins Pubs.

Ehrlich, Fred. Does a Panda Go to School? 2006. (Illus.). 28p. pap. 5.95 (978-1-59354-159-0(7)) Blue Apple Bks.

Eisenson, Adam. Hope. 2005. (Illus.). 35p. (J). 14.95 (978-0-9766157-0-5(3)) Lone Star Pubns.

Elena, Horacio. Un Largo Dia. (SPA.). 32p. (J). 10.00 (978-84-342-2518-3(2)) Parramon Ediciones S.A. ESP. *Dist:* Distribuidora Norma, Inc.

Ellerbee, Linda. Girl Reporter Blows Lid off Town! 2000. (Get Real Ser.: No. 1). (Illus.). (J). (978-0-606-18691-9(3)) Tandem Library Bks.

—Girl Reporter Sinks School! 2000. (gr. 3-6). lib. bdg. 12.40 (978-0-613-21600-5(8)); (Get Real Ser.: No. 2). (Illus.). (J). (978-0-606-18692-6(1)) Tandem Library Bks.

—Girl Reporter Snags Crush! 2000. (Get Real Ser.: No. 4). (Illus.). (J). (978-0-606-18902-6(5)) Tandem Library Bks.

—Girl Reporter Stuck in Jam! 2000. (gr. 3-6). lib. bdg. 12.40 (978-0-613-25334-5(5)); (Get Real Ser.: No. 3). (Illus.). (J). (978-0-606-18901-9(7)) Tandem Library Bks.

Elliott, Laura. Hunter's Best Friend at School: A Hunter & Stripe Story. Munsinger, Lynn, illus. 2005. 32p. (J). (ps-2). reprint ed. pap. 6.99 (978-0-06-075319-1(6), Harper Trophy) HarperCollins Pubs.

Ellis, Ann Dee. This Is What I Did. 2007. 176p. (YA). (gr. 7 up). 16.99 (978-0-316-01363-5(3)) Little Brown & Co.

Ely, Lesley. Looking after Louis. Dunbar, Polly, tr. Dunbar, Polly, illus. 2004. 32p. (J). (gr. 2-5). 15.95 (978-0-8075-4746-5(8)) Whitman, Albert & Co.

Emery, Anne. Dinny Gordon Senior. 2004. (J). per. 9.95 (978-1-59511-000-8(3)) Image Cascade Publishing.

—Senior Year. 2006. (YA). per. 11.95 (***978-1-59511-005-3(4)***) Image Cascade Publishing.

—Sorority Girl. 2006. (YA). per. 11.95 (***978-1-59511-007-7(0)***) Image Cascade Publishing.

Emzer, Counselor. The Day Before Summer Vacation. 2004. 31p. pap. 17.95 (978-1-4137-2680-0(1)) PublishAmerica, Inc.

Engelbreit, Mary. Queen of Hearts. Engelbreit, Mary, illus. 2004. (Ann Estelle Stories Ser.). (Illus.). 32p. (J). (ps-3). 15.99 (978-0-06-008181-2(3)) HarperCollins Pubs.

—Queen of the Class. Engelbreit, Mary, illus. 2004. (Ann Estelle Stories Ser.). (Illus.). 32p. (J). (ps-3). 15.99 (978-0-06-008178-2(3)) HarperCollins Pubs.

Engelbreit, Mary. Queen of the Class. Engelbreit, Mary, illus. 2007. (Ann Estelle Stories Ser.). 32p. (J). pap. 6.99 (***978-0-06-008180-5(5)***, Harper Trophy) HarperCollins Pubs.

English, Karen. Francie. 2002. (Illus.). (J). 25.45 (978-0-7587-0355-2(4)) Book Wholesalers, Inc.

—Francie. 2002. 208p. (J). pap. 5.95 (978-0-374-42459-6(4), Sunburst) Farrar, Straus & Giroux.

—Francie. 2007. 224p. (J). pap. 6.99 (***978-0-312-37383-2(X)***) Square Fish.

—Francie. 2002. (gr. 5-8). lib. bdg. 14.10 (978-0-613-54223-4(1)) Tandem Library Bks.

—Francie. l.t. ed. 2002. 220p. (J). 21.95 (978-0-7862-3717-3(1)) Thomson Gale.

—Nikki & Deja. Freeman-Hines, Laura, illus. 2007. 80p. (J). (gr. 1-5). 15.00 (***978-0-618-75238-6(2)***, Clarion Bks.) Houghton Mifflin Co. Trade & Reference Div.

English, Karen. Speak to Me: And I Will Listen Between the Lines. Bates, Amy June, illus. 2004. 32p. (J). 16.00 (978-0-374-37156-2(3), Farrar, Straus & Giroux (BYR)) Farrar, Straus & Giroux.

Enright, Elizabeth. The Four-Story Mistake. 2008. (Melendy Quartet Ser.). (Illus.). 224p. (J). pap. 6.99 (***978-0-312-37599-7(9)***) Square Fish.

Ensor, Rod. Getting It. 2007. 216p. per. 14.95 (***978-0-595-44800-5(3)***) iUniverse, Inc.

Erik & Isabelle Senior Year at Foresthill High. 2007. (YA). per. 12.00 (***978-0-9755848-3-5(9)***) Foglight Pr.

Erskine, Kathryn. Quaking. 2007. 272p. (YA). (gr. 6 up). 16.99 (***978-0-399-24774-3(2)***, Philomel) Penguin Group (USA) Inc.

Esckilsen, Erik E. Offsides. 2004. 176p. (YA). (gr. 5-9). tchr. ed. 15.00 (978-0-618-46284-1(8), Walter Lorraine) Houghton Mifflin Co. Trade & Reference Div.

Esham, Barbara. Last to Finish A Story about the Smartest Boy in Math Class. Gordon, Mike, illus. 2007. 32p. (J). 16.99 (***978-1-60336-456-0(0)***) Mainstream Connections, Inc.

—Stacey Coolidge's Fancy Smancy Cursive Handwriting. Gordon, Mike, illus. 2007. (J). 16.99 (***978-1-60336-462-1(5)***) Mainstream Connections, Inc.

Esparza-Harris, Mech. Sage. 2006. 69p. pap. 14.95 (978-1-4241-3035-1(2)) PublishAmerica, Inc.

Estep, Joanna, illus. Roadsong, Vol. 1. 2006. 200p. pap. 9.99 (978-1-59816-398-8(1), Tokyopop Adult) TOKYOPOP, Inc.

Evans, Douglas. Math Rashes & Other Classroom Tales. Di Fiori, Larry, illus. 2002. 112p. (J). pap. 4.50 (978-0-439-33902-5(2), Scholastic Paperbacks) Scholastic, Inc.

—Math Rashes & Other Classroom Tales. 2001. (gr. 3-6). lib. bdg. 12.40 (978-0-613-53834-3(X)) Tandem Library Bks.

Evans, Freddi Williams. A Bus of Our Own. Costello, Shawn, illus. 2001. 32p. (J). (gr. 1-5). pap. 6.95 (978-0-8075-0971-5(X)) Whitman, Albert & Co.

Evans, John D. The Cut. 2003. 262p. (YA). (978-1-888725-82-7(6)); (978-1-888725-83-4(4)) Science & Humanities Pr. (BeachHouse Bks.).

Ewing, Lynne. Barbarian. 2004. (Sons of the Dark Ser.: Bk. 1). 272p. (gr. 7-17). 9.99 (978-0-7868-1811-2(5), Volo) Hyperion Bks. for Children.

Fabregat, Antonio-Manuel. Los Cuentos de Mi Escuela. 2001. Tr. of School Stories. (SPA.). (gr. 7-12). lib. bdg. 18.80 (978-0-613-80591-9(7)) Tandem Library Bks.

Faine, Edward Allan. Ned Ventures: Teenage Life in the 1950s. Consalvi, Gerald A., photos by. 2001. 64p. (J). pap. 6.00 (978-0-9654651-7-5(9)) IM Pr.

Falconer, Ian. Olivia Saves the Circus. ed. 2004. (Olivia Ser.). (J). (gr. k-2). spiral bd. (978-0-616-11110-9(X)); spiral bd. (978-0-616-11111-6(8)) Canadian National Institute for the Blind/Institut National Canadien pour les Aveugles.

—Olivia Saves the Circus. Falconer, Ian, illus. (Olivia Ser.). (Illus.). 44p. (J). (ps-2). 2001. 17.95 (978-0-689-82954-3(X), Atheneum/Anne Schwartz Bks.); 2002. 150.00 (978-0-689-85039-4(5), Atheneum) Simon & Schuster Children's Publishing.

Falwell, Cathryn. David's Drawings. 2001. (Illus.). 32p. (J). (ps-3). 16.00 (978-1-58430-031-1(0)) Lee & Low Bks., Inc.

Falwell, Cathryn, illus. & text. David's Drawings. Falwell, Cathryn, text. 2005. 32p. (J). (ps-ps). pap. 7.95 (978-1-58430-261-2(5)) Lee & Low Bks., Inc.

Falzon, Adrienne. What Is an Angel? Salzberg, Helen M., illus. 2004. 27p. pap. 14.95 (978-1-4137-4461-3(3)) PublishAmerica, Inc.

Farber, Erica. The Prince. Mayer, Mercer, illus. 2006. (Critter Kids Adventure Ser.). 32p. (J). (gr. 2-5). pap. 4.95 (978-0-7696-4767-8(7), Gingham Dog Pr.) School Specialty Publishing.

Farmer, Penelope. Charlotte Sometimes. 2007. (Illus.). 192p. (J). (gr. 4-8). 17.95 (978-1-59017-221-6(3), NYR Children's Collection) New York Review of Bks., Inc., The.

Farrar, F. W. Eric: Little by Little. 2nd ed. 2004. 240p. (YA). per. 7.50 (978-1-932774-51-1(3)) Christian, Harvey Pubs. Inc.

Farrar, F. W. Eric or Little by Little (a Tale of Rosl. 2006. 35.99 (***978-1-4219-8395-0(8)***) IndyPublish.com.

Favole, Robert. Monday Redux. 2003. 200p. (YA). 15.99 (978-1-930826-11-3(7)) Flywheel Publishing Co.

Feely, Jenny. Last One Picked. 2000. (gr. k-3). lib. bdg. 11.80 (978-0-613-29802-5(0)) Tandem Library Bks.

Fehler, Gene. Beanball. 2008. 128p. (J). (gr. 7 up). 16.00 (***978-0-618-84348-0(5)***, Clarion Bks.) Houghton Mifflin Co. Trade & Reference Div.

Ferraro, Tina. How to Hook a Hottie. 2008. 208p. (J). pap. (***978-0-385-73438-7(7)***, Delacorte Pr.) Dell Publishing.

—How to Hook a Hottie. 2008. 208p. (YA). (gr. 7). lib. bdg. 11.99 (***978-0-385-90444-5(4)***, Delacorte Bks. for Young Readers) Random Hse. Children's Bks.

—Top Ten Uses for an Unworn Prom Dress. 2007. 240p. (YA). (gr. 7). pap. 7.99 (978-0-385-73368-7(2)); lib. bdg. 12.99 (978-0-385-90383-7(9)) Random Hse. Children's Bks. (Delacorte Bks. for Young Readers).

Ferraro, Tina. Top Ten Uses for an Unworn Prom Dress: A Novel. 2006. 222p. (YA). (***978-1-4287-2694-9(2)***, Delacorte Pr.) Dell Publishing.

Finch, Margo. The Lunch Bunch. Handelman, Dorothy, photos by. 1998. (Real Kids Readers Ser.). (Illus.). 32p. (J). (gr. k-2). pap. 4.99 (978-0-7613-2030-2(X), Millbrook Pr.) Lerner Publishing Group.

Finch, Susan. The Intimacy of Indiana. 2000. (Illus.). 177p. (YA). pap. 5.95 (978-0-936389-79-0(6)) Tudor Pubs., Inc.

Finchler, Judy. Miss Malarkey Won't Be in Today. 2000. (J). (978-0-606-20294-7(3)); lib. bdg. 15.25 (978-0-613-30032-2(7)); (Illus.). (J). (978-0-606-20409-5(1)) Tandem Library Bks.

—Miss Malarkey Won't Be in Today. O'Malley, Kevin, illus. 2000. 32p. (J). (gr. k-4). reprint ed. pap. 6.95 (978-0-8027-7591-7(8)) Walker & Co.

—Testing Miss Malarkey. 2004. (J). (gr. 1-5). 17.95 incl. audio (978-0-8045-6897-5(9)) Spoken Arts, Inc.

—Testing Miss Malarkey. O'Malley, Kevin, illus. 32p. (J). 2003. pap. 6.95 (978-0-8027-7624-2(8)); 2000. 15.95 (978-0-8027-8737-8(1)) Walker & Co.

Finchler, Judy & O'Malley, Kevin. Miss Malarkey Leaves No Reader Behind. O'Malley, Kevin, illus. 2006. (Illus.). 32p. (J). 17.85 (978-0-8027-8085-0(7)); 16.95 (978-0-8027-8084-3(9)) Walker & Co.

—Miss Malarkey's Field Trip. 2006. (Illus.). 32p. (J). pap. 6.95 (978-0-8027-8917-4(X)) Walker & Co.

—Miss Malarkey's Field Trip. O'Malley, Kevin, illus. 2004. (Illus.). 32p. (J). 16.95 (978-0-8027-8912-9(9)) Walker & Co.

Fisch, Sarah & Bridwell, Norman. Backpack Puppy. Durk, Jim, illus. 2005. (J). pap. (***978-0-439-73379-3(0)***) Scholastic, Inc.

Fishbone, Greg. The Penguins of Doom. 2007. (From the Desk of Septina Nash Ser.). (Illus.). 192p. (J). (gr. 3-9). 13.95 (***978-1-933831-03-9(0)***) Blooming Tree Pr.

Fisher, Jane Smith. WJHC: On the Air. 2007. (Illus.). 96p. pap. (978-0-9744235-0-0(5)) Wilson Place Comics.

FitzGerald, Dawn. Getting in the Game. 2007. 160p. (J). pap. 6.99 (***978-0-312-37753-3(3)***) Square Fish.

Fitzgerald, Dawn. Getting in the Game. rev. ed. 2005. 144p. (J). 15.95 (978-1-59643-044-0(3)) Roaring Brook Pr.

—Soccer Chick Rules. 2006. 160p. (J). 16.95 (978-1-59643-137-9(7)) Roaring Brook Pr.

FitzGerald, Dawn. Soccer Chick Rules. 2007. 160p. (J). pap. 6.99 (***978-0-312-37662-8(6)***) Square Fish.

Fitzgerald, Joanne. Yum! Yum! Delicious Nursery Rhymes. 2007. (Illus.). 32p. (J). (ps-1). (***978-1-55041-888-0(2)***) Fitzhenry & Whiteside, Ltd.

Fitzhugh, Louise. Harriet the Spy. 298p. (J). (gr. 3-5). pap. 5.95 (978-0-8072-1535-7(X)); 1999. pap. 38.00 incl. audio (978-0-8072-8069-0(0), YA993SP) Random Hse. Audio Publishing Group. (Listening Library).

—Harriet the Spy. (Illus.). (gr. 5-7). 2001. 320p. pap. 6.50 (978-0-440-41679-1(5), Yearling); 2000. 304p. (J). 15.95 (978-0-385-32783-1(8), Delacorte Bks. for Young Readers) Random Hse. Children's Bks.

Fitzhugh, Louise & Gold, Maya. Harriet the Spy, Double Agent. 2007. 160p. (J). (gr. 4-7). 6.50 (978-0-440-41691-3(4), Yearling) Random Hse. Children's Bks.

Flake, Sharon G. The Broken Bike Boy & the Queen of 33rd Street. Bootman, Colin, illus. 2007. 144p. (gr. 3-7). 15.99 (***978-1-4231-0032-4(8)***, Jump at the Sun) Hyperion Bks. for Children.

—The Skin I'm In. 176p. (gr. 5-17). 2000. pap. 5.99 (978-0-7868-1307-0(5)); 1999. 14.95 (978-0-7868-0444-3(0)) Hyperion Pr.

—The Skin I'm In. 2000. 171p. (J). (gr. 5-9). lib. bdg. 13.94 (978-0-606-17605-7(5)) Tandem Library Bks.

—Skin I'm In. 2000. (gr. 5-8). lib. bdg. 14.15 (978-0-613-28643-5(X)) Tandem Library Bks.

—The Skin I'm In. l.t. ed. 1999. 173p. (J). (gr. 7-12). 20.95 (978-0-7862-2179-0(8)) Thorndike Pr.

Fleischman, Paul. Time Train. 2002. (Illus.). (J). 15.49 (978-0-7587-3814-1(5)) Book Wholesalers, Inc.

Fleming, Candace. The Fabled Fourth Graders of Aesop Elementary School. 2007. 192p. (J). (gr. 2-6). lib. bdg. 18.99 (***978-0-375-93672-2(6)***, Schwartz & Wade Bks.) Random Hse. Children's Bks.

Flesh, Chris P. Me So Pretty! 2007. (Pretty Freekin Scary Ser.: No. 2). 176p. (J). (gr. 3). pap. 4.99 (***978-0-448-44683-7(9)***, Grosset & Dunlap) Penguin Group (USA) Inc.

—You Smell Dead. 2007. (Pretty Freekin Scary Ser.: No. 1). 176p. (J). (gr. 3). pap. 4.99 (***978-0-448-44682-0(0)***, Grosset & Dunlap) Penguin Group (USA) Inc.

Fletcher, Ralph. Spider Boy. 1998. 183p. (J). (ps-7). per. 13.00 (978-0-613-08798-4(4)) Tandem Library Bks.

Fletcher, Ralph J. Flying Solo. 1998. (Illus.). 144p. (J). (gr. 4-6). tchr. ed. 15.00 (978-0-395-87323-6(1), Clarion Bks.) Houghton Mifflin Co. Trade & Reference Div.

—Flying Solo. 2000. (gr. 5-8). lib. bdg. 13.00 (978-0-613-28491-2(7)) Tandem Library Bks.

—Spider Boy. 1998. 192p. (J). (gr. 4-7). 5.99 (978-0-440-41483-4(0), Yearling) Random Hse. Children's Bks.

—Spider Boy. 1998. (978-0-606-13794-2(7)) Tandem Library Bks.

Flinn, Alex. Diva. 2007. 288p. (J). pap. 7.99 (***978-0-06-056846-7(1)***); 2006. 272p. (YA). 16.99 (978-0-06-056843-6(7)); 2006. 272p. (YA). lib. bdg. 17.89 (978-0-06-056845-0(3)) HarperCollins Pubs. (HarperTeen).

Flinn, Alex. Fade to Black. 2006. 208p. (J). pap. 7.99 (978-0-06-056842-9(9), HarperTeen) HarperCollins Pubs.

Flood, Pansie Hart. It's Test Day, Tiger Turcotte. Wummer, Amy, tr. Wummer, Amy, illus. 2004. (Young Reader Fiction Ser.). 72p. (J). (gr. 1-4). pap. 6.95 (978-1-57505-670-8(4)); lib. bdg. 19.93 (978-1-57505-056-0(0), Carolrhoda Bks.) Lerner Publishing Group.

—Sometimey Friend. Marshall, Felicia, illus. 2005. 128p. (J). (gr. 4-6). 15.95 (978-1-57505-866-5(9)) Lerner Publishing Group.

—Tiger's Trouble with Donut Head. Wummer, Amy, illus. 2005. 71p. (J). lib. bdg. 19.93 (978-1-57505-814-6(6), Carolrhoda Bks.) Lerner Publishing Group.

Flower, Jessie Graham. Grace Harlowe's Senior Year at High School. 2006. 156p. pap. 11.99 (978-1-4264-1912-6(0)) BiblioBazaar.

—Grace Harlowe's Senior Year at High School. 2004. reprint ed. pap. 21.95 (978-1-4191-2224-8(X)) Kessinger Publishing, LLC.

Flynn, Pat. Alex Jackson: Dropping In. 2004. (Illus.). 80p. (Orig.). (J). pap. (978-0-7022-3433-0(8)) Univ. of Queensland Pr.

Flynn, Warren. Return Ticket. 2003. (Illus.). 272p. pap. 13.50 (978-1-920731-90-8(3)) Fremantle Pr. AUS. *Dist:* International Specialized Bk. Services.

Fogelin, Adrian. The Big Nothing. 2004. 224p. (J). 14.95 (978-1-56145-326-9(9)) Peachtree Pubs., Ltd.

—Big Nothing. 2006. 224p. (YA). pap. 6.95 (978-1-56145-388-7(9)) Peachtree Pubs., Ltd.

—The Real Question. 2006. 240p. (YA). 15.95 (978-1-56145-383-2(8), Peachtree Junior) Peachtree Pubs., Ltd.

Foley, John. Hoops of Steel. 2007. 240p. (J). (gr. 9 up). pap. 8.95 (978-0-7387-0981-9(6), Flux) Llewellyn Pubns.

Fontes, Justine. My First Day of Preschool. Novak, Matt, illus. 2006. 12p. (J). 6.99 (978-0-689-86477-3(9), Little Simon) Simon & Schuster Children's Publishing.

—Signs of Spring. Hefferan, Rob, illus. 2002. 24p. (J). pap. (978-1-59034-180-3(5)); 14.95 (978-1-59034-189-6(9)) Mondo Publishing.

Forde, Catherine. The Drowning Pond. 2006. 256p. (J). pap. 8.99 (***978-1-4052-2176-4(3)***) Egmont Bks., Ltd. GBR. *Dist:* Independent Pubs. Group.

Forgetful Fred: 6 Small Books. (gr. k-3). 24.00 (978-0-7635-6237-3(8)) Rigby Education.

Forward, Toby. What Did You Do Today? The First Day of School. Thompson, Carol, illus. 2004. 32p. (J). (ps-k). 15.00 (978-0-618-49586-3(X), Clarion Bks.) Houghton Mifflin Co. Trade & Reference Div.

Foster, Kinsley. Wild Abandon Vol. 4: Old Lang Sine. 2000. (YA). pap. 10.95 (978-0-9667634-5-4(9)) What's Inside Pr.

Frampton, David. Beastie ABC. Frampton, David, illus. Date not set. (Illus.). 32p. (J). (ps-1). pap. 5.99 (978-0-06-443653-5(5)) HarperCollins Pubs.

—My Beastie Book of ABC. Frampton, David, illus. 2002. (Illus.). 32p. (J). (ps-1). 15.89 (978-0-06-028824-2(8)) HarperCollins Pubs.

Frank, Christian M. Catholic (Reluctantly) 2007. (YA). pap. 11.95 (***978-1-928832-99-7(7)***) Sophia Institute Pr.

Frank, Lucy. Lucky Stars. (J). 2006. 240p. pap. 5.99 (978-0-689-85934-2(1), Aladdin); 2005. (Illus.). 304p. 16.95 (978-0-689-85933-5(3), Atheneum) Simon & Schuster Children's Publishing.

Frankel, Valerie. American Fringe. 2008. 272p. (gr. 12 up). 9.99 (***978-0-451-22292-3(X)***, N A L Trade) Penguin Group (USA) Inc.

Frankel, Valerie. Fringe Girl in Love. 2007. 256p. (YA). pap. 9.99 (978-0-451-22046-2(3), N A L Trade) Penguin Group (USA) Inc.

Franklin, Emily. All You Need Is Love: The Principles of Love. 2006. 256p. (gr. 12). pap. 9.99 (978-0-451-21961-9(9), N A L Trade) Penguin Group (USA) Inc.

—The Principles of Love. 2005. 256p. (gr. 12-12). pap. 9.99 (978-0-451-21517-8(6), N A L Trade) Penguin Group (USA) Inc.

Franklin, Kristine L. Nerd No More. 1999. (J). (978-0-606-15653-0(4)) Tandem Library Bks.

Fraser, Mary Ann. I. Q. Goes to School. Fraser, Mary Ann, illus. 2004. (Illus.). 32p. (J). (ps-3). pap. 6.95 (978-0-8027-7698-3(1)) Walker & Co.

—I. Q. Goes to the Library. Fraser, Mary Ann, illus. 2003. (Illus.). 32p. (J). (gr. k-3). 15.95 (978-0-8027-8877-1(7)) Walker & Co.

—I. Q., It's Time. Fraser, Mary Ann, illus. 2005. (Illus.). 32p. (J). (ps-3). 16.85 (978-0-8027-8980-8(3)); 15.95 (978-0-8027-8978-5(1)) Walker & Co.

—I.Q. Gets Fit. Fraser, Mary Ann, illus. 2007. (Illus.). 32p. (J). (gr. k-2). 15.95 (978-0-8027-9558-8(7)); 16.85 (978-0-8027-9559-5(5)) Walker & Co.

Frasier, Debra. Miss Alaineus: A Vocabulary Disaster. 2007. (Illus.). 40p. (J). (gr. k-3). pap. 7.00 (***978-0-15-206053-4(7)***, Voyager Bks./Libros Viajeros) Harcourt Children's Bks.

Fredericks, Mariah. Crunch Time. 336p. (YA). 2007. (gr. 7 up). pap. 7.99 (***978-1-4169-3973-3(3)***, Simon Pulse); 2005. (Illus.). 16.99 (978-0-689-86938-9(X), Atheneum) Simon & Schuster Children's Publishing.

—Fame. Watkins, Liselotte, illus. 2008. (In the Cards Ser.). 288p. (J). 15.99 (978-0-689-87656-1(4)) Simon & Schuster Children's Publishing.

—Head Games. 2006. (Illus.). 272p. (YA). pap. 6.99 (978-1-4169-1335-1(1), Simon Pulse) Simon & Schuster Children's Publishing.

—Love. Watkins, Liselotte, illus. 2006. (In the Cards Ser.). 288p. (J). (gr. 5-9). 15.99 (978-0-689-87654-7(8), Atheneum/Richard Jackson Bks.) Simon & Schuster Children's Publishing.

—The True Meaning of Cleavage. (YA). 2003. (Illus.). 224p. 15.95 (978-0-689-85092-9(1), Atheneum/Richard Jackson Bks.); 2004. 240p. reprint ed. pap. 6.99 (978-0-689-86958-7(4), Simon Pulse) Simon & Schuster Children's Publishing.

Freeman, Martha. Fourth Grade Weirdo. 2001. (gr. 3-6). lib. bdg. 12.40 (978-0-613-86227-1(9)); (Illus.). (J). (978-0-606-21195-6(0)) Tandem Library Bks.

—The Trouble with Cats. Smith, Cat Bowman, illus. 2000. 80p. (J). (gr. 4-6). tchr. ed. 15.95 (978-0-8234-1479-6(5)) Holiday Hse., Inc.

French, Jackie. My Dad the Dragon. King, Stephen Michael, illus. 2007. (Funny Families Ser.). (J). (gr. 2-4). 107p. pap. 7.95 (***978-1-59889-436-3(6)***); 112p. lib. bdg. 22.60 (***978-1-59889-343-4(2))*** Stone Arch Bks.

French, Simon. Guess the Baby. Rawlins, Donna, illus. 2002. 32p. (J). (gr. k-3). 14.00 (978-0-618-25989-2(9) , Clarion Bks.) Houghton Mifflin Co. Trade & Reference Div.

French, Vivian. Detective Dan. Bartlett, Alison, illus. 2006. (Read-It! Chapter Books). 48p. (J). (gr. 2-4). 19.95 (978-1-4048-1659-6(3)) Picture Window Bks.

—Princess Alice & the Magical Mirror. Gibb, Sarah, illus. 2007. (J). (Tiara Club Ser.: Vol. 4). 80p. pap. 3.99 (978-0-06-112439-6(7) , Harper Trophy); 67p. (***978-1-4287-2734-2(5))*** HarperCollins Pubs.

—The Princess Alice & the Magical Mirror. Gibb, Sarah, illus. 2007. (Tiara Club Ser.: Vol. 4). 80p. (J). 15.99 (978-0-06-112440-2(0) , Tegen, Katherine Bks) HarperCollins Pubs.

—Princess Charlotte & the Birthday Ball. Gibb, Sarah, illus. 2007. (Tiara Club Ser.). 80p. (J). (gr. 1-4). pap. 3.99 (978-0-06-112428-0(1) , Harper Trophy); 15.99 (978-0-06-112431-0(1) , Tegen, Katherine Bks) HarperCollins Pubs.

—Princess Charlotte & the Enchanted Rose. Gibb, Sarah, illus. 2007. (Tiara Club Ser.: No. 7). 80p. (J). pap. 3.99 (***978-0-06-112441-9(9)*** , Harper Trophy) HarperCollins Pubs.

—Princess Chloe & the Primrose Petticoats. Gibb, Sarah, illus. 2008. (Tiara Club Ser.). 80p. (J). pap. 3.99 (***978-0-06-143484-6(1)*** , Tegen, Katherine Bks) HarperCollins Pubs.

—Princess Daisy & the Dazzling Dragon. Gibb, Sarah, illus. 2007. (Tiara Club Ser.: No.3). 80p. (J). (gr. 1-4). 15.99 (978-0-06-112434-1(6) , Tegen, Katherine Bks); pap. 3.99 (978-0-06-112433-4(8) , Harper Trophy) HarperCollins Pubs.

—Princess Katie & the Silver Pony. Gibb, Sarah, illus. 2007. (Tiara Club Ser.: No.2). 80p. (J). (gr. 1-4). pap. 3.99 (978-0-06-112430-3(3) , Harper Trophy) HarperCollins Pubs.

—Princess Sophia & the Sparkling Surprise. Gibb, Sarah, illus. 2007. (Tiara Club Ser.: Vol. 5). 80p. (J). pap. 3.99 (978-0-06-112437-2(0) , Harper Trophy) HarperCollins Pubs.

French, Vivian. Tiara Club at Ruby Mansions 2: Princess Jessica & the Best-Friend Bracelet, T. Gibb, Sarah, illus. 2008. (Tiara Club Ser.). 80p. (J). pap. 3.99 (***978-0-06-143485-3(X)*** , Harper Trophy) HarperCollins Pubs.

Frey, Hildegard G. The Camp Fire Girls at School or the Woleho Weavers. 2004. reprint ed. pap. 21.95 (978-1-4191-5575-8(X)); pap. 1.99 (978-1-4192-5575-5(4)) Kessinger Publishing, LLC.

Friedman, D. Dina. Playing Dad's Song. 2006. 144p. (YA). 16.00 (978-0-374-37173-9(3)) Farrar, Straus & Giroux.

Friedman, Laurie B. Back to School, Mallory. Schmitz, Tamara, illus. (J). 2005. 175p. (ps-7). pap. 5.95 (978-1-57505-865-8(0)); 2004. 160p. (gr. 2-5). 15.95 (978-1-57505-658-6(5)) Lerner Publishing Group.

Friedman, Laurie B. Honestly, Mallory! Pollak, Barbara, illus. 2007. (Mallory Ser.). 160p. (J). (gr. 2-6). 15.95 (***978-0-8225-6193-4(X)*** , Carolrhoda Bks.) Lerner Publishing Group.

Friedman, Robin. The Girlfriend Project. 2007. 192p. (YA). (gr. 7 up). 15.95 (978-0-8027-9624-0(9)) Walker & Co.

Friedrich, Joachim. The Disappearing Bio Teacher, Bk. 2. 2001. (4 1/2 Friends Mysteries Ser.). (Illus.). 160p. (gr. 3-7). 14.99 (978-0-7868-0698-0(2) , Volo) Hyperion Bks. for Children.

—4 1/2 Friends: And the Disappearing Bio Teacher. Crawford, Elizabeth D., tr. from GER. 2001. 144p. (J). lib. bdg. 15.49 (978-0-7868-2588-2(X) , Volo) Hyperion Bks. for Children.

Friend, Natasha. Bounce. 2007. 192p. (YA). (gr. 6-8). pap. 16.99 (***978-0-439-85350-7(8)*** , Scholastic Pr.) Scholastic, Inc.

Frizzell, Colin. Chill. 2006. 112p. (YA) lib. bdg. 14.95 (978-1-55143-670-8(1)); (gr. 7 up). pap. 8.95 (978-1-55143-507-7(1)) Orca Bk. Pubs. USA.

Frost, Helen. Diamond Willow. 2008. 128p. (J). 16.00 (***978-0-374-31776-8(3))*** Farrar, Straus & Giroux.

Fuqua, Jonathon Scott. King of the Pygmies. 2007. (Illus.). 256p. (YA). (gr. 9). pap. 7.99 (***978-0-7636-3412-4(3))*** Candlewick Pr.

—Reappearance of Sam Webber. 1999. (Illus.). 232p. (YA). pap. 23.95 (978-1-890862-03-9(7)) Bancroft Pr.

—The Reappearance of Sam Webber. 2001. (Illus.). 288p. (J). (gr. 5). reprint ed. pap. 9.99 (978-0-7636-1424-9(6)) Candlewick Pr.

Gaard, Betty. The Theft. 2000. 190p. (YA). (gr. 7 up). pap. 6.49 (978-1-57924-375-3(4) , 124487) Jones, Bob Univ. Pr.

Gaberman, Judith. Who Has the Lucky-Duck in Class 4-B? 2000. 116p. (gr. 4-7). pap. 9.95 (978-0-595-15799-0(8) , Backinprint.com) iUniverse, Inc.

Gaines, Isabel. Pooh's Graduation. 22nd ed. 2000. (Winnie the Pooh Ser.). (Illus.). 37p. (J). (gr. k-3). pap. 3.99 (978-0-7868-4369-5(1)) Disney Pr.

Gallagher, Diana G. Dance Trap: The Complicated Life of Claudia Cristina Cortez. Garvey, Brann, illus. 2008. (J). pap. (***978-1-59889-879-8(5)***); 81p. (gr. 4-8). lib. bdg. 23.93 (***978-1-59889-841-5(8))*** Stone Arch Bks.

—Guilty! The Complicated Life of Claudia Cristina Cortez. Garvey, Brann, illus. 2008. (J). pap. (***978-1-59889-881-1(7)***); 77p. (gr. 4-8). lib. bdg. 23.93 (***978-1-59889-838-5(8))*** Stone Arch Bks.

—Whatever! The Complicated Life of Claudia Cristina Cortez. Garvey, Brann, illus. 2008. (J). pap. (***978-1-59889-880-4(9)***); 81p. (gr. 4-8). lib. bdg. 23.93 (***978-1-59889-839-2(6))*** Stone Arch Bks.

Gallagher, Liz. The Opposite of Invisible. 2008. (YA). (***978-0-375-84152-1(0)***); (***978-0-375-94329-4(3))*** Dell Publishing. (Delacorte Pr.).

Gallagher, Mary Collins. Ginny Morris & Dad's New Girlfriend. Martin, Whitney, illus. 2006. 63p. (J). (gr. 3-5). 14.95 (978-1-59147-386-2(1)); pap. 8.95 (978-1-59147-387-9(X)) American Psychological Assn. (Magination Pr.).

—Nine Is Not an Even Number. Martin, Whitney, illus. 2004. 48p. (J). 14.95 (978-1-59147-157-8(5)); pap. 8.95 (978-1-59147-158-5(3)) American Psychological Assn. (Magination Pr.).

Gallen, Tim. Love, Loss, & Algebra Equations. 2001. 244p. pap. 14.95 (978-0-595-17973-2(8) , Writers Club Pr.) iUniverse, Inc.

Gallo, Donald R. On the Fringe. 2003. (gr. 7-12). lib. bdg. 15.30 (978-0-613-61650-8(2)) Tandem Library Bks.

Gantos, Jack. Jack Adrift: Fourth Grade Without a Clue. 2003. (Jack Henry Ser.). (Illus.). 208p. (J). 16.00 (978-0-374-39987-0(5) , Farrar, Straus & Giroux (BYR)) Farrar, Straus & Giroux.

—Jack Adrift: Fourth Grade Without a Clue. l.t. ed. 2004. 226p. (J). 22.95 (978-0-7862-6387-5(3)) Thorndike Pr.

—Jack Adrift: Fouth Grade Without a Clue. 2005. (Jack Henry Ser.). 208p. (J). pap. 6.95 (978-0-374-43718-3(1) , Farrar, Straus & Giroux (BYR)) Farrar, Straus & Giroux.

—Jack on the Tracks: Four Seasons of Fifth Grade. 2001. (Jack Henry Ser.). 192p. (J). (gr. 5 up). pap. 6.95 (978-0-374-43717-6(3) , Sunburst) Farrar, Straus & Giroux.

—Joey Pigza Swallowed the Key. 1998. (Joey Pigza Ser.). (Illus.). 196p. (J). (gr. 4-7). 16.00 (978-0-374-33664-6(4) , Farrar, Straus & Giroux (BYR)) Farrar, Straus & Giroux.

—Joey Pigza Swallowed the Key. 2000. (J). pap., tchr. ed. (978-0-06-449267-6(2)); 160p. (gr. 5 up). pap. 5.99 (978-0-06-440833-2(7)) HarperCollins Pubs. (Harper Trophy).

—Joey Pigza Swallowed the Key. unabr. ed. 2004. 154p. (J). (gr. 5-9). pap. 29.00 incl. audio (978-0-8072-8166-6(2) , YA120SP, Listening Library) Random Hse. Audio Publishing Group.

—Joey Pigza Swallowed the Key. 2000. (Illus.). (J). 12.64 (978-0-606-18904-0(1)) Tandem Library Bks.

—Joey Pigza Swallowed the Key. l.t. ed. 2000. 174p. (J). 21.95 (978-0-7862-2912-3(8)) Thorndike Pr.

—Rotten Ralph Helps Out. Rubel, Nicole, illus. unabr. ed. 2006. (Readalongs for Beginning Readers Ser.). (J). (gr. k-3). 24.95 incl. audio (978-1-59519-678-1(1)); 28.95 incl. audio compact disk (978-1-59519-679-8(X)); pap. 16.00 incl. audio (978-1-59519-674-3(9)); pap. 18.95 incl. audio compact disk (978-1-59519-675-0(7)); Set. pap. 29.95 incl. audio (978-1-59519-676-7(5)); Set. pap. 31.95 incl. audio compact disk (978-1-59519-677-4(3)) Live Oak Media.

—Rotten Ralph Helps Out: A Rotten Ralph Rotten Reader. Rubel, Nicole, illus. (Rotten Ralph Rotten Readers Ser.). 48p. (J). 2004. pap. 5.95 (978-0-374-46355-7(7) , Sunburst); 2001. (gr. 1-3). 15.00 (978-0-374-36355-0(2) , Farrar, Straus & Giroux (BYR)) Farrar, Straus & Giroux.

—What Would Joey Do? A Dazzling Conclusion to the Joey Pigza Trilogy! 2004. 240p. (J). (gr. 5-9). pap. 36.00 incl. audio (978-1-4000-9020-4(2) , Listening Library) Random Hse. Audio Publishing Group.

Ganz, Yaffa. The Adventures of Jeremy & Heddy Levi. Katz, Avi, illus. 2005. 204p. (J). 16.95 (978-1-930143-50-0(8) , 3507); pap. 12.95 (978-1-930143-51-7(6) , 3516) Pitspopany Pr. (Devora Publishing).

Garcia-Clairac, Santiago. El Libro Invisible (The Invisible Book) Flores, Enrique, illus. 10th ed. 2001. (SPA.). 140p. (J). (gr. 4-6). (978-84-348-6556-3(4)) SM Ediciones.

Garden, Nancy. Endgame. 2006. (Illus.). 304p. (YA). 17.00 (978-0-15-205416-8(2)) Harcourt Children's Bks.

—Holly's Secret. 2000. 144p. (YA). (gr. 3-7). 16.00 (978-0-374-33273-0(8) , Farrar, Straus & Giroux (BYR)) Farrar, Straus & Giroux.

—Molly's Family. Wooding, Sharon, illus. 2004. 32p. (J). 16.00 (978-0-374-35002-4(7) , Farrar, Straus & Giroux (BYR)) Farrar, Straus & Giroux.

—The Year They Burned the Books. 1999. 256p. (YA). (gr. 7-12). 17.00 (978-0-374-38667-2(6) , Farrar, Straus & Giroux (BYR)) Farrar, Straus & Giroux.

Gardner, Graham. Inventing Elliot. 192p. (J). 2005. (gr. 7). pap. 5.99 (978-0-14-240344-0(X) , Puffin); 2004. (gr. 5). 16.99 (978-0-8037-2964-3(2) , Dial) Penguin Group (USA) Inc.

Garfinkle, D. L. Stuck in the 70's. 2007. 192p. (YA). (gr. 7 up). 16.99 (978-0-399-24663-0(0) , Putnam Juvenile) Penguin Group (USA) Inc.

Garfinkle, Debra. Storky: How I Lost My Nickname & Won the Girl. 192p. (YA). 2007. (gr. 7 up). pap. 5.99 (978-0-14-240782-0(8) , Puffin); 2005. (gr. 6). 16.99 (978-0-399-24284-7(8) , Putnam Juvenile) Penguin Group (USA) Inc.

Garland, Michael. Miss Smith Reads Again! Garland, Michael, illus. 2006. (Illus.). 32p. (J). (ps). 15.99 (978-0-525-47722-8(5) , Dutton Juvenile) Penguin Group (USA) Inc.

—Miss Smith Reads Again! 2006. (Illus.). (J). (***978-1-4156-8098-8(1)*** , Dutton Juvenile) Penguin Group (USA) Inc.

Garland, Michael. Miss Smith's Incredible Storybook. Garland, Michael, illus. 32p. (J). 2005. pap. 6.99 (978-0-14-240282-5(6) , Puffin); 2003. (Illus.). 16.99 (978-0-525-47133-2(2) , Dutton Juvenile) Penguin Group (USA) Inc.

—Miss Smith's Incredible Storybook. 2007. 27.95 incl. audio (***978-0-8045-6945-3(2)***); 29.95 incl. audio compact disk (***978-0-8045-4159-6(0))*** Spoken Arts, Inc.

Garland, Robin. Tanglewood, the Gift: Bk. 1. 2005. 133p. pap. 11.95 (978-0-7414-2339-9(1)) Infinity Publishing.

Garland, Sarah. Going to Playschool. 2008. (Illus.). 32p. (J). 9.95 (***978-1-84507-720-4(2))*** Lincoln, Frances Ltd. GBR. *Dist:* Perseus Distribution.

Garsee, Jeannine. Before, after, & Somebody in Between. 2007. 352p. (YA). (gr. 9 up). 16.95 (***978-1-59990-022-3(X))*** Bloomsbury Publishing.

Gatou, Shouji. Full Metal Panic!, Vol. 7. Tateo, Retsu, illus. 2005. 172p. (YA). pap. 9.99 (978-1-4139-0200-6(6)) A. D. Vision, Inc.

—Full Metal Panic! Tateo, Retsu, illus. (YA). Vol. 2. 2003. 200p. pap. (978-1-4139-0006-4(2)); Vol. 3. 2004. 178p. pap. (978-1-4139-0007-1(0)); Vol. 4. 2004. 160p. pap. (978-1-4139-0039-2(9)) ADV Manga.

—Full Metal Panic!, Vol. 6. Tateo, Retsuo, illus. 2004. 172p. (YA). pap. (978-1-4139-0198-6(0)) ADV Manga.

—Full Metal Panic! Overload!, Vol. 5. 2006. (Illus.). 200p. (YA). pap. (978-1-4139-0342-3(8)) ADV Manga.

Gatou, Shouji & Kaisyaku. Full Metal Panic!, Vol. 1. 2003. (Illus.). 168p. (YA). pap. (978-1-4139-0001-9(1) , MFP/001) ADV Manga.

Gatou, Shouji & Tateo, Retsu. Full Metal Panic!, Vol. 5. 2004. (Illus.). 168p. (YA). pap. (978-1-4139-0051-4(8)) ADV Manga.

Gauthier, Gail. The Hero of Ticonderoga. 2002. 240p. (J). (gr. 5-9). pap. 6.99 (978-0-698-11968-0(1) , Putnam Juvenile) Penguin Group (USA) Inc.

—Hero of Ticonderoga. 2002. lib. bdg. 15.30 (978-0-613-60807-7(0)) Tandem Library Bks.

—A Year with Butch & Spike. 2000. (978-0-606-17857-0(0)) Tandem Library Bks.

Gavalda, Anna. 95 Pounds of Hope. Rosner, Gill, tr. from FRE. 2003. (Illus.). 112p. (J). (gr. 3). 14.99 (978-0-670-03672-1(2) , Viking Juvenile) Penguin Group (USA) Inc.

Geist, Ken, ed. Friends Forever: 4 Favorite Stories. 2005. (Scholastic Reader Collection Level 3 Ser.). 160p. (J). pap. 6.99 (978-0-439-76314-1(2) , Cartwheel Bks.) Scholastic, Inc.

Gene, Barbara. Lamar Montgomery & the Freaky Faces Club. 2006. (J). per. 14.95 (978-1-889743-50-9(X)) Robbie Dean Pr.

Geras, Adele. Pictures of the Night. 2005. (Egerton Hall Novels: Vol. 3). 192p. (YA). (gr. 7-17). pap. 6.95 (978-0-15-205543-1(6) , Harcourt Paperbacks) Harcourt Children's Bks.

—The Tower Room. 2005. (Egerton Hall Novels: Vol. 1). 204p. (YA). (gr. 7-17). pap. 6.95 (978-0-15-205537-0(1) , Harcourt Paperbacks) Harcourt Children's Bks.

Gerber, Carole. Jessica Mcbean, Tap Dance Queen. Barton, Patrice, illus. 144p. (J). 2007. per. (978-0-9718348-9-7(X)); 2006. 13.95 (978-0-9718348-7-3(3)) Blooming Tree Pr.

Gerber, Linda. Now & Zen. Pilkington, Roger, ed. 2006. (S. A. S. S. (Students Across the Seven Seas) Ser.). 224p. (YA). (gr. 7). pap. 6.99 (978-0-14-240657-1(0) , Puffin) Penguin Group (USA) Inc.

Gibbs, Lynne. Growing Pains: Schooltime for Sammy. Mitchell, Melanie, illus. 2003. (Growing Pains Ser.). 32p. (J). pap. 4.95 (978-1-57768-931-7(3) , Gingham Dog Pr.) School Specialty Publishing.

—School Time for Sammy. Mitchell, Melanie, illus. 2003. (Growing Pains Ser.). 32p. (J). 12.95 (978-1-57768-482-4(6) , Gingham Dog Pr.) School Specialty Publishing.

Gifaldi, David. Toby Scudder, King of the School. 2005. 208p. (J). (gr. 4-6). pap. 5.95 (978-0-618-55158-3(1) , Clarion Bks.) Houghton Mifflin Co. Trade & Reference Div.

Giff, Patricia Reilly. The Candy Corn Contest. Sims, Blanche, illus. 1999. (J). (gr. 3-6). lib. bdg. 12.40 (978-0-8085-3415-0(7)) Tandem Library Bks.

—Eleven. 2008. 144p. (J). (***978-0-385-73069-3(1)*** , Delacorte Pr.) Dell Publishing.

—Eleven. 2008. 176p. (J). (gr. 3-8). lib. bdg. 18.99 (***978-0-385-90098-0(8)*** , Lamb, Wendy) Random Hse. Children's Bks.

—En las Garras del Dinosaurio. 2000. (SPA.). (YA). (gr. 1 up). 3.95 (978-0-922852-42-0(1)) AIMS International Bks., Inc.

—Fourth-Grade Celebrity. 1999. (J). (gr. 3-6). 21.75 (978-0-8446-7008-9(1)) Smith, Peter Pub., Inc.

—Fourth-Grade Celebrity. 2000. (J). (978-0-606-20018-9(5)) Tandem Library Bks.

—The Secret at the Polk Street School. (J). (gr. 1-2). pap. 3.99 (978-0-8072-1274-5(1) , Listening Library) Random Hse. Audio Publishing Group.

Gilbert, Barbara Snow. Broken Chords. 2001. (J). (978-0-606-21087-4(3)) Tandem Library Bks.

Giles Chambers, Barbara. The Disappearance of Livvy. 2001. per. 9.95 (978-1-58630-088-3(1)) Word Wrangler Publishing, Inc.

Giles, Gail. Playing in Traffic. 2006. (Illus.). 176p. (YA). reprint ed. pap. 6.99 (978-1-4169-0926-2(5) , Simon Pulse) Simon & Schuster Children's Publishing.

—Right Behind You. 2007. 304p. (YA). (gr. 10 up). 15.99 (***978-0-316-16636-2(7))*** Little, Brown Bks. for Young Readers.

Giles, Gail. Shattering Glass. 2004. 215p. (J). (gr. 7 up). pap. 37.00 incl. audio (978-1-4000-9013-6(X) , Listening Library) Random Hse. Audio Publishing Group.

—Shattering Glass. rev. ed. 2002. (Single Titles Ser.: 12). 224p. (YA). (gr. 7 up). 17.95 (978-0-7613-1581-0(0)) Roaring Brook Pr.

—Shattering Glass. 2003. 224p. (YA). pap. 7.99 (978-0-689-85800-0(0) , Simon Pulse) Simon & Schuster Children's Publishing.

—Shattering Glass. 2003. (gr. 7-12). lib. bdg. 15.30 (978-0-613-73394-6(0)) Tandem Library Bks.

Gilles, Almira Astudillo. Willie Wins. Angel, Carl, illus. 2001. 32p. (J). (ps-3). 16.00 (978-1-58430-023-6(X)) Lee & Low Bks., Inc.

Gilson, Jamie. Bug in a Rug. deGroat, Diane, illus. 2003. 80p. (J). pap. 4.95 (978-0-618-31670-0(1) , Clarion Bks.) Houghton Mifflin Co. Trade & Reference Div.

—Bug in a Rug. 1998. 80p. (J). (gr. k-3). tchr. ed. 15.00 (978-0-395-86616-0(2) , Clarion Bks.) Houghton Mifflin Co. Trade & Reference Div.

—Bug in a Rug. 2003. (gr. k-3). lib. bdg. 12.95 (978-0-613-64657-4(6)) Tandem Library Bks.

—Gotcha! Wummer, Amy, illus. 2006. 80p. (J). (gr. k-3). 15.00 (978-0-618-54356-4(2) , Clarion Bks.) Houghton Mifflin Co. Trade & Reference Div.

—It Goes Eeeeeeeeeeeee! 2001. (gr. 3-6). lib. bdg. 12.95 (978-0-613-35528-5(8)) Tandem Library Bks.

Gingold, Janet. Danger, Long Division. 2006. 164p. (YA). pap. 14.99 (978-1-59092-122-7(4) , Blue Works) Windstorm Creative.

—Finch Goes Wild. 2007. 280p. (YA). pap. 14.99 (978-1-59092-385-6(5) , Blue Works) Windstorm Creative.

Glaser, Higashi & Higashi/Glaser Design Inc. Staff. Hello Kitty Hello Beauty! Style Kit. 2006. 16p. (J). (ps-3). 14.95 (978-0-8109-4946-1(6) , Abrams Bks. for Young Readers) Abrams, Harry N. , Inc.

Glassman, Jackie. Our School. 2000. (ps-2). lib. bdg. 11.80 (978-0-613-32314-7(9)) Tandem Library Bks.

Gleitzman, Morris. Sticky Beak. l.t. ed. 2005. 200p. (J). pap. (978-0-7540-6180-9(9) , CLP 374) BBC Audio.

Glover, Sandra. Foxcroft Files. 2003. (Illus.). 128p. (YA). pap. 9.99 (978-1-84270-279-6(3)) Andersen GBR. *Dist:* Independent Pubs. Group.

Going to School. 2005. (J). (978-1-932570-51-9(9)) Literacy Footprints Inc.

Going to School: Individual Title Six-Packs. (Chiquilibros Ser.). (gr. k-1). 23.00 (978-0-7635-0408-3(4)) Rigby Education.

Gold, Bernice. Strange School, Secret Wish. 2005. 112p. (YA). pap., tchr. ed. (978-0-88878-425-4(2) , Sandcastle Bks.) Dundurn Group, The.

Gold, Maya & Fitzhugh, Louise. Harriet the Spy, Double Agent. 2005. 160p. (J). (gr. 5 up). 15.95 (978-0-385-32787-9(0) , Delacorte Bks. for Young Readers) Random Hse. Children's Bks.

Golden Books Staff. Let's Go to School. 2005. (Blue's Clues Ser.). (Illus.). 24p. (J). (ps-2). audio compact disk 9.95 (978-0-375-83282-6(3) , Golden Bks.) Random Hse. Children's Bks.

—Nick Jr. Book Bag. 2006. (Bookbag Ser.). (Illus.). 32p. (J). (ps-2). pap. 4.99 (978-0-375-83717-3(5) , Golden Bks.) Random Hse. Children's Bks.

Golden, Christopher. Body Bags. 1999. (YA). 11.64 (978-0-606-20505-4(5)) Tandem Library Bks.

Goldschmidt, Judy. Raisin Rodriguez & the Big-Time Smooch. 2007. 208p. (YA). pap. 5.99 (978-1-59514-125-5(1) , Razorbill) Penguin Group (USA) Inc.

—The Secret Blog of Raisin Rodriguez. (J). (gr. 5-12). 2006. 224p. pap. 5.99 (978-1-59514-071-5(9)); 2005. 208p. 12.99 (978-1-59514-018-0(2)) Penguin Group (USA) Inc. (Razorbill).

Goldstein, Gary. The Mythfits. 2005. 280p. (YA). (ps-7). pap. 14.99 (978-1-59092-125-8(9) , Blue Works) Windstorm Creative.

Golightly, Holly. School Bites: Blood Drinking 101, 2. ed. 2005. (Illus.). 64p. (YA). per. (978-0-9745367-3-6(3)) BroadSword Comics/ Jim Balent Studios.

Golightly, Holly, creator. School Bites. 2004. 64p. (YA). per. (978-0-9745367-2-9(5) , SB1A) BroadSword Comics/ Jim Balent Studios.

Gonder, Glen W. Micmacs. Gonder, Sharon J., ed. Grove, Gladys, illus. 1999. (Adventures of Willy Whacker Ser.). 125p. (YA). (gr. 6-8). lib. bdg. 8.95 (978-1-58389-003-5(3)) Osage Bend Publishing Co.

Gonzales Bertrand, Diane, et al. Close to the Heart. 2002. (Illus.). 176p. (J). pap. 9.95 (978-1-55885-319-5(7) , Piñata Books) Arte Publico Pr.

Gonzalez, Julie. Imaginary Enemy. 2008. 256p. (J). (gr. 7). 15.99 (***978-0-385-73552-0(9)*** , Delacorte Bks. for Young Readers) Random Hse. Children's Bks.

Gonzalez, Rigoberto & Alvarez, Cecilia Concepcion. Antonio's Card. 2005. (ENG & SPA., Illus.). 32p. (J). 16.95 (978-0-89239-204-9(5)) Children's Bk. Pr.

Goobie, Beth. Hello, Groin. 2006. 224p. (YA). lib. bdg. 17.95 (978-1-55143-459-9(8)) Orca Bk. Pubs. USA.

—The Lottery. 2002. 272p. (J). (gr. 7-12). lib. bdg. 15.95 (978-1-55143-238-0(2)) Orca Bk. Pubs. USA.

Gorbachev, Valeri. Chicken Chickens Go to School. Gorbachev, Valeri, illus. 2003. (Illus.). (J). (ps-1). 28p. 15.95 (978-0-7358-1600-8(X)); 32p. 16.50 (978-0-7358-1767-8(7)) North-South Bks., Inc.

Gordon, Amy. Return to Gill Park. 2006. (Illus.). 240p. (J). (gr. 3-7). 16.95 (978-0-8234-1998-2(3)) Holiday Hse., Inc.

—When JFK Was My Father. 2001. (J). (978-0-606-21520-6(4)) Tandem Library Bks.

Gordon, Lawrence. Haunted High Vol. 2: The Ghost Chronicles. 2000. 162p. (YA). (gr. 6-9). pap. 11.95 (978-0-9653966-1-5(4)) Karmichael Pr.

Gorman, Carol. Dork in Disguise. 2000. (Harper Trophy Bks.). (Illus.). 176p. (J). (gr. 3-7). pap. 5.99 (978-0-06-440891-2(4) , Harper Trophy) HarperCollins Pubs.

—Dork in Disguise. 2000. (J). 12.64 (978-0-606-20049-3(5)); (gr. 3-6). lib. bdg. 14.15 (978-0-613-30359-0(8)) Tandem Library Bks.

—Dork on the Run. 192p. (J). 2003. (Illus.). pap. 5.99 (978-0-06-440970-4(8) , Harper Trophy); 2002. (gr. 3-6). 15.99 (978-0-06-029409-0(4)) HarperCollins Pubs.

—Dork on the Run. 2003. (gr. 3-6). lib. bdg. 14.15 (978-0-613-61371-2(6)) Tandem Library Bks.

—A Midsummer Night's Dork. 224p. (J). 2006. (Illus.). pap. 5.99 (978-0-06-050720-6(9) , Harper Trophy); 2004. 15.99 (978-0-06-050718-3(7)); 2004. lib. bdg. 16.89 (978-0-06-050719-0(5)) HarperCollins Pubs.

S

Goscinny, René. Nicholas & the Gang. 2007. (Illus.). 120p. (J). 19.95 (*978-0-7148-4788-7(7)) Phaidon Pr., Inc.

Goscinny, René & Uderzo, Albert. Asterix Omnibus 2. 2008. (Illus.). 144p. 27.95 (*978-0-7528-9156-9(1)) Orion Bks. Ltd. GBR. *Dist:* Sterling Publishing Co., Inc.

Gosselin, Kim. Sportsercise: A School Story about Exercise-Induced Asthma. Ravanelli, Terry, illus. 2nd ed. 2004. (Children's Asthma Ser.). (J). per. 9.95 (978-1-891383-25-0(6)) JayJo Bks., LLC.

Gott, Barry. Class Worms. 2007. (I'm Going to Read Ser.). (Illus.). 48p. (J). (gr. 3 up). pap. 3.95 (*978-1-4027-4300-9(9)) Sterling Publishing Co., Inc.

Gott, Barry, illus. No! Yes! 2006. (I'm Going to Read Ser.). 24p. (J). pap. 3.95 (978-1-4027-3413-7(1) , 1261646) Sterling Publishing Co., Inc.

Grab, Daphne. Alive & Well in Prague, NY. 2008. 256p. (J). 16.99 (*978-0-06-125670-7(6)); lib. bdg. 17.89 (*978-0-06-125671-4(4)) HarperCollins Pubs. (Geringer, Laura Book).

Grace, Julie. Echoes of the Heart. 2004. 49p. pap. 12.95 (978-1-4137-3042-5(6)) PublishAmerica, Inc.

Grace, N. B. Battle of the Bands. 2007. (High School Musical Ser.: No. 1). 144p. (J). (gr. 3-7). pap. 4.99 (978-1-4231-0611-1(3)) Disney Pr.

—Broadway Dreams. rev. ed. 2007. (High School Musical Ser.: No. 5). 128p. (gr. 3-7). pap. 4.99 (*978-1-4231-0623-4(7)) Disney Pr.

—Crunch Time. Disney Press Staff, ed. 2007. (High School Musical Ser.: No. 4). 128p. (gr. 3-7). pap. 4.99 (*978-1-4231-0614-2(8)) Disney Pr.

—High School Musical: Junior Novel. 2006. 128p. (gr. 4-7). pap. 4.99 (978-1-4231-0422-3(6)) Disney Pr.

Grace, N. B. High School Musical No. 2: The Junior Novel. Disney Press Staff, ed. 2007. 144p. (J). (gr. 4-7). pap. 4.99 (*978-1-4231-0639-5(3)) Disney Pr.

Grace, N. B. & Alfonsi, Alice. Poetry in Motion. Disney Press Staff, ed. rev. ed. 2007. (High School Musical Ser.: No. 3). 128p. (J). (gr. 3-7). pap. 4.99 (*978-1-4231-0613-5(X)) Disney Pr.

Graff, Lisa. Bernetta Wallflower: A Novel. 2008. 256p. (J). 16.99 (*978-0-06-087592-3(5)); lib. bdg. 17.89 (*978-0-06-087593-0(3)) HarperCollins Pubs. (Geringer, Laura Book).

Graff, Lisa. The Thing about Georgie. 2007. 224p. (J). (gr. 3-6). 15.99 (978-0-06-087589-3(5)); lib. bdg. 16.89 (978-0-06-087590-9(9)) HarperCollins Pubs. (Geringer, Laura Book).

Graham, Rosemary. Thou Shalt Not Dump the Skater Dude & Other Commandments I Have Broken. 2005. 224p. (J). (gr. 7). 16.99 (978-0-670-06017-7(8) , Viking Juvenile) Penguin Group (USA) Inc.

—Thou Shalt Not Dump the Skater Dude (Splashproof Edition) 2007. 1p. (YA). (gr. 7). pap. 6.99 (978-0-14-240836-0(0) , Puffin) Penguin Group (USA) Inc.

Grambling, Lois G. Can I Bring My Pterodactyl to School, Ms. Johnson? Love, Judy, illus. 2006. 32p. (J). pap. 6.95 (978-1-58089-141-7(1)) Charlesbridge Publishing, Inc.

—Can I Bring My Pterodactyl to School, Ms. Johnson. Love, Judy, illus. 2006. (J). 16.95 (978-1-58089-044-1(X)) Charlesbridge Publishing, Inc.

Gran, Julia. Big Bug Surprise. 2007. 32p. (J). (ps-3). pap. 12.99 (978-0-439-67609-0(6) , Scholastic Pr.) Scholastic, Inc.

Graves, Bonnie. No Copycats Allowed! 1998. (J). (978-0-606-13664-8(9)) Tandem Library Bks.

Graves, Damien. The Deadly Catch. 2008. (Midnight Library: Vol. 8). 176p. (J). pap. 5.99 (*978-0-439-89395-4(X) , Scholastic Paperbacks) Scholastic, Inc.

Green, Corey. Managing Stan. 2007. 162p. (J). 16.95 (*978-1-934437-01-8(8)); pap. 7.99 (*978-1-934437-02-5(6)) Abligio Bks.

Green, Jessica. Diary of a Would-Be Princess: The Journal of Jillian James, 5B. 2007. (Illus.). 236p. (J). (gr. 4-7). 15.95 (978-1-58089-166-0(7)) Charlesbridge Publishing, Inc.

Greene, Rhonda Gowler. This Is the Teacher. Lester, Mike, illus. 32p. (J). (gr. k). 2004. 15.99 (978-0-525-47125-7(1) , Dutton Juvenile); 2006. reprint ed. pap. 5.99 (978-0-14-240653-3(8) , Puffin) Penguin Group (USA) Inc.

Greene, Stephanie. Owen Foote, Mighty Scientist. Smith, Catharine Bowman, illus. 2004. 96p. (J). (gr. k-3). tchr. ed. 15.00 (978-0-618-43016-1(4) , Clarion Bks.) Houghton Mifflin Co. Trade & Reference Div.

—Queen Sophie Hartley. 2005. 144p. (J). (gr. 3-5). 15.00 (978-0-618-49461-3(8) , Clarion Bks.) Houghton Mifflin Co. Trade & Reference Div.

—Show & Tell. Clayton, Elaine, illus. 2001. 96p. (J). (gr. 7). pap. 3.99 (978-0-439-14553-4(8)) Scholastic, Inc.

Greenfield Educational Center Staff. Small Snail Goes to School. 2000. (I Can Read Ser.: Bk. 7). (CHI & ENG., Illus.). 8p. (J). pap. 2.99 (978-962-563-076-2(7)) Greenfield Enterprises, Ltd. HKG. *Dist:* Cheng & Tsui Co.

—Small Snail Goes to School: Simplified Edition. 2000. (I Can Read Ser.: Bk. 7). (CHI & ENG., Illus.). 8p. (J). pap. 2.99 (978-962-563-212-4(3)) Greenfield Enterprises, Ltd. HKG. *Dist:* Cheng & Tsui Co.

Greenwald, Sheila. Rosy Cole's Memoir Explosion: A Heartbreaking Story about Losing Friends, Annoying Family, & Ruining Romance. 2006. (Rosie Cole Ser.). (Illus.). 112p. (J). 16.00 (978-0-374-36347-5(1)) Farrar, Straus & Giroux.

Gregory, Valiska. A Valentine for Norman Noggs. Winborn, Marsha, illus. 1999. 32p. (J). (gr. k-3). 14.95 (978-0-06-027656-0(8)); 15.89 (978-0-06-027657-7(6)) HarperCollins Pubs.

—Valentine for Norman Noggs. 1999. (978-0-606-18726-8(X)) Tandem Library Bks.

Greig, Allison. Stacey's Adventures. 2006. (Illus.). 64p. pap. (*978-1-84401-035-6(X)) Athena Pr.

Griek, Susan Vande. The Art Room. Milelli, Pascal, illus. 2002. 24p. (J). (ps-2). 15.95 (978-0-88899-449-3(4)) Groundwood Bks. CAN. *Dist:* Perseus Distribution.

Griffin, Adele. Amandine. 2003. 208p. (gr. 5-9). pap. 6.99 (978-0-7868-1441-1(1)) Disney Pr.

—Amandine. 2001. 224p. (gr. 5-9). 15.99 (978-0-7868-0618-8(4)) Hyperion Bks. for Children.

—Amandine. 2003. 199p. (YA). (gr. 7-9). lib. bdg. 15.30 (978-0-613-69042-3(7)) Tandem Library Bks.

Griffis, Molly Levite. The Feester Filibuster. 2002. (Illus.). vi, 236p. (J). pap. 8.95 (978-1-57168-694-7(0) , Eakin Pr.); 224p. 18.95 (978-1-57168-693-0(2)) Eakin Pr.

—The Feester Filibuster. 2002. (gr. 3-6). lib. bdg. 17.60 (978-0-613-79188-5(6)) Tandem Library Bks.

—The Rachel Resistance. 224p. 8.95 (978-1-57168-553-7(7)); 2001. 17.95 (978-1-57168-541-4(3)) Eakin Pr.

Griffith, Amanda. Two Truths & a Lie. 2006. pap. 15.95 (*978-1-4259-4458-2(2)) AuthorHouse.

Grimes, Nikki. Bronx Masquerade. 2003. 176p. (YA). (gr. 6-11). pap. 5.99 (978-0-14-250189-4(1) , Puffin) Penguin Group (USA) Inc.

—Bronx Masquerade. Myers, Chris, illus. 2001. 176p. (J). (gr. 7 up). 16.99 (978-0-8037-2569-0(8) , Dial) Penguin Group (USA) Inc.

—Bronx Masquerade. 2003. (gr. 7-12). lib. bdg. 14.15 (978-0-613-81701-1(X)) Tandem Library Bks.

—Danitra Brown, Class Clown. Lewis, Earl, illus. 2005. 32p. (J). 16.99 (978-0-688-17290-9(3)); lib. bdg. 16.89 (978-0-688-17291-6(1)) HarperCollins Pubs.

Grindley, Sally. It's My School. Chamberlain, Margaret, illus. 2006. 32p. (J). 16.85 (978-0-8027-8087-4(3)); 15.95 (978-0-8027-8086-7(5)) Walker & Co.

Group/McGraw-Hill, Wright. Secrets & Strays, 6 vols. (D-Man Beans Ser.). 47p. (gr. 4-6). 42.50 (978-0-322-06258-0(6)) Wright Group, The.

Grover, Lorie Ann. Hold Me Tight. 2005. 352p. (J). 16.95 (978-0-689-85248-0(7) , McElderry, Margaret K.) Simon & Schuster Children's Publishing.

Groves. Back to School, Bk. 15. Date not set. (Illus.). 32p. (J). pap. 129.15 (978-0-582-18058-1(9)) Addison-Wesley Longman, Ltd. GBR. *Dist:* Trans-Atlantic Pubns., Inc.

Grunwell, Jeanne Marie. Mind Games. 2006. 144p. (YA). (gr. 5-9). pap. 5.95 (978-0-618-68947-7(8)) Houghton Mifflin Co.

—Mind Games. 2003. (Illus.). 144p. (YA). (gr. 5-9). tchr. ed. 15.00 (978-0-618-17672-4(1)) Houghton Mifflin Co. Trade & Reference Div.

Guest, Elissa Haden. Iris & Walter: The School Play. Davenier, Christine, illus. 2003. (Iris & Walter Ser.). 44p. (J). 15.00 (978-0-15-216481-2(2)) Harcourt Children's Bks.

—Iris & Walter: The School Play. Davenier, Christine, illus. 2004. 44p. (J). (gr. 1-4). lib. bdg. 13.15 (978-0-606-30392-7(8)) Tandem Library Bks.

—Iris & Walter & the Field Trip. Davenier, Christine, illus. 2007. (Iris & Walter Ser.). 44p. (J). pap. 5.95 (*978-0-15-205370-3(0) , Harcourt Paperbacks) Harcourt Children's Bks.

—Iris & Walter & the Substitute Teacher. Davenier, Christine, tr. Davenier, Christine, illus. 2004. (Iris & Walter Ser.). 44p. (J). 15.00 (978-0-15-205013-9(2) , Gulliver Bks.) Harcourt Children's Bks.

—The School Play. Davenier, Christine, illus. 2006. (Iris & Walter Ser.). 44p. (J). pap. 5.95 (978-0-15-205668-1(8) , Harcourt Paperbacks) Harcourt Children's Bks.

Gumfounded. 2004. (J). 13.95 (978-0-9759866-0-8(0)) Garr, Sherry B.

Gunn, Robin Jones. Closer Than Ever. 1999. (Sierra Jensen Ser.: Bk. 11). 160p. (YA). (gr. 7-11). pap. 6.99 (978-1-56179-722-6(7)) Bethany Hse. Pubs.

—Only You, Sierra. 1998. (Sierra Jensen Ser.: Bk. 1). 176p. (J). (gr. 7-11). pap. 6.99 (978-1-56179-370-9(1)) Bethany Hse. Pubs.

Gutman, Anne. Gaspard & Lisa, Friends Forever. Hallensleben, Georg, illus. 2003. 32p. (J). (ps-3). 9.95 (978-0-375-82253-7(4) , Knopf Bks. for Young Readers) Random Hse. Children's Bks.

—Lisa in the Jungle. Hallensleben, Georg, illus. 2003. (Misadventures of Gaspard & Lisa Ser.). 32p. (J). (ps-3). 9.95 (978-0-375-82254-4(2) , Knopf Bks. for Young Readers) Random Hse. Children's Bks.

Gutman, Dan. Dr. Carbles Is Losing His Marbles! Paillot, Jim, illus. 2007. (My Weird School Ser.: No.19). 112p. (J). lib. bdg. 15.89 (*978-0-06-123478-1(8)); pap. 3.99 (*978-0-06-123477-4(X) , Harper Trophy) HarperCollins Pubs.

—The Homework Machine. 2006. (Illus.). 160p. (J). (gr. 3-7). 15.95 (978-0-689-87678-3(5)) Simon & Schuster Children's Publishing.

—The Homework Machine. 2006. (YA). 21.95 (978-0-7862-8883-0(3)) Thorndike Pr.

—The Million Dollar Putt. 2006. 176p. (gr. 3-7). 15.99 (978-0-7868-3641-3(5)) Hyperion Bks. for Children.

—Million Dollar Putt. 2007. 176p. (gr. 3-7). pap. 5.99 (*978-0-7868-3642-0(3)) Hyperion Pr.

—Miss Daisy Is Crazy! Paillot, Jim, illus. 2004. (My Weird School Ser.: Bk. 1). 96p. (J). pap. 3.99 (978-0-06-050700-8(4)); lib. bdg. 15.89 (978-0-06-050701-5(2)) HarperCollins Pubs.

—Miss Holly Is Too Jolly! Paillot, Jim, illus. 2006. (My Weird School Ser.: No. 14). 112p. (J). pap. 3.99 (978-0-06-085382-2(4) , Harper Trophy); lib. bdg. 15.89 (978-0-06-085383-9(2)) HarperCollins Pubs.

—Miss Lazar Is Bizarre! Paillot, Jim, illus. 2005. (My Weird School Ser.). 96p. (J). pap. 3.99 (978-0-06-082225-5(2) , Harper Trophy) HarperCollins Pubs.

—Miss Small Is off the Wall! Paillot, Jim, illus. 2005. (My Weird School Ser.). 112p. (J). lib. bdg. 15.89 (978-0-06-074519-6(3)); pap. 3.99 (978-0-06-074518-9(5) , Harper Trophy) HarperCollins Pubs.

—Miss Small Is off the Wall! Paillot, Jim, illus. 2005. 96p. (J). (gr. 2-5). lib. bdg. 11.19 (978-0-606-33326-9(6)) Tandem Library Bks.

—Miss Suki Is Kooky! Paillot, Jim, illus. 2007. (My Weird School Ser.: No. 17). 112p. (J). pap. 3.99 (*978-0-06-123473-6(7) , Harper Trophy); lib. bdg. 15.89 (*978-0-06-123474-3(5)) HarperCollins Pubs.

—Mr. Docker Is off His Rocker! Paillot, Jim, illus. 2006. (My Weird School Ser.). 112p. (J). pap. 3.99 (978-0-06-082227-9(9) , Harper Trophy); lib. bdg. 15.89 (978-0-06-082228-6(7)) HarperCollins Pubs.

—Mr. Hynde Is Out of His Mind! Paillot, Jim, illus. 2005. (My Weird School Ser.). 112p. (J). lib. bdg. 15.89 (978-0-06-074521-9(5)); pap. 3.99 (978-0-06-074520-2(7) , Harper Trophy) HarperCollins Pubs.

—Mr. Hynde Is Out of His Mind! Paillot, Jim, illus. 2005. 97p. (J). (ps-k). lib. bdg. 10.64 (978-0-606-33934-6(5)) Tandem Library Bks.

—Mr. Klutz Is Nuts! Paillot, Jim, illus. 2004. (My Weird School Ser.: Bk. 2). 112p. (J). pap. 3.99 (978-0-06-050702-2(0) , Harper Trophy); lib. bdg. 15.89 (978-0-06-050703-9(9)) HarperCollins Pubs.

—Mr. Louie Is Screwy! Paillot, Jim, illus. 2007. (My Weird School Ser.: No. 20). 112p. (J). lib. bdg. 15.89 (*978-0-06-123480-4(X)); pap. 3.99 (*978-0-06-123479-8(6) , Harper Trophy) HarperCollins Pubs.

—Mr. Macky Is Wacky! Paillot, Jim, illus. 2007. (My Weird School Ser.: No. 15). (J). 112p. lib. bdg. 15.89 (978-0-06-114152-2(6)); 96p. pap. 3.99 (978-0-06-114151-5(8) , Harper Trophy) HarperCollins Pubs.

—Mrs. Cooney Is Loony! Paillot, Jim, illus. 2005. (My Weird School Ser.). 112p. (J). pap. 3.99 (978-0-06-074522-6(3)); lib. bdg. 15.89 (978-0-06-074523-3(1)) HarperCollins Pubs. (Harper Trophy).

—Mrs. Kormel Is Not Normal! Paillot, Jim, illus. 2006. (My Weird School Ser.). 96p. (J). pap. 3.99 (978-0-06-082229-3(5) , Harper Trophy) HarperCollins Pubs.

—Mrs. Patty Is Batty! Paillot, Jim, illus. 2006. (My Weird School Ser.: No. 13). 112p. (J). pap. 3.99 (978-0-06-085380-8(8) , Harper Trophy); lib. bdg. 15.89 (978-0-06-085381-5(6)) HarperCollins Pubs.

—Mrs. Roopy Is Loopy! Paillot, Jim, illus. 2004. (My Weird School Ser.: Bk. 3). 96p. (J). pap. 3.99 (978-0-06-050704-6(7) , Harper Trophy) HarperCollins Pubs.

—Mrs. Yonkers Is Bonkers! 2007. (My Weird School Ser.: No. 18). 112p. (J). lib. bdg. 15.89 (*978-0-06-123476-7(1)) HarperCollins Pubs.

—Mrs. Yonkers Is Bonkers! Paillot, Jim, illus. 2007. (My Weird School Ser.: No. 18). 112p. (J). pap. 3.99 (*978-0-06-123475-0(3) , Harper Trophy) HarperCollins Pubs.

—Ms. Coco Is Loco! Paillot, Jim, illus. 2007. (My Weird School Ser.: No. 16). (J). 96p. pap. 3.99 (978-0-06-114153-9(4) , Harper Trophy); 112p. lib. bdg. 15.89 (978-0-06-114154-6(2)) HarperCollins Pubs.

—Ms. Hannah Is Bananas! Paillot, Jim, illus. 2004. (My Weird School Ser.: Bk. 4). 96p. (J). pap. 3.99 (978-0-06-050706-0(3) , Harper Trophy); lib. bdg. 15.89 (978-0-06-050707-7(1)) HarperCollins Pubs.

—Ms. Hannah Is Bananas! Paillot, Jim, illus. 2005. 84p. (J). (gr. 2-5). lib. bdg. 11.19 (978-0-606-33041-1(0)) Tandem Library Bks.

—Ms. Lagrange Is Strange! Paillot, Jim, illus. 2005. (My Weird School Ser.). 112p. (J). pap. 3.99 (978-0-06-082223-1(6) , Harper Trophy) HarperCollins Pubs.

—My Weird School #21: Ms. Krup Cracks Me Up! 2008. (My Weird School Ser.). 112p. (J). pap. 3.99 (*978-0-06-134605-7(5) , Harper Trophy); lib. bdg. 15.89 (*978-0-06-134606-4(3)) HarperCollins Pubs.

Gutman, Dan. Qwerty Stevens Stuck in Time with Benjamin Franklin. 2002. (Illus.). 192p. (J). (gr. 5-8). 17.95 (978-0-689-84553-6(7)) Simon & Schuster Children's Publishing.

H. Irving Hancock. The High School Captain of the Team: Dick & Co. Leading the Athletic Vanguard. 2007. 156p. pap. 11.99 (*978-1-4264-6386-0(3)) BiblioBazaar.

Haddad, Charles. Meet Calliope Day. 1999. (J). (978-0-606-16452-8(9)) Tandem Library Bks.

Haddix, Margaret Peterson. Because of Anya. 2002. (Illus.). 128p. (J). (gr. 3-6). 16.95 (978-0-689-83298-7(2)) Simon & Schuster Children's Publishing.

—Dexter the Tough. Elliott, Mark, illus. 2007. 144p. (J). (gr. 2-5). 15.99 (978-1-4169-1159-3(6)) Simon & Schuster Children's Publishing.

—The Girl with 500 Middle Names. Hamlin, Janet, illus. 2001. 96p. (J). (gr. 2-5). pap. 4.99 (978-0-689-84136-1(1) , Aladdin) Simon & Schuster Children's Publishing.

—The Girl with 500 Middle Names. 2001. (gr. 3-6). lib. bdg. 11.80 (978-0-613-31244-8(9)); (Illus.). (J). 10.79 (978-0-606-20672-3(8)) Tandem Library Bks.

—The Girl with 500 Middle Names. l.t. ed. 2002. 102p. (J). 21.95 (978-0-7862-4412-6(7)) Thomson Gale.

Hafer, Todd. Stealing Home. 2004. (Spirit of the Game, Sports Fiction Ser.). 144p. (J). pap. 4.99 (978-0-310-70671-7(8)) Zonderkidz.

Hahn, Mary Downing. Janey & the Famous Author. Bush, Timothy, illus. 2005. 48p. (J). (gr. k-3). 15.00 (978-0-618-35408-5(5) , Clarion Bks.) Houghton Mifflin Co. Trade & Reference Div.

Hale, Bruce. The Big Nap. Hale, Bruce, illus. (Chet Gecko Mystery Ser.: No. 4). (Illus.). (J). 2002. 132p. (ps-7). pap. 4.95 (978-0-15-202479-6(4) , Harcourt Paperbacks); 2001. 128p. (gr. 3-7). 15.00 (978-0-15-202521-2(9)) Harcourt Children's Bks.

—The Big Nap. unabr. ed. 2004. (Chet Gecko, Private Eye Ser.: No. 4). 128p. (J). (gr. 3-6). pap. 17.00 incl. audio (978-0-8072-1707-8(7) , S FTR 272 SP, Listening Library) Random Hse. Audio Publishing Group.

—The Big Nap: From the Tattered Casebook of Chet Gecko, Private Eye. 2002. (Chet Gecko Mystery Ser.: No. 4). (J). (gr. 3-6). lib. bdg. 12.95 (978-0-613-50549-9(2)) Tandem Library Bks.

—The Chameleon Wore Chartreuse: A Chet Gecko Mystery. 2001. (Chet Gecko Mystery Ser.: No. 1). (J). (gr. 3-6). lib. bdg. 12.95 (978-0-613-35450-9(8)); (Illus.). 11.60 (978-0-606-21105-5(5)) Tandem Library Bks.

—Farewell, My Lunchbag: A Chet Gecko Mystery. 2002. (Chet Gecko Mystery Ser.: No. 3). (Illus.). 132p. (ps-7). pap. 4.95 (978-0-15-202629-5(0) , Harcourt Paperbacks) Harcourt Children's Bks.

—Farewell, My Lunchbag: A Chet Gecko Mystery. Hale, Bruce, illus. 2001. (Chet Gecko Mystery Ser.: No. 3). (Illus.). 128p. (J). (gr. 3-7). 15.00 (978-0-15-202275-4(9)) Harcourt Children's Bks.

—Farewell, My Lunchbag: A Chet Gecko Mystery. 2002. (Chet Gecko Mystery Ser.: No. 3). (J). (gr. 3-6). lib. bdg. 12.95 (978-0-613-49734-3(1)) Tandem Library Bks.

—Give My Regrets to Broadway: A Chet Gecko Mystery. (Chet Gecko Mystery Ser.: No. 9). (Illus.). (J). (gr. 3-6). 2005. 144p. pap. 4.95 (978-0-15-216730-1(7) , Harcourt Paperbacks); 2004. 136p. 15.00 (978-0-15-216700-4(5)) Harcourt Children's Bks.

—The Hamster of the Baskervilles: A Chet Gecko Mystery. (Chet Gecko Mystery Ser.: No. 5). (Illus.). (J). 2003. 144p. (gr. 3-7). pap. 4.95 (978-0-15-202509-0(X) , Harcourt Paperbacks); 2002. 132p. (gr. 4-7). 14.00 (978-0-15-202503-8(0)) Harcourt Children's Bks.

—Hiss Me Deadly: A Chet Gecko Mystery. Hale, Bruce, illus. 2007. (Chet Gecko Mystery Ser.: No. 13). (Illus.). 144p. (J). (gr. 3-7). 15.00 (*978-0-15-205482-3(0)) Harcourt Children's Bks.

—Key Lardo: A Chet Gecko Mystery. Hale, Bruce, illus. 2007. (Chet Gecko Mystery Ser.: No. 12). (Illus.). 128p. (J). (gr. 3-7). pap. 4.95 (978-0-15-205235-5(6) , Harcourt Paperbacks) Harcourt Children's Bks.

—Key Lardo: A Chet Gecko Mystery. 2006. (Chet Gecko Mystery Ser.: No. 12). (Illus.). 128p. (J). (gr. 3-7). 14.00 (978-0-15-205074-0(4)) Harcourt Children's Bks.

—The Malted Falcon: A Chet Gecko Mystery. (Chet Gecko Mystery Ser.: No. 7). (Illus.). (J). (gr. 3-7). 2004. 132p. pap. 4.95 (978-0-15-216712-7(9) , Harcourt Paperbacks); 2003. 128p. 14.00 (978-0-15-216706-6(4)) Harcourt Children's Bks.

—The Malted Falcon: A Chet Gecko Mystery. 2004. (Chet Gecko Mystery Ser.: No. 7). (J). (gr. 3-6). lib. bdg. 12.95 (978-0-613-71645-1(0)) Tandem Library Bks.

—Murder, My Tweet: A Chet Gecko Mystery. 2004. (Illus.). 117p. (J). (gr. 3-7). per. 12.00 (978-0-606-33413-6(0)) Tandem Library Bks.

—The Mystery of Mr. Nice. 2000. (Chet Gecko Mystery Ser.: No. 2). (Illus.). 112p. (J). (gr. 3-7). 14.00 (978-0-15-202271-6(6)) Harcourt Children's Bks.

—The Mystery of Mr. Nice. 2001. (Chet Gecko Mystery Ser.: No. 2). (J). (gr. 3-7). lib. bdg. 12.95 (978-0-613-35466-0(4)); (Illus.). (978-0-606-21344-8(9)) Tandem Library Bks.

—The Possum Always Rings Twice: A Chet Gecko Mystery. Hale, Bruce, illus. 2007. (Chet Gecko Mystery Ser.: No. 11). (Illus.). 144p. (J). (gr. 3-7). pap. 4.95 (978-0-15-205233-1(X) , Harcourt Paperbacks) Harcourt Children's Bks.

—The Possum Always Rings Twice: A Chet Gecko Mystery. 2006. (Chet Gecko Mystery Ser.: No. 11). (Illus.). 128p. (J). (gr. 3-7). 14.00 (978-0-15-205075-7(2)) Harcourt Children's Bks.

—This Gum for Hire: A Chet Gecko Mystery. (Chet Gecko Mystery Ser.: No. 6). (Illus.). (J). (gr. 3-7). 2003. 144p. pap. 4.95 (978-0-15-202497-0(2) , Harcourt Paperbacks); 2002. 136p. 15.00 (978-0-15-202491-8(3)) Harcourt Children's Bks.

—This Gum for Hire: A Chet Gecko Mystery. 2003. (Chet Gecko Mystery Ser.: No. 6). (J). (gr. 3-6). lib. bdg. 12.95 (978-0-613-59895-8(4)) Tandem Library Bks.

—Trouble Is My Beeswax: A Chet Gecko Mystery. 2004. (Chet Gecko Mystery Ser.: No. 8). (Illus.). 132p. (J). (gr. 3-6). pap. 4.95 (978-0-15-216724-0(2) , Harcourt Paperbacks) Harcourt Children's Bks.

—Trouble Is My Beeswax: A Chet Gecko Mystery. Weinman, Brad, illus. 2003. (Chet Gecko Mystery Ser.: No. 8). 128p. (J). (gr. 3-6). 14.00 (978-0-15-216718-9(8)) Harcourt Children's Bks.

—Trouble Is My Beeswax: A Chet Gecko Mystery. 2004. (Chet Gecko Mystery Ser.: No. 8). (J). (gr. 3-6). lib. bdg. 12.95 (978-0-613-71557-7(8)) Tandem Library Bks.

Hale, Shannon. The Princess Academy. 2007. 336p. (YA). pap. 7.95 (*978-1-59990-073-5(4) , Bloomsbury Children) Bloomsbury Publishing.

—The Princess Academy. l.t. ed. 2006. 400p. (YA). 23.95 (978-0-7862-8733-8(0)) Thorndike Pr.

Haley, Amanda, illus. Music Class. 2006. (I'm Going to Read Ser.). 32p. (J). pap. 3.95 (978-1-4027-3081-8(0)) Sterling Publishing Co., Inc.

Hall, Kirsten. First Day of School: All about Shapes & Sizes. Luedecke, Bev, illus. 2003. (Beastieville Ser.). 32p. (J). (ps-1). 19.50 (978-0-516-22893-8(5) , Children's Pr.) Scholastic Library Publishing.

—Green Thumbs. Burnett, Lindy, illus. 2002. (J). 3.99 (978-0-439-32095-5(X)) Scholastic, Inc.

—My New School. Gott, Barry, illus. 2004. (My First Reader Ser.). 32p. (J). (gr. k-1). pap. 3.95 (978-0-516-25505-7(3) , Children's Pr.) Scholastic Library Publishing.

—My New School. Gott, Barry, tr. Gott, Barry, illus. 2004. (My First Reader Ser.). 31p. (J). 18.50 (978-0-516-24413-6(2) , Children's Pr.) Scholastic Library Publishing.

Hallinan, P. K. Let's Learn All We Can! (J). 2004. (Illus.). 48p. pap. 9.95 (978-0-8249-5491-8(2)); 2002. 24p. 7.95 (978-0-8249-5307-2(X) , Ideals) Ideals Pubns.

—My First Day of School. Hallinan, P. K., illus. 1999. (Illus.). 24p. (ps-3). 6.95 (978-1-57102-154-0(X)) Warehousing & Fulfillment Specialists, LLC (WFS, LLC).

Halpin, Brendan. How Ya Like Me Now. 2007. 208p. (YA). (gr. 7 up). 16.00 (978-0-374-33495-6(1)) Farrar, Straus & Giroux.

Halverson, Deborah. Big Mouth. 2008. 144p. (J). (gr. 5). 15.99 (*978-0-385-73394-6(1)); lib. bdg. 18.99 (*978-0-385-90408-7(8)) Random Hse. Children's Bks. (Delacorte Bks. for Young Readers).

Halvorsen Schreck, Karen. Lucy's Family Tree. Gassler, Stephen, illus. 2006. 40p. (J). 7.95 (*978-0-88448-292-5(8)) Tilbury Hse. Pubs.

Hambrick, Sharon. Arby Jenkins Meets His Match. Thompson, Del, illus. 2000. 120p. (J). (gr. 4-7). 7.49 (978-1-57924-461-3(0)) Jones, Bob Univ. Pr.

—Arby Jenkins, Ready to Roll. 1998. 150p. (J). (gr. 4-7). pap. 7.49 (978-0-89084-958-3(7)) Jones, Bob Univ. Pr.

—Tommy's Rocket. Manning, Maurie, illus. 2003. (Fig Street Kids Ser.). 83p. (J). (gr. 1-2). 7.49 (978-1-59166-186-3(2)) Jones, Bob Univ. Pr.

—The Year of Abi Crim. 2000. (Illus.). 118p. (J). (gr. 4-7). pap. 7.49 (978-1-57924-374-6(6) , 124255) Jones, Bob Univ. Pr.

Hamilton, C. J. An Ordinary School Day. Revell, Cindy, illus. 2004. 24p. (J). (gr. k-4). pap. 6.95 (978-1-55037-828-3(7)) Annick Pr., Ltd. CAN. *Dist:* Firefly Bks., Ltd.

Hamilton, Morse. Yellow Blue Bus Means I Love You. 2000. 192p. (YA). (gr. 7 up). pap. 6.99 (978-0-380-73301-9(3)) HarperCollins Pubs.

—Yellow Bus Means I Love You. 2000. (978-0-606-17984-3(4)) Tandem Library Bks.

Hamilton, Richard. Let's Take over the Kindergarten. Heap, Sue, illus. 2007. 32p. (J). (ps-1). 15.95 (978-1-58234-707-3(7)) Bloomsbury Publishing.

Hamilton, Virginia. Bluish. Dillon, Leo & Dillon, Diane, illus. 1999. 128p. (J). (gr. 4-9). pap. 16.95 (978-0-590-28879-8(2) , Blue Sky Pr., The) Scholastic, Inc.

—Bluish. 2002. (gr. 5-8). lib. bdg. 13.00 (978-0-613-53797-1(1)) Tandem Library Bks.

Hancock, H. Irving. The High School Captain of the Team: Dick & Co. Leading the Athletic Vanguard. l.t. ed. 2007. 172p. pap. 14.99 (*978-1-4264-6460-7(6)) BiblioBazaar.

—The High School Left End: Dick & Co. Grilling on the Football Gridiron. 2007. 156p. pap. 11.99 (*978-1-4264-6385-3(5)); 174p. pap. 14.99 (*978-1-4264-6459-1(2)) BiblioBazaar.

Hanh, Thich Nhat. The Hermit & the Well. Mai, Vo-Dinh, illus. 2004. 36p. (J). 15.00 (978-1-888375-31-2(0)) Parallax Pr.

Hannigan, Katherine. Ida B: ... And Her Plans to Maximize Fun, Avoid Disaster, & (Possibly) Save the World. 256p. 2004. (J). (gr. 4 up). 16.99 (978-0-06-073024-6(2)); 2004. (gr. 4 up). lib. bdg. 16.89 (978-0-06-073025-3(0)); 2007. reprint ed. pap. 5.99 (978-0-06-073026-0(9) , Harper Trophy) HarperCollins Pubs.

Hansen, Joyce. Yellow Bird & Me. 2005. 168p. (J). (gr. 5-9). pap. 6.95 (978-0-618-61116-4(9) , Clarion Bks.) Houghton Mifflin Co. Trade & Reference Div.

Hanson, Bonnie Compton. Meet the Ponytail Girls. 2004. (Ponytail Girls Ser.). (Illus.). 208p. (J). pap. 7.99 (978-1-58411-029-3(5) , Legacy Pr.) Rainbow Pubs. & Legacy Pr.

Hapka, Catherine. Wildcat Spirit. rev. ed. 2007. (High School Musical Ser.: No. 2). 128p. (J). (gr. 3-7). pap. 4.99 (978-1-4231-0612-8(1)) Disney Pr.

Hapka, Cathy & Titlebaum, Ellen. How Not to Start Third Grade. Palen, Debbie, illus. 2007. (Step into Reading Ser.). 48p. (J). (gr. 2-4). 3.99 (*978-0-375-83904-7(6)); lib. bdg. 11.99 (*978-0-375-93904-4(0)) Random Hse. Children's Bks. (Random Hse. Bks. for Young Readers).

Harcourt School Publishers Staff. The ABC's of My School. 3rd ed. 2002. (Trophies English Language Learners Ser.). (Illus.). (gr. 3). pap. 5.10 (978-0-15-327690-3(8)) Harcourt Schl. Pubs.

—The Acting Champ Advanced Level. 3rd ed. 2002. (Trophies Reading Program Ser.). (Illus.). pap. 5.10 (978-0-15 323464-4(4)) Harcourt Schl. Pubs.

—The Balloon Popper: Take-Home Book. 2001. (Collections Ser.). (Illus.). (J). (gr. 6). pap. 1.90 (978-0-15-319543-8(5)) Harcourt Schl. Pubs.

—Before & Now. 3rd ed. 2002. (Trophies English Language Learners Ser.). (Illus.). (gr. 2). pap. 5.10 (978-0-15-327630-9(4)) Harcourt Schl. Pubs.

—The Best Candidate: Take-Home Book. 2001. (Collections Ser.). (Illus.). (J). pap. 1.90 (978-0-15-319533-4(9)) Harcourt Schl. Pubs.

—The Best Candidate Below Level. 3rd ed. 2002. (Trophies Reading Program Ser.). (Illus.). pap. 5.10 (978-0-15-323331-9(1)) Harcourt Schl. Pubs.

—Breaking Away: Take-Home Book. 1999. (Collections Ser.). (Illus.). (J). pap. 1.90 (978-0-15-317286-1(X)) Harcourt Schl. Pubs.

—Career Day: Library Book. 3rd ed. 2002. (Trophies Reading Program Ser.). (Illus.). pap. 14.00 (978-0-15-326532-7(9)) Harcourt Schl. Pubs.

—Collections: The Art Lesson: Grade Level Library. 1999. (Illus.). (J). pap. 4.70 (978-0-15-315205-4(2)) Harcourt Schl. Pubs.

—The Down & Up Fall: Reader's Choice Book. 2001. (Collections Ser.). (Illus.). pap. 13.20 (978-0-15-314366-3(5)) Harcourt Schl. Pubs.

—Fingertips: Take-Home Book. 2001. (Collections Ser.). (Illus.). (J). pap. 1.90 (978-0-15-319565-5(7)) Harcourt Schl. Pubs.

—Fingertips Below Level. 3rd ed. 2002. (Trophies Reading Program Ser.). (Illus.). pap. 5.10 (978-0-15-323423-1(7)) Harcourt Schl. Pubs.

—First Day at School: Pre-Decodable Book. 3rd ed. 2002. (Trophies Reading Program Ser.). (Illus.). (gr. k). pap. 2.90 (978-0-15-325403-1(3)) Harcourt Schl. Pubs.

—Frindle: Reader's Choice Book. 2001. (Collections Ser.). (Illus.). pap. 12.10 (978-0-15-314397-7(5)) Harcourt Schl. Pubs.

—Going to School, Unit 1. 3rd ed. 2003. (Horizons Ser.). (Illus.). (gr. 1). pap. 166.70 (978-0-15-340220-3(2)) Harcourt Schl. Pubs.

—The Hamster in Room 24 Is Missing. 3rd ed. 2002. (Trophies English Language Learners Ser.). (Illus.). pap. 5.10 (978-0-15-327831-0(5)) Harcourt Schl. Pubs.

—A Hat for Sam Advanced Level. 3rd ed. 2002. (Trophies Reading Program Ser.). (Illus.). (J). (gr. 1). pap. 3.70 (978-0-15-323007-3(X)) Harcourt Schl. Pubs.

—High Ropes On Level. 3rd ed. 2002. (Trophies Reading Program Ser.). (Illus.). pap. 5.10 (978-0-15-323447-7(4)) Harcourt Schl. Pubs.

—I Need a Lunch Box: Library Book. 1999. (Collections Ser.). (Illus.). pap. 14.90 (978-0-15-313396-1(1)) Harcourt Schl. Pubs.

—I Want to Be Me. 3rd ed. 2002. (Trophies English Language Learners Ser.). (Illus.). pap. 5.10 (978-0-15-327829-7(3)) Harcourt Schl. Pubs.

—It's Good to Be Me: Take-Home Book. 1999. (Collections Ser.). (Illus.). (J). pap. 1.90 (978-0-15-317194-9(4)) Harcourt Schl. Pubs.

—Keep Well Day Advanced Level. 3rd ed. 2002. (Trophies Reading Program Ser.). (Illus.). pap. 5.10 (978-0-15-323030-1(4)) Harcourt Schl. Pubs.

—The Kid from Brighton Beach Below Level. 3rd ed. 2002. (Trophies Reading Program Ser.). (Illus.). pap. 5.10 (978-0-15-323224-4(2)) Harcourt Schl. Pubs.

—The Kid of Brighton Beach: Take-Home Book. 2001. (Collections Ser.). (Illus.). (J). pap. 1.90 (978-0-15-319486-3(3)) Harcourt Schl. Pubs.

—Letter Perfect Advanced Level. 3rd ed. 2002. (Trophies Reading Program Ser.). (Illus.). pap. 5.10 (978-0-15-323195-7(5)) Harcourt Schl. Pubs.

—The Little Fiddle, 5 Packs., On Level. 3rd ed. 2002. (Trophies Reading Program Ser.). (Illus.). (gr. 1). pap. 20.10 (978-0-15-326839-7(5)) Harcourt Schl. Pubs.

—The Little Fiddle: On Level. 3rd ed. 2002. (Trophies Reading Program Ser.). (Illus.). (J). pap. 4.10 (978-0-15-322989-3(6)) Harcourt Schl. Pubs.

—The Little School in the Valley Below Level. 3rd ed. 2002. (Trophies Reading Program Ser.). (Illus.). pap. 5.10 (978-0-15-323244-2(7)) Harcourt Schl. Pubs.

—Making a Difference On Level. 3rd ed. 2002. (Trophies Reading Program Ser.). (Illus.). pap. 5.10 (978-0-15-323344-9(3)) Harcourt Schl. Pubs.

—Meet Manuel Advanced Level. 3rd ed. 2002. (Trophies Reading Program Ser.). (Illus.). pap. 5.10 (978-0-15-323393-7(1)) Harcourt Schl. Pubs.

—Mi Mayor Deseo: Take-Home Book. 2001. (Vamos Ser.). (SPA., Illus.). (J). pap. 2.80 (978-0-15-319928-8(8)) Harcourt Schl. Pubs.

—Mine - Grade 5. 3rd ed. 2002. (Trophies English Language Learners Ser.). pap. 5.10 (978-0-15-327810-5(2)) Harcourt Schl. Pubs.

—My Greatest Wish: Take-Home Book. 2001. (Collections Ser.). (Illus.). (J). pap. 1.90 (978-0-15-319485-6(5)) Harcourt Schl. Pubs.

—My Greatest Wish Below Level. 3rd ed. 2002. (Trophies Reading Program Ser.). (Illus.). pap. 5.10 (978-0-15-323223-7(4)) Harcourt Schl. Pubs.

—The New Girl: Take-Home Book. 2001. (Collections Ser.). (Illus.). (J). pap. 1.90 (978-0-15-319534-1(7)) Harcourt Schl. Pubs.

—The New Girl Below Level. 3rd ed. 2002. (Trophies Reading Program Ser.). (Illus.). pap. 5.10 (978-0-15-323332-6(X)) Harcourt Schl. Pubs.

—New School: Take-Home Book. 1999. (Signatures Ser.). (Illus.). (J). (gr. 2). pap. 1.90 (978-0-15-313856-0(4)) Harcourt Schl. Pubs.

—The New Teacher: Take-Home Book. 1999. (Signatures Ser.). (Illus.). (J). pap. 1.90 (978-0-15-313916-1(1)) Harcourt Schl. Pubs.

—The Orphan Train Home Advanced Level. 3rd ed. 2002. (Trophies Reading Program Ser.). (Illus.). pap. 5.10 (978-0-15-323126-1(2)) Harcourt Schl. Pubs.

—Paint. 3rd ed. 2002. (Trophies Ser.). pap. 51.00 (978-0-15-327899-0(4)) Harcourt Schl. Pubs.

—Ronda & the Garden of the Gulf On Level. 3rd ed. 2002. (Trophies Reading Program Ser.). (Illus.). pap. 5.10 (978-0-15-323454-5(7)) Harcourt Schl. Pubs.

—School 2501. 3rd ed. 2002. (Trophies English Language Learners Ser.). (Illus.). pap. 5.10 (978-0-15-327834-1(X)) Harcourt Schl. Pubs.

—Science Fair! 3rd ed. 2002. (Trophies English Language Learners Ser.). (Illus.). pap. 5.10 (978-0-15-327751-1(3)) Harcourt Schl. Pubs.

—Science Unfair: Take-Home Book. 2001. (Collections Ser.). (Illus.). (J). pap. 1.90 (978-0-15-319669-0(6)) Harcourt Schl. Pubs.

—Season of the Spider On Level. 3rd ed. 2002. (Trophies Reading Program Ser.). (Illus.). pap. 5.10 (978-0-15-323437-8(7)) Harcourt Schl. Pubs.

—Show & Tell. 3rd ed. 2002. (Trophies English Language Learners Ser.). (Illus.). pap. 5.10 (978-0-15-327634-7(7)) Harcourt Schl. Pubs.

—Silent Observer Level D: Reader. 2001. (Collections Ser.). (Illus.). (J). 5.90 (978-0-15-314376-2(2)) Harcourt Schl. Pubs.

—Somewhere to Go: Take-Home Book. 2001. (Collections Ser.). (Illus.). (J). pap. 1.90 (978-0-15-319547-1(9)) Harcourt Schl. Pubs.

—Sports Day. 3rd ed. 2002. (Trophies English Language Learners Ser.). (Illus.). (J). pap. 3.20 (978-0-15-327572-2(3)) Harcourt Schl. Pubs.

—Stacy's Surprise: Take-Home Book. 1999. (Collections Ser.). (Illus.). (J). pap. 1.90 (978-0-15-317298-4(3)) Harcourt Schl. Pubs.

—Stacy's Surprise Below Level. 3rd ed. 2002. (Trophies Reading Program Ser.). (Illus.). pap. 5.10 (978-0-15-323142-1(4)) Harcourt Schl. Pubs.

—Team Spirit. 3rd ed. 2002. (Illus.). pap. 5.10 (978-0-15-327694-1(0)) Harcourt Schl. Pubs.

—Trofeos On Level: En Mi Escuela. 3rd ed. 2002. (SPA., Illus.). pap. 5.50 (978-0-15-323900-7(X)) Harcourt Schl. Pubs.

Hardin, Suzanne. Dogs at School. Friar, Joanne, illus. 1999. (Books for Young Learners). 16p. (J). (gr. k-2). pap. 5.00 (978-1-57274-256-7(9)) Owen, Richard C. Pubs., Inc.

Hardy, LeAnne. Between Two Worlds: A Novel. 2003. 160p. pap. 6.99 (978-0-8254-2793-0(2)) Kregel Pubns.

Hare, Eric B. Curse Proof. 2007. (Illus.). 95p. (J). (*978-0-8163-2208-4(2)) Pacific Pr. Publishing Assn.

Hargreaves, Roger. Little Miss Brainy. Hargreaves, Roger, illus. 2002. (Mr. Men & Little Miss 3D Ser.). (Illus.). 32p. (J). pap. 3.99 (978-0-8431-7716-9(0) , Price Stern Sloan) Penguin Group (USA) Inc.

Harley Bill. Sarahs Story. Aldridge Eve, illus. 2006. 32p. (J). 6.95 (978-1-58246-178-6(3) , Tricycle Pr.) Ten Speed Pr.

Harmon, Michael. Skate. 2008. 256p. (J). (gr. 9). mass mkt. 6.50 (*978-0-553-49510-2(0) , Laurel Leaf) Random Hse. Children's Bks.

Harmon, Michael B. Skate. 2006. 256p. (YA). (gr. 9). 15.95 (978-0-375-87516-8(6)); 17.99 (978-0-375-97516-5(0)) Random Hse. Children's Bks. (Knopf Bks. for Young Readers).

Harness, Cheryl. Just for You to Know. 2008. (J). pap. (*978-0-06-078315-0(X)) HarperCollins Pubs.

Harold, Gwyneth. Bad Girls in School. 2006. 148p. (YA). pap. (978-0-435-21517-0(5)) Heinemann.

Harper, Charise Mericle. Flashcards of My Life. 2007. 224p. (J). (gr. 3-7). pap. 6.99 (978-0-316-16676-8(6)) Little Brown & Co.

—Just Grace. 2007. (Illus.). 144p. (J). (gr. 1-5). 15.00 (978-0-618-64642-5(6)) Houghton Mifflin Co. Trade & Reference Div.

Harper, Charise Mericle. Still Just Grace. Harper, Charise Mericle, illus. 2007. (Illus.). 152p. (J). (gr. 3-5). 15.00 (*978-0-618-64643-2(4)) Houghton Mifflin Co. Trade & Reference Div.

Harper, Jamie. Miss Mingo & the First Day of School. Harper, Jamie, illus. 2006. (Illus.). 32p. (J). (ps-2). 15.99 (978-0-7636-2410-1(1)) Candlewick Pr.

—Miss Mingo & the First Day of School. 2006. (Illus.). 26p. (J). (*978-1-4156-9174-8(6)) Candlewick Pr.

Harrar, George. Not as Crazy as I Seem. 2003. 208p. (J). (gr. 7). tchr. ed. 15.00 (978-0-618-26365-3(9)) Houghton Mifflin Co. Trade & Reference Div.

—Not As Crazy As I Seem. 2004. 240p. (J). (gr. 7). pap. 6.99 (978-0-618-49480-4(4) , Graphia) Houghton Mifflin Co. Trade & Reference Div.

Harrington, Dylan, Brittany, Huston, Andy & Harrington, Dylan, Brittany, HustonHarrington, Paula, Andy. The Harrington Five & the Case of the School Sandals Err Vandals. 2006. 144p. pap. 11.25 (978-1-4116-7883-5(4)) Lulu.com.

Harris, Robie H. I Am Not Going to School Today! Ormerod, Jan, illus. 2003. 32p. (J). (ps-3). 16.95 (978-0-689-83913-9(8) , McElderry, Margaret K.) Simon & Schuster Children's Publishing.

Harrison, Emma. High School Musical Yearbook. Disney Staff, ed. 2007. 56p. (J). (gr. 1-7). 10.99 (*978-1-4231-0596-1(6)) Disney Pr.

Harrison, Lisi. Best Friends for Never. 2004. (Clique Ser.: Bk. 2). 208p. (J). (gr. 5-8). pap. 9.99 (978-0-316-70131-0(9) , Poppy) Little, Brown Bks. for Young Readers.

—Bratfest at Tiffany's. 2008. (Clique Ser.: No. 9). 300p. (gr. 7-12). pap. 9.99 (*978-0-316-00680-4(7) , Poppy) Little, Brown Bks. for Young Readers.

—The Clique. 2004. (Clique Ser.: No. 1). 220p. (J). (ps-7). lib. bdg. 16.64 (978-0-606-33269-9(3)) Tandem Library Bks.

—The Clique: Second Collection. 2006. (Clique Ser.: Nos. 4-6). (J). (gr. 7-17). pap. 29.99 (978-0-316-06693-8(1) , Poppy) Little, Brown Bks. for Young Readers.

—The Clique Collection. 2006. (Clique Ser.: Nos. 1-3). (J). (gr. 7-17). pap. 29.99 (978-0-316-16705-5(3) , Poppy) Little, Brown Bks. for Young Readers.

—Dial L for Loser. 2006. (Clique Ser.). 272p. (J). (gr. 7-17). pap. 9.99 (978-0-316-11504-9(5) , Poppy) Little, Brown Bks. for Young Readers.

—It's Not Easy Being Mean. 7th rev. ed. 2007. (Clique Ser.: No. 7). 224p. (J). (gr. 7-17). pap. 9.99 (978-0-316-11505-6(3) , Poppy) Little, Brown Bks. for Young Readers.

Harrison, Lisi. Sealed with a Diss. 2007. (Clique Ser.: No. 8). 272p. (J). (gr. 7-17). pap. 9.99 (*978-0-316-11506-3(1) , Poppy) Little, Brown Bks. for Young Readers.

Harry Potter & the Chamber of Secrets. 2002. (Harry Potter Ser.). (Illus.). (J). 15.23 (978-0-7587-4426-5(9)) Book Wholesalers, Inc.

Harry Potter & the Sorcerer's Stone. 2002. (Harry Potter Ser.). (Illus.). (J). 15.23 (978-0-7587-0016-2(4)) Book Wholesalers, Inc.

Hart, Alison. Anna's Blizzard. Bachem, Paul, photos by. 2005. (Illus.). 141p. (J). (gr. 3-5). 12.95 (978-1-56145-349-8(8)) Peachtree Pubs., Ltd.

Hart, Louise. Rosie's Rule. 2004. 96p. pap. 14.95 (978-1-4137-0546-1(4)) PublishAmerica, Inc.

Hart, Tessa & Sergi, Frank. The Snarth Goes to School. Freeman, Pietri, illus. 2000. 48p. (J). (gr. k-5). 18.95 (978-0-9660172-0-5(X)) Brookfield Reader, Inc., The.

Hartinger, Brent. Geography Club. 240p. (J). 2003. 17.99 (978-0-06-001221-2(8)); 2004. reprint ed. pap. 7.99 (978-0-06-001223-6(4) , HarperTeen) HarperCollins Pubs.

—Geography Club. 2004. (gr. 7-12). lib. bdg. 15.30 (978-0-613-71366-5(4)) Tandem Library Bks.

Hartley, Susan. Bienvenido a nuestra Escuela: Fiction-to-Fact Big Book. enl. ed. 2004. (SPA.). (J). pap. 26.00 (978-1-4108-2364-9(4) , 23644) Benchmark Education Co.

Hautman, Pete. Invisible. Hautman, Pete, illus. 160p. (YA). 2005. (gr. 7 up). 16.99 (978-0-689-86800-9(6) , Simon & Schuster Children's Publishing); 2006. reprint ed. pap. 7.99 (978-0-689-86903-7(7) , Simon Pulse) Simon & Schuster Children's Publishing.

—Invisible. l.t. ed. 2005. 192p. (YA). 20.95 (978-0-7862-7909-8(5) , Large Print Pr.) Thorndike Pr.

—Sweetblood. 2003. (Illus.). 192p. (YA). 16.95 (978-0-689-85048-6(4)) Simon & Schuster Children's Publishing.

Hautzig, Deborah. Little Witch Goes to School. Wickstrom, Sylvie K., illus. 1998. (Little Witch Ser.: Vol. 3). 48p. (J). (gr. k-3). pap. 3.99 (978-0-679-88738-6(5) , Random Hse. Bks. for Young Readers) Random Hse. Children's Bks.

—Little Witch Learns to Read. Wickstrom, Sylvie K., illus. 2003. (Step into Reading Ser.). 48p. (J). (gr. 1-3). pap. 3.99 (978-0-375-82179-0(1) , Random Hse. Bks. for Young Readers) Random Hse. Children's Bks.

—Little Witch Learns to Read. 2003. (gr. k-3). lib. bdg. 11.80 (978-0-613-89789-1(7)) Tandem Library Bks.

Havill, Juanita. Jamaica's Blue Marker. O'Brien, Anne Sibley, illus. 2003. 32p. (J). (gr. k-3). pap. 6.95 (978-0-618-36917-1(1)) Houghton Mifflin Co. Trade & Reference Div.

Hawkins, Colin & Hawkins, Jacqui. Mr. Wolf's Nursery Time. 2005. (Illus.). (J). (ps-ps). 31p. pap. 9.99 (978-1-4052-1975-4(0)); 32p. 20.00 (978-1-4052-1101-7(6)) Egmont Bks., Ltd. GBR. *Dist:* Trafalgar Square Publishing, Independent Pubs. Group.

Hawkins-Rodgers, Donzella. No Bulley Destroys Chloe's Hairdo. 2003. (Illus.). 32p. (J). (gr. 3 up). pap. 10.95 (978-1-884242-58-8(8)) Multicultural Pubns.

—No Bulley Destroy's Chloe's Hairdo. Hewins, Shirley, illus. 2003. 32p. (J). (gr. 3 up). lib. bdg. 16.95 (978-1-884242-56-4(1)) Multicultural Pubns.

Hayden, Torey L. The Very Worst Thing. 2003. 176p. (J). (gr. 5 up). 15.99 (978-0-06-029792-3(1)) HarperCollins Pubs.

Hayes, Daniel. Flyers. 1998. (978-0-606-13392-0(5)) Tandem Library Bks.

Hayes, Rosemary. The Amazing Mr Mulch. 2005. (Cambridge Storybooks Ser.). (Illus.). 32p. pap. 7.00 (978-0-521-67479-9(4)) Cambridge Univ. Pr.

Hayes, Sonia. Urban Goddess. 2007. 224p. (YA). per. 9.95 (*978-0-9777573-1-2(5)) NUA Multimedia.

Hays, Anna Jane. Kindergarten Countdown. Davick, Linda, illus. 2007. 24p. (J). (ps-1). 8.99 (978-0-375-84252-8(7) , Knopf Bks. for Young Readers) Random Hse. Children's Bks.

Hayward, Linda. What Homework? O'Rourke, Page Eastburn, illus. 2002. (Science Solves It! Ser.). 32p. (J). (gr. 1-3). 4.99 (978-1-57565-116-3(5)) Kane Pr., The.

—What Homework? 2002. (gr. k-3). lib. bdg. 13.00 (978-0-613-53785-8(8)) Tandem Library Bks.

Haywood, Carolyn. B Is for Betsy. 2004. (Illus.). 144p. (J). 16.00 (978-0-15-205103-7(1) , Harcourt Young Classics); pap. 5.95 (978-0-15-205099-3(X) , Odyssey Classics) Harcourt Children's Bks.

—Back to School with Betsy. 2004. (Illus.). 160p. (J). pap. 5.95 (978-0-15-205101-3(5) , Odyssey Classics) Harcourt Children's Bks.

—Betsy & Billy. 2004. (Illus.). 144p. (J). 16.00 (978-0-15-205104-4(X) , Harcourt Young Classics); pap. 5.95 (978-0-15-205100-6(7) , Odyssey Classics) Harcourt Children's Bks.

Headley, Justina Chen. The Patch. Vane, Mitch, illus. (J). 2007. pap. 7.95 (*978-1-58089-170-7(5)); 2006. 32p. 15.95 (978-1-58089-049-6(0)) Charlesbridge Publishing, Inc.

Hedderwick, Mairi. Katie Morag & the Riddles. 2002. (Illus.). 32p. (J). pap. 9.99 (978-0-09-941418-6(X)) Random Hse. GBR. *Dist:* Independent Pubs. Group.

Heiligman, Deborah. Too Perfect. 1999. (Eek! Stories to Make You Shriek Ser.). (J). (978-0-606-19884-4(9)) Tandem Library Bks.

Helmso, Candy Grant. Cakewalk. Taylor, Stephen, illus. 2003. (Books for Young Learners). 16p. (J). pap. 5.00 net. (978-1-57274-250-5(X) , 2727) Owen, Richard C. Pubs., Inc.

Hemphill, Stephanie. Things Left Unsaid: A Novel in Poems. 2005. 272p. (gr. 7-17). 16.99 (978-0-7868-1850-1(6)) Hyperion Bks. for Children.

—Things Left Unsaid: A Novel in Poems. 2007. 272p. (gr. 7-17). pap. 7.99 (*978-0-7868-3745-8(4)) Hyperion Pr.

Henderson, Aileen Kilgore. The Treasure of Panther Peak. Coyle, Mark, illus. 1998. 160p. (J). (gr. 3-8). pap. 6.95 (978-1-57131-619-6(1)) Milkweed Editions.

Heneghan, James. Hit Squad. 2003. (Orca Soundings Ser.). 96p. (J). (gr. 7-12). pap. 7.95 (978-1-55143-269-4(2)) Orca Bk. Pubs. USA.

—Hit Squad. 2003. (gr. 7-12). lib. bdg. 16.40 (978-0-613-70547-9(5)) Tandem Library Bks.

Heneghan, James. Payback. 2007. 144p. (YA). (gr. 7 up). 17.95 (*978-0-88899-701-2(9)) Groundwood Bks. CAN. *Dist:* Perseus Distribution.

Henkes, Kevin. Chrysanthemum. est. 2004. (Illus.). (J). (gr. k-3). spiral bd. (978-0-616-14575-3(6)) Canadian National Institute for the Blind/Institut National Canadien pour les Aveugles.

—Chrysanthemum Big Book. Henkes, Kevin, illus. 2007. 32p. (J). pap. 24.99 (*978-0-06-111974-3(1) , Harper Festival) HarperCollins Pubs.

—Lilly Adore l'Ecole! pap. 16.95 (978-2-07-054873-6(2)) Gallimard, Editions FRA. *Dist:* Distribooks, Inc.

S

—The Lilly Book & Toy Box. 1998. (Illus.). 160p. (J). 24.95 (978-0-688-16437-9(4) , Harper Festival) HarperCollins Pubs.

—Lilly's Purple Plastic Purse. Henkes, Kevin, illus. 10th anniv. ed. 2006. (Illus.). 40p. (J). (ps-3). 16.99 (978-0-688-12897-5(1)) HarperCollins Pubs.

—Lilly's Purple Plastic Purse. Henkes, Kevin, illus. (Illus.). pap. incl. audio (978-0-87499-688-3(0)); pap. 18.95 incl. audio compact disk (978-1-59112-347-7(X)); pap. incl. audio compact disk (978-1-59112-557-0(X)); pap. 16.95 incl. audio (978-0-87499-686-9(4)); 2000. (J). pap. 28.95 incl. audio compact disk (978-1-59112-348-4(8)) Live Oak Media.

—Wemberly Worried. Henkes, Kevin, illus. (Illus.). pap. 16.95 incl. audio (978-0-87499-806-1(9)); pap. incl. audio (978-0-87499-808-5(5)); pap. 18.95 incl. audio compact disk (978-1-59112-359-0(3)); pap. incl. audio compact disk (978-1-59112-561-7(8)) Live Oak Media.

Hennessy, B. G. & Freeman, Don. Corduroy Goes to School. McCue, Lisa, illus. 2002. 20p. (J). 11.99 (978-0-670-03514-4(9) , Viking Juvenile) Penguin Group (USA) Inc.

Hennessy, Claire. Afterwards. 2005. 188p. (YA). pap. (*978-1-84223-207-1(X)) Poolbeg Pr.

Henry. Biode. 2008. (J). (*978-0-374-30802-5(0)) Farrar, Straus & Giroux.

Henshon, Suzanna E. Spiders on the Ceiling. 2006. (J). (978-0-88092-614-0(7)) Royal Fireworks Publishing Co.

Hergenrader, Christina. Lies & Deceptions. 2003. (Novel Devotions Ser.). 176p. (YA). 6.99 (978-0-7586-0229-9(4)) Concordia Publishing Hse.

—Lies & Deceptions. 2003. (gr. 7-12). lib. bdg. 15.30 (978-0-613-74602-1(3)) Tandem Library Bks.

—Temptations. 2003. (Novel Devotions Ser.). 176p. (YA). 6.99 (978-0-7586-0230-5(8)) Concordia Publishing Hse.

—Temptations. 2003. (gr. 7-12). lib. bdg. 15.30 (978-0-613-74603-8(1)) Tandem Library Bks.

Herman, Gail. I've Got the Back-to-School Blues. Peterson, Stacy, illus. 2002. (All Aboard Reading Ser.). 48p. (J). pap. 3.99 (978-0-448-42832-1(6) , Grosset & Dunlap) Penguin Group (USA) Inc.

—I've Got the Back-to-School Blues. 2002. (gr. k-3). lib. bdg. 11.80 (978-0-613-45285-4(2)) Tandem Library Bks.

—Just Like Mike. 2001. (978-0-606-21277-9(9)) Tandem Library Bks.

—Lucky Goes to School. 2001. (gr. k-3). lib. bdg. 11.80 (978-0-613-35616-9(0)); (Illus.). (J). (978-0-606-21309-7(0)) Tandem Library Bks.

—Mixed-Up Magic. 1999. (Fairy School Ser.). (J). (978-0-606-19281-1(6)) Tandem Library Bks.

—School Play Surprise. 2007. (Hello Reader! Ser.). (Illus.). 32p. (J). pap. 3.99 (978-0-439-78809-0(9)) Scholastic, Inc.

Herman, Gail, et al. School Rules. Peterson, Stacy, illus. 2003. 240p. (J). 9.99 (978-0-448-43336-3(2) , Grosset & Dunlap) Penguin Group (USA) Inc.

Hermes, Patricia. The Wild Year Bk. 3: Joshua's Oregon Trail Diary. 2003. (My America Ser.). (Illus.). 112p. (J). 4.99 (978-0-439-37056-1(6)) Scholastic, Inc.

Herrera, Juan Felipe. Crashboomlove: A Novel in Verse. 2000. (J). 20.60 (978-0-606-19432-7(0)); 1999. (gr. 7-12). lib. bdg. 22.20 (978-0-613-33880-6(4)) Tandem Library Bks.

—CrashBoomLove: A Novel in Verse. 2004. 165p. (gr. 8-12). pap. 14.95 (978-0-8263-2114-5(3)); 1999. 176p. 18.95 (978-0-8263-2113-8(5)) Univ. of New Mexico Pr.

Herrick, Steven. Naked Bunyip Dancing. Norling, Beth, illus. 2008. (J). (*978-1-59078-499-0(5) , Front Street) Boyds Mills Pr.

Hershenhorn, Esther. The Confession$ & $ecret$ of Howard J. Fingerhut. Long, Ethan, illus. 2002. 144p. (J). (gr. 4-6). tchr. ed. 16.95 (978-0-8234-1642-4(9)) Holiday Hse., Inc.

Hershey, Mary. My Big Sister Is So Bossy She Says You Can't Read This Book. 2006. 176p. (gr. 4-7). 5.50 (978-0-553-48797-8(3) , Yearling) Random Hse. Children's Bks.

Hesse, Hermann. Demian. 1999. (gr. 7-12). lib. bdg. 21.10 (978-0-613-16655-3(8)) Tandem Library Bks.

Hest, Amy. The Great Green Notebook of Katie Roberts: Who Just Turned 12 on Monday. Lamut, Sonja, illus. 1998. 112p. (J). (gr. 3-7). 16.99 (978-0-7636-0464-6(X)) Candlewick Pr.

—The Private Notebook of Katie Roberts, Age 11. Lamut, Sonja, illus. ed. 2005. 192p. (J). (gr. 4-7). 10.99 (978-0-7636-2698-3(8)) Candlewick Pr.

Heusler, Marianna. Annabelle's Monsters. 2005. 190p. pap. 19.95 (978-1-4137-6451-2(7)) PublishAmerica, Inc.

Hewett, Lorri. Lives of Our Own. 2000. (J). (978-0-606-19695-6(1)) Tandem Library Bks.

Hiaasen, Carl. Hoot. movie tie-in ed. 2006. 304p. (J). (gr. 5). 6.50 (978-0-440-42170-2(5) , Yearling) Random Hse. Children's Bks.

Hibbett, Myles. Zephyr: Spheres & the Sword of Wonders. 2001. 200p. pap. 14.95 (978-0-595-17452-2(3) , Writer's Showcase Pr.) iUniverse, Inc.

Hickey, Joshalyn M. Good Morning Lovey! Chaveevah, Banks Ferguson, illus. 2005. 28p. (J). 12.00 (978-0-9718939-3-1(4)) BaHar Publishing, L.C.

Hicks, John Bryant. The Day Charlie Lost His Weirdiness. 2nd ed. 2007. (J). per. 5.99 (*978-0-9742829-4-7(4)) Quiet Man Publishing.

Higashi, Sandra & Higashi/Glaser Design Inc. Staff. Hello Kitty, Hello School! Kit: Includes Finger Puppets, Mini Book, & Stage. Hirashima, Jean, illus. 2003. (Hello Kitty Ser.). 16p. (J). (ps-3). 12.95 (978-0-8109-4596-8(7)) Abrams, Harry N. , Inc.

—Hello Kitty's Graduation Day. Hirashima, Jean, illus. 2004. 24p. (J). (ps-3). 12.95 (978-0-8109-4818-1(4)) Abrams, Harry N. , Inc.

High School Musical: All-Access. rev. ed. 2007. 32p. (J). (gr. 2-7). 19.99 (*978-1-4231-1066-8(8)) Disney Pr.

Hileman, Linda L. Dawn's Secret. 2006. (J). per. 9.95 (978-1-59571-117-5(1)) Word Association Pubs.

Hill, David. Time Out. 2001. 128p. (YA). (gr. 6-9). 15.95 (978-0-8126-2899-9(3)) Cricket Bks.

Hill, Eric. Spot Goes to School. Hill, Eric, illus. 2004. (Illus.). (J). (ps-1). (SPA.). 12p. bds. 7.99 (978-0-399-24246-5(5) , Putnam Juvenile); 24p. pap. 6.99 (978-0-14-240167-5(6) , Puffin) Penguin Group (USA) Inc.

—Spot Goes to School. Hill, Eric, illus. 2006. 22p. (J). (ps-k). 12.99 (978-0-399-24613-5(4) , Putnam Juvenile) Penguin Group (USA) Inc.

—Spot Loves School. Hill, Eric, illus. 2008. (Spot Ser.). 10p. (J). (ps-k). bds. 7.99 (*978-0-399-25165-8(0) , Putnam Juvenile) Penguin Group (USA) Inc.

Hill, Eric. Spot Va a la Escuela. Brant Drake, Alexandra, tr. from ENG. 1998. (Spot Ser.). (SPA., Illus.). 20p. (J). (ps). pap. 6.99 (978-0-14-056411-2(X) , Puffin) Penguin Group (USA) Inc.

—Spot Va a la Escuela. 1998. (SPA.). (ps-2). lib. bdg. 15.30 (978-0-613-85730-7(5)) Tandem Library Bks.

Hill, Janet Muirhead. Starlight's Courage: Revised Edition. Lehmkuhl, Pat, illus. 2nd ed. 2007. 170p. (J). per. 9.00 (*978-0-9772525-4-1(X)) Raven Publishing Inc. of Montana.

Hillert, Margaret. Come to School, Dear Dragon. 2002. (Illus.). (J). 15.00 (978-0-7587-9456-7(8)) Book Wholesalers, Inc.

—Come to School, Dear Dragon. Helton, David, illus. rev. ed. 2006. (Beginning to Read Ser.). 32p. (J). lib. bdg. 18.60 (978-1-59953-017-8(1)) Norwood Hse. Pr.

—Who Goes to School? Brooks, Nan, illus. rev. ed. 2006. (Beginning to Read Ser.). 32p. (J). lib. bdg. 18.60 (978-1-59953-032-1(5)) Norwood Hse. Pr.

Hilton, James. Goodbye, Mr. Chips. 2004. 144p. (J). (gr. 7-17). mass mkt. 5.99 (978-0-316-01013-9(8)) Little Brown & Co.

Himelblau, Linda. The Trouble Begins. 2005. 208p. (J). (gr. 3-7). 14.95 (978-0-385-73273-4(2) , Delacorte Bks. for Young Readers) Random Hse. Children's Bks.

Himle, Lisa. Hands As Warm As Toast. Langton, Bruce, illus. 2006. 32p. (J). 17.95 (978-1-58726-298-2(3) , Mitten Pr.) Ann Arbor Media Group, LLC.

Hines-Stephens, Sarah & Mason, Jane. Princess School: Let Down Your Hair. 2004. (Princess School Ser.). 144p. (J). (gr. 4 up). 4.99 (978-0-439-62939-3(X) , Scholastic Paperbacks) Scholastic, Inc.

Hinojosa, Francisco. A Golpe de Calcetin. Barajas, Rafael, illus. 2000. (la Orilla Del Viento Ser.). (SPA.). 46p. (J). (ps-ps). reprint ed. pap. 6.99 (978-968-16-6132-8(X) , 130) Fondo de Cultura Economica USA.

Hirai, Rin. Legendz, Vol. 2. Haruno, Makoto, illus. 2005. (Legendz Ser.). 208p. (YA). pap. 7.99 (978-1-59116-773-0(6)) Viz Media.

Hobbie, Holly. The One & Only. 2006. (Illus.). 32p. (J). (ps-3). 16.99 (978-0-316-36664-9(1)) Little Brown & Co.

Hobbie, Holly. Toot & Puddle: One & Only. 2006. (Illus.). (J). (*978-1-4287-0431-2(0)) Little Brown & Co.

Hobbs, Valerie. How Far Would You Have Gotten If I Hadn't Called You Back? 2003. (J). (gr. 7-12). lib. bdg. 14.15 (978-0-613-72289-6(2)) Tandem Library Bks.

Hodge, Merle. For the Life of Laetitia. 2003. 21.25 (978-0-8446-7246-5(7)) Smith, Peter Pub., Inc.

Hoestlandt, Jo. Robin del Bosque. (SPA.). (J). 7.95 (978-958-04-5041-2(2)) Norma S.A. COL. *Dist:* Distribuidora Norma, Inc.

Hoffman, Mary. Encore, Grace! Allan, June & Binch, Caroline, illus. 2003. 112p. (J). (gr. 2-6). 14.99 (978-0-8037-2951-3(0) , Dial) Penguin Group (USA) Inc.

Hoffman, Mary. Princess Grace. Van Wright, Cornelius & Hu, Ying-Hwa, illus. 2008. 32p. (J). (ps). 16.99 (*978-0-8037-3260-5(0) , Dial) Penguin Group (USA) Inc.

Holder, Nancy. Pretty Little Devils. 2007. (YA). 1p. pap. 6.99 (978-1-59514-152-1(9)); 256p. pap. 6.99 (978-1-59514-149-1(9)) Penguin Group (USA) Inc. (Razorbill).

Holland, Trish. Come Back, Zack! 2008. (Little Golden Book Ser.). (Illus.). 24p. (J). (gr. k-k). 2.99 (*978-0-375-84269-6(1) , Golden Bks.) Random Hse., Inc.

Hollstein, Stephanie. Connections. 2001. 192p. (YA). pap. 13.95 (978-0-595-17152-1(4) , Writers Club Pr.) iUniverse, Inc.

Holm, Jennifer L. Middle School Is Worse Than Meatloaf: A Year Told Through Stuff. Castaldi, Elicia, illus. 2007. 128p. (J). (gr. 3-7). 12.99 (978-0-689-85281-7(9) , Ginne Seo Bks) Simon & Schuster Children's Publishing.

Holm, Jennifer L. & Holm, Matthew. Our Hero. 2005. (Babymouse Ser.). (Illus.). 96p. (J). (gr. 2-5). pap. 5.95 (978-0-375-83230-7(0)); lib. bdg. 12.99 (978-0-375-93230-4(5)) Random Hse. Children's Bks. (Random Hse. Bks. for Young Readers).

Holmes, Elizabeth. Pretty Is. 2007. 224p. (J). (gr. 4-6). 16.99 (978-0-525-47813-3(2) , Dutton Juvenile) Penguin Group (USA) Inc.

Holmes, Lynda. Spring Cleaning. 2006. 55p. pap. 12.95 (978-1-4241-4324-5(1)) PublishAmerica, Inc.

Holmes, Sarah. Letters from Rapunzel. 2007. 192p. (J). (gr. 5-8). 15.99 (978-0-06-078073-9(8)); lib. bdg. 16.89 (978-0-06-078074-6(6)) HarperCollins Pubs.

Holston, Kim R. Spin! 2002. 143p. (YA). pap. 11.95 (978-0-595-22184-4(X) , Writers Club Pr.) iUniverse, Inc.

Holt, Kimberly Willis. Piper Reed, Navy Brat. Davenier, Christine, illus. 2007. 160p. (J). (gr. 3-6). 14.95 (*978-0-8050-8197-8(6) , Holt, Henry & Co. Bks. For Young Readers) Holt, Henry & Co.

—Piper Reed, Navy Brat. Davenier, Christine, illus. 2008. 176p. (J). pap. 6.99 (*978-0-312-38020-5(8)) Square Fish.

Holub, Joan. Big Heart! A Valentine's Day Tale. Terry, Will, illus. 2007. (Ant Hill Ser.). 24p. (J). lib. bdg. 13.89 (*978-1-4169-2562-0(7)); pap. 3.99 (*978-1-4169-0957-6(5)) Simon & Schuster Children's Publishing. (Aladdin).

—Gingerbread Kid Goes to School. 2002. (gr. k-3). lib. bdg. 11.80 (978-0-613-52263-2(X)) Tandem Library Bks.

—The Gingerbread Kid Goes to School, Vol. 1. Palen, Debbie, illus. 2002. (All Aboard Reading Ser.). 32p. (J). mass mkt. 3.99 (978-0-448-42674-7(9) , Grosset & Dunlap) Penguin Group (USA) Inc.

Homework, 6 Packs. (ps-2). 27.00 (978-0-7635-9453-4(9)) Rigby Education.

Honeywood, Varnette P., illus. The Meanest Thing to Say. 2002. (Little Bill Ser.). (J). 11.91 (978-0-7587-1432-9(7)) Book Wholesalers, Inc.

Hoobler, Dorothy & Hoobler, Thomas. The 1960's: Rebels. Hoffman, Robin, illus. 2001. (Century Kids Ser.). 160p. (J). (gr. 5-8). lib. bdg. 22.90 (978-0-7613-1606-0(X) , Twenty-First Century Bks.) Lerner Publishing Group.

Hood, Susan. The New Kid. Handelman, Dorothy, photos by. 1998. (Real Kids Readers Ser.). (Illus.). 32p. (ps-1). lib. bdg. 18.90 (978-0-7613-2014-2(8)); (J). pap. 4.99 (978-0-7613-2039-5(3)) Lerner Publishing Group. (Millbrook Pr.).

—Show & Tell. Handelman, Dorothy, photos by. 1999. (Real Kids Readers Ser.). (Illus.). 32p. (gr. k-2). (J). pap. 4.99 (978-0-7613-2081-4(4)); lib. bdg. 18.90 (978-0-7613-2056-2(3)) Lerner Publishing Group. (Millbrook Pr.).

—Show & Tell. 1999. (J). (978-0-606-19173-9(9)); lib. bdg. 11.80 (978-0-613-16835-9(6)) Tandem Library Bks.

Hooks, Gwendolyn. Nice Wheels. Andriani, Renee, illus. 2005. (My First Reader Ser.). (J). (gr. k-1). 31p. pap. 3.95 (978-0-516-25277-3(1)); 32p. 18.50 (978-0-516-25179-0(1)) Scholastic Library Publishing. (Children's Pr.).

Hooper, Mary & McAllister, Angela. Take a Kiss to School. Hellard, Sue, illus. 2006. 32p. (J). 15.95 (978-1-58234-702-8(6) , Bloomsbury Children) Bloomsbury Publishing.

Hoopmann, Kathy. Blue Bottle Mystery: An Asperger's Adventure. 2001. (gr. 3-6). lib. bdg. 21.05 (978-0-613-84692-9(3)) Tandem Library Bks.

Hopkins, Audrey. Vinny Drake Is One. Flook, Helen, illus. 2007. (Tiger Ser.). 64p. (J). 9.95 (*978-1-84270-437-0(0)) Andersen GBR. *Dist:* Independent Pubs. Group.

Hopkins, Cathy. Recipe for Rebellion: Big Mouth. 2007. (Zodiac Girls Ser.). 192p. (J). (gr. 4-6). pap. 5.95 (978-0-7534-5896-9(9) , Kingfisher) Houghton Mifflin Co. Trade & Reference Div.

Hornik, Laurie Miller. The Secrets of Ms. Snickle's Class. Tilley, Debbie, illus. 2001. 144p. (J). (gr. 4-6). tchr. ed. 15.00 (978-0-618-03435-2(8) , Clarion Bks.) Houghton Mifflin Co. Trade & Reference Div.

—Zoo School. Tilley, Debbie, illus. 2004. 144p. (J). (gr. 3-5). tchr. ed. 16.00 (978-0-618-34204-4(4) , Clarion Bks.) Houghton Mifflin Co. Trade & Reference Div.

Horowitz, Anthony. Point Blank. (Alex Rider Ser.: Bk. 2). 2006. 304p. (J). (gr. 7). pap. 7.99 (978-0-14-240612-0(0) , Puffin); 2002. 208p. (YA). (gr. 5 up). 17.99 (978-0-399-23621-1(X) , Philomel) Penguin Group (USA) Inc.

Horse, Harry, illus. Little Rabbit Goes to School. 2004. 32p. (J). 15.95 (978-1-56145-320-7(X)) Peachtree Pubs., Ltd.

Houston, Julian. New Boy. 2005. 288p. (J). (gr. 7). 16.00 (978-0-618-43253-0(1)) Houghton Mifflin Co. Trade & Reference Div.

Howard, Elizabeth Fitzgerald. Virgie Goes to School with Us Boys. Lewis, Earl, illus. 2002. (J). 25.11 (978-0-7587-3907-0(9)) Book Wholesalers, Inc.

—Virgie Goes to School with Us Boys. Lewis, E. B., illus. 2005. 32p. (J). reprint ed. pap. 6.99 (978-0-689-87793-3(5) , Aladdin) Simon & Schuster Children's Publishing.

Howard, Elizabeth Fitzgerald & Lewis, Earl. Virgie Goes to School with Us Boys. 2000. (Illus.). 32p. (J). (gr. k-3). 17.99 (978-0-689-80076-4(2)) Simon & Schuster Children's Publishing.

Howard, Jo Ann. The Little Boy Who Made a Difference. 2001. 41p. per. 8.95 (978-0-7414-0575-3(X)) Infinity Publishing.

Howe, James. Day the Teacher Went Bananas. 1999. (Illus.). (J). (gr. k-3). lib. bdg. 14.15 (978-0-8335-0697-9(8)) Tandem Library Bks.

—The Misfits. 2002. lib. bdg. 24.00 incl. audio (978-1-932076-12-7(3) , 02010A) Full Cast Audio.

—The Misfits. 2003. 288p. (YA). mass mkt. 5.99 (978-0-689-83956-6(1) , Aladdin) Simon & Schuster Children's Publishing.

—The Misfits. Slota, Gerald, illus. 2001. 288p. (gr. 5-9). 16.95 (978-0-689-83955-9(3) , Atheneum) Simon & Schuster Children's Publishing.

—Pinky & Rex & the School Play. Sweet, Melissa, illus. 1998. (Pinky & Rex Ser.). 48p. (J). (gr. 1-4). pap. 3.99 (978-0-689-81704-5(5) , Aladdin) Simon & Schuster Children's Publishing.

—Pinky & Rex & the School Play. 2006. (J). (gr. 1-4). 24.21 (978-1-59961-078-7(7)) Spotlight.

—Pinky & Rex & the Spelling Bee. 1999. (gr. k-3). lib. bdg. 11.80 (978-0-613-22921-0(5)) Tandem Library Bks.

—Pinky & Rex & the Spelling Bee. 2006. (J). (gr. 1-4). 24.21 (978-1-59961-079-5(5)) Spotlight.

—Totally Joe. 2005. (Illus.). 208p. (J). (gr. 5-9). 16.99 (978-0-689-83957-3(X) , Atheneum) Simon & Schuster Children's Publishing.

Howe, James. Totally Joe. 2007. 208p. (J). (gr. 4-8). pap. 5.99 (*978-0-689-83958-0(8)) Kaplan Bks.

Hubbell, Will. Snow Day Dance. Hubbell, Will, illus. 2005. (Illus.). 32p. (J). (gr. 5-8). 16.95 (978-0-8075-7523-9(2)) Whitman, Albert & Co.

Hudson, Iris. Ask Mia. Sims, Blanche, illus. 2006. (Math Matters Ser.). 32p. (J). (gr. k-3). pap. 4.95 (978-1-57565-188-0(2)) Kane Pr., The.

Hudson, Iris. Mac & the Messmaker. Smath, Jerry, illus. 2005. 32p. (J). lib. bdg. 20.00 (*978-1-4242-1107-4(7)) Fitzgerald Bks.

—Mac & the Messmaker. Smath, Jerry, illus. 2005. (Social Studies Connects). 32p. (J). pap. 4.99 (978-1-57565-158-3(0)) Kane Pr., The.

Hudson, Wade. The Two Tyrones. Page, Mark, illus. 2004. 32p. (J). lib. bdg. 15.00 (*978-1-4242-0239-3(6)) Fitzgerald Bks.

—The Two Tyrones. Page, Mark, illus. 2004. 32p. (J). (gr. 2). lib. bdg. 11.19 (978-0-606-33361-0(4)) Tandem Library Bks.

Huelin, Jodi. Countdown to Valentine's Day. Haskamp, Steve, illus. 2002. 24p. (J). pap. 3.99 (978-0-8431-4882-4(9) , Price Stern Sloan) Penguin Group (USA) Inc.

Hughes, Dawn Marie. Deadwood: Haunted Stories. 2006. 94p. pap. 14.95 (978-1-4241-2600-2(2)) PublishAmerica, Inc.

Hughes, Mark Peter. Lemonade Mouth. 2007. 352p. (J). (gr. 7). 15.99 (978-0-385-73392-2(5)); lib. bdg. 18.99 (978-0-385-90404-9(5)) Random Hse. Children's Bks. (Delacorte Bks. for Young Readers).

Hughes, Monica. Jan's Awesome Party. Freire, Carlos, illus. 2001. (First Novels Ser.: Vol. 18). 57p. (gr. 1-5). (J). (978-0-88780-533-2(7)); 4.95 (978-0-88780-532-5(9)) Formac Publishing Co., Ltd. CAN. *Dist:* Casemate Pubs. & Bk. Distributors, LLC.

Hughes, Pat. Open Ice. 288p. (YA). (gr. 9). 2007. mass mkt. 6.50 (*978-0-553-49444-0(9) , Laurel Leaf); 2005. 15.95 (978-0-385-74675-5(X) , Lamb, Wendy) Random Hse. Children's Bks.

Hughes, Thomas. Tom Brown's School Days. 1998. lib. bdg. 22.95 (978-1-56723-061-1(X)) Yestermorrow, Inc.

—Tom Brown's School Days by an Old Boy. 2004. reprint ed. pap. 1.99 (978-1-4192-9039-8(8)) Kessinger Publishing, LLC.

—Tom Brown's Schooldays. 2002. (Children's Classics). (ENG., Illus.). 352p. (J). (gr. 3-6). pap. (978-1-85326-108-4(4)) Wordsworth Editions, Ltd.

Hughes, Thomas. Tom Browns Schooldays. 2006. pap. (*978-1-4068-1407-1(5)) Echo Library.

Hulme, Joy N. Climbing the Rainbow. 2004. 224p. (J). 15.99 (978-0-380-81572-2(9)); lib. bdg. 16.89 (978-0-06-054304-4(3)) HarperCollins Pubs.

Hunter, Melanie. Dorsello's Key. 2005. 131p. pap. 19.95 (978-1-4137-6294-5(8)) PublishAmerica, Inc.

Hurst, Carol Otis. Torchlight. 2006. 160p. (J). (gr. 4-6). 16.00 (978-0-618-27601-1(7)) Houghton Mifflin Co.

Hurst, Cory Allen. Southern Adversaries. 2002. 114p. pap. 16.95 (978-1-59129-768-0(0)) PublishAmerica, Inc.

Hurwitz, Johanna. Even Stephen. 1998. (Illus.). 128p. (YA). (gr. 5-9). reprint ed. pap. 4.95 (978-0-688-16362-4(9)) HarperCollins Pubs.

—Mostly Monty. McGrory, Anik, illus. 2007. 96p. (J). (gr. 1-4). 15.99 (978-0-7636-2831-4(X)) Candlewick Pr.

—Rip-Roaring Russell. 1999. (Beech Tree Chapter Bks.). (Illus.). 96p. (gr. k-4). mass mkt. 4.95 (978-0-688-16664-9(4)) HarperCollins Pubs.

—Russell Sprouts. 1999. (Beech Tree Chapter Bks.). (Illus.). 80p. (gr. k-4). mass mkt. 4.95 (978-0-688-16667-0(9)) HarperCollins Pubs.

—Spring Break. 1999. (Illus.). 144p. (J). (gr. 2-7). mass mkt. 4.95 (978-0-688-16672-4(5)) HarperCollins Pubs.

—Spring Break. 2001. (gr. 3-6). lib. bdg. 13.00 (978-0-613-37169-8(0)); 1999. (978-0-606-16762-8(5)); 1999. (Illus.). (J). (978-0-606-21452-0(6)) Tandem Library Bks.

—Starting School. Dugan, Karen, illus. 2001. 102p. (J). (ps-ps). per. 10.39 (978-0-606-21464-3(X)) Tandem Library Bks.

Huser, Glen. Skinnybones & the Wrinkle Queen. 192p. 2008. (J). pap. 8.95 (*978-0-88899-733-3(7)); 2006. (gr. 7 up). 16.95 (978-0-88899-732-6(9)) Groundwood Bks. CAN. *Dist:* Perseus Distribution.

Hutchins, H. J. TJ & the Quiz Kids. 2007. (Orca Young Readers Ser.). 144p. (J). (gr. 3-6). pap. (*978-1-55143-731-6(7)) Orca Bk. Pubs.

Hyde, Diana. Sex Without Love. 2001. 304p. pap. 12.95 (978-0-9705435-4-7(9)) Heicron, Inc.

I Can Read Classroom in a Box Level 1. 2007. (I Can Read Bks.). (J). 460.00 (*978-0-06-137567-5(5) , Harper Trophy) HarperCollins Pubs.

I Can Read Classroom in a Box Level 3. 2007. (I Can Read Bks.). (J). 460.00 (*978-0-06-137570-5(5) , Harper Trophy) HarperCollins Pubs.

Ide, Laurie S. & Langcaon, Jeff. Super Puffy. 2004. (Illus.). 32p. (J). 12.95 (978-1-56647-686-7(0)) Mutual Publishing LLC.

Igneri, David S. The Boy & Girl Who Hated History. Wigley, Audrey Watson, illus. deluxe ed. 2000. 60p. (J). (gr. 3-9). 19.50 (978-1-57529-084-3(7)) Kabel Pubs.

Ikids & Hapka, Cathy. Innovative Kids Readers: Clue School - the Lost Lunch Mystery. Larranaga, Ana & Torrey, Richard, illus. 2007. 32p. (J). (gr. 2-17). pap. 6.99 (978-1-58476-541-7(0)) Innovative Kids.

Imperato, Teresa. Fiona's Fairy Magic. Huang, Benrei, illus. 2005. 14p. (J). 10.95 (978-1-58117-322-2(9) , Intervisual/Piggy Toes) Dalmatian Pr.

Impey, Rose. Wanda Witch & Too Many Frogs. McEwen, Katharine, illus. 2006. (Scholastic Reader Ser.). 32p. (J). pap. 3.99 (978-0-439-78451-1(4) , Cartwheel Bks.) Scholastic, Inc.

—Who's a Clever Girl? Amstutz, Andre, illus. 2003. (Yellow Bananas Ser.). 48p. (J). (gr. 3-4). pap. (978-0-7787-0976-3(0)) Crabtree Publishing Co.

—Who's a Clever Girl? 2002. (gr. 3-6). lib. bdg. 12.95 (978-0-613-52935-8(9)) Tandem Library Bks.

Inagaki, Riichiro. Eyeshield 21. 2006. (Eyeshield 21 Ser.). 208p. (YA). Vol. 8. pap. 7.99 (978-1-4215-0637-1(8)); Vol. 9. (Illus.). pap. 7.99 (978-1-4215-0638-8(6)) Viz Media.

Inches, Alison. Off to School with Periwinkle & Blue. Oxley, Jennifer, illus. 2003. (Blue's Clues Ser.). 24p. (J). 5.99 (978-0-689-85498-9(6) , 53560712, Simon Spotlight/Nickelodeon) Simon & Schuster Children's Publishing.

—Spring Is Here! Chernichaw, Ian, illus. 2006. (Blue's Clues Ser.). 16p. (J). pap. 5.99 (978-1-4169-0920-0(6) , Simon Spotlight/Nickelodeon) Simon & Schuster Children's Publishing.

Ingold, Jeanette. Mountain Solo. 320p. (YA). 2005. (gr. 7-17). pap. 6.95 (978-0-15-205358-1(1) , Harcourt Paperbacks); 2003. 17.00 (978-0-15-202670-7(3)) Harcourt Children's Bks.

Irbinskas, Heather. The Lost Kachina. Albert, Robert & Anthis, Brian, illus. 2004. 32p. (J). 15.95 (978-1-885772-33-6(5)) Kiva Publishing, Inc.

Iyengar, Malathi. Romina's Rangoli/By Malathi Michelle Iyengar ; Illustrated by Jennifer Wanardi. Wanardi, Jennifer, illus. 2007. (J). (*978-1-885008-32-9(5)) Shen's Bks.

Jablonski, Carla. Thicker Than Water. 2007. 272p. (YA). (gr. 9-12). pap. 8.99 (978-1-59514-123-1(5) , Razorbill) Penguin Group (USA) Inc.

Jackson, Ellen B. The Cupcake Thief. Sims, Blanche, illus. 2007. (Social Studies Connects). 32p. (J). (gr. 1-3). pap. 4.99 (*978-1-57565-247-4(1)) Kane Pr., The.

Jackson, Kamichi. You're Too Much, Reggie Brown. Goldberg, Jeff A., illus. l.t. ed. 2000. 110p. (J). (gr. 2-5). pap. 5.95 (978-0-615-11287-9(0)) Pen Poised Pr.

Jackson, Teresa Jean. Huggable Harry. 2004. 21p. pap. 14.95 (978-1-4137-1102-8(2)) PublishAmerica, Inc.

Jacobs, John. I Wanna Be. 2006. (Illus.). 144p. 9.95 (978-0-9774659-6-5(9)) Cameo Pubns., LLC.

Jacobson, Jennifer Richard. Andy Shane & the Very Bossy Dolores Starbuckle. Carter, Abby, illus. 64p. (J). (gr. k-3). 2006. 4.99 (978-0-7636-3044-7(6)); 2005. 13.99 (978-0-7636-1940-4(X)) Candlewick Pr.

Jacques, Taryn Elise. What's Wrong with the New Girl? Reilly, Meghan M., illus. 2004. 33p. pap. 17.95 (978-1-4137-1999-4(6)) PublishAmerica, Inc.

Jahn-Clough, Lisa. Me, Penelope. 2007. 208p. (YA). (gr. 7 up). 16.00 (*978-0-618-77366-4(5) , Walter Lorraine) Houghton Mifflin Co. Trade & Reference Div.

James, Brian. Ahoy, Ghost Ship Ahead!, No. 2. Zivoin, Jennifer, illus. 2007. (Pirate School Ser.). 64p. (J). (gr. 1-3). pap. 3.99 (978-0-448-44625-7(1) , Grosset & Dunlap) Penguin Group (USA) Inc.

James, Brian. Treasure Trouble. Zivoin, Jennifer, illus. 2008. (Pirate School Ser.). 64p. (J). (gr. 1-3). 3.99 (*978-0-448-44782-7(7) , Grosset & Dunlap) Penguin Group (USA) Inc.

Janover, Caroline D. The Worst Speller in Jr. High. 2001. 208p. (YA). (gr. 4-7). pap. 13.95 (978-0-595-15328-2(3) , Backinprint.com) iUniverse, Inc.

Janovitz, Marilyn. We Love School. 2007. (Illus.). 36p. (J). (ps). 9.95 (978-0-7358-2112-5(7)) North-South Bks., Inc.

Jarman, Julia. The Magic Backpack. Gon, Adriano, illus. 2004. (Flying Foxes Ser.). 48p. (J). (978-0-7787-1487-3(X)) ; pap. (978-0-7787-1533-7(7)) Crabtree Publishing Co.

Jefferies, Cindy. Rising Star. 2007. (Fame School Ser.: No. 2). 128p. (J). 4.99 (978-0-14-240716-5(X) , Puffin) Penguin Group (USA) Inc.

—Rivals!, No. 4. 2007. (Fame School Ser.). 144p. (YA). (gr. 5). 4.99 (978-0-14-240815-5(8) , Puffin) Penguin Group (USA) Inc.

Jefferies, Cindy. Solo Star #7. 2008. (Fame School Ser.). 128p. (J). (gr. 1-3). pap. 5.99 (*978-0-14-241103-2(5) , Puffin) Penguin Group (USA) Inc.

Jeffs, Stephanie. A Bad Day for Christopher Bear. Thomas, Jacqui, illus. 2004. (Christopher Bear Ser.). 30p. 5.99 (978-0-8066-4367-0(6) , Augsburg Bks.) Augsburg Fortress, Pubs.

—Christopher Bear's First Christmas. Thomas, Jacqui, illus. 2004. (Christopher Bear Ser.). 30p. 5.99 (978-0-8066-4349-6(8) , Augsburg Bks.) Augsburg Fortress, Pubs.

—It's Mine, Christopher Bear! Thomas, Jacqui, illus. 2004. (Christopher Bear Ser.). 32p. 5.99 (978-0-8066-4400-4(1) , Augsburg Bks.) Augsburg Fortress, Pubs.

Jellen, Michelle. Spain or Shine. 2005. (S. A. S. S. (Students Across the Seven Seas) Ser.). (Illus.). 224p. (YA). (gr. 7). pap. 6.99 (978-0-14-240368-6(7) , Puffin) Penguin Group (USA) Inc.

Jenkin-Pearce, Susie, et al. The Hutchinson Book of School Stories. 2005. (Illus.). 127p. (978-0-09-189362-0(3)) Random Hse. Children's Bks.

Jenkins, A. M. Out of Order. 256p. (J). 2005. pap. 6.99 (978-0-06-447374-3(0)); 2003. lib. bdg. 16.89 (978-0-06-623969-9(9)) HarperCollins Pubs.

Jenkins, Jerry B. & Fabry, Chris. Dead End. 2006. (Red Rock Mysteries Ser.). 256p. (J). pap. 5.99 (978-1-4143-0154-9(5) , Tyndale Kids) Tyndale Hse. Pubs.

—Instant Menace. 2006. (Tyndale Kids Ser.). 256p. (J). pap. 5.99 (978-1-4143-0148-8(0)) Tyndale Hse. Pubs.

Jennings, Patrick. Wish Riders. 2006. 288p. (gr. 5-17). 15.99 (978-1-4231-0010-2(7)) Hyperion Pr.

Jeremiah, Omari. Paperboy 3: The School of Doom. Rollins, Bernie, illus. 2006. 75p. pap. 12.99 (978-1-929188-13-0(7)) Morton Bks.

Jiménez, Francisco. La Mariposa. Silva, Simon, illus. (SPA.). 40p. (J). (gr. k-3). 2000. pap. 6.95 (978-0-618-07036-7(2) , HM3550); 2000. pap. 6.95 (978-0-618-07317-7(5)); 1998. tchr. ed. 16.00 (978-0-395-81663-9(7)) Houghton Mifflin Co. Trade & Reference Div.

—La Mariposa. Silva, Simon, illus. 2000. (SPA.). (J). (978-0-606-19813-4(X)) Tandem Library Bks.

Jimenez, Francisco. La Mariposa. Silva, Simon, illus. 2004. 38p. (J). (gr. k-4). reprint ed. pap. 14.00 (978-0-7567-8433-1(6)) DIANE Publishing Co.

Jinkins, Jim. Pinky Dinky Doo: Back to School Is Cool! 2005. (Step into Reading Ser.). (Illus.). 48p. (J). (gr. 1-3). pap. 3.99 (978-0-375-83237-6(8) , Random Hse. Bks. for Young Readers) Random Hse. Children's Bks.

—Pinky Dinky Doo: Pinky Stinky Doo. 2006. (Illus.). 48p. (J). (gr. 1-3). pap. 3.99 (978-0-375-83511-7(3)); lib. bdg. 11.99 (978-0-375-93511-4(8)) Random Hse. Children's Bks. (Random Hse. Bks. for Young Readers).

—Pinky Dinky Doo: Back to School Is Cool! 2005. (Step into Reading Ser.). (Illus.). 48p. (J). (gr. 1-3). lib. bdg. 11.99 (978-0-375-93237-3(2) , Random Hse. Bks. for Young Readers) Random Hse. Children's Bks.

Jinks, Catherine. Evil Genius. 2008. (Illus.). 512p. (YA). pap. 7.95 (*978-0-15-206185-2(1) , Harcourt Paperbacks) Harcourt Children's Bks.

—Evil Genius. 2007. (Illus.). 496p. (YA). (gr. 7 up). 17.00 (978-0-15-205988-0(1)); 486p. (J). (*978-1-4287-3510-1(0)) Harcourt Trade Pubs.

Jocelyn, Marthe. Mable Riley: A Reliable Record of Humdrum, Peril, & Romance. 2007. 288p. (J). (gr. 5). 6.99 (978-0-7636-3287-8(2)) Candlewick Pr.

Johnson, Angela, et al. Tripping over the Lunch Lady. Mercado, Nancy, ed. 2006. 192p. (J). (gr. 5). pap. 5.99 (978-0-14-240624-3(4) , Puffin) Penguin Group (USA) Inc.

Johnson-Choong, Shelly. The Jewelry Box. 2nd ed. 2004. (YA). reprint ed. pap. 10.95 (978-1-932280-40-1(5) , 80405) Granite Publishing & Distribution.

Johnson, Donna. The Story of the Little Red Leaf. Johnson, Emily, illus. l.t. ed. 2006. 22p. (J). 25.00 (*978-0-9778774-0-9(X)) Choicepoint Editions.

Johnson, Doug. Substitute Teacher Plans. Smith, Tammy, illus. rev. ed. 2002. 32p. (J). (gr. k-3). 16.95 (978-0-8050-6520-6(2) , Holt, Henry & Co. Bks. For Young Readers) Holt, Henry & Co.

Johnson, Kathleen Jeffrie. Dumb Love. 2005. 176p. (YA). (gr. 7-17). 16.95 (978-1-59643-062-4(1)) Roaring Brook Pr.

Johnson, Lissa Halls. Bad Girl Days, Vol. 12. 2005. (Brio Girls Ser.). 192p. (YA). pap. 7.99 (978-1-58997-091-5(8)) Focus on the Family Publishing.

—Stuck in the Sky. 2005. (Brio Girls Ser.). 192p. (YA). (gr. 7-11). pap. 7.99 (978-1-56179-951-0(3)) Focus on the Family Publishing.

Johnson, Maureen. The Bermudez Triangle. 384p. (YA). (gr. 9-12). 2007. 7.99 (978-1-59514-155-2(3)); 2005. reprint ed. pap. 7.99 (978-1-59514-033-3(6)) Penguin Group (USA) Inc. (Razorbill).

—Devilish. (YA). (gr. 7 up). 2007. 272p. pap. 8.99 (*978-1-59514-132-3(4)); 2006. 288p. 16.99 (978-1-59514-060-9(3)) Penguin Group (USA) Inc. (Razorbill).

Johnson, Pete. Help! I'm a Classroom Gambler. 2006. (Illus.). 208p. (J). pap. 9.95 (*978-0-440-86627-5(8)) Transworld Publishers Ltd. GBR. *Dist:* Independent Pubs. Group.

Johnson, Richard, illus. The Giant Turnip. 2004. 24p. (J). (TAM, CZE, VIE, SPA & URD.). (978-1-85269-736-5(9)); (TAM, CZE, VIE, SPA & URD.). (978-1-85269-741-9(5)); (TAM, CZE, VIE, SPA & URD.). (978-1-85269-743-3(1)); (TAM, CZE, VIE, SPA & URD.). (978-1-85269-744-0(X)); (TAM, CZE, VIE, SPA & SER.). (978-1-85269-745-7(8)); (TAM, CZE, VIE, SPA & URD.). (978-1-85269-747-1(4)); (CZE, TAM, VIE, SPA & URD.). (978-1-85269-748-8(2)) Mantra Publishing, Ltd.

Johnson, Sandi. My Teacher Is an Alien. Johnson, Britt, ed. Sturgen, Bobbi, illus. 2002. 16p. (J). (gr. k-5). spiral bd. 5.99 (978-1-929063-75-8(X) , 285) Moons & Stars Publishing For Children.

Johnston, Antony. Rosemary's Backpack. Gilbert, Drew, illus. 2002. (YA). per. 12.95 (978-0-9709474-7-5(X)) Cyberosia Publishing.

Johnston, Tony. Off to Kindergarten. Sweet, Melissa, illus. 2007. 32p. (J). (ps-3). 7.99 (*978-0-439-73090-7(2) , Cartwheel Bks.) Scholastic, Inc.

—Sparky & Eddie: Trouble with Rats. Ryan, Susannah, illus. 32p. (J). 1999. pap. 4.95 (978-0-590-47981-3(4)); 1998. 13.95 (978-0-590-47980-6(6)) Scholastic, Inc.

—The Spoon in the Bathroom Wall. 2006. (Illus.). 144p. (J). pap. 5.95 (978-0-15-205625-4(4) , Harcourt Paperbacks) Harcourt Children's Bks.

Johnston, Tony & Johnston, Tony. The Spoon in the Bathroom Wall. 2005. 144p. (J). (ps-7). 16.00 (978-0-15-205292-8(5)) Harcourt Trade Pubs.

Jones, Andrea. The Spitting Twins. Kulka, Joe, illus. 2004. 32p. (J). (978-1-58394-095-2(2) , Frog Ltd.) North Atlantic Bks.

Jones, Carrie. Tips on Having a Gay (ex) Boyfriend. 2008. 264p. (J). pap. 9.95 (*978-0-7387-1341-0(4) , Flux) Llewellyn Pubns.

Jones, Christianne C. Eric Won't Do It. Demski, James, illus. 2005. (Read It! Readers Ser.). 24p. (J). (ps). lib. bdg. 18.60 (978-1-4048-1188-1(5)) Picture Window Bks.

—Joey's First Day. Trover, Zachary, illus. 2005. (Read-It! Readers Ser.). 32p. (J). (gr. k-3). 18.60 (978-1-4048-1174-4(5)) Picture Window Bks.

Jones, Diana Wynne. Year of the Griffin. (J). 2001. 400p. (gr. 7 up). pap. 7.99 (978-0-06-447335-4(X) , Harper Trophy); 2000. 272p. (gr. 5 up). 15.89 (978-0-06-029158-7(3)) HarperCollins Pubs.

—Year of the Griffin. 2001. (gr. 5-8). lib. bdg. 15.30 (978-0-613-44275-6(X)) Tandem Library Bks.

Jones, Jasmine. New Kid in School. 2003. (gr. 3-6). lib. bdg. 13.00 (978-0-613-68268-8(8)) Tandem Library Bks.

Jones, Jasmine, adapted by. All over It: Lizzie Mcguire. 2005. 138p. (J). lib. bdg. 16.92 (*978-1-4242-0690-2(1)) Fitzgerald Bks.

Jones, Jennifer B. Dear Mrs. Ryan, You're Ruining My Life. 2004. 144p. (J). pap. 5.95 (978-0-8027-7653-2(1)) Walker & Co.

—The Short Story of My Life. 2004. 160p. (J). 16.95 (978-0-8027-8905-1(6)) Walker & Co.

Jones, Katina. Cool School Story: Little Lucy & Friends. Ottinger, Jon, illus. Zaidan, Rick, photos by. 2001. (Little Lucy & Friends Ser.). 24p. (J). (ps-3). 9.99 (978-1-57151-700-5(6)) Playhouse Publishing.

Jones, Katina, et al. Cowdog Caper: Little Lucy & Friends. Ottinger, Jon, illus. Zaidan, Rick, photos by. 2001. (Little Lucy & Friends Ser.). 24p. (J). (ps-3). 9.99 (978-1-57151-701-2(4)) Playhouse Publishing.

Jones, Marcia Thornton & Dadey, Debbie. Hide-and-Spook. Tugeau, Jeremy, illus. 2004. 86p. (J). (gr. 2-5). lib. bdg. 11.19 (978-0-606-32926-2(9)) Tandem Library Bks.

—New Ghoul in School. 2004. (Ghostville Elementary Ser.). (Illus.). 96p. mass mkt. 3.99 (978-0-439-42439-4(9) , Scholastic Paperbacks) Scholastic, Inc.

Jones, Marcia Thornton, et al. Ghost Class. Tugeau, Jeremy, illus. 2003. (Ghostville Elementary Ser.). 96p. (J). 3.99 (978-0-439-42437-0(2) , 53616146, Scholastic Paperbacks) Scholastic, Inc.

Jones, Melanie Davis. Field Day. 2004. (Rookie Reader Skill Set Ser.). (Illus.). 31p. (J). (gr. k-2). pap. 4.95 (978-0-516-27772-1(3) , Children's Pr.) Scholastic Library Publishing.

—Field Day. Molnar, Albert, illus. 2003. (Rookie Reader - Level B Ser.). 32p. (J). 19.50 (978-0-516-22880-8(3) , Children's Pr.) Scholastic Library Publishing.

Jones, Melanie Davis & Charnan, Simon. School. 2006. 96p. (J). (gr. 1-2). 8.95 (978-0-516-24554-6(6) , Children's Pr.) Scholastic Library Publishing.

Jones, Miranda. Double Trouble. 2005. 128p. (J). (gr. 1-3). pap. 4.99 (978-0-440-41974-7(3) , Yearling) Random Hse. Children's Bks.

—Little Genie No. 4: Castle Magic. Calver, David, illus. 2004. 144p. (J). (gr. 1-3). 8.95 (978-0-385-73165-2(5) , Delacorte Bks. for Young Readers) Random Hse. Children's Bks.

Jones, Miranda. Meanie Genie. Calver, David, illus. 2008. 128p. (J). lib. bdg. (*978-0-385-90533-6(5)); (gr. 1-4). 4.99 (*978-0-440-42227-3(2)) Random Hse. Children's Bks. (Yearling).

Jones, Patrick. Chasing Tail Lights. 2007. 304p. (YA). (gr. 9 up). 16.95 (*978-0-8027-9628-8(1)) Walker & Co.

—Cheated. 2008. 208p. (YA). 16.95 (*978-0-8027-9699-8(0)) Walker & Co.

Jones, Patrick. Nailed. (YA). 2007. 240p. (gr. 9 up). pap. 7.95 (*978-0-8027-9648-6(6)); 2006. 224p. 16.95 (978-0-8027-8077-5(6)) Walker & Co.

Jones, Traci L. Standing Against the Wind. 2006. 192p. (J). 16.00 (978-0-374-37174-6(1)) Farrar, Straus & Giroux.

Jonjak, Ben. School Shooting. 2002. (ENG.). 116p. 19.95 (*978-0-595-74212-7(2)); 114p. (YA). pap. 9.95 (978-0-595-25291-6(5)) iUniverse, Inc. (Writers Club Pr.).

Jonsberg, Barry. Am I Right or Am I Right? 2007. 256p. (gr. 7). (J). lib. bdg. 18.99 (978-0-375-93637-1(8)); (YA). 15.99 (978-0-375-83637-4(3)) Random Hse. Children's Bks. (Knopf Bks. for Young Readers).

—The Crimes & Punishments of Miss Payne. 2006. 288p. (YA). (gr. 7). pap. 8.95 (978-0-375-84022-7(2) , Knopf Bks. for Young Readers) Random Hse. Children's Bks.

Jordan, Apple. Barbie: School Days. Wolcott, Karen, illus. 2004. (Step into Reading Ser.). 32p. (J). (ps-1). pap. 3.99 (978-0-375-82723-5(4) , Random Hse. Bks. for Young Readers) Random Hse. Children's Bks.

Jordan, Rosa. The Goatnappers. 2007. 224p. (J). (gr. 5-7). 14.95 (*978-1-56145-400-6(1) , Peachtree Junior) Peachtree Pubs., Ltd.

Jordan, Taylor. Movin' on In. Wummer, Amy, illus. 2005. 32p. (J). lib. bdg. 20.00 (*978-1-4242-1108-1(5)) Fitzgerald Bks.

—Movin' on In. Wummer, Amy, illus. 2005. (Social Studies Connects). 32p. (J). pap. 4.99 (978-1-57565-159-0(9)) Kane Pr., The.

Joy, Margaret. Addy the Baddy. (Illus.). 80p. (J). (gr. 3-6). 7.95 (978-0-14-036260-2(6)) Penguin Group (USA) Inc.

Joyal, Lisa. Swahili for Beginners: A Young Adult Novel. 2007. (Illus.). 176p. pap. 9.95 (*978-1-894549-69-1(4)) Sumach Pr. CAN. *Dist:* Univ. of Toronto Pr.

Jukes, Mavis. Planning the Impossible. 2000. (J). (978-0-606-20022-6(3)) Tandem Library Bks.

Jules, Jacqueline. No English. Huntington, Amy, illus. 2007. 32p. (J). 17.95 (*978-1-58726-474-0(9) , Mitten Pr.) Ann Arbor Media Group, LLC.

Just in Time! 2000. (gr. k-3). lib. bdg. 11.80 (978-0-613-25841-8(X)) Tandem Library Bks.

Kabeto, Rita Traut. Weird Steffi. 2001. 164p. pap. 12.95 (978-0-595-19047-8(2)) iUniverse, Inc.

Kalish, Ginny. Rachel Rude Rowdy. 2001. (Illus.). 128p. (J). pap. 15.95 (978-1-56976-127-4(2) , 1148, Zephyr Pr.) Chicago Review Pr., Inc.

Kalman, Maira. Smartypants: Pete in School. 2005. (J). 27.95 incl. audio (978-0-8045-6929-3(0) , SAC6929); 29.95 incl. audio compact disk (978-0-8045-4105-3(1) , SACD4105) Spoken Arts, Inc.

—Smartypants (Pete in School) Kalman, Maira, illus. 2003. (Illus.). 32p. (J). (gr. k-3). 15.99 (978-0-399-23478-1(0) , Putnam Juvenile) Penguin Group (USA) Inc.

Kalomas, Alice & Kerr, Lenora. Sir Wrinkles Goes to School. Utomo, Gabhor, illus. 2005. (J). 16.95 (978-0-9766639-1-1(0)) Sir Wrinkles Pr.

Kamio, Yoko. Boys over Flowers: Hana Yori Dango, Vol. 1. 2003. (Boys over Flowers ~ Hana Yori Dango Ser.). (Illus.). 208p. (YA). pap. 9.95 (978-1-56931-996-3(0)) Viz Media.

Kaneyoshi, Izumi. Doubt!!, Vol. 4. Kaneyoshi, Izumi, illus. 2005. (Doubt Ser.). 192p. (YA). pap. 9.99 (978-1-59116-984-0(4)) Viz Media.

Kann, Elizabeth. Purplicious. Kann, Victoria, illus. 2007. 40p. (J). lib. bdg. 17.89 (*978-0-06-124406-3(6)) HarperCollins Pubs.

Kann, Elizabeth & Kann, Victoria. Purplicious. Kann, Victoria, illus. 2007. 40p. (J). (gr. k-3). 16.99 (*978-0-06-124405-6(8)) HarperCollins Pubs.

Kantor, Melissa. Confessions of a Not It Girl. 2006. 256p. (gr. 7-17). pap. 8.99 (978-0-7868-1808-2(5)) Hyperion Pr.

Kantor, Melissa. If I Have a Wicked Stepmother, Where's My Prince? 2007. 320p. (gr. 7 up). pap. 8.99 (*978-0-7868-0961-5(2)); 2005. 288p. (gr. 7-17). 15.99 (978-0-7868-0960-8(4)); 2005. 283p. (YA). (*978-1-4156-2763-1(0)) Hyperion Pr.

Kapper, R. Jon & D'Andrea, Deborah. Bow Wow Blast Off: Little Lucy & Friends. Ottinger, Jon & Zaidan, Rick, illus. 2001. (Little Lucy & Friends Ser.). 24p. (J). pap. 4.99 (978-1-57151-707-4(3)) Playhouse Publishing.

Kappler, Kathleen. Whitney's School Morning. 2004. 38p. pap. 17.95 (978-1-4137-3711-0(0)) PublishAmerica, Inc.

Karas, G. Brian. The Class Artist. 2001. (Illus.). 32p. (J). 15.89 (978-0-688-17815-4(4)) HarperCollins Pubs.

Karasyov, Carrie & Kargman, Jill. Bittersweet Sixteen. 2007. 240p. (J). pap. 7.99 (*978-0-06-077846-0(6) , HarperTeen) HarperCollins Pubs.

Kargman, Jill & Karasyov, Carrie. Bittersweet Sixteen. 2006. 240p. (J). 15.99 (978-0-06-077844-6(X)); lib. bdg. 16.89 (978-0-06-077845-3(8)) HarperCollins Pubs.

Kassirer, Sue. Math Fair Blues. Smath, Jerry, illus. 2005. (Math Matters Ser.). 32p. (J). (gr. k-2). pap. 4.95 (978-1-57565-104-0(1)) Kane Pr., The.

—Math Fair Blues. 2001. (gr. k-3). lib. bdg. 12.95 (978-0-613-39339-3(2)) Tandem Library Bks.

Katar, Al. Captain Scratch: Island of Sirmanj. 2007. (J). (*978-1-934035-31-3(9)) Trent's Prints.

Katschke. Recess. 1998. 48p. (J). pap. 3.95 (978-0-7868-4301-5(2)) Disney Pr.

Katschke, Judy. If I Were President. 1999. (gr. 3-6). lib. bdg. 11.80 (978-0-613-21748-4(9)) Tandem Library Bks.

Katschke, Judy, adapted by. It's Time for School, Charlie Brown. ed. 2005. (Illus.). 32p. (J). lib. bdg. 15.00 (978-1-59054-948-3(1)) Fitzgerald Bks.

Katz, Alan. Don't Say That Word! Catrow, David, illus. 2007. 40p. (J). (ps-3). 16.99 (978-0-689-86971-6(1) , McElderry, Margaret K.) Simon & Schuster Children's Publishing.

Katz, Danny. Little Lunch Four. Vane, Mitch, illus. 2005. (Little Lunch Ser.). 64p. (J). pap. (978-1-876372-84-2(2)) Black Dog Bks.

Kay, Elizabeth. The Jinx on the Divide. 2005. 384p. (J). pap. 16.99 (978-0-439-72455-5(4) , Chicken Hse., The) Scholastic, Inc.

Kaye, Amy. Real Deal: Focus on This! 2003. (gr. 7-12). lib. bdg. 14.15 (978-0-613-86135-9(3)) Tandem Library Bks.

—Real Deal: Focus on This. 2003. (gr. 7-12). lib. bdg. 14.15 (978-0-613-76910-5(4)) Tandem Library Bks.

—The Used-to-Be It Girl. 2004. mass mkt. 5.99 (978-0-8439-5473-9(6)) Dorchester Publishing Co., Inc.

Kehm, Michelle. Suzi Clue: the Prom Queen Curse: The Prom Queen Curse. 2008. 192p. (YA). 15.99 (*978-0-525-47953-6(8) , Dutton Juvenile) Penguin Group (USA) Inc.

Keizer, Garret. God of Beer. 256p. (J). 2003. pap. 6.99 (978-0-06-447276-0(0)); 2002. (gr. 8 up). 15.95 (978-0-06-029456-4(6)) HarperCollins Pubs.

—God of Beer. 2003. (gr. 7-12). lib. bdg. 15.30 (978-0-613-71500-3(4)) Tandem Library Bks.

Keller, Holly. That's Mine, Horace. Keller, Holly, illus. 2000. (Illus.). 24p. (J). (ps up). 16.99 (978-0-688-17159-9(1)) HarperCollins Pubs.

Kelley, True. The Blabber Report. Kelley, True, illus. 2007. (Illus.). 32p. (J). (gr. k-4). 15.99 (978-0-525-47809-6(4) , Dutton Juvenile) Penguin Group (USA) Inc.

—School Lunch. Kelley, True, illus. 2005. (Illus.). 32p. (J). (ps-ps). 16.95 (978-0-8234-1894-7(4)) Holiday Hse., Inc.

Kellogg, Steven, illus. The Day Jimmy's Boa Ate the Wash. 2002. (Jimmy's Boa Constrictor Ser.). (J). 14.04 (978-0-7587-2356-7(3)) Book Wholesalers, Inc.

Kelly, Claire. Nellie in the News. Hicks, Faith, illus. 2007. 48p. (J). lib. bdg. 23.08 (*978-1-4242-1631-4(1)) Fitzgerald Bks.

Kelly, Katy. Busy Like You Can't Believe. Rex, Adam, illus. 2006. (Lucy Rose Ser.). 176p. (J). (gr. 3-7). 12.95 (978-0-385-73319-9(4) , Delacorte Bks. for Young Readers) Random Hse. Children's Bks.

—Lucy Rose: Here's the Thing about Me. Rex, Adam, illus. (J). (gr. 3-7). 2004. 144p. 12.95 (978-0-385-73203-1(1) , Delacorte Bks. for Young Readers); 2004. 144p. lib. bdg. 14.99 (978-0-385-90234-2(4) , Delacorte Bks. for Young Readers); 2006. 160p. reprint ed. 5.99 (978-0-440-42026-2(1) , Yearling) Random Hse. Children's Bks.

—Lucy Rose: Busy Like You Can't Believe. Rex, Adam, illus. 2006. 176p. (J). (gr. 3-7). lib. bdg. 14.99 (978-0-385-90338-7(3) , Delacorte Bks. for Young Readers) Random Hse. Children's Bks.

Kelly, Theresa. Seaside High, Vol. 2. 1999. (Aloha Cove Ser.: Vol. 2). (Illus.). 272p. (YA). (gr. 8-12). 5.99 (978-0-570-05484-9(2)) Concordia Publishing Hse.

—Seaside High. 1999. (gr. 7-12). lib. bdg. 14.15 (978-0-613-72660-3(X)) Tandem Library Bks.

Kenah, Katharine. The Best Chef in Second Grade. Carter, Abby, illus. 2007. (I Can Read Bks.). 48p. (J). lib. bdg. 16.89 (*978-0-06-053562-9(8)); 15.99 (*978-0-06-053561-2(X)) HarperCollins Pubs.

—The Best Teacher in Second Grade. Carter, Abby, illus. 2007. (I Can Read Bks.). 48p. (J). pap. 3.99 (*978-0-06-053566-7(0) , Harper Trophy) HarperCollins Pubs.

S

Kenner, Julie. The Good Ghouls' Guide to Getting Even. 2007. 256p. (YA). pap. 9.99 (978-0-425-21391-9(9) , Berkley Trade) Penguin Group (USA) Inc.

Kent, Deborah. Belonging. 2000. (gr. 7-12). lib. bdg. 24.55 (978-0-613-84549-6(8)) Tandem Library Bks.

Kent, Deoborah. Belonging. 2001. 210p. (YA). pap. 14.95 (978-0-595-19395-0(1) , People with Disabilities Pr.) iUniverse, Inc.

Kent, Renee Holmes. Robyn Flies Home, Vol. 4. 2004. (Adventures in Misty Falls Ser.: Vol. 4). (Illus.). 100p. (gr. 4-7). pap. 4.99 (978-1-56309-764-5(8) , N007106) New Hope Pubs.

—Tell the Truth, Cassie, Vol. 6. 2004. (Adventures in Misty Falls Ser.: Vol. 6). (Illus.). 100p. (J). (gr. 4-7). pap. 4.99 (978-1-56309-452-1(5) , N007110) New Hope Pubs.

Kephart, Beth. Undercover. 2007. 288p. (gr. 7 up). (J). 16.99 (*978-0-06-123893-2(7)); (YA). lib. bdg. 17.89 (*978-0-06-123894-9(5)) HarperCollins Pubs. (HarperTeen).

Kerr, B. Modern Persona: Valhalla High School. 2007. 296p. (YA). per. 18.95 (*978-0-595-44412-0(1)) iUniverse, Inc.

Kids Can Learn Franklin Staff, ed. Ready for School. 2004. 32p. pap. (978-1-55337-605-7(6)) Kids Can Pr., Ltd.

Kidwell, Leigh-Anne. The Year i Lost My Popularity! 2005. 115p. pap. 16.95 (978-1-4137-8376-6(7)) PublishAmerica, Inc.

Kieda, Alyson. Fightin' Mad: A Tale in Which Sherman Learns to Handle His Anger. Sharp, Dan, illus. 2000. (Stories to Grow By Ser.). 19p. (J). 3.95 (978-1-56822-595-1(4) , Instructional Fair) Schaffer, Frank Pubns.

Kim, Wu-kyung. Su-il vs. Su-il. Park, Jung-eun, tr. from KOR. Kwon, Sawoo, illus. 2005. 164p. (J). pap. 20.00 (978-0-89581-839-3(6)) Jain Publishing Company, Inc.

Kimmel, Cody E. In the Eye of the Storm. Snow, Scott, illus. 2003. (Adventures of Young Buffalo Bill Ser.). 144p. (J). (gr. 3-7). 15.99 (978-0-06-029115-0(X)) HarperCollins Pubs.

Kimmel, E. Cody. In the Eye of the Storm. Snow, Scott, illus. 2003. (Adventures of Young Buffalo Bill Ser.). 144p. (J). (gr. 3-7). lib. bdg. 16.89 (978-0-06-029116-7(8)) HarperCollins Pubs.

Kimmel, Elizabeth Cody. Lily B. on the Brink of Love. (J). 2006. 208p. pap. 5.99 (978-0-06-075545-4(8) , Harper Trophy); 2005. 224p. 15.99 (978-0-06-075541-6(5)); 2005. 192p. lib. bdg. 16.89 (978-0-06-075543-0(1)) HarperCollins Pubs.

—Lily B. on the Brink of Paris. 2006. 192p. (J). (gr. 5-8). 15.99 (978-0-06-083948-2(1)); lib. bdg. 16.89 (978-0-06-083949-9(X)) HarperCollins Pubs.

—Mary Leaves Little House. 2008. (Little House Ser.). 192p. (J). lib. bdg. 16.89 (*978-0-06-000906-9(3)); (gr. 3-7). 15.99 (*978-0-06-000905-2(5)) HarperCollins Pubs.

—Spin the Bottle. 2008. 240p. (J). (gr. 5). 16.99 (*978-0-8037-3191-2(4) , Dial) Penguin Group (USA) Inc.

Kimmel, Elizabeth Cody. Visiting Miss Caples. 2001. (978-0-606-22533-5(1)) Tandem Library Bks.

Kimmel, Haven. Kaline Klattermaster's Tree House. Brown, Peter, illus. 2008. 160p. (J). 15.99 (*978-0-689-87402-4(2) , Atheneum) Simon & Schuster Children's Publishing.

Kindig, Tess. Luv @ First Site. 2004. 128p. (J). pap. 5.99 (978-1-4003-0325-0(7)) Nelson, Thomas Inc.

King, Danny. School for Scumbags. 2008. 288p. pap. 14.95 (*978-1-85242-972-0(0)) Serpent's Tail Ltd. GBR. *Dist:* Consortium Bk. Sales & Distribution.

King, Sophie. The School Run. 2006. 352p. pap. 12.50 (978-0-340-92154-8(4) , Hodder & Stoughton) Hodder General Publishing Division GBR. *Dist:* Trafalgar Square Publishing.

Kinney, Jeff. Diary of a Wimpy Kid. 2007. (Illus.). 224p. (J). (gr. 2-8). 12.95 (*978-0-8109-9313-6(9) , Abrams Bks. for Young Readers) Abrams, Harry N. , Inc.

Kir-On, Calanitte. The Adventures of the Gimmel Gang I: The Fake Mezuza. 2002. 75p. (YA). pap. 8.95 (978-1-931681-21-6(X)) Israel Bk. Shop.

Kirk, Daniel. Keisha Ann Can! Kirk, Daniel, illus. 2008. 32p. (J). (ps-k). 16.99 (*978-0-399-24179-6(5) , Putnam Juvenile) Penguin Group (USA) Inc.

Kirk, David. After School Rules. 2006. (Miss Spider Ser.). 32p. (J). (ps-ps). pap. 3.99 (978-0-448-44412-3(7) , Grosset & Dunlap) Penguin Group (USA) Inc.

Kizer, Amber. Gert Garibaldi's Rants & Raves: One Butt Cheek at a Time. 2007. (YA). 192p. (gr. 7). 15.99 (*978-0-385-73430-1(1)); 304p. (gr. 9). lib. bdg. 18.99 (*978-0-385-90439-1(8)) Random Hse. Children's Bks. (Delacorte Bks. for Young Readers).

Klam, Cheryl. The Pretty One. 2008. 288p. (YA). (gr. 7). pap. 9.99 (*978-0-385-73373-1(9)); lib. bdg. 12.99 (*978-0-385-90388-2(X)) Random Hse. Children's Bks. (Delacorte Bks. for Young Readers).

Klass, David. Dark Angel. 2005. 320p. (YA). (gr. 7). 17.00 (978-0-374-39950-4(6) , Farrar, Straus & Giroux (BYR)) Farrar, Straus & Giroux.

—Dark Angel. 2007. 320p. (J). (gr. 9 up). pap. 7.99 (*978-0-06-088700-1(1) , HarperTeen) HarperCollins Pubs.

Klass, David. You Don't Know Me. 2001. 272p. (YA). (gr. 7 up). 18.00 (978-0-374-38706-8(0) , Farrar, Straus & Giroux (BYR)) Farrar, Straus & Giroux.

—You Don't Know Me. 2002. (gr. 7-12). lib. bdg. 15.30 (978-0-613-53336-2(4)) Tandem Library Bks.

Klass, Sheila S. The Uncivil War. 1999. (978-0-606-17477-0(X)) Tandem Library Bks.

Klein, Abby. Don't Sit on My Lunch! McKinley, John, illus. 2005. 96p. (J). (ps-3). lib. bdg. 11.19 (978-0-606-34119-6(6)) Tandem Library Bks.

—Don't Sit on My Lunch. Mckinley, John, illus. 2005. (Ready, Freddy! Ser.: No. 4). 96p. (J). pap. 15.95 (978-0-439-55601-9(5)); 4th ed. pap. 3.99 (978-0-439-55602-6(3)) Scholastic, Inc. (Blue Sky Pr., The).

—The Pumpkin Elf Mystery. McKinley, John, illus. 2007. (Ready, Freddy! Ser.: No. 11). 96p. (J). pap. 3.99 (*978-0-439-89591-0(X) , Blue Sky Pr., The) Scholastic, Inc.

—Super-secret Valentine. 2007. (Ready, Freddy! Ser.: No. 10). 96p. (J). pap. 3.99 (978-0-439-78459-7(X) , Blue Sky Pr., The) Scholastic, Inc.

—Talent Show Scaredy-Pants. McKinley, John, illus. 2005. (J). pap. (978-0-439-55603-3(1) , Blue Sky Pr., The); 5th ed. (Ready, Freddy! Ser.: No. 5). 96p. pap. 3.99 (978-0-439-55604-0(X)) Scholastic, Inc.

Klein, Abby. 100th Day of School. 2008. (Ready, Freddy! Ser.: No. 13). 96p. (J). pap. 3.99 (*978-0-439-89593-4(6) , Blue Sky Pr., The) Scholastic, Inc.

Klein, Adria F. Max Goes on the Bus. Gallagher-Cole, Mernie, illus. 2005. (Read-It! Readers Ser.). 24p. (J). (ps). lib. bdg. 18.60 (978-1-4048-1176-8(1)) Picture Window Bks.

—Max Goes to School. Gallagher-Cole, Mernie, illus. 2005. (Read-It! Readers Ser.). 24p. (J). (ps). lib. bdg. 18.60 (978-1-4048-1179-9(6)) Picture Window Bks.

Klein, Rachel. The Moth Diaries. 2002. 256p. (YA). (978-1-58243-205-2(8)) Counterpoint.

Kleinberg, Naomi. Elmo's World: Teachers! Nelson, Mary Beth, illus. 2007. 12p. (J). (gr. k-ps). bds. 4.99 (*978-0-375-83788-3(4) , Random Hse. Bks. for Young Readers) Random Hse. Children's Bks.

Kleven, Elisa. The Apple Doll. 2007. (Illus.). 40p. (J). (ps-3). 16.00 (978-0-374-30380-8(0)) Farrar, Straus & Giroux.

Kline, Lisa Williams. The Princesses of Atlantis. 2002. (Illus.). 192p. (J). 16.95 (978-0-8126-2855-5(1)) Cricket Bks.

Kline, Suzy. Herbie Jones & the Class Gift. Williams, Richard, illus. 2002. (Herbie Jones Ser.). 96p. (J). pap. 4.99 (978-0-698-11941-3(X) , Putnam Juvenile) Penguin Group (USA) Inc.

—Herbie Jones & the Second Grade Slippers. Sweeten, Sami, illus. 2006. 64p. (J). (gr. 1-4). 14.99 (978-0-399-23132-2(3) , Putnam Juvenile) Penguin Group (USA) Inc.

—Herbie Jones Moves On. 2003. 80p. (J). (gr. 2-5). 14.99 (978-0-399-23635-8(X) , Putnam Juvenile) Penguin Group (USA) Inc.

—Herbie Jones Sails into Second Grade. Sweeten, Sami, illus. 2006. 64p. (J). (gr. 1-4). 14.99 (978-0-399-22665-6(6) , Putnam Juvenile) Penguin Group (USA) Inc.

—Horrible Harry & the Christmas Surprise. 1998. (Horrible Harry Ser.: No. 5). (Illus.). 64p. (J). (gr. 2-4). pap. 3.99 (978-0-14-130145-7(7) , Puffin) Penguin Group (USA) Inc.

—Horrible Harry & the Dragon War. Remkiewicz, Frank, illus. 2002. 64p. (J). (gr. 1-3). 13.99 (978-0-670-03559-5(9) , Viking Juvenile) Penguin Group (USA) Inc.

—Horrible Harry & the Dungeon. 1998. (Horrible Harry Ser.: No. 7). (Illus.). 64p. (J). (gr. 2-4). pap. 3.99 (978-0-14-038620-2(3) , Puffin) Penguin Group (USA) Inc.

—Horrible Harry & the Dungeon. unabr. ed. 2000. (Horrible Harry Ser.: No. 7). (J). (gr. 2-4). pap. 22.24 incl. audio (978-0-7887-3174-7(2) , 40909X4) Recorded Bks., LLC.

—Horrible Harry & the Goog. Remkiewicz, Frank, illus. 64p. (J). (gr. 2). 2006. pap. 3.99 (978-0-14-240728-8(3) , Puffin); 2005. 13.99 (978-0-670-05992-8(7) , Viking Juvenile) Penguin Group (USA) Inc.

—Horrible Harry & the Holidaze. Remkiewicz, Frank, illus. 2004. (Horrible Harry Ser.). 80p. (J). pap. 3.99 (978-0-14-240205-4(2) , Puffin) Penguin Group (USA) Inc.

—Horrible Harry & the Holidaze. Remkiewicz, Frank, illus. 2004. 67p. (J). (gr. 2-5). per. 11.19 (978-0-606-32710-7(X)) Tandem Library Bks.

—Horrible Harry & the Kickball Wedding. Remkiewicz, Frank, illus. 1999. (Horrible Harry Ser.: No. 6). 64p. (J). (gr. 2-4). pap. 3.99 (978-0-14-130316-1(6) , Puffin) Penguin Group (USA) Inc.

—Horrible Harry & the Mud Gremlins. Remkiewicz, Frank, illus. 2003. 64p. (J). (gr. 2-6). 13.99 (978-0-670-03617-2(X) , Viking Juvenile) Penguin Group (USA) Inc.

—Horrible Harry & the Triple Revenge. Remkiewicz, Frank, illus. (Horrible Harry Ser.). 64p. (J). (gr. 2). 2008. 3.99 (*978-0-14-241081-3(0) , Puffin); 2006. 13.99 (978-0-670-06077-1(1) , Viking Juvenile) Penguin Group (USA) Inc.

—Horrible Harry Bugs the Three Bears. Remkiewicz, Frank, illus. 2008. (J). (gr. 2). 13.99 (*978-0-670-06293-5(6) , Viking Juvenile) Penguin Group (USA) Inc.

—Horrible Harry Cracks the Code. Remkiewicz, Frank, illus. 2007. 80p. (J). 13.99 (978-0-670-06200-3(6) , Viking Juvenile) Penguin Group (USA) Inc.

—Horrible Harry Goes to Sea: Puffine Chapters. Remkiewicz, Frank, illus. (Horrible Harry Ser.). 64p. (J). (gr. 2-5). 2003. pap. 3.99 (978-0-14-250002-6(X) , Puffin); 2001. 13.99 (978-0-670-03516-8(5) , Viking Juvenile) Penguin Group (USA) Inc.

—Horrible Harry Goes to Sea: Puffine Chapters. 2003. (gr. 3-6). lib. bdg. 11.80 (978-0-613-61629-4(4)) Tandem Library Bks.

—Horrible Harry Goes to the Moon. Remkiewicz, Frank, illus. (Horrible Harry Ser.). 64p. (J). 2002. pap. 3.99 (978-0-14-130674-2(2) , Puffin); 2000. (gr. 2-4). 13.99 (978-0-670-88764-4(1) , Viking Juvenile) Penguin Group (USA) Inc.

—Horrible Harry Goes to the Moon. 2002. (gr. 3-6). lib. bdg. 11.80 (978-0-613-45278-6(X)) Tandem Library Bks.

—Horrible Harry Moves up to Third Grade. Remkiewicz, Frank, illus. (Horrible Harry Ser.: No. 10). 64p. (J). (gr. 2-4). 2000. pap. 3.99 (978-0-14-038972-2(5) , Puffin); 1998. 14.99 (978-0-670-87873-4(1) , Viking Juvenile) Penguin Group (USA) Inc.

—Horrible Harry Moves up to Third Grade. 2000. (gr. 3-6). lib. bdg. 11.80 (978-0-613-28522-3(0)); (Horrible Harry Ser.: No. 10). (J). (gr. 2-4). 10.79 (978-0-606-17862-4(7)) Tandem Library Bks.

—Horrible Harry Takes the Cake. Remkiewicz, Frank, illus. (Horrible Harry Ser.). 64p. (J). (gr. 2). 2007. 3.99 (*978-0-14-240939-8(1) , Puffin); 2006. 13.99 (978-0-670-06075-7(5) , Viking Juvenile) Penguin Group (USA) Inc.

—Horrible Harry's Secret. Remkiewicz, Frank, illus. 1998. (Horrible Harry Ser.: No. 4). 64p. (J). (gr. 2-4). pap. 3.99 (978-0-14-130093-1(0) , Puffin) Penguin Group (USA) Inc.

—Marvin & the Mean Words. 1998. (J). (978-0-606-13599-3(5)) Tandem Library Bks.

—Marvin & the Meanest Girl. Sims, Blanche, illus. 2002. (Chapters Ser.). 80p. (J). pap. 4.99 (978-0-698-11967-3(3) , Putnam Juvenile) Penguin Group (USA) Inc.

—Marvin & the Meanest Girl. 2002. (gr. 3-6). lib. bdg. 13.00 (978-0-613-63962-0(6)) Tandem Library Bks.

—Molly Gets Mad. Bluthenthal, Diana Cain, illus. 2001. 1p. (J). (gr. 1-4). 14.99 (978-0-399-23408-8(X) , Putnam Juvenile) Penguin Group (USA) Inc.

—Molly's in a Mess. Bluthenthal, Diana Cain, illus. 2002. (Chapters Ser.). 80p. (J). pap. 4.99 (978-0-698-11928-4(2) , Putnam Juvenile) Penguin Group (USA) Inc.

—Molly's in a Mess. 2002. (gr. 3-6). lib. bdg. 13.00 (978-0-613-64418-1(2)) Tandem Library Bks.

—Song Lee & the "I Hate You" Notes. 2001. (gr. 3-6). lib. bdg. 11.80 (978-0-613-36012-8(5)); (Illus.). (J). (978-0-606-21439-1(9)) Tandem Library Bks.

—Song Lee in Room 2B. Remkiewicz, Frank, illus. 1999. (Song Lee Ser.). 64p. (J). (gr. 2-5). pap. 3.99 (978-0-14-130408-3(1) , Puffin) Penguin Group (USA) Inc.

Kline, Suzy & Kline, Suzy. Herbie Jones & the Class Gift. 2002. (Illus.). 95p. (J). (gr. 4-7). lib. bdg. 13.00 (978-0-613-62518-0(8)) Tandem Library Bks.

—Horrible Harry & the Dragon War. Remkiewicz, Frank, illus. 2003. 64p. (J). (ps-k). pap. 3.99 (978-0-14-250166-5(2) , Puffin) Penguin Group (USA) Inc.

—Horrible Harry & the Holidaze. Remkiewicz, Frank, illus. 2003. (Horrible Harry Ser.). 64p. (J). (gr. 2-k). 13.99 (978-0-670-03642-4(0) , Viking Juvenile) Penguin Group (USA) Inc.

—Horrible Harry & the Kickball Wedding. Remkiewicz, Frank, illus. 1999. 52p. (J). (ps-k). lib. bdg. 11.80 (978-0-7857-9249-9(X)) Tandem Library Bks.

Klinger, Shula. The Kingdom of Strange. 2008. (YA). (*978-0-7614-5395-6(4)) Cavendish, Marshall Corp.

Klise, Kate. Deliver Us from Normal. 2005. 240p. (YA). (gr. 5-9). 16.95 (978-0-439-52322-6(2)) Scholastic, Inc.

—Deliver Us from Normal: Read-Along/Homework Pack. unabr. ed. 2005. (YA). (gr. 5-8). 65.70 incl. audio (978-1-4193-3619-5(3) , 42050) Recorded Bks., LLC.

—Regarding the Bathrooms: A Privy to the Past. Klise, M. Sarah, illus. 2006. (Regarding The ... Ser.). 160p. (YA). 15.00 (978-0-15-205164-8(3)) Harcourt Trade Pubs.

—Regarding the Fountain. Klise, M. Sarah, illus. 1999. 144p. (J). (gr. 3-7). pap. 5.99 (978-0-380-79347-1(4) , Harper Trophy) HarperCollins Pubs.

—Regarding the Fountain: A Tale, in Letters, of Liars & Leaks. Klise, M. Sarah, illus. 1998. 144p. (J). (gr. 4-7). 16.99 (978-0-380-97538-9(6)) HarperCollins Pubs.

—Regarding the Fountain: A Tale, in Letters, of Liars & Leaks. 1999. (978-0-606-16342-2(5)); (gr. 3-6). lib. bdg. 14.15 (978-0-613-17849-5(1)) Tandem Library Bks.

—Regarding the Sink: Where, Oh Where, Did Waters Go? Klise, M. Sarah, illus. 2006. (Regarding The ... Ser.). 144p. (J). pap. 5.95 (978-0-15-205544-8(4) , Harcourt Paperbacks) Harcourt Children's Bks.

Klise, Kate & Klise, M. Sarah. Regarding the Trees: A Splintered Saga Rooted in Secrets. 2007. (Regarding The ... Ser.). (Illus.). 160p. (J). pap. 5.95 (*978-0-15-206090-9(1) , Harcourt Paperbacks) Harcourt Children's Bks.

Klise, Kate & Klise, M. Sarah, illus. Little Rabbit & the Nightmare. 2008. (J). (*978-0-15-205717-6(X)) Harcourt Trade Pubs.

Klise, Kate & Klise, M. Sarah, illus. Regarding the Bees: A Lesson, in Letters, on Honey, Dating, & Other Sticky Subjects. 2007. (Regarding The ... Ser.). 144p. (YA). (gr. 3-7). 15.00 (978-0-15-205711-4(0)) Harcourt Trade Pubs.

Knowlton, Laurie. N 2 Deep. 2004. 128p. (J). pap. 5.99 (978-1-4003-0327-4(3)) Nelson, Thomas Inc.

Knudsen, Michelle. A Slimy Story. Billin-Frye, Paige, illus. 2004. 32p. (J). lib. bdg. 20.00 (*978-1-4242-1150-0(6)) Fitzgerald Bks.

—A Slimy Story. Billin-Frye, Paige, illus. 2004. (Science Solves It! Ser.). 32p. (J). (ps-3). pap. 4.99 (978-1-57565-144-6(0)) Kane Pr., The.

Knudson, Michelle. The Case of Vampire Vivian. Wummer, Amy, illus. 2003. (Science Solves It! Ser.). 32p. (J). 4.99 (978-1-57565-127-9(0)) Kane Pr., The.

Knudson, Mike & Wilkinson, Steve. Raymond & Graham Rule the School. 2008. 128p. (J). (gr. 3-5). 14.99 (*978-0-670-01101-8(0) , Viking Juvenile) Penguin Group (USA) Inc.

Kobayashi, Jin. School Rumble. (JPN., Illus.). (YA). Vol. 1. pap. (978-4-06-363244-6(X)); Vol. 2. 162p. pap. (978-4-06-363290-3(3)); Vol. 3. 158p. pap. (978-4-06-363321-4(7)); Vol. 4. 154p. pap. (978-4-06-363346-7(2)) Kodansha, Ltd.

—School Rumble, Vol. 1. 2006. (Illus.). 192p. (gr. 11). pap. 10.95 (978-0-345-49147-3(5) , Del Rey) Random House Publishing Group.

Koertge, Ronald. Confess-O-Rama. 1998. (978-0-606-13291-6(0)) Tandem Library Bks.

—Stoner & Spaz. 176p. (YA). (gr. 9-12). 2002. 15.99 (978-0-7636-1608-3(7)); 2004. reprint ed. pap. 6.99 (978-0-7636-2150-6(1)) Candlewick Pr.

—Where the Kissing Never Stops. 2005. 256p. (YA). (gr. 9 up). pap. 6.99 (978-0-7636-2696-9(1)); 2nd ed. 16.99 (978-0-7636-2543-6(4)) Candlewick Pr.

Koja, Kathe. Buddha Boy. 2003. 128p. (YA). (gr. 7 up). 16.00 (978-0-374-30998-5(1) , Farrar, Straus & Giroux (BYR)) Farrar, Straus & Giroux.

—Buddha Boy. 2004. 128p. (YA). (gr. 6-11). reprint ed. pap. 5.99 (978-0-14-240209-2(5) , Puffin) Penguin Group (USA) Inc.

—Buddha Boy. l.t. ed. 2003. 113p. (J). 24.95 (978-0-7862-6012-6(2)) Thomson Gale.

—Kissing the Bee. 2007. 128p. (YA). (gr. 9 up). 16.00 (*978-0-374-39938-2(7) , Farrar, Straus & Giroux (BYR)) Farrar, Straus & Giroux.

—Straydog. 2002. (Illus.). 112p. (YA). (gr. 8-10). 16.00 (978-0-374-37278-1(0) , Farrar, Straus & Giroux (BYR)) Farrar, Straus & Giroux.

—Straydog. 2004. 128p. (YA). reprint ed. pap. 5.99 (978-0-14-240071-5(8) , Puffin) Penguin Group (USA) Inc.

Koja, Kathe. Talk. 2005. 144p. (YA). 16.00 (978-0-374-37382-5(5) , Farrar, Straus & Giroux (BYR)) Farrar, Straus & Giroux.

—Talk. 2008. 160p. (YA). pap. 6.99 (*978-0-312-37605-5(7)) Square Fish.

—Talk. l.t. ed. 2006. 183p. (YA). 21.95 (978-0-7862-8811-3(6)) Thorndike Pr.

Kolb, Joseph J. Reservation Dreams. 2004. 185p. pap. 19.95 (978-1-4137-3054-8(X)) PublishAmerica, Inc.

Kompaneyets, Marc. The Squishiness of Things. 2005. (Illus.). 40p. (J). (gr. k-3). 15.95 (978-0-375-82750-1(1) , Knopf Bks. for Young Readers) Random Hse. Children's Bks.

Konigsburg, E. L. Retrato del Sabado. 2002. (SPA.). (gr. 3-6). lib. bdg. 18.75 (978-0-613-64589-8(8)) Tandem Library Bks.

—Throwing Shadows. 1998. 160p. (J). (gr. 5-9). pap. 5.99 (978-0-689-82120-2(4) , Aladdin) Simon & Schuster Children's Publishing.

—The View from Saturday. Konigsburg, E. L., illus. 2002. (Illus.). (J). 25.11 (978-0-7587-0221-0(3)) Book Wholesalers, Inc.

—The View from Saturday. 2000. (J). 11.95 (978-1-56137-936-1(0)) Novel Units, Inc.

—The View from Saturday. 280p. (YA). (gr. 5 up). pap. 4.95 (978-0-8072-1511-1(2) , Listening Library) Random Hse. Audio Publishing Group.

—The View from Saturday. 1998. (Jean Karl Bks.). 176p. (J). (gr. 3-7). reprint ed. pap. 5.99 (978-0-689-81721-2(5) , Aladdin) Simon & Schuster Children's Publishing.

—The View from Saturday. 1998. (J). (978-0-606-13063-9(2)) Tandem Library Bks.

Korelitz, Jean Hanff. Interference Powder. 144p. (J). 2006. pap. 5.95 (978-0-7614-5275-1(3)); 2003. 15.95 (978-0-7614-5139-6(0)) Cavendish, Marshall Corp.

Korman, Gordon. The Chicken Doesn't Skate. 1998. 192p. (J). (gr. 4-8). pap. 4.50 (978-0-590-85301-9(5)) Scholastic, Inc.

—Jake, Reinvented. 2005. 224p. (gr. 7-17). pap. 5.99 (978-0-7868-5697-8(1)) Hyperion Bks. for Children.

—Liar, Liar, Pants on Fire. 1999. (gr. 3-6). lib. bdg. 11.80 (978-0-613-11773-9(5)) Tandem Library Bks.

—Maxx Comedy: The Funniest Kid in America. 2006. 160p. (gr. 3-7). pap. 5.99 (978-0-7868-3895-0(7)) Hyperion Pr.

—No More Dead Dogs. Orig. Title: Touchdown Stage Left. 192p. (gr. 5-9). 2002. (J). pap. 5.99 (978-0-7868-1601-9(5)); 2000. (Illus.). 15.99 (978-0-7868-0531-0(5)) Hyperion Bks. for Children.

—No More Dead Dogs. 2002. Orig. Title: Touchdown Stage Left. (gr. 5-8). lib. bdg. 14.15 (978-0-613-61850-2(5)) Tandem Library Bks.

—Planet of the Nose Pickers. 2000. (gr. 3-6). lib. bdg. 11.80 (978-0-613-26612-3(9)) Tandem Library Bks.

—Schooled. 2007. 224p. (gr. 3-7). 15.99 (*978-0-7868-5692-3(0)) Hyperion Pr.

—The Sixth Grade Nickname Game. 2004. 160p. (gr. 3-7). pap. 5.99 (978-0-7868-5190-4(2)) Hyperion Paperbacks for Children.

—Something Fishy at MacDonald Hall. 2000. (Illus.). 208p. (J). (gr. 4-7). pap. 4.99 (978-0-590-25522-6(3) , Scholastic Paperbacks) Scholastic, Inc.

—The Ultimate Nose Picker Collection. Vaccaro, Victor, illus. 2006. 592p. (gr. 2-6). pap. 9.99 (978-0-7868-3740-3(3)) Hyperion Pr.

Kornblatt, Marc. Understanding Buddy. l.t. ed. 2002. 100p. (J). 21.95 (978-0-7862-3712-8(0)) Thomson Gale.

Koss, Amy Goldman. The Cheat. Nielsen, Cliff, illus. 2003. 176p. (J). (gr. 5-8). 16.99 (978-0-8037-2794-6(1) , Dial) Penguin Group (USA) Inc.

—Poison Ivy. 2006. 176p. (J). 16.95 (978-1-59643-118-8(0)) Macmillan.

Kostecki-Shaw, Jenny Sue. My Travelin' Eye. 2008. 40p. (J). 16.95 (*978-0-8050-8169-5(0)) Holt, Henry & Co.

Koster, Gloria. The Peanut-Free Café. Cocca-Leffler, Maryann, illus. 2006. 32p. (J). 16.95 (978-0-8075-6386-1(2)) Whitman, Albert & Co.

Kovalski, Maryann. Omar on Board. 32p. 2007. pap. (*978-1-55455-033-3(5)); 2005. (Illus.). (J). (978-1-55041-918-4(8)) Fitzhenry & Whiteside, Ltd.

Kowitt, Holly. Ned's Declassified School Survival Guide. 2006. (Teenick Ser.). (Illus.). 96p. (J). pap. 4.99 (978-0-439-83161-1(X)) Scholastic, Inc.

Kraft, Erik P. Miracle Wimp. 2007. 256p. (J). (gr. 7 up). 16.99 (*978-0-316-01165-5(7)) Little, Brown Bks. for Young Readers.

Kraus, Jeanne R. Annie's Plan: Taking Charge of Schoolwork & Homework. Beyl, Charles, illus. 2006. 48p. (J). (gr. 2-5). 14.95 (978-1-59147-481-4(7)); pap. 8.95 (978-1-59147-482-1(5)) American Psychological Assn. (Magination Pr.).

Krensky, Stephen. Big Bad Wolves at School. Sneed, Brad, illus. 2001. 32p. (J). (ps-3). 15.99 (978-0-689-83799-9(2) , Simon & Schuster Children's Publishing) Simon & Schuster Children's Publishing.

—Lionel at School. Natti, Susanna, illus. 2002. (Easy-to-Read, Puffin Ser.). 48p. (J). pap. 3.99 (978-0-14-230137-1(X) , Puffin) Penguin Group (USA) Inc.

—Lionel at School. 2000. (Dial Easy-to-Read Ser.). (Illus.). 48p. (J). (ps-3). 13.99 (978-0-8037-2457-0(8) , Dial) Penguin Group (USA) Inc.

—Lionel at School. Natti, Susanna, illus. 2002. 48p. (J). (ps-ps). lib. bdg. 11.80 (978-0-613-45287-8(9)) Tandem Library Bks.

—Louise Takes Charge. 2000. (gr. 3-6). lib. bdg. 11.80 (978-0-613-85723-9(2)); (Illus.). (J). (978-0-606-18423-6(6)) Tandem Library Bks.

Kress, Adrienne. Alex & the Ironic Gentleman. 2007. 320p. (YA). (gr. 3-7). 16.95 (***978-1-60286-005-6(X)***) Weinstein Bks.

Kristiansson, Leif. Not My Fault. Stenberg, Dick, illus. 2006. 32p. (J). 11.95 (978-0-9762056-6-1(1)) Heryin Publishing Corp.

Kroll, Steven. Patches Lost & Found. Gott, Barry, illus. 2005. 32p. (J). pap. 5.95 (978-0-7614-5217-1(6)) Cavendish, Marshall Corp.

—Patches Lost & Found. Gott, Barry, illus. 2001. 40p. (J). (gr. k-3). 15.95 (978-1-890817-53-4(8)) Winslow Pr.

—Patches Lost & Found. Gott, Barry, illus. 2005. 32p. (J). (gr. k-4). lib. bdg. 13.15 (978-0-606-33744-1(X)) Tandem Library Bks.

Kroll, Virginia L. Ryan Respects. Billin-Frye, Paige, illus. 2006. (Way I ACT Ser.). 24p. (J). 15.95 (978-0-8075-6946-7(1)) Whitman, Albert & Co.

Krosoczka, Jarrett J. Max for President. 2004. (Illus.). 40p. (J). (ps-3). 15.95 (978-0-375-82428-9(6)); lib. bdg. 17.99 (978-0-375-92428-6(0)) Random Hse. Children's Bks. (Knopf Bks. for Young Readers).

Krovatin, Christopher. Heavy Metal & You. 2005. 192p. (J). (gr. 7-12). pap. 16.95 (978-0-439-73648-0(X)) Scholastic, Inc.

Krueger, Kathryn L. Road to Grandma's House. 2005. 128p. pap. 13.95 (978-1-59800-366-6(6)) Outskirts Press, Inc.

Krulik, Nancy E. Anyone but Me, No. 1. John and Wendy Staff, illus. 2006. (Katie Kazoo, Switcheroo Ser.: No. 1). 80p. (J). 2.99 (978-0-448-44259-4(0) , Grosset & Dunlap) Penguin Group (USA) Inc.

—Be Nice to Mice, No. 20. John and Wendy Staff, illus. 2006. (Katie Kazoo, Switcheroo Ser.: No. 20). 80p. (J). (gr. 2-5). mass mkt. 3.99 (978-0-448-44132-0(2) , Grosset & Dunlap) Penguin Group (USA) Inc.

—Be Nice to Mice, No. 20. 2006. (Katie Kazoo, Switcheroo Ser.: No. 20). (Illus.). 78p. (J). (***978-1-4156-7185-6(0)*** , Grosset & Dunlap) Penguin Group (USA) Inc.

—Boys, Boys, Boys. 2000. (gr. 5-8). lib. bdg. 13.00 (978-0-613-31021-5(7)) Tandem Library Bks.

—Can You Get an F in Lunch? 2007. (How I Survived Middle School Ser.: No. 1). 112p. (J). (gr. 4-7). pap. 4.99 (***978-0-439-02555-3(9)***) Scholastic, Inc.

—Drat! You Copycat, No. 7. 2003. (Katie Kazoo, Switcheroo Ser.: No. 7). (gr. 3-6). lib. bdg. 11.80 (978-0-613-62943-0(4)) Tandem Library Bks.

—Drat! You Copycat!, No. 7. 2003. (Katie Kazoo, Switcheroo Ser.: No. 7). (Illus.). 80p. (J). (gr. 2-4). pap. 3.99 (978-0-448-43171-0(8) , Grosset & Dunlap) Penguin Group (USA) Inc.

—Floppy Friends Go to School. Dellorco, Chris, illus. 1999. 32p. (J). (978-0-439-08767-4(8)) Scholastic, Inc.

—Flower Power, No. 27. 2008. (Katie Kazoo, Switcheroo Ser.: No. 27). 80p. (J). (gr. 2-5). 3.99 (***978-0-448-44674-5(X)*** , Grosset & Dunlap) Penguin Group (USA) Inc.

—Free the Worms!, No. 28. John and Wendy Staff, illus. 2008. (Katie Kazoo, Switcheroo Ser.: No. 28). 80p. (J). (gr. 2-5). pap. 3.99 (***978-0-448-44675-2(8)*** , Grosset & Dunlap) Penguin Group (USA) Inc.

—Friends for Never, No. 14. John and Wendy Staff, illus. 2004. (Katie Kazoo, Switcheroo Ser.: No. 14). 80p. (J). (gr. 2-5). pap. 3.99 (978-0-448-43606-7(X) , Grosset & Dunlap) Penguin Group (USA) Inc.

—I Hate Rules! 2003. (Katie Kazoo, Switcheroo Ser.: Vol. 5). (gr. 3-6). lib. bdg. 11.80 (978-0-613-60296-9(X)) Tandem Library Bks.

—I Hate Rules, No. 5. 2003. (Katie Kazoo, Switcheroo Ser.: No. 5). (Illus.). 80p. (J). (gr. 2-6). pap. 3.99 (978-0-448-43100-0(9) , Grosset & Dunlap) Penguin Group (USA) Inc.

—I Heard a Rumor. 2007. (How I Survived Middle School Ser.: No. 3). 112p. (J). pap. 4.99 (***978-0-439-02557-7(5)***) Scholastic, Inc.

—Madame President. 2007. (How I Survived Middle School Ser.: No. 2). 112p. (J). pap. 3.99 (***978-0-439-02556-0(7)***) Scholastic, Inc.

—Major League Mess-up #29. John and Wendy, illus. 2008. (Katie Kazoo, Switcheroo Ser.). 96p. (J). (gr. 2-5). 9.99 (***978-0-448-44676-9(6)*** , Grosset & Dunlap) Penguin Group (USA) Inc.

—New Girl. 2008. (How I Survived Middle School Ser.: No. 4). 112p. (J). pap. 4.99 (***978-0-545-01303-1(8)*** , Scholastic Paperbacks) Scholastic, Inc.

—No Biz Like Show Biz, No. 24. John and Wendy Staff, illus. 2007. (Katie Kazoo, Switcheroo Ser.: No. 24). 80p. (J). pap. 3.99 (978-0-448-44440-6(2) , Grosset & Dunlap) Penguin Group (USA) Inc.

—No Bones about It, No. 12. John and Wendy Staff, illus. 2004. (Katie Kazoo, Switcheroo Ser.: No. 12). 80p. (J). (gr. 2-6). pap. 3.99 (978-0-448-43358-5(3) , Grosset & Dunlap) Penguin Group (USA) Inc.

—No Bones about It. 2004. (Katie Kazoo, Switcheroo Ser.: Vol. 12). (gr. 3-6). lib. bdg. 11.80 (978-0-613-72571-2(9)) Tandem Library Bks.

—No Matzoh for Me. Hendrix, Bryan, illus. 2003. (Reading Railroad Bks.). 32p. (J). (ps-4). pap. 3.49 (978-0-448-43119-2(X) , Grosset & Dunlap) Penguin Group (USA) Inc.

—No Matzoh for Me! 2003. (ps-2). lib. bdg. 11.25 (978-0-613-61648-5(0)) Tandem Library Bks.

—No Messin' with My Lesson, No. 11. John and Wendy Staff, illus. 2004. (Katie Kazoo, Switcheroo Ser.: No. 11). 80p. (J). (gr. 2-6). pap. 3.99 (978-0-448-43357-8(5) , Grosset & Dunlap) Penguin Group (USA) Inc.

—No Messin' with My Lesson, No. 11. 2004. (Katie Kazoo, Switcheroo Ser.: No. 11). (gr. 3-6). lib. bdg. 11.80 (978-0-613-72569-9(7)) Tandem Library Bks.

—On Your Mark, Get Set, Laugh!, No. 13. John and Wendy Staff, illus. 2004. (Katie Kazoo, Switcheroo Ser.: No. 13). 80p. (J). mass mkt. 3.99 (978-0-448-43605-0(1) , Grosset & Dunlap) Penguin Group (USA) Inc.

—Something's Fishy, No. 26. John and Wendy Staff, illus. 2007. (Katie Kazoo, Switcheroo Ser.: No. 26). 80p. (J). (gr. 2-5). pap. 3.99 (***978-0-448-44442-0(9)*** , Grosset & Dunlap) Penguin Group (USA) Inc.

Krulik, Nancy E. A Whirlwind Vacation. John and Wendy Staff, illus. 2005. (Katie Kazoo, Switcheroo Ser.). 160p. (gr. 2-5). mass mkt. 4.99 (978-0-448-43748-4(1) , Grosset & Dunlap) Penguin Group (USA) Inc.

Kuroda, Yosuke & Hayashiya, Shizuru. Onegai Teacher. 2003. No. 2. 120p. pap. 9.95 (978-1-58899-179-9(2)); Vol. 1. (Illus.). 200p. (YA). 9.95 (978-1-58899-196-6(2)) ComicsOne Corp./Dr. Masters.

Kurzweil, Allen. Leon & the Champion Chip. Bertholf, Bret, illus. 2007. 352p. (J). pap. 6.99 (***978-0-06-053935-1(6)*** , Harper Trophy) HarperCollins Pubs.

Kurzweil, Allen. Leon & the Spitting Image. Bertholf, Bret, illus. 320p. (J). (gr. 3 up). 2005. pap. 6.99 (978-0-06-053932-0(1) , Harper Trophy); 2003. 16.99 (978-0-06-053930-6(5)); 2003. lib. bdg. 16.89 (978-0-06-053931-3(3)) HarperCollins Pubs.

Kyi, Tanya Lloyd. My Time as Caz Hazard. 2004. (Orca Young Readers Ser.). 112p. (J). (gr. 7-12). pap. 7.95 (978-1-55143-319-6(2) , 1234557) Orca Bk. Pubs. USA.

—Truth. 2003. (YA). (gr. 7 up). pap. 7.95 (978-1-55143-235-9(8)) Orca Bk. Pubs. USA.

—Truth. 2003. (gr. 7-12). lib. bdg. 16.40 (978-0-613-70627-8(7)) Tandem Library Bks.

Labatt, Mary. Sam Gets Lost. Sarrazin, Marisol, tr. Sarrazin, Marisol, illus. 2004. (Kids Can Read! Ser.: Vol. 1). 32p. (J). (gr. k-3). (978-1-55337-563-0(7)); (978-1-55337-562-3(9)) Kids Can Pr., Ltd.

—Sam Goes to School. Sarrazin, Marisol, illus. 2004. 31p. (J). lib. bdg. 15.38 (***978-1-4242-1160-9(3)***) Fitzgerald Bks.

—Sam Goes to School. Sarrazin, Marisol, tr. Sarrazin, Marisol, illus. 2004. (Kids Can Read! Ser.: Vol. 1). 32p. (J). (gr. k-3). (978-1-55337-565-4(3)); (978-1-55337-564-7(5)) Kids Can Pr., Ltd.

Laguna, Sofie. Too Loud Lily. Argent, Kerry, illus. 2004. 32p. (J). pap. 14.95 (978-0-439-57913-1(9)) Scholastic, Inc.

Laird, Elizabeth. Secret Friends. 2002. (Illus.). 96p. (J). pap. (978-0-340-66473-5(8) , Hodder Children's Books) Hodder Children's Division.

Laird, Elizabeth & Davidson, Roz. Jungle School. Sim, David, illus. 2006. (Green Bananas Ser.). 48p. (J). (gr. k-2). pap. (978-0-7787-1042-4(4)); (978-0-7787-1026-4(2)) Crabtree Publishing Co.

Lakin, Patricia. Max & Mo Go Apple Picking. Floca, Brian, illus. 2007. (Ready-to-Reads Ser.). 32p. (J). pap. 3.99 (***978-1-4169-2535-4(X)***); lib. bdg. 13.89 (***978-1-4169-2536-1(8)***) Simon & Schuster Children's Publishing (Aladdin).

—Max & Mo Make a Snowman. Floca, Brian, illus. 2007. (Ready-to-Reads Ser.). 32p. (J). lib. bdg. 13.89 (***978-1-4169-2538-5(4)***); pap. 3.99 (***978-1-4169-2537-8(6)***) Simon & Schuster Children's Publishing. (Aladdin).

—Max & Mo's First Day at School. Floca, Brian, illus. 2007. (Ready-to-Reads Ser.). 32p. (J). (ps-1). pap. 3.99 (***978-1-4169-2533-0(3)***); lib. bdg. 13.89 (***978-1-4169-2534-7(1)***) Simon & Schuster Children's Publishing. (Aladdin).

Lamba, Marie. What I Meant... 2007. 320p. (gr. 5-11). (J). 16.99 (978-0-375-84091-3(5)); (YA). lib. bdg. 19.99 (978-0-375-94091-0(X)) Random Hse. Children's Bks. (Random Hse. Bks. for Young Readers).

Lambert, Janet. Hi Neighbor: A Sugar Bradley Story. 2003. (J). pap. 9.95 (978-1-930009-82-0(8) , 800-691-7779) Image Cascade Publishing.

—Sweet As Sugar: A Sugar Bradley Story. 2003. (YA). pap. 9.95 (978-1-930009-81-3(X) , 800-691-7779) Image Cascade Publishing.

Laminack, Lester L. Jake's 100th Day of School. Love, Judy, illus. 2006. 32p. (J). (ps-3). 16.95 (978-1-56145-355-9(2) , Peachtree Junior) Peachtree Pubs., Ltd.

—Snow Day! 2007. 32p. (J). (ps-3). 16.95 (***978-1-56145-418-1(4)*** , Peachtree Junior) Peachtree Pubs., Ltd.

Laminack, Lester L. Trevor's Wiggly-Wobbly Tooth. McCord, Kathi Garry, illus. 2002. 32p. (J). pap. 7.95 (978-1-56145-279-8(3)) Peachtree Pubs., Ltd.

—Trevor's Wiggly-Wobbly Tooth. McCord, Kathi G., illus. 1998. 32p. (J). (ps-2). 15.95 (978-1-56145-175-3(4)) Peachtree Pubs., Ltd.

Lamstein, Sarah. Hunger Moon. 2004. (Illus.). 112p. (YA). 15.95 (978-1-932425-05-5(5) , Lemniscaat) Boyds Mills Pr.

Landon, Kristen. Life in the Pit. Johnson, Regan, illus. 2007. 192p. (YA). (gr. 8-12). 16.95 (***978-1-933831-08-4(1)***) Blooming Tree Pr.

Langan, Paul & Blackwell, D. M. Blood Is Thicker. 2007. (Bluford Ser.: No. 8). (Illus.). 176p. (J). pap. 3.99 (***978-0-439-90489-6(7)*** , Scholastic Paperbacks) Scholastic, Inc.

Langcaon, Jeff, illus. My Grandpa's Battleship Missouri Tour. 2007. (J). 14.95 (***978-1-56647-831-1(6)***) Mutual Publishing LLC.

Langston, Laura. The Trouble with Cupid. 2008. 240p. (YA). (gr. 5-8). pap. (***978-1-55455-059-3(9)***) Fitzhenry & Whiteside, Ltd.

Larkin, Jim & Rambo, Lee Elliot. Books for Oliver. Brown, Dan, illus. 2006. (J). (978-1-59336-336-9(2)); pap. (978-1-59336-337-6(0)) Mondo Publishing.

LaRochelle, David. Absolutely, Positively Not. 2005. 219p. (YA). (978-0-439-59110-2(4)); 224p. (J). (gr. 7-12). pap. 16.95 (978-0-439-59109-6(0)) Scholastic, Inc. (Levine, Arthur A. Bks.).

Larsen, C. S. The Chronicles of Marvin Archibald Trekker: Boy Magician Book 1 - Penguins of Choice. l.t. ed. 2006. (Illus.). 163p. (YA). per. 5.99 (978-0-9779844-1-1(9)) KnowledgeGain Inc.

Larsen, Kirsten. Rise & Fall of the Kate Empire. 2002. (gr. 3-6). lib. bdg. 13.00 (978-0-613-68282-4(3)) Tandem Library Bks.

Laser, Michael. Cheater. 2008. 224p. (YA). (gr. 7). 16.99 (***978-0-525-47826-3(4)*** , Dutton Juvenile) Penguin Group (USA) Inc.

Lasky, Kathryn. Show & Tell Bunnies. Hafner, Marylin, illus. 2001. 32p. (J). (ps-3). pap. 5.99 (978-0-7636-1050-0(X)) Candlewick Pr.

—Show & Tell Bunnies. 2001. (ps-2). lib. bdg. 14.15 (978-0-613-44257-2(1)) Tandem Library Bks.

Lauber, Patricia. Purrfectly Purrfect: Life at the Acatemy. Lewin, Betsy, illus. 2000. 80p. (J). (gr. 3-7). 15.89 (978-0-06-029209-6(1)); 15.95 (978-0-688-17299-2(7)) HarperCollins Pubs.

Laurens, Jennifer. Falling for Romeo. 2007. (YA). per. 12.95 (***978-1-933963-94-5(8)***) Grove Creek Publishing, LLC.

LaVerne B, Shaw. Mesa Magic. 2006. 192p. per. 19.95 (***978-1-59879-238-6(5)***) Lifevest Publishing, Inc.

Lawrence, Jan. The Revenge of the Substitute Teacher. 1998. (J). (gr. 3-7). pap. 4.50 (978-0-590-05902-2(5) , Scholastic Paperbacks) Scholastic, Inc.

Lawrence, Michael. The Toilet of Doom. 2004. 256p. (J). pap. 16.95 (978-0-7540-7913-2(9) , Galaxy Children's Large Print) BBC Audiobooks America.

Lay, Kathryn. Crown Me! 2004. 208p. (J). (gr. 4-6). tchr. ed. 16.95 (978-0-8234-1845-9(6)) Holiday Hse., Inc.

Lears, Laurie. Becky the Brave: A Story about Epilepsy. Piazza, Gail, illus. 2002. 32p. (J). (gr. 1-4). 15.95 (978-0-8075-0601-1(X)) Whitman, Albert & Co.

Leblanc, Louise. Maddie Stands Tall. Gay, Marie-Louise, illus. 2005. 61p. (J). lib. bdg. 12.00 (***978-1-4242-1200-2(6)***) Fitzgerald Bks.

—Maddie Stands Tall. Cummins, Sarah, tr. from FRE. Gay, Marie-Louise, illus. 2005. (First Novel Ser.). 64p. (J). (gr. 2-5). (***978-0-88780-683-4(X)***); 4.95 (978-0-88780-682-7(1)) Formac Publishing Co., Ltd. CAN. *Dist:* Casemate Pubs. & Bk. Distributors, LLC.

—Maddie's Big Test. Cummins, Sarah, tr. from FRE. Gay, Marie-Louise, illus. 2006. (First Novel Ser.). 64p. (J). (gr. 2-5). (***978-0-88780-718-3(6)***); 4.95 (***978-0-88780-714-5(3)***) Formac Publishing Co., Ltd. CAN. *Dist:* Casemate Pubs. & Bk. Distributors, LLC.

Lee, Kathy. Phoebe Finds Her Feet. 2004. 128p. 6.49 (978-1-85999-701-7(5)) Scripture Union GBR. *Dist:* Gabriel Resources.

Lekich, John. The Losers' Club. 2002. 256p. (YA). (gr. 8 up). pap. 7.95 (978-1-55037-752-1(3)) Annick Pr., Ltd. CAN. *Dist:* Firefly Bks., Ltd.

LeMieux, Anne Connelly. Dare to Be, M. E.! 1998. (J). (gr. 3-7). pap. 3.99 (978-0-380-72889-3(3)) HarperCollins Pubs.

Lenain, Thierry. Little Zizi. Zolinsky, Daniel, tr. from FRE. Poulin, Stephane, illus. 2008. 32p. (J). 16.95 (***978-1-933693-05-7(3)***) Cinco Puntos Pr.

Lenam, Salva. Hoy Empieza la Escuela, Kiko! Roman, Santi, illus. 2005. (Kiko Ser.). (SPA.). 10p. (J). 3.95 (978-84-95761-76-7(9)) Ediciones Norte, Inc.

Leonard, Elise. Monday Morning Blitz. 2007. (Al's World Ser.). 144p. (J). (gr. 5-9). pap. 5.99 (***978-1-4169-3464-6(2)*** , Aladdin) Simon & Schuster Children's Publishing.

Lerangis, Peter. Boo! Ghosts in the School. 2001. (gr. 3-6). lib. bdg. 11.80 (978-0-613-53484-0(0)) Tandem Library Bks.

Leslie, Robyn. Rinny & the Trail of Clues. 2003. Orig. Title: Miss President & the Trail of Clues. (Illus.). 192p. (J). pap. 7.95 (978-0-9727388-8-0(6)) Sugar Ducky Bks., Inc.

Lester, Helen. Hooway for Wodney Wat. Munsinger, Lynn, illus. 2002. (J). 12.83 (978-1-4046-3507-4(6)) Book Wholesalers, Inc.

—Hooway for Wodney Wat. Munsinger, Lynn, illus. 32p. (J). (gr. k-3). 2002. pap. 5.95 (978-0-618-21612-3(X)); 1999. tchr. ed. 16.00 (978-0-395-92392-4(1)) Houghton Mifflin Co. Trade & Reference Div. (Walter Lorraine).

—Hooway for Wodney Wat. 1999. (gr. k-3). lib. bdg. 12.95 (978-0-613-60682-0(5)) Tandem Library Bks.

—Score One for the Sloths. Munsinger, Lynn, illus. 32p. (J). (gr. k-3). 2003. pap. 5.95 (978-0-618-38006-0(X)); 2001. tchr. ed. 16.00 (978-0-618-10857-2(2)) Houghton Mifflin Co. Trade & Reference Div. (Walter Lorraine).

—Score One for the Sloths. 2003. (gr. k-3). lib. bdg. 14.10 (978-0-613-73024-2(0)) Tandem Library Bks.

—Tackylocks & the Three Bears. Munsinger, Lynn, illus. 32p. (J). (gr. k-3). 2004. 5.95 (978-0-618-43953-9(6)); 2002. tchr. ed. 15.00 (978-0-618-22490-6(4)) Houghton Mifflin Co. Trade & Reference Div. (Walter Lorraine).

Lester, Tyler. Welcome to Dyslexic Park. Russell, Diane & Eskola, Toby Alice, illus. l.t. ed. 1999. 25p. (J). 15.00 (978-0-938911-16-6(3)) Individualized Education Systems/Poppy Lane Publishing.

Lesynski, Loris. Night School. 2001. lib. bdg. 14.10 (978-0-613-50352-5(X)) Tandem Library Bks.

Lethcoe, Jason. Amazing Adventures from Zoom's Academy: The Capture of the Crimson Cape. 2006. (Illus.). 144p. (J). pap. 12.95 (978-0-345-48356-0(1) , Ballantine Bks.) Random House Publishing Group.

—Zoom's Academy. 2006. (Illus.). 304p. (J). pap. 14.95 (978-0-345-49641-6(8) , Ballantine Bks.) Random House Publishing Group.

Let's Learn All We Can! (Illus.). 24p. (J). 5.95 (978-0-8249-5449-9(1)) Ideals Pubns.

Leuck, Laura. My Creature Teacher. Nash, Scott, illus. 2004. 32p. (J). (ps-1). 15.99 (978-0-06-029694-0(1)) HarperCollins Pubs.

Levchuk, Lisa. Everything Beautiful in the World. 2008. (YA). (***978-0-374-32238-0(4)***) Farrar, Straus & Giroux.

Levine, Gail Carson. The Wish. 2005. 256p. (J). (gr. 7 up). pap. 6.50 (978-0-06-075911-7(9) , Harper Trophy) HarperCollins Pubs.

—The Wish. 2001. (gr. 3-6). lib. bdg. 14.15 (978-0-613-44274-9(1)); 2000. (978-0-606-22297-6(9)) Tandem Library Bks.

Levithan, David. Realm of Possibility. 2006. 224p. (YA). (gr. 7). reprint ed. pap. 8.95 (978-0-375-83657-2(8) , Knopf Bks. for Young Readers) Random Hse. Children's Bks.

Levitin, Sonia. Dream Freedom. 2000. 192p. (YA). (gr. 4-7). 17.00 (978-0-15-202404-8(2) , Silver Whistle) Harcourt Trade Pubs.

Levy, Elizabeth. The Creepy Computer Mystery. Brunkus, Denise, illus. 2004. 48p. (J). lib. bdg. 15.00 (978-1-59054-534-8(6)) Fitzgerald Bks.

—A Hare-Raising Tale: A Fletcher Mystery. Gorstein, Mordicai, illus. unabr. ed. 2006. (First Chapter Bks.). (J). (gr. 2-4). pap. 17.95 incl. audio (***978-1-59519-704-7(4)***); pap. 20.95 incl. audio compact disk (***978-1-59519-705-4(2)***) Live Oak Media.

—My Life As a Fifth-Grade Comedian. 1998. 192p. (J). (ps-7). pap. 5.99 (978-0-06-440723-6(3) , Harper Trophy) HarperCollins Pubs.

—My Life As a Fifth-Grade Comedian. 1999. (J). pap., stu. ed. 41.20 incl. audio (978-0-7887-3180-8(7) , 40915) Recorded Bks., LLC.

—Parents' Night Fright. Brunkus, Denise, illus. 1998. (Hello Reader! Ser.). (J). (gr. 2-4). pap. 3.99 (978-0-590-60324-9(8)) Scholastic, Inc.

—Seventh-Grade Tango. 2001. (J). (978-0-606-22571-7(4)) Tandem Library Bks.

—Seventh-Grade Tango. l.t. ed. 2001. (Illus.). 174p. (J). (gr. 3-7). 20.95 (978-0-7862-3105-8(X)) Thorndike Pr.

—The Snack Attack Mystery. Brunkus, Denise, illus. 2004. 48p. (J). lib. bdg. 15.00 (978-1-59054-533-1(8)) Fitzgerald Bks.

—Tackling Dad. 2005. 144p. (J). 16.89 (978-0-06-000050-9(3)); 15.99 (978-0-06-000051-6(1)) HarperCollins Pubs.

Lewin, Betsy. Wiley Learns to Spell. Lewin, Betsy, illus. 1998. (Hello Reader! Ser.). (Illus.). 32p. (J). (ps-1). pap. 3.99 (978-0-590-10835-5(2)) Scholastic, Inc.

—Wiley Learns to Spell. 1998. (Hello Reader! Ser.). (J). (978-0-606-13916-8(8)) Tandem Library Bks.

Lewis, Beverly. Best Friend, Worst Enemy. rev. ed. 2001. (Holly's Heart Ser.: Bk. 1). 160p. (YA). (gr. 6-9). pap. 6.99 (978-0-7642-2500-0(6)) Bethany Hse. Pubs.

—Freshman Frenzy. 2003. (Holly's Heart Ser.: Bk. 11). (Illus.). 160p. (YA). pap. 6.99 (978-0-7642-2618-2(5)) Bethany Hse. Pubs.

—It's a Girl Thing. 2003. (Holly's Heart Ser.: Bk. 14). 160p. (Orig.). (YA). pap. 6.99 (978-0-7642-2621-2(5)) Bethany Hse. Pubs.

—It's a Girl Thing. 2003. (Holly's Heart Ser.: Bk. 14). (Orig.). (gr. 5-8). lib. bdg. 14.15 (978-0-613-87241-6(X)) Tandem Library Bks.

—Mystery Letters. 2003. (Holly's Heart Ser.: Bk. 12). (Illus.). 160p. (YA). reprint ed. pap. 6.99 (978-0-7642-2619-9(3)) Bethany Hse. Pubs.

—Straight-A Teacher. 2002. (Holly's Heart Ser.: Bk. 8). 160p. (YA). pap. 6.99 (978-0-7642-2615-1(0)) Bethany Hse. Pubs.

—The Upside-Down Day. 2001. (Cul-de-Sac Kids Ser.: Vol. 23). (Illus.). 80p. (J). (gr. 2-5). reprint ed. pap. 3.99 (978-0-7642-2128-6(0)) Bethany Hse. Pubs.

Lewis, Doreen. The Bubblegum Babes' Guide to Sixth Grade. 2005. (J). per. 9.95 (978-0-9769193-0-8(3)) Helm Publishing.

Lewis, Jill. A Mom in a Million. Gulbis, Stephen, illus. 2005. 32p. (J). (978-1-84458-368-3(6)) Chrysalis Children's Bks.

Lewis, Jody M. Finding April Hollow. 2006. per. 15.00 (978-0-9772115-1-7(7) , WCP) White Canoe Productions.

Lewis, Maggie. Morgy Makes His Move. Chesworth, Michael, illus. 80p. (J). 2002. (gr. 1-4). pap. 4.95 (978-0-618-19680-7(3)); 1999. (gr. 4-6). tchr. ed. 15.00 (978-0-395-92284-2(4)) Houghton Mifflin Co. Trade & Reference Div.

—Morgy Makes His Move. 1999. (gr. 3-6). lib. bdg. 12.95 (978-0-613-60698-1(1)) Tandem Library Bks.

Lewman, David. Classroom Crack-ups! 2006. (SpongeBob SquarePants Ser.). (Illus.). 48p. (J). pap. 3.99 (978-1-4169-2468-5(X) , Simon Spotlight) Simon & Schuster Children's Publishing.

S

Liberto, Lorenzo. Matt the Rat & His Magic Cloud / Raton Mateo y Su Nube Magica: A Day at School / un Dia de Escuela. Gomez, Rocio, ed. Torres, Irving, illus. 2003. (Matt the Rat Ser. / La Serie de Raton Mateo). (ENG & SPA.). 32p. (J). lib. bdg. 20.00 (978-0-9743668-0-7(3)) Harvest Sun Pr., LLC.

Limb, Sue. Girl, 15, Charming but Insane. 2004. (Girl, 15 Ser.). 214p. (J). (gr. 5). per. 16.00 (978-0-606-33729-8(6)) Tandem Library Bks.

—Girl 15, Charming but Insane. 2007. (Girl, 15 Ser.). 224p. (YA). (gr. 7-11). mass mkt. 5.99 (978-0-440-23896-6(X), Laurel Leaf) Random Hse. Children's Bks.

—Girl, Going on 17: Pants on Fire. (Girl, 15 Ser.). (gr. 5 up). 2007. 256p. (YA). pap. 8.99 (*978-0-385-73219-2(8)); 2006. 240p. (J). 14.95 (978-0-385-73218-5(X)); 2006. 240p. (YA). lib. bdg. 17.99 (978-0-385-90246-5(8)) Random Hse. Children's Bks. (Delacorte Bks. for Young Readers).

Lin, Grace. The Year of the Dog. (Illus.). (J). (gr. 3-7). 2007. 162p. pap. 5.99 (978-0-316-06002-8(X)); 2005. 144p. 14.99 (978-0-316-06000-4(3)) Little Brown & Co.

Lin, Grace. The Year of the Rat. rev. ed. 2008. 208p. (J). (gr. 3-7). 14.99 (*978-0-316-11426-4(X)) Little, Brown Bks. for Young Readers.

Lindgren, Astrid. Pippi Goes to School. 1999. (Pippi Longstocking Storybooks). (Illus.). 64p. (J). (gr. k-2). pap. 5.99 (978-0-14-130236-2(4), Puffin) Penguin Group (USA) Inc.

—Pippi Goes to School. 1999. (J). (gr. k-3). lib. bdg. 14.15 (978-0-613-22923-4(1)) Tandem Library Bks.

Lindquist, N. J. Best of Friends, 4 vols., Vol. 1. 2nd rev. ed. 2000. (Circle of Friends Ser.: Vol. 1). 192p. (gr. 4-12). pap. (978-0-9685495-1-3(9)) That's Life! Communications.

Lion, Melissa. Swollen. 2006. 192p. (YA). pap. 6.50 (978-0-553-49408-2(2), Laurel Leaf) Random Hse. Children's Bks.

—Upstream. 160p. (YA). (gr. 7). 2006. pap. 8.95 (978-0-375-83954-2(2)); 2005. 15.95 (978-0-385-74643-4(1)) Random Hse. Children's Bks. (Lamb, Wendy).

Lipp, Frederick. Fatima. Lindmark, Margaret, illus. 2006. 32p. (J). pap. (978-1-59336-302-4(8)) Mondo Publishing.

Literature Connections English: Nothing but the Truth. 2004. (gr. 6-12). (978-0-395-77536-3(1), 2-80105) McDougal Littell Inc.

Little, Jean. Emma's Magic Winter. Plecas, Jennifer, illus. (I Can Read Bks.). 64p. (J). (ps-3). 2000. pap. 3.99 (978-0-06-443706-6(X), Harper Trophy); 1998. 15.95 (978-0-06-025389-9(4)); 1998. 15.89 (978-0-06-025390-5(8)) HarperCollins Pubs.

—Emma's Magic Winter. 2000. (gr. k-3). lib. bdg. 11.80 (978-0-613-27805-8(4)) Tandem Library Bks.

Little Tiger Goes to School. 1999. (Illus.). 8p. (J). 9.99 (978-1-58048-083-3(7)) Sandvik Publishing.

The Littles Go to School. 2002. (Littles Ser.). (Illus.). (J). 12.17 (978-0-7587-4769-3(1)) Book Wholesalers, Inc.

Littlesugar, Amy. Freedom School, Yes! Cooper, Floyd, illus. 2001. 1p. (J). (ps-3). 16.99 (978-0-399-23006-6(8), Philomel) Penguin Group (USA) Inc.

Lockhart, E. The Boy Book: A Study of Habits & Behaviors, Plus Techniques for Taming Them. (YA). (gr. 7). 2008. 224p. pap. 8.99 (*978-0-385-73209-3(0)); 2006. 208p. 15.95 (978-0-385-73208-6(2)); 2006. 208p. 17.99 (978-0-385-90239-7(5)) Random Hse. Children's Bks. (Delacorte Bks. for Young Readers).

—The Boyfriend List. 2006. 256p. (YA). (gr. 7). reprint ed. pap. 8.95 (978-0-385-73207-9(4), Delacorte Bks. for Young Readers) Random Hse. Children's Bks.

—Dramarama. 2007. 320p. (gr. 7 up). 15.99 (978-0-7868-3815-8(9)) Hyperion Bks. for Children.

—Fly on the Wall. 2007. 192p. (YA). (gr. 7). pap. 8.99 (*978-0-385-73282-6(1), Delacorte Bks. for Young Readers) Random Hse. Children's Bks.

Lockhart, E. Fly on the Wall: How One Girl Saw Everything. 2006. 192p. (YA). (gr. 7). 15.95 (978-0-385-73281-9(3)); lib. bdg. 17.99 (978-0-385-90299-1(9)) Random Hse. Children's Bks. (Delacorte Bks. for Young Readers).

Loehr, Patrick, illus. Mucumber McGee & the Lunch Lady's Liver. 2008. (J). (*978-0-06-082330-6(5)); lib. bdg. (*978-0-06-082331-3(3)) HarperCollins Pubs.

Lombard, Jenny. Drita, My Homegirl. (J). (gr. 4-6). 2008. 144p. pap. 5.99 (*978-0-14-240905-3(7), Puffin); 2006. 176p. 15.99 (978-0-399-24380-6(1), Putnam Juvenile) Penguin Group (USA) Inc.

Lonczak, Heather Suzanne. Mookey the Monkey Gets over Being Teased. Ramsey, Marcy Dunn, illus. 2006. 32p. (J). (gr. k-2). 14.95 (978-1-59147-479-1(5)); pap. 8.95 (978-1-59147-480-7(9)) American Psychological Assn. (Magination Pr.).

London, Jonathan. Froggy Goes to School. Remkiewicz, Frank, illus. 1998. 32p. (J). (ps-1). pap. 5.99 (978-0-14-056247-7(8), Puffin) Penguin Group (USA) Inc.

—Shawn & Keeper: Show & Tell. 2000. (Puffin Easy-to-Read Ser.). (978-0-606-18450-2(3)) Tandem Library Bks.

Longstreet, Barbara, et al. Woodsey School Kids Thanksgiving Feast. 2004. 28p. pap. 14.95 (978-1-4137-1992-5(9)) PublishAmerica, Inc.

Look, Lenore. Ruby Lu, Brave & True. 2004. (Illus.). 104p. (J). lib. bdg. 15.00 (*978-1-4242-0914-9(5)) Fitzgerald Bks.

—Ruby Lu, Brave & True. Wilsdorf, Anne, illus. 2006. (Ready-for-Chapters Ser.). 112p. (J). pap. 3.99 (978-1-4169-1389-4(0), Aladdin) Simon & Schuster Children's Publishing.

Look, Lenore & Wilsdorf, Anne. Ruby Lu, Brave & True. 2004. (Illus.). 176p. (J). (gr. 1-2). 15.95 (978-0-689-84907-7(9), Atheneum/Anne Schwartz Bks.) Simon & Schuster Children's Publishing.

Losier, Dave. Fred's Prayer Machine. 2002. (Illus.). 152p. (J). pap. 11.95 (978-1-929039-07-4(7)) Ambassador Bks., Inc.

Lottridge, Celia B. Wings to Fly. 2007. 144p. (J). pap. 8.95 (*978-0-88899-844-6(9)) Groundwood Bks. CAN. *Dist:* Perseus Distribution.

Love, D. Anne. A Little Rebellion. 2008. 272p. (YA). 16.99 (*978-1-4169-3481-3(2), McElderry, Margaret K.) Simon & Schuster Children's Publishing.

—Picture Perfect. 2007. (YA). 304p. (gr. 7 up). 16.99 (978-0-689-87390-4(5)); 291p. (*978-1-4287-3275-9(6)) Simon & Schuster Children's Publishing. (McElderry, Margaret K.).

—Semiprecious. 2006. 304p. (J). (gr. 5-9). 16.95 (978-0-689-85638-9(5), McElderry, Margaret K.) Simon & Schuster Children's Publishing.

Lowry, Lois. Gooney Bird & the Room Mother. Thomas, Middy Chilman, illus. 2005. 80p. (J). (gr. 3-5). 15.00 (978-0-618-53230-8(7), Walter Lorraine) Houghton Mifflin Co. Trade & Reference Div.

—Gooney Bird & the Room Mother. 2006. 80p. (J). (gr. 2-5). 5.50 (978-0-440-42133-7(0), Yearling) Random Hse. Children's Bks.

—Gooney Bird Greene. Thomas, Middy Chilman, illus. 2002. 96p. (J). (gr. 3-5). tchr. ed. 15.00 (978-0-618-23848-4(4), Walter Lorraine) Houghton Mifflin Co. Trade & Reference Div.

—Gooney Bird Greene. 2004. (Illus.). 96p. (J). (gr. 2-5). reprint ed. pap. 5.50 (978-0-440-41960-0(3), Yearling) Random Hse. Children's Bks.

—Gooney Bird Greene. 2004. (gr. 3-6). lib. bdg. 13.55 (978-0-613-82980-9(8)) Tandem Library Bks.

—Gooney the Fabulous. Thomas, Middy, illus. 2007. 96p. (J). (gr. 2-5). 15.00 (978-0-618-76691-8(X), Walter Lorraine) Houghton Mifflin Co. Trade & Reference Div.

—Zooman Sam. 2002. (J). (gr. 4-6). 20.25 (978-0-8446-7223-6(8)) Smith, Peter Pub., Inc.

—Zooman Sam. 2001. (gr. 3-6). lib. bdg. 13.00 (978-0-613-35480-6(X)); (Illus.). (J). (978-0-606-21544-2(1)) Tandem Library Bks.

Lubar, David. Hidden Talents. 2007. 240p. (J). 2.99 (978-0-7653-5766-3(6), Starscape) Doherty, Tom Assocs., LLC.

—Hidden Talents Sequel. 2008. 320p. (J). 5.99 (978-0-7653-4856-2(X), Tor Bks.) Doherty, Tom Assocs., LLC.

—Sleeping Freshmen Never Lie. (YA). 2007. 288p. pap. 6.99 (978-0-14-240780-6(1), Puffin); 2005. 160p. (gr. 6-10). 16.99 (978-0-525-47311-4(4), Dutton Juvenile) Penguin Group (USA) Inc.

—Wizards of the Game. 2004. 176p. (J). (gr. 5). pap. 5.99 (978-0-14-240215-3(X), Puffin) Penguin Group (USA) Inc.

Lucas, Sally & Lucas, Margeaux. Dancing Dinos Go to School. 2006. (Step into Reading Ser.). (Illus.). 32p. (J). (ps-1). lib. bdg. 11.99 (978-0-375-93241-0(0)); pap. 3.99 (978-0-375-83241-3(6)) Random Hse. Children's Bks. (Random Hse. Bks. for Young Readers).

Luddy, Karon. Spelldown: The Big-Time Dreams of a Small-Town Word Whiz. 2007. 224p. (YA). 15.99 (978-1-4169-1610-9(5)) Simon & Schuster Children's Publishing.

Ludwig, Trudy. Big Mouth. Prevost, Mikela, illus. 2007. (J). (*978-1-58246-240-0(2), Tricycle Pr.) Ten Speed Pr.

Ludwig, Trudy. Just Kidding. Gustavson, Adam, illus. 2006. 32p. (J). 15.95 (978-1-58246-163-2(5), Tricycle Pr.) Ten Speed Pr.

Ludwig Trudy. Solo Bromeando. Gustavson Adam, illus. 2006. (SPA.). 32p. 15.95 (978-1-58246-177-9(5), Tricycle Pr.) Ten Speed Pr.

Lunsford, Susie. The Magical Wishing Well Forest Series. 2006. pap. 25.32 (*978-1-4134-9491-4(9)) Xlibris Corp.

Lupica, Mike. Travel Team. 2004. 288p. (YA). (gr. 3-8). 16.99 (978-0-399-24150-5(7), Philomel) Penguin Group (USA) Inc.

—Travel Team. l.t. ed. 2005. 400p. (J). (ps-7). lib. bdg. 23.95 (978-0-7862-7415-4(8)) Thorndike Pr.

Lutz, Nancie Anne. Patsy Ann Back Again. Lutz, Nancie Anne, illus. 2005. (Illus.). 25p. (J). pap. 14.50 (978-0-9760064-0-4(5)) Dollworks.

Luzzatto, Caroline. Interplanetary Avenger. 2005. (Illus.). 128p. (J). (gr. 3-7). 16.95 (978-0-8234-1933-3(9)) Holiday Hse., Inc.

Lyga, Barry. The Astonishing Adventures of Fanboy & Goth Girl. 2006. 320p. (YA). (gr. 8). 16.95 (978-0-618-72392-8(7)) Houghton Mifflin Co.

—The Astonishing Adventures of Fanboy & Goth Girl. 2007. 320p. (YA). (gr. 9-12). pap. 8.99 (*978-0-618-91652-8(0)) Houghton Mifflin Co. Trade & Reference Div.

—Boy Toy. 2007. 416p. (YA). (gr. 7). 16.95 (*978-0-618-72393-5(5)) Houghton Mifflin Co.

Lynch, Chris. Extreme Elvin. 1999. 240p. (YA). (gr. 7 up). 15.95 (978-0-06-028040-6(9)) HarperCollins Pubs.

—Gold Dust. 2002. 208p. (J). (gr. 5 up). pap. 7.99 (978-0-06-447201-2(9)) HarperCollins Pubs.

—Gold Dust. 2002. (gr. 5-8). lib. bdg. 14.10 (978-0-613-67089-0(2)) Tandem Library Bks.

—Inexcusable. 176p. (YA). 2007. (gr. 9 up). pap. 6.99 (978-1-4169-3972-6(5), Simon Pulse); 2005. (Illus.). (gr. 7 up). 16.95 (978-0-689-84789-9(0), Atheneum) Simon & Schuster Children's Publishing.

—Inexcusable. l.t. ed. 2006. 180p. (YA). 22.95 (978-0-7862-8812-0(4)) Thorndike Pr.

—Sins of the Fathers. 2006. 240p. (J). lib. bdg. 17.89 (978-0-06-074038-2(8), HarperTeen) HarperCollins Pubs.

—Who the Man. 2002. 192p. (J). (gr. 5 up). 15.99 (978-0-06-623938-5(9)) HarperCollins Pubs.

—Who the Man. 2004. (gr. 5-8). lib. bdg. 14.15 (978-0-613-81982-4(9)) Tandem Library Bks.

Lynch, Janet Nichols. Peace Is a Four-Letter Word. 2005. 168p. (YA). pap. 9.95 (978-1-59714-014-0(7), Great Valley Bks.) Heyday Bks.

Lynn, Tracy. Rx. 2005. 272p. (YA). pap. 7.99 (978-1-4169-1155-5(3), Simon Pulse) Simon & Schuster Children's Publishing.

MacBride, Roger Lea. Missouri School Days. Ettlinger, Doris, illus. 2001. (Little House Chapter Bks.). 80p. (J). (gr. 2-5). 14.89 (978-0-06-028555-5(9)); pap. 4.25 (978-0-06-442110-2(4), Harper Trophy) HarperCollins Pubs.

Maccarone, Grace. First Grade Friends: Softball Practice. Lewin, Betsy, illus. 2002. (Hello Reader! Ser.). 32p. (J). (ps-1). pap. 3.99 (978-0-439-20139-1(X), Cartwheel Bks.) Scholastic, Inc.

—Graduation Day Is Here! Brown, Rick, illus. 2006. (Scholastic Reader Ser.). 32p. (J). pap. 3.99 (978-0-439-83298-4(5), Cartwheel Bks.) Scholastic, Inc.

—I See a Leaf. 2002. lib. bdg. 11.80 (978-0-613-63549-3(3)) Tandem Library Bks.

—Mr. Rover Takes Over. 2001. (Illus.). (J). (978-0-606-21338-7(4)); 2000. lib. bdg. 11.80 (978-0-613-35537-7(7)) Tandem Library Bks.

Maccarone, Grace & Pick, Alayne. I See a Leaf. Freeman, Laura, illus. 2002. (Hello Reader! Ser.). 32p. (J). pap. 3.99 (978-0-439-33016-9(5), Cartwheel Bks.) Scholastic, Inc.

Maccarrone, Betsy. First-Grade Friends: The Class Trip. 1999. (Hello Reader! Ser.). (Illus.). (J). 10.79 (978-0-606-18543-1(7)) Tandem Library Bks.

MacCready, Robin. Buried. 2006. 208p. (YA). (gr. 9). 16.99 (978-0-525-47724-2(1), Dutton Juvenile) Penguin Group (USA) Inc.

MacDonald, Alan. High Five Hank. Dupasquier, Philippe, illus. 2006. (Read-It! Chapter Books). 48p. (J). lib. bdg. (*978-1-4048-3121-6(5), 1265808) Picture Window Bks.

MacDonald, Marianne. Secondhand Star. Christelow, Eileen, illus. 1998. (Lots of O'Leary's Ser.). (978-0-606-13769-0(6)) Tandem Library Bks.

MacDowell, Maureen. Tomorrow Is the First Day of School. Hergenrother, Max, illus. 2007. 32p. (J). 15.95 (*978-0-9791463-0-5(5)) Wading River Bks., LLC.

Mackall, Dandi. Larger-Than-Life Lara. 2006. 195p. (J). (gr. 5). 16.99 (978-0-525-47726-6(8), Dutton Juvenile) Penguin Group (USA) Inc.

Mackall, Dandi Daley. Crazy in Love. 2008. 240p. (YA). (gr. 7). pap. 6.99 (*978-0-14-241157-5(4), Puffin) Penguin Group (USA) Inc.

MacKall, Dandi Daley. First Day. Beeke, Tiphanie, illus. 2003. 32p. (J). 16.00 (978-0-15-216577-2(0), Silver Whistle) Harcourt Trade Pubs.

Mackall, Dandi Daley. Grace Notes. 2006. (Faithgirlz Ser.). (Illus.). 128p. (J). pap. 6.99 (978-0-310-71093-6(6)) Zonderkidz.

—Grace under Pressure. 2007. (Faithgirlz!#8482; / Blog On! Ser.). 128p. (J). pap. 6.99 (978-0-310-71263-3(7)) Zonderkidz.

MacKall, Dandi Daley. Kyra's Story. 2003. (gr. 7-12). lib. bdg. 18.80 (978-0-613-76717-0(9)) Tandem Library Bks.

—Kyra's Story. 2003. (Degrees of Guilt Ser.). (YA). pap. 9.99 (978-0-8423-8284-7(4)) Tyndale Hse. Pubs.

—The Presidential Mystery. 1999. (Cinnamon Lake Mysteries Ser.: Vol. 8). 80p. (J). (ps-2). 5.99 (978-0-570-05354-5(4), 12-3405GJ) Concordia Publishing Hse.

Mackall, Dandi Daley. Storm Rising Bk. 4: Blog On! 2006. (Faithgirlz Ser.). (Illus.). 128p. (J). pap. 6.99 (978-0-310-71096-7(0)) Zonderkidz.

—Upsetting Annie. 2007. (Faithgirlz!#8482; / Blog On! Ser.). 128p. (J). pap. 6.99 (978-0-310-71264-0(5)) Zonderkidz.

Mackel, Kathy. Can of Worms. 2000. (Illus.). (J). 10.64 (978-0-606-17962-1(3)); 1999. (gr. 3-6). lib. bdg. 11.80 (978-0-613-23590-7(8)) Tandem Library Bks.

—Eggs in One Basket. (J). 2002. 208p. pap. 6.99 (978-0-380-81399-5(8)); 2000. (Illus.). 195p. (gr. 5-7). 15.95 (978-0-380-97847-2(4)) HarperCollins Pubs.

—From the Horse's Mouth. 2002. 224p. (J). (gr. 3-7). 15.95 (978-0-06-029414-4(0)) HarperCollins Pubs.

Mackey, Weezie Kerr. Throwing a Like Girl. 2007. 272p. (J). (gr. 7 up). 16.99 (*978-0-7614-5342-0(3)) Cavendish, Marshall Corp.

Mackler, Carolyn. The Earth, My Butt & Other Big Round Things. 2003. (Illus.). 256p. (YA). (gr. 9). 15.99 (978-0-7636-1958-9(2)) Candlewick Pr.

—The Earth, My Butt, & Other Big Round Things. 2005. 256p. (YA). (gr. 9 up). reprint ed. pap. 8.99 (978-0-7636-2091-2(2)) Candlewick Pr.

—Vegan Virgin Valentine. 240p. (YA). (gr. 9 up). 2004. (Illus.). 16.99 (978-0-7636-2155-1(2)); 2006. reprint ed. pap. 8.99 (978-0-7636-2613-6(9)) Candlewick Pr.

MacLellan, Erin. Run from the Nun! 2003. 128p. (J). (gr. 4-6). tchr. ed. 16.95 (978-0-8234-1796-4(4)) Holiday Hse., Inc.

MacLeod, Doug. I'm Being Stalked by a Moonshadow. 2007. 212p. (YA). (gr. 8 up). 16.95 (*978-1-59078-501-0(0), Front Street) Boyds Mills Pr.

Madison, Alan. Velma Gratch & the Way Cool Butterfly. Hawkes, Kevin, illus. 2007. 40p. (J). (ps-3). 16.99 (*978-0-375-83597-1(0)); lib. bdg. 19.99 (*978-0-375-93597-8(5)) Random Hse. Children's Bks. (Schwartz & Wade Bks.).

—Velma Gratch & the Way Cool Butterfly. Hawkes, Kevin, illus. 2007. (J). (978-0-689-86921-1(5), Atheneum) Simon & Schuster Children's Publishing.

Madison, Deborah L. A Slimy Frog Who Went to School. 1999. (J). (gr. k-3). pap. 5.95 (978-0-533-13013-9(1)) Vantage Pr., Inc.

Madonna. The English Roses, Too Good to be True. 2006. (Illus.). 64p. (J). (ps-6). 19.95 (978-0-670-06147-1(6)) Callaway Editions, Inc.

Maggiore, Dominick. Dominick's School Bus. 2007. 34p. pap. 7.95 (*978-0-533-15671-9(8)) Vantage Pr., Inc.

Magnus, Kellie. Little Lion Goes to School. Robinson, Michael, illus. l.t. ed. 2003. 16p. (J). 9.99 (978-0-9744211-0-0(3)) Media Magic New York.

Maguire, Gregory. A Couple of April Fools. Clayton, Elaine, illus. 2004. (Hamlet Chronicles Ser.). 192p. (J). (gr. 3-5). tchr. ed. 16.00 (978-0-618-27474-1(X), Clarion Bks.) Houghton Mifflin Co. Trade & Reference Div.

—Four Stupid Cupids. Clayton, Elaine, illus. 2001. 192p. (J). (gr. 4-6). tchr. ed. 16.00 (978-0-395-83895-2(9), Clarion Bks.) Houghton Mifflin Co. Trade & Reference Div.

—Four Stupid Cupids. 2002. (gr. 3-6). lib. bdg. 12.95 (978-0-613-43035-7(2)) Tandem Library Bks.

—Four Stupid Cupids. l.t. ed. 2001. 225p. (J). 21.95 (978-0-7862-3547-6(0)) Thorndike Pr.

—One Final Firecracker. 2007. (Hamlet Chronicles Ser.). 320p. (J). pap. 6.99 (*978-0-06-085284-9(4), Harper Trophy) HarperCollins Pubs.

—One Final Firecracker. Clayton, Elaine, illus. 2005. 240p. (J). (gr. 4-6). 17.00 (978-0-618-27480-2(4), Clarion Bks.) Houghton Mifflin Co. Trade & Reference Div.

—Seven Spiders Spinning: Y Gregory Maguire. l.t. ed. 2002. (J). 21.95 (978-0-7862-4419-5(4)) Thorndike Pr.

—Three Rotten Eggs. Clayton, Elaine, illus. 2002. 192p. (J). (gr. 4-6). 16.00 (978-0-618-09655-8(8), Clarion Bks.) Houghton Mifflin Co. Trade & Reference Div.

—Three Rotten Eggs. l.t. ed. 2005. 281p. 20.95 (978-0-7862-7276-1(7), Large Print Pr.) Thorndike Pr.

Mahony, Mary. Harry Scores A Hat Trick, Pawns, Pucks, & Scoliosis: The Sequel to Stand Tall, Harry. Pasternack, Susan, ed. Larkin, Catherine, illus. 2003. 130p. (YA). (gr. 5-8). per. 14.95 (978-0-9658879-4-6(4)) Redding Pr.

Mahy, Margaret. The Horribly Haunted School. unabr. ed. 1998. (J). pap. 24.95 incl. audio (978-0-7540-6207-3(4)) BBC Audiobooks America.

Malcolm, Jahnna N. Who Framed Mary Bubnik? Mary's Not a Thief or Is She? 2001. (Bad News Ballet Ser.: Vol. 4). Tr. of Quien veut a Mary Bubnik?. 160p. (J). (gr. 4-6). pap. 3.95 (978-0-9700164-3-0(3)) Starcatcher Pr.

Mammay, Judith. It's Time. Fargo, Todd, illus. l.t. ed. 2007. 32p. (J). pap. 9.95 (*978-0-944727-20-1(4)); lib. bdg. 15.95 (*978-0-944727-21-8(2)) Jason & Nordic Pubs. (Turtle Bks.).

—Knowing Joseph. 2008. (Illus.). 256p. (YA). (gr. 2-7). 16.95 (*978-1-933831-05-3(7)) Blooming Tree Pr.

Mangum, Kay Lynn. When the Bough Breaks. 2007. 352p. (YA). pap. 15.95 (*978-1-59038-748-1(1)) Deseret Bk. Co.

Mantell, Paul. Mountain Bike Mania. 2007. 148p. (J). lib. bdg. (*978-1-59953-108-3(9)) Norwood Hse. Pr.

The Marble Patch: Individual Title Six-Packs. 16p. (gr. 2 up). 35.00 (978-0-7635-9239-4(0)) Rigby Education.

Marchetta, Melina. Looking for Alibrandi. 2006. 320p. (YA). (gr. 7). lib. bdg. 17.99 (978-0-375-93694-4(7)); reprint ed. pap. 8.95 (978-0-375-83694-7(2)) Random Hse. Children's Bks. (Knopf Bks. for Young Readers).

—Looking for Alibrandi. 1999. 256p. (YA). (gr. 7-12). pap. 16.95 (978-0-531-30142-5(7)); lib. bdg. 17.99 (978-0-531-33142-2(3)) Scholastic, Inc. (Orchard Bks.).

—Saving Francesca. 256p. (gr. 7). 2004. (J). lib. bdg. 17.99 (978-0-375-92982-3(7)); 2004. (YA). 15.95 (978-0-375-82982-6(2)); 2006. (YA). reprint ed. pap. 8.95 (978-0-375-82983-3(0)) Random Hse. Children's Bks. (Knopf Bks. for Young Readers).

—Saving Francesca. l.t. ed. 2005. 343p. 22.95 (978-0-7862-7309-6(7), Large Print Pr.) Thorndike Pr.

Marcus, Leonard S. & Schwartz, Amy. Oscar: The Big Adventure of a Little Sock Monkey. Schwartz, Amy, illus. 2006. (Illus.). 32p. (J). 16.99 (978-0-06-072622-5(9), Tegen, Katherine Bks); lib. bdg. 17.89 (978-0-06-072623-2(7)) HarperCollins Pubs.

Margulies, Teddy Slater. Show-and-Tell Surprise. 2001. (ps-2). lib. bdg. 11.80 (978-0-613-33054-1(4)) Tandem Library Bks.

Margulies, Teddy Slater & Bridwell, Norman. Clifford & the Show-and-tell Surprise. Studio Orlando Staff, illus. 2001. (Clifford, the Big Red Dog Ser.). 32p. (J). (gr. k-2). pap. 3.99 (978-0-439-21359-2(2)) Scholastic, Inc.

Marineau, Michele. Lean Mean Machines. Ouriou, Susan, tr. from FRE. 2004. (Northern Lights Books for Children Ser.). (Illus.). 128p. (YA). (gr. 4-9). pap. 7.95 (978-0-88995-230-0(2)) Red Deer Pr. CAN. *Dist:* Fitzhenry & Whiteside, Ltd.

—Lean Mean Machines. 2001. (gr. 7-12). lib. bdg. 16.40 (978-0-613-82356-2(7)) Tandem Library Bks.

Marino, Peter. Dough Boy. 176p. (YA). (gr. 7-12). 16.95 (978-0-8234-1873-2(1)) Holiday Hse., Inc.

Marlow, Herb. The Classroom Vandal. 2003. (J). 19.95 (978-1-893595-36-1(6)) Four Seasons Bks., Inc.

Marsden, Carolyn. Bird Springs. 2007. 128p. (J). (gr. 3 up). 14.99 (978-0-670-06193-8(X), Viking Juvenile) Penguin Group (USA) Inc.

—The Quail Club. 2006. 144p. (J). (gr. 3-5). 15.99 (978-0-7636-2635-8(X)) Candlewick Pr.

Marsh, Carole. To the Eight Wonders of the World. 2007. 128p. pap. 5.99 (*978-0-635-06335-9(2)) Gallopade International.

—To the Planet Mars! 2007. 128p. pap. 5.99 (*978-0-635-06336-6(0)) Gallopade International.

Marshall, Catherine. Stage Fright/Goodbye, Sweet Prince/ Brotherly Love. 2005. (Christy Juvenile Ser.). 368p. (J). (gr. 4-7). pap. 9.99 (978-1-4003-0775-3(9)) Nelson, Thomas Inc.

Marshall, James, illus. Miss Nelson Has a Field Day. 2002. (Miss Nelson Ser.). (J). 13.79 (978-0-7587-3145-6(0)) Book Wholesalers, Inc.

Marshall, Rita. I Still Hate to Read! Delessert, Etienne, illus. 2007. (J). (gr. 3 up). (***978-1-56846-174-8(7)*** , Creative Editions) Creative Co., The.

Martin, Ann M. Baby Animal Zoo. Tang, Charles, illus. 1998. (Kids in Ms. Colman's Class Ser.: No. 12). (J). (gr. 1-4). pap. 3.50 (978-0-590-06009-7(0) , Scholastic Paperbacks) Scholastic, Inc.

—Here Today. (J). 2005. 336p. (gr. 5-9). pap. 5.99 (978-0-439-57945-2(7) , Scholastic Paperbacks); 2004. 320p. (gr. 4-7). pap. 16.95 (978-0-439-57944-5(9) , Scholastic Pr.) Scholastic, Inc.

—Karen's Field Day. 1999. (Baby-Sitters Little Sister Ser.: No. 108). 112p. (J). (gr. 3-7). pap. 3.99 (978-0-590-50060-9(0)) Scholastic, Inc.

Martin, Linda. When Dinosaurs Go to School. 2002. (Illus.). 32p. (J). (gr. k-1). pap. 6.95 (978-0-8118-3514-5(6)) Chronicle Bks. LLC.

—When Dinosaurs Go to School. 2002. (ps-2). lib. bdg. 15.25 (978-0-613-51424-8(6)) Tandem Library Bks.

Martínez, Arturo O. Pedrito's World. 2007. (Illus.). 160p. (J). 16.95 (***978-0-89672-600-0(2)*** Texas Tech Univ. Pr.

Marty, Joyce D. I Was in School When...,Dane's Great Day. 2004. (J). 17.00 (978-0-9753992-0-0(9)) Martin Publishing.

Marvin Redpost: Class President. 2002. (Marvin Redpost Ser.). (Illus.). (J). 11.91 (978-0-7587-6195-8(3)) Book Wholesalers, Inc.

Marvin Redpost: Why Pick on Me? 2002. (Marvin Redpost Ser.). (Illus.). (J). 11.91 (978-0-7587-6197-2(X)) Book Wholesalers, Inc.

Mascara. 2002. (SPA.). (J). lib. bdg. 17.95 (978-980-6437-36-4(5)) Playco Editores, C.A.

Masino, Brian & Family, Wayans. Sneaker Madness. 2006. (Thugaboo Ser.). 64p. (J). pap. 4.99 (978-0-439-74598-7(5) , Cartwheel Bks.) Scholastic, Inc.

Mason, Richard. The Red Scarf: A Country Boy's Christmas Story. 2007. 160p. 14.95 (***978-0-87483-850-3(9))*** August Hse. Pubs., Inc.

Mass, Wendy. Heaven Looks a Lot Like the Mall. 2007. 256p. (YA). (gr. 7 up). 16.99 (***978-0-316-05851-3(3))*** Little, Brown Bks. for Young Readers.

—Leap Day. 2006. 224p. (J). (gr. 5-8). pap. 7.99 (978-0-316-05828-5(9)) Little Brown & Co.

—A Mango-Shaped Space. 2005. 240p. (J). (gr. 5-8). pap. 6.99 (978-0-316-05825-4(4)) Little Brown & Co.

Massey, Carol. Not a Friend. 2005. 79p. pap. 9.95 (978-0-7414-2319-1(7)) Infinity Publishing.

Massi, Jeri. Some Through the Fire, 2 vols. 2003. (Great Stories That Teach Eternal Truths Ser.). 496p. pap. 12.99 (978-0-8024-1513-4(X)) Moody Pubs.

Masters, Susan Rowan. The Secret Life of Hubie Hartzel. 2000. 112p. (J). (gr. 4-7). pap. 9.95 (978-0-595-08893-5(7)) iUniverse, Inc.

Matas, Carol. Sparks Fly Upward. 2002. 192p. (YA). (gr. 5-9). 15.00 (978-0-618-15964-2(9) , Clarion Bks.) Houghton Mifflin Co. Trade & Reference Div.

Matas, Carol & Nodelman, Perry. Out of Their Minds. 1998. (Illus.). 192p. (J). (gr. 5-9). 16.00 (978-0-689-81946-9(3)) Simon & Schuster Children's Publishing.

Matlin, Marlee & Cooney, Doug. Leading Ladies. 2007. 288p. (J). (gr. 3-7). 15.99 (***978-0-689-86987-7(8)*** , Simon & Schuster Children's Publishing) Simon & Schuster Children's Publishing.

Matlin, Marlee & Cooney, Doug. Nobody's Perfect. 2006. (Illus.). 240p. (J). (gr. 3-7). 15.95 (978-0-689-86986-0(X) , Simon & Schuster Children's Publishing) Simon & Schuster Children's Publishing.

Matson, Nancy. The Boy Trap. Chesworth, Michael, illus. 1999. 128p. (J). (gr. 3-7). 14.95 (978-0-8126-2663-6(X)) Cricket Bks.

Matt Otra Vez en Problemas! Podra Ayudarlo la Consejera de la Escuela? 2001. 22p. (J). pap. 8.95 (978-0-9713839-2-0(8)) MarLin Bks.

Matthews, L. S. The Outcasts. 2007. 272p. (YA). (gr. 7). 15.99 (***978-0-385-73367-0(4));*** lib. bdg. 18.99 (***978-0-385-90382-0(0))*** Random Hse. Children's Bks. (Delacorte Bks. for Young Readers)

Maude, Rachel. Poseur #1. Compai, illus. 2008. 304p. (J). (gr. 7-17). pap. 9.99 (***978-0-316-06583-2(8)*** , Poppy) Little, Brown Bks. for Young Readers.

Maxwell, Katie. Life, Love, & the Pursuit of Hotties. 2005. 196p. (YA). (gr. 8-12). mass mkt. 5.99 (978-0-8439-5549-1(X)) Dorchester Publishing Co., Inc.

May, Kyla. Introducing Kyla May Miss. Behaves. 2005. (Illus.). 64p. (J). (gr. 4-7). pap. 4.99 (978-0-8431-1370-9(7) , Price Stern Sloan) Penguin Group (USA) Inc.

May, Scott. Sten Gizzle, Time Traveler: The Egyptian Adventure. Farkas, Josh, illus. 2000. 24p. (J). (gr. 1-3). pap. (978-0-9701450-4-8(7)) Long Hill Productions, Inc.

Mayer, Gina. Just a Bully. 1999. (ps-2). lib. bdg. 11.00 (978-0-613-27921-5(2)) Tandem Library Bks.

Mayer, Mercer. Ed-up Morning. 2001. (gr. k-3). lib. bdg. 11.80 (978-0-613-67643-4(2)) Tandem Library Bks.

—Field Day, Vol. 2. 2002. (Little Critter First Readers Ser.). (Illus.). 24p. (J). (gr. k-1). pap. 3.95 (978-1-57768-813-6(9)) School Specialty Publishing.

—Field Day. 2000. (gr. k-3). lib. bdg. 11.80 (978-0-613-67616-8(5)) Tandem Library Bks.

—The Mixed up Morning, Vol. 2. 2002. (Little Critter First Readers Ser.). (Illus.). 24p. (J). (gr. k-1). pap. 3.95 (978-1-57768-808-2(2)) School Specialty Publishing.

—New Fire Truck. 2001. (gr. k-3). lib. bdg. 11.80 (978-0-613-67652-6(1)) Tandem Library Bks.

—The New Fire Truck, Vol. 2. 2002. (Little Critter First Readers Ser.). (Illus.). 24p. (J). (gr. k-1). pap. 3.95 (978-1-57768-843-3(0)) School Specialty Publishing.

—Show & Tell. 2002. (Little Critter First Readers Ser.). (Illus.). 24p. (J). (ps-k). pap. 3.95 (978-1-57768-835-8(X)) School Specialty Publishing.

—Show & Tell. 2001. (gr. k-3). lib. bdg. 11.80 (978-0-613-67668-7(8)) Tandem Library Bks.

Mayfield, Julie. The Magical First Day. Reis, Michael, illus. 1998. (J). pap. 5.95 (978-1-56763-337-5(4)); lib. bdg. 17.25 (978-1-56763-336-8(6)) Ozark Publishing.

Maynard, Joyce. The Cloud Chamber. 288p. (YA). 2006. (gr. 9). pap. 7.99 (978-1-4169-2699-3(2) , Simon Pulse); 2005. (gr. 6-9). 16.95 (978-0-689-87152-8(X) , Atheneum) Simon & Schuster Children's Publishing.

Mazer, Anne. Declaration of Independence. 2000. (Amazing Days of Abby Hayes Ser.: No. 2). (J). 11.64 (978-0-606-19552-2(1)) Tandem Library Bks.

—Good Things Come in Small Packages. 2003. (Amazing Days of Abby Hayes Ser.: No. 12). (Illus.). 112p. mass mkt. 4.99 (978-0-439-48280-6(1) , Scholastic Paperbacks) Scholastic, Inc.

—Good Things Come in Small Packages. 2003. (Amazing Days of Abby Hayes Ser.: No. 12). (gr. 3-6). lib. bdg. 12.40 (978-0-613-72006-9(7)) Tandem Library Bks.

—It's Music to My Ears. 2004. (Amazing Days of Abby Hayes Ser.: No. 14). (Illus.). 110p. (J). lib. bdg. 16.92 (***978-1-4242-0745-9(2))*** Fitzgerald Bks.

—Knowledge Is Power. 2004. (Amazing Days of Abby Hayes Ser.: No. 2). 97p. (J). lib. bdg. 16.92 (***978-1-4242-1198-2(0))*** Fitzgerald Bks.

—Mabel Makes the Grade. 2007. (Sister Magic Ser.). 96p. (J). pap. 3.99 (***978-0-439-87248-5(0)*** , Scholastic Paperbacks) Scholastic, Inc.

—Now You See It, Now You Don't. 2005. (Amazing Days of Abby Hayes Ser.: No. 15). 126p. (J). lib. bdg. 16.92 (***978-1-4242-0751-0(7))*** Fitzgerald Bks.

—Now You See It, Now You Don't. 2005. (Amazing Days of Abby Hayes Ser.: No. 15). (Illus.). 126p. (J). (978-1-4156-0511-0(4)) Scholastic, Inc.

—The Pen Is Mightier Than the Sword. 2001. (Amazing Days of Abby Hayes Ser.: No. 6). (gr. 3-6). lib. bdg. 12.40 (978-0-613-43865-0(5)) Tandem Library Bks.

Mazer, Anne. That's the Way the Cookie Crumbles. 2005. (Amazing Days of Abby Hayes Ser.: No. 16). 119p. (J). lib. bdg. 16.92 (***978-1-4242-0748-0(7))*** Fitzgerald Bks.

Mazer, Norma Fox. Crazy Fish. 2007. (Illus.). 160p. (J). pap. 5.95 (***978-0-15-206373-3(0)*** , Harcourt Paperbacks) Harcourt Children's Bks.

—Crazy Fish. (J). 1999. 160p. (gr. 4-7). pap. 4.50 (978-0-380-73189-3(4) , Harper Trophy); 1998. 192p. (gr. 5-9). 15.00 (978-0-688-16281-8(9)) HarperCollins Pubs.

—Crazy Fish. 1999. (J). (978-0-606-16339-2(5)) Tandem Library Bks.

Mazer, Norma Fox. Ten Ways to Make My Sister Disappear. 2007. (J). (***978-0-439-83984-6(X));*** 160p. (gr. 4-7). pap. 16.99 (***978-0-439-83983-9(1))*** Scholastic, Inc. (Levine, Arthur A. Bks.).

McAllister, Peter. Bites: Dracula Tooth: Beware Pains in the Neck! rev. ed. 2008. (Nibbles, Bites, & Chomps: Ser.). (Illus.). 112p. (J). pap. 3.95 (***978-0-7624-3055-0(9)*** , Running Pr. Kids) Running Pr. Bk. Pubs.

McBratney, Sam. Jimmy Zest, Super Pest. l.t. ed. 2005. (J). pap. (978-0-7540-7888-3(4) , CLP 461) BBC Audio.

—Jimmy Zest, Super Pest. 2004. (J). pap. 24.95 incl. audio (978-0-7540-6278-3(3) , Chivers Children's Audio Bks.) BBC Audiobooks America.

McBrier, Page. Beatrice's Goat. Lohstoeter, Lori, illus. 40p. (J). (ps-3). 2001. 17.99 (978-0-689-82460-9(2) , Atheneum); 2004. reprint ed. 7.99 (978-0-689-86990-7(8) , Aladdin) Simon & Schuster Children's Publishing.

—Beatrice's Goat. unabr. ed. 2005. (J). (ps-3). 29.95 incl. audio compact disk (978-0-8045-4137-4(X)) Spoken Arts, Inc.

McCain, Becky Ray. Nobody Knew What to Do: A Story about Bullying. Leonardo, Todd, illus. 2001. (Concept Book Ser.). 32p. (J). (gr. 1-4). 15.95 (978-0-8075-5711-2(0)) Whitman, Albert & Co.

McCann, Daryl. Rebel Hearts. Scarff, Eileen, ed. 2002. 104p. pap. 17.95 (978-0-7022-3306-7(4)) Univ. of Queensland Pr. AUS. *Dist:* International Specialized Bk. Services.

McCann, Daryl & Forbes, Debbie. Wish You Weren't Here. 2000. 144p. (YA). pap. 14.95 (978-0-7022-3103-2(7)) Univ. of Queensland Pr. AUS. *Dist:* International Specialized Bk. Services.

McClain, Lee. My Abnormal Life. 2005. (YA). mass mkt. 5.99 (978-0-8439-5466-1(3)) Dorchester Publishing Co., Inc.

McClelland, Helen. Visitors for the Chalet School. 2000. 239p. (J). pap. 5.95 (978-0-00-694595-6(3)) Zondervan.

McCombie, Karen. Marshmallow Magic & the Wild Rose Roug. l.t. ed. 2005. pap. 16.95 (978-1-4056-6036-5(8)) BBC Audio Bks. America. *Dist:* BBC Audiobooks America.

McConnell, Edith J. Their Times. 2004. 44p. (J). per. 11.66 (978-1-4116-1370-6(8)) Lulu.com.

McCormick, Angela Barlag. Pie Morgan & the New Girl. 2004. 56p. pap. 12.95 (978-1-4137-1782-2(9)) PublishAmerica, Inc.

McCourt, Lisa. It's Time for School, Stinky Face. Moore, Cyd, illus. 2004. 32p. (J). pap. 15.95 (978-0-439-63574-5(8)); pap. 5.99 (978-0-439-63575-2(6)) Scholastic, Inc.

McCourt, Lisa & Young, Mary. The New Kid & the Cookie Thief. 1998. (Illus.). 32p. (J). (ps-3). 14.95 (978-1-55874-588-9(2)) Health Communications, Inc.

McCully, Emily Arnold. School. McCully, Emily Arnold, illus. 2005. (Illus.). 32p. (J). 15.99 (978-0-06-623856-2(0)); lib. bdg. 16.89 (978-0-06-623857-9(9)) HarperCollins Pubs.

McCurty, Darlene M. I'm Special Too. 2003. 55p. (J). (gr. 4-8). pap. 6.95 (978-0-913543-27-6(6)) African American Images.

McDaniel, Lurlene. The Girl Death Left Behind. 1999. 192p. (YA). (gr. 7-12). pap. 5.50 (978-0-553-57091-5(9) , Laurel Leaf) Random Hse. Children's Bks.

—The Girl Death Left Behind. 1999. (J). 11.64 (978-0-606-16371-2(9)); (gr. 7-12). lib. bdg. 13.00 (978-0-613-16116-9(5)) Tandem Library Bks.

—Hit & Run. 2007. 192p. (YA). (gr. 7). 13.99 (978-0-385-90198-7(4)); 10.99 (978-0-385-73161-4(2)) Random Hse. Children's Bks. (Delacorte Bks. for Young Readers).

—Letting Go of Lisa. (YA). (gr. 7). 2007. 176p. mass mkt. 6.50 (***978-0-440-23868-3(4)*** , Laurel Leaf); 2006. 192p. 10.95 (978-0-385-73159-1(0) , Delacorte Bks. for Young Readers); 2006. 192p. lib. bdg. 12.99 (978-0-385-90196-3(8) , Delacorte Bks. for Young Readers) Random Hse. Children's Bks.

—Prey. 2008. 208p. (YA). (***978-0-385-73453-0(0)*** , Delacorte Pr.) Dell Publishing.

McDonald, Janet. Brother Hood. 2004. 176p. (YA). 16.00 (978-0-374-30995-4(7) , Frances Foster Bks.) Farrar, Straus & Giroux.

—Brother Hood. l.t. ed. 2005. 179p. 20.95 (978-0-7862-7334-8(8) , Large Print Pr.) Thorndike Pr.

McDonald, Janet. Off-Color. 2007. 176p. (YA). (gr. 7 up). 16.00 (***978-0-374-37196-8(2))*** Farrar, Straus & Giroux.

McDonald, Megan. Beetle McGrady Eats Bugs! Manning, Jane K., illus. 2005. 32p. (J). 15.99 (978-0-06-001354-7(0)); lib. bdg. 17.89 (978-0-06-001355-4(9)) HarperCollins Pubs.

—Changes for Julie, Bk. 6. McAliley, Susan, illus. 2007. 104p. (YA). (gr. 3 up). 12.95 (***978-1-59369-355-8(9))*** American Girl Publishing, Inc.

—Changes for Julie, Bk. 6. McAliley, Susan & Hunt, Robert, illus. 2007. 104p. (YA). (gr. 3 up). pap. 6.95 (***978-1-59369-354-1(0))*** American Girl Publishing, Inc.

—Doctor Is In! Reynolds, Peter H., illus. 2006. (Judy Moody Ser.: No. 5). 176p. (J). (gr. 1-5). pap. 5.99 (978-0-7636-2615-0(5)) Candlewick Pr.

—Doctor Is In! Reynolds, Peter H., tr. Reynolds, Peter H., illus. 2004. (Judy Moody Ser.: No. 5). 176p. (J). (gr. 1-5). 15.99 (978-0-7636-2024-0(6)) Candlewick Pr.

—Doctor Is In! Reynolds, Peter, illus. 2004. (Judy Moody Ser.: No. 5). 151p. (J). lib. bdg. 23.08 (***978-1-4242-1145-6(X))*** Fitzgerald Bks.

—Judy Moody Around the World in 8 1/2 Days. Reynolds, Peter H., illus. 2006. (Judy Moody Ser.: No. 7). 176p. (J). (gr. 1-4). 15.99 (978-0-7636-2832-1(8)) Candlewick Pr.

—Judy Moody Predicts the Future. Reynolds, Peter H., illus. 2003. (Judy Moody Ser.: No. 4). 160p. (J). (gr. 1-5). 15.99 (978-0-7636-1792-9(X)) Candlewick Pr.

—Judy Moody Predicts the Future. Reynolds, Peter, illus. 2005. (Judy Moody Ser.: No. 4). 160p. (J). (gr. 1-5). reprint ed. pap. 5.99 (978-0-7636-2343-2(1)) Candlewick Pr.

—Judy Moody Predicts the Future. Reynolds, Peter H., illus. 2005. (Judy Moody Ser.: No. 4). 142p. (J). (ps-k). lib. bdg. 12.64 (978-0-606-33426-6(2)) Tandem Library Bks.

—Judy Moody Saves the World! Reynolds, Peter H., illus. (Judy Moody Ser.: No. 3). 160p. (J). (gr. 1-5). 2004. pap. 5.99 (978-0-7636-2087-5(4)); 2002. 15.99 (978-0-7636-1446-1(7)) Candlewick Pr.

—Julie Tells Her Story, Bk. 2. McAliley, Susan, illus. 2007. 104p. (YA). (gr. 3 up). 12.95 (***978-1-59369-289-6(7))*** American Girl Publishing, Inc.

—Julie Tells Her Story, Bk. 2. McAliley, Susan & Hunt, Robert, illus. 2007. 104p. (YA). (gr. 3 up). pap. 6.95 (***978-1-59369-288-9(9))*** American Girl Publishing, Inc.

—Stink: The Incredible Shrinking Kid. Reynolds, Peter H., illus. (J). (gr. k-3). 2006. 128p. pap. 4.99 (978-0-7636-2891-8(3)); 2005. 112p. 12.99 (978-0-7636-2025-7(4)) Candlewick Pr.

—Stink & the Incredible Super-Galactic Jawbreaker. Reynolds, Peter H., illus. 2007. (Stink Ser.). 144p. (J). (gr. k-3). pap. 4.99 (978-0-7636-3236-6(8)) Candlewick Pr.

—Stink & the Incredible Super-Galactic Jawbreaker. Reynolds, Peter, illus. 2006. 128p. (J). (gr. k-3). 12.99 (978-0-7636-2158-2(7)) Candlewick Pr.

McDonough, Alison. Do the Hokey Pokey. Urbanovic, Jackie, illus. 2001. 112p. (J). (gr. 3-7). 14.95 (978-0-8126-2699-5(0)) Cricket Bks.

McEwan, Jamie. The Heart of Cool. Boynton, Sandra, illus. 2002. (Ready-to-Read Ser.: Level 3). 48p. (J). (gr. 1-4). pap. 3.99 (978-0-689-82178-3(6) , Aladdin) Simon & Schuster Children's Publishing.

—Willy the Scrub. 2005. 64p. (J). pap. 4.99 (978-1-58196-020-4(4)) Darby Creek Publishing.

McFarland, Martha. The Super, Stupendous, & Tremendously Terrific Show-&-Tell Day. Ellis, Dianne, illus. 1998. 32p. (J). (gr. k-3). 12.95 (978-0-9662431-6-1(1)) Viewpoint Pr., Inc.

McFarland, Sandra. Senior Year. 2003. 166p. (J). pap. 19.95 (978-1-59286-388-4(4)) PublishAmerica, Inc.

McGeorge, Constance W. Boomer Goes to School. Whyte, Mary, illus. 1998. 32p. (J). (ps-1). pap. 6.95 (978-0-8118-2020-2(3)) Chronicle Bks. LLC.

—Boomer Va a la Escuela. 1999. Tr. of Boomer Goes to School. (SPA., Illus.). (J). 13.75 (978-0-606-18040-5(0)) Tandem Library Bks.

McGhee, Alison. Countdown to Kindergarten. Bliss, Harry, illus. 2006. 32p. (J). reprint ed. pap. 6.00 (978-0-15-205586-8(X) , Voyager Bks./Libros Viajeros) Harcourt Children's Bks.

—Countdown to Kindergarten. Bliss, Harry, illus. 2002. 32p. (J). (ps-2). 16.00 (978-0-15-202516-8(2) , Silver Whistle) Harcourt Trade Pubs.

—Countdown to Kindergarten. Bliss, Harry, illus. pap. 16.95 incl. audio (978-1-59112-467-2(0)); pap. incl. audio compact disk (978-1-59112-469-6(7)); pap. 18.95 incl. audio compact disk (978-1-59112-927-1(3)); pap. incl. audio (978-1-59112-929-5(X)); 2004. (J). 25.95 incl. audio (978-1-59112-468-9(9)); 2004. (J). 28.95 incl. audio compact disk (978-1-59112-928-8(1)) Live Oak Media.

—Mrs. Watson Wants Your Teeth. Bliss, Harry, illus. 2007. 32p. (J). reprint ed. 16.00 (***978-1-4223-6777-3(0))*** DIANE Publishing Co.

—Mrs. Watson Wants Your Teeth. Bliss, Harry, illus. 2004. 36p. (J). 16.00 (978-0-15-204931-7(2)) Harcourt Children's Bks.

McGinty, Alice B. Eliza's Kindergarten Surprise. Speir, Nancy, illus. 2007. (J). (ps-k). 14.99 (978-0-7614-5351-2(2)) Cavendish, Marshall Corp.

McGowan, Anthony. Hellbent. 2006. 272p. (YA). pap. 8.99 (978-1-4169-0814-2(5) , Simon & Schuster Children's Publishing) Simon & Schuster Children's Publishing.

McGugan, Jim. Josepha: A Prairie Boy's Story. Kimber, Murray, illus. 32p. (J). pap. (978-0-88995-142-6(X)) Red Deer Pr.

—Josepha: A Prairie Boy's Story. 1998. (gr. k-3). lib. bdg. 15.25 (978-0-613-81280-1(8)) Tandem Library Bks.

McGuigan, Mary Ann. Morning in a Different Place. 2008. (J). (***978-1-59078-551-5(7)*** , Front Street) Boyds Mills Pr.

McKain, Kelly. Fairy for a Day. 2008. (Fairy House Ser.: No. 2). 96p. (J). pap. 6.99 (***978-0-545-04238-3(0))*** Scholastic, Inc.

McKay, Hilary. The Birthday Wish. Melling, David, tr. Melling, David, illus. 176p. (J). pap. (978-0-340-87749-4(9) , Hodder Children's Books) Hodder Children's Division.

—Cold Enough for Snow. Melling, David, tr. Melling, David, illus. 2003. 144p. (J). pap. (978-0-340-87750-0(2) , Hodder Children's Books) Hodder Children's Division.

McKay, Sindy. We Both Read-My Day (Picture Book Edition) Johnson, Meredith, illus. 2007. (We Both Read Ser.). 44p. (J). 14.95 (***978-1-60115-005-9(9))*** Treasure Bay, Inc.

McKee, David. Isabel's Noisy Tummy. 2007. (Illus.). 26p. (J). (ps-k). pap. 6.99 (978-1-84270-576-6(8)) Andersen GBR. *Dist:* Independent Pubs. Group.

McKenna, Colleen O'Shaughnessy. Doggone... Third Grade! Roth, Stephanie, illus. 2002. 80p. (J). (gr. 4-6). tchr. ed. 15.95 (978-0-8234-1696-7(8)) Holiday Hse., Inc.

—Third Grade Stinks! Roth, Stephanie, illus. 2001. 104p. (J). (gr. 4-6). tchr. ed. 15.95 (978-0-8234-1595-3(3)) Holiday Hse., Inc.

—Third Grade Wedding Bells. Roth, Stéphanie, illus. 2006. 160p. (J). (gr. 2-5). 15.95 (978-0-8234-1943-2(6)) Holiday Hse., Inc.

McKenna, K. J. Take Three Girls. 2005. 96p. pap. 10.00 (978-1-4116-6290-2(3)) Lulu.com.

McKissack, Fredrick L. & McKissack, Patricia C. Messy Bessey's School Desk. Rau, Dana, ed. Regan, Dana, illus. 1998. (Rookie Reader Skill Set Ser.). 32p. (J). (gr. k-2). pap. 4.95 (978-0-516-26361-8(7) , Children's Pr.) Scholastic Library Publishing.

McKissack, Patricia C. A Friendship for Today. 2007. 240p. (J). (gr. 4-7). pap. 16.99 (978-0-439-66098-3(X) , Scholastic Pr.) Scholastic, Inc.

—Miami Gets It Straight. 2000. (Road to Reading Ser.). (Illus.). (J). (978-0-606-20444-6(X)) Tandem Library Bks.

—Miami Sees It Through. 2002. (gr. k-3). lib. bdg. 11.80 (978-0-613-82723-2(6)) Tandem Library Bks.

McKissack, Patricia C. & McKissack, Frederick. Miami Gets It Straight. Chesworth, Michael, illus. 2004. 89p. (J). (gr. 4-7). lib. bdg. 11.80 (978-0-613-27975-8(1)) Tandem Library Bks.

McKissack, Patricia C. & McKissack, Fredrick L. Messy Bessey's School Desk. Regan, Dana, illus. 1998. (Rookie Readers Ser.). 32p. (J). (gr. 1-2). 19.50 (978-0-516-20827-5(6) , Children's Pr.) Scholastic Library Publishing.

—Miami Jackson Sees It Through. Chesworth, Michael, illus. 2004. (Road to Reading Ser.). 96p. (J). (gr. 2-4). pap. 3.99 (978-0-307-26513-5(7) , Random Hse. Bks. for Young Readers) Random Hse. Children's Bks.

McKissack, Patricia C., et al. Miami Jackson Gets It Straight. 2004. (Road to Reading Ser.). (Illus.). 96p. (J). (gr. k-3). pap. 3.99 (978-0-307-26501-2(3) , Random Hse. Bks. for Young Readers) Random Hse. Children's Bks.

McKissack, Robert L. Try Your Best. Cepeda, Joe, illus. 2004. (Green Light Readers Level 2 Ser.). 24p. (J). 11.95 (978-0-15-205089-4(2)); pap. 3.95 (978-0-15-205090-0(6)) Harcourt Children's Bks. (Green Light Readers).

—Try Your Best. 2004. (gr. k-3). lib. bdg. 11.80 (978-0-613-81420-1(7)) Tandem Library Bks.

McMahen, Chris. Klutzhood. 2007. 160p. (J). (gr. 4-7). pap. (***978-1-55143-710-1(4))*** Orca Bk. Pubs.

McMahon, P. J. The Case of the Psychic Hamster. 2005. (Freaky Joe Club Ser.: No. 4). (Illus.). 153p. (J). (978-1-4155-7725-7(0) , Aladdin) Simon & Schuster Children's Publishing.

McMahon, P. J. Case of the Psychic Hamster. Manders, John, illus. 2005. 153p. (J). lib. bdg. 15.38 (***978-1-4242-0404-5(6))*** Fitzgerald Bks.

McMillan, Bruce. Eating Fractions. McMillan, Bruce, illus. 2002. (Illus.). (J). 25.06 (978-0-7587-2433-5(0)) Book Wholesalers, Inc.

—Mouse Views: What the Class Pet Saw. McMillan, Bruce, illus. 2002. (Illus.). (J). 15.49 (978-0-7587-3182-1(5)) Book Wholesalers, Inc.

McMullan, Kate. Beware! It's Friday the 13th. 2006. (Dragon Slayers' Academy Ser.: No. 13). (Illus.). 107p. (J). (gr. 1-6). 24.21 (978-1-59961-122-8(8)) Spotlight.

—Class Trip to the Cave of Doom. Basso, Bill, illus. 2003. (Dragon Slayers' Academy Ser.: No. 3). 112p. (J). (gr. 1-4). pap. 4.99 (978-0-448-43110-9(6) , Grosset & Dunlap) Penguin Group (USA) Inc.

—Class Trip to the Cave of Doom. 2006. (Dragon Slayers' Academy Ser.: No. 3). (J). (gr. 1-6). 24.21 (978-1-59961-123-5(6)) Spotlight.

S

—Class Trip to the Cave of Doom. 2003. (Dragon Slayers' Academy Ser.: No. 3). (gr. 3-6). lib. bdg. 13.00 (978-0-613-72615-3(4)) Tandem Library Bks.

—Countdown to the Year 1000. Basso, Bill, illus. 2003. (Dragon Slayers' Academy Ser.: No. 8). 112p. (J). pap. 4.99 (978-0-448-43508-4(X) , Grosset & Dunlap) Penguin Group (USA) Inc.

—Countdown to the Year 1000. 2007. (Dragon Slayers' Academy Ser.: No. 8). 112p. (J). (gr. 1-6). 24.21 (*978-1-59961-376-5(X)) Spotlight.

—Countdown to the Year 1000. 2003. (Dragon Slayers' Academy Ser.: No. 8). (gr. 3-6). lib. bdg. 13.00 (978-0-613-72562-0(X)) Tandem Library Bks.

—A Fine Start Bk. 3: Meg's Prairie Diary. 2003. (My America Ser.: No. 3). 112p. (J). pap. 12.95 (978-0-439-37061-5(2)) Scholastic, Inc.

—Fluffy & the Firefighters, Level 3. Smith, Mavis, illus. 2001. (Hello Reader! Ser.). 40p. (J). (gr. 1-3). pap. 3.99 (978-0-439-12917-6(6) , Cartwheel Bks.) Scholastic, Inc.

—Fluffy Goes to School. Smith, Mavis, illus. 1999. (Hello Reader! Ser.: Level 3). 40p. (J). (gr. 1-3). pap. 3.99 (978-0-590-37213-8(0) , Cartwheel Bks.) Scholastic, Inc.

—Fluffy Meets the Groundhog. 2001. 10.79 (978-0-606-22246-4(4)) Tandem Library Bks.

—Fluffy Saves Christmas. Smith, Mavis, illus. 2004. 40p. (J). lib. bdg. 15.00 (978-1-59054-462-4(5)) Fitzgerald Bks.

—Fluffy Saves Christmas, Level 3. Smith, Mavis, illus. 1999. (Hello Reader! Ser.). 40p. (J). (gr. 1-3). pap. 3.99 (978-0-590-52308-0(2) , Cartwheel Bks.) Scholastic, Inc.

—Fluffy, the Secret Santa. Smith, Mavis, illus. 2001. (Hello Reader! Ser.). (J). pap. 3.99 (978-0-439-31942-3(0)) Scholastic, Inc.

—Fluffy's 100th Day at School. 2000. (Hello Reader! Ser.). (J). 10.79 (978-0-606-19562-1(9)) Tandem Library Bks.

—Fluffy's Funny Field Trip. Smith, Mavis, illus. 2004. 40p. (J). lib. bdg. 15.00 (978-1-59054-463-1(3)) Fitzgerald Bks.

—Fluffy's Funny Field Trip. 2001. (Hello Reader! Ser.). (Illus.). (J). 10.79 (978-0-606-21192-5(6)) Tandem Library Bks.

—Fluffy's Happy Halloween. Smith, Mavis, illus. 2004. 40p. (J). lib. bdg. 15.00 (978-1-59054-464-8(1)) Fitzgerald Bks.

—Fluffy's School Bus Adventure. Smith, Mavis, illus. 2004. 40p. (J). lib. bdg. 15.00 (978-1-59054-466-2(8)) Fitzgerald Bks.

—Fluffy's School Bus Adventure. Smith, Mavis, illus. 2001. (Hello Reader! Ser.). 40p. (J). (gr. 1-3). pap. 3.99 (978-0-439-20671-6(5) , Cartwheel Bks.) Scholastic, Inc.

—Fluffy's School Bus Adventure. Smith, Mavis, illus. 2001. (J). (ps-ps). lib. bdg. 11.80 (978-0-613-35512-4(1)) Tandem Library Bks.

—Fluffy's School Bus Adventure. 2001. (Hello Reader! Ser.). (Illus.). (J). 10.79 (978-0-606-21193-2(4)) Tandem Library Bks.

—The Ghost of Sir Herbert Dungeonstone. 2006. (Dragon Slayers' Academy Ser.: No. 12). (J). (gr. 1-6). 24.21 (978-1-59961-124-2(4)) Spotlight.

—Help! It's Parent's Day at DSA, No. 10. Basso, Bill, illus. 2004. (Dragon Slayers' Academy Ser.: No. 10). 112p. (J). (gr. 2-5). pap. 4.99 (978-0-448-43220-5(X) , Grosset & Dunlap) Penguin Group (USA) Inc.

—Help! It's Parent's Day at DSA. 2006. (Dragon Slayers' Academy Ser.: No. 10). (J). (gr. 1-6). 24.21 (978-1-59961-125-9(2)) Spotlight.

—Help! It's Parent's Day at DSA. 2004. (Dragon Slayers' Academy Ser.: No. 10). (gr. 3-6). lib. bdg. 13.00 (978-0-613-72525-5(5)) Tandem Library Bks.

—The New Kid at School. 2006. (Dragon Slayers' Academy Ser.: No. 1). (J). (gr. 1-6). 24.21 (978-1-59961-126-6(0)) Spotlight.

—The New Kid at School. 2003. (Dragon Slayers' Academy Ser.: No. 1). (gr. 3-6). lib. bdg. 13.00 (978-0-613-72614-6(6)) Tandem Library Bks.

—Pig Latin—Not Just for Pigs! Basso, Bill, illus. 2005. (Dragon Slayers' Academy Ser.: No. 14). 112p. (J). (gr. 2-5). pap. 4.99 (978-0-448-43820-7(8) , Grosset & Dunlap) Penguin Group (USA) Inc.

—School! Booth, George, illus. 2008. 128p. (J). 16.95 (*978-0-312-37592-8(1)) Feiwel & Friends.

—A Wedding for Wiglaf? 2003. (Dragon Slayers' Academy Ser.: No. 4). (gr. 3-6). lib. bdg. 13.00 (978-0-613-72540-8(9)) Tandem Library Bks.

—Wheel of Misfortune. Basso, Bill, illus. 2003. (Dragon Slayers' Academy Ser.: No. 7). 112p. (J). pap. 4.99 (978-0-448-43507-7(1) , Grosset & Dunlap) Penguin Group (USA) Inc.

—Wheel of Misfortune. 2007. (Dragon Slayers' Academy Ser.: No. 7). 112p. (J). (gr. 1-6). 24.21 (*978-1-59961-381-9(6)) Spotlight.

McMullan, Kate. 97 Ways to Train a Dragon. Basso, Bill, illus. 2003. (Dragon Slayers' Academy Ser.: No. 9). 112p. (J). (gr. 2-5). pap. 4.99 (978-0-448-43177-2(7) , Grosset & Dunlap) Penguin Group (USA) Inc.

—97 Ways to Train a Dragon. 2003. (Dragon Slayers' Academy Ser.: No. 9). (gr. 3-6). lib. bdg. 13.00 (978-0-613-72474-6(7)) Tandem Library Bks.

McMullan, Kate & Basso, Bill, illus. The New Kid at School. 2003. (Dragon Slayers' Academy Ser.: No. 1). 112p. (J). (gr. 1-4). mass mkt. 4.99 (978-0-448-43108-6(4) , Grosset & Dunlap) Penguin Group (USA) Inc.

McNamara, Margaret. The Counting Race. Gordon, Mike, illus. 2003. (Ready-to-Read Ser.). 32p. (J). pap. 3.99 (978-0-689-85539-9(7) , Aladdin) Simon & Schuster Children's Publishing.

—Counting Race. 2003. (gr. k-3). lib. bdg. 11.80 (978-0-613-66490-5(6)) Tandem Library Bks.

—Dad Goes to School. Gordon, Mike, illus. 2007. (Robin Hill School Ser.). 32p. (J). lib. bdg. 13.89 (978-1-4169-1542-3(7) , Aladdin Library) Simon & Schuster Children's Publishing.

—Election Day. Gordon, Mike, illus. ed. 2005. 32p. (J). lib. bdg. 15.00 (978-1-59054-924-7(4)) Fitzgerald Bks.

—Election Day. Gordon, Mike, illus. 2004. 32p. (J). (ps-ps). lib. bdg. 10.79 (978-0-606-32652-0(9)) Tandem Library Bks.

—Fall Leaf Project. Gordon, Mike, illus. 2006. (Ready-To-Read Ser.). 32p. (J). pap. 3.99 (978-1-4169-1537-9(0)); lib. bdg. 13.89 (978-1-4169-1538-6(9)) Simon & Schuster Children's Publishing. (Aladdin).

—The First Day of School. Gordon, Mike, illus. 2005. (Ready-To-Read Ser.). 32p. (J). (ps-1). pap. 3.99 (978-0-689-86914-3(2)); lib. bdg. 11.89 (978-0-689-86915-0(0)) Simon & Schuster Children's Publishing. (Aladdin).

—First-Grade Bunny. Gordon, Mike, illus. 2005. (Ready-to-Read Ser.). 32p. (J). pap. 3.99 (978-0-689-86427-8(2)); lib. bdg. 11.89 (978-0-689-86428-5(0)) Simon & Schuster Children's Publishing. (Aladdin).

—Groundhog Day. Gordon, Mike, illus. 2006. 32p. (J). lib. bdg. 15.00 (*978-1-4242-0954-5(4)) Fitzgerald Bks.

—Happy Graduation! Gordon, Mike, illus. 2006. (Ready-To-Read Ser.). 32p. (J). (ps-1). lib. bdg. 11.89 (978-1-4169-0510-3(3) , Aladdin) Simon & Schuster Children's Publishing.

—Happy Thanksgiving. Gordon, Mike, illus. 2005. 32p. (J). lib. bdg. 15.00 (*978-1-4242-0953-8(6)) Fitzgerald Bks.

—Happy Thanksgiving. Gordon, Mike, illus. 2005. (Ready-To-Read Ser.). 32p. (J). (ps-3). lib. bdg. 11.89 (978-1-4169-0506-6(5) , Aladdin) Simon & Schuster Children's Publishing.

—How Many Seeds in a Pumpkin? Karas, G. Brian, illus. 2007. 40p. (J). (ps-2). 14.99 (978-0-375-84014-2(1)); lib. bdg. 17.99 (*978-0-375-94014-9(6)) Random Hse. Children's Bks. (Schwartz & Wade Bks.).

—Martin Luther King Jr. Day. Gordon, Mike, illus. 2007. (Robin Hill School Ser.). 32p. (J). pap. 3.99 (*978-1-4169-3494-3(4)); lib. bdg. 13.89 (*978-1-4169-3495-0(2)) Simon & Schuster Children's Publishing. (Aladdin).

—One Hundred Days. 2003. (ps-2). lib. bdg. 11.80 (978-0-613-58162-2(8)) Tandem Library Bks.

—One Hundred Days (Plus One) Gordon, Mike, illus. ed. 2005. 32p. (J). lib. bdg. 15.00 (978-1-59054-968-1(6)) Fitzgerald Bks.

—One Hundred Days (Plus One) Gordon, Mike, illus. 2003. (Ready-to-Reads Ser.). 32p. (J). pap. 3.99 (978-0-689-85535-1(4) , Aladdin) Simon & Schuster Children's Publishing.

—The Playground Problem. Gordon, Mike, illus. 2005. (Ready-to-Read Ser. Level 1). 32p. (J). lib. bdg. 15.00 (978-1-59054-931-5(7)) Fitzgerald Bks.

—The Pumpkin Patch. Gordon, Mike, illus. 2005. (Ready-to-Read Ser. Level 1). 32p. (J). lib. bdg. 15.00 (978-1-59054-932-2(5)) Fitzgerald Bks.

—Robin Hill School #19. Gordon, Mike, illus. 2008. (Robin Hill School Ser.). 32p. (J). lib. bdg. 13.89 (*978-1-4169-5536-8(4) , Aladdin) Simon & Schuster Children's Publishing.

—Too Many Valentines. Gordon, Mike, illus. 2003. (Ready-to-Reads Ser.). 32p. (J). pap. 3.99 (978-0-689-85537-5(0) , Aladdin) Simon & Schuster Children's Publishing.

—Too Many Valentines. 2003. (gr. k-3). lib. bdg. 11.80 (978-0-613-61592-1(1)) Tandem Library Bks.

—A Tooth Story. Gordon, Mike, tr. Gordon, Mike, illus. 2004. (Read-to-Read Ser.). 32p. (J). lib. bdg. 11.89 (978-0-689-86424-7(8) , Aladdin Library) Simon & Schuster Children's Publishing.

—A Tooth Story. Gordon, Mike, illus. 2004. 32p. (J). (ps-ps). lib. bdg. 10.79 (978-0-606-30721-5(4)) Tandem Library Bks.

McNamara, Margaret & Gordon, Mike. Dad Goes to School. 2007. (Robin Hill School Ser.). 32p. (J). pap. 3.99 (978-1-4169-1541-6(9) , Aladdin) Simon & Schuster Children's Publishing.

—Groundhog Day. 2005. (Robin Hill School Ser.). (Illus.). 32p. (J). pap. 3.99 (978-1-4169-0507-3(3) , Aladdin) Simon & Schuster Children's Publishing.

—Happy Graduation! Robin Hill School. 2006. (Ready-To-Read Ser.). (Illus.). 32p. (J). (ps-1). pap. 3.99 (978-1-4169-0509-7(X) , Aladdin) Simon & Schuster Children's Publishing.

—Happy Thanksgiving: Robin Hill School. 2005. (Ready-To-Read Ser.). (Illus.). 32p. (J). (ps-3). pap. 3.99 (978-1-4169-0505-9(7) , Aladdin) Simon & Schuster Children's Publishing.

—The Luck of the Irish. 2007. (Ready-To-Read Ser.). 32p. (J). (SPA.). pap. 3.99 (978-1-4169-1539-3(7) , Aladdin); lib. bdg. 11.89 (978-1-4169-1540-9(0) , Aladdin Library) Simon & Schuster Children's Publishing.

—The Playground Problem. 2004. (Robin Hill School Ser.). (Illus.). 32p. (J). pap. 3.99 (978-0-689-85876-5(0) , Aladdin) Simon & Schuster Children's Publishing.

—A Tooth Story. 2004. (Read-to-Read Ser.). (Illus.). 32p. (J). pap. 3.99 (978-0-689-86423-0(X) , Aladdin) Simon & Schuster Children's Publishing.

McNamee, Graham. Nothing Wrong with a Three-Legged Dog. 2001. (Illus.). (J). (978-0-606-21358-5(9)) Tandem Library Bks.

McNaughton, Colin. Captain Abduls Pirate School. McNaughton, Colin, illus. 2004. (Illus.). 40p. (J). (gr. 1 up). pap. 6.99 (978-0-7636-2540-5(X)) Candlewick Pr.

—When I Grow Up. McNaughton, Colin, illus. 2005. (Illus.). 40p. (J). (ps-1). 12.99 (978-0-7636-2675-4(9)) Candlewick Pr.

McNeal, Laura & McNeal, Tom. Crooked. 2007. 352p. (J). (gr. 7). pap. 7.99 (978-0-375-84191-0(1) , Knopf Bks. for Young Readers) Random Hse. Children's Bks.

—Crushed. (gr. 7). 2007. 336p. (J). pap. 7.99 (978-0-375-83121-8(5)); 2006. 320p. (YA). 15.95 (978-0-375-83105-8(3)); 2006. 320p. (YA). lib. bdg. 17.99 (978-0-375-93105-5(8)) Random Hse. Children's Bks. (Knopf Bks. for Young Readers).

McNeece, Alexander. Sam Iver: Imminent Threat. 2007. 140p. per. 11.95 (*978-0-595-43260-8(3)) iUniverse, Inc.

McNish, Cliff. Angel. 2008. (Exceptional Reading & Language Arts Titles for Upper Grades Ser.). (J). 16.95 (*978-0-8225-8900-6(1) , Carolrhoda Bks.) Lerner Publishing Group.

McOmber, Rachel B., ed. McOmber Phonics Storybooks: The Wizz Kid. rev. ed. (Illus.). (J). (978-0-944991-23-7(8)) Swift Learning Resources.

McPhail, David M. A Bug, a Bear & a Boy Go to School. 1999. (Illus.). (J). 10.79 (978-0-606-20469-9(5)) Tandem Library Bks.

—A Bug, a Bear, & a Boy Go to School. 2004. 32p. (J). lib. bdg. 15.00 (978-1-59054-668-0(7)) Fitzgerald Bks.

Meacham, Margaret. A Fairy's Guide to Understanding Humans. 2007. 160p. (YA). (gr. 5 up). 16.95 (*978-0-8234-2078-0(7)) Holiday Hse., Inc.

Meacham, Margaret. A Mid-Semester Night's Dream. 2004. 160p. (J). (gr. 4-6). tchr. ed. 16.95 (978-0-8234-1815-2(4)) Holiday Hse., Inc.

Mead, Alice & Weber James, Alice. Madame Squidley & Beanie. 2004. 144p. (J). 16.00 (978-0-374-34688-1(7) , Farrar, Straus & Giroux (BYR)) Farrar, Straus & Giroux.

Mead, Richelle. Vampire Academy. 2007. 336p. (J). (gr. 7). pap. 8.99 (*978-1-59514-174-3(X) , Razorbill) Penguin Group (USA) Inc.

Meade, L. T. Red Rose & Tiger Lily or in a Wider Wo. 2004. reprint ed. pap. 28.95 (978-0-7661-8345-2(9)) Kessinger Publishing, LLC.

Meade, T. L. Wild Kitty. 2006. 27.99 (*978-1-4280-2212-6(0)) IndyPublish.com.

Meadowbrook Press. Meadowbrook Kids Three Book Back to School Set. 2005. 250p. pap. 26.85 (978-0-689-05307-8(X)) Meadowbrook Pr.

Mechling, Lauren & Moser, Laura. All Q, No A: More Tales of a 10th-Grade Social Climber. 2006. 288p. (YA). (gr. 7). pap. 7.99 (978-0-618-66378-1(9) , Graphia) Houghton Mifflin Co. Trade & Reference Div.

Mechling, Lauren, et al. The Rise & Fall of a 10th Grade Social Climber. 2005. 304p. (YA). (gr. 7). pap. 7.99 (978-0-618-55519-2(6) , Graphia) Houghton Mifflin Co. Trade & Reference Div.

Medearis, Angela Shelf. The 100th Day of School. Holub, Joan, illus. 2004. 32p. (J). lib. bdg. 15.00 (978-1-59054-394-8(7)) Fitzgerald Bks.

Medearis, Michael & Medearis, Angela Shelf. Daisy & the Doll. Johnson, Larry, illus. 2000. (Family Heritage Ser.). 32p. (J). (gr. 1-5). 14.95 (978-0-916718-15-2(8)) Vermont Folklife Ctr.

Meek, Carol. Believer Boy's Power. 2007. 32p. (J). pap. 9.00 (*978-0-8059-7249-8(8)) Dorrance Publishing Co., Inc.

Mercado, Nancy, ed. Tripping over the Lunch Lady: And Other School Stories. 2004. 192p. (J). 16.99 (978-0-8037-2873-8(5) , Dial) Penguin Group (USA) Inc.

Mercer, Sienna. Fangtastic! 2007. (My Sister the Vampire Ser.: No. 2). 208p. (J). (gr. 3-7). pap. 5.99 (*978-0-06-087115-4(6) , Harper Trophy) HarperCollins Pubs.

Merkel, Ruth. Hannah's Girls: Ann. 2006. 112p. (J). pap. 9.99 (*978-0-8280-1951-4(7)) Review & Herald Publishing Assn.

—Hannah's Girls: Grace, 6. 2006. (Illus.). 128p. (J). pap. 9.99 (*978-0-8280-1953-8(3)) Review & Herald Publishing Assn.

—Hannah's Girls: Marilla, 6 bks. 2006. (Illus.). 144p. (J). pap. 9.99 (*978-0-8280-1952-1(5)) Review & Herald Publishing Assn.

—Hannah's Girls: Ruthie. 2007. 144p. (J). pap. 9.99 (*978-0-8280-1954-5(1)) Review & Herald Publishing Assn.

Merrell, Patrick. Pipsqueaks! Maze School. 1999. (Read with Me Paperback Ser.). (Illus.). 32p. (J). (ps-1). 3.25 (978-0-590-03712-9(9)) Scholastic, Inc.

Messer, Celeste M. The Broken Wing: The Adventures of Andi O'Malley. Hoeffner, Deb, illus. 2004. (Adventures of Andi O'Malley Ser.). 82-92p. (J). (gr. 4-7). 4.95 (978-0-9702171-1-0(0)) AshleyAlan Enterprises.

Metzger, Joanna. The Space Program. Elizalde, Marcelo, illus. 2006. 142p. (J). (978-1-59336-695-7(7)) Mondo Publishing.

Metzger, Steve. Dinofours, Our Holiday Show! Wilhelm, Hans, illus. 2002. (J). 3.50 (978-0-439-38218-2(1)) Scholastic, Inc.

—Five Spooky Ghosts Playing Tricks at School. Harrald-Pilz, Marilee, illus. 2005. (J). (*978-0-439-80381-6(0)) Scholastic, Inc.

—I'll Always Come Back! Allen, Joy, illus. 2002. (J). (978-0-439-42922-1(6)) Scholastic, Inc.

—I'm Having a Bad Day! Wilhelm, Hans, illus. 1998. (Dinofours Ser.: No. 2). 32p. (J). (ps-1). pap. 3.25 (978-0-590-03551-4(7)) Scholastic, Inc.

—It's Apple Picking Day! Wilhelm, Hans, illus. 1998. (Dinofours Ser.: No. 8). (J). (ps-1). 3.25 (978-0-590-03549-1(5)) Scholastic, Inc.

—It's Halloween! Wilhelm, Hans, illus. 1999. (Dinofours Ser.: No. 13). (J). (ps-1). (978-0-439-06326-5(4)) Scholastic, Inc.

—It's Pumpkin Day! Wilhelm, Hans, illus. 2001. (Dinofours Ser.). (J). (ps-1). pap. 3.25 (978-0-439-29569-7(6)) Scholastic, Inc.

—It's Snowing. Wilhelm, Hans, illus. 1998. (Dinofours Ser.: No. 14). (J). (ps-1). pap. 3.25 (978-0-590-03550-7(9)) Scholastic, Inc.

—It's Thanksgiving! Wilhelm, Hans, illus. 2001. (Dinofours Ser.). (J). (ps-1). 3.25 (978-0-439-29570-3(X)) Scholastic, Inc.

—My Seeds Won't Grow! Wilhelm, Hans, illus. 2000. (Dinofours Ser.: No. 18). (J). (ps-1). (978-0-439-06329-6(9)) Scholastic, Inc.

—Rain! Rain! Go Away! Wilhelm, Hans, illus. 2002. (J). pap. 3.25 (978-0-439-29572-7(6)) Scholastic, Inc.

Meunier, Sylvain. Ma Premiere de Classe. Eudes-Pascal, Elisabeth, tr. 2003. (Roman Jeunesse Ser.). (FRE., Illus.). 96p. (J). (gr. 4-7). pap. (978-2-89021-634-1(9)) Diffusion du livre Mirabel.

Meyer, Adam. The Last Domino. 2005. 272p. (YA). (gr. 6). 16.99 (978-0-399-24332-5(1) , Putnam Juvenile) Penguin Group (USA) Inc.

Meyer, Louis A. Curse of the Blue Tattoo: Being an Account of the Misadventures of Jacky Faber, Midshipman & Fine Lady. 2004. (Bloody Jack Adventures Ser.). (Illus.). 496p. (YA). 17.00 (978-0-15-205115-0(5)) Harcourt Children's Bks.

Meyer, Stephenie. Eclipse. rev. ed. 2007. (Twilight Saga Ser.). 640p. (YA). (gr. 7 up). 18.99 (*978-0-316-16020-9(2)) Little, Brown Bks. for Young Readers.

—Twilight. 2005. (Twilight Saga Ser.). 512p. (J). (gr. 9-17). 18.99 (978-0-316-16017-9(2)) Little Brown & Co.

—Twilight. 2006. (Twilight Saga Ser.). 544p. (J). (gr. 9-12). reprint ed. pap. 9.99 (978-0-316-01584-4(9) , Tingley, Megan Bks.) Little, Brown Bks. for Young Readers.

Meyer, Stephenie. The Twilight Collection. rev. ed. 2007. (YA). (gr. 7-17). 55.00 (*978-0-316-00372-8(7)) Little, Brown Bks. for Young Readers.

Miles, Ellen. Penguin's Adventure: The Penguin's Peril. 2007. (Taylor-Made Tales Ser.: No. 4). 112p. (J). pap. 4.99 (978-0-439-59711-1(0) , Scholastic Paperbacks) Scholastic, Inc.

Miller, Edward. Elf Elementary: A Christmas Story. 2004. (Illus.). 32p. (J). (ps-3). 12.95 (978-0-8109-8721-0(X)) Abrams, Harry N., Inc.

Miller, Lee. Ete: (Extraterrestrial Elements) 2006. 80p. pap. 14.95 (978-1-4241-3498-4(6)) PublishAmerica, Inc.

Millman, Isaac. Moses Goes to School. Millman, Isaac, illus. 2000. (Moses Goes To Ser.). (Illus.). 32p. (J). (gr. k-3). 16.00 (978-0-374-35069-7(8) , Farrar, Straus & Giroux (BYR)) Farrar, Straus & Giroux.

—Moses Sees a Play. Millman, Isaac, illus. 2004. (Moses Goes To Ser.). (Illus.). 32p. (J). 16.00 (978-0-374-35066-6(3) , Farrar, Straus & Giroux (BYR)) Farrar, Straus & Giroux.

Millman, M. C. Always Something Else: The whimsical adventures of Elisheva Raskin. 2005. (Illus.). 160p. (J). 14.95 (978-1-932443-23-3(1) , ASEH) Judaica Pr., Inc., The.

—Always Something Else 2. 2006. (Illus.). 160p. (J). 14.95 (978-1-932443-43-1(6) , ASE2H) Judaica Pr., Inc., The.

Mills, Claudia. Alex Ryan, Stop That! 2003. 160p. (J). 16.00 (978-0-374-34655-3(0) , Farrar, Straus & Giroux (BYR)) Farrar, Straus & Giroux.

—Being Teddy Roosevelt. Alley, R. W., illus. 2007. 96p. (J). (gr. 2-5). 16.00 (978-0-374-30657-1(5) , Farrar, Straus & Giroux (BYR)) Farrar, Straus & Giroux.

—Gus & Grandpa & Show-and-Tell. Stock, Catherine, illus. (Gus & Grandpa Ser.). 48p. (J). 2002. pap. 5.95 (978-0-374-42848-8(4) , Sunburst); 2000. (gr. 1-3). 13.00 (978-0-374-32819-1(6) , Farrar, Straus & Giroux (BYR)) Farrar, Straus & Giroux.

—Lizzie at Last. 2002. 152p. (J). (gr. 4-7). lib. bdg. 14.15 (978-0-613-50150-7(0)) Tandem Library Bks.

—Lizzie Mcguire at Last. 2002. 160p. (gr. 3-7). pap. 5.99 (978-0-7868-1672-9(4)) Hyperion Paperbacks for Children.

—Makeovers by Marcia. 2005. 160p. (J). 16.00 (978-0-374-34654-6(2) , Farrar, Straus & Giroux (BYR)) Farrar, Straus & Giroux.

—Standing up to Mr. O. 2000. (978-0-606-18215-7(2)) Tandem Library Bks.

—The Totally Made-Up Civil War Diary of Amanda MacLeish. 2008. 208p. (J). 16.00 (*978-0-374-37696-3(4)) Farrar, Straus & Giroux.

—You're a Brave Man, Julius Zimmerman. 2001. 160p. (gr. 3-7). pap. 5.99 (978-0-7868-1448-0(9)) Hyperion Bks. for Children.

—You're a Brave Man, Julius Zimmerman. 2001. (gr. 3-6). lib. bdg. 14.15 (978-0-613-74974-9(X)); (Illus.). (J). (978-0-606-21539-8(5)) Tandem Library Bks.

—Ziggy's Blue-Ribbon Day. Alley, R. W. & Alley, Robert W., illus. 2005. 32p. (J). (ps-ps). 16.00 (978-0-374-32352-3(6) , Farrar, Straus & Giroux (BYR)) Farrar, Straus & Giroux.

—7 x 9 = Trouble! Karas, G. Brian, illus. 2002. 112p. (J). (gr. 2-3). 16.00 (978-0-374-36746-6(9) , Farrar, Straus & Giroux (BYR)) Farrar, Straus & Giroux.

Mills, David. Sam's First Day. Finlay, Lizzie, illus. 2004. 24p. (J). (TAM, CZE, VIE, SPA & GUJ.). (978-1-85269-630-6(3)); (TAM, CZE, VIE, SPA & GUJ.). (978-1-85269-631-3(1)); (TAM, CZE, VIE, SPA & GUJ.). (978-1-85269-632-0(X)); (TAM, CZE, VIE, SPA & GUJ.). (978-1-85269-633-7(8)); (TAM, CZE, VIE, SPA & GUJ.). (978-1-85269-634-4(6)); (TAM, CZE, VIE, SPA & GUJ.). (978-1-85269-635-1(4)); (TAM, CZE, VIE, SPA & GUJ.). (978-1-85269-636-8(2)); (TAM, CZE, VIE, SPA & GUJ.). (978-1-85269-637-5(0)); (TAM, CZE, VIE, SPA & GUJ.). (978-1-85269-639-9(7)); (TAM, CZE, VIE, SPA & GUJ.). (978-1-85269-640-5(0)); (TAM, CZE, VIE, SPA & GUJ.). (978-1-85269-642-9(7)); (CZE, TAM, VIE, SPA & GUJ.). (978-1-85269-643-6(5)); (TAM, CZE, VIE, SPA & GUJ.). (978-1-85269-645-0(1)); (TAM, CZE, SPA, VIE & GUJ.). (978-1-85269-646-7(X)); (TAM, CZE, VIE, SPA & GUJ.). (978-1-85269-702-0(4)); (POR, TAM, CZE, VIE & SPA.). (978-1-85269-644-3(3)) Mantra Publishing, Ltd.

Mills, David & Finlay, Lizzie. Sam's First Day. 2004. (TAM, CZE, VIE, SPA & GUJ., Illus.). 24p. (J). (978-1-85269-641-2(9)) Mantra Publishing, Ltd.

Mills, Elizabeth. Tick-Tock Sharks. Bettoli, Delana, illus. 2005. 40p. (J). (ps-ps). 9.99 (978-0-439-72308-4(6), Cartwheel Bks.) Scholastic, Inc.

Milord, Susan. Happy School Year! DePalma, Mary Newell, illus. 2008. (J). pap. (***978-0-439-88280-4(X)***, Scholastic Pr.) Scholastic, Inc.

Milord, Susan. Willa the Wonderful. (Illus.). 32p. (J). (gr. k-3). 2005. 5.95 (978-0-618-58543-4(5)); 2003. tchr. ed. 15.00 (978-0-618-27522-9(3)) Houghton Mifflin Co. Trade & Reference Div.

Minsky, Terri. All over It! 2005. (Illus.). 138p. (J). (***978-1-4156-0271-3(9)***) Disney Pr.

Minter, J. Inside Girl: A Novel. 2007. (Insiders Novel Ser.). 240p. (YA). (gr. 7 up). pap. 8.95 (***978-1-59990-086-5(6)***) Bloomsbury Publishing.

—The Sweetest Thing: An Inside Girl Novel. 2007. (Insiders Novel Ser.). 224p. (J). (gr. 7 up). pap. 8.95 (***978-1-59990-087-2(4)***, Bloomsbury Children) Bloomsbury Publishing.

Mitchard, Jacquelyn. Ready, Set, School! Ratz de Tagyos, Paul, illus. 2007. 32p. (J). (ps-1). 16.99 (***978-0-06-050766-4(7)***); lib. bdg. 17.89 (***978-0-06-050767-1(5)***) HarperCollins Pubs.

Mitchell, Anastasia, illus. Josh B'Gosh at School. 1998. 10p. (J). 6.99 (978-1-929174-08-9(X)) Oshkosh B'Gosh, Inc.

Mitchell, Nancy. Global Warning. Christensen, Edie et al, illus. 1999. (Changing Earth Trilogy Ser.: Bk. 3). 178p. (Orig.). (J). (ps-12). mass mkt. 5.95 (978-1-892713-02-5(0)) Lightstream Pubns.

Mitchell, Richard, illus. The Man from Mars. 1999. (J). (978-0-7608-3201-1(3)) Sundance/Newbridge Educational Publishing.

Mlynowski, Sarah. Bras & Broomsticks. 2005. 320p. (YA). (gr. 7). 15.95 (978-0-385-73181-2(7), Delacorte Bks. for Young Readers) Random Hse. Children's Bks.

—Frogs & French Kisses. (gr. 7). 2007. 304p. (YA). pap. 8.99 (***978-0-385-73185-0(X)***); 2006. (Illus.). 288p. (J). 15.95 (978-0-385-73182-9(5)); 2006. (Illus.). 288p. (YA). lib. bdg. 17.99 (978-0-385-90219-9(0)) Random Hse. Children's Bks. (Delacorte Bks. for Young Readers).

Mohr, L. C. Krumbuckets. 2008. (Illus.). 144p. (J). per. 8.95 (978-0-9769417-7-4(5)) Blooming Tree Pr.

—Krumbuckets. Musheno, Erica, illus. 2007. 144p. (J). (gr. 2-7). 13.95 (978-0-9769417-6-7(7)) Blooming Tree Pr.

Mohsenian, Javad. 9/11 Children. 2006. 113p. pap. 10.95 (978-0-7414-3218-6(8)) Infinity Publishing.

Mol, Alien. The Hasty Promise. 2002. (Illus.). 120p. (YA). lib. bdg. 10.95 (978-0-9670728-8-3(3)) Early Foundations Pubs.

Moloney, James. Touch Me. 2000. 256p. (YA). pap. 16.95 (978-0-7022-3151-3(7)) Univ. of Queensland Pr. AUS. *Dist:* International Specialized Bk. Services.

Moncure, Jane Belk. Word Bird's Dinosaur Days. 2002. (New Word Bird Library). (Illus.). 32p. (J). (ps-3). 22.79 (978-1-56766-999-2(9)) Child's World, Inc.

—Word Bird's Rainy-Day Dance. 2002. (New Word Bird Library). (Illus.). 32p. (J). (ps-3). 22.79 (978-1-56766-893-3(3)) Child's World, Inc.

Montanari, Eva. A Very Full Morning. 2006. (Illus.). 32p. (J). (gr. k-3). 16.00 (978-0-618-56318-0(0)) Houghton Mifflin Co. Trade & Reference Div.

Montes, Marisa. A Crazy Mixed-Up Spanglish Day. Cepeda, Joe, illus. 2003. (Get Ready for Gabi Ser.). 128p. (J). pap. 12.95 (978-0-439-51710-2(9), Scholastic Paperbacks) Scholastic, Inc.

—A Crazy Mixed-Up Spanglish Day. 2003. (gr. 3-6). lib. bdg. 11.80 (978-0-613-72003-8(2)) Tandem Library Bks.

Montgomery, Arch. Jake: The Second Novel of the Gunpowder Trilogy. 2004. (YA). 19.95 (978-1-890862-31-2(2)) Bancroft Pr.

Moore, Eva. The Great Shark Escape. 2001. (Magic School Bus Chapter Bks.). (Illus.). (J). 11.79 (978-0-606-21311-0(2)) Tandem Library Bks.

Moore-Mallinos, Jennifer. It's Hard Being a Kid. Fabrega, Marta, illus. 2007. (Live & Learn Ser.). 36p. (J). (gr. k-2). pap. 6.99 (978-0-7641-3586-6(4)) Barron's Educational Series, Inc.

—Ser un nino es Dificil: It's Hard Being a Kid (Spanish Edition) Fabrega, Marta, illus. 2007. (Live & Learn Ser.). 36p. (J). (gr. k-2). pap. 6.99 (978-0-7641-3587-3(2)) Barron's Educational Series, Inc.

Moore, Peter G. Caught in the Act. 2005. 274p. (J). (gr. 7). 16.99 (978-0-670-05990-4(0), Viking Juvenile) Penguin Group (USA) Inc.

Moore, Stephanie Perry. Purity Reigns. 2002. (Laurel Shadrach Ser.: Vol. 1). 240p. (YA). pap. 6.99 (978-0-8024-4035-8(5)) Moody Pubs.

—Purity Reigns. 2002. (gr. 7-12). lib. bdg. 15.30 (978-0-613-90559-6(8)) Tandem Library Bks.

Moorehead, Michael. The Student from Zombie Island: Conquering the Rumor Monster. Parks, Kathy, illus. 2007. 40p. (J). bds. 15.95 net. (***978-1-58985-072-9(6)***) Five Star Pubns., Inc.

Moorhead, Joshua Matthew. Baker's Dozen: In 13 Days, Justin Baker & the World Will Change. 2005. (Fresh Voices Ser.). 218p. (J). (gr. 8-17). pap. 9.95 (978-1-932802-96-2(7), Holy Macro! Bks.) MrExcel.com Publishing.

Mora, Pat. The Rainbow Tulip. Sayles, Elizabeth, illus. 32p. (J). (gr. k-3). 2003. pap. 6.99 (978-0-14-250009-5(7), Puffin); 1999. 16.99 (978-0-670-87291-6(1), Viking Juvenile) Penguin Group (USA) Inc.

Morgan, Melissa J. Ttyl. 2007. 22.78 (978-1-59961-155-6(4)) Spotlight.

Morgan, Michaela. Mouse with No Name. Mikhail, Jess, illus. 2004. 24p. (J). lib. bdg. 22.65 (***978-1-59646-682-1(0)***) Dingles & Co.

—The Thing in the Basement. Weir, Doffy, illus. 2006. 48p. (J). (***978-1-4048-3133-9(9)***) Picture Window Bks.

Morgan, Nicolette. All about Me: Briana's Neighborhood. 2007. 24p. (J). 15.99 (***978-0-9793904-0-1(0)***) It's Me Briana, LLC.

Morgan, Ruth. Batter Splatter! Mikhail, Jess, illus. 2005. 24p. (J). lib. bdg. 22.65 (***978-1-59646-704-0(5)***) Dingles & Co.

Morgenstern, Susie. A Book of Coupons. Rosner, Gill, tr. Bloch, Serge, illus. (J). (gr. 3-6). 2003. 80p. pap. 5.99 (978-0-14-250115-3(8), Puffin); 2001. 64p. 13.99 (978-0-670-89970-8(4), Viking Juvenile) Penguin Group (USA) Inc.

—Secret Letters from 0 to 10. Rosner, Gil, Jr., illus. 2000. 144p. (J). (gr. 3-7). pap. 4.99 (978-0-14-130819-7(2), Puffin) Penguin Group (USA) Inc.

—Secret Letters from 0 to 10. 2000. (978-0-606-18846-3(0)) Tandem Library Bks.

—Secret Letters from 0 To 10. 2000. (gr. 3-6). lib. bdg. 13.00 (978-0-613-28635-0(9)) Tandem Library Bks.

Moriarty, Jaclyn. The Murder of Bindy MacKenzie. (J). 2008. 496p. 8.99 (978-0-439-74052-4(5)); 2006. 352p. pap. 16.99 (978-0-439-74051-7(7)) Scholastic, Inc. (Levine, Arthur A. Bks.).

—The Year of Secret Assignments. (Illus.). 352p. 2004. (J). pap. 16.95 (978-0-439-49881-4(3), Levine, Arthur A. Bks.); 2005. reprint ed. pap. 7.99 (978-0-439-49882-1(1), Scholastic Paperbacks) Scholastic, Inc.

Morin, James F. Rothshield Chasing Shadows. 2006. pap. 14.95 (***978-1-59330-422-5(6)***) Aventine Pr.

Morpurgo, Michael. Snakes & Ladders. Wilson, Anne, illus. 2006. 46p. (J). (978-0-7787-0952-7(3)) Crabtree Publishing Co.

Morris, Rosalind. Drawkcab Brown Stops a Bully. 2004. 35p. pap. 17.95 (978-1-4137-1379-4(3)) PublishAmerica, Inc.

Moser, Lisa. The Monster in the Backpack. Jones, Noah, illus. 2006. 48p. (J). (gr. k-2). 14.99 (978-0-7636-2390-6(3)) Candlewick Pr.

—The Monster in the Backpack: Candlewick Sparks. Jones, Noah Z., illus. 2007. (Candlewick Sparks Ser.). 48p. (J). (gr. k-2). pap. 4.99 (978-0-7636-3307-3(0)) Candlewick Pr.

Moses, Brian. The Playground Snake. Mostyn, David, illus. 2004. (Read-It! Readers Ser.). 32p. (C). (gr. k-3). 18.60 (978-1-4048-0556-9(7)) Picture Window Bks.

Moss, Marissa. The All-New Amelia. Moss, Marissa, illus. 2007. (Amelia's Notebooks). (Illus.). 40p. (J). (gr. 2-5). 9.99 (978-1-4169-0908-8(7), Simon & Schuster/Paula Wiseman Bks.) Simon & Schuster Children's Publishing.

—The All-New Amelia. 1999. (Amelia's Notebooks). (J). (gr. 3-5). 12.75 (978-0-606-19866-0(0)) Tandem Library Bks.

—Amelia Takes Command. 1999. (Amelia's Notebooks). (Illus.). 48p. (J). (ps-7). lib. bdg. 12.75 (978-0-606-19868-4(7)) Tandem Library Bks.

—Amelia Writes Again. Moss, Marissa, illus. 2006. (Amelia's Notebooks). (Illus.). 32p. (J). 9.95 (978-1-4169-0904-0(4), Simon & Schuster/Paula Wiseman Bks.) Simon & Schuster Children's Publishing.

—Amelia Writes Again. 1999. (Amelia's Notebooks). (Illus.). 48p. (gr. 3-5). lib. bdg. 12.75 (978-0-606-17252-3(1)) Tandem Library Bks.

—Amelia's 5th-Grade Notebook. Moss, Marissa, illus. 2006. (Amelia's Notebooks). (Illus.). 40p. (J). 9.95 (978-1-4169-0912-5(5), Simon & Schuster/Paula Wiseman Bks.) Simon & Schuster Children's Publishing.

—Amelia's 6th Grade Notebook. Moss, Marissa, illus. 2005. (Amelia's Notebooks). (Illus.). 80p. (J). (gr. k-8). 9.95 (978-0-689-87040-8(X), Simon & Schuster Children's Publishing) Simon & Schuster Children's Publishing.

—Max's Mystical Logbook. 2004. (J). 12.95 (978-0-439-46663-9(6)) Scholastic, Inc.

—Oh Boy, Amelia! 2001. (Amelia's Notebooks). (Illus.). (J). (978-0-606-21365-3(1)) Tandem Library Bks.

Moss, Marissa. Vote 4 Amelia. Moss, Marissa, illus. 2007. (Amelia's Notebooks). 80p. (J). (gr. 5-8). 9.99 (***978-1-4169-2789-1(1)***, Simon & Schuster/Paula Wiseman Bks.) Simon & Schuster Children's Publishing.

Moss, Miriam. Don't Forget I Love You. Currey, Anna, illus. 2005. 32p. (J). pap. 5.99 (978-0-14-240548-2(5), Puffin) Penguin Group (USA) Inc.

—Pica, Rasca. Durand, Delphine, illus. 2002. (J). (SPA.). 28p. 17.95 (978-84-8488-038-7(9)); (CAT.). 32p. 17.95 (978-84-8488-039-4(7)) Serres, Ediciones, S. L. ESP. *Dist:* Lectorum Pubns., Inc.

—Wibble Wobble. Mockler, Joanna, illus. 2001. 32p. (J). (gr. k-2). tchr. ed. 14.95 (978-1-58925-013-0(3), tiger tales) ME Media LLC.

Moss, Peggy. Say Something. Lyon, Lea, illus. 2005. 32p. (J). (gr. 2-6). 16.95 (978-0-88448-261-1(8)) Tilbury Hse. Pubs.

Moverley, Richard. The Reluctant Rajput. Dean, David, illus. 2005. (Yellow Go Bananas Ser.). 48p. (J). lib. bdg. (978-0-7787-2723-1(8)) Crabtree Publishing Co.

Muldrow, Diane. Deep Freeze. Pollack, Barbara, illus. 2007. (Dish Ser.: No. 12). 160p. (J). (gr. 4-7). pap. 4.99 (***978-0-448-44693-6(6)***, Grosset & Dunlap) Penguin Group (USA) Inc.

—Into the Mix. 2002. (gr. 3-6). lib. bdg. 13.00 (978-0-613-72425-8(9)) Tandem Library Bks.

—Lights! Camera! Cook! Pollak, Barbara, illus. 2007. (Dish Ser.: No. 8). 160p. (J). pap. 4.99 (978-0-448-44533-5(6), Grosset & Dunlap) Penguin Group (USA) Inc.

—On the Back Burner, No. 6. Pollak, Barbara, illus. 2007. (Dish Ser.). 160p. (J). pap. 4.99 (978-0-448-44531-1(X), Grosset & Dunlap) Penguin Group (USA) Inc.

Muldrow, Diane. Winner Takes the Cake. Pollack, Barbara, illus. 2007. (Dish Ser.: No. 11). 160p. (J). (gr. 4-7). pap. 4.99 (***978-0-448-44666-0(9)***, Grosset & Dunlap) Penguin Group (USA) Inc.

Mulford, Carolyn. The Feedsack Dress. 2007. (YA). per. 7.95 (***978-0-9713497-4-2(6)***) Cave Hollow Pr.

Mullican, Judy. Jonah Starts School. Cress, Michelle H., illus. l.t. ed. 2003. (Hrl Big Book Ser.). 8p. (J). (ps-1). pap. 10.95 (978-1-57332-268-3(7)); pap. 10.95 (978-1-57332-269-0(5)) HighReach Learning, Inc.

Mullins, Julie. School Play Stars. Maddock, Monika, illus. 2005. (Girlz Rock! Ser.). (J). pap. (978-1-59336-706-0(6)) Mondo Publishing.

Muluka, B. Kandu & the Lake. 2004. (Illus.). 40p. 13.95 (978-9966-25-165-7(0)) Heinemann Kenya, Limited (East African Educational Publishers Ltd E.A.E.P.) KEN. *Dist:* Michigan State Univ. Pr.

Munoz-Furlong, Anne. Alexander & His Pals Visit the Main Street School. 1999. (J). (gr. k-6). pap. (978-1-882541-07-2(3)) Food Allergy & Anaphylaxis Network.

Munsch, Robert. Get Out of Bed! ed. 2004. (Illus.). (J). (gr. k-3). spiral bd. (978-0-616-04557-2(3)); spiral bd. (978-0-616-03049-3(5)) Canadian National Institute for the Blind/Institut National Canadien pour les Aveugles.

—Get Out of Bed! 2002. (ps-2). lib. bdg. 11.80 (978-0-613-46072-9(3)) Tandem Library Bks.

—Kiss Me, I'm Perfect! 2008. (Candy Apple Ser.). (SPA.). 32p. (J). pap. 3.99 (***978-0-545-02213-2(4)***, Scholastic en Espanol) Scholastic, Inc.

Munsch, Robert. El Traje de Nieve de Tomas. Aguirre, Rigo, tr. from ENG. Martchenko, Michael, illus. 2004. (SPA.). 24p. (J). (ps-2). pap. 5.95 (978-1-55037-854-2(6)) Annick Pr., Ltd. CAN. *Dist:* Firefly Bks., Ltd.

Munsch, Robert, et al. Get Out of Bed! Daniel, Alan & Daniel, Lea, illus. 2002. 32p. (J). pap. 3.99 (978-0-439-38851-1(1)) Scholastic, Inc.

Munsch, Robert N. Kiss Me, I'm Perfect. Martchenko, Michael, illus. 2008. 32p. (J). pap. 3.99 (***978-0-545-01827-2(7)***) Scholastic, Inc.

Murail, Marie-Aude. Sin Azucar, Gracias. 2003. (la Orilla Del Viento Ser.). (SPA.). 104p. (J). 4.99 (978-968-16-6725-2(5)) Fondo de Cultura Economica USA.

Murozumi, Hikaru & Inokuma, Shinobu. The School of Water Business. (Illus.). (YA). 206p. pap. (978-4-09-153102-5(4)); Vol. 4. 2005. (JPN., 205p. mass mkt. (978-4-09-153104-9(0)); Vol. 5. (JPN., 205p. mass mkt. (978-4-09-153105-6(9)) Shogakukan.

Murphy, Jill. A Bad Spell for the Worst Witch. 2000. (Worst Witch Ser.). (J). (978-0-606-19310-8(3)) Tandem Library Bks.

Murphy, Jill. The Worst Witch at School. Murphy, Jill, illus. 2007. (Worst Witch Ser.). (Illus.). 192p. (J). (gr. 3). 6.99 (***978-0-7636-3435-3(2)***) Candlewick Pr.

Murphy, Stuart J. Henry the Fourth. Nash, Scott, illus. 1999. (MathStart Ser.). 40p. (J). (ps up). pap. 5.99 (978-0-06-446719-3(8), Harper Trophy) HarperCollins Pubs.

Murphy, T. M. The Secrets of Cranberry Beach. 2001. (Belltown Mystery Ser.). (Illus.). 156p. (J). 9.95 (978-1-880158-36-4(1)) Townsend, J.N. Publishing.

Murray, Guillermo. Que, Miedo! rev. ed. 2006. (Castillo del Terror Ser.). (SPA.). 112p. (J). (gr. 2-6). pap. 6.95 (978-970-20-0338-0(5)) Castillo, Ediciones, S. A. de C. V. MEX. *Dist:* Macmillan.

Murray, Jaye. Bottled Up. 2004. 224p. (YA). (gr. 6-12). reprint ed. pap. 6.99 (978-0-14-240240-5(0), Puffin) Penguin Group (USA) Inc.

—Bottled Up. 2004. 220p. (J). (gr. 2-13). lib. bdg. 13.04 (978-0-606-32733-6(9)) Tandem Library Bks.

Musolf, Nell. Jessica James. 2003. (J). per. (978-0-9740833-0-8(5)) Port Town Publishing.

Mutter, Mike. Wesley Goes to School. Lawson, Sue, illus. 1999. 33p. (J). (ps-2). pap. 21.00 (978-1-85072-186-4(6)) Sessions, William Ltd. GBR. *Dist:* State Mutual Bk. & Periodical Service, Ltd.

My First Day at School. 2005. (J). 16.95 (978-0-9769004-0-5(8)) Sinanan, Cindy.

My Home Town Has a School. 2000. 20p. (J). 7.95 (978-1-931006-51-4(2)) SteppingStones BookCard Pubns., LLC.

Myers, Anna. Confessions from the Principal's Chair. 2006. 192p. 16.95 (978-0-8027-9560-1(9)) Walker & Co.

Myers, Anna. Wart. 2007. 224p. (J). (gr. 5-9). 16.95 (***978-0-8027-8977-8(3)***) Walker & Co.

Myers, Christopher. Wings. 2001. (YA). (gr. 2-4). 27.90 incl. audio (978-0-8045-6880-7(4), 6880) Spoken Arts, Inc.

Myers, Edward. Duck & Cover. 2004. 200p. (J). per. 11.95 (978-0-9674477-8-0(X)) Montemayor Pr.

—Ice. 2005. 222p. (J). per. 12.95 net. (978-0-9674477-9-7(8)) Montemayor Pr.

Myers, Laurie. Earthquake in the Third Grade. Ritz, Karen, illus. 1998. 64p. (J). (gr. 4-6). pap. 5.95 (978-0-395-92866-0(4), Clarion Bks.) Houghton Mifflin Co. Trade & Reference Div.

—Guinea Pigs Don't Talk. Taylor, Cheryl, illus. 1998. 80p. (J). (gr. 4-6). pap. 5.95 (978-0-395-92865-3(6), Clarion Bks.) Houghton Mifflin Co. Trade & Reference Div.

—Surviving Brick Johnson. Yaccarino, Dan, illus. 2000. 80p. (J). (gr. 4-6). tchr. ed. 15.00 (978-0-395-98031-6(3), Clarion Bks.) Houghton Mifflin Co. Trade & Reference Div.

Myers, Walter Dean. The Beast. 2005. 192p. (YA). (gr. 7-12). 6.99 (978-0-439-36842-1(1), Scholastic Paperbacks) Scholastic, Inc.

—Game. 2008. 240p. (J). 16.99 (***978-0-06-058294-4(4)***); lib. bdg. 17.89 (***978-0-06-058295-1(2)***) HarperCollins Pubs. (HarperTeen).

—Shooter. (J). 2004. 224p. 15.99 (978-0-06-029519-6(8), HarperTeen); 2004. (Illus.). 240p. lib. bdg. 16.89 (978-0-06-029520-2(1), HarperTeen); 2005. 256p. reprint ed. pap. 7.99 (978-0-06-447290-6(6), Amistad) HarperCollins Pubs.

—Shooter. l.t. ed. 2004. 213p. 22.95 (978-0-7862-6969-3(3), Large Print Pr.) Thorndike Pr.

—Slam! 1998. (Point Signature Ser.). 272p. (YA). (gr. 7-12). 5.99 (978-0-590-48668-2(3), Scholastic Paperbacks) Scholastic, Inc.

Myers, Walter Dean & Myers, Walter Dean. Slam! 1998. 266p. (YA). (gr. 7-12). lib. bdg. 14.15 (978-0-613-12111-8(2)) Tandem Library Bks.

Myracle, Lauren. Eleven. 208p. (J). (gr. 3-7). 2004. 16.99 (978-0-525-47165-3(0), Dutton Juvenile); 2005. reprint ed. pap. 6.99 (978-0-14-240346-4(6), Puffin) Penguin Group (USA) Inc.

—The Fashion Disaster That Changed My Life. 2008. 160p. (J). (gr. 5). 6.99 (978-0-14-240717-2(8), Puffin); 2005. 144p. (YA). (gr. 4-6). 15.99 (978-0-525-47222-3(3), Dutton Juvenile) Penguin Group (USA) Inc.

—L8r, G8r. 2007. (Ttyl Ser.). 288p. (J). (gr. 2-8). 15.95 (***978-0-8109-1266-3(X)***, Amulet Bks.) Abrams, Harry N., Inc.

—Rhymes with Witches. (YA). (gr. 8-17). 2006. 272p. pap. 6.95 (978-0-8109-9215-3(9)); 2005. 224p. 16.95 (978-0-8109-5859-3(7), Amulet Bks.) Abrams, Harry N., Inc.

—Thirteen. 2008. 224p. (J). (gr. 5). 15.99 (***978-0-525-47896-6(5)***, Dutton Juvenile) Penguin Group (USA) Inc.

—TTFN (Ta-Ta for Now) (Internet Girls Ser.). 2007. 256p. (J). (gr. 2-8). pap. 6.95 (***978-0-8109-9279-5(5)***); 2006. 240p. (YA). (gr. 9-17). 15.95 (978-0-8109-5971-2(2)) Abrams, Harry N., Inc. (Amulet Bks.).

—Ttyl. (Internet Girls Ser.). (YA). (gr. 8-17). 2005. 234p. pap. 6.95 (978-0-8109-8788-3(0)); 2004. 224p. 15.95 (978-0-8109-4821-1(4), Amulet Bks.) Abrams, Harry N., Inc.

—Twelve. 2007. 208p. (YA). (gr. 5-8). 15.99 (978-0-525-47784-6(5), Dutton Juvenile) Penguin Group (USA) Inc.

S

Nagda, Ann Whitehead. The Perfect Cat-Sitter. Roth, Stephanie, illus. 2007. 96p. (J). (gr. 2-6). 15.95 (***978-0-8234-2112-1(0)***) Holiday Hse., Inc.

Nagda, Ann Whitehead. Tarantula Power! Roth, Stéphanie, illus. 2007. 96p. (J). (gr. 2-5). 15.95 (978-0-8234-1991-3(6)) Holiday Hse., Inc.

Nakajo, Hisaya. Hana-Kimi. 2007. (Hana-Kimi Ser.). 184p. (YA). Vol. 16. pap. 9.99 (978-1-4215-0991-4(1)); Vol. 17. pap. 9.99 (978-1-4215-0992-1(X)) Viz Media.

Nakakuma, Chie. Whazzup, Wolly Ayaka? 2007. 128p. per. 10.95 (***978-0-595-44646-9(9)***) iUniverse, Inc.

Namioka, Lensey. Mismatch. 224p. (gr. 5-9). 2007. (YA). mass mkt. 6.50 (978-0-440-23879-9(X), Laurel Leaf); 2006. (J). 15.95 (978-0-385-73183-6(3), Delacorte Bks. for Young Readers) Random Hse. Children's Bks.

Napoli, Donna Jo. Running Away. 2000. (Angelwings Ser.: No. 10). 96p. (J). (gr. 2-6). pap. 7.95 (978-0-689-83210-9(3), Aladdin) Simon & Schuster Children's Publishing.

—Running Away. 2000. (Angelwings Ser.: No. 10). (Illus.). (J). (978-0-606-20384-5(2)) Tandem Library Bks.

Napoli, Donna Jo & Furrow, Robert. Sly the Sleuth & the Sports Mysteries. Maione, Heather Harms, illus. 2006. 128p. (J). 15.99 (978-0-8037-2994-0(4), Dial) Penguin Group (USA) Inc.

Narayan, Natasha. The Paradise Plot. 2006. 304p. (J). pap. 12.95 (***978-1-4052-1878-8(9)***) Egmont Bks., Ltd. GBR. *Dist:* Independent Pubs. Group.

Nascimbene, Yan. Ocean Deep. 1999. 40p. 18.00 (978-1-56846-161-8(5), Creative Editions) Creative Co., The.

Natti, Susanna, illus. Lionel at School. 2002. (Lionel Ser.). 11.49 (978-1-4046-0491-9(X)) Book Wholesalers, Inc.

Naylor, Phyllis Reynolds. Achingly Alice. 2003. (Alice Ser.). (Illus.). 160p. (YA). mass mkt. 5.99 (978-0-689-86396-7(9), Simon Pulse) Simon & Schuster Children's Publishing.

—Alice Alone. (Alice Ser.). 240p. 2002. mass mkt. 5.99 (978-0-689-85189-6(8), Simon Pulse); 2001. (Illus.). (J). (gr. 5-9). 16.00 (978-0-689-82634-4(6), Atheneum) Simon & Schuster Children's Publishing.

—Alice Alone. 2002. (Alice Ser.). (gr. 5-8). lib. bdg. 13.00 (978-0-613-73352-6(5)) Tandem Library Bks.

—Alice in April. 2002. (Alice Ser.). 176p. (J). pap. 5.99 (978-0-689-81686-4(3), Aladdin) Simon & Schuster Children's Publishing.

—Alice in April. 2002. (Alice Ser.). (gr. 3-6). lib. bdg. 13.00 (978-0-613-88873-8(1)) Tandem Library Bks.

—Alice in Blunderland. 2003. (Alice Ser.). (Illus.). 208p. (J). 15.95 (978-0-689-84397-6(6), Atheneum) Simon & Schuster Children's Publishing.

—Alice on Her Way. 2006. (Alice Ser.). 352p. (YA). mass mkt. 5.99 (978-0-689-87091-0(4), Simon Pulse) Simon & Schuster Children's Publishing.

—Alice on the Outside. (Alice Ser.). 176p. (gr. 5-9). 2000. (YA). mass mkt. 5.99 (978-0-689-80594-3(2), Simon Pulse); 1999. (J). 16.00 (978-0-689-80359-8(1), Atheneum) Simon & Schuster Children's Publishing.

—Alice on the Outside. 2000. (Alice Ser.). (YA). (gr. 5-9). 11.64 (978-0-606-19706-9(0)); (gr. 7-12). lib. bdg. 13.00 (978-0-613-29866-7(7)) Tandem Library Bks.

—All but Alice. 2002. (Alice Ser.). 160p. (J). (gr. 4-7). pap. 5.99 (978-0-689-85044-8(1), Aladdin) Simon & Schuster Children's Publishing.

—All but Alice. 2002. (Alice Ser.). (gr. 7-12). lib. bdg. 13.00 (978-0-613-44999-1(1)) Tandem Library Bks.

—Dangerously Alice. 2007. (Alice Ser.). 304p. (YA). (gr. 9 up). 15.99 (978-0-689-87094-1(9), Atheneum) Simon & Schuster Children's Publishing.

—Including Alice. 2004. (Alice Ser.). 288p. (YA). 15.95 incl. audio compact disk (978-0-689-82637-5(0), Atheneum) Simon & Schuster Children's Publishing.

—Lovingly Alice. (Alice Ser.). (J). 2006. 176p. pap. 5.99 (978-0-689-84400-3(X) , Aladdin); 2006. 166p. (*978-1-4156-5199-5(X) , Aladdin); 2004. (Illus.). 176p. 15.95 (978-0-689-84399-0(2) , Atheneum) Simon & Schuster Children's Publishing.

—Outrageously Alice. 1998. (Alice Ser.). 144p. (J). (gr. 5-9). pap. 5.99 (978-0-689-80596-7(9) , Aladdin) Simon & Schuster Children's Publishing.

—Simply Alice. (Alice Ser.). 240p. (YA). 2003. (Illus.). mass mkt. 5.99 (978-0-689-85965-6(1) , Simon Pulse); 2002. (gr. 6-9). 16.00 (978-0-689-82635-1(4) , Atheneum) Simon & Schuster Children's Publishing.

—Simply Alice. 2003. (Alice Ser.). (gr. 7-12). lib. bdg. 13.00 (978-0-613-73415-8(7)) Tandem Library Bks.

—Starting with Alice. (Alice Ser.). 192p. (J). 2004. (Illus.). pap. 4.99 (978-0-689-84396-9(8) , Aladdin); 2002. 15.95 (978-0-689-84395-2(X) , Atheneum) Simon & Schuster Children's Publishing.

—Starting with Alice. 2004. (gr. 3-6). lib. bdg. 13.00 (978-0-613-87056-6(5)) Tandem Library Bks.

Naylor, Phyllis Reynolds & Naylor, Magdelena R. Achingly Alice. 1999. (Alice Ser.). (YA). (gr. 5-9). 11.64 (978-0-606-16332-3(8)) Tandem Library Bks.

Naylor, Phyllis Reynolds & Vaccaro, Nick. Alice in Blunderland. 2005. (Alice Ser.). (Illus.). 208p. (J). reprint ed. pap. 4.99 (978-0-689-84398-3(4) , Aladdin) Simon & Schuster Children's Publishing.

—Alice on Her Way. 2005. (Alice Ser.). 336p. (YA). 16.99 (978-0-689-87090-3(6) , Atheneum) Simon & Schuster Children's Publishing.

—Including Alice. 2005. (Alice Ser.). 288p. (YA). mass mkt. 5.99 (978-0-689-87074-3(4) , Simon Pulse) Simon & Schuster Children's Publishing.

Neenan, Colin. Idiot! 2005. (Illus.). 160p. (YA). pap. 8.95 (978-0-9746481-1-8(6)) Brown Barn Bks.

—Thick. 2006. 102p. (J). pap. 6.95 (978-0-9746481-9-4(1)) Brown Barn Bks.

Neff, Henry H. The Hound of Rowan. 2007. (Tapestry Ser.: Bk. 1). (Illus.). 414p. (J). (gr. 3-7). 17.99 (978-0-375-83894-1(5) , Random Hse. Bks. for Young Readers) Random Hse. Children's Bks.

—The Hound of Rowan. Neff, Henry H., illus. 2007. (Tapestry Ser.: Bk. 1). (Illus.). 414p. (J). (gr. 3-7). lib. bdg. 20.99 (978-0-375-93894-8(X) , Random Hse. Bks. for Young Readers) Random Hse. Children's Bks.

—The Hound of Rowan. 2007. (J). pap. (978-0-375-83895-8(3)) Random Hse., Inc.

Nellis, Joann Marotta. Spensers Pencil. 2006. pap. 13.99 (*978-1-4259-8451-9(7)) AuthorHouse.

Nelson, Blake. Gender Blender. 2007. 224p. (YA). (gr. 7). pap. 8.99 (*978-0-553-37603-6(9)); 2006. 192p. (J). (gr. 5). 15.95 (978-0-385-74696-0(2)); 2006. 192p. (J). (gr. 5). lib. bdg. 17.99 (978-0-385-90937-2(3)) Random Hse. Children's Bks. (Delacorte Bks. for Young Readers).

—The New Rules of High School. 2004. 240p. (YA). reprint ed. pap. 6.99 (978-0-14-240242-9(7) , Puffin) Penguin Group (USA) Inc.

—Paranoid Park. 2006. 176p. (YA). (gr. 7). 15.99 (978-0-670-06118-1(2) , Viking Juvenile) Penguin Group (USA) Inc.

—Prom Anonymous. 272p. (gr. 7 up). 2007. (YA). pap. 6.99 (978-0-14-240745-5(3) , Puffin); 2006. (J). 16.99 (978-0-670-05945-4(5) , Viking Adult) Penguin Group (USA) Inc.

Nelson, Jim. Crosstown Crush. 2005. 82p. Vol. 1, Bk. 1. (YA). pap. 9.00 (978-1-4116-5266-8(5)); Vol. 1,Bk. 2. pap. 9.00 (978-1-4116-6654-2(2)) Lulu.com.

Nelson, R. A. Breathe My Name. 2007. 288p. (J). (gr. 7). 16.99 (*978-1-59514-094-4(8) , Razorbill) Penguin Group (USA) Inc.

Nelson, R. A. Teach Me. 2007. 272p. (J). pap. 8.99 (978-1-59514-085-2(9) , Razorbill) Penguin Group (USA) Inc.

Nelson, Suzanne. The Sound of Munich. Henderson, Jeanine, illus. 2006. (S. A. S. S. (Students Across the Seven Seas) Ser.). 224p. (J). (gr. 7). pap. 6.99 (978-0-14-240576-5(0) , Puffin) Penguin Group (USA) Inc.

Nelson, Vaunda Micheaux. Beyond Mayfield. 1999. 1p. (J). (gr. 5-9). 15.99 (978-0-399-23355-5(5) , Putnam Juvenile) Penguin Group (USA) Inc.

—Mayfield Crossing. 2002. (gr. 3-6). lib. bdg. 14.15 (978-0-613-43634-2(2)) Tandem Library Bks.

Nemeth, Sally. The Heights, the Depths, & Everything in Between. 2006. 272p. (J). (gr. 5). 17.99 (978-0-375-93458-2(8)); 15.95 (978-0-375-83458-5(3)) Random Hse. Children's Bks. (Knopf Bks. for Young Readers).

Neri, G. Chess Rumble. Watson, Jesse Joshua, illus. 2007. 64p. (J). (gr. 3-7). 18.95 (*978-1-58430-279-7(8)) Lee & Low Bks., Inc.

Nerz, Ryan A. & SparkNotes Editors. Head over Heels. 2004. (SAT Vocabulary Novels Ser.). (Illus.). 240p. pap. 7.95 (978-1-4114-0082-5(8)) Spark Publishing Group.

Ness, Berthetta. Originals: Short Stories for Children. 2007. (YA). pap. (*978-1-57579-351-1(2)) Pine Hill Pr., Inc.

Neubecker, Robert. Wow! School! 2007. 32p. (ps-1). 16.99 (978-0-7868-3896-7(5)) Hyperion Bks. for Children.

Neuschafer-Carlon, Mercedes. Antonio en el Pais del Silencio. (SPA.). 96p. (J). (gr. 3-5). 6.36 (978-84-241-7896-3(3)) Everest de Ediciones y Distribucion, S.L. ESP. *Dist:* Lectorum Pubns., Inc.

Neuschwander, Cindy, et al. Amanda Bean's Amazing Dream: A Mathematical Story. Litzinger, Rosanne, illus. 1998. 40p. (J). (gr. 1-4). pap. 16.95 (978-0-590-30012-4(1)) Scholastic, Inc.

A New School for Megan: Individual Title Six-Packs. 16p. (gr. 2 up). 35.00 (978-0-7635-9234-9(X)) Rigby Education.

Newman, Leslea. Jailbait. 256p. (YA). (gr. 9). 2006. pap. 8.95 (978-0-385-73405-9(0)); 2005. lib. bdg. 17.99 (978-0-385-90230-4(1)) Random Hse. Children's Bks. (Delacorte Bks. for Young Readers).

Nez, John A., illus. One Smart Cookie. 2006. 32p. (J). lib. bdg. 15.95 (978-0-8075-6099-0(5)) Whitman, Albert & Co.

Nicori, Sandi. Minguyaq Elitnauryartuq. Nicori, Sandi & Shantz, Joy, illus. 1998. Tr. of Julie Goes to School. (ESK.). 8p. (J). (gr. k-3). pap. 6.00 (978-1-58084-039-2(6)) Lower Kuskokwim Schl. District.

Nigro, D. M. The Wolfman, the Shrink & the Eighth-Grade Election. 2006. 116p. (J). pap. 13.50 (978-1-931201-66-7(8)) Twilight Times Bks.

Nilsson, Per. You & You & You. Chace, Tara, tr. from SWE. 2005. 301p. (978-1-932425-19-2(5) , Lemniscaat) Boyds Mills Pr.

Nimmo, Jenny. Midnight for Charlie Bone. 2003. (Children of the Red King Ser.: Bk. 1). (J). (gr. 2-6). per. 4.99 (978-0-439-48839-6(7)); 416p. (gr. 4-6). 9.95 (978-0-439-47429-0(9) , Orchard Bks.) Scholastic, Inc.

Nishimori, Hiroyuki. Cheeky Angel, Vol. 13. Nishimori, Hiroyuki, illus. 2006. (Cheeky Angel Ser.). 208p. (YA). pap. 9.99 (978-1-4215-0447-6(2)) Viz Media.

—Cheeky Angel, Vol. 14. 2006. (Cheeky Angel Ser.). 208p. (YA). pap. 9.99 (978-1-4215-0448-3(0)) Viz Media.

Nixon, Joan Lowery. Laugh till You Cry. 2004. 112p. (J). (gr. 5). lib. bdg. 17.99 (978-0-385-90186-4(0) , Delacorte Bks. for Young Readers) Random Hse. Children's Bks.

No es Mi Culpa (It's Not My Fault!) 2006. (Spanish Picture Bks.). (SPA.). 32p. (J). lib. bdg. 15.95 (978-0-8225-6501-7(3) , Ediciones Lerner) Lerner Publishing Group.

Nobisso, Josephine. En Ingles, por Supuesto. Ziborova, Dasha, illus. 2003. Orig. Title: In English, of Course. (SPA.). 32p. 16.95 (978-0-940112-14-8(0)) Gingerbread Hse.

—En ingles, por Supuesto. Ziborova, Dasha, illus. 2003. Orig. Title: In English, of Course. (SPA.). 32p. pap. 8.95 (978-0-940112-16-2(7)) Gingerbread Hse.

—In English, of Course. Ziborova, Dasha, illus. 2003. Tr. of En Ingles, Por Supuesto. 32p. (J). (SPA.). 16.95 (978-0-940112-07-0(8)); pap. 8.95 (978-0-940112-08-7(6)) Gingerbread Hse.

Noble, Trinka Hakes. Jimmy's Boa & the Bungee Jump Slam Dunk. Kellogg, Steven, illus. 2003. 32p. (J). (ps). 16.99 (978-0-8037-2600-0(7) , Dial) Penguin Group (USA) Inc.

—Jimmy's Boa & the Bungee Jump Slam Dunk. Kellogg, Steven, illus. 2005. 32p. (J). pap. 5.99 (978-0-14-240453-9(5) , Puffin) Penguin Group (USA) Inc.

Noble, Trinka Hakes. The Orange Shoes. Ettlinger, Doris, illus. rev. ed. 2007. (General Ser.). 40p. (J). (gr. 1-7). 16.95 (*978-1-58536-277-6(8)) Sleeping Bear Pr.

Nodelman, Perry. Behaving Bradley. 2000. (Illus.). (J). (978-0-606-17911-9(9)) Tandem Library Bks.

—Behaving Bradley. l.t. ed. 2002. 272p. (J). 22.95 (978-0-7862-4779-0(7)) Thorndike Pr.

Noel, Alyson. Saving Zoe: A Novel. 2007. 240p. (YA). (gr. 8 up). pap. 8.95 (*978-0-312-35510-4(6) , St. Martin's Griffin) St. Martin's Pr.

Nolen, Jerdine. Lauren Mcgill's Pickle Museum. Tilley, Debbie, illus. 2006. 29p. (J). (gr. k-4). reprint ed. 16.00 (978-1-4223-5191-8(2)) DIANE Publishing Co.

Norling, Beth. Little School. Norling, Beth, illus. 2003. (Illus.). 32p. (J). (gr. 8-10). 15.95 (978-1-929132-42-3(5)) Kane/Miller Bk. Pubs., Inc.

Norman, Tony. Nervous. Savage, Paul, illus. 2006. 40p. (J). (gr. 2-3). lib. bdg. (978-1-59889-018-1(2)) Stone Arch Bks.

Norris, Shana. Libby Fawcett's Secret Blog. 2008. 208p. (J). 15.95 (*978-0-8109-9474-4(7)) Abrams, Harry N., Inc.

Northway, Jennifer. See You Later, Mom! 2006. (Illus.). 32p. (J). 15.95 (978-1-84507-537-8(4)) Lincoln, Frances Ltd. GBR. *Dist:* Perseus Distribution.

Norton, Tamra. Molly Mormon? Myth or Me? 2002. (Illus.). 170p. (J). pap. 12.95 (978-1-55517-606-8(2) , Bonneville Bks.) Cedar Fort, Inc./CFI Distribution.

Nostlinger. Filo Entra en Accion. 1999. Tr. of Filo Gets into the Action. 15.60 (978-0-606-17656-9(X)) Tandem Library Bks.

Nostlinger, Christine. La Autentica Susi. (SPA.). 176p. (J). 5.20 (978-84-348-2912-1(6)) SM Ediciones ESP. *Dist:* Lectorum Pubns., Inc.

—Nuevas Historias de Franz en la Escuela. (Torre de Papel Ser.). (SPA.). (J). (gr. 2). 7.95 (978-958-04-1013-3(5)) Norma S.A. COL. *Dist:* Distribuidora Norma, Inc.

Nothing Ever Happens 6 Packs. Individual Title. (ps-2). 27.00 (978-0-7635-9467-1(9)) Rigby Education.

Nuhern, G. A. A Christmas List Learn & Have Fun in School & the Magic of Wisdom. 2002. 124p. pap. 10.95 (978-0-595-25320-3(2) , Writers Club Pr.) iUniverse, Inc.

Numeroff, Laura Joffe. If You Take a Mouse to School. ed. 2004. (Illus.). (J). (gr. k-3). spiral bd. (978-0-616-14593-7(4)); spiral bd. (978-0-616-14594-4(2)) Canadian National Institute for the Blind/Institut National Canadien pour les Aveugles.

—If You Take a Mouse to School. Bond, Felicia, illus. 2002. (If You Give... Ser.). 32p. (J). (ps-2). 15.99 (978-0-06-028328-5(9) , Geringer, Laura Book) HarperCollins Pubs.

—If You Take a Mouse to School: Si llevas un raton a la Escuela. Bond, Felicia, illus. 2003. (If You Give... Ser.). (SPA.). 32p. (J). (ps-2). 15.99 (978-0-06-052340-4(9) , Rayo) HarperCollins Pubs.

Oates, Joyce Carol. Big Mouth & Ugly Girl. 2003. (gr. 5-8). lib. bdg. 16.45 (978-0-613-62725-2(3)) Tandem Library Bks.

—Sexy. (J). 2005. 272p. lib. bdg. 17.89 (978-0-06-054150-7(4)); 2005. 272p. (gr. 7 up). 16.99 (978-0-06-054149-1(0)); 2006. 288p. reprint ed. pap. 7.99 (978-0-06-054151-4(2)) HarperCollins Pubs. (HarperTeen).

Oberne, Sharon. Kelsey. 2006. 88p. (YA). pap. 13.95 (978-1-58909-340-9(2)) Bookstand Publishing.

Obstacles in Our Way: Individual Title Six-Packs. (gr. k-1). 23.00 (978-0-7635-9067-3(3)) Rigby Education.

O'Connell, Jenny. The Book of Luke. 2007. 304p. pap. 9.95 (978-1-4165-2040-5(6) , MTV) Simon & Schuster.

O'Connell, Rebecca. Penina Levine Is a Hard-Boiled Egg. Sue, Majella Lue, illus. 2007. 176p. (J). (gr. 4-6). 16.95 (978-1-59643-140-9(7)) Roaring Brook Pr.

O'Connell, Tyne. Dueling Princes: The Calypso Chronicles, Book 3. 2006. 272p. (YA). pap. 7.95 (978-1-58234-900-8(2) , Bloomsbury Children) Bloomsbury Publishing.

—Pulling Princes. 2004. (Illus.). 208p. (J). 16.95 (978-1-58234-957-2(6) , Bloomsbury Children) Bloomsbury Publishing.

—Stealing Princes. 2006. (Calypso Chronicles Ser.: Bk. 2). 304p. (YA). reprint ed. pap. 7.95 (978-1-58234-905-3(3) , Bloomsbury Children) Bloomsbury Publishing.

O'Connor, Barbara. Fame & Glory in Freedom, Georgia. 2003. 112p. (J). 16.00 (978-0-374-32258-8(9) , Farrar, Straus & Giroux (BYR)) Farrar, Straus & Giroux.

—Fame & Glory in Freedom, Georgia. l.t. ed. 2003. 126p. (J). 22.95 (978-0-7862-5994-6(9)) Thorndike Pr.

O'Dell, Kathleen. Agnes Parker... Girl in Progress. Harper, Charise Mericle, illus. 2003. 160p. (J). (gr. 5). 16.99 (978-0-8037-2648-2(1) , Dial) Penguin Group (USA) Inc.

—Agnes Parker... Girl in Progress. 2004. 176p. (J). (gr. 3-6). reprint ed. pap. 5.99 (978-0-14-240228-3(1) , Puffin) Penguin Group (USA) Inc.

—Agnes Parker... Keeping Cool in Middle School. 160p. (J). (gr. 4-6). 2008. pap. 5.99 (*978-0-14-241181-0(7) , Puffin); 2007. 16.99 (978-0-8037-3078-6(0) , Dial) Penguin Group (USA) Inc.

—Bad Tickets. 2007. 240p. (YA). (gr. 7). 15.99 (978-0-375-83801-9(5)); lib. bdg. 18.99 (978-0-375-93801-6(X)) Random Hse. Children's Bks. (Knopf Bks. for Young Readers).

—Ophie Out of Oz. 2005. 192p. (J). (gr. 3). pap. 5.99 (978-0-14-240394-5(6) , Puffin) Penguin Group (USA) Inc.

Off to School: Individual Title Six-Packs. (Story Steps Ser.). (gr. k-2). 29.00 (978-0-7635-9577-7(2)) Rigby Education.

Oh, Jiwon. Mr. Monkey's Classroom. Oh, Jiwon, illus. 2005. (Illus.). 32p. (J). (ps-2). lib. bdg. 15.89 (978-0-06-055722-5(2)) HarperCollins Pubs.

O'Keefe, Susan. My Life & Death by Alexandra Canarsie. 2006. 224p. pap. 7.95 (978-1-56145-387-0(0) , Peachtree Junior) Peachtree Pubs., Ltd.

O'Keefe, Susan Heyboer. My Life & Death, by Alexandra Canarsie. 2002. 217p. (YA). (gr. 7-10). 14.95 (978-1-56145-264-4(5) , Q32889) Peachtree Pubs., Ltd.

Oldfield, Jenny. Watch Out, Wayne. Layton, Neal, illus. (J). mass mkt. 7.99 (978-0-340-85103-6(1) , Hodder & Stoughton) Hodder General Publishing Division GBR. *Dist:* Trafalgar Square Publishing.

Oliver, Lin. The Mighty Mogul. Lindberg, Jeffrey, illus. 1999. (Great Railway Adventures Ser.: Vol. 2;1). 32p. (J). (gr. k-4). 14.95 (978-1-890647-56-8(X)); pap. 14.99 incl. audio (978-1-890647-57-5(8)) RC2 Corp.

Olker, Constance. The Punctuation Pals Meet at School. 2005. (Illus.). 40p. (J). per. 18.95 (978-1-933449-07-4(1)) Nightengale Pr.

—The Punctuation Pals Meet at School. Guzman, Minerva, illus. 2004. (Punctuation Pals Ser.). 24p. (J). (gr. 1 up). 19.95 (978-0-9743348-6-8(3)) Nightengale Pr.

—The Punctuation Pals Meet at School. l.t. ed. 2005. (Illus.). 18p. (J). per. 16.95 (978-0-9761289-4-6(2)) Nightengale Pr.

Olsen, Ashley. Dream Date Debate. 2003. (gr. 5-8). lib. bdg. 13.00 (978-0-613-64706-9(8)) Tandem Library Bks.

—Just Between Us. 2002. (gr. 5-8). lib. bdg. 13.00 (978-0-613-64741-0(6)) Tandem Library Bks.

Olsen, Mary-Kate. Too Good to Be True. 2002. (gr. 5-8). lib. bdg. 13.00 (978-0-613-64774-8(2)) Tandem Library Bks.

Olsen, Sylvia. No Time to Say Goodbye. 2002. (Illus.). 175p. (J). pap. 6.95 (978-1-55039-121-3(6)) Sono Nis Pr. CAN. *Dist:* Orca Bk. Pubs. USA.

—No Time to Say Goodbye: Children's Stories of Kuper Island Residential School. 2002. (gr. 3-6). lib. bdg. 15.25 (978-0-613-78449-8(9)) Tandem Library Bks.

Olson, Gretchen. Call Me Hope. 2007. 288p. (J). (gr. 3-7). 15.99 (*978-0-316-01236-2(X)) Little Brown & Co.

—Call Me Hope: A Novel. 2007. 272p. (J). (*978-1-4287-4131-7(3)) Little Brown & Co.

Olsson, Soren & Jacobsson, Anders. In Ned's Head. Read, Kevin, tr. 2004. 144p. (J). reprint ed. pap. 4.99 (978-0-689-87355-3(7) , Aladdin) Simon & Schuster Children's Publishing.

O'Neill, Alexis. The Recess Queen. Huliska-Beith, Laura, illus. 2002. 32p. (J). (ps-2). pap. 16.95 (978-0-439-20637-2(5) , Scholastic Pr.) Scholastic, Inc.

Onish, Liane. The Alphabet Eurps Visit School. 1999. (Eurps Concept Bks.). (Illus.). 32p. (J). 7.95 (978-1-892522-04-7(7)) Eurpsville USA, Inc.

Orloff, Erica. Balloonatiks: The 1st Goopy, Goofy, Loopy Adventure. 2002. 128p. (J). pap. 5.95 (978-0-9703338-1-0(1) , 174-001) Animagic Entertainment Group, Inc.

Orme, Helen. Moving. 2008. (Siti's Sisters Ser.). 36p. pap. 7.95 (*978-1-84167-689-0(6)) Ransom Publishing Ltd. GBR. *Dist:* International Publishers Marketing.

—Taken for a Ride. 2007. (Siti's Sisters Ser.). (Illus.). 36p. pap. 7.95 (*978-1-84167-596-1(2)) Ransom Publishing Ltd. GBR. *Dist:* International Publishers Marketing.

—Trouble with Teachers. 2007. (Siti's Sisters Ser.). (Illus.). 36p. pap. 7.95 (*978-1-84167-599-2(7)) Ransom Publishing Ltd. GBR. *Dist:* International Publishers Marketing.

—Who's Who? 2008. (Siti's Sisters Ser.). 36p. pap. 7.95 (*978-1-84167-687-6(X)) Ransom Publishing Ltd. GBR. *Dist:* International Publishers Marketing.

Ormerod, Jan. When an Elephant Comes to School. Ormerod, Jan, illus. 2005. (Illus.). 32p. (J). pap. 16.95 (978-0-439-73967-2(5) , Orchard Bks.) Scholastic, Inc.

Oryan, Ellie. Winx Club Alfea School for Fairies Sticker Story. Adriao, Antonio, illus. 2006. 20p. (J). pap. 4.99 (978-0-439-76032-4(1)) Scholastic, Inc.

Osa, Nancy. Cuba 15. 2003. 288p. (YA). (gr. 7). lib. bdg. 17.99 (978-0-385-90086-7(4) , Delacorte Bks. for Young Readers) Random Hse. Children's Bks.

Oshima, Towa. High School Girls. 2005. (YA). Vol. 4. 200p. pap. 9.95 (978-1-59796-084-7(5)); Vol. 5. (Illus.). 208p. pap. 9.95 (978-1-59796-058-8(6)) DrMaster Pubns. Inc.

Owens, Tom. Free to Learn. Pollema-Cahill, Phyllis, illus. 2000. (Cover-to-Cover Bks.). (J). 55p. pap. (978-0-7891-5164-3(2)); 56p. (gr. 1-4). lib. bdg. 16.95 (978-0-7807-9314-9(5)) Perfection Learning Corp.

Oxenbury, Helen. Primer Dia de Escuela (First Day of School) 4th ed. (SPA., Illus.). 24p. (J). 7.50 (978-84-261-2002-1(4)) Juventud, Editorial ESP. *Dist:* AIMS International Bks., Inc.

Packard, Mary. The Missing Tooth. Ulrich, George, illus. 2002. (Hello Reader! Ser.). (J). 3.99 (978-0-439-32094-8(1)) Scholastic, Inc.

Padian, Maria. Brett McCarthy: Work In Progress. 2008. (J). 288p. (*978-0-375-84675-5(1)); (*978-0-375-94675-2(6)) Knopf, Alfred A. Inc.

Pagliarulo, Antonio. The Celebutantes: In the Club. 2008. (YA). (*978-0-385-73473-8(5)); 12.99 (*978-0-385-90472-8(X)) Dell Publishing. (Delacorte Pr.).

Pak, Soyung. Sumi's First Day of School Ever. Kim, Joung Un, illus. 2003. 32p. (J). (ps-3). 15.99 (978-0-670-03522-9(X) , Viking Juvenile) Penguin Group (USA) Inc.

Palatini, Margie. Lab Coat Girl in Cool Fuel. 2000. (L.A.F. Bks.). (Illus.). 96p. (ps-17). 14.49 (978-0-7868-2441-0(7)); Bk. 2. (gr. 2-6). pap. 3.99 (978-0-7868-1347-6(4)) Hyperion Pr.

—Lab Coat Girl in Cool Fuel. 1999. (gr. 3-6). lib. bdg. 11.80 (978-0-613-25908-8(4)) Tandem Library Bks.

—Lab Coat Girl in My Triple Decker Hero. Cole, Henry, illus. 2000. (L.A.F. Bks.). 112p. (gr. 2-6). 14.49 (978-0-7868-2442-7(5)) Disney Pr.

—Lab Coat Girl in My Triple Decker Hero. 2000. (gr. 3-6). lib. bdg. 13.00 (978-0-613-31399-5(2)) Tandem Library Bks.

Papademetriou, Lisa. How to Be a Girly Girl in Just Ten Days. 2007. (Candy Apple Ser.: No. 4). 176p. (J). pap. 4.99 (*978-0-439-89058-8(6)) Scholastic, Inc.

Papademetriou, Lisa. You're in Big Trouble, Brad! Handelman, Dorothy, photos by. 1998. (Real Kids Readers Ser.). (Illus.). 48p. (gr. 1-3). lib. bdg. 18.90 (978-0-7613-2022-7(9)); 32p. (J). (gr. 2-4). pap. 4.99 (978-0-7613-2047-0(4)) Lerner Publishing Group. (Millbrook Pr.).

Papademetriou, Lisa & Tebbetts, Christopher. M or F? 2006. 320p. (YA). (gr. 7-12). reprint ed. pap. 6.99 (978-1-59514-091-3(3) , Razorbill) Penguin Group (USA) Inc.

Papademitriou, Lisa. Sixth-Grade Glommers, Norks, & Me. 2006. 224p. (gr. 5-7). pap. 5.99 (978-0-7868-5170-6(8)) Hyperion Pr.

Pardoe, David. Jasper Tippett's Amazing Journey to Page 42. 2006. (Illus.). 132p. pap. (*978-1-84401-785-0(0)) Athena Pr.

Parente, Peter. Boomer to the Rescue. Ivanov, Aleksey, illus. l.t. ed. 2005. 28p. 15.95 (978-0-9745052-3-7(4) , Peeper & Friends) Tree Of Life Publishing.

Parish, Herman. Amelia Bedelia, Rocket Scientist? Sweat, Lynn, illus. (I Can Read Bks.). 64p. (J). 2007. pap. 3.99 (978-0-06-051889-9(8) , Harper Trophy); 2005. (gr. 1 up). 15.99 (978-0-06-051887-5(1)); 2005. (gr. 1 up). lib. bdg. 16.89 (978-0-06-051888-2(X)) HarperCollins Pubs.

Park, Barbara. Junie B. , First Grader: Shipwrecked. Brunkus, Denise, illus. 2004. 88p. (J). lib. bdg. 18.46 (*978-1-4242-0360-4(0)) Fitzgerald Bks.

—Junie B. , First Grader (at Last!) Brunkus, Denise, illus. (Junie B. Jones Ser.: No. 18). 96p. (J). 2002. (gr. k-3). pap. 3.99 (978-0-375-81516-4(3)); 2001. (gr. k-3). 11.95 (978-0-375-80293-5(2)); 2001. (gr. 1-4). lib. bdg. 13.99 (978-0-375-90293-2(7)) Random Hse. Children's Bks. (Random Hse. Bks. for Young Readers).

—Junie B. , First Grader (at Last!) 2001. (Junie B. Jones Ser.: No. 18). (J). (gr. k-3). lib. bdg. 11.80 (978-0-613-57510-2(5)) Tandem Library Bks.

—Junie B., 1st Grader: Shipwrecked. Brunkus, Denise, illus. 2004. (Junie B. Jones Ser.: No. 23). 96p. (J). (gr. 1-4). 11.95 (978-0-375-82804-1(4) , Random Hse. Bks. for Young Readers) Random Hse. Children's Bks.

—Junie B., First Grader: Aloha-Ha-Ha! Brunkus, Denise, illus. 2007. (Junie B. Jones Ser.: No. 26). 128p. (J). (gr. 1-4). 4.99 (978-0-375-83404-2(4) , Random Hse. Bks. for Young Readers) Random Hse. Children's Bks.

—Junie B., First Grader: Aloha-Ha-Ha! 2006. (Junie B. Jones Ser.: No. 26). (Illus.). 128p. (J). (gr. k-3). lib. bdg. 13.95 (978-0-375-93403-2(0)); (gr. 2-5). 11.95 (978-0-375-83403-5(6)) Random Hse. Children's Bks. (Random Hse. Bks. for Young Readers).

—Junie B., First Grader: Boss of Lunch. Brunkus, Denise, illus. (Junie B. Jones Ser.: No. 19). 96p. (J). 2003. (gr. 1-4). pap. 3.99 (978-0-375-80294-2(0)); 2002. (gr. k-3). 11.95 (978-0-375-81517-1(2)); 2002. (gr. 3-5). lib. bdg. 13.99 (978-0-375-91517-8(6)) Random Hse. Children's Bks. (Random Hse. Bks. for Young Readers).

—Junie B., First Grader: Boss of Lunch. 2002. (Junie B. Jones Ser.: No. 19). (J). (gr. k-3). lib. bdg. 11.80 (978-0-613-63168-6(4)) Tandem Library Bks.

—Junie B., First Grader: Cheater Pants. Brunkus, Denise, tr. Brunkus, Denise, illus. 2004. (Junie B. Jones Ser.: No. 21). 96p. (J). (gr. 1-4). pap. 3.99 (978-0-375-82302-2(6) , Random Hse. Bks. for Young Readers) Random Hse. Children's Bks.

—Junie B., First Grader: Cheater Pants. Brunkus, Denise, illus. 2003. (Junie B. Jones Ser.: No. 21). 96p. (J). (gr. k-3). lib. bdg. 13.99 (978-0-375-92301-2(2)); (gr. 1-4). 11.95 (978-0-375-82301-5(8)) Random Hse. Children's Bks. (Random Hse. Bks. for Young Readers).

—Junie B., First Grader: Dumb Bunny. Brunkus, Denise, illus. 2007. (Junie B. Jones Ser.: No. 27). 128p. (J). (gr. k-3). lib. bdg. 14.99 (978-0-375-93809-2(5) , Random Hse. Bks. for Young Readers) Random Hse. Children's Bks.

—Junie B., First Grader: Jingle Bells, Batman Smells! (P. S. So Does May.) Brunkus, Denise, illus. 2005. (Junie B. Jones Ser.: No. 25). 118p. (J). (gr. k-3). pap. (978-0-375-82809-6(5)) Random Hse., Inc.

—Junie B., First Grader: One-Man Band. Brunkus, Denise, tr. Brunkus, Denise, illus. 2004. (Junie B. Jones Ser.: No. 22). 96p. (J). (gr. k-3). pap. 3.99 (978-0-375-82536-1(3) , Random Hse. Bks. for Young Readers) Random Hse. Children's Bks.

—Junie B., First Grader: Shipwrecked. Brunkus, Denise, illus. (Junie B. Jones Ser.: No. 23). 96p. (J). (gr. k-3). 2005. mass mkt. 3.99 (978-0-375-82805-8(2)); 2004. lib. bdg. 13.99 (978-0-375-92804-8(9)) Random Hse. Children's Bks. (Random Hse. Bks. for Young Readers).

—Junie B. Jones & a Little Monkey Business. Brunkus, Denise, illus. 2007. (Junie B. Jones Ser.: No. 2). 80p. (J). (gr. k-3). 9.99 (978-0-375-84157-6(1) , Random Hse. Bks. for Young Readers) Random Hse. Children's Bks.

—Junie B. Jones & Her Big Fat Mouth. unabr. ed. 2004. (Junie B. Jones Ser.: No. 3). 69p. (J). (gr. k-3). pap. 17.00 incl. audio (978-0-8072-0780-2(2) , LFTR 239 SP, Listening Library) Random Hse. Audio Publishing Group.

—Junie B. Jones & Some Sneaky Peeky Spying. unabr. ed. 2004. (Junie B. Jones Ser.: No. 4). 66p. (J). (gr. k-3). pap. 17.00 incl. audio (978-0-8072-0781-9(0) , LFTR 240 SP, Listening Library) Random Hse. Audio Publishing Group.

—Junie B. Jones & the Stupid Smelly Bus. Brunkus, Denise, illus. 2007. (Junie B. Jones Ser.: No. 1). 80p. (J). (gr. k-3). 9.99 (978-0-375-84156-9(3) , Random Hse. Bks. for Young Readers) Random Hse. Children's Bks.

—Junie B. Jones Is a Beauty Shop Guy. Brunkus, Denise, illus. 2006. (Junie B. Jones Ser.: No. 11). (SPA.). 80p. (J). (gr. k-3). pap. 3.99 (978-0-439-66124-9(2) , Scholastic en Espanol) Scholastic, Inc.

—Junie B. Jones Is a Graduation Girl. Brunkus, Denise, illus. 2001. (Junie B. Jones Ser.: No. 17). 80p. (J). (gr. k-3). pap. 3.99 (978-0-375-80292-8(4)); lib. bdg. 11.99 (978-0-375-90292-5(9)) Random Hse. Children's Bks. (Random Hse. Bks. for Young Readers).

—Junie B. Jones Is a Graduation Girl. 2001. (Junie B. Jones Ser.: No. 17). (Illus.). (J). (gr. k-3). 10.79 (978-0-606-21273-1(6)) Tandem Library Bks.

—Junie B. Jones Is Captain Field Day. Brunkus, Denise, illus. 2001. (Junie B. Jones Ser.: No. 16). 80p. (J). (gr. k-3). lib. bdg. 11.99 (978-0-375-90291-8(0) , Random Hse. Bks. for Young Readers) Random Hse. Children's Bks.

—Junie B. Jones Is Captain Field Day. 2001. (Junie B. Jones Ser.: No. 16). (J). (gr. k-3). lib. bdg. 11.80 (978-0-613-33767-0(0)) Tandem Library Bks.

—Junie B. Jones y el Negocio del Mono. Brunkus, Denise, illus. 2005. (Junie B. Jones Ser.).Tr. of Junie B Jones Little Monkey Business. (SPA.). 80p. (J). pap. 3.99 (978-0-439-42514-8(X) , Scholastic en Espanol) Scholastic, Inc.

—Junie B. Jones y su Gran Bocota. Brunkus, Denise, illus. 2005. (Junie B. Jones Ser.).Tr. of Junie B. Jones Big Fat Mouth. (SPA.). 80p. (J). pap. 3.99 (978-0-439-42516-2(6) , Scholastic en Espanol) Scholastic, Inc.

—Junie B. Jones's Second Boxed Set Ever!, Bks. 5-8. 2002. (Illus.). (J). (gr. 1-4). pap. 15.96 (978-0-375-82265-0(8) , Random Hse. Bks. for Young Readers) Random Hse. Children's Bks.

Park, Frances. Royal Bee. 2000. (gr. 3-6). lib. bdg. 17.60 (978-0-613-29043-2(7)) Tandem Library Bks.

Parker, Roberta N. & Parker, Harvey C. Making the Grade: An Adolescent's Struggle with ADD. DiMatteo, Richard A., illus. 2003. 48p. (J). (gr. 4-7). pap. 11.00 (978-0-9621629-1-6(4)) Specialty Pr., Inc.

Parr, Todd. Otto Goes to School. Parr, Todd, illus. 2005. (Illus.). 24p. (J). (ps-1). 9.99 (978-0-316-83533-6(1)) Little Brown & Co.

Pascal, Francine. The Ruling Class. (YA). 2006. 208p. pap. 8.99 (978-0-689-87333-1(6) , Simon Pulse); 2004. 192p. 14.95 (978-0-689-87332-4(8) , Simon & Schuster/Paula Wiseman Bks.) Simon & Schuster Children's Publishing.

—Terror de la Escuela. Orig. Title: The Bully. (SPA.). 120p. (J). 6.95 (978-84-272-3789-6(8)) Molino, Editorial ESP. *Dist:* AIMS International Bks., Inc.

Passen, Lisa. Attack of the 50-Foot Teacher. 2005. (Illus.). 28p. (J). (gr. k-4). reprint ed. 16.00 (978-0-7567-9665-5(2)) DIANE Publishing Co.

—The Attack of the 50-Foot Teacher. Passen, Lisa, illus. rev. ed. (Illus.). 32p. (J). 2003. (gr. 1-3). pap. 6.95 (978-0-8050-7260-0(8)); 2000. (gr. k-3). 16.00 (978-0-8050-6100-0(2)) Holt, Henry & Co. (Holt, Henry & Co. Bks. For Young Readers).

Passen, Lisa. The Incredible Shrinking Teacher. 2008. (Illus.). 32p. (J). pap. 6.99 (***978-0-312-38017-5(8)***) Square Fish.

Paterson, Katherine. Marvin One Too Many. Brown, Jane Clark, illus. 2002. (J). 23.98 (978-0-7587-6904-6(0)) Book Wholesalers, Inc.

—Marvin One Too Many. Clark Brown, Jane, illus. 2003. 25.95 incl. audio (978-1-59112-254-8(6)); 28.95 incl. audio compact disk (978-1-59112-635-5(5)); pap. 18.95 incl. audio compact disk (978-1-59112-634-8(7)); pap. 31.95 incl. audio compact disk (978-1-59112-636-2(3)) Live Oak Media.

Patneaude, David. Colder Than Ice. 2003. (J). (gr. 4-7). 168p. 15.95 (978-0-8075-8135-3(6)); 167p. pap. 6.95 (978-0-8075-8136-0(4)) Whitman, Albert & Co.

Patricia, Murdoch. Exposure. 2006. 112p. (gr. 3-6). lib. bdg. 14.95 (978-1-55143-523-7(3)); (gr. 7-12). pap. 7.95 (978-1-55143-493-3(8)) Orca Bk. Pubs. USA.

Patterson, James. School's Out - Forever. 2nd ed. 2006. (Maximum Ride Ser.: No. 2). 416p. (J). (gr. 5-17). 16.99 (978-0-316-15559-5(4)) Little Brown & Co.

—School's Out - Forever. 2nd ed. 2007. (Maximum Ride Ser.: No. 2). 368p. (YA). mass mkt. 6.99 (***978-0-446-61889-2(6)***) Little, Brown Bks. for Young Readers.

Patterson, Rebecca & Rees, Mary. The Gordon Star. 2006. (Illus.). 32p. (J). (ps-k). 17.95 (978-0-86264-893-0(9)) Andersen GBR. *Dist:* Independent Pubs. Group.

Pattison, Darcy. 19 Girls & Me. Salerno, Steven, illus. 2006. 32p. (J). (ps). 16.99 (978-0-399-24336-3(4) , Philomel) Penguin Group (USA) Inc.

Pattou, Edith. Mrs. Spitzer's Garden. Tusa, Tricia, illus. 2007. 32p. (J). 9.95 (978-0-15-205802-9(8)) Harcourt Children's Bks.

Paulsen, Gary. The Amazing Life of Birds: The Nineteen Day Puberty Journal of Duane Homer Leech. 2008. 96p. (YA). (gr. 5-9). 6.50 (***978-0-553-49428-0(7)*** , Yearling) Random Hse. Children's Bks.

—The Amazing Life of Birds: The Twenty-Day Puberty Journal of Duane Homer Leech. 2006. (Illus.). 96p. (J). (gr. 5-9). 13.95 (978-0-385-74660-1(1) , Lamb, Wendy) Random Hse. Children's Bks.

—Molly McGinty Has a Good Day. 2004. 112p. (gr. 4-7). lib. bdg. 14.99 (978-0-385-90911-2(X) , Lamb, Wendy) Random Hse. Children's Bks.

—Molly Mcginty Has a Really Good Day. 112p. (gr. 3-7). 2006. 5.50 (978-0-440-41482-7(2) , Yearling); 2004. 12.95 (978-0-385-32588-2(6) , Lamb, Wendy) Random Hse. Children's Bks.

—The Schernoff Discoveries. 1998. 112p. (gr. 5-9). 4.99 (978-0-440-41463-6(6) , Yearling) Random Hse. Children's Bks.

—The Schernoff Discoveries. 1998. (978-0-606-13761-4(0)) Tandem Library Bks.

Pausewang, Gudrun. La Escuela De Los Ninos Felices. Steineke, Inge, illus. 2nd ed. 2002. (SPA.). 28p. (978-84-85334-61-2(2)) Loguez Ediciones ESP. *Dist:* Lectorum Pubns., Inc.

PeachMoon Publishing. Lucky Goes to School. 2007. (J). pap. 9.95 (***978-0-9795831-1-7(X)***) PeachMoon Publishing.

Pearce, Emily Smith. Isabel & the Miracle Baby. 2007. 144p. (YA). (gr. 3 up). 15.95 (***978-1-932425-44-4(6)*** , Front Street) Boyds Mills Pr.

Pearce, Jacqueline. Dog House Blues. 2005. 176p. (J). (gr. 3-7). pap. 6.95 (978-1-55143-360-8(5)) Orca Bk. Pubs. USA.

Pearce, Richard & Story, Ken. Dorkman. 2006. (YA). mass mkt. 8.50 (***978-0-9753367-8-6(9)***) Onstage Publishing, LLC.

Pearsall, Shelley. All of the Above: A Novel. Steptoe, Javaka, illus. 2006. 256p. (J). (gr. 3-7). 15.99 (978-0-316-11524-7(X)) Little Brown & Co.

—All of the Above: A Novel. 2008. 128p. (J). (gr. 3-7). pap. 5.99 (***978-0-316-11526-1(6)***) Little, Brown Bks. for Young Readers.

—All Shook Up. 2008. (J). (***978-0-375-83698-5(5)***); 256p. lib. bdg. (***978-0-375-93698-2(X)***) Knopf, Alfred A. Inc.

Pearson, Mary E. Where Is Max? Walker, Samantha L., illus. 2001. (Rookie Reader Espanol Ser.: Level A). 24p. (J). (gr. k-2). pap. 4.95 (978-0-516-27077-7(X) , Children's Pr.) Scholastic Library Publishing.

—Where Is Max? 2000. (gr. k-3). lib. bdg. 12.95 (978-0-613-54777-2(2)) Tandem Library Bks.

Pearson, Tony. Wesley Harris & the Rotten Patterson Kids. 2004. 117p. pap. 16.95 (978-1-4137-2425-7(6)) PublishAmerica, Inc.

Peck, Richard. The Dreadful Future of Blossom Culp. 2001. 192p. (J). (gr. 4-7). pap. 5.99 (978-0-14-131094-7(4) , Puffin) Penguin Group (USA) Inc.

—The Dreadful Future of Blossom Culp. 2001. 12.64 (978-0-606-21162-8(4)); (gr. 7-12). lib. bdg. 14.15 (978-0-613-35939-9(9)) Tandem Library Bks.

Peel, John. Beware the Metal Children. 1999. (gr. 3-6). lib. bdg. 11.80 (978-0-613-17111-3(X)) Tandem Library Bks.

Pellegrino, Marjorie White, ed. Too Nice. Matthews, Bonnie, illus. 2002. 48p. (YA). (gr. 4-7). 14.95 (978-1-55798-917-8(6)); pap. 8.95 (978-1-55798-918-5(4)) American Psychological Assn. (Magination Pr.).

Penn, Audrey. A. D. D. Not B. A. D. Wyrick, Monica, illus. 2003. (New Child & Family Press Titles Ser.). 32p. pap. 9.95 (978-0-87868-849-4(8) , 8498, Child & Family Pr.) Child Welfare League of America, Inc.

—Un Beso en Mi Mano. 2006. (SPA.). 32p. 16.95 (978-1-933718-01-9(3)) Tanglewood Pr.

—The Kissing Hand. 2007. 32p. (ps-3). 28.95 (***978-1-933718-07-1(2)***) Tanglewood Pr.

—The Kissing Hand. Harper, Ruth E. & Leak, Nancy M., illus. 2006. 32p. 16.95 (978-1-933718-00-2(5)) Tanglewood Pr.

—The Kissing Hand. unabr. ed. 2007. 32p. (J). (ps-3). pap. 9.95 incl. audio compact disk (***978-1-933718-10-1(2)***) Tanglewood Pr.

Penn, Audrey & Wyrick, Monica. A.D.D. Not B.A.D. Penn, Audrey & Wyrick, Monica, illus. 2006. (Illus.). 32p. pap. 7.99 (978-0-9749303-7-4(7)) Tanglewood Pr.

Pennypacker, Sara. Clementine. Frazee, Marla, illus. 2006. 144p. (gr. 1-5). 14.99 (978-0-7868-3882-0(5)) Hyperion Pr.

—Clementine's Letter. Frazee, Marla, illus. rev. ed. 2008. 160p. (J). (gr. 2-7). 14.99 (***978-0-7868-3884-4(1)***) Hyperion Pr.

Pennypacker, Sara. The Talented Clementine. Frazee, Marla, illus. 2007. 144p. (gr. 2-5). 14.99 (978-0-7868-3870-7(1)) Hyperion Bks. for Children.

Per, Sharon Mills. Darkness Before Dawn. 2002. (gr. 7-12). lib. bdg. 14.15 (978-0-613-53804-6(8)) Tandem Library Bks.

—Double Dutch. 2004. (gr. 5-8). lib. bdg. 13.00 (978-0-613-88160-9(5)) Tandem Library Bks.

Perelman-Bernstein, Helen. Heart to Heart. 6th rev. ed. 2007. (High School Musical Ser.: No. 6). 128p. (gr. 3-7). pap. 4.99 (***978-1-4231-0624-1(5)***) Disney Pr.

Peretti, Frank. Hangman's Curse: The Veritas Project - Volume 1. 2008. 352p. (YA). mass mkt. 7.99 (***978-1-4003-1016-6(4)***) Nelson, Thomas Inc.

—Nightmare Academy: The Veritas Project - Volume 2. 2008. 352p. (YA). mass mkt. 7.99 (***978-1-4003-1017-3(2)***) Nelson, Thomas Inc.

Perez, L. King. First Day in Grapes. Casilla, Robert, illus. 2002. 32p. (J). (gr. 1-3). 16.95 (978-1-58430-045-8(0)) Lee & Low Bks., Inc.

Perez, Marlene. Dead Is the New Black. 2008. (Illus.). 204p. (YA). pap. 7.95 (***978-0-15-206408-2(7)*** , Harcourt Paperbacks) Harcourt Children's Bks.

Peters, Julie Anne. Keeping You a Secret. 2005. 272p. (YA). (gr. 9-17). pap. 7.99 (978-0-316-00985-0(7) , Tingley, Megan Bks.) Little, Brown Bks. for Young Readers.

—Keeping You a Secret. 2005. 250p. (YA). (gr. 8-12). per. 14.64 (978-0-606-33459-4(9)) Tandem Library Bks.

—A Snitch in the Snob Squad. 2001. 24p. (J). 5.95 (978-0-316-54561-7(9) , Tingley, Megan Bks.) Little, Brown Bks. for Young Readers.

Petersen, P. J. Can You Keep a Secret? 2000. (Illus.). (J). (978-0-606-18392-5(2)) Tandem Library Bks.

Peterson, John. The Littles Go Around the World, No. 2. Rogers, Jacqueline, illus. 2000. (Littles Ser.). 32p. (J). (gr. 1-5). pap. 3.99 (978-0-439-20300-5(7)) Scholastic, Inc.

Petrillo, Genevieve & Lyon, Lea. Keep Your Ear on the Ball. 2007. (Illus.). 32p. (J). (gr. 3-7). 16.95 (***978-0-88448-296-3(0)***) Tilbury Hse. Pubs.

Petrucha, Stefan. Teen, Inc. 2007. 224p. (YA). (gr. 7 up). 16.95 (***978-0-8027-9650-9(8)***) Walker & Co.

Petrucha, Stefan & Pendleton, Thomas. Crush. 2008. (Wicked Dead Ser.). 224p. (J). pap. 7.99 (***978-0-06-113852-2(5)*** , HarperTeen) HarperCollins Pubs.

Petti, Ken. Zenda 09 Trapped in Time. 2007. 144p. (J). pap. (***978-0-448-44343-0(0)*** , Grosset & Dunlap) Penguin Group (USA) Inc.

Petty, Kate. Starting School. 2007. (***978-1-59604-155-4(2)***) Stargazer Bks.

Pfister, Marcus. The Copycat Fish. 2001. (Rainbow Fish & Friends Ser.). (Illus.). 24p. (J). (ps-3). pap. 3.99 (978-1-59014-000-0(1)) North-South Bks., Inc.

—Fishy Story with Sticker. 2001. (ps-2). lib. bdg. 11.80 (978-0-613-85246-3(X)) Tandem Library Bks.

—Hidden Treasures with Sticker. 2001. (ps-2). lib. bdg. 11.80 (978-0-613-82623-5(X)) Tandem Library Bks.

Phinn, Gervase. What's the Matter, Royston Knapper? (J). 10.99 incl. audio (978-0-85953-556-4(8)) Child's Play-International.

—What's the Matter, Royston Knapper? Fisher, Chris, illus. 2001. 112p. (J). 9.99 (978-0-85953-883-1(4)) Child's Play-International.

Pickles Goes to School. 2002. (J). (978-1-58453-183-8(5)) Pioneer Valley Educational Pr., Inc.

Piercy, Patricia A. The Great Encounter: A Special Meeting Before Columbus. Wilkerson, Napoleon, illus. 2003. 41p. (J). (gr. 2-5). pap. 6.95 (978-0-913543-26-9(8)) African American Images.

Pilkey, Dav. Las Aventuras del Capitan Calzoncillos. 2001. (Captain Underpants Ser.: No. 1). (SPA.). (gr. 3-6). lib. bdg. 13.00 (978-0-613-54408-5(0)) Tandem Library Bks.

—El Capitan Calzoncillos la Ridicula Historia De. 2008. 176p. (J). pap. 4.99 (***978-0-545-02583-6(4)*** , Scholastic en Espanol) Scholastic, Inc.

—El Capitan Calzoncillos y la Furia de la Supermujer Macroelastica. 2003. (Captain Underpants Ser.). (SPA., Illus.). 176p. (J). (gr. 2-5). pap. 4.99 (978-0-439-53820-6(3) , Scholastic en Espanol) Scholastic, Inc.

—Captain Underpants & the Attack of the Talking Toilets. (Captain Underpants Ser.: No. 2). (J). 2004. lib. bdg. 19.95 (978-0-439-68436-1(6) , Scholastic, Inc.); 1999. (Illus.). 144p. (gr. 2-5). pap. 16.95 (978-0-590-63136-5(5) , Blue Sky Pr., The) Scholastic, Inc.

—Captain Underpants & the Attack of the Talking Toilets. Pilkey, Dav, illus. 1999. (Captain Underpants Ser.: No. 2). (Illus.). 144p. (J). (gr. 2-5). pap. 4.99 (978-0-590-63427-4(5)) Scholastic, Inc.

—Captain Underpants & the Attack of the Talking Toilets. collector's ed. 2007. 144p. (J). pap. 9.99 (***978-0-545-02727-4(6)***) Scholastic, Inc.

—Captain Underpants & the Attack of the Talking Toilets. 1999. (Captain Underpants Ser.: No. 2). (Illus.). (J). (gr. 2-5). 11.64 (978-0-606-15830-5(8)); (gr. 3-6). lib. bdg. 13.00 (978-0-613-11382-3(9)) Tandem Library Bks.

—Captain Underpants & the Big, Bad Battle of the Bionic Booger Boy Pt. 1: The Night of the Nasty Nostril Nuggets. 2004. (Captain Underpants Ser.: Bk. 6). (J). lib. bdg. 19.95 (978-0-439-68438-5(2) , Scholastic, Inc.) Scholastic, Inc.

—Captain Underpants & the Big, Bad Battle of the Bionic Booger Boy Pt. 1: The Night of the Nasty Nostril Nuggets. Pilkey, Dav, illus. 2003. (Captain Underpants Ser.: Bk. 6). (Illus.). 176p. (J). 4.99 (978-0-439-37610-5(6) , Blue Sky Pr., The) Scholastic, Inc.

—Captain Underpants & the Big, Bad Battle of the Bionic Booger Boy Pt. 1: The Night of the Nasty Nostril Nuggets. 2003. (Captain Underpants Ser.: Bk. 6). (gr. 3-6). lib. bdg. 13.00 (978-0-613-68836-9(8)) Tandem Library Bks.

—Captain Underpants & the Big, Bad Battle of the Bionic Booger Boy Pt. 2: The Revenge of the Ridiculous Robo-Boogers. 2004. (Captain Underpants Ser.: Bk. 7). (J). lib. bdg. 19.95 (978-0-439-68437-8(4) , Scholastic, Inc.) Scholastic, Inc.

—Captain Underpants & the Big, Bad Battle of the Bionic Booger Boy Pt. 2: The Revenge of the Ridiculous Robo-Boogers. Pilkey, Dav, illus. 2003. (Captain Underpants Ser.). (Illus.). 176p. (J). (gr. 3-6). 4.99 (978-0-439-37612-9(2)); pap. 16.95 (978-0-439-37611-2(4)) Scholastic, Inc. (Blue Sky Pr., The).

—Captain Underpants & the Big, Bad Battle of the Bionic Booger Boy Pt. 2: The Revenge of the Ridiculous Robo-Boogers. 2003. (Captain Underpants Ser.: Bk. 7). lib. bdg. 13.00 (978-0-613-68837-6(6)) Tandem Library Bks.

—Captain Underpants & the Invasion of the Incredibly Naughty Cafeteria Ladies from Outer Space: And the Subsequent Assault of the Equally Evil Lunchroom Zombie Nerds. 2004. (Captain Underpants Ser.: No. 3). (J). lib. bdg. 19.95 (978-0-439-68439-2(0) , Scholastic, Inc.) Scholastic, Inc.

—Captain Underpants & the Invasion of the Incredibly Naughty Cafeteria Ladies from Outer Space: And the Subsequent Assault of the Equally Evil Lunchroom Zombie Nerds. Pilkey, Dav, illus. 1999. (Captain Underpants Ser.: No. 3). (Illus.). 144p. (J). (gr. 2-5). 4.99 (978-0-439-04996-2(2) , Blue Sky Pr., The) Scholastic, Inc.

—Captain Underpants & the Invasion of the Incredibly Naughty Cafeteria Ladies from Outer Space: And the Subsequent Assault of the Equally Evil Lunchroom Zombie Nerds. 1999. (Captain Underpants Ser.: No. 3). (Illus.). 134p. (J). (gr. 2-5). pap. 16.95 (978-0-439-04995-5(4) , Blue Sky Pr., The) Scholastic, Inc.

—Captain Underpants & the Invasion of the Incredibly Naughty Cafeteria Ladies from Outer Space: And the Subsequent Assault of the Equally Evil Lunchroom Zombie Nerds. 1999. (Captain Underpants Ser.: No. 3). (gr. 3-6). lib. bdg. 13.00 (978-0-613-17900-3(5)) Tandem Library Bks.

—Captain Underpants & the Perilous Plot of Professor Poopypants. 2004. (Captain Underpants Ser.: No. 4). (J). lib. bdg. 19.95 (978-0-439-68440-8(4) , Scholastic, Inc.) Scholastic, Inc.

—Captain Underpants & the Perilous Plot of Professor Poopypants. Pilkey, Dav, illus. 2000. (Captain Underpants Ser.: No. 4). (Illus.). 160p. (J). (gr. 2-5). pap. 4.99 (978-0-439-04998-6(9)); pap. 16.95 (978-0-439-04997-9(0)) Scholastic, Inc. (Blue Sky Pr., The).

—Captain Underpants & the Perilous Plot of Professor Poopypants. 2000. (Captain Underpants Ser.: No. 4). (gr. 3-6). lib. bdg. 13.00 (978-0-613-21289-2(4)); (Illus.). (J). (gr. 2-5). 11.64 (978-0-606-18526-4(7)) Tandem Library Bks.

—Captain Underpants & the Preposterous Plight of the Purple Potty People. 2006. 176p. (J). 19.99 (978-0-439-90381-3(5) , Blue Sky Pr., The) Scholastic, Inc.

—Captain Underpants & the Wrath of the Wicked Wedgie Woman. 2004. (Captain Underpants Ser.: No. 5). (J). lib. bdg. 19.95 (978-0-439-68441-5(2) , Scholastic, Inc.) Scholastic, Inc.

—Captain Underpants & the Wrath of the Wicked Wedgie Woman. 2001. (Captain Underpants Ser.: No. 5). (gr. 3-6). lib. bdg. 13.00 (978-0-613-35767-8(1)); (Illus.). (J). 11.64 (978-0-606-21101-7(2)) Tandem Library Bks.

Pilkey, Dav. Captain Underpants Books 1-4 Boxset. 2007. (J). pap. 19.96 (***978-0-545-02287-3(8)*** , Blue Sky Pr., The) Scholastic, Inc.

Pilkey, Dav, illus. Captain Underpants & the Big, Bad Battle of the Bionic Booger Boy Pt. 1: The Night of the Nasty Nostril Nuggets. 2003. (Captain Underpants Ser.: Bk. 6). 176p. (J). pap. 16.95 (978-0-439-37609-9(2) , Blue Sky Pr., The) Scholastic, Inc.

Pin, Isabel. Bumblebee Blues. James, J. Alison, tr. from GER. 2003. (Illus.). 32p. (J). (gr. k-3). 15.95 (978-0-7358-1813-2(4)); lib. bdg. 16.50 (978-0-7358-1814-9(2)) North-South Bks., Inc. (Michael Neugebauer Bks.).

Pinkney, Brian. Jojo's Flying Sidekick. Pinkney, Brian, illus. 1998. (Illus.). 32p. (J). (gr. k-3). pap. 6.99 (978-0-689-82192-9(1) , Aladdin) Simon & Schuster Children's Publishing.

Pinkwater, Daniel M. Big Bob & the Magic Valentine's Day Potato. Pinkwater, Jill, illus. 2000. (Hello Reader! Ser.: Level 3). 32p. (J). (gr. 1-3). 3.99 (978-0-590-63275-1(2) , Cartwheel Bks.) Scholastic, Inc.

—Big Bob & the Magic Valentine's Day Potato. 2000. (Hello Reader! Ser.). (Illus.). (J). (978-0-606-18518-9(6)) Tandem Library Bks.

—Big Bob & the Thanksgiving Potatoes. Pinkwater, Jill, illus. 1999. (Hello Reader! Ser.). 32p. (J). (gr. 1-3). pap. 3.99 (978-0-590-64095-4(X)) Scholastic, Inc.

—Big Bob & the Winter Holiday Potato. 1999. (gr. k-3). lib. bdg. 11.80 (978-0-613-17985-0(4)) Tandem Library Bks.

—The Education of Robert Nifkin. ed. 2005. 192p. (YA). (gr. 7). pap. 6.99 (978-0-618-55208-5(1) , Graphia) Houghton Mifflin Co. Trade & Reference Div.

—The Lunchroom of Doom. 2000. (gr. 3-6). lib. bdg. 11.80 (978-0-613-31437-4(9)) Tandem Library Bks.

—Yo-Yo Man. Davis, Jack E., illus. 2007. 32p. (J). (ps-3). 16.99 (978-0-06-055502-3(5)); lib. bdg. 17.89 (978-0-06-055503-0(3)) HarperCollins Pubs.

Pippenger, Jack G. The Young Rebel. 2007. 292p. 27.95 (***978-0-595-86314-3(0)***); per. 17.95 (***978-0-595-41077-4(4)***) iUniverse, Inc.

Pittar, Gill. Milly, Molly & Henry (book W/dolls) 2006. 28p. pap. (978-1-86972-103-9(9)) Milly Molly Bks.

—Milly, Molly & Jimmy's Seeds (book W/dolls) 2006. 28p. pap. (978-1-86972-091-9(1)) Milly Molly Bks.

S

—Milly, Molly & the Stowaways (book W/dolls) 2006. 28p. pap. (978-1-86972-106-0(3)) Milly Molly Bks.

Pixley, Marcella. Freak. 2007. 144p. (YA). (gr. 7 up). 16.00 (*978-0-374-32453-7(0)) Farrar, Straus & Giroux.

Plourde, Lynn. Book Fair Day. Wickstrom, Thor, illus. (J). 2008. 40p. (gr. 1-3). pap. 6.99 (*978-0-14-241139-1(6) , Puffin); 2006. 34p. (gr. k-3). 16.99 (978-0-525-47696-2(2) , Dutton Juvenile); 2006. (*978-1-4156-8095-7(7) , Dutton Juvenile) Penguin Group (USA) Inc.

—Pajama Day. Wickstrom, Thor, illus. 2005. 40p. (J). (gr. k). 16.99 (978-0-525-47355-8(6) , Dutton Juvenile) Penguin Group (USA) Inc.

—Pajama Day. Wickstrom, Thor, illus. 2007. 40p. (J). pap. 6.99 (978-0-14-240744-8(5) , Puffin) Penguin Group (USA) Inc.

—School Picture Day. Wickstrom, Thor, illus. 40p. (J). (gr. k-3). 2002. 16.99 (978-0-525-46886-8(2) , Dutton Juvenile); 2004. reprint ed. pap. 6.99 (978-0-14-240150-7(1) , Puffin) Penguin Group (USA) Inc.

—Science Fair Day. Wickstrom, Thor, illus. 2008. 40p. (J). (gr. k). 16.99 (*978-0-525-47878-2(7) , Dutton Juvenile) Penguin Group (USA) Inc.

Plourde, Lynn. Teacher Appreciation Day. Wickstrom, Thor, illus. (J). 2005. 40p. pap. 6.99 (978-0-14-240283-2(4) , Puffin); 2003. 36p. 16.99 (978-0-525-47113-4(8) , Dutton Juvenile) Penguin Group (USA) Inc.

Plum-Ucci, Carol. The Body of Christopher Creed. 2000. 256p. (YA). (gr. 7-12). 17.00 (978-0-15-202388-1(7)) Harcourt Children's Bks.

—The Body of Christopher Creed. 2001. 331p. (YA). (gr. 7-17). pap. 6.99 (978-0-7868-1641-5(4) , Volo) Hyperion Bks. for Children.

—The Body of Christopher Creed. 2001. 13.39 (978-0-606-22569-4(2)); (gr. 7-12). lib. bdg. 15.00 (978-0-613-49392-5(3)) Tandem Library Bks.

—The Body of Christopher Creed. l.t. ed. 2001. 352p. (YA). 23.95 (978-0-7862-3509-4(8)) Thorndike Pr.

Podmore, Ron. A Sign to Remember. 2002. (YA). per. 9.95 (978-0-9723537-0-0(4)) Puget Sound Pubns.

Polacco, Patricia. The Lemonade Club. Polacco, Patricia, illus. 2007. (Illus.). 48p. (J). (gr. 1). 16.99 (*978-0-399-24540-4(5) , Philomel) Penguin Group (USA) Inc.

Polacco, Patricia. Mr. Lincoln's Way. Polacco, Patricia, illus. 2001. (Illus.). 40p. (J). (gr. 1-4). 16.99 (978-0-399-23754-6(2) , Philomel) Penguin Group (USA) Inc.

Pollet, Alison. Nobody Was Here: Seventh Grade in the Life of Me, Penelope. (Nobody Was Here Ser.). 2004. 224p. (J). pap. 15.95 (978-0-439-58394-7(2)); 2005. 240p. reprint ed. 5.99 (978-0-439-58395-4(0)) Scholastic, Inc. (Orchard Bks.).

—The Pity Party: 8th Grade in the Life of Me, Cass. (Pity Party Ser.). 160p. (J). 2006. pap. 5.99 (978-0-439-68195-7(2) , Scholastic Paperbacks); 2005. (gr. 5-8). pap. 15.95 (978-0-439-68194-0(4) , Orchard Bks.) Scholastic, Inc.

Poole, Jack. Las Primas de Loreto. 2000. (SPA.). 120p. (gr. 4-7). pap. 7.95 (978-1-58348-610-8(0)) iUniverse, Inc.

Popescu, Petru. Weregirls: Birth of the Pack. rev. ed. 2007. 352p. (YA). (gr. 8 up). pap. 9.95 (*978-0-7653-1641-7(2) , Tor Teen) Doherty, Tom Assocs., LLC.

Poploff, Michelle. The 100th Greatest Day of School. Basso, Bill, tr. Basso, Bill, illus. 2002. 48p. (J). pap. (978-0-439-24405-3(6)) Scholastic, Inc.

Portman, Frank. King Dork. 352p. (YA). (gr. 9). 2007. pap. 8.99 (*978-0-385-73450-9(6)); 2006. (Illus.). 16.95 (978-0-385-73291-8(0)); 2006. (Illus.). lib. bdg. 18.99 (978-0-385-90312-7(X)) Random Hse. Children's Bks. (Delacorte Bks. for Young Readers).

Potter, Ellen. Olivia Kidney & the Secret Beneath the City. 2007. 336p. (YA). (gr. 4 up). 16.99 (978-0-399-24701-9(7) , Philomel) Penguin Group (USA) Inc.

Powell, Jillian. Big Brother at School. Savage, Paul, illus. 2007. (J). 40p. (*978-1-59889-244-4(4)); 33p. (gr. 5-8). lib. bdg. 19.93 (978-1-59889-091-4(3)) Stone Arch Bks.

Powell, Jillian. Recycled! 2004. (Read-It! Readers Ser.). (Illus.). 32p. (C). (gr. k-3). 18.60 (978-1-4048-0068-7(9)) Picture Window Bks.

Powell Zalewski, Amy. Summer School in the City. 2006. (Illus.). 32p. (J). 15.00 (978-0-9773608-2-6(2)) Shiny Red Ball Publishing.

Power, Tim. Tennis Balls & Rotten Shrimp. Bray, Steven, illus. 2006. (Read-It! Chapter Books). 64p. (J). (gr. 2-4). 19.95 (978-1-4048-1664-0(X)) Picture Window Bks.

Powers, J. L. The Confessional. 2007. 304p. (gr. 9). (J). 16.99 (*978-0-375-83872-9(4)); (YA). lib. bdg. 19.99 (*978-0-375-93872-6(9)) Random Hse. Children's Bks. (Knopf Bks. for Young Readers).

Poydar, Nancy. The Bad News Report Card. Poydar, Nancy, illus. 2006. (Illus.). 32p. (J). 16.95 (978-0-8234-1992-0(4)) Holiday Hse., Inc.

—The Biggest Test in the Universe. Poydar, Nancy, illus. 2005. (Illus.). 32p. (J). (ps-ps). 16.95 (978-0-8234-1944-9(4)) Holiday Hse., Inc.

—Bunny Business. 2003. (Illus.). 32p. (J). (gr. k-3). tchr. ed. 16.95 (978-0-8234-1771-1(9)) Holiday Hse., Inc.

—First Day, Hooray! Poydar, Nancy, illus. 1999. (Illus.). 32p. (J). (gr. k-3). tchr. ed. 16.95 (978-0-8234-1437-6(X)) Holiday Hse., Inc.

—The Perfectly Horrible Halloween. Poydar, Nancy, illus. (Illus.). 32p. (J). (gr. k-3). 2005. pap. 6.95 (978-0-8234-1769-8(7)); 2001. tchr. ed. 16.95 (978-0-8234-1592-2(9)) Holiday Hse., Inc.

—Rhyme Time Valentine. Poydar, Nancy, illus. (Illus.). 32p. (J). (gr. k-3). tchr. ed. 16.95 (978-0-8234-1684-4(4)) Holiday Hse., Inc.

Poydar, Nancy. Zip, Zip—Homework! 2008. (J). (*978-0-8234-2090-2(6)) Holiday Hse., Inc.

Pratts, Christine. Tabby Wise for School Secretary. 2005. 61p. pap. 8.99 (978-1-4116-4935-4(4)) Lulu.com.

Preble, Laura. The Queen Geek Social Club. 2006. 336p. (YA). (gr. 12). pap. 9.99 (978-0-425-21164-9(9) , Berkley Trade) Penguin Group (USA) Inc.

Preble, Laura. Queen Geeks in Love. 2007. 304p. (gr. 12 up). 9.99 (*978-0-425-21717-7(5) , Berkley Trade) Penguin Group (USA) Inc.

Preller, James. The Case of the Class Clown. 2001. (Jigsaw Jones Mystery Ser.: No. 12). (Illus.). 80p. (J). (gr. 1-4). pap. 3.99 (978-0-439-18474-8(6)) Scholastic, Inc.

—The Case of the Class Clown. 2001. (Jigsaw Jones Mystery Ser.). (Illus.). (J). 10.79 (978-0-606-20742-3(2)) Tandem Library Bks.

—The Case of the Food Fight. Smith, Jamie C., illus. 2005. (Little Apple Ser.). 75p. (J). (978-1-4156-2391-6(0)) Scholastic, Inc.

—The Case of the Glow-in-the-Dark Ghost. 2004. (Jigsaw Jones Ser.: No. 24). (Illus.). 80p. (J). pap. 3.99 (978-0-439-55998-0(7) , Scholastic Paperbacks) Scholastic, Inc.

—Case of the Kidnapped Candy. 2007. (Jigsaw Jones Ser.: No. 30). (Illus.). 80p. (J). pap. 3.99 (978-0-439-89618-4(5) , Scholastic Paperbacks) Scholastic, Inc.

—Case of the Runaway Dog. 1999. (gr. 3-6). lib. bdg. 11.80 (978-0-613-21301-1(7)) Tandem Library Bks.

—Case of the Secret Valentine. 1999. (gr. 3-6). lib. bdg. 11.80 (978-0-613-16906-6(9)) Tandem Library Bks.

—Case of the Stolen Baseball Card. 1999. (gr. 3-6). lib. bdg. 11.80 (978-0-613-16622-5(1)) Tandem Library Bks.

Preston, Mary Lou. Do You Know What Wildcats Do at School in P. E. Class? Wildcat's First Day in Class. 2006. (J). pap. 8.00 (978-0-8059-7013-5(4)) Dorrance Publishing Co., Inc.

Prevert, Jacques. En Sortant de l'Ecole. (FRE.). (J). pap. (978-2-07-050633-0(9)) Gallimard, Editions FRA. *Dist:* Distribooks, Inc.

Priddy, Roger. First Experiences: My First Day at Preschool. 2003. (Illus.). 16p. (J). bds. 5.95 (978-0-312-49185-7(9) , Priddy Bks.) St. Martin's Pr.

—Let's Get Ready for School. 2006. (Wipe Clean Ser.). 20p. (J). bds. 9.95 (978-0-312-49790-3(3) , Priddy Bks.) St. Martin's Pr.

Principals New Cloth. 1998. (J). pap. 3.95 (978-0-439-04435-6(9)) Scholastic, Inc.

Prinz, Yvonne. Still There, Clare Teacher Guide. 2005. 4p. (J). pap. (978-1-55192-821-0(3)) Raincoast Bk. Distribution CAN. *Dist:* Transition Vendor.

Pritchett, Renee. School's Here, Nothing to Fear. 2006. (ENG.). 28p. per. 12.49 (*978-1-4259-4633-3(X)) AuthorHouse.

Proimos, James. Cowboy Boy. 2003. 96p. (J). 14.95 (978-0-439-41681-8(7) , Scholastic Pr.) Scholastic, Inc.

—The Many Adventures of Johnny Mutton. Proimos, James, illus. 2001. (Johnny Mutton Ser.). (Illus.). 48p. (J). (gr. k-4). pap. 6.00 (978-0-15-202413-0(1) , Harcourt Paperbacks) Harcourt Children's Bks.

Prose, Francine. After. 336p. (J). 2003. (gr. 5 up). lib. bdg. 17.89 (978-0-06-008082-2(5) , Cotler, Joanna Books); 2003. (gr. 5 up). 16.99 (978-0-06-008081-5(7) , Cotler, Joanna Books); 2004. reprint ed. pap. 8.99 (978-0-06-008083-9(3) , HarperTeen) HarperCollins Pubs.

Prose, Francine. Bullyville. 2007. 272p. (J). (gr. 5-8). 16.99 (*978-0-06-057497-0(6)); lib. bdg. 17.89 (*978-0-06-057498-7(4)) HarperCollins Pubs. (HarperTeen).

Pugh, Tracey D. A Show & Tell Lesson. McCracken, Jaime, photos by. l.t. ed. 2006. (Illus.). 32p. (J). 12.95 (978-1-59879-105-1(2)) Lifevest Publishing, Inc.

Pugh, Tracey D. & McCracken, Jaime, photos by. A Show & Tell Lesson. l.t. ed. 2006. (Illus.). 32p. (J). per. 12.95 (978-1-59879-134-1(6)) Lifevest Publishing, Inc.

Pugliano-Martin, Carol. My Little Red Lunchbox Book. Ottinger, Jon, illus. 2004. (Sparkle Shape Bks.). 10p. (J). (ps up). bds. 6.99 (978-1-57151-716-6(2)) Playhouse Publishing.

Pulver, Robin. Author Day for Room 3T. Richards, Chuck, illus. 2005. 32p. (J). (gr. 3-5). 16.00 (978-0-618-35406-1(9) , Clarion Bks.) Houghton Mifflin Co. Trade & Reference Div.

—Nouns & Verbs Have a Field Day. Reed, Lynn Rowe, illus. 32p. (J). (ps-3). 16.95 (978-0-8234-1982-1(7)); 2007. 6.95 (*978-0-8234-2097-1(3)) Holiday Hse., Inc.

—Punctuation Takes a Vacation. Reed, Lynn R., illus. 2003. (J). (gr. k-3). 36p. tchr. ed. 17.95 (978-0-8234-1687-5(9)); 32p. reprint ed. pap. 6.95 (978-0-8234-1820-6(0)) Holiday Hse., Inc.

Pulver, Robin. Silent Letters Loud & Clear. Reed, Lynn Rowe, illus. 2008. (J). (*978-0-8234-2127-5(9)) Holiday Hse., Inc.

Quinn, Zoe. The Caped 6th Grader: Happy Birthday, Hero! 2006. (Illus.). 144p. (J). (gr. 4-7). pap. 4.99 (978-0-440-42079-8(2) , Yearling) Random Hse. Children's Bks.

—The Caped 6th Grader: Happy Birthday, Hero! Spangler, Brie, illus. 2006. 144p. (J). (gr. 4-7). lib. bdg. 11.99 (978-0-385-90304-2(9) , Yearling) Random Hse. Children's Bks.

Rach, W. Dennis. The Goofy Principal at Silly School. 2007. (J). per. (*978-0-9792579-0-2(5)) Rach, W. Dennis.

Radford, Michelle. Almost Fabulous. 2008. 256p. (J). pap. 8.99 (*978-0-06-125235-8(2) , HarperTeen) HarperCollins Pubs.

Rai, Bali. Sold As Seen. 2005. 196p. (J). pap. 9.99 (978-0-340-87729-6(4) , Hodder & Stoughton) Hodder General Publishing Division GBR. *Dist:* Trafalgar Square Publishing.

Raiku, Makoto. Zatch Bell! 2006. (Zatch Bell Ser.). (YA). Vol. 5. 200p. pap. 9.99 (978-1-4215-0283-0(6)); Vol. 6. 184p. pap. 9.99 (978-1-4215-0387-5(5)) Viz Media.

Raiku, Makoto, contrib. by. Zatchbell!, Vol. 3. 2005. 200p. 9.99 (978-1-4215-0208-3(9)) Viz Media.

Raiku, Makoto, creator. Zatch Bell! 2005. 24.98 (978-1-4215-0215-1(1)) Viz Media.

Raintree Steck-Vaughn Staff. El Paseo Escolar de Luis. 1999. (SPA.). (J). pap., stu. ed. 31.05 (978-0-7398-0767-5(6)) Steck-Vaughn.

Rallison, Janette. All's Fair in Love, War, & High School. 2005. 192p. (J). pap. 6.95 (978-0-8027-7725-6(2)) Walker & Co.

—Fame, Glory & Other Things on My to Do List. 2005. 192p. (YA). 16.95 (978-0-8027-8991-4(9)) Walker & Co.

—Fame, Glory, & Other Things on My to Do List. 2007. 208p. (YA). pap. 6.95 (*978-0-8027-9682-0(6)) Walker & Co.

—How to Take the Ex Out of Ex-Boyfriend. 2007. 272p. (YA). (gr. 7 up). 15.99 (978-0-399-24617-3(7) , Putnam Juvenile) Penguin Group (USA) Inc.

—It's a Mall World after All. 2006. 240p. (YA). 16.95 (978-0-8027-8853-5(X)) Walker & Co.

—Life, Love, & the Pursuit of Free Throws. 2006. 192p. (J). pap. 6.95 (978-0-8027-8898-6(X)); 2004. 176p. (YA). 16.95 (978-0-8027-8927-3(7)) Walker & Co.

—Playing the Field. 172p. (J). 2004. pap. 6.95 (978-0-8027-7697-6(3)); 2002. (gr. 5-8). 16.95 (978-0-8027-8804-7(1)) Walker & Co.

Rallison, Janette. Revenge of the Cheerleaders. 2007. (Illus.). 247p. (YA). (gr. 7 up). 16.95 (*978-0-8027-8999-0(4)) Walker & Co.

Rameaka, Thomas. Bee Haven. 2006. (ENG.). 188p. per. 19.95 (*978-1-4241-5646-7(7)) PublishAmerica, Inc.

Ramirez, Linda M. & Salcines, Maria Luisa. Maggie's Visit to the Playroom. Llendler, Christine, illus. l.t. ed. 2000. 16p. (Orig.). (J). pap. 6.95 (978-0-945199-22-9(8) , 956-668-1516) MarLin Bks.

Ramirez, Linda Manning & Salcines, Maria Luisa. Matt's in Trouble... Again! Can the School Counselor Help? Cartee-Cox, Amy, illus. 2001. 20p. pap. 8.95 (978-0-9713839-1-3(X)) MarLin Bks.

Ramona Quimby, Age 8. 2005. (J). (978-1-59564-976-8(X)) Steps To Literacy, LLC.

Ramos, Juan Antonio. El Principe de Blancanieves. (Torre de Papel Ser.). (SPA.). (J). (gr. 4 up). 8.95 (978-958-04-3943-1(5)) Norma S.A. COL. *Dist:* Distribuidora Norma, Inc.

Ramthun, Bonnie. The White Gates. 2008. (J). (*978-0-375-84554-3(2)); pap. (*978-0-375-84555-0(0)); lib. bdg. (*978-0-375-94554-0(7)) Random Hse., Inc.

Randle, Kristen D. Breaking Rank. 2002. (gr. 7-12). lib. bdg. 15.25 (978-0-613-44511-5(2)) Tandem Library Bks.

—Slumming. 2003. (Illus.). 240p. (J). 16.99 (978-0-06-001022-5(3) , HarperTeen) HarperCollins Pubs.

Random House Disney Staff. Finding Nemo: School Days. 2006. (Illus.). 10p. (J). (gr. k-1). bds. 9.99 (978-0-7364-2379-3(6) , RH/Disney) Random Hse. Children's Bks.

Rankin, Laura. Ruthie & the (Not So) Teeny Tiny Lie. Rankin, Laura, illus. 2007. (Illus.). 32p. (J). (ps-2). 15.95 (978-1-59990-010-0(6)) Bloomsbury Publishing.

Ransom, Jeanie Franz. Don't Squeal Unless It's a Big Deal: A Tale of Tattletales. Urbanovic, Jackie, illus. 2005. 32p. (J). 14.95 (978-1-59147-239-1(3)); pap. 8.95 (978-1-59147-240-7(7)) American Psychological Assn. (Magination Pr.).

Rapp, Adam & Boyds Mills Press Staff. Little Chicago. 1998. 256p. (YA). 16.95 (978-1-886910-72-0(3) , Lemniscaat) Boyds Mills Pr.

Rateau, Loy. David's Prayers: A Boy's Perseverance of Conquering the Enemy. 2005. 17.00 (978-0-8059-9834-4(9)) Dorrance Publishing Co., Inc.

Rathmann, Peggy. Officer Buckle & Gloria. Rathmann, Peggy, illus. 2002. (Illus.). (J). 23.64 (978-0-7587-0061-2(X)) Book Wholesalers, Inc.

Rathmann, Peggy. Ruby the Copycat Library. 2007. (J). 18.95 (*978-0-545-00583-8(3)) Scholastic, Inc.

Rathmann, Peggy, et al. Ruby, Mono Ve, Mono Hace. 2003. (Mariposa Ser.). (SPA., Illus.). 32p. (J). (ps-k). pap. 4.95 (978-0-590-50211-5(5) , Scholastic en Espanol) Scholastic, Inc.

Ratner, Susan. Kandoo Kangaroo: Hops into Homeschool. 2000. (Illus.). 20p. (J). (ps-3). pap. 6.99 (978-0-89051-290-6(6) , 303-052) Master Bks.

Rawlinson, Julia. Mule School. Chapman, Lynne, illus. 2008. (J). (*978-1-56148-597-0(7)) Good Bks.

Ray, Belinda & SparkNotes Staff. Sun-Kissed. 2004. (SparkNotes SAT Vocabulary Novels Ser.). (Illus.). 200p. pap. 7.95 (978-1-4114-0080-1(1)) Spark Publishing Group.

Ray, Delia. Ghost Girl: A Blue Ridge Mountain Story. 2003. (Illus.). 224p. (YA). (gr. 5-9). tchr. ed. 15.00 (978-0-618-33377-6(0) , Clarion Bks.) Houghton Mifflin Co. Trade & Reference Div.

—Ghost Girl: A Blue Ridge Mountain Story. 2006. 236p. (YA). 22.95 (978-0-7862-8876-2(0)) Thorndike Pr.

Rayner, Robert J. Walker's Runners. 2002. (gr. 3-6). lib. bdg. 13.55 (978-0-613-78323-1(9)) Tandem Library Bks.

Real Bout High School, Vol. 6. 2005. (YA). pap. 9.99 (978-1-59182-523-4(7)) TOKYOPOP, Inc.

RealBuzz Studios Staff. Hits & Misses. 2007. 128p. (YA). No. 1. pap. 4.97 (978-1-59789-569-9(5)); No. 3. pap. 4.97 (978-1-59789-571-2(7)); No. 4. pap. 4.97 (978-1-59789-572-9(5)) Barbour Publishing, Inc. (Barbour Bks.).

Recess. 2004. (J). (978-1-58453-268-2(8)) Pioneer Valley Educational Pr., Inc.

Recorvits, Helen. My Name Is Yoon. Swiatkowska, Gabi, illus. 2003. 32p. (J). (gr. k-3). 16.00 (978-0-374-35114-4(7) , Farrar, Straus & Giroux (BYR)) Farrar, Straus & Giroux.

—Yoon & the Jade Bracelet. Swiatkowska, Gabriela, illus. 2008. (J). (978-0-374-38689-4(7)) Farrar, Straus & Giroux.

Red & Green Choices by Green Irene: Niki's Next Grade. 2003. (J). per. 14.50 (978-0-9742280-1-3(X)) Green Irene.

Redmon, Angela M., illus. The Adventures of Margaret Mouse: School Days. l.t. ed. 2004. 32p. (J). 6.95 (978-0-9761326-0-8(5)) www.margaretmouse.com publishing co.

Rees, Douglas. Uncle Pirate. Auth, Tony, illus. 2008. 112p. (J). (*978-1-4169-4762-2(0) , McElderry, Margaret K.) Simon & Schuster Children's Publishing.

Rees, Douglas. Vampire High. 2005. 240p. (YA). (gr. 7 up). mass mkt. 5.99 (978-0-440-23834-8(X) , Laurel Leaf) Random Hse. Children's Bks.

Regan, Dana, illus. Messy Bessey's School Desk. 2002. (Messy Bessey Ser.). (J). 12.83 (978-0-7587-7189-6(4)) Book Wholesalers, Inc.

Reindeer Flight School. 2003. (J). per. (978-1-57657-808-7(9)); per. (978-1-57657-920-6(4)) Paradise Pr., Inc.

Reinhardt, Dana. A Brief Chapter in My Impossible Life. (gr. 7). 2007. 256p. (YA). pap. 8.99 (*978-0-375-84691-5(3)); 2006. 240p. (J). 15.95 (978-0-385-74698-4(9)); 2006. 240p. (J). lib. bdg. 17.99 (978-0-385-90940-2(3)) Random Hse. Children's Bks. (Lamb, Wendy).

Reiser, Lynn W. Earthdance. Reiser, Lynn W., illus. 1999. (Illus.). 40p. (J). (gr. k-3). 15.89 (978-0-688-16327-3(0)) HarperCollins Pubs.

Reisman, Michael. Simon Bloom, the Gravity Keeper. 2008. 256p. (J). (gr. 4-12). 15.99 (978-0-525-47922-2(8) , Dutton Juvenile) Penguin Group (USA) Inc.

Reiss, Mike. The Boy Who Looked Like Lincoln. Catrow, David, tr. Catrow, David, illus. 2003. 32p. (J). (ps-6). 10.99 (978-0-8431-0271-0(3) , Price Stern Sloan) Penguin Group (USA) Inc.

—The Boy Who Looked Like Lincoln. Catrow, David, illus. 2006. 32p. (J). (ps). reprint ed. pap. 5.99 (978-0-14-240416-4(0) , Puffin) Penguin Group (USA) Inc.

—The Great Show & Tell Disaster! Cressy, Mike, illus. 2001. 32p. (J). 13.99 (978-0-8431-7680-3(6) , Price Stern Sloan) Penguin Group (USA) Inc.

Reiter, Douglas. Back to School in Cedar Heights. 2006. 79p. pap. 14.95 (978-1-4137-9058-0(5)) PublishAmerica, Inc.

Remkiewicz, Frank, illus. Froggy Goes to School. 2002. (Froggy Ser.). (J). 13.19 (978-0-7587-5334-2(9)) Book Wholesalers, Inc.

—Horrible Harry & the Dungeon. 2002. (Horrible Harry Ser.). (J). 11.49 (978-0-7587-0590-7(5)) Book Wholesalers, Inc.

—Horrible Harry & the Green Slime. 2002. (Horrible Harry Ser.). (J). 11.49 (978-0-7587-0591-4(3)) Book Wholesalers, Inc.

—Horrible Harry & the Purple People. 2002. (Horrible Harry Ser.). (J). 11.49 (978-0-7587-0593-8(X)) Book Wholesalers, Inc.

—Horrible Harry Goes to the Moon. 2002. (Horrible Harry Ser.). (J). 11.49 (978-0-7587-9216-7(6)) Book Wholesalers, Inc.

Rempel, Leah. Hey, Hmong Girl, Whassup? The Journal of Choua Vang. 2004. (Illus.). v, 138p. (YA). pap. (*978-0-9723721-5-2(6)) Hamline Univ. Pr.

Rey, H. A. Curious George & Firefighters. Rey, Margret, illus. 2007. 24p. (J). (ps-k). bds. 9.95 (*978-0-618-89194-8(3)) Houghton Mifflin Co. Trade & Reference Div.

Rey, H. A. & Rey, Margret. Curious George's First Day of School. 2005. (Illus.). 24p. (J). (gr. k-3). 12.95 (978-0-618-60563-7(0)) Houghton Mifflin Co. Trade & Reference Div.

Rey, Margret & Rey, H. A. Curious George's First Day of School. Hines, Anna Grossnickle, illus. 2005. 24p. (J). (gr. k-3). pap. 3.95 (978-0-618-60564-4(9)) Houghton Mifflin Co. Trade & Reference Div.

Reynolds, Marilyn. If You Loved Me. 1999. (True-to-Life Series from Hamilton High: Vol. 7). 32p. (J). pap., tchr. ed. 2.50 (978-1-885356-59-8(5)) Morning Glory Pr., Inc.

—If You Loved Me: True-to-Life Stories from Hamilton High. 1999. (True-to-Life Series from Hamilton High: Vol. 7). 224p. (J). (gr. 7-12). pap. 8.95 (978-1-885356-55-0(2)) Morning Glory Pr., Inc.

—Love Rules. (True-to-Life Series from Hamilton High). 224p. (J). (gr. 8 up). 2003. 18.95 (978-1-885356-75-8(7)); 2001. pap. 9.95 (978-1-885356-76-5(5)) Morning Glory Pr., Inc.

Reynolds, Peter H. The Dot. 2003. (Illus.). 32p. (J). (gr. k). 14.00 (978-0-7636-1961-9(2) , 53509533) Candlewick Pr.

Reynolds, Wendy. Moby for Justice. 2006. 17.00 (*978-0-8059-8861-1(0)) Dorrance Publishing Co., Inc.

Rhae, Sympne. My Name Is Johnson? l.t. ed. 2006. (Illus.). 53p. (J). per. 13.75 (978-0-9770043-9-3(2)) New Global Publishing.

Rice, Bebe Faas. The Place at the Edge of the Earth. 2002. 192p. (YA). (gr. 5-9). tchr. ed. 15.00 (978-0-618-15978-9(9) , Clarion Bks.) Houghton Mifflin Co. Trade & Reference Div.

Richler, Mordecai. Jacob Two-Two Meets the Hooded Fang. Wegner, Fritz, illus. movie tie-in ed. 1999. (Jacob Two-Two Adventures Ser.). 96p. (J). (gr. 3-7). pap. 6.95 (978-0-88776-481-3(9)) Tundra Bks., Inc./Livres Toundra, Inc. CAN. *Dist:* Random Hse., Inc.

—Jacob Two-Two Meets the Hooded Fang. Wegner, Fritz, tr. Wegner, Fritz, illus. 4th ed. 2003. 96p. (J). (gr. 3-7). pap. 6.95 (978-0-88776-686-2(2)) Tundra Bks., Inc./Livres Toundra, Inc. CAN. *Dist:* Random Hse., Inc.

—Jacob Two-Two's First Spy Case. Eyolfson, Norman, illus. 2003. 144p. (J). (gr. 3-7). pap. 6.95 (978-0-88776-694-7(3)) Tundra Bks., Inc./Livres Toundra, Inc. CAN. *Dist:* Random Hse., Inc.

Richter, Jutta. The Cat, or, How I Lost Eternity. Brailovsky, Anna, tr. from GER. 2007. (Illus.). 80p. (J). (gr. 3 up). 14.00 (*978-1-57131-676-9(0)) Milkweed Editions.

Rigby Education Staff. When I Go to School. (Illus.). (J). 20.00 (978-0-7635-6441-4(9) , 764419C99) Rigby Education.

Riggs, Shannon. Not in Room 204. Zollars, Jaime, illus. 2007. 32p. (J). (gr. 1-4). 15.95 (978-0-8075-5764-8(1)) Whitman, Albert & Co.

Rika, Tanaka. Kilala Princess. 20th rev. ed. 2007. (Illus.). pap. 5.99 (***978-1-59816-768-9(5)***, Tokyopop Kids) TOKYOPOP, Inc.

Riker, Richard K. School Days Daze. l.t. ed. 2005. (Illus.). 168p. (J). 15.95 (978-0-9760416-0-3(X)) Safe Harbor Pubns.

Rinaldi, Ann. The Education of Mary: A Little Miss of Color, 1832. 2000. 256p. (gr. 5-9). 15.99 (978-0-7868-0532-7(3), Jump at the Sun) Hyperion Bks. for Children.

—The Education of Mary: A Little Miss of Color, 1832. 2005. 176p. (J). pap. (978-0-7868-1377-3(6)) Hyperion Pr.

—The Staircase. 2002. (gr. 7-12). lib. bdg. 14.15 (978-0-613-59929-0(2)) Tandem Library Bks.

Ripling, Pam. Locker Shock. 2001. 112p. (YA). pap. 14.95 (978-1-59088-970-1(3)) Wings ePress, Inc.

Ripslinger, Jon. Derailed. 2006. 288p. (J). pap. 8.95 (978-0-7387-0888-1(7), Flux) Llewellyn Pubns.

Rivard, Ken. Mom, the School Flooded. Weissmann, Joe, illus. rev. ed. 2007. 24p. (J). (gr. k-2). pap. 6.95 (***978-1-55451-095-5(3)***); lib. bdg. 19.95 (***978-1-55451-096-2(1)***) Annick Pr., Ltd. CAN. *Dist:* Firefly Bks., Ltd.

Rivers, Karen. The Cure for Crushes: And Other Deadly Plagues. 2005. 304p. (J). (gr. 10 up). pap. 6.95 (978-1-55192-779-4(9)) Raincoast Bk. Distribution CAN. *Dist:* Perseus Distribution.

Robb, Diane Burton. The Alphabet War: A Story about Dyslexia. Piazza, Gail, illus. 2004. 32p. (J). (gr. 2-5). 15.95 (978-0-8075-0302-7(9)) Whitman, Albert & Co.

Robberecht, Thierry. Sam's New Friend. Goossens, Philippe, illus. 2008. 32p. (J). (ps-1). 12.00 (***978-0-618-91448-7(X)***, Clarion Bks.) Houghton Mifflin Co. Trade & Reference Div.

Robbins, Jacqui. The New Girl ... & Me. Phelan, Matt, illus. 2006. 32p. (J). (ps-2). 16.95 (978-0-689-86468-1(X), Atheneum) Simon & Schuster Children's Publishing.

Robbins, Jacqui. Two of a Kind. Phelan, Matt, illus. 2008. (J). (***978-1-4169-2437-1(X)***) Simon & Schuster Children's Publishing.

Robert, G. Sillwee Wobbert, Diabetes & Jose at School & Play. 2002. (Illus.). 32p. (J). per. 9.95 (978-0-9704861-5-8(4)) Dream Publishing Co.

Roberts, Barbara A. Phoebe Flower's Adventures: That's What Kids Are For. Sternberg, Kate, illus. 1998. (Phoebe Flower's Adventures Ser.). 68p. (J). (gr. 2-4). pap. 5.95 (978-0-9660366-2-6(X)) Advantage Bks., LLC.

—Phoebe's Best Best Friend. Sternberg, Kate, illus. 2000. (Phoebe Flower's Adventures Ser.). 70p. (J). pap. 5.95 (978-0-9660366-9-5(7)) National Bk. Network.

—Phoebe's Lost Treasure. Sternberg, Kate, illus. 1999. (Phoebe Flower's Adventures Ser.). 68p. (gr. 2-4). pap. 5.95 (978-0-9660366-6-4(2)) National Bk. Network.

Roberts, Laura Peyton. Queen B. 368p. (gr. 7-11). 2007. (YA). mass mkt. 6.50 (***978-0-440-23872-0(2)***, Laurel Leaf); 2006. (J). lib. bdg. 17.99 (978-0-385-90201-4(8), Delacorte Bks. for Young Readers); 2006. (YA). 15.95 (978-0-385-73163-8(9), Delacorte Bks. for Young Readers) Random Hse. Children's Bks.

Roberts, Laura Peyton. The Queen of Second Place. 336p. (gr. 7). 2006. (YA). pap. 5.99 (978-0-440-23871-3(4), Laurel Leaf); 2005. (J). lib. bdg. 17.99 (978-0-385-90200-7(X), Delacorte Bks. for Young Readers); 2005. (YA). 15.95 (978-0-385-73162-1(0), Delacorte Bks. for Young Readers) Random Hse. Children's Bks.

Robertson, Elysia Hill. Tool of Life My Pink School Books. Robertson, Elysia Hill, illus. 2005. (Illus.). 112p. (J). per. 12.95 (978-0-9764444-3-5(7), EJWV-004) E. J. Publishing.

Robins, Eleanor. The Best Week Ever. 2003. (Illus.). 48p. (YA). per. 3.95 (978-1-56254-677-9(5), SP6775) Saddleback Educational Publishing.

—The Easy Way. 2003. (Illus.). 48p. (YA). per. (978-1-56254-683-0(X), SP683X) Saddleback Educational Publishing.

—One Date Too Many. 2003. (Illus.). 48p. (YA). per. (978-1-56254-689-2(9), SP6899) Saddleback Educational Publishing.

—The Right Kind of Win. 2003. (Illus.). 48p. (YA). per. 3.95 (978-1-56254-691-5(0), SP6910) Saddleback Educational Publishing.

—Too Late. 2003. (Illus.). 48p. (YA). per. 3.95 (978-1-56254-693-9(7), SP6937) Saddleback Educational Publishing.

Robley Blake, Colleen. I Can't Wait till I'm Five. 2006. (J). 9.95 (978-0-9767342-0-8(6)) Imaajinn Pubns.

Roche, Denis. The Best Class Picture Ever! Roche, Denis, illus. 2003. (Illus.). 32p. (J). (gr. k-2). pap. 15.95 (978-0-439-26983-4(0)) Scholastic, Inc.

Rockwell, Anne. Welcome to Kindergarten. Rockwell, Anne, illus. 2004. (Illus.). 32p. (J). pap. 6.95 (978-0-8027-7664-8(7)); 15.95 (978-0-8027-8745-3(2)) Walker & Co.

Rockwell, Anne F. Career Day. Rockwell, Lizzy, illus. 2000. 40p. (J). (ps-k). lib. bdg. 17.89 (978-0-06-027566-2(9)); 15.99 (978-0-06-027565-5(0)) HarperCollins Pubs.

—Father's Day. Rockwell, Lizzy, illus. 2005. 40p. (J). (ps-1). 14.99 (978-0-06-051377-1(2)); lib. bdg. 15.89 (978-0-06-051378-8(0)) HarperCollins Pubs.

—First Day of School. 2006. (978-0-06-050191-4(X)); (978-0-06-050192-1(8)) HarperCollins Canada, Ltd.

—Halloween Day. 1999. Orig. Title: Halloween. (Illus.). 40p. (J). (ps-k). pap. 5.95 (978-0-06-443589-5(X), Harper Trophy) HarperCollins Pubs.

—Mother's Day. Rockwell, Lizzy, illus. 2004. 40p. (J). (ps-1). 14.99 (978-0-06-051374-0(8)); 15.89 (978-0-06-051375-7(6)) HarperCollins Pubs.

—Show & Tell Day. Rockwell, Lizzy, illus. 2000. (ps-ps). lib. bdg. 14.10 (978-0-613-22375-1(6)) Tandem Library Bks.

—Show & Tell Day. 2000. (978-0-606-17884-6(8)) Tandem Library Bks.

—Valentine's Day. Rockwell, Lizzy, illus. 2000. 40p. (J). (ps-1). 14.95 (978-0-06-027794-9(7)) HarperCollins Pubs.

—100 School Days. Rockwell, Lizzy, illus. 40p. (J). (ps-1). 2005. pap. 6.99 (978-0-06-443727-1(2)); 2002. 12.99 (978-0-06-029144-0(3)); 2002. lib. bdg. 16.89 (978-0-06-029145-7(1)) HarperCollins Pubs.

Rockwell, Anne F. & Rockwell, Lizzy. Valentine's Day. 2002. (Illus.). 40p. (J). (ps-1). pap. 5.99 (978-0-06-051183-8(4)) HarperCollins Pubs.

Rockwell, Anne F. & Rockwell, Lizzy, illus. Presidents' Day. 2008. 40p. (J). 17.89 (978-0-06-050195-2(2)); 16.99 (978-0-06-050194-5(4)) HarperCollins Pubs.

Roddie, Shen. Baby Goes Too. Stojic, Manya, illus. 2003. 32p. (YA). (978-1-85602-042-0(1)) Chrysalis Children's Bks.

Rodman, Mary Ann. First Grade Stinks! Spiegel, Beth, illus. 2006. 32p. (J). (ps-3). 15.95 (978-1-56145-377-1(3), Peachtree Junior) Peachtree Pubs., Ltd.

—Jimmy's Stars. 2008. 272p. (J). 16.95 (***978-0-374-33703-2(9)***) Farrar, Straus & Giroux.

Rodman, Mary Ann. Yankee Girl. 2004. (Illus.). 224p. (J). 17.00 (978-0-374-38661-0(7), Farrar, Straus & Giroux (BYR)) Farrar, Straus & Giroux.

Rogers, Jacqueline. Kindergarten Count to 100. Rogers, Jacqueline, illus. 2004. (Illus.). 40p. (J). pap. 10.95 (978-0-439-60741-4(8), Cartwheel Bks.) Scholastic, Inc.

—Tiptoe into Kindergarten. Rogers, Jacqueline, illus. (Illus.). (J). (ps-1). 2003. 40p. pap. 6.99 (978-0-439-48592-0(4)); 1999. 32p. pap. 10.95 (978-0-590-46653-0(4)) Scholastic, Inc. (Cartwheel Bks.).

—Tiptoe into Kindergarten. 2003. (gr. k-3). lib. bdg. 14.15 (978-0-613-64686-4(X)) Tandem Library Bks.

Rone, Trenton. Once upon a Hamster. 2003. (YA). spiral bd. 14.95 (978-0-9744437-3-7(5)) Imagination Workshop, The.

Roos, Stephen. The Gypsies Never Came. l.t. ed. 2001. (Juvenile Ser.). 116p. (J). 20.95 (978-0-7862-3469-1(5)) Thorndike Pr.

—Recycling George. 2003. (Illus.). 144p. (J). pap. 4.99 (978-0-689-86351-6(9), Aladdin) Simon & Schuster Children's Publishing.

—Recycling George. 2003. (gr. 3-6). lib. bdg. 13.00 (978-0-613-90717-0(5)) Tandem Library Bks.

—Recycling George. 2003. 22.95 (978-0-7862-5015-8(1)) Thorndike Pr.

Roper, Robert, illus. Dora Goes to School. 2004. (Dora the Explorer Ser.). 24p. (J). pap. 3.99 (978-0-689-86494-0(9), Simon Spotlight/Nickelodeon) Simon & Schuster Children's Publishing.

Rosario, Joann. Secret Swan King. 2004. 27p. (J). pap. 10.00 (978-0-9758746-0-8(8), 1246169) J.G.R. Enterprises.

Rosen, Michael. Totally Wonderful Miss Plumberry. Lee, Chinlun, illus. 2006. 40p. (J). (ps-2). 15.99 (978-0-7636-2744-7(5)) Candlewick Pr.

Rosenberg, Liz. Seventeen: A Novel in Prose Poems. 2002. 160p. (YA). (gr. 9 up). 16.95 (978-0-8126-4915-4(X)) Cricket Bks.

Rosenberry, Vera. Vera's First Day of School. rev. ed. (Illus.). 32p. (J). (ps-2). 2003. pap. 7.95 (978-0-8050-7269-3(1)); 1999. 16.95 (978-0-8050-5936-6(9)) Holt, Henry & Co. (Holt, Henry & Co. Bks. For Young Readers).

—Vera's First Day of School. Rosenberry, Vera, illus. unabr. ed. 2006. (Picture Book Readalong Ser.). (Illus.). (J). (ps-2). 25.95 incl. audio (978-1-59519-662-0(5)); 28.95 incl. audio compact disk (978-1-59519-663-7(3)); pap. 16.95 incl. audio (978-1-59519-658-3(7)); pap. 18.95 incl. audio compact disk (978-1-59519-659-0(5)); pap. 39.95 incl. audio compact disk (978-1-59519-661-3(7)); Set. pap. 37.95 incl. audio (978-1-59519-660-6(9)) Live Oak Media.

—Vera's First Day of School. 2003. (ps-2). lib. bdg. 15.25 (978-0-613-75619-8(3)) Tandem Library Bks.

—Vera's New School. rev. ed. 2006. (Illus.). 32p. (J). 16.95 (978-0-8050-7613-4(1), Holt, Henry & Co. Bks. For Young Readers) Holt, Henry & Co.

Rosensweig, Jay B. & Repka, Janice. The Stupendous Dodgeball Fiasco. Dibley, Glin, illus. 2004. 192p. (J). (gr. 3). 16.99 (978-0-525-47346-6(7), Dutton Juvenile) Penguin Group (USA) Inc.

Ross, Andrea. Chester Earth Ant in School. Ross, Andrea, illus. 1999. (Chester Earth Ant Ser.). (Illus.). 26p. (J). (gr. k-3). pap. 1.95 (978-1-887683-20-3(8)) Storybook Pr. & Productions.

Ross, Jay. Bungalow 29. Klimko, Andrew Frank, illus. 2005. 125p. pap. 12.95 (978-0-9771994-0-2(1)) Visor Bks.

Ross, Tony & Ross, Zoe. Nicky. 2007. (Illus.). 32p. (J). (ps-k). per. 8.95 (***978-1-84270-611-4(X)***) Andersen GBR. *Dist:* Independent Pubs. Group.

Rosten, Carrie. Chloe Leiberman (Sometimes Wong) 2007. 224p. (YA). (gr. 7). pap. 8.99 (978-0-385-73248-2(1), Delacorte Bks. for Young Readers) Random Hse. Children's Bks.

Rothberg, Abraham. Pinocchio's Sister: A Feminist Fable. 2005. 159p. pap. 11.95 (978-1-4116-4347-5(X)) Lulu.com.

Rothstein, Evelyn. My Great Grandpa Dave. 2007. (J). per. 12.95 (***978-0-9786745-1-9(0)***) Marble House Editions.

Rottman, S. L. Shadow of a Doubt. 2005. 224p. (YA). pap. 7.95 (978-1-56145-354-2(4)) Peachtree Pubs., Ltd.

—Slalom. 2004. 256p. (YA). (gr. 7). 16.99 (978-0-670-05913-3(7), Viking Juvenile) Penguin Group (USA) Inc.

—Stetson. 2002. 224p. (J). (gr. 9 up). 16.99 (978-0-670-03542-7(4), Viking Juvenile) Penguin Group (USA) Inc.

Rountree, Wendy. Lost Soul. 2003. 87p. (J). pap. 14.95 (978-1-59129-975-2(6)) PublishAmerica, Inc.

Rouss, Sylvia A. No Rules for Michael. Simon, Susan, illus. 2003. 24p. (J). (ps-1). pap. 6.95 (978-1-58013-044-8(5)) Kar-Ben Publishing.

Rovetch, L. Bob. Hot Dog & Bob & the Dangerously Dizzy Attack of the Alien Hypno Hamsters. Whamond, Dave, illus. 2007. 96p. (J). pap. 4.95 (978-0-8118-5602-7(X)) Chronicle Bks. LLC.

—Hot Dog & Bob & the Exceptionally Eggy Attack of the Game Gators. Whamond, Dave, illus. 2007. 96p. (J). pap. 4.95 (978-0-8118-5604-1(6)) Chronicle Bks. LLC.

Rovetch, Lissa. Hot Dog & Bob Adventure. Whamond, Dave, illus. 2007. 96p. (J). 15.50 (978-0-8118-5601-0(1)) Chronicle Bks. LLC.

—Hot Dog & Bob & the Exceptionally Eggy Attack of the Game Gators. Whamond, Dave, illus. 2007. 96p. (J). 15.50 (978-0-8118-5603-4(8)) Chronicle Bks. LLC.

Rowe, Don. The Sandbox: A Book about Fairness. Archbold, Tim, illus. 2004. (Making Good Choices Ser.). 24p. (C). (gr. k-3). 22.60 (978-1-4048-0665-8(2)) Picture Window Bks.

Rowling, J. K. Harrius Potter et Camera Secretorum. Needham, Peter, tr. from ENG. 2006. Orig. Title: Harry Potter & the Chamber of Secrets. (LAT., Illus.). 300p. (J). 23.95 (978-1-59990-067-4(X), Bloomsbury Children) Bloomsbury Publishing.

—Harry Potter & the Chamber of Secrets. braille ed. 1999. (Harry Potter Ser.: Year 2). 520p. (YA). (gr. 3 up). pap. 17.99 (978-0-939173-35-8(2)) National Braille Pr.

—Harry Potter & the Chamber of Secrets. 2003. 203p. 23.95 (978-7-02-003344-7(X), HAP02) People's Literature Publishing Hse. CHN. *Dist:* China Bks. & Periodicals, Inc.

—Harry Potter & the Chamber of Secrets. unabr. ed. 2004. (Harry Potter Ser.: Year 2). 352p. (J). (gr. 3 up). pap. 46.00 incl. audio (978-0-8072-8207-6(3), S YA 137 SP, Listening Library) Random Hse. Audio Publishing Group.

—Harry Potter & the Chamber of Secrets. (RUS., Illus.). 28.95 (978-5-8451-0947-7(7)) Rosmen-Izdat RUS. *Dist:* Distribooks, Inc.

—Harry Potter & the Chamber of Secrets. 2003. (Harry Potter Ser.: Year 2). 352p. (J). 24.95 (978-0-439-55489-3(6), Levine, Arthur A. Bks.) Scholastic, Inc.

—Harry Potter & the Chamber of Secrets. GrandPré, Mary, illus. (Harry Potter Ser.: Year 2). (J). 2002. 448p. mass mkt. 6.99 (978-0-439-42010-5(5), Levine, Arthur A. Bks.); 2000. 352p. (gr. 3 up). mass mkt. 8.99 (978-0-439-06487-3(2)); 1999. 352p. (gr. 3 up). 22.99 (978-0-439-06486-6(4), Levine, Arthur A. Bks.); 2002. 352p. 75.00 (978-0-439-20353-1(8), Levine, Arthur A. Bks.) Scholastic, Inc.

—Harry Potter & the Chamber of Secrets. GrandPré, Mary, illus. l.t. ed. 2000. (Harry Potter Ser.: Year 2). 464p. (gr. 3 up). 24.95 (978-0-7862-2273-5(5), Large Print Pr.) Thorndike Pr.

—Harry Potter & the Deathly Hallows. braille ed. 2007. (Harry Potter Ser.: Year 7). 34.99 (***978-0-939173-57-0(3)***) National Braille Pr.

—Harry Potter & the Deathly Hallows. GrandPré, Mary, illus. 2007. (Harry Potter Ser.: Year 7). 784p. (J). (gr. 4-7). 34.99 (***978-0-545-01022-1(5)***); 784p. (YA). (gr. 6 up). 39.99 (***978-0-545-02936-0(8)***); 816p. (J). 65.00 (***978-0-545-02937-7(6)***) Scholastic, Inc. (Levine, Arthur A. Bks.).

—Harry Potter & the Deathly Hallows. l.t. ed. 2007. (Harry Potter Ser.: Year 7). (YA). 34.95 (***978-0-7862-9665-1(8)***) Thorndike Pr.

—Harry Potter & the Goblet of Fire. braille ed. 2000. (Harry Potter Ser.: Year 4). 650p. (YA). (gr. 3 up). pap. 25.95 (978-0-939173-37-2(9)) National Braille Pr.

—Harry Potter & the Goblet of Fire. 2003. (Harry Potter Ser.: Year 4). 752p. (J). 30.95 (978-0-439-55490-9(X), Levine, Arthur A. Bks.) Scholastic, Inc.

—Harry Potter & the Goblet of Fire. GrandPré, Mary, illus. (Harry Potter Ser.: Year 4). 752p. (J). (gr. 3 up). 2002. mass mkt. 9.99 (978-0-439-13960-1(0)); 2000. 29.99 (978-0-439-13959-5(7)) Scholastic, Inc. (Levine, Arthur A. Bks.).

—Harry Potter & the Goblet of Fire. 2002. (gr. 3-6). lib. bdg. 17.60 (978-0-613-49674-2(4)) Tandem Library Bks.

—Harry Potter & the Goblet of Fire. GrandPré, Mary, illus. l.t. ed. 2000. (Harry Potter Ser.: Year 4). 936p. (gr. 3 up). 25.95 (978-0-7862-2927-7(6), Large Print Pr.) Thorndike Pr.

—Harry Potter & the Half-Blood Prince, 9 vols. braille ed. 2005. (Harry Potter Ser.: 6). (YA). 29.99 (978-0-939173-39-6(5), HALF) National Braille Pr.

—Harry Potter & the Half-Blood Prince. 2003. (Harry Potter Ser.). 496p. 24.95 (***978-7-02-005323-0(8)***, HAP06) People's Literature Publishing Hse. CHN. *Dist:* China Bks. & Periodicals, Inc.

—Harry Potter & the Half-Blood Prince. GrandPré, Mary, illus. (J). 2005. (Harry Potter Ser.: Year 6). 672p. 34.99 (978-0-439-78677-5(0)); 2005. (Harry Potter Ser.: Year 6). 672p. 29.99 (978-0-439-78454-2(9)); 2005. (Harry Potter Ser.: Year 6). 704p. 60.00 (978-0-439-79132-8(4)); 2006. 672p. reprint ed. pap. 9.99 (978-0-439-78596-9(0)) Scholastic, Inc. (Levine, Arthur A. Bks.).

—Harry Potter & the Half-Blood Prince. 832p. 2007. pap. 14.95 (***978-1-59413-221-6(6)***); 2005. (Harry Potter Ser.: Year 6). 29.95 (978-0-7862-7745-2(9)) Thorndike Pr. (Large Print Pr.).

—Harry Potter & the Order of the Phoenix. 2003. (Harry Potter Ser.). 575p. 25.95 (978-7-02-004327-9(5), HAP05) People's Literature Publishing Hse. CHN. *Dist:* China Bks. & Periodicals, Inc.

—Harry Potter & the Order of the Phoenix. GrandPré, Mary, illus. l.t. ed. 2003. 1232p. (J). (gr. 4-7). pap. 14.95 (978-1-59413-112-7(0), Large Print Pr.) Thorndike Pr.

—Harry Potter & the Prisoner of Azkaban. 2002. (Harry Potter Ser.). (Illus.). (YA). 16.26 (978-0-7587-5662-6(3)) Book Wholesalers, Inc.

—Harry Potter & the Prisoner of Azkaban. braille ed. 1999. (Harry Potter Ser.: Year 3). (YA). (gr. 3 up). pap. 19.95 (978-0-939173-36-5(0)) National Braille Pr.

—Harry Potter & the Prisoner of Azkaban. 2000. (J). tchr. ed. 9.95 (978-1-58130-656-9(3)); stu. ed. 11.95 (978-1-58130-657-6(1)) Novel Units, Inc.

—Harry Potter & the Prisoner of Azkaban. 2004. (Harry Potter Ser.: Year 3). 560p. mass mkt. 7.99 (978-0-439-65548-4(X), Scholastic Paperbacks) Scholastic, Inc.

—Harry Potter & the Prisoner of Azkaban. GrandPré, Mary, illus. (Harry Potter Ser.: Year 3). 448p. (gr. 3 up). 2001. (YA). mass mkt. 8.99 (978-0-439-13636-5(9), Levine, Arthur A. Bks.); 1999. (J). 22.99 (978-0-439-13635-8(0)) Scholastic, Inc.

—Harry Potter & the Prisoner of Azkaban. 2001. (gr. 3-6). lib. bdg. 16.45 (978-0-613-37106-3(2)) Tandem Library Bks.

—Harry Potter & the Prisoner of Azkaban. GrandPré, Mary, illus. l.t. ed. 2000. (Harry Potter Ser.: Year 3). 592p. (gr. 3 up). 24.95 (978-0-7862-2274-2(3), Large Print Pr.) Thorndike Pr.

—Harry Potter & the Sorcerer's Stone. unabr. ed. (Harry Potter Ser.: Year 1). 320p. (gr. 3 up). (YA). pap. 62.00 incl. audio (978-0-8072-1547-0(3)); 2004. (J). pap. 46.00 incl. audio (978-0-8072-8119-2(0), S YA 108 SP) Random Hse. Audio Publishing Group. (Listening Library).

—Harry Potter & the Sorcerer's Stone. GrandPré, Mary, illus. (Harry Potter Ser.: Year 1). (gr. 3 up). 2001. 400p. (J). mass mkt. 6.99 (978-0-439-36213-9(X)); 1999. 320p. (YA). mass mkt. 8.99 (978-0-590-35342-7(X)); 1998. 320p. (J). pap. 22.99 (978-0-590-35340-3(3), Levine, Arthur A. Bks.) Scholastic, Inc.

—Harry Potter & the Sorcerer's Stone. collector's ed. 2000. (Harry Potter Ser.: Year 1). 320p. (YA). (gr. 3 up). 75.00 (978-0-439-20352-4(X)) Scholastic, Inc.

—Harry Potter & the Sorcerer's Stone. GrandPré, Mary, illus. l.t. ed. 1999. (Harry Potter Ser.: Year 1). 422p. (gr. 3 up). 24.95 (978-0-7862-2272-8(7), Large Print Pr.) Thorndike Pr.

—Harry Potter Boxed Set, Bks. 1-7. 2007. (Harry Potter Ser.: Years 1-7). (J). 195.00 (***978-0-545-04425-7(1)***, Levine, Arthur A. Bks.) Scholastic, Inc.

—Harry Potter Boxed Set: Harry Potter & the Sorcerer's Stone; Harry Potter & the Chamber of Secrets; Harry Potter & the Prisoner of Azkaban, 3 vols. GrandPré, Mary, illus. (Harry Potter Ser.: Years 1-3). (YA). 2002. pap. 21.97 (978-0-439-32466-3(1)); 1999. (gr. 3 up). 55.85 (978-0-439-13316-6(5)) Scholastic, Inc. (Levine, Arthur A. Bks.).

—Harry Potter Boxed Set: Harry Potter & the Sorcerer's Stone; Harry Potter & the Chamber of Secrets; Harry Potter & the Prisoner of Azkaban; Harry Potter & the Goblet of Fire, 4 vols. GrandPré, Mary, illus. 2000. (Harry Potter Ser.: Years 1-4). (YA). (gr. 3 up). 85.80 (978-0-641-06631-3(7), Levine, Arthur A. Bks.) Scholastic, Inc.

—Harry Potter Coffret: Harry Potter a l'Ecole des Sorciers; Harry Potter et la Chambre des Secrets; Harry Potter et le Prisonnier d'Azkaban. 1999. (Harry Potter Ser.: Years 1-3). Tr. of Harry Potter Boxed Set: Harry Potter & the Chamber of Secrets; Harry Potter & the Sorcerer's Stone; Harry Potter & the Prisoner of Azkaban. (FRE.). (YA). (gr. 3 up). pap. 43.95 (978-2-07-052929-2(0)) Gallimard, Editions FRA. *Dist:* Distribooks, Inc.

—Harry Potter Coffret: Harry Potter a l'Ecole des Sorciers; Harry Potter et la Chambre des Secrets; Harry Potter et le Prisonnier d'Azkaban; Harry Potter et la Coupe de Feu. 1999. (Harry Potter Ser.: Years 1-3). Tr. of Harry Potter Boxed Set: Harry Potter & the Chamber of Secrets; Harry Potter & the Sorcerer's Stone; Harry Potter & the Prisoner of Azkaban; Harry Potter et la COupe de Feu. (FRE.). 1400p. (YA). (gr. 3 up). pap. 34.95 (978-0-320-03843-3(2)) French & European Pubns., Inc.

—Harry Potter e a Camara Secreta. (POR.). pap. 28.95 (978-85-325-1166-9(X)) Rocco, Editora, Ltda BRA. *Dist:* Distribooks, Inc.

—Harry Potter e a Pedra Filosofal. (POR.). pap. 28.95 (978-85-325-1101-0(5)) Rocco, Editora, Ltda BRA. *Dist:* Distribooks, Inc.

—Harry Potter e a Prisioneiro de Azkaban. (POR.). pap. 29.95 (978-85-325-1206-2(2)) Rocco, Editora, Ltda BRA. *Dist:* Distribooks, Inc.

—Harry Potter e o Calice de Fogo. (POR.). pap. 38.95 (978-85-325-1252-9(6)) Rocco, Editora, Ltda BRA. *Dist:* Distribooks, Inc.

—Harry Potter et la Chambre des Secrets. 1999. (Harry Potter Ser.: Year 2). Tr. of Harry Potter & the Chamber of Secrets. (FRE.). (YA). (gr. 3 up). pap. 13.95 (978-0-320-03778-8(9)) French & European Pubns., Inc.

—Harry Potter et la Chambre des Secrets. 1999. (Harry Potter Ser.: Year 2). Tr. of Harry Potter & the Chamber of Secrets. (FRE., Illus.). 358p. (YA). (gr. 3 up). pap. 16.95 (978-2-07-052455-6(8)) Gallimard, Editions FRA. *Dist:* Distribooks, Inc.

—Harry Potter et le Prisonnier d'Azkaban. 1999. (Harry Potter Ser.: Year 3). Tr. of Harry Potter & the Prisoner of Azkaban. (FRE.). 465p. (YA). (gr. 3 up). pap. 16.95 (978-2-07-052818-9(9)) Gallimard, Editions FRA. *Dist:* Distribooks, Inc.

—Harry Potter et l'Ecole des Sorciers. 3rd ed. 1998. (Harry Potter Ser.: Year 1). Tr. of Harry Potter & the Sorcerer's Stone. (FRE., Illus.). (YA). (gr. 3 up). pap. 14.95 (978-2-07-050142-7(6)) Distribooks, Inc.

S

—Harry Potter et l'Ecole des Sorciers. 1999. (Harry Potter Ser.: Year 1). Tr. of Harry Potter & the Sorcerer's Stone. (FRE.). (YA). (gr. 3 up). pap. 16.95 (978-0-320-03780-1(0)) French & European Pubns., Inc.

—Harry Potter et l'Ecole des Sorciers. 2007. Tr. of Harry Potter & the Sorcerer's Stone. 311p. pap. 14.95 ***(978-2-07-061236-9(8))*** Gallimard, Editions FRA. *Dist:* Distribooks, Inc.

—Harry Potter und der Gefangene von Azkaban. 1999. (Harry Potter Ser.: Year 3). Tr. of Harry Potter & the Prisoner of Azkaban. (GER.). (YA). (gr. 3 up). pap. 34.95 (978-3-551-55169-6(3)) Carlsen Verlag DEU. *Dist:* Distribooks, Inc.

—Harry Potter und der Stein der Weisen. 1999. (Harry Potter Ser.: Year 1). (GER.). 335p. (YA). (gr. 3 up). pap. 34.95 (978-3-551-55167-2(7)) Carlsen Verlag DEU. *Dist:* Distribooks, Inc.

—Harry Potter und die Kammer des Schreckens. 1999. (Harry Potter Ser.: Year 2). Tr. of Harry Potter & Chamber of Secrets. (GER.). (YA). (gr. 3 up). pap. 36.95 (978-3-551-55168-9(5)) Carlsen Verlag DEU. *Dist:* Distribooks, Inc.

—Harry Potter y el Caliz de Fuego. 2001. (SPA.). (gr. 3-6). lib. bdg. 26.35 (978-0-613-35957-3(7)) Tandem Library Bks.

—Harry Potter y el Prisionero de Azkaban. 2004. (Harry Potter Ser.: Year 3). (SPA., Illus.). 360p. (gr. 3 up). 17.95 (978-84-7888-519-0(6) , SAL1889) Emece Editores ESP. *Dist:* Lectorum Pubns., Inc.

—Harry Potter y el Prisionero de Azkaban. 2000. (Harry Potter Ser.: Year 3). (SPA.). (YA). (gr. 3 up). 16.95 (978-0-320-03783-2(5)) French & European Pubns., Inc.

—Harry Potter y el Prisionero de Azkaban. 2001. (SPA.). (gr. 3-6). lib. bdg. 21.10 (978-0-613-35958-0(5)) Tandem Library Bks.

—Harry Potter y la Camara Secreta. 2004. (Harry Potter Ser.: Year 2). (SPA., Illus.). 288p. (YA). (gr. 3 up). 15.95 (978-84-7888-495-7(5) , SAL4595) Emece Editores ESP. *Dist:* Lectorum Pubns., Inc.

—Harry Potter y la Camara Secreta. 1999. (Harry Potter Ser.: Year 2). (SPA.). (YA). (gr. 3 up). 14.95 (978-0-320-03781-8(9)) French & European Pubns., Inc.

—Harry Potter y la Camara Secreta. 2001. (SPA.). (gr. 3-6). lib. bdg. 18.80 (978-0-613-35959-7(3)) Tandem Library Bks.

—Harry Potter y la Piedra Filosofal. 2004. (Harry Potter Ser.: Bk. 1). (SPA., Illus.). 256p. (YA). (gr. 7 up). 15.95 (978-84-7888-445-2(9) , SAL2819) Emece Editores ESP. *Dist:* Lectorum Pubns., Inc.

—Harry Potter y la Piedra Filosofal. 1999. (Harry Potter Ser.: Year 1). (SPA.). (YA). (gr. 3 up). 14.95 (978-0-320-03782-5(7)) French & European Pubns., Inc.

—Harry Potter y la Piedra Filosofal. 2001. (SPA.). (gr. 3-6). lib. bdg. 18.80 (978-0-613-35960-3(7)) Tandem Library Bks.

Rowling, J. K. & Dale, Jim. Harry Potter & the Goblet of Fire. unabr. ed. 2004. (Harry Potter Ser.). 752p. (J). pap. 65.00 incl. audio (978-0-8072-1196-0(6) , S YA 270 SP, Listening Library) Random Hse. Audio Publishing Group.

Roy, Ron. The School Skeleton. Gurney, John Steven, illus. 2003. (A to Z Mysteries Ser.: No. 19). 96p. (J). (gr. 2-5). lib. bdg. 11.99 (978-0-375-91368-6(8)); pap. 3.99 (978-0-375-81368-9(3)) Random Hse. Children's Bks. (Random Hse. Bks. for Young Readers).

—The School Skeleton. Gurney, John Steven, illus. 2003. (A to Z Mysteries Ser.: No. 19). (J). (gr. k-3). lib. bdg. 11.80 (978-0-613-62405-3(X)) Tandem Library Bks.

Rubel, Nicole. Ham & Pickles: First Day of School. 2006. (Illus.). 32p. (J). 16.00 (978-0-15-205039-9(6)) Harcourt Trade Pubs.

Ruby, Laura. Good Girls. 2008. 304p. (J). pap. 8.99 ***(978-0-06-088225-9(5));*** 2006. 288p. (J). lib. bdg. 17.89 (978-0-06-088224-2(7)); 2006. 288p. (YA). 16.99 (978-0-06-088223-5(9)) HarperCollins Pubs. (HarperTeen).

Ruckdeschel, Liz & James, Sara. What If— You Broke All the Rules? A Choose Your Destiny Novel. 2007. (Illus.). 291p. (YA). ***(978-1-4287-5664-9(7)*** , Delacorte Pr.) Dell Publishing.

Ruckdeschel, Liz & James, Sara. What If ... Everyone Knew Your Name. 2006. 352p. (YA). (gr. 7). pap. 8.95 (978-0-385-73296-3(1)); lib. bdg. 10.99 (978-0-385-90317-2(0)) Random Hse. Children's Bks. (Delacorte Bks. for Young Readers).

Rudkin, Nancy. A Dragon at School. 2005. 28p. (J). 9.95 (978-1-4116-3877-8(8)) Lulu.com.

Rue, Nancy. Sophie Loses the Lead, Vol. 11. 2006. (Faithgirlz! Ser.). 144p. (J). pap. 6.99 (978-0-310-71026-4(X)) Zonderkidz.

—Sophie Loves Jimmy, Vol. 10. 2006. (Faithgirlz Ser.). 144p. (J). pap. 6.99 (978-0-310-71025-7(1)) Zonderkidz.

—Sophie's Encore, Vol. 12. 2006. (Faithgirlz! Ser.). (Illus.). 144p. (J). pap. 6.99 (978-0-310-71027-1(8)) Zonderkidz.

Rue, Nancy N. Lily Rules!, No. 8. 2002. (Ywof Library). (Illus.). 128p. (J). pap. 5.99 (978-0-310-70250-4(X)) Zonderkidz.

—Lily Speaks! 2002. (gr. 3-6). lib. bdg. 13.00 (978-0-613-71714-4(7)) Tandem Library Bks.

—Lily the Rebel. 2001. (gr. 3-6). lib. bdg. 13.00 (978-0-613-71721-2(X)) Tandem Library Bks.

—Lily!lights, Action. 2002. (gr. 3-6). lib. bdg. 13.00 (978-0-613-71698-7(1)) Tandem Library Bks.

—Sophie Breaks the Code, Vol. 7. 2005. (Faithgirlz Ser.). (Illus.). 144p. (J). pap. 6.99 (978-0-310-71022-6(7)) Zonderkidz.

—Sophie Flakes Out, Vol. 9. 2006. (Faithgirlz Ser.). (Illus.). 128p. (J). pap. 6.99 (978-0-310-71024-0(3)) Zonderkidz.

—Totally Unfair. 2005. (Invert / 'Nama Beach High Ser.). 160p. (YA). pap. 6.99 (978-0-310-25183-5(4)) Zondervan.

Rue, Nancy N. & Youth Specialties Staff. New Girl in Town. 2004. (Invert / 'Nama Beach High Ser.: No. 1). 176p. (J). pap. 6.99 (978-0-310-24399-1(8)) Zondervan.

Runyon, Brent. Maybe. 2006. 208p. (YA). (gr. 9). 18.99 (978-0-375-93543-5(6)); 16.95 (978-0-375-83543-8(1)) Random Hse. Children's Bks. (Knopf Bks. for Young Readers).

Rupert Goes to School: Level M, 6 vols. 128p. (gr. 2-3). 49.95 (978-0-7699-1028-4(9)) Shortland Pubns. (U. S. A.) Inc.

Rusackas, Francesca. I Love You All Day Long. Burris, Priscilla, illus. 32p. (J). (ps-k). 2002. 12.99 (978-0-06-050276-8(2)); 2004. reprint ed. pap. 6.99 (978-0-06-050278-2(9) , Harper Trophy) HarperCollins Pubs.

Russo, Marisabina. A Portrait of Pia. 2007. (Illus.). 240p. (YA). (gr. 6-8). 17.00 (978-0-15-205577-6(0)) Harcourt Trade Pubs.

Ryan, Darlene. Responsible. 2007. (Orca Soundings Ser.). 112p. (YA). (gr. 7 up). pap. ***(978-1-55143-685-2(X));*** lib. bdg. ***(978-1-55143-687-6(6))*** Orca Bk. Pubs.

Ryan, Pam Muñoz. Becoming Naomi Leon. 2004. 240p. (J). (gr. 4-7). pap. 16.95 (978-0-439-26969-8(5) , Scholastic Pr.) Scholastic, Inc.

Ryan, Sara. Empress of the World. 224p. (YA). (gr. 7). 2003. pap. 7.99 (978-0-14-250059-0(3) , Puffin); 2001. 15.99 (978-0-670-89688-2(8) , Viking Juvenile) Penguin Group (USA) Inc.

Rylant, Cynthia. The Ticky-Tacky Doll. Stevenson, Harvey, illus. 2002. 32p. (J). (gr. k-2). 16.00 (978-0-15-201078-2(5)) Harcourt Children's Bks.

Sabin, E. Rose. A School for Sorcery. rev. ed. 2002. 318p. 17.95 (978-0-7653-0289-2(6) , Forge Bks.) Doherty, Tom Assocs., LLC.

Sachar, Louis. Class President. 1999. (Marvin Redpost Ser.: No. 5). (Illus.). 80p. (J). (gr. k-3). lib. bdg. 11.99 (978-0-679-98999-8(4) , Random Hse. Bks. for Young Readers) Random Hse. Children's Bks.

—Class President. Wummer, Amy, illus. 1999. (Marvin Redpost Ser.: Vol. 5). 80p. (J). (gr. k-3). 3.99 (978-0-679-88999-1(X) , Random Hse. Bks. for Young Readers) Random Hse. Children's Bks.

—Class President. 1999. (Marvin Redpost Ser.: Bk. 5). (J). (978-0-606-16895-3(8)); (gr. 3-6). lib. bdg. 11.80 (978-0-613-16151-0(3)) Tandem Library Bks.

—A Flying Birthday Cake? Wummer, Amy, illus. 1999. (Marvin Redpost Ser.: Bk. 6). (J). (gr. k-3). 96p. lib. bdg. 11.99 (978-0-679-99000-0(3)); 80p. pap. 3.99 (978-0-679-89000-3(9)) Random Hse. Children's Bks. (Random Hse. Bks. for Young Readers).

—A Flying Birthday Cake? 1999. (Marvin Redpost Ser.: Bk. 6). (978-0-606-17524-1(5)) Tandem Library Bks.

—A Flying Birthday Cake. Wummer, Amy, illus. 1999. (Marvin Redpost Ser.: Bk. 6). 76p. (J). (ps-ps). lib. bdg. 11.80 (978-0-613-19523-2(X)) Tandem Library Bks.

—Sideways Stories from Wayside School. McCauley, Adam, illus. rev. ed. 1998. (Wayside School Ser.). 128p. (J). (gr. 5 up). pap. 5.99 (978-0-380-73148-0(7) , Harper Trophy) HarperCollins Pubs.

—Sideways Stories from Wayside School. 124p. (J). (gr. 3-5). pap. 4.99 (978-0-8072-1458-9(2) , Listening Library) Random Hse. Audio Publishing Group.

—Wayside School Gets a Little Stranger. McCauley, Adam, illus. rev. ed. 1998. (Wayside School Ser.). 160p. (J). (gr. 5 up). pap. 6.50 (978-0-380-73149-7(5) , Harper Trophy) HarperCollins Pubs.

—Wayside School Gets a Little Stranger. 150p. (J). (gr. 3-5). pap. 4.99 (978-0-8072-1543-2(0)); 2004. pap. 29.00 incl. audio (978-0-8072-8141-3(7) , S YA 116 SP) Random Hse. Audio Publishing Group. (Listening Library).

—Wayside School Is Falling Down. Schick, Joel, illus. 2002. (J). 14.47 (978-0-7587-5640-4(2)) Book Wholesalers, Inc.

—Wayside School Is Falling Down. McCauley, Adam, illus. rev. ed. 1998. (Wayside School Ser.). 160p. (J). (gr. 5 up). pap. 5.99 (978-0-380-73150-3(9)) HarperCollins Pubs.

—Wayside School Is Falling Down. 179p. (J). (gr. 3-5). pap. 4.99 (978-0-8072-1461-9(2) , Listening Library) Random Hse. Audio Publishing Group.

—Why Pick on Me? 1999. (Marvin Redpost Ser.: Bk. 2). (J). (gr. k-3). lib. bdg. 11.80 (978-0-7857-0343-3(8)) Tandem Library Bks.

Sachs, Marilyn. The Fat Girl. 2nd ed. 2007. 240p. (J). pap. 8.95 (978-0-7387-1000-6(8) , Flux) Llewellyn Pubns.

Sadi, Hendrik E. Ernholder. 2002. 165p. (J). pap. 12.95 (978-0-595-21870-7(9) , Writers Club Pr.) iUniverse, Inc.

Sadler, Marilyn. Honey Bunny's Honey Bear. Bollen, Roger, illus. 2008. (Step into Reading Ser.). (J). (978-0-375-84326-6(4)); lib. bdg. 11.99 (978-0-375-94326-3(9)) Random Hse. Children's Bks.

Saksena, Kate. Hang on in There, Shelley. 2003. 219p. (J). 16.95 (978-1-58234-822-3(7) , Bloomsbury Children) Bloomsbury Publishing.

Sakura & the New Boy. 2001. (gr. 3-6). lib. bdg. 11.80 (978-0-613-33015-2(3)) Tandem Library Bks.

Salant, Sherry Ann. Skipping School. l.t. ed. 2001. 24p. 6.95 (978-0-9712952-0-9(4)) Storywriter Pr.

Saldana, Rene, Jr. Finding Our Way. 2004. 128p. (YA). (gr. 7). pap. 5.99 (978-0-440-23790-7(4) , Laurel Leaf) Random Hse. Children's Bks.

Saltzberg, Barney. Crazy Hair Day. Saltzberg, Barney, illus. 2003. (Illus.). 32p. (J). (gr. k-3). 15.99 (978-0-7636-1954-1(X)) Candlewick Pr.

—Star of the Week. Saltzberg, Barney, illus. 2006. (Illus.). 32p. (J). (gr. k-3). 15.99 (978-0-7636-2914-4(6)) Candlewick Pr.

Salzmann, Mary Elizabeth. Presidential Seal. Nobens, C. A., illus. 2007. (Fact & Fiction Ser.). 24p. (J). pap. (978-1-59928-465-1(0)); 21.35 (978-1-59928-464-4(2)) ABDO Publishing Co.

Sanchez, Alex. Getting It. 2006. 224p. (YA). 16.95 (978-1-4169-0896-8(X)) Simon & Schuster Children's Publishing.

—The God Box. 2007. 272p. (YA). (gr. 7 up). 16.99 ***(978-1-4169-0899-9(4)*** , Simon & Schuster Children's Publishing) Simon & Schuster Children's Publishing.

—Rainbow Boys. (YA). 2003. 272p. 8.99 (978-0-689-85770-6(5) , Simon Pulse); 2001. 256p. (gr. 9 up). 17.00 (978-0-689-84100-2(0)) Simon & Schuster Children's Publishing.

—Rainbow Boys. 2003. (gr. 7-12). lib. bdg. 16.45 (978-0-613-66434-9(5)) Tandem Library Bks.

—Rainbow High. 2003. (Illus.). 272p. (YA). 16.95 (978-0-689-85477-4(3)) Simon & Schuster Children's Publishing.

—So Hard to Say. 240p. 2004. (J). 15.95 (978-0-689-86564-0(3)); 2006. (Illus.). (YA). reprint ed. pap. 7.99 (978-1-4169-1189-0(8) , Aladdin) Simon & Schuster Children's Publishing.

Sanchez, Alex & Frost, Michael. Getting It. 2007. 240p. (YA). pap. 8.99 ***(978-1-4169-0898-2(6)*** , Simon Pulse) Simon & Schuster Children's Publishing.

Sander, Sonia. Let's Go to School. 2006. (Barney Ser.). (Illus.). 6p. (J). bds. 7.99 (978-0-439-82952-6(6) , Scholastic) Scholastic, Inc.

Sander, Sonia & Aboff, Marcie. Get Ready for School. Harpster, Steve, illus. 2006. (Scribble & Sing Ser.). 80p. (J). 4.99 (978-1-4169-2729-7(8) , Simon Scribbles) Simon & Schuster Children's Publishing.

Sandin, Joan. Coyote School News. Sandin, Joan, illus. rev. ed. 2003. (Illus.). 48p. (J). 17.95 (978-0-8050-6558-9(X) , Holt, Henry & Co. Bks. For Young Readers) Holt, Henry & Co.

Santi, Raymond M. Me & Doc. 2004. 182p. pap. 19.95 (978-1-4137-2585-8(6)) PublishAmerica, Inc.

Santomero, Angela C. Blue Goes to School. Levy, David B., illus. 2000. (Blue's Clues Ser.). 24p. (J). (ps-k). pap. 3.99 (978-0-689-83280-2(X) , Simon Spotlight/ Nickelodeon) Simon & Schuster Children's Publishing.

—Blue Goes to School. 2000. (gr. k-3). lib. bdg. 11.25 (978-0-613-24384-1(6)) Tandem Library Bks.

—Blue Va a la Escuela. 2003. Tr. of Blue Goes to School. (SPA.). (ps-2). lib. bdg. 11.25 (978-0-613-90465-0(6)) Tandem Library Bks.

—Blue va a la escuela. Levy, David B., illus. 2003. (Blue's Clues Ser.).Tr. of Blue Goes to School. (SPA.). 24p. (J). 3.99 (978-0-689-86308-0(X) , Libros Para Ninos) Simon & Schuster Children's Publishing.

Sargent, Dave. Sammy Goes to School #8, 10 vols. 2007. (Little Stinker Ser.: 8). (J). lib. bdg. 22.60 ***(978-1-59381-294-2(9))*** Ozark Publishing.

—Sammy Goes to School #8 (PB), 10 vols. 2007. (Little Stinker Ser.: 8). (J). pap. 9.95 ***(978-1-59381-295-9(7))*** Ozark Publishing.

Sargent, Dave & Sargent, Pat. Zeb: (Zebra Dun) Be Prepared, 30, 60. Lenoir, Jane, illus. 2003. (Saddle Up Ser.: Vol. 60). 42p. (J). pap. 6.95 (978-1-56763-718-2(3)); lib. bdg. 22.60 (978-1-56763-717-5(5)) Ozark Publishing.

Sarratt, Carla. Freshman Focus Carter G Woodson High Sc. 2006. 292p. pap. 14.95 ***(978-1-4327-0109-3(6))*** Outskirts Press, Inc.

Sathre, Vivian. Stage Invader. l.t. ed. 2000. (Wishbone Mysteries Ser.: No. 15). (Illus.). 140p. (J). (gr. 4 up). lib. bdg. 23.33 (978-0-8368-2698-2(1)) Stevens, Gareth Inc.

—Stage Invader. 1999. (Wishbone Mysteries Ser.: No. 15). (J). (gr. 2-5). (978-0-606-15826-8(X)) Tandem Library Bks.

Scagliotti, Loti. Silly Number Nonsense. 2006. (Silly Word & Number Stories Ser.). (Illus.). 28p. (J). 12.95 (978-9974-7960-1-0(6)) Hardenville SA URY. *Dist:* Independent Pubs. Group.

Schaefer, Carole Lexa. Someone Says. Morgan, Pierr, illus. 2003. 32p. (J). (gr. k-2). 15.99 (978-0-670-03664-6(1) , Viking Juvenile) Penguin Group (USA) Inc.

Schares, Stephen Jon. Just Plain Crazy. 2000. 124p. (YA). (gr. 4-7). pap. 9.95 (978-0-595-14069-5(6)) iUniverse, Inc.

Schembri, Pamela & Catalanotto, Peter. No More Pumpkins. 2007. (Second Grade Friends Ser.). (Illus.). 64p. (J). (gr. 2-5). 15.95 (978-0-8050-7839-8(8)) Holt, Henry & Co.

Schimel, Lawrence. Little Pirate Goes to School. Perez, Sara Rojo, illus. 2007. 12p. (J). (ps-k). bds. 6.99 (978-1-58476-545-5(3)) Innovative Kids.

Schlepp, Tammy J. Going to School. 2001. 11.79 (978-0-606-22431-4(9)); lib. bdg. 13.00 (978-0-613-45184-0(8)) Tandem Library Bks.

Schmidt, Fran. To Tell or Not to Tell. 2002. (Illus.). (J). (gr. 3-7). pap. (978-1-890276-13-3(8)) Peace Education International.

Schmidt, Gary D. The Wednesday Wars. 2007. 272p. (J). (gr. 5-9). 16.00 (978-0-618-72483-3(4) , Clarion Bks.) Houghton Mifflin Co. Trade & Reference Div.

Schneider, Robyn. Better Than Yesterday. 2007. 240p. (YA). (gr. 9). 15.99 (978-0-385-73345-8(3)); lib. bdg. 18.99 (978-0-385-90362-2(6)) Random Hse. Children's Bks. (Delacorte Bks. for Young Readers).

Scholastic, Inc. Staff. Hello Kitty: My Show-&-Tell Day. 1998. (Sanrio Ser.). (Illus.). 24p. (J). (ps-1). pap. 3.95 (978-0-590-55822-8(6) , Cartwheel Bks.) Scholastic, Inc.

—Let's Go Visit the School. 2007. (Barney Ser.). 24p. (J). pap. 2.99 ***(978-0-545-01715-2(7))*** Scholastic, Inc.

—Show & Tell Surprise. 2007. (Junior Chapter Bk.: No. 5). 48p. (J). 3.99 ***(978-0-439-92732-1(3))*** Scholastic, Inc.

Scholastic, Inc. Staff & Hudson, Wade. The Two Tyrones. Page, Mark, illus. 2004. (Just for You! Ser.). 32p. (gr. k-3). pap. 3.99 (978-0-439-56866-1(8) , Teaching Resources) Scholastic, Inc.

School Days. collector's gif. ed. 2003. (J). bds., act. bk. ed. (978-0-9744302-0-1(X)) School Days.

School Days, Cool Days! Level J, 6 vols. 128p. (gr. 2-3). 41.95 (978-0-7699-0989-9(2)) Shortland Pubns. (U. S. A.) Inc.

The School Play: Individual Title Six-Packs. (ps-2). 27.00 (978-0-7635-9473-2(3)) Rigby Education.

School Time. 2003. (J). per. (978-1-57657-892-6(5)) Paradise Pr., Inc.

Schories, Pat, illus. Biscuit's Graduation Day. 2005. (J). ***(978-1-4155-9660-9(3)*** , Harper Festival) HarperCollins Pubs.

Schott, Kenneth. The (Mis)Adventures of Captain Crazy. 2005. 124p. pap. 17.95 (978-1-4137-8190-8(X)) PublishAmerica, Inc.

Schott, Linda G. Theodore & the Town That Cried. 1999. 62p. (J). (gr. 4-6). pap. 4.99 (978-0-9673859-0-7(3)) Newmark Pr.

Schraff, Anne. The Boy from Planet Nowhere. 1999. 125p. (J). pap. (978-0-7891-4927-5(3)); (gr. 5-12). lib. bdg. 13.95 (978-0-7807-8004-0(3)) Perfection Learning Corp.

—Darkness. 2000. 119p. (J). pap. (978-0-7891-5183-4(9)); (gr. 5-12). lib. bdg. 13.95 (978-0-7807-9367-5(6)) Perfection Learning Corp.

—Howling House. 2000. (gr. 5-8). lib. bdg. 12.95 (978-0-613-51215-2(4)) Tandem Library Bks.

—Lost & Found. Langan, Paul, ed. 2002. (Bluford Ser.: 1). 133p. (J). mass mkt. 4.95 (978-0-944210-02-4(3)) Townsend Pr.

—Whatever Happened to Megan Marie? 2001. (PageTurner Mystery Ser.). 80p. (YA). per. 3.95 (978-1-56254-178-1(1) , SP 1781) Saddleback Educational Publishing.

—Whatever Happened to Megan Marie? 2001. (gr. 7-12). lib. bdg. 11.80 (978-0-613-33232-3(6)); (Illus.). 75p. (J). (gr. 4-7). lib. bdg. 12.15 (978-0-606-21579-4(4)) Tandem Library Bks.

Schrag, Ariel, ed. Stuck in the Middle: Seventeen Comics from an Unpleasant Age. 2007. 224p. (J). (gr. 7 up). pap. 18.99 (978-0-670-06221-8(9) , Viking Juvenile) Penguin Group (USA) Inc.

Schulz, Charles M. It's Time for School, Charlie Brown. 2002. (gr. k-3). lib. bdg. 11.80 (978-0-613-61782-6(7)) Tandem Library Bks.

Schumacher, Julie. The Chain Letter. 2005. 208p. (J). (gr. 5-9). lib. bdg. 17.99 (978-0-385-90205-2(0) , Delacorte Bks. for Young Readers) Random Hse. Children's Bks.

Schwartz, Amy. Annabelle Swift, Kindergartener. Schwartz, Amy, illus. 2002. (Illus.). (J). 14.74 (978-0-7587-1954-6(X)) Book Wholesalers, Inc.

—Annabelle Swift, Kindergartner. 2000. (J). pap. 19.97 incl. audio (978-0-7366-9198-7(7)) Books on Tape, Inc.

—Bea & Mr. Jones: Story & Pictures. 2006. (Illus.). 32p. (J). 13.95 (978-0-15-205811-1(7)) Harcourt Trade Pubs.

—Things I Learned in Second Grade. Schwartz, Amy, illus. 2004. 32p. (J). (ps-2). 15.99 (978-0-06-050936-1(8) , Tegen, Katherine Bks); lib. bdg. 16.89 (978-0-06-050937-8(6)) HarperCollins Pubs.

Schwartz, Amy & Kaye, Randye. Annabelle Swift, Kindergartner. 2004. (Live Oak Readalong Ser.). (Illus.). (J). pap. 18.95 incl. audio compact disk (978-1-59112-687-4(8)) Live Oak Media.

Schwartz, Virginia Frances. 4 Kids in 5E & 1 Crazy Year. 2006. 208p. (J). 16.95 (978-0-8234-1946-3(0)) Holiday Hse., Inc.

Scieszka, Jon. Baloney (Henry P.) Smith, Lane, illus. 2001. 32p. (J). (gr. k-3). 15.99 (978-0-670-89248-8(3) , Viking Juvenile) Penguin Group (USA) Inc.

—Math Curse. ed. 2004. (Illus.). (J). (gr. k-4). spiral bd. (978-0-616-01778-4(2)) Canadian National Institute for the Blind/Institut National Canadien pour les Aveugles.

—Math Curse. Smith, Lane, illus. 2007. 32p. (J). (ps). pap. 9.99 ***(978-0-670-06299-7(5)*** , Viking Juvenile) Penguin Group (USA) Inc.

—Science Verse. Smith, Lane, illus. 40p. (J). 2007. (ps). pap. 9.99 ***(978-0-670-06269-0(3));*** 2004. (gr. 2-8). 16.99 (978-0-670-91057-1(0)) Penguin Group (USA) Inc. (Viking Juvenile).

Scott, C. Anne. Lizard Meets Ivana the Terrible. 2001. (gr. 3-6). lib. bdg. 11.80 (978-0-613-81946-6(2)) Tandem Library Bks.

Scott, C. Anne & Roth, Stephanie. Lizard Meets Ivana the Terrible. 2001. 128p. (J). pap. 3.99 (978-0-439-21999-0(X) , Scholastic Paperbacks) Scholastic, Inc.

Scott, Cynthia A. Lizard Meets Ivana the Terrible. 2001. (978-0-606-22173-3(5)) Tandem Library Bks.

Scott, Kieran. Boy Crazy! Boy of the Year! 2002. (Boy Crazy! Ser.). 128p. (YA). (gr. 7 up). pap. 8.99 (978-0-06-441070-0(6) , Avon) HarperCollins Pubs.

—Brunettes Strike Back. (YA). 2007. 272p. (gr. 7). pap. 7.99 (978-0-14-240778-3(X) , Puffin); 2006. 256p. (gr. 5). 16.99 (978-0-399-24493-3(X) , Putnam Juvenile) Penguin Group (USA) Inc.

—Geek Magnet. 2008. 256p. (YA). (gr. 7). 16.99 ***(978-0-399-24760-6(2)*** , Putnam Juvenile) Penguin Group (USA) Inc.

—I Was a Non-Blonde Cheerleader. 2007. 272p. (YA). (gr. 7). 7.99 ***(978-0-14-240910-7(3)*** , Puffin); 2006. 272p. (YA). (gr. 7). pap. 6.99 (978-0-14-240641-0(4) , Puffin); 2005. 256p. (J). 15.99 (978-0-399-24279-3(1) , Putnam Juvenile) Penguin Group (USA) Inc.

—I was a Non Blonde Cheerleader (Splashproof Edition) 2007. 1p. (J). (gr. 7). pap. 6.99 (978-0-14-240832-2(8) , Puffin) Penguin Group (USA) Inc.

—A Non-Blonde Cheerleader in Love. 2007. 272p. (YA). (gr. 7-10). 16.99 (978-0-399-24494-0(8) , Putnam Juvenile) Penguin Group (USA) Inc.

Scott, Mary Ann. New Girl. 2003. 208p. (YA). (978-1-55041-725-8(8)) Fitzhenry & Whiteside, Ltd.

Scott, Prue. Growth Spurt: Zits Sketchbook 2. 1999. (gr. 7-12). lib. bdg. 19.90 (978-0-613-23720-8(X)) Tandem Library Bks.

Scrimger, Richard. Of Mice & Nutcrackers: A Peeler Christmas. 2001. lib. bdg. 16.40 (978-0-613-53630-1(4)) Tandem Library Bks.

—Of Mice & Nutcrackers: A Peeler Christmas. Hendry, Linda, illus. 2001. 232p. (J). (gr. 3-7). pap. 7.95 (978-0-88776-498-1(3)) Tundra Bks., Inc./Livres Toundra, Inc. CAN. *Dist:* Random Hse., Inc.

Seals, Hollie. When You Can't Find the Words. 2007. 144p. per. 11.95 (*978-0-595-45023-7(7)) iUniverse, Inc.

SeaStar Publishing Staff, ed. School Stories Your Dog Didn't Eat. 2000. (gr. 3-6). lib. bdg. 11.80 (978-0-613-33027-5(7)) Tandem Library Bks.

Sedita, Francesco. Miss Popularity. 2007. (Candy Apple Ser.: No. 3). 144p. (J). pap. 4.99 (*978-0-439-88814-1(X), Scholastic Paperbacks) Scholastic, Inc.

Segal, Douglas. I Can Go to School. 2007. 5p. 10.95 (*978-1-58117-594-3(9), Intervisual/Piggy Toes) Dalmatian Pr.

Segal, Zoe. Confessions of a Tenth-Grade Social Climber. 2005. 290p. (YA). (978-0-618-44981-1(7)) Houghton Mifflin Co.

Seglie, Susan & Schiefelbein, Janis. JR Gets Rady for School: A Visit to the Health Clinic. Papish, Adam, illus. 2001. (J). 4.95 (978-0-9747243-0-0(0)) Seglie, Susan M.

Seidler, Tor. The Silent Spillbills. 1998. 224p. (J). (gr. 3-7). 14.95 (978-0-06-205180-6(6)) HarperCollins Pubs.

—The Tar Pit. 2000. (J). 15.95 (978-0-06-623611-7(8)); lib. bdg. 15.89 (978-0-06-623612-4(6)) HarperCollins Pubs.

—The Tar Pit. 2001. (978-0-606-22299-0(5)) Tandem Library Bks.

Selkowe, Valerie M. Happy Birthday to Me! Sandford, John B., illus. 2001. 32p. (J). (ps-1). 15.89 (978-0-688-16680-9(6)); 15.95 (978-0-688-16679-3(2)) HarperCollins Pubs.

Selzer, Adam. How to Get Suspended & Influence People. 2007. 192p. (J). (gr. 7). 15.99 (978-0-385-73369-4(0)); lib. bdg. 18.99 (978-0-385-90384-4(7)) Random Hse. Children's Bks. (Delacorte Bks. for Young Readers).

Selzer, Adam. Pirates of the Retail Wasteland. 2008. 208p. (YA). (gr. 7). 15.99 (*978-0-385-73482-0(4), Delacorte Bks. for Young Readers) Random Hse. Children's Bks.

Sempe & Goscinny. Los Recreos del Pequeno Nicolas. 2003. (SPA., Illus.). 116p. (J). (gr. 3-5). pap. 9.95 (978-84-204-4814-5(1)) Santillana USA Publishing Co., Inc.

Senate, Melissa. Theodora Twist. 224p. (YA). (gr. 9). 2007. pap. 7.99 (*978-0-385-73302-1(X)); 2006. 15.95 (978-0-385-73301-4(1)); 2006. lib. bdg. 17.99 (978-0-385-90322-6(7)) Random Hse. Children's Bks. (Delacorte Bks. for Young Readers).

Senisi, Ellen B. All Kinds of Friends, Even Green! 2002. (Illus.). 28p. (J). (gr. k-4). 15.95 (978-1-890627-35-5(6)) Woodbine Hse.

—Hurray for Pre-K! Senisi, Ellen B., illus. (Illus.). 32p. (J). (ps-k). 2000. 12.95 (978-0-06-028896-9(5)); 1999. 5.95 (978-0-06-443665-6(9)) HarperCollins Pubs.

Serafin, Jordan. Bella: The Crooked Hat Witch. Rubino, Alisa A., illus. 2004. (J). (978-0-932991-57-7(2)) Place In The Woods, The.

Seuling, Barbara. Oh No, It's Robert. Brewer, Paul, illus. 1999. 128p. (J). (gr. 4-7). 15.95 (978-0-8126-2934-7(5)) Cricket Bks.

—Oh No, It's Robert. Brewer, Paul, illus. 2003. (Oh No, It's Robert Ser.). 128p. (J). pap. 3.99 (978-0-439-23544-0(8), Scholastic Paperbacks) Scholastic, Inc.

—Robert & the Back-to-School Special. Brewer, Paul, illus. 2002. (Robert Bks.). 120p. (J). 15.95 (978-0-8126-2662-9(1)) Cricket Bks.

—Robert & the Great Escape. Brewer, Paul, illus. 2003. (Robert Bks.). 120p. 15.95 (978-0-8126-2700-8(8)) Cricket Bks.

—Robert & the Great Pepperoni. Brewer, Paul, illus. 2001. (Robert Bks.). 128p. (J). (gr. 2-5). 15.95 (978-0-8126-2825-8(X)) Cricket Bks.

—Robert & the Happy Endings. Brewer, Paul, illus. 2007. (Robert Bks.). 160p. (J). (gr. 2-4). 16.95 (978-0-8126-2748-0(2)) Cricket Bks.

—Robert & the Practical Jokes. Brewer, Paul, illus. 2006. (Robert Bks.). 150p. (J). 16.95 (978-0-8126-2741-1(5)) Cricket Bks.

—Robert & the Weird & Wacky Facts. Brewer, Paul, illus. 2002. (Robert Bks.). 112p. (J). (gr. 1-4). 15.95 (978-0-8126-2653-7(2)) Cricket Bks.

—Robert Finds a Way. Brewer, Paul, illus. 2005. (Robert Bks.). 150p. (J). 15.95 (978-0-8126-2734-3(2)) Cricket Bks.

—Robert Takes a Stand. Brewer, Paul, illus. 2004. (Robert Bks.). 120p. (J). 15.95 (978-0-8126-2712-1(1)) Cricket Bks.

Seuss, Dr. & Prelutsky, Jack. Hooray for Diffendoofer Day! Smith, Lane, illus. 1998. 56p. (J). (gr. k-3). 17.00 (978-0-679-89008-9(4)); lib. bdg. 18.99 (978-0-679-99008-6(9)) Random Hse. Children's Bks. (Knopf Bks. for Young Readers).

Seymour, Tres. The Revelation of Saint Bruce. 1998. (Illus.). 128p. (YA). (gr. 7-12). pap. 16.95 (978-0-531-30109-8(5), Orchard Bks.) Scholastic, Inc.

Shalant, Phyllis. The Great Cape Rescue. 2007. (Society of Super Secret Heroes Ser.: Bk. 1). 128p. (J). (gr. 2-4). 15.99 (978-0-525-47404-3(8), Dutton Juvenile) Penguin Group (USA) Inc.

Shan, Darren, pseud. Allies of the Night. 2006. (Cirque du Freak: Bk. 8). 224p. (J). (gr. 5-17). mass mkt. 6.99 (978-0-316-10653-5(4)) Little Brown & Co.

—Allies of the Night. 2004. (Cirque du Freak: Bk. 8). (Illus.). 192p. (J). (gr. 5-17). 15.99 (978-0-316-15570-0(5)) Little, Brown Bks. for Young Readers.

—Tunnels of Blood. 2004. (Cirque du Freak: Bk. 3). (Illus.). 240p. (J). (gr. 3-7). mass mkt. 6.99 (978-0-316-90573-2(9)) Little, Brown Bks. for Young Readers.

Shanahan, Lisa. The Sweet, Terrible, Glorious Year I Truly, Completely Lost It. 2007. 304p. (YA). (gr. 7-10). 15.99 (*978-0-385-73516-2(2)); lib. bdg. 18.99 (*978-0-385-90505-3(X)) Random Hse. Children's Bks. (Delacorte Bks. for Young Readers).

Shann, Taylor. Strange Day. 2003. (J). 13.00 (978-0-9679552-4-7(6)) Mushroom Cloud Pr. of Orlando.

Shannon, David. David Goes to School. Shannon, David, illus. 2002. (Illus.). (J). 25.06 (978-0-7587-2350-5(4)) Book Wholesalers, Inc.

—David Goes to School. Shannon, David, illus. 1999. (Illus.). 32p. (J). (ps-3). pap. 15.95 (978-0-590-48087-1(1), Blue Sky Pr., The) Scholastic, Inc.

—David Va al Colegio. 2000. Tr. of David Goes to School. (SPA., Illus.). 32p. (J). (ps-3). 13.99 (978-84-241-5886-6(5)) Everest de Ediciones y Distribucion, S.L. ESP. *Dist:* Lectorum Pubns., Inc.

—David Va Al Colegio. 1999. (SPA.). (gr. k-3). lib. bdg. 16.40 (978-0-613-64483-9(2)) Tandem Library Bks.

Shapiro, Laurie Gwen. Brand X: The Boyfriend Account. 2006. 240p. (YA). (gr. 7). 15.95 (978-0-385-73288-8(0)); lib. bdg. 17.99 (978-0-385-90309-7(X)) Random Hse. Children's Bks. (Delacorte Bks. for Young Readers).

Sharmat, Marjorie Weinman & Sharmat, Mitchell. The Princess of the Fillmore Street School. Brunkus, Denise, illus. 2nd ed. 2005. 80p. (gr. 1-4). lib. bdg. 11.99 (978-0-385-90291-5(3)); (Olivia Sharp Ser.: Vol. 3). (J). pap. 4.50 (978-0-440-42060-6(1)) Random Hse. Children's Bks. (Yearling).

Shaw, Susan. Safe. 2007. 208p. (J). (gr. 9). 16.99 (*978-0-525-47829-4(9), Dutton Juvenile) Penguin Group (USA) Inc.

Shaw, Tucker. The Hookup Artist. 2007. 208p. (J). pap. 7.99 (978-0-06-075622-5(5), HarperTeen) HarperCollins Pubs.

—The Hookup Artist: Mysterious Mating Rituals of the American Teen. 2006. 208p. (J). lib. bdg. 16.89 (978-0-06-075621-5(7)) HarperCollins Pubs.

Sheldon, Dyan. Confessions of a Teenage Drama Queen. l.t. ed. 2004. 324p. 22.95 (978-0-7862-6903-7(0), Large Print Pr.) Thorndike Pr.

—My Perfect Life. 2002. (Illus.). 224p. (YA). (gr. 7 up). 16.99 (978-0-7636-1839-1(X)) Candlewick Pr.

—Planet Janet. 240p. (YA). (gr. 9 up). 2004. (Illus.). pap. 6.99 (978-0-7636-2556-6(6)); 2003. 14.99 (978-0-7636-2048-6(3)) Candlewick Pr.

Shepard, Sara. Flawless. 2008. (Pretty Little Liars Ser.: Bk. 2). 352p. (J). pap. 8.99 (*978-0-06-088735-3(4), HarperTeen) HarperCollins Pubs.

—Perfect. 2007. (Pretty Little Liars Ser.: Bk. 3). 320p. (YA). (gr. 9 up). 16.99 (*978-0-06-088736-0(2), HarperTeen) HarperCollins Pubs.

—Pretty Little Liars. 2007. (Pretty Little Liars Ser.: Bk. 1). 304p. (J). pap. 8.99 (*978-0-06-088732-2(X), HarperTeen) HarperCollins Pubs.

—Unbelievable. 2008. (Pretty Little Liars Ser.: Bk. 4). 352p. (J). 16.99 (*978-0-06-088739-1(7), HarperTeen) HarperCollins Pubs.

Shepherd, Jodie. Ready for School. 2006. (Sesame Street Ser.). 10p. (J). pap. 10.99 (978-0-7944-1103-9(7)) Reader's Digest Assn., Inc., The.

Sherrard, Valerie. Speechless. 2007. 176p. (YA). pap. 12.99 (*978-1-55002-701-3(8), Boardwalk Bks.) Dundurn Group, The CAN. *Dist:* Univ. of Toronto Pr.

Shinn, Sharon. Dream-maker's Magic. 2006. 272p. (YA). (gr. 7). 16.99 (978-0-670-06070-2(4), Viking Juvenile) Penguin Group (USA) Inc.

Shoup, Barbara. Everything You Want. 2008. 312p. (J). 16.95 (*978-0-7387-1227-7(2), Flux) Llewellyn Pubns.

Shreve, Susan. Jonah, the Whale. 1999. 110p. (J). (ps-7). per. 13.00 (978-0-613-06739-3(8)) Tandem Library Bks.

Shreve, Susan Richards. Blister. 2003. (Illus.). 176p. (J). (gr. 3-7). pap. 4.99 (978-0-439-19314-6(1), Scholastic Paperbacks) Scholastic, Inc.

—Jonah, the Whale. 1999. 128p. (J). (gr. 3-7). pap. 4.99 (978-0-590-37134-6(7), Scholastic Paperbacks) Scholastic, Inc.

—Kiss Me Tomorrow. 2007. 224p. (YA). (gr. 5-8). pap. 5.99 (978-0-439-68048-6(4)); 2006. 220p. (J). (*978-1-4156-5592-4(8)) Scholastic, Inc. (Levine, Arthur A. Bks.).

—Trout & Me. 2004. 144p. (J). (gr. 3-7). reprint ed. pap. 5.50 (978-0-440-41902-0(6), Yearling) Random Hse. Children's Bks.

Shrinking Violet. 2004. 29.95 incl. cd-rom (978-1-55592-497-3(2)) Weston Woods Studios, Inc.

Shubert's Choice. 2004. (YA). 9.00 (978-1-889609-26-3(9)) Loving Guidance, Inc.

Shulman, Mark. Nutsy the Robot Goes to School. Boyce, Katie, illus. 2006. (Nutsy the Robot Ser.). 10p. (J). bds. 15.95 (978-0-7696-4606-0(9), Brighter Child) School Specialty Publishing.

Shulman, Polly. Enthusiasm. (YA). 2007. 208p. (gr. 7 up). 7.99 (*978-0-14-240935-0(9), Puffin); 2006. 212p. (gr. 6). 15.99 (978-0-399-24389-9(5), Putnam Juvenile) Penguin Group (USA) Inc.

Shusterman, Neal. Dread Locks, No. 1. 2006. (Dark Fusion Ser.). 176p. (YA). (gr. 7). pap. 6.99 (978-0-14-240599-4(X), Puffin) Penguin Group (USA) Inc.

—Dread Locks: Dark Fusion # 1. 2005. 176p. (J). (gr. 6-12). 15.99 (978-0-525-47554-5(0), Dutton Juvenile) Penguin Group (USA) Inc.

—The Shadow Club. 2002. 192p. (J). 16.99 (978-0-525-46833-2(1), Dutton Juvenile); pap. 6.99 (978-0-14-230094-7(2), Puffin) Penguin Group (USA) Inc.

—Shadow Club. 2002. (gr. 7-12). lib. bdg. 14.15 (978-0-613-50082-1(2)) Tandem Library Bks.

—Shadow Club Rising. 2003. 208p. (YA). (gr. 7). pap. 6.99 (978-0-14-250089-7(5), Puffin) Penguin Group (USA) Inc.

—Shadow Club Rising. 2003. (gr. 7-12). lib. bdg. 14.15 (978-0-613-67473-7(1)) Tandem Library Bks.

Siebold, Jan. My Nights at the Improv. 2005. 98p. (YA). (gr. 6-9). lib. bdg. 14.95 (978-0-8075-5630-6(0)) Whitman, Albert & Co.

Silverman, Erica. Cowgirl Kate & Cocoa: School Days. Lewin, Betsy, illus. 2007. (Cowgirl Kate & Cocoa Ser.). 48p. (J). 15.00 (978-0-15-205378-9(6)) Harcourt Trade Pubs.

Silverman, Erica. Cowgirl Kate & Cocoa: School Days. Lewin, Betsy, illus. 2008. (Cowgirl Kate & Cocoa Ser.). 48p. (J). pap. 5.95 (*978-0-15-206130-2(4), Harcourt Paperbacks) Harcourt Children's Bks.

Simms, Laura. Rotten Teeth. Catrow, David, illus. 1998. 32p. (J). (gr. k-3). tchr. ed. 16.00 (978-0-395-82850-2(3)) Houghton Mifflin Co. Trade & Reference Div.

—Rotten Teeth. 2002. (gr. k-3). lib. bdg. 14.10 (978-0-613-90722-4(1)) Tandem Library Bks.

Simms, Laura & Catrow, David. Rotten Teeth. 2002. (Illus.). 32p. (J). (gr. k-3). pap. 5.95 (978-0-618-25078-3(6)) Houghton Mifflin Co. Trade & Reference Div.

Simon, Gabriel. Og & His Frogs. Finch, Dianne, illus. l.t. ed. 1998. 32p. (J). (ps-3). lib. bdg. 12.95 (978-0-935343-72-4(5)) Peartree.

Simon, Norma. All Families Are Special. Flavin, Teresa, illus. 2003. 32p. (J). (gr. k-3). 16.95 (978-0-8075-2175-5(2)) Whitman, Albert & Co.

Simpson, Fiona, ed. Zoey 101: Chapter Book. 2006. (Teenick Ser.). 112p. (J). pap. 4.99 (978-0-439-84659-2(5), Scholastic) Scholastic, Inc.

Singletary, Mabel Elizabeth. Something to Jump About! 2008. 150p. pap. 5.99 (*978-0-8024-2252-1(7)) Moody Pubs.

Singleton, Linda Joy. Don't Die, Dragonfly. Karre, Andrew, ed. 2004. 288p. pap. 6.99 (978-0-7387-0526-2(8)) Llewellyn Pubns.

—Witch Ball. 2006. (Seer Ser.: Bk. 3). 264p. pap. 6.99 (978-0-7387-0821-8(6)) Llewellyn Pubns.

Sitomer, Alan Lawrence. Hip-Hop High School. 2006. 368p. (J). (978-0-7868-3831-8(0)); 384p. (gr. 7-17). 16.99 (978-0-7868-5515-5(0)) Hyperion Bks. for Children. (Jump at the Sun).

Skarmeas, Nancy J. My First Day of School. Johnson, Meredith, illus. 2001. 32p. (J). (ps-3). 9.95 (978-0-8249-4198-7(5)) Ideals Pubns.

Skarmeta, Antonio. The Composition. Ruano, Alfonso, illus. 2003. 32p. (J). (gr. 3 up). pap. 5.95 (978-0-88899-550-6(4)) Groundwood Bks. CAN. *Dist:* Perseus Distribution.

—The Composition. Amado, Elisa, tr. from SPA. Ruano, Alfonso, illus. 2000. 32p. (J). (gr. 2-6). 16.95 (978-0-88899-390-8(0), Libros Tigrillo) Groundwood Bks. CAN. *Dist:* Perseus Distribution.

Skeers, Linda. The Impossible Patriotism Project. Hoyt, Ard, illus. 2007. 32p. (J). (ps-3). 16.99 (978-0-8037-3138-7(8), Dial) Penguin Group (USA) Inc.

Skipper, Angelic. Launching Out into the Deep. 2006. 14p. 9.81 (978-1-4116-7345-8(X)) Lulu.com.

Slate, Joseph. Miss Bindergarten Celebrates the Last Day of Kindergarten. Wolff, Ashley, illus. 40p. (J). (ps). 2008. pap. 6.99 (*978-0-14-241060-8(8), Puffin); 2006. 16.99 (978-0-525-47744-0(6), Dutton Juvenile) Penguin Group (USA) Inc.

—Miss Bindergarten Gets Ready for Kindergarten. 2001. (gr. k-3). lib. bdg. 15.30 (978-0-613-35982-5(8)); (Illus.). (J). (978-0-606-21333-2(3)) Tandem Library Bks.

—Miss Bindergarten Has a Wild Day in Kindergarten. Wolff, Ashley, illus. 2006. 40p. (J). (ps). reprint ed. pap. 6.99 (978-0-14-240709-7(7), Puffin) Penguin Group (USA) Inc.

—Miss Bindergarten Takes a Field Trip with Kindergarten. Wolff, Ashley, illus. 2004. 40p. (J). (ps up). pap. 6.99 (978-0-14-240139-2(0), Puffin) Penguin Group (USA) Inc.

—Miss Bindergarten's Wild Day. Wolff, Ashley, illus. 2005. 40p. (J). (ps). 16.99 (978-0-525-47084-7(0), Dutton Juvenile) Penguin Group (USA) Inc.

Slater, David Michael. Comin' Through, Rooney, Ronnie, illus. 2007. (Missy Swiss & More Ser.). 32p. (J). (ps-4). lib. bdg. 27.07 (*978-1-60270-008-6(7), Looking Glass Library) Magic Wagon.

Slegers, Liesbet. Kevin Goes to School. 2002. (On My Way Ser.). (Illus.). 28p. (J). 7.95 (978-1-929132-31-7(X)) Kane/Miller Bk. Pubs., Inc.

Sloan, Glenna. Stealing Time. 1998. 126p. (YA). (gr. 7-17). pap. 9.99 (978-0-88092-266-1(4), 2664) Royal Fireworks Publishing Co.

Smadja, Brigitte. Tarte aux Escargots. pap. 17.95 (978-2-211-03633-7(3)) Archimede Editions FRA. *Dist:* Distribooks, Inc.

Smallcomb, Pam. Camp Buccaneer. Lichtenheld, Tom, illus. 2002. (Ready-for-Chapters Ser.). 64p. (J). (gr. 1-3). lib. bdg. 11.89 (978-0-689-84383-9(6), Aladdin Library) Simon & Schuster Children's Publishing.

—The Last Burp of Mac McGerp. Bromley, Lizzy, illus. 2003. 150p. (J). 15.95 (978-1-58234-856-8(1)); pap. 6.95 (978-1-58234-868-1(5)) Bloomsbury Publishing. (Bloomsbury Children).

Smalls, Irene. Don't Say Ain't. Bootman, Colin, illus. 32p. (J). (gr. k-3). 2004. pap. 6.95 (978-1-57091-382-2(X)); 2003. 15.95 (978-1-57091-381-5(1)) Charlesbridge Publishing, Inc.

—Don't Say Ain't. 2004. (gr. k-3). lib. bdg. 15.25 (978-0-613-70806-7(7)) Tandem Library Bks.

Smith, Greg Leitich. Ninjas, Piranhas, & Galileo. 2005. 192p. (J). (gr. 5-8). pap. 6.99 (978-0-316-01181-5(9)) Little Brown & Co.

Smith, Hawley Willia. The Evolution of Dodd (a Pedagogical Sto. 2006. 77.99 (*978-1-4280-1227-1(3)); pap. 71.99 (*978-1-4280-1225-7(7)) IndyPublish.com.

Smith, James. The Wonderer of Time. 2006. 52p. pap. 12.95 (978-1-4241-3316-1(5)) PublishAmerica, Inc.

Smith, Jane D. Charlie Is a Chicken. 2000. (Illus.). 176p. (J). (gr. 3-7). pap. 4.95 (978-0-06-440824-0(8)) HarperCollins Pubs.

—Charlie Is a Chicken. 2000. (Illus.). (J). (978-0-606-18682-7(4)) Tandem Library Bks.

Smith, Montez Roller. A Summer to Grow On: House upon a Hill Series - Book 1. 2005. 220p. per. 14.95 (978-1-933148-95-3(0)) Tate Publishing & Enterprises, L.L.C.

Smith, Sherri L. Hot, Sour, Salty, Sweet. 2008. 176p. (J). (*978-0-385-73417-2(4)); lib. bdg. (*978-0-385-90431-5(2)) Dell Publishing. (Delacorte Pr.).

Smith, Sherri L. Sparrow. 192p. (YA). (gr. 7). 2008. mass mkt. 6.50 (*978-0-440-23945-1(1), Laurel Leaf); 2006. 15.95 (978-0-385-73324-3(0), Delacorte Bks. for Young Readers); 2006. lib. bdg. 17.99 (978-0-385-90343-1(X), Delacorte Bks. for Young Readers) Random Hse. Children's Bks.

Smith, Stephen D. & Caldwell, Lise. High Hurdles. 2006. 128p. (J). pap. 5.99 (978-0-7847-1439-3(8), 42144) Standard Publishing.

Smith, Stuart. My School's a Zoo! Catrow, David, illus. 2004. 40p. (J). (gr. k-3). 15.99 (978-0-06-028510-4(9)); lib. bdg. 16.89 (978-0-06-028511-1(7)) HarperCollins Pubs.

—My School's a Zoo! 2000. 40p. (J). (gr. k-3). pap. 5.95 (978-0-06-443588-8(1)) HarperCollins Pubs.

Snadowsky, Daria. Anatomy of a Boyfriend. 2007. 272p. (YA). (gr. 9). 16.99 (978-0-385-73320-5(8)); 16.99 (978-0-385-90339-4(1)) Random Hse. Children's Bks. (Delacorte Bks. for Young Readers).

Snicket, Lemony, pseud. Cauchemar a la Scierie. pap. 24.95 (978-2-09-282357-6(4)) Nathan, Fernand FRA. *Dist:* Distribooks, Inc.

Snyder, Jackie. Secret Pal Surprises. 1999. (978-0-606-17743-6(4)) Tandem Library Bks.

Snyder, Susan E. Shivers & Shakes. 2007. (Illus.). 24p. (J). 9.95 (978-0-9767163-5-8(6)) Kotzig Publishing, Inc.

Snyder, Zilpha Keatley. The Unseen. 2005. 208p. 5.99 (978-0-440-41930-3(1), Yearling) Random Hse. Children's Bks.

—The Unseen. l.t. ed. 2005. 276p. 22.95 (978-0-7862-7265-5(1), Large Print Pr.) Thorndike Pr.

Soda, Masahito. Firefighter, Vol. 16. 2006. (Firefighter Daigo of Fire Company M Ser.). 208p. (YA). pap. 9.95 (978-1-4215-0452-0(9)) Viz Media.

Sollinger, Emily. Dora's School Day! Mangano, Tom, illus. 2005. (Dora the Explorer Ser.). 12p. (J). bds. 4.99 (978-0-689-87786-5(2), Simon Spotlight/Nickelodeon) Simon & Schuster Children's Publishing.

—Strawberry Shortcake Goes to School. S. I. Artists Staff, illus. 2003. (Strawberry Shortcake Ser.). 24p. (J). (ps-2). mass mkt. 4.99 (978-0-448-43188-8(2), Grosset & Dunlap) Penguin Group (USA) Inc.

Somebody Moved in Next Door: Individual Chapter Book Title Six-Pack. Vol. 29. 32p. (gr. 5 up). 44.00 (978-0-7578-0978-1(2)) Rigby Education.

Sonenklar, Carol. My Own Worst Enemy. 1999. 152p. (J). (gr. 7 up). tchr. ed. 15.95 (978-0-8234-1456-7(6)) Holiday Hse., Inc.

—My Own Worst Enemy. 2001. 160p. (J). (gr. 3-7). pap. 4.50 (978-0-439-17518-0(6)) Scholastic, Inc.

Sones, Sonya. What My Girlfriend Doesn't Know. 2007. 304p. (YA). (gr. 7 up). 16.99 (978-0-689-87602-8(5)) Simon & Schuster Children's Publishing.

Sonnenblick, Jordan. Drums, Girls & Dangerous Pie. (J). 2006. 29.95 (978-0-439-89550-7(2)); 2005. 288p. pap. 16.99 (978-0-439-75519-1(0), Scholastic Pr.); 2006. 304p. reprint ed. pap. 6.99 (978-0-439-75520-7(4), Scholastic Paperbacks) Scholastic, Inc.

—Drums, Girls & Dangerous Pie. l.t. ed. 2005. 314p. (YA). 21.95 (978-0-7862-8038-4(7)) Thorndike Pr.

Sonnenblick, Jordan. Zen & the Art of Faking It. 2007. 272p. (J). pap. 16.99 (*978-0-439-83707-1(3), Scholastic Pr.) Scholastic, Inc.

Sorrells, Walter. The Silent Room. 2008. 240p. (YA). (gr. 7). pap. 7.99 (*978-0-14-241098-1(5), Puffin) Penguin Group (USA) Inc.

Soto, Gary. Accidental Love. 192p. (YA). 2008. pap. 6.95 (*978-0-15-206113-5(4), Harcourt Paperbacks); 2006. 16.00 (978-0-15-205497-7(9)) Harcourt Children's Bks.

Spafford, Suzy. Tales from Duckport: Back to School? Cool. 2002. (Suzy's Zoo Ser.). 40p. (J). (gr. k-3). pap. 3.99 (978-0-439-38355-4(2)) Scholastic, Inc.

Sparrow, Rebecca. The Year Nick McGowan Came to Stay. 2008. (YA). (*978-0-375-84570-3(4)); lib. bdg. (*978-0-375-94570-0(9)) Knopf, Alfred A. Inc.

Spears, Britney. Mother's Gift. 2003. (gr. 5-8). lib. bdg. 14.15 (978-0-613-72254-4(X)) Tandem Library Bks.

Spinelli, Jerry. Loser. 224p. 2003. pap. 5.99 (978-0-06-054074-6(5)); 2002. (J). (gr. 4-7). 15.99 (978-0-06-000193-3(3), Cotler, Joanna Books); 2002. (Illus.). (J). (gr. 4-6). lib. bdg. 16.89 (978-0-06-000483-5(5), Cotler, Joanna Books) HarperCollins Pubs.

—Loser. 2002. (gr. 3-6). lib. bdg. 14.15 (978-0-613-66899-6(5)) Tandem Library Bks.

—Space Station Seventh Grade. 2001. (J). (gr. 5-8). 22.50 (978-0-8446-7189-5(4)) Smith, Peter Pub., Inc.

—Space Station Seventh Grade: The Newbery Award-Winning Author of Maniac Magee. 2000. 235p. (J). (gr. 4-7). pap. 6.99 (978-0-316-80605-3(6)) Little Brown & Co.

—Star Girl. 2000. 192p. (J). (gr. 5-8). 15.95 (978-0-679-88637-2(0), Knopf Bks. for Young Readers) Random Hse. Children's Bks.

—Stargirl. 2002. (EMC Masterpiece Series Access Editions). xiv, 199p. (YA). 10.95 (978-0-8219-2504-1(0), 35378) EMC/Paradigm Publishing.

—Stargirl. unabr. ed. 2004. 192p. (J). (gr. 7 up). pap. 40.00 incl. audio (978-0-8072-0855-7(8), LYA 323 SP, Listening Library) Random Hse. Audio Publishing Group.

S

—Stargirl. (YA). 2004. 208p. (gr. 5). mass mkt. 6.99 (978-0-440-41677-7(9) , Laurel Leaf); 2000. 192p. (gr. 5-8). lib. bdg. 17.99 (978-0-679-98637-9(5) , Knopf Bks. for Young Readers); 2002. 208p. (gr. 7 up). reprint ed. pap. 8.95 (978-0-375-82233-9(X) , Knopf Bks. for Young Readers) Random Hse. Children's Bks.

—Stargirl. Tino, illus. (SPA.). 224p. (J). (gr. 5-8). pap. 9.95 (978-1-59437-815-7(0)) Santillana USA Publishing Co., Inc.

—Stargirl. 2002. (gr. 7-12). lib. bdg. 17.60 (978-0-613-49417-5(2)) Tandem Library Bks.

—Stargirl. l.t. ed. 2001. 240p. (J). (gr. 8-12). 24.95 (978-0-7862-3218-5(8)) Thorndike Pr.

Spirn, Michele Sobel. I Am the Turkey. Allen, Joy, illus. (I Can Read Bks.). 48p. (J). 2006. pap. 3.99 (978-0-06-053232-1(7)); 2004. 16.89 (978-0-06-053231-4(9)); 2004. 15.99 (978-0-06-053230-7(0)) HarperCollins Pubs.

Spradlin, Michael P. Live & Let Shop. 2006. (Spy Goddess Ser.). (Illus.). 288p. (J). pap. 5.99 (978-0-06-059409-1(8)) HarperCollins Pubs.

—Spy Goddess, Book Two: to Hawaii, with Love. 2008. (Spy Goddess Ser.). 288p. (J). pap. 6.99 (***978-0-06-059412-1(8)*** , HarperTeen) HarperCollins Pubs.

Spradlin, Michael P. To Hawaii, with Love. 2006. (Spy Goddess Ser.). (Illus.). 208p. (J). lib. bdg. 16.89 (978-0-06-059411-4(X)); (YA). 15.99 (978-0-06-059410-7(1)) HarperCollins Pubs.

Spradlin, Michael P., illus. & reader. Live & Let Shop. Spradlin, Michael P., reader. 2005. (Spy Goddess Ser.: Bk. 1). 224p. (gr. 7 up). 15.99 (978-0-06-059407-7(1)) HarperCollins Pubs.

Spyri, Johanna. Rico & Wiseli, Rico & Stineli, & H. 2006. 63.99 (***978-1-4280-3033-6(6)***) IndyPublish.com.

Stadler, Alexander. Beverly Billingsly Takes a Bow. 2007. (Illus.). 32p. (J). (ps-2). pap. 6.00 (978-0-15-205861-6(3) , Voyager Bks./Libros Viajeros) Harcourt Children's Bks.

—Beverly Billingsly Takes a Bow. 2003. (Illus.). 32p. (J). (ps-2). 16.00 (978-0-15-216816-2(8) , Silver Whistle) Harcourt Trade Pubs.

Stahl, Mary Louise. Louie. 2003. 122p. (YA). 20.95 (978-0-595-74889-1(9)); pap. 10.95 (978-0-595-28750-5(6)) iUniverse, Inc.

Stamper, Norm. Breaking Rank: A Top Cop's Street-Smart Approch to Making America a Safe Place - for Everyone. 2005. 384p. 26.00 (978-1-56025-693-9(1) , Nation Bks.) Basic Bks.

Standiford, Natalie. The Dating Game, No. 1. 2005. 224p. (YA). (gr. 8-17). pap. 9.99 (978-0-316-11040-2(X)) Little Brown & Co.

—Dating Game: Breaking Up Is Really, Really Hard to Do, No. 2. 2005. 224p. (YA). (gr. 8-17). pap. 9.99 (978-0-316-11041-9(8)) Little Brown & Co.

—Dating Game: Can True Love Survive High School?, No. 3. 2005. 224p. (YA). (gr. 8-17). pap. 9.99 (978-0-316-11042-6(6)) Little Brown & Co.

—Ex Rating. 4th rev. ed. 2006. (Dating Game Ser.: No. 4). 224p. (J). (gr. 8-17). pap. 9.99 (978-0-316-15876-3(3)) Little Brown & Co.

—Speed Dating. 5th ed. 2006. (Dating Game Ser.: No. 5). 224p. (J). (gr. 8-17). pap. 9.99 (978-0-316-11530-8(4)) Little Brown & Co.

Standish, Burt L. Frank Merriwell in Camp. Rudman, Jack, ed. 2003. (Frank Merriwell Ser.). (YA). (gr. 9 up). 29.95 (978-0-8373-9324-7(8)); pap. 9.95 (978-0-8373-9024-6(9) , FM-024) Merriwell, Frank Inc.

Standish, L. Burt. Frank Merriwell's Chums. 2007. (ENG.). 268p. 97.99 (***978-1-4280-7372-2(8));*** per. 91.99 (***978-1-4280-7378-4(7)***) IndyPublish.com.

Stanley, Diane. The Mysterious Case of the Allbright Academy. 2008. 272p. (J). lib. bdg. 17.89 (***978-0-06-085818-6(4));*** (gr. 3-7). 16.99 (***978-0-06-085817-9(6)***) HarperCollins Pubs.

Stanley, George Edward. Clue of the Left-Handed Envelope. 2000. (gr. 3-6). lib. bdg. 11.80 (978-0-613-31078-9(0)) Tandem Library Bks.

—Cobweb Confession. 2001. (gr. 3-6). lib. bdg. 11.80 (978-0-613-35666-4(7)) Tandem Library Bks.

Star Struck! Individual Title Six-Packs. (Bookweb Ser.). 32p. (gr. 3 up). 34.00 (978-0-7635-3931-3(7)) Rigby Education.

Starke, Ruth. Saving Saddler Street. 2002. (Takeaways Ser.). (Illus.). 160p. (YA). pap. (978-0-7344-0197-7(3) , Lothian Bks.) Hachette Livre Australia.

Stauffacher, Sue. Donutheart. 2006. 208p. (J). (gr. 3-7). 15.95 (978-0-375-83275-8(0)); lib. bdg. 17.99 (978-0-375-93275-5(5)) Random Hse. Children's Bks. (Knopf Bks. for Young Readers).

Staunton, Ted. Sounding Off. 2004. 184p. (J). pap. 7.95 (978-0-88995-293-5(0)) Red Deer Pr. CAN. *Dist:* Fitzhenry & Whiteside, Ltd.

Stead, Rebecca. First Light. 2007. 336p. (J). (gr. 4-7). 15.99 (***978-0-375-84017-3(6));*** lib. bdg. 18.99 (***978-0-375-94017-0(0)***) Random Hse. Children's Bks. (Lamb, Wendy).

Stephen, Smith. Fourth & Long. 2006. 128p. (J). pap. 5.99 (978-0-7847-1471-3(1) , 42142) Standard Publishing.

Stephenson, Lynda. Dancing with Elvis. 331p. (YA). 2006. pap. 8.00 (978-0-8028-5300-4(5)); 2005. (gr. 7). 17.00 (978-0-8028-5293-9(9)) Eerdmans, William B. Publishing Co. (Eerdmans Bks For Young Readers).

Stern, Maggie. George. Sims, Blanche, illus. 1999. 48p. (J). (gr. 1-4). pap. 4.95 (978-0-531-07135-9(9) , Orchard Bks.) Scholastic, Inc.

Stern, Ricki & Worcester, Heidi P. Adventure: Lonely Leader. Bates, Amy June, illus. 2003. (Beryl E. Bean Ser.: No. 3). 64p. (J). lib. bdg. 16.89 (978-0-06-028774-0(8)) HarperCollins Pubs.

Sternberg, Libby. Uncovering Sadie's Secrets. 2005. (YA). (gr. 8-12). mass mkt. 5.99 (978-0-8439-5497-5(3) , SMOOCH) Dorchester Publishing Co., Inc.

Stewart, Trenton Lee. The Mysterious Benedict Society. Ellis, Carson, illus. 2007. 496p. (J). (gr. 3-7). 16.99 (978-0-316-05777-6(0) , Tingley, Megan Bks.) Little, Brown Bks. for Young Readers.

—The Mysterious Benedict Society. 2006. (978-0-307-28440-2(9) , Listening Library) Random Hse. Audio Publishing Group.

Stewart, Trenton Lee. Mysterious Benedict Society 2. 2008. 448p. 16.99 (***978-0-316-05780-6(0)***) Little Brown & Co.

Stiles, Norman. On My Very First School Day I Met... Mayer, Bill, illus. 2005. 32p. (J). (ps). 9.95 (978-0-689-03924-9(7) , Milk & Cookies) ibooks, Inc.

Stine, R. L. Battle of the Dum Diddys. Park, Trip, illus. 2007. (Rotten School Ser.: Vol. 12). 128p. (J). 6.99 (***978-0-06-078833-9(X));*** lib. bdg. 14.89 (***978-0-06-078834-6(8)***) HarperCollins Pubs.

Stine, R. L. The Big Blueberry Barf-Off! Park, Trip, illus. 2005. (Rotten School Ser.). 128p. (J). 6.99 (978-0-06-078586-4(1)); lib. bdg. 14.89 (978-0-06-078587-1(X)) HarperCollins Pubs.

STINE, R. L. Calling All Creeps. 2007. (Goosebumps Ser.). 144p. (J). pap. 4.99 (***978-0-439-92221-0(6)***) Scholastic, Inc.

Stine, R. L. Dudes, the School Is Haunted!, No. 7. Park, Trip, illus. 2006. (Rotten School Ser.). 128p. (J). 6.99 (978-0-06-078817-9(8)); lib. bdg. 14.89 (978-0-06-078818-6(6)) HarperCollins Pubs.

—The Good, the Bad & the Very Slimy. Park, Trip, illus. 2005. (Rotten School Ser.). 128p. (J). lib. bdg. 14.89 (978-0-06-078593-2(4)); 6.99 (978-0-06-078592-5(6)) HarperCollins Pubs.

—Got Cake? Park, Trip, illus. 2007. (Rotten School Ser.: No. 13). 128p. (J). 6.99 (***978-0-06-123269-5(6));*** lib. bdg. 14.89 (***978-0-06-123270-1(X)***) HarperCollins Pubs.

—The Great Smelling Bee. Park, Trip, illus. 2005. (Rotten School Ser.). 128p. (J). lib. bdg. 14.89 (978-0-06-078590-1(X)) HarperCollins Pubs.

—The Haunted School. 2005. (Goosebumps Ser.). 128p. (J). (gr. 3-7). pap. 4.99 (978-0-439-77475-8(6)) Scholastic, Inc.

—The Heinie Prize. Park, Trip, illus. 2006. (Rotten School Ser.). 128p. (J). lib. bdg. 14.89 (978-0-06-078815-5(1)); 6.99 (978-0-06-078814-8(3)) HarperCollins Pubs.

—Lose, Team, Lose! Park, Trip, illus. 2005. (Rotten School Ser.). 128p. (J). lib. bdg. 14.89 (978-0-06-078809-4(7)); 6.99 (978-0-06-078808-7(9)) HarperCollins Pubs.

—The New Girl. 2006. (Fear Street Ser.). 176p. (YA). pap. 5.99 (978-1-4169-1810-3(8) , Simon Pulse) Simon & Schuster Children's Publishing.

—Punk'd & Skunked. Park, Trip, illus. 2007. (Rotten School Ser.: No. 11). 128p. (J). 6.99 (978-0-06-078830-8(5)); lib. bdg. 14.89 (978-0-06-078831-5(3)) HarperCollins Pubs.

—Rottenest Angel. Park, Trip, illus. 2007. (Rotten School Ser.: No. 10). 128p. (J). lib. bdg. 14.89 (978-0-06-078828-5(3)) HarperCollins Pubs.

—The Rottenest Angel. Park, Trip, illus. 2007. (Rotten School Ser.: Vol. 10). 128p. (J). 6.99 (978-0-06-078827-8(5)) HarperCollins Pubs.

—Scream School. 1999. (Goosebumps Series 2000: No. 15). 117p. (gr. 3-7). pap. 3.99 (978-0-590-68519-1(8)) Scholastic, Inc.

—Shake, Rattle, & Hurl! Park, Trip, illus. 2006. (Rotten School Ser.: Vol. 5). 128p. (J). 6.99 (978-0-06-078811-7(9)); lib. bdg. 14.89 (978-0-06-078812-4(7)) HarperCollins Pubs.

Stinson, Kathy. King of the Castle. Charko, Kasia, illus. 2005. (Early Chapter Bks.). 64p. (YA). (gr. 2-5). pap. 5.95 (978-1-896764-35-1(5)) Second Story Pr. CAN. *Dist:* Orca Bk. Pubs. USA.

Stolarz, Laurie Faria. The Blue Is for Nightmares Collection. 2006. 1224p. pap., pap. 29.95 (978-0-7387-0988-8(3) , Flux) Llewellyn Pubns.

—White Is for Magic. Karre, Andrew, ed. 2004. (Blue Is for Nightmares Ser.: Vol. 2). 312p. pap. 8.95 (978-0-7387-0443-2(1)) Llewellyn Pubns.

Stone, Phoebe. Deep down Popular. 2008. (J). 288p. pap. 16.99 (***978-0-439-80245-1(8)); (978-0-439-80244-4(X)***) Scholastic, Inc. (Levine, Arthur A. Bks.).

Stone, Tanya Lee. A Bad Boy Can Be Good for a Girl. 2007. 240p. (YA). (gr. 7-11). pap. 7.99 (978-0-553-49509-6(7) , Lamb, Wendy) Random Hse. Children's Bks.

Stone, Tom B. El Autobus Siniestro. 2002. (Graveyard School Ser.). (SPA.). (J). pap. 5.95 (978-950-24-0873-6(X) , AL30667) Albatros ARG. *Dist:* Lectorum Pubns., Inc.

Straight, Susan. The Friskative Dog. 2007. 160p. (J). (gr. 3-7). 14.99 (978-0-375-83777-7(9)); lib. bdg. 17.99 (978-0-375-93777-4(3)) Random Hse. Children's Bks. (Knopf Bks. for Young Readers).

Strand, Jeff. Elrod Mcbugle on the Loose. 2006. (ENG.). 136p. (YA). per. 9.25 (***978-0-7599-4325-4(7)***) Hard Shell Word Factory.

Strasser, Todd. Con-fidence. 164p. (J). (gr. 4-6). tchr. ed. 16.95 (978-0-8234-1394-2(2)); (YA). (gr. 5 up). pap. 6.95 (***978-0-8234-2061-2(2)***) Holiday Hse., Inc.

—Don't Get Caught in the Girl's Locker Room. 2001. (Don't Get Caught Ser.). (Illus.). (J). 11.15 (978-0-606-21155-0(1)) Tandem Library Bks.

—Give a Boy a Gun. 2002. 208p. (YA). pap. 5.99 (978-0-689-84893-3(5) , Simon Pulse) Simon & Schuster Children's Publishing.

—Give a Boy a Gun. 2002. (gr. 7-12). lib. bdg. 14.15 (978-0-613-73375-5(4)) Tandem Library Bks.

—Help! I'm Trapped in My Lunch Lady's Body. 1999. (Help! I'm Trapped Ser.). 144p. (gr. 4-7). pap. 4.50 (978-0-590-97805-7(5)) Scholastic, Inc.

—Help! I'm Trapped in My Lunch Lady's Body. 1999. (Help! I'm Trapped Ser.). (J). (gr. 4-7). (978-0-606-17543-2(1)) Tandem Library Bks.

Strasser, Todd. How I Changed My Life. 2008. 240p. (YA). mass mkt. 6.99 (***978-1-4169-5409-5(0)*** , Simon Pulse) Simon & Schuster Children's Publishing.

Strauss, Linda Leopold. Really, Truly, Everything's Fine. 2004. 160p. (YA). 15.95 (978-0-7614-5163-1(3)) Cavendish, Marshall Corp.

Strong, Jeremy. Chicken School. l.t. ed. 2005. pap. 16.95 (978-1-4056-6037-2(6)) BBC Audio GBR. *Dist:* BBC Audiobooks America.

—Pandemonium at School. l.t. ed. 2005. (Illus.). 104p. (J). pap. incl. audio (978-0-7540-7862-3(0) , CLP 448) BBC Audio.

—Pandemonium at School. 2004. (J). pap. 24.95 incl. audio (978-0-7540-6272-1(4) , Chivers Children's Audio Bks.) BBC Audiobooks America.

—Stuff: The Life of a Cool Demented Dude. Armstrong, Matthew S., illus. 2007. 240p. (J). (gr. 7 up). 15.99 (978-0-06-084105-8(2) , HarperTeen) HarperCollins Pubs.

—Stuff: The Life of a Cool Demented Dude. Armstrong, Matthew, illus. 2007. 240p. (J). (gr. 7 up). lib. bdg. 16.89 (978-0-06-084106-5(0) , HarperTeen) HarperCollins Pubs.

—Viking at School. Levers, John, illus. l.t. ed. 2000. 96p. (J). pap. (978-0-7540-6093-2(4) , CLP 291) BBC Audio.

—Viking at School. Levers, John, illus. unabr. l.t. ed. 2003. (Read-Along Ser.). 104p. (J). pap. 24.95 incl. audio (978-0-7540-6230-1(9) , RA031, Galaxy Children's Large Print) BBC Audiobooks America.

Stroud, Scott. Grumpy Mr. Grady. 2007. (J). 12.95 (***978-1-60131-008-8(0)***) Big Tent Bks.

Sturges, Philemon. I Love School! Halpern, Shari, illus. 32p. (J). (ps-1). 2004. 12.99 (978-0-06-009284-9(X)); 2004. lib. bdg. 14.89 (978-0-06-009285-6(8)); 2006. reprint ed. pap. 5.99 (978-0-06-009286-3(6) , Harper Trophy) HarperCollins Pubs.

Sturton, Lydia. Are You Listening? 2002. (Takeaways Ser.). (Illus.). 160p. (YA). pap. (978-0-7344-0198-4(1) , Lothian Bks.) Hachette Livre Australia.

Stuve-Bodeen, Stephanie. Babu's Song. Boyd, Aaron, illus. 2003. 32p. (J). 16.95 (978-1-58430-058-8(2)) Lee & Low Bks., Inc.

—Elizabeti's School. Hale, Christy, illus. 2002. 32p. (J). (gr. k-3). 16.95 (978-1-58430-043-4(4)) Lee & Low Bks., Inc.

Stuve-Bodeen, Stephanie. La escuela de Elizabeti. Christy, Hale, illus. 2007. (SPA.). (J). pap. 7.95 (***978-1-60060-235-1(5)***) Lee & Low Bks., Inc.

Suen, Anastasia. Hamster Chase. 2002. (gr. k-3). lib. bdg. 11.80 (978-0-613-71579-9(9)) Tandem Library Bks.

—The Hamster Chase. Eitzen, Allan, illus. 2002. (Easy-to-Read Ser.). 32p. (J). pap. 3.99 (978-0-14-230134-0(5) , Puffin) Penguin Group (USA) Inc.

—Helping Sophia. Ebbeler, Jeffrey, illus. 2007. (Main Street School - Kids with Character Ser.). 32p. (J). (ps-4). lib. bdg. 27.07 (***978-1-60270-030-7(3)*** , Looking Glass Library) Magic Wagon.

—Raising the Flag. Ebbeler, Jeffrey, illus. 2007. (Main Street School - Kids with Character Ser.). 32p. (J). (ps-4). lib. bdg. 27.07 (***978-1-60270-031-4(1)*** , Looking Glass Library) Magic Wagon.

—Scissors, Paper, & Sharing. Ebbeler, Jeffrey, illus. 2007. (Main Street School - Kids with Character Ser.). 32p. (J). (ps-4). lib. bdg. 27.07 (***978-1-60270-032-1(X)*** , Looking Glass Library) Magic Wagon.

—Show Some Respect. Ebbeler, Jeffrey, illus. 2007. (Main Street School - Kids with Character Ser.). 32p. (J). (ps-4). lib. bdg. 27.07 (***978-1-60270-033-8(8)*** , Looking Glass Library) Magic Wagon.

—Times Table Cheat. Ebbeler, Jeffrey, illus. 2007. (Main Street School - Kids with Character Ser.). 32p. (J). (ps-4). lib. bdg. 27.07 (***978-1-60270-034-5(6)*** , Looking Glass Library) Magic Wagon.

Sula, Sondra. Katie: Katie & the Ogre. 2000. mass mkt. 8.95 (978-1-931179-17-1(4)) Long Hill Productions, Inc.

—Katie: Katie & the Ogre. Ruiz, Marcus, illus. 2000. 32p. (J). (gr. 1-3). pap. (978-1-931179-01-0(8)) Long Hill Productions, Inc.

Sumpolec, Sarah Anne. The Alliance. 2004. (Becoming Beka Ser.). 256p. (YA). pap. 12.99 (978-0-8024-6452-1(1)) Moody Pubs.

—The Masquerade. 2003. (Becoming Beka Ser.). 224p. (YA). pap. 12.99 (978-0-8024-6451-4(3)) Moody Pubs.

—The Passage. 2005. (Becoming Beka Ser.). 256p. (J). pap. 12.99 (978-0-8024-6453-8(X)) Moody Pubs.

Super Fly Guy. 2007. 32p. (J). per. (***978-0-439-90374-5(2)***) Scholastic, Inc.

Supplee, Suzanne. When Irish Guys Are Smiling. 2008. (S. A. S. S. (Students Across the Seven Seas) Ser.). 224p. (YA). (gr. 7). pap. 6.99 (***978-0-14-241016-5(0)*** , Puffin) Penguin Group (USA) Inc.

Sutherland, Tui. This Must Be Love. 256p. (J). 2005. pap. 7.99 (978-0-06-056477-3(6) , Harper Trophy); 2004. (gr. 7 up). 15.99 (978-0-06-056475-9(X)); 2004. (gr. 7 up). lib. bdg. 16.89 (978-0-06-056476-6(8)) HarperCollins Pubs.

Swain, Cynthia. Sorting at the Nature Center. 2006. (Early Explorers Ser.). (J). 30.00 (***978-1-4108-6039-2(6)***) Benchmark Education Co.

Swallow, Pamela Curtis. It Only Looks Easy. rev. ed. 2003. 176p. (J). (gr. 3-7). 15.95 (978-0-7613-1790-6(2)) Roaring Brook Pr.

Swan, Bill. Mud Happens. 2005. (Sports Stories Ser.). 112p. (J). (gr. 3-8). (***978-1-55028-899-5(7));*** 7.95 (978-1-55028-898-8(9)) Lorimer, James & Co., Ltd., Pubs. CAN. *Dist:* Casemate Pubs. & Bk. Distributors, LLC.

Sweeney, Joyce. Players. 2005. 220p. (YA). (gr. 7-12). reprint ed. pap. 6.95 (978-0-7614-5236-2(2)) Cavendish, Marshall Corp.

—Waiting for June. 2006. 160p. 5.99 (978-0-7614-5329-1(6)); 2003. 144p. (YA). 15.95 (978-0-7614-5138-9(2)) Cavendish, Marshall Corp.

Sydor, Colleen. Camilla Chameleon. 2007. 32p. pap. (***978-1-55453-164-6(0)***) Kids Can Pr., Ltd.

Synder, Inez. School Tools. 2002. (gr. k-3). lib. bdg. 12.95 (978-0-613-58875-1(4)) Tandem Library Bks.

Tada, Joni Eareckson. Meanest Teacher. 2001. (gr. 3-6). lib. bdg. 14.15 (978-0-613-81758-5(3)) Tandem Library Bks.

Tada, Joni Eareckson & Jensen, Steve. The Meanest Teacher. 2005. (Darcy & Friends Ser.). 144p. (gr. 3-6). pap. 5.99 (978-1-58134-256-7(X) , Crossway Bibles) Crossway Bks.

Tarshis, Lauren. Emma-Jean Lazarus Fell Out of a Tree. 2008. 208p. (YA). (gr. 7). pap. 6.99 (***978-0-14-241150-6(7)*** , Puffin) Penguin Group (USA) Inc.

Taulbert, Clifton L. Little Cliff's First Day of School. Taulbert, Clifton L. & Lewis, Earl, illus. 2003. 32p. (J). (gr. k-3). pap. 6.99 (978-0-14-250082-8(8) , Puffin) Penguin Group (USA) Inc.

—Little Cliff's First Day of School. Lewis, Earl, illus. 2001. 32p. (J). (ps-3). 15.99 (978-0-8037-2557-7(4) , Dial) Penguin Group (USA) Inc.

—Little Cliff's First Day of School. 2003. (gr. k-3). lib. bdg. 15.30 (978-0-613-67561-1(4)) Tandem Library Bks.

Tayler, Kassy. Obsessing Orlando. 2005. (YA). (gr. 8-12). mass mkt. 5.99 (978-0-8439-5603-0(8) , SMOOCH) Dorchester Publishing Co., Inc.

Tayleur, Karen. Promises! David Mortimore Baxter. Garvey, Brann, illus. 2007. 87p. (J). pap. (***978-1-59889-208-6(8)***) Stone Arch Bks.

Taylor, Dan & Taylor, Damon J. Lenny Loses His Lunch: A Lion's Tale. Taylor, Damon J., illus. 2005. (Illus.). 32p. (J). (ps-ps). 10.99 (978-0-8254-3871-4(3)) Kregel Pubns.

Taylor, Kelly. Praise the Moon. 2005. 131p. pap. 19.95 (978-1-4137-8059-8(8)) PublishAmerica, Inc.

Taylor, Mari Jo. Not One of the Robot Children. 2005. 11.00 (978-0-8059-9791-0(1)) Dorrance Publishing Co., Inc.

Teach Us, Amelia Bedelia. 2002. (Amelia Bedelia Ser.). (Illus.). (J). 11.91 (978-0-7587-1726-9(1)) Book Wholesalers, Inc.

Teague, Mark. Secret Shortcut. 1999. (gr. k-3). lib. bdg. 14.15 (978-0-613-22932-6(0)) Tandem Library Bks.

Teal, Joyce Willard. The Point System. 1998. (Illus.). (J). pap. 8.80 (978-1-56763-399-3(4)); lib. bdg. 25.25 (978-1-56763-398-6(6)) Ozark Publishing.

Temple-West, Mariga. Louise & Edna. 2001. 128p. per. 12.75 (978-1-931633-05-5(3)) New World Media, Inc.

TenNapel, Doug & Koelsch, Mike. Fateful Friday. 1998. (Strange Kid Chronicles: No. 5). 80p. (J). (gr. 2-5). pap. 3.99 (978-0-590-05958-9(0)) Scholastic, Inc.

—Just Thursday. 1998. (Strange Kid Chronicles: No. 4). 80p. (J). (gr. 2-5). pap. 3.99 (978-0-590-05957-2(2)) Scholastic, Inc.

—Mighty Monday Madness. 1998. (Strange Kid Chronicles: No. 1). 80p. (J). (gr. 2-5). pap. 3.99 (978-0-590-05953-4(X)) Scholastic, Inc.

—Tuna Fish Tuesday. 1998. (Strange Kid Chronicles: No. 2). 80p. (J). (gr. 2-5). pap. 3.99 (978-0-590-05955-8(6)) Scholastic, Inc.

—Wisenheimer Wednesday. 1998. (Strange Kid Chronicles: No. 3). 80p. (J). (gr. 2-5). pap. 3.99 (978-0-590-05956-5(4)) Scholastic, Inc.

Thacker, Nola. Staying Balanced. 2000. (gr. 3-6). lib. bdg. 13.00 (978-0-613-31754-2(8)) Tandem Library Bks.

Thaler, Mike. The Cafeteria Lady from the Black Lagoon. Lee, Jared D., illus. 1998. (Black Lagoon Ser.). 32p. (J). (ps-3). pap. 3.99 (978-0-590-50493-5(2) , Cartwheel Bks.) Scholastic, Inc.

—The Class Pet from the Black Lagoon. Lee, Jared D., illus. 2003. (J). pap. (978-0-439-55718-4(6)) Scholastic, Inc.

—The Custodian from the Black Lagoon. Lee, Jared D., illus. 2001. (Black Lagoon Ser.). 32p. (J). (ps-3). pap. 3.25 (978-0-439-18874-6(1)) Scholastic, Inc.

—The Custodian from the Black Lagoon. 2001. (Black Lagoon Ser.). (Illus.). (J). 10.05 (978-0-606-22044-6(5)) Tandem Library Bks.

—Custodian from the Black Lagoon. 2001. (gr. k-3). lib. bdg. 10.95 (978-0-613-35667-1(5)) Tandem Library Bks.

—The Field Day from the Black Lagoon. Lee, Jared D., illus. 2008. (Little Apple Ser.). 64p. (J). 3.99 (***978-0-439-68076-9(X)***) Scholastic, Inc.

—Field Day from the Black Lagoon. Lee, Jared D., illus. 2005. 64p. (J). lib. bdg. 15.00 (***978-1-4242-2261-2(3)***) Fitzgerald Bks.

—The Music Teacher from the Black Lagoon. Lee, Jared D., illus. 2000. (Black Lagoon Ser.). 32p. (J). (ps-3). pap. 3.99 (978-0-439-18873-9(3)) Scholastic, Inc.

—The Music Teacher from the Black Lagoon. 2000. (Black Lagoon Ser.). (J). (ps-3). (978-0-606-18882-1(7)) Tandem Library Bks.

—Music Teacher from the Black Lagoon. 2000. (gr. 3-6). lib. bdg. 10.95 (978-0-613-24063-5(4)) Tandem Library Bks.

—The School Secretary from the Black Lagoon. Lee, Jared D., illus. 2006. (J). (***978-0-439-80077-8(3)***) Scholastic, Inc.

—The Teacher from the Black Lagoon. Lee, Jared D., illus. 2004. (YA). (gr. k up). pap. 14.95 incl. audio (978-1-55592-172-9(8)) Weston Woods Studios, Inc.

—The Teacher from the Black Lagoon. Lee, Jared D., illus. 2004. (J). (gr. k-3). pap. 18.95 incl. audio compact disk (978-1-55592-495-9(6)) Weston Woods Studios, Inc.

Tharp, Tim. Knights of the Hill Country. 2006. 240p. (YA). (gr. 7). 16.95 (978-0-375-83653-4(5)); lib. bdg. 18.99 (978-0-375-93653-1(X)) Random Hse. Children's Bks. (Knopf Bks. for Young Readers).

The Book Company. Learn to Count: Bee's School Bus. 2005. (Illus.). 22p. (J). (gr. 2-4). bds. 5.95 (978-1-74047-626-3(3)) Book Co. Publishing Pty, Ltd., The AUS. *Dist:* Penton Overseas, Inc.

The Book Company, ed. School. (Sparkle Bks.). (J). bds. 4.99 (978-1-74047-331-6(0)) Book Co. Publishing Pty, Ltd., The AUS. *Dist:* Penton Overseas, Inc.

Thesman, Jean. Other Ones. 2001. (gr. 5-8). lib. bdg. 14.15 (978-0-613-43861-2(2)) Tandem Library Bks.

Thiel, Annie. Danny Is Moving. 2006. (Playdate Kids Ser.). (Illus.). 32p. 14.95 (978-1-933721-02-6(2)) Playdate Kids Publishing.

Thomas & the School Trip. 2002. (Thomas the Tank Engine Ser.). (Illus.). (J). 11.91 (978-0-7587-1737-5(7)) Book Wholesalers, Inc.

Thomas, Patrick. The Wildsidhe Chronicles Bk. 2: Double Cross. 2002. (J). pap. 7.99 (978-1-890096-14-4(8)) Padwolf Publishing, Inc.

Thomas, Peggy. Snow Dance. Facklam, Paul, illus. 2007. 32p. (J). 15.95 (*978-1-58980-478-4(3)) Pelican Publishing Co., Inc.

Thomas, Rob. Doing Time: Notes from the Underground. 1999. (J). (978-0-606-16336-1(0)) Tandem Library Bks.

—Rats Saw God. 2007. 208p. (YA). pap. 6.99 (978-1-4169-3897-2(4) , Simon Pulse) Simon & Schuster Children's Publishing.

Thompson, Dorothy. Dewey Does Adding & Subtractions Bk. 2: Activity Sports Book. 2004. (Dewey Does Ser.). (Illus.). 44p. (J). (ps-3). pap., act. bk. ed. 4.95 (978-0-9711474-2-3(6)) A B C-123 Publishing.

Thompson, Julian F. Hard Time. 2003. (Illus.). 256p. (YA). 16.95 (978-0-689-85424-8(2) , Atheneum) Simon & Schuster Children's Publishing.

Thompson, Kelly. Lasting. 2005. 120p. pap. 17.95 (978-1-4137-9653-7(2)) PublishAmerica, Inc.

Thompson, Lauren, et al. Mouse's First Day of School. 2003. (Illus.). 32p. (J). (ps-1). 12.95 (978-0-689-84727-1(0)) Simon & Schuster Children's Publishing.

Thompson, Shannon Raines. Mad about Miller. Stone, Kathrine Thompson, ed. Shehan, Terece, illus. 2006. 24p. (YA). 12.95 (978-1-59971-853-8(7)) Aardvark Global Publishing.

—Nuts about Neal. Stone, Kathrine Thompson, ed. Shehan, Terece, illus. 2006. 24p. (YA). 12.95 (978-1-59971-852-1(9)) Aardvark Global Publishing.

Thompson, Tate. Senioritis. 2nd ed. 2003. (YA). per. 13.50 (978-0-943864-47-1(X)) Davenport, May Pubs.

Thompson, Tolya L. Catchin' Cooties Consuelo. Harrold, Brian, illus. 2004. (Smarties Ser.: 3). (SPA.). (J). 16.00 (978-0-9708296-3-4(9)) Savor Publishing Hse., Inc.

Thompson, Vivian L. Neat! Said Jeremy. 2003. 33p. (J). pap. 8.95 (978-0-7414-1579-0(8)) Infinity Publishing.

Thornhill, Samantha. Everybody Hates School Presentations. 2008. (Everybody Hates Chris Ser.). 96p. (J). pap. 5.99 (*978-1-4169-4983-1(6) , Simon Spotlight) Simon & Schuster Children's Publishing.

Tidd, Louise Vitellaro. Did You Hear about Jake? Handelman, Dorothy, photos by. 1999. (Real Kids Readers Ser.). (Illus.). 32p. (gr. k-2). lib. bdg. 18.90 (978-0-7613-2058-6(X)); (J). pap. 4.99 (978-0-7613-2083-8(0)) Lerner Publishing Group. (Millbrook Pr.).

—Did You Hear about Jake? 1999. (J). 10.79 (978-0-606-19153-1(4)); lib. bdg. 11.80 (978-0-613-16658-4(2)) Tandem Library Bks.

Tidd Louise Vitellaro. Lo haré después (I'll Do It Later) 2007. (Lecturas para niños de verdad - Nivel 2 (Real Kids Readers - Level 2) Ser.). (J). pap. 5.95 (*978-0-8225-7805-5(0) , Ediciones Lerner) Lerner Publishing Group.

—¿Ya te enteraste? (Did You Hear about Jake?) 2007. (Lecturas para niños de verdad - Nivel 2 (Real Kids Readers - Level 2) Ser.). (J). pap. 5.95 (*978-0-8225-7802-4(6) , Ediciones Lerner) Lerner Publishing Group.

Tierno, Susan F. Hiciste la Tarea? Alvarado, Ana María, tr. Ramirez, Michael, illus. 2000. (Think-Kids Book Collection).Tr. of Have You Done Your Homework?. (SPA.). 16p. (J). (gr. 1-3). pap. 2.95 (978-1-58237-049-1(4)) Creative Thinkers, Inc.

—Mas Proyectos? Alvarado, Ana María, tr. Schiffman, Jessica, illus. 2000. (Think-Kids Book Collection).Tr. of I Hate Projects. (SPA.). 16p. (J). pap. 2.95 (978-1-58237-041-5(9)) Creative Thinkers, Inc.

—Para Ganarle a Esos... ! Alvarado, Ana María, tr. Ramirez, Michael, illus. 2000. (Think-Kids Book Collection).Tr. of That's a Though Team to Beat!. (SPA.). 16p. (J). (gr. 1-4). pap. 2.95 (978-1-58237-055-2(9)) Creative Thinkers, Inc.

Tildes, Phyllis Limbacher. The Garden Wall. Tildes, Phyllis Limbacher, illus. 2006. (Illus.). (J). 16.95 (978-1-57091-467-6(2) , 1258423); pap. 7.95 (978-1-57091-468-3(0) , 1258423) Charlesbridge Publishing, Inc.

Tilley, Jessica. You Have to Be Smart If You're Going to be Tall. Evans, Leslie, illus. 2006. 46p. (J). per. 16.99 (*978-1-59879-217-1(2)) Lifevest Publishing, Inc.

Timberlake, Amy. That Girl Lucy Moon. 2006. 304p. (gr. 4-7). 15.99 (978-0-7868-5298-7(4)) Hyperion Pr.

Time for School. 2001. (Disney's Winnie the Pooh Ser.). (Illus.). 10p. (J). bds. 7.95 (978-0-7853-4790-3(9)) Publications International, Ltd.

Tindall, Steve. The Quest of the Black Knight. 2006. (ENG.). 168p. (J). per. (978-1-84685-303-6(6) , Exposure Publishing) Meadow Bks.

Tinkler, David. The Headmaster Went Splat! l.t. ed. 2000. (Illus.). 165p. (J). pap. (978-0-7540-6107-6(8) , CLP 302) BBC Audio.

Toader, Alex. Max's Journal: The Adventures of Shark Boy & Lava Girl. Rodriguez, Robert, illus. 2005. 128p. (J). (978-1-933104-03-4(1)) Troublemaker Publishing, LP.

Tobin, C. La Mascota de la Clase. DeMonico, Rick, illus. 2005. (Maya & Miguel Ser.). (SPA.). 80p. (J). (ps-ps). pap. 5.99 (978-0-439-78347-7(X) , Scholastic en Espanol) Scholastic, Inc.

—Teacher's Pet. DeMonico, Rick, illus. 2005. (Maya & Miguel Ser.). 80p. (J). (ps-ps). pap. 5.99 (978-0-439-73385-4(5)) Scholastic, Inc.

Tocher, Timothy. Long Shot. 2001. (J). 137p. (978-0-88166-395-2(6)); 144p. pap. 4.95 (978-0-689-84331-0(3)) Meadowbrook Pr.

Tokio, Marnelle. Room 207. Hendry, Linda, illus. 2006. 120p. (J). (gr. 3-6). pap. 8.95 (978-0-88776-695-4(1)) Tundra Bks., Inc./Livres Toundra, Inc. CAN. *Dist:* Random Hse., Inc.

Tolan, Stephanie S. Surviving the Applewhites. 2004. 224p. (J). (gr. 5 up). pap. 5.99 (978-0-06-441044-1(7) , Harper Trophy) HarperCollins Pubs.

—Surviving the Applewhites. 2004. (YA). (gr. 7-8). tchr. ed. (978-1-58130-867-9(1)); stu. ed. (978-1-58130-868-6(X)) Novel Units, Inc.

—Surviving the Applewhites. 2004. (gr. 5-8). lib. bdg. 14.15 (978-0-613-84148-1(4)) Tandem Library Bks.

—Surviving the Applewhites. l.t. ed. 2005. pap. 10.95 (978-0-7862-7259-4(7) , Large Print Pr.) Thorndike Pr.

Tolliver, Ruby C. Sarita, Be Brave. 1999. 144p. (gr. 3-6). 14.95 (978-1-57168-184-3(1)) Eakin Pr.

Toriyama, Akira. Dragon Ball Z, Vol. 22. Toriyama, Akira, illus. 2005. (Dragon Ball Z Ser.). 192p. (YA). pap. 7.95 (978-1-4215-0051-5(5)) Viz Media.

—Dragon Ball Z. 2006. (Dragon Ball Z Ser.). 208p. (YA). Vol. 24. pap. 7.95 (978-1-4215-0273-1(9)); Vol. 25. pap. 7.95 (978-1-4215-0404-9(9)) Viz Media.

Torres, David M. A Whooper Named Frank. 1999. (Illus.). 96p. 14.95 (978-1-57168-329-8(1)) Eakin Pr.

Torres, J. Sidekicks Vol. 1: The Transfer Student. 2nd ed. 2003. (Illus.). 144p. (YA). pap. 11.95 (978-1-929998-76-0(7)) Oni Pr., Inc.

Tosten, S. Kennedy. Troy's Amazing Universe Bk. 1: M for Mall. 2003. (Illus.). 116p. (YA). (gr. 2 up). pap. 13.95 (978-1-59113-318-6(1)) Booklocker.com, Inc.

Townsend, Michael. Billy Tartle in Say Cheese! Townsend, Michael, illus. 2007. (Illus.). 32p. (J). (gr. k-3). 18.99 (*978-0-375-93932-7(6)); 15.99 (*978-0-375-83932-0(1)) Random Hse. Children's Bks. (Knopf Bks. for Young Readers).

Tracy, Judith. The Wildsidhe Chronicles Bk. 3: Dark Proposal. 2003. (J). pap. 7.99 (978-1-890096-15-1(6)) Padwolf Publishing, Inc.

—The Wildsidhe Chronicles Bk. 4: Legacy. 2002. (J). pap. 7.99 (978-1-890096-16-8(4)) Padwolf Publishing, Inc.

Trailblazers! Individual Title Six-Packs. (Action Packs Ser.). 104p. (gr. 3-5). 44.00 (978-0-7635-2992-5(3)) Rigby Education.

Trapped by a Teacher: Individual Title Six-Packs. (Action Packs Ser.). 128p. (gr. 3-5). 44.00 (978-0-7635-3309-0(2)) Rigby Education.

Trembath, Don. Big Show. 2003. (gr. 3-6). lib. bdg. 15.25 (978-0-613-83710-1(X)) Tandem Library Bks.

Trice, Linda. Kenya's Word. Johnson, Pamela, illus. 32p. (J). 2006. pap. 6.95 (978-1-57091-888-9(0)); 2005. 16.95 (978-1-57091-887-2(2)) Charlesbridge Publishing, Inc.

Tripp, Valerie. Kit Learns a Lesson: A School Story, Bk. 2. Rane, Walter, illus. 2000. (American Girls Collection: Bk. 2). 80p. (J). (gr. 2 up). 6.95 (978-1-58485-018-2(3)); 12.95 (978-1-58485-121-9(X)) American Girl Publishing, Inc.

—Kit Learns a Lesson: A School Story. 2000. (gr. 3-6). lib. bdg. 14.10 (978-0-613-28917-7(X)); (American Girls Collection: Bk. 2). (YA). (gr. 2 up). (978-0-606-18943-9(2)) Tandem Library Bks.

—Lindy's Happy Ending. Allen, Joy, illus. 2005. 48p. (J). (ps-ps). lib. bdg. 10.79 (978-0-606-33674-1(5)) Tandem Library Bks.

Trouble in the Barkers' Class. 2005. (J). 27.95 incl. audio (978-0-8045-6935-4(5)); 29.95 incl. audio compact disk (978-0-8045-4134-3(5)) Spoken Arts, Inc.

Trueit, Trudi. Julep O' Toole: Miss Independent. 2006. (Illus.). 160p. (J). (gr. 3). 15.99 (978-0-525-47637-5(7) , Dutton Juvenile) Penguin Group (USA) Inc.

—Julep O' Toole: Miss Independent: Miss Independent. 2007. 176p. (J). 5.99 (978-0-14-240829-2(8) , Puffin) Penguin Group (USA) Inc.

—Julep O'Toole: What I Really Want to Do Is Direct. 2007. 160p. (J). (gr. 3 up). 16.99 (978-0-525-47781-5(0) , Dutton Juvenile) Penguin Group (USA) Inc.

—Julep O'Toole: Confessions of a Middle Child: Confessions of a Middle Child. 2007. 192p. (J). 5.99 (978-0-14-240798-1(4) , Puffin) Penguin Group (USA) Inc.

Trufant, Robert & Mullins, Tinnesha. Angel Fingers Series: Na'dyd Goes to School. 2004. (Angel Fingers Ser.). (Illus.). 19p. (J). (ps-2). 14.95 (978-0-9760160-0-7(1)) Angel Fingers Foundation.

Tryon, Leslie. Albert's Field Trip. 2001. (gr. 3-6). lib. bdg. 15.30 (978-0-613-49708-4(2)); (Illus.). (J). 13.79 (978-0-606-21018-8(0)) Tandem Library Bks.

Tsuda, Masami. Kare Kano: His & Her Circumstances, 13 vols., Vol. 8. rev. ed. 2004. (Illus.). 192p. pap. 9.99 (978-1-59182-473-2(7) , Tokyopop Kids) TOKYOPOP, Inc.

Tullos, Matt. Dangerous Decisions & Hidden Choices, Vol. 5. 1999. (Summit High Ser.). 186p. pap. 5.99 (978-0-8054-1976-4(4)) B&H Publishing Grp.

—Deleting the Net Threat. 1999. (Summit High Ser.: No. 4). 144p. (J). (gr. 7-9). pap. 4.99 (978-0-8054-1766-1(4)) B&H Publishing Grp.

—Friends to the End. 1999. (Summit High Ser.: No. 6). 144p. (gr. 7-9). pap. 5.99 (978-0-8054-1977-1(2)) B&H Publishing Grp.

—Processing the Computer Conspiracy. 1998. (Summit High Ser.: Vol. 2). 144p. (Orig.). (J). (gr. 7-9). pap. 4.99 (978-0-8054-0181-3(4)) B&H Publishing Grp.

—Wild Lies & Secret Truth. 1999. (Summit High Ser.: Vol. 3). 144p. (J). (gr. 7-9). pap. 4.99 (978-0-8054-1765-4(6)) B&H Publishing Grp.

—Wrong Turn in the Fast Lane. 1998. (Summit High Ser.). 144p. (Orig.). (J). (gr. 7-9). pap. 4.99 (978-0-8054-0180-6(6)) B&H Publishing Grp.

—Wrong Turn in the Fast Lane. 1998. (Orig.). (gr. 7-12). lib. bdg. 14.15 (978-0-613-90148-2(7)) Tandem Library Bks.

Tullson, Diane. Edge. 2002. (Illus.). 212p. (YA). pap. 6.95 (978-0-7737-6230-5(2)) Stoddart Kids CAN. *Dist:* Fitzhenry & Whiteside, Ltd.

—Edge. 2003. (gr. 7-12). lib. bdg. 15.25 (978-0-613-81887-2(3)) Tandem Library Bks.

Uddin, Asma Mobin. My Name Is Bilal. Kiwak, Barbara, illus. 2005. 32p. (J). (ps-17). 15.95 (978-1-59078-175-3(9)) Boyds Mills Pr.

Uegaki, Chieri. Suki's Kimono. Jorisch, Stephane, illus. 32p. (J). 2005. (gr. 3). (978-1-55337-752-8(4)); 2004. (gr. k-3). (978-1-55337-084-0(8)) Kids Can Pr., Ltd.

Ugezene, Esther I. KiKi, the School Truant. 2005. per. 10.00 (978-0-9767678-1-7(3)) Milligan Bks., Inc.

Umansky, Kaye. Sophie & the Wonderful Picture. Currey, Anna, illus. 2004. 30p. (J). 3.95 (978-1-56148-445-4(8)); 9.95 (978-1-56148-437-9(7)) Good Bks.

Umansky, Kaye & Currey, Anna, illus. Sophie & Abigail. 2004. 30p. (J). 3.95 (978-1-56148-444-7(X)); 9.95 (978-1-56148-434-8(2)) Good Bks.

Umezu, Kazuo. Drifting Classroom, Vol. 9. Roman, Annette, ed. Umezu, Kazuo, illus. 2007. (Drifting Classroom Ser.). 192p. (YA). pap. 9.99 (*978-1-4215-0961-7(X)) Viz Media.

Ungerer, Tomi. Keine Kuss fur Mutler. 2000. Tr. of No Kiss for Mother. (GER.). (J). pap. 15.95 (978-3-257-25018-3(5)) Diogenes Verlag AG CHE. *Dist:* Distribooks, Inc.

—No Kiss for Mother. 1998. (Illus.). 40p. (J). (ps-3). pap. 5.95 (978-1-57098-208-8(2)) Rinehart, Roberts Pubs.

Urban, Linda. A Crooked Kind of Perfect. 2007. (Illus.). 224p. (J). (gr. 3-7). 16.00 (*978-0-15-206007-7(3)) Harcourt Children's Bks.

Ure, Jean. Dazzling Danny. 2003. (Illus.). 96p. (J). pap. 7.99 (978-0-00-713370-3(7)) HarperCollins Pubs. Ltd. GBR. *Dist:* Independent Pubs. Group.

Ure, Jean. Sugar & Spice. 2005. (Diary Ser.). (Illus.). 224p. (J). pap. 8.99 (*978-0-00-716137-9(9)) HarperCollins Pubs. Ltd. GBR. *Dist:* Independent Pubs. Group.

Uttley, Tracy. Molly Mcsholly Conquers Kindergarten. 2004. 32p. (J). bds. 15.95 (978-1-59298-077-2(5)) Beaver's Pond Pr., Inc.

Vail, Rachel. Homework Trouble. Bjorkman, Steve, illus. 2002. (Mama Rex & T Ser.). 32p. (J). (gr. k-2). pap. 14.95 (978-0-439-40628-4(5)); pap. 4.99 (978-0-439-33281-1(8)) Scholastic, Inc. (Orchard Bks.).

—If We Kiss. 2005. 272p. (J). 15.99 (978-0-06-056914-3(X)) HarperCollins Pubs.

—If You Only Knew: Zoe. 1998. (Friendship Ring Ser.: No. 1). 240p. (J). (gr. 4-8). pap. 14.95 (978-0-590-03370-1(0)); pap. 4.99 (978-0-590-37451-4(6)) Scholastic, Inc.

—Never Mind! A Twin Novel. 2005. 208p. (J). (gr. 5 up). reprint ed. pap. 5.99 (978-0-06-054316-7(7) , Harper Trophy) HarperCollins Pubs.

—Not That I Care: Morgan. 1998. (Friendship Ring Ser.: No. 3). (J). (gr. 4-8). 59.88 (978-0-590-95214-9(5)); 240p. pap. 4.99 (978-0-590-37453-8(2)); 240p. pap. 14.95 (978-0-590-03476-0(6)) Scholastic, Inc.

—Please, Please, Please. 1998. (Friendship Ring Ser.: No. 2). 240p. (J). (gr. 4-8). pap. 14.95 (978-0-590-00327-8(5)); pap. 4.99 (978-0-590-37452-1(4)) Scholastic, Inc.

—Popularity Contest: Zoe. 2000. (Friendship Ring Ser.: No. 5). (J). (gr. 4-8). (Illus.). 240p. pap. 3.99 (978-0-590-68911-3(8) , Scholastic Paperbacks); Vol. 5. pap. 47.88 (978-0-439-16067-4(7)) Scholastic, Inc.

Vail, Rachel. You, Maybe: The Profound Asymmetry of Love in High School. (J). 2007. 240p. pap. 7.99 (*978-0-06-056919-8(0) , HarperTeen); 2006. 208p. (gr. 2). 15.99 (978-0-06-056917-4(4)); 2006. 208p. (gr. 2). lib. bdg. 16.89 (978-0-06-056918-1(2)) HarperCollins Pubs.

Valdes, Leslie. Dora Goes to School. Roper, Robert, illus. ed. 2005. (Dora the Explorer Ser.: 8). 22p. (J). lib. bdg. 15.00 (978-1-59054-791-5(8)) Fitzgerald Bks.

—Dora Goes to School. 2006. (Dora the Explorer Ser.). (Illus.). (J). (ps-2). 21.35 (978-1-59961-068-9(X)) Spotlight.

Valdes-Rodriguez, Alisa. Haters. 2006. 368p. (J). (gr. 7-17). 16.99 (978-0-316-01307-9(2)) Little Brown & Co.

Valentine, Sally. The Ghost of the Charlotte Lighthouse. 2006. (J). (*978-1-59531-013-2(4)) North Country Bks., Inc.

van Diepen, Allison. Snitch. 2007. 304p. (YA). pap. 6.99 (*978-1-4169-5030-1(3) , Simon Pulse) Simon & Schuster Children's Publishing.

Van Draanen, Wendelin. Attack of the Tagger. Biggs, Brian, illus. unabr. ed. 2006. (Shredderman Ser.: Bk. 2). (J). (gr. 3-6). pap. 24.95 incl. audio (*978-1-59519-758-0(3)); pap. 28.95 incl. audio compact disk (*978-1-59519-759-7(1)) Live Oak Media.

—Attack of the Tagger. 2006. (Shredderman Ser.: Bk. 2). (Illus.). 176p. (gr. 2-5). 5.50 (978-0-440-41913-6(1) , Yearling) Random Hse. Children's Bks.

—Enemy Spy. 2006. (Shredderman Ser.: Bk. 4). 192p. (J). (gr. 2-5). 5.50 (978-0-440-41915-0(8) , Yearling) Random Hse. Children's Bks.

—Meet the Gecko. 2006. (Shredderman Ser.: Bk. 3). 176p. (J). (gr. 2-5). 5.50 (978-0-440-41914-3(X) , Yearling) Random Hse. Children's Bks.

—Meet the Gecko. Biggs, Brian, illus. 2005. (Shredderman Ser.: Bk. 3). 176p. (J). (gr. 2-5). 12.95 (978-0-375-82353-4(0)); lib. bdg. 14.99 (978-0-375-92353-1(5)) Random Hse. Children's Bks. (Knopf Bks. for Young Readers).

—Sammy Keyes & the Dead Giveaway. unabr. ed. 2006. (Sammy Keyes Ser.: Bk. 10). (J). (gr. 5-7). pap. 36.95 incl. audio (*978-1-59519-770-2(2)); pap. 54.95 incl. audio compact disk (*978-1-59519-771-9(0)) Live Oak Media.

—Sammy Keyes & the Dead Giveaway. 2007. (Sammy Keyes Ser.: Bk. 10). 304p. (J). (gr. 5-8). 5.99 (978-0-440-41911-2(5) , Yearling) Random Hse. Children's Bks.

—Secret Identity. Biggs, Brian, illus. unabr. ed. 2006. (Shredderman Ser.: Bk. 1). (J). (gr. 2-4). pap. 24.95 incl. audio (*978-1-59519-762-7(1)); pap. 28.95 incl. audio compact disk (*978-1-59519-763-4(X)) Live Oak Media.

—Secret Identity. Biggs, Brian, illus. (Shredderman Ser.: Bk. 1). 144p. (J). (gr. 2-5). 2004. lib. bdg. 14.99 (978-0-375-92351-7(9) , Knopf Bks. for Young Readers); 2006. reprint ed. 5.50 (978-0-440-41912-9(3) , Yearling) Random Hse. Children's Bks.

S

Van Kersen, Elizabeth. Who's Riley. 2005. (Illus.). 50p. (J). per. 8.99 (978-1-932338-90-4(X)) Lifevest Publishing, Inc.

Van Leeuwen, Jean. Amanda Pig, First Grader. Schweninger, Ann, illus. 2007. 40p. (J). (ps-1). 14.99 (978-0-8037-3181-3(7) , Dial) Penguin Group (USA) Inc.

—Amanda Pig, School Girl. Schweninger, Ann, illus. 1999. (Puffin Easy-to-Read Program Ser.). 48p. (J). (gr. k-3). pap. 3.99 (978-0-14-130357-4(3) , Puffin) Penguin Group (USA) Inc.

—Amanda Pig, School Girl. 1999. (ps-2). lib. bdg. 11.80 (978-0-613-19333-7(4)) Tandem Library Bks.

—Amanda Pig, Schoolgirl. 1999. (Puffin Easy-to-Read Ser.). (J). 10.79 (978-0-606-16779-6(X)) Tandem Library Bks.

—Oliver & Albert, Best Friends Forever. Schweninger, Ann, illus. 2002. (Easy-to-Read Ser.). 48p. (J). pap. 3.99 (978-0-14-230084-8(5) , Puffin) Penguin Group (USA) Inc.

van Stockum, Hilda. A Day on Skates: 2007 Commemorative Edition. van Stockum, Hilda, illus. 2007. (Illus.). 44p. (J). 19.95 (*978-1-932350-18-0(7)) Bethlehem Bks.

Vande Velde, Vivian. Smart Dog. 1998. 160p. (YA). (gr. 3-7). 16.00 (978-0-15-201847-4(6)) Harcourt Children's Bks.

—Smart Dog. 2002. (J). (gr. 4-8). 20.00 (978-0-8446-7231-1(9)) Smith, Peter Pub., Inc.

—Smart Dog. 2000. (978-0-606-18790-9(1)) Tandem Library Bks.

Varela, Barry. Palmer's Gate. 2006. 112p. (J). 16.95 (978-1-59643-073-0(7)) Roaring Brook Pr.

Vaught, Susan. Big Fat Manifesto. 2007. 320p. (YA). 16.95 (*978-1-59990-206-7(0) , Bloomsbury Children) Bloomsbury Publishing.

Vaupel, Robin. My Contract with Henry. 2003. 256p. (J). (gr. 4-6). tchr. ed. 16.95 (978-0-8234-1701-8(8)) Holiday Hse., Inc.

Vega, Denise. Click Here: To Find Out How I Survived Seventh Grade. 2006. 224p. (J). (gr. 5-8). reprint ed. pap. 7.99 (978-0-316-98559-8(7)) Little Brown & Co.

Velasquez, Gloria. Ankiza. 2000. (Roosevelt High School Ser.). 152p. (J). (gr. 2 up). pap. 9.95 (978-1-55885-309-6(X)); (gr. 8-12). pap. 16.95 (978-1-55885-308-9(1)) Arte Publico Pr. (Piñata Books).

—Ankiza. 2000. (gr. 7-12). lib. bdg. 18.75 (978-0-613-59377-9(4)) Tandem Library Bks.

Velasquez, Gloria. Tyrone's Betrayal. 144p. (J). pap. 9.95 (978-1-55885-465-9(7) , Piñata Books) Arte Publico Pr.

Velde, Vivian Vande. Remembering Raquel. 2007. (Illus.). 160p. (YA). (gr. 7 up). 16.00 (*978-0-15-205976-7(8)) Harcourt Trade Pubs.

Velez, Ivan. Dead High Yearbook. McVeigh, Mark, ed. 2007. 80p. (YA). (gr. 7 up). 18.99 (978-0-525-47783-9(7) , Dutton Juvenile) Penguin Group (USA) Inc.

Vic Visits Ground Zero. 2004. (J). (978-0-9761102-0-0(2)) Adams, Evelyn.

Viguie, Debbie. Miss O & Friends: Trouble with a Capital O. Brindak, Hermine, illus. 2006. (Miss O & Friends Ser.). 128p. (J). pap. 5.99 (978-0-8230-2946-4(8)) Watson-Guptill Pubns., Inc.

Villoro, Juan. El Profesor Ziper y la Fabulosa Guitarra Electrica. 1998. (SPA., Illus.). 96p. (J). (gr. 4-7). pap. 9.95 (978-968-29-4003-3(6)) Libros Sin Fronteras.

—El Profesor Ziper y la Fabulosa Guitarra Electrica. El Fisgon, illus. 2003. (SPA.). 96p. (J). (gr. 5-8). pap. 11.95 (978-968-19-0206-3(8)) Santillana USA Publishing Co., Inc.

A Visit to the Schoolhouse. 2003. (J). per. (978-1-57657-903-9(4)) Paradise Pr., Inc.

Vizzini, Ned. Be More Chill. 2004. 304p. (gr. 8-17). 16.95 (978-0-7868-0995-0(7)) Hyperion Bks. for Children.

—Be More Chill. 2005. 304p. (gr. 8-17). pap. 7.99 (978-0-7868-0996-7(5)) Miramax Bks.

Vogel, Jane & Johnson, Lissa Halls. Fast Forward to Normal, Vol. 2. 2005. (Brio Girls Ser.). 192p. (YA). (gr. 7-11). pap. 7.99 (978-1-56179-952-7(1)) Focus on the Family Publishing.

Vogel, Jane, et al. Good-Bye to All That, Vol. 5. 2005. (Brio Girls Ser.). 192p. (YA). pap. 7.99 (978-1-58997-051-9(9)) Focus on the Family Publishing.

Vogelaar, Alie. What Are Your Plans, Margreet?, 5 bks. Van-Brugge, J., tr. from DUT. Kramer, K. J., illus. 2001. 122p. (YA). lib. bdg. 10.95 (978-0-9670728-3-8(2)) Early Foundations Pubs.

Vogiel, Eva. Facing the Music. 2003. 284p. 19.95 (978-1-880582-94-7(5)) Judaica Pr., Inc., The.

Voigt, Cynthia. Bad, Badder, Baddest. 1999. (Bad Girls Ser.). 272p. (J). (gr. 4-7). pap. 4.99 (978-0-439-08096-5(7) , Scholastic Paperbacks) Scholastic, Inc.

—Bad, Badder, Baddest. 1999. (Bad Girls Ser.). (J). (978-0-606-17038-3(3)) Tandem Library Bks.

—Bad Girls, Bad Girls, Whatcha Gonna Do? 2006. (Bad Girls Ser.). 448p. (YA). (gr. 7 up). 17.95 (978-0-689-82474-6(2)) Simon & Schuster Children's Publishing.

Voigt, Cynthia & Marcus, Barry David. Bad Girls in Love. (Bad Girls Ser.). 240p. 2003. (Illus.). (J). pap. 5.99 (978-0-689-86620-3(8) , Aladdin); 2002. (YA). (gr. 4-8). 15.95 (978-0-689-82471-5(8) , Atheneum/Anne Schwartz Bks.) Simon & Schuster Children's Publishing.

Volponi, Paul. Black & White. 2005. 192p. (YA). (gr. 7). 15.99 (978-0-670-06006-1(2) , Viking Adult) Penguin Group (USA) Inc.

Volponi, Paul. The Hand You're Dealt. 2008. 256p. (YA). (*978-1-4169-3989-4(X)) Simon & Schuster Children's Publishing.

von Ziegesar, Cecily. Don't You Forget about Me. 11th ed. 2007. 304p. (YA). (gr. 9 up). pap. 10.99 (*978-0-316-01184-6(3) , Poppy) Little, Brown Bks. for Young Readers.

—Gossip Girl. 2003. (Gossip Girl Ser.: No. 1). 288p. (gr. 8 up). mass mkt. 5.99 (978-0-446-61315-6(0)) Grand Central Publishing.

—Gossip Girl. 208p. 2002. (Gossip Girl Ser.: No. 1). (YA). (gr. 9-17). pap. 10.99 (978-0-316-91033-0(3)); No. 1. 2007. pap. 10.99 (*978-0-316-02456-3(2)) Little, Brown Bks. for Young Readers. (Poppy).

—Gossip Girl. 2002. (Gossip Girl Ser.: No. 1). (YA). (gr. 7-12). lib. bdg. 17.35 (978-0-613-60559-5(4)) Tandem Library Bks.

—Gossip Girl: The Second Collection. 2004. (Gossip Girl Ser.). (YA). (gr. 10-17). pap. 29.99 (978-0-316-01026-9(X) , Poppy) Little, Brown Bks. for Young Readers.

—Gossip Girl: The Third Collection. 2006. (Gossip Girl Ser.). (YA). (gr. 10 up). pap. 29.99 (978-0-316-01653-7(5) , Poppy) Little, Brown Bks. for Young Readers.

—Gossip Girl Collection, 3 bks., Set. 2003. (Gossip Girl Ser.). (YA). (gr. 10-17). pap., pap. 29.99 (978-0-316-72271-1(5) , 53605112, Poppy) Little, Brown Bks. for Young Readers.

—I Like It Like That. 2004. (Gossip Girl Ser.: Bk. 5). 208p. (YA). (gr. 9-17). pap. 10.99 (978-0-316-73518-6(3) , Poppy) Little, Brown Bks. for Young Readers.

—The It Girl, No. 1. 2005. (It Girl Ser.: No. 1). 272p. (J). (gr. 7-17). pap. 9.99 (978-0-316-01185-3(1) , Poppy) Little, Brown Bks. for Young Readers.

—The It Girl Collection. 2006. (It Girl Ser.). (YA). (gr. 10-17). pap. 29.99 (978-0-316-02068-8(0) , Poppy) Little, Brown Bks. for Young Readers.

von Ziegesar, Cecily. It Had to Be You: The Gossip Girl Prequel. 2007. 300p. 16.99 (*978-0-316-02065-7(6) , Tingley, Megan Bks.) Little, Brown Bks. for Young Readers.

Von Ziegesar, Cecily. It Had to Be You: The Gossip Girl Prequel. 2007. 398p. (YA). (gr. 10-12). 17.99 (*978-0-316-01768-8(X) , Poppy) Little, Brown Bks. for Young Readers.

von Ziegesar, Cecily. Nobody Does It Better. 2005. (Gossip Girl Ser.: 7). 240p. (YA). (gr. 9-17). pap. 10.99 (978-0-316-73512-4(4) , Poppy) Little, Brown Bks. for Young Readers.

—Nothing Can Keep Us Together. 2005. (Gossip Girl Ser.: No. 8). 240p. (YA). (gr. 9-17). pap. 9.99 (978-0-316-73509-4(4) , Poppy) Little, Brown Bks. for Young Readers.

—Only in Your Dreams. 9th ed. 2006. (Gossip Girl Ser.: No. 9). 240p. (YA). (gr. 9-17). pap. 9.99 (978-0-316-01182-2(7) , Poppy) Little, Brown Bks. for Young Readers.

—Would I Lie to You. 10th ed. 2006. (Gossip Girl Ser.: No. 10). 208p. (YA). (gr. 9-17). pap. 10.99 (978-0-316-01183-9(5) , Poppy) Little, Brown Bks. for Young Readers.

—You're the One That I Want. 2004. (Gossip Girl Ser.: No. 6). 224p. (YA). (gr. 9-17). pap. 10.99 (978-0-316-73516-2(7) , Poppy) Little, Brown Bks. for Young Readers.

Voorhees, Coert. Los Torres. 2008. 320p. 16.99 (*978-1-4231-0304-2(1)) Hyperion Pr.

Vrettos, A. M. Sight. 2007. 272p. (YA). (gr. 7 up). 16.99 (*978-1-4169-0657-5(6) , McElderry, Margaret K.) Simon & Schuster Children's Publishing.

Waber, Bernard. Evie & Margie. 2006. (Illus.). 32p. (J). (gr. k-3). reprint ed. pap. 6.95 (978-0-618-69338-2(6)) Houghton Mifflin Co.

—Evie & Margie. Waber, Bernard, illus. 2003. (Illus.). 32p. (J). (gr. k-3). 15.00 (978-0-618-34124-5(2) , Walter Lorraine) Houghton Mifflin Co. Trade & Reference Div.

Walde, Christine. The Candy Darlings. 2006. 320p. (YA). (gr. 10). pap. 8.99 (978-0-618-58969-2(4) , Graphia) Houghton Mifflin Co. Trade & Reference Div.

Walden, Mark. The Overlord Protocol. 2008. (H. I. V. E. Ser.). 384p. (J). 15.99 (*978-1-4169-3573-5(8)) Simon & Schuster Children's Publishing.

Waldron, Ann. The Integration of Mary-Larkin Thornhill. 2000. 148p. pap. 10.95 (978-0-595-00069-2(X)) iUniverse, Inc.

Walker, Kate. I Hate Books. Cox, David, illus. 2007. 88p. (J). 16.95 (978-0-8126-2745-9(8)) Cricket Bks.

Walker, Melissa. Violet by Design. 2008. 224p. pap. 9.99 (*978-0-425-21940-9(2) , Berkley Trade) Penguin Group (USA) Inc.

—Violet on the Runway. 2007. 240p. (YA). (gr. 12 up). pap. 9.99 (*978-0-425-21704-7(3) , Berkley Trade) Penguin Group (USA) Inc.

Wallace, Barbara Brooks. Miss Switch Online. 2002. 192p. (J). (gr. 4-6). 16.00 (978-0-689-84376-1(3) , Atheneum) Simon & Schuster Children's Publishing.

—Miss Switch Online. 2003. (gr. 3-6). lib. bdg. 13.00 (978-0-613-91040-8(0)) Tandem Library Bks.

—The Perils of Peppermints. (Illus.). 272p. (J). 2005. pap. 4.99 (978-0-689-85045-5(X) , Aladdin); 2003. 16.95 (978-0-689-85043-1(3) , Atheneum) Simon & Schuster Children's Publishing.

Wallace, Nancy Elizabeth. The Kindness Quilt. 2006. (Illus.). 48p. (J). (gr. k-2). 16.99 (978-0-7614-5313-0(X)) Cavendish, Marshall Corp.

—Recycle Every Day! (Illus.). 32p. (J). 2006. 5.95 (978-0-7614-5290-4(7)); 2003. 16.95 (978-0-7614-5149-5(8)) Cavendish, Marshall Corp.

Wallace, Nancy Elizabeth, illus. Recycle Every Day! 2002. 40p. (J). 15.95 (978-1-58837-018-1(6)) Winslow Pr.

—The Valentine Express. 2004. 32p. (J). 16.95 (978-0-7614-5183-9(8)) Cavendish, Marshall Corp.

Wallace, Rich. Emergency Quarterback: Winning Season. 2005. 128p. (J). (gr. 4-7). 14.99 (978-0-670-06045-0(3) , Viking Adult) Penguin Group (USA) Inc.

—One Good Punch. 2007. 128p. (YA). (gr. 7). 15.99 (*978-0-375-81352-8(7)); lib. bdg. 18.99 (*978-0-375-91352-5(1)) Random Hse. Children's Bks. (Knopf Bks. for Young Readers).

—Shots on Goal. 1998. 160p. (YA). (gr. 7-11). pap. 5.99 (978-0-679-88671-6(0) , Laurel Leaf) Random Hse. Children's Bks.

—Southpaw. 2006. 105p. (J). lib. bdg. 15.38 (*978-1-4242-2166-0(8)) Fitzgerald Bks.

—Southpaw. (Winning Season Ser.: Vol. 6). 128p. (J). 2007. pap. 4.99 (978-0-14-240785-1(2) , Puffin); 2006. (gr. 4). 14.99 (978-0-670-06053-5(4) , Viking Juvenile) Penguin Group (USA) Inc.

Walsh, Jean. Gaffer Samson's Luck. 2003. (J). (gr. 3 up). 20.25 (978-0-8446-7252-6(1)) Smith, Peter Pub., Inc.

Walsh, Marissa. A Field Guide to High School. 2007. 144p. (YA). (gr. 7). lib. bdg. 18.99 (*978-0-385-90427-8(4)); 15.99 (*978-0-385-73410-3(7)) Random Hse. Children's Bks. (Delacorte Bks. for Young Readers).

Walters, Celeste. The Last Race. 2000. (UQP Young Adult Fiction Ser.). 224p. (J). pap. 16.95 (978-0-7022-3172-8(X)) Univ. of Queensland Pr. AUS. *Dist:* International Specialized Bk. Services.

Walters, Eric. Juice. 2006. 112p. (YA). lib. bdg. 14.95 (978-1-55143-588-6(8)) Orca Bk. Pubs. USA.

—Juice. 2005. 101p. (YA). (gr. 7-11). per. 15.90 (978-0-606-33183-8(2)) Tandem Library Bks.

—Laggan Lard Butts. 2006. 112p. (gr. 5-10). pap. 7.95 (978-1-55143-518-3(7)); lib. bdg. 14.95 (978-1-55143-531-2(4)) Orca Bk. Pubs. USA.

Walton, Rick. Bunny School: A Learning Fun-for-All. Miglio, Paige, illus. 2005. 32p. (J). 15.99 (978-0-06-057508-3(5)); lib. bdg. 16.89 (978-0-06-057509-0(3)) HarperCollins Pubs.

Walvoord, Linda. Rosetta, Rosetts, Sit by Me! Velasquez, Eric, illus. 2004. 80p. (J). 14.95 (978-0-7614-5171-6(4)) Cavendish, Marshall Corp.

Warburton, Nick. The Strange Change of Flora Young. l.t. ed. 2005. 192p. (J). pap. (978-0-7540-7853-1(1) , CLP 443) BBC Audio.

Ward, Dan. Meet the Boomer Sisters. 2006. 131p. pap. 13.95 (978-1-4116-6927-7(4)) Lulu.com.

Ward, Nick. No Hay Quien Gane a un Leopardo! Rubies, Carlota, tr. Ward, Nick, illus. 2001. (SPA., Illus.). 32p. (J). (gr. k-3). (978-84-480-1668-5(8) , TM30405) Timun Mas, Editorial S.A. ESP. *Dist:* Lectorum Pubns., Inc.

—No Te Comas a la Maestra. Fabiancic, Miriam, tr. Ward, Nick, illus. 2001. (SPA., Illus.). (J). (gr. k-1). pap. 3.99 (978-0-439-26363-4(8) , SO30706) Scholastic, Inc.

Wardlaw, Lee. 101 Ways to Bug Your Teacher. 256p. 2005. (gr. 5-7). pap. 6.99 (978-0-14-240331-0(8) , Puffin); 2004. (Illus.). (J). (gr. 4). 16.99 (978-0-8037-2658-1(9) , Dial) Penguin Group (USA) Inc.

Ware, Cheryl. Catty-Cornered. Yalowitz, Paul, illus. 1998. 112p. (J). (gr. 4-8). 16.99 (978-0-531-33067-8(2)); pap. 15.95 (978-0-531-30067-1(6)) Scholastic, Inc. (Orchard Bks.).

—Venola in Love. Sorra, Kristin, illus. 2000. 156p. (J). (gr. 3-7). 16.99 (978-0-531-33306-8(X)); pap. 15.95 (978-0-531-30306-1(3)) Scholastic, Inc. (Orchard Bks.).

Warner, Gertrude Chandler. Benny's Saturday Surprise. 2001. (gr. k-3). lib. bdg. 11.80 (978-0-613-35663-3(2)); (Illus.). (J). 10.75 (978-0-606-21084-3(9)) Tandem Library Bks.

Warner, Sally. Best Friend Emma. Harper, Jamie, illus. 2007. 112p. (J). (gr. 2-4). 14.99 (978-0-670-06173-0(5) , Viking Juvenile) Penguin Group (USA) Inc.

—Leftover Lily. 2000. (Illus.). (J). (978-0-606-18238-6(1)) Tandem Library Bks.

—Super Emma. Harper, Jamie, illus. (J). 2008. 112p. (gr. 3). 5.99 (*978-0-14-241088-2(8) , Puffin); 2006. 96p. (gr. 2). 14.99 (978-0-670-06140-2(9) , Viking Juvenile) Penguin Group (USA) Inc.

Washington, Kathleen. The School Bully. 2006. 9.00 (978-0-8059-8201-5(9)) Dorrance Publishing Co., Inc.

Wasserman, Robin. Ghost School. 2003. (gr. k-3). lib. bdg. 11.80 (978-0-613-72194-3(2)) Tandem Library Bks.

—Pride. 2006. (Seven Deadly Sins Ser.). 256p. (YA). pap. 8.99 (978-0-689-87784-1(6) , Simon Pulse) Simon & Schuster Children's Publishing.

—Sloth. 2006. (Seven Deadly Sins Ser.). 256p. (YA). pap. 7.99 (978-1-4169-0718-3(1) , Simon Pulse) Simon & Schuster Children's Publishing.

—Wrath. 2006. (Seven Deadly Sins Ser.). (Illus.). 256p. (YA). pap. 8.99 (978-0-689-87785-8(4) , Simon Pulse) Simon & Schuster Children's Publishing.

Wasserman, Robin & Pyle, Howard. Lust. 2005. (Seven Deadly Sins Ser.). 256p. (YA). pap. 8.99 (978-0-689-87782-7(X) , Simon Pulse) Simon & Schuster Children's Publishing.

Wasserman, Robin, et al. Ghost School. del Sur, Duendes, illus. 2003. (Scooby-Doo Ser.: No. 17). 32p. (J). pap. 3.99 (978-0-439-44227-5(3) , Scholastic Paperbacks) Scholastic, Inc.

Wassner, Gary. The Mystery of the Jubilee Emerald. 2006. (J). pap. (978-1-59336-712-1(0)) Mondo Publishing.

Watase, Yuu. Absolute Boyfriend, Vol. 3. 2007. (Absolute Boyfriend Ser.). (Illus.). 200p. (YA). pap. 8.99 (978-1-4215-1003-3(0)) Viz Media.

Watts, Leander. Beautiful City of the Dead. 2006. 256p. (YA). (gr. 7). 16.00 (978-0-618-59443-6(4)) Houghton Mifflin Co.

—Beautiful City of the Dead. 2007. 256p. (YA). (gr. 7). pap. 7.99 (*978-0-618-59499-3(X)) Houghton Mifflin Co. Trade & Reference Div.

Wax, Wendy. Coolest Girl in School. Artful Doodlers Limited Staff, illus. ed. 2005. 32p. (J). lib. bdg. 15.00 (978-1-59054-982-7(1)) Fitzgerald Bks.

We Need a New School. 2005. (J). (978-1-58453-292-7(0)) Pioneer Valley Educational Pr., Inc.

Weatherford, Carole Boston. Dear Mr. Rosenwald. Christie, Gregory, illus. 2006. 32p. (J). (gr. 2-5). pap. 16.99 (978-0-439-49522-6(9) , Scholastic Pr.) Scholastic, Inc.

Weatherly, Lee. Missing Abby. 2006. 208p. (YA). (gr. 7). mass mkt. 5.99 (978-0-553-49488-4(0) , Laurel Leaf) Random Hse. Children's Bks.

Weaver, Will. Claws. 240p. (J). 2003. lib. bdg. 16.89 (978-0-06-009474-4(5)); 2004. reprint ed. pap. 6.99 (978-0-06-009475-1(3) , HarperTeen) HarperCollins Pubs.

—Claws. 2004. lib. bdg. 15.30 (978-0-613-71445-7(8)) Tandem Library Bks.

Weaver, Will. Defect. 2007. 208p. (YA). (gr. 7 up). 16.00 (*978-0-374-31725-6(9) , Farrar, Straus & Giroux (BYR)) Farrar, Straus & Giroux.

Webb, Mack H., Jr. Danny & the Detention Demons. Espinola, Nicole & Nealon, Eve, illus. l.t. ed. 2007. 52p. (J). per. 15.95 (*978-0-9779576-2-0(4)) Pilinut Pr., Inc.

Webster, Frank V. The Boys of Bellwood School. 2004. reprint ed. pap. 20.95 (978-1-4191-5509-3(1)); pap. 1.99 (978-1-4192-5509-0(6)) Kessinger Publishing, LLC.

Weeks, Sarah. Oggie Cooder #1. 2008. 176p. (J). pap. 16.99 (*978-0-439-92791-8(9) , Scholastic) Scholastic, Inc.

Weight, Janice. Becca. 2004. 54p. pap. 12.95 (978-1-4137-1126-4(X)) PublishAmerica, Inc.

Weil, Zoe. Claude & Medea: The Hellburn Dogs. 2007. 112p. (J). (gr. 4-7). pap. 30.00 (*978-1-59056-105-8(8)) Lantern Bks.

Weinberger, Kimberly. Zany. 2000. (Teacher's Pet Ser.: Vol. 5). (J). pap. 4.95 (978-0-439-13248-0(7)) Scholastic, Inc.

Weinheimer, Beckie. Converting Kate. 2007. 288p. (YA). (gr. 7 up). 16.99 (978-0-670-06152-5(2) , Viking Juvenile) Penguin Group (USA) Inc.

Weir, Joan. Maybe Tomorrow. 2001. 209p. (YA). (gr. 5-9). pap. 5.95 (978-0-7736-7486-8(1)) Stoddart Kids CAN. *Dist:* Fitzhenry & Whiteside, Ltd.

—Maybe Tomorrow. 2001. (gr. 5-8). lib. bdg. 14.10 (978-0-613-63629-2(5)) Tandem Library Bks.

—The Principal's Kid, Vol. 2. 2002. 176p. (J). (gr. 4-7). pap. 6.95 (978-1-896095-98-1(4)) Raincoast Bk. Distribution CAN. *Dist:* Transition Vendor.

Weiss, Ellen. Back to School! S. I. Artists Staff, illus. 2005. (Fisher Price Lift the Flap Bks.). 10p. 7.99 (978-0-7944-0677-6(7)) Reader's Digest Assn., Inc., The.

Welch, Willy. Grumbly Bunnies. Lyon, Tammie, illus. 2004. 28p. (J). bds. 6.95 (978-1-58089-088-5(1)) Charlesbridge Publishing, Inc.

—Grumbly Bunnies. Lyon, Tammie Speer, illus. 2004. 32p. (J). 15.95 (978-1-58089-086-1(5)); pap. 6.95 (978-1-58089-087-8(3)) Charlesbridge Publishing, Inc.

—Grumpy Bunnies. Lyon, Tammie Speer, illus. 2000. 32p. (J). (ps-2). 16.95 (978-1-58089-053-3(9)); pap. 6.95 (978-1-58089-060-1(1)) Charlesbridge Publishing, Inc.

—Grumpy Bunnies. 2000. (Illus.). (J). 13.75 (978-0-606-18749-7(9)) Tandem Library Bks.

Wells, Rosemary. Be My Valentine. Wheeler, Jody & Nez, John, illus. 2001. (Yoko & Friends School Days Ser.: No. 5). 32p. (gr. k-2). 9.99 (978-0-7868-0724-6(5)) Hyperion Bks. for Children.

—Be My Valentine. 2001. (J). (978-0-606-22549-6(8)) Tandem Library Bks.

—Bubble Gum Radar. Wheeler, Jody & Nez, John, illus. 2002. (Yoko & Friends School Days Ser.: Bk. 9). 32p. (gr. k-2). pap. 3.99 (978-0-7868-1528-9(0) , Volo) Hyperion Bks. for Children.

—Discover & Explore: Based on Timothy Goes to School & Other Stories. 2001. (Get Set for Kindergarten Ser.). (Illus.). (J). 12.79 (978-0-606-21150-5(0)) Tandem Library Bks.

—Doris's Dinosaur. Wheeler, Jody & Nez, John, illus. 2001. (Yoko & Friends School Days Ser.: No. 4). 32p. (gr. k-2). 9.99 (978-0-7868-0726-0(1) , Volo) Hyperion Bks. for Children.

—Doris's Dinosaur. 2001. (J). 10.79 (978-0-606-22550-2(1)) Tandem Library Bks.

—Eduardo: El Primer Dia de Colegio. Wells, Rosemary, illus. Orig. Title: Edward's First Day at School. (SPA.). 26p. (J). (ps). pap. 8.95 (978-1-59437-476-0(7)) Santillana USA Publishing Co., Inc.

—Eduardo: El Primer Dia de Colegio. 2003. Orig. Title: Edward's First Day at School. (SPA., Illus.). 22p. (J). (ps-k). 12.95 (978-1-56014-620-9(6)) Santillana USA Publishing Co., Inc.

—Emily's First 100 Days of School. 2000. (Illus.). 64p. (J). (ps-1). 16.99 (978-0-7868-0507-5(2)) Hyperion Bks. for Children.

—Emily's First 100 Days of School. 2000. (Illus.). 64p. (ps-1). pap. 5.99 (978-0-7868-1354-4(7)) Hyperion Paperbacks for Children.

—Emily's First 100 Days of School. 2006. (Illus.). (J). (ps-4). 29.95 incl. audio compact disk (978-0-439-84900-5(4) , WHCD654); 24.95 incl. audio (978-0-439-84898-5(9) , WHRA654); pap. 14.95 incl. audio (978-0-439-84902-9(0) , WPRA654); pap. 18.95 incl. audio compact disk (978-0-439-84903-6(9) , WPCD654) Weston Woods Studios, Inc.

—The Germ Busters. Wheeler, Jody, illus. 2002. (Yoko & Friends School Days Ser.: Bk. 6). 32p. (gr. k-2). pap. 3.99 (978-0-7868-1534-0(5) , Volo) Hyperion Bks. for Children.

—The Germ Busters. (ps-2). 2002. lib. bdg. 11.80 (978-0-613-53188-7(4)); 2001. (J). 10.79 (978-0-606-22551-9(X)) Tandem Library Bks.

—The Halloween Parade. Wheeler, Jody, illus. 2001. (Yoko & Friends School Days Ser.: No. 3). 32p. (gr. k-2). 9.99 (978-0-7868-0723-9(7) , Volo) Hyperion Bks. for Children.

—The Halloween Parade. 2001. (J). 10.79 (978-0-606-22548-9(X)); lib. bdg. 11.80 (978-0-613-53195-5(7)) Tandem Library Bks.

—Make New Friends. Wheeler, Jody, illus. 2003. (Yoko & Friends School Days Ser.: Bk. 11). 32p. (gr. k-2). pap. 3.99 (978-0-7868-1536-4(1)); 9.99 (978-0-7868-0730-7(X)) Hyperion Bks. for Children. (Volo).

—Make New Friends. Wheeler, Jody, illus. 2003. 31p. (J). (ps-ps). lib. bdg. 11.80 (978-0-613-74980-0(4)) Tandem Library Bks.

—Mama, Don't Go! 2001. (Yoko & Friends School Days Ser.: No. 1). (Illus.). 32p. (gr. k-2). 9.99 (978-0-7868-0720-8(2) , Volo) Hyperion Bks. for Children.

—Mama, Don't Go! 2001. (J). (978-0-606-22546-5(3)); lib. bdg. 11.80 (978-0-613-53276-1(7)) Tandem Library Bks.

—Practice Makes Perfect. Wheeler, Jody, illus. 2002. (Yoko & Friends School Days Ser.: No. 10). 32p. (gr. k-2). 9.99 (978-0-7868-0725-3(3)) Disney Pr.

—Practice Makes Perfect. 2002. (gr. k-3). lib. bdg. 11.80 (978-0-613-74979-4(0)) Tandem Library Bks.

—Read Me a Story. Wheeler, Jody & Nez, John, illus. 2002. (Yoko & Friends School Days Ser.: Bk. 8). 32p. (gr. k-2). pap. 3.99 (978-0-7868-1533-3(7) , Volo) Hyperion Bks. for Children.

—The School Play. Wheeler, Jody, illus. 2001. (Yoko & Friends School Days Ser.: No. 2). 32p. (gr. k-2). 9.99 (978-0-7868-0721-5(0)); pap. 3.99 (978-0-7868-1527-2(2)) Hyperion Bks. for Children. (Volo).

—The School Play. 2001. (J). (978-0-606-22547-2(1)); lib. bdg. 11.80 (978-0-613-53555-7(3)) Tandem Library Bks.

—The Secret Birthday. Nez, John & Wheeler, Jody, illus. 2002. (Yoko & Friends School Days Ser.: No. 7). 32p. (gr. k-2). 9.99 (978-0-7868-0729-1(6)) Hyperion Bks. for Children.

—Timothy Goes to School. 2000. (Illus.). 32p. (J). (ps-3). pap. 5.99 (978-0-14-056742-7(9) , Puffin) Penguin Group (USA) Inc.

—Timothy Goes to School. 2000. (gr. k-3). lib. bdg. 14.15 (978-0-8085-3410-5(6)) Tandem Library Bks.

—Timothy's Tales from Hilltop School. Wells, Rosemary, illus. 2004. (Illus.). 64p. (J). (ps up). pap. 7.99 (978-0-14-240156-9(0) , Puffin) Penguin Group (USA) Inc.

—When I Grow Up. Wheeler, Jody, illus. 2003. (Yoko & Friends School Days Ser.: Bk. 12). 32p. (gr. k-2). 9.99 (978-0-7868-0731-4(8) , Volo) Hyperion Bks. for Children.

—The World Around Us: Based on Timothy Goes to School & Other Stories. 2001. (Get Set for Kindergarten Ser.). (Illus.). (J). (978-0-606-21536-7(0)) Tandem Library Bks.

—Yoko. 1998. (Illus.). 32p. (ps-2). 14.95 (978-0-7868-0395-8(9)) Hyperion Pr.

—Yoko's World of Kindness: Golden Rules for a Happy Classroom. Nez, John & Wheeler, Jody, illus. 2005. 160p. (J). (gr. k-2). 19.99 (978-0-7868-5109-6(0)) Hyperion Bks. for Children.

Welton, Jude. Adam's Alternative Sports Day. 2005. (Illus.). 112p. (J). pap. (978-1-84310-300-4(1)) Kingsley, Jessica Ltd.

Wenger, Brahm. Dewey Doo-It at the Jingle Jangle Jamboree: A Musical Storybook Inspired by Arnold Schwarzenegger to Benefit Inner-City Games. 2006. 32p. 18.95 (978-0-9745143-4-5(9)) RandallFraser Publishing.

Wesley, Valerie Wilson. How to (Almost) Ruin Your School Play. Roos, Maryn, illus. 4th rev. ed. 2005. (Willimena Rules! Ser.). 112p. (gr. 2-5). pap. 3.99 (978-0-7868-5259-8(3) , Jump at the Sun) Hyperion Bks. for Children.

—How to Fish for Trouble. Roos, Maryn, illus. 2nd rev. ed. 2004. (Willimena Rules! Ser.: Bk. 2). 96p. (gr. 2-5). pap. 3.99 (978-0-7868-1807-5(7)) Hyperion Bks. for Children.

—How to Lose Your Class Pet. 2003. (gr. 3-6). lib. bdg. 11.80 (978-0-613-68244-2(0)) Tandem Library Bks.

—Willimena, Bk. 2. 2002. 368p. (J). 12.99 (978-0-7868-0466-5(1)) Hyperion Bks. for Children.

—Willimena Rules! Bk. 1: How to Lose Your Class Pet. Roos, Maryn, illus. 2003. 96p. (gr. 2-5). pap. 3.99 (978-0-7868-1322-3(9) , Jump at the Sun) Hyperion Bks. for Children.

West, Tracey. Maximus's School for Super Villains. 2006. (Atomic Betty Ser.: Vol. 2). 80p. (J). pap. 4.99 (978-0-448-44007-1(5) , Grosset & Dunlap) Penguin Group (USA) Inc.

—Me & My Robot No.2: The Show-and-Tell Show-off. Revell, Cindy, illus. 2003. (All Aboard Reading Ser.). 48p. (J). 13.89 (978-0-448-43282-3(X) , Grosset & Dunlap) Penguin Group (USA) Inc.

Weston, Carol. Melanie in Manhattan. 288p. (J). (gr. 3-7). 2006. 5.99 (978-0-440-42040-8(7) , Yearling); 2005. (Illus.). 15.95 (978-0-375-83028-0(6) , Knopf Bks. for Young Readers) Random Hse. Children's Bks.

Weston, Martha. Act I, Act II, Act Normal. rev. ed. 2003. (Roman Mysteries Ser.). 160p. (J). (gr. 5-9). 22.90 (978-0-7613-2859-9(9)) Roaring Brook Pr.

Wetter, Bruce. The Boy with the Lampshade on His Head. 2004. (Illus.). 304p. (J). 16.95 (978-0-689-85032-5(8) , Atheneum) Simon & Schuster Children's Publishing.

Weyn, Suzanne. The Bar Code Tattoo. 2004. (Point Thriller Ser.). 256p. (J). (gr. 7 up). pap. 5.99 (978-0-439-39562-5(3)) Scholastic, Inc.

Wheeler, Lisa. When Pigs Fly. Ansley, Frank, illus. ed. 2005. 48p. (J). lib. bdg. 15.00 (978-1-59054-996-4(1)) Fitzgerald Bks.

Wheeler, Lisa & Ansley, Frank. New Pig in Town. 2003. (Ready-to-Read Ser.). (Illus.). 48p. (J). 14.95 (978-0-689-84950-3(8) , Atheneum/Richard Jackson Bks.) Simon & Schuster Children's Publishing.

Whelan, Gloria. Welcome to Starvation Lake. 2000. (J). (978-0-606-18930-9(0)) Tandem Library Bks.

Whitaker, Zai. Kali & the Rat Snake. Natarajan, Srividya, illus. 2006. 32p. (J). 15.95 (978-1-933605-10-4(3)) Kane/Miller Bk. Pubs., Inc.

Whitcomb, Mary E. Odd Velvet. King, Tara Calahan, illus. 1998. 32p. (J). (ps-3). 14.95 (978-0-8118-2004-2(1)) Chronicle Bks. LLC.

White, Ellen Emerson. The President's Daughter. 2008. (YA). pap. 8.99 (*978-0-312-37488-4(7)) Feiwel & Friends.

White, Russ. Cat Got Your Tongue? A Book of Idioms. Cornelison, Reuel, illus. l.t. ed. 2004. 44p. (J). per. (978-0-9742885-0-5(0) , 00) White, Russ.

Whitta, Gary. Death, Jr. (Illus.). 144p. pap. 14.99 (978-1-58240-526-1(3)) Image Comics.

Whittemore, JoAnne. Escape from Arylon. 2006. 360p. pap. 8.95 (978-0-7387-0869-0(0)) Llewellyn Pubns.

Whittenberg, Allison. Sweet Thang. 160p. (J). (gr. 3-7). 2007. pap. 5.99 (978-0-440-42086-6(5) , Yearling); 2006. 15.95 (978-0-385-73292-5(9) , Delacorte Bks. for Young Readers); 2006. lib. bdg. 17.99 (978-0-385-90313-4(8) , Delacorte Bks. for Young Readers) Random Hse. Children's Bks.

Who Will Look Out for Danny? Individual Title Six-Packs. (Action Packs Ser.). 120p. (gr. 3-5). 44.00 (978-0-7635-8420-7(7)) Rigby Education.

Whybrow, Ian. Harry & the Dinosaurs Go to School. Reynolds, Adrian, illus. 2007. 32p. (J). (ps-2). 15.99 (978-0-375-84180-4(6) , Random Hse. Bks. for Young Readers) Random Hse. Children's Bks.

—Little Wolf's Book of Badness. Ross, Tony, illus. 2005. (Middle Grade Fiction Ser.). 132p. (gr. 3-6). 14.95 (978-1-57505-410-0(8)) Lerner Publishing Group.

—Little Wolf's Haunted Hall for Small Horrors. Ross, Tony, illus. (Middle Grade Fiction Ser.). 132p. (J). 2005. (gr. 3-6). 14.95 (978-1-57505-412-4(4)); 2004. (gr. 2-6). pap. 6.95 (978-1-57505-794-1(8)) Lerner Publishing Group.

Whytock, Cherry. My Cup Runneth Over: The Life of Angelica Cookson Potts. Whytock, Cherry, illus. (YA). 2003. (Illus.). 176p. 14.95 (978-0-689-86546-6(5)); 2004. 192p. reprint ed. mass mkt. 5.99 (978-0-689-86551-0(1) , Simon Pulse) Simon & Schuster Children's Publishing.

Wicke, Ed. Bullies. Warne, Tom, illus. 2nd rev. ed. 2003. 212p. (J). per. 8.99 (978-0-9677652-2-8(6) , BlacknBlue Pr. UK) Blacknblue Pr.

Wierenga, Kathy & Johnson, Lissa Halls. Double Exposure, Vol. 4. 2005. (Brio Girls Ser.). 192p. (YA). pap. 7.99 (978-1-56179-954-1(8)) Focus on the Family Publishing.

Wilcox, Edee. If I'd Only Known. . . 2003. 172p. (YA). pap. 13.95 (978-1-59113-304-9(1)) Booklocker.com, Inc.

Wilcox, Mary. The Hollywood Sisters: Star Quality. 2008. (J). (*978-0-385-90513-8(0)); pap. (*978-0-385-73527-8(8)) Dell Publishing. (Delacorte Pr.).

Wilde, Anne. Million Dollar Girl. 2002. 200p. (YA). per. 8.50 (978-1-59002-002-9(2) , MDG1) Antares Publishing.

Wilde, Jerry. Peace in the Halls: Stories & Activities to Manage Anger & Prevent School Violence. 2003. 112p. (YA). (gr. 4-12). pap. 9.95 (978-0-9657610-4-8(5)) LGR Publishing, Inc.

Wilhelm, Doug. Falling. 2007. 256p. (YA). (gr. 9 up). 17.00 (978-0-374-32251-9(1)) Farrar, Straus & Giroux.

—The Revealers. 224p. (J). 2003. 16.00 (978-0-374-36255-3(6) , Farrar, Straus & Giroux (BYR)); 2005. reprint ed. pap. 6.95 (978-0-374-46243-7(7) , Sunburst) Farrar, Straus & Giroux.

Wilkins, Celia. Little City by the Lake. Andreasen, Dan, illus. 2003. (Little House Ser.). 320p. (J). (gr. 5 up). pap. 6.99 (978-0-06-440735-9(7)) HarperCollins Pubs.

—Little City by the Lake. 2003. (gr. 3-6). lib. bdg. 14.15 (978-0-613-66981-8(9)) Tandem Library Bks.

Wilkins, Rose. So Super Starry. 2006. (YA). 230p. (*978-1-4156-6975-4(9)); 240p. (gr. 7). reprint ed. pap. 6.99 (978-0-14-240581-9(7)) Penguin Group (USA) Inc. (Puffin).

Wilkins, Rose. So Super Stylish. 2006. 288p. (J). (gr. 6). 16.99 (978-0-8037-3064-9(0) , Dial) Penguin Group (USA) Inc.

Wilkowski, Susan. The Bad Luck Chair. 2007. (Illus.). 96p. (J). (gr. 3-5). 15.99 (978-0-525-47794-5(2) , Dutton Juvenile) Penguin Group (USA) Inc.

Will I Have a Friend. 2004. (J). pap. 18.95 incl. audio compact disk (978-0-7882-0994-9(9)); pap. 32.75 incl. audio (978-0-7882-0996-3(5)); pap. 38.75 incl. audio compact disk (978-0-7882-0997-0(3)); pap. 14.95 incl. audio (978-0-7882-0993-2(0)) Weston Woods Studios, Inc.

Willems, Mo. Knuffle Bunny Too: A Case of Mistaken Identity. Willems, Mo, illus. rev. ed. 2007. (Illus.). 48p. (J). (ps-1). 16.99 (*978-1-4231-0299-1(1)) Hyperion Pr.

Williams-Garcia, Rita. No Laughter Here. 144p. (J). (gr. 7 up). 2007. pap. 6.99 (978-0-06-440992-6(9) , Amistad); 2004. 15.99 (978-0-688-16247-4(9)); 2004. lib. bdg. 16.89 (978-0-688-16248-1(7)) HarperCollins Pubs.

Williams, Heather. Nellie Oleson Meets Laura Ingalls. 2007. (Little House Ser.). 240p. (J). lib. bdg. 16.89 (*978-0-06-124249-6(7)); (gr. 3-7). 15.99 (*978-0-06-124248-9(9)) HarperCollins Pubs.

Williams, Jacklyn. Happy Easter, Gus! Cushman, Doug, illus. 2005. (Read-It! Readers Ser.). 32p. (J). (gr. k-3). 18.60 (978-1-4048-0959-8(7)) Picture Window Bks.

—The Haunted Schoolhouse: A Spooky. Cushman, Doug, illus. 2007. 16p. (J). pap. 6.99 (*978-0-689-87150-4(3) , Little Simon) Simon & Schuster Children's Publishing.

Williams, Jacklyn. Welcome to Third Grade, Gus! Cushman, Doug, illus. 2006. (Read-It! Readers Ser.). (J). 19.93 (978-1-4048-2714-1(5)) Picture Window Bks.

Williams, Karen Lynn. One Thing I'm Good At. 1999. 137p. (J). (gr. 3-7). 14.95 (978-0-688-16846-9(9)) HarperCollins Pubs.

Williams, Quan. The Leopard Man. 2005. 183p. pap. 19.95 (978-1-4137-5214-4(4)) PublishAmerica, Inc.

Williams, Rozanne Lanczak. The Author with the Fancy Purple Pen. Maio, Barbara, ed. Richard, Ilene, illus. 2006. (Learn to Write Ser.). (J). 16p. pap. 2.99 (978-1-59198-299-9(5) , 6189); per. 6.99 (*978-1-59198-346-0(0)) Creative Teaching Pr., Inc.

—Emily Santos, Star of the Week. Maio, Barbara, ed. Burris, Priscilla, illus. 2006. (Learn to Write Ser.). (J). 16p. pap. 2.99 (978-1-59198-298-2(7) , 6194); per. 6.99 (*978-1-59198-358-3(4)) Creative Teaching Pr., Inc.

—Room 9 Writes a Report. Maio, Barbara, ed. Lucas, Margeaux, illus. 2006. (Learn to Write Ser.). (J). 16p. pap. 2.99 (978-1-59198-297-5(9) , 6193); per. 6.99 (*978-1-59198-357-6(6)) Creative Teaching Pr., Inc.

—Tess Builds a Snowman. Maio, Barbara & Faulkner, Stacey, eds. Harris, Jenny B., illus. 2006. (Learn to Write Ser.). (J). 8p. pap. 1.99 (978-1-59198-286-9(3) , 6180); per. 4.99 (*978-1-59198-337-8(1)) Creative Teaching Pr., Inc.

—When You Go Walking. Maio, Barbara, ed. Briles, Patty, illus. 2006. (Learn to Write Ser.). 16p. (J). pap. 1.99 (978-1-59198-292-0(8) , 6188) Creative Teaching Pr., Inc.

Williams, Sam. School Bus, Bunny Bus. Trotter, Stuart, illus. 2006. 10p. (J). 12.95 (978-1-905417-17-9(9)) Boxer Bks., Ltd. GBR. *Dist:* Sterling Publishing Co., Inc.

Williams, Suzanne. Master of Minds? Carter, Abby, illus. 2004. 58p. (J). lib. bdg. 15.00 (*978-1-4242-0911-8(0)) Fitzgerald Bks.

Williams, Tara. Benji Martin Is Bashful. Lenoir, Jane, illus. 2001. 36p. (J). (gr. 1-6). lib. bdg. 14.95 (978-0-9705727-1-4(9)) Coastal Publishing Carolina, Inc.

Williamson, Greg. Why Do I Have to Wear Glasses? Popko, Wendy, illus. 2005. (J). 12.99 (978-0-9666076-5-9(1)) Peerless Publishing, L.L.C.

—Why Do I Have to Wear Glasses? Popkp, Wendy, illus. 2005. (J). pap. 7.99 (978-0-9666076-3-5(5)) Peerless Publishing, L.L.C.

Willie Wins. 2007. (J). pap. 7.95 (*978-1-60060-237-5(1)) Lee & Low Bks., Inc.

Willis, Jeanne. Be Gentle, Python! Birchall, Mark, illus. 2005. (Picture Bks.). 28p. (J). (gr. k-2). 7.95 (978-1-57505-508-4(2)) Lerner Publishing Group.

—No Biting, Puma! Birchall, Mark, illus. 2005. (Picture Bks.). 28p. (J). (gr. k-2). 7.25 (978-1-57505-509-1(0)) Lerner Publishing Group.

Willner-Pardo, Gina. Figuring Out Frances. 1999. (Illus.). 144p. (J). (gr. 4-6). tchr. ed. 14.00 (978-0-395-91510-3(4) , Clarion Bks.) Houghton Mifflin Co. Trade & Reference Div.

—My Mom & Other Mysteries of the Universe. 2004. 176p. (YA). (gr. 4-6). tchr. ed. 15.00 (978-0-618-43020-8(2) , Clarion Bks.) Houghton Mifflin Co. Trade & Reference Div.

—Spider Storch, Rotten Runner. Sharratt, Nick, illus. 2001. 88p. (J). (gr. 2-5). lib. bdg. 11.95 (978-0-8075-7594-9(1)) Whitman, Albert & Co.

—Spider Storch's Fumbled Field Trip. Sharratt, Nick, illus. 1998. 68p. (J). (gr. 2-5). pap. 3.95 (978-0-8075-7582-6(8)) Whitman, Albert & Co.

—Spider Storch's Music Mess. Sharratt, Nick, illus. 1998. 80p. (J). (gr. 2-5). pap. 3.95 (978-0-8075-7584-0(4)); lib. bdg. 11.95 (978-0-8075-7583-3(6)) Whitman, Albert & Co.

Willson, Sarah. Cookie Crisis! Ross, Sharon & Bergman, Shannon, illus. ed. 2005. 32p. (J). lib. bdg. 15.00 (978-1-59054-981-0(3)) Fitzgerald Bks.

—Cookie Crisis! Bergman, Shannon & Ross, Sharon, illus. 2005. (Ready-To-Read Ser.). 32p. (J). (ps-ps). pap. 3.99 (978-0-689-86646-3(1) , Simon Spotlight/Nickelodeon) Simon & Schuster Children's Publishing.

Wilson, Bob, illus. Football Fred, Vol. 4. 2003. 72p. (J). pap. (978-0-330-37091-2(X) , Pan) Pan Macmillan.

Wilson, Budge & LaFave, Kim. Duff's Monkey Business. 2000. (New First Novels Ser.). (Illus.). 63p. (gr. 1-5). 4.95 (978-0-88780-498-4(5)); (978-0-88780-499-1(3)) Formac Publishing Co., Ltd. CAN. *Dist:* Casemate Pubs. & Bk. Distributors, LLC.

Wilson, Jacqueline. Best Friends. 2008. (J). (*978-1-59643-278-9(0)) Roaring Brook Pr.

—The Lottie Project. 2002. (J). (gr. 5-8). 20.00 (978-0-8446-7232-8(7)) Smith, Peter Pub., Inc.

—The Lottie Project. 2001. (J). (978-0-606-20774-4(0)) Tandem Library Bks.

—The Lottie Project. 2000. (Illus.). 203p. (J). 17.95 (978-0-385-40703-8(3)) Transworld Publishers Ltd. GBR. *Dist:* Trafalgar Square Publishing.

—Lottie Project. 2001. (gr. 3-6). lib. bdg. 12.40 (978-0-613-33835-6(9)) Tandem Library Bks.

—The Worry Web Site. 2005. 112p. (gr. 3-7). pap. 5.50 (978-0-440-41929-7(8) , Yearling) Random Hse. Children's Bks.

Wilson, Jacqueline & Sharratt, Nick. Candyfloss. 2007. (Illus.). 352p. (J). (gr. 4-7). 14.95 (*978-1-59643-241-3(1)) Roaring Brook Pr.

Wilson, Karma. Sweet Briar Goes to School. Pham, LeUyen, illus. 2005. 32p. (J). pap. 5.99 (978-0-14-240281-8(8) , Puffin) Penguin Group (USA) Inc.

Wilson, Sarah. George Hogglesberry, Grade School Alien. Cameron, Chad, illus. 2004. 38p. (J). 14.95 (978-1-58246-063-5(9) , Tricycle Pr.) Ten Speed Pr.

Wilson, Troy. Perfect Man. Griffiths, Dean, illus. 2005. 32p. (J). (ps-2). 7.95 (978-1-55143-435-3(0)) Orca Bk. Pubs. USA.

Wilt's on Stilts! 2000. 30p. (J). 14.95 (978-0-9708080-0-4(3)) Stilts.

Windle, Jeanette. Jana's Journal: A Novel for Teens. 2002. 256p. pap. 12.99 (978-0-8254-4117-2(X)) Kregel Pubns.

Winerip, Michael. Adam Canfield of the Slash. (Adam Canfield of the Slash Ser.). 336p. (J). (gr. 3-7). 2007. pap. 5.99 (978-0-7636-2794-2(1)); 2005. 15.99 (978-0-7636-2340-1(7)) Candlewick Pr.

Winfield (Edward Str Staff. The Rover Boys at School or the Cadets O. 2006. 26.99 (*978-1-4280-1710-8(0)) IndyPublish.com.

Winfield, Arthur M. The Rover Boys at School. 2004. reprint ed. pap. 1.99 (978-1-4192-8115-0(1)) Kessinger Publishing, LLC.

Winfield, M. Arthur. The Mystery at Putnam Hall or the School. 2006. 96.99 (*978-1-4280-0709-3(1)); pap. 90.99 (*978-1-4280-0711-6(3)) IndyPublish.com.

Wing, Natasha. The Night Before First Grade. Zemke, Deborah, illus. 2005. 32p. (J). (ps-4). 3.99 (978-0-448-43747-7(3) , Grosset & Dunlap) Penguin Group (USA) Inc.

—The Night Before Kindergarten. 2001. (Illus.). (J). (978-0-606-21349-3(X)) Tandem Library Bks.

—The Night Before the 100th Day of School. Pierce, Mindy, illus. 2005. 32p. (J). (ps-4). pap. 3.99 (978-0-448-43923-5(9) , Grosset & Dunlap) Penguin Group (USA) Inc.

—The Night Before Valentine's Day. Petach, Heidi, illus. 2001. (Reading Rainbow Bks.). 32p. (J). (ps-3). mass mkt. 3.99 (978-0-448-42188-9(7) , Grosset & Dunlap) Penguin Group (USA) Inc.

—The Night Before Valentine's Day. 2000. (gr. k-3). lib. bdg. 11.25 (978-0-613-31527-2(8)) Tandem Library Bks.

Winget, Susan. Tucker's Four-Carrot School Day. Winget, Susan, illus. 2005. (Illus.). 40p. (J). (ps-k). 12.99 (978-0-06-054642-7(5)); lib. bdg. 13.89 (978-0-06-054643-4(3)) HarperCollins Pubs.

Winkler, Henry & Oliver, Lin. The Curtain Went Up, My Pants Fell Down. Watson, Jesse Joshua, illus. 2007. (Hank Zipzer Ser.: No. 11). 160p. (J). 13.99 (978-0-448-44268-6(X)); pap. 4.99 (978-0-448-44267-9(1)) Penguin Group (USA) Inc. (Grosset & Dunlap).

—Help! Somebody Get Me Out of Fourth Grade! 2004. (Hank Zipzer Ser.: No. 7). 160p. (J). (gr. 3-8). mass mkt. 4.99 (978-0-448-43619-7(1) , Grosset & Dunlap) Penguin Group (USA) Inc.

—Help! Somebody Get Me Out of Fourth Grade! Heyer, Carol, illus. 2004. (Hank Zipzer Ser.: No. 7). 160p. (J). 12.99 (978-0-448-43613-5(2) , Grosset & Dunlap) Penguin Group (USA) Inc.

—Help! Somebody Get Me Out of Fourth Grade! 2006. (Hank Zipzer Ser.: No. 7). (J). (gr. 3-8). 24.21 (978-1-59961-106-8(6)) Spotlight.

—Help! Somebody Get Me Out of Fourth Grade! Heyer, Carol, illus. 2004. (Hank Zipzer Ser.: No. 7). 156p. (J). (ps-7). lib. bdg. 11.64 (978-0-606-32738-1(X)) Tandem Library Bks.

—Holy Enchilada! Heyer, Carol & Watson, Jesse Joshua, illus. 2004. (Hank Zipzer Ser.: No. 6). 160p. (J). (gr. 3-8). pap. 4.99 (978-0-448-43353-0(2) , Grosset & Dunlap) Penguin Group (USA) Inc.

—Holy Enchilada!, No. 6. Watson, Jesse Joshua, illus. 2004. (Hank Zipzer Ser.: No. 6). 160p. (J). (gr. 3-7). 13.99 (978-0-448-43554-1(3) , Grosset & Dunlap) Penguin Group (USA) Inc.

—Holy Enchilada! 2006. (Hank Zipzer Ser.: No. 6). (J). (gr. 3-8). 24.21 (978-1-59961-105-1(8)) Spotlight.

—Holy Enchilada! 2003. (Hank Zipzer Ser.: No. 6). (gr. 3-6). lib. bdg. 13.00 (978-0-613-72546-0(8)) Tandem Library Bks.

—I Got a "D" in Salami. 2004. (Hank Zipzer Ser.: No. 2). 128p. (J). (gr. 2-6). pap. 29.00 incl. audio (978-1-4000-9007-5(5) , Listening Library) Random Hse. Audio Publishing Group.

—I Got a "D" in Salami. 2006. (Hank Zipzer Ser.: No. 2). (J). (gr. 3-8). 24.21 (978-1-59961-109-9(0)) Spotlight.

—I Got a "D" in Salami. 2003. (Hank Zipzer Ser.: No. 2). (Illus.). 167p. (J). (ps-7). per. 13.00 (978-0-613-63726-8(7)) Tandem Library Bks.

—The Life of Me: Enter at Your Own Risk. Watson, Jesse Joshua, illus. 2008. (Hank Zipzer Ser.: No. 14). 256p. (J). 14.99 (*978-0-448-44377-5(5)); (gr. 3-7). pap. 5.99 (*978-0-448-44376-8(7)) Penguin Group (USA) Inc. (Grosset & Dunlap).

—My Secret Life as a Ping-Pong Wizard. 2006. (Hank Zipzer Ser.: No. 9). (J). (gr. 3-8). 24.21 (978-1-59961-110-5(4)) Spotlight.

—Niagara Falls, or Does It? 2003. (Hank Zipzer Ser.: No. 1). (Illus.). 144p. (J). (gr. 2-5). pap. 4.99 (978-0-448-43162-8(9) , Grosset & Dunlap) Penguin Group (USA) Inc.

—Niagara Falls, or Does It? Carol, Heyer, illus. 2003. (Hank Zipzer Ser.: No. 1). 144p. (J). (gr. 2-5). 12.99 (978-0-448-43232-8(3) , Grosset & Dunlap) Penguin Group (USA) Inc.

—Niagara Falls, or Does It? 2004. (Hank Zipzer Ser.: No. 1). 128p. (J). (gr. 2-6). pap. 29.00 incl. audio (978-1-4000-9006-8(7) , Listening Library) Random Hse. Audio Publishing Group.

—Niagara Falls, or Does It? 2006. (Hank Zipzer Ser.: No. 1). (J). (gr. 3-8). 24.21 (978-1-59961-108-2(2)) Spotlight.

—Niagara Falls, or Does It? 2003. (Hank Zipzer Ser.: No. 1). lib. bdg. 13.00 (978-0-613-63737-4(2)) Tandem Library Bks.

—The Night I Flunked My Field Trip. Heyer, Carol, illus. 2004. (Hank Zipzer Ser.: No. 5). 176p. (J). (gr. 3-7). 13.99 (978-0-448-43502-2(0) , Grosset & Dunlap) Penguin Group (USA) Inc.

—The Night I Flunked My Field Trip. 2006. (Hank Zipzer Ser.: No. 5). (J). (gr. 3-8). 24.21 (978-1-59961-104-4(X)) Spotlight.

—Summer School! What Genius Thought That Up? 2006. (Hank Zipzer Ser.: No. 8). (J). (gr. 3-8). 24.21 (978-1-59961-107-5(4)) Spotlight.

—Summer School! What Genius Thought That Up? 2005. (Hank Zipzer Ser.: No. 8). (Illus.). 157p. (J). (ps-7). per. 11.64 (978-0-606-33097-8(6)) Tandem Library Bks.

—The Zippity Zinger. 2003. (Hank Zipzer Ser.: No. 4). (Illus.). 160p. (J). (gr. 3-8). mass mkt. 4.99 (978-0-448-43193-2(9) , Grosset & Dunlap) Penguin Group (USA) Inc.

—The Zippity Zinger. Heyer, Carol, illus. 2003. (Hank Zipzer Ser.: No. 4). 160p. (J). 13.99 (978-0-448-43287-8(0) , Grosset & Dunlap) Penguin Group (USA) Inc.

—The Zippity Zinger. 2004. (Hank Zipzer Ser.: No. 4). 160p. (J). (gr. 2-6). pap. 29.00 incl. audio (978-1-4000-9009-9(1) , Listening Library) Random Hse. Audio Publishing Group.

—The Zippity Zinger. 2006. (Hank Zipzer Ser.: No. 4). (J). (gr. 3-8). 24.21 (978-1-59961-103-7(1)) Spotlight.

Winner, Ramona Moreno. It's Okay to Be Different! (Esta Bien Ser Diferente!) Velasquez, Nicole, illus. Date not set. (ENG & SPA.). 40p. (J). (gr. k-3). 9.95 (978-0-9651174-0-1(5)) BrainStorm 3000.

Winter, Lisa. Lila Stone: Disaster Prone. 2004. 66p. pap. 14.95 (978-1-4137-1416-6(1)) PublishAmerica, Inc.

Winters, Kay. My Teacher for President. Brunkus, Denise, illus. 2004. 32p. (J). (gr. k). 14.99 (978-0-525-47186-8(3) , Dutton Juvenile) Penguin Group (USA) Inc.

—Teeny Tiny Ghost & the Monster. Munsinger, Lynn, illus. 2006. 32p. (J). pap. 6.99 (978-0-06-443662-5(4) , Harper Trophy) HarperCollins Pubs.

—The Teeny Tiny Ghost & the Monster, Vol. 3. Munsinger, Lynn, illus. 2004. 32p. (J). (ps-3). 14.99 (978-0-06-028884-6(1)) HarperCollins Pubs.

Wiseman, Bernard. Morris Goes to School. Wiseman, Bernard, illus. 2002. (Illus.). (J). 12.34 (978-0-7587-6213-9(5)) Book Wholesalers, Inc.

Wishinsky, Frieda. Give Maggie a Chance. Griffiths, Dean, illus. 32p. (J). 2004. (gr. k-2). pap. (978-1-55041-704-3(5)); 2002. (gr. 1-3). (978-1-55041-682-4(0)) Fitzhenry & Whiteside, Ltd.

—Jennifer Jones Won't Leave Me Alone. Layton, Neal, illus. 2005. 32p. (J). (gr. k-2). 15.95 (978-0-87614-921-8(2)) Lerner Publishing Group.

—Queen of the Toilet Bowl. 2005. (Orca Currents Ser.). (Illus.). 112p. (J). (gr. k-9). pap. 7.95 (978-1-55143-364-6(8)) Orca Bk. Pubs. USA.

—So Long Stinky Queen. 2000. (gr. 3-6). lib. bdg. 11.80 (978-0-613-88778-6(6)) Tandem Library Bks.

Wishnisky, Frieda. Jennifer Jones Won't Leave Me Alone. Layton, Neal, illus. 2005. 32p. (J). (gr. k-2). pap. 6.95 (978-1-57505-921-1(5)) Lerner Publishing Group.

Withrow, Sarah. Box Girl. 2002. 184p. (J). pap. 5.95 (978-0-88899-436-3(2)) Groundwood Bks. CAN. *Dist:* Perseus Distribution.

—Box Girl. 2001. (gr. 5-8). lib. bdg. 14.10 (978-0-613-67071-5(X)) Tandem Library Bks.

—What Gloria Wants. 2006. 176p. pap. 6.95 (978-0-88899-692-3(6)) Groundwood Bks. CAN. *Dist:* Perseus Distribution.

Witschen, Kay. Johnny Coalboy. Luckemeyer, Norma, illus. 2003. (J). per. 5.95 (978-0-9741352-0-5(8)) Dwitt Publishing.

Wittlinger, Ellen. Gracie's Girl. Hamlin, Janet, illus. 2000. 192p. (J). (gr. 3-7). 16.95 (978-0-689-82249-0(9)) Simon & Schuster Children's Publishing.

—Gracie's Girl. l.t. ed. 2002. 224p. (J). 22.95 (978-0-7862-3761-6(9)) Thomson Gale.

—Sandpiper. 2007. 288p. (YA). (gr. 7 up). pap. 6.99 (978-1-4169-3651-0(3) , Simon Pulse) Simon & Schuster Children's Publishing.

Wizner, Jake. Spanking Shakespeare. 2007. (YA). (*978-0-375-84086-9(9)) Random Hse. Children's Bks.

—Spanking Shakespeare. Ewing, Richard, illus. 2007. 287p. (YA). (gr. 9-11). lib. bdg. 18.99 (*978-0-375-94085-9(5)); 15.99 (*978-0-375-84085-2(0)) Random Hse. Children's Bks. (Random Hse. Bks. for Young Readers).

Wodehouse, P. G. Mike at Wrykyn. reprint ed. (J). lib. bdg. 98.00 (978-0-7426-3265-3(2)); 2001. pap. 28.00 (978-0-7426-8265-8(X)) Classic Bks.

Wojciechowski, Susan. Beany & the Meany. Natti, Susanna, illus. 112p. (J). (gr. 1-4). 2006. pap. 4.99 (978-0-7636-2974-8(X)); 2005. 15.99 (978-0-7636-2630-3(9)) Candlewick Pr.

Wojtowicz, Jen. The Boy Who Grew Flowers. Adams, Steve, illus. 2005. 32p. (J). (ps-3). 16.99 (978-1-84148-686-4(8)) Barefoot Bks., Inc.

Wolfer, Dianne. Border Line. 1998. 190p. (J). pap. 11.95 (978-1-86368-208-4(2)) Fremantle Pr. AUS. *Dist:* International Specialized Bk. Services.

S

Wolff, Ashley. Miss Bindergarten Plans a Circus with Kindergarten. Slate, Joseph & Wolff, Ashley, illus. 2002. 40p. (J). 16.99 (978-0-525-46884-4(6) , Dutton Juvenile) Penguin Group (USA) Inc.

Wolff, Nancy. It's Time for School with Tallulah. 2007. (Illus.). 40p. (J). (ps-3). 16.95 (***978-0-8050-7962-3(9))*** Holt, Henry & Co.

Wolff, Patricia Rae. The Toll-Bridge Troll. Root, Kimberly B., illus. 2000. 24p. (J). (ps-2). pap. 7.00 (978-0-15-202105-4(1) , Harcourt Paperbacks) Harcourt Children's Bks.

—Toll-Bridge Troll. 2000. (gr. k-3). lib. bdg. 15.30 (978-0-613-28676-3(6)) Tandem Library Bks.

Wolff, Virginia Euwer. Probably Still Nick Swansen. Katz, illus. 2003. 160p. mass mkt. 10.00 (978-0-689-85227-5(4) , Simon Pulse) Simon & Schuster Children's Publishing.

Wompuse Goes To School. 2000. 24p. (J). pap. 8.00 (978-0-9706316-0-2(X)) Wompuse Publishing Co.

Wong, Janet S. Minn & Jake. Cote, Genevieve, illus. 2003. 160p. (J). (gr. 2-5). 16.00 (978-0-374-34987-5(8) , Farrar, Straus & Giroux (BYR)) Farrar, Straus & Giroux.

Wong, Joyce Lee. Seeing Emily. 2005. (Illus.). 288p. (J). (gr. 7-11). 16.95 (978-0-8109-5757-2(4) , Abrams Bks. for Young Readers) Abrams, Harry N. , Inc.

Wood, Maryrose. My Life, the Musical. 2008. (YA). (***978-0-385-90297-7(2));*** 240p. (gr. 9). 15.99 (***978-0-385-73278-9(3))*** Dell Publishing. (Delacorte Pr.).

Wood, Maryrose. Sex Kittens & Horn Dawgs Fall in Love. 256p. (YA). (gr. 7). 2007. pap. 8.99 (***978-0-385-73277-2(5));*** 2006. 15.95 (978-0-385-73276-5(7)); 2006. lib. bdg. 17.99 (978-0-385-90296-0(4)) Random Hse. Children's Bks. (Delacorte Bks. for Young Readers).

Woodberry, Gareth. Gakeva Gluntok's New School. 2005. 65p. pap. 12.95 (978-1-4137-9894-4(2)) PublishAmerica, Inc.

Woods, Brenda. Emako Blue. 128p. (YA). 2005. (gr. 6). pap. 5.99 (978-0-14-240418-8(7) , Puffin); 2004. (gr. 5-12). 15.99 (978-0-399-24006-5(3) , Putnam Juvenile) Penguin Group (USA) Inc.

Woodson, Jacqueline. Feathers. 2007. 128p. (J). (gr. 3-7). 15.99 (978-0-399-23989-2(8) , Putnam Juvenile) Penguin Group (USA) Inc.

—If You Come Softly. (gr. 5). 2006. 192p. (YA). pap. 5.99 (978-0-14-240601-4(5) , Puffin); 1998. 1p. (J). 16.99 (978-0-399-23112-4(9) , Putnam Juvenile) Penguin Group (USA) Inc.

—If You Come Softly. 2000. 12.64 (978-0-606-17863-1(5)) Tandem Library Bks.

—Maizon at Blue Hill. 2002. 160p. (J). pap. 5.99 (978-0-698-11957-4(6)); 144p. (YA). 16.99 (978-0-399-23756-0(9)) Penguin Group (USA) Inc. (Putnam Juvenile).

—Maizon at Blue Hill. 2002. (gr. 3-6). lib. bdg. 14.15 (978-0-613-50098-2(9)) Tandem Library Bks.

Woodworth, Chris. Georgie's Moon. 2006. 176p. (J). 16.00 (978-0-374-33306-5(8)) Farrar, Straus & Giroux.

Wright, Betty Ren. The Blizzard. Himler, Ronald, illus. 2003. 32p. (J). (gr. k-3). 16.95 (978-0-8234-1656-1(9)) Holiday Hse., Inc.

Wright, Michael. Jake Starts School. 2008. (Illus.). 48p. (J). 16.95 (***978-0-312-36798-5(8))*** Feiwel & Friends.

Wright, Nina. Homefree. 2006. 240p. (J). pap. 8.95 (978-0-7387-0927-7(1) , Flux) Llewellyn Pubns.

Wright, Nina. Sensitive. 2007. 240p. (J). (gr. 4-7). pap. 9.95 (***978-0-7387-1170-6(5)*** , Flux) Llewellyn Pubns.

Wyatt, Leslie J. Poor Is Just a Starting Place. 2005. 192p. (J). (gr. 6-17). 16.95 (978-0-8234-1884-8(7)) Holiday Hse., Inc.

Wynne-Jones, Tim. Rex Zero, the King of Nothing. 2008. 224p. (J). 16.95 (***978-0-374-36259-1(9))*** Farrar, Straus & Giroux.

Yaccarino, Dan. Big Science Fair. 2002. (gr. k-3). lib. bdg. 13.00 (978-0-613-70869-2(5)) Tandem Library Bks.

—First Day on a Strange New Planet. 2000. (Blast Off Boy & Blorp Ser.: Vol. 1). (Illus.). 40p. (gr. k-3). 15.49 (978-0-7868-2499-1(9)) Hyperion Bks. for Children.

—First Day on a Strange New Planet. 2002. (gr. k-3). lib. bdg. 13.00 (978-0-613-74971-8(5)) Tandem Library Bks.

Yang, Dori Jones. The Secret Voice of Gina Zhang. 2000. (978-0-606-21790-3(8)) Tandem Library Bks.

Yang, Gene Luen. American Born Chinese. Pien, Lark, illus. rev. ed. 2006. 240p. (J). pap. 17.95 (978-1-59643-152-2(0) , First Second Bks.) Roaring Brook Pr.

—American Born Chinese, Collector's Edition. rev. ed. 2006. 240p. (J). 29.95 (978-1-59643-208-6(X) , First Second Bks.) Roaring Brook Pr.

Yarbrough, Elizabeth. Where Do Pizzas Grow? Ragsdale, Cathy, illus. 2001. (J). (gr. k-5). lib. bdg. 14.95 (978-1-931650-02-1(0)) Coastal Publishing Carolina, Inc.

Yarnell, Duane. The Winning Basket. 2005. pap. 26.95 (978-1-4191-5930-5(5)) Kessinger Publishing, LLC.

Yashima, Taro. Crow Boy. 2000. (J). pap. 19.97 incl. audio (978-0-7366-9208-3(8)) Books on Tape, Inc.

—Crow Boy. Yashima, Taro, illus. 2004. (Illus.). 34p. (J). (gr. k-3). reprint ed. pap. 14.00 (978-0-7567-7102-7(1)) DIANE Publishing Co.

—Crow Boy. Yashima, Taro, illus. (Illus.). 28.95 incl. audio compact disk (978-1-59112-802-1(1)); pap. 35.95 incl. audio compact disk (978-1-59112-803-8(X)) Live Oak Media.

—Crow Boy. 2005. (Illus.). (J). pap. 18.95 incl. audio compact disk (978-1-59112-801-4(3)) Live Oak Media.

Yates, Alma J. Sammy's Song: A Novel. 2005. 272p. (J). (***978-1-59156-945-9(1))*** Covenant Communications.

Yeager, Barbara. Confirmation. 2006. 21.95 (***978-1-4259-7010-9(9));*** pap. 12.00 (***978-1-4259-7009-3(5))*** AuthorHouse.

Yee, Lisa. Stanford Wong Flunks Big Time. (Illus.). (J). 2007. 320p. pap. 5.99 (978-0-439-62248-6(4)); 2005. 304p. (gr. 5-7). pap. 16.99 (978-0-439-62247-9(6)) Scholastic, Inc. (Levine, Arthur A. Bks.).

Yolen, Jane. How Do Dinosaurs Go to School? Teague, Mark, illus. 2007. 40p. (J). (ps-2). 16.99 (***978-0-439-02081-7(6))*** Scholastic, Inc.

Yoo, David. Girls for Breakfast. 304p. (YA). (gr. 9). 2005. 15.95 (978-0-385-73192-8(2) , Delacorte Bks. for Young Readers); 2005. lib. bdg. 17.99 (978-0-385-90227-4(1) , Delacorte Bks. for Young Readers); 2006. reprint ed. pap. 5.99 (978-0-440-23883-6(8) , Laurel Leaf) Random Hse. Children's Bks.

Yoon, Salina. School Bus. Yoon, Salina, illus. 2005. (Illus.). 10p. (J). (ps-1). bds. 5.99 (978-0-8431-1394-5(4) , Price Stern Sloan) Penguin Group (USA) Inc.

Yoon, Salina, illus. My Little Shimmery School Days, 4. 2002. 12p. (J). 5.95 (978-1-58117-165-5(X) , Intervisual/Piggy Toes) Dalmatian Pr.

Yoyo. Ready for School. 2005. 40p. bds. 6.95 (978-90-5843-890-4(2)) YoYo Bks. BEL. *Dist:* National Bk. Network.

Zarr, Sara. Sweethearts. 2008. 224p. (J). 16.99 (***978-0-316-01455-7(9))*** Little, Brown Bks. for Young Readers.

Zemach, Kaethe. Ms. Mccaw Learns To Draw. (J). 2008. 32p. pap. 16.99 (978-0-439-82914-4(3)); 2006. (978-0-439-82915-1(1)) Scholastic, Inc. (Levine, Arthur A. Bks.).

Zevin, Gabrielle. Memoirs of a Teenage Amnesiac. 2007. 288p. (YA). (gr. 9 up). 17.00 (***978-0-374-34946-2(0)*** , Farrar, Straus & Giroux (BYR)) Farrar, Straus & Giroux.

Zidrou. Ducoboo: In the Corner! Godi, illus. 2007. 48p. pap. 9.99 (***978-1-905460-26-7(0))*** CineBook GBR. *Dist:* Biblio Distribution.

Ziefert, Harriet. Schools Have Learn. 2004. (Illus.). 36p. 15.95 (978-1-59354-056-2(6)) Blue Apple Bks.

Ziefert, Harriet & Boon, Emilie. Little Hippo's New School. Ziefert, Harriet & Boon, Emilie, illus. 1998. (Little Hippo Ser.). (Illus.). (J). (ps). (978-0-7894-3106-6(8)) Dorling Kindersley Publishing, Inc.

Ziegesar, Cecily von. Gossip Girl #2: You Know You Love Me: A Gossip Girl Novel. 2008. 240p. pap. 10.99 (***978-0-316-02661-1(1)*** , Poppy) Little, Brown Bks. for Young Readers.

Zoehfeld, Kathleen Weidner & Random House Disney Staff. Time for School, Pooh. Cuddy, Robbin, illus. 2001. 24p. (J). (gr. k-3). pap. 3.25 (978-0-7364-1179-0(8) , RH/Disney) Random Hse. Children's Bks.

Zollman, Pam. Don't Bug Me! 2001. (Illus.). 144p. (J). (gr. 4-6). tchr. ed. 15.95 (978-0-8234-1584-7(8)) Holiday Hse., Inc.

Zucker, Jonny. Steel Eyes. Savage, Paul, illus. 2006. (Keystone Books (Stone Arch)). 33p. (J). (978-1-59889-019-8(0)) Stone Arch Bks.

Zydek, Heather. Basil's Search for Miracles. 2007. 160p. pap. 13.95 (***978-1-888212-86-0(1))*** Conciliar Pr.

The 15 Best Things about Being the New Kid. 2006. (J). pap. 5.95 (978-0-8225-6473-7(4) , First Avenue Editions) Lerner Publishing Group.

SCHOOLS—MANAGEMENT AND ORGANIZATION

see School Management And Organization

SCHOOLS, MILITARY

see Military Education

SCHUBERT, FRANZ, 1797-1828

Ekker, Ernst A. Franz Schubert: Un Album Musical. Eisenburger, Doris, illus. 2002. (Coleccion Joven Musica).Tr. of Franz Schubert: A Musical Picture Book. (SPA.). 32p. (YA). 20.76 incl. audio compact disk (978-84-89804-29-6(X)) Loguez Ediciones ESP. *Dist:* Lectorum Pubns., Inc.

Kreissle Von Hellborn, Heinrich. Franz Schubert: A Musical Biography. 2001. 287p. (YA). reprint ed. 98.00 (978-0-7222-5510-0(1)) Library Reprints, Inc.

—The Life of Franz Schubert, 2 vols., set. 2001. (YA). reprint ed. 250.00 (978-0-7222-5509-4(8)) Library Reprints, Inc.

Summerer, Eric Michael. Franz Peter Schubert. 2006. (Primary Source Library of Famous Composers). (Illus.). 32p. (J). 21.95 (978-1-4042-2768-2(7) , PowerKids Pr.) Rosen Publishing Group, Inc., The.

Wheeler, Opal & Deucher, Sybil. Franz Schubert & his Merry Friends. Greenwalt, Mary, illus. 2007. 128p. (J). pap. 12.95 (***978-1-933573-13-7(9))*** Zeezok Publishing.

SCHULZ, CHARLES M., 1922-2000

Carlson, Cheryl. Charles M. Schulz. 2005. (First Biographies Ser.). (Illus.). 24p. (J). 15.93 (978-0-7368-3638-8(1) , Pebble Bks.) Capstone Pr., Inc.

—Charles M Schulz. (First Biographies Ser.). 24p. (J). pap. 5.95 (978-0-7368-5090-2(2)) Capstone Pr., Inc.

Marvis, Barbara J. Charles Schulz. 2004. (Robbie Reader Ser.). (Illus.). 32p. (J). (gr. 1-4). lib. bdg. 25.70 (978-1-58415-289-7(3)) Mitchell Lane Pubs., Inc.

Schuman, Michael A. Charles M. Schulz: Cartoonist & Creator of Peanuts. 2002. (People to Know Ser.). (Illus.). 128p. (J). (gr. 6-12). lib. bdg. 26.60 (978-0-7660-1846-4(6)) Enslow Pubs., Inc.

Whiting, Jim. Charles Schulz. l.t. ed. 2002. (Real-Life Reader Biography Ser.). (Illus.). 32p. (gr. 3-8). lib. bdg. 15.95 (978-1-58415-131-9(5)) Mitchell Lane Pubs., Inc.

Woods, Mae. Charles Schulz. 2000. (Children's Authors Ser.). (Illus.). 24p. (J). (gr. k-6). lib. bdg. 21.35 (978-1-57765-425-4(0) , Checkerboard Library) ABDO Publishing Co.

SCHUMANN, CLARA, 1819-1896

Allman, Barbara. Her Piano Sang: A Story about Clara Schumann. 2003. (Creative Minds Biographies Ser.). (Illus.). 64p. (J). (gr. 3-6). pap. 22.60 (978-1-57505-151-2(6)) Lerner Publishing Group.

Reich, Susanna. Clara Schumann: Piano Virtuoso. (Illus.). 128p. (J). 2005. (gr. 3-5). pap. 9.95 (978-0-618-55160-6(3)); 1999. (gr. 4-6). tchr. ed. 18.00 (978-0-395-89119-3(1)) Houghton Mifflin Co. Trade & Reference Div. (Clarion Bks.).

SCHUMANN, ROBERT, 1810-1856

Fuller-Maitland, John A. Schumann. 2001. 150p. (YA). reprint ed. 88.00 (978-0-7222-5194-2(7)) Library Reprints, Inc.

Niecks, Frederick. Robert Schumann. 2001. 336p. (YA). reprint ed. 98.00 (978-0-7222-5515-5(2)) Library Reprints, Inc.

Reissmann, August. The Life & Works of Robert Schumann. 2001. 276p. (YA). reprint ed. 98.00 (978-0-7222-5517-9(9)) Library Reprints, Inc.

Schumann, Robert. The Letters of Robert Schumann. 2001. 299p. (YA). reprint ed. 98.00 (978-0-7222-5512-4(8)) Library Reprints, Inc.

—The Life of Robert Schumann Told in His Letters, 2 vols., set. 2001. (YA). reprint ed. 250.00 (978-0-7222-5514-8(4)) Library Reprints, Inc.

Von Wasielewski, Wilhelm J. The Life of Robert Schumann. 2001. 299p. (YA). reprint ed. 98.00 (978-0-7222-5518-6(7)) Library Reprints, Inc.

Wheeler, Opal. Robert Schumann & Mascot Ziff. 2006. (Illus.). (J). per. 12.95 (978-1-933573-06-9(6) , 4483) Zeezok Publishing.

Wilcox, Judy. Robert Schumann & Mascot Ziff. 2006. (Illus.). (J). stu. ed. 4.95 (978-1-933573-07-6(4)) Zeezok Publishing.

SCIENCE

see also Astronomy; Bacteriology; Biology; Botany; Chemistry; Crystallography; Ethnology; Fossils; Geology; Mathematics; Meteorology; Mineralogy; Natural History; Physics; Physiology; Space Sciences; Zoology

also headings beginning with the word Scientific

Abegglen, Sue R. Science Skills Made Easy. 1999. (Illus.). 96p. (YA). (gr. 5). pap. 10.95 (978-1-58037-095-0(0)) Twain, Mark Media, Inc. Pubs.

Abruscato, Joseph. Whizbangers & Wonderments: Science Activities for Children. 1999. (Illus.). 312p. (C). pap. 34.40 (978-0-205-28409-2(4)) Allyn & Bacon, Inc.

Accelerated Curriculum for Science Grade 11 Exit Taks Student Edition. 2005. (Region IV ESC Resources for Science Ser.). spiral bd. (978-1-932797-27-5(0)) Region IV Education Service Ctr.

Acercate a las ciencias: Recursos para el Maestro. 2000. (McGraw-Hill Ciencias Ser.). (ENG & SPA.). (gr. 1 up). (978-0-02-277208-6(1)); (gr. 2 up). (978-0-02-277209-3(X)); (gr. 3 up). (978-0-02-277211-6(1)); (gr. 4 up). (978-0-02-277212-3(X)); (gr. 5 up). (978-0-02-277213-0(8)) Macmillan/McGraw-Hill Schl. Div.

Acoma: la ciudad del Cielo. 2000. (McGraw-Hill Ciencias Ser.). (ENG & SPA.). (gr. 3 up). (978-0-02-279643-3(6)) Macmillan/McGraw-Hill Schl. Div.

ACT Science Reasoning Victory Student Textbook. 2nd ed. 2005. per. (978-1-58894-034-6(9)) Cambridge Educational Services, Inc.

Adios, muneco de Nieve! 2000. (McGraw-Hill Ciencias Ser.). (ENG & SPA.). (gr. 1 up). (978-0-02-279558-0(0)) Macmillan/McGraw-Hill Schl. Div.

Adonde se Fueron? 2000. (McGraw-Hill Ciencias Ser.). (ENG & SPA.). (gr. 1 up). (978-0-02-279572-6(3)) Macmillan/McGraw-Hill Schl. Div.

¿Adonde Van los Residuos? (Coleccion Primeros Pasos en la Ciencia). (SPA., Illus.). (J). (gr. 1-3). pap. (978-950-724-216-8(3) , LMA8222) Lumen ARG. *Dist:* Lectorum Pubns., Inc.

The Adventurers, 6 bks., Set. 2001. (J). (gr. k-2). lib. bdg. 111.60 (978-1-57103-316-1(5)) Rourke Publishing, LLC.

Agarrate! 2000. (McGraw-Hill Ciencias Ser.). (ENG & SPA.). (gr. 3 up). (978-0-02-279626-6(6)) Macmillan/McGraw-Hill Schl. Div.

Agua. (Coleccion Jugando Con la Ciencia). (SPA., Illus.). 39p. (J). pap. 9.95 (978-950-11-0682-4(9) , SGM333) Sigmar ARG. *Dist:* Continental Bk. Co., Inc.

Agua Science, 6 vols.Tr. of Water Science. (SPA.). (gr. k-2). 28.95 (978-0-7368-3127-7(4) , Yellow Umbrella Bks.) Capstone Pr., Inc.

Aire. (Coleccion Jugando Con la Ciencia). (SPA., Illus.). 39p. (J). pap. 9.95 (978-950-11-0681-7(0) , SGM341) Sigmar ARG. *Dist:* Continental Bk. Co., Inc.

Alas de Papel. 2000. (McGraw-Hill Ciencias Ser.). (ENG & SPA.). (gr. 1 up). (978-0-02-279569-6(3)) Macmillan/McGraw-Hill Schl. Div.

Allen, Margaret. Dr. Maggie's Play & Discover, Grades Preschool-2: Science. Corker, Joanne, ed. Sopp Rae, Terri, illus. 1998. (Dr. Maggie's Play & Discover Early-Childhood Ser.). 72p. pap., tchr. ed. 12.98 (978-1-57471-359-6(0) , 2347) Creative Teaching Pr., Inc.

El alunizaje que nunca Sucedio. 2000. (McGraw-Hill Ciencias Ser.). (ENG & SPA.). (gr. 5 up). (978-0-02-279682-2(7)) Macmillan/McGraw-Hill Schl. Div.

Amazing Science, 12 bks. Incl. Air : Outside, Inside, & All Around. Stille, Darlene R. Boyd, Sheree, illus. (C). 22.60 (978-1-4048-0248-3(7)); Dirt : The Scoop on Soil. Rosinsky, Natalie M. Boyd, Sheree, illus. (C). 22.60 (978-1-4048-0012-0(3)); Electricity : Bulbs, Batteries, & Sparks. Stille, Darlene R. Boyd, Sheree, illus. (C). 22.60 (978-1-4048-0245-2(2)); Energy : Heat, Light, & Food. Stille, Darlene R. Boyd, Sheree, illus. (C). 22.60 (978-1-4048-0249-0(5)); Light : Shadows, Mirrors, & Rainbows. Rosinsky, Natalie M. Boyd, Sheree, illus. (C). 22.60 (978-1-4048-0013-7(1)); Magnets : Pulling Together, Pushing Apart. Rosinsky, Natalie M. Boyd, Sheree, illus. (C). 22.60 (978-1-4048-0014-4(X)); Matter : See It, Touch It, Taste It, Smell It. Stille, Darlene R. Boyd, Sheree, illus. (C). 22.60 (978-1-4048-0246-9(0) , 1229495); Motion : Push & Pull, Fast & Slow. Stille, Darlene R. Boyd, Sheree, tr. Boyd, Sheree, illus. (J). 22.60 (978-1-4048-0250-6(9)); Rocks : Hard, Soft, Smooth, & Rough. Rosinsky, Natalie M. John, Matthew, illus. (C). 22.60 (978-1-4048-0015-1(8)); Sound : Loud, Soft, High, & Low. Rosinsky, Natalie M. John, Matthew, illus. (C). 22.60 (978-1-4048-0016-8(6)); Temperature : Heating Up & Cooling Down. Stille, Darlene R. Boyd, Sheree, illus. (C). 22.60 (978-1-4048-0247-6(9)); Water : Up, Down, & All Around. Rosinsky, Natalie M. John, Matthew, illus. (C). 22.60 (978-1-4048-0017-5(4)); 24p. (gr. k-4). 2004. 2003. 271.20 (978-1-4048-0244-5(4)) Picture Window Bks.

Ana Pinta. 2000. (McGraw-Hill Ciencias Ser.). (ENG & SPA.). (gr. 1 up). (978-0-02-279568-9(5)) Macmillan/McGraw-Hill Schl. Div.

Angliss, Sarah. Science Now. 2001. (Datafiles Ser.). (Illus.). 84p. (J). (gr. 3-7). 15.95 (978-1-57145-481-2(0) , Silver Dolphin Bks.) Advantage Pubs. Group.

Animal Eaters of the Pond: 6 Each of 1 Student Book, 6 vols. (Sunshinetm Science Ser.). 24p. (gr. 1-2). 41.95 (978-0-7802-2696-8(8)) Wright Group, The.

Animal Eaters of the Pond: Big Book. (Sunshinetm Science Ser.). 24p. (gr. 1-2). 37.50 (978-0-7802-2782-8(4)) Wright Group, The.

Animal Fibers: 6 Each of 1 Student Book, 6 vols. (Sunshinetm Science Ser.). 24p. (gr. 1-2). 41.95 (978-0-7802-1434-7(X)) Wright Group, The.

Animal Fibers: Big Book. (Sunshinetm Science Ser.). 24p. (gr. 1-2). 37.50 (978-0-7802-1435-4(8)) Wright Group, The.

Animales Nocturnos de la Selva. (Coleccion Ventana Transparente). (SPA., Illus.). (J). (gr. 3-5). (978-950-11-1280-1(2) , SG5231) Sigmar ARG. *Dist:* Lectorum Pubns., Inc.

Animals & Their Teeth, 6 vols. (Sunshinetm Science Ser.). 24p. (gr. 1-2). 41.95 (978-0-7802-1443-9(9)) Wright Group, The.

Animals & Their Teeth: Big Book. (Sunshinetm Science Ser.). 24p. (gr. 1-2). 37.50 (978-0-7802-1444-6(7)) Wright Group, The.

Ani's Rocket Ride: Internet Coach for Early Learning Network 50. 2000. (J). cd-rom 699.00 (978-1-931872-00-3(7)) APTE, Inc.

Apgar, Cheryl. Layer It! With Science: Interactive Layer Books that Promote Reading, Writing, & Listening. Samoiloff, Sheri, ed. Tom, Darcy, illus. 2002. 80p. (J). (gr. k-1). pap. 10.99 (978-1-57471-817-1(7) , CTP 3373) Creative Teaching Pr., Inc.

Applin, D. G., et al. AQA Modular Science for GCSE. 2003. (Illus.). 320p. pap. (978-0-7487-7286-5(3)) Nelson Thornes Ltd.

Aqui, alla, y en todas partes Science. (SPA.). (gr. k-2). 19.95 (978-0-7368-3110-9(X)) Red Brick Learning.

El arbol: Cuaderno de Evaluacion: Unit 1: el arbol (A Tree) 2000. (McGraw-Hill Ciencias Ser.). (ENG & SPA.). (gr. 1 up). (978-0-02-278627-4(9)) Macmillan/McGraw-Hill Schl. Div.

El arbol: Recursos para el maestro con clave de Respuestas: Unit 1: el arbol (A Tree) 2000. (McGraw-Hill Ciencias Ser.). (ENG & SPA.). (gr. 1 up). (978-0-02-278678-6(3)) Macmillan/McGraw-Hill Schl. Div.

Ardley. The Science Book of Things. 1998. (978-0-8172-9808-1(8)) Steck-Vaughn.

Ardley, Neil. The Science Book Of... Class Library. 1998. (Illus.). (YA). (978-0-8172-9817-3(7)) Steck-Vaughn.

—The Science Book of... Class Library, 14 vols. 2003. (Illus.). (J). (978-0-7398-8059-3(4)) Steck-Vaughn.

Arnold, Brian. Quick Revision KS3 Science. 2007. 46p. pap. 9.95 (***978-0-340-94308-3(4)*** , Hodder Murray) Hodder Education GBR. *Dist:* Trans-Atlantic Pubns., Inc.

Arnold, Nick. Esa Fascinante Arqueologia. 2003. (Coleccion Esa Gran Cultura).Tr. of Awesome Archaeology. (SPA., Illus.). 160p. (YA). (gr. 5-8). 7.96 (978-84-272-2139-0(8)) Molino, Editorial ESP. *Dist:* Lectorum Pubns., Inc.

—The Stunning Science of Everything: Science with the Squishy Bits Left In! De Saulles, Tony, illus. 2006. 96p. (J). (gr. 4-8). pap. 10.99 (978-0-439-87777-0(6) , Scholastic Reference) Scholastic, Inc.

Arnold, Nick & De Saulles, Tony. Esas Funestas Fuerzas. De Saulles, Tony, tr. 2003. (Coleccion Esa Horrible Cienca). (SPA., Illus.). 160p. (YA). (978-84-272-2054-6(5) , ML8313) Molino, Editorial ESP. *Dist:* Lectorum Pubns., Inc.

—Ese Voluminoso Cerebro. De Saulles, Tony, tr. 2003. (Coleccion Esa Horrible Cienca). (SPA., Illus.). 158p. (YA). (978-84-272-2065-2(0) , ML31376) Molino, Editorial ESP. *Dist:* Lectorum Pubns., Inc.

Arriba, arriba! Al espacio! la historia de Mae Jemison. 2000. (McGraw-Hill Ciencias Ser.). (ENG & SPA.). (gr. 3 up). (978-0-02-279644-0(4)) Macmillan/McGraw-Hill Schl. Div.

Asimov, Isaac & Hantula, Richard. Science Fiction: Vision of Tomorrow? 2004. (Isaac Asimov's 21st Century Library of the Universe). (Illus.). 32p. (J). lib. bdg. 24.67 (978-0-8368-3952-4(8)) Stevens, Gareth Inc.

Atlas de la Prehistoria. (Coleccion Atlas del Saber). (SPA., Illus.). (YA). (gr. 4 up). 20.95 (978-950-11-0889-7(9) , SGM74) Sigmar ARG. *Dist:* Continental Bk. Co., Inc.

Atlas de la Tierra. (Coleccion Atlas del Saber). (SPA., Illus.). (YA). (gr. 4 up). 20.95 (978-950-11-0916-0(X) , SGM16) Sigmar ARG. *Dist:* Continental Bk. Co., Inc.

Atlas de los Pueblos. (Coleccion Atlas del Saber). (SPA., Illus.). (YA). (gr. 4 up). 20.95 (978-950-11-0917-7(8) , SGM73) Sigmar ARG. *Dist:* Continental Bk. Co., Inc.

Atlas del Espacio. (Coleccion Atlas del Saber). (SPA., Illus.). (YA). (gr. 4 up). 20.95 (978-950-11-0887-3(2) , SGM72) Sigmar ARG. *Dist:* Continental Bk. Co., Inc.

Atlas Visual de las Ciencias. 2001. Tr. of Visual Atlas of Science. (SPA.). 1080p. 70.00 incl. cd-rom (978-84-494-1308-7(7) , GML07104-176346) Oceano Grupo Editoria, S.A. ESP. *Dist:* Thomson Gale.

Baeuerle, Patrick A. & Landa, Norbert. Microexplorers - Physical Science Series, 4 bks. (Illus.). (J). (gr. k-6). lib. bdg. 75.80 (978-1-56674-946-6(8)) Forest Hse. Publishing Co., Inc.

Bailey, Gerry. High-Tech Information. Boulter, Steve & Smith, Jan, illus. 2005. (Crafty Inventions Ser.). 48p. (C). (gr. 4-6). 26.60 (978-1-4048-1041-9(2)) Picture Window Bks.

Bailey, Jacqui. Science Works, 4 bks. Lilly, Matthew, illus. Incl. Charged Up : The Story of Electricity. 23.93 (978-1-4048-0568-2(0)); Drop in the Ocean : The Story of Water. 23.93 (978-1-4048-0566-8(4)); Monster Bones : The Story of a Dinosaur Fossil. 23.93 (978-1-4048-0565-1(6)); Sun Up, Sun Down : The Story of Day & Night. 23.93 (978-1-4048-0567-5(2)); 32p. (J). (gr. 3-6). 2004. (Illus.). 2004. 90.40 (978-1-4048-0571-2(0)) Picture Window Bks.

Bajo las Estrellas. 2000. (McGraw-Hill Ciencias Ser.). (ENG & SPA.). (gr. 1 up). (978-0-02-279556-6(1)) Macmillan/McGraw-Hill Schl. Div.

Baker, Christopher W. Scientific Visualization: The New Eyes of Science. 2000. (New Century Technology Ser.: 8). (Illus.). 48p. (gr. 5-8). lib. bdg. 23.90 (978-0-7613-1351-9(6) , Millbrook Pr.) Lerner Publishing Group.

Ballet! Puf! Leveled Books. 2000. (McGraw-Hill Ciencias Ser.). (ENG & SPA.). (gr. 4 up). (978-0-02-279664-8(9)) Macmillan/McGraw-Hill Schl. Div.

Baredes, Carla & Lotersztain, Ileana. Preguntas que Ponen los Pelos de Punta: Sobre el Aqua y el Fuego. Basile, Javier, illus. 2004. (SPA.). pap. (978-987-98042-1-6(X)) Iamique, Ediciones.

—Preguntas que Ponen los Pelos de Punta: Sobre la Luz y los Colores. Basile, Javier, illus. 2002. (Preguntas Que Ponen los Pelos de Punta Ser.: Vol. 3). (SPA.). 60p. pap. (978-987-98042-2-3(8)) Iamique, Ediciones.

—Preguntas que Ponen los Pelos de Punta: Sobre la Tierra y el Sol. Basile, Javier, illus. 2004. (SPA.). pap. (978-987-98042-0-9(1)) Iamique, Ediciones.

Barnes, John, et al. Science, Maths & Technology. 2003. (Illus.). 184p. pap. (978-0-7487-7121-9(2)) Nelson Thornes Ltd.

Barr, George. Science Projects for Young People. 1998. (Illus.). 153p. (J). (gr. 5-8). reprint ed. pap. 5.95 (978-0-486-25235-3(3) , 25235-3) Dover Pubns., Inc.

Barra, Nancy. Carlos & His Friends. Zuman, John, ed. Rooney, Veronica, illus. 2002. (Sunflower/Girasol Ser.). 35p. (J). 5.95 (978-1-58332-056-3(3)) Intercultural Center for Research in Education (I N C R E).

—Monica & the Summer Party. Zuman, John, ed. Deming, Linda, illus. 2002. (Sunflower/Girasol Ser.). 38p. (J). 5.95 (978-1-58332-052-5(0)) Intercultural Center for Research in Education (I N C R E).

—Monica Goes to the Zoo. Zuman, John, ed. Deming, Linda, illus. 2002. (Sunflower/Girasol Ser.). 30p. (J). 5.95 (978-1-58332-048-8(2)) Intercultural Center for Research in Education (I N C R E).

—Natalia & Her Grandma. Zuman, John, ed. Deming, Linda, illus. 2002. (Sunflower/Girasol Ser.). 38p. (J). 5.95 (978-1-58332-060-0(1)) Intercultural Center for Research in Education (I N C R E).

Basic Science Mysteries: Activities, Quizzes & Tests. 2003. Vol. 1. spiral bd. (978-1-928629-92-4(X)); Vol. 2. spiral bd. (978-1-928629-93-1(8)) Paradigm Accelerated Curriculum.

Basic Science Mysteries: Text. 2003. Vol. 1. spiral bd. (978-1-928629-90-0(3)); Vol. 2. spiral bd. (978-1-928629-91-7(1)) Paradigm Accelerated Curriculum.

Basic Science Mysteries Full Kit (with TRK) 2005. (Illus.). 796p. (YA). 75.00 (978-1-59476-096-9(9)) Paradigm Accelerated Curriculum.

Bates, Robin, et al. Images, 23 bks., Set. (Illus.). (J). (gr. 2-12). (978-0-88682-399-3(4) , Creative Education) Creative Co., The.

Batido Supersonico. 2000. (McGraw-Hill Ciencias Ser.). (ENG & SPA.). (gr. 3 up). (978-0-02-279645-7(2)) Macmillan/McGraw-Hill Schl. Div.

Baumann, Anne-Sophie. Where Does It Come From? Daigen, Al, tr. from FRE. Barborini, Robert & Chollat, Emilie, illus. 2006. (Explore Your World Ser.). 28p. (J). (ps-1). 15.95 (978-1-55407-009-1(0)) Firefly Bks., Ltd.

Baxen, Jean & Sinclair, Peta-Jane. Science & Technology Matters Grade 6 Learner's Book. 2002. 112p. (gr. 6). pap. 5.05 (978-0-521-78839-7(0)) Cambridge Univ. Pr.

Be a Plant Scientist: Level L, 6 vols. (Take-Twostm Ser.). 16p. 36.95 (978-0-322-03403-7(5)) Wright Group, The.

Be a Scientist. 2000. (McGraw-Hill Science Ser.). (gr. 6 up). stu. ed. (978-0-02-278959-6(6)) Macmillan/McGraw-Hill Schl. Div.

Be a Scientist, Gr 3. 2000. (McGraw-Hill Science Ser.). (gr. 3 up). (978-0-02-278953-4(7)) Macmillan/McGraw-Hill Schl. Div.

Be a Scientist Pupil Edition. 2000. (McGraw-Hill Science Ser.). (gr. 3 up). (978-0-02-278956-5(1)); (gr. 4 up). (978-0-02-278957-2(X)); (gr. 5 up). (978-0-02-278958-9(8)) Macmillan/McGraw-Hill Schl. Div.

Beacon Science. 2004. per. (978-1-932948-04-2(X)) Student Pr. Initiative.

Beals, Kevin & Willard, Carolyn. Mystery Festival. Bergman, Lincoln et al, eds. Baker, Lisa H. et al, illus. Hoyt, Richard, photos by. rev. ed. 1998. (Great Explorations in Math & Science Ser.). 268p. (J). (gr. 2-8). pap. 25.50 (978-0-924886-10-2(2) , GEMS) Univ. of California, Berkeley, Lawrence Hall of Science.

Beare, Emma. Tell Me about Science & Technology. 2006. (Tell Me About Ser.). 224p. (J). (gr. 3-6). 18.95 (978-0-7696-4289-5(6)) School Specialty Publishing.

—Tell Me about the World. 2006. (Tell Me About Ser.). 224p. (J). (gr. 3-6). 18.95 (978-0-7696-4290-1(X)) School Specialty Publishing.

Beat the Stuyvesant High School Exam (SSHSAT) l.t. ed. 2001. per. 30.00 (978-0-9706484-0-2(5) , Beat The Test) Trademark Universal, Inc.

Beginning to End Set 1. 2007. 170.80 (978-1-59679-833-5(5) , Buddy Bks.) ABDO Publishing Co.

Benchmark Education Staff, compiled by. Bloom & Grow & Simple Systems. 2005. spiral bd. 225.00 (*978-1-4108-5804-7(9)) Benchmark Education Co.

—Read & Achieve Science Small Group Set. 2005. spiral bd. 3500.00 (*978-1-4108-3814-8(5)); spiral bd. 500.00 (*978-1-4108-4165-0(0)); spiral bd. 3500.00 (*978-1-4108-4166-7(9)) Benchmark Education Co.

—Read & Achieve Science Whole Group Set. 2005. spiral bd. 2275.00 (*978-1-4108-4163-6(4)); spiral bd. 5275.00 (*978-1-4108-4164-3(2)) Benchmark Education Co.

—Science & Technology. 2006. spiral bd. 115.00 (*978-1-4108-6923-4(7)); 2006. spiral bd. 105.00 (*978-1-4108-6935-7(0)); 2005. spiral bd. 60.00 (*978-1-4108-3843-8(9)); 2005. spiral bd. 115.00 (*978-1-4108-3854-4(4)); 2005. spiral bd. 55.00 (*978-1-4108-3855-1(2)); 2005. spiral bd. 110.00 (*978-1-4108-3866-7(8)); 2005. spiral bd. 42.00 (*978-1-4108-3880-3(3)); 2005. spiral bd. 235.00 (*978-1-4108-4520-7(6)); 2005. spiral bd. 255.00 (*978-1-4108-5444-5(2)); 2005. spiral bd. 145.00 (*978-1-4108-5445-2(0)); 2005. spiral bd. 170.00 (*978-1-4108-5855-9(3)); 2005. spiral bd. 130.00 (*978-1-4108-5856-6(1)); 2005. spiral bd. 125.00 (*978-1-4108-3842-1(0)) Benchmark Education Co.

—Science As Inquiry. 2005. spiral bd. 80.00 (*978-1-4108-3918-3(4)); spiral bd. 55.00 (*978-1-4108-3919-0(2)); spiral bd. 85.00 (*978-1-4108-5848-1(0)) Benchmark Education Co.

—Science as Inquiry. 2005. spiral bd. 85.00 (*978-1-4108-4516-0(8)); spiral bd. 145.00 (*978-1-4108-5435-3(3)) Benchmark Education Co.

—Science Classroom Library. 2005. spiral bd. 390.00 (*978-1-4108-6019-4(1)) Benchmark Education Co.

—Science in Personal & Social Perspectives. 2006. spiral bd. 205.00 (*978-1-4108-6929-6(6)); 2006. spiral bd. 295.00 (*978-1-4108-6944-9(X)); 2006. spiral bd. 185.00 (*978-1-4108-6948-7(2)); 2005. spiral bd. 80.00 (*978-1-4108-3857-5(9)); 2005. spiral bd. 225.00 (*978-1-4108-3862-9(5)); 2005. spiral bd. 75.00 (*978-1-4108-3863-6(3)); 2005. spiral bd. 35.00 (*978-1-4108-3877-3(3)); 2005. spiral bd. 300.00 (*978-1-4108-4519-1(2)); 2005. spiral bd. 375.00 (*978-1-4108-5442-1(6)); 2005. spiral bd. 335.00 (*978-1-4108-5443-8(4)); 2005. spiral bd. 245.00 (*978-1-4108-5853-5(7)); 2005. spiral bd. 185.00 (*978-1-4108-5854-2(5)); 2005. spiral bd. 140.00 (*978-1-4108-3856-8(0)) Benchmark Education Co.

—Science in Personal Social Perspectives. 2005. spiral bd. 125.00 (*978-1-4108-3846-9(3)); spiral bd. 90.00 (*978-1-4108-3847-6(1)) Benchmark Education Co.

—Science Standards Set. 2006. 140.00 (*978-1-4108-6938-8(5)); 2006. pap. 350.00 (*978-1-4108-6952-4(0)); 2006. pap. 215.00 (*978-1-4108-6953-1(9)); 2006. spiral bd. 785.00 (*978-1-4108-6937-1(7)); 2006. spiral bd. 1075.00 (*978-1-4108-6940-1(7)); 2006. spiral bd. 195.00 (*978-1-4108-6941-8(5)); 2006. spiral bd. 2065.00 (*978-1-4108-6950-0(4)); 2006. spiral bd. 1195.00 (*978-1-4108-6951-7(2)); 2005. spiral bd. 6110.00 (*978-1-4108-5446-9(9)) Benchmark Education Co.

—Science Strands Set. 2005. spiral bd. 2580.00 (*978-1-4108-5459-9(0)); spiral bd. 695.00 (*978-1-4108-5562-6(7)) Benchmark Education Co.

—Science, Technology & Society. 2005. spiral bd. 185.00 (*978-1-4108-3753-0(X)) Benchmark Education Co.

—Science, Technology, & Society. 2005. spiral bd. 70.00 (*978-1-4108-3954-1(0)); spiral bd. 80.00 (*978-1-4108-3961-9(3)); spiral bd. 80.00 (*978-1-4108-3962-6(1)); spiral bd. 145.00 (*978-1-4108-4499-6(4)); spiral bd. 110.00 (*978-1-4108-5425-4(6)); spiral bd. 115.00 (*978-1-4108-5841-2(3)); spiral bd. 74.00 (*978-1-4108-5842-9(1)) Benchmark Education Co.

—Science Text Set. 2005. 110.00 (*978-1-4108-3819-3(6)); 165.00 (*978-1-4108-3823-0(4)); 50.00 (*978-1-4108-3825-4(0)); 40.00 (*978-1-4108-3841-4(2)); spiral bd. 715.00 (*978-1-4108-3818-6(8)); spiral bd. 4475.00 (*978-1-4108-3820-9(X)); spiral bd. 1025.00 (*978-1-4108-3822-3(6)); spiral bd. 315.00 (*978-1-4108-3824-7(2)); spiral bd. 175.00 (*978-1-4108-3839-1(0)); spiral bd. 200.00 (*978-1-4108-3840-7(4)) Benchmark Education Co.

—Science Texts Set. 2005. (Navigators Ser.). (J). spiral bd. 875.00 (*978-1-4108-5309-7(8)) Benchmark Education Co.

—Science Theme: Science in Personal & Social Perspectives. 2005. spiral bd. 115.00 (*978-1-4108-5313-4(6)) Benchmark Education Co.

—Science Themes. 2006. spiral bd. 2460.00 (*978-1-4108-7022-3(7)); spiral bd. 1295.00 (*978-1-4108-7037-7(5)); spiral bd. 1295.00 (*978-1-4108-7064-3(2)); spiral bd. 689.00 (*978-1-4108-7084-1(7)); spiral bd. 975.00 (*978-1-4108-7109-1(6)); spiral bd. 939.00 (*978-1-4108-7123-7(1)); spiral bd. 995.00 (*978-1-4108-7138-1(X)); spiral bd. 695.00 (*978-1-4108-7150-3(9)) Benchmark Education Co.

—Spanish Science Standard Set. 2005. spiral bd. 3455.00 (*978-1-4108-5857-3(X)) Benchmark Education Co.

Bender, Lionel. Science Safety: Being Careful. Davis, Jon, illus. 2006. (Amazing Science Ser.). (J). (978-1-4048-2198-9(8)) Picture Window Bks.

Bennett, Andrea T. & Kessler, James H. Sunlight, Skyscrapers, & Soda-Pop: The Wherever-You-Look Science Book. Sarecky, Melody, illus. 2003. (J). 12.95 (978-0-8412-3870-1(7)) American Chemical Society.

Bennett, Paul. En el Oceano. Nunez, Olga, tr. 2001. (Natural World Ser.). (SPA.). 32p. (J). (gr. 4-7). pap. (978-968-5308-26-7(8) , Silver Dolphin en Español) Advanced Marketing, S. de R. L. de C. V.

Beres, Samantha. 101 Things Every Kid Should Know about Science. 1998. (Illus.). 96p. (J). (gr. 3-7). pap. 9.95 (978-1-56565-916-2(3) , 09163W) Lowell Hse. Juvenile.

Bergethon, Peter R. Describing My World: Student Science Journal. 2000. (Illus.). 139p. (J). (gr. 1-3). pap. (978-1-58447-003-8(8)) Symmetry Learning Systems.

—Exploring My World: Marty's Miraculous Monday. 1999. (Illus.). 73p. (J). (gr. k-1). pap. (978-1-58447-001-4(1)) Symmetry Learning Systems.

—Marty's Miraculous Monday. Bacon, Edith N., photos by. 1999. (Illus.). 36p. (J). (gr. k-4). pap. (978-1-58447-004-5(6)) Symmetry Learning Systems.

—Marty's Miraculous Monday Reader. Date not set. (Illus.). (J). (gr. k-3). pap. (978-1-58447-011-3(9)) Symmetry Learning Systems.

—Measuring My World: Student Science Journal. Date not set. (Illus.). (J). pap. (978-1-58447-006-9(2)) Symmetry Learning Systems.

—Understanding My World: Student Science Journal. Date not set. (Illus.). (J). pap. (978-1-58447-008-3(9)) Symmetry Learning Systems.

Bernardy, Catherine J., et al. Let's Investigate, 12 Vol., Set. (Illus.). 384p. (J). 167.40 (978-0-88682-667-3(5)) Creative Co., The.

The Best of You Can with Beakman & Jax. 2002. 255p. (J). pap. 12.99 (978-0-88724-800-9(4) , WG 3008) Carson-Dellosa Publishing Co., Inc.

Big Book Collection. 2003. (gr. k up). 138.60 (978-0-328-00683-0(1)); (gr. 1 up). 138.60 (978-0-328-00684-7(X)); (gr. 2 up). 138.60 (978-0-328-00685-4(8)); (gr. 3 up). 138.60 (978-0-328-00686-1(6)) Addison-Wesley Educational Pubs., Inc.

Billings. Weird Science. 1998. (Wild Side Ser.). (Illus.). (YA). (gr. 6-12). 13.00 (978-0-89061-798-4(8) , R0798-8E) Jamestown.

Bingham, Jane, et al. Science Answers, 6 bks., Set 2. 2004. (J). (gr. 3-5). lib. bdg. 162.43 (978-1-4034-4769-2(1)) Heinemann Library.

Bittner, Linda Howard, illus. Kids Ask What? 2006. 32p. (J). (*978-1-4127-1360-3(9)) Publications International, Ltd.

Bizony, Piers. Invisible Worlds: Exploring the Unseen. 2004. (Illus.). 232p. 34.95 (978-0-297-84342-9(7) , Weidenfeld & Nicolson) Orion Publishing Group, Ltd. GBR. *Dist:* Sterling Publishing Co., Inc.

BJU Staff. Science Activity Manual St Gr6. 2004. pap. 15.00 (978-1-59166-008-8(4)) Jones, Bob Univ. Pr.

—Science Student Notebook Grd 1. 2004. pap. 7.50 (978-1-57924-927-4(2)) Jones, Bob Univ. Pr.

—Science Student Notebook Grd 3. 2004. pap. 7.50 (978-1-57924-929-8(9)) Jones, Bob Univ. Pr.

—Science Student Text Grd 1. 2004. 23.50 (978-1-57924-908-3(6)) Jones, Bob Univ. Pr.

—Science Student Text Grd 3. 2004. 23.50 (978-1-57924-914-4(0)) Jones, Bob Univ. Pr.

—Science Student Text Grd 6. 2004. pap. 17.00 (978-1-59166-006-4(8)) Jones, Bob Univ. Pr.

Blastoff! - Group 2, 5 bks., Set. 142.50 (978-0-7614-1400-1(2) , Benchmark Bks.) Cavendish, Marshall Corp.

Block, Cheryl. The Rainbow Web. 2005. (Illus.). 32p. (J). 19.95 (978-0-9761625-0-6(4)) Block Publishing.

Bocknek, Jonathan. The Science of the Sky. 2000. (Living Science Ser.). (Illus.). 32p. (J). (gr. 2 up). lib. bdg. 24.67 (978-0-8368-2574-9(8)) Stevens, Gareth Inc.

Body Numbers, 6 pack. (Discovery World Ser.). 16p. (gr. 1-2). 28.00 (978-0-7635-8467-2(3)) Rigby Education.

Body Parts: KinderFacts Individual Title Six-Packs. (Kinderstarters Ser.). 8p. (ps-1). 21.00 (978-0-7635-8741-3(9)) Rigby Education.

Body Talk: Individual Title Six-Packs. (Story Steps Ser.). (gr. k-2). 32.00 (978-0-7635-9815-0(1)) Rigby Education.

Bones Sets: 1 Each of 3 Big Books. (Sunshinetm Science Ser.). (gr. 1-2). 93.95 (978-0-7802-0530-7(8)) Wright Group, The.

Bones Sets: 1 Each of 3 Student Books. (Sunshinetm Science Ser.). (gr. 1-2). 17.95 (978-0-7802-0271-9(6)) Wright Group, The.

Book Studio Staff. Attract! 2006. (Cool Kits Ser.). 1p. (J). 7.99 (978-0-7566-2428-6(2)) Dorling Kindersley Publishing, Inc.

—Spark! 2006. (Cool Kits Ser.). 1p. (J). 7.99 (978-0-7566-2429-3(0)) Dorling Kindersley Publishing, Inc.

Books Are Fun Exclusive Let's Start Science 5 Set. 2005. (J). lib. bdg. (978-1-59566-165-4(4)) QEB Publishing Inc.

Boring, Mel & Dendy, Leslie. Guinea Pig Scientists: Bold Self-Experimenters in Science & Medicine. Mordan, C. B., illus. rev. ed. 2005. 224p. (J). 19.95 (978-0-8050-7316-4(7) , Holt, Henry & Co. Bks. For Young Readers) Holt, Henry & Co.

Bosak, Susan V. Science Is... A Source Book of Fascinating Facts, Projects & Activities. 2nd ed. 2000. (Illus.). 515p. (gr. 3-9). pap. 35.00 (978-0-590-74070-8(9)) Scholastic Canada, Ltd. CAN. *Dist:* Firefly Bks., Ltd.

Botha, Tommy C. I., et al. Natural Sciences Matters Grade 7 Learner's Book. 2005. 144p. pap. 13.50 (978-0-521-67070-8(5)) Cambridge Univ. Pr.

—Natural Sciences Matters Grade 7 Learner's Book Afrikaans Translation. 2005. (AFR.). 144p. pap. 13.50 (978-0-521-67072-2(1)) Cambridge Univ. Pr.

Bowler, Sue. Restless Earth. 2002. (gr. 7-12). lib. bdg. 15.30 (978-0-613-55757-3(3)) Tandem Library Bks.

Branigan, Carrie. First Steps in Science: Big Story Book. 2003. (Illus.). 24p. (J). 75.00 (978-0-7487-6865-3(3)) Nelson Thornes Ltd. GBR. *Dist:* Trans-Atlantic Pubns., Inc.

—First Steps in Science: Image Bank. 2003. (Illus.). 96p. (J). 150.00 (978-0-7487-6866-0(1)) Nelson Thornes Ltd. GBR. *Dist:* Trans-Atlantic Pubns., Inc.

Branzei, Sylvia. Grossology. Keely, Jack, illus. 2002. 80p. mass mkt. 9.99 (978-0-8431-4914-2(0) , Price Stern Sloan) Penguin Group (USA) Inc.

Bredeson, Carmen. Despegue: Liftoff! 2005. (Rookie Espanol: Ciencias Ser.). (SPA., Illus.). 32p. (J). (gr. k-2). pap. 5.95 (978-0-516-25510-1(X) , Children's Pr.) Scholastic Library Publishing.

Brocker, Susan & Furgang, Kathy. Pioneers in Medicine. 2004. (Navigators Ser.). (J). pap. 42.00 (978-1-4108-0422-8(4)) Benchmark Education Co.

Bronson, Cary. I am Not a Flying Elephant Fish! A Children's Science Book on the Butterfly. Gomer, William, illus. l.t. ed. 2004. 32p. (J). lib. bdg. 14.95 (978-0-9746094-0-9(4)) Connect With Your Kid Bks.

Brown Bag Science Set Gr. 1-2. 2004. (J). (978-1-57022-470-6(6)) ECS Learning Systems, Inc.

Brown Bag Science Set Gr. 3-4. 2004. (J). (978-1-57022-471-3(4)) ECS Learning Systems, Inc.

Brown, Jordan. Easy Hyperstudio Projects That Fit Right into Your Curriculum: 10 Super-Cool Projects with Step-by-Step Reproducible Directions That Use the Power of HyperStudio to Motivate All Kids & Liven up Learning. 2001. 96p. (gr. 3). pap. 12.95 (978-0-439-13114-8(6)) Scholastic, Inc.

Brushing Well, 6 vols. (gr. k-2). 28.95 (978-0-7368-8137-1(9)) Red Brick Learning.

Buckley, Arabella. The Fairy-Land of Science (Yesterday's Classics) 2006. (Illus.). 244p. (J). per. 10.95 (978-1-59915-024-6(7)) Yesterday's Classics.

Buckley, Arabella Burton. The Fairy-Land of Science. fac. ed. 2000. 258p. pap. 18.95 (978-1-4021-0038-3(8) , Elibron Classics) Adamant Media.

—The Fairy-Land of Science. 2001. 250p. im. lthr. 24.95 (978-1-57179-145-0(0)) Scientists of New Atlantis.

—The Fairy Land of Science. 2004. reprint ed. pap. 20.95 (978-1-4191-6179-7(2)) Kessinger Publishing, LLC.

Buenos Dias. 2000. (McGraw-Hill Ciencias Ser.). (ENG & SPA.). (gr. k up). (978-0-02-279704-1(1)) Macmillan/McGraw-Hill Schl. Div.

Building Science Skills. 2002. 80p. (J). (gr. 4-6). pap. 9.99 (978-0-7424-0251-5(7) , IF19216) School Specialty Publishing.

Bulging Brains. (YA). (gr. 5-8). pap. (978-0-439-14976-1(2)) Scholastic GBR. *Dist:* Lectorum Pubns., Inc.

Bulloch, Ivan & James, Diane. Jardiniers en Herbe. 2000. (Watch It Ser.). (FRE., Illus.). 32p. (J). (gr. 2-6). 12.95 (978-1-58728-139-6(2) , Two Can Publishing) T&N Children's Publishing.

Bumcrot, Curt & Dunlap, Shiree. Testing Targets: For Science of the Physical Creation. Zyp, Nicole & Robinson, Heldi, eds. 2004. 19p. (YA). (gr. 9-12). pap. 5.00 (978-1-888786-44-6(2)) Basic Skills Assessment & Educational Services.

Burger, Nicolette, et al. Science Matters Learner's Book Grade 8. 2000. 152p. pap. 9.00 (978-0-521-59561-2(4)) Cambridge Univ. Pr.

Burkett, Katherine. Eureka. 2002. (Mad Science Ser.: No. 1). (Illus.). 96p. (J). (gr. 3-7). pap. 4.50 (978-0-439-22856-5(5)) Scholastic, Inc.

Burton, Jane & Taylor, Kim. The Nature & Science of Numbers. 2001. (Exploring the Science of Nature Ser.). (Illus.). 32p. (J). (gr. 3 up). lib. bdg. 24.67 (978-0-8368-2193-2(9)) Stevens, Gareth Inc.

Burton, Margie, et al. Children As Young Scientists. Adams, Alison, ed. 1999. (Early Connections Ser.). 16p. (gr. k-2). pap. 4.50 (978-1-58344-055-1(0)) Benchmark Education Co.

Calhoun, Yael, ed. Environmental Issues. 2005. (Illus.). 100+p. (gr. 9-13). pap. 191.70 (978-0-7910-8321-5(7) , Chelsea Hse.) Facts On File, Inc.

California Science Explorer: Teaching Resource Box Grade Eight 2001C. 1999. (J). (gr. 6-8). (978-0-13-050309-1(6)) Prentice Hall PTR.

California Science Explorer: Teaching Resource Box Grade Seven 2001C. 1999. (J). (gr. 6-8). (978-0-13-050308-4(8)) Prentice Hall PTR.

Callella, Trisha & Marks, Marilyn. Integrating Science with Reading Instruction 1-2: 12 Complete Science Units. Walter, LaDawn, ed. Rader, Catherine & Grayson, Rick, illus. 2002. 136p. (J). (gr. 1-2). pap. 16.99 (978-1-57471-806-5(1) , CTP 2814) Creative Teaching Pr., Inc.

—Integrating Science with Reading Instruction 3-4: 12 Complete Science Units. Walter, LaDawn, ed. Campbell, Jenny & Grayson, Rick, illus. 2002. 144p. (J). (gr. 3-4). pap., act. bk. ed. 16.99 (978-1-57471-807-2(X) , CTP 2815) Creative Teaching Pr., Inc.

—Integrating Science with Reading Instruction 5-6: 12 Complete Science Units. Walter, LaDawn, ed. Grayson, Rick & Campbell, Jenny, illus. 2002. 144p. (J). (gr. 5-6). pap., act. bk. ed. 16.99 (978-1-57471-808-9(8) , CTP 2816) Creative Teaching Pr., Inc.

Cambridge Educational, prod. Eureka! an Encyclopedia Hyb Lb. (YA). cd-rom 224.95 (978-0-7365-4338-5(4)) Films Media Group.

Cambridge Studios. Interactive World Issues, Set. 2nd ed. 2003. (C). (gr. 6-12). cd-rom 51.25 (978-0-07-255648-3(X) , 9780072556483) Glencoe/McGraw-Hill.

Canizares, Susan. Make It Move. 2000. (J). pap. 2.50 (978-0-439-08121-4(1)) Scholastic, Inc.

—Push & Pull. 1999. (Science Emergent Readers Ser.). (J). pap. 10.01 (978-0-439-08119-1(X)) Scholastic, Inc.

—Science, Tools & Magic, Vol.12. 1999. (Learning Center Emergent Readers Ser.). (J). pap. 2.50 (978-0-439-04603-9(3)) Scholastic, Inc.

Canizares, Susan & Chessen, Betsey. Science Outside. 1999. (J). pap. (978-0-439-04604-6(1)) Scholastic, Inc.

Cannon, William, Jr. Marine Science. 2008. (Twentieth-Century Science Ser.). 272p. (gr. 6-12). 49.50 (978-0-8160-5534-0(3)) Facts On File, Inc.

S

Capeci, Anne. MSB Science Reader: Has A Heart. Bracken, Carolyn, illus. 2006. 32p. (J). pap. 3.99 (978-0-439-68402-6(1) , Cartwheel Bks.) Scholastic, Inc.

Carlson, Dale. In & Out of Your Mind: Teen Science: Human Bites. Khairnar, Kishore, ed. 2002. (Illus.). 256p. 14.95 (978-1-884158-27-8(7)) Bick Publishing Hse.

—In & Out of Your Mind: Teen Science: Human Bites. Khairnar, Kishore, ed. Nicklaus, Carol, illus. 2002. 218p. (YA). (gr. 8-12). per. 24.55 (978-0-613-57061-9(8)) Tandem Library Bks.

El Carrito de Ana. 2000. (McGraw-Hill Ciencias Ser.). (ENG & SPA.). (gr. 1 up). (978-0-02-279557-3(X)) Macmillan/McGraw-Hill Schl. Div.

Los castores construyen Diques. 2000. (McGraw-Hill Ciencias Ser.). (ENG & SPA.). (gr. 1 up). (978-0-02-279559-7(6)) Macmillan/McGraw-Hill Schl. Div.

Cells & Things. 2004. (Illus.). lib. bdg. 7.95 (978-0-8225-4371-8(0)) Lerner Publishing Group.

Chahrour, Janet Parks. Flash! Bang! Pop! Fizz! Exciting Science for Curious Minds. 2005. (Illus.). 144p. (J). (gr. 5-9). pap. 16.99 (978-0-7641-1142-6(6)) Barron's Educational Series, Inc.

Challoner, Jack. Sound & Light. 2001. (Hands-On Science Ser.). (Illus.). (J). (978-0-606-21442-1(9)) Tandem Library Bks.

—Start-Up Science, 8 bks., Set. Incl. Big & Small. lib. bdg. 24.26 (978-0-8172-4319-7(4)); Fast & Slow. lib. bdg. 24.26 (978-0-8172-4320-3(8)); Floating & Sinking. lib. bdg. 16.98 (978-0-8172-4317-3(8)); Hot & Cold. lib. bdg. 24.76 (978-0-8172-4323-4(2)); Light & Dark. lib. bdg. 24.76 (978-0-8172-4321-0(6)); Loud & Quiet. lib. bdg. 24.26 (978-0-8172-4318-0(6)); Push & Pull. lib. bdg. 24.26 (978-0-8172-4316-6(X)); Wet & Dry. lib. bdg. 24.26 (978-0-8172-4322-7(4)); 32p. (J). (gr. 1-4). 1996. (Illus.). Set lib. bdg. 135.84 (978-0-8172-4324-1(0)) Raintree.

Chancellor, Deborah & Murrell, Deborah. Everything You Need to Know: An Encyclopedia for Inquiring Young Minds. 2007. (Illus.). 320p. (J). (ps-3). 24.95 (***978-0-7534-6089-4(0)*** , Kingfisher) Houghton Mifflin Co. Trade & Reference Div.

Chang, Maria L. Science Graphic Organizers & Mini-Lessons. 2006. 48p. pap. 10.99 (978-0-439-54896-0(9) , Teaching Resources) Scholastic, Inc.

Chasse, Betsy & Captured Light Distribution, creators. The Little Book of Bleeps. 2004. (Illus.). 14.95 (978-0-9761074-0-8(6)) Captured Light Distribution, LLC.

Chelsea Clubhouse Science Exploration. (Illus.). (J). 418.50 (978-0-7910-7274-5(6) , Chelsea Hse.) Facts On File, Inc.

Chemicals, Health, Environment & Me Kit. 2000. (Illus.). (J). tchr. ed., ring bd. (978-1-887725-68-2(7)) Lab-Aids, Inc.

Chickadee Magazine Editors & Penrose, Gordon. Science Fun: Hands-On Science with Dr. Zed. 1998. (Illus.). 80p. (J). (ps-3). pap. 12.95 (978-1-895688-74-0(4)) Firefly Bks., Ltd.

Christopher, Garrett. Look at These Animals: A Content Area Reader-science. 2005. (Sadlier Phonics Reading Program). (Illus.). 16p. (YA). (ps-2). 25.20 (978-0-8215-7812-4(X)) Sadlier, William H. Inc.

Christopher Lee Publications Staff. Newton's Science Terms Made Easy. 2002. (Newton's... Made Easy Flippers Ser.). (Illus.). 50p. (J). pap. 7.95 (978-1-59125-163-7(X)) Penton Overseas, Inc.

Churchill, E. Richard. Amazing Science Experiments. Garbot, Dave & Gallagher, Jack, illus. 2005. (No Sweat Science Ser.). 128p. (gr. 4-7). pap. 5.95 (978-1-4027-2331-5(8)) Sterling Publishing Co., Inc.

Cicadas, 6 vols. (gr. k-2). 28.95 (978-0-7368-9107-3(2)) Red Brick Learning.

El cielo: Cuaderno de Evaluacion: Unit 2: el cielo (the Sky) 2000. (McGraw-Hill Ciencias Ser.). (ENG & SPA.). (gr. 1 up). (978-0-02-278628-1(7)) Macmillan/McGraw-Hill Schl. Div.

El cielo: Recursos para el maestro con clave de Respuestas: Unit 2: el cielo (the Sky) 2000. (McGraw-Hill Ciencias Ser.). (ENG & SPA.). (gr. 1 up). (978-0-02-278679-3(1)) Macmillan/McGraw-Hill Schl. Div.

Ciencias. (Enciclopedias Everest Internacional Ser.). (SPA., Illus.). (YA). (gr. 5-8). 41.95 (978-84-241-9405-5(5) , EV7495) Everest de Ediciones y Distribucion, S.L. ESP. *Dist:* Lectorum Pubns., Inc.

Ciencias Naturales. (Coleccion Ciencas Naturales Ser.). (SPA., Illus.). (J). Bk. 1. (gr. 1). pap. 8.95 (978-968-416-500-7(5) , FN5005); Bk. 2. (gr. 2). pap. 10.95 (978-968-416-489-5(0) , FN4890); Bk. 3. (gr. 3). pap. 10.95 (978-968-416-490-1(4) , FN4904); Bk. 4. (gr. 4). pap. 10.95 (978-968-416-491-8(2) , FN4912); Bk. 5. (gr. 5). pap. 11.95 (978-968-416-492-5(0) , FN4920); Bk. 6. (gr. 6). pap. 12.95 (978-968-416-493-2(9) , FN4939) Fernandez USA Publishing.

Cientificos! (SPA.). (J). Vol. 7. wbk. ed. 15.00 (978-958-04-6435-8(9)); Vol. 8. wbk. ed. 15.00 (978-958-04-6436-5(7)); Vol. 9. wbk. ed. 15.00 (978-958-04-6437-2(5)) Norma S.A. COL. *Dist:* Distribuidora Norma, Inc.

Cientificos! Ciencia Integrada 1. (SPA.). (J). 30.00 (978-958-04-5245-4(8)) Norma S.A. COL. *Dist:* Distribuidora Norma, Inc.

Cientificos! Ciencia Integrada 2. (SPA.). (J). 30.00 (978-958-04-5246-1(6)) Norma S.A. COL. *Dist:* Distribuidora Norma, Inc.

Cientificos! Ciencia Integrada 3. (SPA.). (J). 30.00 (978-958-04-5247-8(4)) Norma S.A. COL. *Dist:* Distribuidora Norma, Inc.

Cientificos! Ciencia Integrada 4. 35.00 (978-958-04-5248-5(2)) Norma S.A. COL. *Dist:* Distribuidora Norma, Inc.

Cientificos! Ciencia Integrada 5. (SPA.). (J). 40.00 (978-958-04-5249-2(0)) Norma S.A. COL. *Dist:* Distribuidora Norma, Inc.

Cientificos! Ciencia Integrada 6. (SPA.). (J). 45.00 (978-958-04-5250-8(4)) Norma S.A. COL. *Dist:* Distribuidora Norma, Inc.

Circular Movement, 6 vols. (gr. k-2). 28.95 (978-0-7368-8614-7(1)) Red Brick Learning.

The Circulatory System, 6 vols. (gr. k-2). 28.95 (978-0-7368-8800-4(4)) Red Brick Learning.

Clark, John Owen Edward. The New Encyclopedia of Science, 9 vols. 2nd ed. 2003. (Illus.). (J). (978-0-19-521959-3(7)); (978-0-19-521960-9(0)); (978-0-19-521961-6(9)) Oxford Univ. Pr., Inc.

Clarke, Phil, et al. Mysteries & Marvels of Science - Internet Linked. 2005. (Mysteries & Marvels Ser.). 96p. (J). 19.95 (978-0-7945-0922-4(3) , Usborne) EDC Publishing.

Clarke, Phillip, et al. The Usborne Internet-Linked Mysteries & Marvels of Science. Furnival, Keith, illus. 2005. 96p. (J). (***978-0-439-81568-0(1)***) Scholastic, Inc.

Clasificacion de los seres vivos: Cuaderno de Evaluacion: Unit 1: Clasificacion de los seres vivos (Classifying Living Things) 2000. (McGraw-Hill Ciencias Ser.). (ENG & SPA.). (gr. 4 up). (978-0-02-278660-1(0)) Macmillan/McGraw-Hill Schl. Div.

Clasificacion de los seres vivos: Recursos para el maestro con clave de Respuestas: Unit 1: Clasificacion de los seres vivos (Classifying Living Things) 2000. (McGraw-Hill Ciencias Ser.). (ENG & SPA.). (gr. 4 up). (978-0-02-278699-1(6)) Macmillan/McGraw-Hill Schl. Div.

Clendenin, Priscilla. No Scare Science Fair: An Extra Out of the Ordinary Guide to Doing a Science Fair Project. Clendenin, Stephen P. & Uriz, Tony, illus. l.t. ed. 1998. Orig. Title: So You Have to Do a Science Fair Project.... 67p. (J). (gr. 1-8). pap. 15.95 (978-0-9679713-0-8(6)) Ribbitt Productions.

Cleveland, Don. How Do We Know How the Brain Works. 2005. (Great Scientific Questions & the Scientists Who Answered Them Ser.). (Illus.). 112p. (J). (gr. 7-12). lib. bdg. 26.50 (978-1-4042-0078-4(9)) Rosen Publishing Group, Inc., The.

Clouds, Rain, & Fog: 6 Each of 1 Student Book, 6 vols. (Sunshinetm Science Ser.). 24p. (gr. 1-2). 41.95 (978-0-7802-1373-9(4)) Wright Group, The.

Clouds, Rain, & Fog: Big Book. (Sunshinetm Science Ser.). 24p. (gr. 1-2). 37.50 (978-0-7802-1374-6(2)) Wright Group, The.

Cloyd, J. B. Rocks We Use: A Content Area Reader. 2005. (Emergent/Early (Prek-2) Science Package Ser.). 12p. (YA). (ps-2). 25.20 (978-0-8215-7813-1(8)) Sadlier, William H. Inc.

CNN Staff, prod. Issues in Science. 2000. (Primary Source Science Collection). (YA). (gr. 5-8). pap. incl. VHS (978-0-7398-3215-8(8)) Raintree.

Cobb, Vicki. Don't Try This at Home! Science Fun for Kids on the Go. 1999. (Illus.). (J). (978-0-606-17964-5(X)) Tandem Library Bks.

Cohen, Paul S. & Sorrentino, Anthony V. New York City Science Grade 6. 2007. (J). pap. (***978-1-56765-908-5(X)*** , R66P) AMSCO Schl. Pubns., Inc.

—New York City Science Grade 6 Hardbound. 2007. (J). (***978-1-56765-909-2(8)*** , R66H) AMSCO Schl. Pubns., Inc.

Cole, Joanna. The Magic School Bus & the Electric Field Trip: Literature Unit. Chaney, Howard, illus. 1999. (Magic School Bus Ser.). 48p. (J). (gr. 1-4). pap., tchr. ed. 7.99 (978-1-57690-082-6(7) , TCA2082) Teacher Created Materials, Inc.

—The Magic School Bus Answers Questions. 1999. (Magic School Bus Ser.). (J). (gr. 1-4). (978-0-606-15832-9(4)) Tandem Library Bks.

Collison, Paul, et al. Nelson Modular Science. (Illus.). (YA). Bk. 1. 2nd ed. 2005. 296p. pap. 36.50 (978-0-7487-6856-1(4)); Bk. 2. 2002. 256p. pap. 36.50 (978-0-7487-6247-7(7)) Nelson Thornes Ltd. GBR. *Dist:* Trans-Atlantic Pubns., Inc.

Colvard, Mary & Dirksen, Howard, contrib. by. Science I Essential Interactions: Computer Generated Assessment. 2000. (Illus.). (YA). (gr. 7-12). pap. 79.95 (978-1-930799-08-0(X)) Centre Pointe Learning, Inc.

—Science I Essential Interactions: Overhead Transparencies. 2000. (Illus.). 40p. (YA). (gr. 7-12). pap. 65.95 (978-1-930799-07-3(1)) Centre Pointe Learning, Inc.

—Science II Essential Interactions. 2000. (Illus.). 432p. (YA). (gr. 7-12). 47.95 (978-1-930799-10-3(1)) Centre Pointe Learning, Inc.

—Science II Essential Interactions: Computer Generated Assessment. 2000. (YA). (gr. 7-12). pap. 79.95 (978-1-930799-18-9(7)) Centre Pointe Learning, Inc.

—Science III Essential Interactions. 2000. (Illus.). 592p. (YA). (gr. 7-12). 48.95 (978-1-930799-20-2(9)) Centre Pointe Learning, Inc.

—Science IV Essential Interactions. 2000. (J). pap. 79.95 (978-1-930799-35-6(7)); (Illus.). 736p. tchr. ed. 48.95 (978-1-930799-28-8(4)) Centre Pointe Learning, Inc.

Combined Test Preparation & Practice Book: Assessment. 2000. (McGraw-Hill Science Ser.). (gr. 3 up). (978-0-02-279511-5(1)); (gr. 4 up). (978-0-02-279512-2(X)); (gr. 5 up). (978-0-02-279513-9(8)); (gr. 6 up). (978-0-02-279514-6(6)) Macmillan/McGraw-Hill Schl. Div.

Los combustibles fosiles nos dan Calor. 2000. (McGraw-Hill Ciencias Ser.). (ENG & SPA.). (gr. 2 up). (978-0-02-279611-2(8)) Macmillan/McGraw-Hill Schl. Div.

Comiendo bien Science, 6 vols.Tr. of Eating Well Science. (SPA.). (gr. k-2). 28.95 (978-0-7368-3050-8(2) , Yellow Umbrella Bks.) Capstone Pr., Inc.

Como haces un arco Iris? 2000. (McGraw-Hill Ciencias Ser.). (ENG & SPA.). (gr. 1 up). (978-0-02-279565-8(0)) Macmillan/McGraw-Hill Schl. Div.

Como la palanca cambio el Mundo: Leveled Books. 2000. (McGraw-Hill Ciencias Ser.). (ENG & SPA.). (gr. 4 up). (978-0-02-279648-8(7)) Macmillan/McGraw-Hill Schl. Div.

Como mantenerse sano: Cuaderno de Evaluacion: Unit 7: Como mantenerse sano (Human Body: Keeping Healthy) 2000. (McGraw-Hill Ciencias Ser.). (ENG & SPA.). (gr. 3 up). (978-0-02-278730-1(5)) Macmillan/McGraw-Hill Schl. Div.

Como mantenerse sano: Recursos para el maestro con clave de Respuestas: Unit 7: Como mantenerse sano (Human Body: Keeping Healthy) 2000. (McGraw-Hill Ciencias Ser.). (ENG & SPA.). (gr. 3 up). (978-0-02-278729-5(1)) Macmillan/McGraw-Hill Schl. Div.

Como se calientan? Science, 6 vols.Tr. of Keeping Warm Science. (SPA.). (gr. k-2). 28.95 (978-0-7368-3144-4(4) , Yellow Umbrella Bks.) Capstone Pr., Inc.

Como se mueve?: Cuaderno de Evaluacion: Unit 4: Como se mueve? (Watch it Move) 2000. (McGraw-Hill Ciencias Ser.). (ENG & SPA.). (gr. 2 up). (978-0-02-278641-0(4)) Macmillan/McGraw-Hill Schl. Div.

Complete Set. (Investigate Science Ser.). (gr. 1-3). 170.08 (978-0-7565-0724-4(3)); (gr. 2-4). 510.24 (978-0-7565-0711-4(1)) Compass Point Bks.

Concept Summaries: Language Support Cantonese: Student & Teacher Support Resources. 2000. (McGraw-Hill Science Ser.). (gr. 2 up). (978-0-02-279457-6(3)); (gr. 3 up). (978-0-02-279458-3(1)); (gr. 4 up). (978-0-02-279459-0(X)); (gr. 5 up). (978-0-02-279461-3(1)) Macmillan/McGraw-Hill Schl. Div.

Concept Summaries: Language Support Hmong: Student & Teacher Support Resources. 2000. (McGraw-Hill Science Ser.). (gr. 2 up). (978-0-02-279464-4(6)); (gr. 3 up). (978-0-02-279465-1(4)); (gr. 4 up). (978-0-02-279466-8(2)); (gr. 5 up). (978-0-02-279467-5(0)) Macmillan/McGraw-Hill Schl. Div.

Concept Summaries: Language Support Khmer: Student & Teacher Support Resources. 2000. (McGraw-Hill Science Ser.). (gr. 2 up). (978-0-02-279471-2(9)); (gr. 3 up). (978-0-02-279472-9(7)); (gr. 4 up). (978-0-02-279473-6(5)); (gr. 5 up). (978-0-02-279474-3(3)) Macmillan/McGraw-Hill Schl. Div.

Concept Summaries: Language Support Vietnamese: Student & Teacher Support Resources. 2000. (McGraw-Hill Science Ser.). (gr. 2 up). (978-0-02-279477-4(8)); (gr. 3 up). (978-0-02-279478-1(6)); (gr. 4 up). (978-0-02-279479-8(4)); (gr. 5 up). (978-0-02-279481-1(6)) Macmillan/McGraw-Hill Schl. Div.

Conexion Curricular: Student & Teacher Support Resources. 2000. (McGraw-Hill Ciencias Ser.). (ENG & SPA.). (gr. k up). (978-0-02-279042-4(X)); (gr. 1 up). (978-0-02-279043-1(8)); (gr. 2 up). (978-0-02-279044-8(6)); (gr. 3 up). (978-0-02-279045-5(4)); (gr. 4 up). (978-0-02-279046-2(2)); (gr. 5 up). (978-0-02-279047-9(0)) Macmillan/McGraw-Hill Schl. Div.

Conley, Kate A. Greek Arts & Sciences. 2005. (Life in Ancient Days: Greece Ser.). (J). (978-1-59197-866-4(1)) ABDO Publishing Co.

Conoce tu mundo: Cuaderno de Actividades: Unit 1: Conoce tu mundo (Learn about Your World) 2000. (McGraw-Hill Ciencias Ser.). (ENG & SPA.). (gr. k up). (978-0-02-278989-3(8)) Macmillan/McGraw-Hill Schl. Div.

Cook, Sherry & Johnson, Terri. Andy Acid, 26 vols. Kuhn, Jesse, illus. l.t. ed. 2006. (Quirkles—Exploring Phonics through Science Ser.: 1). 32p. (J). 7.99 (978-1-933815-00-8(0) , Quirkles, The) Creative 3, LLC.

—Botanist Bert, 26 vols. Kuhn, Jesse, illus. l.t. ed. 2006. (Quirkles—Exploring Phonics through Science Ser.: 2). 32p. (J). 7.99 (978-1-933815-01-5(9) , Quirkles, The) Creative 3, LLC.

—Colorful Caroline, 26 vols. Kuhn, Jesse, illus. l.t. ed. 2006. (Quirkles—Exploring Phonics through Science Ser.: 3). 32p. (J). 7.99 (978-1-933815-02-2(7) , Quirkles, The) Creative 3, LLC.

—Density Dan, 26 vols. Kuhn, Jesse, illus. l.t. ed. 2006. (Quirkles—Exploring Phonics through Science Ser.: 4). 32p. (J). 7.99 (978-1-933815-03-9(5) , Quirkles, The) Creative 3, LLC.

—Friction Fred, 26 vols. Kuhn, Jesse, illus. l.t. ed. 2006. (Quirkles—Exploring Phonics through Science Ser.: 6). 32p. (J). 7.99 (978-1-933815-05-3(1) , Quirkles, The) Creative 3, LLC.

Cooke, Andrew, et al. Spectrum Year 7: Class Book. 2002. (Spectrum Key Stage 3 Science Ser.). (Illus.). 184p. pap. 12.95 (978-0-521-75004-2(0)) Cambridge Univ. Pr.

—Spectrum Year 8: Class Book. 2003. (Spectrum Key Stage 3 Science Ser.). (Illus.). 168p. pap. 12.95 (978-0-521-75007-3(5)) Cambridge Univ. Pr.

—Spectrum Year 9: Class Book. 2003. (Spectrum Key Stage 3 Science Ser.). (Illus.). 184p. pap. 13.50 (978-0-521-75010-3(5)) Cambridge Univ. Pr.

Cooper, Kay. Too Many Rabbits. Moffatt, Judith, illus. 2001. 48p. (J). (ps-3). pap. 5.99 (978-0-590-96748-8(7)) Scholastic, Inc.

Corals, 6 vols. (gr. k-2). 28.95 (978-0-7368-8255-2(3)) Red Brick Learning.

Corliss, William R. Scientific Anomalies & other Provocative Phenomena. 2003. (Illus.). 300p. (Orig.). (YA). (gr. 9-12). pap. 17.95 (978-0-915554-45-4(3)) Sourcebook Project, The.

Corrigan, Patricia. Bringing Science to Life: A Guide from the St. Louis Science Center. 2007. 128p. (J). pap. 16.00 (***978-1-933370-16-3(5)***) Reedy Pr.

Coupe, Robert. Attack & Defense. 2002. (Junior Adventure Ser.). (Illus.). 32p. (J). (gr. 3 up). lib. bdg. (978-1-59084-174-7(3)) Mason Crest Pubs.

—Every Body Tells a Story. 2002. (Junior Adventure Ser.). (Illus.). 32p. (J). (gr. 3 up). lib. bdg. (978-1-59084-188-4(3)) Mason Crest Pubs.

—Features & Flight. 2002. (Junior Adventure Ser.). (Illus.). 32p. (J). (gr. 3 up). lib. bdg. (978-1-59084-164-8(6)) Mason Crest Pubs.

—Sky Watch. 2002. (Junior Adventure Ser.). (Illus.). 32p. (J). (gr. 3 up). lib. bdg. (978-1-59084-171-6(9)) Mason Crest Pubs.

—Travelers & Traders. 2002. (Junior Adventure Ser.). (Illus.). 32p. (J). (gr. 3 up). lib. bdg. (978-1-59084-183-9(2)) Mason Crest Pubs.

—Up & Away. 2002. (Junior Adventure Ser.). (Illus.). 32p. (J). (gr. 3 up). lib. bdg. (978-1-59084-184-6(0)) Mason Crest Pubs.

Cover Your Bases. 2004. (YA). ring bd. (978-0-9747576-0-5(8)) Event-Based Science Institute, Inc.

Crafty Inventions. 2005. (C). (gr. 4-6). 319.20 (978-1-4048-1057-0(9)) Picture Window Bks.

Crochemore, Maxime & Gasieniec, Leszek, eds. Matching Patterns. 2001. 278p. (YA). pap. 89.00 (978-1-903398-07-4(X)) Hermes science pubns. FRA. *Dist:* International Specialized Bk. Services.

Cross-Curricular Projects Book: Student & Teacher Support Resources. 2000. (McGraw-Hill Science Ser.). (gr. 4 up). (978-0-02-277723-4(7)); (gr. 5 up). (978-0-02-277724-1(5)) Macmillan/McGraw-Hill Schl. Div.

Cuaderno Cientificos! 4, Vol. 4. (SPA.). (J). wbk. ed. 15.00 (978-958-04-5346-8(2)) Norma S.A. COL. *Dist:* Distribuidora Norma, Inc.

Cuaderno Cientificos! 5, Vol. 5. (SPA.). (J). wbk. ed. 15.00 (978-958-04-5347-5(0)) Norma S.A. COL. *Dist:* Distribuidora Norma, Inc.

Cuaderno Cientificos! 6, Vol. 6. (SPA.). (J). wbk. ed. 15.00 (978-958-04-5348-2(9)) Norma S.A. COL. *Dist:* Distribuidora Norma, Inc.

Cuaderno de actividades con clave de Respuestas: Student & Teacher Support Resources. 2000. (McGraw-Hill Ciencias Ser.). (ENG & SPA.). (gr. k-1). (978-0-02-279156-8(6)); (978-0-02-279868-0(4)) Macmillan/McGraw-Hill Schl. Div.

Cuaderno de evaluacion con clave de Respuestas: Assessment. 2000. (McGraw-Hill Ciencias Ser.). (ENG & SPA.). (gr. k up). (978-0-02-279157-5(4)); (gr. 1 up). (978-0-02-278626-7(0)); (gr. 2 up). (978-0-02-278637-3(6)); (gr. 3 up). (978-0-02-278648-9(1)); (gr. 4 up). (978-0-02-278659-5(7)); (gr. 5 up). (978-0-02-278670-0(8)) Macmillan/McGraw-Hill Schl. Div.

Cuaderno de Practica: Student & Teacher Support Resources. 2000. (McGraw-Hill Ciencias Ser.). (ENG & SPA.). (gr. 1 up). (978-0-02-277353-3(3)); (gr. 2 up). (978-0-02-277354-0(1)); (gr. 3 up). (978-0-02-277355-7(X)); (gr. 4 up). (978-0-02-277356-4(8)); (gr. 5 up). (978-0-02-277357-1(6)) Macmillan/McGraw-Hill Schl. Div.

Cuaderno de practica con clave de Respuestas: Student & Teacher Support Resources. 2000. (McGraw-Hill Ciencias Ser.). (ENG & SPA.). (gr. 1 up). (978-0-02-279028-8(4)); (gr. 2 up). (978-0-02-279029-5(2)); (gr. 3 up). (978-0-02-279031-8(4)); (gr. 4 up). (978-0-02-279032-5(2)); (gr. 5 up). (978-0-02-279033-2(0)) Macmillan/McGraw-Hill Schl. Div.

Cuando Zeke esta solo en Casa. 2000. (McGraw-Hill Ciencias Ser.). (ENG & SPA.). (gr. 2 up). (978-0-02-279608-2(8)) Macmillan/McGraw-Hill Schl. Div.

El cuerpo humano: como eres?: Cuaderno de Evaluacion: Unit 6: el cuerpo humano: como eres? (Human Body: Being You) 2000. (McGraw-Hill Ciencias Ser.). (ENG & SPA.). (gr. 1 up). (978-0-02-278632-8(5)) Macmillan/McGraw-Hill Schl. Div.

El cuerpo humano: como eres?: Recursos para el maestro con clave de Respuestas: Unit 6: el cuerpo humano: como eres? (Human Body: Being You) 2000. (McGraw-Hill Ciencias Ser.). (ENG & SPA.). (gr. 1 up). (978-0-02-278683-0(X)) Macmillan/McGraw-Hill Schl. Div.

El cuerpo humano: corazon y pulmones: Cuaderno de Evaluacion: Unit 6: el cuerpo humano: corazon y pulmones (Human Body: Heart & Lungs) 2000. (McGraw-Hill Ciencias Ser.). (ENG & SPA.). (gr. 2 up). (978-0-02-278643-4(0)) Macmillan/McGraw-Hill Schl. Div.

El cuerpo humano: corazon y pulmones: Recursos para el maestro con clave de Respuestas: Unit 6: el cuerpo humano: corazon y pulmones (Human Body: Heart & Lungs) 2000. (McGraw-Hill Ciencias Ser.). (ENG & SPA.). (gr. 2 up). (978-0-02-278690-8(2)) Macmillan/McGraw-Hill Schl. Div.

El cuerpo humano: su movimiento: Cuaderno de Evaluacion: Unit 7: el cuerpo humano: su movimiento (Human Body: A Body in Motion) 2000. (McGraw-Hill Ciencias Ser.). (ENG & SPA.). (gr. 4 up). (978-0-02-278732-5(1)) Macmillan/McGraw-Hill Schl. Div.

El cuerpo humano: su movimiento: Recursos para el maestro con clave de Respuestas: Unit 7: el cuerpo humano: su movimiento (Human Body: A Body in Motion) 2000. (McGraw-Hill Ciencias Ser.). (ENG & SPA.). (gr. 4 up). (978-0-02-278731-8(3)) Macmillan/McGraw-Hill Schl. Div.

El cuerpo humano: sus sistemas: Cuaderno de Evaluacion: Unit 7: el cuerpo humano: sus sistemas (Human Body: Pathways) 2000. (McGraw-Hill Ciencias Ser.). (ENG & SPA.). (gr. 5 up). (978-0-02-278735-6(6)) Macmillan/McGraw-Hill Schl. Div.

El cuerpo humano: sus sistemas: Recursos para el maestro con clave de Respuestas: Unit 7: el cuerpo humano: sus sistemas (Human Body: Pathways) 2000. (McGraw-Hill Ciencias Ser.). (ENG & SPA.). (gr. 5 up). (978-0-02-278734-9(8)) Macmillan/McGraw-Hill Schl. Div.

Cullen, David. Big Book of Science. Leeks, David, illus. 2004. 48p. (J). 7.99 (978-1-85854-532-5(3)) Brimax Books Ltd. GBR. *Dist:* Byeway Bks.

Cut & Paste: Science. 2003. pap. 11.99 (978-0-7439-3706-1(6)) Teacher Created Materials, Inc.

Cutting Machines, 6 vols. (Sunshinetm Science Ser.). 24p. (gr. 1-2). 31.50 (978-0-7802-0302-0(X)); 36.95 (978-0-7802-0553-6(7)) Wright Group, The.

Daily Problems & Weekly Puzzlers-Science. 64p. (gr. 1 up). 7.99 (978-1-56451-290-1(8) , ID5941); (gr. 2 up). 7.99 (978-1-56451-291-8(6) , ID5942); (gr. 3 up). 7.99 (978-1-56451-272-7(X) , ID5943); (gr. 4 up). 7.99 (978-1-56451-273-4(8) , ID5944); (gr. 5 up). 7.99 (978-1-56451-274-1(6) , ID5945); (gr. 6 up). 7.99 (978-1-56451-275-8(4) , ID5946) School Specialty Publishing.

The Dairy Group, 6 vols. (gr. k-2). 28.95 (978-0-7368-8748-9(2)) Red Brick Learning.

Dalgleish, Sharon. Bright Ideas. 2002. (Junior Adventure Ser.). (Illus.). 32p. (J). (gr. 3 up). lib. bdg. (978-1-59084-162-4(X)) Mason Crest Pubs.

—Hidden World. 2002. (Junior Adventure Ser.). (Illus.). 32p. (J). (gr. 3 up). lib. bdg. (978-1-59084-190-7(5)) Mason Crest Pubs.

—How Things Work. 2002. (Junior Adventure Ser.). (Illus.). 32p. (J). (gr. 3 up). lib. bdg. (978-1-59084-192-1(1)) Mason Crest Pubs.

—Out & About. 2002. (Junior Adventure Ser.). (Illus.). 32p. (J). (gr. 3 up). lib. bdg. (978-1-59084-178-5(6)) Mason Crest Pubs.

—Out & About. 1999. (Explorers Ser.). (Illus.). 32p. (J). (978-0-7699-0484-9(X)) Shortland Pubns. (U. S. A.) Inc.

—Sharks & Rays. 2002. (Junior Adventure Ser.). (Illus.). 32p. (J). (gr. 3 up). lib. bdg. (978-1-59084-170-9(0)) Mason Crest Pubs.

Daronco, Mickey & Ohanesian, Diane. A Sight to See. 2nd rev. ed. 2003. (BuildUp Ser.). (J). pap. 22.00 (978-1-4108-0762-5(2)) Benchmark Education Co.

DataWonder! Science. 2000. (SPA.). (gr. k-6). 39.00 (978-0-201-65888-0(7)) Addison-Wesley Educational Pubs., Inc.

Davidson, Avelyn. Dollars & Sense: Economics & Science. (Shockwave: Economics & Geography Ser.). (J). 2008. 32p. pap. 6.95 ***978-0-531-18836-1(1));** 2007. (Illus.). 36p. (gr. 4-6). lib. bdg. 25.00 ***978-0-531-17750-1(5))** Scholastic Library Publishing. (Children's Pr.).

Davidson, Gary, des. Mesozoic & Cenozoic, 2 vols. 2004. (Time Line Companion Bks.). (Illus.). (J). per. 8.50 (978-0-9745560-1-7(7)) Azoka Co., The.

—Paleozoic Era, 2 vols. 2004. (Time Line Companion Bks.). (Illus.). 65p. (J). per. (978-0-9745560-0-0(9)) Azoka Co., The.

Day Two PSAE Student Textbook. 3rd ed. 2005. per. (978-1-58894-035-3(7)) Cambridge Educational Services, Inc.

Days We Celebrate, 6 vols. (Book2WebTM Ser.). (gr. 4-8). 36.50 (978-0-322-02846-3(9)) Wright Group, The.

de Panafieu, Jean Baptiste & Desplanche, Vincent. Charles Darwin. Gonzalez Batlle, Jorge, tr. 2007. (Tras los pasos de ... Ser.). (SPA., Illus.). 128p. (J). pap. 14.95 (978-84-89396-83-8(3)) Blume ESP. *Dist:* Independent Pubs. Group.

De Waard, Nancy & De Waard, E. John. Science Challenge: 190 Fun & Creative Brainteasers for Kids. 2005. (Illus.). 192p. (J). (ps-k). Level 1. pap. (978-1-59647-067-5(4) , EAS002); Level 2. pap. (978-1-59647-068-2(2) , EAS002) Good Year Bks.

Density. 2001. (Physical Science Ser.). (J). (gr. k-12). vinyl bd. 4.95 (978-1-58845-126-2(7)) School Specialty Publishing.

El desastre del bizcochuelo Blanco: Leveled Books. 2000. (McGraw-Hill Ciencias Ser.). (ENG & SPA.). (gr. 4 up). (978-0-02-279660-0(6)) Macmillan/McGraw-Hill Schl. Div.

El dia que me Cai. 2000. (McGraw-Hill Ciencias Ser.). (ENG & SPA.). (gr. 1 up). (978-0-02-279561-0(8)) Macmillan/McGraw-Hill Schl. Div.

Diagram Group. Science Diagrams on File Set. 2005. (Diagrams Ser.). 580p. (gr. 9-12). ring bd. 1810.00 (978-0-8160-6427-4(X)) Facts On File, Inc.

—Science Visual Resources Set. 2006. (Science Visual Resources Ser.). 208p. (gr. 6-12). 396.00 (978-0-8160-6161-7(0)) Facts On File, Inc.

Diagram Group, contrib. by. Forensic Science Experiments on File. 2004. (Experiments Ser.). 288p. (J). (gr. 6-12). 185.00 (978-0-8160-5106-9(2)) Facts On File, Inc.

Diakanastasis, Maria, et al. Cambridge Senior Hospitality. 2006. pap. 36.75 (978-0-521-68933-5(3)) Cambridge Univ. Pr.

Diario Cientifico: Student & Teacher Support Resources. 2000. (McGraw-Hill Ciencias Ser.). (ENG & SPA.). (gr. 1 up). (978-0-02-278623-6(6)); (gr. 2 up). (978-0-02-278634-2(1)); (gr. 3 up). (978-0-02-278645-8(7)); (gr. 4 up). (978-0-02-278656-4(2)); (gr. 5 up). (978-0-02-278667-0(8)) Macmillan/McGraw-Hill Schl. Div.

Diario cientifico con clave de Respuestas: Student & Teacher Support Resources. 2000. (McGraw-Hill Ciencias Ser.). (ENG & SPA.). (gr. 1 up). (978-0-02-279035-6(7)); (gr. 2 up). (978-0-02-279036-3(5)); (gr. 3 up). (978-0-02-279037-0(3)); (gr. 4 up). (978-0-02-279038-7(1)); (gr. 5 up). (978-0-02-279039-4(X)) Macmillan/McGraw-Hill Schl. Div.

Un Dibujo. 2000. (McGraw-Hill Ciencias Ser.). (ENG & SPA.). (gr. k up). (978-0-02-279702-7(5)) Macmillan/McGraw-Hill Schl. Div.

Different Kinds of Bread: 6 Each of 1 Student Book, 6 vols. (Sunshinetm Science Ser.). 24p. (gr. 1-2). 41.95 (978-0-7802-2726-2(3)) Wright Group, The.

Different Kinds of Bread: Big Book. (Sunshinetm Science Ser.). 24p. (gr. 1-2). 37.50 (978-0-7802-2797-2(2)) Wright Group, The.

The Digestive System, 6 vols. (gr. k-2). 28.95 (978-0-7368-8801-1(2)) Red Brick Learning.

Dino-Mite! 2003. (Science Card Games Ser.). (gr. 2-3). 9.99 (978-0-7682-1977-7(9) , J53005) School Specialty Publishing.

Discover Series: Science, Nature, Wildlife, 11 bks. (Illus.). (J). (gr. 3-6). lib. bdg. 175.45 (978-1-56674-935-0(2)) Forest Hse. Publishing Co., Inc.

Discovering Science: Includes: Electricity & Magnetism; Energy; Hot & Cold; Light & Dark; Matter; Sound, 6 bks., Set. 2000. (Illus.). (J). (gr. 3-5). 154.14 (978-0-7398-2975-2(0)) Raintree.

Discovery Channel & Staff. Gluttons. 2004. (Planet's Most Extreme Ser.). (Illus.). 48p. (J). (gr. 4-7). 24.95 (978-1-4103-0378-3(0) , Blackbirch Pr., Inc.) Thomson Gale.

—Jumpers. 2004. (Planet's Most Extreme Ser.). (Illus.). 48p. (J). (gr. 4-7). 24.95 (978-1-4103-0377-6(2) , Blackbirch Pr., Inc.) Thomson Gale.

Discovery Channel School Science: Sets I, II, III, IV, 40 bks. Incl. Bacteria. 2003. lib. bdg. 24.67 (978-0-8368-3366-9(X)); Birds. Gareth Stevens Publishing Staff, contrib. by. 2002. lib. bdg. 24.67 (978-0-8368-3210-5(8)); Cells. Lewin, Benjamin, ed. 2003. lib. bdg. 24.67 (978-0-8368-3367-6(8)); Chemistry. Gareth Stevens Publishing Staff, contrib. by. 2003. lib. bdg. 24.67 (978-0-8368-3355-3(4)); Conservation & Natural Resources. Ball, Jackie. 2004. lib. bdg. 24.67 (978-0-8368-3377-5(5)); Earthquakes. Ball, Jackie. 2004. lib. bdg. 24.67 (978-0-8368-3378-2(3)); Earth's History. Ball, Jackie. 2004. lib. bdg. 24.67 (978-0-8368-3379-9(1)); Ecology. Ball, Jackie. 2004. lib. bdg. 24.67 (978-0-8368-3380-5(5)); Electricity. Gareth Stevens Publishing Staff, contrib. by. 2003. lib. bdg. 24.67 (978-0-8368-3356-0(2)); Elements. Gareth Stevens Publishing Staff, contrib. by. 2003. lib. bdg. 24.67 (978-0-8368-3357-7(0)); Evolution. Gareth Stevens Publishing Staff, contrib. by. 2002. lib. bdg. 24.67 (978-0-8368-3211-2(6)); Fish & Amphibians. Gareth Stevens Publishing Staff, contrib. by. 2002. lib. bdg. 24.67 (978-0-8368-3212-9(4)); Forces & Gravity. Gareth Stevens Publishing Staff, contrib. by. 2003. lib. bdg. 24.67 (978-0-8368-3368-3(6)); Forensics. Gareth Stevens Publishing Staff, contrib. by. 2003. lib. bdg. 24.67 (978-0-8368-3369-0(4)); Genetics. Gareth Stevens Publishing Staff, contrib. by. 2003. lib. bdg. 24.67 (978-0-8368-3370-6(8)); Health. Gareth Stevens Publishing Staff, contrib. by. 2002. lib. bdg. 24.67 (978-0-8368-3213-6(2)); Heat. Gareth Stevens Publishing Staff, contrib. by. 2003. lib. bdg. 24.67 (978-0-8368-3358-4(9)); Human Biology. Gareth Stevens Publishing Staff, contrib. by. 2002. lib. bdg. 24.67 (978-0-8368-3214-3(0)); Insects. Gareth Stevens Publishing Staff, contrib. by. 2002. lib. bdg. 24.67 (978-0-8368-3215-0(9)); Invertebrates. Gareth Stevens Publishing Staff, contrib. by. 2002. lib. bdg. 24.67 (978-0-8368-3216-7(7)); Land & Water. Burgan, Michael. 2004. lib. bdg. 24.67 (978-0-8368-3381-2(3)); Light. Gareth Stevens Publishing Staff, contrib. by. 2003. lib. bdg. 24.67 (978-0-8368-3359-1(7)); Magnetism. Gareth Stevens Publishing Staff, contrib. by. 2003. lib. bdg. 24.67 (978-0-8368-3360-7(0)); Mammals. Gareth Stevens Publishing Staff, contrib. by. 2002. lib. bdg. 24.67 (978-0-8368-3217-4(5)); Mapping Earth. Ball, Jackie. 2004. lib. bdg. 24.67 (978-0-8368-3382-9(1)); Matter. Gareth Stevens Publishing Staff, contrib. by. 2003. lib. bdg. 24.67 (978-0-8368-3361-4(9)); Nuclear Energy. Gareth Stevens Publishing Staff, contrib. by. 2003. lib. bdg. 24.67 (978-0-8368-3362-1(7)); Oceans. 2004. lib. bdg. 24.67 (978-0-8368-3383-6(X)); Plants. Gareth Stevens Publishing Staff, contrib. by. 2002. lib. bdg. 24.67 (978-0-8368-3218-1(3)); Protists & Fungi. Gareth Stevens Publishing Staff, contrib. by. 2003. lib. bdg. 24.67 (978-0-8368-3371-3(6)); Reptiles. Gareth Stevens Publishing Staff, contrib. by. 2002. lib. bdg. 24.67 (978-0-8368-3219-8(1)); Rocks & Minerals. Prokos, Anna. 2004. lib. bdg. 24.67 (978-0-8368-3384-3(8)); Solar System. Gareth Stevens Publishing Staff, contrib. by. 2003. lib. bdg. 24.67 (978-0-8368-3372-0(4)); Sound. Gareth Stevens Publishing Staff, contrib. by. 2003. lib. bdg. 24.67 (978-0-8368-3363-8(5)); Space Exploration. Gareth Stevens Publishing Staff, contrib. by. 2003. lib. bdg. 24.67 (978-0-8368-3373-7(2)); Structures. Gareth Stevens Publishing Staff, contrib. by. 2003. lib. bdg. 24.67 (978-0-8368-3364-5(3)); Universe. Gareth Stevens Publishing Staff, contrib. by. 2003. lib. bdg. 24.67 (978-0-8368-3374-4(0)); Viruses. Gareth Stevens Publishing Staff, contrib. by. 2003. lib. bdg. 24.67 (978-0-8368-3375-1(9)); Volcanoes. 2004. lib. bdg. 24.67 (978-0-8368-3385-0(6)); Weather & Climate Change. Howell, Laura. 2004. lib. bdg. 24.67 (978-0-8368-3386-7(4)); 32p. (J). (gr. 5 up). (Illus.). 2004. Set lib. bdg. 986.80 (978-0-8368-4166-4(2)) Stevens, Gareth Inc.

Discovery Channel School Science Set 2: Physical Science, 10 bks. 2002. (Illus.). (J). (gr. 5 up). lib. bdg. 246.70 (978-0-8368-3354-6(6)) Stevens, Gareth Inc.

Discovery Channel School Science Set 4: Our Planet Earth, 10 bks. 2004. (Illus.). (J). (gr. 5 up). lib. bdg. 246.70 (978-0-8368-3376-8(7)) Stevens, Gareth Inc.

Dobson. Holt Science Spectacular: Physical Science. 6th ed. 2006. stu. ed. 79.33 (978-0-03-039093-7(1)) Harcourt Schl. Pubs.

Doherty, Edith J. S. SMILE Science: Scientific Method Integrated Learning Experience. 2000. 90p. (J). spiral bd. 16.95 (978-0-945984-99-3(5) , Zephyr Pr.) Chicago Review Pr., Inc.

Los domingos por la Manana. 2000. (McGraw-Hill Ciencias Ser.). (ENG & SPA.). (gr. 2 up). (978-0-02-279620-4(7)) Macmillan/McGraw-Hill Schl. Div.

Donde viven los seres vivos?: Cuaderno de Evaluacion: Unit 6: Donde viven los seres vivos? (Living Things Live) 2000. (McGraw-Hill Ciencias Ser.). (ENG & SPA.). (gr. 3 up). (978-0-02-278654-0(6)) Macmillan/McGraw-Hill Schl. Div.

Donde viven los seres vivos?: Recursos para el maestro con clave de Respuestas: Unit 6: Donde viven los seres vivos? (Living Things Live) 2000. (McGraw-Hill Ciencias Ser.). (ENG & SPA.). (gr. 3 up). (978-0-02-278697-7(X)) Macmillan/McGraw-Hill Schl. Div.

Dorling Kindersley Publishing Staff. Big Book of Knowledge. 2002. (Illus.). 480p. (J). (gr. 4-7). pap. 17.99 (978-0-7894-8501-4(X)) Dorling Kindersley Publishing, Inc.

—Big Book of Knowledge. 2002. (gr. 3-6). lib. bdg. 28.05 (978-0-613-75146-9(9)) Tandem Library Bks.

—Cool Stuff Science Kit. 2007. 32p. (J). (gr. 5). pap. 19.99 (978-0-7566-2219-0(0)) Dorling Kindersley Publishing, Inc.

—DK Science Kit. 2002. 1p. (J). (gr. 3-12). 29.99 (978-0-7894-8866-4(3)) Dorling Kindersley Publishing, Inc.

—Science Encyclopedia. 2nd ed. 2003. (Pockets Ser.). (Illus.). 512p. (J). pap. 12.99 (978-0-7894-9602-7(X)) Dorling Kindersley Publishing, Inc.

Dotlich, Rebecca Kai. What Is Science? Yoshikawa, Sachiko, illus. rev. ed. 2006. 32p. (J). 16.95 (978-0-8050-7394-2(9) , Holt, Henry & Co. Bks. For Young Readers) Holt, Henry & Co.

Doudna, Kelly. It's My Mission to Make a Definition! (Illus.). 24p. (J). 2007. 19.93 (978-1-59928-600-6(9)); 2006. (978-1-59928-601-3(7)) ABDO Publishing Co.

Douglas, Kathy M. Simple Centers. 1999. 240p. (J). (gr. k up). pap. 16.99 (978-1-56822-305-6(6) , IF8666) School Specialty Publishing.

Douglas, Vincent. Daily Learning Drills: Grade 4. 2003. (Daily Learning Drills Ser.). (Illus.). 416p. (J). (gr. 4-4). pap., wbk. ed. 10.95 (978-0-7696-3094-6(4) , American Education Publishing) School Specialty Publishing.

—Daily Learning Drills: Grade 5. 2003. (Daily Learning Drills Ser.). (Illus.). 416p. (J). (gr. 5-5). pap., wbk. ed. 10.95 (978-0-7696-3095-3(2) , American Education Publishing) School Specialty Publishing.

—Daily Learning Drills: Grade 6. 2003. (Daily Learning Drills Ser.). (Illus.). 416p. (J). (gr. 6-6). pap. 10.95 (978-0-7696-3096-0(0) , Brighter Child) School Specialty Publishing.

—Science And Social Studies Fun Fact Cards. 2004. (Flash Card Collection). 324p. (C). 16.95 (978-1-58845-664-9(1)) School Specialty Publishing.

Douglas, Vincent & School Specialty Publishing Staff. The Complete Book of Science, Grades 5-6. 2005. (Complete Book Ser.). (Illus.). 352p. (J). pap. 14.95 (978-0-7696-3945-1(3) , American Education Publishing) School Specialty Publishing.

—Science Fact Book. 2003. (Notebook Reference Ser.). (Illus.). 128p. (J). (gr. 4-8). pap. 4.95 (978-1-57768-966-9(6)) School Specialty Publishing.

—Science Fact Book. Notebk Referenc, ed. 2nd rev. ed. 2006. (Notebook Reference Ser.). 144p. (J). pap. 3.95 (978-0-7696-4346-5(9) , American Education Publishing) School Specialty Publishing.

—Science, Grade 3. 2004. (Illus.). 40p. (J). pap. 2.99 (978-0-7696-3853-9(8) , Brighter Child) School Specialty Publishing.

—Science, Grade 4. 2004. (Illus.). 40p. (J). pap. 2.99 (978-0-7696-3854-6(6) , Brighter Child) School Specialty Publishing.

—Science, Grade 5. 2004. (Illus.). 40p. (J). pap. 2.99 (978-0-7696-3855-3(4) , Brighter Child) School Specialty Publishing.

—Science, Grade 6. 2004. (Illus.). 40p. (J). pap. 2.99 (978-0-7696-3856-0(2) , Brighter Child) School Specialty Publishing.

—Tell Me about Science & Technology. 2004. (Tell Me Ser.). (Illus.). 224p. (J). pap. 14.95 (978-0-7696-3382-4(X) , Waterbird Bks.) School Specialty Publishing.

Drew, David. All Sorts of Things. Harradine, Dona, tr. Falla, Dominique, illus. 1999. (Hello! Lote Ser.). (IND.). 17p. (J). pap. 29.99 (978-0-7339-0874-3(8)); pap. 5.99 (978-0-7339-0875-0(6)) Pearson Education Australia AUS. *Dist:* Cheng & Tsui Co.

—All Sorts of Things. Batt, Deleece, tr. Falla, Dominique, illus. 1999. (Hello! Lote Ser.). (JPN.). 17p. (J). pap. 29.99 (978-0-7339-0873-6(X)); pap. 5.99 (978-0-7339-0890-3(X)) Pearson Education Australia AUS. *Dist:* Cheng & Tsui Co.

Drohan, Michele Ingber & Levchuck, Caroline M. Environment. 2001. (It's All about! Ser.). (Illus.). 32p. (J). (gr. 2-5). lib. bdg. 25.27 (978-1-58952-160-5(9)) Rourke Publishing, LLC.

DynaNotes Grade 8 Science TAKS Review Guide. 2006. (YA). pap. (978-1-933854-28-1(6)) DynaStudy, Inc.

DynaNotes Grade 8 Science TAKS Review Guide Transparency Set. 2006. (YA). trans. (978-1-933854-32-8(4)) DynaStudy, Inc.

DynaNotes Laboratory Review Guide. 2007. (J). pap. ***978-1-933854-61-8(8))** DynaStudy, Inc.

DynaNotes Laboratory Review Guide Transparency Set. 2007. (J). trans. ***978-1-933854-69-4(3))** DynaStudy, Inc.

DynaNotes Mass Transparency Set. 2007. (J). trans. ***978-1-933854-53-3(7))** DynaStudy, Inc.

Early Fluency Set 2: 1 Each of 8 Big Books. (Sunshinetm Science Ser.). (gr. 1-2). 296.50 (978-0-7802-1764-5(0)) Wright Group, The.

Early Fluency Set 2: 1 Each of 8 Big Books, 1 Each of 8 Student Books, 1 Teacher Guide, & 1 Duplicate Masters Book. (Sunshinetm Science Ser.). (gr. 1-2). 391.50 (978-0-7802-1763-8(2)) Wright Group, The.

Early Fluency Set 2: 1 Each of 8 Student Books. (Sunshinetm Science Ser.). (gr. 1-2). 55.95 (978-0-7802-1765-2(9)) Wright Group, The.

Early Fluency Set 3. (Sunshinetm Science Ser.). (gr. 1-2). 296.50 (978-0-7802-1767-6(5)) Wright Group, The.

Early Fluency Set 3: 1 Each of Student Books. (Sunshinetm Science Ser.). (gr. 1-2). 55.95 (978-0-7802-1768-3(3)) Wright Group, The.

Early Fluency Set 4: 1 Each of 8 Big Books. (Sunshinetm Science Ser.). (gr. 1-2). 296.50 (978-0-7802-2800-9(6)) Wright Group, The.

Early Fluency Set 4: 1 Each of 8 Student Books. (Sunshinetm Science Ser.). (gr. 1-2). 55.96 (978-0-7802-2801-6(4)) Wright Group, The.

Early Fluency Set 5: 1 Each of 8 Big Books. (Sunshinetm Science Ser.). (gr. 1-2). 296.50 (978-0-7802-2803-0(0)) Wright Group, The.

Early Fluency Set 5: 1 Each of 8 Student Books. (Sunshinetm Science Ser.). (gr. 1-2). 55.95 (978-0-7802-2804-7(9)) Wright Group, The.

Early Fluency Set 6: 1 Each of 8 Big Books. (Sunshinetm Science Ser.). (gr. 1-2). 296.50 (978-0-7802-2806-1(5)) Wright Group, The.

Early Fluency Set 6: 1 Each of 8 Big Books, 1 Each of 8 Student Books, 1 Teacher Guide, & 1 Duplicate Master Book. (Sunshinetm Science Ser.). (gr. 1-2). 391.50 (978-0-7802-2805-4(7)) Wright Group, The.

Early Fluency Set 6: 1 Each of 8 Student Books. (Sunshinetm Science Ser.). (gr. 1-2). 55.95 (978-0-7802-2807-8(3)) Wright Group, The.

Early Science Package. 2005. (Emergent/Early (Prek-2) Science Package Ser.). (YA). (ps-2). 126.00 (978-0-8215-7861-2(8)) Sadlier, William H. Inc.

Earth & Space Classroom Library. (gr. k-2). lib. bdg. 54.95 (978-0-7368-3284-7(X)) Red Brick Learning.

Earth & Space Complete Unit. (gr. k-2). 311.95 (978-0-7368-3283-0(1)) Red Brick Learning.

Eating Well Science, 6 vols. (gr. k-2). 28.95 (978-0-7368-3014-0(6) , Yellow Umbrella Bks.) Capstone Pr., Inc.

Eberle, Laura. Rats, Bulls, & Flying Machines. Davis, Matthew, ed. 2001. 39p. instr.'s gde. ed. (978-1-890517-49-6(6)) Core Knowledge Foundation.

Echols, Jean C., et al. Eggs Eggs Everywhere. Bergman, Lincoln et al, eds. Baker, Lisa H. et al, illus. Hoyt, Richard, photos by. rev. ed. 1998. (Great Explorations in Math & Science Ser.). 84p. (J). (ps-1). pap. 13.50 (978-0-924886-13-3(7) , GEMS) Univ. of California, Berkeley, Lawrence Hall of Science.

Ehlke, Paul. Clouds: Science Information in American Sign Language: A Paws Science Adventure. 2003. (J). cd-rom 29.95 (978-0-9752933-2-4(X)) Institute for Disabilities Research & Training, Inc.

Ehrlich, Robert. What If? Mind-Boggling Science Questions for Kids. 1998. (Illus.). 192p. (gr. 3-7). pap. 13.95 (978-0-471-17608-4(7) , Jossey-Bass) Wiley, John & Sons, Inc.

Elementary Science. 2004. 2. 444.00 (978-0-531-14701-6(0)); 3. 895.00 (978-0-531-12329-4(4)) Scholastic Library Publishing.

The Elements - Group 3, 4 bks., Set. Incl. Aluminum. Farndon, John. lib. bdg. 25.64 (978-0-7614-0947-2(5)); Copper. Beatty, Richard. lib. bdg. 25.64 (978-0-7614-0945-8(9)); Phosphorus. Beatty, Richard. lib. bdg. 25.64 (978-0-7614-0946-5(7)); Sulfur. Beatty, Richard. lib. bdg. 25.64 (978-0-7614-0948-9(3)); 32p. (J). (gr. 3-5). (Illus.). 2000. Set lib. bdg. 102.57 (978-0-7614-0944-1(0) , Benchmark Bks.) Cavendish, Marshall Corp.

Emergent Science Package. 2005. (Emergent/Early (Prek-2) Science Package Ser.). (YA). (ps-2). 135.00 (978-0-8215-7877-3(4)) Sadlier, William H. Inc.

Emergent Set: 1 Each of 8 Student Books. (Sunshinetm Science Ser.). (gr. 1-2). 48.95 (978-0-7802-0568-0(5)) Wright Group, The.

Emergent Set: 1 Each of Student Books, Vol. 2. (Sunshinetm Science Ser.). (gr. 1-2). 48.95 (978-0-7802-0570-3(7)) Wright Group, The.

Emergent/Early Science Package. 2005. (YA). (ps-2). 243.00 (978-0-8215-7887-2(1)) Sadlier, William H. Inc.

Empujar y halar Science, 6 vols.Tr. of Push & Pull Science. (SPA.). (gr. k-2). 28.95 (978-0-7368-3034-8(0) , Yellow Umbrella Bks.) Capstone Pr., Inc.

En movimiento!: Cuaderno de Evaluacion: Unit 4: en movimiento! (on the Move) 2000. (McGraw-Hill Ciencias Ser.). (ENG & SPA.). (gr. 1 up). (978-0-02-278630-4(9)) Macmillan/McGraw-Hill Schl. Div.

Enciclopedia Ilustrada de Ciencia Naturaleza (Understanding Science & Nature), 16 bks. Incl. Comportamiento de los Animales (Animal Behavior) 17.95 (978-0-7835-3358-2(6)); Cuerpo Humano (Human Body) 17.95 (978-0-7835-3350-6(0)); Era de la Computadora. 17.95 (978-0-7835-3375-9(6)); Espacio y Planetas. 17.95 (978-0-7835-3370-4(5)); Estructura de la Materia (Structure of Matter) 17.95 (978-0-7835-3383-4(7)); Evolucion de la Vida. 17.95 (978-0-7835-3354-4(3)); Fuerzas Fisicas (Physical Forces) 17.95 (978-0-7835-3395-7(0)); Geografia. 17.95 (978-0-7835-3387-2(X)); Insectos y Aranas. 17.95 (978-0-7835-3398-8(5)); Maquinas e Inventos (Machines & Inventions) 17.95 (978-0-7835-3400-8(0)); Mundo Submarino (Underwater World) 17.95 (978-0-7835-3397-1(7)); Planeta Tierra (Planet Earth) 17.95 (978-0-7835-3396-4(9)); Plantas (Plant Life) 17.95 (978-0-7835-3399-5(3)); Tiempo y Clima (Weather & Climate) 17.95 (978-0-7835-3366-7(7)); Transporte y la Navegacion (Transportation) 17.95 (978-0-7835-3379-7(9)); 152p. (YA). (gr. 6 up). 1996. (Illus.). Set lib. bdg. 319.20 (978-0-7835-3391-9(8)) Time-Life, Inc.

Energy Chain: Individual Title Six-Packs. (Bookweb Ser.). 32p. (gr. 4 up). 34.00 (978-0-7635-3744-9(6)) Rigby Education.

England, Nicholas M., et al. Science Matters Year 9. 1998. 302p. pap. 20.25 (978-0-7336-0724-0(1)) Cambridge Univ. Pr.

England, Nick, et al. Science Matters Year 10. 1998. 256p. pap. 20.25 (978-0-7336-0726-4(8)) Cambridge Univ. Pr.

Englehart, Deirdre. Magnets. 2000. (Inquiry Science Ser.). 32p. (J). (gr. 2-3). pap. 4.99 (978-1-56822-948-5(8) , IF20855) School Specialty Publishing.

—Write about Physical Science: The Test Connection. 2003. (Write about Science Ser.). 64p. (J). (gr. 3-5). pap. 9.99 (978-0-7424-1918-6(5) , FS99243, Schaffer, Frank) Schaffer, Frank Pubns.

Un equipo Ganador. 2000. (McGraw-Hill Ciencias Ser.). (ENG & SPA.). (gr. 2 up). (978-0-02-279624-2(X)) Macmillan/McGraw-Hill Schl. Div.

Equipo Staff. 1000 Preguntas y Respuestas. (SPA., Illus.). 96p. (J). (gr. 3-5). (978-84-305-8671-4(7) , SU2565) Susaeta Ediciones, S.A. ESP. *Dist:* Lectorum Pubns., Inc.

Es una emergencia! Vamos al Hospital! Leveled Books. 2000. (McGraw-Hill Ciencias Ser.). (ENG & SPA.). (gr. 4 up). (978-0-02-279656-3(8)) Macmillan/McGraw-Hill Schl. Div.

Esbensen, Barbara Juster. Sponges Are Skeletons, Stage 2. 1998. (Let's-Read-and-Find-Out Science Ser.). (978-0-606-13796-6(3)) Tandem Library Bks.

Essential Words Science Glossary (Intermediate) Intermediate/Middle School. 2005. (Illus.). 98p. (J). per. 19.95 (978-0-9764217-3-3(9)) New Leaf Educ., Inc.

Essential Words Science(Intermediate) Intermediate/Middle School. 2005. (Illus.). 37p. (J). 8.95 (978-0-9764217-2-6(0)) New Leaf Educ., Inc.

Esta Viva! Leveled Books. 2000. (McGraw-Hill Ciencias Ser.). (ENG & SPA.). (gr. 4 up). (978-0-02-279646-4(0)) Macmillan/McGraw-Hill Schl. Div.

El estanque: Cuaderno de Evaluacion: Unit 5: el estanque (A Pond) 2000. (McGraw-Hill Ciencias Ser.). (ENG & SPA.). (gr. 1 up). (978-0-02-278631-1(7)) Macmillan/McGraw-Hill Schl. Div.

El estanque: Recursos para el maestro con clave de Respuestas: Unit 5: el estanque (A Pond) 2000. (McGraw-Hill Ciencias Ser.). (ENG & SPA.). (gr. 1 up). (978-0-02-278682-3(1)) Macmillan/McGraw-Hill Schl. Div.

Evans, David & Williams, Claudette. Make It Change. (Let's Explore Science Ser.). (Illus.). (J). 12.95 (978-0-590-74511-6(5)) Scholastic, Inc.

Everyday Science. 2000. (Finditquick Ser.). (Illus.). 32p. (J). pap. 6.99 (978-0-307-10540-0(7) , Golden Bks.) Random Hse. Children's Bks.

Everyday Science New Releases: Animals, Habitats, Health, Life Cycles, Movement, Plants, Seasons, Senses, 8 bks. 2003. (Illus.). (J). (gr. 1 up). lib. bdg. 180.80 (978-0-8368-3712-4(6)) Stevens, Gareth Inc.

Everything Is Matter! Science, 6 vols. (gr. k-2). 28.95 (978-0-7368-3019-5(7) , Yellow Umbrella Bks.) Capstone Pr., Inc.

Exploring Science, 8 titles, Set. 2005. lib. bdg. 202.16 (978-0-7565-1398-6(7)) Compass Point Bks.

Fabrica de Sonidos. 2000. (McGraw-Hill Ciencias Ser.). (ENG & SPA.). (gr. 5 up). (978-0-02-279669-3(X)) Macmillan/McGraw-Hill Schl. Div.

Facts on File, Inc. Staff, ed. Science in Focus, 6 Vols., Set. 2006. (Science in Focus Ser.). 48p. 162.00 (978-0-7910-9444-0(8) , Chelsea Clubhouse) Facts On File, Inc.

The Facts on File Science Handbook Set. 2003. (Science Handbook Ser.). (gr. 6-12). 350.00 (978-0-8160-4930-1(0)) Facts On File, Inc.

Falk, John H. & Rosenberg, Kristi S. Bite-Sized Science: Activities for Children in 15 Minutes or Less. Matthews, Bonnie, illus. 1999. 128p. (J). pap. 14.95 (978-1-55652-348-9(3)) Chicago Review Pr., Inc.

Farndon, John & Adams, Simon. Science & Technology. 2004. (History Detectives Ser.). (Illus.). 64p. pap. 7.99 (978-1-84215-898-2(8) , Southwater) Anness Publishing GBR. *Dist:* National Bk. Network.

Fast & Faster! Science, 6 vols. (gr. k-2). 28.95 (978-0-7368-1746-2(8) , Yellow Umbrella Bks.) Capstone Pr., Inc.

Faucets & Water Sets: 1 Each of 3 Student Books. (Sunshinetm Science Ser.). (gr. 1-2). 20.95 (978-0-7802-2815-3(4)) Wright Group, The.

Fiero, Alex & Wagner, Joan. Science: Big 8 Review. Garnsey, Wayne, ed. 2000. (ENG., Illus.). 288p. (YA). (gr. 5-11). per. 17.95 (978-0-935487-71-8(9) , Big 8 Reviews) N&N Publishing Co., Inc.

Finton, Nancy. Read & Write Science Mini-Journals: Reproducible Booklets with Easy Hands-on Activities & Quick Writing Prompts That Teach Key Science Topics. 2003. 48p. (gr. 2-4). pap. 10.99 (978-0-439-41532-3(2) , Teaching Resources) Scholastic, Inc.

First Look Science, 8 bks. Set. Incl. And Everyone Shouted, "Pull!" A First Look at Forces & Motion. Llewellyn, Claire. Abel, Simone, illus. 22.60 (978-1-4048-0656-6(3)); Case of the Missing Caterpillar : A First Look at the Life Cycle of a Butterfly. Godwin, Sam. Abel, Simone, illus. 22.60 (978-1-4048-0655-9(5)); Drop Goes Plop : A First Look at the Water Cycle. Godwin, Sam. Abel, Simone, illus. 22.60 (978-1-4048-0657-3(1)); From Little Acorns- A First Look at the Life Cycle of a Tree. Godwin, Sam. Abel, Simone, illus. 22.60 (978-1-4048-0658-0(X)); Hen Can't Help It : A First Look at the Life Cycle of a Chicken. Godwin, Sam. Abel, Simone, illus. 22.60 (978-1-4048-0653-5(9)); Paint a Sun in the Sky : A First Look at the Seasons. Llewellyn, Claire. Wood, Amanda, illus. 22.60 (978-1-4048-0659-7(8)); Take a Walk on the Rainbow : A First Look at Colour. Moss, Miriam. Wood, Amanda, illus. 22.60 (978-1-4048-0660-3(1)); Trouble with Tadpoles : A First Look at the Life Cycle of a Frog. Godwin, Sam. Abel, Simone, illus. 22.60 (978-1-4048-0654-2(7)); 32p. (C). (gr. k-3). 2004. 180.80 (978-1-4048-0661-0(X)) Picture Window Bks.

First-Time Science, Vol. 2. 2004. 728.00 (978-0-516-27715-8(4)) Scholastic Library Publishing.

Fischer, Stephen David & Carroll, Joseph. Science Detective Beginning: Higher-Order Thinking. Reading, & Writing in Science. 2005. (J). pap. 18.99 (978-0-89455-834-4(X)) Critical Thinking Bks. & Software.

Fleming, Christine. Art As Science. 2007. (Shockwave: Arts & Culture Ser.). (Illus.). 36p. (J). (gr. 4-6). lib. bdg. 25.00 (***978-0-531-17784-6(X)*** , Children's Pr.) Scholastic Library Publishing.

Flip Chart. 2003. (gr. 3 up). suppl. ed. 262.50 (978-0-673-59353-5(3)) Addison-Wesley Educational Pubs., Inc.

Float or Sink? 2005. (Emergent/Early (Prek-2) Science Package Ser.). 12p. (YA). (ps-2). 25.20 (978-0-8215-7840-7(5)) Sadlier, William H. Inc.

Floating & Sinking, 6 vols. (Sunshinetm Science Ser.). 24p. (gr. 1-2). 31.50 (978-0-7802-0296-2(1)); 36.95 (978-0-7802-0547-5(2)) Wright Group, The.

Force & Energy. 2001. (Inquiry Science Ser.). 32p. (gr. 4-5). 4.99 (978-1-56822-951-5(8) , IF20858) School Specialty Publishing.

Forte, Imogene. Ready to Learn Beginning Science. 2003. (Illus.). 64p. per. 7.95 (978-0-86530-598-4(6)) Incentive Pubns., Inc.

—Ready to Learn Following Directions. 2003. (Illus.). 64p. per. 7.95 (978-0-86530-596-0(X)) Incentive Pubns., Inc.

—Science Fun. 2004. (Fun Things to Make & Do Ser.). (Illus.). (J). per. 9.95 (978-0-86530-620-2(6)) Incentive Pubns., Inc.

Forte, Imogene & Schurr, Sandra. Standards-Based Science Graphic Organizers & Rubrics. 2004. 128p. (J). per. 13.95 (978-0-86530-628-8(1)) Incentive Pubns., Inc.

Fossils & Minerals & Crystals & Rocks. 2002. (Illus.). 48p. (J). 2.99 (978-0-88724-803-0(9) , WG 3032) Carson-Dellosa Publishing Co., Inc.

Foster, Patience. Pocket Scientist. 2004. 290p. (J). 8.95 (978-0-7945-0209-6(1)) EDC Publishing.

Foster, Ruth. Nonfiction Reading Comprehension: Science. 2006. 144p. pap. 15.99 (978-1-4206-8021-8(8)); pap. 15.99 (978-1-4206-8026-3(9)) Austin & Company, Inc.

Fowler, Allan. Lands of Grass. 2000. (gr. k-3). lib. bdg. 12.95 (978-0-613-54725-3(X)) Tandem Library Bks.

—Science, Rookie Read-About Science: Habitats & Ecosystems. 2004. (Illus.). 228.00 (978-0-516-29319-6(2)) Scholastic Library Publishing.

Frank, Marjorie Slavick, et al. Science Instant Readers: Collection. 1999. (Harcourt Science Ser.). (gr. 1 up). pap. 35.20 (978-0-15-316226-8(0)); (gr. 2 up). pap. 35.20 (978-0-15-316227-5(9)) Harcourt Schl. Pubs.

—Science Instant Readers Bk. 2: What Do You See? 1999. (Harcourt Science Ser.). (gr. 1 up). pap. 15.50 (978-0-15-316200-8(7)) Harcourt Schl. Pubs.

—Science Instant Readers Bk. 10: Changes Around Us. 1999. (Harcourt Science Ser.). (gr. 2 up). pap. 15.50 (978-0-15-316220-6(1)) Harcourt Schl. Pubs.

—Science Leveled Libraries: Strings Around the World. 3rd ed. 2002. (Harcourt Science Ser.). (gr. 5 up). pap. 25.60 (978-0-15-327414-5(X)) Harcourt Schl. Pubs.

Freeman, Marcia S. La Ciencia Se Encuentra en la Ciudad. 2005. (Ciencia Citadina Ser.). (SPA.). (978-1-59515-669-3(0)) Rourke Publishing, LLC.

—Science in the City. 2006. (City Science Ser.). (Illus.). 24p. (gr. k-3). 14.95 (978-1-59515-412-5(4)) Rourke Publishing, LLC.

—You Are a Scientist. 2005. (Everything Science Ser.). (Illus.). 24p. (gr. 1-4). 14.95 (978-1-59515-126-1(5)) Rourke Publishing, LLC.

Frith, Alex. See Inside Science. 2007. 16p. (J). bds. 12.99 (978-0-7945-1549-2(5) , Usborne) EDC Publishing.

From Flowers to Fruit: 6 Each of 1 Student Book, 6 vols. (Sunshinetm Science Ser.). 24p. (gr. 1-2). 41.95 (978-0-7802-2686-9(0)) Wright Group, The.

From Flowers to Fruit: Big Book. (Sunshinetm Science Ser.). 24p. (gr. 1-2). 37.50 (978-0-7802-2777-4(8)) Wright Group, The.

Frost, Helen. Fats, Oils & Sweets, 6 vols. Saunders-Smith, Gail, ed. (gr. k-2). 28.95 (978-0-7368-8744-1(X)) Red Brick Learning.

—What Are Inclined Planes? Saunders-Smith, Gail, ed. 2001. (Looking at Simple Machines Ser.). (Illus.). 24p. (J). (gr. k-1). lib. bdg. 15.93 (978-0-7368-0845-3(0) , Pebble Bks.) Capstone Pr., Inc.

Fry. Fry Readability Scale. (YA). (gr. 9-12). pap. (978-0-89061-282-8(X)) Jamestown.

Fuchs, Menucha. The Little Scientists: Exploring the World. Goldfield, Zelda, tr. from HEB. Miri, illus. 1999. (Children's Learning Ser.: Vol. 3). 48p. (J). (gr. k-3). pap. 4.95 (978-1-880582-45-9(7)) Judaica Pr., Inc., The.

Una fuerza Especial. 2000. (McGraw-Hill Ciencias Ser.). (ENG & SPA.). (gr. 5 up). (978-0-02-279689-1(4)) Macmillan/McGraw-Hill Schl. Div.

Funston, Sylvia. The Book of You: The Science & Fun! of Why You Look, Feel & Act the Way You Do. Denti, Susanna, illus. Duclos, Gilbert, photos by. 2000. 48p. (J). (gr. 3-7). pap. (978-1-895688-96-2(5)) Maple Tree Pr. CAN. *Dist:* Firefly Bks., Ltd.

Furgang, Kathy. Working with Electricity & Magnetism. 2004. (Navigators Ser.). (J). pap. 42.00 (978-1-4108-0438-9(0)) Benchmark Education Co.

El Futuro ya llego: Leveled Books. 2000. (McGraw-Hill Ciencias Ser.). (ENG & SPA.). (gr. 4 up). (978-0-02-279666-2(5)) Macmillan/McGraw-Hill Schl. Div.

Fyfe, Aileen, ed. & intro. Science for Children, 7 vols. Fyfe, Aileen, intro. fac. ed. 2003. (Popular Science in the Nineteenth Century Ser.). (Illus.). 3057p. 825.00 (978-1-84371-021-9(8) , Thoemmes Continuum) Continuum International Publishing Group, Ltd. GBR. *Dist:* Chicago Distribution Ctr.

Gail Stewart. Written Communication. 2004. (Yesterday & Today Ser.). (Illus.). 32p. 23.70 (978-1-56711-834-6(8) , Blackbirch Pr., Inc.) Thomson Gale.

Gallant, Roy A. The Story of Science - Group 1, 4 bks., Set. Incl. Dance of the Continents. (YA). 1999. lib. bdg. 29.93 (978-0-7614-0962-5(9)); Early Humans. (J). 1999. lib. bdg. 29.93 (978-0-7614-0960-1(2) , Benchmark Bks.); Earth's Place in Space. (J). 2000. lib. bdg. 28.50 (978-0-7614-0963-2(7) , Benchmark Bks.); Ever Changing Atom. (YA). 2000. lib. bdg. 29.93 (978-0-7614-0961-8(0) , Benchmark Bks.); 80p. (gr. 5 up). (Illus.). 2000. Set lib. bdg. 114.00 (978-0-7614-0959-5(9) , Benchmark Bks.) Cavendish, Marshall Corp.

—The Story of Science - Group 2, 4 bks., Set. Incl. Eyes on the Universe. 2000. lib. bdg. 29.93 (978-0-7614-1154-3(2)); Life Stories of Stars. 2000. lib. bdg. 29.93 (978-0-7614-1152-9(6)); Origins of Life. 2000. lib. bdg. 29.93 (978-0-7614-1151-2(8)); Tales Fossils Tell. 2001. lib. bdg. 29.93 (978-0-7614-1153-6(4)); 80p. (J). (gr. 5 up). (Illus.). 2001. Set lib. bdg. 119.71 (978-0-7614-1150-5(X) , Benchmark Bks.) Cavendish, Marshall Corp.

Ganeri, Anita. Science Questions & Answers: Bumper Edition. 1998. (Illus.). 192p. (J). 30.00 (978-0-237-51925-4(9) , Evans Brothers, Limited) Evans Publishing Group GBR. *Dist:* Independent Pubs. Group.

La Gansa de Invierno. 2000. (McGraw-Hill Ciencias Ser.). (ENG & SPA.). (gr. 3 up). (978-0-02-279633-4(9)) Macmillan/McGraw-Hill Schl. Div.

Gardner, Robert. Yesterday's Science, Today's Technology. (Illus.). 96p. (978-0-7613-3114-8(X) , Twenty-First Century Bks.) Lerner Publishing Group.

Garras, alas y otras cosas Utiles. 2000. (McGraw-Hill Ciencias Ser.). (ENG & SPA.). (gr. 3 up). (978-0-02-279625-9(8)) Macmillan/McGraw-Hill Schl. Div.

Gateways to Science for Grade 3 Student Edition. 2007. lib. bdg. (***978-1-933521-11-4(2)***) Region IV Education Service Ctr.

Gateways to Science for Grade 4 Student Edition. 2007. lib. bdg. (***978-1-933521-13-8(9)***) Region IV Education Service Ctr.

Gateways to Science for Grade 5 - Spanish. 2005. stu. ed., per. (978-1-933049-12-0(X)) Region IV Education Service Ctr.

Gateways to Science Grade 6. 2005. (Region IV ESC Resources for Science Ser.). stu. ed., per. (978-1-932797-73-2(4)) Region IV Education Service Ctr.

Gateways to Science Grade 7. 2005. (Region IV ESC Resources for Science Ser.). stu. ed., per. (978-1-932797-75-6(0)) Region IV Education Service Ctr.

Gateways to Science Grade 8 - Student Edition. 2005. (Region IV ESC Resources for Science Ser.). stu. ed., per. (978-1-932797-77-0(7)) Region IV Education Service Ctr.

Gatlin, Connie. Mystery Science: Case of the Missing Lunch. 2005. 48p. 10.95 (978-1-59363-111-6(1)) Prufrock Pr.

Gay, Kathlyn. Science in Ancient Greece. rev. ed. 1999. (Science of the Past Ser.). (Illus.). 64p. (J). (gr. 5-7). pap. 8.95 (978-0-531-15929-3(9) , Watts, Franklin) Scholastic Library Publishing.

Gaydos, Nora. Simply Science Vol. 2: Independent. Sams, B. B., illus. 2006. (Now I'm Reading! Ser.). 74p. (J). (ps-2). 16.99 (978-1-58476-433-5(3) , IKIDS) Innovative Kids.

—Simply Science - Independent. Montgomery, Lee, illus. 2003. (Now I'm Reading! Ser.). 128p. (J). (ps-2). 16.99 (978-1-58476-169-3(5)) Innovative Kids.

Getting Cold! Getting Hot!, 6 vols. (Sunshinetm Science Ser.). 24p. (gr. 1-2). 37.50 (978-0-7802-1405-7(6)); 41.95 (978-0-7802-1404-0(8)) Wright Group, The.

Getting Rid of Waste Water: 6 Each of 1 Student Book, 6 vols. (Sunshinetm Science Ser.). 24p. (gr. 1-2). 41.95 (978-0-7802-2692-0(5)) Wright Group, The.

Getting Rid of Waste Water: Big Book. (Sunshinetm Science Ser.). 24p. (gr. 1-2). 37.50 (978-0-7802-2780-4(8)) Wright Group, The.

Getting the Water We Need: 6 Each of 1 Student Book, 6 vols. (Sunshinetm Science Ser.). 24p. (gr. 1-2). 41.95 (978-0-7802-2690-6(9)) Wright Group, The.

Getting the Water We Need: Big Book. (Sunshinetm Science Ser.). 24p. (gr. 1-2). 37.50 (978-0-7802-2779-8(4)) Wright Group, The.

Giant Balloons: Individual Title Six-Packs. (Rigby Focus Ser.). 16p. (gr. 1 up). 28.00 (978-0-7578-5330-2(7)); 30.00 (978-0-7578-5562-7(8)) Rigby Education.

Giesecke, Ernestine. Outside My Window, 4 bks., Set. 1999. (Illus.). 24p. (J). (gr. 1-3). lib. bdg. 85.44 (978-1-57572-685-4(8)) Heinemann Library.

El Globo Perdido. 2000. (McGraw-Hill Ciencias Ser.). (ENG & SPA.). (gr. 1 up). (978-0-02-279566-5(9)) Macmillan/McGraw-Hill Schl. Div.

Glover, David. Living Science. (Make It Work! Science Ser.). (gr. 3-6). 2004. (Illus.). 192p. 24.95 (978-1-58728-378-9(6)); 2001. (J). pap. 19.95 (978-1-58728-286-7(0)) T&N Children's Publishing. (Two Can Publishing).

—Science: Science Around Us. 2001. (gr. k-3). lib. bdg. 19.90 (978-0-613-90914-3(3)) Tandem Library Bks.

Godlewski, Lorraine, et al. Preparing for the Science RCT. 1998. (WPCO's Science Ser.). (Illus.). 155p. (J). pap., stu. ed. 4.75 (978-0-937323-08-3(X)) United Publishing Co.

Gonsalves, Philip & Kopp, Jaine. Build It! Festival. Bergman, Lincoln et al, eds. Craig, Rose et al, illus. Hoyt, Richard & Goodman, Jan M., photos by. 1999. (Great Explorations in Math & Science Ser.). 224p. (J). (gr. k-6). pap., tchr. ed. 25.50 (978-0-924886-38-6(2) , GEMS) Univ. of California, Berkeley, Lawrence Hall of Science.

Gordon, Charlotte & Gordon, Michael. Mysteries in Time Science Activity Book. 2000. (Mysteries in Time Ser.). (Illus.). 80p. (J). (gr. 3-7). pap. 8.95 (978-1-893110-22-9(2)) Silver Moon Pr.

Gorman, Jacqueline Laks. X Science, 6 bks. Incl. Bermuda Triangle. lib. bdg. 22.00 (978-0-8368-3196-2(9)); Bigfoot. lib. bdg. 22.00 (978-0-8368-3197-9(7)); ESP. lib. bdg. 22.00 (978-0-8368-3198-6(5)); Ghosts. lib. bdg. 22.00 (978-0-8368-3199-3(3)); Loch Ness Monster. lib. bdg. 22.00 (978-0-8368-3200-6(0)); UFOs. lib. bdg. 22.00 (978-0-8368-3201-3(9)); (YA). (gr. 2 up). (Illus.). 24p. 2002. Set lib. bdg. 132.00 (978-0-8368-3195-5(0)) Stevens, Gareth Inc.

Gottlieb. Matter, Motion & Machines. 2004. pap., tchr. ed. 17.60 incl. cd-rom (978-0-7398-9185-8(5)); (Illus.). pap. 15.60 incl. cd-rom (978-0-7398-9179-7(0)) Steck-Vaughn.

Gow, Mary. Robert Boyle: Pioneer of Experimental Chemistry. 2005. (Great Minds of Science Ser.). (Illus.). 128p. (J). lib. bdg. 26.60 (978-0-7660-2501-1(2)) Enslow Pubs., Inc.

Gr 4 Mttr O/T Move Sci Pe. 2000. (McGraw-Hill Science Ser.). (gr. 4 up). (978-0-02-278216-0(8)) Macmillan/McGraw-Hill Schl. Div.

Gr 5 Matter, Sci Pe. 2000. (McGraw-Hill Science Ser.). (gr. 5 up). (978-0-02-278226-9(5)) Macmillan/McGraw-Hill Schl. Div.

The Grain Group, 6 vols. (gr. k-2). 28.95 (978-0-7368-8746-5(6)) Red Brick Learning.

Grambo, Rebecca L. The Kids' Fun-Filled Nature Question & Answer Book. Tallarico, Tony, illus. 2000. 93p. (J). (978-1-56156-839-0(2)) Kidsbooks, Inc.

El gran Chiquitin. 2000. (McGraw-Hill Ciencias Ser.). (ENG & SPA.). (gr. 1 up). (978-0-02-279574-0(X)) Macmillan/McGraw-Hill Schl. Div.

La gran inundacion de Johnstown. 2000. (McGraw-Hill Ciencias Ser.). (ENG & SPA.). (gr. 5 up). (978-0-02-279679-2(7)) Macmillan/McGraw-Hill Schl. Div.

Granowsky, Alvin, et al. Take-Home Books Blackline Masters: Content Area Readers-Science. 2002. (Sadlier Phonics Reading Program). (Illus.). 32p. (J). per. (978-0-8215-7856-8(1) , Sadlier-Oxford) Sadlier, William H. Inc.

Great Minds of Science, 19 bks., Set. (Illus.). (J). (gr. 4-10). lib. bdg. 398.05 (978-0-89490-566-7(X)) Enslow Pubs., Inc.

Great Scientific Questions & the Scientists Who Answered Them Set 1, 8 bks., Set. Incl. How Do We Know How Stars Shine? Cobb, Allan B. lib. bdg. 26.50 (978-0-8239-3380-8(6)); How Do We Know the Age of the Earth? Caes, Charles J. lib. bdg. 26.50 (978-0-8239-3381-5(4)); How Do We Know the Age of the Universe? Germadnik, Mary Lynn. lib. bdg. 26.50 (978-0-8239-3382-2(2)); How Do We Know the Laws of Motion? Roberts, Jeremy. lib. bdg. 26.50 (978-0-8239-3383-9(0)); How Do We Know the Laws of Thermodynamics? Moran, Jeffrey B. lib. bdg. 26.50 (978-0-8239-3384-6(9)); How Do We Know the Nature of the Atom? Goldstein, Natalie. lib. bdg. 26.50 (978-0-8239-3385-3(7)); How Do We Know the Size of the Solar System? Turiel, Isaac. lib. bdg. 26.50 (978-0-8239-3386-0(5)); How Do We Know the Speed of Light? Caes, Charles J. lib. bdg. 26.50 (978-0-8239-3387-7(3)); 112p. (YA). (gr. 4-6). 2001. (Illus.). 2000. Set lib. bdg. 212.00 (978-0-8239-9423-6(6)) Rosen Publishing Group, Inc., The.

Greenwood, Rosie. I Wonder Why Volcanoes Blow Their Tops & Other Questions about Natural Disasters. 2004. (I Wonder Why Ser.). (Illus.). 32p. (J). (gr. k-3). 11.95 (978-0-7534-5751-1(2) , Kingfisher) Houghton Mifflin Co. Trade & Reference Div.

Gribbin, Mary & Gribbin, John. The Science of Philip Pullman's "His Dark Materials" 2005. 224p. (J). (gr. 7). lib. bdg. 17.99 (978-0-375-93144-4(9) , Knopf Bks. for Young Readers) Random Hse. Children's Bks.

Griffith, Saul & Bonsen, Joost. Howtoons: The Possibilities Are Endless. Dragotta, Nick, illus. 2007. 112p. (J). (gr. 3-7). pap. 15.99 (978-0-06-076158-5(X) , ReganBooks) HarperCollins Pubs.

Groessen und Masse. (Duden-Schuelerhilfen Ser.). (GER.). 96p. (J). (gr. 4-5). (978-3-411-02610-4(3)) Bibliographisches Institut & F. A. Brockhaus AG DEU. *Dist:* International Bk. Import Service, Inc.

Grolier Educational Staff, contrib. by. The New Book of Popular Science, 6 vols. (Illus.). (J). 2003. 279.00 (978-0-7172-1224-8(6)); 2002. 3,798p. (978-0-7172-1223-1(8)); Set. 2000. 3100p. (gr. 6-12). lib. bdg. 269.00 (978-0-7172-1222-4(X)) Scholastic Library Publishing. (Grolier).

Group/McGraw-Hill, Wright. Cold Facts about Ice Ages, 6 vols. (Book2WebTM Ser.). (gr. 4-8). 36.50 (978-0-322-04434-0(0)) Wright Group, The.

—Dreams of Flight, 6 vols. (Book2WebTM Ser.). (gr. 4-8). 36.50 (978-0-322-04433-3(2)) Wright Group, The.

—Earth & Physical Science: Color & Light, 6 vols. (Book2WebTM Ser.). (gr. 4-8). 36.50 (978-0-322-04429-6(4)) Wright Group, The.

—Earth & Physical Science: Exploring Electricity, 6 vols. (Book2WebTM Ser.). (gr. 4-8). 36.50 (978-0-322-04428-9(6)) Wright Group, The.

—Famous Shipwrecks, 6 vols. (Book2WebTM Ser.). (gr. 4-8). 36.50 (978-0-322-04458-6(8)) Wright Group, The.

—Inventors Create Tomorrow, 6 vols. (Book2WebTM Ser.). (gr. 4-8). 36.50 (978-0-322-04469-2(3)) Wright Group, The.

—Mountain Majesty, 6 vols. (Book2WebTM Ser.). (gr. 4-8). 36.50 (978-0-322-04440-1(5)) Wright Group, The.

—People on the Path Toward Human Rights, 6 vols. (Book2WebTM Ser.). (gr. 4-8). 36.50 (978-0-322-04466-1(9)) Wright Group, The.

—Wonder World Complete Sets: Science Set - 1 Each of 97 Titles. (Wonder Worldtm Ser.). (gr. k-6). 501.95 (978-0-322-06714-1(6)) Wright Group, The.

—Wonder World Early & Upper Emergent Sets: Science Set - 1 Each of 49 Titles. (Wonder Worldtm Ser.). (gr. k-6). 229.50 (978-0-322-06721-9(9)) Wright Group, The.

—Wonder World Early Fluency & Fluency: Science Set - 1 Each of 48 Titles. (Wonder Worldtm Ser.). (gr. k-6). 299.50 (978-0-322-06717-2(0)) Wright Group, The.

Groves, Marcia & Findon, Joanna. Science & Technology in the Middle Ages. 2004. (Medieval World Ser.). (Illus.). 32p. (J). (978-0-7787-1354-8(7)); pap. (978-0-7787-1386-9(5)) Crabtree Publishing Co.

El guardian del Rio. 2000. (McGraw-Hill Ciencias Ser.). (ENG & SPA.). (gr. 5 up). (978-0-02-279674-7(6)) Macmillan/McGraw-Hill Schl. Div.

Los guardianes del Agua: Leveled Books. 2000. (McGraw-Hill Ciencias Ser.). (ENG & SPA.). (gr. 4 up). (978-0-02-279655-6(X)) Macmillan/McGraw-Hill Schl. Div.

Hall, Godfrey. Changes. 1998. (Find Out about Ser.). (Illus.). 24p. (J). (ps-3). (978-0-563-39615-4(6)) BBC Worldwide.

Hands: Level B, 6 vols. 8p. 24.95 (978-0-7802-8915-4(3)) Wright Group, The.

Hands on Projects. 2005. 80p. (J). per. 2.95 (978-1-59441-272-1(3) , RB-904005) Carson-Dellosa Publishing Co., Inc.

Hands-on Science-20 Themes. 2005. 208p. (gr. 1-3). 19.99 (978-1-55799-935-1(X) , EMC 5000) Evan-Moor Educational Pubs.

Hands-On Science, Math, & Technology. 112p. (gr. 5-8). 14.99 (978-0-7682-0218-2(3) , GA13018) School Specialty Publishing.

Handwerker, Mark J. Ready-to-Use Physical Science Activities for Grades 5-12. 2000. (Secondary Science Curriculum Activities Library: Vol. 1). (Illus.). 240p. (J). pap. 27.50 (978-0-13-029113-4(7) , Addison Wesley) Benjamin-Cummings Publishing Co.

Hann, Judith. How Science Works: 100 Ways Parents & Kids Can Share the Secrets of Science. 1999. (Reader's Digest Ser.). (Illus.). 192p. (gr. 12-7). pap. 16.95 (978-0-7621-0249-5(7)) Reader's Digest Assn., Inc., The.

Hansen, Merrily P. A Close-Up Look at Plants: A Content Area Reader-Science. 2005. (Sadlier Phonics Reading Program). (Illus.). 16p. (YA). (ps-2). 25.20 (978-0-8215-7811-7(1)) Sadlier, William H. Inc.

Harcourt School Publishers Staff. Changes Around Us: Science Reader. 1999. (SPA., Illus.). (J). pap. 3.70 (978-0-15-316125-4(6)) Harcourt Schl. Pubs.

—Los Cinco Patitos. 2000. (SPA., Illus.). pap. 82.60 (978-0-15-315097-5(1)) Harcourt Schl. Pubs.

—Collections, Grade K Unit 2: Instant Reader's Teacher's Guide. 2000. (Harcourt Science Ser.). (gr. 2 up). pap., tchr. ed. 22.00 (978-0-15-317829-0(9)) Harcourt Schl. Pubs.

—Harcourt Ciencias: CA Edition. 2001. (SPA., Illus.). (J). (gr. 1). 46.70 (978-0-15-321457-8(0)); (J). (gr. 1). pap., wbk. ed. 6.80 (978-0-15-321473-8(2)); (J). (gr. 2). 48.00 (978-0-15-321458-5(9)); (J). (gr. 2). pap., wbk. ed. 6.80 (978-0-15-321474-5(0)); (J). (gr. 3). 51.70 (978-0-15-321459-2(7)); (gr. 3). pap., wbk. ed. 9.10 (978-0-15-321475-2(9)); (J). (gr. 4). 55.00 (978-0-15-321460-8(0)); (gr. 4). pap., wbk. ed. 9.90 (978-0-15-321476-9(7)); (J). (gr. 5). 55.60 (978-0-15-321461-5(9)); (gr. 5). pap., wbk. ed. 9.90 (978-0-15-321477-6(5)) Harcourt Schl. Pubs.

—Harcourt Ciencias: CA Edition Take-Home Book. 2001. (SPA., Illus.). (gr. 1). pap. 28.30 (978-0-15-321496-7(1)); (gr. 2). pap. 28.30 (978-0-15-321497-4(X)); (gr. 3). pap. 33.90 (978-0-15-321498-1(8)); (gr. 4). pap. 33.90 (978-0-15-321499-8(6)); (gr. 5). pap. 33.90 (978-0-15-321500-1(3)) Harcourt Schl. Pubs.

—Harcourt Ciencias: CA Unit Big Book Extension Chapters. 2001. (SPA., Illus.). (J). pap. 168.30 (978-0-15-321524-7(0)); pap. 168.30 (978-0-15-321529-2(1)) Harcourt Schl. Pubs.

—Harcourt Ciencias Unit C: CA Unit Big Book. 2001. (SPA., Illus.). (J). pap. 168.30 (978-0-15-321523-0(2)); pap. 217.20 (978-0-15-321528-5(3)) Harcourt Schl. Pubs.

—Harcourt Ciencias Unit A: CA Unit Big Book. 2001. (SPA., Illus.). (J). (gr. 1). pap. 241.60 (978-0-15-321521-6(6)); (gr. 2). pap. 192.80 (978-0-15-321526-1(7)) Harcourt Schl. Pubs.

—Harcourt Ciencias Unit B: CA Unit Big Book. 2001. (SPA., Illus.). (J). pap. 168.30 (978-0-15-321522-3(4)); pap. 168.30 (978-0-15-321527-8(5)) Harcourt Schl. Pubs.

—Harcourt Ciencias, Grade 1: CA Edition. 2001. (SPA.). tchr. ed. 121.00 (978-0-15-321463-9(5)); pap., tchr. ed., wbk. ed. 24.60 (978-0-15-321478-3(3)) Harcourt Schl. Pubs.

—Harcourt Ciencias, Grade 2: CA Assessment Guide. 2001. pap. 57.50 (978-0-15-321484-4(8)) Harcourt Schl. Pubs.

—Harcourt Ciencias, Grade 2: CA Edition. 2001. (SPA.). tchr. ed. 121.00 (978-0-15-321464-6(3)); pap., tchr. ed., wbk. ed. 24.60 (978-0-15-321479-0(1)) Harcourt Schl. Pubs.

—Harcourt Ciencias, Grade 2: CA Teaching Resources. 2001. pap., tchr. ed. 51.80 (978-0-15-321469-1(4)) Harcourt Schl. Pubs.

—Harcourt Ciencias, Grade 3: CA Assessment Guide. 2001. pap. 57.50 (978-0-15-321485-1(6)) Harcourt Schl. Pubs.

—Harcourt Ciencias, Grade 3: CA Edition. 2001. (SPA.). tchr. ed. 155.60 (978-0-15-321465-3(1)); pap., tchr. ed., wbk. ed. 24.90 (978-0-15-321480-6(5)) Harcourt Schl. Pubs.

—Harcourt Ciencias, Grade 4: CA Assessment Guide. 2001. pap. 66.20 (978-0-15-321486-8(4)) Harcourt Schl. Pubs.

—Harcourt Ciencias, Grade 4: CA Edition. 2001. (SPA.). tchr. ed. 155.60 (978-0-15-321466-0(X)); pap., tchr. ed., wbk. ed. 25.70 (978-0-15-321481-3(3)) Harcourt Schl. Pubs.

—Harcourt Ciencias, Grade 5: CA Assessment Guide. 2001. pap. 66.20 (978-0-15-321487-5(2)) Harcourt Schl. Pubs.

—Harcourt Ciencias, Grade 5: CA Edition. 2001. (SPA.). tchr. ed. 164.20 (978-0-15-321467-7(8)); pap., tchr. ed., wbk. ed. 25.70 (978-0-15-321482-0(1)) Harcourt Schl. Pubs.

—Harcourt Science: Activities: South Carolina Edition. 2001. (Illus.). (gr. 1). pap. 23.10 (978-0-15-321245-1(4)); (gr. 2). pap. 23.10 (978-0-15-321246-8(2)); (gr. 3). pap. 23.10 (978-0-15-321247-5(0)); (gr. 4). pap. 23.10 (978-0-15-321248-2(9)); (gr. 5). pap. 23.10 (978-0-15-321249-9(7)) Harcourt Schl. Pubs.

—Harcourt Science: Arkansas Test Preparation. 2001. (Illus.). (gr. 1). pap. 13.20 (978-0-15-321172-0(5)); (gr. 2). pap. 13.20 (978-0-15-321173-7(3)); (gr. 3). pap. 13.20 (978-0-15-321174-4(1)); (gr. 4). pap. 13.90 (978-0-15-321175-1(X)); (gr. 5). pap. 13.90 (978-0-15-321176-8(8)); (gr. 6). pap. 13.90 (978-0-15-321177-5(6)) Harcourt Schl. Pubs.

—Harcourt Science: CA Big Book Extension Chapter. 2000. (Illus.). pap. 207.90 (978-0-15-317901-3(5)); pap. 207.90 (978-0-15-317907-5(4)) Harcourt Schl. Pubs.

—Harcourt Science: CA Expeditions. 2001. (Illus.). (gr. 1). pap. 75.70 (978-0-15-321167-6(9)); (gr. 2). pap. 75.70 (978-0-15-321168-3(7)); (gr. 3). pap. 75.70 (978-0-15-321169-0(5)); (gr. 4). pap. 75.70 (978-0-15-321170-6(9)); (gr. 5). pap. 75.70 (978-0-15-321171-3(7)) Harcourt Schl. Pubs.

—Harcourt Science: CA Standardized Test Preparation. 2001. (Illus.). (gr. 1). pap. 9.20 (978-0-15-321156-0(3)); (gr. 2). pap. 9.20 (978-0-15-321157-7(1)); (gr. 3). pap. 9.20 (978-0-15-321158-4(X)); (gr. 4). pap. 9.60 (978-0-15-321159-1(8)); (gr. 5). pap. 9.60 (978-0-15-321161-4(X)) Harcourt Schl. Pubs.

—Harcourt Science: CA Take-Home Book. 1999. (Illus.). (gr. 3). pap. 35.00 (978-0-15-317682-1(2)); (gr. 4). pap. 35.00 (978-0-15-317683-8(0)); (gr. 5). pap. 35.00 (978-0-15-317684-5(9)) Harcourt Schl. Pubs.

—Harcourt Science: CA Workbook. 1999. (Illus.). (gr. 1). pap., wbk. ed. 8.60 (978-0-15-317672-2(5)); (gr. 2). pap., wbk. ed. 8.60 (978-0-15-317674-6(1)) Harcourt Schl. Pubs.

—Harcourt Science: California Edition. 1999. (Illus.). (gr. 1). 50.00 (978-0-15-317649-4(0)); (gr. 2). 50.00 (978-0-15-317651-7(2)); (gr. 3). 58.00 (978-0-15-317652-4(0)); (gr. 4). 60.30 (978-0-15-317654-8(7)); (gr. 5). 65.00 (978-0-15-317655-5(5)) Harcourt Schl. Pubs.

—Harcourt Science: Changes Around Us Reader. 1999. (Illus.). pap. 3.10 (978-0-15-314873-6(X)) Harcourt Schl. Pubs.

—Harcourt Science: Energy & Motion. 2000. (Illus.). pap. 17.10 (978-0-15-315703-5(8)) Harcourt Schl. Pubs.

—Harcourt Science: FCAT Practice. 2001. (Illus.). (gr. 1). pap. 9.10 (978-0-15-320578-1(4)); (gr. 2). pap. 9.10 (978-0-15-320579-8(2)); (gr. 6). pap. 9.60 (978-0-15-320595-8(4)) Harcourt Schl. Pubs.

—Harcourt Science: FCAT Practice Book. 2000. (Illus.). (gr. 3). pap. 9.30 (978-0-15-319594-5(0)); (gr. 4). pap. 9.30 (978-0-15-319597-6(5)); (gr. 5). pap. 9.30 (978-0-15-319599-0(1)) Harcourt Schl. Pubs.

—Harcourt Science: Florida Activities. 1999. (Illus.). (gr. 1). pap. 20.20 (978-0-15-318331-7(4)); (gr. 2). pap. 20.20 (978-0-15-318332-4(2)); (gr. 3). pap. 20.20 (978-0-15-318333-1(0)); (gr. 4). pap. 20.20 (978-0-15-318334-8(9)); (gr. 5). pap. 20.20 (978-0-15-318335-5(7)) Harcourt Schl. Pubs.

—Harcourt Science: Heat Changes Things Reader. 1999. (Illus.). pap. 3.10 (978-0-15-314860-6(8)) Harcourt Schl. Pubs.

—Harcourt Science: How Does a Plant Grow Reader. 1999. (Illus.). (gr. 2). pap. 3.10 (978-0-15-314863-7(2)) Harcourt Schl. Pubs.

—Harcourt Science: Jeff's Magnet Reader. 1999. (Illus.). pap. 3.10 (978-0-15-314862-0(4)) Harcourt Schl. Pubs.

—Harcourt Science: Motion Reader. 1999. (Illus.). pap. 3.10 (978-0-15-314874-3(8)) Harcourt Schl. Pubs.

—Harcourt Science: National Edition. 2000. (Illus.). (gr. 1). 52.30 (978-0-15-317496-4(X)); (gr. 2). 52.30 (978-0-15-317497-1(8)) Harcourt Schl. Pubs.

—Harcourt Science: Ohio Proficiency Test Activity Book. 1999. (Illus.). (gr. 3-4). pap. 29.00 (978-0-15-319057-5(4)); (gr. 5-6). pap. 29.00 (978-0-15-319058-2(2)) Harcourt Schl. Pubs.

—Harcourt Science: PACT Test Preparation: South Carolina Edition. 2001. (Illus.). (gr. 1). pap. 9.10 (978-0-15-321255-0(1)); (gr. 2). pap. 9.10 (978-0-15-321256-7(X)); (gr. 3). pap. 9.10 (978-0-15-321257-4(8)); (gr. 4). pap. 9.50 (978-0-15-321258-1(6)); (gr. 5). pap. 9.50 (978-0-15-321259-8(4)) Harcourt Schl. Pubs.

—Harcourt Science: Physical Science Instant Reader CD-ROM Teacher's Guide. 2nd ed. 2003. (Harcourt Science Ser.). (gr. k up). tchr. ed. 8.00 incl. cd-rom (978-0-15-324957-0(9)) Harcourt Schl. Pubs.

—Harcourt Science: Practice for Stanford 9. (Illus.). 2000. (gr. 4). pap. 9.50 (978-0-15-319062-9(0)); 2000. (gr. 5). pap. 9.50 (978-0-15-319063-6(9)); 2000. (gr. 6). pap. 9.50 (978-0-15-319064-3(7)); 1999. (gr. 3). pap. 9.50 (978-0-15-319061-2(2)) Harcourt Schl. Pubs.

—Harcourt Science: Push It or Pull It Reader. 1999. (Illus.). pap. 3.10 (978-0-15-314861-3(6)) Harcourt Schl. Pubs.

—Harcourt Science: Reuse & Recycle Reader. 1999. (Illus.). pap. 3.10 (978-0-15-314866-8(7)) Harcourt Schl. Pubs.

—Harcourt Science: Seasons Reader. 1999. (Illus.). pap. 3.10 (978-0-15-314857-6(8)) Harcourt Schl. Pubs.

—Harcourt Science: Sink or Float Reader. 1999. pap. 3.10 (978-0-15-314859-0(4)) Harcourt Schl. Pubs.

—Harcourt Science: Solids, Liquids & Gases Reader. 1999. (Illus.). pap. 3.10 (978-0-15-314872-9(1)) Harcourt Schl. Pubs.

—Harcourt Science: Standardized Test Preparation. 2001. (Illus.). (gr. 1). pap. 9.20 (978-0-15-320582-8(2)); (gr. 2). pap. 9.20 (978-0-15-320583-5(0)); (gr. 3). pap. 9.20 (978-0-15-320584-2(9)); (gr. 4). pap. 9.60 (978-0-15-320585-9(7)); (gr. 5). pap. 9.60 (978-0-15-320586-6(5)); (gr. 6). pap. 9.60 (978-0-15-320587-3(3)); 2nd ed. (gr. 4 up). pap. 9.10 (978-0-15-334073-4(8)) Harcourt Schl. Pubs.

—Harcourt Science: TAAS Practice. 2001. (Illus.). (J). (gr. 1). pap. 5.80 (978-0-15-320913-0(5)); (J). (gr. 2). pap. 5.80 (978-0-15-320914-7(3)); (J). (gr. 3). pap. 6.00 (978-0-15-320915-4(1)); (gr. 4). pap. 9.30 (978-0-15-320916-1(X)) Harcourt Schl. Pubs.

—Harcourt Science: Take-Home Book. 1999. (Illus.). (gr. 3). pap. 35.00 (978-0-15-315425-6(X)); (gr. 4). pap. 35.00 (978-0-15-315426-3(8)); (gr. 5). pap. 35.00 (978-0-15-315431-7(4)); (gr. 6). pap. 35.00 (978-0-15-315432-4(2)) Harcourt Schl. Pubs.

—Harcourt Science: Test Preparation: Georgia Edition. 2nd ed. 2002. (Illus.). (gr. 1). pap. 10.20 (978-0-15-332644-8(1)); (gr. 2). pap. 10.20 (978-0-15-332646-2(8)); (gr. 3). pap. 10.20 (978-0-15-332647-9(6)); (gr. 4). pap. 10.60 (978-0-15-332648-6(4)); (gr. 5). pap. 10.60 (978-0-15-332649-3(2)) Harcourt Schl. Pubs.

—Harcourt Science: Test Preparation: Oregon Edition. 2nd ed. 2002. (Illus.). (gr. 1). pap. 94.00 (978-0-15-329393-1(4)); (gr. 2). pap. 94.00 (978-0-15-329394-8(2)); (gr. 3). pap. 94.00 (978-0-15-329395-5(0)); (gr. 4). pap. 98.00 (978-0-15-329396-2(9)); (gr. 5). pap. 98.00 (978-0-15-329397-9(7)); (gr. 6). pap. 98.00 (978-0-15-329399-3(3)) Harcourt Schl. Pubs.

—Harcourt Science: The Garden Reader. 1999. (Illus.). pap. 2.90 (978-0-15-314843-9(8)) Harcourt Schl. Pubs.

—Harcourt Science: The House Book Reader. 1999. (Illus.). pap. 2.90 (978-0-15-314846-0(2)) Harcourt Schl. Pubs.

—Harcourt Science: The Moon Reader. 1999. (Illus.). pap. 3.10 (978-0-15-314870-5(5)) Harcourt Schl. Pubs.

—Harcourt Science: The Water Cycle Reader. 1999. (Illus.). pap. 3.10 (978-0-15-314871-2(3)) Harcourt Schl. Pubs.

—Harcourt Science: Water at Work Reader. 1999. (Illus.). pap. 3.10 (978-0-15-314867-5(5)) Harcourt Schl. Pubs.

—Harcourt Science: Water Changes Reader. 1999. (Illus.). pap. 2.90 (978-0-15-314847-7(0)) Harcourt Schl. Pubs.

—Harcourt Science: What Is a Food Chain Reader. 1999. pap. 3.10 (978-0-15-314865-1(9)) Harcourt Schl. Pubs.

—Harcourt Science Bk. 7: Instant Reader. 2nd ed. 2002. (Illus.). (J). pap. 2.40 (978-0-15-324504-6(2)) Harcourt Schl. Pubs.

—Harcourt Science Bk. 8: Instant Reader. 2nd ed. 2002. (Illus.). (J). pap. 2.40 (978-0-15-324505-3(0)) Harcourt Schl. Pubs.

—Harcourt Science Bk. 9: Instant Reader. 2nd ed. 2002. (Illus.). (J). pap. 2.40 (978-0-15-324506-0(9)) Harcourt Schl. Pubs.

—Harcourt Science Bk. 10: Instant Reader. 2nd ed. 2002. (Illus.). (J). pap. 2.40 (978-0-15-324507-7(7)) Harcourt Schl. Pubs.

—Harcourt Science Bk. 11: Instant Reader. 2nd ed. 2002. (Illus.). (J). pap. 2.40 (978-0-15-324508-4(5)) Harcourt Schl. Pubs.

—Harcourt Science Bk. 12: Instant Reader. 2nd ed. 2002. (Illus.). (J). pap. 2.40 (978-0-15-324509-1(3)) Harcourt Schl. Pubs.

—Harcourt Science Level C: Modular Big Book, Soft-Cover. 1999. (Illus.). pap. 104.40 (978-0-15-315670-8(8)); (gr. 1). pap. 93.10 (978-0-15-315664-9(3)) Harcourt Schl. Pubs.

—Harcourt Science Level D: Modular Big Book, Soft-Cover. 1999. (Illus.). pap. 104.40 (978-0-15-315665-6(1)); (gr. 2). pap. 104.40 (978-0-15-315671-7(6)) Harcourt Schl. Pubs.

—Harcourt Science Level A: Modular Big Book. 1999. (Illus.). (gr. 2). pap. 115.70 (978-0-15-315668-7(6)) Harcourt Schl. Pubs.

—Harcourt Science Level A: Modular Big Book, Soft-Cover. 1999. (Illus.). (gr. 1). pap. 115.70 (978-0-15-315662-5(7)) Harcourt Schl. Pubs.

—Harcourt Science Level B: Modular Big Book, Soft-Cover. 1999. (Illus.). pap. 104.40 (978-0-15-315663-2(5)); pap. 104.40 (978-0-15-315669-4(4)) Harcourt Schl. Pubs.

—Harcourt Science Level E: Modular Big Book, Soft-Cover. 1999. (Illus.). pap. 104.40 (978-0-15-315672-4(4)); (gr. 1). pap. 104.40 (978-0-15-315666-3(X)) Harcourt Schl. Pubs.

—Harcourt Science Level F: Modular Big Book, Soft-Cover. 1999. (Illus.). pap. 104.40 (978-0-15-315667-0(8)); pap. 104.40 (978-0-15-315673-1(2)) Harcourt Schl. Pubs.

—Harcourt Science Unit C: CA Big Book. 2000. (Illus.). pap. 207.90 (978-0-15-317899-3(X)) Harcourt Schl. Pubs.

—Harcourt Science Unit C: Living Planet. 2000. (Illus.). pap. 17.10 (978-0-15-315706-6(2)) Harcourt Schl. Pubs.

—Harcourt Science Unit C: CA Big Book. 2000. (Illus.). pap. 268.80 (978-0-15-317904-4(X)) Harcourt Schl. Pubs.

—Harcourt Science Unit D: Cycles in Earth & Space. 2000. (Illus.). pap. 17.10 (978-0-15-315707-3(0)) Harcourt Schl. Pubs.

—Harcourt Science Unit D: The Solar System & Beyond. 2000. (Illus.). pap. 17.10 (978-0-15-315701-1(1)) Harcourt Schl. Pubs.

—Harcourt Science Unit A: CA Big Book. 2000. (Illus.). (gr. 2). pap. 238.30 (978-0-15-317902-0(3)) Harcourt Schl. Pubs.

—Harcourt Science Unit A: Processes of Living Things. 2000. (Illus.). (gr. 5). pap. 17.10 (978-0-15-315698-4(8)) Harcourt Schl. Pubs.

—Harcourt Science Unit A: World of Living Things. 2000. (Illus.). (gr. 6). pap. 17.10 (978-0-15-315704-2(6)) Harcourt Schl. Pubs.

—Harcourt Science Unit A, Chapters 1-5: CA Big Book. 2000. (Illus.). (gr. 1). pap. 299.30 (978-0-15-317896-2(5)) Harcourt Schl. Pubs.

—Harcourt Science Unit B: CA Big Book. 2000. (Illus.). pap. 207.90 (978-0-15-317898-6(1)); pap. 207.90 (978-0-15-317903-7(1)) Harcourt Schl. Pubs.

—Harcourt Science Unit B: Living Things Grow & Respond. 2000. (Illus.). pap. 17.10 (978-0-15-315705-9(4)) Harcourt Schl. Pubs.

—Harcourt Science Unit B: Systems & Interactions in Nature. 2000. (Illus.). pap. 17.10 (978-0-15-315699-1(6)) Harcourt Schl. Pubs.

—Harcourt Science Unit E: Building Blocks of Matter. 2000. (Illus.). pap. 17.10 (978-0-15-315702-8(X)) Harcourt Schl. Pubs.

—Harcourt Science Unit E: Matter & Energy. 2000. (Illus.). pap. 17.10 (978-0-15-315708-0(9)) Harcourt Schl. Pubs.

—Harcourt Science Unit F: Forces & Machines. 2000. (Illus.). pap. 17.10 (978-0-15-315709-7(7)) Harcourt Schl. Pubs.

—Harcourt Science Activity Book. 2nd ed. 2002. (Illus.). (ps). pap. 5.00 (978-0-15-335183-9(7)) Harcourt Schl. Pubs.

—Harcourt Science Big Book Collection. 3rd ed. 2002. (Harcourt Science Ser.). (Illus.). (gr. k-6). pap. 400.00 (978-0-15-335318-5(X)) Harcourt Schl. Pubs.

—Harcourt Science, Grade 1. 1999. pap., tchr. ed., wbk. ed. 22.50 (978-0-15-314971-9(X)) Harcourt Schl. Pubs.

—Harcourt Science, Grade 1: Arkansas Test Preparation. 2001. pap., tchr. ed. 22.80 (978-0-15-321178-2(4)) Harcourt Schl. Pubs.

—Harcourt Science, Grade 1: CA Graphic Organizer Chart. 2001. 83.20 (978-0-15-321214-7(4)) Harcourt Schl. Pubs.

—Harcourt Science, Grade 1: CA Standardized Test Preparation. 2001. pap., tchr. ed. 20.20 (978-0-15-321162-1(8)) Harcourt Schl. Pubs.

—Harcourt Science, Grade 1: CA Workbook. 1999. pap., tchr. ed., wbk. ed. 22.50 (978-0-15-317889-4(2)) Harcourt Schl. Pubs.

—Harcourt Science, Grade 1: California Edition. 1999. tchr. ed. 152.40 (978-0-15-317666-1(0)) Harcourt Schl. Pubs.

—Harcourt Science, Grade 1: FCAT Practice. 2001. pap., tchr. ed. 18.00 (978-0-15-320580-4(6)) Harcourt Schl. Pubs.

—Harcourt Science, Grade 1: Florida Planner. 2000. pap. 20.30 (978-0-15-318326-3(8)) Harcourt Schl. Pubs.

—Harcourt Science, Grade 1: Oklahoma Planning Guide. 2000. pap. 15.30 (978-0-15-319851-9(6)) Harcourt Schl. Pubs.

—Harcourt Science, Grade 1: PACT Test Preparation: South Carolina Edition. 2001. pap., tchr. ed. 22.80 (978-0-15-321250-5(0)) Harcourt Schl. Pubs.

—Harcourt Science, Grade 1: Planning Guide: Georgia Edition. 2nd ed. 2002. pap. 16.70 (978-0-15-332638-7(7)) Harcourt Schl. Pubs.

—Harcourt Science, Grade 1: Planning Guide: South Carolina Edition. 2001. pap. 15.30 (978-0-15-321240-6(3)) Harcourt Schl. Pubs.

—Harcourt Science, Grade 1: Standardized Test Preparation. 2001. pap., tchr. ed. 27.60 (978-0-15-320588-0(1)) Harcourt Schl. Pubs.

—Harcourt Science, Grade 1: TAAS Practice. 1999. pap., tchr. ed. 30.50 (978-0-15-318341-6(1)) Harcourt Schl. Pubs.

—Harcourt Science, Grade 1: Test Preparation: Georgia Edition. 2nd ed. 2002. pap., tchr. ed. 29.70 (978-0-15-332653-0(0)) Harcourt Schl. Pubs.

—Harcourt Science, Grade 1: Test Preparation: Oregon Edition. 2nd ed. 2002. pap., tchr. ed. 27.60 (978-0-15-329402-0(7)) Harcourt Schl. Pubs.

—Harcourt Science, Grade 1 Vol. 3: Physical Science: Louisiana Edition. 2nd ed. 2002. tchr. ed. 100.70 (978-0-15-328355-0(6)) Harcourt Schl. Pubs.

—Harcourt Science, Grade 2. 1999. pap., tchr. ed., wbk. ed. 22.50 (978-0-15-314972-6(8)) Harcourt Schl. Pubs.

—Harcourt Science, Grade 2: Arkansas Test Preparation. 2001. pap., tchr. ed. 22.80 (978-0-15-321179-9(2)) Harcourt Schl. Pubs.

—Harcourt Science, Grade 2: CA Standardized Test Preparation. 2001. pap., tchr. ed. 20.20 (978-0-15-321163-8(6)) Harcourt Schl. Pubs.

—Harcourt Science, Grade 2: CA Workbook. 1999. pap., tchr. ed., wbk. ed. 22.50 (978-0-15-317891-7(4)) Harcourt Schl. Pubs.

—Harcourt Science, Grade 2: California Edition. 1999. tchr. ed. 152.40 (978-0-15-317667-8(9)) Harcourt Schl. Pubs.

—Harcourt Science, Grade 2: FCAT Practice. 2001. pap., tchr. ed. 18.00 (978-0-15-320581-1(4)) Harcourt Schl. Pubs.

—Harcourt Science, Grade 2: Florida Planner. 2000. pap. 20.30 (978-0-15-318327-0(6)) Harcourt Schl. Pubs.

—Harcourt Science, Grade 2: Oklahoma Planning Guide. 2000. pap. 15.30 (978-0-15-319852-6(4)) Harcourt Schl. Pubs.

—Harcourt Science, Grade 2: PACT Test Preparation: South Carolina Edition. 2001. pap., tchr. ed. 22.80 (978-0-15-321251-2(9)) Harcourt Schl. Pubs.

—Harcourt Science, Grade 2: Planning Guide: Arkansas Edition. 2001. pap. 14.40 (978-0-15-321186-7(5)) Harcourt Schl. Pubs.

—Harcourt Science, Grade 2: Planning Guide: South Carolina Edition. 2001. pap. 15.30 (978-0-15-321241-3(1)) Harcourt Schl. Pubs.

—Harcourt Science, Grade 2: Standardized Test Preparation. 2001. pap., tchr. ed. 27.60 (978-0-15-320589-7(X)) Harcourt Schl. Pubs.

—Harcourt Science, Grade 2: TAAS Practice. 1999. pap., tchr. ed. 30.50 (978-0-15-318342-3(X)) Harcourt Schl. Pubs.

—Harcourt Science, Grade 2: Test Preparation: Oregon Edition. 2nd ed. 2002. pap., tchr. ed. 27.60 (978-0-15-329403-7(5)) Harcourt Schl. Pubs.

—Harcourt Science, Grade 2 Vol. 2: Earth Science: Louisiana Edition. 2nd ed. 2002. tchr. ed. 100.70 (978-0-15-328357-4(2)) Harcourt Schl. Pubs.

—Harcourt Science, Grade 3. 1999. pap., tchr. ed., wbk. ed. 26.50 (978-0-15-314973-3(6)) Harcourt Schl. Pubs.

—Harcourt Science, Grade 3: Arkansas Test Preparation. 2001. pap., tchr. ed. 22.80 (978-0-15-321180-5(6)) Harcourt Schl. Pubs.

—Harcourt Science, Grade 3: CA Standardized Test Preparation. 2001. pap., tchr. ed. 23.10 (978-0-15-321164-5(4)) Harcourt Schl. Pubs.

—Harcourt Science, Grade 3: CA Workbook. 1999. pap., tchr. ed., wbk. ed. 26.50 (978-0-15-317892-4(2)) Harcourt Schl. Pubs.

—Harcourt Science, Grade 3: California Edition. 1999. tchr. ed. 177.90 (978-0-15-317668-5(7)) Harcourt Schl. Pubs.

—Harcourt Science, Grade 3: FCAT Practice. 2000. pap., tchr. ed. 20.20 (978-0-15-318322-5(5)) Harcourt Schl. Pubs.

—Harcourt Science, Grade 3: Florida Planner. 2000. pap. 20.30 (978-0-15-318328-7(4)) Harcourt Schl. Pubs.

S

—Harcourt Science, Grade 3: Oklahoma Planning Guide. 2000. pap. 15.30 (978-0-15-319850-2(8)) ; pap. 15.30 (978-0-15-319853-3(2)) Harcourt Schl. Pubs.

—Harcourt Science, Grade 3: PACT Test Preparation, South Carolina Edition. 2001. pap., tchr. ed. 22.80 (978-0-15-321252-9(7)) Harcourt Schl. Pubs.

—Harcourt Science, Grade 3: Planning Guide: Arkansas Edition. 2001. pap. 14.40 (978-0-15-321187-4(3)) Harcourt Schl. Pubs.

—Harcourt Science, Grade 3: Planning Guide: South Carolina Edition. 2001. pap. 15.30 (978-0-15-321242-0(X)) Harcourt Schl. Pubs.

—Harcourt Science, Grade 3: TAAS Practice. 1999. pap., tchr. ed. 30.50 (978-0-15-318343-0(8)) Harcourt Schl. Pubs.

—Harcourt Science, Grade 3: Test Preparation: Georgia Edition. 2nd ed. 2002. pap., tchr. ed. 29.70 (978-0-15-332656-1(5)) Harcourt Schl. Pubs.

—Harcourt Science, Grade 3: Test Preparation: Oregon Edition. 2nd ed. 2002. pap., tchr. ed. 27.60 (978-0-15-329404-4(3)) Harcourt Schl. Pubs.

—Harcourt Science, Grade 3 Vol. 1: Life Science: Tennessee Edition, Vol. 1. 2nd ed. 2002. tchr. ed. 110.60 (978-0-15-328340-6(8)) Harcourt Schl. Pubs.

—Harcourt Science, Grade 3 Vol. 3: Physical Science: Louisiana Edition. 2nd ed. 2002. tchr. ed. 104.30 (978-0-15-328361-1(0)) Harcourt Schl. Pubs.

—Harcourt Science, Grade 3 Vol. 3: Physical Science: Tennessee Edition. 2nd ed. 2002. tchr. ed. 110.60 (978-0-15-328342-0(4)) Harcourt Schl. Pubs.

—Harcourt Science, Grade 4. 1999. pap., tchr. ed., wbk. ed. 26.50 (978-0-15-314974-0(4)) Harcourt Schl. Pubs.

—Harcourt Science, Grade 4: Arkansas Test Preparation. 2001. pap., tchr. ed. 23.50 (978-0-15-321181-2(4)) Harcourt Schl. Pubs.

—Harcourt Science, Grade 4: CA Standardized Test Preparation. 2001. pap., tchr. ed. 23.10 (978-0-15-321165-2(2)) Harcourt Schl. Pubs.

—Harcourt Science, Grade 4: CA Teacher's Guide to the Explorations CD-Rom. 1999. pap., tchr. ed. 8.50 (978-0-15-317516-9(8)) Harcourt Schl. Pubs.

—Harcourt Science, Grade 4: CA Workbook. 1999. pap., tchr. ed., wbk. ed. 26.50 (978-0-15-317893-1(0)) Harcourt Schl. Pubs.

—Harcourt Science, Grade 4: California Edition. 1999. tchr. ed. 177.90 (978-0-15-317669-2(5)) Harcourt Schl. Pubs.

—Harcourt Science, Grade 4: FCAT Practice. 1999. (Illus.). pap., tchr. ed. 20.20 (978-0-15-318323-2(3)) Harcourt Schl. Pubs.

—Harcourt Science, Grade 4: Florida Planner. 2000. pap. 20.30 (978-0-15-318329-4(2)) Harcourt Schl. Pubs.

—Harcourt Science, Grade 4: Oklahoma Planning Guide. 2000. pap. 15.30 (978-0-15-319854-0(0)) Harcourt Schl. Pubs.

—Harcourt Science, Grade 4: PACT Test Preparation: South Carolina Edition. 2001. pap., tchr. ed. 23.50 (978-0-15-321253-6(5)) Harcourt Schl. Pubs.

—Harcourt Science, Grade 4: Planning Guide: Arkansas Edition. 2001. pap. 14.40 (978-0-15-321188-1(1)) Harcourt Schl. Pubs.

—Harcourt Science, Grade 4: Planning Guide: Georgia Edition. 2nd ed. 2002. pap. 16.70 (978-0-15-332642-4(5)) Harcourt Schl. Pubs.

—Harcourt Science, Grade 4: Planning Guide: South Carolina Edition. 2001. pap. 15.30 (978-0-15-321243-7(8)) Harcourt Schl. Pubs.

—Harcourt Science, Grade 4: Standardized Test Preparation. 2001. pap., tchr. ed. 29.30 (978-0-15-320591-0(1)) Harcourt Schl. Pubs.

—Harcourt Science, Grade 4: TAAS Practice. 1999. pap., tchr. ed. 30.50 (978-0-15-318344-7(6)) Harcourt Schl. Pubs.

—Harcourt Science, Grade 4: Test Preparation: Georgia Edition. 2nd ed. 2002. pap., tchr. ed. 31.70 (978-0-15-332657-8(3)) Harcourt Schl. Pubs.

—Harcourt Science, Grade 4: Test Preparation: Oregon Edition. 2nd ed. 2002. pap., tchr. ed. 29.30 (978-0-15-329405-1(1)) Harcourt Schl. Pubs.

—Harcourt Science, Grade 4 Vol. 1: Life Science: Louisiana Edition. 2nd ed. 2002. tchr. ed. 104.30 (978-0-15-328362-8(9)) Harcourt Schl. Pubs.

—Harcourt Science, Grade 4 Vol. 1: Life Science: Tennessee Edition. 2nd ed. 2002. tchr. ed. 110.60 (978-0-15-328343-7(2)) Harcourt Schl. Pubs.

—Harcourt Science, Grade 4 Vol. 2: Earth Science: Louisiana Edition. 2nd ed. 2002. tchr. ed. 104.30 (978-0-15-328363-5(7)) Harcourt Schl. Pubs.

—Harcourt Science, Grade 4 Vol. 3: Physical Science: Louisiana Edition. 2nd ed. 2002. tchr. ed. 104.30 (978-0-15-328364-2(5)) Harcourt Schl. Pubs.

—Harcourt Science, Grade 4 Vol. 3: Physical Science: Tennessee Edition. 2nd ed. 2002. tchr. ed. 110.60 (978-0-15-328345-1(9)) Harcourt Schl. Pubs.

—Harcourt Science, Grade 5. 1999. pap., tchr. ed., wbk. ed. 29.20 (978-0-15-314975-7(2)) Harcourt Schl. Pubs.

—Harcourt Science, Grade 5: Arkansas Test Preparation. 2001. pap., tchr. ed. 23.50 (978-0-15-321182-9(2)) Harcourt Schl. Pubs.

—Harcourt Science, Grade 5: CA Standardized Test Preparation. 2001. pap., tchr. ed. 23.10 (978-0-15-321166-9(0)) Harcourt Schl. Pubs.

—Harcourt Science, Grade 5: CA Workbook. 1999. pap., tchr. ed., wbk. ed. 29.20 (978-0-15-317894-8(9)) Harcourt Schl. Pubs.

—Harcourt Science, Grade 5: California Edition. 1999. tchr. ed. 181.40 (978-0-15-317671-5(7)) Harcourt Schl. Pubs.

—Harcourt Science, Grade 5: FCAT Practice. 1999. pap., tchr. ed. 20.20 (978-0-15-318324-9(1)) Harcourt Schl. Pubs.

—Harcourt Science, Grade 5: Florida Planner. 2000. pap. 20.30 (978-0-15-318330-0(6)) Harcourt Schl. Pubs.

—Harcourt Science, Grade 5: Oklahoma Planning Guide. 2000. pap. 15.30 (978-0-15-319855-7(9)) Harcourt Schl. Pubs.

—Harcourt Science, Grade 5: PACT Test Preparation: South Carolina Edition. 2001. pap., tchr. ed. 23.50 (978-0-15-321254-3(3)) Harcourt Schl. Pubs.

—Harcourt Science, Grade 5: Planning Guide: Arkansas Edition. 2001. pap. 14.40 (978-0-15-321189-8(X)) Harcourt Schl. Pubs.

—Harcourt Science, Grade 5: Planning Guide: Georgia Edition. 2nd ed. 2002. pap. 16.70 (978-0-15-332643-1(3)) Harcourt Schl. Pubs.

—Harcourt Science, Grade 5: Planning Guide: Kentucky Edition. 2nd ed. 2002. pap. 16.70 (978-0-15-332673-8(5)) Harcourt Schl. Pubs.

—Harcourt Science, Grade 5: Planning Guide: South Carolina Edition. 2001. pap. 15.30 (978-0-15-321244-4(6)) Harcourt Schl. Pubs.

—Harcourt Science, Grade 5: Standardized Test Preparation. 2001. pap., tchr. ed. 29.30 (978-0-15-320592-7(X)) Harcourt Schl. Pubs.

—Harcourt Science, Grade 5: TAAS Practice. 1999. pap., tchr. ed. 30.50 (978-0-15-318345-4(4)) Harcourt Schl. Pubs.

—Harcourt Science, Grade 5: Test Preparation: Georgia Edition. 2nd ed. 2002. pap., tchr. ed. 31.70 (978-0-15-332658-5(1)) Harcourt Schl. Pubs.

—Harcourt Science, Grade 5: Test Preparation: Oregon Edition. 2nd ed. 2002. pap., tchr. ed. 29.30 (978-0-15-329406-8(X)) Harcourt Schl. Pubs.

—Harcourt Science, Grade 5 Vol. 1: Life Science: Louisiana Edition. 2nd ed. 2002. tchr. ed. 107.90 (978-0-15-328365-9(3)) Harcourt Schl. Pubs.

—Harcourt Science, Grade 5 Vol. 1: Life Science: Tennessee Edition. 2nd ed. 2002. tchr. ed. 114.50 (978-0-15-328346-8(7)) Harcourt Schl. Pubs.

—Harcourt Science, Grade 5 Vol. 3: Physical Science: Louisiana Edition. 2nd ed. 2002. tchr. ed. 107.90 (978-0-15-328367-3(X)) Harcourt Schl. Pubs.

—Harcourt Science, Grade 5 Vol. 3: Physical Science: Tennessee Edition. 2nd ed. 2002. tchr. ed. 114.50 (978-0-15-328348-2(3)) Harcourt Schl. Pubs.

—Harcourt Science, Grade 6. 1999. pap., tchr. ed., wbk. ed. 29.20 (978-0-15-314976-4(0)) Harcourt Schl. Pubs.

—Harcourt Science, Grade 6: Arkansas Test Preparation. 2001. pap., tchr. ed. 23.50 (978-0-15-321183-6(0)) Harcourt Schl. Pubs.

—Harcourt Science, Grade 6: FCAT Practice. 2001. pap., tchr. ed. 20.90 (978-0-15-320596-5(2)) Harcourt Schl. Pubs.

—Harcourt Science, Grade 6: Oklahoma Planning Guide. 2000. pap. 15.30 (978-0-15-319856-4(7)) Harcourt Schl. Pubs.

—Harcourt Science, Grade 6: Planning Guide: Arkansas Edition. 2001. pap. 14.40 (978-0-15-321190-4(3)) Harcourt Schl. Pubs.

—Harcourt Science, Grade 6: Planning Guide: Kentucky Edition. 2nd ed. 2002. pap. 16.70 (978-0-15-332674-5(3)) Harcourt Schl. Pubs.

—Harcourt Science, Grade 6: Standardized Test Preparation. 2001. pap., tchr. ed. 29.30 (978-0-15-320593-4(8)) Harcourt Schl. Pubs.

—Harcourt Science, Grade 6: Test Preparation: Oregon Edition. 2nd ed. 2002. pap., tchr. ed. 29.30 (978-0-15-329407-5(8)) Harcourt Schl. Pubs.

—Harcourt Science, Grade K: California Edition. 1999. tchr. ed. 121.80 (978-0-15-317665-4(2)) Harcourt Schl. Pubs.

—Harcourt Science, Grade K: Florida Planner. 2000. pap. 20.30 (978-0-15-318325-6(X)) Harcourt Schl. Pubs.

—Harcourt Science, Grade K: Planning Guide: Arkansas Edition. 2001. pap. 14.40 (978-0-15-321184-3(9)) Harcourt Schl. Pubs.

—Harcourt Science, Grade K: Planning Guide: Georgia Edition. 2nd ed. 2002. pap. 16.70 (978-0-15-332637-0(9)) Harcourt Schl. Pubs.

—Harcourt Science, Grade K: Planning Guide: Kentucky Edition. 2nd ed. 2002. pap. 16.70 (978-0-15-332659-2(X)) Harcourt Schl. Pubs.

—Harcourt Science Instant Reader Bk. 1. 2nd ed. 2002. (Illus.). (J). pap. 2.40 (978-0-15-325271-6(5)) Harcourt Schl. Pubs.

—Harcourt Science Instant Reader Bk. 2. 2nd ed. 2002. (Illus.). (J). pap. 2.40 (978-0-15-325272-3(3)) Harcourt Schl. Pubs.

—Harcourt Science Instant Reader Bk. 3. 2nd ed. 2002. (Illus.). (J). pap. 2.40 (978-0-15-325273-0(1)) Harcourt Schl. Pubs.

—Harcourt Science Instant Reader Bk. 4. 2nd ed. 2002. (Illus.). (J). pap. 2.40 (978-0-15-325274-7(X)) Harcourt Schl. Pubs.

—Harcourt Science Instant Reader Bk. 5. 2nd ed. 2002. (Illus.). (J). pap. 2.40 (978-0-15-325275-4(8)) Harcourt Schl. Pubs.

—Harcourt Science Instant Reader Bk. 6. 2nd ed. 2002. (Illus.). (J). pap. 2.40 (978-0-15-325276-1(6)) Harcourt Schl. Pubs.

—Harcourt Science Leveled Library. 2nd ed. 2002. (Harcourt Science Ser.). (Illus.). (gr. 3 up). pap. 61.30 (978-0-15-334256-1(0)); (gr. 4 up). pap. 61.30 (978-0-15-334257-8(9)); (gr. 5 up). pap. 61.30 (978-0-15-334258-5(7)); (gr. 6 up). pap. 61.30 (978-0-15-334259-2(5)) Harcourt Schl. Pubs.

—Holt Science, Grade 1: TAAS Practice. 2000. (SPA.). pap., tchr. ed. 37.60 (978-0-15-318351-5(9)) Harcourt Schl. Pubs.

—Holt Science, Grade 2: TAAS Practice. 2000. (SPA.). pap., tchr. ed. 37.60 (978-0-15-318352-2(7)) Harcourt Schl. Pubs.

—Holt Science, Grade 3: TAAS Practice. 2000. (SPA.). pap., tchr. ed. 37.60 (978-0-15-318353-9(5)) Harcourt Schl. Pubs.

—Holt Science, Grade 4: TAAS Practice. 1999. (SPA.). pap., tchr. ed. 37.60 (978-0-15-318354-6(3)) Harcourt Schl. Pubs.

—Holt Science, Grade 5: TAAS Practice. 2000. (SPA.). pap., tchr. ed. 37.60 (978-0-15-318355-3(1)) Harcourt Schl. Pubs.

—A Hot Day: Science Reader. 1999. (SPA., Illus.). (J). pap. 3.70 (978-0-15-316113-1(2)) Harcourt Schl. Pubs.

—Jeff's Magnet: Science Reader. 2000. (SPA., Illus.). (J). pap. 3.70 (978-0-15-316115-5(9)) Harcourt Schl. Pubs.

—One, Two, Three, What Do You See. 3rd ed. 2002. (Trophies English Language Learners Ser.). (Illus.). (J). (gr. 1). pap. 3.20 (978-0-15-327566-1(9)) Harcourt Schl. Pubs.

—Push It or Pull It: Science Reader. 1999. (SPA., Illus.). (J). pap. 3.70 (978-0-15-316114-8(0)) Harcourt Schl. Pubs.

—Seasons: Science Reader. 1999. (SPA., Illus.). (J). pap. 3.70 (978-0-15-316111-7(6)) Harcourt Schl. Pubs.

—Sink or Float: Science Reader. 1999. (SPA., Illus.). (J). pap. 3.70 (978-0-15-316112-4(4)) Harcourt Schl. Pubs.

—Spanish Science Vols. 12: Instant Reader Package. 1999. (Harcourt Ciencias Ser.). (SPA., Illus.). (gr. 1 up). pap. 50.80 (978-0-15-316958-8(3)); (gr. 2 up). pap. 50.80 (978-0-15-316959-5(1)) Harcourt Schl. Pubs.

—What Do You See: Science Reader. 2000. (SPA., Illus.). (J). pap. 3.70 (978-0-15-316102-5(7)) Harcourt Schl. Pubs.

Harmer, Andrea J. Nanotechnology for Grades 1-6+ Introducing Nan & Bucky Dog. 2005. (ENG.). 44p. (J). (ps-7). per. 24.00 (978-1-4208-1903-8(8)) AuthorHouse.

Harris, Nicholas, ed. High-Tech Science. 2002. (Blackbirch Visual Encyclopedia Ser.). (Illus.). 64p. (J). 38.70 (978-1-56711-522-2(5) , Blackbirch Pr., Inc.) Thomson Gale.

Harris, Nicholas & Helbrough, Emma. Everyday Science. 2006. 32p. (gr. 2-4). 23.70 (978-1-4103-0351-6(9) , Blackbirch Pr., Inc.) Thomson Gale.

Haslam, Andrew. Machines. 2004. (Make It Work! Science Ser.). (Illus.). 48p. (gr. 3-6). (J). pap. 6.95 (978-1-58728-357-4(3)); 12.95 (978-1-58728-368-0(9)) T&N Children's Publishing. (Two Can Publishing).

Hassard, Jack. Science As Inquiry. 2004. (Illus.). 280p. pap. (978-0-673-57731-3(7)) Good Year Bks.

Hauck, Max M. Science vs. Crime. 2008. (Essentials of Forensic Science Ser.). 176p. (gr. 6-12). 35.00 (978-0-8160-5508-1(4)) Facts On File, Inc.

Haycack, Cara, adapted by. Maya & Miguel: Un Novio Para Abuelita. 2005. (Maya & Miguel Ser.). (SPA., Illus.). 80p. (J). 5.99 (978-0-439-74901-5(8) , Scholastic en Espanol) Scholastic, Inc.

Hazlo mover! Science, 6 vols.Tr. of Make It Move! Science. (SPA.). (gr. k-2). 28.95 (978-0-7368-3052-2(9) , Yellow Umbrella Bks.) Capstone Pr., Inc.

HB Staff. Science Anytime, 1995. 95th ed. 2002. (gr. 4). pap., wbk. ed. 11.00 (978-0-15-306786-0(1)) Harcourt Schl. Pubs.

Head, Honor. My Pet, 6 bks., Set. Burton, Jane, photos by. Incl. Guinea Pig. lib. bdg. 25.69 (978-0-7398-2888-5(6)); Hamsters & Gerbils. lib. bdg. 25.69 (978-0-7398-2886-1(X)); Kitten. lib. bdg. 25.69 (978-0-7398-2884-7(3)); Puppy. lib. bdg. 25.69 (978-0-7398-2885-4(1)); Rabbit. lib. bdg. 25.69 (978-0-7398-2887-8(8)); Rats & Mice. lib. bdg. 25.69 (978-0-7398-2889-2(4)); (Illus.). 32p. (J). (gr. 3-5). 2000. Set lib. bdg. 154.14 (978-0-7398-2890-8(8)) Raintree.

Hensley, Wendie & Licata, Annette. Painless Junior Science. 2007. (Painless Junior Ser.). (Illus.). 208p. pap. 8.99 ***(978-0-7641-3719-8(0))*** Barron's Educational Series, Inc.

Here, There, & Everywhere Science. (gr. k-2). 19.95 (978-0-7368-1796-7(4)) Red Brick Learning.

Hewitt, Sally. Light & Dark. Moller, Ray, illus. 1998. (It's Science! Ser.). 32p. (J). (gr. k-3). 23.50 (978-0-516-20842-8(X) , Children's Pr.) Scholastic Library Publishing.

—Listen Up!, 5 vols. 2005. (QEB Let's Start! Science Ser.). (Illus.). 24p. (J). (gr. 1-4). lib. bdg. 15.95 (978-1-59566-086-2(0)) QEB Publishing Inc.

—Look Here!, 5 vols. 2005. (QEB Let's Start! Science Ser.). (Illus.). 24p. (J). (gr. 1-4). lib. bdg. 15.95 (978-1-59566-087-9(9)) QEB Publishing Inc.

—Smell That!, 5 vols. 2005. (QEB Let's Start! Science Ser.). (Illus.). 24p. (J). (gr. 1-4). lib. bdg. 15.95 (978-1-59566-088-6(7)) QEB Publishing Inc.

—Tastes Good!, 5 vols. 2005. (QEB Let's Start! Science Ser.). (Illus.). 24p. (J). (gr. 1-4). lib. bdg. 15.95 (978-1-59566-089-3(5)) QEB Publishing Inc.

—Touch That!, 5 vols. 2005. (QEB Let's Start! Science Ser.). (Illus.). 24p. (J). (gr. 1-4). lib. bdg. 15.95 (978-1-59566-090-9(9)) QEB Publishing Inc.

Hex, Kathleen. A Taste of Science. 2003. 96p. (J). (gr. 3-5). pap. 10.99 (978-0-7682-2742-0(9) , FS99245) Schaffer, Frank Pubns.

Hil, Mcgraw. Gr 3 Matter & Energy Sci. 2000. (McGraw-Hill Science Ser.). (gr. 3 up). (978-0-02-278209-2(5)) Macmillan/McGraw-Hill Schl. Div.

—Gr 4 Clssfyng Lv Thngs Sc. 2000. (McGraw-Hill Science Ser.). (gr. 4 up). (978-0-02-278215-3(X)) Macmillan/McGraw-Hill Schl. Div.

—Gr 4 Elec & Mag Sci Pe. 2000. (McGraw-Hill Science Ser.). (gr. 4 up). (978-0-02-278219-1(2)) Macmillan/McGraw-Hill Schl. Div.

—Gr 5 Th Enrgy Snd & Lgt. 2000. (McGraw-Hill Science Ser.). (gr. 5 up). (978-0-02-278225-2(7)) Macmillan/McGraw-Hill Schl. Div.

—Gr 6 Forces Sci Pe. 2000. (McGraw-Hill Science Ser.). (gr. 6 up). (978-0-02-278233-7(8)) Macmillan/McGraw-Hill Schl. Div.

—Gr 6 Science Journal. 2000. (McGraw-Hill Science Ser.). (gr. 6 up). (978-0-02-278123-1(4)) Macmillan/McGraw-Hill Schl. Div.

—Gr3-6 Science Assmnt Reso. 2000. (McGraw-Hill Science Ser.). (gr. 6 up). (978-0-02-278115-6(3)) Macmillan/McGraw-Hill Schl. Div.

—Gr4 Science Practice Wkbk. 2000. (McGraw-Hill Science Ser.). (gr. 4 up). wbk. ed. (978-0-02-277708-1(3)) Macmillan/McGraw-Hill Schl. Div.

—Gr6 Prprty O/Mtr & Enrgy. 2000. (McGraw-Hill Science Ser.). (gr. 6 up). (978-0-02-278231-3(1)) Macmillan/McGraw-Hill Schl. Div.

—Sciasmtbk Matter & Energy. 2000. (McGraw-Hill Science Ser.). (gr. 3 up). (978-0-02-277749-4(0)) Macmillan/McGraw-Hill Schl. Div.

—Sciasmtbk Matter on the M. 2000. (McGraw-Hill Science Ser.). (gr. 4 up). (978-0-02-277756-2(3)) Macmillan/McGraw-Hill Schl. Div.

—Sciasmtbk Prprty O Mttr & 2000. (McGraw-Hill Science Ser.). (gr. 6 up). (978-0-02-277771-5(7)) Macmillan/McGraw-Hill Schl. Div.

—Sciasmtbk Rocks & Resourc. 2000. (McGraw-Hill Science Ser.). (gr. 3 up). (978-0-02-277752-4(0)) Macmillan/McGraw-Hill Schl. Div.

—Sciasmtbk T Enrgy of Snd. 2000. (McGraw-Hill Science Ser.). (gr. 5 up). (978-0-02-277765-4(2)) Macmillan/McGraw-Hill Schl. Div.

—Trfpaswak Forces. 2000. (McGraw-Hill Science Ser.). (gr. 6 up). (978-0-02-277654-1(0)) Macmillan/McGraw-Hill Schl. Div.

—Trfpaswak Matter & Energy. 2000. (McGraw-Hill Science Ser.). (gr. 3 up). (978-0-02-277631-2(1)) Macmillan/McGraw-Hill Schl. Div.

—Trfpaswak Prpty O/Mttr & 2000. (McGraw-Hill Science Ser.). (gr. 6 up). (978-0-02-277652-7(4)) Macmillan/McGraw-Hill Schl. Div.

Hilltree, Angela. ABC Coloring Book: Creation Science & Geology. 2004. (Illus.). 26p. (J). 6.50 ***(978-1-931941-10-5(6))*** Media Angels, Inc.

La Historia de la Via Lactea, Unidad 2: Superlibros (Big Books) 2001. (Aventuras A Traves Del Tiempo Ser.). (ENG & SPA.). (gr. 3 up). (978-0-02-147874-3(0)) Macmillan/McGraw-Hill Schl. Div.

Hixson, Bryce. Newton Take 3. Hixson, Bryce, illus. 2003. (Illus.). (J). per. 14.95 (978-0-9660965-3-8(3)) Loose In The Lab.

—What's Up? Hixson, Bryce, illus. 2003. (Illus.). (J). per. 14.95 (978-1-931801-05-8(3)) Loose In The Lab.

—50 Science Zingers! Hixson, Bryce, illus. 2002. (Illus.). (J). per. 14.95 (978-1-931801-00-3(2)) Loose In The Lab.

HM Group Staff. HMS Science. 2000. 128p. pap. 12.95 (978-0-8108-3808-6(7)); 176p. pap., tchr. ed. 17.95 (978-0-8108-3809-3(5)) Scarecrow Pr., Inc.

Hola! 2000. (McGraw-Hill Ciencias Ser.). (ENG & SPA.). (gr. k up). (978-0-02-279701-0(7)) Macmillan/McGraw-Hill Schl. Div.

Hola: Aventuras (Adventure Books) 2000. (Aventuras A Traves Del Tiempo Ser.). (ENG & SPA.). (gr. k up). (978-0-02-148659-5(X)) Macmillan/McGraw-Hill Schl. Div.

Holden, Arianne. Science. (Playschool Ser.). (Illus.). 2003. 32p. pap. 5.99 (978-1-84215-668-1(3) , Southwater); 1999. 48p. 7.95 (978-1-85967-832-9(7)) Anness Publishing GBR. *Dist:* National Bk. Network.

Hollenbeck, Kathleen M. Early Themes: Ocean Life. 2002. pap. 9.95 (978-0-439-18838-8(5)) Scholastic, Inc.

Holman. Science Spectacular: Enhanced Online Edition. 2002. 74.13 (978-0-03-072484-8(8)) Holt, Rinehart & Winston.

Holmes. Gateway Science, Level K. 5th ed. (J). 23.61 (978-0-07-029942-9(0)) Macmillan/McGraw-Hill Schl. Div.

Holt, Rinehart and Winston Staff. Answers to Study Guide: Holt Science & Technology: Texas Edition. 2nd ed. 2002. (SPA.). (YA). (gr. 7). pap. 11.40 (978-0-03-069208-6(3)); (gr. 8). pap. 11.40 (978-0-03-069209-3(1)) Holt, Rinehart & Winston.

—The Character of Living Things Resources: Texas Edition. 2nd ed. 2001. (Holt Science & Technology Ser.: No. 3). (Illus.). pap. 26.00 (978-0-03-064861-8(0)) Holt, Rinehart & Winston.

—Classification: Chapter Resources: Tennessee Edition. 3rd ed. 2003. (Holt Science & Technology Ser.). pap. 11.40 (978-0-03-069162-1(1)) Holt, Rinehart & Winston.

—Environmental Science Chptr. 8: Population & Communities. 4th ed. Date not set. pap. 11.20 (978-0-03-068067-0(0)) Holt, Rinehart & Winston.

—Environmental Science Chptr. 9: The Human Population. 4th ed. Date not set. pap. 11.20 (978-0-03-068068-7(9)) Holt, Rinehart & Winston.

—Environmental Science Chptr. 11: Water. 4th ed. Date not set. pap. 11.20 (978-0-03-068071-7(9)) Holt, Rinehart & Winston.

—Harcourt Science & Technology: Strategies & Practice Answer Key. 4th ed. 2004. (Illus.). pap. 6.00 (978-0-03-019863-2(1)) Holt, Rinehart & Winston.

—Holt Ciencias y Technologia: Directed Reading Worksheets Answer Key: Texas Edition. 2nd ed. 2001. (gr. 6). pap. 12.00 (978-0-03-064627-0(8)) Holt, Rinehart & Winston.

—Holt Ciencias y Technologia: Directed Reading Worksheets: Texas Edition. 2nd ed. 2001. (J). pap. 20.00 (978-0-03-064628-7(6)) Holt, Rinehart & Winston.

—Holt Ciencias y Technologia: Life. 2000. 75.80 (978-0-03-064749-9(5)) Holt, Rinehart & Winston.

—Holt Ciencias y Technologia: Study Guide with Answer Key: Texas Edition. 2nd ed. 2001. (J). (gr. 6). pap., stu. ed. 10.60 (978-0-03-064447-4(X)) Holt, Rinehart & Winston.

—Holt Ciencias y Technologia. 2nd ed. 2001. (J). pap., stu. ed. 15.60 (978-0-03-064451-1(8)) Holt, Rinehart & Winston.

—Holt Environmental Science: Spanish Student Edition. 4th ed. 2004. 74.20 (978-0-03-068063-2(8)) Holt, Rinehart & Winston.

—Holt Science & Technology. 4th annot. ed. 2004. tchr. ed. 128.80 (978-0-03-073173-0(9)); tchr. ed. 128.80 (978-0-03-073174-7(7)); tchr. ed. 128.80 (978-0-03-073176-1(3)) Holt, Rinehart & Winston.

—Holt Science & Technology: Chapter Resources. 5th ed. 2005. pap. 87.36 (978-0-03-030632-7(9)) Holt, Rinehart & Winston.

—Holt Science & Technology: Custom A, C, D, F, I. 2nd ed. 2002. 73.00 (978-0-03-070032-3(9)) Holt, Rinehart & Winston.

—Holt Science & Technology: Custom A, F, K, M. 2nd ed. 2002. 65.60 (978-0-03-070041-5(8)) Holt, Rinehart & Winston.

—Holt Science & Technology: Custom B, E, J, L, M. 2nd ed. 2002. 73.00 (978-0-03-070033-0(7)) Holt, Rinehart & Winston.

—Holt Science & Technology: Custom C, D, J, K. 2nd ed. 2002. 65.60 (978-0-03-070034-7(5)) Holt, Rinehart & Winston.

—Holt Science & Technology: Custom E, F, H, I, O. 2nd ed. 2002. 73.00 (978-0-03-070036-1(1)) Holt, Rinehart & Winston.

—Holt Science & Technology: Custom Edition: C, F, G, I, M. 2nd ed. 2002. 88.60 (978-0-03-070991-3(1)) Holt, Rinehart & Winston.

—Holt Science & Technology: Custom F, G, L, N, H. 2nd ed. 2002. (YA). 73.00 (978-0-03-070028-6(0)) Holt, Rinehart & Winston.

—Holt Science & Technology: Custom G, L, M, N. 2nd ed. 2002. 65.60 (978-0-03-070037-8(X)) Holt, Rinehart & Winston.

—Holt Science & Technology: Custom K, L, C, F, G. 2nd ed. 2002. 73.00 (978-0-03-070029-3(9)) Holt, Rinehart & Winston.

—Holt Science & Technology: Custom M, I, A, B, E. 2nd ed. 2002. 73.00 (978-0-03-070031-6(0)) Holt, Rinehart & Winston.

—Holt Science & Technology: Datasheets for Labs: Texas Edition - Grade 7. 2001. pap. 17.93 (978-0-03-064499-3(2)) Holt, Rinehart & Winston.

—Holt Science & Technology: Datasheets for Labs: Texas Edition - Grade 8. 2001. pap. 17.93 (978-0-03-064501-3(8)) Holt, Rinehart & Winston.

—Holt Science & Technology: Directed Reading Answer Key. 4th ed. 2004. (Illus.). pap. 11.20 (978-0-03-037018-2(3)); pap. 11.20 (978-0-03-037019-9(1)); pap. 11.20 (978-0-03-037021-2(3)) Holt, Rinehart & Winston.

—Holt Science & Technology: Directed Reading Worksheets. 4th ed. 2004. pap. 15.00 (978-0-03-036992-6(4)); pap. 15.00 (978-0-03-036993-3(2)); pap. 15.00 (978-0-03-036994-0(0)) Holt, Rinehart & Winston.

—Holt Science & Technology: Earth: Critical Thinking & Problem Worksheets. 2000. pap. 11.60 (978-0-03-054388-3(6)) Holt, Rinehart & Winston.

—Holt Science & Technology: Enhanced Online Edition. 2002. 74.53 (978-0-03-072489-3(9)) Holt, Rinehart & Winston.

—Holt Science & Technology: Enhanced Online Edition - Short Course. 5th ed. 2004. (J). (gr. k). 18.60 (978-0-03-030493-4(8)); (gr. 1). 18.60 (978-0-03-030496-5(2)); (gr. 2). 18.60 (978-0-03-030501-6(2)) Holt, Rinehart & Winston.

—Holt Science & Technology: Life: Critical Thinking & Problem Worksheets. 2000. pap. 11.60 (978-0-03-054378-4(9)) Holt, Rinehart & Winston.

—Holt Science & Technology: Life: Study Guide with Answer Key - California Edition. 2000. pap. 10.80 (978-0-03-055649-4(X)) Holt, Rinehart & Winston.

—Holt Science & Technology: Online Edition Update, Level G. 2nd ed. 2003. 2.60 (978-0-03-037243-8(7)) Holt, Rinehart & Winston.

—Holt Science & Technology: Physical Science. 5th ed. 2004. (Illus.). pap., stu. ed. 17.13 (978-0-03-030161-2(0)) Holt, Rinehart & Winston.

—Holt Science & Technology: Physical Science: Reading & Comprehension Guide. 5th ed. 2004. pap. 17.13 (978-0-03-036063-3(3)) Holt, Rinehart & Winston.

—Holt Science & Technology: Physical Science: Special Needs Workbook. 5th ed. 2004. pap., wbk. ed. 17.13 (978-0-03-036056-5(0)) Holt, Rinehart & Winston.

—Holt Science & Technology: Physics: Critical Thinking & Problem Worksheets. 2000. pap. 11.60 (978-0-03-054398-2(3)) Holt, Rinehart & Winston.

—Holt Science & Technology: Program Introduction Booklet. 5th ed. 2004. (Illus.). 4.33 (978-0-03-030162-9(9)) Holt, Rinehart & Winston.

—Holt Science & Technology: Test Practice Guide - Texas Edition - Grade 7. 2nd ed. 2001. pap. 21.66 (978-0-03-064837-3(8)) Holt, Rinehart & Winston.

—Holt Science & Technology: Texas Edition. 2001. (J). (gr. 6). 72.60 (978-0-03-064361-3(9)); 2nd ed. 2002. (SPA.). (YA). (gr. 7). pap., stu. ed. 16.00 (978-0-03-069201-7(6)); 2nd ed. 2002. (SPA.). (YA). (gr. 8). pap., stu. ed. 16.00 (978-0-03-069202-4(4)) Holt, Rinehart & Winston.

—Holt Science & Technology: Texas Edition - Grade 6. 2001. pap., stu. ed. 16.26 (978-0-03-064493-1(3)) Holt, Rinehart & Winston.

—Holt Science & Technology: Texas Edition - Grade 8. 2001. pap., stu. ed. 16.26 (978-0-03-064488-7(7)) Holt, Rinehart & Winston.

—Holt Science & Technology: With Answer Key: Texas Edition. 2001. (J). pap., stu. ed. 10.60 (978-0-03-064471-9(2)); (YA). (gr. 7). pap., stu. ed. 10.60 (978-0-03-064472-6(0)); (YA). (gr. 8). pap., stu. ed. 10.60 (978-0-03-064473-3(9)) Holt, Rinehart & Winston.

—Holt Science & Technology Chptr. 1: World of Science: Chapter Resources - Tennessee Edition. 3rd ed. 2003. (J). (gr. 6). pap. 11.40 (978-0-03-069106-5(0)); (YA). (gr. 7). pap. 11.40 (978-0-03-069129-4(X)); (YA). (gr. 8). pap. 11.40 (978-0-03-069158-4(3)) Holt, Rinehart & Winston.

—Holt Science & Technology Chptr. 20: Elements & Compounds: Chapter Resources - Tennessee Edition. 3rd ed. 2003. (YA). pap. 11.40 (978-0-03-069153-9(2)) Holt, Rinehart & Winston.

—Holt Science & Technology Chptr. 22: The Periodic Table: Chapter Resources - Tennessee Edition. 3rd ed. 2003. (YA). pap. 11.40 (978-0-03-069156-0(7)) Holt, Rinehart & Winston.

—Holt Science & Technology, Grade 7: Reinforcement Worksheets: Texas Edition. 2nd ed. 2001. pap. 21.61 (978-0-03-065983-6(3)) Holt, Rinehart & Winston.

—Holt Science & Technology, Grade 8: Reinforcement Worksheets: Texas Edition. 2nd ed. 2001. pap. 21.61 (978-0-03-065986-7(8)) Holt, Rinehart & Winston.

—Life Science. 5th ed. 2004. (Holt Science & Technology Ser.). (SPA., Illus.). 75.80 (978-0-03-021179-9(4)) Holt, Rinehart & Winston.

—Life Science: Directed Reading & Vocabulary Workbook. 5th ed. 2004. (Holt Science & Technology Ser.). (SPA., Illus.). pap., wbk. ed. 17.13 (978-0-03-036057-2(9)) Holt, Rinehart & Winston.

—Life Science: Study Guide. 5th ed. 2004. (Holt Science & Technology Ser.). (SPA., Illus.). pap., stu. ed. 17.13 (978-0-03-030151-3(3)) Holt, Rinehart & Winston.

—NJ One-Stope Lesson Planner 2002. 2002. (Holt Science & Technology Ser.). (J). cd-rom 100.00 (978-0-03-072168-7(7)) Holt, Rinehart & Winston.

—Physical Science. 5th ed. 2004. (Holt Science & Technology Ser.). (SPA., Illus.). 75.80 (978-0-03-021272-7(3)) Holt, Rinehart & Winston.

—Physical Science: Chapter Resources. 5th ed. 2004. (Holt Science & Technology Ser.). (Illus.). pap. 290.13 (978-0-03-030126-1(2)) Holt, Rinehart & Winston.

—Physical Science: Directed Reading & Vocabulary Workbook. 5th ed. 2004. (Holt Science & Technology Ser.). (SPA., Illus.). pap., wbk. ed. 17.13 (978-0-03-036059-6(5)) Holt, Rinehart & Winston.

—Physical Science: Science Tutorials. 5th ed. 2005. (Holt Science & Technology Ser.). 49.26 (978-0-03-038804-0(X)) Holt, Rinehart & Winston.

—Physical Science: Study Guide. 5th ed. 2004. (Holt Science & Technology Ser.). (SPA., Illus.). pap., stu. ed. 17.13 (978-0-03-030157-5(2)) Holt, Rinehart & Winston.

—Science: High School: Reading & Content Areas - Georgia Edition. 2nd ed. 2002. pap., tchr. ed. 41.93 (978-0-03-068031-1(X)) Holt, Rinehart & Winston.

—Science: High School: Reading & Content Areas - Kentucky Edition. 2nd ed. 2002. pap., tchr. ed. 41.93 (978-0-03-068032-8(8)) Holt, Rinehart & Winston.

—Science: High School Standard Test Preparation: Missouri Edition. 2001. pap. 13.46 (978-0-03-067579-9(0)) Holt, Rinehart & Winston.

—Science: Reading & Content Areas for Middle School: Alabama Edition. 2nd ed. 2002. pap. 41.53 (978-0-03-067474-7(3)) Holt, Rinehart & Winston.

—Science Plus 2002: Level Green. 2001. stu. ed. 77.80 (978-0-03-064529-7(8)) Holt, Rinehart & Winston.

—Science Skills Workshop: Reading/Content Area. 2nd ed. 2002. pap. 34.13 (978-0-03-064424-5(0)) Holt, Rinehart & Winston.

—Science Spectacular: Strategies & Practice Answer Key. 4th ed. 2004. (Illus.). pap. 12.80 (978-0-03-020482-1(8)) Holt, Rinehart & Winston.

Hosley, Maria. First Science. 2007. (Illus.). 24p. (J). 21.35 (978-1-59679-802-1(5) , Buddy Bks.) ABDO Publishing Co.

How Are They Built?, 6 bks., Set. (J). (gr. 4-8). lib. bdg. 179.57 (978-1-58952-133-9(1)) Rourke Publishing, LLC.

How Birds Live: 6 Each of 1 Student Book, 6 vols. (Sunshinetm Science Ser.). 24p. (gr. 1-2). 41.95 (978-0-7802-1398-2(X)) Wright Group, The.

How Bread Is Made: 6 Each of 1 Student Book, 6 vols. (Sunshinetm Science Ser.). 24p. (gr. 1-2). 41.95 (978-0-7802-2724-8(7)) Wright Group, The.

How Bread Is Made: Big Book. (Sunshinetm Science Ser.). 24p. (gr. 1-2). 37.50 (978-0-7802-2796-5(4)) Wright Group, The.

How Can We See in the Dark?, 6 vols. (Sunshinetm Science Ser.). 24p. (gr. 1-2). 31.50 (978-0-7802-0305-1(4)); 36.95 (978-0-7802-0556-7(1)) Wright Group, The.

Hubble Science Cards. 2003. (Illus.). 44p. 7.99 (978-0-9741147-0-5(7)) Phlare, Inc.

El Huerto de Juan. 2000. (McGraw-Hill Ciencias Ser.). (ENG & SPA.). (gr. 2 up). (978-0-02-279607-5(X)) Macmillan/McGraw-Hill Schl. Div.

Hughes, Colin & Wade, Winnie. How to Be a Wizard at Science Investigations. (J). (gr. 3-6). pap. (978-1-876367-30-5(X)) Wizard Bks.

—How to Be Brilliant at Living Things. 2004. (Illus.). 48p. pap. 30.00 (978-1-897675-66-3(6)) Brilliant Pubns. GBR. *Dist:* Parkwest Pubns., Inc.

Human Body: a Body in Motion Assessment Book: Unit 7: Human Body: a Body in Motion. 2000. (McGraw-Hill Science Ser.). (gr. 4 up). (978-0-02-277762-3(8)) Macmillan/McGraw-Hill Schl. Div.

Human Body: a Body in Motion Teacher Resources for Practice & Support with Answer Key: Unit 7: Human Body: a Body in Motion. 2000. (McGraw-Hill Science Ser.). (gr. 4 up). (978-0-02-277643-5(5)) Macmillan/ McGraw-Hill Schl. Div.

Human Body: Response & Change Assessment Book: Unit 7: Human Body: Response & Change. 2000. (McGraw-Hill Science Ser.). (gr. 6 up). (978-0-02-277777-7(6)) Macmillan/McGraw-Hill Schl. Div.

Human Body: Response & Change Teacher Resources for Practice & Support with Answer Key: Unit 7: Human Body: Response & Change. 2000. (McGraw-Hill Science Ser.). (gr. 6 up). (978-0-02-277658-9(3)) Macmillan/McGraw-Hill Schl. Div.

Humphrey, Melanie Friedersdorf. Where Do Falling Stars Go? 3rd ed. 1999. (Illus.). 48p. (J). (ps-1). pap. 14.95 (978-0-9658061-6-9(2)) Peaceful Village Publishing.

Hunter, Rebecca M. Discovering Science, 12 bks., Set. Incl. Electricity & Magnetism. (gr. 3-5). 2000. lib. bdg. 25.69 (978-0-7398-2970-7(X)); Energy. (gr. 3-5). 2000. lib. bdg. 25.69 (978-0-7398-2971-4(8)); Hot & Cold. (gr. 3-5). 2000. lib. bdg. 25.69 (978-0-7398-2972-1(6)); Light & Dark. (gr. 3-5). 2000. lib. bdg. 25.69 (978-0-7398-2973-8(4)); Matter. (gr. 3-5). 2000. lib. bdg. 25.69 (978-0-7398-2969-1(6)); Pollution & Conservation. (gr. 3-7). 2001. lib. bdg. 25.69 (978-0-7398-3246-2(8)); Rocks, Minerals & Fossils. (gr. 4-7). 2001. lib. bdg. 25.69 (978-0-7398-3250-9(6)); Seasons. (gr. 3-7). 2001. lib. bdg. 25.69 (978-0-7398-3247-9(6)); Sound. (gr. 3-5). 2000. lib. bdg. 25.69 (978-0-7398-2974-5(2)); Space. (gr. 4-7). 2001. lib. bdg. 25.69 (978-0-7398-3248-6(4)); Volcanoes & Earthquakes. (gr. 4-7). 2001. lib. bdg. 25.69 (978-0-7398-3249-3(2)); Weather. (gr. 4-7). 2001. lib. bdg. 25.69 (978-0-7398-3245-5(X)); 32p. (J). (Illus.). 2001. Set lib. bdg. 308.28 (978-0-7398-3278-3(6)) Raintree.

Hurd. Physical Science. 3rd ed. (J). 59.47 (978-0-13-982158-5(9)) Prentice Hall (Schl. Div.).

Hyde, Philip, III. The Football of Time: Why Globalization Isn't Working. Hyde, Philip, III, illus. l.t. ed. 2002. (Illus.). 116p. per. (978-0-9668013-1-6(8)) Groundwork Ideas Pr.

Ida y Vuelta, Antes y Ahora. 2000. (McGraw-Hill Ciencias Ser.). (ENG & SPA.). (gr. 3 up). (978-0-02-279641-9(X)) Macmillan/McGraw-Hill Schl. Div.

Imanes y mas Imanes! Leveled Books. 2000. (McGraw-Hill Ciencias Ser.). (ENG & SPA.). (gr. 4 up). (978-0-02-279653-2(3)) Macmillan/McGraw-Hill Schl. Div.

Un incendio Voraz. 2000. (McGraw-Hill Ciencias Ser.). (ENG & SPA.). (gr. 5 up). (978-0-02-279686-0(X)) Macmillan/McGraw-Hill Schl. Div.

Ingenio. 2000. (McGraw-Hill Ciencias Ser.). (ENG & SPA.). (gr. 5 up). (978-0-02-279681-5(9)) Macmillan/McGraw-Hill Schl. Div.

Innes, Brian. The Cosmic Joker. 1999. (Unsolved Mysteries Ser.). 48p. (YA). (gr. 3 up). lib. bdg. 25.69 (978-0-8172-5487-2(0)) Raintree.

—Forensic Science. 2002. (Crime & Detection Ser.). (Illus.). 96p. (J). (gr. 7 up). lib. bdg. 22.95 (978-1-59084-373-4(8)) Mason Crest Pubs.

An Inside Look, 12 bks. Incl. Discovering Prehistory. Wood, Robert Muir. 2001. lib. bdg. 26.00 (978-0-8368-2900-6(X)); Discovering the Universe. Clark, Stuart. 2000. lib. bdg. 26.00 (978-0-8368-2724-8(4)); Environment. Allaby, Michael. 2000. lib. bdg. 26.00 (978-0-8368-2725-5(2)); Exploring the Oceans. Hall, Stephen. 2000. lib. bdg. 26.00 (978-0-8368-2726-2(0)); Inside the Human Body. Weston, Steve, illus. 2001. lib. bdg. 26.00 (978-0-8368-2901-3(8)); Superstructures. Brooks, Philip. 2002. lib. bdg. 26.00 (978-0-8368-3177-1(2)); World of Animal Life. Weston, Steve, illus. 2001. lib. bdg. 26.00 (978-0-8368-2902-0(6)); World of Computers & Communication. Graham, Ian. 2000. lib. bdg. 26.00 (978-0-8368-2727-9(9)); World of Flight. Howatson, Ian & Quigley, Sebastian, illus. 2001. lib. bdg. 26.00 (978-0-8368-2903-7(4)); World of Insect Life. Legg, Gerald. 2002. lib. bdg. 26.00 (978-0-8368-3179-5(9)); World of Plant Life. Legg, Gerald. 2002. lib. bdg. 26.00 (978-0-8368-3180-1(2)); World's Weather. Allaby, Michael. 2002. lib. bdg. 26.00 (978-0-8368-3178-8(0)); 48p. (J). (gr. 4 up). (Illus.). Set lib. bdg. 312.00 (978-0-8368-3347-8(3)) Stevens, Gareth Inc.

Instructional Resources. 2003. (gr. 6 up). suppl. ed. 47.95 (978-0-673-59337-5(1)) Addison-Wesley Educational Pubs., Inc.

Integrated Course 1: Integrated Course 1 PE. l.t. ed. 2005. (YA). (gr. 6-8). (978-0-618-42299-9(4) , 2-01157) McDougal Littell Inc.

Integrated Course 2: Integrated Course 2 PE. l.t. ed. 2005. (YA). (gr. 6-8). (978-0-618-42301-9(X) , 2-01159) McDougal Littell Inc.

Integrated Course 3: Integrated Course 3 PE. l.t. ed. 2005. (YA). (gr. 6-8). (978-0-618-42303-3(6) , 2-01161) McDougal Littell Inc.

Interactive Transparency Package. 2003. (gr. k up). suppl. ed. 109.15 (978-0-673-59454-9(8)); (gr. 1 up). suppl. ed. 109.15 (978-0-673-59455-6(6)); (gr. 2 up). suppl. ed. 109.15 (978-0-673-59456-3(4)); (gr. 3 up). suppl. ed. 109.15 (978-0-673-59457-0(2)); (gr. 4 up). suppl. ed. 109.15 (978-0-673-59458-7(0)); (gr. 5 up). suppl. ed. 109.15 (978-0-673-59459-4(9)); (gr. 6 up). suppl. ed. 109.15 (978-0-673-59460-0(2)) Addison-Wesley Educational Pubs., Inc.

Intermediate Science, 2. 2004. 987.50 (978-0-531-12330-0(8)) Scholastic Library Publishing.

Investigating Science, 4 bks. Incl. Archaeology : The Study of Our Past. Devereux, Paul. lib. bdg. 24.67 (978-0-8368-3228-0(0)); Astronomy : The Study of the Universe. Mahoney, Terry. lib. bdg. 24.67 (978-0-8368-3229-7(9)); Ecology : The Study of Living Things. Jennings, Terry J. lib. bdg. 24.67 (978-0-8368-3230-3(2)); Genetics : The Study of Heredity. Graham, Ian. lib. bdg. 24.67 (978-0-8368-3231-0(0)); 36p. (J). (gr. 4 up). (Illus.). 2002. Set lib. bdg. 98.68 (978-0-8368-3227-3(2)) Stevens, Gareth Inc.

The Invisible World. 2005. 32p. pap. 197.55 (978-0-7910-8323-9(3) , Chelsea Hse.) Facts On File, Inc.

Iopeners: Big Book Collection, 20 vols. 2005. (J). (gr. k up). 525.95 (978-0-7652-4972-2(3)); (gr. 1 up). 587.50 (978-0-7652-4976-0(6)) Modern Curriculum Pr.

Iopeners: Classroom Library. 2005. (J). (gr. k up). 440.50 (978-0-7652-4969-2(3)); (gr. 1 up). 518.50 (978-0-7652-4973-9(1)); (gr. 2 up). 518.50 (978-0-7652-4977-7(4)); (gr. 3 up). 616.50 (978-0-7652-4980-7(4)); (gr. 4 up). 616.50 (978-0-7652-4983-8(9)); (gr. 5 up). 694.50 (978-0-7652-4986-9(3)); (gr. 6 up). 694.50 (978-0-7652-4989-0(8)) Modern Curriculum Pr.

Iopeners: Science Library, 10 vols. 2005. (J). (gr. k up). 220.95 (978-0-7652-4970-8(7)); (gr. 1 up). 259.95 (978-0-7652-4974-6(X)); (gr. 2 up). 259.95 (978-0-7652-4978-4(2)); (gr. 3 up). 308.50 (978-0-7652-4981-4(2)); (gr. 4 up). 308.50 (978-0-7652-4984-5(7)); (gr. 5 up). 347.50 (978-0-7652-4987-6(1)); (gr. 6 up). 347.50 (978-0-7652-4990-6(1)) Modern Curriculum Pr.

Is it Floating?, 6 vols. (Sunshinetm Science Ser.). 24p. (gr. 1-2). 31.50 (978-0-7802-0295-5(3)); 36.95 (978-0-7802-0546-8(4)) Wright Group, The.

Issues, Evidence & You Complete Materials Package. 2003. (Illus.). (YA). tchr. ed., ring bd. (978-1-887725-71-2(7)) Lab-Aids, Inc.

Issues, Evidence & You Complete Materials Package: Includes Teacher's Guide & Student Books. 2003. (Illus.). (YA). (978-1-887725-72-9(5)) Lab-Aids, Inc.

Issues, Evidence & You Complete Materials Package for Chicago Public Schools. 2003. (Illus.). (YA). ring bd. (978-1-887725-84-2(9)) Lab-Aids, Inc.

Jacobs, Daniel. For Your Information. Date not set. (Early Science Big Bks.). (Illus.). 16p. (J). (ps-2). pap. 16.95 (978-1-58273-123-0(3)) Sundance/Newbridge Educational Publishing.

El Jardin del Senor Hobson. 2000. (McGraw-Hill Ciencias Ser.). (ENG & SPA.). (gr. 2 up). (978-0-02-279621-1(5)) Macmillan/McGraw-Hill Schl. Div.

Jason Science Adventure: Aquatic Field Study. 2004. (J). (978-0-9763809-0-0(0)) JASON Project, The.

Jefferis, David. Megastructures. 2002. (Young Library). (Illus.). 32p. (J). lib. bdg. 25.69 (978-0-7398-6324-4(X)) Raintree.

Jenkins, Martin. The Art of Science: A Pop-Up Adventure in Art. Young, Jay, illus. 1999. 41p. (YA). (gr. 7-9). reprint ed. 28.00 (978-0-7567-5831-8(9)) DIANE Publishing Co.

Jeunesse. ¿Donde Esta? 1999. (Coleccion Mundo Maravilloso). (SPA., Illus.). 40p. (J). (gr. 2-4). (978-84-348-4037-9(5) , SM5787) SM Ediciones ESP. *Dist:* Lectorum Pubns., Inc.

Johnson, Keith, et al. Spotlight Science: Assessment Resource Bank 7. rev. ed. 2000. (Illus.). 188p. (J). (gr. 6-9). ring bd. 167.50 (978-0-7487-5537-0(3)) Nelson Thornes Ltd. GBR. *Dist:* Trans-Atlantic Pubns., Inc.

—Spotlight Science: NC 2000 Sc 1 Supplement. 2000. (Illus.). 64p. (YA). (gr. 6-9). pap. 72.50 (978-0-7487-5538-7(1)) Nelson Thornes Ltd. GBR. *Dist:* Trans-Atlantic Pubns., Inc.

—Spotlight Science 7: Spiral Students Book. 2nd rev. ed. 2000. (Illus.). 160p. (J). pap. 27.50 (978-0-7487-5534-9(9)) Nelson Thornes Ltd. GBR. *Dist:* Trans-Atlantic Pubns., Inc.

—Spotlight Science Key Stage 3/S1-S2: Spotlight Science 9, Pupils Book. 1998. (Illus.). 160p. pap., stu. ed. 25.50 (978-0-7487-1564-0(9)) State Mutual Bk. & Periodical Service, Ltd.

Jonathan Chapman. 2000. (McGraw-Hill Ciencias Ser.). (ENG & SPA.). (gr. 5 up). (978-0-02-279676-1(2)) Macmillan/McGraw-Hill Schl. Div.

Julia Morgan, una gran Arquitecta: Leveled Books. 2000. (McGraw-Hill Ciencias Ser.). (ENG & SPA.). (gr. 4 up). (978-0-02-279665-5(7)) Macmillan/McGraw-Hill Schl. Div.

The Jumbo Book of Short-n-Simple Science: Easy Science Activities for School & Home. 128p. (gr. 1-3). 10.99 (978-1-56451-357-1(2) , ID5800); (gr. 3-6). 10.99 (978-1-56451-358-8(0) , ID5801) School Specialty Publishing.

Junior Adventure, 36 vols., Set. 2002. (Illus.). 32p. (YA). (gr. 3 up). lib. bdg. (978-1-59084-161-7(1)) Mason Crest Pubs.

Just the Facts, 6 bks., Set 2. 2002. (YA). (gr. 6-8). lib. bdg. 153.84 (978-1-58810-575-2(X)) Heinemann Library.

Kain, Kathleen E. Surprise Explosions: The Science Spiders(TM) Make Chemicals React. 1999. (Illus.). 32p. (J). (gr. k-3). pap. 5.95 (978-1-892221-02-5(0) , RW0562) Ranch Works.

Kalman, Bobbie. El Ciclo de Vida de la Abeja. 2005. (Serie Ciclos de Vida Ser.). (SPA., Illus.). 32p. (J). (978-0-7787-8666-5(8)); pap. (978-0-7787-8712-9(5)) Crabtree Publishing Co.

Kalman, Bobbie & Langille, Jacqueline. Que Es el Ciclo de Vida? 2005. (Ciencia de los Seres Vivos Ser.). (SPA., Illus.). 32p. (J). (ps). pap. (978-0-7787-8800-3(8)) Crabtree Publishing Co.

Kaplan Staff & Shulman, Mark. Flip-O-Matic: Instant Science for Ages 9-12. 2006. (G - Reference,Information & Interdisciplinary Subjects Ser.). 256p. pap. 10.00 (978-1-4195-4181-0(1)) Kaplan Publishing.

Karapetian, Marjam. Bilingual Content Dictionary: English to Spanish. 2004. (SPA & ENG.). 13.95 (978-0-9764829-4-9(0)); 15.95 (978-0-9764829-5-6(9)) WizdomInc.

Keeping Warm Science, 6 vols. (gr. k-2). 28.95 (978-0-7368-1747-9(6) , Yellow Umbrella Bks.) Capstone Pr., Inc.

Keller, Rebecca. Real Science-4-Kids: Textbook. 2001. (J). spiral bd. 29.95 (978-1-931796-00-2(9) , RS01) Access Research Network.

Kerrod, Robin. 1000 Questions & Answers. Kingfisher Publications, Inc. Staff, ed. 2006. (Illus.). 288p. (J). (gr. 5-9). vinyl bd. 12.95 (978-0-7534-5947-8(7) , Kingfisher) Houghton Mifflin Co. Trade & Reference Div.

S

Kerrod, Robin & Holgate, Sharon Ann. The Way Science Works: Discover the Secrets of Science with Exciting, Accessible Experiments. Parsons, Jayne, ed. 2002. (Illus.). 160p. (J). (gr. 5 up). 24.99 (978-0-7894-8562-5(1)) Dorling Kindersley Publishing, Inc.

Kidd, J. S. & Kidd, Renee A. Science & Society, 6 vols., Set. Incl. Quarks & Sparks : The Story of Nuclear Power. 160p. 1999. 25.00 (978-0-8160-3587-8(3)); Shades of Green : The Clash of Agricultural Science & Environmental Science. 144p. 1997. 25.00 (978-0-8160-3583-0(0)); (Illus.). (YA). (gr. 7-12). 1999. 125.00 o.p. (978-0-8160-4103-9(2)) Facts On File, Inc.

Kids Publishing Science Staff. It's Alive! All about the Living World. 1999. (J). (gr. 2-6). pap. 6.95 (978-1-891418-20-4(3)) Science Kids.

—Mix It Up! The Science of Chemistry. 1999. (J). (gr. 2-6). pap. 6.95 (978-1-891418-15-0(7)) Science Kids.

Kingfisher Larousse Chambers Staff. Fascinating Facts: About the Earth, Space, Wild Animals & People. 1999. (Illus.). 96p. (J). (gr. 3-7). pap. (978-0-7534-5265-3(0)) Kingfisher Publications, plc.

Kinser, Kathy. Doomed to Disappear? Endangered Species. 2004. (Navigators Ser.). (J). pap. 42.00 (978-1-4108-0418-1(6)) Benchmark Education Co.

Knapp, Brian J. Adapting & Surviving, Vol. 19. Woodroffe, David, illus. 2003. (J). lib. bdg. (978-0-7172-5853-6(X) , Grolier) Scholastic Library Publishing.

—Changing Circuits, Vol. 25. Woodroffe, David, illus. 2003. (J). lib. bdg. (978-0-7172-5859-8(9) , Grolier) Scholastic Library Publishing.

—Changing from Solids to Liquids to Gases, Vol. 16. Woodroffe, David, illus. 2003. (J). lib. bdg. (978-0-7172-5850-5(5) , Grolier) Scholastic Library Publishing.

—Changing Materials, Vol. 22. Woodroffe, David, illus. 2003. (J). lib. bdg. (978-0-7172-5856-7(4) , Grolier) Scholastic Library Publishing.

—Changing Sounds, Vol. 18. Woodroffe, David, illus. 2003. (J). lib. bdg. (978-0-7172-5852-9(1) , Grolier) Scholastic Library Publishing.

—Dissolving, Vol. 21. Woodroffe, David, illus. 2003. (J). lib. bdg. (978-0-7172-5855-0(6) , Grolier) Scholastic Library Publishing.

—Earth & Beyond, Vol. 17. Woodroffe, David, illus. 2003. (J). lib. bdg. (978-0-7172-5851-2(3) , Grolier) Scholastic Library Publishing.

—Food, Teeth & Eating, Vol. 1. Woodroffe, David, illus. 2003. (J). lib. bdg. (978-0-7172-5835-2(1) , Grolier) Scholastic Library Publishing.

—Forces in Action, Vol. 23. Woodroffe, David, illus. 2003. (J). lib. bdg. (978-0-7172-5857-4(2) , Grolier) Scholastic Library Publishing.

—Friction, Vol. 11. Woodroffe, David, illus. 2003. (J). lib. bdg. (978-0-7172-5845-1(9) , Grolier) Scholastic Library Publishing.

—Gases Around Us, Vol. 15. Woodroffe, David, illus. 2003. (J). lib. bdg. (978-0-7172-5849-9(1) , Grolier) Scholastic Library Publishing.

—Habitats, Vol. 8. Woodroffe, David, illus. 2003. (J). lib. bdg. (978-0-7172-5842-0(4) , Grolier) Scholastic Library Publishing.

—Helping Plants Grow Well, Vol. 2. Woodroffe, David, illus. 2003. (J). lib. bdg. (978-0-7172-5836-9(X) , Grolier) Scholastic Library Publishing.

—How We See Things, Vol. 24. Woodroffe, David, illus. 2003. (J). lib. bdg. (978-0-7172-5858-1(0) , Grolier) Scholastic Library Publishing.

—Keeping Healthy, Vol. 13. Woodroffe, David, illus. 2003. (J). lib. bdg. (978-0-7172-5847-5(5) , Grolier) Scholastic Library Publishing.

—Keeping Warm & Cool, Vol. 9. Woodroffe, David, illus. 2003. (J). lib. bdg. (978-0-7172-5843-7(2) , Grolier) Scholastic Library Publishing.

—Life Cycles, Vol. 14. Woodroffe, David, illus. 2003. (J). lib. bdg. (978-0-7172-5848-2(3) , Grolier) Scholastic Library Publishing.

—Light & Shadows, Vol. 6. Woodroffe, David, illus. 2003. (J). lib. bdg. (978-0-7172-5840-6(8) , Grolier) Scholastic Library Publishing.

—Microbes, Vol. 20. Woodroffe, David, illus. 2003. (J). lib. bdg. (978-0-7172-5854-3(8) , Grolier) Scholastic Library Publishing.

—Moving & Growing, Vol. 7. Woodroffe, David, illus. 2003. (J). lib. bdg. (978-0-7172-5841-3(6) , Grolier) Scholastic Library Publishing.

—Properties of Materials, Vol. 3. Woodroffe, David, illus. 2003. (J). lib. bdg. (978-0-7172-5837-6(8) , Grolier) Scholastic Library Publishing.

—Rocks & Soils, Vol. 4. Woodroffe, David, illus. 2003. (J). lib. bdg. (978-0-7172-5838-3(6) , Grolier) Scholastic Library Publishing.

—Science Matters!, 25 vols. Woodroffe, David, illus. Incl. Vol. 1. Food, Teeth & Eating. lib. bdg. (978-0-7172-5835-2(1)); Vol. 2. Helping Plants Grow Well. lib. bdg. (978-0-7172-5836-9(X)); Vol. 3. Properties of Materials. lib. bdg. (978-0-7172-5837-6(8)); Vol. 4. Rocks & Soils. lib. bdg. (978-0-7172-5838-3(6)); Vol. 5. Springs & Magnets. lib. bdg. (978-0-7172-5839-0(4)); Vol. 6. Light & Shadows. lib. bdg. (978-0-7172-5840-6(8)); Vol. 7. Moving & Growing. lib. bdg. (978-0-7172-5841-3(6)); Vol. 8. Habitats. lib. bdg. (978-0-7172-5842-0(4)); Vol. 9. Keeping Warm & Cool. lib. bdg. (978-0-7172-5843-7(2)); Vol. 10. Solids & Liquids. lib. bdg. (978-0-7172-5844-4(0)); Vol. 11. Friction. lib. bdg. (978-0-7172-5845-1(9)); Vol. 12. Simple Electricity. lib. bdg. (978-0-7172-5846-8(7)); Vol. 13. Keeping Healthy. lib. bdg. (978-0-7172-5847-5(5)); Vol. 14. Life Cycles. lib. bdg. (978-0-7172-5848-2(3)); Vol. 15. Gases Around Us. lib. bdg. (978-0-7172-5849-9(1)); Vol. 16. Changing from Solids to Liquids to Gases. lib. bdg. (978-0-7172-5850-5(5)); Vol. 17. Earth & Beyond. lib. bdg. (978-0-7172-5851-2(3)); Vol. 18. Changing Sounds. lib. bdg. (978-0-7172-5852-9(1)); Vol. 19. Adapting & Surviving. lib. bdg. (978-0-7172-5853-6(X)); Vol. 20. Microbes. lib. bdg. (978-0-7172-5854-3(8)); Vol. 21. Dissolving. lib. bdg. (978-0-7172-5855-0(6)); Vol. 22. Changing Materials. lib. bdg. (978-0-7172-5856-7(4)); Vol. 23. Forces in Action. lib. bdg. (978-0-7172-5857-4(2)); Vol. 24. How We See Things. lib. bdg. (978-0-7172-5858-1(0)); Vol. 25. Changing Circuits. lib. bdg. (978-0-7172-5859-8(9)); (J). 2003. (Illus.). 2002. 309.00 (978-0-7172-5834-5(3) , Grolier) Scholastic Library Publishing.

—Simple Electricity, Vol. 12. Woodroffe, David, illus. 2003. (J). lib. bdg. (978-0-7172-5846-8(7) , Grolier) Scholastic Library Publishing.

—Solids & Liquids, Vol. 10. Woodroffe, David, illus. 2003. (J). lib. bdg. (978-0-7172-5844-4(0) , Grolier) Scholastic Library Publishing.

—Springs & Magnets, Vol. 5. Woodroffe, David, illus. 2003. (J). lib. bdg. (978-0-7172-5839-0(4) , Grolier) Scholastic Library Publishing.

Kohl, Herbert R. & Kohl, Judith. The View from the Oak: The Private Worlds of Other Creatures. 2000. (Illus.). 112p. (gr. 4-7). pap. 14.95 (978-1-56584-636-4(2)) New Pr., The.

Kohl, MaryAnn F. & Potter, Jean. Science Arts: Discovering Science Through Art Experiences. Dery, K. Whelan, illus. 2003. (Bright Ideas for Learning Ser.: Vol. 4). 144p. (Orig.). (J). (ps-5). pap. 18.95 (978-0-935607-04-8(8)) Bright Ring Publishing, Inc.

Kopp, Jaine, et al. Treasure Boxes. Klofkorn, Lisa, illus. Hoyt, Richard, photos by. 2002. (Great Explorations in Math & Science Ser.). 102p. reprint ed. pap., tchr. ed. 16.00 (978-0-924886-64-5(1) , GEMS) Univ. of California, Berkeley, Lawrence Hall of Science.

Koss, Larry. The UFO Library, 2 bks. Incl. Could UFOs Be Real? lib. bdg. 21.26 (978-1-56065-093-5(1)); If UFOs Are Real. Schuessler, John & Haines, Richard F. lib. bdg. 21.26 (978-1-56065-094-2(X)); 48p. (J). (gr. 3-4). 1991. (Illus.). Set lib. bdg. 45.52 (978-1-56065-665-4(4) , Capstone High-Interest Bks.) Capstone Pr., Inc.

Kramer, Alan. Under the Sea with Jacques Cousteau. 2004. (Reader's Theater Ser.). (J). pap. 22.00 (978-1-4108-0801-1(7)) Benchmark Education Co.

—The Wright Brothers at Kitty Hawk. 2004. (Reader's Theater Ser.). (J). pap. 22.00 (978-1-4108-0794-6(0)) Benchmark Education Co.

Krautwurst, Terry. Night Science for Kids: Exploring the World after Dark. 2005. (Illus.). 144p. (J). pap. 12.95 (978-1-57990-670-2(2)) Lark Bks.

Kroutil Artists, creator. The Elements: A Fun, Easy to Learn, Introduction to the Elements in Character! 2004. (YA). per. 24.95 (978-1-932689-00-6(1)) EDGEucation Publishing.

Lab Manual. 2003. (gr. 1 up). stu. ed., lab manual ed. 6.30 (978-0-673-59338-2(X)); (gr. 2 up). stu. ed., lab manual ed. 6.30 (978-0-673-59339-9(8)); (gr. 3 up). stu. ed., lab manual ed. 5.95 (978-0-673-59340-5(1)) Addison-Wesley Educational Pubs., Inc.

Ladders, 4 vols. , Set. 1999. 32p. (J). (gr. k-3). 43.00 (978-0-7166-7715-4(6)) World Bk., Inc.

Ladders Series, 6 vols., Set. 2000. 192p. (J). (gr. k-3). (978-0-7166-7722-2(9)) World Bk., Inc.

Ladizinsky, Eric. Magical Science. Bild, Linda, illus. 2nd rev. ed. 1998. 80p. (J). (gr. 4-7). pap. 6.95 (978-1-56565-980-3(5) , 09805W) Lowell Hse. Juvenile.

Lakeshore Learning Materials Staff, contrib. by. Big Book Science Packet - Complete Set, 6 vols., Set. 2000. (J). pap. 179.00 (978-1-929255-77-1(2)) Lakeshore Learning Materials.

—Introducing Science Concepts Activity Kits - Complete Set, 3 vols., Set. 2000. (J). pap. 69.00 (978-1-929255-71-9(3)) Lakeshore Learning Materials.

Lauw, Darlene & Puay, Lim Cheng. Science Alive!, 12 bks. Incl. Air. 2002. lib. bdg. (978-0-7787-0566-6(8)); Earth & the Solar System. 2002. lib. bdg. (978-0-7787-0569-7(2)); Electricity. 2001. lib. bdg. (978-0-7787-0561-1(7)); Heat. 2002. lib. bdg. (978-0-7787-0559-8(5)); Human Body. 2002. lib. bdg. (978-0-7787-0568-0(4)); Light. 2002. lib. bdg. (978-0-7787-0560-4(9)); Magnets. 2002. lib. bdg. (978-0-7787-0563-5(3)); Materials. 2002. lib. bdg. (978-0-7787-0564-2(1)); Motion. 2002. lib. bdg. (978-0-7787-0558-1(7)); Sound. 2002. lib. bdg. (978-0-7787-0562-8(5)); Water. 2002. lib. bdg. (978-0-7787-0567-3(6)); Weather. 2002. lib. bdg. (978-0-7787-0565-9(X)); 32p. (J). (gr. 4-5). (Illus.). 2002. (978-0-7787-0556-7(0)) Crabtree Publishing Co.

—Science Alive!, 12 bks. Incl. Air. 2002. pap. (978-0-7787-0612-0(5)); Earth & the Solar System. 2002. pap. (978-0-7787-0615-1(X)); Electricity. 2001. pap. (978-0-7787-0607-6(9)); Heat. 2002. pap. (978-0-7787-0605-2(2)); Human Body. 2002. pap. (978-0-7787-0614-4(1)); Light. 2002. pap. (978-0-7787-0606-9(0)); Magnets. 2002. pap. (978-0-7787-0609-0(5)); Materials. 2002. pap. (978-0-7787-0610-6(9)); Motion. 2002. pap. (978-0-7787-0604-5(4)); Sound. 2002. pap. (978-0-7787-0608-3(7)); Water. 2002. pap. (978-0-7787-0613-7(3)); Weather. 2002. pap. (978-0-7787-0611-3(7)); 32p. (J). (gr. 4-5). (Illus.). 2002. Set pap. (978-0-7787-0602-1(8)) Crabtree Publishing Co.

Layton, Neal. The Story of Everything: From the Big Bang Until Now in 11 Pop-up Spreads. 2007. (Illus.). 22p. (J). 18.99 (978-0-7641-5985-5(2)) Barron's Educational Series, Inc.

LeapFrog Staff, compiled by. 3rd Grade Science: Quantum Pad Book. 2002. (Fundamentals Ser.). (YA). (gr. 4 up). spiral bd. 14.99 (978-1-58605-831-9(2)) LeapFrog Enterprises, Inc.

—4th Grade Science: Quantum Pad Book. 2002. (Fundamentals Ser.). (YA). (gr. 4 up). spiral bd. 14.99 (978-1-58605-832-6(0)) LeapFrog Enterprises, Inc.

Leather, Harry & Leather, Jan. Cambridge Checkpoints VCE Biology Unit 4 2004. 2003. (Cambridge Checkpoints Ser.). pap. 11.00 (978-0-521-54143-5(3)) Cambridge Univ. Pr.

Lemonick, Michael D. Science Alive, No. 1. 2005. 48p. (J). (978-0-7868-2106-8(X)) Hyperion Bks. for Children.

—Science Alive, No. 2. 2005. (J). (978-0-7868-0134-3(4)) Hyperion Pr.

Let's Look at Rocks Science, 6 vols. (gr. k-2). 28.95 (978-0-7368-3015-7(4) , Yellow Umbrella Bks.) Capstone Pr., Inc.

Levantar, empujar, y jalar: Cuaderno de Evaluacion: Unit 2: Levantar, empujar, y jalar (Lift It, Push It, Pull It) 2000. (McGraw-Hill Ciencias Ser.). (ENG & SPA.). (gr. 3 up). (978-0-02-278650-2(3)) Macmillan/McGraw-Hill Schl. Div.

Levantar, empujar, y jalar: Recursos para el maestro con clave de Respuestas: Unit 2: Levantar, empujar, y jalar (Lift It, Push It, Pull It) 2000. (McGraw-Hill Ciencias Ser.). (ENG & SPA.). (gr. 3 up). (978-0-02-278693-9(7)) Macmillan/McGraw-Hill Schl. Div.

Leveled Books Deluxe Package. 2000. (McGraw-Hill Ciencias Ser.). (ENG & SPA.). (gr. 3 up). (978-0-02-279281-7(3)); (gr. 4 up). (978-0-02-279283-1(X)) Macmillan/McGraw-Hill Schl. Div.

Leveled Books Deluxe Package: Leveled Books. 2000. (McGraw-Hill Ciencias Ser.). (ENG & SPA.). (gr. 5 up). (978-0-02-279285-5(6)) Macmillan/McGraw-Hill Schl. Div.

Leveled Books Package. 2000. (McGraw-Hill Ciencias Ser.). (ENG & SPA.). (gr. 3 up). (978-0-02-279279-4(1)); (gr. 4 up). (978-0-02-279282-4(1)) Macmillan/McGraw-Hill Schl. Div.

Leveled Books Package: Leveled Books. 2000. (McGraw-Hill Ciencias Ser.). (ENG & SPA.). (gr. 5 up). (978-0-02-279284-8(8)) Macmillan/McGraw-Hill Schl. Div.

Leveled Reader Collection. 2003. (gr. k up). 198.00 (978-0-673-65126-6(6)); (gr. 1 up). 198.00 (978-0-673-65127-3(4)); (gr. 2 up). 198.00 (978-0-673-65128-0(2)); (gr. 3 up). 231.00 (978-0-673-65129-7(0)); (gr. 4 up). 231.00 (978-0-673-65130-3(4)); (gr. 5 up). 231.00 (978-0-673-65131-0(2)); (gr. 6 up). 231.00 (978-0-673-65132-7(0)) Addison-Wesley Educational Pubs., Inc.

Levy, Nathan & Michels, Dia L. 101 Things Everyone Should Know about Science- Test Booklet. 2007. (101 Things Everyone Should Know Ser.). 16p. (J). pap. 2.95 (978-0-9678020-4-6(0)) Science, Naturally!.

Lewis Howard Latimer: Una mente Creadora! Leveled Books. 2000. (McGraw-Hill Ciencias Ser.). (ENG & SPA.). (gr. 4 up). (978-0-02-279652-5(5)) Macmillan/McGraw-Hill Schl. Div.

Lewis Tilden, Thomasine E. Mind Readers: Science Examines ESP. 2008. (24/7: Science Behind the Scenes: Mystery Files Ser.). 64p. (J). pap. 7.95 (***978-0-531-17532-3(4)*** , Watts, Franklin) Scholastic Library Publishing.

Libro del Estudiante. (MacMillan/McGraw-Hill Matematicas Ser.). (ENG & SPA.). 2002. (gr. 4 up). (978-0-02-111540-2(0)); 2002. (gr. 5 up). (978-0-02-111541-9(9)); 2002. (gr. 6 up). (978-0-02-111542-6(7)); 2000. (gr. 1 up). (978-0-02-277145-4(X)); 2000. (gr. 2 up). (978-0-02-277146-1(8)); 2000. (gr. 3 up). (978-0-02-277147-8(6)); 2000. (gr. 4 up). (978-0-02-277148-5(4)); 2000. (gr. 5 up). (978-0-02-277149-2(2)); 1999. (gr. k up). (978-0-02-110716-2(5)); 1999. (gr. 1 up). (978-0-02-110631-8(2)); 1999. (gr. 2 up). (978-0-02-110632-5(0)); 1999. (gr. 3 up). (978-0-02-110633-2(9)); 1999. (gr. 4 up). (978-0-02-110634-9(7)); 1999. (gr. 5 up). (978-0-02-110635-6(5)); 1999. (gr. 6 up). (978-0-02-110636-3(3)) Macmillan/McGraw-Hill Schl. Div.

Life Cycle of a Frog. 2002. 21.95 (978-1-57572-535-2(5) , 91023) Heinemann Library.

Life Science: EEdition : Life Science. 2005. (gr. 6-12). cd-rom (978-0-618-42031-5(2) , 2-01145) McDougal Littell Inc.

Life Science: Life Science PE. l.t. ed. 2005. (YA). (gr. 6-8). (978-0-618-30367-0(7) , 2-01002) McDougal Littell Inc.

Lift It, Push It, Pull It Assessment Book: Unit 2: Lift It, Push It, Pull It. 2000. (McGraw-Hill Science Ser.). (gr. 3 up). (978-0-02-277748-7(2)) Macmillan/McGraw-Hill Schl. Div.

Lift It, Push It, Pull It Pupil Edition: Unit 2: Lift It, Push It, Pull It. 2000. (McGraw-Hill Science Ser.). (gr. 3 up). (978-0-02-278207-8(9)) Macmillan/McGraw-Hill Schl. Div.

Light & Shadow Science, 6 vols. (gr. k-2). 28.95 (978-0-7368-1748-6(4) , Yellow Umbrella Bks.) Capstone Pr., Inc.

Light & Sound. (Illus.). lib. bdg. incl. cd-rom (978-0-7398-1392-8(7)) Raintree.

Literature Library. (Literature Library). 2003. (gr. k up). 105.85 (978-0-673-59585-0(4)); 2003. (gr. 1 up). 105.85 (978-0-673-59586-7(2)); 2003. (gr. 2 up). 105.85 (978-0-673-59587-4(0)); 2003. (gr. 3 up). 105.85 (978-0-673-59588-1(9)); 2003. (gr. 4 up). 35.30 (978-0-673-59589-8(7)); 2003. (gr. 5 up). 35.30 (978-0-673-59590-4(0)); 2003. (gr. 6 up). 35.30 (978-0-673-59591-1(9)); 2000. (SPA.). (gr. k up). 112.90 (978-0-673-59592-8(7)); 2000. (SPA.). (gr. 1 up). 112.90 (978-0-673-59593-5(5)); 2000. (SPA.). (gr. 2 up). 112.90 (978-0-673-59594-2(3)); 2000. (SPA.). (gr. 3 up). 112.90 (978-0-673-59595-9(1)); 2000. (SPA.). (gr. 4 up). 37.65 (978-0-673-59596-6(X)); 2000. (SPA.). (gr. 5 up). 37.65 (978-0-673-59597-3(8)); 2000. (SPA.). (gr. 6 up). 37.65 (978-0-673-59598-0(6)) Addison-Wesley Educational Pubs., Inc.

Littlefield, Cindy A. Awesome Science. 2006. (Illus.). 120p. (J). pap. 12.95 (978-0-8249-6796-3(8) , Williamson Bks.) Ideals Pubns.

Living on the Edge Series, 5 bks., Set. 128.21 (978-0-7614-1436-0(3) , Benchmark Bks.) Cavendish, Marshall Corp.

Living Science, 24 bks. Incl. Science of Air. Dann, Sarah. 2000. lib. bdg. 24.67 (978-0-8368-2569-5(1)); Science of Animals. Seidlitz, Lauri. 1999. lib. bdg. 24.67 (978-0-8368-2464-3(4)); Science of Birds. Parker, Janice. 1999. lib. bdg. 24.67 (978-0-8368-2465-0(2)); Science of Energy. Dann, Sarah. 2000. lib. bdg. 24.67 (978-0-8368-2571-8(3)); Science of Fire. Craats, Rennay. 2000. lib. bdg. 24.67 (978-0-8368-2680-7(9)); Science of Insects. Parker, Janice. 1999. lib. bdg. 23.93 (978-0-8368-2466-7(0)); Science of Light & Color. Miller-Schroeder, Patricia. 2000. lib. bdg. 24.67 (978-0-8368-2679-1(5)); Science of Liquids & Solids. McLuskey, Krista. 2001. lib. bdg. 24.67 (978-0-8368-2789-7(9)); Science of Magnets. Bocknek, Jonathan. 1999. lib. bdg. 23.93 (978-0-8368-2572-5(1)); Science of Plants. Bocknek, Jonathan. 1999. lib. bdg. 23.93 (978-0-8368-2467-4(9)); Science of Primates. Paterson, Samantha. 2001. lib. bdg. 24.67 (978-0-8368-2790-3(2)); Science of Reptiles. Parker, Janice. 2000. lib. bdg. 24.67 (978-0-8368-2681-4(7)); Science of Seasons. Strudwick, Leslie. 2001. lib. bdg. 24.67 (978-0-8368-2791-0(0)); Science of Senses. Miller-Schroeder, Patricia. 1999. lib. bdg. 24.67 (978-0-8368-2573-2(X)); Science of Soil. Bocknek, Jonathan. 1999. lib. bdg. 23.93 (978-0-8368-2468-1(7)); Science of Sound. Craats, Rennay. 2000. lib. bdg. 24.67 (978-0-8368-2682-1(5)); Science of Structures. Parker, Janice. 2001. lib. bdg. 24.67 (978-0-8368-2792-7(9)); Science of the Environment. Miller-Schroeder, Patricia. 2001. lib. bdg. 24.67 (978-0-8368-2788-0(0)); Science of the Human Body. Seidlitz, Lauri. 1999. lib. bdg. 24.67 (978-0-8368-2570-1(5)); Science of the Sky. Bocknek, Jonathan. 2000. lib. bdg. 24.67 (978-0-8368-2574-9(8)); Science of Tools. Munro, Andrea. 2001. lib. bdg. 24.67 (978-0-8368-2793-4(7)); Science of Underwater Life. Miller-Schroeder, Patricia. 2000. lib. bdg. 24.67 (978-0-8368-2683-8(3)); Science of Water. Parker, Janice. 1999. lib. bdg. 24.67 (978-0-8368-2469-8(5)); Science of Weather. Parker, Janice. 2000. lib. bdg. 24.67 (978-0-8368-2684-5(1)); 32p. (J). (gr. 2 up). (Illus.). Set lib. bdg. 468.73 (978-0-8368-2866-5(6)) Stevens, Gareth Inc.

Living Things Assessment Book: Unit 1: Living Things. 2000. (McGraw-Hill Science Ser.). (gr. 3 up). (978-0-02-277747-0(4)) Macmillan/McGraw-Hill Schl. Div.

Living Things Pupil Edition: Unit 1: Living Things. 2000. (McGraw-Hill Science Ser.). (gr. 3 up). (978-0-02-278206-1(0)) Macmillan/McGraw-Hill Schl. Div.

Llewellyn, Claire. Caliente y Frio. (Coleccion de Lado a Lado). (SPA., Illus.). (J). (gr. k-3). (978-970-656-279-1(6) , CM30003) Publicaciones Citem, S.A. de C.V. MEX. *Dist:* Lectorum Pubns., Inc.

—Dia y Noche. (Coleccion de Lado a Lado). (SPA., Illus.). (978-970-656-281-4(8) , CM30004) Publicaciones Citem, S.A. de C.V. MEX. *Dist:* Lectorum Pubns., Inc.

—Diminuto y Enorme. (Coleccion de Lado a Lado). (SPA., Illus.). 11.16 (978-970-656-280-7(X) , CM30005) Publicaciones Citem, S.A. de C.V. MEX. *Dist:* Lectorum Pubns., Inc.

—Push & Pull. 2005. (Illus.). 24p. (YA). (gr. 1 up). lib. bdg. 22.80 (978-1-932889-36-9(1)) Sea-To-Sea Pubns.

—Tierra y Mar. (Coleccion de Lado a Lado). (SPA., Illus.). (J). (gr. k-3). (978-970-656-282-1(6) , CM30006) Publicaciones Citem, S.A. de C.V. MEX. *Dist:* Lectorum Pubns., Inc.

Lo que hacen las computadoras Science, 6 vols.Tr. of What Computers Do Science. (SPA.). (gr. k-2). 28.95 (978-0-7368-3054-6(5) , Yellow Umbrella Bks.) Capstone Pr., Inc.

Locker, Thomas. Sky Tree: Seeing Science Through Art. 2001. (gr. k-3). lib. bdg. 15.30 (978-0-613-44259-6(8)) Tandem Library Bks.

Londt, Claire, et al. English Matters for Zambia Basic Education Grade 3 Pupil's Book. 2nd ed. 2007. pap., stu. ed. 5.75 (978-0-521-68755-3(1)) Cambridge Univ. Pr.

A Look into Space: Individual Title Six-Packs. (Discovery World Ser.). 12p. (gr. k-1). 28.00 (978-0-7635-8452-8(5)) Rigby Education.

Lopatka, Michael. The A. P. Environmental Science: Student Resource Edition. 2nd ed. 2002. (YA). stu. ed., per. 21.95 (978-0-9723218-0-8(2) , BKAPESSG02) Awesome Guides, Inc.

Lopatka, Michaell. The Ultimate Guide to Science Fair Projects: High School Edition. 2nd ed. 2002. (YA). per. 12.95 (978-0-9723218-1-5(0) , BKUGSFPHS02) Awesome Guides, Inc.

—The Ultimate Guide to Science Fair Projects: Middle School Edition. 2nd ed. 2002. (YA). per. 12.95 (978-0-9723218-2-2(9) , BKUGSFPMS02) Awesome Guides, Inc.

Lorenz Editors. Simple Science: With over 50 Reusable Stickers. 2001. (Sticker Fun Ser.). (Illus.). 16p. pap. 2.95 (978-0-7548-0796-4(7) , Lorenz Bks.) Anness Publishing, Inc.

Los arboles son impresionantes! Science, 6 vols.Tr. of Trees Are Terrific! Science. (SPA.). (gr. k-2). 28.95 (978-0-7368-3036-2(7) , Yellow Umbrella Bks.) Capstone Pr., Inc.

Lowell, Laura & Willard, Carolyn. Sifting Through Science. Bergman, Lincoln et al, eds. Klofkorn, Lisa et al, illus. Hoyt, Richard & Bradley, Laurence, photos by. 1999. (Great Explorations in Math & Science Ser.). 104p. (J). (gr. k-2). pap., tchr. ed. 13.50 (978-0-924886-46-1(3) , GEMS) Univ. of California, Berkeley, Lawrence Hall of Science.

Lunis, Natalie. Backyard Scientist. Date not set. (Thinking Like a Scientist Ser.). (Illus.). 20p. (J). pap. 16.95 (978-1-58273-107-0(1)) Sundance/Newbridge Educational Publishing.

—A Closer Look. Date not set. (Thinking Like a Scientist Ser.). (Illus.). 20p. (J). pap. 16.95 (978-1-58273-109-4(8)) Sundance/Newbridge Educational Publishing.

Lunis, Natalie & White, Nancy. Being a Scientist. Date not set. (Thinking Like a Scientist Ser.). (Illus.). 20p. (J). pap. 16.95 (978-1-58273-085-1(7)) Sundance/Newbridge Educational Publishing.

—Exploring Everyday Wonders. Date not set. (Thinking Like a Scientist Ser.). (Illus.). 20p. (J). pap. 16.95 (978-1-58273-368-5(6)) Sundance/Newbridge Educational Publishing.

—Popcorn Science. Date not set. (Thinking Like a Scientist Ser.). (Illus.). 20p. (J). pap. 16.95 (978-1-58273-370-8(8)) Sundance/Newbridge Educational Publishing.

—A World of Change. Date not set. (Thinking Like a Scientist Ser.). (Illus.). 20p. (J). pap. 16.95 (978-1-58273-077-6(6)) Sundance/Newbridge Educational Publishing.

Luz. (Coleccion Jugando Con la Ciencia). (SPA., Illus.). 39p. (J). pap. 9.95 (978-950-11-0683-1(7) , SGM35X) Sigmar ARG. *Dist:* Continental Bk. Co., Inc.

Luz y sombra Science, 6 vols.Tr. of Light & Shadow Science. (SPA.). (gr. k-2). 28.95 (978-0-7368-3145-1(2) , Yellow Umbrella Bks.) Capstone Pr., Inc.

Lyon, Tammie, illus. Kids Ask: Why? 2005. 32p. (J). (978-1-4127-1130-2(4) , 5550700) Publications International, Ltd.

MacDonald, Fiona. Science, Crafts & Technology. 2001. (Through the Ages Ser.). (Illus.). 64p. (gr. 3-7). 12.95 (978-0-7548-0850-3(5)) Anness Publishing GBR. *Dist:* National Bk. Network.

Make It Move! Science, 6 vols. (gr. k-2). 28.95 (978-0-7368-3016-4(2) , Yellow Umbrella Bks.) Capstone Pr., Inc.

Maquinas Constructoras. 2000. (McGraw-Hill Ciencias Ser.). (ENG & SPA.). (gr. 3 up). (978-0-02-279627-3(4)) Macmillan/McGraw-Hill Schl. Div.

Maravilla de los Pantanos. 2000. (McGraw-Hill Ciencias Ser.). (ENG & SPA.). (gr. 5 up). (978-0-02-279677-8(0)) Macmillan/McGraw-Hill Schl. Div.

Marcom Group Ltd, prod. Science Fair Win Labpak. (YA). cd-rom 222.50 (978-0-7365-4357-6(0)) Films Media Group.

Markle, Sandra. Make Fake Blood & 18 More Spooky Special Effects! Brace, Eric, illus. 2004. (Science Dares You! Ser.). 64p. (J). (978-0-439-44431-6(4)) Scholastic, Inc.

Mascotas Chiquitas. 2000. (McGraw-Hill Ciencias Ser.). (ENG & SPA.). (gr. k up). (978-0-02-279705-8(X)) Macmillan/McGraw-Hill Schl. Div.

Mast, Steven. God's Wonderful World: Science 5. 2004. (God's World Science Ser.). (Illus.). 272p. (gr. 5 up). 12.85 (978-0-7399-0614-9(3) , 14501) Rod & Staff Pubs., Inc.

—God's Wonderful World: Science 5 Tests. 2004. (God's World Science Ser.). 31p. (gr. 5 up). 1.95 (978-0-7399-0615-6(1) , 14511) Rod & Staff Pubs., Inc.

Math & Science Excelerator (Ages 8-12), 4 Cds. 2003. cd-rom 29.99 (978-1-59150-266-1(7)) TOPICS Entertainment.

A Matter of Time. 2001. (YA). (gr. 6-12). pap. incl. audio (978-0-8224-3281-4(1)) Globe Fearon Educational Publishing.

Mayes, Susan. Starting Point Science (Combined Volume) rev. ed. 2007. 96p. (J). 13.99 (978-0-7945-1626-0(2) , Usborne) EDC Publishing.

Maynard, Christopher. Science Fun at Home. 2005. (Illus.). 96p. (J). pap. 9.99 (978-0-7566-1794-3(4)) Dorling Kindersley Publishing, Inc.

McCarthy, Sue, et al. Science Matters: Grade 8. 2000. 244p. (gr. 8). pap., tchr. ed. 11.05 (978-0-521-66525-4(6)) Cambridge Univ. Pr.

McDonald. Life in Outer Space. 1999. (Illus.). (J). pap. (978-0-7398-2498-6(8)) Steck-Vaughn.

McFall, Sally, ed. Pro/Con, 12 vols. 2002. (Illus.). (YA). (978-0-7172-5928-1(5)); (978-0-7172-5929-8(3)); (978-0-7172-5930-4(7)); (978-0-7172-5931-1(5)); (978-0-7172-5932-8(3)); (978-0-7172-5933-5(1)); (978-0-7172-5754-6(1)); (978-0-7172-5755-3(X)); (978-0-7172-5756-0(8)); (978-0-7172-5757-7(6)); (978-0-7172-5758-4(4)); (978-0-7172-5759-1(2)) Scholastic Library Publishing. (Grolier).

—Pro/Con 3, 12 vols. 2004. (Illus.). (YA). 339.00 (978-0-7172-5927-4(7) , Grolier) Scholastic Library Publishing.

McGee, Sherry & Kelsey, Kim. AppleJill "The World Is Science" Johnson, Jo, illus. 1999. (Applekid's Chapter Bks.). 12p. (J). (gr. 1-6). pap. 4.99 (978-0-9673591-1-3(2)) Apple Bk. Ctr.

McGraw-Hill - Jamestown Education Staff. Jamestown Education: Reading Science, Strategies for English Language Learners, High Beginning. 2005. pap. 15.96 (978-0-07-872914-0(9) , 9780078729140) Glencoe/McGraw-Hill.

—The Outer Edge: Cool Science. 2005. pap. 16.64 (978-0-07-869053-2(6) , 9780078690532) Glencoe/McGraw-Hill.

—Timed Readings Plus in Science. 2002. (gr. 6-12). Bk. 1. pap. 16.64 (978-0-07-827370-4(6) , 9780078273704); Bk. 2. pap. 16.64 (978-0-07-827371-1(4) , 9780078273711); Bk. 3. pap. 16.64 (978-0-07-827372-8(2) , 9780078273728); Bk. 4. pap. 16.64 (978-0-07-827373-5(0) , 9780078273735); Bk. 5. pap. 16.64 (978-0-07-827374-2(9) , 9780078273742); Bk. 6. pap. 16.64 (978-0-07-827375-9(7) , 9780078273759); Bk. 7. pap. 16.64 (978-0-07-827376-6(5) , 9780078273766); Bk. 8. pap. 16.64 (978-0-07-827377-3(3) , 9780078273773); Bk. 9. pap. 16.64 (978-0-07-827378-0(1) , 9780078273780); Bk. 10. pap. 16.64 (978-0-07-827379-7(X) , 9780078273797) Jamestown.

McGraw-Hill Science Newsroom: Primary. 2000. (McGraw-Hill Ciencias Ser.). (SPA & ENG.). (gr. k up). (978-0-02-277914-6(0)); (gr. 1 up). (978-0-02-277915-3(9)); (gr. 2 up). (978-0-02-277916-0(7)) Macmillan/McGraw-Hill Schl. Div.

Mcgraw-Hill Science Staff. Grade 3 Science. 2000. (McGraw-Hill Science Ser.). (gr. 3 up). (978-0-02-277435-6(1)) Macmillan/McGraw-Hill Schl. Div.

—Grade 3 Science Cross-Curricular Project. 2000. (McGraw-Hill Science Ser.). (gr. 3 up). (978-0-02-277722-7(9)) Macmillan/McGraw-Hill Schl. Div.

—Grade 3 Science Practice Workbook. 2000. (McGraw-Hill Science Ser.). (gr. 3 up). wbk. ed. (978-0-02-277707-4(5)) Macmillan/McGraw-Hill Schl. Div.

—Grade 5 Science. 2000. (McGraw-Hill Science Ser.). (gr. 5 up). (978-0-02-277437-0(8)) Macmillan/McGraw-Hill Schl. Div.

—Grade 5 Science Practice Workbook. 2000. (McGraw-Hill Science Ser.). (gr. 5 up). wbk. ed. (978-0-02-277709-8(1)) Macmillan/McGraw-Hill Schl. Div.

—Grade 6 Science. 2000. (McGraw-Hill Science Ser.). (gr. 6 up). (978-0-02-277438-7(6)) Macmillan/McGraw-Hill Schl. Div.

—Grade 6 Science Practice Workbook. 2000. (McGraw-Hill Science Ser.). (gr. 6 up). wbk. ed. (978-0-02-277711-1(3)) Macmillan/McGraw-Hill Schl. Div.

McGraw-Hill Staff. The Air Around You. 2nd ed. 2004. (Glencoe Science Ser.). stu. ed. 20.64 (978-0-07-861758-4(8) , 9780078617584) Glencoe/McGraw-Hill.

—Glencoe Science, Level Blue. 2003. stu. ed. 74.64 (978-0-07-828242-3(X)) Glencoe/McGraw-Hill.

—Glencoe Science: An Introduction to the Life, Earth & Physical Sciences. 2002. stu. ed. 81.32 (978-0-07-830616-7(7) , 9780078306167) Glencoe/McGraw-Hill.

—Glencoe Science: From Bacteria to Plants. 2001. stu. ed. 20.64 (978-0-07-825560-1(0) , 9780078255601); 2nd ed. 2004. (C). stu. ed. 20.64 (978-0-07-861737-9(5) , 9780078617379) Glencoe/McGraw-Hill.

—Glencoe Science: Level Blue, Reinforcement. 2004. pap., stu. ed. 11.96 (978-0-07-867169-2(8) , 9780078671692) Glencoe/McGraw-Hill.

—Glencoe Science: Level Green, Reinforcement. 2004. pap., stu. ed. 11.96 (978-0-07-867188-3(4) , 9780078671883) Glencoe/McGraw-Hill.

—Glencoe Science: Level Red Reinforcement. 2004. (C). pap., stu. ed. 11.96 (978-0-07-867216-3(3) , 9780078672163) Glencoe/McGraw-Hill.

—Glencoe Science: Motion, Forces, & Energy, 2nd ed. 2004. (C). stu. ed. 20.64 (978-0-07-861770-6(7) , 9780078617706) Glencoe/McGraw-Hill.

—Life Science Animations. 2nd ed. 2004. (gr. 6-12). cd-rom (978-0-07-248438-0(1)) Glencoe/McGraw-Hill.

—The Nature of Matter. 2nd ed. 2004. (Glencoe Science Ser.). stu. ed. 20.64 (978-0-07-861765-2(0) , 9780078617652) Glencoe/McGraw-Hill.

—Science Level Red, Mastering Standardized Tests, SE. 2004. pap. 10.64 (978-0-07-867208-8(2) , 9780078672088) Glencoe/McGraw-Hill.

—Science Level Red, Reading Essentials. 2004. (C). pap., stu. ed. 34.64 (978-0-07-867214-9(7) , 9780078672149) Glencoe/McGraw-Hill.

McHugh, Michael J. & Arwine, David K. Our Father's World. 1999. (God's Creation Ser.: Vol. 2). (Illus.). 112p. (J). (gr. 1-2). pap., wbk. ed. 8.95 (978-1-930092-05-1(9) , CLP69510) Christian Liberty Pr.

McMorrow, Annalisa. Leapin' Lizards & Other Reptiles. 1999. (Illus.). 80p. (J). pap. 9.95 (978-1-57612-110-8(0)) Monday Morning Bks., Inc.

Meacham, Nancy. Agua: Libro de Actividades de Descubrimeinto Cientifico. Zuman, John & Barra, Nancy, eds. Deming, Linda, illus. 2002. (SPA.). 20p. (J). 5.00 (978-1-58332-006-8(7)) Intercultural Center for Research in Education (I N C R E).

Measurement of Matter. 2001. (Physical Science Ser.). (J). (gr. k-12). vinyl bd. 4.95 (978-1-58845-130-9(5)) School Specialty Publishing.

Meissner, David. Habitat Rescue. 2004. (Navigators Ser.). (J). pap. 38.00 (978-1-4108-0411-2(9)) Benchmark Education Co.

Mellett, Peter. Matter & Materials. 2001. (Hands-On Science Ser.). (Illus.). (J). (978-0-606-21318-9(X)) Tandem Library Bks.

Mendelsohn, Everett. Life Sciences in the Twentieth Century. 2000. (Scribner Science Reference Ser.: Vol. 2). (Illus.). 207p. (YA). (gr. 7 up). 115.00 (978-0-684-80647-1(9) , GML00502-172407) Thomson Gale.

Mercer, Bobby. The Leaping, Sliding, Sprinting, Riding Science Book: 50 Super Sports Science Activities. LaBaff, Tom, illus. 2007. 80p. (J). 14.95 (978-1-57990-785-3(7) , 1262286) Lark Bks.

Mi estacion Favorita. 2000. (McGraw-Hill Ciencias Ser.). (ENG & SPA.). (gr. k up). (978-0-02-279699-0(1)) Macmillan/McGraw-Hill Schl. Div.

Mi hogar: la Tierra: Cuaderno de Actividades: Unit 4: Mi hogar: la Tierra (A Home Called Earth) 2000. (McGraw-Hill Ciencias Ser.). (ENG & SPA.). (gr. k up). (978-0-02-278994-7(4)) Macmillan/McGraw-Hill Schl. Div.

Mi Papalote. 2000. (McGraw-Hill Ciencias Ser.). (ENG & SPA.). (gr. 1 up). (978-0-02-279567-2(7)) Macmillan/McGraw-Hill Schl. Div.

Mi Paseo. 2000. (SPA.). (J). (978-1-58453-109-8(6)) Pioneer Valley Educational Pr., Inc.

Michels, Michael, et al. Cooperative Learning & Science High School Activities. 2005. per. (***978-1-879097-74-2(5)***) Kagan Publishing.

Middle Grades Science. 2004. 520.00 (978-0-531-14703-0(7)) Scholastic Library Publishing.

Miles Kelly Staff. Science: Family Flip Quiz. 2003. (Flip Quiz Ser.). (Illus.). 152p. (J). spiral bd. 12.95 (978-1-84236-073-6(6)) Miles Kelly Publishing, Ltd. GBR. *Dist:* Independent Pubs. Group.

Miller, Brendan D. & Willard-Holt, Colleen. Dare to Differentiate: Content-Based Enrichment Strategies for Upper & Middle School Science. 2000. 80p. (YA). spiral bd. 18.00 (978-0-910609-41-8(1)) Gifted Education Pr.

Miller Molengraft, Lisa. Simple Centers. 1999. 240p. (J). (gr. 1 up). pap. 16.99 (978-1-56822-306-3(4) , IF8667); (gr. 2 up). pap. 16.99 (978-1-56822-307-0(2) , IF8668) School Specialty Publishing.

Miller, Ray. Sloppy Slimy Sticky Soggy Dripping Moving Science. 1999. 24p. (J). (gr. 3-7). 7.95 (978-0-590-18725-1(2)) Scholastic, Inc.

Milner, Bryan & Martin, Jean. Core Science Homework. 1999. (Core Science Ser.). (Illus.). 96p. pap. 12.00 (978-0-521-66660-2(0)) Cambridge Univ. Pr.

Minibeasts up Close, 6 vols., Set 2. 2004. pap. 40.50 (978-1-4109-1541-2(7)) Raintree.

Miremos a las rocas Science, 6 vols.Tr. of Let's Look at Rocks Science. (SPA.). (gr. k-2). 28.95 (978-0-7368-3051-5(0) , Yellow Umbrella Bks.) Capstone Pr., Inc.

Mitchell Lane Publishers. A Robbie Reader-Science Biography, 5 vols., Set. 2005. (Robbie Reader Ser.). (Illus.). 32p. (gr. 1-4). lib. bdg. 128.50 (978-1-58415-351-1(2)) Mitchell Lane Pubs., Inc.

MoCasins: Level A. 8p. 20.95 (978-0-322-00624-9(4)) Wright Group, The.

Modern Staff. Apple Tree. 2003. 38.95 (978-0-8136-4107-2(1)) Modern Curriculum Pr.

Modules: Physical Science. 2005. (gr. 6-12). cd-rom (978-0-618-42032-2(0) , 2-01146) McDougal Littell Inc.

Modules: Physical Science; Content Review CD-ROM: Physical Science. 2005. (gr. 6-12). cd-rom (978-0-618-42026-1(6) , 2-01140) McDougal Littell Inc.

Modules: Physical Science; Diversity of Living Things. 2005. (gr. 6-12). lab manual ed. (978-0-618-43724-5(X) , 2-01217) McDougal Littell Inc.

Modules: Physical Science; Ecology Unit. 2005. (gr. 6-12). lab manual ed. (978-0-618-43728-3(2) , 2-01221) McDougal Littell Inc.

Modules: Physical Science; English Learners Package. 2005. (gr. 6-12). (978-0-618-41579-3(3) , 2-01131) McDougal Littell Inc.

Modules: Physical Science; How Stuff Works Express Magazine. 2005. (gr. 6-12). (978-0-618-41615-8(3) , 2-01137) McDougal Littell Inc.

Modules: Physical Science; Lab Generator. 2005. (gr. 6-12). cd-rom (978-0-618-42033-9(9) , 2-01147) McDougal Littell Inc.

Modules: Physical Science; Life over Time. 2005. (gr. 6-12). lab manual ed. (978-0-618-43731-3(2) , 2-01224) McDougal Littell Inc.

Modules: Physical Science; Process & Lab Skills PE. 2005. (gr. 6 up). (978-0-618-41364-5(2) , 2-01113); (gr. 7 up). (978-0-618-41365-2(0) , 2-01114); (gr. 8 up). (978-0-618-41366-9(9) , 2-01115) McDougal Littell Inc.

Modules: Physical Science; Science Toolkit. 2005. (gr. 6-12). (978-0-618-41583-0(1) , 2-01134) McDougal Littell Inc.

Modules: Physical Science; Standardized Test Practice PE. 2005. (gr. 6-12). cd-rom (978-0-618-41372-0(3) , 2-01121); (gr. 7 up). (978-0-618-41371-3(5) , 2-01120) McDougal Littell Inc.

Modules: Physical Science; Visual Glossary. 2005. (gr. 6-12). (978-0-618-41587-8(4) , 2-01136) McDougal Littell Inc.

Moehlenpah, Arlo. Creation Versus Evolution: Scientific & Religious Considerations. 2003. 36p. (YA). (978-0-9667054-6-1(7)) Doing Good Ministries.

Mom, Science. The Science in Your Shoes: And 49 Other Places in a Kid's Everyday Life. Mom, Science & Girl, Science, illus. 1999. 12p. (J). (gr. 3-6). pap. 10.95 (978-0-9659630-2-2(0)) Tomorrow's Girl.

Monde, Mathew. Integrated Science for Zambia Basic Education Grade 1 Pupil's Book. 2005. 48p. pap. 3.70 (978-0-521-67362-4(3)) Cambridge Univ. Pr.

Monde, Mathews. Integrated Science for Zambia Basic Education Grade 2 Pupil's Book. 2008. pap., stu. ed. 4.00 (978-0-521-69110-9(9)) Cambridge Univ. Pr.

—Integrated Science for Zambia Basic Education Grade 2 Teacher's Guide. 2008. pap., tchr. ed. 4.00 (978-0-521-69111-6(7)) Cambridge Univ. Pr.

Montgomery, Sy. The Snake Scientist. Bishop, Nic, photos by. 2001. (Scientists in the Field Ser.). (Illus.). 48p. (J). (gr. 3-5). pap., pap. 6.95 (978-0-618-11119-0(0)) Houghton Mifflin Co. Trade & Reference Div.

Moog. Bonding & Structure with Student Solutions Manual. 2003. (YA). pap., pap. 35.16 (978-0-618-44714-5(8) , 387213) Houghton Mifflin College Div.

Moor, Jo Ellen. Giant Science Resource Book. Evans, Marilyn, ed. 1998. (Illus.). 304p. (J). (gr. 1-6). pap., tchr. ed. 24.95 (978-1-55799-696-1(2) , EMC 398) Evan-Moor Educational Pubs.

Moore, Suzanne & Henry, Lucia Kemp. Toss & Learn Games: Science. 2003. (Toss & Learn Games Ser.). (Illus.). 48p. (ps-k). 10.99 (978-0-439-47118-3(4) , Teaching Resources) Scholastic, Inc.

Morter, Peter. Atlas Visual de los Descubrimientos. (SPA., Illus.). 412p. (YA). (gr. 5-8). 29.95 (978-84-216-1814-1(8) , BU4892) Bruño, Editorial ESP. *Dist:* Lectorum Pubns., Inc.

Mother Goose Cares about Math & Science: Professional Development Manual. 2004. (978-0-9753985-2-4(0)) Mother Goose Programs.

El Motin del Amistad: Libros Aventuras (Adventure Books) 2003. (MacMillan/McGraw-Hill. Estudios Sociales Ser.). (ENG & SPA.). (gr. 5 up). (978-0-02-150125-0(4)) Macmillan/McGraw-Hill Schl. Div.

Movimiento. (Coleccion Jugando Con la Ciencia). (SPA., Illus.). 39p. (J). pap. 9.95 (978-950-11-0684-8(5) , SGM325) Sigmar ARG. *Dist:* Continental Bk. Co., Inc.

El movimiento de las Mareas: Leveled Books. 2000. (McGraw-Hill Ciencias Ser.). (ENG & SPA.). (gr. 4 up). (978-0-02-279654-9(1)) Macmillan/McGraw-Hill Schl. Div.

Muerto de Frio. 2000. (McGraw-Hill Ciencias Ser.). (ENG & SPA.). (gr. 5 up). (978-0-02-279672-3(X)) Macmillan/McGraw-Hill Schl. Div.

Muestranos tus alas Science, 6 vols.Tr. of Show Us Your Wings Science. (SPA.). (gr. k-2). 28.95 (978-0-7368-3035-5(9) , Yellow Umbrella Bks.) Capstone Pr., Inc.

El Mundo de la Ciencia. (Coleccion Lo Sabias?). (SPA., Illus.). 44p. (J). 12.95 (978-950-11-0940-5(2) , SGM9402) Sigmar ARG. *Dist:* Continental Bk. Co., Inc.

Murphy, Lisa. Even More Fizzle Bubble Pop & Wow! Simple Science for Young Children. rev. ed. 2004. Orig. Title: Fizzle Bubble Pop & Wow!. (Illus.). 116p. pap. 19.95 (978-0-9706634-2-9(0)) Learning Through Adventure Co., The.

Murphy, Patricia J. Push & Pull. 2002. (Rookie Read-About Science Ser.). (Illus.). 32p. (J). (gr. 1-2). pap. 4.95 (978-0-516-26864-4(3) , Children's Pr.) Scholastic Library Publishing.

Museums: Collections to Share, 6 vols. (Book2WebTM Ser.). (gr. 4-8). 36.50 (978-0-322-02986-6(4)) Wright Group, The.

My Big Book of Science. 2004. (Illus.). 48p. (J). pap. 5.99 (978-1-85854-843-2(8)) Brimax Books Ltd. GBR. *Dist:* Byeway Bks.

My Feet: Big Book: Level C. 8p. 20.95 (978-0-322-00364-4(4)) Wright Group, The.

My Pet. 2005. (Emergent/Early (Prek-2) Science Package Ser.). 12p. (YA). (ps-2). 25.20 (978-0-8215-7836-0(7)) Sadlier, William H. Inc.

My World of Science: Set 1. (Illus.). (J). (gr. 1-2). 96.00 (978-1-4042-3379-9(2)) Rosen Publishing Group, Inc., The.

My World of Science: Set 2. (Illus.). (J). (gr. 1-2). 96.00 (978-1-4042-3289-1(3)) Rosen Publishing Group, Inc., The.

My World of Science Set 1. (ENG & SPA., Illus.). (J). (gr. 4-8). 96.00 (978-1-4042-7568-3(1) , Buenas Letra) Rosen Publishing Group, Inc., The.

Mystery Science: The Case of the Missing Lunch. 2002. (J). per. 10.95 (978-1-883055-54-7(7)) Dandy Lion Pubns.

Natural Science Mysteries Full Kit. 2005. (Illus.). 856p. (YA). 75.00 (978-1-59476-097-6(7)) Paradigm Accelerated Curriculum.

Nature's Fury: Lightning!, Killer Quake! & Hurricane!, 3 cass.; set. gif. ed. 2004. (NOVA Ser.). (gr. 7 up). 49.95 incl. VHS (978-1-884738-68-5(0) , WG027) WGBH Boston Video.

NCPTA Staff. Home Learning 11 Sats Practical Science. (Illus.). 32p. pap. 6.99 (978-0-340-71046-3(2) , Coronet) Hodder General Publishing Division GBR. *Dist:* Trafalgar Square Publishing.

Nelson, Robin. Float & Sink. 2004. (First Step Nonfiction Ser.). (Illus.). 24p. (J). (gr. k-2). lib. bdg. 18.60 (978-0-8225-5135-5(7)) Lerner Publishing Group.

—Magnets. 2005. (Forces & Motion Ser.). (Illus.). 22p. (J). pap. (978-0-8225-5298-7(1) , Lerner Pubns.) Lerner Publishing Group.

—Push & Pull. 2005. (Forces & Motion Ser.). (Illus.). 22p. (J). pap. (978-0-8225-5299-4(X)) Lerner Publishing Group.

—Se Congela y Se Derrite. 2003. (First Step Nonfiction Ser.). (SPA., Illus.). 24p. (J). (gr. k-2). lib. bdg. 18.60 (978-0-8225-4865-2(8)) Lerner Publishing Group.

Njeleshi, Chansa. Integrated Science for Zambia Basic Education Grade 5 Pupil's Book. 2006. pap., stu. ed. 6.00 (978-0-521-69108-6(7)) Cambridge Univ. Pr.

Njeleshi, Chansa. Integrated Science for Zambia Basic Education Grade 6 Pupil's Book. 2006. pap., stu. ed. 3.99 (***978-0-521-70091-7(4)***) Cambridge Univ. Pr.

No lo puedo Creer! 2000. (McGraw-Hill Ciencias Ser.). (ENG & SPA.). (gr. 3 up). (978-0-02-279635-8(5)) Macmillan/McGraw-Hill Schl. Div.

Nobleman, Marc Tyler. Felix Explores Our World. 1999. (Illus.). 304p. (J). (gr. 4-7). pap., act. bk. ed. 8.95 (978-0-7892-0596-4(3)) Abbeville Pr., Inc.

La noche de la Huida. 2000. (McGraw-Hill Ciencias Ser.). (ENG & SPA.). (gr. 3 up). (978-0-02-279629-7(0)) Macmillan/McGraw-Hill Schl. Div.

Norris, Jill. Science Experiments for Young Learners. Davis, Cindy, illus. 2000. 256p. (J). (gr. k-2). pap., tchr. ed. 24.95 (978-1-55799-779-1(9) , EMC 866) Evan-Moor Educational Pubs.

Nos comimos un arco Iris. 2000. (McGraw-Hill Ciencias Ser.). (ENG & SPA.). (gr. k up). (978-0-02-279709-6(2)) Macmillan/McGraw-Hill Schl. Div.

Nos divertimos Science, 6 vols.Tr. of On All Kinds of Days Science. (SPA.). (gr. k-2). 28.95 (978-0-7368-3126-0(6) , Yellow Umbrella Bks.) Capstone Pr., Inc.

Nsrc. Science & Technology for Children Books, Microworlds. 2004. (Illus.). 64p. (J). (978-1-933008-04-2(0)) National Science Resources Ctr.

Nuestro Arbol. 2000. (McGraw-Hill Ciencias Ser.). (ENG & SPA.). (gr. 1 up). (978-0-02-279555-9(3)) Macmillan/McGraw-Hill Schl. Div.

Nuestro hogar el Desierto. 2000. (McGraw-Hill Ciencias Ser.). (ENG & SPA.). (gr. k up). (978-0-02-279698-3(3)) Macmillan/McGraw-Hill Schl. Div.

Nuestros cinco sentidos Science, 6 vols.Tr. of Our Five Senses Science. (SPA.). (gr. k-2). 28.95 (978-0-7368-3146-8(0) , Yellow Umbrella Bks.) Capstone Pr., Inc.

Nuevo Investiguemos 1: Ciencias Naturales y de la Salud. (SPA.). (J). (gr. 1). (978-958-02-1575-2(8)) Editorial Voluntad S.A. COL. *Dist:* Distribuidora Norma, Inc.

Nuevo Investiguemos 2: Ciencias Naturales y de la Salud. (SPA.). (J). (gr. 2). (978-958-02-1576-9(6)) Editorial Voluntad S.A. COL. *Dist:* Distribuidora Norma, Inc.

Nuevo Investiguemos 3: Ciencias Naturales y de la Salud. (SPA.). (J). (gr. 3). (978-958-02-1577-6(4)) Editorial Voluntad S.A. COL. *Dist:* Distribuidora Norma, Inc.

Nuevo Investiguemos 4: Ciencias Naturales y de la Salud. (SPA.). (J). (gr. 4). (978-958-02-1578-3(2)) Editorial Voluntad S.A. COL. *Dist:* Distribuidora Norma, Inc.

Nuevo Investiguemos 5: Ciencias Naturales y de la Salud. (SPA.). (J). (gr. 5). (978-958-02-1579-0(0)) Editorial Voluntad S.A. COL. *Dist:* Distribuidora Norma, Inc.

Nuevo Investiguemos 6: Ciencias Naturales y de la Salud. (SPA.). (978-958-02-1534-9(0)) Editorial Voluntad S.A. COL. *Dist:* Distribuidora Norma, Inc.

Nuevo Investiguemos 8: Ciencias Naturales y de la Salud. (SPA.). (YA). (gr. 8). (978-958-02-1536-3(7)) Editorial Voluntad S.A. COL. *Dist:* Distribuidora Norma, Inc.

Nye, Bill. Bill Nye the Science Guy's Consider the Following. 2000. (Illus.). (J). 17.39 (978-0-606-18254-6(3)) Tandem Library Bks.

Los observadores del Cielo. 2000. (McGraw-Hill Ciencias Ser.). (ENG & SPA.). (gr. 5 up). (978-0-02-279668-6(1)) Macmillan/McGraw-Hill Schl. Div.

The Ocean Science, 6 vols. (gr. k-2). 28.95 (978-0-7368-2997-7(0) , Yellow Umbrella Bks.) Capstone Pr., Inc.

El oceano Science, 6 vols.Tr. of Ocean Science. (SPA.). (gr. k-2). 28.95 (978-0-7368-3033-1(2) , Yellow Umbrella Bks.) Capstone Pr., Inc.

Oceanor Staff. Quimica - Atlas Visual. 1999. (SPA.). (gr. 3-6). lib. bdg. 20.00 (978-0-613-80881-1(9)) Tandem Library Bks.

Oh, Soo & Yoon, Seok. Exploring the Human Body. 2005. (Illus.). 192p. (J). pap. 12.95 (978-981-05-2242-1(8)) Youngjin.com Publishing Co., Ltd. KOR. *Dist:* Transition Vendor.

O'Leary, Nancy K. & Shelly, Susan. The Complete Idiot's Guide' to Science Fair Projects. 2003. (Complete Idiot's Guide Ser.). (Illus.). 368p. (gr. 12). pap. 16.95 (978-1-59257-137-6(9) , Alpha Bks.) Penguin Group (USA) Inc.

Las Olimpiadas: a jugar Limpio! Leveled Books. 2000. (McGraw-Hill Ciencias Ser.). (ENG & SPA.). (gr. 4 up). (978-0-02-279657-0(6)) Macmillan/McGraw-Hill Schl. Div.

Oliver, Clare. Tell Me Who Lives in Space? And More about Space. 2004. (Illus.). 32p. (J). pap. (978-1-84458-057-6(1)) Chrysalis Children's Bks.

O'Mara, Anna. Ecosystems, 4 bks. Incl. Deserts. lib. bdg. 18.60 (978-1-56065-338-7(8)); Mountains. lib. bdg. 18.60 (978-1-56065-337-0(X)); Oceans. lib. bdg. 18.60 (978-1-56065-339-4(6)); Rain Forests. lib. bdg. 18.60 (978-1-56065-336-3(1)); 24p. (J). (gr. 2-3). 1996. (Illus.). Set lib. bdg. 74.40 (978-1-56065-630-2(1) , Bridgestone Bks.) Capstone Pr., Inc.

On All Kinds of Days Science, 6 vols. (gr. k-2). 28.95 (978-0-7368-1740-0(9) , Yellow Umbrella Bks.) Capstone Pr., Inc.

One Each of 8 Big Books. (Sunshinetm Science Ser.). (gr. 1-2). 250.50 (978-0-7802-0567-3(7)) Wright Group, The.

O'Neil, Sarah. Floating & Sinking. 1999. (gr. k-3). lib. bdg. 11.80 (978-0-613-19353-5(9)) Tandem Library Bks.

Operation: Top Secret. 2005. (J). per. (978-1-932855-33-3(5)) becker&mayer! books.

Organization Skills. 2004. 80p. (J). (gr. 6-8). pap. 10.99 (978-0-7696-3328-2(5) , MH1032) School Specialty Publishing.

Orme, David. Extreme Science. 2008. (Trailblazers Ser.). (Illus.). 36p. pap. 7.95 (***978-1-84167-648-7(9)***) Ransom Publishing Ltd. GBR. *Dist:* International Publishers Marketing.

El oso polar y el Jaguar: Leveled Books. 2000. (McGraw-Hill Ciencias Ser.). (ENG & SPA.). (gr. 4 up). (978-0-02-279651-8(7)) Macmillan/McGraw-Hill Schl. Div.

O'Toole, Mitch & McKenzie, Carol. Science Skills 1. 2000. (Australian Secondary Science Ser.). 160p. pap. 21.00 (978-0-521-57504-1(4)) Cambridge Univ. Pr.

—Science Skills 2. 2000. (Australian Secondary Science Ser.). 160p. pap. 21.00 (978-0-521-57503-4(6)) Cambridge Univ. Pr.

—Science Skills 3. 2000. (Australian Secondary Science Ser.). 160p. pap. 31.00 (978-0-521-57502-7(8)) Cambridge Univ. Pr.

—Science Skills 4. 2000. (Australian Secondary Science Ser.). 160p. pap. 31.00 (978-0-521-57501-0(X)) Cambridge Univ. Pr.

Ottaviani, Jim. Two-Fisted Science: Stories about Scientists. Chadwick, Paul et al, illus. 2001. 128p. (YA). (gr. 4-7). pap. 14.95 (978-0-9660106-2-6(0)) GT Labs.

Our Five Senses Science, 6 vols. (gr. k-2). 28.95 (978-0-7368-1749-3(2) , Yellow Umbrella Bks.) Capstone Pr., Inc.

Outdoor Science Classroom. 2005. 96p. (J). per. 10.99 (978-1-59441-198-4(0) , CD-104107) Carson-Dellosa Publishing Co., Inc.

Owen, Andy & Ashwell, Miranda. Science Topics, 5 bks., Set. 1999. (Illus.). 32p. (YA). (gr. 7-9). pap. 113.95 (978-1-57572-771-4(4)) Heinemann Library.

Owl Magazine Editors. You Asked? Over 300 Great Questions & Astounding Answers. 2004. (Illus.). 160p. (J). pap. 14.95 (978-1-897066-16-4(3)) Maple Tree Pr. CAN. *Dist:* Perseus Distribution.

Oxlade, Chris. Can Science Solve?, 13 bks. (J). (gr. 4-7). Set. 2003. lib. bdg. 296.27 (978-1-58810-670-4(5)); Set 2. 2002. lib. bdg. 113.95 (978-1-58810-669-8(1)) Heinemann Library.

—Mail. 2001. 32p. (J). (ps-3). lib. bdg. 21.36 (978-1-58810-064-1(2)) Heinemann Library.

Oxlade, Chris. The Mystery of Crop Circles. (Can Science Solve? Ser.). (Illus.). 32p. (J). 2006. lib. bdg. 29.29 (***978-1-4034-8333-1(7)***); 1999. (gr. 4-7). lib. bdg. 22.79 (978-1-57572-804-9(4)); 2nd ed. 2006. pap. 7.85 (***978-1-4034-8342-3(6)***); Set 1. 2002. (gr. 4-7). pap. 7.50 (978-1-58810-308-6(0) , 91036) Heinemann Library.

Oxlade, Chris & Wallace, Holly. Can Science Solve?, 8 vols., Set 1. 1999. 32p. (J). (gr. 4-7). lib. bdg. 182.32 (978-1-57572-813-1(3)) Heinemann Library.

Packard, Mary. Morse Code. Nichols, Cathy, ed. Watling, J., illus. 2000. 16p. (YA). (978-1-884270-14-7(X)) Hall, Nancy Inc.

Padilla, Michael J., et al. Adventures in Life, Earth, & Physical Science, 3 vols. 2004. 866p. (YA). (gr. 6-8). 433.00 (978-0-13-115416-2(8)) Prentice Hall Pr.

—Discoveries in Life, Earth, & Physical Science, 3 vols. 2004. 858p. (YA). (gr. 6-8). 429.00 (978-0-13-115415-5(X)) Prentice Hall Pr.

—Investigations in Life, Earth, & Physical Science, 3 vols. 2004. 890p. (YA). (gr. 6-8). 445.00 (978-0-13-115414-8(1)) Prentice Hall Pr.

El paraiso del Panqueque. 2000. (McGraw-Hill Ciencias Ser.). (ENG & SPA.). (gr. k up). (978-0-02-279703-4(3)) Macmillan/McGraw-Hill Schl. Div.

Parker, Andrew & Stamford, Jane. Starting Science Bk. 1: Materials. 2nd ed. 1999. (Illus.). 31p. (J). (gr. 1-3). pap., wbk. ed. 24.00 (978-0-7217-3606-8(8)) Schofield & Sims Ltd. GBR. *Dist:* State Mutual Bk. & Periodical Service, Ltd.

—Starting Science Bk. 2: Living Things. 2nd ed. 1999. (Illus.). 31p. (J). (gr. 1-3). pap., wbk. ed. 24.00 (978-0-7217-3607-5(6)) Schofield & Sims Ltd. GBR. *Dist:* State Mutual Bk. & Periodical Service, Ltd.

—Starting Science Bk. 3: Light, Sound, Movement & Electricity. 1999. (Illus.). 31p. (J). (gr. 1-3). pap., wbk. ed. 24.00 (978-0-7217-3608-2(4)) Schofield & Sims Ltd. GBR. *Dist:* State Mutual Bk. & Periodical Service, Ltd.

Parker, Janice. Engines, Elevators & X-Rays: The Science of Machines. 1999. (Science @ Work Ser.). (Illus.). 48p. (J). (gr. 4-6). pap. 27.12 (978-0-7398-0142-0(2)) Raintree.

Parker, Steve. Quimica Elemental - Jugando Con la Ciencia. 1998. (SPA.). (gr. 3-6). lib. bdg. 19.65 (978-0-613-83050-8(4)) Tandem Library Bks.

—Science Files - Set I - Materials: Glass; Metals; Plastics; Rocks & Minerals; Textiles; Wood, 6 bks. 2002. (Illus.). (J). (gr. 3 up). lib. bdg. 148.02 (978-0-8368-3081-1(4)) Stevens, Gareth Inc.

—20th Century Science & Technology, 6 bks. Incl. 1900-20 : A Shrinking World. lib. bdg. 26.00 (978-0-8368-2942-6(5)); 1920-40 : Atoms to Automation. lib. bdg. 26.00 (978-0-8368-2943-3(3)); 1940-60 : The Nuclear Age. lib. bdg. 26.00 (978-0-8368-2944-0(1)); 1960s : Space & Time. lib. bdg. 26.00 (978-0-8368-2945-7(X)); 1970-90 : Computers & Chips. lib. bdg. 26.00 (978-0-8368-2946-4(8)); 1990-2000 : The Electronic Age. lib. bdg. 26.00 (978-0-8368-2947-1(6)); 32p. (J). (gr. 5 up). 2001. (Illus.). Set lib. bdg. 156.00 (978-0-8368-2941-9(7)) Stevens, Gareth Inc.

Las partes de las Plantas. 2000. (McGraw-Hill Ciencias Ser.). (ENG & SPA.). (gr. k up). (978-0-02-279693-8(2)) Macmillan/McGraw-Hill Schl. Div.

Pascoe, Elaine. How & Why, 12 bks. Kuhn, Dwight, photos by. Incl. Animals Are Poisonous. lib. bdg. 20.67 (978-0-8368-3002-6(4)); Animals Grow New Parts. lib. bdg. 20.67 (978-0-8368-3003-3(2)); Animals Hatch from Eggs. lib. bdg. 20.67 (978-0-8368-3004-0(0)); Animals Hide. lib. bdg. 20.67 (978-0-8368-3005-7(9)); Animals Prepare for Winter. lib. bdg. 20.67 (978-0-8368-3006-4(7)); Birds Build Nests. lib. bdg. 20.67 (978-0-8368-3007-1(5)); Birds Use Their Beaks. lib. bdg. 20.67 (978-0-8368-3008-8(3)); Insects Grow & Change. lib. bdg. 20.67 (978-0-8368-3009-5(1)); Insects Visit Flowers. lib. bdg. 20.67 (978-0-8368-3010-1(5)); Plants Eat Insects. lib. bdg. 20.67 (978-0-8368-3011-8(3)); Seeds Travel. lib. bdg. 20.67 (978-0-8368-3012-5(1)); Spiders Spin Silk. lib. bdg. 20.67 (978-0-8368-3013-2(X)); 24p. (J). (gr. 1 up). (Illus.). 2002. Set lib. bdg. 248.04 (978-0-8368-3001-9(6)) Stevens, Gareth Inc.

Un paseo Mojado. 2000. (McGraw-Hill Ciencias Ser.). (ENG & SPA.). (gr. 1 up). (978-0-02-279564-1(2)) Macmillan/McGraw-Hill Schl. Div.

Pasternak, Ceel. Cool Careers for Girls as Environmentalists. 2001. (Cool Careers for Girls Ser.: Vol. 11). (Illus.). 144p. pap. 12.95 (978-1-57023-172-8(9)) Impact Pubns.

Pathfinders, 8 vols. 2000. (Illus.). 64p. 135.00 (978-1-58209-553-0(1)) Books Are Fun, Ltd.

Pauli, Gunter. Bear & the Fox. Salazar, Pamela, illus. 2007. 33p. pap. 9.95 (***978-958-692-840-3(3)***) Marion Institute.

—Can Apples Fly. Salazar, Pamela, illus. 2007. 33p. pap. 9.95 (***978-958-692-854-0(3)***) Marion Institute.

—Cold Feet. Salazar, Pamela, illus. 2007. 33p. pap. 9.95 (***978-958-692-861-8(6)***) Marion Institute.

—Desert Witch. Salazar, Pamela, illus. 2007. 33p. pap. 9.95 (***978-958-692-844-1(6)***) Marion Institute.

—Red Rice. Salazar, Pamela, illus. 2007. 33p. pap. 9.95 (***978-958-692-831-1(4)***) Marion Institute.

—Tree Candy. Salazar, Pamela, illus. 2007. 33p. pap. 9.95 (***978-958-692-836-6(5)***) Marion Institute.

Pearce, Q. L. Activities for Science Centers. 2004. 80p. (J). (gr. 1 up). pap. 10.99 (978-0-7424-2851-5(6) , IFG99222); (gr. 2 up). pap. 10.99 (978-0-7424-2852-2(4) , IFG99223) School Specialty Publishing.

Pearce, Querida L. The Science Almanac for Kids. 1998. (Illus.). 128p. (J). (gr. 3-7). 12.95 (978-1-56565-683-3(0) , 06830W) Lowell Hse. Juvenile.

Peces que Enganan. 2000. (McGraw-Hill Ciencias Ser.). (ENG & SPA.). (gr. 2 up). (978-0-02-279623-5(1)) Macmillan/McGraw-Hill Schl. Div.

Pentland, Peter & Stoyles, Pennie. Party Science. 2003. (Science & Scientists Ser.). (Illus.). 32p. (gr. 4-8). lib. bdg. 27.00 (978-0-7910-7015-4(8) , Chelsea Hse.) Facts On File, Inc.

Perry, Phyllis J. Science Fair Success with Plants. 1999. (Science Fair Success Ser.). (Illus.). 104p. (YA). (gr. 6-12). lib. bdg. 26.60 (978-0-7660-1170-0(4)) Enslow Pubs., Inc.

Personas que han dejado huella: Dr Errol Crook. 2000. (McGraw-Hill Ciencias Ser.). (ENG & SPA.). (gr. 5 up). (978-0-02-279688-4(6)) Macmillan/McGraw-Hill Schl. Div.

Petheram, Louise, et al. Ascent! 2003. Bk. 2. 200p. pap. (978-0-7487-6795-3(9)); Bk. 3. 240p. pap. (978-0-7487-6796-0(7)) Nelson Thornes Ltd.

—Ascent! 1 Bk. 1: Key Stage 3 Science. 2002. (Illus.). 192p. (J). (gr. 2-4). pap. 24.50 (978-0-7487-6792-2(4)) Nelson Thornes Ltd. GBR. *Dist:* Trans-Atlantic Pubns., Inc.

PH Inc. Staff. Parade of Life: Animals. 2nd ed. (J). pap., act. bk. ed. (978-0-13-225616-2(9)) Prentice Hall (Schl. Div.).

—PH Science Ecology Earth. (J). pap., act. bk. ed. (978-0-13-225582-0(0)) Prentice Hall (Schl. Div.).

—PH Science Evolution. 2nd ed. (J). pap., act. bk. ed. (978-0-13-225541-7(3)) Prentice Hall (Schl. Div.).

Physical, Module B. 2003. (gr. 3 up). suppl. ed. 15.50 (978-0-328-03436-9(3)); (gr. 4 up). suppl. ed. 15.50 (978-0-328-03440-6(1)); (gr. 5 up). suppl. ed. 16.00 (978-0-328-03444-4(4)); (gr. 6 up). suppl. ed. 16.00 (978-0-328-03448-2(7)) Addison-Wesley Educational Pubs., Inc.

Physical Science: Physical Science PE. 2005. (gr. 6-12). (978-0-618-30369-4(3) , 2-01004) McDougal Littell Inc.

Physical Science: Physical Science Unit Resource Materials. 2005. (gr. 6-12). (978-0-618-41242-6(5) , 2-01097) McDougal Littell Inc.

Physical Science Classroom Library. (gr. k-2). lib. bdg. 54.95 (978-0-7368-9309-1(1)) Red Brick Learning.

Physical Science Complete Unit. (gr. k-2). 311.95 (978-0-7368-9310-7(5)) Red Brick Learning.

Physical Science-Flip Chart. 2001. 10p. (J). (gr. k-12). spiral bd. 12.95 (978-1-58845-180-4(1)) School Specialty Publishing.

Physical Science Syllabus & Tests. 1999. 18p. (YA). ring bd. 2.50 (978-1-57896-056-9(8) , 1540, Hewitt Homeschooling Resources) Hewitt Research Foundation, Inc.

El Picnic. 2000. (McGraw-Hill Ciencias Ser.). (ENG & SPA.). (gr. k up). (978-0-02-279706-5(8)) Macmillan/McGraw-Hill Schl. Div.

Pinguinos: Aves que Nadan: Leveled Books. 2000. (McGraw-Hill Ciencias Ser.). (ENG & SPA.). (gr. 4 up). (978-0-02-279662-4(2)) Macmillan/McGraw-Hill Schl. Div.

Pistas del pasado: Cuaderno de Evaluacion: Unit 2: Pistas del pasado (Clues from the Past) 2000. (McGraw-Hill Ciencias Ser.). (ENG & SPA.). (gr. 2 up). (978-0-02-278639-7(2)) Macmillan/McGraw-Hill Schl. Div.

Pistas del pasado: Recursos para el maestro con clave de Respuestas: Unit 2: Pistas del pasado (Clues from the Past) 2000. (McGraw-Hill Ciencias Ser.). (ENG & SPA.). (gr. 2 up). (978-0-02-278686-1(4)) Macmillan/McGraw-Hill Schl. Div.

Un planeta Ileno de agua: Cuaderno de Evaluacion: Unit 6: un planeta Ileno de agua (Earth's Water) 2000. (McGraw-Hill Ciencias Ser.). (ENG & SPA.). (gr. 4 up). (978-0-02-278665-6(1)) Macmillan/McGraw-Hill Schl. Div.

Un planeta Ileno de agua: Recursos para el maestro con clave de Respuestas: Unit 6: un planeta Ileno de agua (Earth's Water) 2000. (McGraw-Hill Ciencias Ser.). (ENG & SPA.). (gr. 4 up). (978-0-02-278705-9(4)) Macmillan/McGraw-Hill Schl. Div.

Plant Eaters of the Pond: 6 Each of 1 Student Book, 6 vols. (Sunshinetm Science Ser.). 24p. (gr. 1-2). 41.95 (978-0-7802-2698-2(4)) Wright Group, The.

Plant Eaters of the Pond: Big Book. (Sunshinetm Science Ser.). 24p. (gr. 1-2). 37.50 (978-0-7802-2783-5(2)) Wright Group, The.

Platt, Richard & Biesty, Stephen. Stephen Biesty's Incredible Cross-Sections Book. (Illus.). (J). pap. 24.95 (978-0-590-73870-5(4)) Scholastic, Inc.

Pluckrose, Henry. Let's Explore, 12 bks. Incl. Air. lib. bdg. 23.33 (978-0-8368-2957-0(3)); Day & Night. lib. bdg. 23.33 (978-0-8368-2958-7(1)); Discovering Shapes. lib. bdg. 23.33 (978-0-8368-2959-4(X)); Earth. lib. bdg. 23.33 (978-0-8368-2960-0(3)); Fire. lib. bdg. 23.33 (978-0-8368-2961-7(1)); Measuring Size. lib. bdg. 23.33 (978-0-8368-2962-4(X)); My Day. lib. bdg. 23.33 (978-0-8368-2963-1(8)); Numbers & Counting. lib. bdg. 23.33 (978-0-8368-2964-8(6)); Seasons. lib. bdg. 23.33 (978-0-8368-2965-5(4)); Sorting & Sets. lib. bdg. 23.33 (978-0-8368-2966-2(2)); Time. lib. bdg. 23.33 (978-0-8368-2967-9(0)); Water. lib. bdg. 23.33 (978-0-8368-2968-6(9)); 32p. (J). (gr. 1 up). 2001. (Illus.). Set lib. bdg. 279.96 (978-0-8368-2956-3(5)) Stevens, Gareth Inc.

Pocket Chart Science: Weather. 2000. (J). pap. 9.95 (978-1-56911-700-2(4)) Learning Resources, Inc.

Pocket Library, 3 vols., Set. 2000. (J). 29.95 (978-0-7525-3734-4(2)) Parragon, Inc.

Pocket Science. 2000. 128p. (J). 9.99 (978-0-7525-3969-0(8)) Parragon, Inc.

Pocket Scientist: The Blue Book. 2004. (Illus.). 290p. (J). 8.99 (978-0-7945-0148-8(6) , Usborne) EDC Publishing.

Poco a Poco. 2000. (McGraw-Hill Ciencias Ser.). (ENG & SPA.). (gr. 1 up). (978-0-02-279563-4(4)) Macmillan/McGraw-Hill Schl. Div.

El poder de la Clorofila. 2000. (McGraw-Hill Ciencias Ser.). (ENG & SPA.). (gr. 5 up). (978-0-02-279667-9(3)) Macmillan/McGraw-Hill Schl. Div.

The Pond: 6 Each of 1 Student Book, 6 vols. (Sunshinetm Science Ser.). 24p. (gr. 1-2). 41.95 (978-0-7802-2694-4(1)) Wright Group, The.

The Pond: Big Book. (Sunshinetm Science Ser.). 24p. (gr. 1-2). 37.50 (978-0-7802-2781-1(6)) Wright Group, The.

Pond Life Sets: 1 Each of 3 Big Books. (Sunshinetm Science Ser.). (gr. 1-2). 111.50 (978-0-7802-2820-7(0)) Wright Group, The.

Pond Life Sets: 1 Each of 3 Student Books. (Sunshinetm Science Ser.). (gr. 1-2). 20.95 (978-0-7802-2821-4(9)) Wright Group, The.

Por que la tortuga tiene Caparazon? Leveled Books. 2000. (McGraw-Hill Ciencias Ser.). (ENG & SPA.). (gr. 4 up). (978-0-02-279661-7(4)) Macmillan/McGraw-Hill Schl. Div.

Porter, Andrew, et al. Science Companion. 2nd ed. 1998. (Illus.). (J). (gr. 3-5). 144p. pap. 24.00 (978-0-7487-3003-2(6)); 189p. pap. 29.00 (978-0-7487-3002-5(8)) State Mutual Bk. & Periodical Service, Ltd.

Power & Light for Kids: Facilitator's Guide. 2005. (J). pap., tchr. ed. 8.95 (978-0-8309-1133-2(2)) Herald Publishing Hse.

Prentice-Hall Staff. Building Block. (J). pap., act. bk. ed. (978-0-13-402140-9(1)) Prentice Hall (Schl. Div.).

—Learning System Integrated Science, Bk. 1. (J). pap., act. bk. ed. 21.97 (978-0-13-402199-7(1)) Prentice Hall (Schl. Div.).

—Things Fall Apart. 2nd ed. (J). stu. ed. (978-0-13-716846-0(2)) Prentice Hall (Schl. Div.).

Preteen Pressures Series, 8 bks., Set. 2000. (Preteen Pressures Ser.). (Illus.). 205.52 (978-0-7398-4205-8(6)) Steck-Vaughn.

Pretests: Identifying Misconceptions: Assessment. 2000. (McGraw-Hill Science Ser.). (gr. 3 up). (978-0-02-279486-6(7)); (gr. 4 up). (978-0-02-279487-3(5)); (gr. 5 up). (978-0-02-279488-0(3)) Macmillan/McGraw-Hill Schl. Div.

Priddy, Roger. IQ Assortment: Bug, space, dino, Body. 2006. (J). 179.40 (978-0-312-49721-7(0) , Priddy Bks.) St. Martin's Pr.

Primal Pictures Staff, et al. PowerAnatomy: An On-Line. 10th ed. 2004. pap., lab manual ed. 24.95 (978-0-471-44558-6(4)) Wiley, John & Sons, Inc.

Primary Sources of Revolutionary Scientific Discoveries & Theories, 8 bk. set. 2005. (YA). (gr. 5-8). lib. bdg. 234.00 (978-1-4042-0373-0(7)) Rosen Publishing Group, Inc., The.

Princeton Review Publishing Staff. Science Smart Junior: Discovering the Secrets of Science. 2002. (Smart Junior Guides). (Illus.). 304p. (J). pap. 12.00 (978-0-375-76262-8(0) , Princeton Review) Random Hse. Information Group.

Prism the Rainbow Pony. 2004. (Region IV ESC Resources for Science Ser.). per. (978-1-932797-90-9(4)) Region IV Education Service Ctr.

Problemas en el Parque Forestal. 2000. (McGraw-Hill Ciencias Ser.). (ENG & SPA.). (gr. 5 up). (978-0-02-279678-5(9)) Macmillan/McGraw-Hill Schl. Div.

Profiles in Science, 15 bks., Set. Incl. Curious Bones : Mary Anning & the Birth of Paleontology. Goodhue, Thomas W. (Illus.). 112p. (YA). (gr. 6-12). 2004. lib. bdg. 23.95 (978-1-883846-93-0(5) , First Biographies); Double Stars : The Story of Caroline Herschel. Venkatraman, Padma. 160p. (YA). (gr. 6-12). 2007. lib. bdg. 27.95 (***978-1-59935-042-4(4)***); Galileo Galilei & the Science of Motion. Boerst, William J. (Illus.). 144p. (YA). (gr. 6-12). 2004. lib. bdg. 26.95 (978-1-931798-00-6(1)); Ibn Al-Haytham : First Scientist. Steffens, Bradley. (Illus.). 128p. (YA). (gr. 6-12). 2006. lib. bdg. 27.95 (978-1-59935-024-0(6)); Johannes Kepler : Discovering the Laws of Celestial Motion. Boerst, William J. (Illus.). 144p. (YA). (gr. 6-12). 2004. lib. bdg. 26.95 (978-1-883846-98-5(6) , First Biographies); Lise Meitner : Discoverer of Nuclear Fission. Barron, Rachel Stiffler. (Illus.). 112p. (YA). (gr. 6-12). 2004. lib. bdg. 23.95 (978-1-883846-52-7(8) , First Biographies); Louis Pasteur & the Founding of Microbiology. Ackerman, Jane. (Illus.). 144p. (YA). (gr. 6-12). 2004. 26.95 (978-1-931798-13-6(3)); New Elements : The Story of Marie Curie. Yannuzzi, Della A. (Illus.). 144p. (YA). (gr. 6-12). 2006. lib. bdg. 27.95 (978-1-59935-023-3(8)); Nicholas Copernicus & the Founding of Modern Astronomy. Boerst, William J. (Illus.). 144p. (YA). (gr. 6-12). 2004. lib. bdg. 26.95 (978-1-883846-99-2(4) , First Biographies); Nikola Tesla & the Taming of Electricity. Aldrich, Lisa J. (Illus.). 160p. (J). (ps-7). 2005. lib. bdg. 26.95 (978-1-931798-46-4(X)); Rosalind Franklin & the Structure of Life. Polcovar, Jane. 144p. (J). (gr. 6-12). 2006. lib. bdg. 27.95 (978-1-59935-022-6(X)); Scheduling the Heavens : The Story of Edmond Halley. Fox, Mary Virginia. (Illus.). 144p. (YA). (gr. 6-12). 2006. lib. bdg. 27.95 (***978-1-59935-021-9(1)***); Skeptical Chemist : The Story of Robert Boyle. Baxter, Roberta. (Illus.). 128p. (YA). (gr. 6-12). 2006. lib. bdg. 27.95 (978-1-59935-025-7(4)); Tycho Brahe : Mapping the Heavens. Boerst, William J. (Illus.). 144p. (YA). (gr. 6-12). 2004. 26.95 (978-1-883846-97-8(8) , First Biographies); 2007. Set lib. bdg. 413.25 (***978-1-59935-033-2(5)***) Reynolds, Morgan Inc.

Un proyecto de ciencias para George. 2000. (McGraw-Hill Ciencias Ser.). (ENG & SPA.). (gr. 2 up). (978-0-02-279618-1(5)) Macmillan/McGraw-Hill Schl. Div.

Pruebas Preliminares: Assessment. 2000. (McGraw-Hill Ciencias Ser.). (ENG & SPA.). (gr. k up). (978-0-02-279844-4(7)); (gr. 1 up). (978-0-02-279845-1(5)); (gr. 2 up). (978-0-02-279846-8(3)); (gr. 3 up). (978-0-02-279847-5(1)); (gr. 4 up). (978-0-02-279848-2(X)); (gr. 5 up). (978-0-02-279849-9(8)) Macmillan/McGraw-Hill Schl. Div.

Pupil Edition. 2003. (gr. 1 up). 32.50 (978-0-328-03421-5(5)); (gr. 2 up). 32.90 (978-0-328-03422-2(3)) Addison-Wesley Educational Pubs., Inc.

Pupil Edition. 2000. (McGraw-Hill Science Ser.). (gr. 4 up). (978-0-02-277436-3(X)) Macmillan/McGraw-Hill Schl. Div.

Pupil Workbook. 2003. (gr. k up). wbk. ed. 5.25 (978-0-328-03420-8(7)) Addison-Wesley Educational Pubs., Inc.

Push & Pull, 6 vols. (gr. k-2). 28.95 (978-0-7368-8615-4(X)) Red Brick Learning.

Push & Pull Science, 6 vols. (gr. k-2). 28.95 (978-0-7368-2998-4(9) , Yellow Umbrella Bks.) Capstone Pr., Inc.

QEB Start Reading & Writing National Book Stores Edition: What's in the Sky? 2006. (J). per. (978-1-59566-266-8(9)) QEB Publishing Inc.

Quadrillion Media Staff. Science. 1999. (Start Me Up Ser.). (J). pap. 3.95 (978-1-58185-105-2(7)) Quadrillion Media LLC.

Que hay de Nuevo? 2000. (McGraw-Hill Ciencias Ser.). (ENG & SPA.). (gr. 1 up). (978-0-02-279573-3(1)) Macmillan/McGraw-Hill Schl. Div.

Que hay en el espacio? Science, 6 vols.Tr. of What Is in Space? Science. (SPA.). (gr. k-2). 28.95 (978-0-7368-3129-1(0) , Yellow Umbrella Bks.) Capstone Pr., Inc.

Que hay en la Tierra? 2000. (McGraw-Hill Ciencias Ser.). (ENG & SPA.). (gr. k up). (978-0-02-279696-9(7)) Macmillan/McGraw-Hill Schl. Div.

Que se hunde? Que Flota? 2000. (McGraw-Hill Ciencias Ser.). (ENG & SPA.). (gr. k up). (978-0-02-279695-2(9)) Macmillan/McGraw-Hill Schl. Div.

Querida llama. 2000. (McGraw-Hill Ciencias Ser.). (ENG & SPA.). (gr. 2 up). (978-0-02-279619-8(3)) Macmillan/McGraw-Hill Schl. Div.

Quetzals. 2002. pap. (978-0-7398-5815-8(7)) Steck-Vaughn.

Quien construye? Science, 6 vols.Tr. of Who Builds? Science. (SPA.). (gr. k-2). 28.95 (978-0-7368-3037-9(5) , Yellow Umbrella Bks.) Capstone Pr., Inc.

Un Quimico en la Cocina: Experimentos que Puedes Realizar en la Casa: Leveled Books. 2000. (McGraw-Hill Ciencias Ser.). (ENG & SPA.). (gr. 4 up). (978-0-02-279647-1(9)) Macmillan/McGraw-Hill Schl. Div.

Quinley, Elliott. Science & Technology Words: Vocabulary in Context. 2002. (Illus.). 112p. per., wbk. ed. 8.95 (978-1-56254-400-3(4) , SP 4004) Saddleback Educational Publishing.

Raintree. Itlp 2004 Grade 4 Science Stat. 2004. pap. (978-1-4109-1570-2(0)); pap. (978-1-4109-1619-8(7)) Harcourt Schl. Pubs.

—Itlp 2004 Grades 2-4 Science S. 2004. pap. (978-1-4109-1567-2(0)); pap. (978-1-4109-1569-6(7)); pap. (978-1-4109-1571-9(9)) Harcourt Schl. Pubs.

—Science Starters, 8 bks., Set. 1999. (J). (gr. k-4). lib. bdg. 205.52 (978-0-8172-5334-9(3)) Raintree.

Raintree Fusion, 30 bks. 2005. (J). 550.10 (978-1-4109-1944-1(7)) Raintree.

Raintree Steck-Vaughn Staff. It's All Relative: Arkansas Edition, 31 bks., Set. 2003. 821.06 (978-1-4109-0170-5(X)) Raintree.

—Life Science. 1999. (J). (gr. 1). pap. (978-0-8172-3841-4(7)); (gr. 2). pap. (978-0-8172-3842-1(5)); (gr. 3). pap. (978-0-8172-3843-8(3)); (gr. 4). pap. (978-0-8172-3844-5(1)); (gr. 6). pap. (978-0-8172-3846-9(8)) Steck-Vaughn.

—Physical Science. 1999. pap. (978-0-8172-3761-5(5)); (J). (gr. 1). pap. (978-0-8172-3760-8(7)); (J). (gr. 3). pap. (978-0-8172-3762-2(3)); (J). (gr. 4). pap. (978-0-8172-3763-9(1)); (J). (gr. 5). pap. (978-0-8172-3764-6(X)); (J). (gr. 6). pap. (978-0-8172-3765-3(8)) Steck-Vaughn.

—Read All about It Science: Level A. 2000. (Illus.). (J). pap., tchr. ed. 5.80 (978-0-8114-3714-1(0)) Steck-Vaughn.

—Science World, 4 bks., Set. 1999. (Illus.). (J). lib. bdg. 102.76 (978-0-7398-1326-3(9)) Raintree.

—Think Like a Scientist. 1999. (J). pap. 35.60 (978-0-7398-0894-8(X)) Steck-Vaughn.

Raintree Steck-Vaughn Staff, contrib. by. Basic Skills in Science. 1999. (YA). (gr. 9-12). pap. 14.48 (978-0-7398-0989-1(X)) Steck-Vaughn.

Raintree Steck-Vaughn Staff, ed. Raintree Steck-Vaughn Illustrated Science Encyclopedia, 26 vols., Set. 2000. (Illus.). (J). lib. bdg. incl. cd-rom (978-0-7398-1843-5(0)) Raintree.

Ramsden, Eileen, et al. Key Science 4, Bk. 2. 1998. (Illus.). 480p. (YA). (gr. 9-11). pap. 48.00 (978-0-7487-0494-1(9)) State Mutual Bk. & Periodical Service, Ltd.

Randolph, J. A. Science Tools. Date not set. (Thinking Like a Scientist Ser.). (Illus.). 20p. (J). pap. 16.95 (978-1-58273-113-1(6)) Sundance/Newbridge Educational Publishing.

Rapido y mas rapido Science, 6 vols.Tr. of Fast & Faster! Science. (SPA.). (gr. k-2). 28.95 (978-0-7368-3143-7(6) , Yellow Umbrella Bks.) Capstone Pr., Inc.

La rata Mochilera: Leveled Books. 2000. (McGraw-Hill Ciencias Ser.). (ENG & SPA.). (gr. 4 up). (978-0-02-279658-7(4)) Macmillan/McGraw-Hill Schl. Div.

Read & Understand: Science. 2002. (J). (gr. 2-3). per. 14.99 (978-1-55799-855-2(8) , EMC 3303); (gr. 3-4). per. 14.99 (978-1-55799-856-9(6) , EMC 3304); (gr. 4-6). per. 14.99 (978-1-55799-857-6(4) , EMC 3305); (Illus.). (gr. 1-2). per. 14.99 (978-1-55799-854-5(X) , EMC 3302) Evan-Moor Educational Pubs.

Read & Understand Spanish / English, Science. 2005. (J). 29.99 (978-1-59673-077-9(3) , EMC 5312) Evan-Moor Educational Pubs.

Reader dsm-3 sink or float Ea. 2004. (J). (978-1-59242-525-9(9)) Delta Education, LLC.

Reading First Through Science Grade 1. 2005. (978-0-9766802-8-4(9)) Educational Tools, Inc.

Reading First Through Science Grade 2. 2005. (978-0-9766802-7-7(0)) Educational Tools, Inc.

Reading First Through Science Grade 4. 2005. (978-0-9766802-6-0(2)) Educational Tools, Inc.

The Reading Room Collection: Science. (J). (gr. 2-3). 79.50 (978-1-4042-3384-3(9)) Rosen Publishing Group, Inc., The.

Recursos de Evaluacion: Assessment. 2000. (McGraw-Hill Ciencias Ser.). (ENG & SPA.). (gr. k-2). (978-0-02-279049-3(7)); (gr. 3-5). (978-0-02-279051-6(9)) Macmillan/McGraw-Hill Schl. Div.

Recursos para el maestro con clave de Respuestas: Student & Teacher Support Resources. 2000. (McGraw-Hill Ciencias Ser.). (ENG & SPA.). (gr. 1 up). (978-0-02-278677-9(5)); (gr. 2 up). (978-0-02-278684-7(8)); (gr. 3 up). (978-0-02-278691-5(0)); (gr. 4 up). (978-0-02-278698-4(8)); (gr. 5 up). (978-0-02-278706-6(2)) Macmillan/McGraw-Hill Schl. Div.

Refrence Library & Index, Space Explorer, 4 vols. 2004. 800p. 235.00 (978-0-7876-9208-7(5) , Greenhaven Pr., Inc.) Thomson Gale.

El Regreso de las Aguilas! 2000. (McGraw-Hill Ciencias Ser.). (ENG & SPA.). (gr. 5 up). (978-0-02-279685-3(1)) Macmillan/McGraw-Hill Schl. Div.

Rescate en la playa primer Encuentro. 2000. (McGraw-Hill Ciencias Ser.). (ENG & SPA.). (gr. 3 up). (978-0-02-279640-2(1)) Macmillan/McGraw-Hill Schl. Div.

The Restless Earth Assessment Book: Unit 5: the Restless Earth. 2000. (McGraw-Hill Science Ser.). (gr. 6 up). (978-0-02-277775-3(X)) Macmillan/McGraw-Hill Schl. Div.

The Restless Earth Pupil Edition: Unit 5: the Restless Earth. 2000. (McGraw-Hill Science Ser.). (gr. 6 up). (978-0-02-278235-1(4)) Macmillan/McGraw-Hill Schl. Div.

Riley, Peter D. Everyday Science, 16 bks. Moller, Ray, photos by. Incl. Animals. 2003. lib. bdg. 23.33 (978-0-8368-3713-1(4)); Changing Forms. 2002. lib. bdg. 23.33 (978-0-8368-3246-4(9)); Electricity. 2002. lib. bdg. 23.33 (978-0-8368-3247-1(7)); Floating & Sinking. 2002. lib. bdg. 23.33 (978-0-8368-3248-8(5)); Habitats. 2003. lib. bdg. 23.33 (978-0-8368-3714-8(2)); Health. 2003. lib. bdg. 23.33 (978-0-8368-3715-5(0)); Life Cycles. 2003. lib. bdg. 23.33 (978-0-8368-3716-2(9)); Light & Dark. 2002. lib. bdg. 23.33 (978-0-8368-3249-5(3)); Magnets. 2002. lib. bdg. 23.33 (978-0-8368-3250-1(7)); Materials. 2002. lib. bdg. 23.33 (978-0-8368-3251-8(5)); Movement. 2003. lib. bdg. 23.33 (978-0-8368-3717-9(7)); Plants. 2003. lib. bdg. 23.33 (978-0-8368-3718-6(5)); Pushing & Pulling. 2002. lib. bdg. 23.33 (978-0-8368-3252-5(3)); Seasons. 2003. lib. bdg. 23.33 (978-0-8368-3719-3(3)); Senses. 2003. lib. bdg. 23.33 (978-0-8368-3720-9(7)); Sound. 2002. lib. bdg. 23.33 (978-0-8368-3253-2(1)); 32p. (J). (gr. 1 up). (Illus.). 2002. Set lib. bdg. 373.28 (978-0-8368-3878-7(5)) Stevens, Gareth Inc.

Ring, Susan. Design It! Build It! Date not set. (Early Science Big Bks.). (Illus.). 16p. (J). (ps-2). pap. 16.95 (978-1-58273-121-6(7)) Sundance/Newbridge Educational Publishing.

El rio, un Hogar. 2000. (McGraw-Hill Ciencias Ser.). (ENG & SPA.). (gr. 2 up). (978-0-02-279614-3(2)) Macmillan/McGraw-Hill Schl. Div.

Ripley, Catherine. Why? The Best Ever Question & Answer Book about Nature, Science, & the World Around You. Ritchie, Scot, illus. 2004. 192p. (J). 19.95 (978-1-897066-17-1(1)) Maple Tree Pr. CAN. *Dist:* Perseus Distribution.

Rita y Eduardo Construyen. 2000. (McGraw-Hill Ciencias Ser.). (ENG & SPA.). (gr. k up). (978-0-02-279708-9(4)) Macmillan/McGraw-Hill Schl. Div.

Roberts, Don & Roberts, Susan. Things That Scratch: The Story of Abrasives. (Illus.). 60p. (YA). (gr. 8 up). pap. 24.95 (978-1-57555-169-2(1)); pap. 14.95 (978-1-57555-170-8(5)) Cedar Bay Pr., L.L.C.

Roberts, Janette, et al. Science Matters Learner's Book Grade 7. 1999. pap. 8.00 (978-0-521-59562-9(2)) Cambridge Univ. Pr.

Las rocas tambien Cambian: Leveled Books. 2000. (McGraw-Hill Ciencias Ser.). (ENG & SPA.). (gr. 4 up). (978-0-02-279649-5(5)) Macmillan/McGraw-Hill Schl. Div.

Rocas y recursos: Cuaderno de Evaluacion: Unit 5: Rocas y recursos (Rocks & Resources) 2000. (McGraw-Hill Ciencias Ser.). (ENG & SPA.). (gr. 3 up). (978-0-02-278653-3(8)) Macmillan/McGraw-Hill Schl. Div.

Rocas y recursos: Recursos para el maestro con clave de Respuestas: Unit 5: Rocas y recursos (Rocks & Resources) 2000. (McGraw-Hill Ciencias Ser.). (ENG & SPA.). (gr. 3 up). (978-0-02-278696-0(1)) Macmillan/McGraw-Hill Schl. Div.

Rohrer, Lesa. Write about Physical Science: The Test Connection. 2003. (Write about Science Ser.). 64p. (J). (gr. 6-8). pap. 9.99 (978-0-7424-1919-3(3) , FS99244, Schaffer, Frank) Schaffer, Frank Pubns.

Rohrig, Brian. Pure Slime: 50 Incredible Ways to Make Slime Using Household Substances. 2004. (Illus.). 232p. (YA). per. 12.95 (978-0-9718480-5-4(X)) FizzBang Science.

Rollins, Barbara B. & Dahl, Michael. A Bloody Trail: Analyzing Blood. 2004. (Forensic Crime Solvers Ser.). (Illus.). 32p. (J). 22.60 (978-0-7368-2418-7(9)) Capstone Pr., Inc.

—Cause of Death. 2004. (Forensic Crime Solvers Ser.). (Illus.). 32p. (J). 22.60 (978-0-7368-2420-0(0)) Capstone Pr., Inc.

Romer, Ruth. Welcome to Waterworld. 2004. (Reader's Theater Ser.). (J). pap. 22.00 (978-1-4108-0796-0(7)) Benchmark Education Co.

Romer, Ruth & Kramer, Candice. Farflings from Farflung. 2004. (Reader's Theater Ser.). (J). pap. 22.00 (978-1-4108-0797-7(5)) Benchmark Education Co.

Rookie Read-About Science, 6 Bks. 2004. 114.00 (978-0-516-23719-0(5) , Children's Pr.) Scholastic Library Publishing.

Rookie Read-About Science: Life Science, 6 bks., Set. Incl. Tiny Life in a Puddle. Early, Bobbi. 20.50 (978-0-516-25272-8(0)); Tiny Life in the Air. Taylor-Butler, Christine. 20.50 (978-0-516-25273-5(9)); Tiny Life in Your Home. Trumbauer, Lisa. 20.50 (978-0-516-25274-2(7)); Tiny Life on Plants. Lindstrom, Karin. 20.50 (978-0-516-25297-1(6)); Tiny Life on the Ground. Wade, Mary Dodson. 20.50 (978-0-516-25298-8(4)); Tiny Life on Your Body. Taylor-Butler, Christine. 20.50 (978-0-516-25299-5(2)); (Illus.). 31p. (J). (ps-ps). 2005. 2005. 117.00 (978-0-516-25395-4(6) , Children's Pr.) Scholastic Library Publishing.

Rookie Read-About Science Accelerated Reader Series. 2004. Vol. 1. pap. 798.00 (978-0-516-29706-4(6)); Vol. 2. pap. 798.00 (978-0-516-29707-1(4)) Scholastic Library Publishing. (Children's Pr.).

Rosinsky, Natalie M. Amazing Science: Dirt; Light; Magnets; Rocks; Sound; Water, 6 bks. Boyd, Sheree, illus. 2003. (J). (gr. k-4). lib. bdg. 127.56 (978-1-4048-0077-9(8)) Picture Window Bks.

Rossouw, Andre J. & Bitline S. A. 1010. Natural Sciences Matters Grade 8 Learner's Book Afrikaans Translation. 2006. 160p. pap. 14.00 (978-0-521-67894-0(3)) Cambridge Univ. Pr.

Rossouw, Andre J., et al. Natural Sciences Matters Grade 8 Learner's Book. 2006. 160p. pap. 14.00 (978-0-521-67892-6(7)) Cambridge Univ. Pr.

Rough Cuts. 2001. (J). cd-rom 199.95 (978-1-56791-301-9(6)) Environmental Media Corp.

Rourke Publishing Staff. Rourke's World of Science Encyclopedia, 10 vols., Set. 2007. (J). (gr. 3-8). 329.95 (***978-1-60044-646-7(9)** , 1-6467) Rourke Publishing, LLC.

Royston, Angela. My World of Science Series, 11 bks. 2003. (Illus.). (J). (gr. k-2). Set. lib. bdg. 478.59 (978-1-4034-0862-4(9)); Set 2. lib. bdg. 250.69 (978-1-4034-0861-7(0)) Heinemann Library.

Saffer, Barbara. ABC Science Riddles. Johnson, Jennifer, illus. 2004. (ABC Riddles Ser.). 32p. (J). (ps-3). (978-0-939217-55-7(4)) Peel Productions, Inc.

—Science Questions & Answers: The Human Body. 1998. (Gifted & Talented Ser.). (Illus.). 64p. (J). (gr. 1-3). pap. 5.95 (978-1-56565-910-0(4) , 09104W) Lowell Hse. Juvenile.

Saffer, Barbara & Hlodan, Oksana. Science Questions & Answers. 2001. (Gifted & Talented Ser.). (Illus.). 248p. (J). (gr. 1-3). pap. 12.95 (978-0-7373-0471-8(5)) Lowell Hse.

Salvemos los Animales. 2000. (McGraw-Hill Ciencias Ser.). (ENG & SPA.). (gr. 2 up). (978-0-02-279613-6(4)) Macmillan/McGraw-Hill Schl. Div.

Sang, David, et al. Scientifica - Higher. 2005. (Illus.). 240p. (YA). Bk. 8. pap., stu. ed. 29.50 (978-0-7487-7988-8(4)); Bk. 9. pap., stu. ed. 29.50 (978-0-7487-7996-3(5)) Nelson Thornes Ltd. GBR. *Dist:* Trans-Atlantic Pubns., Inc.

Sarver, Amy. Science at the Grocery. 2004. (National Geographic Reading Expeditions Ser.). (Illus.). 24p. (J). pap. (978-0-7922-4567-4(9)) National Geographic Society.

—Science at the Mall. 2004. (National Geographic Reading Expeditions Ser.). (Illus.). 24p. (J). pap. (978-0-7922-4569-8(5)) National Geographic Society.

Schaefer, Lola M. What's up, What's Down? Bash, Barbara, illus. 2002. 32p. (J). 16.99 (978-0-06-029757-2(3)); lib. bdg. 17.89 (978-0-06-029758-9(1)) HarperCollins Pubs.

Schaefer, Lola M. & Miller, Heather. Ruedas, Alas y Agua, 9 bks., Set. 2003. Tr. of Wheels, Wings, & Water. (SPA., Illus.). (J). (ps-1). lib. bdg. 166.50 (978-1-4034-0924-9(2)) Heinemann Library.

Schaffer, Frank. Science Made Simple. 2001. (Made Simple Ser.). 80p. (J). (gr. 1-3). pap. 10.99 (978-0-7647-0167-2(3) , FS23211); pap. 10.99 (978-0-7647-0169-6(X) , FS23213) Schaffer, Frank Pubns.

Schifferrdanoff, Valerie. Irresistible Science Pocket Charts. 2001. 64p. (J). pap. 10.95 (978-0-439-04384-7(0)) Scholastic, Inc.

Scholastic, Inc. Staff. Amazing Air Racers. Im, Angela, ed. 2003. 24p. (J). pap. 9.99 (978-0-439-40965-0(9) , Tangerine Pr.) Scholastic, Inc.

—Weird Science. Nagler, Michelle, ed. 2004. (Ripley's Believe It or Not! Ser.: No. 9). (Illus.). 96p. (J). pap. 4.99 (978-0-439-56421-2(2)) Scholastic, Inc.

Scholastic Library Publishing Staff, ed. Rookie Read-About Science, Vol. 3. 2004. 570.00 (978-0-516-22910-2(9)) Scholastic Library Publishing.

School Specialty Pub. Science Cycles: Inquiry Learning with Intriguing Investigations & Stories. 2002. 80p. (J). (gr. 3-6). pap. 10.99 (978-0-7424-0248-5(7) , IF19215) School Specialty Publishing.

School Specialty Publishing. Activities for Science Centers. 2004. 80p. (J). (gr. k up). pap. 10.99 (978-0-7424-2850-8(8) , IFG99224) School Specialty Publishing.

—Earth Science at Home: It's Everyplace You Are! 2004. (It's Everyplace You Are! Ser.). 48p. (J). (gr. k-2). pap. 6.99 (978-0-7682-2656-0(2) , FS99287); (gr. 3-5). pap. 6.99 (978-0-7682-2657-7(0) , FS99286) Schaffer, Frank Pubns.

—Funtastic Frogs Science Activities. 2004. 192p. (J). (gr. k-2). pap. 18.99 (978-0-7424-2769-3(2) , ID99075) School Specialty Publishing.

—Inquiry Science, Grades 2-3. 2006. (Inquiry Science Ser.). 96p. (J). (gr. 2-3). pap. 12.99 (978-0-7682-3372-8(0) , Schaffer, Frank) Schaffer, Frank Pubns.

—Inquiry Science, Grades 4-5. 2006. (Inquiry Science Ser.). 96p. (J). (gr. 4-5). pap. 12.99 (978-0-7682-3374-2(7) , Schaffer, Frank) Schaffer, Frank Pubns.

—Inquiry Science, Grades K-1. 2006. (Inquiry Science Ser.). 96p. (J). (gr. k-1). pap. 12.99 (978-0-7682-3370-4(4) , Schaffer, Frank) Schaffer, Frank Pubns.

—Life Science at Home: It's Everyplace You Are! 2004. (It's Everyplace You Are! Ser.). 48p. (J). (gr. k-2). pap. 6.99 (978-0-7682-2666-9(X) , FS99295); (gr. 3-5). pap. 6.99 (978-0-7682-2667-6(8) , FS99294) Schaffer, Frank Pubns.

—Make Your Own Emergent Readers: Science. 2006. (Make Your Own Emergent Readers Ser.). 64p. (J). (gr. k-2). pap. 8.99 (978-0-7682-3380-3(1) , Schaffer, Frank) Schaffer, Frank Pubns.

—Physical Science at Home: It's Everyplace You Are! 2004. (It's Everyplace You Are! Ser.). 48p. (J). (gr. k-2). pap. 6.99 (978-0-7682-2676-8(7) , FS99303); (gr. 3-5). pap. 6.99 (978-0-7682-2677-5(5) , FS99302) Schaffer, Frank Pubns.

—Science, Grade 3. 2006. (Skills for Scholars Ser.). 80p. (C). pap. 4.99 (***978-0-7696-4943-6(2)** , Schaffer, Frank) Schaffer, Frank Pubns.

—Science, Grade 4. 2006. (Skills for Scholars Ser.). 80p. (C). pap. 4.99 (***978-0-7696-4944-3(0)** , Schaffer, Frank) Schaffer, Frank Pubns.

—Science, Grade 5. 2006. (Skills for Scholars Ser.). 80p. (C). pap. 4.99 (***978-0-7696-4945-0(9)** , Schaffer, Frank) Schaffer, Frank Pubns.

—Science, Grade 6. 2006. (Skills for Scholars Ser.). 80p. (C). pap. 4.99 (***978-0-7696-4946-7(7)** , Schaffer, Frank) Schaffer, Frank Pubns.

—Science Made Simple. 2001. (Made Simple Ser.). 80p. (J). (gr. 5 up). pap. 10.99 (978-0-7647-0171-9(1) , FS23215); (gr. 6 up). pap. 10.99 (978-0-7647-0172-6(X) , FS23216) Schaffer, Frank Pubns.

—Spectrum Science Test Practice, Grade 3. 2006. (Spectrum Science Test Practice Ser.). 96p. (J). pap. 9.95 (978-0-7696-8063-7(1) , Schaffer, Frank) Schaffer, Frank Pubns.

—Spectrum Science Test Practice, Grade 4. 2006. (Spectrum Science Test Practice Ser.). 96p. (J). pap. 9.95 (978-0-7696-8064-4(X) , Schaffer, Frank) Schaffer, Frank Pubns.

—Spectrum Science Test Practice, Grade 5. 2006. (Spectrum Science Test Practice Ser.). 96p. (J). pap. 9.95 (978-0-7696-8065-1(8) , Schaffer, Frank) Schaffer, Frank Pubns.

—Spectrum Science Test Practice, Grade 6. 2006. (Spectrum Science Test Practice Ser.). 96p. (J). pap. 9.95 (978-0-7696-8066-8(6) , Schaffer, Frank) Schaffer, Frank Pubns.

—Spectrum Science Test Practice, Grade 7. 2006. (Spectrum Science Test Practice Ser.). 96p. (J). pap. 9.95 (978-0-7696-8067-5(4) , Schaffer, Frank) Schaffer, Frank Pubns.

—Spectrum Science Test Practice, Grade 8. 2006. (Spectrum Science Test Practice Ser.). 96p. (J). pap. 9.95 (978-0-7696-8068-2(2) , Schaffer, Frank) Schaffer, Frank Pubns.

—Using the Media: Fact, Fiction, & Opinion. 2004. 64p. (J). (gr. 6-8). pap. 8.99 (978-0-7696-3401-2(X) , MH1034) School Specialty Publishing.

School Zone Publishing Company Staff & Giglio, Judith. Summer Scholar Grade 1. deluxe ed. 2000. (Deluxe Wkbks.). (Illus.). 64p. (J). (gr. 1). pap., wbk. ed. 3.79 (978-0-88743-832-5(6) , 02232) School Zone Publishing Co.

School Zone Publishing Company Staff & Hall, M. C. Summer Scholar Grade 3. deluxe ed. 2000. (Deluxe Wkbks.). (Illus.). 64p. (J). (gr. 3). pap., wbk. ed. 3.79 (978-0-88743-834-9(2) , 02234) School Zone Publishing Co.

School Zone Publishing Company Staff & Kupecky, Jere M. Summer Scholar Grade 2. Carmona, Lisa, ed. Sandford, John, illus. deluxe ed. 2000. (Deluxe Wkbks.). 64p. (J). (gr. 2). pap., wbk. ed. 3.79 (978-0-88743-833-2(4) , 02233) School Zone Publishing Co.

School Zone Staff. Science 2-3 Big Get Ready! 2006. 320p. (J). (gr. 2-3). pap. 9.99 (***978-1-58947-317-1(5)**) School Zone Publishing Co.

Schwartz, David M. Q Is for Quark: A Science Alphabet Book. Doner, Kim, illus. 2004. 64p. (YA). (gr. 4-8). tchr. ed. 15.95 (978-1-58246-021-5(3) , Tricycle Pr.) Ten Speed Pr.

—Q Is for Quark, Grades 4-8: A Science Alphabet Book. Doner, Kim, illus. 2001. 64p. tchr. ed. 2.95 (978-1-58246-049-9(3) , Tricycle Pr.) Ten Speed Pr.

Schwartz, Linda. Primary Science Quiz Whiz, Vol. 429. Van-Blaricum, Pam, ed. Mason, Mark, illus. 2004. 128p. (J). (gr. 1-3). pap. 14.99 (978-0-88160-372-9(4) , LW-429) Creative Teaching Pr., Inc.

—Social Studies & Science Quiz Whiz 3-5, Vol. 432. Van-Blaricum, Pam, ed. Armstrong, Beverly, illus. 2004. 128p. (J). (gr. 3-5). pap. 10.99 (978-0-88160-375-0(9) , LW-432) Creative Teaching Pr., Inc.

Science, Set. 2004. (gr. 6). tchr. ed., stu. ed. 47.95 (978-1-58095-765-6(X) , SCI0615); (Illus.). (gr. 5). tchr. ed., stu. ed. 47.95 (978-1-58095-762-5(5) , SCI0515) Alpha Omega Pubns., Inc. (Lifepac).

Science: Chemistry, 11 vols., Set. 2004. (Illus.). (gr. 11). tchr. ed., stu. ed. 47.95 (978-1-58095-780-9(3) , SCI1115, Lifepac) Alpha Omega Pubns., Inc.

Science: Physics, 11 vols., Set. 2004. (Illus.). (gr. 12). tchr. ed., stu. ed. 47.95 (978-1-58095-783-0(8) , SCI1215, Lifepac) Alpha Omega Pubns., Inc.

Science: Practice & Assessment. 2000. (SPA.). (gr. k up). cd-rom 39.00 (978-0-673-59407-5(6)); (gr. 1 up). cd-rom 39.00 (978-0-673-59408-2(4)); (gr. 2 up). cd-rom 39.00 (978-0-673-59409-9(2)); (gr. 3 up). cd-rom 39.00 (978-0-673-59410-5(6)); (gr. 4 up). cd-rom 39.00 (978-0-673-59411-2(4)); (gr. 5 up). cd-rom 39.00 (978-0-673-59412-9(2)); (gr. 6 up). cd-rom 39.00 (978-0-673-59413-6(0)) Addison-Wesley Educational Pubs., Inc.

Science: Production Studio, 3 disc. 2000. (SPA & ENG.). (gr. k-6). cd-rom 69.96 (978-0-673-59431-0(9)) Addison-Wesley Educational Pubs., Inc.

Science: Student Testing Kit. 2004. (Illus.). (J). (gr. 1-8). stu. ed. 5.00 (978-0-7403-0045-5(8) , SD001); (YA). (gr. 7-12). pap., stu. ed. 5.00 (978-0-7403-0046-2(6) , SD002) Alpha Omega Pubns., Inc.

Science @ Work, 4 vols., set. 2003. 108.60 (978-0-7398-6997-0(3)) Raintree.

Science @ Work, 12 bks., Set. Incl. Allergies, Asthma & Exercise : The Science of Health. 1999. pap. 27.12 (978-0-7398-0140-6(6)); Boomerangs, Blades & Basketballs : The Science of Sports. Creighton, Jayne, contrib. by. 1999. lib. bdg. 27.12 (978-0-7398-0132-1(5));

S

Circuits, Shocks & Lightning : The Science of Electricity. Peters, Celeste A. 1999. pap. 27.12 (978-0-7398-0143-7(0)); Cockroaches, Cocoons & Honeycombs : The Science of Insects. Parker, Janice. 1998. 27.12 (978-0-7398-0135-2(X)); Comets, Stardust & Supernovas : The Science of Space. Willett, Edward. 1999. 27.12 (978-0-7398-0134-5(1)); Engines, Elevators & X-Rays : The Science of Machines. Parker, Janice. 1999. pap. 27.12 (978-0-7398-0142-0(2)); Forgeries, Fingerprints & Forensics : The Science of Crime. Parker, Janice, contrib. by. 1999. 27.12 (978-0-7398-0133-8(3)); Messengers, Morse Code & Modems : The Science of Communication. Parker, Janice. 2000. lib. bdg. 27.12 (978-0-7398-0138-3(4)); Peppers, Popcorn & Pizza : The Science of Food. Peters, Celeste A., contrib. by. 1998. lib. bdg. 27.12 (978-0-7398-0136-9(8)); Scales, Slime & Salamanders : The Science of Reptiles & Amphibians. Miller-Schroeder, Patricia. 1999. lib. bdg. 27.12 (978-0-7398-0141-3(4)); Sunburns, Twisters & Thunderclaps : The Science of Weather. Parker, Janice. 1999. lib. bdg. 27.12 (978-0-7398-0131-4(7)); Wings, Wheels & Keels : The Science of Transportation. Miller-Schroeder, Patricia. 1999. lib. bdg. 27.12 (978-0-7398-0139-0(2)); 48p. (J). (gr. 4-6). (Illus.). 1999. Set pap. 325.44 (978-0-7398-0144-4(9)) Raintree.

Science Activities. 2005. (ENG & SPA.). 304p. (gr. 1-3). 24.99 (978-1-55799-860-6(4) , EMC 5306) Evan-Moor Educational Pubs.

Science Add-on Set, Early Level. (gr. k-2). 57.95 (978-0-7368-3069-0(3) , Yellow Umbrella Bks.) Capstone Pr., Inc.

Science Add-on Set, Emergent Level. (gr. k-2). 57.95 (978-0-7368-1787-5(5) , Yellow Umbrella Bks.) Capstone Pr., Inc.

Science Advantage 2000: Educational Pack. 2000. (YA). cd-rom 19.99 (978-1-58263-144-8(1)) Encore Software, Inc.

Science Advantage 2000: Lab Pack (5) 2000. (YA). cd-rom 79.99 (978-1-58263-145-5(X)) Encore Software, Inc.

Science Adventures, 4 bks., Set. Incl. In the Deep Sea. Collard, Sneed B., III. 44p. (gr. 3-7). lib. bdg. 25.64 (978-0-7614-1952-5(7)); In the Rain Forest Canopy. Collard, Sneed B., III. 44p. (gr. 3-7). lib. bdg. 25.64 (978-0-7614-1954-9(3)); In the Wild. Collard, Sneed B., III. 44p. (gr. 4-7). lib. bdg. 28.50 (978-0-7614-1955-6(1)); On the Coral Reef. Collard, Sneed B. 43p. 25.64 (978-0-7614-1953-2(5)); (Illus.). (J). 2005. 2005. (978-0-7614-1951-8(9) , Benchmark Bks.) Cavendish, Marshall Corp.

Science & Life Issues Complete Materials Package for Chicago Public Schools. 2001. (Illus.). (YA). ring bd. (978-1-887725-83-5(0)) Lab-Aids, Inc.

Science & Life Issues Complete Materials Package W/Teacher's Guide & Student Books, 2 volumes. 2001. (Illus.). (YA). ring bd. (978-1-887725-53-8(9)) Lab-Aids, Inc.

Science & Scientists. 2005. 32p. pap. 84.00 (978-0-7910-9170-8(8)); 2003. (Illus.). (gr. 4-8). lib. bdg. 113.70 (978-0-7910-7060-4(3)) Facts On File, Inc. (Chelsea Hse.).

Science & Sustainability Complete Materials Package with Teacher's Guide & 28 Student Books, 2 vols., 2001. (Illus.). 1000p. ring bd. (978-1-887725-87-3(3)) Lab-Aids, Inc.

Science & Sustainability Complete Materials Package W/Teacher's Manual & Student Books, 2 volumes. 2001. (Illus.). (YA). ring bd. (978-1-887725-59-0(8)) Lab-Aids, Inc.

Science & Sustainability Essentials Materials Package, 2 vols. 2001. 1000p. ring bd. (978-1-887725-88-0(1)); (Illus.). (YA). (978-1-887725-63-7(6)) Lab-Aids, Inc.

Science & Technology. 2000. (Quick Start Masters Technology Ser.). (J). (gr. 1-2). (978-0-7725-2361-7(4)); (gr. 3-5). (978-0-7725-2365-5(7)); (gr. 5-6). (978-0-7725-2369-3(X)) Thomson Nelson.

Science & Technology for Children Books, MicroWorlds Set, 8 vols. 2004. (Illus.). 64p. (J). (978-1-933008-16-5(4)) National Science Resources Ctr.

Science & Technology for Children Books, Physical Sciences & Technology Library, 6 vols. 2004. (Illus.). 64p. (J). (978-1-933008-26-4(1)) National Science Resources Ctr.

Science & Technology for Children Books, Science Library, 12 vols. 2004. (Illus.). 64p. (J). (978-1-933008-24-0(5)) National Science Resources Ctr.

Science & Technology in Focus, 6 Vols., Set. 2006. 192-208p. (gr. 6-12). 210.00 (978-0-8160-6781-7(3)) Facts On File, Inc.

Science & Technology in Focus Set 1. 2004. (Science & Technology in Focus Ser.). 208-240p. (gr. 9-12). 175.00 (978-0-8160-5836-5(9)) Facts On File, Inc.

Science & You. (Illus.). (J). 502.60 (978-0-7910-7275-2(4) , Chelsea Hse.) Facts On File, Inc.

Science at the Edge. (Illus.). (YA). (gr. 6-8). Set 1. 2002. lib. bdg. 167.16 (978-1-58810-465-6(6)); Set 2. 2003. lib. bdg. 111.44 (978-1-58810-869-2(4)) Heinemann Library.

Science at Work, 6 vols. 1998. 162.72 (978-0-7398-0137-6(6)); Set 1. 2003. (Illus.). 434.24 (978-1-4109-0705-9(8)) Raintree.

Science Big Books, English. (gr. k-2). 112.95 (978-0-7368-3246-5(7)) Red Brick Learning.

Science Big Books, Spanish. (SPA.). (gr. k-2). 37.95 (978-0-7368-3247-2(5)) Red Brick Learning.

Science Centers. 2005. (J). 21.99 (978-1-59673-090-8(0) , EMC 5004) Evan-Moor Educational Pubs.

Science Centers, 1-2. 2004. (J). (gr. 1-2). per. 19.99 (978-1-55799-961-0(9) , EMC 5002) Evan-Moor Educational Pubs.

Science Centers, 3-4. 2004. (J). (gr. 3-4). per. 19.99 (978-1-55799-962-7(7) , EMC 5003) Evan-Moor Educational Pubs.

Science Explorer. 1999. (YA). (gr. 6-9). pap., act. bk. ed. (978-0-13-436367-7(1)) Prentice Hall (Schl. Div.).

Science Explorer: North Carolina Resource Pro 2000C. 1999. (J). (gr. 6-8). (978-0-13-050862-1(4)) Prentice Hall PTR.

Science Fact Files, 10 bks., Set. Incl. Communications. Graham, Ian. 2001. lib. bdg. 27.12 (978-0-7398-1014-9(6)); Criminal Investigation. Woodford, Chris. Kossmann, Walter, ed. 2001. lib. bdg. 27.12 (978-0-7398-1016-3(2)); Earth's Resources. Parker, Steve. 2001. lib. bdg. 27.12 (978-0-7398-1009-5(X)); Electricity & Magnetism. Parker, Steve. 2000. lib. bdg. 27.12 (978-0-7398-1010-1(3)); Forces & Motion. Lafferty, Peter. 2000. lib. bdg. 27.12 (978-0-7398-1007-1(3)); Genetics. Beatty, Richard. 2001. lib. bdg. 27.12 (978-0-7398-1015-6(4)); Human Body. Farndon, John. 2001. lib. bdg. 27.12 (978-0-7398-1013-2(8)); Light & Sound. Parker, Steve. 2000. lib. bdg. 27.12 (978-0-7398-1011-8(1)); Solar System. Cooper, Christopher. 2000. lib. bdg. 27.12 (978-0-7398-1006-4(5)); Weather. Oxlade, Chris. 2000. lib. bdg. 27.12 (978-0-7398-1008-8(1)); 48p. (J). (gr. 4-7). (Illus.). 2001. Set lib. bdg. 271.20 (978-0-7398-1017-0(0)) Raintree.

Science Fact Files: Includes: Communications; Criminal Investigation; Genetics; The Human Body, 4 bks., Set. 2001. (Illus.). (J). (gr. 4-7). lib. bdg. 108.48 (978-0-7398-3446-6(0)) Raintree.

Science Fact Files; Includes: The Earth's Resources; Electricity & Magnetism; Forces & Motion; Light & Sound; The Solar System; Weather, 6 bks., Set. 1998. (Illus.). (J). (gr. 4-7). 113.88 (978-0-7398-1012-5(X)) Raintree.

Science Fact Files Series, 6 bks., Set. 2000. (Science Fact Files Ser.). (Illus.). 162.72 (978-0-7398-4255-3(2)) Steck-Vaughn.

Science Files: Set I - Earth; Set II - Materials; Set III - Energy, 18 bks. Incl. Coal. Parker, Steve. 2004. lib. bdg. 24.67 (978-0-8368-4029-2(1)); Deserts. Ganeri, Anita. 2003. lib. bdg. 24.67 (978-0-8368-3566-3(2)); Forests. Ganeri, Anita. 2003. lib. bdg. 24.67 (978-0-8368-3567-0(0)); Glass. Parker, Steve. 2002. lib. bdg. 24.67 (978-0-8368-3082-8(2)); Islands. Oxlade, Chris. 2003. lib. bdg. 24.67 (978-0-8368-3568-7(9)); Metals. Parker, Steve. 2002. lib. bdg. 24.67 (978-0-8368-3083-5(0)); Mountains. Oxlade, Chris. 2003. lib. bdg. 24.67 (978-0-8368-3569-4(7)); Nuclear Energy. Parker, Steve. 2004. lib. bdg. 24.67 (978-0-8368-4030-8(5)); Oceans. Ganeri, Anita. 2003. lib. bdg. 24.67 (978-0-8368-3570-0(0)); Oil & Gas. Parker, Steve. 2004. lib. bdg. 24.37 (978-0-8368-4031-5(3)); Plastics. Parker, Steve. 2002. lib. bdg. 24.67 (978-0-8368-3084-2(9)); Rivers & Lakes. Oxlade, Chris. 2003. lib. bdg. 24.67 (978-0-8368-3571-7(9)); Rocks & Minerals. Parker, Steve. 2002. lib. bdg. 24.67 (978-0-8368-3085-9(7)); Solar Power. Parker, Steve. 2004. lib. bdg. 24.67 (978-0-8368-4032-2(1)); Textiles. Parker, Steve. 2002. lib. bdg. 24.67 (978-0-8368-3086-6(5)); Water Power. Parker, Steve. 2004. lib. bdg. 24.67 (978-0-8368-4033-9(X)); Wind Power. Parker, Steve. 2004. lib. bdg. 24.67 (978-0-8368-4034-6(8)); Wood. Parker, Steve. 2002. lib. bdg. 24.67 (978-0-8368-3087-3(3)); 32p. (J). (gr. 3 up). (Illus.). 2002. Set lib. bdg. 444.06 (978-0-8368-4169-5(7)) Stevens, Gareth Inc.

Science Fun. 2005. (Little Celebrations Thematic Packages Ser.). (J). (gr. k-3). 133.50 (978-0-673-75382-3(4)) Celebration Pr.

Science Journal Book: Student & Teacher Support Resources. 2000. (McGraw-Hill Science Ser.). (gr. 3 up). (978-0-02-278119-4(6)); (gr. 4 up). (978-0-02-278121-7(8)); (gr. 5 up). (978-0-02-278122-4(6)) Macmillan/McGraw-Hill Schl. Div.

Science Links. 2005. (Illus.). 32p. (gr. 3-5). pap. 414.00 (978-0-7910-7415-2(3) , Chelsea Hse.) Facts On File, Inc.

Science Made Simple. 2007. 478.32 (978-1-59928-578-8(9) , SandCastle) ABDO Publishing Co.

Science Matters. (J). (gr. 2). (978-0-8374-1466-9(0) , 542); (gr. 3). (978-0-8374-1467-6(9) , 543); (gr. 4). (978-0-8374-1468-3(7) , 544); (gr. 5). (978-0-8374-1469-0(5) , 545); (gr. 6). (978-0-8374-1470-6(9) , 546) Weekly Reader Corp.

Science News for Kids, 6-Volume Set. 2006. 180.00 (978-0-7910-9292-7(5) , Chelsea Clubhouse) Facts On File, Inc.

Science of Chaos. 2000. (Illus.). 126p. (YA). (gr. 8-11). reprint ed. 20.00 (978-0-7881-9057-5(1)) DIANE Publishing Co.

Science Practice Answer Key: Student & Teacher Support Resources. 2000. (McGraw-Hill Science Ser.). (gr. 3 up). (978-0-02-277715-9(6)); (gr. 4 up). (978-0-02-277716-6(4)); (gr. 5 up). (978-0-02-277717-3(2)) Macmillan/McGraw-Hill Schl. Div.

Science Program, Early Level. (gr. k-2). 348.95 (978-0-7368-3068-3(5) , Yellow Umbrella Bks.) Capstone Pr., Inc.

Science Program, Emergent Level. (gr. k-2). 348.95 (978-0-7368-1788-2(3) , Yellow Umbrella Bks.) Capstone Pr., Inc.

Science Puzzles & Games. 2002. (Home Workbooks Ser.). 64p. pap. 2.49 (978-0-88724-742-2(3) , CD-4544) Carson-Dellosa Publishing Co., Inc.

Science Quest. 148.02 (978-0-8368-4552-5(8)) Stevens, Gareth Inc.

Science Reading Stories. (J). (gr. 2). (978-0-8374-0622-0(6) , 656); (gr. 3). (978-0-8374-0623-7(4) , 657); (gr. 4). (978-0-8374-0624-4(2) , 658); (gr. 5). (978-0-8374-0625-1(0) , 659) Weekly Reader Corp.

Science Set, 8 vols. (Content Collections). (gr. k-2). 276.08 (978-0-7362-2269-3(3)) Hampton-Brown Bks.

Science Spanish Content Area Standard Set. 2005. spiral bd. 2500.00 (***978-1-4108-4530-6(3))*** Benchmark Education Co.

Science Stories, 4 bks. (J). (gr. 2-4). lib. bdg. 59.80 (978-1-56674-934-3(4)) Forest Hse. Publishing Co., Inc.

Science stories foss spanish models & designs ea Cr05. 2005. (J). (978-1-59242-592-1(5)) Delta Education, LLC.

Science View. 2005. (Illus.). 32p. (gr. 4-8). pap. 168.00 (978-0-7910-8445-8(0) , Chelsea Hse.) Facts On File, Inc.

Scientific American, inc Staff, contrib. by. Scientific American: Cutting-Edge Science, 6 bks., Set. Incl. Extreme Engineering. (Illus.). (gr. 9-12). lib. bdg. 31.95 (***978-1-4042-0986-2(7));*** Fighting Infectious Diseases. (Illus.). (gr. 9-12). lib. bdg. 31.95 (978-1-4042-0988-6(3)); Future of the Web. (Illus.). (gr. 9-12). lib. bdg. 31.95 (***978-1-4042-0989-3(1));*** Nanotech Revolution. (Illus.). (gr. 7-12). lib. bdg. 31.95 (***978-1-4042-0990-9(5)*** , 1267059); Tackling Cancer. (gr. 9-12). lib. bdg. 31.95 (***978-1-4042-0987-9(5));*** 21st Century Robotics. (Illus.). (gr. 9-12). lib. bdg. 31.95 (***978-1-4042-0985-5(9));*** 101p. (YA). 2006. 2007. Set lib. bdg. 191.70 (***978-1-4042-0939-8(5))*** Rosen Publishing Group, Inc., The.

Scientifica 7. 2004. (Illus.). 240p. (YA). pap., stu. ed. 29.50 (978-0-7487-7980-2(9)) Nelson Thornes Ltd. GBR. *Dist:* Trans-Atlantic Pubns., Inc.

Scientists of the Biomes et, Set. 2001. (Illus.). (J). pap. (978-0-7398-4942-2(5)) Steck-Vaughn.

Scott, Foresman and Company Staff. Discover Science (J). (gr. 1). pap. 12.34 (978-0-673-42490-7(1)); (gr. 2). pap. 12.90 (978-0-673-42491-4(X)); (gr. 3). pap. 14.59 (978-0-673-42492-1(8)) Addison Wesley Schl. (Scott Foresman).

—Discover Science. (J). (gr. 4). pap. 16.06 (978-0-673-42493-8(6)); (gr. 5). pap. 17.00 (978-0-673-42494-5(4)); (gr. 6). pap. 17.62 (978-0-673-42495-2(2)) Addison Wesley Schl. (Scott Foresman).

Se mueve?: Cuaderno de Actividades: Unit 6: Se mueve? (Make Things Move) 2000. (McGraw-Hill Ciencias Ser.). (ENG & SPA.). (gr. k up). (978-0-02-278996-1(0)) Macmillan/McGraw-Hill Schl. Div.

Seddon, Tony, et al. Lower Secondary Science for Trinidad & Tobago, Bk. 1. 2007. 184p. pap., stu. ed. 15.95 (978-0-521-60717-9(5)) Cambridge Univ. Pr.

Seddon, Tony, et al. Our Science 2 Trinidad & Tobago. 2007. (Illus.). 216p. pap. (***978-0-521-60715-5(9))*** Cambridge Univ. Pr.

Seeds Grow, 6 vols. (Sunshinetm Science Ser.). 24p. (gr. 1-2). 31.50 (978-0-7802-0290-0(2)); 36.95 (978-0-7802-0541-3(3)) Wright Group, The.

Seeing, 6 vols. (gr. k-2). 28.95 (978-0-7368-8584-3(6)) Red Brick Learning.

La Seguridad en los Desportes de Verano. 2000. (McGraw-Hill Ciencias Ser.). (ENG & SPA.). (gr. 5 up). (978-0-02-279675-4(4)) Macmillan/McGraw-Hill Schl. Div.

Los seres vivos: Cuaderno de Evaluacion: Unit 1: Los seres vivos (Living Things) 2000. (McGraw-Hill Ciencias Ser.). (ENG & SPA.). (gr. 3 up). (978-0-02-278649-6(X)) Macmillan/McGraw-Hill Schl. Div.

Los seres vivos: Recursos para el maestro con clave de Respuestas: Unit 1: Los seres vivos (Living Things) 2000. (McGraw-Hill Ciencias Ser.). (ENG & SPA.). (gr. 3 up). (978-0-02-278692-2(9)) Macmillan/McGraw-Hill Schl. Div.

Serpientes y largatos Science, 6 vols.Tr. of Snakes & Lizards Science. (SPA.). (gr. k-2). 28.95 (978-0-7368-3053-9(7) , Yellow Umbrella Bks.) Capstone Pr., Inc.

Setford, Steve & Dorling Kindersley Publishing Staff. Science Facts. 2nd ed. 2004. (Pocket Guides Ser.). (Illus.). 160p. (J). pap. 6.99 (978-0-7566-0207-9(6)) Dorling Kindersley Publishing, Inc.

Shake & Learn Science. 2001. (YA). spiral bd. 119.95 incl. audio compact disk (978-0-9746001-2-3(1)) Salt Productions, Inc.

Shapiro, Irwin I., et al. ARIES Exploring Light & Color: Filters, Lenses, & Cameras: Science Journal. 2000. (Aries Ser.). Orig. Title: Project Aries: Light & Color. (Illus.). (J). (gr. 3-8). pap. 3.80 (978-1-57091-251-1(3)) Charlesbridge Publishing, Inc.

Shell, Barry. Sensational Scientists: The Journeys & Discoveries of 24 Men & Women of Science. 2nd rev. ed. 2006. (Illus.). 208p. (J). pap. 15.95 (978-1-55192-727-5(6)) Raincoast Bk. Distribution CAN. *Dist:* Perseus Distribution.

Shevick, Ed. Great Scientists in Action. Wheeler, Ron, illus. 2004. (Science Action Labs Ser.). 64p. (J). pap. 9.95 (978-1-57310-436-4(1) , 1238118) Teaching & Learning Co.

Shevick, Edward. Air Science: Active Science with Air. Mitchell, Judy, ed. Jones, Marguerite, illus. 1998. (Science Action Labs Ser.). 64p. (gr. 4-8). pap., tchr. ed. 8.95 (978-1-57310-142-4(7)) Teaching & Learning Co.

Shields, Charles J. Standardized Test Practice for 6th Grade. 1999. 96p. (J). (gr. 6). pap., tchr. ed. 11.99 (978-1-57690-681-1(7) , TCA2681) Teacher Created Materials, Inc.

Show Us Your Wings Science, 6 vols. (gr. k-2). 28.95 (978-0-7368-2999-1(7) , Yellow Umbrella Bks.) Capstone Pr., Inc.

Show What You Know on the FCAT 8, Science Student Self Study Workbook. 2006. (YA). per. 16.95 (978-1-59230-178-2(9)) Englefield & Assocs., Inc.

Show What You Know on the OGT, Science Student Self Study Workbook. 2007. (YA). per. 18.95 (***978-1-59230-274-1(2))*** Englefield & Assocs., Inc.

Sian Revision Work: Plane & Simple. 2004. (Science in A Nutshell(R) Ser.). (J). (978-1-59242-089-6(3)) Delta Education, LLC.

Sientes Como Se Mueve la Tierra? Leveled Books. 2000. (McGraw-Hill Ciencias Ser.). (ENG & SPA.). (gr. 4 up). (978-0-02-279650-1(9)) Macmillan/McGraw-Hill Schl. Div.

Silva Lee, Alfonso. Mi Isla y Yo: La Naturaleza de Cuba. Hayskar, Bonnie J., ed. Lago, Alexis, illus. 2010. (SPA.). 32p. (J). pap. 9.95 (978-1-929165-22-3(6)) PANGAEA.

Silver, Donald M. & Wynne, P. J. Lift & Look Science Mini-Books & Manipulatives. 2000. pap. 10.95 (978-0-590-68567-2(8)) Scholastic, Inc.

Silverstein, Alvin, et al. Science Concepts, 10 vols. 2004. (Science & Technology Ser.). (Illus.). 64p. (YA). (gr. 5-8). (978-0-7613-3093-6(3) , Twenty-First Century Bks.) Lerner Publishing Group.

Simon, Charnan. Solids, Liquids, Gases. 2000. (Simply Science Ser.). (Illus.). 32p. (J). (gr. 3 up). lib. bdg. 19.93 (978-0-7565-0037-5(0)) Compass Point Bks.

Simon, Seymour. Destination: Jupiter. (Illus.). 32p. (J). 2000. (gr. k up). pap. 6.99 (978-0-06-443759-2(0) , Harper Trophy); 1998. (gr. 5 up). 15.95 (978-0-688-15620-6(7)) HarperCollins Pubs.

—Destination: Jupiter. 2000. (gr. 3-6). lib. bdg. 15.30 (978-0-613-33691-8(7)) Tandem Library Bks.

—Seymour Simon Event Kit. 2000. (J). (978-0-06-029309-3(8)) HarperCollins Pubs.

Sinclair, Peta-Jane. Science & Technology Matters: Grade 5. 2001. (gr. 5). pap., tchr. ed. 9.20 (978-0-521-78841-0(2)) Cambridge Univ. Pr.

—Science & Technology Matters: Grade 5 Learner's Book. 2001. (gr. 5). pap., tchr. ed. 6.90 (978-0-521-78838-0(2)) Cambridge Univ. Pr.

Singer, Marilyn. What Stinks? 2006. (Illus.). 64p. (J). 17.95 (978-1-58196-035-8(2)) Darby Creek Publishing.

Sink & Float. 2001. (Inquiry Science Ser.). 32p. (gr. k-1). 4.99 (978-1-56822-676-7(4) , IF20847) School Specialty Publishing.

Sitarski, Anita. Cold Light: Creatures, Discoveries, & Inventions That Glow. 2007. (Illus.). 40p. (YA). (gr. 4 up). 16.95 (***978-1-59078-468-6(5))*** Boyds Mills Pr.

Sloan, Peter. Floating. 1999. (gr. k-3). lib. bdg. 11.80 (978-0-613-30407-8(1)) Tandem Library Bks.

Small Worlds, 10 bks. Incl. Coral Reef. Green, Jen. 2002. (978-0-7787-0138-5(7)); Dead Log. Green, Jen. 1999. lib. bdg. (978-0-7787-0136-1(0)); Freshwater Pond. Hibbert, Adam. 1999. lib. bdg. (978-0-7787-0133-0(6)); In a Backyard. Green, Jen. 2002. lib. bdg. (978-0-7787-0141-5(7)); In a House. Green, Jen. 2002. lib. bdg. (978-0-7787-0140-8(9)); On the Tundra. Green, Jen. 2002. lib. bdg. (978-0-7787-0139-2(5)); Rain Forest Tree. Kite, Lorien. 1999. lib. bdg. (978-0-7787-0132-3(8)); Saguaro Cactus. Green, Jen. 1999. lib. bdg. (978-0-7787-0134-7(4)); Tidal Pool. Steele, Philip. 1999. lib. bdg. (978-0-7787-0135-4(2)); Under a Stone. Green, Jen. 1999. lib. bdg. (978-0-7787-0137-8(9)); 32p. (J). (gr. 3-4). (Illus.). 1999. (978-0-7787-0131-6(X)); Set pap. (978-0-7787-0145-3(X)) Crabtree Publishing Co.

SmartLab. SmartLab Catalog Fall 2005. 2005. pap. 0.01 (978-1-932855-30-2(0)) becker&mayer! books.

Smith, Alastair. Tures & Compounds. 2002. (gr. 3-6). lib. bdg. 18.75 (978-0-613-75097-4(7)) Tandem Library Bks.

Smooth or Rough? Individual Title Six-Packs. (Rigby Focus Ser.). 16p. (gr. k up). 26.00 (978-0-7578-5293-0(9)); 28.00 (978-0-7578-5527-6(X)) Rigby Education.

Sneider, Cary I. Oobleck: What Do Scientists Do? Bergman, Lincoln & Fairwell, Kay, eds. Baker, Lisa H. & Peterson, Adria M., illus. rev. ed. 1998. (Great Explorations in Math & Science Ser.). 40p. (J). (gr. 4-8). pap. 10.50 (978-0-924886-09-6(9) , GEMS) Univ. of California, Berkeley, Lawrence Hall of Science.

Sneider, Cary I. & Barber, Jacqueline. Paper Towel Testing. Bergman, Lincoln & Fairwell, Kay, eds. Bevilacqua, Carol, illus. Hoyt, Richard, photos by. rev. ed. 1998. (Great Explorations in Math & Science Ser.). 48p. (Orig.). (YA). (gr. 5-8). pap. 10.50 (978-0-924886-11-9(0) , GEMS) Univ. of California, Berkeley, Lawrence Hall of Science.

Sobey, Ed. Rocket-Powered Science. 2005. 112p. pap. (978-1-59647-055-2(0)) Good Year Bks.

Sobey, Edwin J. C. Fantastic Flying Fun with Science: 69 Projects You Can Fly, Spin, Launch, & Ride. 2000. (Illus.). 90p. (J). (gr. 5 up). pap. 11.95 (978-0-07-134800-3(X)) McGraw-Hill Cos., The.

—Wacky Water Fun with Science: 69 Projects You Can Float, Sink, Squirt & Sail. 1999. (Illus.). 88p. (J). (gr. 5 up). pap. 11.95 (978-0-07-134809-6(3) , 9780071348096) McGraw-Hill Cos., The.

Soil. 2001. (Inquiry Science Ser.). 32p. (gr. k-1). 4.99 (978-1-56822-945-4(3) , IF20852) School Specialty Publishing.

El sol Science, 6 vols.Tr. of Sun Science. (SPA.). (gr. k-2). 28.95 (978-0-7368-3147-5(9) , Yellow Umbrella Bks.) Capstone Pr., Inc.

Solway, Andrew. A History of Super Science: Atoms & Elements. 2005. (Illus.). 32p. (J). (978-1-4109-1951-9(X)); (gr. 3-5). lib. bdg. 28.21 (978-1-4109-1920-5(X)) Steck-Vaughn.

Some Kids Are Deaf, 6 vols. (gr. k-2). 28.95 (978-0-7368-8817-2(9)) Red Brick Learning.

Some Kids Wear Leg Braces, 6 vols. (gr. k-2). 28.95 (978-0-7368-8819-6(5)) Red Brick Learning.

Sonido. (Coleccion Jugando Con la Ciencia). (SPA., Illus.). 39p. (J). pap. 9.95 (978-950-11-0831-6(7) , SGM317) Sigmar ARG. *Dist:* Continental Bk. Co., Inc.

La sorpresa del Anochecer. 2000. (McGraw-Hill Ciencias Ser.). (ENG & SPA.). (gr. 2 up). (978-0-02-279616-7(9)) Macmillan/McGraw-Hill Schl. Div.

Space Missions, 6 vols. (gr. 2-5). 36.95 (978-0-7368-4610-3(7)) Red Brick Learning.

Spanish Science Add-on Set, Early Level. (SPA.). (gr. k-2). 57.95 (978-0-7368-3071-3(5) , Yellow Umbrella Bks.) Capstone Pr., Inc.

Spanish Science Add-on Set, Emergent Level. (SPA.). (gr. k-2). 57.95 (978-0-7368-3156-7(8) , Yellow Umbrella Bks.) Capstone Pr., Inc.

Spanish Science Program, Early Level. (SPA.). (gr. k-2). 348.95 (978-0-7368-3070-6(7) , Yellow Umbrella Bks.) Capstone Pr., Inc.

Spanish Science Program, Emergent Level. (SPA.). (gr. k-2). 348.95 (978-0-7368-3155-0(X) , Yellow Umbrella Bks.) Capstone Pr., Inc.

Splish, Splash! 2005. (Emergent/Early (Prek-2) Science Package Ser.). 12p. (YA). (ps-2). 25.20 (978-0-8215-7838-4(3)) Sadlier, William H. Inc.

Spyglass Books Complete Set. (Spyglass Books-Around the World Ser.). (gr. 1-2). 1514.68 (978-0-7565-0803-6(7)) Compass Point Bks.

Stanbury, Jean. How to Dazzle at Being a Scientist. 2004. (Illus.). 48p. pap. 30.00 (978-1-897675-52-6(6)) Brilliant Pubns. GBR. *Dist:* Parkwest Pubns., Inc.

Start & Stop, 6 vols. (gr. k-2). 28.95 (978-0-7368-8616-1(8)) Red Brick Learning.

Staton, Hilarie. Science & Stories K-3. 2005. 152p. (gr. k-3). pap. (978-1-59647-082-8(8)) Good Year Bks.

Stazzer, James. Weird New Science Mega-Mouth Discovered: Bizarre Real-Life Monsters, Myths & Future Animals, No. 1. 1999. (Weird New Science Ser.: Vol. 1). (Illus.). 128p. (YA). (gr. 4-7). pap. 4.95 (978-1-902618-36-4(X)) Element Children's Bks.

Steck-Vaughn Staff. Access Science. 2004. pap., tchr. ed. 5.95 (978-0-7398-8936-7(2)); (Illus.). pap. 14.96 (978-0-7398-8930-5(3)) Steck-Vaughn.

—At-Home Workbooks: General Science. 2004. (Illus.). pap., wbk. ed. 5.99 (978-0-7398-8514-7(6)); (gr. 1). pap., wbk. ed. 5.99 (978-0-7398-8513-0(8)); (gr. 2). pap., wbk. ed. 5.99 (978-0-7398-8515-4(4)); (gr. 3). pap., wbk. ed. 5.99 (978-0-7398-8516-1(2)); (gr. 4). pap., wbk. ed. 5.99 (978-0-7398-8517-8(0)) Steck-Vaughn.

—Berrent Espanol Success Science: Answer Key - Steck Vaughn. 2002. (SPA.). (J). pap. (978-0-7398-3986-7(1)) Steck-Vaughn.

—Best of Science, Vol. 1. 2000. (Illus.). (J). (gr. 2). pap. (978-0-7398-3390-2(1)); (gr. 3). pap. (978-0-7398-3391-9(X)); (gr. 4). pap. (978-0-7398-3392-6(8)) Steck-Vaughn.

—Creepy Creatures. 2003. pap. 4.10 (978-0-7398-7629-9(5)) Steck-Vaughn.

—Focus on Science. 2004. Level C. pap., tchr. ed. 13.50 incl. cd-rom (978-0-7398-9152-0(9)); Level C. (Illus.). pap. 14.70 incl. cd-rom (978-0-7398-9146-9(4)); Level D. pap., tchr. ed. 13.50 incl. cd-rom (978-0-7398-9153-7(7)); Level D. (Illus.). pap. 14.70 incl. cd-rom (978-0-7398-9147-6(2)); Level A. pap. 13.10 incl. cd-rom (978-0-7398-9144-5(8)); Level A. pap., tchr. ed. 13.50 incl. cd-rom (978-0-7398-9150-6(2)); Level B. pap., tchr. ed. 13.50 incl. cd-rom (978-0-7398-9151-3(0)); Level B. (Illus.). pap. 13.10 incl. cd-rom (978-0-7398-9145-2(6)); Level E. pap., tchr. ed. 13.50 incl. cd-rom (978-0-7398-9154-4(5)); Level E. (Illus.). pap. 15.60 incl. cd-rom (978-0-7398-9148-3(0)); Level F. pap., tchr. ed. 13.50 incl. cd-rom (978-0-7398-9155-1(3)); Level F. (Illus.). pap. 15.60 incl. cd-rom (978-0-7398-9149-0(9)) Steck-Vaughn.

—GED Exercises: Science. 2000. pap. 11.67 (978-0-7398-3602-6(1)) Steck-Vaughn.

—Higher Scores on Science Standard Tests. 2000. (Illus.). (J). (gr. 2). pap. (978-0-7398-3419-0(3)); (gr. 3). pap. 7.99 (978-0-7398-3420-6(7)); (gr. 4). pap. (978-0-7398-3421-3(5)); (gr. 5). pap. (978-0-7398-3422-0(3)); (gr. 6). pap. (978-0-7398-3423-7(1)) Steck-Vaughn.

—Life, Earth & Physical Science: Complete Science Series. 2001. (Illus.). pap. 1396.70 (978-0-7398-6267-4(7)) Steck-Vaughn.

—Light & Sound: Classroom Edition. 1999. (Illus.). (J). pap. (978-0-7398-1925-8(9)) Steck-Vaughn.

—PU Extended Complete Collection Level 1. 2003. (Illus.). pap. 599.00 (978-0-7398-8913-8(3)) Steck-Vaughn.

—PU Extended Complete Collection Level 2. 2003. (Illus.). pap. 729.00 (978-0-7398-8914-5(1)) Steck-Vaughn.

—Science. 2003. (J). (gr. 1). pap. (978-0-7398-7933-7(2)); (gr. 2). pap. (978-0-7398-7934-4(0)); (gr. 3). pap. 16.99 (978-0-7398-7935-1(9)); (gr. 4). pap. 16.99 (978-0-7398-7936-8(7)); (gr. 5). pap. 16.99 (978-0-7398-7937-5(5)); (gr. 6). pap. (978-0-7398-7938-2(3)) Steck-Vaughn.

—Science Level H-J: Hello, Hello! 2003. (Illus.). pap. (978-0-7398-7635-0(X)) Steck-Vaughn.

—Science Level C: Answer Key. 2000. (Strategies for Success Ser.). (Illus.). (J). pap. (978-0-7398-3991-1(8)) Steck-Vaughn.

—Science Level D: Answer Key. 2000. (Strategies for Success Ser.). (Illus.). (J). pap. (978-0-7398-3992-8(6)) Steck-Vaughn.

—Science Level F: Answer Key. 2000. (Strategies for Success Ser.). (Illus.). (J). pap. (978-0-7398-3982-9(9)) Steck-Vaughn.

—Science Level G: Answer Key. 2000. (Strategies for Success Ser.). (Illus.). (J). pap. (978-0-7398-3983-6(7)) Steck-Vaughn.

—Science Level H: Answer Key. 2000. (Strategies for Success Ser.). (Illus.). (J). pap. (978-0-7398-3984-3(5)) Steck-Vaughn.

—Shutterbug Science Starter Set Level A-I. 2002. (Illus.). pap. 240.00 (978-0-7398-7812-5(3)); pap. 240.00 (978-0-7398-7813-2(1)) Steck-Vaughn.

—What Goes up Must Come Down. 2003. pap. 4.10 (978-0-7398-7632-9(5)) Steck-Vaughn.

Stiffler, Lee Anne, et al. Integrated Science: (6th Grade): Patterns & Cycles. 2000. 50.00 (978-0-89089-775-1(1)) Carolina Academic Pr.

Stille, Darlene R. Solids, Liquids, & Gases. 2004. (Science Around Us Ser.). 32p. (J). (gr. 2-6). 27.07 (978-1-59296-225-9(4)) Child's World, Inc.

The Story of Science - Group 3, 4 bks., Set. 119.71 (978-0-7614-1424-7(X) , Benchmark Bks.) Cavendish, Marshall Corp.

Strang, Craig, et al. On Sandy Shores. Bergman, Lincoln et al, eds. Baker, Lisa H. et al, illus. Hoyt, Richard & Bradley, Laurence, photos by. 1999. (Great Explorations in Math & Science Ser.). 212p. (J). (gr. 2-4). pap., tchr. ed. 18.00 (978-0-924886-33-1(1) , GEMS) Univ. of California, Berkeley, Lawrence Hall of Science.

Un sueno sobre Ruedas. 2000. (McGraw-Hill Ciencias Ser.). (ENG & SPA.). (gr. 2 up). (978-0-02-279617-4(7)) Macmillan/McGraw-Hill Schl. Div.

The Sun Science, 6 vols. (gr. k-2). 28.95 (978-0-7368-1750-9(6) , Yellow Umbrella Bks.) Capstone Pr., Inc.

Sunshine Science Early Fluency Sets 1-3: 1 Each of 24 Big Books from Sets 1-3. (gr. 1-2). 845.95 (978-0-7802-1370-8(X)) Wright Group, The.

Sunshine Science Early Fluency Sets 1-3: 1 Each of 24 Student Books from Sets 1-3. (gr. 1-2). 167.95 (978-0-7802-1371-5(8)) Wright Group, The.

Sunshine Science Early Fluency Sets 4-6: 1 Each of 24 Big Books from Sets 4-6. (gr. 1-2). 845.95 (978-0-7802-2924-2(X)) Wright Group, The.

Sunshine Science Early Fluency Sets 4-6: 1 Each of 24 Student Books from Sets 4-6. (gr. 1-2). 167.95 (978-0-7802-3189-4(9)) Wright Group, The.

Sunshine Science Emergent Sets: 1 Each of 24 Big Books from Sets 1-3. (gr. 1-2). 750.50 (978-0-7802-2751-4(4)) Wright Group, The.

Sunshine Science Emergent Sets: 1 Each of 24 Student Books from Sets 1-3. (gr. 1-2). 146.50 (978-0-7802-1944-1(9)) Wright Group, The.

Super Science Themes. 128p. (ps-1). 10.99 (978-0-7424-0247-8(9) , IF19108) School Specialty Publishing.

Superlibro: Acercate a las Ciencias. 2000. (McGraw-Hill Ciencias Ser.). (ENG & SPA.). (gr. k-2). (978-0-02-277177-5(8)); (gr. 3-5). (978-0-02-278997-8(9)) Macmillan/McGraw-Hill Schl. Div.

Superlibro de Como se Mueve? Unit 4: Como se mueve? (Watch it Move) 2000. (McGraw-Hill Ciencias Ser.). (ENG & SPA.). (gr. 2 up). (978-0-02-277174-4(3)) Macmillan/McGraw-Hill Schl. Div.

Superlibro de el Cielo: Unit 2: el cielo (the Sky) 2000. (McGraw-Hill Ciencias Ser.). (ENG & SPA.). (gr. 1 up). (978-0-02-277165-2(4)) Macmillan/McGraw-Hill Schl. Div.

Superlibro de el Estanque: Unit 5: el estanque (A Pond) 2000. (McGraw-Hill Ciencias Ser.). (ENG & SPA.). (gr. 1 up). (978-0-02-277168-3(9)) Macmillan/McGraw-Hill Schl. Div.

Superlibro de en Movimiento! Unit 4: en movimiento! (on the Move) 2000. (McGraw-Hill Ciencias Ser.). (ENG & SPA.). (gr. 1 up). (978-0-02-277167-6(0)) Macmillan/McGraw-Hill Schl. Div.

Superlibro de Materia y mas Materia: Unit 3: Materia y mas materia (Matter, Matter Everywhere) 2000. (McGraw-Hill Ciencias Ser.). (ENG & SPA.). (gr. 1 up). (978-0-02-277166-9(2)) Macmillan/McGraw-Hill Schl. Div.

Superlibro de Pistas del Pasado: Unit 2: Pistas del pasado (Clues from the Past) 2000. (McGraw-Hill Ciencias Ser.). (ENG & SPA.). (gr. 2 up). (978-0-02-277172-0(7)) Macmillan/McGraw-Hill Schl. Div.

Superlibro de Se Mueve? Unit 6: Se mueve? (Make Things Move) 2000. (McGraw-Hill Ciencias Ser.). (ENG & SPA.). (gr. k up). (978-0-02-277163-8(8)) Macmillan/McGraw-Hill Schl. Div.

Superlibro de Todo Cambia: Unit 3: Todo cambia (Changes all Around) 2000. (McGraw-Hill Ciencias Ser.). (ENG & SPA.). (gr. 2 up). (978-0-02-277173-7(5)) Macmillan/McGraw-Hill Schl. Div.

Survivors Science, 6 vols., Set. 2004. 179.57 (978-1-4109-0230-6(7)) Harcourt Schl. Pubs.

Sussman, Art. Dr. Art's Guide to Science: Connecting Atoms, Galaxies & Everything in Between. 2006. (Illus.). 256p. 22.95 (978-0-7879-8326-0(8) , Jossey-Bass) Wiley, John & Sons, Inc.

Suzuki, David T. & Hehner, Barbara. Descubre el Cuerpo Humano. 2004. (Juego de la Ciencia Ser.). (SPA., Illus.). 96p. 14.99 (978-84-9754-033-9(6) , 87813) Ediciones Oniro S.A. ESP. *Dist:* Bilingual Pubns. Co., The, Lectorum Pubns., Inc.

Suzuki, David T. & Helmer, Barbara. Descubre los Sentidos. 2002. (Juego de la Ciencia Ser.). (SPA., Illus.). 94p. 11.50 (978-84-9754-032-2(8) , 87812) Ediciones Oniro S.A. ESP. *Dist:* Bilingual Pubns. Co., The, Lectorum Pubns., Inc.

Swain, Cynthia. Cliff. 2003. (BuildUp Ser.). (J). pap. 22.00 (978-1-4108-0745-8(2)) Benchmark Education Co.

—What Do You Think? 2003. (BuildUp Ser.). (J). pap. 22.00 (978-1-4108-0758-8(4)) Benchmark Education Co.

Swanson, Diane. Nibbling on Einstein's Brain: The Good, the Bad & the Bogus in Science. Clark, Warren, illus. 2001. 112p. (J). (gr. 3-7). pap. 14.95 (978-1-55037-686-9(1)) Annick Pr., Ltd. CAN. *Dist:* Firefly Bks., Ltd.

—Nibbling on Einstein's Brain: The Good, the Bad & the Bogus in Science. 2001. (gr. 3-6). lib. bdg. 24.55 (978-0-613-51177-3(8)) Tandem Library Bks.

—Turn It Loose: The Scientist in Absolutely Everybody. Clark, Warren, illus. 2004. 112p. (J). (gr. 5). 29.95 (978-1-55037-851-1(1)); pap. 14.95 (978-1-55037-850-4(3)) Annick Pr., Ltd. CAN. *Dist:* Firefly Bks., Ltd.

Sweeney, Kathie. Science Questions & Answers: Animals. Nolte, Larry, illus. 1999. (Science Questions & Answers Ser.). 63p. (J). (gr. 1-3). pap. 5.95 (978-0-7373-0056-7(6)) Lowell Hse. Juvenile.

Sylvia Earle: en aguas Profundas: Leveled Books. 2000. (McGraw-Hill Ciencias Ser.). (ENG & SPA.). (gr. 4 up). (978-0-02-279663-1(0)) Macmillan/McGraw-Hill Schl. Div.

TAKS Science Preparation Elementary - Student Edition. 2003. (Region IV ESC Resources for Science Ser.). stu. ed., per., wbk. ed. (978-1-932524-62-8(2)) Region IV Education Service Ctr.

TAKS Science Preparation Elementary - Student Edition - Spanish. 2004. (SPA.). stu. ed., per., wbk. ed. (978-1-932524-87-1(8)) Region IV Education Service Ctr.

TAKS Science Preparation Grade 10. 2004. (Region IV ESC Resources for Science Ser.). stu. ed., per., wbk. ed. (978-1-932524-63-5(0)) Region IV Education Service Ctr.

TAKS Science Preparation Grade 11 Exit. 2004. (Region IV ESC Resources for Science Ser.). stu. ed., per., wbk. ed. (978-1-932524-64-2(9)) Region IV Education Service Ctr.

Tang, Greg. Math Fables Too: Making Science Count. Morley, Taia, illus. 2007. 40p. (J). (ps-k). pap. 16.99 (***978-0-439-78351-4(8)*** , Scholastic Pr.) Scholastic, Inc.

Tarjetas de Ilustraciones: Student & Teacher Support Resources. 2000. (McGraw-Hill Ciencias Ser.). (ENG & SPA.). (gr. k up). (978-0-02-279138-4(8)); (gr. 1 up). (978-0-02-279139-1(6)) Macmillan/McGraw-Hill Schl. Div.

Tarsitano, Frank. Raintree Steck-Vaughn Illustrated Science Encyclopedia Annual, 1998. 1999. (Raintree Steck-Vaughn Illustrated Science Encyclopedia Annual Ser.). (Illus.). 96p. (J). (gr. 4-7). lib. bdg. (978-0-8172-5721-7(7)) Raintree.

Tasting, 6 vols. (gr. k-2). 28.95 (978-0-7368-8586-7(2)) Red Brick Learning.

Taylor, Kim. Action. (Illus.). 32p. (YA). (gr. 3 up). lib. bdg. 27.10 (978-1-931983-72-3(0)) Chrysalis Education.

—Cold. (Illus.). 32p. (YA). (gr. 3 up). lib. bdg. 27.10 (978-1-931983-73-0(9)) Chrysalis Education.

—Pattern. (Illus.). 32p. (YA). (gr. 3 up). lib. bdg. 27.10 (978-1-931983-76-1(3)) Chrysalis Education.

—Structure. (Illus.). 32p. (YA). (gr. 3 up). lib. bdg. 27.10 (978-1-931983-78-5(X)) Chrysalis Education.

Teeth, 6 vols. (Sunshinetm Science Ser.). 24p. (gr. 1-2). 37.50 (978-0-7802-1402-6(1)); 41.95 (978-0-7802-1401-9(3)) Wright Group, The.

Teeth Sets: 1 Each of 3 Student Books. (Sunshinetm Science Ser.). (gr. 1-2). 20.95 (978-0-7802-1751-5(9)) Wright Group, The.

Thimmesh, Catherine. The Sky's the Limit: Stories of Discovery by Women & Girls. Sweet, Melissa, illus. 2005. 73p. (J). (gr. 4-8). reprint ed. 16.00 (978-0-7567-9631-0(8)) DIANE Publishing Co.

—The Sky's the Limit: Stories of Discovery by Women & Girls. Sweet, Melissa, illus. 80p. (J). (gr. 5-9). 2004. pap. 7.95 (978-0-618-49489-7(8)); 2002. 16.00 (978-0-618-07698-7(0)) Houghton Mifflin Co. Trade & Reference Div.

Thompson, Gene. Kitchen Science. Date not set. (Thinking Like a Scientist Ser.). (Illus.). 20p. (J). pap. 16.95 (978-1-58273-097-4(0)) Sundance/Newbridge Educational Publishing.

Thomson Gale Staff, ed. First Library of Knowledge, 12 vols., Set. 2005. 384p. 282.80 (978-1-4103-0742-2(5) , Blackbirch Pr., Inc.) Thomson Gale.

Thomson, Ruth. Take My Plant for a Walk? 2001. (Why Can't I Ser.). (Illus.). 30p. (J). lib. bdg. 24.25 (978-1-930643-02-4(0)) Chrysalis Education.

Tiempo y clima: Cuaderno de Evaluacion: Unit 2: Tiempo y clima (Weather & Climate) 2000. (McGraw-Hill Ciencias Ser.). (ENG & SPA.). (gr. 5 up). (978-0-02-278672-4(4)) Macmillan/McGraw-Hill Schl. Div.

La Tierra y sus recursos: Cuaderno de Evaluacion: Unit 5: la Tierra y sus recursos (Earth & Its Resources) 2000. (McGraw-Hill Ciencias Ser.). (ENG & SPA.). (gr. 5 up). (978-0-02-278675-5(9)) Macmillan/McGraw-Hill Schl. Div.

La Tierra y sus recursos: Recursos para el maestro con clave de Respuestas: Unit 5: la Tierra y sus recursos (Earth & Its Resources) 2000. (McGraw-Hill Ciencias Ser.). (ENG & SPA.). (gr. 5 up). (978-0-02-278712-7(7)) Macmillan/McGraw-Hill Schl. Div.

Tilley, Rebecca & Willard, Carolyn. Secret Formulas. Bergman, Lincoln et al, eds. Baker, Lisa H. et al, illus. Hoyt, Richard & Bradley, Laurence, photos by. rev. ed. 1998. (Great Explorations in Math & Science Ser.). 160p. (J). (gr. 1-3). pap. 16.00 (978-0-924886-08-9(0) , GEMS) Univ. of California, Berkeley, Lawrence Hall of Science.

Time-Life Books Editors. Science Starter. 1999. (Illus.). 88p. (J). (gr. 1-4). 14.95 (978-0-8094-4881-4(5)) Time-Life, Inc.

Time-Life Staff. Things Around Us. 1999. (Illus.). 88p. (J). (ps-2). 14.95 (978-0-8094-4845-6(9)) Time-Life, Inc.

Tocci, Salvatore. Experiments with Solids, Liquids, & Gases. 2002. (True Bks.). (Illus.). 48p. (J). (gr. 3-5). pap. 6.95 (978-0-516-27352-5(3) , Children's Pr.) Scholastic Library Publishing.

—Experiments with Solids, Liquids, & Gases. 2001. (gr. 3-6). lib. bdg. 15.25 (978-0-613-54213-5(4)) Tandem Library Bks.

—High-Tech IDs: From Finger Scans to Voice Patterns. 2000. (Single Title Science Pb Ser.). (Illus.). 128p. (gr. 8-12). pap. 8.95 (978-0-531-16462-4(4) , Watts, Franklin) Scholastic Library Publishing.

Toda clase de Plantas. 2000. (McGraw-Hill Ciencias Ser.). (ENG & SPA.). (gr. k up). (978-0-02-279692-1(4)) Macmillan/McGraw-Hill Schl. Div.

Toda clase de Rocas. 2000. (McGraw-Hill Ciencias Ser.). (ENG & SPA.). (gr. k up). (978-0-02-279694-5(0)) Macmillan/McGraw-Hill Schl. Div.

Todo cambia: Cuaderno de Evaluacion: Unit 3: Todo cambia (Changes all Around) 2000. (McGraw-Hill Ciencias Ser.). (ENG & SPA.). (gr. 2 up). (978-0-02-278640-3(6)) Macmillan/McGraw-Hill Schl. Div.

Todo cambia: Recursos para el maestro con clave de Respuestas: Unit 3: Todo cambia (Changes all Around) 2000. (McGraw-Hill Ciencias Ser.). (ENG & SPA.). (gr. 2 up). (978-0-02-278687-8(2)) Macmillan/McGraw-Hill Schl. Div.

Todo es materia! Science, 6 vols.Tr. of Everything Is Matter! Science. (SPA.). (gr. k-2). 28.95 (978-0-7368-3055-3(3) , Yellow Umbrella Bks.) Capstone Pr., Inc.

Todo sobre Huevos. 2000. (McGraw-Hill Ciencias Ser.). (ENG & SPA.). (gr. 2 up). (978-0-02-279615-0(0)) Macmillan/McGraw-Hill Schl. Div.

Tools & Ideas Complete Materials Package W/Teacher's Guide & Student Books. 2001. (Illus.). (YA). ring bd. (978-1-887725-58-3(X)) Lab-Aids, Inc.

Top That Publishing Staff, ed. Electric Science. 2004. (Top That! Labs Ser.). (Illus.). 24p. (J). (978-1-84510-152-7(9)) Top That! Publishing PLC.

—Lets Go Bubbletastic. 2005. (Illus.). 48p. (978-1-84510-548-8(6)) Top That! Publishing PLC.

—Mirror Science. 2004. (Top That! Labs Ser.). (Illus.). 24p. (J). (978-1-84510-155-8(3)) Top That! Publishing PLC.

Transparencias: Student & Teacher Support Resources. 2000. (McGraw-Hill Ciencias Ser.). (ENG & SPA.). (gr. 1 up). (978-0-02-279149-0(3)); (gr. 2 up). (978-0-02-279151-3(5)); (gr. 3 up). (978-0-02-279152-0(3)); (gr. 4 up). (978-0-02-279153-7(1)); (gr. 5 up). (978-0-02-279154-4(X)) Macmillan/McGraw-Hill Schl. Div.

Trees Are Terrific! Science, 6 vols. (gr. k-2). 28.95 (978-0-7368-3000-3(6) , Yellow Umbrella Bks.) Capstone Pr., Inc.

Trefil, James. (WCS)Sciences. 4th ed. 2004. pap., stu. ed. 71.95 (978-0-471-72701-9(6)) Wiley, John & Sons, Inc.

—(WCS)Sciences: With eGrade Set. 4th ed. 2004. pap., stu. ed. 71.95 (978-0-471-72702-6(4)) Wiley, John & Sons, Inc.

S

True Books: Science, 4. 2004. 423.00 (978-0-516-24712-0(3)) Scholastic Library Publishing.

True Books Science. 2004. Vol. 3. 1128.00 (978-0-516-22901-0(X)); Vol. 4. 752.00 (978-0-516-27713-4(8)) Scholastic Library Publishing.

True Books Science Accelerated Reader Series, 50 bks., Vol. 1. 2004. pap. 1175.00 (978-0-516-29710-1(4) , Children's Pr.) Scholastic Library Publishing.

Trumbauer, Lisa. Everyone Is a Scientist. 2000. (Yellow Umbrella Books). (Illus.). 16p. (J). (gr. 1). lib. bdg. 14.60 (978-0-7368-0722-7(5) , Pebble Bks.) Capstone Pr., Inc.

Tuxworth, Nicola. A First Book about Mixing & Matching. 1999. (Look & Learn Ser.). (Illus.). 24p. (J). (gr. 1 up). lib. bdg. 22.00 (978-0-8368-2371-4(0)) Stevens, Gareth Inc.

—A First Book about Patterns. 1999. (Look & Learn Ser.). (Illus.). 24p. (J). (gr. 1 up). lib. bdg. 22.00 (978-0-8368-2288-5(9)) Stevens, Gareth Inc.

—Look & Learn, 6 bks. Incl. First Book about Animal Homes. lib. bdg. 22.00 (978-0-8368-2285-4(4)); First Book about Bodies. lib. bdg. 22.00 (978-0-8368-2286-1(2)); First Book about Colors. lib. bdg. 22.00 (978-0-8368-2287-8(0)); First Book about Growing. lib. bdg. 22.00 (978-0-8368-2370-7(2)); First Book about Mixing & Matching. lib. bdg. 22.00 (978-0-8368-2371-4(0)); First Book about Patterns. lib. bdg. 22.00 (978-0-8368-2288-5(9)); 24p. (J). (gr. 1 up). (Illus.). 1999. Set lib. bdg. 132.00 (978-0-8368-2284-7(6)) Stevens, Gareth Inc.

Ulysses S Grant, 6 vols. (gr. 2-5). 39.95 (978-0-7368-4606-6(9)) Red Brick Learning.

Uncharted, Unexplored, & Unexplained: Scienctific Advancements of the 19th Century, 16 Bks, Set. 2004. (Illus.). (gr. 4-8). lib. bdg. 319.20 (978-1-58415-322-1(9)) Mitchell Lane Pubs., Inc.

Uncharted, Unexplored, & Unexplained: Scientific Advancements of the 19th Century, 26 vols., Set. Incl. Alexander Graham Bell & the Story of the Telephone. Bankston, John. (gr. 4-8). 2004. lib. bdg. 29.95 (978-1-58415-243-9(5)); Antoine Lavoisier : Father of Modern Chemistry. Kjelle, Marylou. (gr. 4-8). 2004. lib. bdg. 29.95 (978-1-58415-309-2(1)); Auguste & Louis Lumiere & the Rise of Motion Pictures. Whiting, Jim. (gr. 4-8). 2005. lib. bdg. 29.95 (978-1-58415-365-8(2)); Charles Babbage & the Story of the First Computer. Sherman, Josepha. (gr. 4-8). 2005. lib. bdg. 29.95 (978-1-58415-372-6(5)); Charles Darwin & the Origin of the Species. Whiting, Jim. (gr. 8). 2005. lib. bdg. 29.95 (978-1-58415-364-1(4)); Dmitri Mendeleyev & the Periodic Table. Zannos, Susan. (gr. 4-8). 2004. lib. bdg. 29.95 (978-1-58415-267-5(2)); Florence Nightingale & the Advancement of Nursing. Hinman, Bonnie. (gr. 4-8). 2004. lib. bdg. 29.95 (978-1-58415-257-6(5)); Friedrich Miescher & the Story of Nucleic Acid. Tracy, Kathleen. (gr. 4-8). 2005. lib. bdg. 29.95 (978-1-58415-369-6(5)); George Eastman & Photographic Film. Mattern, Joanne. (gr. 4-8). 2004. lib. bdg. 29.95 (978-1-58415-258-3(3)); Gregor Mendel & the Discovery of the Gene. Bankston, John. (gr. 4-8). 2004. lib. bdg. 29.95 (978-1-58415-266-8(4)); Guglielmo Marconi & Radio Waves. Zannos, Susan. (gr. 4-8). 2004. lib. bdg. 29.95 (978-1-58415-265-1(6)); Henry Bessemer : Making Steel from Iron. Tracy, Kathleen. (gr. 4-8). 2005. lib. bdg. 29.95 (978-1-58415-366-5(0)); Henry Cavendish & the Discovery of Hydrogen. Sherman, Josepha. (gr. 4-8). 2005. lib. bdg. 29.95 (978-1-58415-368-9(7)); J. J. Thomson & the Discovery of Electrons. Sherman, Josepha. (gr. 4-8). 2005. lib. bdg. 29.95 (978-1-58415-370-2(9)); James Watt & the Steam Engine. Whiting, Jim. (gr. 4-8). 2005. lib. bdg. 29.95 (978-1-58415-371-9(7)); John Dalton & the Atomic Theory. Kjelle, Marylou. (gr. 4-8). 2004. lib. bdg. 29.95 (978-1-58415-308-5(3)); Joseph Lister & the Story of Antiseptics. Bankston, John. (gr. 4-8). 2004. lib. bdg. 29.95 (978-1-58415-262-0(1)); Joseph Priestly & the Discovery of Oxygen. Conley, Kate A. (gr. 4-8). 2005. lib. bdg. 29.95 (978-1-58415-367-2(9)); Karl Benz & the Single Cylinder Engine. Bankston, John. (gr. 4-8). 2004. lib. bdg. 29.95 (978-1-58415-244-6(3)); Louis Daguerre & the Story of the Daguerreotype. Bankston, John. (gr. 4-8). 2004. lib. bdg. 29.95 (978-1-58415-247-7(8)); Louis Pasteur : Fighter Against Contagious Disease. Kjelle, Marylou Morano. (gr. 4-8). 2005. lib. bdg. 29.95 (978-1-58415-363-4(6) , 1244912); Michael Faraday & the Discovery of Electromagnetism. Zannos, Susan. (gr. 4-8). 2004. lib. bdg. 29.95 (978-1-58415-307-8(5));

Pierre & Marie Curie & the Discovery of Radium. Tracy, Kathleen. (gr. 4-8). 2004. lib. bdg. 29.95 (978-1-58415-310-8(5)); Robert Koch & the Study of Anthrax. Tracy, Kathleen. (gr. 4-8). 2004. lib. bdg. 29.95 (978-1-58415-261-3(3)); Samuel Morse & the Telegraph. Zannos, Susan. (gr. 4-8). 2004. lib. bdg. 29.95 (978-1-58415-269-9(9)); Thomas Edison : Great Inventor. Thatcher Murcia, Rebecca. (gr. 4-8). 2004. lib. bdg. 29.95 (978-1-58415-306-1(7)); (Illus.). 48p. (J). 2005. Set lib. bdg. 778.70 (978-1-58415-410-5(1)) Mitchell Lane Pubs., Inc.

Under Your Skin: Investigator Slide Strip Sets: the Muscular & Skeletal Systems. 2000. (J). pap. 6.95 (978-1-56911-785-9(3)) Learning Resources, Inc.

Understanding Differences Set. (gr. k-2). 114.95 (978-0-7368-9033-5(5)) Red Brick Learning.

The Unexplained, 4 bks. Incl. Disappearances. Fuchs, Carol A. lib. bdg. 21.26 (978-1-56065-041-6(9)); Ghosts & Poltergeists. Meier, Gisela. lib. bdg. 21.26 (978-1-56065-040-9(0)); Magic & Magicians. Burgess, Mike. lib. bdg. 21.26 (978-1-56065-044-7(3)); Mythical Beasts. Marx, Doug. lib. bdg. 21.26 (978-1-56065-046-1(X)); 48p. (J). (gr. 3-4). 1991. (Illus.). Set lib. bdg. 85.04 (978-1-56065-666-1(2) , Capstone High-Interest Bks.) Capstone Pr., Inc.

Unlocking the Secrets of Science: Profiling 20th Century Achievers in Science, Medicine, & Technology, 30 vols., set. (Illus.). 56p. (J). (gr. 5-6). 718.00 (978-1-58415-163-0(3)) Mitchell Publishing, Inc.

Up in the Air: 6 Each of 1 Anthology, 6 vols. (Wildcats Ser.). 32p. (J). (gr. 2-8). (978-0-322-00596-9(5)) Wright Group, The.

UXL Staff. U-X-L Complete Life Science Resource, 3 vols., Set. 2001. (Illus.). 608p. (J). 181.00 (978-0-7876-4851-0(5) , GML00502-114895, UXL) Thomson Gale.

Vamos de Paseo. 2000. (McGraw-Hill Ciencias Ser.). (ENG & SPA.). (gr. 1 up). (978-0-02-279571-9(5)) Macmillan/McGraw-Hill Schl. Div.

VanCleave, Janice Pratt. Janice VanCleave's Every Kid Set. 2002. (Illus.). 2042p. pap. 96.95 (978-0-471-42339-3(4) , Wiley) Wiley, John & Sons, Inc.

VanVoorst, Jennifer. Tu eres un cientifico! Science. (SPA.). (gr. k-2). 19.95 (978-0-7368-2981-6(4)) Red Brick Learning.

Vecchione, Glen. Experimentos Sencillos con Animales y Plantas. 2004. (Juego de la Ciencia Ser.: Vol. 8). (SPA., Illus.). 130p. 12.50 (978-84-9754-007-0(7) , 87808) Ediciones Oniro S.A. ESP. *Dist:* Bilingual Pubns. Co., The, Latin American Bk. Source, Inc., Lectorum Pubns., Inc., Libros Sin Fronteras.

—Experimentos Sencillos con la Electricidad. Elena, Horacio, tr. Elena, Horacio, illus. 2004. (Juego de la Ciencia Ser.: Vol. 10). (SPA.). 124p. 10.99 (978-84-9754-024-7(7) , 87810) Ediciones Oniro S.A. ESP. *Dist:* Latin American Bk. Source, Inc., Lectorum Pubns., Inc.

—Experimentos Sencillos de Quimica en la Cocina. 2004. (Juego de la Ciencia Ser.). (SPA.). 128p. 9.99 (978-84-95456-96-0(6) , 87807) Ediciones Oniro S.A. ESP. *Dist:* Bilingual Pubns. Co., The, Lectorum Pubns., Inc., Libros Sin Fronteras.

—The Little Giant Book of Science Facts. Harris, Joel C. & Harris, Sharon, illus. 2004. 352p. pap. 6.95 (978-1-4027-0653-0(7) , 1234564) Sterling Publishing Co., Inc.

Vecchione, Glen. Science Facts. Harris, Joel & Harris, Sharon, illus. 2007. 360p. (J). pap. 6.95 ***(978-1-4027-4981-0(3))*** Sterling Publishing Co., Inc.

Vete, Lluvia! 2000. (McGraw-Hill Ciencias Ser.). (ENG & SPA.). (gr. k up). (978-0-02-279707-2(6)) Macmillan/McGraw-Hill Schl. Div.

Viaje en un tren Flotante. 2000. (McGraw-Hill Ciencias Ser.). (ENG & SPA.). (gr. 2 up). (978-0-02-279609-9(6)) Macmillan/McGraw-Hill Schl. Div.

Un viaje Espeleologico! 2000. (McGraw-Hill Ciencias Ser.). (ENG & SPA.). (gr. 5 up). (978-0-02-279673-0(8)) Macmillan/McGraw-Hill Schl. Div.

Viaje por el cuerpo Humano. 2000. (McGraw-Hill Ciencias Ser.). (ENG & SPA.). (gr. 2 up). (978-0-02-279610-5(X)) Macmillan/McGraw-Hill Schl. Div.

Un viaje sobre el Serengeti. 2000. (McGraw-Hill Ciencias Ser.). (ENG & SPA.). (gr. 3 up). (978-0-02-279628-0(2)) Macmillan/McGraw-Hill Schl. Div.

Vibrations, 6 vols. (gr. k-2). 28.95 (978-0-7368-8617-8(6)) Red Brick Learning.

Videos: Actividad de Exploracion: Technology. 2000. (McGraw-Hill Ciencias Ser.). (ENG & SPA.). (gr. 1 up). (978-0-02-277418-9(1)); (gr. 2 up). (978-0-02-277419-6(X)); (gr. 3 up). (978-0-02-277421-9(1)); (gr. 4 up). (978-0-02-277422-6(X)); (gr. 5 up). (978-0-02-277423-3(8)) Macmillan/McGraw-Hill Schl. Div.

Videos: Maraton Mental: Technology. 2000. (McGraw-Hill Ciencias Ser.). (ENG & SPA.). (gr. 3 up). (978-0-02-278740-0(2)); (gr. 4 up). (978-0-02-278741-7(0)); (gr. 5 up). (978-0-02-278742-4(9)) Macmillan/McGraw-Hill Schl. Div.

Vorderman, Carol. Grades 3-4. 2006. (Learn Science! Ser.). 96p. (J). pap. 10.99 (978-0-7566-2104-9(6)) Dorling Kindersley Publishing, Inc.

—Grades 5-6. 2006. (Learn Science! Ser.). (Illus.). 96p. (J). pap. 10.99 (978-0-7566-2105-6(4)) Dorling Kindersley Publishing, Inc.

—Grades K-2. 2006. (Learn Science! Ser.). 96p. (J). pap. 10.99 (978-0-7566-2103-2(8)) Dorling Kindersley Publishing, Inc.

Vriesenga, Daryl. Science Enrichment. 1999. (100+ Seriestm Ser.). 128p. (J). (gr. 1-2). pap. 12.99 (978-0-88012-913-8(1) , IF8757); (gr. 3-4). pap. 12.99 (978-0-88012-914-5(X) , IF8758); (gr. 5-6). pap. 12.99 (978-0-88012-915-2(8) , IF8759) School Specialty Publishing.

Wagner, Douglas, et al. Stepping into Natural Science & Technology Matters Grade 4 Facilitator's Guide. 2nd rev. ed. 2004. 152p. (AFR.). pap. 14.45 (978-0-521-54449-8(1)); pap. 14.45 (978-0-521-54447-4(5)) Cambridge Univ. Pr.

—Stepping into Natural Science & Technology Matters Grade 4 Learner's Book. rev. ed. 2000. 168p. pap. (978-0-947465-87-2(1)); 2nd ed. 2004. 152p. pap., stu. ed. 8.85 (978-0-521-54446-7(7)) Cambridge Univ. Pr.

—Stepping into Natural Science & Technology Matters Grade 4 Learner's Book (Afrikaans Translation) 2nd rev. ed. 2004. (AFR.). 152p. pap. 8.85 (978-0-521-54448-1(3)) Cambridge Univ. Pr.

—Stepping into Natural Science & Technology Matters Grade 5 Facilitators Guide. 2nd rev. ed. 2000. 178p. pap. (978-0-947465-65-0(0)); 3rd rev. ed. 2004. (AFR.). 128p. pap. 14.35 (978-0-521-54641-6(9)) Cambridge Univ. Pr.

—Stepping into Natural Science & Technology Matters Grade 5 Facilitator's Guide Afrikaans Translation. 2nd rev. ed. 2004. (AFR.). 128p. pap. 14.35 (978-0-521-54643-0(5)) Cambridge Univ. Pr.

—Stepping into Natural Science & Technology Matters Grade 5 Learner's Book. 2nd rev. ed. 2004. 176p. pap. 9.25 (978-0-521-54640-9(0)); 2000. pap. (978-0-947465-66-7(9)) Cambridge Univ. Pr.

—Stepping into Natural Science & Technology Matters Grade 5 Learner's Book Afrikaans Translation. 2nd rev. ed. 2004. (AFR.). 176p. pap. 9.25 (978-0-521-54642-3(7)) Cambridge Univ. Pr.

—Stepping into Natural Science & Technology Matters Grade 6 Facilitators Guide. 2000. 158p. pap. (978-0-947465-77-3(4)) Cambridge Univ. Pr.

—Stepping into Natural Science & Technology Matters Grade 6 Facilitator's Guide. 2nd rev. ed. 2004. 168p. pap. 14.35 (978-0-521-54645-4(1)) Cambridge Univ. Pr.

Walch. Assessment Strategies for Science. 2004. 54p. 24.99 (978-0-8251-5174-3(0)); 80p. 24.99 (978-0-8251-5175-0(9)) Walch Publishing.

Walker, Colin, et al. Los Seres Vivos. (Coleccion Conceptos de Ciencia en Big Books). (SPA., Illus.). (J). (gr. k-3). 12.00 net. (978-0-8136-6704-1(6) , MD7209) Modern Curriculum Pr.

—La Superficie de la Tierra. (Coleccion Conceptos de Ciencia en Big Books). (SPA., Illus.). (J). (gr. k-3). 12.00 (978-0-8136-6754-6(2) , MD7212) Modern Curriculum Pr.

Walker, David. A Leaf in Time. Balkwill, Fran, ed. Rolph, Mic, illus. 1999. (Making Sense of Science Ser.). 32p. (J). (gr. 3-7). pap. (978-1-85578-097-2(6)) Portland Pr., Ltd.

Walker, Pam. Ask the Science Expert. 2001. (100+ Seriestm Ser.). 128p. (J). (gr. 6-8). pap. 12.99 (978-0-7424-0138-9(3) , IF8753) School Specialty Publishing.

—Inexpensive Science Experiments. 2000. 96p. (J). (gr. 5-8). pap. 10.99 (978-1-56822-957-7(7) , IF19310) School Specialty Publishing.

Walking, Walking: Big Book: Level D. 8p. 20.95 (978-0-322-00626-3(0)) Wright Group, The.

Walkingsticks, 6 vols. (gr. k-2). 28.95 (978-0-7368-9110-3(2)) Red Brick Learning.

Wall Chart. 2003. (gr. 2 up). suppl. ed. 81.90 (978-0-673-59356-6(8)); (gr. 3 up). suppl. ed. 81.90 (978-0-673-65118-1(5)) Addison-Wesley Educational Pubs., Inc.

Wallace, Holly. Mystery of Loch Ness Monster, Set 1. 2002. (Can Science Solve? Ser.). (Illus.). 32p. (J). (gr. 4-7). pap. 7.50 (978-1-58810-309-3(9) , 91039) Heinemann Library.

Warbrick, Sarah. What Is Bendy? 1998. (What Is—? Ser.). (J). 14.60 (978-1-57572-049-4(3)) Heinemann Library.

—What Is Bouncy & Stretchy? 1998. (What Is—? Ser.). (J). 14.60 (978-1-57572-050-0(7)) Heinemann Library.

—What Is See Through? 1998. (What Is—? Ser.). (J). 14.60 (978-1-57572-051-7(5)) Heinemann Library.

—What Is Squishy? 1998. (What Is—? Ser.). (J). 14.60 (978-1-57572-048-7(5)) Heinemann Library.

—What Is Sticky? 1998. (What Is—? Ser.). (J). 14.60 (978-1-57572-052-4(3)) Heinemann Library.

Warm up to Science for Grade 5. 2005. spiral bd. (978-1-933049-16-8(2)) Region IV Education Service Ctr.

Warm up to Science for Grade 8. 2005. spiral bd. (978-1-933049-15-1(4)) Region IV Education Service Ctr.

Warm up to Science for Integrated Physics & Chemistry. 2005. spiral bd. (978-1-933049-14-4(6)) Region IV Education Service Ctr.

Warming up! Cooling Off! 6 Each of 1 Student Book, 6 vols. (Sunshinetm Science Ser.). 24p. (gr. 1-2). 41.95 (978-0-7802-1407-1(2)) Wright Group, The.

Warming up! Cooling Off! Big Book. (Sunshinetm Science Ser.). 24p. (gr. 1-2). 37.50 (978-0-7802-1408-8(0)) Wright Group, The.

Warthogs, 6 vols. (gr. 2-5). 36.95 (978-0-7368-8417-4(3)) Red Brick Learning.

Wasps, 6 vols. (gr. k-2). 28.95 (978-0-7368-9111-0(0)) Red Brick Learning.

Water Science, 6 vols. (gr. k-2). 28.95 (978-0-7368-1745-5(X) , Yellow Umbrella Bks.) Capstone Pr., Inc.

Watts Library, 8 bks. 2004. 64p. (J). (gr. 5-7). 192.00 (978-0-531-16711-3(9)) Scholastic Library Publishing.

Weiner, Esther. Twenty-Five Science Mini-Books. 1999. 72p. (J). (gr. k-4). pap. 9.95 (978-0-590-49507-3(0)) Scholastic, Inc.

Weird & Wacky Science, 6 bks., Set. (Illus.). (YA). (gr. 4-10). lib. bdg. 113.70 (978-0-89490-662-6(3)) Enslow Pubs., Inc.

Weird & Wonderful Wildlife, 12 vols., Set. 2002. (Junior Adventure Ser.). (Illus.). 32p. (J). (gr. 3 up). lib. bdg. (978-1-59084-240-9(5)) Mason Crest Pubs.

Weird Careers in Science. 2005. (Illus.). 64p. (gr. 4-8). pap. 175.00 (978-0-7910-9088-6(4) , Chelsea Hse.) Facts On File, Inc.

Weird Science. (Eyes on Adventure Ser.). 32p. (J). (gr. 1). pap. (978-1-882210-82-4(4)) Action Publishing, Inc.

Wells, Robert E. Como Se Mide el Tiempo? 2004. (SPA.). 176p. (J). 15.99 (978-84-261-3287-1(1)) Juventud, Editorial ESP. *Dist:* Lectorum Pubns., Inc.

—What's Older Than a Giant Tortoise? Wells, Robert E., illus. 2004. (Illus.). 32p. (J). (gr. 2-5). 15.95 (978-0-8075-8831-4(8)) Whitman, Albert & Co.

What? Where? Why?, 6 bks. Incl. Do French Fries Come from France? Randall, Ronne. lib. bdg. 20.67 (978-0-8368-3787-2(8)); What Makes Weather? Orme, Helen. lib. bdg. 20.67 (978-0-8368-3788-9(6)); What's So Good about Vegetables? Randall, Ronne. lib. bdg. 20.67 (978-0-8368-3789-6(4)); Why Do Plants Grow in Spring? Orme, Helen. lib. bdg. 20.67 (978-0-8368-3790-2(8)); Why Don't Worms Have Legs? Vaughan, Jenny. lib. bdg. 20.67 (978-0-8368-3791-9(6)); Why Is the Sun So Bright? Orme, Helen. lib. bdg. 20.67 (978-0-8368-3792-6(4)); 24p. (J). (gr. 1 up). (Illus.). 2003. Set lib. bdg. 124.02 (978-0-8368-3786-5(X)) Stevens, Gareth Inc.

What About, 24 bks., Set. 2001. (Illus.). (J). pap. (978-0-7398-5722-9(3)) Steck-Vaughn.

What Are Inclined Planes?, 6 vols. (gr. k-2). 28.95 (978-0-7368-9220-9(6)) Red Brick Learning.

What Are Levers?, 6 vols. (gr. k-2). 28.95 (978-0-7368-9221-6(4)) Red Brick Learning.

What Are Pulleys?, 6 vols. (gr. k-2). 28.95 (978-0-7368-9222-3(2)) Red Brick Learning.

What Are Screws?, 6 vols. (gr. k-2). 28.95 (978-0-7368-9223-0(0)) Red Brick Learning.

What Are Wedges?, 6 vols. (gr. k-2). 28.95 (978-0-7368-9224-7(9)) Red Brick Learning.

What Computers Do Science, 6 vols. (gr. k-2). 28.95 (978-0-7368-3018-8(9) , Yellow Umbrella Bks.) Capstone Pr., Inc.

What Goes into Bread? 6 Each of 1 Student Book, 6 vols. (Sunshinetm Science Ser.). 24p. (gr. 1-2). 41.95 (978-0-7802-2728-6(X)) Wright Group, The.

What Goes into Bread? Big Book. (Sunshinetm Science Ser.). 24p. (gr. 1-2). 37.50 (978-0-7802-2798-9(0)) Wright Group, The.

What Is an Insect? Science, 6 vols. (gr. k-2). 28.95 (978-0-7368-1744-8(1) , Yellow Umbrella Bks.) Capstone Pr., Inc.

What Is in Space? Science, 6 vols. (gr. k-2). 28.95 (978-0-7368-1741-7(7) , Yellow Umbrella Bks.) Capstone Pr., Inc.

What Is Rock? 6 Each of 1 Student Book, 6 vols. (Sunshinetm Science Ser.). 24p. (gr. 1-2). 41.95 (978-0-7802-2718-7(2)) Wright Group, The.

What Is Rock? Big Book. (Sunshinetm Science Ser.). 24p. (gr. 1-2). 37.50 (978-0-7802-2793-4(X)) Wright Group, The.

What Is Soil? 6 Each of 1 Student Book, 6 vols. (Sunshinetm Science Ser.). 24p. (gr. 1-2). 41.95 (978-0-7802-2722-4(0)) Wright Group, The.

What Is Soil? Big Book. (Sunshinetm Science Ser.). 24p. (gr. 1-2). 37.50 (978-0-7802-2795-8(6)) Wright Group, The.

What Is the Weather Today? 2005. (Emergent/Early (Prek-2) Science Package Ser.). 12p. (YA). (ps-2). 25.20 (978-0-8215-7839-1(1)) Sadlier, William H. Inc.

What Is this Skeleton?, 6 vols. (Sunshinetm Science Ser.). 24p. (gr. 1-2). 31.50 (978-0-7802-0298-6(8)); 36.95 (978-0-7802-0550-5(2)) Wright Group, The.

What Kind of Day Is It? Set. (gr. k-2). 172.95 (978-0-7368-9048-9(3)) Red Brick Learning.

What Kind of Sound? Science, 6 vols. (gr. k-2). 28.95 (978-0-7368-1742-4(5) , Yellow Umbrella Bks.) Capstone Pr., Inc.

What Makes Light?, 6 vols. (Sunshinetm Science Ser.). 24p. (gr. 1-2). 31.50 (978-0-7802-0304-4(6)); 36.95 (978-0-7802-0555-0(3)) Wright Group, The.

What Plants & Animals Need Set C, 6 vols. (Phonics Readers Ser.). (gr. k-2). 17.50 (978-0-7368-3215-1(7)) Red Brick Learning.

What will Float?, 6 vols. (Sunshinetm Science Ser.). 24p. (gr. 1-2). 31.50 (978-0-7802-0297-9(X)); 36.95 (978-0-7802-0548-2(0)) Wright Group, The.

Where Living Things Live Assessment Book: Unit 6: Living Things Live. 2000. (McGraw-Hill Science Ser.). (gr. 3 up). (978-0-02-277753-1(9)) Macmillan/McGraw-Hill Schl. Div.

Where Living Things Live Pupil Edition: Unit 6: Living Things Live. 2000. (McGraw-Hill Science Ser.). (gr. 3 up). (978-0-02-278213-9(3)) Macmillan/McGraw-Hill Schl. Div.

Where Living Things Live Teacher Resources for Practice & Support with Answer Key: Unit 6: Living Things Live. 2000. (McGraw-Hill Science Ser.). (gr. 3 up). (978-0-02-277634-3(6)) Macmillan/McGraw-Hill Schl. Div.

White, Nancy. Push, Pull, Play the Game: A Content Area Reader-science. 2005. (Sadlier Phonics Reading Program). (Illus.). 20p. (YA). (ps-2). 25.20 (978-0-8215-7815-5(4)) Sadlier, William H. Inc.

Who Builds? Science, 6 vols. (gr. k-2). 28.95 (978-0-7368-3001-0(4) , Yellow Umbrella Bks.) Capstone Pr., Inc.

Who Needs Plants? Science, 6 vols. (gr. k-2). 28.95 (978-0-7368-1751-6(4) , Yellow Umbrella Bks.) Capstone Pr., Inc.

Whose Baby Are You? 2003. (Science Card Games Ser.). (gr. k-1). 9.99 (978-0-7682-1973-9(6) , J53001) School Specialty Publishing.

Willis, Shirley. Dime por Que Es Mojada la Lluvia. 1999. (Coleccion los Estupendos). (SPA., Illus.). 32p. (J). (gr. 2-4). 20.00 (978-0-531-11849-8(5) , OD30029, Watts, Franklin) Scholastic Library Publishing.

—Dime por Que Es Mojada la Lluvia. 2000. (Estupendos Ser.). (J). 12.75 (978-0-606-20150-6(5)) Tandem Library Bks.

—Dime Que Tan Lejos Esta de Aqui. 1999. (Coleccion los Estupendos). (SPA., Illus.). 32p. (J). (gr. 2-4). 20.00 (978-0-531-11842-9(8) , OD30041, Watts, Franklin) Scholastic Library Publishing.

—Dime Que Tan Rapidamente Va. 1999. (Coleccion los Estupendos). (SPA., Illus.). 32p. (J). (gr. 2-4). 20.00 (978-0-531-11843-6(6) , OD30045, Watts, Franklin) Scholastic Library Publishing.

Willis, Tammy A. Super Science. Kirchner, Barbara, ed. 2007. (J). per. ***(978-1-57332-466-3(3))*** HighReach Learning, Inc.

Wolf, Cathrine, ed. Inside Space Jam. Date not set. 64p. (Orig.). (J). (gr. 4-8). pap. 3.95 (978-1-886749-19-1(1)) Sports Illustrated For Kids.

Wolf, Sophie. I Know How Seeds Grow. Wolf, Sophie, illus. 2001. (J). spiral bd. 6.00 (978-0-939195-29-9(1)) Parent Child Pr., Inc.

Wollard, Kathy & Solomon, Debra. El Libro de Los Porqués 2: Las Preguntas Mas Difíciles y Las Respuestas Mas Faciles Sobre Las Personas, Los Animales y Las Cosas. Solomon, Debra, tr. 2004. (SPA., Illus.). 208p. 28.99 (978-84-9754-047-6(6) , 87432) Ediciones Oniro S.A. ESP. *Dist:* Bilingual Pubns. Co., The, Lectorum Pubns., Inc.

Wonderful Ears: 6 Each of 1 Student Book, 6 vols. (Sunshinetm Science Ser.). 24p. (gr. 1-2). 41.95 (978-0-7802-1416-3(1)) Wright Group, The.

Wonderful Ears: Big Book. (Sunshinetm Science Ser.). 24p. (gr. 1-2). 37.50 (978-0-7802-1417-0(X)) Wright Group, The.

Wonderful Eyes, 6 vols. (Sunshinetm Science Ser.). 24p. (gr. 1-2). 37.50 (978-0-7802-1414-9(5)); 42.95 (978-0-7802-1413-2(7)) Wright Group, The.

Wonders of the World. (Eyes on Adventure Ser.). 32p. (J). (gr. 1). pap. (978-1-882210-65-7(4)) Action Publishing, Inc.

Words to Know Cards: Student & Teacher Support Resources. 2000. (McGraw-Hill Science Ser.). (gr. 3 up). (978-0-02-277897-2(7)); (gr. 4 up). (978-0-02-277898-9(5)); (gr. 5 up). (978-0-02-277899-6(3)) Macmillan/McGraw-Hill Schl. Div.

World Book, Inc. Staff. World Book's Young Scientist, 10 vols., Vol. 10. 2004. (Illus.). 1,280p. (gr. 3-8). pap., tchr. ed. 249.00 (978-0-7166-2750-0(7) , 60031) World Bk., Inc.

World Book, Inc. Staff, contrib. by. World Book's Science & Nature Guides, 12 vols. 2004. (World Book's Science & Nature Guides Ser.). (Illus.). 80p. (gr. 5-9). 319.00 (978-0-7166-4208-4(5) , SKU 30119) World Bk., Inc.

World Book, Inc. Staff, ed. Science Year in Review: 2000-2001. 2001. 352p. (978-0-7166-0553-9(8) , 20078) World Bk., Inc.

—The World Book Encyclopedia of Science. (YA). 2001. cd-rom (978-0-7166-3397-6(3)); set. 1999. (Illus.). 1223p. (gr. 6 up). (978-0-7166-3396-9(5)) World Bk., Inc.

—World Book's Young Scientist, 10 vols. 2000. (Illus.). 1280p. (J). (978-0-7166-2797-5(3)) World Bk., Inc.

World of Science. Date not set. (Illus.). 256p. (J). 12.98 (978-1-4054-1635-1(1)) Parragon, Inc.

Yellow Umbrella Books - Science: Animal Ears; Everyone Is a Scientist; Food for Thought; How Things Move; Let's Make Butter; Looking at Ants; Models; Seasons; Stars; The Water Cycle; What Grows from a Tree?; What Hatches?, 12 bks. 2001. (Illus.). (J). (gr. 1). lib. bdg. 175.20 (978-0-7368-0755-5(1) , Pebble Bks.) Capstone Pr., Inc.

Yellow Umbrella Books: Science, 12 bks. Incl. Animal Ears. Trumbauer, Lisa. 2000. lib. bdg. 14.60 (978-0-7368-0723-4(3)); Everyone Is a Scientist. Trumbauer, Lisa. 2000. lib. bdg. 14.60 (978-0-7368-0722-7(5)); Fast & Faster. Rubin, Alan. 2003. lib. bdg. 14.60 (978-0-7368-2018-9(3)); Food for Thought. Trumbauer, Lisa. 2000. lib. bdg. 14.60 (978-0-7368-0729-6(2)); How Things Move. Curry, Don L. 2000. lib. bdg. 14.60 (978-0-7368-0724-1(1)); Keeping Warm. Rubin, Alan. 2003. lib. bdg. 14.60 (978-0-7368-2019-6(1)); Let's Make Butter. Christian, Eleanor & Roth-Singer, Lyzz. 2000. lib. bdg. 14.60 (978-0-7368-0728-9(4)); Light & Shadow. Ring, Susan. 2003. lib. bdg. 14.60 (978-0-7368-2020-2(5)); Looking at Ants. Christian, Eleanor & Roth-Singer, Lyzz. 2000. lib. bdg. 14.60 (978-0-7368-0725-8(X)); Models. Schaefer, Lola M. 2000. lib. bdg. 14.60 (978-0-7368-0731-9(4)); Our Five Senses. Catala, Ellen. 2003. lib. bdg. 14.60 (978-0-7368-2021-9(3)); Seasons. Trumbauer, Lisa. 2000. lib. bdg. 14.60 (978-0-7368-0732-6(2)); Stars. Curry, Don L. 2000. lib. bdg. 14.60 (978-0-7368-0726-5(8)); Sun. Ring, Susan. 2003. lib. bdg. 14.60 (978-0-7368-2022-6(1)); Water Cycle. Curry, Don L. 2000. lib. bdg. 14.60 (978-0-7368-0727-2(6)); What Grows from a Tree? Schaefer, Lola M. 2000. lib. bdg. 14.60 (978-0-7368-0730-2(6)); What Hatches? Curry, Don L. 2000. lib. bdg. 14.60 (978-0-7368-0721-0(7)); Who Needs Plants? Trumbauer, Lisa. 2003. lib. bdg. 14.60 (978-0-7368-2023-3(X)); 16p. (J). (gr. 1). (Illus.). Set lib. bdg. 262.80 (978-0-7368-2033-2(7) , Pebble Bks.) Capstone Pr., Inc.

Yong, Tohmoh J., et al. Tune in CM1 Pupil's Workbook. 2007. pap., stu. ed. 1.13 (978-0-521-69596-1(1)) Cambridge Univ. Pr.

—Tune in CM1 Teacher's Book. 2007. pap., tchr. ed. 5.65 (978-0-521-69597-8(X)) Cambridge Univ. Pr.

—Tune in CM2 Pupil's Book. 2007. pap., stu. ed. 2.64 (978-0-521-69598-5(8)) Cambridge Univ. Pr.

Yoon, Paul. At the Amusement Park. 2005. (Illus.). 192p. (J). pap. 12.95 (978-981-05-2243-8(6)) Youngjin.com Publishing Co., Ltd. KOR. *Dist:* Transition Vendor.

You & Your Teeth. (Sunshinetm Science Ser.). 24p. (gr. 1-2). 37.50 (978-0-7802-1441-5(2)); Set. 41.95 (978-0-7802-1440-8(4)) Wright Group, The.

You Are a Scientist Science. (gr. k-2). 19.95 (978-0-7368-2904-5(0)) Red Brick Learning.

Young Explorers in Science. (J). 105.00 (978-0-8136-4363-2(5)) Modern Curriculum Pr.

Your Senses, 6 vols. (gr. k-2). 28.95 (978-0-7368-8596-6(X)) Red Brick Learning.

Zev, Marc, et al. 101 Things Everyone Should Know about Math. 2009. 128p. pap. 9.95 (978-0-9678020-3-9(2)) Science, Naturally!.

Zigzag Movement, 6 vols. (gr. k-2). 28.95 (978-0-7368-8618-5(4)) Red Brick Learning.

Los zorros del Desierto. 2000. (McGraw-Hill Ciencias Ser.). (ENG & SPA.). (gr. 3 up). (978-0-02-279638-9(X)) Macmillan/McGraw-Hill Schl. Div.

21st Century Science, 8 bks. Incl. Climate & the Environment. World Almanac Library Staff, contrib. by. 2002. lib. bdg. 32.67 (978-0-8368-5006-2(8)); Exploring the Universe. Fredette, Nathalie & Lafleur, Claude. 2001. lib. bdg. 32.67 (978-0-8368-5001-7(7)); Inside the Earth. Fredette, Nathalie & Lafleur, Claude. 2001. lib. bdg. 32.67 (978-0-8368-5002-4(5)); Major Systems of the Body. Gareth Stevens Publishing Staff, contrib. by. 2002. lib. bdg. 32.67 (978-0-8368-5007-9(6)); Our Planet Today. Fredette, Nathalie & Lafleur, Claude. 2001. lib. bdg. 32.67 (978-0-8368-5003-1(3)); Solar System & the Stars. Fredette, Nathalie & Lafleur, Claude. 2001. lib. bdg. 32.67 (978-0-8368-5004-8(1)); Structure of the Body. Gareth Stevens Publishing Staff, contrib. by. 2002. lib. bdg. 32.67 (978-0-8368-5008-6(4)); Understanding the Weather. World Almanac Library Staff, contrib. by. 2002. lib. bdg. 32.67 (978-0-8368-5009-3(2)); 64p. (J). (gr. 5 up). (Illus.). 2001. Set lib. bdg. 261.36 (978-0-8368-5367-4(9) , World Almanac Library) Stevens, Gareth Inc.

100 Things You Should Know About, 15 vols., Set. (Illus.). 48p. (gr. 3 up). lib. bdg. (978-1-59084-444-1(0)) Mason Crest Pubs.

1000 Things You Should Know About, 13 vols., Set. (Illus.). 64p. (gr. 3 up). lib. bdg. (978-1-59084-460-1(2)) Mason Crest Pubs.

SCIENCE—DATA PROCESSING

Allen-Conn, B. J. & Rose, Kim. Powerful Ideas in the Classroom Using Squeak to Enhance Math & Science Learning. 2003. (Illus.). 86p. per. (978-0-9743131-0-8(6)) Viewpoints Research Institute, Inc.

Group/McGraw-Hill, Wright. Caretakers of the Earth, 6 vols. (Book2WebTM Ser.). (gr. 4-8). 36.50 incl. 5.25 hd (978-0-322-04470-8(7)) Wright Group, The.

SCIENCE—DICTIONARIES

Allaby, Michael, et al. The New Encyclopedia of Science, 9 vols., Set. Allaby, Michael, ed. 2nd rev. ed. 2003. (Illus.). 1472p. (YA). (gr. 6 up). 399.00 (978-0-19-521918-0(X)) Oxford Univ. Pr., Inc.

American Heritage Dictionary Editors. The American Heritage Student Science Dictionary. 2002. (Illus.). 384p. (gr. 7-12). 18.00 (978-0-618-18919-9(X) , J-06390) Houghton Mifflin Co. Trade & Reference Div.

Berger, Melvin. Scholastic Science Dictionary. Bonner, Hannah, illus. 2000. 224p. (YA). (gr. 4 up). pap. 19.95 (978-0-590-31321-6(5) , Scholastic Reference) Scholastic, Inc.

Blachford, Stacey & McGrath, Kimberley A., contrib. by. The Gale Encyclopedia of Science, 6 vols., Vol. 1. 2nd ed. 2001. (Illus.). xviii, 4140p. (J). (978-0-7876-4371-3(8)) Thomson Gale.

Bruno, Leonard C. UXL Complete Life Science Resource. Carnagie, Julie L., ed. 2001. (Illus.). xxxvii, 608p. (J). Vol. 1. (978-0-7876-4852-7(3)); Vol. 2. (978-0-7876-4853-4(1)) Thomson Gale. (UXL).

Clark, John Owen Edward. The New Encyclopedia of Science, 9 vols. 2nd ed. 2003. (Illus.). (J). (978-0-19-521962-3(7)); (978-0-19-521963-0(5)); (978-0-19-521964-7(3)); (978-0-19-521965-4(1)); (978-0-19-521966-1(X)) Oxford Univ. Pr., Inc.

Craig, A. & Rosney, C. Science Encyclopedia. 2004. (Encyclopedias Ser.). (Illus.). 128p. (J). 7.95 (978-0-7945-0007-8(2)) EDC Publishing.

Delta science dictionary gr3-4 single Title. 2003. 64p. (J). (gr. 3-4). (978-1-59242-297-5(7)) Delta Education, LLC.

Delta science dictionary gr5-6 single Title. 2003. 80p. (J). (gr. 5-6). (978-1-59242-299-9(3)) Delta Education, LLC.

Dictionary of Science Words: Individual Title Six-Packs. (Discovery World Ser.). 24p. (gr. 1-2). 33.00 (978-0-7635-8482-5(7)) Rigby Education.

DK Publishing Staff, contrib. by. Encyclopedia of Science. 2006. (Illus.). 448p. (J). (***978-1-4287-0373-5(X)***) Dorling Kindersley Publishing, Inc.

Dorling Kindersley Publishing Staff. The Concise Encyclopedia of Science. 2000. (978-0-606-17805-1(8)) Tandem Library Bks.

—Encyclopedia of Science. 2006. (Illus.). 448p. (J). pap. 19.99 (978-0-7566-2220-6(4)) Dorling Kindersley Publishing, Inc.

—Online Encyclopedia: Science. 2nd ed. 2006. (Illus.). 384p. (J). pap. 19.99 (978-0-7566-2222-0(0)) Dorling Kindersley Publishing, Inc.

—Visual Encyclopedia of Science. 2005. (Illus.). 512p. (J). pap. 12.99 (978-0-7566-0700-5(0) , 1241879) Dorling Kindersley Publishing, Inc.

The Facts on File Science Dictionaries Set. 2005. (Science Dictionary Ser.). 240-496p. (gr. 9). 995.00 (978-0-8160-6321-5(4)) Facts On File, Inc.

Firth, Rachel. First Encyclopedia of Science. 2004. (First Encyclopedias Ser.). (Illus.). 64p. (J). (gr. 3 up). pap. 9.99 (978-0-7945-0273-7(3) , Usborne); lib. bdg. 17.95 (978-1-58086-472-5(4)) EDC Publishing.

—Little Encyclopedia of Science - Internet Linked. 2005. 64p. (J). 6.99 (978-0-7945-1095-4(7) , Usborne) EDC Publishing.

Firth, Rachel, et al. The Usborne First Encyclopedia of Science. Hancock, David, illus. 2002. 64p. (J). (978-0-439-56059-7(4)) Scholastic, Inc.

Ganeri, Anita. The Little Science Encyclopedia. 2001. (Kingfisher Little Encyclopedias Ser.). (Illus.). 112p. (J). (gr. k-3). pap. 11.95 (978-0-7534-5402-2(5) , Kingfisher) Houghton Mifflin Co. Trade & Reference Div.

—Little Science Encyclopedia. 2001. (gr. k-3). lib. bdg. 21.05 (978-0-613-90911-2(9)) Tandem Library Bks.

Grolier Educational Staff, contrib. by. Computers & the Internet, 12 vols., Vol. 10. 2001. (J). (978-0-7172-5605-1(7) , Grolier) Scholastic Library Publishing.

—Earth & Space, 12 vols., Vol. 9. 2001. (J). (978-0-7172-5604-4(9) , Grolier) Scholastic Library Publishing.

—Earthquakes & Volcanoes, 12 vols., Vol. 11. 2001. (J). (978-0-7172-5606-8(5) , Grolier) Scholastic Library Publishing.

—Electricity & Magnetism, 12 vols., Vol. 8. 2001. (J). (978-0-7172-5603-7(0) , Grolier) Scholastic Library Publishing.

—Elements, 12 vols., Vol. 2. 2001. (J). (978-0-7172-5597-9(2) , Grolier) Scholastic Library Publishing.

—Forces, 12 vols., Vol. 4. 2001. (J). (978-0-7172-5599-3(9) , Grolier) Scholastic Library Publishing.

—Heat & Energy, 12 vols., Vol. 12. 2001. (J). (978-0-7172-5607-5(3) , Grolier) Scholastic Library Publishing.

—Light & Sound, 12 vols., Vol. 5. 2001. (J). (978-0-7172-5600-6(6) , Grolier) Scholastic Library Publishing.

—Plants, 12 vols., Vol. 7. 2001. (J). (978-0-7172-5602-0(2) , Grolier) Scholastic Library Publishing.

—Rocks, Minerals, & Soil, 12 vols., Vol. 3. 2001. (J). (978-0-7172-5598-6(0) , Grolier) Scholastic Library Publishing.

—Visual Science Encyclopedia, 12 vols. Incl. Vol. 1. Weather. (978-0-7172-5596-2(4)); Vol. 2. Elements. (978-0-7172-5597-9(2)); Vol. 3. Rocks, Minerals, & Soil. (978-0-7172-5598-6(0)); Vol. 4. Forces. (978-0-7172-5599-3(9)); Vol. 5. Light & Sound. (978-0-7172-5600-6(6)); Vol. 6. Water. (978-0-7172-5601-3(4)); Vol. 7. Plants. (978-0-7172-5602-0(2)); Vol. 8. Electricity & Magnetism. (978-0-7172-5603-7(0)); Vol. 9. Earth & Space. (978-0-7172-5604-4(9)); Vol. 10. Computers & the Internet. (978-0-7172-5605-1(7)); Vol. 11. Earthquakes & Volcanoes. (978-0-7172-5606-8(5)); Vol. 12. Heat & Energy. (978-0-7172-5607-5(3)); (J). 576p. 2001. 279.00 (978-0-7172-5595-5(6) , Grolier) Scholastic Library Publishing.

—Water, 12 vols., Vol. 6. 2001. (J). (978-0-7172-5601-3(4) , Grolier) Scholastic Library Publishing.

—Weather, 12 vols., Vol. 1. 2001. (J). (978-0-7172-5596-2(4) , Grolier) Scholastic Library Publishing.

Holt, Rinehart and Winston Staff. Holt Science & Technology. 5th ed. 2003. (Illus.). 75.80 (978-0-03-066476-2(4)); 75.80 (978-0-03-066478-6(0)); 75.80 (978-0-03-066481-6(0)) Holt, Rinehart & Winston.

—Holt Science & Technology: Custom Edition - C, F & K. 2nd ed. 2003. (Illus.). 62.66 (978-0-03-036086-2(2)) Holt, Rinehart & Winston.

—Holt Science & Technology: Custom Edition - E, H-I & M. 2nd ed. 2003. (Illus.). 75.40 (978-0-03-036199-9(0)) Holt, Rinehart & Winston.

—Holt Science & Technology: Custom Edition - F, I & K-M. 2nd ed. 2003. (Illus.). (J). 86.00 (978-0-03-036084-8(6)) Holt, Rinehart & Winston.

—Holt Science & Technology: Custom Edition - H-J & O. 2nd ed. 2003. (Illus.). 75.40 (978-0-03-036198-2(2)) Holt, Rinehart & Winston.

—Holt Science & Technology: Custom Edition, C-D & K-L. 2nd ed. 2003. (Illus.). (J). 75.40 (978-0-03-036083-1(8)) Holt, Rinehart & Winston.

—Holt Science & Technology: Online Edition Upgrade. 2nd ed. 2003. Level I. 10.60 (978-0-03-037203-2(8)); Level I. 2.60 (978-0-03-037246-9(1)); Level L. 10.60 (978-0-03-037207-0(0)); Level L. 2.60 (978-0-03-037249-0(6)); Level C. 10.60 (978-0-03-037196-7(1)); Level C. 2.60 (978-0-03-037238-4(0)); Level D. 10.60 (978-0-03-037197-4(X)); Level D. 2.60 (978-0-03-037239-1(9)); Level M. 10.60 (978-0-03-037208-7(9)); Level M. 2.60 (978-0-03-037251-3(8)); Level A. 10.60 (978-0-03-037193-6(7)); Level A. 2.60 (978-0-03-037236-0(4)); Level B. 10.60 (978-0-03-037194-3(5)); Level B. 2.60 (978-0-03-037237-7(2)); Level E. 10.60 (978-0-03-037198-1(8)); Level E. 2.60 (978-0-03-037241-4(0)); Level F. 10.60 (978-0-03-037199-8(6)); Level F. 2.60 (978-0-03-037242-1(9)); Level G. 10.60 (978-0-03-037201-8(1)); Level H. 10.60 (978-0-03-037202-5(X)); Level H. 2.60 (978-0-03-037244-5(5)); Level J. 10.60 (978-0-03-037204-9(6)); Level J. 2.60 (978-0-03-037247-6(X)); Level K. 10.60 (978-0-03-037206-3(2)); Level K. 2.60 (978-0-03-037248-3(8)); Level N. 10.60 (978-0-03-037209-4(7)); Level N. 2.60 (978-0-03-037252-0(6)); Level O. 10.60 (978-0-03-037211-7(9)); Level O. 2.60 (978-0-03-037253-7(4)) Holt, Rinehart & Winston.

How It Works: Science & Technology, 20 vols. 3rd ed. 2003. (J). (978-0-7614-7315-2(7)); (978-0-7614-7316-9(5)); (978-0-7614-7317-6(3)); (978-0-7614-7318-3(1)); (978-0-7614-7319-0(X)); (978-0-7614-7320-6(3)); (978-0-7614-7321-3(1)); (978-0-7614-7322-0(X)); (978-0-7614-7323-7(8)); (978-0-7614-7324-4(6)); (978-0-7614-7325-1(4)); (978-0-7614-7326-8(2)); (978-0-7614-7327-5(0)); (978-0-7614-7328-2(9)); (978-0-7614-7329-9(7)); (978-0-7614-7330-5(0)); (978-0-7614-7331-2(9)); (978-0-7614-7332-9(7)); (978-0-7614-7333-6(5)); (978-0-7614-7346-6(7)) Cavendish, Marshall Corp.

Illingworth, Valerie. Penguin Dictionary of Physics. 2000. (gr. 7-12). lib. bdg. 26.90 (978-0-613-64994-0(X)) Tandem Library Bks.

Jugendhandbuch Naturwissen: Bausteine des Lebens, 6 vols., Vol. 1. (GER.). 144p. (J). pap. 750.00 (978-3-499-16203-9(2) , M-7486) French & European Pubns., Inc.

Kingfisher Editors & Taylor, Charles, eds. The Kingfisher Science Encyclopedia. 2006. (Illus.). 496p. (J). (gr. 5-9). 24.95 (978-0-7534-5886-0(1) , Kingfisher) Houghton Mifflin Co. Trade & Reference Div.

Larousse Mexico Staff, ed. Mi Primer Larousse de las Ciencias de la vida y de las Tierra. 2006. (Mi Primer Larousse Ser.). 160p. (gr. k-3). 19.95 (978-970-22-1231-7(6)) Larousse, Ediciones, S. A. de C. V. MEX. *Dist:* Houghton Mifflin Co. Trade & Reference Div.

McGrath, Kimberley A. & Blachford, Stacey. The Gale Encyclopedia of Science, 6 vols. 2nd ed. 2001. (Illus.). xviii, 4140p. (J). Vol. 2. (978-0-7876-4372-0(6)); Vol. 3. (978-0-7876-4373-7(4)); Vol. 4. (978-0-7876-4374-4(2)); Vol. 5. (978-0-7876-4375-1(0)); Vol. 6. (978-0-7876-4376-8(9)) Thomson Gale.

Myers, Jack. What Happened to the Mammoths? And Other Explorations of Science in Action. Rice, John, illus. 2004. 64p. (YA). (gr. 4-6). 17.95 (978-1-56397-801-2(6)) Boyds Mills Pr.

Nagel, Rob. U-X-L Encyclopedia of Science Vol. 1: A - As, 10 vols. 2nd ed. 2001. (Illus.). (J). (978-0-7876-5433-7(7) , UXL) Thomson Gale.

—U-X-L Encyclopedia of Science Vol. 2: At - Car, 10 vols. 2nd ed. 2001. (Illus.). (J). (978-0-7876-5434-4(5) , UXL) Thomson Gale.

—U-X-L Encyclopedia of Science Vol. 3: Cat - Cy, 10 vols. 2nd ed. 2001. (Illus.). (J). (978-0-7876-5435-1(3) , UXL) Thomson Gale.

—U-X-L Encyclopedia of Science Vol. 5: En - G, 10 vols. 2nd ed. 2001. (Illus.). (J). (978-0-7876-5437-5(X) , UXL) Thomson Gale.

—U-X-L Encyclopedia of Science Vol. 6: H- Mar, 10 vols. 2nd ed. 2001. (Illus.). (J). (978-0-7876-5438-2(8) , UXL) Thomson Gale.

—U-X-L Encyclopedia of Science Vol. 7: Mas - O, 10 vols. 2nd ed. 2001. (Illus.). (J). (978-0-7876-5439-9(6) , UXL) Thomson Gale.

—U-X-L Encyclopedia of Science Vol. 8: P - Ra, 10 vols. 2nd ed. 2001. (Illus.). (J). (978-0-7876-5440-5(X) , UXL) Thomson Gale.

—U-X-L Encyclopedia of Science Vol. 9: Re - St, 10 vols. 2nd ed. 2001. (Illus.). (J). (978-0-7876-5441-2(8) , UXL) Thomson Gale.

—U-X-L Encyclopedia of Science Vol. 10: Su - Z, 10 vols. 2nd ed. 2001. (Illus.). (J). (978-0-7876-5775-8(1) , UXL) Thomson Gale.

The New Book of Popular Science 2008, 6 vols., Set. 2008. (YA). (gr. 7-12). lib. bdg. 299.00 (***978-0-7172-1226-2(2)***) Scholastic Library Publishing.

O'Daly, Anne. Encyclopedia of Life Sciences, 13 vols. 2nd ed. 2004. (Illus.). (***978-0-7614-7443-2(9)); (978-0-7614-7444-9(7)); (978-0-7614-7445-6(5)); (978-0-7614-7446-3(3)); (978-0-7614-7447-0(1)); (978-0-7614-7448-7(X)); (978-0-7614-7449-4(8)); (978-0-7614-7450-0(1)); (978-0-7614-7451-7(X)); (978-0-7614-7452-4(8)); (978-0-7614-7453-1(6)); (978-0-7614-7454-8(4)); (978-0-7614-7455-5(2)***) Cavendish, Marshall Corp.

Oxlade, C. Illustrated Dictionary of Science. rev. ed. 2007. (Illustrated Dictionaries Ser.). 382p. (J). 29.99 (***978-0-7945-1847-9(8)*** , Usborne) EDC Publishing.

Oxlade, Chris. Illustrated Dictionary of Science. 2004. (Illustrated Dictionaries Ser.). (Illus.). 382p. (J). lib. bdg. 37.95 (978-1-58086-363-6(9)) EDC Publishing.

Pickett, Joseph P. & American Heritage Dictionary Editors, eds. The American Heritage Children's Science Dictionary. 2003. (Illus.). 288p. (gr. 4-6). 17.95 (978-0-618-35401-6(8)) Houghton Mifflin Co. Trade & Reference Div.

Popular Science Magazine Staff. Popular Science: Almanac for Kids. rev. ed. 2004. (Illus.). 256p. (J). pap. 11.99 (978-1-931933-69-8(3)) Time, Inc. Home Entertainment.

Priddy, Roger. My Big Science Book: Simple, Fun Experiments for All Young Scientists. rev. ed. 2004. (Smart Kids Ser.). (Illus.). 80p. (J). 14.95 (978-0-312-49176-5(X) , Priddy Bks.) St. Martin's Pr.

Rigby Education Staff. Discovery World Red Dictionary. (Discovery World Ser.). (Illus.). 12p. (gr. 1-2). 31.00 (978-0-7635-2707-5(6)) Rigby Education.

Rogers, Kirsteen. Human Body. 2002. (gr. 3-6). lib. bdg. 18.75 (978-0-613-75096-7(9)) Tandem Library Bks.

—Usborne Internet-Linked Science Encyclopedia. 2003. (gr. 3-6). lib. bdg. 30.35 (978-0-613-86942-3(7)) Tandem Library Bks.

Scarborough & Moyle. Mi Primera Enciclopedia de las Ciencias. 2000. (My First Encyclopedias Ser.).Tr. of My First Encyclopedia of Science. (SPA., Illus.). 40p. (J). 19.95 (978-84-488-0513-5(5)) Beascoa, Ediciones S.A. ESP. *Dist:* Distribooks, Inc.

Scholastic Library Publishing Staff, contrib. by. The New Book of Popular Science, 6 vols., Set. 2006. (Illus.). (J). (gr. 7-12). 279.00 (978-0-7172-1225-5(4) , Grolier) Scholastic Library Publishing.

Serres. Dictionary of the Sciences. 2002. (Illus.). 1100p. (978-0-12-637245-8(4) , Academic Pr.) Elsevier Science & Technology Bks.

Steck-Vaughn Staff. Rise: With '99 Annual & Macintosh, 25 vols., set. 1999. (Illus.). (J). pap. 692.81 incl. cd-rom (978-0-7398-1844-2(9)) Raintree.

—Rise: With '99 Annual & Windows, 25 vols., set. 1999. (Illus.). (J). pap. 692.81 incl. cd-rom (978-0-7398-1845-9(7)) Raintree.

Stockley, Corinne, et al. The Usborne Illustrated Dictionary of Science: A Complete Reference Guide to Physics, Chemistry & Biology. Rogers, Kirsteen, ed. Smith, G. & Chen, Kuo Kang, trs. 2004. (Illustrated Dictionaries Ser.). (Illus.). 382p. (J). pap. 29.95 (978-0-7945-0064-1(1) , Usborne) EDC Publishing.

—The Usborne Illustrated Dictionary of Science: Physics, Chemistry & Biology Facts. 1998. (Illus.). 384p. (YA). (gr. 7-11). lib. bdg. 32.95 (978-1-58086-025-3(7)) EDC Publishing.

Tachell, Judy. Science Encyclopedia. 2004. (Library of Science Ser.). (Illus.). 448p. (J). pap. 19.99 (978-0-7945-0331-4(4) , Usborne) EDC Publishing.

Tatchell, Judy. Science Encyclopedia. 2004. (Library of Science Ser.). (Illus.). 448p. (J). (gr. 4 up). 39.95 (978-0-7460-3833-8(X)); lib. bdg. 47.95 (978-1-58086-337-7(X)) EDC Publishing.

Usborne Books Staff, ed. The Usborne Illustrated Dictionary of Science: A Complete Reference Guide to Physics, Chemistry & Biology. rev. ed. 1999. (Illustrated Dictionaries Ser.). (Illus.). 384p. (YA). (gr. 7 up). lib. bdg. 37.95 (978-1-58086-224-0(1)) EDC Publishing.

Ward, Brian R. First Fun Science Encyclopedia. 2003. (Illus.). 48p. (J). (gr. 3 up). lib. bdg. (978-1-59084-554-7(4)) Mason Crest Pubs.

World Book, Inc. Staff. The World Book Encyclopedia of Science, 8 vols., Set. 1999. (Illus.). 1223p. (YA). (gr. 6-12). 189.00 (978-0-7166-3394-5(9) , 1380) World Bk., Inc.

World Book, Inc. Staff, ed. The World Book Encyclopedia of Science. (YA). 2001. cd-rom (978-0-7166-3397-6(3)); set. 1999. (Illus.). 1223p. (gr. 6 up). (978-0-7166-3396-9(5)) World Bk., Inc.

—World Book Encyclopedia of Science, 8 vols., Vol. 8. 2001. (Illus.). 12p. (J). (gr. 6 up). incl. cd-rom (978-0-7166-3358-7(2) , 60040) World Bk., Inc.

S

SCIENCE—EXPERIMENTS

see also Science Projects

see also particular branches of science with the subdivision Experiments, e.g. Chemistry—Experiments, etc.

Abruscato, Joseph. Whizbangers & Wonderments: Science Activities for Children. 1999. (Illus.). 312p. (C). pap. 34.40 (978-0-205-28409-2(4)) Allyn & Bacon, Inc.

Adams, Richard C. Ideas for Science Projects. rev. ed. 1998. (Experimental Science Ser.). 128p. (YA). (gr. 8-12). pap. 9.95 (978-0-531-15882-1(9) , Watts, Franklin) Scholastic Library Publishing.

Adams, Richard C. & Gardner, Robert. Energy Projects for Young Scientists. rev. ed. 2003. (Project for Young Scientists Ser.). (Illus.). 160p. (YA). (gr. 9-12). pap. 9.95 (978-0-531-16380-1(6) , Watts, Franklin) Scholastic Library Publishing.

Adams, Richard C. & Goodwin, Peter. Physics Projects for Young Scientists. 2000. (Projects for Young Scientists Ser.). (Illus.). 128p. (YA). (gr. 9-12). rev. ed. 23.50 (978-0-531-11667-8(0)); 2nd rev. ed. pap. 6.95 (978-0-531-16461-7(6)) Scholastic Library Publishing. (Watts, Franklin).

Andrews, Georgina & Knighton, Kate. 100 Science Experiments - Internet Linked. 2006. 96p. (J). 15.99 (978-0-7945-1076-3(0)) EDC Publishing.

—(100 Science Experiments) - Spanish. 2006. 96p. (J). 15.99 (978-0-7460-7408-4(5) , Usborne) EDC Publishing.

Angliss, Sarah. Electricity & Magnets. Le Jars, David, illus. 2001. (Hands-On Science Ser.). 40p. (J). (gr. 3-5). pap. 6.95 (978-0-7534-5349-0(5) , Kingfisher) Houghton Mifflin Co. Trade & Reference Div.

—Electricity & Magnets. 2001. (Hands-On Science Ser.). (Illus.). (J). 13.75 (978-0-606-21172-7(1)) Tandem Library Bks.

Angliss, Sarah & Graham, John. Force & Motion, Sound & Light, Electricity & Magnets, Matter & Materials. Le Jars, David, illus. 2002. (Hands-On Ser.). 160p. (J). (gr. 3-5). pap. 12.95 (978-0-7534-5440-4(8) , Kingfisher) Houghton Mifflin Co. Trade & Reference Div.

Ardley, Neil. The Science Book of Hot & Cold. 1998. (Illus.). (978-0-8172-9801-2(0)) Steck-Vaughn.

—101 Great Science Experiments. 120p. (J). 2006. pap. 7.99 (978-0-7566-1918-3(1)); 2000. (Illus.). (gr. 4-7). 18.00 (978-0-7894-4921-4(8)) Dorling Kindersley Publishing, Inc.

Armentrout, David & Armentrout, Patricia. Una Cuna. 2002. (Como Podemos Utilizar Maquinas Simples? Ser.). (SPA.), (J). 26.60 (978-1-58952-438-5(1)) Rourke Publishing, LLC.

—A Lever. 2003. (How Can I Experiment with Simple Machines? Ser.). (Illus.). 32p. (gr. 1-4). 19.95 (978-1-58952-334-0(2)) Rourke Publishing, LLC.

—Un Plano Inclinado. 2002. (Como Podemos Utilizar Maquinas Simples? Ser.). (SPA.). (J). 26.60 (978-1-58952-434-7(9)) Rourke Publishing, LLC.

—A Pulley. 2003. (How Can I Experiment with Simple Machines? Ser.). (Illus.). 32p. (gr. 1-4). 19.95 (978-1-58952-335-7(0)) Rourke Publishing, LLC.

—A Screw. 2003. (How Can I Experiment with Simple Machines? Ser.). (Illus.). 32p. (gr. 1-4). 19.95 (978-1-58952-336-4(9)) Rourke Publishing, LLC.

—Un Tornillo. 2002. (Como Podemos Utilizar Maquinas Simples? Ser.). (SPA.). (J). 26.60 (978-1-58952-437-8(3)) Rourke Publishing, LLC.

—A Wedge. 2003. (How Can I Experiment with Simple Machines? Ser.). (Illus.). 32p. (gr. 1-4). 19.95 (978-1-58952-337-1(7)) Rourke Publishing, LLC.

Arner, Elizabeth. Weather Detectives. 2004. (Illus.). (J). (gr. 4-6). 40.00 (978-1-57336-404-1(5) , I2065) Interaction Pubs., Inc.

Barber, Jacqueline, et al. Dry Ice Investigations. Stone, Florence et al, eds. Bevilacqua, Carol et al, illus. Hoyt, Richard et al, photos by. 1999. (Great Explorations in Math & Science Ser.). 212p. (YA). (gr. 6-8). pap. 21.00 (978-0-924886-15-7(3) , GEMS) Univ. of California, Berkeley, Lawrence Hall of Science.

Bardhan-Quallen, Sudipta. Last-Minute Science Fair Projects: When Your Bunsen's Not Burning but the Clock's Really Ticking. 2006. (Illus.). 112p. (J). 19.95 (978-1-4027-1690-4(7) , 1262284) Sterling Publishing Co., Inc.

Bartholomew, Alan. Electric Mischief: Battery-Powered Gadgets Kids Can Build. Bartholomew, Lynn, illus. 2004. (Kids Can Do It Ser.). 48p. (J). (gr. 4-6). (978-1-55074-925-0(0)); (978-1-55074-923-6(4)) Kids Can Pr., Ltd.

—Electric Mischief: Battery-Powered Gadgets Kids Can Build. 2002. (gr. 3-6). lib. bdg. 14.10 (978-0-613-67883-4(4)) Tandem Library Bks.

Batson, Ernie & Batson, Mary. A Handful of Lightning. 1999. (Illus.). 53p. (J). (gr. k-6). spiral bd. 15.95 (978-0-9702880-2-8(6)) Sun R.A.Y.S., LLC.

Beck, Esther. Cool Odor Decoders: Fun Science Projects about Smells. 2007. (Cool Science Ser.). (Illus.). 32p. (J). (gr. k-6). lib. bdg. 24.21 (***978-1-59928-909-0(1)*** , Checkerboard Library) ABDO Publishing Co.

—Cool Sensory Suspense: Fun Science Projects about the Senses. 2007. (Cool Science Ser.). (Illus.). 32p. (J). (gr. k-6). lib. bdg. 24.21 (***978-1-59928-910-6(5)*** , Checkerboard Library) ABDO Publishing Co.

—Cool Spy Supplies: Fun Top Secret Science Projects. 2007. (Cool Science Ser.). (Illus.). 32p. (J). (gr. k-6). lib. bdg. 24.21 (***978-1-59928-911-3(3)*** , Checkerboard Library) ABDO Publishing Co.

Belvins, Wiley. You Can Use a Magnifying Glass. 2004. (Rookie Read-About Science Ser.). (Illus.). 31p. (J). (gr. 1-2). pap. 4.95 (978-0-516-27328-0(0) , Children's Pr.) Scholastic Library Publishing.

Bennett, Andrea T. & Kessler, James H. Apples, Bubbles, & Crystals: Your Science ABCs. Sarecky, Melody, illus. 2004. (J). (978-0-8412-3944-9(4)) American Chemical Society.

Bingham, Jane. El Libro de los Experimentos Cientificos. (SPA., Illus.). (YA). (gr. 5-8). pap. (978-950-724-263-2(5) , LMA8241) Lumen ARG. *Dist:* Lectorum Pubns., Inc.

Bittinger, Gayle. Investigation Station. Barr, Marilynn G., illus. 1998. (Kinderstation Ser.). 160p. (J). pap. 15.95 (978-1-57029-190-6(X) , WPH 04504, Totline Pubns.) Schaffer, Frank Pubns.

Blakey, Nancy. Lotions, Potions, & Slime: Mudpies & More! Watts, Melissah, illus. 2004. 120p. (J). (ps-7). 9.95 (978-1-883672-21-8(X) , Tricycle Pr.) Ten Speed Pr.

Blobaum, Cindy. Geology Rocks! 50 Hands-On Activities to Explore the Earth. 1999. (Kaleidoscope Kids Bks.). (Illus.). 96p. (J). (gr. 2-8). pap. 12.95 (978-1-885593-29-0(5) , Williamson Bks.) Ideals Pubns.

Bombaugh, Ruth. Science Fair Success. exp. rev. ed. 1999. (Science Fair Success Ser.). (Illus.). 128p. (YA). (gr. 6-12). lib. bdg. 26.60 (978-0-7660-1163-2(1)) Enslow Pubs., Inc.

Bradley, Kimberly Brubaker. Pop! A Book about Bubbles. 2001. (gr. k-3). lib. bdg. 13.00 (978-0-613-49346-8(X)) Tandem Library Bks.

Brandolini, Anita J. Fizz, Bubble & Flash! Element Explorations & Atom Adventures for Hands-On Science Fun! 2004. (Kids Can Bks.). (Illus.). 128p. (J). pap. 12.95 (978-1-885593-83-2(X) , Williamson Bks.) Ideals Pubns.

Branzei, Sylvia. Hands-on Grossology. 2003. (gr. 3-6). lib. bdg. 14.15 (978-0-613-67550-5(9)) Tandem Library Bks.

Brunelle, Lynn. Pop Bottle Science. Meisel, Paul, illus. 2004. 128p. (J). pap. 14.95 (978-0-7611-2980-6(4) , 12980) Workman Publishing Co., Inc.

Bryant-Mole, Karen & Ansary, Mir Tamim. Floating & Sinking. 2002. (Illus.). 24p. (J). (gr. 1-3). pap. 6.50 (978-1-4034-0049-9(0) , 91493) Heinemann Library.

—Hot & Cold. 2002. (Illus.). 24p. (J). (gr. 1-3). pap. 6.50 (978-1-4034-0051-2(2) , 91495) Heinemann Library.

—Magnets. 2002. (Science All Around Me Ser.). (Illus.). 24p. (J). (gr. 1-3). pap. 6.50 (978-1-4034-0052-9(0) , 91496) Heinemann Library.

Brynie, Faith Hickman. Six-Minute Nature Experiments. Whittingham, Kim, illus. 2006. 80p. (J). (gr. 4-8). reprint ed. pap. 11.00 (978-1-4223-5105-5(X)) DIANE Publishing Co.

Burke. Think Like a Scientist. 1999. (Illus.) (J). pap. 5.65 (978-0-7398-0863-4(X)) Steck-Vaughn.

Buttitta, Hope. It's Not Magic, It's Science! 50 Science Tricks that Mystify, Dazzle & Astound. La Baff, Tom & Lundgren, Orrin, illus. 2007. 80p. pap. 7.95 (978-1-57990-883-6(7)) Lark Bks.

Buttitta, Hope P. It's Not Magic, It's Science! 50 Science Tricks That Mystify, Dazzle & Astound! 2005. (Illus.). 80p. 14.95 (978-1-57990-622-1(2)) Lark Bks.

Capeci, Anne. Now You See It! 2002. (Mad Science Ser.: No. 2). 96p. (J). (gr. 3-7). pap. 4.50 (978-0-439-22857-2(3)) Scholastic, Inc.

—Now You See It! 2002. (gr. 3-6). lib. bdg. 12.40 (978-0-613-81719-6(2)) Tandem Library Bks.

Castaldo, Nancy F. Rainy Day Play: Explore, Create, Discover, Pretend. 2005. (Illus.). 144p. (J). pap. 12.95 (978-1-55652-563-6(X)) Chicago Review Pr., Inc.

Chahrour, Janet Parks. Zap! Blink! Taste! Think! Exciting Life Science for Curious Minds. Gurvin, Abe, illus. 2003. 200p. (J). (gr. 5-10). pap. 14.95 (978-0-7641-1912-5(5)) Barron's Educational Series, Inc.

Chickadee Magazine Editors & Penrose, Gordon. Science Fun: Hands-On Science with Dr. Zed. 1998. (Illus.). 80p. (J). (ps-3). pap. 12.95 (978-1-895688-74-0(4)) Firefly Bks., Ltd.

Church, Jok. El Mundo de Beakman y Jax: Experimentos Divertidos; Mas Experimentos Divertidos, 2 vols. Clark, Gerardo Hernandez, tr. 2002. (SPA.). 127p. pap. (978-970-643-415-9(1)) Selector, S.A. de C.V. MEX. *Dist:* Lectorum Pubns., Inc.

Churchill, E. Richard. 365 Super Science Experiments with Everyday Materials. 2001. (gr. 3-6). lib. bdg. 22.20 (978-0-613-75606-8(1)); (978-0-606-22740-7(7)) Tandem Library Bks.

Ciencia con Todo: Experimentos Simples con las Cosas Que Nos Rodean. (Coleccion Pura Ciencia).Tr. of Everyday Science. (SPA.). (YA). (gr. 5-8). pap. 9.56 (978-950-24-0746-3(6)) Albatros ARG. *Dist:* Lectorum Pubns., Inc.

Ciencia en Segundos: Experimentos Que Puedes Hacer en 10 Minutos o Menos.Tr. of Science in Seconds. (SPA.). (YA). (gr. 5-8). pap. 9.56 (978-950-24-0748-7(2)) Albatros ARG. *Dist:* Lectorum Pubns., Inc.

Ciencia Magica: Experimentos Extranos y Asombrosos. (SPA.). (YA). (gr. 5-8). pap. (978-950-24-0747-0(4)) Albatros ARG. *Dist:* Lectorum Pubns., Inc.

Clarke, Silvana. Back-to-Nature Science Experiments. 2001. (Mother Nature's Ser.). (Illus.). 64p. (J). (gr. 3-7). pap. 6.95 (978-0-7373-0338-4(7) , 03387W) Lowell Hse.

Cleland, JoAnn. I Can Make Colors. 2007. (J). (978-1-59515-925-0(8)) Rourke Publishing, LLC.

Cobb, Allan B. Super Science Projects about Animals in Their Habitats. 2005. (Psyched for Science Ser.). (Illus.). 48p. (YA). (gr. 5-8). lib. bdg. 23.95 (978-0-8239-3175-0(7) , SCADHO) Rosen Publishing Group, Inc., The.

—Super Science Projects about Energy & Motion. 2005. (Psyched for Science Ser.). (Illus.). 48p. (YA). (gr. 5-8). lib. bdg. 23.95 (978-0-8239-3176-3(1) , SCENMO) Rosen Publishing Group, Inc., The.

—Super Science Projects about Oceans. 2005. (Psyched for Science Ser.). (Illus.). 48p. (YA). (gr. 5-8). lib. bdg. 23.95 (978-0-8239-3174-3(9) , SCOCEA) Rosen Publishing Group, Inc., The.

—Super Science Projects about Sound. 2005. (Psyched for Science Ser.). (Illus.). 48p. (YA). (gr. 5-8). lib. bdg. 23.95 (978-0-8239-3176-7(5) , SCSOUN) Rosen Publishing Group, Inc., The.

Cobb, Vicki. I Face the Wind. Gorton, Julia, illus. 2003. (Science Play Ser.). 40p. (J). (ps-k). 15.99 (978-0-688-17840-6(5)); lib. bdg. 16.89 (978-0-688-17841-3(3)) HarperCollins Pubs.

—See for Yourself: More Than 100 Experiments for Science Fairs & Projects. Klug, Dave, illus. 2001. 192p. (gr. 4-7). (J). pap. 16.95 (978-0-439-09010-0(5)); (YA). pap. 7.95 (978-0-439-09011-7(3)) Scholastic, Inc. (Scholastic Reference).

—See for Yourself: More Than 100 Experiments for Science Fairs & Projects. 2001. (Illus.). (J). (978-0-606-21585-5(9)) Tandem Library Bks.

—Sources of Forces: Science Fun with Force Fields. Haefele, Steve, illus. 2002. (Science Fun with Vicki Cobb Ser.). 48p. (gr. 3-6). lib. bdg. 24.90 (978-0-7613-1574-2(8) , Millbrook Pr.) Lerner Publishing Group.

—Whirlers & Twirlers: Science Fun with Spinning. Haefele, Steve, illus. 2001. (Science Fun with Vicki Cobb Ser.). 64p. (gr. 3-6). lib. bdg. 24.90 (978-0-7613-1573-5(X) , Millbrook Pr.) Lerner Publishing Group.

Cobb, Vicki & Darling, Kathy. You Gotta Try This! Absolutely Irresistible Science. Kelley, True, illus. 1999. 144p. (J). (gr. 3 up). 15.99 (978-0-688-15740-1(8)) HarperCollins Pubs.

Dalton, Cindy Devine. Electricity. 2001. (How Can I Experiment With? Ser.). (Illus.). 32p. (gr. 1-4). 19.95 (978-1-58952-011-0(4)) Rourke Publishing, LLC.

—How Can I Experiment With?, 6 bks., Set. 2001. (How Can I Experiment with Ser.). (gr. 1-4). 119.70 (978-1-58952-009-7(2)) Rourke Publishing, LLC.

DiSpezio, Michael A. No-Sweat Science: Optical Illusion Experiments. Gallagher, Jack, illus. 2007. 128p. (J). pap. 5.95 (978-1-4027-2336-0(9)) Sterling Publishing Co., Inc.

DiSpezio, Michael Anthony. Experimentos Sencillos Sobre Ilusiones Opticas. 2002. (Juego de la Ciencia Ser.). (SPA.). 128p. 12.25 (978-84-95456-95-3(8) , 87806) Ediciones Oniro S.A. ESP. *Dist:* Bilingual Pubns. Co., The, Latin American Bk. Source, Inc., Lectorum Pubns., Inc., Libros Sin Fronteras.

Experimentos Sencillos Sobre Ilusiones Opticas. 2002. (SPA.). (gr. 3-6). lib. bdg. 20.75 (978-0-613-82669-3(8)) Tandem Library Bks.

Dixon, Malcolm & Smith, Karen. Electricity. 1998. (Young Scientists Ser.). (Illus.). 32p. (J). (ps-3). lib. bdg. 16.95 (978-1-887068-67-3(8)) Smart Apple Media.

—Forces & Movement. 1998. (Young Scientists Ser.). (Illus.). 32p. (J). (ps-3). lib. bdg. 16.95 (978-1-887068-68-0(6)) Smart Apple Media.

—Light & Color. 1998. (Young Scientists Ser.). (Illus.). 32p. (J). (ps-3). lib. bdg. 16.95 (978-1-887068-70-3(8)) Smart Apple Media.

—Plants Around Us. 1998. (Young Scientists Ser.). (Illus.). 32p. (J). (ps-3). lib. bdg. 16.95 (978-1-887068-71-0(6)) Smart Apple Media.

—Sound & Music. 1998. (Young Scientists Ser.). (Illus.). 32p. (J). (ps-3). lib. bdg. 16.95 (978-1-887068-72-7(4)) Smart Apple Media.

Doudna, Kelly. Don't be Hasty with Science Safety. 2007. (Illus.). 24p. (J). 19.93 (978-1-59928-580-1(0) , SandCastle) ABDO Publishing Co.

—I'll Use a Hand Lens with My Friends! (Illus.). 24p. (J). 2007. 19.93 (978-1-59928-586-3(X)); 2006. pap. (978-1-59928-587-0(8)) ABDO Publishing Co.

—I'm on a Roll with Variable Control. 2007. (Illus.). 24p. (J). 19.93 (978-1-59928-590-0(8) , SandCastle) ABDO Publishing Co.

—I'm on a Roll with Variable Control! 2006. (Illus.). 24p. (J). (978-1-59928-591-7(6)) ABDO Publishing Co.

—It's a Date, Let's Investigate! (Illus.). 24p. (J). 2007. 19.93 (978-1-59928-596-2(7)); 2006. pap. (978-1-59928-597-9(5)) ABDO Publishing Co.

—It's an Event When We Experiment. 2007. (Illus.). 24p. (J). 19.93 (978-1-59928-598-6(3) , SandCastle) ABDO Publishing Co.

—It's an Event When We Experiment! 2006. (Illus.). 24p. (J). (978-1-59928-599-3(1)) ABDO Publishing Co.

Douglas, Vincent & School Specialty Publishing Staff. Experiments You Can Do in Your Backyard. 2003. (Science Experiments Ser.). (Illus.). 96p. (J). (gr. 5-8). 16.95 (978-1-57768-624-8(1) , Waterbird Bks.) School Specialty Publishing.

—Experiments You Can Do in Your Kitchen. Pearce, Q. L., tr. 2003. (Science Experiments Ser.). (Illus.). 96p. (J). (gr. 5-8). 16.95 (978-1-57768-623-1(3) , Waterbird Bks.) School Specialty Publishing.

Ebner, Aviva. Junior Science Experiments on File. (Experiments Ser.). (gr. 4-9). 2006. 280p. 185.00 (978-0-8160-6187-7(4)); 2005. 576p. ring bd. 370.00 (978-0-8160-5738-2(9)); Set. 2006. 864p. 555.00 (978-0-8160-6188-4(2)); Vol. 2. 2005. (Illus.). 266p. 185.00 (978-0-8160-5737-5(0)) Facts On File, Inc.

Echols, Jean C. Buzzing a Hive. Bergman, Lincoln & Fairwell, Kay, eds. Baker, Lisa H., illus. Curtis, Elizabeth et al, photos by. 1999. (Great Explorations in Math & Science Ser.). 146p. (J). pap., tchr. ed. 16.00 (978-0-924886-39-3(0) , GEMS) Univ. of California, Berkeley, Lawrence Hall of Science.

Ecociencia: Experimentos Ecologicos para Chicos.Tr. of Projects for a Healthy Planet. (SPA.). (YA). (gr. 5-8). pap. 9.56 (978-950-24-0745-6(8)) Albatros ARG. *Dist:* Lectorum Pubns., Inc.

Edom, Helen. Science with Plants. rev. ed. 2007. 24p. (J). pap. 5.99 (978-0-7945-1485-3(5) , Usborne) EDC Publishing.

—Science with Water. rev. ed. 2007. 24p. (J). pap. 5.99 (978-0-7945-1484-6(7) , Usborne) EDC Publishing.

Egan, Lorraine Hopping. Today's Weather Is... A Book of Experiments. Johnson, Meredith, illus. 2000. 32p. (J). (gr. 2-4). pap. 4.95 (978-1-57255-809-0(1)) Mondo Publishing.

—Today's Weather Is... A Book of Experiments. 2000. (978-0-606-22658-5(3)) Tandem Library Bks.

Englehart, Deirdre. Inexpensive science exper Age4. 2004. 80p. (C). pap. 10.99 (***978-0-7424-2791-4(9)*** , Instructional Fair) Schaffer, Frank Pubns.

—Inexpensive science exper gr K-1. 2004. 80p. (C). pap. 10.99 (***978-0-7424-2789-1(7)*** , Instructional Fair) Schaffer, Frank Pubns.

Exploratorium Staff, et al. Exploratopia: More Than 400 Kid-Friendly Explorations & Experiments for Curious Minds. Gorski, Jason, illus. 2006. 384p. (J). (gr. 3-7). 29.99 (978-0-316-61281-4(2)) Little, Brown Bks. for Young Readers.

Factastic Challenge, Grades 1-2. 2005. (J). spiral bd. 15.95 (978-1-932855-17-3(3)) becker&mayer! books.

Factastic Challenge, Grades 3-4. 2005. (J). spiral bd. 15.95 (978-1-932855-18-0(1)) becker&mayer! books.

Factastic Challenge, Grades 5-6. 2005. (J). spiral bd. 15.95 (978-1-932855-19-7(X)) becker&mayer! books.

Facts on File, Inc. Staff. More Science Experiments on File Set. 2005. (Experiments Ser.). 288-320p. (gr. 6-12). 1295.00 (978-0-8160-6426-7(1)) Facts On File, Inc.

Falk, John H., et al. Bubble Monster: And Other Science Fun. 2003. (Illus.). 176p. (J). (ps-3). pap. 17.95 (978-1-55652-301-4(7)) Chicago Review Pr., Inc.

Farndon, John. Buoyancy. 2002. (Science Experiments Ser.). (J). 25.64 (978-0-7614-1467-4(3) , Benchmark Bks.) Cavendish, Marshall Corp.

—Color. 2000. (Science Experiments Ser.). (Illus.). 32p. (J). (gr. 3-5). lib. bdg. 25.64 (978-0-7614-1092-8(9) , Benchmark Bks.) Cavendish, Marshall Corp.

—Gravity, Weight & Balance. 2001. (Science Experiments Ser.). (Illus.). 32p. (J). (gr. 3-5). lib. bdg. 25.64 (978-0-7614-1340-0(5) , Benchmark Bks.) Cavendish, Marshall Corp.

—Levers, Wheels & Pulleys. 2001. (Science Experiments Ser.). (Illus.). 32p. (J). (gr. 3-5). lib. bdg. 25.64 (978-0-7614-1341-7(3) , Benchmark Bks.) Cavendish, Marshall Corp.

—Magnetism. 2001. (Science Experiments Ser.). (Illus.). 32p. (J). (gr. 3-5). lib. bdg. 25.64 (978-0-7614-1343-1(X) , Benchmark Bks.) Cavendish, Marshall Corp.

—Rocks & Minerals. 2002. (Science Experiments Ser.). (J). 25.64 (978-0-7614-1468-1(1) , Benchmark Bks.) Cavendish, Marshall Corp.

—Science Experiments - Group 1, 6 bks., Set. Incl. Color. 2000. lib. bdg. 25.64 (978-0-7614-1092-8(9)); Electricity. 2000. lib. bdg. 25.64 (978-0-7614-1086-7(4)); Light & Optics. 2000. lib. bdg. 25.64 (978-0-7614-1090-4(2)); Sound & Hearing. 2000. lib. bdg. 25.64 (978-0-7614-1091-1(0)); Water. 2001. lib. bdg. 25.64 (978-0-7614-1087-4(2)); Weather. 2001. lib. bdg. 25.64 (978-0-7614-1089-8(9)); 32p. (J). (gr. 3-5). (Illus.). 2000. Set lib. bdg. 153.86 (978-0-7614-1088-1(0) , Benchmark Bks.) Cavendish, Marshall Corp.

—Solids, Liquids & Gases. 2001. (Science Experiments Ser.). (Illus.). 32p. (J). (gr. 3-5). lib. bdg. 25.64 (978-0-7614-1338-7(3) , Benchmark Bks.) Cavendish, Marshall Corp.

Fauteux, Nicole & Simon, Seymour. In the Water: Hands-on Early-Learning Science Activities. Cushman, Doug, illus. 2003. (Let's Try It Out Ser.). 32p. (J). pap. 6.99 (978-0-689-86012-6(9) , Aladdin) Simon & Schuster Children's Publishing.

Fox, Tom. Snowball Launchers, Giant-Pumpkin Growers, & Other Cool Contraptions. 2006. (Illus.). 128p. (J). pap. 9.95 (978-0-8069-5515-5(5)) Sterling Publishing Co., Inc.

Frank, Marjorie Slavick, et al. PreK Program: Activity Books. 2nd ed. 2002. (Harcourt Science Ser.). (gr. k-6). pap., act. bk. ed. 24.90 (978-0-15-335320-8(1)) Harcourt Schl. Pubs.

Frankel Hauser, Jill. Science Play. Kline, Michael, illus. 2007. 144p. 16.99 (978-0-8249-6799-4(2) , Williamson Bks.) Ideals Pubns.

Frauenfelder, Mark. Mad Professor: Concoct Extremely Weird Science Projects. Frauenfelder, Mark, illus. 2002. (Illus.). 80p. pap. 14.95 (978-0-8118-3554-1(5)) Chronicle Bks. LLC.

Fredericks, Anthony D. Nature Experiments. Gallagher, Jack, illus. 2005. 128p. pap. 5.95 (978-1-4027-2158-8(7)) Sterling Publishing Co., Inc.

—Simple Nature Experiments with Everyday Materials. Zweifel, Frances, illus. 2004. 128p. (J). (gr. 4-8). reprint ed. pap. 6.00 (978-0-7567-7727-2(5)) DIANE Publishing Co.

Frederickson, A. Experimentos Sencillos con la Naturaleza. 2004. (Juego de la Ciencia Ser.). (SPA., Illus.). 128p. 9.99 (978-84-95456-48-9(6) , 87801) Ediciones Oniro S.A. ESP. *Dist:* Bilingual Pubns. Co., The, Lectorum Pubns., Inc., Libros Sin Fronteras.

Gadd, Ken. Gcse Applied Science Double Award. 2003. (Illus.). vi, 345p. (YA). pap. 47.50 (978-0-7487-7044-1(5)) Nelson Thornes Ltd. GBR. *Dist:* Trans-Atlantic Pubns., Inc.

Gardner, Robert. Bicycle Science Projects: Physics on Wheels. 2004. (Science Fair Success Ser.). (Illus.). 112p. (J). lib. bdg. 26.60 (978-0-7660-1630-9(7)) Enslow Pubs., Inc.

—Experimenting with Water. 2004. (Illus.). 144p. (gr. 5-8). pap. 7.95 (978-0-486-43400-1(1)) Dover Pubns., Inc.

—Far-Out Science Projects with Height & Depth: How High Is up? How Low Is Down? 2003. (Sensational Science Experiments Ser.). (Illus.). 48p. (J). (gr. 1-4). lib. bdg. 23.93 (978-0-7660-2016-0(9)) Enslow Pubs., Inc.

—Forces & Motion Science Fair Projects Using Water Balloons, Pulleys, & Other Stuff. 2004. (Physics! Best Science Projects Ser.). (Illus.). 128p. (J). lib. bdg. 26.60 (978-0-7660-2129-7(7)) Enslow Pubs., Inc.

—Health Science Projects about Nutrition. 2002. (Science Projects Ser.). (Illus.). 112p. (YA). (gr. 6-11). lib. bdg. 26.60 (978-0-7660-1442-8(8)) Enslow Pubs., Inc.

—It's about Time! Science Projects: How Long Does It Take? 2003. (Sensational Science Experiments Ser.). (Illus.). 48p. (J). (gr. 1-4). lib. bdg. 23.93 (978-0-7660-2012-2(6)) Enslow Pubs., Inc.

—Light, Sound, & Waves Science Fair Projects Using Sunglasses, Guitars, & Other Stuff. 2004. (Physics! Best Science Projects Ser.). (Illus.). 128p. (J). lib. bdg. 26.60 (978-0-7660-2126-6(2)) Enslow Pubs., Inc.

—Planet Earth Science Fair Projects Using the Moon, Stars, Beach Balls, Frisbees, & Other Far-Out Stuff. 2005. (Earth Science! Best Science Projects Ser.). (Illus.). 128p. (J). lib. bdg. 26.60 (978-0-7660-2362-8(1) , 1238538) Enslow Pubs., Inc.

—Really Hot Science Projects with Temperature: How Hot Is It? How Cold Is It? 2003. (Sensational Science Experiments Ser.). (Illus.), 48p. (J). lib. bdg. 23.93 (978-0-7660-2015-3(0)) Enslow Pubs., Inc.

—Science Fair Projects - Planning, Presenting, Succeeding. 1999. (Science Projects Ser.). (Illus.). 104p. (YA). (gr. 6-12). lib. bdg. 26.60 (978-0-89490-949-8(5)) Enslow Pubs., Inc.

—Science Fair Projects about the Properties of Matter Using Marbles, Water, Balloons, & More. 2004. (Physics! Best Science Projects Ser.). (Illus.). 128p. (J). lib. bdg. 26.60 (978-0-7660-2128-0(9)) Enslow Pubs., Inc.

—Science Project Ideas in the House. rev. ed. 2002. (Science Project Ideas Ser.). (Illus.). 128p. (J). (gr. 4-9). lib. bdg. 26.60 (978-0-7660-1705-4(2)) Enslow Pubs., Inc.

—Science Projects about Math. 1999. (Science Projects Ser.). (Illus.). 112p. (YA). (gr. 6-12). lib. bdg. 26.60 (978-0-89490-950-4(9)) Enslow Pubs., Inc.

—Science Projects about Physics in the Home. 1999. (Science Projects Ser.). (Illus.). 112p. (YA). (gr. 6-12). lib. bdg. 26.60 (978-0-89490-948-1(7)) Enslow Pubs., Inc.

—Science Projects about Plants. 1999. (Science Projects Ser.). (Illus.). 112p. (YA). (gr. 6-12). lib. bdg. 26.60 (978-0-89490-952-8(5)) Enslow Pubs., Inc.

—Science Projects about the Environment & Ecology. 1999. (Science Projects Ser.). (Illus.). 112p. (YA). (gr. 6-12). lib. bdg. 26.60 (978-0-89490-951-1(7)) Enslow Pubs., Inc.

—Science Projects about the Physics of Toys & Games. 2000. (Science Projects Ser.). (Illus.). 128p. (YA). (gr. 6-12). lib. bdg. 26.60 (978-0-7660-1165-6(8)) Enslow Pubs., Inc.

—Sizzling Science Projects with Heat & Energy. 2006. (Fantastic Physical Science Experiments Ser.). (Illus.). 48p. (J). lib. bdg. 23.93 (978-0-7660-2586-8(1) , Enslow Elementary) Enslow Pubs., Inc.

—Split-Second Science Projects with Speed: How Fast Does It Go? 2003. (Sensational Science Experiments Ser.). (Illus.). 48p. (J). (gr. 1-4). lib. bdg. 23.93 (978-0-7660-2017-7(7)) Enslow Pubs., Inc.

—Super-Sized Science Projects with Volume: How Much Space Does It Take Up? 2003. (Sensational Science Experiments Ser.). (Illus.). 48p. (J). lib. bdg. 23.93 (978-0-7660-2014-6(2)) Enslow Pubs., Inc.

Gardner, Robert & Conklin, Barbara Gardner. Health Science Projects about Sports Performance. 2002. (Science Projects Ser.). (Illus.). 112p. (YA). (gr. 6-12). lib. bdg. 26.60 (978-0-7660-1441-1(X)) Enslow Pubs., Inc.

Garrett, Ginger. Scientists Ask Questions. (Rookie Read-About Science Ser.). (J). 2005. (Illus.). 32p. (gr. 1-2). pap. 4.95 (978-0-516-24662-8(3)); 2004. 20.50 (978-0-516-23614-8(8)) Scholastic Library Publishing. (Children's Pr.).

Gerwitz, Felice. An Insider's Guide to Successful Science Fair Projects. 2002. (YA). per. 6.50 (978-1-931941-03-7(3)) Media Angels, Inc.

Gingold, Janet. My Adventure as a Scientist: Advanced My Adventure. 2007. 44p. (J). pap. 8.99 (978-1-59092-408-2(8) , Orchard Academy Pr.) Windstorm Creative.

Glass, Susan. Prove It! The Scientific Method in Action. 2006. (Illus.). 48p. (J). (978-1-4034-8359-1(0)); pap. (978-1-4034-8363-8(9)) Heinemann Library.

—Watch Out! Science Tools & Safety. 2006. (Illus.). 48p. (J). pap. (978-1-4034-8364-5(7)); lib. bdg. (978-1-4034-8360-7(4)) Heinemann Library.

Glover, David. Batteries, Bulbs, & Wires. 2002. (Young Discoverers Ser.). (Illus.). 32p. (J). (gr. k-3). pap. 7.95 (978-0-7534-5510-4(2) , Kingfisher) Houghton Mifflin Co. Trade & Reference Div.

—Color & Light. 2001. (Experiments in Science Ser.). (Illus.). (J). (978-0-7894-7464-3(6)) Dorling Kindersley Publishing, Inc.

—Electricity: American Edition. 2001. (Experiments in Science Ser.). (Illus.). (J). (978-0-7894-7462-9(X)) Dorling Kindersley Publishing, Inc.

—Forces & Movements. 2001. (Experiments in Science Ser.). (Illus.). (J). (978-0-7894-7463-6(8)) Dorling Kindersley Publishing, Inc.

—How Do Things Grow? Martin, Linda, ed. 2001. (Experiments in Science Ser.). (Illus.). 128p. (J). 24.95 (978-0-7894-7848-1(X)) Dorling Kindersley Publishing, Inc.

—How Does It Work? Martin, Linda, ed. 2001. (Experiments in Science Ser.). (Illus.). 128p. (J). 24.99 (978-0-7894-7849-8(8)) Dorling Kindersley Publishing, Inc.

—Living Science. (Make It Work! Science Ser.). (gr. 3-6). 2004. (Illus.). 192p. 24.95 (978-1-58728-378-9(6)); 2001. (J). pap. 19.95 (978-1-58728-286-7(0)) T&N Children's Publishing. (Two Can Publishing).

—Plants. 2001. (Experiments in Science Ser.). (Illus.). (J). (978-0-7894-7471-1(9)) Dorling Kindersley Publishing, Inc.

—Solids & Liquids: Science Facts & Experiments. 2002. (gr. k-3). lib. bdg. 16.40 (978-0-613-90580-0(6)) Tandem Library Bks.

—Sound & Light: Science Facts & Experiments. 2002. (Young Discoverers Ser.). (Illus.). 32p. (J). (gr. k-3). pap. 7.95 (978-0-7534-5512-8(9) , Kingfisher) Houghton Mifflin Co. Trade & Reference Div.

—Testing Materials. 2001. (Experiments in Science Ser.). (Illus.). (J). (978-0-7894-7465-0(4)) Dorling Kindersley Publishing, Inc.

—Using Materials. 2001. (Experiments in Science Ser.). (Illus.). (J). (978-0-7894-7467-4(0)) Dorling Kindersley Publishing, Inc.

—What Is It Made Of? Martin, Linda, ed. 2001. (Experiments in Science Ser.). (Illus.). 128p. (J). 24.95 (978-0-7894-7850-4(1)) Dorling Kindersley Publishing, Inc.

—Wonderful Water. 2001. (Experiments in Science Ser.). (Illus.). (J). (978-0-7894-7468-1(9)) Dorling Kindersley Publishing, Inc.

Gold-Dworkin, Heidi. Exploring Light & Color. 2000. (gr. 3-6). lib. bdg. 22.20 (978-0-613-27811-9(9)) Tandem Library Bks.

—Fun with Mixing & Chemistry. 2000. (J). (gr. 3-6). lib. bdg. 22.20 (978-0-613-27844-7(5)) Tandem Library Bks.

Gold-Dworkin, Heidi, et al. Exploring Light & Color. 1999. (Little Scientists Ser.). (Illus.). 58p. (J). (gr. k-3). pap. 12.95 (978-0-07-134821-8(2) , 9780071348218) McGraw-Hill Cos., The.

Goldstein, Natalie. The First-Timer's Guide to Science Experiments. Manwaring, Kerry, illus. 1999. (First - Timers Guides). 80p. (J). (gr. 1-4). pap. 8.95 (978-0-7373-0069-7(8) , 00698W) McGraw-Hill/Contemporary.

—Super More Science Fair Projects. Yamamoto, Neal, illus. 2000. (Fifty Nifty Ser.). 96p. (J). (gr. 3-7). pap. 6.95 (978-0-7373-0368-1(9) , 03689W, Roxbury Park Juvenile) Lowell Hse. Juvenile.

Goodstein, Madeline. Fish Tank Physics Projects. 2002. (Science Fair Success Ser.). (Illus.). 128p. (YA). (gr. 6-12). lib. bdg. 26.60 (978-0-7660-1624-8(2)) Enslow Pubs., Inc.

Goodstein, Madeline P. Plastics & Polymers Science Fair Projects Using Hair Gel, Soda Bottles, & Slimy Stuff. 2004. (Chemistry! Best Science Projects Ser.). (Illus.). 128p. (J). lib. bdg. 26.60 (978-0-7660-2123-5(8)) Enslow Pubs., Inc.

—Water Science Fair Projects Using Ice Cubes, Super Soakers, & Other Wet Stuff. 2004. (Chemistry! Best Science Projects Ser.). (Illus.). 128p. (J). lib. bdg. 26.60 (978-0-7660-2124-2(6)) Enslow Pubs., Inc.

Gore, Gordon R. Experimenting with Energy: Hands-On Science Activities. 2000. (Experimenting with... Ser.). (Illus.). 48p. (J). pap. (978-1-55244-044-5(3)) Trifolium Bks., Inc.

Gould, Alan. Hot Water & Warm Homes from Sunlight. Gould, Alan et al, illus. Sneider, Cary I., photos by. rev. ed. 2005. (Great Explorations in Math & Science Ser.). 80p. 13.50 (978-1-931542-04-3(X) , GEMS) Univ. of California, Berkeley, Lawrence Hall of Science.

Graham, John. Forces & Motion: Over 40 Fantastic Experiments. 2001. (Hands-On Science Ser.). (Illus.). (J). 13.75 (978-0-606-21194-9(2)) Tandem Library Bks.

Graham, John & Angliss, Sarah. Forces & Motion: Over 40 Fantastic Experiments. 2001. (Hands-On Science Ser.). (Illus.). 40p. (J). (gr. 3-5). pap. 6.95 (978-0-7534-5348-3(7) , Kingfisher) Houghton Mifflin Co. Trade & Reference Div.

Green, Joey. Mad Scientist Handbook. 2000. (gr. 5-8). lib. bdg. 21.05 (978-0-613-26091-6(0)) Tandem Library Bks.

—The Mad Scientist Handbook: The Do-It-Yourself Guide to Making Your Own Rock Candy, Anti-Gravity Machine, Edible Glass, Rubber & Fake Blood. 2000. (Illus.). (J). (978-0-606-18425-0(2)) Tandem Library Bks.

—The Mad Scientist Handbook No. 1: The Do-It-Yourself Guide to Making Your Own Rock Candy, Anti-Gravity Machine, Edible Grass, Rubber Eggs, Fake Blood, Green Slime & Much, Much More. 2000. (Illus.). 1p. (gr. 7-12). pap. 12.95 (978-0-399-52593-3(9) , Perigee Trade) Penguin Group (USA) Inc.

Griffith, Dave. General Science Student Workbook. 1999. (Illus.). (J). pap. 12.00 (978-1-886998-11-7(6)) Pasco Scientific.

—Math in Science. 1999. (Illus.). (YA). pap., stu. ed., wbk. ed. 12.00 (978-1-886998-15-5(9)) Pasco Scientific.

Grolier Educational Staff, contrib. by. Chemical Reactions, 10 vols., Vol. 1. 2002. (Illus.). 64p. (J). (978-0-7172-5609-9(X) , Grolier) Scholastic Library Publishing.

—Ecology & Plants, 10 vols., Vol. 2. 2002. (Illus.). 64p. (J). (978-0-7172-5610-5(3) , Grolier) Scholastic Library Publishing.

—Electricity & Magnetism, 10 vols., Vol. 3. 2002. (Illus.). 64p. (J). (978-0-7172-5611-2(1) , Grolier) Scholastic Library Publishing.

—Force & Motion, 10 vols., Vol. 4. 2002. (Illus.). 64p. (J). (978-0-7172-5612-9(X) , Grolier) Scholastic Library Publishing.

—Heat & Energy, 10 vols., Vol. 5. 2002. (Illus.). 64p. (J). (978-0-7172-5613-6(8) , Grolier) Scholastic Library Publishing.

—Light, 10 vols., Vol. 6. 2002. (Illus.). 64p. (J). (978-0-7172-5614-3(6) , Grolier) Scholastic Library Publishing.

—Materials, 10 vols., Vol. 7. 2002. (Illus.). 64p. (J). (978-0-7172-5615-0(4) , Grolier) Scholastic Library Publishing.

—Science Activities, 10 vols., Set. Incl. Vol. 1. Chemical Reactions. (978-0-7172-5609-9(X)); Vol. 2. Ecology & Plants. (978-0-7172-5610-5(3)); Vol. 3. Electricity & Magnetism. (978-0-7172-5611-2(1)); Vol. 4. Force & Motion. (978-0-7172-5612-9(X)); Vol. 5. Heat & Energy. (978-0-7172-5613-6(8)); Vol. 6. Light. (978-0-7172-5614-3(6)); Vol. 7. Materials. (978-0-7172-5615-0(4)); Vol. 8. Sound. (978-0-7172-5616-7(2)); Vol. 9. Structure & Matter. (978-0-7172-5617-4(0)); Vol. 10. Weather & Climate. (978-0-7172-5618-1(9)); (J). (Illus.). 64p. 2002. 365.00 (978-0-7172-5608-2(1) , Grolier) Scholastic Library Publishing.

—Sound, 10 vols., Vol. 8. 2002. (Illus.). 64p. (J). (978-0-7172-5616-7(2) , Grolier) Scholastic Library Publishing.

—Structure & Matter, 10 vols., Vol. 9. 2002. (Illus.). 64p. (J). (978-0-7172-5617-4(0) , Grolier) Scholastic Library Publishing.

—Weather & Climate, 10 vols., Vol. 10. 2002. (Illus.). 64p. (J). (978-0-7172-5618-1(9) , Grolier) Scholastic Library Publishing.

Gunter, Veronika & Newcomb, Rain. Pet Science: Purr-Fectly Woof-Worthy Activities for You & Your Pets. 2006. (Illus.). 80p. (J). 14.95 (978-1-57990-786-0(5)) Lark Bks.

Hacker, Randi. Detective & Spy Science: Experiment Log. 2001. (Mad Science Ser.). (Illus.). 48p. (J). (978-0-439-22335-5(0)) Scholastic, Inc.

Haduch, Bill. Science Fair Success Secrets: How to Win Prizes, Have Fun, & Think Like a Scientist. Scheuer, Philip, illus. 2002. 128p. (J). pap. 10.99 (978-0-525-46534-8(0) , Dutton Juvenile) Penguin Group (USA) Inc.

—Science Fair Success Secrets: How to Win Prizes, Have Fun, & Think Like a Scientist. 2002. (gr. 3-6). lib. bdg. 19.95 (978-0-613-72584-2(0)) Tandem Library Bks.

Hansen, Amy. KidSource: Science Experiments. Moran, Mike, illus. 2000. 112p. (J). (gr. 3-7). pap. 9.95 (978-0-7373-0342-1(5) , 03425W, Roxbury Park Juvenile) Lowell Hse. Juvenile.

Harcourt School Publishers Staff. A Cool Experiment: Take-Home Book. 1999. (Collections Ser.). (Illus.). (J). pap. 1.90 (978-0-15-317232-8(0)) Harcourt Schl. Pubs.

—Harcourt Science: Assessment Guide. (Illus.). 1999. (gr. 6). pap. 59.30 (978-0-15-313190-5(X)); 1999. (gr. 1). pap. 49.80 (978-0-15-313184-4(5)); 1999. (gr. 2). pap. 49.80 (978-0-15-313186-8(1)); 1999. (gr. 3). pap. 52.80 (978-0-15-313187-5(X)); 1999. (gr. 4). pap. 56.00 (978-0-15-313188-2(8)); 1999. (gr. 5). pap. 59.30 (978-0-15-313189-9(6)); 2nd ed. 2002. (gr. 1 up). pap. 49.80 (978-0-15-323705-8(8)); 2nd ed. 2002. (gr. 2 up). pap. 49.80 (978-0-15-323706-5(6)); 2nd ed. 2002. (gr. 4 up). pap. 56.00 (978-0-15-323708-9(2)); 2nd ed. 2002. (gr. 5 up). pap. 59.30 (978-0-15-323709-6(0)); 2nd ed. 2002. (gr. 6 up). pap. 59.30 (978-0-15-323710-2(4)) Harcourt Schl. Pubs.

—Harcourt Science Unit Big Book Collection. 2nd ed. 2002. (Illus.). (gr. 1). pap. 866.90 (978-0-15-325375-1(4)); (gr. 1 up). pupil's gde. ed. 1066.70 (978-0-15-325373-7(8)); (gr. 2). pap. 866.90 (978-0-15-325376-8(2)); (gr. 2 up). pupil's gde. ed. 1066.70 (978-0-15-325374-4(6)) Harcourt Schl. Pubs.

—Harcourt Science Unit Books Unit C. 2nd ed. 2002. (Harcourt Science Ser.). (Illus.). (gr. 3 up). pap., pupil's gde. ed. 15.60 (978-0-15-325379-9(7)); (gr. 4 up). pap., pupil's gde. ed. 15.60 (978-0-15-325385-0(1)); (gr. 5 up). pap., pupil's gde. ed. 16.10 (978-0-15-325391-1(6)); (gr. 6 up). pap., pupil's gde. ed. 16.10 (978-0-15-325397-3(5)) Harcourt Schl. Pubs.

—Harcourt Science Unit Books Unit D. 2nd ed. 2002. (Harcourt Science Ser.). (Illus.). (gr. 3 up). pap., pupil's gde. ed. 15.60 (978-0-15-325380-5(0)); (gr. 4 up). pap., pupil's gde. ed. 15.60 (978-0-15-325386-7(X)); (gr. 5 up). pap., pupil's gde. ed. 16.10 (978-0-15-325392-8(4)); (gr. 6 up). pap., pupil's gde. ed. 16.10 (978-0-15-325398-0(3)) Harcourt Schl. Pubs.

—Harcourt Science Unit Books Unit A. 2nd ed. 2002. (Harcourt Science Ser.). (Illus.). (gr. 3 up). pap., pupil's gde. ed. 15.60 (978-0-15-325377-5(0)); (gr. 4 up). pap., pupil's gde. ed. 15.60 (978-0-15-325383-6(5)); (gr. 5 up). pap., pupil's gde. ed. 16.10 (978-0-15-325389-8(4)); (gr. 6 up). pap., pupil's gde. ed. 16.10 (978-0-15-325395-9(9)) Harcourt Schl. Pubs.

—Harcourt Science Unit Books Unit B. 2nd ed. 2002. (Harcourt Science Ser.). (Illus.). (gr. 3 up). pap., pupil's gde. ed. 15.60 (978-0-15-325378-2(9)); (gr. 4 up). pap., pupil's gde. ed. 15.60 (978-0-15-325384-3(3)); (gr. 5 up). pap., pupil's gde. ed. 16.10 (978-0-15-325390-4(8)); (gr. 6 up). pap., pupil's gde. ed. 16.10 (978-0-15-325396-6(7)) Harcourt Schl. Pubs.

—Harcourt Science Unit Books Unit E. 2nd ed. 2002. (Harcourt Science Ser.). (Illus.). (gr. 3 up). pap., pupil's gde. ed. 15.60 (978-0-15-325381-2(9)); (gr. 4 up). pap., pupil's gde. ed. 15.60 (978-0-15-325387-4(8)); (gr. 5 up). pap., pupil's gde. ed. 16.10 (978-0-15-325393-5(2)); (gr. 6 up). pap., pupil's gde. ed. 16.10 (978-0-15-325399-7(1)) Harcourt Schl. Pubs.

—Harcourt Science Unit Books Unit F. 2nd ed. 2002. (Harcourt Science Ser.). (Illus.). (gr. 3 up). pap., pupil's gde. ed. 15.60 (978-0-15-325382-9(7)); (gr. 4 up). pap., pupil's gde. ed. 15.60 (978-0-15-325388-1(6)); (gr. 5 up). pap., pupil's gde. ed. 16.10 (978-0-15-325394-2(0)); (gr. 6 up). pap., pupil's gde. ed. 16.10 (978-0-15-325400-0(9)) Harcourt Schl. Pubs.

Harlow, Rosie. Energy & Power: Environmental Facts & Experiments. 2002. (Young Discoverers Ser.). (Illus.). 32p. (J). (gr. k-3). pap. 7.95 (978-0-7534-5502-9(1) , Kingfisher) Houghton Mifflin Co. Trade & Reference Div.

—Energy & Power: Environmental Facts & Experiments. 2002. (gr. k-3). lib. bdg. 16.40 (978-0-613-90900-6(3)) Tandem Library Bks.

Harris, Elizabeth Snoke. Yikes! Wow! Yuck! Fun Experiments for Your First Science Fair. Thompson, Nora, illus. 2008. 112p. (J). 12.95 ***(978-1-57990-930-7(2))*** Lark Bks.

Hartley, Pamela. Dirty Thirty: 30 Science Experiments to Try in Your Bathtub. Wise, Noreen, ed. Wethington, Liz, illus. 2001. (Gold Mixed Collection). 128p. (YA). (gr. 2 up). pap. 9.95 (978-1-58584-478-4(0)) Huckleberry Pr.

Hartzog, Daniel. Everyday Science Experiments in the Car. 2000. (Science Surprises Ser.). (Illus.). 24p. (J). (gr. k-4). lib. bdg. 19.95 (978-0-8239-5459-9(5) , PowerKids Pr.) Rosen Publishing Group, Inc., The.

—Everyday Science Experiments with Food. 2000. (Science Surprises Ser.). (Illus.). 24p. (J). (gr. k-4). lib. bdg. 19.95 (978-0-8239-5460-5(9) , PowerKids Pr.) Rosen Publishing Group, Inc., The.

Hartzog, John D. Everyday Science Experiments in the Backyard. 2000. (Science Surprises Ser.). (Illus.). 24p. (J). (gr. k-4). lib. bdg. 19.95 (978-0-8239-5455-1(2) , PowerKids Pr.) Rosen Publishing Group, Inc., The.

Haslam, Andrew. Building. 2004. (Make It Work! Science Ser.). (Illus.). 48p. (gr. 3-6). 12.95 (978-1-58728-375-8(1) , Two Can Publishing) T&N Children's Publishing.

—Cartes et Plans. 2000. (Make It Work! Geography Ser.). (FRE., Illus.). 48p. (J). (gr. 3-6). pap. 6.95 (978-1-58728-186-0(4) , Two Can Publishing) T&N Children's Publishing.

—Earth. 2004. (Make It Work! Science Ser.). (Illus.). 48p. (J). (gr. 3-6). 12.95 (978-1-58728-376-5(X) , Two Can Publishing) T&N Children's Publishing.

Haslam, Andrew, et al. Building. (Make It Work! Ser.). (Illus.). 48p. (J). pap. 15.95 (978-0-590-24332-2(2)) Scholastic, Inc.

—Building. 2004. (Make It Work! Science Ser.). (Illus.). 48p. (J). (gr. 3-6). pap. 6.95 (978-1-58728-351-2(4) , Two Can Publishing) T&N Children's Publishing.

Hauser, Jill Frankel. Gizmos & Gadgets: Creating Science Contraptions That Work (& Knowing Why) Kline, Michael, illus. 1999. 144p. (J). (ps-9). per. 22.20 (978-0-613-16357-6(5)) Tandem Library Bks.

—Science Play! Beginning Discoveries for 2- to 6-Year-Olds. 1998. (Little Hands Bks.: Vol. 8). (Illus.). 140p. (J). (ps-3). pap. 12.95 (978-1-885593-20-7(1) , Williamson Bks.) Ideals Pubns.

Heating. 2004. (Illus.). 24p. (J). (ps-ps). pap. 5.75 (978-1-4034-5103-3(6)) Heinemann Library.

Hewitt, Sally. Plants. (Illus.). 32p. (YA). (gr. 2 up). lib. bdg. 27.10 (978-1-932333-30-5(4)) Chrysalis Education.

—Plants. 2001. (gr. 5-8). lib. bdg. 17.60 (978-0-613-45214-4(3)) Tandem Library Bks.

Highlights for Children Editorial Staff. The Highlights U. S. A. Big Book of Science Secrets: 101 Amazing Experiments. 2003. (Illus.). 144p. (J). (gr. 5-7). pap., stu. ed. 8.95 (978-1-56397-651-3(X)) Boyds Mills Pr.

Hoffman, Jane. Backyard Scientist A Science Wonderland for the Very Young: Simple, fun-to-do Science Experiments Ages 2 To 7. 2005. (Illus.). 56p. (J). pap. 8.95 (978-0-9618663-8-9(1)) Backyard Scientist, Inc.

Holt, Rinehart and Winston Staff. Animals Science Kit: Non-Consumable Edition, Module B. 2nd ed. 2002. (Holt Science & Technology Ser.). pap. 527.40 (978-0-03-067613-0(4)) Harcourt Schl. Pubs.

—Astronomy Science Kit: Consumable Edition, Module J. 2nd ed. 2002. (Holt Science & Technology Ser.). 141.86 (978-0-03-067642-0(8)) Holt, Rinehart & Winston.

—Astronomy Science Kit: Non-Consumable Edition, Module J. 2nd ed. 2002. (Holt Science & Technology Ser.). 349.86 (978-0-03-067623-9(1)) Holt, Rinehart & Winston.

—Holt Science & Technology: Inquiry Labs. 2001. pap. 14.60 (978-0-03-054419-4(X)); 5th ed. 2004. (Illus.). pap. 14.60 (978-0-03-035184-6(7)) Holt, Rinehart & Winston.

—Holt Science & Technology: Labs You Can Eat. 5th ed. 2004. (Illus.). pap. 14.60 (978-0-03-035183-9(9)) Holt, Rinehart & Winston.

—Weather Science Kit: Consumable Edition, Module I. 2nd ed. 2002. (Holt Science & Technology Ser.). 142.73 (978-0-03-067641-3(X)) Holt, Rinehart & Winston.

Hopwood, James. Cool Distance Assistants: Fun Science Projects to Propel Things. 2007. (Cool Science Ser.). (Illus.). 32p. (J). (gr. k-6). lib. bdg. 24.21 ***(978-1-59928-906-9(7)*** , Checkerboard Library) ABDO Publishing Co.

—Cool Dry Ice Devices: Fun Science Projects with Dry Ice. 2007. (Cool Science Ser.). (Illus.). 32p. (J). (gr. k-6). lib. bdg. 24.21 ***(978-1-59928-907-6(5)*** , Checkerboard Library) ABDO Publishing Co.

How to Do Science Experiments with Children. 2005. 304p. (gr. 2-4). 29.99 (978-1-55799-936-8(8) , EMC 5001) Evan-Moor Educational Pubs.

Hunter, Rebecca M. Matter. 2000. (Discovering Science Ser.). (Illus.). 32p. (J). (gr. 3-5). lib. bdg. 25.69 (978-0-7398-2969-1(6)) Raintree.

Inventions in Land Vehicles. 2005. (Illus.). 28p. (J). pap. 15.95 incl. audio (978-0-9724983-0-2(3)) Jazwares Distribution, Inc.

Jackson, Dorothy M. & Nankivell-Aston, Sally. Science Experiments with Forces. 2000. (Science Experiments Ser.). (Illus.). 32p. (J). (gr. 3-6). 22.00 (978-0-531-14582-1(4) , Watts, Franklin) Scholastic Library Publishing.

—Science Experiments with Simple Machines. 2000. (Science Experiments Ser.). (Illus.). 32p. (J). (gr. 3-6). 22.00 (978-0-531-14579-1(4) , Watts, Franklin) Scholastic Library Publishing.

Jacobs Krieger, Melanie. Using Statistics in Science Projects, Internet Enhanced. 2002. (Science Fair Success Ser.). (Illus.). 144p. (YA). (gr. 6-12). lib. bdg. 26.60 (978-0-7660-1629-3(3)) Enslow Pubs., Inc.

Janice VanCleave's Insects & Spiders: Mind-Boggling Experiments You Can Turn into Science Fair Projects. 2002. (Janice Vancleave Ser.). (Illus.). (J). 19.72 (978-0-7587-4629-0(6)) Book Wholesalers, Inc.

Jones, Lorraine. Super Science Projects about Weather & Natural Forces. 2005. (Psyched for Science Ser.). (Illus.). 48p. (YA). (gr. 5-8). lib. bdg. 23.95 (978-0-8239-3105-7(6) , SCWENA) Rosen Publishing Group, Inc., The.

Der Jugend Brockhaus: Natur und Technik. (GER., Illus.). 640p. (YA). (gr. 5-11). (978-3-7653-1851-1(5)) Brockhaus, F. A., GmbH DEU. *Dist:* International Bk. Import Service, Inc.

Kain, Kathleen E. First Science Fair: The Science Spiders Experiment with Cupcakes. 1999. (Illus.). 32p. (J). (gr. k-3). pap. 5.95 (978-1-892221-03-2(9) , RW0563) Ranch Works.

Kauffman, Dorothy. Science Lab. 2005. (Content Area Readers Ser.). 24p. 4.95 (978-0-19-430955-4(X)) Oxford Univ. Pr., Inc.

Keller, Rebecca. Real Science-4-Kids: Laboratory Manual. 2001. spiral bd. 9.95 (978-1-931796-02-6(5)) Access Research Network.

Kerrod, Robin. The Sea. 2000. (Fantastic Facts Ser.). (Illus.). 64p. (gr. 2-7). pap. 6.95 (978-1-84215-321-5(8) , Southwater) Anness Publishing GBR. *Dist:* National Bk. Network.

—The Sea. Sweet, Stephen & Whetton, John, illus. 1998. (Young Scientist Concepts & Projects Ser.). 68p. (J). (gr. 4 up). lib. bdg. 26.60 (978-0-8368-2164-2(5)) Stevens, Gareth Inc.

Kerrod, Robin & Holgate, Sharon Ann. The Way Science Works: Discover the Secrets of Science with Exciting, Accessible Experiments. Parsons, Jayne, ed. 2002. (Illus.). 160p. (J). (gr. 5 up). 24.99 (978-0-7894-8562-5(1)) Dorling Kindersley Publishing, Inc.

Knighton, Kate. 50 Science Things to Make & Do. 2007. (Activity Cards Ser.). 50p. (J). 9.99 ***(978-0-7945-1698-7(X)*** , Usborne) EDC Publishing.

Krautwurst, Terry. Night Science for Kids: Exploring the World after Dark. 2003. (Illus.). 144p. (J). (gr. 3-9). 19.95 (978-1-57990-411-1(4)) Lark Bks.

Krautwurst, Terry, et al. Science Smart: Cool Projects for Exploring the Marvels of the Planet Earth. 2004. (Illus.). 400p. (J). pap. 12.98 (978-1-4027-1436-8(X)) Sterling Publishing Co., Inc.

Ladd, Karol. The Glad Scientist Explores the Human Body. 2004. (Glad Scientist Ser.). pap., act. bk. ed. 6.99 (978-0-8054-0829-4(0)) B&H Publishing Grp.

Ladizinsky, Eric. More Magical Science: Magic Tricks for Young Scientists. rev. ed. 2000. (Illus.). 80p. (J). (gr. 4-7). pap. 6.95 (978-0-7373-0513-5(4)) Lowell Hse. Juvenile.

LaFosse, Michael. Making Origami Science Experiments Step by Step. 2004. (Kid's Guide to Origami Ser.). (Illus.). 24p. (J). lib. bdg. 21.25 (978-0-8239-6705-6(0) , PowerKids Pr.) Rosen Publishing Group, Inc., The.

Lauw, Darlene. Electricity. 2002. (gr. 3-6). lib. bdg. 16.40 (978-0-613-52838-2(7)) Tandem Library Bks.

—Heat. 2002. (gr. 3-6). lib. bdg. 16.40 (978-0-613-52851-1(4)) Tandem Library Bks.

—Magnets. 2002. (gr. 3-6). lib. bdg. 16.40 (978-0-613-52877-1(8)) Tandem Library Bks.

—Motion. 2002. (gr. 3-6). lib. bdg. 16.40 (978-0-613-52883-2(2)) Tandem Library Bks.

Lauw, Darlene & Puay, Lim Cheng. Electricity. 2001. (Science Alive! Ser.). (Illus.). 32p. (J). (gr. 4-5). pap. (978-0-7787-0607-6(9)); lib. bdg. (978-0-7787-0561-1(7)) Crabtree Publishing Co.

—Heat. 2002. (Science Alive! Ser.). (Illus.). 32p. (J). (gr. 4-5). pap. (978-0-7787-0605-2(2)); lib. bdg. (978-0-7787-0559-8(5)) Crabtree Publishing Co.

—Magnets. 2002. (Science Alive! Ser.). (Illus.). 32p. (J). (gr. 4-5). pap. (978-0-7787-0609-0(5)); lib. bdg. (978-0-7787-0563-5(3)) Crabtree Publishing Co.

—Motion. 2002. (Science Alive! Ser.). (Illus.). 32p. (J). (gr. 4-5). pap. (978-0-7787-0604-5(4)); lib. bdg. (978-0-7787-0558-1(7)) Crabtree Publishing Co.

Lemke, Donald. Lessons in Science Safety with Max Axiom, Super Scientist. 2007. (Illus.). 32p. (J). ***(978-0-7368-7887-6(4))*** Capstone Pr., Inc.

Lemke, Donald B. & Adamson, Thomas K. Lessons in Science Safety with Max Axiom, Super Scientist. Smith, Tod & Anderson, Bill, illus. 2007. 32p. (J). ***(978-0-7368-6834-1(8))*** Capstone Pr., Inc.

Lemonick, Michael D. Science Alive, No. 1. 1998. 48p. (J). (978-0-7868-0133-6(6)) Hyperion Pr.

S

Leonard, Sue, ed. Kitchen Science: With over 50 Fantastic Experiments. 2004. (Illus.). 48p. (J). (gr. k-8). reprint ed. 13.00 (978-0-7567-7285-7(0)) DIANE Publishing Co.

Let's Go! Elementary Science. 2004. spiral bd. 30.00 (*978-1-929075-38-6(3)*) Vernier Software & Technology.

Let's Investigate, 6 bks. (J). (gr. 2-6). lib. bdg. 86.70 (978-1-56674-929-9(8)) Forest Hse. Publishing Co., Inc.

Levine, Shar. Bathtub Science. 2003. (Illus.). 80p. pap. 10.95 (978-0-8069-7243-5(2)) Sterling Publishing Co., Inc.

—Quick-but-Great Science Fair Projects. 2001. (978-0-606-22742-1(3)) Tandem Library Bks.

Levine, Shar & Johnstone, Leslie. The Amazing Human Body. Harpster, Steve, illus. 2006. (First Science Experiments Ser.). 48p. (J). 14.95 (978-1-4027-2437-4(3)) Sterling Publishing Co., Inc.

—Bathtub Science. 2006. (Illus.). 80p. (J). pap. 9.95 (978-1-4027-4094-7(8)) Sterling Publishing Co., Inc.

—Build Your Own Remote Control. 2001. 24p. (J). pap. 14.95 (978-0-9700346-5-6(2)) becker&mayer! books.

—First Science Experiments with Nature, Senses, Weather & Machines. Harpster, Steve, illus. 2005. 192p. (978-1-4027-2922-5(7)) Sterling Publishing Co., Inc.

—Kitchen Science. 2005. (Illus.). 80p. pap. 9.95 (978-1-4027-2232-5(X)) Sterling Publishing Co., Inc.

—Magnet Power! Harpster, Steve, illus. 2006. (First Science Experiments Ser.). 48p. (J). 14.95 (978-1-4027-2438-1(1)) Sterling Publishing Co., Inc.

—Nature Science. Garbot, Dave, illus. 2007. 80p. (J). pap. 9.95 (978-1-4027-4516-4(8)) Sterling Publishing Co., Inc.

—Sports Science. 2006. (Illus.). 80p. (gr. 2-5). 19.95 (978-1-4027-1520-4(X) , 1252963) Sterling Publishing Co., Inc.

—Super Senses. Harpster, Steve, illus. 2005. (First Science Experiments Ser.). 48p. (J). (ps). pap. 4.95 (978-1-4027-2767-2(4)) Sterling Publishing Co., Inc.

—Wonderful Weather. Harpster, Steve, illus. 2005. (First Science Experiments Ser.). 48p. (J). (ps). pap. 4.95 (978-1-4027-2768-9(2)) Sterling Publishing Co., Inc.

Littlefield, Cindy A. Awesome Ocean Science: Investigating the Secrets of the Underwater World. 2004. (Kids Can Bks.). (Illus.). 120p. (J). (gr. 3-5). pap. 12.95 (978-1-885593-71-9(6) , Williamson Bks.) Ideals Pubns.

Lobb, Janice. Bump! Thump! How Do We Jump? Experiments in the Kitchen. Savage, Ann & Utton, Peter, illus. 2002. (At Home with Science Ser.). 32p. (J). pap. 5.95 (978-0-7534-5461-9(0) , Kingfisher) Houghton Mifflin Co. Trade & Reference Div.

—Munch! Crunch! What's for Lunch? Experiments in the Kitchen. Savage, Ann & Utton, Peter, illus. 2002. (At Home with Science Ser.). 32p. (J). pap. 5.95 (978-0-7534-5460-2(2) , Kingfisher) Houghton Mifflin Co. Trade & Reference Div.

Loret, John & Tanacredi, John T. Experiment Central: Understanding Scientific Principles Through Projects, 4 vols., Set. 2000. (Illus.). lxxxi, 773p. (J). (gr. 4-7). lib. bdg. 235.00 (978-0-7876-2892-5(1) , GML00502-112457, UXL) Thomson Gale.

Loret, John & Tanacredi, John T., contrib. by. Experiment Central: Understanding Scientific Principles Through Projects, 4 vols. 2000. (Illus.). lxxxi, 773p. (J). (978-0-7876-2894-9(8)); (978-0-7876-2895-6(6)); (978-0-7876-2896-3(4)) Thomson Gale. (UXL).

Lunis, Natalie & White, Nancy. Let's Experiment! Date not set. (Thinking Like a Scientist Ser.). (Illus.). 20p. (J). pap. 16.95 (978-1-58273-111-7(X)) Sundance/Newbridge Educational Publishing.

Madgwick, Wendy. Up in the Air. 1998. (Science Starters Ser.). (Illus.). 32p. (J). (gr. k-4). lib. bdg. 25.70 (978-0-8172-5325-7(4)) Raintree.

—Water Play. 1998. (Science Starters Ser.). (Illus.). 32p. (J). (gr. k-4). lib. bdg. 25.69 (978-0-8172-5326-4(2)) Raintree.

Mandell, Muriel. No-Sweat Science: Super Science Experiments. Gallagher, Jack, illus. 2005. (No Sweat Science Ser.). 128p. pap. 5.95 (978-1-4027-2149-6(8)) Sterling Publishing Co., Inc.

—No-Sweat Science: Simple Experiments in Time. Gallagher, Jack, illus. 2007. 96p. (J). pap. 5.95 (978-1-4027-2335-3(0)) Sterling Publishing Co., Inc.

Markle, Sandra. Magic. Smith, Jamie, tr. Smith, Jamie, illus. 2001. (Super Science Ser.). 61p. (J). pap. (978-0-439-28136-2(9)) Scholastic, Inc.

—Super Cool Science: South Pole Stations, Past, Present, & Future. 1998. (Illus.). 32p. (J). (gr. 3-7). 16.95 (978-0-8027-8470-4(4)) Walker & Co.

Martin, Patricia A. Fink. Rivers & Streams. 1999. (Exploring Ecosystems Ser.). (Illus.). 144p. (YA). (gr. 8-12). 24.50 (978-0-531-11523-7(2) , Watts, Franklin) Scholastic Library Publishing.

—Woods & Forests. 2000. (Exploring Ecosystems Ser.). (Illus.). 144p. (YA). (gr. 8-12). pap. 6.95 (978-0-531-16459-4(4) , Watts, Franklin) Scholastic Library Publishing.

Martineau, Susan. Slimy Science & Awesome Experiments: Amazing Tests & Tricks. Ursell, Martin, illus. 2001. 24p. (J). (gr. 2-7). pap. 6.95 (978-0-7373-0578-4(9)) Lowell Hse.

Mason, Adrienne. Living Things. Boudreau, Ray, photos by. 2000. (Illus.). 32p. (J). (gr. k-4). lib. bdg. 14.10 (978-0-613-26042-8(2)) Tandem Library Bks.

Matloff, Gregory L. More Telescope Power: All New Activities & Projects for Young Astronomers. 2002. (Illus.). 128p. pap. 12.95 (978-0-471-40985-4(5) , Wiley) Wiley, John & Sons, Inc.

Meacham, Nancy. Aire: Libro de Actividades de Descubrimiento Cientifico. Zuman, John & Barra, Nancy, eds. Deming, Linda, illus. 2002. (Sunflower/Girasol Ser.). (SPA.). 20p. (J). 5.00 (978-1-58332-014-3(8)) Intercultural Center for Research in Education (I N C R E).

Meiani, Antonella. Air. 2003. (Experimenting with Science Ser.). (Illus.). 40p. (J). (gr. 4-8). lib. bdg. 23.93 (978-0-8225-0082-7(5)) Lerner Publishing Group.

—Magnetism. 2003. (Experimenting with Science Ser.). (Illus.). 40p. (J). (gr. 4-8). lib. bdg. 23.93 (978-0-8225-0085-8(X)) Lerner Publishing Group.

—Water. 2003. (Experimenting with Science Ser.). (Illus.). 40p. (J). (gr. 4-8). 23.93 (978-0-8225-0083-4(3)) Lerner Publishing Group.

Mellett, Peter. Flight. Bowyer, Dave, illus. 1998. (Young Scientist Concepts & Projects Ser.). 68p. (J). (gr. 4 up). lib. bdg. 27.33 (978-0-8368-2162-8(9)) Stevens, Gareth Inc.

Mellett, Peter & Angliss, Sarah. Matter & Materials. 2001. (Hands-On Science Ser.). (Illus.). 40p. (J). (gr. 3-5). pap. 6.95 (978-0-7534-5350-6(9) , Kingfisher) Houghton Mifflin Co. Trade & Reference Div.

Meredith, Susan. Science in the Kitchen. rev. ed. 2007. 24p. (J). pap. 5.99 (978-0-7945-1405-1(7) , Usborne) EDC Publishing.

Merrill, Amy French. Everyday Physical Science Experiments with Gases. 2002. (Science Surprises Ser.). (Illus.). 24p. (J). lib. bdg. 19.95 (978-0-8239-5803-0(5) , PowerKids Pr.) Rosen Publishing Group, Inc., The.

—Everyday Physical Science Experiments with Gravity. 2002. (Science Surprises Ser.). 24p. (J). lib. bdg. 19.95 (978-0-8239-5805-4(1) , PowerKids Pr.) Rosen Publishing Group, Inc., The.

—Everyday Physical Science Experiments with Liquids. 2002. (Science Surprises Ser.). (Illus.). 24p. (J). lib. bdg. 19.95 (978-0-8239-5801-6(9) , PowerKids Pr.) Rosen Publishing Group, Inc., The.

—Everyday Physical Science Experiments with Magnetism. 2002. (Science Surprises Ser.). (Illus.). 24p. (J). lib. bdg. 19.95 (978-0-8239-5800-9(0) , PowerKids Pr.) Rosen Publishing Group, Inc., The.

—Everyday Physical Science Experiments with Solids. 2002. (Science Surprises Ser.). 24p. (J). lib. bdg. 19.95 (978-0-8239-5802-3(7) , PowerKids Pr.) Rosen Publishing Group, Inc., The.

Mixing. 2004. (Illus.). 24p. (J). (ps-ps). pap. 5.75 (978-1-4034-5104-0(4)) Heinemann Library.

More Junior Science Experiments on File Set. 2005. (Experiments Ser.). 578p. (gr. 4-9). 370.00 (978-0-8160-6425-0(3)) Facts On File, Inc.

Moredock, Janet, et al. Handy Homework Helper. 2005. (Illus.). 128p. (J). (*978-1-4127-1179-1(7)*) Publications International, Ltd.

Morgan, Sally. Butterflies, Bugs, & Worms. 2002. (Young Discoverers Ser.). (Illus.). 32p. (J). (gr. k-3). pap. 7.95 (978-0-7534-5499-2(8) , Kingfisher) Houghton Mifflin Co. Trade & Reference Div.

—Flowers, Trees, & Fruits. 2002. (Young Discoverers Ser.). (Illus.). 32p. (J). (gr. k-3). pap. 7.95 (978-0-7534-5500-5(5) , Kingfisher) Houghton Mifflin Co. Trade & Reference Div.

Muller, Eric. While You're Waiting for the Food to Come: A Tabletop Science Activity Book. Doty, Eldon C., illus. 1999. xii, 84p. (J). (gr. 3-7). pap. 15.95 (978-0-531-30199-9(0) , Orchard Bks.) Scholastic, Inc.

Murphy, Brian. Air. 2004. (Experiment with Ser.). (SPA., Illus.). 32p. (gr. 2-5). (J). pap. 5.95 (978-1-58728-113-6(9)); 9.95 (978-1-58728-244-7(5)) T&N Children's Publishing. (Two Can Publishing).

—Experimenta Con el Agua. 2004. (Experiment with Ser.).Tr. of Experiment with Air. (SPA., Illus.). 32p. (gr. 2-5). 9.95 (978-1-58728-437-3(5)); (J). pap. 5.95 (978-1-58728-436-6(7)) Quayside. (Creative Publishing International).

—Experimenta Con el Aire. 2004. (Experiment with Ser.).Tr. of Experiment With Air. (SPA., Illus.). 32p. (gr. 2-5). 9.95 (978-1-58728-435-9(9) , Creative Publishing International) Quayside.

—Experimenta Con el Aire. 2004. (Experiment with Ser.).Tr. of Experiment With Air. (SPA., Illus.). 32p. (J). (gr. 2-5). pap. 5.95 (978-1-58728-434-2(0) , Two Can Publishing) T&N Children's Publishing.

—Movement. 2004. (Experiment with Ser.). (SPA., Illus.). 32p. (J). (gr. 2-5). 9.95 (978-1-58728-248-5(8)); pap. 5.95 (978-1-58728-116-7(3)) T&N Children's Publishing. (Two Can Publishing).

—Water. 2004. (Experiment with Ser.). (SPA., Illus.). 32p. (gr. 2-5). (J). pap. 5.95 (978-1-58728-119-8(8)); 9.95 (978-1-58728-242-3(9)) T&N Children's Publishing. (Two Can Publishing).

Nankivell-Aston, Sally. Science Experiments with Color. 2000. (J). (978-0-606-19789-2(3)) Tandem Library Bks.

—Science Experiments with Light. 2000. (Science Experiments Ser.). (Illus.). 32p. (J). (gr. 3-5). pap. 6.95 (978-0-531-15429-8(7) , Watts, Franklin) Scholastic Library Publishing.

—Science Experiments with Magnets. 2000. (Science Experiments Ser.). (Illus.). 32p. (J). (gr. 3-6). pap. 6.95 (978-0-531-15430-4(0) , Watts, Franklin) Scholastic Library Publishing.

—Science Experiments with Simple Machines. 2000. (gr. 3-6). lib. bdg. 15.25 (978-0-613-50731-8(2)) Tandem Library Bks.

—Science Experiments with Sound. 2000. (gr. 3-6). lib. bdg. 15.25 (978-0-613-62699-6(0)) Tandem Library Bks.

—Science Experiments with Water. 2000. (Science Experiments Ser.). (Illus.). 32p. (J). (gr. 3-6). pap. 6.95 (978-0-531-15432-8(7) , Watts, Franklin) Scholastic Library Publishing.

Nankivell-Aston, Sally & Jackson, Dorothy. Science Experiments with Simple Machines. 2000. (Science Experiments Ser.). (Illus.). 32p. (YA). (gr. 3-6). pap. 6.95 (978-0-531-15445-8(9) , Watts, Franklin) Scholastic Library Publishing.

—Science Experiments with Sound. 2000. (Science Experiments Ser.). (Illus.). 32p. (J). (gr. 3-6). 22.00 (978-0-531-14578-4(6) , Watts, Franklin) Scholastic Library Publishing.

Nankivell-Aston, Sally & Jackson, Dorothy M. Science Experiments with Light. 2000. (Science Experiments Ser.). (Illus.). 32p. (J). (gr. 3-6). 22.00 (978-0-531-14577-7(8) , Watts, Franklin) Scholastic Library Publishing.

Nash, Kimberley. How to Write Lab Reports for Science Fairs & Classroom Experiments. 1999. (Illus.). 96p. (gr. 3-12). spiral bd., wbk. ed. 14.95 (978-0-9653723-3-6(2) , #21010) Resurrection Resources LLC.

—More Lab Reports - Level One: Level One. 1999. (Illus.). 68p. (J). (gr. 3-6). spiral bd., wbk. ed. 11.00 (978-0-9653723-4-3(0) , #22010) Resurrection Resources LLC.

—More Lab Reports - Level Two: Level Two. 1999. (ENG., Illus.). 123p. (J). (gr. 7-12). spiral bd., wbk. ed. 13.00 (978-0-9653723-5-0(9) , #22020) Resurrection Resources LLC.

Nayer, Judy. Projects for Preschoolers-Science. 1999. (Judy Bks.). (Illus.). 48p. (J). (gr. k-1). mass mkt. 4.99 (978-0-7681-0078-5(X) , 67308, McClanahan Bk.) Learning Horizons, Inc.

Naylor, Brenda & Naylor, Stuart. Bungee Jumpers & Other Science Questions, 4 vols. Mitchell, Ged, illus. 32p. (J). pap. 11.99 (978-0-340-76441-1(4) , Hodder & Stoughton) Hodder General Publishing Division GBR. *Dist:* Trafalgar Square Publishing.

—The Snowman's Coat & Other Science Questions, 4 vols. Mitchell, Ged, illus. 32p. (J). pap. (978-0-340-75755-0(8) , Hodder & Stoughton) Hodder General Publishing Division.

Naylor, Brenda, et al. Upside down Seeds & Other Science Questions, 4 vols. Mitchell, Ged, illus. 32p. (J). pap. 11.99 (978-0-340-76445-9(7) , Hodder & Stoughton) Hodder General Publishing Division GBR. *Dist:* Trafalgar Square Publishing.

Newman, Marjorie. Ideas for a Windy Day. 1999. (Ideas Activity Bks.). (Illus.). 12p. (J). (ps-3). pap. 5.99 (978-0-89051-245-6(0)) Master Bks.

Nye, Bill. Bill Nye the Science Guy's Big Blast of Science. 2000. (Illus.). 176p. (YA). pap. 16.95 (978-0-201-60864-9(2)) Basic Bks.

—Bill Nye the Science Guy's Consider the Following. 2000. (Illus.). (J). 17.39 (978-0-606-18254-6(3)) Tandem Library Bks.

—Bill Nye the Science Guy's Consider the Following: A Way Cool Set of Q'S, A'S, & Ideas. 2000. (gr. 3-6). lib. bdg. 19.65 (978-0-613-12519-2(3)) Tandem Library Bks.

—Bill Nye the Science Guy's Consider the Following: A Way Cool Set of Science Questions, Answers, & Ideas to Ponder. Kimball, Anton, illus. 2000. 112p. (gr. 4-7). pap. 10.99 (978-0-7868-1443-5(8)) Hyperion Bks. for Children.

Nye, Bill & Saunders, Ian G. Bill Nye the Science Guy's Great Big Dinosaur Dig. Koelsch, Michael, illus. 2002. 48p. (gr. 2-5). 16.99 (978-0-7868-0542-6(0)) Hyperion Bks. for Children.

Oxlade, Chris. Earth: 30 Great Science Experiments & Projects. 2003. (Hands-On Science Ser.). (Illus.). 64p. (gr. 3-7). pap. 10.99 (978-1-84215-770-1(1) , Southwater) Anness Publishing GBR. *Dist:* National Bk. Network.

—Nature: 30 Great Science Experiments & Projects. 2003. (Hands-On Science Ser.). (Illus.). 64p. (gr. 3-7). pap. 10.99 (978-1-84215-824-1(4) , Southwater) Anness Publishing GBR. *Dist:* National Bk. Network.

—Transport: 40 Great Science Experiments & Projects. 2004. (Hands-On Science Ser.). (Illus.). 64p. pap. 10.99 (978-1-84215-857-9(0) , Southwater) Anness Publishing GBR. *Dist:* National Bk. Network.

—150 Great Science Experiments: Ingenious, Easy-to-Do Projects Explore & Explain the Wonders of Science & Technology. 2002. (Illus.). 256p. 29.95 (978-0-7548-0843-5(2)) Anness Publishing GBR. *Dist:* National Bk. Network.

Oxlade, Chris, et al. 300 Science & History Projects. 2006. (Illus.). 512p. pap. 19.99 (978-1-84476-310-8(2) , Southwater) Anness Publishing GBR. *Dist:* National Bk. Network.

Packard, Mary & Discovery Staff. MythBusters: Don't Try This at Home. 2005. (Illus.). 144p. pap. 14.95 (978-0-7879-8369-7(1) , Jossey-Bass) Wiley, John & Sons, Inc.

Parker, Steve. Light. 2004. (Science View Ser.). (Illus.). 32p. (J). (gr. 4-8). 28.00 (978-0-7910-8209-6(1) , Chelsea Hse.) Facts On File, Inc.

—The Science of Air: Projects & Experiments on Air & Flight. 2005. (Tabletop Scientist Ser.). (Illus.). 32p. (J). (gr. 4-7). lib. bdg. 27.79 (978-1-4034-7280-9(7)) Heinemann Library.

—The Science of Water: Projects with Experiments with Water & Power. 2005. (Tabletop Scientist Ser.). (Illus.). 32p. (J). (gr. 4-7). lib. bdg. 29.29 (978-1-4034-7282-3(3)) Heinemann Library.

—Sound. 2004. (Science View Ser.). (Illus.). 32p. (J). (gr. 4-8). 28.00 (978-0-7910-8210-2(5) , Chelsea Hse.) Facts On File, Inc.

—Tiempo y Clima - Jugando Con la Ciencia. 1998. (SPA.). (gr. 3-6). lib. bdg. 19.65 (978-0-613-89837-9(0)) Tandem Library Bks.

Parker, Steve & Parker, Jane. I Can Experiment: Fun to Do Simple Science Projects for Young Children. 2000. (Show Me How Ser.). (Illus.). 48p. (ps-2). pap. 7.95 (978-0-7548-0098-9(9)) Anness Publishing, Inc.

Pascoe, Elaine. Bugs. Kuhn, Dwight, illus. Kuhn, Dwight, photos by. 2003. 48p. (J). 23.70 (978-1-56711-458-4(X) , Blackbirch Pr., Inc.) Thomson Gale.

—Flowers. 2003. (Illus.). 48p. (J). 24.95 (978-1-56711-432-4(6) , Blackbirch Pr., Inc.) Thomson Gale.

—Snails & Slugs. Kuhn, Dwight, photos by. 1998. (Nature Close-Up Ser.). (Illus.). 48p. (J). (gr. 4-8). 23.70 (978-1-56711-181-1(5) , Blackbirch Pr., Inc.) Thomson Gale.

—Spittlebugs & Other Sap Tappers. 2003. (Illus.). 48p. (J). 24.95 (978-1-56711-430-0(X) , Blackbirch Pr., Inc.) Thomson Gale.

Pearce, Querida L. Backyard Science Experiments. Sheppard, Sophie, illus. 1999. (Roxbury Park Bks.). 64p. (J). (gr. 4-7). pap. 8.95 (978-0-7373-0283-7(6) , 02836W, Roxbury Park) Lowell Hse.

—Kitchen Science Experiments. 1999. (Illus.). 64p. (J). (gr. 4-7). pap. 8.95 (978-0-7373-0285-1(2) , 02852W, Roxbury Park) Lowell Hse.

—Super Science Experiments. Artenstein, Michael, ed. Gleeson, Tony, illus. 1999. (Roxbury Park Bks.). 96p. (J). (gr. 3-7). pap. 7.95 (978-0-7373-0073-4(6) , 00736W) McGraw-Hill/Contemporary.

—60 Super Simple More Science Experiments. 1999. (Sixty Super Simple Ser.). (Illus.). 80p. (J). (gr. 3-7). pap. 6.95 (978-0-7373-0233-2(X) , 0233XW) McGraw-Hill/Contemporary.

—60 Super Simple Science Experiments. Abbett, Leo, illus. 1998. (Sixty Super Simple Ser.). 80p. (J). (gr. 3-7). pap. 6.95 (978-1-56565-688-8(1) , 06881W) Lowell Hse. Juvenile.

—60 Super Simple Still More Science Experiments. 2000. (Illus.). 80p. (J). (gr. 2-6). pap. 6.95 (978-0-7373-0534-0(7)) Lowell Hse. Juvenile.

Pederson, Bridget. Don't Be Hasty with Science Safety! 2006. (Illus.). 24p. (J). (978-1-59928-581-8(9)) ABDO Publishing Co.

Pentland, Peter & Stoyles, Pennie. Party Science. 2003. (Science & Scientists Ser.). (Illus.). 32p. (gr. 4-8). lib. bdg. 27.00 (978-0-7910-7015-4(8) , Chelsea Hse.) Facts On File, Inc.

Perry, Phyllis J. Science Fair Success with Plants. 1999. (Science Fair Success Ser.). (Illus.). 104p. (YA). (gr. 6-12). lib. bdg. 26.60 (978-0-7660-1170-0(4)) Enslow Pubs., Inc.

Peterson, Carol. Jump into Science: Themed Science Fairs. 2007. (Illus.). 152p. (J). pap. 30.00 (*978-1-59158-413-1(2)* , TIP4132, Teacher Ideas Pr.) Libraries Unlimited, Inc.

Physical Science with Vernier. 2007. spiral bd. 45.00 (*978-1-929075-47-8(2)*) Vernier Software & Technology.

Pilger, Mary Anne. Science Experiments Index for Young People. 3rd ed. 2001. 294p. (YA). 67.95 (978-1-56308-899-5(1)) Libraries Unlimited, Inc.

—Science Experiments Index for Young People: Fourth Edition. 4th rev. ed. 2005. 212p. 62.00 (978-1-59158-237-3(7) , LU2377) Libraries Unlimited, Inc.

Popular Science Editors. Backyard Laboratory. 2007. (Experiment with Science Ser.). 32p. (J). pap. 7.95 (*978-0-531-18757-9(8)*); (Illus.). (gr. 3-6). lib. bdg. 25.00 (*978-0-531-18542-1(7)*) Scholastic Library Publishing. (Children's Pr.).

—Try It with Food. 2007. (Experiment with Science Ser.). 32p. (J). pap. 7.95 (*978-0-531-18761-6(6)*); (Illus.). (gr. 3-6). lib. bdg. 25.00 (*978-0-531-18544-5(3)*) Scholastic Library Publishing. (Children's Pr.).

Potter, Jean. Science in Seconds at the Beach: Exciting Experiments You Can Do in Ten Minutes. 1998. (gr. 3-6). lib. bdg. 22.20 (978-0-613-81940-4(3)) Tandem Library Bks.

—Science in Seconds at the Beach: Exciting Experiments You Can Do in Ten Minutes or Less. 1998. (Illus.). 122p. (gr. 4-7). pap. 13.95 (978-0-471-17899-6(3) , Wiley) Wiley, John & Sons, Inc.

Press, H. J. Science Experiments. 2007. (Illus.). 360p. (J). pap. 6.95 (*978-1-4027-4990-2(2)*) Sterling Publishing Co., Inc.

Prochnow, Dave & Prochnow, Kathy. How? 1999. (Experiments for Young Scientists Ser.). (Illus.). 152p. (YA). (gr. 4-7). lib. bdg. 25.25 (978-0-7910-4846-7(2) , Chelsea Hse.) Facts On File, Inc.

Ragsdale, Tyraine D. Science of Grand Hank Lab Book of Experiments. 2005. pap. 24.95 (978-0-9767236-0-8(3)) Grand Hank Productions, Inc.

Rainis, Kenneth G. Forgery: Crime-Solving Science Experiments. 2006. (Forensic Science Projects Ser.). (Illus.). 128p. (YA). (gr. 5 up). lib. bdg. 31.93 (978-0-7660-1961-4(6)) Enslow Pubs., Inc.

—Microscope Science Projects & Experiments: Magnifying the Hidden World. 2003. (Science Fair Success Ser.). (Illus.). 128p. (J). lib. bdg. 26.60 (978-0-7660-2090-0(8)) Enslow Pubs., Inc.

—Nature Projects for Young Scientists. rev. ed. (Project for Young Scientists Ser.). (Illus.). 192p. (gr. 9-12). 2003. (YA). pap. 9.95 (978-0-531-16381-8(4)); 2002. (J). pap. 23.50 (978-0-531-11724-8(3)) Scholastic Library Publishing. (Watts, Franklin).

Rainis, Kenneth G. & Nassis, George. Biotechnology Projects for Young Scientists. 1998. (Projects for Young Scientists Ser.). (Illus.). 160p. (J). (gr. 9-12). 25.00 (978-0-531-11419-3(8) , Watts, Franklin) Scholastic Library Publishing.

Raintree Steck-Vaughn Staff. Light & Dark. 2000. (Science Starters Ser.). (Illus.). 32p. (J). (gr. k-4). lib. bdg. 25.70 (978-0-8172-5331-8(9)) Raintree.

—Super Materials. 2000. (Science Starters Ser.). (J). (gr. k-4). lib. bdg. 25.70 (978-0-8172-5330-1(0)) Raintree.

—Think Like a Scientist. 1999. (J). pap. 35.60 (978-0-7398-0894-8(X)) Steck-Vaughn.

Reid, Struan. The Science & History Project Book. 2004. (Illus.). 512p. 45.00 (978-0-7548-1445-0(9) , Lorenz Bks.) Anness Publishing GBR. *Dist:* National Bk. Network.

Rhatigan, Joe & Gunter, Veronika. Cool Chemistry Concoctions: 50 Formulas that Fizz, Foam, Splatter & Ooze. La Baff, Tom, illus. 2007. 80p. pap. 7.95 (978-1-57990-882-9(9)) Lark Bks.

Rhatigan, Joe & Gunter, Veronika Alice. Cool Chemistry Concoctions: 50 Formulas That Fizz, Foam, Splatter & Ooze. LaBaff, Tom, illus. 2005. 80p. (J). 14.95 (978-1-57990-620-7(6)) Lark Bks.

Riley, Peter D. Changing Forms. Moller, Ray, photos by. 2002. (Everyday Science Ser.). (Illus.). 32p. (J). (gr. 1 up). lib. bdg. 23.33 (978-0-8368-3246-4(9)) Stevens, Gareth Inc.

—Forces & Movement. 2005. (Illus.). 32p. (J). (gr. 4-7). lib. bdg. 27.10 (978-1-58340-712-7(X)) Smart Apple Media.

Rillero, Peter. 1001 Ways to Explore Science & Nature. (Illus.). 640p. 2005. per. 12.98 (978-0-7853-8348-2(4), 3447900); 2003. (J). per. (978-0-7853-8933-0(4)) Publications International, Ltd.

Robinson, Richard. Science Magic in the Bedroom: Amazing Tricks with Ordinary Stuff. Rowe, Alan, illus. 2002. (Science Magic Ser.). 96p. (J). pap. 4.99 (978-0-689-84335-8(6), Aladdin) Simon & Schuster Children's Publishing.

—Science Magic in the Kitchen. 2001. (gr. 3-6). lib. bdg. 13.00 (978-0-613-73321-2(5)); (Illus.). (J). (978-0-606-21422-3(4)) Tandem Library Bks.

Robinson, Tom. Everything Kids' Magical Science Experiments Book: Dazzle your friends & family by making magical things Happen! 2007. (Illus.). 144p. (J). pap. 7.95 (***978-1-59869-426-0(X)***) Adams Media Corp.

—Everything Kids' Science Experiments Book: Boil Ice, Float Water, Measure Gravit. 2001. (gr. 3-6). lib. bdg. 15.25 (978-0-613-51249-7(9)) Tandem Library Bks.

—The Everything' Kids' Science Experiments Book: Boil Ice, Float Water, Measure Gravity—Challenge the World Around You! 2001. (Everything Kids Ser.). (Illus.). 144p. (J). (gr. 3-7). 6.95 (978-1-58062-557-9(6)) Adams Media Corp.

—Kids' Science Experiments Book. 2001. (978-0-606-22485-7(8)) Tandem Library Bks.

Rogers, Kirsteen. Human Body. 2002. (gr. 3-6), lib. bdg. 18.75 (978-0-613-75096-7(9)) Tandem Library Bks.

Rohrig, Brian. 39 Dazzling Experiments with Dry Ice. 2003. (Illus.). 104p. (YA). per. (978-0-9718480-3-0(3)) FizzBang Science.

—39 Dazzling Experiments with the Mega-Magnet. 2003. (Illus.). 136p. (YA). per. (978-0-9718480-4-7(1)) FizzBang Science.

Rosner, Marc Alan. Science Fair Success Using the Internet. 1999. (Science Fair Success Ser.). (Illus.). 112p. (YA). (gr. 6-12). lib. bdg. 26.60 (978-0-7660-1172-4(0)) Enslow Pubs., Inc.

Ross, Michael Elsohn. Kitchen Lab. Seeley, Tim, illus. 2003. (You Are the Scientist Ser.). 48p. (J). (gr. 3-6). lib. bdg. 23.93 (978-0-87614-625-5(6)) Lerner Publishing Group.

—Sandbox Scientist: Real Science Activities for Little Kids. Lloyd, Mary A., illus. 2003. 208p. (J). (ps-3). pap. 12.95 (978-1-55652-248-2(7)) Chicago Review Pr., Inc.

—What's the Matter in Mr. Whisker's Room? Meisel, Paul, illus. 2004. 48p. (J). (gr. 1-5). 16.99 (978-0-7636-1349-5(5)) Candlewick Pr.

Ross, Michael Elsohn. What's the Matter in Mr. Whiskers' Room. Meisel, Paul, illus. 2007. 48p. (J). (gr. 1-5). pap. 7.99 (***978-0-7636-3566-4(9)***) Candlewick Pr.

Roza, Greg. Heads or Tails? 2004. (PowerMath Ser.). (Illus.). 24p. (J). lib. bdg. 21.25 (978-0-8239-8971-3(2), PowerKids Pr.) Rosen Publishing Group, Inc., The.

—Heads or Tails? Exploring Probability Through Games. 2004. (PowerMath Ser.). (Illus.). 24p. (J). pap. (978-0-8239-8894-5(5), PowerKids Pr.) Rosen Publishing Group, Inc., The.

—Where We Play Sports: Measuring the Perimeters of Polygons. 2004. (PowerMath Ser.). (Illus.). 24p. (J). lib. bdg. (978-0-8239-8895-2(3)); lib. bdg. 21.25 (978-0-8239-8972-0(0)) Rosen Publishing Group, Inc., The. (PowerKids Pr.).

Rushin, John W. Science Fair Projects. 1999. (YA). (gr. 5). 9.95 (978-1-58037-100-1(0)) Twain, Mark Media, Inc. Pubs.

Rybolt, Thomas R. Soda Pop Science Projects: Experiments with Carbonated Soft Drinks. 2004. (Science Fair Success Ser.). (Illus.). 104p. (J). lib. bdg. 26.60 (978-0-7660-2089-4(4)) Enslow Pubs., Inc.

Rybolt, Thomas R. & Mebane, Robert C. Science Experiments for Young People, 5 bks., Set. (Illus.). (YA). (gr. 4-9). lib. bdg. 99.75 (978-0-89490-448-6(5)) Enslow Pubs., Inc.

Saffer, Barbara. Backyard Science Experiments. 2000. (Gifted & Talented Ser.). (Illus.). 64p. (J). (gr. 1-3). pap. 5.95 (978-0-7373-0497-8(9)) Lowell Hse. Juvenile.

—Kitchen Science Experiments. Abbett, Leo, illus. 2000. (Gifted & Talented Ser.). 64p. (J). (gr. 1-3). pap. 5.95 (978-0-7373-0374-2(3), 03743W, Roxbury Park Juvenile) Lowell Hse. Juvenile.

Savage, Paul. Let's Experiment. 2002. (Csiro Molecular Science Ser.). (Illus.). 120p. pap. 35.00 (978-0-643-06801-8(5)) CSIRO Publishing AUS. *Dist:* Antipodes Bks. & Beyond.

Schofield, Tracey Ann. 101 Science Activities for Emerging Einsteins. Mitchell, Judy, ed. Glikin, Alex, illus. 2001. 96p. (J). (gr. 3-6). pap. 10.95 (978-1-57310-301-5(2)) Teaching & Learning Co.

School Specialty Publishing. Air. 2005. (Science Search Lab Ser.). (J). (gr. 3-5). pap. 24.95 (978-0-7682-2831-1(X), Ideal School Supply) Schaffer, Frank Pubns.

Science Anytime. 2000. (Switched on Schoolhouse Ser.). (Illus.). (J). (gr. 3-7). pap. 66.95 (978-0-7403-0226-8(4), SOS300S) Alpha Omega Pubns., Inc.

Science Experiments. 2004. (gr. 4). pap. 14.95 (978-0-7403-0221-3(3), SV0401); (gr. 6). pap. 14.95 (978-1-58095-902-5(4), SV0601); (gr. 7). pap. 14.95 (978-1-58095-903-2(2), SV0701); (gr. 8). pap. 14.95 (978-1-58095-904-9(0), SV0801) Alpha Omega Pubns., Inc. (Lifepac).

Science Experiments - Group 3, 6 bks., Set. 153.86 (978-0-7614-1465-0(7), Benchmark Bks.) Cavendish, Marshall Corp.

Science Experiments Kid Kit. 2004. (Illus.). 64p. (J). 18.95 (978-1-58086-419-0(8)) EDC Publishing.

Science Play. 2007. (Illus.). 144p. pap. 12.99 (978-0-8249-6798-7(4), Williamson Bks.) Ideals Pubns.

Science Stories Foss Spanish Ideas & Inventions EA CR05. 2005. (J). (978-1-59242-588-4(7)) Delta Education, LLC.

Science with Light & Mirrors Kid Kit. (Illus.). 24p. (J). 14.95 (978-1-58086-451-0(1)) EDC Publishing.

Science with Magnets Kid Kit. 2004. (Kid Kits Ser.). (Illus.). 24p. (J). 14.95 (978-1-58086-420-6(1)) EDC Publishing.

Shevick, Edward. Science Action Labs: Air Science. Mitchell, Judy, ed. Rojas, Mary Galan, illus. 2002. 64p. (J). (gr. 1-3). pap. 8.95 (978-1-57310-361-9(6)) Teaching & Learning Co.

—Science Action Labs: Astronomy. Mitchell, Judy, ed. Rojas, Mary Galan, illus. 2002. 64p. (J). (gr. 1-3). pap. 8.95 (978-1-57310-362-6(4)) Teaching & Learning Co.

—Science Action Labs: Earth Science. Mitchell, Judy, ed. Rojas, Mary Galan, illus. 2002. 64p. (J). (gr. 1-3). pap. 8.95 (978-1-57310-363-3(2)) Teaching & Learning Co.

—Science Fun: Activities to Encourage Students to Think & Solve Problems. Mitchell, Judy, ed. Jones, Marguerite, illus. 1998. (Science Action Labs Ser.). 64p. (gr. 4-8). pap., tchr. ed. 8.95 (978-1-57310-140-0(0)) Teaching & Learning Co.

Sian Phys&Chml Changes. 2004. (Science in A Nutshell(R) Ser.). (J). (978-1-59242-055-1(9)) Delta Education, LLC.

Simon, Seymour. Let's Try It Out in the Air. 2003. (gr. k-3). lib. bdg. 15.30 (978-0-613-67150-7(3)) Tandem Library Bks.

Simon, Seymour & Fauteux, Nicole. Let's Try It Out in the Air: Hands-on Early-Learning Science Activities. Cushman, Doug, illus. 2003. (Let's Try It Out Ser.). 32p. (J). pap. 6.99 (978-0-689-86011-9(0), Aladdin) Simon & Schuster Children's Publishing.

Smith, Alastair. Gran Libro de los Experiementos. 1999. (SPA.). (gr. 5-8). lib. bdg. 24.55 (978-0-613-70607-0(2)) Tandem Library Bks.

Sobey, Edwin J. C. Fantastic Flying Fun with Science: 69 Projects You Can Fly, Spin, Launch, & Ri. 2000. (gr. 5-8). lib. bdg. 21.05 (978-0-613-71530-0(6)) Tandem Library Bks.

—How to Build Your Own Prize-Winning Robot. 2002. (Science Fair Success Ser.). (Illus.). 128p. (YA). (gr. 6-12). lib. bdg. 26.60 (978-0-7660-1627-9(7)) Enslow Pubs., Inc.

Somervill, Barbara A. Communicating Valid Conclusions. 2007. (Scientific Processes Ser.). (Illus.). 24p. (J). pap. (978-1-4042-2195-6(6)); lib. bdg. (978-1-4042-3486-4(1)) Rosen Publishing Group, Inc., The. (PowerKids Pr.).

—Planning Investigations. 2007. (Understanding Scientific Inquiry Ser.). pap. (978-1-4042-2192-5(1)); lib. bdg. (978-1-4042-3483-3(7)) Rosen Publishing Group, Inc., The. (PowerKids Pr.).

Spangler, Steve. Secret Science: 25 Science Experiments Your Teacher Doesn't Know About. 2007. (Illus.). 144p. (J). pap. 9.95 (978-1-933317-75-5(2)) Silverleaf Pr.

Spilsbury, Richard & Spilsbury, Louise. What Are Forces & Motion? Exploring Science with Hands-On Activities. 2008. (In Touch with Basic Science Ser.). 32p. (J). (gr. 3-4). lib. bdg. 22.60 (***978-0-7660-3095-4(4)***) Enslow Pubs., Inc.

—What Is Solids, Liquids, & Gases? Exploring Science with Hands-On Activities. 2008. (In Touch with Basic Science Ser.). 32p. (J). (gr. 3-4). lib. bdg. 22.60 (***978-0-7660-3094-7(6)***) Enslow Pubs., Inc.

—What Is Sound? Exploring Science with Hands-On Activities. 2008. (In Touch with Basic Science Ser.). 32p. (J). (gr. 3-4). lib. bdg. 22.60 (***978-0-7660-3098-5(9)***) Enslow Pubs., Inc.

Steck-Vaughn Staff. Science Projects. 2002. (Illus.). (J). (gr. 1-2). pap. (978-0-7398-6909-3(4)); (gr. 3-4). pap. (978-0-7398-6910-9(8)); (gr. 5-6) pap. (978 0-7398-6911-6(6)) Steck-Vaughn.

Stille, Darlene R. Hot & Cold. 2001. (Simply Science Ser.). (Illus.). 32p. (J). (gr. 3 up). lib. bdg. 19.93 (978-0-7565-0090-0(7)) Compass Point Bks.

Stillinger, Doug. Klutz Battery Science. 2003. (Illus.). 56p. (J). spiral bd. 19.95 (978-1-59174-251-7(X), 53643124) Klutz.

Super Science Concoctions. 2007. (Illus.). 160p. 16.99 (***978-0-8249-6802-1(6));*** pap. 12.99 (***978-0-8249-6803-8(4)***) Ideals Pubns. (Williamson Bks.).

Surprise Station. 2004. 9.99 (978-0-7644-1644-6(8)); 2004. 9.99 (978-0-7644-1715-3(0)); 2003. 9.99 (978-0-7644-1626-2(X)) Group Publishing, Inc. (Flagship Church Resources).

Swenson. Growing Science Fair Projects. Date not set. (J). (978-0-8069-0497-9(6)) Sterling Publishing Co., Inc.

Talmadge, Ellen. Unearthing Garden Mysteries Vol. 1: Experiments for Kids. Curtis, Bruce, photos by. 2004. (Illus.). 96p. (J). (gr. 4-7). 17.95 (978-1-55591-993-1(6)) Fulcrum Publishing.

A Taste of Science: 18 Edible Science Experiments. 96p. (gr. 5-8). 9.99 (978-0-7424-0124-2(3), IF19318) School Specialty Publishing.

Thomas, Lyndall. Plants. 1999. (Interfact Reference Ser.). (Illus.). 48p. (J). (gr. 2-8). 15.00 (978-0-7166-7239-5(1), 1544) World Bk., Inc.

Tocci, Salvatore. Experiments with a Hand Lens. 2002. (True Bks.). (J). (Illus.). 48p. (gr. 3-5). pap. 6.95 (978-0-516-26994-8(1), Children's Pr.); (978-0-531-12155-9(0), Watts, Franklin); (Illus.). 48p. (gr. 3-5). 25.00 (978-0-516-22506-7(5), Children's Pr.) Scholastic Library Publishing.

—Experiments with Colors. 2003. (True Book Ser.). (Illus.). 48p. (J). 25.00 (978-0-516-22785-6(8), Children's Pr.) Scholastic Library Publishing.

—Experiments with Electricity. 2002. (True Bks.). (Illus.). 48p. (J). (gr. 3-5). pap. 6.95 (978-0-516-27348-8(5), Children's Pr.) Scholastic Library Publishing.

—Experiments with Electricity. 2001. (gr. 3-6). lib. bdg. 15.25 (978-0-613-54208-1(8)) Tandem Library Bks.

—Experiments with Foods. 2003. (True Book Ser.). (Illus.). 48p. (J). 25.00 (978-0-516-22787-0(4), Children's Pr.) Scholastic Library Publishing.

—Experiments with Friction. (True Bks.). (Illus.). 48p. (J). (gr. 3-5). 2003. pap. 6.95 (978-0-516-29363-9(X)); 2002. pap. 25.00 (978-0-516-22512-8(X)) Scholastic Library Publishing. (Children's Pr.).

—Experiments with Gravity. 2002. (True Book Ser.). (Illus.). 48p. (J). (gr. 3-5). pap. 25.00 (978-0-516-22513-5(8), Children's Pr.) Scholastic Library Publishing.

—Experiments with Magic. 2003. (True Book Ser.). (Illus.). 48p. (J). 25.00 (978-0-516-22788-7(2), Children's Pr.) Scholastic Library Publishing.

—Experiments with Motion. 2003. (True Book Ser.). (Illus.). 48p. (J). 25.00 (978-0-516-22603-3(7), Children's Pr.) Scholastic Library Publishing.

—Experiments with Plants. (True Books Ser.). (Illus.). 48p. (J). (gr. 3-5). 2002. pap. 6.95 (978-0-516-27351-8(5)); Set. 2001. 25.00 (978-0-516-22252-3(X)) Scholastic Library Publishing. (Children's Pr.).

—Experiments with Simple Machines. 2003. (True Books Ser.). (Illus.). 48p. (J). 25.00 (978-0-516-22604-0(5), Children's Pr.) Scholastic Library Publishing.

—Experiments with Solids, Liquids, & Gases. 2002. 13.75 (978-0-606-22879-4(9)) Tandem Library Bks.

—Experiments with the Sun & the Moon. 2003. (True Bks.). (gr. 3-5). pap. 6.95 (978-0-516-27469-0(4), Children's Pr.) Scholastic Library Publishing.

—Experiments with the Sun & the Moon. 2003. (gr. 3-6). lib. bdg. 15.25 (978-0-613-67892-6(3)) Tandem Library Bks.

—Experiments with Weather. 2003. (True Book Ser.). (Illus.). 48p. (J). 25.00 (978-0-516-22790-0(4), Children's Pr.) Scholastic Library Publishing.

—How to Do a Science Fair Project. rev. ed. 1998. (Experimental Science Ser.). 144p. (J). (gr. 8-12). pap. 9.95 (978-0-531-15881-4(0), Watts, Franklin) Scholastic Library Publishing.

—Plant Projects for Young Scientists. 2000. (Projects for Young Scientists Ser.). (Illus.). 144p. (YA). (gr. 9-12). 23.50 (978-0-531-11704-0(9), Watts, Franklin) Scholastic Library Publishing.

—Science Fair Success Using Household Products. 2002. (Science Fair Success Ser.). (Illus.). 112p. (YA). (gr. 6-12). lib. bdg. 26.60 (978-0-7660-1626-2(9)) Enslow Pubs., Inc.

—Science Fair Success Using Supermarket Products. 2000. (Science Fair Success Ser.). (Illus.). 128p. (YA). (gr. 6-12). lib. bdg. 26.60 (978-0-7660-1288-2(3)) Enslow Pubs., Inc.

Top That Publishing Staff, ed. Safe & Simple Science Tricks. 2004. (Fun Kits Ser.). (Illus.). 48p. (J). (978-1-904748-75-5(9)) Top That! Publishing PLC.

Two-Can Publishing Ltd. Staff. Experiment with Movement. 2001. (gr. 3-6). lib. bdg. 14.10 (978-0-613-84873-2(X)) Tandem Library Bks.

—Experiment with Water. 2001. (gr. 3-6). lib. bdg. 14.10 (978-0-613-83316-5(3)) Tandem Library Bks.

VanCeave, Janice. Janice VanCleave's Big Book of Play & Find Out Science Projects. 2007. (Illus.). 224p. pap. 19.95 (***978-0-7879-8928-6(2)***) Wiley, John & Sons, Inc.

VanCleave, Janice Pratt. Engineering for Every Kid: Easy Activities That Make Learning Science Fun. 2007. (Science for Every Kid Ser.). 224p. pap. 14.95 (978-0-471-47182-0(8), Jossey-Bass) Wiley, John & Sons, Inc.

—Great Science Projects from Real Kids. 2006. (Illus.). 144p. pap. 14.95 (978-0-471-47204-9(2), Jossey-Bass) Wiley, John & Sons, Inc.

—Janice VanCleave's 203 Icy, Freezing, Frosty, Cool, & Wild Experiments. 1999. (Illus.). 128p. (gr. 3-7). pap. 12.95 (978-0-471-25223-8(9), Wiley) Wiley, John & Sons, Inc.

—Janice VanCleave's 203 Icy, Freezing, Frosty, Cool & Wild Experiments. 1999. (Illus.). 122p. (J). (ps-7). per. 22.20 (978-0-613-25780-0(4)) Tandem Library Bks.

—Janice VanCleaves A+ Projects in Astronomy: Winning Experiments for Science Fairs & Extra Credit. 2001. (Illus.). 224p. 32.50 (978-0-471-32816-2(2)); (VanCleave a+ Science Projects Ser.: Vol. 3). pap. 12.95 (978-0-471-32820-9(0)) Wiley, John & Sons, Inc. (Wiley).

—Janice VanCleave's A+ Projects in Earth Science: Winning Experiments for Science Fairs & Extra Credit. 1998. (Illus.). 234p. (YA). (gr. 7-12). lib. bdg. 22.20 (978-0-613-16516-7(0)) Tandem Library Bks.

—Janice VanCleave's A+ Projects in Earth Science: Winning Experiments for Science Fairs & Extra Credit. 1998. (VanCleave a+ Science Projects Ser.: Vol. 1). (Illus.). 240p. (gr. 7-12). pap. 12.95 (978-0-471-17770-8(9), Wiley) Wiley, John & Sons, Inc.

—Janice VanCleave's A+ Projects in Physics: Winning Experiments for Science Fairs & Extra Credit. 2003. (VanCleave a+ Science Projects Ser.). 240p. pap. 12.95 (978-0-471-33098-1(1), Wiley) Wiley, John & Sons, Inc.

—Janice VanCleave's A+ Science Fair Projects. 2003. (Illus.). 160p. pap. 14.95 (978-0-471-33102-5(3), Wiley) Wiley, John & Sons, Inc.

—Janice VanCleave's Food & Nutrition for Every Kid: Easy Activities That Make Learning Science Fun. 1999. (Science for Every Kid Ser.: Vol. 117). (Illus.). 240p. (gr. 3-7). pap. 12.95 (978-0-471-17665-7(6), Wiley) Wiley, John & Sons, Inc.

—Janice VanCleave's Magnets: Mind-Boggling Experiments You Can Turn into Science Fair Projects. 2002. (Janice Vancleave Ser.). (Illus.). (J). 19.72 (978-0-7587-4630-6(X)) Book Wholesalers, Inc.

—Janice VanCleave's Play & Find Out about Bugs: Easy Experiments for Young Children. 1999. (Play & Find Out Ser.: Vol. 9). (Illus.). 122p. (ps-2). pap. 12.95 (978-0-471-17663-3(X), Wiley) Wiley, John & Sons, Inc.

—Janice VanCleave's Solar System: Mind-Boggling Experiments You Can Turn into Science Fair Projects. 1999. (Spectacular Science Project Ser.: Vol. 14). (Illus.). 96p. (gr. 3-7). pap. 10.95 (978-0-471-32204-7(0), Wiley-Interscience) Wiley, John & Sons, Inc.

VanCleave, Janice Pratt. Janice VanCleave's Super Science Challenges: Hands-On Science Inquiry Projects for School, Science Fair, or Just Plain Fun! 2007. 160p. pap. 14.95 (***978-0-471-47183-7(6)***, Jossey-Bass) Wiley, John & Sons, Inc.

Vecchione, Glen. Experimentos Sencillos con la Luz y el Sonido. Elena, Horacio, tr. Elena, Horacio, illus. 2004. (Juego de la Ciencia Ser.). (SPA.). 124p. 10.99 (978-84-9754-043-8(3), 87814) Ediciones Oniro S.A. ESP. *Dist:* Bilingual Pubns. Co., The, Lectorum Pubns., Inc.

—Experimentos Sencillos Sobre Las Leyes de la Naturaleza. Elena, Horacio, tr. Elena, Horacio, illus. (Juego de la Ciencia Ser.). (SPA.). 128p. 5.20 (978-84-9754-025-4(5), 87811) Ediciones Oniro S.A. ESP. *Dist:* Bilingual Pubns. Co., The.

S

—100 First Prize Make-It-Yourself Science Fair Projects. 1998. (Illus.). 192p. (J). (gr. 4-7). 19.95 (978-0-8069-0703-1(7)) Sterling Publishing Co., Inc.

Voth, Danna. Kidsource: Science Fair Handbook. 1998. (Illus.). 112p. (J). (gr. 3-7). pap. 9.95 (978-1-56565-514-0(1), 05141W) Lowell Hse. Juvenile.

Walker, Pam & Wood, Elaine. Science Experiments on File, 3 Vols. (Experiments Ser.). (gr. 6-12). Set. 2006. 288p. 555.00 (978-0-8160-6069-6(X)); Vol. 2. 2nd rev. ed. 2005. 352p. 185.00 (978-0-8160-5735-1(4)); Vol. 3. 2006. 320p. (YA). ring bd. 185.00 (978-0-8160-6068-9(1)) Facts On File, Inc.

—Science Experiments on File Set. 2nd rev. ed. 2005. (Experiments Ser.). 640p. (gr. 6-12). 370.00 (978-0-8160-5736-8(2)) Facts On File, Inc.

Wells, Rosemary. Discover & Explore: Based on Timothy Goes to School & Other Stories. Koelsch, Michael, illus. 2001. 24p. (J). (ps-k). 13.99 (978-0-670-91035-9(X), Viking Juvenile) Penguin Group (USA) Inc.

West, Krista. Hands-On Projects about Changes in the Earth. 2002. (Great Earth Science Projects Ser.). (Illus.). 24p. (J). lib. bdg. 19.95 (978-0-8239-5844-3(2), PowerKids Pr.) Rosen Publishing Group, Inc., The.

—Hands-On Projects about Earth & Space. 2002. (Great Earth Science Projects Ser.). (Illus.). 24p. (J). lib. bdg. 19.95 (978-0-8239-5843-6(4)) Rosen Publishing Group, Inc., The.

—Hands-On Projects about Oceans. 2002. (Great Earth Science Projects Ser.). (Illus.). 24p. (J). lib. bdg. 19.95 (978-0-8239-5846-7(9), PowerKids Pr.) Rosen Publishing Group, Inc., The.

—Hands-On Projects about Rocks, Minerals & Fossils. 2002. (Great Earth Science Projects Ser.). (Illus.). 24p. (J). lib. bdg. 19.95 (978-0-8239-5842-9(6), PowerKids Pr.) Rosen Publishing Group, Inc., The.

—Hands-On Projects about Weather & Climate. 2002. (Great Earth Science Projects Ser.). (Illus.). 24p. (J). lib. bdg. 19.95 (978-0-8239-5845-0(0), PowerKids Pr.) Rosen Publishing Group, Inc., The.

Whitehouse, Patricia. Empujar. 2003. Tr. of Pushing. 5.25 (978-1-4034-3456-2(5)) Heinemann Library.

—Floating. 2003. (Illus.). 24p. (J). pap. (978-1-4034-3467-8(0)); lib. bdg. 18.50 (978-1-4034-0904-1(8)) Heinemann Library.

—Flotar. 2003. Tr. of Floating. 24p. pap. 5.25 (978-1-4034-3457-9(3)) Heinemann Library.

—Investigations, 4 bks., Set. 2004. (J). (ps-1). lib. bdg. 82.57 (978-1-4034-5101-9(X)) Heinemann Library.

—Matter & Energy. 2007. (J). (***978-1-4034-7917-4(8)***) Heinemann Library.

—Mezclar. 2004. 24p. (J). (ps-1). lib. bdg. 20.64 (978-1-4034-5113-2(3)) Heinemann Library.

—Pulling. 2003. (Illus.). 24p. (J). pap. (978-1-4034-3468-5(9)); lib. bdg. 18.50 (978-1-4034-0909-6(9)) Heinemann Library.

—Pushing. 2003. (Illus.). 24p. (J). pap. (978-1-4034-3469-2(7)); lib. bdg. 18.50 (978-1-4034-0908-9(0)) Heinemann Library.

—Resbalar. 2003. 24p. pap. 5.25 (978-1-4034-3458-6(1)) Heinemann Library.

—Rolling. 2003. (Illus.). 24p. (J). pap. (978-1-4034-3470-8(0)); lib. bdg. 18.50 (978-1-4034-0907-2(2)) Heinemann Library.

—Sliding. 2003. (Illus.). 24p. (J). pap. (978-1-4034-3471-5(9)); lib. bdg. 18.50 (978-1-4034-0906-5(4)) Heinemann Library.

—Tirar. 2003. Tr. of Pulling. 24p. pap. 5.25 (978-1-4034-3460-9(3)) Heinemann Library.

Whitehouse, Patricia, tr. Cooling. 2004. (J). pap. (978-1-4034-5102-6(8)); lib. bdg. (978-1-4034-5097-5(8)) Heinemann Library.

—Heating. 2004. (J). lib. bdg. (978-1-4034-5098-2(6)) Heinemann Library.

—Mixing. 2004. (J). lib. bdg. (978-1-4034-5099-9(4)) Heinemann Library.

Whiting Woodfield, Marilee. Inexpensive science exper G 2-3. 2004. 80p. (C). pap. 10.99 (***978-0-7424-2790-7(0)***, Instructional Fair) Schaffer, Frank Pubns.

Whitley, Peggy J. & Goodwin, Susan Williams. 99 Jumpstarts for Kids' Science Research. 2005. (Illus.). 264p. pap. 35.00 (978-1-59158-261-8(X), LU261X) Libraries Unlimited, Inc.

Wiese, Jim. Head to Toe Science: Over 40 Eye-Popping, Spine-Tingling, Heart-Pounding Activit. 2000. (gr. 3-6). lib. bdg. 22.20 (978-0-613-25472-4(4)) Tandem Library Bks.

—Head to Toe Science: Over 40 Eye-Popping, Spine-Tingling, Heart-Pounding Activities That Teach Kids about the Human Body. Cash-Walsh, Tina, illus. 2000. 128p. (gr. 3-7). pap. 12.95 (978-0-471-33203-9(8), Wiley-IEEE Pr.) Wiley, John & Sons, Inc.

—Magic Science: 50 Jaw-Dropping, Mind-Boggling, Head-Scratching Activities for Kids. 1998. (gr. 3-6). lib. bdg. 22.20 (978-0-613-89256-8(9)) Tandem Library Bks.

—Magic Science: 50 Jaw-Dropping, Mind-Boggling, Head-Scratching Activities for Kids. 1998. (Illus.). 128p. (gr. 3-7). pap. 12.95 (978-0-471-18239-9(7), Wiley) Wiley, John & Sons, Inc.

Wiese, Jim & Shems, Ed. Weird Science: 40 Strange-Acting, Bizarre-Looking, & Barely Believable Activities for Kids. 2004. (Illus.). 128p. pap. 12.95 (978-0-471-46229-3(2), Jossey-Bass) Wiley, John & Sons, Inc.

Williams, John. Water Projects. 1998. (Design & Create Ser.). (Illus.). 32p. (J). (gr. 2-5). lib. bdg. 17.98 (978-0-8172-4890-1(0)) Raintree.

Williams, Zella. Do-It-Yourself Science, 6 bks., Set. Incl. Experiments about Planet Earth. lib. bdg. 23.95 (978-1-4042-3662-2(7), PowerKids Pr.); Experiments about the Natural World. lib. bdg. 23.95 (978-1-4042-3661-5(9), PowerKids Pr.); Experiments on Rocks & the Rock Cycle. lib. bdg. 23.95 (978-1-4042-3660-8(0)); Experiments on the Weather. lib. bdg. 23.95 (978-1-4042-3663-9(5)); Experiments with Physical Science. lib. bdg. 23.95 (978-1-4042-3659-2(7)); Experiments with Solids, Liquids, & Gases. lib. bdg. 23.95 (978-1-4042-3658-5(9), PowerKids Pr.); (Illus.). 24p. (J). (gr. 2-5). 2007. 2007. Set lib. bdg. 143.70 (***978-1-4042-3605-9(8)**, PowerKids Pr.) Rosen Publishing Group, Inc., The.

Willis, Shirley. Dime Como Flotan los Barcos. 2000. (Estupendos Ser.). (J). 12.75 (978-0-606-20147-6(5)) Tandem Library Bks.

Wilson, Jim. Ray's Reflections. Cordel, Betty, ed. Richmond, Brenda, illus. 2000. 122p. (J). (gr. 4-8). pap., wbk. ed. 18.95 (978-1-881431-84-8(3), 1316) AIMS Education Foundation.

Wood, Robert W. McGraw-Hill Big Book of Science Activities. 1999. (gr. 3-6). lib. bdg. 25.70 (978-0-613-71525-6(X)) Tandem Library Bks.

—The McGraw-Hill Big Book of Science Activities: Fun & Easy Experiments for Kids. 3rd ed. 1999. (Illus.). 512p. (C). (gr. 4-7). pap. 15.95 (978-0-07-071873-9(3), 9780070718739) McGraw-Hill Cos., The.

—What? 1999. (Experiments for Young Scientists Ser.). (Illus.). ix, 143p. (YA). (gr. 4-7). lib. bdg. 25.25 (978-0-7910-4847-4(0), Chelsea Hse.) Facts On File, Inc.

—When? 1999. (Experiments for Young Scientists Ser.). (Illus.). 152p. (J). (gr. 3-8). lib. bdg. 25.25 (978-0-7910-4850-4(0), Chelsea Hse.) Facts On File, Inc.

—Where? 1999. (Experiments for Young Scientists Ser.). (Illus.). 152p. (YA). (gr. 4-7). lib. bdg. 22.95 (978-0-7910-4848-1(9), Chelsea Hse.) Facts On File, Inc.

—Who? 1999. (Experiments for Young Scientists Ser.). (Illus.). 152p. (YA). (gr. 4-7). lib. bdg. 25.25 (978-0-7910-4851-1(9), Chelsea Hse.) Facts On File, Inc.

Wood, Robert W., et al. Why? 1999. (Experiments for Young Scientists Ser.). (Illus.). 152p. (YA). (gr. 4-7). lib. bdg. 25.25 (978-0-7910-4849-8(7), Chelsea Hse.) Facts On File, Inc.

Zubrowski, Bernie. Making Waves: Finding Out about Rhythmic Motion. 2001. 73p. spiral bd. 9.00 (978-1-58651-901-8(8)) Pitsco/Pitsco LEGO Dacta.

—Mirrors: Finding Out about the Properties of Light. 2001. 59p. spiral bd. 9.00 (978-1-58651-903-2(4)) Pitsco/Pitsco LEGO Dacta.

150 + Easy Science Experiments. 1999. (Illus.). 128p. (YA). (gr. 5). pap. 11.95 (978-1-58037-107-0(8)) Twain, Mark Media, Inc. Pubs.

SCIENCE—EXPERIMENTS—FICTION

Anderson, M. T. The Astonishing Life of Octavian Nothing, Traitor to the Nation. 2006. (Pox Party Ser.: Vol. 1). (Illus.). 368p. (YA). (gr. 9). 17.99 (978-0-7636-2402-6(0)) Candlewick Pr.

Anderson, M. T. Astonishing Life of Octavian Nothing, Traitor to the Nation: The Pox Party. rev. l.t. ed. 2007. (Astonishing Life of Octavian Nothing Ser.). 500p. (YA). 23.95 (***978-0-7862-9552-4(X)**) Thorndike Pr.

Baldacci, David. The Mystery of Silas Finklebean. Harrington, Patrick, illus. 2nd ed. 2006. (Freddy & the French Fries Ser.: No. 2). 176p. (J). (gr. 3-7). pap. 4.99 (978-0-316-05900-8(5)) Little Brown & Co.

Baldacci, David & Baldacci, Rudy. Fries Alive! 2006. (Freddy & the French Fries Ser.). (Illus.). 192p. (J). (gr. 3-7). pap. 4.99 (978-0-316-05901-5(3)) Little Brown & Co.

Benton, Jim. Attack of the 50-Ft. Cupid. Benton, Jim, illus. 2003. (Franny K. Stein, Mad Scientist Ser.: Bk. 2). (Illus.). 112p. (J). (gr. 2-5). 14.95 (978-0-689-86292-2(X)) Simon & Schuster Children's Publishing.

—Franny K. Stein's Crate of Danger Set: Lunch Walks among Us; Attack of the 50-Ft. Cupid; the Invisible Fran; the Fran That Time Forgot. Benton, Jim, illus. 2005. (Franny K. Stein, Mad Scientist Ser.). 448p. (J). pap. 14.99 (978-1-4169-1402-0(1), Aladdin) Simon & Schuster Children's Publishing.

—Lunch Walks among Us. Benton, Jim, illus. (Franny K. Stein, Mad Scientist Ser.: Bk. 2). (Illus.). 112p. (J). 2004. (gr. 2-5). mass mkt. 3.99 (978-0-689-86295-3(4), Aladdin); 2003. 15.99 (978-0-689-86291-5(1)) Simon & Schuster Children's Publishing.

Burkett, Kathy. Out of This World! Ethan Flask & Professor Von Offel Take on Space Science. 2003. (gr. 3-6). lib. bdg. 12.40 (978-0-613-72121-9(7)) Tandem Library Bks.

Clements, Andrew. Jake Drake, Know-It-All. l.t. ed. 2002. (Juvenile Ser.). (Illus.). 76p. (J). 21.95 (978-0-7862-4139-2(X)) Thomson Gale.

Clements, Andrew. Know-It-All. Pedersen, Janet, illus. 2007. (Jake Drake Ser.: No. 2). 112p. (J). pap. 3.99 (***978-1-4169-3931-3(8)**, Aladdin) Simon & Schuster Children's Publishing.

Cook, Robin. Vector. 2000. (gr. 7-12). lib. bdg. 16.45 (978-0-613-22563-2(5)) Tandem Library Bks.

David, James F. Ship of the Damned. 2001. (gr. 7-12). lib. bdg. 15.30 (978-0-613-42792-0(0)) Tandem Library Bks.

Dewin, Howie. Dexter's Ink. Kurtz Art Studio Staff, illus. 2002. (Dexter's Laboratory Chapter Bks.: No. 1). 64p. (J). (gr. 1-4). pap. 3.99 (978-0-439-38579-4(2)) Scholastic, Inc.

Dowell, Frances O'Roark. Phineas L. MacGuire ... Erupts! The First Experiment. McDaniels, Preston, illus. 2006. (From the Highly Scientific Notebooks of Phineas L. MacGuire Ser.). 176p. (J). (gr. 3-7). 15.95 (978-1-4169-0195-2(7)) Simon & Schuster Children's Publishing.

—Phineas L. MacGuire ... Erupts! The First Experiment. McDaniels, Preston, illus. 2007. (From the Highly Scientific Notebooks of Phineas L. MacGuire Ser.). 176p. (J). pap. 4.99 (***978-1-4169-4734-9(5)**, Aladdin) Simon & Schuster Children's Publishing.

Dowell, Frances O'Roark. Phineas L. MacGuire... Gets Slimed! The Second Experiment. McDaniels, Preston L., illus. 2007. (From the Highly Scientific Notebooks of Phineas L. MacGuire Ser.). 208p. (J). (gr. 3-7). 16.99 (978-1-4169-0196-9(5)) Simon & Schuster Children's Publishing.

Egan, Tim. The Experiments of Doctor Vermin. Egan, Tim, illus. 2002. (Illus.). 32p. (J). (gr. k-3). tchr. ed. 15.00 (978-0-618-13224-9(4)) Houghton Mifflin Co. Trade & Reference Div.

Grunwell, Jeanne Marie. Mind Games. 2006. 144p. (YA). (gr. 5-9). pap. 5.95 (978-0-618-68947-7(8)) Houghton Mifflin Co.

Harcourt School Publishers Staff. Will Ants Come? On Level. 3rd ed. 2002. (Trophies Reading Program Ser.). (Illus.). (J). pap. 3.20 (978-0-15-322975-6(6)) Harcourt Schl. Pubs.

Howe, James. It Came from Beneath the Bed! 2003. (Tales from the House of Bunnicula Ser.). (gr. 3-6). lib. bdg. 11.80 (978-0-613-66415-8(9)) Tandem Library Bks.

—It Came from Beneath the Bed! 2004. (Tales from the House of Bunnicula Ser.). 112p. (J). (gr. 3-6). pap. 17.00 incl. audio (978-1-4000-8632-0(9), Listening Library) Random Hse. Audio Publishing Group.

Knudsen, Michelle. A Moldy Mystery. Gott, Barry, illus. 2006. (Science Solves It! Ser.). 32p. (J). (978-1-57565-167-5(X)) Kane Pr., The.

Parish, Herman. Amelia Bedelia, Rocket Scientist? Sweat, Lynn, illus. (I Can Read Bks.). 64p. (J). 2007. pap. 3.99 (978-0-06-051889-6(8), Harper Trophy); 2005. (gr. 1 up). 15.99 (978-0-06-051887-5(1)); 2005. (gr. 1 up). lib. bdg. 16.89 (978-0-06-051888-2(X)) HarperCollins Pubs.

Pollack, Pam & Belviso, Meg. Dr. Dee Dee & Dexter Hyde. Kurtz Art Studio Staff, illus. 2002. (Dexter's Laboratory Chapter Bks.: No. 3). 64p. (J). (gr. 1-4). pap. 3.99 (978-0-439-43422-5(X)) Scholastic, Inc.

Seuling, Barbara. Robert & the Happy Endings. Brewer, Paul, illus. 2007. (Robert Bks.). 160p. (J). (gr. 2-4). 16.95 (978-0-8126-2748-0(2)) Cricket Bks.

Stefan, V., creator. Tom Leanius, Little Science Genius. 2002. (Series on Science for Children). (J). per. (978-1-889545-51-6(1)) Stefan Univ. Pr., The.

Taylor-Butler, Christine. Step by Step. Miller, Susan, illus. 2006. 32p. (J). (gr. k-1). pap. 3.95 (978-0-516-24974-2(6), Children's Pr.) Scholastic Library Publishing.

SCIENCE—FICTION

see Science Fiction

SCIENCE—HISTORY

Anderson, Margaret J. & Stephenson, Karen F. Scientists of the Ancient World. 1999. (Collective Biographies Ser.). (Illus.). 104p. (YA). (gr. 6-12). lib. bdg. 26.60 (978-0-7660-1111-3(9)) Enslow Pubs., Inc.

Atkinson, Mary. The Earth Is Flat! Science Facts & Fictions. 2007. (Shockwave: Science in Practice Ser.). (Illus.). 36p. (J). (gr. 4-6). lib. bdg. 25.00 (***978-0-531-17580-4(4)**, Children's Pr.) Scholastic Library Publishing.

Balchin, Jon. Science: 100 Scientists Who Changed the World. 2003. (Illus.). 224p. 18.95 (978-1-59270-017-2(9)) Enchanted Lion Bks., LLC.

Benchmark Education Staff, compiled by. HIST & Nature of Science. 2006. spiral bd. 145.00 (***978-1-4108-6949-4(0)**); 2005. spiral bd. 60.00 (***978-1-4108-3849-0(8)**); 2005. spiral bd. 145.00 (***978-1-4108-3865-0(X)**); 2005. spiral bd. 42.00 (***978-1-4108-3878-0(1)**); 2005. spiral bd. 42.00 (***978-1-4108-3879-7(X)**); 2005. spiral bd. 135.00 (***978-1-4108-4515-3(X)**); 2005. spiral bd. 185.00 (***978-1-4108-5436-0(1)**); 2005. spiral bd. 185.00 (***978-1-4108-5437-7(X)**); 2005. spiral bd. 85.00 (***978-1-4108-5849-8(9)**); 2005. spiral bd. 165.00 (***978-1-4108-5850-4(2)**); 2005. spiral bd. 180.00 (***978-1-4108-3848-3(X)**) Benchmark Education Co.

—Scientific Achievements. 2006. spiral bd. 119.00 (***978-1-4108-7130-5(4)**) Benchmark Education Co.

Beshore, George W. Science in Ancient China. 1998. (Science of the Past Ser.). (Illus.). 64p. (J). (gr. 5-7). pap. 8.95 (978-0-531-15914-9(0), Watts, Franklin) Scholastic Library Publishing.

—Science in Ancient China. 1998. (gr. 3-6). lib. bdg. 17.60 (978-0-613-72684-9(7)) Tandem Library Bks.

Biesty, Stephen & Platt, Richard. Stephen Biesty's Incredible Explosions: Exploded Views of Astonishing Things. (Illus.). 32p. (J). pap. 22.99 (978-0-590-24893-8(6)) Scholastic, Inc.

Craig, Diane. Science History Is No Mystery! 2006. (Illus.). 24p. (J). (978-1-59928-617-4(3)) ABDO Publishing Co.

Doudna, Kelly. Science History Is No Mystery. 2007. (Illus.). 24p. (J). 19.93 (978-1-59928-616-7(5), Sand-Castle) ABDO Publishing Co.

Farndon, John. Religion, Science, Medicine & Warfare. 2001. (Illustrated Encyclopedia Ser.). (Illus.). 256p. (gr. 3-7). pap. 19.95 (978-1-84215-518-9(0), Southwater) Anness Publishing GBR. *Dist:* National Bk. Network.

Gjertsen, Derek & Allaby, Michael, eds. Makers of Science, 5 vols., Set. 2001. (Illus.). 480p. (YA). (gr. 5-9). 225.00 (978-0-19-521680-6(6)) Oxford Univ. Pr., Inc.

Gow, Mary. Robert Hooke: Creative Genius, Scientist, Inventor. 2006. (Great Minds of Science Ser.). (Illus.). 128p. (J). (gr. 4-10). lib. bdg. 31.93 (978-0-7660-2547-9(0)) Enslow Pubs., Inc.

Hakim, Joy. The Story of Science: Newton at the Center. 2005. (Smithsonian's Story of Science Ser.). (Illus.). 463p. (YA). (gr. 7 up). 24.95 (978-1-58834-161-7(5)) Smithsonian Institution Pr.

Harris, Jacqueline L. Science in Ancient Rome. 1998. (Illus.). 64p. (J). (ps-6). lib. bdg. 17.60 (978-0-613-19128-9(5)) Tandem Library Bks.

Hatt, Christine. Scientists & Their Discoveries. 2001. (Documenting History Ser.). (Illus.). 64p. (J). (gr. 8-12). 24.50 (978-0-531-14614-9(6), Watts, Franklin) Scholastic Library Publishing.

Herold, Vickey. Discover Science During the Renaissance. 2006. pap. 39.00 (***978-1-4108-6467-3(7)**) Benchmark Education Co.

—Science During the Renaissance. 2006. pap. 42.00 (***978-1-4108-6464-2(2)**) Benchmark Education Co.

January, Brendan. Science in Colonial America. 1999. (Science of the Past Ser.). (Illus.). 64p. (J). (gr. 5-7). pap. 8.95 (978-0-531-15940-8(X), Watts, Franklin) Scholastic Library Publishing.

—Science in Colonial America. 1999. (gr. 5-8). lib. bdg. 17.60 (978-0-613-50830-8(0)) Tandem Library Bks.

Kudlinski, Kathleen V. Boy, Were We Wrong about Dinosaurs! Schindler, S. D., illus. 2005. 32p. (J). (ps-4). 15.99 (978-0-525-46978-0(8), Dutton Juvenile) Penguin Group (USA) Inc.

Lorenz Books Staff, et al. Science & Technology: Humanity's Quest for Knowledge & Explanations, 4 vols. 2000. (Exploring History Ser.). (Illus.). 64p. (gr. 3-7). 12.95 (978-0-7548-0454-3(2), Lorenz Bks.) Anness Publishing GBR. *Dist:* National Bk. Network.

McGowen, Tom. The Beginnings of Science. 1998. (Single Titles Ser.). (Illus.). 80p. (gr. 5-8). lib. bdg. 26.90 (978-0-7613-3016-5(X), Millbrook Pr.) Lerner Publishing Group.

Milestones in Modern Science, 6 Vols. 180.00 (978-0-8368-5850-1(6)) Stevens, Gareth Inc.

Moss, Carol. Science in Mesopotamia. rev. ed. 1999. (Science of the Past Ser.). (Illus.). 64p. (J). (gr. 5-7). pap. 8.95 (978-0-531-15930-9(2), Watts, Franklin) Scholastic Library Publishing.

Parker, Steve. 1900-20: A Shrinking World. 2001. (Twentieth Century Science & Technology Ser.). (Illus.). 32p. (J). (gr. 5 up). lib. bdg. 26.00 (978-0-8368-2942-6(5)) Stevens, Gareth Inc.

—1920-40: Atoms to Automation. 2001. (Twentieth Century Science & Technology Ser.). (Illus.). 32p. (J). (gr. 5 up). lib. bdg. 26.00 (978-0-8368-2943-3(3)) Stevens, Gareth Inc.

—1940-60: The Nuclear Age. 2001. (Twentieth Century Science & Technology Ser.). (Illus.). 32p. (J). (gr. 5 up). lib. bdg. 26.00 (978-0-8368-2944-0(1)) Stevens, Gareth Inc.

—1960s: Space & Time. 2001. (Twentieth Century Science & Technology Ser.). (Illus.). 32p. (J). (gr. 5 up). lib. bdg. 26.00 (978-0-8368-2945-7(X)) Stevens, Gareth Inc.

Platt, Richard. Stephen Biesty's Incredible Explosions: Exploded Views of Astonishing Things. Biesty, Stephen, illus. 2004. 32p. (J). (gr. 2-8). reprint ed. 20.00 (978-0-7567-7680-0(5)) DIANE Publishing Co.

Ross, Frank. Oracle Bones, Stars, & Wheelbarrows: Ancient Chinese Science & Technology. (gr. 5-8). lib. bdg. 15.25 (978-0-8335-6082-7(4)) Tandem Library Bks.

Scientific Revolution: PowerPoints in World History. 2005. cd-rom 49.95 net. (978-1-56004-215-0(X)) Social Studies Schl. Service.

Scientific Revolution DBA. 2003. spiral bd. 16.95 (978-1-56004-168-9(4)) Social Studies Schl. Service.

Spangenburg, Ray & Moser, Diane. The Birth of Science: Ancient Times to 1699. 2nd ed. 2004. (Facts on File Science Library). (Illus.). 256p. (J). (gr. 6-12). 40.00 (978-0-8160-4851-9(7)) Facts On File, Inc.

—Modern Science, 1896-1945. 2nd ed. 2004. (History of Science Ser.). (Illus.). 224p. (J). (gr. 6-12). 40.00 (978-0-8160-4854-0(1)) Facts On File, Inc.

—The Rise of Reason: 1700-1799. 2nd ed. 2004. (History of Science Ser.). (Illus.). 224p. (J). (gr. 6-12). 40.00 (978-0-8160-4852-6(5)) Facts On File, Inc.

—Science Frontiers, 1946-2001. 2nd ed. 2004. (Facts on File Science Library). (Illus.). 272p. (J). (gr. 6-12). 40.00 (978-0-8160-4855-7(X)) Facts On File, Inc.

Spangenburg, Ray & Moser, Diane K. The Great Age of Synthesis: 1800-1895. 2nd ed. 2004. (Facts on File Science Library). (Illus.). 208p. (J). (gr. 6-12). 40.00 (978-0-8160-4853-3(3)) Facts On File, Inc.

—The History of Science, 5 vols., Set. 2004. (History of Science Ser.). 208-272p. (gr. 6-12). 200.00 (978-0-8160-4850-2(9)) Facts On File, Inc.

Stiffler, Leanne. Science Rediscovered: A Daily Chronicle of Highlights in the History of Science. 1998. (Illus.). 112p. (J). (gr. 6-8). pap. (978-0-89089-940-3(1)) Carolina Academic Pr.

Strom, Laura Layton. The Egyptian Science Gazette. 2007. (Shockwave: Science in Practice Ser.). (Illus.). 36p. (J). (gr. 4-6). lib. bdg. 25.00 (***978-0-531-17582-8(0)**, Children's Pr.) Scholastic Library Publishing.

VanCleave, Janice Pratt. Janice VanCleave's Science Through the Ages. 2002. (Illus.). 128p. pap. 12.95 (978-0-471-33097-4(3), Wiley) Wiley, John & Sons, Inc.

Whitfield, Peter. Atoms & Galaxies: Modern Physical Science, 10 vols., Vol. 9. 2003. (Illus.). (J). (978-0-7172-5711-9(8), Grolier) Scholastic Library Publishing.

—The Eighteenth Century, 10 vols., Vol. 6. 2003. (Illus.). (J). (978-0-7172-5708-9(8), Grolier) Scholastic Library Publishing.

—The European Renaissance, 10 vols., Vol. 4. 2003. (Illus.). (J). (978-0-7172-5706-5(1), Grolier) Scholastic Library Publishing.

—Geology & Evolution in the Nineteenth Century, 10 vols., Vol. 8. 2003. (Illus.). (J). (978-0-7172-5710-2(X), Grolier) Scholastic Library Publishing.

—History of Science, 10 vols. Incl. Vol. 1. Science in Ancient Civilizations. (978-0-7172-5703-4(7)); Vol. 2. Islamic & Western Medieval Science. (978-0-7172-5704-1(5)); Vol. 3. Traditions of Science Outside Europe. (978-0-7172-5705-8(3)); Vol. 4. European Renaissance. (978-0-7172-5706-5(1)); Vol. 5. Scientific Revolution. (978-0-7172-5707-2(X)); Vol. 6. Eighteenth Century. (978-0-7172-5708-9(8)); Vol. 7. Physical Science in the Nineteenth Century. (978-0-7172-5709-6(6)); Vol. 8. Geology & Evolution in the Nineteeth Century. (978-0-7172-5710-2(X)); Vol. 9. Atoms & Galaxies: Modern Physical Science. (978-0-7172-5711-9(8)); Vol. 10. Twentieth-Century Life Sciences. (978-0-7172-5712-6(6)); (J). (Illus.). 800p. 2003. 279.00 (978-0-7172-5729-4(0), Grolier) Scholastic Library Publishing.

—Islamic & Western Medieval Science, 10 vols., Vol. 2. 2003. (Illus.). (J). (978-0-7172-5704-1(5), Grolier) Scholastic Library Publishing.

—Physical Science in the Nineteenth Century, 10 vols., Vol. 7. 2003. (Illus.). (J). (978-0-7172-5709-6(6), Grolier) Scholastic Library Publishing.

—Science in Ancient Civilizations, 10 vols., Vol. 1. 2003. (Illus.). (J). (978-0-7172-5703-4(7), Grolier) Scholastic Library Publishing.

—The Scientific Revolution, 10 vols., Vol. 5. 2003. (Illus.). (J). (978-0-7172-5707-2(X), Grolier) Scholastic Library Publishing.

—Traditions of Science Outside Europe, 10 vols., Vol. 3. 2003. (Illus.). (J). (978-0-7172-5705-8(3), Grolier) Scholastic Library Publishing.

—Twentieth-Century Life Sciences, 10 vols., Vol. 10. 2003. (Illus.). (J). (978-0-7172-5712-6(6), Grolier) Scholastic Library Publishing.

Wiese, Jim. Ancient Science: 40 Time-Traveling, World-Exploring, History-Making Activities F. 2003. (gr. 3-6). lib. bdg. 22.20 (978-0-613-89252-0(6)) Tandem Library Bks.

Wood, Geraldine. Science of the Early Americas. 1999. (gr. 5-8). lib. bdg. 17.60 (978-0-613-54346-0(7)) Tandem Library Bks.

Woods, Geraldine. Science of the Early Americas. 1999. (Science of the Past Ser.). (Illus.). 64p. (J). (gr. 5-7). pap. 8.95 (978-0-531-15941-5(8), Watts, Franklin) Scholastic Library Publishing.

SCIENCE—METHODOLOGY

see also Logic

Brown, Stephanie Gwyn. Professor Aesop's the Crow & the Pitcher. 2004. (Illus.). 30p. (J). tchr. ed. 15.95 (978-1-58246-087-1(6), Tricycle Pr.) Ten Speed Pr.

Chappell, Rachel M. Solving Science Questions: A Book about the Scientific Process. 2008. (J). (***978-1-60044-542-2(X)**) Rourke Publishing, LLC.

Cowles, Rose, illus. Science Detectives. 2006. 48p. (978-1-55337-995-9(0)); (978-1-55337-994-2(2)) Kids Can Pr., Ltd.

Doudna, Kelly. I'll Use Information for My Explanation! (Illus.). 24p. (J). 2007. 19.93 (978-1-59928-588-7(6)); 2006. (978-1-59928-589-4(4)) ABDO Publishing Co.

—It's a Date, Let's Investigate! (Illus.). 24p. (J). 2007. 19.93 (978-1-59928-596-2(7)); 2006. pap. (978-1-59928-597-9(5)) ABDO Publishing Co.

—It's Not Strange, I Know about Change. 2007. (Illus.). 24p. (J). 19.93 (978-1-59928-604-4(1), SandCastle) ABDO Publishing Co.

—It's Not Too Late, Let's Communicate! (Illus.). 24p. (J). 2007. 19.93 (978-1-59928-606-8(8)); 2006. pap. (978-1-59928-607-5(6)) ABDO Publishing Co.

—We Are Wise, Let's Hypothesize! (Illus.). 24p. (J). 2007. 19.93 (978-1-59928-622-8(X)); 2006. pap. (978-1-59928-623-5(8)) ABDO Publishing Co.

Exploratorium Staff, et al. Exploratopia: More Than 400 Kid-Friendly Explorations & Experiments for Curious Minds. Gorski, Jason, illus. 2006. 384p. (J). (gr. 3-7). 29.99 (978-0-316-61281-4(2)) Little, Brown Bks. for Young Readers.

Glass, Susan. Analyze This! Understanding the Scientific Method. 2006. (Illus.). 48p. (J). (978-1-4034-8362-1(0)); lib. bdg. (978-1-4034-8358-4(2)) Heinemann Library.

—Prove It! The Scientific Method in Action. 2006. (Illus.). 48p. (J). (978-1-4034-8359-1(0)); pap. (978-1-4034-8363-8(9)) Heinemann Library.

Holly Wallace. The Mystery of the Loch Ness Monster. 2nd ed. 2006. (Can Science Solve? Ser.). (Illus.). 32p. (J). pap. (***978-1-4034-8346-1(9)**) Heinemann Library.

Jerome, Kate Boehm. Thinking It Through. 2004. (National Geographic Reading Expeditions Ser.). (Illus.). 24p. (J). pap. (978-0-7922-4593-3(8)) National Geographic Society.

Lemke, Donald B. Investigating the Scientific Method with Max Axiom, Super Scientist. Smith, Tod, illus. 2008. (J). (***978-1-4296-1329-3(7)**) Capstone Pr., Inc.

Magner, Laura. The Scientific Method in Fairy Tale Forest. 2007. pap. 14.95 (***978-1-931334-94-5(3)**) Pieces of Learning.

Nye, Bill. Bill Nye the Science Guy's Big Blast of Science. 2000. (Illus.). 176p. (YA). pap. 16.95 (978-0-201-60864-9(2)) Basic Bks.

Pederson, Bridget. It's Not Strange, I Know about Change! 2006. (Illus.). 24p. (J). (978-1-59928-605-1(X)) ABDO Publishing Co.

Porchetta, Renato L. Universal Methodology: Semantics - the Mosaic Thinking. 2005. (Illus.). 300p. (YA). lib. bdg. 100.00 (978-0-9769931-0-0(4)) Ce Code Efficiency, Inc.

Rosinsky, Natalie M. How Scientists Work. 2004. (Illus.). 32p. (J). (gr. 3 up). 21.26 (978-0-7565-0596-7(8)) Compass Point Bks.

Somervill, Barbara A. Collecting Information. 2007. (Scientific Processes Ser.). (Illus.). 24p. (J). pap. (978-1-4042-2193-2(X)); lib. bdg. (978-1-4042-3484-0(5)) Rosen Publishing Group, Inc., The. (PowerKids Pr.).

—Communicating Valid Conclusions. 2007. (Scientific Processes Ser.). (Illus.). 24p. (J). pap. (978-1-4042-2195-6(6)); lib. bdg. (978-1-4042-3486-4(1)) Rosen Publishing Group, Inc., The. (PowerKids Pr.).

—Constructing Explanations. 2007. (Scientific Processes Ser.). (Illus.). 24p. (J). pap. (978-1-4042-2194-9(8)); lib. bdg. (978-1-4042-3485-7(3)) Rosen Publishing Group, Inc., The. (PowerKids Pr.).

—Forming Hypotheses. 2007. (Understanding Scientific Inquiry Ser.). (Illus.). 24p. (J). pap. (978-1-4042-2191-8(3)); lib. bdg. (978-1-4042-3482-6(9)) Rosen Publishing Group, Inc., The. (PowerKids Pr.).

—Organizing & Evaluating Information. 2007. (Scientific Processes Ser.). (Illus.). 24p. (J). pap. (978-1-4042-2196-3(4) , PowerKids Pr.) Rosen Publishing Group, Inc., The.

—Planning Investigations. 2007. (Understanding Scientific Inquiry Ser.). pap. (978-1-4042-2192-5(1)); lib. bdg. (978-1-4042-3483-3(7)) Rosen Publishing Group, Inc., The. (PowerKids Pr.).

Wallace, Holly. The Mystery of the Loch Ness Monster. 2006. (Can Science Solve? Ser.). (Illus.). 32p. (J). (***978-1-4034-8337-9(X)***) Heinemann Library.

SCIENCE—PHILOSOPHY

Beck, Esther. I'll Help My Chums Learn about Systems! 2006. (Illus.). 24p. (J). (978-1-59928-585-6(1)) ABDO Publishing Co.

Doudna, Kelly. I'll Help My Chums Learn about Systems. 2007. (Illus.). 24p. (J). 19.93 (978-1-59928-584-9(3) , SandCastle) ABDO Publishing Co.

Harding, Sandra & Figueroa, Robert, eds. Science & Other Cultures: Diversity in the Philosophy of Science & Technology. 2003. 304p. (gr. 13 up). 32.00 (978-0-415-93992-8(5)) Routledge.

SCIENCE—POETRY

Lewis, J. Patrick. Scien-Trickery: Riddles in Science. Remkiewicz, Frank, illus. 2007. 32p. (J). pap. 6.00 (978-0-15-205849-4(4) , Voyager Bks./Libros Viajeros) Harcourt Children's Bks.

Lewis, J. Patrick & Remkiewicz, Frank. Scien-Trickery: Riddles in Science. 2004. (Illus.). 32p. (J). 16.00 (978-0-15-216681-6(5) , Silver Whistle) Harcourt Trade Pubs.

Shields, Carol Diggory. BrainJuice: Science, Fresh Squeezed! 2003. (Illus.). 64p. (J). 14.95 (978-1-59354-005-0(1)) Handprint Bks.

SCIENCE—RESEARCH

Cherfas, Jeremy. El Genoma Humano. Yanez, Cecilia, tr. 2003. (Essential Science Ser.). (SPA.). 72p. (J). pap. 6.95 (978-970-690-599-4(5)) Planeta Mexicana Editorial S. A. de C. V. MEX. *Dist:* Lectorum Pubns., Inc.

Garlick, Mark A. El Universo en Expansion. Barois, Valerian Stoopen, tr. 2003. (Ciencia para Todos Ser.). (SPA.). 72p. (J). pap. 6.95 (978-970-690-600-7(2)) Planeta Mexicana Editorial S. A. de C. V. MEX. *Dist:* Lectorum Pubns., Inc.

Tudge, Colin. Alimentos para el Futuro. Barois, Lorena Stoopen, tr. 2003. (Essential Science Ser.). (SPA.). 72p. (J). pap. 6.95 (978-970-690-603-8(7)) Planeta Mexicana Editorial S. A. de C. V. MEX. *Dist:* Lectorum Pubns., Inc.

World Book's Science Year in Review. 2002. 352p. (978-0-7166-0555-3(4) , 20120) World Bk., Inc.

SCIENCE—SOCIAL ASPECTS

see Science and Civilization

SCIENCE—STUDY AND TEACHING

see also Nature Study

Brown, Sam Ed. Bubbles, Rainbows, & Worms: Science Experiments for Preschool Children. rev. ed. 2004. (Illus.). 96p. (J). pap. 14.95 (978-0-87659-241-0(8) , 10243) Gryphon Hse., Inc.

Building Blocks of Science: Human Bodyworks Teacher's Guide (Firsthand Learning) 2007. ring bd. (***978-0-89278-337-3(0)***) Carolina Biological Supply Co.

Building Blocks of Science: Light Teacher's Guide. 2007. (Illus.). ring bd. (***978-0-89278-339-7(7)***) Carolina Biological Supply Co.

Building Blocks of Science: Understanding Cells & DNA Teacher's Guide (Firsthand Learning) 2007. ring bd. (***978-0-89278-338-0(9)***) Carolina Biological Supply Co.

Chang, Maria L. Science. 2002. (Internet Scavenger Hunts Ser.). (Illus.). 64p. (gr. 4-8). pap. 10.95 (978-0-439-13846-8(9)) Scholastic, Inc.

Chappell, Jackie. Do You Think It's Funny When- 2007. (J). (978-1-59515-933-5(9)) Rourke Publishing, LLC.

Clausen-Grace, Nicki. Haircuts Don't Hurt. 2007. (J). (978-1-59515-931-1(2)) Rourke Publishing, LLC.

—What Can You Make? 2007. (J). (978-1-59515-932-8(0)) Rourke Publishing, LLC.

Cleland, JoAnn. I Can Make Colors. 2007. (J). (978-1-59515-925-0(8)) Rourke Publishing, LLC.

Dodd, Julia, et al. Passing the Georgia High School Graduation Test in Science. 1999. (Illus.). 224p. (J). pap. 12.00 (978-0-89892-185-4(6)) Contemporary Publishing Co. of Raleigh, Inc.

Fossils & Minerals & Crystals & Rocks. 2002. (Illus.). 48p. (J). 2.99 (978-0-88724-803-0(9) , WG 3032) Carson-Dellosa Publishing Co., Inc.

Fredericks, Anthony D. Exploring the Universe: Science Activities for Kids. Shea, Shawn, illus. 2000. 124p. (gr. 4-6). pap. 16.95 (978-1-55591-976-4(6)) Fulcrum Publishing.

Grolier Educational Staff, contrib. by. Chemical Reactions, 10 vols., Vol. 1. 2002. (Illus.). 64p. (J). (978-0-7172-5609-9(X) , Grolier) Scholastic Library Publishing.

—Ecology & Plants, 10 vols., Vol. 2. 2002. (Illus.). 64p. (J). (978-0-7172-5610-5(3) , Grolier) Scholastic Library Publishing.

—Electricity & Magnetism, 10 vols., Vol. 3. 2002. (Illus.). 64p. (J). (978-0-7172-5611-2(1) , Grolier) Scholastic Library Publishing.

—Force & Motion, 10 vols., Vol. 4. 2002. (Illus.). 64p. (J). (978-0-7172-5612-9(X) , Grolier) Scholastic Library Publishing.

—Heat & Energy, 10 vols., Vol. 5. 2002. (Illus.). 64p. (J). (978-0-7172-5613-6(8) , Grolier) Scholastic Library Publishing.

—Light, 10 vols., Vol. 6. 2002. (Illus.). 64p. (J). (978-0-7172-5614-3(6) , Grolier) Scholastic Library Publishing.

—Materials, 10 vols., Vol. 7. 2002. (Illus.). 64p. (J). (978-0-7172-5615-0(4) , Grolier) Scholastic Library Publishing.

—Science Activities, 10 vols., Set. Incl. Vol. 1. Chemical Reactions. (978-0-7172-5609-9(X)); Vol. 2. Ecology & Plants. (978-0-7172-5610-5(3)); Vol. 3. Electricity & Magnetism. (978-0-7172-5611-2(1)); Vol. 4. Force & Motion. (978-0-7172-5612-9(X)); Vol. 5. Heat & Energy. (978-0-7172-5613-6(8)); Vol. 6. Light. (978-0-7172-5614-3(6)); Vol. 7. Materials. (978-0-7172-5615-0(4)); Vol. 8. Sound. (978-0-7172-5616-7(2)); Vol. 9. Structure & Matter. (978-0-7172-5617-4(0)); Vol. 10. Weather & Climate. (978-0-7172-5618-1(9)); (J). (Illus.). 64p. 2002. 365.00 (978-0-7172-5608-2(1) , Grolier) Scholastic Library Publishing.

—Sound, 10 vols., Vol. 8. 2002. (Illus.). 64p. (J). (978-0-7172-5616-7(2) , Grolier) Scholastic Library Publishing.

—Structure & Matter, 10 vols., Vol. 9. 2002. (Illus.). 64p. (J). (978-0-7172-5617-4(0) , Grolier) Scholastic Library Publishing.

—Weather & Climate, 10 vols., Vol. 10. 2002. (Illus.). 64p. (J). (978-0-7172-5618-1(9) , Grolier) Scholastic Library Publishing.

Harcombe, Elnora S. Science Teaching/Science Learning: Constructivist Learning in Urban Classrooms. 2001. (Ways of Knowing in Science & Mathematics Ser.). (Illus.). 1p. (J). pap. 24.95 (978-0-8077-4033-0(0)) Teachers College Pr., Teachers College, Columbia Univ.

Harcourt School Publishers Staff. Harcourt Ciencias. 1999. (Harcourt Ciencias Ser.). (SPA., Illus.). (gr. 4 up). pupil's gde. ed. 73.40 (978-0-15-314806-4(3)); (gr. 5 up). pupil's gde. ed. 74.10 (978-0-15-314807-1(1)); (gr. 3 up). pupil's gde. ed. 68.90 (978-0-15-314805-7(5)) Harcourt Schl. Pubs.

—Harcourt Ciencias: CA & National Activity Book. 2000. (Harcourt Ciencias Ser.). (SPA., Illus.). pap., act. bk. ed. 8.30 (978-0-15-321397-7(3)) Harcourt Schl. Pubs.

—Harcourt Ciencias: CA & National Big Book. 2003. (Harcourt Ciencias Ser.). (SPA., Illus.). 221.70 (978-0-15-321531-5(3)) Harcourt Schl. Pubs.

—Harcourt Ciencias: CA & National Instant Readers Collection, 6 vols. 2001. (Harcourt Ciencias Ser.). (SPA., Illus.). pap. 24.90 (978-0-15-321411-0(2)) Harcourt Schl. Pubs.

—Harcourt Ciencias: CA Unit Big Book Collection. 2001. (SPA., Illus.). (J). pap. 746.50 (978-0-15-321525-4(9)); pap. 746.50 (978-0-15-321530-8(5)) Harcourt Schl. Pubs.

—Harcourt Ciencias: Explorar la Superficie de la Tierra Big Book. 2000. (Harcourt Ciencias Ser.). (SPA., Illus.). (gr. 2 up). pap., pupil's gde. ed. 119.50 (978-0-15-316837-6(4)) Harcourt Schl. Pubs.

—Harcourt Ciencias: Practice for Stanford 9. 2001. (SPA., Illus.). (gr. 1). pap. 9.80 (978-0-15-321191-1(1)); (gr. 2). pap. 9.80 (978-0-15-321192-8(X)); (gr. 3). pap. 12.70 (978-0-15-321193-5(8)); (gr. 4). pap. 12.70 (978-0-15-321194-2(6)); (gr. 5). pap. 12.70 (978-0-15-321195-9(4)) Harcourt Schl. Pubs.

—Harcourt Ciencias: TAAS Practice Test. 2001. (SPA., Illus.). (gr. 1). pap. 13.10 (978-0-15-321324-3(8)); (gr. 2). pap. 13.90 (978-0-15-321325-0(6)); (gr. 3). pap. 13.90 (978-0-15-321326-7(4)); (gr. 4). pap. 15.30 (978-0-15-321327-4(2)); (gr. 5). pap. 15.30 (978-0-15-321328-1(0)) Harcourt Schl. Pubs.

—Harcourt Ciencias: Take-Home Book. 1999. (Harcourt Ciencias Ser.). (SPA., Illus.). (gr. 1 up). pap. 28.60 (978-0-15-316171-1(X)); (gr. 2 up). pap. 28.60 (978-0-15-316172-8(8)); (gr. 3 up). pap. 34.30 (978-0-15-316173-5(6)); (gr. 4 up). pap. 34.30 (978-0-15-316174-2(4)) Harcourt Schl. Pubs.

—Harcourt Ciencias: Workbook with Translation. 1999. (Harcourt Ciencias Ser.). (SPA & ENG., Illus.). (gr. 1 up). pap., wbk. ed. 9.50 (978-0-15-315044-9(0)); (gr. 2 up). pap., wbk. ed. 9.50 (978-0-15-315045-6(9)); (gr. 3 up). pap., wbk. ed. 10.20 (978-0-15-315046-3(7)); (gr. 4 up). pap., wbk. ed. 10.20 (978-0-15-315047-0(5)); (gr. 5 up). pap., wbk. ed. 11.20 (978-0-15-315048-7(3)) Harcourt Schl. Pubs.

—Harcourt Ciencias Book 1: CA & National Instant Reader. 2001. (SPA., Illus.). pap. 4.30 (978-0-15-321399-1(X)) Harcourt Schl. Pubs.

—Harcourt Ciencias Book 2: CA & National Instant Reader. 2001. (SPA., Illus.). pap. 4.30 (978-0-15-321400-4(7)) Harcourt Schl. Pubs.

—Harcourt Ciencias Book 3: CA & National Instant Reader. 2001. (SPA., Illus.). pap. 4.30 (978-0-15-321401-1(5)) Harcourt Schl. Pubs.

—Harcourt Ciencias Book 4: CA & National Instant Reader. 2001. (SPA., Illus.). pap. 4.30 (978-0-15-321402-8(3)) Harcourt Schl. Pubs.

—Harcourt Ciencias Book 5: CA & National Instant Reader. 2001. (SPA., Illus.). pap. 4.30 (978-0-15-321403-5(1)) Harcourt Schl. Pubs.

—Harcourt Ciencias Book 6: CA & National Instant Reader. 2001. (SPA., Illus.). pap. 4.30 (978-0-15-321404-2(X)) Harcourt Schl. Pubs.

—Harcourt Ciencias Unit C: Nuestra Tierra Big Book. 2000. (Harcourt Ciencias Ser.). (SPA., Illus.). (gr. 1 up). pap., pupil's gde. ed. 108.40 (978-0-15-316831-4(5)) Harcourt Schl. Pubs.

—Harcourt Ciencias Unit D: Clima y Estaciones Big Book. 2000. (Harcourt Ciencias Ser.). (SPA., Illus.). (gr. 1 up). pap., pupil's gde. ed. 119.50 (978-0-15-316832-1(3)) Harcourt Schl. Pubs.

—Harcourt Ciencias Unit D: El Espacio y el Clima Big Book. 2000. (Harcourt Ciencias Ser.). (SPA., Illus.). (gr. 2 up). pap., pupil's gde. ed. 119.50 (978-0-15-316838-3(2)) Harcourt Schl. Pubs.

—Harcourt Ciencias Unit A: Los Seres Vivos Crecen y Cambian Big Book. 1999. (Harcourt Ciencias Ser.). (SPA., Illus.). (gr. 2 up). pap., pupil's gde. ed. 130.60 (978-0-15-316835-2(8)) Harcourt Schl. Pubs.

—Harcourt Ciencias Unit B: Los Hogares de los Seres Vivos Big Book. 2000. (Harcourt Ciencias Ser.). (SPA., Illus.). (gr. 2 up). pap., pupil's gde. ed. 119.50 (978-0-15-316836-9(6)) Harcourt Schl. Pubs.

—Harcourt Ciencias Unit B: Soft Cover Book Collection. 2000. (Harcourt Ciencias Ser.). (SPA., Illus.). (gr. 1 up). pap., pupil's gde. ed. 716.70 (978-0-15-320518-7(0)); (gr. 2 up). pap., pupil's gde. ed. 727.80 (978-0-15-320519-4(9)) Harcourt Schl. Pubs.

—Harcourt Ciencias Unit B: Todos Vivimos Juntos Big Book. 2000. (Harcourt Ciencias Ser.). (SPA., Illus.). (gr. 1 up). pap., pupil's gde. ed. 119.50 (978-0-15-316830-7(7)) Harcourt Schl. Pubs.

—Harcourt Ciencias Unit E: Explorar la Materia Big Book. 2000. (Harcourt Ciencias Ser.). (SPA., Illus.). (gr. 2 up). pap., pupil's gde. ed. 119.50 (978-0-15-316839-0(0)) Harcourt Schl. Pubs.

—Harcourt Ciencias Unit E: La Materia y Energia Big Book. 2000. (Harcourt Ciencias Ser.). (SPA., Illus.). (gr. 1 up). pap., pupil's gde. ed. 119.50 (978-0-15-316833-8(1)) Harcourt Schl. Pubs.

—Harcourt Ciencias Unit F: La Energia en Movimiento Big Book. 2000. (Harcourt Ciencias Ser.). (SPA., Illus.). (gr. 2 up). pap., pupil's gde. ed. 119.50 (978-0-15-316840-6(4)) Harcourt Schl. Pubs.

—Harcourt Ciencias Unit F: La Energia y Fuerzas Big Book. 2000. (Harcourt Ciencias Ser.). (SPA., Illus.). (gr. 1 up). pap., pupil's gde. ed. 119.50 (978-0-15-316834-5(X)) Harcourt Schl. Pubs.

—Harcourt Ciencias, Grade 1: Grade Level Set: Texas/National Edition. 2003. (Harcourt Ciencias Ser.). (SPA.). (gr. 1 up). tchr. ed. 145.10 (978-0-15-315172-9(2)) Harcourt Schl. Pubs.

—Harcourt Ciencias, Grade 1: Workbook with Translation. 1999. (Harcourt Ciencias Ser.). (SPA & ENG.). (gr. 1 up). pap., tchr. ed., wbk. ed. 22.70 (978-0-15-315051-7(3)) Harcourt Schl. Pubs.

—Harcourt Ciencias, Grade 2: Grade Level Set: Texas/National Edition. 2003. (Harcourt Ciencias Ser.). (SPA.). (gr. 2 up). tchr. ed. 145.10 (978-0-15-315173-6(0)) Harcourt Schl. Pubs.

—Harcourt Ciencias, Grade 2: Workbook with Translation. 1999. (Harcourt Ciencias Ser.). (SPA & ENG.). (gr. 2 up). pap., tchr. ed., wbk. ed. 22.70 (978-0-15-315052-4(1)) Harcourt Schl. Pubs.

—Harcourt Ciencias, Grade 3: Grade Level Set: Texas/National Edition. 1999. (Harcourt Ciencias Ser.). (SPA.). (gr. 3 up). tchr. ed. 222.30 (978-0-15-315174-3(9)) Harcourt Schl. Pubs.

—Harcourt Ciencias, Grade 3: Workbook with Translation. 1999. (Harcourt Ciencias Ser.). (SPA & ENG.). (gr. 3 up). pap., tchr. ed., wbk. ed. 22.90 (978-0-15-315053-1(X)) Harcourt Schl. Pubs.

—Harcourt Ciencias, Grade 3 Unit A&B: Life Science. 2003. (Harcourt Ciencias Ser.). (SPA.). (gr. 3 up). tchr. ed. 67.40 (978-0-15-314808-8(X)) Harcourt Schl. Pubs.

—Harcourt Ciencias, Grade 3 Unit E&F: Physical Science. 2003. (Harcourt Ciencias Ser.). (SPA.). (gr. 3 up). tchr. ed. 67.40 (978-0-15-314810-1(1)) Harcourt Schl. Pubs.

—Harcourt Ciencias, Grade 4: Grade Level Set: Texas/National Edition. 1999. (Harcourt Ciencias Ser.). (SPA.). (gr. 4 up). tchr. ed. 222.30 (978-0-15-315175-0(7)) Harcourt Schl. Pubs.

—Harcourt Ciencias, Grade 4: Workbook with Translation. 1999. (Harcourt Ciencias Ser.). (SPA & ENG.). (gr. 4 up). pap., tchr. ed., wbk. ed. 23.80 (978-0-15-315054-8(8)) Harcourt Schl. Pubs.

—Harcourt Ciencias, Grade 4 Unit A&B: Life Science. 2003. (Harcourt Ciencias Ser.). (SPA.). (gr. 4 up). tchr. ed. 67.40 (978-0-15-314811-8(X)) Harcourt Schl. Pubs.

—Harcourt Ciencias, Grade 4 Unit E&F: Physical Science. 2003. (Harcourt Ciencias Ser.). (SPA.). (gr. 4 up). tchr. ed. 67.40 (978-0-15-314813-2(6)) Harcourt Schl. Pubs.

—Harcourt Ciencias, Grade 5: Grade Level Set: Texas/National Edition. 1999. (Harcourt Ciencias Ser.). (SPA.). (gr. 5 up). tchr. ed. 230.90 (978-0-15-315176-7(5)) Harcourt Schl. Pubs.

—Harcourt Ciencias, Grade 5: Workbook with Translation. 1999. (Harcourt Ciencias Ser.). (SPA & ENG.). (gr. 5 up). pap., tchr. ed., wbk. ed. 23.80 (978-0-15-315055-5(6)) Harcourt Schl. Pubs.

—Harcourt Ciencias, Grade 5 Unit A&B: Life Science. 2003. (Harcourt Ciencias Ser.). (SPA.). (gr. 5 up). tchr. ed. 70.00 (978-0-15-314814-9(4)) Harcourt Schl. Pubs.

—Harcourt Ciencias, Grade 5 Unit E&F: Physical Science. 2003. (Harcourt Ciencias Ser.). (SPA.). (gr. 5 up). tchr. ed. 70.00 (978-0-15-315037-1(8)) Harcourt Schl. Pubs.

—Harcourt Science. (Illus.). 2001. (gr. 5). pap., wbk. ed. 11.00 (978-0-15-313182-0(9)); 2001. (gr. 5). 64.10 (978-0-15-311208-9(5)); 1999. (gr. 6). 64.90 (978-0-15-311209-6(3)); 1999. (gr. 6). pap., wbk. ed. 11.00 (978-0-15-313183-7(7)); 1999. (gr. 3). 59.00 (978-0-15-311206-5(9)); 1999. (gr. 3). pap., wbk. ed. 11.00 (978-0-15-313180-6(2)); 1999. (gr. 4). 59.00 (978-0-15-311207-2(7)); 1999. (gr. 4). pap., wbk. ed. 11.00 (978-0-15-313181-3(0)); 2nd ed. 2003. (gr. 3 up). wbk. ed. 8.70 (978-0-15-323713-3(9)); 2nd ed. 2003. (gr. 4 up). wbk. ed. 8.70 (978-0-15-323714-0(7)); 2nd ed. 2003. (gr. 5 up). wbk. ed. 9.60 (978-0-15-323715-7(5)); 2nd ed. 2003. (gr. 6 up). wbk. ed. 9.60 (978-0-15-323716-4(3)); 2nd ed. 2002. (gr. 4 up). pupil's gde. ed. 57.00 (978-0-15-322921-3(7)); 2nd ed. 2002. (gr. 1 up). pupil's gde. ed. 50.50 (978-0-15-322918-3(7)); 2nd ed. 2002. (gr. 1 up). pap., wbk. ed. 9.10 (978-0-15-323711-9(2)); 2nd ed. 2002. (gr. 2 up). pupil's gde. ed. 50.50 (978-0-15-322919-0(5)); 2nd ed. 2002. (gr. 2 up). pap., wbk. ed. 9.10 (978-0-15-323712-6(0)); 2nd ed. 2002. (gr. 3 up). pupil's gde. ed. 55.40 (978-0-15-322920-6(9)); 2nd ed. 2002. (gr. 6 up). pupil's gde. ed. 62.50 (978-0-15-322923-7(3)); 2nd ed. 2001. (gr. 5 up). pupil's gde. ed. 62.50 (978-0-15-322922-0(5)) Harcourt Schl. Pubs.

—Harcourt Science: Animals in Plants Reader. 1999. (Illus.). pap. 3.10 (978-0-15-314853-8(5)) Harcourt Schl. Pubs.

—Harcourt Science: Assessment Guide. (Illus.). 1999. (gr. 6). pap. 59.30 (978-0-15-313190-5(X)); 1999. (gr. 1). pap. 49.80 (978-0-15-313184-4(5)); 1999. (gr. 2). pap. 49.80 (978-0-15-313186-8(1)); 1999. (gr. 3). pap. 52.80 (978-0-15-313187-5(X)); 1999. (gr. 4). pap. 56.00 (978-0-15-313188-2(8)); 1999. (gr. 5). pap. 59.30 (978-0-15-313189-9(6)); 2nd ed. 2002. (gr. 1 up). pap. 49.80 (978-0-15-323705-8(8)); 2nd ed. 2002. (gr. 2 up). pap. 49.80 (978-0-15-323706-5(6)); 2nd ed. 2002. (gr. 4 up). pap. 56.00 (978-0-15-323708-9(2)); 2nd ed. 2002. (gr. 5 up). pap. 59.30 (978-0-15-323709-6(0)); 2nd ed. 2002. (gr. 6 up). pap. 59.30 (978-0-15-323710-2(4)) Harcourt Schl. Pubs.

—Harcourt Science: Assesssment Guide. 2nd ed. 2002. (Harcourt Science Ser.). (Illus.). (gr. 3 up). pap. 52.80 (978-0-15-323707-2(4)) Harcourt Schl. Pubs.

—Harcourt Science: Big Book. (Harcourt Science Ser.). (Illus.). (gr. k-6). 2nd ed. 2002. 219.80 (978-0-15-324502-2(6)); Level C. 2000. 177.80 (978-0-15-318049-1(8)); Level C. 2000. 188.70 (978-0-15-318070-5(6)); Level D. 2000. 188.70 (978-0-15-318050-7(1)); Level D. 2000. 188.70 (978-0-15-318079-8(X)); Level A. 2000. 215.90 (978-0-15-318044-6(7)); Level A. 2000. 209.70 (978-0-15-318065-1(X)); Level B. 2000. 188.70 (978-0-15-318048-4(X)); Level B. 2000. 188.70 (978-0-15-318066-8(8)); Level E. 2000. 188.70 (978-0-15-318062-0(5)); Level E. 2000. 188.70 (978-0-15-318080-4(3)); Level F. 2000. 188.70 (978-0-15-318063-7(3)); Level F. 2000. 188.70 (978-0-15-318081-1(1)) Harcourt Schl. Pubs.

—Harcourt Science: Big Book Grade Level Set. 1999. (Illus.). (gr. 2). 1153.00 (978-0-15-318064-4(1)); (gr. 1). 1148.20 (978-0-15-318043-9(9)) Harcourt Schl. Pubs.

—Harcourt Science: TAAS Practice Book. 2001. (Illus.). (gr. 5). pap. 9.30 (978-0-15-320917-8(8)) Harcourt Schl. Pubs.

—Harcourt Science: Take Home Book. 2nd ed. 2002. (Harcourt Science Ser.). (Illus.). (gr. 1 up). pap. 27.40 (978-0-15-324483-4(6)); (gr. 2 up). pap. 27.40 (978-0-15-324484-1(4)); (gr. 3 up). pap. 32.80 (978-0-15-324485-8(2)); (gr. 4 up). pap. 32.80 (978-0-15-324486-5(0)); (gr. 5 up). pap. 32.80 (978-0-15-324487-2(9)); (gr. 6 up). pap. 32.80 (978-0-15-324488-9(7)) Harcourt Schl. Pubs.

—Harcourt Science: Texas Edition. 1999. (Illus.). (gr. 1). pap. 58.70 (978-0-15-311204-1(2)); (gr. 2). pap. 62.10 (978-0-15-311205-8(0)) Harcourt Schl. Pubs.

—Harcourt Science Big Book. 1999. (Illus.). pap. 230.90 (978-0-15-315413-3(6)) Harcourt Schl. Pubs.

—Harcourt Science Big Book Unit C. 2nd ed. 2002. (Illus.). 144.50 (978-0-15-325369-0(X)); pap. 144.50 (978-0-15-325363-8(0)); (gr. 1 up). pupil's gde. ed. 177.80 (978-0-15-325351-5(7)); (gr. 2 up). pupil's gde. ed. 177.80 (978-0-15-325357-7(6)) Harcourt Schl. Pubs.

—Harcourt Science Big Book Unit D. 2nd ed. 2002. (Illus.). pap. 144.50 (978-0-15-325364-5(9)); pap. 144.50 (978-0-15-325370-6(3)); (gr. 1 up). pupil's gde. ed. 177.80 (978-0-15-325352-2(5)); (gr. 2 up). pupil's gde. ed. 177.80 (978-0-15-325358-4(4)) Harcourt Schl. Pubs.

—Harcourt Science Big Book Unit A. 2nd ed. 2002. (Illus.). (J). (gr. 1). pap. 132.00 (978-0-15-325361-4(4)); (gr. 1 up). pupil's gde. ed. 180.70 (978-0-15-325349-2(5)); (J). (gr. 2). pap. 132.00 (978-0-15-325367-6(3)); (gr. 2 up). pupil's gde. ed. 180.70 (978-0-15-325355-3(X)) Harcourt Schl. Pubs.

—Harcourt Science Big Book Unit B. 2nd ed. 2002. (Illus.). 144.50 (978-0-15-325368-3(1)); pap. 144.50 (978-0-15-325362-1(2)); (gr. 1 up). pupil's gde. ed. 177.80 (978-0-15-325350-8(9)); (gr. 2 up). pupil's gde. ed. 177.80 (978-0-15-325356-0(8)) Harcourt Schl. Pubs.

—Harcourt Science Big Book Unit E. 2nd ed. 2002. (Illus.). pap. 144.50 (978-0-15-325365-2(7)); pap. 144.50 (978-0-15-325371-3(1)); (gr. 1 up). pupil's gde. ed. 177.80 (978-0-15-325353-9(3)); (gr. 2 up). pupil's gde. ed. 177.80 (978-0-15-325359-1(2)) Harcourt Schl. Pubs.

—Harcourt Science Big Book Unit F. 2nd ed. 2002. (Illus.). pap. 144.50 (978-0-15-325366-9(5)); pap. 144.50 (978-0-15-325372-0(X)); (gr. 1 up). pupil's gde. ed. 177.80 (978-0-15-325354-6(1)); (gr. 2 up). pupil's gde. ed. 177.80 (978-0-15-325360-7(6)) Harcourt Schl. Pubs.

—Harcourt Science, Grade 1. 2nd ed. 2002. (Harcourt Science Ser.). (gr. 1 up). pap., tchr. ed., wbk. ed. 22.50 (978-0-15-323717-1(1)) Harcourt Schl. Pubs.

S

—Harcourt Science, Grade 1: Teaching Resource. 2nd ed. 2002. (Harcourt Science Ser.). (gr. 1 up). tchr. ed. 44.80 (978-0-15-324477-3(1)) Harcourt Schl. Pubs.

—Harcourt Science, Grade 2. 2nd ed. 2002. (Harcourt Science Ser.). (gr. 2 up). pap., tchr. ed., wbk. ed. 22.50 (978-0-15-323718-8(X)) Harcourt Schl. Pubs.

—Harcourt Science, Grade 2: Teaching Resource. 2nd ed. 2002. (Harcourt Science Ser.). (gr. 2 up). tchr. ed. 44.80 (978-0-15-324478-0(X)) Harcourt Schl. Pubs.

—Harcourt Science, Grade 3. 2nd ed. 2002. (Harcourt Science Ser.). (gr. 3 up). pap., tchr. ed., wbk. ed. 26.50 (978-0-15-323719-5(8)) Harcourt Schl. Pubs.

—Harcourt Science, Grade 3: Teaching Resource. 2nd ed. 2002. (Harcourt Science Ser.). (gr. 3 up). tchr. ed. 44.80 (978-0-15-324479-7(8)) Harcourt Schl. Pubs.

—Harcourt Science, Grade 4. 2nd ed. 2002. (Harcourt Science Ser.). (gr. 4 up). pap., tchr. ed., wbk. ed. 26.50 (978-0-15-323720-1(1)) Harcourt Schl. Pubs.

—Harcourt Science, Grade 4: Teaching Resource. 2nd ed. 2002. (Harcourt Science Ser.). (gr. 4 up). tchr. ed. 51.20 (978-0-15-324480-3(1)) Harcourt Schl. Pubs.

—Harcourt Science, Grade 5. 2nd ed. 2002. (Harcourt Science Ser.). (gr. 5 up). pap., tchr. ed., wbk. ed. 29.20 (978-0-15-323721-8(X)) Harcourt Schl. Pubs.

—Harcourt Science, Grade 5: Teaching Resource. 2nd ed. 2002. (Harcourt Science Ser.). (gr. 5 up). tchr. ed. 51.20 (978-0-15-324481-0(X)) Harcourt Schl. Pubs.

—Harcourt Science, Grade 6. 2nd ed. 2002. (Harcourt Science Ser.). (gr. 6 up). pap., tchr. ed., wbk. ed. 29.20 (978-0-15-323722-5(8)) Harcourt Schl. Pubs.

—Harcourt Science, Grade 6: Teaching Resource. 2nd ed. 2002. (Harcourt Science Ser.). (gr. 6 up). tchr. ed. 51.20 (978-0-15-324482-7(8)) Harcourt Schl. Pubs.

—Harcourt Science, Grade K: Teaching Resource. 2nd ed. 2002. (Harcourt Science Ser.). (gr. k-6). tchr. ed. 28.20 (978-0-15-324476-6(3)) Harcourt Schl. Pubs.

—Harcourt Science Unit Big Book Collection. 2nd ed. 2002. (Illus.). (gr. 1). pap. 866.90 (978-0-15-325375-1(4)); (gr. 1 up). pupil's gde. ed. 1066.70 (978-0-15-325373-7(8))); (gr. 2). pap. 866.90 (978-0-15-325376-8(2)); (gr. 2 up). pupil's gde. ed. 1066.70 (978-0-15-325374-4(6)) Harcourt Schl. Pubs.

—Harcourt Science Unit Books Unit C. 2nd ed. 2002. (Harcourt Science Ser.). (Illus.). (gr. 3 up). pap., pupil's gde. ed. 15.60 (978-0-15-325379-9(7)); (gr. 4 up). pap., pupil's gde. ed. 15.60 (978-0-15-325385-0(1)); (gr. 5 up). pap., pupil's gde. ed. 16.10 (978-0-15-325391-1(6)); (gr. 6 up). pap., pupil's gde. ed. 16.10 (978-0-15-325397-3(5)) Harcourt Schl. Pubs.

—Harcourt Science Unit Books Unit D. 2nd ed. 2002. (Harcourt Science Ser.). (Illus.). (gr. 3 up). pap., pupil's gde. ed. 15.60 (978-0-15-325380-5(0)); (gr. 4 up). pap., pupil's gde. ed. 15.60 (978-0-15-325386-7(X)); (gr. 5 up). pap., pupil's gde. ed. 16.10 (978-0-15-325392-8(4)); (gr. 6 up). pap., pupil's gde. ed. 16.10 (978-0-15-325398-0(3)) Harcourt Schl. Pubs.

—Harcourt Science Unit Books Unit A. 2nd ed. 2002. (Harcourt Science Ser.). (Illus.). (gr. 3 up). pap., pupil's gde. ed. 15.60 (978-0-15-325377-5(0)); (gr. 4 up). pap., pupil's gde. ed. 15.60 (978-0-15-325383-6(5)); (gr. 5 up). pap., pupil's gde. ed. 16.10 (978-0-15-325389-8(4)); (gr. 6 up). pap., pupil's gde. ed. 16.10 (978-0-15-325395-9(9)) Harcourt Schl. Pubs.

—Harcourt Science Unit Books Unit B. 2nd ed. 2002. (Harcourt Science Ser.). (Illus.). (gr. 3 up). pap., pupil's gde. ed. 15.60 (978-0-15-325378-2(9)); (gr. 4 up). pap., pupil's gde. ed. 15.60 (978-0-15-325384-3(3)); (gr. 5 up). pap., pupil's gde. ed. 16.10 (978-0-15-325390-4(8)); (gr. 6 up). pap., pupil's gde. ed. 16.10 (978-0-15-325396-6(7)) Harcourt Schl. Pubs.

—Harcourt Science Unit Books Unit E. 2nd ed. 2002. (Harcourt Science Ser.). (Illus.). (gr. 3 up). pap., pupil's gde. ed. 15.60 (978-0-15-325381-2(9)); (gr. 4 up). pap., pupil's gde. ed. 15.60 (978-0-15-325387-4(8)); (gr. 5 up). pap., pupil's gde. ed. 16.10 (978-0-15-325393-5(2)); (gr. 6 up). pap., pupil's gde. ed. 16.10 (978-0-15-325399-7(1)) Harcourt Schl. Pubs.

—Harcourt Science Unit Books Unit F. 2nd ed. 2002. (Harcourt Science Ser.). (Illus.). (gr. 3 up). pap., pupil's gde. ed. 15.60 (978-0-15-325382-9(7)); (gr. 4 up). pap., pupil's gde. ed. 15.60 (978-0-15-325388-1(6)); (gr. 5 up). pap., pupil's gde. ed. 16.10 (978-0-15-325394-2(0)); (gr. 6 up). pap., pupil's gde. ed. 16.10 (978-0-15-325400-0(9)) Harcourt Schl. Pubs.

—Living or Nonliving: Science Reader. 1999. (SPA., Illus.). (J). (gr. 1). pap. 3.70 (978-0-15-316098-1(5)) Harcourt Schl. Pubs.

Hartzog, Daniel. Everyday Science Experiments in the Kitchen. 2000. (Science Surprises Ser.). (Illus.). 24p. (J). (gr. k-4). lib. bdg. 19.95 (978-0-8239-5456-8(0) , PowerKids Pr.) Rosen Publishing Group, Inc., The.

Holt, Rinehart and Winston Staff. Holt Science & Technology: Science Skills Worksheets. 5th ed. 2004. (Illus.). pap., wbk. ed. 11.60 (978-0-03-035197-6(9)) Holt, Rinehart & Winston.

—Holt Science & Technology: Strategies & Practice Answer Key. 4th ed. 2004. (Illus.). pap. 6.00 (978-0-03-020022-9(9)); pap. 6.00 (978-0-03-019892-2(5)) Holt, Rinehart & Winston.

—Science Spectrum: Florida FCAT Test Preparation Workbook. 2002. (J). pap. 11.17 (978-0-03-070404-8(9)) Holt, Rinehart & Winston.

—Standard Test Preparation Workbook: South Carolina Edition - Science. 2002. (J). pap. 11.00 (978-0-03-069041-9(2)) Holt, Rinehart & Winston.

Jones, Glenda. Science & Technology Matters: Grade 4 Learner's Book. 2000. 96p. (gr. 4). pap., tchr. ed. 7.35 (978-0-521-78837-3(4)) Cambridge Univ. Pr.

Khanna, Sudarshan, et al. Toys & Tales with Everyday Materials. 2003. (Illus.). 144p. 10.99 (978-81-86211-42-7(X)) Penguin Group (USA) Inc.

Lopatka, Michael, creator. A. P. Environmental Science. 2002. (YA). lib. bdg., stu. ed., wbk. ed. 15.95 (978-0-9703694-6-8(8)) Awesome Guides, Inc.

McCarthy, Sue, et al. Science Matters: Grade 9. 2001. (gr. 9). pap., tchr. ed. 9.65 (978-0-521-66524-7(8)) Cambridge Univ. Pr.

McGraw-Hill Staff. Mosquito Island: Grade 6+ Life Science. 1999. (J). (gr. 6-7). pap. 14.95 (978-1-57768-002-4(2)) School Specialty Publishing.

McMorrow, Annalisa. Bats: A Science Discovery Book. Chalk, Philip, illus. 1999. 48p. (J). (gr. 3-6). pap. 7.95 (978-1-57612-076-7(7) , MM2090) Monday Morning Bks., Inc.

—Rain Forest: A Science Discovery Book. Barr, Marilynn G., illus. 1999. 48p. (J). (gr. 3-6). pap. 7.95 (978-1-57612-078-1(3) , MM2093) Monday Morning Bks., Inc.

—Whales. Chalk, Philip, illus. 1999. 48p. (J). (gr. 3-6). pap. 7.95 (978-1-57612-077-4(5) , No. MM2091) Monday Morning Bks., Inc.

Miles Kelly Staff. Science. 2003. (Info Bank Ser.). (Illus.). 96p. (J). 7.95 (978-1-84236-152-8(X)) Miles Kelly Publishing, Ltd. GBR. *Dist:* Independent Pubs. Group.

—Science & Maths. 2003. (Flip Quiz Ser.). (Illus.). 38p. (J). (gr. 10-11). spiral bd. 5.95 (978-1-84236-032-3(9)); (gr. 11-12). spiral bd. 5.95 (978-1-84236-033-0(7)); (gr. 7-9). spiral bd. 5.95 (978-1-84236-030-9(2)); (gr. 9-10). spiral bd. 5.95 (978-1-84236-031-6(0)) Miles Kelly Publishing, Ltd. GBR. *Dist:* Independent Pubs. Group.

Moredock, Janet, et al. Handy Homework Helper. 2005. (Illus.). 128p. (J). (***978-1-4127-1179-1(7)***) Publications International, Ltd.

Niles, Lori, ed. Amazing Science Devotions for Children's Ministry. 1998. (Illus.). 96p. (gr. k-6). pap. 15.99 (978-0-7644-2105-1(0) , Flagship Church Resources) Group Publishing, Inc.

Schaefer, Lola M. What Is Big, Big, Big? 2007. (J). (978-1-59515-930-4(4)) Rourke Publishing, LLC.

—What Is Good for You? 2007. (J). (978-1-59515-926-7(6)) Rourke Publishing, LLC.

Schaefer, Ted. When Is Your Birthday? 2007. (J). (978-1-59515-945-8(2)) Rourke Publishing, LLC.

School Zone Publishing Company Staff. First Grade Scholar. rev. ed. 2001. (Super-Deluxe Wkbks.). (Illus.). 128p. (J). (gr. k-1). pap. 7.99 (978-1-58947-009-5(5) , 02460) School Zone Publishing Co.

—Grades 3-4 Big Get Ready! 2002. (Big Get Ready Ser.). (Illus.). 320p. (J). (gr. 3-4). pap. 9.99 (978-1-58947-017-0(6) , 06320) School Zone Publishing Co.

School Zone Staff, ed. Third Grade Scholar. 2005. (Illus.). 128p. (J). (gr. k-3). pap. 7.99 (978-1-58947-015-6(X) , 02466) School Zone Publishing Co.

Science. 2000. (Little Books for Little Hands). (Illus.). 80p. (J). (ps-2). pap. 9.95 (978-1-58273-375-3(9)) Sundance/Newbridge Educational Publishing.

Spilsbury, Richard & Spilsbury, Louise. What Are Forces & Motion? Exploring Science with Hands-On Activities. 2008. (In Touch with Basic Science Ser.). 32p. (J). (gr. 3-4). lib. bdg. 22.60 (***978-0-7660-3095-4(4)***) Enslow Pubs., Inc.

—What Is Solids, Liquids, & Gases? Exploring Science with Hands-On Activities. 2008. (In Touch with Basic Science Ser.). 32p. (J). (gr. 3-4). lib. bdg. 22.60 (***978-0-7660-3094-7(6)***) Enslow Pubs., Inc.

—What Is Sound? Exploring Science with Hands-On Activities. 2008. (In Touch with Basic Science Ser.). 32p. (J). (gr. 3-4). lib. bdg. 22.60 (***978-0-7660-3098-5(9)***) Enslow Pubs., Inc.

Stone, Barry, et al. Examining GCSE Science. 2nd ed. 1998. (Illus.). 310p. (YA). (gr. 9-11). pap. 39.00 (978-0-7487-0568-9(6)) State Mutual Bk. & Periodical Service, Ltd.

Suzuki, David T. & Helmer, Barbara. Descubre las Plantas. 2004. (Juego de la Ciencia Ser.). (SPA., Illus.). 96p. 14.99 (978-84-9754-062-9(X) , 87817) Ediciones Oniro S.A. ESP. *Dist:* Bilingual Pubns. Co., The, Lectorum Pubns., Inc.

VanCleave, Janice. Janice VanCleave's Big Book of Play & Find Out Science Projects. 2007. (Illus.). 224p. pap. 19.95 (***978-0-7879-8928-6(2)***) Wiley, John & Sons, Inc.

Walker, Pam & Wood, Elaine. Crime Scene Investigations: Real-Life Science Activities for the Elementary Grades. 1999. 272p. pap. 29.95 (978-0-7879-6687-4(8) , Jossey-Bass) Wiley, John & Sons, Inc.

Wawrychuk, Carol & McSweeney, Cherie. Insects & Spiders: Active Learning about Nature. Chalk, Philip, illus. 1999. 48p. (J). (ps-1). pap. 7.95 (978-1-57612-074-3(0) , MM2088) Monday Morning Bks., Inc.

Weikart, Cindy. The Ohio Graduation Test: Science Study Guide. 2004. 288p. pap., stu. ed. 16.95 (978-1-882203-30-7(5)) Orange Frazer Pr.

Wiese, Jim. Ancient Science: 40 Time-Traveling, World-Exploring, History-Making Activities for Kids. 2003. (Illus.). 128p. pap. 12.95 (978-0-471-21595-0(3) , Wiley) Wiley, John & Sons, Inc.

SCIENCE—VOCATIONAL GUIDANCE

Cherry Lake Publishing, compiled by. Cool Science Centers. 2008. lib. bdg. (***978-1-60279-109-1(0)***) Cherry Lake Publishing.

Davis, Wendy & Knight, Bertram T. Working at a Marine Institute. 1998. (Working Here Ser.). (Illus.). 32p. (J). (gr. 2-4). 23.50 (978-0-516-21223-4(0) , Children's Pr.) Scholastic Library Publishing.

Devantier, Alecia T. & Turkington, Carol. Extraordinary Jobs in Health & Science. 2006. (Extraordinary Jobs Ser.). 176p. (J). (gr. 6-12). 35.00 (978-0-8160-5858-7(X) , Ferguson Publishing Co.) Facts On File, Inc.

Ferguson. Discovering Careers for Your Future. 2nd ed. 2004. (Discovering Careers for Your Future Ser.). (Illus.). 96p. (J). (gr. 4-9). 21.95 (978-0-8160-5571-5(8) , Ferguson Publishing Co.) Facts On File, Inc.

French, Lloyd C. On the Job with an Explorer. 2003. (Adventures in Science Professions Ser.). (J). pap. (978-1-58417-123-2(5)); lib. bdg. (978-1-58417-060-0(3)) Lake Street Pubs.

Glass, Susan. Prove It! The Scientific Method in Action. 2006. (Illus.). 48p. (J). (978-1-4034-8359-1(0)); pap. (978-1-4034-8363-8(9)) Heinemann Library.

Hoyt, Beth Caldwell & Ritter, Erica. The Ultimate Girls' Guide to Science: From Backyard Experiments to Winning the Nobel Prize. Palen, Debbie, illus. 2004. 128p. (J). (gr. 4-12). pap. (978-1-58270-092-2(3)) Beyond Words Publishing, Inc.

Mahaney, Ian F. Energy in Action, 6 bks., Set. Incl. Electricity. lib. bdg. 21.25 (978-1-4042-3478-9(0)); Heat. lib. bdg. 21.25 (978-1-4042-3477-2(2)); Light. lib. bdg. 21.25 (978-1-4042-3476-5(4)); Solar Energy. lib. bdg. 21.25 (978-1-4042-3479-6(9)); Sound Waves. lib. bdg. 21.25 (978-1-4042-3480-2(2)); Water Power. lib. bdg. 21.25 (978-1-4042-3481-9(0)); (Illus.). 24p. (J). (gr. 4-6). 2007. , PowerKids Pr. 2007. Set lib. bdg. 127.50 (978-1-4042-3504-5(3)) Rosen Publishing Group, Inc., The.

Maze, Stephanie. I Want to Be an Environmentalist. 2000. (J). (978-0-606-20164-3(5)) Tandem Library Bks.

Objects in the Sky, 6 bks., Set. Incl. Exploring Comets. Way, Jennifer. lib. bdg. 21.25 (978-1-4042-3469-7(1) , PowerKids Pr.); Exploring Earth. Olien, Rebecca. lib. bdg. 21.25 (978-1-4042-3465-9(9)); Exploring Meteors. Olien, Rebecca. lib. bdg. 21.25 (978-1-4042-3468-0(3) , PowerKids Pr.); Exploring the Moon. Olien, Rebecca. lib. bdg. 21.25 (978-1-4042-3466-6(7) , PowerKids Pr.); Exploring the Planets in Our Solar System. Olien, Rebecca. lib. bdg. 21.25 (978-1-4042-3467-3(5) , PowerKids Pr.); Exploring the Sun. Olien, Rebecca. lib. bdg. 21.25 (978-1-4042-3464-2(0) , PowerKids Pr.); (Illus.). 24p. (J). (gr. 4-6). 2007. 2007. Set lib. bdg. 127.50 (978-1-4042-3502-1(7) , PowerKids Pr.) Rosen Publishing Group, Inc., The.

Pasternak, Ceel. Cool Careers for Girls as Environmentalists. 2001. (Cool Careers for Girls Ser.: Vol. 11). (Illus.). 144p. pap. 12.95 (978-1-57023-172-8(9)) Impact Pubns.

Reeves, Diane Lindsey. Career Ideas for Kids Who Like Science. 2nd rev. ed. 2007. (Career Ideas for Kids Ser.). 192p. (J). (gr. 4-9). 32.95 (***978-0-8160-6549-3(7)*** , Checkmark Bks.) Facts On File, Inc.

—Career Ideas for Kids Who Like Science. 1998. (gr. 5-8). lib. bdg. 22.20 (978-0-613-76189-5(8)) Tandem Library Bks.

Reeves, Diane Lindsey & Clasen, Lindsey. Career Ideas for Kids Who Like Science. 2nd rev. ed. (Career Ideas for Kids Ser.). 192p. (J). (gr. 4-9). pap. 16.95 (***978-0-8160-6550-9(0)*** , Checkmark Bks.) Facts On File, Inc.

Ring, Susan. Scientists at Work. 2005. (Yellow Umbrella Books for Early Readers). (Illus.). 16p. (J). (978-0-7368-5267-8(0)); (978-0-7368-5303-3(0)) Capstone Pr., Inc.

Zannos, Susan. Careers in Science & Medicine. 2001. (Latinos at Work Ser.). (Illus.). 96p. (YA). (gr. 5-12). lib. bdg. 22.95 (978-1-58415-084-8(X)) Mitchell Lane Pubs., Inc.

SCIENCE—YEARBOOKS

Yearbooks in Science. (Illus.). 80p. (YA). (978-0-7613-3113-1(1) , Twenty-First Century Bks.) Lerner Publishing Group.

SCIENCE AND CIVILIZATION

Focus on Science & Society, 8 bks. Incl. Animal Testing : The Animal Rights Debate. Hayhurst, Chris. (YA). 2000. lib. bdg. 26.50 (978-0-8239-3213-9(3) , FSANTE); Biological & Chemical Weapons : The Debate over Modern Warfare. Cobb, Allan B. (YA). 2000. lib. bdg. 26.50 (978-0-8239-3214-6(1) , FSWEAP); Euthanasia : Debate Over the Right to Die. Cavan, Seamus & Dolan, Sean. (YA). 2000. lib. bdg. 26.50 (978-0-8239-3215-3(X) , FSEUTH); Fertility Technology : The Baby Debate. Williams, Kara. (YA). 2003. lib. bdg. 26.50 (978-0-8239-3210-8(9) , FSFETE); Genetic Engineering : The Cloning Debate. Stanley, Debbie. (YA). 2000. lib. bdg. 26.50 (978-0-8239-3211-5(7) , FSGEEN); New Medications : The Debate over Approval & Access. Stanley, Debbie. (YA). 2000. lib. bdg. 26.50 (978-0-8239-3212-2(5) , FSNEME); Organ Transplant : The Debate over Who, How & Why. Winters, Adam. (YA). 2000. lib. bdg. 26.50 (978-0-8239-3209-2(5) , FSORTR); Scientifically Engineered Foods : The Debate over What's on Your Plate. Cobb, Allan B. (J). 2000. lib. bdg. 26.50 (978-0-8239-3208-5(7) , FSENFO); 64p. (gr. 4-6). (Illus.). 1999. Set lib. bdg. 212.00 (978-0-8239-9322-2(1)) Rosen Publishing Group, Inc., The.

Haywood, John. Science & Technology. 2004. (Illus.). 64p. pap. 8.99 (978-1-84215-956-9(9) , Southwater) Anness Publishing GBR. *Dist:* National Bk. Network.

Kidd, J. S. & Kidd, Renee A. Science & Society Set. 2nd rev. ed. 2006. (Science & Society Ser.). 176-176p. (gr. 6-12). 175.00 (978-0-8160-5603-3(X)) Facts On File, Inc.

SCIENCE AND RELIGION

see Religion and Science

SCIENCE AND SPACE

see Space Sciences

SCIENCE FICTION

see also Time Travel

Abalos, Rafael. Bufo Sonador en la Galazia de la Tristeza. 2000. (SPA., Illus.). 240p. 19.95 (978-84-8306-356-9(5)) Debate, Editorial ESP. *Dist:* Libros Sin Fronteras.

Abbott, Tony. The Hawk Bandits of Tarkoom. 2001. (gr. 3-6). lib. bdg. 11.80 (978-0-613-32634-6(2)) Tandem Library Bks.

—In the Ice Caves of Krog. Adams, Gil, illus. 2003. (Secrets of Droon Ser.: No. 20). 128p. mass mkt. 3.99 (978-0-439-56040-5(3) , Scholastic Paperbacks) Scholastic, Inc.

—In the Ice Caves of Krog. 2003. (gr. 3-6). lib. bdg. 11.80 (978-0-613-66360-1(8)) Tandem Library Bks.

—The Isle of Mists. Merrell, David, illus. 2004. 121p. (J). lib. bdg. 15.38 (***978-1-4242-0313-0(9)***) Fitzgerald Bks.

—The Mask of Maliban. 2001. (gr. 3-6). lib. bdg. 11.80 (978-0-613-35785-2(X)) Tandem Library Bks.

—Wizard or Witch. Merrell, David & Jessell, Tim, illus. 2004. (Secrets of Droon Ser.: Special Edition #2). 176p. (J). pap. 5.99 (978-0-439-56049-8(7)) Scholastic, Inc.

Abnett, Dan. Eisenhorn. Gascoigne, Marc, ed. 2005. 768p. pap. 10.99 (978-1-84416-156-0(0) , Games Workshop) Simon & Schuster.

Abnett, Dan & Williams, Anthony. This Ghost Is Toast! 2007. (Real Ghostbusters Ser.). (Illus.). 96p. pap. 8.95 (***978-1-84576-143-1(X)***) Titan Bks. Ltd. GBR. *Dist:* Random Hse., Inc.

The Abominable Snowman, 6 Vols., Pack. (Bookweb Ser.). 32p. (gr. 3 up). 34.00 (978-0-7635-3935-1(X)) Rigby Education.

Abrams, Pete. The Bug, the Witch, & the Robot. 2001. (Sluggy Freelance Ser.: No. 6). 178p. pap. 12.95 (978-1-929462-37-7(9)) Plan Nine Publishing, Inc.

Adams, Lucas. Future Odyssey. 2002. 164p. pap. 14.95 (978-1-891429-35-4(3)) Armadillo Publishing Corp.

Addison-Wesley Publishing Staff. Et Level 2: The Extraterrestrial. 2002. (Illus.). 48p. (C). pap. 9.00 (978-0-582-51747-9(8)) Pearson ESL.

Adlington, L. J. The Diary of Pelly D. 2008. 304p. (J). pap. 8.99 (***978-0-06-076617-7(4)*** , HarperTeen); 2005. 288p. (YA). (gr. 8 up). 16.99 (978-0-06-076615-3(8)); 2005. 288p. (YA). (gr. 8 up). lib. bdg. 17.89 (978-0-06-076616-0(6)) HarperCollins Pubs.

Adventures Beyond the Solar System: Planetron & Me. 2005. (J). audio, cd-rom 24.95 (978-0-9771381-5-9(1)) Williams, Geoffrey T.

Adventures in the Solar System: Planetron & Me. 2005. (J). audio, cd-rom 24.95 (978-0-9771381-4-2(3)) Williams, Geoffrey T.

Alcock, Vivien. The Monster Garden. 2000. 176p. (J). (gr. 5-9). pap. 4.95 (978-0-618-00337-2(1)) Houghton Mifflin Co. Trade & Reference Div.

—Monster Garden. 2000. (gr. 3-6). lib. bdg. 12.95 (978-0-8335-4263-2(X)) Tandem Library Bks.

Alden, Paul, et al. The Imperial Perspective. 2004. 144p. pap. 17.95 (978-1-59307-128-8(0)) Dark Horse Comics.

Alex de Campi & Edo Fuijkschot. Agent Boo, Vol. 1. 2006. (Illus.). 96p. pap. 4.99 (978-1-59816-802-0(9) , Tokyopop Kids) TOKYOPOP, Inc.

Alexander, Claudia. Windows to Adventure Bk. 1: Which of the Mountains Is Greatest of All? Kindert, Jennifer, illus. 2004. 32p. (J). 18.95 (978-0-9726290-0-3(9)) Blue Pheonix Bks.

Alexander, Lloyd. The Chronicles of Prydain. rev. ed. 1999. (Chronicles of Prydain Ser.: Bk. 3). (Illus.). 224p. (J). (gr. 3-7). 19.95 (978-0-8050-6132-1(0) , Holt, Henry & Co. Bks. For Young Readers) Holt, Henry & Co.

Alexander, Lloyd, et al. Firebirds: An Anthology of Original Fantasy & Science Fiction. Vess, Charles, illus. 2005. 432p. (YA). (gr. 6-11). pap. 8.99 (978-0-14-240320-4(2) , Puffin) Penguin Group (USA) Inc.

The Alien Next Door. 2005. (J). audio, cd-rom 24.95 (978-0-9771381-6-6(0)) Williams, Geoffrey T.

Allie, Scott. Planet of the Apes Movie Adaptation. 2001. (gr. 7-12). lib. bdg. 15.25 (978-0-613-79091-8(X)) Tandem Library Bks.

Allred, Mike. The Atomics: Spaced Out & Grounded in Snap City. 2003. (Illus.). 112p. pap. 12.95 (978-1-929998-67-8(8)) Oni Pr., Inc.

—Superman. 1998. Tr. of Madman Hullabaloo!. (gr. 7-12). lib. bdg. 17.60 (978-0-613-79001-7(4)) Tandem Library Bks.

Allred, Mike & Allred, Laura. Red Rocket 7. 1998. (Illus.). 208p. (YA). (gr. 7 up). pap. 29.95 (978-1-56971-347-1(2)) Dark Horse Comics.

Ames, Mildred. Anna to the Infinite Power. 2003. (J). pap. 2.75 (978-0-590-42707-4(5)) Scholastic, Inc.

Ammann, Michael. Exos. 2003. 108p. (YA). pap. 9.95 (978-0-595-27121-4(9) , Writers Club Pr.) iUniverse, Inc.

Amodeo, John, et al. The Crystal Planet. 2004. (Zenda Ser.: 3). 144p. (J). (gr. 5 up). pap. 4.99 (978-0-448-43255-7(2) , Grosset & Dunlap) Penguin Group (USA) Inc.

—The Impossible Butterfly. 2004. (Zenda Ser.: 5). 144p. (J). (gr. 12-12). pap. 4.99 (978-0-448-43257-1(9) , Grosset & Dunlap) Penguin Group (USA) Inc.

Amory, Jay. The Fledging of Az Gabrielson. 2006. (YA). pap. 19.95 (***978-0-575-07879-6(0)***) Orion Publishing Group, Ltd. GBR. *Dist:* Independent Pubs. Group.

Amy, Mary Lucille & Matthews, Katherine Amy. Earthly Travels: The Origin of Gemsacs, 3 vols., Set. Travers, Kirsten, illus. unabr. ed. 2000. 38p. (YA). (gr. k up). pap. (978-0-9702494-0-1(3)) Nature's Tools, Inc.

Anderson, Brian. The Adventures of Commander Zack Proton & the Red Giant. Holgate, Doug, illus. 2006. (Adventures of Commander Zack Proton Ser.). 128p. (J). (gr. 2-5). pap. 3.99 (978-1-4169-1364-1(5) , Aladdin) Simon & Schuster Children's Publishing.

—The Adventures of Commander Zack Proton & the Warlords of Nibblecheese. Holgate, Doug, illus. 2006. (Adventures of Commander Zack Proton Ser.). 112p. (J). pap. 3.99 (978-1-4169-1365-8(3) , Aladdin) Simon & Schuster Children's Publishing.

Anderson, J. A. Dragon Fire No.1: The Starriders Saga. 2002. (gr. 7-12). lib. bdg. 16.40 (978-0-613-84083-5(6)) Tandem Library Bks.

Anderson, Kevin J. The Shards of Alderaan. 1999. (Star Wars Ser.: No. 7). (978-0-606-14313-4(0)) Tandem Library Bks.

Anderson, Kevin J., et al. The Fall of the Sith Empire. 1998. (Star Wars Ser.). (Illus.). 136p. (YA). (gr. 7 up). pap. 14.95 (978-1-56971-320-4(0)) Dark Horse Comics.
—Knights of the Old Republic. Johnston, Janine & Roach, David, illus. (Star Wars Ser.). 136p. (YA). (gr. 7 up). pap. 14.95 (978-1-56971-020-3(1)) Dark Horse Comics.
Anderson, M. T. Feed. braille ed. 2003. (J). (gr. 2). spiral bd. (978-0-616-15869-2(6)) Canadian National Institute for the Blind/Institut National Canadien pour les Aveugles.
—Feed. (YA). (gr. 9 up). 2004. 320p. pap. 7.99 (978-0-7636-2259-6(1)); 2002. 240p. 16.99 (978-0-7636-1726-4(1)) Candlewick Pr.
—Feed. 2004. 320p. (J). (gr. 7 up). pap. 38.00 incl. audio (978-1-4000-9022-8(9) , Listening Library) Random Hse. Audio Publishing Group.
—Feed. 2004. 299p. (YA). (gr. 9-12). lib. bdg. 16.65 (978-0-613-99702-7(6)) Tandem Library Bks.
Anderson, M. T. & Moore, Stephen. Whales on Stilts! Thrilling Tales. Cyrus, Kurt, illus. 2005. (M. T. Anderson's Thrilling Tales Ser.). 208p. (J). 15.00 (978-0-15-205340-6(9)) Harcourt Children's Bks.
Andrews, Jerome. The Initiation. 2006. 40p. pap. 8.50 (978-1-4116-9167-4(9)) Lulu.com.
Anghelides, Peter & Cole, Stephen. The Ancestor Cell. 2001. (Doctor Who Ser.). (Illus.). 288p. (J). pap. 6.95 (978-0-563-53809-7(0)) BBC Worldwide Americas.
Annie Auerbach & MikeNorton. The Good, the Bad & the Gassy. 2006. (Illus.). 96p. pap. 4.99 (978-1-59816-049-9(4) , Tokyopop Kids) TOKYOPOP, Inc.
Ant, Exupery. Journee avec le Petit Prince. pap. 10.95 (978-2-07-054268-0(8)) Gallimard, Editions FRA. *Dist:* Distribooks, Inc.
Anthony, David & David, Charles. Early Winter's Orb: Knightscares #3. 2005. (Illus.). 208p. (J). pap. 5.99 (978-0-9728461-2-7(3)) Sigil Publishing.
Aoki, Toshinao & Toda, Akihito. Pikachu's Day. Itoh, Benimaru & Himeno, Kagemaru, illus. 1999. (Pokemon Tales Ser.: No. 4). 18p. (YA). (ps-k). 4.95 (978-1-56931-386-2(5)) Viz Media.
Applegate, Katherine. The Absolute. 2001. (Animorphs Ser.: No. 51). (Illus.). 160p. (J). (gr. 3-7). pap. 4.99 (978-0-439-11525-4(6)) Scholastic, Inc.
—Aftermath. 2003. (Remnants Ser.: No. 12). 176p. (J). pap. 4.99 (978-0-590-88522-5(7) , Scholastic Paperbacks) Scholastic, Inc.
—Aftermath. 2003. (Remnants Ser.: No. 12). (gr. 3-6). lib. bdg. 13.00 (978-0-613-66345-8(4)) Tandem Library Bks.
—Animorphs Boxed Set: The Change; The Unknown; The Escape; The Warning, No. 4. 2001. (Animorphs Ser.). (J). (gr. 3-7). 19.96 (978-0-590-28434-9(7) , Scholastic Paperbacks) Scholastic, Inc.
—Animorphs Boxed Set: The Invasion; The Visitor; The Encounter; The Message, No. 1. 2001. (Animorphs Ser.). (J). (gr. 3-7). 19.96 (978-0-590-38187-1(3)) Scholastic, Inc.
—Animorphs Boxed Set: The Separation; The Illusion; The Prophecy; The Proposal; The Mutation; The Weakness; The Arrival; The Hidden; The Other; The Familiar; The Journey, 12 bks. l.t. ed. Incl. Arrival. 148p. 2001. lib. bdg. 23.33 (978-0-8368-2771-2(6)); Conspiracy. 138p. 2000. lib. bdg. 23.33 (978-0-8368-2754-5(6)); Familiar. 143p. 2001. lib. bdg. 23.33 (978-0-8368-2774-3(0)); Hidden. 121p. 2001. lib. bdg. 23.33 (978-0-8368-2772-9(4)); Illusion. 156p. 2000. lib. bdg. 23.33 (978-0-8368-2755-2(4)); Journey. 139p. 2001. lib. bdg. 23.33 (978-0-8368-2775-0(9)); Mutation. 142p. 2000. lib. bdg. 23.33 (978-0-8368-2756-9(2)); Other. 130p. 2001. lib. bdg. 23.33 (978-0-8368-2773-6(2)); Prophecy. 141p. 2000. lib. bdg. 23.33 (978-0-8368-2757-6(0)); Proposal. 147p. 2000. lib. bdg. 23.33 (978-0-8368-2758-3(9)); Separation. 158p. 2000. lib. bdg. 23.33 (978-0-8368-2759-0(7)); Weakness. (Illus.). 129p. 2001. lib. bdg. 23.33 (978-0-8368-2770-5(8)); (J). (gr. 4 up). (Animorphs Ser.: Nos. 32-42). 2001. Set lib. bdg. 279.96 (978-0-8368-2862-7(3)) Stevens, Gareth Inc.
—Animorphs Boxed Set: The Threat; The Solution; The Pretender; The Suspicion, 4 vols., No. 6. 2001. (Animorphs Ser.: Nos. 21-24). (J). (gr. 3-7). 19.96 (978-0-590-28543-8(2)) Scholastic, Inc.
—Animorphs Boxed Set: The Weakness; the Arrival; the Hidden; the Other, No. 10. 2000. (Animorphs Ser.: Nos. 37-40). (Illus.). (J). (gr. 3-7). 19.96 (978-0-439-10688-7(5) , Scholastic Paperbacks) Scholastic, Inc.
—Animorphs Series Boxed Set. 1998. (Animorphs Ser.). (J). (gr. 3-7). pap. 143.64 (978-0-590-51066-0(5)) Scholastic, Inc.
—The Arrival. l.t. ed. 2001. (Animorphs Ser.: No. 38). 148p. (J). (gr. 4 up). lib. bdg. 23.33 (978-0-8368-2771-2(6)) Stevens, Gareth Inc.
—The Arrival. 2000. (Animorphs Ser.: No. 38). (gr. 3-6). lib. bdg. 13.00 (978-0-613-21111-6(1)); (Illus.). (J). 11.64 (978-0-606-18509-7(7)) Tandem Library Bks.
—The Attack. 1999. (Animorphs Ser.: No. 26). (gr. 3-6). lib. bdg. 13.00 (978-0-613-11262-8(8)); (J). (978-0-606-15834-3(0)) Tandem Library Bks.
—Back to Before. 2000. (Animorphs Ser.: No. 4). (Illus.). 192p. (J). (gr. 3-7). pap. 5.99 (978-0-439-17307-0(8) , Scholastic Paperbacks) Scholastic, Inc.
—Brave the Betrayal. 2000. (EverWorld Ser.: No. 8). (Illus.). (J). (gr. 4-7). 11.64 (978-0-606-18541-7(0)) Tandem Library Bks.
—Breakdown. 2002. (Remnants Ser.: No. 6). (Illus.). 176p. (J). (gr. 7-12). pap. 4.99 (978-0-590-88195-1(7)) Scholastic, Inc.
—The Conspiracy. l.t. ed. 2000. (Animorphs Ser.: No. 31). 138p. (J). (gr. 4 up). lib. bdg. 23.33 (978-0-8368-2754-5(6)) Stevens, Gareth Inc.
—The Conspiracy. 1999. (Animorphs Ser.: No. 31). (Illus.). (J). (gr. 3-7). 11.64 (978-0-606-16928-8(8)) Tandem Library Bks.
—The Deception. 2000. (Animorphs Ser.: No. 46). (Illus.). 160p. (J). (gr. 3-7). pap. 4.99 (978-0-439-11520-9(5)) Scholastic, Inc.
—The Deception. 2000. (Animorphs Ser.: No. 46). (J). (gr. 3-7). (978-0-606-19529-4(7)) Tandem Library Bks.
—The Decision. 1998. (Animorphs Ser.: No. 18). (J). (gr. 3-7). 11.64 (978-0-606-13138-4(8)) Tandem Library Bks.
—The Departure. 1998. (Animorphs Ser.: No. 19). 176p. (J). (gr. 3-7). pap. 4.99 (978-0-590-49451-9(1) , Scholastic Paperbacks) Scholastic, Inc.
—The Departure. 1998. (Animorphs Ser.: No. 19). (J). (gr. 3-7). 11.64 (978-0-606-13139-1(6)) Tandem Library Bks.
—Destination Unknown. 2001. (Remnants Ser.: No. 2). 160p. (J). (gr. 4-7). 4.99 (978-0-590-88074-9(8) , Scholastic Paperbacks) Scholastic, Inc.
—Destination Unknown. 2001. (Remnant Ser.: No. 2). (Illus.). (J). 11.64 (978-0-606-21399-8(6)) Tandem Library Bks.
—Discover the Destroyer. (EverWorld Ser.: No. 5). 2000. (gr. 7-12). lib. bdg. 13.00 (978-0-613-21502-2(8)); 1999. (Illus.). (J). (gr. 4-7). 11.64 (978-0-606-18539-4(9)) Tandem Library Bks.
—The Discovery. 1998. (Animorphs Ser.: No. 20). 153p. (J). (gr. 3-7). pap. 4.99 (978-0-590-49637-7(9) , Scholastic Paperbacks) Scholastic, Inc.
—The Discovery. 1998. (Animorphs Ser.: No. 20). (J). (gr. 3-7). (978-0-606-13140-7(X)) Tandem Library Bks.
—The Ellimist Chronicles. 2000. (Animorphs Ser.). (Illus.). 288p. (J). (gr. 3-7). pap. 5.99 (978-0-439-21798-9(9)) Scholastic, Inc.
—The Ellimist Chronicles. 2000. (Animorphs Ser.). (J). (gr. 3-7). (978-0-606-19533-1(5)) Tandem Library Bks.
—El Encuentro. 1999. (Animorphs Ser.: Vol. 3). (SPA., Illus.). (J). (gr. 4-7). pap. 4.99 (978-0-439-08627-1(2) , SO1649) Scholastic, Inc.
—El Encuentro. 1999. (Animorphs Ser.: No. 3). (J). (gr. 3-7). (978-0-606-17286-8(6)) Tandem Library Bks.
—Enter the Enchanted. 1999. (EverWorld Ser.: No. 3). (J). (gr. 4-7). 11.64 (978-0-606-17279-0(3)) Tandem Library Bks.
—Entertain the End. 2001. (EverWorld Ser.: No. 12). 176p. (YA). (gr. 4-7). pap. 4.99 (978-0-590-87996-5(0)) Scholastic, Inc.
—Entertain the End. 2001. (EverWorld Ser.). (Illus.). (J). (978-0-606-21183-3(7)) Tandem Library Bks.
—The Experiment. 1999. (Animorphs Ser.: No. 28). 160p. (J). (gr. 3-7). pap. 4.99 (978-0-590-76261-8(3)) Scholastic, Inc.
—The Experiment. 1999. (Animorphs Ser.: No. 28). (gr. 3-6). lib. bdg. 13.00 (978-0-613-16892-2(5)); (J). (978-0-606-16608-9(4)) Tandem Library Bks.
—The Exposed. 1999. (Animorphs Ser.: No. 27). (J). (gr. 3-7). (978-0-606-16589-1(4)) Tandem Library Bks.
—The Extreme. 1999. (Animorphs Ser.: No. 25). 146p. (J). (gr. 3-7). pap. 4.99 (978-0-590-76258-8(3)) Scholastic, Inc.
—The Familiar. l.t. ed. 2001. (Animorphs Ser.: No. 41). 143p. (J). (gr. 4 up). lib. bdg. 23.33 (978-0-8368-2774-3(0)) Stevens, Gareth Inc.
—The Familiar. 2000. (Animorphs Ser.: No. 41). (Illus.). (J). (gr. 3-7). 11.64 (978-0-606-18512-7(7)) Tandem Library Bks.
—Fear the Fantastic. 2000. (EverWorld Ser.: No. 6). (Illus.). 192p. (J). (gr. 4-7). pap. 4.99 (978-0-590-87764-0(X)) Scholastic, Inc.
—Fear the Fantastic. 2000. (EverWorld Ser.: No. 6). (Illus.). (J). (gr. 4-7). 11.64 (978-0-606-18540-0(2)) Tandem Library Bks.
—The First Journey. 1999. (Animorphs Ser.: No. 1). (J). (gr. 3-7). (978-0-606-16606-5(8)) Tandem Library Bks.
—Gateway to the Gods. 7th ed. 2000. (EverWorld Ser.: No. 7). (Illus.). 192p. (J). (gr. 4-7). pap. 4.99 (978-0-590-87766-4(6)) Scholastic, Inc.
—Gateway to the Gods. 2000. (EverWorld Ser.: No. 7). (Illus.). (J). (gr. 4-7). (978-0-606-18872-2(X)) Tandem Library Bks.
—The Hidden. l.t. ed. 2001. (Animorphs Ser.: No. 39). 121p. (J). (gr. 4 up). lib. bdg. 23.33 (978-0-8368-2772-9(4)) Stevens, Gareth Inc.
—The Hork-Bajir Chronicles. 1998. (Animorphs Ser.). (J). (gr. 3-7). (Illus.). 206p. pap. 13.95 (978-0-439-04291-8(7)); 12.95 (978-0-590-38198-7(9)) Scholastic, Inc.
—The Hork-Bajir Chronicles. 1999. (Animorphs Ser.). (J). (gr. 3-7). (978-0-606-17284-4(X)) Tandem Library Bks.
—The Illusion. l.t. ed. 2000. (Animorphs Ser.: No. 33). 156p. (J). (gr. 4 up). lib. bdg. 23.33 (978-0-8368-2755-2(4)) Stevens, Gareth Inc.
—The Illusion. 1999. (Animorphs Ser.: No. 33). (J). (gr. 3-7). 11.64 (978-0-606-17287-5(4)) Tandem Library Bks.
—In the Time of Dinosaurs. 1998. (Animorphs Ser.: No. 2). 229p. (J). (gr. 3-7). pap. 4.99 (978-0-590-95615-4(9) , Scholastic Paperbacks) Scholastic, Inc.
—In the Time of Dinosaurs. 1998. (Animorphs Ser.: No. 2). (J). (gr. 3-7). (978-0-606-13142-1(6)) Tandem Library Bks.
—Inside the Illusion. 2000. (EverWorld Ser.: No. 9). (J). (gr. 4-7). 11.64 (978-0-606-19558-4(0)) Tandem Library Bks.
—L' Invasion. 1999. (Animorphs Ser.: No. 1). Tr. of Invasion. (FRE & SPA.). 128p. (J). (gr. 3-7). pap. 4.99 (978-0-439-05602-1(0)) Scholastic, Inc.
—La Invasion. 1999. (Animorphs Ser.: No. 1). Tr. of Invasion. (J). (gr. 3-7). (978-0-606-16607-2(6)) Tandem Library Bks.
—The Journey. l.t. ed. 2001. (Animorphs Ser.: No. 42). 139p. (J). (gr. 4 up). lib. bdg. 23.33 (978-0-8368-2775-0(9)) Stevens, Gareth Inc.
—The Journey. 2000. (Animorphs Ser.: No. 42). (Illus.). (J). (gr. 3-7). 11.64 (978-0-606-18860-9(6)) Tandem Library Bks.
—Land of Loss. 1999. (EverWorld Ser.: No. 2). 192p. (J). (gr. 4-7). pap. 4.99 (978-0-590-87751-0(8)) Scholastic, Inc.
—Land of Loss. 1999. (EverWorld Ser.: No. 2). (J). (gr. 4-7). (978-0-606-16927-1(X)) Tandem Library Bks.
—El Mensaje. 1999. (Animorphs Ser.: No. 4). (SPA., Illus.). 164p. (J). (gr. 3-7). pap. 4.99 (978-0-439-07883-4(X) , SO5398) Scholastic, Inc.
—El Mensaje. 1999. No. 4. (J). (978-0-606-17290-5(4)) Tandem Library Bks.
—The Message. 2000. (Animorphs Ser.: No. 4). (Illus.). (J). (gr. 3-7). 11.64 (978-0-606-18510-3(0)) Tandem Library Bks.
—The Mutation. l.t. ed. 2000. (Animorphs Ser.: No. 36). 142p. (J). (gr. 4 up). lib. bdg. 23.33 (978-0-8368-2756-9(2)) Stevens, Gareth Inc.
—The Mutation. 1999. (Animorphs Ser.: No. 36). (Illus.). (J). (gr. 3-7). (978-0-606-18507-3(0)) Tandem Library Bks.
—The Next Passage. 2000. (Animorphs Ser.: No. 2). (Illus.). 128p. (J). (gr. 3-7). pap. 4.99 (978-0-439-14263-2(6)) Scholastic, Inc.
—The Next Passage. 2000. (Animorphs Ser.: No. 2). (Illus.). (J). (gr. 3-7). (978-0-606-18506-6(2)) Tandem Library Bks.
—No Place Like Home. 2002. (Remnants Ser.: No. 9). 176p. (J). (gr. 4-8). pap. 4.99 (978-0-590-88492-1(1) , Scholastic Paperbacks) Scholastic, Inc.
—Nowhere Land. 2002. (Remnants Ser.: No. 4). 176p. (J). (gr. 4-8). pap. 4.99 (978-0-590-88193-7(0) , Scholastic Paperbacks) Scholastic, Inc.
—The Other. 2000. (Animorphs Ser.: No. 40). (Illus.). 144p. (J). (gr. 3-7). pap. 4.99 (978-0-439-10679-5(6)) Scholastic, Inc.
—The Other. l.t. ed. 2001. (Animorphs Ser.: No. 40). 130p. (J). (gr. 4 up). lib. bdg. 23.33 (978-0-8368-2773-6(2)) Stevens, Gareth Inc.
—The Other. 2000. (Animorphs Ser.: No. 40). (Illus.). (J). (gr. 3-7). (978-0-606-18511-0(9)) Tandem Library Bks.
—The Prophecy. l.t. ed. 2000. (Animorphs Ser.: No. 34). 141p. (J). (gr. 4 up). lib. bdg. 23.33 (978-0-8368-2757-6(0)) Stevens, Gareth Inc.
—The Prophecy. 1999. (Animorphs Ser.: No. 34). (J). (gr. 3-7). (978-0-606-17283-7(1)) Tandem Library Bks.
—The Proposal. l.t. ed. 2000. (Animorphs Ser.: No. 35). 147p. (J). (gr. 4 up). lib. bdg. 23.33 (978-0-8368-2758-3(9)) Stevens, Gareth Inc.
—The Proposal. 1999. (Animorphs Ser.: No. 35). (gr. 3-6). lib. bdg. 13.00 (978-0-613-21114-7(6)); (J). (978-0-606-17289-9(0)) Tandem Library Bks.
—Realm of the Reaper. 1999. (EverWorld Ser.: No. 4). (J). (gr. 4-7). (978-0-606-17541-8(5)) Tandem Library Bks.
—The Resistance. 2000. (Animorphs Ser.: No. 47). (J). (gr. 3-7). (978-0-606-19530-0(0)) Tandem Library Bks.
—The Revelation. 2000. (Animorphs Ser.: No. 45). (Illus.). 144p. (J). (gr. 3-7). pap. 4.99 (978-0-439-11519-3(1)) Scholastic, Inc.
—Search for Senna. 1999. (EverWorld Ser.: No. 1). (J). (gr. 4-7). (978-0-606-16926-4(1)) Tandem Library Bks.
—The Separation. 1999. (Animorphs Ser.: No. 32). 176p. (J). (gr. 3-7). pap. 4.99 (978-0-439-07032-4(5)) Scholastic, Inc.
—The Separation. l.t. ed. 2000. (Animorphs Ser.: No. 32). 158p. (J). (gr. 4 up). lib. bdg. 23.33 (978-0-8368-2759-0(7)) Stevens, Gareth Inc.
—The Separation. 1999. (Animorphs Ser.: No. 32). (gr. 3-6). lib. bdg. 13.00 (978-0-613-16895-3(X)); (J). (978-0-606-17060-4(X)) Tandem Library Bks.
—The Sickness. 1999. (Animorphs Ser.: No. 29). 176p. (J). (gr. 3-7). pap. 4.99 (978-0-590-76262-5(1)) Scholastic, Inc.
—The Sickness. 1999. (Animorphs Ser.: No. 29). (J). (978-0-606-16618-8(1)); (gr. 3-6). lib. bdg. 13.00 (978-0-613-16896-0(8)) Tandem Library Bks.
—The Solution. 1998. (Animorphs Ser.: No. 22). 152p. (J). (gr. 3-7). pap. 4.99 (978-0-590-76255-7(9)) Scholastic, Inc.
—Survival. 2003. (Remnants Ser.: No. 13). (gr. 3-6). lib. bdg. 13.00 (978-0-613-66387-8(X)) Tandem Library Bks.
—The Suspicion. 1998. (Animorphs Ser.: No. 24). 176p. (J). (gr. 3-7). pap. 4.99 (978-0-590-76257-1(5)) Scholastic, Inc.
—The Test. 2000. (Animorphs Ser.: No. 43). (Illus.). (J). (gr. 3-7). (978-0-606-18861-6(4)) Tandem Library Bks.
—Them. 2001. (Remnants Ser.: No. 3). 208p. (J). pap. 4.99 (978-0-590-88078-7(0) , Scholastic Paperbacks) Scholastic, Inc.
—The Threat. 1998. (Animorphs Ser.: No. 21). (J). (gr. 3-7). (978-0-606-13141-4(8)) Tandem Library Bks.
—The Underground. 1998. (Animorphs Ser.: No. 17). (J). (gr. 3-7). (978-0-606-13137-7(X)) Tandem Library Bks.
—Understand the Unknown. 2000. (EverWorld Ser.: No. 10). 208p. (J). (gr. 4-7). pap. 4.99 (978-0-590-87986-6(3)) Scholastic, Inc.
—Understand the Unknown. 2000. (EverWorld Ser.: No. 10). (J). (gr. 4-7). (978-0-606-19557-7(2)); (978-0-606-19917-9(9)) Tandem Library Bks.
—El Visitante. 1999. (Animorphs Ser.: No. 2). (SPA., Illus.). 192p. (J). (gr. 3-7). pap. 4.99 (978-0-439-07163-5(1) , SO5396) Scholastic, Inc.
—El Visitante. 1999. (Animorphs Ser.: No. 2). (J). (gr. 3-7). (978-0-606-16929-5(6)) Tandem Library Bks.
—Visser. 1999. (Animorphs Ser.). 208p. (J). (gr. 3-7). pap. 12.95 (978-0-439-08764-3(3)) Scholastic, Inc.
—The Warning. 1998. (Animorphs Ser.: No. 16). (J). (gr. 3-7). (978-0-606-13136-0(1)) Tandem Library Bks.
—The Weakness. l.t. ed. 2001. (Animorphs Ser.: No. 37). (Illus.). 129p. (J). (gr. 4 up). lib. bdg. 23.33 (978-0-8368-2770-5(8)) Stevens, Gareth Inc.
—The Weakness. 2000. (Animorphs Ser.: No. 37). (gr. 3-6). lib. bdg. 13.00 (978-0-613-21115-4(4)); (Illus.). (J). (978-0-606-18508-0(9)) Tandem Library Bks.
Appleton, Victor. Into the Abyss. 2007. (Tom Swift, Young Inventor Ser.). 160p. (J). (gr. 4-7). 27.07 (***978-1-59961-350-5(6))*** Spotlight.
—Tom Swift & His Airship. 2004. (Tom Swift Original Ser.: No. 3). 216p. (J). (ps-3). 17.95 (978-1-55709-177-2(3)) Applewood Bks.
—Tom Swift & His Airship. 2000. (Tom Swift Original Ser.: Vol. No. 3). 118p. (gr. 3-7). 19.95 (978-1-57646-359-8(1)); 118p. (gr. 3-7). pap. 7.95 (978-1-57646-203-4(X)); 186p. pap. 12.99 (978-1-57646-360-4(5)) Quiet Vision Publishing.
—Tom Swift & His Electric Rifle. 2006. 18.99 (***978-1-4280-3261-3(4))*** IndyPublish.com.
—Tom Swift & His Motor Boat. 2004. (Tom Swift Original Ser.: No. 2). 212p. (J). (ps-3). 14.95 (978-1-55709-176-5(5)) Applewood Bks.
—Tom Swift & His Motor Boat. 2000. (Tom Swift Original Ser.: Vol. No. 2). 112p. (gr. 3-7). 19.95 (978-1-57646-356-7(7)); 112p. (gr. 3-7). pap. 7.95 (978-1-57646-202-7(1)); 182p. pap. 12.99 (978-1-57646-357-4(5)) Quiet Vision Publishing.
—Tom Swift & His Motor Cycle. 2004. (Tom Swift Original Ser.: No. 1). 206p. (J). (ps-3). 17.95 (978-1-55709-175-8(7)) Applewood Bks.
—Tom Swift & His Motor Cycle. 2000. (Tom Swift Original Ser.: Vol. No. 1). 114p. (gr. 3-7). 19.95 (978-1-57646-353-6(2)); 114p. (gr. 3-7). pap. 7.95 (978-1-57646-201-0(3)); 180p. pap. 12.99 (978-1-57646-354-3(0)) Quiet Vision Publishing.
—Tom Swift & His MotorCycle. 2006. 18.99 (***978-1-4280-3267-5(3))*** IndyPublish.com.
—Tom Swift & the Electronic Hydrolung. 2007. 94.99 (***978-1-4280-5319-9(0));*** pap. 88.99 (***978-1-4280-5318-2(2))*** IndyPublish.com.
—Tom Swift & the Visitor from Planet X. 2006. 95.99 (***978-1-4280-1626-2(0));*** pap. 88.99 (***978-1-4280-1622-4(8))*** IndyPublish.com.
Apps, Roy. The Time Spinner. 2003. (Illus.). 128p. (J). pap. 9.99 (978-1-84270-231-4(9)) Andersen GBR. *Dist:* Independent Pubs. Group.
Archer, Chris. Shape-Shifter. 1998. 135p. (J). (gr. 4-7). per. 11.80 (978-0-613-73006-8(2)) Tandem Library Bks.
Archibald, G. K. The World Wide Websters: First Contact. 2002. 134p. (J). pap. 10.95 (978-0-595-24201-6(4) , Writers Club Pr.) iUniverse, Inc.
Armentrout, James & Macon, Steven, eds. Alien Alerts Journal Winter 2003, 2004. (Illus.). 64p. pap. 5.00 (978-1-57688-038-8(9) , 80389, Otherworlds Sci-Fi) Branch & Vine Pubs., LLC.
—Alien Alerts Magazine: Spring 2003. 2003. (Illus.). 40p. (YA). pap. 5.00 (978-1-57688-014-2(1) , 80141) Branch & Vine Pubs., LLC.
Armstrong, Jennifer. The Keepers of the Flame. 2003. (gr. 7-12). lib. bdg. 14.15 (978-0-613-67205-4(4)) Tandem Library Bks.
—The Kiln. 2004. (Fire-Us Ser.: No. 3). 256p. (J). (gr. 7 up). pap. 5.99 (978-0-06-447271-5(X)) HarperCollins Pubs.
Armstrong, Jennifer & Butcher, Nancy. The Kiln. 2003. (Fire-Us Ser.: Bk. 3). 208p. (J). (gr. 7 up). 15.99 (978-0-06-008050-1(7)) HarperCollins Pubs.
—The Kindling. 2002. (Fire-Us Ser.: Bk. 1). 224p. (J). (gr. 7 up). 15.99 (978-0-06-008048-8(5)); 16.89 (978-0-06-029411-3(6)) HarperCollins Pubs.
Arnold, Hap. Secret of Spring Mill. 2001. (gr. 7-12). lib. bdg. 16.45 (978-0-613-77893-0(6)) Tandem Library Bks.
Arnold, Michelle Lee. Mathew Sunburst & the Keepers of the Sky. 2003. 141p. (J). pap. 13.95 (978-0-7414-1575-2(5)) Infinity Publishing.
, Asah, Asah & , Kooma, Kooma. The 7 Big Secrets of Planet WU. 2006. 68p. (J). 22.73 (978-1-4116-9101-8(6)) Lulu.com.
Asimov, Isaac. Isaac Asimov Collected Short Stories. Court, Robert, illus. 2001. (Great Author Ser.). (J). (978-0-9709033-5-8(9)) Peterson Publishing Co., Inc.
Asimov, Isaac & Asimov, Janet. Norby & the Lost Princess. 129p. (J). lib. bdg. 20.90 (978-0-8027-6593-2(9)) Walker & Co.
Asimov, Isaac & Hantula, Richard. Science Fiction: Vision of Tomorrow? 2004. (Isaac Asimov's 21st Century Library of the Universe). (Illus.). 32p. (J). lib. bdg. 24.67 (978-0-8368-3952-4(8)) Stevens, Gareth Inc.
Asimov, Janet & Asimov, Isaac. Norby & the Court Jester. l.t. ed. 1999. 168p. 24.95 (978-0-7838-8610-7(1)) Thorndike Pr.
At Space Camp, Vol. 2. 2005. (Early Library). (YA). (ps-3). 23.94 (978-0-8215-8945-8(8)) Sadlier, William H. Inc.
Auerbach, Annie. No Parent's Day. 2001. (gr. k-3). lib. bdg. 11.25 (978-0-613-43945-9(7)) Tandem Library Bks.
Auerbach, Annie. The Quest for Energon. 2007. (Transformers Ser.). 64p. (J). pap. 4.99 (***978-0-06-088834-3(2)*** , Harper Entertainment) HarperCollins Pubs.
Augarde, Steve. The Various. 2004. (Illus.). 448p. (J). (gr. 5). 16.95 (978-0-385-75029-5(3)); (gr. 7). lib. bdg. 18.99 (978-0-385-75037-0(4)) Random Hse. Children's Bks. (Fickling, David Bks.).
Avi. Avi Mid Grade 2. 2008. 208p. (J). 16.99 (***978-0-06-000015-8(5));*** lib. bdg. 17.89 (***978-0-06-000016-5(3))*** HarperCollins Pubs.
Avi. Poppy's Return. Floca, Brian, illus. (Poppy Stories Ser.). (J). 2006. 256p. pap. 5.99 (978-0-06-000014-1(7) , Harper Trophy); 2005. 240p. lib. bdg. 16.89 (978-0-06-000013-4(9)) HarperCollins Pubs.

S

AWRP Meet Superkids. (J). pap., stu. ed. (978-0-201-21600-4(0)) Addison-Wesley Longman, Inc.

Bagley, Mark, illus. Ultimate Spider-Man: Double Trouble. 2002. (Ultimate Spider-Man Ser.). 27.19 (978-1-4046-2382-8(5)) Book Wholesalers, Inc.

—Ultimate Spider-Man: Learning Curve. 2002. 21.09 (978-1-4046-2220-3(9)) Book Wholesalers, Inc.

—Ultimate Spider-Man: Legacy. 2002. (Ultimate Spider-Man Ser.). 20.83 (978-1-4046-2353-8(1)) Book Wholesalers, Inc.

—Ultimate Spider-Man: Power & Responsibility. 2002. (YA). 23.04 (978-1-4046-0900-6(8)) Book Wholesalers, Inc.

Bailey-Peiffer, Stefanie & Bailey-Yarbrough, Caroline. Modie & the Power of the BellKeys. 2004. pap. 8.95 (978-0-9762502-0-3(9)) Hudson Bks.

Bailey, Peter, illus. The Kingfisher Treasury of Magical Stories. 2003. (Kingfisher Treasury of Stories Ser.: Vol. 16). 160p. (J). (gr. k-3). pap. 5.95 (978-0-7534-5624-8(9) , Kingfisher) Houghton Mifflin Co. Trade & Reference Div.

Baker, Kage. The Life of the World to Come. rev. ed. 2005. (Company Ser.). 416p. mass mkt. 6.99 (978-0-7653-5432-7(2) , Tor Bks.) Doherty, Tom Assocs., LLC.

Balian, Lorna. Un Fiasco de Bruja. 2004. Tr. of Humbug Witch. (SPA., Illus.). 32p. (J). (ps). pap. 4.95 (978-1-59572-011-5(1)) Star Bright Bks., Inc.

Banim, Lisa. Case of the Missing She-Geek. 2004. 125p. (J). lib. bdg. 16.92 (***978-1-4242-0683-4(9)***) Fitzgerald Bks.

Banyai, Istvan. Re-Zoom. 1998. (Picture Puffin Ser.). (Illus.). 64p. (J). (gr. k-3). pap. 7.99 (978-0-14-055694-0(X) , Puffin) Penguin Group (USA) Inc.

Barlow, Dave. The Seekers. 2004. 48p. 3.95 (978-0-9725230-4-2(9)) Wandering Sage Bookstore & More, LLC.

Barlow, Steve & Skidmore, Steve. The Doomsday Virus. Buckley, Harriet, illus. 2008. (J). pap. (***978-1-59889-907-8(4)***); lib. bdg. (***978-1-59889-871-2(X)***) Stone Arch Bks.

—The Hunt. 2003. (Outernet Ser.: No. 5). 192p. (J). pap. 4.99 (978-0-439-43018-0(6) , Chicken Hse., The) Scholastic, Inc.

—Star Bores: May the Farce Be with You. 2004. 416p. 9.95 (978-0-00-719208-3(8)) HarperCollins Pubs. Ltd. GBR. *Dist:* Independent Pubs. Group.

—Stone Me! Ross, Tony, illus. 2005. (Mad Myths Ser.). 122p. (J). pap. 5.95 (978-1-903015-43-8(X)) Barn Owl Bks, London GBR. *Dist:* Independent Pubs. Group.

Barlow, Steve L. & Skidmore, Steve. Friend or Foe? 2002. (Outernet Ser.: No. 1). (Illus.). 176p. (J). (gr. 3-7). pap. 4.99 (978-0-439-34351-0(8)) Scholastic, Inc.

—Odyssey. 2002. (Outernet Ser.: No. 3). 192p. (J). (gr. 3-7). pap. 4.99 (978-0-439-34353-4(4) , Chicken Hse., The) Scholastic, Inc.

Barnes, Emma. Jessica Haggerthwaite Media Star. Archbold, Tim, illus. l.t. ed. 2005. 269p. (J). (ps-7). pap. (978-1-4056-6001-3(5)) BBC Audio.

Barnes, Steven. Iron Shadows. 2000. (gr. 7-12). lib. bdg. 15.30 (978-0-613-27904-8(2)) Tandem Library Bks.

Baron, Mike, et al. The Last Command: X-Wing Rogue Squadron. (Star Wars Ser.). (Illus.). 144p. (YA). (gr. 7 up). pap. 17.95 (978-1-56971-378-5(2)) Dark Horse Comics.

Barrera, J. Mario. Nine Moons. 2005. (ENG & SPA., Illus.). (YA). cd-rom 21.99 (978-0-9752725-2-7(7)) Orion-Cosmos.

Base, Graeme. The Worst Bana in the Universe: A Totally Cosmic Music Adventure. 1999. (Illus.). 46p. (YA). reprint ed. 20.00 (978-0-7567-6078-6(X)) DIANE Publishing Co.

The Bash Street Kids Annual 2004. annual 2003. (Illus.). 96p. (978-0-85116-815-9(9)) Thomson, D.C. & Co., Ltd. GBR. *Dist:* APG Sales and Fulfillment.

Baum, L. Frank. The Wonderful Wizard of Oz. 2005. (Great Classics for Children Ser.). 160p. (J). 5.99 (978-1-4037-1394-0(4)) Dalmatian Pr.

Bawden, Nina. Off the Road. 1998. (Illus.). 192p. (J). (gr. 5-9). 16.00 (978-0-395-91321-5(7) , Clarion Bks.) Houghton Mifflin Co. Trade & Reference Div.

—Off the Road. 2001. (J). (978-0-606-21364-6(3)); (gr. 5-8). lib. bdg. 14.15 (978-0-613-35993-1(3)) Tandem Library Bks.

Baxendale, Trevor. Eater of Wasps. 2001. (Doctor Who Ser.). (Illus.). 288p. (J). pap. 6.95 (978-0-563-53832-5(5)) BBC Worldwide Americas.

Baxter, Stephen. The Web: Gulliverzone. 2005. 128p. (J). (gr. 4-6). mass mkt. 5.99 (978-0-7653-4941-5(8) , Tor Bks.) Doherty, Tom Assocs., LLC.

Bayo, Ignacio Fernandez & Roy, Antonio Clavo. Enchufate a la Energia! 2001. (Barco de Vapor). (SPA.). 126p. (YA). (978-84-348-7823-5(2)) SM Ediciones ESP. *Dist:* AIMS International Bks., Inc.

Beals, Kevin, et al. Messages from Space: The Solar System & Beyond. Bergman, Lincoln et al, eds. Craig, Rose et al, illus. Sneider, Cary et al, photos by. 2000. (Great Explorations in Math & Science Ser.). 192p. (J). (gr. 4-7). otabind 18.00 (978-0-924886-17-1(X) , GEMS) Univ. of California, Berkeley, Lawrence Hall of Science.

Bechard, Margaret. Spacer & Rat. 2005. 192p. (YA). (gr. 7). 16.95 (978-1-59643-058-7(3)) Roaring Brook Pr.

Beechen, Adam. No More Mr Smart Guy. 2003. (gr. k-3). lib. bdg. 11.80 (978-0-613-66370-0(5)) Tandem Library Bks.

—Ufo! Saunders, Zina, illus. ed. 2005. 32p. (J). lib. bdg. 15.00 (978-1-59054-988-9(0)) Fitzgerald Bks.

Beecroft, Simon. Greatest Battles. 2008. (Dk Readers Ser.). 48p. (J). (ps-12). 14.99 (***978-0-7566-3606-7(X)***); pap. 3.99 (***978-0-7566-3603-6(5)***) Dorling Kindersley Publishing, Inc.

—Ready, Set, Podrace! 2007. (DK Readers: Level 1 (Paperback) Ser.). (Illus.). 32p. (J). (gr. 4-7). pap. 3.99 (***978-0-7566-3274-8(9)***); (ps-3). 14.99 (***978-0-7566-3275-5(7)***) Dorling Kindersley Publishing, Inc.

Bell, David. Pink Alert! 2007. (Dawn Gray Trilogy Ser.). 260p. pap. 11.95 (***978-1-84167-581-7(4)***) Ransom Publishing Ltd. GBR. *Dist:* International Publishers Marketing.

Bell, Hilari. A Matter of Profit. 2001. 288p. (J). (gr. 7 up). 16.99 (978-0-06-029513-4(9)) HarperCollins Pubs.

—A Matter of Profit. 2003. (gr. 7-12). lib. bdg. 15.30 (978-0-613-60391-1(5)) Tandem Library Bks.

—Rise of a Hero. 2006. (Farsala Trilogy Ser.: No. 2). 592p. (YA). pap. 6.99 (978-0-689-85417-0(X) , Simon Pulse) Simon & Schuster Children's Publishing.

Bellairs, John. The Eyes of the Killer Robot. 1998. (Johnny Dixon Mystery Ser.). 12.64 (978-0-606-13371-5(2)) Tandem Library Bks.

Bendis, Brian Michael. Avengers Disassembled HC. 2007. (Illus.). 184p. 24.99 (978-0-7851-2294-4(X)) Marvel Enterprises, Inc.

—Daredevil, Vol. 5. (Illus.). 256p. 29.99 (978-0-7851-2110-7(2)) Marvel Enterprises, Inc.

—Secrets & Lies, Vol. 3. (Illus.). 128p. 19.99 (978-0-7851-1939-5(6)) Marvel Enterprises, Inc.

—Sentry. (Illus.). 152p. pap. 14.99 (978-0-7851-1672-1(9)) Marvel Enterprises, Inc.

Benford, Gregory. Cosm. 1999. (J). (978-0-606-15930-2(4)) Tandem Library Bks.

Bennett, Jeffrey. Max Goes to Mars: A Science Adventure. Okamoto, Alan, illus. 2003. (Science Adventures with Max the Dog Ser.). 32p. (J). 16.95 (978-0-9721819-1-4(1)) Big Kid Science.

—Max Goes to the Moon. Okamoto, Alan, illus. 2003. (Science Adventures with Max the Dog Ser.). 32p. (J). (ps-7). 16.95 (978-0-9721819-0-7(3)) Big Kid Science.

Benton, Jim. The Fran That Time Forgot. Benton, Jim, illus. 2005. (Franny K. Stein, Mad Scientist Ser.: Bk. 4). (Illus.). 112p. (J). mass mkt. 3.99 (978-0-689-86298-4(9) , Aladdin); 14.95 (978-0-689-86294-6(6) , Simon & Schuster Children's Publishing) Simon & Schuster Children's Publishing.

—The Invisible Fran. Benton, Jim, illus. 2005. (Franny K. Stein, Mad Scientist Ser.: Bk. 3). (Illus.). 112p. (J). (gr. 2-5). pap. 3.99 (978-0-689-86297-7(0) , Aladdin) Simon & Schuster Children's Publishing.

Bergen, Lara Rice. General Jar Jar. Thompson, Dana et al, illus. 1999. (Lucas Books). 32p. (J). (978-0-439-10160-8(3)) Scholastic, Inc.

Bernard, Patricia. Techno Terror. 2000. (gr. 7-12). lib. bdg. 12.10 (978-0-613-29093-7(3)) Tandem Library Bks.

Besser, Kenneth/R. Arnie Carver & the Plague of Demeverde. 2007. (Illus.). x, 338p. (J). (***978-1-934316-02-3(4)***) RTMC Organization, LLC.

Best, Jessie. Land of Notion, Bk. 1. 2005. 177p. pap. 19.95 (978-1-4137-8606-4(5)) PublishAmerica, Inc.

Beyond the Black Hole: Individual Title Six-Packs. (Bookweb Ser.). 32p. (gr. 4 up). 34.00 (978-0-7635-3733-3(0)) Rigby Education.

Bichoman Vuelve de la Tumba. (Fantasmas de Fear Street Coleccion). (SPA.). (YA). (gr. 5-8). pap. 7.95 (978-950-04-1718-1(9) , EM9292) Emecé Editores S.A. ARG. *Dist:* Lectorum Pubns., Inc., Planeta Publishing Corp.

Bishop, David. Amorality Tale. 2001. (Doctor Who Ser.: No. 3). 224p. pap. 6.95 (978-0-563-53850-9(3)) BBC Worldwide Americas.

Bisson, Terry. Crossfire. 2002. (Star Wars Ser.: Vol. 2). 144p. (J). pap. 9.95 (978-0-439-33928-5(6) , Scholastic Paperbacks) Scholastic, Inc.

—Crossfire. 2003. (Star Wars Ser.: Vol. 2). (gr. 7-12). lib. bdg. 13.00 (978-0-613-63273-7(7)) Tandem Library Bks.

—The Fight to Survive. Bolinger, Peter, illus. 2003. (Star Wars Ser.). 160p. (J). 5.99 (978-0-439-54880-9(2) , Scholastic Paperbacks) Scholastic, Inc.

—The Fight to Survive. 2003. (Star Wars Ser.). (gr. 3-6). lib. bdg. 13.00 (978-0-613-72154-7(3)) Tandem Library Bks.

—Miracle Man. 1998. (X-Files Ser.). 144p. (J). pap. 4.50 (978-0-06-447192-3(6)) HarperCollins Pubs.

Black, Jake. Leonardo Returns. Jourdan, Diego, illus. 2007. (Teenage Mutant Ninja Turtles Ser.). 32p. (J). pap. 3.99 (978-1-4169-4056-2(1) , Simon Spotlight) Simon & Schuster Children's Publishing.

Blackman, Haden, et al. Victories & Sacrifices Vol. 2. 2003. (Illus.). 112p. (YA). pap. 14.95 (978-1-56971-969-5(1)) Dark Horse Comics.

Blackmore, Nancy J. The Story of Big Bone Lick. McFerron, Mark, illus. 1998. 72p. (J). 24.95 (978-0-9666172-0-7(7)); per. 14.95 (978-0-9666172-1-4(5)) Thoroughbred Publishing, L.L.C.

Blackout! Individual Title Six-Packs. (Bookweb Ser.). 32p. (gr. 4 up). 34.00 (978-0-7635-3728-9(4)) Rigby Education.

Bleatham, Graham & Denham, Sam, eds. Thunderbirds Classic Comics. 2002. (Illus.). 160p. (J). 27.50 (978-1-84222-731-2(9)) Carlton Bks., Ltd. GBR. *Dist:* Independent Pubs. Group.

Blishen, Edward. Science Fiction Stories. 2003. (gr. 3-6). lib. bdg. 15.25 (978-0-613-90169-7(X)) Tandem Library Bks.

Block, Francesca Lia, et al. Firebirds Rising: An Anthology of Original Science Fiction & Fantasy. November, Sharyn, ed. 2006. (Firebird Ser.). 544p. (YA). (gr. 7). 19.99 (978-0-14-240549-9(3) , Puffin) Penguin Group (USA) Inc.

Blum, Jonathan & Orman, Kate. Year of Intelligent Tigers. 2001. (Doctor Who Ser.). (Illus.). 288p. (J). pap. 6.95 (978-0-563-53831-8(7)) BBC Worldwide Americas.

Blundell, Judy. Star Wars: The Last of the Jedi #9. 2008. 160p. pap. 5.99 (***978-0-439-68142-1(1)***) Scholastic, Inc.

Blundell, Judy & Watson, Jude. Against the Empire. 2007. (Star Wars Ser.: No. 8). 160p. (J). pap. 5.99 (***978-0-439-68141-4(3)***) Scholastic, Inc.

Blythe, William. Solar Element Saga: The Legacy of Mirgard. 2004. 175p. pap. 19.95 (978-1-4137-2460-8(4)) PublishAmerica, Inc.

Bondoux, Anne-Laure. The Destiny of Linus Hoppe. Temerson, Catherine, tr. from FRE. 2005. 160p. (J). (gr. 3-7). lib. bdg. 17.99 (978-0-385-90255-7(7) , Delacorte Bks. for Young Readers) Random Hse. Children's Bks.

Bondoux, Anne-Laure. The Second Life of Linus Hoppe. Temerson, Catherine, tr. 2007. 208p. (gr. 4-7). 5.99 (***978-0-440-42039-2(3)*** , Yearling) Random Hse. Children's Bks.

Bone, Ian. Time Trap. 2006. 176p. 5.99 (978-0-440-42034-7(2) , Yearling) Random Hse. Children's Bks.

Book Company Staff. Magic Planet. Schimmel, Schim, illus. 2002. (Pop-up Bks.). 14p. (J). 15.95 (978-1-74047-187-9(3)) Book Co. Publishing Pty, Ltd., The AUS. *Dist:* Penton Overseas, Inc.

Bracken, E E. No Place Like Loam: A Michael O'Brien Story. 2002. 143p. pap. 10.95 (978-0-595-25688-4(0)); (ENG.). 144p. (gr. 2-13). 20.95 (***978-0-595-65261-7(1)***) iUniverse, Inc. (Writers Advantage Pr.).

Bradbury, Ray. Ray Bradbury Collected Short Stories. Court, Robert, illus. 2001. (Great Author Ser.). (J). (978-0-9709033-2-7(4)) Peterson Publishing Co., Inc.

Bradley, Marion Zimmer. Traitor's Sun. 2000. (gr. 7-12). lib. bdg. 16.45 (978-0-613-28110-2(1)) Tandem Library Bks.

Brake, Colin. Escape Velocity. 2001. (Doctor Who Ser.). (Illus.). 288p. (J). pap. 6.95 (978-0-563-53825-7(2)) BBC Worldwide Americas.

Bramscher, Cynthia. Night of the Corn Maiden. 2003. 211p. pap. 19.95 (978-1-59286-704-2(9)) PublishAmerica, Inc.

Brand, Christianna. Nanny McPhee: Based on the Collected Tales of Nurse Matilda. Ardizzone, Edward, illus. 2005. 300p. (J). pap. 7.95 (978-1-58234-671-7(2)) Bloomsbury Publishing.

Braver, Gary. Elixir. 2001. (978-0-606-21174-1(8)) Tandem Library Bks.

Breslin, Theresa. Dream Master Gladiator. l.t. ed. 2005. (J). pap. (978-0-7540-7884-5(1) , CLP 460) BBC Audio.

Breslin, Theresa. Starship Rescue. Buckley, Harriet, illus. 2007. 64p. (J). (***978-1-59889-267-3(3)***) Stone Arch Bks.

Brett, Jan. Hedgie Blasts Off! Brett, Jan, illus. 2006. (Illus.). 32p. (J). (ps-3). 16.99 (978-0-399-24621-0(5) , Putnam Juvenile) Penguin Group (USA) Inc.

Bright, J. E. Digimon No. 3: Andromon's Attack. 2000. (Digimon Ser.: No. 3). 96p. (gr. 4-7). pap. 4.50 (978-0-06-107188-1(9) , Harper Entertainment) HarperCollins Pubs.

—The Quest for Crests. 2001. (Digimon Ser.). (Illus.). 96p. (J). (gr. 1-4). pap. 4.50 (978-0-06-107199-7(4) , Harper Entertainment) HarperCollins Pubs.

—Return to Infinity Mountain. 2000. (Digimon Ser.). 144p. (J). (gr. 1-4). pap. 8.95 (978-0-06-107196-6(X) , Harper Entertainment) HarperCollins Pubs.

Brin, Susannah. Alien Encounter. rev. ed. 1999. (Take Ten Ser.). 64p. (YA). (gr. 4-12). pap. 3.95 (978-1-58659-051-2(0)) Artesian Pr.

Brocato, Bert & Brocato, Tim. QuizQuester & the Captive of the Illusionist. 2002. (Illus.). 181p. pap. 8.95 (978-0-9718432-0-2(1)) QuizQuester Pr. LLC.

Broderick, Damien. Time Zones. 2005. (Thrillogy Ser.). (Illus.). 48p. (gr. 4-8). 17.50 (978-0-7910-8870-8(7)) Facts On File, Inc.

—Time Zones. 2000. (gr. 7-12). lib. bdg. 12.10 (978-0-613-29108-8(5)) Tandem Library Bks.

Brooks, Walter R. Freddy & the Flying Saucer Plans. unabr. ed. 2000. (J). pap. 66.95 incl. audio (978-0-7887-3639-1-6) , 41004X4) Recorded Bks., LLC.

Brouwer, Sigmund. Alien Pursuit. 2000. (gr. 5-8). lib. bdg. 13.00 (978-0-613-76892-4(2)) Tandem Library Bks.

—Countdown. 2001. (gr. 5-8). lib. bdg. 13.00 (978-0-613-76821-4(3)) Tandem Library Bks.

—Hammerhead. 2001. (gr. 3-6). lib. bdg. 13.00 (978-0-613-76893-1(0)) Tandem Library Bks.

—Last Stand. 2002. (gr. 3-6). lib. bdg. 13.00 (978-0-613-76883-2(3)) Tandem Library Bks.

—Manchurian Sector. 2002. (gr. 3-6). lib. bdg. 13.00 (978-0-613-76880-1(9)) Tandem Library Bks.

—Mission 2: Alien Pursuit. 2000. (Mars Diaries Ser.: Mission 2). (Illus.). 144p. (J). (gr. 5-9). mass mkt. 4.99 (978-0-8423-4305-3(9)) Tyndale Hse. Pubs.

—Moon Racer. 2001. (gr. 5-8). lib. bdg. 13.00 (978-0-613-76814-6(0)) Tandem Library Bks.

—Oxygen Level Zero Level Zero. 2000. (gr. 5-8). lib. bdg. 10.65 (978-0-613-76779-8(9)) Tandem Library Bks.

—Robot War. 2001. (gr. 5-8). lib. bdg. 13.00 (978-0-613-76822-1(1)) Tandem Library Bks.

—Sole Survivor. 2001. (gr. 3-6). lib. bdg. 13.00 (978-0-613-76817-7(5)) Tandem Library Bks.

—Time Bomb. 2000. (gr. 5-8). lib. bdg. 13.00 (978-0-613-76816-0(7)) Tandem Library Bks.

Brown, Joseph F. Dark Things, Vol. 2. Lewis, Jason, illus. 2001. 169p. (J). (gr. 5-8). 9.99 (978-0-88092-460-3(8) , 4608) Royal Fireworks Publishing Co.

Brown, Michele. New Tales from Alice's Wonderland: The Queen of Hearts & the Wibbly Wobbly Jelly. Martyr, Paula, illus. 24p. (J). pap. 7.95 (978-0-233-99536-6(6)) Andre Deutsch GBR. *Dist:* Trans-Atlantic Pubns., Inc.

Bruce, Jonathan C. There Is a Season. 2001. 324p. pap. 17.95 (978-0-595-17565-9(1) , Writers Club Pr.) iUniverse, Inc.

Bruce, Karl. Annie Apple & the Teleportation Phantoms from Outer Space. 2006. (YA). pap. 16.00 (978-0-8059-7156-9(4)) Dorrance Publishing Co., Inc.

Bryant, Tod. Lost on the Moon: The Adventure of Will Dare. 2003. 151p. pap. 19.95 (978-1-59129-491-7(6)) PublishAmerica, Inc.

BubbleGirl, Season. A Doggy Diary. 2006. 93p. (J). per. (***978-0-9775120-0-3(2)***) Carpe Diem Publishing.

Buckeridge, Anthony. According to Jennings. 2002. 177p. pap. 8.95 (978-0-7551-0165-8(0)) House of Stratus, Inc. GBR. *Dist:* Midpoint Trade Bks., Inc.

Bundy, Kim. Aiko. Less, Sally, illus. 2000. 32p. (J). 7.95 net. (978-0-9706654-0-9(7)) Sprite Pr.

Bunting, Eve. Wanna Buy an Alien? Bush, Timothy, illus. 2000. 96p. (J). (gr. 4-6). tchr. ed. 14.00 (978-0-395-69719-1(0) , Clarion Bks.) Houghton Mifflin Co. Trade & Reference Div.

Burkett & Watson. Emergency in Escape Pod Four. 1999. (Star Wars Science Adventures Ser.). (978-0-606-16615-7(7)) Tandem Library Bks.

Burkett, Kathy. Whiz Bang, Zoom! Ethan Flask & Professor Von Offel's Energetic Experiments. 2001. (Mad Science Ser.). 66p. (J). pap. (978-0-439-27089-2(8)) Scholastic, Inc.

Burkett, Kathy & Korman, Gordon. What's the Big Idea? Ethan Flask & Professor Von Offel's Ingenious Inventions. 2001. (Mad Science Ser.). (Illus.). 65p. (J). pap. (978-0-439-23581-5(2)) Scholastic, Inc.

Burns, Dal. The Adventures of Phoo. 2006. 148p. pap. 19.95 (978-1-4241-1773-4(9)) PublishAmerica, Inc.

Burns, Laura J. & Burge, Constance M. Sweet Talkin' Demon. 2006. (Charmed Ser.). 192p. (YA). pap. 6.99 (978-1-4169-1469-3(2) , Simon Spotlight Entertainment) Simon & Schuster.

Burris, Ronal S., Jr. A Martian Adventure: We Can Go. 1999. 196p. (gr. 4-7). pap. 13.95 (978-0-9668591-2-6(X) , Writers Club Pr.) iUniverse, Inc.

Burroughs, Edgar Rice. At the Earth's Core. 2001. Tr. of 184. (gr. 3-6). lib. bdg. 9.50 (978-0-613-88729-8(8)) Tandem Library Bks.

Busiek, Kurt. Marvels. 2001. (gr. 5-8). lib. bdg. 30.35 (978-0-613-53688-2(6)) Tandem Library Bks.

Butler, Octavia E. Lilith's Brood. 2000. (gr. 7-12). lib. bdg. 23.40 (978-0-613-27941-3(7)) Tandem Library Bks.

Butler, Susan. The Hermit Thrush Sings. unabr. ed. 2000. (YA). pap. 69.95 incl. audio (978-0-7887-3798-5(8) , 41042X4) Recorded Bks., LLC.

Butler, Ted D. Menace Beyond the Moon: Book Two of the Belt Republic Series. 2005. 280p. (YA). pap. 14.99 (978-1-59092-235-4(2) , Blue Works) Windstorm Creative.

—2176: The Birth of the Belt Republic. 2005. 280p. (YA). pap. 14.99 (978-1-59092-234-7(4) , Blue Works) Windstorm Creative.

Butterfield, Moira. Time Capsule. 1999. (Illus.). 24p. (YA). (gr. 3 up). pap. 8.95 (978-1-902618-64-7(5)) Element Children's Bks.

Byng, Georgia. Molly Moon Detiene el Mundo. 2004. (SPA.). 358p. (gr. 5-8). 18.99 (978-84-348-9610-9(9)) SM Ediciones ESP. *Dist:* Lectorum Pubns., Inc.

—Molly Moon's Incredible Book of Hypnotism. 2nd ed. 2005. 432p. (J). (gr. 7 up). pap. 6.99 (978-0-06-075976-6(3) , Harper Trophy) HarperCollins Pubs.

Cabot, Meg. Haunted. 2005. (Mediator Ser.: Bk. 5). 288p. (J). (gr. 7 up). pap. 6.99 (978-0-06-075164-7(9)) HarperCollins Pubs.

Calero, Dennis. You're Not the Captain of Me! 2006. 272p. pap. 9.95 (978-1-59687-375-9(2)) ibooks, Inc.

Calleja, Seve. El Planeta del Tesoro. 2003. (Disney Collection). (SPA.). 96p. (J). 6.95 (978-84-670-0305-5(7)) Espasa Calpe, S.A. ESP. *Dist:* Planeta Publishing Corp.

Cameron, Eleanor. The Wonderful Flight to the Mushroom Planet. 2000. (J). (gr. 4-8). 22.50 (978-0-8446-7139-0(8)) Smith, Peter Pub., Inc.

Campbell, Hazel D. Ramgoat Dashalong. 2004. 74p. 5.99 (978-976-610-269-2(4)) Penguin Group (USA) Inc.

Campbell, Joanna. Star in Danger. 1999. (gr. 3-6). lib. bdg. 13.00 (978-0-613-22437-6(X)) Tandem Library Bks.

Carbajal, Xavier Joseph. Captain Nemo, Set. abr. ed. 1999. (Captain Nemo Legacy Ser.: Vol. 13). (YA). (gr. 6 up). pap. 18.95 incl. audio (978-0-9654507-7-5(5) , 97-92534) New Future Publishing.

Card, Orson Scott. First Meetings: In the Enderverse. rev. ed. 2004. 224p. (YA). 6.99 (978-0-7653-4798-5(9) , Tor Bks.) Doherty, Tom Assocs., LLC.

Card, Orson Scott, ed. Future on Ice. rev. ed. 1998. 432p. (YA). (gr. 7 up). 24.95 (978-0-312-86694-5(1) , Tor Bks.) Doherty, Tom Assocs., LLC.

Carey, Mike, et al. Mirror Mirror. 2006. (Illus.). 152p. (YA). pap. 16.99 (978-0-7851-1902-9(7)) Marvel Enterprises, Inc.

Carlson, Dale Bick. The Mountain of Truth. Nicklaus, Carol, illus. 2nd ed. 2005. 169p. (gr. 8-12). reprint ed. pap. 14.95 (978-1-884158-30-8(7)) Bick Publishing Hse.

Carlson, Dale Bick, et al, illus. The Human Apes. 2nd ed. 2005. 155p. (gr. 8-12). reprint ed. pap. 14.95 (978-1-884158-31-5(5)) Bick Publishing Hse.

Carman, Patrick. Atherton. 2nd ed. 2008. 304p. 16.99 (***978-0-316-16672-0(3)***) Little Brown & Co.

—Atherton: The House of Power. 2007. (Illus.). 330p. (J). (***978-1-4287-4140-9(2)***) Little Brown & Co.

Carroll, Michael. Gathering. 2008. (Quantum Prophecy Ser.). 224p. (YA). (gr. 5). 16.99 (***978-0-399-24726-2(2)*** , Philomel) Penguin Group (USA) Inc.

Carson, D. Mathew. Cyber Angel. 2006. pap. 8.95 (978-0-533-15218-6(6)) Vantage Pr., Inc.

Cart, Michael, ed. Tomorrowland: Ten Stories about the Future. 1999. 198p. (YA). (gr. 6-12). pap. 15.95 (978-0-590-37678-5(0)) Scholastic, Inc.

Carter, Mike. Access to the Universe. 2005. (Illus.). 160p. (Orig.). pap. (978-0-7344-0696-5(7) , Lothian Bks.) Hachette Livre Australia.

—Space Games. 2002. (Illus.). 160p. (YA). pap. (978-0-7344-0273-8(2) , Lothian Bks.) Hachette Livre Australia.

Carter, Timothy. Epoch. 2007. 312p. (J). (gr. 7 up). pap. 8.95 (***978-0-7387-1066-2(0)***) Llewellyn Pubns.

Cartoon Network Staff, contrib. by. Dexter's Laboratory Science Fair Showdown: Cartoon Network. 2000. (Illus.). 48p. (J). (ps-3). pap. 3.99 (978-0-307-10775-6(2) , Golden Bks.) Random Hse. Children's Bks.

Caswell, Brian. Messengers of the Great Orff. 1998. (Alien Zones Ser.: Bk. 2). 89p. (J). 8.95 (978-0-7022-2989-3(X)) Univ. of Queensland Pr. AUS. *Dist:* International Specialized Bk. Services.

—The View from Ararat. 1999. (UQP Young Adult Fiction Ser.). (Illus.). 268p. (Orig.). (J). (gr. 9 up). pap. 14.95 (978-0-7022-3067-7(7)) Univ. of Queensland Pr. AUS. *Dist:* International Specialized Bk. Services.

Cave, Patrick. Sharp North. 2006. (Illus.). 528p. (J). 16.95 (978-1-4169-1222-4(3) , Atheneum) Simon & Schuster Children's Publishing.

Center for Learning Network Staff. Slaughterhouse-Five: Curriculum Unit. 2005. (Novel Ser.). 76p. (YA). tchr. ed., spiral bd. 19.95 (978-1-56077-789-2(3)) Ctr. for Learning, The.

Chadwick, Paul. Darklighter. 2004. (Star Wars Ser.: Vol. 2). 144p. (YA). pap. 17.95 (978-1-56971-975-6(6)) Dark Horse Comics.

—Depths. 2005. (Illus.). 208p. (YA). pap. 12.95 (978-1-59307-343-5(7)) Dark Horse Comics.

Chang, Monica. Daughter of Gredien. 2002. 234p. pap. 19.95 (978-1-59129-949-3(7)) PublishAmerica, Inc.

Channell, Jim. Quien Vive en el Arbol? 2000. (SPA., Illus.). 10p. (J). (ps-k). 7.95 (978-84-392-8315-7(6)) Lectorum Pubns., Inc.

—Quien Vive en el Jardin? 2000. (SPA., Illus.). 10p. (J). (ps-k). 7.95 (978-84-392-8320-1(2)) Lectorum Pubns., Inc.

—Quien Vive en el Rio? 2000. (SPA., Illus.). (J). (ps-k). bds. 7.95 (978-84-392-8313-3(X)) Lectorum Pubns., Inc.

Chartrand, Kenneth. A Martian's Dream of Christmas. 2006. 48p. pap. 12.95 (978-1-4241-4123-4(0)) PublishAmerica, Inc.

Chase, Jeffrey Scott. Andy the Alien. 2006. (J). pap. 16.00 (978-0-8059-7081-4(9)) Dorrance Publishing Co., Inc.

Chesterfield, Sadie. Optimus Prime Versus Megatron. Staples, Val, illus. 2007. (Transformers Ser.). 24p. (J). pap. 3.99 (***978-0-06-088824-4(5)*** , Harper Entertainment) HarperCollins Pubs.

Chiaramonti, Gregory. Probie: the Space Probe, Mission One: the Ocean of Europa. 2007. 32p. (J). 16.72 (***978-0-615-13848-0(9)***) Chiaramonti, Gregory.

Childress, Jamie. Galactic Treasure Hunt: Lost City of Atlantis. Braun, Chris, illus. 2006. 120p. (J). pap. 4.99 (978-1-931882-62-0(2)) Adventures Unlimited Pr.

—Galactic Treasure Hunt: Lost City of the Moon. Braun, Chris, illus. 2005. 115p. (J). (ps-7). pap. 4.99 (978-1-931882-45-3(2)) Adventures Unlimited Pr.

Cho, Takara. Warrior Chosen, Tekkan Wing: First Blood. 2002. 198p. (YA). pap. 13.95 (978-0-595-25017-2(3) , Writers Club Pr.) iUniverse, Inc.

Choyce, Lesley. Deconstructing Dylan. 2006. 180p. (YA). pap. 12.99 (***978-1-55002-603-0(8)*** , Boardwalk Bks.) Dundurn Group, The CAN. *Dist:* Univ. of Toronto Pr.

Christopher, John. The City of Gold & Lead. 2003. (Tripods Ser.). (Illus.). 224p. (YA). mass mkt. 5.99 (978-0-689-85666-2(0) , Simon Pulse) Simon & Schuster Children's Publishing.

—The City of Gold & Lead. 2000. (J). (gr. 5-9). 20.25 (978-0-8446-7141-3(X)) Smith, Peter Pub., Inc.

—City of Gold & Lead. 2003. (gr. 7-12). lib. bdg. 13.00 (978-0-613-73349-6(5)) Tandem Library Bks.

—The City of Gold & Lead. l.t. ed. 2001. 205p. (J). (978-0-7540-4456-7(4) , Macmillan Reference USA) Thomson Gale.

—The City of Gold & Lead. l.t. ed. 2001. (Tripods Trilogy Ser.: Vol. 2). (Illus.). 205p. (J). 26.95 (978-0-7838-9290-0(X)) Thorndike Pr.

—The Pool of Fire. 35th anniv. ed. 2003. (Tripods Ser.). (Illus.). 192p. (YA). 16.95 (978-0-689-85506-1(0)) Simon & Schuster Children's Publishing.

—The Pool of Fire. l.t. ed. 2001. (Tripods Trilogy Ser.). 205p. (J). 26.95 (978-0-7838-9289-4(6)) Thorndike Pr.

—The White Mountains. 2002. (Illus.). (J). 13.40 (978-0-7587-5563-6(5)) Book Wholesalers, Inc.

—The White Mountains. 2003. (Tripods Ser.). 208p. (YA). pap. 5.99 (978-0-689-85672-3(5) , Simon Pulse) Simon & Schuster Children's Publishing.

—White Mountains. 2003. (gr. 7-12). lib. bdg. 13.00 (978-0-613-73385-4(1)) Tandem Library Bks.

—The White Mountains: The Tripods Trilogy. l.t. ed. 2000. 168p. (J). 25.95 (978-0-7838-9170-5(9)) Thorndike Pr.

Christopher, John & Burleson, Joe. The Pool of Fire. 2003. (Tripods Ser.). (Illus.). 224p. (YA). mass mkt. 5.99 (978-0-689-85669-3(5) , Simon Pulse) Simon & Schuster Children's Publishing.

Ciencin, Scott & Burge, Constance M. Light of the World. 2006. (Charmed Ser.). 256p. (YA). pap. 6.99 (978-1-4169-1470-9(6) , Simon Spotlight Entertainment) Simon & Schuster.

Clamp. Fugue. Olsen, Lillian, tr. 2002. (X/1999 Ser.: Vol. 10). (Illus.). 180p. (YA). pap. 9.95 (978-1-56931-896-6(4)) Viz Media.

Clapham, Mark & Miller, John. Twilight of the Gods. 2000. 256p. (J). pap. 6.95 (978-0-426-20536-4(7)) Virgin Bks. Ltd. GBR. *Dist:* London Bridge.

Claremont, Chris. New Mutants Classic, Vol. 1. 2006. (Illus.). 240p. pap. 24.99 (978-0-7851-2194-7(3)) Marvel Enterprises, Inc.

—Wolverine by Claremont & Miller Premiere HC. 2007. (Illus.). 144p. 19.99 (978-0-7851-2329-3(6)) Marvel Enterprises, Inc.

—X-Men. 2005. (Essential Ser.: Vol. 2). (Illus.). 584p. pap. 16.99 (978-0-7851-2007-0(6)) Marvel Enterprises, Inc.

—X-Men: the Dark Phoenix Saga (New Printing) TPB: The Dark Phoenix Saga (New Printing) TPB. 2006. (Illus.). 200p. pap. 24.99 (978-0-7851-2213-5(3)) Marvel Enterprises, Inc.

Clement, Hal. Half Life. 2000. (gr. 7-12). lib. bdg. 15.30 (978-0-613-27864-5(X)) Tandem Library Bks.

Clements, Andrew. Jake Drake, Know-It-All. 2001. (gr. 3-6). lib. bdg. 11.80 (978-0-613-35670-1(5)) Tandem Library Bks.

—Things Not Seen. 2006. 272p. (YA). pap. 10.00 (978-0-14-240731-8(3) , Puffin); 2002. 176p. (J). (gr. 6-9). 15.99 (978-0-399-23626-6(0) , Philomel); 2004. 251p. (J). reprint ed. pap. 6.99 (978-0-14-240076-0(9) , Puffin) Penguin Group (USA) Inc.

—Things Not Seen. 2004. 256p. (J). (gr. 4-7). pap. 38.00 incl. audio (978-1-4000-9014-3(8) , Listening Library) Random Hse. Audio Publishing Group.

Coffin, Bill & Siembieda, Kevin. Century Station. Breaux, Wayne, Jr. et al, illus. 2nd ed. 2000. (Heroes Unlimited Ser.). 224p. (YA). (gr. 8). pap. 20.95 (978-1-57457-040-3(4) , 517) Palladium Bks., Inc.

—Library of Bletherad. Smith, Wayne & Marciniszyn, Alex, eds. Breaux, Wayne, Jr. et al, illus. 2000. (Palladium Sourcebook Ser.). 160p. (YA). (gr. 8 up). pap. 16.95 (978-1-57457-047-2(1) , 466) Palladium Bks., Inc.

Cohen, Elly, illus. Peg Bearskin. 2003. (J). pap. (978-0-9688712-7-0(5)) Running the Goat.

Cole, Bob. Power Reading: Chapter/Sci-Fi/Dr. Little. Sirrell, Terri, illus. 2004. 25p. (J). (gr. 3-4). vinyl bd. 39.95 (978-1-883186-63-0(3) , PPSF1) National Reading Styles Institute, Inc.

—Power Reading: Chapter/Sci-Fi/Dr. Little 2. Ford, David, illus. 2005. 25p. (J). (gr. 3-4). vinyl bd. 39.95 (978-1-883186-76-0(5) , PPSF4) National Reading Styles Institute, Inc.

—Power Reading: Chapter/Sci-Fi/Superhero. Ford, David, illus. 2004. 25p. (J). (gr. 3-4). vinyl bd. 39.95 (978-1-883186-62-3(5) , PPSF2) National Reading Styles Institute, Inc.

—Power Reading: Chapter/Sci-Fi/Time Warp. Ford, David, illus. 2004. 25p. (J). (gr. 4 up). vinyl bd. 39.95 (978-1-883186-60-9(9) , PPSF3) National Reading Styles Institute, Inc.

—Power Reading: Chapter/Sci-Fi/Time Warp 2. Ford, David, illus. 2005. 52p. (J). (gr. 4 up). vinyl bd. 39.95 (978-1-883186-75-3(7) , PPSF5) National Reading Styles Institute, Inc.

Cole, Joanna & Capeci, Anne. The Giant Germ. Degen, Bruce, illus. 2001. (Magic School Bus Chapter Bks.: No. 6). 80p. (J). (gr. 1-4). pap. 4.99 (978-0-439-20420-0(8)) Scholastic, Inc.

Cole, Steve. Riddle of the Raptors. Fowkes, Charlie, illus. 2006. (Astrosaurs Ser.). 144p. (J). (gr. 3-7). pap. 4.99 (978-0-689-87841-1(9) , Aladdin) Simon & Schuster Children's Publishing.

Cole, T. M. A Slip in Time: The Book of Eventide. Cole, Raymond A., illus. 2006. (YA). per. 10.75 (978-0-9777677-0-0(1)) Silver Cloak Pubns.

Colfer, Eoin. Airman. rev. ed. 2008. 416p. 17.99 (***978-1-4231-0750-7(0)***) Hyperion Bks. for Children.

—The Lost Colony. rev. ed. 2008. (Artemis Fowl Ser.: Bk. 5). 400p. (J). (gr. 2-7). pap. 7.99 (***978-0-7868-4959-8(2)***) Miramax Bks.

Collins, Dennis. Spinley's Spaceship. 2007. (Illus.). (J). per. 8.99 (***978-1-60247-100-9(2)***) Tate Publishing & Enterprises, L.L.C.

Collins, Suzanne. Gregor & the Prophecy of Bane. 2005. (Underland Chronicles: Bk. 2). 304p. (J). (gr. 3-6). 6.99 (978-0-439-65076-2(3)) Scholastic, Inc.

Condon, Bill. Time Travelers: The Jungle Goes Bananas, Sherwood Forest Goes to Pieces, the Wild West Goes Crazy. 2005. (Triple Play Ser.). (Illus.). 48p. (gr. 4-8). 41.85 (978-0-7910-9076-3(0)) Facts On File, Inc.

Conly, Jane Leslie. The Rudest Alien on Earth. rev. ed. 2002. 272p. (J). (gr. 5-8). 16.95 (978-0-8050-6069-0(3) , Holt, Henry & Co. Bks. For Young Readers) Holt, Henry & Co.

Connely, Chris L. & Vaughan, Mark. An Alien from Earth. 2003. 175p. per. 9.95 (978-0-9745544-0-2(5)) Lewis Lynn Bks.

Conner, Jimmie L. The Adventures of Captain Computerman & His Sidekick Mouseman: The Saving of the Toy Websites. 2005. 77p. pap. 14.95 (978-1-4137-7457-3(1)) PublishAmerica, Inc.

Cook, Robin. Abduction. 2000. (gr. 7-12). lib. bdg. 16.45 (978-0-613-33574-4(0)) Tandem Library Bks.

Cook, Sherry & Johnson, Terri. Gilbert Gas, 26 vols. Kuhn, Jesse, illus. l.t. ed. 2006. (Quirkles—Exploring Phonics through Science Ser.: 7). 32p. (J). 7.99 (978-1-933815-06-0(X) , Quirkles, The) Creative 3, LLC.

—Inquisitive Inman, 26 vols. Kuhn, Jesse, illus. l.t. ed. 2006. (Quirkles—Exploring Phonics through Science Ser.: 9). 32p. (J). 7.99 (978-1-933815-08-4(6) , Quirkles, The) Creative 3, LLC.

—Kitchen Chemistry Kal, 26 vols. Kuhn, Jesse, illus. l.t. ed. 2006. (Quirkles—Exploring Phonics through Science Ser.: 11). 32p. (J). 7.99 (978-1-933815-10-7(8) , Quirkles, The) Creative 3, LLC.

—Mary Motion, 26 vols. Kuhn, Jesse, illus. l.t. ed. 2006. (Quirkles—Exploring Phonics through Science Ser.: 13). 32p. (J). 7.99 (978-1-933815-12-1(4) , Quirkles, The) Creative 3, LLC.

—Ollie Oxygen, 26 vols. Kuhn, Jesse, illus. l.t. ed. 2006. (Quirkles—Exploring Phonics through Science Ser.: 15). 32p. (J). 7.99 (978-1-933815-14-5(0) , Quirkles, The) Creative 3, LLC.

—Pressure Pete, 26 vols. Kuhn, Jesse, illus. l.t. ed. 2006. (Quirkles—Exploring Phonics through Science Ser.: 16). 32p. (J). 7.99 (978-1-933815-15-2(9) , Quirkles, The) Creative 3, LLC.

—Quincy Quake, 26. Kuhn, Jesse, illus. l.t. ed. 2006. (Quirkles—Exploring Phonics through Science Ser.: 17). 32p. (J). 7.99 (978-1-933815-16-9(7) , Quirkles, The) Creative 3, LLC.

—Zany Science Zeke, 26. Kuhn, Jesse, illus. l.t. ed. 2006. (Quirkles—Exploring Phonics through Science Ser.: 26). 32p. (J). 7.99 (978-1-933815-25-1(6) , Quirkles, The) Creative 3, LLC.

Cooney, Caroline B. Prisoner of Time. 1999. 224p. (YA). (gr. 7-12). pap. 5.50 (978-0-440-22019-0(X) , Laurel Leaf) Random Hse. Children's Bks.

Cooper, Clare. Stonehead. 2000. 132p. (J). pap. 12.95 (978-1-85902-782-0(2)) Beekman Bks., Inc.

Cooper, Susan. The Boggart. 2005. 208p. (ps-7). pap. 2.99 (978-1-4169-0527-1(8) , Aladdin) Simon & Schuster Children's Publishing.

—Green Boy. 2002. (Illus.). 208p. (J). (gr. 4-6). 16.00 (978-0-689-84751-6(3) , McElderry, Margaret K.) Simon & Schuster Children's Publishing.

Cotes, Gilles. OGM et Chant de Mais. Begin, Jean-Guy, illus. 2004. (FRE.). 112p. (J). (978-2-89599-002-4(6)) Editions de la Paix CAN. *Dist:* World of Reading, Ltd.

Counter, Ben. Grey Knights. 2004. 416p. mass mkt. 7.99 (978-1-84416-087-7(4) , Games Workshop) Simon & Schuster.

Cousineau, Craig S. Skippy & Oaf: The Battle Against Oxygen Radicals. 2007. (Illus.). 48p. (J). pap. 8.95 (978-1-933255-27-9(7)) DNA Pr.

Coville, Bruce. Aliens Ate My Homework. 179p. (J). (gr. 4-6). pap. 3.99 (978-0-8072-1503-6(1) , Listening Library) Random Hse. Audio Publishing Group.

—Aliens Ate My Homework. Coville, Katherine, illus. 2007. (Alien Adventures Ser.). 192p. (J). pap. 5.99 (978-1-4169-3883-5(4) , Aladdin) Simon & Schuster Children's Publishing.

—Aliens Stole My Body. 1998. (Bruce Coville's Alien Adventures Ser.). (J). (gr. 3-7). 11.64 (978-0-606-13115-5(9)) Tandem Library Bks.

—Bruce Coville's Strange Worlds. 2000. (Illus.). 208p. (J). (gr. 3-7). pap. 4.99 (978-0-380-80256-2(2)) HarperCollins Pubs.

—Bruce Coville's Strange Worlds. 2000. (Illus.). (J). (978-0-606-17960-7(7)) Tandem Library Bks.

—Bruce Coville's UFOs. 2000. (Illus.). (J). 11.64 (978-0-606-18679-7(4)) Tandem Library Bks.

—Don't Fry My Veeblax! Sansekers, Tony, illus. 2000. (I Was a Sixth Grade Alien Ser.: Vol. 6). (J). 10.64 (978-0-606-19849-3(0)) Tandem Library Bks.

—A Glory of Unicorns. Berenzy, Alix, illus. 1998. 198p. (J). (gr. 4-9). pap. 16.95 (978-0-590-95943-8(3)) Scholastic, Inc.

—I Left My Sneakers in Dimension X. Coville, Katherine, illus. 2007. (Alien Adventures Ser.). 192p. (J). pap. 5.99 (978-1-4169-3882-8(6) , Aladdin) Simon & Schuster Children's Publishing.

—I Lost My Grandfather's Brain. unabr. ed. 2004. (I Was a Sixth Grade Alien Ser.). 160p. (J). (gr. 3-6). pap. 29.00 incl. audio (978-0-8072-8385-1(1) , YA180SP, Listening Library) Random Hse. Audio Publishing Group.

—I Lost My Grandfather's Brain. 1999. (I Was a Sixth Grade Alien Ser.). (Illus.). (J). 10.64 (978-0-606-18306-2(X)) Tandem Library Bks.

—I Was a Sixth Grade Alien. (I Was a Sixth Grade Alien Ser.). 170p. (J). (gr. 4-6). pap. 3.99 (978-0-8072-8202-1(2)); 2004. (gr. 3-6). pap. 29.00 incl. audio (978-0-8072-8201-4(4) , S YA 138 SP) Random Hse. Audio Publishing Group. (Listening Library).

—I Was a Sixth Grade Alien. 1999. (I Was a Sixth Grade Alien Ser.). (J). 11.64 (978-0-606-17089-5(8)) Tandem Library Bks.

—The Monsters of Morley Manor: A Madcap Adventure. 240p. (YA). (gr. 3-6). 2003. pap. 5.95 (978-0-15-204705-4(0) , Magic Carpet Bks.); 2001. 16.00 (978-0-15-216382-2(4)) Harcourt Children's Bks.

—The Monster's Ring. Coville, Katherine, illus. 2003. (Magic Shop Bks.). 128p. mass mkt. 5.99 (978-0-689-85692-1(X) , Aladdin) Simon & Schuster Children's Publishing.

—My Teacher Flunked the Planet. Pierard, John, illus. 2005. (My teacher Bks.). 176p. (J). (ps-7). pap. 4.99 (978-1-4169-0331-4(3) , Aladdin) Simon & Schuster Children's Publishing.

—My Teacher Fried My Brains. 2005. (Illus.). 136p. (J). (***978-1-4156-1080-0(0)*** , Aladdin) Simon & Schuster Children's Publishing.

—My Teacher Fried My Brains. Pierard, John, illus. 2005. 138p. (J). (gr. 3-7). lib. bdg. 12.04 (978-0-606-33890-5(X)) Tandem Library Bks.

—My Teacher Is an Alien. unabr. ed. 2004. (My Teacher Is an Alien Ser.). 123p. (J). (gr. 3-6). pap. 29.00 incl. audio (978-0-8072-8029-4(1) , S YA 971 SP, Listening Library) Random Hse. Audio Publishing Group.

—My Teacher Is an Alien. 2005. (Illus.). 123p. (J). (***978-1-4156-1082-4(7)*** , Aladdin) Simon & Schuster Children's Publishing.

—My Teacher Is an Alien. Wimmer, Mike, illus. 2005. (My teacher Bks.). 128p. (J). (ps-7). pap. 5.99 (978-1-4169-0334-5(8) , Aladdin) Simon & Schuster Children's Publishing.

—Peanut Butter Lover Boy. 2000. (I Was a Sixth Grade Alien Ser.). (Illus.). (J). (978-0-606-18307-9(8)) Tandem Library Bks.

—The Search for Snout. Coville, Katherine, illus. 2007. (Rod Allbright & the Galactic Patrol Ser.). 224p. (J). pap. 5.99 (***978-1-4169-4980-0(1)*** , Aladdin) Simon & Schuster Children's Publishing.

Coville, Bruce. Zombies of the Science Fair. 2000. (I Was a Sixth Grade Alien Ser.). (Illus.). (J). (978-0-606-18308-6(6)) Tandem Library Bks.

Cowell, Cressida. Heroic Misadventures of Hiccup the Viking, the: the First Collection Boxed Set. 2007. (gr. 3-7). 28.99 (***978-0-316-00592-0(4)***) Little, Brown Bks. for Young Readers.

Craig, Joe. Jimmy Coates: Target. 2007. 272p. (J). 15.99 (978-0-06-077266-6(2)); lib. bdg. 16.89 (978-0-06-077267-3(0)) HarperCollins Pubs.

Cravens, Dave. Crusaders of a Dying Breed. 2000. 200p. (YA). pap. 9.95 (978-1-893652-91-0(2) , Writers Club Pr.) iUniverse, Inc.

Crew, Gary. Gothic Hospital. 2002. (Illus.). 160p. (YA). pap. (978-0-7344-0232-5(5) , Lothian Bks.) Hachette Livre Australia.

Crew, Gary & Tan, Shaun. The Viewer. 2003. (Illus.). 32p. (gr. 1-6). 16.95 (978-1-894965-02-6(7)) Simply Read Bks. CAN. *Dist:* Perseus Distribution.

Crilley, Mark. Akiko, Vol. 6. 2003. (Illus.). 136p. pap. 14.95 (978-1-57989-057-5(1)) Sirius Entertainment, Inc.

—Akiko Vol. 7: The Battle for Boach's Keep. 2004. (Illus.). 144p. pap. 14.95 (978-1-57989-064-3(4)) Sirius Entertainment, Inc.

—Akiko & the Alpha Centauri 5000. Crilley, Mark, illus. 2004. (Illus.). 176p. (gr. 3). pap. 5.50 (978-0-440-41892-4(5) , Yearling) Random Hse. Children's Bks.

—Akiko & the Intergalactic Zoo. Crilley, Mark, illus. 2003. (Illus.). 160p. (gr. 3 up). pap. 5.50 (978-0-440-41891-7(7) , Yearling) Random Hse. Children's Bks.

—Akiko & the Intergalactic Zoo. 2003. (gr. k-3). lib. bdg. 13.00 (978-0-613-82973-1(5)) Tandem Library Bks.

—Akiko & the Journey to Toog. Crilley, Mark, illus. (Illus.). (gr. 3 up). 2005. 192p. 5.50 (978-0-440-41893-1(3) , Yearling); 2003. 176p. 9.95 (978-0-385-73042-6(X) , Delacorte Bks. for Young Readers) Random Hse. Children's Bks.

—Akiko in the Castle of Alia Rellapor. Crilley, Mark, illus. 2002. (Illus.). 176p. (gr. 3). pap. 5.50 (978-0-440-41657-9(4) , Yearling) Random Hse. Children's Bks.

—Akiko in the Castle of Alia Rellapor. 2002. (gr. 3-6). lib. bdg. 13.00 (978-0-613-49540-0(3)) Tandem Library Bks.

—Akiko in the Sprubly Islands. Crilley, Mark, illus. 2001. (Akiko Ser.: Vol. 2). (Illus.). 176p. (J). (gr. 3-3). pap. 5.50 (978-0-440-41651-7(5) , Yearling) Random Hse. Children's Bks.

—Akiko in the Sprubly Islands. 2001. (Illus.). 146p. (J). (gr. 4-7). lib. bdg. 13.00 (978-0-613-42696-1(7)) Tandem Library Bks.

—Akiko on the Planet Smoo. Crilley, Mark, illus. 2001. (Akiko Ser.: Vol. 1). (Illus.). 176p. (J). (gr. 3-3). pap. 5.50 (978-0-440-41648-7(5) , Yearling) Random Hse. Children's Bks.

—Akiko on the Planet Smoo. 2001. (gr. 3-6). lib. bdg. 13.00 (978-0-613-42697-8(5)) Tandem Library Bks.

—Akiko Pocket-Size. 2004. (Illus.). 192p. pap. 11.95 (978-1-57989-067-4(9)); Vol. 2. 128p. pap. 9.95 (978-1-57989-068-1(7)); Vol. 3. 128p. pap. 9.95 (978-1-57989-069-8(5)) Sirius Entertainment, Inc.

—Akiko: The Training Master. Crilley, Mark, illus. 2006. (Illus.). 224p. (gr. 3). 5.50 (978-0-440-41894-8(1) , Yearling) Random Hse. Children's Bks.

—Bornstone's Elixir. 2001. (gr. 3-6). lib. bdg. 22.20 (978-0-613-50412-6(7)) Tandem Library Bks.

—Flights of Fancy. exp. ed. 2007. (Illus.). 264p. pap. 24.95 (***978-1-57989-088-9(1)***) Sirius Entertainment, Inc.

Crilley, Mark. The Training Master. Crilley, Mark, illus. 2005. (Akiko Ser.). (Illus.). 224p. (J). (gr. 3). 9.95 (978-0-385-73043-3(8) , Delacorte Bks. for Young Readers) Random Hse. Children's Bks.

Crispin, A. C. The Paradise Snare. 1998. (Star Wars: Vol. 1) (gr. 7-12). lib. bdg. 15.30 (978-0-613-70932-3(2)) Tandem Library Bks.

Crook, Carol. The Prophetic End Time Temple. Crook, Carol, illus. 2000. (Illus.). 88p. (YA). (gr. 10 up). stu. ed., spiral bd. 23.50 (978-0-939399-60-4(1)) Books of Truth.

Cross, Gillian. The Black Room: The Lost. 2006. (Dark Ground Ser.). 256p. (YA). (gr. 6). 16.99 (978-0-525-47487-6(0) , Dutton Juvenile) Penguin Group (USA) Inc.

Crow, E. J. The Eye Pocket: The Fantastic Society of Peculiar Adventurers. 2006. (Illus.). 48p. (J). pap. 7.95 (978-1-933255-17-0(X)) DNA Pr.

Crowson, Andrew & Ward, Beck. Spaceman Sam. 2005. 8p. (J). 12.95 (978-0-7624-2408-5(7) , Running Pr. Kids) Running Pr. Bk. Pubs.

Cunningham, Mary. The Magic Medallion. 2006. 160p. (YA). pap. 9.99 (978-1-59080-460-5(0)) Echelon Press Publishing.

A Cup of Tea, A Piece of Pie. 2004. (J). 14.95 (978-0-9747363-4-1(1)) Kelly, Kimberly.

Curley, Marianne. The Dark. 2005. (Guardians of Time Trilogy: Bk. 2). 336p. (J). pap. 8.95 (978-1-58234-664-9(X) , Bloomsbury Children) Bloomsbury Publishing.

Czerneda, Julie. Odyssey. Normand, Jean-Pierre, illus. 2002. 128p. pap. (978-1-55244-080-3(X)) Trifolium Bks., Inc.

—Packing Fraction: And Other Tales of Science & Imagination. 1999. (gr. 7-12). lib. bdg. 12.95 (978-0-613-35429-5(X)) Tandem Library Bks.

Czerneda, Julie E. Explorer. 2001. (gr. 5-8). lib. bdg. 21.05 (978-0-613-86413-8(1)) Tandem Library Bks.

Czerneda, Julie E., ed. Explorer. Normand, Jean-Pierre, illus. 2001. (Tales from the Wonder Zone Ser.). 128p. (J). (gr. 4 up). pap. 15.95 (978-1-55244-022-3(2)) Trifolium Bks., Inc. CAN. *Dist:* Fitzhenry & Whiteside, Ltd.

S

Czerneda, Julie E., ed. Polaris: A Celebration of Polar Science. Normand, Jean-Pierre, illus. 2007. 160p. pap. 14.95 (*978-0-88995-372-7(4)) Red Deer Pr. CAN. *Dist:* Fitzhenry & Whiteside, Ltd.

Dabb, Andrew, et al. Depth. 2007. (G. I. Joe SIGMA 6 Ser.). 24p. (J). (gr. 3-6). 21.35 (*978-1-59961-370-3(0)) Spotlight.

Dadey, Debbie & Jones, Marcia Thornton. Phantoms Don't Drive Sports Cars. Gurney, John Steven, illus. 1998. (Adventures of the Bailey School Kids Ser.: No. 32). 80p. (J). (gr. 2-4). pap. 3.99 (978-0-590-18982-8(4), Scholastic Paperbacks) Scholastic, Inc.

Dahl, Michael. Worm Tunnel. 1999. (Illus.). (J). (978-0-606-21798-9(3)) Tandem Library Bks.

Dahl, Roald. Charlie & the Great Glass Elevator. Blake, Quentin, illus. 2007. 176p. (J). (gr. 2). 6.99 (*978-0-14-241032-5(2), Puffin) Penguin Group (USA) Inc.

—Charlie & the Great Glass Elevator. Blake, Quentin, illus. 2001. 176p. (J). (gr. 3-7). 15.95 (978-0-375-81525-6(2), Knopf Bks. for Young Readers) Random Hse. Children's Bks.

—Charlie & the Great Glass Elevator. Blake, Quentin, illus. 2005. (Puffin Modern Classics Ser.). 176p. (J). (gr. 3-6). pap. 6.99 (978-0-14-240412-6(8), Puffin) Penguin Group (USA) Inc.

—Volando Solo. 2000. (SPA.). 192p. (J). (978-84-204-4583-0(5)) Aguilar, S. A. de Ediciones-Grupo Santillana.

D'Alessandro, James. Time in a Bottle. 2002. 475p. pap. 21.95 (978-1-59129-390-3(1)) PublishAmerica, Inc.

Daley, Michael J. Space Station Rat. 2005. 144p. (J). 15.95 (978-0-8234-1866-4(9)) Holiday Hse., Inc.

Dalkey, Kara. Reunion, Bk. 2. 2002. (Water Ser.: No. 2). 240p. (J). (gr. 5 up). pap. 5.99 (978-0-06-440809-7(4)) HarperCollins Pubs.

—Reunion. 2002. (gr. 7-12). lib. bdg. 13.00 (978-0-613-62644-6(3)) Tandem Library Bks.

Dalmatian Press Staff. Storm Power: Ninja Storm. 2003. (Power Rangers Ninja Storm Ser.). 24p. (J). pap. 2.99 (978-1-4037-0355-2(8)) Dalmatian Pr.

—There's No I in Team: Ninja Storm. 2003. (Power Rangers Ninja Storm Ser.). 24p. (J). pap. 2.99 (978-1-4037-0354-5(X)) Dalmatian Pr.

Daly, Joseph M. Strange Town Volume One: The Woods Behind Trevor Malone's House. 2007. 265p. (YA). pap. (*978-0-9779921-0-2(1)) Wolfs Corner Publishing.

D'Ambrosio, Michael. Fractured Time: Book One of the Fractured Time Trilogy. 2004. 198p. (YA). 24.95 (978-0-595-75830-2(4)); pap. 14.95 (978-0-595-30996-2(8)) iUniverse, Inc.

Danvers, Dennis. The Watch. 2003. 356p. (YA). (gr. 8-12). per. 25.70 (978-0-613-58394-7(9)) Tandem Library Bks.

Danziger, Paula. This Place Has No Atmosphere. 2006. 176p. (J). (gr. 5). 5.99 (978-0-14-240680-9(5), Puffin) Penguin Group (USA) Inc.

Dark Horse Comics Staff & Lucas, George. The Empire Strikes Back. 1999. (Star Wars Manga Ser.: No. 4). (Illus.). 96p. (J). (gr. 3 up). pap. 9.95 (978-1-56971-393-8(6)); pap. 9.95 (978-1-56971-392-1(8)); pap. 9.95 (978-1-56971-390-7(1)) Dark Horse Comics.

—Episode I: The Phantom Menace. 1999. (Star Wars Manga Ser.: No. 1). (Illus.). 88p. (J). (gr. 3 up). pap. 9.95 (978-1-56971-483-6(5)) Dark Horse Comics.

—Episode I: The Phantom Menace Manga. 2000. (Star Wars Manga Ser.: No. 2). (Illus.). 88p. (J). (gr. 3 up). pap. 9.95 (978-1-56971-484-3(3)) Dark Horse Comics.

Darvill-Evans, Paul. Asylum. 2001. (Doctor Who Ser.). (Illus.). 288p. (J). pap. 6.95 (978-0-563-53833-2(3)) BBC Worldwide Americas.

—Instruments of Darkness. 2001. (Doctor Who Ser.). (Illus.). 288p. (J). pap. 6.95 (978-0-563-53828-8(7)) BBC Worldwide Americas.

Dashner, James. A Gift of Ice. 2004. (Jimmy Fincher Saga Ser.: 2). 208p. (J). pap. 14.95 (978-1-55517-753-9(0), 1232041, Bonneville Bks.) Cedar Fort, Inc./CFI Distribution.

David, Charles. Skull in the Birdcage: Knightscares #2. 2003. 208p. (J). per. 5.99 (978-0-9728461-1-0(5)) Sigil Publishing.

David, Peter. Peter David, Vol. 3. 2006. (Illus.). 192p. pap. 19.99 (978-0-7851-2095-7(5)) Marvel Enterprises, Inc.

—Survival. 1999. 11.10 (978-0-7857-2419-3(2)) CRC Pr. LLC.

—Wolverine Classic, Vol. 3. 2006. (Illus.). 144p. (YA). pap. 14.99 (978-0-7851-2053-7(X)) Marvel Enterprises, Inc.

David, Peter, et al. The Return of the Worthy. 2007. (Illus.). 160p. pap. 19.95 (*978-1-84576-319-0(X)) Titan Bks. Ltd. GBR. *Dist:* Random Hse., Inc.

Davids, Paul & Davids, Hollace. The Lost City of the Jedi. 1999. (Star Wars Ser.: Bk. 2). (Illus.). 94p. (J). (gr. 4-7). reprint ed. pap. 10.00 (978-0-7881-6480-4(5)) DIANE Publishing Co.

—Star Wars, 3 bks. l.t. ed. Incl. Prophets of the Dark Side. lib. bdg. 22.60 (978-0-8368-1994-6(2)); Queen of the Empire. lib. bdg. 22.60 (978-0-8368-1993-9(4)); Zorba the Hutt's Revenge. lib. bdg. 22.60 (978-0-8368-1991-5(8)); 112p. (J). (gr. 4 up). 1997. Set lib. bdg. 67.80 (978-0-8368-1988-5(8)) Stevens, Gareth Inc.

Davidson, Ellen. When the Third Moon Wanes. 2004. 123p. pap. 17.95 (978-1-4137-2233-8(4)) PublishAmerica, Inc.

Davidson, Ellen Dee. Stolen Voices. 2005. 192p. (YA). (gr. 7-10). pap. 9.95 (978-1-897073-16-2(X)) Lobster Pr. CAN. *Dist:* Univ. of Toronto Pr.

Davila, Andrew. Prophecies of the Ancient. 2003. 110p. (YA). pap. 9.95 (978-0-595-26851-1(X)) iUniverse, Inc.

DC Comics Staff, et al. See No Evil. 2nd ed. 2002. (Smallville Ser.: No. 2). 192p. (J). (gr. 7-17). mass mkt. 5.99 (978-0-316-17301-8(0)) Little, Brown Bks. for Young Readers.

de Brunhoff, Laurent. Babar Visits Another Planet. 2003. (Illus.). 32p. (J). (ps-3). 16.95 (978-0-8109-4244-8(5)) Abrams, Harry N., Inc.

DeAndrea, William L. & DeAndrea, Matthew. The Pizza That Time Forgot. 1999. (J). (gr. 3-7). pap. 3.99 (978-0-380-79155-2(2)) HarperCollins Pubs.

Deary, Terry. Vanished! 2004. (Classified Ser.). 96p. (J). (gr. 5-9). pap. 4.95 (978-0-7534-5825-9(X), Kingfisher) Houghton Mifflin Co. Trade & Reference Div.

Degen, Bruce, illus. Commander Toad & the Dis-Asteroid. 2002. (Commander Toad Ser.). (J). 13.19 (978-0-7587-1076-5(3)) Book Wholesalers, Inc.

—Commander Toad & the Intergalactic Spy. 2002. (Commander Toad Ser.). (J). 13.19 (978-0-7587-1079-6(8)) Book Wholesalers, Inc.

—Commander Toad & the Planet of the Grapes. 2002. (Commander Toad Ser.). (J). 13.19 (978-0-7587-1078-9(X)) Book Wholesalers, Inc.

—Commander Toad & the Space Pirates. 2002. (Commander Toad Ser.). (J). 13.19 (978-0-7587-1080-2(1)) Book Wholesalers, Inc.

—Commander Toad & the Voyage Home. 2002. (Commander Toad Ser.). (J). 13.19 (978-0-7587-1077-2(1)) Book Wholesalers, Inc.

Denning, Troy. Tempest. 2006. (Star Wars Ser.: Bk. 3). 416p. mass mkt. 7.99 (978-0-345-47752-1(9), Del Rey) Random House Publishing Group.

Denton, Terry. The Eye of Ulam. 2003. (Storymaze Ser.: Vol. 2). (Illus.). 132p. (J). (gr. 3-5). pap. 6.95 (978-1-86508-358-2(5)) Allen & Unwin AUS. *Dist:* Independent Pubs. Group.

—The Ultimate Wave. Denton, Terry, illus. 2003. (Storymaze Ser.: Vol. 1). (Illus.). 144p. (J). (gr. 3-5). pap. 5.95 (978-1-86508-378-0(X)) Allen & Unwin AUS. *Dist:* Independent Pubs. Group.

Despain, Kellene. A Certain Kind of Treasure. 2000. (Illus.). 215p. (J). (gr. 5-9). per. 7.95 (978-0-9679046-0-3(9)) Gray Hse. Bks.

Desrosiers, Sylvie. Qui Veut Entrer dans la Peau d'un Chien? Sylvestre, Daniel, illus. 2002. (Roman Jeunesse Ser.). (FRE.). 96p. (J). (gr. 4-7). pap. (978-2-89021-576-4(8)) Diffusion du livre Mirabel.

Di Maggio, S. J. Rob's Trilogy. 2006. 196p. (YA). per. 13.95 (978-0-9786593-1-8(7)) Omniland Bks.

Dickins, Grampa. The Creation & Adventures of Little One-time: In a World of Hurt, 5 vols. Clay, Charlotte, illus. l.t. ed. 2002. 112p. (J). pap. 14.95 (978-0-9678054-0-5(6)) Child Development Publishing Co.

Dickinson, John. The Cup of the World. 2007. 432p. (YA). (gr. 7-11). mass mkt. 6.99 (978-0-553-49489-1(9), Laurel Leaf) Random Hse. Children's Bks.

Dicks, Terrance. Star Quest. 2004. 256p. pap. 24.99 (978-1-84435-066-7(5)) Reynolds & Hearn GBR. *Dist:* Independent Pubs. Group.

Dietz, William C. & Dorman, Dave. Dark Forces: Jedi Knight. 2004. (Star Wars Ser.). 128p. (YA). (gr. 7 up). pap. 14.95 (978-1-56971-433-1(9)) Dark Horse Comics.

Diggs, Dylan. Palladium: Second Contact. 2006. (J). mass mkt. 3.80 (978-1-886366-13-8(6), 5,000) Sights Productions.

—Palladium: Trust No One. 2006. (J). mass mkt. 3.80 (978-1-886366-14-5(4)) Sights Productions.

DiTerlizzi, Tony. Jimmy Zangwow's Out-of-This-World Moon-Pie Adventure. DiTerlizzi, Tony, illus. 2003. (Illus.). 40p. (J). pap. 6.99 (978-0-689-85563-4(X), Aladdin) Simon & Schuster Children's Publishing.

—Jimmy Zangwow's Out-of-This-World Moon-Pie Adventure. 2003. (gr. k-3). lib. bdg. 15.30 (978-0-613-61784-0(3)) Tandem Library Bks.

DiTerlizzi, Tony & Black, Holly. El Arbol Metalico. Abreu, Carlos, tr. 2005. (Escritura desatada Ser.). (SPA., Illus.). 128p. (J). (gr. 4-7). 12.95 (978-84-666-1658-4(6)) Ediciones B ESP. *Dist:* Independent Pubs. Group.

Dixon, Chuck. Old Friends, New Enemies. Land, Greg, illus. rev. ed. 2003. (Birds of Prey Ser.: Vol. 2). 224p. pap. 17.95 (978-1-56389-939-3(6)) DC Comics.

—Perdition's Gate, Vol. 6. Eaglesham, Dale et al, illus. 2004. (Sigil Ser.: Vol. 6). 160p. (YA). pap. 15.95 (978-1-59314-048-9(7)) CrossGeneration Comics, Inc.

—Resurrection, Vol. 5. Cariello, Sergio et al, illus. 2004. (Crux Ser.: Vol. 5). 160p. (YA). pap. 15.95 (978-1-59314-053-3(3)) CrossGeneration Comics, Inc.

Dixon, George. The Adventures of Yin & Yang. 2002. (Illus.). 193p. (YA). mass mkt. 9.95 (978-0-9721833-2-1(5)) Sleepy D Publishing.

DK Publishing. Star Wars Ultimate Blueprints Collections. 2008. 10p. (J). (gr. 5-12). 19.99 (*978-0-7566-3869-6(0)) Dorling Kindersley Publishing, Inc.

Dobbyn, Nigel, et al. Digimon: Adventures in the Digital World. 2001. 88p. (YA). (gr. 4-7). pap. 9.95 (978-1-56971-532-1(7)) Dark Horse Comics.

Dodd, Quentin. Beatnik Rutabagas from Beyond the Stars. 2001. (Illus.). 224p. (J). (gr. 4-6). 17.00 (978-0-374-30515-4(3), Farrar, Straus & Giroux (BYR)) Farrar, Straus & Giroux.

—The Princess of Neptune. 2004. 224p. (J). 17.00 (978-0-374-36119-8(3), Farrar, Straus & Giroux (BYR)) Farrar, Straus & Giroux.

Donkin, Andrew. Transformers Armada: The Awakening. 2003. (Dk Readers Ser.). (Illus.). 48p. pap. 3.99 (978-0-7894-9741-3(7)) Dorling Kindersley Publishing, Inc.

—Transformers Armada: The Awakening. 2003. (gr. k-3). lib. bdg. 11.80 (978-0-613-75248-0(1)) Tandem Library Bks.

—Transformers Armada: The Quest. 2003. (gr. k-3). lib. bdg. 11.80 (978-0-613-75249-7(X)) Tandem Library Bks.

Donkin, Andrew & Dorling Kindersley Publishing Staff. Megatron Returns. 2005. (Dk Readers Ser.). (Illus.). 48p. (J). (ps-12). pap. 3.99 (978-0-7566-1152-1(0)); 12.99 (978-0-7566-1151-4(2)) Dorling Kindersley Publishing, Inc.

—Terrorcon Attack. 2005. (Dk Readers Ser.). (Illus.). 48p. (J). (ps-k). 14.99 (978-0-7566-1149-1(0)) Dorling Kindersley Publishing, Inc.

—Transformers Armada: The Quest. 2003. (Readers Ser.). 48p. (J). 12.99 (978-0-7894-9804-5(9)) Dorling Kindersley Publishing, Inc.

Donkin, Andrew, et al. Terrorcon Attack. 2005. (Dk Readers Ser.). (Illus.). 48p. (J). (ps-7). pap. 3.99 (978-0-7566-1150-7(4)) Dorling Kindersley Publishing, Inc.

Dorling Kindersley Publishing Staff. Revenge of the Sith. 2005. (Ultimate sticker Bks.). 16p. (J). pap. 6.99 (978-0-7566-1130-9(X)) Dorling Kindersley Publishing, Inc.

Doyle, Arthur Conan. The Lost World & Other Thrilling Tales. 2001. (gr. 7-12). lib. bdg. 17.65 (978-0-613-64299-6(6)) Tandem Library Bks.

Doyle, Bill. Trapped! The 2031 Journal of Otis Fitzmorgan. Pamituan, Macky, illus. 2006. 141p. (J). lib. bdg. 18.46 (*978-1-4242-1738-0(5)) Fitzgerald Bks.

The Dragon Compass: Individual Title Six-Packs. (Bookweb Ser.). 32p. (gr. 6 up). 34.00 (978-0-7578-0898-2(0)) Rigby Education.

Draper, Sharon M. The Space Mission Adventure. Watson, Jesse Joshua, illus. 2006. (Ziggy & the Black Dinosaurs Ser.). 128p. (J). lib. bdg. 11.89 (978-1-4169-2458-6(2), Aladdin Library); pap. 4.99 (978-0-689-87914-2(8), Aladdin) Simon & Schuster Children's Publishing.

Driggs, Scout. Power Up! 2004. (Astro Boy Ser.). (Illus.). 24p. (J). pap. 3.50 (978-0-06-072525-9(7), Harper Festival) HarperCollins Pubs.

Driscoll, Laura. Blast off Kid. 2003. (gr. k-3). lib. bdg. 12.95 (978-0-613-79278-3(5)) Tandem Library Bks.

Druga-Marchetti, Jacqueline. The Nerdfly. 2001. (gr. 7-12). lib. bdg. 19.90 (978-0-613-81921-3(7)) Tandem Library Bks.

—The Nerdfly. 2001. 136p. pap. 10.95 (978-0-595-20241-6(1), Writers Club Pr.) iUniverse, Inc.

Duane, Diane. High Wizardry. (Young Wizards Ser.: Bk. 3). (YA). 2003. 372p. (ps-7). pap. 6.95 (978-0-15-204941-6(X)); 2001. 368p. (gr. 5 up). pap. 6.95 (978-0-15-216244-3(5)) Harcourt Children's Bks. (Magic Carpet Bks.).

—High Wizardry. 2000. (YA). (gr. 5 up). pap. 58.25 incl. audio (978-0-7887-3799-2(6), 41043) Recorded Bks., LLC.

—High Wizardry. 2003. (gr. 3-6). lib. bdg. 15.25 (978-0-613-71634-5(5)); 2001. (gr. 5-8). lib. bdg. 15.25 (978-0-613-36065-4(6)) Tandem Library Bks.

—Wizard's Holiday. (Young Wizards Ser.: Bk. 7). (YA). 2005. 448p. (gr. 8-12). pap. 6.95 (978-0-15-205207-2(0), Magic Carpet Bks.); 2003. 432p. 17.00 (978-0-15-204771-9(9)) Harcourt Children's Bks.

Duey, Kathleen. Journey Home. 2003. (gr. 3-6). lib. bdg. 11.80 (978-0-613-90472-8(9)) Tandem Library Bks.

—Rex. Epstein, Eugene, illus. Gould, Robert, photos by. 2000. (Time Soldiers Ser.: Bk. 1). 48p. (J). (ps-5). 12.95 (978-1-929945-18-4(3)) Big Guy Bks., Inc.

—Rex. Epstein, Eugene, illus. Gould, Robert, photos by. 2005. (Time Soldiers Ser.: Bk. 1). 96p. (J). (gr. 3-4). pap. 5.95 (978-1-929945-53-5(1)) Big Guy Bks., Inc.

—Rex 2. Epstein, Eugene, illus. Gould, Robert, photos by. (Time Soldiers Ser.: Bk. 2). (J). 2005. (ENG.). 96p. (gr. 3-4). pap. 5.95 (978-1-929945-54-2(X)); 2nd rev. ed. 2000. 48p. (ps-5). 12.95 (978-1-929945-19-1(1)) Big Guy Bks., Inc.

—Rex, Rex 2, Patch, Set. Epstein, Eugene, illus. Gould, Robert, photos by. gif. ed. 2003. (Time Soldiers Ser.). 144p. (J). 32.95 (978-1-929945-23-8(X)) Big Guy Bks., Inc.

Duey, Kathleen & Gould, Robert. Rex. Windler-Cheren, Victoria, tr. Epstein, Eugene, illus. Gould, Robert, photos by. 2003. (Time Soldiers Ser.: Bk. 1). (SPA.). 48p. (J). pap. 8.95 (978-1-929945-35-1(3)) Big Guy Bks., Inc.

Duncan, Lois. A Gift of Magic. 1999. 240p. (YA). (gr. 7-9). mass mkt. 5.99 (978-0-440-22847-9(6), Laurel Leaf) Random Hse. Children's Bks.

Dunn, Mary. Magical Message Machine: Book One. 2007. 120p. (YA). pap. 14.99 (978-1-59092-402-0(9), Blue Works) Windstorm Creative.

DuPrau, Jeanne. The People of Sparks. 2004. 352p. (J). (gr. 2). 17.99 (978-0-375-92824-6(3)); (gr. 5-8). 15.95 (978-0-375-82824-9(9)) Random Hse. Children's Bks. (Random Hse. Bks. for Young Readers).

Durant, Alan. Gamer. Mason, Sue, illus. 2008. (J). pap. (*978-1-59889-908-5(2)); lib. bdg. (*978-1-59889-872-9(8)) Stone Arch Bks.

—Gamer: Next Level. Mason, Sue, illus. 2008. (J). pap. (*978-1-59889-909-2(0)); lib. bdg. (*978-1-59889-873-6(6)) Stone Arch Bks.

Dutcher, David. Feebie Brainiac & the Lysis Virus. 2005. (Illus.). 248p. (YA). (gr. 7). pap. 11.95 (978-1-933255-14-9(5)) DNA Pr.

Dwyer, Tom. What the Man in the Moon Saw. Buziak, Cari, illus. 2000. (J). cd-rom 9.95 (978-1-58338-701-6(3)) CrossroadsPub.com.

Eason, Alethea. Hungry. 2007. 208p. (J). (gr. 5 up). 15.99 (*978-0-06-082554-6(5)); lib. bdg. 16.89 (*978-0-06-082555-3(3)) HarperCollins Pubs. (Eos).

Edginton, Ian. Scarlet Traces. 2003. 88p. (YA). 14.95 (978-1-56971-940-4(3)) Dark Horse Comics.

Edington, Ian & Allie, Scott. Old Gods. Sibar, Adrian et al, illus. 2001. (Planet of the Apes Ser.: Vol. 1). 56p. pap. 6.95 (978-1-56971-583-3(1)) Dark Horse Comics.

Egan, Greg. Diaspora. 1999. (Illus.). (J). (978-0-606-18687-2(5)) Tandem Library Bks.

Egan, Kate. Keeping Hope. rev. ed. 2005. (W. I. T. C. H. Ser.: Bk. 18). (Illus.). 144p. (gr. 3-7). pap. 4.99 (978-0-7868-5279-6(8), Volo) Hyperion Bks. for Children.

Egan, Kate. Transformers: The Movie Storybook. Matere, Marcelo, illus. 2007. (Transformers Ser.). 48p. (J). pap. 8.99 (*978-0-06-088836-7(9), Harper Entertainment) HarperCollins Pubs.

Elish, Dan. Attack of the Frozen Woodchucks. 2008. 256p. (J). 17.89 (*978-0-06-113871-3(1), Geringer, Laura Book) HarperCollins Pubs.

—Attack of the Frozen Woodchucks. Call, Greg, illus. 2008. 256p. (J). 16.99 (*978-0-06-113870-6(3), Geringer, Laura Book) HarperCollins Pubs.

Ellis, LaRene R. Stones' Quest: In Search of Its Master, 6 vols. 2005. (Stones' Quest Ser.: 1). (Illus.). 485p. (YA). pap. 19.95 (978-0-9754622-0-1(2)) Gathering Place Pubs., Inc.

Ellis, Sarah. Odd Man Out. 2008. 168p. (J). pap. 8.95 (*978-0-88899-703-6(5)); 2006. 160p. (gr. 4-7). 16.95 (978-0-88899-702-9(7)) Groundwood Bks. CAN. *Dist:* Perseus Distribution.

Ellis, Warren. Switchblade Honey. 2003. (Illus.). 88p. (gr. 11 up). pap. 9.95 (978-1-932051-13-1(9)) A i T/Planet Lar.

Ellis, Warren & Carey, Mike. Ultimate Fantastic Four, Vol. 2. 2006. (Illus.). 240p. 29.99 (978-0-7851-2058-2(0)) Marvel Enterprises, Inc.

Elmer, Robert. About-Face Space Race. 2001. (AstroKids Ser.). (Illus.). 112p. (J). (gr. 2-6). pap. 4.99 (978-0-7642-2360-0(7)) Bethany Hse. Pubs.

—Astrokids, Vols. 1-5. 2001. (AstroKids Ser.). (J). pap. 25.99 (978-0-7642-8851-7(2)) Bethany Hse. Pubs.

—The Great Galaxy Goof. 2000. (Astrokids Ser.: Vol. 1). (Illus.). 112p. (J). (gr. 2-6). pap. 5.99 (978-0-7642-2356-3(9)) Bethany Hse. Pubs.

—Miko's Muzzy Mess. 2001. (SpaceKids Ser.: Vol. 4). (Illus.). 112p. (J). (gr. 2-6). pap. 4.99 (978-0-7642-2359-4(3)) Bethany Hse. Pubs.

—Miko's Muzzy Mess. 2001. (gr. 3-6). lib. bdg. 13.00 (978-0-613-85064-3(5)) Tandem Library Bks.

—Wired Wonder Woof. 2001. (SpaceKids Ser.: Vol. 3). (Illus.). 112p. (J). (gr. 2-6). pap. 4.99 (978-0-7642-2358-7(5)) Bethany Hse. Pubs.

—Wired Wonder Woof. 2001. (gr. 3-6). lib. bdg. 13.00 (978-0-613-82426-2(1)) Tandem Library Bks.

—The Zero-G Headache. 2000. (Astrokids Ser.: Vol. 2). (Illus.). 112p. (J). (gr. 2-6). pap. 4.99 (978-0-7642-2357-0(7)) Bethany Hse. Pubs.

Emert, Phyllis Raybin. Mysteries of the Lost & Hidden Treasure, Vol. 1. Jael, illus. 1999. (J). mass mkt. 2.99 (978-0-8125-4360-5(2), Tor Bks.) Doherty, Tom Assocs., LLC.

Emmet, Laura. Julie Trent & the Lightning. 2003. 148p. pap. 11.95 (978-0-595-27380-5(7)) iUniverse, Inc.

—Julie Trent & the Tempest. 2003. 136p. pap. 11.95 (978-0-595-27418-5(8)) iUniverse, Inc.

Ende, Michael. La Historia Interminable. (SPA.). 432p. (YA). (gr. 5-8). 13.95 (978-84-204-2522-1(2), LEC5222) Alfaguara, Ediciones, S.A.- Grupo Santillana ESP. *Dist:* Lectorum Pubns., Inc.

—La Historia Interminable. Quadflieg, Roswitha & Saenz, Miguel, trs. Quadflieg, Roswitha, illus. (SPA.). 424p. (J). 9.95 (978-84-204-3226-7(1)) Alfaguara, Ediciones, S.A.- Grupo Santillana ESP. *Dist:* Santillana USA Publishing Co., Inc.

—La Historia Interminable. 2003. (SPA., Illus.). 420p. (J). (gr. 5-8). pap. 12.95 (978-968-19-0254-4(8)) Santillana USA Publishing Co., Inc.

Engdahl, Sylvia. Enchantress from the Stars. 2003. (Firebird Ser.). 304p. (YA). (gr. 6). pap. 6.99 (978-0-14-250037-8(2), Puffin) Penguin Group (USA) Inc.

—Enchantress from the Stars. 2003. (gr. 7-12). lib. bdg. 15.30 (978-0-613-61619-5(7)) Tandem Library Bks.

—Journey Between Worlds. 2007. 240p. (YA). (gr. 7). pap. 7.99 (978-0-14-240828-5(X), Puffin) Penguin Group (USA) Inc.

Engdahl, Sylvia Louise. Enchantress from the Stars. Dillon, Leo & Dillon, Diane, illus. 2001. 288p. (YA). (gr. 6-11). reprint ed. 18.95 (978-0-8027-8764-4(9)) Walker & Co.

Engineering is Elementary Team. Kwame's Sound: An Acoustical Engineering Story. 2005. (J). lib. bdg. 15.99 (*978-0-9774084-2-9(6)) Museum of Science.

—Michelle's MVP Award: A Chemical Engineering Story. 2005. (J). lib. bdg. 15.99 (*978-0-9774084-7-4(7)) Museum of Science.

—A Reminder for Emily: An Electrical Engineering Story. 2006. (J). lib. bdg. 15.99 (*978-0-9774084-3-6(4)) Museum of Science.

Englehart, Steve & Warner, John. Captain America & the Falcon: Nomad TPB: Nomad TPB. 2007. (Illus.). 192p. pap. 24.99 (978-0-7851-2197-8(8)) Marvel Enterprises, Inc.

Epner, Paul. There's a Dachshund in My Bed! Reed, Bill, illus. 2004. 56p. (J). 16.95 (978-0-9743335-8-8(1)) Imaginative Publishing, Ltd.

Espinosa, Frank. The Journey to the Hidden Sea. (Illus.). 304p. (YA). pap. 19.99 (978-1-58240-585-8(9)) Image Comics.

Eubanks, Sandra & Weihl, M. J. Melanie Joy of Upland. 2004. 48p. pap. 12.95 (978-1-4137-0015-2(2)) PublishAmerica, Inc.

Ewing, Lynne. Possession Bk. 8. 2002. 288p. (J). (gr. 7-17). 9.99 (978-0-7868-0850-2(0), Volo) Hyperion Bks. for Children.

Faerber, Jay, et al. Captain Universe Universal Heroes. 2006. (Illus.). 136p. (YA). pap. 13.99 (978-0-7851-1857-2(8)) Marvel Enterprises, Inc.

Fardell, John. Flight of the Silver Turtle. 2006. 212p. (J). (gr. 3). 15.99 (978-0-399-24382-0(8), Putnam Juvenile) Penguin Group (USA) Inc.

—Seven Professors of the Far North. 2006. 240p. (J). pap. 6.99 (978-0-14-240735-6(6), Puffin) Penguin Group (USA) Inc.

—The Seven Professors of the Far North. 2005. (Illus.). 192p. (YA). (gr. 3-7). 14.99 (978-0-399-24381-3(X), Putnam Juvenile) Penguin Group (USA) Inc.

Farmer, Nancy. Ear, the Eye & the Arm. 2002. (gr. 7-12). lib. bdg. 15.30 (978-0-613-45032-4(9)) Tandem Library Bks.

—The House of the Scorpion. (J). 2002. 400p. 17.95 (978-0-689-85222-0(3) , Atheneum/Richard Jackson Bks.); 2004. (Illus.). 416p. reprint ed. pap. 9.99 (978-0-689-85223-7(1) , Simon Pulse) Simon & Schuster Children's Publishing.

—The House of the Scorpion. l.t. ed. 2003. 515p. (J). 24.95 (978-0-7862-5048-6(8)) Thorndike Pr.

Farmer, Penelope. Charlotte Sometimes. 2007. (Illus.). 192p. (J). (gr. 4-8). 17.95 (978-1-59017-221-6(3) , NYR Children's Collection) New York Review of Bks., Inc., The.

Farshtey, Greg. Bionicle Adventures: Web of the Visorak. 7th ed. 2005. (Bionicle Ser.). 112p. (J). 4.99 (978-0-439-69619-7(4)) Scholastic, Inc.

—Bionicle Encyclopedia (with Stickers) 2005. (Illus.). 128p. (J). pap. 6.99 (978-0-439-74561-1(6)) Scholastic, Inc.

—Dark Destiny. 2006. 128p. (J). pap. 4.99 (978-0-439-78795-6(5)) Scholastic, Inc.

—Search for the Golden City. 2007. (Lego Ser.: No. 3). (Illus.). 64p. (J). pap. 3.99 (***978-0-439-89203-2(1)***) Scholastic, Inc.

Farshtey, Greg. Time Trap. 2005. (Bionicle Adventures Ser.). 144p. (J). pap. 4.99 (978-0-439-74559-8(4)) Scholastic, Inc.

Farshtey, Greg, et al. Bionicle Collector's Sticker Book. 2003. (Bionicle Ser.). (Illus.). 48p. (J). 5.99 (978-0-439-50120-0(2)) Scholastic, Inc.

Feldstein, Al. The EC Archives Vol. 2: Weird Science. 2007. (Illus.). 212p. (YA). 49.95 (***978-1-888472-69-1(3)***) Gemstone Publishing, Inc.

Fernandez, Roberto Peredo. Acoyani: El Nino y el Poeta. Arte y Diseno, Tane, illus. 2nd rev. ed. 2006. (Castillo de la Lectura Naranja Ser.). (SPA.). 166p. (J). pap. 7.95 (978-970-20-0146-1(3)) Castillo, Ediciones, S. A. de C. V. MEX. *Dist:* Macmillan.

Fickling, Phillip. Fillmore & Geary Take Off! Shulman, Mark, illus. 2003. 40p. (J). lib. bdg. (978-1-58717-258-8(5) , SeaStar Bks.) Chronicle Bks. LLC.

Figueroa, Acton. I Am Astro. 2004. (Festival Reader Ser.). (Illus.). 32p. (J). pap. 3.99 (978-0-06-072526-6(5) , Harper Festival) HarperCollins Pubs.

—Invisible Robot. 2004. (Festival Reader Ser.). (Illus.). 32p. (J). pap. 3.99 (978-0-06-072527-3(3) , Harper Festival) HarperCollins Pubs.

—Rocket Ball. 2004. (Astro Boy Ser.). (Illus.). 24p. (J). pap. 3.50 (978-0-06-072524-2(9) , Harper Festival) HarperCollins Pubs.

Fix, Philippe. Serafin und seine Wundermaschine. Ibach, Sabine, tr. from FRE. 1999. (Taschenbuecher Ser.). (GER., Illus.). 40p. (J). pap. (978-3-257-25046-6(0)) Diogenes Verlag AG CHE. *Dist:* International Bk. Import Service, Inc.

Fleischman, Paul. Time Train. 2002. (Illus.). (J). 15.49 (978-0-7587-3814-1(5)) Book Wholesalers, Inc.

Fleury, Mike Stevenson. Natural Disaster 2222. 2003. (ENG.). 112p. 19.95 (***978-0-595-65436-9(3) ;*** 108p. (YA). pap. 9.95 (978-0-595-25921-2(9)) iUniverse, Inc. (Writers Club Pr.).

Flexer, Michael. Edmund's Struggle: Under the Spell of the White Witch. Baynes, Pauline, illus. 2006. (Narnia Ser.). 96p. (J). 14.99 (978-0-06-085232-0(1)) HarperCollins Pubs.

—Edmund's Struggle: Under the Spell of the White Witch. Baynes, Pauline, illus. 2006. (Narnia Ser.). 96p. (J). pap. 3.99 (978-0-06-085231-3(3) , Harper Trophy) HarperCollins Pubs.

—Lucy's Adventure: The Search for Aslan. Baynes, Pauline, illus. 2006. (Narnia Ser.). 96p. (J). 14.99 (978-0-06-085234-4(8)) HarperCollins Pubs.

Fontenay, Charles L. Kipton & the Delusions of Tante Else, 18 vols. 1999. (Kipton Chronicles Ser.: Bk. 17). 189p. (YA). (gr. 6-9). 9.99 (978-0-88092-456-6(X) , 456-X) Royal Fireworks Publishing Co.

—Kipton & the Matter Transmitter, 18 vols. 1999. (Kipton Chronicles Ser.: Vol. 15). 190p. (YA). (gr. 6). 9.99 (978-0-88092-455-9(1)) Royal Fireworks Publishing Co.

—Kipton & the Monorail Murder, 18 vols. 1998. (Kipton Chronicles Ser.: Bk. 12). 185p. (YA). (gr. 5 up). 9.99 (978-0-88092-418-4(7) , 4187) Royal Fireworks Publishing Co.

—Kipton & the Riddle of Sandstone, 18 vols. 1999. (Kipton Chronicles Ser.: No. 18). 185p. (YA). (gr. 8-12). pap. 9.99 (978-0-88092-457-3(8) , 4578) Royal Fireworks Publishing Co.

—Kipton at the Martian Games, 18 vols. 1998. (Kipton Chronicles Ser.: Bk. 14). 187p. (J). (gr. k-8). pap. 9.99 (978-0-88092-396-5(2) , 3962) Royal Fireworks Publishing Co.

—Kipton on Phobos, 18 vols. 1999. (Kipton Chronicles Ser.: Bk. 13). 188p. (J). (gr. 5 up). pap. 9.99 (978-0-88092-416-0(0) , 4160) Royal Fireworks Publishing Co.

Fools Bounty. 2003. (Star Wars Ser.: Vol. 5). (Illus.). 376p. (Orig.). (J). (gr. 3 up). pap. 29.95 (978-1-56971-906-0(3)) Dark Horse Comics.

Foon, Dennis. Freewalker. 2004. (Longlight Legacy Ser.). 320p. (YA). (gr. 6). 19.95 (978-1-55037-885-6(6)); pap. 9.95 (978-1-55037-884-9(8)) Annick Pr., Ltd. CAN. *Dist:* Firefly Bks., Ltd.

—The Keeper's Shadow. 2006. (Longlight Legacy Ser.). 412p. (YA). (gr. 6-12). 19.95 (978-1-55451-028-3(7)); pap. 12.95 (978-1-55451-027-6(9)) Annick Pr., Ltd. CAN. *Dist:* Firefly Bks., Ltd.

Forbeck, Matt. Prophecy of the Dragons, Pt. 1. ed. 2006. 192p. (YA). pap. 5.99 (978-0-7869-4031-8(X) , Mirrorstone) Wizards of the Coast.

Ford, Linda. The Santa Season. 2002. 93p. (J). (978-0-439-43532-1(3)) Scholastic, Inc.

The Forgotten Armory 2. 2005. (Illus.). 12p. 8.99 (978-1-933300-00-9(0)) Wandering Sage Bookstore & More, LLC.

Forward, Toby. Travelling Backwards. 2003. (Illus.). 128p. (J). 9.99 (978-1-84270-293-2(9)) Andersen GBR. *Dist:* Independent Pubs. Group.

Foster, Alan Dean. Approaching Storm. 2003. (gr. 7-12). lib. bdg. 15.30 (978-0-613-62586-9(2)) Tandem Library Bks.

Fotonovel Publications Staff. Dinosaur. 2000. (Illus.). 176p. (J). pap. 7.95 (978-0-89752-012-6(2)) Fotonovel Pubns.

Fountain of Ecstasy. 2000. (YA). spiral bd. 19.95 (978-0-9740227-0-3(5)) Kendrick, G. David Properties.

Fox, Helen. Eager. 2004. 288p. (gr. 3-7). 15.95 (978-0-385-74672-4(5) , Lamb, Wendy) Random Hse. Children's Bks.

—Eager's Nephew. 304p. (gr. 3-7). 2007. 5.99 (***978-0-553-48796-1(5)*** , Yearling); 2006. (J). 15.95 (978-0-385-74673-1(3) , Lamb, Wendy) Random Hse. Children's Bks.

Fox, Jennifer & Frantz, Jennifer. Meet the Autobots. Guidi, Guido, illus. 2007. (I Can Read Bks.). 32p. (J). pap. 3.99 (***978-0-06-088831-2(8)*** , Harper Trophy) HarperCollins Pubs.

—Transformers: Meet the Decepticons. Guidi, Guido, illus. 2007. (I Can Read Bks.). 32p. (J). pap. 3.99 (***978-0-06-088828-2(8)*** , Harper Trophy) HarperCollins Pubs.

Fox, Michael H. Theater Boy: Part I of the Tomorrowteens Series. 2004. 189p. pap. 19.95 (978-1-4137-1797-6(7)) PublishAmerica, Inc.

Francis, Pauline & Wyndham, John. The Day of the Triffids. 2003. (Fast Track Classics Ser.). (Illus.). 48p. (YA). pap. 9.99 (978-0-237-52536-1(4) , Evans Brothers, Limited) Evans Publishing Group GBR. *Dist:* Independent Pubs. Group.

Fraser, Jess, illus. The Legend of the Cosmic Cowboy. 2007. (J). cd-rom 12.99 (***978-0-9795190-7-9(1)***) Color & Learn.

French, Vivian. Space Dog Visits Planet Earth. Heap, Sue, illus. 2000. (Space Dog Ser.: No. 4). 64p. (J). (ps-3). pap. 3.99 (978-0-439-13086-8(7) , Scholastic Paperbacks) Scholastic, Inc.

French, Vivian & Heap, Sue. Space Dog Finds Treasure. 2000. (Space Dog Ser.: No. 2). (Illus.). 64p. (J). (ps-3). pap. 3.99 (978-0-439-13084-4(0)) Scholastic, Inc.

—Space Dog Meets Space Cat. 2000. (Space Dog Ser.: No. 3). (Illus.). 64p. (J). (ps-3). pap. 3.99 (978-0-439-13085-1(9)) Scholastic, Inc.

—Space Dog to the Rescue. 2000. (Space Dog Ser.: No. 1). (Illus.). 64p. (J). (ps-3). pap. 3.99 (978-0-439-13083-7(2)) Scholastic, Inc.

Friedman, Michael Jan, et al. Convergence. Erwin, Steve et al, illus. 2007. 176p. pap. 22.95 (***978-1-84576-320-6(3)***) Titan Bks. Ltd. GBR. *Dist:* Random Hse., Inc.

Friesner, Esther M. Men in Black II: The Official Novelization. 2002. (gr. 7-12). lib. bdg. 15.30 (978-0-613-56978-1(4)) Tandem Library Bks.

Fujishima, Kosuke. Mara Strikes Back. 2000. (Oh My Goddess! Ser.: Vol. 8). (Illus.). 176p. (J). (gr. 3 up). pap. 14.95 (978-1-56971-449-2(5)) Dark Horse Comics.

Fullerton, Charlotte. Aqua Planet. 2006. (Sonic X Ser.). (Illus.). 48p. (J). (gr. 1-3). pap. 4.99 (978-0-448-44254-9(X) , Grosset & Dunlap) Penguin Group (USA) Inc.

—Desperately Seeking Sonic. 2007. (Sonic X Ser.). 48p. (J). pap. 4.99 (978-0-448-44479-6(8) , Grosset & Dunlap) Penguin Group (USA) Inc.

Furey, Maggie. Web 6: Sorceress. 1998. 98p. (J). pap. 7.99 (978-1-85881-551-0(7)) Orion Children's Bks. GBR. *Dist:* Independent Pubs. Group.

Gaarder, Jostein. Hello? Is Anybody There? Gardner, Sally, illus. l.t. ed. 2002. 152p. (J). 16.95 (978-0-7540-7814-2(0) , Galaxy Children's Large Print) BBC Audiobooks America.

Gage, Brian. The Saddest Little Robot. Otoshi, Kathryn, tr. Otoshi, Kathryn, illus. 2003. 90p. (J). 12.99 (978-1-932360-05-9(0)) Penguin Group (USA) Inc.

The Galactic Adventures of Team Energy: Episode I: Dr. Slouch & the Candy Factory. 2007. (J). 16.95 (***978-0-9778776-1-4(2)***) LGE Performance Systems, Inc.

Galada, Lee. A World of Difference. 2005. (Fresh Voices Ser.). 154p. (J). pap. 5.95 (978-1-932802-98-6(3) , Holy Macro! Bks.) MrExcel.com Publishing.

Gallagher, Diana G. Spaceship Blue Typhoon. 2005. (Sonic X Ser.). 48p. (J). (gr. 1-3). pap. 4.99 (978-0-448-43997-6(2) , Grosset & Dunlap) Penguin Group (USA) Inc.

Gallagher, John. Buzzboy Vol. 2: Monsters, Dreams, & Milkshakes. 2004. 144p. pap. 11.95 (978-0-9721831-1-6(6)) sky-dog.

Gallagher, Michael. X-Men, Magneto's Master Plan. Severin, Marie, illus. 24p. (YA). (gr. k up). 12.95 (978-0-9627001-6-3(9)) Futech Educational Products, Inc.

—X-Men, Scourge of the Savage Land. Severin, Marie, illus. 24p. (YA). (gr. k up). 12.95 (978-0-9627001-7-0(7)) Futech Educational Products, Inc.

Garcia-Weed, Barbara. Zeroid & the Gold-Fanged Frock. 2003. pap. 13.95 (978-0-533-13491-5(9)) Vantage Pr., Inc.

Gardiner, John Reynolds. Alto Secreto. (SPA.). 96p. (YA). (gr. 5-8). (978-84-279-3396-5(7) , NG3489) Noguer y Caralt Editores, S. A. ESP. *Dist:* Lectorum Pubns., Inc.

Gardner, J. J. The Perils of Quadrant X. 1998. (Lost in Space Ser.: Vol. 3). (J). (gr. 3-7). pap. 3.99 (978-0-590-18940-8(9) , Scholastic Paperbacks) Scholastic, Inc.

Gardner, Sally. Magical Kids: The Strongest Girl in the World & the Invisible Boy. 2007. (Illus.). 224p. (J). (gr. 2-5). 15.99 (978-0-8037-3158-5(2) , Dial) Penguin Group (USA) Inc.

Gass, Kenneth. Trilobites! 2005. 110p. per. 18.99 net. (978-0-9634906-8-1(0) , SQP) Specialized Quality Pubns.

Gear, Kathleen O'Neal. The Visitant. 2000. (gr. 7-12). lib. bdg. 15.30 (978-0-613-28126-3(8)) Tandem Library Bks.

Gehrt, Linda. My Trip, My Spaceship. 2004. 26p. pap. 14.95 (978-1-4137-3392-1(1)) PublishAmerica, Inc.

Geiger, Beth & Fuerst, Jeffrey B. Return to Earth: Reader's Theater Levels N-U (30-50) Wolk-Stanley, Jessica, illus. ed. 2004. (Reader's Theater Ser.). 16p. (J). pap. 22.00 (978-1-4108-2306-9(7) , A23067) Benchmark Education Co.

Geras, Adele. Family Photographs. 2000. (Fabulous Fantoras Ser.: Vol. 2). (Illus.). 160p. (J). (gr. 3-7). pap. 4.95 (978-0-380-79358-7(X) , Harper Trophy) HarperCollins Pubs.

Gerber, Steve, et al. Omega: The Unknown Classic. 2005. (Illus.). 224p. (YA). pap. 29.99 (978-0-7851-2009-4(2)) Marvel Enterprises, Inc.

Gerritsen, Tess. Gravity: A Novel of Medical Suspense. 2000. (gr. 7-12). lib. bdg. 16.45 (978-0-613-36378-5(7)) Tandem Library Bks.

Gerwitz, Felice & Gerwitz, Christina. Dinosaur Quest at Diamond Peak, 3, Vol. 2. 2nd rev. ed. 2007. (Truth Seeker's Mystery Ser.). 208p. (YA). per. 8.99 (***978-1-931941-11-2(4)***) Media Angels, Inc.

—The Missing Link: Found, 3, Vol. 1. 2nd rev. ed. 2004. (Truth Seeker's Mystery Ser.). 208p. (YA). per. 8.99 (***978-1-931941-08-2(4)***) Media Angels, Inc.

Gibbons, Gail. Planet Earth/Inside Out. Gibbons, Gail, illus. 1998. (Illus.). 32p. (J). (ps-3). pap. 6.99 (978-0-688-15849-1(8) , Harper Trophy) HarperCollins Pubs.

Gilden, Mel. Britney Spears Is a Three-Headed Alien: The Inside Story. 2001. (gr. 7-12). lib. bdg. 18.80 (978-0-613-82444-6(X)) Tandem Library Bks.

—Britney Spears Is a Three-Headed Alien: The Inside Story. 2001. 208p. pap. 9.99 (978-0-7434-2383-0(6)) ibooks, Inc.

Gill, Margaret. The Brain Changers. 2004. 160p. (YA). pap. 12.95 (978-0-595-31161-3(X)) iUniverse, Inc.

Gioseffi, Anthony P. Mainframe. 2007. 144p. per. 11.95 (***978-0-595-44953-8(0)***) iUniverse, Inc.

Glass, Julie. The Fly on the Ceiling: A Math Myth. Walz, Richard, illus. 1998. (Step into Reading & Math Step 3 Bks.). 48p. (J). (gr. k-3). pap. 3.99 (978-0-679-88607-5(9) , Random Hse. Bks. for Young Readers) Random Hse. Children's Bks.

Glassman, Peter & Wells, H. G. The War of the Worlds. Kidd, Tom, illus. 2001. (Books of Wonder). 240p. 24.99 (978-0-688-13137-1(9)) HarperCollins Pubs.

Glicksman, Caroline. Eric & the Red Planet: A Space Adventure with Numbers. 2004. (Illus.). 32p. (J). pap. 8.99 (978-0-09-945640-7(0) , Arrow Bks., Ltd.) Random Hse. GBR. *Dist:* Independent Pubs. Group.

The Globster of Glassy Beach. 2001. 56p. (J). per. 6.95 (978-0-941367-25-7(8)) Peach Blossom Pubns.

Glur, D. L' Empire Contre Attaque.Tr. of Empire Strikes Back. (FRE.). (J). pap. 11.95 (978-2-265-06729-5(6)) Fleuve Noir FRA. *Dist:* Distribooks, Inc.

Goldberg, Dennis. Double Bubble Trouble. 2007. (J). 14.95 (***978-1-933769-19-6(X)***) Level 4 Press, Inc.

Golden, Christopher. Surrogates. 2001. (gr. 7-12). lib. bdg. 18.75 (978-0-613-79090-1(1)) Tandem Library Bks.

Gollub, Matthew. Moon Was at a Fiesta. 2002. (gr. k-3). lib. bdg. 15.25 (978-0-613-70980-4(2)) Tandem Library Bks.

Gonzalez, Mary. The House That Was. 2003. 49p. pap. 12.95 (978-1-4137-0872-1(2)) PublishAmerica, Inc.

Goobie, Beth. Fixed. 2005. 288p. (YA). (gr. 7-12). lib. bdg. 16.95 (978-1-55143-374-5(5)) Orca Bk. Pubs. USA.

—Flux. 2004. 224p. (J). (gr. 7-12). lib. bdg. 16.95 (978-1-55143-314-1(1)) Orca Bk. Pubs. USA.

Goodstuff, "Scoop. Doomuche. 2005. 86p. pap. 14.95 (978-1-4137-7858-8(5)) PublishAmerica, Inc.

Graham, Craig. Peter's Destiny: The Battle for Narnia. Baynes, Pauline, illus. 2006. (Narnia Ser.). 96p. (J). pap. 3.99 (978-0-06-085235-1(6) , Harper Trophy) HarperCollins Pubs.

Graham, Denise. Eye of Fortune. 2004. (Dungeons & Dragons Ser.: Bk. 04). (Illus.). 192p. (J). pap. 5.99 (978-0-7869-3169-9(8)) Wizards of the Coast.

Grantham, Jared. Ashley & the Mooncorn People. 2002. 64p. (J). 16.00 (978-1-58597-134-3(0)) Leathers Publishing.

Grayson, Devin. Batman: The Copycat Crime. 2003. (gr. k-3). lib. bdg. 11.80 (978-0-613-71996-4(4)) Tandem Library Bks.

Grayson, Devin, et al. Batman No. 2: The Copycat Crime. 2003. (Reader Ser.). (Illus.). 40p. (J). pap. 3.99 (978-0-439-47097-1(8) , Cartwheel Bks.) Scholastic, Inc.

Greenburg, Dan. Attack of the Evil Elvises. Pamintuan, Macky, illus. 2007. (Weird Planet Ser.: No. 4). 96p. (J). (gr. 2-4). lib. bdg. 11.99 (978-0-375-93347-9(6)); 3.99 (978-0-375-83347-2(1)) Random Hse. Children's Bks. (Random Hse. Bks. for Young Readers).

—Chilling with the Great Ones. Pamintuan, Macky, illus. 2006. 96p. (J). (gr. 2-5). lib. bdg. 11.99 (978-0-375-93346-2(8)); (Weird Planet Ser.: No. 3). (gr. 1-4). pap. 3.99 (978-0-375-83346-5(3)) Random Hse. Children's Bks. (Random Hse. Bks. for Young Readers).

—Dude, Where's My Spaceship? Pamintuan, Macky, illus. 2006. 96p. (J). (gr. 2-5). lib. bdg. 11.99 (978-0-375-93344-8(1) , Random Hse. Bks. for Young Readers) Random Hse. Children's Bks.

—Dude, Where's My Spaceship? Pamintuan, Macky, illus. 2006. 81p. (J). (***978-1-4156-6704-0(7)***) Random Hse., Inc.

—Dude Where's My Spaceship. Calver, Dave & Pamintuan, Macky, illus. 2006. (Weird Planet Ser.: No. 1). 96p. (J). (gr. 2-5). pap. 3.99 (978-0-375-83344-1(7) , Random Hse. Bks. for Young Readers) Random Hse. Children's Bks.

—Hang a Left at Venus. Davis, Jack E., illus. 1999. (Zack Files Ser.: No. 15). 64p. (J). (gr. 2-5). pap. 4.99 (978-0-448-41875-9(4) , Grosset & Dunlap) Penguin Group (USA) Inc.

—Hang a Left at Venus. 1999. (gr. 3-6). lib. bdg. 13.00 (978-0-613-14785-9(5)); (Zack Files Ser.: No. 15). (J). (gr. 2-5). 11.79 (978-0-606-17781-8(7)) Tandem Library Bks.

—Lost in Las Vegas. Pamintuan, Macky, illus. 2006. 96p. (J). (gr. 2-5). pap. 3.99 (978-0-375-83345-8(5)); lib. bdg. 11.99 (978-0-375-93345-5(X)) Random Hse. Children's Bks. (Random Hse. Bks. for Young Readers).

—Weird Planet: Lights, Camera... Liftoff! Pamintuan, Macky, illus. 2007. (Weird Planet Ser.: No. 5). 96p. (J). (gr. 2-5). pap. 3.99 (***978-0-375-84336-5(1)*** , Random Hse. Bks. for Young Readers) Random Hse. Children's Bks.

—Weird Planet No. 5: Lights, Camera... Liftoff! Pamintuan, Macky, illus. 2007. (Stepping Stone Bks.). 96p. (J). (gr. 2-5). lib. bdg. 11.99 (***978-0-375-94336-2(6)*** , Random Hse. Bks. for Young Readers) Random Hse. Children's Bks.

Greene, Janice. Escape from Earth. 2001. (PageTurner Science Fiction Ser.). 80p. (YA). per. 3.95 (978-1-56254-131-6(5) , SP 1315) Saddleback Educational Publishing.

—Escape from Earth. 2001. (gr. 7-12). lib. bdg. 11.80 (978-0-613-34198-1(8)) Tandem Library Bks.

—Under Siege. 2001. (PageTurner Science Fiction Ser.). 80p. (YA). per. 3.95 (978-1-56254-134-7(X) , SP 134X) Saddleback Educational Publishing.

—Under Siege. 2001. (gr. 7-12). lib. bdg. 11.80 (978-0-613-34520-0(7)); (Illus.). (J). (978-0-606-21577-0(8)) Tandem Library Bks.

Greenwood, Kerry. Alien Invasions. 2005. (Thrillogy Ser.). (Illus.). 48p. (gr. 4-8). 17.50 (978-0-7910-8865-4(0)) , Facts On File, Inc.

—Alien Invasions. 2000. (gr. 7-12). lib. bdg. 12.10 (978-0-613-28728-9(2)) Tandem Library Bks.

Greeson, Ewell. Aegis. 2003. 436p. (YA). per. 19.95 (978-1-59453-024-1(6) , 1701) Airleaf Publishing & Bookselling.

Gregory, David. Visions of Reality. 2007. 236p. per. 15.95 (***978-0-595-44969-9(7)***) iUniverse, Inc.

Grell, Mike, et al. Magic-The Gathering: Gerrard's Quest. 1999. 112p. (YA). (gr. 9 up). pap. 12.95 (978-1-56971-403-4(7)) Dark Horse Comics.

Gresh, Lois H. & Gresh, Danny. Chuck Farris & the Tower of Darkness: An Action Story about Play Station 2. 2001. (Chuck Farris Ser.). 253p. (J). (gr. 4-9). pap. 6.95 (978-1-55022-440-5(9) , misFit) ECW Pr. CAN. *Dist:* Independent Pubs. Group.

Griffiths, Andy. Final Conflict. 2005. (Butt Wars Ser.). 304p. (J). pap. 5.99 (978-0-439-74750-9(3) , Scholastic Paperbacks) Scholastic, Inc.

Grisham, Jonathan. The Death of the Universe. 2005. (YA). per. (978-1-933594-16-3(0)) Faith Baptist Church Publns.

Grosset and Dunlap Staff & Miller, Edward. Rockets. Jarnow, Jill, ed. 2001. (Sticker Stories Ser.). (Illus.). 1p. (J). (ps-3). pap. 4.99 (978-0-448-42461-3(4) , Grosset & Dunlap) Penguin Group (USA) Inc.

Gruber, Michael. The Witch's Boy. 2005. 384p. (gr. 6-9). (J). lib. bdg. 17.89 (978-0-06-076165-3(2)); (YA). 16.99 (978-0-06-076164-6(4)) HarperCollins Pubs. (HarperTeen).

Gruenwald, Mark, et al. Essential Official Handbook of the Marvel Universe - TPB, 3 vols., Vol. 2. deluxe ed. 2006. (Illus.). 480p. pap. 16.99 (978-0-7851-1935-7(3)) Marvel Enterprises, Inc.

—Squadron Supreme: Death of a Universe. 2006. (Illus.). 240p. (YA). pap. 24.99 (978-0-7851-2091-9(2)) Marvel Enterprises, Inc.

Guibert, Emmanuel. Sardine in Outer Space, Vol. 2. Sfar, Joann, illus. 2nd rev. ed. 2006. (Sardine in Outer Space Ser.). 128p. (J). pap. 12.95 (978-1-59643-127-0(X) , First Second Bks.) Roaring Brook Pr.

Guibert, Emmanuel. Sardine in Outer Space 3. Brizzi, Elisabeth & Siegel, Alexis, trs. from FRE. Sfar, Joann, illus. 3rd rev. ed. 2007. (Sardine in Outer Space Ser.). 112p. (J). (gr. 1-5). pap. 12.95 (***978-1-59643-128-7(8)*** , First Second Bks.) Roaring Brook Pr.

Guillen, Michael. Dr. Universe, Vol. 3. 2000. (J). pap. 10.00 (978-0-517-88563-5(8)); lib. bdg. 16.99 (978-0-517-88564-2(6)) Random Hse. Children's Bks. (Random Hse. Bks. for Young Readers).

Guillet, Jean-Pierre. La Puce Cosmique et le Rayon Bleuge. Guillet, Francois, illus. 2004. (Des 9 Ans. Ser.). (FRE.). 120p. (J). (978-2-922565-98-0(X)) Editions de la Paix CAN. *Dist:* World of Reading, Ltd.

Gully, Mario & Hammond, Marc. Reality Bites. 2006. (Illus.). 120p. (YA). pap. 12.99 (978-1-58240-580-3(8)) Image Comics.

Gutman, Dan. Mr. Docker Is off His Rocker! Paillot, Jim, illus. 2006. (My Weird School Ser.). 112p. (J). pap. 3.99 (978-0-06-082227-9(9) , Harper Trophy); lib. bdg. 15.89 (978-0-06-082228-6(7)) HarperCollins Pubs.

—Virtually Perfect. 128p. (gr. 3-7). 1999. pap. 4.99 (978-0-7868-1316-2(4)); 2003. pap. 5.99 (978-0-7868-1745-0(3)) Hyperion Bks. for Children.

—Virtually Perfect. 2003. (gr. 3-6). lib. bdg. 14.15 (978-0-613-75029-5(2)); 1999. (978-0-606-16673-7(4)) Tandem Library Bks.

Guzzo, Anthony V. & Guzzo, Sandra E. Jason & the Time Modem: The Archimedes Challenge. 2001. (Illus.). 150p. (J). (gr. 4-7). pap. 9.95 (978-0-9643692-1-4(4)) Dandelion Pr.

Hadcroft, Will. Anne Droyd & Century Lodge. 2004. 282p. (J). pap. (978-1-84310-282-3(X)) Kingsley, Jessica Ltd.

Haddix, Margaret Peterson. Among the Barons. (Shadow Children Ser.). (J). (gr. 3-7). 2003. 192p. 16.95 (978-0-689-83906-1(5)); 2004. 208p. reprint ed. pap. 5.99 (978-0-689-83910-8(3) , Aladdin) Simon & Schuster Children's Publishing.

—Among the Betrayed. l.t. ed. 2006. (Shadow Children Ser.). 205p. (YA). 22.95 (978-0-7862-8279-1(7)) Thorndike Pr.

—Among the Brave. (Shadow Children Ser.). (Illus.). 240p. (J). (gr. 3-7). 2005. pap. 5.99 (978-0-689-85795-9(0) , Aladdin); 2004. 15.95 (978-0-689-85794-2(2)) Simon & Schuster Children's Publishing.

—Among the Enemy. (Shadow Children Ser.). (J). 2006. 240p. pap. 5.99 (978-0-689-85797-3(7) , Aladdin); 2005. 224p. (gr. 3-7). 16.95 (978-0-689-85796-6(9) , Simon & Schuster Children's Publishing) Simon & Schuster Children's Publishing.

—Among the Free. (Shadow Children Ser.). 208p. (J). 2007. pap. 5.99 (*978-0-689-85799-7(3) , Aladdin); 2006. (gr. 3-7). 16.95 (978-0-689-85798-0(5) , Simon & Schuster Children's Publishing) Simon & Schuster Children's Publishing.

—Among the Hidden. 2002. (Shadow Children Ser.). (YA). (gr. 7-8). stu. ed. (978-1-58130-779-5(9)) Novel Units, Inc.

—Among the Hidden. Nielsen, Cliff, illus. 2000. (Shadow Children Ser.). 160p. (J). (gr. 3-7). mass mkt. 5.99 (978-0-689-82475-3(0) , Aladdin) Simon & Schuster Children's Publishing.

—Among the Hidden. 1998. (Shadow Children Ser.). 160p. (J). (gr. 3-7). 16.95 (978-0-689-81700-7(2)) Simon & Schuster Children's Publishing.

—Among the Hidden. 2000. (Shadow Children Ser.). (gr. 3-6). lib. bdg. 13.00 (978-0-613-23618-8(1)) Tandem Library Bks.

—Among the Impostors. (Shadow Children Ser.). (J). (gr. 3-7). 2002. 192p. mass mkt. 5.99 (978-0-689-83908-5(1) , Aladdin); 2001. (Illus.). 176p. 16.95 (978-0-689-83904-7(9)) Simon & Schuster Children's Publishing.

—Among the Impostors. 2002. (Shadow Children Ser.). (gr. 3-6). lib. bdg. 13.00 (978-0-613-61844-1(0)) Tandem Library Bks.

—Running Out of Time. 2005. 192p. (J). pap. 2.99 (978-1-4169-0531-8(6) , Aladdin) Simon & Schuster Children's Publishing.

—Turnabout. 240p. 2007. (YA). mass mkt. 5.99 (978-1-4169-3653-4(X) , Simon Pulse); 2002. (gr. 5-9). mass mkt. 5.99 (978-0-689-84037-1(3) , Aladdin) Simon & Schuster Children's Publishing.

—Turnabout. Nielsen, Cliff, illus. 2000. 240p. (YA). (gr. 7-12). 17.00 (978-0-689-82187-5(5)) Simon & Schuster Children's Publishing.

—Turnabout. 2002. (gr. 5-8). lib. bdg. 14.15 (978-0-613-45116-1(3)) Tandem Library Bks.

Halam, Ann. Dr Franklin's Island. 2003. (gr. 7-12). lib. bdg. 13.55 (978-0-613-72267-4(1)) Tandem Library Bks.

—Siberia: A Novel. 2006. 272p. (YA). (gr. 7). mass mkt. 5.99 (978-0-553-49414-3(7) , Laurel Leaf) Random Hse. Children's Bks.

Haldeman, Joe. The Forever War. 2003. (gr. 7-12). lib. bdg. 23.40 (978-0-613-68423-1(0)) Tandem Library Bks.

Hale, Bruce. The Adventures of Space Gecko. (Illus.). (J). 8.95 (978-0-9621280-2-8(3)) Words & Pictures Publishing, Inc.

—How the Gecko Lost His Tail. Hale, Bruce, illus. 1999. (Moki the Gecko Ser.). Orig. Title: The Adventures of Space Gecko. (Illus.). 32p. (J). (gr. k-6). 8.95 (978-0-9621280-8-0(2)) Words & Pictures Publishing, Inc.

Hambrick, Sharon. Tommy's Rocket. Manning, Maurie, illus. 2003. (Fig Street Kids Ser.). 83p. (J). (gr. 1-2). 7.49 (978-1-59166-186-3(2)) Jones, Bob Univ. Pr.

Hamel, Mike. The Sword & the Flute: Matterhorn, the Brave Series. 2007. 176p. (J). pap. 12.99 (978-0-89957-833-0(0)) AMG Pubs.

—Talis Hunters: Matterhorn, the Brave Series, Vol. 2. 2007. 176p. (J). pap. 12.99 (978-0-89957-834-7(9)) AMG Pubs.

Hamilton, John. Time Travel. 2007. (World of Science Fiction Ser.). (Illus.). 32p. (J). 24.21 (978-1-59679-996-7(X)) ABDO Publishing Co.

Hamme. Thorgal Child of the Stars. Rosinski, Grzegorz, illus. 2007. 96p. pap. 14.99 (*978-1-905460-23-6(6)) CineBook GBR. *Dist:* Biblio Distribution.

Hancock, Niel. Squaring the Circle. 4th rev. ed. 2004. (Circle of Light Ser.: Vol. 4). (Illus.). 368p. (J). 5.99 (978-0-7653-4618-6(4) , Tor Bks.) Doherty, Tom Assocs., LLC.

Hand, Elizabeth. Hunted. Bollinger, Peter, illus. 2003. (Star Wars Ser.: Vol. 4). 160p. (J). pap. 5.99 (978-0-439-33930-8(8) , Scholastic Paperbacks) Scholastic, Inc.

—Hunted. 2003. (Star Wars Ser.: Vol. 4). (gr. 7-12). lib. bdg. 13.00 (978-0-613-66359-5(4)) Tandem Library Bks.

—Maze of Deception. Bolinger, Peter, illus. 2003. (Star Wars Ser.: Vol. 3). 144p. (J). pap. 5.99 (978-0-439-44245-9(1)) Scholastic, Inc.

—Maze of Deception. 2003. (Star Wars Ser.: Vol. 3). (gr. 7-12). lib. bdg. 13.00 (978-0-613-66366-3(7)) Tandem Library Bks.

Hand, Elizabeth. A New Threat. 2004. (Star Wars Ser.: Vol. 5). 139p. (J). lib. bdg. 20.00 (*978-1-4242-0781-7(9)) Fitzgerald Bks.

—A New Threat. Bollinger, Peter, illus. 2004. (Star Wars Ser.: Vol. 5). 144p. (J). 5.99 (978-0-439-33931-5(6) , Scholastic Paperbacks) Scholastic, Inc.

Hansen, Lynne. Reckless Revolution. 2007. (YA). (*978-1-4114-9672-9(8)) Spark Publishing Group.

—Shades of Blue & Gray. 2007. (YA). pap. (*978-1-4114-9674-3(4)) Spark Publishing Group.

—A Time for Witches. 2007. (YA). (*978-1-4114-9671-2(X)) Spark Publishing Group.

Hapka, C. A. Beware the Bohrok. 2003. (gr. 3-6). lib. bdg. 13.00 (978-0-613-87587-5(7)) Tandem Library Bks.

Hapka, C.A., et al. Mask of Light. 2003. (Bionicle Ser.). (Illus.). 128p. (J). 4.99 (978-0-439-50118-7(0)) Scholastic, Inc.

Hapka, Catherine. Astro Boy Color, Bk. 1. Merkel, Joe F., illus. 2004. (Astro Boy Ser.). 32p. (J). pap., act. bk. ed. 4.99 (978-0-06-072522-8(2) , Harper Festival) HarperCollins Pubs.

—Astro Boy Color & Sticker Book, Bk. 2. Farley, Rick, illus. 2004. (Astro Boy Ser.). 32p. (J). pap. 4.99 (978-0-06-072523-5(0) , Harper Festival) HarperCollins Pubs.

Hapka, Cathy. Beware the Bohrok: Chronicles 2. 2003. (Bionicle Chronicles: No. 2). 96p. (J). (gr. 2-5). 4.99 (978-0-439-50117-0(2)) Scholastic, Inc.

—Tale of the Toa. 2003. (Bionicle Chronicles: Bk. 1). 128p. (J). (gr. 2-5). pap. 4.99 (978-0-439-50116-3(4)) Scholastic, Inc.

Harcourt School Publishers Staff. Adrift in Space Advanced Level. 3rd ed. 2002. (Trophies Reading Program Ser.). (Illus.). pap. 5.10 (978-0-15-323488-0(1)) Harcourt Schl. Pubs.

—The Crystal Radio Advanced Level. 3rd ed. 2002. (Trophies Reading Program Ser.). (Illus.). pap. 5.10 (978-0-15-323287-9(0)) Harcourt Schl. Pubs.

—The Encounter Advanced Level. 3rd ed. 2002. (Trophies Reading Program Ser.). (Illus.). pap. 5.10 (978-0-15-323385-2(0)) Harcourt Schl. Pubs.

—The Green Book. 1998. (Illus.). pap. 13.50 (978-0-15-307562-9(7)) Harcourt Schl. Pubs.

—Rock Hounds Advanced Level. 3rd ed. 2002. (Trophies Reading Program Ser.). (Illus.). pap. 5.10 (978-0-15-323218-3(8)) Harcourt Schl. Pubs.

—Taking Chances: Take-Home Book. 2001. (Collections Ser.). (Illus.). (J). pap. 1.90 (978-0-15-319517-4(7)) Harcourt Schl. Pubs.

—Trapped in the Future Advanced Level. 3rd ed. 2002. (Trophies Reading Program Ser.). (Illus.). pap. 5.10 (978-0-15-323395-1(8)) Harcourt Schl. Pubs.

—Wilderness School. 3rd ed. 2002. (Trophies Reading Program Ser.). (Illus.). pap. 5.10 (978-0-15-323476-7(8)) Harcourt Schl. Pubs.

Harold y el lapiz color Morado 15: Leveled Books. 2001. (McGraw-Hill. Lectura Ser.). (ENG & SPA.). (gr. 1 up). (978-0-02-187992-2(3)) Macmillan/McGraw-Hill Schl. Div.

HarperEntertainment Staff, contrib. by. Map of File Island. 2000. (Digimon Ser.). (J). (gr. 1-6). pap. 7.95 (978-0-06-107194-2(3) , Harper Entertainment) HarperCollins Pubs.

Harperfestival. Good Boy! The Movie Novel. 2003. (gr. 3-6). lib. bdg. 13.00 (978-0-613-71420-4(2)) Tandem Library Bks.

Harpur, James. Warriors. 2007. 32p. (J). (gr. 3-9). 21.99 (*978-1-4169-3951-1(2) , Atheneum) Simon & Schuster Children's Publishing.

Harras, Bob, et al. Galactic Storm Vol. 1. 2006. (Avengers Ser.). (Illus.). 280p. (YA). pap. 29.99 (978-0-7851-2044-5(0)) Marvel Enterprises, Inc.

Harris, Ann Marie, ed. Short-Circuit Chef. 2006. (Teen Titans Ser.). 32p. (J). pap. 3.99 (978-0-439-78961-5(3)) Scholastic, Inc.

Harris, Christine. It Came from the Lab. 2000. (gr. 7-12). lib. bdg. 12.10 (978-0-613-28901-6(3)) Tandem Library Bks.

Harrison, Emma & Burge, Constance M. Something Wiccan This Way Comes. 2003. (Charmed Ser.). (Illus.). 224p. (YA). pap. 5.99 (978-0-689-85554-2(0) , Simon Pulse) Simon & Schuster Children's Publishing.

Hastings, Jan. Amaranthus. 2004. 200p. pap. 19.95 (978-1-4137-5110-9(5)) PublishAmerica, Inc.

Hatten, Patrick. Survival Planet: Green's World. 2002. 196p. (J). per. 6.99 (978-0-9723111-0-6(6)) Galaxsis Publishing.

Hautman, Pete. Hole in the Sky. 2005. (Illus.). 224p. (YA). reprint ed. mass mkt. 5.99 (978-0-689-84428-7(X) , Simon Pulse) Simon & Schuster Children's Publishing.

—Mr. Was. 1998. 256p. (YA). (gr. 7-12). mass mkt. 5.99 (978-0-689-81914-8(5) , Simon Pulse) Simon & Schuster Children's Publishing.

—No Limit. 2005. 224p. (YA). reprint ed. mass mkt. 5.99 (978-1-4169-0504-2(9) , Simon Pulse) Simon & Schuster Children's Publishing.

Hautman, Pete. Rash. 2007. 272p. (YA). pap. 8.99 (*978-0-689-86904-4(5) , Simon Pulse) Simon & Schuster Children's Publishing.

Hawking, Stephen & Hawking, Lucy. George's Secret Key to the Universe. Parsons, Gary, illus. 2007. 304p. (J). (gr. 3 up). 17.99 (*978-1-4169-5462-0(7)) Simon & Schuster Children's Publishing.

Hay DeSimone, Corkey. The Planet Hue. Hay DeSimone, Corkey, illus. 2003. 12.50 (978-0-9747921-0-1(1)) Gentle Giraffe Pr.

Hayahibara, Megumi & Toda, Akihito. Jigglypuff's Magic Lullaby. Himeno, Kagemaru, illus. 2000. (Pokemon Tales Ser.: No. 11). 18p. (YA). (ps-k). 4.95 (978-1-56931-442-5(X)) Viz Media.

Hearn, Julie & Yankus, Marc. Sign of the Raven. 2005. (Illus.). 336p. (YA). 16.95 (978-0-689-85734-8(9) , Atheneum) Simon & Schuster Children's Publishing.

Hearn, Lian. Across the Nightingale Floor: Journey to Inuyama. 2005. (Tales of the Otori Trilogy: Episode 2). 276p. (YA). (gr. 6-11). reprint ed. pap. 6.50 (978-0-14-240433-1(0) , Puffin) Penguin Group (USA) Inc.

—Across the Nightingale Floor: The Sword of the Warrior. 2005. (Tales of the Otori Trilogy Ser.: Episode 1). 276p. (YA). (gr. 6-11). pap. 6.50 (978-0-14-240324-2(5) , Puffin) Penguin Group (USA) Inc.

—Battle for Marnyama. 2006. (Brilliance of the Moon Ser.: Episode 1). (Illus.). 256p. (YA). (gr. 7). pap. 6.50 (978-0-14-240623-6(6) , Puffin) Penguin Group (USA) Inc.

—Scars of Victory. 2006. (Brilliance of the Moon Ser.: Episode 2). (Illus.). 320p. (YA). (gr. 7). pap. 6.50 (978-0-14-240594-9(9) , Puffin) Penguin Group (USA) Inc.

Hein, Connie L. Toliver in Time; for a Journey West: History in a Nutshell. Theobald, Denise, illus. l.t. ed. 2005. 28p. (J). lib. bdg. 17.95 (978-0-9740855-6-2(1)); per. 9.95 (978-0-9740855-7-9(X)) Still Water Publishing.

Heinberg, Allan. Sidekicks. 2006. (Young Avengers Ser.: Vol. 1). (Illus.). 144p. (YA). pap. 14.99 (978-0-7851-2018-6(1)) Marvel Enterprises, Inc.

Heller, Sarah E. Two of a Kind. Batcheller, Keith, illus. 2000. (Pokemon Junior Chapter Bks.: No. 5). 48p. (J). (ps-3). pap. 3.99 (978-0-439-15431-4(6)) Scholastic, Inc.

Hello Mars! 2005. (J). audio, cd-rom 24.95 (978-0-9771381-6-6(X)) Williams, Geoffrey T.

Henderson, J. A. Bunker 10. 2007. (Illus.). 272p. (YA). (gr. 7 up). 17.00 (*978-0-15-206240-8(8)) Harcourt Children's Bks.

Henderson, Jason & Salvaggio, Tony. Psy-Comm. 2007. (Kaplan SAT/ACT Score-Raising Manga Ser.). 192p. pap. 9.99 (*978-1-4277-5496-7(9)) Kaplan Publishing.

Henighan, Tom. Mercury Man. 2004. 200p. pap. 9.99 (978-1-55002-508-8(2)) Dundurn Group, The CAN. *Dist:* Univ. of Toronto Pr.

Hennelly, Nilsson. Rafters. 1998. (Rafters Ser.: Vol. 1). 128p. (J). (gr. 3-7). pap. 12.95 (978-1-56565-616-1(4) , 06164W, Roxbury Park Juvenile) Lowell Hse. Juvenile.

Henry. Biode. 2008. (J). (*978-0-374-30802-5(0)) Farrar, Straus & Giroux.

Herman, Gail. Friend for E T. 2002. (gr. k-3). lib. bdg. 11.25 (978-0-613-87767-1(5)) Tandem Library Bks.

—Obi-Wan's Bongo Adventure. 1999. (Illus.). 32p. (J). (978-0-439-10159-2(X)) Scholastic, Inc.

Herman, Gail & Cole, Joanna. Earthquake. Gangloff, Hope, tr. Gangloff, Hope, illus. 2003. 90p. (J). (978-0-439-42938-2(2)) Scholastic, Inc.

Hernandez, Lea. Cathedral Child. 2002. (Illus.). (YA). per. 10.95 (978-0-9709474-5-1(3)) Cyberosia Publishing.

Hinkler Books Staff, reader. Barney's Outer Space Adventure. 2004. (J). 9.99 incl. audio compact disk (978-1-86515-996-6(4)) Hinkler Bks. Pty, Ltd. AUS. *Dist:* Penton Overseas, Inc.

Hoena, B. A. & Harpster, Steve. Invaders from the Great Goo Galaxy. 2007. (Graphic Sparks Ser.). (Illus.). (J). 19.93 (978-1-59889-052-5(2)) Stone Arch Bks.

Hoffman, Mary. City of Flowers. 2005. (Illus.). 250p. (YA). (gr. 7-12). 17.95 (978-1-58234-887-2(1) , Bloomsbury Children) Bloomsbury Publishing.

—City of Masks. 2002. (Illus.). 256p. (J). (gr. 7-12). 17.95 (978-1-58234-791-2(3) , Bloomsbury Children) Bloomsbury Publishing.

—City of Stars. (Illus.). 2003. (Stravaganza Ser.: Vol. 2). 300p. (J). 17.95 (978-1-58234-839-1(1)); 2005. 464p. (YA). reprint ed. pap. 7.95 (978-1-58234-982-4(7)) Bloomsbury Publishing. (Bloomsbury Children).

—Trace in Space. (Illus.). 118p. (J). pap. 8.99 (978-0-340-62669-6(0) , Hodder & Stoughton) Hodder General Publishing Division GBR. *Dist:* Trafalgar Square Publishing.

Hoffman, Nina Kiriki. Spirits That Walk in Shadow. 2006. 320p. (YA). (gr. 7 up). 17.99 (978-0-670-06071-9(2) , Viking Juvenile) Penguin Group (USA) Inc.

Holder, Nancy. Queen of the Slayers. 2005. (Buffy the Vampire Slayer Ser.). 352p. (YA). pap. 9.99 (978-1-4169-0241-6(4) , Simon Spotlight Entertainment) Simon & Schuster.

Holt, Rinehart and Winston Staff. Anthology of Science Fiction. 2000. (Illus.). pap. 25.73 (978-0-03-052947-4(6)) Holt, Rinehart & Winston.

Homzie, H. B. & Phillips, Matt. Who Let the Dogs Out?, Vol. 2. 2002. (Alien Clones from Outer Space Ser.). 80p. (J). pap. 3.99 (978-0-689-82343-5(6) , Aladdin) Simon & Schuster Children's Publishing.

Homzie, H.B. Who Let the Dogs Out? Homzie, H.B., illus. 2002. (gr. k-3). lib. bdg. 11.80 (978-0-613-57589-8(X)) Tandem Library Bks.

Homzie, Hillary. Two Heads Are Better Than One. 2002. (gr. k-3). lib. bdg. 11.80 (978-0-613-57587-4(3)) Tandem Library Bks.

Homzie, Hillary & Phillips, Matthew. Two Heads Are Better Than One, Vol. 1. 2002. (Alien Clones from Outer Space Ser.). 80p. (J). pap. 3.99 (978-0-689-82342-8(8) , Aladdin) Simon & Schuster Children's Publishing.

Hongo, Akiyoshi. Digimon Zero Two, 2 vols., Vol. 2. 2nd rev. ed. 2004. (Illus.). 192p. pap. 9.99 (978-1-59182-668-2(3)) TOKYOPOP, Inc.

Hood, Robert. Gadgets & Gizmos. 2005. (Thrillogy Ser.). (Illus.). 48p. (gr. 4-8). 17.50 (978-0-7910-8866-1(9)) Facts On File, Inc.

—Gadgets & Gizmos. 2000. (gr. 7-12). lib. bdg. 12.10 (978-0-613-28848-4(3)) Tandem Library Bks.

Hoover, H. M. Another Heaven, Another Earth. 2002. (gr. 7-12). lib. bdg. 14.15 (978-0-613-70761-9(3)) Tandem Library Bks.

Hopkins, Cathy. Brat Princess. 2007. (Zodiac Girls Ser.). 192p. (J). (gr. 4-7). pap. 5.95 (*978-0-7534-6132-7(3) , Kingfisher) Houghton Mifflin Co. Trade & Reference Div.

—Discount Diva. 2007. (Zodiac Girls Ser.). 184p. (J). (gr. 4-7). pap. 5.95 (*978-0-7534-6131-0(5) , Kingfisher) Houghton Mifflin Co. Trade & Reference Div.

House, David James. The Key to Space. 2006. (ENM.). 364p. (YA). 24.95 (978-0-9777086-0-4(8)) House, David.

Howard, Mary. Superstition Mountain. 2003. 78p. pap. 11.95 (978-1-59129-978-3(0)) PublishAmerica, Inc.

Howe, James. Screaming Mummies of the Pharaoh's Tomb II. Helquist, Brett, illus. 2003. (Tales from the House of Bunnicula Ser.). 112p. (J). pap. 3.99 (978-0-689-83954-2(5) , Aladdin) Simon & Schuster Children's Publishing.

Hrdlitschka, Shelley. Sun Signs. 2005. 208p. (J). (gr. 7-12). pap. 7.95 (978-1-55143-338-7(9)); lib. bdg. 16.95 (978-1-55143-388-2(5)) Orca Bk. Pubs. USA.

Hubbard, L. Ron. Battlefield Earth. 2002. (gr. 7-12). lib. bdg. 16.45 (978-0-613-70670-4(6)) Tandem Library Bks.

Hubert, Jerry. They Were Not Gods: A Space-Age Fairytale. 2003. 170p. (YA). 23.95 (978-0-595-66091-9(6)); pap. 13.95 (978-0-595-29970-6(9)) iUniverse, Inc.

Hudlin, Reginald & Romita, John. Bad Mutha. 2006. (Illus.). 96p. pap. 10.99 (978-0-7851-1750-6(4)) Marvel Enterprises, Inc.

Huff, Tanya. Valor's Choice. 2000. (SPA.). (gr. 7-12). lib. bdg. 15.30 (978-0-613-28123-2(3)) Tandem Library Bks.

Huggins-Cooper, Lynn. Alien Invaders/Invasores Extraterrestres. de la Vega, Eida, tr. Leick, Bonnie, illus. 2005. Tr. of Invasores Extraterrestres. (SPA & ENG.). 32p. (J). (gr. 1-3). 16.95 (978-0-9724973-9-8(0) , 626999) Raven Tree Pr.

—Alien Invaders/Invasores Extraterrestres. Leick, Bonnie, illus. 2005. Tr. of Invasores Extraterrestres. (SPA & ENG.). 32p. (J). pap. 4.99 (978-0-9741992-7-6(3) , 626999) Raven Tree Pr.

Hughes, Carol. Toots Underground. 2001. (gr. 3-6). lib. bdg. 11.80 (978-0-613-53657-8(6)) Tandem Library Bks.

Hughes, Monica. Invitation to the Game. l.t. ed. 2001. 184p. (J). 26.95 (978-0-7838-9600-7(X) , Hall, G. K. & Co.) Thomson Gale.

—The Isis Trilogy. ed. 2006. 568p. (J). (gr. 4-7). (978-0-88776-792-0(3)) Tundra Bks., Inc./Livres Toundra, Inc. CAN. *Dist:* Random Hse., Inc.

—The Keeper of the Isis Light. 2000. Orig. Title: Summerspell. (J). (978-0-606-19715-1(X)) Tandem Library Bks.

—The Keeper of the Isis Light. l.t. ed. 2000. Orig. Title: Summerspell. (Illus.). 213p. (YA). 25.95 (978-0-7838-9295-5(0)) Thorndike Pr.

—Space Trap. (J). pap. 7.95 (978-0-88899-202-4(5)) Groundwood Bks. CAN. *Dist:* Transition Vendor.

Hunt, Gene. Accidental Space Ship. 2006. 150p. (J). (gr. 4-6). 16.95 (978-1-59354-119-4(8)) Handprint Bks.

Hunter, Erin. A Dangerous Path. 2005. (Warriors Ser.: Bk. 5). 336p. (gr. 5 up). pap. 6.99 (978-0-06-052565-1(7)) HarperCollins Pubs.

—The Lost Warrior. 2007. (Warriors Manga Ser.: No. 1). (J). (*978-0-06-124061-4(3)) HarperCollins Pubs.

Hunter, Erin. Moonrise. 2005. (Warriors Ser.: Bk. 2). (Illus.). 304p. (gr. 5 up). (J). lib. bdg. 17.89 (978-0-06-074453-3(7)); (YA). 15.99 (978-0-06-074452-6(9)) HarperCollins Pubs.

Hunter, Melanie. Dorsello's Key. 2005. 131p. pap. 19.95 (978-1-4137-6294-5(8)) PublishAmerica, Inc.

Hurd, Thacher. Moo Cow Kaboom. Hurd, Thacher, illus. unabr. ed. 2006. (Picture Book Readalong Ser.). (J). 25.95 incl. audio (978-1-59519-498-5(3)); 28.95 incl. audio compact disk (978-1-59519-502-9(5)) Live Oak Media.

Hutchins, Hazel. Sarah & the Magic Science Project. Delezenne, Christine, illus. 2005. 152p. (J). (gr. 3-6). 18.95 (978-1-55037-931-0(3)); pap. 7.95 (978-1-55037-930-3(5)) Annick Pr., Ltd. CAN. *Dist:* Firefly Bks., Ltd.

Hutchinson, Emily. The Time Machine. Hagerty, Carol, ed. 1998. (Classics Ser.: Set II). (Illus.). 77p. (YA). (gr. 5-12). pap. 7.95 (978-1-56254-279-5(6) , SP2796) Saddleback Educational Publishing.

Hyland, Tony. Film & Fiction Robots. 2007. (J). (*978-1-59920-120-7(8)) Smart Apple Media.

Iacobucci, Vincent. The Little Book All about Fluguls. ed. 2006. (Illus.). (J). (*978-0-9779390-0-8(6)) Flugul Pubng.

Imakuni, Tomoaki & Toda, Akihito. Come Out, Squirtle!, Vol. 2. Kimura, Naoyo & Himeno, Kagemaru, illus. 1999. (Pokemon Tales Ser.: No. 2). 18p. (YA). (ps-k). 4.95 (978-1-56931-384-8(9)) Viz Media.

Inagaki, Misao. Ring. 2002. (Illus.). 152p. Vol. 1. pap. (978-1-56931-789-1(5)); Vol. 2. pap. (978-1-56931-802-7(6)) Viz Media.

Into the Black Hole. 1999. (SmartReader Ser.). (J). pap., tchr. ed. 19.95 incl. audio (978-0-7887-0279-2(3) , 79319T3) Recorded Bks., LLC.

iPAM. Alien, Him. 2007. 240p. per. 15.95 (*978-0-595-45867-7(X)) iUniverse, Inc.

It Came from the Lab. 2005. (Thrillogy Ser.). (Illus.). 48p. (gr. 4-8). 17.50 (978-0-7910-8867-8(7)) Facts On File, Inc.

Jackson-Beavers, Rose, et al. A Hole in My Heart. 2004. (YA). per. 10.95 (978-0-9753634-0-9(9)) Prioritybooks Pubns.

Jackson, Paul B. Luke & Mcnashty's Treasure. 2006. 96p. pap. 14.95 (978-1-4241-2909-6(5)) PublishAmerica, Inc.

Jacques, Brian. Redwall: The Graphic Novel. Blevins, Bret, illus. 2007. (Redwall Ser.). 148p. (YA). (gr. 3 up). 12.99 (*978-0-399-24481-0(6) , Philomel) Penguin Group (USA) Inc.

Jaffe, Charlotte & Doherty, Barbara. The Space Race. 2003. (Illus.). (J). (gr. 2-3). 60.00 (978-1-57336-395-2(2) , 15077) Interaction Pubs., Inc.

Jaffe, Elizabeth. Alien Alert, Vol. 2. Steck, Jim, illus. 2005. 32p. (J). (ps-7). lib. bdg. 12.04 (978-0-606-33922-3(1)) Tandem Library Bks.

James, B. J. Supertwins Meet the Dangerous Dino-Robots. 2003. (gr. k-3). lib. bdg. 11.80 (978-0-613-72179-0(9)) Tandem Library Bks.

Janicke, Gregory. The Dark Mystery of the Shadow Beasts. 2004. (Illus.). 168p. (978-983-58-0993-4(3)) Times Edition.

Jank, Sandy Dawson. The Shimmering Ones. 2002. (gr. 7-12). lib. bdg. 20.55 (978-0-613-77909-8(6)) Tandem Library Bks.

Jansson, Tove. Moominvalley in November. Hart, Kingsley, tr. Jansson, Tove, illus. 2003. (Moomintrolls Ser.). (Illus.). 176p. (J). 17.00 (978-0-374-35013-0(2) , Farrar, Straus & Giroux (BYR)) Farrar, Straus & Giroux.

—Moominvalley in November. 2003. (gr. 5-8). lib. bdg. 14.10 (978-0-613-71871-4(2)) Tandem Library Bks.

Jeapes, Ben. The Ark. 2000. 352p. (YA). (gr. 8-12). pap. 4.99 (978-0-439-21917-4(5)) Scholastic, Inc.

—The Xenocide Mission. 400p. (gr. 7). 2004. (YA). mass mkt. 6.50 (978-0-440-23785-3(8) , Laurel Leaf); 2002. (J). 15.95 (978-0-385-75007-3(2) , Fickling, David Bks.) Random Hse. Children's Bks.

—Xenocide Mission. 2004. (gr. 7-12). lib. bdg. 14.75 (978-0-613-72334-3(1)) Tandem Library Bks.

Jenkins, Paul. Decimation: Generation M TPB: Generation M TPB. 2006. (Illus.). 120p. pap. 13.99 (978-0-7851-1958-6(2)) Marvel Enterprises, Inc.

Jinks, Catherine. Evil Genius. 2008. (Illus.). 512p. (YA). pap. 7.95 (*978-0-15-206185-2(1) , Harcourt Paperbacks) Harcourt Children's Bks.

—Evil Genius. 2007. (Illus.). 496p. (YA). (gr. 7 up). 17.00 (978-0-15-205988-0(1)); 486p. (J). (*978-1-4287-3510-1(0)) Harcourt Trade Pubs.

Johansen, K. V. The Drone War: A Cassandra Virus Novel. 2007. (Cassandra Virus Ser.). 150p. (YA). pap. 9.95 (*978-0-9739505-2-6(8)) Sybertooth Inc. CAN. *Dist:* Lightning Source, Inc.

Johns, Geoff. Rogues. rev. ed. 2003. (Flash Ser.). (Illus.). 144p. pap. 14.99 (978-1-56389-950-8(7)) DC Comics.

Johnson, Bob. The Squatland Chronicles: The Lost Mine of the Mechanical Spider. 2006. (Illus.). 56p. (J). per. 11.00 (*978-1-60002-185-5(9) , 3977, Airleaf Publishing) Airleaf Publishing & Bookselling.

Johnson, David. Trapped in Space. Liew, Sonny, illus. 2007. (J). 80p. (*978-1-59889-354-0(8)); 74p. pap. (*978-1-59889-449-3(8)) Stone Arch Bks.

Johnson, Jennifer. The Battle for the Zephyr Badge. 2001. (Pokemon Chapter Bks.: Vol. 20). (Illus.). 96p. (J). (gr. 2-7). pap. 4.50 (978-0-439-24397-1(1)) Scholastic, Inc.

Johnson, Sandi. Chip Dude from Space. Johnson, Britt, ed. Sturgen, Bobbi, illus. l.t. ed. 2002. 23p. (J). (gr. k-5). spiral bd. 5.99 (978-1-929063-81-9(4) , 254) Moons & Stars Publishing For Children.

Johnston, Antony. Rosemary's Backpack. Gilbert, Drew, illus. 2002. (YA). per. 12.95 (978-0-9709474-7-5(X)) Cyberosia Publishing.

Johse, Jill Taylor. Beyond the Third Floor. 2003. (gr. 7-12). lib. bdg. 22.20 (978-0-613-86202-8(3)) Tandem Library Bks.

—Beyond the Third Floor. 2003. 166p. (YA). pap. 12.95 (978-0-595-28006-3(4)) iUniverse, Inc.

Jolley, Dan. Alex Unlimited: The Vosarak Code. 2007. (Illus.). 224p. (YA). (gr. 8 up). pap. 7.99 (*978-1-4278-0122-7(3) , TOKYOPOP Kids) TOKYOPOP, Inc.

Jones, A. Starship. (Hunter & Moon Mystery Ser.: Vol. 5). 169p. (J). pap. 8.99 (978-0-340-70964-1(2) , Hodder & Stoughton) Hodder General Publishing Division GBR. *Dist:* Trafalgar Square Publishing.

—Thunderbolt. (Hunter & Moon Mystery Ser.: Vol. 5). (Illus.). 171p. (J). pap. 8.99 (978-0-340-70963-4(4) , Hodder & Stoughton) Hodder General Publishing Division GBR. *Dist:* Trafalgar Square Publishing.

Jones, Diana Wynne. Aunt Maria. 2003. (gr. 5-8). lib. bdg. 14.15 (978-0-613-68403-3(6)) Tandem Library Bks.

—Cart & Cwidder & Drowned Ammet, Vol. 1. 2005. (Dalemark Quartet Ser.). (Illus.). 560p. (J). (gr. 7 up). reprint ed. pap. 7.99 (978-0-06-076369-5(8)) HarperCollins Pubs.

—Hexwood. 2002. 464p. (J). (gr. 7 up). 16.99 (978-0-06-029888-3(X)) HarperCollins Pubs.

—Hexwood. 2002. (gr. 5-8). lib. bdg. 15.30 (978-0-613-68430-9(3)) Tandem Library Bks.

—Howl's Moving Castle. 2001. (gr. 5-8). lib. bdg. 15.30 (978-0-613-37151-3(8)) Tandem Library Bks.

—A Tale of Time City. 2002. 336p. (J). (gr. 5 up). 16.95 (978-0-06-029884-5(7)) HarperCollins Pubs.

—Tale of Time City. 2001. (gr. 5-8). lib. bdg. 15.25 (978-0-613-53654-7(1)) Tandem Library Bks.

Jones, Miranda. Double Trouble. Calver, David, illus. 2004. (Little Genie Ser.). 128p. (J). (gr. 1-3). 8.95 (978-0-385-73138-6(8) , Delacorte Bks. for Young Readers) Random Hse. Children's Bks.

—Make a Wish. Calver, David, illus. 2004. (Little Genie Ser.). 128p. (gr. 1-3). 8.95 (978-0-385-73137-9(X) , Delacorte Bks. for Young Readers) Random Hse. Children's Bks.

Kahn, J. Le Retour du Jedi, Vol. II.Tr. of Return of the Jedi. (FRE.). (J). pap. 11.95 (978-2-265-06728-8(8)) Fleuve Noir FRA. *Dist:* Distribooks, Inc.

Kain, Kathleen E. Acid Attack: The Science Spiders(TM) Demonstrate Acids & Bases. 1999. (Illus.). 32p. (J). (gr. k-3). pap. 5.95 (978-1-892221-07-0(1) , RW0567) Ranch Works.

—The Experience: The Science Spiders Learn Colors. 1999. (Illus.). 32p. (J). (gr. k-3). pap. 5.95 (978-1-892221-01-8(2) , RW0561) Ranch Works.

—Secret Tricks: The Science Spiders(TM) Investigate Air Pressure. 1999. (Illus.). 32p. (J). (gr. k-3). pap. 5.95 (978-1-892221-05-6(5) , RW0565) Ranch Works.

Kanan. Galaxy Angel Party, Vol. 2. 2005. (Galaxy Angel Ser.). Orig. Title: Galaxy Angel Anthology. (Illus.). 208p. pap. 9.99 (978-1-932480-27-6(7) , Broccoli Bks. Deluxe) Broccoli International USA, Inc.

Katschke, Judy. The Adventures of Astro. 2004. (Astro Boy Ser.). (Illus.). 64p. (J). pap. 4.99 (978-0-06-072528-0(1) , Harper Festival) HarperCollins Pubs.

Katz, Z. L. Aliens Are Everywhere. 2002. (gr. 3-6). lib. bdg. 11.80 (978-0-613-50402-7(X)) Tandem Library Bks.

—Back in Black. 2002. (gr. 3-6). lib. bdg. 11.80 (978-0-613-50408-9(9)) Tandem Library Bks.

Kawahara, Yumiko. Dolls. Kawahara, Yumiko, illus. (Dolls Ser.). (Illus.). (YA). 1. 2004. 200p. pap. 9.99 (978-1-59116-508-8(3)); Vol. 2. 2005. 216p. pap. 9.99 (978-1-59116-670-2(5)) Viz Media.

Kawamura, Kunimi & Toda, Akihito. Lapras Makes a Friend. Aoki, Toshinao & Himeno, Kagemaru, illus. 2000. (Pokemon Tales Ser.: No. 12). 18p. (YA). (ps-k). 4.95 (978-1-56931-443-2(8)) Viz Media.

Kaye, Marilyn. Amy, Number Seven. 1999. (Replica Ser.: No. 1). (J). (gr. 4-7). (978-0-606-15933-3(9)) Tandem Library Bks.

—And the Two Shall Meet. 1999. (Replica Ser.: No. 6). (J). (gr. 4-7). (978-0-606-16376-7(X)) Tandem Library Bks.

—Another Amy. 1999. (Replica Ser.: No. 3). (J). (gr. 4-7). (978-0-606-16003-2(5)) Tandem Library Bks.

—The Beginning. 2000. (Replica Ser.: No. 14). (gr. 3-6). lib. bdg. 12.40 (978-0-613-28251-2(5)) Tandem Library Bks.

—The Best of the Best. 1999. (Replica Ser.: No. 7). (978-0-606-16377-4(8)) Tandem Library Bks.

—The Convergence. 1999. (Last on Earth Ser.: 2). (YA). (978-0-606-16367-5(0)) Tandem Library Bks.

—The Fever. 1999. (Replica Ser.: No. 9). (J). (gr. 4-7). (978-0-606-17482-4(6)) Tandem Library Bks.

—Mystery Mother. 1999. (Replica Ser.: No. 8). (J). (gr. 4-7). (978-0-606-17481-7(8)) Tandem Library Bks.

—Perfect Girls. 1999. (Replica Ser.: No. 4). (J). (gr. 4-7). (978-0-606-16372-9(7)) Tandem Library Bks.

—Pursuing Amy. 1999. (Replica Ser.: No. 2). (J). (gr. 4-7). (978-0-606-15934-0(7)) Tandem Library Bks.

—The Return. 1999. (Last on Earth Ser.: 3). (J). (978-0-606-16368-2(9)) Tandem Library Bks.

—Secret Clique. 1999. (Replica Ser.: No. 5). (J). (gr. 4-7). (978-0-606-16373-6(5)) Tandem Library Bks.

Keaney, Brian. The Hollow People. Ceccoli, Nicoletta, illus. 2007. (Promises of Dr. Sigmundus: Bk. 1). 240p. (YA). (gr. 7-12). lib. bdg. 19.99 (*978-0-375-94332-4(3) , Knopf Bks. for Young Readers) Random Hse. Children's Bks.

—The Hollow People. 2007. (Promises of Dr. Sigmundus: Bk. 1). (Illus.). 224p. (YA). (gr. 7-12). 16.99 (*978-0-375-84332-7(9) , Knopf Bks. for Young Readers) Random Hse. Children's Bks.

Kelly, Joe. Golden Perfect. rev. ed. 2003. (Justice League Adventures Ser.: Vol. 10). (Illus.). 128p. pap. 14.99 (978-1-56389-941-6(8)) DC Comics.

Kelly, Marylee A. NoWhere Land. 2002. 136p. pap. 10.95 (978-0-595-25359-3(8) , Writers Club Pr.) iUniverse, Inc.

Kernaghan, Eileen. The Alchemist's Daughter. 2005. (Illus.). 192p. (YA). pap. 13.95 (978-1-894345-79-8(7)) Thistledown Pr., Ltd. CAN. *Dist:* Literary Pr. Group of Canada.

Kerner, Charlotte. Blueprint. Crawford, Elizabeth D., tr. from GER. 2003. (Young Adult Fiction Ser.). 192p. (YA). (gr. 9-12). 16.95 (978-0-8225-0080-3(9) , Carolrhoda Bks.) Lerner Publishing Group.

Kerr, P. B. The Akhenaten Adventure. 2005. (Children of the Lamp Ser.: 1). (Illus.). 384p. mass mkt. 2.99 (978-0-439-77135-1(8)) Scholastic, Inc.

—One Small Step. 2008. 304p. (J). 16.99 (978-1-4169-4213-9(0)) Simon & Schuster Children's Publishing.

Kesel, Barbara. Radiant, Vol. 2. Perez, George et al, illus. 2004. (Solus Ser.: Vol. 2). 160p. (YA). pap. 15.95 (978-1-59314-057-1(6)) CrossGeneration Comics, Inc.

Keyes, Daniel. Flowers for Algernon. unabr. ed. 1998. (YA). Class Set. 133.70 incl. audio (978-0-7887-2549-4(1) , 46719); Homework Set. (gr. 7). 67.24 incl. audio (978-0-7887-2244-8(1) , 40728) Recorded Bks., LLC.

Keystone Books. (Illus.). 40p. (YA). (gr. 2-3). lib. bdg. 259.09 (978-1-59889-020-4(4)) Stone Arch Bks.

King, Kristin. Project: Noah's Ark. 2005. 201p. pap. 19.95 (978-1-4137-6521-2(1)) PublishAmerica, Inc.

King-Smith, Dick. The Water Horse. Parkins, David, illus. 2000. 128p. (J). (gr. 3-5). pap. 5.50 (978-0-375-80352-9(1) , Yearling) Random Hse. Children's Bks.

King, Stephen. Long Walk. 1999. (gr. 7-12). lib. bdg. 16.45 (978-0-613-17350-6(3)) Tandem Library Bks.

Kirk, David. Nova's Ark: David Kirk's Nova the Robot. 2005. (Nova the Robot Ser.). 40p. pap. 7.99 (978-0-448-43816-0(X)) Penguin Group (USA) Inc.

Kirkman, Robert. Freedom Ring, Vol. 4. 2007. (Illus.). 168p. pap. 17.99 (978-0-7851-1990-6(6)) Marvel Enterprises, Inc.

—Marvel Zombies HC. 2006. (Illus.). 136p. 19.99 (978-0-7851-2277-7(X)) Marvel Enterprises, Inc.

Kirkman, Robert. Marvel Zombies HC (Spider-Man Cover) 2006. (Illus.). 136p. 19.99 (*978-0-7851-2608-9(2)) Marvel Enterprises, Inc.

Kitamura, Satoshi. Yo y Mi Gato? (Los Especiales de A la Orilla Del Viento Ser.). (SPA., Illus.). 36p. (J). (gr. k-3). 13.99 (978-968-16-6234-9(2) , FC30958) Fondo de Cultura Economica USA.

Kizuki, Sumiyashi & Toda, Akihito. Snorlax's Snack. Himeno, Kagemaru, illus. 2000. (Pokemon Tales Ser.: No. 10). 18p. (YA). (ps-k). 4.95 (978-1-56931-441-8(1)) Viz Media.

Klass, David. Firestorm. 2006. (Caretaker Trilogy Ser.: Bk. 1). 304p. (YA). 17.00 (978-0-374-32307-3(0) , Frances Foster Bks.) Farrar, Straus & Giroux.

—Firestorm: The Caretaker Trilogy: Book 1. 2008. (Caretaker Trilogy Ser.). 320p. (YA). pap. 8.99 (*978-0-312-38018-2(6)) Square Fish.

—Whirlwind. 2008. (Caretaker Trilogy Ser.). 304p. (YA). 17.95 (*978-0-374-32308-0(9)) Farrar, Straus & Giroux.

Klause, Annette Curtis. Alien Secrets. 1999. 240p. (YA). (gr. 5-12). mass mkt. 5.99 (978-0-440-22851-6(4) , Laurel Leaf) Random Hse. Children's Bks.

—Alien Secrets. 1999. (gr. 5-8). lib. bdg. 13.55 (978-0-613-72273-5(6)) Tandem Library Bks.

Kline, Suzy. Horrible Harry & the Purple People. 1999. (Horrible Harry Ser.: No. 8). (Illus.). (J). (gr. 2-4). pap. 3.99 (978-0-14-038223-5(2) , Puffin) Penguin Group (USA) Inc.

—Horrible Harry & the Purple People. 1999. (Horrible Harry Ser.: No. 8). (J). (gr. 2-4). pap. 30.99 incl. audio (978-0-7887-3643-8(4) , 41009) Recorded Bks., LLC.

—Horrible Harry & the Purple People. 1999. (gr. 3-6). lib. bdg. 11.80 (978-0-613-19515-7(9)) Tandem Library Bks.

Kline, Suzy & Kline, Suzy. Horrible Harry & the Purple People. Remkiewicz, Frank, illus. 1999. (Horrible Harry Ser.: No. 8). 51p. (gr. 2-4). lib. bdg. 10.79 (978-0-606-16785-7(4)) Tandem Library Bks.

Knife & Packer. Captain Fact: Space Adventure. 2004. (Illus.). 103p. (J). (*978-1-4156-0561-5(0)) Hyperion Bks. for Children.

Knife and Packer Staff. Space Adventure. 2005. (Captain Fact Ser.: Bk. 1). (Illus.). 112p. (gr. 2-5). pap. 4.99 (978-0-7868-5511-7(8) , Volo) Hyperion Bks. for Children.

Knight, Ernest C. Bean Head & the Imagination Machine. l.t. ed. 2002. (Illus.). 42p. per. 12.99 (978-0-9724680-7-7(2)) Lifevest Publishing, Inc.

Knudsen, Michelle. A Moldy Mystery. Gott, Barry, illus. 2006. 32p. (J). lib. bdg. 20.00 (*978-1-4242-1096-1(8)) Fitzgerald Bks.

Kochalka, James. Fantastic Butterflies. 2002. (Illus.). 168p. (YA). pap. 14.95 (978-1-891867-18-7(0) , JUN021979) Alternative Comics.

Koehler, Karen. The Maiden No. 1: Out of the Ashes. 2003. 248p. (gr. 4-12). pap. 15.00 (978-0-9679220-3-4(8) , Black Death Bks.) KHP Industries.

Korman, Gordon. Planet of the Nose Pickers. 2000. (gr. 3-6). lib. bdg. 11.80 (978-0-613-26612-3(9)) Tandem Library Bks.

Kostick, Conor. Epic. 384p. 2008. (J). (gr. 4-6). pap. 9.99 (*978-0-14-241159-9(0) , Puffin); 2007. (YA). (gr. 7 up). 17.99 (978-0-670-06179-2(4) , Viking Juvenile) Penguin Group (USA) Inc.

—Saga. 2008. 368p. (YA). (gr. 7). 18.99 (*978-0-670-06280-5(4) , Viking Juvenile) Penguin Group (USA) Inc.

Kowitt, Holly. Shooting Stars. 2003. (gr. k-3). lib. bdg. 11.80 (978-0-613-72168-4(3)) Tandem Library Bks.

Krulik, Nancy E. Gotcha! Gotcha Back!, No. 19. John and Wendy Staff, illus. 2006. (Katie Kazoo, Switcheroo Ser.: No. 19). 80p. (J). (gr. 2-5). pap. 3.99 (978-0-448-43768-2(6) , Grosset & Dunlap) Penguin Group (USA) Inc.

—Super Special on Thin Ice. John and Wendy Staff, illus. 2007. (Katie Kazoo, Switcheroo Ser.). 160p. (J). (gr. 2-5). pap. 4.99 (*978-0-448-44447-5(X) , Grosset & Dunlap) Penguin Group (USA) Inc.

Krulik, Nancy E. The Virus. 1999. (Lost in Space the New Journeys Ser.: Vol. 6). (Illus.). 128p. (gr. 3-7). pap. 3.99 (978-0-590-18943-9(3)) Scholastic, Inc.

Kubler, Annie, illus. Head, Shoulders, Knees & Toes ... 2003. 12p. (J). (ps). bds. 4.99 (978-0-85953-728-5(5)) Child's Play-International.

Kusaka, Hidenori. Desperado Pikachu. MATO Staff, illus. 2000. (Pokemon Adventures Ser.: Vol. 1). 206p. (YA). (gr. 4-7). pap. 13.95 (978-1-56931-507-1(8)) Viz Media.

—Legendary Pokemon. MATO Staff, illus. 2000. (Pokemon Adventures Ser.: Vol. 2). 216p. (YA). (gr. 4-7). pap. 14.95 (978-1-56931-508-8(6)) Viz Media.

—Yellow Caballero: The Seafoam Encounter. MATO Staff, illus. 2002. (Pokemon Adventures Ser.: Vol. 5). 49p. (YA). pap. 4.95 (978-1-56931-726-6(7)) Viz Media.

Kusaka, Hidenori & Ono, Toshihiro. Ghastly Ghosts, Vol. 5. MATO Staff, illus. 2000. (Pokemon Adventures Ser.: No. 5). 200p. (YA). (gr. 4-7). pap. 5.95 (978-1-56931-409-8(8)) Viz Media.

—Mysterious Mew, Vol. 1. MATO Staff, illus. 1999. (Pokemon Adventures Ser.: No. 1). 200p. (YA). (gr. 4-7). pap. 5.95 (978-1-56931-387-9(3)) Viz Media.

—The Snorlax Stop. MATO Staff, illus. 1999. (Pokemon Adventures Ser.: No. 4). 200p. (YA). (gr. 4-7). pap. 5.95 (978-1-56931-408-1(X)) Viz Media.

—Wanted Pikachu. MATO Staff, illus. 1999. (Pokemon Adventures Ser.: No. 2). 200p. (YA). (gr. 4-7). pap. 5.95 (978-1-56931-388-6(1)) Viz Media.

Kyle, Craig & Yost, Christopher. Childhood's End, Vol. 1. 2006. (Illus.). 104p. (YA) pap. 10.99 (978 0 7851-1831-2(4)) Marvel Enterprises, Inc.

La Fevers, Robin. The Forging of the Blade. 2004. (Lowthar's Blade Ser.: Bk. 1). (Illus.). 144p. (J). (gr. 2). 15.99 (978-0-525-47349-7(1) , Dutton Juvenile) Penguin Group (USA) Inc.

LaHaye, Tim & Jenkins, Jerry B. Assassins: Assignment: Jerusalem, Target: Antichrist. 1999. (Left Behind Ser.: Bk. 6). (gr. 7-12). lib. bdg. 24.60 (978-0-613-28378-6(3)) Tandem Library Bks.

—A Dangerous Plan: Race Against Time. 2002. (Left Behind Ser.: Bk. 20). (gr. 5-8). lib. bdg. 14.15 (978-0-613-57401-3(X)) Tandem Library Bks.

Land, David, et al. Star Wars Infinities: The Empire Strikes Back. Fabbri, Davide & Vecchia, Christian Della, illus. 2003. 96p. (YA). (gr. 3 up). pap. 12.95 (978-1-56971-904-6(7)) Dark Horse Comics.

Lanse, Hal W. Penelope Quagmire & the Planet of the Zombies. (J). 2004. 15.00 (978-1-893896-26-0(9)); 2002. (Illus.). (gr. 3-7). pap. 10.50 (978-1-893896-65-9(X)) ImaJinn Bks.

Lasenby, Jack. The Shaman & the Droll. 1999. (Travellers Ser.: Bk. 3). 220p. pap. 13.00 (978-1-877135-32-3(1)) Longacre Pr. NZL. *Dist:* Pacific Island Bks.

Lasky, Kathryn. The Capture. 2007. (Guardians of Ga'Hoole Ser.: Bk. 1). 240p. (J). (gr. 3-7). pap. 2.99 (*978-0-545-01034-4(9)) Scholastic, Inc.

—The First Collier. 2006. (Guardians of Ga'Hoole Ser.: Bk. 9). 208p. (J). (gr. 4-7). pap. 4.99 (978-0-439-79568-5(0) , Scholastic Paperbacks) Scholastic, Inc.

—The Rescue. 2003. (Guardians of Ga'Hoole Ser.: Bk. 3). (J). (gr. 3-6). lib. bdg. 13.00 (978-0-613-72136-3(5)) Tandem Library Bks.

—Star Split. 2001. (YA). (978-0-606-21456-8(9)) Tandem Library Bks.

Lavoie, Rejean. Des Legumes Pour Frank Einstein. Begin, Jean-Guy, illus. 2004. (Des 9 Ans. Ser.: Vol. 44). (FRE.). 120p. (J). 8.95 (978-2-89599-006-2(9)) Editions de la Paix CAN. *Dist:* World of Reading, Ltd.

Lawrence, David. El Niño Escarabajo. 2004. (SPA.). 32p. (978-84-7720-794-8(1)) Obelisco, Ediciones S.A.

Lawrence, Michael. A Crack in the Line. 2005. (Withern Rise Ser.). 352p. (J). pap. 7.99 (978-0-06-072479-5(X) , HarperTeen) HarperCollins Pubs.

—Small Eternities. (Withern Rise Ser.). 336p. 2006. (J). pap. 7.99 (978-0-06-072482-5(X) , HarperTeen); 2005. (J). 15.99 (978-0-06-072480-1(3)); 2005. (YA). 16.89 (978-0-06-072481-8(1)) HarperCollins Pubs.

—The Underwood See. 2007. (Withern Rise Ser.). 384p. (J). 16.99 (978-0-06-072483-2(8)) HarperCollins Pubs.

Lawson, Julie. White Jade Tiger. rev. ed. 2005. 168p. (YA). (gr. 3-8). reprint ed. pap., tchr. ed. 6.95 (978-0-88878-332-5(9)) Beach Holme Pubs., Ltd. CAN. *Dist:* Literary Pr. Group of Canada.

Layne, Steven L. Mergers. 2006. 200p. (YA). (gr. 5-12). 15.95 (978-1-58980-183-7(0)) Pelican Publishing Co., Inc.

—This Side of Paradise. 224p. 2005. (YA). (gr. 5-9). pap. 9.95 (978-1-58980-254-4(3)); 2004. 15.99 (978-1-58980-096-0(6)) Pelican Publishing Co., Inc.

Le Guin, Ursula K. The Eye of the Heron. 2003. 192p. (J). 5.99 (978-0-7653-4612-4(5) , Starscape) Doherty, Tom Assocs., LLC.

—The Telling. 2001. (gr. 7-12). lib. bdg. 23.40 (978-0-613-55545-6(7)) Tandem Library Bks.

Lectorum Publications Staff. ESA Inmensa Galaxia. 1999. Tr. of Gobsmacking Galaxy. (SPA.). (gr. k-3). lib. bdg. 18.75 (978-0-613-83085-0(7)) Tandem Library Bks.

Lee, Ingrid. George Most Wanted. Denis, Stephane, illus. 2005. (Orca Echoes Ser.). 64p. (J). (gr. 2-3). pap. 4.99 (978-1-55143-472-8(5)) Orca Bk. Pubs. USA.

Lee, Quinlan B. Boohbah Bibbly Bobbly Bubbles. 2005. (Boohbah Ser.). (Illus.). 25p. (J). pap. 3.99 (978-0-439-69160-4(5)) Scholastic, Inc.

Lee, Stan. Essential Silver Surfer Volume 1 TPB. 2nd ed. 2005. (Illus.). 528p. pap. 16.99 (978-0-7851-2008-7(4)) Marvel Enterprises, Inc.

Lee, Stan, et al. John Buscema. 2007. (Marvel Visionaries Ser.). (Illus.). 368p. 34.99 (978-0-7851-2161-9(7)) Marvel Enterprises, Inc.

Lee, Tanith. Indigara: Firebird Novella. 2007. 192p. (YA). (gr. 7 up). 11.99 (*978-0-14-240922-0(7) , Puffin) Penguin Group (USA) Inc.

Leeds, Jonathan M. Hyperlink. 2001. (YA). pap. (978-1-56765-064-8(3) , R693P) AMSCO Schl. Pubns., Inc.

Leinster, Murray. Space Tug. 2006. 95.99 (*978-1-4280-4342-8(X)); pap. 89.99 (*978-1-4280-4295-7(4)) Indy-Publish.com.

Leloup, Roger. Yoko Tsuno: On the Edge of Life. Spear, Luke, tr. from FRE. 2007. (Illus.). 48p. pap. 9.99 (*978-1-905460-32-8(5)) CineBook GBR. *Dist:* Biblio Distribution.

Lemieux, Jean. Toby Shoots for Infinity. Casson, Sophie, illus. 2005. 61p. (J). lib. bdg. 12.00 (*978-1-4242-1201-9(4)) Fitzgerald Bks.

L'Engle, Madeleine. A Swiftly Tilting Planet. 228p. (YA). (gr. 5 up). pap. 5.50 (978-0-8072-1495-4(7) , Listening Library) Random Hse. Audio Publishing Group.

—A Swiftly Tilting Planet. 2007. 224p. (J). 6.99 (978-0-312-36860-9(7)); pap. 6.99 (978-0-312-36856-2(9)) Square Fish.

—A Wind in the Door. 211p. (YA). (gr. 5 up). pap. 5.50 (978-0-8072-1466-4(3) , Listening Library) Random Hse. Audio Publishing Group.

—A Wind in the Door. 2007. 224p. (J). 6.99 (978-0-312-36859-3(3)); pap. 6.99 (978-0-312-36854-8(2)) Square Fish.

—A Wrinkle in Time. 2002. (J). 15.00 (978-0-7587-6754-7(4)) Book Wholesalers, Inc.

—A Wrinkle in Time, 2 vols., Set. 20.00 (978-0-89064-014-2(9)) National Assn. for Visually Handicapped.

—A Wrinkle in Time. 211p. (YA). (gr. 5 up). pap. 5.99 (978-0-8072-1460-2(4) , Listening Library) Random Hse. Audio Publishing Group.

—A Wrinkle in Time. 2007. 224p. (J). 6.99 (978-0-312-36755-8(4)); pap. 6.99 (978-0-312-36754-1(6)) Square Fish.

—A Wrinkle in Time. l.t. ed. 2005. 273p. pap. 10.95 (978-0-7862-7335-5(6) , Large Print Pr.); 1998. 208p. (J). (gr. 4-7). 24.95 (978-0-7838-8371-7(4)) Thorndike Pr.

Lennon, Joan. Questors. 2007. 368p. (J). (gr. 5-9). 16.99 (*978-1-4169-3658-9(0) , McElderry, Margaret K.) Simon & Schuster Children's Publishing.

Lente, Fred Van, et al. Untold Tales of the New Universe TPB. 2006. (Illus.). 152p. pap. 15.99 (978-0-7851-2185-5(4)) Marvel Enterprises, Inc.

Leonard, Paul & Walters, Nick. Dry Pilgrimage. 1998. (New Adventures Ser.). 292p. mass mkt. 5.95 (978-0-426-20525-8(1)) Virgin Bks. Ltd. GBR. *Dist:* London Bridge.

Levithan, David. Journey Through the Lost Canyon. 2000. (Pokemon Challenge Ser.: No. 1). 128p. (J). (gr. 4-7). pap. 5.99 (978-0-439-15407-9(3)) Scholastic, Inc.

Levy, Stuart. The Case of the Crystal Stone, 4 vols., Vol. 2. 2008. (Juvenile Favorite Ser.). (Illus.). 192p. (gr. 4-7). mass mkt. 9.99 (978-1-59182-264-6(5)) TOKYOPOP, Inc.

—Karma Club, 4 vols., Vol. 3. 2005. (Illus.). 128p. (J). (gr. 4-7). pap. 4.99 (978-1-59182-265-3(3)) TOKYOPOP, Inc.

L'Homme, Erik. Book of Stars 1: Quadehar the Sorcerer. 2006. 288p. (J). pap. 5.99 (978-0-439-53648-6(0) , Scholastic Paperbacks) Scholastic, Inc.

Libiran, L. J. Dragon Skurfers. 2002. (gr. 7-12). lib. bdg. 22.85 (978-0-613-78052-0(3)) Tandem Library Bks.

S

Liefeld, Rob, et al. Wolverine, Vol. 3. 2006. (Illus.). 112p. pap. 12.99 (978-0-7851-2065-0(3)) Marvel Enterprises, Inc.

Literature Connections English: A Wrinkle in Time, Source-Book. 2004. (gr. 6-12). (978-0-395-78351-1(8) , 2-70233) McDougal Littell Inc.

Literature Connections English: The Giver. 2004. (gr. 6-12). (978-0-395-77529-5(9) , 2-80098) McDougal Littell Inc.

Littlewood, Karin, illus. Science Fiction Stories. 2003. (Red Hot Reads Ser.). 256p. (J). (gr. 4-8). pap. 6.95 (978-0-7534-5677-4(X) , Kingfisher) Houghton Mifflin Co. Trade & Reference Div.

Lively, Penelope. A Martian in the Supermarket. Bartlett, Alison, illus. 2002. mass mkt. 8.99 (978-0-340-85569-0(X) , Coronet) Hodder General Publishing Division GBR. *Dist:* Trafalgar Square Publishing.

Lively, Penelope, et al. A Martian Comes to Stay. (Illus.). mass mkt. 8.99 (978-0-340-85568-3(1) , Coronet) Hodder General Publishing Division GBR. *Dist:* Trafalgar Square Publishing.

Lobdell, Scott & Robinson, James. X-Men: Zero Tolerance. Madureira, Joe & Yu, Leinil Francis, illus. 2000. (Marvels Finest Ser.). 336p. (J). pap. 24.95 (978-0-7851-0738-5(X) , Marvel's Finest) Marvel Enterprises, Inc.

Locke, Terry. Spencer Hurley & the Aliens: Book One: the Abduction. 2007. (Spencer Hurley & the Aliens Ser.: 1). (Illus.). 224p. (YA). 12.95 (978-0-9786940-0-5(7) , SHAB1V1E1CB) Dream Workshop Publishing Co., LLC, The.

Lockyer, John. The Lullabob: Individual Title Six-Packs. Hoit, Richard, illus. (Sails Literacy Ser.). 20p. (gr. 4 up). 27.00 (978-0-7578-0793-0(3)) Rigby Education.

Loesch, Joe. The Tuskegee Airmen: Raiders of the Skies with Buffalo Biff & Farley's Raiders. Hutchinson, Cheryl, ed. 2004. (Backyard Adventure Ser.). (Illus.). 56p. (J). bds. 16.95 incl. audio compact disk (978-1-932332-27-8(8)) Toy Box Productions.

Lofficier, Randy & Lofficier, Jean-Marc. Robonocchio. Pijuan Aragon, Miren, tr. Martiniere, Stephan, illus. 2004. (SPA.). 128p. (YA). per. 14.95 (978-1-932983-25-8(2) , Black Coat Pr.) HollywoodComics.com, LLC.

Lojeski, Lynne & O'Donnell, Thomas. Sneak Force, Mission Infinity: The Legend. 2004. (J). lib. bdg. 28.95 (978-1-932303-17-9(0)) Media Creations, Inc.

Longyear, Barry B. The Homecoming. 2002. 146p. pap. 12.95 (978-0-595-21309-2(X) , Backinprint.com) iUniverse, Inc.

Lorimer, Janet. Bugged! 2001. (PageTurner Science Fiction Ser.). 80p. (YA). per. 3.95 (978-1-56254-130-9(7) , SP 1307) Saddleback Educational Publishing.

—Bugged! 2001. (gr. 7-12). lib. bdg. 11.80 (978-0-613-34096-0(5)) Tandem Library Bks.

—A Deadly Game. 2001. (PageTurner Spy Ser.). 80p. (YA). per. 3.95 (978-1-56254-136-1(6) , SP 1366) Saddleback Educational Publishing.

—Flashback. 2001. (PageTurner Science Fiction Ser.). 80p. (YA). per. 3.95 (978-1-56254-132-3(3) , SP 1323) Saddleback Educational Publishing.

—Flashback. 2001. (gr. 7-12). lib. bdg. 11.80 (978-0-613-34211-7(9)) Tandem Library Bks.

—Murray's Nightmare. 2001. (PageTurner Science Fiction Ser.). 80p. (YA). per. 3.95 (978-1-56254-133-0(1) , SP 1331) Saddleback Educational Publishing.

—Murray's Nightmare. 2001. (gr. 7-12). lib. bdg. 11.80 (978-0-613-34374-9(3)) Tandem Library Bks.

Lovhaug, Lewis J. Angel Armor: The Cassandra Conflict. 2004. 188p. (YA). pap. 13.95 (978-0-595-30869-9(4)) iUniverse, Inc.

Lowachee, Karin. War Child. 2002. (gr. 3-6). lib. bdg. 15.30 (978-0-613-52925-9(1)) Tandem Library Bks.

Lowenstein, Sallie. Evan's Voice. 1998. (Illus.). 192p. (YA). (gr. 6-12). pap. 15.00 (978-0-9658486-1-9(2)) Lion Stone Bks.

Lowry, Lois. Gathering Blue. 2000. (Illus.). 224p. (YA). (gr. 7 up). 16.00 (978-0-618-05581-4(9) , Mariner Bks.) Houghton Mifflin Co. Trade & Reference Div.

—Gathering Blue. (YA). (gr. 7). 2006. 240p. pap. 8.95 (978-0-385-73256-7(2) , Delacorte Bks. for Young Readers); 2005. 224p. mass mkt. 6.99 (978-0-553-49478-5(3) , Bantam Bks. for Young Readers); 2002. 224p. mass mkt. 6.50 (978-0-440-22949-0(9) , Laurel Leaf) Random Hse. Children's Bks.

—Gathering Blue. 2002. (gr. 5-8). lib. bdg. 14.75 (978-0-613-57593-5(8)) Tandem Library Bks.

—Gathering Blue. l.t. ed. 2000. 256p. (J). (gr. 8-12). 22.95 (978-0-7862-3048-8(7)) Thorndike Pr.

—The Giver. 2002. (EMC Masterpiece Series Access Editions). xvi, 202p. (J). 10.95 (978-0-8219-2406-8(0) , 35362) EMC/Paradigm Publishing.

—The Giver. 180p. (gr. 5 up). (YA). pap. 5.99 (978-0-8072-8314-1(2)); 2004. (J). pap. 38.00 incl. audio (978-0-8072-8313-4(4) , YA159SP) Random Hse. Audio Publishing Group. (Listening Library).

—The Giver. (YA). (gr. 7). 2006. 208p. pap. 8.95 (978-0-385-73255-0(4) , Delacorte Bks. for Young Readers); 2002. 208p. mass mkt. 6.50 (978-0-440-23768-6(8) , Laurel Leaf); 1999. 192p. mass mkt. 7.50 (978-0-553-57133-2(8) , Bantam Bks. for Young Readers) Random Hse. Children's Bks.

—The Giver. 2002. (gr. 7-12). lib. bdg. 14.75 (978-0-613-72266-7(3)) Tandem Library Bks.

—The Giver. l.t. ed. 2004. 226p. pap. 10.95 (978-0-7862-7153-5(1) , Large Print Pr.); 23.95 (978-0-7862-7154-2(X)) Thorndike Pr.

—Messenger. 2004. 176p. (YA). (gr. 7 up). tchr. ed. 16.00 (978-0-618-40441-4(4) , Walter Lorraine) Houghton Mifflin Co. Trade & Reference Div.

—Messenger. 2006. (YA). 192p. (gr. 7). pap. 8.95 (978-0-385-73253-6(8) , Delacorte Bks. for Young Readers); 176p. pap. 6.50 (978-0-440-23912-3(5) , Laurel Leaf) Random Hse. Children's Bks.

—Messenger. l.t. ed. 2004. 184p. 23.95 (978-0-7862-6686-9(4) , Large Print Pr.) Thorndike Pr.

—Passeur. pap. 22.95 (978-2-211-02166-1(2)) Archimede Editions FRA. *Dist:* Distribooks, Inc.

Lubbert, Constance L. True Colors. 2000. 328p. (YA). pap. 15.95 (978-0-595-14530-0(2)) iUniverse, Inc.

Lucas, ed. Star Wars Balance of the Force: Big Best Book to Color. 2005. (Big Best Book to Color Ser.). (Illus.). 80p. (J). pap. 2.99 (978-1-4037-1204-2(2)) Dalmatian Pr.

—Star Wars Beware of the Dark Side: Bright Idea Book to Color. rev. ed. 2005. (Bright Idea Book to Color Ser.). (Illus.). 32p. (J). 4.49 (978-1-4037-1290-5(5)) Dalmatian Pr.

—Star Wars Droids: Sticker Book to Color. 2005. (Illus.). 32p. (J). pap. 2.99 (978-1-4037-1392-6(8)) Dalmatian Pr.

—Star Wars Episode III: Power of the Empire. rev. ed. 2005. (Illus.). 400p. (J). 5.99 (978-1-4037-1283-7(2)) Dalmatian Pr.

—Star Wars Sticker Book Asst: In a Galaxy Far Far Away. 2005. (Illus.). 32p. (J). pap. 2.99 (978-1-4037-1003-1(1)) Dalmatian Pr.

Lucas, George. La Guerre des Etoiles, Tome 1.Tr. of Star Wars. (FRE.). (J). pap. 11.95 (978-2-265-06730-1(X)) Fleuve Noir FRA. *Dist:* Distribooks, Inc.

—Return of the Jedi. 1999. (Star Wars Manga Ser.: No. 4). 96p. (J). (gr. 3 up). pap. 9.95 (978-1-56971-397-6(9)); pap. 9.95 (978-1-56971-396-9(0)); pap. 9.95 (978-1-56971-395-2(2)); pap. 9.95 (978-1-56971-394-5(4)) Dark Horse Comics.

Luckett, Dave. Girl the Queen & the Castle. 2004. (Rhianna Ser.: No. 3). 144p. (J). pap. 4.99 (978-0-439-41189-9(0) , Scholastic Paperbacks) Scholastic, Inc.

Lunn, John. The Aquanauts. 2005. 228p. (J). (gr. 6-9). pap. 8.95 (978-0-88776-727-2(3)) Tundra Bks., Inc./Livres Toundra, Inc. CAN. *Dist:* Random Hse., Inc.

—The Mariner's Curse. 2004. (gr. 3-6). lib. bdg. 18.75 (978-0-613-77349-2(7)) Tandem Library Bks.

Lupini, Valerie Rolfe. The Whistle. 2005. 200p. (J). (gr. 4-8). pap. 7.95 (978-0-88995-314-7(7)) Red Deer Pr. CAN. *Dist:* Fitzhenry & Whiteside, Ltd.

Lusted, Marcia Amidon. Time's Passage. 2000. (gr. 7-12). lib. bdg. 19.90 (978-0-613-84093-4(3)) Tandem Library Bks.

—Time's Passage. 2000. 172p. (YA). (gr. 7-12). pap. 10.95 (978-0-595-13882-1(9)) iUniverse, Inc.

Luther, John & Novak. Existenz. 235p. (978-0-671-03308-8(5) , Free Pr.) Simon & Schuster.

Lyons, Suzanne. Pete Discovers Gravity. ed. 2003. (Early Connections Ser.). (J). pap. 35.00 (978-1-4108-1559-0(5)) Benchmark Education Co.

Ma, Jyoti. Sparkling Together: Starbright & His Earthling Friends. Devi, Chandra, illus. 2004. 96p. pap. 19.95 (978-0-932040-54-1(3)) Integral Yoga Pubns.

Ma, Wing Shing. Black Leopard, Vol. 1. 2005. (Illus.). 160p. (YA). pap. 14.95 (978-1-58899-333-5(7)) ComicsOne Corp./Dr. Masters.

Macan, Darko, et al. Vader's Quest. (Star Wars Ser.). (Illus.). 96p. (YA). (gr. 7 up). pap. 11.95 (978-1-56971-415-7(0)) Dark Horse Comics.

Macaulay, David. The Way We Work. 2006. (Illus.). 352p. (J). 40.00 (978-0-618-23378-6(4) , Walter Lorraine) Houghton Mifflin Co. Trade & Reference Div.

Macaw, Grant. Vigil's End: Book One of the Ninth Day of Man. 2005. 310p. (YA). (gr. 7). pap. 11.95 (978-1-933255-13-2(7)) DNA Pr.

MacHado, Ana Maria. Un Deseo Loco. (Torre de Papel Ser.). (SPA.). (YA). (gr. 6 up). 8.95 (978-958-04-4529-6(X) , NR30565) Norma S.A. COL. *Dist:* Distribuidora Norma, Inc., Lectorum Pubns., Inc.

—From Another World. Baeta, Luisa, tr. from POR. Brandao, Lucia, illus. 2005. 128p. (J). 15.95 (978-0-88899-597-1(0)) Groundwood Bks. CAN. *Dist:* Perseus Distribution.

MacHale, D. J. Pendragon: The Merchant of Death; the Lost City of Faar; the Never War. 2004. (Pendragon Ser.: Bks. 1-3). (Illus.). 1136p. (J). 15.95 (978-0-689-03808-2(9) , Aladdin) Simon & Schuster Children's Publishing.

—The Reality Bug, Vol. 4. 2003. (Pendragon Ser.: Bk. 4). 384p. pap. 6.99 (978-0-7434-3734-9(9) , Aladdin) Simon & Schuster Children's Publishing.

Mackel, Kathy. Can of Worms. 2000. (Illus.). (J). 10.64 (978-0-606-17962-1(3)); 1999. (gr. 3-6). lib. bdg. 11.80 (978-0-613-23590-7(8)) Tandem Library Bks.

—Eggs in One Basket. (J). 2002. 208p. pap. 6.99 (978-0-380-81399-5(8)); 2000. (Illus.). 195p. (gr. 5-7). 15.95 (978-0-380-97847-2(4)) HarperCollins Pubs.

—From the Horse's Mouth. 2002. 224p. (J). (gr. 3-7). 15.95 (978-0-06-029414-4(0)) HarperCollins Pubs.

Madronero, Ester. La Bruja Colorea. 5th ed. 2000. (SPA., Illus.). 36p. (J). (ps-k). 6.95 (978-84-241-5972-6(1)) Everest de Ediciones y Distribucion, S.L. ESP. *Dist:* Lectorum Pubns., Inc.

Magnificent Staff. The Road to Paradise. Clouche, Armelle, ed. Heyer, Marilee, illus. 2000. 88p. (J). (gr. 4-7). 16.95 (978-0-615-11546-7(2)) Armelle Prod.

Magrs, Paul. Sick Building. 2007. 256p. (***978-1-84607-269-7(7)***) Random Hse.

Major, David L. The Day of the Nefilim. 2002. 343p. (YA). pap. (978-0-9579858-9-6(4)) Metropolis Ink.

Malley, Gemma. The Declaration. 2007. 320p. (J). (gr. 5 up). 16.95 (***978-1-59990-119-0(6)***) Bloomsbury Publishing.

Mantlo, Bill, et al. Champions Classic, Vol. 2. 2007. (Illus.). 216p. pap. 19.99 (978-0-7851-2098-8(X)) Marvel Enterprises, Inc.

Manzi, Edward Reynolds. The Time Trav-lrz: Tanya Takes Room 215. 2003. 156p. (YA). pap. 13.95 (978-1-58736-177-7(9) , Starbound Bks.) Wheatmark.

Margolis, Dawn. Men in Black: Official Agents' Handbook. 2004. (Illus.). 64p. (gr. 4-7). 5.00 (978-1-55704-345-0(0)) Newmarket Pr.

Marino, Ricardo. En el Ultimo Planeta. 2002. (SPA.). 184p. (J). pap. 11.95 (978-1-4000-0034-0(3)) Random Hse., Inc.

Marley, Louise. Singer in the Snow. 2007. (Firebird Ser.). 320p. (YA). pap. 7.99 (978-0-14-240748-6(8) , Puffin) Penguin Group (USA) Inc.

Marois, André. Les Voleurs d'Espoir. 2001. (Roman + Ser.). (FRE.). 160p. (YA). (gr. 8). pap. (978-2-89021-540-5(7)) Diffusion du livre Mirabel.

Marsden, John. Out of Time. 2007. 128p. (YA). 6.99 (978-0-7653-5303-0(2) , Tor Teen) Doherty, Tom Assocs., LLC.

Martin, Gary & Pennebaker, H. I. Professor Tyme's Timeless Tales: Revenge of the Sargasso Sea Ogre. 2006. (ENG.). 160p. per. 19.95 (***978-1-4241-5701-3(3)***) PublishAmerica, Inc.

Marz, Ron & Robinson, James. Wildstorm Rising. 1999. (Orig.). (YA). pap. 19.95 (978-1-56389-588-3(9)) DC Comics.

Maselli, Christopher P. N. Escape from Jungle Island. 1998. (Commander Kellie & the Superkids' Early Adventures Ser.). (J). pap. (978-1-57562-217-0(3)) Copeland, Kenneth Pubns.

—In Pursuit of the Enemy. 1998. (Commander Kellie & the Superkids' Early Adventures Ser.). (J). pap. (978-1-57562-218-7(1)) Copeland, Kenneth Pubns.

—The Mysterious Presence. 1998. (Commander Kellie & the Superkids' Early Adventures Ser.). pap. (978-1-57562-215-6(7)) Copeland, Kenneth Pubns.

—The Quest for the Second Half. 1998. (Commander Kellie & the Superkids' Early Adventures Ser.). (J). pap. (978-1-57562-216-3(5)) Copeland, Kenneth Pubns.

Mashima, Hiro. En Espanol, Vol. 5. 2006. (SPA., Illus.). 192p. reprint ed. pap. 10.95 (978-1-59497-179-2(X)) Public Square Bks.

—Rave Master. 2006. (SPA., Illus.). reprint ed. Vol. 7. 200p. pap. 10.95 (978-1-59497-199-0(4)); Vol. 8. 186p. pap. 10.95 (978-1-59497-200-3(1)); Vol. 9. 192p. pap. 10.95 (978-1-59497-201-0(X)) Public Square Bks.

—Rave Master (En Español) 2006. (SPA., Illus.). reprint ed. Vol. 1. 192p. pap. 10.95 (978-1-59497-175-4(7)); Vol. 2. 192p. pap. 10.95 (978-1-59497-176-1(5)); Vol. 3. 184p. pap. 10.95 (978-1-59497-177-8(3)); Vol. 4. 192p. pap. 10.95 (978-1-59497-178-5(1)); Vol. 6. 200p. pap. 10.95 (978-1-59497-180-8(3)) Public Square Bks.

Mason, Jane & Stephens, Sarah. Obi-Wan's Foe. Edwards, Tommy Lee, illus. 2005. (Star Wars Ser.). 48p. (J). (gr. 2-5). pap. 3.99 (978-0-375-82609-2(2) , LucasBooks for Young Readers) Random Hse. Children's Bks.

Masters, Anthony. The Desert Pirates. Buckley, Harriet, illus. 2008. (J). pap. (***978-1-59889-906-1(6)***); lib. bdg. (***978-1-59889-870-5(1)***) Stone Arch Bks.

Matas, Carol. More Minds. 1998. (978-0-606-13622-8(3)) Tandem Library Bks.

—Of Two Minds. 1998. (978-0-606-13672-3(X)) Tandem Library Bks.

Mattern, Joanne. Batter Up! 2005. 40.00 (***978-1-4108-4193-3(6)***) Benchmark Education Co.

Matthews, Steve. Brain-in-A-Box. 1999. (gr. 3-6). lib. bdg. 12.60 (978-0-613-19342-9(3)) Tandem Library Bks.

Maupin Schmid, Susan. Lost Time. 2008. 224p. (J). (gr. 5-8). 16.99 (***978-0-399-24460-5(3)*** , Philomel) Penguin Group (USA) Inc.

Mazer, Anne. The Oxboy. 2000. 112p. reprint ed. pap. 6.95 (978-0-89255-240-5(9)) Persea Bks., Inc.

—The Oxboy. 2000. (YA). (978-0-606-19473-0(8)) Tandem Library Bks.

McBride, Earvin, Jr. The Blockheads from Planet Ecto. 2nd unabr. ed. 2003. (Earvin MacBride's Amazing Sci-Fi & Adventure Heroes Ser.). (Illus.). 41p. (YA). (gr. 7-12). pap. 4.95 (978-1-892511-10-2(X) , Disposition Sketch Bks.) MacBride, E. J. Pubn., Inc.

McCaffrey, Anne. Dragonsinger. 2003. (Harper Hall Trilogy: Vol. 2). (gr. 7-12). lib. bdg. 15.30 (978-0-613-66494-3(9)) Tandem Library Bks.

—Dragonsong. 2006. (Harper Hall Trilogy: Vol. 1). 208p. (J). pap. 2.99 (978-1-4169-2499-9(X) , Aladdin) Simon & Schuster Children's Publishing.

—Freedom's Ransom. 2003. (gr. 7-12). lib. bdg. 15.30 (978-0-613-59808-8(3)) Tandem Library Bks.

—The Masterharper of Pern. 1999. (Pern Ser.). (gr. 7-12). lib. bdg. 15.30 (978-0-613-37699-0(4)) Tandem Library Bks.

—The Tower & the Hive. 2000. (gr. 7-12). lib. bdg. 15.30 (978-0-613-28107-2(1)) Tandem Library Bks.

McCall, Bruce. Marveltown Forever. 2008. (J). (***978-0-374-39925-2(5)***) Farrar, Straus & Giroux.

McClain, Lee. My Alternate Life. 2004. (YA). mass mkt. 5.99 (978-0-8439-5451-7(5)) Dorchester Publishing Co., Inc.

McIntyre, Vonda N. Nautilus. (Illus.). (YA). mass mkt. (978-0-671-03683-6(1) , Pocket) Simon & Schuster.

—Starfarers. (Illus.). (YA). mass mkt. (978-0-671-03681-2(5) , Pocket) Simon & Schuster.

McKay, Amanda. Not Sally Marshall Again! 2000. 200p. (J). pap. 12.95 (978-0-7022-3169-8(X)) Univ. of Queensland Pr. AUS. *Dist:* International Specialized Bk. Services.

McKeever, Sean. Doom with a View. 2007. 21.35 (978-1-59961-208-9(9)) Spotlight.

—Sentinel Vol. 3: Past Imperfect Digest. 2006. (Illus.). 120p. pap. 7.99 (978-0-7851-1914-2(0)) Marvel Enterprises, Inc.

McKinley, Robin. Dragonhaven. 2007. 342p. (J). (gr. 5 up). 17.99 (***978-0-399-24675-3(4)*** , Putnam Juvenile) Penguin Group (USA) Inc.

McKinney, Brandon, illus. Star Wars - Episode II: Attack of the Clones. 2002. (Star Wars Ser.). 348p. 9.95 (978-0-8118-3418-6(2)) Chronicle Bks. LLC.

McKinty, Adrian. The Lighthouse War. 2007. 403p. (J). (gr. 7-17). 16.95 (***978-0-8109-9354-9(6)***) Abrams, Harry N. , Inc.

McNaughton, Janet. The Secret under My Skin. (J). 2006. 368p. pap. 6.99 (978-0-06-008991-7(1)); 2005. 272p. (gr. 7 up). 15.99 (978-0-06-008989-4(X)); 2005. 272p. (gr. 7 up). lib. bdg. 16.89 (978-0-06-008990-0(3)) HarperCollins Pubs.

McOmber, Rachel B., ed. McOmber Phonics Storybooks: Tale of the Green Glob. rev. ed. (Illus.). (J). (978-0-944991-65-7(3)) Swift Learning Resources.

McPhail, David M. Tinker & Tom & the Star Baby. 2000. (Illus.). 32p. (J). (ps-3). pap. 5.95 (978-0-316-56389-5(7)) Little Brown & Co.

—Tinker & Tom & the Star Baby. McPhail, David M., illus. 1998. (Illus.). 32p. (J). (ps-3). 14.95 (978-0-316-56349-9(8)) Little Brown & Co.

Mears, Richard Chase. Saint Nick & the Space Nicks. Westerfield, William Stephen, illus. l.t. ed. 2004. 32p. 16.95 (978-0-9754056-0-4(8)) Tuxedo Blue, LLC.

Medina, Rick. Humaliens: Lexicon's Mission. 1999. 150p. (J). (gr. 4-7). pap. 4.99 (978-1-892587-00-8(9)) Dualstar, Inc.

—Humaliens Vol. 2: The Clone Formula. 1999. 150p. (J). (gr. 4-7). pap. 4.99 (978-1-892587-01-5(7)) Dualstar, Inc.

Meehan, William. Amulets of Acacia. 2003. 184p. pap. 13.95 (978-0-595-27163-4(4)) iUniverse, Inc.

Meredith Books Staff & Forlini, Victoria, eds. Batman Begins Color & Activity Book with Paints: Fighting for Justice. 2005. (ENG.). 32p. (J). pap., act. bk. ed. 3.99 (978-0-696-22394-5(5)) Meredith Bks.

—The Sweet Treats Contest: Deluxe Sound Storybook. 2004. (Strawberry Shortcake Ser.). (ENG., Illus.). 22p. (J). (gr. k-3). 15.95 (978-0-696-22242-9(6)) Meredith Bks.

Metzger, Joanna. The Space Program. Elizalde, Marcelo, illus. 2006. 142p. (J). (978-1-59336-695-7(7)) Mondo Publishing.

Michaels, Bill. Meowth, the Big Mouth. Batcheller, Keith, illus. 2000. (Pokemon Junior Chapter Bks.: No. 2). 48p. (J). (ps-3). pap. 3.99 (978-0-439-15417-8(0)) Scholastic, Inc.

—Surf's up, Pikachu! Batcheller, Keith, illus. 2000. (Pokemon Junior Chapter Bks.: No. 1). 48p. (J). (ps-3). pap. 3.99 (978-0-439-15405-5(7)) Scholastic, Inc.

Michaels, Bill & West, Tracey. Bulbasaur's Bad Day. Batcheller, Keith, illus. 2000. (Pokemon Junior Chapter Bks.: No. 4). 48p. (J). (ps-3). pap. 3.99 (978-0-439-15427-7(8)) Scholastic, Inc.

Michalowski, Mark. Wetworld. 2007. 256p. (***978-1-84607-271-0(9)***) Random Hse.

Michelinie, David, et al. Freemind - The Origin. 2003. (Freemind Ser.). (Illus.). 112p. 14.95 (978-0-9744225-0-3(9)) Future Comics.

Mick Morris Myth Solver #3 Champ... A Wave of Terror! Five Ways to Finish. 2006. (J). mass mkt. 6.99 (***978-0-9774119-2-4(3)*** , Five Ways to Finish) Team B Creative LLC.

Milam, Mary Kay. The Zooming Star Babies. Date not set. (J). pap. (978-1-890622-65-7(6)) Leathers Publishing.

Milky, D. J. Karma Club, 4 vols., Vol. 1. 2007. (Juvenile Favorite Ser.). (Illus.). 184p. (gr. 2-8). pap. 9.99 (978-1-59182-263-9(7) , Tokyopop Kids) TOKYOPOP, Inc.

Millar, Mark. Ultimate Fantastic Four Volume 5: Crossover TPB: Crossover TPB. 2006. (Illus.). 144p. pap. 12.99 (978-0-7851-1802-2(0)) Marvel Enterprises, Inc.

—Ultimate X-Men: The Tomorrow People. 2002. (gr. 5-8). lib. bdg. 24.55 (978-0-613-53690-5(8)) Tandem Library Bks.

Millar, Mark & Romita, John. Enemy of the State, Vol. 2. 2006. (Illus.). 176p. pap. 16.99 (978-0-7851-1627-1(3)) Marvel Enterprises, Inc.

Miller, Wiley. The Extraordinary Adventures of Ordinary Basil: The Impossible Flight to Helios. 2006. (Illus.). 128p. (J). pap. 14.99 (978-0-439-85665-2(5) , Blue Sky Pr., The) Scholastic, Inc.

Miller, Wiley. The Extraordinary Adventures of Ordinary Basil Vol. 2: Island of the Volcano Monkeys. 2008. (Extraordinary Adventures of Ordinary Bas Ser.). 128p. (J). pap. 14.99 (***978-0-439-86132-8(2)*** , Blue Sky Pr., The) Scholastic, Inc.

Miller, Wray. Cerulean Blue. 2003. 506p. (YA). per. 18.95 (978-0-9723948-1-9(8)) MillerWrite, Inc.

Milliron, Kerry. Podracing Book Plus Magnets. 2000. (J). 8.99 (978-0-375-80522-6(2) , Random Hse. Bks. for Young Readers) Random Hse. Children's Bks.

Mills, Eva. Simon & the Aliens. 1999. (gr. 3-6). lib. bdg. 12.60 (978-0-613-30734-5(8)) Tandem Library Bks.

Mindler, Jason. Giralon. 2003. 122p. (YA). 20.95 (978-0-595-74854-9(6)); pap. 10.95 (978-0-595-28581-5(3)) iUniverse, Inc. (Writers Club Pr.).

Mission of the Artist. 2000. 361p. pap. 12.95 (978-0-9700181-0-6(X)) Cordova, Barbara Joy.

Mitchell, N. J. W. Hannah, the Witch, & the Unicorn: A Sequel to the Adventures of Princess Nightshade & Fuzbud & the Wizard. 2002. 154p. (J). pap. 11.95 (978-0-595-21186-9(0) , Writer's Showcase Pr.) iUniverse, Inc.

Mizobuchi, Makoto & Uemaya, Michiro. Zoids New Century. 2002. (Zoids Ser.). (Illus.). 200p. (YA). pap. 9.95 (978-1-56931-786-0(0)) Viz Media.

Mlynowski, Sarah. Bras & Broomsticks. 2006. 320p. (YA). (gr. 7). reprint ed. pap. 8.95 (978-0-385-73184-3(1) , Delacorte Bks. for Young Readers) Random Hse. Children's Bks.

Modesitt, L. E., Jr. Gravity Dreams. 2000. (gr. 7-12). lib. bdg. 15.30 (978-0-613-27861-4(5)) Tandem Library Bks.

Moench, Doug, et al. Essential Moon Knight, Vol. 1. 2006. (Illus.). 536p. pap. 16.99 (978-0-7851-2092-6(0)) Marvel Enterprises, Inc.

Moesta, Rebecca. Vader's Fortress. 1999. (Star Wars Ser.: No. 5). (978-0-606-14362-2(9)) Tandem Library Bks.

Mohr, L. C. Krumbuckets. 2008. (Illus.). 144p. (J). per. 8.95 (978-0-9769417-4-7(5)) Blooming Tree Pr.

—Krumbuckets. Musheno, Erica, illus. 2007. 144p. (J). (gr. 2-7). 13.95 (978-0-9769417-6-7(7)) Blooming Tree Pr.

Moloney, James. The Scorpion's Tail. 2005. (Doomsday Rats Ser.: Bk. 2). 192p. 14.95 (978-0-207-19666-9(4) , Angus & Robertson) HarperCollins Pubs. AUS. *Dist:* Consortium Bk. Sales & Distribution.

Monda, Joseph, creator. The Unnaturals. 2007. (Illus.). 32p. (YA). 3.00 (***978-0-615-15138-0(8)***) Wild Mind Creations.

Montgomery, R. A. Beyond Escape. 2007. (Choose Your Own Adventure Ser.: No. 15). (Illus.). 144p. (J). mass mkt. 5.99 (978-1-933390-15-4(8) , CHCL15) Chooseco LLC.

—Beyond Escape. 2005. (Illus.). 118p. (J). pap. (***978-0-7608-9703-4(4)***) Sundance/Newbridge Educational Publishing.

—Escape. 2005. (Illus.). 127p. (J). pap. (***978-0-7608-9696-9(8)***) Sundance/Newbridge Educational Publishing.

—Forecast from Stonehenge. 2007. (Choose Your Own Adventure Ser.: No. 19). (Illus.). 144p. (J). mass mkt. 6.99 (***978-1-933390-19-2(0)***) Chooseco LLC.

—Prisoner of the Ant People. 2006. (Choose Your Own Adventure Ser.: No. 10). (Illus.). 144p. (J). mass mkt. 5.99 (978-1-933390-10-9(7) , CHCL10) Chooseco LLC.

—Space & Beyond. 2006. (Choose Your Own Adventure Ser.: No. 3). (Illus.). 144p. (J). mass mkt. 5.99 (978-1-933390-03-1(4) , CHCL03) Chooseco LLC.

—War with the Evil Power Master. 2006. (Choose Your Own Adventure Ser.: No. 12). (Illus.). 144p. (J). mass mkt. 5.99 (978-1-933390-12-3(3) , CHCL12) Chooseco LLC.

—War with the Evil Power Master. 2005. (Illus.). 123p. (J). pap. (***978-0-7608-9700-3(X)***) Sundance/Newbridge Educational Publishing.

Morden, Simon. The Lost Art. 2008. 528p. (J). (gr. 7). lib. bdg. 19.99 (***978-0-385-75148-3(6)*** , Fickling, David Bks.) Random Hse. Children's Bks.

Mordenga, Michael P. Spirit Box. 2007. 280p. per. 17.95 (***978-0-595-43785-6(0)***) iUniverse, Inc.

Moreau, Chris. The Professor's Telescope. Marek, Jane, illus. 2006. (YA). 10.95 (978-0-9785399-0-0(7)); cd-rom 7.95 (978-0-9785399-2-4(3)) Windows of Discovery.

Morris, Gilbert. City of the Cyborgs, Vol. 4. 2000. (Seven Sleepers the Lost Chronicles Ser.: Vol. 4). (Illus.). 144p. (J). (gr. 7-12). pap. 5.99 (978-0-8024-3670-2(6)) Moody Pubs.

—Savage Game of Lord Zarak, Vol. 2. 2000. (Seven Sleepers the Lost Chronicles Ser.: Vol. 2). (Illus.). 160p. (J). (gr. 7-12). pap. 5.99 (978-0-8024-3668-9(4)) Moody Pubs.

—Terrible Beast of Zor. 2000. (gr. 3-6). lib. bdg. 14.15 (978-0-613-88615-4(1)) Tandem Library Bks.

Morse, Scott. Day I Tried to Live, Bk. 2. 2000. (Soulwind Ser.: Vol. 2). (Illus.). 104p. (YA). pap. 8.50 (978-0-9667127-6-6(5)) Oni Pr., Inc.

Morvan, Jean-David. Artifice/Maximum (in)Security, 67 vols. Buchet, Philippe, illus. 2005. 96p. pap. 14.95 (978-1-56163-420-0(4)) NBM Publishing Co.

Mueller, Richard. Zoonauts: The Secret of Animalville. Gosline, Sheldon, ed. Dal Chele, Egido Victor, illus. 2003. 210p. (J). 14.95 (978-0-9719496-6-9(2)) Shangri-La Pubns.

Munzel, Alexander. Allí Donde Florece el Cardo Sagrado/ Where the Holy Thistle Blooms. 2003. (SPA., Illus.). 196p. (J). per. (978-0-9672566-2-7(3)) Technical Software, Inc.

Myers, Bill. My Life as a Human Hairball, Vol. 15. 1998. (Incredible Worlds of Wally McDoogle Ser.: No. 15). 128p. (J). (gr. 3-7). pap. 6.99 (978-0-8499-4024-8(9)) Nelson, Thomas Inc.

Nelson, O. T. The Girl Who Owned a City. unabr. ed. 1998. (J). (gr. 7). 50.75 incl. audio (978-0-7887-2664-4(1) , 40824) Recorded Bks., LLC.

Nerz, A. Ryan. Invasion of the Black Gears! 2000. (Digimon Ser.: No. 2). (Illus.). 96p. (J). (gr. 4-7). pap. 4.50 (978-0-06-107187-4(0) , Harper Entertainment) HarperCollins Pubs.

Nettrour, Nelani. Nunkey's Adventures, Bk. 1. Nettrour, Autumn, illus. 2003. 70p. (J). pap. 11.95 (978-1-929381-17-3(4) , Third Millennium Publishing) Sci Fi-Arizona, Inc.

Nevins, Paul. Dante's War. 2003. 168p. (YA). pap. 12.95 (978-0-595-26743-9(2) , Writers Club Pr.) iUniverse, Inc.

Nguyen, Taohuu. Mighty Mite 3: Good Mites, Bad Mites. Nguyen, Taohuu, illus. 2007. (J). 14.95 (***978-0-9790302-3-9(4)***) Amazing Factory, The.

Nichol, Barbara. Dippers. Moser, Barry, illus. 2001. 32p. (J). (gr. 3-7). pap. 7.95 (978-0-88776-549-0(1) , Main St. Bks.) Broadway Bks.

Nicholas, Mark & Christine, Jane. Space Academy, Stargate Search. 2002. (Kirsten Chronicles: 2). 236p. pap. 14.95 (978-0-595-22174-5(2) , Writers Club Pr.) iUniverse, Inc.

Nicholas, Mark & Christinw, Jane. Space Academy. 2001. (Kirsten Chronicles: Vol. 1). 156p. pap. 11.95 (978-0-595-19179-6(7) , Writers Club Pr.) iUniverse, Inc.

Nicholson, William. Viento en Llamas: Siervos del Maestro. Manero Jimenez, Laura, tr. 2005. (Escritura desatada Ser.). (SPA.). 384p. (J). 17.95 (978-84-666-1178-7(9)) Ediciones B ESP. *Dist:* Independent Pubs. Group.

Nicieza, Fabian. Right of Power, Vol. 3. 2006. (Illus.). 184p. pap. 17.99 (978-0-7851-1832-9(2)) Marvel Enterprises, Inc.

Nicieza, Mariano. Phazer: A Man Lost in Alternative Universes. Olivetti, Ariel, illus. 2003. (YA). per. 14.95 (978-0-9740212-7-0(X)) Cedar Grove Bks.

Niles, Steve. The War of the Worlds. 2005. (Illus.). 48p. 15.99 (978-1-933239-37-8(9)) Diamond Bk. Distributors.

Niles, Steve, et al. Marvel Monsters. 2006. (Illus.). 224p. 20.99 (978-0-7851-2141-1(2)) Marvel Enterprises, Inc.

Nimoy, Leonard. Leonard Nimoy's Primortals Vol. 1, No. 1: Origins. Chambers, James et al, eds. Eaton, Scot & Barreiro, Mike, illus. 36p. (Orig.). (YA). pap. 2.25 (978-0-9645175-1-6(5)) Big Entertainment, Inc.

Nix, Garth. Abhorsen Trilogy Set: Sabriel; Lirael; Abhorsen. 2005. (Old Kingdom Ser.: Nos. 1-3). (J). pap. 23.99 (978-0-06-073419-0(1)) HarperCollins Pubs.

—Above the Veil. Rawlings, Steve, illus. 2001. (Seventh Tower Ser.: Bk. 4). 256p. (J). (gr. 3-7). pap. 4.99 (978-0-439-17685-9(9) , Scholastic Pr.) Scholastic, Inc.

—Above the Veil. (Seventh Tower Ser.: Bk. 4). 2001. 248p. (gr. 3-6). lib. bdg. 13.00 (978-0-613-35751-7(5)); 2000. (Illus.). (J). 11.64 (978-0-606-21426-1(7)) Tandem Library Bks.

—Grim Tuesday. 2004. (Keys to the Kingdom Ser.: No. 2). 336p. (J). 5.99 (978-0-439-43655-7(9) , Scholastic Paperbacks) Scholastic, Inc.

—Grim Tuesday. 2004. (Keys to the Kingdom Ser.: No. 2). (gr. 3-6). lib. bdg. 14.15 (978-0-613-70969-9(1)) Tandem Library Bks.

—Into Battle. Rawlings, Steve, illus. 2001. (Seventh Tower Ser.: Bk. 5). 208p. (J). pap. 5.99 (978-0-439-17686-6(7)) Scholastic, Inc.

—Into Battle. 2001. (Seventh Tower Ser.: Bk. 5). (gr. 3-6). lib. bdg. 13.00 (978-0-613-35750-0(7)) Tandem Library Bks.

—Mister Monday. 2003. (Keys to the Kingdom Ser.: No. 1). 368p. (J). 6.99 (978-0-439-55123-6(4) , Scholastic Paperbacks) Scholastic, Inc.

—Mister Monday. 2003. (Keys to the Kingdom Ser.: No. 1). (gr. 3-6). lib. bdg. 14.15 (978-0-613-67341-9(7)) Tandem Library Bks.

Noah's Freezer. 2005. (978-0-9765358-0-5(7)) Strategic Dreamers, LLC.

Nono, Auntie. Solar System Song. Shirasu, Nori, illus. 2004. (J). bds. 1.25 (978-0-9754098-0-0(8)) Accordian Bks.

Noriss, Andrew. Aquila. 1999. (J). pap. 29.95 incl. audio (978-0-7540-6213-4(9)) BBC Audiobooks America.

Norman, Tony. Sky Bikers. Savage, Paul, illus. 2008. (J). pap. (***978-1-59889-903-0(1)***); 33p. (YA). (gr. 5-9). lib. bdg. 21.26 (***978-1-59889-851-4(5)***) Stone Arch Bks.

Norriss, Andrew. Aquila. l.t. ed. 2005. 232p. (J). pap. (978-0-7540-6052-9(7) , CLP 259) BBC Audio.

Norton, Andre. The Defiant Agents & Key Out of Time, 2 vols. 2001. (Time Traders II Ser.). 384p. (J). 19.00 (978-0-671-31968-7(X)) Baen Bks.

—Steel Magic. 2005. (Magic Bks.: Bk. 1). 128p. (J). 5.99 (978-0-7653-5297-2(4) , Starscape) Doherty, Tom Assocs., LLC.

Norton, Andre. Time Traders. 2007. 95.99 (***978-1-4280-5221-5(6)***); pap. 89.99 (***978-1-4280-5202-4(X)***) Indy-Publish.com.

Norton, Andre Alice. The Time Traders. 2006. pap. (***978-1-4068-3561-8(7)***) Echo Library.

Nybo, B. J. Elmo Jackson Great Yellow Ball. 2005. (978-0-9742322-0-1(3)) New Art & Vision, LLC.

Oberne, Sharon. Kelsey. 2006. 88p. (YA). pap. 13.95 (978-1-58909-340-9(2)) Bookstand Publishing.

Obie, Christopher R. Dumisai & the Enchanted Journey. 2003. (J). pap. (978-0-9718530-0-3(2)) Ancestral Light Publishing.

O'Brien, Patrick & O'Malley, Kevin. Captain Raptor & the Space Pirates. O'Brien, Patrick, illus. 2007. (Illus.). 32p. (J). (gr. k-3). 17.85 (***978-0-8027-9572-4(2)***); 16.95 (***978-0-8027-9571-7(4)***) Walker & Co.

O'Brien, Robert C. Z for Zachariah. 2002. (Illus.). (J). 13.40 (978-0-7587-4827-0(2)) Book Wholesalers, Inc.

—Z for Zachariah. l.t. ed. 2002. (LRS Large Print Cornerstone Ser.). (J). (gr. 5-7). pap. 32.95 (978-1-58118-105-0(1)) LRS.

—Z for Zachariah. 2001. mass mkt. 4.99 (978-0-689-84453-9(0) , Simon Pulse) Simon & Schuster Children's Publishing.

—Z for Zachariah. 2001. (YA). 22.00 (978-0-8446-7182-6(7)) Smith, Peter Pub., Inc.

Odgers, Sally. Translations in Celadon. 1999. 140p. (J). (gr. 7-12). 7.95 (978-0-7322-5908-2(8)) HarperCollins Pubs.

—Translations in Celadon. 1999. (gr. 7-12). lib. bdg. 16.40 (978-0-613-73234-5(0)) Tandem Library Bks.

Ogilvy, Ian. Measle & the Mallockee. 2006. 384p. (J). lib. bdg. 16.89 (978-0-06-058692-8(3)) HarperCollins Pubs.

—Measle & the Wrathmonk. 2005. 224p. (J). reprint ed. pap. 5.99 (978-0-06-058687-4(7) , Harper Trophy) HarperCollins Pubs.

Ohnogi, Hiroshi. Rahxephon Novel. 2006. (Illus.). (YA). Vol. 3. 208p. pap. 7.95 (***978-1-59796-002-1(0)***); Vol. 4. 200p. pap. 7.95 (***978-1-59796-003-8(9)***); Vol. 5. 200p. pap. 7.95 (***978-1-59796-004-5(7)***) DrMaster Pubns. Inc.

Oliver, Chad. Far from This Earth & Other Stories. Olson, Priscilla, ed. Dennis, Jane, illus. 2003. (NESFA's Choice Ser.: 25). 480p. 24.00 (978-1-886778-48-1(5) , NESFA Pr.) New England Science Fiction Assn., Inc.

—A Star Above It & Other Stories. Olson, Priscilla, ed. Dennis, Jane, illus. 2003. (NESFA's Choice Ser.: 24). 480p. 24.00 (978-1-886778-45-0(0) , NESFA Pr.) New England Science Fiction Assn., Inc.

The Ologies Collection. 2006. (J). 79.96 (***978-0-7636-3509-1(X)***) Candlewick Pr.

Olsen, Lance. Freaknest. 2000. (Speculative Writers Ser.: Vol. 23). 258p. (J). pap. 12.00 (978-1-877655-35-7(X)) Wordcraft of Oregon, LLC.

O'Malley, Kevin. Captain Raptor & the Moon Mystery. O'Brien, Patrick, illus. 2005. 32p. (J). 17.85 (978-0-8027-8936-5(6)); 16.95 (978-0-8027-8935-8(8)) Walker & Co.

Ono, Toshihiro. Electric Pikachu Boogaloo, Vol. 4. Ono, Toshihiro, illus. 2000. (Pokemon Ser.). (Illus.). 168p. (YA). (gr. 4-7). pap. 12.95 (978-1-56931-436-4(5)) Viz Media.

—Pikachu Shocks Back. Ono, Toshihiro, illus. 1999. (Pokemon Ser.). (Illus.). 168p. (YA). (gr. 4-7). pap. 12.95 (978-1-56931-411-1(X)) Viz Media.

—Surf's up, Pikachu, Vol. 3. Ono, Toshihiro, illus. 1999. (Pokemon Ser.). (Illus.). 167p. (YA). (ps-3). pap. 12.95 (978-1-56931-494-4(2)) Viz Media.

Oppel, Kenneth. Dead Water Zone. 2007. 208p. (J). (gr. 7 up). pap. 6.99 (***978-0-06-123442-2(7)*** , Eos) HarperCollins Pubs.

Orban, Marianne. To Earn a Star. 2000. 172p. (YA). pap. 14.95 (978-0-595-17080-7(3)) iUniverse, Inc.

Orme, David. Boffin Boy & the Deadly Swarm. 2007. (Boffin Boy Ser.). (Illus.). 36p. pap. 7.95 (***978-1-84167-625-8(X)***) Ransom Publishing Ltd. GBR. *Dist:* International Publishers Marketing.

—Boffin Boy & the Ice Caves of Pluto. 2007. (Boffin Boy Ser.). (Illus.). 36p. pap. 7.95 (***978-1-84167-626-5(8)***) Ransom Publishing Ltd. GBR. *Dist:* International Publishers Marketing.

—Boffin Boy & the Invaders from Space. 2007. (Boffin Boy Ser.). (Illus.). 36p. pap. 7.95 (***978-1-84167-613-5(6)***) Ransom Publishing Ltd. GBR. *Dist:* International Publishers Marketing.

—Boffin Boy & the Lost City. 2007. (Boffin Boy Ser.). (Illus.). 36p. pap. 7.95 (***978-1-84167-617-3(9)***) Ransom Publishing Ltd. GBR. *Dist:* International Publishers Marketing.

—Boffin Boy & the Monsters from the Deep. 2007. (Boffin Boy Ser.). (Illus.). 36p. pap. 7.95 (***978-1-84167-615-9(2)***) Ransom Publishing Ltd. GBR. *Dist:* International Publishers Marketing.

—Boffin Boy & the Red Wolf. 2007. (Boffin Boy Ser.). (Illus.). 36p. pap. 7.95 (***978-1-84167-616-6(0)***) Ransom Publishing Ltd. GBR. *Dist:* International Publishers Marketing.

—Boffin Boy & the Temples of Mars. 2007. (Boffin Boy Ser.). (Illus.). 36p. pap. 7.95 (***978-1-84167-623-4(3)***) Ransom Publishing Ltd. GBR. *Dist:* International Publishers Marketing.

—Boffin Boy & the Time Warriors. 2007. (Boffin Boy Ser.). (Illus.). 36p. pap. 7.95 (***978-1-84167-622-7(5)***) Ransom Publishing Ltd. GBR. *Dist:* International Publishers Marketing.

—Boffin Boy & the Wizard of Edo. 2007. (Boffin Boy Ser.). (Illus.). 36p. pap. 7.95 (***978-1-84167-614-2(4)***) Ransom Publishing Ltd. GBR. *Dist:* International Publishers Marketing.

—Monster Planet. Savage, Paul, illus. 2008. (J). pap. (***978-1-59889-900-9(7)***); 32p. (YA). (gr. 5-9). lib. bdg. 21.26 (***978-1-59889-848-4(5)***) Stone Arch Bks.

—Space Explorers. 2004. (Shades Ser.). 64p. (J). pap. 7.99 (978-0-237-52646-7(8) , Evans Brothers, Limited) Evans Publishing Group GBR. *Dist:* Independent Pubs. Group.

—Space Games. Savage, Paul, illus. 2007. 40p. (J). (***978-1-59889-246-8(0)***) Stone Arch Bks.

—Space Pirates. Savage, Paul, illus. 2006. 40p. (J). (gr. 2-3). lib. bdg. (978-1-59889-016-7(6)) Stone Arch Bks.

—Space Wreck. Savage, Paul, illus. 2006. 33p. (J). (978-1-59889-015-0(8)) Stone Arch Bks.

Osborne, Mary Pope. Medianoche en la Luna. 2004. (Coleccion la Casa Del Arbol the Magic Tree House Ser.).Tr. of Midnight on the Moon. (SPA.). (J). pap. 4.95 (978-1-930332-69-0(6)) Lectorum Pubns., Inc.

—Night of the New Magicians. Murdocca, Sal, illus. (Magic Tree House Ser.: No. 35). (J). 2007. 144p. (gr. 2-5). pap. 4.99 (978-0-375-83036-5(7)); 2006. 128p. (gr. k-3). 11.95 (978-0-375-83035 8(9)); 2006. 128p. (gr. k-3). lib. bdg. 13.99 (978-0-375-93035-5(3)) Random Hse. Children's Bks. (Random Hse. Bks. for Young Readers).

Ostow, Micol. Mumble's Journey: The Junior Novelization-Happy Feet. 2006. 96p. (J). (gr. 1-3). pap. 4.99 (978-0-8431-2104-9(1) , Price Stern Sloan) Penguin Group (USA) Inc.

Ostrander, John, et al. Star Wars': The Stark Hyperspace War. 2003. (Illus.). 120p. (YA). pap. 12.95 (978-1-56971-985-5(3)) Dark Horse Comics.

Otomo, Katsuhiro. Hipira: The Little Vampire. 2005. (Illus.). 48p. 13.95 (978-1-59582-002-0(7)) DH Pr.

Owens, Everett. Regeneration. 1999. (X-Files Young Adult Ser.: No. 14). 144p. (YA). (gr. 7 up). 13.95 (978-0-06-447190-9(X)) HarperCollins Pubs.

Owens, M. T. The Great Tome. 2006. (YA). per. 11.99 (978-0-9768589-2-8(4)) Montage Publishing International.

Palatini, Margie. Lab Coat Girl in Cool Fuel. 2000. (L.A.F. Bks.). (Illus.). 96p. (ps-17). 14.49 (978-0-7868-2441-0(7)); Bk. 2. (gr. 2-6). pap. 3.99 (978-0-7868-1347-6(4)) Hyperion Pr.

—Lab Coat Girl in Cool Fuel. 1999. (gr. 3-6). lib. bdg. 11.80 (978-0-613-25908-8(4)) Tandem Library Bks.

Paolini, Christopher. Eldest. 2005. (Inheritance Trilogy Ser.: Bk. 2). (Illus.). 704p. (YA). (gr. 7 up). lib. bdg. 24.99 (978-0-375-92670-9(4) , Knopf Bks. for Young Readers) Random Hse. Children's Bks.

—Eldest: Inheritance. 2005. (Inheritance Trilogy: Bk. 2). (Illus.). 704p. (YA). (gr. 7 up). 21.00 (978-0-375-82670-2(X) , Knopf Bks. for Young Readers) Random Hse. Children's Bks.

—Eldest/Eragon Boxed Set, Set. 2005. (Inheritance Trilogy Ser.). 1232p. (YA). (gr. 7 up). 39.95 (978-0-375-83658-9(6) , Knopf Bks. for Young Readers) Random Hse. Children's Bks.

—Eragon. movie tie-in ed. 2006. (Inheritance Trilogy Ser.: Bk. 1). (Illus.). 528p. (YA). (gr. 7 up). pap. 10.95 (978-0-375-84054-8(0) , Knopf Bks. for Young Readers) Random Hse. Children's Bks.

Parisi, Mark. Science Fiction Picture Show. 2001. (Off the Mark Ser.: Vol. 3). 128p. pap. 9.95 (978-1-929462-33-9(6)) Plan Nine Publishing, Inc.

Parker, George. The Atomic Kid: Adventures in the Anti-world. 2003. 318p. (J). (ps-7). per. 14.95 (978-1-59453-090-6(4) , 1868) Airleaf Publishing & Bookselling.

Parker, Jeff. The Bird, the Beast & the Lizard. 2007. (X-Men: First Class Ser.). 24p. (J). (gr. 2-6). 21.35 (***978-1-59961-398-7(0)***) Spotlight.

—The Leader Has a Big Head. 2007. (Avengers Ser.). 24p. (J). (gr. 2-6). 21.35 (***978-1-59961-384-0(0)***) Spotlight.

—The Master of Sound. 2007. (Fantastic Four Set II Ser.). 24p. (J). (gr. 2-6). 21.35 (***978-1-59961-391-8(3)***) Spotlight.

—The Masters of Evil. 2007. (Avengers Ser.). 24p. (J). (gr. 2-6). 21.35 (***978-1-59961-385-7(9)***) Spotlight.

—The Replacements. 2007. (Avengers Ser.). 24p. (J). (gr. 2-6). 21.35 (***978-1-59961-386-4(7)***) Spotlight.

Parker, John. Gwoppy. 2003. 79 p. pap. 14.95 (978-1-4137-0795-3(5)) PublishAmerica, Inc.

Passarella, John. Avatar. 2001. (gr. 7-12). lib. bdg. 14.15 (978-0-613-63176-1(5)) Tandem Library Bks.

Pati, Geeta. Finny's Voyage Through the Universe: The. 2005. (ENG.). 64p. per. 10.95 (***978-1-59526-019-2(6)***) Media Creations, Inc.

Patterson, James. Saving the World & Other Extreme Sports. 3rd ed. 2008. (Maximum Ride Novel Ser.). 432p. mass mkt. 7.99 (***978-0-446-19404-4(2)***); 2007. (Maximum Ride Ser.: No. 3). 416p. (J). (gr. 5 up). 16.99 (***978-0-316-15560-1(8)***) Little, Brown Bks. for Young Readers.

Patterson, James. School's Out - Forever. 2006. (Maximum Ride Ser.: No. 2). 414p. (YA). 16.99 (978-0-316-01449-6(4)); 2nd ed. 416p. (J). (gr. 5-17). 16.99 (978-0-316-15559-5(4)) Little Brown & Co.

—School's Out - Forever. 2nd ed. 2007. (Maximum Ride Ser.: No. 2). 368p. (YA). mass mkt. 6.99 (***978-0-446-61889-2(6)***) Little, Brown Bks. for Young Readers.

Paulsen, Gary. The Schernoff Discoveries. 1998. (978-0-606-13761-4(0)) Tandem Library Bks.

—The Time Hackers. 2005. 96p. (J). (gr. 4-7). lib. bdg. 17.99 (978-0-385-90896-2(2)); (gr. 5). 13.95 (978-0-385-74659-5(8)) Random Hse. Children's Bks. (Lamb, Wendy).

—The Transall Saga. 1998. (J). (978-0-385-43196-5(1)) Dell Distributing.

—The Transall Saga. 1999. 256p. (J). (gr. 5-7). mass mkt. 6.99 (978-0-440-21976-7(0) , Laurel Leaf) Random Hse. Children's Bks.

—The Transall Saga. 1999. 248p. lib. bdg. 12.64 (978-0-606-17349-0(8)) Tandem Library Bks.

—Transall Saga. 1999. (gr. 7-12). lib. bdg. 14.15 (978-0-613-22948-7(7)) Tandem Library Bks.

—The Transall Saga. l.t. ed. 1999. 312p. (YA). (gr. 7-12). 21.95 (978-0-7862-2187-5(9)) Thorndike Pr.

—The White Fox Chronicles. 2002. (gr. 5-8). lib. bdg. 13.55 (978-0-613-67131-6(7)) Tandem Library Bks.

Pausacker, Jenny. Freedom Fighters: Mindfire, Starfight, Endgame. 2005. (Triple Play Ser.). (Illus.). 48p. (gr. 4-8). 41.85 (978-0-7910-9073-2(6)) Facts On File, Inc.

Pearson. Alien Draw. 214p. (J). pap. (978-0-340-68077-3(6) , Hodder & Stoughton) Hodder General Publishing Division.

Peck, Richard. The Great Interactive Dream Machine. 1998. (Puffin Novel Ser.). 160p. (J). (gr. 5-9). pap. 6.99 (978-0-14-038264-8(X) , Puffin) Penguin Group (USA) Inc.

Peel, John. Betrayal. 1999. (Twenty Ninety-Nine Ser.: Bk. 2). 160p. (J). (gr. 3-7). pap. 4.99 (978-0-439-06031-8(1)) Scholastic, Inc.

—Beware the Metal Children. 1999. (gr. 3-6). lib. bdg. 11.80 (978-0-613-17111-3(X)) Tandem Library Bks.

—Book of Magic, Vol. 3. Karre, Andrew, ed. 2004. (Diadem Worlds of Magic Ser.). 208p. pap. 4.99 (978-0-7387-0615-3(9)) Llewellyn Pubns.

—Book of Names. Karre, Andrew, ed. 2004. (Diadem Worlds of Magic Ser.). 208p. pap. 6.99 (978-0-7387-0617-7(5)) Llewellyn Pubns.

—Book of Signs, Vol. 2. Karre, Andrew, ed. 2004. (Diadem Worlds of Magic Ser.). (Illus.). 208p. pap. 5.99 (978-0-7387-0616-0(7)) Llewellyn Pubns.

—Change. 1999. (Outer Limits Ser.: No. 12). 128p. (J). (gr. 4-7). 3.99 (978-0-8125-7569-9(5) , Tor Bks.) Doherty, Tom Assocs., LLC.

—Doomsday. 1999. (Twenty Ninety-Nine Ser.: Bk. 1). (J). (gr. 3-7). 59.88 (978-0-439-09277-7(9)); 192p. pap. 4.99 (978-0-439-06030-1(3)) Scholastic, Inc.

—Firestorm. 2000. (Twenty Ninety-Nine Ser.: Bk. 6). (Illus.). 160p. (J). (gr. 3-7). pap. 4.99 (978-0-439-06035-6(4)) Scholastic, Inc.

—The Innocent. 1998. (Outer Limits Ser.: No. 6). 128p. (J). (gr. 4-7). pap. 3.99 (978-0-8125-6455-6(3) , Tor Bks.) Doherty, Tom Assocs., LLC.

—Meltdown. 2000. (Twenty Ninety-Nine Ser.: Bk. 5). 160p. (J). (gr. 3-7). pap. 4.99 (978-0-439-06034-9(6)) Scholastic, Inc.

—Traitor. 2000. (Twenty Ninety-Nine Ser.: Bk. 3). (Illus.). 160p. (J). (gr. 3-7). pap. 4.99 (978-0-439-06032-5(X) , Scholastic Paperbacks) Scholastic, Inc.

Peel, John & Peel, John. Twice the Trouble! 2001. 145p. (J). (gr. 3-6). per. 13.00 (978-0-613-70906-4(3)) Tandem Library Bks.

Pepper, Dennis. The Young Oxford Book of Timewarp Stories. 2002. (Illus.). 224p. (YA). (gr. 5). 15.95 (978-0-19-278167-3(7)) Oxford Univ. Pr., Inc.

S

Peterseil, Yaacov. Jewish Sci-Fi Stories for Kids: An Anthology of Short Stories. 1999. (Jewish Stories for Kids Ser.). (Illus.). 190p. (J). (gr. 3-7). 16.95 (978-0-943706-73-3(4)); pap. 12.95 (978-0-943706-74-0(2)) Pitspopany Pr. (Devora Publishing).

Peterson Haddix, Margaret. Among the Brave. 2004. (Shadow Children Ser.). 132p. (J). lib. bdg. 20.00 (*978-1-4242-0392-5(9)) Fitzgerald Bks.

Peterson, John. Littles First Readers: The Littles & the Big Blizzard. Rogers, Jacqueline, illus. 2001. (J). (978-0-606-19929-2(2)) Tandem Library Bks.

Petri, Michelle. The Fvantom: Omegapocalypse. 2007. 212p. per. 14.95 (*978-0-595-45723-6(1)) iUniverse, Inc.

Petrucha, Stefan. Future Imperfect. 2007. (Timetripper Ser.: No. 4). 240p. (J). pap. 5.99 (978-1-59514-087-6(5) , Razorbill) Penguin Group (USA) Inc.

Pfeffer, Susan Beth. Life As We Knew It. 2006. (Illus.). 352p. (J). 17.00 (978-0-15-205826-5(5)) Harcourt Children's Bks.

Philbrick, Rodman. The Last Book in the Universe. unabr. ed. 2004. 224p. (J). (gr. 5-9). pap. 36.00 incl. audio (978-0-8072-8844-3(6) , LYA 272 SP, Listening Library) Random Hse. Audio Publishing Group.

—The Last Book in the Universe. 2005. 240p. mass mkt. 2.99 (978-0-439-77133-7(1)); 2002. 224p. (J). (gr. 4-7). pap. 5.99 (978-0-439-08759-9(7) , Scholastic Paperbacks) Scholastic, Inc.

—The Last Book in the Universe. 2001. (gr. 5-8). lib. bdg. 13.00 (978-0-613-45598-5(3)) Tandem Library Bks.

Phillips, John A., Jr. Jahjep & Chip. Licon, Melissa, illus. l.t. ed. 2002. 28p. (978-0-9727968-0-4(0)) Jahjep Bks.

Phillips, Terrie. The Ski Trip. 2006. (Illus.). 38p. (J). lib. bdg. 12.95 (*978-0-9789449-0-2(9)) Tbooks Publishing Co.

Pickering, David & Dorling Kindersley Publishing Staff. The Ultimate Star Wars Episode I. 1999. (Ultimate Sticker Bks.). (Illus.). 16p. (J). (gr. 3-7). pap. 6.95 (978-0-7894-3964-2(6)) Dorling Kindersley Publishing, Inc.

Pierce, Tamora. Alanna: The First Adventure. unabr. ed. 2004. (Song of the Lioness Ser.: Bk. 1). 216p. (J). (gr. 6 up). pap. 36.00 incl. audio (978-0-8072-8772-9(5) , YA263SP, Listening Library) Random Hse. Audio Publishing Group.

—Alanna: The First Adventure. 2005. (Song of the Lioness Ser.: Bk. 1). (Illus.). 304p. (YA). pap. 6.99 (978-0-689-87855-8(9) , Simon Pulse) Simon & Schuster Children's Publishing.

—Alanna: The First Adventure. 1999. (Song of the Lioness Ser.: Bk. 1). (J). (gr. 5 up). 20.50 (978-0-8446-7002-7(2)) Smith, Peter Pub., Inc.

—Sandry's Book. 1999. (Circle of Magic Ser.: No. 1). (Illus.). (J). (978-0-606-20509-2(8)) Tandem Library Bks.

Pilkey, Dav. El Capitan Calzoncillos y el Ataque de los Inodoros Parlantes. 2001. (Captain Underpants Ser.). (SPA.). (gr. 3-6). lib. bdg. 13.00 (978-0-613-54409-2(9)) Tandem Library Bks.

—El Capitan Calzoncillos y el Perverso Plan del Profesor Pipicaca. 2002. (Captain Underpants Ser.: No. 4). (SPA.). (gr. 3-6). lib. bdg. 13.00 (978-0-613-50414-0(3)) Tandem Library Bks.

—El Capitan Calzoncillos y la Invasion de las Horribles Camareras. 2002. (Captain Underpants Ser.). (SPA.). (gr. 3-6). lib. bdg. 13.00 (978-0-613-50415-7(1)) Tandem Library Bks.

—Mighty Robot vs. the Jurassic Jackrabbits from Jupiter. 2002. (Ricky Ricotta Ser.: No. 5). (ps-2). lib. bdg. 11.80 (978-0-613-50493-5(3)) Tandem Library Bks.

—Ricky Ricotta Y el Poderoso Robot Contra Los Mecamonos de Marte. 2002. (Ricky Ricotta Ser.: No. 4). (ps-2). lib. bdg. 11.80 (978-0-613-45613-5(0)) Tandem Library Bks.

Pillsbury, Samuel H. The Invasion of Planet Wampetter. Angorn, Matthew, illus. 2003. (Planet Wampetter Adventure Ser.). 133p. (J). (gr. 3-8). 15.00 (978-0-9622036-6-4(1)); pap. 8.95 (978-1-930085-05-3(2)) Perspective Publishing, Inc.

Planet of the Apes. movie tie-in ed. 2001. 160p. (J). pap. 4.99 (978-0-06-093768-3(8) , Harper Entertainment) HarperCollins Pubs.

Pocket Books Staff. Intruder. 2000. (gr. 7-12). lib. bdg. 14.15 (978-0-613-73179-9(4)) Tandem Library Bks.

Pohl, Frederik. Far Shore of Time. 2000. (gr. 7-12). lib. bdg. 15.30 (978-0-613-27821-8(6)) Tandem Library Bks.

Pollack, Pamela & Belviso, Meg. Mimi's Crest of Sincerity. 2001. (Digimon Ser.: No. 7). (Illus.). 96p. (J). (gr. 1-4). pap. 4.50 (978-0-06-107203-1(6) , Harper Entertainment) HarperCollins Pubs.

Pottle, Bill T. DreamQuest. 2003. 274p. (YA). pap. 16.95 (978-0-595-26804-7(8) , Writers Club Pr.) iUniverse, Inc.

Pow, Tom. The Pack. 2006. 240p. (YA). 16.95 (978-1-59643-159-1(8)) Roaring Brook Pr.

PowerMark Issue 3 Vol. 1, Issue 3: Under Fire. 2001. 32p. (J). pap. 2.95 (978-0-9705669-2-8(1)) PowerMark Productions.

Pratchett, Terry. The Bromeliad: Truckers, Diggers, & Wings. 2003. 512p. (J). (gr. 5 up). 18.99 (978-0-06-009493-5(1)); 18.89 (978-0-06-054855-1(X)) HarperCollins Pubs.

—Diggers. 2004. (Bromeliad Trilogy Ser.). 224p. (J). (gr. 5 up). reprint ed. pap. 5.99 (978-0-06-009494-2(X) , Harper Trophy) HarperCollins Pubs.

—Hogfather. 2000. (gr. 5-8). lib. bdg. 15.30 (978-0-613-57222-4(X)) Tandem Library Bks.

—The Last Continent. 1999. (gr. 7-12). lib. bdg. 15.30 (978-0-613-27928-4(X)) Tandem Library Bks.

—Truckers. 2004. (Bromeliad Trilogy Ser.). 288p. (J). (gr. 5 up). reprint ed. pap. 6.99 (978-0-06-009496-6(6) , Harper Trophy) HarperCollins Pubs.

—Wings. 2004. (Bromeliad Trilogy Ser.). 224p. (J). (gr. 5 up). reprint ed. pap. 5.99 (978-0-06-009495-9(8) , Harper Trophy) HarperCollins Pubs.

Preston, Douglas & Child, Lincoln. The Ice Limit. 2001. (gr. 7-12). lib. bdg. 16.45 (978-0-613-49415-1(6)) Tandem Library Bks.

Preuss, Paul. Venus Prime, Vol. 1. 1999. (Arthur C. Clarke's Venus Prime Ser.: Vol. 1). (Illus.). 336p. pap. 14.00 (978-0-671-03888-5(5)) ibooks, Inc.

Price, Susan. The Sterkarm Handshake. 2000. 448p. (J). (gr. 4-7). 17.95 (978-0-06-028959-1(7)); 18.89 (978-0-06-029392-5(6)) HarperCollins Pubs.

—The Sterkarm Handshake. 2000. (978-0-606-21707-1(X)) Tandem Library Bks.

—A Sterkarm Kiss. 2004. 288p. (J). (gr. 7 up). 16.99 (978-0-06-072197-8(9)) HarperCollins Pubs.

Prior, Natalie Jane & Dawson, Kathy. Lily Quench & the Magician's Pyramid, Vol. 5. 2004. (Illus.). 176p. (Orig.). (J). (gr. 3 up). pap. 4.99 (978-0-14-240163-7(3) , Puffin) Penguin Group (USA) Inc.

Psycho Backho: Arc of Fury - the Cataclysm. 2005. (YA). per. (978-1-59620-003-6(0)) Science of Knowledge Pr.

Pullman, Philip. The Amber Spyglass. 2002. (His Dark Materials Ser.: Bk. 3). (YA). (gr. 7-12). lib. bdg. 21.05 (978-0-613-71927-8(1)) Tandem Library Bks.

—La Daga. Gallart Iglesias, Maria Dolores, tr. 7th ed. 2005. (Escritura desatada Ser.). (SPA., Illus.). 288p. (YA). (gr. 7-11). 13.95 (978-84-406-8409-7(6)) Ediciones B ESP. *Dist:* Independent Pubs. Group.

—His Dark Materials Trilogy: The Golden Compass; The Subtle Knife; The Amber Spyglass. 2003. (His Dark Materials Ser.: Bks. 1-3). (YA). pap. 22.50 (978-0-440-41951-8(4) , Yearling) Random Hse. Children's Bks.

Radcliffe, Wil. Noggle Stones. 2003. (gr. 7-12). lib. bdg. 25.70 (978-0-613-89756-3(0)) Tandem Library Bks.

Ragnar. Izzy's Very Important Job. Ragnar, illus. 2005. (Illus.). 32p. 9.00 (978-0-9729388-2-2(6)) Baby Tattoo Bks.

Raham, Gary, et al. The Deep Time Diaries: As Recorded by Neesha & Jon Olifee. 2000. (Illus.). 96p. (J). (gr. 3-4). pap. 17.95 (978-1-55591-415-8(2)) Fulcrum Publishing.

Raintree Steck-Vaughn Staff. The Science Fair Surprise. 1999. (J). pap. 35.60 (978-0-7398-0893-1(1)) Steck-Vaughn.

Ralles, H. J. Darok 10. 2005. 230p. (J). pap. 9.95 (978-1-929976-31-7(3)) Top Pubns., Ltd.

—Darok 9. 2002. 229p. pap. 9.95 (978-1-929976-10-2(0)) Top Pubns., Ltd.

—Keeper of the Colony. 2006. (YA). pap. 10.95 (978-1-929976-35-5(6)) Top Pubns., Ltd.

—Keeper of the Realm, Vol. 2. 2003. (Illus.). 248p. (J). pap. 9.95 (978-1-929976-21-8(6)) Top Pubns., Ltd.

Ralph, Brian. Crum Bums. 2007. (Illus.). 208p. (YA). pap. 15.00 (*978-1-60309-002-5(9)) Top Shelf Productions.

Random House Staff. Revenge of the Sith Movie Storybook. 2005. 48p. (J). (gr. 3). pap. 7.99 (978-0-375-82612-2(2) , LucasBooks for Young Readers) Random Hse. Children's Bks.

Ransom, Candice. Giant in the Garden. 2007. (Time Spies Ser.: Bk. 3). (Illus.). 128p. (J). (gr. 1-5). pap. 4.99 (978-0-7869-4074-5(3) , Mirrorstone) Wizards of the Coast.

—Magician in the Trunk. 2007. (Time Spies Ser.: Bk. 4). (Illus.). 128p. (J). (gr. 1-5). 4.99 (978-0-7869-4070-7(0) , Mirrorstone) Wizards of the Coast.

—Secret in the Tower. Call, Greg, illus. 2006. 128p. (J). (gr. 2-4). pap. 4.99 (978-0-7869-4027-1(1) , Mirrorstone) Wizards of the Coast.

Raphael, Elaine. Asteroid Alert. 2000. (2050 : No. 1). (J). (gr. 1-4). (978-0-606-19522-5(X)) Tandem Library Bks.

—Rescue in Space. Bolognese, Don, illus. 2000. (2050: No. 2). 48p. (J). (gr. 1-4). pap. 3.99 (978-0-439-07816-0(4) , Cartwheel Bks.) Scholastic, Inc.

—Rescue in Space. 2000. (2050 : No. 2). (J). (gr. 1-4). (978-0-606-19523-2(8)) Tandem Library Bks.

Raphael, Elaine & Bolognese, Don. Asteroid Alert. Bolognese, Don, illus. 2000. (Two Thousnd Fifty: No. 1). (Illus.). 48p. (J). (ps-3). pap. 3.99 (978-0-439-07815-3(6) , Cartwheel Bks.) Scholastic, Inc.

Rau, Dana Meachen. Mi Lugar Preferido: My Special Space. Kim, Julie J., illus. 2005. (Rookie Reader(R) Espanol Ser.). 32p. (gr. k-2). 19.50 (978-0-516-25250-6(X) , Children's Pr.) Scholastic Library Publishing.

Rawson, Christopher. Gnomes & Goblins. Cartwright, Stephen, illus. 2004. (Young Reading Series One Ser.). 48p. (J). (gr. 2 up). pap. 5.95 (978-0-7945-0407-6(8) , Usborne) EDC Publishing.

Read Magazine Editorial Staff. Read into the Millennium: Stories of the Future. 1999. (Best of READ Ser.). 160p. (gr. 5 up). lib. bdg. 24.90 (978-0-7613-0962-8(4) , Millbrook Pr.) Lerner Publishing Group.

Rector, Rebecca Kraft. Tria & the Great Star Rescue. 2003. (gr. 3-6). lib. bdg. 13.00 (978-0-613-86232-5(5)) Tandem Library Bks.

Rees, Celia. Pirates! 2005. 384p. (YA). (gr. 9-12). reprint ed. pap. 8.95 (978-1-58234-665-6(8) , Bloomsbury Children) Bloomsbury Publishing.

Reeve, Philip. A Darkling Plain. 2007. (Hungry City Chronicles Ser.). 576p. (J). (gr. 7 up). 18.99 (*978-0-06-089055-1(X)); lib. bdg. 19.89 (*978-0-06-089056-8(8)) HarperCollins Pubs.

—Infernal Devices. (Hungry City Chronicles Ser.). (J). 2007. 448p. (gr. 7 up). pap. 8.99 (*978-0-06-082637-6(1) , Eos); 2006. 368p. 16.99 (978-0-06-082635-2(5)); 2006. 368p. lib. bdg. 17.89 (978-0-06-082636-9(3)) HarperCollins Pubs.

—Larklight: A Rousing Tale of Dauntless Pluck in the Farthest Reaches of Space. Wyatt, David, illus. 2007. 416p. (J). (gr. 5 up). pap. 7.95 (*978-1-59990-145-9(5) , Bloomsbury Children) Bloomsbury Publishing.

—Mortal Engines. (Hungry City Chronicles Ser.). (gr. 7 up). 2003. 320p. (J). lib. bdg. 17.89 (978-0-06-008208-6(9)); 2004. 384p. reprint ed. pap. 6.99 (978-0-06-008209-3(7)) HarperCollins Pubs.

—Mortal Engines. 2001. 304p. (YA). (978-0-439-99345-6(8)) Scholastic, Inc.

—Predator's Gold. (Hungry City Chronicles Ser.). (J). 2004. 336p. (gr. 7 up). 16.99 (978-0-06-072193-0(6)); 2004. 336p. (gr. 7 up). lib. bdg. 17.89 (978-0-06-072194-7(4)); 2006. 416p. reprint ed. pap. 7.99 (978-0-06-072196-1(0)) HarperCollins Pubs.

Reeve, Philip. Starcross: An Intergalactic Adventure of Spies & Time Travel. Wyatt, David, illus. 2007. 320p. (J). (gr. 5 up). 16.95 (*978-1-59990-121-3(8) , Bloomsbury Children) Bloomsbury Publishing.

Reeve, Philip & Yancey, Rick. Larklight: A Rousing Tale of Dauntless Pluck in the Farthest Reaches of Space. Wyatt, David, illus. 2006. 250p. (YA). 16.95 (978-1-59990-020-9(3) , Bloomsbury Children) Bloomsbury Publishing.

Reid, Kate. Operation Timewarp. 2003. 195p. pap. 9.99 (978-1-84255-203-2(1)) Orion Children's Bks. GBR. *Dist:* Trafalgar Square Publishing.

Reilly, Matthew. Crash Course. Raimondi, Pablo, illus. 2006. (Hover Car Racer Ser.). 240p. (J). pap. 5.99 (978-1-4169-0226-3(0)); pap. 2.99 (978-1-4169-2503-3(1)) Simon & Schuster Children's Publishing. (Aladdin).

—Full Throttle. Raimondi, Pablo, illus. 2007. (Hover Car Racer Ser.). 224p. (J). 9.95 (978-1-4169-0227-0(9)) Simon & Schuster Children's Publishing.

Reinhart, Matthew. Star Wars: A Pop-Up Guide to the Galaxy. 2007. (Illus.). 6p. (J). pap. 32.99 (*978-0-439-88282-8(6) , Orchard Bks.) Scholastic, Inc.

Reisman, Michael. Simon Bloom, the Gravity Keeper. 2008. 256p. (J). (gr. 4-12). 15.99 (978-0-525-47922-2(8) , Dutton Juvenile) Penguin Group (USA) Inc.

Reiss, Kathryn. Paint by Magic. 2003. (Time Travel Mystery Ser.). 288p. (J). (gr. 5 up). pap. 6.95 (978-0-15-204925-6(8) , Harcourt Paperbacks) Harcourt Children's Bks.

—Paint by Magic. 2002. (gr. 5-8). lib. bdg. 14.10 (978-0-613-70531-8(9)) Tandem Library Bks.

—Time Windows. 2000. 272p. (YA). (gr. 7 up). pap. 6.95 (978-0-15-202399-7(2) , Harcourt Paperbacks) Harcourt Children's Bks.

—Time Windows. 2000. (978-0-606-20334-0(6)); (gr. 3-6). lib. bdg. 14.15 (978-0-613-30159-6(5)) Tandem Library Bks.

Renick, Sam X. The Adventures of Sammy the Saver In: Will Sammy Ride the World's First Space Coaster?, Vol. 2. Alvarado, Juan, illus. 2003. 32p. (J). pap. 8.95 (978-0-9713664-1-1(1)) It's A Habit! Co., The.

Rennie, Gordon, et al. Starship Troopers. 1998. (Illus.). 152p. (YA). pap. 14.95 (978-1-56971-314-3(6)) Dark Horse Comics.

Resnick, Mike. The World Behind the Door: An Encounter with Salvador Dali. 2007. (Illus.). 144p. (YA). 16.95 (*978-0-8230-0416-4(3)) Watson-Guptill Pubns., Inc.

Rex, Adam. The True Meaning of Smekday. Rex, Adam, illus. rev. ed. 2007. 432p. (gr. 2-7). 16.99 (*978-0-7868-4900-0(2)) Hyperion Pr.

Reynolds, David West & Luceno, James. Star Wars: The Complete Visual Dictionary. 2006. (Illus.). 272p. (J). (ps-12). 40.00 (978-0-7566-2238-1(7)) Dorling Kindersley Publishing, Inc.

Rhino Records Staff. Junior Jedi Training Manual. 1999. (Star Wars Ser.). (Illus.). 24p. (J). pap. 5.98 incl. audio (978-0-7379-0002-6(4) , R4 75669); pap. 9.98 incl. audio compact disk (978-0-7379-0003-3(2) , R2 75669) Rhino Entertainment Co, A Warner Music Group Co.

Richards, Douglas E. Captured! 2007. 160p. (J). pap. 7.95 (*978-1-933255-33-0(1)) DNA Pr.

Richards, J. & Lane, A. Banquo's Legacy. 2001. (Doctor Who Ser.). (Illus.). 288p. (J). pap. 6.95 (978-0-563-53808-0(2)) BBC Worldwide Americas.

Richards, Justin. The Burning. 2001. (Doctor Who Ser.). (Illus.). 288p. (J). pap. 6.95 (978-0-563-53812-7(0)) BBC Worldwide Americas.

—The Joy Device. 1999. 256p. (J). mass mkt. 6.95 (978-0-426-20535-7(9)) Virgin Bks. Ltd. GBR. *Dist:* London Bridge.

Richards, L. B. Charley Tooth Bites Back. 2005. (YA). pap. 12.95 (978-0-8439-5137-0(0)) Dorchester Publishing Co., Inc.

Richardson, Fay Lapka. Dark Is a Color. 2004. 264p. (J). pap. 12.95 (978-0-9744989-6-6(3)) Fox Song Bks.

Ridley, Susan. Suzie's Adventures in Space: the Forbidden Planet. 2007. 80p. pap. 8.99 (*978-0-615-15328-5(3)) Arts & Health Publishing.

Ring, Vicky L. Who's There? 2001. (gr. 7-12). lib. bdg. 31.55 (978-0-613-78009-4(4)) Tandem Library Bks.

Ripley, Virginia. The Little Troll's Big Adventure. Dintzer, Josh, illus. 1999. 32p. (J). (gr. k-2). pap. 12.00 (978-0-9674612-0-5(0)) Strike Publishing.

Ritchie, Thelma. Terra Nova: Settling the Red Planet. 2005. 208p. pap. 16.95 (978-1-933148-25-0(X)) Tate Publishing & Enterprises, L.L.C.

Roberts, Rachel. All's Fairy in Love & War. 2003. (Avalon Ser.: Vol. 2). 200p. (J). pap. 4.99 (978-1-59315-011-2(3)) Perseus Bks. Group.

—All's Fairy in Love & War. 2003. (gr. 3-6). lib. bdg. 13.00 (978-0-613-79959-1(3)) Tandem Library Bks.

—Ghost Wolf. 2004. (Avalon Ser.: Vol. 3). 200p. (J). pap. 4.99 (978-1-59315-012-9(1)) Perseus Bks. Group.

—Heart of Avalon. 2005. (Avalon Ser.: Vol. 4). 224p. (J). pap. 5.99 (978-1-59315-013-6(X)) Perseus Bks. Group.

Robertson, M. P., illus. The Egg. 2001. 32p. (J). (ps-3). 15.99 (978-0-8037-2546-1(9) , Dial) Penguin Group (USA) Inc.

Robinson, Kim Stanley. The Martians. 2000. (gr. 7-12). lib. bdg. 15.30 (978-0-613-35420-2(6)) Tandem Library Bks.

Robson, Jenny. Savannah 2116 Ad. 2005. 144p. pap. (*978-0-624-04230-3(8)) Tafelberg Pubs., Ltd.

Rockwell, Carey. Revolt on Venus. 2006. 95.99 (*978-1-4280-5054-9(X)); pap. 89.99 (*978-1-4280-5053-2(1)) IndyPublish.com.

—Sabotage in Space. 2006. 95.99 (*978-1-4280-3661-1(X)); pap. 89.99 (*978-1-4280-3670-3(9)) IndyPublish.com.

—The Space Pioneers. 2006. 95.99 (*978-1-4280-4341-1(1)); pap. 89.99 (*978-1-4280-4388-6(8)) IndyPublish.com.

—Stand by for Mars! 2007. (ENG.). 208p. per. 89.99 (*978-1-4280-7416-3(3)) IndyPublish.com.

—Treachery in Outer Space. 2006. 95.99 (*978-1-4280-4384-8(5)); pap. 89.99 (*978-1-4280-4383-1(7)) IndyPublish.com.

Rodda, Emily. Dread Mountain. 2001. (Deltora Quest Ser.: No. 5). 144p. (J). pap. 4.99 (978-0-439-25327-7(6) , Scholastic Paperbacks) Scholastic, Inc.

—Dread Mountain. 2001. (gr. 5-8). lib. bdg. 13.00 (978-0-613-35715-9(9)) Tandem Library Bks.

—The Forests of Silence. 2001. (Deltora Quest Ser.: No. 1). (Illus.). 144p. (J). (gr. 3-7). pap. 5.99 (978-0-439-25323-9(3)) Scholastic, Inc.

—Isle of the Dead. 2004. 195p. (J). lib. bdg. 16.92 (*978-1-4242-0273-7(6)) Fitzgerald Bks.

—The Lake of Tears. 2001. (Deltora Quest Ser.: No. 2). (Illus.). 144p. (J). (gr. 3-7). pap. 4.99 (978-0-439-25324-6(1)) Scholastic, Inc.

—The Lake of Tears. 2001. (gr. 5-8). lib. bdg. 13.00 (978-0-613-35736-4(1)) Tandem Library Bks.

—The Maze of the Beast. 2001. (Deltora Quest Ser.: No. 6). (Illus.). 144p. (J). pap. 4.99 (978-0-439-25328-4(4) , Scholastic Paperbacks) Scholastic, Inc.

—Return to Del. (Illus.). (J). 2002. 136p. (978-0-439-41951-2(4)); 2001. (Deltora Quest Ser.: No. 8). 144p. (gr. 8). pap. 4.99 (978-0-439-25330-7(6)) Scholastic, Inc.

—Return to Del. 2001. (gr. 5-8). lib. bdg. 13.00 (978-0-613-43874-2(4)) Tandem Library Bks.

—Shadowgate. 2004. 195p. (J). lib. bdg. 16.92 (*978-1-4242-0274-4(4)) Fitzgerald Bks.

—The Shifting Sands. 2001. (Deltora Quest Ser.: No. 4). (Illus.). 144p. (J). (gr. 4-7). pap. 4.99 (978-0-439-25326-0(8)) Scholastic, Inc.

—The Shifting Sands. 2001. (gr. 5-8). lib. bdg. 13.00 (978-0-613-35752-4(3)) Tandem Library Bks.

—The Valley of the Lost. 2001. (Deltora Quest Ser.: No. 7). (Illus.). 143p. (J). pap. 4.99 (978-0-439-25329-1(2) , Scholastic Paperbacks) Scholastic, Inc.

Rodriguez, Robert. New Kind of Super Spy. 2003. (gr. 3-6). lib. bdg. 13.00 (978-0-613-68269-5(6)) Tandem Library Bks.

Roe, David & Reader's Digest Staff. Transformers Mix & Match. 2007. 12p. (J). bds. 14.99 (*978-0-7944-1286-9(6)) Reader's Digest Assn., Inc., The.

Roman, Steven A. & Timmons, Stan. Doctor Doom, 3 vols., Bk. 1. 2000. (Chaos Engine Trilogy Ser.: Vol. 1). (Illus.). 384p. (gr. 4-7). pap. (978-0-7434-0019-0(4)) ibooks, Inc.

—X-Men: Magneto, 3 vols. 2002. (Chaos Engine Ser.: Bk. 2). (Illus.). 320p. (gr. 4-7). pap. (978-0-7434-0023-7(2)) ibooks, Inc.

Rose, Malcolm. Lost Bullet. 2007. (Traces Ser.). 212p. (J). (gr. 5-9). pap. 5.95 (978-0-7534-5980-5(9) , Kingfisher) Houghton Mifflin Co. Trade & Reference Div.

—Roll Call. 2007. (Traces Ser.). 224p. (J). (gr. 5-9). pap. 5.95 (978-0-7534-5981-2(7) , Kingfisher) Houghton Mifflin Co. Trade & Reference Div.

Ross, Christine Johanson. A Snowflake Dream. 2001. (gr. k-3). lib. bdg. 28.00 (978-0-613-74534-5(5)) Tandem Library Bks.

Ruditis, Paul. Meteor Shower Messenger. 2005. (Sonic X Ser.). 48p. (J). (gr. 1-3). pap. 4.99 (978-0-448-43996-9(4) , Grosset & Dunlap) Penguin Group (USA) Inc.

Ruditis, Paul & Burge, Constance M. Leo Rising. 2007. (Charmed Ser.). 224p. (YA). pap. 6.99 (*978-1-4169-3669-5(6) , Simon Spotlight Entertainment) Simon & Schuster.

Ryan, Kevin. Nightscape. 2003. (Roswell Ser.). (Illus.). 208p. (YA). pap. 5.99 (978-0-689-85521-4(4) , Simon Pulse) Simon & Schuster Children's Publishing.

—Nightscape. 2003. (gr. 7-12). lib. bdg. 14.15 (978-0-613-66528-5(7)) Tandem Library Bks.

Rymer, Alta M. Stars of Obron: Chambo Returns. Rymer, Alta M., illus. (Tales of Planet Artembo Ser.: Bk. 3). (Illus.). 56p. (Orig.). (J). (gr. 5-7). pap. 20.00 (978-0-9600792-3-0(8)) Rymer Bks.

Sadamoto, Yoshiyuki. Neon Genesis Evangelion, Vol. 10. 2007. (Neon Genesis Evangelion Ser.). 200p. (YA). pap. 9.99 (978-1-4215-1160-3(6)) Viz Media.

—Neon Genesis Evangelion Vol. 2. Sadamoto, Yoshiyuki, illus. collector's ed. 2002. (Neon Genesis Evangelion Ser.). (Illus.). 168p. (YA). pap. 15.95 (978-1-56931-344-2(X)) Viz Media.

Sadler, Marilyn. Zenon Kar, Girl of the 21st Century No. 1: Bobo Crazy. 2001. (Stepping Stone Bks.). (Illus.). (J). 10.79 (978-0-606-21007-2(5)) Tandem Library Bks.

—Zenon Kar, Girl of the 21st Century No. 2: Spaceball Stars. 2001. (Stepping Stone Bks.). (Illus.). (J). (978-0-606-21542-8(5)) Tandem Library Bks.

Sage, Alison. Susan's Journey: Step Through the Wardrobe. Baynes, Pauline, illus. 2006. (Narnia Ser.). 96p. (J). 14.99 (978-0-06-085238-2(0)); pap. 3.99 (978-0-06-085237-5(2) , Harper Trophy) HarperCollins Pubs.

Sahovey, Judith Galardi. Return to Thrae. 2002. (gr. 7-12). lib. bdg. 25.15 (978-0-613-78044-5(2)) Tandem Library Bks.

Saint-Exupéry, Antoine de. A Day with The Little Prince. 2003. (Illus.). (J). bds. (978-0-15-204727-6(1) , Red Wagon Bks.) Harcourt Children's Bks. CAN. *Dist:* Harcourt Trade Pubs.

Saito, Chiho. To Sprout. Be-Papas, illus. 2003. (Revolutionary Girl Utena Ser.: Vol. 3). 200p. (YA). pap. 9.95 (978-1-56931-812-6(3)) Viz Media.

Salvatore, R. A. Vector Prime. 2000. (Star Wars Ser.: Bk. 1). (gr. 7-12). lib. bdg. 15.90 (978-0-613-29377-8(0)) Tandem Library Bks.

Sampson, Fay. Finnglas & the Stones of Choosing, Vol. 4. 2003. 176p. (J). (gr. 5-8). pap. 7.99 (978-0-7459-4760-0(3) , Lion) Lion Hudson plc GBR. *Dist:* Independent Pubs. Group.

—Finnglas of the Horses, Vol. 3. rev. ed. 2002. 144p. (J). (gr. 5-8). pap. 7.99 (978-0-7459-4761-7(1) , Lion) Lion Hudson plc GBR. *Dist:* Independent Pubs. Group.

Sander, Heather. Robbie Packford - Alien Monster. 2004. (Robbie Packford Ser.). (Illus.). 96p. (J). (gr. 3-7). pap. 6.95 (978-1-55143-259-5(5)) Orca Bk. Pubs. USA.

Sands, Karen & Frank, Marietta. Back in the Spaceship Again: Juvenile Science Fiction Series since 1945. 1999. (Contributions to the Study of Science Fiction & Fantasy Ser.: No. 84). (Illus.). 166p. 105.00 (978-0-313-30192-6(1) , GM0192, Greenwood Pr.) Greenwood Publishing Group, Inc.

Santana, Gabriela. Cuentos de Viajes Espaciales para Ninos. 1999. (Stories for Children Ser.).Tr. of Stories of Space Travel for Kids. (SPA., Illus.). 125p. (J). 7.95 (978-970-643-182-0(9)) Selector, S.A. de C.V. MEX. *Dist:* Libros Sin Fronteras.

Sasaki, Chris & Wells, H. G. The War of the Worlds. Akib, Jamel, illus. 2007. (Classic Starts Ser.). 151p. (J). (****978-1-4287-4208-6(5)***) Sterling Publishing Co., Inc.

Satten, Sandra C. In the Thirteenth Year. Spark, illus. 1999. 72p. (YA). (ps up). pap. 7.95 (978-1-881283-24-9(0)) Alef Design Group.

Saunders, Catherine. The Story of Darth Vader. 2008. (Dk Readers Ser.). 48p. (J). 14.99 (****978-0-7566-3605-0(1)***); pap. 3.99 (****978-0-7566-3602-9(7)***) Dorling Kindersley Publishing, Inc.

Sava, Scott C. Eds Terrestrials. 2005. (Illus.). 80p. 19.99 (978-1-933428-64-2(3)) Alias Enterprises LLC.

Saxton, Curtis. Revenge of the Sith: Incredible Cross-Sections. Jenssen, Hans & Chasemore, Richard, illus. 2005. (Star Wars Ser.). 32p. (J). 19.99 (978-0-7566-1129-3(6) , 1241620) Dorling Kindersley Publishing, Inc.

Scanlan, S. Red Alert! Oops! 2001. 136p. (J). pap. 10.95 (978-0-595-18805-5(2) , Writers Club Pr.) iUniverse, Inc.

Schade, Susan. Faradawn. Buller, Jon, illus. 2007. (Fog Mound Ser.: No. 2). 208p. (J). (gr. 3-7). 15.99 (978-0-689-87686-8(6)) Simon & Schuster Children's Publishing.

—Travels of Thelonious. Buller, Jon, illus. 2007. (Fog Mound Ser.: No. 1). 224p. (J). (gr. 3-7). pap. 7.99 (978-0-689-87685-1(8) , Simon & Schuster Children's Publishing) Simon & Schuster Children's Publishing.

Schade, Susan & Buller, Jon. Space Dog Jack & the Haunted Spaceship. 2002. (Hello Reader! Ser.). (Illus.). 32p. (J). pap. 3.99 (978-0-439-32315-4(0) , Cartwheel Bks.) Scholastic, Inc.

—The Travels of Thelonious. 2006. (Fog Mound Ser.: No. 1). (Illus.). 224p. (J). (gr. 3-7). 14.95 (978-0-689-87684-4(X)) Simon & Schuster Children's Publishing.

Schanback, Mindy. Princess from Another Planet. 2005. 254p. (J). (gr. 5-9). 16.95 (978-0-8234-1847-3(2)) Holiday Hse., Inc.

Schleich, James J. The Sound Man. (Illus.). 64p. (J). pap. 7.00 (978-0-615-12142-0(X)) Schleich, James.

Schmitz, James H. Trigger & Friends. 2001. 480p. mass mkt. 6.99 (978-0-671-31966-3(3)) Baen Bks.

Schneider, John Lee. Extinction: Dragons of Earth: A Novel. 2005. 173p. (YA). pap. (978-1-890109-79-0(7) , Cross Time) Crossquarter Publishing Group.

Scholastic, Inc. Staff. The Big Bang Theory. 2002. (Butt-Ugly Martians Chapter Bks.: No. 1). 80p. (J). (gr. k-7). pap. 4.99 (978-0-439-37023-3(X)) Scholastic, Inc.

—Bionicle Chronicles: Box Set 1-4: Tales of the Masks; Makuta's Revenge; Beware the Bohrok; Tale of the Toa. 2004. (Bionicle Ser.). (Illus.). 620p. (J). (gr. 4-7). 19.96 (978-0-439-69053-9(6)) Scholastic, Inc.

—Lost in Space: Digest. 1998. (Illus.). (J). (gr. 3-7). pap. 3.98 (978-0-590-18934-7(4)) Scholastic, Inc.

Scholastic, Inc. Staff, ed. Chicken Soup for Little Souls: The Never Forgotten Doll. Date not set. (Star Wars Ser.). (J). pap. 4.95 (978-0-590-39635-6(8)) Scholastic, Inc.

Scholastic, Inc. Staff & Farshtey, Greg. Mystery of Metru Nui: Bionicle Adventures. 2004. (Bionicle Adventures Ser.: Vol. 1). (Illus.). 96p. (J). 4.99 (978-0-439-60731-5(0)) Scholastic, Inc.

Schooley, Bob. Kim Possible Cine-Manga, 9 vols., Vol. 7. McCorkle, Mark, illus. 2004. 96p. pap. 7.99 (978-1-59182-570-8(9) , Tokyopop Kids) TOKYOPOP, Inc.

—Kim Possible Cine-Manga: Sink or Swim & Number One, 9 vols., Vol. 6. McCorkle, Mark, illus. 2004. 96p. pap. 7.99 (978-1-59182-569-2(5) , Tokyopop Kids) TOKYOPOP, Inc.

Schuler, Betty Jo. Double Trouble Ditto Box. Cummins, Sandy, ed. 2002. (Shadows Trilogy Ser.). 48p. (J). mass mkt. (978-1-876962-68-5(2)) Writers Exchange E-Publishing Australia.

Schusterman, Neal. The Dark Side of Nowhere. unabr. ed. 2004. 192p. (J). (gr. 4-7). pap. 36.00 incl. audio (978-0-8072-8757-6(1) , YA258SP, Listening Library) Random Hse. Audio Publishing Group.

Schut, A. J. Harmony Island. 2002. 176p. pap. 19.95 (978-1-59129-798-7(2)) PublishAmerica, Inc.

Schwartz, Ellen. Starshine & the Fanged Vampire Spider. 2000. (Starshine Ser.: Vol. 4). 182p. (J). (gr. 3-7). pap. 6.95 (978-1-896095-60-8(7) , Polestar Book Pubs.) Raincoast Bk. Distribution CAN. *Dist:* Transition Vendor.

Science Fiction. 2001. (Illus.). 48p. (J). (ps-3). 12.95 (978-0-439-23810-6(2)) Scholastic, Inc.

Science Fiction Collection. (Fiction Collections). 160.77 (978-1-59889-043-3(3)) Stone Arch Bks.

Scieszka, Jon. Baloney (Henry P.) Smith, Lane, illus. 2005. 40p. (J). (gr. k-3). pap. 5.99 (978-0-14-240430-0(6) , Puffin) Penguin Group (USA) Inc.

—It's All Greek to Me. Smith, Lane, illus. 2004. (Time Warp Trio Ser.: No. 8). 96p. (J). (gr. 2-6). pap. 4.99 (978-0-14-240116-3(1) , Puffin) Penguin Group (USA) Inc.

—It's All Greek to Me. 2001. (Time Warp Trio Ser.: No. 8). (Illus.). (J). 11.79 (978-0-606-20730-0(9)) Tandem Library Bks.

Scieszka, Jon. Science Verse. Smith, Lane, illus. 2007. 40p. (J). (ps). pap. 9.99 (****978-0-670-06269-0(3)*** , Viking Juvenile) Penguin Group (USA) Inc.

Scion: Conflict of Conscience. 2002. (Scion Ser.). 28.47 (978-1-4046-1029-3(4)) Book Wholesalers, Inc.

Scion: Divided Loyalties. 2002. (Scion Ser.). (Illus.). 24.38 (978-1-4046-1563-2(6)) Book Wholesalers, Inc.

Scrimger, Richard. The Nose from Jupiter. 1998. (Illus.). 156p. (J). (ps-6). per. 16.40 (978-0-613-10237-7(1)) Tandem Library Bks.

Seal, Gyla B. & Taylor, January. Power Vector. 1998. 236p. (J). pap. 9.99 (978-0-88092-441-2(1) , 4411) Royal Fireworks Publishing Co.

Seidler, Tor. Brainboy & the DeathMaster. 320p. (J). 2005. pap. 6.99 (978-0-06-440935-3(X) , Harper Trophy); 2003. (gr. 3 up). 16.99 (978-0-06-029181-5(8)); 2003. (gr. 3 up). lib. bdg. 17.89 (978-0-06-029182-2(6)) HarperCollins Pubs.

Sennell, Joles. El Bosque Encantado. 4th ed. 1998. (Espasa Juvenil Ser.: Vol. 62). (SPA., Illus.). 116p. (J). (gr. 4-7). 7.95 (978-84-239-9033-7(8)) i.b.d., Ltd.

Service, Pamela F. My Cousin, the Alien. 2008. (J). lib. bdg. (****978-0-8225-7627-3(9)*** , Carolrhoda Bks.) Lerner Publishing Group.

Seto, Andy. Saint Legend, Vol. 4. 2003. (Illus.). 120p. (YA). (gr. 8 up). pap. 13.95 (978-1-58899-213-0(6)) ComicsOne Corp./Dr. Masters.

Shackelford, Mary Alice. Sojo. 2004. 87p. pap. 14.95 (978-1-4137-2276-5(8)) PublishAmerica, Inc.

Sharon, Lynn. Angelicum: Jewish Sci-Fi. 1999. pap. 9.95 (978-0-943706-63-4(7)) Pitspopany Pr.

Shasek, Judy & Schulz, Wendy Anderson. E-Wally & the Quest. 2001. (Adventures of E-Wally Ser.). 133p. (J). per. 9.95 (978-0-9711818-0-9(2)) Net Works Publishing.

Shearer, Alex. Child for the Afternoon (Pb) 2005. 282p. (J). pap. (****978-0-330-43190-3(0)*** , Macmillan Children's Bks.) Pan Macmillan.

Shortall, Leonard, illus. Encyclopedia Brown Keeps the Peace. 2002. (Encyclopedia Brown Ser.: No. 6). (J). 12.87 (978-0-7587-0848-9(3)) Book Wholesalers, Inc.

—Encyclopedia Brown Saves the Day. 2002. (Encyclopedia Brown Ser.). (J). 12.87 (978-0-7587-0850-2(5)) Book Wholesalers, Inc.

—Encyclopedia Brown Solves Them All. 2002. (Encyclopedia Brown Ser.: No. 5). (J). 12.87 (978-0-7587-0862-5(9)) Book Wholesalers, Inc.

Shudo, Takeshi & Sonoda, Hideki. Pokemon the First Movie. 2000. (Pokemon Ser.). (Illus.). 208p. (YA). (gr. 4-7). pap. 15.95 (978-1-56931-505-7(1)) Viz Media.

Shusterman, Neal. Unwind. 2007. 352p. (YA). (gr. 8 up). 16.99 (****978-1-4169-1204-0(5)*** , Simon & Schuster Children's Publishing) Simon & Schuster Children's Publishing.

Siembieda, Kevin. Rifter, No. 6. 1999. 112p. (YA). pap. 7.95 (978-1-57457-024-3(2)) Palladium Bks., Inc.

—Rifter, No. 11. Smith, Wayne & Marciniszyn, Alex, eds. Breaux, Wayne, Jr. et al, illus. 2000. (Rifter Ser.: vol. 11). 112p. (YA). (gr. 8 up). pap. 7.95 (978-1-57457-043-4(9) , 111) Palladium Bks., Inc.

—Rifter Number Nine. Smith, Wayne & Osten, James, eds. Breaux, Wayne, Jr. et al, illus. 2000. (Rifter Ser.). 112p. (YA). pap. 7.95 (978-1-57457-037-3(4) , 109) Palladium Bks., Inc.

—Rifter Number Twelve. Smith, Wayne & Marciniszyn, Alex, eds. Breaux, Wayne, Jr. et al, illus. 2000. (Rifter Ser.: Vol. 12). 112p. (YA). (gr. 8 up). pap. 7.95 (978-1-57457-044-1(7) , 112) Palladium Bks., Inc.

—Rifts Coalition Wars: Siege on Tolkeen - Sorcerers Revenge. Marciniszyn, Alex & Smith, Wayne, eds. Dorman, Dave et al, illus. 2000. 112p. (YA). (gr. 8 up). pap. 12.95 (978-1-57457-050-2(1) , 841) Palladium Bks., Inc.

—Rifts Coalition Wars Vol. 5: Shadows of Evil, 6 vols. Dorman, Dave, illus. 2001. (Rifts RPG Ser.: Vol. Five). 112p. (YA). pap. 12.95 (978-1-57457-052-6(8)) Palladium Bks., Inc.

Siembieda, Kevin & Coffin, Bill. Rifts Coalition Wars: Siege on Tolkeen - CS Overkill. Marciniszyn, Alex & Smith, Wayne, eds. Zeleznik, John et al, illus. 2000. 112p. (YA). (gr. 8 up). pap. 12.95 (978-1-57457-046-5(3) , 840) Palladium Bks., Inc.

Silberberg, Alan. Pond Scum. 2007. 288p. (gr. 3-7). pap. 5.99 (978-0-7868-5635-0(1)) Hyperion Pr.

Simmons, Monica. Aster City: 2Kul4Skul - The Hyperspace Hero. Ward, Jon, illus. 1998. (Aster Planet Chronicles Ser.: Vol. 5). 32p. (J). (gr. k-4). 15.95 (978-0-9658128-6-3(3)) Long Wind Publishing.

—Aster Desert: C. D. Romina in the Silicon Valley. Ward, Jon, illus. 1998. (Aster Planet Chronicles Ser.: Vol. 3). 32p. (J). (gr. k-4). 15.95 (978-0-9658128-4-9(7)) Long Wind Publishing.

—Aster Jungle: Furrdinand the Furrballer. Ward, Jon, illus. 1998. (Aster Planet Chronicles Ser.: Vol. 2). 32p. (J). (gr. k-4). 15.95 (978-0-9658128-3-2(9)) Long Wind Publishing.

—Aster Ocean: Dolfina the Bottlenoze Dolf. Ward, Jon, illus. 1998. (Aster Planet Chronicles Ser.: Vol. 4). 32p. (J). (gr. k-4). 15.95 (978-0-9658128-5-6(5)) Long Wind Publishing.

Simon, Seymour. The Gigantic Ants & Other Cases. 1998. (Einstein Anderson, Science Detective Ser.). (Illus.). (J). (gr. 3-6). pap. 3.99 (978-0-380-72657-8(2)) HarperCollins Pubs.

—The Invisible Man & Other Cases. rev. ed. 1998. (Einstein Anderson, Science Detective Ser.: Vol. 7). (Illus.). 96p. (J). (gr. 3-7). 14.95 (978-0-688-14447-0(0)) HarperCollins Pubs.

—The On-Line Spaceman & Other Cases. 1998. (Einstein Anderson, Science Detective Ser.). (Illus.). 96p. (J). (gr. 3-6). reprint ed. pap. 3.99 (978-0-380-72662-2(9)) HarperCollins Pubs.

Simons, Jamie & Scollon, E. W. All Hands on Deck. Evans, Michael, illus. 1998. (Goners Ser.: No. 3). 144p. (J). (gr. 3-7). pap. 3.99 (978-0-380-79732-5(1)) HarperCollins Pubs.

—Double Trouble. Evans, Michael, illus. 1999. (Goners Ser.: No. 9). 160p. (J). (gr. 3-7). pap. 3.99 (978-0-380-80725-3(4)) HarperCollins Pubs.

—The Hunt is On. Evans, Michael, illus. 1998. (Goners Ser.: No. 2). 144p. (J). (gr. 3-7). pap. 3.99 (978-0-380-79730-1(5)) HarperCollins Pubs.

—Rabid Transit, No. 5. Evans, Michael, illus. 1998. (Goners Ser.: No. 5). (J). (gr. 3-7). pap. 3.99 (978-0-380-79734-9(8)) HarperCollins Pubs.

—Spitting Image. Evans, Michael, illus. 1998. (Goners Ser.: No. 4). 160p. (J). (gr. 3-7). pap. 3.99 (978-0-380-79733-2(X)) HarperCollins Pubs.

—Under Loch & Key. Evans, Michael, illus. 1998. (Goners Ser.: No. 6). 144p. (J). (gr. 3-7). pap. 3.99 (978-0-380-79735-6(6)) HarperCollins Pubs.

Simonson, Louise, et al. X-Factor. 2007. (Essential Ser.: Vol. 2). (Illus.). 544p. pap. 16.99 (978-0-7851-2099-5(8)) Marvel Enterprises, Inc.

Sinclair, Peter. The Universe Is Made of Stories: Alex's Restaurant. 2001. 152p. pap. 12.95 (978-1-929462-34-6(4)) Plan Nine Publishing, Inc.

Singer, Maurene. A Place in the Sky. Marino, Natalie, illus. 2005. 52p. (J). 16.00 (978-0-9759382-0-1(7)) Carousel Pubns., Inc.

Singer, Nicky. GemX. 2008. (YA). (****978-0-8234-2108-4(2)***) Holiday Hse., Inc.

Singleton, Linda Joy. Regeneration: The Search. l.t. ed. 2002. 240p. (J). 23.95 (978-0-7862-3868-2(2)) Thorndike Pr.

—Regeneration: The Truth. l.t. ed. 2002. 266p. (YA). 23.95 (978-0-7862-3869-9(0)) Thorndike Pr.

Sinykin, Sheri Cooper. A Matter of Time. 1998. (Accelerated Reader Bks.). 208p. (J). (gr. 5-9). lib. bdg. 14.95 (978-0-7614-5019-1(X) , Cavendish Children's Bks.) Cavendish, Marshall Corp.

Skillchecks for Science Fiction. rev. ed. 2005. (Fastback Ser.). 32p. (J). (gr. 6-12). pap. 5.95 (978-0-13-024450-5(3)) Globe Fearon Educational Publishing.

Skrimager, R. J. The Making: Volume One of the Golden Isle. 2003. 380p. (YA). pap. 20.95 (978-0-595-26705-7(X) , Writers Club Pr.) iUniverse, Inc.

Skurzynski, Gloria. The Choice. 2006. (Virtual War Chronologs Ser.: Bk. 4). 240p. (YA). 16.95 (978-0-689-84267-2(8) , Atheneum) Simon & Schuster Children's Publishing.

—The Revolt. 2005. (Virtual War Chronologs Ser.: Bk. 3). 256p. (J). 16.95 (978-0-689-84265-8(1) , Atheneum) Simon & Schuster Children's Publishing.

Skvarch, Angela & Skvarch, Jeffrey. Dinosaurs in Space. 2004. 48p. (J). per. 9.95 (978-1-932560-35-0(1)) Media Creations, Inc.

Slade, Arthur. The Invasion of the IQ Snatchers. 2007. (Arthur Slade's Canadian Chills Ser.: No. 3). 120p. (YA). (gr. 4 up). 6.95 (****978-1-55050-361-6(8)***) Coteau Bks. CAN. *Dist:* Fitzhenry & Whiteside, Ltd.

Slattery, Tom. Open 25 Hours: Science Fiction, Fantasy & Ghost Stories. 2000. 144p. pap. 9.95 (978-0-595-14022-0(X)) iUniverse, Inc.

Sleator, William. The Boxes. 2000. 208p. (J). (gr. 3-7). pap. 5.99 (978-0-14-130810-4(9) , Puffin) Penguin Group (USA) Inc.

—The Boxes. 2000. (gr. 5-8). lib. bdg. 14.15 (978-0-613-28428-8(3)); (Illus.). (J). 12.64 (978-0-606-18833-3(9)) Tandem Library Bks.

—The Boy Who Reversed Himself. 1998. 176p. (J). (gr. 5-9). pap. 5.99 (978-0-14-038965-4(2) , Puffin) Penguin Group (USA) Inc.

—The Duplicate. 1999. (gr. 5-8). lib. bdg. 14.15 (978-0-8335-5902-9(8)) Tandem Library Bks.

—House of Stairs. 2001. (YA). 20.75 (978-0-8446-7186-4(X)) Smith, Peter Pub., Inc.

—The Night the Heads Came. 1998. (J). (978-0-606-13663-1(0)) Tandem Library Bks.

—Parasite Pig. 2004. (Illus.). 224p. (J). (gr. 7). pap. 6.99 (978-0-14-240086-9(6) , Puffin) Penguin Group (USA) Inc.

Slott, Dan. She-Hulk Volume 4: Laws of Attraction TPB: Laws of Attraction TPB. 2007. (Illus.). 192p. pap. 19.99 (978-0-7851-2218-0(4)) Marvel Enterprises, Inc.

Smith, Bryon. Night Visions Bk. 5: The Adventures of Megan Martin. 2003. 524p. (YA). pap. 20.00 (978-0-9745434-1-3(1)) Sweetgrass Pr., L.L.C.

—A Space in Time: The Adventures of Megan Martin. 2003. pap. 18.00 (978-0-9723376-5-6(2)) Sweetgrass Pr., L.L.C.

Smith, Dean Wesley & Rusch, Kristine Kathryn. Little Green Men. 2002. (Roswell Ser.: Vol. 3). 208p. (YA). pap. 6.99 (978-0-7434-1836-2(0) , Simon Pulse) Simon & Schuster Children's Publishing.

Smith, J. E. Complex City: All in a Day's Work. 2003. 120p. per. 12.95 (978-0-9728070-0-5(4)) Better Comics.

Smith, Larry. Cloud Realm. 2003. (Chronicles of Ingarde: Bk. 1). 218p. (YA). pap. 15.95 (978-0-595-30149-2(5)) iUniverse, Inc.

Soesbee, Ree. Pillar of Flame. 2007. (Elements Ser.: Vol. 1). (Illus.). 256p. (J). (gr. 5-9). pap. 5.99 (978-0-7869-4248-0(7) , Mirrorstone) Wizards of the Coast.

Sohn, Emily. A Crash Course in Forces & Motion with Max Axiom, Super Scientist. 2007. (Graphic Library). (Illus.). 32p. (J). (****978-0-7368-7890-6(4)*** , 1264931) Capstone Pr., Inc.

Solitaire, Jenna. Keeper of the Winds. 2006. (Guardian of the Boards Ser.). 256p. (YA). 6.99 (978-0-7653-5357-3(1) , Tor Teen) Doherty, Tom Assocs., LLC.

Souhami, Jessica. In the Dark Dark Wood. 2004. (Illus.). 24p. (J). 15.95 (978-1-84507-199-8(9)) Lincoln, Frances Ltd. GBR. *Dist:* Perseus Distribution.

Space Monster Saves the Day. 2007. (J). per. (****978-1-932570-61-8(6)***) Literacy Footprints Inc.

Spaceboy Chapter Books. 2007. (J). per. (****978-1-932570-60-1(8)***) Literacy Footprints Inc.

Spaziante, Patrick, illus. Meet Leatherhead. 2005. (Teenage Mutant Ninja Turtles Ser.). 24p. pap. 3.99 (978-0-689-87711-7(0) , Simon Spotlight) Simon & Schuster Children's Publishing.

Spinner, Stephanie & Bisson, Terry. Be First in the Universe. 2000. 144p. (gr. 3-7). 14.95 (978-0-385-32687-2(4) , Delacorte Bks. for Young Readers) Random Hse. Children's Bks.

Spire, Hazel. Secret of the Seventh Gate. 2001. 123p. (YA). (gr. 7-17). pap. 9.99 (978-0-88092-541-9(8) , 5418) Royal Fireworks Publishing Co.

Spirn, Michele. Racing Against the Light. 2001. (YA). pap. (978-1-56765-066-2(X) , R695P) AMSCO Schl. Pubns., Inc.

Spring, Manda. Emerald & the Magic of Raynon. 2004. 118p. pap. 16.95 (978-1-4137-3708-0(0)) PublishAmerica, Inc.

Springham, James. Earth-n-Bones: Blue Things. 2006. 54p. pap. 12.95 (978-1-4137-9738-1(5)) PublishAmerica, Inc.

—Earth-n-Bones: Toxic. 2005. 56p. pap. 12.95 (978-1-4137-9755-8(5)) PublishAmerica, Inc.

Star Maker. 2001. 32p. (J). (gr. k-3). 15.00 (978-0-06-025315-8(0)) HarperCollins Pubs.

Starlin, Jim. Infinity War. 2006. (Illus.). 400p. (YA). pap. 29.99 (978-0-7851-2105-3(6)) Marvel Enterprises, Inc.

Steck-Vaughn Staff. The Science Fair Surprise/Think Like a Scientist. 1999. (Take Me Home Ser.). (J). pap. 11.30 (978-0-7398-0942-6(3)) Steck-Vaughn.

Steele, Alexander. Unleashed in Space. 1999. (Super Adventures of Wishbone Ser.: No. 3). (J). (gr. 4-7). (978-0-606-19032-9(5)) Tandem Library Bks.

Steele, Allen. Oceanspace. 2001. (J). (978-0-606-21362-2(7)) Tandem Library Bks.

Steele, Michael Anthony. Digging to the Center of the Earth. Punchatz, Don, illus. l.t. ed. 1999. (Adventures of Wishbone Ser.: No. 17). (J). (gr. 4 up). lib. bdg. 22.60 (978-0-8368-2595-4(0)) Stevens, Gareth Inc.

—Winx Club: Secret Powers. 2005. (Winx Club Ser.). (Illus.). 120p. (J). 4.99 (978-0-439-68511-5(7)) Scholastic, Inc.

Stein, Erin K. Sam's New Car. Staples, Val, illus. 2007. (Transformers Ser.). 24p. (J). pap. 3.99 (****978-0-06-088823-7(7)*** , Harper Entertainment) HarperCollins Pubs.

Steinberg, David. Mac Attack! Smith, Brian, illus. 2008. 96p. (J). (gr. 3-6). pap. 5.99 (****978-0-448-44699-8(5)*** , Grosset & Dunlap) Penguin Group (USA) Inc.

Stephens, J. B. The Big Empty. 2004. (Big Empty Ser.: Bk. 1). 240p. (YA). (gr. 7-12). pap. 6.99 (978-1-59514-006-7(9) , Razorbill) Penguin Group (USA) Inc.

Stephenson, Larry K. & Weinbrenner, Patti. The Butterfly King: A Legend for the New Millennium. Stephenson, Larry K., illus. 1999. (Illus.). v, 45p. (J). (gr. 4). 19.95 (978-0-9672202-0-8(3)) Jewel Box & Friends.

Stephenson, Neal. Snow Crash. 2000. (Illus.). 468p. (gr. 7-12). per. 23.40 (978-0-613-36162-0(8)) Tandem Library Bks.

Sterling, Bruce. Distraction. 1999. (Illus.). 532p. lib. bdg 13.64 (978-0-606-17995-9(X)) Tandem Library Bks.

Stern, Steven L. The Earth Project. 2001. (YA). pap. (978-1-56765-068-6(6) , R697P) AMSCO Schl. Pubns., Inc.

Stevermer, Caroline & Collin, Frances. River Rats. 2005. (Illus.). 320p. (YA). (gr. 7-12). pap. 6.95 (978-0-15-205554-7(1) , Magic Carpet Bks.) Harcourt Children's Bks.

Stewart, Paul & Riddell, Chris. Blobheads. 2005. (Read-along Ser.). (Illus.). (J). audio (978-0-7540-6285-1(6)) BBC Audio.

—Stormchaser. 2004. (Edge Chronicles Ser.: Bk. 2). (Illus.). 400p. (gr. 5-7). (J). lib. bdg. 14.99 (978-0-385-75071-4(4)); 12.95 (978-0-385-75070-7(6)) Random Hse. Children's Bks. (Fickling, David Bks.).

—Vox. 2005. (Edge Chronicles Ser.: Bk. 6). (Illus.). 400p. (J). (gr. 5-7). 12.95 (978-0-385-75080-6(3)); lib. bdg. 14.99 (978-0-385-75081-3(1)) Random Hse. Children's Bks. (Fickling, David Bks.).

Stewart, Trenton Lee. The Mysterious Benedict Society. Ellis, Carson, illus. 2007. 496p. (J). (gr. 3-7). 16.99 (978-0-316-05777-6(0) , Tingley, Megan Bks.) Little, Brown Bks. for Young Readers.

—The Mysterious Benedict Society. 2006. (978-0-307-28440-2(9) , Listening Library) Random Hse. Audio Publishing Group.

Stewart, Trenton Lee. Mysterious Benedict Society 2. 2008. 448p. 16.99 (****978-0-316-05780-6(0)***) Little Brown & Co.

Stier, Roy E. Son of Bunyon & the Swamp Angel. 2002. (J). pap. 11.95 (978-1-58151-082-9(9)) BookPartners, Inc.

Stine, R. L. Attack of the Mutant. 2004. (Goosebumps Ser.). 144p. (J). 4.99 (978-0-439-66215-4(X)) Scholastic, Inc.

Stoddard, Michael Eugene. The Porthole to Time. 1999. 176p. (YA). pap. 9.95 (978-0-9675924-0-4(2)) Stoddard, Michael Eugene.

S

Stohler, Dee. Conquest of Quagmire. 2004. 142p. pap. 19.95 (978-1-4137-4868-0(6)) PublishAmerica, Inc.

Stone, David Lee. The Shadewell Shenanigans. 3rd rev. ed. 2006. (Illmore Chronicles: Bk. 3). 320p. (gr. 6-9). 16.99 (978-0-7868-3795-3(0)) Hyperion Pr.

Stories Beyond Time & Space. (J). pap. 15.50 (978-0-8359-0158-1(0)) Globe Fearon Educational Publishing.

Straczynski, J. M. Hyperion. 2006. (Illus.). 120p. pap. 14.99 (978-0-7851-1895-4(0)) Marvel Enterprises, Inc.

Stradley, Randy, et al. Jedi Council: Acts of War. 2001. (Star Wars Ser.). 96p. (YA). (gr. 7 up). pap. 12.95 (978-1-56971-539-0(4)) Dark Horse Comics.

Strahan, Jonathan. The Starry Rift. 2008. (J). (gr. 7). 19.99 (*978-0-670-06059-7(3) , Viking Juvenile) Penguin Group (USA) Inc.

Strasser, Dirk. Lost in Space. 2000. (gr. 7-12). lib. bdg. 12.10 (978-0-613-28937-5(4)) Tandem Library Bks.

Strasser, Todd. Anakin Skywalker. 1999. (Star Wars Episode 1 : Vol. 1). (Illus.). 112p. (J). (gr. 4-7). pap. 5.99 (978-0-590-52093-5(8)) Scholastic, Inc.

—Anakin Skywalker. 1999. (gr. 3-6). lib. bdg. 14.15 (978-0-613-16588-4(8)) Tandem Library Bks.

Strasshofer, Craig. Picture Me in the Future. Thompson, Jennifer, photos by. 2000. (Picture Me Ser.). (Illus.). 10p. (J). (ps-2). bds. 6.99 (978-1-57151-585-8(2)) Playhouse Publishing.

Strauss, Elizabeth. Message on a Rocket. 2000. (gr. k-3). lib. bdg. 11.80 (978-0-613-29696-0(6)) Tandem Library Bks.

Strickland, Brad & Fuller, Thomas E. Missing! 2004. (Mars Year One Ser.: No. 2). (Illus.). 176p. (J). pap. 4.99 (978-0-689-86401-8(9) , Aladdin) Simon & Schuster Children's Publishing.

Stromberg, Ronica. The Glass Inheritance. Dodge, Chris, illus. 2001. 126p. (J). (gr. 4-6). 9.99 (978-0-88092-543-3(4) , 5434) Royal Fireworks Publishing Co.

Stroud, David Wayne. Wiggles the White Blood Cell. Stroud, David Wayne, illus. 2005. (Illus.). (J). 14.95 (978-0-9762835-1-5(4)) Shooting Star Publishing.

Sullivan, Michael J. The Ultimate Adventures New Digidestined, 2. 2001. (Digimon Ser.). 96p. (J). (gr. 4-7). pap. 4.50 (978-0-06-107206-2(0) , Harper Entertainment) HarperCollins Pubs.

Sumerak, Marc. Big Trouble at the Big Top. 2007. 21.35 (978-1-59961-219-5(4)) Spotlight.

—Costumes On. 2007. 21.35 (978-1-59961-220-1(8)) Spotlight.

Suter, Joanne. War of the Worlds. 2003. (gr. 7-12). lib. bdg. 15.25 (978-0-613-65749-5(7)) Tandem Library Bks.

Sutherland, Tui. Shadow Falling. 2007. (Avatars Ser.: Bk. 2). 368p. (YA). (gr. 7 up). 16.99 (*978-0-06-085146-0(5)); (J). lib. bdg. 17.89 (*978-0-06-085147-7(3)) HarperCollins Pubs. (Eos).

—So This Is How It Ends. 2007. (Avatars Ser.: Bk. 1). 512p. (J). pap. 6.99 (*978-0-06-075029-9(4) , Eos) HarperCollins Pubs.

Sweeny, Sheila. Scyther, Heart of a Champion. 2000. (Pokemon Chapter Bks.: No.12). (Illus.). (J). (gr. 2-7). pap. 128.88 (978-0-439-21190-1(5)); No. 12. 96p. pap. 4.50 (978-0-439-16945-5(3)) Scholastic, Inc.

Swindells, Robert. Timesnatch. 2000. (Illus.). 171p. (J). pap. 8.99 (978-0-440-86322-9(8)) Transworld Publishers Ltd. GBR. *Dist:* Trafalgar Square Publishing.

—World-Eater. l.t. ed. 2005. 200p. (J). pap. (978-0-7540-6192-2(2) , CLP 386) BBC Audio.

Sykes, Harold S. The Beacon of Airport Seven. 2004. reprint ed. pap. 15.95 (978-1-4191-5375-4(7)); pap. 1.99 (978-1-4192-5375-1(1)) Kessinger Publishing, LLC.

Tajin, Satoshi, et al. Pokemon Tv Animation Comic: I Choose You! Ono, Toshihiro, illus. 1999. (Pokemon Ser.). 128p. (YA). (gr. 2-7). pap. 10.95 (978-1-56931-455-5(1)) Viz Media.

Takahashi, Kazuki. Yu-Gi-Oh! Vol. 3: Capsule Monster Chess, 3. Sengupta, Anita, tr. Takahashi, Kazuki, illus. 2003. (Yu-Gi-Oh! Ser.). (Illus.). 216p. (YA). pap. 7.95 (978-1-59116-179-0(7)) Viz Media.

Takahashi, Rumiko. Inu-Yasha, Vol. 13. Takahashi, Rumiko, illus. 2003. (Inuyasha Ser.). (Illus.). 192p. (YA). pap. 8.95 (978-1-56931-808-9(5)) Viz Media.

Takashi, Toshiko & Toda, Akihito. Fly on, Butterfree. Kimura, Naoyo & Himeno, Kagemaru, illus. 1999. (Pokemon Tales Ser.: No. 7). 18p. (YA). (ps-k). 4.95 (978-1-56931-420-3(9)) Viz Media.

Tamura, Yumi. Chicago Book of Justice, Vol. 2. Tamura, Yumi, illus. 2003. (Chicago Ser.: Vol. 2). (Illus.). 200p. (YA). pap. 15.95 (978-1-56931-829-4(8)) Viz Media.

Tan, Shaun. The Lost Thing. (Illus.). 32p. pap. (978-0-7344-0388-9(7)); 2002. (YA). (978-0-7344-0074-1(8)) Hachette Livre Australia. (Lothian Bks.).

—The Lost Thing. 2004. (Illus.). 32p. (J). 16.95 (978-1-894965-10-1(8)) Simply Read Bks. CAN. *Dist:* Perseus Distribution.

Tartakovsky, Genndy. Dexter's Laboratory: Zappo Change-O. Tartakovsky, Genndy, illus. 2001. 24p. (J). (ps-k). pap. 2.99 (978-0-307-99812-5(6) , Golden Bks.) Random Hse. Children's Bks.

Tavicat Staff, illus. Sushi Girl 1. 19th rev. ed. 2000. (Sushi Girl Ser.). 96p. (gr. 8-12). pap. 9.95 (978-1-892213-25-9(7) , Pocket Mixx) Mixx Entertainment, Inc.

Taylor, Cora. On Wings of Evil. 2005. 250p. (J). (gr. k-17). (978-1-55041-929-0(3)) Fitzhenry & Whiteside, Ltd.

Taylor, G. P. El Hechicero de las Sombras. Attrache, Ismael, tr. 2005. (SPA.). 328p. pap. 9.95 (978-950-511-910-3(0)) Santillana USA Publishing Co., Inc.

Taylor, G. P. Wormwood. 2004. (Illus.). 320p. (J). pap. (*978-0-571-22150-9(5)) Faber & Faber, Ltd.

—Wormwood. 2004. (Illus.). 272p. (J). (gr. 3-6). 17.99 (978-1-59185-626-9(4)) Strang Communications Co.

Teacher Talk: Individual Title Six-Packs. (ps-2). 27.00 (978-0-7635-9477-0(6)) Rigby Education.

Techno Terror. 2005. (Thrillogy Ser.). (Illus.). 48p. (gr. 4-8). 17.50 (978-0-7910-8869-2(3)) Facts On File, Inc.

Teitelbaum, Michael. The Story of the X-Men: How It All Began. O'Neill, Cynthia, ed. 2000. (Dorling Kindersley Readers Ser.). (Illus.). 32p. (J). (gr. 4-7). pap. 3.99 (978-0-7894-6697-6(X)) Dorling Kindersley Publishing, Inc.

—The Story of the X-Men: How It All Began. 2000. (978-0-606-22326-3(6)) Tandem Library Bks.

Teitelbaum, Michael & Dorling Kindersley Publishing Staff. The Story of the X-Men: How It All Began. 2000. (Dorling Kindersley Readers Ser.). (Illus.). 32p. (J). (gr. 4-7). 12.99 (978-0-7894-6696-9(1)) Dorling Kindersley Publishing, Inc.

Teply, George. Lost Crown of Meleor. 2000. (gr. k-3). lib. bdg. 15.25 (978-0-613-30013-1(0)) Tandem Library Bks.

Testa, Dom. Galahad 1: The Comet's Curse. 2005. 224p. (YA). per. 8.95 (978-0-9760564-0-9(2)) Profound Impact Group.

—Galahad 2: The Web of Titan. 2006. (YA). per. 8.95 (978-0-9760564-1-6(0)) Profound Impact Group.

Testa, Dom. Galahad 3: The Cassini Code. 2008. 272p. (YA). pap. 9.95 (*978-0-9760564-4-7(5)) Profound Impact Group.

Tezuka, Osamu. Astro Boy. (YA). Vol. 5. 2002. (Illus.). 216p. pap. 9.95 (978-1-56971-680-9(3) , 378471); Vol. 6. 2002. (Illus.). 232p. pap. 9.95 (978-1-56971-681-6(1) , 378472); Vol. 12. 2003. (Illus.). 224p. pap. 9.95 (978-1-56971-813-1(X)); Vol. 13. 2003. (Illus.). 224p. (gr. 9 up). pap. 9.95 (978-1-56971-894-0(6)); Vol. 19. 2003. 208p. pap. 9.95 (978-1-56971-900-8(4)); Vol. 20. 2003. 224p. pap. 9.95 (978-1-56971-901-5(2)); Vol. 21. 2003. 232p. pap. 9.95 (978-1-56971-902-2(0)); Vol. 22. 2003. 216p. pap. 9.95 (978-1-56971-903-9(9)) Dark Horse Comics.

—The Dawn. Tezuka, Osamu, illus. 2003. (Phoenix Ser.: Vol. 1). (Illus.). 344p. (YA). pap. 15.95 (978-1-56931-868-3(9)) Viz Media.

—Nextworld. 2003. (YA). Vol. 1. (Illus.). 160p. pap. 13.95 (978-1-56971-866-7(0)); Vol. 2. 152p. pap. 13.95 (978-1-56971-867-4(9)) Dark Horse Comics.

—Phoenix Vol. 3: Yamato/Space. Tezuka, Osamu, illus. 2003. (Phoenix Ser.). (Illus.). 336p. (YA). pap. 15.95 (978-1-59116-100-4(2)) Viz Media.

Thaler, Mike. Science Fair from the Black Lagoon. Lee, Jared D., illus. 2004. 64p. (J). lib. bdg. 15.00 (*978-1-4242-2259-9(1)) Fitzgerald Bks.

Thomas, Lynne N. Sneak Force: Mission 1 the Legend. 2003. 148p. pap. 9.95 (*978-1-932303-18-6(9) , Llumina Pr.) Media Creations, Inc.

Thomas, Nigel. Tom Travis: The Lost People of Orion. 2006. 193p. pap. 19.95 (978-1-4241-0382-9(7)) PublishAmerica, Inc.

Thomas, Patrick. The Wildsidhe Chronicles Bk. 1: Welcome to the Wildsidhe. 2002. (J). pap. 7.99 (978-1-890096-12-0(1)) Padwolf Publishing, Inc.

Thomas, Roy. Rogues in the House & Other Stories. 2003. (Chronicles of Conan Ser.: Vol. 2). 144p. (YA). pap. 15.95 (978-1-59307-023-6(3)) Dark Horse Comics.

—Roy Thomas. 2006. (Marvel Visionaries Ser.). (Illus.). 352p. (YA). 34.99 (978-0-7851-2088-9(2)) Marvel Enterprises, Inc.

Thomas, Roy, et al. Avengers. 2006. (Marvel Essentials Ser.: Vol. 5). (Illus.). 552p. pap. 16.99 (978-0-7851-2087-2(4)) Marvel Enterprises, Inc.

Thompson, Kate. Fourth World. 2005. 316p. (YA). (ps-7). 16.95 (978-1-58234-650-2(X) , Bloomsbury Children) Bloomsbury Publishing.

Thompson, Kate. Origins. 2007. (Missing Link Trilogy Ser.: Bk. 3). 320p. (YA). (gr. 7 up). 17.95 (*978-1-58234-652-6(6) , Bloomsbury Children) Bloomsbury Publishing.

Thompson, Kirk Robert. Paradise Lost: Earth First. 2004. 384p. (YA). per. 18.95 (978-0-9716681-3-3(2)) Magic Valley Pubs.

Thorpe, Kiki. Treasure Planet: Jim's Journal. 2002. (ps-2). lib. bdg. 11.80 (978-0-613-50576-5(X)) Tandem Library Bks.

Thorsland, Dan, et al. The Kalarba Adventures. Hughes, Bill et al, illus. (Star Wars Ser.). 200p. (J). (gr. 3 up). pap. 17.95 (978-1-56971-064-7(3)) Dark Horse Comics.

Thrillogy. 2006. (Illus.). (gr. 4-8). 77.70 (978-0-7910-9070-1(1)) Facts On File, Inc.

Titlebaum, Ellen. Down Under. 1999. (gr. 3-6). lib. bdg. 13.00 (978-0-613-73082-2(8)) Tandem Library Bks.

Tocco, John V. Elfinbright: The Tale of the Forever Present. Smith, Nancy Velick, illus. 2001. 32p. 16.95 (978-0-9711665-0-9(1)) Favorite Uncle Bks., LLC.

—Meet the Gizmos: The First Kids on the International Space Station. Tocco, Douglas, illus. 2003. 32p. 16.95 (978-0-9711665-2-3(8)); per. 9.95 (978-0-9711665-3-0(6)) Favorite Uncle Bks., LLC.

Toda, Akihito. Bulbasaur's Trouble, Vol. 3. Itoh, Benimaru & Himeno, Kagemaru, illus. 1999. (Pokemon Tales Ser.: No. 3). 18p. (YA). (ps-k). 4.95 (978-1-56931-385-5(7)) Viz Media.

—Charmander Sees a Ghost. Himeno, Kagemaru, illus. 1999. (Pokemon Tales Ser.: No. 1). 18p. (YA). (ps-k). 4.95 (978-1-56931-383-1(0)) Viz Media.

—Meet Mew! Himeno, Kagemaru, illus. 2000. (Pokemon Tales Ser.: No. 9). 18p. (YA). (ps-k). 4.95 (978-1-56931-440-1(3)) Viz Media.

Tomizawa, Hitoshi. Alien Nine: Emulators. Pannone, Frank, ed. Jackson, Laura & Kobayashi, Yoko, trs. from JPN. Tomizawa, Hitoshi, illus. 2004. (Illus.). 248p. pap. 9.99 (978-1-58664-924-1(8) , CMX 65004G, CPM Manga) Central Park Media Corp.

Torres, J. Birthquake. 2003. (Jason & the Argobots Ser.: Vol. 1). (Illus.). 112p. pap. 11.95 (978-1-929998-55-5(4)) Oni Pr., Inc.

Torrey, Michele. The Case of the Gasping Garbage. Johansen Newman, Barbara & Newman, Barbara, illus. 2001. (Doyle & Fossey, Science Detectives Ser.). 112p. (J). (gr. 3-6). 14.99 (978-0-525-46657-4(6) , Dutton Juvenile) Penguin Group (USA) Inc.

Trondheim, Lewis. Kaput & Zosky. 2008. 80p. (J). pap. 13.95 (*978-1-59643-132-4(6) , First Second Bks.) Roaring Brook Pr.

Tsukirino, Yumi. Magical Pokemon Vol. 3: Pokemon Holiday. Tsukirino, Yumi, illus. 2000. (Magical Pokemon Journey Ser.: No. 3). (Illus.). 40p. (YA). (ps-3). pap. 4.95 (978-1-56931-457-9(8)) Viz Media.

Tuazon, Noel & Keating, Scott A., illus. Elk's Run. 2007. 224p. 19.95 (978-0-345-49511-2(X) , Villard Bks.) Random House Publishing Group.

Tunnell, Michael O. Moon Without Magic. 2007. 240p. (YA). (gr. 7). 17.99 (*978-0-525-47729-7(2) , Dutton Juvenile) Penguin Group (USA) Inc.

Turtledove, Harry. Second Contact. 2000. (Illus.). (J). (978-0-606-18095-5(8)) Tandem Library Bks.

Ueyama, Michiro. Chaotic Century. Ueyama, Michiro, illus. (Zoids Ser.). (Illus.). (YA). Vol. 7. 2002. 80p. pap. 5.95 (978-1-56931-766-2(6)); Vol. 8. 2002. 72p. pap. 5.95 (978-1-56931-767-9(4)); Vol. 9. 2002. 72p. pap. 5.95 (978-1-56931-768-6(2)); Vol. 10. 2002. 70p. pap. 5.95 (978-1-56931-857-7(3)); Vol. 11. 2004. 82p. pap. 5.95 (978-1-56931-858-4(1)); Vol. 12. 2003. 72p. pap. 5.95 (978-1-56931-867-6(0)) Viz Media.

Uncle Henry. Biode. Uncle Henry, illus. 100th ed. 2004. (Illus.). 216p. pap. 7.99 (978-1-932568-02-8(6) , UHB003) Uncle Henry Bks.

Valdés, Zoé. Los Aretes de la Luna. 2nd ed. 2000. (SPA., Illus.). 72p. (J). (gr. 3-5). 6.36 net. (978-84-241-7888-8(2)) Lectorum Pubns., Inc.

Valentine, James. JumpMan Rule #2: Don't Even Think about It. 2005. (Illus.). 288p. (J). 14.95 (978-0-689-87353-9(0)) Simon & Schuster Children's Publishing.

—The Past Is Gone. 2007. (Timejumpers Ser.). 288p. (J). pap. 5.99 (978-1-4169-3955-9(5) , Aladdin) Simon & Schuster Children's Publishing.

Valentine, James. The Present Never Happens. 2007. (TimeJumpers Ser.). 304p. (J). pap. 5.99 (*978-1-4169-3956-6(3) , Aladdin) Simon & Schuster Children's Publishing.

Van Belkom, Edo. Wolf Pack. 2004. 184p. (J). (gr. 6). pap. 8.95 (978-0-88776-669-5(2)) Tundra Bks., Inc./Livres Toundra, Inc. CAN. *Dist:* Random Hse., Inc.

Van Draanen, Wendelin. Meet the Gecko. Biggs, Brian, illus. 2005. (Shredderman Ser.: Bk. 3). 176p. (J). (gr. 2-5). 12.95 (978-0-375-82353-4(0)); lib. bdg. 14.99 (978-0-375-92353-1(5)) Random Hse. Children's Bks. (Knopf Bks. for Young Readers).

Van Pelt, James. Strangers & Beggars: Stories. 2002. (gr. 7-12). lib. bdg. 28.05 (978-0-613-60619-6(1)) Tandem Library Bks.

Vande Velde, Vivian. Heir Apparent. (Illus.). 336p. 2002. (YA). (gr. 3-7). 17.00 (978-0-15-204560-9(0)); 2004. (J). reprint ed. pap. 6.95 (978-0-15-205125-9(2) , Magic Carpet Bks.) Harcourt Children's Bks.

—Now You See It... 2005. (Illus.). 288p. (YA). 17.00 (978-0-15-205311-6(5)) Harcourt Children's Bks.

—User Unfriendly. 2001. (978-0-606-22618-9(4)) Tandem Library Bks.

Vargas, George. The Prophecy of the Ages: Of War & Choices. 2004. 458p. (YA). pap. 24.95 (978-0-595-29607-1(6)) iUniverse, Inc.

Vargas, Jay. Cantaleya. Vargas, Jay, illus. 2000. (Illus.). 112p. (YA). (gr. 4 up). pap. 11.99 (978-0-9674768-0-3(1)) Creative Endeavors Publishing.

—Cantaleya. 2000. 108p. (gr. 4-7). pap. 9.95 (978-0-595-09916-0(5)) iUniverse, Inc.

Varsell, Linda. Ends of Rainbow. Curtis, E., illus. 2003. 260p. (J). per. 8.00 (978-0-9725479-5-6(9)) Rainbow Communications.

—The Humane Touch. Curtis, E., illus. 2003. 316p. per. 10.00 (978-0-9728737-0-3(8)) Rainbow Communications.

—The Rainbow Breakers. Curtis, E., illus. 2003. 232p. per. 7.00 (978-0-9725479-3-2(2)) Rainbow Communications.

—The Rainbow Circle. Curtis, E., illus. 2003. 428p. (J). per. 10.00 (978-0-9725479-9-4(1)) Rainbow Communications.

—The Rainbow Dreamers. Curtis, E., illus. 2003. 262p. per. 8.00 (978-0-9725479-4-9(0)) Rainbow Communications.

—The Rainbow Makers. Curtis, E., illus. 2003. 148p. per. 6.00 (978-0-9725479-2-5(4)) Rainbow Communications.

—The Rainbow Planet. Curtis, E., illus. 2003. 162p. (J). per. 6.00 (978-0-9725479-7-0(5)) Rainbow Communications.

—The Rainbow Remnants. Curtis, E., illus. 2003. 204p. (J). per. 7.00 (978-0-9725479-8-7(3)) Rainbow Communications.

—The Rainbow Rescue. Curtis, E., illus. 2003. 200p. (J). per. 7.00 (978-0-9725479-6-3(7)) Rainbow Communications.

—With a Human Touch. Curtis, E., illus. 2003. 178p. per. 6.00 (978-0-9725479-0-1(8)) Rainbow Communications.

Vaughan, Brian K. Escape to New York. 2006. (Runaways Ser.: Vol. 5). (Illus.). 144p. pap. 7.99 (978-0-7851-1901-2(9)) Marvel Enterprises, Inc.

—Magnetic North. 2006. (Illus.). 128p. (YA). pap. 12.99 (978-0-7851-1906-7(X)) Marvel Enterprises, Inc.

—Ultimate X Men, Vol. 5. 2006. (Illus.). 296p. (YA). 29.99 (978-0-7851-2103-9(X)) Marvel Enterprises, Inc.

Vaupel, Robin. The Rules of the Universe by Austin W. Hale. 2007. 192p. (YA). (gr. 5 up). 16.95 (978-0-8234-1811-4(1)) Holiday Hse., Inc.

Verne, Jules. Journey to the Center of the Earth. 2002. (Great Illustrated Classics Ser.). (Illus.). 240p. (J). (gr. 3-8). 21.35 (978-1-57765-689-0(X) , ABDO & Daughters) ABDO Publishing Co.

—Journey to the Center of the Earth. Calaguian, Val, illus. 2nd ed. 1998. (Illustrated Classic Book Ser.). 61p. (J). (gr. 3 up). reprint ed. pap. 4.95 (978-1-56767-259-6(0)) Educational Insights, Inc.

—Jules Verne/Journey to the Center of the Earth. 2005. (Illus.). 48p. (gr. 5-8). 25.50 (978-0-7910-9105-0(8)) Facts On File, Inc.

—Twenty Thousand Leagues under the Sea. 2005. (Illus.). 32p. (C). pap. 9.00 (*978-0-582-85494-9(6)) Pearson ESL.

—Voyage au Centre de la Terre.Tr. of Voyage to the Center of the Earth. (FRE.). (J). pap. 14.95 (978-2-07-051437-3(4)) Gallimard, Editions FRA. *Dist:* Distribooks, Inc.

—20,000 Leagues under the Sea. Dillon, Leo & Dillon, Diane, illus. 2000. (Books of Wonder). 384p. (gr. 4-7). 24.99 (978-0-688-10535-8(1)) HarperCollins Pubs.

—20,000 Leagues under the Sea. 2003. (gr. 5-8). lib. bdg. 13.00 (978-0-613-66744-9(1)) Tandem Library Bks.

—20,000 Leagues under the Sea. 2004. (Fast Track Classics Ser.). (Illus.). 48p. (J). pap. 9.99 (978-0-237-52688-7(3) , Evans Brothers, Limited) Evans Publishing Group GBR. *Dist:* Independent Pubs. Group.

—20,000 Leagues under the Sea: Retold from the Jules Verne Original. Andreasen, Dan, illus. 2006. (Classic Starts Ser.). 160p. 4.95 (978-1-4027-2533-3(7)) Sterling Publishing Co., Inc.

Viz Comics Staff & Toda, Akihito. Pokemon Tales Gift Box Set 2: Psyduck's Tongue Twisters; Where's Clefairy's Voice?; Fly on, Butterfree; Dragonite's Christmas. Himeno, Kagemaru, illus. 2000. (Pokemon Tales Ser.: Nos. 5-8). 18p. (YA). (ps-k). pap. 19.95 (978-1-56931-526-2(4)) Viz Media.

Viz Media Staff. The Year's Best Articles, 2003. 2003. (Best of Animerica Ser.). (Illus.). 96p. (YA). pap. 12.95 (978-1-56931-899-7(9)) Viz Media.

Wada, Junko. I'm Not Pikachu! Pokemon Tales Movie Special. Aoki, Toshinao, illus. 1999. (Pokemon Tales Movie Special Ser.: No. 1). 18p. (YA). (ps-k). 4.95 (978-1-56931-422-7(5)) Viz Media.

Wada, Junko & Ono, Toshihiro. Pikachu Unparalleled Adventure. Aoki, Toshinao, illus. 2000. (Pokemon Tales Movie Special Ser.: No. 2). 200p. (YA). (ps-k). pap. 4.95 (978-1-56931-485-2(3)) Viz Media.

Wada, Junko & Toda, Akihito. Diglett's Birthday Party. Arai, Yasukazu & Himeno, Kagemaru, illus. 2000. (Pokemon Tales Ser.: No. 14). 18p. (YA). (ps-k). 4.95 (978-1-56931-487-6(X)) Viz Media.

—Dragonite's Christmas. Kimura, Naoyo & Himeno, Kagemaru, illus. 1999. (Pokemon Tales Ser.: No. 8). 18p. (YA). (ps-k). 4.95 (978-1-56931-421-0(7)) Viz Media.

—Eevee's Weather Report. Yamashita, Masako & Himeno, Kagemaru, illus. 2000. (Pokemon Tales Ser.: No. 13). 18p. (YA). (ps-k). 4.95 (978-1-56931-486-9(1)) Viz Media.

Waddington-Feather, John. Quill's Adventures in Mereful. 2004. 87p. pap. 14.95 (978-1-4137-1632-0(6)) PublishAmerica, Inc.

Wagner, John. Predator vs. Judge Dredd. 1998. (Predator Ser.). (Illus.). 80p. (YA). (gr. 9 up). pap. 9.95 (978-1-56971-345-7(6)) Dark Horse Comics.

Waid, Mark. Fantastic Four, Vol. 3. 2005. (Illus.). 256p. (YA). 29.99 (978-0-7851-2011-7(4)) Marvel Enterprises, Inc.

—Kingdom Come. Ross, Alex, illus. 2002. (YA). 22.40 (978-1-4046-0894-8(X)) Book Wholesalers, Inc.

Walden, Mark. The Overlord Protocol. 2008. (H. I. V. E. Ser.). 384p. (J). 15.99 (*978-1-4169-3573-5(8)) Simon & Schuster Children's Publishing.

Wall, Cynthia. A Spark to the Past. 1998. 184p. (J). (gr. 5-8). pap. 6.95 (978-0-931625-34-3(3)) DIMI Pr.

Walley, Chris. The Dark Foundations. 2006. (Lamb among the Stars Ser.). (Illus.). 560p. (YA). 19.99 (978-1-4143-0767-1(5) , Thirsty(?)) Tyndale Hse. Pubs.

Walters, Nick. Superior Beings. 2001. (Illus.). 288p. (J). pap. 6.95 (978-0-563-53830-1(9)) BBC Worldwide Americas.

Warrington, Dean Grey. Perfiction. 2007. 188p. per. 13.95 (*978-0-595-43758-0(3)) iUniverse, Inc.

Wasserman, Robin. Truth. 2007. (Chasing Yesterday Ser.). 240p. (J). pap. 5.99 (*978-0-439-93342-1(0) , Scholastic Paperbacks) Scholastic, Inc.

Waters, Galadriel, ed. The Plot Thickens... Harry Potter Investigated by Fans for Fans. Rogers, Melissa & Heran, Michelle, illus. 2005. 300p. (YA). pap. 18.95 (978-0-9723936-3-8(3)) Wizarding World Pr.

Watkins, Shelagh. Mr. Planemaker's Flying Machine. 2005. 197p. pap. 19.95 (978-1-4137-7136-7(X)) PublishAmerica, Inc.

Watson, Jacqueline. Mattie-Jo-Calico. 2003. 109p. pap. 16.95 (978-1-59286-920-6(3)) PublishAmerica, Inc.

Watson, Jude. The Captive Temple. 2000. (Star Wars Ser.: Bk. 7). (J). (gr. 4-7). 11.64 (978-0-606-19619-2(6)) Tandem Library Bks.

—The Changing of the Guard. Buelow, Alice & Mattingly, David, illus. 2004. (Star Wars Ser.: No. 8). 160p. (J). 5.99 (978-0-439-33924-7(3) , Scholastic Paperbacks) Scholastic, Inc.

—The Dangerous Rescue. 2001. (Star Wars Ser.: Bk. 13). (Illus.). (J). (gr. 4-7). 11.64 (978-0-606-21457-5(7)) Tandem Library Bks.

—The Dark Rival. 1999. (Star Wars Ser.: No. 2). (J). (gr. 4-7). 11.64 (978-0-606-16650-8(5)) Tandem Library Bks.

—Dark Warning. 2nd ed. 2005. (Star Wars Ser.: No. 2). 160p. (J). (ps-7). pap. 5.99 (978-0-439-68135-3(9) , Scholastic Paperbacks) Scholastic, Inc.

—The Day of Reckoning. 2000. (Star Wars Ser.: Bk. 8). (J). (gr. 4-7). 12.64 (978-0-606-19620-8(X)) Tandem Library Bks.

—Death on Naboo. 2006. (Star Wars Ser.: No. 4). 135p. (J). lib. bdg. 13.00 (*978-1-4242-0777-0(0)) Fitzgerald Bks.

—Death on Naboo. 2006. (Star Wars Ser.: No. 4). 160p. (J). pap. 5.99 (978-0-439-68137-7(5)) Scholastic, Inc.
—Deception. Nielsen, Cliff, illus. ed. 2001. (Star Wars Ser.: Bk. 1 Special Edition). 192p. (J). (gr. 4-7). pap. 5.99 (978-0-439-13938-0(4)) Scholastic, Inc.
—Deceptions. 2001. (Star Wars Ser.). (Illus.). (J). (gr. 4-7). 12.64 (978-0-606-21459-9(3)) Tandem Library Bks.
—The Defenders of the Dead. 1999. (Star Wars Ser.: Bk. 5). 11.64 (978-0-606-18608-7(5)) Tandem Library Bks.
—The Desperate Mission. 2005. (Star Wars Ser.: No. 1). 168p. (J). lib. bdg. 20.00 (***978-1-4242-0774-9(6)***) Fitzgerald Bks.
—The Desperate Mission. 2005. (Star Wars Ser.: No. 1). (J). 160p. mass mkt. 5.99 (978-0-439-68134-6(0) , Scholastic Paperbacks); 168p. (978-1-4155-9754-5(5)) Scholastic, Inc.
—The Evil Experiment. 2000. (Star Wars Ser.: Bk. 12). (J). (gr. 4-7). 12.64 (978-0-606-19938-4(1)) Tandem Library Bks.
—The False Peace. Buelow, Alicia, illus. 2004. (Star Wars Ser.: No. 9). 160p. (J). 5.99 (978-0-439-33925-4(1) , Scholastic Paperbacks) Scholastic, Inc.
—The Fight for Truth. 2000. (Star Wars Ser.: Bk. 9). (J). (gr. 4-7). 11.64 (978-0-606-19621-5(8)) Tandem Library Bks.
—The Final Showdown. Mattingly, David, illus. 2004. (Star Wars Ser.: No. 10). 144p. (J). (gr. 4-7). 5.99 (978-0-439-33926-1(X)) Scholastic, Inc.
—The Hidden Past. 1999. (Star Wars Ser.: Bk. 3). (J). (gr. 4-7). 11.64 (978-0-606-17040-6(5)) Tandem Library Bks.
—Legacy of the Jedi. Mattingly, David, illus. 2003. (Star Wars Ser.). 208p. (J). (gr. 3-7). pap. 12.95 (978-0-439-53666-0(9)) Scholastic, Inc.
—Legacy of the Jedi / Secrets of the Jedi. 2006. (Star Wars Ser.). 416p. (J). pap. 7.99 (978-0-439-85146-6(7) , Scholastic) Scholastic, Inc.
—The Mark of the Crown. 1999. (Star Wars Ser.: Bk. 4). 144p. (J). (gr. 4-7). pap. 4.99 (978-0-590-51934-2(4)) Scholastic, Inc.
—The Mark of the Crown. 1999. (Star Wars Ser.: Bk. 4). (J). (gr. 4-7). (978-0-606-19617-8(X)) Tandem Library Bks.
—Path to Truth. 2001. (Star Wars Ser.). 176p. (J). (gr. 3-6). pap. 12.95 (978-0-439-24204-2(5)) Scholastic, Inc.
—Return of the Dark Side. 2006. (Star Wars Ser.: No. 6). 160p. (J). pap. 5.99 (978-0-439-68139-1(1)) Scholastic, Inc.
—The School of Fear. Buelow, Alice & Mattingly, David, illus. 2003. (Star Wars Ser.: No. 5). 144p. (J). (gr. 3-7). 4.99 (978-0-439-33921-6(9)) Scholastic, Inc.
—Secret Weapon. 2007. (Star Wars Ser.: No. 7). 149p. (J). pap. 5.99 (978-0-439-68140-7(5) , Scholastic Paperbacks) Scholastic, Inc.
—Secrets of the Jedi. 2005. (Star Wars Ser.). 208p. (J). 12.95 (978-0-439-53667-7(7) , Scholastic Paperbacks) Scholastic, Inc.
—The Shadow Trap. 2003. (Star Wars Ser.: No. 6). (gr. 3-6). lib. bdg. 13.00 (978-0-613-66381-6(0)) Tandem Library Bks.
—The Shattered Peace. Nielsen, Cliff, illus. 2000. (Star Wars Ser.: Bk. 10). 144p. (J). (gr. 3-7). pap. 4.99 (978-0-590-52084-3(9)) Scholastic, Inc.
—The Shattered Peace. 2000. (Star Wars Ser.: Bk. 10). (J). (gr. 4-7). (978-0-606-19615-4(3)) Tandem Library Bks.
—The Ties That Bind. 2001. (Star Wars Ser.: Bk. 14). (Illus.). 136p. (J). (ps-7). lib. bdg. 11.64 (978-0-606-21458-2(5)) Tandem Library Bks.
—The Trail of the Jedi. 2002. (Star Wars Ser.: No. 2). 144p. (J). (gr. 3 up). pap. 5.99 (978-0-439-33918-6(9)) Scholastic, Inc.
—The Uncertain Path. 2000. (Star Wars Ser.: Bk. 6). (Illus.). 144p. (J). (gr. 4-7). pap. 5.99 (978-0-590-51969-4(7)) Scholastic, Inc.
—The Uncertain Path. 2000. (Star Wars Ser.: Bk. 6). (J). (gr. 4-7). (978-0-606-19618-5(8)) Tandem Library Bks.
—Underworld. 2005. (Star Wars Ser.: No. 3). 137p. (J). lib. bdg. 20.00 (***978-1-4242-0776-3(2)***) Fitzgerald Bks.
—Underworld. 3rd ed. 2005. (Star Wars Ser.: No. 3). 137p. (J). (gr. 4-7). pap. 5.99 (978-0-439-68136-0(7)) Scholastic, Inc.
—The Way of the Apprentice. 2002. (Star Wars Ser.: No. 1). 176p. (J). (gr. 3 up). mass mkt. 5.99 (978-0-439-33917-9(0)) Scholastic, Inc.
—The Way of the Apprentice. 2002. (Star Wars Ser.: No. 1). (gr. 3-6). lib. bdg. 13.00 (978-0-613-50655-7(3)) Tandem Library Bks.
Watson, Jude & Blondell, Judy. The Death of Hope. Nielsen, Cliff, illus. 2001. (Star Wars Ser.: Bk. 15). 144p. (J). (gr. 4-7). pap. 4.99 (978-0-439-13934-2(1)) Scholastic, Inc.
Waugh, Sylvia. Carrera Espacial. (SPA.). (YA). 8.95 (978-958-04-6028-2(0)) Norma S.A. COL. *Dist:* Distribuidora Norma, Inc.
—Space Race. 2001. 256p. (gr. 5 up). 5.50 (978-0-440-41714-9(7) , Yearling) Random Hse. Children's Bks.
—Space Race. 2001. (gr. 5-8). lib. bdg. 13.00 (978-0-613-88327-6(6)) Tandem Library Bks.
—Space Race. l.t. ed. 2001. 300p. (J). 20.95 (978-0-7862-3606-0(X)) Thorndike Pr.
Way, Daniel. Planet Hulk Prelude. 2006. (Illus.). 144p. pap. 13.99 (978-0-7851-1953-1(1)) Marvel Enterprises, Inc.
Webb, Catherine. Mirror Wakes. 2005. 314p. (Orig.). (J). pap. 9.99 (978-1-904233-09-1(0) , Atom Books) Little, Brown Bk. Group Ltd. GBR. *Dist:* Trafalgar Square Publishing.
Weber, Lou, ed. Star Wars: Revenge of the Sith: Play-a-Sound. 2004. (Illus.). 24p. (J). 15.98 (978-1-4127-3487-5(8) , 7262800) Publications International, Ltd.
Webster, David. Book One of the Naxos Island Mages: The Grand Adventure. 2003. 200p. 24.95 (978-0-595-75137-2(7)) iUniverse, Inc.
—Book One of the Naxos Island Mages: The Grand Adventure. 2003. 200p. pap. 14.95 (978-0-595-29933-1(4)) iUniverse, Inc.
Weigel, Jeff, illus. Atomic Ace & the Robot Rampage. 2006. 32p. (J). 15.95 (978-0-8075-0484-0(X)); pap. 6.95 (978-0-8075-0485-7(8)) Whitman, Albert & Co.
Wein, Elizabeth. The Sunbird. 2006. 208p. (YA). (gr. 7 up). pap. 6.99 (978-0-14-240171-2(4) , Puffin) Penguin Group (USA) Inc.
Weinman, Logan & Bennett, Jeffrey. Max's Ice Age Adventure. 2007. (Science Adventures Written by Kids Ser.). (Illus.). 32p. (J). pap. 12.00 (***978-0-9721819-2-1(X)***) Big Kid Science.
Weis, Margaret & Hickman, Tracy. To the Gates of Palanthas. 2003. (Dragonlance Ser.: Pt. 4). (Illus.). 256p. (YA). pap. 5.99 (978-0-7869-3096-8(9)) Wizards of the Coast.
Weiss, Bobbi J. G. & Weiss, David Cody. Brain Power. Mateu, Francesc, illus. 2003. (Dexter's Laboratory Ser.: No. 2). 24p. (J). pap. 3.50 (978-0-439-44942-7(1) , Scholastic Paperbacks) Scholastic, Inc.
—Deceptions. 1998. (Star Trek, The Next Generation: No. 14). (J). (gr. 3-6). (978-0-606-13812-3(9)) Tandem Library Bks.
Weller, Duncan, illus. Spacesnake. 2004. 32p. (J). 16.95 (978-1-894965-09-5(4)) Simply Read Bks. CAN. *Dist:* Perseus Distribution.
Wells, H. G. Classic Starts: the War of the Worlds. Akib, Jamel, illus. 2007. (Classic Starts Ser.). 160p. (J). 4.95 (978-1-4027-3688-9(6)) Sterling Publishing Co., Inc.
—The Invisible Man. Marcos, Pablo, illus. 2002. (Great Illustrated Classics Ser.). 240p. (J). (gr. 3-8). 21.35 (978-1-57765-817-7(5) , ABDO & Daughters) ABDO Publishing Co.
—The Lost World. 2004. (Fast Track Classics Ser.). (Illus.). 48p. (J). pap. 8.99 (978-0-237-52404-3(X) , Evans Brothers, Limited) Evans Publishing Group GBR. *Dist:* Independent Pubs. Group.
—The Magic Shop. Roca, Francois, illus. 2005. 32p. (J). (gr. 1-4). lib. bdg. 16.85 (978-1-933327-06-8(5)) Purple Bear Bks., Inc.
—The Time Machine. Lynch, Brendan, illus. 2002. (Great Illustrated Classics Ser.). 240p. (J). (gr. 3-8). 21.35 (978-1-57765-804-7(3) , ABDO & Daughters) ABDO Publishing Co.
—The Time Machine. 1999. (Saddleback Classics). (Illus.). (J). (978-0-606-21574-9(3)) Tandem Library Bks.
—The Time Machine. 2004. (Fast Track Classics Ser.). (Illus.). 48p. (J). pap. 8.99 (978-0-237-52406-7(6) , Evans Brothers, Limited) Evans Publishing Group GBR. *Dist:* Independent Pubs. Group.
—The Time Machine. Howell, Troy, illus. 2008. (Classic Starts Ser.). 160p. (J). 5.95 (***978-1-4027-4582-9(6)***) Sterling Publishing Co., Inc.
—Time Machine. abr. ed. 1999. (gr. 7-12). lib. bdg. 15.25 (978-0-613-33147-0(8)) Tandem Library Bks.
—The Time Machine. unabr. ed. 2002. (YA). pap. incl. audio compact disk (978-1-58472-338-7(6) , In Audio) Sound Room Pubs., Inc.
—The War of the Worlds. 2005. (Aladdin Classics Ser.). xv, 308p. (J). (***978-1-4155-9579-4(8)*** , Aladdin) Simon & Schuster Children's Publishing.
—The War of the Worlds. 2004. (Fast Track Classics Ser.). (Illus.). 48p. (J). pap. 8.99 (978-0-237-52405-0(8) , Evans Brothers, Limited) Evans Publishing Group GBR. *Dist:* Independent Pubs. Group.
—The War of the Worlds. Lynch, Brendan, illus. 2005. (Great Illustrated Classics Ser.). 238p. (J). (gr. 3-8). 21.35 (978-1-59679-253-1(1) , ABDO & Daughters) ABDO Publishing Co.
Wells, H. G. & Geary, Rick. The Invisible Man. (Classics Illustrated Ser.). (Illus.). 52p. (YA). pap. 4.95 (978-1-57209-020-0(0)) Classics International Entertainment, Inc.
Wells, H. G. & Roca, Francois. The Magic Shop. ed. 2005. (Illus.). 32p. (J). 15.95 (978-1-933327-02-0(2)) Purple Bear Bks., Inc.
Wells, H. G., et al. The Island of Dr. Moreau. (Illus.). 52p. (YA). pap. 4.95 (978-1-57209-012-5(X)) Classics International Entertainment, Inc.
Werley-Prieto, Elizabeth. Racing Through Time on a Flying Machine. 1999. (Publish-a-Book Ser.). (Illus.). 32p. (J). (gr. 1-6). pap. 8.50 (978-0-7398-0054-6(X)) Steck-Vaughn.
Werlin, Nancy. Double Helix. 2005. 256p. (YA). (gr. 3-6). pap. 6.99 (978-0-14-240327-3(X) , Puffin) Penguin Group (USA) Inc.
West, Cathy. All Growed Up. 2001. (gr. k-3). lib. bdg. 14.15 (978-0-613-43915-2(5)) Tandem Library Bks.
West, Terry M. The Legend of the Ghost Pokemon. 2000. (Pokemon Challenge Ser.: No. 2). (Illus.). 128p. (YA). (gr. 4-7). pap. 5.99 (978-0-439-15419-2(7)) Scholastic, Inc.
West, Tracey. Attack of the Prehistoric Pokemon. 1999. (Pokemon Chapter Bks.: No. 3). (Illus.). 80p. (J). (gr. 2-7). pap. 4.99 (978-0-439-13550-4(8)) Scholastic, Inc.
—Attack of the Prehistoric Pokemon. 1999. (gr. 3-6). lib. bdg. 12.40 (978-0-613-22685-1(2)); (Pokemon Chapter Bks.: No. 3). (J). (gr. 2-7). (978-0-606-19535-5(1)) Tandem Library Bks.
—Charizard, Go! 2000. (Pokemon Chapter Bks.: No. 6). (Illus.). 96p. (J). (gr. 2-7). pap. 4.50 (978-0-439-15421-5(9)) Scholastic, Inc.
—Donut Disaster. 2002. (gr. k-3). lib. bdg. 11.80 (978-0-613-72064-9(4)) Tandem Library Bks.
—The Four-Star Challenge. 2000. (Pokemon Chapter Bks.: No. 11). (Illus.). 80p. (J). (gr. 2-7). pap. 4.50 (978-0-439-16944-8(5)) Scholastic, Inc.
—I Choose You! 1999. (Pokemon Chapter Bks.: No. 1). (J). (gr. 2-7). (978-0-606-19568-3(8)) Tandem Library Bks.
—Island of the Giant Pokemon. 1999. (Pokemon Chapter Bks.: No. 2). (J). (gr. 2-7). (978-0-606-19570-6(X)) Tandem Library Bks.
—Maximus's School for Super Villains. 2006. (Atomic Betty Ser.: Vol. 2). 80p. (J). pap. 4.99 (978-0-448-44007-1(5) , Grosset & Dunlap) Penguin Group (USA) Inc.
—Night in the Haunted Tower. 1999. (Pokemon Chapter Bks.: No. 4). (Illus.). 80p. (J). (gr. 2-7). pap. 4.50 (978-0-439-13742-3(X)) Scholastic, Inc.
—Night in the Haunted Tower. 1999. (Pokemon Chapter Bks.: No. 4). (J). (gr. 2-7). (978-0-606-19585-0(8)) Tandem Library Bks.
—The Pet Store Sprite. 2006. (Pixie Tricks Ser.: No. 3). (Illus.). 80p. (J). (gr. 1-4). pap. 3.99 (978-0-439-17978-2(5) , Scholastic Paperbacks) Scholastic, Inc.
—Psyduck Ducks Out. 2000. (Pokemon Chapter Bks.: Vol. 15). (Illus.). 96p. (J). (gr. 2-7). pap. 4.50 (978-0-439-20091-2(1)) Scholastic, Inc.
—Race to Danger. 2000. (Pokemon Chapter Bks.: Vol. 13). (Illus.). 96p. (J). (gr. 2-7). pap. 4.50 (978-0-439-20089-9(X)) Scholastic, Inc.
—Return of the Squirtle Squad. 2000. (Pokemon Chapter Bks.: No. 8). (Illus.). 96p. (J). (gr. 2-7). pap. 4.50 (978-0-439-15429-1(4)) Scholastic, Inc.
—Secret of the Pink Pokemon. 2000. (Pokemon Chapter Bks.: No. 10). (Illus.). 96p. (J). (gr. 2-7). pap. 4.50 (978-0-439-16943-1(7)) Scholastic, Inc.
—Splashdown in Cerulean City. 2000. (Pokemon Chapter Bks.: No. 7). (Illus.). 96p. (J). (gr. 2-7). pap. 4.50 (978-0-439-15426-0(X)) Scholastic, Inc.
—Sporty Sprite. 2006. (Pixie Tricks Ser.: No. 6). (Illus.). 96p. (J). (gr. 6). mass mkt. 3.99 (978-0-439-17982-9(3) , Scholastic Paperbacks) Scholastic, Inc.
—Talent Showdown. 2000. (Pokemon Chapter Bks.: Vol. 14). (Illus.). 96p. (J). (gr. 2-7). pap. 4.50 (978-0-439-20090-5(3)) Scholastic, Inc.
West, Tracey, adapted by. I Choose You! 1999. (Pokemon Chapter Bks.: No. 1). (Illus.). 80p. (J). (gr. 2-7). pap. 4.50 (978-0-439-10464-7(5)) Scholastic, Inc.
West, Tracey & Michaels, Bill. Save Our Squirtle! 2000. (Pokemon Junior Chapter Bks.: No. 3). (Illus.). 48p. (J). (ps-3). pap. 3.99 (978-0-439-15420-8(0)) Scholastic, Inc.
Westerfeld, Scott. Blue Noon. (Midnighters Ser.: Vol. 3). 384p. 2007. (J). pap. 6.99 (978-0-06-051959-9(2)); 2006. (YA). 16.99 (978-0-06-051957-5(6)) HarperCollins Pubs.
—Extras. 2007. (Uglies Trilogy Ser.). 417p. (YA). (gr. 7-12). 16.99 (***978-1-4169-5117-9(2)*** , Simon Pulse) Simon & Schuster Children's Publishing.
—The Last Days. 2006. 304p. (YA). (gr. 9-12). 16.99 (978-1-59514-062-3(X) , Razorbill) Penguin Group (USA) Inc.
—The Secret Hour. (Midnighters Ser.). 304p. (gr. 7 up). 2004. (J). lib. bdg. 17.89 (978-0-06-051952-0(5)); 2005. (Illus.). (YA). reprint ed. pap. 6.99 (978-0-06-051953-7(3)) HarperCollins Pubs.
—Specials. (YA). 2007. 400p. (gr. 7 up). pap. 9.99 (***978-1-4169-4795-0(7)*** , Simon Pulse); 2006. (978-1-4169-2165-3(6)); 2006. 384p. (gr. 7 up). 15.95 (978-0-689-86540-4(6) , Simon Pulse) Simon & Schuster Children's Publishing.
—Touching Darkness. (Midnighters Ser.). 336p. 2005. (J). (gr. 7 up). lib. bdg. 16.89 (978-0-06-051955-1(X)); 2005. (YA). (gr. 7 up). 15.99 (978-0-06-051954-4(1)); 2006. (YA). reprint ed. pap. 6.99 (978-0-06-051956-8(8)) HarperCollins Pubs.
—Uglies. 2005. 448p. (YA). (gr. 7 up). pap. 8.99 (978-0-689-86538-1(4) , Simon Pulse) Simon & Schuster Children's Publishing.
Westerfeld, Scott. The Uglies Trilogy: Uglies, Pretties, Specials. 2007. 1216p. (YA). pap. 25.99 (***978-1-4169-3640-4(8)*** , Simon Pulse) Simon & Schuster Children's Publishing.
Westover, Alli. My Daddy Works at NASA. 2005. (J). 15.95 (978-1-888237-59-7(7)) Baxter Pr.
WeWrite Kids Staff. A Goo Idea! Brodland, Rita, ed. Freeman, Troy, illus. 2002. (WeWrite Kids! Ser.). 64p. (J). (gr. k-4). pap. 8.95 (978-1-57635-058-4(4)) WeWrite LLC.
Weyn, Suzanne. The Bar Code Revolution. 2006. 272p. (J). pap. 6.99 (978-0-439-80385-4(3) , Scholastic Paperbacks) Scholastic, Inc.
—The Bar Code Tattoo. 2004. (Point Thriller Ser.). 256p. (J). (gr. 7 up). pap. 5.99 (978-0-439-39562-5(3)) Scholastic, Inc.
Whitman, John. Adventures on File Island. 2000. (Digimon Ser.: No. 1). (Illus.). 96p. (J). (gr. 4-7). pap. 4.50 (978-0-06-107186-7(2) , Harper Entertainment) HarperCollins Pubs.
—City of the Dead. l.t. ed. 1998. (Star Wars Ser.: No. 2). 144p. (J). (gr. 4 up). lib. bdg. 22.60 (978-0-8368-2236-6(6)) Stevens, Gareth Inc.
—Eaten Alive. l.t. ed. 1998. (Star Wars Ser.: No. 1). 144p. (J). (gr. 4 up). lib. bdg. 22.60 (978-0-8368-2235-9(8)) Stevens, Gareth Inc.
—Legend Digidestined. 2001. (Digimon Ser.). (Illus.). 96p. (J). (gr. 4-7). pap. 4.50 (978-0-06-107198-0(6) , Harper Entertainment) HarperCollins Pubs.
—Leomon's Challenge. 2000. (Digimon Ser.: No. 4). 96p. (J). (gr. 1-6). pap. 4.50 (978-0-06-107189-8(7) , Harper Entertainment) HarperCollins Pubs.
—The Nightmare Machine. l.t. ed. 1998. (Star Wars Ser.: No. 4). 144p. (J). (gr. 4 up). lib. bdg. 22.60 (978-0-8368-2238-0(2)) Stevens, Gareth Inc.
Wiesner, David. June 29, 1999. Wiesner, David, illus. 2002. (Illus.). (J). 13.77 (978-0-7587-2912-5(X)) Book Wholesalers, Inc.
Wilce, Ysabeau S. Flora Segunda: The Magickal Mishaps of a Girl of Spirit, Her Glass-Gazing Sidekick, Two Ominous Butlers (One Blue), a House with Eleven Thousand Rooms, & a Red Dog. 2008. 448p. (J). pap. 7.95 (978-0-15-205439-7(1)) Harcourt Trade Pubs.
Wild, Kate. Fight Game. 2007. 288p. (J). (gr. 4-7). 16.99 (***978-0-439-87175-4(1)***) Scholastic, Inc.
Wiley. The Extraordinary Adventures of Ordinary Basil: Island of the Volcano Monkeys. 2007. (J). pap. (***978-0-439-86133-5(0)***) Blue Sky Pr.
Wilkens, S. G. Transformers: The Junior Novel. 2007. (Transformers Ser.). 144p. (J). pap. 4.99 (***978-0-06-088835-0(0)*** , Harper Entertainment) HarperCollins Pubs.
Wilkinson, Carole. Out of Orbit. 2000. (Fact Meets Fiction Ser.). (Illus.). 96p. (J). (978-0-7608-4948-4(X)) Sundance/Newbridge Educational Publishing.
Willett, Edward. Andy Nebula: Interstellar Rock Star. 1999. (Out of This World Ser.). 176p. (YA). (gr. 6-8). pap. 5.95 (978-1-896184-52-4(9)) Roussan Pubs., Inc./ Roussan Editeur, Inc. CAN. *Dist:* Orca Bk. Pubs. USA.
Williams, Heather L. & Muench-Williams, Heather. Caillou Learns about Space. Storch, Ellen N., illus. l.t. ed. 2005. (Hrl Board Book Ser.). (J). (ps-k). bds. 10.95 (978-1-57332-308-6(X)) HighReach Learning, Inc.
Williams, Mark London. Ancient Fire: Danger Boy Episode 1. 2006. 232p. (J). (gr. 4-8). pap. 4.99 (978-0-7636-3092-8(6)) Candlewick Pr.
—City of Ruins, No. 4. 2007. 288p. (J). (gr. 4-8). 12.99 (978-0-7636-2871-0(9)) Candlewick Pr.
—Dragon Sword. (Danger Boy Ser.: Vol. 2). (Illus.). 288p. (J). (gr. 4-8). 2007. 4.99 (978-0-7636-3290-8(2)); 2004. 12.99 (978-0-7636-2153-7(6)) Candlewick Pr.
—Trail of Bones. Koelsch, Michael, illus. 2005. (Danger Boy Ser.: No. 3). 320p. (J). (gr. 4-8). 12.99 (978-0-7636-2154-4(4)) Candlewick Pr.
Williams, Mark London. Trail of Bones: Danger Boy Episode 3. 2007. (Illus.). 320p. (J). (gr. 4-8). 5.99 (***978-0-7636-3410-0(7)***) Candlewick Pr.
Williams, Suzanne. Human or Alien? Carter, Abby, illus. 2004. (Ready-for-Chapters Ser.). 64p. (J). pap. 3.99 (978-0-689-86337-0(3) , Aladdin) Simon & Schuster Children's Publishing.
Wilson, Greg. Three Sensible Adventures. Lytle, William S., illus. 1999. 56p. (J). (gr. k-3). lib. bdg. 18.95 (978-1-55037-599-2(7)) Annick Pr., Ltd. CAN. *Dist:* Firefly Bks., Ltd.
—Three Sensible Adventures. 1999. (gr. k-3). lib. bdg. 16.40 (978-0-613-27242-1(0)) Tandem Library Bks.
Windham, Ryder. Beware the Dark Side. 2007. (Dk Readers Ser.). 48p. (J). (ps-12). 14.99 (***978-0-7566-3115-4(7)***); pap. 3.99 (***978-0-7566-3114-7(9)***) Dorling Kindersley Publishing, Inc.
—The Cavern of the Screaming Skulls. 2002. 104p. (J). (978-0-439-45880-1(3)) Scholastic, Inc.
—Empire Strikes Back. novel ed. 2004. (Star Wars Ser.). 176p. (J). (gr. 4-7). pap. 5.99 (978-0-439-68124-7(3)) Scholastic, Inc.
—Galactic Crisis. 2005. (Dk Readers Ser.). (Illus.). 48p. (J). 14.99 (978-0-7566-1162-0(8) , 1241629) Dorling Kindersley Publishing, Inc.
—The Hostage Princess. 2002. 90p. (J). (978-0-439-45881-8(1)) Scholastic, Inc.
—Hunt the Sun Runner Game Book. 2002. 108p. (J). (978-0-439-45908-2(7)) Scholastic, Inc.
—Journey Through Space. 2005. (Dk Readers Ser.). (Illus.). 32p. (J). (ps-12). 14.99 (978-0-7566-1158-3(X) , 1241627); pap. 3.99 (978-0-7566-1159-0(8) , 1241627) Dorling Kindersley Publishing, Inc.
—A New Hope. 2004. (Star Wars Ser.). 172p. (J). (gr. 4-7). pap. 5.99 (978-0-439-68123-0(5)) Scholastic, Inc.
—Rise & Fall of Darth Vader. 2007. (Star Wars Ser.). 208p. (J). pap. 15.99 (***978-0-439-68132-2(4)***) Scholastic, Inc.
—The Shape-Shifter Strikes. 2003. 85p. (J). (978-0-439-45884-9(6)) Scholastic, Inc.
—Star Wars: Galactic Crisis. 2005. (Dk Readers Ser.). (Illus.). 48p. (J). (ps-12). pap. 3.99 (978-0-7566-1163-7(6) , 1241629) Dorling Kindersley Publishing, Inc.
—The Warlords of Balmorra. 2003. 97p. (J). (978-0-439-45903-7(6)) Scholastic, Inc.
Windham, Ryder & Beecroft, Simon. I Want to Be A Jedi. 2007. (Dk Readers Ser.). 48p. (J). (ps-12). 14.99 (***978-0-7566-3113-0(0)***); pap. 3.99 (***978-0-7566-3112-3(2)***) Dorling Kindersley Publishing, Inc.
Windsor-Smith, Barry. Wolverine Weapon X Premiere. 2007. (Illus.). 152p. 19.99 (***978-0-7851-2327-9(X)***) Marvel Enterprises, Inc.
Wolfe, D. K. Flap Doodle & the Incredible Kibbll Caper. 2005. (Illus.). 247p. (J). (gr. 4-6). 16.95 (978-1-59810-031-0(9)) Jeriger Pr.
Wolverton, Dave. The Rising Force. 1999. (Star Wars Ser.: Bk. 1). (J). (gr. 4-7). (978-0-606-16649-2(1)) Tandem Library Bks.
Wood, Audrey. The Christmas Adventure of Space Elf Sam. Wood, Bruce Robert, illus. 1998. 40p. (J). (ps-4). pap. 15.95 (978-0-590-03143-1(0) , Blue Sky Pr., The) Scholastic, Inc.
Wooding, Chris. Storm Thief. 320p. 2007. (J). pap. 8.99 (***978-0-439-86514-2(X)*** , Scholastic Paperbacks); 2006. (YA). pap. 16.99 (978-0-439-86513-5(1) , Orchard Bks.) Scholastic, Inc.
Woods, Tonita. Mystical Forest of Wise. 2001. 120p. pap. 10.95 (978-0-595-19147-5(9) , Writers Club Pr.) iUniverse, Inc.
Woodward/Amit, Kay/Ofra. Countdown! 2006. (Illus.). 32p. (J). lib. bdg. 9.00 (***978-1-4242-0879-1(3)***) Fitzgerald Bks.
Wookie World. 2003. (Star Wars Ser.: Vol. 6). (Illus.). 360p. pap. 29.95 (978-1-56971-907-7(1)) Dark Horse Comics.

S

Wrede, Patricia C. Attack of the Clones. 2002. (Star Wars Ser.). (Illus.). 176p. (J). (gr. 4-6). 5.99 (978-0-439-13928-1(7)) Scholastic, Inc.

—Revenge of the Sith. 2005. (Star Wars Ser.). (Illus.). 192p. (J). pap. 5.99 (978-0-439-13929-8(5) , Scholastic Paperbacks) Scholastic, Inc.

—Star Wars: Episode II: Attack of the Clones. unabr. ed. 2002. (YA). (gr. 3 up). pap. 35.00 incl. audio (978-0-8072-0857-1(4) , LYA 369 SP, Listening Library) Random Hse. Audio Publishing Group.

Wriede, Marilyn. Windows to the Worlds: Azra. Wriede, Valerie, illus. 2001. 160p. (J). (gr. 3-6). pap. 6.95 (978-0-9710098-0-6(5)) Wriede, Peter.

Wright Johnson, Shelli. Falcon in the Nest: A Story of Bes Adventure. 2004. 273p. pap. 21.95 (978-1-4137-5263-2(2)) PublishAmerica, Inc.

Wyatt, Valerie. Earthlings Inside & Out. 1999. (gr. 3-6). lib. bdg. 15.25 (978-0-613-16346-0(X)) Tandem Library Bks.

—Earthlings Inside & Out: A Space Alien Studies the Human Body. Petricic, Dusan, illus. unabr. ed. 1999. 64p. (J). (gr. 4-6). (978-1-55074-513-9(1)) Kids Can Pr., Ltd.

Wylie, Philip. When Worlds Collide. 1999. (gr. 7-12). lib. bdg. 25.70 (978-0-613-35377-9(3)) Tandem Library Bks.

Wyndham, John. The Midwich Cuckoos. 2004. (Fast Track Classics Ser.). (Illus.). 48p. (J). pap. 9.99 (978-0-237-52689-4(1) , Evans Brothers, Limited) Evans Publishing Group GBR. *Dist:* Independent Pubs. Group.

X-Men. 2003. (J). (978-1-57657-859-9(3)) Paradise Pr., Inc.

Yaccarino, Dan. First Day on a Strange New Planet. (Blast Off Boy & Blorp Ser.). (Illus.). 40p. (gr. k-3). 2002. pap. 4.99 (978-0-7868-1428-2(4)); 2000. 15.49 (978-0-7868-2499-1(9)) Hyperion Bks. for Children.

—First Day on a Strange New Planet. 2002. (gr. k-3). lib. bdg. 13.00 (978-0-613-74971-8(5)) Tandem Library Bks.

—Primer Dia en un Planeta Extrano. Yaccarino, Dan, illus. 2002. (Torre de Papel Ser.). (SPA., Illus.). 34p. (J). 7.95 (978-958-04-6865-3(6)) Norma S.A. COL. *Dist:* Distribuidora Norma, Inc.

Yackety-Yak, the Alien's Back. 2005. (Illus.). (J). lib. bdg. 27.10 (978-1-59389-141-1(5)) Chrysalis Education.

Yaeger, Stephen S. Ian & the Woodins. 2001. 152p. (Orig.). pap. 11.95 (978-0-595-18366-1(2) , Writers Club Pr.) iUniverse, Inc.

Yamamoto, Kazuyuki & Toda, Akihito. First Prize for Starmie. Kimura, Naoyo & Himeno, Kagemaru, illus. 2000. (Pokemon Tales Ser.: No. 15). 18p. (YA). (ps-k). 4.95 (978-1-56931-489-0(6)) Viz Media.

—Seel to the Rescue. Himeno, Kagemaru, illus. 2000. (Pokemon Tales Ser.: No. 16). 18p. (YA). (ps-k). 4.95 (978-1-56931-488-3(8)) Viz Media.

Yamamoto, Lani. Albert. Yamamoto, Lani, illus. 2004. (Illus.). 32p. (J). 10.95 (978-1-58536-251-6(4)) Sleeping Bear Pr.

Yasuhiko, Yoshikazu. Gundam No. 9, No. 10: The Origin. 2004. (gr. 7-12). lib. bdg. 16.40 (978-0-613-88462-4(0)) Tandem Library Bks.

—Origin. 2003. (gr. 3-6). lib. bdg. 16.40 (978-0-613-79041-3(3)) Tandem Library Bks.

Yenkavitch, Joseph. On a Distant World. 2001. 280p. pap. 14.99 (978-1-883573-84-3(X) , Blue Works) Windstorm Creative.

Yep, Laurence. The Star Maker. Date not set. 32p. (J). (gr. k-3). lib. bdg. 15.89 (978-0-06-025316-5(9)) HarperCollins Pubs.

Yolen, Jane. Commander Toad & the Voyage Home. Degen, Bruce, illus. 1998. 64p. (J). (gr. 2-5). pap. 5.99 (978-0-698-11602-3(X) , Putnam Juvenile) Penguin Group (USA) Inc.

—Commander Toad & the Voyage Home. 1999. (Illus.). (J). (978-0-606-15489-5(2)) Tandem Library Bks.

Yolen, Jane & Nielsen Hayden, Patrick. The Year's Best Science Fiction & Fantasy for Teens: First Annual Collection. 2005. 288p. (YA). 17.95 (978-0-7653-1383-6(9) , Tor Teen) Doherty, Tom Assocs., LLC.

Yolen, Jane & Stemple, Adam. Pay the Piper: A Rock 'n' Roll Fairy Tale. 2005. 176p. (J). (gr. k-9). 16.95 (978-0-7653-1158-0(5) , Starscape) Doherty, Tom Assocs., LLC.

Yoon, Salina. Fire Truck. Yoon, Salina, illus. 2005. (Illus.). 10p. (J). (ps-1). bds. 5.99 (978-0-8431-1395-2(2) , Price Stern Sloan) Penguin Group (USA) Inc.

Yoshizaki, Mine. Sgt. Frog, 6 vols., Vol. 2. Fukami, Yuko, tr. from JPN. rev. ed. 2004. (Illus.). 192p. pap. 9.99 (978-1-59182-704-7(3) , Tokyopop Adult) TOKYOPOP, Inc.

—Sgt. Frog, 6 vols., Vol. 3. rev. ed. 2004. (Illus.). 192p. pap. 9.99 (978-1-59182-705-4(1) , Tokyopop Adult) TOKYOPOP, Inc.

Yoshizaki, Mine, creator. Sgt. Frog, 6 vols. 2004. (Illus.). Vol. 4. rev. ed. 188p. pap. 9.99 (978-1-59182-706-1(X)); Vol. 5. 5th rev. ed. 192p. pap. 9.99 (978-1-59182-707-8(8)) TOKYOPOP, Inc. (Tokyopop Adult).

Yukimura, Makoto. Planetes, 3 vols. 2003. (Illus.). 192p. pap. 9.99 (978-1-59182-262-2(9) , Tokyopop Adult) TOKYOPOP, Inc.

—Planetes, 3 vols., Vol. 2. Nakamara, Yuki, tr. from JPN. Yukimura, Makoto, illus. rev. ed. 2004. (Illus.). 192p. pap. 9.99 (978-1-59182-509-8(1) , Tokyopop Adult) TOKYOPOP, Inc.

—Planetes, 3 vols., Vol. 3. rev. ed. 2004. (Illus.). 240p. pap. 9.99 (978-1-59182-510-4(5) , Tokyopop Adult) TOKYOPOP, Inc.

—Planetes, Vol. 4.2. Yukimura, Makoto, illus. rev. ed. 2005. (Illus.). 200p. pap. 9.99 (978-1-59532-467-2(4) , Tokyopop Adult) TOKYOPOP, Inc.

Yukimura, Makoto, creator. Planetes, Vol. 4. rev. ed. 2004. (Illus.). 208p. pap. 9.99 (978-1-59532-208-1(6) , Tokyopop Adult) TOKYOPOP, Inc.

Yume, Hajime & Toda, Akihito. Psyduck's Tongue Twisters. Himeno, Kagemaru, illus. 1999. (Pokemon Tales Ser.: No. 5). 18p. (YA). (ps-k). 4.95 (978-1-56931-418-0(7)) Viz Media.

Z for Zachariah. 1999. (YA). 9.95 (978-1-56137-888-3(7)); (J). 11.95 (978-1-56137-889-0(5)) Novel Units, Inc.

Zahn, Timothy. Dragon & Herdsman. 2007. (Dragonback Ser.). 304p. (J). mass mkt. 5.99 ***(*978-0-7653-5276-7(1)*** , Starscape) Doherty, Tom Assocs., LLC.

—Dragon & Slave: The Third Dragonback Adventure. rev. ed. 2005. (Dragonback Ser.). 304p. (J). 17.95 (978-0-7653-0126-0(1) , Tor Bks.) Doherty, Tom Assocs., LLC.

—Dragon & Soldier. 2005. (Dragonback Ser.). 304p. (J). 5.99 (978-0-7653-5017-6(3) , Starscape) Doherty, Tom Assocs., LLC.

Zahn, Timothy, et al. Mara Jade: By the Emperor's Hand. (Star Wars Ser.). 144p. (YA). (gr. 7 up). pap. 15.95 (978-1-56971-401-0(0)) Dark Horse Comics.

Zeman, Ludmila, illus. & retold by. The Last Quest of Gilgamesh. Zeman, Ludmila, retold by. 1998. (J). (ps-7). lib. bdg. 17.60 (978-0-613-09459-7(X)) Tandem Library Bks.

Zoehfeld, Kathleen Weidner. Billy. 2001. (Rolie Polie Olie Ser.). (Illus.). 12p. (J). (gr. k-2). bds. 3.99 (978-0-7364-1023-6(6)) Mouse Works.

SCIENCE FICTION—HISTORY AND CRITICISM

Bloom, Harold. Frankenstein. 2007. (Bloom's Guides). 160p. (YA). (gr. 9 up). 30.00 ***(*978-0-7910-9358-0(1)*** , Chelsea Hse.) Facts On File, Inc.

Bloom, Harold. George Orwell's 1984. 2004. (gr. 7-12). lib. bdg. 18.75 (978-0-613-70824-1(5)) Tandem Library Bks.

Bloom, Harold, intro. George Orwell's 1984. (Bloom's Guides Ser.). (Illus.). (gr. 9-13). 2004. 112p. pap. 30.00 (978-0-7910-7766-5(7)); 2003. 80p. 30.00 (978-0-7910-7567-8(2)) Facts On File, Inc. (Chelsea Hse.).

Czerneda, Julie E., ed. Stardust. Normand, Jean-Pierre, illus. 2001. (Tales from the Wonder Zone Ser.). 128p. (J). (gr. 4 up). pap. 11.95 (978-1-55244-018-6(4)) Trifolium Bks., Inc. CAN. *Dist:* Fitzhenry & Whiteside, Ltd.

Datnow, Claire L. American Science Fiction & Fantasy Writers. 1999. (Collective Biographies Ser.). (Illus.). 128p. (YA). (gr. 6-12). lib. bdg. 26.60 (978-0-7660-1090-1(2)) Enslow Pubs., Inc.

Hamilton, John. The Final Frontier. 2007. (World of Science Fiction Ser.). (Illus.). 32p. (J). (gr. 4-6). lib. bdg. 24.21 (978-1-59679-987-5(0) , ABDO & Daughters) ABDO Publishing Co.

—Future Societies. 2007. (Illus.). 32p. (J). 24.21 (978-1-59679-988-2(9) , ABDO & Daughters) ABDO Publishing Co.

—The Golden Age & Beyond. 2007. (World of Science Fiction Ser.). (Illus.). 32p. 24.21 (978-1-59679-989-9(7)) ABDO Publishing Co.

—Man-Made Horrors. 2007. (ENG., Illus.). 32p. (YA). lib. bdg. 24.21 ***(*978-1-59928-769-0(2)*** , ABDO & Daughters) ABDO Publishing Co.

—Modern Masters of Science Fiction. 2007. (World of Science Fiction Ser.). (Illus.). 32p. (J). (gr. 4-6). lib. bdg. 24.21 (978-1-59679-990-5(0) , ABDO & Daughters) ABDO Publishing Co.

—New Worlds. 2007. (Illus.). 32p. (J). 24.21 (978-1-59679-991-2(9) , ABDO & Daughters) ABDO Publishing Co.

—Pioneers of Science Fiction. 2007. (World of Science Fiction Ser.). 32p. 24.21 (978-1-59679-992-9(7)) ABDO Publishing Co.

—Spaceships. 2007. (World of Science Fiction Ser.). (Illus.). 32p. (J). 24.21 (978-1-59679-995-0(1)) ABDO Publishing Co.

—Weapons of Science Fiction. 2007. (Illus.). 32p. (J). 24.21 (978-1-59679-997-4(8) , ABDO & Daughters) ABDO Publishing Co.

Judson, Karen. Isaac Asimov: Master of Science Fiction. 1998. (People to Know Ser.). (Illus.). 112p. (YA). (gr. 6-12). lib. bdg. 26.60 (978-0-7660-1031-4(7)) Enslow Pubs., Inc.

L'Engle, Madeleine. Una Arruga en el Tiempo. 2003. (SPA., Illus.). 206p. (J). (gr. 5-8). pap. 12.95 (978-84-204-4074-3(4) , KZ744) Santillana USA Publishing Co., Inc.

Loos, Pamela. Reading the Giver. 2005. (Engaged Reader Ser.). (Illus.). 75p. (J). (gr. 4-8). lib. bdg. 25.00 (978-0-7910-8830-2(8) , Chelsea Hse.) Facts On File, Inc.

Miller, Ron. The History of Science Fiction. 2001. (Single Titles Social Studies Ser.). (Illus.). 144p. (YA). (gr. 8-12). pap. 13.95 (978-0-531-13979-0(4)); 30.00 (978-0-531-11866-5(5)) Scholastic Library Publishing. (Watts, Franklin).

—History of Science Fiction. 2001. (gr. 7-12). lib. bdg. 23.40 (978-0-613-57643-7(8)) Tandem Library Bks.

Nichols, Joan K. Mary Shelley: Frankenstein's Creator - The First Science Fiction Writer. 1998. (Barnard Biography Ser.: No. 3). (Illus.). 150p. (YA). (gr. 7-12). pap. 6.95 (978-1-57324-087-1(7) , Red Wheel) Red Wheel/Weiser.

Sanderson, Jeannette & Lowry, Lois. Giver. 2003. (Bookfiles Ser.). 64p. (J). pap. 4.99 (978-0-439-46356-0(4)) Scholastic, Inc.

SCIENCE PROJECTS

Anderson, Maxine. Amazing Leonardo da Vinci: Inventions You Can Build Yourself. 2006. (Build It Yourself Ser.). (Illus.). 128p. (J). pap. 14.95 (978-0-9749344-2-6(9)) Nomad Pr.

Bardhan-Quallen, Sudipta. Championship Science Fair Projects: 100 Sure-to-Win Experiments. 2004. (Illus.). 208p. (J). 19.95 (978-1-4027-1138-1(7)) Sterling Publishing Co., Inc.

—Last-Minute Science Fair Projects: When Your Bunsen's Not Burning but the Clock's Really Ticking. 2006. (Illus.). 112p. (J). 19.95 (978-1-4027-1690-4(7) , 1262284) Sterling Publishing Co., Inc.

Barrow, Lloyd H. Science Fair Projects Investigating Earthworms. 2000. (Science Fair Success Ser.). (Illus.). 104p. (YA). (gr. 6-12). lib. bdg. 26.60 (978-0-7660-1291-2(3)) Enslow Pubs., Inc.

Beck, Esther. Cool Odor Decoders: Fun Science Projects about Smells. 2007. (Cool Science Ser.). (Illus.). 32p. (J). (gr. k-6). lib. bdg. 24.21 ***(*978-1-59928-909-0(1)*** , Checkerboard Library) ABDO Publishing Co.

—Cool Sensory Suspense: Fun Science Projects about the Senses. 2007. (Cool Science Ser.). (Illus.). 32p. (J). (gr. k-6). lib. bdg. 24.21 ***(*978-1-59928-910-6(5)*** , Checkerboard Library) ABDO Publishing Co.

—Cool Spy Supplies: Fun Top Secret Science Projects. 2007. (Cool Science Ser.). (Illus.). 32p. (J). (gr. k-6). lib. bdg. 24.21 ***(*978-1-59928-911-3(3)*** , Checkerboard Library) ABDO Publishing Co.

Berda, Marty, et al, eds. Science Projects for All Students, 2 vols., Set. 2002. (J). (gr. 4-9). 370.00 (978-0-8160-5097-0(X)) Facts On File, Inc.

Bochinski, Julianne Blair. More Award-Winning Science Fair Projects. 2003. (gr. 7-12). lib. bdg. 24.55 (978-0-613-81939-8(X)) Tandem Library Bks.

—More Award-Winning Science Fair Projects. DiBiase, Judy, illus. 2003. 228p. pap. 14.95 (978-0-471-27337-0(6) , Wiley) Wiley, John & Sons, Inc.

Bochinski, Julianne Blair & DiBiase, Judy. More Award-Winning Science Fair Projects. 2003. (Illus.). 228p. 29.95 (978-0-471-27338-7(4) , Cliff Notes) Wiley, John & Sons, Inc.

Boldt, Mark. U-Do Book Project "Science Fair" Vol. 7: An Asthma Action Plan U-Do Book. 2001. (Illus.). 24p. (J). (gr. k-8). pap. (978-0-9662556-6-9(6)) Boldt.Entertainment.

Bombaugh, Ruth. Science Fair Success. exp. rev. ed. 1999. (Science Fair Success Ser.). (Illus.). 128p. (YA). (gr. 6-12). lib. bdg. 26.60 (978-0-7660-1163-2(1)) Enslow Pubs., Inc.

Bonnet, Bob. Chemistry. Bonnet, Bob, illus. 2001. (Illus.). (J). (978-0-606-21421-6(6)) Tandem Library Bks.

Bonnet, Robert L. & Keen, Dan. Gigantic Book of Winning Science Fair Projects. 2005. (Illus.). 368p. (J). pap. (978-1-4027-2923-2(5) , Sterling/Main St.) Sterling Publishing Co., Inc.

Brown, Patrica A. & Krelle, Ginger R. Classroom Hydroponic Plant Factory, Vol. 2. 2nd rev. ed. 2004. (Illus.). 102p. (YA). (gr. 7-12). pap. 19.95 (978-0-9669557-1-2(4)) Foothill-Hydroponics.

Brynie, Faith Hickman. Parent's Crash Course: Elementary School Science Fair Projects. 2005. (Illus.). 256p. pap. 16.99 (978-0-7645-9934-7(8) , Cliff Notes) Wiley, John & Sons, Inc.

Carlson, Laurie. Thomas Edison for Kids: His Life & Ideas, 21 Activities. 2006. (For Kids Ser.). (Illus.). 160p. (J). pap. 14.95 (978-1-55652-584-1(2) , 1248637) Chicago Review Pr., Inc.

Carson, Mary Kay. Weather Projects for Young Scientists: Experiments & Science Fair Ideas. 2007. (Illus.). 144p. (J). pap. 14.95 (978-1-55652-629-9(6)) Chicago Review Pr., Inc.

Cobb, Allan B. Super Science Projects about Energy & Motion. 2005. (Psyched for Science Ser.). (Illus.). 48p. (YA). (gr. 5-8). lib. bdg. 23.95 (978-0-8239-3116-3(1) , SCENMO) Rosen Publishing Group, Inc., The.

—Super Science Projects about Light & Optics. 2005. (Psyched for Science Ser.). (Illus.). 48p. (YA). (gr. 5-8). lib. bdg. 23.95 (978-0-8239-3177-4(3) , SCLIOP) Rosen Publishing Group, Inc., The.

—Super Science Projects about Oceans. 2005. (Psyched for Science Ser.). (Illus.). 48p. (YA). (gr. 5-8). lib. bdg. 23.95 (978-0-8239-3174-3(9) , SCOCEA) Rosen Publishing Group, Inc., The.

—Super Science Projects about Sound. 2005. (Psyched for Science Ser.). (Illus.). 48p. (YA). (gr. 5-8). lib. bdg. 23.95 (978-0-8239-3176-7(5) , SCSOUN) Rosen Publishing Group, Inc., The.

DiSpezio, Michael Anthony. Super Sensational Science Fair Projects. Toye, Derek, illus. 2003. 96p. (J). 19.95 (978-0-8069-4409-8(9)) Sterling Publishing Co., Inc.

Friedhoffer, Bob. More Scientific American Simple Science Fair Projects. 2006. (Scientific American Science Fair Projects Ser.). (Illus.). 48p. (gr. 3-5). 27.00 (978-0-7910-9055-8(8) , Chelsea Hse.) Facts On File, Inc.

—More Scientific American Winning Science Fair Projects. 2006. (Scientific American Science Fair Projects Ser.). (Illus.). 48p. (gr. 5-7). 27.00 (978-0-7910-9057-2(4) , Chelsea Hse.) Facts On File, Inc.

—Scientific American Simple Science Fair Projects. 2006. (Scientific American Science Fair Projects Ser.). (Illus.). 48p. (gr. 3-5). 27.00 (978-0-7910-9054-1(X) , Chelsea Hse.) Facts On File, Inc.

—Scientific American Winning Science Fair Projects. 2006. (Scientific American Science Fair Projects Ser.). (Illus.). 48p. (gr. 5-7). 27.00 (978-0-7910-9056-5(6) , Chelsea Hse.) Facts On File, Inc.

Gabrielson, Curt. Stomp Rockets, Catapults, & Kaleidoscopes: 30+ Amazing Science Projects You Can Build for Less Than $1. 2008. 192p. (J). (gr. 4 up). pap. 16.95 ***(*978-1-55652-737-1(3))*** Chicago Review Pr., Inc.

Galus, Pamela J. Science Fair Projects: An Inquiry-Based Guide, Grades 3-5. Armbrust, Janet, illus. 2003. 80p. per. 9.99 (978-0-88724-948-8(5) , CD-7332) Carson-Dellosa Publishing Co., Inc.

—Science Fair Projects: An Inquiry-Based Guide, Grades 5-8. Armbrust, Janet, illus. 2003. 80p. per. 9.99 (978-0-88724-949-5(3) , CD-7333) Carson-Dellosa Publishing Co., Inc.

Gardner, Robert. Bicycle Science Projects: Physics on Wheels. 2004. (Science Fair Success Ser.). (Illus.). 112p. (J). lib. bdg. 26.60 (978-0-7660-1630-9(7)) Enslow Pubs., Inc.

—Chemistry Projects with a Laboratory You Can Build. 2007. (Build-a-Lab! Science Experiments Ser.). (Illus.). 128p. (J). (gr. 5). lib. bdg. 31.93 (978-0-7660-2805-0(4)) Enslow Pubs., Inc.

—Chemistry Science Fair Projects Using Acids, Bases, Metals, Salts, & Inorganic Stuff. 2004. (Chemistry! Best Science Projects Ser.). (Illus.). 128p. (J). lib. bdg. 26.60 (978-0-7660-2210-2(2)) Enslow Pubs., Inc.

—Earth-Shaking Science Projects about Planet Earth. LaBaff, Tom, illus. 2007. (Rockin' Earth Science Experiments Ser.). 48p. (J). (gr. 3-4). lib. bdg. 23.93 ***(*978-0-7660-2733-6(3)*** , Enslow Elementary) Enslow Pubs., Inc.

—Electricity & Magnetism Science Fair Projects Using Batteries, Balloons, & Other Hair-Raising Stuff. 2004. (Physics! Best Science Projects Ser.). (Illus.). 128p. (J). lib. bdg. 26.60 (978-0-7660-2127-3(0)) Enslow Pubs., Inc.

—Far-Out Science Projects about Earth's Sun & Moon. LaBaff, Tom, illus. 2007. (Rockin' Earth Science Experiments Ser.). 48p. (J). (gr. 3-6). lib. bdg. 23.93 (978-0-7660-2736-7(8) , Enslow Elementary) Enslow Pubs., Inc.

—Meteorology Projects with a Weather Station You Can Build. 2008. (Build-a-Lab! Science Experiments Ser.). (Illus.). 128p. (J). (gr. 5 up). lib. bdg. 31.93 ***(*978-0-7660-2807-4(0))*** Enslow Pubs., Inc.

—Physics Projects with a Light Box You Can Build. 2007. (Build-a-Lab! Science Experiments Ser.). (Illus.). 128p. (J). (gr. 5). lib. bdg. 31.93 ***(*978-0-7660-2810-4(0))*** Enslow Pubs., Inc.

—Planet Earth Science Fair Projects Using the Moon, Stars, Beach Balls, Frisbees, & Other Far-Out Stuff. 2005. (Earth Science! Best Science Projects Ser.). (Illus.). 128p. (J). lib. bdg. 26.60 (978-0-7660-2362-8(1) , 1238538) Enslow Pubs., Inc.

—Science Fair Projects about the Properties of Matter Using Marbles, Water, Balloons, & More. 2004. (Physics! Best Science Projects Ser.). (Illus.). 128p. (J). lib. bdg. 26.60 (978-0-7660-2128-0(9)) Enslow Pubs., Inc.

—Science Project Ideas about Kitchen Chemistry. rev. ed. 2002. (Science Project Ideas Ser.). (Illus.). 128p. (J). (gr. 4-9). lib. bdg. 26.60 (978-0-7660-1706-1(0)) Enslow Pubs., Inc.

—Science Project Ideas about Space Science. rev. ed. 2002. (Science Project Ideas Ser.). (Illus.). 128p. (J). (gr. 4-9). lib. bdg. 26.60 (978-0-7660-1707-8(9)) Enslow Pubs., Inc.

—Science Projects about Methods of Measuring. 2000. (Science Projects Ser.). (Illus.). 128p. (YA). (gr. 6-12). lib. bdg. 26.60 (978-0-7660-1169-4(0)) Enslow Pubs., Inc.

—Science Projects about Physics in the Home. 1999. (Science Projects Ser.). (Illus.). 112p. (YA). (gr. 6-12). lib. bdg. 26.60 (978-0-89490-948-1(7)) Enslow Pubs., Inc.

—Science Projects about Solids, Liquids & Gases. 2000. (Science Projects Ser.). (Illus.). 128p. (YA). (gr. 6-12). lib. bdg. 26.60 (978-0-7660-1168-7(2)) Enslow Pubs., Inc.

—Science Projects about Sound. 2000. (Science Projects Ser.). (Illus.). 112p. (YA). (gr. 6-12). lib. bdg. 26.60 (978-0-7660-1166-3(6)) Enslow Pubs., Inc.

—Science Projects about the Environment & Ecology. 1999. (Science Projects Ser.). (Illus.). 112p. (YA). (gr. 6-12). lib. bdg. 26.60 (978-0-89490-951-1(7)) Enslow Pubs., Inc.

—Science Projects about the Physics of Sports. 2000. (Science Projects Ser.). (Illus.). 128p. (YA). (gr. 6-12). lib. bdg. 26.60 (978-0-7660-1167-0(4)) Enslow Pubs., Inc.

—Science Projects about the Science Behind Magic. 2000. (Science Projects Ser.). (Illus.). 128p. (YA). (gr. 6-12). lib. bdg. 26.60 (978-0-7660-1164-9(X)) Enslow Pubs., Inc.

—Smashing Science Projects about Earth's Rocks & Minerals. LaBaff, Tom, illus. 2007. (Rockin' Earth Science Experiments Ser.). 48p. (J). (gr. 3-4). lib. bdg. 23.93 (978-0-7660-2731-2(7) , Enslow Elementary) Enslow Pubs., Inc.

—Sound Projects with a Music Lab You Can Build. 2008. (Build-a-Lab! Science Experiments Ser.). (Illus.). 104p. (J). (gr. 5 up). lib. bdg. 31.93 ***(*978-0-7660-2809-8(7))*** Enslow Pubs., Inc.

—Stellar Science Projects about Earth's Sky. LaBaff, Tom, illus. 2007. (Rockin' Earth Science Experiments Ser.). 48p. (J). (gr. 3-6). lib. bdg. 23.93 (978-0-7660-2732-9(5) , Enslow Elementary) Enslow Pubs., Inc.

—Super Science Projects about Earth's Soil & Water. LaBaff, Tom, illus. 2007. (Rockin' Earth Science Experiments Ser.). 48p. (J). (gr. 4-6). lib. bdg. 23.93 (978-0-7660-2735-0(X) , Enslow Elementary) Enslow Pubs., Inc.

—Weather Science Fair Projects Using Sunlight, Rainbows, Ice Cubes, & More. 2005. (Earth Science! Best Science Projects Ser.). (Illus.). 128p. (J). lib. bdg. 26.60 (978-0-7660-2361-1(3)) Enslow Pubs., Inc.

—Wild Science Projects about Earth's Weather. LaBaff, Tom, illus. 2007. (Rockin' Earth Science Experiments Ser.). 48p. (J). lib. bdg. 23.93 (978-0-7660-2734-3(1) , Enslow Elementary) Enslow Pubs., Inc.

Gardner, Robert & Conklin, Barbara Gardner. Chemistry Science Fair Projects Using French Fries, Gumdrops, Soap, & Other Organic Stuff. 2004. (Chemistry! Best Science Projects Ser.). (Illus.). 128p. (J). lib. bdg. 26.60 (978-0-7660-2211-9(0)) Enslow Pubs., Inc.

—Health Science Projects about Psychology. 2002. (Science Projects Ser.). (Illus.). 112p. (YA). (gr. 6-12). lib. bdg. 26.60 (978-0-7660-1439-8(8)) Enslow Pubs., Inc.

Goodstein, Madeline. Science Fair Success Using Newton's Laws of Motion. 2002. (Science Fair Success Ser.). (Illus.). 128p. (YA). (gr. 6-12). lib. bdg. 26.60 (978-0-7660-1628-6(5)) Enslow Pubs., Inc.

—Sports Science Projects: The Physics of Balls in Motion. 1999. (Science Fair Success Ser.). (Illus.). 128p. (YA). (gr. 6-12). lib. bdg. 26.60 (978-0-7660-1174-8(7)) Enslow Pubs., Inc.

Haduch, Bill. Science Fair Success Secrets: How to Win Prizes, Have Fun, & Think Like a Scientist. Scheuer, Philip, illus. 2002. 128p. (J). pap. 10.99 (978-0-525-46534-8(0) , Dutton Juvenile) Penguin Group (USA) Inc.

—Science Fair Success Secrets: How to Win Prizes, Have Fun, & Think Like a Scientist. 2002. (gr. 3-6). lib. bdg. 19.95 (978-0-613-72584-2(0)) Tandem Library Bks.

Halls, Kelly Milner. Astronomy & Space. 2006. (Science Fair Projects Ser.). (Illus.). 48p. (J). (gr. 6-9). lib. bdg. 30.00 (978-1-4034-7908-2(9)) Heinemann Library.

—Cells & Systems. 2006. (J). (978-1-4034-7909-9(7)) Heinemann Library.

—Forces & Motion. 2006. (Science Fair Projects Ser.). (Illus.). 48p. (YA). (gr. 6-9). lib. bdg. 30.00 (978-1-4034-7910-5(0)) Heinemann Library.

—Rocks & Minerals. 2006. (Illus.). 48p. (J). (978-1-4034-7911-2(9)) Heinemann Library.

Harrington, Philip S. & Pascuzzi, Edward. Astronomy for All Ages: Discovering the Universe Through Activities for Children & Adults. 2nd ed. 2000. (Illus.). 224p. pap. 19.95 (978-0-7627-0809-3(3)) Globe Pequot Pr., The.

Harris, Elizabeth Snoke. Crime Scene Science Fair Projects. 2006. (Illus.). 112p. (J). (gr. 6-10). 19.95 (978-1-57990-765-5(2)) Lark Bks.

—First Place Science Fair Projects for Inquisitive Kids. 2005. (Illus.). 128p. (J). 19.95 (978-1-57990-493-7(9)) Lark Bks.

Harris, Elizabeth Snoke. Yikes! Wow! Yuck! Fun Experiments for Your First Science Fair. Thompson, Nora, illus. 2008. 112p. (J). 12.95 (***978-1-57990-930-7(2)***) Lark Bks.

Hewitt, Sally. Nature for Fun Projects. 2000. (978-0-606-20486-6(5)) Tandem Library Bks.

Holt, Rinehart and Winston Staff. Holt Science & Technology: Eco-Labs & Field Activities. 2001. pap. 11.60 (978-0-03-054418-7(1)) Holt, Rinehart & Winston.

—Holt Science & Technology: Long-Term Projects & Research Ideas. 5th ed. 2004. (Illus.). pap. 11.13 (978-0-03-035191-4(X)) Holt, Rinehart & Winston.

—Holt Science & Technology: Science Fair Guide. 5th ed. 2004. (Illus.). pap. 11.60 (978-0-03-035199-0(5)) Holt, Rinehart & Winston.

Hopwood, James. Cool Distance Assistants: Fun Science Projects to Propel Things. 2007. (Cool Science Ser.). (Illus.). 32p. (J). (gr. k-6). lib. bdg. 24.21 (***978-1-59928-906-9(7)*** , Checkerboard Library) ABDO Publishing Co.

—Cool Dry Ice Devices: Fun Science Projects with Dry Ice. 2007. (Cool Science Ser.). (Illus.). 32p. (J). (gr. k-6). lib. bdg. 24.21 (***978-1-59928-907-6(5)*** , Checkerboard Library) ABDO Publishing Co.

—Cool Gravity Activities: Fun Science Projects about Balance. 2007. (Cool Science Ser.). (Illus.). 32p. (J). (gr. k-6). lib. bdg. 24.21 (***978-1-59928-908-3(3)*** , Checkerboard Library) ABDO Publishing Co.

Iritz, Maxine Haren. More Blue Ribbon Science Fair Projects. 1999. (gr. 3-6). lib. bdg. 22.20 (978-0-613-71529-4(2)) Tandem Library Bks.

Janice Vancleave's Guide to More of the Best Science Fair Projects. 2002. (Janice Vancleave Ser.). (Illus.). (J). 24.00 (978-0-7587-5215-4(6)) Book Wholesalers, Inc.

Janice Vancleave's Help! My Science Project Is Due Tomorrow! Easy Experiments You Can Do Overnight. 2002. (Janice Vancleave Ser.). (Illus.). (J). 23.98 (978-0-7587-9960-9(8)) Book Wholesalers, Inc.

Jones, Lorraine. Super Science Projects about Weather & Natural Forces. 2005. (Psyched for Science Ser.). (Illus.). 48p. (YA). (gr. 5-8). lib. bdg. 23.95 (978-0-8239-3105-7(6) , SCWENA) Rosen Publishing Group, Inc., The.

Kauffman, Dorothy. Science Lab. 2005. (Content Area Readers Ser.). 24p. 4.95 (978-0-19-430955-4(X)) Oxford Univ. Pr., Inc.

Levine, Shar. Quick-but-Great Science Fair Projects. 2001. (978-0-606-22742-1(3)) Tandem Library Bks.

Levine, Shar & Johnstone, Leslie. First Science Experiments with Nature, Senses, Weather & Machines. Harpster, Steve, illus. 2005. 192p. (978-1-4027-2922-5(7)) Sterling Publishing Co., Inc.

Lopez, Delano. Amazing Solar System Projects You Can Build Yourself. 2008. (Build It Yourself Ser.). 128p. (J). pap. 14.95 (***978-0-9792268-1-6(3)***) Nomad Pr.

Markle, Sandra. Build a Room Alarm & 16 More Electrifying Projects! Brace, Eric, illus. 2003. (Science Dares You! Ser.). 64p. (J). (978-0-439-44432-3(2)) Scholastic, Inc.

McFarren, Kathleen & Graf, Mike. Science Fair Projects & Activities: Creative Ideas Using Easy-to-Find Materials. Valko, Diane & Corbin, Hillam, illus. 2005. 144p. (J). pap. 18.99 (978-0-88160-376-7(7) , LW407, Learning Works, The) Creative Teaching Pr., Inc.

Mebane, Robert C. & Rybolt, Thomas R. Adventures with Science, 5 bks., Set. Incl. Bk. I. Adventures with Atoms & Molecules : Chemistry Experiments for Young People. 82p. pap. 11.93 (978-0-7660-1224-0(7)); Bk. II. Adventures with Atoms & Molecules : Chemistry Experiments for Young People. 96p. pap. 11.93 (978-0-7660-1225-7(5)); Bk. III. Adventures with Atoms & Molecules : Chemistry Experiments for Young People. 96p. pap. 11.93 (978-0-7660-1226-4(3)); Bk. IV. Adventures with Atoms & Molecules : Chemistry Experiments for Young People. 96p. pap. 11.93 (978-0-7660-1227-1(1)); Bk. V. Adventures with Atoms & Molecules : Chemistry Experiments for Young People. 96p. pap. 11.93 (978-0-7660-1228-8(X)); (YA). (gr. 4-9). (Illus.). 1998. Set pap. 49.75 (978-0-7660-1324-7(3)) Enslow Pubs., Inc.

Moorman, Thomas & Moorman, Tom. How to Make Your Science Project Scientific. rev. ed. 2002. (Illus.). 112p. pap. 12.95 (978-0-471-41920-4(6) , Jossey-Bass) Wiley, John & Sons, Inc.

Nankivell-Aston, Sally. Science Experiments with Electricity. 2000. (gr. 3-6). lib. bdg. 15.25 (978-0-613-50728-8(2)) Tandem Library Bks.

Nankivell-Aston, Sally & Jackson, Dorothy. Science Experiments with Electricity. 2000. (Science Experiments Ser.). (Illus.). 32p. (YA). (gr. 3-6). pap. 6.95 (978-0-531-15443-4(2) , Watts, Franklin) Scholastic Library Publishing.

Neuhaus, Richard A. Science Projects - How to Collect, Analyze, & Present Your Data: An Intuitive Approach to the Statistics for the High School Student. Gormley, Julia A., illus. 2007. 184p. (YA). spiral bd. 24.95 (***978-0-9794500-0-6(4)***) Gormley Publishing.

Peterson, Carol. Jump into Science: Themed Science Fairs. 2007. (Illus.). 152p. (J). pap. 30.00 (***978-1-59158-413-1(2)*** , TIP4132, Teacher Ideas Pr.) Libraries Unlimited, Inc.

Psyched for Science, 6 bks. Incl. Super Science Projects about Animals in Their Habitats. Cobb, Allan B. lib. bdg. 23.95 (978-0-8239-3175-0(7) , SCADHO); Super Science Projects about Energy & Motion. Cobb, Allan B. lib. bdg. 23.95 (978-0-8239-3116-3(1) , SCENMO); Super Science Projects about Light & Optics. Cobb, Allan B. lib. bdg. 23.95 (978-0-8239-3177-4(3) , SCLIOP); Super Science Projects about Oceans. Cobb, Allan B. lib. bdg. 23.95 (978-0-8239-3174-3(9) , SCOCEA); Super Science Projects about Sound. Cobb, Allan B. lib. bdg. 23.95 (978-0-8239-3176-7(5) , SCSOUN); Super Science Projects about Weather & Natural Forces. Jones, Lorraine. lib. bdg. 23.95 (978-0-8239-3105-7(6) , SCWENA); 48p. (YA). (gr. 5-8). 2005. (Illus.). Set lib. bdg. 143.70 Rosen Publishing Group, Inc., The.

Rainis, Kenneth G. Cell & Microbe Science Fair Projects Using Microscopes, Mold, & More. 2005. (Biology! Best Science Projects Ser.). (Illus.). 128p. (J). (gr. 6-12). lib. bdg. 26.60 (978-0-7660-2369-7(9)) Enslow Pubs., Inc.

—Crime-Solving Science Projects: Forensic Science Experiments. 2000. (Science Fair Success Ser.). (Illus.). 128p. (YA). (gr. 6-12). lib. bdg. 26.60 (978-0-7660-1289-9(1)) Enslow Pubs., Inc.

—Microscope Science Projects & Experiments: Magnifying the Hidden World. 2003. (Science Fair Success Ser.). (Illus.). 128p. (J). lib. bdg. 26.60 (978-0-7660-2090-0(8)) Enslow Pubs., Inc.

—Nature Projects for Young Scientists. rev. ed. 2002. (Projects for Young Scientist Ser.). (Illus.). 192p. (J). (gr. 9-12). pap. 23.50 (978-0-531-11724-8(3) , Watts, Franklin) Scholastic Library Publishing.

Rhatigan, Joe & Newcomb, Rain. Prize-Winning Science Fair Projects for Curious Kids. 2006. (Illus.). 112p. (ps-17). pap., pap. 7.95 (978-1-57990-750-1(4)) Lark Bks.

Rhatigan, Joe, et al. Gross Me Out! 50 Nasty Projects to Disgust Your Friends & Repulse Your Family. Meyer, Clay, illus. 2005. 112p. (ps-7). pap. 7.95 (978-1-57990-752-5(0)) Lark Bks.

Riley, Karen. Agarranderas Plasticas y Otras Cosas: Plastic Rings & Other Things. 2003. (ENG & SPA., Illus.). 16p. (J). (gr. 2-5). pap. 4.50 (978-0-9708135-2-7(X)) S.C.R.A.P. Gallery.

Rompella, Natalie. Chemistry. 2007. (J). (***978-1-4034-7914-3(3)***) Heinemann Library.

Rosner, Marc Alan. Science Fair Success Using the Internet. rev. ed. 2006. (Science Fair Success Ser.). (Illus.). 112p. (J). (gr. 6-12). lib. bdg. 26.60 (978-0-7660-2425-0(3)) Enslow Pubs., Inc.

Rubin, Joel. Weather. 2007. (J). (***978-1-4034-7912-9(7)***) Heinemann Library.

Rybolt, Thomas R. & Mebane, Robert C. Environmental Science Fair Projects: Using Water, Feathers, Sunlight, Balloons, & More. 2005. (Earth Science! Best Science Projects Ser.). (Illus.). 128p. (J). (gr. 6-13). lib. bdg. 26.60 (978-0-7660-2364-2(8)) Enslow Pubs., Inc.

Rybolt, Thomas R. & Rybolt, Leah M. Science Fair Success with Scents, Aromas, & Smells. 2002. (Science Fair Success Ser.). (Illus.). 112p. (YA). (gr. 6-12). lib. bdg. 26.60 (978-0-7660-1625-5(0)) Enslow Pubs., Inc.

Sarquis, Mickey & Woodward, Linda. Science Projects for Holidays Throughout the Year. 1999. 374p. (J). pap. 23.95 (978-1-883822-30-9(0)) Terrific Science Pr.

Science Fair Success, 16 bks., Set. Incl. Crime-Solving Science Projects : Forensic Science Experiments. Rainis, Kenneth G. 128p. 2000. lib. bdg. 26.60 (978-0-7660-1289-9(1)); How to Enter & Win an Invention Contest. Sobey, Edwin J. C. 104p. 1999. lib. bdg. 26.60 (978-0-7660-1173-1(9)); How to Excel in Science Competitions. Krieger, Melanie Jacobs. 128p. 1999. lib. bdg. 26.60 (978-0-7660-1292-9(1)); Science Fair Projects Investigating Earthworms. Barrow, Lloyd H. 104p. 2000. lib. bdg. 26.60 (978-0-7660-1291-2(3)); Bombaugh, Ruth. 128p. 1999. lib. bdg. 26.60 (978-0-7660-1163-2(1)); Science Fair Success in the Hardware Store. Tocci, Salvatore. 128p. 2000. lib. bdg. 26.60 (978-0-7660-1287-5(5)); Science Fair Success Using Supermarket Products. Tocci, Salvatore. 128p. 2000. lib. bdg. 26.60 (978-0-7660-1288-2(3)); Science Fair Success Using the Internet. Rosner, Marc Alan. 112p. 1999. lib. bdg. 26.60 (978-0-7660-1172-4(0)); Science Fair Success with Plants. Perry, Phyllis J. 104p. 1999. lib. bdg. 26.60 (978-0-7660-1170-0(4)); Sports Science Projects : The Physics of Balls in Motion. Goodstein, Madeline. 128p. 1999. lib. bdg. 26.60 (978-0-7660-1174-8(7)); (YA). (gr. 6-12). (Illus.). 2000. Set lib. bdg. 335.20 (978-0-7660-1406-0(1)) Enslow Pubs., Inc.

Scientific American Science Fair Projects, 4 Vols., Set. 2006. 108.00 (978-0-7910-9097-8(3) , Chelsea Clubhouse) Facts On File, Inc.

Suzuki, David. Eco-Fun: Great Projects, Experiments & Games for a Greener Earth. 2001. (J). (978-0-606-21168-0(3)) Tandem Library Bks.

Tocci, Salvatore. Science Fair Success in the Hardware Store. 2000. (Science Fair Success Ser.). (Illus.). 128p. (YA). (gr. 6-12). lib. bdg. 26.60 (978-0-7660-1287-5(5)) Enslow Pubs., Inc.

—Science Fair Success Using Household Products. 2002. (Science Fair Success Ser.). (Illus.). 112p. (YA). (gr. 6-12). lib. bdg. 26.60 (978-0-7660-1626-2(9)) Enslow Pubs., Inc.

Van Vleet, Carmella. Amazing Ben Franklin Inventions You Can Build Yourself. 2007. (Build It Yourself Ser.). 128p. (J). (gr. 4-7). pap. 14.95 (***978-0-9771294-7-8(0)***) Nomad Pr.

VanCleave, Janice. Janice VanCleave's Big Book of Play & Find Out Science Projects. 2007. (Illus.). 224p. pap. 19.95 (***978-0-7879-8928-6(2)***) Wiley, John & Sons, Inc.

VanCleave, Janice Pratt. Great Science Projects from Real Kids. 2006. (Illus.). 144p. pap. 14.95 (978-0-471-47204-9(2) , Jossey-Bass) Wiley, John & Sons, Inc.

—Help! My Science Project Is Due Tomorrow! Easy Experiments You Can Do Overnight. 2001. (Illus.). 128p. pap. 14.95 (978-0-471-33100-1(7) , Capstone) Wiley, John & Sons, Inc.

—Janice VanCleaves A+ Projects in Astronomy: Winning Experiments for Science Fairs & Extra Credit. 2001. (Illus.). 224p. 32.50 (978-0-471-32816-2(2) , Wiley) Wiley, John & Sons, Inc.

—Janice VanCleave's A+ Projects in Earth Science: Winning Experiments for Science Fairs & Extra Credit. 1998. (VanCleave a+ Science Projects Ser.: Vol. 1). (Illus.). 240p. (gr. 7-12). pap. 12.95 (978-0-471-17770-8(9) , Wiley) Wiley, John & Sons, Inc.

—Janice VanCleave's A+ Projects in Physics: Winning Experiments for Science Fairs & Extra Credit. 2003. (VanCleave a+ Science Projects Ser.). (Illus.). 240p. 27.95 (978-0-471-39070-6(8) , Wiley) Wiley, John & Sons, Inc.

—Janice VanCleave's A+ Science Fair Projects. 2003. (Illus.). 160p. pap. 14.95 (978-0-471-33102-5(3) , Wiley) Wiley, John & Sons, Inc.

—Janice VanCleave's A+ Science Fair Workbook & Project Journal. 2003. (Illus.). 352p. (gr. 7-12). pap. 19.95 (978-0-471-46719-9(7)) Wiley, John & Sons, Inc.

—Janice VanCleave's Microscopes & Magnifying Lenses: Mind-Boggling Chemistry & Biology Experiments You Can Turn into Science Fair Projects. 2002. (Janice Vancleave Ser.). (Illus.). (J). 19.72 (978-0-7587-4631-3(8)) Book Wholesalers, Inc.

—Janice VanCleave's Science Project Workbook, Grades 3-6. 2003. (Illus.). 512p. pap. 19.95 (978-0-471-46647-5(6)) Wiley, John & Sons, Inc.

VanCleave, Janice Pratt. Janice VanCleave's Super Science Challenges: Hands-On Science Inquiry Projects for School, Science Fair, or Just Plain Fun! 2007. 160p. pap. 14.95 (***978-0-471-47183-7(6)*** , Jossey-Bass) Wiley, John & Sons, Inc.

Vecchione, Glen. Blue Ribbon Science Fair Projects. 2005. (Illus.). 224p. (J). (gr. 7-11). 19.95 (978-1-4027-1073-5(9)) Sterling Publishing Co., Inc.

—100 Amazing Award-Winning Science Fair Projects. 2005. (Illus.). 208p. (J). pap. 7.95 (978-1-4027-1910-3(8)) Sterling Publishing Co., Inc.

—100 Amazing First-Prize Science Fair Projects. 2005. (Science Fair Projects Ser.). (Illus.), 208p. (J). pap. 7.95 (978-1-4027-1911-0(6)) Sterling Publishing Co., Inc.

—100 Amazing First-Prize Science Fair Projects. 2005. (Illus.). 208p. (J). (gr. k-9). lib. bdg. 14.60 (978-0-606-33863-9(2)) Tandem Library Bks.

—100 Amazing Make-It-Yourself Science Fair Projects. 2005. (Science Fair Projects Ser.). (Illus.). 224p. (J). pap. 7.95 (978-1-4027-1912-7(4)) Sterling Publishing Co., Inc.

—100 First Prize Make-It-Yourself Science Fair Projects. 1998. (Illus.). 192p. (J). (gr. 4-7). 19.95 (978-0-8069-0703-1(7)) Sterling Publishing Co., Inc.

West, Krista. Hands-On Projects about Saving the Earth's Resources. 2002. (Great Earth Science Projects Ser.). (Illus.). 24p. (J). lib. bdg. 19.95 (978-0-8239-5847-4(7) , PowerKids Pr.) Rosen Publishing Group, Inc., The.

Whitehouse, Patricia. Plants. 2007. (J). (***978-1-4034-7918-1(6)***) Heinemann Library.

Wiese, Jim. Head to Toe Science: Over 40 Eye-Popping, Spine-Tingling, Heart-Pounding Activit. 2000. (gr. 3-6). lib. bdg. 22.20 (978-0-613-25472-4(4)) Tandem Library Bks.

—Magic Science: 50 Jaw-Dropping, Mind-Boggling, Head-Scratching Activities for Kids. 1998. (gr. 3-6). lib. bdg. 22.20 (978-0-613-89256-8(9)) Tandem Library Bks.

—Magic Science: 50 Jaw-Dropping, Mind-Boggling, Head-Scratching Activities for Kids. 1998. (Illus.). 128p. (J). (gr. 3-7). pap. 12.95 (978-0-471-18239-9(7) , Wiley) Wiley, John & Sons, Inc.

SCIENCE PROJECTS—FICTION

Alfonsi, Alice, adapted by. What You See Is What You Get. novel ed. 2004. (That's So Raven Ser.: Bk. 1). (Illus.). 144p. (gr. 3-7). pap. 4.99 (978-0-7868-4639-9(9)) Disney Pr.

Brown, Marc. Arthur's Science Fair Trouble. Brown, Marc, illus. 2003. (Arthur Ser.). (Illus.). 24p. (J). (gr. k-3). pap. 3.99 (978-0-375-81003-9(X)); lib. bdg. 11.99 (978-0-375-91003-6(4)) Random Hse. Children's Bks. (Random Hse. Bks. for Young Readers).

—Arthur's Science Fair Trouble. 2003. (Arthur Ser.). (gr. k-3). lib. bdg. 11.80 (978-0-613-70564-6(5)) Tandem Library Bks.

Burkett, Kathy. Mucus Attack! 2002. (Mad Science Ser.: No. 3). 96p. (J). (gr. 3-7). pap. 4.50 (978-0-439-22858-9(1)) Scholastic, Inc.

Carr, Roger. Can-Rolling Race. 2001. (gr. k-3). lib. bdg. 11.65 (978-0-613-33344-3(6)) Tandem Library Bks.

Clements, Andrew. Know-It-All. Pedersen, Janet, illus. 2007. (Jake Drake Ser.: No. 2). 112p. (J). pap. 3.99 (***978-1-4169-3931-3(8)*** , Aladdin) Simon & Schuster Children's Publishing.

Cole, Joanna. The Magic School Bus & the Science Fair Expedition. 2006. (Magic School Bus Ser.). 56p. (J). pap. 21.99 (978-0-439-90380-6(7)) Scholastic, Inc.

Cox, Judy. That Crazy Eddie & the Science Project of Doom. Simms, Blanche, illus. 2005. 96p. (J). 15.95 (978-0-8234-1931-9(2)) Holiday Hse., Inc.

Dean, Pamela. Juniper, Gentian, & Rosemary. 1998. 352p. (YA). (gr. 10 up). 24.95 (978-0-312-86004-2(8) , Tor Bks.) Doherty, Tom Assocs., LLC.

Dixon, Franklin W. All Eyes on First Prize. 1999. (Hardy Boys Are: No. 14). (J). (gr. 2-4). (978-0-606-19046-6(5)) Tandem Library Bks.

Dorros, Arthur. The Fungus That Ate My School. Catrow, David, illus. 32p. (J). (ps-ps). 2005. 5.99 (978-0-439-75539-9(5) , Scholastic Paperbacks); 2000. pap. 15.95 (978-0-590-47704-8(8) , Scholastic Reference) Scholastic, Inc.

Gilson, Jamie. It Goes Eeeeeeeeeeeee! 2001. (gr. 3-6). lib. bdg. 12.95 (978-0-613-35528-5(8)) Tandem Library Bks.

Greene, Stephanie. Owen Foote, Mighty Scientist. Smith, Catharine Bowman, illus. 2004. 96p. (J). (gr. k-3). tchr. ed. 15.00 (978-0-618-43016-1(4) , Clarion Bks.) Houghton Mifflin Co. Trade & Reference Div.

Grunwell, Jeanne Marie. Mind Games. 2006. 144p. (YA). (gr. 5-9). pap. 5.95 (978-0-618-68947-7(8)) Houghton Mifflin Co.

—Mind Games. 2003. (Illus.). 144p. (YA). (gr. 5-9). tchr. ed. 15.00 (978-0-618-17672-4(1)) Houghton Mifflin Co. Trade & Reference Div.

Harcourt School Publishers Staff. The Science Fair. 3rd ed. 2002. (Trophies English Language Learners Ser.). (Illus.). pap. 5.10 (978-0-15-327815-0(3)) Harcourt Schl. Pubs.

Johnston, Tony. Sparky & Eddie: Trouble with Rats. Ryan, Susannah, illus. 32p. (J). 1999. pap. 4.95 (978-0-590-47981-3(4)); 1998. 13.95 (978-0-590-47980-6(6)) Scholastic, Inc.

Kerley, Barbara. Greetings from Planet Earth. 2007. (Illus.). 256p. (J). (gr. 4-7). pap. 16.99 (978-0-439-80203-1(2) , Scholastic Pr.) Scholastic, Inc.

Komechak, Marilyn Gilbert. Paisano Pete: Snake-Killer Bird. 2003. (Illus.). 100p. (J). 9.95 (978-1-57168-770-8(X) , Eakin Pr.) Eakin Pr.

Korman, Gordon. The Chicken Doesn't Skate. 1998. 192p. (J). (gr. 4-8). pap. 4.50 (978-0-590-85301-9(5)) Scholastic, Inc.

Krulik, Nancy E. Be Nice to Mice, No. 20. John and Wendy Staff, illus. 2006. (Katie Kazoo, Switcheroo Ser.: No. 20). 80p. (J). (gr. 2-5). mass mkt. 3.99 (978-0-448-44132-0(2) , Grosset & Dunlap) Penguin Group (USA) Inc.

—Be Nice to Mice, No. 20. 2006. (Katie Kazoo, Switcheroo Ser.: No. 20). (Illus.). 78p. (J). (***978-1-4156-7185-6(0)*** , Grosset & Dunlap) Penguin Group (USA) Inc.

Layne, Steven L. Thomas's Sheep & the Spectacular Science Project. Board, Perry, illus. 2004. 32p. (J). pap. 15.95 (978-1-58980-210-0(1)) Pelican Publishing Co., Inc.

Lundy, Charlotte. Thank You, Moses. Waldrep, Evelyn L., ed. James, Margaret Ray, illus. 1999. 32p. (ps-3). 15.95 (978-0-9670280-3-3(5)) Bay Light Publishing.

Matlin, Marlee & Cooney, Doug. Nobody's Perfect. 2006. (Illus.). 240p. (J). (gr. 3-7). 15.95 (978-0-689-86986-0(X) , Simon & Schuster Children's Publishing) Simon & Schuster Children's Publishing.

Matson, Nancy. The Boy Trap. Chesworth, Michael, illus. 1999. 128p. (J). (gr. 3 7). 14.95 (978-0-8126-2663-6(X)) Cricket Bks.

Mayer, Mercer. Just a School Project. Mayer, Mercer, illus. 2004. (Little Critter Ser.). (Illus.). 24p. (J). (ps-2). pap. 3.99 (978-0-06-053946-7(1) , Harper Festival) HarperCollins Pubs.

Mayer, Mercer. Little Critter: Just a School Project (Spanish Edition) Tan solo un proyecto Escolar. Mayer, Mercer, illus. 2007. (Little Critter Ser.). (SPA.). 24p. (J). pap. 3.99 (***978-0-06-089241-8(2)*** , Rayo) HarperCollins Pubs.

McMullan, Kate. Pearl & Wagner: Two Good Friends. Alley, R. W., illus. 2003. (Easy-to-Read Ser.). 48p. (J). (gr. k-3). 13.99 (978-0-8037-2573-7(6) , Dial) Penguin Group (USA) Inc.

Newhouse, Mark H. The Rockhound Science Mysteries, 3 vols. (J). 2002. pap. 19.95 incl. cd-rom (978-0-9704629-8-5(0)); 2002. cd-rom 14.95 (978-0-9704629-5-4(6)); Bk. 1. 2000. (Illus.). 48p. cd-rom 5.95 (978-0-9704629-7-8(2)); Bk. 2. 2000. pap. 5.95 (978-0-9704629-6-1(4)); Vol. 1. 2nd rev. ed. 2002. (Illus.). 48p. reprint ed. pap. 5.95 (978-0-9704629-4-7(8)) Earthkids Publishing.

—The Rockhound Science Mysteries. 2000. (J). Bk. 1. (gr. 2-7). 39.95 incl. cd-rom, audio compact disk ; Bk. 1. (gr. 2-7). cd-rom 199.00 ; Bk. 2. (gr. 2-7). 199.00 incl. cd-rom, audio compact disk ; Bk. 2. (gr. 3-6). 39.95 incl. cd-rom ; Bk. 3. (gr. 2-7). 199.00 incl. cd-rom, audio compact disk ; Bk. 3. (gr. 4-7). 39.95 incl. cd-rom, audio compact disk Educational Activities, Inc.

Palatini, Margie. Lab Coat Girl in My Triple Decker Hero. Cole, Henry, illus. 2000. (L.A.F. Bks.). 112p. (gr. 2-6). 14.49 (978-0-7868-2442-7(5)) Disney Pr.

—Lab Coat Girl in My Triple Decker Hero. 2000. (gr. 3-6). lib. bdg. 13.00 (978-0-613-31399-5(2)) Tandem Library Bks.

S

Parish, Herman. Amelia Bedelia, Rocket Scientist? Sweat, Lynn, illus. (I Can Read Bks.). 64p. (J). 2007. pap. 3.99 (978-0-06-051889-9(8) , Harper Trophy); 2005. (gr. 1 up). 15.99 (978-0-06-051887-5(1)); 2005. (gr. 1 up). lib. bdg. 16.89 (978-0-06-051888-2(X)) HarperCollins Pubs.

Perry, Phyllis Jean. The Alien, the Giant, & Rocketman. Francis, Guy, illus. 2006. (J). pap. (978-1-59336-723-7(6)) Mondo Publishing.

Plourde, Lynn. Science Fair Day. Wickstrom, Thor, illus. 2008. 40p. (J). (gr. k). 16.99 (***978-0-525-47878-2(7)*** , Dutton Juvenile) Penguin Group (USA) Inc.

Preller, James. Case of the Stinky Science Project. 2000. (gr. 3-6). lib. bdg. 11.80 (978-0-613-24496-1(6)) Tandem Library Bks.

Rue, Nancy N. Sophie & the Scoundrels, Bk. 3. Chen, Grace, illus. 2005. (Faithgirlz Ser.). 128p. (J). pap. 6.99 (978-0-310-70758-5(7)) Zonderkidz.

Schraff, Anne. The Experiment: Set 1. 2002. 32p. (YA). 2.95 (978-1-56254-408-9(X) , SP 408X) Saddleback Educational Publishing.

Shevick, Edward. Science Action Labs: Water Science. Mitchell, Judy, ed. Rojas, Mary Galan, illus. 2002. 64p. (J). pap. 8.95 (978-1-57310-364-0(0)) Teaching & Learning Co.

Sierra, Judy. The Secret Science Project That Almost Ate the School. Gammell, Stephen, illus. 2006. 32p. (J). (gr. 1-4). 16.95 (978-1-4169-1175-3(8) , Simon & Schuster Children's Publishing) Simon & Schuster Children's Publishing.

Simon, Seymour. The Mysterious Lights & Other Cases. Schindler, S. D., illus. (Einstein Anderson, Science Detective Ser.). 96p. (J). (gr. 3-6). 1999. pap. 3.99 (978-0-380-72660-8(2)); 1998. 14.95 (978-0-688-14445-6(4)) HarperCollins Pubs.

—The Mysterious Lights & Other Cases. 1999. (Einstein Anderson, Science Detective Ser.). (J). (gr. 3-6). (978-0-606-16354-5(9)) Tandem Library Bks.

Smith, Greg Leitich. Ninjas, Piranhas, & Galileo. 2005. 192p. (J). (gr. 5-8). pap. 6.99 (978-0-316-01181-5(9)) Little Brown & Co.

Veit, Wilbert, Jr. The Music of Sunlight: The First Molecular Adventure. Hamblin, Randy, illus. 2000. v, 169p. (YA). (gr. 6-13). pap. 19.95 (978-0-9678081-4-7(6)) Sunlight Bks.

Wojciechowski, Susan. Beany & the Meany. Natti, Susanna, illus. 112p. (J). (gr. 1-4). 2006. pap. 4.99 (978-0-7636-2974-8(X)); 2005. 15.99 (978-0-7636-2630-3(9)) Candlewick Pr.

Yaccarino, Dan. The Big Science Fair. 2002. (Blast off Boy & Blorp Ser.: Bk. 3). (Illus.). 40p. (gr. k-3). 15.99 (978-0-7868-0580-8(3)) Disney Pr.

SCIENTIFIC APPARATUS AND INSTRUMENTS

see also names of groups of instruments, e.g. Aeronautical Instruments; Astronomical Instruments; Chemical Apparatus; Electric Apparatus and Appliances; Meteorological Instruments

Blevins, Wiley. You Can Use a Magnifying Glass. 2003. (Rookie Read. . . Science Ser.). (Illus.). 32p. (J). 20.50 (978-0-516-22871-6(4) , Children's Pr.) Scholastic Library Publishing.

Clark, John Owens Edward. Electrical Measurement, 9 vols., Vol. 4. 2002. (Illus.). (J). (978-0-7172-5632-7(4) , Grolier) Scholastic Library Publishing.

—Force & Pressure, 9 vols., Vol. 3. 2002. (Illus.). (J). (978-0-7172-5631-0(6) , Grolier) Scholastic Library Publishing.

—Length & Distance, 9 vols., Vol. 1. 2002. (Illus.). (J). (978-0-7172-5629-7(4) , Grolier) Scholastic Library Publishing.

—Measuring Time, 9 vols., Vol. 2. 2002. (Illus.). (J). (978-0-7172-5630-3(8) , Grolier) Scholastic Library Publishing.

—Scientific Analysis, 9 vols., Vol. 8. 2002. (Illus.). (J). (978-0-7172-5636-5(7) , Grolier) Scholastic Library Publishing.

—Scientific Classification, 9 vols., Vol. 9. 2002. (Illus.). (J). (978-0-7172-5637-2(5) , Grolier) Scholastic Library Publishing.

—Under the Microscope: Science Tools, 9 vols., Set. Incl. Vol. 1. Length & Distance. (978-0-7172-5629-7(4)); Vol. 2. Measuring Time. (978-0-7172-5630-3(8)); Vol. 3. Force & Pressure. (978-0-7172-5631-0(6)); Vol. 4. Electrical Measurement. (978-0-7172-5632-7(4)); Vol. 5. Using Visible Light. (978-0-7172-5633-4(2)); Vol. 6. Using Invisible Light. (978-0-7172-5634-1(0)); Vol. 7. Using Sound. (978-0-7172-5635-8(9)); Vol. 8. Scientific Analysis. (978-0-7172-5636-5(7)); Vol. 9. Scientific Classification. (978-0-7172-5637-2(5)); (J). (Illus.). 432p. 2002. 239.00 (978-0-7172-5628-0(6) , Grolier) Scholastic Library Publishing.

—Using Invisible Light, 9 vols., Vol. 6. 2002. (Illus.). (J). (978-0-7172-5634-1(0) , Grolier) Scholastic Library Publishing.

—Using Sound, 9 vols., Vol. 7. 2002. (Illus.). (J). (978-0-7172-5635-8(9) , Grolier) Scholastic Library Publishing.

—Using Visible Light, 9 vols., Vol. 5. 2002. (Illus.). (J). (978-0-7172-5633-4(2) , Grolier) Scholastic Library Publishing.

Coppin, Brigitte. The Compass: Steering Towards the New World. Didelot, Jean-Luc, illus. 2000. 47p. (YA). (gr. 6-8). pap. 10.00 (978-0-7881-6878-9(9)) DIANE Publishing Co.

Eboch, Chris. Science Tools: Using Machines & Instruments. Davis, Jon, illus. 2007. (Amazing Science Ser.). (J). 23.93 (978-1-4048-2199-6(6)) Picture Window Bks.

Furgang, Kathy. Instrumentos para medir en ciencias & Science Measuring Tools. 2005. spiral bd. 88.00 (***978-1-4108-5727-9(1)***) Benchmark Education Co.

Glass, Susan. Watch Out! Science Tools & Safety. 2006. (Illus.). 48p. (J). pap. (978-1-4034-8364-5(7)); lib. bdg. (978-1-4034-8360-7(4)) Heinemann Library.

Goldberg, Jan. Earth Imaging Satellites. 2003. (Library of Satellites). (Illus.). 64p. (YA). (gr. 5-8). lib. bdg. 26.50 (978-0-8239-3853-7(0) , Rosen Central) Rosen Publishing Group, Inc., The.

Holt, Rinehart and Winston Staff. Holt Science & Technology: Calculator for Biological Science Labs. 5th ed. 2004. (Illus.). pap. 14.60 (978-0-03-035177-8(4)) Holt, Rinehart & Winston.

Hossell, Karen Price. Sonar. 2003. (Communicating Ser.). 48p. (J). (gr. 3-5). pap. 8.50 (978-1-58810-944-6(5) , 91583) Heinemann Library.

Hyland, Tony. Scientific & Medical Robots. 2007. (J). (***978-1-59920-118-4(6)***) Smart Apple Media.

Martin, Elena. Seeing Is Believing. 2005. (Yellow Umbrella Books for Early Readers). (Illus.). 17p. (J). (978-0-7368-5263-0(8)); (978-0-7368-5299-9(9)) Capstone Pr., Inc.

Richardson, Adele D. Compasses. 2004. (First Facts Ser.). (Illus.). 24p. (J). 15.95 (978-0-7368-2520-7(7)) Capstone Pr., Inc.

Rivera, Sheila. Eyedropper. 2006. (First Step Nonfiction Ser.). (Illus.). 8p. (J). lib. bdg. (978-0-8225-5712-8(6) , Lerner Pubns.) Lerner Publishing Group.

—Tweezers. 2007. (First Step Nonfiction Ser.). (J). lib. bdg. (978-0-8225-6851-3(9)) Lerner Publishing Group.

Science Tools. (First Facts Ser.). (Illus.). (J). (gr. 1-2). lib. bdg. 106.30 (978-0-7368-2567-2(3)) Capstone Pr., Inc.

Sloan, Peter. Instruments. 1999. (gr. k-3). lib. bdg. 11.80 (978-0-613-30520-4(5)) Tandem Library Bks.

SCIENTIFIC DISCOVERIES

see Discoveries in Science

SCIENTIFIC EDUCATION

see Science—Study and Teaching

SCIENTIFIC EXPEDITIONS

see also names of regions explored, e.g. Antarctic Regions; Arctic Regions; and names of expeditions

Lewin, Ted. The Search for the Lost City: The Discovery of Machu Picchu. Lewin, Ted, illus. 2003. (Illus.). 48p. (J). (gr. 3-6). 17.99 (978-0-399-23302-9(4) , Philomel) Penguin Group (USA) Inc.

SCIENTIFIC EXPERIMENTS

see Science—Experiments

also particular branches of science with the subdivision Experiments, e.g. Chemistry—Experiments

SCIENTIFIC INSTRUMENTS

see Scientific Apparatus and Instruments

SCIENTIFIC MANAGEMENT

see Management

SCIENTIFIC RECREATIONS

see also Mathematical Recreations

Ardley, Neil. 101 Great Science Experiments. 2006. 120p. (J). pap. 7.99 (978-0-7566-1918-3(1)) Dorling Kindersley Publishing, Inc.

Barr, George. Outdoor Science Projects for Young People. 1998. Orig. Title: Young Scientist Takes a Walk: Guide to Outdoor Observations. (Illus.). 160p. (J). reprint ed. pap. 3.95 (978-0-486-26855-2(1) , 26855-1) Dover Pubns., Inc.

Blum, Raymond, et al. Giant Book of Science Fun/Giant Book of Math Fun: Flip Book. Sterling Publishing Company Staff, ed. (Illus.). 512p. pap. 9.98 (978-1-4027-0469-7(0)) Sterling Publishing Co., Inc.

Buttitta, Hope P. It's Not Magic, It's Science! 50 Science Tricks That Mystify, Dazzle & Astound! 2005. (Illus.). 80p. 14.95 (978-1-57990-622-1(2)) Lark Bks.

Cobb, Vicki & Darling, Kathy. You Gotta Try This! Absolutely Irresistible Science. Kelley, True, illus. 1999. 144p. (J). (gr. 3 up). 15.99 (978-0-688-15740-1(8)) HarperCollins Pubs.

Falk, John H., et al. Bubble Monster: And Other Science Fun. 2003. (Illus.). 176p. (J). (ps-3). pap. 17.95 (978-1-55652-301-4(7)) Chicago Review Pr., Inc.

Gardner, Martin. Smart Science Tricks. Steimle, Bob, illus. 2005. 144p. (J). (gr. k-9). pap. 5.95 (978-1-4027-2220-2(6)) Sterling Publishing Co., Inc.

Gardner, Robert. Science Project Ideas in the House. rev. ed. 2002. (Science Project Ideas Ser.). (Illus.). 128p. (J). (gr. 4-9). lib. bdg. 26.60 (978-0-7660-1705-4(2)) Enslow Pubs., Inc.

El Libro de los Acertijos Cientificos. (Coleccion Acertijos). (SPA.). (YA). (gr. 5-8). (978-950-724-614-2(2) , LM8237) Lumen ARG. *Dist:* Lectorum Pubns., Inc.

Markle, Sandra. Magic. Smith, Jamie, tr. Smith, Jamie, illus. 2001. (Super Science Ser.). 61p. (J). pap. (978-0-439-28136-2(9)) Scholastic, Inc.

Moche, Dinah L. More Magic Science Tricks. 2000. (Orig.). (J). pap. 1.95 (978-0-590-40399-3(0)) Scholastic, Inc.

Nye, Bill. Bill Nye the Science Guy's Consider the Following. 2000. (Illus.). (J). 17.39 (978-0-606-18254-6(3)) Tandem Library Bks.

—Bill Nye the Science Guy's Consider the Following: A Way Cool Set of Q'S, A'S, & Ideas. 2000. (gr. 3-6). lib. bdg. 19.65 (978-0-613-12519-2(3)) Tandem Library Bks.

—Bill Nye the Science Guy's Consider the Following: A Way Cool Set of Science Questions, Answers, & Ideas to Ponder. Kimball, Anton, illus. 2000. 112p. (gr. 4-7). pap. 10.99 (978-0-7868-1443-5(8)) Hyperion Bks. for Children.

Popular Science Editors. Backyard Laboratory. 2007. (Experiment with Science Ser.). 32p. (J). pap. 7.95 (***978-0-531-18757-9(8)***); (Illus.). (J). (gr. 3-6). lib. bdg. 25.00 (***978-0-531-18542-1(7)***) Scholastic Library Publishing. (Children's Pr.).

Press, Judy. Little Hands Sea Life Art & Activities: Creative Learning Experiences for 3- to 7-Year Olds. 2004. (Williamson's Little Hands Book Ser.). (Illus.). 128p. (J). 12.95 (978-1-885593-94-8(5) , Williamson Bks.) Ideals Pubns.

Recio, Belinda. Inventor's Workshop: Explore Your Creativity! 2nd ed. 2001. (Illus.). 96p. (J). pap. 22.95 (978-0-7624-1213-6(5) , Running Pr. Kids) Running Pr. Bk. Pubs.

VanCleave, Janice Pratt. Janice VanCleave's Super Science Challenges: Hands-On Science Inquiry Projects for School, Science Fair, or Just Plain Fun! 2007. 160p. pap. 14.95 (***978-0-471-47183-7(6)*** , Jossey-Bass) Wiley, John & Sons, Inc.

Yount, Lisa. Antoni van Leeuwenhoek: First to See Microscopic Life. 2001. (Great Minds of Science Ser.). (Illus.). 128p. (YA). (gr. 4-10). pap. 13.26 (978-0-7660-1866-2(0)) Enslow Pubs., Inc.

SCIENTISTS

see also Science—Vocational Guidance

also classes of scientists, e.g. Astronomers; Chemists; Geologists; Mathematicians; Naturalists; Physicists, etc.; and names of scientists

Abbey, Cherie D., ed. Biography Today: Profiles of People of Interest to Young Readers. (Scientists & Inventors Ser.: Vol. 9). 2004. (J). (gr. 3 up). lib. bdg. (978-0-7808-0711-2(1)); 2003. (YA). lib. bdg. (978-0-7808-0656-6(5)); 2002. 200p. (YA). lib. bdg. (978-0-7808-0636-8(0)); 2002. 200p. (YA). lib. bdg. (978-0-7808-0514-9(3)) Omnigraphics, Inc.

Ackerman, Jane. Louis Pasteur & the Founding of Microbiology. 2004. (Profiles in Science Ser.). (Illus.). 144p. (YA). (gr. 6-12). 26.95 (978-1-931798-13-6(3)) Reynolds, Morgan Inc.

Adler, David A. B. Franklin, Printer. 2001. (Illus.). 136p. (J). (gr. 4-6). tchr. ed. 19.95 (978-0-8234-1675-2(5)) Holiday Hse., Inc.

Akaeva, Mairam. Stars of Science: Innovators from All over the Globe, Bekbolotov, Ilyas, tr. 2002. 216p. (J). pap. 30.00 (978-1-59267-001-7(6)) Global Scholarly Pubns.

Allan, Tony. Isaac Newton. (Groundbreakers Ser.). (Illus.). 48p. (J). (gr. 5-7). 2002. pap. 8.50 (978-1-58810-992-7(5) , 91467); 2001. lib. bdg. 25.64 (978-1-58810-053-5(7)) Heinemann Library.

Allen, John. Robert Boyle: Father of Chemistry. 2005. (Giants of Science Ser.). (Illus.). 64p. (J). (ps-7). lib. bdg. 26.20 (978-1-56711-887-2(9) , Blackbirch Pr., Inc.) Thomson Gale.

Alphin, Elaine Marie. Germ Hunter: A Story about Louis Pasteur. Verstraete, Elaine, illus. 2003. 64p. (J). 6.95 (978-0-87614-929-4(8)); lib. bdg. 22.60 (978-1-57505-179-6(6)) Lerner Publishing Group. (Carolrhoda Bks.).

—Germ Hunter: A Story about Louis Pasteur. 2003. (gr. 3-6). lib. bdg. 14.10 (978-0-613-77207-5(5)) Tandem Library Bks.

Anderson, Margaret J. Isaac Newton: The Greatest Scientist of All Time. 2001. (Great Minds of Science Ser.). (Illus.). 128p. (YA). (gr. 4-10). pap. 10.95 (978-0-7660-1872-3(5)) Enslow Pubs., Inc.

Anderson, Margaret J. & Stephenson, Karen F. Aristotle: Philosopher & Scientist. 2004. (Great Minds of Science Ser.). (Illus.). 112p. (J). lib. bdg. 26.60 (978-0-7660-2096-2(7)) Enslow Pubs., Inc.

—Scientists of the Ancient World. 1999. (Collective Biographies Ser.). (Illus.). 104p. (YA). (gr. 6-12). lib. bdg. 26.60 (978-0-7660-1111-3(9)) Enslow Pubs., Inc.

Armentrout, David & Armentrout, Patricia. Louis Pasteur. 2002. (Discover Someone Who Made a Difference Discovery Library Ser.). (Illus.). 24p. (gr. 2-5). 14.95 (978-1-58952-056-1(4)) Rourke Publishing, LLC.

—Louis Pasteur. Sarfatti, Esther & de la Vega, Eida, trs. 2001. (Personas que Cambiaron la Historia Ser.). (SPA., Illus.). 24p. (J). (gr. 1-4). lib. bdg. 19.27 (978-1-58952-170-4(6) , RK5237) Rourke Publishing, LLC.

Baigrie, Brian S. The Renaissance & the Scientific Revolution. 2000. (Scribner Science Reference Ser.: Vol. 1). (Illus.). 210p. (YA). (gr. 7 up). 115.00 (978-0-684-80646-4(0) , GML00502-172406) Thomson Gale.

Balchin, Jon. Science: 100 Scientists Who Changed the World. 2003. (Illus.). 224p. 18.95 (978-1-59270-017-2(9)) Enchanted Lion Bks., LLC.

Bank Street Staff & Jakab, E. A. M. Louis Pasteur: Hunting Killer Germs. 2000. (Ideas on Trial Ser.). (Illus.). 122p. (C). (gr. 5-10). pap. 8.95 (978-0-07-134334-3(2) , 9780071343343) McGraw-Hill Cos., The.

Bankston, John. Alexander Fleming & the Story of Penicillin. l.t. ed. 2002. (Unlocking the Secrets of Science Ser.). (Illus.). 56p. (gr. 4-10). lib. bdg. 25.70 (978-1-58415-106-7(4)) Mitchell Lane Pubs., Inc.

—Francis Crick & James Watson: Pioneers in DNA Research. l.t. ed. 2002. (Unlocking the Secrets of Science Ser.). (Illus.). 56p. (gr. 4-10). lib. bdg. 17.95 (978-1-58415-122-7(6)) Mitchell Lane Pubs., Inc.

—Gerhard Domagk & the Discovery of Sulfa. l.t. ed. 2002. (Unlocking the Secrets of Science Ser.). (Illus.). 56p. (gr. 4-10). lib. bdg. 25.70 (978-1-58415-115-9(3)) Mitchell Lane Pubs., Inc.

—Gregor Mendel & the Discovery of the Gene. 2004. (Uncharted, Unexplored, & Unexplained Ser.). (Illus.). 48p. (J). (gr. 4-8). lib. bdg. 29.95 (978-1-58415-266-8(4)) Mitchell Lane Pubs., Inc.

Barter, James E. Jonas Salk. 2002. (Importance of Ser.). (Illus.). 120p. (J). (gr. 4-12). 32.45 (978-1-56006-968-3(6) , Lucent Bks.) Thomson Gale.

Baxter, Roberta. Skeptical Chemist: The Story of Robert Boyle. 2006. (Profiles in Science Ser.). (Illus.). 128p. (YA). (gr. 6-12). lib. bdg. 27.95 (978-1-59935-025-7(4)) Reynolds, Morgan Inc.

Beardsley, Laura E. Benjamin Franklin. 2007. (Essential Lives Ser.). (ENG., Illus.). 112p. (YA). (gr. 8-12). lib. bdg. 32.79 (***978-1-59928-840-6(0)*** , Essential Library) ABDO Publishing Co.

Benge, Janet & Benge, Geoff. Benjamin Franklin: A Useful Life. 2005. (Illus.). 197p. (J). (978-1-932096-14-9(0)) Emerald Bks.

Binns, Tristan Boyer. Alfred Nobel. 2004. (Great Life Stories Ser.). (Illus.). 111p. (J). 30.50 (978-0-531-12328-7(6) , Watts, Franklin) Scholastic Library Publishing.

Birch, Beverley & Fleming, Alexander. Alexander Fleming: Pioneer with Antibiotics. 2002. (Giants of Science Ser.). (Illus.). 64p. (J). 26.20 (978-1-56711-656-4(6) , Blackbirch Pr., Inc.) Thomson Gale.

Boekhoff, P. M. Galileo. 2003. (Inventors & Creators Ser.). (Illus.). 48p. (J). 23.70 (978-0-7377-1891-1(9) , Greenhaven Pr., Inc.) Thomson Gale.

Boekhoff, P. M. & Kallen, Stuart A. Benjamin Franklin. 2006. (Illus.). 48p. (J). (gr. 4-8). 17.00 (978-1-4223-5322-6(2)) DIANE Publishing Co.

—Steve Irwin. 2003. (Famous People Ser.). (Illus.). 48p. (J). 26.20 (978-0-7377-1890-4(0) , Greenhaven Pr., Inc.) Thomson Gale.

Boerst, William J. Isaac Newton: Organizing the Universe. 2004. (Great Scientists Ser.). (Illus.). 144p. (YA). (gr. 6-12). 26.95 (978-1-931798-01-3(X)) Reynolds, Morgan Inc.

Bortz, Fred. Beyond Jupiter: The Story of Planetary Astronomer Heidi Hammel. 2005. (Women's Adventures in Science Ser.). (Illus.). 110p. (YA). (gr. 7-9). 31.00 (978-0-531-16775-5(5) , Watts, Franklin) Scholastic Library Publishing.

Bowdish, Lynea. George Washington Carver. 2004. (Rookie Biographies Ser.). (Illus.). 31p. (J). 20.50 (978-0-516-23610-0(5) , Children's Pr.) Scholastic Library Publishing.

Brashares, Ann. Linus Torvalds: Software Rebel. 2001. (Techies Ser.: up). (Illus.). 80p. (J). (gr. 5 up). lib. bdg. 23.90 (978-0-7613-1960-3(3) , Twenty-First Century Bks.) Lerner Publishing Group.

Braun. Scientists of Rivers, Lakes & Ponds. 2001. (Scientists of the Biomes Ser.). (Illus.). (J). pap. (978-0-7398-4939-2(5)) Steck-Vaughn.

Brown, Don. Odd Boy Out: Young Albert Einstein. 2004. (Illus.). 32p. (J). (gr. k-3). 16.00 (978-0-618-49298-5(4)) Houghton Mifflin Co. Trade & Reference Div.

—Teedie: The Boyhood Adventures of Teddy Roosevelt. 2008. 32p. (J). (gr. k-3). 16.00 (978-0-618-17999-2(2)) Houghton Mifflin Co. Trade & Reference Div.

Bruchac, Joseph. Rachel Carson: Preserving a Sense of Wonder. Locker, Thomas, illus. 2004. (Thomas Locker Images of Conservation Ser.). 32p. (J). 17.95 (978-1-55591-482-0(9)) Fulcrum Publishing.

Burgan, Michael. Robert Hooke: Natural Philosopher & Scientific Explorer. 2007. (J). lib. bdg. (***978-0-7565-3315-1(5)***) Compass Point Bks.

Byman, Jeremy. Carl Sagan: In Contact with the Cosmos. 2004. (Great Scientists Ser.). (Illus.). 112p. (YA). (gr. 6-12). 21.95 (978-1-883846-55-8(2) , First Biographies) Reynolds, Morgan Inc.

Chanko, Pamela. Scientists. 1999. (J). pap. 10.01 (978-0-439-04601-5(7)) Scholastic, Inc.

Chronicle Books LLC Staff. Kid Who Named Pluto. 2008. 88p. (J). pap. 7.99 (978-0-8118-5451-1(5)) Chronicle Bks. LLC.

Clark, Brenda, illus. Franklin & His Friend. 2002. (Franklin Ser.). 12.40 (978-1-4046-2101-5(6)) Book Wholesalers, Inc.

Collard, Sneed B., III. Benjamin Franklin: The Man Who Could Do Just about Anything. 2006. (American Heroes Ser.). (Illus.). 48p. (J). (gr. 3-5). lib. bdg. 28.50 (***978-0-7614-2161-0(0)*** , Benchmark Bks.) Cavendish, Marshall Corp.

—A Firefly Biologist at Work. 2001. (gr. 3-6). lib. bdg. 15.25 (978-0-613-54218-0(5)) Tandem Library Bks.

—Lizard Island: Science & Scientists on Australia's Great Barrier Reef. (Single Title Science Pb Ser.). (Illus.). 144p. (YA). (gr. 9-12). 2001. pap. 12.95 (978-0-531-16559-1(1)); 2000. 26.00 (978-0-531-11719-4(7)) Scholastic Library Publishing. (Watts, Franklin).

Collier, James Lincoln. The Benjamin Franklin You Never Knew. 2004. (You Never Knew Ser.). (Illus.). 80p. (J). 25.50 (978-0-516-24427-3(2) , Children's Pr.) Scholastic Library Publishing.

Conlan, Kathy. Under the Ice. 2004. (Illus.). 56p. (J). (gr. 4-6). (978-1-55337-060-4(0)) Kids Can Pr., Ltd.

Crompton, Samuel Willard. Emanuel Swedenborg. 2004. (Spiritual Leaders & Thinkers Ser.). (Illus.). 120p. (gr. 9-13). 30.00 (978-0-7910-8102-0(8) , Chelsea Hse.) Facts On File, Inc.

Cullen, J. Heather. Barbara McClintock. 2003. (Women in the Science Ser.). (Illus.). 122p. pap. 30.00 (978-0-7910-7522-7(2)); 112p. (gr. 6-12). 30.00 (978-0-7910-7248-6(7)) Facts On File, Inc. (Chelsea Hse.).

Cullen, Katherine, et al. Pioneers in Science Set. 2005. (Pioneers in Science Ser.). 192-192p. (gr. 6-12). 239.60 (978-0-8160-5460-2(6)) Facts On File, Inc.

Cullen, Katherine E. Science, Technology, & Society: The People Behind the Science. 2005. (Pioneers in Science Ser.). (Illus.). 192p. (J). (gr. 6-12). 29.95 (978-0-8160-5468-8(1)) Facts On File, Inc.

Cummings, Pat & Cummings, Linda. Talking with Adventurers. 1998. (Illus.). 96p. (J). (gr. 3-5). 19.95 (978-0-7922-7068-3(1) , National Geographic Children's Bks.) National Geographic Society.

Davis, Wendy & Knight, Bertram T. Working at a Marine Institute. 1998. (Working Here Ser.). (Illus.). 32p. (J). (gr. 2-4). 23.50 (978-0-516-21223-4(0) , Children's Pr.) Scholastic Library Publishing.

De Angelis, Gina & Bianco, David J. Computers: Processing the Data. 2005. (Innovators Ser.: Vol. 13). (Illus.). 144p. (J). (gr. 5 up). lib. bdg. 24.95 (978-1-881508-87-8(0)) Oliver Pr., Inc.

Deary, Terry. The Nuclear Winter Man. 2004. (Classified Ser.). 96p. (J). (gr. 5-8). pap. 4.95 (978-0-7534-5827-3(6) , Kingfisher) Houghton Mifflin Co. Trade & Reference Div.

Don Nardo. The Trial of Galileo. 2004. (Famous Trials Ser.). (Illus.). 112p. (J). 29.95 (978-1-59018-423-3(8)) Thomson Gale.

Donlan, Leni. A Life Well Lived: Ben Franklin. 2007. (J). ***(*978-1-4109-2698-2(2));*** pap. ***(*978-1-4109-2709-5(1))*** Steck-Vaughn.

Doris. Life at the Top. 1999. (Illus.). (J). pap. (978-0-7398-2480-1(5)) Steck-Vaughn.

Driscoll, Laura. George Washington Carver. Weber, Jill, illus. 2003. (Smart about Scientists Ser.). 32p. (J). (gr. k-5). pap. 5.99 (978-0-448-43243-4(9) , Grosset & Dunlap) Penguin Group (USA) Inc.

Edelson, Edward. Francis Crick & James Watson: And the Building Blocks of Life. 1998. (Oxford Portraits in Science Ser.). (Illus.). 112p. (YA). (gr. 9 up). 30.00 (978-0-19-511451-5(5)) Oxford Univ. Pr., Inc.

Endres, Hollie J. Scientists Try, Try Again. 2007. (Shockwave: Life Stories Ser.). (Illus.). 36p. (J). (gr. 4-6). lib. bdg. 25.00 ***(*978-0-531-17744-0(0)*** , Children's Pr.) Scholastic Library Publishing.

Espinosa, Rod. Benjamin Franklin. 2007. (Bio-Graphics Ser.). (Illus.). 32p. (J). (gr. 3-6). lib. bdg. 27.07 ***(*978-1-60270-066-6(4)*** , Graphic Planet) Magic Wagon.

Fandel, Jennifer. Louis Pasteur. 2003. (World Was Never the Same Ser.). (J). (978-1-58417-266-6(5)) Lake Street Pubs.

Farndon, John. Great Scientists. 2007. (DK Eyewitness Bks.). 72p. (J). (gr. 3-8). 15.99 incl. cd-rom (978-0-7566-2974-8(8)) Dorling Kindersley Publishing, Inc.

Feinstein, Stephen. Louis Pasteur: The Father of Microbiology. 2008. (Inventors Who Changed the World Ser.). 128p. (J). (gr. 6 up). lib. bdg. 33.27 ***(*978-1-59845-078-1(6)*** , MyReportLinks.com Bks.) Enslow Pubs., Inc.

Feinstein, Stephen. Read about Benjamin Franklin. 2006. (I Like Biographies! Ser.). (Illus.). 24p. (J). lib. bdg. 21.26 (978-0-7660-2596-7(9) , Enslow Elementary) Enslow Pubs., Inc.

Fish, Bruce. Benjamin Franklin: American Statesman, Scientist & Writer. 1999. (Colonial Leaders Ser.). (Illus.). 80p. (gr. 3 up). (J). pap. 8.95 (978-0-7910-5690-5(2)); (YA). 27.50 (978-0-7910-5347-8(4)) Facts On File, Inc. (Chelsea Hse.).

Fleming, Candace. Ben Franklin's Almanac. 2003. (Illus.). 128p. (J). (gr. 5-9). 19.95 (978-0-689-83549-0(3) , Atheneum/Anne Schwartz Bks.) Simon & Schuster Children's Publishing.

Fleming, Thomas. Sterling Point Books: Ben Franklin: Inventing America. 2007. (Sterling Point Bks.). (Illus.). 192p. (J). 12.95 (978-1-4027-4523-2(0)); pap. 6.95 (978-1-4027-4143-2(X)) Sterling Publishing Co., Inc.

Fleming, Thomas J. Benjamin Franklin: Inventing America. 2007. (Sterling Point Bks.). (Illus.). viii, 177p. (J). ***(*978-1-4287-2411-2(7))*** Sterling Publishing Co., Inc.

Forbes, Charlotte & Forbes, Charlotte. Those Amazing Scientists. Pillion, Dean, illus. 2007. 26p. (J). ***(*978-0-9772799-1-3(X))*** Trilogy Pubns. LLC.

Fortey, Jackie. Great Scientists. 2007. (DK Eyewitness Bks.). 72p. (J). (gr. 3-8). lib. bdg. 19.99 (978-0-7566-2973-1(X)) Dorling Kindersley Publishing, Inc.

Fradin, Dennis Brindell. Nicolaus Copernicus: The Earth Is a Planet. Buhler, Cynthia von, tr. Buhler, Cynthia von, illus. 2003. 32p. (J). (gr. 2-6). 15.95 (978-1-59336-006-1(1)); pap. (978-1-59336-007-8(X)) Mondo Publishing.

—Who Was Ben Franklin? 2002. (gr. 3-6). lib. bdg. 13.00 (978-0-613-43654-0(7)) Tandem Library Bks.

Frisch, Aaron. Albert Einstein. 2005. (Illus.). 48p. (J). (gr. 5-9). 21.95 (978-1-58341-328-9(6) , Creative Education) Creative Co., The.

Garretson, Gregory. Severo Ochoa. (Biografías Hispanoamericanas Ser.). 64p. (J). 2006. (SPA.). lib. bdg. 32.86 ***(*978-1-4109-2126-0(3));*** 2005. (Illus.). pap. 9.50 (978-1-4109-1306-7(6)); 2004. (Illus.). (gr. 4-6). 32.86 (978-1-4109-1298-5(1)) Raintree.

Gaustad, Edwin S. Benjamin Franklin: Inventing America. 2006. 143p. (J). (gr. 4-8). reprint ed. 22.00 (978-1-4223-5227-4(7)) DIANE Publishing Co.

Gillis, Jennifer Blizin. Benjamin Franklin. 2004. (Illus.). 32p. (J). pap. 6.50 (978-1-4034-5332-7(2)); lib. bdg. 22.79 (978-1-4034-5324-2(1)) Heinemann Library.

Gjertsen, Derek & Allaby, Michael, eds. Makers of Science, 5 vols., Set. 2001. (Illus.). 480p. (YA). (gr. 5-9). 225.00 (978-0-19-521680-6(6)) Oxford Univ. Pr., Inc.

Glass, Maya. Benjamin Franklin: Early American Genius. 2003. (Primary Sources of Famous People in American History Ser.). (Illus.). 32p. (YA). pap. (978-0-8239-4175-9(2)) Rosen Publishing Group, Inc., The.

Gogerly, Liz. Sigmund Freud. 2003. (20th Century History Makers Ser.). (Illus.). 112p. (J). lib. bdg. 32.85 (978-0-7398-6142-4(5)) Raintree.

Goldish, Meish. Fossil Tales. 2003. (On the Job Ser.). (Illus.). 32p. (gr. 3-5). 23.00 (978-0-7910-7411-4(0) , Chelsea Hse.) Facts On File, Inc.

Gomez, Rebecca. Albert Einstein. 2003. (First Biographies Ser.). (Illus.). 32p. (J). (gr. k-4). lib. bdg. 22.78 (978-1-57765-946-4(5)) ABDO Publishing Co.

Goodridge, Catherine. Jane Goodall. ed. 2004. (SPA.). (J). pap. 5.00 (978-1-4108-2426-4(8) , A24268) Benchmark Education Co.

Gordon, Karen. Selman Waksman & the Discovery of Streptomycin. l.t. ed. 2002. (Unlocking the Secrets of Science Ser.). (Illus.). 56p. (gr. 4-10). lib. bdg. 25.70 (978-1-58415-138-8(2)) Mitchell Lane Pubs., Inc.

Gow, Mary. Robert Boyle: Pioneer of Experimental Chemistry. 2005. (Great Minds of Science Ser.). (Illus.). 128p. (J). lib. bdg. 26.60 (978-0-7660-2501-1(2)) Enslow Pubs., Inc.

—Robert Hooke: Creative Genius, Scientist, Inventor. 2006. (Great Minds of Science Ser.). (Illus.). 128p. (J). (gr. 4-10). lib. bdg. 31.93 (978-0-7660-2547-9(0)) Enslow Pubs., Inc.

Graham, Amy. Thomas Edison: Wizard of Light & Sound. 2007. (Inventors Who Changed the World Ser.). (Illus.). 128p. (J). lib. bdg. 33.27 (978-1-59845-052-1(2) , MyReportLinks.com Bks.) Enslow Pubs., Inc.

Great Life Stories: Inventors & Scientists, 3 bks. 2004. (J). 88.50 (978-0-531-12397-3(9) , Children's Pr.); (Illus.). 118.00 (978-0-531-19329-7(2)) Scholastic Library Publishing.

Great Scientific Questions & the Scientists Who Answered Them. 2005. (Illus.). 112p. (gr. 7-12). lib. bdg. 319.20 (978-1-4042-0356-3(7)) Rosen Publishing Group, Inc., The.

Gregson, Susan R. Benjamin Franklin. 2000. (Let Freedom Ring Ser.). (Illus.). 48p. (J). (gr. 3-4). lib. bdg. 22.60 (978-0-7368-1031-9(5) , Bridgestone Bks.) Capstone Pr., Inc.

Guidici, Cynthia. Mario Molina. (Hispanic-American Biographies Ser.). (Illus.). 64p. (J). 2005. pap. 9.50 (978-1-4109-1304-3(X)); 2004. (gr. 4-6). 32.86 (978-1-4109-1296-1(5)) Raintree.

Hacker, Carlotta. Scientists. 1998. (Women in Profile Ser.). (Illus.). 48p. (J). (gr. 4). pap. (978-0-7787-0028-9(3)); lib. bdg. (978-0-7787-0006-7(2)) Crabtree Publishing Co.

Hamilton, Janet. James Watson: Solving the Mystery of DNA. 2004. (Nobel Prize-Winning Scientists Ser.). (Illus.). 104p. (J). lib. bdg. 26.60 (978-0-7660-2258-4(7)) Enslow Pubs., Inc.

—Lise Meitner: Pioneer of Nuclear Fission. 2002. (Great Minds of Science Ser.). (Illus.). 128p. (J). (gr. 4-10). lib. bdg. 26.60 (978-0-7660-1756-6(7)) Enslow Pubs., Inc.

Hantula, Richard. Alexander Fleming. 2003. (Trailblazers of the Modern World Ser.). (Illus.). 48p. (J). (gr. 5 up). pap. 14.95 (978-0-8368-5243-1(5)); lib. bdg. 30.00 (978-0-8368-5083-3(1)) Stevens, Gareth Inc. (World Almanac Library).

—Jonas Salk. 2004. (Trailblazers of the Modern World Ser.). (Illus.). 48p. (J). (gr. 5 up). pap. 11.95 (978-0-8368-5260-8(5)); lib. bdg. 30.00 (978-0-8368-5100-7(5)) Stevens, Gareth Inc. (World Almanac Library).

Harcourt School Publishers Staff. Dreams of the Deep Below Level. 3rd ed. 2002. (Trophies Reading Program Ser.). (Illus.). pap. 5.10 (978-0-15-323427-9(X)) Harcourt Schl. Pubs.

—The Rain Forest Is a Home: Take-Home Book. 2001. (Collections Ser.). (J). pap. 1.90 (978-0-15-319492-4(8)) Harcourt Schl. Pubs.

Harness, Cheryl. The Remarkable Benjamin Franklin. 2005. (Illus.). 48p. (J). (gr. 2 up). 17.95 (978-0-7922-7882-5(8)); 27.90 (978-0-7922-7884-9(4)) National Geographic Society. (National Geographic Children's Bks.).

Harris, Laurie Lanzen. Biography for Beginners: Inventors. 2006. (J). (978-1-931360-27-2(8)) Favorable Impressions.

Harris, Laurie Lanzen, ed. Biography Today: Profiles of People of Interest to Young Readers. (Illus.). (YA). (gr. 4 up). 2001. (Scientists & Inventors Ser.: Vol. 5). 200p. lib. bdg. (978-0-7808-0434-0(1)); 1999. (Scientist Inventors Ser.: Vol. 3). 206p. lib. bdg. (978-0-7808-0364-0(7)) Omnigraphics, Inc.

Hasan, Heather. Mendel & the Laws of Genetics. 2004. (Primary Sources of Revolutionary Scientific Discoveries & Theories Ser.). (Illus.). 64p. (J). lib. bdg. 29.25 (978-1-4042-0309-9(5)) Rosen Publishing Group, Inc., The.

Hasday, Judy L. Albert Einstein: The Giant of 20th Century Science. 2004. (Nobel Prize-Winning Scientists Ser.). (Illus.). 128p. (J). lib. bdg. 26.60 (978-0-7660-2185-3(8)) Enslow Pubs., Inc.

Hatt, Christine. Scientists & Their Discoveries. 2001. (Documenting History Ser.). (Illus.). 64p. (J). (gr. 8-12). 24.50 (978-0-531-14614-9(6) , Watts, Franklin) Scholastic Library Publishing.

Haven, Kendall F. Women at the Edge of Discovery: 40 True Science Adventures. 2003. 296p. (J). (gr. 4-9). pap. 34.00 (978-1-59158-015-7(3) , LU0153) Libraries Unlimited, Inc.

Higgins, Maria Mihalik. Sterling Biographies: Benjamin Franklin: Revolutionary Inventor. 2007. (Sterling Biographies Ser.). (Illus.). 128p. (J). 12.95 ***(*978-1-4027-4952-0(X))*** Sterling Publishing Co., Inc.

Hitchcock, Susan Tyler. Sylvia A. Earle: Deep Sea Explorer. 2004. (Women Explorers Ser.). (Illus.). 120p. 30.00 (978-0-7910-7712-2(8) , Chelsea Hse.) Facts On File, Inc.

Ingram, Scott. Nicolaus Copernicus: Father of Modern Astronomy. 2004. (Illus.). 64p. (J). 26.20 (978-1-56711-489-8(X) , Blackbirch Pr., Inc.) Thomson Gale.

Inventors & Scientists, 2 bks., Set. 2005. (YA). 59.00 (978-0-531-18750-0(0)) Scholastic Library Publishing.

Jackson, Ellen B. Looking for Life in the Universe: The Search for Extraterrestrial Intelligence. Bishop, Nic, photos by. 2005. (Scientists in the Field Ser.). (Illus.). 64p. (J). (gr. 4-6). pap. 6.95 (978-0-618-54886-6(6)) Houghton Mifflin Co. Trade & Reference Div.

Jenner, Caryn. Thomas Edison. 2007. 48p. (J). (gr. 3-4). 14.99 (978-0-7566-2947-2(0)); pap. 3.99 (978-0-7566-2946-5(2)) Dorling Kindersley Publishing, Inc.

Jones, Lynda. Great Black Heroes: Five Brilliant Scientists. 2000. (gr. 3-6). lib. bdg. 11.80 (978-0-613-21631-9(8)); (Hello Reader! Ser.: Level 4). (Illus.). (J). 10.79 (978-0-606-18544-8(5)) Tandem Library Bks.

Kahn, Jetty. Women in Physical Science Careers. 1998. (Short Biographies Ser.). (Illus.). 48p. (J). (gr. 3-4). lib. bdg. 22.60 (978-0-7368-0015-0(8) , Bridgestone Bks.) Capstone Pr., Inc.

Kelly, Jack. Benjamin Franklin. Tafalla, Ortiz, illus. 2005. (Heroes of America Ser.). 240p. (J). (gr. 3-8). lib. bdg. 21.35 (978-1-59679-257-9(4)) ABDO Publishing Co.

Kent, Deborah. Mario Molina: Chemist & Nobel Prize Winner. 2004. (Proud Heritage: the Hispanic Library Ser.). (Illus.). 40p. (J). (gr. 3-7). 28.50 (978-1-59296-170-2(3)) Child's World, Inc.

Kepnes, Caroline. Stephen Crane. 2004. (Classic Storytellers Ser.). (Illus.). 48p. (J). (gr. 4-8). lib. bdg. 20.95 (978-1-58415-272-9(9)) Mitchell Lane Pubs., Inc.

Kjelle, Marylou Morano. Raymond Damadian & the Development of the MRI. l.t. ed. 2002. (Unlocking the Secrets of Science Ser.). (Illus.). 56p. (gr. 4-10). lib. bdg. 25.70 (978-1-58415-141-8(2)) Mitchell Lane Pubs., Inc.

Klare, Roger. Gregor Mendel: Father of Genetics. 2001. (Great Minds of Science Ser.). (Illus.). 128p. (YA). (gr. 4-10). pap. 10.95 (978-0-7660-1871-6(7)) Enslow Pubs., Inc.

Koestler-Grack, Rachel A. Mary Baker Eddy. 2004. (Spiritual Leaders & Thinkers Ser.). (Illus.). 120p. (gr. 9-13). 30.00 (978-0-7910-7866-2(3) , Chelsea Hse.) Facts On File, Inc.

Kozar, Richard. Inventors & Their Discoveries. 1999. (Costume, Tradition & Culture). (Illus.). 64p. (YA). (gr. 5 up). 28.00 (978-0-7910-5163-4(3) , Chelsea Hse.) Facts On File, Inc.

Kurtz, Jane. Mister Bones: Dinosaur Hunter. Haverfield, Mary, illus. 2004. (Ready-to-Read Ser.). 32p. (J). pap. 3.99 (978-0-689-85960-1(0) , Aladdin) Simon & Schuster Children's Publishing.

Lalley. Grassland Scientists. 2001. (Scientists of the Biomes Ser.). (Illus.). (J). pap. (978-0-7398-4937-8(9)) Steck-Vaughn.

—Ocean Scientists. 2001. (Scientists of the Biomes Ser.). (Illus.). (J). pap. (978-0-7398-4938-5(7)) Steck-Vaughn.

Landau, Elaine. Meet Ben Franklin with Elaine Landau. 2006. (Explore Colonial America with Elaine Landau Ser.). (Illus.). 48p. (J). lib. bdg. 23.93 (978-0-7660-2555-4(1) , Enslow Elementary) Enslow Pubs., Inc.

Lassieur, Allison. Benjamin Banneker: Astronomer & Mathematician. 2006. (Fact Finders Ser.). (Illus.). 32p. (J). (978-0-7368-5432-0(0)) Capstone Pr., Inc.

—Marie Curie: A Scientific Pioneer. 2003. (Great Life Stories Ser.). (Illus.). 112p. (J). 30.50 (978-0-531-12270-9(0) , Watts, Franklin) Scholastic Library Publishing.

Lehn, Barbara. What Is A Scientist? 1999. 3. (Illus.). 32p. (J). (gr. k-3). pap. 7.95 (978-0-7613-1298-7(6) , Millbrook Pr.) Lerner Publishing Group.

—What Is A Scientist? Krauss, Carol, photos by. 1998. (What Is...? Ser.). (Illus.). 32p. (gr. k-3). lib. bdg. 21.90 (978-0-7613-1272-7(2) , Millbrook Pr.) Lerner Publishing Group.

Levine, Ellen. Up Close: Rachel Carson: Rachel Carson. 2008. (Up Close Ser.). 208p. (J). (gr. 6). pap. 6.99 ***(*978-0-14-241046-2(2)*** , Puffin) Penguin Group (USA) Inc.

The Life & Contributions of Leonardo Da Vinci. 2006. 58p. (J). pap. (978-0-935047-60-8(3)) Americas Group, The.

MacDonald, Fiona & Birch, Beverley. Louis Pasteur: Father of Modern Medicine. 2001. (Giants of Science Ser.). (Illus.). 64p. (J). (gr. 5-8). 27.44 (978-1-56711-336-5(2) , Blackbirch Pr., Inc.) Thomson Gale.

Mara, Wil. Benjamin Franklin. rev. ed. 2006. (Rookie Biography Ser.). (Illus.). 31p. (J). (978-0-531-12450-5(9)) Children's Pr., Ltd.

—Dian Fossey: Among the Gorillas. 2004. (Great Life Stories Ser.). (Illus.). 127p. (J). 30.50 (978-0-531-12059-0(7) , Watts, Franklin) Scholastic Library Publishing.

—Thomas Alva Edison. 2004. (Rookie Biographies Ser.). (Illus.). 31p. (J). 20.50 (978-0-516-21843-4(3) , Children's Pr.) Scholastic Library Publishing.

Marcovitz, Hal. Benjamin Franklin: Scientist, Inventor, Printer, & Statesman. 2006. (Leaders of the American Revolution Ser.). (Illus.). 176p. (J). (gr. 5-8). 30.00 (978-0-7910-9219-4(4) , Chelsea Hse.) Facts On File, Inc.

Marsh, Carole. Aldo Leopold. 2002. (One Thousand Readers Ser.). (Illus.). 12p. (J). (gr. k-4). 2.95 (978-0-635-01546-4(3) , 15463) Gallopade International.

Martin, Jacqueline Briggs. Snowflake Bentley. ed. 2004. (Illus.). (J). (ps-3). spiral bd. (978-0-616-01714-2(6)) Canadian National Institute for the Blind/Institut National Canadien pour les Aveugles.

—Snowflake Bentley. Azarian, Mary, illus. 1998. 32p. (J). (gr. k-3). lib. bdg., tchr. ed. 16.00 (978-0-395-86162-2(4)) Houghton Mifflin Co. Trade & Reference Div.

Mason, Antony & da Vinci, Leonardo. Leonardo da Vinci. 2004. (Lives of the Artists Ser.). (Illus.). 48p. (J). (gr. 5 up). pap. 29.26 (978-0-8368-5604-0(X)); lib. bdg. 30.00 (978-0-8368-5599-9(X)) Stevens, Gareth Inc. (World Almanac Library).

Mason, Paul. Galileo. (Groundbreakers Ser.). (Illus.). 48p. (J). (gr. 5-7). 2002. pap. 8.50 (978-1-58810-991-0(7) , 91466); 2001. lib. bdg. 25.64 (978-1-58810-052-8(9)) Heinemann Library.

Mayer, Cassie. Benjamin Franklin. 2007. (J). ***(*978-1-4034-9970-7(5));*** pap. ***(*978-1-4034-9979-0(9))*** Heinemann Library.

McCartin, Brain. Thomas Paine: "Common Sense" & Revolutionary Pamphleteering. 2005. (Library of American Lives & Times). (Illus.). 112p. (J). (gr. 4-8). lib. bdg. 31.95 (978-0-8239-5729-3(2)) Rosen Publishing Group, Inc., The.

McCurdy, Michael. So Said Ben. 2007. (Illus.). 32p. (YA). (gr. 4 up). 17.95 ***(*978-1-56846-147-2(X)*** , Creative Editions) Creative Co., The.

McCutcheon, Marc. The Kid Who Named Pluto: And the Stories of Other Extraordinary Young People in Science. Cannell, Jon, illus. 2004. 88p. (J). 15.95 (978-0-8118-3770-5(X)) Chronicle Bks. LLC.

McDonough, Yona Zeldis. The Life of Benjamin Franklin: An American Original. Zeldis, Malcah, illus. 2006. 48p. (J). 17.95 (978-0-8050-7856-5(8)) Holt, Henry & Co.

McLeese, Don. Benjamin Franklin. 2005. (Heroes of the American Revolution Ser.). (Illus.). 32p. (gr. 2-5). 19.95 (978-1-59515-216-9(4)) Rourke Publishing, LLC.

Michael White. Issac Newton. 2005. (Gigantes de Ciencia Ser.). (gr. 5-7). 28.70 (978-1-4103-0502-2(3) , Blackbirch Pr., Inc.) Thomson Gale.

Miles, Victoria. Wild Science: Amazing Encounters Between Animals & the People Who Study Them. 2004. (Illus.). 168p. (J). pap. 18.95 (978-1-55192-618-6(0)) Raincoast Bk. Distribution CAN. *Dist:* Perseus Distribution.

Montgomery, Sy. The Tarantula Scientist. Bishop, Nic, photos by. 2004. (Scientists in the Field Ser.). (Illus.). 80p. (J). (gr. 3-5). tchr. ed. 18.00 (978-0-618-14799-1(3)) Houghton Mifflin Co. Trade & Reference Div.

Moore, Jo Ellen. Learning to Be a Scientist. Davis, Cindy et al, illus. 2000. (ScienceWorks for Kids Ser.). 80p. (J). (gr. k-1). pap. 9.95 (978-1-55799-776-0(4) , EMC 872) Evan-Moor Educational Pubs.

Nardo, Don. Scientists of Ancient Greece. 1998. (History Makers Ser.). (Illus.). 128p. (YA). (gr. 7-10). 27.45 (978-1-56006-362-9(9) , Lucent Bks.) Thomson Gale.

New York Public Library Staff & Callan, Jim. The New York Public Library Amazing Scientists: A Book of Answers for Kids. 2001. (New York Public Library Books for Kids: Vol. 10). (Illus.). 176p. pap. 12.95 (978-0-471-39289-7(8) , Wiley) Wiley, John & Sons, Inc.

Nichols, Catherine. Leonardo Da Vinci. 2006. (Primary Source Library of Famous Artists). (Illus.). 32p. (J). 21.95 (978-1-4042-2762-0(8) , PowerKids Pr.) Rosen Publishing Group, Inc., The.

Notable Scientists Set. 2005. (Notable Scientists Ser.). 240-400p. (gr. 6-12). 450.00 (978-0-8160-5967-6(5)) Facts On File, Inc.

Oleksy, Walter. Hispanic-American Scientists. 1998. (American Profiles Ser.). (Illus.). 160p. (YA). (gr. 5-12). 25.00 (978-0-8160-3704-9(3)) Facts On File, Inc.

Olson, Kay Melchisedech. Benjamin Franklin: An American Genius. Purcell, Gordon & Schulz, Barbara, illus. 2005. (Graphic Library). 32p. (J). (gr. 3-7). lib. bdg. 25.26 (978-0-7368-4629-5(8)) Capstone Pr., Inc.

Orozco, Julia & Mulfinger, George. Christian Men of Science. 2004. (Illus.). 304p. (YA). pap. 14.99 (978-1-932307-22-1(2) , Ambassador-Emerald, International) Emerald Hse. Group, Inc.

Orr, Tamra. Forensic Science Investigator. 2008. (J). pap. 7.95 ***(*978-1-60279-081-0(7))*** Cherry Lake Publishing.

Parker, Steve. Alexander Fleming. (Groundbreakers Ser.). 48p. pap. 8.50 (978-1-4034-4060-0(3)); 2001. (Illus.). (J). (gr. 5-7). lib. bdg. 25.64 (978-1-58810-050-4(2)) Heinemann Library.

Parker, Steve, et al. Scientists & Inventors, 16 bks. (Illus.). (J). (gr. 5-7). Set 1-2. lib. bdg. 410.24 (978-1-58810-183-9(5)); Set 2. 2001. lib. bdg. 153.24 (978-1-58810-009-2(X)) Heinemann Library.

Parks, Deborah A. Nature's Machines: The Story of Biomechanist Mimi Koehl. 2005. (Women's Adventures in Science Ser.). (Illus.). 118p. (YA). (gr. 7-9). 31.00 (978-0-531-16780-9(1) , Watts, Franklin) Scholastic Library Publishing.

Parks, Peggy J. Benjamin Franklin: Genius Inventor & Electricity Pioneer. 2002. (Giants of Science Ser.). (Illus.). 64p. (J). 26.20 (978-1-56711-658-8(2) , Blackbirch Pr., Inc.) Thomson Gale.

—Jonas Salk: Polio Vaccine Pioneer. 2003. (Giants of Science Ser.). (Illus.). 64p. (J). 26.20 (978-1-56711-475-1(X) , Blackbirch Pr., Inc.) Thomson Gale.

Patent, Dorothy Hinshaw. A Polar Bear Biologist at Work. 2001. (Wildlife Conservation Society Bks.). (Illus.). 48p. (J). (gr. 4-6). 24.50 (978-0-531-11850-4(9) , Watts, Franklin) Scholastic Library Publishing.

—Secrets of the Ice Man. 1999. (Frozen in Time Ser.). (Illus.). 72p. (J). (gr. 5-9). lib. bdg. 28.50 (978-0-7614-0782-9(0) , Benchmark Bks.) Cavendish, Marshall Corp.

Petrie, Kristin. Jacques Cousteau. 2004. (Explorers Set I Ser.). (J). (gr. k-6). lib. bdg. 22.78 (978-1-59197-599-1(9)) ABDO Publishing Co.

Polcovar, Jane. Rosalind Franklin & the Structure of Life. 2006. (Profiles in Science Ser.). 144p. (J). (gr. 6-12). lib. bdg. 27.95 (978-1-59935-022-6(X)) Reynolds, Morgan Inc.

Polking, Kirk. Oceanographers & Explorers of the Sea. 1999. (Collective Biographies Ser.). (Illus.). 128p. (YA). (gr. 6-12). lib. bdg. 20.95 (978-0-7660-1113-7(5)) Enslow Pubs., Inc.

Price-Groff, Claire. Thomas Alva Edison: Inventor & Entrepreneur. 2003. (Great Life Stories Ser.). 128p. (J). 30.50 (978-0-531-12275-4(1) , Watts, Franklin) Scholastic Library Publishing.

Proffitt, Pamela, ed. Notable Women Scientists. 1999. (Illus.). xxvi, 668p. (J). (gr. 6). 130.00 (978-0-7876-3900-6(1) , GML00502-113696, Gale Research International, Ltd.) Thomson Gale.

Puerta, German. Galileo Galilei - Y Sin Embargo se Mueve. 2005. 108p. pap. (978-958-30-1700-1(0)) Panamericana Editorial.

Randolph, Ryan P. Benjamin Franklin: Inventor, Writer & Patriot. 2005. (Library of American Lives & Times). (Illus.). 112p. (YA). (gr. 4-8). lib. bdg. 31.95 (978-0-8239-5751-4(9)) Rosen Publishing Group, Inc., The.

Rau, Dana Meachen. Albert Einstein. 2003. (Compass Point Early Biographies Ser.). (Illus.). 32p. (J). (gr. 2 up). lib. bdg. 21.26 (978-0-7565-0416-8(3)) Compass Point Bks.

S

Rausch, Monica. Benjamin Franklin. 2006. (J). (ENG & SPA.). pap. (***978-0-8368-7988-9(0)**); (ENG & SPA.). lib. bdg. (***978-0-8368-7981-0(3)***); (Illus.). 24p. pap. (***978-0-8368-7689-5(X)***); (Illus.). 24p. lib. bdg. (***978-0-8368-7682-6(2)***) Stevens, Gareth Inc. (Weekly Reader Early Learning Library).

Reed, Jennifer. Leonardo da Vinci: Genius of Art & Science. 2005. (Great Minds of Science Ser.). (Illus.). 128p. (J). lib. bdg. 26.60 (978-0-7660-2500-4(4)) Enslow Pubs., Inc.

Reid, Struan & Fara, Patricia. El Libro de los Cientificos: Desde Arquimedes a Einstein. (SPA.). (YA). (gr. 5-8). pap. (978-950-724-272-4(4) , LMA8234) Lumen ARG. *Dist:* Lectorum Pubns., Inc.

Riggs, Ernestine G. & Gholar, Cheryl, contrib. by. Careers with Character, 18 vols., Set. 2002. (Careers with Character Ser.). (Illus.). 96p. (J). (gr. 7 up). (978-1-59084-327-7(4)) Mason Crest Pubs.

Riley, Gail Blasser. Benjamin Franklin & Electricity. 2004. (Cornerstones of Freedom Ser.). (Illus.). 48p. (J). 26.00 (978-0-516-24240-8(7) , Children's Pr.) Scholastic Library Publishing.

Riley, John B. Benjamin Franklin: A Photo Biography. l.t. ed. 2004. (First Biographies Ser.). (Illus.). 24p. (YA). (gr. 5 up). 16.95 (978-1-883846-64-0(1) , First Biographies) Reynolds, Morgan Inc.

Rinaldo, Denise. Jane Goodall: With a Discussion of Responsibility. 2003. (Values in Action Ser.). (J). (978-1-59203-062-0(9)) Learning Challenge, Inc.

—Leonardo Da Vinci: With a Discussion of Imagination. 2003. (Values in Action Ser.). (J). (978-1-59203-066-8(1)) Learning Challenge, Inc.

Ring, Susan. Scientists at Work. (Illus.). 16p. (J). (gr. k-2). 2006. 15.93 (978-0-7368-5837-3(7) , Yellow Umbrella Bks.); 2005. (978-0-7368-5303-3(0)); 2005. (978-0-7368-5267-8(0)) Capstone Pr., Inc.

Robbins, Louise E. Louis Pasteur & the Hidden World of Microbes. 2001. (Oxford Portraits in Science Ser.). (Illus.). 144p. (YA). 30.00 (978-0-19-512227-5(5)) Oxford Univ. Pr., Inc.

Robert Goddard, 6 vols. (gr. k-2). 28.95 (978-0-7368-8756-4(3)) Red Brick Learning.

Rosinsky, Natalie M. How Scientists Work. 2004. (Illus.). 32p. (J). (gr. 3 up). 21.26 (978-0-7565-0596-7(8)) Compass Point Bks.

Salas, Laura Purdie. Discovering Nature's Laws: A Story about Isaac Newton. Reynolds, Emily C. S., tr. Reynolds, Emily C. S., illus. 2004. (Creative Minds Biography Ser.). 64p. (J). (gr. 4-8). lib. bdg. 22.60 (978-1-57505-183-3(4)) Lerner Publishing Group.

Satterfield, Kathryn Hoffman. Benjamin Franklin A Man of Many Talents. 2005. 44p. (J). lib. bdg. 15.00 (***978-1-4242-0846-3(7)***) Fitzgerald Bks.

Schaefer, Lola M. Jane Goodall. (First Biographies Ser.). 24p. (J). pap. 5.95 (978-0-7368-5085-8(6)) Capstone Pr., Inc.

Schaefer, Lola M. & Schaefer, Wyatt S. Jane Goodall. 2004. (First Biographies Ser.). 24p. (J). lib. bdg. 15.93 (978-0-7368-2083-7(3) , Pebble Bks.) Capstone Pr., Inc.

Schraff, Anne. Charles Drew: Pioneer in Medicine. 2003. (Famous Inventors Ser.). (Illus.). 32p. (J). (gr. 1-4). lib. bdg. 22.60 (978-0-7660-2008-5(8)) Enslow Pubs., Inc.

Science Adventures, 4 bks., Set. Incl. In the Deep Sea. Collard, Sneed B., III. 44p. (gr. 3-7). lib. bdg. 25.64 (978-0-7614-1952-5(7)); In the Rain Forest Canopy. Collard, Sneed B., III. 44p. (gr. 3-7). lib. bdg. 25.64 (978-0-7614-1954-9(3)); In the Wild. Collard, Sneed B., III. 44p. (gr. 4-7). lib. bdg. 28.50 (978-0-7614-1955-6(1)); On the Coral Reef. Collard, Sneed B. 43p. 25.64 (978-0-7614-1953-2(5)); (Illus.). (J). 2005. 2005. (978-0-7614-1951-8(9) , Benchmark Bks.) Cavendish, Marshall Corp.

Science & Scientists. 2005. 32p. pap. 84.00 (978-0-7910-9170-8(8)); 2003. (Illus.). (gr. 4-8). lib. bdg. 113.70 (978-0-7910-7060-4(3)) Facts On File, Inc. (Chelsea Hse.).

Scientist Who Made History: F02, 6 bks. 2002. 162.72 (978-0-7398-5274-3(4)) Raintree.

Scientists & Inventors, 10 bks., Set 1. 2000. (Illus.). (J). (gr. 5-7). lib. bdg. 256.40 (978-1-58810-132-7(0)) Heinemann Library.

Scientists Who Made History. 2002. (Illus.). 216.96 (978-0-7398-4848-7(8)); 108.48 (978-0-7398-4847-0(X)) Raintree.

Senker, Cath. Rosalind Franklin. 2002. (Scientists Who Made History Ser.). (Illus.). 48p. (J). 27.12 (978-0-7398-5226-2(4)) Raintree.

Shell, Barry. Great Canadian Scientists. 1998. (Illus.). 200p. (gr. 5-9). pap. 14.95 (978-1-896095-36-3(4)) Raincoast Bk. Distribution CAN. *Dist:* Perseus Distribution.

—Sensational Scientists: The Journeys & Discoveries of 24 Men & Women of Science. 2nd rev. ed. 2006. (Illus.). 208p. (J). pap. 15.95 (978-1-55192-727-5(6)) Raincoast Bk. Distribution CAN. *Dist:* Perseus Distribution.

Silverthorne, Elizabeth. Louis Pasteur. 2004. (Heroes & Villains Ser.). (Illus.). 112p. (J). (gr. 7-10). 29.95 (978-1-59018-308-3(8) , Lucent Bks.) Thomson Gale.

Smith, Linda Wasmer. Louis Pasteur: Disease Fighter. (Great Minds of Science Ser.). (Illus.). 128p. (gr. 4-10). 2001. (YA). pap. 13.26 (978-0-7660-1874-7(1)); 2007. (J). lib. bdg. 31.93 (***978-0-7660-2792-3(9)***) Enslow Pubs., Inc.

Snedden, Robert. Scientists & Discoveries. 2000. (Microlife Ser.). 48p. (YA). (gr. 6-8). lib. bdg. 22.79 (978-1-57572-244-3(5)) Heinemann Library.

Snowflake Bentley. 2004. 29.95 incl. cd-rom (978-1-55592-624-3(X)); 24.95 incl. audio (978-1-55592-622-9(3)) Weston Woods Studios, Inc.

Souza, Dorothy M. John Wesley Powell. 2004. (Watts Library). (Illus.). 64p. (J). (gr. 5-7). pap. 8.95 (978-0-531-16653-6(8)); 25.50 (978-0-531-12289-1(1)) Scholastic Library Publishing. (Watts, Franklin).

Spangenburg, Ray & Moser, Diane Kit. Rita Levi-Montalcini: Seeking the Secrets of Growth. 2008. (Makers of Modern Science Ser.). 160p. (gr. 6-12). 29.95 (***978-0-8160-6171-6(8)*** , Chelsea Hse.) Facts On File, Inc.

Spengler, Kremena. Louis Pasteur. 2003. (Photo-Illustrated Biographies Ser.). (Illus.). 24p. (J). lib. bdg. 19.93 (978-0-7368-2225-1(9) , Bridgestone Bks.) Capstone Pr., Inc.

Spilsbury, Louise & Spilsbury, Richard. Scientists at Work: Insect Investigators: Entomologists Paperback. 2007. (Illus.). 32p. (J). (***978-0-431-14932-5(1)***) Heinemann Library.

Stanley, George Edward. Leonardo Da Vinci: Young Artist, Writer, & Inventor. 2005. (Childhood of World Figures Ser.). 166p. (J). (978-1-4156-3039-6(9) , Aladdin) Simon & Schuster Children's Publishing.

Steck-Vaughn Staff. Jane Goodall: A Good & True Heart. 2002. pap. (978-0-7398-6152-3(2)) Steck-Vaughn.

Stephen, Krensky. Dk Bio: Benjamin Franklin Hc. 2007. 128p. 14.99 (***978-0-7566-3529-9(2)***) Dorling Kindersley Publishing, Inc.

—Dk Bio: Benjamin Franklin Pb. 2007. 128p. pap. 4.99 (***978-0-7566-3528-2(4)***) Dorling Kindersley Publishing, Inc.

The Story of Benjamin Franklin. 2002. (Illus.). 24p. (J). (ps-k). 6.95 (978-0-8249-4227-4(2)) Ideals Pubns.

Streissguth, Tom. Benjamin Franklin. 2005. (Bios for Challenged Readers Ser.). (Illus.). 112p. (J). (gr. 6-12). lib. bdg. 27.93 (978-0-8225-2210-2(1)) Lerner Publishing Group.

Strom, Laura Layton. Leonardo da Vinci: Artist & Scientist. 2007. (Shockwave: Life Stories Ser.). 36p. (J). (gr. 3-5). pap. 6.95 (***978-0-531-18798-2(5)*** , Children's Pr.) Scholastic Library Publishing.

Strom, Laura Layton & Leonardo. Leonardo Da Vinci: Artist & Scientist. 2007. (Shockwave: Life Stories Ser.). (Illus.). 36p. (J). (gr. 4-6). lib. bdg. 25.00 (***978-0-531-17771-6(8)*** , Children's Pr.) Scholastic Library Publishing.

Sullivan, Anne Marie. Sir Isaac Newton: Famous English Scientist. 2002. (Great Names Ser.). (Illus.). 32p. (J). (gr. 3 up). lib. bdg. (978-1-59084-139-6(5)) Mason Crest Pubs.

Thayer, William M. From Boyhood to Manhood - the Life of Be. 2006. pap. (***978-1-4068-0906-0(3)***) Echo Library.

Time for Kids Editors. Benjamin Franklin: A Man of Many Talents. 2005. (Time for Kids Ser.). (Illus.). 48p. (J). 14.99 (978-0-06-057610-3(3)); pap. 3.99 (978-0-06-057609-7(X)) HarperCollins Pubs.

Tiner. 100 Scientists Who Shaped World History. 2000. (100 Ser.). (J). (978-0-606-20099-8(1)) Tandem Library Bks.

Tiner, John Hudson. 100 Scientists Who Changed the World. 2003. (People Who Changed the World Ser.). (Illus.). 112p. (J). (gr. 5 up). lib. bdg. 30.00 (978-0-8368-5471-8(3) , World Almanac Library) Stevens, Gareth Inc.

—100 Scientists Who Shaped World History. 2000. (100 Ser.). (Illus.). 112p. (J). (gr. 7-12). 7.95 (978-0-912517-39-1(5)) Bluewood Bks.

—100 Scientists Who Shaped World History. 2000. (978-0-606-20347-0(8)); (gr. 7-12). lib. bdg. 16.40 (978-0-613-67511-6(8)) Tandem Library Bks.

Tracy, Kathleen. Robert Koch & the Study of Anthrax. 2004. (Uncharted, Unexplored, & Unexplained Ser.). (Illus.). 48p. (J). (gr. 4-8). lib. bdg. 29.95 (978-1-58415-261-3(3)) Mitchell Lane Pubs., Inc.

—William Hewlett: Pioneer of the Computer Age. 2002. (Unlocking the Secrets of Science Ser.). (J). (978-1-58415-178-4(1)); (Illus.). 56p. (gr. 4-10). lib. bdg. 25.70 (978-1-58415-142-5(0)) Mitchell Lane Pubs., Inc.

Tremblay, E. A. Rachel Carson. 2003. (Women in the Science Ser.). (Illus.). 118p. pap. 30.00 (978-0-7910-7520-3(6)); 112p. (gr. 6-12). 30.00 (978-0-7910-7244-8(4)) Facts On File, Inc. (Chelsea Hse.).

Trumbauer, Lisa. Everyone Is a Scientist. 2000. (Yellow Umbrella Books). (Illus.). 16p. (J). (gr. 1). lib. bdg. 14.60 (978-0-7368-0722-7(5) , Pebble Bks.) Capstone Pr., Inc.

Unlocking the Secrets of Science: Set of 15 Scientists. (Illus.). (J). (gr. 4-10). lib. bdg. (978-1-58415-233-0(8)) Mitchell Lane Pubs., Inc.

Unwin, Mike. Scientists at Work: Pack A of 6 Paperback. 2007. (Illus.). 32p. (J). (***978-0-431-14936-3(4)***) Heinemann Library.

—Scientists at Work: Secrets of the Deep: Marine Biologists Hardback. 2007. (Illus.). 32p. (J). (***978-0-431-14928-8(3)***) Heinemann Library.

—Secrets of the Deep: Marine Biologists. 2007. (J). (***978-1-4034-9952-3(7)***); pap. (***978-1-4034-9959-2(4)***) Heinemann Library.

What Do Scientists Do? Big Book: Level E. 8p. 20.95 (978-0-322-00346-0(6)) Wright Group, The.

Whiting, Jim. Benjamin Franklin. 2006. (Profiles in American History Ser.). (Illus.). 48p. (J). (gr. 4-8). lib. bdg. 20.95 (978-1-58415-435-8(7)) Mitchell Lane Pubs., Inc.

Williams, Brian. Faraday: Pioneer of Electricity. Antram, David, illus. 2003. (Explosion Zone Ser.). 32p. (J). pap. 6.95 (978-0-7641-2592-8(3)) Barron's Educational Series, Inc.

Williams, Judith. Exploring the Rain Forest Treetops with a Scientist. 2004. (I Like Science! Ser.). (Illus.). 24p. (J). lib. bdg. 21.26 (978-0-7660-2294-2(3)) Enslow Pubs., Inc.

—Saving Endangered Animals with a Scientist. 2004. (I Like Science! Ser.). (Illus.). 24p. (J). (gr. 2-4). lib. bdg. 21.26 (978-0-7660-2276-8(5)) Enslow Pubs., Inc.

Wilson, Camilla. George Washington Carver: The Genius Behind the Peanut. 2003. (Scholastic Biography Ser.). (Illus.). 101p. (J). pap. (978-0-439-28722-7(7)) Scholastic, Inc.

Witteman, Barbara. Leonardo Da Vinci. 2003. (Masterpieces, Artists & Their Works). (Illus.). 24p. (J). lib. bdg. 19.93 (978-0-7368-2228-2(3) , Bridgestone Bks.) Capstone Pr., Inc.

World Book's Biographical Encyclopedia of Scientists, 8 vols. 2005. 1,536p. (YA). (gr. 6 up). 329.00 (978-0-7166-7601-0(X) , 20170) World Bk., Inc.

Yannuzzi, Della. Gregor Mendel: Genetics Pioneer. 2004. (Great Life Stories Ser.). (Illus.). 111p. (J). 30.50 (978-0-531-12263-1(8) , Watts, Franklin) Scholastic Library Publishing.

Yount, Lisa. Antoni Van Leeuwenhoek: First to See Microscopic Life. 2008. (J). (***978-0-7660-3012-1(1)***) Enslow Pubs., Inc.

—Asian-American Scientists. 1998. (American Profiles Ser.). (Illus.). 144p. (J). (gr. 5-12). 25.00 (978-0-8160-3756-8(6)) Facts On File, Inc.

—Medical Technology. annot. ed. 1998. (Milestones in Discovery & Invention Ser.). (Illus.). 160p. (J). (gr. 6-12). 25.00 (978-0-8160-3568-7(7)) Facts On File, Inc.

—William Harvey: Discoverer of How Blood Circulates. 2001. (Great Minds of Science Ser.). (Illus.). 128p. (YA). (gr. 4-10). pap. 10.95 (978-0-7660-1876-1(8)) Enslow Pubs., Inc.

Zannos, Susan. Dmitri Mendeleyev & the Periodic Table. 2004. (Uncharted, Unexplored, & Unexplained Ser.). (Illus.). 48p. (J). (gr. 4-8). lib. bdg. 29.95 (978-1-58415-267-5(2)) Mitchell Lane Pubs., Inc.

—The Life & Times of Archimedes. 2004. (Biography from Ancient Civilizations Ser.). (Illus.). 48p. (J). (gr. 4-8). lib. bdg. 29.95 (978-1-58415-242-2(7)) Mitchell Lane Pubs., Inc.

—Paul Ehrlich & Modern Drug Development. 2002. (Unlocking the Secrets of Science Ser.). (Illus.). 56p. (gr. 4-10). lib. bdg. 17.95 (978-1-58415-121-0(8)) Mitchell Lane Pubs., Inc.

SCIENTISTS—FICTION

Abela, Deborah. In Search of the Time & Space Machine. Murphy, Jobi, illus. 2005. (Spy Force Ser.). vi, 248p. (Orig.). (J). 14.95 (978-1-74051-765-2(2) , Simon & Schuster Children's Publishing) Simon & Schuster Children's Publishing.

—Mission: In Search of the Time & Space Machine. O'Connor, George, illus. (Spy Force Ser.). (J). (gr. 4-7). 2006. 240p. pap. 2.99 (978-1-4169-2501-9(5) , Aladdin); 2005. 224p. 9.95 (978-0-689-87357-7(3) , Simon & Schuster Children's Publishing) Simon & Schuster Children's Publishing.

—Mission: in Search of the Time & Space Machine. O'Connor, George, illus. 2006. (Spy Force Ser.). 240p. (J). pap. 5.99 (978-1-4169-2752-5(2) , Aladdin) Simon & Schuster Children's Publishing.

Anderson, M. T. & Moore, Stephen. Whales on Stilts! Thrilling Tales. Cyrus, Kurt, illus. 2005. (M. T. Anderson's Thrilling Tales Ser.). 208p. (J). 15.00 (978-0-15-205340-6(9)) Harcourt Children's Bks.

Barnett, Gary W. Princess of the Lights: Fantasy Adventure. 2007. 324p. 29.95 (***978-0-595-68957-6(4)***); per. 19.95 (***978-0-595-44705-3(8)***) iUniverse, Inc.

Benton, Jim. Attack of the 50-Ft. Cupid. 2004. (Franny K. Stein, Mad Scientist Ser.: Bk. 2). (Illus.). 112p. (J). (gr. 2-5). pap. 3.99 (978-0-689-86296-0(2) , Aladdin) Simon & Schuster Children's Publishing.

Brinley, Bertrand R. The Big Chunk of Ice: The Last Known Adventure of the Mad Scientists' Club. Geer, Charles, illus. 2005. 275p. (J). (gr. 3-7). 18.95 (978-1-930900-29-5(5)) Purple Hse. Pr.

Brouwer, Sigmund. Robot War. 2001. (gr. 5-8). lib. bdg. 13.00 (978-0-613-76822-1(1)) Tandem Library Bks.

Buller, Jon. Growling Grizzly. 2002. (gr. k-3). lib. bdg. 11.80 (978-0-613-72092-2(X)) Tandem Library Bks.

Cole, Joanna. The Magic School Bus & the Science Fair Expedition. Degen, Bruce, illus. 2006. (Magic School Bus Ser.). 56p. (J). pap. 15.99 (978-0-590-10824-9(7) , Scholastic) Scholastic, Inc.

Dadey, Debbie & Jones, Marcia Thornton. Dragons Don't Throw Snowballs. Gurney, John Steven, illus. 2006. (Little Apple Ser.). 75p. (J). (978-1-4156-4913-8(8)) Scholastic, Inc.

Davies, Jacqueline. Where the Ground Meets the Sky. 2002. 224p. (YA). (gr. 5-9). 14.95 (978-0-7614-5105-1(6) , Cavendish Children's Bks.) Cavendish, Marshall Corp.

Del Amo, Montserrat. Montes, Pajaros y Amigos. (SPA.). 104p. (YA). (gr. 5-8). (978-84-207-2788-2(1) , GS6293) Grupo Anaya, S.A. ESP. *Dist:* Lectorum Pubns., Inc.

Dexter & Missy the Kitten. 2004. (J). per. 15.99 (978-0-9753533-1-8(4)) Golden Eagle Publishing Hse., Inc.

Dexter Rescues Matt the Duckling. 2004. (J). per. 15.99 (978-0-9753533-3-2(0)) Golden Eagle Publishing Hse., Inc.

Dexter the Hamster Gets Lost. 2004. (J). per. 15.99 (978-0-9753533-2-5(2)) Golden Eagle Publishing Hse., Inc.

Hughes, Susan. Not-Quite World Famous Scientist. 2002. (gr. 3-6). lib. bdg. 12.95 (978-0-613-90068-3(5)) Tandem Library Bks.

Kimpton, Diana. Edison's Fantastic Phonograph. Robertson, M. P., illus. 2004. 32p. (J). pap. 7.95 (978-1-84507-262-9(6)) Lincoln, Frances Ltd. GBR. *Dist:* Perseus Distribution.

Larry, H. I. Zac Power #1: Poison Island. Oswald, Ash, illus. 2008. (Zac Power Ser.). 96p. (J). pap. 3.99 (***978-0-312-34659-1(X)***) Feiwel & Friends.

Latorre, Jose Maria. La Incognita del Volcan. Ibarz, Miguel, illus. 2000. (Periscopio Ser.).Tr. of Mystery of the Volcano. (SPA.). 236p. (YA). (gr. 9 up). (978-84-236-5517-5(2)) Edebé ESP. *Dist:* Baker & Taylor Bks.

Lumry, Amanda & Hurwitz, Laura. Operation Orangutan. 2007. 36p. 15.95 (978-0-9748411-4-4(5)) Eaglemont Pr.

The Mad Scientist, 6 vols. (Woodland Mysteriestm Ser.). 133p. (gr. 3-7). 42.50 (978-0-7802-7928-5(X)) Wright Group, The.

Marsh, Carole. The Earthshaking Earthquake MYST. 2007. 128p. pap. 5.99 (***978-0-635-06339-7(5)***) Gallopade International.

—The Horrendous Hurricane MYST. 2007. 128p. pap. 5.99 (***978-0-635-06340-3(9)***) Gallopade International.

—The Treacherous Tornado Mystery! 2007. 128p. pap. 5.99 (***978-0-635-06338-0(7)***) Gallopade International.

Montgomery, R. A. The Brilliant Dr. Wogan. 2005. (Illus.). 112p. (J). pap. (***978-0-7608-9705-8(0)***) Sundance/Newbridge Educational Publishing.

Morgan, Harry. The Monteverdi Mystery. 2006. per. (***978-1-84685-409-5(1)*** , Exposure Publishing) Meadow Bks.

Nishimura, Kae. I Am Dodo: Not a True Story. Nishimura, Kae, illus. 2005. (Illus.). 32p. (J). (ps-k). 15.00 (978-0-618-33614-2(1) , Clarion Bks.) Houghton Mifflin Co. Trade & Reference Div.

Onion Head Monster Attacks. 2007. (YA). per. 12.95 (***978-0-9793676-0-1(3)***) Friedrich, Paul.

Onion Head Monster Attacks (XL) 2006. per. 19.99 (***978-0-9793676-3-2(8)***) Friedrich, Paul.

Osorio, Rick. The Great Adventure of Sally Rock & el Lobo. 2007. (ENG.). 96p. per. 14.95 (***978-1-4241-5869-0(9)***) PublishAmerica, Inc.

The Perfect Person, 6 Packs. (Bookweb Ser.). 32p. (gr. 4 up). 34.00 (978-0-7635-3734-0(9)) Rigby Education.

The Perfect Pet, 6 Packs. (Bookweb Ser.). 32p. (gr. 5 up). 34.00 (978-0-7635-3781-4(0)) Rigby Education.

Reiche, Dietlof. Freddy in Peril. Brownjohn, John & Cepeda, Joe, trs. from GER. Cepeda, Joe, illus. 2004. (Golden Hamster Saga: Bk. 2). 208p. (J). pap. 16.95 (978-0-439-53155-9(1)) Scholastic, Inc.

Reiche, Dietlof & Brownjohn, John. Freddy in Peril: Book Two in the Golden Hamster Saga. Cepeda, Joe, illus. 2004. 202p. (J). pap. (978-0-439-64984-1(6)) Scholastic, Inc.

Rose, Malcolm. Framed! 2007. (Traces Ser.). 232p. (J). (gr. 5). pap. 5.95 (***978-0-7534-5971-3(X)*** , Kingfisher) Houghton Mifflin Co. Trade & Reference Div.

Springham, James. Earth-n-Bones: Toxic. 2005. 56p. pap. 12.95 (978-1-4137-9755-8(5)) PublishAmerica, Inc.

Tezuka, Osamu. Metropolis. 2003. (Illus.). 169p. (YA). (gr. 8 up). pap. 13.95 (978-1-56971-864-3(4)) Dark Horse Comics.

Thomas, Carroll, creator. Under the Open Sky: A Matty Trescott Novel. 2005. (Illus.). 184p. (J). per. 12.95 (978-0-9762091-2-6(8)) Antrim Hse.

Weston, Martha. The Dinosaurs Meet Dr. Clock: A Holiday House Reader. 2002. (Reader Level 1 Ser.). (Illus.). 32p. (J). (gr. k-3). tchr. ed. 14.95 (978-0-8234-1661-5(5)) Holiday Hse., Inc.

Woolfe, Angela. Avril Crump & Her Amazing Clones. 2008. (Illus.). 192p. (J). pap. 9.95 (***978-1-4052-0747-8(7)***) Egmont Bks., Ltd. GBR. *Dist:* Independent Pubs. Group.

—Avril Crump & Her Amazing Clones. 2005. (Avril Crump Ser.). 224p. (J). 9.95 (978-0-439-65130-1(1) , Orchard Bks.) Scholastic, Inc.

—Avril Crump & the Clone Countdown. 2006. 224p. (J). 9.99 (978-0-439-65132-5(8) , Orchard Bks.) Scholastic, Inc.

Woolfe, Angela. Avril Crump & the Slumber Code. 2008. (Illus.). 256p. (J). pap. 9.95 (***978-1-4052-1893-1(2)***) Egmont Bks., Ltd. GBR. *Dist:* Independent Pubs. Group.

Young, Emma. STORM: the Infinity Code: The Infinity Code. 2008. (J). (gr. 5). 16.99 (***978-0-8037-3265-0(1)*** , Dial) Penguin Group (USA) Inc.

SCIENTISTS, AFRICAN AMERICAN

see African American Scientists

SCILLY, ISLES OF (ENGLAND)—FICTION

Llewellyn, Sam. Pegleg. 2001. (Illus.). 173p. pap. (978-0-7551-0011-8(5)) House of Stratus, Inc.

Morpurgo, Michael. The Wreck of the Zanzibar. l.t. ed. 2003. (J). 16.95 (978-0-7540-7846-3(9) , Galaxy Children's Large Print) BBC Audiobooks America.

SCOOBY-DOO (FICTITIOUS CHARACTER)—FICTION

Balaban, Mariah, ed. Scooby-doo Pirates Ahoy. 2006. (Scooby-doo 8x8 Video Tie-in Ser.). (J). 24p. pap. 3.99 (978-0-439-83993-8(9)); 64p. pap. 3.99 (978-0-439-83992-1(0)) Scholastic, Inc.

—Scooby Doo Sudoku. 2006. 24p. (J). pap. 4.99 (978-0-439-87921-7(3)) Scholastic, Inc.

Barbo, Maria S. Catnapped Caper. del Sur, Duendes, illus. 2000. (Scooby-Doo! Picture Clue Book Ser.: No. 1). 32p. (J). (ps-3). pap. 3.99 (978-0-439-16010-0(3) , Scholastic Paperbacks) Scholastic, Inc.

Brewster, Joy. The Roller Ghoster. del Sur, Duendes, illus. 2004. (Scooby-Doo Mysteries Ser.). 48p. (J). (gr. 1 up). pap. 3.99 (978-0-439-70128-0(7)) Scholastic, Inc.

—Roller-Ghoster: Junior Chapter Book. del Sur, Duendes, illus. 2004. (Scooby-Doo Ser.). 48p. (J). mass mkt. 3.99 (978-0-439-55710-8(0) , Scholastic Paperbacks) Scholastic, Inc.

Brewster, Joy & Gelsey, James. Mean Green Mystery Machine, Vol. 2. del Sur, Duendes, illus. 2004. (Scooby-Doo Mysteries Ser.). 48p. (J). (gr. 1 up). pap. 3.99 (978-0-439-70129-7(5)) Scholastic, Inc.

Crime Sniffers. 2001. (Scooby-Doo Ser.). (Illus.). 32p. (J). (ps-3). pap. 4.99 (978-0-307-29905-5(8) , Golden Bks.) Random Hse. Children's Bks.

Cunningham, Scott. Scooby Doo & the Hungry Ghost. del Sur, Duendes, illus. 2005. 12p. (J). (ps-3). pap. 8.99 (978-0-439-74882-7(8)) Scholastic, Inc.

Dalmatian Press Staff. Clues on the Loose! Mystery Magnet Book. (Scooby-Doomt! Ser.). 4p. (J). 9.99 (978-1-4037-0610-2(7)) Dalmatian Pr.

—Monsters Ahead Scooby BBBTC. 2004. 96p. pap. 2.99 (978-1-4037-0830-4(4)) Dalmatian Pr.

—The Mystery Machine Adventure! Shaped Board Book. 2003. (Scooby-Doo! Ser.). (Illus.). 6p. (J). bds. 4.99 (978-1-57759-898-5(9)) Dalmatian Pr.

—The Pyramid Mystery. 2003. (Scooby-Doo! Ser.). (Illus.). 10p. (J). 9.99 (978-1-57759-899-2(7)) Dalmatian Pr.

—Scooby Doo: A Dog's Best Friend. 2005. (Big Best Book to Color Ser.). (Illus.). 80p. (J). pap. 2.99 (978-1-4037-1179-3(8)) Dalmatian Pr.

—Scooby-Doo: Key Chain Book. rev. ed. 2003. (Scooby-Doo! Ser.). 48p. (J). 3.99 (978-1-4037-0195-4(4)) Dalmatian Pr.

—Scooby Doo Fun Kit. 2005. (J). 9.99 (978-1-4037-1261-5(1)) Dalmatian Pr.

—Scooby Doo Jingle Chills. 2004. 32p. pap. 2.99 (978-1-4037-0107-7(5)) Dalmatian Pr.

—Scooby-Doo Mystery Revealed: Amazing Marker. 2004. (Scooby-Doo Ser.). (Illus.). 48p. (J). spiral bd. 4.99 (978-1-4037-0818-2(5)) Dalmatian Pr.

—Scooby Doo Shadow Mystery: Window Board Book. 2003. (Scooby-Doo! Ser.). (Illus.). 14p. (J). bds. 7.99 (978-1-4037-0332-3(9)) Dalmatian Pr.

—Scooby Doodles: Walter Foster How to Draw Book with Mini Booklet & Gel Pen. 2003. (Scooby-Doo! Ser.). 32p. (J). pap. 4.99 (978-1-4037-0182-4(2)) Dalmatian Pr.

—Scooby Spooked BBBTC. 2004. 96p. pap. 2.99 (978-1-4037-0829-8(0)) Dalmatian Pr.

Dalmatian Press Staff, ed. Midnight Snack! Fuzzy Book to Color. 2004. (Scooby-Dootm! Ser.). (Illus.). 32p. (J). pap. 4.49 (978-1-4037-0619-5(0)) Dalmatian Pr.

—Scooby Doo Pirates Ahoy! 2006. 48p. (J). 2.99 (978-1-4037-2431-1(8)) Dalmatian Pr.

Danko, Dan. Scooby-Doo: The Complete Movie Scrapbook. 2002. (gr. k-3). lib. bdg. 14.15 (978-0-613-50741-7(X)) Tandem Library Bks.

Davis, Dan, illus. Scooby-Doo & the Samurai Ghost. 2005. (Scooby-Doo Ser.). 24p. (J). 3.99 (978-0-439-69644-9(5)) Scholastic, Inc.

del Sur, Duendes. Catnapped Caper. 2000. (gr. k-3). lib. bdg. 11.80 (978-0-613-24507-4(5)) Tandem Library Bks.

—Search for Scooby Snacks. 2000. (gr. k-3). lib. bdg. 11.80 (978-0-613-26871-4(7)) Tandem Library Bks.

del Sur, Duendes, illus. Pizza Place Ghost. 2001. (Scooby-Doo! Picture Clue Book Ser.: No. 4). 32p. (J). (gr. 5). pap. 3.99 (978-0-439-20495-8(X)) Scholastic, Inc.

Draw Your Own Scooby-Doo Coloring Clues. 2001. (Scooby-Doo Ser.). (Illus.). 32p. (J). (ps-3). pap. 4.99 (978-0-307-10372-7(2) , Golden Bks.) Random Hse. Children's Bks.

Erwin, Vicki B. Scooby-Doo! The Case of the Spinning Spider. 2001. (Collect the Clues Mystery Ser.). (Illus.). 59p. (J). pap. (978-0-439-23167-1(1)) Scholastic, Inc.

Fernandes, Lindsay. Spooky Scooby Doo! Fernandes, Lindsay, ed. 2004. (Ultimate Sticker Bks.). (Illus.). 16p. (J). pap. 6.99 (978-0-7566-0301-4(3)) Dorling Kindersley Publishing, Inc.

Flatau, Carole, ed. Scooby-Doo's Upbeat Songs: Level Three for Early Intermediate Students. 2000. (Looney Tunes Piano Library). (J). 5.95 (978-0-7692-8438-5(8) , Warner Bros. Pubns.) Alfred Publishing Co., Inc.

Fontes, Justine & Reader's Digest Staff. Scooby-Doo Mysterious Message Storybook Scooby Clues. 2007. 32p. (J). 12.99 (***978-0-7944-1304-0(8)***) Reader's Digest Assn., Inc., The.

—Scooby-Doo the Haunted Mysteries Storybook & DVD. 2007. (Readers Book & DVD Ser.). 32p. (J). 17.99 (***978-0-7944-1302-6(1)***) Reader's Digest Assn., Inc., The.

Gelsey, James. The Baseball Boogeyman. 2004. (Illus.). 44p. (J). (***978-0-439-55713-9(5)***) Scholastic, Inc.

—Cactus Creature. del Sur, Duendes, illus. 2005. (Scooby-Doo Mysteries Ser.: No. 32). 64p. (J). (ps-k). pap. 3.99 (978-0-439-56116-7(7) , Scholastic Paperbacks) Scholastic, Inc.

—Deep Sea Diver. del Sur, Duendes, illus. 2003. (Scooby-Doo Mysteries Ser.: No. 26). 64p. (J). pap. 3.99 (978-0-439-42073-0(3) , Levine, Arthur A. Bks.) Scholastic, Inc.

—Deep Sea Diver. 2003. (gr. 3-6). lib. bdg. 11.80 (978-0-613-58165-3(2)) Tandem Library Bks.

—The Devilish Donut. 2007. (Scooby-Doo Case Files Ser.: No. 1). 80p. (J). pap. 3.99 (978-0-439-81418-8(9)) Scholastic, Inc.

—Gruesome Goblin. del Sur, Duendes, illus. 2004. (Scooby-Doo Mysteries Ser.: No. 29). 64p. (J). pap. 3.99 (978-0-439-42076-1(8) , Scholastic Paperbacks) Scholastic, Inc.

—Hoopster Horror. del Sur, Duendes, illus. 2005. (Scooby-Doo Ser.: No. 31). 64p. (J). pap. 3.99 (978-0-439-54606-5(0)) Scholastic, Inc.

—The Scary Scooby. 2007. (Scooby-Doo Case Files Ser.). 80p. (J). pap. 3.99 (***978-0-439-91594-6(5)***) Scholastic, Inc.

—Scooby-Doo! & the Cactus Creature. 2005. (Illus.). 58p. (J). lib. bdg. 15.00 (***978-1-4242-0304-8(X)***) Fitzgerald Bks.

—Scooby-Doo! & the Cactus Creature. 2005. (Illus.). 58p. (J). (***978-1-4155-9742-2(1)***) Scholastic, Inc.

—Scooby-Doo & the Carnival Creeper. 1999. (Scooby-Doo Mysteries Ser.: No. 7). (Illus.). 64p. (J). (ps-3). 3.99 (978-0-439-11346-5(6)) Scholastic, Inc.

—Scooby-Doo & the Farmyard Fright. del Sur, Duendes, illus. 2001. (Scooby-Doo Mysteries Ser.: No. 17). 64p. (J). (ps-3). pap. 3.99 (978-0-439-18881-4(4)) Scholastic, Inc.

—Scooby-Doo & the Groovy Ghost. 8th ed. 2000. (Scooby-Doo Mysteries Ser.: No. 8). (Illus.). 64p. (J). (ps-3). pap. 3.99 (978-0-439-11347-2(4) , Scholastic Paperbacks) Scholastic, Inc.

—Scooby-Doo & the Groovy Ghost. 2000. (gr. 3-6). lib. bdg. 11.80 (978-0-613-22338-6(1)) Tandem Library Bks.

—Scooby-Doo! & the Gruesome Goblin. 2004. (Illus.). 60p. (J). lib. bdg. 15.00 (***978-1-4242-0303-1(1)***) Fitzgerald Bks.

—Scooby-Doo & the Haunted Castle. 1998. (Scooby-Doo Mysteries Ser.: No. 1). (Illus.). 64p. (ps-3). pap. 3.99 (978-0-590-81909-1(7)) Scholastic, Inc.

—Scooby-Doo & the Haunted Castle: Scooby-Doo Y el Castillo Hechizado. 2002. (Scooby-Doo Mysteries Ser.: No. 1). (SPA., Illus.). 64p. (J). (gr. 2-4). mass mkt. 3.99 (978-0-439-40984-1(5) , Scholastic en Espanol) Scholastic, Inc.

—Scooby-Doo & the Headless Horseman. 2002. (gr. 3-6). lib. bdg. 11.80 (978-0-613-58166-0(0)) Tandem Library Bks.

—Scooby-Doo! & the Hoopster Horror. 2005. (Illus.). 61p. (J). lib. bdg. 15.00 (***978-1-4242-0305-5(8)***) Fitzgerald Bks.

—Scooby-Doo & the Monster Menace. 2006. (Scooby-Doo Mysteries Ser.: No. 34). (Illus.). 64p. (J). pap. 3.99 (978-0-439-81417-1(0) , Scholastic) Scholastic, Inc.

—Scooby-Doo & the Mummy's Curse. 1998. (Scooby-Doo Mysteries Ser.: No. 2). (Illus.). 64p. (ps-3). pap. 3.99 (978-0-590-81910-7(0)) Scholastic, Inc.

—Scooby-Doo & the Phony Fortune-Teller. del Sur, Duendes, illus. 2001. (Scooby-Doo Mysteries Ser.: No. 15). 64p. (J). (ps-3). pap. 3.99 (978-0-439-18879-1(2)) Scholastic, Inc.

—Scooby-Doo & the Scary Skateboarder. del Sur, Duendes, illus. 2006. (Scooby-Doo Mysteries Ser.). 64p. (J). pap. 3.99 (978-0-439-56117-4(5)) Scholastic, Inc.

—Scooby-Doo & the Snow Monster. 1999. (Scooby-Doo Mysteries Ser.: No. 3). (Illus.). 57p. (J). (ps-3). 3.99 (978-0-590-81914-5(3) , Scholastic Paperbacks) Scholastic, Inc.

—Scooby-Doo & the Spooky Strikeout. 2000. (gr. 3-6). lib. bdg. 11.80 (978-0-613-26854-7(7)) Tandem Library Bks.

—Scooby-Doo! & the Spooky Strikeout. del Sur, Duendes, illus. 2000. (Scooby-Doo Mysteries Ser.: No. 10). 64p. (J). (ps-3). 3.99 (978-0-439-11349-6(0)) Scholastic, Inc.

—Scooby-Doo & the Sunken Ship. 1999. (Scooby-Doo Mysteries Ser.: No. 4). (Illus.). 64p. (J). (ps-3). pap. 3.99 (978-0-590-81917-6(8)) Scholastic, Inc.

—Scooby-Doo & the Sunken Ship. 1999. (gr. 3-6). lib. bdg. 11.80 (978-0-613-17004-8(0)) Tandem Library Bks.

—Scooby-Doo & the Vampire's Revenge. 1999. (Scooby-Doo Mysteries Ser.: No. 6). (Illus.). 64p. (J). (ps-3). mass mkt. 3.99 (978-0-439-08278-5(1)) Scholastic, Inc.

—Scooby-Doo & the Vampire's Revenge. 1999. (gr. 3-6). lib. bdg. 11.80 (978-0-613-17940-9(4)) Tandem Library Bks.

—Scooby Doo! & the Zombie's Treasure. 2000. (gr. 3-6). lib. bdg. 11.80 (978-0-613-27677-1(9)) Tandem Library Bks.

—Scooby-Doo! & You. del Sur, Duendes, illus. 2001. (Collect the Clues Mystery Ser.). 60p. (J). (978-0-439-23155-8(8)) Scholastic, Inc.

—Scooby-Doo! & You: The Case of Dr. Jenkins & Mr. Hyde. 2001. (Collect the Clues Mystery Ser.). (Illus.). 60p. (J). pap. (978-0-439-23157-2(4)) Scholastic, Inc.

—Scooby-Doo! & You: The Case of the Seaweed Monster. 2001. (Collect the Clues Mystery Ser.). (Illus.). 60p. (J). pap. (978-0-439-23153-4(1)) Scholastic, Inc.

—Scooby-Doo! & You: The Case of the Singing Ghost. 2001. (Collect the Clues Mystery Ser.). (Illus.). 61p. (J). pap. (978-0-439-23163-3(9)) Scholastic, Inc.

—Scooby-Doo y el Castillo Hechizado. 2002. Tr. of Scooby-Doo & the Haunted Castle. (SPA.). (gr. k-3). lib. bdg. 13.00 (978-0-613-82494-1(6)) Tandem Library Bks.

—Scooby-Doo y la Maldicion de la Momia. 2003. (Scooby-Doo Mysteries Ser.: No. 2). (SPA., Illus.). 64p. (J). (gr. 2-4). pap. 3.99 (978-0-439-40985-8(3) , Scholastic en Espanol) Scholastic, Inc.

—Scooby-Doo y la Maldicion de la Momia. 2003. (SPA.). (gr. k-3). lib. bdg. 11.80 (978-0-613-87302-4(5)) Tandem Library Bks.

—Scooby-Doo!TM & the Fairground Phantom. del Sur, Duendes, illus. 2000. (Scooby-Doo Mysteries Ser.: No. 11). 64p. (J). (ps-3). 3.99 (978-0-439-10664-1(8)) Scholastic, Inc.

—Scooby-Doo!TM & the Headless Horseman. 2002. (Scooby-Doo Mysteries Ser.: No. 25). (Illus.). 64p. (J). (gr. 1-4). 3.99 (978-0-439-42072-3(5)) Scholastic, Inc.

—Seashore Slimer. del Sur, Duendes, illus. 2002. (Scooby-Doo Mysteries Ser.: No. 22). 64p. (J). (gr. 4-6). pap. 3.99 (978-0-439-28488-2(0)) Scholastic, Inc.

—Snow Monster, Bk. 3. 2004. (Scooby-Doo Mysteries Ser.). 64p. (J). pap. 3.99 (978-0-439-55115-1(3) , Scholastic en Espanol) Scholastic, Inc.

—The Summer Camp Cyclops. 2007. (Scooby-Doo Case Files Ser.: No. 2). 80p. (J). pap. 3.99 (***978-0-439-91592-2(9)***) Scholastic, Inc.

—Sunken Ship: Scooby-Doo y el Barco Hundido. 2004. (Scooby-Doo Ser.). (ENG & SPA.). 64p. (J). mass mkt. 3.99 (978-0-439-55116-8(1) , Scholastic en Espanol) Scholastic, Inc.

—Witch Doctor. del Sur, Duendes, illus. 2003. (Scooby Doo Mystery Ser.). 64p. (J). (gr. k-3). 3.99 (978-0-439-42075-4(X) , Scholastic Paperbacks) Scholastic, Inc.

—Witch Doctor. 2003. (gr. k-3). lib. bdg. 11.80 (978-0-613-72125-7(X)) Tandem Library Bks.

—The Zombie's Treasure. 2000. (Scooby-Doo Mysteries Ser.: No. 9). (Illus.). 64p. (J). (ps-3). pap. 3.99 (978-0-439-11348-9(2)) Scholastic, Inc.

Golden Books Staff. The Beast of Blueberry Heights. 2000. (Scooby-Doo Ser.). (Illus.). 12p. (J). (ps-3). pap. 9.99 (978-0-307-10143-3(6) , 10143, Golden Bks.) Random Hse. Children's Bks.

—Ghoul's Inn. 2000. (Scooby-Doo Ser.). (Illus.). 16p. (J). (ps-3). pap. 3.99 (978-0-307-15400-2(9) , 15400, Golden Bks.) Random Hse. Children's Bks.

—Jeepers, It's the Creeper! 2000. (Scooby-Doo Ser.). (Illus.). 64p. (J). (ps-3). pap. 2.99 (978-0-307-29051-9(4) , 29051, Golden Bks.) Random Hse. Children's Bks.

—Mummy's Tomb Maze Book. 2000. (Scooby-Doo Ser.). (Illus.). 8p. (J). (ps-3). 9.99 (978-0-307-11127-2(X) , 11127, Golden Bks.) Random Hse. Children's Bks.

—Trouble Ahead. 2000. (Scooby-Doo Ser.). (Illus.). 56p. (J). (ps-3). pap. 3.99 (978-0-307-27610-0(4) , 27610, Golden Bks.) Random Hse. Children's Bks.

Golden Books Staff, ed. The Haunted Carnival. 1999. (Scooby-Doo Ser.). (Illus.). 16p. (J). (ps-3). bds. 2.99 (978-0-307-99504-9(6) , Golden Bks.) Random Hse. Children's Bks.

Goodman, David & Copp, Rick. Scooby-Doo & the Hex Files. 1999. (Scooby-Doo Movie Storybooks). (Illus.). 32p. (J). (ps-3). pap. 3.50 (978-0-439-08787-2(2)) Scholastic, Inc.

Herman, Gail. The Apple Thief. del Sur, Duendes, illus. 2002. (Scooby-Doo! Reader Ser.: Bk. 13). 32p. (J). 3.99 (978-0-439-34115-8(9)) Scholastic, Inc.

—The Big Bad Blizzard. 2007. (Scooby-Doo Reader Ser.: No. 21). 32p. (J). pap. 3.99 (***978-0-439-78810-6(2)***) Scholastic, Inc.

—The Camping Caper. del Sur, Duendes, illus. 2006. (Scooby-Doo! Reader Ser.: No. 18). 32p. (J). pap. 3.99 (978-0-439-80942-9(8)) Scholastic, Inc.

—Disappearing Donuts. del Sur, Duendes, illus. 2000. (Scooby-Doo! Reader Ser.: No. 2). 32p. (J). (ps-3). pap. 3.99 (978-0-439-16168-8(1)) Scholastic, Inc.

—Fall Fright. del Sur, Duendes, illus. 2005. (Hello Reader! Ser.). 32p. (J). pap. (978-0-439-78358-3(5)) Scholastic, Inc.

—The Haunted Halloween Party. 2007. (Scooby-Doo! Reader Ser.: No. 20). 32p. (J). pap. 3.99 (***978-0-439-78811-3(0)***) Scholastic, Inc.

—Howling on the Playground. del Sur, Duendes, illus. 2000. (Scooby-Doo! Reader Ser.: No. 3). 32p. (J). (ps-3). 3.99 (978-0-439-16169-5(X)) Scholastic, Inc.

—Map in the Mystery Machine. del Sur, Duendes, illus. 2000. (Scooby-Doo! Reader Ser.: No. 1). 32p. (J). (ps-3). 3.99 (978-0-439-16167-1(3)) Scholastic, Inc.

—The Mixed-Up Museum. del Sur, Duendes, illus. 2001. (Scooby-Doo! Reader Ser.: No. 6). 32p. (J). (ps-3). pap. 3.99 (978-0-439-20228-2(0)) Scholastic, Inc.

—Mummies at the Mall. del Sur, Duendes, illus. 2002. (Scooby-Doo! Reader Ser.: Vol. 11). 32p. (J). (ps-3). pap. 3.99 (978-0-439-34114-1(0)) Scholastic, Inc.

—Scooby Doo: Mummies at the Mall. 2002. (gr. k-3). lib. bdg. 11.80 (978-0-613-51319-7(3)) Tandem Library Bks.

—Scooby-Doo: Racecar Monster. 2001. (gr. k-3). lib. bdg. 11.80 (978-0-613-43872-8(8)) Tandem Library Bks.

—Scooby Doo: Sea Monster Scare. 2002. (gr. k-3). lib. bdg. 11.80 (978-0-613-51324-1(X)) Tandem Library Bks.

—Scooby Doo! Shiny Spooky Knights. 2000. (gr. k-3). lib. bdg. 11.80 (978-0-613-33053-4(6)) Tandem Library Bks.

—Scooby-Doo! Snack Snatcher. 2001. (gr. k-3). lib. bdg. 11.80 (978-0-613-36675-5(1)) Tandem Library Bks.

—Scooby Doo! The Haunted Ski Lodge. 2001. (gr. k-3). lib. bdg. 11.80 (978-0-613-43831-5(0)) Tandem Library Bks.

—Scooby-Doo & Aliens Too! del Sur, Duendes, illus. 2000. (Scooby-Doo Movie Storybooks). 32p. (J). (ps-3). 3.50 (978-0-439-17701-6(4)) Scholastic, Inc.

—Scooby-Doo & Aliens Too! 2000. (gr. k-3). lib. bdg. 11.25 (978-0-613-33034-3(X)) Tandem Library Bks.

—Scooby Doo! & the Football Fright. 2002. (gr. k-3). lib. bdg. 11.80 (978-0-613-58152-3(0)) Tandem Library Bks.

—Scooby Doo! & the Howling on the Playground. 2000. (gr. k-3). lib. bdg. 11.80 (978-0-613-32658-2(X)) Tandem Library Bks.

—Scooby Doo! & the Map in the Mystery Machine. 2000. (gr. k-3). lib. bdg. 11.80 (978-0-613-26117-3(8)) Tandem Library Bks.

—Scooby-Doo on Zombie Island. 1998. (Scooby-Doo Movie Storybooks). (Illus.). 32p. (J). (ps-3). pap. 3.50 (978-0-590-38652-4(2)) Scholastic, Inc.

—Scooby Doo! Valentine's Day Dognapping. 2002. (gr. k-3). lib. bdg. 11.80 (978-0-613-54717-8(9)) Tandem Library Bks.

—A Scooby-Rific Reader. del Sur, Duendes, illus. 2005. (Scooby Doo Ser.). 290p. (J). (978-0-681-15349-3(0)) Scholastic, Inc.

—Sea Monster Scare. del Sur, Duendes, illus. 2002. (Scooby-Doo! Reader Ser.: No. 12). 32p. (J). (gr. k-2). 3.99 (978-0-439-31831-0(9)) Scholastic, Inc.

—The Secret Santa Mystery. del Sur, Duendes, illus. 2003. (Scooby-Doo! Reader Ser.). 32p. (J). pap. 3.99 (978-0-439-45619-7(3) , Scholastic Paperbacks) Scholastic, Inc.

—Shiny Spooky Knights. del Sur, Duendes, illus. 2001. (Scooby-Doo! Reader Ser.: No. 5). 32p. (J). (ps-3). 3.99 (978-0-439-20227-5(2)) Scholastic, Inc.

—Snack Snatcher. del Sur, Duendes, illus. 2001. (Scooby-Doo! Reader Ser.: No. 7). 32p. (J). (ps-3). 3.99 (978-0-439-20229-9(9)) Scholastic, Inc.

—Thanksgiving Mystery. 2006. (Hello Reader! Ser.: No. 17). (Illus.). 32p. (J). pap. 3.99 (978-0-439-78359-0(3)) Scholastic, Inc.

Herman, Gail & del Sur, Duendes. Football Fright. 2002. (Scooby-Doo! Reader Ser.: No. 14). (Illus.). 32p. (J). (gr. k-3). pap. 3.99 (978-0-439-34116-5(7)) Scholastic, Inc.

Herman, Gail & Nagler, Michelle H. The Haunted Pumpkins. del Sur, Duendes, illus. 2001. (Scooby-Doo! Picture Clue Book Ser.: No. 8). 32p. (J). (ps-3). pap. 3.99 (978-0-439-31836-5(X)) Scholastic, Inc.

Hurley, Jo. Scooby-Doo! & the Phantom Prankster. 2005. (Illus.). 44p. (***978-0-439-73708-1(7)***) Scholastic, Inc.

—Scooby-Doo Case Files 04. 2008. 80p. pap. 3.99 (***978-0-545-00668-2(6)*** , Scholastic) Scholastic, Inc.

Ip, Ivy S. Clues at the Carnival. 2001. (ps-2). lib. bdg. 11.80 (978-0-613-54137-4(5)) Tandem Library Bks.

IScooby-Doo! el caso de las Scooby-galletas Misteriosas. 2005. Tr. of Scooby Doo! The Case of the Disappearing Scooby Snacks. (SPA.). 12p. (J). 4.95 (978-1-58117-330-7(X) , Intervisual/Piggy Toes) Dalmatian Pr.

Knight, K. R. Scary Mine. 2003. (Scooby-Doo! Ser.). 5p. (J). bds. 5.99 (978-1-4037-0186-2(5)) Dalmatian Pr.

LeapFrog Staff, compiled by. Scooby Doo & the Disappearing Donuts. 2001. (J). (ps-2). spiral bd. 14.99 (978-1-58605-107-5(5)) LeapFrog Enterprises, Inc.

—Scooby Doo & the Haunted Castle. 2001. (J). (ps-2). spiral bd. 14.99 (978-1-58605-108-2(3)) LeapFrog Enterprises, Inc.

—Scooby Doo & the Zombie's Treasure. 2001. (J). (ps-2). spiral bd. 14.99 (978-1-58605-218-8(7)) LeapFrog Enterprises, Inc.

Leon McCann, Jesse. Haunted Halloween: Sticker Storybook. del Sur, Duendes, illus. 2004. (Scooby-Doo Ser.). 24p. (J). pap. 5.99 (978-0-439-60699-8(3) , Scholastic Paperbacks) Scholastic, Inc.

—Scooby-Doo & the Soccer Monster. del Sur, Duendes, illus. 2004. (Scooby Doo Ser.). 24p. (J). pap. 5.99 (978-0-439-54602-7(8)) Scholastic, Inc.

—Scooby-Doo & the Trick-or-Treat Thief. del Sur, Duendes, illus. 2002. (Scooby Doo Ser.). 32p. (J). pap. 5.99 (978-0-439-44294-7(X)) Scholastic, Inc.

Lou Weber Staff, ed. Scooby Doo Message in a Bottle Sound Book. 2004. (Illus.). 24p. 15.98 (978-1-4127-0600-1(9) , 7222600) Publications International, Ltd.

Markas, Jenny. Monster of Mexico. Mackenzie, Kevin, illus. movie tie-in ed. 2003. (Scooby-Doo Ser.). 80p. (J). pap. 4.99 (978-0-439-44919-9(7) , Scholastic Paperbacks) Scholastic, Inc.

—Scooby-Doo & the Monster of Mexico Jr Novelization. 2003. (gr. k-3). lib. bdg. 13.00 (978-0-613-66378-6(0)) Tandem Library Bks.

—Scooby-Doo! & You: The Case of the Headless Henry. 2001. (Collect the Clues Mystery Ser.). (Illus.). 60p. (J). (978-0-439-23162-6(0)) Scholastic, Inc.

—Scooby-Doo! & You: The Case of the Leaping Lion. 2001. (Collect the Clues Mystery Ser.). (Illus.). 62p. (J). (978-0-439-23154-1(X)) Scholastic, Inc.

McCann, Jesse Leon. And the Fishy Phantom. 2006. (Scooby-doo 8x8 Ser.). 24p. (J). pap. 3.99 (978-0-439-78807-6(2) , Scholastic Paperbacks) Scholastic, Inc.

—Ghastly Giant. del Sur, Duendes, illus. 2003. (Scooby Doo Ser.). 32p. (J). pap. 3.50 (978-0-439-45523-7(5)) Scholastic, Inc.

—Ghastly Giant. 2003. (gr. k-3). lib. bdg. 11.25 (978-0-613-66376-2(4)) Tandem Library Bks.

—Haunted Halloween Mask. 2003. (gr. k-3). lib. bdg. 14.15 (978-0-613-72207-0(8)) Tandem Library Bks.

—The Mystery Mall. 1998. (Scooby-Doo 3-D Storybooks: No. 2). (Illus.). 16p. (J). (ps-3). pap. 5.99 (978-0-590-38656-2(5)) Scholastic, Inc.

—Scooby-Doo & Santa's Bake Shop. del Sur, Duendes, illus. 2000. (Scooby-Doo Ser.). 24p. (J). (ps-3). pap. 5.99 (978-0-439-20999-1(4)) Scholastic, Inc.

—Scooby-Doo! & Santa's Bake Shop. 2000. (gr. 3-6). lib. bdg. 14.15 (978-0-613-54349-1(1)) Tandem Library Bks.

—Scooby-Doo & the Alien Invaders. 2000. (Golden Book Ser.). (Illus.). 32p. (J). (ps-3). pap. 3.99 (978-0-307-10474-8(5) , 10474, Golden Bks.) Random Hse. Children's Bks.

—Scooby-Doo & the Alien Invaders. 2000. (gr. k-3). lib. bdg. 11.25 (978-0-613-33035-0(8)) Tandem Library Bks.

—Scooby-Doo & the Creepy Carnival. 1998. (Scooby-Doo 3-D Storybooks: No. 1). (Illus.). 16p. (J). (ps-3). pap 5.99 (978-0-590-38654-8(9)) Scholastic, Inc.

—Scooby Doo & the Creepy Chef. Davis, Dan, illus. 2005. (Scooby-Doo Ser.). 24p. (J). pap. 3.99 (978-0-439-69643-2(7) , Scholastic Paperbacks) Scholastic, Inc.

—Scooby-Doo! & the Creepy Chef. 2005. (Illus.). 24p. (J). (978-1-4155-9752-1(9)) Scholastic, Inc.

—Scooby-Doo & the Cyber Chase. 2001. (gr. k-3). lib. bdg. 11.25 (978-0-613-50734-9(7)) Tandem Library Bks.

—Scooby-Doo! & the Eerie Ice Monster. 2000. (gr. k-3). lib. bdg. 14.15 (978-0-613-54351-4(3)) Tandem Library Bks.

—Scooby-Doo & the Fantastic Puppet Factory. 2000. (gr. k-3). lib. bdg. 11.25 (978-0-613-26852-3(0)) Tandem Library Bks.

—Scooby-Doo & the Halloween Hotel Haunt: A Glow in the Dark Mystery! del Sur, Duendes, illus. 1999. (Scooby-Doo Ser.). 24p. (J). (ps-3). pap. 5.99 (978-0-439-11768-5(2)) Scholastic, Inc.

—Scooby-Doo & the Haunted Lab: Scooby-Doo Decoder Book. del Sur, Duendes, illus. 2002. (Scooby-Doo Ser.). 32p. (J). (ps-3). pap. 5.99 (978-0-439-40789-2(3)) Scholastic, Inc.

—Scooby-Doo & the Legend of Vampire Rock. 2003. (gr. 3-6). lib. bdg. 11.25 (978-0-613-58167-7(9)) Tandem Library Bks.

—Scooby-Doo & the Loch Ness Monster. del Sur, Duendes, illus. 2004. (Scooby Doo Ser.). 32p. (J). pap. 3.50 (978-0-439-60697-4(7) , Scholastic Paperbacks) Scholastic, Inc.

—Scooby Doo! & the Monster of Mexico. 2003. (Scooby-Doo Ser.). (Illus.). 32p. (J). 3.50 (978-0-439-44946-5(4) , Scholastic Paperbacks) Scholastic, Inc.

—Scooby-Doo & the Monster of Mexico. 2003. (gr. 3-6). lib. bdg. 11.25 (978-0-613-66377-9(2)) Tandem Library Bks.

S

—Scooby-Doo & the Phantom Cowboy. McCann, Jesse Leon & del Sur, Duendes, illus. 2002. (Scooby-Doo Ser.). 32p. (J). (ps-3). pap. 3.50 (978-0-439-36586-4(4)) Scholastic, Inc.

—Scooby-Doo & the Phantom Cowboy. 2002. (gr. k-3). lib. bdg. 11.25 (978-0-613-50736-3(3)) Tandem Library Bks.

—Scooby-Doo & the Rock 'n' Roll Zombie. 2007. (Scooby-doo 8x8 Ser.). 24p. (J). pap. 3.99 (978-0-439-78808-3(0)) Scholastic, Inc.

—Scooby-Doo & the Tiki's Curse. 2004. (Scooby-Doo Ser.). (Illus.). 24p. (J). 3.50 (978-0-439-54604-1(4) , Scholastic Paperbacks) Scholastic, Inc.

—Scooby-Doo & the Weird Water Park. 2000. (Scooby-Doo Original Titles Ser.: No. 3). (Illus.). 32p. (J). (ps-3). 3.50 (978-0-439-17253-0(5)) Scholastic, Inc.

—Scooby-Doo & the Weird Water Park. 2000. (gr. k-3). lib. bdg. 11.25 (978-0-613-26855-4(5)) Tandem Library Bks.

—Scooby-Doo & the Werewolf. del Sur, Duendes, illus. 2004. (Scooby-Doo Ser.). 24p. (J). (gr. 1 up). 3.50 (978-0-439-45524-4(3)) Scholastic, Inc.

—Scooby-Doo! & You. del Sur, Duendes, illus. 2001. (Collect the Clues Mystery Ser.). 60p. (J). (978-0-439-23156-5(6)) Scholastic, Inc.

—Scooby-Doo! & You: The Case of the Mad Mermaid. 2001. (Collect the Clues Mystery Ser.). (Illus.). 62p. (J). pap. (978-0-439-23164-0(7)) Scholastic, Inc.

—Scooby-Doo y el Monstruo de Mexico. 2003. (Scooby Doo Ser.). (SPA., Illus.). 32p. (J). pap. 3.50 (978-0-439-55565-4(5) , Scholastic en Espanol) Scholastic, Inc.

—Scooby-Doo!TM & the Eerie Ice Monster. 2000. (Scooby-Doo Ser.). (Illus.). 24p. (J). (ps-3). 5.99 (978-0-439-20667-9(7)) Scholastic, Inc.

—Scooby-Doo!TM & the Fantastic Puppet Factory. 2000. (Scooby-Doo Original Titles Ser.: No. 4). (Illus.). 32p. (J). (ps-3). 3.50 (978-0-439-17254-7(3)) Scholastic, Inc.

—Scooby-Doo!TM in Jungle Jeopardy. 2001. (Scooby-Doo Original Titles Ser.: No. 2). (Illus.). 32p. (J). (ps-3). 3.99 (978-0-439-26075-6(2)) Scholastic, Inc.

—Scooby-Doo!TM in Jungle Jeopardy. 2001. (gr. k-3). lib. bdg. 11.25 (978-0-613-43886-5(8)) Tandem Library Bks.

McCann, Jesse Leon, adapted by. Scooby-Doo & the Alien Invaders. 2000. (Scooby-Doo Movie Storybooks). (Illus.). 32p. (J). (ps-3). 3.50 (978-0-439-17700-9(6)) Scholastic, Inc.

McCann, Jesse Leon, et al. Haunted Halloween Mask. del Sur, Duendes, illus. 2003. (Scooby-Doo Ser.). 24p. (J). pap. 5.99 (978-0-439-44937-3(5) , Scholastic Paperbacks) Scholastic, Inc.

Monsters Unleashed. Scooby Doo: The Ultimate Sticker Book. 2004. (Ultimate Sticker Bks.). (Illus.). 16p. (J). pap. 6.99 (978-0-7566-0302-1(1)) Dorling Kindersley Publishing, Inc.

Musacchia, Vince, illus. Scooby-Doo! The Case of the Disappearing Scooby Snacks. 2005. (Media Favorites!! Ser.). 22p. (J). 9.95 (978-1-58117-214-0(1) , Intervisual/Piggy Toes) Dalmatian Pr.

Mystery Adventures. 2001. (Scooby-Doo Ser.). (Illus.). 70p. (J). (ps-3). pap. 2.99 (978-0-307-33765-8(0) , Golden Bks.) Random Hse. Children's Bks.

The Mystery Machine Adventure. 2001. (Scooby-Doo Ser.). (Illus.). 12p. (J). (ps-3). bds. 5.99 (978-0-307-20038-9(8) , Golden Bks.) Random Hse. Children's Bks.

Nagler, Michelle H. Haunted Pumpkins. 2001. (gr. k-3). lib. bdg. 11.80 (978-0-613-54532-7(X)) Tandem Library Bks.

Publishing Company Staff. Scooby-Doo! 2000. (Illus.). (J). pap. 3.99 (978-0-307-44532-2(1) , Golden Bks.) Random Hse. Children's Bks.

Reader's Digest Staff. Scooby-Doo Magnetic Mystery. 2007. 16p. (J). 14.99 (***978-0-7944-1353-8(6)**) Reader's Digest Assn., Inc., The.

Scholastic Editorial Staff. Scooby Doo Reader 2 in 1 Bind-Up. 2007. 64p. (J). pap. 4.99 (***978-0-545-00115-1(3)**) Scholastic, Inc.

—Super Spooky Double Storybook. 2008. (Puppy Place Ser.). 48p. (J). pap. 4.99 (***978-0-545-03153-0(2)**) Scholastic, Inc.

Scholastic, Inc. Staff. Scooby Doo Storybook Collection, 8 vols., Set. 2002. (Scooby-Doo Ser.). (Illus.). 256p. (J). (ps-1). 10.99 (978-0-439-51320-3(0) , Scholastic Paperbacks) Scholastic, Inc.

Scholastic, Inc. Staff & McCann, Jesse Leon. Aloha Scooby-Doo. del Sur, Duendes, illus. 2005. (Scooby Doo Ser.). 24p. (J). 3.50 (978-0-439-70429-8(4) , Scholastic Paperbacks) Scholastic, Inc.

Scholastic, Inc. Staff & Weyn, Suzanne. Scooby-doo. novel movie tie-in ed. 2005. (Scooby Doo Ser.). (Illus.). 88p. (J). pap. 3.99 (978-0-439-70428-1(6) , Scholastic Paperbacks) Scholastic, Inc.

Scholastic, Inc. Staff, et al. Scooby-Doo & the Witch's Ghost. 1999. (Scooby-Doo Movie Storybooks). (Illus.). 32p. (J). (ps-3). pap. 3.50 (978-0-439-08786-5(4)) Scholastic, Inc.

Scooby: Cool Ghoul Collection, 3 vols. 2001. (J). (978-1-58805-145-5(5)) DS-Max USA, Inc.

Scooby-Do! Scooby. . . Don't! 2005. (Media Favorites!! Ser.). 14p. (J). 10.95 (978-1-58117-215-7(X) , Intervisual/Piggy Toes) Dalmatian Pr.

Scooby-Doo! 2000. (Scooby-Doo Ser.). (J). (ps-3). 1.99 (978-0-307-28915-5(X) , Golden Bks.) Random Hse. Children's Bks.

Scooby Doo - Large Picture Puzzle Board Book (English) 1999. (Scooby-Doo Ser.). (J). (ps-3). bds. (978-1-58805-002-1(5)) DS-Max USA, Inc.

Scooby-Doo & the Case of the Disappearing Scooby Snacks. 2004. (Media Favorites!! Ser.). 12p. (J). 4.95 (978-1-58117-329-1(6) , Intervisual/Piggy Toes) Dalmatian Pr.

Scooby Doo & the Pirate Ghost. 2001. (Illus.). (J). 15.98 (978-0-7853-4875-7(1)) Publications International, Ltd.

Scooby-Doo Mystery Mania Box Set with Coloring Books. 2000. (Scooby-Doo Ser.). (J). (ps-3). (978-1-58805-136-3(6)) DS-Max USA, Inc.

Scooby Doo Storybook Box Set. 2003. (Illus.). 14.00 (978-0-439-55194-6(3)) Scholastic, Inc.

Scooby Doo to the Rescue. 2007. 48p. pap. 3.99 (***978-1-4037-3716-8(9)**) Dalmatian Pr.

Scooby Doo Where Are You? 2001. (Look & Find Ser.). (J). lib. bdg. 15.95 (978-1-56674-298-6(6)) Forest Hse. Publishing Co., Inc.

Scooby Doo 8X8. Scooby-Doo Museum Madness. 2008. (Scooby-doo 8x8 Ser.). 24p. (J). pap. 3.99 (***978-0-545-00669-9(4)** , Scholastic) Scholastic, Inc.

Scooby Doo's Halloween Tricks & Treats. 2006. (Illus.). 128p. 4.95 (978-0-7624-2827-4(9)) Running Pr. Bk. Pubs.

Scooby-Doo's Upbeat Songs: Level Three for Early Intermediate Students. 2000. (Looney Tunes Piano Library). 24p. (J). 12.95 (978-0-7692-9609-8(2) , Warner Bros. Pubns.) Alfred Publishing Co., Inc.

Smith, Geof. Scooby-Doo! & the Cyber Chase. 2001. 16p. (J). (ps-3). pap. 3.99 (978-0-307-25301-9(5) , Golden Bks.) Random Hse. Children's Bks.

Snack-A-Thon! 2001. (Scooby-Doo Ser.). (Illus.). 16p. (J). (ps-3). pap. 3.99 (978-0-307-28332-0(1) , Golden Bks.) Random Hse. Children's Bks.

Soderberg, Erin. Dinosaur Dig. del Sur, Duendes, illus. 2000. (Scooby-Doo! Picture Clue Book Ser.: No. 3). 32p. (J). (ps-3). 3.99 (978-0-439-20231-2(0)) Scholastic, Inc.

—Spooky Sports Day. 2002. (gr. k-3). lib. bdg. 11.80 (978-0-613-63348-2(2)) Tandem Library Bks.

Tyo, Courtney. Shamrock Scare. del Sur, Duendes, illus. 2004. (Scooby-Doo Ser.: No. 19). 32p. (J). pap. 3.99 (978-0-439-55715-3(1) , Scholastic Paperbacks) Scholastic, Inc.

Wasserman, Robin. Ghost School. 2003. (gr. k-3). lib. bdg. 11.80 (978-0-613-72194-3(2)) Tandem Library Bks.

—Search for Scooby Snacks. del Sur, Duendes, illus. 2000. (Scooby-Doo! Picture Clue Book Ser.: No. 2). 32p. (J). (ps-3). pap. 3.99 (978-0-439-16166-4(5) , Scholastic Paperbacks) Scholastic, Inc.

Wasserman, Robin, et al. Ghost School. del Sur, Duendes, illus. 2003. (Scooby-Doo Ser.: No. 17). 32p. (J). pap. 3.99 (978-0-439-44227-5(3) , Scholastic Paperbacks) Scholastic, Inc.

Weber, Lou. Scooby-Doo Fishy Phonics Mystery Active Point. 2006. 24p. (J). 19.98 (978-1-4127-3172-0(0) , 7233000) Publications International, Ltd.

Weber, Lou, ed. Scooby Doo Mystery Time. 2005. 10p. (J). bds. 16.98 (978-1-4127-3031-0(7) , 7226600) Publications International, Ltd.

Weyn, Suzanne. Loch Ness Monster. 2004. (Scooby Doo Ser.). (Illus.). 80p. (J). pap. 3.99 (978-0-439-60698-1(5) , Scholastic Paperbacks) Scholastic, Inc.

—Scooby-Doo! And the Curse of Cleopatra. 2005. (Illus.). 88p. (J). (gr. 4-7). pap. 3.99 (978-0-439-74419-5(9) , Scholastic Paperbacks) Scholastic, Inc.

—Scooby-Doo! & You: The Case of the Batty Vampire. 2001. (Collect the Clues Mystery Ser.). (Illus.). 59p. (J). pap. (978-0-439-23168-8(X)) Scholastic, Inc.

—Scooby-Doo Movie Novelization. 2002. (gr. k-3). lib. bdg. 13.00 (978-0-613-50739-4(8)) Tandem Library Bks.

Weyn, Suzanne & Erwin, Vicky Berger. Scooby-Doo's Super Case Book. 2002. (Scooby-Doo Mysteries Ser.). (Illus.). 144p. (J). 4.50 (978-0-439-40788-5(5)) Scholastic, Inc.

Wigand, Molly. Scooby-Doo: That's Snow Ghost. Neely, Scott & Phong, Thomas, illus. 2001. 24p. (J). (ps-k). pap. 2.99 (978-0-307-96012-2(9) , Golden Bks.) Random Hse. Children's Bks.

SCOPES, JOHN THOMAS, 1900-1970

Crewe, Sabrina & Uschan, Michael V. The Scopes "Monkey" Trial. 2005. (Events That Shaped America Ser.). (Illus.). 32p. (J). lib. bdg. 24.67 (978-0-8368-3415-4(1)) Stevens, Gareth Inc.

Fitzgerald, Stephanie. The Scopes Trial: The Battle over Teaching Evolution. 2006. 96p. (978-0-7565-2018-2(5)) Compass Point Bks.

Graves, Renee. The Scopes Trial. 2007. (Cornerstones of Freedomtrade;, Second Ser.). 48p. (J). pap. 5.95 (***978-0-531-18769-2(1)*** , Children's Pr.) Scholastic Library Publishing.

Hanson, Freya Ottem. The Scopes Monkey Trial: A Headline Court Case. 2000. (Headline Court Cases Ser.). (Illus.). 128p. (YA). (gr. 6-12). lib. bdg. 26.60 (978-0-7660-1388-9(X)) Enslow Pubs., Inc.

Johnson, Anne Janette. The Scopes "Monkey Trial" 2006. (Defining Moments Ser.). (Illus.). 246p. (YA). (gr. 9 up). lib. bdg. 49.00 (978-0-7808-0955-0(6)) Omnigraphics, Inc.

Uschan, Michael V. The Scopes "Monkey" Trial. 2004. (Landmark Events in American History Ser.). (Illus.). 48p. (J). pap. 11.95 (978-0-8368-5424-4(1)) ; lib. bdg. 30.00 (978-0-8368-5396-4(2)) Stevens, Gareth Inc. (World Almanac Library).

SCORPIONS

Clarke, Penny. Spiders, Insects, & Minibeasts. 2003. (gr. 3-6). lib. bdg. 15.25 (978-0-613-54362-0(9)) Tandem Library Bks.

Claybourne, Anna. Spiders & Scorpions. 2004. (Awesome Bugs Ser.). (J). lib. bdg. 27.10 (978-1-932799-53-8(2)) Stargazer Bks.

Grolier Educational Staff. Scorpions. 2001. (Nature's Children Ser.). (Illus.). 48p. (J). (978-0-7172-5547-4(6) , Grolier) Scholastic Library Publishing.

Halfmann, Janet. Scorpions. 2002. (Nature's Predators Ser.). (Illus.). 48p. (J). (gr. 3-5). 26.20 (978-0-7377-1390-9(9) , Kidhaven) Thomson Gale.

Krul Araujo, Paige, ed. Scorpions. 2006. (Real Thing Ser.). (Illus.). 48p. (J). pap. 8.99 (978-0-439-78793-2(9) , Tangerine Pr.) Scholastic, Inc.

Lassieur, Allison. Scorpions: The Sneaky Stingers. 2001. (Animals in Order Ser.). (Illus.). 48p. (J). (gr. 4-6). pap. 6.95 (978-0-531-16497-6(7) , Watts, Franklin) Scholastic Library Publishing.

Lassieur, Allison & Savage, Stephen. Scorpions: The Sneaky Stingers. Gonzales, Jose, illus. 2000. (Animals in Order Ser.). 48p. (J). (gr. 4-6). 26.50 (978-0-531-11651-7(4) , Watts, Franklin) Scholastic Library Publishing.

Murray, Peter. Scorpions. 2007. (New Naturebooks Ser.). 32p. (J). (gr. 1-5). 27.07 (***978-1-59296-852-7(X)***) Child's World, Inc.

Murray, Peter. Spiders & Scorpions. 2004. (Science Around Us Ser.). 32p. (J). (gr. 2-6). 27.07 (978-1-59296-273-0(4)) Child's World, Inc.

Rankin, Wayne & Walls, Jerry G. Tarantulas & Scorpions. 1999. (Basic Domestic Reptile & Amphibian Library). (Illus.). 64p. (YA). (gr. 4-7). lib. bdg. 19.75 (978-0-7910-5081-1(5) , Chelsea Hse.) Facts On File, Inc.

Richardson, Adele D. Scorpions. 2002. (Predators in the Wild Ser.). (Illus.). 32p. (J). (gr. 3-4). lib. bdg. 21.26 (978-0-7368-1318-1(7) , Capstone High-Interest Bks.) Capstone Pr., Inc.

Ripple, William John. Scorpions. 2005. (Desert Animals Ser.). (Illus.). 24p. (J). 15.93 (978-0-7368-3637-1(3)) Capstone Pr., Inc.

Solway, Andrew. Deadly Spiders & Scorpions. 2004. (J). 29.93 (978-1-4034-5767-7(0)) ; pap. 8.50 (978-1-4034-5773-8(5)) Heinemann Library.

Thomas, Isabel. Scorpion vs. Tarantula. 2006. (Illus.). 32p. (J). (978-1-4109-2396-7(7)) ; pap. (978-1-4109-2403-2(3)) Steck-Vaughn.

SCOTLAND

Adil, Janeen. Scotland: A Question & Answer Book. 2007. 32p. (J). (***978-0-7368-6773-3(2)***) Capstone Pr., Inc.

Brassey, Richard. The Story of Scotland. 1999. (Illus.). 32p. (J). pap. 12.00 (978-1-85881-549-7(5)) Dolphin Paperbacks GBR. *Dist:* Trafalgar Square Publishing.

Britton, Tamara L. Scotland. 2003. (Countries Ser.). (Illus.). 40p. (J). (gr. k-6). lib. bdg. 22.78 (978-1-57765-843-6(4)) ABDO Publishing Co.

Cane, Graeme & Hull, Lise. Welcome to Scotland. 2002. (Welcome to My Country Ser.). (Illus.). 48p. (J). (gr. 2 up). lib. bdg. 26.00 (978-0-8368-2539-8(X)) Stevens, Gareth Inc.

Dendinger, Roger. Scotland. 2002. (Modern World Nations Ser.). (Illus.). 150p. (gr. 6-12). 30.00 (978-0-7910-6782-6(3) , Chelsea Hse.) Facts On File, Inc.

Ganeri, Anita & Oxlade, Chris. A Visit to Scotland. 2003. (Visit to Ser.). (Illus.). 32p. (J). lib. bdg. 22.79 (978-1-4034-0966-9(8)) Heinemann Library.

Griffiths, Jonathan. Scotland. 1999. (Festivals of the World Ser.). (Illus.). 32p. (J). (gr. 3 up). lib. bdg. 24.67 (978-0-8368-2034-8(7)) Stevens, Gareth Inc.

Grolier Educational Staff, contrib. by. Scotland. 2003. (Illus.). 32p. (J). (978-0-7172-5800-0(9) , Grolier) Scholastic Library Publishing.

Hull, Lisa. Scotland. 2001. (Countries of the World Ser.). (Illus.). 96p. (J). (gr. 6 up). lib. bdg. 30.00 (978-0-8368-2339-4(7)) Stevens, Gareth Inc.

Jamison, Margaret Mary Elizabeth Tague. Memories of Maryhill. 2000. (Illus.). 140p. (J). (ps-12). pap. 25.00 (978-0-9712359-0-8(2)) Jamison Publishing.

Jarvie, Frances. Festivals in Scotland. Galloway, Fhiona, illus. 1999. (Scottie Bks.). 40p. (J). (gr. 3-7). pap. 6.95 (978-0-11-495271-6(X)) Stationery Office, The GBR. *Dist:* Balogh International, Inc.

Kirkby, Mandy. Pick Your Brains about Scotland. Williams, Caspar, illus. 2005. (Pick Your Brains Ser.). 128p. pap. 9.95 (978-1-86011-223-2(4)) Cadogan Guides GBR. *Dist:* Globe Pequot Pr., The.

Lace, William W. Scotland. 2000. (Modern Nations of the World Ser.). (Illus.). 112p. (J). (gr. 7-10). 29.95 (978-1-56006-703-0(9) , Lucent Bks.) Thomson Gale.

Levy, Patricia. Scotland. 2000. (Cultures of the World Ser.). (Illus.). 128p. (J). (gr. 5-12). lib. bdg. 37.07 (978-0-7614-1159-8(3) , Benchmark Bks.) Cavendish, Marshall Corp.

McKirdy, Alan. Scottish Landscapes. Ellery, Craig, illus. 1999. 40p. (J). (gr. 3-7). pap. 6.95 (978-0-11-495772-8(X)) Stationery Office, The GBR. *Dist:* Balogh International, Inc.

O'Neill, Judith. Leaving the Island. 1998. (Cambridge Reading Ser.). (Illus.). 32p. (gr. 2-6). pap. 9.00 (978-0-521-63745-9(7)) Cambridge Univ. Pr.

Ruth, Angie. My Adventure in Scotland. 2007. 44p. (J). 8.99 (978-1-59092-433-4(9) , Orchard Academy Pr.) Windstorm Creative.

Shakespeare, William & Roth, Robert R., eds. Macbeth. 2002. (Simply Shakespeare Ser.). (Illus.). 288p. pap. 8.99 (978-0-7641-2086-2(7)) Barron's Educational Series, Inc.

Stein, R. Conrad. Scotland. 2001. (Enchantment of the World, Second Ser.). (Illus.). 144p. (J). (gr. 5-9). 36.00 (978-0-516-21112-1(9) , Children's Pr.) Scholastic Library Publishing.

Watts, Cedric. Macbeth. Shakespeare, William, ed. 2001. 118p. audio compact disk (978-1-903342-15-2(5)) Wordsworth Educational.

Zocchi, Judy. In Scotland. Brodie, Neale, illus. 2005. (Global Adventures II Ser.). 32p. (J). per. 9.95 (978-1-59646-149-9(7)) Dingles & Co.

—In Scotland/en Escocia. Brodie, Neale, illus. 2005. (Global Adventures II Ser.).Tr. of En Escocia. (ENG & SPA.). 32p. (J). per. 9.95 (978-1-59646-151-2(9)) Dingles & Co.

SCOTLAND—FICTION

Aiken, Joan. The Witch of Clatteringshaws. 2005. 144p. (J). (gr. 5). lib. bdg. 17.99 (978-0-385-90252-6(2) , Delacorte Bks. for Young Readers) Random Hse. Children's Bks.

—The Witch of Clatteringshaws. 2006. 160p. (gr. 4-7). 5.99 (978-0-440-42037-8(7) , Yearling) Random Hse. Children's Bks.

Benz, Derek & Lewis, J. S. The Rise of the Black Wolf. 2007. (Grey Griffins Ser.: No. 2). 320p. (J). (gr. 4-7). pap. 12.99 (978-0-439-83774-3(X) , Orchard Bks.) Scholastic, Inc.

Blackford. The Eskdale Herd Boy A Scottish Tale for the Instruction & Amusement of Young Persons. 2004. reprint ed. pap. 15.95 (978-1-4191-6125-4(3)) Kessinger Publishing, LLC.

Blackmore, R. D. Lorna Doone. 1999. lib. bdg. 21.95 (978-1-56723-172-4(1)) Yestermorrow, Inc.

Blackmore, Richard D. Lorna Doone: A Romance of Exmoor. Shuttleworth, Sally, ed. 1999. (Oxford World's Classics Ser.). (Illus.). 720p. 13.95 (978-0-19-283627-4(7)) Oxford Univ. Pr., Inc.

Blyton, Enid. The Sea of Adventure. 7th rev. ed. 2003. (Adventure Series [3] Ser.). 192p. (J). pap. 9.99 (978-0-330-30173-2(X)) Pan Macmillan GBR. *Dist:* Trafalgar Square Publishing.

Bond, Doug. Crown & Covenant, 3 bks. Bird, Matthew, illus. 2004. (Crown & Covenant Ser.). (J). per. 26.99 (978-0-87552-671-3(3)) P & R Publishing.

Brooks, Felicity. King Arthur. rev. ed. 2007. 144p. (J). pap. 4.99 (***978-0-7945-1483-9(9)*** , Usborne) EDC Publishing.

Brown, Ruth, retold by. The Ghost of Greyfriar's Bobby. 1999. (Illus.). (J). pap. 5.99 (978-0-14-056190-6(0) , Puffin) Penguin Group (USA) Inc.

Butler, Berwyn. Dinky the Doorknob: The Adventures of Sir Dinkum Wilhelm, the Third Earl of Surridge. 2005. (J). per. 11.99 (***978-1-933732-02-2(4)*** , Round Rock Chapter Bks.) MidAmerica Publishing Co.

Butler, Berwyn & McClean, Shorty. Dinky the Doorknob. 2006. (J). lib. bdg. 21.95 (***978-1-933732-04-6(0)*** , Round Rock Chapter Bks.) MidAmerica Publishing Co.

Cheshire, Simon. The Prince & the Snowgirl. 2007. 176p. (J). (gr. 7). pap. 8.99 (978-0-385-73342-7(9)) ; lib. bdg. 12.99 (978-0-385-90359-2(6)) Random Hse. Children's Bks. (Delacorte Bks. for Young Readers).

Cooney, Caroline B. Enter Three Witches: A Story of Macbeth. 2007. 288p. (J). (gr. 7 up). pap. 16.99 (978-0-439-71156-2(8) , Scholastic Pr.) Scholastic, Inc.

Cooney, Caroline B. & Shakespeare, William. Enter Three Witches: A Story of Macbeth. 2007. 281p. (***978-1-4287-3716-7(2)*** , Scholastic Pr.) Scholastic, Inc.

Del Negro, Janice. Lucy Dove. 2001. (gr. 3-6). lib. bdg. 15.25 (978-0-613-75135-3(3)) Tandem Library Bks.

Del Negro, Janice & Dorling Kindersley Publishing Staff. Lucy Dove. Gore, Leonid, illus. 2001. 32p. (J). (gr. 3-6). pap. 6.95 (978-0-7894-8084-2(0)) Dorling Kindersley Publishing, Inc.

Derwent, Lavinia. Sula. (Illus.). 144p. pap. 10.00 (978-0-86315-487-4(5)) Floris Bks. GBR. *Dist:* SteinerBooks, Inc.

Dickinson, Peter & Dickinson, Peter. Inside Grandad. 2005. 128p. (J). (gr. 4-7). 5.50 (978-0-553-48782-4(5) , Yearling) Random Hse. Children's Bks.

Downer, Ann. The Dragon of Never-Was. Rayyan, Omar, illus. 2006. 320p. (J). (gr. 3-6). 16.95 (978-0-689-85571-9(0) , Atheneum) Simon & Schuster Children's Publishing.

Duncan, Jane. Janet Reachfar & the Kelpie. Hedderwick, Mairi, illus. 2002. 32p. (J). (gr. k-3). pap. 7.95 (978-1-84158-210-8(7)) Birlinn, Ltd. GBR. *Dist:* Interlink Publishing Group, Inc.

Dunkle, Clare B. By These Ten Bones. rev. ed. 2005. 240p. (YA). (gr. 6-9). 16.95 (978-0-8050-7496-3(1) , Holt, Henry & Co. Bks. For Young Readers) Holt, Henry & Co.

Dunrea, Olivier. Hanne's Quest. 2006. (Illus.). 96p. (J). (gr. 3). 16.99 (978-0-399-24216-8(3) , Philomel) Penguin Group (USA) Inc.

Ehrenhaft, Daniel. Drawing a Blank: Or How I Tried to Solve a Mystery, End a Feud, & Land the Girl of My Dreams. Ristow, Trevor, illus. 2006. 336p. (J). 16.99 (978-0-06-075252-1(1)) ; lib. bdg. 16.89 (978-0-06-075253-8(X)) HarperCollins Pubs.

Flaherty, Alice. The Luck of the Loch Ness Monster: A Tale of Picky Eating. Magoon, Scott, illus. 2007. 40p. (J). (gr. 3-5). 16.00 (***978-0-618-55644-1(3)***) Houghton Mifflin Co.

Forde, Catherine. Fat Boy Swim. 2004. 240p. (J). (gr. 7). lib. bdg. 17.99 (978-0-385-90237-3(9) , Delacorte Bks. for Young Readers) Random Hse. Children's Bks.

Glencoe McGraw-Hill Staff & McGraw-Hill - Jamestown Education Staff. Topics from the Restless, Bk. 2. unabr. ed. 1999. (Wordsworth Classics Ser.). (gr. 10 up). pap. 24.64 (978-0-89061-117-3(3) , 9780890611173) Jamestown.

Gliori, Debi. Pure Dead Batty. 2007. (Illus.). 320p. (J). (gr. 4-7). 6.50 (***978-0-440-42074-3(1)*** , Yearling) Random Hse. Children's Bks.

—Pure Dead Frozen. 2007. (J). (gr. 5). 320p. 15.99 (***978-0-375-83317-5(X)***); 304p. lib. bdg. 18.99 (***978-0-375-93317-2(4)***) Random Hse. Children's Bks. (Knopf Bks. for Young Readers).

—Pure Dead Magic. 2002. (Illus.). 208p. (gr. 5). mass mkt. 6.50 (978-0-440-41849-8(6) , Yearling) Random Hse. Children's Bks.

—Pure Dead Wicked. 2003. 240p. (gr. 5). 6.50 (978-0-440-41936-5(0) , Yearling) Random Hse. Children's Bks.

Greiman, Lois. The MacGowan Betrothal: Highland Rogues. 2001. 384p. mass mkt. 5.99 (978-0-380-81541-8(9)) HarperCollins Pubs.

Griffin, Adele. Witch Twins & the Ghost of Glenn Bly. Rogers, Jacqueline, illus. 2005. 128p. (gr. 2-6). pap. 5.99 (978-0-7868-5496-7(0)) Hyperion Bks. for Children.

Harcourt School Publishers Staff. The Visit Advanced Level. 3rd ed. 2002. (Trophies Reading Program Ser.). (Illus.). pap. 5.10 (978-0-15-323294-7(3)) Harcourt Schl. Pubs.

Hedderwick, Mairi. Katie Morag & the Riddles. 2002. (Illus.). 32p. (J). pap. 9.99 (978-0-09-941418-6(X)) Random Hse. GBR. *Dist:* Independent Pubs. Group.

Hergé. The Black Island. (Illus.). 62p. (J). 19.95 (978-0-8288-5012-4(7)) French & European Pubns., Inc.

—L' Ile Noire. 1999. (Tintin Ser.).Tr. of Black Island. (FRE., Illus.). (J). (gr. 4-7). pap. 21.95 (978-2-203-00106-0(2)) Casterman, Editions FRA. *Dist:* Distribooks, Inc.

—L' Ile Noire.Tr. of Black Island. (FRE., Illus.). (J). (gr. 7-9). ring bd. 19.95 (978-0-8288-5039-1(9)) French & European Pubns., Inc.

Howell, Gill. Selkie Child. Keen, Sophie, illus. 2005. 24p. (J). lib. bdg. 22.65 (***978-1-59646-750-7(9)***) Dingles & Co.

Jardine, Quintin. Wearing Purple. 1999. (Oz Blackstone Mysteries Ser.). 344p. pap. 9.99 (978-0-7472-5666-3(7)) Headline Bk. Publishing GBR. *Dist:* Independent Pubs. Group.

Kane, James. Tom & Katie's Greatest Adventure. 2005. 73p. pap. 14.95 (978-1-4241-0776-6(8)) PublishAmerica, Inc.

Kellerhals-Stewart, Heather. Brave Highland Heart. ed. 2004. (Illus.). (J). (gr. k-3). spiral bd. (978-0-616-01688-6(3)) Canadian National Institute for the Blind/Institut National Canadien pour les Aveugles.

—Brave Highland Heart. Zimmermann, H. Werner, illus. 1998. 15p. (J). (gr. k-3). 15.95 (978-0-7737-3099-1(0)) Stoddart Kids CAN. *Dist:* Fitzhenry & Whiteside, Ltd.

King-Smith, Dick. The Water Horse. Parkins, David, illus. 2000. 128p. (J). (gr. 3-5). pap. 5.50 (978-0-375-80352-9(1) , Yearling) Random Hse. Children's Bks.

—Water Horse. 2000. (gr. 3-6). lib. bdg. 13.00 (978-0-613-24003-1(0)) Tandem Library Bks.

Knight, Caitlyn. Anastasia: the Tapestry of the Silver Unicorns. 2007. 386p. pap. 19.98 (***978-0-615-15145-8(0)***) Neugard, S.L.

Knight, Eric. Lassie Come-Home. Kirmse, Marguerite, illus. rev. ed. 2003. 256p. (J). (gr. 4-12). 18.95 (978-0-8050-7206-8(3) , Holt, Henry & Co. Bks. For Young Readers) Holt, Henry & Co.

Lang, Andrew. Prince Ricardo of Pantouflia: Being the. 2006. (Illus.). pap. 24.95 (***978-1-4286-0645-6(9)***) Kessinger Publishing, LLC.

Leaf, Munro. Wee Gillis. Lawson, Robert, illus. ed. 2006. (New York Review Children's Collection). 80p. (J). (ps). 14.95 (978-1-59017-206-3(X) , NYR Children's Collection) New York Review of Bks., Inc., The.

Lindenbaum, Pija. Mini Mia & Her Darling Uncle. Dysseg-aard, Elisabeth Kallick, tr. from SWE. 2007. (Illus.). 40p. (J). (ps-3). 16.00 (***978-91-29-66734-9(8)***) R & S Bks. SWE. *Dist:* Macmillan.

MacDonald, George. Ranald Bannerman's Boyhood. 2006. 63.99 (***978-1-4280-3039-8(5)***) IndyPublish.com.

MacDonald, George. Sir Gibbie. Lindskoog, Kathryn, ed. Wynne, Patrick, illus. 2001. (Classics for Young Readers Ser.). 224p. (J). (gr. 3-6). pap. 7.99 (978-0-87552-726-0(4)) P & R Publishing.

MacPhail, Catherine. Dark Waters. 2005. 176p. (YA). pap. 6.95 (978-1-58234-986-2(X)); 2003. 177p. (J). (gr. 5 up). 15.95 (978-1-58234-846-9(4)) Bloomsbury Publishing. (Bloomsbury Children).

Maddux, Marlaine. The Loch Pt. 1: Facing the Future, 3 vols. Huddleston, Courtney, illus. 2000. (Mythics Ser.). 64p. (J). (gr. 3-6). 17.95 (978-0-9673683-3-7(2)) Penny-Farthing Pr., Inc.

Maxwell, Katie. They Wear What under Their Kilts? 2004. (Illus.). (YA). mass mkt. 5.99 (978-0-8439-5258-2(X)) Dorchester Publishing Co., Inc.

—They Wear What under Their Kilts? 2004. (gr. 7-12). lib. bdg. 14.15 (978-0-613-76906-8(6)) Tandem Library Bks.

McGoldrick, May. Avon True Romance: An Tess & the Highlander. 2002. (gr. 7-12). lib. bdg. 13.00 (978-0-613-71370-2(2)) Tandem Library Bks.

McKeown, Adam. Macbeth. 2005. pap. (978-1-4027-2476-3(4)) Sterling Publishing Co., Inc.

McLean, Allan Campbell. The Hill of the Red Fox. 2nd ed. 2006. (Kelpies Ser.). 272p. (J). pap. 11.95 (978-0-86315-556-7(1)) Floris Bks. GBR. *Dist:* SteinerBooks, Inc.

Morrison, P. R. Wave Traveller. 2007. 300p. (J). (gr. 3-7). 16.95 (***978-1-59990-123-7(4)***) Bloomsbury Publishing.

Nicholson, Mike. Catscape. 2006. 192p. (YA). pap. 9.99 (978-0-86315-531-4(6)) Floris Bks. GBR. *Dist:* Steiner-Books, Inc.

Paul, Colette. Whoever You Chose to Love. 2004. 256p. pap. (978-0-297-84717-5(1) , Weidenfeld & Nicolson) Orion Publishing Group, Ltd.

Pelley, Kathleen. The Giant King. Manning, Maurie, tr. Manning, Maurie, illus. 2003. (New Child & Family Press Titles Ser.). 32p. (ps-4). 14.95 (978-0-87868-880-7(3) , 8803, Child & Family Pr.) Child Welfare League of America, Inc.

Perkins, Lucy Fitch. Scotch Twins. 2006. 62.99 (***978-1-4280-3717-5(9)***); pap. 55.99 (***978-1-4280-3713-7(6)***) IndyPublish.com.

Perkins, Lucy Fitch. The Scotch Twins. 2004. reprint ed. pap. 15.95 (978-1-4191-8160-3(2)); pap. 1.99 (978-1-4192-8160-0(7)) Kessinger Publishing, LLC.

Peyton, K. M. Stealaway. Wyatt, David, illus. 2004. 96p. (J). 12.95 (978-0-8126-2722-0(9)) Cricket Bks.

Ransome, Arthur. Great Northern? 2003. (Swallows & Amazons Ser.). (Illus.). 352p. (J). pap. 14.95 (978-1-56792-259-2(7)) Godine, David R. Pub.

Rees, Gwyneth. Fairy Dust. 2005. (Read-along Ser.). (Illus.). (J). audio (978-0-7540-6286-8(4)) BBC Audio.

Ryan, Margaret. Wild Kat Mccrumble. 2005. (Kat Mccrumble Ser.). 208p. (J). pap. (978-0-340-88402-7(9) , Hodder Children's Books) Hodder Children's Division.

Spirn, Michele Sobel. The Bridges in Edinburgh. 2004. (Going to Ser.). 144p. pap. 6.95 (978-1-893577-11-4(2)) Four Corners Publishing Co., Inc.

Stevenson, Robert Louis. Kidnapped. 2006. per. 8.95 (978-1-57646-970-5(0)) Quiet Vision Publishing.

—Kidnapped. Kennedy, Cam, illus. 2007. 64p. (J). (gr. 5). pap. 11.95 (***978-0-88776-843-9(1)***); Tundra Bks., Inc./Livres Toundra, Inc. CAN. *Dist:* Random Hse., Inc.

Stevenson, Robert Louis. Kidnapped. unabr. ed. 2000. (Dover Juvenile Classics Ser.). (Illus.). 256p. (J). (gr. 4-7). pap. 2.50 (978-0-486-41026-5(9)) Dover Pubns., Inc.

Stoddart, Lady. The Eskdale Herd Boy: A Scottish Tale for the Instruction & Amusement of Young Persons. 2005. reprint ed. pap. 20.95 (978-1-4179-6691-2(2)) Kessinger Publishing, LLC.

Strachan, Linda. Ghost of Glamis. 2005. (Illus.). 32p. pap. 9.00 (978-0-9546701-9-1(1)) GW Publishing GBR. *Dist:* Wilson & Assocs.

—Serach for Loch Ness Monster. 2005. (Illus.). 32p. pap. 9.00 (978-0-9546701-5-3(9)) GW Publishing GBR. *Dist:* Wilson & Assocs.

—Skye Surprise. 2005. (Illus.). 32p. pap. 9.00 (978-0-9546701-8-4(3)) GW Publishing GBR. *Dist:* Wilson & Assocs.

Sutcliff, Rosemary. Sword Song. 2005. (Illus.). 288p. (J). pap. 6.95 (978-0-374-46984-9(9) , Farrar, Straus & Giroux (BYR)) Farrar, Straus & Giroux.

Swoish, Tammy. Hot Scots, Castles, & Kilts. 2008. (YA). (gr. 7). 208p. pap. 7.99 (***978-0-385-73447-9(6)***); 224p. lib. bdg. 10.99 (***978-0-385-90450-6(9)***) Random Hse. Children's Bks. (Delacorte Bks. for Young Readers).

Thomas, Jerry D. Detective Zack Secret of Blackloch Castle. 1998. (Detective Zack Ser.: Vol. 10). (Illus.). 126p. (J). (gr. 3-6). pap. 6.99 (978-0-8163-1399-0(7)) Pacific Pr. Publishing Assn.

Tracey, Rhian. When Isla Meets Luke Meets Isla. 2003. 160p. (YA). pap. 12.95 (978-0-7475-6344-0(6)) Bloomsbury Publishing Plc GBR. *Dist:* Independent Pubs. Group.

The Travels of Jimm Pigg. 2001. 32p. (J). per. 9.95 (978-0-9713900-0-3(2)) Hynes Enterprises, Inc.

Walton, O. F. Saved at Sea: A Young Boy in a Dramatic Rescue. (Illus.). 144p. (J). mass mkt. 5.99 (978-1-85792-795-5(8) , Christian Heritage) Christian Focus Pubns. GBR. *Dist:* Riverside.

Watson, Sally. Witch of the Glens. 2004. (YA). pap. 12.95 (978-1-59511-001-5(1) , 800-691-7779) Image Cascade Publishing.

Watson, T. E. Glen Robbie: A Scottish Fairy Tale. Ferchaud, Steve, illus. ed. 2006. (J). lib. bdg. 22.95 (978-1-58478-013-7(4) , Highland Children's Pr.) Heather & Highlands Publishing.

—The Man Who Spoke with Cats. Ferchaud, Steve, illus. 2006. (J). lib. bdg. 18.95 (978-1-58478-019-9(3) , Highland Children's Pr.) Heather & Highlands Publishing.

Wiggin, Kate Douglas. Penelope's Experiences in Scotland. 2004. reprint ed. pap. 21.95 (978-1-4191-4071-6(X)); pap. 1.99 (978-1-4192-4071-3(X)) Kessinger Publishing, LLC.

Wiley, Melissa. Beyond the Heather Hills. Graef, Renee, illus. 2003. (Little House Ser.). 208p. (J). pap. 6.99 (978-0-06-440715-1(2)) HarperCollins Pubs.

—Beyond the Heather Hills. 2003. (gr. 3-6). lib. bdg. 14.15 (978-0-613-62171-7(9)) Tandem Library Bks.

—Down to the Bonny Glen: Martha Years. 2001. (Martha Years Ser.). (Illus.). (J). 12.64 (978-0-606-21160-4(8)) Tandem Library Bks.

—The Far Side of the Loch. Graef, Renee, illus. (Little House). (J). (gr. 3-6). 2001. lib. bdg. (978-0-06-028556-2(7)); 2000. 256p. pap. 6.99 (978-0-06-440713-7(6) , Harper Trophy); 2000. 256p. 15.89 (978-0-06-028203-5(7)); 2000. 256p. 15.95 (978-0-06-027984-4(2)) HarperCollins Pubs.

—The Far Side of the Loch. 2000. (Little House Ser.). (Illus.). (J). 12.64 (978-0-606-18689-6(1)) Tandem Library Bks.

—Far Side of the Loch. 2000. (gr. 3-6). lib. bdg. 14.15 (978-0-613-25131-0(8)) Tandem Library Bks.

—The Far Side of the Loch Bk. 2: The Martha Years. 2007. (Little House Ser.). 160p. (J). pap. 5.99 (***978-0-06-114818-7(0)*** , Harper Trophy) HarperCollins Pubs.

—Little House in the Highlands. 2007. (Little House Ser.). 144p. (J). pap. 5.99 (***978-0-06-114817-0(2)*** , Harper Trophy) HarperCollins Pubs.

—Little House in the Highlands. Andreasen, Dan & Graef, Renee, illus. 1999. (Little House Ser.). 288p. (J). (gr. 3-7). pap. 6.99 (978-0-06-440712-0(8) , Harper Trophy) HarperCollins Pubs.

—Little House in the Highlands. Graef, Renee, illus. 1999. (Little House). 271p. (J). (gr. 4-7). 15.89 (978-0-06-028202-8(9)) HarperCollins Pubs.

—Little House in the Highlands. 1999. (Little House Ser.). 271p. (J). (978-0-606-15838-1(3)); (gr. 3-6). lib. bdg. 14.15 (978-0-613-11795-1(6)) Tandem Library Bks.

Wiley, Melissa, et al. Little House in the Highlands. Graef, Renee, illus. 1999. (Little House Ser.). 288p. (J). (gr. 3-7). 16.95 (978-0-06-027983-7(4)) HarperCollins Pubs.

Yolen, Jane. The Bagpiper's Ghost. 2003. (Tartan Magic Ser.: Bk. 3). (Illus.). 144p. (J). pap. 5.95 (978-0-15-204913-3(4) , Magic Carpet Bks.) Harcourt Children's Bks.

—Bagpiper's Ghost. 2003. (gr. 3-6). lib. bdg. 6.95 (978-0-613-70524-0(6)) Tandem Library Bks.

—The Wizard's Map. 1999. (Tartan Magic Ser.: Bk. 1). 144p. (YA). (gr. 3-7). 16.00 (978-0-15-202067-5(5)) Harcourt Children's Bks.

—Wizard's Map. 2002. (gr. 3-6). lib. bdg. 14.10 (978-0-613-53882-4(X)) Tandem Library Bks.

Yolen, Jane & Harris, Robert J. Girl in a Cage. 2002. (Illus.). 240p. (YA). (gr. 6-10). 18.99 (978-0-399-23627-3(9) , Philomel) Penguin Group (USA) Inc.

SCOTLAND—HISTORY

Burnett, Allan. Macbeth & All That. 2007. (Illus.). 128p. pap. 4.95 (***978-1-84158-574-1(2)***) Birlinn, Ltd. GBR. *Dist:* Interlink Publishing Group, Inc.

Capt, E. Raymond. Isle of Iona. 2003. 160p. per. 11.95 (978-0-934666-58-9(X)) Artisan Pubs.

Carruth, J. A., text. Mary Queen of Scots. (Scotland in Words & Pictures Ser.). (Illus.). 32p. pap. 3.95 (978-0-7117-0147-2(4)) Jarrold Publishing GBR. *Dist:* 7 Hills Bk. Distributors.

Douglas, Elizabeth. Mary, Queen of Scots. Philip, Carrie, illus. 1999. (Scottie Bks.). 40p. (J). (gr. 3-7). pap. 8.95 (978-0-11-494265-6(X)) NMS Enterprises Ltd. - Publishing GBR. *Dist:* Antique Collectors' Club, Balogh International, Inc.

English, Anna Bruce. Let's Explore Edinburgh Old Town. McLeod, Cinders, illus. 2001. (Let's Explore Ser.). 58p. (ps-7). per. 8.95 (978-0-946487-98-1(7)) Luath Pr. Ltd. GBR. *Dist:* Ingram Pub. Services.

Israel, Fred L., intro. Scottish Clans & Tartans. 1999. (Looking into the Past). (Illus.). 64p. (YA). (gr. 5 up). lib. bdg. 19.75 (978-0-7910-4676-0(1) , Chelsea Hse.) Facts On File, Inc.

Jarvie, Frances. The Romans in Scotland. Philip, Carrie, illus. 1999. (Scottie Bks.). 40p. (J). (gr. 3-7). pap. 6.95 (978-0-11-494277-9(3)) Stationery Office, The GBR. *Dist:* Balogh International, Inc.

Jarvie, Gordon & Jarvie, Frances. Scotland's Vikings. Galloway, Fhiona, illus. 1999. (Scottie Bks.). 40p. (J). (gr. 3-7). pap. 6.95 (978-0-11-495813-8(0)) Stationery Office, The GBR. *Dist:* Balogh International, Inc.

Jarvie, Gordon & Whelan, Olwyn. Scottish Castles. 2004. (Scottie Bks.). (Illus.). 41p. (J). (gr. 3-7). pap. 8.95 (978-0-11-494276-2(5)) NMS Enterprises Ltd. - Publishing GBR. *Dist:* Antique Collectors' Club.

Kamm, Antony. The Jacobites. Steel, Ewan, illus. 1999. (Scottie Bks.). 40p. (J). (gr. 3-7). pap. 6.95 (978-0-11-495250-1(7)) Stationery Office, The GBR. *Dist:* Balogh International, Inc.

Kings & Queens of Scotland. 2002. 192p. 3.95 (978-1-85534-915-5(9)) Geddes & Grosset, Ltd. GBR. *Dist:* CPG Publishing, Inc.

Marshall, H. E. Scotland's Story. rev. ed. 2006. (Illus.). 368p. (***978-1-902984-77-3(3)***) Galore Park Publishing Ltd.

Marshall, H.E. Scotland's Story (Yesterday's Classics) Skelton, J. R. et al, illus. 2005. 552p. (J). per. 17.95 (978-1-59915-056-7(5)) Yesterday's Classics.

Orme, Helen. Edinburgh Castle: Scotland's Haunted Fortress. 2006. (Castles, Palaces, & Tombs Ser.). (Illus.). 32p. (J). lib. bdg. 25.27 (978-1-59716-248-7(5)) Bearport Publishing Co., Inc.

Paterson, Judy. The History of Scotland for Children. Collins, Sally J., illus. 136p. (J). (gr. 3-6). 2001. pap. (978-1-871512-63-2(8)); 2000. (978-1-871512-56-4(5)) Glowworm Bks., Ltd.

Sir William Wallace. 2002. 192p. 3.95 (978-1-85534-925-4(6)) Geddes & Grosset, Ltd. GBR. *Dist:* CPG Publishing, Inc.

Zocchi, Judy. In Scotland. Brodie, Neale, illus. 2005. (Global Adventures I Ser.). 32p. (J). pap. 9.95 (978-1-59646-147-5(0)); lib. bdg. 20.65 (978-1-59646-012-6(1)) Dingles & Co.

—In Scotland/en Escocia. Brodie, Neale, illus. 2005. (Global Adventures I Ser.).Tr. of En Escocia. (ENG & SPA.). 32p. (J). pap. 9.95 (978-1-59646-150-5(0)); lib. bdg. (978-1-59646-013-3(X)) Dingles & Co.

SCOTLAND—HISTORY—FICTION

Banks, Lynne Reid. The Dungeon. 2002. 288p. (J). (gr. 7 up). 16.99 (978-0-06-623782-4(3)) HarperCollins Pubs.

Birch, Beverley & Shakespeare, William. Macbeth. 2007. (Illus.). 80p. 13.95 (***978-0-7502-4965-2(X)*** , Hodder Wayland) Hodder Children's Division GBR. *Dist:* Independent Pubs. Group.

Bond, Douglas. King's Arrow. Bird, Matthew, illus. 2003. (Crown & Covenant Ser.). 208p. (J). per. 10.99 (978-0-87552-743-7(4)) P & R Publishing.

—Rebel's Keep. Bird, Matthew, illus. 2004. (Crown & Covenant Ser.). 285p. (J). per. 9.99 (978-0-87552-744-4(2)) P & R Publishing.

Breslin, Theresa. Remembrance. 2004. 304p. (YA). (gr. 7). mass mkt. 6.50 (978-0-440-23778-5(5) , Laurel Leaf) Random Hse. Children's Bks.

Cameron, Ian. Stirling Bridge. (Illus.). 32p. pap. 6.95 (978-1-899827-07-7(2)) Scottish Children's Pr. GBR. *Dist:* Wilson & Assocs.

Douglas, Bond. Duncan's War. 2002. (Crown & Covenant Ser.). (Illus.). 277p. (J). per. 10.99 (978-0-87552-742-0(6)) P & R Publishing.

Frost, Helen. The Braid. 2006. (Illus.). 112p. (YA). (gr. 7 up). 16.00 (978-0-374-30962-6(0) , Frances Foster Bks.) Farrar, Straus & Giroux.

Hendry, Frances. Quest for a Queen: The Falcon. 2006. pap. (***978-1-905665-06-8(7)***) Pollinger In Print.

Henty, G. A. Bonnie Prince Charlie: A Tale of Fontenoy & Culloden. 2006. 280p. pap. 13.99 (978-1-4264-2121-1(4)); 268p. pap. 16.99 (978-1-4264-2189-1(3)) BiblioBazaar.

—In Freedom's Cause: A Story of Wallace & Bruce. 2002. 320p. (J). (gr. 4-7). pap. 6.95 (978-0-486-42362-3(X)) Dover Pubns., Inc.

—In Freedom's Cause: A Story of Wallace & Bruce. 2004. reprint ed. pap. 1.99 (978-1-4192-2572-7(3)) Kessinger Publishing, LLC.

—In Freedom's Cause: A Story of Wallace & Bruce. 2000. (Illus.). 337p. (J). pap. 14.99 (978-1-887159-35-7(5)) Preston-Speed Pubns.

—In Freedom's Cause: A Story of Wallace & Bruce. 2004. 176p. (YA). pap. 8.95 (978-1-57646-886-9(0)) Quiet Vision Publishing.

Hunter, Mollie. The King's Swift Rider: A Novel on Robert the Bruce. 1998. 256p. (J). (gr. 7 up). 16.95 (978-0-06-027186-2(8)) HarperCollins Pubs.

—The King's Swift Rider: A Novel on Robert the Bruce. 2000. (Illus.). (J). (978-0-606-18701-5(4)) Tandem Library Bks.

—The Thirteenth Member. 2002. (Kelpies Ser.). (Illus.). 160p. (J). pap. (978-0-86315-405-8(0)) Floris Bks. GBR. *Dist:* SteinerBooks, Inc.

Jenkins, Sara D. The Prose Marmion a Tale of the Scottish. 2004. reprint ed. pap. 15.95 (978-1-4191-7925-9(X)) Kessinger Publishing, LLC.

—The Prose Marmion A Tale of the Scottish Border. 2004. reprint ed. pap. 1.99 (978-1-4192-7925-6(4)) Kessinger Publishing, LLC.

Lightwood, Donald. The Long Revenge. 128p. pap. 7.95 (978-1-899827-94-7(3)) Scottish Children's Pr. GBR. *Dist:* Wilson & Assocs.

Marston, Hope Irvin. Against the Tide: The Valor of Margaret Wilson. 2007. (J). pap. (***978-1-59638-061-5(6)***) P & R Publishing.

Morgan, Nicola. Fleshmarket. 2004. 224p. (YA). (gr. 9). lib. bdg. 17.99 (978-0-385-90192-5(5) , Delacorte Bks. for Young Readers) Random Hse. Children's Bks.

Stevenson, Robert Louis. Kidnapped. 2002. (Great Illustrated Classics Ser.). (Illus.). 240p. (J). (gr. 3-8). 21.35 (978-1-57765-690-6(3) , ABDO & Daughters) ABDO Publishing Co.

—Kidnapped. 1999. (Illus.). 208p. 19.95 (978-1-85149-708-9(0)) Antique Collectors' Club.

—Kidnapped. 2000. (Classics Ser.). 240p. mass mkt. 3.95 (978-0-451-52768-4(2) , Signet Classics) Penguin Group (USA) Inc.

—Kidnapped. 1998. (Children's Classics). (ENG.). 224p. (YA). (ps up). pap. (978-1-85326-117-6(3) , 1173WW) Wordsworth Editions, Ltd.

—Secuestrado. 1999. (SPA.). 360p. (978-950-03-7852-9(3) , 4000) Losada.

Stevenson, Robert Louis, intro. Kidnapped: Catriona. 2007. 480p. pap. 15.00 (***978-1-84697-033-7(4)***) BirlinnPolygon GBR. *Dist:* Interlink Publishing Group, Inc.

Stevenson, Robert Louis & Wyeth, N. C. Kidnapped. 2004. (Scribner Storybook Classic Ser.). (Illus.). 64p. (J). 18.95 (978-0-689-86542-8(2) , Atheneum) Simon & Schuster Children's Publishing.

Strachan, Linda. Edinburgh Adventure. 2005. (Illus.). 32p. pap. 9.00 (978-0-9546701-7-7(5)) GW Publishing GBR. *Dist:* Wilson & Assocs.

Sutcliff, Rosemary. The Mark of the Horse Lord. 2006. 256p. (YA). pap. 10.95 (978-1-932425-62-8(4) , Lemniscaat) Boyds Mills Pr.

Weigand, Edith S. If Mandy Ruled the World. 2003. (Illus.). 16p. 7.95 (978-0-9618904-9-0(5)) Zhera Pubns.

Wiley, Melissa. Down to the Bonny Glen. 2008. (Little House Ser.). 160p. (J). pap. 5.99 (***978-0-06-114819-4(9)*** , Harper Trophy) HarperCollins Pubs.

—Down to the Bonny Glen. Graef, Renee, illus. 2001. (Little House Ser.). 336p. (J). (gr. 3-7). pap. 6.99 (978-0-06-440714-4(4) , Harper Trophy) HarperCollins Pubs.

—Down to the Bonny Glen. 2001. (gr. 3-6). lib. bdg. 14.15 (978-0-613-35803-3(1)) Tandem Library Bks.

—Down to the Bonny Glen: Martha Years. Graef, Renee, illus. 2001. (Little House Ser.). 336p. (J). (gr. 3-7). 16.95 (978-0-06-027985-1(0)); 16.89 (978-0-06-028204-2(5)) HarperCollins Pubs.

Yolen, Jane. Queen's Own Fool: A Novel of Mary Queen of Scots. 2001. (gr. 7-12). lib. bdg. 16.45 (978-0-613-44410-1(8)) Tandem Library Bks.

Yolen, Jane & Harris, Robert J. The Rogues. 2007. 277p. (J). (gr. 6-9). 18.99 (***978-0-399-23898-7(0)*** , Philomel) Penguin Group (USA) Inc.

SCOTLAND—KINGS AND RULERS

Burnett, Allan. Macbeth & All That. 2007. (Illus.). 128p. pap. 4.95 (***978-1-84158-574-1(2)***) Birlinn, Ltd. GBR. *Dist:* Interlink Publishing Group, Inc.

Douglas, Elizabeth. Scottish Kings & Queens. Salgado, Adrienne, illus. 1999. (Scottie Bks.). 40p. (J). (gr. 3-7). pap. 8.95 (978-0-11-495753-7(3)) NMS Enterprises Ltd. - Publishing GBR. *Dist:* Antique Collectors' Club.

SCOTT, DRED, 1809-1858

Blue, Rose & Naden, Corinne J. Dred Scott: Person or Property? 2004. (Supreme Court Milestones Ser.). (Illus.). 128p. (J). 37.07 (978-0-7614-1841-2(5) , Benchmark Bks.) Cavendish, Marshall Corp.

Dred Scott & Freedom. 2000. (My Ancestors—My Heroes Ser.: Vol. 22). (J). (gr. 3-4). (978-1-893091-21-4(X)) Parker Publishing Co.

Gunderson, Cory Gideon. The Dred Scott Decision. 2005. (American Moments Ser.). (Illus.). 48p. (J). (gr. 4-8). lib. bdg. 25.65 (978-1-59197-283-9(3)) ABDO Publishing Co.

January, Brendan. The Dred Scott Decision. De Capua, Sarah, ed. 1998. (Cornerstones of Freedom Ser.). (Illus.). 32p. (J). (gr. 4-6). pap. 5.95 (978-0-516-26457-8(5) , Children's Pr.) Scholastic Library Publishing.

McNeese, Tim. Dred Scott V. Sandford. 2006. (Great Supreme Court Decisions Ser.). (Illus.). 120p. (J). (gr. 5-8). 30.00 (978-0-7910-9236-1(4) , Chelsea Hse.) Facts On File, Inc.

Rosen, Daniel. Dred Scott & the Supreme Court. 2006. (Navigators Ser.). (J). pap. 42.00 (*978-1-4108-6258-7(5)) Benchmark Education Co.

Swain, Gwenyth. Dred & Harriet Scott: A Family's Struggle for Freedom. 2004. (Illus.). 102p. pap. 12.95 (978-0-87351-483-5(1) , Borealis Bk.) Minnesota Historical Society Pr.

SCOTT, ROBERT FALCON, 1868-1912

Gogerly, Liz. Amundsen & Scott's Race to the South Pole. 2007. (J). (*978-1-4034-9761-1(3)) Heinemann Library.

Harcourt School Publishers Staff. Antarctica Below Level: The Race for the South Pole. 3rd ed. 2002. (Trophies Reading Program Ser.). (Illus.). pap. 5.10 (978-0-15-323409-5(1)) Harcourt Schl. Pubs.

McNeil, Niki, et al. HOCPP 1132 Robert Falcon Scott. 2006. spiral bd. 18.50 (*978-1-60308-132-0(1)) In the Hands of a Child.

Pipe, Jim. The Race to the South Pole. 2006. (Stories from History Ser.). 48p. (J). 14.95 (*978-0-7696-4722-7(7)); pap. 6.95 (*978-0-7696-4702-9(2)) School Specialty Publishing.

Riddle, John. Robert F. Scott: British Explorer of the South. 2002. (Great Names Ser.). (Illus.). 32p. (J). (gr. 3 up). lib. bdg. (978-1-59084-146-4(8)) Mason Crest Pubs.

SCOTTISH POETRY

Aigner-Clark, Julie. Baby Einstein Poemas Preciosos: Pretty Poems & Wonderful Words. Zaidi, Nadeem, illus. 2004. (SPA.). 10p. (J). 9.95 (978-970-718-210-3(5) , Silver Dolphin Bks.) Advantage Pubs. Group.

Boyd, Betty & Elder, Mike, eds. A Hantle O Rhymes. 2004. (Illus.). 96p. pap. 9.95 (978-1-901663-73-0(6)) NMS Enterprises Ltd. - Publishing GBR. *Dist:* Antique Collectors' Club.

McClintock, R. Princess & the Goblin. 2002. 40p. (J). (ps-3). 14.95 (978-0-06-028228-8(2)) HarperCollins Pubs.

Stevenson, Robert Louis. A Child's Garden of Verses. Tudor, Tasha, illus. 1999. 72p. (J). (ps-3). 20.99 (978-0-689-82382-4(7)) Simon & Schuster Children's Publishing.

—A Child's Garden of Verses. Wildsmith, Brian, illus. 2008. 80p. (J). 19.95 (978-1-59572-057-3(X)) Star Bright Bks., Inc.

—A Child's Garden of Verses Vol. 2. Stevenson, Robert Louis, ed. Kliros, Thea, illus. unabr. ed. 1998. (Dover Children's Thrift Classics Ser.). 96p. (J). (gr. 3-6). reprint ed. pap. 2.00 (978-0-486-27301-3(6)) Dover Pubns., Inc.

—Poetry For Young People: Robert Louis Stevenson. 2003. cd-rom 19.00 (978-0-931968-62-4(3)) B & R Samizdat Express.

—Robert Louis Stevenson. Schoonmaker, Frances, ed. Corvino, Lucy, illus. 2000. (Poetry for Young People Ser.). 48p. (gr. 3-7). 14.95 (978-0-8069-4956-7(2)) Sterling Publishing Co., Inc.

SCOUTS AND SCOUTING

see also Boy Scouts; Girl Scouts

Balloon Books Staff, ed. Scout in the Woods: 85 Removable Stickers. 2003. (Sticker Story Bks.). (Illus.). 18p. (J). (ps-1). pap. 4.95 (978-1-4027-0101-6(2) , Balloon Bks.) Sterling Publishing Co., Inc.

—Scout Super Sticker Book: 180 Removable Stickers. 2003. (Sticker Story Bks.). (Illus.). 18p. (J). (ps-1). pap. 4.95 (978-1-4027-0102-3(0) , Balloon Bks.) Sterling Publishing Co., Inc.

Boraas, Tracey. Kit Carson: Mountain Man. 2002. (Let Freedom Ring Ser.). (Illus.). 48p. (J). (gr. 3-4). lib. bdg. 22.60 (978-0-7368-1349-5(7) , Bridgestone Bks.) Capstone Pr., Inc.

Boy Scouts of America Staff. Bear Cub Scout Book. rev. ed. 1998. 264p. (J). (gr. 3). 4.95 (978-0-8395-3107-4(9)) Boy Scouts of America.

—Wolf Cub Scout Book. rev. ed. 1998. (Illus.). 232p. (J). (gr. 2). pap. 4.95 (978-0-8395-3106-7(0)) Boy Scouts of America.

Bryan, Roy. Aid to Patrol Leadership. 3rd ed. 2001. (Illus.). 110p. (J). pap. (978-0-9711543-0-8(9)) Corinthian Enterprise Co.

Calvert, Patricia. Kit Carson: He Led the Way. 2006. (Great Explorations Ser.). (Illus.). 80p. (J). lib. bdg. 32.79 (978-0-7614-2223-5(4) , Benchmark Bks.) Cavendish, Marshall Corp.

DK Publishing Staff. Century of Scouting: Cub Scout Activity Series. 2007. (J). (gr. 12). pap. 2.49 (*978-0-7566-3306-6(0)) Dorling Kindersley Publishing, Inc.

Kalar, Bonnie. The Scouts. Spreen, Kathe, illus. Date not set. 8p. (J). (ps-2). pap. (978-1-891619-26-7(8)) Corona Pr.

Palmer, Rosemary Gudmundson. Jim Bridger: Trapper, Trader, & Guide. 2006. (J). (978-0-7565-1870-7(9)) Compass Point Bks.

Studio 2b: Focus - Express It. 2004. (YA). pap. (978-0-88441-671-5(2)) Girl Scouts of the USA.

Studio 2b Focus - Don't Sweat It. 2004. (YA). pap. (978-0-88441-669-2(0)) Girl Scouts of the USA.

Studio 2b Focus - Mind Your Own Business. 2004. (YA). pap. (978-0-88441-668-5(2)) Girl Scouts of the USA.

STUDIO 2B Guide for Councils Phase II: Strategies & Models. 2004. (YA). (978-0-88441-686-9(0)) Girl Scouts of the USA.

Wiese, Jim & Melton, H. Keith. The Spy's Guide to Scouting & Reconnaissance. 2003. (Illus.). 48p. (J). (978-0-439-33647-5(3)) Scholastic, Inc.

SCOUTS AND SCOUTING—FICTION

Berenstain, Stan & Berenstain, Jan. The Berenstain Bear Scouts & the Evil Eye. 1998. (Berenstain Bear Scouts Ser.). (J). (gr. 3-6). pap. 3.99 (978-0-590-94488-5(6) , Scholastic Paperbacks) Scholastic, Inc.

—The Berenstain Bear Scouts & the Missing Merit Badges. 1998. (Berenstain Bear Scouts Ser.). (Illus.). 32p. (J). (gr. 3-6). pap. 3.50 (978-0-590-56390-1(4)) Scholastic, Inc.

—The Berenstain Bear Scouts & the Missing Merit Badges. 1998. (Berenstain Bear Scouts Ser.). (J). (gr. 3-6). (978-0-606-13191-9(4)) Tandem Library Bks.

—The Berenstain Bear Scouts & the Really Big Disaster. 1998. (Berenstain Bear Scouts Ser.). (Illus.). 32p. (J). (gr. 3-6). pap. 3.99 (978-0-590-94481-6(9) , Scholastic Paperbacks) Scholastic, Inc.

—The Berenstain Bear Scouts & the Ripoff Queen. 1998. (Berenstain Bear Scouts Ser.). (Illus.). 112p. (J). (gr. 3-6). pap. 3.99 (978-0-590-94493-9(2)) Scholastic, Inc.

—The Berenstain Bear Scouts & the Search for Naughty Ned. 1998. (Berenstain Bear Scouts Ser.). (Illus.). 32p. (J). (gr. 3-6). pap. 3.50 (978-0-590-56509-7(5)) Scholastic, Inc.

—The Berenstain Bear Scouts & the Search for Naughty Ned. 1998. (Berenstain Bear Scouts Ser.). (J). (gr. 3-6). (978-0-606-13193-3(0)) Tandem Library Bks.

—The Berenstain Bear Scouts & the Stinky Milk Mystery. 1999. (Berenstain Bear Scouts Ser.). (Illus.). 32p. (J). (gr. 3-6). pap. 3.50 (978-0-590-56524-0(9) , Cartwheel Bks.) Scholastic, Inc.

—The Berenstain Bear Scouts & the Stinky Milk Mystery. 1999. (Berenstain Bear Scouts Ser.). (J). (gr. 3-6). (978-0-606-16597-6(5)) Tandem Library Bks.

—The Berenstain Bear Scouts & the White-Water Mystery. 1999. (Berenstain Bear Scouts Ser.). 32p. (J). (gr. 3-6). pap. 3.50 (978-0-590-56522-6(2)) Scholastic, Inc.

—The Berenstain Bear Scouts & the White-Water Mystery. 1999. (Berenstain Bear Scouts Ser.). (J). (gr. 3-6). (978-0-606-16598-3(3)) Tandem Library Bks.

—The Berenstain Bear Scouts Scream Their Heads Off. 1998. (Berenstain Bear Scouts Ser.). (Illus.). 32p. (J). (gr. 3-6). pap. 3.99 (978-0-590-94484-7(3) , Scholastic Paperbacks) Scholastic, Inc.

—The Berenstain Bear Scouts Scream Their Heads Off. 1998. (Berenstain Bear Scouts Ser.). (J). (gr. 3-6). (978-0-606-13194-0(9)) Tandem Library Bks.

—Los Osos Scouts Berenstain y el Desastre Colosal. 1998. (Berenstain Bear Scouts Ser.).Tr. of Berenstain Bear Scouts & the Really Big Disaster. (SPA.). (J). (gr. 3-6). pap. 3.50 (978-0-590-94482-3(7) , Scholastic Paperbacks) Scholastic, Inc.

Delton, Judy. Molly for Mayor. 1999. (Pee Wee Scouts Ser.: No. 39). (J). (gr. 2-5). (978-0-606-18787-9(1)) Tandem Library Bks.

—Pedal Power. Tiegreen, Alan, illus. 1998. (Pee Wee Scouts Ser.: No. 35). (J). (gr. 2-5). (978-0-606-13700-3(9)) Tandem Library Bks.

—Send in the Clowns! 1999. (Pee Wee Scouts Ser.: No. 38). (J). (gr. 2-5). (978-0-606-16713-0(7)) Tandem Library Bks.

—Wild, Wild West. 1999. (Pee Wee Scouts Ser.: No. 37). (J). (gr. 2-5). (978-0-606-16585-3(1)) Tandem Library Bks.

GSUSA Staff. Octavia's Girl Scout Journey Activity Guide. 2001. (978-0-88441-624-1(0)) Girl Scouts of the USA.

Welcom to the Nature Scouts. 2003. (J). per. (978-1-57657-874-2(7)) Paradise Pr., Inc.

SCRIPTURES, HOLY

see Bible

SCROOGE, EBENEZER (FICTITIOUS CHARACTER)—FICTION

Barks, Carl, et al. Uncle Scrooge, No. 352. 2006. 64p. pap. 6.95 (978-1-888472-22-6(7)) Gemstone Publishing, Inc.

—Uncle Scrooge #349. 2006. 64p. pap. 6.95 (978-1-888472-13-4(8)) Gemstone Publishing, Inc.

—Uncle Scrooge #351. 2006. 64p. pap. 6.95 (978-1-888472-15-8(4)) Gemstone Publishing, Inc.

A Christmas Carol. 2004. (J). cd-rom 7.99 (978-0-9740847-9-4(4)) GiGi Bks.

A Christmas Carol. 2003. (Illus.). 32p. (J). 9.98 (978-1-4054-0997-1(5)); 4.98 (978-1-4054-0980-3(0)) Parragon, Inc.

Dickens, Charles. A Christmas Carol. Blake, Quentin, illus. 2001. 160p. (J). pap. 8.99 (978-1-86205-130-0(5) , Pavilion Bks., Ltd.) Anova Bks. GBR. *Dist:* Trafalgar Square Publishing.

—A Christmas Carol. Wheatcroft, Andrew, illus. 2006. (Read & Listen Bks.). 64p. (J). 9.99 (978-0-7566-1831-5(2)) Dorling Kindersley Publishing, Inc.

—A Christmas Carol. Morrissey, Dean, illus. 2001. 80p. (J). (gr. 2-5). 17.89 (978-0-06-028578-4(8)) HarperCollins Pubs.

—A Christmas Carol. Zwerger, Lisbeth, illus. 2001. (ENG & GER.). 72p. (J). (ps up). 19.95 (978-0-7358-1259-8(4)) North-South Bks., Inc.

—A Christmas Carol. 2004. 224p. (YA). pap. 29.00 incl. audio (978-1-4000-9005-1(9) , Listening Library) Random Hse. Audio Publishing Group.

—A Christmas Carol. 2000. (Illus.). 144p. (J). (gr. 4-7). pap. 5.99 (978-0-439-10133-2(6)) Scholastic, Inc.

—A Christmas Carol. 1998. (Children's Classics). (ENG., Illus.). 96p. (YA). (ps up). pap. (978-1-85326-121-3(1) , 1211WW) Wordsworth Editions, Ltd.

—A Christmas Carol. 2003. (Illus.). 48p. (978-0-7502-3666-9(3) , Hodder Wayland) Hodder Children's Division.

—A Christmas Carol. Lo Famia, Jon, illus. 2nd ed. 1998. (Illustrated Classic Book Ser.: Vol. III). 61p. (J). reprint ed. pap. 4.95 (978-1-56767-241-1(8)) Educational Insights, Inc.

—A Christmas Carol. Stemach, Jerry et al, eds. Ham, Jeff, illus. l.t. ed. 2000. (Start-to-Finish? Books: Vol. 6). 116p. (J). pap. 65.00 incl. audio, cd-rom (978-1-58702-395-8(4)) Johnston, Don Inc.

—A Christmas Carol. l.t. ed. 1999. (Large Print Heritage Ser.). 140p. (YA). (gr. 7-12). lib. bdg. 24.95 (978-1-58118-041-1(1) , 22510) LRS.

—A Christmas Carol, Level 2. 2001. (Illus.). v, 38p. (C). pap. 9.00 (978-0-582-42120-2(9)) Longman Publishing Group.

—A Christmas Carol. abr. ed. 2001. (Illus.). 144p. pap. 4.99 (978-0-14-230055-8(1) , Puffin) Penguin Group (USA) Inc.

—A Christmas Carol. unabr. ed. 2002. (YA). pap. 45.00 incl. audio compact disk (978-1-58472-229-8(0) , In Audio) Sound Room Pubs., Inc.

Dickens, Charles & Birmingham, Christian. A Christmas Carol. 2000. (Miniature Editionstm Ser.). (Illus.). 128p. (gr. 4-7). 4.95 (978-0-7624-0831-3(6) , Running Pr. Miniature Editions) Running Pr. Bk. Pubs.

Dickens, Charles & Innocenti, Roberto. A Christmas Carol. 2005. (Illus.). 152p. 35.00 (978-1-56846-182-3(8)) Creative Co., The.

Dickens, Charles & Sims, L. A Christmas Carol. (Young Reading Ser.: Vol. 2). 64p. (J). (gr. 2 up). lib. bdg. 13.95 (978-1-58086-790-0(1) , Usborne) EDC Publishing.

Dickens, Charles & Skarmeas, Nancy J. A Christmas Carol. Flint, Russ, illus. abr. ed. 1998. 48p. (J). (gr. 4-7). 14.00 (978-0-8249-4096-6(2) , Candy Cane Pr.) Ideals Pubns.

Dickens, Charles & Wheatcroft, Andrew. A Christmas Carol. 2000. (Read & Listen Ser.). (Illus.). 64p. (J). pap. incl. cd-rom (978-0-7894-6363-0(6)) Dorling Kindersley Publishing, Inc.

Resnick, Jane Parker. A Christmas Carol: A Young Reader's Edition of the Classic Holiday Tale. Birmingham, Christian, illus. 2000. (Courage Children's Ser.). 56p. (J). (gr. 4-7). 9.98 (978-0-7624-0848-1(0) , Courage Bks.) Running Pr. Bk. Pubs.

Rosa, Don, et al. Uncle Scrooge #350. 2006. 64p. pap. 6.95 (978-1-888472-14-1(6)) Gemstone Publishing, Inc.

SCUBA DIVING

Here are entered works on free diving with the use of a self-contained underwater breathing apparatus. Works on free diving with the use of mask, fins and snorkel are entered under Skin Diving.

Giacobello, John. Scuba Divers: Life under Water. 2005. (Extreme Careers Ser.). (Illus.). 64p. (J). (gr. 5-8). 26.50 (978-0-8239-3368-6(7)) Rosen Publishing Group, Inc., The.

Gilkerson, Patricia. My Adventure Scuba Diving. 2006. 44p. (J). 8.99 (978-1-59092-286-6(7) , Orchard Academy Pr.) Windstorm Creative.

Huntrods, David. For the Love of Scuba. 2006. (For the Love of Sports Ser.). (978-1-59036-382-9(5)); (978-1-59036-383-6(3)) Weigl Pubs., Inc.

Lopatka, Michael. Scuba Divers Sign Language: A Guide to Underwater Communications of Tropical Reef Inhabitants. 2003. (Illus.). 75p. 12.95 (978-0-9723218-9-1(6) , 0-9723218-9-6) Awesome Guides, Inc.

Mason, Paul. Snorkeling & Diving. 2007. (J). (*978-1-59920-128-3(3)) Smart Apple Media.

Ryback, Carol. Scuba Diving. 2005. (Illus.). 24p. (J). pap. (978-0-8368-4549-5(8)); (YA). lib. bdg. 22.00 (978-0-8368-4542-6(0)) Stevens, Gareth Inc.

SCULPTORS

Burby, Liza N. A Day in the Life of a Sculptor. 1999. (Kids' Career Library). (Illus.). 24p. (J). (gr. 3). lib. bdg. 18.75 (978-0-8239-5305-9(X) , PowerKids Pr.) Rosen Publishing Group, Inc., The.

Connolly, Sean. Henry Moore. 2006. (Heinemann First Library). (Illus.). 32p. (J). lib. bdg. (*978-1-4034-8491-8(0)) Heinemann Library.

Di Cagno, Gabriella. Michelangelo. 2008. (YA). lib. bdg. 24.95 net. (*978-1-934545-01-0(5)) Oliver Pr., Inc.

FitzGerald, Dawn. Vinnie & Abraham. Stock, Catherine, illus. 2007. 48p. (J). (gr. k-3). 15.95 (978-1-57091-658-8(6)) Charlesbridge Publishing, Inc.

Harcourt School Publishers Staff. Stefan the Sculptor Advanced Level. 3rd ed. 2002. (Trophies Reading Program Ser.). (Illus.). pap. 5.10 (978-0-15-323021-9(5)) Harcourt Schl. Pubs.

—Trofeos Advanced Level: Stefan Es Escultor. 3rd ed. 2002. (SPA., Illus.). pap. 6.80 (978-0-15-323932-8(8)) Harcourt Schl. Pubs.

Morrison, Taylor. The Buffalo Nickel. Morrison, Taylor, illus. 2006. (Illus.). 32p. (J). (gr. 4-8). reprint ed. 16.00 (*978-1-4223-5858-0(5)) DIANE Publishing Co.

—The Buffalo Nickel. 2002. (Illus.). 32p. (J). (gr. 1-5). 16.00 (978-0-618-10855-8(6) , Walter Lorraine) Houghton Mifflin Co. Trade & Reference Div.

Oliver, Clare. Henry Moore. 2003. (gr. 5-8). lib. bdg. 15.25 (978-0-613-59496-7(7)) Tandem Library Bks.

Oliver, Clare & O'Reilly, Sally. Henry Moore. 2003. (Artists in Their Time Ser.). (Illus.). 48p. (J). (gr. 5-7). pap. 6.95 (978-0-531-16643-7(0) , Watts, Franklin) Scholastic Library Publishing.

O'Reilly, Sally. Henry Moore. 2003. (Artists in Their Time Ser.). (Illus.). 48p. (J). 23.50 (978-0-531-12241-9(7) , Watts, Franklin) Scholastic Library Publishing.

Richard Tames. Auguste Rodin. 2nd ed. 2006. (Heinemann First Library). (Illus.). 32p. (J). pap. (*978-1-4034-8499-4(6)) Heinemann Library.

Schaefer, A. R. Alexander Calder. (Life & Work of. . . Ser.). (Illus.). 32p. (J). (gr. k-2). 2003. lib. bdg. 22.79 (978-1-4034-0287-5(6)); 2002. pap. 6.50 (978-1-4034-0493-0(3)) Heinemann Library.

Shea, Pegi Deitz. Patience Wright: America's First Sculptor, & Revolutionary Spy. Andersen, Bethanne, illus. 2007. (J). (*978-1-4287-3694-8(8)) Holt, Henry & Co.

Stone, Amy. Maya Lin. 2003. (Raintree Biographies Ser.). (Illus.). 32p. (J). lib. bdg. 25.70 (978-0-7398-6863-8(2)) Raintree.

—Maya Lin. 2003. (gr. 3-6). lib. bdg. 15.90 (978-0-613-78165-7(1)) Tandem Library Bks.

Tames, Richard. Auguste Rodin. (Heinemann First Library). 32p. (J). 2006. (Illus.). lib. bdg. (*978-1-4034-8488-8(0)); 2000. lib. bdg. 21.36 (978-1-57572-342-6(5)); Set 1. 2002. (Illus.). pap. 6.50 (978-1-58810-288-1(2) , 91051) Heinemann Library.

Tiger, Caroline & Noguchi, Isamu. Isamu Noguchi. 2007. (Asian Americans of Achievement Ser.). (Illus.). 112p. (J). (gr. 6-12). 30.00 (978-0-7910-9276-7(3) , Chelsea Hse.) Facts On File, Inc.

Wallis, Jeremy. Henry Moore. 2001. (Creative Lives Ser.). (J). 26.50 (978-1-58810-204-1(1)) Heinemann Library.

SCULPTORS—FICTION

Bedard, Michael. The Clay Ladies. braille ed. 2004. (J). (gr. k-3). spiral bd. (978-0-616-01544-5(5)) Canadian National Institute for the Blind/Institut National Canadien pour les Aveugles.

—The Clay Ladies. 2001. (978-0-606-21845-0(9)) Tandem Library Bks.

Harcourt School Publishers Staff. The Masterpiece: Take-Home Book. 2001. (Collections Ser.). (Illus.). (J). pap. 1.90 (978-0-15-319499-3(5)) Harcourt Schl. Pubs.

Sappey, Maureen. Letters from Vinnie. 2007. 248p. (J). (gr. 4-6). pap. 10.95 (*978-1-59078-538-6(X)) Boyds Mills Pr.

Stanley, Diane. The Trouble with Wishes. Stanley, Diane, illus. 2007. (Illus.). 32p. (J). (gr. 2-4). 16.99 (978-0-06-055451-4(7) , HarperCollins); lib. bdg. 17.89 (978-0-06-055452-1(5)) HarperCollins Pubs.

Wishinsky, Frieda. Each One Special. (gr. k-3). 2001. lib. bdg. 16.40 (978-0-613-33891-2(X)); 2000. (J). 14.75 (978-0-606-20203-9(X)) Tandem Library Bks.

SCULPTURE

see also Bronzes; Mobiles (Sculpture); Modeling; Monuments

Bryant, Lorinda Munson. Childrens Book of Celebrated Sculpture. 2006. pap. 19.95 (*978-1-4304-4158-8(5)) Kessinger Publishing, LLC.

Bryant, Lorinda Munson. The Children's Book of Celebrated Sculpture. 2005. reprint ed. pap. 19.95 (978-1-4179-0273-6(6)) Kessinger Publishing, LLC.

Burby, Liza N. A Day in the Life of a Sculptor. 1999. (Kids' Career Library). (Illus.). 24p. (J). (gr. 3). lib. bdg. 18.75 (978-0-8239-5305-9(X) , PowerKids Pr.) Rosen Publishing Group, Inc., The.

Civardi, Anne. What Is a Sculpture? 2005. (Illus.). 30p. (J). (gr. 3-7). lib. bdg. 27.10 (978-1-932889-87-1(6)) Sea-To-Sea Pubns.

Civardi, Annie. Sculpture: Three Dimensions in Art. 2005. (Artventures Ser.). (Illus.). 32p. (J). (gr. 4-7). lib. bdg. 27.10 (978-1-58340-624-3(7)) Smart Apple Media.

Dean, Arlan. Terra-Cotta Soldiers: Army of Stone. 2005. (High Interest Bks.). (Illus.). 48p. (YA). (gr. 7-12). pap. 6.95 (978-0-516-25093-9(0) , Children's Pr.) Scholastic Library Publishing.

Fritz, Jean. Leonardo's Horse. Talbott, Hudson, illus. 2001. 48p. (J). (gr. 1-6). 18.99 (978-0-399-23576-4(0) , Putnam Juvenile) Penguin Group (USA) Inc.

Herr, Joelle. Crazy Cat Lady: A Magnetic Sculpture Kit. 2007. 32p. pap. 6.95 (978-0-7624-2974-5(7) , Running Pr. Miniature Editions) Running Pr. Bk. Pubs.

Jakab, Cheryl. Stone. 2006. (Illus.). 32p. (J). (978-1-58340-779-0(0)) Smart Apple Media.

Krempel, Ulrich. Niki's World: Niki de Saint Phalle. 2004. (Adventures in Art Ser.). (Illus.). 30p. (J). 14.95 (978-3-7913-3068-6(3)) Prestel Publishing.

May, S. & Whitely, H. Shape. 2004. (Children's Art Ser. from the National Gallery of Victoria Ser.). (Illus.). 28p. 9.95 (978-0-7241-0239-6(0)) National Gallery of Victoria AUS. *Dist:* Antique Collectors' Club.

Nardo, Don. Sculpture. 2006. (Eye on Art Ser.). 112p. (J). (gr. 7-10). 32.45 (978-1-59018-966-5(3) , Lucent Bks.) Thomson Gale.

QEB Let's Start! Art National Book Stores Edition: Sculpture. 2006. (J). per. (978-1-59566-302-3(9)) QEB Publishing Inc.

Raczka, Bob. 3-D ABC: A Sculptural Alphabet. 2006. (Bob Raczka's Art Adventures Ser.). (Illus.). 32p. (J). (gr. k-3). lib. bdg. 23.93 (978-0-7613-9456-3(7) , Millbrook Pr.) Lerner Publishing Group.

Roca, Nuria. Que Es el Arte? Pintura y Escultura. 2004. (Libros Que Es el Arte? Ser.). (SPA.). 36p. (J). pap. 6.95 (978-0-7641-2704-5(7)) Barron's Educational Series, Inc.

SCULPTURE—FICTION

Campos, Tito. Muffler Man/el hombre Mofle. Vigil-Pion, Evangelina, tr. Alvarez, Lamberto & Alvarez, Beto, illus. 2001. Tr. of Hombre Mofle. (ENG & SPA.). 32p. (J). (ps-3). 14.95 (978-1-55885-318-8(9) , Piñata Books) Arte Publico Pr.

Dadey, Debbie & Jones, Marcia Thornton. Dragons Don't Throw Snowballs. Gurney, John Steven, illus. 2006. (Little Apple Ser.). 75p. (J). (978-1-4156-4913-8(8)) Scholastic, Inc.

Fisher, Marcy Heller. The Outdoor Museum: The Magic of Michigan's Marshall M. Fredericks. Woomer, Christine Collins, illus. 2001. (Great Lakes Bks.). 72p. (J). (gr. 3-7). 18.95 (978-0-8143-2969-6(1) , Great Lakes Bks.); 29.95 (978-0-8143-2932-0(2)) Wayne State Univ. Pr.

Lee, Ingrid. Dragon Tide. Meister, Soizik, illus. 2006. 32p. (ps-2). 17.95 (978-1-55143-352-3(4)) Orca Bk. Pubs. USA.

Reynolds, Aaron. Metal Man. Hoppe, Paul, illus. 2008. (J). (*978-1-58089-150-9(0)) Charlesbridge Publishing, Inc.

Whalen, Sharla Scannell. Best Friends under the Sun. 2000. (Faithful Friends Ser.). (Illus.). 64p. (J). (gr. 4). lib. bdg. 21.35 (978-1-57765-228-1(2) , ABDO & Daughters) ABDO Publishing Co.

SCULPTURE—HISTORY

Harcourt School Publishers Staff. The Elgin Marbles. 3rd ed. 2002. (Horizons Ser.). (Illus.). (J). pap. 7.30 (978-0-15-333622-5(6)) Harcourt Schl. Pubs.

Patent, Dorothy Hinshaw. The Incredible Story of China's Buried Warriors. 2000. (Frozen in Time Ser.). (Illus.). (J). (gr. 5-9). lib. bdg. 27.07 (978-0-7614-0783-6(9) , Benchmark Bks.) Cavendish, Marshall Corp.

SCULPTURE, RELIGIOUS
see Christian Art and Symbolism

SCULPTURE—TECHNIQUE
see also Modeling

Cranium. Super Sculpting. 2007. (Play It Again Book Ser.). (Illus.). 44p. (J). (gr. 1). 9.99 ***(978-0-316-01205-8(X))*** Little, Brown Bks. for Young Readers.

Cranium Inc. Staff. The Cranium Ultimate Book of Fantastic Fun & Games. 2007. 54p. (J). (ps-3). 19.99 ***(978-0-316-01208-9(4))*** Little, Brown Bks. for Young Readers.

Luxbacher, Irene. 123 I Can Sculpt! 2007. (Starting Art Ser.). 24p. (J). (ps-2). pap. ***(978-1-55453-151-6(9))*** Kids Can Pr., Ltd.

—123 I Can Sculpt! Luxbacher, Irene, illus. 2007. (Starting Art Ser.). (Illus.). 23p. (J). (ps-2). ***(978-1-55453-038-0(5))*** Kids Can Pr., Ltd.

Reid, Barbara. Fun with Modeling Clay. Reid, Barbara, illus. 1998. (Kids Can Do It Ser.). (Illus.). 134p. (J). (gr. 4-6). (978-1-55074-510-8(7)) Kids Can Pr., Ltd.

Thomas, Isabel. Action Art: Sculpting. 2005. (Heinemann Read & Learn Ser.). (Illus.). 24p. (J). (978-1-4034-6921-2(0)); pap. (978-1-4034-6927-4(X)) Heinemann Library.

Watt, Fiona. Complete Book of Art Ideas. 2005. (Art Ideas Ser.). 288p. (J). 39.95 (978-0-7945-0900-2(2) , Usborne) EDC Publishing.

SEA
see Ocean

SEA ANIMALS
see Marine Animals

SEA FISHERIES
see Fisheries

SEA HORSES

Berger, Melvin & Berger, Gilda. Caballitos de Mar: Sea Horses. 2006. (SPA & ENG., Illus.). (J). ***(978-0-439-87988-0(4))*** Scholastic, Inc.

Butterworth, Christine. Sea Horse: The Shyest Fish in the Sea. Lawrence, John, illus. 2006. 32p. (J). (ps-3). 16.99 (978-0-7636-2989-2(8)) Candlewick Pr.

Clinging Sea Horses 6-Pack. 2004. (Illus.). (J). lib. bdg. 39.99 (978-0-8225-5192-8(6)) Lerner Publishing Group.

Coldiron, Deborah. Sea Horses. 2007. (Underwater World Ser.). (ENG., Illus.). 32p. (J). (gr. k-4). lib. bdg. 24.21 ***(978-1-59928-821-5(4)*** , Buddy Bks.) ABDO Publishing Co.

George, Twig C. Seahorses. (ps-ps). 2005. (Illus.). 31p. (J). pap. 8.95 (978-0-8225-3390-0(1)); 2003. 32p. lib. bdg. 24.90 (978-0-7613-2869-8(6) , Millbrook Pr.) Lerner Publishing Group.

Gilkerson, Patricia. My Adventure with Sea Horses. 2007. 44p. (J). 8.99 (978-1-59092-465-5(7) , Orchard Academy Pr.) Windstorm Creative.

Herriges, Ann. Sea Horses. 2006. (Blastoff! Readers Ser.). (Illus.). 24p. (J). (gr. k-3). lib. bdg. 16.95 (978-1-60014-020-4(3)) Bellwether Media.

Hirschmann, Kris. Sea Horses. 2004. (Illus.). (gr. 4-7). 26.20 (978-0-7377-2344-1(0)) Thomson Gale.

Is it a Fish? 6 Each of 1, 6 vols. (Sunshinetm Science Ser.). 24p. (gr. 1-2). 41.95 (978-0-7802-1428-6(5)) Wright Group, The.

Is it a Fish? Big Book. (Sunshinetm Science Ser.). 24p. (gr. 1-2). 37.50 (978-0-7802-1429-3(3)) Wright Group, The.

James, Sylvia M. Seahorses. 2002. (Illus.). 24p. (J). (gr. k-3). pap. 6.00 (978-1-59034-034-9(5)) Mondo Publishing.

Jango-Cohen, Judith. Clinging Sea Horses. (Pull Ahead Bks.). (Illus.). 32p. (gr. k-3). 2005. lib. bdg. 22.60 (978-0-8225-3764-9(8)); 2003. (J). pap. 5.95 (978-0-8225-3767-0(2)) Lerner Publishing Group.

—Clinging Sea Horses. 2001. (gr. k-3). lib. bdg. 14.10 (978-0-613-58828-7(2)) Tandem Library Bks.

Kalman, Bobbie. The Life Cycle of a Sea Horse. 2004. (Life Cycle Ser.). (Illus.). 32p. (J). (978-0-7787-0663-2(X)); pap. (978-0-7787-0693-9(1)) Crabtree Publishing Co.

Landau, Elaine. Sea Horses. 1999. (True Bks.). (Illus.). 48p. (J). (gr. 3-5). pap. 6.95 (978-0-516-26503-2(2) , Children's Pr.) Scholastic Library Publishing.

Lindeen, Carol. Caballitos de Mar: Sea Horses. 2007. (SPA.). 24p. (J). ***(978-0-7368-7647-6(2))*** Capstone Pr., Inc.

Lindeen, Carol K. Sea Horses. 2005. (Under the Sea Ser.). (Illus.). 24p. (J). 19.93 (978-0-7368-3662-3(4)) Capstone Pr., Inc.

Otfinoski, Steven. Seahorses. 2007. (Animals Animals Ser.). 48p. (J). (gr. 4-7). lib. bdg. 28.50 (978-0-7614-2529-8(2)) Cavendish, Marshall Corp.

Rhodes, Mary Jo & Hall, David. Seahorses & Sea Dragons. 2006. (Undersea Encounters Ser.). (Illus.). 48p. (J). (gr. 3-5). pap. 6.95 (978-0-516-25351-0(4) , Children's Pr.) Scholastic Library Publishing.

—Seahorses & Sea Dragons. Hall, David, photos by. 2005. (Undersea Encounters Ser.). (Illus.). 48p. (J). (ps-7). 27.00 (978-0-516-24393-1(4) , Children's Pr.) Scholastic Library Publishing.

Schaefer, Lola M. El Caballito de Mar. 2002. (Animales Acorazados (Musty-Crusty Animals) Ser.). (SPA.). 24p. (J). (ps-1). lib. bdg. 18.50 (978-1-58810-858-6(9)); (Illus.). pap. 5.25 (978-1-58810-820-3(1) , 91557) Heinemann Library.

—Musty-Crusty Animals 123. 2002. (Musty-Crusty Animals Ser.). (Illus.). 24p. (J). (ps-1). pap. 5.25 (978-1-58810-728-2(0) , 91379); lib. bdg. 17.08 (978-1-58810-519-6(9)) Heinemann Library.

—Musty-Crusty Animals ABC. 2002. (Musty-Crusty Animals Ser.). (Illus.). 24p. (J). (ps-1). pap. 5.25 (978-1-58810-727-5(2) , 91380); lib. bdg. 17.08 (978-1-58810-518-9(0)) Heinemann Library.

—Sea Horses, Vol. 2. 2005. (Ocean Life Ser.). 24p. (YA). (gr. k-3). pap. (978-0-7368-8220-0(0) , Pebble Bks.) Capstone Pr., Inc.

Sea Horses, 6 vols. (gr. k-2). 28.95 (978-0-7368-8260-6(X)) Red Brick Learning.

Sea Horses Oceans Alive. 2006. (Illus.). 24p. (J). (gr. k-2). 18.50 ***(978-0-531-17872-0(2))*** Scholastic Library Publishing.

Seahorse. 2000. (Portable Pets Ser.). (Illus.). 12p. (J). (ps). bds. 6.95 (978-0-8109-5659-4(4)) Abrams, Harry N., Inc.

Walker, Sally M. Sea Horses. (Early Bird Nature Bks.). (Illus.). (J). 2004. 47p. 25.26 (978-0-8225-3051-0(1) , Lerner Pubns.); 1999. 48p. (gr. 3-6). lib. bdg. 25.26 (978-1-57505-317-2(9) , Carolrhoda Bks.) Lerner Publishing Group.

Wyllie, Jim. Cedric the Seahorse. Wyllie, Margaret, illus. 2001. 24p. (J). (ps-3). 7.95 (978-1-85149-709-6(9)) Antique Collectors' Club.

SEA HORSES—FICTION

Blackstone, Stella. Secret Seahorse. Beaton, Clare, illus. 2005. (ps-ps). lib. bdg. 14.19 (978-0-606-33158-6(1)) Tandem Library Bks.

Carle, Eric. Mister Seahorse. Carle, Eric, illus. 2004. (Illus.). 32p. (J). (ps-2). 17.99 (978-0-399-24269-4(4) , Philomel) Penguin Group (USA) Inc.

Lee, Julia Elizabeth. Seahorses Down Under. Weiser, Robert, ed. (Defenders of Wildlife Ser.). (Illus.). 50+p. (J). (gr. k-3). lib. bdg. 9.95 (978-0-9666857-0-1(9)) Dawn of Day Childrens Publishing Co., Inc.

Salzmann, Mary Elizabeth. Sea Horse Races. Nobens, C. A., illus. 2007. (Fact & Fiction Ser.). 24p. (J). pap. (978-1-59928-469-9(3)); 21.35 (978-1-59928-468-2(5)) ABDO Publishing Co.

Smiley, Minerva J. Billy's Search for Florida Undersea Treasure. Smiley, Russ, illus. 2002. 44p. (J). lib. bdg. 16.95 (978-0-89317-047-9(X) , RS-047X, Windward Publishing) Finney Co., Inc.

Steele, Margaret. Wuz Da Nite Befo: A Pidgin Christmas Story in Hawaii. Chang, Roy, illus. 2005. 24p. 10.95 (978-1-56647-750-5(6)) Mutual Publishing LLC.

Voyage to Shelter Cove. 2006. (Illus.). (J). pap., act. bk. ed. 2.00 (978-0-9724425-5-8(3) , White Tiger Pr.) Homes for the Homeless, Inc.

Walker, Sally M. Seahorse Reef: A Story of the South Pacific. Petruccio, Steven James, illus. 2005. 32p. (J). (ps-2). pap. 6.95 (978-1-56899-938-8(0) , S4020) Soundprints.

Wyllie, Jim & Wyllie, Miggie. Cedric's Day at the Castle. 2003. (Illus.). 24p. (J). (ps-1). pap. 7.95 (978-1-85149-712-6(9)) Antique Collectors' Club.

SEA IN ART
see Marine Painting

SEA LIFE
see Seafaring Life
also names of countries with the subhead Navy, e.g., United States—Navy

SEA LIONS
see Seals (Animals)

SEA MOSSES
see Algae

SEA POETRY
see also Sea Songs

Anderson, Sara. Octopus Oyster Hermit Crab Snail: A Poem of the Sea. 2005. (Illus.). 32p. (J). (gr. 1-3). 16.95 (978-1-59354-079-1(5)) Handprint Bks.

Sturges, Philemon. Down to the Sea in Ships. Laroche, Giles, illus. 2005. 32p. (J). (ps-3). 16.99 (978-0-399-23464-4(0) , Putnam Juvenile) Penguin Group (USA) Inc.

SEA POWER
see also Disarmament; Naval History; Warships
also names of countries with the subhead Navy or the subdivision History, Naval, e.g. United States—Navy; United States—History, Naval, etc.

Mueller, Richard. Naval Warfare of the Future. 2005. (Library of Future Weaponry). (Illus.). 64p. (YA). (978-1-4042-0526-0(8)) Rosen Publishing Group, Inc., The.

SEA ROUTES
see Trade Routes

SEA SHELLS
see Shells

SEA SHORE
see Seashore

SEA SONGS

Bullen, Frank T. Songs of Sea Labour Chanties. 2001. 35p. (YA). reprint ed. 88.00 (978-0-7222-6110-1(1)) Library Reprints, Inc.

King, Stanton H. King's Book of Chanties. 2001. 26p. (YA). reprint ed. 88.00 (978-0-7222-6111-8(X)) Library Reprints, Inc.

Marston, George W. Shanties: Tunes by Doris Allen. 2001. (YA). reprint ed. 150.00 (978-0-7222-6112-5(8)) Library Reprints, Inc.

Rouse, William H. D. Latin Chanties Written for Ancient Traditional Airs. 2001. 31p. (YA). reprint ed. 88.00 (978-0-7222-6113-2(6)) Library Reprints, Inc.

Terry, Richard R. The Shanty Book: Sailor Shanties, 2 vols., set. 2001. (YA). reprint ed. 250.00 (978-0-7222-6116-3(0)) Library Reprints, Inc.

Whall, W. B. Ships, Sea Songs & Shanties. 2001. 131p. (YA). reprint ed. 88.00 (978-0-7222-6117-0(9)) Library Reprints, Inc.

SEA STORIES

Abbott, Tony. Pirates of the Purple Dawn. 2007. (Secrets of Droon Ser.: No. 29). 128p. (J). pap. 3.99 (978-0-439-90250-2(9) , Scholastic Paperbacks) Scholastic, Inc.

Ardizzone, Edward. Little Tim & the Brave Sea Captain. Ardizzone, Edward, illus. 2000. (Tim Bks.). (Illus.). 48p. (J). (ps-3). 15.95 (978-0-688-17678-5(X)) HarperCollins Pubs.

—Ship's Cook Ginger. 2008. (Illus.). 48p. (J). 16.95 ***(978-1-84507-574-3(9))*** Lincoln, Frances Ltd. GBR. *Dist:* Perseus Distribution.

—Tims Friend Towser. 2000. (J). 15.89 (978-0-06-029205-8(9)) HarperCollins Pubs.

Ardizzone, Edward. Tims Friend Towser. 2008. (Illus.). 48p. (J). 16.95 ***(978-1-84507-560-6(9))*** Lincoln, Frances Ltd. GBR. *Dist:* Perseus Distribution.

Avi. The True Confessions of Charlotte Doyle. Murray, Ruth E., illus. 1999. 239p. (J). 17.90 (978-0-03-054709-6(1)) Holt, Rinehart & Winston.

—The True Confessions of Charlotte Doyle. l.t. ed. 2005. 337p. pap. 10.95 (978-0-7862-7252-5(X) , Large Print Pr.) Thorndike Pr.

Babbitt, Natalie. The Eyes of the Amaryllis. 2007. 144p. (J). pap. 6.99 ***(978-0-312-37008-4(3))*** Square Fish.

Barbour, Ralph Henry. The Adventure Club Afloat. 2006. 78.99 ***(978-1-4280-1948-5(0))*** IndyPublish.com.

Bledsoe, Glen & Bledsoe, Karen, compiled by. Classic Sea Stories. 1999. (Roxbury Park Bks.). (Illus.). 123p. (J). (gr. 3-7). pap. 5.95 (978-0-7373-0041-3(8) , 00418W) McGraw-Hill/Contemporary.

Brown, Margaret Wise. The Sailor Dog. Williams, Garth, illus. 2001. (Little Golden Bks.). 24p. (J). (gr. k-k). 2.99 (978-0-307-00143-6(1) , 98284, Golden Bks.) Random Hse. Children's Bks.

Burt Dow: Deep Water Man. 2004. (J). 24.95 incl. audio (978-1-56008-021-3(3)); pap. 18.95 incl. audio compact disk (978-1-55592-374-7(7)); pap. 38.75 incl. audio compact disk (978-1-55592-376-1(3)); pap. 32.75 incl. audio (978-1-55592-197-2(3)) Weston Woods Studios, Inc.

Capdevila, Roser. Moby Dick. 2002. (Cuentos Fantasticos de las Tres Mellizas Coleccion: Vol. 1). (SPA.). (J). (gr. k-2). pap. 5.95 (978-1-930332-38-6(6) , LC6629) Lectorum Pubns., Inc.

Chizuru, Mio. The Pirate & the Princess Volume 1: the Timelight Stone: The Timelight Stone. 2007. 110p. (J). pap. 5.99 ***(978-1-933164-43-4(3))*** Seven Seas Entertainment, LLC.

—The Pirate & the Princess Volume 2: the Red Crystal: The Red Crystal. 2007. 110p. (J). pap. 5.99 ***(978-1-933164-44-1(1))*** Seven Seas Entertainment, LLC.

Collins, Terry. Deep-Sea Tales: 6 Salty Sea Stories. 2005. (Spongebob Squarepants Ser.). (Illus.). 336p. (J). pap. 7.99 (978-0-689-87704-9(8) , Simon Spotlight/Nickelodeon) Simon & Schuster Children's Publishing.

Conrad, Joseph & West, Clare. Lord Jim. 2nd abr. ed. 2000. (Bookworms Ser.). (Illus.). 6.50 (978-0-19-423037-7(6)) Oxford Univ. Pr., Inc.

Cooper, Susan. Victory. 2007. 224p. (J). pap. 6.99 ***(978-1-4169-1478-5(1)*** , Aladdin) Simon & Schuster Children's Publishing.

Creech, Sharon. The Wanderer. 2002. (gr. 3-6). lib. bdg. 14.15 (978-0-613-49702-2(3)) Tandem Library Bks.

Cummings, Mary. And the Baker's Boy Went to Sea. 2006. (Illus.). 195p. (YA). 16.95 (978-0-9774855-0-5(1)) Sparkling Pr.

Cussler, Clive & Kemprecos, Paul. Serpent: A Novel from the NUMA Files. 1999. (gr. 7-12). lib. bdg. 25.75 (978-0-613-26898-1(9)) Tandem Library Bks.

Dale, Jenny. The Sea Dog. 2002. (Puppy Patrol Ser.: No. 13). 128p. (J). (gr. 3-6). pap. 3.99 (978-0-439-21814-6(4) , Scholastic Paperbacks) Scholastic, Inc.

Dalmatian Press Staff, adapted by. Moby Dick. 2002. (Spot the Classics Ser.). (Illus.). 180p. (J). (gr. k-5). 4.99 (978-1-57759-547-2(5)) Dalmatian Pr.

—Moby Dick. (J). 9.95 (978-1-56156-308-1(0)) Kidsbooks, Inc.

Davidson, Halsey. Navy Boys Behind the Big Guns or Sinking. 2006. 95.99 ***(978-1-4280-1601-9(5))***; pap. 89.99 ***(978-1-4280-1600-2(7))*** IndyPublish.com.

Demas, Corinne. The Boy Who Was Generous with Salt. Hays, Michael, illus. 2002. 32p. (J). (gr. k-3). 15.95 (978-0-7614-5099-3(8) , Cavendish Children's Bks.) Cavendish, Marshall Corp.

—If Ever I Return Again. (gr. 5 up). 2000. (Illus.). 208p. (J). lib. bdg. 15.89 (978-0-06-028718-4(7)); 2000. 208p. (J). 15.95 (978-0-06-028717-7(9)); 1999. (Illus.). 196p. (YA). pap. 4.95 (978-0-06-440844-8(2)) HarperCollins Pubs.

Dowswell, Paul. Powder Monkey: Adventures of a Young Sailor. 2006. 288p. (YA). pap. 7.95 (978-1-58234-748-6(4) , Bloomsbury Children) Bloomsbury Publishing.

—Prison Ship: Adventures of a Young Sailor. 2006. 300p. (YA). 16.95 (978-1-58234-676-2(3) , Bloomsbury Children) Bloomsbury Publishing.

Edens, Cooper, compiled by. Sea Stories: A Classic Illustrated Edition. 2007. (Illus.). 148p. (J). 19.95 (978-0-8118-5634-8(8)) Chronicle Bks. LLC.

Forester, C. S. & Border, Rosemary. Mr. Midshipman Hornblower. 2nd abr. ed. 2000. (Hornblower Ser.: No. 1). (Illus.). 96p. 6.25 (978-0-19-423041-4(4)) Oxford Univ. Pr., Inc.

Foster, Evelyn. The Mermaid of Cafur. Whelan, Olwyn, illus. 1999. 32p. (J). (gr. k-3). 15.95 (978-1-902283-40-1(6)) Barefoot Bks., Inc.

Fowles, Shelley, illus. The Seven Voyages of Sinbad. 2008. 64p. (J). 18.95 ***(978-1-84507-531-6(5))*** Lincoln, Frances Ltd. GBR. *Dist:* Perseus Distribution.

Guiberson, Brenda Z. Tales of the Haunted Deep. Godwin, Laura, ed. Guiberson, Brenda Z., illus. rev. ed. 2000. (Redfeather Chapter Bk.). (Illus.). 80p. (J). (gr. 3-6). 16.95 (978-0-8050-6057-7(X) , Holt, Henry & Co. Bks. For Young Readers) Holt, Henry & Co.

Hagerty, Carol, ed. Moby Dick. 1998. (Classics Ser.: Set II). 77p. (YA). (gr. 5-12). pap. 7.95 (978-1-56254-258-0(3) , SP2583) Saddleback Educational Publishing.

Hamilton, Tisha. The Search for Dead Man's Chest: Storybook with Spyglass. 2006. (Pirates of the Caribbean Ser.). (Illus.). 40p. (J). pap. 24.99 (978-0-7944-1101-5(0)) Reader's Digest Assn., Inc., The.

Hancock, Irving H. Dave Darrin's First Year at Annapolis. 2006. 78.99 ***(978-1-4219-9882-4(3))***; pap. 72.99 ***(978-1-4219-9880-0(7))*** IndyPublish.com.

—Dave Darrin's Fourth Year at Annapolis (2006. 78.99 ***(978-1-4219-9801-5(7))***; pap. 72.99 ***(978-1-4219-9805-3(X))*** IndyPublish.com.

—Dave Darrin's Second Year at Annapolis O. 2006. 95.99 ***(978-1-4280-1562-3(0))***; pap. 89.99 ***(978-1-4280-1578-4(7))*** IndyPublish.com.

—Dave Darrin's Third Year at Annapolis or. 2006. 95.99 ***(978-1-4219-7420-0(7))***; pap. 89.99 ***(978-1-4219-7419-4(3))*** IndyPublish.com.

Hawes, Charles Boardman. The Dark Frigate. 2005. pap. 27.95 (978-1-4179-3209-2(0)) Kessinger Publishing, LLC.

Hendrickson, Jean A. Tales of the Sea Patrol. 2001. (Angell Ser.). (Illus.). 32p. (J). (gr. k up). pap. (978-1-929953-03-5(8)) Gates & Bridges Inc.

Hesse, Karen. Stowaway. unabr. ed. 2004. 328p. (J). (gr. 5-9). pap. 48.00 incl. audio (978-0-8072-8760-6(1) , LYA 259 SP, Listening Library) Random Hse. Audio Publishing Group.

S

—Stowaway. Parker, Robert Andrew, illus. 2002. 320p. (J). (gr. 5-9). pap. 6.99 (978-0-689-83989-4(8) , Aladdin) Simon & Schuster Children's Publishing.

—Stowaway. Parker, Robert Andrew & Prato, Rodica, illus. 2000. 328p. (J). (gr. 5-9). 17.95 (978-0-689-83987-0(1) , McElderry, Margaret K.) Simon & Schuster Children's Publishing.

—Stowaway. 2002. (gr. 5-8). lib. bdg. 15.30 (978-0-613-45110-9(4)) Tandem Library Bks.

Hodgson, William Hope. The Sea Horses. 2004. reprint ed. pap. 1.99 (978-1-4192-8166-2(6)) Kessinger Publishing, LLC.

Hoffman, Alice. The Foretelling. l.t. ed. 2006. 156p. 23.95 (978-0-7862-8285-2(1)) Thorndike Pr.

Holt, Rinehart and Winston Staff. Goodbye, Vietnam. 2nd ed. 2002. pap., stu. ed. 13.20 (978-0-03-066514-1(0)) Holt, Rinehart & Winston.

—Goodbye, Vietnam: With Connections. 2nd ed. 2001. 14.64 (978-0-03-066513-4(2)) Holt, Rinehart & Winston.

Horn, Sandra A. Stormteller: Little Weather Doll. (Illus.). (J). mass mkt. 8.99 (978-0-340-75736-9(1) , Hodder & Stoughton) Hodder General Publishing Division GBR. *Dist:* Trafalgar Square Publishing.

Horrigan, David J. The Spark in the Sea: Adventures in Marine Science, 1. 2003. 152p. pap. 24.00 (978-0-9743712-0-7(3) , 001) Home Planet Bks.

Ita, Sam. Moby-Dick: A Pop-up Book. 2007. (Illus.). 8p. (J). 24.95 ***(978-1-4027-4528-7(1))*** Sterling Publishing Co., Inc.

Kehl, Mark. Scary Sea Stories, Vol. II. 2000. (Scary Sea Stories Ser.: Vol. 2). (Illus.). 96p. (J). (gr. 3-7). pap. 5.95 (978-0-7373-0400-8(6) , 04006W, Roxbury Park Juvenile) Lowell Hse. Juvenile.

Lasky, Kathryn. Pirate Bob. Clark, David, illus. 2006. (J). 15.95 (978-1-57091-595-6(4)) Charlesbridge Publishing, Inc.

Lassen C R Staff. Bountiful Sea. 2002. (Illus.). 20p. (J). 8.95 (978-1-74047-139-8(3)) Book Co. Publishing Pty, Ltd., The AUS. *Dist:* Leonard, Hal Corp.

Lindgren, Astrid. Pippi in the South Seas. (Pippi Longstocking Ser.). 125p. (J). (gr. 3-5). pap. 3.99 (978-0-8072-1392-6(6) , Listening Library) Random Hse. Audio Publishing Group.

Lombardi, Kristine. Summer under the Sea. 2006. 12p. (J). pap. 12.99 (978-0-7944-1102-2(9)) Reader's Digest Assn., Inc., The.

Lunn, John. The Mariner's Curse. 2004. 216p. (J). (gr. 4-7). pap. 8.95 (978-0-88776-672-5(2)) Tundra Bks., Inc./Livres Toundra, Inc. CAN. *Dist:* Random Hse., Inc.

Melville, Herman. Cities of the Fantastic: Brusel. Eisner, Will, illus. 2003. (Cities of the Fantastic Ser.). 120p. 19.95 (978-1-56163-291-6(0)) NBM Publishing Co.

—Herman Melville/Moby Dick. Niño, Alex, illus. 2005. 48p. (gr. 5-8). 25.50 (978-0-7910-9106-7(6)) Facts On File, Inc.

—Moby Dick. 2002. (Great Illustrated Classics Ser.). (Illus.). 240p. (J). (gr. 3-8). 21.35 (978-1-57765-695-1(4) , ABDO & Daughters) ABDO Publishing Co.

—Moby Dick. Giordano, Dick, illus. 2002. 48p. (J). (gr. 5). tchr. ed. 16.00 (978-0-618-26571-8(6)) Houghton Mifflin Co. Trade & Reference Div.

—Moby Dick. 2000. (Coleccion "Clasicos Juveniles" Ser.). (SPA.). 228p. (YA). pap. 12.95 (978-0-595-13218-8(9)) iUniverse, Inc.

—Moby Dick. 2003. (Illus.). 32p. 7.95 (978-1-56163-294-7(5)) NBM Publishing Co.

—Moby Dick. Eisner, Will, illus. 2003. 32p. (gr. 4-7). 15.95 (978-1-56163-293-0(7)) NBM Publishing Co.

—Moby Dick. Nino, Alex, illus. 2nd ed. 1998. (Illustrated Classic Book Ser.). 61p. (J). (gr. 3 up). reprint ed. pap. 4.95 (978-1-56767-235-0(3)) Educational Insights, Inc.

—Moby Dick. adapted ed. (YA). (gr. 5-12). pap. 8.50 (978-0-8359-0225-0(0)) Globe Fearon Educational Publishing.

—Moby Dick. 2nd ed. 2003. (Historias de Siempre Ser.). (SPA., Illus.). 92p. (J). (gr. 5-8). pap. 9.95 (978-84-204-5732-1(9)) Santillana USA Publishing Co., Inc.

—Moby Dick, Grades 5-12. adapted ed. pap., tchr. ed. 4.95 (978-0-8359-0123-9(8)) Globe Fearon Educational Publishing.

Melville, Herman & Schwartz, Lew Sayre. Moby Dick. Giordano, Dick, illus. 2002. 48p. (J). pap. 6.95 (978-0-618-26572-5(4)) Houghton Mifflin Co. Trade & Reference Div.

Melville, Herman, et al. Moby Dick. (Classics Illustrated Ser.). (Illus.). 52p. (YA). pap. 4.95 (978-1-57209-003-3(0)) Classics International Entertainment, Inc.

Meyer, L. A. Under the Jolly Roger: Being an Account of the Further Nautical Adventures of Jacky Faber. 2007. (Bloody Jack Adventures Ser.). (Illus.). 544p. (YA). pap. 6.95 (978-0-15-205873-9(7) , Harcourt Paperbacks) Harcourt Children's Bks.

Meyer, Louis A. Bloody Jack: Being an Account of the Curious Adventures of Mary Jacky Faber, Ship's Boy. 2002. (Bloody Jack Adventures Ser.). (Illus.). 336p. (YA). (gr. 6-9). 17.00 (978-0-15-216731-8(5)) Harcourt Children's Bks.

Meyer, Louis A. & Nielsen, Cliff. In the Belly of the Bloodhound: Being an Account of a Particularly Peculiar Adventure in the Life of Jacky Faber. 2006. (Bloody Jack Adventures Ser.). (Illus.). 528p. (J). (gr. 8 up). 17.00 (978-0-15-205557-8(6)) Harcourt Children's Bks.

Molloy, Michael. Peter Raven under Fire. 2007. 512p. (J). 8.99 (***978-0-439-72457-9(0)***) Scholastic, Inc.

Murawski, Kevin, illus. Harold & the Purple Crayon: Under the Sea. 2004. 32p. (J). (ps-ps). lib. bdg. 10.79 (978-0-606-29924-4(6)) Tandem Library Bks.

Niedworok, Claudio O. Seafarers: Chronicles of the Suspense & Romance of the Sea. Knight, Tori, ed. Cooper, Paul, illus. Date not set. 80p. (Orig.). (YA). pap. 11.95 (978-1-882133-05-5(6)) Barefoot Pr.

Plum-Ucci, Carol. The She. 2003. (Illus.). 288p. (YA). 17.00 (978-0-15-216819-3(2)) Harcourt Children's Bks.

Posner-Sanchez, Andrea & Golden Books Staff. Sea Captain Ned. 2004. (Illus.). 24p. (J). (ps-2). pap. 3.99 (978-0-375-82954-3(7) , Golden Bks.) Random Hse. Children's Bks.

Pryor, Bonnie. Hannah Pritchard: Girl Pirate of the Revolution. 2008. (Historical Fiction Adventures (HFA) Ser.). (Illus.). 160p. (J). (gr. 3-6). lib. bdg. 27.93 (***978-0-7660-2851-7(8)***) Enslow Pubs., Inc.

Riordan, James, ed. Stories from the Sea. Hall, Amanda, illus. 2002. 79p. (J). (gr. 4-6). 20.00 (978-0-7567-5638-3(3)) DIANE Publishing Co.

Ruby, Anne. Children of the Sea. Meier, Ty, illus. 2007. (YA). per. (978-0-9787881-0-0(9)) Seachild.

Scott, James, adapted by. Moby Dick: Reproducible Teaching Unit. 2001. 110p. (YA). (gr. 7-12). tchr. ed., ring bd. 29.50 (978-1-58049-283-6(5) , TU169) Prestwick Hse., Inc.

Shanower, Eric. Thousand Ships. 2001. (gr. 7-12). lib. bdg. 30.35 (978-0-613-65633-7(4)) Tandem Library Bks.

Skogan, Joan. The Good Companion. McCallum, Stephen, illus. 1998. 32p. (J). (ps-3). 15.95 (978-1-55143-134-5(3)) Orca Bk. Pubs. USA.

Smith, Barbara. Ghost Stories of the Sea, Vol. 1. rev. ed. 2003. (Ghost Stories Ser.). (Illus.). 224p. (J). (gr. 4). pap. (978-1-894877-23-7(3)) Lone Pine Publishing.

Smith, Barbara Sweetland. Science under Sail: Russia's Great Voyages to America, 1728-1867. 2000. (J). pap. (978-1-885267-02-3(9)) Anchorage Museum of History & Art.

Smith, Barbara Sweetland & Matthews, Donna. Science under Sail: Russia's Great Voyages to America, 1728-1867. 2000. (J). (gr. 4-8). pap. (978-1-885267-03-0(7)) Anchorage Museum of History & Art.

Souhami, Jessica. Sausages. 2006. (Illus.). 32p. (ps-2). 15.95 (978-1-84507-397-8(5)) Lincoln, Frances Ltd. GBR. *Dist:* Perseus Distribution.

Soundprints. Ocean Adventures: Story-Time Treasury. 2005. (Smithsonian Institution Story-Time Treasures Ser.). (Illus.). 256p. (J). (ps-2). 14.95 (978-1-59069-226-4(8) , HT1001) Studio Mouse LLC.

Steele, Alexander. Moby Dog. l.t. ed. 1999. (Adventures of Wishbone Ser.: No. 10). (Illus.). 144p. (J). (gr. 4 up). lib. bdg. 22.60 (978-0-8368-2306-6(0)) Stevens, Gareth Inc.

Stevenson, Robert Louis. Secuestrado. 3rd ed. (Coleccion Clasicos en Accion). (SPA., Illus.). 80p. (YA). (gr. 5-8). 15.95 (978-84-241-5781-4(8) , EV1487) Everest de Ediciones y Distribucion, S.L. ESP. *Dist:* Lectorum Pubns., Inc.

—Secuestrado. 2002. (Clover Ser.). (SPA., Illus.). 156p. (YA). 11.50 (978-84-392-8006-4(8) , EV5548) Lectorum Pubns., Inc.

Taylor, Theodore. The Odyssey of Ben O'Neal. 2004. (Illus.). 264p. (J). pap. 5.95 (978-0-15-205295-9(X) , Odyssey Classics) Harcourt Children's Bks.

—Rogue Wave: And Other Red-Blooded Sea Stories. 2009. (Illus.). 192p. (YA). pap. 6.95 (***978-0-15-206254-5(8)*** , Harcourt Paperbacks) Harcourt Children's Bks.

Taylor, Theodore. Rogue Wave & Other Red-Blooded Sea Stories. 1998. (978-0-606-13746-1(7)) Tandem Library Bks.

Thornton, Duncan. The Star-Glass: The Return of Kalifax & Captain Jenny. Noblet, Yves, illus. 2003. (Kalifax Trilogy Ser.). 432p. (J). (gr. 5-7). pap. 10.95 (978-1-55050-269-5(7)) Coteau Bks. CAN. *Dist:* Fitzhenry & Whiteside, Ltd.

Torrey, Michele. Voyage of Plunder. 208p. (J). 2007. (gr. 4-7). pap. 5.99 (978-0-440-41887-0(9) , Yearling); 2005. (gr. 5-7). 15.95 (978-0-375-82383-1(2) , Knopf Bks. for Young Readers) Random Hse. Children's Bks.

Townsend, John. Mysteries of the Deep. 2004. (Out There Ser.). (Illus.). 56p. (J). 28.56 (978-1-4109-0562-8(4)) Raintree.

Troncale, Steven L. Yankee Boys of War. 2003. 171p. pap. 19.95 (978-1-59286-879-7(7)) PublishAmerica, Inc.

Verne, Jules. Twenty Thousand Leagues under the Sea. l.t. ed. 2006. 592p. pap. (978-1-84702-222-6(7)) Echo Library.

—20,000 Leagues under the Sea. 2003. (gr. 5-8). lib. bdg. 13.00 (978-0-613-66744-9(1)) Tandem Library Bks.

—20,000 Leagues under the Sea: Retold from the Jules Verne Original. Andreasen, Dan, illus. 2006. (Classic Starts Ser.). 160p. 4.95 (978-1-4027-2533-3(7)) Sterling Publishing Co., Inc.

Wensel, Bill. Adventure Is Adventure: The Sea Stories of Captain Bill. 2002. 185p. per. 14.95 net. (978-1-931934-09-1(6)) Back Yard Pub.

Wheeler, Lisa. Seadogs: An Epic Ocean Operetta. Siegel, Mark, illus. 2006. 40p. (J). reprint ed. 7.99 (978-1-4169-4103-3(7) , Aladdin) Simon & Schuster Children's Publishing.

YKids Staff. Treasure Island. 2007. (Manga Literary Classics Ser.). 148p. (J). (gr. 4-7). pap. 14.95 (***978-981-05-4942-8(3)***) Youngjin (Singapore) Pte Ltd. SGP. *Dist:* Independent Pubs. Group.

Young, Joseph R. Legend of the Lost Josephine Mine: A Fascinating Adventure. 2001. 221p. (J). pap. 13.95 (978-1-55517-550-4(3) , Bonneville Bks.) Cedar Fort, Inc./CFI Distribution.

Zuhdi, Darla. A South Sea Adventure, Vol. 4. 2005. (Cat Detectives Present Ser.: 4). (Illus.). 104p. (J). per. 6.99 (978-0-9706062-6-6(5)) Aloha Publications.

SEA WAVES

see Ocean Waves

SEAFARING LIFE

Anastasio, Dina. Hiding in the Sea. 2003. (Early Connections Ser.). (J). pap. 33.00 (978-1-4108-1080-9(1)) Benchmark Education Co.

Brewster, Joy. El mundo bajo las Olas. Hanner, Albert, illus. ed. 2004. (SPA.). 32p. (J). pap. 6.00 (978-1-4108-2339-7(3) , A23393) Benchmark Education Co.

Brown, Susan. Vida Marina/Sea Life. 2005. 80p. (J). per. 9.99 (978-1-59441-437-4(8) , FI-704008) Carson-Dellosa Publishing Co., Inc.

Crompton, Samuel Willard. Francis Drake & the Oceans of the World. 2005. (Explorers of New Worlds Ser.). (Illus.). 160p. (J). (gr. 4-8). 30.00 (978-0-7910-8615-5(1) , Chelsea Hse.) Facts On File, Inc.

Duder, Tessa, ed. Down to the Sea Again: True Sea Stories for Young Newzealanders. 2005. 256p. (J). (978-1-86950-476-2(3)) HarperCollins Pubs. New Zealand NZL. *Dist:* HarperCollins Canada, Ltd.

Greenfield, Eloise. How They Got Over: African Americans & the Call of the Sea. Gilchrist, Jan Spivey, illus. 2003. 128p. (J). (gr. 3-5). 16.99 (978-0-06-028991-1(0)) HarperCollins Pubs.

Hirschi, Ron. Swimming with Humuhumu: A Young Snorkeler's First Guide to Hawaiian Sea Life. Yee, Tammy, illus. 32p. (J). 14.99 (978-0-931548-67-3(5) , 25098-000) Island Heritage Publishing.

Lithgow, John & Blackaby, Susan. Drop, Drip, an Underwater Trip: Level 3. 2007. (Lithgow Palooza Readers Ser.). (Illus.). 32p. (J). (gr. 1-2). pap. 3.95 (978-0-7696-4253-6(5)) School Specialty Publishing.

Moore, Robin. The Man with the Silver Oar. 2002. 192p. (J). (gr. 5 up). 15.89 (978-0-06-000048-6(1)) HarperCollins Pubs.

O'Hara, Megan, ed. A Whaling Captain's Daughter: The Diary of Laura Jernegan, 1868-1871. 1999. (Diaries, Letters & Memoirs Ser.). (Illus.). 32p. (J). (gr. 2-7). pap. 21.00 (978-0-516-21851-9(4) , Children's Pr.) Scholastic Library Publishing.

Petrillo, Valerie. Sailors, Whalers, Fantastic Sea Voyages: An Activity Guide to North American Sailing Life. 2003. (Illus.). 224p. (J). pap. 14.95 (978-1-55652-475-2(7)) Chicago Review Pr., Inc.

Sohl, Marcia & Dackerman, Gerald. Two Years Before the Mast: Student Activity Book. Cruz, Ernesto R, illus. (Now Age Illustrated Ser.). (J). (gr. 4-12). stu. ed. 1.25 (978-0-88301-294-9(4)) Pendulum Pr., Inc.

Walker, Pam & Wood, Elaine. Life in the Sea Set, 6 vols. 2005. (Life in the Sea Ser.). 112-112p. (gr. 4-9). 210.00 (978-0-8160-5700-9(1)) Facts On File, Inc.

SEALS (ANIMALS)

Andersen, Ashley C. & Shriver, Chelsea. Sea Lion Swims. 2005. (Let's Go to the Zoo! Ser.). (Illus.). 16p. (J). (ps). bds. 5.95 (978-1-56899-976-0(3) , B9010) Soundprints.

Antarctic Seals, 6 vols., Pack. 16p. (gr. 3 up). 36.00 (978-0-7635-9688-0(4)) Rigby Education.

Bonner, W. Nigel. Seals & Sea Lions of the World. 2nd ed. 2004. (Of the World Ser.). (Illus.). 224p. (YA). (gr. 6-12). 35.00 (978-0-8160-5717-7(6)) Facts On File, Inc.

Crossingham, John & Kalman, Bobbie. Seals & Sea Lions. 2005. (Living Ocean Ser.). (Illus.). 32p. (J). (ps-3). lib. bdg. (978-0-7787-1301-2(6)); pap. (978-0-7787-1323-4(7)) Crabtree Publishing Co.

Fetty, Margaret. Sea Lions. 2006. (Smart Animals! Ser.). (Illus.). 32p. (J). (gr. 3-7). lib. bdg. 25.27 (978-1-59716-274-6(4)) Bearport Publishing Co., Inc.

Haller, Christine A. Chippy: The sea lion that lost its Way. Lund, Nancy M., illus. 2006. 20p. (J). 11.95 (978-0-9771129-0-6(X)) Oxbow Bks.

Hewett, Joan. A Harbor Seal Pup Grows Up. Hewett, Richard, photos by. (Baby Animals Ser.). (Illus.). 32p. (gr. k-3). 2005. lib. bdg. 21.27 (978-1-57505-166-6(4)); 2003. (J). pap. 6.95 (978-0-8225-0092-6(2)) Lerner Publishing Group.

—Harbor Seal Pup Grows Up. 2002. (gr. k-3). lib. bdg. 15.25 (978-0-613-55720-7(4)) Tandem Library Bks.

Hirschi, Ron. Seals. 2002. (Animals, Animals Ser.). (Illus.). 47p. (J). 25.64 (978-0-7614-1445-2(2) , Benchmark Bks.) Cavendish, Marshall Corp.

Hodge, Judith. Seals, Sea Lions & Walruses. 2001. (Animals of the Ocean Ser.). (Illus.). (J). lib. bdg. 15.95 (978-1-56674-301-3(X)) Forest Hse. Publishing Co., Inc.

Hodgkins, Fran. The Orphan Seal: A True Story. Peterson, Dawn, illus. 2000. 32p. (gr. 1-5). pap. 9.95 (978-0-89272-471-0(4)) Down East Bks.

Johnson, Jinny. Sea Lions. 2006. (Illus.). 32p. (J). (978-1-58340-903-9(3)) Smart Apple Media.

Kalman, Bobbie. Endangered Monk Seals. 2004. (Earth's Endangered Animals Ser.). (Illus.). 32p. (J). (978-0-7787-1851-2(4)); pap. (978-0-7787-1897-0(2)) Crabtree Publishing Co.

Kalman, Bobbie & Crossingham, John. Les Phoques et les Otaries. 2007. (FRE.). 32p. pap. 8.95 (***978-2-89579-165-2(1)***) Editions Banjo CAN. *Dist:* Crabtree Publishing Co.

Lang, Aubrey. Baby Seal. Lynch, Wayne, photos by. 2002. (Nature Babies Ser.). (Illus.). 36p. (J). (gr. k-3). (978-1-55041-685-5(5)) Fitzhenry & Whiteside, Ltd.

Leon, Vicki. A Colony of Seals: The Captivating Life of a Deep Sea Diver. 2nd ed. 2005. (Jean-Michel Cousteau Presents Ser.). (Illus.). 48p. pap. 8.95 (978-0-9766134-0-4(9)) London Town Pr.

Lindeen, Carol K. Seals. 2005. (Under the Sea Ser.). (Illus.). 24p. (J). 19.93 (978-0-7368-3663-0(2)) Capstone Pr., Inc.

Lynch, Wayne. Seals. 2002. (gr. 3-6). lib. bdg. 16.40 (978-0-613-55895-2(2)) Tandem Library Bks.

Lynch, Wayne, photos by. Baby Seal. (Nature Babies Ser.). (Illus.). 36p. (J). (gr. k-3). pap. (978-1-55041-726-5(6)) Fitzhenry & Whiteside, Ltd.

Macken, JoAnn Early. Sea Lions. 2002. (Weekly Reader Early Learning Library). (Illus.). 24p. (J). (ps up). pap. 5.95 (978-0-8368-3287-7(6)); lib. bdg. 19.33 (978-0-8368-3274-7(4)) Stevens, Gareth Inc. (Weekly Reader Early Learning Library).

McGee, John F., illus. Seals. Lynch, Wayne, photos by. 2004. (Our Wild World Ser.). 48p. (J). (gr. 2-5). ring bd. 10.95 (978-1-55971-827-1(7)); pap. 7.95 (978-1-55971-826-4(9)) T&N Children's Publishing. (NorthWord Bks. for Young Readers).

Miller, David. Seals & Sea Lions. rev. ed. 1998. (WorldLife Library). (Illus.). 72p. (gr. 5 up). pap. 17.95 (978-0-89658-371-9(6)) Voyageur Pr., Inc.

Parker, Steve. Seal. 2003. (Illus.). 48p. (J). lib. bdg. 28.56 (978-0-7398-6058-8(5)) Raintree.

Piasetsky, Lorne. Fur Seals & Other Pinnipeds, Vol. 2. World Book, Inc. Staff, ed. 2002. (World Book's Animals of the World Ser.: Set 1). 64p. (J). (978-0-7166-1239-1(9)) World Bk., Inc.

Rustad, Martha E. H. Seals. Saunders-Smith, Gail, ed. 2001. (Ocean Life Ser.). (Illus.). 24p. (J). (gr. k-1). lib. bdg. 15.93 (978-0-7368-0860-6(4) , Pebble Bks.) Capstone Pr., Inc.

Schaefer, Lola M. Seals, Vol. 2. 2005. (Ocean Life Ser.). 24p. (YA). (gr. k-3). pap. (978-0-7368-9083-0(1) , Pebble Bks.) Capstone Pr., Inc.

Schemenauer, Elma & Switzer, Merebeth. Pronghorns. 1999. (Getting to Know ... Nature's Children Ser.). (Illus.). 47p. (J). (978-0-7172-8842-7(0) , Grolier) Scholastic Library Publishing.

Seals, 6 vols. (gr. k-2). 28.95 (978-0-7368-9104-2(8)) Red Brick Learning.

Sexton, Colleen. Seals. 2007. (Illus.). 24p. (J). lib. bdg. 16.95 (978-1-60014-056-3(4)) Bellwether Media.

—Seals. 2007. (Blastoff! Readers Ser.). (Illus.). 24p. (J). (gr. k-2). 18.50 (***978-0-531-17564-4(2)*** , Children's Pr.) Scholastic Library Publishing.

Shivley, Julie. Baby Seal. Sharp, Chris & Seaworld, Chris, illus. Seaworld, Chris, photos by. 2005. (Seaworld Animal Library: Vol. 3). 26p. (J). (ps-k). bds. 6.95 (978-0-8249-6617-1(1)) Ideals Pubns.

Solway, Andrew. Sea Hunters: Dolphins, Whales, & Seals. 2005. (Illus.). 48p. (J). (978-1-4034-6569-6(X)); pap. (978-1-4034-6575-7(4)) Heinemann Library.

Soundprints Staff, ed. Oceanic Collection III: Beluga Whale, Harp Seal, Walrus & Lobster Books, 4 micro bks. (Smithsonian Oceanic Collection). (Illus.). 128p. (J). (ps-2). 18.95 (978-1-56899-633-2(0)) Soundprints.

Stille, Darlene. I Am a Seal: The Life of an Elephant Seal. Ouren, Todd, illus. 2004. (I Live in the Ocean Ser.). 24p. (J). (gr. k-2). lib. bdg. 22.60 (978-1-4048-0598-9(2)) Picture Window Bks.

Stone, Lynn M. Seals. 2001. (Wildlife in Danger Ser.). (Illus.). 24p. (gr. 1-4). 14.95 (978-1-58952-022-6(X)) Rourke Publishing, LLC.

Stone, Tanya Lee. Sea Lions. 2003. (Wild Wild World Ser.). (Illus.). 24p. (J). 22.45 (978-1-4103-0036-2(6) , Blackbirch Pr., Inc.) Thomson Gale.

The Story of Small Fry: Individual Title Six-Packs. (Action Packs Ser.). 104p. (gr. 3-5). 44.00 (978-0-7635-8405-4(3)) Rigby Education.

Townsend, Emily Rose. Seals. 2004. (Polar Animals Ser.). (Illus.). 24p. (J). (gr. k-1). lib. bdg. 15.93 (978-0-7368-2359-3(X) , Pebble Bks.) Capstone Pr., Inc.

Vogel, Julia. Polar Animals. McGee, John F., illus. 2004. (Our Wild World Ser.). 192p. (J). (gr. 2-5). ring bd. 16.95 (978-1-55971-832-5(3) , NorthWord Bks. for Young Readers) T&N Children's Publishing.

Wexo, John Bonnett. Seals & Sea Lions. rev. ed. 2003. (Illus.). 24p. (J). (gr. 1-7). 10.95 (978-1-932396-00-3(4) , Zoo Bks.) Wildlife Education, Ltd.

Whitehouse, Patricia. El Leon Marino. 2003. (Animales del Zoologico (Zoo Animals) Ser.). (Illus.). 24p. (ps-1). (J). lib. bdg. 17.08 (978-1-4034-0407-7(0)); (SPA., pap. 5.25 (978-1-4034-0655-2(3)) Heinemann Library.

Wildlife Education, Ltd. Staff. Seals & Sea Lions. Stuart, Walter, illus. 2001. (Zoobooks Ser.). 18p. (Orig.). (YA). (gr. 5 up). pap. 2.95 (978-0-937934-33-3(X)) Wildlife Education, Ltd.

Wilsdon, Christina. Seals. 2007. (J). (***978-1-59939-127-4(9)*** , Reader's Digest Young Families, Inc.) Reader's Digest Children's Publishing, Inc.

SEALS (ANIMALS)—FICTION

Bos, Maarten. Webster's Wardrobe. 1998. (Illus.). 20p. (J). (ps-k). pap. 8.95 (978-0-531-30097-8(8) , Orchard Bks.) Scholastic, Inc.

Brin, Susannah. Seal Killers. 2000. (gr. 5-8). lib. bdg. 11.80 (978-0-613-51223-7(5)) Tandem Library Bks.

—The Seal Killers. Taylor, Marjorie, illus. rev. ed. 1999. (Take Ten Ser.). 50p. (YA). (gr. 4-12). pap. 3.95 (978-1-58659-014-7(6)) Artesian Pr.

Call of the Selkie: Individual Title Six-Packs. (Action Packs Ser.). 104p. (gr. 3-5). 44.00 (978-0-7635-2991-8(5)) Rigby Education.

Chapman, Jason. Ted, Bo, & Diz: The First Adventure. 2007. 28p. (J). (ps-2). 16.00 (***978-1-56148-592-5(6)***) Good Bks.

Coffey, Maria. A Seal in the Family. Fernandes, Eugenie, illus. 1999. 32p. (J). (ps-2). pap. 6.95 (978-1-55037-580-0(6)); lib. bdg. 17.95 (978-1-55037-581-7(4)) Annick Pr., Ltd. CAN. *Dist:* Firefly Bks., Ltd.

—Seal in the Family. 1999. (gr. 3-6). lib. bdg. 15.25 (978-0-613-26867-7(9)) Tandem Library Bks.

Cook, Sherry & Johnson, Terri. Susie Sound, 26. Kuhn, Jesse, illus. l.t. ed. 2006. 32p. (J). 7.99 (978-1-933815-18-3(3) , Quirkles, The) Creative 3, LLC.

Doherty, Berlie. Daughter of the Sea. 2000. (Illus.). (J). (978-0-606-18102-0(4)) Tandem Library Bks.

Foreman, Michael. Seal Surfer. 2007. (Illus.). 36p. (J). pap. 9.95 (978-1-84270-578-0(4)) Andersen GBR. *Dist:* Independent Pubs. Group.

Harris, Sue. The Little Seal. Boey, Stephanie, illus. 2007. 28p. (J). (ps). pap. 15.99 (***978-0-525-47839-3(6)*** , Dutton Juvenile) Penguin Group (USA) Inc.

He Who Listens: Individual Title Six-Packs. (Literatura 2000 Ser.). (gr. 2-3). 33.00 (978-0-7635-0171-6(9)) Rigby Education.

Hoff, Syd. Sammy the Seal. Hoff, Syd, illus. 2002. (Illus.). (J). 12.34 (978-0-7587-4577-4(X)) Book Wholesalers, Inc.

—Sammy the Seal. 2000. (I Can Read Bks.). (Illus.). 64p. (J). (ps-1). pap. 3.99 (978-0-06-444270-1(5) , Harper Trophy) HarperCollins Pubs.

—Sammy the Seal. Hoff, Syd, illus. rev. ed. 2000. (I Can Read Bks.). (Illus.). 64p. (J). (ps-1). 16.99 (978-0-06-028545-6(1)); lib. bdg. 16.89 (978-0-06-028546-3(X)) HarperCollins Pubs.

—Sammy the Seal, Class Set. unabr. ed. 2000. (J). pap. 168.80 incl. audio (978-0-7887-4447-1(X) , 47138) Recorded Bks., LLC.

—Sammy the Seal. 2000. (I Can Read Bks.). (978-0-606-17825-9(2)) Tandem Library Bks.

Hollenbeck, Kathleen M. Islands of Ice: The Story of a Harp Seal. Genzo, John Paul, illus. (Smithsonian Oceanic Collection). (J). (ps-2). 2005. 32p. 4.95 (978-1-56899-966-1(6) , B4071); 2005. 32p. 9.95 (978-1-56899-970-8(4) , PB4071); 2005. 32p. 15.95 (978-1-56899-965-4(8) , B4021); 2001. 13p. 29.95 (978-1-56899-969-2(0)) Soundprints.

Horn, S. Silkie. (Illus.). 89p. pap. 7.95 (978-0-340-67265-5(X) , Hodder & Stoughton) Hodder General Publishing Division GBR. *Dist:* Trafalgar Square Publishing.

Howell, Gill. Selkie Child. Keen, Sophie, illus. 2005. 24p. (J). lib. bdg. 22.65 (***978-1-59646-750-7(9)***) Dingles & Co.

Jobling, Brenda. Pirate the Seal. 1998. (Animal Tales Ser.). (978-0-606-13710-2(6)) Tandem Library Bks.

Jones, Chuck. The White Seal. Jones, Chuck, illus. 2006. (Illus.). 32p. (J). 8.95 (978-0-8249-6598-3(1) , Ideals Children's Bks.) Ideals Pubns.

MacGregor, Jill. Swim Safe Little Seals. 2006. (Illus.). 31p. (J). 14.95 (978-0-9774062-0-3(2)) Seal Publishing, LLC.

Massey, Jane. Sea Creatures. 2000. (Touch & Fit Ser.). (Illus.). 10p. (J). (ps-k). bds. 12.95 (978-1-57145-417-1(9) , Silver Dolphin Bks.) Advantage Pubs. Group.

McKnew Jr., Thomas I. The Legend of Seal Beach. 2007. 28p. 14.94 (***978-0-615-15593-7(6)***) VideoPresence-.com, A.

Mitton, Tony. Playful Little Penguins. Parker-Rees, Guy, illus. 2007. 32p. (J). (ps-1). 15.95 (***978-0-8027-9710-0(5)***) Walker & Co.

Morris, Jackie. The Seal Children. 2004. (Illus.). 32p. (J). 16.95 (978-1-84507-040-3(2)) Lincoln, Frances Ltd. GBR. *Dist:* Perseus Distribution.

Patterson, Sherri, et al. No-No & the Secret Touch: The Gentle Story of a Little Seal Who Learns to Stay Safe, Say "No" & Tell! Krupp, Marian N., illus. unabr. ed. 70p. (J). (gr. 1-6). pap. 14.95 incl. audio (978-0-9632276-2-1(9)) National Self-Esteem Resources & Development Ctr.

Resnicoff, Stanley. Stanley, the Seal of Approval. 2001. (Illus.). (J). (978-0-606-21455-1(0)) Tandem Library Bks.

The Right Place for Jupiter: Individual Title Six-Packs. (gr. 3 up). 35.00 (978-0-7635-9672-9(8)) Rigby Education.

Rumford, James. Dog-of-the-Sea-Waves. 2004. (ENG & HAW., Illus.). 48p. (J). (gr. k-3). tchr. ed. 16.00 (978-0-618-35611-9(8)) Houghton Mifflin Co. Trade & Reference Div.

Salzmann, Mary Elizabeth. Presidential Seal. Nobens, C. A., illus. 2007. (Fact & Fiction Ser.). 24p. (J). pap. (978-1-59928-465-1(0)); 21.35 (978-1-59928-464-4(2)) ABDO Publishing Co.

Shaw-MacKinnon, Margaret & Gal, Laszlo. Tiktala. (Illus.). 30p. 13.95 (978-0-7737-2920-9(8)) Stoddart Kids CAN. *Dist:* Fitzhenry & Whiteside, Ltd.

Simmons, Jane. Ebb & Flo & the Baby Seal. Simmons, Jane, illus. 2002. (Illus.). 32p. (J). 16.95 (978-0-689-84368-6(2) , McElderry, Margaret K.) Simon & Schuster Children's Publishing.

Stadler, John. One Seal. Stadler, John, illus. 1999. (Illus.). 32p. (J). (ps-2). 16.99 (978-0-531-33195-8(4)); pap. 15.95 (978-0-531-30195-1(8)) Scholastic, Inc. (Orchard Bks.).

SEAMANSHIP

see also Navigation

Mosenthal, Basil. Young Sailor: How to Be a Good Sailor & Have Fun! 2nd ed. 2003. (Illus.). 36p. pap. 12.95 (978-0-7136-6395-2(2)) A & C Black GBR. *Dist:* MBI Distribution Services.

Mosenthal, Basil & Pelling, Sue. Getting Afloat. 2003. (Illus.). 80p. pap. 7.95 (978-0-7136-5278-9(0)) A & C Black GBR. *Dist:* MBI Distribution Services.

Pike, Dag. Practical Motor Cruising. 2003. (Illus.). 192p. 22.95 (978-0-229-11827-4(5)) A & C Black GBR. *Dist:* MBI Distribution Services.

SEAMEN

see Sailors

SEARCH AND RESCUE OPERATIONS

see Rescue Work

SEASCAPES

see Marine Painting

SEASHORE

Amery, Heather. What's Happening at the Seaside? Cartwright, Stephen, illus. rev. ed. 2006. 16p. (J). pap. 5.99 (978-0-7945-1290-3(9) , Usborne) EDC Publishing.

Anderson, Sheila. Coast. 2008. (First Step Nonfiction - Landforms Ser.). (J). lib. bdg. 18.60 (***978-0-8225-8595-4(2)*** , Lerner Pubns.) Lerner Publishing Group.

Arnosky, Jim. Beach Combing: Exploring the Seashore. 2004. (Illus.). 32p. (J). (gr. 2-7). 15.99 (978-0-525-47104-2(9) , Dutton Juvenile) Penguin Group (USA) Inc.

Atseriak, Liz, et al. At the Beach. Curtis, Katie, illus. l.t. ed. 1999. 8p. (J). (gr. k-3). pap. 6.00 (978-1-58084-050-7(7)) Lower Kuskokwim Schl. District.

—Cenami. Curtis, Katie, illus. l.t. ed. 1999. Tr. of At the Beach. (ESK.). 8p. (J). (gr. k-3). pap. 6.00 (978-1-58084-116-0(3)) Lower Kuskokwim Schl. District.

—Higyami (At the Beach) Curtis, Katie, illus. l.t. ed. 1999. (ESK.). 8p. (J). (gr. k-3). pap. 6.00 (978-1-58084-134-4(1)) Lower Kuskokwim Schl. District.

—Imarpiim Ceniini (At the Beach) Curtis, Katie, illus. l.t. ed. 1999. (ESK.). 8p. (J). (gr. k-3). pap. 6.00 (978-1-58084-051-4(5)) Lower Kuskokwim Schl. District.

—Sigyami (At the Beach) Curtis, Katie, illus. l.t. ed. 1999. (ESK.). 8p. (J). (gr. k-3). pap. 6.00 (978-1-58084-127-6(9)) Lower Kuskokwim Schl. District.

—Sirrami (At the Beach) Curtis, Katie, illus. l.t. ed. 1999. (ESK.). 8p. (J). (gr. k-3). pap. 6.00 (978-1-58084-141-2(4)) Lower Kuskokwim Schl. District.

—Tagium Sinaani (at the Beach) Curtis, Katie, illus. l.t. ed. 1999. (ESK.). 8p. (J). (gr. k-3). pap. 6.00 (978-1-58084-121-4(X)) Lower Kuskokwim Schl. District.

Bedford, Kate. Seashores. 2005. (Illus.). 32p. (J). (gr. 3-7). lib. bdg. 27.10 (978-1-59604-038-0(6)) Stargazer Bks.

Beylon, Cathy. At the Beach. 2004. 32p. (J). pap. 2.95 (978-0-486-43643-2(8)) Dover Pubns., Inc.

Blaxland, Beth. Sea Shores. 2001. (Water Worlds Ser.). (Illus.). 32p. (J). (gr. 4 up). 28.00 (978-0-7910-6568-6(5) , 010356, Chelsea Hse.) Facts On File, Inc.

Burgess, Thornton W. Burgess Sea Shore Book for Children. (J). 26.95 (978-0-8488-0403-9(1)) Amereon LTD.

Burton, Margie & French, Tammy, Cathy - Jones. Playas limpias & Clean Beaches. 2005. spiral bd. 66.00 (***978-1-4108-5625-8(9)***) Benchmark Education Co.

Capogna, Vera Vullo. Did You Ever Wonder about Things You Find at the Beach? 1998. (Did You Ever Wonder? Ser.). (Illus.). 32p. (J). (gr. k-3). lib. bdg. 22.79 (978-0-7614-0851-2(7) , Benchmark Bks.) Cavendish, Marshall Corp.

Christian, Sandra J. Lifeguards. 2002. (Community Helpers Ser.). (Illus.). 92p. (J). (gr. 1-2). 18.60 (978-0-7368-1129-3(X) , Bridgestone Bks.) Capstone Pr., Inc.

Crossingham, John & Kalman, Bobbie. Cadenas Alimentarias de la Costa Marina. 2006. (Cadenas Alimentarias Ser.). (SPA., Illus.). 32p. (J). pap. (978-0-7787-8547-7(5)) Crabtree Publishing Co.

Darling, Kathy. Seashore Babies. 2002. (gr. k-3). lib. bdg. 15.25 (978-0-613-63529-5(9)) Tandem Library Bks.

—Seashore Babies. Darling, Tara, photos by. 2002. (Illus.). 32p. (J). pap. 6.95 (978-0-8027-7534-4(9)) Walker & Co.

Day. Oceans & Beaches. 2003. (Biomes Atlas Ser.). (Illus.). 64p. pap. 9.50 (978-1-4109-0013-5(4)); (J). pap. 48.30 (978-1-4109-0248-1(X)) Raintree.

Day, Trevor. Oceans & Beaches. 2003. (Biomes Atlases Ser.). (Illus.). 64p. (J). lib. bdg. 31.42 (978-0-7398-5512-6(3)) Raintree.

Dorling Kindersley Publishing Staff. Beach. 2004. (Dk Picture Stickers Ser.). 16p. (J). pap. 3.99 (978-0-7566-0247-5(5)) Dorling Kindersley Publishing, Inc.

—Shoreline. 2000. (978-0-606-17813-6(9)) Tandem Library Bks.

Dorling Kindersley Publishing Staff, ed. Seashore. 2004. (Dk Eyewitness Books Ser.). (Illus.). 72p. (J). (ps-12). 15.99 (978-0-7566-0721-0(3)) Dorling Kindersley Publishing, Inc.

Dunn, Mary. My Adventure Building the Eiffel Tower. 2007. 44p. (J). 8.99 (978-1-59092-413-6(4) , Orchard Academy Pr.) Windstorm Creative.

Emmer, Rae. Community Service. 2002. (Reading Power Ser.). (Illus.). 24p. (J). (gr. 1). lib. bdg. 17.25 (978-0-8239-5967-9(8) , PowerKids Pr.) Rosen Publishing Group, Inc., The.

Fowler, Allan. Living near the Sea. 2000. (Rookie Read-About Geography Ser.). (Illus.). 32p. (J). (gr. 1-2). pap. 5.95 (978-0-516-27053-1(2) , Children's Pr.) Scholastic Library Publishing.

—Living near the Sea. 2000. (gr. k-3). lib. bdg. 14.10 (978-0-613-54736-9(5)) Tandem Library Bks.

From Rocks to Sand: Level L, 6 vols. (Wonder Worldtm Ser.). 16p. 34.95 (978-0-7802-4575-4(X)) Wright Group, The.

Fun at the Beach: Individual Title Six-Packs. (Rigby Focus Ser.). 16p. (gr. k up). 26.00 (978-0-7578-5297-8(1)); 28.00 (978-0-7578-5531-3(8)) Rigby Education.

Galko, Francine. Seashore Animals. 2003. (Animals in Their Habitats Ser.). (Illus.). 32p. (J). (gr. k-2). lib. bdg. 21.36 (978-1-4034-0185-4(3)); pap. 6.95 (978-1-4034-0442-8(9)) Heinemann Library.

Greenaway, Theresa, ed. Ocean: A Foldout Book & Wall Chart. 2005. (Illus.). 12p. (J). (gr. k-4). reprint ed. 10.00 (978-0-7567-8533-8(2)) DIANE Publishing Co.

Gresko, Marcia S. Tide Pools. 2001. (Kidhaven Science Library). (Illus.). 48p. (J). (gr. 3-5). 26.20 (978-0-7377-0748-9(8) , LML00102-178567, Kidhaven) Thomson Gale.

Halpern, Monica. All about Tide Pools. 2007. (Science Chapters Ser.). 48p. (J). (gr. 1-4). lib. bdg. 17.90 (***978-1-4263-0184-1(7)*** , National Geographic Children's Bks.) National Geographic Society.

Harcourt School Publishers Staff. Salt & Sand. 3rd ed. 2002. (Trophies English Language Learners Ser.). (Illus.). pap. 5.10 (978-0-15-327658-3(4)) Harcourt Schl. Pubs.

Hill, Mary. Let's Go to the Beach. 2004. (Wel-Weekend Fun Ser.). (Illus.). 24p. (J). 18.00 (978-0-516-23994-1(5) , Watts, Franklin); pap. 4.95 (978-0-516-25921-5(0) , Children's Pr.) Scholastic Library Publishing.

Holland, Gini. I Live near the Ocean. 2004. (Weekly Reader Early Learning Library). (Illus.). 24p. (gr. k up). (J). pap. 5.95 (978-0-8368-4089-6(5)); (YA). lib. bdg. 19.33 (978-0-8368-4082-7(8)) Stevens, Gareth Inc. (Weekly Reader Early Learning Library).

—I Live near the Ocean/Vivo cerca del Mar. Coffey, Colleen & Carrillo, Consuelo, trs. 2004. (Weekly Reader Early Learning Library). (SPA & ENG., Illus.). 24p. (J). (gr. k up). pap. 5.95 (978-0-8368-4137-4(9)); lib. bdg. 19.33 (978-0-8368-4130-5(1)) Stevens, Gareth Inc. (Weekly Reader Early Learning Library).

Hooper, Roseanne. Life on the Coastlines, 1 vols. 2001. (World Book Ecology Ser.). 32p. (J). (978-0-7166-5229-8(3)) World Bk., Inc.

Huggins-Cooper, Lynn. Seashore. McNicholas, Shelagh & Burroughs, Dave, trs. McNicholas, Shelagh & Burroughs, Dave, illus. 2004. 30p. (J). lib. bdg. (978-1-58340-446-1(5)) Smart Apple Media.

I Feel Hot, 6 Packs. (ps-2). 23.00 (978-0-7635-9014-7(2)) Rigby Education.

Jarrell, Pamela R. Diving at the Reef. Ruminski, Jeff, illus. 2002. (Big Bks.). 8p. (J). (ps-1). pap. 10.95 (978-1-57332-200-3(8)); pap. 10.95 (978-1-57332-201-0(6)) HighReach Learning, Inc.

Johansson, Philip. The Seashore: A Saltwater Web of Life. 2007. (Wonderful Water Biomes Ser.). (Illus.). 48p. (J). (gr. 3-4). lib. bdg. 23.93 (***978-0-7660-2811-1(9)*** , Enslow Elementary) Enslow Pubs., Inc.

Kent, Lorna, illus. At the Beach. 2004. 8p. (J). bds. 3.99 (978-1-85854-087-0(9)) Brimax Books Ltd. GBR. *Dist:* Byeway Bks.

Kerrigan, Michael. Coastlines. 2004. (Geography Fact Files Ser.). (J). lib. bdg. 28.50 (978-1-58340-424-9(4)) Smart Apple Media.

Kingsley, Charles. Glaucus or the Wonders of the Shore. 2004. reprint ed. pap. 15.95 (978-1-4191-2183-8(9)); pap. 1.99 (978-1-4192-2183-5(3)) Kessinger Publishing, LLC.

LeapFrog Staff, compiled by. At the Shore. 2001. (J). (ps-2). spiral bd. 14.95 (978-1-58605-056-6(7)) LeapFrog Enterprises, Inc.

Litchfield, Jo. Beach. 2004. (Look & Say Board Books Ser.). (Illus.). 10p. (J). 7.95 (978-0-7945-0703-9(4) , Usborne) EDC Publishing.

Llewellyn, Claire. Seashore & Tides. 2007. (Illus.). 24p. (J). (***978-1-59771-019-0(9)***) Sea-To-Sea Pubns.

Macken, JoAnn Early. Beaches. 2005. (Illus.). 24p. (J). pap. (978-0-8368-4889-2(6)); lib. bdg. 19.33 (978-0-8368-4882-3(9)) Stevens, Gareth Inc.

—Beaches: Playas. 2005. (SPA., Illus.). 24p. (J). (978-0-8368-6034-4(9)) Stevens, Gareth Inc.

—Beaches/Playas. 2005. (SPA., Illus.). 24p. (ps-17). lib. bdg. 19.33 (978-0-8368-6027-6(6)) Stevens, Gareth Inc.

McFarlane, Sheryl. A Pod of Orcas: A Seaside Counting Book. Wakelin, Kirsti, illus. 2006. 28p. (J). pap. 7.95 (978-1-55041-722-5(3)) Fitzhenry & Whiteside, Ltd. CAN. *Dist:* F & W Pubns., Inc.

McFarlane, Sheryl & Hartmann, Barbara. A Pod of Orcas: A Seaside Counting Book. Wakelin, Kirsti Anne, illus. 2002. 24p. (J). (978-1-55041-681-7(2)) Fitzhenry & Whiteside, Ltd.

Milbourne, Anna. On the Seashore. 2006. 24p. (J). 9.99 (978-0-7945-1069-5(8) , Usborne) EDC Publishing.

Morgan, Sally. A Tide on the Seashore. 2000. (Life In... Ser.). (Illus.). 32p. (J). (gr. 2-6). lib. bdg. 16.95 (978-1-929298-87-7(0)) Chrysalis Education.

Morris. Earth's Changing Coasts 6-Pack. 2003. (Illus.). pap. 40.50 (978-1-4109-0404-1(0)) Raintree.

Mullarkey, Lisa. Splashing by the Shore: Beach Activities for Kids. Dixon, Debra Spina, illus. 2007. 64p. (J). (gr. 1-3). pap. 9.95 (978-1-58685-884-1(X)) Gibbs Smith, Publisher.

Murray, W. On the Beach. (Sunstart Ser.: No. 747-2). (Illus.). 50p. (J). (ps-5). 3.50 (978-0-7214-8001-5(2) , Dutton Juvenile) Penguin Group (USA) Inc.

National Geographic Society Staff. Seashore Life. 2002. (My First Pocket Guides Ser.). (Illus.). 80p. (J). (gr. 1-5). pap. 5.95 (978-0-7922-6576-4(9) , National Geographic Children's Bks.) National Geographic Society.

Newman-D'Amico, Fran. Seashore Fun. 1998. (Illus.). 32p. (J). pap. 2.95 (978-0-486-40352-6(1)) Dover Pubns., Inc.

O'Brien, John & Bilkins, Maxi. The Beach Patrol, rev. ed. 2004. (Illus.). 32p. (J). 15.95 (978-0-8050-6911-2(9) , Holt, Henry & Co. Bks. For Young Readers) Holt, Henry & Co.

Oceans: Individual Title Six-Packs. (On Deck Ser.: Vol. 2). 24p. (gr. 4-5). 35.00 (978-0-7578-5827-7(9)) Rigby Education.

Oliver, Clare. Life in a Tide Pool. 2002. (Microhabitats Ser.). (Illus.). 32p. (J). lib. bdg. 25.69 (978-0-7398-4332-1(X)) Raintree.

On the Beach: Individual Title-Six Packs. (Chiquilibros Ser.). (gr. k-1). 23.00 (978-0-7635-0448-9(3)) Rigby Education.

Otten, Jack. Watch Me Build a Sandcastle. 2002. (Welcome Books). (Illus.). 24p. (J). (ps-k). 18.00 (978-0-516-23946-0(5)); pap. 4.95 (978-0-516-23496-0(X)) Scholastic Library Publishing. (Children's Pr.).

—Watch Me Build a Sandcastle. 2002. (gr. k-3). lib. bdg. 12.95 (978-0-613-58809-6(6)) Tandem Library Bks.

Parker, Steve & Dorling Kindersley Publishing Staff. Seashore. 2004. (Eyewitness Books). (Illus.). 72p. (J). lib. bdg. 19.99 (978-0-7566-0720-3(5)) Dorling Kindersley Publishing, Inc.

Patrizzi, Barbara. O Is for Oystercatcher: A Book of Seaside ABCs. Patrizzi, Barbara, illus. 2005. (Illus.). 55p. (978-1-59322-008-2(1)) Down The Shore Publishing.

Peterson, Roger T. & Kricher, John C. Peterson First Guide to Seashores. Morrison, Gordon, illus. 2nd ed. 1998. (First Guides). 228p. pap. 5.95 (978-0-395-91180-8(X)) Houghton Mifflin Co. Trade & Reference Div.

La Playa: Individual Title Six-Packs. (Literatura 2000 Ser.). (SPA.). (ps-1). 28.00 (978-0-7635-1001-5(7)) Rigby Education.

Pledger, Maurice, illus. By the Seashore: A Touch-and-Feel Adventure, , 2002. (Nature Trail Bks.). 16p. (J). (ps-1). 12.95 (978-1-57145-322-8(9)) Advantage Pubs. Group.

Potter, Jean. Science in Seconds at the Beach: Exciting Experiments You Can Do in Ten Minutes. 1998. (gr. 3-6). lib. bdg. 22.20 (978-0-613-81940-4(3)) Tandem Library Bks.

Procter, Alice. At the Beach: The Parts of a Day. 2007. (I Can Tell Time Ser.). 24p. (J). (gr. k-2). lib. bdg. 19.93 (***978-0-8368-8388-6(8)***) Stevens, Gareth Inc.

Proctor, Alice. At the Beach: The Parts of a Day. 2007. (J). pap. (***978-0-8368-8393-0(4)***) Stevens, Gareth Inc.

Pryor, Kimberley Jane. Rocky Shores. 2007. (J). (***978-1-59920-139-9(9)***) Smart Apple Media.

Raintree Steck-Vaughn Staff. Beach Creatures. 2000. (Illus.). (J). pap. 29.12 (978-0-8172-6457-4(4)) Steck-Vaughn.

Rau, Dana Meachen. At the Beach. 2007. (Fun Time Ser.). 24p. (J). lib. bdg. 22.79 (***978-0-7614-2609-7(4)*** , Benchmark Bks.) Cavendish, Marshall Corp.

Richter, Abigail. By the Ocean: Learning the Long O Sound. (PowerPhonics Ser.). (Illus.). (J). 2002. 24p. (gr. 1). lib. bdg. 18.50 (978-0-8239-5922-8(8)); 2001. 23p. pap. 26.40 (978-0-8239-8267-7(X)) Rosen Publishing Group, Inc., The. (PowerKids Pr.).

Rigby Education Staff. Look up, Look down, Look All Around. (Illus.). 8p. (J). bds. 3.95 (978-0-7635-6504-6(0) , 765040C99) Rigby Education.

Ring, Elizabeth. Shorelands. 2004. (Illus.). 48p. (J). (gr. 2-4). 24.95 (978-1-4103-0316-5(0) , Blackbirch Pr., Inc.) Thomson Gale.

Royston, Angela. Coasts. 2004. (Heinemann First Library). (Illus.). 32p. (J). 24.21 (978-1-4034-5595-6(3)) Heinemann Library.

Saunders, G. & Swallow, S. Seashore. 2004. (Spotter's Guides Sticker Bks.). (Illus.). 32p. (J). (gr. 2 up). pap. 7.95 (978-0-7945-0185-3(0) , Usborne) EDC Publishing.

Schwartz, David M. At the Seashore. Kuhn, Dwight, photos by. 1998. (Springboards into Science Ser.). (Illus.). 24p. (J). (gr. 1 up). lib. bdg. 19.93 (978-0-8368-2224-3(2)) Stevens, Gareth Inc.

Serafini, Frank. Looking Closely along the Shore. 2008. (Illus.). 40p. (***978-1-55453-141-7(1)***) Kids Can Pr., Ltd.

Shannon, George. Sea Gifts. Azarian, Mary, illus. 2000. 32p. (ps-3). pap. 7.95 (978-1-56792-109-0(4)) Godine, David R. Pub.

Shorelines. 2001. (J). cd-rom 69.95 (978-1-56791-298-2(2)) Environmental Media Corp.

Skelton, Olivia. The Atlantic Coast. 2000. (Ecosystems of North America Ser.). (Illus.). 64p. (YA). (gr. 6 up). lib. bdg. 28.50 (978-0-7614-0903-8(3) , Benchmark Bks.) Cavendish, Marshall Corp.

Smith, Alastair & Howell, Laura. On the Beach. 2004. (Luxury Lift-the-Flap Ser.). 16p. (J). (gr. 1 up). 11.95 (978-0-7945-0740-4(9) , Usborne) EDC Publishing.

Smith, Carrie & Swain, Cameron. Fun at the Beach. 2006. (Early Explorers Ser.). (J). 30.00 (***978-1-4108-6021-7(3)***) Benchmark Education Co.

Soffer, Ruth. Shore Birds: Stained Glass Coloring Book. 2001. (Dover Little Activity Bks.). (Illus.). 8p. (J). (ps up). pap. 1.50 (978-0-486-41617-5(8)) Dover Pubns., Inc.

Squire, Ann O. Animals of the Sea & Shore. 2001. (gr. 3-6). lib. bdg. 15.25 (978-0-613-51613-6(3)) Tandem Library Bks.

Stanley, Mandy. At the Beach. 2002. (All Aboard Ser.). (Illus.). 12p. (J). (gr. 4-6). bds. 4.95 (978-0-7534-5444-2(0) , Kingfisher) Houghton Mifflin Co. Trade & Reference Div.

—Vamos a la Playa. 2003. (Classic Collections). (SPA., Illus.). 12p. (J). (ps-k). bds. 3.95 (978-0-7534-5689-7(3) , Kingfisher) Houghton Mifflin Co. Trade & Reference Div.

Steele, Phillip W. Changing Coastlines. 2004. (Earth's Changing Landscape Ser.). (Illus.). 46p. (J). lib. bdg. 28.50 (978-1-58340-476-8(7)) Smart Apple Media.

Stewart, Jacqueline. The Glaciers' Treasure Trove: A Field Guide to the Lake Michigan Riviera. 2003. (Illus.). 155p. spiral bd. 19.95 (978-0-9727484-7-6(4)) Lexicus Pr.

Stone, Lynn M. High Tide, Low Tide. 2007. (Illus.). 24p. (J). (978-1-60044-178-3(5)) Rourke Publishing, LLC.

Taylor, Barbara. Coastal Habitats. 2006. (Exploring Habitats Ser.). (Illus.). 36p. (J). lib. bdg. (978-0-8368-7252-1(5)) Stevens, Gareth Inc.

Theodorou, Rod. Along the Seashore. 2000. (Amazing Journeys Ser.). (Illus.). 32p. (J). (gr. 3-5). lib. bdg. 22.79 (978-1-57572-483-6(9)) Heinemann Library.

Thomas, Maryann. Summer at the Beach: Learning the EA Sound. (PowerPhonics Ser.). (Illus.). (J). 2002. 24p. (gr. 1). lib. bdg. 18.50 (978-0-8239-5950-1(3)); 2001. 23p. pap. 26.40 (978-0-8239-8295-0(5)) Rosen Publishing Group, Inc., The. (PowerKids Pr.).

Unstead, Sue. Seashore. 2006. (Illus.). 32p. (J). (***978-0-439-91178-8(8)*** , Scholastic) Scholastic, Inc.

Vogel, Carole G. Shifting Shores. 2003. (Restless Sea Ser.). (gr. 5-8). pap. 12.95 (978-0-531-16683-3(X)); (Illus.). 80p. (J). 30.50 (978-0-531-12322-5(7)) Scholastic Library Publishing. (Watts, Franklin).

—Shifting Shores. 2003. (gr. 5-8). lib. bdg. 22.20 (978-0-613-67855-1(9)) Tandem Library Bks.

Waldron, Melanie. Coasts. 2007. (J). (***978-1-4034-9605-8(6)***) Heinemann.

Walker, Jane. La Costa. 2001. (SPA., Illus.). 32p. (J). (ps-3). 10.95 (978-84-263-3171-7(8)) Lectorum Pubns., Inc.

Walker, Pam & Wood, Elaine. The Coast. 2005. (Life in the Sea Ser.). (Illus.). 132p. (J). (gr. 4-9). 35.00 (978-0-8160-5701-6(X)) Facts On File, Inc.

Waters, Jo. A Walk on the Beach. 2006. (Illus.). 24p. (J). (978-1-4109-2290-8(1)); pap. 5.75 (978-1-4109-2295-3(2)) Steck-Vaughn.

When the Tide Goes Out: Individual Title, 6 packs. (Story Steps Ser.). (gr. k-2). 20.00 (978-0-7635-9590-6(X)) Rigby Education.

Wickings, Ruth. By the Seaside. 2006. (World at Your Feet Ser.). (Illus.). 10p. 9.95 (978-1-84560-024-2(X)) Mercury Bks. Ltd. GBR. *Dist:* International Publishers Marketing.

Wilkes, Angela. Question Time: Seashore. 2001. (Explore & Discover Ser.). (Illus.). (J). (978-0-606-21391-2(0)) Tandem Library Bks.

—The Seashore. 2001. (Question Time Ser.). (Illus.). 32p. (J). (gr. k-3). tchr. ed. 11.95 (978-0-7534-5339-1(8) , Kingfisher) Houghton Mifflin Co. Trade & Reference Div.

—Seashore. 2001. (Question Time Ser.). (Illus.). 32p. (J). (gr. k-3). 6.95 (978-0-7534-5407-7(6) , Kingfisher) Houghton Mifflin Co. Trade & Reference Div.

Wolfe, Frances. Where I Live. 2001. (Illus.). 32p. (J). (ps-1). 14.95 (978-0-88776-529-2(7)) Tundra Bks., Inc./Livres Toundra, Inc. CAN. *Dist:* Random Hse., Inc.

Wynne, Patricia J. Seashore. 2005. 48p. (J). (gr. 3-6). pap., act. bk. ed. 4.95 (978-0-486-44434-5(1)) Dover Pubns., Inc.

Yolen, Jane. Welcome to the Sea of Sand. 1999. (978-0-606-16796-3(X)) Tandem Library Bks.

SEASHORE—FICTION

Adler, David A. Young Cam Jansen & the Double Beach Mystery. Natti, Susanna, illus. (Young Cam Jansen Ser.: No. 8). 32p. (J). (gr. k-2). 2003. pap. 3.99 (978-0-14-250079-8(8) , Puffin); 2002. 13.99 (978-0-670-03531-1(9) , Viking Juvenile) Penguin Group (USA) Inc.

Aigner-Clark, Julie. What Does Violet See? Sand & Sea. Zaidi, Nadeem, illus. 2002. (Baby Einstein Ser.). 16p. (ps-ps). 5.99 (978-0-7868-0873-1(X)) Disney Pr.

Andrei, Julie. Seagulls at the Seashore. Andrei, Julie, illus. 2003. (Illus.). 32p. (J). 14.00 (978-0-8059-5521-7(6)) Dorrance Publishing Co., Inc.

Apsley, Brenda, ed. Kevin's Seaside Picnic. 2000. (Let's Start! Teacher's Pets Ser.). (Illus.). 32p. (J). (ps-1). 6.95 (978-1-57145-438-6(1) , Silver Dolphin Bks.) Advantage Pubs. Group.

Arena, Felice & Kettle, Phil. Hit the Beach. Vane, Mitch, illus. 2004. (J). pap. (978-1-59336-361-1(3)) Mondo Publishing.

At the Beach. 2004. (Out & about Ser.). 12p. (J). bds. 4.99 (978-1-85997-807-8(X)) Byeway Bks.

Axelrod, Amy. Pigs on a Blanket. McGinley-Nally, Sharon, illus. 1998. 40p. (J). (ps-3). 6.99 (978-0-689-82252-0(9) , Aladdin) Simon & Schuster Children's Publishing.

Banks, Kate. A Gift from the Sea. Hallensleben, Georg, illus. 2001. 40p. (J). (gr. 3-6). 16.00 (978-0-374-32566-4(9) , Farrar, Straus & Giroux (BYR)) Farrar, Straus & Giroux.

Barclay, Jane. Going on a Journey to the Sea. Barrette, Doris, illus. 2001. 32p. (J). (ps-1). 16.95 (978-1-894222-34-1(2)) Lobster Pr. CAN. *Dist:* Univ. of Toronto Pr.

Barlow, Galon L., Jr. The Adventures of Levi & Nathan from the Cape of Cod to the Outer Banks. Guthrie, Adam C., illus. l.t. ed. 1998. (YA). (gr. 6 up). mass mkt. 7.95 (978-0-9666020-2-9(1)) Farewell Pr.

Barron, T. A. The Lost Years of Merlin. unabr. ed. 2004. (Lost Years of Merlin Ser.). 284p. (J). (gr. 5-9). pap. 46.00 incl. audio (978-0-8072-8766-8(0) , YA261SP, Listening Library) Random Hse. Audio Publishing Group.

Bassede, Francine. George's Store at the Shore. Barth, Dominic, tr. 1998. (Illus.). 32p. (J). (ps-1). 15.99 (978-0-531-33083-8(4) , Orchard Bks.) Scholastic, Inc.

Beach Ball. 2004. (J). 5.99 (978-0-7566-0250-5(5)) Dorling Kindersley Publishing, Inc.

Bella & Rosie Beach Stories. 2007. (J). per. (***978-1-932570-83-0(7)***) Literacy Footprints Inc.

Berenstain, Stan & Berenstain, Jan. The Berenstain Bears by the Sea. Berenstain, Stan & Berenstain, Jan, illus. 2002. (Berenstain Bears Ser.). (Illus.). (J). (gr. k-3). 11.91 (978-0-7587-0969-1(2)) Book Wholesalers, Inc.

—The Berenstain Bears by the Sea. 1998. (Berenstain Bears Ser.). (Illus.). 32p. (ps-2). (J). pap. 3.99 (978-0-679-88719-5(9)); lib. bdg. 11.99 (978-0-679-98719-2(3)) Random Hse. Children's Bks. (Random Hse. Bks. for Young Readers).

—The Berenstain Bears by the Sea. 1998. (Berenstain Bears Ser.). (Illus.). (J). (gr. k-3). lib. bdg. 11.80 (978-0-613-07341-7(X)) Tandem Library Bks.

—The Berenstain Bears Go on Vacation. 2006. (Berenstain Bears Ser.: No. 1). (Illus.). 32p. (J). 9.99 (978-0-06-057431-4(3)); Bk. 1. lib. bdg. 15.89 (978-0-06-057432-1(1)) HarperCollins Pubs.

Berenstain, Stan & Berenstain, Jan. The Berenstain Bears' Seashore Treasure. Berenstain, Stan, illus. 2005. (Illus.). 30p. (J). lib. bdg. 13.85 (***978-1-4242-0814-2(9))** Fitzgerald Bks.

—The Berenstain Bears' Seashore Treasure. Berenstain, Stan & Berenstain, Jan, illus. 2005. (Berenstain Bears Ser.). (Illus.). 32p. (J). (gr. k-3). 15.99 (978-0-06-058340-8(1) , Harper Festival) HarperCollins Pubs.

—The Berenstain Bears' Seashore Treasure. 2005. (Berenstain Bears Ser.). (Illus.). 32p. (J). (ps). pap. 3.99 (978-0-06-058341-5(X) , Harper Festival) HarperCollins Pubs.

Billington, Rachel. There's More to Life. 2007. 240p. pap. 10.95 (***978-0-340-88247-4(6))** Hodder Children's Division GBR. *Dist:* Independent Pubs. Group.

Biro, Maureen Boyd. Walking with Maga. Guevara, Linda L., ed. Wheeler, Joyce, illus. 2002. 32p. (J). (ps-3). 16.95 (978-0-9700863-4-1(2)) All About Kids Publishing.

Blackaby, Susan. El Lugar de Luis. Gallagher-Cole, Mernie, illus. 2006. (Read-It! Readers en Espanol Ser.).Tr. of Place for Mike. (SPA.). 32p. (J). (ps-3). 19.95 (978-1-4048-1688-6(7)) Picture Window Bks.

Blackstone, Stella. Secret Seahorse. Beaton, Clare, illus. 24p. (J). 2005. pap. 6.99 (978-1-84148-937-7(9)); 2005. 15.99 (978-1-84148-704-5(X)); 2004. per. 6.99 (978-1-905236-15-2(8)) Barefoot Bks., Inc.

Blumberg, Margie. Sunny Bunnies. Goulding, June, illus. 2008. 32p. (J). 15.00 (***978-0-9624166-4-4(9))** MB Publishing, LLC.

Blumenthal, Deborah. The Pink House at the Seashore. Chayka, Doug, illus. 2005. 32p. (J). (gr. 3-5). 16.00 (978-0-618-37886-9(3) , Clarion Bks.) Houghton Mifflin Co. Trade & Reference Div.

Borkin, Jeff. Blue's Beach Day. Craig, Karen, illus. 2004. (Blue's Clues Ser.: Vol. 9). 24p. (J). pap. 3.99 (978-0-689-86499-5(X) , Simon Spotlight/Nickelodeon) Simon & Schuster Children's Publishing.

Branford, Henrietta & Beardshaw, Rosalind. Splash! (Illus.). 32p. (J). 19.99 (978-0-340-85550-8(9)) Macmillan Publishers Ltd. GBR. *Dist:* Trafalgar Square Publishing.

Briant, Ed. A Day at the Beach. Briant, Ed, illus. 2006. (Illus.). 32p. (J). 16.99 (978-0-06-079981-6(1)) HarperCollins Pubs.

Brooks, Brian. Oopsy Daisy's Bad Day. Brooks, Brian, illus. 2007. (Illus.). 62p. (J). reprint ed. 13.00 (***978-1-4223-9004-7(7))** DIANE Publishing Co.

Brouillet, Chrystine. Une Plage Trop Chaude. 2002. (Roman Plus Ser.). (FRE.). 160p. (YA). (gr. 8 up). pap. (978-2-89021-148-3(7)) Diffusion du livre Mirabel.

Bryant, Megan E. Strawberry Shortcake at the Beach. 2003. (Strawberry Shortcake Ser.). (Illus.). 32p. (J). (ps-2). mass mkt. 3.99 (978-0-448-43187-1(4) , Grosset & Dunlap) Penguin Group (USA) Inc.

Bulion, Leslie. Uncharted Waters. 2006. 155p. (J). 14.95 (978-1-56145-365-8(X) , Peachtree Junior) Peachtree Pubs., Ltd.

The Busy Beach. 2003. (J). 10.99 (978-0-89610-768-7(X)) Island Heritage Publishing.

Byars, Betsy. The Animal, the Vegetable, & John D. Jones. 150p. (J). (gr. 4-6). pap. 3.50 (978-0-8072-1414-5(0) , Listening Library) Random Hse. Audio Publishing Group.

Chapman, Jason. Ted, Bo, & Diz: The First Adventure. 2007. 28p. (J). (ps-2). 16.00 (***978-1-56148-592-5(6))** Good Bks.

Clark, Joyce. Katie. 2006. 196p. (***978-1-4122-0067-7(9))** Trafford Publishing.

Clements, Andrew. Because Your Daddy Loves You. Alley, R. W., tr. Alley, R. W., illus. 2005. 32p. (J). (gr. k-3). 16.00 (978-0-618-00361-7(4) , Clarion Bks.) Houghton Mifflin Co. Trade & Reference Div.

Cocca-Leffler, Maryann. Clams All Year. 1998. (J). (978-0-606-13277-0(5)) Tandem Library Bks.

Come Away from the Water, Shirley. 2004. (J). pap. 14.95 incl. audio (978-1-56008-183-8(X)) Weston Woods Studios, Inc.

Come Away from the Water Shirley, 2004. (J). 24.95 incl. audio (978-1-56008-182-1(1)) Weston Woods Studios, Inc.

Condra, Estelle. See the Ocean. Crockett-Blassingame, Linda, illus. 2002. 32p. (gr. k-3). 9.95 (978-1-59093-067-0(3)) Warehousing & Fulfillment Specialists, LLC (WFS, LLC).

Cooper, Elisha. Beach. 2006. (Illus.). 40p. (J). pap. 16.99 (978-0-439-68785-0(3) , Orchard Bks.) Scholastic, Inc.

Coplans, Peta. Cat & Dog. 2000. (Illus.). (J). pap. (978-0-14-056140-1(4) , Puffin) Penguin Group (USA) Inc.

Coste, Marion. Wild Beach. Gray, Cissy, illus. 2005. 32p. (J). pap. 8.25 (978-0-89317-062-2(3) , WW-623); lib. bdg. 17.95 (978-0-89317-061-5(5) , WW-0615) Finney Co., Inc. (Windward Publishing).

Counts, Elizabeth. Buffy Visits the Beach. 1998. (Illus.). 24p. (J). (gr. k-2). pap. 7.00 (978-0-8059-4472-3(9)) Dorrance Publishing Co., Inc.

Crockett-Blassingame, Linda, illus. See the Ocean. 2006. 32p. (J). 14.95 (978-0-9778143-0-5(0)) Inclusive Books LLC.

Cummings, Priscilla. Meet Chadwick & His Chesapeake Bay Friends. Cohen, A. R., illus. 1999. 30p. (J). (ps-3). 11.95 (978-0-87033-516-7(2) , Tidewater Pubs.) Cornell Maritime Pr., Inc.

Dad at the Beach: Individual Title Six-Packs. (Sails Literacy Ser.). (gr. 1-2). 36.00 (978-0-7578-6714-9(6)) Rigby Education.

Davies, Jacqueline. The House Takes a Vacation. White, Lee, illus. 2006. (J). 16.99 (978-0-7614-5331-4(8)) Cavendish, Marshall Corp.

Dodd, Anne W. The Story of the Sea Glass. Owens, Mary Beth, illus. 1999. 32p. (gr. k-3). 15.95 (978-0-89272-416-1(1)) Down East Bks.

Dodd, Lynley. The Smallest Turtle. Dodd, Lynley, illus. 2000. (Gold Star First Readers Ser.). (Illus.). 32p. (J). (gr. 1 up). lib. bdg. 22.00 (978-0-8368-2692-0(2)) Stevens, Gareth Inc.

Dower, Laura. Hit the Beach. 2nd rev. ed. 2006. (From the Files of Madison Finn Ser.: Bk. 2). 272p. (gr. 3-7). pap. 5.99 (978-0-7868-3780-9(2)) Hyperion Pr.

Doyle, Malachy. Riley, Kylie & Smiley. Evans, Fran, illus. 2002. 48p. pap. 11.95 (978-1-84323-118-9(2)) Beekman Bks., Inc.

Eastman, Peter Anthony. Fred & Ted Like to Fly. 2007. (Beginner Books(R) Ser.). (Illus.). 48p. (J). (gr. k-3). 8.99 (978-0-375-84064-7(8)); lib. bdg. 12.99 (978-0-375-94064-4(2)) Random Hse. Children's Bks. (Random Hse. Bks. for Young Readers).

Edelson, Madelyn. The Proud Beech: A Long Island Folk Tale. Tucker, Diane, illus. 2004. 48p. (J). pap. 14.95 (978-0-9658920-7-0(7)) Edelson, Madelyn.

Ehrlich, H. M. Louie's Goose. Bolam, Emily, illus. 32p. (J). (gr. k-3). 2002. pap. 5.95 (978-0-618-26008-9(0)); 2000. tchr. ed. 15.00 (978-0-618-03023-1(9)) Houghton Mifflin Co. Trade & Reference Div. (Walter Lorraine).

—Louie's Goose. 2002. (gr. k-3). lib. bdg. 14.10 (978-0-613-72913-0(7)) Tandem Library Bks.

Finale, Frank. A Gull's Story: A Tale of Learning about Life, the Shore & the ABCs. Valente, George C., ed. Moore, Margie, illus. 2007. 36p. (J). 22.00 (978-0-9632906-3-2(0)) Jersey Shore Pubns.

—A Gull's Story, Part 2: Counting at the Shore. Moore, Margie, illus. 2007. (J). 22.00 (978-0-9777077-0-6(9)) Jersey Shore Pubns.

Finale, Frank. A Gull's Story, Part 3: Colors at the Shore. Moore, Margie, illus. 2007. (J). 22.00 (***978-0-9777077-2-0(5))** Jersey Shore Pubns.

Finley, Judith S. As the Waters Cover the Sea: A Visit to the Seashore. Fleet, Eric C., photos by. l.t. ed. 1998. (Caitlyn & Eryn Ser.: No. 1). (Illus.). 20p. (J). (gr. k-2). pap. 6.00 (978-0-9665424-0-0(1)) Master Design, The.

Forrester, Sandra. The Witches of Sea-Dragon Bay: The Adventures of Beatrice Bailey. 2003. (Illus.). 224p. (J). pap. 4.95 (978-0-7641-2633-8(4)) Barron's Educational Series, Inc.

Forton-Barnes, Therese. Zaki & Venus. 2007. 13.95 (***978-1-59526-388-9(8))** Media Creations, Inc.

Franco, Betsy. Shells. Sorra, Kristin, illus. 2000. (Rookie Readers Ser.). 32p. (J). (gr. 1-2). 19.50 (978-0-516-22012-3(8) , Children's Pr.) Scholastic Library Publishing.

Frazee, Marla. A Couple of Boys Go to Antarctica (Sort Of) 2008. 40p. (J). 16.00 (***978-0-15-206020-6(0))** Harcourt Trade Pubs.

G Studios & Crouch, Cheryl. Solo Act. 2007. (Chosen Girls' Ser.). 144p. (J). pap. 6.99 (978-0-310-71270-1(X)) Zonderkidz.

Gallup, Tracy. Shell Crazy. Gallup, Tracy, illus. 2007. (Crazy Little Ser.). (Illus.). 40p. (J). 9.95 (***978-1-934133-14-9(0))** Mackinac Island Pr., Inc.

Gamble, Adam. Good Night Beach. Kelly, Cooper, illus. 2007. (Good Night Our World Ser.). 20p. (J). (ps). bds. 7.95 (***978-1-60219-002-3(X))** Our World of Books.

Gauthier, Bertrand. Just Me & My Dad, 2 bks. Sylvestre, Daniel, illus. Incl. Zachary in Camping Out. lib. bdg. 19.93 (978-0-8368-1012-7(0)); Zachary in the Winner. lib. bdg. 19.93 (978-0-8368-1009-7(0)); 24p. (J). (gr. 2 up). 1993. (Illus.). Set lib. bdg. 39.86 (978-0-8368-1006-6(6)) Stevens, Gareth Inc.

Gay, Marie-Louise. Stella, Star of the Sea. 2004. (Illus.). (J). 7.95 (978-0-88899-572-8(5)) Groundwood Bks. CAN. *Dist:* Transition Vendor.

—Stella, Star of the Sea. Gay, Marie-Louise, illus. 1999. (Stella Ser.). (Illus.). 32p. (J). (ps-k). 15.95 (978-0-88899-337-3(4) , Libros Tigrillo) Groundwood Bks. CAN. *Dist:* Perseus Distribution.

Gelsey, James. Sunken Ship: Scooby-Doo y el Barco Hundido. 2004. (Scooby-Doo Ser.). (ENG & SPA.). 64p. (J). mass mkt. 3.99 (978-0-439-55116-8(1) , Scholastic en Espanol) Scholastic, Inc.

Gray, Rita. The Wild Little Horse. Wolff, Ashley, illus. 2005. 32p. (J). (ps-ps). 15.99 (978-0-525-47455-5(2) , Dutton Juvenile) Penguin Group (USA) Inc.

Greenberg, Melanie Hope. The Mermaid Parade. Greenberg, Melanie Hope, illus. 2008. 32p. (J). (ps-k). 16.99 (***978-0-399-24708-8(4)** , Putnam Juvenile) Penguin Group (USA) Inc.

Hardin, Suzanne. No Se Permiten Perros. Romo, Alberto, tr. Friar, Joanne, illus. 1998. (Books for Young Learners).Tr. of No Dogs Allowed. (SPA.). 12p. (J). (gr. k-2). pap. 5.00 (978-1-57274-201-7(1) , A2886) Owen, Richard C. Pubs., Inc.

Hassett, John & Hassett, Ann. Can't Catch Me. Hassett, John & Hassett, Ann, illus. 2006. (Illus.). 32p. (J). (gr. k-3). 16.00 (978-0-618-70490-3(6)) Houghton Mifflin Co.

Hautzig, Deborah. Little Witch Loves to Write. Wickstrom, Sylvie, illus. 2004. (Stepping into Reading Ser.: Vol. 3). 48p. (J). (gr. 1-3). pap. 3.99 (978-0-375-82893-5(1) , Random Hse. Bks. for Young Readers) Random Hse. Children's Bks.

Heady, Heather. What's at the Beach? Storch, Ellen N., illus. l.t. ed. 2005. 10p. (J). (ps-k). pap. 10.95 (978-1-57332-355-0(1)) HighReach Learning, Inc.

Hennessy, B. G. Corduroy Goes to the Beach. McCue, Lisa, illus. 2006. 20p. (J). (gr. 1). 11.99 (978-0-670-06052-8(6) , Viking Juvenile) Penguin Group (USA) Inc.

Hillert, Margaret. Let's Go, Dear Dragon. Kock, Carl, illus. rev. ed. 2006. (Beginning to Read Ser.). 32p. (J). lib. bdg. 18.60 (978-1-59953-021-5(X)) Norwood Hse. Pr.

Hoffman, Basia. The Ocean & Pebbles. Solcyk, Phyllis, illus. l.t. ed. 1999. 32p. (J). (ps-2). pap. (978-1-890582-02-9(6)) Creations by Basia.

Hofmeister, Alan, et al. The Shell. (Reading for All Learners Ser.). (Illus.). (J). pap. (978-1-56861-103-7(X)) Swift Learning Resources.

Holm, Jennifer L. & Holm, Matthew. Beach Babe! 2006. (Babymouse Ser.). (Illus.). 96p. (J). (gr. 2-5). pap. 5.95 (978-0-375-83231-4(9) , Random Hse. Bks. for Young Readers) Random Hse. Children's Bks.

Hope, Laura Lee. The Bobbsey Twins at the Seashore. 2000. (J). 24.95 (978-0-8488-2852-3(6)) Amereon LTD.

—Freddie & Flossie at the Beach. 2006. (Ready-To-Read Ser.). (J). (ps-2). 21.35 (978-1-59961-098-6(1)) Spotlight.

Hoppner, Gabi. Beach Fun. 2004. (What A Series of Fun! Ser.). (Illus.). 10p. (J). bds. 3.99 (978-1-59384-053-2(5)) Parklane Publishing.

Hortten, Jacqueline Faye. Pu Beach. Maximilian Press Staff, illus. l.t. unabr. ed. 2002. 48p. (J). (gr. k-5). pap. 12.50 (978-1-930211-42-1(2)) Maximilian Pr. Pubs.

Howe, James. La Mirona. 1999. Tr. of Watcher. (J). (978-0-606-20217-6(X)) Tandem Library Bks.

—The Watcher. 1999. 192p. (YA). (gr. 7-12). pap. 8.99 (978-0-689-82662-7(1) , 076714008007, Simon Pulse) Simon & Schuster Children's Publishing.

—The Watcher. 1999. (978-0-606-16319-4(0)) Tandem Library Bks.

Hubbell, Patricia. Sea, Sand, Me! Ernst, Lisa Campbell, illus. 2001. 32p. (J). (ps-3). 16.99 (978-0-688-17378-4(0)) HarperCollins Pubs.

Huneck, Stephen. Sally Goes to the Beach. Huneck, Stephen, illus. 2000. (Illus.). 38p. (J). (ps-3). 17.95 (978-0-8109-4186-1(4)) Abrams, Harry N., Inc.

Hutchings, Amy & Hutchings, Richard. Our Day at the Seashore. 2001. (Illus.). (J). (978-0-439-22353-9(9)) Scholastic, Inc.

Inkpen, Mick. Sandcastle. Inkpen, Mick, illus. 2002. (Kipper Ser.). (Illus.). (J). 12.30 (978-0-7587-6470-6(7)) Book Wholesalers, Inc.

Jerome, Kate Boehm. Maggie's Rocky Shore Adventure. Garry-McCord, Kathleen, illus. 2002. (J). (978-1-878244-41-3(8)) Monterey Bay Aquarium.

Jessup, Harley. Grandma Summer. 2001. (Illus.). (J). (978-0-606-21800-9(9)) Tandem Library Bks.

Kalar, Bonnie. A Trip to the Beach. Spreen, Kathe, illus. Date not set. 12p. (J). (ps-2). pap. (978-1-891619-42-7(X)) Corona Pr.

Kettle, Shey. Surf Girls. Thomas, Meredith, illus. 2005. (Girlz Rock! Ser.). (J). pap. (978-1-59336-708-4(2)) Mondo Publishing.

Kittinger, Jo & Miller, Pam. Beach. 2006. 88p. (J). (gr. 1-2). 8.95 (978-0-516-29687-6(6) , Children's Pr.) Scholastic Library Publishing.

Kittinger, Jo S. Going to the Beach. Warren, Shari, illus. 2003. (Rookie Reader Skill Set Ser.). 24p. (J). (gr. k-2). pap. 4.95 (978-0-516-27370-9(1) , Children's Pr.) Scholastic Library Publishing.

—Going to the Beach. 2002. (gr. k-3). lib. bdg. 12.95 (978-0-613-59490-5(8)) Tandem Library Bks.

Knutson, Kimberley. Beach Babble. 1998. (Accelerated Reader Bks.). (Illus.). 32p. (J). (ps-k). 15.95 (978-0-7614-5026-9(2) , Cavendish Children's Bks.) Cavendish, Marshall Corp.

Komaiko, Leah. Just My Dad & Me. Greene, Jeffrey, illus. 1999. (Trophy Picture Bk.). 32p. (J). (ps-2). pap. 5.95 (978-0-06-443562-8(8) , Harper Trophy) HarperCollins Pubs.

—Just My Dad & Me. 1999. (J). (978-0-606-16691-1(2)); lib. bdg. 14.10 (978-0-613-18259-1(6)) Tandem Library Bks.

Koss, Amy Goldman. Kailey. Howe, Philip, illus. 2003. (American Girl of Today Ser.). 152p. (J). pap. 6.95 (978-1-58485-591-0(6)) American Girl Publishing, Inc.

—Kailey. 2003. (gr. 3-6). lib. bdg. 15.25 (978-0-613-86379-7(8)) Tandem Library Bks.

Kotzwinkle, William, et al. Walter the Farting Dog: Banned from the Beach. Colman, Audrey, illus. 2007. 32p. (J). (gr. k up). 16.99 (978-0-525-47812-6(4) , Dutton Juvenile) Penguin Group (USA) Inc.

Kurtz, Carmen. Veva y el Mar.Tr. of Veva & the Sea. (SPA.). 144p. (J). (gr. 3-5). (978-84-279-3129-9(8)) Noguer y Caralt Editores, S. A. ESP. *Dist:* Lectorum Pubns., Inc.

Landry, Leo. Sea Surprise. 2005. (Illus.). 64p. (J). 15.95 (978-0-8050-6645-6(4) , Holt, Henry & Co. Bks. For Young Readers) Holt, Henry & Co.

Landstrom, Olof & Landstrom, Lena. Will Goes to the Beach. Wilberg, Carla, tr. from SWE. Landstrom, Olof & Landstrom, Lena, illus. 2001. (Illus.). 28p. (J). (ps-1). pap. 4.95 (978-91-29-65305-2(3)) R & S Bks. SWE. *Dist:* Macmillan.

Lantz, Frances L. Sea for Yourself. 2004. (Luna Bay Ser.: No. 8). 176p. mass mkt. 4.99 (978-0-06-059520-3(5) , Harper Entertainment) HarperCollins Pubs.

LeapFrog Staff. Imagination Desk Counting Day at the Beach. 2003. (Illus.). 9.99 (978-1-59319-025-5(5)) LeapFrog Enterprises, Inc.

Lester, Alison. Magic Beach. 2006. (Illus.). 32p. (J). (ps-k). pap. 7.95 (978-1-74114-488-8(4)) Allen & Unwin AUS. *Dist:* Independent Pubs. Group.

Lewis, Rob. Grandpa at the Beach. Lewis, Rob, illus. 1998. (Mondo Ser.). (Illus.). 48p. (J). (gr. 1-5). pap. 4.50 (978-1-57255-552-5(1)) Mondo Publishing.

Lies, Brian. Bats at the Beach. 2006. (Illus.). 32p. (J). (gr. k-3). 16.00 (978-0-618-55744-8(X)) Houghton Mifflin Co.

Lilienstein, Jennel. Day at the Beach. 2003. (Illus.). 36p. (J). 8.99 (978-0-9741215-1-2(7)) Stories of My Life, The.

Lubar, David. Dunk. (YA). (gr. 7-10). 2002. 256p. tchr. ed. 15.00 (978-0-618-19455-1(X) , Clarion Bks.); 2004. 272p. reprint ed. pap. 6.99 (978-0-618-43909-6(9) , Graphia) Houghton Mifflin Co. Trade & Reference Div.

Luciani, Brigitte. How Will We Get Beach?/¿Como Iremos a la Playa? An English-Spanish Guessing-Game Story. Tharlet, Eve, illus. 2006. (ENG & SPA.). 36p. (J). (ps-1). 15.95 (978-0-7358-2037-1(6)) North-South Bks., Inc.

Lynch, Chris. The Gravedigger's Cottage. 2004. 208p. (J). (gr. 7 up). 15.99 (978-0-06-623940-8(0)) HarperCollins Pubs.

Macveety, Sue Maney. Singing Sea/el Mar Que Canta. Zantay, Valerie, tr. 2005. (SPA., Illus.). 36p. per. 15.99 (978-1-4134-7275-2(3)) Xlibris Corp.

Maddox, Tony & Wen, Dref. Ffred ar y Dwr. 2005. (WEL., Illus.). 28p. (978-1-85596-666-6(2)) Dref Wen.

Marquess, Dana. Night of the Lighted Freedom: A Firefly Fantasy. 2006. (Illus.). 32p. (J). 19.95 (978-1-932278-06-4(0)) Mayhaven Publishing.

Mathers, Petra. Lottie's New Beach Towel. Mathers, Petra, illus. 2001. (Illus.). 32p. (J). (ps-3). 6.99 (978-0-689-84441-6(7) , Aladdin) Simon & Schuster Children's Publishing.

—Lottie's New Beach Towel. 1998. (Illus.). 32p. (J). (ps-3). 15.00 (978-0-689-81606-2(5) , Atheneum/Anne Schwartz Bks.) Simon & Schuster Children's Publishing.

Matheson, Shirlee Smith. Fastback Beach. 2003. (Orca Soundings Ser.). 96p. (J). (gr. 7-12). pap. 7.95 (978-1-55143-267-0(6)) Orca Bk. Pubs. USA.

Mayer, Mercer. Beach Day. 2002. (Little Critter First Readers Ser.). (Illus.). 24p. (J). (ps-k). pap. 3.95 (978-1-57768-844-0(9)) School Specialty Publishing.

—Beach Day. 2003. (gr. k-3). lib. bdg. 11.80 (978-0-613-67599-4(1)) Tandem Library Bks.

—Just Grandma & Me. Mayer, Mercer, illus. 2001. (Little Critter Ser.). (Illus.). 24p. (J). (gr. k-k). reprint ed. pap. 3.29 (978-0-307-11893-6(2) , 11893, Random Hse. Bks. for Young Readers) Random Hse. Children's Bks.

McCarty, Peter. Hondo & Fabian. unabr. ed. 2006. (Illus.). (J). (ps-3). 24.95 incl. audio (978-0-439-84905-0(5) , WHRA688); 29.95 incl. audio compact disk (978-0-439-84906-7(3) , WHCD688) Weston Woods Studios, Inc.

McKay, Hilary. The Amber Cat. 1999. (YA). pap., stu. ed. 41.00 incl. audio (978-0-7887-3635-3(3) , 41000) Recorded Bks., LLC.

—The Amber Cat. 1999. 'p. (J). 11.64 (978-0-606-16326-2(3)) Tandem Library Bks.

Metzger, Steve. It's Beach Day! Wilhelm, Hans, illus. 1998. (Dinofours Ser.: No. 9). 32p. (J). (ps-1). pap. 3.25 (978-0-590-03267-4(4)) Scholastic, Inc.

Milbourne, A. & Wells, R. Bunny on the Beach. 2004. (Look-Through Board Bks.). (Illus.). 10p. (J). (ps). 4.95 (978-0-7945-0147-1(8) , Usborne) EDC Publishing.

Miller, Ruth. I Went to the Bay. Gourbault, Martine, illus. unabr. ed. 1999. 24p. (J). (gr. k-3). (978-1-55074-498-9(4)) Kids Can Pr., Ltd.

Milord, Susan. Pebble. Milord, Susan, illus. 2007. 32p. (J). lib. bdg. 16.89 (978-0-06-085808-7(7) , Julie Andrews Collection) HarperCollins Pubs.

—Pebble. 2007. 32p. (J). (ps-2). 15.99 (978-0-06-085807-0(9) , Julie Andrews Collection) HarperCollins Pubs.

Montanari, Eva, illus. Carlo Castlecrusher. 2006. 40p. (J). 16.50 (978-1-933327-16-7(2)); 15.95 (978-1-933327-15-0(4)) Purple Bear Bks., Inc.

Montgomery, L. M. Along the Shore: Tales by the Sea. (YA). 22.95 (978-0-8488-2655-0(8)) Amereon LTD.

Murphy, Elspeth Campbell. Mystery of the Sand Castle. 1998. (gr. 3-6). lib. bdg. 11.80 (978-0-613-86064-2(0)) Tandem Library Bks.

A New Friend at the Beach. 2007. (J). per. (***978-1-932570-87-8(X))** Literacy Footprints Inc.

Norman, Tony. Sky Bikers. Savage, Paul, illus. 2008. (J). pap. (***978-1-59889-903-0(1)**); 33p. (YA). (gr. 5-9). lib. bdg. 21.26 (***978-1-59889-851-4(5))** Stone Arch Bks.

Nugent, Matthew. The Mystery of the Sinking Sand. Nugent, Louise M., illus. 2002. 136p. (J). (gr. 4-10). per. 14.95 (978-0-9705812-2-8(X)) CBI Pr.

Nugent, Matthew A. The Legend of Goose Rocks Beach. Nugent, Louise, illus. 2001. 84p. (YA). (gr. 3-8). pap. 14.95 (978-0-9705812-0-4(3)) CBI Pr.

Obiols, Anna. Dali & the Path of Dreams. Dunn, Andrew, tr. from SPA. Subirana, Joan, illus. 2007. 32p. (J). pap. 7.95 (***978-1-84507-777-8(6))** Lincoln, Frances Ltd. GBR. *Dist:* Perseus Distribution.

O'Connor, George. Ker-splash! O'Connor, George, illus. 2005. (Illus.). 40p. (J). 14.95 (978-0-689-87682-0(3)) Simon & Schuster Children's Publishing.

Olker, Constance. The Punctuation Pals Go to the Beach. 2005. (Illus.). 36p. (J). per. 18.95 (978-1-933449-12-8(8)) Nightengale Pr.

Paratore, Coleen. Catching the Sun. Catalanotto, Peter, illus. 2008. (J). (***978-1-57091-720-2(5))** Charlesbridge Publishing, Inc.

Parvensky Barwell, Catherine A. Tommi Goes to the Beach, 4 vols. Barwell, Matthew W. & Parvensky, Mary T., eds. 2006. (Illus.). 40p. (J). (978-0-9774409-2-4(3) , TL003) ILT Publishing.

Petrucha, Stefan. Snared. 2008. (Wicked Dead Ser.: No.3). 224p. (J). pap. 7.99 (***978-0-06-113851-5(7)** , Harper-Teen) HarperCollins Pubs.

Plowden, Sally H. Turtle Tracks. Plowden, Tee, illus. 2002. 32p. (J). (gr. 4-6). 14.95 (978-0-9679016-6-4(9)) Palmetto Conservation Foundation.

Rau, Dana Meachen. Stroll by the Sea. 2000. (Adventurers Ser.). (Illus.). 24p. (J). (gr. k-2). lib. bdg. 19.27 (978-1-57103-320-8(3)) Rourke Publishing, LLC.

Raven, Margot Theis. Circle Unbroken. Lewis, E.B., illus. 2007. 48p. (J). pap. 6.99 (***978-0-312-37603-1(0)***) Square Fish.

Renaud, Anne. How the Sea Came to Marissa. Durland, Maud, illus. 2006. 32p. (J). (978-1-58270-129-5(6)) Beyond Words Publishing, Inc.

Repp, Gloria. Booklinks, Level 2. 1998. 149p. (J). (gr. 4-7). pap. 7.49 (978-1-57924-000-4(3) , 106484) Jones, Bob Univ. Pr.

—Trouble at Silver Pines Inn. 1998. lib. bdg. 14.70 (978-0-613-86050-5(0)) Tandem Library Bks.

Rey, H. A. & Rey, Margret. Curious George Goes to the Beach. 1999. (Curious George Ser.). (Illus.). (J). (gr. k-3). 24p. tchr. ed. 12.95 (978-0-395-97834-4(3)); 32p. pap. 3.95 (978-0-395-97838-2(6)) Houghton Mifflin Co. Trade & Reference Div.

Rey, Margret. Curious George Goes to the Beach. 1999. (gr. k-3). lib. bdg. 11.80 (978-0-613-21392-9(0)) Tandem Library Bks.

The Right Place for Jupiter: Individual Title Six-Packs. (gr. 3 up). 35.00 (978-0-7635-9672-9(8)) Rigby Education.

Roberts, Willo Davis. Twisted Summer. 1998. (978-0-606-13089-6(0)) Tandem Library Bks.

ROBERTSON, M. P. The Sandcastle. 2008. (Illus.). 32p. (J). pap. 7.95 (***978-1-84507-800-3(4)***) Lincoln, Frances Ltd. GBR. *Dist:* Perseus Distribution.

Robertson, Mark. Big Brave Brian. 2007. (Illus.). 32p. (J). (ps-2). 16.95 (***978-1-84507-559-0(5)***) Lincoln, Frances Ltd. GBR. *Dist:* Perseus Distribution.

Rotner, Shelley. Senses at the Seashore. 2006. (Illus.). (J). 22.60 (978-0-7613-2897-1(1) , Millbrook Pr.) Lerner Publishing Group.

Rudisill, J. J., et al, illus. Wimzie's Beach Trip. 1999. (Wimzie's House Bks.). 24p. (J). pap. 3.99 (978-0-88724-543-5(9) , CD-4849) Carson-Dellosa Publishing Co., Inc.

Rylant, Cynthia. Henry & Mudge & the Forever Sea. Stevenson, Sucie, illus. 2000. (Henry & Mudge Ser.). 28.95 incl. audio compact disk (978-1-59112-575-4(8)); pap. 31.95 incl. audio compact disk (978-1-59112-574-7(X)) Live Oak Media.

—The Octopus. McDaniels, Preston, illus. 2005. (Lighthouse Family Ser.). 64p. (J). 15.99 (978-0-689-86246-5(6)) Simon & Schuster Children's Publishing.

Sage, Molly. At the Beach. 2007. (Illus.). 6p. (J). pap. 6.99 (***978-1-85602-497-6(0)***) Anova Bks. GBR. *Dist:* Independent Pubs. Group.

Santillo, LuAnn. The Snack Shack. Santillo, LuAnn, ed. 2003. (Half-Pint Kids Readers Ser.). (Illus.). 7p. (J). (ps-1). pap. (978-1-59256-086-8(5)) Half-Pint Kids, Inc.

Schertle, Alice. All You Need for a Beach. Lavallee, Barbara, illus. 2004. 32p. (J). 16.00 (978-0-15-216755-4(2) , Silver Whistle) Harcourt Trade Pubs.

Schroder, Jack. A Fun Day at the Beach. 2005. 170p. (YA). per. 6.95 net. (978-0-9763810-0-6(1)) Catalpa Pr.

Scott, Janine. Fun in the Sun. Forss, Ian, illus. 2006. (Farmer Claude & Farmer Maude Ser.). 32p. (J). (gr. k-2). 22.60 (978-1-4048-1697-8(6) , 1253180) Picture Window Bks.

Sea Story. (Illus.). (J). (978-0-399-22488-1(2) , Philomel) Penguin Group (USA) Inc.

Seashore Touch & See Hi? 2004. (J). 8.99 (978-0-89610-999-5(2)) Island Heritage Publishing.

Silverhardt, Lauryn. A Day at the Beach. Fruchter, Jason, illus. 2003. (Dora the Explorer Ser.). 22p. (J). bds. 4.99 (978-0-689-85482-8(X) , Simon Spotlight/Nickelodeon) Simon & Schuster Children's Publishing.

Smax, Willy & Ludlow, Keren. Benny Goes to the Seaside. 2000. (Illus.). 24p. (J). pap. 4.99 (978-1-85881-700-2(5)) Orion Children's Bks. GBR. *Dist:* Trafalgar Square Publishing.

Smith, Carrie. Going to the Beach. ed. 2004. (Shared Connections Ser.). (J). pap. 27.00 (978-1-4108-1639-7(7)) Benchmark Education Co.

Spinelli, Eileen. Summerhouse Time. Lew-Vriethoff, Joanne, illus. 2007. 224p. (J). (gr. 3-7). lib. bdg. 15.99 (978-0-375-94061-3(8) , Knopf Bks. for Young Readers) Random Hse. Children's Bks.

Spinelli, Eileen & Lisker, Emily, illus. Summerhouse Time. 2001. (J). 16.00 (978-0-689-82418-0(1) , Simon & Schuster Children's Publishing) Simon & Schuster Children's Publishing.

Spinelli, Patti. Mackenzie & Emma Visit York Beach. Spinelli, Patti, illus. 2003. (J). (978-0-9742328-0-5(7)) Spinelli, Patti.

Staffier, Jane Sarah. Casey's Day at the Beach. Staffier, Jane Sarah, illus. l.t. ed. 1999. (Casey the Beacon Hill Cat Ser.). (Illus.). 28p. (gr. k-5). spiral bd. 9.95 (978-1-928895-00-8(X)) B.A.B., Ltd.

Stewart, Sarah. The Friend. Small, David, illus. 2004. 48p. (J). 16.00 (978-0-374-32463-6(8) , Farrar, Straus & Giroux (BYR)) Farrar, Straus & Giroux.

—The Friend. Small, David, illus. unabr. ed. 2007. (Picture Book Readalong Ser.). (J). (ps-3). 28.95 incl. audio compact disk (***978-1-59519-918-8(7) ;*** 25.95 incl. audio (***978-1-59519-914-0(4)***) Live Oak Media.

Stilton, Geronimo. Surf's up, Geronimo! 2005. (Geronimo Stilton Ser.: No. 20). (Illus.). 109p. (J). (978-1-4156-0622-3(6)) Scholastic, Inc.

Stockland, Patricia M. At the Beach. Muehlenhardt, Amy Bailey, illus. 2004. (Read-It! Readers Ser.). 32p. (C). (gr. k-3). 18.60 (978-1-4048-0651-1(2)) Picture Window Bks.

Swallow, Su. Matt's Sand & Sea Dragon. Raga, Silvia, illus. 2006. (Lightning Readers Ser.). 32p. (J). pap. 3.95 (978-0-7696-4196-6(2) , Gingham Dog Pr.) School Specialty Publishing.

Swarta, Donna. At the Beach. Ferri, Francesca, illus. 2006. 6p. (J). 15.99 (978-0-7641-7923-5(3)) Barron's Educational Series, Inc.

Takhar, Jodi. Four Seasons of Fun. Takhar, Jodi & Jones, Paul, illus. 14p. (J). (ps-3). 19.95 (978-1-886000-02-5(6)) Takhar's, Jodi Spilt Milk Collection.

Taylor, Eleanor. Beep, Beep, Let's Go! 2005. (Illus.). 32p. (J). 15.95 (978-1-58234-973-2(8)) Bloomsbury Publishing.

Thompson, Kay & Fry, Sonali. Eloise Goes to the Beach. Lyon, Tammie, illus. 2007. (Eloise Ser.). 12p. (J). 7.99 (978-1-4169-3344-1(1) , Little Simon) Simon & Schuster Children's Publishing.

Trimble, Marcia. Malinda Martha & Her Skipping Stones. Grell, Susi, illus. 1999. 32p. (J). (ps-3). 15.95 (978-1-891577-72-7(7)) Images Pr.

—The Smiling Stone. Arciero, Susan, illus. 1998. 32p. (J). (ps-2). lib. bdg. 15.95 (978-1-891577-37-6(9)) Images Pr.

A Trip to the Beach. 2007. (J). per. (***978-1-932570-85-4(3)***) Literacy Footprints Inc.

Tyler, Jenny & Cartwright, S. Duck by the Sea. 2004. (SPA.). 6p. (J). vinyl bd. 7.95 (978-0-7945-0569-1(4)) EDC Publishing.

Tym, Kate. We Love the Seaside. 2007. (J). lib. bdg. 16.95 (***978-1-59566-369-6(X)***) QEB Publishing Inc.

Van Dusen, Chris. Down to the Sea with Mr. Magee. (Illus.). 36p. (J). 2006. pap. 6.95 (978-0-8118-5225-8(3)); 2000. 14.95 (978-0-8118-2499-6(3)) Chronicle Bks. LLC.

Vasiliu, Mircea. A Day at the Beach. 2007. (Illus.). 36p. (J). 7.95 (***978-1-59091-068-9(0)***) Eastern National.

Wagner, Jenny. High Hopes on Sea. Rogers, Gregory, illus. 2005. (UQP Children's Fiction Ser.). 80p. (Orig.). (J). pap. 16.95 (978-0-7022-3525-2(3)) Univ. of Queensland Pr. AUS. *Dist:* International Specialized Bk. Services.

Waite, Lance. A Day with Dad at the Beach. 2008. (J). 15.99 (***978-1-60131-016-3(1)***) Big Tent Bks.

Wallace, Karen. A Day at Seagull Beach. 1999. (Eyewitness Readers). (Illus.). 32p. (J). (gr. 5-1). pap. 3.99 (978-0-7894-4002-0(4)) Dorling Kindersley Publishing, Inc.

—A Day at Seagull Beach. 1999. (J). 10.75 (978-0-606-18989-7(0)) Tandem Library Bks.

—Day at Seagull Beach. 1999. (gr. k-3). lib. bdg. 11.80 (978-0-613-17163-2(2)) Tandem Library Bks.

Wallace, Karen & Dorling Kindersley Publishing Staff. A Day at Seagull Beach. 1999. (Eyewitness Readers). (Illus.). 32p. (J). (ps-4). 14.99 (978-0-7894-4003-7(2)) Dorling Kindersley Publishing, Inc.

Warner, Gertrude Chandler. The Mystery of the Pirate's Map. 1999. (Boxcar Children Ser.: No. 70). (J). (gr. 2-5). (978-0-606-18763-3(4)) Tandem Library Bks.

Warner, Gertrude Chandler, creator. The Mystery of the Pirate's Map, Vol. 70. (Boxcar Children Ser.: No.70). (Illus.). (J). (gr. 2-5). 2004. 14.95 (978-0-8075-5453-1(7)); 1999. 128p. pap. 4.50 (978-0-8075-5454-8(5)) Whitman, Albert & Co.

Warren, Rick. Made for a Purpose AMS. 2004. (J). 287.82 (978-0-310-60329-0(3)) Zonderkidz.

Wells, Carolyn. Marjorie at Seacote. 2006. 29.95 (***978-1-55742-656-7(2) ;*** pap. 14.95 (***978-1-55742-653-6(8)***) Wildside Pr.

Wen, Dref. Traeth Prysur. 2005. Tr. of Busy Beach. (WEL., Illus.). 10p. (978-1-85596-661-1(1)) Dref Wen.

White, Amanda. Sand Sister. Morales, Yuyi, illus. 2004. 32p. (J). 16.99 (978-1-84148-617-8(5)) Barefoot Bks., Inc.

Yee, Brenda S. The Sand Castle. 1999. lib. bdg. (978-0-688-16195-8(2)) HarperCollins Pubs.

—Sand Castle. Kliros, Thea, illus. 1999. 24p. (J). (ps-3). 16.99 (978-0-688-16194-1(4)) HarperCollins Pubs.

SEASONS

see also names of the seasons, e.g. Autumn, etc.

Aigner-Clark, Julie. Seasons Discovery Cards. Zaidi, Nadeem, illus. 2005. (Baby Einstein Ser.). 16p. (ps-17). 9.99 (978-0-7868-5479-0(0)) Hyperion Bks. for Children.

Art for All Seasons. 2004. (J). per. 24.99 (978-1-55799-953-5(8) , EMC 2001) Evan-Moor Educational Pubs.

Art, Henry W. & Robbins, Michael W. WoodsWalk: Peepers, Porcupines, & Exploding Puff Balls! 2003. (Illus.). 128p. (J). (gr. 3-7). pap. 14.95 (978-1-58017-452-7(3) , 67452, Storey Kids) Storey Publishing, LLC.

Attwood, Jilly. Seasons of the Year. 2005. (Illus.). 24p. (J). (ps-1). lib. bdg. 21.36 (978-1-4109-1640-2(5)) Heinemann Library.

—Talking about Time: Seasons of the Year. 2005. (Illus.). 24p. (J). pap. 5.99 (978-1-4109-1646-4(4)) Heinemann Library.

Barnett, Michelle Noble, et al. Theme Pockets - January: The Four Seasons; Penguins; Famous Americans. Evans, Marilyn, ed. Larsen, Jo, illus. 1999. (Making Books with Pockets Ser.). 96p. (J). pap., tchr. ed. 12.99 (978-1-55799-698-5(9) , EMC 584) Evan-Moor Educational Pubs.

Benchmark Education Staff. Weather & Climate. 2005. 2.00 (***978-1-4108-4635-8(0)***) Benchmark Education Co.

Benchmark Education Staff, compiled by. Weather & Season. 2006. spiral bd. 249.00 (***978-1-4108-7031-5(6)***) Benchmark Education Co.

Berendes, Mary. Seasons & Weather. 2007. (WordBooks/Libros de Palabras Ser.). (SPA & ENG.). 24p. (J). 19.93 (***978-1-59296-801-5(5)***) Child's World, Inc.

Bernard, Robin. A Tree for All Seasons. 1999. (J). (978-0-7922-9427-6(0)); pap. (978-0-7922-9435-1(1)) National Geographic Society.

—Tree for All Seasons. 2001. (Illus.). 16p. (J). (gr. 3-7). pap. 5.95 (978-0-7922-6674-7(9) , National Geographic Children's Bks.) National Geographic Society.

—Tree for All Seasons. 2001. (ps-2). lib. bdg. 14.10 (978-0-613-56662-9(9)) Tandem Library Bks.

Branley, Franklyn M. Sunshine Makes the Seasons. Rex, Michael, illus. 2005. (Let's-Read-and-Find-Out Science Ser.). 40p. (J). (gr. k-4). pap. 5.99 (978-0-06-059205-9(2)) HarperCollins Pubs.

Branley, Franklyn Mansfield. Sunshine Makes the Seasons. Rex, Michael, illus. 2005. (Let's-Read-and-Find-Out Science Ser.). (J). (ps-ps). 31p. 15.99 (978-0-06-059203-5(6)); 40p. lib. bdg. 16.89 (978-0-06-059204-2(4)) HarperCollins Pubs.

Brighter Vision Publishing Staff. Fun with Seasons Activity Book. 2000. (Learning Adventures Grade 1 Ser.). (Illus.). (J). (gr. 1-2). pap. 2.25 (978-1-55254-065-7(0)) Brighter Vision Pubns.

Bruno, Janet, et al. Seasons. Wolkoff, Stacey, ed. Yuh, Catherine, illus. 2000. (Primary Theme Ser.). 32p. (gr. k-3). pap., tchr. ed. 7.99 (978-1-57471-684-9(0) , 2458) Creative Teaching Pr., Inc.

El Buho. 2002. Tr. of Owl. (SPA., Illus.). 22p. (J). 6.50 (978-84-246-1735-6(5)) La Galera, S.A. Editorial ESP. *Dist:* AIMS International Bks., Inc.

Burningham, John. Las Estaciones. (SPA., Illus.). (J). (gr. k-3). (978-84-88342-14-0(4) , KK7662) S.A. Kokinos ESP. *Dist:* Lectorum Pubns., Inc.

Cannon, Shannon. The Seasons. 2003. (Compass Point Phonics Readers Ser.). (Illus.). 16p. (J). (gr. 1 up). 13.26 (978-0-7565-0527-1(5)) Compass Point Bks.

Cash, Megan Montague. What Makes the Seasons? Cash, Megan Montague, illus. 2003. (Illus.). 40p. (J). (ps-3). 15.99 (978-0-670-03598-4(X) , Viking Juvenile) Penguin Group (USA) Inc.

Changing Seasons. 2002. (Illus.). (J). pap. 5.43 (978-0-7398-5924-7(2)) Steck-Vaughn.

Childrens Press Staff. Weather & Seasons. 1998. (Rookie Read-About Science Ser.). pap. 23.22 (978-0-516-29990-7(5) , Children's Pr.) Scholastic Library Publishing.

Christian Bulletin Board Idea Book: Holidays & Seasons. 2006. 144p. (J). (gr. 1-6). 15.99 (978-1-4206-7070-7(0)) Teacher Created Resources, Inc.

Cicciarelli, Joellyn. October. 1998. (Illus.). 96p. (J). (gr. k-3). pap., tchr. ed. 10.99 (978-1-57471-351-0(5) , 2377) Creative Teaching Pr., Inc.

Coder, Kelly, ed. Investigating Science - Weather & the Seasons. 2003. 48p. 9.95 (978-1-56234-548-8(6) , Mailbox Bks., The) Education Ctr., Inc.

DeGezelle, Terri. The Bridgestone Science Library: Seasons, 4 bks. Incl. Autumn. lib. bdg. 18.60 (978-0-7368-1409-6(4)); Spring. lib. bdg. 18.60 (978-0-7368-1410-2(8)); Summer. lib. bdg. 18.60 (978-0-7368-1411-9(6)); Winter. lib. bdg. 18.60 (978-0-7368-1412-6(4)); 24p. (J). (gr. 1-2). 2002. (Illus.). 2002. Set lib. bdg. 74.40 (978-0-7368-1413-3(2) , Bridgestone Bks.) Capstone Pr., Inc.

Dolan, Graham. The Greenwich Guide to the Seasons. 2001. 48p. (J). (gr. 2-4). lib. bdg. 22.79 (978-1-58810-044-3(8)) Heinemann Library.

Dorling Kindersley Publishing Staff. Four Seasons. 2004. (Baby Genius Ser.). (Illus.). 16p. (J). bds. 6.99 (978-0-7566-0266-6(1)) Dorling Kindersley Publishing, Inc.

Droop, Constanza. Que? Como? Por que?: Las estaciones del Ano: What? How? Why?: the Seasons of the Year, Spanish-Lanuage Edition. 2007. (Illus.). 16p. (J). 9.95 (***978-970-718-492-3(2)*** , Silver Dolphin en Español) Advanced Marketing, S. de R. L. de C. V. MEX. *Dist:* Perseus Distribution.

Eckart, Edana. Watching the Seasons. 2004. (Wel-Watching Nature Ser.). (J). 18.00 (978-0-516-27600-7(X)); 24p. pap. 4.95 (978-0-516-25937-6(7)) Scholastic Library Publishing. (Children's Pr.).

Las Estaciones del Ano, 4 vols. 2006. (SPA.). (J). (gr. k-2). 69.08 (978-0-8225-3322-1(7) , Ediciones Lerner) Lerner Publishing Group.

Evans, David & Williams, Claudette. Seasons & Weather. (Let's Explore Science Ser.). (Illus.). (J). 12.95 (978-0-590-74592-5(1)) Scholastic, Inc.

The Four Seasons. 16.95 incl. audio compact disk (978-0-9700489-5-0(5)) Little Fiddle Co., Inc., The.

Frank, Marjorie Slavick, et al. Science Instant Readers Bk. 8: Seasons. 1999. (Harcourt Science Ser.). (gr. 1 up). pap. 15.50 (978-0-15-316206-0(6)) Harcourt Schl. Pubs.

Freeman, Marcia S. Seasons of the Year. 2005. (Everything Science Ser.). (Illus.). 24p. (gr. 1-4). 14.95 (978-1-59515-123-0(0)) Rourke Publishing, LLC.

Ganeri, Anita. Season to Season. 2005. (Nature's Patterns Ser.). (Illus.). 32p. (J). pap. (978-1-4109-1320-3(1)); lib. bdg. 16.95 (978-1-4034-5897-1(9)) Heinemann Library.

Geisert, Bonnie. Prairie Town. Geisert, Arthur, illus. 1998. (Small Town U. S. A. Ser.). 32p. (J). (gr. k-3). tchr. ed. 16.00 (978-0-395-85907-0(7) , Walter Lorraine) Houghton Mifflin Co. Trade & Reference Div.

Geisert, Bonnie & Geisert, Arthur. River Town. 1999. (Small Town U. S. A. Ser.). (Illus.). 32p. (J). (gr. k-3). tchr. ed. 16.00 (978-0-395-90891-4(4) , Walter Lorraine) Houghton Mifflin Co. Trade & Reference Div.

George, Jean Craighead. Spring Moon. 2003. (J). (gr. 3-7). 20.75 (978-0-8446-7242-7(4)) Smith, Peter Pub., Inc.

Gibbons, Gail. The Reasons for Seasons. Gibbons, Gail, illus. 2002. (Illus.). (J). 15.49 (978-0-7587-3501-0(4)) Book Wholesalers, Inc.

Glaser, Linda. It's Fall! Swan, Susan, illus. 2001. (Celebrate the Seasons! Ser.). 32p. (J). (gr. 1-3). pap. 7.95 (978-0-7613-1342-7(7) , First Avenue Editions) Lerner Publishing Group.

Gold-Dworkin, Heidi. Learning about the Changing Seasons. 2000. (gr. 3-6). lib. bdg. 22.20 (978-0-613-27930-7(1)) Tandem Library Bks.

Gold, Kimberley. Four Seasons. (Flip Flap Fun Book Ser.). (Illus.). 10p. (J). bds. (978-2-89393-934-6(1)) Phidal Publishing, Inc./Editions Phidal, Inc.

Goodings, Christina. Look What I Made! 2001. (Illus.). 48p. (J). 16.99 (978-0-7459-4473-9(6) , Lion) Lion Hudson plc GBR. *Dist:* Independent Pubs. Group.

Gould, Alan, et al. The Real Reasons for Seasons: Sun-Earth Connections. Bergman, Lincoln et al, eds. Gould, Alan & Baker, Lisa H., illus. Hoyt, Richard & Bradley, Laurence, photos by. 2000. (Great Explorations in Math & Science Ser.). 140p. (YA). pap. 25.50 (978-0-924886-45-4(5) , GEMS) Univ. of California, Berkeley, Lawrence Hall of Science.

Gutierrez, Javiera. El Baul de Mis Amigos: Un Libro Sobre el Tiempo y las Estaciones. Maddonni, Karina, illus. (Coleccion el Baul Ser.). (SPA.). 10p. (J). (gr. k-1). (978-950-46-1160-8(5)) Santillana USA Publishing Co., Inc.

Hall, Margaret. Las Estaciones Del Año: Seasons of the Year. 2008. (ENG & SPA.). (J). (***978-1-4296-0045-3(4)***) Capstone Pr., Inc.

Hall, Margaret. The Seasons of the Year. 2007. (Pebble Plus Ser.). (Illus.). 24p. (J). 19.93 (978-0-7368-6341-4(9)) Capstone Pr., Inc.

Harcourt School Publishers Staff. Harcourt Science: Seasons Reader. 1999. (Illus.). pap. 3.10 (978-0-15-314857-6(8)) Harcourt Schl. Pubs.

—Harcourt Science: See the Seasons Reader. 1999. (Illus.). pap. 2.90 (978-0-15-314845-3(4)) Harcourt Schl. Pubs.

—What Season Is It? 3rd ed. 2002. (Trophies English Language Learners Ser.). (Illus.). (J). pap. 4.10 (978-0-15-327589-0(8)) Harcourt Schl. Pubs.

—What Season Is It? - 5 Pack - Grade 1. 3rd ed. 2002. (Trophies English Language Learners Ser.). 20.10 (978-0-15-327623-1(1)) Harcourt Schl. Pubs.

—Winter, Spring, Summer, Fall. 3rd ed. 2002. (Trophies English Language Learners Ser.). (Illus.). pap. 5.10 (978-0-15-327700-9(9)) Harcourt Schl. Pubs.

S

Haydon, Julie. The Seasons: Individual Title, 6 packs. (Rigby Focus Ser.). 16p. (gr. k up). 28.00 (978-0-7578-5530-6(X)) Rigby Education.

—The Seasons: Individual Title Six-Packs. (Rigby Focus Ser.). 16p. (gr. k up). 26.00 (978-0-7578-5296-1(3)) Rigby Education.

Heuninck, Ronald. Rain or Shine. Heuninck, Ronald, illus. (Illus.). 12p. (J). pap. 5.50 (978-0-86315-089-0(6) , 20269) Floris Bks. GBR. *Dist:* Gryphon Hse., Inc.

Hudson, Cheryl Willis. Book of Seasons. Simpson, Howard, illus. (Afro-Bets Ser.). (J). pap. 4.95 (978-0-940975-15-6(7)) Just Us Bks., Inc.

Hunter, Rebecca M. Seasons. 2001. (Discovering Science Ser.). (Illus.). 32p. (J). (gr. 3-7). lib. bdg. 25.69 (978-0-7398-3247-9(6)) Raintree.

Is It Spring? 2003. (YA). (978-0-8374-0009-9(0)); lib. bdg. (978-0-8374-0008-2(2)) Weekly Reader Corp.

Jackson, Ellen B. The Spring Equinox: The Greening of the Earth. 2003. (Illus.). 32p. (J). (gr. 3-6). pap. 7.95 (978-0-7613-1983-2(2) , Millbrook Pr.) Lerner Publishing Group.

—The Spring Equinox: The Greening of the Earth. Ellis, Jan Davey, illus. 2001. 4. 32p. (gr. 2). 14.95 (978-0-7613-1644-2(2) , Millbrook Pr.) Lerner Publishing Group.

Jeunesse, Gallimard & Grant, Donald. Four Seasons. 2001. (Look-It-Up Ser.). (Illus.). 14p. (J). bds. 4.95 (978-0-439-29725-7(7) , Cartwheel Bks.) Scholastic, Inc.

Jones, Annie. The Four Seasons: Uncovering Nature. 2006. (Uncovering Ser.). (Illus.). 52p. (J). (gr. 3-12). 16.95 (978-1-55407-137-1(2)) Firefly Bks., Ltd.

Jordan, Sara. Celebrate Seasons. Howard, Joan, ed. Filipov, Alex, illus. 1999. 50p. (J). (gr. k-4). pap. 14.95 incl. audio (978-1-894262-02-6(6) , JMP118K) Jordan Music Productions, Inc.

Just for Journaling: Holidays & Seasons. 2004. 128p. (J). per. 11.99 (978-1-59441-004-8(6) , DJ-604000) Carson-Dellosa Publishing Co., Inc.

Kalman, Bobbie & MacAulay, Kelley. Changing Seasons. 2005. (Nature's Changes Ser.). (Illus.). 32p. (J). (978-0-7787-2275-5(9)); pap. (978-0-7787-2309-7(7)) Crabtree Publishing Co.

Kniffke, Sophie. El Tiempo. (Coleccion Mundo Maravilloso).Tr. of Seasons & Weather. (SPA., Illus.). 40p. (J). (gr. 2-4). (978-84-348-3470-5(7) , SM5473) SM Ediciones ESP. *Dist:* Lectorum Pubns., Inc.

Latta, Sara L. What Happens in Fall? 2006. (I Like the Seasons! Ser.). (Illus.). 24p. (J). lib. bdg. 21.26 (978-0-7660-2417-5(2) , Enslow Elementary) Enslow Pubs., Inc.

—What Happens in Spring? 2006. (I Like the Seasons! Ser.). (Illus.). 24p. (J). lib. bdg. 21.26 (978-0-7660-2419-9(9) , Enslow Elementary) Enslow Pubs., Inc.

—What Happens in Summer? 2006. (I Like the Seasons! Ser.). (Illus.). 24p. (J). lib. bdg. 21.26 (978-0-7660-2416-8(4) , Enslow Elementary) Enslow Pubs., Inc.

—What Happens in Winter? 2006. (I Like the Seasons! Ser.). (Illus.). 24p. (J). lib. bdg. 21.26 (978-0-7660-2418-2(0) , Enslow Elementary) Enslow Pubs., Inc.

Lin, Grace. Our Seasons. McKneally, Ranida T., illus. 2007. 32p. (J). (gr. k-3). pap. 6.95 (***978-1-57091-361-7(7)***) Charlesbridge Publishing, Inc.

Lin, Grace & McKneally, Rainda T. Our Seasons. Lin, Grace, illus. 2006. (Illus.). (J). 15.95 (978-1-57091-360-0(9)) Charlesbridge Publishing, Inc.

Linde, Barbara M. Weather & Climate. 2005. 39.00 (***978-1-4108-4587-0(7)***) Benchmark Education Co.

Llewellyn, Claire. Paint a Sun in the Sky: A First Look at the Seasons. Wood, Amanda, illus. 2004. (First Look Science Ser.). 32p. (C). (gr. k-3). 22.60 (978-1-4048-0659-7(8)) Picture Window Bks.

—Seasons. 2006. (Illus.). 24p. (J). (978-1-59771-017-6(2)) Sea-To-Sea Pubns.

Locker, Thomas. Sky Tree: Seeing Science Through Art. 2001. (978-0-606-22281-5(2)) Tandem Library Bks.

Lucas, Diane. Walking with the Seasons in Kakadu. Searle, Ken, illus. 2005. 32p. (J). pap. 9.95 (978-1-74114-471-0(X)) Allen & Unwin AUS. *Dist:* Independent Pubs. Group.

Lynn, Sara. Rain & Shine: A First Look at Seasons. James, Diane, illus. rev. ed. 2000. (Play & Discover Ser.). 32p. (J). (ps). pap. 4.95 (978-1-58728-046-7(9) , Two Can Publishing) T&N Children's Publishing.

Maslowski, Stephen. Through the Seasons, 4 vols., set. 2001. (Illus.). (J). (gr. 2-7). lib. bdg. 59.80 (978-1-58340-015-9(X)) Smart Apple Media.

Maurer, Tracy. A to Z of Seasons. 2002. 114.00 (978-1-58952-195-7(1)) Rourke Publishing, LLC.

McCarroll, Tolbert. A Winter Walk: Glimpses of the Sacred in Ordinary Life. 2006. (Illus.). 160p. 14.95 (978-0-8245-2416-6(0)) Crossroad Publishing Co.

McKay, Sindy. We Both Read-about the Seasons. 2001. (We Both Read Ser.). (Illus.). 44p. (J). (gr. 1 up). 7.99 (978-1-891327-27-8(5)); pap. 3.99 (978-1-891327-28-5(3)) Treasure Bay, Inc.

Mitchell, Judy, ed. Seasons. Rojas, Mary Galan, illus. 2001. (Pictures to Color Ser.). 32p. (J). (ps-k). pap. 4.95 (978-1-57310-266-7(0)) Teaching & Learning Co.

Morris, Neil. Seasons. 2002. (Our World Ser.). (Illus.). 32p. (J). lib. bdg. 24.25 (978-1-930643-77-2(2)) Chrysalis Education.

Morrison, Gordon. Nature in the Neighborhood. 2004. (Illus.). 32p. (J). (gr. 3-5). tchr. ed. 16.00 (978-0-618-35215-9(5) , Walter Lorraine) Houghton Mifflin Co. Trade & Reference Div.

—Oak Tree. 2005. (Illus.). 32p. (J). (gr. k-3). 6.95 (978-0-618-60918-5(0) , Walter Lorraine) Houghton Mifflin Co. Trade & Reference Div.

My First Book of Seasons. (Butterfly Bks.). (ARA., Illus.). (J). 14.95 (978-0-86685-711-6(7)) International Bk. Ctr., Inc.

Nakagawa, Rieko. Guri & Gura's Playtime Book of Seasons. Yamawaki, Yuriko, illus. 2003. 32p. 12.95 (978-0-8048-3358-5(3)) Tuttle Publishing.

Nichols, Catherine. An Arctic Year. 2002. (We Can Read about Nature Ser.). (Illus.). 32p. (J). 21.36 (978-0-7614-1430-8(4) , Benchmark Bks.) Cavendish, Marshall Corp.

On All Kinds of Days. 2006. (Yellow Umbrella Science Ser.). 8,16p. (J). 6.50 (978-0-7368-1704-2(2)) Red Brick Learning.

Pebble Books: Our Seasons & Weather. 2005. (YA). (gr. k-3). 712.80 (978-0-7368-4219-8(5) , Pebble Bks.) Capstone Pr., Inc.

Perez, Marlene. Colors of the Seasons. ed. 2004. (Shared Connections Ser.). (J). pap. 27.00 (978-1-4108-1628-3(1)) Benchmark Education Co.

—Colors of the Seasons (Big Book) ed. 2004. (Shared Connections Ser.). (J). pap., instr.'s gde. ed. 27.00 (978-1-4108-1604-7(4)) Benchmark Education Co.

Pipe, Jim. Seasons. 2004. (Earthwise Ser.). (J). lib. bdg. 27.10 (978-1-932799-48-4(6)) Stargazer Bks.

Pipe, Jim. Seasons: Why Do Leaves Fall? 2007. (Science Starters Ser.). (Illus.). 32p. (J). ***978-1-59604-081-6(5)*** Stargazer Bks.

Price. Season to Season. 1999. (Illus.). (J). pap. (978-0-8172-6421-5(3)) Steck-Vaughn.

—Theme Pack: Seasons. 2002. (Pair-It Bks.). (J). pap. (978-0-7398-6373-2(8)) Steck-Vaughn.

Primm & Petelinsek. Seasons/Estaciones. 2004. (Talking Hands, Listening Eyes Ser.). (ENG & SPA., Illus.). 24p. (J). (ps-3). 21.36 (978-1-59296-023-1(5)) Child's World, Inc.

Provensen, Alice. Year at Maple Hill Farm. 2001. (ps-2). lib. bdg. 15.30 (978-0-613-90198-7(3)) Tandem Library Bks.

Provensen, Alice & Provensen, Martin. A Book of Seasons. 32p. (J). Random Hse. Children's Bks.

Quiri, Patricia Ryon. Seasons. 2000. (Simply Science Ser.). (Illus.). 32p. (J). (gr. 3 up). lib. bdg. 19.93 (978-0-7565-0034-4(6)) Compass Point Bks.

Raintree Steck-Vaughn Staff. Las Estaciones del Año. 1999. (SPA.). (J). pap., stu. ed. 31.05 (978-0-7398-0756-9(0)) Steck-Vaughn.

Randolph, Joanne. All about the Seasons. 2008. (J). lib. bdg. ***978-1-4042-3768-1(2)*** , PowerKids Pr.) Rosen Publishing Group, Inc., The.

Rigby Education Staff. Discovery World Yel Seasons. (Discovery World Ser.). (Illus.). 12p. (gr. k-1). 23.00 (978-0-7635-2694-8(0)) Rigby Education.

Riley, Peter D. Seasons. Moller, Ray, photos by. 2003. (Everyday Science Ser.). (Illus.). 32p. (J). (gr. 1 up). lib. bdg. 23.33 (978-0-8368-3719-3(3)) Stevens, Gareth Inc.

Rius, Maria. Las Cuatro Estaciones: El Otono. 1999. (Four Seasons Ser.).Tr. of Four Seasons. (SPA., Illus.). 32p. (J). (ps-k). pap. 6.95 (978-0-7641-0892-1(1)) Barron's Educational Series, Inc.

—Four Seasons: Fall. 1998. (Four Seasons Ser.). (Illus.). 32p. (J). (ps-k). pap. 6.95 (978-0-7641-0552-4(3)) Barron's Educational Series, Inc.

—Summer. 1998. (Four Seasons Ser.). (Illus.). 32p. (J). (ps-k). pap. 6.95 (978-0-7641-0556-2(6)) Barron's Educational Series, Inc.

Rockwell, Anne F. Four Seasons Make a Year. Halsey, Megan, illus. 2004. 32p. (J). 16.85 (978-0-8027-8885-6(8)); 15.95 (978-0-8027-8883-2(1)) Walker & Co.

Royston, Angela. Looking at Weather & Seasons: How Do They Change? 2008. (Looking at Science: How Things Change Ser.). 32p. (J). (gr. 1-3). lib. bdg. 22.60 ***978-0-7660-3093-0(8)*** Enslow Pubs., Inc.

Saunders-Smith, Gail. Weather & the Seasons Science. (gr. k-2). 19.95 (978-0-7368-9219-3(2)) Red Brick Learning.

Schlepp, Tammy J. Seasons. 2001. (978-0-606-22442-0(4)) Tandem Library Bks.

Scholastic, Inc. Staff. Seasons & Holidays. 2004. (Biggie Patterns Ser.). 48p. pap. 10.99 (978-0-439-46840-4(X)) Scholastic, Inc.

School Specialty Publishing. Phonemic Awareness & Beginning Phonics: Weather & Seasons. 2004. 96p. (J). pap. 10.99 (978-1-57029-494-5(1) , WPH99044, Totline Pubns.) Schaffer, Frank Pubns.

Seasons. 2001. (Stick'n Learn Stories Ser.). (Illus.). 96p. (J). (ps-3). pap. 6.95 (978-1-55254-231-6(9)) Brighter Vision Pubns.

Seasons, Vol. 4. 2005. (Our Seasons & Weather Ser.). (YA). (gr. k-3). 118.80 (978-0-7368-4201-3(2) , Pebble Bks.) Capstone Pr., Inc.

Seasons, 4 vols., Set. 2006. (Blastoff! Readers Ser.). (Illus.). (J). (gr. k-2). 74.00 ***978-0-531-16879-0(4)*** Scholastic Library Publishing.

Seasons. 2001. (Let's Explore Ser.). (Illus.). 32p. (J). (gr. 1 up). lib. bdg. 23.33 (978-0-8368-2965-5(4)) Stevens, Gareth Inc.

Seasons: Individual Title, 6 packs. (Discovery World Ser.). 12p. (gr. k-1). 28.00 (978-0-7635-8445-0(2)) Rigby Education.

The Seasons: Individual Title Two-Packs. (Chiquilibros Ser.). (ps-1). 12.00 (978-0-7635-8543-3(2)) Rigby Education.

Seasons Set. (gr. k-2). 114.95 (978-0-7368-9046-5(7)) Red Brick Learning.

The Seasons Set C, 6 vols. (Phonics Readers Ser.). (gr. k-2). 17.50 (978-0-7368-3204-5(1)) Red Brick Learning.

Seasons/Weather - PowerPhonics Skill Set III, 6 bks. Incl. Clouds : Learning the CL Sound. Tanner, Susan. lib. bdg. 18.50 (978-0-8239-5942-6(2)); I Like Winter : Learning the ER Sound. Moskal, Greg. lib. bdg. 18.50 (978-0-8239-5939-6(2)); It Grows in Spring : Learning the GR Sound. Leigh, Autumn. lib. bdg. 18.50 (978-0-8239-5941-9(4)); Rain : Learning the AI Sound. Vastola, Pam. lib. bdg. 18.50 (978-0-8239-5943-3(0)); Summer at the Beach : Learning the EA Sound. Thomas, Maryann. lib. bdg. 18.50 (978-0-8239-5950-1(3)); When Leaves Turn : Learning the UR Sound. Sheffield, Sarah. lib. bdg. 18.50 (978-0-8239-5940-2(6)); 24p. (J). (gr. 1). 2002. (Illus.). 2001. Set lib. bdg. 108.00 (978-0-8239-7211-1(9) , PowerKids Pr.) Rosen Publishing Group, Inc., The.

Seelig, Renate, illus. Mein Kleiner Brockhaus: Jahreszeiten. (GER.). 28p. (J). (ps up). (978-3-7653-2571-7(6)) Brockhaus, F. A., GmbH DEU. *Dist:* International Bk. Import Service, Inc.

Sesame Street Seasons Toddler Time. 2007. (J). pap. 2.95 ***978-1-59545-145-3(5)*** Learning Horizons, Inc.

Sheffield, Sarah. When Leaves Turn: Learning the UR Sound. 2002. (PowerPhonics Ser.). (Illus.). (J). 23p. lib. bdg. (978-0-8239-8285-1(8)); 24p. (gr. 1). lib. bdg. 18.50 (978-0-8239-5940-2(6)) Rosen Publishing Group, Inc., The. (PowerKids Pr.).

Simon, Seymour. Summer Across America. 1999. (J). (978-0-7868-0181-7(6)) Hyperion Pr.

Sipiera, Paul P. & Sipiera, Diane M. The Seasons. 1999. (True Bks.). (Illus.). 48p. (J). (gr. 3-5). pap. 6.95 (978-0-516-26439-4(7) , Children's Pr.) Scholastic Library Publishing.

Slade, Suzanne. Seasonal Cycles. 2007. (Illus.). 24p. (J). (978-1-4042-2388-2(6)); pap. (978-1-4042-2198-7(0)) Rosen Publishing Group, Inc., The. (PowerKids Pr.).

Smith, Ian. Scholastic Clubs Animal Kingdom Pack (5 x PB QAL Titles) 2004. (QEB Start Talking Ser.). (Illus.). 24p. (J). per. 15.95 (978-1-59566-162-3(X)) QEB Publishing Inc.

Steck-Vaughn Staff. Seasons in Color. 2000. pap. (978-0-7398-4487-8(3)) Steck-Vaughn.

—Winter, Spring, Summer, Fall. 2000. pap. (978-0-7398-4486-1(5)) Steck-Vaughn.

Stewart, David. Seasons. 2002. (gr. k-3). lib. bdg. 15.25 (978-0-613-53079-8(9)) Tandem Library Bks.

Stewart, Melissa. Why Do the Seasons Change? 2006. (Tell Me Why, Tell Me How Ser.). (Illus.). 32p. (J). lib. bdg. 28.50 (978-0-7614-2112-2(2) , Benchmark Bks.) Cavendish, Marshall Corp.

Stille, Darlene R. Fall. 2001. (Simply Science Ser.). (Illus.). 32p. (J). (gr. 3 up). lib. bdg. 19.93 (978-0-7565-0093-1(1)) Compass Point Bks.

Stone, Lynn M. Season to Season. 2007. (Illus.). 24p. (J). (978-1-60044-181-3(5)) Rourke Publishing, LLC.

Strawberry Shortcake Seasons of the Year. 2004. (J). 4.99 ***978-1-58610-900-4(6)*** Learning Horizons, Inc.

Strudwick, Leslie. The Science of Seasons. 2001. (Living Science Ser.). (Illus.). 32p. (J). (gr. 2 up). lib. bdg. 24.67 (978-0-8368-2791-0(0)) Stevens, Gareth Inc.

—The Science of Seasons. 2003. (Living Science Ser.). (Illus.). 32p. (J). (gr. 1-3). pap. 7.95 (978-1-930954-16-8(6)) Weigl Pubs., Inc.

—Science of Seasons. 2001. (gr. k-3). lib. bdg. 16.40 (978-0-613-80424-0(4)) Tandem Library Bks.

Taylor, Barbara & Walpole, Brenda. I Wonder Why the Sun Rises & Other Questions about Time & Seasons. 2006. (I Wonder Why Ser.). 32p. (J). (gr. k-3). pap. 6.95 (978-0-7534-5964-5(7) , Kingfisher) Houghton Mifflin Co. Trade & Reference Div.

Thomas, Eric, illus. Through the Seasons, 4 bks. Incl. Autumn : Signs of the Season Around North America. Finnegan, Mary Pat. 22.60 (978-1-4048-0000-7(X)); Spring : Signs of the Season Around North America. Gerard, Valerie J. 22.60 (978-1-4048-0002-1(6)); Summer : Signs of the Season Around North America. Gerard, Valerie J. 22.60 (978-1-4048-0003-8(4)); Winter : Signs of the Season Around North America. Finnegan, Mary Pat. 22.60 (978-1-4048-0001-4(8)); 24p. (C). (gr. k-1). 2004. (Illus.). 2002. 90.40 (978-1-4048-0075-5(1)) Picture Window Bks.

Thomas, Isabel. The Day the Earth Stood Still. 2005. (Illus.). 32p. (J). lib. bdg. (978-1-4109-1930-4(7)) Steck-Vaughn.

—The Day the Earth Stood Still: The Earth's Movement in Space. 2005. (Illus.). 32p. (J). (gr. 3-5). pap. 7.85 (978-1-4109-1961-8(7)) Steck-Vaughn.

El tiempo y las estaciones: Cuaderno de Actividades: Unit 5: el tiempo y las estaciones (Weather & Seasons) 2000. (McGraw-Hill Ciencias Ser.). (ENG & SPA.). (gr. k up). (978-0-02-278995-4(2)) Macmillan/McGraw-Hill Schl. Div.

Trumbauer, Lisa. Seasons. 2000. (Yellow Umbrella Books). (Illus.). 16p. (J). (gr. 1). lib. bdg. 14.60 (978-0-7368-0732-6(2) , Pebble Bks.) Capstone Pr., Inc.

—A Year in the Desert. 2005. (Yellow Umbrella Ser.). (Illus.). 16p. (J). (978-0-7368-5266-1(2)); (978-0-7368-5302-6(2)) Capstone Pr., Inc.

Wardlaw, Trevor P. What Is the Holiday? A Book of Learning for the Seasons. 1999. 50p. (J). (gr. k-3). pap. 9.95 (978-0-7392-0378-1(9) , PO3597) Morris Publishing.

Weather & Seasons. (Make Your Own Emergent Readers Ser.). 48p. (gr. k-2). 8.99 (978-0-7682-0018-8(0) , FS69006) Schaffer, Frank Pubns.

Weather & Seasons. 2004. lib. bdg. 152.00 (978-0-516-29321-9(4) , Children's Pr.) Scholastic Library Publishing.

Weather & Seasons Classroom Library. (gr. k-2). lib. bdg. 128.95 (978-0-7368-1828-5(6)) Red Brick Learning.

Weather & Seasons Complete Unit. (gr. k-2). 642.95 (978-0-7368-1829-2(4)) Red Brick Learning.

Whitehouse, Patricia. Las Estaciones, 5 vols., Set. 2003. (SPA.). (J). (ps-1). lib. bdg. 92.50 (978-1-4034-0338-4(0)) Heinemann Library.

—Las Estaciones 1 2 3. (Las Estaciones (Seasons) Ser.). 24p. pap. 5.25 (978-1-4034-0548-7(4)) Heinemann Library.

—Primavera. (Las Estaciones (Seasons) Ser.). 24p. pap. 5.25 (978-1-4034-0550-0(6)) Heinemann Library.

—Season 1 2 3. 2002. (Seasons Ser.). (Illus.). 24p. (J). pap. 5.25 (978-1-4034-0538-8(7)) Heinemann Library.

—Seasons, 6 vols., Set. 2003. (Illus.). (J). (ps-1). lib. bdg. 102.48 (978-1-58810-875-3(9)) Heinemann Library.

—Seasons 123. 2003. (Seasons Ser.). (Illus.). 24p. (J). (ps-1). lib. bdg. 17.08 (978-1-58810-896-8(1)) Heinemann Library.

—Seasons A B C. 2002. (Seasons Ser.). (Illus.). 24p. (J). pap. 5.25 (978-1-4034-0539-5(5)) Heinemann Library.

—Seasons ABC. 2003. (Seasons Ser.). (Illus.). 24p. (J). (ps-1). lib. bdg. 17.08 (978-1-58810-895-1(3)) Heinemann Library.

—Verano. (Las Estaciones (Seasons) Ser.). 24p. pap. 5.25 (978-1-4034-0552-4(2)) Heinemann Library.

Wilkes, Angela. Book of the Seasons. 2001. 96p. (Illus.). (YA). (gr. 1 up). lib. bdg. 24.95 (978-1-58086-331-5(0)); (J). lib. bdg. 24.95 (978-1-58086-595-1(X)) EDC Publishing.

—Lluvia y Sol. 2004. (Ladders Ser.).Tr. of Rain & Sunshine. (SPA., Illus.). 32p. (ps-3). 12.95 (978-1-58728-405-2(7) , Two Can Publishing) T&N Children's Publishing.

Winter in the Woods. 2003. (YA). (978-0-8374-0007-5(4)); lib. bdg. (978-0-8374-0006-8(6)) Weekly Reader Corp.

Woodhull, Anne Love. Every Season. Rotner, Shelley, illus. Rotner, Shelley, photos by. 2007. 32p. (J). (ps-3). 16.95 (978-1-59643-136-2(9)) Roaring Brook Pr.

Yolen, Jane. Welcome to the Icehouse. Regan, Laura, illus. 1998. 1p. (J). (ps-3). 16.99 (978-0-399-23011-0(4) , Putnam Juvenile) Penguin Group (USA) Inc.

Yolen, Jane & Christiana, David. The Book of Fairy Holidays. 1998. (J). (978-0-590-60356-0(6) , Blue Sky Pr., The) Scholastic, Inc.

4 Seasons of Fun. 2000. (Illus.). (J). (ps-1). 4.95 (978-2-89543-009-4(8)) Presswer Adventure CAN. *Dist:* Hushion Hse. Publishing, Ltd.

SEASONS—FICTION

Aignier-Clark, Julie. Peek-a-Boo Bard. 2008. 10p. 9.99 ***978-1-4231-0860-3(4)*** Hyperion Bks. for Children.

Allred, Sylvester. Rascal, the Tassel-Eared Squirrel. Iverson, Diane, illus. 2007. (J). ***978-0-938216-88-9(0)*** Grand Canyon Assn.

Anderson, Derek. Blue Burt & Wiggles. Anderson, Derek, illus. 2006. (Illus.). 32p. (J). (ps-3). 14.95 (978-1-4169-0593-6(6) , Simon & Schuster Children's Publishing) Simon & Schuster Children's Publishing.

Banks, Kate. The Great Blue House. Hallensleben, Georg, illus. 2005. 40p. (J). 16.00 (978-0-374-32769-9(6) , Farrar, Straus & Giroux (BYR)) Farrar, Straus & Giroux.

Berger, Samantha. It's Spring! 2001. (Hello Reader! Ser.). (Illus.). (J). (978-0-606-21257-1(4)) Tandem Library Bks.

Berger, Samantha & Chanko, Pamela. It's Spring. Sweet, Melissa, illus. 2003. 30p. (J). bds. 5.99 (978-0-439-44238-1(9) , Cartwheel Bks.) Scholastic, Inc.

Berger, Samantha, et al. It's Spring! 2001. (Hello Reader! Ser.). (Illus.). 32p. (J). (gr. k-2). pap. 3.99 (978-0-439-08754-4(6)) Scholastic, Inc.

Blackaby, Susan. A Year of Fun. Magnuson, Natalie, illus. 2005. (Read-It! Readers Ser.). 32p. (J). (gr. k-3). 18.60 (978-1-4048-1009-9(9)) Picture Window Bks.

Brennan, Martin. I Saw It in the Garden. Monroe, Michael Glenn, illus. 2006. 32p. (J). 17.95 (978-1-58726-296-8(7) , Mitten Pr.) Ann Arbor Media Group, LLC.

Bridwell, Norman. Clifford Celebrates the Year. 2002. (Clifford Ser.). (Illus.). 256p. (J). pap. 10.99 (978-0-439-46770-4(5)) Scholastic, Inc.

Brown. Little Bear Friendship Box: Love Song of Fall. 2002. (J). bds. (978-0-7868-0898-4(5)) Hyperion Bks. for Children.

Brown, Kerry Hannula. Tupaq the Dreamer. Sapport, Linda, illus. 2001. 32p. (J). (ps-3). 15.95 (978-0-7614-5076-4(9) , Cavendish Children's Bks.) Cavendish, Marshall Corp.

Bruna, Dick. Let's Learn: Seasons of the Year. 2004. (Illus.). 24p. pap. 4.99 (978-1-59226-168-0(X)) Big Tent Entertainment, Inc.

Bunting, Eve. Moonstick: The Seasons of the Sioux. Sandford, John B., illus. 2000. (Trophy Picture Bk.). 32p. (J). (gr. k-4). pap. 6.99 (978-0-06-443619-9(5) , Harper Trophy) HarperCollins Pubs.

—Moonstick: The Seasons of the Sioux. 2000. (978-0-606-18706-0(5)); (gr. 3-6). lib. bdg. 14.10 (978-0-613-34014-4(0)) Tandem Library Bks.

Burg, Annegret. Autumn Walk. Asbury, Kelly, illus. 2003. (Small Seasons Ser.). 20p. (J). (ps-k). 5.99 (978-0-06-009741-7(8)) HarperCollins Pubs.

Burrowes, Adjoa J. Grandma's Purple Flowers. 2000. (Illus.). 32p. (J). (ps-3). 15.95 (978-1-880000-73-1(3)) Lee & Low Bks., Inc.

Buscaglia, Leo. The Fall of Freddie the Leaf: A Story of Life for All Ages. annot. rev. ed. 2002. (Illus.). 30p. (J). 14.95 (978-0-8050-7195-5(4)) SLACK, Inc.

Carr, Jan. Dappled Apples. Donohue, Dorothy, illus. 2001. 32p. (J). (gr. k-3). tchr. ed. 15.95 (978-0-8234-1583-0(X)) Holiday Hse., Inc.

Christenson, Lisa & Christenson, Emme Jo. Seasons on the Sofa. Christenson, Lisa & Christenson, Emme Jo, illus. 2006. per. (978-0-9725311-3-9(0)) Pickled Eggs Pr.

Chronicle Books LLC Staff. Taro Gomi Seasons Pb. 2007. 376p. (J). pap. 16.95 ***978-0-8118-6019-2(1)*** Chronicle Bks. LLC.

Cochran, Jean M. Off I Go. Gullens, Lee, illus. 2007. 32p. (J). 16.95 ***978-0-9792035-1-0(1)*** Pleasant St. Pr.

Coulton, Mia. Danny & the Four Seasons. Coulton, Mia, photos by. 2001. (J). 4.95 (978-0-9713518-5-1(6)) Maryruth Bks., Inc.

Cousins, Lucy. Maisy's Seasons. 2002. (Maisy Ser.). (Illus.). 12p. (J). (gr. k-k). bds. 8.99 (978-0-7636-1914-5(0)) Candlewick Pr.

Crilley, Mark. Autumn. Crilley, Mark, illus. 2007. (Miki Falls Ser.). 176p. (J). (gr. 7 up). pap. 7.99 ***978-0-06-084618-3(6)*** , HarperTeen) HarperCollins Pubs.

Curry, Don L. In My Backyard. Oleary, Brown Erin, illus. 2004. (Rookie Reader Skill Set Ser.). 24p. (J). (gr. k-2). pap. 4.95 (978-0-516-26825-5(2) , Children's Pr.) Scholastic Library Publishing.

de Brunhoff, Laurent. Babar's Busy Year. 2005. (Illus.). 24p. (J). (ps-1). 9.95 (978-0-8109-5864-7(3)) Abrams, Harry N. , Inc.

—Meet Babar & His Family. 2002. (Babar Ser.). (Illus.). 30p. (J). (ps-3). 9.95 (978-0-8109-0555-9(8)) Abrams, Harry N. , Inc.

de Paola, Tomie. Four Friends in Autumn. 2004. (Illus.). 32p. (J). 14.95 (978-0-689-85980-9(5)) Simon & Schuster Children's Publishing.

Deady, Kathleen W. All Year Long. Bronson, Linda, illus. 2004. (Carolrhoda Picture Books Ser.). 32p. (J). (ps-3). 15.95 (978-1-57505-537-4(6)) Lerner Publishing Group.

Derby, Sally. Mi Escalera. de la Vega, Eida, tr. Burrowes, Adjoa J., illus. 1998. (SPA & ENG.). 32p. (J). (ps-3). 15.95 (978-1-880000-74-8(1) , LW7547); pap. 6.95 (978-1-880000-75-5(X) , LW7771) Lee & Low Bks., Inc.

—My Steps. Burrowes, Adjoa J., illus. 1999. 32p. (J). (gr. 1-4). (978-1-880000-84-7(9)); (ps-4). 15.95 (978-1-880000-40-3(7)) Lee & Low Bks., Inc.

Disney Publishing Staff. My Favorite Season, 15 vols. 2003. (It's Fun to Learn Ser.). (Illus.). 32p. (J). (ps-3). 3.99 (978-1-57973-129-8(5)) Advance Pubs. LLC.

Donahue, Jill L. Cass the Monkey. Muehlenhardt, Amy Bailey, illus. 2006. (Read-It! Readers Ser.). (J). 19.93 (978-1-4048-2407-2(3)) Picture Window Bks.

Dorling Kindersley Publishing Staff. Colorful Day. 2003. (ps-2). lib. bdg. 11.80 (978-0-613-75173-5(6)) Tandem Library Bks.

—Colorful Days. 2003. (Readers Ser.). (Illus.). (J). 32p. 12.99 (978-0-7894-9798-7(0)); 1p. pap. 3.99 (978-0-7894-9799-4(9)) Dorling Kindersley Publishing, Inc.

Dorling Kindersley Publishing Staff, ed. Dias Colоridos. 2004. (Dk Readers Ser.).Tr. of Colorful Days. (SPA.). 32p. (J). 12.99 (978-0-7566-0638-1(1)) Dorling Kindersley Publishing, Inc.

Doty, Linda. In Search of the Robin. 2003. 35p. pap. 17.95 (978-1-4137-0231-6(7)) PublishAmerica, Inc.

Ehrlich, Gretel. A Blizzard Year. Kiesler, Kate A., illus. 2001. 128p. (gr. 4-8). pap. 5.99 (978-0-7868-1245-5(1)) Hyperion Bks. for Children.

—A Blizzard Year. 2001. (J). (gr. 4-8). 12.64 (978-0-606-22572-4(2)) Tandem Library Bks.

Emerson, Carl. Old Oak & the Autumn Leaf. Doerrfeld, Cori, illus. 2007. (J). (978-1-4048-2624-3(6)) Picture Window Bks.

Erdrich, Louise. The Birchbark House. Erdrich, Louise, illus. 2002. (Illus.). 256p. (gr. 4-17). pap. 6.99 (978-0-7868-1454-1(3)) Hyperion Paperbacks for Children.

—The Birchbark House. 2002. (gr. 5-8). lib. bdg. 15.00 (978-0-613-59384-7(7)) Tandem Library Bks.

—The Game of Silence. 2005. (Illus.). 272p. (J). lib. bdg. 16.89 (978-0-06-029790-9(5)); 15.99 (978-0-06-029789-3(1)) HarperCollins Pubs.

—The Game of Silence. l.t. ed. 2000. 272p. (YA). (gr. 7-12). 20.95 (978-0-7862-2178-3(X)) Thorndike Pr.

Estes, Don. Willy & Friends traveling through the Seasons: The continuing story of Willy the little fire Jeep. Glass, Eric, illus. 2006. (J). (978-1-883551-75-9(7) , Maple Corners Press) Attic Studio Publishing Hse.

Ewart, Claire. The Giant. Ewart, Claire, illus. 2003. (Illus.). 32p. (J). (ps-3). 16.95 (978-0-8027-8835-1(1)) Walker & Co.

Fall Is Pumpkin Time! 2004. (YA). (978-0-8374-0011-2(2)); lib. bdg. (978-0-8374-0010-5(4)) Weekly Reader Corp.

Fraggalosch, Audrey. Let's Explore, Moose! Forest, Crista, illus. 2005. (Soundprints' Read-and-Discover Ser.). 32p. (J). (ps-1). pap. 3.95 (978-1-59249-151-3(0) , S2017) Soundprints.

Gershator, Phillis. Listen, Listen. Jay, Alison, illus. 2008. 32p. (J). (ps-4). 16.99 ***978-1-84686-084-3(9)*** Barefoot Bks., Inc.

Godwin, Laura. The Best Fall of All. Chapman, Jane, illus. 2002. (Happy Honey Ser.). 32p. (J). pap. 3.99 (978-0-689-84763-9(7) , Aladdin); 14.95 (978-0-689-84713-4(0) , McElderry, Margaret K.) Simon & Schuster Children's Publishing.

Gomi, Taro. Spring Is Here/Llego la Primavera. (Illus.). (J). 2006. (ENG & SPA.). 40p. pap. 6.95 (978-0-8118-4760-5(8)); 1999. 34p. bds. 6.95 (978-0-8118-2331-9(8)) Chronicle Bks. LLC.

Gray, Libba Moore. My Mama Had a Dancing Heart. Colon, Raul, illus. 2001. pap. 35.95 incl. audio compact disk (978-1-59112-543-3(X)) Live Oak Media.

—My Mama Had a Dancing Heart. 1999. (gr. k-3). lib. bdg. 14.10 (978-0-613-28968-9(4)) Tandem Library Bks.

Halfmann, Janet. Barney's Four Seasons. Davis, Guy, ed. Sharp, Chris, illus. 1999. 80p. (J). (ps-3). 1.99 (978-1-57064-465-8(9)) Scholastic, Inc.

Hall, Kirsten. Good Times: All about the Seasons. Luedecke, Bev, illus. (Beastieville Ser.). (J). (gr. k-1). 2005. 32p. pap. 3.95 (978-0-516-25518-7(5)); 2004. 19.50 (978-0-516-23648-3(2)) Scholastic Library Publishing. (Children's Pr.).

Hall, Zoe. Fall Leaves Fall! Halpern, Shari, illus. 1999. (J). pap. (978-0-590-10080-9(7)) Scholastic, Inc.

Halperin, Wendy Anderson, illus. Untitled Picture Book. 2003. (J). 16.99 (978-0-689-82552-1(8) , Atheneum) Simon & Schuster Children's Publishing.

Harshman, Marc & Ryan, Cheryl. Red Are the Apples. Zahares, Wade, illus. 2007. 32p. (J). pap. 6.00 (***978-0-15-206065-7(0)*** , Voyager Bks./Libros Viajeros) Harcourt Children's Bks.

Hoberman, Mary Ann. Right Outside My Window. Wilton, Nicholas, illus. 2002. 24p. (J). pap. (978-1-59034-181-0(3)); 15.95 (978-1-59034-194-0(5)) Mondo Publishing.

Holub, Joan. Five Little Fairies. Couri, Kathy, illus. 2008. 12p. (J). 9.99 (978-1-4169-3906-1(7) , Little Simon) Simon & Schuster Children's Publishing.

Hope, Laura Lee. Freddie & Flossie & the Leaf Monster. Ruppert, Larry, illus. 2005. 32p. (J). lib. bdg. 15.00 (***978-1-4242-0965-1(X)***) Fitzgerald Bks.

—Freddie & Flossie & the Leaf Monster. 2006. (Ready-To-Read Ser.). 32p. (J). (ps-2). 21.35 (978-1-59961-099-3(X)) Spotlight.

Howard-Parham, Pam. Caillou's Spring Discoveries. Gray, Stacy A., illus. 2006. (J). pap. (978-1-57332-374-1(8)) HighReach Learning, Inc.

Howell, Will C. I Call It Sky. Ward, John, illus. 1999. 32p. (J). (ps-1). 15.95 (978-0-8027-8686-9(3)); lib. bdg. 16.85 (978-0-8027-8687-6(1)); 15.95 (978-0-8027-8677-7(4)); lib. bdg. 16.85 (978-0-8027-8678-4(2)) Walker & Co.

Howker, Janni. Walk with a Wolf. 2002. (gr. k-3). lib. bdg. 14.15 (978-0-613-74757-8(7)) Tandem Library Bks.

—Walk with a Wolf: Read & Wonder. Fox-Davies, Sarah, illus. 2002. (Read & Wonder Bks.). 32p. (J). (ps-3). pap. 6.99 (978-0-7636-1872-8(1)) Candlewick Pr.

Hubery, Julia. A Friend for All Seasons. Matsuoka, Mei, illus. 2007. 32p. (J). (ps-2). 15.99 (***978-1-4169-2685-6(2)***) Simon & Schuster Children's Publishing.

Inches, Alison. Hello, Spring! Chernichaw, Ian, illus. 2004. (Blue's Clues Ser.: Vol. 8). 24p. (J). pap. 3.99 (978-0-689-86316-5(0) , Simon Spotlight/Nickelodeon) Simon & Schuster Children's Publishing.

Jane, Pamela. Fall Is Here! Counting 1 to 10. Haskamp, Steve, illus. 2005. 20p. (J). 8.99 (978-0-689-87470-3(7) , Little Simon) Simon & Schuster Children's Publishing.

Kindley, Jeff. Scamper's Year. Rader, Laura, illus. 1999. (Bank Street Reader Collection). 48p. (J). (ps-2). lib. bdg. 22.60 (978-0-8368-1777-5(X)) Stevens, Gareth Inc.

Kinsey-Warnock, Natalie. From Dawn till Dusk. Azarian, Mary, illus. 2002. 40p. (J). (gr. k-3). tchr. ed. 16.00 (978-0-618-18655-6(7)) Houghton Mifflin Co. Trade & Reference Div.

—From Dawn till Dusk. Azarian, Mary, illus. 2006. 40p. (J). (gr. k-3). reprint ed. pap. 6.95 (978-0-618-73750-5(2)) Houghton Mifflin Co. Trade & Reference Div.

Knudsen, Michelle. Autumn Is for Apples. Denise, Fernando, illus. 2001. 24p. (J). (ps-1). pap. 3.25 (978-0-375-81090-9(0) , Random Hse. Bks. for Young Readers) Random Hse. Children's Bks.

Koopmans, Loek. Frog, Bee & Snail Look for Snow. 2006. Orig. Title: Samen Op Zoek. (Illus.). 28p. (J). 15.95 (978-0-86315-559-8(6)) Floris Bks. GBR. *Dist:* Steiner-Books, Inc.

Kroner, David. Seasons. 2007. 72p. pap. 6.95 (***978-1-882190-54-6(8)***) Polar Bear & Co.

Kusugak, Michael Arvaarluk. Arctic Stories. Krykorka, Vladyana Langer, illus. 1998. 40p. (J). (gr. k-4). pap. 7.95 (978-1-55037-452-0(4)) Annick Pr., Ltd. CAN. *Dist:* Firefly Bks., Ltd.

—Arctic Stories. 1999. (J). (978-0-606-16482-5(0)) Tandem Library Bks.

Lagonegro, Melissa. The Fairest of the Fall. Emslie, Peter, illus. 2003. (Disney Princess Ser.). 24p. (J). (gr. k-3). pap. 3.25 (978-0-7364-2148-5(3) , RH/Disney) Random Hse. Children's Bks.

Lee, Jeanie. Now It's Fall! Valerio, Geraldo, illus. 2007. (Flips & Flaps Book Ser.). 12p. (J). (ps-2). 9.99 (***978-1-4169-0934-7(6)*** , Little Simon) Simon & Schuster Children's Publishing.

Lee, Nancy. Hoover's Funny Little Kids. 2005. (J). spiral bd. 8.95 (978-0-9748087-8-9(4)) Journey Pubns., LLC.

Leep, Jennifer. Precious Moments: The Four Seasons, 4 bks. , Set. Butcher, Sam, illus. 1999. 12p. (J). (ps-k). bds. 16.95 (978-1-57145-362-4(8) , Silver Dolphin Bks.) Advantage Pubs. Group.

Lister, Mary. The Winter King & the Summer Queen. Mayo, Diana, illus. 2002. 32p. (J). (gr. 1-3). 16.99 (978-1-84148-357-3(5)) Barefoot Bks., Inc.

London, Jonathan. Park Beat: Rhymin' Through the Seasons. Hubbard, Woodleigh Marx, illus. 2001. 32p. (J). (ps-3). 15.95 (978-0-688-13994-0(9)) HarperCollins Pubs.

Maio, Barbara & Faulkner, Stacey, eds. Seasons. Second-grade students, illus. 2006. (Learn to Write Ser.). 8p. (J). pap. 1.99 (978-1-59198-291-3(X) , 6185) Creative Teaching Pr., Inc.

Manutoli, Sophie. Mer'em Ayuqucia. Smart, B. George & Horesh, David, illus. 1998. Tr. of Water in All Forms. (ESK.). 12p. (J). (gr. k-3). pap. 6.00 (978-1-58084-044-6(2)) Lower Kuskokwim Schl. District.

McNamara, Margaret. Fall Leaf Project. Gordon, Mike, illus. 2006. (Ready-To-Read Ser.). 32p. (J). pap. 3.99 (978-1-4169-1537-9(0)); lib. bdg. 13.89 (978-1-4169-1538-6(9)) Simon & Schuster Children's Publishing. (Aladdin).

Messinger, Carla & Katz, Susan. When the Shadbush Blooms. Fadden, David Kanietakeron, illus. 2007. 32p. (J). (ps-2). 15.95 (978-1-58246-192-2(9) , Tricycle Pr.) Ten Speed Pr.

Metzger, Steve. It's Fall! Wilhelm, Hans, illus. 2000. (Dinofours Ser.: No. 11). (J). (ps-1). pap. (978-0-439-17958-4(0)) Scholastic, Inc.

Milne, A. A. Slide & Seek Numbers: A Sliding Window Book. 1999. (Illus.). 8p. (J). 10.99 (978-0-7868-3241-5(X)) Disney Pr.

Mioduchowska, Anna. In Between Season. 67p. (J). 12.95 (978-1-895836-56-1(5)) River Bks. CAN. *Dist:* Coteau Bks.

Moss, Marissa. Amelia's 5th-Grade Notebook. Moss, Marissa, illus. 2006. (Amelia's Notebooks). (Illus.). 40p. (J). 9.95 (978-1-4169-0912-5(5) , Simon & Schuster/ Paula Wiseman Bks.) Simon & Schuster Children's Publishing.

Muller, Gerda. The Circle of Seasons. 1999. 48p. (J). pap. 4.99 (978-0-14-055887-6(X) , Puffin) Penguin Group (USA) Inc.

Mullican, Judy & Linke, Don, Jr. In the Fall. l.t. ed. 1999. (Cuddle Bks.). (Illus.). 6p. (J). (ps-k). pap. 10.95 (978-1-57332-146-4(X)) HighReach Learning, Inc.

Nelson, Ray, et al. Jenny's Autumn Book. Siegel, Joseph & Habecker, Mary Beth, eds. Peeples, Aaron et al, illus. 2000. 32p. (J). (gr. 1-3). pap. 12.00 (978-1-883772-50-5(8)) Flying Rhinoceros, Inc.

Nettrour, Nelani. Jodi & the Seasons. Nettrour, Heather, illus. l.t. ed. 2004. 88p. pap. 11.95 (978-1-932657-16-6(9)) Third Millennium Pubns.

Nidey, Kelli. When Autumn Falls. Swan, Susan, illus. 32p. (J). 2006. pap. 6.95 (978-0-8075-0491-8(2)); 2004. 15.95 (978-0-8075-0490-1(4)) Whitman, Albert & Co.

Onish, Liane. The Alphabet Eurps & the 4 Seasons. 1999. (Eurps Concept Bks.). (Illus.). (J). 7.95 (978-1-892522-08-5(X)) Eurpsville USA, Inc.

Owens, Katherine. Tree Seasons Ball, 1 bk. l.t. ed. 2004. (Illus.). 40p. (J). per. 19.99 (978-0-9760419-0-0(1) , TREESEASONSBALL) ThatsMyLife Co.

Page, Nick & Claire. The Autumn Princess. 2006. (Read with Me (Make Believe Ideas) Ser.). (Illus.). 32p. (J). (gr. k-2). 3.95 (978-1-84610-171-7(9)) Make Believe Ideas GBR. *Dist:* Ingram Pub. Services.

Pickering, Jimmy. It's Fall. 2003. (Illus.). 32p. (J). (ps-3). 16.95 (978-1-931290-15-9(6)) Tallfellow Pr.

Plourde, Lynn. Wild Child. Couch, Greg, illus. 2003. 32p. (J). pap. 7.99 (978-0-689-86349-3(7) , Aladdin) Simon & Schuster Children's Publishing.

Polacco, Patricia. For the Love of Autumn. Polacco, Patricia, illus. 2008. 40p. (J). (gr. 1-4). 16.99 (***978-0-399-24541-1(3)*** , Philomel) Penguin Group (USA) Inc.

Posner, Renee & Quinton, Sasha. Suzy Season Loves Spring. D'Argo, Laura, illus. (Be Mine Bears Ser.). (J). bds. 4.99 (978-1-58209-350-5(4)) Books Are Fun, Ltd.

Pugliano-Martin, Carol. Glooscap Makes the Seasons: A Canadian Legend. 2006. spiral bd. 42.00 (***978-1-4108-7159-6(2)***) Benchmark Education Co.

—Ready for Fall! 2006. (Early Explorers Ser.). (J). 34.00 (***978-1-4108-6103-0(1)***) Benchmark Education Co.

Raczka, Bob. Who Loves the Fall? Stead, Judy, illus. 2007. 29p. (ps-1). 16.95 (***978-0-8075-9037-9(1)***) Whitman, Albert & Co.

Random House Disney Staff. Weather Watcher. 2006. 96p. (J). (ps-2). pap. 2.99 (978-0-7364-2407-3(5) , Golden/ Disney) Random Hse. Children's Bks.

Random House Disney Staff & Lagonegro, Melissa. Sweethearts in the Snow. Emslie, Peter & Marrucchi, Elisa, illus. 2003. (Disney Princess Ser.). 24p. (J). (ps-2). pap. 3.25 (978-0-7364-2170-6(X) , RH/Disney) Random Hse. Children's Bks.

Rau, Dana Meachen. In the Yard, Level A. 2001. (Early Reader Ser.). (Illus.). 24p. (J). (gr. k up). lib. bdg. 18.60 (978-0-7565-0116-7(4)) Compass Point Bks.

Ringler, Matt. One Little, Two Little, Three Little Apples. Kennedy, Anne, illus. 2005. (J). pap. (***978-0-439-77500-7(0)***) Scholastic, Inc.

Rogers, Alan. Green Bear. 2004. (Little Giants Ser.). (Illus.). 16p. (ps-k). (J). pap. 3.95 (978-1-58728-159-4(7)); 5.95 (978-1-58728-152-5(X)) T&N Children's Publishing. (Two Can Publishing).

Rohmann, Eric. A Kitten Tale. 2008. (J). (***978-0-517-70915-3(5));*** lib. bdg. (***978-0-517-70916-0(3)***) Knopf, Alfred A. Inc.

Root, Phyllis. Mouse Goes Out. Croft, James, illus. 2002. (Brand New Readers Ser.). (J). (ps-2). 48p. 12.99 (978-0-7636-1351-8(7)); 32p. pap. 5.99 (978-0-7636-1352-5(5)) Candlewick Pr.

Rosenberry, Vera. Run - Jump - Whiz - Splash. Rosenberry, Vera, illus. 1999. (Illus.). 32p. (J). (gr. k-3). tchr. ed. 15.95 (978-0-8234-1378-2(0)) Holiday Hse., Inc.

Rouillard, Wendy W. Barnaby-Seasons in the Park. Rouillard, Wendy W., ed. 2000. (Barnaby Ser.: Vol. 5). (Illus.). 32p. (J). 15.95 (978-0-9642836-9-5(7)) Barnaby & Co.

Rousseau, Bonney Jo. The Plano Seasons. 1999. iv, 147p. (YA). (gr. 7-12). pap. 11.00 (978-0-9667395-4-1(X)) Escapr Pr.

Rucki, Ani. When the Earth Wakes. 1998. (Illus.). 32p. (J). (ps-2). pap. 15.95 (978-0-590-05951-0(3)) Scholastic, Inc.

Ruffenach, Jessie, ed. Baby Learns about Seasons. Thomas, Peter, tr. from ENG. Blacksheep, Beverly, illus. 2005. (NAV & ENG.). 16p. (J). bds. 7.95 (978-1-893354-61-6(X)) Salina Bookshelf.

Russell, Ching Yeung. Moon Festival. 2003. (gr. k-3). lib. bdg. 17.60 (978-0-613-59335-9(9)) Tandem Library Bks.

Ryan, Susan Jane. Esmeralda & the Enchanted Pond. Cook, Sandra, illus. 2001. 48p. (J). (gr. 2-5). 14.95 (978-1-56164-236-6(3)) Pineapple Pr., Inc.

Ryan, Susan Jane & Cook, Sandra G. Esmeralda & the Enchanted Pond. 2001. (Illus.). 48p. (gr. 4-7). pap., act. bk. ed. 5.00 (978-1-56164-247-2(9)) Pineapple Pr., Inc.

Rylant, Cynthia. Henry & Mudge under the Yellow Moon. Stevenson, Sucie, illus. 1998. (Henry & Mudge Ser.). 28.95 incl. audio compact disk (978-1-59112-585-3(5)); pap. 31.95 incl. audio compact disk (978-1-59112-584-6(7)) Live Oak Media.

—Seasons with Henry & Mudge. Stevenson, Sucie, illus. 2000. (Henry & Mudge Ser.). pap. 68.95 incl. audio compact disk (978-1-59112-855-7(2)) Live Oak Media.

—This Year's Garden. Szilagyi, Mary, illus. 1998. (J). pap. 4.95 (978-0-87628-397-4(0)) Ctr. for Applied Research in Education, The.

—This Year's Garden. 1999. (Illus.). (J). (ps-2). lib. bdg. 12.95 (978-0-8085-9240-2(8)) Tandem Library Bks.

Rylant, Cynthia & Siegel, Mark. Long Night Moon. 2004. (Illus.). 40p. (J). 16.95 (978-0-689-85426-2(9)) Simon & Schuster Children's Publishing.

Sargent, David M., Jr. Autumn's Emergency. Huff, Jeane Lirley, illus. 2003. (Doggie Tails Ser.). 32p. (J). lib. bdg. 19.95 (978-1-56763-845-5(7)) Ozark Publishing.

Savard, Remi & Germain, Catherine. First Spring. Kellough, Donald, tr. from FRE. Coté, Geneviève, illus. 2006. 44p. (J). 16.95 (978-1-894965-34-7(5)) Simply Read Bks. CAN. *Dist:* Perseus Distribution.

Schertle, Alice. Very Hairy Bear. Phelan, Matt, illus. 2007. 32p. (J). (ps-2). 16.00 (978-0-15-216568-0(1)) Harcourt Trade Pubs.

Schubert, Leda. Here Comes Darrell. Azarian, Mary, illus. 2005. 32p. (J). (gr. k-3). 16.00 (978-0-618-41605-9(6)) Houghton Mifflin Co. Trade & Reference Div.

Schulman, Janet. A Bunny for All Seasons. So, Meilo, illus. 2003. 32p. (J). (gr. k-1). 9.95 (978-0-375-82256-8(9) , Knopf Bks. for Young Readers) Random Hse. Children's Bks.

Sklansky, Amy E. My Daddy & Me. Hoyt, Ard, illus. 2005. 24p. (J). 3.50 (978-0-439-74046-3(0) , Cartwheel Bks.) Scholastic, Inc.

Spinelle, Nancy. Seasons. 2005. (Illus.). (J). pap. 4.95 (978-1-57874-105-2(X)) Kaeden Corp.

Spinelli, Eileen. I Know It's Autumn. Hayashi, Nancy, tr. Hayashi, Nancy, illus. 2004. 32p. (J). (ps-2). 16.99 (978-0-06-029422-9(1)); lib. bdg. 17.89 (978-0-06-029423-6(X)) HarperCollins Pubs.

Stein, David Ezra. Leaves. Stein, David Ezra, illus. 2007. (Illus.). 32p. (J). (ps-2). 15.99 (978-0-399-24636-4(3) , Putnam Juvenile) Penguin Group (USA) Inc.

Stewart, Paul. A Little Bit of Winter. Riddell, Chris, illus. 1999. 32p. (J). (ps-2). 14.95 (978-0-06-028278-3(9)) HarperCollins Pubs.

Stewart, Sarah. The Money Tree. Small, David, illus. 2004. (J). (ps-ps). lib. bdg. 14.15 (978-0-606-29981-7(5)) Tandem Library Bks.

Stoeke, Janet Morgan. Waiting for May. Stoeke, Janet Morgan, illus. 2005. (Illus.). 32p. (J). (gr. k-ps). 16.99 (978-0-525-47098-4(0) , Dutton Juvenile) Penguin Group (USA) Inc.

Stout, Steve. The Day It Rained Leaves: A Starved Rock Park Adventure. Funk, Charles, illus. 2002. (Orig.). (J). (gr. k-5). pap. 9.95 (978-0-9609296-3-4(0)) Utica Hse. Publishing Co.

Stringer, Lauren. Winter Is the Warmest Season. 2006. (Illus.). 40p. (J). 16.00 (978-0-15-204967-6(3)) Harcourt Trade Pubs.

Summer Is a Special Season. 2004. (YA). (978-0-8374-0013-6(9)); lib. bdg. (978-0-8374-0012-9(0)) Weekly Reader Corp.

Tafuri, Nancy. Snowy Flowy Blowy: A Twelve Months Rhyme. 1999. (Illus.). (J). pap. (978-0-590-18974-3(3)) Scholastic Reading Counts.

Taylor, Theodore. Hello, Arctic! Chodos-Irvine, Margaret, illus. 2002. 40p. (J). (gr. k-2). 17.00 (978-0-15-201577-0(9)) Harcourt Children's Bks.

Tibo, Gilles. Simon Says: Seasons. 2006. (Illus.). 48p. (J). (ps-3). 17.95 (978-0-88776-793-7(1)) Tundra Bks., Inc./ Livres Toundra, Inc. CAN. *Dist:* Random Hse., Inc.

Van Laan, Nancy. Busy, Busy Moose. Rusch, Amy, illus. 2003. 48p. (J). (gr. k-3). tchr. ed. 15.00 (978-0-395-96091-2(6)) Houghton Mifflin Co. Trade & Reference Div.

Van Laan, Nancy. Busy, Busy Moose. Rusch, Amy, illus. 2007. 48p. (J). (gr. k-3). 6.95 (***978-0-618-80907-3(4)***) Houghton Mifflin Co. Trade & Reference Div.

Wallace, Nancy Elizabeth. Leaves! Leaves! Leaves! 2003. (Illus.). 40p. (J). 16.95 (978-0-7614-5140-2(4)) Cavendish, Marshall Corp.

Waters, Tony. Cinnamon's Busy Year. Guevara, Linda L. & Merrill, Libby, eds. Waters, Tony, illus. 2003. (Illus.). 32p. (J). (ps-3). pap. 5.95 (978-0-9710278-2-4(X)) All About Kids Publishing.

Watt, Fiona. Hide-And-Seek Bunnies. Danson, Lesley, illus. 2007. (Touchy-Feely Flap Bks). 10p. (J). bds. 16.99 (***978-0-7945-1566-9(5)*** , Usborne) EDC Publishing.

Weiss, Ellen. Winter Spring Summer Fall: A Touch & Feel Seasons Book. Bennett, Andy, illus. 2006. (PBS Kids(R) Ser.). 10p. (J). 6.95 (***978-1-57791-312-2(4)***) Brighter Minds Children's Publishing.

Williams, Rozanne Lanczak. Seasons. Maio, Barbara & Faulkner, Stacey, eds. 2006. (J). per. 4.99 (***978-1-59198-342-2(8)***) Creative Teaching Pr., Inc.

Willson, Sarah. Hooray for Fall! 2003. (ps-2). lib. bdg. 11.80 (978-0-613-73399-1(1)) Tandem Library Bks.

Wilson, Sarah. Friends & Pals & Brothers, Too. Landry, Leo, illus. 2008. 32p. (J). 16.95 (***978-0-8050-7643-1(3)***) Holt, Henry & Co.

Zanimo & Perkes, Carolyn. My Seasons. 2000. (Maki's Words Ser.). (Illus.). 24p. (J). (ps-k). pap. (978-1-894363-55-6(8)) Dominique & Friends.

Zeman, Ludmila. The First Red Maple Leaf. Zeman, Ludmila, illus. 1999. (Illus.). 24p. (J). (gr. k-3). reprint ed. pap. 9.95 (978-0-88776-419-6(3)) Tundra Bks., Inc./ Livres Toundra, Inc. CAN. *Dist:* Random Hse., Inc.

SEASONS—LEGENDS

Old, Wendie. The Groundhog Day Book of Facts & Fun. Billin-Frye, Paige, illus. 2004. 40p. (J). (gr. 3-6). 15.95 (978-0-8075-3066-5(2)) Whitman, Albert & Co.

SEASONS—POETRY

Burton, Michael H. In the Light of a Child: A Journey Through the 52 Weeks of the Year in Both Hemispheres for Children & for the Child in Each Human Being. 1998. 64p. pap. 14.95 (978-0-88010-450-0(3)) Steiner-Books, Inc.

Roemer, Heidi. Come to My Party: And Other Shape Poems. Takahashi, Hideko, tr. Takahashi, Hideko, illus. rev. ed. 2004. 32p. (J). 17.95 (978-0-8050-6620-3(9) , Holt, Henry & Co. Bks. For Young Readers) Holt, Henry & Co.

Salas, Laura Purdie. Shrinking Days, Frosty Nights: Poems about Fall. 2008. (***978-1-4296-1205-0(3)***) Capstone Pr., Inc.

Seasons Come Seasons Go. 2nd ed. 2005. per. (978-0-9763958-0-5(0)) Aceybee Publishing.

Siebert, Diane. Spring, Summer, Autumn, Winter. Burckhardt, Marc, illus. 2005. (J). (978-1-59336-299-7(4)); pap. (978-1-59336-300-0(1)) Mondo Publishing.

Thomas, Patricia. Nature's Paintbox: A Seasonal Gallery of Art & Verse. Orback, Craig, illus. 2007. (Millbrook Picture Books Ser.). 32p. (J). (gr. 2-5). 16.95 (***978-0-8225-6807-0(1)*** , Millbrook Pr.) Lerner Publishing Group.

Zolotow, Charlotte. Seasons: A Book of Poems. Blegvad, Erik, illus. 2002. (I Can Read Bks.). 64p. (J). (gr. k-3). 14.95 (978-0-06-026698-1(8)) HarperCollins Pubs.

—Seasons: A Book of Poems. 2003. (gr. k-3). lib. bdg. 11.80 (978-0-613-62189-2(1)) Tandem Library Bks.

SEATTLE, CHIEF, 1790-1866

Carew-Miller, Anna. Chief Seattle: Great Chief. 2002. (Great Names Ser.). (Illus.). 32p. (YA). (gr. 3 up). lib. bdg. (978-1-59084-154-9(9)) Mason Crest Pubs.

SEATTLE (WASH.)

Filer, Patricia & Fulton, Cathy. Welcome to the Greenland: A Children's Activity Guide to the Birthplace of Seattle. 2003. (Illus.). 40p. (J). spiral bd. 24.95 (978-0-9727759-5-3(1)) Capturing Memories.

Seattle Sold C 2005. 2004. 372p. (YA). pap. 15.00 (978-1-58553-965-9(1) , 05GC0009) Entertainment Publications, Inc.

Stein, R. Conrad. Seattle. 1999. (Cities of the World Ser.). (Illus.). 64p. (gr. 4-9). pap. 9.95 (978-0-516-26463-9(X) , Children's Pr.) Scholastic Library Publishing.

SEATTLE (WASH.)—FICTION

Brown, Marc. Buster & the Giant Pumpkin. 2005. (Postcards from Buster Ser.). (Illus.). 32p. (J). (gr. 1-4). 14.99 (978-0-316-15887-9(9)) Little Brown & Co.

—Buster & the Giant Pumpkin. 2005. (Postcards from Buster Ser.). (Illus.). 32p. (J). (gr. 1-4). pap., pap. 3.99 (978-0-316-00111-3(2)) Little, Brown Bks. for Young Readers.

Caletti, Deb. The Nature of Jade. 2007. (YA). 304p. (gr. 7 up). 16.99 (978-1-4169-1005-3(0)); 288p. (***978-1-4287-2344-3(7)***) Simon & Schuster Children's Publishing. (Simon & Schuster Children's Publishing).

Cosgrove, Stephen. Wheedle on the Needle. James, Robin, illus. ed. 2002. (Serendipity Ser.). 32p. (J). reprint ed. pap. 4.99 (978-0-8431-4872-5(1) , Price Stern Sloan) Penguin Group (USA) Inc.

—Wheedle on the Needle. 2002. (gr. k-3). lib. bdg. 13.00 (978-0-613-64617-8(7)) Tandem Library Bks.

De Guzman, Michael. The Bamboozlers. 2005. 176p. (J). (gr. 5-8). 16.00 (978-0-374-30512-3(9)) Farrar, Straus & Giroux.

Ennis, Judith. Kalakala Comes Home: No Dream Is Too Big! McCoy, Lisa et al, eds. Ingram, Dean, tr. Wilburn, Kathy, photos by. l.t. ed. 2000. (Illus.). 50p. (J). 18.95 (978-0-9660092-7-9(4)) Puget Sound Pr.

Gallagher, Liz. The Opposite of Invisible. 2008. (YA). (***978-0-375-84152-1(0));*** (***978-0-375-94329-4(3)***) Dell Publishing. (Delacorte Pr.).

Gamble, Adam & Steere, Jay. Good Night Seattle. Veno, Joe, illus. 2007. (Good Night Our World Ser.). 20p. (J). bds. 9.95 (***978-1-60219-014-6(3)***) Our World of Books.

Hobbs, William. Jackie's Wild Seattle. 208p. (J). (gr. 5 up). 2004. pap. 5.99 (978-0-380-73311-8(0) , Harper Trophy); 2003. 16.99 (978-0-688-17474-3(4)); 2003. lib. bdg. 16.89 (978-0-06-051631-4(3)) HarperCollins Pubs.

Johns, Linda. Hannah West on Millionaire's Row. 2007. (Hannah West Ser.). 160p. (J). (gr. 5). 6.99 (***978-0-14-240824-7(7)*** , Puffin) Penguin Group (USA) Inc.

Kehret, Peg. Abduction! (J). 2006. 224p. (gr. 4). pap. 6.99 (978-0-14-240617-5(1) , Puffin); 2004. 192p. (gr. 5). reprint ed. 16.99 (978-0-525-47294-0(0) , Dutton Juvenile) Penguin Group (USA) Inc.

Kirkpatrick, Katherine. The Voyage of the Continental. 2002. (Illus.). 256p. (J). (gr. 7 up). tchr. ed. 16.95 (978-0-8234-1580-9(5)) Holiday Hse., Inc.

S

Lockhart, E. The Boyfriend List. (gr. 7). 2005. 240p. (J). lib. bdg. 17.99 (978-0-385-90238-0(7)); 2006. 256p. (YA). reprint ed. pap. 8.95 (978-0-385-73207-9(4)) Random Hse. Children's Bks. (Delacorte Bks. for Young Readers).

—The Boyfriend List: (15 Guys, 11 Shrink Appointments, 4 Ceramic Frogs, & Me, Ruby Oliver) 2005. 240p. (YA). (gr. 7). 15.95 (978-0-385-73206-2(6) , Delacorte Bks. for Young Readers) Random Hse. Children's Bks.

Losi, Carol A. Salt & Pepper at the Pike Place Market. Meissner, Amy, illus. 2004. 32p. (J). 15.95 (978-1-55868-800-1(5)); pap. 8.95 (978-1-55868-801-8(3)) Graphic Arts Ctr. Publishing Co. (West Winds Pr.).

Loyd, Mark. Big Ben: A Little Known Story. Loyd, Mark, illus. ed. 2005. (J). (978-0-9773317-1-0(7)) Too Fun Publshing.

Meyer, Stephenie. Eclipse. rev. ed. 2007. (Twilight Saga Ser.). 640p. (YA). (gr. 7 up). 18.99 (***978-0-316-16020-9(2))*** Little, Brown Bks. for Young Readers.

Mochizuki, Ken. Beacon Hill Boys. 208p. (J). 2004. (gr. 7 up). 5.99 (978-0-439-24906-5(6)); 2002. (gr. 9 up). pap. 16.95 (978-0-439-26749-6(8) , Scholastic Pr.) Scholastic, Inc.

Powell, Randy. Run If You Dare. 2001. 192p. (YA). (gr. 7 up). 16.00 (978-0-374-39981-8(6) , Farrar, Straus & Giroux (BYR)) Farrar, Straus & Giroux.

—Run If You Dare. 2006. 192p. (YA). pap. 6.95 (978-0-374-46375-5(1)) Macmillan.

—Run If You Dare. l.t. ed. 2001. 216p. (J). 22.95 (978-0-7862-3716-6(3)) Thorndike Pr.

—Tribute to Another Dead Rock Star. 224p. (YA). 2003. pap. 5.95 (978-0-374-47968-8(2) , Sunburst); 1999. (gr. 7-12). 17.00 (978-0-374-37748-9(0) , Farrar, Straus & Giroux (BYR)) Farrar, Straus & Giroux.

—Tribute to Another Dead Rock Star. l.t. ed. 2000. 224p. (J). 21.95 (978-0-7862-2191-2(7)) Thorndike Pr.

Skewes, John & Schwartz, Robert. Larry Gets Lost in Seattle. 2007. (Illus.). 32p. 16.95 (***978-1-57061-483-5(0))*** Sasquatch Bks.

Warner, Gertrude Chandler. The Seattle Puzzle. 2007. (Boxcar Children Mysteries Ser.: No. 111). 128p. (J). (gr. 2-7). pap. 4.50 (***978-0-8075-5561-3(4));*** lib. bdg. 14.95 (***978-0-8075-5560-6(6))*** Whitman, Albert & Co.

Wilson, Barbara. A Clear Spring. 2002. (Girls First! Ser.: Vol. 1). 112p. 12.50 (978-1-55861-277-8(7)) Feminist Pr. at The City Univ. of New York.

SEATTLE SEAHAWKS (FOOTBALL TEAM)

Gilbert, Sara. The History of the Seattle Seahawks. 2004. (NFL Today Ser.). (Illus.). 32p. 18.95 (978-1-58341-314-2(6) , Creative Education) Creative Co., The.

Seattle Seahawks Staff. Seattle Seahawks. CWC Sports Inc, ed. 1998. (NFL Team Yearbooks Ser.). (J). (gr. 1-12). pap. 9.99 (978-1-891613-16-6(2)) Everett Sports Publishing & Marketing.

SEAWEED

see Algae

SECONDARY EDUCATION

see Education, Secondary

SECONDARY SCHOOLS

see Education, Secondary; High Schools; Public Schools

SECRET SERVICE

see also Detectives; Spies

also subdivision Secret Service under individual wars, e.g. World War, 1939-1945—Secret Service.

Beyer, Mark. The Secret Service. 2003. (High-Top Secret Ser.). (Illus.). 48p. (J). 23.00 (978-0-516-24313-9(6)); (YA). (gr. 7-12). pap. 6.95 (978-0-516-24376-4(4)) Scholastic Library Publishing. (Children's Pr.).

—Secret Service. 2003. (gr. 7-12). lib. bdg. 15.25 (978-0-613-59717-3(6)) Tandem Library Bks.

Caravantes, Peggy. Petticoat Spies: Six Women Spies of the US Civil War. 2004. (Notable Americans Ser.). (Illus.). 112p. (YA). (gr. 6-12). 23.95 (978-1-883846-88-6(9) , First Biographies) Reynolds, Morgan Inc.

Gaines, Ann Graham. The U. S. Secret Service. 2001. (Your Government Ser.). (Illus.). 64p. (J). (gr. 4-7). 25.00 (978-0-7910-5990-6(1) , Chelsea Hse.) Facts On File, Inc.

Inside the World's Most Famous Intelligence Agencies. 2005. (Illus.). (gr. 7-12). lib. bdg. 159.00 (978-0-8239-4061-5(6)) Rosen Publishing Group, Inc., The.

Lough, Loree. Nathan Hale. 1999. (Revolutionary War Leaders Ser.). (Illus.). 80p. (gr. 3 up). (J). 31.00 (978-0-7910-5361-4(X)); (YA). pap. 27.50 (978-0-7910-5704-9(6)) Facts On File, Inc. (Chelsea Hse.).

—Nathan Hale: Revolutionary Hero. 2000. (Illus.). 80p. (J). (gr. 3-17). lib. bdg. 17.60 (978-0-613-43357-0(2)) Tandem Library Bks.

Miller, Connie Colwell. The Secret Service: Protecting Our Leaders. 2008. (***978-1-4296-1275-3(4))*** Capstone Pr., Inc.

Polisar, Patti. Inside France's DGSE: The General Directorate for External Security. 2005. (Illus.). 63p. (gr. 4-8). reprint ed. 20.00 (978-0-7567-8670-0(3)) DIANE Publishing Co.

Schiel, Katy. Inside Germany's BND: The Federal Intelligence Service. 2005. (Illus.). 63p. (YA). (gr. 4-8). reprint ed. 20.00 (978-0-7567-8669-4(X)) DIANE Publishing Co.

Seidman, David. Secret Service: Life Protecting the President. 2005. (Extreme Careers Ser.). (Illus.). 64p. (YA). (gr. 5-8). 26.50 (978-0-8239-3636-6(8)) Rosen Publishing Group, Inc., The.

Souter, Gerry. Secret Service Agent & Careers in Federal Protection. 2006. (Homeland Security & Counterterrorism Careers Ser.). (Illus.). 128p. (J). lib. bdg. 31.93 (978-0-7660-2651-3(5)) Enslow Pubs., Inc.

Suib, Stella. Inside Russia's SVR: The Foreign Intelligence Service. 2005. (Illus.). 63p. (YA). reprint ed. 26.00 (978-0-7567-8668-7(1)) DIANE Publishing Co.

Zemlicka, Shannon. Nathan Hale: Patriot Spy. 2002. (On My Own Biographies Ser.). (Illus.). 48p. (J). lib. bdg. 23.93 (978-0-87614-597-5(7) , Carolrhoda Bks.) Lerner Publishing Group.

SECRET SERVICE—FICTION

Babbitt, Natalie. Tuck Everlasting. l.t. ed. 2004. 152p. pap. 10.95 (978-0-7862-6322-6(9)) Thorndike Pr.

Beriot, Louis. L' Enfant Secret. l.t. ed. 2002. (French Ser.). (FRE., Illus.). 542p. 30.99 (978-2-84011-464-2(X)) Ulverscroft Large Print Bks. GBR. *Dist:* Ulverscroft Large Print Bks., Ltd.

Cox, Joseph J. Grobar & the Mind Control Potion. Becker, Rebecca J., illus. 2005. 168p. (J). per. 9.95 (978-0-9764659-3-5(0)) Suckerfish Bks.

Goldsmann, Henri. Secret Agent Spanky Sheep in the mystery of: the Pooperous Pizza Plunderer. 2006. 140p. pap. 11.99 (978-1-4116-8094-4(4)) Lulu.com.

Groot, Bob de & Turk. The Laughing Thief. 2007. (Illus.). 48p. pap. 9.99 (***978-1-905460-07-6(4))*** CineBook GBR. *Dist:* Biblio Distribution.

Groot, De. Clifton: Black Moon. Spear, Luke, tr. from FRE. Rodrigue, illus. 2007. 48p. pap. 9.99 (***978-1-905460-30-4(9))*** CineBook GBR. *Dist:* Biblio Distribution.

Jones, Veda Boyd. Emma's Secret: The Cincinnati Epidemic. 2005. (Sisters in Time Ser.). 141p. (J). (***978-1-4156-0074-0(0))*** Barbour Publishing, Inc.

Kelly, John & Simkins, Kate. The Spy-Catcher Gang. Inklink, illus. 2008. 48p. (J). (gr. 3-4). 14.99 (***978-0-7566-3850-4(X));*** pap. 3.99 (***978-0-7566-3849-8(6))*** Dorling Kindersley Publishing, Inc.

Krailing, Tessa. Beastly Basil. Phillips, Mike, illus. 2006. 48p. (J). lib. bdg. (***978-1-4048-3113-1(4))*** Picture Window Bks.

Linamen, Karen Scalf. Princess Madison & the Paisley Puppy. 2007. (Princess Madison Trilogy Ser.). (Illus.). 32p. (J). 12.99 (978-0-8007-1841-1(0)) Revell.

McPherson, F. M. Secrets. 2005. 267p. (gr. 7-12). pap. 9.99 (978-1-932815-30-6(9)) Medallion Pr., Inc.

Richardson, Nigel. The Wrong Hands. 2008. 272p. (YA). (gr. 7). mass mkt. 6.50 (***978-0-553-49500-3(3)*** , Laurel Leaf) Random Hse. Children's Bks.

Van Draanen, Wendelin. Sammy Keyes & the Dead Giveaway. unabr. ed. 2006. (Sammy Keyes Ser.: Bk. 10). (J). (gr. 5-7). pap. 36.95 incl. audio (***978-1-59519-770-2(2));*** pap. 54.95 incl. audio compact disk (***978-1-59519-771-9(0))*** Live Oak Media.

—Sammy Keyes & the Dead Giveaway. 2007. (Sammy Keyes Ser.: Bk. 10). 304p. (J). (gr. 5-8). 5.99 (978-0-440-41911-2(5) , Yearling) Random Hse. Children's Bks.

Whatley, Bruce. Clinton Gregory's Secret. 2008. 32p. (J). 15.95 (***978-0-8109-9364-8(3)*** , Abrams Bks. for Young Readers) Abrams, Harry N. , Inc.

SECRET WRITING

see Cryptography

SECRETARIES

Firestone, Mary. School Secretaries. 2003. (Community Helpers Ser.). (Illus.). 24p. (J). (gr. 1-2). lib. bdg. 19.93 (978-0-7368-1617-5(8) , Bridgestone Bks.) Capstone Pr., Inc.

Vogel, Elizabeth. Meet the School Secretary. 2002. (PowerKids Readers Ser.). (Illus.). 24p. (J). (gr. 1). lib. bdg. 16.00 (978-0-8239-6036-1(6) , PowerKids Pr.) Rosen Publishing Group, Inc., The.

SECRETARIES—FICTION

Thaler, Mike. The School Secretary from the Black Lagoon. Lee, Jared D., illus. 2006. (J). (***978-0-439-80077-8(3))*** Scholastic, Inc.

SECTS

see also names of churches and sects, e.g. Methodist Church, etc.

Cole, Michael D. The Siege at Waco: Deadly Inferno. 1999. (American Disasters Ser.). (Illus.). 48p. (YA). (gr. 4-10). lib. bdg. 23.93 (978-0-7660-1218-9(0)) Enslow Pubs., Inc.

De Angelis, Gina. Jonestown Massacre: Tragic End of a Cult. 2002. (American Disasters Ser.). (Illus.). 48p. (J). (gr. 4-10). lib. bdg. 23.93 (978-0-7660-1784-9(2)) Enslow Pubs., Inc.

Foundation for Religious Freedom Staff, ed. "Cult" Alert: A Practical Handbook for Saving Families. 1999. (Illus.). 104p. (YA). (gr. 8-12). pap. 4.95 (978-1-928575-03-0(X)) Foundation for Religious Freedom.

Goodnough, David. Cult Awareness. 2000. (Hot Issues Ser.). (Illus.). 64p. (YA). (gr. 6-12). lib. bdg. 27.93 (978-0-7660-1196-0(8)) Enslow Pubs., Inc.

Karson, Jill. Cults. 2000. (Contemporary Issues Companion Ser.). (Illus.). 144p. (YA). (gr. 10 up). lib. bdg. 24.95 (978-0-7377-0162-3(5) , Greenhaven Pr., Inc.) Thomson Gale.

Kjelle, Marylou Morano. The Waco Siege. 2002. (Great Disasters, Reforms & Ramifications Ser.). (Illus.). 112p. (J). 30.00 (978-0-7910-6739-0(4) , Chelsea Hse.) Facts On File, Inc.

Mason, Claire. New Religious Movements. 2003. (21st Century Debates Ser.). (Illus.). 64p. (J). lib. bdg. 28.56 (978-0-7398-6032-8(1)) Raintree.

SECURITIES

see also Bonds; Investments; Stocks

Thurston, Cheryl M. Capitalization: Teaching Correct Capitalization to Kids Who Aren't Crazy about Writing in the First Place. Howard, Zach, illus. 2000. (Teaching the Boring Stuff Ser.). 47p. pap. 12.95 (978-1-877673-43-6(9) , CAP-BWK03) Cottonwood Pr., Inc.

SECURITIES EXCHANGE

see Stock Exchanges

SECURITY (PSYCHOLOGY)

Espeland, Pamela & Verdick, Elizabeth. People Who Care about You: The Support Assets. 2004. (Adding Assets Series for Kids: Bk. 1). (Illus.). 80p. (J). (gr. 3-7). pap. 9.95 (978-1-57542-162-9(3)) Free Spirit Publishing, Inc.

Schulz, Charles M. Seguridad es un Pulgar y una Manta. (SPA.). (J). 7.00 (978-84-7655-664-1(0) , PI3929) Plaza Joven, S.A. ESP. *Dist:* Lectorum Pubns., Inc.

SECURITY (PSYCHOLOGY)—FICTION

Cooper, Ilene. Jake's Best Thumb. Muñoz, Claudio, illus. 2008. 32p. (J). (ps). 16.99 (***978-0-525-47788-4(8)*** , Dutton Juvenile) Penguin Group (USA) Inc.

Rylant, Cynthia. The Stars Will Still Shine. Beeke, Tiphanie, illus. 2005. 40p. (J). lib. bdg. 16.89 (978-0-06-054640-3(9)); 15.99 (978-0-06-054639-7(5)) HarperCollins Pubs.

Shaw, Susan. Safe. 2007. 208p. (J). (gr. 9). 16.99 (***978-0-525-47829-4(9)*** , Dutton Juvenile) Penguin Group (USA) Inc.

Spinelli, Eileen. A Safe Place Called Home. Hale, Christy, illus. 2001. 32p. (J). (gr. k-3). 15.95 (978-0-7614-5085-6(8) , Cavendish Children's Bks.) Cavendish, Marshall Corp.

SECURITY, INTERNATIONAL

see also Disarmament; International Organization

Bauder, Julia. Is Iran a Threat to Global Security? 2006. (Illus.). 128p. (gr. 10-12). 21.20 (978-0-7377-3527-7(9)); pap. 29.95 (978-0-7377-3526-0(0)) Thomson Gale. (Greenhaven Pr., Inc.).

Docalavich, Heather. UN Action Against Terrorism: Fighting Fear. 2007. (United Nations Ser.). (Illus.). 88p. (J). (gr. 5 up). lib. bdg. 21.95 (978-1-4222-0067-4(1)) Mason Crest Pubs.

Gerdes, Louise, ed. Rogue Nations. 2006. (Opposing Viewpoints Ser.). (Illus.), 244p. (YA). (gr. 6 up). pap. 24.95 (978-0-7377-3422-5(1) , Greenhaven Pr., Inc.) Thomson Gale.

Libal, Autumn. International Security: Peacekeeping & Peace-Building Around the World. 2007. (United Nations Ser.). 88p. (J). (gr. 5 up). lib. bdg. 21.95 (978-1-4222-0071-1(X)) Mason Crest Pubs.

SEDITION

see Political Crimes and Offenses; Revolutions

SEEDS

Aston, Dianna Hutts. A Seed Is Sleepy. Long, Sylvia, illus. 2007. 40p. (J). (gr. k-5). 16.95 (978-0-8118-5520-4(1)) Chronicle Bks. LLC.

Balsavar, Deepa & Kaushal, Tara. The Seed. 2005. (HIN & ENG., Illus.). (J). (***978-81-8146-110-0(X))*** Tulika Pubs.

Berger, Melvin & Berger, Gilda. Seed to Plant. 2004. (Illus.). (J). (978-0-439-57486-0(2)) Scholastic, Inc.

Blackaby, Susan. Plant Packages: A Book about Seeds. DeLage, Charlene, illus. 2004. (Growing Things Ser.). 24p. (C). (gr. k-2). 22.60 (978-1-4048-0108-0(1)) Picture Window Bks.

Blowing in the Wind. 2002. (Illus.). (J). pap. 3.74 (978-0-7398-5836-3(X)) Steck-Vaughn.

Bodach, Vijaya. Seeds. 2007. (Illus.). 24p. (J). 19.93 (978-0-7368-6346-9(X) , Pebble Bks.) Capstone Pr., Inc.

Boyston, Angela. Flowers, Fruits & Seeds. 1999. (Plants Ser.). (Illus.). 32p. (J). (gr. k-3). lib. bdg. 21.36 (978-1-57572-822-3(2)) Heinemann Library.

Branigan, Carrie & Dunne, Richard. Flowers & Seeds. 2005. (World of Plants Ser.). (Illus.). 31p. (J). (gr. 2-5). lib. bdg. 27.10 (978-1-58340-612-0(3)) Smart Apple Media.

Burns, Diane L. Berries, Nuts & Seeds. Garrow, Linda, illus. 2000. (Young Naturalist Field Guides Ser.). 40p. (J). (gr. 3 up). lib. bdg. 24.67 (978-0-8368-2144-4(0)) Stevens, Gareth Inc.

Burton, Jane & Taylor, Kim. The Nature & Science of Seeds. Burton, Jane & Taylor, Kim, photos by. 1999. (Exploring the Science of Nature Ser.). (Illus.). 32p. (J). (gr. 3 up). lib. bdg. 24.67 (978-0-8368-2184-0(X)) Stevens, Gareth Inc.

Carle, Eric. The Tiny Seed. Carle, Eric, illus. 2001. (Illus.). 40p. (J). (ps-3). pap. 7.99 (978-0-689-84244-3(9) , Aladdin) Simon & Schuster Children's Publishing.

—The Tiny Seed. 2001. (gr. k-3). lib. bdg. 15.30 (978-0-613-35001-3(4)) Tandem Library Bks.

Cartw, Paul. Where Are the Seeds/Ww/E. (Wonder Worldtm Ser.). 16p. 29.95 (978-0-7802-2042-3(0)) Wright Group, The.

Edwards, Nicola. Seeds. 2005. (Little Hands Ser.). (Illus.). 24p. (J). (gr. 1 up). lib. bdg. 22.80 (978-1-59389-212-8(8)) Chrysalis Education.

Esparza, June F. Tiny Seedlings . . . Their Journey. 1999. (Illus.). 264p. 10.00 (978-0-9647161-2-4(7)) Thoughts in Motion.

Fanning, Regine. Seed Surprise. Pagels, Tianna, illus. 1999. 8p. (J). (gr. k-2). pap. 3.75 (978-1-880612-89-7(5) , Seedling Pubns.) Continental Pr., Inc.

Farndon, John. Seeds. 2005. (Illus.). 24p. (J). (gr. 2-4). 23.70 (978-1-4103-0419-3(1) , Blackbirch Pr., Inc.) Thomson Gale.

Fowler, Allan. From Seed to Plant. 2001. (Rookie Read-About Science Ser.). (Illus.). 32p. (J). (gr. 1-2). pap. 4.95 (978-0-516-27307-5(8)); 19.50 (978-0-516-21682-9(1)) Scholastic Library Publishing. (Children's Pr.).

—From Seed to Plant. 2001. (gr. k-3). lib. bdg. 12.95 (978-0-613-54501-3(X)) Tandem Library Bks.

Godwin, Sam. A Seed in Need: A First Look at the Plant Cycle. Abel, Simone, illus. 2004. (First Look Science Ser.). 32p. (C). (gr. k-3). 22.60 (978-1-4048-0920-8(1)) Picture Window Bks.

Grieveson, Margaret. Flowers & Seeds. 2005. (Illus.). 32p. (J). (gr. 3-7). lib. bdg. 27.10 (978-1-59604-039-7(4)) Stargazer Bks.

Heller, Ruth. The Reason for a Flower. 1999. (Ruth Heller's World of Nature Ser.). (Illus.). 48p. (J). (ps-3). pap. 6.99 (978-0-698-11559-0(7) , Putnam Juvenile) Penguin Group (USA) Inc.

—The Reason for a Flower. (FRE.). (J). 6.99 (978-0-590-71999-5(8)) Scholastic, Inc.

Jordan, Helene J. Como Crece una Semilla. Krupinski, Loretta, illus. 2006. (Let's-Read-and-Find-Out Science Ser.). (SPA.). 32p. (J). pap. 6.99 (978-0-06-088716-2(8)) HarperCollins Pubs.

—How a Seed Grows. Krupinski, Loretta, illus. rev. ed. 2000. (Let's-Read-and-Find-Out Science Ser.). 32p. (J). (ps-1). 15.89 (978-0-06-020185-2(1)) HarperCollins Pubs.

Kababik, Dana. From Seed to Flower. 2003. (Grow up! Ser.). (J). (978-1-58417-170-6(7)); pap. (978-1-58417-176-8(6)) Lake Street Pubs.

Kite, L. Patricia. Dandelion Adventures. Hariton, Anca, illus. 1998. (Our World Ser.). 32p. (ps-1). lib. bdg. 21.90 (978-0-7613-0037-3(6) , Millbrook Pr.) Lerner Publishing Group.

Macken, JoAnn Early. Flip, Float, Fly: Seeds on the Move. Paparone, Pamela, illus. 2008. (J). (***978-0-8234-2043-8(4))*** Holiday Hse., Inc.

Mann, Rachel. Plants Grow from Seeds. 2003. (Compass Point Phonics Readers Ser.). (Illus.). 16p. (J). (gr. 1 up). 13.26 (978-0-7565-0519-6(4)) Compass Point Bks.

Marzollo, Jean. Soy una Semilla. Moffatt, Judith, illus. 2002. (Coleccion "Hola, Lector" Ser.). (SPA.). 32p. (J). (ps-1). pap. 3.99 (978-0-439-08698-1(1) , SO0770, Scholastic en Espanol) Scholastic, Inc.

Medearis, Angela Shelf. Seeds Grow! 2000. (Hello Reader! Ser.). (978-0-606-18606-3(9)) Tandem Library Bks.

Mitchell, Melanie S. Seeds. 2003. (First Step Nonfiction Ser.). (Illus.). 8p. (J). pap. 3.95 (978-0-8225-3920-9(9) , Lerner Pubns.) Lerner Publishing Group.

Morgan, Sally. Flowers, Fruits & Seeds. (Looking at Plants Ser.). (Illus.). 32p. (J). lib. bdg. 24.25 (978-1-931983-10-5(0)) Chrysalis Education.

O'Donnell, Kerri. So Many Seeds: Learning the S Sound. (PowerPhonics Ser.). (Illus.). (J). 2002. 24p. (gr. 1). lib. bdg. 18.50 (978-0-8239-5908-2(2)); 2001. 23p. pap. 26.40 (978-0-8239-8253-0(X)) Rosen Publishing Group, Inc., The. (PowerKids Pr.).

Ohanesian, Diane C. Seeds & Plants: Grades 2 & 3. (Illus.). (J). pap., wbk. ed. 4.99 (978-0-88743-961-2(6)) School Zone Publishing Co.

Pascoe, Elaine. How & Why Seeds Travel. Kupperstein, Joel, ed. Kuhn, Dwight, photos by. 2000. (How & Why Ser.). (Illus.). 16p. (J). (gr. 1-3). pap. 2.99 (978-1-57471-658-0(1) , 2977) Creative Teaching Pr., Inc.

—Plants with Seeds. Kuhn, Dwight, illus. Kuhn, Dwight, photos by. 2003. (Kids Guide to the Classification of Living Things Ser.). (Illus.). 24p. (J). lib. bdg. 21.25 (978-0-8239-6314-0(4) , PowerKids Pr.) Rosen Publishing Group, Inc., The.

—Seeds Travel. Kuhn, Dwight, photos by. 2002. (Springboards into Science Ser.). (Illus.). 24p. (J). (gr. 1 up). lib. bdg. 20.67 (978-0-8368-3012-5(1)) Stevens, Gareth Inc.

Picture Window Books, contrib. by. Plant Packages. (Growing Things Ser.). 24p. (J). pap. 7.95 (978-1-4048-0384-8(X)) Picture Window Bks.

Plants & Seeds, 6 vols. (Sunshinetm Science Ser.). 24p. (gr. 1-2). 31.50 (978-0-7802-0291-7(0)); 36.95 (978-0-7802-0542-0(1)) Wright Group, The.

Plants Grow from Seeds Set B, 6 vols. (Phonics Readers Ser.). (gr. k-2). 17.50 (978-0-7368-3207-6(6)) Red Brick Learning.

Reid, Barbara. Seed to Sunflower: A First Look Board Book. Crysler, Ian, photos by. 2004. (Illus.). 12p. (J). (gr. k-2). reprint ed. 10.00 (978-0-7567-7853-8(0)) DIANE Publishing Co.

Richards, Jean. A Fruit Is a Suitcase for Seeds. 2006. (Illus.). (J). pap. 6.95 (978-0-8225-5991-7(9) , First Avenue Editions) Lerner Publishing Group.

—A Fruit Is a Suitcase for Seeds. Hariton, Anca, illus. 2002. (Our World Ser.). 32p. (ps-1). lib. bdg. 21.90 (978-0-7613-1622-0(1) , Millbrook Pr.) Lerner Publishing Group.

Rigby Education Staff. From Here to There. (Sails Literacy Ser.). (Illus.). 16p. (gr. 2-3). 27.00 (978-0-7635-9958-4(1) , 699581C99) Rigby Education.

Robbins, Ken. Seeds. Robbins, Ken, illus. 2005. (Illus.). 32p. (J). (gr. 1-4). 16.99 (978-0-689-85041-7(7) , Atheneum) Simon & Schuster Children's Publishing.

Roemer, Heidi. What Kinds of Seeds Are There? Kassian, Olena, illus. 2006. 32p. 16.95 (978-1-55971-955-1(9) , NorthWord Bks. for Young Readers) T&N Children's Publishing.

Royston, Angela. El Frijol. Abello, Patricia, tr. 2003. (Ciclo de la Vida de... Ser.).Tr. of Bean. (SPA & ENG., Illus.). 32p. (J). lib. bdg. 22.79 (978-1-4034-3014-4(4)) Heinemann Library.

Saunders, Gail. Seeds. 1998. (Growing Flowers Ser.). (Illus.). 24p. (J). (ps-3). pap. 13.25 (978-0-516-21324-8(5) , Children's Pr.) Scholastic Library Publishing.

Schaefer, Lola M. Pick, Pull, Snap! Where Once a Flower Bloomed. George, Lindsay B., illus. 2003. 32p. (J). 15.99 (978-0-688-17834-5(0)) HarperCollins Pubs.

School Zone Publishing Company Staff. Seeds & Plants. (Illus.). (J). 19.99 incl. audio compact disk (978-0-88743-922-3(5)) School Zone Publishing Co.

School Zone Publishing Company Staff & Hall, Julie. Weather, Seeds, Plants. deluxe ed. 2000. (Deluxe Wkbks.). (Illus.). 64p. (J). (gr. 2-4). pap., wbk. ed. 4.16 (978-0-88743-861-5(X) , 02261) School Zone Publishing Co.

Scraper, Katherine. A Seed Needs Help. 2006. (Early Explorers Ser.). (J). 30.00 (***978-1-4108-6026-2(4))*** Benchmark Education Co.

Seed Dispersal. 2001. (Botany Ser.). (J). (gr. k-12). vinyl bd. 4.95 (978-1-58845-140-8(2)) School Specialty Publishing.

Seed Formation. 2001. (Botany Ser.). (J). (gr. k-12). vinyl bd. 4.95 (978-1-58845-142-2(9)) School Specialty Publishing.

Seeds. (Early Intervention Levels Ser.). 23.10 (978-0-7362-0011-0(8)) Hampton-Brown Bks.

Seeds, 6 vols. (gr. k-2). 28.95 (978-0-7368-8002-2(X)) Red Brick Learning.

Seeds Grow, 6 vols. (Sunshinetm Science Ser.). 24p. (gr. 1-2). 31.50 (978-0-7802-0290-0(2)); 36.95 (978-0-7802-0541-3(3)) Wright Group, The.

Seeds, Seeds, Seeds, 6 vols. (Sunshinetm Science Ser.). 24p. (gr. 1-2). 31.50 (978-0-7802-0289-4(9)); 36.95 (978-0-7802-0540-6(5)) Wright Group, The.

Sian revision seed Mysteries. 2004. (J). (978-1-59242-065-0(6)) Delta Education, LLC.

Stone, Lynn M. Seeds. 2008. (J). ***(978-1-60044-555-2(1))*** Rourke Publishing, LLC.

This Little Seed: Individual Title Six-Packs. (Rigby Focus Ser.). 16p. (gr. k up). 26.00 (978-0-7578-5290-9(4)); 28.00 (978-0-7578-5524-5(5)) Rigby Education.

Thomson, Ruth. Bean. 2007. (J). lib. bdg. ***(978-1-4042-3714-8(3)*** , PowerKids Pr.) Rosen Publishing Group, Inc., The.

Vegetales y Semillas. (Vamos a Crear Ser.). (SPA., Illus.). (J). 12.00 (978-84-342-2316-5(3)) Parramon Ediciones S.A. ESP. *Dist:* Distribuidora Norma, Inc., Lectorum Pubns., Inc.

Walker, Jane. Las Flores. 2001. (SPA., Illus.). 32p. (J). (ps-3). 10.95 (978-84-263-3169-4(6)) Lectorum Pubns., Inc.

Whitehouse, Patricia. Seeds. 2002. (Plants Ser.). (Illus.). 24p. (J). (ps-1). lib. bdg. 17.08 (978-1-58810-525-7(3)) Heinemann Library.

—Las Semillas. 2002. (Plantas (Plants) Ser.). (SPA.). 24p. (J). (ps-1). lib. bdg. 17.08 (978-1-58810-779-4(5)); (Illus.). pap. 5.25 (978-1-58810-826-5(0) , 91650) Heinemann Library.

Worth, Bonnie. Oh Say Can You Seed? All about Flowering Plants. Ruiz, Aristides, illus. 2001. (Cat in the Hat's Learning Library). 48p. (J). (gr. k-3). 8.99 (978-0-375-81095-4(1) , Random Hse. Bks. for Young Readers) Random Hse. Children's Bks.

SEEING EYE DOGS

see Guide Dogs

SEGREGATION IN EDUCATION

see also Discrimination in Education

Bridges, Ruby. Through My Eyes. 1999. (Illus.). 64p. (J). (gr. 3-7). pap. 16.95 (978-0-590-18923-1(9)) Scholastic, Inc.

Bridges, Ruby & Maccarone, Grace. Let's Read About—Ruby Bridges. Van Wright, Cornelius & Hu, Ying-Hwa, illus. 2003. (Scholastic First Biographies Ser.). (J). (978-0-439-51362-3(6)) Scholastic, Inc.

Clark, Carolyn. Little Rock Nine. 2002. (Illus.). 16p. (J). (978-0-439-35188-1(X)) Scholastic, Inc.

Conaway, Judith. Brown V. Board of Education: The Case for Integration. 2006. 96p. lib. bdg. (978-0-7565-2448-7(2)) Compass Point Bks.

Fitzgerald, Stephanie. Little Rock Nine: Struggle for Integration. 2006. (J). (978-0-7565-2011-3(8)) Compass Point Bks.

Fradin, Judith Bloom & Fradin, Dennis Brindell. The Power of One: Daisy Bates & the Little Rock Nine. 2004. (Illus.). 192p. (YA). (gr. 5-9). tchr. ed. 19.00 (978-0-618-31556-7(X) , Clarion Bks.) Houghton Mifflin Co. Trade & Reference Div.

Gold, Susan Dudley. Brown V. Board of Education: Separate but Equal? 2004. (Supreme Court Milestones Ser.). (Illus.). 143p. (J). 37.07 (978-0-7614-1842-9(3) , Benchmark Bks.) Cavendish, Marshall Corp.

Good, Diane L. Brown v. Board of Education. 2007. (Cornerstones of Freedomtrade;, Second Ser.). 48p. (J). (gr. 4-6). pap. 5.95 ***(978-0-531-18686-2(5)*** , Children's Pr.) Scholastic Library Publishing.

Good, Diane L. Brown vs. Board of Education: A Civil Rights Milestone. 2004. (Cornerstones of Freedom Ser.). (J). 26.00 (978-0-516-24225-5(3) , Children's Pr.) Scholastic Library Publishing.

Harcourt School Publishers Staff. A Certain Courage. 3rd ed. 2002. (Horizons Ser.). (Illus.). (J). pap. 7.30 (978-0-15-333589-1(0)) Harcourt Schl. Pubs.

Haskins, Jim. Separate but Not Equal: The Dream & the Struggle. 2002. (978-0-606-22269-3(3)) Tandem Library Bks.

Kelso, Richard. Days of Courage: The Little Rock Story. 2001. (Nonfiction Bookbag Ser.). (J). (gr. 6-7). per. 8.45 (978-1-58830-208-3(3)) Metropolitan Teaching & Learning Co.

Koestler-Grack, Rachel A. Going to School During the Civil Rights Movement. 2001. (Blue Earth Books). (Illus.). 32p. (J). (gr. 3-4). lib. bdg. 22.60 (978-0-7368-0799-9(3) , Bridgestone Bks.) Capstone Pr., Inc.

Lucas, Eileen. Cracking the Wall: The Story of the Little Rock Nine. Anthony, Mark, illus. 2007. pap. 16.95 incl. audio ***(978-1-59519-937-9(3));*** pap. 18.95 incl. audio compact disk ***(978-1-59519-941-6(1))*** Live Oak Media.

—Cracking the Wall (4 PB/1 Cass) Anthony, Mark, illus. 2007. pap. 37.95 incl. audio ***(978-1-59519-939-3(X))*** Live Oak Media.

—Cracking the Wall (4 PB/1 CD) Anthony, Mark, illus. 2007. pap. 39.95 incl. audio compact disk ***(978-1-59519-943-0(8))*** Live Oak Media.

Miller, Jake. Brown vs. Board of Education of Topeka: Challenging School Segregation in the Supreme Court. 2004. (Library of the Civil Rights Movement Ser.). (Illus.). 24p. (J). lib. bdg. 19.95 (978-0-8239-6250-1(4)) Rosen Publishing Group, Inc., The.

Miller, Mara. School Desegregation & the Story of the Little Rock Nine. 2008. (From Many Cultures, One History Ser.). (Illus.). 128p. (J). (gr. 5 up). lib. bdg. 31.93 ***(978-0-7660-2835-7(6))*** Enslow Pubs., Inc.

Plessy vs. Ferguson Separate but Equal. 2000. (My Ancestors—My Heroes Ser.: Vol. 21). (J). (gr. 3-4). (978-1-893091-20-7(1)) Parker Publishing Co.

Polakow, Amy. Daisy Bates: Civil Rights Crusader. 2002. (Illus.). 128p. (J). 25.00 (978-0-208-02513-5(8) , Linnet Bks.) Shoe String Pr., Inc.

Rappaport, Doreen. The School Is Not White! A True Story of the Civil Rights Movement. James, Curtis, illus. 2005. 32p. (gr. 2-7). 16.99 (978-0-7868-1838-9(7) , Jump at the Sun) Hyperion Bks. for Children.

SEGREGATION IN EDUCATION—FICTION

Schraff, Anne. Strawberry Autumn. 1999. (Passages Ser.). (Illus.). 135p. (J). (gr. 5-12). lib. bdg. 13.95 (978-0-7807-8985-2(7)) Perfection Learning Corp.

Sharenow, Robert. My Mother the Cheerleader. 2007. 304p. (gr. 7 up). (J). lib. bdg. 17.89 (978-0-06-114897-2(0)); (YA). 16.99 (978-0-06-114896-5(2)) HarperCollins Pubs. (Geringer, Laura Book).

Waldron, Ann. The Integration of Mary-Larkin Thornhill. 2000. 148p. pap. 10.95 (978-0-595-00069-2(X)) iUniverse, Inc.

Walvoord, Linda. Rosetta, Rosetts, Sit by Me! Velasquez, Eric, illus. 2004. 80p. (J). 14.95 (978-0-7614-5171-6(4)) Cavendish, Marshall Corp.

Weatherford, Carole Boston. Dear Mr. Rosenwald. Christie, Gregory, illus. 2006. 32p. (J). (gr. 2-5). pap. 16.99 (978-0-439-49522-6(9) , Scholastic Pr.) Scholastic, Inc.

Woods, Brenda. The Red Rose Box. 2002. 160p. (YA). (gr. 4-6). 16.99 (978-0-399-23702-7(X) , Putnam Juvenile) Penguin Group (USA) Inc.

SEINE RIVER AND VALLEY

Rawlins, Carol B. The Seine River. 2001. (World of Water Ser.). (Illus.). 64p. (J). (gr. 5-7). 25.50 (978-0-531-11853-5(3) , Watts, Franklin) Scholastic Library Publishing.

—Seine River. 2001. (gr. 3-6). lib. bdg. 17.60 (978-0-613-37534-4(3)) Tandem Library Bks.

SEISMOGRAPHY

see Earthquakes

SEISMOLOGY

see Earthquakes

SELECTION, NATURAL

see Natural Selection

SELECTIVE SERVICE

see Military Service, Compulsory

SELF-ACCEPTANCE

Cook, Kerri Beth. The Wannabe Honeybee. Cook, Kerri Beth, illus. 2002. (Illus.). 50p. (J). (ps-2). pap. 12.95 (978-0-9719300-0-1(7)) KBCottontop Publishing.

Huber, Cheri. There Is Nothing Wrong with You for Teens. Shiver, June, illus. 2001. 276p. (gr. 9 up). pap. 12.00 (978-0-9636255-9-5(4)) Keep it Simple Bks.

Kelly, Dorothy A. Developing a Sense of Self: A Workbook of Tenets & Tactics for Adolescent Girls. 2006. (Illus.). 146p. (J). pap. 29.99 (978-0-87101-366-8(5) , NASW Pr.) National Assn. of Social Workers/NASW Pr.

Kim, Jeannie. The Whole You. 2003. (Whole You Ser.: No. 1). 160p. (J). (gr. 3-7). pap. 4.99 (978-0-439-40463-1(0) , Scholastic Paperbacks) Scholastic, Inc.

Kirberger, Kimberly. No Body's Perfect: Stories by Teens about Body Image, Self-Acceptance, & the S. 2003. (gr. 5-8). lib. bdg. 22.20 (978-0-613-61510-5(7)) Tandem Library Bks.

—No Body's Perfect: Stories by Teens about Body Image, Self-Acceptance, & the Search for Identity. 2003. (No Body's Perfect Ser.). 304p. (YA). 12.95 (978-0-439-42638-1(3) , Scholastic Paperbacks) Scholastic, Inc.

—No Body's Perfect Journal. 2003. 336p. (J). (gr. 5 up). pap. 8.95 (978-0-439-42639-8(1) , Scholastic Paperbacks) Scholastic, Inc.

Le Jeune, Veronique, et al. Feeling Freakish? How to be Comfortable in Your Own Skin, 4 vols. Princess, H., illus. 2004. (Sunscreen Ser.). 112p. (J). (gr. 6-11). pap. 9.95 (978-0-8109-9164-4(0) , Amulet Bks.) Abrams, Harry N. , Inc.

Mastromarino, Diane. The Girl's Guide to Loving Yourself: A Book about Falling in Love with the One Person Who Matters Most - You. 64p. pap. 9.95 (978-0-88396-751-5(0) , Blue Mountain Pr.) Blue Mountain Arts Inc.

Noll, Kathy. Taking the Bully by the Horns: Children's Version of Best-Selling Book, Nasty People. Carter, Jay, ed. Cusimano, Flora & Broderbund, illus. 2nd aut. ed. 1998. Orig. Title: Nasty Kids. 80p. (J). (gr. 4-9). pap. 12.95 (978-0-937004-11-1(1)) Unicorn Pr.

Parr, Todd. The Okay Book. 2004. (Illus.). 24p. (J). (ps-ps). bds. 6.99 (978-0-316-90809-2(6)) Little, Brown Bks. for Young Readers.

Renaud, Andrea, creator. The Goal Keeper. 2001. (YA). cd-rom 18.00 (978-0-9717041-0-7(4)) A Happy Friend, Inc. CAN. *Dist:* Century Bk. Distribution.

Richmond, Marianne. Hooray for You! A Celebration of You-ness. Richmond, Marianne, illus. 2001. (Illus.). 40p. (J). (gr. 3 up). per. 15.95 (978-0-931674-44-0(1)) Marianne Richmond Studios, Inc.

Taylor, Jeannie St. John. You Wouldn't Love Me If You Knew. 2004. (Illus.). 32p. 17.00 (978-0-687-07325-2(1)) Abingdon Pr.

Wandberg, Robert, et al. Self-Acceptance: Building Confidence. 2000. (Contemporary Issues Ser.). (Illus.). 64p. (YA). (gr. 4-6). lib. bdg. 23.93 (978-0-7368-1024-1(2) , LifeMatters Bks.) Capstone Pr., Inc.

A Wanderer's Handbook: An Owner's Manual for ETs & Other Spiritual Outsiders. 2001. 565p. (YA). pap. 24.95 (978-0-945007-16-6(7)) L/L Research.

Weedn, Lisa. Finding My Groove: Who I Am & Where I'm Going. Weedn, Flavia M., illus. 2001. 64p. (gr. 8 up). pap. 14.95 (978-0-7683-2237-8(5)) CEDCO Publishing.

—Getting Real: Listen to My Heart & Finding Peace with Who I Am. Weedn, Flavia M., illus. 2001. 144p. (YA). (gr. 7-12). pap. 9.95 (978-0-7683-2236-1(7)) CEDCO Publishing.

SELF-ACCEPTANCE—FICTION

Ackerman, Karen. Bean's Big Day. Mombourquette, Paul, tr. Mombourquette, Paul, illus. 2004. 32p. (J). (gr. k-3). (978-1-55337-444-2(4)) Kids Can Pr., Ltd.

Anderson, M. T. Burger Wuss. Butler, David, illus. 2001. 208p. (YA). (gr. 9 up). pap. 6.99 (978-0-7636-1567-3(6)) Candlewick Pr.

—Burger Wuss. 2001. 13.64 (978-0-606-22539-7(0)); (gr. 7-12). lib. bdg. 14.15 (978-0-613-44380-7(2)) Tandem Library Bks.

Araki, Mie. Perfect Tail. 2004. (Illus.). 32p. (J). 14.95 (978-0-8118-4266-2(5)) Chronicle Bks. LLC.

Augarde, Steve. Celandine. 496p. (J). (gr. 5). 2008. 6.99 ***(978-0-440-42216-7(7)*** , Yearling); 2006. 16.95 (978-0-385-75048-6(X) , Fickling, David Bks.); 2006. lib. bdg. 18.99 (978-0-385-75049-3(8) , Fickling, David Bks.) Random Hse. Children's Bks.

Baker, Keith. Sometimes. 2003. (Green Light Readers Level 1 Ser.). (Illus.). 24p. (J). 11.95 (978-0-15-204807-5(3)); pap. 3.95 (978-0-15-204847-1(2)) Harcourt Children's Bks. (Green Light Readers).

—Sometimes. 1999. (Green Light Readers Ser.). (978-0-606-16510-5(X)); lib. bdg. 11.80 (978-0-613-64597-3(9)) Tandem Library Bks.

—Sometimes/Algunas Veces. Campoy, F. Isabel & Ada, Alma Flor, trs. from ENG. 2007. (Green Light Readers Level 1 Ser.). (ENG & SPA., Illus.). 28p. (J). 12.95 (978-0-15-205959-0(8)); pap. 3.95 (978-0-15-205961-3(X)) Harcourt Trade Pubs.

Barnes, Laura T. Twist & Ernest. Camburn, Carol A., illus. 2002. (Ernest Ser.: Vol. 1). 32p. (J). (ps-3). 15.95 (978-0-9674681-0-5(8)) Barnesyard Bks.

Barrett, Anna Pearl. Neecie Loves Trouble. Edwards, Lana C., ed. Peguero, Phillip, illus. 1999. (Neecie Ser.: Vol. 2). 48p. (J). (gr. 2-5). 9.95 (978-0-9661330-1-1(3)) Over the Rainbow Productions.

Bevan, Jan Atchley. Corky the Bathtub Who Couldn't Swallow. Yovanovic, Christine, illus. l.t. ed. 2001. 48p. (J). pap. 12.95 (978-0-9653895-4-9(5)) Bookmark Publishing.

Bingham, Kelly. Shark Girl. 2007. (Illus.). 288p. (YA). (gr. 7 up). 16.99 ***(978-0-7636-3207-6(4))*** Candlewick Pr.

Bingham, Kelly L. Shark Girl. 2007. 276p. (YA). ***(978-1-4287-4705-0(2))*** Candlewick Pr.

Bloomfield, Denise. More Than A Spoonful. 2007. 28p. (J). mass mkt. 12.95 ***(978-0-9778113-0-4(1))*** HeartFelt Stories LLC.

Blume, Judy. Otherwise Known As Sheila the Great. (Fudge Ser.). (J). 2007. 144p. 5.99 (978-0-14-240879-7(4) , Puffin); 2002. (Illus.). 128p. 15.99 (978-0-525-46928-5(1) , Dutton Juvenile) Penguin Group (USA) Inc.

Boulden, James. Buddy Learns from His Mistakes: Student Involvement Pack. 2003. (Illus.). 21p. (J). 24.95 (978-1-892421-78-4(X)) Boulden Publishing.

Brinkerhoff, Shirley. Balancing Act. 1998. (Nikki Sheridan Ser.: Vol. 4). 208p. (J). (gr. 9-12). pap. 5.99 (978-1-56179-559-8(3)) Bethany Hse. Pubs.

Brown, Stephanie. Thea the Yellow Tomato. Brown, Stephanie, illus. l.t. ed. 1998. (Illus.). 32p. (J). (gr. k-4). 14.95 (978-0-9638152-6-2(1)) Freedom Publishing Co.

Burns, Marilyn. Greedy Triangle, The (Bkshelf) 2008. 32p. pap. 6.99 ***(978-0-545-04220-8(8)*** , Scholastic Paperbacks) Scholastic, Inc.

Campbell, Louisa. Biglet. 2002. (Illus.). 32p. (ps-1). 5.99 (978-0-7868-3363-4(7)) Disney Pr.

Carter, Catherine. Anna's Choice. Pittman, Gail, illus. 2005. 24p. (J). (gr. 3-7). 12.95 (978-1-893062-79-5(1)) Quail Ridge Pr., Inc.

Cavanna, Betty. Going on Sixteen. 1998. 192p. (YA). (gr. 7-12). reprint ed. pap. 5.95 (978-0-688-16324-2(6)) HarperCollins Pubs.

Changizi, Mandana S. The Plain Blue Caterpillar. 2000. (Illus.). 16p. (J). (ps-5). pap. 9.95 (978-0-9637240-9-0(6)) Biographical Publishing Co.

Charlton-Trujillo, E. E. Prizefighter en Mi Casa. (J). (gr. 5-7). 2007. 192p. 5.99 ***(978-0-440-42117-7(9)*** , Yearling); 2006. 224p. 15.95 (978-0-385-73325-0(9) , Delacorte Bks. for Young Readers); 2006. 224p. lib. bdg. 17.99 (978-0-385-90344-8(8) , Delacorte Bks. for Young Readers) Random Hse. Children's Bks.

Chen, Zhiyuan & Chen, Chih-Yuan. The Featherless Chicken. 2006. (Illus.). 40p. (J). 16.95 (978-0-9762056-9-2(6)) Heryin Publishing Corp.

Ciddor, Anna. Runestone. 2007. (Viking Magic Ser.). (Illus.). 192p. (Orig.). (J). (gr. 4-7). pap. 7.95 ***(978-1-86508-689-7(4))*** Allen & Unwin AUS. *Dist:* Independent Pubs. Group.

Claverie, Jean & Chapouton, Anne Marie. Julian. 2003. (Illus.). 28p. (978-84-85334-71-1(X)) Loguez Ediciones ESP. *Dist:* Lectorum Pubns., Inc.

Collins, Ross. Medusa Jones. 2008. (J). ***(978-0-439-90101-7(4));*** 144p. pap. 16.99 ***(978-0-439-90100-0(6))*** Scholastic, Inc. (Levine, Arthur A. Bks.).

Cosgrove, Stephen. Minikin. 2000. (gr. k-3). lib. bdg. 13.00 (978-0-613-33659-8(3)) Tandem Library Bks.

Curen, Cathi. The Secret Journey. 1998. (Illus.). 80p. (J). (gr. 2-4). pap. 5.95 (978-0-9667442-0-0(9)) Curen Enterprises.

Cuyler, Margery. From Here to There. Pak, Yu Cha, illus. rev. ed. 1999. 32p. (J). (ps-2). 17.95 (978-0-8050-3191-1(X) , Holt, Henry & Co. Bks. For Young Readers) Holt, Henry & Co.

Dole, Mayra Lazara. Down to the Bone. 2008. 384p. (J). 16.99 ***(978-0-06-084310-6(1));*** lib. bdg. 17.89 ***(978-0-06-084311-3(X))*** HarperCollins Pubs. (HarperTeen).

Drachman, Eric. A Frog Thing. Muscarello, James, illus. 2006. 32p. 18.95 (978-0-9703809-3-7(3)) Kidwick Bks.

Duvoisin, Roger. Donkey-Donkey. 2007. 56p. (J). (gr. k-1). 15.99 (978-0-375-84065-4(6)); lib. bdg. 18.99 (978-0-375-94065-1(0)) Random Hse. Children's Bks. (Knopf Bks. for Young Readers).

Ebeling, Vicki. The Winners Group. 2007. (J). per. 7.95 (978-0-9779768-0-5(7)) Pier Avenue Publishing.

Emerson, Carl. Falling Freddy, the Fainting Goat. Trover, Zachary, illus. 2007. (Animal Underdogs Ser.). 32p. (J). (ps-4). lib. bdg. 27.07 ***(978-1-60270-015-4(X)*** , Looking Glass Library) Magic Wagon.

Estefan, Gloria & Garland, Michael. The Magically Mysterious Adventures of Noelle the Bulldog. 32p. 2006. pap. 6.99 (978-0-06-082625-3(8)); 2005. (Illus.). 17.99 (978-0-06-082623-9(1)) HarperCollins Pubs. (Rayo).

Flesher, Vivienne. Alfred's Nose. Flesher, Vivienne, illus. 2008. 32p. (J). 16.99 ***(978-0-06-084313-7(6));*** lib. bdg. 17.89 ***(978-0-06-084314-4(4))*** HarperCollins Pubs.

Frank, E. R. Wrecked. 256p. (YA). (gr. 7 up). 2007. pap. 8.99 (978-0-689-87384-3(0) , Simon Pulse); 2005. (Illus.). 16.99 (978-0-689-87383-6(2) , Atheneum) Simon & Schuster Children's Publishing.

Gawade, Akansha A. This Is Who I Am. 2006. (J). pap. 8.00 (978-0-8059-6886-6(5)) Dorrance Publishing Co., Inc.

Gehret, Jeanne. Eagle Eyes: A Child's Guide to Paying Attention. Covert, Susan, illus. 3rd rev. ed. 2003. 40p. (J). (gr. 1-5). pap. 9.95 (978-1-884281-11-2(7)) Verbal Images Pr.

Giff, Patricia Reilly. All the Way Home. 2003. (Illus.). 176p. (J). (gr. 3-7). pap. 5.99 (978-0-440-41182-6(3) , Yearling) Random Hse. Children's Bks.

—Fourth-Grade Celebrity. 1999. (J). (gr. 3-6). 21.75 (978-0-8446-7008-9(1)) Smith, Peter Pub., Inc.

Gorman, Carol. Dork in Disguise. 2000. (J). 12.64 (978-0-606-20049-3(5)) Tandem Library Bks.

Goss, Leon. I'm Good, I'm Beautiful, I'm Smart. Mailey, Maria C. & Neuburger, Jenny, illus. 2005. (J). per. (978-1-933156-02-6(3) , VisionQuest Kids) GSVQ Publishing.

Graves, Keith. Loretta: Ace Pinky Scout. 2002. (Loretta Ser.). (Illus.). (J). 40p. (gr. 2-5). pap. 16.95 (978-0-439-36831-5(6) , Scholastic Pr.); pap. (978-0-439-36832-2(4)) Scholastic, Inc.

Green-Armytage, Stephen. Dudley: The Little Terrier That Could. 1999. (Illus.). 32p. (gr. 8-17). 12.95 (978-0-8109-4098-7(1)) Abrams, Harry N. , Inc.

Green, George & Brooke, Amy/ J. George Green's, the Lion Who Couldn't Roar. 2007. (J). per. 17.99 ***(978-1-933156-14-9(7)*** , Visikid Bks.) GSVQ Publishing.

Hacker, Michael. Who Am I? Dillard, Karen, illus. 2000. 24p. (J). (ps). 7.99 (978-1-56309-736-2(2)) New Hope Pubs.

Harrison, Jim. The Boy Who Ran to the Woods. Pohrt, Tom, illus. 2000. 32p. (J). (gr. 4-7). 18.95 (978-0-87113-822-4(0) , Atlantic Monthly Pr.) Grove/Atlantic, Inc.

Headley, Justina Chen. The Patch. Vane, Mitch, illus. (J). 2007. pap. 7.95 ***(978-1-58089-170-7(5));*** 2006. 32p. 15.95 (978-1-58089-049-6(0)) Charlesbridge Publishing, Inc.

Henkes, Kevin. The Birthday Room. Henkes, Kevin, illus. 1999. (Illus.). 160p. (J). (gr. 3 up). 19.99 (978-0-688-16733-2(0)) HarperCollins Pubs.

—The Birthday Room. 2001. (gr. 5-8). lib. bdg. 14.15 (978-0-613-44190-2(7)) Tandem Library Bks.

Henshon, Suzanna E. Spiders on the Ceiling. 2006. (J). (978-0-88092-614-0(7)) Royal Fireworks Publishing Co.

Hill, Karen. Ava, the One & Only. Roos, Maryn, illus. 2005. 24p. (J). 9.99 (978-1-4169-0511-0(1) , Little Simon) Simon & Schuster Children's Publishing.

Hodgson, Mona Gansberg. Goofy Glasses. 2000. (ps-2). lib. bdg. 13.00 (978-0-613-72834-8(3)) Tandem Library Bks.

Hodgson, Mona Gansberg & Sharp, Chris. Goofy Glasses. 2000. (Desert Critter Friends Ser.: Vol. 10). (Illus.). 48p. (J). (ps-2). 4.99 (978-0-570-07011-5(2)) Concordia Publishing Hse.

Hogan, Mary. Pretty Face. 2008. 224p. (J). 16.99 ***(978-0-06-084111-9(7));*** lib. bdg. 17.89 ***(978-0-06-084112-6(5))*** HarperCollins Pubs. (HarperTeen).

Kent, Renee Holmes. Robyn Flies Home, Vol. 4. 2004. (Adventures in Misty Falls Ser.: Vol. 4). (Illus.). 100p. (gr. 4-7). pap. 4.99 (978-1-56309-764-5(8) , N007106) New Hope Pubs.

Kimmel, Elizabeth Cody. Lily B. on the Brink of Love. (J). 2006. 208p. pap. 5.99 (978-0-06-075545-4(8) , Harper Trophy); 2005. 224p. 15.99 (978-0-06-075541-6(5)); 2005. 192p. lib. bdg. 16.89 (978-0-06-075543-0(1)) HarperCollins Pubs.

Knapp, J. Richard. Bobby's Story: An Amazing Story of Teen Courage. 2006. 234p. (YA). per. 12.95 (978-0-9774761-7-6(0) , Books To Believe In) Thornton Publishing.

Koertge, Ronald. Stoner & Spaz. 176p. (YA). (gr. 9-12). 2002. 15.99 (978-0-7636-1608-3(7)); 2004. reprint ed. pap. 6.99 (978-0-7636-2150-6(1)) Candlewick Pr.

Lanier, Bob. It's All in the Name. 2003. (gr. k-3). lib. bdg. 11.80 (978-0-613-66643-5(7)) Tandem Library Bks.

—Stuck in the Middle. 2003. (gr. k-3). lib. bdg. 11.80 (978-0-613-84844-2(6)) Tandem Library Bks.

Lanier, Bob & Goodyear, Heather. It's All in the Name. 2003. (Hey L'il D! Ser.: No. 1). (Illus.). 96p. (J). pap. 3.99 (978-0-439-40899-8(7) , Scholastic Paperbacks) Scholastic, Inc.

—Stuck in the Middle. Grover, Desire, illus. 2003. (Hey L'il D! Ser.: No. 3). 80p. (J). pap. 3.99 (978-0-439-40901-8(2) , Scholastic Paperbacks) Scholastic, Inc.

S

Le Guin, Ursula K. Very Far Away from Anywhere Else. 2004. 144p. (YA). pap. 6.95 (978-0-15-205208-9(9), Harcourt Paperbacks) Harcourt Children's Bks.

Leppard, Laura Jennifer. The Duchess of Sao Paulo. 2006. 49p. (J). pap. 17.89 (978-1-4116-6635-1(6)) Lulu.com.

Leverich, Kathleen. The New You. 1998. 112p. (YA). (gr. 5 up). 15.00 (978-0-688-16076-0(X)) HarperCollins Pubs.

—New You. 2000. (978-0-606-18587-5(9)) Tandem Library Bks.

Levine, Gail Carson. Fairest. 2006. 336p. (J). (gr. 3-9). 16.99 (978-0-06-073408-4(6)); lib. bdg. 17.89 (978-0-06-073409-1(4)) HarperCollins Pubs.

—Fairest. l.t. rev. ed. 2007. 356p. (YA). 23.95 (*978-0-7862-9270-7(9)) Thorndike Pr.

Lewis, Catherine. Postcards to Father Abraham. Yeomans, Jane, illus. 2000. 304p. (YA). (gr. 7-12). 17.95 (978-0-689-82852-2(7), Atheneum) Simon & Schuster Children's Publishing.

Linko, G. J. Frank's Fear. 2004. (Seekers Ser.: No. 6). 108p. 5.99 (978-0-8066-4187-4(8), Augsburg Bks.) Augsburg Fortress, Pubs.

Lovell, Patty. Stand Tall, Molly Lou Melon. Catrow, David, illus. 2001. 32p. (J). (ps-3). 15.99 (978-0-399-23416-3(0), Putnam Juvenile) Penguin Group (USA) Inc.

—Stand Tall, Molly Lou Melon. 2002. (J). (gr. k-3). 25.95 incl. audio (978-0-8045-6891-3(X)) Spoken Arts, Inc.

Lucado, Max. If Only I Had a Green Nose. Martinez, Sergio, illus. 2005. (Wemmicks Ser.). 28p. 6.99 (978-1-58134-533-9(X)); 31p. 15.99 (978-1-58134-397-7(3)) Crossway Bks. (Crossway Bibles).

—Punchinello & the Most Marvelous Gift: And, Your Special Gift. Martinez, Sergio, illus. 2007. (J). (*978-1-58134-877-4(0)) Crossway Bks.

—You Are Mine. Martinez, Sergio, illus. 2005. (Wemmicks Ser.). 28p. bds. 6.99 (978-1-58134-429-5(5), Crossway Bibles) Crossway Bks.

—You Are Mine: Read & Sing Along. Martinez, Sergio, illus. 2005. (Wemmicks Ser.). 32p. (ps-3). 15.99 (978-1-58134-276-5(4), Crossway Bibles) Crossway Bks.

—You Are Mine & If Only I Had A Green Nose, vol. 2. 2006. (Illus.). 64p. (J). 19.99 (978-1-58134-805-7(3)) Crossway Bks.

—Your Special Gift. Wenzel, David, illus. 2006. 31p. (J). 15.99 (978-1-58134-698-5(0)) Crossway Bks.

Lynch, Chris. Extreme Elvin. 1999. 240p. (YA). (gr. 7 up). 15.95 (978-0-06-028040-6(9)) HarperCollins Pubs.

Mac, Carrie. Crush. 2006. 112p. (gr. 3-6). lib. bdg. 14.95 (978-1-55143-521-3(7)) Orca Bk. Pubs. USA.

MacDonald, Alan. The Pig in a Wig. Hess, Paul, illus. 2003. 32p. (J). (gr. k-3). pap. 6.95 (978-1-56145-299-6(8), Q32523) Peachtree Pubs., Ltd.

—Pig in a Wig. 1999. (gr. k-3). lib. bdg. 16.40 (978-0-613-68926-7(7)) Tandem Library Bks.

Mackler, Carolyn. Love & Other Four-Letter Words. 2002. (Laurel-Leaf Books). 256p. (YA). (gr. 7). pap. 5.99 (978-0-440-22831-8(X), Laurel Leaf) Random Hse. Children's Bks.

Markes, Julie. Good Thing You're Not an Octopus! Smith, Maggie, illus. 40p. (J). (ps-1). 2006. pap. 6.99 (978-0-06-443586-4(5), Harper Trophy); 2001. 15.99 (978-0-06-028465-7(X)) HarperCollins Pubs.

May, Kara. Joe Lion's Big Boots. Allen, Jonathan, illus. 2005. (I Am Reading Ser.). 48p. (J). (gr. k-3). pap. 3.95 (978-0-7534-5856-3(X), Kingfisher) Houghton Mifflin Co. Trade & Reference Div.

McEwan, Jamie. The Heart of Cool. Boynton, Sandra, illus. 2002. (Ready-to-Read Ser.: Level 3). 48p. (J). (gr. 1-4). pap. 3.99 (978-0-689-82178-3(6), Aladdin) Simon & Schuster Children's Publishing.

Mendez, Phil. The Black Snowman. Byard, Carole M., illus. 2005. 48p. (J). (ps-3). pap. 5.99 (978-0-439-76993-8(0), Scholastic Paperbacks) Scholastic, Inc.

Metzger, Steve. I'm the Winner! Wilhelm, Hans, illus. 1999. (Dinofours Ser.: No. 7). (J). (ps-1). 3.25 (978-0-439-06327-2(2)) Scholastic, Inc.

Mills, Claudia. You're a Brave Man, Julius Zimmerman. 2001. 160p. (gr. 3-7). pap. 5.99 (978-0-7868-1448-0(9)) Hyperion Bks. for Children.

Moore, Julianne. Freckleface Strawberry. Pham, LeUyen, illus. 2007. 32p. (J). (ps-3). 16.95 (*978-1-59990-107-7(2)) Bloomsbury Publishing.

Moore, Julianne & Pham, LeUyen. Freckleface Strawberry. 2007. (Illus.). 32p. (J). 17.85 (*978-1-59990-137-4(4)) Bloomsbury Publishing.

Morgan, Nicola. Chicken Friend. 2005. 160p. (J). (gr. 4-7). 15.99 (978-0-7636-2735-5(6)) Candlewick Pr.

Murrell, Diane, illus. Oliver Onion: The Onion Who Learns to Accept & Be Himself. 2004. (J). (978-1-931282-64-2(1)) Autism Asperger Publishing Co.

Nanette. Little Red. 2004. (Life on Granny's Farm Ser.). (J). 12.95 (978-0-9741269-1-3(8)) St. Bernard Publishing, LLC.

—Oinky the Yellow Pig. 2004. (Life on Granny's Farm Ser.). (J). 12.95 (978-0-9741269-4-4(2)) St. Bernard Publishing, LLC.

Oke, Janette. The Impatient Turtle. Munger, Nancy, illus. rev. ed. 2000. (Animal Friends Ser.). 64p. (Orig.). (J). (gr. 1-5). pap. 6.99 (978-0-7642-2407-2(7)) Bethany Hse. Pubs.

O'Neill, Peggy. Little Squarehead. Freeman, Denise, illus. 2001. 32p. (J). (ps up). 15.95 (978-0-935699-21-0(X), 093569921x) Illumination Arts Publishing Co., Inc.

Petty, Dini. The Queen, the Bear & the Bumblebee. Cowles, Rose, illus. 32p. (J). 19.95 (978-1-55285-151-7(6)) Whitecap Bks., Ltd. CAN. Dist: Graphic Arts Ctr. Publishing Co.

Pfister, Marcus. Just the Way You Are. Pfister, Marcus, illus. 2002. (Illus.). 32p. (J). (gr. k-3). 15.95 (978-0-7358-1615-2(8)) North-South Bks., Inc.

—Somos Como Somos. Almohar, Ariel, tr. Pfister, Marcus, illus. 2002. (SPA., Illus.). 32p. (J). (gr. k-3). 15.95 (978-0-7358-1654-1(9), NS31596) North-South Bks., Inc.

Pitino, Donna Marie. Too-Tall Tina. Woodruff, Liza, illus. 2005. 32p. (J). lib. bdg. 13.00 (*978-1-4242-1076-3(3)) Fitzgerald Bks.

—Too-Tall Tina. Woodruff, Liza, illus. 2005. (Math Matters Ser.). 32p. (J). pap. 4.95 (978-1-57565-150-7(5)) Kane Pr., The.

Pixley, Marcella. Freak. 2007. 144p. (YA). (gr. 7 up). 16.00 (*978-0-374-32453-7(0)) Farrar, Straus & Giroux.

Powell, Jillian. Tall Tilly. Archbold, Tim, illus. 2005. 32p. (J). (gr. 1-2). lib. bdg. 11.15 (978-0-606-33587-4(0)) Tandem Library Bks.

Price, Marjorie Baker. Merinda & the Magic Mirror: Children's Self Help Coloring Book. Price, David & Price, David, illus. 2002. 30p. (J). spiral bd. 4.95 (978-0-9713013-9-9(5)) Centering Pubns.

Priddy, Roger. Rainbow Rob. 2006. (Illus.). 20p. (J). bds. 12.95 (978-0-312-49791-0(1), Priddy Bks.) St. Martin's Pr.

Prue, Sally. Playing with Fire. 2005. 208p. (J). (gr. 7-12). pap. 5.99 (978-0-439-48635-4(1), Scholastic Paperbacks) Scholastic, Inc.

Radunsky, Vladimir. I Love You Dude. 2005. (Illus.). 48p. (J). (gr. 2-5). 16.00 (978-0-15-205176-1(7), Gulliver Bks.) Harcourt Children's Bks.

Reider, Katja. Rosalie & Truffle; A Story of Love. Bucker, Jutta, illus. 2005. (ENG & GER.). 64p. (ps-3). 9.95 (978-0-8109-5984-2(4)) Abrams, Harry N., Inc.

—Todo Empezo Con Caracol. 1999. (SPA.). (gr. k-3). lib. bdg. 15.25 (978-0-613-29109-5(3)) Tandem Library Bks.

Reider, Katja & Von Roehl, Angela. Todo Empezo Con Caracol. 1999. (978-0-606-17757-3(4)) Tandem Library Bks.

Richardson, John. Grunt. Rogers, Emma, illus. 2002. 32p. (J). (gr. k-3). 15.00 (978-0-618-15974-1(6), Clarion Bks.) Houghton Mifflin Co. Trade & Reference Div.

Ritter, John. Choosing up Sides. 2000. (gr. 5-8). lib. bdg. 14.15 (978-0-613-28444-8(5)) Tandem Library Bks.

Roos, Stephen. The Gypsies Never Came. l.t. ed. 2001. (Juvenile Ser.). 116p. (J). 20.95 (978-0-7862-3469-1(5)) Thorndike Pr.

Rosenthal, Amy Krouse & Lichtenheld, Tom. The OK Book. Rosenthal, Amy Krouse & Lichtenheld, Tom, illus. 2007. (Illus.). 40p. (ps-2). 12.99 (*978-0-06-115255-9(2)); lib. bdg. 14.89 (*978-0-06-115256-6(0)) HarperCollins Pubs.

Ryan, Patrick. Saints of Augustine. 2007. 320p. (J). lib. bdg. 17.89 (*978-0-06-085811-7(7)); (gr. 7 up). 16.99 (*978-0-06-085810-0(9)) HarperCollins Pubs. (HarperTeen).

Sargent, Dave & Sargent, Pat. Cammie Camel: Endurance, 56 bks, Vol. 42. Lenoir, Jane, illus. 2000. (Animal Pride Ser.). 36p. (J). lib. bdg. 19.95 (978-1-56763-525-6(3)) Ozark Publishing.

Sargent, Dave, et al. Cammie Camel: Endurance, 17, 42. 2000. (Animal Pride Ser.: 42). (Illus.). (J). pap. 6.95 (978-1-56763-526-3(1)) Ozark Publishing.

Savageau, Cheryl. Muskrat Will Be Swimming. Hynes, Robert, illus. 2006. 32p. (J). pap. (978-0-88448-280-2(4)) Tilbury Hse. Pubs.

Shavick, Andrea. You'll Grow Soon, Alex. Ayto, Russell, illus. 2000. 32p. (J). (ps-3). 15.95 (978-0-8027-8736-1(3)) Walker & Co.

Sherman, Denise Privette. Samantha Salisbury Worthington. Privette, Betty S., illus. 2002. (J). 19.95 (978-0-9722221-0-5(3)) Wordsmith Pr.

Small, David. Imogene's Antlers. Small, David, illus. 2002. (Illus.). (J). 14.79 (978-0-7587-2836-4(0)) Book Wholesalers, Inc.

—Imogene's Antlers. 2000. (J). pap. 19.97 incl. audio (978-0-7366-9207-6(X)) Books on Tape, Inc.

—Imogene's Antlers. 2005. (Illus.). (J). pap. 18.95 incl. audio compact disk (978-1-59112-723-9(8)) Live Oak Media.

—Imogene's Antlers. Small, David, illus. 2005. (Illus.). (J). (gr. 1-6). pap. 16.95 incl. audio (978-0-87499-322-6(9)) Live Oak Media.

—Imogene's Antlers. Boughton, Simon, ed. Small, David, illus. 2000. (Illus.). 32p. (J). (ps-3). 15.95 (978-0-375-81048-0(X), Crown Books For Young Readers) Random Hse. Children's Bks.

Sonenklar, Carol. My Own Worst Enemy. 1999. 152p. (J). (gr. 7 up). tchr. ed. 15.95 (978-0-8234-1456-7(6)) Holiday Hse., Inc.

Spinelli, Jerry. Loser. 224p. 2003. pap. 5.99 (978-0-06-054074-6(5)); 2002. (J). (gr. 4-7). 15.99 (978-0-06-000193-3(3), Cotler, Joanna Books); 2002. (Illus.). (J). (gr. 4-6). lib. bdg. 16.89 (978-0-06-000483-5(5), Cotler, Joanna Books) HarperCollins Pubs.

—Loser. 2002. (gr. 3-6). lib. bdg. 14.15 (978-0-613-66899-6(5)) Tandem Library Bks.

Springer, Nancy. Dusssie. 2007. 176p. (J). (gr. 5-9). 16.95 (*978-0-8027-9649-3(4)) Walker & Co.

Steele, D. Kelley. Fire in Her Hair: A Story of Friendship. James, Margaret Ray, illus. l.t. ed. 2002. 40p. (J). (gr. 1-6). 18.95 (978-0-9711534-0-0(X)) Hidden Path Pubn., Inc.

Stevens, Janet & Crummel, Susan Stevens. Jackalope. Stevens, Janet, illus. 2003. (Illus.). 56p. (J). (gr. k-3). 17.00 (978-0-15-216736-3(6)) Harcourt Children's Bks.

Storm, Hannah, frwd. Buddy Booby's Birthmark. 2006. (Illus.). 36p. (J). 15.99 (*978-0-9794413-0-1(7)); per. 8.99 (*978-0-9794413-1-8(5)) E & D Bks., Ltd.

Sweeney, Jacqueline. Little Honu. Hart, G. K. & Hart, Vikki, illus. Hart, G. K. & Hart, Vikki, photos by. 2002. (We Can Read! Ser.). 32p. (J). 21.36 (978-0-7614-1512-1(2), Benchmark Bks.) Cavendish, Marshall Corp.

Terry, Michael. Rhino's Horns. 2001. (Illus.). 32p. (J). (ps up). 19.99 (978-0-7475-5051-8(4)) Bloomsbury Publishing Plc GBR. Dist: Independent Pubs. Group.

—Rhinos Horns. 2003. (Illus.). (J). (978-1-58234-796-7(4), Bloomsbury Children) Bloomsbury Publishing.

Tokio, Marnelle. More Than You Can Chew. 2003. (gr. 7-12). lib. bdg. 18.75 (978-0-613-77305-8(5)) Tandem Library Bks.

—More Than You Can Chew. 2003. (Illus.). 240p. (J). (gr. 9 up). pap. 9.95 (978-0-88776-639-8(0)) Tundra Bks., Inc./Livres Toundra, Inc. CAN. Dist: Random Hse., Inc.

Townsend, Wendy. Lizard Love. 2008. (J). (*978-1-932425-34-5(9), Front Street) Boyds Mills Pr.

Ulmer, Mari P. Adventures of the Little Green Dragon. Maass, Mary K., illus. 1998. (Weewisdom Bks.). 64p. (J). (ps-3). 17.95 (978-0-87159-228-6(2)) Unity Schl. of Christianity.

van Holst Pellekaan, Karen. Coco the Koala. De Backker, Vera, illus. 2000. (Coco the Koala Ser.). 29p. (J). (ps up). lib. bdg. 23.33 (978-0-8368-2729-3(5)) Stevens, Gareth Inc.

Walter, Debbie. Introducing Russell. Walter, Debbie, illus. 2007. (Illus.). 68p. (J). per. 6.95 (*978-0-9766315-2-1(0)) Moose Run Productions.

Weaver, Will. Defect. 2007. 208p. (YA). (gr. 7 up). 16.00 (*978-0-374-31725-6(9), Farrar, Straus & Giroux (BYR)) Farrar, Straus & Giroux.

Welsh, David J. The Boy Who Burned Too Brightly: A Modern Allegory. Bolt, Brandon, illus. 2001. 67p. 19.95 (978-0-9656442-0-4(0)) Alisam Pr.

Wheeler, Kathryn. Patty Saves the Day! A Tale in Which Patty Discovers Her True Gift. Myers, Darcy, illus. 2000. (Stories to Grow By Ser.). 19p. (J). (978-0-7424-0012-2(3), Instructional Fair) Schaffer, Frank Pubns.

Wilson, Diane Lee. Black Storm Comin' (J). 2006. 240p. pap. 5.99 (978-0-689-87138-2(4), Aladdin); 2005. 304p. (gr. 5-9). 17.99 (978-0-689-87137-5(6), McElderry, Margaret K.) Simon & Schuster Children's Publishing.

Winter, Laurel. Growing Wings. 2002. (Firebird Ser.). 224p. (YA). pap. 6.99 (978-0-14-230219-4(8), Puffin) Penguin Group (USA) Inc.

—Growing Wings. 2002. (gr. 5-8). lib. bdg. 15.30 (978-0-613-56405-2(7)) Tandem Library Bks.

Wojtowicz, Jen. The Boy Who Grew Flowers. Adams, Steve, illus. 2005. 32p. (J). (ps-3). 16.99 (978-1-84148-686-4(8)) Barefoot Bks., Inc.

Wolff, Virginia. Probably Still Nick Swansen. 2002. (gr. 5-8). lib. bdg. 16.45 (978-0-613-57323-8(4)) Tandem Library Bks.

Wolff, Virginia Euwer. Probably Still Nick Swansen. 2002. 160p. (YA). pap. 7.99 (978-0-689-85226-8(6), Simon Pulse) Simon & Schuster Children's Publishing.

SELF-CONFIDENCE

see also Self-reliance

Arnold, Ellen. Brilliant Brain Battles Bad Guys. Farber, Deborah, illus. 2001. (MI Strategies for Kids Ser.). 32p. (J). (gr. 1-5). pap. 7.00 (978-1-56976-111-3(6), 1140, Zephyr Pr.) Chicago Review Pr., Inc.

Barry, Douglas. Wisdom for a High School Grad. 2005. 176p. 14.95 (978-0-7624-2340-8(4), Running Pr.) Running Pr. Bk. Pubs.

Canfield, Jack L., et al. Chicken Soup for the Preteen Soul II: Stories about Taking Charge, Making a Difference & Moving Through the Preteen Years for Kids Ages 9-13. 2004. 384p. (YA). pap. 14.95 (978-0-7573-0150-6(9)) Health Communications, Inc.

Chinn, Jacqueline. How Can I Be Special? Mondragon, Manny, illus. 2003. (J). pap. 15.95 (978-0-929526-55-3(4)) Double B Pubns.

Dreaming Bigger Dreams. 2005. (YA). per. (978-1-59872-127-0(5)) Instantpublisher.com.

Drohan, Michele Ingber. Learning about Strength of Character from the Life of Muhammad Ali. 1999. (Character Building Book Ser.). (Illus.). 24p. (J). (gr. 3). lib. bdg. 18.75 (978-0-8239-5347-9(5), PowerKids Pr.) Rosen Publishing Group, Inc., The.

Everly, Nita. Early Social Behavior Books Can You Keep Trying? 2007. (J). spiral bd. 11.95 (*978-0-7606-0738-1(9)) LinguiSystems, Inc.

Green, Edna. My Special Thoughts. 2003. (J). (ps-5). bds. 11.95 (978-0-9743019-0-7(6)) My Special Thoughts.

Harris, Destiny. Beauty Secrets for Girls: Beauty Secrets for Girls. 2004. (J). per. (978-0-9754380-2-2(6), 100) Harris, Pleshette Communications Inc. Publishing.

Ignoffo, Matthew. Everything You Need to Know about Self-Confidence. rev. ed. 1999. (Need to Know Library). (Illus.). 64p. (YA). (gr. 7-12). lib. bdg. 25.25 (978-0-8239-3037-1(8), NTSECO) Rosen Publishing Group, Inc., The.

Jeffers, Susan. I Can Handle It! 50 Confidence-Building Stories to Empower Your Child. 2006. 160p. pap. 9.95 (978-0-9777618-0-7(0)) Jeffers Pr.

Kiyosaki, Robert T. & Lechter, Sharon L. Rich Dad Poor Dad for Teens: The Secrets about Money—That You Don't Learn in School! 2004. (Rich Dad Ser.). 160p. pap. 14.99 (978-0-446-69321-9(9)) Little Brown & Co.

Naik, Anita. Self Esteem. 2nd ed. 2005. (Illus.). 144p. (YA). pap. 12.00 (978-0-340-88395-2(2), Hodder & Stoughton) Hodder General Publishing Division GBR. Dist: Trafalgar Square Publishing.

Schwartz, Stuart B. & Conley, Craig. Building Self Confidence. (Life Skills-Career Bks.). 48p. pap. 6.95 (978-0-7368-8506-5(4), LifeMatters Bks.) Capstone Pr., Inc.

Sheldon, Jodi. Living on My Own I Can Do Everything, 8 vols., Vol. 3. 2002. (Illus.). (J). per. (978-1-932062-21-2(0)) Hability Solution Services, Inc.

Straight Talk about Self-Confidence. (YA). (gr. 6-8). 69.95 (978-1-55942-197-3(5), 9239V9) Marsh Media.

Summers, Barbara, ed. Open the Unusual Door: True Life Stories of Challenge, Adventure, & Success by Black Americans. Triplett, Gina, illus. 2005. 224p. (YA). (gr. 7 up). pap. 7.99 (978-0-618-58531-1(1), Graphia) Houghton Mifflin Co. Trade & Reference Div.

Williams-Kinsey, Rose & Williams, Carolyn. Be a Dreamer the Positive Path: A Dream Lasts Forever. Williams-Kinsey, Rose et al, illus. Nelson, Melvin L. et al, illus. 1998. (J). (ps up). pap. (978-0-9628539-0-6(9)) Be A Dreamer Pubs.

SELF-CONFIDENCE—FICTION

Aboff, Marcie. Giant Jelly Bean Jar. 2004. (gr. k-3). lib. bdg. 11.80 (978-0-613-89801-0(X)) Tandem Library Bks.

Allen, Debbie. Dancing in the Wings. Nelson, Kadir A., illus. (J). (gr. k-2). 2003. 32p. pap. 6.99 (978-0-14-250141-2(7), Puffin); 2000. 1p. 16.99 (978-0-8037-2501-0(9), Dial) Penguin Group (USA) Inc.

—Dancing in the Wings. 2003. (gr. k-3). lib. bdg. 15.30 (978-0-613-86700-9(9)) Tandem Library Bks.

An, Na. The Fold. 2008. 192p. (J). (gr. 5). 16.99 (*978-0-399-24276-2(7), Putnam Juvenile) Penguin Group (USA) Inc.

Anderson, Jodi Lynn. May Bird among the Stars, Bk. 2. 272p. (J). 2007. pap. 5.99 (978-1-4169-0608-7(8), Aladdin); 2006. 16.95 (978-0-689-86924-2(X), Atheneum) Simon & Schuster Children's Publishing.

Averbuch, Gloria. Turn for Lucas. Guterman, Yaacov, illus. 2006. 32p. (J). 17.95 (978-1-58726-291-3(6), Mitten Pr.) Ann Arbor Media Group, LLC.

Bache, Ellyn. Daddy & the Pink Flash. Tornatore, Carol, illus. 2003. 32p. 14.95 (978-1-889199-11-5(7)) Banks Channel Bks.

Baicker, Karen. I Can Do It Too! Wilson-Max, Ken, illus. 2003. 24p. (J). 13.95 (978-1-929766-83-3(1)) Handprint Bks.

Bandsuh, Jim. Helmet Hank. 2007. (J). per. 15.99 (*978-1-933156-19-4(8), Visikid Bks.) GSVQ Publishing.

Banks, Steven. King of the Creeps. 2006. 176p. (YA). (gr. 7). 15.95 (978-0-375-83291-8(2), Knopf Bks. for Young Readers) Random Hse. Children's Bks.

Benton, Jim. Howard Hubbins Half Hour Hero. 2008. (J). pap. (*978-0-06-059774-0(7)) HarperCollins Pubs.

Bledsoe, Lucy Jane. Hoop Girlz. 2002. (Illus.). 128p. (J). (gr. 4-6). tchr. ed. 16.95 (978-0-8234-1691-2(7)) Holiday Hse., Inc.

Bloom, Stephanie. The Drummer Who Lost His Beat. Keylon, Joe, illus. 2005. 40p. (J). lib. bdg. 16.95 (978-1-931969-47-5(7)) Bloom & Grow Bks.

Blume, Lesley. Cornelia & the Audacious Escapades of the Somerset Sisters. 2006. 272p. (J). (gr. 3-7). 15.95 (978-0-375-83523-0(7), Knopf Bks. for Young Readers) Random Hse. Children's Bks.

Blume, Lesley M. M. Cornelia & the Audacious Escapades of the Somerset Sisters. 2006. 272p. (J). (gr. 3-7). lib. bdg. 17.99 (978-0-375-93523-7(1), Knopf Bks. for Young Readers) Random Hse. Children's Bks.

Boyce, Katie. Hector the Hermit Crab. Boyce, Katie, illus. 2003. (Illus.). 32p. (J). (ps-1). 15.95 (978-1-58234-800-1(6), Bloomsbury Children) Bloomsbury Publishing.

Brennan-Nelson, Denise. Buzzy the Bumblebee. Monroe, Michael Glenn, illus. 32p. (J). (gr. k-3). 2003. pap. 6.95 (978-1-58536-166-3(6)); 1999. 15.00 (978-1-886947-82-5(1)) Sleeping Bear Pr.

—Buzzy the Bumblebee. 2003. (gr. k-3). lib. bdg. 15.25 (978-0-613-79710-8(8)) Tandem Library Bks.

Brian, Kate. Megan Meade's Guide to the McGowan Boys. 2005. (Illus.). 272p. (YA). 15.99 (978-1-4169-0030-6(6)) Simon & Schuster Children's Publishing.

—Megan Meade's Guide to the McGowan Boys. 2006. 288p. (YA). pap. 8.99 (978-1-4169-0031-3(4), Simon Pulse) Simon & Schuster Children's Publishing.

Brightwood, Laura, illus. The Woodsman & His Ax. Brightwood, Laura, . 2007. (J). DVD (*978-1-934409-07-7(3)) 3-C Institute for Social Development.

Brown, Marc. Arthur & the Goalie Ghost. Brown, Marc, illus. 5th ed. 2001. (Arthur Good Sports Ser.: Bk. 5). (Illus.). 64p. (J). (gr. 2-4). 14.95 (978-0-316-12042-5(1)); pap. 3.95 (978-0-316-12146-0(0)) Little, Brown Bks. for Young Readers.

Bruel, Nick. Little Red Bird. 2008. 32p. (J). 16.95 (*978-1-59643-339-7(6)) Roaring Brook Pr.

Bunting, Eve. I Don't Want to Go to Camp. Cocca-Leffler, Maryann, illus. 2003. 32p. (J). (ps up). pap. 8.95 (978-1-59078-074-9(4)) Boyds Mills Pr.

—One Green Apple. Lewin, Ted, illus. 2006. 32p. (J). (gr. k-3). 16.00 (978-0-618-43477-0(1), Clarion Bks.) Houghton Mifflin Co. Trade & Reference Div.

Burch, Christian. The Manny Files. 2006. (Illus.). 304p. (J). (gr. 4-7). 15.95 (978-1-4169-0039-9(X), Atheneum) Simon & Schuster Children's Publishing.

Cabot, Meg. The Princess Diaries, Volume IX: Princess Mia (International Edition) 2008. (Princess Diaries). 288p. (J). pap. 12.00 (*978-0-06-156819-0(8), HarperTeen) HarperCollins Pubs.

—Princess Mia. 2008. (Princess Diaries: Vol. 9). 288p. (J). lib. bdg. 17.89 (*978-0-06-072462-7(5)) HarperCollins Pubs.

Choyce, Lesley. Carrie Loses Her Nerve. Thurman, Mark, illus. 2003. (First Novel Ser.). 64p. (J). (gr. 1-5). 4.95 (978-0-88780-591-2(4)); (*978-0-88780-592-9(2)) Formac Publishing Co., Ltd. CAN. Dist: Casemate Pubs. & Bk. Distributors, LLC.

—Carrie Loses Her Nerve. 2003. (gr. k-3). lib. bdg. 11.80 (978-0-613-88546-1(5)) Tandem Library Bks.

Christopher, Matt. Fairway Phenom. 2003. (gr. 3-6). lib. bdg. 12.40 (978-0-613-71602-4(7)) Tandem Library Bks.

—The Lucky Baseball Bat: 50th Anniversary Commemorative Edition. Henneberger, Robert, illus. anniv. ed. 2004. 128p. (J). (gr. 2-4). pap. 4.99 (978-0-316-01012-2(X)) Little Brown & Co.

Church, Caroline Jayne. Digby Takes Charge. 2007. 32p. (J). (ps-2). 14.99 (978-1-4169-3441-7(3) , McElderry, Margaret K.) Simon & Schuster Children's Publishing.

Civardi, Anne, et al. More Nightlights: Stories for You to Read to Your Child to Encourage Calm, Confidence & Creativity. 2007. (Illus.). 144p. pap. 14.95 (978-1-84483-407-5(7)) Duncan Baird Pubs. GBR. *Dist:* Sterling Publishing Co., Inc.

Clarke, Nicole & Henderson, Mel. Write Here, Right Now, No. 1. 2006. (Flirt Ser.: No. 1). 224p. (J). (gr. 7-10). pap. 6.99 (978-0-448-44263-1(9) , Grosset & Dunlap) Penguin Group (USA) Inc.

Colon, Suzan. Smallville No.9: Temptation Book. 2004. (gr. 7-12). lib. bdg. 14.15 (978-0-613-71778-6(3)) Tandem Library Bks.

Cornish, D. M. Lamplighter: Monster Blood Tattoo, Book 2: Monster Blood Tattoo, Book 2. 2008. 400p. (YA). (gr. 7). 18.99 ***(978-0-399-24639-5(8)*** , Putnam Juvenile) Penguin Group (USA) Inc.

Cornish, D. M. Monster Blood Tattoo: Foundling. 2006. 404p. (YA). (gr. 4 up). 18.99 (978-0-399-24638-8(X) , Putnam Juvenile) Penguin Group (USA) Inc.

Cosgrove, Stephen. Mizz Buggly: Doing Your Best. Arroyo, Fian, illus. 2004. (J). (978-1-58804-380-1(0)) PCI Educational Publishing.

Courtenay, Bryce. The Power of One. 2005. 304p. (J). (gr. 5-12). lib. bdg. 17.99 (978-0-385-90274-8(3) , Delacorte Bks. for Young Readers) Random Hse. Children's Bks.

Craig, Gary. You Can Be Anything. Craig, Gary, illus. 2006. 32p. (J). 14.95 (978-0-9786813-1-9(2)) Elora Pr.

Crane, E. M. Skin Deep. 2008. (YA). ***(978-0-385-73479-0)*** , Delacorte Pr.) Dell Publishing.

Cuyler, Margery. Biggest, Best Snowman. Hillenbrand, Will, illus. 2004. (Bookshelf Ser.). 32p. (J). (gr. k-ps). pap. 5.99 (978-0-439-66940-5(5) , Scholastic Paperbacks) Scholastic, Inc.

—Biggest, Best Snowman, Library Edition. 2007. (J). 18.95 ***(978-0-545-01780-0(7))*** Scholastic, Inc.

—Biggest Best Snowman, The (Readalong) 2007. (J). 9.95 ***(978-0-545-01484-7(0))*** Scholastic, Inc.

Cuyler, Margery. Bookshelf: Biggest, Best Snowman. Hillenbrand, Will, illus. 1998. (J). (ps-2). pap. 15.95 (978-0-590-13493-4(0)) Scholastic, Inc.

Cuyler, Margery & Hillenbrand, Will. Bookshelf: Biggest, Best Snowman. 1998. (Illus.). 32p. (J). (ps-2). pap. 15.95 (978-0-590-13922-9(3)) Scholastic, Inc.

Danzig, Marsha. The Tiniest Acorn: A Story to Grow By. 1999. (Illus.). 32p. 12.95 (978-0-88391-001-6(2)) Fell, Frederick Pubs., Inc.

deGroat, Diane. Liar, Liar, Pants on Fire. deGroat, Diane, illus. 2006. (Illus.). 27p. (J). (gr. k-4). reprint ed. 16.00 (978-0-7567-9987-8(2)) DIANE Publishing Co.

Dion. Fishing with Balloons. 2004. (Illus.). 68p. (J). (978-1-881929-34-5(5)) Oxton Hse., Pubs.

Duffey, Betsy. How to Be Cool in the Third Grade. Wilson, Janet, illus. 1999. (Chapters Ser.). 80p. (J). (gr. 2-5). pap. 4.99 (978-0-14-130466-3(9) , Puffin) Penguin Group (USA) Inc.

Eastwood, J. G. Dragon: Enter the Realm. 2007. (YA). per. ***(978-0-9792030-7-7(4))*** Light Sword Publishing LLC.

Edwards, Pamela Duncan. The Worrywarts. Cole, Henry, illus. 32p. (J). (ps-1). 2003. pap. 6.99 (978-0-06-443516-1(4)); 1999. 15.95 (978-0-06-028150-2(2)) HarperCollins Pubs.

—The Worrywarts. 1999. (Illus.). (J). (978-0-606-22071-2(2)) Tandem Library Bks.

Efaw, Amy. Battle Dress. (J). (gr. 7 up). 2003. 400p. pap. 6.99 (978-0-06-053520-9(2)); 2000. (Illus.). 304p. 16.99 (978-0-06-027943-1(5)) HarperCollins Pubs.

—Battle Dress. 2004. (Illus.). 382p. (YA). (gr. 8-12). per. 14.04 (978-0-606-30102-2(X)); 2000. (gr. 7-12). lib. bdg. 15.30 (978-0-613-68406-4(0)) Tandem Library Bks.

Ering, Timothy B. Necks Out for Adventure: The True Story of Edwin Wiggleskin. 2007. 48p. (J). ***(978-0-7636-2355-5(5))*** Candlewick Pr.

Fermin, Alice. The Snail & the Rose Tree. Adaptation of a Hans Christian Andersen Story. Barrera, Sandra A., tr. 1999. Tr. of Caracol y el Rosal. (ENG & SPA.). 36p. (J). (ps-3). 14.95 (978-0-931722-16-5(0)) Corona Publishing, Co.

Flinn, Alex. Diva. 2007. 288p. (J). pap. 7.99 ***(978-0-06-056846-7(1));*** 2006. 272p. (YA). 16.99 (978-0-06-056843-6(7)); 2006. 272p. (YA). lib. bdg. 17.89 (978-0-06-056845-0(3)) HarperCollins Pubs. (HarperTeen).

Foard, Sheila Wood. Harvey Girl. 2006. (Illus.). viii, 152p. (J). (978-0-89672-570-6(7)) Texas Tech Univ. Pr.

Forman, Gayle. Sisters in Sanity. 2007. 304p. (J). lib. bdg. 17.89 ***(978-0-06-088748-3(6));*** (YA). (gr. 7 up). 16.99 ***(978-0-06-088747-6(8))*** HarperCollins Pubs. (HarperTeen).

Friedman, D. Dina. Playing Dad's Song. 2006. 144p. (YA). 16.00 (978-0-374-37173-9(3)) Farrar, Straus & Giroux.

Geras, Adele. Other Echoes. 2005. 144p. (J). (gr. 7). 15.95 (978-0-385-75054-7(4) , Fickling, David Bks.) Random Hse. Children's Bks.

Geter, Maurice. My Friend Buddy. Geter, Maurice, illus. 2006. (Illus.). 24p. (J). (978-1-4120-9646-1(4)) Trafford Publishing.

Gibbs, Lynne. Quiet as a Mouse. Mitchell, Melanie, illus. 2003. (Growing Pains Ser.). 32p. (J). pap. 4.95 (978-1-57768-928-7(3)); 12.95 (978-1-57768-481-7(8)) School Specialty Publishing. (Gingham Dog Pr.).

Giblin, James Cross. The Boy Who Saved Cleveland: Based on a True Story. Dooling, Michael, illus. rev. ed. 2006. 80p. (J). 15.95 (978-0-8050-7355-3(8) , Holt, Henry & Co. Bks. For Young Readers) Holt, Henry & Co.

Going, K. L. The Liberation of Gabriel King. (J). (gr. 3 up). 2007. 160p. pap. 6.99 (978-0-14-240766-0(6) , Puffin); 2005. 192p. 15.99 (978-0-399-23991-5(X) , Putnam Juvenile) Penguin Group (USA) Inc.

Goobie, Beth. Sticks & Stones. 2006. 96p. (YA). lib. bdg. 14.95 (978-1-55143-562-6(4)) Orca Bk. Pubs. USA.

Goss, Michael Anthony. The Bat Who Wore Glasses. Longabough, Kristen, illus. 2005. (J). pap. (978-1-933156-13-2(9)); per. (978-1-933156-06-4(6)) GSVQ Publishing. (VisionQuest Kids).

Graham, Rosemary. Thou Shalt Not Dump the Skater Dude & Other Commandments I Have Broken. 2005. 224p. (J). (gr. 7). 16.99 (978-0-670-06017-7(8) , Viking Juvenile) Penguin Group (USA) Inc.

—Thou Shalt Not Dump the Skater Dude (Splashproof Edition) 2007. 1p. (YA). (gr. 7). pap. 6.99 (978-0-14-240836-0(0) , Puffin) Penguin Group (USA) Inc.

Grambling, Lois G. Daddy Will Be There. Kessell, Walter G., illus. 1998. 24p. (J). (ps-3). 15.99 (978-0-688-14983-3(9)) HarperCollins Pubs.

Grannis, Greg. Lottie Bright & the Starmaker's Universe. Vargas, Robert, illus. 2006. (ENG.). 272p. (J). pap. ***(978-0-9778205-9-7(9))*** Helm Publishing.

Grant, Crystal. Warrior Boy. 2007. (ENG.). 92p. per. 14.95 ***(978-1-4241-3978-1(3))*** PublishAmerica, Inc.

Greene, Stephanie. Queen Sophie Hartley. 2005. 144p. (J). (gr. 3-5). 15.00 (978-0-618-49461-3(8) , Clarion Bks.) Houghton Mifflin Co. Trade & Reference Div.

Guanci, Anne Marie. David & the Worry Beast: Helping Children Cope with Anxiety. Attia, Caroline, illus. 2007. (Let's Talk Ser.). 48p. (J). pap. 8.95 (978-0-88282-275-4(6)) New Horizon Pr. Pubs., Inc.

Haas, Jessie. Will You, Won't You? 2000. 176p. (J). (gr. 5 up). 15.89 (978-0-06-029197-6(4)) HarperCollins Pubs.

Haddix, Margaret Peterson. The Girl with 500 Middle Names. Hamlin, Janet, illus. 2001. 96p. (J). (gr. 2-5). pap. 4.99 (978-0-689-84136-1(1) , Aladdin) Simon & Schuster Children's Publishing.

—The Girl with 500 Middle Names. 2001. (gr. 3-6). lib. bdg. 11.80 (978-0-613-31244-8(9)); (Illus.). (J). 10.79 (978-0-606-20672-3(8)) Tandem Library Bks.

—The Girl with 500 Middle Names. l.t. ed. 2002. 102p. (J). 21.95 (978-0-7862-4412-6(7)) Thomson Gale.

Hale, Shannon. The Princess Academy. 2007. 336p. (YA). pap. 7.95 ***(978-1-59990-073-5(4)*** , Bloomsbury Children) Bloomsbury Publishing.

—The Princess Academy. l.t. ed. 2006. 400p. (YA). 23.95 (978-0-7862-8733-8(0)) Thorndike Pr.

Ham, David A. & Sibley, Janice B. Magic Baseball Cap. Bostick, Blair, illus. 2006. 48p. (J). 16.95 (978-0-9746920-2-9(6)) CRM Pubs., LLC.

Harcourt School Publishers Staff. Fly Away! Take-Home Book. 1999. (Collections Ser.). (Illus.). (J). pap. 1.90 (978-0-15-317210-6(X)) Harcourt Schl. Pubs.

Hest, Amy. Make the Team, Baby Duck! Barton, Jill, illus. 2002. (Baby Duck Books! Ser.). 32p. (J). (ps-1). 16.99 (978-0-7636-1541-3(2)) Candlewick Pr.

—You Can Do It, Sam. Jeram, Anita, illus. 2003. 32p. (J). (ps). 15.99 (978-0-7636-1934-3(5)) Candlewick Pr.

Hilbert, Richard A. The Duck King. Peck, Christopher Scott, illus. 2000. (J). 9.95 (978-0-8362-5254-5(3)) Andrews McMeel Publishing.

Hoffman, Mary. City of Stars. 2003. (Stravaganza Ser.: Vol. 2). (Illus.). 300p. (J). 17.95 (978-1-58234-839-1(1) , Bloomsbury Children) Bloomsbury Publishing.

Hogan, Mary. Susanna Hits Hollywood. 2008. (YA). ***(978-0-385-73514-8(6));*** 256p. lib. bdg. ***(978-0-385-90503-9(3))*** Dell Publishing. (Delacorte Pr.).

—Susanna Sees Stars. 2007. 256p. (YA). (gr. 7). pap. 7.99 ***(978-0-385-73513-1(8));*** lib. bdg. 10.99 ***(978-0-385-90502-2(5))*** Random Hse. Children's Bks. (Delacorte Bks. for Young Readers).

Hopkins, Cathy. Mates, Dates & Chocolate Cheats. 2005. (Mates, Dates Ser.). (Illus.). 224p. (YA). mass mkt. 5.99 (978-0-689-87696-7(3) , Simon Pulse) Simon & Schuster Children's Publishing.

Hughes, Dean. Now We're Talking. 1999. (Scrappers Ser.: No. 4). (J). (gr. 3-7). (978-0-606-16297-5(6)) Tandem Library Bks.

Hurwitz, Johanna. Starting School. Dugan, Karen M., illus. 1998. 144p. (J). (gr. 2 up). 15.00 (978-0-688-15685-5(1)) HarperCollins Pubs.

Jellen, Michelle. Spain or Shine. 2005. (S. A. S. S. (Students Across the Seven Seas) Ser.). (Illus.). 224p. (YA). (gr. 7). pap. 6.99 (978-0-14-240368-6(7) , Puffin) Penguin Group (USA) Inc.

Johnson, Kathleen A. A Voice Came to Me. 2006. lib. bdg. 17.95 (978-0-9785623-0-4(5)) Voice of Light Pubns.

Jolley, Dan. Alex Unlimited: The Vosarak Code. 2007. (Illus.). 224p. (YA). (gr. 8 up). pap. 7.99 ***(978-1-4278-0122-7(3)*** , Tokyopop Kids) TOKYOPOP, Inc.

Jones, Carrie. Tips on Having a Gay (ex) Boyfriend. 2008. 264p. (J). pap. 9.95 ***(978-0-7387-1341-0(4)*** , Flux) Llewellyn Pubns.

Jones, Traci L. Standing Against the Wind. 2006. 192p. (J). 16.00 (978-0-374-37174-6(1)) Farrar, Straus & Giroux.

Jordan, Deloris & Jordan, Michael. Michael's Golden Rules. Nelson, Kadir, illus. 2007. 32p. (J). 16.99 (978-0-689-87016-3(7) , Simon & Schuster/Paula Wiseman Bks.) Simon & Schuster Children's Publishing.

Karbo, Karen. Minerva Clark Gets a Clue. 2006. 256p. (J). pap. 6.95 (978-1-58234-747-9(6) , Bloomsbury Children) Bloomsbury Publishing.

Knudson, Mike & Wilkinson, Steve. Raymond & Graham Rule the School. 2008. 128p. (J). (gr. 3-5). 14.99 ***(978-0-670-01101-8(0) ,*** Viking Juvenile) Penguin Group (USA) Inc.

Komaiko, Leah. Malibu Carmie. 2007. 256p. (YA). (gr. 7-11). mass mkt. 5.99 (978-0-440-42014-9(8) , Laurel Leaf) Random Hse. Children's Bks.

Konigsburg, E. L. Throwing Shadows. 1998. 160p. (J). (gr. 5-9). pap. 5.99 (978-0-689-82120-2(4) , Aladdin) Simon & Schuster Children's Publishing.

—The View from Saturday. Konigsburg, E. L., illus. 2002. (Illus.). (J). 25.11 (978-0-7587-0221-0(3)) Book Wholesalers, Inc.

—The View from Saturday. 2000. (J). 11.95 (978-1-56137-936-1(0)) Novel Units, Inc.

—The View from Saturday. 280p. (YA). (gr. 5 up). pap. 4.95 (978-0-8072-1511-1(2) , Listening Library) Random Hse. Audio Publishing Group.

—The View from Saturday. 1998. (Jean Karl Bks.). 176p. (J). (gr. 3-7). reprint ed. pap. 5.99 (978-0-689-81721-2(5) , Aladdin) Simon & Schuster Children's Publishing.

—The View from Saturday. 1998. (J). (978-0-606-13063-9(2)) Tandem Library Bks.

Krensky, Stephen. Arthur Makes the Team. 1998. (Arthur Chapter Bks. : Bk. 3). (J). (gr. 3-6). pap. 3.95 (978-0-316-10536-1(8)); (Illus.). 64p. (gr. 2-4). pap. 4.25 (978-0-316-11551-3(7)) Little, Brown Bks. for Young Readers.

—Arthur Makes the Team. 1998. (Arthur Chapter Bks.: Bk. 3). (J). (gr. 3-6). 11.05 (978-0-606-13152-0(3)) Tandem Library Bks.

Krensky, Stephen & LeapFrog Staff. Arthur Makes the Team. 2001. (Arthur Chapter Bks. : Bk. 3). (J). (ps-2). spiral bd. 14.99 (978-1-58605-130-3(X)) LeapFrog Enterprises, Inc.

Krishnaswami, Uma. The Happiest Tree: A Yoga Story. Jeyaveeran, Ruth, illus. 2005. 32p. (J). 16.95 (978-1-58430-237-7(2)) Lee & Low Bks., Inc.

Kroll, Steven. When I Dream of Heaven. 2004. 156p. (J). lib. bdg. 16.92 ***(978-1-4242-0770-1(3))*** Fitzgerald Bks.

Kylie's Song: Evaluation Guide. 2006. (J). (978-1-55942-414-1(1)) Marsh Media.

Langston, Laura. Exit Point. 2006. 112p. (YA). (gr. 3-6). lib. bdg. 14.95 (978-1-55143-525-1(X)); (gr. 7-12). pap. 7.95 (978-1-55143-505-3(5)) Orca Bk. Pubs. USA.

Larsen, Ramonita. Yes, I Can Do It: Si, lo Puedo Hacer. Larsen, Ramonita, illus. l.t. ed. 2006. (Illus.). 25p. (J). per. 10.99 ***(978-1-59879-292-8(X))*** Lifevest Publishing, Inc.

Larson, Del. Quin's Dream: Reaching for Space. 2003. (Illus.). 94p. per. 14.25 (978-1-932301-55-7(0) , 1286) Airleaf Publishing & Bookselling.

Levine, Gail Carson. The Two Princesses of Bamarre. (J). 2003. 256p. (gr. 5 up). pap. 6.99 (978-0-06-440966-7(X)); 2001. 256p. (gr. 5 up). 17.99 (978-0-06-029315-4(2)); 2001. 256p. (gr. 5 up). lib. bdg. 17.89 (978-0-06-029316-1(0)); 2004. (Illus.). 304p. (gr. 7 up). reprint ed. pap. 6.99 (978-0-06-057580-9(8)) HarperCollins Pubs.

—The Two Princesses of Bamarre. 2003. (Illus.). (gr. 7-12). lib. bdg. 14.15 (978-0-613-67233-7(X)) Tandem Library Bks.

Lewis, Paul Owen. Grasper. 1999. (gr. 3-6). lib. bdg. 16.40 (978-0-613-70971-2(3)) Tandem Library Bks.

Litty, Julie. Chloe & the Magic Baton. Litty, Julie, illus. 2006. 32p. (J). (ps-3). 16.99 (978-0-698-40039-9(9) , Minedition) Penguin Group (USA) Inc.

Lonczak, Heather Suzanne. Mookey the Monkey Gets over Being Teased. Ramsey, Marcy Dunn, illus. 2006. 32p. (J). (gr. k-2). 14.95 (978-1-59147-479-1(5)); pap. 8.95 (978-1-59147-480-7(9)) American Psychological Assn. (Magination Pr.).

Lubar, David. Sleeping Freshmen Never Lie. (YA). 2007. 288p. pap. 6.99 (978-0-14-240780-6(1) , Puffin); 2005. 160p. (gr. 6-10). 16.99 (978-0-525-47311-4(4) , Dutton Juvenile) Penguin Group (USA) Inc.

Ludwig, Trudy. Just Kidding. Gustavson, Adam, illus. 2006. 32p. (J). 15.95 (978-1-58246-163-2(5) , Tricycle Pr.) Ten Speed Pr.

Ludwig Trudy. Solo Bromeando. Gustavson Adam, illus. 2006. (SPA.). 32p. 15.95 (978-1-58246-177-9(5) , Tricycle Pr.) Ten Speed Pr.

Lyssenko, Taras. Wendy's Fear of Heights. 2003. 14p. (J). (978-0-9740542-0-9(8)) Prairie Shore Creative, Inc.

Maddox, Jake. On the Line. Tiffany, Sean, illus. 2007. (Jake Maddox Sports Story Ser.). 65p. (J). (gr. 4-8). lib. bdg. 21.26 (978-1-59889-062-4(X)) Stone Arch Bks.

Maddox, Jake. Slam Dunk Shoes. Tiffany, Sean, illus. 2008. (J). ***(978-1-59889-842-2(6));*** pap. ***(978-1-59889-894-1(9))*** Stone Arch Bks.

Magnus, Kellie. Little Lion Goes to School. Robinson, Michael, illus. l.t. ed. 2003. 16p. (J). 9.99 (978-0-9744211-0-0(3)) Media Magic New York.

Mahony, Mary. Harry Scores A Hat Trick, Pawns, Pucks, & Scoliosis: The Sequel to Stand Tall, Harry. Pasternack, Susan, ed. Larkin, Catherine, illus. 2003. 130p. (YA). (gr. 5-8). per. 14.95 (978-0-9658879-4-6(4)) Redding Pr.

Maier, Inger M. When Lizzie Was Afraid: Of Trying New Things. Candon, Jennifer, illus. 2005. 32p. (J). 14.95 (978-1-59147-170-7(2)); pap. 8.95 (978-1-59147-171-4(0)) American Psychological Assn. (Magination Pr.).

Manson, Ainslie. Ballerinas Don't Wear Glasses. Griffiths, Dean, illus. 2001. 32p. (J). (ps-2). 6.95 (978-1-55143-176-5(9)) Orca Bk. Pubs. USA.

—Ballerinas Don't Wear Glasses. 2000. (gr. 3-6). lib. bdg. 15.25 (978-0-613-53944-9(3)) Tandem Library Bks.

Marzollo, Jean & Marzollo, Dan. Basketball Buddies, Level 3. Kelley, True, illus. 1998. (Hello Reader! Ser.). 32p. (J). (gr. 1-3). pap. (978-0-590-38401-8(5)) Scholastic, Inc.

Matthews, L. S. The Outcasts. 2007. 272p. (YA). (gr. 7). 15.99 ***(978-0-385-73367-0(4));*** lib. bdg. 18.99 ***(978-0-385-90382-0(0))*** Random Hse. Children's Bks. (Delacorte Bks. for Young Readers).

Mayer, Melody. The Nannies: Friends with Benefits. 2006. (Nannies Ser.). 288p. (YA). (gr. 9). pap. 8.95 (978-0-385-73284-0(8)); lib. bdg. 10.99 (978-0-385-90301-1(4)) Random Hse. Children's Bks. (Delacorte Bks. for Young Readers).

McKay, Hilary. Permanent Rose. (J). (gr. 3-7). 2005. 240p. 16.99 (978-1-4169-0372-7(0) , McElderry, Margaret K.); 2006. 256p. reprint ed. pap. 5.99 (978-1-4169-2804-1(9) , Aladdin) Simon & Schuster Children's Publishing.

McKee, David. Elmer & the Kangaroo. McKee, David, illus. 2000. (Elmer Bks.). (Illus.). 32p. (J). (ps up). 15.99 (978-0-688-17951-9(7)) HarperCollins Pubs.

McKissack, Robert L. Try Your Best. Cepeda, Joe, illus. 2004. (Green Light Readers Level 2 Ser.). 24p. (J). 11.95 (978-0-15-205089-4(2)); pap. 3.95 (978-0-15-205090-0(6)) Harcourt Children's Bks. (Green Light Readers).

—Try Your Best. 2004. (gr. k-3). lib. bdg. 11.80 (978-0-613-81420-1(7)) Tandem Library Bks.

Mills, Joyce C. & Crowley, Richard J. Sammy the Elephant & Mr. Camel: A Story to Help Children Overcome Bedwetting. Pillo, Cary, illus. 2nd ed. 2005. 32p. (J). 14.95 (978-1-59147-247-6(4)); pap. 8.95 (978-1-59147-248-3(2)) American Psychological Assn. (Magination Pr.).

Minou: Evaluation Guide. 2006. (J). (978-1-55942-416-5(8)) Marsh Media.

Moore-Malinos, Jennifer & Roca, Nuria. Winning Isn't Everything! Fabrega, Marta, illus. 2007. (Live & Learn Ser.). 32p. (J). (ps-2). pap. 6.99 ***(978-0-7641-3791-4(3))*** Barron's Educational Series, Inc.

Myers, Anna. Hoggee. 2004. 160p. (J). 16.95 (978-0-8027-8926-6(9)) Walker & Co.

Nanette. Blue the Frog. 2004. (Life on Granny's Farm Ser.). (J). 12.95 (978-0-9741269-2-0(6)) St. Bernard Publishing, LLC.

Napoli, Donna Jo. One Leap Forward. 1999. (Angelwings Ser.: No. 4). (Illus.). 96p. (J). (gr. 2-5). pap. 7.95 (978-0-689-82986-4(8) , Aladdin) Simon & Schuster Children's Publishing.

—One Leap Forward. 1999. (Angelwings Ser.: No. 4). (Illus.). (J). (978-0-606-17907-2(0)) Tandem Library Bks.

Naylor, Phyllis Reynolds. Including Alice. 2004. (Alice Ser.). 288p. (YA). 15.95 incl. audio compact disk (978-0-689-82637-5(0) , Atheneum) Simon & Schuster Children's Publishing.

Naylor, Phyllis Reynolds & Vaccaro, Nick. Including Alice. 2005. (Alice Ser.). 288p. (YA). mass mkt. 5.99 (978-0-689-87074-3(4) , Simon Pulse) Simon & Schuster Children's Publishing.

Nelson, Blake. Prom Anonymous. 272p. (gr. 7 up). 2007. (YA). pap. 6.99 (978-0-14-240745-5(3) , Puffin); 2006. (J). 16.99 (978-0-670-05945-4(5) , Viking Adult) Penguin Group (USA) Inc.

Oates, Joyce Carol. Sexy. (J). 2005. 272p. lib. bdg. 17.89 (978-0-06-054150-7(4)); 2005. 272p. (gr. 7 up). 16.99 (978-0-06-054149-1(0)); 2006. 288p. reprint ed. pap. 7.99 (978-0-06-054151-4(2)) HarperCollins Pubs. (HarperTeen).

O'Dell, Kathleen. Agnes Parker... Keeping Cool in Middle School. 160p. (J). (gr. 4-6). 2008. pap. 5.99 ***(978-0-14-241181-0(7)*** , Puffin); 2007. 16.99 (978-0-8037-3078-6(0) , Dial) Penguin Group (USA) Inc.

Okimoto, Jean Davies. Jason's Women. 2000. 220p. (gr. 4-7). pap. 12.95 (978-0-595-00797-4(X) , Backinprint-.com) iUniverse, Inc.

Oram, Hiawyn. The Wrong Overcoat. Birchall, Mark, illus. 2000. (Picture Bks.). 32p. (J). (ps-3). lib. bdg. 15.95 (978-1-57505-453-7(1) , Carolrhoda Bks.) Lerner Publishing Group.

Paros, Jennifer. Violet Bing & the Grand House. 2007. 112p. (J). (gr. 1-4). 14.99 (978-0-670-06151-8(4) , Viking Juvenile) Penguin Group (USA) Inc.

Paulsen, Gary. Molly McGinty Has a Good Day. 2004. 112p. (gr. 4-7). lib. bdg. 14.99 (978-0-385-90911-2(X) , Lamb, Wendy) Random Hse. Children's Bks.

—Molly Mcginty Has a Really Good Day. 112p. (gr. 3-7). 2006. 5.50 (978-0-440-41482-7(2) , Yearling); 2004. 12.95 (978-0-385-32588-2(6) , Lamb, Wendy) Random Hse. Children's Bks.

Pearsall, Shelley. All of the Above: A Novel. Steptoe, Javaka, illus. 2006. 256p. (J). (gr. 3-7). 15.99 (978-0-316-11524-7(X)) Little Brown & Co.

—All of the Above: A Novel. 2008. 128p. (J). (gr. 3-7). pap. 5.99 ***(978-0-316-11526-1(6))*** Little, Brown Bks. for Young Readers.

Pearson, Tracey Campbell. Myrtle. Pearson, Tracey Campbell, illus. 2004. (Illus.). 32p. (J). 15.00 (978-0-374-35157-1(0) , Farrar, Straus & Giroux (BYR)) Farrar, Straus & Giroux.

Pennington, Beverly. Jonathan's Discovery. 2005. 32p. (J). per. 12.95 (978-1-56167-920-1(8)) American Literary Pr.

Pequeña the Burro: Evaluation Guide. 2006. (J). (978-1-55942-420-2(6)) Marsh Media.

Peters, Alison. Tomorrow's Olympian. Islip, Coralie, illus. 2006. (Read-It! Chapter Books). 64p. (J). (gr. 2-4). 19.95 (978-1-4048-1665-7(8)) Picture Window Bks.

Phipps, Ben. I'm a Winner You're a Winner: Remembering How Great You Are. 2006. (J). per. 9.95 (978-0-9779374-0-0(2)) One Source Publishing, LLC.

Prue, Sally. The Devil's Toenail. 2004. (Illus.). 208p. (J). 16.95 (978-0-439-48634-7(3)) Scholastic, Inc.

Radford, Michelle. Almost Fabulous. 2008. 256p. (J). pap. 8.99 ***(978-0-06-125235-8(2)*** , HarperTeen) HarperCollins Pubs.

Reichman, Justin. The Green. 2003. (Dream Series Ser.: Vol. 9). 160p. 9.95 (978-0-9708992-9-3(7)) Scobre Pr. Corp.

Reynolds, Peter. Ish. Reynolds, Peter, illus. 2004. (Illus.). 32p. (J). (gr. k up). 14.00 (978-0-7636-2344-9(X)) Candlewick Pr.

Reynolds, Peter H. The Dot. 2003. (Illus.). 32p. (J). (gr. k). 14.00 (978-0-7636-1961-9(2) , 53509533) Candlewick Pr.

Richards, Barbara. Barbie Com: Ballet Buddies. 2000. (gr. 3-6). lib. bdg. 11.80 (978-0-613-27723-5(6)) Tandem Library Bks.

Rodda, Emily. The Flower Fairies. Vitale, Raoul, illus. 2003. (Fairy Realm Ser.: No. 2). 128p. (J). 8.99 (978-0-06-009586-4(5)); lib. bdg. 15.89 (978-0-06-009587-1(3)) HarperCollins Pubs.

Rodgers, Frank. Little T & Lizard the Wizard. 2007. (Read-It! Chapter Books). (J). 21.26 (978-1-4048-2725-7(0)) Picture Window Bks.

Saltzberg, Barney. Star of the Week. Saltzberg, Barney, illus. 2006. (Illus.). 32p. (J). (gr. k-3). 15.99 (978-0-7636-2914-4(6)) Candlewick Pr.

Sargent, Dave & Sargent, Pat. Ding Bat: Accuracy, 56 vols., 44. Lenoir, Jane, illus. 2001. (Cherokee Indian Legend Ser.: Vol. 44). 36p. (J). lib. bdg. 19.95 (978-1-56763-529-4(6)) Ozark Publishing.

—Ding Bat: Accuracy, 17 bks, 44. Huff, Jean Lirley, illus. 2000. (Animal Pride Ser.: 44). 42p. (J). pap. 6.95 (978-1-56763-530-0(X)) Ozark Publishing.

Schafer, Milton. I'm Big! Lew-Vriethoff, Joanne, illus. 2006. (J). (*978-1-4156-8150-3(3) , Dial) Penguin Group (USA) Inc.

Sebra, Diane. Making Mountains Out of Moles. 2003. 120p. (YA). pap. 9.95 (978-1-55517-712-6(3) , 77123, Bonneville Bks.) Cedar Fort, Inc./CFI Distribution.

Sheldon, Dyan. Sophie Pitt-Turnbull Discovers America. 192p. (YA). (gr. 7). 2007. pap. 7.99 (*978-0-7636-3295-3(3)); 2005. 15.99 (978-0-7636-2740-9(2)) Candlewick Pr.

Shields, Gillian. The Actual Real Reality of Jennifer James: A Reality TV Novel. 2006. 384p. (J). lib. bdg. 17.89 (978-0-06-082241-5(4) , Tegen, Katherine Bks) HarperCollins Pubs.

Sisters of Isis3 & Ewing, Lynne. Enchantress. 3rd rev. ed. 2007. 256p. (gr. 7 up). 9.99 (*978-1-4231-0684-5(9)) Hyperion Bks. for Children.

Small, Tanya. What You Say Is What You Are. 2007. pap. 7.50 (*978-0-9705090-1-7(4)) MorningGlory Publishing.

Sometimes a Stranger. 2000. (Katie Rose/Stacy Belford Ser.). (YA). (gr. 5-9). per. 12.95 (978-1-930009-17-2(8)) Image Cascade Publishing.

Sonenklar, Carol. Mighty Boy. 1999. 128p. (J). (gr. 3-7). 16.99 (978-0-531-33203-0(9)); pap. 15.95 (978-0-531-30203-3(2)) Scholastic, Inc. (Orchard Bks.).

Sorenson, Margo. Ambrose & the Cathedral Dream. Szegedi, Katalin, illus. 2006. 30p. (J). (978-0-8146-3004-4(9)) Liturgical Pr.

Spelman, Cornelia Maude. When I Feel Good about Myself. Parkinson, Kathy, illus. 2003. (Way I Feel Ser.). 24p. (J). (ps-1). 15.95 (978-0-8075-8887-1(3)) Whitman, Albert & Co.

Standish, Burt L. Frank Merriwell's Confidence. Rudman, Jack, ed. 2003. (Frank Merriwell Ser.). 29.95 (978-0-8373-9349-0(3)); pap. 9.95 (978-0-8373-9049-9(4)) Merriwell, Frank Inc.

Strasser, Todd. Con-fidence. 164p. (J). (gr. 4-6). tchr. ed. 16.95 (978-0-8234-1394-2(2)); (YA). (gr. 5 up). pap. 6.95 (*978-0-8234-2061-2(2)) Holiday Hse., Inc.

Strom, Kellie. Sadie the Air Mail Pilot. 2007. 32p. (J). (gr. k-3). 16.99 (*978-0-385-75027-1(7)); lib. bdg. 19.99 (*978-0-385-75041-7(2)) Random Hse. Children's Bks. (Fickling, David Bks.).

Swift, Amanda. Big Bones. 2007. 144p. (J). pap. 9.95 (*978-0-689-87547-2(9)) Simon & Schuster, Ltd. GBR. *Dist:* Independent Pubs. Group.

Taylor-Butler, Christine. I Am Smart. Borlasca, Hector, illus. (J). (gr. k-1). 2006. 32p. pap. 3.95 (978-0-516-24971-1(1)); 2005. 31p. 18.50 (978-0-516-25176-9(7)) Scholastic Library Publishing. (Children's Pr.).

Thomas, Charolette. Franklin Finds a Friend. 2006. (ENG.). 40p. per. 16.99 (*978-1-4259-6209-8(2)) AuthorHouse.

Thomas, Jane Resh. Blind Mountain. 2006. 128p. (J). (gr. 4-6). 15.00 (978-0-618-64872-6(0) , Clarion Bks.) Houghton Mifflin Co. Trade & Reference Div.

Thompson, Lauren. Wee Little Chick. Butler, John, illus. 2008. (Wee Little Ser.). 32p. (J). 14.99 (*978-1-4169-3468-4(5)) Simon & Schuster Children's Publishing.

Tocher, Timothy. Playing for Pride. 2002. (J). 110p. (978-0-88166-424-9(3)); 120p. pap. 4.95 (978-0-689-02453-5(3)) Meadowbrook Pr.

Torrey, Richard L. Beans Baker, Num. 5. Torrey, Richard L., illus. 2001. (Road to Reading Ser.). (Illus.). 48p. (J). (gr. 1-3). pap. 3.99 (978-0-307-26335-3(5) , Random Hse. Bks. for Young Readers) Random Hse. Children's Bks.

—Beans Baker, No. 5. 2001. (gr. k-3). lib. bdg. 11.80 (978-0-613-42993-1(1)); (Illus.). (J). 10.79 (978-0-606-20564-1(0)) Tandem Library Bks.

van Genechten, Guido. Kangaroo Christine. van Genechten, Guido, illus. 2006. (Illus.). 32p. (J). 6.95 (978-1-58925-396-4(5) , tiger tales) ME Media LLC.

Vaught, Susan. Big Fat Manifesto. 2007. 320p. (YA). 16.95 (*978-1-59990-206-7(0) , Bloomsbury Children) Bloomsbury Publishing.

Verville, Linda. For Pete's Sake. Pelletier, Melissa, illus. 2002. 24p. (J). (gr. k-5). pap. 7.95 (978-0-9721472-0-0(9)) For Pete's Sake Publishing.

Vision, David & Vision, Mutiya Sahar. If Only I Could! Alcantara, Ignacio, illus. 2005. 32p. (J). 17.00 (978-0-9659538-8-7(2)) Soul Vision Works Publishing.

Vizzini, Ned. Be More Chill. 2004. 304p. (gr. 8-17). 16.95 (978-0-7868-0995-0(7)) Hyperion Bks. for Children.

—Be More Chill. 2005. 304p. (gr. 8-17). pap. 7.99 (978-0-7868-0996-7(5)) Miramax Bks.

Wade, Rebecca. The Theft & the Miracle. 2007. 368p. (J). (gr. 5-9). 16.99 (978-0-06-077493-6(2)); lib. bdg. 17.89 (978-0-06-077495-0(9)) HarperCollins Pubs.

Wallace, Rich. Dunk under Pressure, Vol. 7. 2007. 120p. (J). pap. 4.99 (978-0-14-240858-2(1) , Puffin) Penguin Group (USA) Inc.

—Dunk under Pressure: Winning Season 7. 2006. (Winning Season Ser.). 128p. (J). (gr. 4-6). 14.99 (978-0-670-06095-5(X) , Viking Juvenile) Penguin Group (USA) Inc.

—The Roar of the Crowd. 2005. (Winning Season Ser.: Bk. 1). 112p. (YA). (gr. 3-7). pap. 4.99 (978-0-14-240443-0(8) , Puffin) Penguin Group (USA) Inc.

—Roar of the Crowd. 2004. 101p. (J). lib. bdg. 15.38 (*978-1-4242-2165-3(X)) Fitzgerald Bks.

—Second String Center. 2007. (Winning Season Ser.). 128p. (J). (gr. 4). 14.99 (*978-0-670-06150-1(6) , Viking Juvenile) Penguin Group (USA) Inc.

Welty, Tony. Ricardo the Fierce. 2006. 24p. per. 11.99 (*978-1-59886-697-1(4)) Tate Publishing & Enterprises, L.L.C.

Wigington, Patti. Summer's Ashes. 2007. 208p. (YA). pap. 15.00 (*978-0-9766805-9-8(9)) Keene Publishing.

Wilcox, Mary. The Hollywood Sisters: Backstage Pass. 2006. 256p. (J). (gr. 5). 7.95 (978-0-385-73354-0(2)); lib. bdg. 9.99 (978-0-385-90369-1(3)) Random Hse. Children's Bks. (Delacorte Bks. for Young Readers).

Wilkerson, L. Kobie, 3rd, reader. Fred & Mary. 2008. (Illus.). 32p. (J). 24.95 incl. DVD, audio compact disk (*978-0-9796679-0-9(9)) Gye Nyame Pr.

Wilkinson, Carole. Garden of the Purple Dragon. 2007. 368p. (gr. 3-7). 16.99 (*978-1-4231-0338-7(6)) Hyperion Pr.

Wilson, Sarah. George Hogglesberry, Grade School Alien. Cameron, Chad, illus. 2004. 38p. (J). 14.95 (978-1-58246-063-5(9) , Tricycle Pr.) Ten Speed Pr.

Wishinsky, Frieda. Just Mabel. Heap, Sue, illus. (I Am Reading Ser.). (J). 2004. 48p. (gr. 1-3). pap. 3.95 (978-0-7534-5742-9(3)); 2001. 3.95 (978-0-7534-5353-7(3)) Houghton Mifflin Co. Trade & Reference Div. (Kingfisher).

Wong, Janet S. Minn & Jake. Cote, Genevieve, illus. 2003. 160p. (J). (gr. 2-5). 16.00 (978-0-374-34987-5(8) , Farrar, Straus & Giroux (BYR)) Farrar, Straus & Giroux.

Wurtz, K. D. Digby in Disguise. Carrier, Tracey Dahle, illus. 2001. (Digby in Disguise Ser.: Vol. 1). (J). (978-0-9712840-1-2(6)) Boyds Collection Ltd., The.

SELF-CONTROL

Burch, Regina G. Think Before You Act: Learning about Self-Discipline & Self-Control K-3. Hamaguchi, Carla, ed. Leary, Catherine, illus. 2002. (Character Education Readers). 16p. (J). (gr. k-3). pap. 2.99 (978-1-57471-833-1(9) , CTP 3132) Creative Teaching Pr., Inc.

Doron. Look in the Mirror... 2005. 228p. pap. 15.00 (978-1-4116-0109-3(2)) Lulu.com.

—Look in the Mirror. 2nd ed. 2005. 335p. pap. 16.56 (978-1-4116-0197-0(1)) Lulu.com.

Doudna, Kelly. Keep Your Cool! 2007. (Character Concepts Ser.). (Illus.). 24p. (J). (gr. k-3). lib. bdg. 19.93 (*978-1-59928-736-2(6)) ABDO Publishing Co.

Miller, Connie Colwell. Self-Discipline. 2005. (First Facts Ser.). (Illus.). 24p. (J). (ps-7). lib. bdg. 21.26 (978-0-7368-4281-5(0)) Capstone Pr., Inc.

PowerXpress Living God's Word Self-Control. 2005. 115.00 (978-0-687-06261-4(6)) Abingdon Pr.

Purcell, Sherry L. Teaching Self Discipline. 2004. 325p. (gr. 4-6). spiral bd. 49.00 incl. audio compact disk (978-1-57861-493-6(7) , IEP RESOURCES) Attainment Co., Inc.

SELF-CULTURE

see also Books and Reading

Andrews, Andy. Letters from American Heroes. 2003. (Never Give up & Go for It! Ser.). (Illus.). 48p. (J). pap. 3.99 (978-1-57759-776-6(1)) Dalmatian Pr.

—Letters from Celebrity Heroes. 2003. (Never Give up & Go for It! Ser.). (Illus.). 48p. (J). pap. 3.99 (978-1-57759-777-3(X)) Dalmatian Pr.

—Letters from Inspirational Heroes. 2003. (Never Give up & Go for It! Ser.). (Illus.). 48p. (J). pap. 3.99 (978-1-57759-778-0(8)) Dalmatian Pr.

—Letters from Sports Heroes. 2003. (Never Give up & Go for It! Ser.). (Illus.). 48p. (J). pap. 3.99 (978-1-57759-779-7(6)) Dalmatian Pr.

Asugha, Ruby. Little Sisters, Listen Up! A Message of Hope for Girls Growing up in Poverty Racism, & Despair. 2004. 138p. 9.95 (978-1-889322-61-2(X) , 25-017) Boys Town Pr.

Bishop, John. Goal Setting for Students: Winner of three national parenting book Awards. 2003. (Illus.). (YA). pap. 11.95 (978-0-9743700-0-2(2)) Accent On Success.

Bright Ideas: Level O, 6 vols. (Explorers Ser.). 32p. (gr. 3-6). 44.95 (978-0-7699-0598-3(6)) Shortland Pubns. (U. S. A.) Inc.

Cox, Scott, Sr. Love Your Ego As Your SELF. 2004. (J). per. 12.95 (978-0-9753817-1-7(7)) Unlimited Horizons.

Douglas, Marianne. How to Deal When Your Middle Name Is Stress: Real Teens - Real Advice. 2004. (J). per. 4.95 (978-1-59196-643-2(4)) Instantpublisher.com.

Erlbach, Arlene. Real Kids Taking the Right Risks: Plus, How You Can, Too! 1998. Orig. Title: Worth the Risk: True Stories about Risk Takers: Plus How You Can Be One, Too. (Illus.). 136p. (YA). (gr. 5-10). pap. 12.95 (978-1-57542-051-6(1)) Free Spirit Publishing, Inc.

Gabe, Janice E. Making the Grade: The Teen's Guide to Homework Success. Word Works Staff, illus. 2000. 72p. (YA). pap. 7.95 (978-0-9639023-1-3(8)) Professional Resource Pubns.

Ideal Instructional Fair Staff. Who I Am is Up to Me: Developing Character Education in the Middle School. 1998. 96p. (gr. 5-8). 9.99 (978-1-56822-622-4(5) , IF2523) School Specialty Publishing.

Kise, Jane A. G. & Johnson, Kevin. Find Your Fit Discovery. 1999. (LifeKeys 4 Teens Ser.). 32p. (YA). (gr. 8-12). reprint ed. pap. 8.99 (978-0-7642-2289-4(9)) Bethany Hse. Pubs.

Renaud, Andrea. The Goal Keeper Journal. 2003. (Illus.). 160p. (YA). per. (978-0-9717041-1-4(2)) A Happy Friend, Inc.

Stone, Penny. Complicated Mourning & Grief Blocks: How to Move Forward Past Our Pain. 2004. (New Line of Grief Guides(R) Ser.). 64p. pap. 15.00 (978-1-891400-10-0(X)) Champion Pr., Ltd.

—My World Is Upside Down: Making Sense of Life after Confronting Death. 2004. (New Line of Grief Guides(R) Ser.). 9.95 (978-1-891400-24-7(X)) Champion Pr., Ltd.

—Surviving the Loss of a Parent. 2005. (New Line of Grief Guides(R) Ser.). 9.95 (978-1-891400-57-5(6)) Champion Pr., Ltd.

—Taste of Cultures: Italy. 2004. (New Line of Grief Guides(R) Ser.). 9.95 (978-1-891400-76-6(2)) Champion Pr., Ltd.

Vander Zee, Ruth. Discover Your Gifts: And Learn How to Use Them. 1999. (Discover Ser.). 32p. stu. ed. 4.75 (978-1-56212-366-6(1) , 120400); 40p. 9.50 (978-1-56212-365-9(3) , 120405) CRC Pubns. (Faith Alive Christian Resources).

SELF-DEFENSE

see also Boxing; Judo; Karate

Chaiet, Donna. Staying Safe at Home. 1998. (Get Prepared Library of Violence Prevention for Young Women). (Illus.). 64p. (YA). (gr. 7-12). lib. bdg. 16.95 (978-0-8239-2740-1(7)) Rosen Publishing Group, Inc., The.

—Staying Safe on Dates. 1998. (Get Prepared Library of Violence Prevention for Young Women). (Illus.). 64p. (YA). (gr. 7-12). lib. bdg. 16.95 (978-0-8239-2739-5(3)) Rosen Publishing Group, Inc., The.

—Staying Safe on the Streets. 1998. (Get Prepared Library of Violence Prevention for Young Women). (Illus.). 64p. (YA). (gr. 7-12). lib. bdg. 16.95 (978-0-8239-2741-8(5)) Rosen Publishing Group, Inc., The.

Chaline, Eric. Martial Arts for Women. 2002. (Martial & Fighting Arts Ser.). (Illus.). 96p. (J). (gr. 7 up). lib. bdg. (978-1-59084-395-6(9)) Mason Crest Pubs.

Dahl, Michael. Do Salamanders Spit? A Book about How Animals Protect Themselves. Ayers, Franklin, illus. 2004. (Animals All Around Ser.). 24p. (J). (gr. k-2). 22.60 (978-1-4048-0291-9(6) , 1229502) Picture Window Bks.

Escher, Ursula. Self-Defense for Kids: Learn Practical & Effective Techniques to Help You Defend Yourself. 2004. (Illus.). 47p. (J). (ps-12). pap. 6.95 (978-0-9718609-5-7(5)) High Mountain Publishing.

Holt, Rinehart and Winston Staff. Holt Science & Technology Chapter 27: Life Science: Body Defenses. 5th ed. 2004. (Illus.). pap. 12.86 (978-0-03-030256-5(0)) Holt, Rinehart & Winston.

Johnson, Nathan. Martial Arts for Children. 2002. (Martial & Fighting Arts Ser.). (Illus.). 96p. (J). (gr. 7 up). lib. bdg. (978-1-59084-396-3(7)) Mason Crest Pubs.

Knotts, Bob. Martial Arts. 2000. (gr. 3-6). lib. bdg. 15.25 (978-0-613-54004-9(2)) Tandem Library Bks.

Lebell, Gene. Gene Lebell's Grappling & Self-Defense for the Young Adult. 2002. (gr. 7-12). lib. bdg. 22.20 (978-0-613-84440-6(8)) Tandem Library Bks.

Levigne, Heather. Martial Arts in Action. 2000. (Sports in Action Ser.). (Illus.). 32p. (J). (gr. 3-4). (978-0-7787-0169-9(7)); pap. (978-0-7787-0181-1(6)) Crabtree Publishing Co.

—Martial Arts in Action. 2001. (gr. 3-6). lib. bdg. 14.10 (978-0-613-32820-3(5)) Tandem Library Bks.

McNab, Chris. Martial Arts for People with Disabilities. 2004. (Martial & Fighting Arts Ser.). (Illus.). 96p. (J). (gr. 7). lib. bdg. (978-1-59084-399-4(1)) Mason Crest Pubs.

Morris, Neil. Get Going! Martial Arts: The Ancient Arts of Self-Defense, 4 bks., Set. 2001. (Illus.). (J). (gr. 4-6). lib. bdg. 91.16 (978-1-58810-007-8(3)) Heinemann Library.

Olson, Marcy. Tae Kwon Do. 2000. (World of Sports Ser.). (Illus.). 32p. (J). (gr. 4-7). lib. bdg. 16.95 (978-1-887068-55-0(4)) Smart Apple Media.

Rodgers, Thomas. Safety Activities for Kids. 2004. (Illus.). 24p. (J). 2.95 (978-1-55864-134-1(3) , K1343, KIDSRIGHTS) JIST Publishing.

Searle, Michael. Kaijudo Master's Guide. 2005. (Duel Masters Ser.). (Illus.). 80p. (J). pap. 6.99 (978-0-439-69113-0(3) , Scholastic Paperbacks) Scholastic, Inc.

Stark, Evan. Everything You Need to Know about Street Gangs. rev. ed. 2000. (Need to Know Library). (Illus.). 64p. (YA). (gr. 4-6). lib. bdg. 25.25 (978-0-8239-3305-1(9) , NTSTGA) Rosen Publishing Group, Inc., The.

Williamson, Wendy. Christian Martial Arts 101. 2004. per. 17.95 (978-0-9721328-2-4(1)); per. 15.95 (978-0-9721328-1-7(3)) Agapy Publishing.

SELF-ESTEEM

Abraham, Adam E. I Am My Body, Not! Litster, Marie, illus. 2000. 60p. (J). (gr. 1-6). lib. bdg. 19.95 (978-0-9700209-1-8(0) , Phaelos Bks.) Phaelos Publishing.

Alexander, Jenny. Bullies, Bigmouths & So-Called Friends. 2003. (Illus.). mass mkt. (978-0-340-87565-0(8) , Hodder Children's Books) Hodder Children's Division.

Allenbaugh, Kay. Chocolate for a Teen's Spirit: Inspiring Stories for Young Women about Hope, Strength, & Wisdom. 2002. (Illus.). 256p. pap. 12.00 (978-0-7432-2289-1(X) , Fireside) Simon & Schuster.

Amos, Janine. ¡Es Mio! Coffee, Carol & Carrillo, Consuelo, trs. Spenceley, Annabel, illus. 2002. (Weekly Reader Early Learning Library). (SPA.). 32p. (J). (ps up). lib. bdg. 23.33 (978-0-8368-3678-3(2)) Stevens, Gareth Inc.

—¡No Digas Eso! Coffee, Carol & Carrillo, Consuelo, trs. Spenceley, Annabel, illus. 2002. (Weekly Reader Early Learning Library). (SPA.). 32p. (J). (ps up). lib. bdg. 23.33 (978-0-8368-3679-0(0)) Stevens, Gareth Inc.

—¡Quitate de Aqui! Coffee, Carol & Carrillo, Consuelo, trs. Spenceley, Annabel, illus. 2002. (Weekly Reader Early Learning Library). (SPA.). 32p. (J). (ps up). lib. bdg. 23.33 (978-0-8368-3682-0(0)) Stevens, Gareth Inc.

Apel, Melanie Ann. Let's Talk about When You Think Nobody Likes You. 2002. (Let's Talk Library). (Illus.). 24p. (J). lib. bdg. 18.75 (978-0-8239-5862-7(0) , PowerKids Pr.) Rosen Publishing Group, Inc., The.

Asgedom, Mawi. Code: The 5 Secrets of Teen Success. 2003. (gr. 7-12). lib. bdg. 18.80 (978-0-613-70576-9(9)) Tandem Library Bks.

—The Code: The 5 Secrets of Teen Success. 2003. (Illus.). 160p. (J). (gr. 7-17). pap. 9.99 (978-0-316-73689-3(9)) Little Brown & Co.

Baker, Sandy. DoodleLoops about Me. 2007. (DoodleLoops Ser.). 48p. pap. 7.99 (*978-0-7682-3329-2(1) , Schaffer, Frank) Schaffer, Frank Pubns.

Barrington Jones, Barbara & Thomas, Janet. Dear Barbara: Answers to the Most-Asked Questions from Teenage Girls. 1998. (YA). pap. 13.95 (978-1-57345-369-1(2)) Deseret Bk. Co.

Berry, Joy Wilt. Criticism - Rejection: Get over It! Bartholomew, illus. rev. ed. 2000. (Winning Skills Ser.: Vol. 3). 48p. (YA). (gr. 4-7). pap. 2.95 (978-1-58634-162-6(6)) Goldstar Publishing, Inc.

Biscoe, Celia, illus. Don't Worry, Spike... about the Dark! 2007. 12p. (J). (ps-k). pap. 3.99 (*978-0-7566-3096-6(7)) Dorling Kindersley Publishing, Inc.

Black, Jessica L. We Can Do Most Anything. Cress, Michelle H., illus. l.t. ed. 2003. (HRL Board Book Ser.). 10p. (J). (ps-k). bds. 10.95 (978-1-57332-263-8(6)) HighReach Learning, Inc.

Brashich, Audrey. All Made Up: A Girl's Guide to Seeing Through Celebrity Culture & Celebrating Real Beauty. 2006. (Illus.). 160p. (J). pap. 9.95 (978-0-8027-7744-7(9)) Walker & Co.

—All Made Up: A Girl's Guide to Seeing Through Celebrity Culture & Celebrating Real Beauty. Banner, Shawn, illus. 2006. 160p. (J). 16.95 (978-0-8027-8074-4(1)) Walker & Co.

Brookes, Derek & Brookes, Michelle. Praisin U: How I Love Ya! 2001. (J). pap. 3.29 (978-3-905332-31-5(0)) Aurora Production AG CHE. *Dist:* Activated Ministries.

—Praisin U: Inline Praise! 2001. (J). pap. 3.29 (978-3-905332-32-2(9)) Aurora Production AG CHE. *Dist:* Activated Ministries.

—Praisin U: You're Tops! 2001. (J). pap. 3.29 (978-3-905332-30-8(2)) Aurora Production AG CHE. *Dist:* Activated Ministries.

Brooks, Susan. Any Girl Can Rule the World. 1998. 224p. (gr. 8-12). pap. 12.95 (978-1-57749-068-5(1)) Fairview Pr.

Bundschuh, Rick, et al. Secret Power for Girls Video Devotionals. 2003. (YA). 19.99 incl. VHS (978-0-310-24771-5(3)) Zondervan.

Burns, Peggy. Playground Survival. 2004. (Kids' Guides Ser.). (Illus.). 32p. (J). (gr. 1-4). lib. bdg. 25.64 (978-1-4109-0572-7(1)) Raintree.

Cattrall, Kim. Being a Girl: Navigating the Ups & Downs of Teen Life. Briamonte, Amy, illus. 2006. 128p. (J). (gr. 7-17). 18.99 (978-0-316-01102-0(9)) Little Brown & Co.

Chinn, Jacqueline. How Can I Be Special? Mondragon, Manny, illus. 2003. (J). pap. 15.95 (978-0-929526-55-3(4)) Double B Pubns.

Clayton, Lawrence & Morrison, Jaydene. Coping with a Learning Disability. rev. ed. 1999. (Coping Ser.). (Illus.). 121p. (YA). (gr. 7-12). lib. bdg. 26.50 (978-0-8239-2887-3(X) , COLEDI) Rosen Publishing Group, Inc., The.

Coffey, Colleen & Carrillo, Consuelo, trs. Niños Educados, 6 bks. Spenceley, Annabel, illus. Incl. ¡Es Mio! Amos, Jamie. pap. 7.93 (978-0-8368-3692-9(8)); ¡No Digas! Amos, Janine. pap. 7.93 (978-0-8368-3693-6(6)); ¡No Funciona! Amos, Janine. pap. 7.93 (978-0-8368-3694-3(4)); ¡No Hagas Eso! Amos, Janine. pap. 7.93 (978-0-8368-3695-0(2)); ¡Quitate de Aqui! Amos, Janine. pap. 7.93 (978-0-8368-3696-7(0)); ¡Vete! Amos, Janine. pap. 7.93 (978-0-8368-3697-4(9)); 32p. (J). (ps up). (SPA., Illus.). 2003. pap. (978-0-8368-3691-2(X) , Weekly Reader Early Learning Library) Stevens, Gareth Inc.

Common. Mirror & Me. West, Lorraine, illus. 2005. 40p. (J). pap. 9.95 (978-0-9768674-0-1(0)) Hip Hop Schl. House.

Cook, Kerri Beth. The Wannabe Honeybee. Cook, Kerri Beth, illus. 2002. (Illus.). 50p. (J). (ps-2). pap. 12.95 (978-0-9719300-0-1(7)) KBCottontop Publishing.

Cordes, Helen. Girl Power in the Mirror: Your Body, Your Self. 1999. (Girl Power Ser.). (Illus.). 64p. (YA). (gr. 6-9). lib. bdg. (978-0-8225-2691-9(3) , Lerner Pubns.) Lerner Publishing Group.

Costanzo, Charlene A. The Twelve Gifts of Birth. Ackison, Wendy Wassink, illus. Reger, Jill, photos by. 1998. 64p. (J). (ps-3). 19.95 (978-1-891836-12-1(9)) Featherfew.

—The Twelve Gifts of Birth. Ackison, Wendy Wassink, illus. Reger, Jill, photos by. 2001. 64p. 19.95 (978-0-06-621104-6(2) , Rayo) HarperCollins Pubs.

Dalfin, Chaim. Teenagers Farbreng. 2000. 144p. (YA). pap. 12.00 (978-1-880880-34-0(2)) Jewish Enrichment Pr.

DiMarco, Hayley. Mean Girls: Facing Your Beauty Turned Beast. 2004. 208p. (YA). (gr. 7-9). pap. 14.99 (978-0-8007-5913-1(3)) Revell.

Doron. Look in the Mirror... 2005. 228p. pap. 15.00 (978-1-4116-0109-3(2)) Lulu.com.

—Look in the Mirror. 2nd ed. 2005. 335p. pap. 16.56 (978-1-4116-0197-0(1)) Lulu.com.

Dunn, Michael P. What's the Big Secret? 2003. (Illus.). 192p. per. 13.95 (978-0-9724924-3-0(7)) Big Secret, The.

Espeland, Pamela & Verdick, Elizabeth. Proud to Be You. 2006. (Illus.). 80p. (J). (gr. 3-7). pap. 9.95 (978-1-57542-202-2(6)) Free Spirit Publishing, Inc.

Falconer, Ian, creator. Dream Big: Starring Olivia. 2006. (Olivia Ser.). (Illus.). 64p. 9.95 (978-0-7407-5818-8(7)) Andrews McMeel Publishing.

Gammon, Shana. Watching the Winners. 1999. (Illus.). 98p. (YA). pap. 12.95 (978-1-890306-19-9(3)) Warwick Hse. Publishing.

Girls Can Do Hood Christian Educational Curriculum Book. 2005. (J). 19.95 (978-1-59210-365-2(0)) Whispering Pine Pr., Inc.

Happy to Be Me: A Kid's Book about Self-Esteem. 2001. 32p. (J). per. 6.95 (978-0-87029-355-9(9)) Abbey Pr.

Hinds, Maurene J. Focus on Body Image: How You Feel about How You Look. 2002. (Teen Issues Ser.). (Illus.). 64p. (YA). (gr. 6-12). lib. bdg. 22.60 (978-0-7660-1915-7(2)) Enslow Pubs., Inc.

Hodge, Aleta S. The Value Book. 2002. 230p. 13.95 (978-0-9648316-3-6(5)) Money Counsel, Inc.

Holyoke, Nancy. The Big Book of Help. Nash, Scott, illus. 2004. 180p. pap. 9.95 (978-1-58485-966-6(0) , American Girl) American Girl Publishing, Inc.

How to Be a S. T. A. R. The Young Person's Guide to Finding Success & Living Your Dreams. 2nd ed. 2003. (J). (978-0-9728626-0-8(9)) Gems International, LLC.

Kalman, Izzy C. Bullies to Buddies: How to Turn Your Enemies into Friends! 2005. (Illus.). 128p. (YA). per. 15.00 (978-0-9706482-1-1(9)) Wisdom Pages, The.

Kaufman, Gershen & Raphael, Lev. Defiendete! Desarrolla tu Poder Personal y Autoestima. 2005. (SPA., Illus.). 112p. (J). pap. 11.95 (978-968-860-226-3(4)) Editorial Pax MEX. *Dist:* Independent Pubs. Group.

Kaufman, Gershen, et al. Stick up for Yourself! Every Kid's Guide to Personal Power & Positive Self-Esteem. 2nd rev. ed. 2004. (Illus.). 128p. (YA). (gr. 3-7). pap. 11.95 (978-1-57542-068-4(6)) Free Spirit Publishing, Inc.

Keep Empowering Yourself Successfully: Raising Your Self Esteem. 2004. (YA). (978-0-9762009-1-8(0)) Keep Empowering Yourself Successfully.

Kent, Susan, et al, contrib. by. Learning How to Feel Good about Yourself. 2001. (Violence Prevention Library). (Illus.). 24p. (J). (gr. 3). lib. bdg. 18.75 (978-0-8239-5615-9(6) , PowerKids Pr.) Rosen Publishing Group, Inc., The.

Ketch, Susan & Scraper, Katherine. It's Snack Time! Futrell, Ashley, ed. 2005. 128p. (J). per. 11.99 (978-1-59441-043-7(7) , CD-104043) Carson-Dellosa Publishing Co., Inc.

Kirberger, Kimberly. No Body's Perfect Journal. 2003. 336p. (J). (gr. 5 up). pap. 8.95 (978-0-439-42639-8(1) , Scholastic Paperbacks) Scholastic, Inc.

Koubek, Christine Wickert. Friends, Cliques & Peer Pressure: Be True to Yourself. 2002. (Teen Issues Ser.). (Illus.). 64p. (YA). (gr. 6-12). lib. bdg. 22.60 (978-0-7660-1669-9(2)) Enslow Pubs., Inc.

Kunjufu, Jawanza & Prescott, Folami. Eighth Grade: Self-Esteem Through Culture Leads to Academic Excellence. 2003. (SETCLAE Ser.). 60p. (J). pap. 9.95 (978-0-913543-93-1(4)) African American Images.

—High School: Self-Esteem Through Culture Leads to Academic Excellence. 2003. (SETCLAE Ser.). 60p. (J). pap. 9.95 (978-0-913543-94-8(2)) African American Images.

—Kindergarten: Self-Esteem Through Culture Leads to Academic Excellence. 2003. (SETCLAE Ser.). 60p. (J). pap. 9.95 (978-0-913543-85-6(3)) African American Images.

—SETCLAE, Fifth Grade: Self-Esteem Through Culture Leads to Academic Excellence. 2003. (SETCLAE Ser.). 60p. (J). pap. 9.95 (978-0-913543-90-0(X)) African American Images.

—SETCLAE, First Grade: Self-Esteem Through Culture Leads to Academic Excellence. 2003. (SETCLAE Ser.). 60p. (J). pap. 9.95 (978-0-913543-86-3(1)) African American Images.

—SETCLAE, Fourth Grade: Self-Esteem Through Culture Leads to Academic Excellence. 2003. (SETCLAE Ser.). 60p. (J). pap. 9.95 (978-0-913543-89-4(6)) African American Images.

—SETCLAE, Second Grade: Self-Esteem Through Culture Leads to Academic Excellence. 2003. (SETCLAE Ser.). 60p. (J). pap. 9.95 (978-0-913543-87-0(X)) African American Images.

—SETCLAE, Seventh Grade: Self-Esteem Through Culture Leads to Academic Excellence. 2003. (SETCLAE Ser.). 60p. (J). pap. 9.95 (978-0-913543-92-4(6)) African American Images.

—SETCLAE, Sixth Grade: Self-Esteem Through Culture Leads to Academic Excellence. 2003. (SETCLAE Ser.). 60p. (J). pap. 9.95 (978-0-913543-91-7(8)) African American Images.

—SETCLAE, Third Grade: Self-Esteem Through Culture Leads to Academic Excellence. 2003. (SETCLAE Ser.). 60p. (J). pap. 9.95 (978-0-913543-88-7(8)) African American Images.

Lansky, Bruce. I'm Glad I'm Me. Blough, Tim, illus. 2003. 22p. (J). bds. 9.95 (978-0-689-02452-8(5)) Meadowbrook Pr.

Le Jeune, Veronique, et al. Feeling Freakish? How to be Comfortable in Your Own Skin, 4 vols. Princess, H., illus. 2004. (Sunscreen Ser.). 112p. (J). (gr. 6-11). pap. 9.95 (978-0-8109-9164-4(0) , Amulet Bks.) Abrams, Harry N. , Inc.

Lishinski, Ann King. Let Your Light Shine. Morello, Charles, ed. Lishinski, Jamie, illus. 2003. (J). pap. 9.95 (978-0-9709575-0-4(5)) Singing River Pubns.

Mastromarino, Diane. The Girl's Guide to Loving Yourself: A Book about Falling in Love with the One Person Who Matters Most - You. 64p. pap. 9.95 (978-0-88396-751-5(0) , Blue Mountain Pr.) Blue Mountain Arts Inc.

McCloud, Carol. Have You Filled a Bucket Today? A Guide to Daily Happiness for Kids. Messing, Dave, illus. 2006. (J). pap. 9.95 (978-0-9785075-1-0(7) , Ferne Pr.) Nelson Publishing & Marketing.

McNulty, John. I Am Your Self-Esteem. Gilmour, Karen, illus. 2006. 32p. (J). lib. bdg. (***978-0-9769580-5-5(8)***) I Am Your Playground LLC.

Medina, Sarah. Proud. Brooker, Jo, illus. 2007. (Feelings Ser.). 24p. (J). (ps-k). 5.99 (978-1-4034-9303-3(0)); lib. bdg. 21.36 (978-1-4034-9296-8(4)) Heinemann Library.

Moe, Barbara. Understanding the Causes of a Negative Body Image. 1999. (Teen Eating Disorder Prevention Library). 144p. (gr. 7-12). pap. 6.95 (978-1-56838-262-3(6)) Hazelden Publishing & Educational Services.

Moka & Daly, Melissa. Just Us Girls: Secrets to Feeling Good about Yourself, Inside & Out, 4 vols. Heliot, Eric, illus. 2004. (Sunscreen Ser.). 112p. (J). (gr. 6-11). pap. 9.95 (978-0-8109-9161-3(6)) Abrams, Harry N. , Inc.

Morgan, Richard. Well Done! A Confidence-Building Book. 2005. (Illus.). 24p. (J). pap. 3.95 (978-0-7641-3158-5(3)) Barron's Educational Series, Inc.

Morse, Philip C. Kick Out Stress - Teen Stress Reduction Program: Improving Self-Esteem, Optimizing Performance in School & Sports & Improving Physical & Emotional Health. 2004. (YA). (gr. 8-12). pap. (978-0-9748548-0-9(8)) Mind/Body Workshops.

Naik, Anita. Self Esteem. 2nd ed. 2005. (Illus.). 144p. (YA). pap. 12.00 (978-0-340-88395-2(2) , Hodder & Stoughton) Hodder General Publishing Division GBR. *Dist:* Trafalgar Square Publishing.

Newman, Jill. If I Called You a Duck Would You Quack? A Kid's Eye View of Self Esteem: How It Goes Away & How to Get It Back! Miller, Allison M., illus. 1999. 16p. (J). (gr. k-5). pap. 12.95 (978-0-9674262-0-4(0)) Newman, Jill.

O'Keefe, Susan. Be the Star That You Are: A Book for Kids Who Feel Different. Alley, R. W., illus. 2005. (Elf-Help Books for Kids). (J). per. 7.95 (978-0-87029-391-7(5)) Abbey Pr.

Onuoha-Ezemma, Glory. Don't Make Fun of My Name: My Name Is Special to My Parents & Me. unabr. ed. 2003. (Illus.). 47p. (J). (gr. k-6). pap. 9.95 (978-0-9661598-6-8(1)) Ekwike Bks. & Publishing.

Penchina, Sharon & Hoffman, Stuart, creators. I AM Inside of ME. 2006. (J). (978-0-9740684-9-7(7)) 2 Imagine.

Penchina, Sharon R. I Am a Lovable Me: Self Esteem Affirmations for Children. 2006. (I Am a Lovable Me! Ser.). (Illus.). 48p. 15.95 (978-0-9740684-5-9(4)) 2 Imagine.

Powell, Jillian. Self-Esteem. 2005. (It's Your Health Ser.). (Illus.). 45p. (J). (gr. 6-9). lib. bdg. 29.95 (978-1-58340-589-5(5)) Smart Apple Media.

PowerXpress Living God's Word Self-Esteem. 2005. 115.00 (978-0-687-00119-4(6)) Abingdon Pr.

Pryor, Tamara & Konek, Jana. Respect Self Value People Middle School Student Lesson & Activity Guide. 2002. (Illus.). XV, 173p. (YA). (gr. 6-8). pap. 55.00 (978-0-9722617-0-8(2)) Healing Path Foundation.

Raatma, Lucia. Self-Respect. 2002. (Character Education Ser.). (Illus.). 24p. (J). (gr. 1-2). lib. bdg. 18.60 (978-0-7368-1133-0(8) , Bridgestone Bks.) Capstone Pr., Inc.

Raica-Klotz, Helen. Empower Me! 12 Sessions for Building Self-Esteem in Girls. 1999. 64p. (gr. 4-7). pap. 34.95 (978-0-89390-448-7(1)) Resource Pubns., Inc.

Renaud, Andrea, creator. The Goal Keeper. 2001. (YA). cd-rom 18.00 (978-0-9717041-0-7(4)) A Happy Friend, Inc. CAN. *Dist:* Century Bk. Distribution.

Richmond, Marianne. Hooray for You! A Celebration of You-ness. Richmond, Marianne, illus. 2001. (Illus.). 40p. (J). (gr. 3 up). per. 15.95 (978-0-931674-44-0(1)) Marianne Richmond Studios, Inc.

Rimm, Sylvia. See Jane Win for Girls: A Smart Girl's Guide to Success. 2004. (Illus.). 144p. (YA). (gr. 4-8). pap. 13.95 (978-1-57542-122-3(4)) Free Spirit Publishing, Inc.

—See Jane Win for Girls: A Smart Girl's Guide to Success. 2003. (gr. 7-12). lib. bdg. 23.40 (978-0-613-67161-3(9)) Tandem Library Bks.

Rothenberg, B. Annye. Mommy & Daddy Are Always Supposed to Say Yes— Aren't They? Eldridge, Marion, illus. 2007. 40p. (J). pap. 9.95 (***978-0-9790420-0-3(3)***) Pefecting Parenting Pr.

Rotner, Shelley & Kelly, Sheila M. What I Can Do? A Book about Discovering What You Do Well. 2001. (Contemporary Issues for Young Children Ser.). (Illus.). 24p. (gr. k-3). lib. bdg. 22.90 (978-0-7613-2119-4(5) , Millbrook Pr.) Lerner Publishing Group.

Schoenberg, Jill. Journal Buddies: A Girl's Journal for Sharing & Celebrating Magnificence (2nd Edition) 2007. (J). per. 16.95 (***978-0-9768623-0-7(1)***) Blue Sky at Night Publishing.

Self-Esteem Garden. 2003. (978-1-57543-116-1(5)) MAR*CO Products, Inc.

The Self-Esteem Handbook for Kids. 2004. (J). 24.95 (978-0-9725836-0-2(2)) Long Life Publishing Co.

Sommer, Carl. If Only I Were. . ., 1 bk. 2003. (Another Sommer-Time Story Ser.). (Illus.). 48p. (J). 16.95 incl. audio compact disk (978-1-57537-502-1(8)); (gr. 1-4). 16.95 incl. audio (978-1-57537-551-9(6)) Advance Publishing, Inc.

Standard Publishing Staff. Self Esteem. 2006. cd-rom 24.99 (978-0-7847-1886-5(5)) Standard Publishing.

Sunderland, Margot, et al. Helping Children with Low Self-esteem: A Guidebook. (Illus.). 96p. spiral bd. (978-0-86388-466-5(0) , 002-5153) Speechmark Publishing Ltd.

Teolis, Beth. Ready-to-Use Self Esteem & Conflict Solving Activities, Grades 4-8. Giguere, Carol & Li, Alexander, illus. 2002. (J-B Ed Ser.). 336p. (gr. 4-8). pap. 29.95 (978-0-13-045256-6(4) , Jossey-Bass) Wiley, John & Sons, Inc.

Thayer, Eva. The MeLand 3: Songs & Raps for 3-4-5 Year Olds. 2001. (J). 12.95 incl. audio compact disk (978-1-931228-02-2(7)) Tes Publishing Co.

Tubbs, Janet. Self-Esteem, 2000. (Spud Packs Ser.). (Illus.). 16p. (J). (ps-4). pap. 19.95 (978-1-881185-22-2(2)) Arcadia Pr.

Vaughn, Wendy. For Children of the World with Love. 2003. 63p. pap. 9.95 (978-1-4137-0124-1(8)) PublishAmerica, Inc.

Weiss, Stefanie Iris. Coping with the Beauty Myth: A Guide for Real Girls. (Coping Ser.). (Illus.). (YA). (gr. 7-12). 2005. 192p. lib. bdg. 26.50 (978-0-8239-3757-8(7)); 2000. 112p. lib. bdg. 25.25 (978-0-8239-3033-3(5) , COBEAU) Rosen Publishing Group, Inc., The.

Wilde, Jerry. Hot Stuff to Help Kids Cheer U. 2007. 80p. (J). pap. 9.95 (***978-1-4022-0926-0(6)*** , Sourcebooks Jabberwocky) Sourcebooks, Inc.

Woods, Earl & Tiger Woods Foundation Staff. Start Something: You Can Make a Difference. 2006. 144p. pap. 14.00 (978-1-4165-3704-5(X)) Simon & Schuster.

SELF-ESTEEM—FICTION

Abromovitz, Jaime. Baby Dreamer Ding-A-Ling: Ding-A-Lings. 2004. (Illus.). (J). per. 9.95 (978-0-9762587-1-1(4)) StoryGirl Productions, LLC.

—Dreamer Ding-A-Ling: Ding-A-Lings: the Banana Phone. 2004. (Illus.). (J). per. 9.95 (978-0-9762587-0-4(6)) StoryGirl Productions, LLC.

—Zazzy-Q Ding-A-Ling: Ding-A-Lings: the Magic Wand. 2004. (Illus.). (J). per. 9.95 (978-0-9762587-2-8(2)) StoryGirl Productions, LLC.

Alma, Ann. Summer of Changes. 2002. (Sports Stories Ser.). (Illus.). 172p. (J). (gr. 3-7). pap. 6.95 (978-1-55039-120-6(8)) Sono Nis Pr. CAN. *Dist:* Orca Bk. Pubs. USA.

Amos, Janine. Niños Educados: Es Mío!; No Digas Eso!; No Funciona!; No Hagas Eso!; Quítate de Aquí!; Vete!, 6 bks. Coffee, Carol & Carrillo, Consuelo, trs. 2002. (SPA., Illus.). (J). (ps up). lib. bdg. 127.60 (978-0-8368-3677-6(4)) Stevens, Gareth Inc.

Anderson, Carolyn. Granny's Farm Friends. 2005. (J). per. 39.95 (978-1-59453-550-5(7) , Airleaf Publishing) Airleaf Publishing & Bookselling.

Appelt, Kathi. Incredible Me! Karas, G. Brian, illus. 2003. 32p. (J). (ps-1). 15.99 (978-0-06-028622-4(9)) HarperCollins Pubs.

Arterburn, Stephen & Hunt, Angela Elwell. Shane. 2004. (Young Believer on Tour Ser.). (J). pap. 3.99 (978-0-8423-8339-4(5)) Tyndale Hse. Pubs.

Austin, M. O. Boy Named Joe. 2006. pap. 12.99 (***978-1-4259-6217-3(3)***) AuthorHouse.

Avi & Vail, Rachel. Never Mind! A Twin Novel. 2005. 200p. (J). (gr. k-9). per. 12.64 (978-0-606-33941-4(8)) Tandem Library Bks.

Banting, Celia. I Only Said Yes So That They'd Like Me. 2006. 224p. (YA). per. 14.99 (***978-0-9786648-1-7(7)***) Wighita Pr.

Barkan, Joanne. Celebrate! Your Amazing Achievements. 2007. 16p. (J). bds. 14.99 (978-0-7944-1231-9(9)) Reader's Digest Assn., Inc., The.

Beaudoin, Sean. Going Nowhere Faster. 2007. 240p. (J). (gr. 8 up). 16.99 (***978-0-316-01415-1(X)***) Little, Brown Bks. for Young Readers.

Beaumont, Karen. I Like Myself! Catrow, David, illus. 2004. 32p. (J). 16.00 (978-0-15-202013-2(6)) Harcourt Children's Bks.

Bellingham, Brenda. Lilly Takes the Lead. MacDonald, Clarke, illus. 2006. (First Novels Ser.: Vol. 34). 64p. (gr. 2-5). (***978-0-88780-703-9(8));*** (J). 4.95 (978-0-88780-701-5(1)) Formac Publishing Co., Ltd. CAN. *Dist:* Casemate Pubs. & Bk. Distributors, LLC.

Belton, Sandra. Pictures for Miss Josie. Andrews, Benny, illus. 2003. 40p. (J). (gr. k-3). 17.99 (978-0-688-17480-4(9)) HarperCollins Pubs.

Benjamin, A. H. & Holstien, Elisabeth. A Duck So Small. 1998. (Illus.). 32p. (J). (ps-3). 14.95 (978-1-888444-30-8(4) , 21028) Little Tiger Pr.

Bishop, Brett & Olson, Laura. Clayton's Path. Eagle, Mona, illus. 2001. 40p. (J). (gr. k-6). pap. 12.95 (978-0-9700035-3-9(6)) Apogee Publishing.

Blume, Judy. Jugo de Pecas. Navarro, Cristina, illus. (SPA.). 36p. (J). (gr. 3-5). pap. 8.95 (978-1-58986-630-0(4)) Santillana USA Publishing Co., Inc.

Bo, Ben. The Edge. 2003. (Young Adult Fiction Ser.). 144p. (J). (gr. 9-12). 14.95 (978-0-8225-3307-8(3)) Lerner Publishing Group.

Bogert, Betsy. The Big Happy Bear: For Children of All Sizes. 2002. 144p. (J). pap. 11.95 (978-0-595-22155-4(6) , Writers Club Pr.) iUniverse, Inc.

Booth, Teena. Falling from Fire. 2004. 208p. (YA). (gr. 7). pap. 5.99 (978-0-440-22960-5(X) , Laurel Leaf) Random Hse. Children's Bks.

—Falling from Fire. 2004. (gr. 7-12). lib. bdg. 13.55 (978-0-613-72339-8(2)) Tandem Library Bks.

Bright, Paul. Nobody Laughs at a Lion! Buckingham, Matt, illus. 2005. 28p. (J). 16.00 (978-1-56148-471-3(7)) Good Bks.

Brimner, Larry Dane. Unsinkable! Tripp, Christine, illus. (Rookie Choices Ser.). 32p. (J). (gr. 1-2). 2003. pap. 5.95 (978-0-516-27790-5(1)); 2002. pap. 20.50 (978-0-516-22543-2(X)) Scholastic Library Publishing. (Children's Pr.).

Broski, Julie. Being Me. Vigla, Vincent, illus. 2006. (Rookie Reader Skill Set Ser.). 32p. (J). (gr. k-2). 19.50 (978-0-516-24975-9(4) , Children's Pr.) Scholastic Library Publishing.

Brown, Corinne. Wishful Watoosi: The Horse That Wished He Wasn't. 2006. (Illus.). 32p. (J). 16.95 (978-0-9721057-2-9(7) , 3000) Cowgirl Peg Enterprises LLC.

Brudos, Susan E. & Rubino, Alisa A., illus. Wayne's Trail. 2004. (J). pap. (978-0-932991-62-1(9)) Place In The Woods, The.

Byrd, Jeff, illus. A Tale of Two Tails, el Perro con Dos Colas: A children's story in English & Spanish. 2004. Tr. of Perro con Dos Colas. (SPA.). (J). (ps-3). per. 14.95 (978-0-9746024-0-0(X)) One Arm Publishing.

Carlson, Nancy. Piensa en Grande! 2005. (Libros Ilustrados (Picture Bks.)). (SPA., Illus.). 32p. (J). (ps-ps). lib. bdg. 15.95 (978-0-8225-3192-0(5) , Ediciones Lerner) Lerner Publishing Group.

—Think Big! 2005. (Illus.). 28p. (J). (ps-ps). 15.95 (978-1-57505-622-7(4) , Carolrhoda Bks.) Lerner Publishing Group.

Carman, Debby. I'm Maximum Cat That's a Fact. 2006. (J). (978-0-9777340-2-3(1)) Faux Paw Media Group.

—Kittywimpuss, Got Game. 2006. (J). (978-0-9777340-4-7(8)) Faux Paw Media Group.

Cattanach, Ann. Malpas the Dragon. Renouf, Michael, illus. 2007. 24p. (***978-1-84310-572-5(1)***) Kingsley, Jessica Ltd.

Clarissa - Evaluation Guide: Evaluation Guide. 2006. (J). (978-1-55942-402-8(8)) Marsh Media.

Clarke, Jane & Gale, Cathy. Plodney Creeper, Supersloth. 2006. (Blue Bananas Ser.). (Illus.). 48p. (J). pap. (978-0-7787-0896-4(9)) Crabtree Publishing Co.

Clevenger, Lee. IncrediBoy: Be Careful What You Wish. 2004. 267p. (J). pap. 12.95 (978-0-9764052-0-7(2)) Thomas Max Publishing.

Codell, Esmé Raji. Sahara Special. (J). (gr. 3-7). 2004. 192p. pap. 5.99 (978-0-7868-1611-8(2)); 2003. (Illus.). 208p. lib. bdg. 16.49 (978-0-7868-2627-8(4)) Hyperion Bks. for Children.

—Sahara Special. 2003. (gr. 3-6). lib. bdg. 14.10 (978-0-613-65611-5(3)) Tandem Library Bks.

Cohn, Rachel. You Know Where to Find Me. 2008. 208p. (YA). 15.99 (***978-0-689-87859-6(1)*** , Simon & Schuster Children's Publishing) Simon & Schuster Children's Publishing.

Conner, Wendy Simpson. Princess of the Moon. (Illus.). (J). 16.95 (978-1-889599-20-5(4)) Interstellar Publishing Co.

Couric, Katie. The Blue Ribbon Day. Priceman, Marjorie, illus. 2004. 32p. (J). (gr. k-2). 15.95 (978-0-385-50142-2(0) , Doubleday) Doubleday Publishing.

Craig, Stephanie. This Is Me. 2005. 168p. (YA). pap. 7.00 (978-0-14-131399-3(4) , Penguin Global) Penguin Group (USA) Inc.

Crane, Stephen. The Red Badge of Courage: With a Discussion of Self-Esteem. Clift, Eva, illus. 2003. (Values in Action Illustrated Classics Ser.). 190p. (J). (978-1-59203-034-7(3)) Learning Challenge, Inc.

Curtis, Jamie Lee. I'm Gonna Like Me: Letting off a Little Self-Esteem. Cornell, Laura, illus. 2002. (J). (ps-3). 32p. 16.99 (978-0-06-028761-0(6)); 40p. lib. bdg. 17.89 (978-0-06-028762-7(4)) HarperCollins Pubs. (Cotler, Joanna Books).

Daniels, Lucy. The Horseshoe Trilogies: Where There's Hope. 2003. (gr. 3-6). lib. bdg. 13.00 (978-0-613-90437-7(0)) Tandem Library Bks.

Danziger, Paula. I, Amber Brown. Ross, Tony, illus. 1999. (Amber Brown Ser.: No. 8). 144p. (J). (gr. 3-6). 14.99 (978-0-399-23180-3(3) , Putnam Juvenile) Penguin Group (USA) Inc.

—I, Amber Brown. 2004. (Amber Brown Ser.: No. 8). 144p. (J). (gr. 2-4). pap. 17.00 incl. audio (978-0-8072-2064-1(7) , Listening Library) Random Hse. Audio Publishing Group.

—I, Amber Brown. 2000. (Amber Brown Ser.: No. 8). (gr. 3-6). lib. bdg. 11.80 (978-0-613-28528-5(X)) Tandem Library Bks.

Dessen, Sarah. Keeping the Moon. 1999. (Illus.). 288p. (J). (gr. 7-12). 16.99 (978-0-670-88549-7(5) , Viking Juvenile) Penguin Group (USA) Inc.

—Keeping the Moon. 2000. (J). (978-0-606-20047-9(9)) Tandem Library Bks.

Dowell, Frances O'Roark. Chicken Boy. Krause, George, photos by. 2007. 208p. (J). (gr. 5 up). pap. 5.99 (978-1-4169-3482-0(0) , Aladdin) Simon & Schuster Children's Publishing.

—Chicken Boy. 2005. (Illus.). 208p. (J). 15.95 (978-0-689-85816-1(7) , Atheneum) Simon & Schuster Children's Publishing.

—Chicken Boy. l.t. ed. 2006. 169p. (YA). 22.95 (978-0-7862-8280-7(0)) Thorndike Pr.

Doyle, Malachy & Walker, Sholto. Long Gray Norris. 2006. (Yellow Bananas Ser.). (Illus.). 48p. (J). pap. (978-0-7787-1002-8(5)) Crabtree Publishing Co.

Dreiling, Christy. Holes in My Socks. 2005. pap. 16.95 (978-0-9771891-0-6(4)) Holes In My Socks Publishing.

Dubovoy, Silvia. Turquesita. (SPA.). (J). pap. (978-968-6465-18-1(9)) Casa de Estudios de Literatura y Talleres Artisticos Amaquemecan A.C. MEX. *Dist:* Lectorum Pubns., Inc.

Ellsworth, Mark R. The Quiniela of Angels. 2006. 19p. (YA). per. 8.95 (***978-1-59453-841-4(7)*** , 3319, Airleaf Publishing) Airleaf Publishing & Bookselling.

Emerson, Carl. Nosy Arnie the Anteater. Trover, Zachary, illus. 2007. (Animal Underdogs Ser.). 32p. (J). (ps-4). lib. bdg. 27.07 (***978-1-60270-016-1(8)*** , Looking Glass Library) Magic Wagon.

—Opie the Opossum Wakes Up. Trover, Zachary, illus. 2007. (Animal Underdogs Ser.). 32p. (J). (ps-4). lib. bdg. 27.07 (***978-1-60270-017-8(6)*** , Looking Glass Library) Magic Wagon.

S

Ewart, Franzeska G. Speak up, Spike. Oliver, Mark, illus. 2005. (Yellow Go Bananas Ser.). (J). 48p. pap. (978-0-7787-2744-6(0)); 42p. lib. bdg. (978-0-7787-2722-4(X)) Crabtree Publishing Co.

Fierstein, Harvey & Cole, Henry. The Sissy Duckling. 2002. (Illus.). 40p. (J). (ps-3). 16.00 (978-0-689-83566-7(3)) Simon & Schuster Children's Publishing.

Fine, Anne. Notso Hotso. Ross, Tony, illus. 2006. 96p. (J). 15.00 (978-0-374-35550-0(9)) Farrar, Straus & Giroux.

Flake, Sharon G. The Skin I'm In. 176p. (gr. 5-17). 2000. pap. 5.99 (978-0-7868-1307-0(5)); 1999. 14.95 (978-0-7868-0444-3(0)) Hyperion Pr.

—The Skin I'm In. 2000. 171p. (J). (gr. 5-9). lib. bdg. 13.94 (978-0-606-17605-7(5)) Tandem Library Bks.

—Skin I'm In. 2000. (gr. 5-8). lib. bdg. 14.15 (978-0-613-28643-5(X)) Tandem Library Bks.

—The Skin I'm In. l.t. ed. 1999. 173p. (J). (gr. 7-12). 20.95 (978-0-7862-2179-0(8)) Thorndike Pr.

Fleischman, Paul. Breakout. 2003. 160p. 15.95 (978-0-8126-2696-4(6)) Cricket Bks.

—Breakout. 2005. 144p. (YA). reprint ed. pap. 6.99 (978-0-689-87189-4(9) , Simon Pulse) Simon & Schuster Children's Publishing.

Francis, Davy. Jim the Elephant. Brundige, Britt, ed. Francis, Davy, illus. 2001. (Illus.). 10p. (J). (gr. k-5). spiral bd. 5.99 (978-1-929063-78-9(4) , 251) Moons & Stars Publishing For Children.

Freschet, Gina. Feet Man & Mr. Tiny. 2006. (Illus.). 32p. (J). 16.00 (978-0-374-32294-6(5)) Farrar, Straus & Giroux.

Froese, Deborah. Out of the Fire: A Young Adult Novel. 2002. 288p. (J). (gr. 8-11). pap. 7.95 (978-1-894549-09-7(0)) Sumach Pr. CAN. *Dist:* Orca Bk. Pubs. USA.

Frost, Helen. Keesha's House. l.t. ed. 2005. 173p. (YA). (gr. 7-12). per. 20.95 (978-0-7862-7697-4(5) , Large Print Pr.) Thorndike Pr.

Gallucci, Susie. Believe I-Can. Sellers, Amy, illus. 2006. (J). (***978-0-9776074-1-9(0)***) Pounce To Success International, Inc.

—Dream I-Can. Sellers, Amy, illus. 2006. (J). (***978-0-9776074-2-6(9)***) Pounce To Success International, Inc.

Garcia, Mary. Play with Me: Togetherness Time for Your Preschooler & You. ed. (J). 2007. 16.95 (***978-0-9790931-2-8(0)***); 2006. 16.95 (***978-0-9790931-0-4(4)***) SMARTseeds Co., LLC, The.

—Play with Me: Togetherness Time for Your Preschooler & You: St. Valentine's Day. ed. 2007. (J). (***978-0-9790931-1-1(2)***) SMARTseeds Co., LLC, The.

Garon, Risa J. Snowman. 2000. (Illus.). 5p. (J). pap. 5.00 (978-0-9729415-0-1(9)) National Family Resiliency Ctr., Inc.

Gemmen, Heather. Quit Looking at Me! Lagares, Luciano, illus. 2003. (Tough Stuff for Kids Ser.). 32p. (J). pap., pap. 5.99 (978-0-7814-3852-0(7) , 0781438527) Cook, David C. Publishing Co.

Gershon, Dann. Extra Large. Robinson, David, illus. 1999. (Hangin' with the Hombeez Ser.: Vol. 3). 40p. (J). (gr. k-6). 14.95 (978-0-9656985-5-9(6)) Noware Bks.

Gifaldi, David. Toby Scudder, King of the School. 2005. 208p. (J). (gr. 4-6). pap. 5.95 (978-0-618-55158-3(1) , Clarion Bks.) Houghton Mifflin Co. Trade & Reference Div.

Ginolfi, Arthur. Tiny Snowflake Picture Book. Max, Louise Reinoehl, illus. 2003. 32p. (J). 7.99 (978-1-4003-0205-5(6)) Nelson, Thomas Inc.

Goobie, Beth. Something Girl. 112p. 2006. (YA). lib. bdg. 14.95 (978-1-55143-560-2(8)); 2005. (J). (gr. 7-12). pap. 7.95 (978-1-55143-347-9(8)) Orca Bk. Pubs. USA.

Gordon, David. The Ugly Truckling. Gordon, David, illus. 2004. (Illus.). 32p. (J). (ps-2). lib. bdg. 16.89 (978-0-06-054601-4(8) , Geringer, Laura Book) HarperCollins Pubs.

Goss, Leon. Selfus Esteemus Personalitus Low. Tunell, Ken, illus. 2005. (J). pap. (978-1-933156-08-8(2) , VisionQuest Kids) GSVQ Publishing.

Goss, Leon, 3rd. Selfus Esteemus Personalitus Low. Tunell, Ken, illus. ed. 2005. 32p. (J). per. 17.95 (978-1-933156-00-2(7) , VisionQuest Kids) GSVQ Publishing.

Graves, Keith. Three Nasty Gnarlies. Graves, Keith, illus. 2003. (Illus.). 40p. (J). pap. 16.95 (978-0-439-24090-1(5)) Scholastic, Inc.

Greene, Bette. Summer of My German Soldier. 2006. (Puffin Modern Classics Ser.). 240p. (J). (gr. 5). pap. 6.99 (978-0-14-240651-9(1) , Puffin) Penguin Group (USA) Inc.

Greenwald, Lisa & Paley, Sasha. Huge. 2007. 272p. (YA). 15.99 (978-1-4169-3517-9(7)) Simon & Schuster Children's Publishing.

Gregory, Valiska. Valentine for Norman Noggs. 1999. (978-0-606-18726-8(X)) Tandem Library Bks.

Griffin, Saundra J. Which Should I Be? 2004. 21p. pap. 14.95 (978-1-4137-3167-5(8)) PublishAmerica, Inc.

Grossman, Linda Sky. Charlene's Choice. Bockus, Petra, illus. (I'm a Great Little Kid Ser.). 24p. (ps-3). 2002. 12.95 (978-1-896764-53-5(3)); 2001. pap. 4.95 (978-1-896764-47-4(9)) Second Story Pr. CAN. *Dist:* Orca Bk. Pubs. USA, Univ. of Toronto Pr.

—It's No Joke, My Telephone Broke. Bockus, Petra, illus. (I'm a Great Little Kid Ser.). 24p. (ps-3). 2002. 12.95 (978-1-896764-51-1(7)); 2001. pap. 4.95 (978-1-896764-45-0(2)) Second Story Pr. CAN. *Dist:* Orca Bk. Pubs. USA, Univ. of Toronto Pr.

—Now I See How Great I Can Be. Bockus, Petra, illus. (I'm a Great Little Kid Ser.). 24p. (ps-3). 2002. 12.95 (978-1-896764-52-8(5)); 2001. pap. 4.95 (978-1-896764-46-7(0)) Second Story Pr. CAN. *Dist:* Orca Bk. Pubs. USA, Univ. of Toronto Pr.

Gunn, Robin Jones. With This Ring. 1998. (Sierra Jensen Ser.: Bk. 6). 160p. (J). (gr. 7-11). pap. (978-1-56179-540-6(2)) Focus on the Family Publishing.

Hagerup, Klaus. Markus & Diana. Chace, Tara, tr. from NOR. 2006. 192p. (J). 17.95 (978-1-932425-59-8(4) , Front Street) Boyds Mills Pr.

Haig-Brown, Roderick L. Starbuck Valley Winter. 2nd unabr. ed. 240p. (YA). pap. 14.95 (***978-1-55017-247-8(6)***) Harbour Publishing Co., Ltd. CAN. *Dist:* Graphic Arts Ctr. Publishing Co.

Hale, Shannon. River Secrets. 2006. (Illus.). 304p. (J). 17.95 (978-1-58234-901-5(0)) Bloomsbury Publishing.

Halley, Marilyn. Apple-Green Eyes. 2005. pap. 8.00 (978-0-8059-6681-7(1)) Dorrance Publishing Co., Inc.

Han, Jenny. Shug. 256p. 2007. (J). pap. 5.99 (***978-1-4169-0943-9(5)*** , Aladdin); 2006. (Illus.). (YA). (gr. 5-9). 16.99 (978-1-4169-0942-2(7)) Simon & Schuster Children's Publishing.

Harris, Devon D. Yes I Can. 2006. (Illus.). 48p. (J). (978-0-9764082-4-6(4)) Waterhouse Publishing.

Haseltine, Dan. The One the Only Magnificent Me. Tanis, Joel Schoon, illus. 2007. 32p. (J). 14.95 (***978-1-934133-21-7(3)***) Mackinac Island Pr., Inc.

Hawley, Bobby. By Golly, Molly, You're Right. 2006. 48p. pap. 12.95 (978-1-4241-2085-7(3)) PublishAmerica, Inc.

Hayes, Sonia. Ms. Thang. 2006. (ENG.). 192p. (YA). per. 9.95 (978-0-9777573-0-5(7)) NUA Multimedia.

Hayes, Sonia. Urban Goddess. 2007. 224p. (YA). per. 9.95 (***978-0-9777573-1-2(5)***) NUA Multimedia.

Headley, Justina Chen. Nothing but the Truth (And a Few White Lies) 2006. 256p. (J). (gr. 5-9). 16.99 (978-0-316-01128-0(2)) Little Brown & Co.

—Nothing but the Truth (And a Few White Lies) 2007. 256p. (J). (gr. 7 up). pap. 7.99 (***978-0-316-01131-0(2)***) Little, Brown Bks. for Young Readers.

Heling, Kathryn & Hembrook, Deborah. I Wish I Had Freckles Like Abby/Quisiera tener pecas como Abby. de la Vega, Eida, tr. Adamson, Bonnie, illus. 2006. Tr. of Quisiera tener pecas como Abby. (SPA.). (J). 4.99 (978-0-9770906-6-2(3)) Raven Tree Pr.

—I Wish I Had Freckles Like Abby/Quisiera tener pecas como Abby. de la Vega, Eida, tr. Parins, Kris, illus. 2005. Tr. of Quisiera tener pecas como Abby. (SPA & ENG.). 32p. (J). 16.95 (978-0-9724973-8-1(2) , 626999) Raven Tree Pr.

—I Wish I Had Glasses Like Rosa/Quisiera tener lentes como Rosa. de la Vega, Eida, tr. Adamson, Bonnie, illus. Tr. of Quisiera tener lentes como Rosa. (SPA.). (J). 2006. 4.99 (978-0-9770906-5-5(5)); 2005. 32p. 16.95 (978-0-9724973-7-4(4) , 626999) Raven Tree Pr.

Hernandez, Jo Ann Yolanda. The Throw-Away Piece. 246p. (Orig.). (YA). pap. 9.95 (978-1-55885-353-9(7) , Piñata Books) Arte Publico Pr.

Hobbs, Valerie. Letting Go of Bobby James: Or How I Found My Self of Steam. 2004. 144p. (YA). 16.00 (978-0-374-34384-2(5) , Frances Foster Bks.) Farrar, Straus & Giroux.

Hoog, Mark E. Dream Machine: Another Growing Field Adventure. Aukerman, Robert J., illus. 2007. 32p. 16.95 (978-0-9770391-1-1(0) , 5000) Growing Field Bks.

Howard, Jo Ann. The Little Boy Who Made a Difference. 2001. 41p. per. 8.95 (978-0-7414-0575-3(X)) Infinity Publishing.

Hubbard, Coleen. The Flying Angels. Rabinowitz, Sandy & Keiffer, Christa, illus. l.t. ed. 1999. (Treasured Horses Collection). 128p. (J). (gr. 4 up). lib. bdg. 23.33 (978-0-8368-2401-8(6)) Stevens, Gareth Inc.

Hunter, Alixander. The Handicapped Squirrel. l.t. ed. 1998. (Illus.). 32p. 19.95 (978-0-9665582-0-3(0)) Alixander Group.

Jabar, Cynthia. Wow! It Sure Is Good to Be You! Jabar, Cynthia, illus. 2006. (Illus.). 32p. (J). (gr. k-3). 9.95 (978-0-618-58132-0(4)) Houghton Mifflin Co.

Jacobson, Jennifer. Winnie (Dancing) on Her Own. Geis, Alissa Imre, illus. 2003. 112p. (J). (gr. 3-5). pap. 5.95 (978-0-618-36921-8(X)) Houghton Mifflin Co. Trade & Reference Div.

Jacono, Mary Kaye. Lenny's Gift. 2005. 27p. pap. 10.95 (978-0-7414-2602-4(1)) Infinity Publishing.

Jeram, Anita. You're All My Favorites Book & Toy Gift Set. Jeram, Anita, illus. 2004. (Illus.). 32p. (J). (ps-2). 15.99 (978-0-7636-2442-2(X)) Candlewick Pr.

Johnson, Kathleen A. A Voice Came to Me. 2006. lib. bdg. 17.95 (978-0-9785623-0-4(5)) Voice of Light Pubns.

Johnson, Lissa Halls. Bad Girl Days, Vol. 12. 2005. (Brio Girls Ser.). 192p. (YA). pap. 7.99 (978-1-58997-091-5(8)) Focus on the Family Publishing.

Jones, Patrick. Chasing Tail Lights. 2007. 304p. (YA). (gr. 9 up). 16.95 (***978-0-8027-9628-8(1)***) Walker & Co.

Kelleher, Victor. Dogboy. 2006. (YA). (gr. 9 up). 16.95 (978-1-932425-76-5(4) , Lemniscaat) Boyds Mills Pr.

Kline, Suzy. Herbie Jones & the Second Grade Slippers. Sweeten, Sami, illus. 2006. 64p. (J). (gr. 1-4). 14.99 (978-0-399-23132-2(3) , Putnam Juvenile) Penguin Group (USA) Inc.

—Marvin & the Mean Words. 1998. (J). (978-0-606-13599-3(5)) Tandem Library Bks.

Klise, Kate. Deliver Us from Normal. 2006. 256p. (YA). (gr. 5-9). pap. 5.99 (978-0-439-52323-3(0) , Scholastic Paperbacks) Scholastic, Inc.

Kobert, Michael Gilead & Donato, Dona. Who Goes with That Nose? The Wild Adventures of Juicy Coppertoes. Fuller, Laurie, illus. 2005. 40p. (J). per. 9.95 (978-0-9770700-0-8(X)) Giggling Gorilla Productions, LLC.

Koller, Jackie French. A Wizard Named Nell. Guay, Rebecca, illus. 2003. (Keepers Ser.: Bk. 1). 208p. pap. 11.95 (978-0-689-85591-7(5) , Aladdin) Simon & Schuster Children's Publishing.

Korman, Gordon. Liar, Liar, Pants on Fire. 1999. (gr. 3-6). lib. bdg. 11.80 (978-0-613-11773-9(5)) Tandem Library Bks.

Krauser, Susan A. Lilith A. Wilith. 2002. (J). lib. bdg. 16.95 (978-0-9717860-0-4(3)) Lilith & Co.

Lane, Deborah Jean. I Am an Individual. 2004. pap. 8.00 (978-0-8059-6527-8(0)) Dorrance Publishing Co., Inc.

Larsen, Ramonita. Yes, I Can Do It: Si, lo Puedo Hacer. Larsen, Ramonita, illus. l.t. ed. 2006. (Illus.). 25p. (J). per. 10.99 (***978-1-59879-292-8(X)***) Lifevest Publishing, Inc.

Lea, Audry. Scott the Dot. 2005. (Illus.). 32p. (J). (978-1-4120-4927-6(X)) Trafford Publishing.

Lekich, John. The Losers' Club. 2002. 256p. (YA). (gr. 8 up). pap. 7.95 (978-1-55037-752-1(3)) Annick Pr., Ltd. CAN. *Dist:* Firefly Bks., Ltd.

Lite, Lori. The Affirmation Web: A Believe in Yourself Adventure. Botelho, Helder, illus. 2003. 32p. (J). (gr. k-6). pap. 10.95 (978-1-886941-25-0(4) , 0942) Specialty Pr., Inc.

Livingston, Irene. Finklehopper Frog Cheers. Lies, Brian, illus. 2005. 32p. (J). 14.95 (978-1-58246-138-0(4) , Tricycle Pr.) Ten Speed Pr.

Lobel, Gillian. Does Anybody Love Me? Beardshaw, Rosalind, illus. 2002. 28p. (J). (gr. k-3). 16.00 (978-1-56148-368-6(0)) Good Bks.

Love, D. Anne. A Little Rebellion. 2008. 272p. (YA). 16.99 (***978-1-4169-3481-3(2)*** , McElderry, Margaret K.) Simon & Schuster Children's Publishing.

Lucado, Max. Hermie: A Common Caterpillar. 2002. (Max Lucado's Hermie & Friends Ser.). 16p. (J). bds. 6.99 (978-1-4003-0126-3(2)) Nelson, Thomas Inc.

—You Are Mine & Best of All, 2 vols. 2006. (Illus.). 64p. (J). 19.99 (978-1-58134-804-0(5)) Crossway Bks.

—You Are Special. Martinez, Sergio, illus. rev. ed. 2007. 32p. 19.99 (***978-1-58134-894-1(0)***) Crossway Bks.

Lucado, Max. You Are Special: A Story for Everyone. Martinez, Sergio, illus. gif. ed. 2005. (Wemmicks Ser.). 46p. (ps-3). 10.99 (978-1-58134-405-9(8) , Crossway Bibles) Crossway Bks.

Lucado, Max, creator. Hermie, A Common Caterpillar. 2006. 38p. (J). bds. 12.99 (978-1-4003-0888-0(7)) Nelson, Thomas Inc.

MacMillan, Ian C. Khala Maninge - the Little Elephant That Cried a Lot: An African Fable. MacMillan, Eric G., illus. 2nd ed. 2003. lib. bdg. 5.00 (978-0-9729698-0-2(2)) Maninge Mali.

Madison, Alan. Velma Gratch & the Way Cool Butterfly. Hawkes, Kevin, illus. 2007. 40p. (J). (ps-3). lib. bdg. 19.99 (***978-0-375-93597-8(5)*** , Schwartz & Wade Bks.) Random Hse. Children's Bks.

—Velma Gratch & the Way Cool Butterfly. Hawkes, Kevin, illus. 2007. (J). (978-0-689-86921-1(5) , Atheneum) Simon & Schuster Children's Publishing.

Magsamen, Sandra. When I Grow up I Want to Be Me. 2002. (Illus.). 22p. (J). pap. 19.95 (978-0-439-39886-2(X) , Orchard Bks.) Scholastic, Inc.

Maier, Inger M. When Lizzie Was Afraid: Of Trying New Things. Candon, Jennifer, illus. 2005. 32p. (J). 14.95 (978-1-59147-170-7(2)); pap. 8.95 (978-1-59147-171-4(0)) American Psychological Assn. (Magination Pr.).

Mangum, Kay Lynn. When the Bough Breaks. 2007. 352p. (YA). pap. 15.95 (***978-1-59038-748-1(1)***) Deseret Bk. Co.

Marbury, Ja'Nitta. It's Okay to Be Me: Coloring the Self-Esteem of Children. Marbury, Ja'Nitta, illus. l.t. ed. 2001. Tr. of Esta Bien de Ser Como Yo!. (SPA., Illus.). 33p. (J). pap. 20.00 (978-0-9718307-1-4(1)) Shades of Me Publishing.

—Shades of Me: Coloring the Self-Esteem of African American Children. Marbury, Ja'Nitta, illus. l.t. ed. 2002. (Illus.). 22p. (J). pap. 20.00 (978-0-9718307-2-1(X)) Shades of Me Publishing.

Marino, Peter. Dough Boy. 2007. 176p. (YA). (gr. 7 up). pap. 6.95 (***978-0-8234-2096-4(5)***) Holiday Hse., Inc.

Mark, Hoog. Your Song: The First Growing Field Adventure. 2007. (Illus.). 48p. (J). 16.95 (***978-0-9770391-2-8(9)***) Growing Field Bks.

Mayfield, Sue & Padua, Rochelle. I Can You Can Toucan! 2006. (Green Bananas Ser.). (Illus.). 48p. (J). pap. (978-0-7787-1048-6(3)) Crabtree Publishing Co.

Mazer, Anne. Every Cloud Has a Silver Lining. Gesue, Monica, illus. 2000. (Amazing Days of Abby Hayes Ser.: No. 1). 128p. (gr. 4-7). mass mkt. 4.99 (978-0-439-14977-8(0)) Scholastic, Inc.

—Every Cloud Has a Silver Lining. 2000. (Amazing Days of Abby Hayes Ser.: No. 1). (J). 11.79 (978-0-606-19559-1(9)); (gr. 3-6). lib. bdg. 12.40 (978-0-613-25048-1(6)) Tandem Library Bks.

Medearis, Michael & Medearis, Angela Shelf. Daisy & the Doll. Johnson, Larry, illus. 2000. (Family Heritage Ser.). 32p. (J). (gr. 1-5). 14.95 (978-0-916718-15-2(8)) Vermont Folklife Ctr.

Mills, Claudia. Ziggy's Blue-Ribbon Day. Alley, R. W. & Alley, Robert W., illus. 2005. 32p. (J). (ps-ps). 16.00 (978-0-374-32352-3(6) , Farrar, Straus & Giroux (BYR)) Farrar, Straus & Giroux.

Mills, Joyce C. Little Tree: A Story for Children with Serious Medical Illness. Sebern, Brian, illus. 2nd ed. 2003. 32p. (J). pap. 8.95 (978-1-59147-042-7(0)); 14.95 (978-1-59147-041-0(2)) American Psychological Assn. (Magination Pr.).

Moore, Martha A. Matchit. 2003. (Illus.). 208p. (J). (gr. 3-7). pap. 4.99 (978-0-440-41716-3(3) , Yearling) Random Hse. Children's Bks.

Myers, Christopher A. Wings. Myers, Christopher A., illus. 2000. (Illus.). 40p. (J). (gr. 1-3). pap. 16.95 (978-0-590-03377-0(8)) Scholastic, Inc.

Na, An. Wait for Me. 2007. 192p. (YA). (gr. 7 up). 7.99 (***978-0-14-240918-3(9)*** , Puffin) Penguin Group (USA) Inc.

Nanette. The Black Alligator. 2004. (Life on Granny's Farm Ser.). (J). 12.95 (978-0-9741269-3-7(4)) St. Bernard Publishing, LLC.

Naylor, Phyllis Reynolds. Alice Alone. (Alice Ser.). 240p. 2002. mass mkt. 5.99 (978-0-689-85189-6(8) , Simon Pulse); 2001. (Illus.). (J). (gr. 5-9). 16.00 (978-0-689-82634-4(6) , Atheneum) Simon & Schuster Children's Publishing.

—Alice Alone. 2002. (Alice Ser.). (gr. 5-8). lib. bdg. 13.00 (978-0-613-73352-6(5)) Tandem Library Bks.

—Ice. 1998. 256p. (YA). (gr. 7-12). mass mkt. 12.95 (978-0-689-81872-1(6) , Simon Pulse) Simon & Schuster Children's Publishing.

—Ice. 1998. (J). 11.64 (978-0-606-12970-1(7)) Tandem Library Bks.

Newman, Leslea. Jailbait. 2005. 256p. (YA). (gr. 9-12). lib. bdg. 17.99 (978-0-385-90230-4(1) , Delacorte Bks. for Young Readers) Random Hse. Children's Bks.

Nolan, Allia. What I Do Best! 2006. (Illus.). 14p. (J). 14.99 (978-0-7944-1131-2(2)) Reader's Digest Assn., Inc., The.

Nolan, Lucy. Jack Quack. Wesson, Andrea, illus. 32p. (J). 2005. pap. 5.95 (978-0-7614-5153-2(6)); 2001. 15.95 (978-0-7614-5091-7(2) , Cavendish Children's Bks.) Cavendish, Marshall Corp.

Otto, Gina. Cassandra's Angel. Joost, Trudy, illus. 2001. 32p. (ps-3). 15.95 (978-0-935699-20-3(1)) Illumination Arts Publishing Co., Inc.

Owens, Connie S. I know I am Special! 2003. pap. 5.99 (978-1-59317-010-3(6)) Warner Pr. Pubs.

Papademetriou, Lisa. Rani in the Mermaid Lagoon. Clarke, Judith, illus. 2006. (Stepping Stone Bks.). 128p. (J). (gr. 2-4). 5.99 (978-0-7364-2375-5(3) , RH/Disney) Random Hse. Children's Bks.

Parr, Todd. It's Okay to Be Different. Parr, Todd, illus. 2001. (Illus.). 32p. (J). (ps-1). 15.99 (978-0-316-66603-9(3) , Tingley, Megan Bks.) Little, Brown Bks. for Young Readers.

Paterson, Katherine. Lyddie. 2003. (Espasa Juvenil Ser.: Vol. 18). (SPA., Illus.). (J). (gr. 9-12). pap. (978-84-239-9015-3(X) , EC6561) Espasa Calpe, S.A. ESP. *Dist:* Lectorum Pubns., Inc.

—Lyddie. 2004. 192p. (J). (gr. 5). pap. 6.99 (978-0-14-240254-2(0) , Puffin) Penguin Group (USA) Inc.

Patricia, Murdoch. Exposure. 2006. 112p. (J). (gr. 3-6). lib. bdg. 14.95 (978-1-55143-523-7(3)); (gr. 7-12). pap. 7.95 (978-1-55143-493-3(8)) Orca Bk. Pubs. USA.

Pellegrino, Marjorie White, ed. Too Nice. Matthews, Bonnie, illus. 2002. 48p. (YA). (gr. 4-7). 14.95 (978-1-55798-917-8(6)); pap. 8.95 (978-1-55798-918-5(4)) American Psychological Assn. (Magination Pr.).

Pendziwol, Jean E. Marja's Skis. Marton, Jirina, illus. 2007. 32p. (J). (ps-3). 17.95 (***978-0-88899-674-9(8)***) Groundwood Bks. CAN. *Dist:* Perseus Distribution.

Penn, Audrey. A Kiss Goodbye. Gibson, Barbara Leonard, illus. 2007. 32p. (ps-3). 16.95 (***978-1-933718-04-0(8)***) Tanglewood Pr.

—A Kiss Goodbye. Gibson, Barbara, illus. 2007. 32p. 16.95 (***978-1-933718-03-3(X)***) Tanglewood Pr.

Pesko, Mila. Little Mary of the Rose & the Giant Baked Bean. 2007. per. 14.95 (***978-1-932762-75-4(2)***) Elderberry Press, Inc.

Phillips, Sally Kahler. Nonsense! 2006. (Illus.). 32p. (J). (ps-2). 14.95 (978-0-375-83306-9(4) , Random Hse. Bks. for Young Readers) Random Hse. Children's Bks.

Pielichaty, Helena. Starring Alex ... 2006. (Girls of Avenue Z Ser.). 128p. (J). pap. 4.99 (978-1-4169-0063-4(2) , Aladdin) Simon & Schuster Children's Publishing.

Pilling, Ann. The Year of the Worm. 176p. (J). (gr. 4-7). pap. 7.50 (978-0-7459-4294-0(6) , Lion) Lion Hudson plc GBR. *Dist:* Trafalgar Square Publishing.

Plante, Raymond. Marilou's Long Nose. Cummins, Sarah, tr. from FRE. Favreau, Marie-Claude, illus. 2000. (First Novels Ser.). 64p. (gr. 1-5). 4.95 (978-0-88780-528-8(0)); (978-0-88780-529-5(9)) Formac Publishing Co., Ltd. CAN. *Dist:* Casemate Pubs. & Bk. Distributors, LLC.

—Marilou's Long Nose. 2001. (gr. k-3). lib. bdg. 11.80 (978-0-613-88933-9(9)) Tandem Library Bks.

Plummer, Deborah. The Adventures of the Little Tin Tortoise: A Self-Esteem Story with Activities for Teachers, Parents & Carers. 2005. (Illus.). 92p. (978-1-84310-406-3(7)) Kingsley, Jessica Ltd.

Pokeberry, P. J. The Huckenpuck Papers: The Tales of a Family's Secret & a Young Girls Search for Self-Esteem. 2003. (Illus.). 87p. (J). pap. 8.95 (978-0-943962-03-0(X)) Viewpoint Pr.

Pressler, Mirjam. Let Sleeping Dogs Lie. Macki, Erik J., tr. from GER. 2007. 208p. (YA). (gr. 7 up). 16.95 (***978-1-932425-84-0(5)*** , Front Street) Boyds Mills Pr.

Rayburn, Tricia. The Melting of Maggie Bean. 2007. 256p. (J). (gr. 4-8). pap. 5.99 (978-1-4169-3348-9(4) , Aladdin) Simon & Schuster Children's Publishing.

Reiss, Mike. The Boy Who Looked Like Lincoln. Catrow, David, illus. Catrow, David, illus. 2003. 32p. (J). (ps-6). 10.99 (978-0-8431-0271-0(3) , Price Stern Sloan) Penguin Group (USA) Inc.

—The Boy Who Looked Like Lincoln. Catrow, David, illus. 2006. 32p. (J). (ps). reprint ed. pap. 5.99 (978-0-14-240416-4(0) , Puffin) Penguin Group (USA) Inc.

Reynolds, Cynthia Furlong. Grammie's Secret Cupboard. Dodson, Bert, illus. 2007. 32p. (J). 17.95 (***978-1-58726-310-1(6)*** , Mitten Pr.) Ann Arbor Media Group, LLC.

Richardson, Charisse K. The Real Lucky Charm. Velasquez, Eric, illus. 2005. 80p. (J). (gr. 2-5). 16.99 (978-0-8037-3105-9(1) , Dial); pap. 4.99 (978-0-14-240431-7(4) , Puffin) Penguin Group (USA) Inc.

Richardson, Wanda Thomas. Beautiful Me. Gary, Kelli M., ed. Higgins, John & Holmes, Gregory L., illus. 2001. 24p. (Orig.). (J). (gr. 3-8). pap. 7.99 (978-0-9673084-1-8(0)) JCW Enterprises, Inc.

Roberts, Barbara A. Phoebe's Lost Treasure. Sternberg, Kate, illus. 1999. (Phoebe Flower's Adventures Ser.). 68p. (gr. 2-4). pap. 5.95 (978-0-9660366-6-4(2)) National Bk. Network.

Rue, Nancy N. Lily & the Creep. 2001. (gr. 3-6). lib. bdg. 13.00 (978-0-613-71718-2(X)) Tandem Library Bks.

Rue, Nancy N. & Youth Specialties Staff. New Girl in Town. 2004. (Invert / 'Nama Beach High Ser.: No. 1). 176p. (J). pap. 6.99 (978-0-310-24399-1(8)) Zondervan.

Seidler, Tor. Brothers below Zero. McCarty, Peter, illus. 2003. 144p. (J). (gr. 5 up). pap. 5.99 (978-0-06-440936-0(8) , Harper Trophy) HarperCollins Pubs.

—Brothers below Zero. 2002. (Illus.). 144p. (J). (gr. 3 up). 14.95 (978-0-06-029179-2(6) , Geringer, Laura Book) HarperCollins Pubs.

—Brothers below Zero. McCarty, Peter, illus. 2002. 144p. (J). (gr. 5 up). lib. bdg. 15.89 (978-0-06-029180-8(X) , Geringer, Laura Book) HarperCollins Pubs.

—Brothers below Zero. 2003. (gr. 3-6). lib. bdg. 14.15 (978-0-613-57705-2(1)) Tandem Library Bks.

—The Tar Pit. 2000. (J). 15.95 (978-0-06-623611-7(8)); lib. bdg. 15.89 (978-0-06-623612-4(6)) HarperCollins Pubs.

—The Tar Pit. 2001. (978-0-606-22299-0(5)) Tandem Library Bks.

Sequins. 2001. (J). (978-0-9700756-8-0(5)) Pajo Publishing Co.

Shannon, David. Un Caso Grave de Rayas. 2002. (SPA., Illus.). 32p. (J). (gr. k-4). pap. 3.99 (978-0-439-40986-5(1) , Scholastic en Espanol) Scholastic, Inc.

Shaw, Janet Beeler. Kaya's Hero. 2002. (gr. 3-6). lib. bdg. 14.10 (978-0-613-46224-2(6)) Tandem Library Bks.

—Kaya's Hero Bk. 3: A Story of Giving. Farnsworth, Bill & McAliley, Susan, illus. 2002. (American Girls Collection: Bk. 3). 88p. (gr. 2-7). (J). 12.95 (978-1-58485-428-9(6)); 6.95 (978-1-58485-427-2(8)) American Girl Publishing, Inc.

Shay, Ruth Ann. The Littlest Susan. Mertes, Charles, illus. 2000. 32p. (J). (ps-4). lib. bdg. 20.00 (978-0-9701167-0-3(5)) Guided Pen Pr.

Silver, Rita. Best Friends. 2006. 17.00 (978-0-8059-9932-7(9)) Dorrance Publishing Co., Inc.

Small, David. Fenwick's Suit. 2005. (Illus.). 32p. (J). (ps-ps). pap. 6.95 (978-0-374-42296-7(6) , Farrar, Straus & Giroux (BYR)) Farrar, Straus & Giroux.

Small, Tanya. What You Say Is What You Are. 2007. pap. 7.50 (***978-0-9705090-1-7(4)***) MorningGlory Publishing.

Smillie, Bryan. A Time for Evron. Rooth, Mike, illus. 2004. 190p. 11.95 (978-0-9689516-0-6(0)) Shabrya Publishing CAN. *Dist:* Hushion Hse. Publishing, Ltd.

Smith, Suzanne C. Peter Cottontail & the Easter Bunny Imposter. Brittingham, Geoffrey, illus. 24p. (J). pap. 3.25 (978-0-8249-5372-0(X) , Ideals) Ideals Pubns.

Sohaili, Monira. Stories from Earth & Beyond: Enchanting & Inspirational Stories. 2006. (Illus.). 94p. per. 9.95 (978-1-60002-044-5(5) , 2833, Airleaf Publishing) Airleaf Publishing & Bookselling.

Sones, Sonya. What My Girlfriend Doesn't Know. 2007. 304p. (YA). (gr. 7 up). 16.99 (978-0-689-87602-8(5)) Simon & Schuster Children's Publishing.

Starks, Kimberly. Real Girls, Inc. 2005. 68p. pap. 14.95 (978-1-4137-7133-6(5)) PublishAmerica, Inc.

Stoehr, Shelley. Crosses. 2003. (gr. 7-12). lib. bdg. 23.40 (978-0-613-86660-6(6)) Tandem Library Bks.

—Crosses. 2003. 161p. (YA). pap. 13.95 (978-0-595-26952-5(4) , Backinprint.com) iUniverse, Inc.

Stuart, Kelly. Cowgirls Can Do! Amazing Things, Too! Clarke, Cynthia & Clarke, Bradley, illus. 2002. (Can Do! Bks.). 32p. 14.95 (978-0-9709987-4-3(0)) Bright Sky Pr.

Sunderland, Margot & Hancock, Nicky. Ruby & the Rubbish Bin: A Story for Children with Low Self-Esteem. Armstrong, Nicky, tr. Armstrong, Nicky, illus. 32p. pap. (978-0-86388-462-7(8) , 002-5146) Speechmark Publishing Ltd.

Tanaka, Usa. Give Me That! 2007. 32p. 15.95 (***978-0-9741319-0-0(3)***) 4N Publishing LLC.

Thompson, Kay. Eloise's What I Absolutely Love Love Love. Knight, Hilary, illus. 2004. 32p. (J). 9.95 (978-0-689-84965-7(6) , Simon & Schuster Children's Publishing) Simon & Schuster Children's Publishing.

Tillman, Nancy. On the Night You Were Born. 2006. (Illus.). 32p. (J). (gr. k-2). 16.95 (978-0-312-34606-5(9) , Feiwel & Friends) Feiwel & Friends.

Trimble, Marcia. Moonbeams for Santa. Bingham, Sid, illus. 2001. 32p. (J). (ps-4). 15.95 (978-1-891577-89-5(1)) Images Pr.

Wagele, Elizabeth. Finding the Birthday Cake: Helping Children Raise Their Self-Esteem. Wagele, Elizabeth, illus. 2007. (Let's Talk Ser.). (Illus.). 48p. (J). pap. 8.95 (978-0-88282-277-8(2)) New Horizon Pr. Pubs., Inc.

Walker, Melissa. Violet on the Runway. 2007. 240p. (YA). (gr. 12 up). pap. 9.99 (***978-0-425-21704-7(3)*** , Berkley Trade) Penguin Group (USA) Inc.

Wallace, Karen. Clever Cat. Axworthy, Ann, illus. 2004. (Read-It! Readers Ser.). 32p. (C). (gr. k-3). 18.60 (978-1-4048-0560-6(5)) Picture Window Bks.

Weedn, Flavia M. Flavia & the Dream Maker. 1999. (Illus.). 48p. (J). (ps-3). 14.95 (978-0-7683-2102-9(6)) CEDCO Publishing.

Weeks, Sarah. I'm a Pig. Berry, Holly, illus. 2005. 32p. (J). (ps-2). lib. bdg. 16.89 (978-0-06-074344-4(1)); 15.99 (978-0-694-01075-2(8)) HarperCollins Pubs. (Geringer, Laura Book).

Weeks, Sarah. Oggie Cooder #1. 2008. 176p. (J). pap. 16.99 (***978-0-439-92791-8(9)*** , Scholastic) Scholastic, Inc.

West, Greta. Never Good Enough. 2000. 48p. (J). pap. 8.00 (978-0-8059-4705-2(1)) Dorrance Publishing Co., Inc.

What Do You See When You Look at Me? 2003. (J). 12.00 (978-0-9724442-7-9(0)) LightHouse Pr.

When I Grow up I'm Going to Be A Hockey Star. 2004. (J). 16.95 (978-0-9763931-0-8(7)) Great Northern Adventure Co., Inc.

White, Amanda. Rip & Rap. Harter, Debbie, illus. 2002. 24p. (J). (gr. k-2). 14.99 (978-1-84148-944-5(1)) Barefoot Bks., Inc.

Whytock, Cherry. My Cup Runneth Over: The Life of Angelica Cookson Potts. 2005. 192p. (YA). mass mkt. 3.99 (978-1-4169-0521-9(9) , Simon Pulse) Simon & Schuster Children's Publishing.

Wild, Margaret. Fox. Brooks, Ron, illus. 2006. 32p. (J). pap. 7.95 (978-1-933605-15-9(4)) Kane/Miller Bk. Pubs., Inc.

Williams, Ted. Curly Hare Gets It Straight. 2001. (Kiss a Me Teacher Creature Stories Ser.). (Illus.). (J). (978-1-890343-35-4(8)) Kiss A Me Productions, Inc.

Wilson, Troy. Perfect Man. Griffiths, Dean, illus. 2005. 32p. (J). (ps-2). 7.95 (978-1-55143-435-3(0)) Orca Bk. Pubs. USA.

Windle, Jeanette. Jana's Journal. 2002. (gr. 7-12). lib. bdg. 22.25 (978-0-613-88253-8(9)) Tandem Library Bks.

—Jana's Journal: A Novel for Teens. 2002. 256p. pap. 12.99 (978-0-8254-4117-2(X)) Kregel Pubns.

Withers, Pam. Breathless. 2005. (Orca Soundings Ser.). 112p. (J). (gr. 7-12). pap. 7.95 (978-1-55143-480-3(6)) Orca Bk. Pubs. USA.

Yamanaka, Lois-Ann. Name Me Nobody. 2000. 240p. (gr. 8-17). pap. 5.99 (978-0-7868-1466-4(7)) Disney Pr.

—Name Me Nobody. 2000. (gr. 7-12). lib. bdg. 14.15 (978-0-613-31521-0(9)) Tandem Library Bks.

Yep, Laurence. When the Circus Came to Town. Wang, Suling, illus. 2001. 128p. (J). (ps-1). 14.99 (978-0-06-029325-3(X)); lib. bdg. 15.89 (978-0-06-029326-0(8)) HarperCollins Pubs.

—When the Circus Came to Town. 2004. (gr. 3-6). lib. bdg. 14.15 (978-0-613-86716-0(5)) Tandem Library Bks.

Yep, Laurence & Yep, Laurence. When the Circus Came to Town. Wang, Suling, illus. 2004. 128p. (J). (ps-k). pap. 5.99 (978-0-06-440965-0(1) , Harper Trophy) HarperCollins Pubs.

Young, Karen Romano. Cobwebs. 400p. 2005. (YA). pap. 7.99 (978-0-06-441028-1(5) , HarperTeen); 2004. (J). (gr. 7 up). lib. bdg. 16.89 (978-0-06-029762-6(X)) HarperCollins Pubs.

Zarr, Sara. Story of a Girl. 2007. 208p. (J). (gr. 7-17). 16.99 (978-0-316-01453-3(2)) Little Brown & Co.

Zobel-Nolan, Allia. What I Like about Me! A Book Celebrating Differences. 2005. (Illus.). 14p. (J). 14.99 (978-0-7944-0763-6(3)) Reader's Digest Assn., Inc., The.

Zoehfeld, Kathleen Weidner. Curious You: You're on Your Way! Rey, H. A., illus. 2008. 32p. (gr. k). 12.95 (***978-0-618-91975-8(9)***) Houghton Mifflin Co.

Zusak, Markus. I Am the Messenger. 368p. (YA). 2005. (gr. 9). 16.95 (978-0-375-83099-0(5)); 2005. (gr. 9). lib. bdg. 18.99 (978-0-375-93099-7(X)); 2006. (gr. 7). reprint ed. pap. 8.95 (978-0-375-83667-1(5)) Random Hse. Children's Bks. (Knopf Bks. for Young Readers).

SELF-GOVERNMENT

see Democracy

SELF-INSTRUCTION

see Self-Culture

SELF-MUTILATION

Lee, Jordan. Coping with Self-Mutilation. 1999. (Coping Skills Library). 128p. (YA). (gr. 6 up). pap. 6.95 (978-1-56838-253-1(7)) Hazelden Publishing & Educational Services.

Nadelson, Carol C. & Reinburg, Claire E., eds. Cutting the Pain Away: Understanding Self-Mutilation. 1999. (Encyclopedia of Psychological Disorders Ser.). (Illus.). 88p. (YA). (gr. 6 up). 35.00 (978-0-7910-4951-8(5) , Chelsea Hse.) Facts On File, Inc.

Simpson, Carolyn & Clarke, Alicia. Coping with Self-Mutilation: A Helping Book for Teens Who Hurt Themselves. 1999. (Coping Ser.). (Illus.). 104p. (YA). (gr. 7-12). lib. bdg. 26.50 (978-0-8239-2559-9(5) , COSEMU) Rosen Publishing Group, Inc., The.

Winkler, Kathleen. Cutting & Self-Mutilation: When Teens Injure Themselves. 2003. (Teen Issues Ser.). (Illus.). 64p. (YA). (gr. 6-12). lib. bdg. 22.60 (978-0-7660-1956-0(X)) Enslow Pubs., Inc.

SELF-MUTILATION—FICTION

Carlson, Melody. Blade Silver: Color Me Scarred. 2005. 197p. (YA). (gr. 8-12). pap. 12.99 (978-1-57683-535-7(9)) NavPress Publishing Group.

Jablonski, Carla. Thicker Than Water. 2007. 272p. (YA). (gr. 9-12). pap. 8.99 (978-1-59514-123-1(5) , Razorbill) Penguin Group (USA) Inc.

McCormick, Patricia. Cut. unabr. ed. 2004. 168p. (J). (gr. 7 up). pap. 36.00 incl. audio (978-0-8072-0868-7(X) , LYA 320 SP, Listening Library) Random Hse. Audio Publishing Group.

—Cut. 2002. (Illus.). 160p. (J). (gr. 7 up). pap. 6.99 (978-0-439-32459-5(9) , PUSH) Scholastic, Inc.

—Cut. 2002. 13.64 (978-0-606-22261-7(8)); (gr. 7-12). lib. bdg. 15.30 (978-0-613-49394-9(X)) Tandem Library Bks.

Stoehr, Shelley. Crosses. 2003. (gr. 7-12). lib. bdg. 23.40 (978-0-613-86660-6(6)) Tandem Library Bks.

—Crosses. 2003. 161p. (YA). pap. 13.95 (978-0-595-26952-5(4) , Backinprint.com) iUniverse, Inc.

Wilson, Dawn. Saint Jude. 2000. (Illus.). 171p. (YA). (gr. 6-12). pap. 15.95 (978-0-936389-68-4(0)) Tudor Pubs., Inc.

SELF-PERCEPTION

Apel, Melanie Ann. Let's Talk about When You Think Nobody Likes You. 2002. (Let's Talk Library). (Illus.). 24p. (J). lib. bdg. 18.75 (978-0-8239-5862-7(0) , PowerKids Pr.) Rosen Publishing Group, Inc., The.

Barrington Jones, Barbara & Thomas, Janet. Dear Barbara: Answers to the Most-Asked Questions from Teenage Girls. 1998. (YA). pap. 13.95 (978-1-57345-369-1(2)) Deseret Bk. Co.

Brighter Vision Publishing Staff. About Me. 2000. (My Discovery Bks.). (Illus.). 20p. (J). (ps). pap. 2.95 (978-1-55254-209-5(2)) Brighter Vision Pubns.

Carroll, Joan. Smile a Seven Step Journey Toward Self-Discovery & Leadership Empowerment. Glevicky, Greg, illus. 2000. 100p. (YA). pap. 9.95 (978-1-881223-18-4(3)) Zulema Enterprises.

Charlip, Remy & Moore, Lilian. Hooray for Me! Williams, Vera B., illus. 2004. 40p. (YA). (ps up). 14.95 (978-1-883672-43-0(0) , Tricycle Pr.) Ten Speed Pr.

Chiu, Christina. Eating Disorder Survivors Tell Their Stories. 1999. (Teen Eating Disorder Prevention Library). 64p. (YA). (gr. 3-10). pap. 6.95 (978-1-56838-259-3(6)) Hazelden Publishing & Educational Services.

Davis, Brangien. What's Real, What's Ideal: Overcoming a Negative Body Image. 1999. (Teen Eating Disorder Prevention Library). 64p. (YA). (gr. 3-10). pap. 6.95 (978-1-56838-258-6(8)) Hazelden Publishing & Educational Services.

Douglas, Ann & Douglas, Julie. Body Talk: The Straight Facts on Fitness, Nutrition, & Feeling Great about Yourself! Davila, Claudia, illus. 2nd ed. 2006. (Girl Zone Ser.). 64p. (J). 19.95 (978-1-897066-62-1(7)); pap. 9.95 (978-1-897066-61-4(9)) Maple Tree Pr. CAN. *Dist:* Perseus Distribution.

Espeland, Pamela. Knowing Me, Knowing You: The I-Sight Way to Understand Yourself & Others. 2004. (Illus.). 128p. (YA). (gr. 8-12). pap. 13.95 (978-1-57542-090-5(2)) Free Spirit Publishing, Inc.

Freidmann, Frank. Who Am I? McCormick, Joe, illus. 1998. 20p. (ps-3). pap. 4.99 (978-1-58169-018-7(5) , Evergreen Pr.) Genesis Communications, Inc.

Funston, Sylvia. The Book of You: The Science & Fun! of Why You Look, Feel & Act the Way You Do. Denti, Susanna, illus. Duclos, Gilbert, photos by. 2000. 48p. (J). (gr. 3-7). (978-1-895688-95-5(7)) Maple Tree Pr. CAN. *Dist:* Firefly Bks., Ltd.

Huber, Cheri. There Is Nothing Wrong with You for Teens. Shiver, June, illus. 2001. 276p. (gr. 9 up). pap. 12.00 (978-0-9636255-9-5(4)) Keep it Simple Bks.

Kelly, Dorothy A. Developing a Sense of Self: A Workbook of Tenets & Tactics for Adolescent Girls. 2006. (Illus.). 146p. (J). pap. 29.99 (978-0-87101-366-8(5) , NASW Pr.) National Assn. of Social Workers/NASW Pr.

Lazear, Jonathon. Come On, Get Happy. 2004. (Illus.). 384p. (978-0-00-717532-1(9) , HarperElement) HarperCollins Pubs. Ltd.

Marks, James Lynn. I Have an Idea! 2000. (Education Through Creation Ser.: Bk. 1). (Illus.). 16p. (J). (ps-6). pap. 9.95 (978-0-9706412-0-5(6) , 1001) Seventh Sun Productions.

McGraw-Hill Staff & School Specialty Publishing Staff. I Am Special. 2001. (Homework Helpers Activity Bks.). (Illus.). 56p. (J). (gr. k-1). pap., act. bk. ed. 2.99 (978-0-7682-0683-8(9) , FS109012, Schaffer, Frank) Schaffer, Frank Pubns.

Meister, Cari. What Can I Be? 2004. (Rookie Reader Skill Set Ser.). 23p. (J). (gr. k-2). pap. 4.95 (978-0-516-27810-0(X) , Children's Pr.) Scholastic Library Publishing.

Mirriam-Goldberg, Caryn. Write Where You Are: How to Use Writing to Make Sense of Your Life: A Guide for Teens. 2004. (Illus.). 168p. (YA). (gr. 7-12). pap. 14.95 (978-1-57542-060-8(0)) Free Spirit Publishing, Inc.

Moe, Barbara. Understanding the Causes of a Negative Body Image. 1999. (Teen Eating Disorder Prevention Library). 144p. (gr. 7-12). pap. 6.95 (978-1-56838-262-3(6)) Hazelden Publishing & Educational Services.

Orr, Tamra B. When the Mirror Lies: Anorexia, Bulimia, & Other Eating Disorders. 2006. (Illus.). 144p. (J). (gr. 9-12). 30.50 (978-0-531-16791-5(7)); pap. 17.95 (***978-0-531-17977-2(X)***) Scholastic Library Publishing. (Watts, Franklin).

Phillips, Karen. It's All about Me! 2006. (Illus.). 70p. (YA). spiral bd. 14.95 (978-1-57054-225-1(2)) Klutz.

Rue, Nancy N. The Uniquely Me Book: It's a God Thing! 2002. (Ywof Library Ser.). 112p. (J). pap. 7.99 (978-0-310-70248-1(8)) Zonderkidz.

Shaw, Tucker. Who Do You Think You Are? 12 Methods for Analyzing the True You. Gonzalez, Chuck, illus. 2001. 159p. (YA). (gr. 7-12). pap. 7.99 (978-0-14-131091-6(X) , Puffin) Penguin Group (USA) Inc.

Wandberg, Robert. Self-Direction: Taking Positive Risks, Following Your Dreams. 2000. (Contemporary Issues Ser.). (Illus.). 64p. (J). (gr. 4-6). lib. bdg. 23.93 (978-0-7368-0696-1(2) , LifeMatters Bks.) Capstone Pr., Inc.

Willett, Edward. Negative Body Image. 2006. (Danger Zone Ser.). (Illus.). 64p. (J). (gr. 7-12). lib. bdg. 27.95 (***978-1-4042-1995-3(1)***) Rosen Publishing Group, Inc., The.

SELF-PERCEPTION—FICTION

Almond, David. Secret Heart. 2004. 224p. (YA). (gr. 7). pap. 5.99 (978-0-440-41827-6(5) , Laurel Leaf) Random Hse. Children's Bks.

Angelou, Maya. Cedric of Jamaica. Rockwell, Lizzy, illus. 2005. (Random House Pictureback Book Ser.). (J). (978-0-375-83269-7(6)); lib. bdg. (978-0-375-93269-4(0)) Random Hse., Inc.

Arrington, Aileen. Paper Heart. 2006. 113p. (J). 16.95 (978-1-932425-61-1(6) , Lemniscaat) Boyds Mills Pr.

Auerbach, Annie. Spongebob Superstar, Vol. 5. 2004. 64p. (J). (gr. 2-5). pap. 17.00 incl. audio (978-1-4000-8628-3(0) , Listening Library) Random Hse. Audio Publishing Group.

Bang, Molly Garrett. Tiger's Fall. Bang, Molly Garrett, illus. rev. ed. 2001. (Illus.). 112p. (J). (gr. 4-7). 15.95 (978-0-8050-6689-0(6) , Holt, Henry & Co. Bks. For Young Readers) Holt, Henry & Co.

Barnwell, Ysaye M. No Mirrors in My Nana's House. Saint James, Synthia, illus. 1998. 32p. (J). (gr. k-3). 18.00 (978-0-15-201825-2(5)) Harcourt Children's Bks.

—No Mirrors in My Nana's House: Musical CD & Book. Saint James, Synthia, illus. 2005. 32p. (J). reprint ed. 8.00 (978-0-15-205243-0(7) , Voyager Bks./Libros Viajeros) Harcourt Children's Bks.

Bencastro, Mario. A Promise to Keep. Giersbach-Rascon, Susan, tr. from SPA. 2005. 134p. (J). (gr. 3-7). pap. 9.95 (978-1-55885-457-4(6) , Piñata Books) Arte Publico Pr.

Bennett, Cherie. Life in the Fat Lane. 1999. 272p. (YA). (gr. 7-12). pap. 5.99 (978-0-440-22029-9(7) , Laurel Leaf) Random Hse. Children's Bks.

—Life in the Fat Lane. 1999. (YA). (gr. 7 up). pap., stu. ed. 57.24 incl. audio (978-0-7887-2665-1(X) , 40825) Recorded Bks., LLC.

—Life in the Fat Lane. 1999. (YA). (978-0-606-16720-8(X)); (gr. 7-12). lib. bdg. 13.00 (978-0-613-16143-5(2)) Tandem Library Bks.

—Life in the Fat Lane. l.t. ed. 2000. 351p. (YA). (gr. 8-12). 21.95 (978-0-7862-2887-4(3)) Thorndike Pr.

Bernasconi, Pablo. The Wizard, the Ugly, & the Book of Shame. Bernasconi, Pablo, illus. 2005. (Illus.). 32p. (J). (ps-3). 16.95 (978-1-58234-673-1(9)) Bloomsbury Publishing.

Bloomfield, Denise. More Than A Spoonful. 2007. 28p. (J). mass mkt. 12.95 (***978-0-9778113-0-4(1)***) HeartFelt Stories LLC.

Borden, Louise. A. Lincoln & Me. 2000. (J). 12.79 (978-0-606-19625-3(0)) Tandem Library Bks.

—A Lincoln & Me. 2001. (gr. k-3). lib. bdg. 14.15 (978-0-613-33661-1(5)) Tandem Library Bks.

Borden, Louise W. A. Lincoln & Me. Lewin, Ted, illus. 2001. 32p. (J). (gr. 4). pap. 5.99 (978-0-590-45715-6(2)) Scholastic, Inc.

Brian, Kate. Sweet 16. 2007. 288p. (YA). pap. 8.99 (***978-1-4169-0033-7(0)*** , Simon Pulse) Simon & Schuster Children's Publishing.

Brightwood, Laura, illus. Look What You've Done. Brightwood, Laura, . 2007. (J). DVD (***978-1-934409-03-9(0)***) 3-C Institute for Social Development.

Broski, Julie. Being Me. Vigla, Vincent, illus. 2006. (Rookie Reader Skill Set Ser.). 32p. (J). (gr. k-2). 19.50 (978-0-516-24975-9(4) , Children's Pr.) Scholastic Library Publishing.

Brown, Devin. Not Exactly Normal. 2006. 238p. (J). pap. 8.00 (978-0-8028-5287-8(4) , Eerdmans Bks For Young Readers) Eerdmans, William B. Publishing Co.

Brown, Lisa. How to Be. Brown, Lisa, illus. 2006. (Illus.). 32p. (J). 15.99 (978-0-06-054635-9(2)); lib. bdg. 16.89 (978-0-06-054636-6(0)) HarperCollins Pubs.

Bullard, Lisa. Marvelous Me: Inside & Out. Wesley, Omarr, illus. 2004. (All about Me Ser.). 24p. (C). (gr. k-1). 21.26 (978-1-4048-0042-7(5)) Picture Window Bks.

Burns, Suzanne. The Moon Painters. 2003. 192p. 14.00 (978-1-894942-36-2(1)) Zumaya Pubns. LLC.

Cabot, Meg. Perfect Princess. McLaren, Chesley, illus. 2004. (Princess Diaries). 160p. (J). (gr. 7 up). 12.99 (978-0-06-052679-5(3)) HarperCollins Pubs.

Caletti, Deb. Honey, Baby, Sweetheart. 320p. (YA). 2005. pap. 7.99 (978-0-689-86474-2(4) , Simon Pulse); 2004. 15.95 (978-0-689-86765-1(4)) Simon & Schuster Children's Publishing.

—Honey, Baby, Sweetheart. l.t. ed. 2005. 367p. 22.95 (978-0-7862-7308-9(9) , Large Print Pr.) Thorndike Pr.

Cameron, Ann. Secret Life of Amanda K Woods. 1999. (gr. 3-6). lib. bdg. 14.15 (978-0-613-23031-5(0)) Tandem Library Bks.

Cameron, Peter. Someday This Pain Will Be Useful to You. 2007. 240p. (YA). (gr. 9 up). 16.00 (978-0-374-30989-3(2)) Farrar, Straus & Giroux.

Cann, Kate. Spanish Holiday: Or, How I Transformed the Worst Vacation Ever into the Best Sum. 2004. (gr. 7-12). lib. bdg. 14.15 (978-0-613-71954-4(9)) Tandem Library Bks.

Carlson, Melody. Becoming Me. 2000. (Diary of a Teenage Girl Ser.: Bk. 1). (Illus.). 256p. (YA). pap. 12.99 (978-1-57673-735-4(7) , Multnomah) WaterBrook Pr.

Castellucci, Cecil. Beige. 2007. (Illus.). 304p. (YA). (gr. 9 up). 16.99 (***978-0-7636-3066-9(7)***) Candlewick Pr.

Castellucci, Cecil. The Queen of Cool. 2006. 176p. (YA). (gr. 9). 15.99 (978-0-7636-2720-1(8)) Candlewick Pr.

—The Queen of Cool. l.t. rev. ed. 2007. 172p. (YA). 22.95 (***978-0-7862-9551-7(1)***) Thorndike Pr.

Charlip, Remy & Moore, Lilian. Hooray for Me! 2007. (Illus.). 40p. (J). pap. 7.95 (***978-1-58246-201-1(1)*** , Tricycle Pr.) Ten Speed Pr.

Chiazzo, Chi. Makinga. 2000. 101p. 9.95 (978-978-34301-4-3(9)) College Pr. Pubs. NGA. *Dist:* Michigan State Univ. Pr.

Christopher, Matt. Center Court Sting. 1998. 160p. (J). (gr. 3-7). pap. 4.99 (978-0-316-14205-2(0)) Little Brown & Co.

—Center Court Sting. 1998. 140p. (J). (ps-7). per. 12.40 (978-0-613-11395-3(0)) Tandem Library Bks.

—Slam Dunk. 2004. (Illus.). 128p. (J). (gr. 4-7). pap. 4.99 (978-0-316-60762-9(2)) Little Brown & Co.

Christopher, Matt & #1 Sports Writer for Kids Staff. Center Court Sting. 1998. 160p. (J). (gr. 3-7). 15.95 (978-0-316-14278-6(6)) Little Brown & Co.

Clifton, Dorinda. Everybody Is Somebody. 2006. (J). 6.95 (978-0-9771973-2-3(8)) Bedbug Pr., Inc.

Clinton, Cathryn. The Eyes of Van Gogh. 2007. (Illus.). 224p. (YA). (gr. 9 up). 16.99 (***978-0-7636-2245-9(1)***) Candlewick Pr.

Coburn, Jake. Prep. 2005. 192p. (YA). (gr. 7). pap. 5.99 (978-0-14-240307-5(5) , Puffin) Penguin Group (USA) Inc.

Coles, William E., Jr. Another Kind of Monday. 1999. 246p. per. 14.64 (978-0-606-16357-6(3)) Tandem Library Bks.

Condon, Bill. A Waste of Space. Tulloch, Coral, illus. 1999. (Supa Doopers Ser.). 64p. (J). (978-0-7608-3294-3(3)) Sundance/Newbridge Educational Publishing.

—Waste of Space. 1999. (gr. 3-6). lib. bdg. 12.60 (978-0-613-30846-5(8)) Tandem Library Bks.

Connelly, Wendy. Fiona the Firefly! 2003. (Illus.). (J). 12.95 (978-1-929039-16-6(6)) Ambassador Bks., Inc.

S

Cooper, Patrick. I Is Someone Else. 304p. (YA). 2007. (gr. 7-11). mass mkt. 6.50 (978-0-440-23919-2(2) , Laurel Leaf); 2006. (Illus.). (gr. 9). 16.95 (978-0-385-73269-7(4) , Delacorte Bks. for Young Readers); 2006. (Illus.). (gr. 9). lib. bdg. 18.99 (978-0-385-90286-1(7) , Delacorte Bks. for Young Readers) Random Hse. Children's Bks.

Copeland, Cynthia L. The 15 Best Things about Being the New Kid. Vargo, Sharon Hawkins, illus. 2006. (Silly Millies Ser.). 32p. (J). 21.27 (978-0-7613-2889-6(0) , Millbrook Pr.) Lerner Publishing Group.

Coyle, Carmela LaVigna. Do Princesses Wear Hiking Boots? Gordon, Mike & Gordon, Carl, illus. 2003. 32p. (J). 15.95 (978-0-87358-828-7(2) , Rising Moon Bks. for Young Readers) Northland Publishing.

Crutcher, Chris. Deadline. 2007. 320p. (gr. 9 up). (J). 16.99 (***978-0-06-085089-0(2)***); (YA). lib. bdg. 17.89 (***978-0-06-085090-6(6)***) HarperCollins Pubs. (Greenwillow Bks.).

Dalton, Annie & Dalton, Maria. Invisible Threads. 2006. 208p. (YA). (gr. 9). 15.95 (978-0-385-73286-4(4)); lib. bdg. 17.99 (978-0-385-90303-5(0)) Random Hse. Children's Bks. (Delacorte Bks. for Young Readers).

Davidson, Dana. Jason & Kyra. 2005. 352p. (gr. 7-17). pap. 5.99 (978-0-7868-3653-6(9) , Jump at the Sun) Hyperion Bks. for Children.

Davies, Nicola. Tangled Webs. 2000. 120p. (YA). pap. 12.95 (978-1-85902-847-6(0)) Beekman Bks., Inc.

Duder, Tessa. Tiggie Thompson All at Sea. 2001. 232p. (YA). pap. (978-0-14-131323-8(4) , Puffin) Penguin Group (USA) Inc.

Durrant, George D. Shakespeare's Best Work: A Novel of Unexpected Family Ties & Uncommon Faith. 2003. 130p. (YA). pap. 10.95 (978-1-55517-709-6(3) , 77093, Bonneville Bks.) Cedar Fort, Inc./CFI Distribution.

Emerson, Carl. Sally the Salamander's Lost Tail. Trover, Zachary, illus. 2007. (Animal Underdogs Ser.). 32p. (J). (ps-4). lib. bdg. 27.07 (***978-1-60270-018-5(4)*** , Looking Glass Library) Magic Wagon.

Erlbruch, Wolf. The Big Question. Reynolds, Michael, tr. from FRE. 2005. (Illus.). 52p. (ps-7). pap. 14.95 (978-1-933372-03-7(6)) Europa Editions, Inc.

Evangelista, Beth. Gifted. 192p. (J). 2007. pap. 6.95 (***978-0-8027-9644-8(3)***); 2005. (gr. 5-9). 16.95 (978-0-8027-8994-5(3)) Walker & Co.

Fisher, Dorothy Canfield. Understood Betsy. Root, Kimberly B., illus. rev. ed. 1999. 240p. (J). (gr. 4-6). 17.95 (978-0-8050-6073-7(1) , Holt, Henry & Co. Bks. For Young Readers) Holt, Henry & Co.

—Understood Betsy. 2004. reprint ed. pap. 1.99 (978-1-4192-9201-9(3)); pap. 24.95 (978-1-4179-0955-1(2)) Kessinger Publishing, LLC.

—Understood Betsy. 1999. (Hardscrabble Bks.). 182p. (J). reprint ed. pap. 9.95 (978-0-87451-920-4(9)) Univ. Pr. of New England.

Fleischman, Paul. Breakout. 2005. (Illus.). 137p. (YA). (gr. 7-12). lib. bdg. 15.60 (978-1-4176-6932-5(2)) Tandem Library Bks.

Fletcher, Christine. Tallulah Falls. (YA). 2007. 400p. pap. 7.95 (***978-1-59990-095-7(5)***); 2006. 304p. 16.95 (978-1-58234-662-5(3)) Bloomsbury Publishing. (Bloomsbury Children).

Friedrich, Molly. You're Not My Real Mother! Hale, Christy, tr. Hale, Christy, illus. 2004. 32p. (J). (ps-3). 15.99 (978-0-316-60553-3(0) , Tingley, Megan Bks.) Little, Brown Bks. for Young Readers.

Gagne, Michel. Insanely Twisted Rabbits. 2001. (Illus.). 32p. 14.95 (978-0-9666404-4-1(6)) Gagne International Pr.

Gantos, Jack. Best in Show for Rotten Ralph: A Rotten Ralph Rotten Reader. Rubel, Nicole, illus. 2005. (Rotten Ralph Reader Ser.: No. 4). 48p. (J). 15.00 (978-0-374-36358-1(7) , Farrar, Straus & Giroux (BYR)) Farrar, Straus & Giroux.

—Jack on the Tracks: Four Seasons of Fifth Grade. 1999. (Jack Henry Ser.). (Illus.). 192p. (J). (gr. 5-9). 16.00 (978-0-374-33665-3(2) , Farrar, Straus & Giroux (BYR)) Farrar, Straus & Giroux.

Gerber, Linda. Now & Zen. Pilkington, Roger, ed. 2006. (S. A. S. S. (Students Across the Seven Seas) Ser.). 224p. (YA). (gr. 7). pap. 6.99 (978-0-14-240657-1(0) , Puffin) Penguin Group (USA) Inc.

Gordon, Amy. Magic by Heart. Gustavson, Adam, illus. 2007. 128p. (J). (gr. 3-7). 16.95 (***978-0-8234-1995-1(9)***) Holiday Hse., Inc.

Goss, Leon. Selfus Esteemus Personalitus Low. Tunell, Ken, illus. 2005. (J). pap. (978-1-933156-08-8(2) , VisionQuest Kids) GSVQ Publishing.

Goss, Leon, 3rd. Selfus Esteemus Personalitus Low. Tunell, Ken, illus. ed. 2005. 32p. (J). per. 17.95 (978-1-933156-00-2(7) , VisionQuest Kids) GSVQ Publishing.

Gould, Jason. Jinx. 2004. 215p. (YA). (gr. 9-17). per. 14.04 (978-0-606-30072-8(4)) Tandem Library Bks.

Graves, Keith. Three Nasty Gnarlies. Graves, Keith, illus. 2003. (Illus.). 40p. (J). pap. 16.95 (978-0-439-24090-1(5)) Scholastic, Inc.

Green, John. An Abundance of Katherines. 256p. (YA). 2008. pap. 8.99 (***978-0-14-241070-7(5)*** , Puffin); 2006. (gr. 9). 16.99 (978-0-525-47688-7(1) , Dutton Juvenile) Penguin Group (USA) Inc.

Greene, Stephanie. Moose's Big Idea. Matthieu, Joe, illus. 2005. 51p. (J). (gr. 1-3). 14.95 (978-0-7614-5212-6(5)) Cavendish, Marshall Corp.

Griffin, Adele. My Almost Epic Summer. 2008. 176p. (YA). (gr. 7). pap. 6.99 (***978-0-14-240805-6(0)*** , Puffin); 2006. 192p. (J). (gr. 4). 15.99 (978-0-399-23784-3(4) , Putnam Juvenile) Penguin Group (USA) Inc.

Griffin, Adele. My Almost Epic Summer (Splashproof Ed.) 2007. 1p. (YA). (gr. 7). pap. 6.99 (978-0-14-240860-5(3) , Puffin) Penguin Group (USA) Inc.

Grimes, Nikki. Dark Sons. 2005. 224p. (gr. 7-17). 15.99 (978-0-7868-1888-4(3)) Hyperion Bks. for Children.

Grover, Lorie Ann. On Pointe. 2004. 320p. (J). 17.99 (978-0-689-86525-1(2) , McElderry, Margaret K.) Simon & Schuster Children's Publishing.

Hacker, Michael. Who Am I? Dillard, Karen, illus. 2000. 24p. (J). (ps). 7.99 (978-1-56309-736-2(2)) New Hope Pubs.

Halpern, Julie. Get Well Soon. 2007. 208p. (YA). (gr. 7 up). 16.95 (***978-0-312-36795-4(3)***) Feiwel & Friends.

Hayes, Sonia. Ms. Thang. 2006. (ENG.). 192p. (YA). per. 9.95 (978-0-9777573-0-5(7)) NUA Multimedia.

Hayes, Sonia. Urban Goddess. 2007. 224p. (YA). per. 9.95 (***978-0-9777573-1-2(5)***) NUA Multimedia.

Henkes, Kevin. Olive's Ocean. 224p. (J). 2003. (gr. 5 up). 15.99 (978-0-06-053543-8(1) , 53396925); 2003. (gr. 5 up). lib. bdg. 16.89 (978-0-06-053544-5(X)); 2005. (gr. k-9). reprint ed. pap. 6.99 (978-0-06-053545-2(8) , Harper Trophy) HarperCollins Pubs.

Hill, Elizabeth Starr. Wildfire! Shepperson, Rob, illus. 2004. 80p. (J). 16.00 (978-0-374-37712-6(7) , Farrar, Straus & Giroux (BYR)) Farrar, Straus & Giroux.

Hill, Karen. I Am Good at Being Me. Graef, Renee, illus. 2005. 24p. (J). 3.99 (978-1-4169-0319-2(4)); 9.99 (978-1-4169-0512-7(X)) Simon & Schuster Children's Publishing. (Little Simon).

Hoffman, Alice. Indigo. 96p. (J). 2003. pap. 5.99 (978-0-439-25636-0(4) , Scholastic Paperbacks); 2002. (Illus.). (gr. 5 up). pap. 16.95 (978-0-439-25635-3(6) , Scholastic Pr.) Scholastic, Inc.

Holm, Jennifer L. An Adventure. 2002. (Boston Jane Ser.). 288p. (J). (gr. k-17). pap. 6.99 (978-0-06-440849-3(3)) HarperCollins Pubs.

Holman, Sandy Lynne. Grandpa, Is Everything Black Bad? Holman, Sandy Lynne, ed. Kometiani, Lela, illus. 1998. 32p. (J). (gr. 2-6). lib. bdg. 18.95 (978-0-9644655-0-3(7)) Culture C.O.-O.P., The.

Horvath, Polly. The Vacation. 2005. 208p. (J). 16.00 (978-0-374-38070-0(8) , Farrar, Straus & Giroux (BYR)) Farrar, Straus & Giroux.

Hurwin, Davida Wills. Circle the Soul Softly. 2006. 176p. (J). 15.99 (978-0-06-077505-6(X)); lib. bdg. 16.89 (978-0-06-077506-3(8)) HarperCollins Pubs.

Jaffe, Gail Lois. The Enchanted Mirror. Holmes, Jon, ed. 32p. (YA). (gr. 6 up). 24.95 (978-0-9667476-0-7(7)) Papillon Pr., Inc.

Jenkins, A. M. Out of Order. 256p. (J). 2005. pap. 6.99 (978-0-06-447374-3(0)); 2003. lib. bdg. 16.89 (978-0-06-623969-9(9)) HarperCollins Pubs.

Johnson, Vincent L. Of Corn Silk & Black Braids. Crockett, Linda, illus. 2005. 32p. (J). (gr. k-3). 17.95 (978-0-9657033-2-1(0)) Marzetta Bks.

Jones, Christianne C. Emma's New Look. 2007. (Illus.). 24p. (J). (***978-1-4048-1230-7(X)***) Picture Window Bks.

—Emma's New Look. Yilmaz, Necdet, illus. 2006. (Read It! Readers Ser.). 32p. (J). (gr. 1-2). 19.93 (***978-1-4048-3138-4(X)***) Picture Window Bks.

Jones, Diana Wynne. The Merlin Conspiracy. 480p. (J). (gr. 5 up). 2004. pap. 6.99 (978-0-06-052320-6(4) , Harper Trophy); 2003. 17.89 (978-0-06-052319-0(0)); 2003. 16.99 (978-0-06-052318-3(2)) HarperCollins Pubs.

Jones, Jennifer B. The Short Story of My Life. 2004. 160p. (J). 16.95 (978-0-8027-8905-1(6)) Walker & Co.

Jones, Patrick. Nailed. (YA). 2007. 240p. (gr. 9 up). pap. 7.95 (***978-0-8027-9648-6(6)***); 2006. 224p. 16.95 (978-0-8027-8077-5(6)) Walker & Co.

Jones, Patrick. Things Change. (J). 2004. 216p. 16.95 (978-0-8027-8901-3(3)); 2006. 228p. reprint ed. pap. 7.95 (978-0-8027-7746-1(5)) Walker & Co.

Juby, Susan. Alice MacLeod, Realist at Last. 2006. 320p. (J). pap. 8.99 (978-0-06-051552-2(X) , HarperTeen) HarperCollins Pubs.

Kashino, Mark. The Journey of Mobius & Sidh: An Interactive Journey of Self Discovery. Kashino, Mark, illus. 2nd l.t. ed. 2001. 48p. 19.95 (978-0-9715709-0-0(6) , KEI Publishing) Kashino Enterprises, Inc.

Kipling, Rudyard. Captains Courageous. Landgraf, Ken, illus. 2002. (Great Illustrated Classics Ser.).Tr. of 200. 240p. (J). (gr. 3-8). 21.35 (978-1-57765-683-8(0) , ABDO & Daughters) ABDO Publishing Co.

—Captains Courageous. 1999. (Dover Juvenile Classics Ser.).Tr. of 200. (J). (Illus.). 176p. (gr. 4-7). pap. 2.50 (978-0-486-40786-9(1)); (978-0-04-864078-9(6)) Dover Pubns., Inc.

—Captains Courageous. 1999. Tr. of 200. (gr. 3-6). lib. bdg. 10.10 (978-0-613-90755-2(8)) Tandem Library Bks.

Klass, David. You Don't Know Me. 2001. 272p. (YA). (gr. 7 up). 18.00 (978-0-374-38706-8(0) , Farrar, Straus & Giroux (BYR)) Farrar, Straus & Giroux.

—You Don't Know Me. 2002. (gr. 7-12). lib. bdg. 15.30 (978-0-613-53336-2(4)) Tandem Library Bks.

Klinger, Shula. The Kingdom of Strange. 2008. (YA). (***978-0-7614-5395-6(4)***) Cavendish, Marshall Corp.

Klise, Kate. Deliver Us from Normal. 2005. 240p. (YA). (gr. 5-9). 16.95 (978-0-439-52322-6(2)) Scholastic, Inc.

—Deliver Us from Normal: Read-Along/Homework Pack. unabr. ed. 2005. (YA). (gr. 5-8). 65.70 incl. audio (978-1-4193-3619-5(3) , 42050) Recorded Bks., LLC.

Koertge, Ron. Boy Girl Boy. 2007. (Illus.). 180p. (YA). (gr. 9 up). pap. 6.95 (978-0-15-205865-4(6) , Harcourt Paperbacks) Harcourt Children's Bks.

Koertge, Ronald. Boy Girl Boy. 2005. 176p. (YA). (gr. 9-17). 16.00 (978-0-15-205325-3(5)) Harcourt Children's Bks.

Kogler, Jennifer Anne. Ruby Tuesday. 2005. 320p. (J). (gr. 7 up). 15.99 (978-0-06-073956-0(8)) HarperCollins Pubs.

Koja, Kathe. Going Under. 2006. 128p. (YA). 16.00 (978-0-374-30393-8(2) , Frances Foster Bks.) Farrar, Straus & Giroux.

Koja, Kathe. Talk. 2005. 144p. (YA). 16.00 (978-0-374-37382-5(5) , Farrar, Straus & Giroux (BYR)) Farrar, Straus & Giroux.

—Talk. 2008. 160p. (YA). pap. 6.99 (***978-0-312-37605-5(7)***) Square Fish.

—Talk. l.t. ed. 2006. 183p. (YA). 21.95 (978-0-7862-8811-3(6)) Thorndike Pr.

Korman, Gordon. Jake, Reinvented. 2005. 224p. (gr. 7-17). pap. 5.99 (978-0-7868-5697-8(1)) Hyperion Bks. for Children.

Lantz, Francess L. Fade Far Away. 1999. 176p. (YA). (gr. 7-12). pap. 6.99 (978-0-380-79372-3(5)) HarperCollins Pubs.

—Fade Far Away. 1999. (J). (978-0-606-16361-3(1)) Tandem Library Bks.

Lenain, Thierry. Little Zizi. Zolinsky, Daniel, tr. from FRE. Poulin, Stephane, illus. 2008. 32p. (J). 16.95 (***978-1-933693-05-7(3)***) Cinco Puntos Pr.

Levy, Elizabeth. My Life As a Fifth-Grade Comedian. 1998. 192p. (J). (ps-7). pap. 5.99 (978-0-06-440723-6(3) , Harper Trophy) HarperCollins Pubs.

—My Life As a Fifth-Grade Comedian. 1999. (J). pap., stu. ed. 41.20 incl. audio (978-0-7887-3180-8(7) , 40915) Recorded Bks., LLC.

Lowry, Brigid. Follow the Blue. 2004. 205p. (J). (gr. 7 up). tchr. ed. 16.95 (978-0-8234-1827-5(8)) Holiday Hse., Inc.

—Follow the Blue. 2006. 208p. (YA). pap. 8.95 (978-0-312-34297-5(7) , St. Martin's Griffin) St. Martin's Pr.

Lowry, Lois. Anastasia Elige Profesion. 2003. Tr. of Anastasia's Chosen Career. (SPA.). 188p. (J). 9.95 (978-84-239-9066-5(4)) Espasa Calpe, S.A. ESP. *Dist:* Planeta Publishing Corp.

Luper, Eric. Big Slick. 2007. 240p. (YA). (gr. 9 up). 16.00 (***978-0-374-30799-8(7)***) Farrar, Straus & Giroux.

Lyga, Barry. The Astonishing Adventures of Fanboy & Goth Girl. 2006. 320p. (YA). (gr. 8). 16.95 (978-0-618-72392-8(7)) Houghton Mifflin Co.

—The Astonishing Adventures of Fanboy & Goth Girl. 2007. 320p. (YA). (gr. 9-12). pap. 8.99 (***978-0-618-91652-8(0)***) Houghton Mifflin Co. Trade & Reference Div.

Lynch, Chris. Me, Dead Dad, & Alcatraz. 3rd ed. 2005. 240p. (J). 15.99 (978-0-06-059709-2(7)) HarperCollins Pubs.

Mackall, Dandi Daley. Just Jazz Bk. 3: Blog On! 2006. (Faithgirlz Ser.). (Illus.). 128p. (J). pap. 6.99 (978-0-310-71095-0(2)) Zonderkidz.

—Love, Annie. 2006. (Faithgirlz Ser.: Bk. 2). 128p. (J). pap. 6.99 (978-0-310-71094-3(4)) Zonderkidz.

—Storm Rising Bk. 4: Blog On! 2006. (Faithgirlz Ser.). (Illus.). 128p. (J). pap. 6.99 (978-0-310-71096-7(0)) Zonderkidz.

Mackler, Carolyn. The Earth, My Butt & Other Big Round Things. 2003. (Illus.). 256p. (YA). (gr. 9). 15.99 (978-0-7636-1958-9(2)) Candlewick Pr.

—The Earth, My Butt, & Other Big Round Things. 2005. 256p. (YA). (gr. 9 up). reprint ed. pap. 8.99 (978-0-7636-2091-2(2)) Candlewick Pr.

—Love & Other Four-Letter Words. 2005. 256p. (YA). (gr. 7). pap. 7.95 (978-0-385-73266-6(X) , Delacorte Bks. for Young Readers) Random Hse. Children's Bks.

—Love & Other Four-Letter Words. 2002. (gr. 7-12). lib. bdg. 13.55 (978-0-613-72272-8(8)) Tandem Library Bks.

Maclean, Christine. Mary Margaret, Center Stage. Vicky, Lowe, illus. 2007. 176p. (J). (gr. 3). pap. 5.99 (978-0-14-240768-4(2) , Puffin) Penguin Group (USA) Inc.

—Mary Margaret, Center Stage. 2006. (Illus.). 160p. (J). (gr. 3). 15.99 (978-0-525-47597-2(4) , Dutton Juvenile) Penguin Group (USA) Inc.

Mallat, Kathy. Mama Love. Mallat, Kathy, illus. 2004. (Illus.). 24p. (J). 15.95 (978-0-8027-8902-0(1)) Walker & Co.

Manning, Sarra. Pretty Things (Splashproof Ed.) 2007. 1p. (YA). (gr. 7). pap. 6.99 (978-0-14-240859-9(X) , Puffin) Penguin Group (USA) Inc.

Marvelous Me. (All about Me Ser.). 24p. (J). 6.95 (978-1-4048-0157-8(X)) Picture Window Bks.

Matcheck, Diane. The Sacrifice. 1999. (978-0-606-17598-2(9)) Tandem Library Bks.

May, Eleanor. The Real Me. Gott, Barry, illus. 2006. (Social Studies Connects). 32p. (J). (gr. k-3). pap. 4.99 (978-1-57565-186-6(6)) Kane Pr., The.

McKee, David. The Conquerors. 2004. (Illus.). 25p. (J). (gr. k-3). 16.95 (978-1-59354-078-4(7)) Handprint Bks.

McNamara, Margaret. How Many Seeds in a Pumpkin? Karas, G. Brian, illus. 2007. 40p. (J). (ps-2). 14.99 (978-0-375-84014-2(1)); lib. bdg. 17.99 (***978-0-375-94014-9(6)***) Random Hse. Children's Bks. (Schwartz & Wade Bks.).

Meehl, Brian. Out of Patience. 2008. 304p. 6.50 (***978-0-440-42090-3(3)*** , Yearling) Dell Bks. for Young Readers CAN. *Dist:* Random Hse., Inc.

—Out of Patience. 2006. 304p. (gr. 4-7). (J). 15.95 (978-0-385-73299-4(6)); lib. bdg. 17.99 (978-0-385-90320-2(0)) Random Hse. Children's Bks. (Delacorte Bks. for Young Readers).

—Out of Patience. l.t. ed. 2006. (J). 22.95 (978-0-7862-8968-4(6)) Thorndike Pr.

Messer, Celeste M. Andi's Choice. Hoeffner, Deb, illus. 2004. 82-92p. 4.95 (978-0-9702171-6-5(1)) AshleyAlan Enterprises.

Mills, Claudia. Makeovers by Marcia. 2005. 160p. (J). 16.00 (978-0-374-34654-6(2) , Farrar, Straus & Giroux (BYR)) Farrar, Straus & Giroux.

Minter, J. Hold on Tight. 2006. (Insiders Novel Ser.: Bk. 5). 256p. (YA). pap. 8.95 (978-1-58234-719-6(0) , Bloomsbury Children) Bloomsbury Publishing.

Montgomery, L. M. Anne of the Island. Date not set. mass mkt. (978-0-8125-6563-8(0) , Tor Bks.) Doherty, Tom Assocs., LLC.

—Anne of the Island. 2006. (ENG.). pap. (***978-1-4068-2171-0(3)***); pap. (***978-1-4068-3175-7(1)***) Echo Library.

—Anne of the Island. 2006. (ENG.). 102.99 (***978-1-4219-3295-8(4)***) IndyPublish.com.

—Anne of the Island. 2004. reprint ed. pap. 1.99 (978-1-4192-0718-1(0)); pap. 30.95 (978-1-4179-0885-1(8)) Kessinger Publishing, LLC.

—Anne of the Island. (Twelve-Point Ser.). 2001. 240p. lib. bdg. 25.00 (978-1-58287-157-8(4)); 2004. 396p. 26.00 (978-1-58287-640-5(1)) North Bks.

—Anne of the Island. abr. ed. 1998. (Avonlea Ser.: No. 4). 304p. (J). (gr. 5-8). pap. 4.99 (978-0-14-036777-5(2) , Puffin) Penguin Group (USA) Inc.

—Anne of the Island. 2000. (Anne of Green Gables Ser.: Vol. No. 3). (gr. 5-8). 182p. 24.95 (978-1-57646-309-3(5)); 182p. pap. 14.99 (978-1-57646-308-6(7)); 336p. pap. 19.99 (978-1-57646-310-9(9)) Quiet Vision Publishing.

—Anne of the Island. 2001. (gr. 7-12). lib. bdg. 30.40 (978-0-613-79774-0(4)) Tandem Library Bks.

—Anne of the Island Book & Charm. 2005. (Charming Classics). 304p. (J). pap. 6.99 (978-0-06-075859-2(7) , Harper Festival) HarperCollins Pubs.

Moss, Marissa. The All-New Amelia. Moss, Marissa, illus. 2007. (Amelia's Notebooks). (Illus.). 40p. (J). (gr. 2-5). 9.99 (978-1-4169-0908-8(7) , Simon & Schuster/Paula Wiseman Bks.) Simon & Schuster Children's Publishing.

—The All-New Amelia. 1999. (Amelia's Notebooks). (J). (gr. 3-5). 12.75 (978-0-606-19866-0(0)) Tandem Library Bks.

Moss, Thylias. I Want to Be. 1998. (978-0-606-13511-5(1)) Tandem Library Bks.

Munsch, Robert. Makeup Mess. ed. 2004. (Illus.). (J). (gr. k-3). spiral bd. (978-0-616-11125-3(8)) Canadian National Institute for the Blind/Institut National Canadien pour les Aveugles.

—Makeup Mess. Martchenko, Michael, illus. ed. 2004. (J). (gr. k-3). spiral bd. (978-0-616-11124-6(X)) Canadian National Institute for the Blind/Institut National Canadien pour les Aveugles.

Myers, Walter Dean. Monster. Myers, Christopher A., illus. 1999. (Amistad Ser.). 288p. (J). (gr. 7 up). 16.99 (978-0-06-028077-2(8)) HarperCollins Pubs.

—Monster. Myers, Christopher, illus. (Newbery Honor Roll Ser.). (J). 1999. 288p. (gr. 7 up). lib. bdg. 17.89 (978-0-06-028078-9(6)); 2001. 304p. reprint ed. pap. 7.99 (978-0-06-440731-1(4) , Amistad) HarperCollins Pubs.

Myracle, Lauren. Twelve. 2008. 224p. (YA). (gr. 5-8). 6.99 (***978-0-14-241091-2(8)*** , Puffin) Penguin Group (USA) Inc.

Nash, Andy. Tatum & Her Tiger: For Kids Blessed with Passion. 2007. (J). (***978-0-8127-0451-8(7)***) Autumn Hse. Publishing Co.

Naylor, Phyllis Reynolds. Dangerously Alice. 2007. (Alice Ser.). 304p. (YA). (gr. 9 up). 15.99 (978-0-689-87094-1(9) , Atheneum) Simon & Schuster Children's Publishing.

—The Grooming of Alice. Elliott, Mark, illus. (Alice Ser.). 224p. (J). (gr. 5-9). 2001. pap. 4.99 (978-0-689-84618-2(5) , Aladdin); 2000. 16.99 (978-0-689-82633-7(8) , Atheneum) Simon & Schuster Children's Publishing.

—The Grooming of Alice. 2001. (Alice Ser.). 11.64 (978-0-606-22125-2(5)) Tandem Library Bks.

Neasi, Barbara J. Muchas Veces Yo. Ochoa, Ana, illus. 2003. (Rookie Reader Espanol Ser.). (SPA & ENG.). 31p. (J). 19.50 (978-0-516-25894-2(X) , Children's Pr.) Scholastic Library Publishing.

—So Many Me's. 2004. (Rookie Reader Espanol Ser.). (J). (gr. k-2). pap. 4.95 (978-0-516-27786-8(3) , Children's Pr.) Scholastic Library Publishing.

Newbery, Linda. The Shell House. 2004. 352p. (YA). (gr. 7-11). reprint ed. mass mkt. 6.50 (978-0-440-23786-0(6) , Laurel Leaf) Random Hse. Children's Bks.

Niemann, Christoph. The Police Cloud. 2007. 40p. (J). (ps-2). 15.99 (978-0-375-83963-4(1)); lib. bdg. 17.99 (978-0-375-93963-1(6)) Random Hse. Children's Bks. (Schwartz & Wade Bks.).

Nolan, Han. Send Me down a Miracle. 2003. 276p. (YA). pap. 6.95 (978-0-15-204680-4(1)) Harcourt Children's Bks.

—Send Me down a Miracle. 2003. (gr. 7-12). lib. bdg. 15.25 (978-0-613-59926-9(8)) Tandem Library Bks.

Noonan, Brandon. Plenty Porter. 2006. 240p. (YA). (gr. 7-17). 16.95 (978-0-8109-5996-5(8)) Abrams, Harry N. , Inc.

Okamoto, Kazuhiro. Translucent Volume 1. 2007. (Illus.). 192p. (J). pap. 9.95 (***978-1-59307-647-4(9)***) Dark Horse Comics.

Partridge, Juliet. That's Me!, 6 vols., Pack. 2001. (Cambridge Storybooks Ser.). (Illus.). 8p. pap. 16.00 (978-0-521-00771-9(2)) Cambridge Univ. Pr.

—That's Me! ELT Edition. Sweeten, Sami, illus. 2001. (Cambridge Storybooks Ser.). 8p. pap. 3.00 (978-0-521-00682-8(1)) Cambridge Univ. Pr.

Paulsen, Gary. The Amazing Life of Birds: The Nineteen Day Puberty Journal of Duane Homer Leech. 2008. 96p. (YA). (gr. 5-9). 6.50 (***978-0-553-49428-0(7)*** , Yearling) Random Hse. Children's Bks.

—The Amazing Life of Birds: The Twenty-Day Puberty Journal of Duane Homer Leech. 2006. (Illus.). 96p. (J). (gr. 5-9). 13.95 (978-0-385-74660-1(1) , Lamb, Wendy) Random Hse. Children's Bks.

—Dogsong. 1999. (YA). 9.95 (978-1-56137-342-0(7)) Novel Units, Inc.

—Dogsong. 192p. 2007. (J). pap. 6.99 (978-1-4169-3962-7(8) , Aladdin); 2007. (YA). mass mkt. 6.99 (978-1-4169-3919-1(9) , Simon Pulse); 2000. (YA). (gr. 7 up). 17.99 (978-0-689-83960-3(X) , Atheneum/Richard Jackson Bks.) Simon & Schuster Children's Publishing.

—Dogsong. 1999. (J). 11.64 (978-0-606-16328-6(X)) Tandem Library Bks.

—Dogsong. l.t. ed. 2000. (Illus.). 184p. (J). (gr. 8-12). 21.95 (978-0-7862-2845-4(8)) Thorndike Pr.

Pennypacker, Sara. The Talented Clementine. Frazee, Marla, illus. 2007. 144p. (gr. 2-5). 14.99 (978-0-7868-3870-7(1)) Hyperion Bks. for Children.

Peters, Julie Anne. Far from Xanadu. 2007. 288p. (YA). (gr. 7 up). pap. 7.99 (***978-0-316-15971-5(9)***) Little, Brown Bks. for Young Readers.

Polacco, Patricia. Gracias, Senor Falker. Mlawer, Teresa, tr. from ENG. 2001. (SPA., Illus.). (J). (gr. 1-3). lib. bdg. 17.00 (978-1-930332-03-4(3) , LC30185) Lectorum Pubns., Inc.

—Thank You, Mr. Falker. 1998. (Illus.). 40p. (J). (gr. k-4). 16.99 (978-0-399-23166-7(8) , Philomel) Penguin Group (USA) Inc.

Rae, Nan, illus. Suma the Elephant. 2006. 80p. 18.00 (978-0-9762544-0-9(9)) Garden Fleetfoot Pr.

Rahlens, Holly-Jane. Prince William, Maximilian Minsky, & Me. (YA). (gr. 7-11). 2007. 320p. pap. 7.99 (***978-0-7636-3299-1(6)***); 2005. 160p. 16.99 (978-0-7636-2704-1(6)) Candlewick Pr.

Rallison, Janette. All's Fair in Love, War, & High School. 2005. 192p. (J). pap. 6.95 (978-0-8027-7725-6(2)) Walker & Co.

Randle, Kristen D. Slumming. 2003. (Illus.). 240p. (J). 16.99 (978-0-06-001022-5(3) , HarperTeen) HarperCollins Pubs.

Rau, Dana Meachen. Yahoo for You, Level B. Pillo, Cary, illus. 2002. (Compass Point Early Reader Ser.). 32p. (J). (gr. k up). lib. bdg. 18.60 (978-0-7565-0177-8(6)) Compass Point Bks.

Resau, Laura. What the Moon Saw. l.t. rev. ed. 2007. 300p. (YA). 22.95 (***978-0-7862-9278-3(4)***) Thorndike Pr.

Reynolds, Peter H. So Few of Me. 2006. (Illus.). 32p. (J). (gr. k-12). 14.00 (978-0-7636-2623-5(6)) Candlewick Pr.

Richardson, Wanda Thomas. Beautiful Me. Gary, Kelli M., ed. Higgins, John, illus. rev. ed. 2002. 32p. (Orig.). (J). (gr. 3-7). pap. 8.99 (978-0-9673084-3-2(7) , JCW 2002-1001) JCW Enterprises, Inc.

—Handsome Me. Gary, Kelli M., ed. Higgins, John, illus. (Orig.). (J). (gr. 3-8). 2001. 24p. pap. 7.99 (978-0-9673084-0-1(2) , JCW2001-1002); 2002. 32p. pap. 8.99 (978-0-9673084-2-5(9) , JCW 2002-1002) JCW Enterprises, Inc.

Roter, Jordan. Girl in Development. 2008. 320p. (YA). (gr. 7). pap. 7.99 (***978-0-14-240822-3(0)*** , Puffin) Penguin Group (USA) Inc.

Roter, Jordan. Girl of Development (Splashproof Ed) 2007. 1p. (YA). (gr. 7). pap. 7.99 (978-0-14-240838-4(7) , Puffin) Penguin Group (USA) Inc.

Rubel, Nicole. It's Hot & Cold in Miami. 2006. (Illus.). 208p. (J). 17.00 (978-0-374-33611-0(3)) Farrar, Straus & Giroux.

Rue, Nancy N. Lily & the Creep. 2001. (gr. 3-6). lib. bdg. 13.00 (978-0-613-71718-2(X)) Tandem Library Bks.

Salmansohn, Karen. Girl Wonders. 2007. 128p. (J). 6.95 (***978-1-58246-162-5(7)*** , Tricycle Pr.) Ten Speed Pr.

—One Puppy, Three Tales Bk. 1: Alexandra Rambles On! 2004. (Alexandra Rambles on! Ser.: Bk. 1). (Illus.). 70p. (J). (gr. 4-6). 12.95 (978-1-58246-044-4(2) , Tricycle Pr.) Ten Speed Pr.

—Wherever I Go, There I Am. 2004. (Alexandra Rambles on! Ser.). (Illus.). 70p. (YA). (gr. 4-7). 12.95 (978-1-58246-079-6(5) , Tricycle Pr.) Ten Speed Pr.

Scheunemann, Pam. Crocodile Tears. Chawla, Neena, illus. 2007. (Fact & Fiction Ser.). 24p. (J). (978-1-59928-437-8(5)); 21.35 (978-1-59928-436-1(7)) ABDO Publishing Co.

Schneider, Christine. Picky Mrs. Pickle. 2001. (978-0-606-22744-5(X)) Tandem Library Bks.

Schulte, Mary. Who Do I Look Like? Roos, Maryn, illus. 2006. (Rookie Reader Skill Set Ser.). 32p. (J). (gr. k-2). 19.50 (978-0-516-24978-0(9) , Children's Pr.) Scholastic Library Publishing.

Schulte, Mary & Roos, Maryn. Who Do I Look Like? 2006. (Illus.). 32p. (YA). pap. 4.95 (978-0-516-24758-8(1) , Children's Pr.) Scholastic Library Publishing.

Seidler, Tor. Rat's Tale. 1999. (978-0-606-16698-0(X)); (gr. 3-6). lib. bdg. 15.25 (978-0-613-12367-9(0)) Tandem Library Bks.

Shaskan, Trisha Speed. This Is Anna. 2007. (Illus.). 24p. (J). (***978-1-4048-1244-4(X)***) Picture Window Bks.

—This Is Anna. Senturk, Burak, illus. 2006. 24p. (J). (***978-1-4048-3168-1(1)***) Picture Window Bks.

Shimko, Bonnie. Kat's Promise. 2006. 288p. (J). 17.00 (978-0-15-205473-1(1)) Harcourt Children's Bks.

Shusterman, Neal. Full Tilt. 208p. (YA). 2004. mass mkt. 5.99 (978-0-689-87325-6(5) , Simon Pulse); 2003. (Illus.). 16.95 (978-0-689-80374-1(5)) Simon & Schuster Children's Publishing.

—Full Tilt. l.t. ed. 2003. 243p. (J). 22.95 (978-0-7862-5886-4(1)) Thorndike Pr.

—The Schwa Was Here. 2006. 240p. (J). (gr. 3). reprint ed. pap. 5.99 (978-0-14-240577-2(9) , Puffin) Penguin Group (USA) Inc.

Smallman, Steve. Bumbletum. Warnes, Tim, illus. 2006. 32p. (J). 15.95 (978-1-58925-060-4(5) , tiger tales) ME Media LLC.

Snider, Cindy Gay. Finding Anna Bee. Chambers, Mary, illus. 2007. (J). pap. (***978-0-8361-9392-3(X)***) Herald Pr.

Sonnenblick, Jordan. Notes from the Midnight Driver. 2007. 288p. (J). pap. 6.99 (***978-0-439-75781-2(9)*** , Scholastic Paperbacks); 2006. 272p. (YA). pap. 16.99 (978-0-439-75779-9(7) , Scholastic Pr.) Scholastic, Inc.

Steig, William. Toby, Who Are You? Euvremer, Teryl, illus. 2004. 32p. (J). (ps-3). 14.99 (978-0-06-000705-8(2)); lib. bdg. 15.89 (978-0-06-000706-5(0)) HarperCollins Pubs. (Cotler, Joanna Books).

Stewart, Sharon. Spider's Web. 1998. 160p. (J). (gr. 4-9). pap. 7.95 (978-0-88995-177-8(2)) Red Deer Pr. CAN. *Dist:* Fitzhenry & Whiteside, Ltd.

Tashjain, Janet. Multiple Choice. rev. ed. 1999. (Illus.). 192p. (YA). (gr. 5-10). 16.95 (978-0-8050-6086-7(3) , Holt, Henry & Co. Bks. For Young Readers) Holt, Henry & Co.

Then I'm Me! l.t. ed. 2002. (Illus.). 28p. (J). pap. 10.00 (978-1-888562-05-7(6)) Pelican Pr.

Thomas, Rob. Satellite Down. 1999. (978-0-606-17319-3(6)) Tandem Library Bks.

Van Draanen, Wendelin. Flipped. 224p. (gr. 5-9). 2003. (J). pap. 8.95 (978-0-375-82544-6(4)); 2001. (J). 14.95 (978-0-375-81174-6(5)); 2001. lib. bdg. 16.99 (978-0-375-91174-3(X)) Random Hse. Children's Bks. (Knopf Bks. for Young Readers).

Velmans, Hester. Isabel of the Whales. 2006. 192p. (gr. 4-7). 5.99 (978-0-440-42025-5(3) , Yearling) Random Hse. Children's Bks.

Vision, Mutiya Sahar. Disabilities?! Alcantara, Ignacio, illus. 2005. 40p. (J). mass mkt. 17.00 (978-0-9659538-9-4(0)) Soul Vision Works Publishing.

Vizzini, Ned. Be More Chill. 2004. 304p. (gr. 8-17). 16.95 (978-0-7868-0995-0(7)) Hyperion Bks. for Children.

—Be More Chill. 2005. 304p. (gr. 8-17). pap. 7.99 (978-0-7868-0996-7(5)) Miramax Bks.

Vrettos, Adrienne Maria. Skin. 2007. 272p. (YA). pap. 6.99 (***978-1-4169-0656-8(8)*** , Simon Pulse); 2006. (Illus.). 240p. (J). (gr. 7 up). 16.95 (978-1-4169-0655-1(X) , McElderry, Margaret K.) Simon & Schuster Children's Publishing.

Wallace, Karen. The Unrivalled Spangles. 2006. 224p. (YA). 16.95 (978-1-4169-1503-4(6)) Simon & Schuster Children's Publishing.

Walter, Mildred Pitts. Suitcase. Flavin, Teresa, illus. 1999. 112p. (J). (gr. 3 up). 16.99 (978-0-688-16547-5(8)) HarperCollins Pubs.

Wax, Wendy & Artful Doodlers Limited Staff. Coolest Girl in School. 2005. (Ready-To-Read Ser.). (Illus.). 32p. (J). (ps-ps). pap. 3.99 (978-0-689-86647-0(X) , Simon Spotlight/Nickelodeon) Simon & Schuster Children's Publishing.

Weatherly, Lee. Kat Got Your Tongue. 2007. 208p. (YA). (gr. 7-9). lib. bdg. 18.99 (978-0-385-75122-3(2)); 15.99 (978-0-385-75117-9(6)) Random Hse. Children's Bks. (Fickling, David Bks.).

Weinheimer, Beckie. Converting Kate. 2007. 288p. (YA). (gr. 7 up). 16.99 (978-0-670-06152-5(2) , Viking Juvenile) Penguin Group (USA) Inc.

Wetter, Bruce. The Boy with the Lampshade on His Head. 2004. (Illus.). 304p. (J). 16.95 (978-0-689-85032-5(8) , Atheneum) Simon & Schuster Children's Publishing.

Wilcox, Mary. The Hollywood Sisters: Star Quality. 2008. (J). (***978-0-385-90513-8(0)***); pap. (***978-0-385-73527-8(8)***) Dell Publishing. (Delacorte Pr.).

Wild, Margaret. Jinx. Gould, Jason, photos by. 2004. (Illus.). 224p. (YA). reprint ed. pap. 11.95 (978-0-689-86541-1(4) , Simon Pulse) Simon & Schuster Children's Publishing.

—Jinx. 2004. (gr. 7-12). lib. bdg. 15.30 (978-0-613-73451-6(3)) Tandem Library Bks.

Wilhelm, Hans. No Me Gusta Mi Mono. Wilhelm, Hans, illus. 2002. (Coleccion "Hola, Lector" Ser.). (SPA., Illus.). 32p. (J). (ps-1). pap. 3.99 (978-0-439-22645-5(7) , SO5389, Scholastic en Espanol) Scholastic, Inc.

Williams-Garcia, Rita. Fast Talk on a Slow Track. 1998. 192p. (J). (gr. 7-12). pap. 6.99 (978-0-14-130231-7(3) , Puffin) Penguin Group (USA) Inc.

Williams, Karen Lynn. One Thing I'm Good At. 1999. 137p. (J). (gr. 3-7). 14.95 (978-0-688-16846-9(9)) HarperCollins Pubs.

Wolff, Patricia Rae. A New Improved Santa. Cravath, Lynne W., illus. 2002. 32p. (J). (gr. k-2). pap. 15.95 (978-0-439-35249-9(5) , Orchard Bks.) Scholastic, Inc.

Wolfson, Jill. What I Call Life. rev. ed. 2005. (Illus.). 272p. (J). (ps-7). 16.95 (978-0-8050-7669-1(7)) Holt, Henry & Co.

—What I Call Life. 2008. 288p. (J). pap. 6.99 (***978-0-312-37752-6(5)***) Square Fish.

Wong, Joyce Lee. Seeing Emily. 2005. (Illus.). 288p. (J). (gr. 7-11). 16.95 (978-0-8109-5757-2(4) , Abrams Bks. for Young Readers) Abrams, Harry N. , Inc.

Wright, Betty Ren. The Wish Master. 2000. (Illus.). 112p. (J). (gr. 4-6). tchr. ed. 15.95 (978-0-8234-1611-0(9)) Holiday Hse., Inc.

Wurtz, K. D. Digby in Disguise. Carrier, Tracey Dahle, illus. 2001. (Digby in Disguise Ser.: Vol. 1). (J). (978-0-9712840-1-2(6)) Boyds Collection Ltd., The.

Yaccarino, Dan. Unlovable. rev. ed. 2004. (Illus.). 32p. (J). reprint ed. pap. 6.95 (978-0-8050-7532-8(1) , Owlet Paperbacks for Young Readers) Holt, Henry & Co.

Zeises, Lara M. Anyone but You. 256p. (YA). (gr. 9). 2007. mass mkt. 6.50 (***978-0-440-23858-4(7)*** , Laurel Leaf); 2005. 15.95 (978-0-385-73145-4(0) , Delacorte Bks. for Young Readers) Random Hse. Children's Bks.

Ziegler, Jennifer. Alpha Dog. 2006. 336p. (YA). (gr. 7). pap. 7.95 (978-0-385-73285-7(6)); lib. bdg. 9.99 (978-0-385-90302-8(2)) Random Hse. Children's Bks. (Delacorte Bks. for Young Readers).

The 15 Best Things about Being the New Kid. 2006. (J). pap. 5.95 (978-0-8225-6473-7(4) , First Avenue Editions) Lerner Publishing Group.

SELF-RELIANCE

see also Self-confidence

All by Myself. 2002. (J). pap. 3.74 (978-0-7398-5843-1(2)) Steck-Vaughn.

Dyer, Wayne W. & Dyer, Summer. 10 Secrets for Success & Inner Peace for Teens. 2004. 12.95 (978-1-4019-0270-4(7) , 2707, Hay Hse. Lifestyles) Hay Hse., Inc.

Falconer, Ian, creator. Dream Big: Starring Olivia. 2006. (Olivia Ser.). (Illus.). 64p. 9.95 (978-0-7407-5818-8(7)) Andrews McMeel Publishing.

Navarra, Tova. The Kids' Guidebook: Great Advice to Help Kids Cope. Kerr, Tom, illus. 2nd ed. 2002. 128p. (J). (gr. 2-7). pap. 10.95 (978-0-7641-2066-4(2)) Barron's Educational Series, Inc.

Noll, Kathy. Taking the Bully by the Horns: Children's Version of Best-Selling Book, Nasty People. Carter, Jay, ed. Cusimano, Flora & Broderbund, illus. 2nd aut. ed. 1998. Orig. Title: Nasty Kids. 80p. (J). (gr. 4-9). pap. 12.95 (978-0-937004-11-1(1)) Unicorn Pr.

SELF-RELIANCE—FICTION

Aliki. All by Myself! Aliki, illus. (Illus.). 32p. (J). (ps-1). 2003. pap. 6.99 (978-0-06-446253-2(6)); 2000. 16.99 (978-0-06-028929-4(5)) HarperCollins Pubs.

—All by Myself! 2003. (gr. k-3). lib. bdg. 14.15 (978-0-613-65685-6(7)) Tandem Library Bks.

Asch, Frank & Asch, Devin. Baby Duck's New Friend. 2001. (Illus.). 40p. (J). (ps-k). 15.00 (978-0-15-202257-0(0) , Gulliver Bks.) Harcourt Children's Bks.

Auch, M. J. One-Handed Catch. 2006. 256p. (J). 16.95 (978-0-8050-7900-5(9) , Holt, Henry & Co. Bks. For Young Readers) Holt, Henry & Co.

Bea, Holly. Lucy Goose Goes to Texas. Boddy, Joe, illus. 2005. 32p. (J). 15.95 (978-1-932073-15-7(9)) New World Library.

Best, Cari & Davenier, Christine. Sally Jean, the Bicycle Queen. 2006. (Illus.). 32p. (J). (gr. k-2). 16.00 (978-0-374-36386-4(2) , Nelanie Kroupa Bks.) Farrar, Straus & Giroux.

Brokaw, Nancy Steele. Leaving Emma. 1999. 144p. (J). (gr. 4-6). tchr. ed. 15.00 (978-0-395-90699-6(7) , Clarion Bks.) Houghton Mifflin Co. Trade & Reference Div.

Cameron, Ann. Gloria Rising. 2004. 112p. (J). (gr. 1-4). pap. 4.99 (978-0-440-41998-3(0) , Random Hse. Bks. for Young Readers) Random Hse. Children's Bks.

Carlson, Nancy. I Like Me! Carlson, Nancy, illus. 2002. (Illus.). (J). 13.19 (978-0-7587-2804-3(2)) Book Wholesalers, Inc.

Clark, Emma Chichester. What Shall We Do, Blue Kang? 2002. (Illus.). 32p. (J). (978-1-84270-185-0(1)) Andersen GBR. *Dist:* Random Hse. of Canada, Ltd.

Coles, Michael Joseph, et al. The Land of Caring Bou. Banks, Timothy, illus. 2006. (J). (978-0-87483-814-5(2)) August Hse. Pubs., Inc.

Connor, Leslie. Waiting for Normal. 2008. 304p. (J). 16.99 (***978-0-06-089088-9(6)***); lib. bdg. 17.89 (***978-0-06-089089-6(4)***) HarperCollins Pubs.

Cross, Gillian. The Nightmare Game. 2007. 272p. (J). (gr. 7). 18.99 (***978-0-525-47923-9(6)*** , Dutton Juvenile) Penguin Group (USA) Inc.

Dahl, Michael. The Princess & the Tower. Zhurkina, Svetlana A., illus. 2005. (Read-It! Readers Ser.). 32p. (J). (ps). lib. bdg. 18.60 (978-1-4048-1184-3(2)) Picture Window Bks.

Disney Staff. Pooh Can, Can You? 1999. (Learn & Grow Busy Book Ser.: Vol. 1). (Illus.). 12p. (J). (ps-k). 6.99 (978-0-7364-0135-7(0)) Mouse Works.

Dorfman, Craig. I Knew You Could! A Book for All the Stops in Your Life. Ong, Cristina, illus. 2003. (Little Engine That Could Ser.). 32p. (J). (gr. 1-2). 11.99 (978-0-448-43148-2(3) , Grosset & Dunlap) Penguin Group (USA) Inc.

Dorfman, Craig. I Knew You Could! Celebrate All the Stops in Your Life. Ong, Cristina, illus. 2008. (Little Engine That Could Ser.). 32p. (J). (ps). 12.99 (***978-0-448-44813-8(0)*** , Grosset & Dunlap) Penguin Group (USA) Inc.

Doyon, Stephanie. Leaving Home. 1999. (On the Road Ser.: No.1). (978-0-606-18626-1(3)) Tandem Library Bks.

Farnes, Catherine. Over the Divide. 2001. 146p. (J). (gr. 7-12). 6.49 (978-1-57924-646-4(X)) Jones, Bob Univ. Pr.

—Over the Divide. 2001. (gr. 7-12). lib. bdg. 14.70 (978-0-613-85517-4(5)) Tandem Library Bks.

Firth, Barbara, illus. Good Job, Little Bear. 2002. (Little Bear Picture Bks.). (J). 23.40 (978-0-7587-2616-2(3)) Book Wholesalers, Inc.

George, Jean Craighead. My Side of the Mountain. rev. ed. 1999. (Illus.). 176p. (J). (gr. 3-7). 15.99 (978-0-525-46346-7(1) , Dutton Juvenile) Penguin Group (USA) Inc.

Hautman, Pete. Rash. 2006. 256p. (YA). (gr. 7 up). 16.99 (978-0-689-86801-6(4) , Simon & Schuster Children's Publishing) Simon & Schuster Children's Publishing.

Horvath, Polly. Everything on a Waffle. 2001. 160p. (J). (gr. 5 up). 16.00 (978-0-374-32236-6(8) , Farrar, Straus & Giroux (BYR)) Farrar, Straus & Giroux.

—Everything on a Waffle. (Illus.). (J). pap. 8.95 (978-0-88899-442-4(7)) Groundwood Bks. CAN. *Dist:* Transition Vendor.

—Everything on a Waffle. 2008. 176p. (J). pap. 6.99 (***978-0-312-38004-5(6)***) Square Fish.

Howard, Elizabeth Fitzgerald. The Train to Lulu's. 1998. (J). pap. 4.95 (978-0-87628-336-3(9)) Simon & Schuster.

Konigsburg, E. L. From the Mixed-Up Files of Mrs. Basil E. Frankweiler. 35th anniv. ed. 2002. (gr. 5-8). lib. bdg. 14.15 (978-0-613-73358-8(4)) Tandem Library Bks.

—From the Mixed-Up Files of Mrs. Basil E. Frankweiler. l.t. ed. 2005. (Illus.). 205p. (J). 22.95 (978-0-7862-7297-6(X) , Large Print Pr.) Thorndike Pr.

Larson, Kirby. Hattie Big Sky. 2006. 304p. (J). (gr. 7). 15.95 (978-0-385-73313-7(5)); lib. bdg. 17.99 (978-0-385-90332-5(4)) Random Hse. Children's Bks. (Delacorte Bks. for Young Readers).

—Hattie Big Sky. l.t. ed. 2007. 400p. (YA). 23.95 (***978-0-7862-9697-2(6)***) Thorndike Pr.

Laybourn, Emma. Missing Magic. 2007. 192p. (J). (gr. 4 up). 16.99 (978-0-8037-3219-3(8) , Dial) Penguin Group (USA) Inc.

Le Guin, Ursula K. Jane on Her Own. 2003. (Catwings Ser.: No. 4). 48p. (J). pap. 3.99 (978-0-439-55192-2(7)) Scholastic, Inc.

Louthain, J. A. Tagger: Alone along the Mystic River. 2002. (Illus.). 215p. (YA). per. 14.95 (978-0-9679416-0-8(1) , 0-1) Alexie Bks.

Morgan, Nicola. The Passionflower Massacre. 2007. (J). pap. (***978-0-340-87734-0(0)*** , Hodder Children's Books) Hodder Children's Division.

Mothershead, Martha Fulford. Petoskey Stone Soup. Clarkson, Janet M., illus. 2006. 32p. (J). 18.95 (978-0-9785465-0-2(4)) Whaleback Pr.

Napoli, Donna Jo. On Her Own. 1999. (Angelwings Ser.: No. 3). Orig. Title: Room to Grow. (Illus.). 96p. (J). (gr. 2-5). pap. 7.95 (978-0-689-82985-7(X) , Aladdin) Simon & Schuster Children's Publishing.

—On Her Own. 1999. (Angelwings Ser.: No. 3). Orig. Title: Room to Grow. (Illus.). (J). (978-0-606-17906-5(2)) Tandem Library Bks.

Parrott, Darcie. Ladybug's Walk. 2007. 32p. (J). 10.95 (***978-0-9772692-8-0(0)***) Historical Pages Co.

Paterson, Katherine. Lyddie. 2005. 192p. (J). (ps-7). pap. 3.99 (978-0-14-240438-6(1) , Puffin) Penguin Group (USA) Inc.

—The Same Stuff as Stars. 2002. (Illus.). 256p. (J). (gr. 5-9). tchr. ed. 15.00 (978-0-618-24744-8(0) , Clarion Bks.) Houghton Mifflin Co. Trade & Reference Div.

—The Same Stuff As Stars. 2004. 288p. (J). reprint ed. pap. 6.99 (978-0-06-055712-6(5) , Harper Trophy) HarperCollins Pubs.

Paulsen, Gary. Brian's Return. unabr. ed. 2004. (Middle Grade Cassette Librariestm Ser.). 115p. (J). (gr. 5-9). pap. 29.00 incl. audio (978-0-8072-0658-4(X) , S YA 292 SP, Listening Library) Random Hse. Audio Publishing Group.

—Brian's Return. (GLB Reprints Ser.). (gr. 5). 2004. 128p. (YA). lib. bdg. 17.99 (978-0-385-90223-6(9) , Delacorte Bks. for Young Readers); 1999. 128p. (J). 15.95 (978-0-385-32500-4(2) , Delacorte Bks. for Young Readers); 2001. 144p. (J). reprint ed. pap. 5.99 (978-0-440-41379-0(6) , Laurel Leaf) Random Hse. Children's Bks.

—Brian's Return. 2001. (gr. 7-12). lib. bdg. 13.55 (978-0-613-33796-0(4)) Tandem Library Bks.

—Brian's Winter. 2004. (GLB Reprints Ser.). 144p. (YA). (gr. 5). lib. bdg. 17.99 (978-0-385-90222-9(0) , Delacorte Bks. for Young Readers) Random Hse. Children's Bks.

—The River. unabr. ed. 2004. (Middle Grade Cassette Librariestm Ser.). 132p. (J). (gr. 5-9). pap. 29.00 incl. audio (978-0-8072-8704-0(0) , S YA 241 SP, Listening Library) Random Hse. Audio Publishing Group.

—The River. 2004. (GLB Reprints Ser.). 144p. (YA). (gr. 5). lib. bdg. 17.99 (978-0-385-90221-2(2) , Delacorte Bks. for Young Readers) Random Hse. Children's Bks.

Petrillo, Genevieve & Lyon, Lea. Keep Your Ear on the Ball. 2007. (Illus.). 32p. (J). (gr. 3-7). 16.95 (***978-0-88448-296-3(0)***) Tilbury Hse. Pubs.

Pierce, Tamora & Sherman, Josepha. Young Warriors: Stories of Strength. 2006. 336p. (J). (gr. 7-11). pap. 8.95 (978-0-375-82963-5(6) , Random Hse. Bks. for Young Readers) Random Hse. Children's Bks.

Polette, Keith. Isabel & the Hungry Coyote/Isabel y el Coyote Hambriento. de la Vega, Eida, tr. Szegedy, Esther, illus. 2006. Tr. of Isabel y el coyote Hambriento. (SPA.). (J). 4.99 (978-0-9770906-4-8(7)) Raven Tree Pr.

Rapp, Adam. The Buffalo Tree. (J). 2002. 192p. (gr. 5 up). pap. 6.95 (978-0-06-001226-7(9) , HarperTeen); 1998. 336p. (gr. 7 up). pap. 11.00 (978-0-06-440711-3(X) , Harper Trophy) HarperCollins Pubs.

Reynolds, Marilynn. The Prairie Fire. Kilby, Don, illus. 2001. 32p. (J). (ps-2). 6.95 (978-1-55143-175-8(0)) Orca Bk. Pubs. USA.

Schulz, Kathy. I Need a Little Help. 2004. (Rookie Reader Skill Set Ser.). (Illus.). 23p. (J). (gr. k-2). pap. 4.95 (978-0-516-27833-9(9) , Children's Pr.) Scholastic Library Publishing.

—I Need a Little Help. Losa, Ann, illus. 2003. (Rookie Reader - Level a Ser.). 24p. (J). 19.50 (978-0-516-22877-8(3) , Children's Pr.) Scholastic Library Publishing.

—I Need a Little Help. Iosa, Ann, illus. 2004. 24p. lib. bdg. 12.15 (978-0-606-30160-2(7)) Tandem Library Bks.

Stratton-Porter, Gene. A Girl of the Limberlost. 2003. (Twelve-Point Ser.). (J). lib. bdg. 25.00 (978-1-58287-232-2(5)) North Bks.

Stratton Porter, Gene. A Girl of the Limberlost. 2006. 336p. (YA). 21.95 (***978-1-934169-30-8(7)***); pap. 10.95 (***978-1-934169-31-5(5)***) Norilana Bks.

Stratton-Porter, Gene. A Girl of the Limberlost. (J). reprint ed. lib. bdg. 33.95 (978-0-89190-948-4(6) , Rivercity Pr.) Amereon LTD.

—A Girl of the Limberlost. Benda, Wladyslaw T., illus. 2005. reprint ed. pap. 38.95 (978-0-7661-9424-3(8)) Kessinger Publishing, LLC.

—A Girl of the Limberlost. l.t. ed. 2004. (Large Print Ser.). 463p. 26.00 (978-1-58287-716-7(5)) North Bks.

Tierno, Susan F. I Did My Best. Ramirez, Michael, illus. 1998. (Think-Kids Book Collection). 16p. (J). (gr. 1-4). pap. 2.95 (978-1-58237-011-8(7)) Creative Thinkers, Inc.

—Lo Hice Bien! Alvarado, Ana María, tr. Ramirez, Michael, illus. 2000. (Think-Kids Book Collection).Tr. of I Did My Best Ser.. (SPA.). 16p. (J). pap. 2.95 (978-1-58237-040-8(0)) Creative Thinkers, Inc.

Van Genechten, Guido. Alex & the Tart. 2005. (Illus.). 32p. (J). (ps). 6.95 (978-1-58925-393-3(0) , tiger tales) ME Media LLC.

Van Leeuwen, Jean. Cabin on Trouble Creek. 2004. 224p. (J). (gr. 4). 16.99 (978-0-8037-2548-5(5) , Dial) Penguin Group (USA) Inc.

S

Waber, Bernard. Betty's Day Off. Date not set. (J). (978-0-618-46875-1(7)) Houghton Mifflin Co.

Waddell, Martin. Sleep Tight, Little Bear. Firth, Barbara, illus. 2005. 32p. (J). (ps-1). 15.99 (978-0-7636-2439-2(X)) Candlewick Pr.

Wels, Barbara. Finwood & Lisa. 144p. pap. 11.95 (978-0-7022-2502-4(9)) Univ. of Queensland Pr. AUS. *Dist:* International Specialized Bk. Services.

Wiles, Deborah. Love, Ruby Lavender. (Illus.). (J). 2001. 200p. (gr. 3-7). 16.00 (978-0-15-202314-0(3)); 2005. 228p. reprint ed. pap. 5.95 (978-0-15-205478-6(2)) Harcourt Children's Bks. (Gulliver Bks.).

—Love, Ruby Lavender. 2004. 216p. (J). (gr. 3-7). pap. 36.00 incl. audio (978-0-8072-2096-2(5) , Listening Library) Random Hse. Audio Publishing Group.

Wyss, Thelma Hatch. Ten Miles from Winnemucca. 2002. 144p. (J). (gr. 7 up). 15.95 (978-0-06-029783-1(2)) HarperCollins Pubs.

Zile, Susan Van. Cay. 2002. (Literature Circle Guides Ser.). 32p. pap. 5.95 (978-0-439-35535-3(4)) Scholastic, Inc.

SELF-RESPECT

Asher, Sandy, ed. With All My Heart, with All My Mind: Thirteen Stories about Growing up Jewish. 2004. Orig. Title: Today I Am. 164p. (J). (gr. 4-8). reprint ed. pap. 18.00 (978-0-7567-7692-3(9)) DIANE Publishing Co.

Egbufoama, Caius. Showbar Kingdom: My Wishes. 1998. 16p. (J). (gr. k-3). pap. 6.00 (978-0-8059-4235-4(1)) Dorrance Publishing Co., Inc.

Espeland, Pamela & Verdick, Elizabeth. Making Every Day Count: Daily Readings for Young People on Solving Problems, Setting Goals & Feeling Good about Yourself. 1998. 408p. (YA). (gr. 6 up). pap. 10.95 (978-1-57542-047-9(3)) Free Spirit Publishing, Inc.

Huegel, Kelly. Young People & Chronic Illness: True Stories, Help & Hope. Bratvold, Gretchen & Verdick, Elizabeth, eds. 1998. (Illus.). 208p. (YA). (gr. 5-9). pap. 14.95 (978-1-57542-041-7(4)) Free Spirit Publishing, Inc.

Hughes, Morgan. An Introduction to Track & Field. 1999. (Illus.). 48p. (J). (gr. 4-8). lib. bdg. 27.93 (978-1-57103-288-1(6)) Rourke Publishing, LLC.

Johnson, Lois Walfrid. You're Worth More Than You Think. rev. ed. 1999. (Let's Talk about It Stories for Kids Ser.). 176p. (J). (gr. 3-8). pap. 7.99 (978-1-55661-651-8(1)) Bethany Hse. Pubs.

Lewis, Barbara A. Being Your Best: Character Building for Kids 7-10. 2004. (Laugh & Learn Ser.). (Illus.). 172p. (J). (gr. 4-7). pap. 14.95 (978-1-57542-063-9(5)) Free Spirit Publishing, Inc.

Moe, Barbara. Understanding Negative Body Image. 1999. (Teen Eating Disorder Prevention Book Ser.). (Illus.). 192p. (YA). (gr. 7-12). lib. bdg. 25.25 (978-0-8239-2865-1(9) , E2BOIM) Rosen Publishing Group, Inc., The.

The Need to Know Library: Guidance for Today's Problems, 8 bks. Incl. Everything You Need to Know about Bipolar Disorder & Manic Depressive Illness. Sommers, Michael A. (J). (gr. 4-6). 2000. lib. bdg. 25.25 (978-0-8239-3106-4(4) , NTBIDI); Everything You Need to Know about Deafness. Basinger, Carol. (J). (gr. 7-12). 2005. lib. bdg. 25.25 (978-0-8239-3165-1(X) , NTDEAF); Everything You Need to Know about Diabetes. Apel, Melanie Ann. (YA). (gr. 7-12). 2005. lib. bdg. 25.25 (978-0-8239-3090-6(4) , NTDIAB); Everything You Need to Know about Effective Communication at School & at Work. Sommers, Annie Leah. (YA). (gr. 7-12). 2005. lib. bdg. 25.25 (978-0-8239-3227-6(3) , NTEFCO); Everything You Need to Know about Family Court. Bianchi, Anne. (YA). (gr. 7-12). 2005. lib. bdg. 25.25 (978-0-8239-3163-7(3) , NTFACO); Everything You Need to Know about Hepatitis. Aronson, Virginia. (YA). (gr. 7-12). 2005. lib. bdg. 25.25 (978-0-8239-3100-2(5) , NTHEPA); Everything You Need to Know about Media Violence. Edgar, Kathleen J. (YA). (gr. 4-6). 2000. lib. bdg. 25.25 (978-0-8239-3108-8(0) , NTMEVI); Everything You Need to Know about Schizophrenia. Friedman, Michelle S. (YA). (gr. 7-12). 2005. lib. bdg. 25.25 (978-0-8239-3091-3(2) , NTSCHI); 64p. (Illus.). Set lib. bdg. 202.00 (978-0-8239-9282-9(9)) Rosen Publishing Group, Inc., The.

Riehecky, Janet. Respect. 2005. (Illus.). 24p. (J). 21.26 (978-0-7368-3682-1(9)) Capstone Pr., Inc.

Romain, Trevor. Cliques, Phonies, & Other Baloney. Romain, Trevor, illus. 1998. (Laugh & Learn Ser.). (Illus.). 136p. (YA). (gr. 3-8). pap. 8.95 (978-1-57542-045-5(7)) Free Spirit Publishing, Inc.

—Cliques, Phonies, & Other Baloney. 1998. (gr. 5-8). lib. bdg. 18.75 (978-0-613-87131-0(6)) Tandem Library Bks.

Rubly-Burggraff, Roberta. Magnum Opus: My Own Journal. Robbins-Ptak, Elizabeth, illus. 1999. 72p. (Orig.). (YA). (gr. 7-12). pap. 5.95 (978-0-937997-14-7(5)) Pflaum Publishing Group.

Schwartz, Stuart B. Building Self-Confidence. 1998. (J). lib. bdg. (978-0-516-21295-1(8) , Children's Pr.) Scholastic Library Publishing.

Shepherd, Kenneth R. Drugs & Low Self-Esteem. 1999. (Drug Abuse Prevention Library). (Illus.). 64p. (YA). (gr. 7-12). lib. bdg. 25.25 (978-0-8239-2826-2(8) , DRSEES) Rosen Publishing Group, Inc., The.

Stinnett, Leia A. Mommy! Why Is Everyone Staring at Me? Stinnett, Leia A., illus. 2001. (Little Angel Bks.). (Illus.). (J). (gr. k-12). pap., stu. ed. 6.95 (978-1-880737-11-8(6)) Crystal Journeys Publishing.

Story Rhyme Staff. Self-Esteem: Stories, Poetry & Activity Pages. Story Rhyme Staff, illus. Date not set. (Illus.). 28p. (YA). (gr. 4-9). ring bd. 19.95 (978-1-56820-107-8(9)) Story Time Stories That Rhyme.

Wood 'n' Barnes Publishing Staff. The Me I See: Answering Life's Questions. 1999. (Illus.). 110p. (YA). spiral bd. 27.95 (978-1-885473-25-7(7)) Wood 'N' Barnes.

SELKIRK, ALEXANDER, 1676-1721

Kraske, Robert. Marooned: The Strange but True Adventures of Alexander Selkirk, the Real Robinson Crusoe. Parker, Robert Andrew, illus. 2005. 128p. (J). (gr. 5-9). 15.00 (978-0-618-56843-7(3) , Clarion Bks.) Houghton Mifflin Co. Trade & Reference Div.

SELLING

see Sales Personnel

SENATORS—UNITED STATES

see Legislators—United States; United States—Congress—Senate—Biography

SENEGAL

Berg, Elizabeth. Senegal. 1999. (Cultures of the World Ser.). (Illus.). 128p. (gr. 5-12). lib. bdg. 37.07 (978-0-7614-0872-7(X) , Benchmark Bks.) Cavendish, Marshall Corp.

Brownlie, Alison. Senegal. 1998. (Worldfocus Ser.). (Illus.). 32p. (J). pap. (978-1-57572-076-0(0)) Heinemann Library.

Gioanni, Alain. Ballel: A Child of Senegal. 2005. (Children of the World Ser.). 24p. (J). (gr. 2-4). 22.45 (978-1-4103-0285-4(7) , Blackbirch Pr., Inc.) Thomson Gale.

Gritzner, Janet H. Senegal. 2004. (Modern World Nations Ser.). (Illus.). 120p. (J). (gr. 6-12). 30.00 (978-0-7910-8023-8(4) , Chelsea Hse.) Facts On File, Inc.

Mulroy, Tanya. Senegal. 2007. (J). (978-1-4222-0091-9(4)) Mason Crest Pubs.

SENSES AND SENSATION

see also Hearing; Smell; Touch; Vision

Ackroyd, Dorothea. What Do You See? 1999. bds. 3.95 (978-1-58185-205-9(3)) Quadrillion Media LLC.

Adoff, Arnold. Touch the Poem. Desimini, Lisa, illus. 2000. 32p. (J). (ps-3). pap. 16.95 (978-0-590-47970-7(9) , Blue Sky Pr., The) Scholastic, Inc.

Aliki. My Five Senses. Aliki, illus. rev. ed. 2000. (Let's-Read-and-Find-Out Science Ser.). (Illus.). 32p. (J). (ps-1). 15.89 (978-0-690-04794-3(0)) HarperCollins Pubs.

Andrews, Georgina. That's Not My Mermaid. 2006. 10p. (J). bds. 9.99 (978-0-7945-1083-1(3) , Usborne) EDC Publishing.

Apel, Melanie Ann. Cocaine & Your Nose (Rev) The Incredibly Disgusting Story. rev. ed. 2005. (Illus.). 48p. (J). (ps-ps). lib. bdg. 25.25 (978-1-4042-0632-8(9) , Rosen Central) Rosen Publishing Group, Inc., The.

Baby Shakespeare. (Baby Einstein Ser.). (Illus.). 28p. (J). (ps). pap. 19.98 incl. audio, VHS (978-1-892309-15-0(7)) Baby Einstein Co., LLC, The.

Ballard, Carol. Ears. 2003. (Body Focus Ser.). (Illus.). 48p. (J). lib. bdg. 27.07 (978-1-4034-0749-8(5)); pap. (978-1-4034-3297-1(X)) Heinemann Library.

—Eyes. 2003. (Body Focus Ser.). (Illus.). 48p. (J). lib. bdg. 27.07 (978-1-4034-0750-4(9)); pap. (978-1-4034-3298-8(8)) Heinemann Library.

Barraclough, Sue. What Can I Taste? 2005. (Illus.). 24p. (J). (978-1-4109-2166-6(2)); pap. (978-1-4109-2172-7(7)) Heinemann Library.

—What Can I Taste? 2005. (J). (978-1-4034-7081-2(2)); pap. (978-1-4034-7087-4(1)) Steck-Vaughn.

Beaumont, Susanna. Baby Senses Taste. 2005. (Baby Senses Ser.). (Illus.). 12p. (ps-k). per., bds. 5.95 (978-1-905051-50-2(6)) Make Believe Ideas GBR. *Dist:* Ingram Pub. Services.

Beck, Esther. Cool Sensory Suspense: Fun Science Projects about the Senses. 2007. (Cool Science Ser.). (Illus.). 32p. (J). (gr. k-6). lib. bdg. 24.21 ***(*978-1-59928-910-6(5)** , Checkerboard Library) ABDO Publishing Co.

Bellamy, Rufus. The Senses. 2004. (Body Science Ser.). (J). lib. bdg. 27.10 (978-1-58340-459-1(7)) Smart Apple Media.

Benchmark Education Staff, compiled by. Senses. 2006. spiral bd. 85.00 ***(*978-1-4108-7033-9(2))*** Benchmark Education Co.

Bentley, Joyce. Soft. 2006. (Things Around Us Ser.). (J). (978-1-59389-278-4(0)) Chrysalis Education.

—Wet. 2006. (Things Around Us Ser.). (J). (978-1-59389-279-1(9)) Chrysalis Education.

Berger, Melvin & Berger, Gilda. You Taste with Your Tongue. 2003. (Illus.). 16p. (J). pap. (978-0-439-56692-6(4)) Scholastic, Inc.

BHB International Staff. My First Picture Book. 1998. (Images Ser.). (Illus.). 136p. (ps-k). pap. 9.95 (978-2-215-06190-8(1)) Continental Enterprises Group, Inc. (CEG).

Brighter Vision Publishing Staff. Senses. 1999. (Learning Adventures Kindergarten Ser.). (Illus.). (J). (gr. k-1). pap. 2.25 (978-1-55254-060-2(X) , BV12022) Brighter Vision Pubns.

Bulloch, Ivan & James, Diane. Avis aux Cinq Sens. 2000. (My Turn Ser.). (Illus.). 12p. (J). (ps-k). bds. 6.95 (978-1-58728-168-6(6) , Two Can Publishing) T&N Children's Publishing.

Burstein, John. Patterns: What's on the Wall? 2003. (Weekly Reader Early Learning Library). (Illus.). 24p. (J). (gr. 1 up). pap. 7.93 (978-0-8368-3831-2(9) , Weekly Reader Early Learning Library) Stevens, Gareth Inc.

Burton, Margie, et al. My Five Senses. Evento, Susan, ed. 1998. (Early Connections Ser.). 16p. (J). (gr. k-2). pap. 4.25 (978-1-892393-64-7(6)) Benchmark Education Co.

Butler, John. Whose Nose & Toes? 2004. (Illus.). 20p. (J). (ps-ps). 10.99 (978-0-670-05904-1(8) , Viking Juvenile) Penguin Group (USA) Inc.

Byles, Monica. Senses. 2004. (Interfact Ser.). (SPA., Illus.). 48p. (J). (gr. 3-6). 14.95 incl. cd-rom (978-1-58728-463-2(4) , Two Can Publishing) T&N Children's Publishing.

Canizares, Susan. Look Listen & Learn. 1999. (J). 2.50 (978-0-439-04605-3(X)) Scholastic, Inc.

Casado, Dami & Casado, Alicia. El Gusto. 2005. (Sentidos y Algo Mas). (SPA.). 10p. (978-84-272-6414-4(3)) Molino, Editorial.

—El Oido. 2005. (Sentidos y Algo Mas). (SPA & ESP.). 16p. 8.99 (978-84-272-6412-0(7)) Molino, Editorial ESP. *Dist:* Santillana USA Publishing Co., Inc.

—La Palabra. 2005. (Sentidos y Algo Mas). (SPA & ESP.). 16p. 8.99 (978-84-272-6416-8(X)) Molino, Editorial ESP. *Dist:* Santillana USA Publishing Co., Inc.

—El Tacto. 2005. (Sentidos y Algo Mas). (SPA & ESP.). 16p. 8.99 (978-84-272-6415-1(1)) Molino, Editorial ESP. *Dist:* Santillana USA Publishing Co., Inc.

—La Vista. 2005. (Sentidos y Algo Mas). (SPA & ESP.). 16p. 8.99 (978-84-272-6411-3(9)) Molino, Editorial ESP. *Dist:* Santillana USA Publishing Co., Inc.

Cassan, Adolfo. The Senses. 2005. (Inside the Human Body Ser.). (Illus.). 32p. (J). (gr. 4-8). 28.00 (978-0-7910-9013-8(2) , Chelsea Clubhouse) Facts On File, Inc.

Catala, Ellen. Our Five Senses. 2003. (Yellow Umbrella Books for Early Readers). (Illus.). (J). 17p. (978-0-7368-1713-4(1)); 16p. (gr. 1). lib. bdg. 14.60 (978-0-7368-2021-9(3) , Pebble Bks.) Capstone Pr., Inc.

Caviezel, Giovanni. My Own Five Senses. 2005. (Illus.). 10p. (J). bds. 10.99 (978-0-7641-5870-4(8)) Barron's Educational Series, Inc.

Chancellor, Deborah. I Wonder Why Lemons Taste Sour & Other Questions about Senses. 2007. 32p. (J). (gr. k-3). 12.95 (978-0-7534-6088-7(2) , Kingfisher) Houghton Mifflin Co. Trade & Reference Div.

Chara, Kathleen A. & Chara, Paul J. Sensory Smarts: A Book for Kids with ADHD or Autism Spectrum Disorders Struggling with Sensory Integration Problems. Berns, Joel M., illus. 2004. 64p. (J). pap. (978-1-84310-783-5(X)) Kingsley, Jessica Ltd.

Ciboul, Adele. The Five Senses. Bell, Anthea, tr. from FRE. Collinet, Clementine et al, illus. 2006. (Explore Your World Ser.). 28p. (J). (ps-1). 15.95 (978-1-55407-007-7(4)) Firefly Bks., Ltd.

Cobb, Vicki. Feeling Your Way: Discover Your Sense of Touch. 2003. (Five Senses Ser.). 32p. pap. 7.95 (978-0-7613-1980-1(8) , Millbrook Pr.) Lerner Publishing Group.

—Feeling Your Way: Discover Your Sense of Touch. Lewis, Cynthia C., illus. 2001. (Five Senses Ser.: 4). 32p. (gr. 2-4). lib. bdg. 22.90 (978-0-7613-1657-2(4) , Millbrook Pr.) Lerner Publishing Group.

—Feeling Your Way: Discover Your Sense of Touch. 2003. (gr. k-3). lib. bdg. 16.40 (978-0-613-88971-1(1)) Tandem Library Bks.

—Follow Your Nose: Discover Your Sense of Smell. (Five Senses Ser.). (Illus.). 32p. 2003. pap. 7.95 (978-0-7613-1978-8(6)); 2000. (gr. 2-4). lib. bdg. 22.90 (978-0-7613-1521-6(7)) Lerner Publishing Group. (Millbrook Pr.).

—Follow Your Nose: Discover Your Sense of Smell. 2003. (gr. k-3). lib. bdg. 16.40 (978-0-613-88969-8(X)) Tandem Library Bks.

—How to Really Fool Yourself: Illusions for All Your Senses. Wolk-Stanley, Jessica, illus. 1999. 120p. (J). (ps-7). per. 22.20 (978-0-613-16515-0(2)) Tandem Library Bks.

—How to Really Fool Yourself: Illusions for All Your Senses. 1999. (Illus.). 128p. (gr. 3-7). pap. 12.95 (978-0-471-31592-6(3) , Wiley-VCH) Wiley, John & Sons, Inc.

—Open Your Eyes: Discover Your Sense of Sight. 2003. (Five Senses Ser.). 32p. pap. 7.95 (978-0-7613-1982-5(4) , Millbrook Pr.) Lerner Publishing Group.

—Open Your Eyes: Discover Your Sense of Sight. Lewis, Cynthia C., illus. 2002. 32p. (gr. 2-4). lib. bdg. 22.90 (978-0-7613-1705-0(8) , Millbrook Pr.) Lerner Publishing Group.

—Open Your Eyes: Discover Your Sense of Sight. 2003. (gr. k-3). lib. bdg. 16.40 (978-0-613-91016-3(8)) Tandem Library Bks.

—Perk up Your Ears: Discover Your Sense of Hearing. 2003. (Five Senses Ser.). 32p. pap. 7.95 (978-0-7613-1981-8(6) , Millbrook Pr.) Lerner Publishing Group.

—Your Tongue Can Tell: Discover Your Sense of Taste. (Five Senses Ser.). 32p. 2003. pap. 7.95 (978-0-7613-1979-5(4)); 2000. (Illus.). (gr. 2-4). lib. bdg. (978-0-7613-1473-8(3)) Lerner Publishing Group. (Millbrook Pr.).

Cobb, Vicky. On the Tip of Your Tongue. 1998. 48p. (J). (ps-3). 14.95 (978-0-7868-0143-5(3)); 14.89 (978-0-7868-2116-7(7)) Hyperion Bks. for Children.

Cole, Joanna. Explores the Senses. Degen, Bruce, illus. 2001. (Magic School Bus Ser.). 48p. (J). (gr. 1-4). 5.99 (978-0-590-44698-3(3)) Scholastic, Inc.

—The Magic School Bus Explores the Senses. Degen, Bruce, illus. 1999. (Magic School Bus Ser.). 47p. (J). (gr. 1-4). pap. 15.95 (978-0-590-44697-6(5)) Scholastic, Inc.

—The Magic School Bus Explores the Senses. 2001. (Illus.). (J). (978-0-606-21312-7(0)); 1999. lib. bdg. 13.00 (978-0-613-59331-1(6)) Tandem Library Bks.

Collins, Andrew. See, Hear, Smell, Taste, Touch: Using Your Five Senses. 2006. (National Geographic Science Chapters Ser.). (Illus.). 48p. (gr. 1-4). 17.90 (978-0-7922-5943-5(2) , National Geographic Children's Bks.) National Geographic Society.

Conrad, Marjorie. Five Senses, Grades K-2. Blocher, Wendy, ed. Yuh, Catherine, illus. 1999. (Primary Theme Ser.). 32p. pap., tchr. ed. 7.99 (978-1-57471-628-3(X) , 2442) Creative Teaching Pr., Inc.

Daoust, Cidny, ed. Investigating Science - Five Senses. 2003. 48p. 9.95 (978-1-56234-542-6(7) , Mailbox Bks., The) Education Ctr., Inc.

del Moral, Susana. Baby Einstein: Que Flota? Baby Einstein: What Floats?, Spanish-Language Edition. Zaidi, Nadeem, illus. 2006. 8p. (J). 6.95 ***(*978-970-718-453-4(1)*** , Silver Dolphin en Español) Advanced Marketing, S. de R. L. de C. V. MEX. *Dist:* Perseus Distribution.

Devaney, Sherri. Super Senses. 2005. (Planet's Most Extreme Ser.). (Illus.). 48p. (gr. 3-7). 24.95 (978-1-4103-0398-1(5) , Blackbirch Pr., Inc.) Thomson Gale.

Diagram Group. The Senses. 2005. (Illus.). 112p. (J). (978-0-8160-5987-4(X)) Facts On File, Inc.

DK Publishing Staff. Baby Senses. 2007. (Let's Play Ser.). (Illus.). 16p. (J). 9.99 (978-0-7566-2597-9(1)) Dorling Kindersley Publishing, Inc.

Douglas, Lloyd G. My Ears. 2004. (Wel-My Body Ser.). (J). 18.00 (978-0-516-24062-6(5)); 24p. pap. 4.95 (978-0-516-22126-7(4)) Scholastic Library Publishing. (Children's Pr.).

—My Eyes. 2004. (Wel-My Body Ser.). (J). 18.00 (978-0-516-24060-2(9)); 24p. pap. 4.95 (978-0-516-22127-4(2)) Scholastic Library Publishing. (Children's Pr.).

—My Nose. 2004. (Wel-My Body Ser.). (J). 18.00 (978-0-516-24063-3(3) , Children's Pr.) Scholastic Library Publishing.

Dubovoy, Silvia. Orejas. 2002. (SPA.). (gr. k-3). lib. bdg. 15.25 (978-0-613-64569-0(3)) Tandem Library Bks.

Editions Phidal Staff, ed. Senses. (Jump Ser.). (Illus.). 32p. (J). (gr. 2-7). pap. 4.95 (978-1-882210-30-5(1)) Action Publishing, Inc.

—Senses. 2004. (Illus.). lib. bdg. 7.95 (978-0-8225-5162-1(4)) Lerner Publishing Group.

Ehrlich, Fred. You Can't Taste a Pickle W/ Ea. 2006. (Illus.). 40p. pap. 6.95 (978-1-59354-172-9(4)) Blue Apple Bks.

Einhorn, Kama. Sesame Subjects: My First Book about the Five Senses. Moroney, Christopher, illus. 2006. (Sesame Street Ser.). 24p. (J). (gr. k). 7.99 (978-0-375-83516-2(4) , Random Hse. Bks. for Young Readers) Random Hse. Children's Bks.

Endres, Hollie J. Nuestros cinco Sentidos. 2005. Tr. of Our Five Senses. (SPA., Illus.). 16p. (J). (gr. 1 up). lib. bdg. 15.93 (978-0-7368-4138-2(5)) Capstone Pr., Inc.

Equipo Staff. El Tacto. (Coleccion Mundo Maravilloso). (SPA., Illus.). 42p. (J). (gr. 2-4). (978-84-348-5207-5(1) , SM8406) SM Ediciones ESP. *Dist:* Lectorum Pubns., Inc.

Falk, Laine. Let's Explore the Five Senses with City Dog & Country Dog. 2007. (Let's Find Out Early Learning Bks.). (Illus.). 24p. (J). (ps-k). 18.00 (978-0-531-14873-0(4) , Children's Pr.) Scholastic Library Publishing.

The Five Senses/Opposites & Position Words, 4 bks., Set. Incl. Let's Explore the Five Senses with City Dog & Country Dog. Falk, Laine. 18.00 (978-0-531-14873-0(4)); Let's Find Rain Forest Animals : Up, down, Around. Behrens, Janice. 18.00 ***(*978-0-531-14874-7(2));*** Let's Play a Five Senses Guessing Game. Miller, Amanda. 18.00 (978-0-531-14871-6(8)); Let's Talk about Opposites, Morning to Night. Falk, Laine. 18.00 (978-0-531-14872-3(6)); (Illus.). 24p. (J). (ps-k). (Let's Find Out Early Learning Bks.). 2007. 72.00 ***(*978-0-531-17574-3(X)*** , Children's Pr.) Scholastic Library Publishing.

Freymann, Saxton & Elffers, Joost. Vegetal Como Eres. 2001. (Illus.). (J). (978-0-606-21500-8(X)) Tandem Library Bks.

Frost, Helen. The Senses, 6 bks. Saunders-Smith, Gail, ed. Incl. Hearing. lib. bdg. 15.93 (978-0-7368-0382-3(3)); Seeing. lib. bdg. 15.93 (978-0-7368-0383-0(1)); Smelling. lib. bdg. 15.93 (978-0-7368-0384-7(X)); Tasting. lib. bdg. 15.93 (978-0-7368-0385-4(8)); Touching. lib. bdg. 15.93 (978-0-7368-0386-1(6)); Your Senses. lib. bdg. 15.93 (978-0-7368-0387-8(4)); 24p. (J). (gr. k-1). 1999. (Illus.). 2000. Set lib. bdg. 95.58 (978-0-7368-0450-9(1) , Pebble Bks.) Capstone Pr., Inc.

—Tasting. Saunders-Smith, Gail, ed. 1999. (Senses Ser.). (Illus.). 24p. (J). (gr. k-1). lib. bdg. 15.93 (978-0-7368-0385-4(8) , Pebble Bks.) Capstone Pr., Inc.

—Tasting. 1999. pap. 13.25 (978-0-516-21912-7(X) , Children's Pr.) Scholastic Library Publishing.

Furgang, Kathy. My Eyes. 2001. (My Body Ser.). (Illus.). 24p. (J). lib. bdg. 19.95 (978-0-8239-5573-2(7) , PowerKids Pr.) Rosen Publishing Group, Inc., The.

—My Nose. 2001. (My Body Ser.). (Illus.). 24p. (J). lib. bdg. 19.95 (978-0-8239-5576-3(1) , PowerKids Pr.) Rosen Publishing Group, Inc., The.

Galvin, Laura Gates. JoJo's Circus My Five Senses Travel Pack. 2006. 10 x 6p. 12.99 (978-1-59069-478-7(3)) Studio Mouse LLC.

Ganeri, Anita. Your Senses. Shott, Steve, photos by. 2003. (How Your Body Works). (Illus.). 32p. (J). (gr. 2 up). lib. bdg. 23.33 (978-0-8368-3636-3(7)) Stevens, Gareth Inc.

Gardner, Robert. Health Science Projects about Your Senses. 2001. (Science Projects Ser.). (Illus.). 112p. (YA). (gr. 6-12). lib. bdg. 26.60 (978-0-7660-1437-4(1)) Enslow Pubs., Inc.

Gates, Phil. Animal Senses: South African Edition. 1999. (Cambridge Reading Routes Ser.). (Illus.). 24p. pap. 5.50 (978-0-521-77891-6(3)) Cambridge Univ. Pr.

Glover, David & Glover, Penny. Senses. 2005. (Illus.). 30p. (J). (gr. 3-7). lib. bdg. 27.10 (978-1-58340-692-2(1)) Smart Apple Media.

Godwin, Sam. It All Makes Sense. 2002. (Little Bees Ser.). (Illus.). 31p. (J). lib. bdg. 24.25 (978-1-58340-223-8(3)) Smart Apple Media.

Gordon, Sharon. Hearing. 2002. (Rookie Read-About Health Ser.). (Illus.). 32p. (J). (gr. k-2). pap. 5.95 (978-0-516-25989-5(X) , Children's Pr.) Scholastic Library Publishing.

—Hearing. 2001. (gr. k-3). lib. bdg. 14.10 (978-0-613-50700-4(2)) Tandem Library Bks.

—Tasting. (Rookie Read-About Health Ser.). (Illus.). 32p. (J). (gr. k-2). 2002. pap. 5.95 (978-0-516-25992-5(X)); 2001. 20.50 (978-0-516-22293-6(7)) Scholastic Library Publishing. (Children's Pr.).

—Tasting. 2001. (gr. k-3). lib. bdg. 14.10 (978-0-613-50752-3(5)) Tandem Library Bks.

—Touching. 2002. (Rookie Read-About Health Ser.). (Illus.). 32p. (J). (gr. k-2). pap. 5.95 (978-0-516-25993-2(8) , Children's Pr.) Scholastic Library Publishing.

—Touching. 2001. (gr. k-3). lib. bdg. 14.10 (978-0-613-50757-8(6)) Tandem Library Bks.

Granowsky, Alvin. Sounds. 2001. (ps-2). lib. bdg. 13.00 (978-0-613-45225-0(9)) Tandem Library Bks.

Green, Jen. Brain & Senses. 2005. (Illus.). 32p. (J). (gr. 3-7). lib. bdg. 27.10 (978-1-59604-050-2(5)) Stargazer Bks.

Group/McGraw-Hill, Wright. Nuestros Cinco Sentidos, 6 vols. (First Explorers. Primeros Exploradores Nonfiction Sets Ser.). (SPA.). (gr. 1-2). 29.95 (978-0-7699-1476-3(4)) Shortland Pubns. (U. S. A.) Inc.

El Gusto (Tasting) 2006. (SPA.). (J). 18.60 (978-0-8225-6224-5(3) , Ediciones Lerner) Lerner Publishing Group.

Haddon, Jean. Make Sense! 2006. (Silly Millies Ser.). (J). 21.27 (978-0-7613-3403-3(3) , Millbrook Pr.) Lerner Publishing Group.

Hall, Kirsten. Animal Taste. 2005. (Illus.). 24p. (J). pap. (978-0-8368-4811-3(X)); lib. bdg. 19.33 (978-0-8368-4805-2(5)) Stevens, Gareth Inc.

—Animal Taste: El Gusto en Los Animales. 2005. (ENG & SPA., Illus.). 24p. (J). pap. (978-0-8368-4823-6(3)); lib. bdg. 19.33 (978-0-8368-4817-5(9)) Stevens, Gareth Inc.

—Animal Touch: El Tacto en Los Animales. 2005. (ENG & SPA., Illus.). 24p. pap. (978-0-8368-4824-3(1)); lib. bdg. 19.33 (978-0-8368-4818-2(7)) Stevens, Gareth Inc.

—Animals & Their Senses. 24p. (YA). 96.65 (978-0-8368-4801-4(2)); 96.65 (978-0-8368-4813-7(6)) Stevens, Gareth Inc.

Hanel, Rachael. Smell. 2003. 24p. (J). lib. bdg. 21.35 (978-1-58340-306-8(X)) Smart Apple Media.

Harcourt School Publishers Staff. The Five Senses. 3rd ed. 2002. (Trophies English Language Learners Ser.). (Illus.). pap. 5.10 (978-0-15-327699-6(1)) Harcourt Schl. Pubs.

Hartley, Karen, et al. Hearing in Living Things. 2000. (Senses Ser.). (Illus.). 32p. (J). (gr. k-2). lib. bdg. 21.36 (978-1-57572-246-7(1)) Heinemann Library.

—Seeing in Living Things. 2000. (Senses Ser.). (J). (gr. k-2). lib. bdg. 21.36 (978-1-57572-247-4(X)) Heinemann Library.

—Senses in Living Things. 2000. (Senses Ser.). (Illus.). 32p. (J). 21.95 (978-1-58810-134-1(7)) Heinemann Library.

—The Sixth Sense & other Special Senses. 2000. (Senses Ser.). 32p. (J). (gr. k-2). lib. bdg. 21.36 (978-1-57572-248-1(8)) Heinemann Library.

—Smelling in Living Things. 2000. 32p. (J). (gr. k-2). lib. bdg. 21.36 (978-1-57572-249-8(6)) Heinemann Library.

—Tasting in Living Things. 2000. (Senses Ser.). (Illus.). 32p. (J). (gr. k-2). lib. bdg. 21.36 (978-1-57572-250-4(X)) Heinemann Library.

—Touching in Living Things. 2000. (Senses Ser.). 32p. (J). (gr. k-2). lib. bdg. 21.36 (978-1-57572-251-1(8)) Heinemann Library.

Hathon, Elizabeth. Oh, Baby! 1999. (Touch & Feel Ser.). (Illus.). 12p. (J). (ps-k). bds. 6.99 (978-0-448-41897-1(5) , Grosset & Dunlap) Penguin Group (USA) Inc.

Haydon, Julie. The Five Senses: Individual Title Six-Packs. (Rigby Focus Ser.). 16p. (gr. k up). 26.00 (978-0-7578-5292-3(0)); 28.00 (978-0-7578-5526-9(1)) Rigby Education.

Henderson, Kathy. Look at You! A Baby Body Book. Howard, Paul, illus. 2007. 40p. (J). (ps). 15.99 (978-0-7636-2745-4(3)) Candlewick Pr.

Hewitt, Sally. The Five Senses. 1999. (It's Science! Ser.). (Illus.). 32p. (J). (gr. k-3). 23.50 (978-0-516-21179-4(X) , Children's Pr.) Scholastic Library Publishing.

—Five Senses. 1999. (It's Science! Ser.). (Illus.). 32p. (J). (gr. k-3). pap. 6.95 (978-0-516-26447-9(8) , Children's Pr.) Scholastic Library Publishing.

Hickman, Pamela. Animal Senses: How Animals See, Hear, Taste, Smell & Feel. Stephens, Pat, illus. 2004. (Animal Behavior Ser.). 40p. (J). (gr. 4-6). (978-1-55074-425-5(9)) Kids Can Pr., Ltd.

—How Animals Use Their Senses. Stephens, Pat, illus. 2006. 32p. (978-1-55337-903-4(9)); (978-1-55337-902-7(0)) Kids Can Pr., Ltd.

Hidalgo, Maria. Taste. 2003. 24p. (J). lib. bdg. 21.35 (978-1-58340-305-1(1)) Smart Apple Media.

—Touch. 2003. 24p. (J). lib. bdg. 21.35 (978-1-58340-307-5(8)) Smart Apple Media.

Howells, Shelley. Making Sense of Your Senses. 2004. (Navigators Ser.). (J). pap. 38.00 (978-1-4108-0407-5(0)) Benchmark Education Co.

Howells, Shelley. Tus sentidos tienen sentido & Making Sense of Your Senses. 2005. spiral bd. 77.00 ***(978-1-4108-5677-7(1))*** Benchmark Education Co.

Jarrell, Jane & Saathoff, Deborah. My Five Senses. 2000. (One-Stop Thematic Units Ser.). (Illus.). 64p. (J). (gr. k-1). 9.50 (978-0-570-05258-6(0)) Concordia Publishing Hse.

Johnson, Jinny. Senses. 2004. (Kingfisher Young Knowledge Ser.). (Illus.). 48p. (J). (gr. k-3). 9.95 (978-0-7534-5771-9(7) , Kingfisher) Houghton Mifflin Co. Trade & Reference Div.

Kalman, Bobbie. How Does It Feel? 2007. (Looking at Nature Ser.). (Illus.). 24p. (J). (ps-2). pap. ***(978-0-7787-3334-8(3))*** Crabtree Publishing Co.

Kashman, Nancy & Mora, Janet. The Sensory Connection: Sensory & Communication Strategies That Work, 1. 2nd ed. 2005. Orig. Title: An OT & SLP Team Approach. 192p. per. 19.95 (978-1-931615-21-1(7)) Sensory Resources.

Katz, Karen. A Potty for Me! Katz, Karen, illus. 2004. (Illus.). 28p. (J). tchr. ed. 7.99 (978-0-689-87423-9(5) , Little Simon) Simon & Schuster Children's Publishing.

—Wiggle Your Toes. Katz, Karen, illus. 2006. (Illus.). 14p. (J). 8.99 (978-1-4169-0365-9(8) , Little Simon) Simon & Schuster Children's Publishing.

Kauffman, Dorothy. Use Your Senses. 2005. (Content Area Readers Ser.). 24p. 4.95 (978-0-19-430954-7(1)) Oxford Univ. Pr., Inc.

Klingel, Cynthia Fitterer & Noyed, Robert B. Ears. Andersen, Gregg, photos by. 2002. (Weekly Reader Early Learning Library). (Illus.). 24p. (J). (ps up). pap. 5.95 (978-0-8368-3151-1(9)); lib. bdg. 19.33 (978-0-8368-3062-0(8)) Stevens, Gareth Inc. (Weekly Reader Early Learning Library).

—Ears/Orejas. Acosta, Tatiana & Gutiérrez, Guillermo, trs. Andersen, Gregg, photos by. 2002. (Weekly Reader Early Learning Library). (Illus.). 24p. (J). (ps up). (SPA & ENG.). pap. (978-0-8368-3320-1(1)); (ENG & SPA., lib. bdg. 19.33 (978-0-8368-3071-2(7)) Stevens, Gareth Inc. (Weekly Reader Early Learning Library).

—Eyes. Andersen, Gregg, photos by. 2002. (Weekly Reader Early Learning Library). (Illus.). 24p. (J). (ps up). pap. 5.95 (978-0-8368-3152-8(7)); lib. bdg. 19.33 (978-0-8368-3063-7(6)) Stevens, Gareth Inc. (Weekly Reader Early Learning Library).

—Eyes/Ojos. Acosta, Tatiana & Gutiérrez, Guillermo, trs. Andersen, Gregg, photos by. 2002. (Weekly Reader Early Learning Library). (ENG & SPA., Illus.). 24p. (J). (ps up). pap. (978-0-8368-3321-8(X)); lib. bdg. 19.33 (978-0-8368-3072-9(5)) Stevens, Gareth Inc. (Weekly Reader Early Learning Library).

—Mouth. Andersen, Gregg, photos by. 2002. (Weekly Reader Early Learning Library). (Illus.). 24p. (J). (ps up). pap. 5.95 (978-0-8368-3156-6(X)); lib. bdg. 19.33 (978-0-8368-3067-5(9)) Stevens, Gareth Inc. (Weekly Reader Early Learning Library).

—Mouth/Boca. Acosta, Tatiana & Gutiérrez, Guillermo, trs. Andersen, Gregg, photos by. 2002. (Weekly Reader Early Learning Library). (Illus.). 24p. (J). (ps up). pap. (978-0-8368-3325-6(2)); (ENG & SPA., lib. bdg. 19.33 (978-0-8368-3076-7(8)) Stevens, Gareth Inc. (Weekly Reader Early Learning Library).

—Nose. Andersen, Gregg, photos by. 2002. (Weekly Reader Early Learning Library). (Illus.). 24p. (J). (ps up). pap. 5.95 (978-0-8368-3157-3(8)); lib. bdg. 19.33 (978-0-8368-3068-2(7)) Stevens, Gareth Inc. (Weekly Reader Early Learning Library).

—Nose/Nariz. Acosta, Tatiana & Gutiérrez, Guillermo, trs. Andersen, Gregg, photos by. 2002. (Weekly Reader Early Learning Library). (Illus.). 24p. (J). (ps up). (SPA & ENG.). pap. (978-0-8368-3326-3(0)); (ENG & SPA., lib. bdg. 19.33 (978-0-8368-3077-4(6)) Stevens, Gareth Inc. (Weekly Reader Early Learning Library).

Layton, Neil. Go Wild with Noises. 2004. (Illus.). 12p. (J). bds. (978-1-84458-043-9(1)) Chrysalis Children's Bks.

Levine, Shar & Johnstone, Leslie. First Science Experiments with Nature, Senses, Weather & Machines. Harpster, Steve, illus. 2005. 192p. (978-1-4027-2922-5(7)) Sterling Publishing Co., Inc.

Libra, Anna. Why Does Loud Music Hurt My Ears? An Inside Look at the Ear. 2003. (J). pap. (978-1-58417-072-3(7)); lib. bdg. (978-1-58417-009-9(3)) Lake Street Pubs.

—Why Does That Taste Bad? An Inside Look at the Tongue. 2003. (J). pap. (978-1-58417-069-3(7)); lib. bdg. (978-1-58417-006-8(9)) Lake Street Pubs.

Llewellyn, Claire. Seeing. 2004. (Body in Action Ser.). (J). pap. (978-1-58340-438-6(4)) Smart Apple Media.

Look, Listen, Taste, Touch, & Smell. (Amazing Body Ser.). 24p. (J). 7.95 (978-1-4048-0508-8(7)) Picture Window Bks.

MacKenzie, Catherine. Smell. 2000. 16p. (J). (ps-3). (978-1-85792-564-7(5) , Christian Focus) Christian Focus Pubns.

—Taste. 2000. 16p. (J). (ps-3). (978-1-85792-561-6(0) , Christian Focus) Christian Focus Pubns.

Mackill, Mary. Special Animal Senses. 2006. (Heinemann Read & Learn Ser.). (Illus.). 24p. (J). (978-1-4034-7378-3(1)); pap. (978-1-4034-7385-1(4)) Steck-Vaughn.

—Tasting. 2006. (Super Senses Ser.). (ENG & SPA., Illus.). 24p. (J). (978-1-4034-7379-0(X)); pap. (978-1-4034-7386-8(2)) Steck-Vaughn.

Make Sense! 2006. (J). pap. 5.95 (978-0-8225-6472-0(6) , First Avenue Editions) Lerner Publishing Group.

Mason, Paul. Animal Spies. 2007. (J). ***(978-1-4109-2975-4(2)); pap. (978-1-4109-2996-9(5))*** Steck-Vaughn.

McKendry, Sam. Are You Ticklish? Bilingual Edition. 2006. 12p. 10.95 (978-1-58117-472-4(1) , Intervisual/Piggy Toes) Dalmatian Pr.

McNeil, Niki, et al. HOCPP 1067 the Five Senses. 2006. spiral bd. 15.50 ***(978-1-60308-067-5(8))*** In the Hands of a Child.

Miller, Amanda. Let's Play a Five Senses Guessing Game. 2007. (Let's Find Out Early Learning Bks.). (Illus.). 24p. (J). (ps-k). 18.00 (978-0-531-14871-6(8) , Children's Pr.) Scholastic Library Publishing.

Miller, Margaret. My Five Senses. 1998. (Illus.). 24p. (J). (ps). 6.99 (978-0-689-82009-0(7) , Aladdin) Simon & Schuster Children's Publishing.

—My Five Senses. 1998. (978-0-606-13631-0(2)) Tandem Library Bks.

Miller-Schroeder, Patricia. The Science of Senses. 1999. (Living Science Ser.). (Illus.). 32p. (J). (gr. 2 up). lib. bdg. 24.67 (978-0-8368-2573-2(X)) Stevens, Gareth Inc.

Miller-Schroeder, Patricia. Senses. 2007. (J). ***(978-1-59036-715-5(4)); (978-1-59036-716-2(2))*** Weigl Pubs., Inc.

Mitchell, Melanie S. Ears. 2003. (First Step Nonfiction Ser.). (Illus.). 8p. (J). pap. 3.95 (978-0-8225-3910-0(1) , Lerner Pubns.) Lerner Publishing Group.

Molter, Carey. The Five Senses. l.t. ed. 2001. (Senses Ser.). (Illus.). 24p. (J). (ps-3). lib. bdg. 19.93 (978-1-57765-631-9(8) , SandCastle) ABDO Publishing Co.

—Sense of Hearing. l.t. ed. 2001. (Senses Ser.). (Illus.). 24p. (J). (ps-3). lib. bdg. 19.93 (978-1-57765-627-2(X) , SandCastle) ABDO Publishing Co.

—Sense of Sight. l.t. ed. 2001. (Senses Ser.). (Illus.). 24p. (J). (ps-3). lib. bdg. 19.93 (978-1-57765-626-5(1) , SandCastle) ABDO Publishing Co.

—Sense of Taste. l.t. ed. 2001. (Senses Ser.). (Illus.). 24p. (J). (ps-3). lib. bdg. 19.93 (978-1-57765-629-6(6) , SandCastle) ABDO Publishing Co.

—The Senses, Set. l.t. ed. Incl. Five Senses. lib. bdg. 19.93 (978-1-57765-631-9(8)); Sense of Hearing. lib. bdg. 19.93 (978-1-57765-627-2(X)); Sense of Sight. lib. bdg. 19.93 (978-1-57765-626-5(1)); Sense of Smell. lib. bdg. 19.93 (978-1-57765-628-9(8)); Sense of Taste. lib. bdg. 19.93 (978-1-57765-629-6(6)); Sense of Touch. lib. bdg. 19.93 (978-1-57765-630-2(X)); 24p. (J). (ps-3). 2001. (Illus.). 2001. Set lib. bdg. 119.58 (978-1-57765-515-2(X) , SandCastle) ABDO Publishing Co.

Morgan, Sally. Animals & Their World. 2002. (Young Discoverers Ser.). (Illus.). 32p. (J). (gr. k-3). pap. 7.95 (978-0-7534-5498-5(X) , Kingfisher) Houghton Mifflin Co. Trade & Reference Div.

Murphy, Brian. Experiment with Senses. 2001. (Experiment with Ser.). (J). (gr. 2-7). 9.95 (978-1-58728-247-8(X)); pap. 5.95 (978-1-58728-118-1(X)) T&N Children's Publishing. (Two Can Publishing).

Murphy, Patricia J. Taste. 2003. (True Bks.). (gr. 3-5). pap. 6.95 (978-0-516-26971-9(2) , Children's Pr.) Scholastic Library Publishing.

—Taste. 2003. (gr. 3-6). lib. bdg. 15.25 (978-0-613-67987-9(3)) Tandem Library Bks.

Nelson, Robin. Hearing. 2005. (First Step Nonfiction Ser.). (Illus.). 24p. (gr. k-2). lib. bdg. 17.27 (978-0-8225-1264-6(5)) Lerner Publishing Group.

—Seeing. 2005. (First Step Nonfiction Ser.). (Illus.). 24p. (gr. k-2). lib. bdg. 17.27 (978-0-8225-1262-2(9)) Lerner Publishing Group.

—Smelling. 2005. (Senses Ser.). (Illus.). 24p. (gr. k-2). lib. bdg. 17.27 (978-0-8225-1263-9(7)) Lerner Publishing Group.

—Tasting. 2005. (Senses Ser.). (Illus.). 24p. (gr. k-2). lib. bdg. 17.27 (978-0-8225-1265-3(3)) Lerner Publishing Group.

—Touching. 2005. (First Step Nonfiction Ser.). (Illus.). 24p. (gr. k-2). lib. bdg. 17.27 (978-0-8225-1266-0(1)) Lerner Publishing Group.

The Nervous System/The Senses/The Skin. 2006. (World Book's Human Body Works). (Illus.). 48p. (J). (978-0-7166-4430-9(4)) World Bk., Inc.

Nettleton, Pamela Hill. Look, Listen, Taste, Touch & Smell: Learning about Your Five Senses. Shipe, Becky, illus. 2004. (Amazing Body Ser.). 24p. (C). (gr. k-3). 22.60 (978-1-4048-0257-5(6)) Picture Window Bks.

Nunn, Daniel. Noses. 2006. (Illus.). 24p. (J). (978-1-4034-8476-5(7)); pap. (978-1-4034-8481-9(3)) Heinemann Library.

O'Brien-Palmer, Michelle. Sense-Abilities: Fun Ways to Explore the Senses. 1998. (Illus.). 176p. (J). (ps-3). pap. 14.95 (978-1-55652-327-4(0)) Chicago Review Pr., Inc.

Oleksy, Walter. The Head & Neck: Learning How We Use Our Muscles. 2002. (3-D Library of the Human Body). (Illus.). 48p. (YA). (gr. 5-8). lib. bdg. 26.50 (978-0-8239-3531-4(0) , Rosen Central) Rosen Publishing Group, Inc., The.

Oliendo. (Coleccion Mil Preguntas). (SPA., Illus.). 24p. (J). pap. 4.50 (978-950-11-0659-6(4) , SGM628) Sigmar ARG. *Dist:* Continental Bk. Co., Inc.

Olson, Karen W. Eyes, Ears, Nose & Mouth. George, Leonard, Jr., illus. 2006. 20p. (J). pap. 10.95 (978-1-894778-34-3(0)) Theytus Bks., Ltd. CAN. *Dist:* Orca Bk. Pubs. USA.

Our Five Senses Science. (gr. k-2). 19.95 (978-0-7368-7105-1(5)) Red Brick Learning.

Our Senses. (Early Intervention Levels Ser.). 23.10 (978-0-7362-0030-1(4)); Vol. 4. 3.85 (978-1-56334-978-2(7)) Hampton-Brown Bks.

Oyendo. (Coleccion Mil Preguntas). (SPA., Illus.). 24p. (J). pap. 5.50 (978-950-11-0662-6(4) , SGM624) Sigmar ARG. *Dist:* Continental Bk. Co., Inc.

Paine, Penelope C. Gift of Taste. Maeno, Itoko, illus. 2006. 24p. per. 5.95 (978-0-9707944-6-8(0)) Paper Posie.

Parker, Steve. The Senses. 2004. (Our Bodies Ser.). (Illus.). 48p. (J). lib. bdg. 28.56 (978-0-7398-6624-5(9)) Raintree.

Pat Them Gently w/ Plush. 2007. 14.95 ***(978-1-58117-626-1(0)*** , Intervisual/Piggy Toes) Dalmatian Pr.

Pavisic, Jenny. Acidin y Acidon. Graullera, Fabiola, illus. 2001. (SPA.). 28p. (J). (gr. k-3). lib. bdg. 7.95 (978-968-19-0630-6(6)) Aguilar Editorial MEX. *Dist:* Santillana USA Publishing Co., Inc.

Petersen, Christine. Does Everyone Have ADHD? A Teen's Guide to Diagnosis & Treatment. 2006. (Health & Human Disease Ser.). (Illus.). 144p. (J). (gr. 9-12). 30.50 (978-0-531-16794-6(1) , Watts, Franklin) Scholastic Library Publishing.

Phidal Publishing Staff, ed. Senses. (Turn & Learn Ser.). 12p. (J). (978-2-7643-0140-1(5)) Phidal Publishing, Inc./Editions Phidal, Inc.

Piggy Toes Press Staff. Dog Walk. 2006. 14p. 9.95 (978-1-58117-481-6(0) , Intervisual/Piggy Toes) Dalmatian Pr.

Popular Science Editors. Making Sense of Senses. 2007. (Experiment with Science Ser.). 32p. (J). pap. 7.95 ***(978-0-531-18760-9(8));*** (Illus.). (gr. 3-6). lib. bdg. 25.00 ***(978-0-531-18540-7(0))*** Scholastic Library Publishing. (Children's Pr.).

Priddy, Roger. Quack! Quack! rev. ed. 2004. (Baby Touch & Feel Ser.). (Illus.). 14p. (J). bds. 8.95 (978-0-312-49250-2(2) , Priddy Bks.) St. Martin's Pr.

Pringle, Laurence P. Explore Your Senses, 5 bks., Set. Incl. Hearing. lib. bdg. 25.64 (978-0-7614-0735-5(9)); Sight. lib. bdg. 25.64 (978-0-7614-0734-8(0)); Smell. lib. bdg. 25.64 (978-0-7614-0737-9(5)); Taste. lib. bdg. 25.64 (978-0-7614-0736-2(7)); Touch. lib. bdg. 25.64 (978-0-7614-0738-6(3)); 32p. (J). (gr. 4-8). (Illus.). 2000. Set lib. bdg. 128.21 (978-0-7614-0733-1(2) , Benchmark Bks.) Cavendish, Marshall Corp.

—Hearing. 2000. (Explore Your Senses Ser.). (Illus.). 32p. (J). (gr. 4-8). lib. bdg. 25.64 (978-0-7614-0735-5(9) , Benchmark Bks.) Cavendish, Marshall Corp.

—Sight. 2000. (Explore Your Senses Ser.). (Illus.). 32p. (J). (gr. 4-8). lib. bdg. 25.64 (978-0-7614-0734-8(0) , Benchmark Bks.) Cavendish, Marshall Corp.

—Smell. 2000. (Explore Your Senses Ser.). (Illus.). 32p. (J). (gr. 4-8). lib. bdg. 25.64 (978-0-7614-0737-9(5) , Benchmark Bks.) Cavendish, Marshall Corp.

—Taste. 2000. (Explore Your Senses Ser.). (Illus.). 32p. (J). (gr. 4-8). lib. bdg. 25.64 (978-0-7614-0736-2(7) , Benchmark Bks.) Cavendish, Marshall Corp.

—Touch. 2000. (Explore Your Senses Ser.). (Illus.). 32p. (J). (gr. 4-8). lib. bdg. 25.64 (978-0-7614-0738-6(3) , Benchmark Bks.) Cavendish, Marshall Corp.

Pryor, Kimberley Jane. Hearing. 2003. (Senses Ser.). (Illus.). 32p. (gr. 2-4). 23.00 (978-0-7910-7554-8(0) , Chelsea Hse.) Facts On File, Inc.

—Seeing. 2003. (Senses Ser.). (Illus.). 32p. (gr. 2-4). 23.00 (978-0-7910-7555-5(9) , Chelsea Hse.) Facts On File, Inc.

—Smelling. 2003. (Senses Ser.). (Illus.). 32p. (gr. 2-4). 23.00 (978-0-7910-7556-2(7) , Chelsea Hse.) Facts On File, Inc.

—Tasting. 2003. (Senses Ser.). (Illus.). 32p. (gr. 2-4). 23.00 (978-0-7910-7557-9(5) , Chelsea Hse.) Facts On File, Inc.

—Touching. 2003. (Senses Ser.). (Illus.). 32p. (gr. 2-4). 23.00 (978-0-7910-7558-6(3) , Chelsea Hse.) Facts On File, Inc.

—Your Senses. 2003. (Senses Ser.). (Illus.). 32p. (J). (gr. 2-4). 23.00 (978-0-7910-7559-3(1) , Chelsea Hse.) Facts On File, Inc.

Ramos & Arago. El Pastel de Chocolate. (SPA.). 32p. (J). 10.00 (978-84-342-2515-2(8)) Parramon Ediciones S.A. ESP. *Dist:* Distribuidora Norma, Inc.

Read about the Five Sense Collection. 2005. (J). pap. ***(978-1-60015-011-1(X))*** Steps To Literacy, LLC.

Riley, Peter D. Senses. Moller, Ray, photos by. 2003. (Everyday Science Ser.). (Illus.). 32p. (J). (gr. 1 up). lib. bdg. 23.33 (978-0-8368-3720-9(7)) Stevens, Gareth Inc.

Robert, Naima Bint & Petrova-Browning, Nina. Welcome to the World, Baby. Brazell, Derek, illus. 2005. (ENG & BUL.). 32p. (J). pap. 12.95 (978-1-84444-721-3(9)) Mantra Lingua GBR. *Dist:* Mantra Publishing, Ltd.

Roca, Nuria. Aprendamos sobre los 5 Sentidos: The 5 Senses (Spanish Edition) Curto, Rosa M., illus. 2006. (Let's Learn About Ser.). (SPA.). 36p. (J). pap. 6.99 (978-0-7641-3313-8(6)) Barron's Educational Series, Inc.

—The 5 Senses. Curto, Rosa M., illus. 2006. (Let's Learn About Ser.). 36p. (J). pap. 6.99 (978-0-7641-3312-1(8)) Barron's Educational Series, Inc.

Rofé, April, illus. The SENSEsational Alphabet: See-Read, Touch-Feel, Scratch & Smell, Hear-Learn, Have Fun! 2006. (J). (978-0-9779189-1-1(2)) Waldenhouse Pub., Inc.

Romanek, Trudee. Wow! The Most Interesting Book You'll Ever Read about the Five Senses. Cowles, Rose, illus. 2005. (Mysterious You Ser.). 40p. (YA). (gr. 4-9). (978-1-55337-630-9(7)); (978-1-55337-629-3(3)) Kids Can Pr., Ltd.

Ross, Veronica. The Senses. 2002. (My Healthy Body Ser.). (Illus.). 32p. (J). lib. bdg. 24.25 (978-1-930643-81-9(0)) Chrysalis Education.

Royston. The Senses. 2004. (My Amazing Body Ser.). (Illus.). pap. 7.50 (978-1-4109-0952-7(2)) Raintree.

—The Senses 6-Pack. 2004. (My Amazing Body Ser.). (Illus.). pap. 40.50 (978-1-4109-0959-6(X)) Raintree.

Royston, Angela. The Senses. 2004. (My Amazing Body Ser.). (Illus.). 32p. 25.70 (978-1-4109-0483-6(0)) Raintree.

—Taste. 2005. (Illus.). 32p. (J). (gr. 1 up). lib. bdg. 27.10 (978-1-59389-202-9(0)) Chrysalis Education.

Rybolt, Thomas R. & Rybolt, Leah M. Science Fair Success with Scents, Aromas, & Smells. 2002. (Science Fair Success Ser.). (Illus.). 112p. (YA). (gr. 6 12). lib. bdg. 26.60 (978-0-7660-1625-5(0)) Enslow Pubs., Inc.

Saab, Carl Y. Seeing, Hearing, & Smelling the World. 2007. (Brain Works). 104p. (J). (gr. 5-8). 32.95 (978-0-7910-8945-3(2) , Chelsea Hse.) Facts On File, Inc.

Scholasctic Clubs US Five Senses Pack: Let's Start Science. 2006. (J). 34.75 (978-1-59566-323-8(1)) QEB Publishing Inc.

Schuh, Mari. The Sense of Hearing. 2007. (Illus.). 24p. (J). lib. bdg. 19.95 (978-1-60014-070-9(X)) Bellwether Media.

—The Sense of Sight. 2007. (Illus.). 24p. (J). lib. bdg. 19.95 (978-1-60014-071-6(8)) Bellwether Media.

—The Sense of Smell. 2007. (Illus.). 24p. (J). lib. bdg. 19.95 (978-1-60014-072-3(6)) Bellwether Media.

—The Sense of Taste. 2007. (Illus.). 24p. (J). lib. bdg. 19.95 (978-1-60014-073-0(4)) Bellwether Media.

—The Sense of Touch. 2007. (Illus.). 24p. (J). lib. bdg. 19.95 (978-1-60014-074-7(2)) Bellwether Media.

Scott, Janine. Animal Senses. 2002. (Spyglass Books). (Illus.). 24p. (J). (gr. 1 up). lib. bdg. 18.60 (978-0-7565-0229-4(2)) Compass Point Bks.

—Our Senses. 2003. (Spyglass Books). (Illus.). 24p. (J). (gr. 1 up). lib. bdg. 18.50 (978-0-7565-0450-2(3)) Compass Point Bks.

Sensational!, 6 Pack. (Bookweb Ser.). 32p. (gr. 3 up). 34.00 (978-0-7635-3949-8(X)) Rigby Education.

The Senses. 2005. (First Facts Ser.). (Illus.). (J). (gr. 1-2). lib. bdg. 106.30 (978-0-7368-4415-4(5)) Capstone Pr., Inc.

The Senses, 6 vols., Set. 2005. (Senses Ser.). (Illus.). 32p. (gr. 2-4). pap. 138.00 (978-0-7910-7553-1(2) , Chelsea Hse.) Facts On File, Inc.

The Senses Set. (gr. k-2). 172.95 (978-0-7368-9036-6(X)) Red Brick Learning.

S

Sherman, Josepha. The Ear: Learning How We Hear. 2002. (3-D Library of the Human Body). (Illus.). 48p. (YA). (gr. 5-8). lib. bdg. 26.50 (978-0-8239-3529-1(9) , Rosen Central) Rosen Publishing Group, Inc., The.

Shott, Steve & Gorton, Steve, photos by. Playtime. 2001. (Touch & Feel Ser.). (Illus.). 12p. (J). (ps-3). bds. 6.99 (978-0-7894-7419-3(0)) Dorling Kindersley Publishing, Inc.

Sian revision smell taste Touch. 2004. (J). (978-1-59242-069-8(9)) Delta Education, LLC.

Sights & Sounds. (YA). (gr. 8). 48.95 (978-0-673-72661-2(4) , Scott Foresman) Addison Wesley Schl.

Silver Dolphin en Español Editors. Baby Senses: el Gusto? Baby Senses: Taste, Spanish-Language Edition. 2007. (Illus.). 8p. (J). bds. 5.95 (***978-970-718-473-2(6)*** , Silver Dolphin en Español) Advanced Marketing, S. de R. L. de C. V. MEX. *Dist:* Perseus Distribution.

—Baby Senses: el Olfato: Baby Senses: Smell, Spanish-Language Edition. 2007. (Illus.). 8p. (J). bds. 5.95 (***978-970-718-471-8(X)*** , Silver Dolphin en Español) Advanced Marketing, S. de R. L. de C. V. MEX. *Dist:* Perseus Distribution.

—Baby Senses: la Vista: Baby Senses: Sight, Spanish-Langage Edition. 2007. (Illus.). 8p. (J). bds. 5.95 (***978-970-718-472-5(8)*** , Silver Dolphin en Español) Advanced Marketing, S. de R. L. de C. V. MEX. *Dist:* Perseus Distribution.

Silverstein, Alvin. Earaches. 2002. (gr. 3-6). lib. bdg. 15.25 (978-0-613-54181-7(2)) Tandem Library Bks.

Silverstein, Alvin, et al. Can You See the Chalkboard? 2001. (My Health Ser.). (Illus.). 48p. (J). (gr. 3-5). pap. 6.95 (978-0-531-13969-1(7) , Watts, Franklin) Scholastic Library Publishing.

—Earaches. 2002. (My Health Ser.). (Illus.). 48p. (J). (gr. 3-5). pap. 6.95 (978-0-531-15562-2(5) , Watts, Franklin) Scholastic Library Publishing.

—Hearing. 2001. (Senses & Sensors Ser.). (Illus.). 64p. (gr. 5-8). lib. bdg. 25.90 (978-0-7613-1666-4(3) , Millbrook Pr.) Lerner Publishing Group.

—Seeing. 2001. (Senses & Sensors Ser.). (Illus.). 64p. (gr. 5-8). lib. bdg. 25.90 (978-0-7613-1663-3(9) , Millbrook Pr.) Lerner Publishing Group.

—Senses & Sensors, 4 vols. 2004. (Illus.). 64p. (YA). (gr. 5-8). (978-0-7613-3301-2(0) , Twenty-First Century Bks.) Lerner Publishing Group.

—Smelling & Tasting. 2002. (Senses & Sensors Ser.). (Illus.). 64p. (gr. 5-8). lib. bdg. 25.90 (978-0-7613-1667-1(1) , Millbrook Pr.) Lerner Publishing Group.

Simon, Seymour. Eyes & Ears. (Illus.). (J). 2005. 32p. pap. 6.99 (978-0-06-073302-5(0) , Harper Trophy); 2003. 15.99 (978-0-688-15303-8(8)) HarperCollins Pubs.

—Out of Sight: Pictures of Hidden World. 2000. (gr. 3-6). lib. bdg. 15.25 (978-0-613-44470-5(1)) Tandem Library Bks.

—Out of Sight: Pictures of Hidden Worlds. 2002. (Illus.). 48p. (J). (gr. k up). 6.95 (978-1-58717-149-9(X) , SeaStar Bks.) Chronicle Bks. LLC.

Siy, Alexandra. Sneeze! Siy, Alexandra & Kunkel, Dennis, photos by. 2007. (J). (gr. 2-5). 48p. 16.95 (***978-1-57091-653-3(5));*** 40p. pap. 6.95 (***978-1-57091-654-0(3))*** Charlesbridge Publishing, Inc.

Slater, Teddy. Busy Bunnies' Five Senses. Swanson, Maggie, illus. 2000. (Hello Reader! Science Ser.). 32p. (J). (gr. 1-3). pap. 3.99 (978-0-439-09910-3(2)) Scholastic, Inc.

—Busy Bunnies' Five Senses. 1999. (Hello Reader! Ser.). (Illus.). (J). (978-0-606-18520-2(8)) Tandem Library Bks.

Smart Kids Publishing Staff. What's That Sound. Sharp, Chris, illus. 2005. 10p. (J). (ps-k). 12.95 (978-0-8249-6624-9(4) , Candy Cane Pr.) Ideals Pubns.

Sounds & Hearing. 2005. (J). (978-0-9767850-0-2(5)) Success for All Foundation.

Stewart, Melissa. Use Your Senses. 2004. (Investigate Science Ser.). 32p. (J). (gr. 1 up). lib. bdg. 21.26 (978-0-7565-0636-0(0)) Compass Point Bks.

Stihler, Cherie B. Squishy, Squishy: A Book about My Five Senses. Rose, Heidi, illus. 2005. 23p. (J). pap. 5.95 (978-0-8198-7078-0(1) , 332-374) Pauline Bks. & Media.

Stonehouse, Bernard & Bertram, Esther. The Truth about Animal Senses. Francis, John, illus. 2002. (Animals Exposed! Ser.). 48p. (J). pap. (978-0-439-51807-9(5)) Scholastic, Inc.

Stradling, Jan. Sense This: Level I, 6 vols. (First Explorers Ser.). 24p. (gr. 1-2). 29.95 (978-0-7699-1452-7(7)) Shortland Pubns. (U. S. A.) Inc.

Tatchell, Judy. How Do Your Senses Work? 1998. (Flip Flap Ser.). (Illus.). 16p. (J). (gr. 2 up). lib. bdg. 15.95 (978-1-58086-647-7(6) , Usborne) EDC Publishing.

—How Do Your Senses Work? Wheatley, Maria, illus. rev. ed. 2004. (Flip Flaps Ser.). 16p. (J). (gr. 2 up). pap. 7.95 (978-0-7945-0642-1(9) , Usborne) EDC Publishing.

Thames, Susan. Our Senses. 2008. (J). (***978-1-60044-513-2(6))*** Rourke Publishing, LLC.

Touch It. 2002. (Illus.). (J). pap. 3.74 (978-0-7398-5838-7(6)) Steck-Vaughn.

Treays, Rebecca. Understanding Your Senses. 2005. (Illus.). 31p. (J). pap. (978-0-439-79805-1(1)) Scholastic, Inc.

Trumbauer, Lisa. Animal Ears. 2000. (Yellow Umbrella Books). (Illus.). 16p. (J). (gr. 1). lib. bdg. 14.60 (978-0-7368-0723-4(3) , Pebble Bks.) Capstone Pr., Inc.

Tullet, Hervé. The Five Senses. 2005. (Illus.). 144p. (J). (ps-3). pap., pap. 16.50 (978-1-85437-581-0(4)) Tate Gallery Publishing, Ltd. GBR. *Dist:* Hachette Bk. Group.

Tyler, Jenny. Jugamos Al Escondite? 2004. (Titles in Spanish Ser.). (SPA., Illus.). 10p. (J). 15.95 (978-0-7460-6114-5(5) , Usborne) EDC Publishing.

Van der Meer, Ron & Van der Meer, Atie. Amazing Animal Senses. Motoyama, Keiko, illus. 2001. 12p. (J). (gr. k-3). 12.95 (978-1-58117-087-0(4) , Intervisual/Piggy Toes) Dalmatian Pr.

—Your Amazing Senses. Motoyama, Keiko, illus. 2001. 12p. (J). (gr. k-3). 12.95 (978-1-58117-088-7(2) , Intervisual/ Piggy Toes) Dalmatian Pr.

Viegas, Jennifer. The Mouth & Nose: Learning How We Taste & Smell. 2002. (3-D Library of the Human Body). (Illus.). 48p. (YA). (gr. 5-8). lib. bdg. 26.50 (978-0-8239-3535-2(3) , Rosen Central) Rosen Publishing Group, Inc., The.

Vv. Como Funcionan Nuestros Sentidos. (SPA.). 92p. (J). 10.00 (978-84-342-1809-3(7)) Parramon Ediciones S.A. ESP. *Dist:* Distribuidora Norma, Inc.

Walt & Wells. Este No Es Mi Dinosaurio. 2004. (Touchy-Feely Board Bks.).Tr. of This Is Not My Dinosaur. (SPA., Illus.). 12p. (J). (ps up). 7.95 (978-0-7460-5079-8(8)) EDC Publishing.

Watt, Fiona. Baby Monster Cloth Bk. Wells, Rachel, illus. 2007. 10p. (J). 10.99 (978-0-7945-1428-0(6) , Usborne) EDC Publishing.

—Cuddly Baby Board Book. 2006. 10p. (J). bds. 8.99 (978-0-7945-1070-1(1) , Usborne) EDC Publishing.

—Esta No Es Mi Muneca. Wells, Rachel, illus. 2005. (Titles in Spanish Ser.). (SPA.). 10p. (J). 7.95 (978-0-7460-6102-2(1) , Usborne) EDC Publishing.

—Este No es Mi Sirenita. 2006. 10p. (J). bds. 9.99 (978-0-7460-7386-5(0) , Usborne) EDC Publishing.

—Este no es michigan Monstruo. 2005. (SPA.). 10p. (J). 7.95 (978-0-7460-6633-1(3) , Usborne) EDC Publishing.

—Hide-and-seek baby board Book. 2005. 10p. (J). 8.99 (978-0-7945-1055-8(8) , Usborne) EDC Publishing.

—Ratoncitos Navidenos. Wells, Rachel, illus. 2005. (SPA.). 10p. (J). per. 11.95 (978-0-7460-6890-8(5) , Usborne) EDC Publishing.

—Snuggletime Busy Baby. MacKinnon, Catherine-Anne, illus. 2005. 10p. (J). (ps-ps). per. 8.99 (978-0-7945-1054-1(X) , Usborne) EDC Publishing.

—Thats Not My Robot. Wells, Rachel, illus. 2005. 10p. (J). bds. 7.95 (978-0-7945-1169-2(4) , Usborne) EDC Publishing.

Williamson, Sarah A. Fun with My 5 Senses: Activities to Build Learning Readiness. 2nd rev. ed. 1998. (Little Hands Bks.: Vol. 5). Orig. Title: Stop, Look & Listen Exploring the World Around You. (Illus.). 141p. (J). (ps-3). pap. 12.95 (978-1-885593-19-1(8) , Williamson Bks.) Ideals Pubns.

Woodward, Kay. Our Senses, 5 Vols. 110.00 (978-0-8368-4405-4(X)) Stevens, Gareth Inc.

—Taste. 2005. (Illus.). 24p. (J). lib. bdg. 22.00 (978-0-8368-4409-2(2)) Stevens, Gareth Inc.

Yates, Irene. Touch. 2002. (All about Sen.). (Illus.). 32p. (J). lib. bdg. 24.25 (978-1-931983-01-3(1)) Chrysalis Education.

Young, Laurie. I See a Monster. 2006. (J). 10.95 (978-1-58117-483-0(7) , Intervisual/Piggy Toes) Dalmatian Pr.

SENSES AND SENSATION—FICTION

Aigner-Clark, Julie. Baby Einstein: Baby Mozart Music Is Everywhere!, Spanish-Language Edition. Zaidi, Nadeem, illus. 2005. (Baby Einstein: Libros de Carton Ser.). (SPA.). 16p. (J). bds. 7.95 (978-970-718-309-4(8) , Silver Dolphin en Español) Advanced Marketing, S. de R. L. de C. V. MEX. *Dist:* Perseus Distribution.

—Baby Einstein: La casa de Violet Violet's House, Spanish-Language Edition. Zaidi, Nadeem, illus. 2005. (Baby Einstein: Libros de Carton Ser.). (SPA.). 10p. (J). bds. 9.95 (978-970-718-305-6(5) , Silver Dolphin en Español) Advanced Marketing, S. de R. L. de C. V. MEX. *Dist:* Perseus Distribution.

—Baby Noah's Touch & Feel Discovery Cards. Zaidi, Nadeem, illus. 2006. 10p. (J). (ps-17). 9.99 (978-1-4231-0060-7(3)) Baby Einstein Co., LLC, The.

Amelio-Ortiz, Osvaldo P. Anita Takes Notes. 2005. (Illus.). 28p. (J). (ps-ps). 12.95 (978-9974-7816-8-9(X)) Hardenville SA URY. *Dist:* Independent Pubs. Group.

Ardley, Neil & Challoner, Jack. Senses. 2000. (J). (gr. 4-6). 11.00 (978-0-8172-9807-4(X)) Steck-Vaughn.

Baker, Keith. Sometimes. 2003. (Green Light Readers Level 1 Ser.). (Illus.). 24p. (J). 11.95 (978-0-15-204807-5(3)); pap. 3.95 (978-0-15-204847-1(2)) Harcourt Children's Bks. (Green Light Readers).

—Sometimes. 1999. (Green Light Readers Ser.). (978-0-606-16510-5(X)); lib. bdg. 11.80 (978-0-613-64597-3(9)) Tandem Library Bks.

—Sometimes/Algunas Veces. Campoy, F. Isabel & Ada, Alma Flor, trs. from ENG. 2007. (Green Light Readers Level 1 Ser.). (ENG & SPA., Illus.). 28p. (J). 12.95 (978-0-15-205959-0(8)); pap. 3.95 (978-0-15-205961-3(X)) Harcourt Trade Pubs.

Becker, Bonny. Tickly Prickly. Halpern, Shari, photos by. 1999. (Growing Tree Ser.). (Illus.). 24p. (J). (ps up). 9.95 (978-0-694-01239-8(4) , Harper Festival) Harper-Collins Pubs.

Book Company Staff. Are You a Dinosaur? 2003. (Novelty Bks.). (J). 12.95 (978-1-74047-319-4(1)) Book Co. Publishing Pty, Ltd., The AUS. *Dist:* Penton Overseas, Inc.

—Are You a Frog? 2003. (Novelty Bks.). (Illus.). (J). 12.95 (978-1-74047-318-7(3)) Book Co. Publishing Pty, Ltd., The AUS. *Dist:* Penton Overseas, Inc.

Coll, Ivar Da. Cinco Amigos. (SPA.). (J). bds. (978-958-04-4909-6(0)) Norma S.A. COL. *Dist:* Lectorum Pubns., Inc.

Coulton, Mia. Danny's Five Senses. Coulton, Mia, photos by. 2002. (J). 4.95 (978-0-9720295-0-6(8)) Maryruth Bks., Inc.

Davis, Caroline, illus. My Pets. 2007. 12p. (J). (ps). bds. 6.95 (***978-1-58925-824-2(X)*** , tiger tales) ME Media LLC.

Delval, Marie-Helene. Burrito escucha los Ruidos. Courtin, Thierry, illus. 2004. (Palabras menudas Ser.). (SPA.). 14p. 5.95 (978-84-7864-710-1(4)) Combel Editorial, S.A. ESP. *Dist:* Independent Pubs. Group.

—A Tigreton le gusta Moverse. Courtin, Thierry, illus. 2004. (Palabras menudas Ser.). (SPA.). 14p. 5.95 (978-84-7864-709-5(0)) Combel Editorial, S.A. ESP. *Dist:* Independent Pubs. Group.

Doudna, Kelly. Rabbit Ears. Nobens, C. A., illus. 2006. (Fact & Fiction Ser.). 24p. (J). pap. (***978-1-59679-962-2(5))*** ABDO Publishing Co.

Duvoisin, Roger. Donkey-Donkey. 2007. 56p. (J). (gr. k-1). 15.99 (978-0-375-84065-4(6)); lib. bdg. 18.99 (978-0-375-94065-1(0)) Random Hse. Children's Bks. (Knopf Bks. for Young Readers).

Faulkner, Keith. The Five Senses. Lambert, Jonathan, illus. 2002. 14p. (J). pap. 9.95 (978-0-439-38882-5(1) , Scholastic Pr.) Scholastic, Inc.

Flesher, Vivienne. Alfred's Nose. Flesher, Vivienne, illus. 2008. 32p. (J). 16.99 (***978-0-06-084313-7(6));*** lib. bdg. 17.89 (***978-0-06-084314-4(4))*** HarperCollins Pubs.

George, Kristine O'Connell. Up! Nakata, Hiroe, illus. 2005. 32p. (J). (gr. k-ps). 15.00 (978-0-618-06489-2(3) , Clarion Bks.) Houghton Mifflin Co. Trade & Reference Div.

Hall, Kirsten. A Perfect Day: All about the Five Senses. Luedecke, Bev, illus. (Beastieville Ser.). (J). (gr. k-1). 2005. 32p. pap. 3.95 (978-0-516-25521-7(5)); 2004. 19.50 (978-0-516-24437-2(X)) Scholastic Library Publishing. (Children's Pr.).

Harcourt School Publishers Staff. My Cats 5-Pack, Below Level. 3rd ed. 2002. (Illus.). (gr. 1). pap. 20.10 (978-0-15-326807-6(7)) Harcourt Schl. Pubs.

—Trofeos Below Level: Mis Gatos. 3rd ed. 2002. (SPA., Illus.). pap. 5.50 (978-0-15-323868-0(2)) Harcourt Schl. Pubs.

Kranowitz, Carol Stock. The Goodenoughs Get in Sync: A Story for Kids about the Tough Day When Filibuster Grabbed Darwin's Rabbit's Foot... Wylie, T. J., illus. 2004. 86p. (J). 14.95 (978-1-931615-17-4(9) , 978-1-931615-17-4) Sensory Resources.

Ladd, Debbie. Don't Pick Your Nose, one. 2003. (Illus.). 24p. (J). 12.95 (978-0-9727615-1-2(9)) Deb on Air Bks.

Lears, Laurie. Ian's Walk: A Story about Autism. 2003. (gr. k-3). lib. bdg. 15.25 (978-0-613-75728-7(9)) Tandem Library Bks.

—Ian's Walk: A Story about Autism. Ritz, Karen, illus. 2004. 32p. (J). (gr. 1-4). pap. 6.95 (978-0-8075-3481-6(1)) Whitman, Albert & Co.

LeSieg, Theo. The Eye Book. Mathieu, Joe, illus. 1999. (Bright & Early Bks.). 36p. (J). (gr. k-1). lib. bdg. 11.99 (978-0-375-90033-4(0) , Random Hse. Bks. for Young Readers) Random Hse. Children's Bks.

LeSieg, Theo., ed. & illus. The Eye Book. LeSieg, Theo., illus. Mathieu, Joe, illus. (J). (gr. k-ps). 2001. 24p. bds. 4.99 (978-0-375-81240-8(7)); 1999. 36p. 8.99 (978-0-375-80033-7(6)) Random Hse. Children's Bks. (Random Hse. Bks. for Young Readers).

Loupy, Christophe. Hugs & Kisses Touch & Feel. Tharlet, Eve, illus. 2005. 14p. (J). (ps up). bds. 6.95 (978-0-7358-2019-7(8)) North-South Bks., Inc.

Mandy, et al. Hattie's House. (Illus.). (J). 2005. (URD, ENG, VIE, CHI & BEN.). 24p. 9.95 (978-1-84059-156-9(0)); 2000. (GUJ, ENG, VIE, URD & CHI., 16p. pap. 9.95 (978-1-84059-154-5(4)); 2000. (TUR, ENG, VIE, CHI & BEN., 16p. pap. 9.95 (978-1-84059-155-2(2)); 2000. (BEN, ENG, VIE, CHI & GUJ., 16p. pap. 9.95 (978-1-84059-152-1(8)) Milet Publishing.

—Hattie's House. Wood, Kim Marie, tr. from ENG. 2000. (Senses Ser.). (VIE, ENG, URD, TUR & CHI., Illus.). 16p. (J). pap. 9.95 (978-1-84059-157-6(9)) Milet Publishing.

—Rosie's Room. Datta, Kanai, tr. from ENG. 2000. (Senses Ser.). (BEN, ENG, VIE, CHI & GUJ., Illus.). 16p. (J). pap. 9.95 (978-1-84059-158-3(7)) Milet Publishing.

Mass, Wendy. A Mango-Shaped Space. 2005. 240p. (J). (gr. 5-8). pap. 6.99 (978-0-316-05825-4(4)) Little Brown & Co.

Nash, Naomi. Senses Working Overtime. 2005. (YA). (gr. 11-17). mass mkt. 5.99 (978-0-8439-5404-3(3)) Dorchester Publishing Co., Inc.

Newgarden, Mark & Cash, Megan Montague. Bow-Wow hears Things. 2008. (Illus.). 18p. (J). bds. 4.95 (***978-0-15-205841-8(9)*** , Red Wagon Bks.) Harcourt Children's Bks.

Newman, Dolores A. Papa, How Do You Know? 2000. (Illus.). 32p. (J). pap. 9.95 (978-0-9676438-0-9(5)) Sanctuary Pr.

O'Brien, Gerry. Bubba Begonia, You'll Be Sorry. 2006. (Illus.). 64p. 6.95 (***978-1-894838-23-8(8))*** Acorn Pr., The CAN. *Dist:* Univ. of Toronto Pr.

Patricelli, Leslie. Binky. Patricelli, Leslie, illus. 2005. (Illus.). 24p. (J). (gr. k-ps). bds. 6.99 (978-0-7636-2364-7(4)) Candlewick Pr.

—Blankie. Patricelli, Leslie, illus. 2005. (Illus.). 24p. (J). (gr. k-ps). bds. 6.99 (978-0-7636-2363-0(6)) Candlewick Pr.

Raintree Steck-Vaughn Staff, contrib. by. My Five Senses. 2000. (Read All about It Ser.). (J). (ps-3). pap. 4.95 (978-0-8114-3712-7(4)) Steck-Vaughn.

Raschka, Chris. Five for a Little One. Raschka, Chris, illus. 2006. (Illus.). 48p. (J). (ps-k). 16.95 (978-0-689-84599-4(5) , Atheneum/Richard Jackson Bks.) Simon & Schuster Children's Publishing.

Rau, Dana Meachen. Uncle's Bakery, Level B. Baskin, Janie, illus. 2001. (Compass Point Early Reader Ser.). 32p. (J). (gr. k up). lib. bdg. 18.60 (978-0-7565-0119-8(9)) Compass Point Bks.

Rotner, Shelley. Senses at the Seashore. 2006. (Illus.). (J). 22.60 (978-0-7613-2897-1(1) , Millbrook Pr.) Lerner Publishing Group.

Rouss, Sylvia A. Sammy Spider's First Israel: A Book about the Five Senses. Kahn, Katherine Janus, illus. 2002. 32p. (J). (ps-3). pap. 7.95 (978-1-58013-035-6(6)) Kar-Ben Publishing.

—Sammy Spider's First Israel: A Book about the Five Senses. 2002. lib. bdg. 16.40 (978-0-613-81763-9(X)) Tandem Library Bks.

Ruffenach, Jessie, ed. Baby Learns about Senses. Thomas, Peter, tr. from ENG. Blacksheep, Beverly, illus. 2005. (NAV & ENG.). 16p. (J). bds. 7.95 (978-1-893354-63-0(6)) Salina Bookshelf.

Ryan, Pam Muñoz. Hello, Ocean. Astrella, Mark, illus. 2001. Tr. of Hola Mar. 32p. (J). (ps-3). 16.95 (978-0-88106-987-7(6)); pap. 6.95 (978-0-88106-988-4(4)) Charlesbridge Publishing, Inc.

—Hello, Ocean. 2001. Tr. of Hola Mar. (Illus.). (J). 13.75 (978-0-606-20698-3(1)) Tandem Library Bks.

—Hello, Ocean: Hola Mar. Canetti, Yanitzia, tr. Astrella, Mark, illus. 2004. (ENG & SPA.). 32p. (J). (gr. k-3). pap. 7.95 (978-1-57091-372-3(2)) Charlesbridge Publishing, Inc.

Saltzberg, Barney. Peekaboo, Blueberry! 2008. (Illus.). 14p. (J). bds. 8.95 (***978-0-15-206062-6(6)*** , Red Wagon Bks.) Harcourt Children's Bks.

Shannon, David. Diaper David Book. Shannon, David, illus. 2005. (David Smells! Ser.). (Illus.). 12p. (J). (ps). bds. 6.99 (978-0-439-69138-3(9) , Blue Sky Pr., The) Scholastic, Inc.

Stojic, Manya. Rain. Stojic, Manya, illus. 2000. (Illus.). 32p. (J). (gr. k-3). 15.95 (978-0-517-80085-0(3) , Crown Books For Young Readers) Random Hse. Children's Bks.

Taylor, Alastair. Mr. Blewitt's Nose. 2005. (J). (gr. k-3). 16.00 (978-0-618-58111-5(1)); (Illus.). 32p. 16.00 (978-0-618-42353-8(2)) Houghton Mifflin Co. Trade & Reference Div.

Topek, Susan R. Shalom, Shabbat: A Book for Havdalah. Ephraim, Shelly S., illus. 1998. 12p. (J). (ps up). 5.95 (978-1-58013-010-3(0)) Kar-Ben Publishing.

Tymms, Jean. The Me Book. Gergely, Tibor, illus. 2005. (Golden Sturdy Book Ser.). 24p. (J). (gr. k-k). bds. 5.99 (978-0-375-83366-3(8) , Golden Bks.) Random Hse. Children's Bks.

Vonthron, Satanta C. Marsy's Perfect Eyesight. Teeple, Jackie, illus. 1.t. ed. 2005. (J). (ps-k). pap. 10.95 (978-1-57332-344-4(6)); pap. 10.95 (978-1-57332-345-1(4)) HighReach Learning, Inc.

Wagner, Brian. 10 Things Not to Do with Your Eyeball. 2005. 20p. 9.99 (978-1-4116-5977-3(5)) Lulu.com.

Whose Ears. 2005. (J). bds. 5.99 (978-1-933200-06-4(5)) Family Bks. at Home.

Whose Feet. 2005. (J). bds. 5.99 (978-1-933200-02-6(2)) Family Bks. at Home.

Whose Nose. 2005. (J). bds. 5.99 (978-1-933200-03-3(0)) Family Bks. at Home.

SEPARATION (LAW)

see Divorce

SEPARATION ANXIETY—FICTION

Barclift, Betty. Gypsy Summer: A Novel. 2003. 160p. (J). pap. 6.99 (978-0-8254-2038-2(5)) Kregel Pubns.

Dowell, Frances O'Roark. Shooting the Moon. 2008. 176p. (J). 16.99 (***978-1-4169-2690-0(9))*** Simon & Schuster Children's Publishing.

Edwards, Becky. My First Day at Nursery School. 2004. (Illus.). 32p. (J). (ps-1). pap. 6.95 (978-1-58234-909-1(6) , Bloomsbury Children) Bloomsbury Publishing.

—My First Day at Nursery School. Flintoft, Anthony, illus. 2002. 32p. (J). 15.95 (978-1-58234-761-5(1) , Bloomsbury Children) Bloomsbury Publishing.

Freed, Shirley & Moon, Louise. Grandma, Kitty & Me. Morelan, Bill, ed. Harrell, Rob, illus. 2003. 8p. (J). (gr. 1 up). pap. 3.99 (978-1-58938-107-0(6)) Concerned Communications.

Freeman, Suzanne. The Cuckoo's Child. 249p. (YA). (gr. 5-8). pap. 5.95 (978-0-8072-1510-4(4) , Listening Library) Random Hse. Audio Publishing Group.

Greene, Marjorie. Cassie's Big Day. 2003. (Illus.). (J). 16.95 (978-0-9741764-0-6(0)) Greene, Marjorie A.

Howe, James. Pinky & Rex Go to Camp. 1999. (Pinky & Rex Ser.). (J). (gr. 1-4). (978-0-606-16306-4(9)) Tandem Library Bks.

Howe, James & Sweet, Melissa. Pinky & Rex Go to Camp. 1999. (Pinky & Rex Ser.). (Illus.). 48p. (J). (gr. 1-4). pap. 3.99 (978-0-689-82588-0(9) , 076714003996, Aladdin) Simon & Schuster Children's Publishing.

Kaufmann, Nancy. Bye, Bye! Spetter, Jung-Hee, illus. 2004. 32p. (J). (ps-1). 14.95 (978-1-886910-95-9(2) , Lemniscaat) Boyds Mills Pr.

Keselman, Gabriela. Cuando Viene Papa? Gusti, illus. 2000. (Tren Azul Ser.).Tr. of When Will Dad Be Back?. (SPA.). 32p. (J). (ps-2). (978-84-236-5493-2(1)) Edebé ESP. *Dist:* Baker & Taylor Bks.

Maier, Inger M. When Fuzzy Was Afraid: Of Losing His Mother. Candon, Jennifer, illus. 2005. 32p. (J). 14.95 (978-1-59147-168-4(0)); pap. 8.95 (978-1-59147-169-1(9)) American Psychological Assn. (Magination Pr.).

Metzger, Steve. I'll Always Come Back! Allen, Joy, illus. 2002. (J). (978-0-439-42922-1(6)) Scholastic, Inc.

Pando, Nancy J. I Don't Want to Go to School: Helping Children Cope with Separation Anxiety. Voerg, Kathy, illus. 2005. (Let's Talk Ser.). 48p. (J). pap. 8.95 (978-0-88282-254-9(3)) New Horizon Pr. Pubs., Inc.

Pappas, Debra. Mom, Dad, Come Back Soon. Koeller, Carol, illus. 2002. 32p. (J). (ps-2). 14.95 (978-1-55798-799-0(8)); pap. 8.95 (978-1-55798-798-3(X)) American Psychological Assn. (Magination Pr.).

Peck, Judith. The Bright Blue Button & the Button-Hole. Stasolla, Mario, illus. 2004. 28p. (J). 18.95 (978-0-9746119-5-2(6)) Imagination Arts Pubns.

SEPTEMBER 11 TERRORIST ATTACKS, 2001

SEQUOIA NATIONAL FOREST (CALIF.)

S

SEQUOYAH, 1770?-1843

SERIALS (PUBLICATIONS)

see Periodicals

SERMON ON THE MOUNT

SERMONS

—Bible Warnings: Sermons to Children. 2006. pap. 25.00 (*978-1-59925-083-0(7)*) Solid Ground Christian Bks.

Smith, Rodney Gipsy. The Lost Christ. 2003. (Illus.). 32p. 2.99 (978-1-931393-05-8(2)) Christian Life Bks.

Staf, Edie. Christmas Novena: For Home or Classroom. 22p. (J). (gr. 2-8). pap. 1.50 (978-0-8198-1456-2(3) , 332-032) Pauline Bks. & Media.

Vanissery, Matthew. Awesome Homilies: The Power of His Word. 2004. 236p. pap. 29.95 (978-0-9759906-0-5(8)) Vanissery, Matthew.

Wezeman, Phyllis Vos & Liechty, Anna L. Tell Me a Story: 30 Children's Sermons Based on Best-Loved Books. 2005. (New Brown Bag Ser.). (Illus.). 96p. pap. 12.00 (978-0-8298-1635-8(6)) Pilgrim Pr., The/United Church Pr.

Wezeman, Phyllis Vos, et al. Wipe the Tears: 30 Children's Sermons on Death. 2005. (New Brown Bag Ser.). (Illus.). 96p. 10.00 (978-0-8298-1520-7(1)) Pilgrim Pr., The/United Church Pr.

SERPENTS

see Snakes

SERRA, JUNIPERO, 1713-1784

Heinrichs, Ann. The California Missions. 2002. (We the People Ser.). (Illus.). 48p. (J). (gr. 4 up). lib. bdg. 22.60 (978-0-7565-0208-9(X)) Compass Point Bks.

Hernandez, Natalie. Las Aventuras con Padre Serra. Hernandez, Tony Y., tr. Nolan, Claudia, illus. 1999. (ENG & SPA.). 112p. (Orig.). (J). (gr. 3-8). pap. 9.95 (978-0-9644386-1-3(5)) Santa Ines Pubns.

SERVICE, COMPULSORY MILITARY

see Military Service, Compulsory

SERVICE STATIONS

Hiner, Mark. Village Garage. Thatcher, Fran, illus. 2001. 3p. (J). 16.95 (978-1-902413-62-4(8)) Van der Meer, a Div. of PHPC GBR. *Dist:* Abbeville Pr., Inc.

Lee, Debra. Sylvia's Garage. Jabar, Cynthia, illus. Evans, Douglas, photos by. 2001. (Doors to Discovery Ser.). 8p. (J). pap. 7.76 (978-0-322-04831-7(1)) Wright Group, The.

Sundance, ed. At the Gas Station. 2000. (ps-2). lib. bdg. 11.65 (978-0-613-37620-4(X)) Tandem Library Bks.

SET THEORY

see also Arithmetic; Number Theory

Baker, Alan. Little Rabbits' First Number Book. 1998. (Little Rabbit Bks.). (Illus.). 32p. (J). (gr. k-ps). tchr. ed. 11.95 (978-0-7534-5167-0(0) , Kingfisher) Houghton Mifflin Co. Trade & Reference Div.

Bauer, David. Let's Sort. 2003. (Yellow Umbrella Books). (Illus.). 16p. (J). (gr. 1). lib. bdg. 14.60 (978-0-7368-2014-1(0) , Pebble Bks.) Capstone Pr., Inc.

—Let's Sort. 2003. (J). (978-0-7368-1701-1(8)) Yellow Umbrella Pr.

Doudna, Kelly. Use Your Eye, Let's Classify! (Illus.). 24p. (J). 2007. 19.93 (978-1-59928-620-4(3)); 2006. pap. (978-1-59928-621-1(1)) ABDO Publishing Co.

GER Set Square. 2006. (J). 2.90 (*978-1-934046-11-1(6)*) Global Education Resources, LLC.

Hoban, Tana. More, Fewer, Less. Hoban, Tana, photos by. 1998. (Illus.). 32p. (J). (ps-3). 15.99 (978-0-688-15693-0(2)) HarperCollins Pubs.

Kirkby, David. Sorting. 1998. (Mini Math Ser.). (Illus.). (J). (978-1-57572-006-7(X)) Heinemann Library.

Kompelien, Tracy. There Is Order on the Border. 2007. (Math Made Fun Ser.). (Illus.). 24p. (J). 19.93 (978-1-59928-547-4(9) , SandCastle) ABDO Publishing Co.

—There Is Order on the Border! 2006. (Math Made Fun Ser.). (Illus.). 24p. (J). (978-1-59928-548-1(7)) ABDO Publishing Co.

Koomen, Michele. Sets: Sorting into Groups. 2001. (Exploring Math Ser.). (Illus.). 24p. (J). (gr. 1-2). lib. bdg. 18.60 (978-0-7368-0822-4(1) , Bridgestone Bks.) Capstone Pr., Inc.

Lacapa, Kathleen & Lacapa, Michael. Less Than Half, More Than Whole. Lacapa, Michael, illus. 1998. (Illus.). 32p. (J). (gr. 1-3). 7.95 (978-0-87358-731-0(6) , Rising Moon Bks. for Young Readers) Northland Publishing.

Marks, Jenny L. Sorting Toys. 2007. (Sorting Ser.). (Illus.). 32p. (J). (gr. k-3). lib. bdg. 23.93 (978-0-7368-6737-5(6)) Capstone Pr., Inc.

Murphy. Seaweed Soup Big Book. 2002. (Illus.). pap. (978-0-7398-6787-7(3)) Steck-Vaughn.

Murphy, Stuart J. Dave's down-to-Earth Rock Shop. 2000. (gr. k-3). lib. bdg. 13.00 (978-0-613-21409-4(9)) Tandem Library Bks.

—Seaweed Soup. Remkiewicz, Frank, illus. 2001. (MathStart Ser.). 40p. (J). (ps up). pap. 5.99 (978-0-06-446736-0(8) , Harper Trophy) HarperCollins Pubs.

—3 Little Firefighters. Lum, Bernice, illus. 2003. (MathStart Ser.: Vol. 46). 40p. (J). 15.99 (978-0-06-000118-6(6)) HarperCollins Pubs.

—3 Little Firefighters. 2003. (gr. k-3). lib. bdg. 13.00 (978-0-613-68469-9(9)) Tandem Library Bks.

Patilla, Peter. Patterns. 1999. (Math Links Ser.). 32p. (J). (gr. k-2). lib. bdg. 21.36 (978-1-57572-967-1(9)) Heinemann Library.

—Sorting: (Or Handling Data) 1999. (Math Links Ser.). 32p. (J). (gr. k-2). lib. bdg. 14.95 (978-1-57572-969-5(5)) Heinemann Library.

Pluckrose, Henry. Sorting & Sets. 2001. (Let's Explore Ser.). (Illus.). 32p. (J). (gr. 1 up). lib. bdg. 23.33 (978-0-8368-2966-2(2)) Stevens, Gareth Inc.

Pluckrose, Henry Arthur. Sorting & Sets. 2006. (Illus.). 32p. (J). (978-1-59771-038-1(5)) Sea-To-Sea Pubns.

Realtime Associates and Mazer Corporation Staff & LeapFrog Staff, compiled by. Define a Set by Its Elements. 2002. (J). (gr. 4). 66.75 (978-1-58605-463-2(5) , LeapFrog Schl. Hse.) LeapFrog Enterprises, Inc.

Ribke, Simone T. Grouping at the Dog Show. 2006. 32p. (gr. 1-2). (YA). pap. 5.95 (978-0-516-28100-1(3)); (Illus.). (J). 20.50 (978-0-516-24959-9(2)) Scholastic Library Publishing. (Children's Pr.).

Roy, Jennifer Rozines & Roy, Gregory. Sorting at the Ocean. 2005. (Math All Around Ser.). (J). 25.64 (978-0-7614-1998-3(5) , Benchmark Bks.) Cavendish, Marshall Corp.

Sets. 2001. (Early Math Ser.). (J). (gr. k-12). vinyl bd. 4.95 (978-1-58845-067-8(8)) School Specialty Publishing.

Tang, Greg. Math-Terpieces. 2003. (J). pap. (978-0-439-44389-0(X)) Scholastic, Inc.

—Math-Terpieces: The Art of Problem-Solving. Paprocki, Greg, illus. 2003. 32p. (J). pap. 16.95 (978-0-439-44388-3(1)) Scholastic, Inc.

Trumbauer, Lisa. Vamos a Clasificar. 2005. Tr. of Let's Sort. (SPA., Illus.). 16p. (J). (gr. k-1). lib. bdg. 15.93 (978-0-7368-4131-3(8)) Capstone Pr., Inc.

Weekly Reader Early Learning Library (Firm) Staff, contrib. by. I Know Same & Different. 2006. (I'm Ready for Math Ser.). (Illus.). 16p. (J). pap. (978-0-8368-6481-6(6)); lib. bdg. 16.67 (978-0-8368-6476-2(X)) Stevens, Gareth Inc.

—I Know Same & Different: Igual y Diferente. 2006. (ENG & SPA., Illus.). 16p. (J). pap. 4.50 (978-0-8368-6491-5(3)); lib. bdg. 16.67 (978-0-8368-6486-1(7)) Stevens, Gareth Inc.

Whitehouse, Patricia. Agrupemos Alimentos. 2002. (Colores Para Comer (The Colors We Eat) Ser.).Tr. of Sorting Foods. 24p. (J). (ps-1). pap. 5.25 (978-1-58810-840-1(6) , 91577); (SPA.). lib. bdg. 18.50 (978-1-58810-793-0(0)) Heinemann Library.

SETS (MATHEMATICS)

see Set Theory

SETTLEMENTS, SOCIAL

see Social Settlements

SEUSS, DR., 1904-1991

Carlson, Cheryl. Dr Seuss. (First Biographies Ser.). 24p. (J). pap. 5.95 (978-0-7368-5091-9(0)) Capstone Pr., Inc.

Kudlinski, Kathleen. Dr. Seuss: Young Author & Artist. Henderson, Meryl, illus. 2005. 184p. (J). lib. bdg. 18.46 (*978-1-4242-2201-8(X)*) Fitzgerald Bks.

Rau, Dana Meachen. Dr. Seuss. 2003. (Rookie Biographies Ser.). (gr. 1-2). pap. 4.95 (978-0-516-26964-1(X)); (Illus.). 32p. (J). 20.50 (978-0-516-22593-7(6)) Scholastic Library Publishing. (Children's Pr.).

—Dr. Seuss. 2003. lib. bdg. 12.95 (978-0-613-67612-0(2)) Tandem Library Bks.

SEVEN WONDERS OF THE WORLD

Bergin, Mark. Wonders of the World. 1999. (Fast Forward Ser.). (Illus.). 32p. (J). (gr. 4-8). pap. 9.95 (978-0-531-15424-3(6) , Watts, Franklin) Scholastic Library Publishing.

Curlee, Lynn. The Seven Wonders of the Ancient World. Curlee, Lynn, illus. 2002. (Illus.). 40p. (J). (gr. 3-7). 18.99 (978-0-689-83182-9(X) , Atheneum) Simon & Schuster Children's Publishing.

Freund, Lisa. The Las siete maravillas naturales del mundo & Seven Natural Wonders. 2005. spiral bd. 77.00 (*978-1-4108-5671-5(2)*) Benchmark Education Co.

Gonzales, Doreen. Seven Wonders of the Modern World: A MyReportLinks. com Book. 2005. (Seven Wonders of the World Ser.). (Illus.). 48p. (J). lib. bdg. 25.26 (978-0-7660-5292-5(3) , MyReportLinks.com Bks.) Enslow Pubs., Inc.

Kenah, Katharine. Amazing Creations: Level 2. 2006. (Extreme Readers Ser.). (Illus.). 32p. (J). (gr. k-1). pap. 3.95 (978-0-7696-4336-6(1)) School Specialty Publishing.

Laliberte, Michelle. Seven Wonders of the Ancient World. 2005. (Seven Wonders of the World Ser.). (Illus.). 48p. (J). (gr. 4-10). lib. bdg. 25.26 (978-0-7660-5293-2(1) , MyReportLinks.com Bks.) Enslow Pubs., Inc.

Lynette, Rachel. The Great Wall of China. 2004. (Great Structures in History Ser.). (Illus.). 48p. (J). (gr. 4-7). 26.20 (978-0-7377-1558-3(8)) Thomson Gale.

Piano, Maureen. My Adventure to the Wonders of the World. 2006. 44p. (J). 8.99 (978-1-59092-445-7(2) , Orchard Academy Pr.) Windstorm Creative.

Steele, Philip. Wonders of the World. 2007. (Kingfisher Knowledge Ser.). (Illus.). 64p. (J). (gr. 3-5). 12.95 (978-0-7534-5979-9(5) , Kingfisher) Houghton Mifflin Co. Trade & Reference Div.

Sullivan, Erin Ash. The Las siete maravillas del mundo antiguo & Seven Wonders of the Ancient World. 2005. spiral bd. 88.00 (*978-1-4108-5728-6(X)*) Benchmark Education Co.

Tagliapietra, Ron. The Seven Wonders of the World. 1999. (Illus.). 238p. (J). pap. 6.95 (978-1-57924-234-3(0)) Jones, Bob Univ. Pr.

Top That Publishing Staff, ed. 7 Wonders of World. 2004. (Know How Know Why Ser.). (Illus.). 48p. (J). pap. (978-1-84510-073-5(5)) Top That! Publishing PLC.

The Wonders of the World. 2005. pap. 65.85 (978-0-7910-9180-7(5) , Chelsea Hse.) Facts On File, Inc.

SEWAGE DISPOSAL

see also Refuse and Refuse Disposal; Water—Pollution

Lopatka, Michael. Wastwater Treatment. 2002. (YA). (gr. 9-12). cd-rom 24.95 (978-0-9703694-4-4(1)) Awesome Guides, Inc.

SEWING

see also Dressmaking; Embroidery; Needlework

Alvarez, Beverly. Kids Can Sew: Fun & Easy Projects for Your Small Stitcher. 2004. (Illus.). 128p. (J). pap. 16.95 (978-0-7641-2771-7(3)) Barron's Educational Series, Inc.

Carlson, Laurie M. Queen of Inventions: How the Sewing Machine Changed the World. 2003. (Illus.). 32p. lib. bdg. 22.90 (978-0-7613-2706-6(1) , Millbrook Pr.) Lerner Publishing Group.

Cherry, Winky. My First Doll Book Level 3: Hand Sewing. Palmer, Pati & Wisner, Linda, eds. Cherry, Winky, illus. 2003. (My First Sewing Book Ser.). (Illus.). 40p. (J). (gr. k-5). pap. 14.95 (978-0-935278-36-1(2)) Palmer-Pletsch Assocs.

—My First Machine Sewing Book Level 4: Straight Stitching. Black, Lynette R. et al, eds. 2003. (My First Sewing Book Ser.). (Illus.). 40p. (Orig.). (J). (gr. k-6). pap. 12.95 (978-0-935278-40-8(0)) Palmer-Pletsch Assocs.

—My First Sewing Book Level 1: Hand Sewing. Cherry, Winky, illus. 2003. (My First Sewing Book Ser.). Orig. Title: Is That Sew?. (Illus.). 40p. (J). (ps-6). pap. 14.95 (978-0-935278-29-3(X)) Palmer-Pletsch Assocs.

Davis, Tina. See & Sew: A Sewing Book for Children. 2006. 150p. 19.95 (978-1-58479-491-2(7)) Stewart, Tabori & Chang.

Dorling Kindersley Publishing Staff. Basic Sewing. 2004. (101 Essential Tips Ser.). (Illus.). 72p. (gr. 12). pap. 5.00 (978-0-7566-0612-1(8)) Dorling Kindersley Publishing, Inc.

Hantman, Clea. I Wanna Make My Own Clothes. Houshyar, Azadeh, illus. 2006. 144p. (J). pap. 9.99 (978-0-689-87462-8(6) , Aladdin) Simon & Schuster Children's Publishing.

Kane, Barbara. Quilting: Design & Make Your Own Patchwork Projects. 2005. (Illus.). 64p. (YA). (gr. 5-9). spiral bd. 21.95 (978-1-57054-215-2(5)) Klutz.

King, Nancy Jo. 60 Simple Clothing Crafts for Making Wearable Art. McCready, Lynne, photos by. 2002. (Get Crafty Ser.). (Illus.). 96p. (gr. 3-9). pap. 7.95 (978-0-9678285-4-1(6)) Lunchbox Pr.

Klutz Press Staff. Simple Sewing. 1999. (Illus.). 56p. (J). (gr. 4-7). spiral bd. 19.95 (978-1-57054-317-3(8) , 51275983) Klutz.

Lyons, Mary E. Stitching Stars: The Story Quilts of Harriet Powers. 1998. (J). pap. 6.99 (978-0-87628-344-8(X)) Ctr. for Applied Research in Education, The.

McAllister, Buff. Sewing with Felt: Learn Basic Stitches to Create More Than 60 Colorful Projects. Schneider, Hank, photos by. 2003. (Illus.). 88p. (YA). spiral bd. 19.95 (978-1-56397-999-6(3)) Boyds Mills Pr.

Milligan, Lynda & Smith, Nancy. The Best of Sewing Machine Fun for Kids. 2004. (Best Crafts for Kids Ser.). (Illus.). 128p. pap. 16.95 (978-1-57120-254-3(4) , 10361) C&T Publishing.

Ross, Kathy. Things to Make for Your Doll. Garvin, Elaine, illus. 2003. 48p. (J). (gr. k-2). lib. bdg. (978-0-7613-2861-2(0) , Millbrook Pr.); pap. 7.95 (978-0-7613-1781-4(3) , First Avenue Editions) Lerner Publishing Group.

Sadler, Ann. Sewing.Tr. of Couture. (FRE., Illus.). (J). (gr. k-5). pap. 7.99 (978-0-590-24055-0(2)) Scholastic, Inc.

Sadler, Judy Ann. The Jumbo Book of Needlecrafts. Bradford, June et al, illus. 2005. (Jumbo Bks.). 208p. (YA). (gr. 3 up). (978-1-55337-793-1(1)) Kids Can Pr., Ltd.

—Simply Sewing. Kurisu, Jane, illus. 2005. (Kids Can Do It Ser.). 48p. (YA). (gr. 3 up). (978-1-55337-660-6(9)); (978-1-55337-659-0(5)) Kids Can Pr., Ltd.

Warwick, Ellen. Stuff to Hold Your Stuff. Lum, Bernice, illus. 2006. 80p. (YA). (gr. 6 up). spiral bd. (978-1-55337-745-0(1)) Kids Can Pr., Ltd.

Zent, Sheila. Sew Teen: Make Your Own Cool Clothes. Howell, Don, photos by. 2006. (Illus.). 128p. (YA). (gr. 7 up). pap. 17.95 (978-1-931543-90-3(9)) Sixth&Spring Bks.

SEX

see also Reproduction

also headings beginning with the word Sexual

Ayer, Eleanor H. La Paternidad Adolescente. 2002. (Todo lo Que Necesitas Saber Ser.). (SPA & ENG., Illus.). 64p. (YA). lib. bdg. 26.50 (978-0-8239-3585-7(X) , Buenas Letra) Rosen Publishing Group, Inc., The.

Bailey, Jacqui. Sex, Puberty, & All That Stuff: A Guide to Growing Up. McCafferty, Jan, illus. 2004. 112p. (J). pap. 12.95 (978-0-7641-2992-6(9)) Barron's Educational Series, Inc.

Bartosch, Janet, et al. God's Gift of Sexuality. ldr.'s ed. 1998. 248p. pap. 17.95 (978-1-57895-059-1(7) , Witherspoon Pr.) Curriculum Publishing, Presbyterian Church (U. S. A.).

Brewer, Janet N. In God's Image. Watkins, Virginia, ed. Pullen, Pip, illus. Carr, Geoffrey, photos by. 1998. 32p. (J). (ps-1). stu. ed. 14.99 (978-1-57895-055-3(4)) Bridge Resources.

Burrows, David. Sex & Dating: A Guide to Relationships for Teens & Young Adults y Dave Burrows. 2001. (gr. 7-12). lib. bdg. 19.95 (978-0-613-85880-9(8)) Tandem Library Bks.

Butler, Brian, et al. Theology of the Body for Teens: Student Workbook. 2006. per. 14.95 (*978-1-932927-86-3(7)*) Ascension Pr.

Cart, Michael. Necessary Noise: Stories about Our Families as They Really Are. Noruzi, Charlotte, illus. 2003. 256p. (J). (gr. 12 up). lib. bdg. 16.89 (978-0-06-027500-6(6)) HarperCollins Pubs.

Choosing the Best Path. 3rd ed. 2004. (978-0-9724890-2-7(9)) Choosing The Best Publishing.

Constant. Sex. 2004. (Teen Issues Ser.). (Illus.). 56p. (J). 28.56 (978-0-4109-0613-7(2)); pap. 8.95 (978-1-4109-0884-1(4)) Harcourt Schl. Pubs.

Cross, Craig, et al. Questions You Can't Ask Your Mama about Sex. 2005. (Invert Ser.). 128p. (YA). pap. 9.99 (978-0-310-25812-4(X)) Zondervan.

Custom Curricul Staff. What about Sex, Drugs, And... ? 2004. (Custom Curriculum Ser.). 256p. pap., pap. 19.99 (978-0-7814-4093-6(9) , 0781440939) Cook, David C. Publishing Co.

Degrassi Talks Sex, 1. 1999. (J). pap. (978-1-55120-000-2(7)) Mint Pubs., Inc.

Elliot, Elisabeth. Passion & Purity: Learning to Bring Your Love Life under Christ's Control. 2nd ed. 2002. 192p. (gr. 13 up). pap. 11.99 (978-0-8007-5818-9(8)) Revell.

Endersbe, Julie. Healthy Sexuality: What Is It? (Perspectives on Healthy Sexuality Ser.). pap. 8.95 (978-0-7368-8851-6(9) , LifeMatters Bks.) Capstone Pr., Inc.

Forssberg, Manne. Sex for Guys. Lundin, Maria, tr. from SWE. 2007. (Groundwork Guides). 144p. 15.95 (*978-0-88899-770-8(1)*) Groundwood Bks. CAN. *Dist:* Perseus Distribution.

Garth, Lakita. The Naked Truth: About Sex, Love & Relationships. 2007. (Illus.). 164p. 14.99 (978-0-8307-4328-5(6) , Regal Bks.) Gospel Light Pubns.

Gay & Lesbian Writers. (Illus.). (gr. 9-13). pap. (978-0-7910-8395-6(0)); 2005. 144p. pap. 210.00 (978-0-7910-8477-9(9)) Facts On File, Inc. (Chelsea Hse.).

Gerdes, Louise. What are the Causes of Prostitution? 2007. (At Issue Ser.). 128p. (J). (gr. 10-12). pap. 21.20 (*978-0-7377-2738-8(1)* , Greenhaven Pr., Inc.) Thomson Gale.

Gross, Craig & Foster, Mike. Questions You Can't Ask Your Mama: 68 1/2 Questions for Craig & Mike. 2003. (C). per. 11.99 (978-0-9741849-0-6(X)) Fireproof Ministries.

Harris, H. Robie. Its Perfectly Normal: Changing Bodies, Growing up, Sex, & Sexual Health. Emberley, Michael, illus. 10th anniv. ed. 2004. 96p. (J). (gr. 5 up). 22.99 (978-0-7636-2610-5(4)) Candlewick Pr.

Harris, Robie H. Its Perfectly Normal: A Book about Changing Bodies, Growing Up, Sex, & Sexual Health. Emberley, Michael, illus. 10th anniv. ed. 2004. 96p. (gr. 5 up). pap. 10.99 (978-0-7636-2433-0(0)) Candlewick Pr.

—Sexo: Que es? Desarrollo, Cambios Corporales, Sexo y Salud Sexual. Saslavsky, Irene, tr. Emberley, Michael, illus. 2005. (SPA.). 89p. pap. 12.99 (978-84-8488-181-0(4)) Serres, Ediciones, S. L. ESP. *Dist:* Lectorum Pubns., Inc.

—Sexo... Que Es? 2003. (SPA., Illus.). (YA). (gr. 7-8). pap. (978-84-95040-35-0(2) , RR7144) Serres, Ediciones, S. L. ESP. *Dist:* Lectorum Pubns., Inc.

—Sexo... Que Es? Emberley, Michael, illus. 2000. (YA). (gr. 5-8). (SPA.). 90p. 17.95 (978-84-88061-90-4(0)); 2nd ed. (CAT.). 96p. pap. 17.95 (978-84-95040-28-2(X)) Serres, Ediciones, S. L. ESP. *Dist:* Lectorum Pubns., Inc.

Hickman, Pamela. Animals & Their Mates: How Animals Attract, Fight for & Protect Each Other. Stephens, Pat, illus. 2005. (Animal Behavior Ser.). 40p. (YA). (gr. 2-6). (978-1-55337-546-3(7)); (978-1-55337-545-6(9)) Kids Can Pr., Ltd.

Human Sexuality: Human Sexuality (Windows/Macintosh) 36p. (gr. 7-12). cd-rom 126.00 (978-1-59070-357-1(X)) Goodheart-Willcox Pub.

Hunter-Geboy, Carol, et al. God's Gift of Sexuality - Older Youth Guide. rev. ed. 1998. 88p. (YA). (gr. 9-12). pap. 7.95 (978-1-57895-061-4(9) , Witherspoon Pr.) Curriculum Publishing, Presbyterian Church (U. S. A.).

—God's Gift of Sexuality - Younger Youth Guide. rev. ed. 1998. 56p. (J). (gr. 6-8). pap. 7.95 (978-1-57895-062-1(7) , Witherspoon Pr.) Curriculum Publishing, Presbyterian Church (U. S. A.).

Jones, Stan And Brenna & Jones, Brenna. The Story of Me (Revised) 2007. 48p. pap. 9.99 (978-1-60006-013-7(7)) NavPress Publishing Group.

Learning about Sex Series, 7 vols. exp. rev. abr. ed. Incl. How You Are Changing. Graver, Jane. 64p. (J). (gr. 3-6). 10.99 (978-0-570-03564-0(3)); Love, Sex & God. Ameiss, Bill. 128p. (YA). (gr. 9-12). 10.99 (978-0-570-03566-4(X)); Sex & the New You. Bimler, Richard W. 64p. (YA). 10.99 (978-0-570-03565-7(1)); Where Do Babies Come from? Hummel, Ruth. (Illus.). 32p. (J). (gr. 1-3). 10.99 (978-0-570-03563-3(5)); Why Boys & Girls Are Different. Greene, Carol. (Illus.). 32p. (J). (ps-k). 10.99 (978-0-570-03562-6(7)); 1998. 74.99 incl. VHS (978-0-570-03569-5(4)) Concordia Publishing Hse.

Lickona, Tom & Lickona, Judy. Sex, Love & You: Making the Right Decision. rev. ed. 2003. (Illus.). 192p. 12.95 (978-0-87793-987-0(X)) Ave Maria Pr.

Lookadoo, Justin & Morgan, Hayley. The Dirt on Sex: A Dateable Book. 2004. (Dirt Ser.). (Illus.). 120p. (YA). (gr. 10-12). reprint ed. pap. 9.99 (978-0-8007-5916-2(8)) Revell.

Luadzers, Darcy. Virgin Sex for Girls: A No-Regrets Guide to Safe & Healthy Sex. 2006. 320p. (J). 13.95 (978-1-57826-229-8(1) , Hatherleigh Pr.) Hatherleigh Co., Ltd., The.

—Virgin Sex for Guys: A No-Regrets Guide to Safe & Healthy Sex. 2006. 320p. 13.95 (978-1-57826-230-4(5) , Hatherleigh Pr.) Hatherleigh Co., Ltd., The.

Luster, Ivon. The Power in Sex. Lattiboudeaine, Michael & Peterson, Carlisle, eds. 1998. 140p. (Orig.). (YA). (gr. 10). pap. 12.95 (978-1-889448-50-3(8)) Great House Publishers Grp., Inc., The.

Manning, Mick & Granstrom, Brita. How Did I Begin? (Illus.). 31p. (J). pap. (978-0-7496-3409-4(X) , Franklin Watts) Hodder Children's Division.

Mathis, Teresea A. & Smith-Rex, Susan J. Getting Your Life on Track: A Female Teen's Guide to Saying No to Sex. 2001. (Illus.). 72p. (J). pap. 11.95 (978-1-930572-14-0(X)) Educational Media Corp.

Mayall, Beth. What's Your Guy-Q? 25+ Cool Quizzes to Help Discover the Real You! 2000. 128p. (YA). (gr. 7-12). pap. 4.99 (978-0-439-11466-0(7)) Scholastic, Inc.

Moore, Stephanie Perry. Staying Pure. 2000. (gr. 7-12). lib. bdg. 15.30 (978-0-613-90878-8(3)) Tandem Library Bks.

Morris, Marilyn. Teens, Sex & Choices. McEowen, Shannan, illus. 2000. 210p. (YA). (gr. 6 up). pap. 13.95 (978-0-9648113-6-2(7) , 0723) Charles Rivers Publishing Co.

National Campaign to Prevent Teen Pregnancy Staff, ed. Voices Carry: Teens Speak Out on Sex & Teen Pregnancy. 2000. (Illus.). 35p. (YA). pap. 5.00 (978-1-58671-030-9(3)) National Campaign to Prevent Teen Pregnancy.

Naylor, Phyllis Reynolds. Alice on the Outside. (Alice Ser.). 176p. (gr. 5-9). 2000. (YA). mass mkt. 5.99 (978-0-689-80594-3(2) , Simon Pulse); 1999. (J). 16.00 (978-0-689-80359-8(1) , Atheneum) Simon & Schuster Children's Publishing.

—Alice on the Outside. 2000. (Alice Ser.). (YA). (gr. 5-9). 11.64 (978-0-606-19706-9(0)); (gr. 7-12). lib. bdg. 13.00 (978-0-613-29866-7(7)) Tandem Library Bks.

Ouffy, Jan. Recuerdos de las Montanas. 2000. (Reunited Ser.: Vol. 3). (SPA.). (J). (gr. 8-12). mass mkt. 3.99 (978-0-7899-0804-9(2)) Spanish Hse. Distributors.

Park, Jane & Muller, Kathryn. Just the Facts: What Science Has Found Out about Teenage Sexuality & Pregnancy in the U. S. Card, Josephina T. & Gibson, Anjalique C., eds. 2nd rev. ed. 1998. (Illus.). vii, 133p. (YA). (gr. 6-12). pap. (978-0-9666901-0-1(9)) Sociometrics Corp.

Planned Parenthood Federation of America, Inc. Staff. Teensex? It's Okay to Say: No Way! 2003. (YA). pap. 3.00 net. (978-0-934586-79-5(9)) Planned Parenthood Federation of America, Inc.

Pogany, Susan Browning. Sex Smart: 501 Reasons to Hold off on Sex. 1998. (gr. 7-12). lib. bdg. 24.55 (978-0-613-79261-5(0)) Tandem Library Bks.

Roleff, Tamara. Prostitution. 2006. (Contemporary Issues Companion Ser.). (Illus.). 244p. (gr. 10-12). pap. 36.20 (978-0-7377-2462-2(5) , Greenhaven Pr., Inc.) Thomson Gale.

Rose, Lyman Hinckley. Pure & Chased. 2004. ix, 86p. (978-1-55517-774-4(3)) Cedar Fort, Inc./CFI Distribution.

Scheer, Scott. Talking to Teens about Dating & Sex. 2002. (YA). per. (978-1-931600-09-5(0)) Faith Printing Co.

Scherrer, David L. & Klepacki, Linda M. Fearless Love: Making Sexual Choices That Honor God. 2004. (Worth Waiting for Ser.). (Illus.). 176p. (YA). (gr. 13 up). 19.99 (978-0-7814-4076-9(9) , 0781440769) Cook, David C. Publishing Co.

Schiffer, Howard B. First Love : Remembrances. 2004. (YA). 29.95 (978-0-9723639-2-1(0)) Heartful Loving Pr.

Sex & Purity. ldr.'s ed. 1998. (Cross Training Ser.: Vol. 2). 64p. (YA). (gr. 10-12). pap. 15.00 incl. VHS (978-1-57405-018-9(4)) CharismaLife Pubs.

Smith, Louis. Sexual Sins of the Bible: Everything You Want to Know, but Wouldn't Ask! 2004. 200p. pap. 14.99 (978-0-9744519-1-6(6)) Smith, Kasper.

Stenzel, Pam. Sex Has a Price Tag: Discussions about Sexuality, Spirituality, & Self Respect. 2003. (gr. 7-12). lib. bdg. 18.80 (978-0-613-86016-1(0)) Tandem Library Bks.

Stenzel, Pam & Kirgiss, Crystal. Sex Has a Price Tag: Discussions about Sexuality, Spirituality, & Self Respect. 2003. (Studentware Ser.). (Illus.). 144p. (YA). pap. 9.99 (978-0-310-24971-9(6)) Zondervan.

Theisen, Michael. Sexuality: Challenges & Choices. Zanzig, Thomas, ed. Thiewes, Sam, illus. 2003. (Horizons Program : Level 1, Minicourse 2). 68p. (Orig.). (YA). (gr. 9). pap., stu. ed. 9.95 (978-0-88489-348-6(0)) St. Mary's Pr.

Vitale, Ann E. Drug Therapy & Sexual Disorders. 2003. (Encyclopedia of Psychiatric Drugs & Their Disorders Ser.). (Illus.). 128p. (J). lib. bdg. (978-1-59084-575-2(7)) Mason Crest Pubs.

Wilcox, Brad. Growing Up: Gospel Answers about Maturation & Sex. 2000. (Illus.). xii, 132p. (J). pap. 10.95 (978-1-57345-821-4(X)) Deseret Bk. Co.

SEX—FICTION

Angelchild, P. Erotic Memoirs Volume 1. 2007. pap. (***978-1-84747-127-7(7)***) Chipmunkapublishing.

Banting, Celia. I Only Said Yes So That They'd Like Me. 2006. 224p. (YA). per. 14.99 (***978-0-9786648-1-7(7)***) Wighita Pr.

Burgess, Melvin. Doing It. 336p. (YA). 2006. reprint ed. pap. 6.95 (978-0-8050-8079-7(1)); 2004. 15.95 (978-0-8050-7565-6(8)) Holt, Henry & Co. (Holt, Henry & Co. Bks. For Young Readers).

Cabot, Meg. Ready or No. 2008. 256p. (J). pap. 7.99 (***978-0-06-147996-0(9)*** , HarperTeen) HarperCollins Pubs.

Henderson, Lauren. Kiss Me Kill Me. 2008. 256p. (YA). (gr. 9). 15.99 (***978-0-385-73487-5(5)*** , Delacorte Bks. for Young Readers) Random Hse. Children's Bks.

Ruby, Laura. Good Girls. 2008. 304p. (J). pap. 8.99 (***978-0-06-088225-9(5)***); 2006. 288p. (J). lib. bdg. 17.89 (978-0-06-088224-2(7)); 2006. 288p. (YA). 16.99 (978-0-06-088223-5(9)) HarperCollins Pubs. (HarperTeen).

Zarr, Sara. Story of a Girl. 2007. 208p. (J). (gr. 7-17). 16.99 (978-0-316-01453-3(2)) Little Brown & Co.

SEX CRIMES

see also Child Sexual Abuse; Incest; Rape

McDowell, Josh & Stewart, Ed. Friendship 911 Collection: My Friend Is Struggling With... Past Sexual Abuse. 2000. (Friendship 911 Ser.). (Illus.). 64p. (gr. 8-12). pap. 7.98 (978-0-8499-3797-2(3)) Nelson, Thomas Inc.

Penney, Betty. Tell Your Mother. 2004. 32p. (J). pap. 8.95 (978-0-9631975-4-2(1)) Morgan, E. A.

Quigley, Ann. Sexual Harassment. 2006. (Illus.). 244p. (gr. 10-12). 34.95 (978-0-7377-3289-4(X)); pap. 23.70 (978-0-7377-3290-0(3)) Thomson Gale. (Greenhaven Pr., Inc.).

SEX CRIMES—FICTION

Cummings, Priscilla. What Mr. Mattero Did. 2007. 224p. (J). (gr. 3). pap. 6.99 (978-0-14-240856-8(5) , Puffin) Penguin Group (USA) Inc.

Hooper, Mary. Amy. 2004. 176p. (J). (gr. 5-10). reprint ed. pap. 6.95 (978-1-58234-915-2(0) , Bloomsbury Children) Bloomsbury Publishing.

Kleven, Sandy. The Right Touch: A Read-Aloud Story to Help Prevent Child Sexual Abuse. Bergsma, Jody Lynn, illus. 1998. (Jody Bergsma Collection). 32p. (ps-3). 15.95 (978-0-935699-10-4(4)) Illumination Arts Publishing Co., Inc.

Polak, Monique. On the Game. 2005. (SideStreets Ser.). 184p. (YA). (gr. 7-12). (***978-1-55028-877-3(6)***); 7.95 (978-1-55028-876-6(8)) Lorimer, James & Co., Ltd., Pubs. CAN. *Dist:* Casemate Pubs. & Bk. Distributors, LLC.

Riggs, Shannon. Not in Room 204. Zollars, Jaime, illus. 2007. 32p. (J). (gr. 1-4). 15.95 (978-0-8075-5764-8(1)) Whitman, Albert & Co.

Stang, Debra L. Visiting Grandma. 2003. 136p. (YA). pap. 12.95 (978-1-59113-322-3(X)) Booklocker.com, Inc.

SEX INSTRUCTION

Ameiss, Bill. Love, Sex, & God. 1998. (gr. 7-12). lib. bdg. 19.95 (978-0-613-72727-3(4)) Tandem Library Bks.

Amos, Janine. Is Helen Pregnant? 2003. (Body Matters Ser.). (Illus.). 32p. (YA). 19.99 (978-1-84234-107-0(3) , Cherrytree Books) Evans Publishing Group GBR. *Dist:* Independent Pubs. Group.

Annunziata, Jane & Nemiroff, Marc A. Sex & Babies: First Facts. Ortakales, Denise & Patrolia, Maureen Tracy, illus. 2003. 48p. (YA). (gr. 3-5). 14.95 (978-1-55798-809-6(9)); pap. 8.95 (978-1-55798-808-9(0)) American Psychological Assn. (Magination Pr.).

Ballman, Swanee. Where Do Babies Come From? 2003. (Illus.). 32p. (J). per. 6.95 (978-1-59094-023-5(7) , 1590940237) Jawbone Publishing Corp.

Basso, Michael J. The Underground Guide to Teenage Sexuality. 2nd ed. 2003. (Illus.). 272p. pap. 16.95 (978-1-57749-131-6(9)) Fairview Pr.

Bell, Alison. Your Body, Yourself Q & A: Questions & Answers about Your Changing Body. 1999. (Teen Body Book Ser.). (Illus.). 191p. (J). (gr. 4-8). pap. 9.95 (978-0-7373-0190-8(2) , 01902W) McGraw-Hill/ Contemporary.

Bethel, Glynis & Bethel, Orlando. Be a Model for the Gospel: Sex Talk! Questions & Biblical Answers about Sex. 1998. (Illus.). 80p. (YA). (gr. 6-12). pap. 6.00 (978-0-9675738-0-9(7)) New Life Gospel Productions, Inc.

Bourgeois, Paulette & Martyn, Kim. Changes in You & Me: A Book about Puberty Mostly for Boys. rev. ed. 2005. (Illus.). 64p. (J). pap. 16.95 (***978-1-55263-668-8(2)***) Key Porter Bks. CAN. *Dist:* Perseus Distribution.

—Changes in You & Me: A Book about Puberty Mostly for Girls. Phillips, Louise, illus. rev. ed. 2005. 64p. (J). pap. 16.95 (***978-1-55263-670-1(4)***) Key Porter Bks. CAN. *Dist:* Perseus Distribution.

Brewer, Janet N. In God's Image. Watkins, Virginia, ed. Pullen, Pip, illus. Carr, Geoffrey, photos by. 1998. 32p. (J). (ps-1). stu. ed. 14.99 (978-1-57895-055-3(4)) Bridge Resources.

Brown, Laurie Krasny. What's the Big Secret? Talking about Sex with Girls & Boys. Brown, Marc, illus. 2000. 32p. (J). (ps-3). pap. 6.99 (978-0-316-10183-7(4)) Little Brown & Co.

—What's the Big Secret? Talking about Sex with Girls & Boys. 2000. (gr. k-3). lib. bdg. 14.95 (978-0-613-28695-4(2)) Tandem Library Bks.

Brynie, Faith Hickman. 101 Questions about Sex & Sexuality: With Answers for the Curious, Cautious, & Confused. 2003. (Single Titles Ser.). (Illus.). 176p. (gr. 7 up). lib. bdg. 27.90 (978-0-7613-2310-5(4) , Twenty-First Century Bks.) Lerner Publishing Group.

Byers, Ann. Sexually Transmitted Diseases. 1999. (Hot Issues Ser.). (Illus.). 64p. (YA). (gr. 6-12). lib. bdg. 27.93 (978-0-7660-1192-2(5)) Enslow Pubs., Inc.

Carey, Joely. Boys & Sex. 2002. (gr. 7-12). lib. bdg. 15.25 (978-0-613-81891-9(1)) Tandem Library Bks.

Christenson, Larry. The Wonderful Way Babies Are Made. rev. ed. 2000. (Backyard Ser.). (Illus.). 48p. reprint ed. 15.99 (978-0-7642-2341-9(0)) Bethany Hse. Pubs.

Clausener-Petit, Magali & Daly, Melissa. Sex Explained: Honest Answers to Your Questions about Guys & Girls, Your Changing Body, & What Really Happens During Sex, 4 vols. Soledad, illus. 2004. (Sunscreen Ser.). 112p. (J). (gr. 6-11). pap. 9.95 (978-0-8109-9162-0(4)) Abrams, Harry N. , Inc.

Culp, Bruce & Culp, Melody. The Value of the Gift: A Spiritual Guide to Love & Intimacy, for Young Adults. l.t. ed. 2000. 96p. (YA). (gr. 7 up). pap. 8.95 (978-0-9672616-1-4(9)) Oak Hammock Publishing.

Curran, Christine Perdan. Sexually Transmitted Diseases. 1998. (Diseases & People Ser.). (Illus.). 128p. (YA). (gr. 6-12). lib. bdg. 26.60 (978-0-7660-1050-5(3)) Enslow Pubs., Inc.

Daldry, Jeremy. The Teenage Guy's Survival Guide: The Real Deal on Girls, Growing up, & Other Guy Stuff. 1999. (978-0-606-17234-9(3)) Tandem Library Bks.

Drill, Esther. Deal with It! a Whole New Approach to Your Body, Brain & Life As a Gurl. 1999. (gr. 7-12). lib. bdg. 26.85 (978-0-613-23702-4(1)) Tandem Library Bks.

Duerksen, Carol. God's Gift of Sex. 2000. (Fast Lane Bible Studies Ser.). 52p. (YA). pap. 9.95 (978-0-87303-400-5(7)) Faith & Life Pr.

Gitchel, Sam & Foster, Lorri. Let's talk about S-E-X: A Guide for Kids 9-12 & Their Parents. 2nd ed. 2005. (Illus.). 100p. pap. 9.99 (978-1-931863-18-6(0)) Book Peddlers.

Gravelle, Karen. What's Going on down There? Answers to Questions Boys Find Hard to Ask. 1998. (gr. 5-8). lib. bdg. 17.60 (978-0-613-75331-9(3)) Tandem Library Bks.

Gravelle, Karen, et al. Que Pasa Por Alla Abajo? Respuestas Faciles a Preguntas Dificiles para un Adolescente. Leighton, Robert, illus. 2003. (ENG & SPA.). 158p. (YA). (gr. 5-9). pap. 8.95 (978-0-8027-7649-5(3)) Walker & Co.

—What's Going on down There? Answers to Questions Boys Find Hard to Ask. Leighton, Robert, illus. 1998. (gr. 5-9). 128p. (J). 15.95 (978-0-8027-8671-5(5)); 160p. (YA). pap. 8.95 (978-0-8027-7540-5(3)) Walker & Co.

Graver, Jane. How You Are Changing. 1998. (Learning about Sex Ser.: Vol. 3). 64p. (J). (gr. 3-6). 10.99 (978-0-570-03564-0(3)) Concordia Publishing Hse.

Grimes, Janice D. Before You Were Born - Our Wish for A Baby: Version 1: in Vitro Fertilization. 2004. (Illus.). 18p. (J). 14.97 (978-0-9755028-0-8(8)) X, Y, & Me LLC.

—Before You Were Born - Our Wish for A Baby: Version 10: Male Partners. 2004. (Illus.). 18p. (J). 14.97 (978-0-9755028-9-1(1)) X, Y, & Me LLC.

—Before You Were Born - Our Wish for A Baby: Version 2: Donor Insemination. 2004. (Illus.). 18p. (J). 14.97 (978-0-9755028-1-5(6)) X, Y, & Me LLC.

—Before You Were Born - Our Wish for A Baby: Version 4: Traditional Surrogate. 2004. (Illus.). 18p. (J). 14.97 (978-0-9755028-3-9(2)) X, Y, & Me LLC.

—Before You Were Born - Our Wish for A Baby: Version 5: Gestational Carrier. 2004. (Illus.). 18p. (J). 14.97 (978-0-9755028-4-6(0)) X, Y, & Me LLC.

—Before You Were Born - Our Wish for A Baby: Version 6: Frozen Embryo. 2004. (Illus.). 18p. (J). 14.97 (978-0-9755028-5-3(9)) X, Y, & Me LLC.

—Before You Were Born - Our Wish for A Baby: Version 7: Embryo Donation. 2004. (Illus.). 18p. (J). 14.97 (978-0-9755028-6-0(7)) X, Y, & Me LLC.

—Before You Were Born - Our Wish for A Baby: Version 8: Donor Sperm (IVF) 2004. (Illus.). 18p. (J). 14.97 (978-0-9755028-7-7(5)) X, Y, & Me LLC.

—Before You Were Born - Our Wish for A Baby: Version 9: Female Partners. 2004. (Illus.). 18p. (J). 14.97 (978-0-9755028-8-4(3)) X, Y, & Me LLC.

Harris, Robie H. Es Alucinante! Emberley, Michael, illus. 2000. Tr. of It's So Amazing!. (J). (CAT.). 80p. (gr. k-2). pap. 17.95 (978-84-95040-33-6(6)); (SPA.). 84p. (gr. 3-5). 17.95 (978-84-95040-32-9(8) , RR4476) Serres, Ediciones, S. L. ESP. *Dist:* Lectorum Pubns., Inc.

—It's NOT the Stork! A Book about Girls, Boys, Babies, Bodies, Families & Friends. Emberley, Michael, illus. 2006. 64p. (J). (ps-3). 16.99 (978-0-7636-0047-1(4)) Candlewick Pr.

—It's So Amazing! A Book about Eggs, Sperm, Birth, Babies & Families. Emberley, Michael, illus. 1999. 80p. (J). (gr. 2-5). 22.99 (978-0-7636-0051-8(2)) Candlewick Pr.

—It's So Amazing! A Book about Eggs, Sperm, Birth, Babies, & Families. 2002. (gr. k-3). lib. bdg. 19.95 (978-0-613-74790-5(9)) Tandem Library Bks.

—It's So Amazing! A Book about Eggs, Sperm, Birth, Babies & Families. Emberley, Michael, illus. 5th anniv. ed. 2004. 88p. (J). (gr. 2 up). reprint ed. pap. 10.99 (978-0-7636-1321-1(5)) Candlewick Pr.

Hickling, Meg. Boys, Girls & Body Science: A First Book about Facts of Life. LaFave, Kim, illus. unabr. ed. 2002. 32p. (ps-2). 18.95 (978-1-55017-236-2(0)) Harbour Publishing Co., Ltd. CAN. *Dist:* Graphic Arts Ctr. Publishing Co.

Hirschmann, Kris. Your Sexuality. 2007. (Ripped from the Headlines Ser.). 64p. (J). (gr. 5). 23.95 (***978-1-60217-009-4(6)***) Erickson Pr.

Horner, Susan. What Is God's Design for My Body? 2004. (Miracle of Creation Ser.). (Illus.). 64p. (J). pap. 5.99 (978-0-8024-0923-2(7)) Moody Pubs.

Huard, Donald V. Teenagers: "Safe" Sex Isn't, but Abstinence Is. . . 1998. 58p. (YA). (gr. 7-12). mass mkt. 3.95 (978-0-9661606-2-8(2)) Huard Pubns.

In God's Image: Young Children & Sexuality, Guide for Congregations. 7.99 (978-1-57895-057-7(0)) Bridge Resources.

In God's Image: Young Children & Sexuality, Parent's Guide. 6.99 (978-1-57895-056-0(2)) Bridge Resources.

Jukes, Mavis. The Guy Book: An Owner's Manual: Maintenance, Safety, & Operating Instructions for Boys. 2002. (Illus.). 160p. (YA). (gr. 7 up). 12.95 (978-0-679-89028-7(9) , Crown Books For Young Readers) Random Hse. Children's Bks.

Kelly, Bill. You Ought to Know: A Guy's Guide to Sex. 2005. (Guys' Guides Ser.). (Illus.). 48p. (J). (gr. 5-8). lib. bdg. 23.95 (978-0-8239-3084-5(X) , GUYOSH) Rosen Publishing Group, Inc., The.

Kemp, Kristen. Healthy Sexuality. 2005. (Life Balance Ser.). (Illus.). 80p. (J). (gr. 5-8). pap. 6.95 (978-0-531-16689-5(9) , Watts, Franklin) Scholastic Library Publishing.

Kurre, Don. Sexuality. Cannizzo, Karen A., ed. 2000. (Conversations with Teens Ser.). 16p. (YA). pap. 7.95 (978-0-937997-66-6(8)) Pflaum Publishing Group.

Lange, Donna. Taking Responsibility: A Teen's Guide to Contraception & Pregnancy. 2004. (Science of Health Ser.). (Illus.). 128p. (J). (978-1-59084-841-8(1)) Mason Crest Pubs.

Lickona, Tom & Lickona, Judy. Sex, Love & You: Making the Right Decision. rev. ed. 2003. (Illus.). 192p. 12.95 (978-0-87793-987-0(X)) Ave Maria Pr.

Lieberman, E. James & Troccoli, Karen L. Like It Is: A Teen Sex Guide. 1998. (Illus.). 216p. (C). (gr. 6 up). pap. 29.95 (978-0-7864-0526-8(0)) McFarland & Co., Inc. Pubs.

Lookadoo, Justin & DiMarco, Hayley. The Dateable Rules: A Guide to the Sexes. 2004. (Illus.). 176p. (YA). reprint ed. pap. 11.99 (978-0-8007-5915-5(X)) Revell.

Luadzers, Darcy. Virgin S.e.x: A Girl's No-Regrets Guide to Happy, Healthy Sex... the First Time & Every Time. 2004. 261p. (YA). per. 18.95 (978-0-9742532-7-5(8)) Palmetto Tree Pr.

Madaras, Lynda. What's Happening to My Body? Book for Girls. 2000. (gr. 3-6). lib. bdg. 22.20 (978-0-613-45351-6(4)) Tandem Library Bks.

Madaras, Lynda & Madaras, Area. My Body, My Self for Boys. (Illus.). 112p. 2nd ed. 2000. (gr. 4-7). reprint ed. 12.95 (978-1-55704-440-2(6) , Newmarket Shooting Scripts); 3rd rev. ed. 2007. (YA). pap. 12.95 (***978-1-55704-767-0(7)***) Newmarket Pr.

—My Body, My Self for Girls. 3rd rev. ed. 2007. (Illus.). 128p. (YA). pap. 12.95 (***978-1-55704-766-3(9)***) Newmarket Pr.

—What's Happening to my Body? A Growing-Up Guide for Parents & Daughters. 3rd ed. 2001. (Illus.). 304p. (gr. 4-7). reprint ed. 24.95 (978-1-55704-448-8(1) , Newmarket Shooting Scripts) Newmarket Pr.

—What's Happening to My Body? A Growing-Up Guide for Parents & Sons. 3rd ed. 2001. (Illus.). 288p. (gr. 4-7). 24.95 (978-1-55704-447-1(3) , Newmarket Shooting Scripts) Newmarket Pr.

—The "What's Happening to My Body?" Book for Boys: A Growing-Up Guide for Parents & Sons. Sullivan, Simon & Aher, Jackie, illus. 3rd ed. 2000. (What's Happening to My Body? Ser.). 288p. (gr. 4-7). reprint ed. 12.95 (978-1-55704-443-3(0) , Newmarket Shooting Scripts) Newmarket Pr.

—The What's Happening to My Body? Book for Girls: A Growing-Up Guide for Parents & Daughters. Sullivan, Simon & Aher, Jackie, illus. 3rd ed. 2000. 304p. (gr. 4-7). reprint ed. pap. 12.95 (978-1-55704-444-0(9) , Newmarket Shooting Scripts) Newmarket Pr.

—The What's Happening to My Body Book for Boys. 3rd ed. 2007. (Illus.). 272p. (YA). 24.95 (***978-1-55704-769-4(3)***); pap. 12.95 (***978-1-55704-765-6(0)***) Newmarket Pr.

—The What's Happening to My Body Book for Girls. 3rd rev. ed. 2007. (Illus.). 304p. (YA). 24.95 (***978-1-55704-768-7(5)***); pap. 12.95 (***978-1-55704-764-9(2)***) Newmarket Pr.

Marsh, Carole. 25 Most Asked Questions about Sex: Questions Kids Ask Parents & Teachers Today ... & the Honest Answers! 2001. (Illus.). 48p. (J). (gr. 1-12). pap. 7.95 (978-0-635-00263-1(9)) Gallopade International.

Martyn Kim. All the Way: Sex for the First Time. 2004. (Illus.). 216p. (J). pap. 14.95 (978-1-894549-26-4(0)) Sumach Pr. CAN. *Dist:* Orca Bk. Pubs. USA.

Mast, Coleen Kelly. Sex Respect: The Option of True Sexual Freedom: A Public Health Workbook for Students. Forrestal, Julienne, ed. 2001. (Illus.). 143p. (Orig.). (YA). (gr. 8-12). pap. 12.95 (978-0-945745-11-2(7)) Respect, Inc.

McCoy, Kathy & Wibbelsman, Charles. Growing & Changing: A Handbook for Preteens. rev. ed. 2003. (Illus.). 224p. (gr. 12). pap. 14.95 (978-0-399-52898-9(9) , Perigee Trade) Penguin Group (USA) Inc.

Morris, Marilyn. Teens, Sex & Choices. McEowen, Shannan, illus. 2000. 210p. (YA). (gr. 6 up). pap. 13.95 (978-0-9648113-6-2(7) , 0723) Charles Rivers Publishing Co.

Morrison, Jan. A Safe Place: Beyond Sexual Abuse. 2002. 208p. (Orig.). (YA). pap. 13.99 (978-0-87788-747-8(0) , Shaw) WaterBrook Pr.

The Need to Know Library: Facts of Life, 8 vols. 1999. (Illus.). (J). (gr. 4-6). lib. bdg. 143.60 (978-0-8239-9001-6(X)) Rosen Publishing Group, Inc., The.

Nystrom, Carolyn. Before I Was Born. rev. ed. 2007. 40p. pap. 9.99 (978-1-60006-014-4(5)) NavPress Publishing Group.

O'Donnell, Kerri. The Reproductive System. 2001. (Insider's Guide to the Body Ser.). (Illus.). 48p. (YA). (gr. 5-8). lib. bdg. 23.95 (978-0-8239-3334-1(2) , Rosen Central) Rosen Publishing Group, Inc., The.

Paonessa, Mary. Growth & Development with Friends, 8 vols. 3rd rev. ed. 2003. (Human Growth & Development Ser.). (Illus.). 41p. (J). (gr. 5 up). pap. 9.00 (978-0-9711721-0-4(2) , 388) Paon Pubns.

—Growth & Development with Friends & School, 8 vols. 3rd ed. 2003. (Human Growth & Development Ser.). (Illus.). (J). (gr. 7 up). 112p. pap., tchr. ed. 15.00 (978-0-9711721-5-9(3) , 393); 91p. pap. (978-0-9711721-4-2(5) , 392) Paon Pubns.

Pardes, Bronwen. Doing It Right: Making Smart, Safe, & Satisfying Choices about Sex. 2007. (Illus.). 160p. (J). (gr. 9 up). pap. 14.99 (978-1-4169-1823-3(X) , Simon Pulse) Simon & Schuster Children's Publishing.

Pavanel, Jane. The Sex Book: An Alphabet of Smarter Love. Cunningham, Grant, illus. 2001. (Millennium Generation Ser.). 200p. (J). (gr. 8-12). pap. 14.95 (978-1-894222-30-3(X)) Lobster Pr. CAN. *Dist:* Univ. of Toronto Pr.

—Sex Book: An Alphabet of Smarter Love. 2001. (gr. 7-12). lib. bdg. 24.55 (978-0-613-60608-0(6)) Tandem Library Bks.

Peacock, Judith. Birth Control & Protection: Options for Teens. 2000. (Perspectives on Healthy Sexuality Ser.). (Illus.). 64p. (J). (gr. 4-6). lib. bdg. 23.93 (978-0-7368-0715-9(2) , LifeMatters Bks.) Capstone Pr., Inc.

Perspectives on Healthy Sexuality, 6 bks. Incl. Abstinence : Postponing Sexual Involvement. Peacock, Judith. 2000. lib. bdg. 23.93 (978-0-7368-0713-5(6)); Birth Control & Protection : Options for Teens. Peacock, Judith. 2000. lib. bdg. 23.93 (978-0-7368-0715-9(2)); Dating & Sex : Defining & Setting Boundaries. Peacock, Judith. 2000. lib. bdg. 23.93 (978-0-7368-0716-6(0)); Sexually Transmitted Diseases : How Are They Prevented? Endersbe, Julie. 1999. lib. bdg. 23.93 (978-0-7368-0276-5(2)); Teen Fathers : Getting Involved. Endersbe, Julie. 1999. lib. bdg. 23.93 (978-0-7368-0269-7(X)); Teen Mothers : Raising a Baby. Endersbe, Julie. 1999. lib. bdg. 23.93 (978-0-7368-0270-3(3)); 64p. (J). (gr. 4-6). (Illus.). 2001. Set lib. bdg. 143.58 (978-0-7368-1691-5(7) , LifeMatters Bks.) Capstone Pr., Inc.

Planned Parenthood Federation of America, Inc. Staff. A Young Woman's Guide to Sexuality. 2003. (Illus.). (YA). pap. 3.00 net. (978-1-930996-17-5(9)) Planned Parenthood Federation of America, Inc.

S

Pogany, Susan Browning. Sex Smart: 501 Reasons to Hold Off on Sex. 1998. 192p. (gr. 8-12). pap. 14.95 (978-1-57749-043-2(6)) Fairview Pr.

Ritchie, James. Created by God: About Human Sexuality for Older Girls & Boys. 2004. (Illus.). (gr. 5-6). tchr. ed. 49.95 (978-0-687-07408-2(8)) Abingdon Pr.

Roleff, Tamara L. Sex. 2001. (Teen Decisions Ser.). (Illus.). 170p. (YA). (gr. 10 up). lib. bdg. 36.20 (978-0-7377-0494-5(2) , Greenhaven Pr., Inc.) Thomson Gale.

Roleff, Tamara L., ed. Sex. 2001. (Teen Decisions Ser.). (Illus.). 170p. (YA). (gr. 10 up). pap. 24.95 (978-0-7377-0493-8(4) , Greenhaven Pr., Inc.) Thomson Gale.

—Sex Education. 1998. (At Issue Ser.). (Illus.). 96p. (YA). (gr. 9-12). pap. 17.45 (978-0-7377-0008-4(4) , Greenhaven Pr., Inc.) Thomson Gale.

Ryder, Verdene. Human Sexuality: Responsible Life Choices. 2000. (gr. 7-12). lib. bdg. 40.85 (978-0-613-88169-2(9)) Tandem Library Bks.

Ryder, Verdene & Smith, Peggy B. Human Sexuality: Responsible Life Choices. 2004. 236p. (gr. 7-12). pap. 25.50 (978-1-59070-302-1(2)); 1998. (Illus.). 197p. (J). (gr. 8-12). 29.00 (978-1-56637-455-2(3)) Goodheart-Willcox Pub.

Saltz, Gail. Changing You! A Guide to Body Changes & Sexuality. Cravath, Lynne Avril, illus. 2007. 48p. (J). (gr. 1). 16.99 (***978-0-525-47817-1(5)*** , Dutton Juvenile) Penguin Group (USA) Inc.

Schiffer, Howard B. How to Be the Best Lover - a Guide for Teenage Boys. 2004. (YA). 19.95 (978-0-9723639-0-7(4)) Heartful Loving Pr.

Stanley, Deborah A., ed. Sexual Health Information for Teens: Health Tips about Sexual Development, Human Reporduction & Sexually Transmitted Diseases. 2003. (Teen Health Ser.). (Illus.). 391p. (gr. 7 up). (978-0-7808-0445-6(7)) Omnigraphics, Inc.

Straight Talk about Sexual Choices & Consequences. 2002. (YA). (gr. 6-8). tchr. ed. 69.95 (978-1-55942-179-9(7) , 9230V9) Marsh Media.

Watkins, James. When Can I Start Dating? The Why Files. 2000. (ENG., Illus.). 222p. (YA). (gr. 7-12). pap. 9.99 (978-0-570-05249-4(1)) Concordia Publishing Hse.

Westheimer, Ruth K. Dr. Ruth Talks to Kids: Where You Came from, How Your Body Changes, & What Sex Is All About. 1998. (J). 13.64 (978-0-606-13345-6(3)) Tandem Library Bks.

Wright, Sally Ann. Where Do Babies Come From? Ayres, Honor, illus. 2007. 29p. (J). 9.95 (978-0-8198-8311-7(5)) Pauline Bks. & Media.

Zep. What's Going on down There? All the Stuff Your Body Won't Tell You about Sex. Zimmerman, Dwight, ed. 2005. (Illus.). 96p. pap. 14.95 (978-1-4165-0458-0(3)) ibooks, Inc.

SEX INSTRUCTION—FICTION

Berenstain, Stan & Berenstain, Jan. The Birds, the Bees, & the Berenstain Bears. 2000. (Berenstain Bears First Time Bks.). (Illus.). 32p. (J). (gr. k-3). pap. 3.99 (978-0-679-88959-5(0) , Random Hse. Bks. for Young Readers) Random Hse. Children's Bks.

—The Birds, the Bees, & the Berenstain Bears. 1999. (Berenstain Bears First Time Bks.). (J). (gr. k-2). (978-0-679-88971-7(X)) Random Hse., Inc.

SEX ROLE

Abrahams, George & Ahlbrand, Sheila. Boy v. Girl? How Gender Shapes Who We Are, What We Want, & How We Get Along. 2004. (Illus.). 208p. (YA). (gr. 5-10). pap. 14.95 (978-1-57542-104-9(6)) Free Spirit Publishing, Inc.

Brooks, Susan. Any Girl Can Rule the World. 1998. 224p. (gr. 8-12). pap. 12.95 (978-1-57749-068-5(1)) Fairview Pr.

Connolly, Sean. Gender Equality. 2005. (Campaigns for Change Ser.). (Illus.). 48p. (J). (gr. 6-9). lib. bdg. 29.95 (978-1-58340-515-4(1)) Smart Apple Media.

Corey, Shana. You Forgot Your Skirt, Amelia Bloomer! McLaren, Chesley, illus. 2000. 40p. (J). (gr. k-3). pap. 16.95 (978-0-439-07819-1(9) , Scholastic Reference) Scholastic, Inc.

Forbes, Jeff Donaldson. Everything You Need to Know about Sexual Identity. 2005. (Need to Know Library). (Illus.). 64p. (YA). (gr. 7-12). lib. bdg. 25.25 (978-0-8239-3089-0(0) , NTSEID) Rosen Publishing Group, Inc., The.

Harris, Robie H. It's NOT the Stork! A Book about Girls, Boys, Babies, Bodies, Families & Friends. Emberley, Michael, illus. 2006. 64p. (J). (ps-3). 16.99 (978-0-7636-0047-1(4)) Candlewick Pr.

Haughton, Emma. Equality of the Sexes? 2005. (Illus.). 32p. (J). (gr. 5-9). lib. bdg. 27.10 (978-1-932889-58-1(2)) Sea-To-Sea Pubns.

Libal, Autumn. Women in the World of Southeast Asia. 2005. (Women's Issues, Global Trends Ser.). (Illus.). 112p. (J). lib. bdg. (978-1-59084-867-8(5)) Mason Crest Pubs.

Roberts, Jeremy. The Real Deal: A Guy's Guide to Being a Guy. 2005. (Guys' Guides Ser.). (Illus.). 48p. (YA). (gr. 5-8). lib. bdg. 23.95 (978-0-8239-3104-0(8) , GUREDE) Rosen Publishing Group, Inc., The.

Ross, Mandy. The Changing Role of Women. 2002. (20th-Century Perspectives Ser.). (Illus.). 48p. (J). (gr. 5-7). lib. bdg. 27.07 (978-1-58810-660-5(8)) Heinemann Library.

—Changing Role of Women. 2002. (gr. 5-8). lib. bdg. 16.40 (978-0-613-58200-1(4)) Tandem Library Bks.

—The Changing Role of Women, Set 2. 2002. (20th Century Perspectives Ser.). (Illus.). 48p. (J). (gr. 5-7). pap. 7.95 (978-1-58810-920-0(8) , 91511) Heinemann Library.

Swisher, Clarice. Women of Victorian England. 2004. (Illus.). 112p. (YA). (gr. 7-12). lib. bdg. 32.45 (978-1-59018-571-1(4) , Lucent Bks.) Thomson Gale.

Winfield, Cynthia. Gender Identity: The Ultimate Teen Guide. 2006. (It Happened to Me Ser.: No. 16). (Illus.). 232p. 43.00 (978-0-8108-4907-5(0)) Scarecrow Pr., Inc.

SEX ROLE—FICTION

Abraham, Susan Gonzales. Cecilia's Year. 2004. (Latino Fiction for Young Adults Ser.). (Illus.). 160p. (J). (gr. 5 up). 16.95 (978-0-938317-87-6(3)) Cinco Puntos Pr.

Abraham, Susan Gonzales & Abraham, Denise Gonzales. Cecilia's Year. 2007. (Latino Fiction for Young Adults Ser.). 210p. (J). pap. 11.95 (978-1-933693-02-6(9)) Cinco Puntos Pr.

Avi. The Secret School. 2001. 160p. (YA). (gr. 3-7). 16.00 (978-0-15-216375-4(1)) Harcourt Children's Bks.

—The True Confessions of Charlotte Doyle. Murray, Ruth E., illus. 1999. 239p. (J). 17.90 (978-0-03-054709-6(1)) Holt, Rinehart & Winston.

Ayres, Katherine. Silver Dollar Girl. 2002. (Illus.). 208p. (gr. 3-7). pap. 5.50 (978-0-440-41705-7(8) , Yearling) Random Hse. Children's Bks.

—Silver Dollar Girl. 2002. (gr. 3-6). lib. bdg. 13.00 (978-0-613-64685-7(1)) Tandem Library Bks.

Baguley, Elizabeth. Meggie Moon. Mabire, Gregoire, illus. 2005. 28p. (J). (ps-ps). 16.00 (978-1-56148-474-4(1)) Good Bks.

Bajoria, Paul. The Printer's Devil. 2007. 400p. (J). (gr. 4-8). pap. 6.99 (978-0-316-10678-8(X)) Little Brown & Co.

Banks, Kate. Mama's Coming Home. Bogacki, Tomek, illus. 2003. 32p. (J). (ps-1). 16.00 (978-0-374-34747-5(6) , Farrar, Straus & Giroux (BYR)) Farrar, Straus & Giroux.

Berenstain, Stan & Berenstain, Jan. The Berenstain Bears Play Ball. l.t. ed. 1998. (Berenstain Bears Ser.). (Illus.). 48p. (J). (ps-3). pap. 10.95 (978-0-590-94732-9(X)) Scholastic, Inc.

Bildner, Phil. Playing the Field. 2006. (Illus.). 192p. (YA). 15.95 (978-1-4169-0284-3(8)) Simon & Schuster Children's Publishing.

Bognomo, Joel Ebouerne. Madoulina: A Girl Who Wanted to Go to School. 2003. (Illus.). 32p. (J). (gr. 2-4). 14.95 (978-1-56397-769-5(9)); pap. 8.95 (978-1-56397-822-7(9)) Boyds Mills Pr.

—Madoulina: A Girl Who Wanted to Go to School. 1999. (978-0-606-17704-7(3)); lib. bdg. 17.60 (978-0-613-23339-2(5)) Tandem Library Bks.

Bower, Tamara. How the Amazon Queen Fought the Prince of Egypt. Bower, Tamara, illus. 2005. (Illus.). 40p. (J). (gr. 2-6). 17.99 (978-0-689-84434-8(4) , Atheneum) Simon & Schuster Children's Publishing.

Brooks, Bruce. Dooby. 1998. (Wolfbay Wings Ser.: No. 8). (Illus.). (J). 128p. (gr. 5 up). pap. 4.50 (978-0-06-440708-3(X)); 32p. (ps-1). 14.89 (978-0-06-027898-4(6)) HarperCollins Pubs.

Browning, Leah. Dancing with the Wind. 2000. 80p. (J). (978-0-936389-54-7(0)) Tudor Pubs., Inc.

Buckner, Arlene. Elphina. Klementz-Harte, Lauren, illus. 1998. 32p. (J). (gr. k-2). 17.95 (978-1-890309-56-5(7)) Tern Bk. Co., Inc., The.

Burch, Christian. The Manny Files. 2006. (Illus.). 304p. (J). (gr. 4-7). 15.95 (978-1-4169-0039-9(X) , Atheneum) Simon & Schuster Children's Publishing.

Butler, Dori Hillestad. Sliding into Home. Casale, Paul, illus. 2003. (Peachtree Junior Publication Ser.). 192p. (J). 14.95 (978-1-56145-222-4(X)) Peachtree Pubs., Ltd.

Capeci, Anne. Missing! Casale, Paul, illus. 2005. 144p. (J). 12.95 (978-1-56145-334-4(X)) Peachtree Pubs., Ltd.

Carlson, Nancy. Louanne Pig in Making the Team. 2005. (Illus.). 32p. (J). (ps-ps). lib. bdg. 15.95 (978-1-57505-914-3(2)) Lerner Publishing Group.

Chambers, Aidan. This Is All: The Pillow Book of Cordelia Kenn. 2006. 816p. (J). (gr. 8-17). 19.95 (978-0-8109-7060-1(0) , Amulet Bks.) Abrams, Harry N. , Inc.

Cheng, Andrea. The Lace Dowry. 2005. 120p. (J). 16.95 (978-1-932425-20-8(9) , Lemniscaat) Boyds Mills Pr.

Clifford, Mary Louise. The Shalamar Code. 2006. 192p. (J). (gr. 7 up). pap. 8.95 (978-0-7387-0934-5(4) , Flux) Llewellyn Pubns.

Collins, Pat L. The Fattening Hut. 2003. 192p. (YA). (gr. 7 up). tchr. ed. 15.00 (978-0-618-30955-9(1)) Houghton Mifflin Co. Trade & Reference Div.

Collins, Pat Lowery. The Fattening Hut. 2005. 192p. (YA). (gr. 7). pap. 7.99 (978-0-618-55209-2(X) , Graphia) Houghton Mifflin Co. Trade & Reference Div.

Collison, Linda. Star-Crossed. 2006. (Illus.). 416p. (YA). (gr. 9). 16.95 (978-0-375-83363-2(3)); lib. bdg. 18.99 (978-0-375-93363-9(8)) Random Hse. Children's Bks. (Knopf Bks. for Young Readers).

Cooney, Caroline B. Prisoner of Time. 1999. (978-0-606-16455-9(3)) Tandem Library Bks.

Corey, Shana. Players in Pigtails. Gibbon, Rebecca, illus. 2006. 28p. (YA). (gr. 8-11). reprint ed. 17.00 (***978-1-4223-5848-1(8)***) DIANE Publishing Co.

—Players in Pigtails. 2006. 40p. (J). pap. 6.99 (978-0-439-18306-2(5) , Scholastic Paperbacks) Scholastic, Inc.

—Players in Pigtails. Gibbon, Rebecca, illus. 2003. 40p. (J). pap. 16.95 (978-0-439-18305-5(7)) Scholastic, Inc.

Cristaldi, Kathryn. Baseball Ballerina. Carter, Abby, illus. 2002. (J). 11.91 (978-0-7587-0907-3(2)) Book Wholesalers, Inc.

Day, Karen. No Cream Puffs. 2008. 160p. (J). (gr. 5). 15.99 (***978-0-375-83775-3(2)***); lib. bdg. 18.99 (***978-0-375-93775-0(7)***) Random Hse. Children's Bks. (Lamb, Wendy).

Dines, Carol. The Queen's Soprano. 2007. (Illus.). 336p. (YA). pap. 6.95 (***978-0-15-206102-9(9)*** , Harcourt Paperbacks) Harcourt Children's Bks.

Dole, Mayra L. Drum, Chavi, Drum ! / Toca, Chavi, Toca! Tonel, illus. 2003. Tr. of Toca, Chavi, Toca!. (ENG & SPA.). 32p. (J). 16.95 (978-0-89239-186-8(3)) Children's Bk. Pr.

Dow, Unity. Far & Beyon' 2002. 208p. (YA). (gr. 7 up). pap. 11.95 (978-1-879960-64-0(8)) Aunt Lute Bks.

Durrant, Lynda. My Last Skirt: The Story of Jennie Hodgers, Union Soldier. 2006. 192p. (J). (gr. 5). 16.00 (978-0-618-57490-2(5) , Clarion Bks.) Houghton Mifflin Co. Trade & Reference Div.

—My Last Skirt: The Story of Jennie Hodgers, Union Soldier. 2006. 245p. (YA). 21.95 (978-0-7862-8880-9(9)) Thorndike Pr.

Ellis, Deborah. The Breadwinner. 2002. (gr. 3-6). lib. bdg. 14.10 (978-0-613-44488-0(4)) Tandem Library Bks.

Ellison, Laura. Hard Rock, Hard Times: Coming of Age in Butte Montana, 1911-1917. 2005. 195p. (YA). per. (978-0-9722217-7-1(8)) Horse Creek Pubns.

Evans, Lauralee. The King's Heir. 2006. (YA). (***978-1-55517-865-9(0)*** , Bonneville Bks.) Cedar Fort, Inc./CFI Distribution.

Ferreiro-Esteban, Carmen. Two Moon Princess. 2007. 300p. (gr. 5 up). 15.95 (***978-1-933718-12-5(9)***) Tanglewood Pr.

Fisher, Linda C. A Will of Her Own. 2006. (YA). pap. (978-0-88092-641-6(4)); lib. bdg. (978-0-88092-640-9(6)) Royal Fireworks Publishing Co.

FitzGerald, Dawn. Getting in the Game. 2007. 160p. (J). pap. 6.99 (***978-0-312-37753-3(3)***) Square Fish.

Fitzgerald, Dawn. Getting in the Game. rev. ed. 2005. 144p. (J). 15.95 (978-1-59643-044-0(3)) Roaring Brook Pr.

Florie, Christine. Cori Plays Football. Tripp, Christine, illus. 2005. (Rookie Reader Ser.). 31p. (J). (ps-ps). 19.50 (978-0-516-24864-6(2) , Children's Pr.) Scholastic Library Publishing.

Friesner, Esther M. Nobody's Princess. (gr. 7-11). 2008. 336p. (J). pap. 7.99 (978-0-375-87529-8(8)); 2007. 320p. (J). lib. bdg. 19.99 (978-0-375-97528-8(4)); 2007. 320p. (YA). 16.99 (978-0-375-87528-1(X)) Random Hse. Children's Bks. (Random Hse. Bks. for Young Readers).

Friesner, Esther M. Nobody's Prize. 2008. (J). (***978-0-375-87531-1(X)***); (***978-0-375-87533-5(6)***); pap. (***978-0-375-87532-8(8)***); lib. bdg. (***978-0-375-97531-8(4)***) Random Hse., Inc.

Gag, Wanda. Gone Is Gone or the Story of a Man Who Wanted to Do Housework. 2003. (Illus.). 64p. 14.95 (978-0-8166-4243-4(5)) Univ. of Minnesota Pr.

Geeslin, Campbell. Elena's Serenade. Juan, Ana, illus. 2004. 40p. (J). 17.95 (978-0-689-84908-4(7) , Atheneum) Simon & Schuster Children's Publishing.

Gonzales Bertrand, Diane, et al. Close to the Heart. 2002. (Illus.). 176p. (J). pap. 9.95 (978-1-55885-319-5(7) , Piñata Books) Arte Publico Pr.

Grambling, Lois G. Nicky Jones & the Roaring Rhinos. Geer, William J., illus. 2004. 32p. (J). 6.95 (978-1-877810-14-5(2)) Rayve Productions, Inc.

Gray, Dianne E. Together Apart. 2002. 208p. (J). (gr. 5-9). tchr. ed. 16.00 (978-0-618-18721-8(9)) Houghton Mifflin Co. Trade & Reference Div.

Green, Connie Jordan. The War at Home. 2nd ed. 2003. 144p. (J). pap. (978-0-916078-75-1(2)) Iris Publishing Group, Inc., The.

Gregerson, Jonathan, illus. Minerva's Dream. 1999. (J). 30.00 (978-0-8172-7282-1(8)) Steck-Vaughn.

Haddix, Margaret Peterson. Just Ella. 2000. (J). pap., stu. ed. 61.00 incl. audio (978-0-7887-4337-5(6) , 41132) Recorded Bks., LLC.

—Just Ella. 2007. 240p. (YA). mass mkt. 5.99 (978-1-4169-3649-7(1) , Simon Pulse) Simon & Schuster Children's Publishing.

—Just Ella. Milot, René, illus. 2001. 240p. (YA). (gr. 6-9). pap. 5.99 (978-0-689-83128-7(5) , Aladdin) Simon & Schuster Children's Publishing.

—Just Ella. Milot, Rene, illus. 2001. 224p. mass mkt. 4.99 (978-0-689-84917-6(6) , Aladdin) Simon & Schuster Children's Publishing.

—Just Ella. Milot, René, illus. 1999. 192p. (YA). (gr. 7 up). 17.00 (978-0-689-82186-8(7)) Simon & Schuster Children's Publishing.

Hahn, Mary Downing. The Gentleman Outlaw & Me: A Story of the Old West. 2007. 224p. (YA). (gr. 7-9). pap. 6.95 (978-0-618-83000-8(6) , Clarion Bks.) Houghton Mifflin Co. Trade & Reference Div.

Harlow, Joan Hiatt. Midnight Rider. 2006. 384p. (J). pap. 5.99 (978-0-689-87010-1(8) , Aladdin) Simon & Schuster Children's Publishing.

Harlow, Joan Hiatt & Minor, Wendell. Midnight Rider. 2005. (Illus.). 416p. (J). 15.95 (978-0-689-87009-5(4) , McElderry, Margaret K.) Simon & Schuster Children's Publishing.

Hawes, Louise. Vanishing Point. 2007. 240p. (YA). (gr. 5). pap. 7.99 (***978-0-618-74788-7(5)***) Houghton Mifflin Co. Trade & Reference Div.

Hill, Pamela Smith. Ghost Horses. 1999. 224p. (J). (gr. 4-7). pap. 4.50 (978-0-380-72942-5(3)) HarperCollins Pubs.

—Ghost Horses. 1999. (J). (978-0-606-16340-8(9)) Tandem Library Bks.

Hill, Susanna Leonard. Punxsutawney Phyllis. Ebbeler, Jeffrey, illus. 32p. (J). pap. 6.95 (978-0-8234-2040-7(X)); 17.95 (978-0-8234-1872-5(3)) Holiday Hse., Inc.

Hoffman, Alice. The Foretelling. (J). (gr. 8-17). 2005. 176p. 16.99 (978-0-316-01018-4(9)); 2006. 192p. reprint ed. pap. 7.99 (978-0-316-15409-3(1)) Little Brown & Co.

—The Foretelling. l.t. ed. 2006. 156p. 23.95 (978-0-7862-8285-2(1)) Thorndike Pr.

Holm, Jennifer L. Our Only May Amelia. (Harper Trophy Bks.). (Illus.). (J). 2001. 272p. (gr. 4 up). pap. 5.99 (978-0-06-440856-1(6) , Harper Trophy); 1999. 253p. (gr. k-9). per. 15.89 (978-0-06-028354-4(8)); 1999. 272p. (gr. 4 up). 18.99 (978-0-06-027822-9(6)) HarperCollins Pubs.

—Our Only May Amelia. unabr. ed. 2004. 253p. (J). (gr. 5-9). pap. 36.00 incl. audio (978-0-8072-8366-0(5) , YA191SP, Listening Library) Random Hse. Audio Publishing Group.

—Our Only May Amelia. 2001. (Illus.). 251p. (J). (gr. k-9). lib. bdg. 14.15 (978-0-613-35995-5(X)) Tandem Library Bks.

—Our Only May Amelia. l.t. ed. 2000. (Illus.). 261p. (J). (ps up). 21.95 (978-0-7862-2742-6(7)) Thorndike Pr.

Holohan, Maureen. Ice Cold. 1999. (Broadway Ballplayers Ser.: No. 6). (Illus.). 164p. (J). (gr. 4-8). (978-0-9659091-5-0(8)) Broadway Ballplayers, Inc.

Homan, Lynn M. & Reilly, Thomas. Girls Fly! Shepherd, Rosalie M., tr. Shepherd, Rosalie M., illus. 2003. 32p. (J). pap. 14.95 (978-1-58980-154-7(7)) Pelican Publishing Co., Inc.

Impey, Rose. Who's a Clever Girl? Amstutz, Andre, illus. 2003. (Yellow Bananas Ser.). 48p. (J). (gr. 3-4). pap. (978-0-7787-0976-3(0)) Crabtree Publishing Co.

—Who's a Clever Girl? 2002. (gr. 3-6). lib. bdg. 12.95 (978-0-613-52935-8(9)) Tandem Library Bks.

Johnson, Angela. Just Like Josh Gibson. Peck, Beth, illus. 32p. (J). 2004. 15.95 (978-0-689-82628-3(1)); 2007. reprint ed. 6.99 (978-1-4169-2728-0(X) , Aladdin) Simon & Schuster Children's Publishing.

Johnson, Tim. Never So Green. 2002. 240p. (YA). 18.00 (978-0-374-35509-8(6) , Farrar, Straus & Giroux (BYR)) Farrar, Straus & Giroux.

Kay, Alan N. No Girls Allowed. 2003. (Young Heroes of History: Vol. 5). (Illus.). 140p. (J). pap. 6.95 (978-1-57249-324-7(0) , White Mane Kids) White Mane Publishing Co., Inc.

Keehn, Sally M. Anna Sunday. 2002. 272p. (YA). (gr. 5-9). 18.99 (978-0-399-23875-8(1) , Philomel) Penguin Group (USA) Inc.

Kellerhals-Stewart, Heather. Skookum Sal, Birling Gal. Blaine, Janice, illus. unabr. ed. 32p. (YA). 18.95 (***978-1-55017-285-0(9)***) Harbour Publishing Co., Ltd. CAN. *Dist:* Graphic Arts Ctr. Publishing Co.

Kessler, Christina. Our Secret, Siri Aang. 2007. 224p. (YA). (gr. 5). pap. 6.99 (***978-0-14-240840-7(9)*** , Puffin) Penguin Group (USA) Inc.

Kessler, Cristina. The Best Beekeeper of Lalibela: A Tale from Africa. Jenkins, Leonard, illus. 2006. 32p. (J). 16.95 (978-0-8234-1858-9(8)) Holiday Hse., Inc.

—Our Secret Siri Aang. 2004. 240p. (YA). (gr. 5). 16.99 (978-0-399-23985-4(5) , Philomel) Penguin Group (USA) Inc.

Kinsey-Warnock, Natalie. A Doctor Like Papa. Bernardin, James, illus. 2002. 80p. (J). 14.99 (978-0-06-029319-2(5)) HarperCollins Pubs.

—A Doctor Like Papa. 2002. (gr. 3-6). lib. bdg. 13.00 (978-0-613-68417-0(6)) Tandem Library Bks.

Kittinger, Jo S. Cuando Sea Grande. Lucas, Margeaux, illus. 2005. (Rookie Reader Espanol Ser.). (SPA & ESP.). 23p. (J). (gr. k-2). pap. 4.95 (978-0-516-24692-5(5) , Children's Pr.) Scholastic Library Publishing.

Korman, Gordon. Nick's a Chick. 2000. (gr. 3-6). lib. bdg. 13.00 (978-0-613-31525-8(1)) Tandem Library Bks.

—No Girly-Girls Allowed! 2000. (gr. 3-6). lib. bdg. 13.00 (978-0-613-31529-6(4)) Tandem Library Bks.

Kroll, Virginia L. Girl, You're Amazing! Potter, Melisande, illus. 2001. 32p. (J). (gr. k-4). 15.95 (978-0-8075-2930-0(3)) Whitman, Albert & Co.

Krulik, Nancy E. Boys, Boys, Boys. 2000. (gr. 5-8). lib. bdg. 13.00 (978-0-613-31021-5(7)) Tandem Library Bks.

Kubler, Annie. Man's Work. 2000. (All in a Day Boardbooks Ser.). (Illus.). 14p. (J). (ps-k). bds. 3.99 (978-0-85953-587-8(8)) Child's Play-International.

Kupchella, Rick. Girls Can! Make it Happen. Brown, Marilyn, illus. 2004. 40p. (J). 16.95 (978-0-9726504-3-4(1)) Tristan Publishing, Inc.

Kurtz, Jane. Bicycle Madness. Peck, Beth, illus. rev. ed. 2003. 128p. (J). 15.95 (978-0-8050-6981-5(X) , Holt, Henry & Co. Bks. For Young Readers) Holt, Henry & Co.

Lavender, William. Aftershocks. 2006. (Illus.). 352p. (YA). 17.00 (978-0-15-205882-1(6)) Harcourt Children's Bks.

Lawrence, Michael. The Toilet of Doom. 2004. 256p. (J). pap. 16.95 (978-0-7540-7913-2(9) , Galaxy Children's Large Print) BBC Audiobooks America.

Lee, Tanith. Piratica: Being a Daring Tale of a Singular Girl's Adventure upon the High Seas. (Piratica Ser.: Vol. 1). 304p. (gr. 6). 2006. (YA). pap. 6.99 (978-0-14-240644-1(9) , Puffin); 2004. (Illus.). (J). 17.99 (978-0-525-47324-4(6) , Dutton Juvenile) Penguin Group (USA) Inc.

Lynch, Chris. Wolf Gang. 1998. (He-Man Women Haters Club Ser.). 128p. (YA). (gr. 3-7). pap. 4.50 (978-0-06-440659-8(8)) HarperCollins Pubs.

Matas, Carol. Rosie in New York City: Gotcha! 2003. (Aladdin Historical Fiction Ser.). (Illus.). 128p. (J). (gr. 3-6). pap. 9.95 (978-0-689-85714-0(4) , Aladdin) Simon & Schuster Children's Publishing.

—Rosie in New York City: Gotcha! 2003. (gr. 5-8). lib. bdg. 13.00 (978-0-613-66469-1(8)) Tandem Library Bks.

Matson, Nancy. The Boy Trap. Chesworth, Michael, illus. 1999. 128p. (J). (gr. 3-7). 14.95 (978-0-8126-2663-6(X)) Cricket Bks.

McCaffrey, Laura Williams. Alia Waking. 2003. 224p. (J). (gr. 5-9). tchr. ed. 16.00 (978-0-618-19461-2(4) , Clarion Bks.) Houghton Mifflin Co. Trade & Reference Div.

McCully, Emily Arnold. Beautiful Warrior: The Legend of the Nun's Kung Fu. McCully, Emily Arnold, illus. 2nd ed. 1998. (Illus.). 40p. (J). (ps-3). pap. 19.99 (978-0-590-37487-3(7)) Scholastic, Inc.

McElroy, Lisa Tucker. Love, Lizzie: Letters to a Military Mom. Paterson, Diane, illus. 2005. 32p. (J). (gr. k-3). lib. bdg. 15.95 (978-0-8075-4777-9(8)) Whitman, Albert & Co.

McMullan, Kate. The Ghost of Sir Herbert Dungeonstone. 2006. (Dragon Slayers' Academy Ser.: No. 12). (J). (gr. 1-6). 24.21 (978-1-59961-124-2(4)) Spotlight.

McNamara, Margaret. The Playground Problem. Gordon, Mike, illus. 2005. (Ready-to-Read Ser. Level 1). 32p. (J). lib. bdg. 15.00 (978-1-59054-931-5(7)) Fitzgerald Bks.

McNamara, Margaret & Gordon, Mike. The Playground Problem. 2004. (Robin Hill School Ser.). (Illus.). 32p. (J). pap. 3.99 (978-0-689-85876-5(0) , Aladdin) Simon & Schuster Children's Publishing.

Meyer, L. A. Under the Jolly Roger: Being an Account of the Further Nautical Adventures of Jacky Faber. 2007. (Bloody Jack Adventures Ser.). (Illus.). 544p. (YA). pap. 6.95 (978-0-15-205873-9(7) , Harcourt Paperbacks) Harcourt Children's Bks.

—Under the Jolly Roger: Being an Account of the Further Nautical Adventures of Jacky Faber. 2005. (Bloody Jack Adventures Ser.). (Illus.). 528p. (YA). (gr. 7-17). 17.00 (978-0-15-205345-1(X)) Harcourt Trade Pubs.

Meyer, Louis A. Bloody Jack: Being an Account of the Curious Adventures of Mary Jacky Faber, Ship's Boy. 2002. (Bloody Jack Adventures Ser.). (Illus.). 336p. (YA). (gr. 6-9). 17.00 (978-0-15-216731-8(5)) Harcourt Children's Bks.

—Curse of the Blue Tattoo: Being an Account of the Misadventures of Jacky Faber, Midshipman & Fine Lady. 2004. (Bloody Jack Adventures Ser.). (Illus.). 496p. (YA). 17.00 (978-0-15-205115-0(5)) Harcourt Children's Bks.

Moss, Marissa. Oh Boy, Amelia! 2001. (Amelia's Notebooks). (Illus.). (J). (978-0-606-21365-3(1)) Tandem Library Bks.

Namioka, Lensey. Ties That Bind, Ties That Break. 2000. 160p. (YA). (gr. 7 up). pap. 5.99 (978-0-440-41599-2(3) , Laurel Leaf) Random Hse. Children's Bks.

—Ties That Bind, Ties That Break. 2000. (gr. 7-12). lib. bdg. 13.00 (978-0-613-28377-9(5)) Tandem Library Bks.

Napoli, Donna Jo. Bound. 192p. (YA). 2004. (Illus.). (gr. 6 up). 16.95 (978-0-689-86175-8(3) , Atheneum); 2006. (gr. 7 up). reprint ed. pap. 5.99 (978-0-689-86178-9(8) , Simon Pulse) Simon & Schuster Children's Publishing.

—Daughter of Venice. 2003. 288p. (YA). (gr. 7). pap. 6.50 (978-0-440-22928-5(6) , Laurel Leaf) Random Hse. Children's Bks.

—Daughter of Venice. 2003. (gr. 7-12). lib. bdg. 13.55 (978-0-613-72327-5(9)) Tandem Library Bks.

—No Fair! Ben-Ami, Doren & Klementz-Harte, Lauren, illus. 2000. (Angelwings Ser.: No. 6). 96p. (J). (gr. 2-5). pap. 7.95 (978-0-689-83206-2(0) , Aladdin) Simon & Schuster Children's Publishing.

—No Fair! 2000. (Angelwings Ser.: No. 6). (Illus.). (J). (978-0-606-17909-6(7)) Tandem Library Bks.

Nelson, Blake. Gender Blender. 2007. 224p. (YA). (gr. 7). pap. 8.99 (***978-0-553-37603-6(9));*** 2006. 192p. (J). (gr. 5). 15.95 (978-0-385-74696-0(2)); 2006. 192p. (J). (gr. 5). lib. bdg. 17.99 (978-0-385-90937-2(3)) Random Hse. Children's Bks. (Delacorte Bks. for Young Readers).

Nixon, Joan Lowery. Ann's Story, 1747. 2004. (J). (978-0-87935-198-4(5)) Colonial Williamsburg Foundation.

—Land of Dreams. l.t. ed. 2001. (Ellis Island Stories Ser.). 153p. (J). (gr. 4 up). lib. bdg. 23.33 (978-0-8368-2810-8(0)) Stevens, Gareth Inc.

—Maria's Story, 1773. 2004. (J). (978-0-87935-227-1(2)) Colonial Williamsburg Foundation.

Numeroff, Laura Joffe & Munsinger, Lynn. What Mommies Do Best: What Daddies Do Best. 1998. (Illus.). 40p. (J). (ps-3). 13.95 (978-0-689-80577-6(2)) Simon & Schuster Children's Publishing.

Osborne, Mary Pope. Hour of the Olympics. unabr. ed. 2004. (Magic Tree House Ser. : No. 16). 70p. (J). (gr. k-3). pap. 17.00 incl. audio (978-0-8072-0785-7(3) , LFTR 244 SP, Listening Library) Random Hse. Audio Publishing Group.

—Hour of the Olympics. Murdocca, Sal, illus. 1998. (Magic Tree House Ser.: No. 16). 96p. (J). (gr. k-3). lib. bdg. 11.99 (978-0-679-99062-8(3)); mass mkt. 3.99 (978-0-679-89062-1(9)) Random Hse. Children's Bks. (Random Hse. Bks. for Young Readers).

Osterlund, Anne. Aurelia. 2008. 288p. (YA). (gr. 7). pap. 8.99 (***978-0-14-240579-6(5)*** , Puffin) Penguin Group (USA) Inc.

Papademetriou, Lisa. My Pen Pal, Pat. Handelman, Dorothy, photos by. 1998. (Real Kids Readers Ser.). (Illus.). 48p. (gr. 1-3). lib. bdg. 18.90 (978-0-7613-2023-4(7)); 32p. (J). (gr. 2-4). pap. 4.99 (978-0-7613-2048-7(2)) Lerner Publishing Group. (Millbrook Pr.).

Park, Linda Sue. Seesaw Girl. Tseng, Jean & Tseng, Mou-Sien, illus. 1999. 96p. (J). (gr. 4-6). tchr. ed. 14.00 (978-0-395-91514-1(7) , Clarion Bks.) Houghton Mifflin Co. Trade & Reference Div.

—Seesaw Girl. Tseng, Jean & Tseng, Mou-Sien, illus. 2001. 112p. (gr. 4-7). 5.50 (978-0-440-41672-2(8) , Yearling) Random Hse. Children's Bks.

—Seesaw Girl. Tseng, Jean & Tseng, Mou-Sien, illus. 2001. 96p. (J). (gr. 4-7). lib. bdg. 12.40 (978-0-613-35470-7(2)) Tandem Library Bks.

—Seesaw Girl. 1999. (Illus.). (J). (978-0-606-20902-1(6)) Tandem Library Bks.

Pattison, Darcy. 19 Girls & Me. Salerno, Steven, illus. 2006. 32p. (J). (ps). 16.99 (978-0-399-24336-3(4) , Philomel) Penguin Group (USA) Inc.

Perkins, Mitali. Rickshaw Girl. Hogan, Jamie, illus. 2007. 91p. (J). (gr. 2-5). 13.95 (978-1-58089-308-4(2)) Charlesbridge Publishing, Inc.

Pierce, Tamora. Alanna: The First Adventure. Heyer, illus. 2002. (Song of the Lioness Ser.: Bk. 1). 240p. (YA). 11.95 (978-0-689-85323-4(8) , Atheneum) Simon & Schuster Children's Publishing.

—First Test. 2000. (Protector of the Small Ser.: No. 1). (Illus.). 256p. (YA). (gr. 7-11). mass mkt. 6.50 (978-0-679-88917-5(5) , Laurel Leaf) Random Hse. Children's Bks.

—First Test. 2000. (Protector of the Small Ser.: No. 1). (gr. 5-8). lib. bdg. 14.15 (978-0-613-25184-6(9)) Tandem Library Bks.

—Page. (Protector of the Small Ser.: No. 2). 2001. 288p. (YA). (gr. 7-11). mass mkt. 6.50 (978-0-679-88918-2(3) , Laurel Leaf); 2000. (Illus.). 272p. (gr. 5-9). lib. bdg. 17.99 (978-0-679-98915-8(3) , Random Hse. Bks. for Young Readers) Random Hse. Children's Bks.

—Page. 2001. (Protector of the Small Ser.: No. 2). (gr. 5-8). lib. bdg. 13.55 (978-0-613-50483-6(6)) Tandem Library Bks.

—Squire. 2002. (Protector of the Small Ser.: No. 3). 432p. (YA). (gr. 7-11). mass mkt. 6.50 (978-0-679-88919-9(1) , Laurel Leaf) Random Hse. Children's Bks.

—Squire. 2002. (Protector of the Small Ser.: No. 3). (gr. 5-8). lib. bdg. 14.15 (978-0-613-49349-9(4)) Tandem Library Bks.

Players in Pigtails. 2004. 29.95 incl. cd-rom (978-0-7882-0518-7(8)); 24.95 incl. audio (978-0-7882-0517-0(X)) Weston Woods Studios, Inc.

Pryor, Bonnie. Hannah Pritchard: Girl Pirate of the Revolution. 2008. (Historical Fiction Adventures (HFA) Ser.). (Illus.). 160p. (J). (gr. 3-6). lib. bdg. 27.93 (***978-0-7660-2851-7(8)***) Enslow Pubs., Inc.

Qamar, Amjed. Beneath My Mother's Feet. 2008. 208p. (J). (***978-1-4169-4728-8(0)***) Simon & Schuster Children's Publishing.

Reich, Susanna. Penelope Bailey Takes the Stage. 2006. 208p. (J). 16.95 (978-0-7614-5287-4(7)) Cavendish, Marshall Corp.

Richardson, V. A. The Moneylender's Daughter. 2006. (Illus.). 300p. (YA). 17.95 (978-1-58234-885-8(5) , Bloomsbury Children) Bloomsbury Publishing.

Rinaldi, Ann. Girl in Blue. 2005. 320p. (J). pap. 5.99 (978-0-439-67646-5(0) , Scholastic Paperbacks) Scholastic, Inc.

Roberts, Kristi. My Thirteenth Season. rev. ed. 2005. (Illus.). 160p. (J). 15.95 (978-0-8050-7495-6(3) , Holt, Henry & Co. Bks. For Young Readers) Holt, Henry & Co.

Ross, Eileen. Nellie & the Bandit. Kono, Erin Eitter, illus. 2005. 32p. (J). 16.00 (978-0-374-35508-1(8) , Farrar, Straus & Giroux (BYR)) Farrar, Straus & Giroux.

Rudisill, J. J., et al, illus. The Boys Against the Girls. 1999. (Wimzie's House Bks.). 24p. (J). pap. 3.99 (978-0-88724-515-2(3) , CD-4840) Carson-Dellosa Publishing Co., Inc.

Ryan, Pam Muñoz. Riding Freedom. Selznick, Brian, illus. 2007. 144p. (J). (gr. 3-7). mass mkt. 4.99 (978-0-439-08796-4(1) , Scholastic Paperbacks) Scholastic, Inc.

—Riding Freedom. Selznick, Brian, illus. 1999. 138p. per. 11.64 (978-0-606-17445-9(1)) Tandem Library Bks.

Salisbury, Linda G. The Wild Women of Lake Anna: A Bailey Fish Adventure. 2005. (Illus.). 159p. (J). (978-1-881539-37-7(7)) Tabby Hse. Bks.

Sayres, Meghan Nuttall. Anahita's Woven Riddle. 2006. 368p. (YA). (gr. 5-9). 16.95 (978-0-8109-5481-6(8)) Abrams, Harry N. , Inc.

Selman, Marty. Nick's a Chick. Weizman, Daniel, ed. 2000. (Jersey Ser.: 3). (Illus.). 128p. (gr. 3-7). pap. 4.99 (978-0-7868-4423-4(X)) Disney Pr.

—Nick's a Chick. 2000. (Jersey Ser.). (Illus.). (J). (978-0-606-20738-6(4)) Tandem Library Bks.

Shickman, Allan Richard. Zan-Gah: A Prehistoric Adventure. 2007. 160p. pap. 9.95 (***978-0-9790357-0-8(8)***) Earthshaker Bks.

Sinclair, Jay. No Girly-Girls Allowed! 2000. (Jersey Ser.). (Illus.). (J). (978-0-606-20737-9(6)) Tandem Library Bks.

Skinner, Constance Lindsay. Becky Landers: Frontier Warrior. 2006. (Living History Library). 200p. (J). pap. 13.95 (978-1-932350-06-7(3)) Bethlehem Bks.

Spinner, Stephanie. Quiver. 192p. (YA). (gr. 7). 2002. lib. bdg. 17.99 (978-0-375-91489-8(7) , Knopf Bks. for Young Readers); 2005. reprint ed. pap. 5.99 (978-0-440-23819-5(6) , Laurel Leaf) Random Hse. Children's Bks.

Springer, Nancy. Rowan Hood: Outlaw Girl of Sherwood Forest. 2002. (Tales of Rowan Hood Ser.: No. 1). (gr. 5-8). lib. bdg. 14.15 (978-0-613-53860-2(9)) Tandem Library Bks.

Stanley, Diane. Bella at Midnight. Ibatoulline, Ba, illus. 2008. 304p. (J). pap. 6.99 (***978-0-06-077575-9(0)*** , Harper Trophy) HarperCollins Pubs.

—Bella at Midnight. Ibatoulline, Bagram, illus. 2006. 288p. (J). (gr. 5-8). 16.99 (978-0-06-077573-5(4)); lib. bdg. 16.89 (978-0-06-077574-2(2)) HarperCollins Pubs.

Staples, Suzanne Fisher. Haveli. 2006. 21.50 (978-0-8446-7291-5(2)) Smith, Peter Pub., Inc.

—Jameel & the House of Djinn. 2008. 224p. (YA). 16.95 (***978-0-374-39936-8(0)***) Farrar, Straus & Giroux.

Staples, Suzanne Fisher. Shabanu: Daughter of the Wind. 3rd ed. (J). pap. 3.99 (978-0-13-800053-0(0)) Prentice Hall (Schl. Div.).

—Shabanu: Daughter of the Wind. 2003. 288p. (YA). (gr. 7). pap. 6.99 (978-0-440-23856-0(0) , Laurel Leaf) Random Hse. Children's Bks.

—Shabanu: Daughter of the Wind. 2003. (gr. 7-12). lib. bdg. 14.75 (978-0-613-72260-5(4)) Tandem Library Bks.

Stewart, Jennifer J. Close Encounters of a Third World Kind. 2004. 128p. (J). (gr. 4-6). tchr. ed. 16.95 (978-0-8234-1850-3(2)) Holiday Hse., Inc.

Stites, Clara. Lixia of Gold Mountain: A Story of Early California. 2003. (Illus.). 64p. (J). pap. 8.95 (978-1-56474-421-0(3)) Fithian Pr.

Stolz, Joelle. The Shadows of Ghadames. 128p. (gr. 3-7). 2006. 5.99 (978-0-440-41949-5(2) , Yearling); 2004. (J). 15.95 (978-0-385-73104-1(3) , Delacorte Bks. for Young Readers) Random Hse. Children's Bks.

Stone, Jeff. Crane. 2007. (Five Ancestors Ser.: Bk. 4). 248p. (J). pap. (***978-0-375-83078-5(2)***) Random Hse., Inc.

Stratton Porter, Gene. A Daughter of the Land. 2007. 340p. 22.95 (***978-1-934169-46-9(3));*** pap. 11.95 (***978-1-934169-47-6(1)***) Norilana Bks.

Sturtevant, Katherine. At the Sign of the Star. 144p. (YA). 2002. pap. 6.95 (978-0-374-40458-1(5) , Sunburst); 2000. (gr. 5 up). 16.00 (978-0-374-30449-2(1) , Farrar, Straus & Giroux (BYR)) Farrar, Straus & Giroux.

—At the Sign of the Star. 2002. (gr. 3-6). lib. bdg. 14.10 (978-0-613-71732-8(5)) Tandem Library Bks.

—A True & Faithful Narrative. 2006. 256p. (YA). 17.00 (978-0-374-37809-7(6)) Farrar, Straus & Giroux.

—A True & Faithful Narrative. l.t. ed. 2006. 289p. (YA). 21.95 (978-0-7862-9081-9(1)) Thorndike Pr.

Sykes, Shelley & Szymanski, Lois. A Whisper of War. 2003. (J). 5.95 (978-1-57249-327-8(5) , White Mane Kids) White Mane Publishing Co., Inc.

Testa, Maria. Some Kind of Pride. 2003. 128p. (gr. 3-7). 4.99 (978-0-440-41669-2(8) , Yearling) Random Hse. Children's Bks.

—Some Kind of Pride. 2003. (gr. 3-6). lib. bdg. 13.00 (978-0-613-62119-9(0)) Tandem Library Bks.

Thomas, Carroll. Ring Out Wild Bells: A Matty Trescott Novel. 2001. (Illus.). viii, 169p. (J). 9.95 (978-1-57525-291-9(0)) Smith and Kraus Publishers, Incorporated.

—The Town on Rambling Creek: A Matty Trescott Novel. 2004. (Illus.). ix, 185p. (J). (978-1-57525-376-3(3)) Smith and Kraus Publishers, Incorporated.

Thomas, Carroll, creator. Under the Open Sky: A Matty Trescott Novel. 2005. (Illus.). 184p. (J). per. 12.95 (978-0-9762091-2-6(8)) Antrim Hse.

Thomson, Sarah L. The Secret of the Rose. 2006. 304p. (J). 16.99 (978-0-06-087250-2(0)); lib. bdg. 17.89 (978-0-06-087251-9(9)) HarperCollins Pubs.

Turtleback Books, creator. Evvy's Civil War. 2004. 209p. (YA). (gr. 8-12). per. 13.64 (978-0-606-30114-5(3)) Tandem Library Bks.

Vick, Helen Hughes. Shadow. 1998. (Courage of the Stone Ser.). 128p. (gr. 4-9). 15.95 (978-1-57098-218-7(X)) Rinehart, Roberts Pubs.

Wallace, Karen. Princess Gusty Ox's Strange Change. Flook, Helen, illus. 2007. (J). lib. bdg. (***978-1-4048-3708-9(6)***) Picture Window Bks.

Walter, Mildred Pitts. Justin & the Best Biscuits in the World. Stock, Catherine, illus. 2002. (J). 13.40 (978-0-7587-0371-2(6)) Book Wholesalers, Inc.

—Justin & the Best Biscuits in the World. 1999. (Illus.). 128p. (J). (gr. 3-5). pap. 4.99 (978-0-679-89448-3(9)) Knopf, Alfred A. Inc.

Watts, Leander. Wild Ride to Heaven. 2003. 176p. (YA). (gr. 5-9). tchr. ed. 16.00 (978-0-618-26805-4(7)) Houghton Mifflin Co. Trade & Reference Div.

Weil, Sylvie. My Guardian Angel. 208p. (J). 2007. pap. 5.99 (***978-0-439-57682-6(2)*** , Scholastic Paperbacks); 2004. (gr. 4-7). pap. 16.95 (978-0-439-57681-9(4) , Levine, Arthur A. Bks.) Scholastic, Inc.

Whelan, Gloria. Chu Ju's House. 2004. 240p. (J). (gr. 5 up). 16.99 (978-0-06-050724-4(1)); lib. bdg. 17.89 (978-0-06-050725-1(X)) HarperCollins Pubs.

Whitney, Kim Ablon. See You down the Road: A Novel. 2004. 192p. (J). (gr. 7). lib. bdg. 17.99 (978-0-375-92467-5(1) , Knopf Bks. for Young Readers) Random Hse. Children's Bks.

Williams, Susan. Wind Rider. 2006. 320p. (J). 16.99 (978-0-06-087236-6(5)); (YA). lib. bdg. 17.89 (978-0-06-087237-3(3)) HarperCollins Pubs.

Willis, Jeanne. I Want to Be a Cowgirl. Ross, Tony, illus. rev. ed. 2002. 32p. (J). 15.95 (978-0-8050-6997-6(6) , Holt, Henry & Co. Bks. For Young Readers) Holt, Henry & Co.

Wilson, Diane Lee. Firehorse. 2006. 336p. (J). (gr. 7 up). 16.95 (978-1-4169-1551-5(6) , McElderry, Margaret K.) Simon & Schuster Children's Publishing.

Yim, Shirin. Ruby's Wish. Blackall, Sophie, illus. 2002. 36p. (J). (gr. k-3). 15.95 (978-0-8118-3490-2(5)) Chronicle Bks. LLC.

SEXUAL ABSTINENCE

Ayer, Eleanor H. It's Okay to Say No: Choosing Sexual Abstinence. rev. ed. 2005. (Teen Pregnancy Prevention Library). (Illus.). 64p. (YA). (gr. 7-12). lib. bdg. 23.95 (978-0-8239-3239-9(7) , TPOKNO) Rosen Publishing Group, Inc., The.

Butler, Brian, et al. Theology of the Body for Teens: Student Workbook. 2006. per. 14.95 (***978-1-932927-86-3(7)***) Ascension Pr.

Gitchel, Sam & Foster, Lorri. Let's talk about S-E-X: A Guide for Kids 9-12 & Their Parents. 2nd ed. 2005. (Illus.). 100p. pap. 9.99 (978-1-931863-18-6(0)) Book Peddlers.

Herman, Doug. Come Clean. 2004. (Illus.). (YA). pap. 8.99 (978-0-8423-8358-5(1)) Tyndale Hse. Pubs.

—Time for a Pure Revolution. 2004. pap. 13.99 (978-0-8423-8357-8(3)) Tyndale Hse. Pubs.

Kreiner, Anna. In Control: Learning to Say No to Sexual Pressure. rev. ed. 1999. (Teen Pregnancy Prevention Library). (Illus.). 64p. (YA). (gr. 4-6). lib. bdg. 23.95 (978-0-8239-2996-2(5) , TPINCO) Rosen Publishing Group, Inc., The.

Long, Mike. Teenagers: Everyone Is Not Doing It. 2001. 112p. (J). (gr. 8-12). pap. 9.95 (978-0-915463-87-9(3)) Jameson Bks., Inc.

McPherson, Miles. I Don't Want Your Sex for Now. 2001. 128p. (J). pap. 9.99 (978-0-7642-2369-3(0)) Bethany Hse. Pubs.

Peacock, Judith. Abstinence: Postponing Sexual Involvement. 2000. (Perspectives on Healthy Sexuality Ser.). (Illus.). 64p. (J). (gr. 4-6). lib. bdg. 23.93 (978-0-7368-0713-5(6) , LifeMatters Bks.) Capstone Pr., Inc.

Pogany, Susan Browning. Sex Smart: 501 Reasons to Hold Off on Sex. 1998. 192p. (gr. 8-12). pap. 14.95 (978-1-57749-043-2(6)) Fairview Pr.

Rose, Lyman Hinckley. Pure & Chased. 2004. ix, 86p. (978-1-55517-774-4(3)) Cedar Fort, Inc./CFI Distribution.

Sommers, Michael A. & Sommers, Annie Leah. Everything You Need to Know about Virginity. 2005. (Need to Know Library). (Illus.). 64p. (YA). (gr. 7-12). lib. bdg. 25.25 (978-0-8239-3115-6(3) , NTVIRG) Rosen Publishing Group, Inc., The.

The True Love Waits Youth Bible. 2004. (Illus.). 1294p. pap. 19.99 (978-1-55819-621-6(8)) B&H Publishing Grp.

Ware, Jim. No Apologies: The Truth about Life, Love & Sex. 1999. (Life on the Edge Ser.). 240p. (YA). (gr. 9-12). pap. 5.99 (978-1-56179-654-0(9)) Focus on the Family Publishing.

SEXUAL ABSTINENCE—FICTION

Gunn, Robin Jones. With This Ring. 1998. (Sierra Jensen Ser.: Bk. 6). 160p. (J). (gr. 7-11). pap. (978-1-56179-540-6(2)) Focus on the Family Publishing.

Reynolds, Marilyn. If You Loved Me. 1999. (True-to-Life Series from Hamilton High: Vol. 7). 32p. (J). pap., tchr. ed. 2.50 (978-1-885356-59-8(5)) Morning Glory Pr., Inc.

—If You Loved Me: True-to-Life Stories from Hamilton High. 1999. (True-to-Life Series from Hamilton High: Vol. 7). 224p. (J). (gr. 7-12). pap. 8.95 (978-1-885356-55-0(2)) Morning Glory Pr., Inc.

SEXUAL EDUCATION

see Sex Instruction

SEXUAL ETHICS

see also Birth Control

Barrington Jones, Barbara & Thomas, Janet. Dear Barbara: Answers to the Most-Asked Questions from Teenage Girls. 1998. (YA). pap. 13.95 (978-1-57345-369-1(2)) Deseret Bk. Co.

Bethel, Glynis & Bethel, Orlando. Be a Model for the Gospel: Sex Talk! Questions & Biblical Answers about Sex. 1998. (Illus.). 80p. (YA). (gr. 6-12). pap. 6.00 (978-0-9675738-0-9(7)) New Life Gospel Productions, Inc.

Endersbe, Julie. Healthy Sexuality: What Is It? (Perspectives on Healthy Sexuality Ser.). pap. 8.95 (978-0-7368-8851-6(9) , LifeMatters Bks.) Capstone Pr., Inc.

Gilbert, Laura. Everything You Need to Know about Compulsive Sexual Behavior. 2001. (Need to Know Library). (Illus.). 64p. (YA). (gr. 4-6). lib. bdg. 25.25 (978-0-8239-3290-0(7)) Rosen Publishing Group, Inc., The.

Havelin, Kate. Dating: "What Is a Healthy Relationship?" 1999. (Perspectives on Relationships Ser.). (Illus.). 64p. (J). (gr. 4-6). lib. bdg. 23.93 (978-0-7368-0292-5(4) , LifeMatters Bks.) Capstone Pr., Inc.

Hormachea, David. Cartas Al Joven Tentado: Consejos Practicos para Evitar las Caídas Sexuales. 2002. (SPA.). 160p. pap. 9.99 (978-0-88113-714-9(6)) Grupo Nelson.

Joy, Donald M. Becoming a Man: A Celebration of Sexuality, Responsibility & the Christian Young Man. 2nd ed. 2001. (ENG.). 125p. pap. 12.99 (978-1-928915-18-8(3)) Evangel Publishing Hse.

Lickona, Tom & Lickona, Judy. Sex, Love & You: Making the Right Decision. rev. ed. 2003. (Illus.). 192p. 12.95 (978-0-87793-987-0(X)) Ave Maria Pr.

Lieberman, E. James & Troccoli, Karen L. Like It Is: A Teen Sex Guide. 1998. (Illus.). 216p. (C). (gr. 6 up). pap. 29.95 (978-0-7864-0526-8(0)) McFarland & Co., Inc. Pubs.

Marcovitz, Hal. Teens & Sex. 2004. (Gallup Youth Survey, Major Issues & Trends Ser.). (Illus.). 112,128p. (YA). (gr. 7-9). lib. bdg. 22.95 (978-1-59084-722-0(9)) Mason Crest Pubs.

McGowan, Keith. Sexual Harassment. 1998. (Overview Ser.). (Illus.). 112p. (YA). (gr. 6-9). lib. bdg. 29.95 (978-1-56006-507-4(9) , LML00902-177867, Lucent Bks.) Thomson Gale.

Mucciolo, Gary. Everything You Need to Know about Birth Control. rev. ed. 2000. (Need to Know Library). (Illus.). 64p. (YA). (gr. 4-6). lib. bdg. 25.25 (978-0-8239-3301-3(6)) Rosen Publishing Group, Inc., The.

Peacock, Judith. Dating & Sex: Defining & Setting Boundaries. (Perspectives on Healthy Sexuality Ser.). pap. 8.95 (978-0-7368-8845-5(4)); 2000. (Illus.). 64p. (J). (gr. 4-6). lib. bdg. 23.93 (978-0-7368-0716-6(0)) Capstone Pr., Inc. (LifeMatters Bks.).

Polish, Daniel F. Drugs, Sex, & Integrity: What Does Judaism Say? 1998. (gr. 7-12). lib. bdg. 21.10 (978-0-613-90995-2(X)) Tandem Library Bks.

Roleff, Tamara L. Sex. 2001. (Teen Decisions Ser.). (Illus.). 170p. (YA). (gr. 10 up). lib. bdg. 36.20 (978-0-7377-0494-5(2) , Greenhaven Pr., Inc.) Thomson Gale.

Roleff, Tamara L., ed. Sex. 2001. (Teen Decisions Ser.). (Illus.). 170p. (YA). (gr. 10 up). pap. 24.95 (978-0-7377-0493-8(4) , Greenhaven Pr., Inc.) Thomson Gale.

Rose, Lyman Hinckley. Pure & Chased. 2004. ix, 86p. (978-1-55517-774-4(3)) Cedar Fort, Inc./CFI Distribution.

Ryder, Verdene. Human Sexuality: Responsible Life Choices. 2000. (gr. 7-12). lib. bdg. 40.85 (978-0-613-88169-2(9)) Tandem Library Bks.

Ryder, Verdene & Smith, Peggy B. Human Sexuality: Responsible Life Choices. 2004. 236p. (gr. 7-12). pap. 25.50 (978-1-59070-302-1(2)); 1998. (Illus.). 197p. (J). (gr. 8-12). 29.00 (978-1-56637-455-2(3)) Goodheart-Willcox Pub.

Sommers, Michael A. & Sommers, Annie Leah. Everything You Need to Know about Virginity. 2005. (Need to Know Library). (Illus.). 64p. (YA). (gr. 7-12). lib. bdg. 25.25 (978-0-8239-3115-6(3) , NTVIRG) Rosen Publishing Group, Inc., The.

The True Love Waits Youth Bible. 2004. (Illus.). 1294p. pap. 19.99 (978-1-55819-621-6(8)) B&H Publishing Grp.

Ware, Jim. No Apologies: The Truth about Life, Love & Sex. 1999. (Life on the Edge Ser.). 240p. (YA). (gr. 9-12). pap. 5.99 (978-1-56179-654-0(9)) Focus on the Family Publishing.

S

Wilcox, Brad. Growing Up: Gospel Answers about Maturation & Sex. 2000. (Illus.). xii, 132p. (J). pap. 10.95 (978-1-57345-821-4(X)) Deseret Bk. Co.

Williams, Mary E., ed. The Sexual Revolution. 2002. (American Social Movements Ser.). (Illus.). 240p. (J). 36.20 (978-0-7377-1052-6(7)); pap. 24.95 (978-0-7377-1051-9(9)) Thomson Gale. (Greenhaven Pr., Inc.).

SEXUAL ETHICS—FICTION

Cann, Kate. Grecian Holiday: Or, How I Turned down the Best Possible Thing Only to Have The. 2002. (gr. 7-12). lib. bdg. 14.15 (978-0-613-71506-5(3)) Tandem Library Bks.

—Grecian Holiday: Or, How I Turned down the Best Possible Thing Only to Have the Time of My Life. 2002. 352p. (J). (gr. 8 up). pap. 5.99 (978-0-06-447302-6(3)) HarperCollins Pubs.

—Sex. 2001. (Love Trilogy). 240p. (YA). (gr. 7 up). pap. (978-0-06-440870-7(1) , HarperTeen) HarperCollins Pubs.

Goobie, Beth. Hello, Groin. 2006. 224p. (YA). lib. bdg. 17.95 (978-1-55143-459-9(8)) Orca Bk. Pubs. USA.

Hamilton, Elizabeth L. Date with Responsibility. 2004. (Character-in-Action Ser.: No. 2). (Illus.). 384p. (YA). per. 19.95 (978-0-9713749-0-4(2) , Character-in-Action) Quiet Impact, Inc.

Johnson, Kathleen Jeffrie. The Parallel Universe of Liars. 2004. 240p. (YA). (gr. 9). reprint ed. pap. 5.99 (978-0-440-23852-2(8) , Laurel Leaf) Random Hse. Children's Bks.

Kleven, Sandy. The Right Touch: A Read-Aloud Story to Help Prevent Child Sexual Abuse. Bergsma, Jody Lynn, illus. 1998. (Jody Bergsma Collection). 32p. (ps-3). 15.95 (978-0-935699-10-4(4)) Illumination Arts Publishing Co., Inc.

Moore, Stephanie Perry. Totally Free, Vol. 2. 2002. (Laurel Shadrach Ser.: Vol. 2). 208p. (YA). pap. 6.99 (978-0-8024-4036-5(3)) Moody Pubs.

—Totally Free. 2002. (gr. 3-6). lib. bdg. 15.30 (978-0-613-90336-3(6)) Tandem Library Bks.

Ratcliffe, Jane. The Free Fall. rev. ed. 2001. (Illus.). 192p. (YA). (gr. 9-12). 16.95 (978-0-8050-6667-8(5) , Holt, Henry & Co. Bks. For Young Readers) Holt, Henry & Co.

Ruditis, Paul. Rainbow Party. 2005. 256p. (YA). (gr. 9 up). pap. 12.95 (978-1-4169-0235-5(X) , Simon Pulse) Simon & Schuster Children's Publishing.

SEXUAL HARASSMENT

Bouchard, Elizabeth. Everything You Need to Know about Sexual Harassment. rev. ed. 2001. (Need to Know Library). (Illus.). 64p. (YA). (gr. 4-6). lib. bdg. 25.25 (978-0-8239-3466-9(7)) Rosen Publishing Group, Inc., The.

Goodnough, David. Stalking. 2000. (Hot Issues Ser.). (Illus.). 64p. (YA). (gr. 6-12). lib. bdg. 27.93 (978-0-7660-1364-3(2)) Enslow Pubs., Inc.

McGowan, Keith. Sexual Harassment. 1998. (Overview Ser.). (Illus.). 112p. (YA). (gr. 6-9). lib. bdg. 29.95 (978-1-56006-507-4(9) , LML00902-177867, Lucent Bks.) Thomson Gale.

Paonessa, Mary. Growth & Development with Friends & School, 8 vols. 3rd ed. 2003. (Human Growth & Development Ser.). (Illus.). (J). (gr. 7 up). 112p. pap., tchr. ed. 15.00 (978-0-9711721-5-9(3) , 393); 91p. pap. (978-0-9711721-4-2(5) , 392) Paon Pubns.

Shaw, Victoria. Coping with Sexual Harassment & Gender Bias. 2005. (Coping Ser.). (Illus.). 192p. (YA). (gr. 7-12). lib. bdg. 26.50 (978-0-8239-3267-2(2) , COSEHA) Rosen Publishing Group, Inc., The.

Stanley, Debbie. Everything You Need to Know about Student-on-Student Sexual Harassment. 2005. (Need to Know Library). (Illus.). 64p. (YA). (gr. 7-12). lib. bdg. 25.25 (978-0-8239-3281-8(8) , NTSTHA) Rosen Publishing Group, Inc., The.

Tamar's Dilemma: An Overview of Sexual Exploitation. 2003. 32p. (YA). per. (978-0-9746327-0-4(8) , 1196490) Trammel, Crystal.

SEXUAL HARASSMENT—FICTION

Banting, Celia. I only said I was telling the Truth. 2006. 240p. (YA). per. 14.99 (***978-0-9786648-4-8(1)***) Wighita Pr.

Chambers, Aidan. This Is All: The Pillow Book of Cordelia Kenn. 2006. 816p. (J). (gr. 8-17). 19.95 (978-0-8109-7060-1(0) , Amulet Bks.) Abrams, Harry N. , Inc.

Goobie, Beth. Sticks & Stones. 2006. 96p. (YA). lib. bdg. 14.95 (978-1-55143-562-6(4)) Orca Bk. Pubs. USA.

West-Smith, Sandy. Who Will Teach Johnny. 2006. (J). (978-1-56167-914-0(3)) American Literary Pr.

—Who Will Teach Missy: The Difference Between Good Touches & Bad Touches? 2006. 24p. (J). pap. 9.95 (978-1-56167-913-3(5) , Shooting Star Edition) American Literary Pr.

Woodson, Marion. Charlotte's Vow. 2006. 144p. (J). pap., tchr. ed. 5.95 (978-0-88878-413-1(9) , Sandcastle Bks.) Dundurn Group, The CAN. *Dist:* Univ. of Toronto Pr.

SEXUALLY TRANSMITTED DISEASES

AIDS & Other STDs. 2001. (YA). (gr. 6-12). pap. 11.50 (978-0-8359-0766-8(X)) Globe Fearon Educational Publishing.

Breguet, Amy. Chlamydia. 2006. (Library of Sexual Health). (Illus.). 64p. (J). lib. bdg. (978-1-4042-0909-1(3)) Rosen Publishing Group, Inc., The.

Byers, Ann. Sexually Transmitted Diseases. 1999. (Hot Issues Ser.). (Illus.). 64p. (YA). (gr. 6-12). lib. bdg. 27.93 (978-0-7660-1192-2(5)) Enslow Pubs., Inc.

Cefrey, Holly. Syphilis & Other Sexually Transmitted Diseases. 2002. (Epidemics Ser.). (Illus.). 64p. (YA). (gr. 7-12). lib. bdg. 26.50 (978-0-8239-3488-1(8)) Rosen Publishing Group, Inc., The.

Connolly, Sean. STDs. 2002. (Just the Facts Ser.). (Illus.). 56p. (J). (gr. 6-8). lib. bdg. 25.64 (978-1-58810-681-0(0)) Heinemann Library.

Curran, Christine Perdan. Sexually Transmitted Diseases. 1998. (Diseases & People Ser.). (Illus.). 128p. (YA). (gr. 6-12). lib. bdg. 26.60 (978-0-7660-1050-5(3)) Enslow Pubs., Inc.

Egendorf, Laura. Sexually Transmitted Diseases. 2007. (At Issue Ser.). 128p. (gr. 10-12). 29.95 (***978-0-7377-1975-8(3)***); pap. 21.20 (***978-0-7377-1976-5(1)***) Thomson Gale. (Greenhaven Pr., Inc.).

Endersbe, Julie. Sexually Transmitted Diseases: How Are They Prevented? 1999. (Perspectives on Healthy Sexuality Ser.). (Illus.). 64p. (J). (gr. 4-6). lib. bdg. 23.93 (978-0-7368-0276-5(2) , LifeMatters Bks.) Capstone Pr., Inc.

Grapes, Bryan J., ed. Sexually Transmitted Diseases. 2001. (Current Controversies Ser.). (Illus.). 158p. lib. bdg. 36.20 (978-0-7377-0687-1(2)); (YA). (gr. 7-12). pap. 24.95 (978-0-7377-0686-4(4)) Thomson Gale. (Greenhaven Pr., Inc.).

Haerens, Margaret, ed. Sexually Transmitted Diseases. 2006. (Opposing Viewpoints Ser.). 244p. (YA). (gr. 10 up). pap. 24.95 (978-0-7377-3334-1(9)); lib. bdg. 36.20 (978-0-7377-3333-4(0)) Thomson Gale. (Greenhaven Pr., Inc.).

Hunter, Miranda & Hunter, William. Staying Safe: A Teen's Guide to Sexually Transmitted Diseases. 2004. (Science of Health Ser.). (Illus.). 128p. (J). (978-1-59084-852-4(7)) Mason Crest Pubs.

Kolesnikow, Tassia. Sexually Transmitted Diseases. 2003. (Diseases & Disorders Ser.). (Illus.). 112p. (J). (gr. 6-9). 32.45 (978-1-56006-910-2(4) , Lucent Bks.) Thomson Gale.

Little, Marjorie. Sexually Transmitted Diseases. 1999. (Twenty-First Century Health & Wellness Ser.). (Illus.). 106p. (YA). (gr. 7-11). 36.00 (978-0-7910-5528-1(0) , Chelsea Hse.) Facts On File, Inc.

McGraw-Hill Staff. Teen Health Course 3, Modules, Healthy Relationships & Sexuality. 5th ed. 2002. (Three-Level Middle School Health Ser.). (C). (gr. 8 up). 15.32 (978-0-07-826211-1(9) , 9780078262111) Glencoe/McGraw-Hill.

Michaud, Christopher. Gonorrhea. 2006. (Library of Sexual Health). (Illus.). 64p. (J). lib. bdg. (978-1-4042-0908-4(5)) Rosen Publishing Group, Inc., The.

Planned Parenthood Federation of America, Inc. Staff. The Condom. 2003. (YA). pap. 3.00 net. (978-0-934586-80-1(2)) Planned Parenthood Federation of America, Inc.

—Sexually Transmitted Infections: The Facts. 2003. (YA). pap. 3.00 net. (978-0-934586-82-5(9)) Planned Parenthood Federation of America, Inc.

Silverstein, Alvin, et al. The STDs Update. 2006. (Disease Update Ser.). (Illus.). 128p. (YA). (gr. 5 up). lib. bdg. 31.93 (978-0-7660-2484-7(9)) Enslow Pubs., Inc.

Slade, Suzanne. The Phases of the Moon. 2007. (Cycles in Nature Ser.). (Illus.). 24p. (J). (gr. 4-6). lib. bdg. 21.25 (978-1-4042-3488-8(8) , PowerKids Pr.) Rosen Publishing Group, Inc., The.

Whelan, Jo. Sexually Transmitted Diseases. 2001. (Health Issues Ser.). (Illus.). 64p. (YA). (gr. 6-8). lib. bdg. 28.54 (978-0-7398-4420-5(2)) Raintree.

Winters, Adam. Syphilis. 2006. (Library of Sexual Health). (Illus.). 64p. (J). (978-1-4042-0906-0(9)) Rosen Publishing Group, Inc., The.

Woods, Samuel G. Everything You Need to Know about STD (Sexually Transmitted Disease) rev. ed. 2000. (Need to Know Library). (Illus.). 64p. (J). (gr. 4-6). lib. bdg. 25.25 (978-0-8239-3280-1(X) , NTSTDS) Rosen Publishing Group, Inc., The.

Woods, Samuel O. Everything You Need to Know about STD (Sexually Transmitted Disease) rev. ed. 2005. (Need to Know Library). (Illus.). 64p. (YA). (gr. 4-6). lib. bdg. 25.25 (978-0-8239-3766-0(6)) Rosen Publishing Group, Inc., The.

WSTDTV: Being Informed Is the First Step to HIV/STD Prevention. 2004. (YA). cd-rom (978-0-9754754-8-5(7)) Academic Edge, Inc.

Yancey, Diane. STDs: What You Don't Know Can Hurt You. 2002. (Medical Library). (Illus.). 128p. (gr. 7 up). lib. bdg. 26.90 (978-0-7613-1957-3(3) , Twenty-First Century Bks.) Lerner Publishing Group.

SHACKLETON, ERNEST HENRY, SIR, 1874-1922

Armstrong, Jennifer. Shipwreck at the Bottom of the World: The Extraordinary True Story of Shackleton & the Endurance. Boughton, Simon, ed. 2000. 144p. (J). (gr. 5-7). 12.95 (978-0-375-81049-7(8) , Crown Books For Young Readers) Random Hse. Children's Bks.

—Shipwreck at the Bottom of the World: The Extraordinary True Story of Shackleton & the Endurance. 2000. (gr. 5-8). lib. bdg. 21.05 (978-0-613-30126-8(9)) Tandem Library Bks.

Calvert, Patricia. Sir Ernest Shackleton: By Endurance We Conquer. 2002. (Great Explorations Ser.). (Illus.). 80p. (J). 29.93 (978-0-7614-1485-8(1) , Benchmark Bks.) Cavendish, Marshall Corp.

Fine, Jil. The Shackleton Expedition. 2002. (Survivors Ser.). (Illus.). 48p. (J). (gr. 7-12). 24.00 (978-0-516-23904-0(X) , Children's Pr.) Scholastic Library Publishing.

—Shackleton Expedition. 2002. (gr. 7-12). lib. bdg. 15.25 (978-0-613-58800-3(2)) Tandem Library Bks.

Green, Jen. You Wouldn't Want to Be a Polar Explorer. 2001. (gr. 3-6). lib. bdg. 18.75 (978-0-613-44276-3(8)) Tandem Library Bks.

—You Wouldn't Want to Be a Polar Explorer! An Expedition You'd Rather Not Go On. Antram, David, illus. 2001. (You Wouldn't Want to Ser.). 32p. (J). (gr. 2-5). 28.50 (978-0-531-14601-9(4) , Watts, Franklin) Scholastic Library Publishing.

Hoena, B. A. Shackleton & the Lost Antarctic Expedition. Hoover, Dave & Barnett, Charles, illus. 2006. (Graphic Library). 32p. (J). (978-0-7368-5482-5(7)) Capstone Pr., Inc.

Hooper, Meredith & Robertson, M. P. The Endurance: Shackleton's Perilous Expedition in Antarctica. 2001. (Illus.). 32p. 16.95 (978-0-7892-0704-3(4)) Abbeville Pr., Inc.

Johnson, Rebecca L. Ernest Shackleton: Gripped by the Antarctic. 2003. (Trailblazers Biographies Ser.). (Illus.). 112p. (J). (gr. 5-9). 30.60 (978-0-87614-920-1(4)) Lerner Publishing Group.

Kimmel, Elizabeth Cody. Ice Story: Shackleton's Lost Expedition. 1999. (Illus.). 128p. (J). (gr. 4-6). tchr. ed. 19.00 (978-0-395-91524-0(4) , Clarion Bks.) Houghton Mifflin Co. Trade & Reference Div.

McCurdy, Michael. Trapped by the Ice! Shackleton's Amazing Antarctic Adventure. McCurdy, Michael, illus. 2002. (Illus.). 40p. (J). pap. 8.95 (978-0-8027-7633-4(7)) Walker & Co.

—Trapped by the Ice: Shackleton's Amazing Antarctic Adventure. 2002. (gr. 3-6). lib. bdg. 17.60 (978-0-613-75493-4(X)) Tandem Library Bks.

Penner, Lucille Recht. Ice Wreck. LaFleur, David, illus. 2004. (Stepping Stones Ser.). 48p. (J). (gr. k-3). pap. 3.99 (978-0-307-26408-4(4) , Random Hse. Bks. for Young Readers) Random Hse. Children's Bks.

Roop, Connie, et al. Escape from the Ice: Shackleton & the Endurance. 2001. (Hello Reader! Ser.). (Illus.). 48p. (J). (gr. 2-4). pap. 3.99 (978-0-439-20640-2(5) , Cartwheel Bks.) Scholastic, Inc.

Smith, Michael. Boss: The Remarkable Adventures of Ernest Shackleton, Heroic Antarctic Explorer. Brady, Annie, illus. 2005. (SPA.). 128p. pap. 12.95 (978-1-903464-57-1(9)) Collins Pr., The IRL. *Dist:* Dufour Editions, Inc.

White, Matt. Endurance: Shipwreck & Survival on a Sea of Ice. 2001. (Illus.). 64p. (J). pap. (978-0-7368-9500-2(0)); (gr. 4-5). lib. bdg. 22.60 (978-0-7368-4000-2(1) , Capstone High-Interest Bks.) Capstone Pr., Inc.

Worsley, Frank Arthur. Shackleton's Boat Journey: The Narrative from the Captain of the 'Endurance' 1998. (Illus.). 224p. (gr. 3). pap. 13.95 (978-0-393-31864-7(8) , Norton Paperbacks) Norton, W. W. & Co., Inc.

SHADES AND SHADOWS

see Shadows

SHADOW PANTOMIMES AND PLAYS

see Shadow Shows

SHADOW SHOWS

Adams, Elizabeth. Me & My Shadows: Shadow Puppet Fun for Kids of All Ages. l.t. ed. 2002. (J). spiral bd. 16.96 (978-1-888725-78-0(8) , 1-888725-78-8, MacroPrint-Books) Science & Humanities Pr.

Adams, Elizabeth & Banis, Bud. Me & My Shadows: Shadow Puppet Fun for Kids of All Ages. 2000. (Illus.). 73p. (J). per. 12.95 (978-1-888725-44-5(3) , Beach-House Bks.) Science & Humanities Pr.

Bryant, Jill. Making Shadow Puppets. 2002. (gr. 3-6). lib. bdg. 14.10 (978-0-613-87154-9(5)) Tandem Library Bks.

Bryant, Jill & Heard, Catherine. Making Shadow Puppets. Watson, Laura, illus. 2004. (Kids Can Do It Ser.). 40p. (J). (gr. 4-6). (978-1-55337-029-1(5)); (978-1-55337-028-4(7)) Kids Can Pr., Ltd.

Klutz Press Staff, creator. Shadow Games. 2005. (Illus.). 24p. (YA). (gr. 4-7). spiral bd. 9.95 (978-1-59174-160-2(2)) Klutz.

Lilly, Melinda. Me & My Shadow. 2006. (Rourke Discovery Library). (Illus.). 24p. (gr. 1-4). 14.95 (978-1-59515-403-3(5) , 1244274) Rourke Publishing, LLC.

Llewellyn, Claire. Shadow Play Pack of 6 American English Edition, 6 bks., Set. 2000. (Cambridge Reading Ser.). (Illus.). 12p. pap. 28.00 (978-0-521-79903-4(1)) Cambridge Univ. Pr.

SHADOWS

Bauer, David. Luz y Sombra. 2005. Tr. of Light & Shadow. (SPA., Illus.). 16p. (J). (gr. 1 up). lib. bdg. 15.93 (978-0-7368-4137-5(7)) Capstone Pr., Inc.

Berge, Claire. Whose Shadow Is This? A Look at Animal Shapes - Round, Long, & Pointy. Alderman, Derrick & Shea, Denise, illus. 2004. (Whose Is It? Ser.). 24p. (C). (gr. k-2). 22.60 (978-1-4048-0609-2(1)) Picture Window Bks.

Flux, Paul. Line & Tone. 2007. (Illus.). 32p. (J). (***978-1-4034-9630-0(7)***) Heinemann Library.

—Line & Tone (2nd Edition) 2007. (Illus.). 32p. (J). (***978-1-4034-9636-2(6)***) Heinemann Library.

Lilly, Melinda. Me & My Shadow. 2006. (Rourke Discovery Library). (Illus.). 24p. (gr. 1-4). 14.95 (978-1-59515-403-3(5) , 1244274) Rourke Publishing, LLC.

Madgwick, Wendy. Light & Dark. 1999. (Science Starters Ser.). (Illus.). 32p. (gr. k-4). pap. 7.95 (978-0-8172-5882-5(5)) Steck-Vaughn.

Montgomery, Rutherford G. Pekan the Shadow. Nenninger, J. D., illus. 2004. (Classic Ser.). 164p. (gr. 4-7). pap. 13.95 (978-0-87004-406-9(0)) Caxton Pr.

Otto, Carolyn B. Shadows. (Scholastic Science Readers Ser.). (Illus.). 32p. (J). (gr. k-1). 2001. pap. 3.99 (978-0-439-29583-3(1) , Scholastic Reference); 2000. (978-0-439-20548-1(4)) Scholastic, Inc.

—Shadows. 2001. (Scholastic Science Ser.). (Illus.). (J). (978-0-606-21415-5(1)) Tandem Library Bks.

Riley, Peter D. Light & Dark. Moller, Ray, photos by. 2002. (Everyday Science Ser.). (Illus.). 32p. (J). (gr. 1 up). lib. bdg. 23.33 (978-0-8368-3249-5(3)) Stevens, Gareth Inc.

Ring, Susan. Light & Shadow. 2003. (Yellow Umbrella Books). (Illus.). 16p. (J). (gr. 1). lib. bdg. 14.60 (978-0-7368-2020-2(5) , Pebble Bks.) Capstone Pr., Inc.

—Light & Shadow. 2003. (J). (978-0-7368-1712-7(3)) Yellow Umbrella Pr.

Royston, Angela. Light & Dark. (My World of Science Ser.). (Illus.). 32p. (J). (gr. k-2). 2002. pap. 6.95 (978-1-4034-0041-3(5) , 91485); 2001. lib. bdg. 21.36 (978-1-58810-242-3(4)) Heinemann Library.

Shaw, Gina. Shadows Everywhere. Holub, Joan, illus. 1999. (Hello Reader! Science Ser.). (J). 20.01 (978-0-590-52296-0(5)) Scholastic, Inc.

Swinburne, Stephen R. Guess Whose Shadow? 2003. (Illus.). 32p. (YA). (gr. k-2). 15.95 (978-1-56397-724-4(9)) Boyds Mills Pr.

—Guess Whose Shadow? Swinburne, Stephen R., photos by. 2003. (Illus.). 32p. (YA). (gr. k-2). pap. 9.95 (978-1-59078-017-6(5)) Boyds Mills Pr.

—Guess Whose Shadow? 2002. (ps-2). lib. bdg. 17.60 (978-0-613-79876-1(7)) Tandem Library Bks.

Waters, Jennifer. Bright Lights & Shadowy Shapes. 2002. (Spyglass Books). (Illus.). 24p. (J). (gr. 1 up). 18.60 (978-0-7565-0227-0(6)) Compass Point Bks.

SHADOWS—FICTION

Allen, Lisa & Sharp, Julis. Time for Bed - The Secret of Shadows: Shadow Theater Inside. Johnson, Vickie, illus. 26p. (J). (ps-2). pap. (978-1-56021-355-0(8) , 206) W.J. Fantasy, Inc.

Alvarez, Leticia Herrera. El Pais de las Sombras. Martinez, Enrique & Graullera, Fabiola, illus. 2003. (SPA.). 48p. (J). (gr. 3-5). pap. 7.95 (978-968-19-0535-4(0)) Santillana USA Publishing Co., Inc.

Asch, Frank. Moonbear's Shadow. Asch, Frank, illus. 2002. (Moonbear Ser.). (Illus.). (J). 14.47 (978-0-7587-6647-2(5)) Book Wholesalers, Inc.

—Moonbear's Shadow. Asch, Frank, illus. 2000. (Moonbear Ser.). 32p. (J). (ps-k). 6.99 (978-0-689-83519-3(1) , Aladdin) Simon & Schuster Children's Publishing.

—Moonbear's Shadow. 2000. (978-0-606-18625-4(5)); 1999. lib. bdg. 15.30 (978-0-8335-2452-2(6)) Tandem Library Bks.

Auerbach, Joshua. Baby Shadows, 1. Auerbach, Joshua, illus. 2003. (Illus.). 8p. (J). bds. 10.00 (978-0-9744928-0-3(9)) Baby Shadows.

Barry, Dave & Pearson, Ridley. Peter & the Shadow Thieves. rev. ed. 2007. 592p. (gr. 5 up). pap. 8.99 (***978-1-4231-0855-9(8)*** , Disney Editions) Disney Pr.

Berger, Barbara Helen. The Jewel Heart. 1998. (978-0-606-13537-5(5)) Tandem Library Bks.

Calvert, Deanna. Shadows. Lester, Mike, illus. 2004. (Rookie Reader Espanol Ser.). 24p. (J). (gr. k-2). pap. 4.95 (978-0-516-25840-9(0) , Children's Pr.) Scholastic Library Publishing.

—Las Sombras. Lester, Mike, illus. 2005. (Rookie Reader Espanol Ser.). (SPA & ESP.). 23p. (J). (gr. k-2). pap. 4.95 (978-0-516-24697-0(6) , Children's Pr.) Scholastic Library Publishing.

Cosgrove, Stephen. Snugg N. Flitter: Facing Your Fears. Arroyo, Fian, illus. 2004. (J). (978-1-58804-377-1(0)) PCI Educational Publishing.

Di Fiori, Larry. Jackie & the Shadow Snatcher. 2006. (Illus.). 32p. (J). (gr. k-3). 15.95 (978-0-375-87515-1(8) , Knopf Bks. for Young Readers) Random Hse. Children's Bks.

Di Fiori, Lawrence. Jackie & the Shadow Snatcher. 2006. (Illus.). 32p. (J). (gr. k-3). lib. bdg. 17.99 (978-0-375-97515-8(2) , Knopf Bks. for Young Readers) Random Hse. Children's Bks.

Drake, David. Cricket Loses His Shadow. 2002. (Cricket of Dew Drop Dell Ser.). (Illus.). 36p. (J). 3.49 (978-1-885631-63-3(4) , Family Of Man Pr., The) Hutchison, G.F. Pr.

Ewart, Franzeska G. Shadowflight. 2001. (Illus.). 81p. (J). pap. 7.50 (978-0-7497-4380-2(8)) Egmont Bks., Ltd. GBR. *Dist:* Independent Pubs. Group.

Freeman, Don. Gregory's Shadow. Freeman, Don, illus. (Illus.). 2005. (J). pap. 18.95 incl. audio compact disk (978-1-59112-488-7(3)); 2003. 28.95 incl. audio compact disk (978-1-59112-537-2(5)); 2003. pap. 39.95 incl. audio compact disk (978-1-59112-536-5(7)) Live Oak Media.

—Gregory's Shadow. Freeman, Don, illus. (Illus.). 32p. (J). (gr. k-2). 2002. pap. 6.99 (978-0-14-230196-8(5) , Puffin); 2000. 15.99 (978-0-670-89328-7(5) , Viking Juvenile) Penguin Group (USA) Inc.

Harcourt School Publishers Staff. Inside & Outside Together. 3rd ed. 2002. (Trophies English Language Learners Ser.). (Illus.). pap. 5.10 (978-0-15-327758-0(0)) Harcourt Schl. Pubs.

Hayward, Linda. Monster Bug. Palmisciano, Diane, illus. 2004. 32p. (J). lib. bdg. 20.00 (***978-1-4242-1097-8(6)***) Fitzgerald Bks.

Hedrick, Georgia. Share Me a Shadow. l.t. ed. 2002. 48p. (J). cd-rom 12.95 (978-0-9706612-7-2(4)) JetKor.

Jones, Elisabeth. Moonlight & Shadow. Coplestone, James, illus. 2002. 32p. (J). 15.95 (978-1-929927-42-5(8)) Ragged Bears USA.

Lewin, Betsy. Groundhog Day. 2000. (Hello Reader! Ser.). (Illus.). (J). pap. 10.01 (978-0-439-10802-7(0)) Scholastic, Inc.

Medearis, Angela Shelf. Lights Out! Tadgell, Nicole, illus. 2004. 32p. (J). lib. bdg. 15.00 (***978-1-4242-0221-8(3)***) Fitzgerald Bks.

Meomi (Firm) Staff, contrib. by. The Octonauts & the Sea of Shade. 2007. 36p. (J). (ps-3). 15.95 (***978-1-59702-010-7(9)***) Immedium.

Powell, Jillian. Henry & the Hand-Me-Downs. Worsley, Belinda, illus. 2005. 32p. (J). lib. bdg. 9.00 (***978-1-4242-0886-9(6)***) Fitzgerald Bks.

—Henry & the Hand-Me-Downs, Level 1. Worsley, Belinda, illus. 2005. (Lightning Readers Ser.). 32p. (J). (ps-k). pap., pap. 3.95 (978-0-7696-4209-3(8) , Gingham Dog Pr.) School Specialty Publishing.

—Henry y las Cosas Usadas, Level 1. Worsley, Belinda, illus. 2005. (Lightning Readers Ser.). 32p. (J). (ps-3). pap., pap. 3.95 (978-0-7696-4229-1(2) , Gingham Dog Pr.) School Specialty Publishing.

Scholastic, Inc. Staff, et al. Lights Out! Tadgell, Nicole, illus. 2004. (Just for You! Ser.). 32p. (J). (gr. k-1). pap. 3.99 (978-0-439-56868-5(4) , Teaching Resources) Scholastic, Inc.

Thorn, Nikki. A Shadow of My Own. 2002. 115p. (J). pap. 9.95 (978-0-595-21887-5(3) , Writers Club Pr.) iUniverse, Inc.

Welling, Peter J. Andrew McGroundhog & His Shady Shadow. 2001. (Illus.). 32p. (J). (gr. k-3). 15.95 (978-1-56554-711-7(X)) Pelican Publishing Co., Inc.

Zarraonandia, Thomas. Johnny Jingle. l.t. ed. 2002. 33p. (J). per. (978-1-59196-173-4(4)) Instantpublisher.com.

—Johnny Jingle. Zarraonandia, Thomas, illus. 2nd ed. 2003. (Illus.). 30p. (J). (ps-7). per. 20.00 (978-0-9741070-0-4(X)) Zarraonandia, Anne.

SHAKERS

Capek, Michael. A Personal Tour of a Shaker Village. 2001. (How It Was Ser.). (Illus.). 64p. (J). (gr. 4-6). lib. bdg. (978-0-8225-3584-3(X) , Lerner Pubns.) Lerner Publishing Group.

Lawson, Rose Mary. Shaker Paper Dolls. McGraw, Marjorie, illus. 1998. 16p. (Orig.). (J). (gr. 2-5). pap. 5.00 (978-0-9655018-2-8(5)) Knot Garden Pr.

Raschka, Chris. Simple Gifts. Raschka, Chris, illus. 2003. (Illus.). pap. 41.95 incl. audio (978-0-87499-642-5(2)); pap. 43.95 incl. audio compact disk (978-1-59112-604-1(5)) Live Oak Media.

Thorne-Thomsen, Kathleen. A Shaker's Dozen: Counting Book. Thorne-Thomsen, Kathleen, illus. Rocheleau, Paul, photos by. 2003. (Illus.). 27p. (J). (gr. k-13). reprint ed. 16.00 (978-0-7567-9041-7(7)) DIANE Publishing Co.

Turner, Ann. Shaker Hearts. Minor, Wendell, illus. 2006. 35p. (J). (gr. 4-8). pap. 11.00 ***978-1-4223-5856-6(9))** DIANE Publishing Co.

Turner, Ann Warren. Shaker Hearts. Minor, Wendell, photos by. 2002. (Illus.). 32p. (J). pap. 10.95 (978-1-56792-231-8(7)) Godine, David R. Pub.

SHAKESPEARE, WILLIAM, 1564-1616

Aliki. William Shakespeare & the Globe. Aliki, illus. (Illus.). 48p. (J). 2000. (gr. 4-7). pap. 6.99 (978-0-06-443722-6(1) , Harper Trophy); 1999. (gr. 7 up). lib. bdg. 17.89 (978-0-06-027821-2(8)) HarperCollins Pubs.

—William Shakespeare & the Globe. 2000. (gr. 3-6). lib. bdg. 15.25 (978-0-613-30192-3(7)) Tandem Library Bks.

Andrews, John F., contrib. by. Shakespeare's World & Work: An Encyclopedia for Students, 3 vols., Set. 2001. (Illus.). 750p. (YA). (gr. 4-7). lib. bdg. 375.00 (978-0-684-80629-7(0) , Charles Scribner's Sons) Thomson Gale.

Ashworth, Leon. William Shakespeare. (British History Makers Ser.). 32p. 2004. (Illus.). (YA). pap. 11.99 (978-1-84234-284-8(3) , Cherrytree Books); 2001. 19.99 (978-1-84234-083-7(2) , Cherrytree Books); 1999. (Illus.). pap. 12.95 (978-1-84234-030-1(1) , Evans Brothers, Limited) Evans Publishing Group GBR. *Dist:* Independent Pubs. Group.

Brassey, Richard. Shakespeare, Vol. 3. (Illus.). 24p. (J). pap. 8.99 (978-1-84255-228-5(7)) Dolphin Paperbacks GBR. *Dist:* Trafalgar Square Publishing.

Burdett, Lois. Much Ado about Nothing: For Kids. 2002. (gr. 3-6). lib. bdg. 17.60 (978-0-613-51175-9(1)) Tandem Library Bks.

Carew-Miller, Anna. William Shakespeare: Great English Playwright & Poet. 2002. (Great Names Ser.). (Illus.). 32p. (YA). (gr. 3 up). lib. bdg. (978-1-59084-157-0(3)) Mason Crest Pubs.

Chastain, Emma & SparkNotes Staff. Shakespeare. 2004. (SparkNotes 101 Ser.). (Illus.). 568p. pap. 14.95 (978-1-4114-0027-6(5)) Spark Publishing Group.

Chrisp, Peter. A Shakespearean Theater. Hook, Adam, illus. 2000. (Look Inside Ser.). 32p. (J). (gr. 4-7). lib. bdg. 25.69 (978-0-7398-2381-1(7)) Raintree.

Claybourne, A. & Treays, R. World of Shakespeare. 2004. (Internet-Linked Library of Science). (Illus.). 64p. (J). pap. 9.95 (978-0-7945-0014-6(5) , Usborne); lib. bdg. 17.95 (978-1-58086-391-9(4)) EDC Publishing.

Cromwell Productions Limited, prod. The Interactive Shakespeare Library. (Interactive Shakespeare Library). (YA). cd-rom 499.95 (978-0-7365-7147-0(7)) Films Media Group.

Davidson, Rebecca Piatt. All the World's a Stage. Lobel, Anita, illus. 2003. 32p. (J). 16.89 (978-0-06-029627-8(5)) HarperCollins Pubs.

Doder, Joshua. Time Traveler's Guide to Shakespeare's London. 2004. (Timetraveller's Guides). (Illus.). 96p. (J). pap. 8.99 (978-1-904153-10-8(0)) Watling St., Ltd. GBR. *Dist:* Independent Pubs. Group.

Dommermuth-Costa, Carol. William Shakespeare. 2001. (Biography Ser.). (Illus.). 112p. (J). (gr. 6-12). lib. bdg. 27.93 (978-0-8225-4996-3(4) , Lerner Pubns.) Lerner Publishing Group.

Dorling Kindersley Publishing Staff, ed. Shakespeare. 2004. (Dk Eyewitness Books Ser.). (Illus.). 72p. (J). 15.99 (978-0-7566-0723-4(X)) Dorling Kindersley Publishing, Inc.

Edcon Staff. The Tempest Worktext: Level 2. 2004. 72p. (YA). act. bk. ed. 9.95 (978-1-55576-327-5(8) , EDSC-201B) AV Concepts Corp.

Elgin, Kathy. Crime & Punishment. Hook, Adam, illus. 2004. (Changing Times Ser.). 32p. 26.60 (978-0-7565-0885-2(1)) Compass Point Bks.

—Daily Life. 2004. (Changing Times Ser.). (Illus.). 32p. (J). 26.60 (978-0-7565-0886-9(X)) Compass Point Bks.

—Health & Disease. 2004. (Changing Times Ser.). (Illus.). 32p. (J). 26.60 (978-0-7565-0887-6(8)) Compass Point Bks.

Fandel, Jennifer. William Shakespeare. 2003. (Voices of Poetry Ser.). (Illus.). 48p. 19.95 (978-1-58341-283-1(2) , Creative Education) Creative Co., The.

Gibson, Rex. The Language of Shakespeare. 2001. (Literacy in Context Ser.). (Illus.). 64p. (gr. 6-9). tchr. ed. 26.00 (978-0-521-80565-0(1)) Cambridge Univ. Pr.

Green, John & Negri, Paul. Great Scenes from Shakespeare's Plays. 2000. 64p. (J). pap. 3.95 (978-0-486-40960-3(0)) Dover Pubns., Inc.

Greenhill, Wendy & Wignall, Paul. Shakespeare: A Life. 2006. (Illus.). 32p. (978-1-4034-8609-7(3)) Heinemann Library.

—Shakespeare: Man of the Theater. 2000. (Illus.). 196p. (J). (gr. 8 up). lib. bdg. 28.50 (978-1-57572-282-5(8)) Heinemann Library.

Greenhill, Wendy & Wignall, Paul, contrib. by. Shakespeare: A Life. 2000. (Shakespeare Library). (Illus.). 32p. (J). lib. bdg. 21.36 (978-1-57572-287-0(9)) Heinemann Library.

Hilliam, David. William Shakespeare: England's Greatest Playwright & Poet. 2004. (Rulers, Scholars, & Artists of Renaissance Europe Ser.). (Illus.). 112p. lib. bdg. 31.95 (978-1-4042-0318-1(4)) Rosen Publishing Group, Inc., The.

Lamb, Charles & Lamb, Mary. Shakespeare Cuenta. (Advanced Reading Ser.). (SPA.). 136p. (gr. 5-8). 2003. (J). 11.95 (978-84-239-7082-7(5) , EC3412); 6th ed. (Illus.). (YA). 7.96 (978-84-239-8860-0(0)) Espasa Calpe, S.A. ESP. *Dist:* Lectorum Pubns., Inc., Planeta Publishing Corp., Lectorum Pubns., Inc.

Lebscky, Ibi. William. Cardoni, Paolo, illus. (Coleccion Seran Famosos).Tr. of Little Wim. Shakespeare. (SPA.). 28p. (J). (gr. 2-4). 10.36 (978-84-233-1663-2(7)) Ediciones Destino ESP. *Dist:* Lectorum Pubns., Inc.

Mannis, Celeste & Davidson, Mannis. Who Was William Shakespeare? John, Obrien, illus. 2006. (Who Was... ? Ser.). 112p. (J). (gr. 2-5). pap. 4.99 (978-0-448-43904-4(2) , Grosset & Dunlap) Penguin Group (USA) Inc.

Mayhew, James, illus. Shakespeare's Storybook: Folk Tales That Inspired the Bard. 2001. 80p. (J). (gr. 3 up). 19.99 (978-1-84148-307-8(9)) Barefoot Bks., Inc.

Mittelstaedt, Walt. A Student's Guide to William Shakespeare. 2005. (Understanding Literature Ser.). (Illus.). 192p. (J). lib. bdg. 27.93 (978-0-7660-2284-3(6)) Enslow Pubs., Inc.

Mulherin, Jennifer & Frost, Abigail. As You Like It. 2002. (Illus.). 31p. pap. (978-1-84234-043-1(3)) Evans Publishing Group.

—Richard III. 2003. (Illus.). 32p. (J). pap. 11.99 (978-1-84234-049-3(2)) Evans Publishing Group GBR. *Dist:* Independent Pubs. Group.

Nardo, Don. Great Elizabethan Playwrights. 2002. (Lucent Library of Historical Eras). (Illus.). 112p. (J). 32.45 (978-1-59018-017-4(8) , Lucent Bks.) Thomson Gale.

Nettleton, Pamela Hill. William Shakespeare: Playwright & Poet. 2004. (Signature Lives Ser.). (Illus.). 112p. (J). 30.60 (978-0-7565-0816-6(9) , 1240125) Compass Point Bks.

Page, Philip & Pettit, Marilyn. Richard III. 2005. (Illus.). 64p. pap. (978-0-340-88811-7(3)) Cambridge Univ. Pr.

Rosen, Michael. Shakespeare: His Work & His World. Ingpen, Robert R., illus. 2006. 96p. (J). (gr. 7-11). pap. 9.99 (978-0-7636-3201-4(5)) Candlewick Pr.

Ross, Stewart. William Shakespeare. 2004. (Illus.). 48p. (J). lib. bdg. 28.56 (978-0-7398-6630-6(3)) Raintree.

Ryan Patrick. Shakespeares Storybk. Mayhew James, illus. 2006. 0080p. 16.99 (978-1-905236-86-2(7)) Barefoot Bks., Inc.

Shakespeare, William. Richard II. 1999. (gr. 7-12). lib. bdg. 12.95 (978-0-613-17477-0(1)) Tandem Library Bks.

—Romeo & Juliet: The Inessential Shakespeare. Hort, John & Hort, Leela, eds. 2003. 52p. (J). (gr. 8-12). pap. 7.00 (978-0-948662-02-7(6)) Kabet Pr. GBR. *Dist:* Empire Publishing Service.

—Twelfth Night: The Inessential Shakespeare. Hort, John & Hort, Leela, eds. 2003. 52p. (YA). (gr. 8-12). pap. 7.00 (978-0-948662-00-3(X)) Kabet Pr. GBR. *Dist:* Empire Publishing Service.

Shakespeare, William, et al. Hamlet. (Classics Illustrated Ser.). (Illus.). 52p. (YA). pap. 4.95 (978-1-57209-004-0(9)) Classics International Entertainment, Inc.

Shuter, Jane. Shakespeare's Birthplace. 2003. (Visiting the Past Ser.). (Illus.). 32p. (J). (gr. 5-7). lib. bdg. 25.64 (978-1-58810-708-4(6)) Heinemann Library.

Stanley, Diane & Vennema, Peter. Bard of Avon: The Story of William Shakespeare. Stanley, Diane, illus. 1998. (Illus.). 48p. (J). (ps-3). pap. 7.99 (978-0-688-16294-8(0) , Harper Trophy) HarperCollins Pubs.

—Bard of Avon: The Story of William Shakespeare. Stanley, Diane, illus. 1998. (Illus.). (J). (ps-ps). lib. bdg. 15.30 (978-0-613-09937-0(0)) Tandem Library Bks.

Thrasher, Thomas E. William Shakespeare. 1998. (Importance of Ser.). (Illus.). 112p. (YA). (gr. 7-10). 27.45 (978-1-56006-374-2(2) , Lucent Bks.) Thomson Gale.

Turk, Ruth. The Play's the Thing: A Story about William Shakespeare. Harvey, Lisa, illus. 64p. (J). pap. 6.95 (978-1-57505-857-3(X)) Lerner Publishing Group.

Whiting, Jim. William Shakespeare. 2006. (Poets & Playwrights Ser.). (Illus.). 112p. (YA). (gr. 6-12). lib. bdg. 37.10 (978-1-58415-426-6(8)) Mitchell Lane Pubs., Inc.

Williams, Colleen Madonna Flood. My Adventure with Shakespeare. 2007. 44p. (J). 8.99 (978-1-59092-467-9(3) , Orchard Academy Pr.) Windstorm Creative.

World Microfilms Productions, prod. Shakespeare. (YA). cd-rom 99.95 (978-0-7365-0250-4(5)) Films Media Group.

SHAKESPEARE, WILLIAM, 1564-1616—ADAPTATIONS

Aagesen, Colleen & Blumberg, Margie. Shakespeare for Kids: His Life & Times: 21 Activities. 1999. (For Kids Ser.). (Illus.). 160p. (J). (gr. 4 up). pap. 16.95 (978-1-55652-347-2(5)) Chicago Review Pr., Inc.

Anderson, Peggy L. & Anderson, Judith D., adapted by. The Taming of the Shrew. 2000. (Streamlined Shakespeare Ser.). 96p. (J). (gr. 4-8). pap. 7.00 (978-1-57128-164-7(9)) High Noon Bks.

Birch, Beverley. Shakespeare's Tales. Lambert, Stephen, illus. 2003. 128p. pap. (978-0-340-79891-1(2) , Hodder Children's Books) Hodder Children's Division.

—Shakespeare's Tales. Lambert, Stephen, illus. 2002. 128p. (YA). (gr. 5). (978-0-340-79725-9(8) , Hodder & Stoughton) Hodder General Publishing Division.

Blackman, Malorie. Naughts & Crosses. 2005. (Illus.). 400p. (YA). (gr. 9 up). 15.95 (978-1-4169-0016-0(0)) Simon & Schuster Children's Publishing.

Burdett, Lois. Much Ado about Nothing for Kids. 2002. (Shakespeare Can Be Fun Ser.). (Illus.). 64p. (J). (gr. 2-3). lib. bdg. 19.95 (978-1-55209-411-2(1)); pap. 8.95 (978-1-55209-413-6(8)) Firefly Bks., Ltd.

—Romeo & Juliet for Kids. 1998. (Shakespeare Can Be Fun Ser.). (Illus.). 64p. (J). (gr. 2-7). pap. 8.95 (978-1-55209-229-3(1)); lib. bdg. 19.95 (978-1-55209-244-6(5)) Firefly Bks., Ltd.

Coville, Bruce. William Shakespeare's Romeo & Juliet. Nolan, Dennis, illus. 1999. 40p. (J). (ps-k). 17.99 (978-0-8037-2462-4(4) , Dial) Penguin Group (USA) Inc.

Coville, Bruce & Shakespeare, William. Hamlet. Gore, Leonid, illus. 2004. 40p. (J). (gr. 3). 18.99 (978-0-8037-2708-3(9) , Dial) Penguin Group (USA) Inc.

Fiedler, Lisa. Romeo's Ex: Rosalind's Story. rev. ed. 2006. 256p. (YA). 16.95 (978-0-8050-7500-7(3) , Holt, Henry & Co. Bks. For Young Readers) Holt, Henry & Co.

Garfield, Leon. Shakespeare Stories. Foreman, Michael, illus. 1998. 288p. (YA). (gr. 7-9). pap. 19.95 (978-0-395-86140-0(3)) Houghton Mifflin Co. Trade & Reference Div.

—Shakespeare Stories II. Foreman, Michael, illus. 2000. 288p. (YA). (gr. 7-7). pap. 17.00 (978-0-395-89109-4(4)) Houghton Mifflin Co. Trade & Reference Div.

Isaac, Megan Lynn. Heirs to Shakespeare: Reinventing the Bard in Young Adult Literature. 2000. (Young Adult Literature Ser.). 155p. (YA). (gr. 7-12). pap. 19.50 (978-0-86709-494-7(X) , 0494, Boynton/Cook) Heinemann.

King Lear. 1999. (YA). 9.95 (978-1-56137-923-1(9)) Novel Units, Inc.

King Lear. 2006. (Classics Ser.). (YA). per. (978-1-56254-853-7(0)) Saddleback Educational Publishing.

Klein, Lisa & Shakespeare, William. Ophelia. 2006. 336p. (YA). 16.95 (978-1-58234-801-8(4)) Bloomsbury Publishing.

Lamb, Charles. Tales from Shakespeare, 2 vols. (J). reprint ed. lib. bdg. 196.00 (978-0-7426-2085-8(9)) Classic Bks.

Lamb, Charles & Lamb, Mary. Tales from Shakespeare. Jolivet, Joelle, illus. 2007. 180p. 17.95 ***978-0-8109-9453-9(4)** , Abrams Image) Abrams, Harry N. , Inc.

—Tales from Shakespeare. 2007. 352p. (gr. 12). pap. 5.95 ***978-0-451-53064-6(0)** , Signet Classics) Penguin Group (USA) Inc.

Matthews, Andrew & Barrett, Angela. The Random House Book of Shakespeare Stories. 2003. (Illus.). 128p. (J). (gr. 3-7). 20.95 (978-0-375-81610-9(0) , Random Hse. Bks. for Young Readers) Random Hse. Children's Bks.

Much Ado about Nothing. 1999. (YA). 11.95 (978-1-56137-926-2(3)) Novel Units, Inc.

Mulherin, Jennifer & Frost, Abigail. Best Loved Plays of Shakespeare. 1999. (Illus.). 160p. (J). (gr. 5-9). 24.95 (978-1-887734-62-2(7)) Star Bright Bks., Inc.

—Macbeth. 2002. (Illus.). 32p. pap. (978-1-84234-060-8(3)) Evans Publishing Group.

—A Midsummer Night's Dream. 2002. (Illus.). 32p. (J). pap. (978-1-84234-058-5(1)) Evans Publishing Group.

—Romeo & Juliet. 2002. (Illus.). 32p. pap. (978-1-84234-057-8(3)) Evans Publishing Group.

Nesbit, E. The Children's Shakespeare. Klep, Rolf, illus. 2000. 117p. (J). (gr. 4-7). reprint ed. 12.95 (978-0-89733-485-3(X)) Academy Chicago Pubs., Ltd.

—Shakespeare's Stories for Young Readers. 2006. 80p. pap. 4.95 (978-0-486-44762-9(6)) Dover Pubns., Inc.

Olster, Fredi & Hamilton, Rick. Much Ado about Nothing: A Workbook for Students & Teachers. 1998. (Young Actors Ser.). 160p. (YA). (gr. 7-12). pap. 19.95 (978-1-57525-143-1(4)) Smith and Kraus Publishers, Incorporated.

Packer, Tina & Dillon, Diane. Tales from Shakespeare. De Marcken, Gail et al, illus. 2004. 192p. (J). pap. 24.95 (978-0-439-32107-5(7)) Scholastic, Inc.

Page, Philip & Petit, Marilyn, eds. Macbeth. Page, Philip, illus. 2005. (Picture This! Shakespeare Ser.). (Illus.). 64p. pap. 7.99 (978-0-7641-3140-0(0)) Barron's Educational Series, Inc.

—A Midsummer Night's Dream. 2005. (Picture This! Shakespeare Ser.). (Illus.). 64p. pap. 7.95 (978-0-7641-3142-4(7)) Barron's Educational Series, Inc.

—Romeo & Juliet. Page, Philip, illus. 2005. (Picture This! Shakespeare Ser.). (Illus.). 64p. pap. 7.99 (978-0-7641-3144-8(3)) Barron's Educational Series, Inc.

—Twelfth Night. 2005. (Picture This! Shakespeare Ser.). (Illus.). 64p. pap. 7.95 (978-0-7641-3147-9(8)) Barron's Educational Series, Inc.

Robert, Thando Bint, adapted by. Macbeth: Dual Language Set. 2004. (J). (ARA & ENG.). cd-rom (978-1-84444-469-4(4)); (BEN & ENG.). cd-rom (978-1-84444-470-0(8)); (CHI & ENG.). cd-rom (978-1-84444-471-7(6)); cd-rom (978-1-84444-472-4(4)); (ENG & FRE.). cd-rom (978-1-84444-473-1(2)); (ENG & SOM.). cd-rom (978-1-84444-474-8(0)); (ENG & TUR.). cd-rom (978-1-84444-475-5(9)); (ENG & URD.). cd-rom (978-1-84444-476-2(7)) Mantra Publishing, Ltd.

Rosen, Michael & Shakespeare, William. Shakespeare's Romeo & Juliet. Ray, Jane, tr. Ray, Jane, illus. 2003. 80p. (J). (gr. 7). 17.99 (978-0-7636-2258-9(3)) Candlewick Pr.

Sanderson, Jeannette, et al. Shakespeare. ed. 2003. 96p. pap. 13.95 (978-0-439-36601-4(1) , Teaching Resources) Scholastic, Inc.

Scott, James. The Taming of the Shrew: Side by Side. 2002. (YA). (gr. 7-12). pap., wbk. ed. 6.75 (978-1-58049-509-7(5) , DE08A) Prestwick Hse., Inc.

Shakespeare, William. As You Like It: Classicscript. Landes, William-Alan, ed. abr. ed. 2003. (Shakespeare Ser.: Vol. 2). 60p. (YA). (gr. 4-12). pap. 6.50 (978-0-88734-532-6(8)) Players Pr., Inc.

—A Midsummer Night's Dream. Camillo, Fred, illus. 1998. (Illustrated Classic Book Ser.). 61p. (J). (gr. 3 up). pap. 4.95 (978-1-56767-245-9(0)) Educational Insights, Inc.

—Othello. 1998. (978-0-606-13009-7(8)) Tandem Library Bks.

—Shakespeare. 2003. (Plays for Young People Ser.). 96p. pap. 16.95 (978-1-84002-313-8(9) , Oberon Bks.) Theatre Communications Group, Inc.

—Tales of William Shakespeare: The Comedies. Bryant, Laura J., illus. 2001. (Cover-to-Cover Timeless Classics Ser.). 83p. (J). pap. (978-0-7891-5288-6(6)); (gr. 1-4). lib. bdg. 13.95 (978-0-7807-9683-6(7)) Perfection Learning Corp.

—Twelfth Night: Classicscript. Landes, William-Alan, ed. abr. ed. 2003. (Shakespeare Ser.: Vol. 3). 68p. (YA). (gr. 4-12). pap. 6.50 (978-0-88734-530-2(1)) Players Pr., Inc.

—90-Minute Shakespeare. 2001. (J). 80p. pap. 9.95 (978-1-57525-238-4(4)); 9.95 (978-1-57525-290-2(2)) Smith and Kraus Publishers, Incorporated.

Shakespeare, William & Lester, Julius. Othello. 1998. 176p. (J). (gr. 7-12). pap. 5.99 (978-0-590-41966-6(8) , Scholastic Paperbacks) Scholastic, Inc.

Shakespeare, William & Williams, Marcia. Tales from Shakespeare. Williams, Marcia, illus. 2004. (Illus.). 40p. (J). (gr. 3-7). reprint ed. pap. 7.99 (978-0-7636-2323-4(7)) Candlewick Pr.

Shakespeare, William, et al. Tales from Shakespeare. Green Elliott, Elizabeth Shippen, illus. 1999. (Children's Classics Ser.). 384p. (J). 6.99 (978-0-517-20574-7(2) , Children's Classics) Random Hse. Value Publishing.

Tempest. 1999. (YA). 11.95 (978-1-56137-628-5(0)) Novel Units, Inc.

SHAKESPEARE, WILLIAM, 1564-1616—ANTONY AND CLEOPATRA

Mulherin, Jennifer & Frost, Abigail. Antony & Cleopatra. 2002. (Illus.). 31p. pap. (978-1-84234-045-5(X)) Evans Publishing Group.

SHAKESPEARE, WILLIAM, 1564-1616—AS YOU LIKE IT

Shakespeare, William. As You Like It: Classicscript. Landes, William-Alan, ed. abr. ed. 2003. (Shakespeare Ser.: Vol. 2). 60p. (YA). (gr. 4-12). pap. 6.50 (978-0-88734-532-6(8)) Players Pr., Inc.

SHAKESPEARE, WILLIAM, 1564-1616—CRITICISM AND INTERPRETATION

Gleed, Paul. Bloom's How to Write about William Shakespeare. 2007. (Bloom's How to Write about Literature Ser.). 256p. (YA). (gr. 9 up). 45.00 ***978-0-7910-9484-6(7)** , Chelsea Hse.) Facts On File, Inc.

The Merchant of Venice. 1998. 44p. (YA). 11.95 (978-1-58130-567-8(2) , NU5672SP) Novel Units, Inc.

Mulherin, Jennifer & Frost, Abigail. Hamlet. 2002. (Illus.). 32p. pap. (978-1-84234-033-2(6)) Evans Publishing Group.

—The Merchant of Venice. 2002. (Illus.). 32p. pap. (978-1-84234-059-2(X)) Evans Publishing Group.

—Twelfth Night. 2002. (Illus.). 32p. pap. (978-1-84234-047-9(6)) Evans Publishing Group.

Novy, Marianne L. Engaging with Shakespeare: Responses of George Eliot & Other Women Novelists. 1998. 286p. (J). reprint ed. pap. 24.95 (978-0-87745-650-6(X)) Univ. of Iowa Pr.

Palfrey, Simon. Doing Shakespeare: Arden Shakespeare. 2004. 224p. (C). pap. 19.99 (978-1-904271-54-3(5) , Arden Shakespeare, The) Thomson Learning EMEA, Ltd. GBR. *Dist:* CENGAGE Learning.

Shakespeare, William. Anthony & Cleopatra: Review. 1999. lib. bdg. 12.95 (978-0-613-64223-1(6)) Tandem Library Bks.

—Othello: Modern English Version Side-by-Side with Full Original Text. Holste, Gayle, ed. 2002. (Shakespeare Made Easy Ser.). 240p. (YA). pap. 6.95 (978-0-7641-2058-9(1)) Barron's Educational Series, Inc.

Solomon, Susan & Lipson, Greta B. Romeo & Juliet: Plainspoken. Lipson, Greta B., ed. Kropa, Susan, illus. 2003. 256p. (gr. 7-12). 18.99 (978-0-86653-283-9(8) , GA659) School Specialty Publishing.

SHAKESPEARE, WILLIAM, 1564-1616—FICTION

Blackwood, Gary. Shakespeare's Scribe. 2002. 272p. (J). pap. 6.99 (978-0-14-230066-4(7) , Puffin) Penguin Group (USA) Inc.

Blackwood, Gary L. The Shakespeare Stealer. 2000. 224p. (YA). (gr. 4-8). pap. 6.99 (978-0-14-130595-0(9) , Puffin) Penguin Group (USA) Inc.

—The Shakespeare Stealer. 2000. (ps-7). 216p. (J). lib. bdg. 14.15 (978-0-613-28638-1(3)); (978-0-606-17870-9(8)) Tandem Library Bks.

—Shakespeare's Scribe. Blackwood, Gary L., illus. 2002. (Illus.). (YA). 13.19 (978-1-4046-0844-3(3)) Book Wholesalers, Inc.

—Shakespeare's Scribe. 2002. (gr. 3-6). lib. bdg. 14.15 (978-0-613-59017-4(1)) Tandem Library Bks.

—Shakespeare's Spy. 288p. (J). 2005. (gr. 5-9). pap. 6.99 (978-0-14-240311-2(3) , Puffin); Vol. 3. 2003. (gr. 4-6). 16.99 (978-0-525-47145-5(6) , Dutton Juvenile) Penguin Group (USA) Inc.

S

Blackwood, Gary L. & Alcorn, Stephen. The Shakespeare Stealer. 1998. 208p. (J). (gr. 4-6). 16.99 (978-0-525-45863-0(8) , Dutton Juvenile) Penguin Group (USA) Inc.

Broach, Elise. Shakespeare's Secret. 2007. 272p. (J). pap. 5.99 (*978-0-312-37132-6(2)*) Square Fish.

Cheaney, J. B. The True Prince. 2004. 352p. (J). (gr. 5). reprint ed. pap. 6.50 (978-0-440-41940-2(9) , Yearling) Random Hse. Children's Bks.

—The True Prince. 2004. (gr. 5-8). lib. bdg. 14.15 (978-0-613-89784-6(6)) Tandem Library Bks.

Chute, Marchette. The Wonderful Winter. 2002. 256p. 12.95 (978-0-9714612-1-5(X)) Green Mansion Pr. LLC.

Cooper, Susan. King of Shadows. 2005. 192p. (J). pap. 2.99 (978-1-4169-0532-5(4) , Aladdin) Simon & Schuster Children's Publishing.

—King of Shadows. Clapp, John, illus. 192p. (J). (gr. 5-9). 2001. mass mkt. 5.99 (978-0-689-84445-4(X) , Aladdin); 1999. 16.00 (978-0-689-82817-1(9) , McElderry, Margaret K.) Simon & Schuster Children's Publishing.

—King of Shadows. l.t. ed. 2000. (Thorndike Press Large Print Juvenile Ser.). (Illus.). 246p. (J). (gr. 8-12). 21.95 (978-0-7862-2706-8(0)) Thorndike Pr.

Dakos, Kalli & Desmarteau, Alicia. Our Principal Promised to Kiss a Pig. DiRocco, Carl, illus. 2004. 32p. (J). (gr. 2-5). 15.95 (978-0-8075-6629-9(2)) Whitman, Albert & Co.

Deary, Terry. Top Ten Shakespeare Stories. Tickner, Michael, illus. 1999. (Top Ten Ser.). 192p. (J). (gr. 6-12). pap. 4.50 (978-0-439-08387-4(7)) Scholastic, Inc.

Durrant, George D. Shakespeare's Best Work: A Novel of Unexpected Family Ties & Uncommon Faith. 2003. 130p. (YA). pap. 10.95 (978-1-55517-709-6(3) , 77093, Bonneville Bks.) Cedar Fort, Inc./CFI Distribution.

Elise Broach. Shakespeare's Secret. l.t. ed. 2006. 350p. (J). 22.95 (978-0-7862-8735-2(7)) Thorndike Pr.

Fisher, Linda C. A Will of Her Own. 2006. (YA). pap. (978-0-88092-641-6(4)); lib. bdg. (978-0-88092-640-9(6)) Royal Fireworks Publishing Co.

Forward, Toby. Shakespeare's Globe: An Interactive Pop-Up Theatre. Wijngaard, Juan, illus. 2005. 14p. (J). (gr. 3). 19.99 (978-0-7636-2694-5(5)) Candlewick Pr.

Hassinger, Peter W. Shakespeare's Daughter. 2004. (Illus.). 320p. (J). (gr. 5 up). 15.99 (978-0-06-028467-1(6) , Geringer, Laura Book) HarperCollins Pubs.

Kositsky, Lynne. A Question of Will. 2001. (Out of This World Ser.). (Illus.). 144p. (YA). (gr. 7 up). pap. 5.95 (978-1-896184-66-1(9)) Roussan Pubs., Inc./Roussan Editeur, Inc. CAN. *Dist:* Orca Bk. Pubs. USA.

Lawlor, Laurie. The Two Loves of Will Shakespeare. 2006. 256p. (YA). 16.95 (978-0-8234-1901-2(0)) Holiday Hse., Inc.

Meyer, Carolyn. Loving Will Shakespeare. 2006. 272p. (YA). 17.00 (978-0-15-205451-9(0)) Harcourt Children's Bks.

Ortiz, Michael J. Swan Town: The Secret Journal of Susanna Shakespeare. 2006. 208p. (J). lib. bdg. 16.89 (978-0-06-058127-5(1)); (Illus.). 15.99 (978-0-06-058126-8(3)) HarperCollins Pubs.

Random House Value Publishing Staff, ed. Shakespeare, Illustrated Stories for Children. 1999. 6.99 (978-0-517-20430-6(4)) Random Hse. Value Publishing.

Ranulfo. Joker. 2006. 208p. (J). 15.99 (978-0-06-054158-3(X)); lib. bdg. 16.89 (978-0-06-054159-0(8)) HarperCollins Pubs. (Cotler, Joanna Books).

Schmidt, Gary D. The Wednesday Wars. 2007. 272p. (J). (gr. 5-9). 16.00 (978-0-618-72483-3(4) , Clarion Bks.) Houghton Mifflin Co. Trade & Reference Div.

Selfors, Suzanne. Saving Juliet. 2008. 256p. (YA). 16.95 (*978-0-8027-9740-7(7)*) Walker & Co.

Shakespeare, William. MacBeth. 2006. (J). (gr. 3-8). 24.21 (978-1-59961-117-4(1)) Spotlight.

Shanahan, Lisa. The Sweet, Terrible, Glorious Year I Truly, Completely Lost It. 2007. 304p. (YA). (gr. 7-10). 15.99 (*978-0-385-73516-2(2)*); lib. bdg. 18.99 (*978-0-385-90505-3(X)*) Random Hse. Children's Bks. (Delacorte Bks. for Young Readers).

Sutherland, Tui. This Must Be Love. 256p. (J). 2005. pap. 7.99 (978-0-06-056477-3(6) , Harper Trophy); 2004. (gr. 7 up). 15.99 (978-0-06-056475-9(X)); 2004. (gr. 7 up). lib. bdg. 16.89 (978-0-06-056476-6(8)) HarperCollins Pubs.

Swan. Stories from Shakespeare, Level 3. 2001. (Illus.). 64p. (C). pap. 9.00 (978-0-582-42694-8(4)) Longman Publishing Group.

SHAKESPEARE, WILLIAM, 1564-1616—HAMLET

Bloom, Harold. William Shakespeare's Hamlet. 2004. (gr. 7-12). lib. bdg. 18.75 (978-0-613-70829-6(6)) Tandem Library Bks.

Burdett, Lois. Hamlet for Kids. 2000. (Shakespeare Can Be Fun Ser.). (Illus.). 64p. (J). (gr. 2-4). pap. 8.95 (978-1-55209-530-0(4)); lib. bdg. 19.95 (978-1-55209-522-5(3)) Firefly Bks., Ltd.

—Hamlet for Kids. 2000. (gr. 3-6). lib. bdg. 17.60 (978-0-613-51149-0(2)); (Illus.). (J). (978-0-606-18136-5(9)) Tandem Library Bks.

Foster, Cass. Hamlet. 2000. (gr. 7-12). lib. bdg. 17.60 (978-0-613-80141-6(5)) Tandem Library Bks.

Foster, Cass, abr. Hamlet. 6th ed. 2000. (Sixty-Minute Shakespeare Ser.). (Illus.). 75p. (J). (gr. 8-12). pap. 8.99 (978-1-877749-40-7(0)) Five Star Pubns., Inc.

Holt, Rinehart and Winston Staff. Tragedy of Hamlet of Denmark with Connection. 2001. 16.80 (978-0-03-095769-7(9)) Holt, Rinehart & Winston.

Mulherin, Jennifer & Frost, Abigail. Hamlet. 2002. (Illus.). 32p. pap. (978-1-84234-033-2(6)) Evans Publishing Group.

Scott, James. Hamlet: The World's Great Drama - Drama Centered Language Arts Activities. abr. ed. 1999. 40p. (YA). (gr. 7). pap. 3.50 (978-1-58049-374-1(2) , GD09A) Prestwick Hse., Inc.

Shakespeare, William. Hamlet. Mueller, Jenny, ed. 2002. (Simply Shakespeare Ser.). (Illus.). 346p. pap. 8.99 (978-0-7641-2084-8(0)) Barron's Educational Series, Inc.

—Hamlet. Cruz, Ernesto R, illus. 2nd ed. 1998. (Illustrated Classic Book Ser.). 61p. (J). (gr. 3 up). reprint ed. pap. 4.95 (978-1-56767-257-2(4)) Educational Insights, Inc.

SHAKESPEARE, WILLIAM, 1564-1616—JULIUS CAESAR

Julius Caesar Study Guide. 2002. (Illus.). 48p. (YA). per. 17.95 (978-1-56254-606-9(6) , SP6066) Saddleback Educational Publishing.

Literature Connections English: Julius Caesar. 2004. (gr. 6-12). (978-0-395-77542-4(6) , 2-80111) McDougal Littell Inc.

Mulherin, Jennifer & Frost, Abigail. Julius Caesar. 2002. (Illus.). 31p. (J). pap. (978-1-84234-048-6(4)) Evans Publishing Group.

Ouellet, Jocelyne. Julien Cesar. Paquin, Marc-Etienne, illus. 2001. (Des 9 Ans Ser.: vol. 20). (FRE & ENG.). 111p. (J). 8.95 (978-2-922565-31-7(9)) Editions de la Paix CAN. *Dist:* World of Reading, Ltd.

Shakespeare, William, ed. Julius Caesar. 1998. 44p. (YA). 11.95 (978-1-56137-304-8(4) , NU3044SP) Novel Units, Inc.

SHAKESPEARE, WILLIAM, 1564-1616—KING HENRY IV

Shakespeare, William. Henry V. 2000. (Shakespeare Made Easy Ser.). (Illus.). (J). 13.60 (978-0-606-20700-3(7)) Tandem Library Bks.

SHAKESPEARE, WILLIAM, 1564-1616—KING HENRY V

Mulherin, Jennifer & Frost, Abigail. Henry V. 2002. (Illus.). 32p. pap. (978-1-84234-050-9(6)) Evans Publishing Group.

SHAKESPEARE, WILLIAM, 1564-1616—KING LEAR

Mulherin, Jennifer & Frost, Abigail. King Lear. 2002. (Illus.). 31p. pap. (978-1-84234-046-2(8)) Evans Publishing Group.

Shakespeare, William. King Lear. unabr. ed. 1998. (Wordsworth Classics Ser.). (YA). (gr. 6-12). 5.27 (978-0-89061-095-4(9) , R0959WW) Jamestown.

—King Lear. Fraser, Russell A., ed. 1998. 275p. (gr. 7-12). lib. bdg. 11.80 (978-0-613-18207-2(3)) Tandem Library Bks.

—King Lear: Classicscript. Landes, William-Alan, ed. 2003. (Shakespeare Ser.: Vol. 8). 71p. (YA). (gr. 6-12). pap. 6.50 (978-0-88734-537-1(9)) Players Pr., Inc.

—King Lear: The Quarto & the Folio Texts. 2000. (gr. 7-12). lib. bdg. 14.15 (978-0-613-64231-6(7)) Tandem Library Bks.

Shakespeare, William & SparkNotes Staff. King Lear. Crowther, John, ed. 2003. (No Fear Shakespeare Ser.). (Illus.). 320p. pap. 6.95 (978-1-58663-853-5(X)) Spark Publishing Group.

SHAKESPEARE, WILLIAM, 1564-1616—KING RICHARD II

Shakespeare, William. Richard II. 1998. (Oxford School Shakespeare Ser.). (Illus.). 168p. (YA). (gr. 6 up). 8.95 (978-0-19-832003-6(5)) Oxford Univ. Pr., Inc.

SHAKESPEARE, WILLIAM, 1564-1616—MACBETH

Burnett, Allan. Macbeth & All That. 2007. (Illus.). 128p. pap. 4.95 (*978-1-84158-574-1(2)*) Birlinn, Ltd. GBR. *Dist:* Interlink Publishing Group, Inc.

Cannoy, Lynne, illus. The Young Reader's Shakespeare: Macbeth. 2004. (Young Reader's Shakespeare Ser.). 80p. (J). 14.95 (978-1-4027-1116-9(6)) Sterling Publishing Co., Inc.

Cunningham, Patrick. How to Dazzle at Macbeth. 2004. (Illus.). 48p. pap. 30.00 (978-1-897675-93-9(3)) Brilliant Pubns. GBR. *Dist:* Parkwest Pubns., Inc.

Edcon Staff. Macbeth Worktext: Level 4. 2003. 72p. (YA). act. bk. ed. 9.95 (978-1-55576-331-2(6) , EDSC401B) AV Concepts Corp.

Foster, Cass, abr. Macbeth With Related Readings. 2000. (Sixty-Minute Shakespeare Ser.). (Illus.). 69p. (YA). (gr. 8-12). pap. 8.99 (978-1-877749-41-4(9)) Five Star Pubns., Inc.

The Great Gatsby. 2002. (Understanding Great Literature Ser.). 112p. (YA). (gr. 8-11). lib. bdg. 29.95 (978-1-56006-997-3(X) , Lucent Bks.) Thomson Gale.

Literature Connections English: Macbeth. 2004. (gr. 6-12). (978-0-395-77553-0(1) , 2-80122) McDougal Littell Inc.

Macbeth Study Guide. 2002. (Illus.). 48p. (YA). per. (978-1-56254-611-3(2) , SP6112) Saddleback Educational Publishing.

Mulherin, Jennifer & Frost, Abigail. Macbeth. 2002. (Illus.). 32p. pap. (978-1-84234-060-8(3)) Evans Publishing Group.

Shakespeare, William. Macbeth. 1998. 44p. (YA). 11.95 (978-1-56137-437-3(7) , NU4377SP) Novel Units, Inc.

—Macbeth. Tamai, Tony Leonard, illus. 2005. (Puffin Graphics Ser.). 176p. (J). (gr. 4). pap. 9.99 (978-0-14-240409-6(8) , Puffin) Penguin Group (USA) Inc.

Shakespeare, William, ed. Macbeth. 2004. (Classic Retelling Ser.). (Illus.). 176p. (gr. 6-12). 13.32 (978-0-618-03147-4(2) , 2-00141) McDougal Littell Inc.

—Macbeth. 2002. (gr. 7-12). lib. bdg. 17.60 (978-0-613-52701-9(1)) Tandem Library Bks.

—Macbeth. 2001. (English Ser.). (C). mass mkt. 9.95 (978-0-17-443525-9(8)) Thomson Wadsworth.

Shakespeare, William & Roth, Robert R., eds. Macbeth. 2002. (Simply Shakespeare Ser.). (Illus.). 288p. pap. 8.99 (978-0-7641-2086-2(7)) Barron's Educational Series, Inc.

SparkNotes Staff. Macbeth. Shakespeare, William & Crowther, John, eds. 2003. (No Fear Shakespeare Ser.). (Illus.). 240p. pap. 5.95 (978-1-58663-846-7(7)) Spark Publishing Group.

Watts, Cedric. Macbeth. Shakespeare, William, ed. 2001. 118p. audio compact disk (978-1-903342-15-2(5)) Wordsworth Educational.

SHAKESPEARE, WILLIAM, 1564-1616—MERCHANT OF VENICE

Lamb, Mary. The Merchant of Venice. Kallay, Dusan, illus. 1999. (J). 14.95 (978-962-7609-10-0(2)) Reader's Digest Children's Publishing, Inc.

The Merchant of Venice. 1998. 44p. (YA). 11.95 (978-1-58130-567-8(2) , NU5672SP) Novel Units, Inc.

Shakespeare, William. The Merchant of Venice: Texts & Contexts. 2000. (Classics Library). (ENG., Illus.). 128p. pap. (978-1-84022-431-3(2)) Wordsworth Editions, Ltd.

Shakespeare, William & SparkNotes Staff. The Merchant of Venice: Texts & Contexts. Crowther, John, ed. 2003. (No Fear Shakespeare Ser.). (Illus.). 256p. pap. 5.95 (978-1-58663-850-4(5)) Spark Publishing Group.

Swisher, Clarice. Readings on "The Merchant of Venice" 2000. (Literary Companion to American Literature Ser.). (Illus.). 224p. (YA). (gr. 9-12). pap. (978-0-7377-0178-4(1) , Greenhaven Pr., Inc.) Thomson Gale.

SHAKESPEARE, WILLIAM, 1564-1616—MIDSUMMER NIGHT'S DREAM

Foster, Cass, abr. A Midsummer Night's Dream. 2000. (Sixty-Minute Shakespeare Ser.). (Illus.). 75p. (YA). (gr. 6 up). pap. 8.99 (978-1-877749-37-7(0)) Five Star Pubns., Inc.

Greenhill, Wendy, contrib. by. A Midsummer Night's Dream. 2000. (Illus.). 32p. (J). (gr. 5-7). lib. bdg. 21.36 (978-1-57572-284-9(4)) Heinemann Library.

Greenhill, Wendy & Wignall, Paul. A Midsummer Night's Dream. rev. ed. 2006. (Shakespeare Library). (Illus.). 32p. (J). lib. bdg. 29.29 (978-1-4034-8607-3(7)) Heinemann Library.

Jurksaitis, Dinah. A Midsummer Night's Dream. Jurksaitis, Dinah & Beal, Duncan, eds. 2004. (Nelson Thornes Shakespeare Ser.). 144p. (YA). pap. 13.95 (978-0-7487-8604-6(X)) Nelson Thornes Ltd. GBR. *Dist:* Trans-Atlantic Pubns., Inc.

Mulherin, Jennifer & Frost, Abigail. A Midsummer Night's Dream. 2002. (Illus.). 32p. (J). pap. (978-1-84234-058-5(1)) Evans Publishing Group.

Shakespeare, William. A Midsummer Night's Dream. Camillo, Fred, illus. 1998. (Illustrated Classic Book Ser.). 61p. (J). (gr. 3 up). pap. 4.95 (978-1-56767-245-9(0)) Educational Insights, Inc.

—A Midsummer Night's Dream. 1999. (English Ser.). (C). mass mkt. 9.95 (978-0-17-443529-7(0)) Thomson Wadsworth.

Walker, Geof. William Shakespeare's 'A Midsummer Night's Dream' - a playscript for younger Students. 2006. 49p. pap. 19.45 (978-1-4116-4407-6(7)) Lulu.com.

SHAKESPEARE, WILLIAM, 1564-1616—MUCH ADO ABOUT NOTHING

Foster, Cass. Much Ado about Nothing. 2000. (gr. 7-12). lib. bdg. 17.60 (978-0-613-80143-0(1)) Tandem Library Bks.

Foster, Cass, abr. Much Ado about Nothing. 2000. (Sixty-Minute Shakespeare Ser.). (Illus.). 69p. (YA). (gr. 8-12). pap. 8.99 (978-1-877749-42-1(7)) Five Star Pubns., Inc.

Green, Lawrence. Much Ado about Nothing. Beal, Duncan & Jurksaitis, Dinah, eds. 2004. (Illus.). 160p. (YA). pap. 14.95 (978-0-7487-8603-9(1)) Nelson Thornes Ltd. GBR. *Dist:* Trans-Atlantic Pubns., Inc.

Mulherin, Jennifer & Frost, Abigail. Much Ado about Nothing. 2002. (Illus.). 31p. pap. (978-1-84234-035-6(2)) Evans Publishing Group.

Petit, Marilyn & Page, Philip. Livewire Shakespeare Much Ado About Nothing. 2005. (Illus.). 64p. pap. (978-0-340-88808-7(3)) Cambridge Univ. Pr.

SHAKESPEARE, WILLIAM, 1564-1616—OTHELLO

Edcon Staff. Othello Worktext: Level 5. 2002. (YA). act. bk. ed. 9.95 (978-1-55576-337-4(5) , EDSC-501B) AV Concepts Corp.

Nardo, Don. Readings on "Othello" 2000. (Literary Companion to American Literature Ser.). (Illus.). 190p. (YA). (gr. 9-12). pap. 22.45 (978-0-7377-0186-9(2) , Greenhaven Pr., Inc.) Thomson Gale.

Shakespeare, William. Othello. 1998. (978-0-606-13009-7(8)) Tandem Library Bks.

—Othello: Classicscript. Landes, William Alan, ed. abr. ed. 2003. (Shakespeare Ser.: Vol. 9). 64p. (YA). (gr. 4-12). pap. 6.50 (978-0-88734-538-8(7)) Players Pr., Inc.

—Othello: Modern English Version Side-by-Side with Full Original Text. Holste, Gayle, ed. 2002. (Shakespeare Made Easy Ser.). 240p. (YA). pap. 6.95 (978-0-7641-2058-9(1)) Barron's Educational Series, Inc.

Shakespeare, William & Lester, Julius. Othello. 1998. 176p. (J). (gr. 7-12). pap. 5.99 (978-0-590-41966-6(8) , Scholastic Paperbacks) Scholastic, Inc.

SHAKESPEARE, WILLIAM, 1564-1616—QUOTATIONS

Pollinger, Gina. Treasury of Shakespeare's Verse. 2000. (J). (978-0-606-19438-9(X)) Tandem Library Bks.

Shakespeare, William. A Treasury of Shakespeare's Verse. Pollinger, Gina, ed. Clark, Emma Chichester, illus. 2006. 96p. (J). (gr. 4-8). reprint ed. pap. 12.00 (978-1-4223-5444-5(X)) DIANE Publishing Co.

SHAKESPEARE, WILLIAM, 1564-1616—ROMEO AND JULIET

Burdett, Lois. Romeo & Juliet for Kids. 1998. (Shakespeare Can Be Fun Ser.). (Illus.). 64p. (J). (gr. 2-7). pap. 8.95 (978-1-55209-229-3(1)) Firefly Bks., Ltd.

Foster, Cass. Romeo & Juliet. 2000. (gr. 7-12). lib. bdg. 17.60 (978-0-613-80041-9(9)) Tandem Library Bks.

Foster, Cass, abr. Romeo & Juliet. 2000. (Sixty-Minute Shakespeare Ser.). (Illus.). 65p. (YA). (gr. 8-12). pap. 8.99 (978-1-877749-38-4(9)) Five Star Pubns., Inc.

Greenhill, Wendy, contrib. by. Romeo & Juliet. 2000. (Shakespeare Library). (Illus.). 32p. (J). lib. bdg. 21.36 (978-1-57572-285-6(2)) Heinemann Library.

Greenhill, Wendy & Wignall, Paul. Romeo & Juliet. rev. ed. 2006. (Shakespeare Library). (Illus.). 32p. (J). lib. bdg. 29.29 (978-1-4034-8608-0(5)) Heinemann Library.

Larousse Mexico Staff, ed. Romeo y Julieta. 2004. (Encuentro Con la Lectura Ser.). (SPA., Illus.). 48p. (gr. 4-9). pap. 6.50 (978-970-22-0530-2(1)) Larousse, Ediciones, S. A. de C. V. MEX. *Dist:* Houghton Mifflin Co. Trade & Reference Div.

McKeown, Adam & Shakespeare, William. Romeo & Juliet. 2004. (Young Reader's Shakespeare Ser.). (Illus.). 80p. (J). 14.95 (978-1-4027-0004-0(0)) Sterling Publishing Co., Inc.

Mulherin, Jennifer & Frost, Abigail. Romeo & Juliet. 2002. (Illus.). 32p. pap. (978-1-84234-057-8(3)) Evans Publishing Group.

Shakespeare, William. Romeo & Juliet. Mueller, Jenny, ed. 2002. (Simply Shakespeare Ser.). (Illus.). 288p. pap. 8.99 (978-0-7641-2085-5(9)) Barron's Educational Series, Inc.

—Romeo & Juliet. Redondo, Nestor, illus. 2nd ed. 1998. (Illustrated Classic Book Ser.). 61p. (J). (gr. 3 up). reprint ed. pap. 4.95 (978-1-56767-269-5(8)) Educational Insights, Inc.

—Romeo & Juliet. 2004. (Classic Retelling Ser.). (Illus.). 176p. (J). (gr. 6-12). 13.32 (978-0-618-03146-7(4) , 2-00140) McDougal Littell Inc.

—Romeo & Juliet. 2004. (Interfact Shakespeare Ser.). (Illus.). 112/144p. (J). (gr. 6-10). pap. 19.95 incl. cd-rom (978-1-58728-383-3(2) , Two Can Publishing) T&N Children's Publishing.

—Romeo & Juliet. Watts, Cedric, ed. 2000. (ENG., Illus.). 160p. pap. (*978-1-84022-433-7(9)*) Wordsworth Editions, Ltd.

Shakespeare, William & McCallum, Alistair. Romeo & Juliet. 2000. (Oxford Bookworms Playscripts Ser.). (Illus.). 6.50 (978-0-19-422852-7(5)) Oxford Univ. Pr., Inc.

Shakespeare, William & SparkNotes Staff. Romeo & Juliet. Crowther, John, ed. 2003. (No Fear Shakespeare Ser.). (Illus.). 304p. pap. 5.95 (978-1-58663-845-0(9)) Spark Publishing Group.

Shakespeare, William & Watts, Cedric. Romeo & Juliet. 2001. 160p. audio compact disk (978-1-903342-16-9(3)) Wordsworth Educational.

Shakespeare, William, et al. Romeo & Juliet. 1999. (Literature Made Easy Ser.). (Illus.). 96p. pap. 5.95 (978-0-7641-0832-7(8)) Barron's Educational Series, Inc.

Thrasher, Thomas E. Romeo & Juliet. 2001. (Understanding Great Literature Ser.). (Illus.). 112p. (J). (gr. 8-11). lib. bdg. 27.45 (978-1-56006-787-0(X) , Lucent Bks.) Thomson Gale.

SHAKESPEARE, WILLIAM, 1564-1616—STAGE HISTORY

Aliki. William Shakespeare & the Globe. 2000. (J). (978-0-606-20008-0(8)) Tandem Library Bks.

Chrisp, Peter. Welcome to the Globe! The Story of Shakespeare's Theater. Martin, Linda, ed. 2000. (Readers Ser.). (Illus.). 48p. (J). (gr. 3-5). pap. 3.99 (978-0-7894-6640-2(6)) Dorling Kindersley Publishing, Inc.

—Welcome to the Globe! The Story of Shakespeare's Theater. 2000. (Eyewitness Readers Ser.). (J). (978-0-606-20130-8(0)) Tandem Library Bks.

—Welcome to the Globe! the Story of Shakespeare's Theater. 2000. (gr. k-3). lib. bdg. 11.80 (978-0-613-33212-5(1)) Tandem Library Bks.

Chrisp, Peter & Dorling Kindersley Publishing Staff. Welcome to the Globe! The Story of Shakespeare's Theater. 2000. (Eyewitness Readers). (Illus.). 48p. (J). (gr. 2-4). 12.99 (978-0-7894-6641-9(4)) Dorling Kindersley Publishing, Inc.

Greenhill, Wendy. Shakespeare's Theater. 2006. (Illus.). 32p. (978-1-4034-8610-3(7)) Heinemann Library.

Greenhill, Wendy, contrib. by. Shakespeare's Theater. 2000. (Illus.). 32p. (J). lib. bdg. 21.36 (978-1-57572-286-3(0)) Heinemann Library.

Ross, Stewart. Look Around a Shakespearean Theater. 2007. (*978-1-84193-722-9(3)*) Smart Apple Media.

SHAKESPEARE, WILLIAM, 1564-1616—TAMING OF THE SHREW

Lamb, Mary. The Taming of the Shrew. Urdiales, Alberto, illus. 1999. (J). 14.95 (978-962-7609-09-4(9)) Reader's Digest Children's Publishing, Inc.

Mulherin, Jennifer & Frost, Abigail. The Taming of the Shrew. 2001. (Illus.). 32p. (J). pap. 11.99 (978-1-84234-051-6(4)) Evans Publishing Group GBR. *Dist:* Independent Pubs. Group.

SHAKESPEARE, WILLIAM, 1564-1616—TEMPEST

Burningham. The Tempest. abr. ed. 1998. (Graphic Shakespeare Ser.). (Illus.). 72p. pap., stu. ed. 7.99 (978-0-237-51910-0(0) , Evans Brothers, Limited) Evans Publishing Group GBR. *Dist:* Independent Pubs. Group.

Mulherin, Jennifer & Frost, Abigail. The Tempest. 2002. (Illus.). 32p. pap. (978-1-84234-044-8(1)) Evans Publishing Group.

Shakespeare, William. The Tempest. Ermitage, Kathleen, ed. 2002. (Simply Shakespeare Ser.). (Illus.). 288p. pap. 8.99 (978-0-7641-2087-9(5)) Barron's Educational Series, Inc.

—The Tempest. 2002. (gr. 7-12). lib. bdg. 17.60 (978-0-613-52731-6(3)) Tandem Library Bks.

The Tempest Study Guide. 2003. (Illus.). 48p. (YA). per. 17.95 (978-1-56254-639-7(2) , SP6392) Saddleback Educational Publishing.

Walker, Geof. William Shakespeare's 'the Tempest' - a playscript for younger Students. 2006. 40p. pap. 19.46 (978-1-4116-7138-6(4)) Lulu.com.

SHAKESPEARE, WILLIAM, 1564-1616—TWELFTH NIGHT

Burningham. Twelfth Night. abr. ed. 1998. (Graphic Shakespeare Ser.). (Illus.). 64p. pap., stu. ed. 8.99 (978-0-237-51909-4(7) , Evans Brothers, Limited) Evans Publishing Group GBR. *Dist:* Independent Pubs. Group.

Foster, Cass. Twelfth Night. 2000. (gr. 7-12). lib. bdg. 17.60 (978-0-613-80042-6(7)) Tandem Library Bks.

Foster, Cass, abr. Twelfth Night. 6th ed. 2000. (Sixty-Minute Shakespeare Ser.). (Illus.). 75p. (J). (gr. 8-12). pap. 8.99 (978-1-877749-39-1(7)) Five Star Pubns., Inc.

King, Neil, ed. Twelfth Night. 1998. (Illus.). 96p. pap. 21.00 (978-0-7487-3480-1(5)) State Mutual Bk. & Periodical Service, Ltd.

Shakespeare, William. Twelfth Night. Higgins, Fitzgerald, ed. 2002. (Simply Shakespeare Ser.). (Illus.). 288p. pap. 8.95 (978-0-7641-2088-6(3)) Barron's Educational Series, Inc.

—Twelfth Night: Or, What You Will. unabr. ed. 1998. (Wordsworth Classics Ser.). (YA). (gr. 6-12). 5.27 (978-0-89061-010-7(X) , R010XWW) Jamestown.

Walker, Geof. William Shakespeare's 'Twelfth Night' - a playscript for younger Students. 2006. 52p. pap. 19.51 (978-1-4116-7137-9(6)) Lulu.com.

SHAPE

see Size and Shape

SHARES OF STOCK

see Stocks

SHARING—FICTION

Ahmed, Said Salah. The Lion's Share/Qayb Libaax: A Somali Folktale. Dupre, Kelly, illus. 2006. 32p. (J). (ps-3). pap. 7.95 (*978-1-931016-13-1(5)) Minnesota Humanities Commission.

Albee, Sarah. One for Me, One for You: A Book about Sharing. Craig, Karen, illus. 2006. (Blue's Clues Ser.). 24p. (J). pap. 3.99 (978-1-4169-1300-9(9) , Simon Spotlight/Nickelodeon) Simon & Schuster Children's Publishing.

Alberts, Katharine O. Boo on the Loose. 2006. (J). 14.00 (978-0-8059-7071-5(1)) Dorrance Publishing Co., Inc.

Alexander, Martha. I Sure Am Glad to See You, Blackboard Bear. Alexander, Martha, illus. 2nd rev. ed. 2004. (Illus.). 30p. (J). (gr. k-3). reprint ed. 11.00 (978-0-7567-7153-9(6)) DIANE Publishing Co.

Becker, Shelly. Mine! Mine! Mine! Takahashi, Hideko, illus. 2006. 32p. (J). 14.95 (978-1-4027-2538-8(8)) Sterling Publishing Co., Inc.

Bethers, Linda, retold by. Christmas Oranges. 2004. 13p. pap. 3.95 (978-1-57734-546-6(0) , 01114387) Covenant Communications, Inc.

Bodden, Michelle, adapted by. Obara the Gatekeeper. 2007. (J). 14.95 (*978-0-9753089-1-2(2)) Water Daughter Publishing.

Brimner, Larry Dane. Everybody's Best Friend. 2002. (gr. k-3). lib. bdg. 14.10 (978-0-613-59470-7(3)) Tandem Library Bks.

Bryan-Brown, Kim. The Leaf That Was Left. Curren, Cindy, illus. l.t. ed. 2006. 32p. (J). 16.95 (978-0-9772564-0-2(5)) Them Potatoes.

Carmi, Giora. A Circle of Friends. Carmi, Giora, illus. 2003. (Illus.). 40p. (J). 15.95 (978-1-932065-00-8(8)) Star Bright Bks., Inc.

Carmi, Giora, illus. A Circle of Friends. 2006. 40p. pap. 5.95 (978-1-59572-060-3(X)) Star Bright Bks., Inc.

Cohen, Miriam. Mine! A Backpack Baby Story. 2005. (ENG & SPA., Illus.). 12p. (J). (ps-ps). per. 5.95 (978-1-59572-019-1(7)) Star Bright Bks., Inc.

Cooper, Helen. Pumpkin Soup. 2005. (Illus.). 32p. (J). (ps-ps). pap. 6.95 (978-0-374-46031-0(0) , Farrar, Straus & Giroux (BYR)) Farrar, Straus & Giroux.

Cosgrove, Stephen. Big Bubba Bigg, Jr: Dealing with Bullies. Arroyo, Fian, illus. 2004. (J). (978-1-58804-352-8(5)) PCI Educational Publishing.

Coxon, Michele. It's Mine. 2002. (Illus.). 16p. (J). 13.95 (978-1-903285-05-3(4)); pap. 5.95 (978-1-903285-04-6(6)) Happy Cat Bks. GBR. *Dist:* Star Bright Bks., Inc.

Dalmatian Press Staff. Sesame Street Big Steps for Little Monsters Treasury. 2005. (Illus.). 80p. (J). 4.99 (978-1-4037-1041-3(4)) Dalmatian Pr.

Dixon, Annabelle. Joe's Car: A Book about Friendship. Archbold, Tim, illus. 2004. (Making Good Choices Ser.). 24p. (J). (gr. k-3). 22.60 (978-1-4048-0662-7(8)) Picture Window Bks.

Dooley, Phyllis & Duncan, Alice Faye. Christmas Soup. Gilchrist, Jan Spivey, illus. 2005. 32p. (J). (ps-3). 15.99 (978-0-310-70930-5(X)) Zonderkidz.

Exclaim Entertainment. It's Fun to Share. 2007. (BOZ#8482; Ser.). 14p. (J). 4.99 (*978-0-310-71405-7(2)) Zonderkidz.

Fanning, Tena. Booger Boogie. 2007. 32p. (ps-3). 14.95 (*978-1-933721-13-2(8)) Playdate Kids Publishing.

Fielder, Barbara L. & Broady, Brianna. Missy, the Kitty, Learns about Sharing. (Illus.). 13p. (J). 6.95 (978-0-9639986-2-0(5)) Fielder Group.

Freed, Shirley & Moon, Louise. I Share My Toys. Morelan, Bill, ed. Harrell, Rob, illus. 2003. 8p. (J). (-k). pap. 3.99 (978-1-58938-100-1(9)) Concerned Communications.

Fuller, Bob. Tea for Two. 2007. (Paddywhack Lane Ser.). 24p. (J). pap. 3.99 (978-0-448-44509-0(3) , Grosset & Dunlap) Penguin Group (USA) Inc.

Gibbs, Lynne. Ping Won't Share. Mitchell, Melanie, illus. 2003. (Growing Pains Ser.). 32p. (J). pap. 4.95 (978-1-57768-927-0(5)); 12.95 (978-1-57768-480-0(X)) School Specialty Publishing. (Gingham Dog Pr.).

Glassman, Jackie. Berry Best Friends' Picnic. 2003. (gr. k-3). lib. bdg. 11.80 (978-0-613-64020-6(9)) Tandem Library Bks.

Goodspeed, Judy. Perky Turkey Finds a Friend. 2006. (Illus.). 24p. (J). lib. bdg. 24.95 (978-0-9778651-2-3(6)) Dragonfly Publishing, Inc.

Hallinan, P. K. Let's Play As a Team. 2003. (Illus.). 28p. (J). 7.95 (978-0-8249-5452-9(1)) Ideals Pubns.

Hamilton Geller, Diana. Simon Says. Finger, Matthew, illus. 2000. 16p. (J). pap. 5.95 (978-1-891846-23-6(X)) Business Word, The.

Hamilton, Richard & Williams, Sophy. Polly's Picnic. 2003. (Illus.). 32p. (J). (ps-2). 16.95 (978-1-58234-819-3(7) , Bloomsbury Children) Bloomsbury Publishing.

Harrington, Sean P. Patterson & the Great Green Greedy Galumpus. 2000. (Illus.). 20p. (J). (gr. k-4). pap. 10.95 (978-0-9672290-2-7(2)) Harrington, Denis J. Pub.

Harris, Tumeka. The Goody Bag. Sea Breeze Productions, ed. Miller, Linzi, illus. 2006. 36p. (J). 14.95 (978-0-9769366-2-6(3)) Volare, LLC.

Horowitz, Alena Netia. The Tlytiettlym Tree. Horowitz, Alena Netia & De La Fuente, Mary, illus. l.t. ed. 2003. 64p. (J). per. 12.95 (978-0-923550-42-4(9)) Tetrahedron Publishing LLC.

Hughes, Shirley. Annie Rose Is My Little Sister. Hughes, Shirley, illus. 2003. (Illus.). 32p. (J). (ps-2). 15.99 (978-0-7636-1959-6(0)) Candlewick Pr.

Hulme, Joy N. Mary Clare Likes to Share: A Math Reader. Rockwell, Lizzy, illus. 2006. (Step into Reading Ser.). 32p. (J). (ps-2). lib. bdg. 11.99 (978-0-375-93421-6(9)); 3.99 (978-0-375-83421-9(4)) Random Hse. Children's Bks. (Random Hse. Bks. for Young Readers).

Idle, Molly Schaar. Emma's Gift. 2004. (Illus.). 32p. bds. 14.00 (978-0-687-02294-6(0)) Abingdon Pr.

Jaekel, Susan M., illus. Stone Soup: A Tale about Sharing. 2006. (J). (978-1-59939-080-2(9) , Reader's Digest Young Families, Inc.) Reader's Digest Children's Publishing, Inc.

Kittinger, Jo S. A Lunch with Punch. 2004. (Rookie Reader Espanol Ser.). (Illus.). 31p. (J). (gr. k-2). pap. 4.95 (978-0-516-27785-1(5) , Children's Pr.) Scholastic Library Publishing.

—A Lunch with Punch. Medoff, Jack, illus. 2003. (Rookie Reader - Level B Ser.). 32p. (J). 19.50 (978-0-516-22879-2(X) , Children's Pr.) Scholastic Library Publishing.

Kortepeter, Paul. Oliver's Red Toboggan. Wheeler, Susan, illus. 2006. 28p. (J). (ps). 15.99 (978-0-525-47752-5(7) , Dutton Juvenile) Penguin Group (USA) Inc.

Kroll, Steven. Jungle Bullies. Nguyen, Vincent, illus. 2006. 32p. (J). 16.99 (978-0-7614-5297-3(4)) Cavendish, Marshall Corp.

LaReau, Kara. Ugly Fish. Magoon, Scott, illus. 2006. 40p. (J). (ps-2). 16.00 (978-0-15-205082-5(5)) Harcourt Trade Pubs.

Larsen, Kirsten. It's Sharing Day. Zalme, Ron, illus. 2007. (Dora the Explorer Ser.). 24p. (J). pap. 3.99 (978-1-4169-1575-1(3) , Simon Spotlight/Nickelodeon) Simon & Schuster Children's Publishing.

Let's Share. 2003. (Illus.). 24p. (J). bds. 7.95 (978-0-8249-5451-2(3)) Ideals Pubns.

Lucado, Max, creator. To Share or Nut to Share. 2006. (Max Lucado's Hermie & Friends Ser.). (Illus.). 24p. (J). bds. 12.99 (978-1-4003-0776-0(7)) Nelson, Thomas Inc.

Ludmila's Way - Teaching Guide. 2003. (J). 17.95 (978-1-55942-192-8(4)) Marsh Media.

Ludmila's Way: Evaluation Guide. 2006. (J). (978-1-55942-415-8(X)) Marsh Media.

Maccarone, Grace. El Almuerzo Sorpresa. Lewin, Betsy, illus. 2000. (Coleccion "Hola, Lector" Ser.). (SPA.). (J). (ps-1). pap. 3.20 net. (978-0-439-08696-7(5) , SO5844) Scholastic, Inc.

MacDonald, Alan. Contest Crazy. Brown, Judy, illus. 2006. (Read-It! Chapter Books). 48p. (J). lib. bdg. (*978-1-4048-3134-6(7) , 1265803) Picture Window Bks.

Maisner, Heather. It's My Turn! Stephenson, Kristina, illus. 2005. (First Time Stories Ser.). 24p. (J). (gr. k-ps). pap. 3.95 (978-0-7534-5740-5(7) , Kingfisher) Houghton Mifflin Co. Trade & Reference Div.

Mattern, Joanne. The Tricky Garden. 2005. 22.00 (*978-1-4108-4191-9(X)) Benchmark Education Co.

McKissack, Pat. The All-I'll-Ever-Want Christmas Doll. Pinkney, Jerry, illus. 2007. (J). (*978-0-375-83615-2(2) , Schwartz & Wade Bks.) Random Hse. Children's Bks.

McKissack, Patricia. The All-I'll-Ever-Want Christmas Doll. Pinkney, Jerry, illus. 2007. 40p. (J). (ps-3). lib. bdg. 19.99 (*978-0-375-93759-0(5)); 16.99 (*978-0-375-83759-3(0)) Random Hse. Children's Bks. (Schwartz & Wade Bks.).

McKissack, Patricia C. El Closet de Bessey, la Desordenada. 2002. Tr. of Messy Bessey's Closet. (SPA.). (gr. k-3). lib. bdg. 12.95 (978-0-613-59460-8(6)) Tandem Library Bks.

—Messy Bessey's Closet. 2001. (gr. k-3). lib. bdg. 12.95 (978-0-613-54440-5(4)) Tandem Library Bks.

McNease, Mitzy. Chester's Presents. Cox, Kim, illus. ed. 2006. 28p. (J). 10.96 (978-0-9779488-0-2(3)) Blancmange Publishing.

Meade, David. Shapes & Sharing. Byers, Brian, illus. 2005. 22p. (J). (gr. k-5). bds. 6.95 (978-1-59125-518-5(X) , Penton Kids) Penton Overseas, Inc.

Metzger, Steve. That's My Dino! Wilhelm, Hans, illus. 2002. (J). (978-0-439-32052-8(6)) Scholastic, Inc.

Moodie, Fiona. Noko's Suprise Party. 2008. (Illus.). 32p. (J). 16.95 (*978-1-84507-587-3(0)) Lincoln, Frances Ltd. GBR. *Dist:* Perseus Distribution.

Moss, Miriam. It's My Turn Smudge! Chapman, Lynne, illus. 2002. 24p. (J). (ps-2). (978-1-86233-287-4(8) , Gullane Children's Bks.) Pinwheel.

Muller, Lisa M. Master smokey & mr. Duck. 2006. 15p. (J). 9.99 (978-1-4276-0027-1(9)) Aardvark Global Publishing.

Muttini, Pablo. Rotas y partidas, son mas ricas Compartidas. Amelio-Ortiz, Osvaldo P., illus. 2005. (SPA.). 28p. (J). 14.95 (978-84-933955-7-5(9)) Hardenville SA URY. *Dist:* Independent Pubs. Group.

Myers, Bill. My Life as a Belching Baboon with Bad Breath. 2006. (Incredible Worlds of Wally McDoogle Ser.). pap. 6.99 (978-1-4003-0907-8(7)) Nelson, Thomas Inc.

Nicholson, Doris. A Day with Grandma. 2006. 9.00 (978-0-8059-9914-3(0)) Dorrance Publishing Co., Inc.

Niland, Deborah. When I Was a Baby. Niland, Deborah, illus. 2007. (Illus.). 24p. (J). (ps). pap. 4.99 (*978-1-933605-49-4(9)) Kane/Miller Bk. Pubs., Inc.

Oram, Hiawyn. Mine! Rees, Mary, illus. 2005. 32p. (J). (ps-7). pap. 7.95 (978-1-84507-451-7(3)) Lincoln, Frances Ltd. GBR. *Dist:* Perseus Distribution.

Pants, S. & Brooke, Samantha. Caring & Sharing. 2007. (Care Bears Ser.). 24p. (J). pap. 3.99 (978-0-439-89468-5(9)) Scholastic, Inc.

Parent, Nancy. The Day Nobody Shared. Johnson, Jay, illus. 2003. (Care Bears Ser.). 24p. (J). 3.50 (978-0-439-45157-4(4) , Scholastic Paperbacks) Scholastic, Inc.

Parker, David. I Can Share! Dubin, Jill, illus. 2005. (J). (978-0-439-73587-2(4)) Scholastic, Inc.

Peterson, Doug. West Slide Story: A Lesson in Making Peace. Big Idea Design Staff, illus. 2006. (VeggieTown Values Ser.: Bk. 7). 32p. (J). pap. 3.99 (978-0-310-70742-4(0)) Zonderkidz.

Prestine, Joan Singleton. It's Hard to Share My Teacher: Picture Book & Resource Guide, 2 bks., Set. 2001. (Kids Have Feelings, Too Ser.). (J). (ps-3). 14.99 (978-1-56417-773-5(4) , FE0061, Fearon Teacher Aids) Schaffer, Frank Pubns.

Quigley's Village Staff. Spike & the Big Blue Bubble Babble Balloon Machine: Sharing. 1998. (Quigley's Village Ser.: Vol. 6). (J). (ps-2). 12.19 incl. VHS (978-0-310-58179-6(6) , V6757) Zondervan.

Ramsey, Dave. The Big Birthday Surprise: Junior Discovers Giving. Ramsey, Marshall, illus. 2003. 26p. (J). 9.99 (978-0-9726323-2-4(8)) Lampo Group Inc., The.

Rau, Dana Meachen. Let's Share. 2004. (Compass Point Early Reader Ser.). (J). 18.60 (978-0-7565-0573-8(9)) Compass Point Bks.

—Let's Share. Favereau, Beatrice, illus. 2004. (Read-It! Readers Ser.). 32p. (C). (gr. k-3). 18.60 (978-1-4048-0647-4(4)) Picture Window Bks.

Richter, Dana. Pooh Take Your Turn. Baker, Darrell, illus. 2002. (J). 7.95 (978-0-7853-6039-1(5)) Publications International, Ltd.

Roitman, Tanya. Who Lives Here? Roitman, Tanya, illus. 2007. (Illus.). 32p. 12.95 (978-1-59354-599-4(1)) Blue Apple Bks.

Rose, Gill. William & the Guinea-Pig: A Book about Responsibility. Archbold, Tim, illus. 2004. (Making Good Choices Ser.). 24p. (C). (gr. k-3). 22.60 (978-1-4048-0664-1(4)) Picture Window Bks.

Rowe, Don. The Sandbox: A Book about Fairness. Archbold, Tim, illus. 2004. (Making Good Choices Ser.). 24p. (C). (gr. k-3). 22.60 (978-1-4048-0665-8(2)) Picture Window Bks.

Russell, Cheryl & Brouch, Dan. The Story of the Starhearts. l.t. ed. 1999. 30p. (J). (ps-3). 15.95 (978-0-9713181-0-6(7)) StarHeart Productions.

Rylant, Cynthia. Poppleton Has Fun. 2000. (Poppleton Ser.). (J). (gr. k-3). (978-0-606-19603-1(X)) Tandem Library Bks.

Santillo, LuAnn. Gum. Santillo, LuAnn, ed. 2003. (Half-Pint Kids Readers Ser.). (Illus.). 7p. (J). (ps-1). pap. (978-1-59256-087-5(3)) Half-Pint Kids, Inc.

Savadier, Elivia. Will Sheila Share? 2008. 24p. (J). 12.95 (*978-1-59643-289-5(6)) Roaring Brook Pr.

Schmauss, Judy Kentor. Luke's Mule. 2006. (Reader's Clubhouse Set B Ser.). (Illus.). 24p. (J). pap. 3.99 (978-0-7641-3297-1(0)) Barron's Educational Series, Inc.

Schneider, Richard H. The Christmas Pea Coat. Bond, Higgins, illus. 2004. 32p. (J). 14.95 (978-0-8249-5474-1(2)) Ideals Pubns.

Shaw, Francesca. Sharing: How Kindness Grows. 2006. (Illus.). 14p. (J). bds. 14.99 (978-0-7944-1143-5(6)) Reader's Digest Assn., Inc., The.

Soleim, Heather. God's Incredible Creatures: The Gift of Sharing. Greisen, Steve, ed. Hedgecock, Sean, illus. ed. 2005. 24p. (J). bds. 14.95 (978-0-9707422-9-2(0)) Reel Productions, LLC.

Sowards, Ben, illus. Christmas Oranges. 2004. 32p. 17.95 (978-1-59156-098-2(5)) Covenant Communications, Inc.

Spelvin, Justin. It's My Party! A Book about Sharing. Marantz, Larissa & DiPaolo, Katharine, illus. 2006. (LazyTown Ser.). 24p. (J). pap. 3.99 (978-1-4169-1536-2(2) , Simon Spotlight/Nickelodeon) Simon & Schuster Children's Publishing.

Stein, Mathilde. Mine! Hout, Mies van, illus. 2007. 28p. (J). (ps-1). 16.95 (*978-1-59078-506-5(1)) Boyds Mills Pr.

Suen, Anastasia. Scissors, Paper, & Sharing. Ebbeler, Jeffrey, illus. 2007. (Main Street School - Kids with Character Ser.). 32p. (J). (ps-4). lib. bdg. 27.07 (*978-1-60270-032-1(X) , Looking Glass Library) Magic Wagon.

Talley, Linda. Ludmila's Way. Chase, Andra, illus. 2003. (J). 17.95 (978-1-55942-190-4(8)) Marsh Media.

Thomas, Jerry D. & Thomas, Kitty. More Than Two Hands Full: A Mixed-Up Max Story about Sharing. 2002. (Illus.). 32p. (J). (978-0-8163-1953-4(7)) Pacific Pr. Pubns.

Weiss, Ellen. Twins Have a Fight. Williams, Sam, tr. Williams, Sam, illus. 2004. (Ready-to-Read Ser.). 24p. (J). pap. 3.99 (978-0-689-86515-2(5) , Aladdin) Simon & Schuster Children's Publishing.

Weninger, Brigitte. A Ball for All. Tharlet, Eve, illus. 2006. 32p. (J). (ps-3). 16.99 (978-0-698-40049-8(6) , Minedition) Penguin Group (USA) Inc.

Willems, Mo. The Pigeon Finds a Hot Dog! 2004. (Illus.). 40p. (ps-1). 12.99 (978-0-7868-1869-3(7)) Hyperion Bks. for Children.

Williams, Karen Lynn & Mohammed, Khadra. Four Feet, Two Sandals. Chayka, Doug, illus. 2007. 32p. (J). (gr. 2-5). 17.00 (978-0-8028-5296-0(3) , Eerdmans Bks For Young Readers) Eerdmans, William B. Publishing Co.

Yerrid, Gable. Marley's Treasure. Fitzgerald, Jennifer, illus. 2007. 28p. (J). 15.95 (*978-0-9767442-6-9(0)) Yorkville Pr.

Zatz, Lia. Mamita Monstruo. Guevara, Angeles Godinez, tr. Furnari, Eva, illus. 2003. (ENG & SPA.). 32p. pap. 6.95 (978-85-7416-173-0(X)) Callis Editora Ltda BRA. *Dist:* Independent Pubs. Group.

Ziefert, Harriet. Be Fair! Share! Whitehead, Peter, illus. 2006. (I'm Going to Read Ser.). 32p. (J). (ps-1). pap. 3.95 (978-1-4027-3422-9(0)) Sterling Publishing Co., Inc.

SHARKS

Animal Lives: Sharks. 2006. pap. 4.99 (978-1-4206-8160-4(5)) Teacher Created Materials, Inc.

Animals & the Environment: Incl. Lizards (4 bks.), Sharks (4 bks.), Snakes (12 bks.), 20 bks. (Illus.). (J). (gr. 3-4). lib. bdg. (978-1-56065-810-8(X) , Capstone High-Interest Bks.) Capstone Pr., Inc.

Arnold, Caroline. Giant Shark: Megalodon, the Super Prehistoric Predator. Caple, Laurie A., illus. 2000. 32p. (J). (gr. 4-6). tchr. ed. 16.00 (978-0-395-91419-9(1) , Clarion Bks.) Houghton Mifflin Co. Trade & Reference Div.

Arnosky, Jim. All about Sharks. Arnosky, Jim, illus. 2003. (Illus.). 32p. (J). pap. 15.95 (978-0-590-48166-3(5)) Scholastic, Inc.

Baldwin, Carol. Sharks. 2003. (Sea Creatures Ser.). (Illus.). 32p. (J). pap. 6.95 (978-1-4034-3566-8(9)); (gr. 3-5). lib. bdg. 22.79 (978-1-4034-0958-4(7)) Heinemann Library.

Balfour, Barbara. Great White Sharks. 2006. (Amazing Animals Ser.). (J). (978-1-59036-391-1(4)); (978-1-59036-397-3(3)) Weigl Pubs., Inc.

Barnes, Julia. 101 Facts about Sharks. 2004. (One Hundred One Facts about Predators Ser.). (Illus.). 32p. (J). (gr. 3 up). lib. bdg. 23.33 (978-0-8368-4039-1(9)) Stevens, Gareth Inc.

Bauman, Amy & Corrigan, Patricia. The Wonder of Sharks. 2000. (Animal Wonders Ser.). (Illus.). 48p. (J). (gr. 1 up). lib. bdg. 26.00 (978-0-8368-2665-4(5)) Stevens, Gareth Inc.

BBC Discovery Channel Staff. Seas of Life: Shark Watch! 2002. (978-0-606-22274-7(X)) Tandem Library Bks.

BBC Staff, contrib. by. Shark Watch! 2002. (Blue Planet Ser.). (Illus.). 48p. (J). (gr. 3-7). pap. 8.95 (978-0-439-33413-6(6)) Scholastic, Inc.

Benchley, Peter. Shark Life: True Stories about Sharks & the Sea. 208p. (J). 2007. (gr. 4-7). pap. 6.99 (978-0-440-41954-9(9) , Yearling); 2005. (Illus.). (gr. 4-7). 15.95 (978-0-385-73109-6(4) , Delacorte Bks. for Young Readers); 2005. (Illus.). (gr. 5). lib. bdg. 17.99 (978-0-385-90135-2(6) , Delacorte Bks. for Young Readers) Random Hse. Children's Bks.

Berger, Gilda & Berger, Melvin. Sharks & Other Wild Water Animals. 2006. (Scholastic Reader Collection Level 3 Ser.). 160p. (J). pap. 6.99 (978-0-439-84802-2(4) , Cartwheel Bks.) Scholastic, Inc.

Berger, Melvin. Chomp! A Book about Sharks. 1999. (Hello Reader! Science Ser.). (Illus.). 40p. (J). (gr. 1-3). pap. 3.99 (978-0-590-52298-4(1)) Scholastic, Inc.

—Chomp! a Book about Sharks. 1999. (gr. k-3). lib. bdg. 11.80 (978-0-613-13376-0(5)) Tandem Library Bks.

—What Do Sharks Eat for Dinner? 2000. (gr. 3-6). lib. bdg. 14.10 (978-0-613-35801-9(5)) Tandem Library Bks.

—What Do Sharks Eat for Dinner? Questions & Answers about Sharks. 2001. (Question & Answer Ser.). (Illus.). (J). (978-0-606-21516-9(6)) Tandem Library Bks.

Berger, Melvin & Berger, Gilda. Chomp! A Book about Sharks. 1999. (Hello Reader! Ser.). (J). 10.79 (978-0-606-17037-6(5)) Tandem Library Bks.

—Sharks. 2003. (Scholastic Readers Ser.). (Illus.). (J). pap. (978-0-439-47388-0(8)) Scholastic, Inc.

—What Do Sharks Eat for Dinner? Questions & Answers about Sharks. Rice, John, illus. (Question & Answer Ser.). 48p. (J). 2001. (gr. 2-4). pap. 6.99 (978-0-439-22905-0(7) , Scholastic Reference); 2000. (978-0-439-19372-6(9)) Scholastic, Inc.

Berger, Melvin, et al. What Do Sharks Eat for Dinner? Questions & Answers about Sharks. 2000. (Question & Answer Ser.). (Illus.). 48p. (J). pap. (978-0-439-19373-3(7)) Scholastic, Inc.

Berkowitz, Henry. Sharks: An Educational Coloring Book. 2001. (Illus.). 32p. (J). (ps-3). pap. 4.95 (978-0-932855-60-2(1)) Winner Enterprises.

Betz, Adrienne. Sharks! 2005. 32p. (J). lib. bdg. 13.85 (*978-1-4242-0860-9(2)) Fitzgerald Bks.

Betz, Adrienne & Time for Kids Editors. Sharks! 2005. (Time for Kids Science Scoops Ser.). (Illus.). 32p. (J). 14.99 (978-0-06-057633-2(2)); pap. 3.99 (978-0-06-057632-5(4)) HarperCollins Pubs. (Harper Trophy).

Bienert, Kristin, ed. Shark Attack. 2007. 48p. (J). pap. 6.99 (*978-0-696-23692-1(3)) Meredith Bks.

Bredeson, Carmen. Great White Sharks up Close. 2006. (Zoom in on Animals! Ser.). (Illus.). 24p. (J). lib. bdg. 21.26 (978-0-7660-2495-3(4) , Enslow Elementary) Enslow Pubs., Inc.

S

Bright, Michael. Sharks, 3 vols. 2000. (Nature Watch Ser.). (Illus.). 64p. (gr. 4-7). 14.99 (978-0-7548-0702-5(9) , Lorenz Bks.) Anness Publishing GBR. *Dist:* National Bk. Network.

—Sharks. Howard, Colin, illus. 2001. (Trackpack Ser.). 32p. (J). 4.99 (978-0-439-37480-4(4)) Scholastic, Inc.

Bright, Michael & Fergusson, Ian K. Sharks. 2003. (Nature Fact File Ser.). (Illus.). 64p. (gr. 3-7). pap. 7.99 (978-1-84215-736-7(1) , Southwater) Anness Publishing GBR. *Dist:* National Bk. Network.

Bright, Michael & Kerrod, Robin. Giants of the Ocean. 2004. (Illus.). 128p. pap. 17.99 (978-1-84215-989-7(5) , Southwater) Anness Publishing GBR. *Dist:* National Bk. Network.

Brocker, Susan. Sharks: Animals of the Ocean. 1998. (Animals of the Ocean Ser.: No. 3). (Illus.). 32p. (J). (gr. 2-6). lib. bdg. 14.95 (978-1-56674-232-0(3)) Forest Hse. Publishing Co., Inc.

Brooks, Bruce. Shark. 1998. (Wolfbay Wings Ser.: No. 6). (J). (gr. 4-7). (978-0-606-13926-7(5)) Tandem Library Bks.

Bulletpoints Sharks. 2005. (Illus.). (J). per. 4.99 (978-1-933581-07-1(7)) Byeway Bks.

Burnham, Brad. The Great White Shark. 2001. (Underwater World of Sharks Ser.). (Illus.). 24p. (J). lib. bdg. 18.75 (978-0-8239-5583-1(4) , PowerKids Pr.) Rosen Publishing Group, Inc., The.

—The Hammerhead Shark. 2001. (Underwater World of Sharks Ser.). (Illus.). 24p. (J). lib. bdg. 18.75 (978-0-8239-5584-8(2) , PowerKids Pr.) Rosen Publishing Group, Inc., The.

—The Mako Shark. 2001. (Underwater World of Sharks Ser.). (Illus.). 24p. (J). lib. bdg. 18.75 (978-0-8239-5585-5(0) , PowerKids Pr.) Rosen Publishing Group, Inc., The.

—The Sand Tiger Shark. 2001. (Underwater World of Sharks Ser.). (Illus.). 24p. (J). lib. bdg. 18.75 (978-0-8239-5707-1(1) , PowerKids Pr.) Rosen Publishing Group, Inc., The.

—The Tiger Shark. 2001. (Underwater World of Sharks Ser.). 24p. (J). (gr. 3). lib. bdg. 18.75 (978-0-8239-5586-2(9) , PowerKids Pr.) Rosen Publishing Group, Inc., The.

—The Whale Shark. 2001. (Underwater World of Sharks Ser.). (Illus.). 24p. (J). (gr. 3). lib. bdg. 18.75 (978-0-8239-5587-9(7) , PowerKids Pr.) Rosen Publishing Group, Inc., The.

Candelaria, Michael. Sharks! 2003. (World Discovery Science Readers Ser.). (Illus.). 32p. (J). (978-0-439-56629-2(0)) Scholastic, Inc.

Capuzzo, Michael. Close to Shore: The Terrifying Shark Attacks of 1916. 2003. (Illus.). 144p. (J). (gr. 5 up). 16.95 (978-0-375-82231-5(3) , Crown Books For Young Readers) Random Hse. Children's Bks.

—Close to Shore: The Terrifying Shark Attacks of 1916. 2002. (gr. 7-12). lib. bdg. 24.55 (978-0-613-62735-1(0)) Tandem Library Bks.

Carr, Karen & Diffily, Deborah. Jurassic Shark. Carr, Karen, illus. 2004. (Illus.). 32p. (J). (ps-3). 17.99 (978-0-06-008249-9(6)); lib. bdg. 18.89 (978-0-06-008250-5(X)) HarperCollins Pubs.

Carrier, Jeffrey. Discovering Sharks. rev. ed. 2006. (Illus.). 48p. pap. 9.95 (978-0-7603-2562-9(6)) Voyageur Pr., Inc.

Carwardine, Mark. Great White Shark. 2000. (Natural World Ser.). (Illus.). 48p. (J). (gr. 4-7). pap. 9.95 (978-0-7398-2029-2(X)) Steck-Vaughn.

Cerullo, Mary M. The Truth about Great White Sharks. Wertz, Michael, illus. Rotman, Jeffrey L., photos by. 2000. 48p. (J). (gr. 3-7). 15.95 (978-0-8118-2467-5(5)) Chronicle Bks. LLC.

Cerullo, Mary M. & Wertz, Michael. Truth about Great White Sharks. Rotman, Jeffrey L., photos by. 2006. (Illus.). 54p. (J). pap. 6.95 (978-0-8118-5759-8(X)) Chronicle Bks. LLC.

Chessen, Betsey. Sharks. 1998. (Science Emergent Readers Ser.). (J). 3.25 (978-0-590-63881-4(5)) Scholastic, Inc.

—Sharks: Tiburones. 2002. (Science Emergent Readers Ser.). (Illus.). (J). pap. (978-0-439-41162-2(9)) Scholastic, Inc.

Clarke, Catriona. Sharks - Internet Referenced (Level 2) 2007. 32p. (J). 4.99 (978-0-7945-1581-2(9) , Usborne) EDC Publishing.

Clarke, Ginjer. Sharks. Petruccio, Steven James, illus. 2001. (All Aboard Reading Ser.). 32p. (J). (ps-3). mass mkt. 3.99 (978-0-448-42490-3(8) , Grosset & Dunlap) Penguin Group (USA) Inc.

—Sharks. 2001. (gr. k-3). lib. bdg. 11.80 (978-0-613-35621-3(7)); (Illus.). (J). (978-0-606-21431-5(3)) Tandem Library Bks.

Clarke, Penny. Sharks. Bergin, Mark, illus. 2002. (Scary Creatures Ser.). 32p. (J). (gr. 2-4). pap. 6.95 (978-0-531-14846-4(7)); pap. 22.50 (978-0-531-14672-9(3)) Scholastic Library Publishing. (Watts, Franklin).

—Sharks. 2002. (gr. 3-6). lib. bdg. 15.25 (978-0-613-53646-2(0)) Tandem Library Bks.

Clarke, Phil. Sharks. 2005. (Illus.). 16p. (J). (gr. 1 up). 11.99 (978-0-7945-1109-8(0) , Usborne) EDC Publishing.

Clarke, Phillip & Furnival, Keith. Sharks. Scott, Peter David, illus. 2005. (J). ***978-0-439-86358-2(9))** Scholastic, Inc.

Cole & Leeson. El Tiburon. 2002. (Animales Marinos Salvajes Serie).Tr. of Wild Marine Animals: The Shark. (SPA.). 24p. (J). (gr. 3-5). 24.94 (978-1-4103-0008-9(0) , Blackbirch Pr., Inc.) Thomson Gale.

Cole, Joanna. Great Shark Escape. 2000. (gr. 3-6). lib. bdg. 11.80 (978-0-613-35778-4(7)) Tandem Library Bks.

Crossingham, John. El Ciclo de Vida del Tiburon. 2007. (SPA.). 32p. (J). (gr. 2-3). ***978-0-7787-8673-3(0))** Crabtree Publishing Co.

Crossingham, John & Kalman, Bobbie. The Life Cycle of a Shark. 2005. (Life Cycle Ser.). (Illus.). 32p. (J). (gr. k-6). (978-0-7787-0669-4(9)); pap. (978-0-7787-0699-1(0)) Crabtree Publishing Co.

Dalgleish, Sharon. Sharks & Rays. 1999. (Explorers Ser.). (Illus.). 32p. (J). (978-0-7699-0467-2(X)) Shortland Pubns. (U. S. A.) Inc.

Davies, Nicola. Surprising Sharks. Croft, James, illus. 2003. 32p. (J). (gr. k). 15.99 (978-0-7636-2185-8(4)) Candlewick Pr.

—Surprising Sharks: Read & Wonder. Croft, James, illus. 2005. 32p. (J). (gr. k-ps). reprint ed. pap. 6.99 (978-0-7636-2742-3(9)) Candlewick Pr.

Deady, Kathleen W. Great White Sharks. 2001. (Predators in the Wild Ser.). (Illus.). 48p. (J). (gr. 3-4). lib. bdg. 21.26 (978-0-7368-0786-9(1) , Capstone High-Interest Bks.) Capstone Pr., Inc.

Dorling Kindersley Publishing Staff. Sharks. 2nd rev. ed. 2003. (DK Pockets Ser.). (Illus.). 128p. (J). pap. 6.99 (978-0-7894-9592-1(9)) Dorling Kindersley Publishing, Inc.

—Tiburon. 2004. (Dk Eyewitness Books Ser.).Tr. of Shark. 72p. (J). (SPA.). 15.99 (978-0-7566-0636-7(5)); lib. bdg. 19.99 (978-0-7566-0795-1(7)) Dorling Kindersley Publishing, Inc.

—1001 Facts about Sharks. 2002. (gr. 3-6). lib. bdg. 17.60 (978-0-613-75143-8(4)) Tandem Library Bks.

Dorling Kindersley Publishing Staff, ed. Shark. 2004. (Dk Eyewitness Books Ser.). (Illus.). 72p. (J). 15.99 (978-0-7566-0725-8(6)) Dorling Kindersley Publishing, Inc.

—Shark & Whale. 2004. (Ultimate Sticker Bks.). 16p. (J). pap. 6.99 (978-0-7566-0237-6(8)) Dorling Kindersley Publishing, Inc.

—Shark Tale. 2004. (Ultimate Sticker Bks.). (Illus.). 16p. (J). pap. 6.99 (978-0-7566-0553-7(9)) Dorling Kindersley Publishing, Inc.

Dubowski, Cathy East. Shark Attack! 1998. (Eyewitness Readers). (Illus.). 48p. (J). (gr. 2-3). pap. 3.99 (978-0-7894-3440-1(7)) Dorling Kindersley Publishing, Inc.

Equipo Staff. Tiburones. 2004. Tr. of Sharks. (SPA., Illus.). 64p. (J). pap. 8.95 (978-0-7460-4515-2(8)) EDC Publishing.

Evert, Laura. Sharks. 2004. (Our Wild World Ser.). (Illus.). 48p. (J). (gr. 2-5). pap. 7.95 (978-1-55971-779-3(3) , NorthWord Bks. for Young Readers) T&N Children's Publishing.

—Sharks. 2001. (gr. 3-6). lib. bdg. 16.40 (978-0-613-55896-9(0)) Tandem Library Bks.

Field, Nancy H. Discovering Sharks & Rays. Maydak, Michael S., illus. 2003. (Discovering Nature Library). 40p. (J). (gr. 2-6). pap. 7.95 (978-0-941042-33-8(2)) Dog-Eared Pubns.

Fine, John Christopher. Diving with Sharks. 2000. (J). (978-0-531-11785-9(5) , Watts, Franklin) Scholastic Library Publishing.

Fitzgerald, Patrick J. Shark Attacks. 2000. (High Interest Bks.). (Illus.). 48p. (YA). (gr. 7-12). pap. 6.95 (978-0-516-23518-9(4) , Children's Pr.) Scholastic Library Publishing.

—Shark Attacks. 2000. (gr. 7-12). lib. bdg. 15.25 (978-0-613-52181-9(1)) Tandem Library Bks.

Gaines, Richard Marshall. When Sharks Attack! 2006. (When Wild Animals Attack! Ser.). (Illus.). 48p. (J). (gr. 4-10). lib. bdg. 23.93 (978-0-7660-2664-3(7)) Enslow Pubs., Inc.

Gareth Stevens Publishing Staff, contrib. by. Sharks. 2004. (All about Wild Animals Ser.). (Illus.). 32p. (J). lib. bdg. 23.33 (978-0-8368-4188-6(3)) Stevens, Gareth Inc.

Gentle, Victor & Perry, Janet. Baby Sharks. 2001. (Sharks Ser.). (Illus.). 24p. (J). (gr. 2 up). lib. bdg. 22.00 (978-0-8368-2824-5(0)) Stevens, Gareth Inc.

—Chasing Sharks. 2001. (Sharks Ser.). (Illus.). 24p. (J). (gr. 2 up). lib. bdg. 22.00 (978-0-8368-2825-2(9)) Stevens, Gareth Inc.

—Killer Sharks, Killer People. 2001. (Sharks Ser.). (Illus.). 24p. (J). (gr. 2 up). lib. bdg. 22.00 (978-0-8368-2826-9(7)) Stevens, Gareth Inc.

—Shark Camouflage & Armor. 2001. (Sharks Ser.). (Illus.). 24p. (J). (gr. 2 up). lib. bdg. 22.00 (978-0-8368-2827-6(5)) Stevens, Gareth Inc.

—Sharks, 6 bks. Incl. Baby Sharks. lib. bdg. 22.00 (978-0-8368-2824-5(0)); Chasing Sharks. lib. bdg. 22.00 (978-0-8368-2825-2(9)); Killer Sharks, Killer People. lib. bdg. 22.00 (978-0-8368-2826-9(7)); Shark Camouflage & Armor. lib. bdg. 22.00 (978-0-8368-2827-6(5)); Very Big Sharks. lib. bdg. 22.00 (978-0-8368-2828-3(3)); World's Strangest Sharks. lib. bdg. 22.00 (978-0-8368-2829-0(1)); 24p. (J). (gr. 2 up). 2001. (Illus.). Set lib. bdg. 132.00 (978-0-8368-2823-8(2)) Stevens, Gareth Inc.

—Very Big Sharks. 2001. (Sharks Ser.). (Illus.). 24p. (J). (gr. 2 up). lib. bdg. 22.00 (978-0-8368-2828-3(3)) Stevens, Gareth Inc.

—The World's Strangest Sharks. 2001. (Sharks Ser.). (Illus.). 24p. (J). (gr. 2 up). lib. bdg. 22.00 (978-0-8368-2829-0(1)) Stevens, Gareth Inc.

Getting to Know Sharks. 2005. (Fluent Library). (YA). (ps-3). 29.34 (978-0-8215-8963-2(6)) Sadlier, William H. Inc.

Gibbons, Gail. Sharks. Gibbons, Gail, illus. 2002. (Illus.). (J). 15.49 (978-0-7587-3605-5(3)) Book Wholesalers, Inc.

Gibbons, Lynn & Coode, Chris. Sharks. 2007. (Up Close Ser.). (Illus.). 24p. (J). (gr. 3-5). lib. bdg. 23.95 (***978-1-4042-3762-9(3)** , PowerKids Pr.) Rosen Publishing Group, Inc., The.

Gibbons, Lynn & Coode, Chris. 3D Sharks. 2001. (Illus.). 16p. (J). pap. (978-1-84193-007-7(5)) Arcturus Publishing.

Gilkerson, Patricia. My Adventure with Sharks. 2006. 44p. (J). 8.99 (978-1-59092-468-6(1) , Orchard Academy Pr.) Windstorm Creative.

Gilpin, Daniel. Life-Size Sharks & Other Underwater Creatures. Knowelden, Martin, illus. 2005. (Life-Size Ser.). 28p. (J). (ps-7). 9.95 (978-1-4027-2537-1(X)) Sterling Publishing Co., Inc.

Goldish, Meish. Whale Shark: The World's Biggest Fish. 2007. (SuperSized! Ser.). (J). lib. bdg. 21.28 (978-1-59716-397-2(X)) Bearport Publishing Co., Inc.

Gordon, David George. Uncover a Shark. Pringle, Betsy Henry, ed. Bonadonna, Davide & Kitzmuller, Christian, illus. 2004. (Uncover Ser.). 16p. (J). 18.95 (978-1-59223-115-7(2) , Silver Dolphin Bks.) Advantage Pubs. Group.

Gordon, Sharon. Guess Who Bites. 2004. (SPA & ENG.). (J). 21.36 (978-0-7614-1766-8(4) , Benchmark Bks.) Cavendish, Marshall Corp.

Gordon, Sharon. Guess Who Bites: Adivina Quién Muerde. 2007. (SPA & ENG.). (J). (***978-0-7614-2882-4(8)); (*978-0-7614-2865-7(8))** Cavendish, Marshall Bks., Ltd.

Great White Sharks, 6 bks. 2005. (Animal Predators Ser.). (Illus.). 40p. (J). (gr. 3-6). pap. 46.95 (978-0-8225-5488-2(7)) Lerner Publishing Group.

Guiberson, Brenda Z. Sharks. 2002. (Scholastic Science Readers Ser.). (Illus.). 32p. (J). pap. (978-0-439-26985-8(7) , Scholastic Reference) Scholastic, Inc.

Gussoni, Clizia. The Awesome Book of Sharks! McDonnell, Luke, illus. 2006. 288p. pap. 9.95 (978-0-7624-2644-7(6) , Running Pr. Kids) Running Pr. Bk. Pubs.

Hall, Howard. A Frenzy of Sharks: The Surprising Life of a Perfect Predator. Leon, Vicki, ed. 2nd ed. 2006. (Jean-Michel Cousteau Presents Ser.). (Illus.). 48p. (J). pap. 8.95 (978-0-9766134-4-2(1)) London Town Pr.

Healy, Nick. World's Deadliest Sharks. 2006. (Edge Books, the World's Top Tens). (Illus.). 32p. (J). (978-0-7368-5453-5(3)) Capstone Pr., Inc.

Huggins-Cooper, Lynn. Savage Sharks. 2006. (J). (978-1-58340-933-6(5)) Smart Apple Media.

Johnston, Marianne. Prehistoric Sharks & Modern-Day Sharks. 2000. (Prehistoric Animals & Their Modern-Day Relatives Ser.). 24p. (J). (gr. k-4). lib. bdg. 18.75 (978-0-8239-5206-9(1) , PowerKids Pr.) Rosen Publishing Group, Inc., The.

Kalman, Bobbie. Spectacular Sharks. 2003. (gr. 3-6). lib. bdg. 15.25 (978-0-613-59138-6(0)) Tandem Library Bks.

—Tiburones Espectaculares. 2006. (SPA., Illus.). 32p. pap. (978-0-7787-8415-9(0)) Crabtree Publishing Co.

Kalman, Bobbie & Aloian, Molly. Spectacular Sharks. (Living Ocean Ser.). (Illus.). 32p. 2006. (gr. 3-4). pap. (978-0-7787-1320-3(2)); 2003. (J). (gr. 2-9). (978-0-7787-1298-5(2)) Crabtree Publishing Co.

King, H. Elizabeth. Kemo Shark. Date not set. 14p. (J). pap. 2.95 (978-0-9647798-0-8(3)) Kidscope, Inc.

Kite, L. Patricia. Watching Sharks in the Oceans. 2006. (Heinemann First Library). (Illus.). 32p. (J). (978-1-4034-7233-5(5)); pap. (978-1-4034-7246-5(7)) Heinemann Library.

Klein, Adam G. Basking Sharks. 2006. (Checkerboard Animal Library). (Illus.). 24p. (J). (gr. k-6). 21.35 (978-1-59679-285-2(X) , Checkerboard Library) ABDO Publishing Co.

—Common Sawsharks. 2006. (Illus.). 24p. (J). (gr. k-6). 21.35 (978-1-59679-286-9(8) , Checkerboard Library) ABDO Publishing Co.

—Lantern Sharks. 2006. (Checkerboard Animal Library). (Illus.). 24p. (J). (gr. k-6). 21.35 (978-1-59679-287-6(6) , Checkerboard Library) ABDO Publishing Co.

—Mako Sharks. 2006. (Illus.). 24p. (J). (gr. k-6). 21.35 (978-1-59679-288-3(4) , Checkerboard Library) ABDO Publishing Co.

—Seal Sharks. 2006. (Checkerboard Animal Library). (Illus.). 24p. (J). (gr. k-6). 21.35 (978-1-59679-289-0(2) , Checkerboard Library) ABDO Publishing Co.

—Sharks Set II. 2006. (J). (gr. k-6). 128.10 (978-1-59679-284-5(1) , Checkerboard Library) ABDO Publishing Co.

—Thresher Sharks. 2006. (Checkerboard Animal Library). (Illus.). 24p. (J). (gr. k-6). 21.35 (978-1-59679-290-6(6) , Checkerboard Library) ABDO Publishing Co.

Kris Hirschmann. The Whale Shark. 2004. (Illus.). 48p. (J). 26.20 (978-0-7377-2059-4(X) , Kidhaven) Thomson Gale.

Landau, Elaine. Scary Sharks. 2003. (Fearsome, Scary, & Creepy Animals Ser.). (Illus.). 48p. (J). (gr. 1-4). lib. bdg. 23.93 (978-0-7660-2058-0(4)) Enslow Pubs., Inc.

Le Bloas-Julienne, Renée. The Shark: Silent Hunter. 2007. (Animal Close-Ups Ser.). Orig. Title: Le Requin. (Illus.). 26p. (J). pap. 6.95 (978-1-57091-631-1(4)) Charlesbridge Publishing, Inc.

Lee, Justin. How to Draw Sharks. 2002. (Kid's Guide to Drawing Ser.). (Illus.). 24p. (J). lib. bdg. 21.25 (978-0-8239-5788-0(8) , PowerKids Pr.) Rosen Publishing Group, Inc., The.

Legg, Gerald. Sharks. 1998. (Worldwise Ser.: Vol. 21). (Illus.). 40p. (J). (gr. 3-5). 24.00 (978-0-531-14461-9(5) , Watts, Franklin) Scholastic Library Publishing.

Less, Emma. Little Scribbles: Shark Fun. Harpster, Steve, illus. 2007. (Little Scribbles Ser.). 12p. (J). bds. 5.95 (978-1-4027-3807-4(2)) Sterling Publishing Co., Inc.

Lewis, Brenda Ralph. Sharks. 2006. (Nature's Monsters Ser.). (Illus.). 32p. (J). lib. bdg. 23.33 (978-0-8368-6178-5(7)) Stevens, Gareth Inc.

Lindeen, Carol K. Sharks. 2005. (Under the Sea Ser.). (Illus.). 24p. (J). lib. bdg. 19.93 (978-0-7368-2602-0(5) , Pebble Bks.) Capstone Pr., Inc.

Lingemann, Linda. Survival in the Sea: The Story of a Hammerhead Shark. Marchesi, Stephen, illus. 1999. (Smithsonian Oceanic Collection: No. 18). 32p. (J). (ps-2). 15.95 (978-1-56899-769-8(8)) Soundprints.

Llewellyn, Claire. The Best Book of Sharks. 2005. (Best Book of... Ser.). 32p. (J). (gr. k-3). pap. 6.95 (978-0-7534-5875-4(6) , Kingfisher) Houghton Mifflin Co. Trade & Reference Div.

—The Best Book of Sharks. Grinaway, Ray & Stewart, Roger, illus. 1999. (Best Book of... Ser.). 32p. (J). (gr. k-3). tchr. ed. 12.95 (978-0-7534-5173-1(5) , Kingfisher) Houghton Mifflin Co. Trade & Reference Div.

Locke, Ian. Deadly Deep. Rowe, Alan, illus. 17th ed. 2003. 60p. (J). pap. 3.99 (978-0-330-37500-9(8) , Pan) Pan Macmillan GBR. *Dist:* Trafalgar Square Publishing.

Lopez, Gary. Sharks. 2006. (New Naturebooks). (Illus.). 32p. (J). (gr. 1-5). 27.07 (978-1-59296-649-3(7)) Child's World, Inc.

MacQuitty, Miranda. Shark. 2008. (DK Eyewitness Bks.). 72p. (J). (gr. 3-8). 15.99 (***978-0-7566-3778-1(3))** Dorling Kindersley Publishing, Inc.

MacQuitty, Miranda & Dorling Kindersley Publishing Staff. Shark. 2004. (Eyewitness Books). (Illus.). 72p. (J). lib. bdg. 19.99 (978-0-7566-0724-1(8)) Dorling Kindersley Publishing, Inc.

Mallory, Kenneth. Swimming with Hammerhead Sharks. Mallory, Kenneth, photos by. (Scientists in the Field Ser.). (Illus.). 48p. (J). (gr. 4-6). 2002. pap. 5.95 (978-0-618-25079-0(4)); 2001. tchr. ed. 16.00 (978-0-618-05543-2(6)) Houghton Mifflin Co. Trade & Reference Div.

—Swimming with Hammerhead Sharks. 2002. (gr. 3-6). lib. bdg. 12.95 (978-0-613-90723-1(X)) Tandem Library Bks.

Markle, Sandra. Great White Sharks. (Animal Predators Ser.). 40p. (J). 2005. (gr. 4-6). pap. 7.95 (978-1-57505-747-7(6)); 2004. (Illus.). (gr. 3-6). lib. bdg. 25.26 (978-1-57505-731-6(X)) Lerner Publishing Group.

—Outside & Inside Sharks. 1999. (978-0-606-16310-1(7)) Tandem Library Bks.

Markle, Sandra. Tough, Toothy Baby Sharks. 2007. (J). 32p. 17.85 (***978-0-8027-9594-6(3));** (Illus.). 31p. 16.95 (***978-0-8027-9593-9(5))** Walker & Co.

Mattern, Joanne. Sharks. 2001. (Animals Animals Ser.). (Illus.). 48p. (J). (gr. 3). lib. bdg. 25.64 (978-0-7614-1261-8(1)) Cavendish, Marshall Corp.

Maydak, Michael S., illus. Wild Stickers - Sharks & Rays. 2003. 4p. (J). 2.50 (978-0-941042-34-5(0)) Dog-Eared Pubns.

McNeil, Niki, et al. HOCPP 1085 Sharks. 2006. spiral bd. 19.50 (***978-1-60308-085-9(6))** In the Hands of a Child.

Miller, Jonathan. Sharks. 2004. (Discovery Program Ser.). (SPA., Illus.). 64p. (J). (gr. 2 up). pap. 8.95 (978-0-7460-3723-2(6)); lib. bdg. 16.95 (978-1-58086-335-3(3)) EDC Publishing.

Morgan, Sally. Sharks. 2004. (QEB Animal Lives Ser.). (Illus.). 32p. (J). lib. bdg. 18.95 (978-1-59566-034-3(8)) QEB Publishing Inc.

Mugford, Simon. Shark. 2004. (Twenty4Sevens Ser.). (Illus.). 48p. (J). pap. (978-0-439-68102-5(2)) Scholastic, Inc.

Mugford, Simon & Priddy, Roger. Sharks & Other Dangers of the Deep. rev. ed. 2005. (Illus.). 32p. (J). (ps-3). bds. 6.95 (978-0-312-49534-3(X) , Priddy Bks.) St. Martin's Pr.

Murray, Julie. Great White Sharks. 2002. (Buddy Book Ser.). (Illus.). 24p. (J). (gr. k-4). lib. bdg. 21.35 (978-1-57765-706-4(3)) ABDO Publishing Co.

—Hammerhead Sharks. 2005. (Animal Kingdom Set Ii Ser.). (Illus.). 24p. (J). (gr. k-4). lib. bdg. 21.35 (978-1-59197-319-5(8)) ABDO Publishing Co.

—Tiger Sharks. 2005. (Animal Kingdom Set Ii Ser.). (Illus.). 24p. (J). (gr. k-4). lib. bdg. 21.35 (978-1-59197-336-2(8)) ABDO Publishing Co.

Nelson, Kristin L. Hunting Sharks. 2003. (Pull Ahead Bks.). (Illus.). 32p. (J). (gr. 2-6). 22.60 (978-0-8225-4671-9(X) , Lerner Pubns.) Lerner Publishing Group.

—Hunting Sharks. 2003. (gr. k-3). lib. bdg. 14.10 (978-0-613-58947-5(5)) Tandem Library Bks.

O'Donnell, Kerri. Hammerhead Sharks. 2006. (Illus.). 24p. (J). lib. bdg. (978-1-4042-3529-8(9) , PowerKids Pr.) Rosen Publishing Group, Inc., The.

Orme, David. Sea Killers. 2007. (Trailblazers Ser.). (ACE., Illus.). 36p. pap. 7.95 (***978-1-84167-592-3(X))** Ransom Publishing Ltd. GBR. *Dist:* International Publishers Marketing.

Osborne, Mary Pope & Boyce, Natalie Pope. Dolphins & Sharks. Murdocca, Sal, illus. 2003. (Magic Tree House Research Guide Ser.: No. 9). 128p. (J). (gr. k-3). pap. 4.99 (978-0-375-82377-0(8) , Random Hse. Bks. for Young Readers) Random Hse. Children's Bks.

—Dolphins & Sharks: A Nonfiction Companion to Dolphins at Daybreak. Murdocca, Sal, illus. 2003. (Magic Tree House Research Guide Ser.: No. 9). 128p. (J). (gr. k-3). lib. bdg. 11.99 (978-0-375-92377-7(2) , Random Hse. Bks. for Young Readers) Random Hse. Children's Bks.

Otfinoski, Steven. Hammerheads & Other Sharks, Vol. 3. World Book, Inc. Staff, ed. 2002. (World Book's Animals of the World Ser.: Set 1). 64p. (J). (978-0-7166-1240-7(2)) World Bk., Inc.

Palazzo-Craig, Janet. Sharks! 2001. (Planet Reader Ser.). (Illus.). (J). (978-0-606-20911-3(5)) Tandem Library Bks.

Palmer, Sarah. Tiburones Nodrizas (Nurse Sharks) (Tiburones Ser.). (SPA., Illus.). 24p. (J). (gr. 1-4). lib. bdg. 18.60 (978-0-86593-205-0(0)) Rourke Publishing, LLC.

Parker, Steve. Encyclopedia of Sharks. 2002. (gr. 7-12). lib. bdg. 36.15 (978-0-613-65550-7(8)) Tandem Library Bks.

—10 Things You Should Know about Sharks. Gallagher, Belinda & Borton, Paula, eds. Butler, John, illus. 2004. (10 Things You Should Know Ser.). (J). 6.99 (978-1-84236-118-4(X)) Miles Kelly Publishing, Ltd. GBR. *Dist:* Independent Pubs. Group.

Parker, Steven. See-Through Sharks. 2005. 32p. 15.95 (978-0-7624-2720-8(5)) Running Pr. Bk. Pubs.

Perrine, Doug. Sharks. rev. ed. 2002. (WorldLife Library Ser.). (Illus.). 72p. (J). pap. 17.95 (978-0-89658-604-8(9)) Voyageur Pr., Inc.

Pope, Deidre. Sharks. 2001. (Let's Investigate Ser.). (Illus.). 32p. (J). 18.95 (978-1-58341-193-3(3) , Creative Education) Creative Co., The.

Pope, Joyce & Smart, Brian Hunter. 1,001 Facts about Sharks. Grabham, Sue, ed. 2002. (Backpack Book Ser.). (Illus.). 192p. (J). (gr. k-3). pap. 8.99 (978-0-7894-8449-9(8)) Dorling Kindersley Publishing, Inc.

Priddy, Roger. Sharks: And Other Dangers of the Deep. l.t. rev. ed. 2005. 32p. (J). 9.95 (978-0-312-49533-6(1) , Priddy Bks.) St. Martin's Pr.

Pringle, Laurence P. Sharks! Strange & Wonderful. Henderson, Meryl, illus. 32p. 2003. (J). (gr. 2-4). 15.95 (978-1-56397-863-0(6)); 2001. (gr. 1-4). 15.95 (978-1-56397-209-6(3)) Boyds Mills Pr.

Raatma, Lucia. Sharks. 2001. (First Reports). (Illus.). 48p. (J). (gr. 3 up). lib. bdg. 21.26 (978-0-7565-0056-6(7)) Compass Point Bks.

Randolph, Joanne. The Great White Shark: King of the Ocean. 2007. (Sharks Ser.). (Illus.). 24p. (J). (gr. k-5). lib. bdg. 21.25 (978-1-4042-3624-0(4) , 1266081, PowerKids Pr.) Rosen Publishing Group, Inc., The.

—The Hammerhead Shark: Coastal Killer. 2007. (Sharks Ser.). (Illus.). 24p. (J). (gr. k-5). lib. bdg. 21.25 (978-1-4042-3625-7(2) , 1266082, PowerKids Pr.) Rosen Publishing Group, Inc., The.

—The Mako Shark: Built for Speed. 2007. (Sharks Ser.). (Illus.). 24p. (J). (gr. k-5). lib. bdg. 21.25 (978-1-4042-3627-1(9)) Rosen Publishing Group, Inc., The.

—Sharks: Hunters of the Deep, 4 bks., Set. Incl. Great White Shark : King of the Ocean. lib. bdg. 21.25 (978-1-4042-3624-0(4) , 1266081, PowerKids Pr.); Hammerhead Shark : Coastal Killer. lib. bdg. 21.25 (978-1-4042-3625-7(2) , 1266082, PowerKids Pr.); Mako Shark : Built for Speed. lib. bdg. 21.25 (978-1-4042-3627-1(9)); Whale Shark : Gentle Giant. lib. bdg. 21.25 (978-1-4042-3626-4(0) , PowerKids Pr.); (Illus.). 24p. (J). (gr. k-5). 2007. 2007. Set lib. bdg. 85.00 (978-1-4042-3599-1(X) , PowerKids Pr.) Rosen Publishing Group, Inc., The.

—The Whale Shark: Gentle Giant. 2007. (Sharks Ser.). (Illus.). 24p. (J). (gr. k-5). lib. bdg. 21.25 (978-1-4042-3626-4(0) , PowerKids Pr.) Rosen Publishing Group, Inc., The.

Richardson, Adele D. Sharks: Hunters of the Deep. 2001. (Wild World of Animals Ser.). (Illus.). 24p. (J). (gr. 1-2). lib. bdg. 18.60 (978-0-7368-0828-6(0) , Bridgestone Bks.) Capstone Pr., Inc.

Riehecky, Janet. Megalodon. 2006. (Pebble Plus Ser.). (Illus.). 24p. (J). (978-0-7368-5354-5(5) , Pebble Bks.) Capstone Pr., Inc.

—Megalodonte: Megalodon. 2007. (ENG & SPA.). (J). (978-0-7368-7639-1(1)) Capstone Pr., Inc.

Robinson, Claire. Shark. 1999. (In the Wild Ser.). (Illus.). 24p. (J). (gr. k-2). lib. bdg. 21.36 (978-1-57572-863-6(X)) Heinemann Library.

—Sharks. 2002. (In the Wild Ser.). (Illus.). 24p. (J). (gr. k-2). pap. 6.95 (978-1-58810-323-9(4) , 91048) Heinemann Library.

—Sharks. 1999. (In the Wild Ser.). (Illus.). (J). (978-0-606-22019-4(4)) Tandem Library Bks.

Rockwell, Anne F. Little Shark. Halsey, Megan, illus. 2005. 32p. (J). 16.85 (978-0-8027-8956-3(0)); 15.95 (978-0-8027-8955-6(2)) Walker & Co.

Rustad, Martha E. Sharks, Vol. 2. 2005. (Ocean Life Ser.). 24p. (YA). (gr. k-3). pap. (978-0-7368-9084-7(X) , Pebble Bks.) Capstone Pr., Inc.

Rustad, Martha E. H. Sharks. Saunders-Smith, Gail, ed. 2001. (Ocean Life Ser.). (Illus.). 24p. (J). (gr. k-1). lib. bdg. 15.93 (978-0-7368-0861-3(2) , Pebble Bks.) Capstone Pr., Inc.

Sandler, Michael. Bethany Hamilton: Follow Your Dreams! 2007. (Defining Moments Ser.). (Illus.). 32p. (J). (gr. 3-6). lib. bdg. 25.27 (978-1-59716-270-8(1)) Bearport Publishing Co., Inc.

Savage, Stephen. Sharks. (Inside Access Ser.). (Illus.). (J). (gr. k-3). 2007. 32p. 9.95 (978-0-7534-6064-1(5)); 2002. 36p. tchr. ed. 11.95 (978-0-7534-5437-4(8)) Houghton Mifflin Co. Trade & Reference Div. (Kingfisher).

—Sharks. 2002. (gr. k-3). lib. bdg. 15.25 (978-0-613-90171-0(1)) Tandem Library Bks.

—Sharks: Explore & Discover. Grinaway, Ray et al, illus. 2002. (Question Time Ser.). 32p. (J). (gr. k-3). pap. 6.95 (978-0-7534-5441-1(6) , Kingfisher) Houghton Mifflin Co. Trade & Reference Div.

Savage, Stephen & Parker, Steven. See-Through Sharks. Ferring, Rod, illus. 2005. 32p. 15.95 (978-0-7624-2407-8(9) , Running Pr. Kids) Running Pr. Bk. Pubs.

Seelig, Tina L. Shark Cards. 2007. (Games for Your Brain Ser.). (Illus.). 61p. (J). (gr. k up). 9.95 (978-0-8118-5772-7(7)) Chronicle Bks. LLC.

Sexton, Colleen. Sharks. 2007. (Illus.). 24p. (J). lib. bdg. 19.95 (978-1-60014-057-0(2)) Bellwether Media.

Shark: Level 2, 6 vols. (Fluency Strand Ser.). (gr. 4-8). 45.00 (978-1-4045-1210-8(1)) Wright Group, The.

Shark Stencilling Book: Learn How to Draw Sharks & Discover Shark Facts at Your Fingertips! 2007. (Illus.). 24p. (J). (gr. 3-7). bds. 12.95 (978-1-59125-553-6(8) , Penton Kids) Penton Overseas, Inc.

Sharks! (Creatures Corner Ser.). 16p. (J). (978-2-7643-0121-0(9)) Phidal Publishing, Inc./Editions Phidal, Inc.

Sharks. (Eyes on Nature Ser.). 32p. (J). (gr. 1). pap. (978-1-882210-55-8(7)) Action Publishing, Inc.

Sharks: Hunters of the Deep, 6 vols. (Book2WebTM Ser.). (gr. 4-8). 36.50 (978-0-322-02973-6(2)) Wright Group, The.

Sharks: Level M, 6 vols. (Wonder Worldtm Ser.). 16p. 34.95 (978-0-7802-2906-8(1)) Wright Group, The.

Sharks & Other Dangerous Fish. 2002. (Wild, Wild World Ser.). 32p. (J). 9.95 (978-0-7525-4686-5(4)) Parragon, Inc.

Sharks & Rays: Level O, 6 vols. (Explorers Ser.). 32p. (gr. 3-6). 44.95 (978-0-7699-0590-7(0)) Shortland Pubns. (U. S. A.) Inc.

Sharks Learning Kits Know It Alls. 2001. (Illus.). 24p. (YA). (ps up). 7.95 (978-1-58610-510-5(8) , 85011) Learning Horizons, Inc.

Sharon the Shark 6 Packs. Set D. (gr. k-3). 29.00 (978-0-7635-0553-0(6)) Rigby Education.

Sieswerda, Paul L. Sharks. 2001. (Animalways Ser.). (Illus.). 112p. (J). (gr. 5 up). lib. bdg. 31.36 (978-0-7614-1267-0(0) , Benchmark Bks.) Cavendish, Marshall Corp.

Simon, Seymour. Incredible Sharks. 2003. (See More Readers). (Illus.). 32p. (J). 14.50 (978-1-58717-238-0(0)); pap. 3.95 (978-1-58717-239-7(9)) Chronicle Bks. LLC. (SeaStar Bks.).

—Seemore Incredible Sharks. 2006. 32p. (J). (SPA.). 14.50 (978-0-8118-5494-8(9)); pap. 3.95 (978-0-8118-5495-5(7)) Chronicle Bks. LLC.

—Sharks. 2006. 32p. (J). 17.99 (978-0-06-087712-5(X)); (Illus.). pap. 6.99 (978-0-06-087713-2(8)) HarperCollins Pubs.

—Sharks. 2005. (Illus.). 24p. (J). (978-0-439-77699-8(6)) Scholastic, Inc.

Solway, Andrew. Sharks & Other Fish. 2006. (Illus.). 48p. (J). (978-1-4034-8221-1(7)); pap. (978-1-4034-8228-0(4)) Heinemann Library.

Sovak, Jan. Learning about Sharks. 1999. (Illus.). 16p. (J). (gr. 3-5). pap. 1.50 (978-0-486-40768-5(3)) Dover Pubns., Inc.

Spilsbury, Louise & Spilsbury, Richard. Great White Shark. 2004. (Animals under Threat Ser.). (Illus.). 48p. (J). lib. bdg. (978-1-4034-4860-6(4)) Heinemann Library.

—The Great White Shark. 2004. (Animals under Threat Ser.). (Illus.). 48p. (J). pap. 8.50 (978-1-4034-5434-8(5)) Heinemann Library.

—Shark Snacks: Food Chains & Webs. 2005. (Illus.). 32p. (J). (978-1-4109-1973-1(0)); lib. bdg. (978-1-4109-1942-7(0)) Steck-Vaughn.

Steffens, Ezekiel. Sharks. 2006. (Animals Attack! Ser.). (J). (978-0-7377-1544-6(8) , Greenhaven Pr., Inc.) Thomson Gale.

Stille, Darlene. I Am a Shark: The Life of a Great Hammerhead Shark. Ouren, Todd, illus. 2004. (I Live in the Ocean Ser.). 24p. (J). (gr. k-2). lib. bdg. 22.60 (978-1-4048-0599-6(0)) Picture Window Bks.

Stone, Tanya Lee. Sharks. 2003. (Wild Wild World Ser.). 24p. (YA). 24.94 (978-1-56711-822-3(4) , Blackbirch Pr., Inc.) Thomson Gale.

Strong, Mike. Shark! The Truth Behind the Terror. 2002. (High Five Reading Ser.). (Illus.). 48p. (J). pap. (978-0-7368-9525-5(6)) Capstone Pr., Inc.

—Shark! The Truth Behind the Terror. 2002. (High Five Reading Ser.). (Illus.). 48p. (J). (gr. 2-3). lib. bdg. 22.60 (978-0-7368-9547-7(7) , Capstone High-Interest Bks.) Capstone Pr., Inc.

—Shark! the Truth behind the Terror, 6 vols. (gr. 4 up). 49.95 (978-0-7368-9536-1(1) , High Five) Red Brick Learning.

Swanson, Diane. Sharks. 2003. (Welcome to the World of Animals Ser.). (Illus.). 32p. (J). (gr. 3 up). lib. bdg. 23.33 (978-0-8368-3563-2(8)) Stevens, Gareth Inc.

—Sharks. 2001. (Welcome to the World Ser.). (Illus.). 32p. (J). (ps-2). pap. 5.95 (978-1-55285-170-8(2)) Whitecap Bks., Ltd. CAN. *Dist:* Firefly Bks., Ltd.

—Welcome to the World of Sharks. 2001. (Welcome to the World Ser.). (Illus.). 32p. (J). (ps-2). 9.95 (978-1-55285-315-3(2)) Whitecap Bks., Ltd. CAN. *Dist:* Firefly Bks., Ltd.

Taylor, Leighton. Great White Sharks. 2006. (Early Bird Nature Books). (Illus.). 47p. (J). (ps-7). 25.26 (978-0-8225-2868-5(1) , Lerner Pubns.) Lerner Publishing Group.

Thomas, Isabel. Shark vs. Killer Whale. 2006. (Illus.). 32p. (J). (978-1-4109-2392-9(4)); pap. (978-1-4109-2399-8(1)) Steck-Vaughn.

Thomson, Sarah L. Amazing Sharks! (I Can Read Bks.). (Illus.). 32p. (J). 2006. pap. 3.99 (978-0-06-054456-0(2) , Harper Trophy); 2005. 15.99 (978-0-06-054458-4(9)); 2005. lib. bdg. 16.89 (978-0-06-054457-7(0)) HarperCollins Pubs.

Los Tiburones Blancos (Great White Sharks) 2006. (Animales Depredadores (Animal Predators) Ser.). (SPA.). 40p. (J). lib. bdg. 25.26 (978-0-8225-6490-4(4) , Ediciones Lerner) Lerner Publishing Group.

Los tiburones blancos (Great White Sharks) 2006. (J). pap. 7.95 (978-0-8225-6627-4(3) , Ediciones Lerner) Lerner Publishing Group.

Los Tiburones y Las Rayas, 6 vols. (Explorers. Exploradores Nonfiction Sets Ser.). (SPA.). 32p. (gr. 3-6). 44.95 (978-0-7699-0626-3(5)) Shortland Pubns. (U. S. A.) Inc.

Toms, Kate. Marc the Shark: Bathtime Buddy. 2005. (Illus.). 12p. (ps-ps). 9.95 (978-1-84610-019-2(4)) Make Believe Ideas GBR. *Dist:* Ingram Pub. Services.

Top That Publishing Staff, ed. Sharks. 2006. (Illus.). 48p. (978-1-84510-011-7(5)) Top That! Publishing PLC.

Trimble, Irene. Sharks. Maydak, Mike, illus. 2005. 24p. (J). (ps-ps). pap. 5.99 incl. audio compact disk (978-1-58610-932-5(4)) Learning Horizons, Inc.

Twist, Clint. Shark & Other Sea Creatures Dictionary: An a to Z of Sea Life. 2002. (Illus.). 64p. (J). (978-0-439-46133-7(2)) Scholastic, Inc.

Vadon, Catherine. Meet the Shark. 2007. 45p. ***(978-1-58728-598-1(3)*** , Two Can Publishing) T&N Children's Publishing.

Wagner, Kathi & Wagner, Obe. The Everything Kids' Sharks Book. 2005. (Illus.). 144p. pap. 6.95 (978-1-59337-304-7(X)) Adams Media Corp.

Ward, Nathalie. Do Sharks Ever... ? What You Really Want to Know about Sharks. Morgan, Tessa, illus. 1999. 32p. (J). (ps-5). pap. 9.95 (978-0-89272-438-3(2)) Down East Bks.

Westwood, Brett. Great White Shark: Habitats, Life Cycles, Food Chains, Threats. 2000. (Natural World Ser.). (Illus.). 48p. (J). (gr. 3-7). lib. bdg. 27.12 (978-0-7398-1061-3(8)) Raintree.

Wexo, John Bonnett. Sharks. (Zoobooks). (Illus.). 24p. (J). (gr. 1-7). 2001. 15.95 (978-1-888153-31-6(8) , 229-7); 2003. 10.95 (978-1-932396-05-8(5) , Zoo Bks.) Wildlife Education, Ltd.

Whitecap Books Staff. Sharks. 2000. (Investigate Ser.). (Illus.). 64p. (J). (gr. 1-7). pap. 3.95 (978-1-55285-070-1(6)) Whitecap Bks., Ltd. CAN. *Dist:* Firefly Bks., Ltd.

Wildlife Education, Ltd. Staff. Sharks: Hunters of the Deep. Hoopes, Barbara, illus. 1998. (Zoobooks Ser.). 18p. (J). pap. 2.95 (978-0-937934-15-9(1)) Wildlife Education, Ltd.

Wilsdon, Christina. Sharks. 2007. (J). ***(978-1-59939-130-4(9)*** , Reader's Digest Young Families, Inc.) Reader's Digest Children's Publishing, Inc.

Wlodarski, Loran. Sharks! From Fear to Fascination, 1. 1999. (Education Department Publications). (Illus.). 68p. (gr. 4-12). per. 7.99 (978-1-893698-02-4(5) , B06, SeaWorld Education Dept.) SeaWorld, Inc.

Wood, Ira. Sharks: Learning the SH Sound. (PowerPhonics Ser.). (Illus.). (J). 2002. 24p. (gr. 1). lib. bdg. 18.50 (978-0-8239-5921-1(X)); 2001. 23p. pap. 26.40 (978-0-8239-8266-0(1)) Rosen Publishing Group, Inc., The. (PowerKids Pr.).

Woods, Bob. Shark Attack! 2006. (Boys Rock! Ser.). (Illus.). 32p. (J). (gr. 1-5). 24.21 (978-1-59296-734-6(5)) Child's World, Inc.

Woog, Adam. The Shark. 2001. (Endangered Animals & Habitats Ser.). (Illus.). 96p. (YA). (gr. 4-12). 27.45 (978-1-56006-462-6(5) , Lucent Bks.) Thomson Gale.

Yin, Robert, illus. & photos by. Sharks & Rays. Yin, Robert, photos by. 1999. 24p. (J). (978-0-7685-0357-9(4)) Dominie Pr., Inc.

Zoehfeld, Kathleen Weidner. Great White Shark: Ruler of the Sea. 2005. (Illus.). 32p. (J). (ps-2). 8.95 incl. audio (978-1-59249-224-4(X) , SC4006); pap. 6.95 (978-1-59249-196-4(0) , S4006) Soundprints.

Zollman, Pam. A Shark Pup Grows Up. 2005. (Scholastic News Nonfiction Readers Ser.). (Illus.). 24p. (J). (gr. 1-2). 19.00 (978-0-516-24945-2(2) , Children's Pr.) Scholastic Library Publishing.

SHARKS—FICTION

Alten, Steve. Trench. 2000. (gr. 5-8). lib. bdg. 15.30 (978-0-613-50383-9(X)) Tandem Library Bks.

Aoki, Takao. Beyblade. 2006. (Beyblade Ser.). 208p. (YA). Vol. 11. pap. 7.99 (978-1-4215-0437-7(5)); Vol. 12. pap. 7.99 (978-1-4215-0438-4(3)) Viz Media.

Ballantyne, R. The Coral Island. 2006. pap. 14.95 ***(978-1-55742-666-6(X))*** Wildside Pr.

Beserra, Donna. Twirly Shirley In Hurricane Shirley. 2005. 22p. (J). 8.00 (978-0-9729484-4-9(9)) Seventh Street Pr.

Bollback, Anthony G. The Tiger Shark Strikes Again, Vol. 5. 2000. 109p. (J). (gr. 4-9). pap. 7.95 (978-1-885729-20-0(0)) Toccoa Falls College Pr.

Bradley, Timothy J. Paleo Sharks: Survival of the Strangest. 2007. (Illus.). 48p. (J). (gr. 4-7). 15.95 (978-0-8118-4878-7(7)) Chronicle Bks. LLC.

Briny Town: Shark Showdown (Interactive Cd-rom) 2000. cd-rom 9.95 (978-1-931179-60-7(3)) Long Hill Productions, Inc.

Chronicle Books LLC Staff. Castaway Pirates. 2008. (J). 19.99 (978-0-8118-5923-3(1)) Chronicle Bks. LLC.

Clarke, Jane. Gilbert in Deep. Fuge, Charles, illus. 2007. 32p. (J). (ps-2). 12.95 ***(978-1-4027-5125-7(7))*** Sterling Publishing Co., Inc.

Clarke, Jane. Gilbert the Great. Fuge, Charles, illus. 2005. 32p. (J). 12.95 (978-1-4027-2169-4(2)) Sterling Publishing Co., Inc.

Cole, Joanna. The Great Shark Escape. Degen, Bruce, illus. 2001. (Magic School Bus Ser.: No. 7). 96p. (J). pap. 4.99 (978-0-439-20421-7(6) , Scholastic Paperbacks) Scholastic, Inc.

Coombs, Bob. Ted P Bear - A Bitter Tale. 2005. 83p. (YA). pap. 8.69 (978-1-4116-4260-7(0)) Lulu.com.

Cottringer, Anne. Mary Is Scary. Gale, Cathy, illus. 2007. 32p. (J). pap. 9.99 ***(978-0-7475-7927-4(X))*** Bloomsbury Publishing Plc GBR. *Dist:* Independent Pubs. Group.

Cox, Phil Roxbee. Shark in the Park. Cartwright, Stephen, illus. rev. ed. 2006. 16p. (J). pap. 6.99 (978-0-7945-1509-6(6) , Usborne) EDC Publishing.

Cruz, Stefanie. Delta & Dawn: Mother & Baby Whales' Journey. Toppenberg, Lily, illus. 2007. 32p. (J). lib. bdg. 15.95 ***(978-0-9791233-2-0(1))*** Big Tomato Pr.

Cullimore, Stan. Killer Sharks. Savage, Paul, illus. 2006. 40p. (J). (gr. 2-3). lib. bdg. (978-1-59889-013-6(1)) Stone Arch Bks.

Czekaj, Jef. Grampa & Julie: Shark Hunters. 2004. (Illus.). 128p. pap. 14.95 (978-1-891830-52-5(X)) Top Shelf Productions.

Delittle, Cathy. Blue Sharks in My Bathtub. Delittle, Cathy, illus. 1998. (Illus.). 10p. (J). (ps-1). spiral bd. 7.95 (978-1-892633-02-6(7) , GOCD210) Delittle Storyteller Co.

Dexter, Anthony. The Adventures of Manny the Manatee. 2004. 45p. pap. 19.95 (978-1-4137-2751-7(4)) PublishAmerica, Inc.

Galloway, Ruth. Smiley Shark. Galloway, Ruth, illus. (Illus.). 32p. (J). 2005. 6.95 (978-1-58925-391-9(4)); 2003. tchr. ed. 15.95 (978-1-58925-028-4(1)) ME Media LLC. (tiger tales).

Geist, Ken & Grace, Will. The Three Little Fish & the Big Bad Shark. Gorton, Julia, illus. 2007. 32p. (J). (ps-1). pap. 6.99 ***(978-0-439-71962-9(3))*** Scholastic, Inc.

George, Jean Craighead. Shark Beneath the Reef. (J). pap. 3.50 (978-0-13-800038-7(7)) Prentice Hall (Schl. Div.).

George, Twig C. Swimming with Sharks. Chen, Yong, illus. 1999. (Trophy Chapter Bks.). 128p. (J). (gr. 4-7). 14.89 (978-0-06-027758-1(0)) HarperCollins Pubs.

—Swimming with Sharks. Chen, Yong, photos by. 1999. (Trophy Chapter Bks.). (Illus.). 128p. (J). (gr. 4-7). 14.95 (978-0-06-027757-4(2)) HarperCollins Pubs.

Great White Man Eating Shark. 2004. (J). pap. 14.95 incl. audio (978-0-7882-0690-0(7)) Weston Woods Studios, Inc.

Haksteen, Herman. The Shark & the Blue Bottom Fishing Boat. Cadieux, Judy, illus. ltd. ed. 2000. 26p. (J). (ps-5). pap. 9.95 (978-0-9701700-0-2(9)) Internet Pubs., Inc.

Hall, Kirsten. I'm So Scared! Eugenie, illus. 2002. (My First Hello Reader! Ser.). (J). 2.95 (978-0-439-32098-6(4)) Scholastic, Inc.

Hanson, Anders. Lone Shark. Haberstroh, Anne, illus. (Fact & Fiction Ser.). 24p. (J). 2007. 21.35 (978-1-59928-452-1(9)); 2006. (978-1-59928-453-8(7)) ABDO Publishing Co.

Harvey, M. A. The Shark Island Mystery: Dare to Take the Test. 2004. (Illus.). 128p. (J). pap. (978-1-84458-147-4(0)) Chrysalis Children's Bks.

James, Brian. The Shark Who Was Afraid of Everything. 2006. (Illus.). 32p. (J). pap. 5.99 (978-0-439-78672-0(X) , Cartwheel Bks.) Scholastic, Inc.

—The Shark Who Was Afraid of Everything. McNally, Bruce J., illus. 2002. (J). (978-0-439-36865-0(0)) Scholastic, Inc.

Janacone, Matt. Finny the Friendly Shark. Druschel, Bob, illus. 2005. 40p. (J). per. 20.99 (978-1-58939-655-5(3)) Virtualbookworm.com Publishing, Inc.

Laird, Donivee Martin. The Magic Shark Learns to Cook. Johnson, Carol Ann, illus. 2004. 48p. (J). 9.95 (978-1-57306-233-6(2)) Bess Pr., Inc.

Lingemann, Linda. Survival in the Sea: The Story of a Hammerhead Shark, Includes toy. Marchesi, Stephen, illus. 1999. (Smithsonian Oceanic Collection: Vol. 18). 32p. (J). (ps-3). 29.95 incl. audio (978-1-56899-773-5(6)) Soundprints.

—Survival in the Sea: The Story of a Hammerhead Shark-Micro Edition. Marchesi, Stephen, illus. 1999. (Smithsonian Oceanic Collection: Vol. 18). 32p. (J). (ps-3). 4.95 (978-1-56899-770-4(1)) Soundprints.

Little Shark's First Hunt. 2002. (Oceanic Mini Bks.). (Illus.). 32p. (J). (978-1-59069-006-2(0) , H1007) Studio Mouse LLC.

Lloyd, Sam. Yummy Yummy! Food for My Tummy. Tickle, Jack, illus. 2004. 32p. (J). tchr. ed. 15.95 (978-1-58925-035-2(4) , tiger tales) ME Media LLC.

Maden, Mary. The Great Pirate Adventure. Schroeder, Eric, ed. 1999. (Outer Banks Animals Adventure Ser.: Vol. 7). (Illus.). 24p. (J). (gr. k-6). pap. 5.95 (978-1-890479-56-5(X)) Dog & Pony Publishing.

Maestro, Betsy & Maestro, Giulio. A Sea Full of Sharks.Tr. of Mer Pleine de Requins. (FRE., Illus.). (J). pap. 7.99 (978-0-590-74409-6(7)) Scholastic, Inc.

Mahy, Margaret. The Great White Man-Eating Shark: A Cautionary Tale. Allen, Jonathan, illus. 2002. (J). 13.19 (978-0-7587-2659-9(7)) Book Wholesalers, Inc.

Martin, Rafe. The Shark God. Shannon, David, illus. 2007. 32p. (J). (ps-3). pap. 5.99 ***(978-0-590-39570-0(X))*** Scholastic, Inc.

McGovern, Ann. Adventures of the Shark Lady: Eugene Clark Around the World. 1999. (Illus.). 96p. (gr. 3-7). pap. 4.50 (978-0-590-45712-5(8)) Scholastic, Inc.

Metzger, Steve. Big Shark's Valentine Surprise. Hohnstadt, Cedric, illus. 2007. (J). pap. ***(978-0-439-92251-7(8))*** Scholastic, Inc.

Metzger, Steve. Five Little Sharks Swimming in the Sea. Bryant, Laura, illus. 2005. 32p. (J). pap. 5.99 (978-0-439-73767-8(2)) Scholastic, Inc.

Mills, Elizabeth. Tick-Tock Sharks. Bettoli, Delana, illus. 2005. 40p. (J). (ps-ps). 9.99 (978-0-439-72308-4(6) , Cartwheel Bks.) Scholastic, Inc.

Moore, Eva. The Great Shark Escape. 2001. (Magic School Bus Chapter Bks.). (Illus.). (J). 11.79 (978-0-606-21311-0(2)) Tandem Library Bks.

Morgan, Michaela. Shy Shark. Gomez, Elena, illus. 2005. 24p. (J). lib. bdg. 22.65 ***(978-1-59646-722-4(3))*** Dingles & Co.

Murphy, Stuart J. Shark Swimathon. 2001. (gr. k-3). lib. bdg. 13.00 (978-0-613-31686-6(X)) Tandem Library Bks.

Page, Nick & Claire. Jonah the Moaner. 2006. (Read with Me (Make Believe Ideas) Ser.). (Illus.). (J). (gr. k-2). 32p. 3.95 (978-1-84610-167-0(0)); 12p. pap. 4.95 (978-1-84610-183-0(2)) Make Believe Ideas GBR. *Dist:* Ingram Pub. Services.

Pfister, Marcus. El Pez Arco Iris al Rescate! Pfister, Marcus, illus. 1998. (Rainbow Fish Ser.). Orig. Title: Regenbogenfisch, Komm Hilf Mir!. (SPA., Illus.). 12p. (J). (ps-3). bds. 9.95 (978-1-55858-885-1(X)) North-South Bks., Inc.

—Rainbow Fish to the Rescue! Minibook & Audio Package. James, J. Alison, tr. from GER. Pfister, Marcus, illus. 1998. (Rainbow Fish Ser.).Tr. of Regenbogenfisch, Komm Hilf Mir!. (ENG & SPA., Illus.). 12p. (J). (ps-3). bds. 9.95 (978-1-55858-880-6(9)) North-South Bks., Inc.

Raintree Steck-Vaughn Staff. Los Grandes Tiburones Blancos. 1999. (SPA.). (J). pap., stu. ed. 31.05 (978-0-7398-0754-5(4)) Steck-Vaughn.

Salisbury, Graham. Shark Bait. 1999. (978-0-606-16449-8(9)) Tandem Library Bks.

Scholastic, Inc. Staff & McCann, Jesse Leon. Shark Tale. Edwards, Ken, illus. 2004. (Shark Tale Ser.). 48p. (J). (gr. 2-5). pap. 3.99 (978-0-439-64162-3(4)) Scholastic, Inc.

S

Schwarz, Viviane. Shark & Lobster's Amazing Undersea Adventure. Schwarz, Viviane & Stewart, Joel, illus. 2006. 40p. (J). (ps-1). 15.99 (978-0-7636-2910-6(3)) Candlewick Pr.

—Shark & Lobster's Amazing Undersea Adventure. Stewart, Joel, illus. 2006. 34p. (J). ***978-1-4156-8140-4(6))*** Candlewick Pr.

Stanley, George Edward. Adam Sharp No. 3: Swimming with Sharks. 2003. (gr. k-3). lib. bdg. 11.80 (978-0-613-82722-5(8)) Tandem Library Bks.

Stephens, Ann Marie. Christmas for Bly & Ray. Bolan, Michael P., illus. 2003. 45p. (J). per. 11.95 (978-0-9729285-0-2(2) , 0-9729285-0-2) Kinkachoo Pr., The.

—A Surprise for Ray. Bolan, Michael P., illus. 2003. 47p. (J). per. 11.95 (978-0-9729285-1-9(0) , 0-9729285-1-0) Kinkachoo Pr., The.

Sula, Sondra Robert. Briny Town: Shark Showdown. 2000. mass mkt. 8.95 (978-1-931179-12-6(3)) Long Hill Productions, Inc.

Tate, Suzanne. Great Sharky Shark: A Tale of a Big Hunter. Melvin, James, illus. 2004. (Suzanne Tate's Nature Ser.). 32p. (J). per. 10.95 (978-1-878405-46-3(2)) Nags Head Art, Inc.

Ward, Nick. Don't Eat the Babysitter. 2006. 32p. (J). (gr. k-3). 9.95 (978-0-385-75062-2(5) , Fickling, David Bks.) Random Hse. Children's Bks.

Warner, Gertrude Chandler. Great Shark Mystery. 2003. (gr. 3-6). lib. bdg. 11.80 (978-0-613-75720-1(3)) Tandem Library Bks.

Wurzburg, Robert. Dogshark Readers: Red Set. 2005. (Illus.). 96p. (ps-ps). 14.95 (978-1-59354-074-6(4)) Handprint Bks.

SHAVUOT—FICTION

Brooks, David, illus. My Shabbat. 2005. (Soft Shapes Ser.). 8p. (J). (ps-ps). 8.99 (978-1-58476-351-2(5)) Innovative Kids.

Rouss, Sylvia A. Sammy Spider's First Shavuot. Kahn, Katherine, illus. 2008. (J). lib. bdg. ***978-0-8225-7224-4(9))*** Kar-Ben Publishing.

SHAW, GEORGE BERNARD, 1856-1950

Summers, Ann. The George Bernard Shaw Papers. 2005. (British Library - Catalogue of Additions to the Manuscripts). (Illus.). 330p. 100.00 ***978-0-7123-4887-4(5))*** British Library, The GBR. *Dist:* Chicago Distribution Ctr.

SHAYS' REBELLION, 1786-1787

Hull, Mary E. Shays' Rebellion & the Constitution in American History. 2000. (In American History Ser.). (Illus.). 112p. (YA). (gr. 5-12). lib. bdg. 26.60 (978-0-7660-1418-3(5)) Enslow Pubs., Inc.

SHEEP

see also Dolly (Sheep)

Bannor, Brett. Bighorn Sheep. 2002. (Endangered Animals & Habitats Ser.). (Illus.). 112p. (J). 27.45 (978-1-56006-887-7(6) , Lucent Bks.) Thomson Gale.

Beck, Isabel L., et al. Trophies Kindergarten: The Big Ram. 2003. (Trophies Ser.). (gr. k-6). 13.80 (978-0-15-329540-9(6)) Harcourt Schl. Pubs.

Bell, Rachael. Sheep. (Farm Animals Ser.). 32p. 2003. pap. 6.95 (978-1-4034-4040-2(9)); 2000. (Illus.). (J). lib. bdg. 21.36 (978-1-57572-533-8(9)) Heinemann Library.

The Bighorn Sheep. (Wildlife of North America Ser.). 48p. (YA). 7.95 (978-0-7368-8484-6(X)) Capstone Pr., Inc.

The Bighorn Sheep, 6 vols. (gr. 4 up). 39.95 (978-0-7368-8496-9(3)) Red Brick Learning.

Blake, Anne Catharine. Sheep Sleep. 2001. (ENG., Illus.). 20p. (J). (ps-k). bds. 4.99 (978-0-570-07166-2(6)) Concordia Publishing Hse.

Bolam, Emily. Chunky Farm Sheep. 2000. (Chunky Farm Bks.). (Illus.). 14p. (J). (ps-k). bds. 5.99 (978-0-7641-5321-1(8)) Barron's Educational Series, Inc.

Brady, Peter. Ovejas. Schon, Isabel, ed. Ferrer, Martín Luis Guzman, tr. from ENG. Munoz, William, illus. 1998. (Coleccion Primeros Lectores). (SPA.). 24p. (J). (gr. k-3). lib. bdg. 18.60 (978-1-56065-790-3(1) , CAP2405, Bridgestone Bks.) Capstone Pr., Inc.

Casey's Lamb: First Grade Guided Reading Level C. (On Our Way to English Ser.). (gr. 1 up). 27.75 (978-0-7578-7037-8(6)) Rigby Education.

Dalgleish, Sharon. Sheep. 2005. (Farm Animals Ser.). (Illus.). 32p. (J). (gr. 2-4). 23.00 (978-0-7910-8271-3(7) , Chelsea Hse.) Facts On File, Inc.

DK Publishing. Lamb. 2007. (See How They Grow Ser.). 24p. (J). pap. 3.99 ***978-0-7566-3373-8(7))*** Dorling Kindersley Publishing, Inc.

Doubleday Entertainment USA - Sheep: Down on the Farm. 2006. (J). per. 6.95 (978-1-59566-227-9(8)) QEB Publishing Inc.

Feinstein, Stephen. The Bighorn Sheep: Help Save This Endangered Species! 2007. (Saving Endangered Species Ser.). (Illus.). 128p. (J). (gr. 5). lib. bdg. 33.27 ***978-1-59845-042-2(5)*** , MyReportLinks.com Bks.) Enslow Pubs., Inc.

Frisch, Aaron. Bighorns. 2001. (Kings of the Mountain Ser.). (Illus.). 24p. (J). lib. bdg. 14.95 (978-1-58340-016-6(8)) Smart Apple Media.

Green, Emily. Sheep. 2007. (Blastoff! Readers Ser.). 24p. (J). (gr. k-2). 18.50 ***978-0-531-17555-2(3)*** , Children's Pr.) Scholastic Library Publishing.

Green, Emily K. Sheep. 2007. (Illus.). 24p. (J). lib. bdg. 16.95 (978-1-60014-069-3(6)) Bellwether Media.

Harcourt School Publishers Staff. Little Big Horns On Level. 3rd ed. 2002. (Trophies Reading Program Ser.). (Illus.). pap. 5.10 (978-0-15-323265-7(X)) Harcourt Schl. Pubs.

Harder Tangvald, Christine. Jesus' Little Lamb. Stewart, Jennifer, ed. Garris, Norma, illus. 1999. (Patty Cake Devotions Ser.). 14p. (J). (ps). bds. 3.99 (978-0-7847-0978-8(5) , 04292, Bean Sprouts) Standard Publishing.

Hudak, Heather C. Sheep. 2006. (J). (978-1-59036-428-4(7)); (978-1-59036-435-2(X)) Weigl Pubs., Inc.

Ivy, Bill, et al. Bighorn Sheep. 1999. (Getting to Know ... Nature's Children Ser.). (Illus.). 47p. (J). (978-0-7172-8836-6(6) , Grolier) Scholastic Library Publishing.

Macken, JoAnn Early. Bighorn Sheep. 2006. (Illus.). 24p. (J). pap. 5.95 (978-0-8368-6322-2(4)); lib. bdg. 19.33 (978-0-8368-6315-4(1)) Stevens, Gareth Inc.

—Bighorn Sheep: Carnero de Canada. 2006. (ENG & SPA., Illus.). 24p. (J). pap. (978-0-8368-6453-3(0)); lib. bdg. 19.33 (978-0-8368-6446-5(8)) Stevens, Gareth Inc.

—Sheep: Las Ovejas. 2004. (ENG & SPA., Illus.). 24p. (J). pap. (978-0-8368-4297-5(9)); lib. bdg. 19.33 (978-0-8368-4290-6(1)) Stevens, Gareth Inc.

—Sheep/JoAnn Early Macken. 2004. (Animals That Live on the Farm Ser.). (Illus.). 24p. (J). pap. (978-0-8368-4283-8(9)); (YA). lib. bdg. 19.33 (978-0-8368-4276-0(6)) Stevens, Gareth Inc.

Marie, Christian. Little Sheep. 2006. (Born to Be Wild Ser.). (Illus.). 23p. (J). lib. bdg. 22.00 (978-0-8368-6169-3(8)) Stevens, Gareth Inc.

Mattern, Joanne. The Bighorn Sheep. 1998. (Wildlife of North America Ser.). (Illus.). 48p. (J). (gr. 3-4). lib. bdg. 21.26 (978-0-7368-0028-0(X) , Capstone High-Interest Bks.) Capstone Pr., Inc.

Miller, Heather. My Sheep. 2000. (Welcome Bks.). (Illus.). 24p. (J). (ps-2). 17.00 (978-0-516-23110-5(3) , Children's Pr.) Scholastic Library Publishing.

—My Sheep. 2000. (gr. k-3). lib. bdg. 12.95 (978-0-613-58871-3(1)) Tandem Library Bks.

Miller, Sara Swan. Sheep. 2000. (True Bks.). (Illus.). 48p. (J). (gr. 3-5). 25.00 (978-0-516-21580-8(9) , Children's Pr.) Scholastic Library Publishing.

—Sheep. 2000. (gr. 3-6). lib. bdg. 15.25 (978-0-613-54656-0(3)) Tandem Library Bks.

Murray, Julie. Sheep. 2005. (Animal Kingdom Set Ii Ser.). (Illus.). 24p. (J). (gr. k-4). lib. bdg. 21.35 (978-1-59197-335-5(X)) ABDO Publishing Co.

—Sheep to Sweater. 2007. (Illus.). 24p. (J). 21.35 (978-1-59679-914-1(5) , Buddy Bks.) ABDO Publishing Co.

Nelson, Robin. From Sheep to Sweater. 2003. (Start to Finish Ser.). (Illus.). 24p. (J). 18.60 (978-0-8225-0716-1(1) , Lerner Pubns.) Lerner Publishing Group.

Powell, Jillian. From Lamb to Sheep. 2001. (How Do They Grow? Ser.). (Illus.). 32p. (J). lib. bdg. 25.69 (978-0-7398-4425-0(3)) Raintree.

Powell, R. This Little Lamb. Curry, Peter, illus. 2004. (Mini Movers Ser.). 14p. (J). bds. 3.50 (978-0-7641-5742-4(6)) Barron's Educational Series, Inc.

Ray, Hannah. Sheep. Davidson, Chris, illus. 2006. (Down on the Farm Ser.). 24p. (J). (gr. k-2). lib. bdg. 15.95 (978-1-59566-182-1(4)) QEB Publishing Inc.

Royston, Angela. Lamb. 2004. (J). lib. bdg. 27.10 (978-1-59389-161-9(X)) Chrysalis Education.

Schuh, Mari C. Sheep on the Farm. 2001. (On the Farm Ser.). (Illus.). 24p. (J). (gr. k-1). lib. bdg. 15.93 (978-0-7368-0994-8(5) , Pebble Bks.) Capstone Pr., Inc.

Sheep, 6 vols., Pack. 16p. (gr. 2 up). 36.00 (978-0-7635-9212-7(9)) Rigby Education.

Sheep Gets Lost. 2004. bds. 5.99 (978-0-8254-7286-2(5)) Kregel Pubns.

Sheep Have Lambs. (Animals & Their Young Ser.). 24p. (J). 7.95 (978-0-7565-1247-7(6)) Compass Point Bks.

Sheep on the Farm, 6 vols. (gr. k-2). 28.95 (978-0-7368-9231-5(1)) Red Brick Learning.

Sibylle, Rieckhoff & Rieckhoff, Jurgen. Roberta. 2004. (Illus.). 32p. (J). 15.95 (978-1-84507-324-4(X)) Lincoln, Frances Ltd. GBR. *Dist:* Perseus Distribution.

Simmons, Paula & Salsbury, Darrell L. Your Sheep: A Kid's Guide to Raising & Showing. Steege, Gwen, ed. 2003. (Illus.). 120p. (J). (gr. 4-7). pap. 14.95 (978-0-88266-769-0(6) , 66769) Storey Publishing, LLC.

Stockland, Patricia M. In the Sheep Pasture. Ouren, Todd, illus. 2007. (Barnyard Buddies Ser.). 24p. (J). (ps-2). lib. bdg. 25.65 ***978-1-60270-026-0(5)*** , Looking Glass Library) Magic Wagon.

Stone, Lynn M. Sheep Have Lambs. 2000. (Animals & Their Young Ser.). (Illus.). 24p. (J). (gr. 1 up). lib. bdg. 18.60 (978-0-7565-0004-7(4)) Compass Point Bks.

—Wool. 2002. (Harvest to Home Ser.). (Illus.). 24p. (gr. 2-5). 14.95 (978-1-58952-131-5(5)) Rourke Publishing, LLC.

Top That Publishing Staff, ed. Wacky Sheep. 2004. (Wacky Animals Ser.). (Illus.). 10p. (J). pap. (978-1-84510-089-6(1)) Top That! Publishing PLC.

Urbigkit, Cat. The Shepherd's Trail. 2008. (J). ***978-1-59078-509-6(6))*** Boyds Mills Pr.

Wilsdon, Christina. Sheep. 2006. (J). (978-1-59939-079-6(5) , Reader's Digest Young Families, Inc.) Reader's Digest Children's Publishing, Inc.

Wolfman, Judy. Life on a Sheep Farm. Winston, David Lorenz, illus. Winston, David Lorenz, photos by. 2004. (Life on a Farm Ser.). 48p. (J). (gr. 2-5). lib. bdg. 23.93 (978-1-57505-192-5(3)) Lerner Publishing Group.

SHEEP—FICTION

Aesop. The Wolf in Sheep's Clothing: A Tale about Appearances. 2006. (J). (978-1-59939-086-4(8) , Reader's Digest Young Families, Inc.) Reader's Digest Children's Publishing, Inc.

Alphabetical Sleepy Sheep. 2005. (J). bds. 7.95 (978-0-9749305-7-2(1)); (ENG.). bds. 7.95 (978-0-9749305-4-1(7)) Castle Pacific Publishing.

Amery, H. The Naughty Sheep. 2004. (Keyring Pack Ser.). 16p. (J). pap. 6.95 (978-0-7945-0067-2(6) , Usborne) EDC Publishing.

—Where's Woolly? Cartwright, Stephen, illus. 2004. (Treasury of Farmyard Tales Ser.). 16p. (J). (gr. 1 up). lib. bdg. 15.95 (978-1-58086-531-9(3)) EDC Publishing.

Amery, H. & Cartwright, Stephen. The Naughty Sheep. 16p. (J). lib. bdg. 13.95 (978-1-58086-720-7(0) , Usborne) EDC Publishing.

Amery, Heather. Naughty Sheep. Tyler, Jenny, ed. Cartwright, Stephen, illus. rev. ed. 2004. (Farmyard Tales Readers Ser.). 16p. (J). pap. 5.95 (978-0-7945-0749-7(2) , Usborne) EDC Publishing.

—Woolly the Sheep. Cartwright, Stephen, illus. 2004. (Young Farmyard Tales Board Books Ser.). 10p. (J). bds. 3.95 (978-0-7945-0467-0(1) , Usborne) EDC Publishing.

Animal I can hear s/s - Sheep. 2005. (J). bds. (978-1-4194-0060-5(6)) Paradise Pr., Inc.

Apperley, Dawn. Hello Little Lamb. Apperley, Dawn, illus. 2000. (Hello Bks.). (Illus.). 12p. (J). bds. 3.95 (978-1-86233-190-7(1)) David & Charles Children's Bks. GBR. *Dist:* Sterling Publishing Co., Inc.

Baa, Baa Black Sheep. 2003. (J). per. (978-1-57657-799-8(6)) Paradise Pr., Inc.

Banta, Byron. Tales from the High Meadows. 2005. 48p. (J). per. 13.99 (978-1-58930-149-8(8)) Selah Publishing Group, LLC.

Bee, Granny. Laffy the Lamb. Sohn, Jeana, illus. 2006. (J). lib. bdg. 16.95 (978-1-932367-00-3(4)) BookBound Publishing.

Beeke, Joel & Kleyn, Diana. How God Used a Drought & an Umbrella. Anderson, Jeff, illus. (Building on the Rock Ser.). 176p. (J). pap. (978-1-85792-818-1(0) , Christian Focus) Christian Focus Pubns. GBR. *Dist:* Riverside.

Bergna, Monica, illus. Juguemos en el Bosque. 2004. (SPA.). 28p. (J). (gr. k up). pap. 6.50 (978-980-257-282-3(9)) Ekare, Ediciones VEN. *Dist:* Lectorum Pubns., Inc., Iaconi, Mariuccia Bk. Imports.

Bester, Maryanne. Three Friends & a Taxi. Bester, Shayle, illus. 2007. 24p. (J). pap. 12.00 ***978-1-77009-265-5(X))*** Jacana Media ZAF. *Dist:* Independent Pubs. Group.

Blair, Eric. El Pastorcito Mentiroso: Version de la Fabula de Esopo. Silverman, Dianne, illus. 2006. (Read-It! Readers en Espanol Ser.).Tr. of Boy Who Cried Wolf: A Retelling of Aesop's Fable. (SPA.). 32p. (J). (ps-3). 19.95 (978-1-4048-1616-9(X)) Picture Window Bks.

Blake, Anne Catharine. Sheep Lost. 1998. (ENG., Illus.). 20p. (J). (ps). bds. 4.99 (978-0-570-05091-9(X)) Concordia Publishing Hse.

Blyton, Enid. Don't Be Silly Mr Twiddle! (Illus.). 111p. (J). pap. 7.95 (978-0-7475-3858-5(1)) Bloomsbury Publishing Plc GBR. *Dist:* Trafalgar Square Publishing.

Brenner, Barbara & Hooks, William H. Lion & Lamb Step Out. Degen, Bruce, illus. 1998. (Bank Street Reader Collection). 48p. (J). (gr. 2-4). lib. bdg. 22.60 (978-0-8368-1772-0(9)) Stevens, Gareth Inc.

—Ups & Downs with Lion & Lamb. Degen, Bruce, illus. 1999. (Bank Street Reader Collection). 48p. (J). (gr. 2-4). lib. bdg. (978-0-8368-1783-6(4)) Stevens, Gareth Inc.

Brown, Margaret Wise. The Little Lost Lamb. Date not set. 40p. (J). (ps-3). 15.89 (978-0-06-027291-3(0)); 14.99 (978-0-06-027290-6(2)) HarperCollins Pubs.

—The Little Lost Lamb. 2020. 32p. (J). pap. 5.99 (978-0-7868-1258-5(3)) Hyperion Paperbacks for Children.

—The Little Lost Lamb. 2000. 32p. (J). (ps-1). 14.95 (978-0-7868-0372-9(X)) Hysolli Production Co.

—Sheep Don't Count Sheep. Huang, Benrei, illus. 2003. 32p. (J). (ps). 14.95 (978-0-689-83346-5(6) , McElderry, Margaret K.) Simon & Schuster Children's Publishing.

Brown, Richard. A Welsh Lamb. 2005. (Cambridge Storybooks Ser.). 32p. pap. 7.00 (978-0-521-67482-9(4)) Cambridge Univ. Pr.

Butler, Dori. A Sheep in Wolf's Clothing. 2006. 23.00 ***978-1-4108-6185-6(6))*** Benchmark Education Co.

Butterfield, Moira. Do Frogs Fly? Canals, Sonia, illus. 2007. (Animal Flappers Bks.). 16p. (J). (gr. k-k). 7.99 (978-0-7641-6027-1(3)) Barron's Educational Series, Inc.

Calhoun, Mary. Henry the Christmas Cat. Ingraham, Erick, illus. 2004. 32p. (J). (ps-3). 15.99 (978-0-688-16560-4(5)) HarperCollins Pubs.

Cansino, Eliacer. Nube y las Ninos(Delicado, Federico, illus. 2000. (SPA.). 80p. (J). (gr. 3-5). (978-84-207-1283-3(3)) Grupo Anaya, S.A. ESP. *Dist:* Lectorum Pubns., Inc.

Caple, Kathy. The Friendship Tree. Caple, Kathy, illus. (House Readers Ser.). (Illus.). 32p. (J). (gr. k-3). tchr. ed. 15.95 (978-0-8234-1376-8(4)) Holiday Hse., Inc.

Carle, Eric. Little Cloud. Carle, Eric, illus. 1998. (Illus.). 28p. (J). (ps-k). bds. 6.99 (978-0-399-23191-9(9) , Philomel) Penguin Group (USA) Inc.

Carrick, Carol. Valentine. 2001. (J). (978-0-606-20966-3(2)); lib. bdg. 14.10 (978-0-613-31853-2(6)) Tandem Library Bks.

Casey's Lamb: First Grade Guided Reading Level C. (On Our Way to English Ser.). (gr. 1 up). 27.75 (978-0-7578-7037-8(6)) Rigby Education.

Christian, Focus. God's Zoo TNT Ministries. Charnick, Tim, illus. 2005. 96p. pap. (978-1-84550-069-6(5) , Christian Focus) Christian Focus Pubns.

Christie, Jacky. The Shepherd's Bell Sheep. 2006. (ENG.). 36p. (J). per. 16.99 (978-1-4141-0418-8(9)) Pleasant Word.

The Christmas Star. 2005. (Illus.). 28p. (J). (ps-k). bds. 7.95 (978-0-8249-6620-1(1)) Ideals Pubns.

Clark, Carol Toledo. Cheii's Sheepcamp. 2005. 16.95 (978-0-533-15141-7(4)) Vantage Pr., Inc.

Coe, Frances. Sleepy Little Lamb: With Soft Cloth Blanket. Elgar, Rebecca, illus. 1999. (Little Blanket Bks.). 10p. (J). (ps). bds. 3.95 (978-0-7641-5176-7(2)) Barron's Educational Series, Inc.

Colorful Sleepy Sheep. ed. 2005. (J). bds. 7.95 (978-0-9749305-5-8(5)) Castle Pacific Publishing.

Cosgrove, Stephen. Minikin. 2000. (gr. k-3). lib. bdg. 13.00 (978-0-613-33659-8(3)) Tandem Library Bks.

Cox, Phil Roxbee. Sam Sheep Can't Sleep. Cartwright, Stephen, illus. rev. ed. 2006. 16p. (J). pap. 6.99 (978-0-7945-1508-9(8) , Usborne) EDC Publishing.

Cox, Phil Roxbee & Cartwright, S. Sam Sheep Can't Sleep. 2004. (Phonics Board Bks.). 10p. (J). 4.99 (978-0-7945-0060-3(9) , Usborne) EDC Publishing.

—Ted's Shed, Toad Makes a Road, Fat Cat on a Mat & Sam Sheep Can't Sleep. 2004. (Easy Words to Read Ser.). (Illus.). 16p. (J). (gr. 1 up). pap. 9.95 (978-0-7945-0245-4(8) , Usborne) EDC Publishing.

The Crippled Lamb. 2004. (Max Lucado Ser.). 32p. 19.99 incl. DVD (978-1-4003-0181-2(5)) Nelson, Thomas Inc.

Croteau, Marie-Danielle. The Amazing Story of the Little Black Sheep. Cote, Genevieve, illus. 1999. 32p. (J). (ps up). pap. (978-1-894363-16-7(7)) Dominique & Friends.

Dakin, Glenn. Wallace & Gromit Curse of the Were-Rabbit: The Essential Guide. 2005. (Illus.). 48p. (J). (ps-7). 12.99 (978-0-7566-1153-8(9)) Dorling Kindersley Publishing, Inc.

Daniels, Lucy. Lamb Lessons. Howard, Paul, illus. 2000. (Animal Ark Pets Ser.: No. 11). 128p. (J). (gr. 3-6). pap. 3.99 (978-0-439-05168-2(1)) Scholastic, Inc.

Davies, Gill & Freeman, Tina. Lucy Lamb. 2004. (Tales from Yellow Barn Farm Ser.). (Illus.). 24p. (J). 3.99 (978-1-85854-322-2(3)) Brimax Books Ltd. GBR. *Dist:* Byeway Bks.

DePrisco, Dorothea. One Little Sheep. 2006. 12p. (J). 12.95 (978-1-58117-488-5(8) , Intervisual/Piggy Toes) Dalmatian Pr.

Dillon, Sally Pierson & Williams, Sharon Dalton. From Growlies to Bleats: How to Be All that We Can Be. 2002. (J). (gr. 1-5). pap. 7.97 (978-0-9714167-3-4(7)) Kingdom Ambassador Ministries.

Dohaney, Rainy. Tinka. Dohaney, Rainy, illus. 2003. (Illus.). 40p. (J). 15.95 (978-0-689-85261-9(4) , Atheneum/Anne Schwartz Bks.) Simon & Schuster Children's Publishing.

Dorling Kindersley Publishing Staff. Wallace & Gromit: Curse of the Were-Rabbit. 2005. (Ultimate sticker Bks.). (Illus.). 16p. (J). 6.99 (978-0-7566-1154-5(7)) Dorling Kindersley Publishing, Inc.

Doudna, Kelly. Lamb Chops. Chawla, Neena, illus. 2006. (Fact & Fiction Ser.). 24p. (J). 21.35 (978-1-59679-947-9(1) , SandCastle); pap. (978-1-59679-948-6(X)) ABDO Publishing Co.

Durkee, Noura. The King, the Prince & the Naughty Sheep. Durkee, Noura, illus. 1999. (Illus.). 24p. (J). (gr. 1-5). 16.00 (978-1-879402-58-4(0)) Tahrike Tarsile Quran, Inc.

Edwards, David. The Pen That Pa Built. Wolff, Ashley, illus. 2007. 32p. (J). (ps-1). 14.95 ***978-1-58246-153-3(8)*** , Tricycle Pr.) Ten Speed Pr.

Eglin, Lorna. A Boy of Two Worlds. 2006. 208p. mass mkt. (978-1-84550-126-6(8)) Christian Focus Pubns.

Enderle, Judith Ross. Six Creepy Sheep. 2001. (ps-2). lib. bdg. 17.60 (978-0-613-78778-9(1)); (Illus.). (J). (978-0-606-20918-2(2)) Tandem Library Bks.

Ennis, Scott. Feed My Sheep. 2005. 23p. 7.49 (978-1-4116-6287-2(3)) Lulu.com.

Entara Ltd., photos by. Sheep on the Loose. 2007. (Jakers! Ser.). 24p. (J). (ps-1). pap. 3.99 ***978-1-4169-3819-4(2)*** , Simon Spotlight) Simon & Schuster Children's Publishing.

Eversole, Robyn. Red Berry Wool. 2002. (gr. k-3). lib. bdg. 15.25 (978-0-613-75727-0(0)) Tandem Library Bks.

—Red Berry Wool. Coffey, Timothy, illus. 2004. 32p. (J). (gr. k-3). pap. 6.95 (978-0-8075-6918-4(6)) Whitman, Albert & Co.

Fernleigh Books Staff. Little Lamb. 2007. 32p. (J). pap. 4.99 (978-0-439-90661-6(X) , Cartwheel Bks.) Scholastic, Inc.

Following Isabella - Evaluation Guide: Evaluation Guide. 2006. (J). (978-1-55942-406-6(0)) Marsh Media.

Following Isabella - Teaching Guide. 2000. 17.95 (978-1-55942-169-0(X)) Marsh Media.

Forrester, Sandra. Dust from Old Bones. 1999. (Illus.). xi, 164p. (J). (gr. 5-9). 16.00 (978-0-688-16202-3(9)) HarperCollins Pubs.

—House of Lamb. 1999. (J). 15.99 (978-0-525-67584-6(1) , Dutton Juvenile) Penguin Group (USA) Inc.

Fraggalosch, Audrey. Trails above the Tree Line: A Story of a Rocky Mountain Meadow. Bond, Higgins, illus. (Soundprints' Wild Habitats Ser.). (J). 2005. 36p. (gr. 1-4). 15.95 (978-1-56899-941-8(0) , B7021); 2005. 36p. (gr. 1-4). 19.95 incl. reel tape (978-1-56899-943-2(7) , BC7021); 2005. 32p. (gr. 1-4). pap. 6.95 (978-1-56899-942-5(9) , S7021); 2002. 36p. 26.95 (978-1-56899-945-6(3) , Little Soundprints) Soundprints.

French, Jackie. Pete the Sheep-Sheep. Whatley, Bruce, illus. 2005. 32p. (J). (gr. k-3). 14.00 (978-0-618-56862-8(X) , Clarion Bks.) Houghton Mifflin Co. Trade & Reference Div.

Friend, Catherine. Quiet Ruby. 2000. (Brand New Readers Ser.). (Illus.). (J). (978-0-7636-1075-3(5)) Candlewick Pr.

—Ruby Apple Tree. 2000. (Brand New Readers Ser.). (Illus.). (J). (978-0-7636-1076-0(3)) Candlewick Pr.

—Ruby, Buzz Buzz. 2000. (Brand New Readers Ser.). (Illus.). (J). (978-0-7636-1073-9(9)) Candlewick Pr.

—Ruby Eats Hay. 2000. (Brand New Readers Ser.). (Illus.). (J). (978-0-7636-1069-2(0)) Candlewick Pr.

—Ruby Is Hungry. 2000. (Brand New Readers Ser.). (Illus.). (J). (978-0-7636-1067-8(4)) Candlewick Pr.

—Ruby Jumps. 2000. (Brand New Readers Ser.). (Illus.). (J). (978-0-7636-1068-5(2)) Candlewick Pr.

—Ruby Yuck. 2000. (Brand New Readers Ser.). (Illus.). (J). (978-0-7636-1070-8(4)) Candlewick Pr.

—Rubys Bathtub. 2000. (Brand New Readers Ser.). (Illus.). (J). (978-0-7636-1074-6(7)) Candlewick Pr.

Gerstein, Mordicai. The White Ram: A Story of Abraham & Isaac. Gerstein, Mordicai, illus. 2006. (Illus.). 32p. (J). (gr. 1-5). 16.95 (978-0-8234-1897-8(9)) Holiday Hse., Inc.

Giff, Patricia Reilly. Leones Perezosos, Corderos Afortunados. 2000. (SPA.). (YA). (gr. 1 up). 3.95 (978-0-922852-47-5(2)) AIMS International Bks., Inc.

Goldsack, Gaby. Little Lamb. Davies, Kate, illus. 2000. (Fluffy Tales Ser.). 12p. (ps-k). 6.99 (978-0-7847-0577-3(1) , 03721, Bean Sprouts) Standard Publishing.

Gonzalez Jensen, Margarita. Botas Negras. Sanchez, Enrique O., illus. (SPA.). (J). (gr. 2-4). 3.96 net. (978-0-590-26842-4(2)) Scholastic, Inc.

Gormley, Greg. Rocky & the Lamb. Chapman, Lynne, illus. 2006. 32p. (J). 12.99 (978-0-7641-5939-8(9)) Barron's Educational Series, Inc.

Griver, Jeanette A. Curio, a Shetland Sheepdog Meets the Crow: A Story of Friendship For Children of All Ages, 2004. (Illus.). 44p. (J). pap. 6.95 (978-0-929948-04-1(1)) Compsych Systems, Inc., Pubns. Div.

Gummelt, Donna & Melchiorre, Dondino. Cow Puppies. Wall, Randy Hugh, ed. Varela, Juan D., tr. Varela, Juan D., illus. 2006. Tr. of Cachorros Vaqueros. (SPA.). 32p. (J). 14.95 (978-0-9764798-7-1(7)) Story Store Collection Publishing.

Gunzi, Christiane. On the Farm. 2005. (Feels Real Bks.). (Illus.). 10p. (J). bds. 4.95 (978-0-7641-5856-8(2)) Barron's Educational Series, Inc.

Hanlin, Beverly Austin. Little Lamb: A Christmas Story. 2006. (J). pap. 8.00 (978-0-8059-7128-6(9)) Dorrance Publishing Co., Inc.

Harcourt School Publishers Staff. The Pig Who Cried Help: Take-Home Book. 1999. (Collections Ser.). (Illus.). (J). pap. 1.90 (978-0-15-317311-0(4)) Harcourt Schl. Pubs.

Harper, Stephan J. The Black Sheep, Beach, Mary FitzGerald, illus. l.t. ed. 2005. 32p. (J). lib. bdg. 16.95 (978-0-9741800-1-4(7)) Inspire Press, Inc.

Hathorn, Libby & Magerl, Caroline. Over the Moon. 2005. (Illus.). 32p. (978-0-7344-0480-0(8) , Lothian Bks.) Hachette Livre Australia.

Heap, Sue. Four Friends in the Garden. Heap, Sue, illus. 2004. (Illus.). 32p. (J). (gr. k-ps). 15.99 (978-0-7636-2371-5(7)) Candlewick Pr.

Hedrick, Helen Groves. Baas on the Bus. 2000. (J). 12.00 (978-0-8059-5003-8(6)) Dorrance Publishing Co., Inc.

Helakoski, Leslie. Woolbur. Harper, Lee, illus. 2008. 32p. (J). 17.89 (*978-0-06-084727-2(1)); 16.99 (*978-0-06-084726-5(3)) HarperCollins Pubs.

Hobbs, Valerie. Sheep. 2006. 128p. (J). 16.00 (978-0-374-36777-0(9) , Farrar, Straus & Giroux (BYR)) Farrar, Straus & Giroux.

Hughes, Mair Wynn & Jones, Steven. Dwyn Afalau. 2005. (WEL., Illus.). 15p. pap. (978-0-86243-457-1(2)) Y Lolfa.

ImageBooks Staff. Finger Puppet Friends: Little Duck, Little Ladybug, Little Lamb, & Little Bee. 2007. (Illus.). 48p. (J). (ps). bds. 22.95 (978-0-8118-5805-2(7)) Chronicle Bks. LLC.

Imai, Ayano. The 108th Sheep. Imai, Ayano, illus. 2007. (Illus.). 32p. (J). (ps-2). 15.95 (978-1-58925-063-5(X) , tiger tales) ME Media LLC.

Inkpen, Mick. If I Had a Sheep. 2000. (Illus.). 22p. (J). bds. (978-0-333-72253-4(1) , Macmillan Children's Bks.) Pan Macmillan.

Jeanne-Marie Counts Her Sheep. 2003. (Illus.). 32p. (J). mass mkt. 9.99 (978-0-9740599-0-7(0) , 1) Omnibus Publishing.

Kelly, Mij. One More Sheep. Ayto, Russell, illus. 2006. 30p. (J). 16.95 (978-1-56145-378-8(1) , Peachtree Junior) Peachtree Pubs., Ltd.

Kempter, C. & Weldin, F. Dear Little Lamb. 2006. (Illus.). 32p. (J). 16.95 (978-0-7358-2086-9(4)) North-South Bks., Inc.

Keylocke, Andrew, illus. Lazy Larry. 2004. (Crazy Racers Ser.). 12p. (J). bds. 4.95 (978-0-7641-5747-9(7)) Barron's Educational Series, Inc.

Kimpton, Diana. The Lamb-A-Roo. Beardshaw, Rosalind, illus. 2006. 32p. (J). 15.95 (978-0-7696-4619-0(0) , Gingham Dog Pr.) School Specialty Publishing.

Kitamura, Satoshi. Cuando los Borregos No Pueden Dormir. Kitamura, Satoshi, illus. 2nd ed. 2003. (Picture Books Collection). (SPA., Illus.). 26p. (J). (gr. k-3). pap. 12.95 (978-84-372-2182-3(X)) Santillana USA Publishing Co., Inc.

—When Sheep Can't Sleep (Cuando los Borregos no Pueden Dormir) (SPA.). (J). (gr. 1-6). 19.95 (978-84-372-6605-3(X)) Santillana USA Publishing Co., Inc.

Krone, Thelma Smith. Nosey. 2007. (J). 7.95 (*978-1-56167-974-4(7)) American Literary Pr.

Lakeshore Learning Materials Staff, contrib. by. Sheep on a Ship Packet. 2000. (J). pap. 19.95 (978-1-929255-18-4(7)) Lakeshore Learning Materials.

Lamb Who Loved to Laugh. 2001. (ps-2). lib. bdg. 9.80 (978-0-613-32754-1(3)) Tandem Library Bks.

Lammie, Karen J., illus. Baa! 2005. (On the Farm Ser.). 10p. (J). (ps-ps). bds. 4.95 (978-0-7641-5826-1(0)) Barron's Educational Series, Inc.

Landstrom, Olof. Boo & Baa Get Wet. 2000. (978-0-606-22355-3(X)) Tandem Library Bks.

—Boo & Baa in the Woods. 2000. (978-0-606-22354-6(1)) Tandem Library Bks.

Layne, Steven L. Thomas's Sheep & the Spectacular Science Project. Board, Perry, illus. 2004. 32p. (J). pap. 15.95 (978-1-58980-210-0(1)) Pelican Publishing Co., Inc.

Leche para Ovejita: Individual Title Six-Packs. (Coleccion Pm Ser.).Tr. of Baby lamb's first drink. (SPA.). 16p. (gr. 1 up). 26.00 (978-0-7578-2960-4(0)) Rigby Education.

The Legend of Teton Tony: King of the Mountain Rams. 2005. (Illus.). 32p. (J). 14.95 (978-0-9767265-0-0(5)) Fisher Enterprises.

Lenz Mulligan Rights and Co. Staff & van der Put, Klaartje. Little Lamb: Finger Puppet Book. 2006. (Illus.). 12p. (J). bds. 6.95 (978-0-8118-5235-7(0)) Chronicle Bks. LLC.

Lewis, Kim. Emma's Lamb. ed. 2004. (J). (gr. k-3). spiral bd. (978-0-616-07563-0(4)) Canadian National Institute for the Blind/Institut National Canadien pour les Aveugles.

—Little Baa. 2004. (Illus.). 24p. (J). (gr. k-ps). bds. 6.99 (978-0-7636-2472-9(1)) Candlewick Pr.

—Little Baa. Lewis, Kim, illus. 2001. (Illus.). 32p. (J). (gr. k-k). 15.99 (978-0-7636-1447-8(5)) Candlewick Pr.

The Little Lost Lamb. 2002. (Illus.). 12p. (J). 10.99 (978-0-8254-7249-7(0)) Kregel Pubns.

Little Softy Sheep. 2002. (J). (978-1-931312-93-6(1)) Soft-Play, Inc.

The Littlest Lamb: Lap Book. (Pebble Soup Explorations Ser.). 16p. (ps up). 21.00 (978-0-7578-1658-1(4)) Rigby Education.

The Littlest Lamb: Small Book. (Pebble Soup Explorations Ser.). 16p. (ps up). 5.00 (978-0-7578-1698-7(3)) Rigby Education.

Livingstone, Star. Harley. Bang, Molly, illus. 2003. 64p. (J). (gr. 1-4). pap. 5.95 (978-1-58717-150-5(3) , SeaStar Bks.) Chronicle Bks. LLC.

—Harley. 2003. (gr. k-3). lib. bdg. 12.95 (978-0-613-65127-1(8)) Tandem Library Bks.

Lodge, Jo. Sheep. 2003. (Cosy Cuddlers Ser.). (Illus.). 8p. (ps). 7.99 (978-0-333-98754-4(3)) Macmillan Publishers Ltd. GBR. *Dist:* Independent Pubs. Group.

Lucado, Max. The Crippled Lamb. Bonham, Liz, illus. collector's ed. 2004. 30p. (J). (gr. k-4). reprint ed. 18.00 (978-0-7567-8021-0(7)) DIANE Publishing Co.

—The Crippled Lamb. Bonham, Liz, illus. (J). (ps-2). 2005. 20p. bds., bds. 15.99 (978-1-4003-0695-4(7)); 1999. 16p. bds. 6.99 (978-0-8499-7502-8(6)) Nelson, Thomas Inc.

—The Crippled Lamb. collector's ed. 2006. 32p. (J). 19.99 (978-1-4003-0877-4(1)) Nelson, Thomas Inc.

Lucy Lamb. 2006. (J). per. 3.99 (978-1-934004-16-6(2)) Byeway Bks.

Lunn, Janet. Amos's Sweater. LaFave, Kim, illus. 2007. 32p. pap. 6.95 (*978-0-88899-845-3(7)) Groundwood Bks. CAN. *Dist:* Perseus Distribution.

Lyon, George Ella & Anderson, Stephanie. Weaving the Rainbow. 2004. (Illus.). 40p. (J). 16.95 (978-0-689-85169-8(3) , Atheneum/Richard Jackson Bks.) Simon & Schuster Children's Publishing.

MacKall, Dandi Daley. Little Shepherds First Christm. 2004. 32p. (J). 6.99 (978-0-7586-0324-1(X)) Concordia Publishing Hse.

Maier, Inger M. When Fuzzy Was Afraid: Of Losing His Mother. Candon, Jennifer, illus. 2005. 32p. (J). 14.95 (978-1-59147-168-4(0)); pap. 8.95 (978-1-59147-169-1(9)) American Psychological Assn. (Magination Pr.).

—When Fuzzy Was Afraid of Big & Loud Things. Candon, Jennifer, illus. 2005. 32p. (J). 14.95 (978-1-59147-322-0(5)); pap. 8.95 (978-1-59147-323-7(3)) American Psychological Assn. (Magination Pr.).

—When Lizzie Was Afraid: Of Trying New Things. Candon, Jennifer, illus. 2005. 32p. (J). 14.95 (978-1-59147-170-7(2)); pap. 8.95 (978-1-59147-171-4(0)) American Psychological Assn. (Magination Pr.).

Matthews-Dodd, Melissa. Chase Coming Home. 2003. (J). pap. 9.95 (978-0-7414-1522-6(4)) Infinity Publishing.

McAllister, Margaret. Emily & the Lamb. Vince, Dawn, illus. 2005. 24p. (J). lib. bdg. 22.65 (*978-1-59646-756-9(8)) Dingles & Co.

McMillan, Bruce. How the Ladies Stopped the Wind. Gunnella, illus. 2007. 32p. (J). (gr. k-3). 16.00 (*978-0-618-77330-5(4)) Houghton Mifflin Co.

McPhail, David M. The Day the Sheep Showed Up. 1998. (Hello Reader! Ser.). (Illus.). 32p. (J). (gr. k-2). pap. 3.99 (978-0-590-84910-4(7)) Scholastic, Inc.

—The Day the Sheep Showed Up. 1998. (Hello Reader! Ser.). (J). 10.79 (978-0-606-13318-0(6)) Tandem Library Bks.

McQueen, Lucinda. Little Lamb's Easter Surprise. 1999. (Illus.). 10p. (J). (ps-1). pap. 3.50 (978-0-590-41968-0(4)) Scholastic, Inc.

Michaels, Nina. Love from Woolly: A Lift-the-Flap Book of Woolly Gifts. Smee, Nicola, illus. 2007. 12p. (J). (ps). 9.95 (978-1-905417-21-6(7)) Boxer Bks., Ltd. GBR. *Dist:* Sterling Publishing Co., Inc.

Mitchell, Melanie. Mommy & Baby: Farm. 2006. (Illus.). 10p. (J). bds. 6.95 (978-0-8027-8061-4(X)) Walker & Co.

More Than a Meal. (Early Intervention Levels Ser.). 28.56 (978-0-7362-1049-2(0)) Hampton-Brown Bks.

Mustaine Hettinger, Cynthia. Travis, the Shetland Sheep. Ramsey, Jayne, illus. 2004. (Electra's Acres Ser.: Bk. 5). 32p. (J). per. 14.95 (978-0-9746330-6-0(2)) Anton Berkshire Publishing.

Nation, Kay. Jamie Learns to Love. 2006. pap. 10.00 (*978-1-4257-0534-3(0)) Xlibris Corp.

Odziemek, John. Catching Wayward Sheep. 2006. 128p. 21.99 (978-1-4141-0563-5(0)) Pleasant Word.

Oke, Janette. Maury Had a Little Lamb. Munger, Nancy, illus. rev. ed. 2001. (Janette Oke's Animal Friends Ser.). 80p. (Orig.). (J). (gr. 1-5). pap. 6.99 (978-0-7642-2457-7(3)) Bethany Hse. Pubs.

—Maury Had a Little Lamb. 2001. (Orig.). (gr. 3-6). lib. bdg. 14.15 (978-0-613-82431-6(8)) Tandem Library Bks.

Old MacDonald's Sheep. 2002. 16p. (J). pap. 2.98 (978-0-7525-7058-7(7)) Parragon, Inc.

Ommen, Sylvia Van. The Surprise. 2007. 24p. (J). (ps). 15.95 (978-1-932425-85-7(3) , Front Street) Boyds Mills Pr.

Palatini, Margie. Bad Boys. Cole, Henry, illus. 40p. (J). (ps-2). 2003. 15.99 (978-0-06-000102-5(X)); 2003. lib. bdg. 16.89 (978-0-06-000103-2(8)); 2006. reprint ed. pap. 6.99 (978-0-06-000104-9(6) , Tegen, Katherine Bks) HarperCollins Pubs.

Pearson, Tracey Campbell. Little Bo-Peep. 2004. (Mother Goose Board Bks.). (Illus.). 14p. (J). bds. 5.95 (978-0-374-30859-9(4) , Farrar, Straus & Giroux (BYR)) Farrar, Straus & Giroux.

Peters, Andrew. Sheep Don't Go to School. 1999. (Illus.). 96p. pap. 15.95 (978-1-85224-408-8(9)) Bloodaxe Bks. GBR. *Dist:* Dufour Editions, Inc.

Pete's Sheep. 2004. (Illus.). (J). (978-1-59577-007-3(0)) Starfall Education.

Phelps, Karen. Grass Is Always Greener, the & Let Sleeping Dogs Lie: Two Original Fairy Tales. 2006. spiral bd. 23.00 (*978-1-4108-7155-8(X)) Benchmark Education Co.

Powers, John. The Lion Who Couldn't Roar. Colavecchio, Alan, illus. 2002. 32p. (J). 13.95 (978-1-929039-10-4(7)) Ambassador Bks., Inc.

Proimos, James. Johnny Mutton, He's So Him! 2004. (Johnny Mutton Ser.). (Illus.). 48p. (J). reprint ed. pap. 5.95 (978-0-15-216766-0(8) , Harcourt Paperbacks) Harcourt Children's Bks.

—Johnny Mutton, He's So Him! 2004. (gr. 3-6). lib. bdg. 14.10 (978-0-613-71558-4(6)) Tandem Library Bks.

—The Many Adventures of Johnny Mutton. Proimos, James, illus. 2001. (Johnny Mutton Ser.). (Illus.). 48p. (J). (gr. k-4). pap. 6.00 (978-0-15-202413-0(1) , Harcourt Paperbacks) Harcourt Children's Bks.

—Many Adventures of Johnny Mutton. 2001. (gr. k-3). lib. bdg. 14.15 (978-0-613-35535-3(0)) Tandem Library Bks.

—Mutton Soup: More Adventures of Johnny Mutton. 2004. (Johnny Mutton Ser.). (Illus.). 48p. (J). 16.00 (978-0-15-216772-1(2)) Harcourt Children's Bks.

Rand, Gloria & Rand, Ted. Mary Was a Little Lamb. rev. ed. 2004. (Illus.). 32p. (J). 16.95 (978-0-8050-6816-0(3) , Holt, Henry & Co. Bks. For Young Readers) Holt, Henry & Co.

Raum, Elizabeth. The Christmas Star. Johnson, Meredith, illus. 2007. 32p. (J). pap. 3.99 (*978-0-8249-5567-0(6) , Ideals Children's Bks.) Ideals Pubns.

Raum, Elizabeth. Follow That Star: A Christmas Story. Johnson, Meredith, ed. Johnson, Meredith, illus. 2001. 32p. (J). 12.95 (978-0-8249-4136-9(5) , Candy Cane Pr.) Ideals Pubns.

Reader's Digest Editors. Fuzzy Little Lamb. 2004. (Small Miracles Ser.: No. 2). 10p. (J). 5.99 (978-1-4003-0315-1(X)) Nelson, Thomas Inc.

Rix, Jamie. Giddy Goat. Chapman, Lynne, illus. 2003. 32p. (J). (gr. k-3). 14.95 (978-0-7696-3161-5(4) , Gingham Dog Pr.) School Specialty Publishing.

Rock, Michelle L. Nighttime Adventures Counting Sheep. Longmore, Nickolai, illus. 2006. 32p. (J). 3.99 net. (978-0-9771700-1-2(2)) Mystic Arts, LLC.

Root, Phyllis. Ten Sleepy Sheep. Gaber, Susan, illus. 2004. 32p. (J). (gr. k-k). 15.99 (978-0-7636-1545-1(5)) Candlewick Pr.

Roth, Carol. Who Will Tuck Me in Tonight? Gorbachev, Valeri, illus. 2003. 32p. (J). 15.95 (978-0-7358-1772-2(3)); 16.50 (978-0-7358-1773-9(1)) North-South Bks., Inc.

—Who Will Tuck Me in Tonight Sp. 2007. (J). 16.50 (978-0-7358-2108-8(9)); (Illus.). pap. 6.95 (978-0-7358-2107-1(0)) North-South Bks., Inc.

Rothstein, Gloria L. Sheep Asleep. Date not set. 224p. (J). (ps-1). pap. 4.99 (978-0-06-443717-2(5)) HarperCollins Pubs.

Rundstrom, T. S. Cherry the Sheep Finds Her Sheep Sound. Miller, Bryan & Marshall, H. Keene, illus. 2002. (J). per. 16.00 (978-1-932062-10-6(6)) Hability Solution Services, Inc.

—Sherman the Sheep: A Sheep Adventure Story about Dreams, Doing Stuff & Happiness. Miller, Bryan & Marshall, H. Keene, illus. l.t. ed. 2002. per. (978-1-932062-00-7(9) , 02-0232SH) Hability Solution Services, Inc.

Rundstrom, Teressa. Cherry the Sheep Finds Her Sheep Sound. Miller, Bryan & Marshall, H. Keene, illus. 2004. 25p. (J). per. (978-1-932062-40-3(8)) Hability Solution Services, Inc.

—Sherman the Sheep. Marshall, H. Keene & Miller, Bryan, illus. 2002. 35p. (J). per. (978-1-932062-38-0(6)) Hability Solution Services, Inc.

Rwakasisi, Rose. How Goats Lost Their Beautiful Tails. 2004. (Illus.). 19p. pap. 9.95 (978-9970-02-436-0(1)) Fountain Pubs. Ltd. UGA. *Dist:* Michigan State Univ. Pr.

Salazar, Martinez Lydia. Lily, the Lost & Found Lamb. 2004. (Illus.). 32p. (ps-3). pap. 5.00 (978-0-687-09218-5(3)) Abingdon Pr.

Sam's Winter Book Adventure Pack. 2001. (978-1-883772-33-8(8)) Flying Rhinoceros, Inc.

Samuel, Janet, intro. Sneaky Sheep. 2007. 8p. 14.95 (*978-1-58117-560-8(4) , Intervisual/Piggy Toes) Dalmatian Pr.

Sanders, Scott Russell. Warm as Wool. Cogancherry, Helen, illus. 2007. (J). lib. bdg. 18.00 (*978-1-59098-421-5(8)) Wooster Bk. Co., The.

Santillo, LuAnn. Shag. Santillo, LuAnn, ed. 2003. (Half-Pint Readers Ser.). (Illus.). 7p. (J). (ps-1). pap. (978-1-59256-068-4(7)) Half-Pint Kids, Inc.

Sargent, Dave & Sargent, David M., Jr. Petie Pelican: Be Proud of Yourself, 19, 14. Lenoir, Jane, illus. 2003. (Feather Tales Ser.: 14). 42p. (J). pap. 6.95 (978-1-56763-746-5(9)) Ozark Publishing.

Savitsky, Steven, illus. Dora Had a Little Lamb. 2007. (Dora the Explorer Ser.). 24p. (J). pap. 3.99 (*978-1-4169-3368-7(9) , Simon Spotlight/Nickelodeon) Simon & Schuster Children's Publishing.

Schroeder, Lisa. Baby Can't Sleep. Garofoli, Viviana, illus. 2005. 32p. (J). (ps). 12.95 (978-1-4027-2171-7(4)) Sterling Publishing Co., Inc.

Scotton, Rob. Russell & the Lost Treasure. Scotton, Rob, illus. 2006. (Illus.). 32p. (J). 15.99 (978-0-06-059851-8(4)); lib. bdg. 16.89 (978-0-06-059852-5(2)) HarperCollins Pubs.

—Russell the Sheep. 2005. (Illus.). 40p. (J). (ps-2). 15.99 (978-0-06-059848-8(4)) HarperCollins Pubs.

—Russell the Sheep. Scotton, Rob, illus. 2005. (Illus.). 40p. (J). (ps-ps). lib. bdg. 17.89 (978-0-06-059849-5(2)) HarperCollins Pubs.

—Russell the Sheep Mini Book & Plush. Scotton, Rob, illus. 2006. 32p. (J). 14.99 (978-0-06-112540-9(7) , Harper Festival) HarperCollins Pubs.

Scotton, Rob. Russell's Christmas Magic. Scotton, Rob, illus. 2007. 32p. (J). lib. bdg. 17.89 (*978-0-06-059855-6(7)) HarperCollins Pubs.

Scraper, Katherine. The Boy Who Cried Wolf: An Aesop's Fable. 2006. 42.00 (*978-1-4108-6166-5(X)) Benchmark Education Co.

Sengel. Sheeps Surprise. 1998. pap. (978-0-8172-5656-2(3)) Steck-Vaughn.

Shapely Sleepy Sheep. ed. 2005. (J). bds. 7.95 (978-0-9749305-6-5(3)) Castle Pacific Publishing.

Shaw, Nancy. Sheep in a Jeep. Apple, Margot, illus. 2002. (J). 12.83 (978-0-7587-3608-6(8)) Book Wholesalers, Inc.

—Sheep in a Shop. Apple, Margot, illus. 2002. (J). 12.81 (978-0-7587-3609-3(6)) Book Wholesalers, Inc.

—Sheep on a Ship. Apple, Margot, illus. 2002. (J). 12.81 (978-0-7587-3611-6(8)) Book Wholesalers, Inc.

—Sheep Out to Eat. Apple, Margot, illus. 2002. (J). 12.81 (978-0-7587-3612-3(6)) Book Wholesalers, Inc.

—Sheep Take a Hike. Apple, Margot, illus. 2002. (J). 12.81 (978-0-7587-3613-0(4)) Book Wholesalers, Inc.

—Sheep Trick or Treat. 2000. (J). (978-0-606-19428-0(2)) Tandem Library Bks.

Shaw, Nancy E. Sheep Blast off! HC. Apple, Margot, illus. 2008. 32p. (J). 15.00 (*978-0-618-13168-6(X)) Houghton Mifflin Co. Trade & Reference Div.

—Sheep in a Jeep. Apple, Margot, illus. 1999. (Carry-Along Book & Cassette Favorites Ser.). 1p. (J). (gr. k-3). pap. 9.95 incl. audio (978-0-395-95990-9(X)) Houghton Mifflin Co. Trade & Reference Div.

—Sheep Out to Eat. Apple, Margot, illus. 2005. 13p. (J). (gr. k-ps). bds. 5.95 (978-0-618-58339-3(4)) Houghton Mifflin Co. Trade & Reference Div.

—Sheep Trick or Treat. Apple, Margot, illus. 2000. 32p. (J). (gr. k-3). pap. 5.95 (978-0-618-07035-0(4)) Houghton Mifflin Co. Trade & Reference Div.

—Sheep Trick or Treat. Apple, Margot, illus. 2005. 13p. (J). (gr. k-ps). bds. 5.95 (978-0-618-58120-7(0)) Houghton Mifflin Co. Trade & Reference Div.

Sheep Wants to Jump. 2002. (J). 4.98 (978-0-7525-7219-2(9)) Parragon, Inc.

Simon, Mary Manz. Lamb Is Joyful. Harris, Phyllis & Clearwater, Linda, illus. 2006. (First Virtuestm for Toddlers Ser.). 20p. (J). 5.99 (978-0-7847-1575-8(0) , 04069) Standard Publishing.

Smallman, Steve. The Lamb Who Came for Dinner. Dreidemy, Joelle, illus. 2007. 32p. (J). (ps-2). 15.95 (*978-1-58925-067-3(2) , tiger tales) ME Media LLC.

Snow, Ravay L. Hildegarde & the Great Green Shirt Factory. Snow, Ravay L., illus. 2005. (Hildegarde Ser.). (Illus.). 32p. (J). 16.95 (978-1-932362-10-7(X)) Snowbound Pr., Inc.

Sollinger, Emily. Find the Sheep, Piggley! A Jakers! Counting Book. Entara Ltd. Staff, photos by. 2006. (Jakers! Ser.). 14p. (J). 7.99 (978-1-4169-0613-1(4) , Simon Spotlight) Simon & Schuster Children's Publishing.

Sundgaard, Arnold & Sundgaard, Carle. The Lamb & the Butterfly. Carle, Eric, illus. 1999. 32p. (J). (ps-1). pap. 16.95 (978-0-531-05779-7(8) , Orchard Bks.) Scholastic, Inc.

Suzie Sheep & her Friends. 2004. (Play Pals Ser.) (Illus.). 12p. (J). bds. (978-1-84229-649-3(3)) Top That! Publishing PLC.

Talley, Linda. Following Isabella - Kit. Chase, Andra, illus. 2001. (Key Concepts in Personal Development Ser.). 32p. (J). pap., tchr. ed. 89.95 incl. VHS (978-1-55942-170-6(3) , 9388K3) Marsh Media.

Teddy Bear-Sheep. 2003. (J). per. (978-1-57657-163-7(7)) Paradise Pr., Inc.

Theobald, Joseph. Marvin Wanted More! Theobald, Joseph, illus. (Illus.). 32p. (J). 2005. pap. 12.99 (978-0-7475-6481-2(7)); 2004. 16.99 (978-0-7475-5631-2(8)) Bloomsbury Publishing Plc GBR. *Dist:* Independent Pubs. Group.

Theobald, Joseph. Marvin Wanted More. Theobald, Joseph, illus. 2007. 32p. (J). pap., pap. 13.99 incl. audio compact disk (*978-0-7475-8873-3(2)) Bloomsbury Publishing Plc GBR. *Dist:* Independent Pubs. Group.

—Marvin Wanted More. 2003. (Board Book Ser.). (Illus.). 24p. (ps). 9.99 (978-0-7475-7561-0(4)) Bloomsbury Publishing Plc GBR. *Dist:* Independent Pubs. Group.

Thomas Nelson Publishing Staff. The Greatest Shepherd of All: A Really Woolly Christmas Story. 2006. (Illus.). 32p. (J). 7.99 (978-1-4003-0964-1(6)) Nelson, Thomas Inc.

—Really Woolly Furry Friends. 2007. 12p. (J). bds. 7.99 (978-1-4003-0988-7(3)) Nelson, Thomas Inc.

Tich, Jan. Pope & Ba. 2006. (Adventures in Unusual Places Ser.). (Illus.). 28p. (J). 12.95 (978-9974-7925-8-6(4)) Hardenville SA URY. *Dist:* Independent Pubs. Group.

Tyrrell, Melissa. Busy Little Lamb. Tom-Nellis, Susan, illus. 1998. (Baby Buddy Bks.: Vol. 4). 12p. (YA). (ps up). bds. 4.95 (978-1-888443-71-4(5) , Intervisual/Piggy Toes) Dalmatian Pr.

Van Patter, Bruce. Farley Found It. (Illus.). (J). 16.95 (978-1-59078-351-1(4)) Boyds Mills Pr.

S

Vanderklip, Michael. Christmas Star. 2006. (Christmas Minis Ser.). 14p. 3.99 (978-0-310-70847-6(8)) Zondervan.

Waddell, Martin. Tough Ronald. Mould, Chris, illus. 2006. (Read-It! Chapter Books). 64p. (J). lib. bdg. (*978-1-4048-3127-8(4)*, 1265816) Picture Window Bks.

Warden, Evelyn. Oh, Please, Cricket. 2006. 144p. pap. 19.95 (978-1-4241-1860-1(3)) PublishAmerica, Inc.

Weare, Tim. I'm a Little Sheep. 2005. (Illus.). 7p. (J). (ps-6). bds. 7.95 (978-1-904613-54-1(3), Buster Bks.) O'Mara, Michael Bks., Ltd. GBR. *Dist:* Independent Pubs. Group.

Weeks, Sarah. Baa-Choo! Manning, Jane, illus. (I Can Read Bks.). 32p. (J). (ps-3). 2006. pap. 3.99 (978-0-06-443740-0(X)); 2004. 15.99 (978-0-06-029236-2(9)); 2004. lib. bdg. 16.89 (978-0-06-029237-9(7)) HarperCollins Pubs.

—Counting Ovejas. Diaz, David, illus. 2006. (ENG & SPA.). 40p. (J). (ps-1). 17.99 (978-0-689-86750-7(6), Atheneum) Simon & Schuster Children's Publishing.

Westera, Marleen & Forest, Nancy. Sheep & Goat. Ommen, Sylvia Van, illus. (J). 16.95 (978-1-932425-81-9(0), Lemniscaat) Boyds Mills Pr.

Whybrow, Ian. Little Farmer Joe. Birmingham, Christian, illus. 2003. 32p. (J). (ps-k). pap. 7.95 (978-0-7534-5593-7(5), Kingfisher) Houghton Mifflin Co. Trade & Reference Div.

Willis, Jeanne. Misery Moo. Ross, Tony, illus. rev. ed. 2005. 32p. (J). 16.95 (978-0-8050-7672-1(7)) Holt, Henry & Co.

Ziefert, Harriet & Bolam, Emily. Buzzy Had a Little Lamb. 2005. (Illus.). 32p. (J). 9.95 (978-1-59354-068-5(X)) Blue Apple Bks.

SHELLEY, PERCY BYSSHE, 1792-1822

Bloom, Harold. Percy Shelley. 2001. (Bloom's Major Poets Ser.). 120p. (J). (gr. 8 up). 31.95 (978-0-7910-5930-2(8), Chelsea Hse.) Facts On File, Inc.

SHELLFISH

see Mollusks

SHELLS

see also Mollusks

Andersen, Honey. My Shells. 2000. (gr. k-3). lib. bdg. 11.80 (978-0-613-29705-9(9)) Tandem Library Bks.

Arthur, Alex. Shell. 2000. (Eyewitness Bks.). (Illus.). 64p. (J). (gr. 4-7). 15.99 (978-0-7894-5830-8(6)) Dorling Kindersley Publishing, Inc.

Berkes, Marianne Collins. Seashells by the Seashore. Noreika, Robert, illus. 2004. (Sharing Nature with Children Book Ser.). 32p. (J). (ps-5). 16.95 (978-1-58469-035-1(6)); pap. 8.95 (978-1-58469-034-4(8)) Dawn Pubns.

—Seashells by the Seashore. 2002. (gr. k-3). lib. bdg. 17.60 (978-0-613-62835-8(7)) Tandem Library Bks.

Bown, Deni & Dorling Kindersley Publishing Staff. Shells. 1998. (Eyewitness Explorers Ser.). (Illus.). 64p. (J). (gr. 4-7). pap. 5.99 (978-0-7894-2984-1(5)) Dorling Kindersley Publishing, Inc.

Burton, Jane & Taylor, Kim. The Nature & Science of Shells. Burton, Jane & Taylor, Kim, photos by. 1999. (Exploring the Science of Nature Ser.). (Illus.). 32p. (J). (gr. 3 up). lib. bdg. 24.67 (978-0-8368-2185-7(8)) Stevens, Gareth Inc.

Cassie, Brian. Shells. 2000. (National Audubon Society First Field Guides). (Illus.). 160p. (J). (gr. 3 up). pap. 8.95 (978-0-590-64258-3(8)) Scholastic, Inc.

—Shells. 2000. (National Audubon Society First Field Guide Ser.). (J). (978-0-606-19583-6(1)) Tandem Library Bks.

Franco, Betsy. Shells. Sorra, Kristin, illus. 2001. (Rookie Reader Skill Set Ser.). 32p. (J). (gr. k-2). pap. 4.95 (978-0-516-27080-7(X), Children's Pr.) Scholastic Library Publishing.

—Shells. 2000. (gr. k-3). lib. bdg. 12.95 (978-0-613-54657-7(1)) Tandem Library Bks.

Fredlee. The Magic of Seashells. Gray, Cissy, illus. 2002. 36p. (J). pap. 6.95 (978-0-89317-049-3(6), WW-0496, Windward Publishing) Finney Co., Inc.

Garrow, Linda, illus. Young Naturalist Field Guides, 5 bks. Incl. Berries, Nuts & Seeds. Burns, Diane L. 2000. lib. bdg. 24.67 (978-0-8368-2144-4(0)); Frogs, Toads & Turtles. Burns, Diane L. 1999. lib. bdg. 24.67 (978-0-8368-2145-1(9)); Rabbits, Squirrels & Chipmunks. Boring, Mel. 1999. lib. bdg. 24.67 (978-0-8368-2146-8(7)); Tracks, Scats & Signs. Dendy, Leslie. 1999. lib. bdg. 24.67 (978-0-8368-2147-5(5)); Wildflowers, Blooms & Blossoms. Burns, Diane L. 2000. lib. bdg. 24.67 (978-0-8368-2148-2(3)); 40p. (J). (gr. 3 up). (Illus.). Set lib. bdg. 123.35 (978-0-8368-2658-6(2)) Stevens, Gareth Inc.

Hansen, Judith. Seashells in My Pocket: AMC Family Guide to Exploring Nature along the Atlantic Coast from Maine to Florida. Sabaka, Donna R., illus. 3rd ed. 2008. (ENG.). 160p. pap. 14.95 (978-1-929173-61-7(X)) Appalachian Mountain Club Bks.

Mayer, Cassie. Shells. 2006. (Illus.). 24p. (J). (978-1-4034-8375-1(2)); pap. (978-1-4034-8381-2(7)) Heinemann Library.

Parker, Steve & Dorling Kindersley Publishing Staff. Seashore. 2004. (Eyewitness Books). (Illus.). 72p. (J). lib. bdg. 19.99 (978-0-7566-0720-3(5)) Dorling Kindersley Publishing, Inc.

Peterson, Roger T. & Douglass, Jackie Leatherbury. Peterson First Guide to Shells of North America. Douglass, John, illus. 2nd ed. 1998. (Peterson First Guides). 128p. pap. 5.95 (978-0-395-91182-2(6)) Houghton Mifflin Co. Trade & Reference Div.

Richardson, Adele D. Seashells. (Illus.). 32p. pap. 8.95 (978-0-89812-320-3(8)); 2000. (J). pap. 10.60 (978-0-89812-008-0(X), Creative Paperbacks) Creative Co., The.

—Seashells. 1998. (Let's Investigate Ser.: Vol. 12). (Illus.). 32p. (J). (ps-3). lib. bdg. (978-0-88682-996-4(8), Creative Education) Creative Co., The.

Robinson, W. Wright. How Shellmakers Build Their Amazing Homes. DeRubbio, Jennifer, illus. 1999. (Animal Architects Ser.). 64p. (J). (gr. 5-9). 24.95 (978-1-56711-379-2(6), Blackbirch Pr., Inc.) Thomson Gale.

Salzmann, Mary Elizabeth. Cool Shells. 2007. (Checkerboard Science Library). (Illus.). 32p. (J). 22.78 (978-1-59679-772-7(X)) ABDO Publishing Co.

Salzmann, Mary Elizabeth. What Has a Shell? 2007. (Creature Features Ser.). (ENG., Illus.). 24p. (J). (ps-3). lib. bdg. 24.21 (*978-1-59928-871-0(0)*, Super SandCastle) ABDO Publishing Co.

Sea Shells of the United States & Canada. 2004. (World Book's Science & Nature Guides Ser.). (Illus.). 80p. (J). (978-0-7166-4218-3(2)) World Bk., Inc.

Shells. Date not set. (Illus.). 8p. (J). (gr. k-2). pap. 3.75 (978-1-58323-015-2(7), Seedling Pubns.) Continental Pr., Inc.

Squire, Ann O. Seashells. 2002. (True Bks.). (Illus.). 48p. (J). (gr. 3-5). pap. 6.95 (978-0-516-26986-3(0), Children's Pr.) Scholastic Library Publishing.

—Seashells. 2002. (gr. 3-6). lib. bdg. 15.25 (978-0-613-54353-8(X)) Tandem Library Bks.

Ward, Helen. Old Shell, New Shell: A Coral. 2002. (Illus.). 40p. (gr. k-2). lib. bdg. 24.90 (978-0-7613-2708-0(8), Millbrook Pr.) Lerner Publishing Group.

—Old Shell, New Shell: A Coral Reef Tale. 2002. (Illus.). 40p. (gr. k-2). (978-0-7613-1635-0(3), Millbrook Pr.) Lerner Publishing Group.

Yin, Robert, illus. & photos by. Seashells. Yin, Robert, photos by. 1999. 24p. (J). 6.50 (978-0-7685-0355-5(8)) Dominie Pr., Inc.

SHEPARD, ALAN B. (ALAN BARTLETT), 1923-1998

Benge, Janet & Benge, Geoff. Alan Shepard: Higher & Faster. 2007. (J). (*978-1-932096-41-5(8)*) YWAM Publishing.

SHEPHERDS

Pastores en el Campo (Shepherd's Fields) (SPA.). (J). (978-0-7899-0877-3(8), 496236) Editorial Unilit.

Peregrinos & Extranjeros. El Buen Pastor (The Good Shepherd) (SPA.). (J). 1.59 (978-1-56063-854-4(0), 494016) Editorial Unilit.

Urbigkit, Cat. The Shepherd's Trail. 2008. (J). (*978-1-59078-509-6(6)*) Boyds Mills Pr.

—Young Shepherd. 2006. (Illus.). 32p. (J). 15.95 (978-1-59078-364-1(6)) Boyds Mills Pr.

Urbigkit, Cat. A Young Shepherd. 2006. (Illus.). (J). (*978-1-4156-6559-6(1)*) Boyds Mills Pr.

SHEPHERDS—FICTION

Banks, Celia. Jacob's Promise. 2006. pap. 13.99 (978-0-9764460-6-4(5)) HonorNet.

Blackford. The Eskdale Herd Boy A Scottish Tale for the Instruction & Amusement of Young Persons. 2004. reprint ed. pap. 15.95 (978-1-4191-6125-4(3)) Kessinger Publishing, LLC.

Calhoun, Mary. A Shepherd Boy's Christmas. Colon, Raul, illus. 2001. 32p. (J). (ps-4). 15.95 (978-0-688-15176-8(0)) HarperCollins Pubs.

—A Shepherd's Gift. Colon, Raul, illus. 2001. 32p. (J). (ps-4). 15.89 (978-0-688-15177-5(9)) HarperCollins Pubs.

—A Shepherd's Gift: El Regalo del Pastor. 2001. (SPA., Illus.). 32p. (J). (ps-4). 15.89 (978-0-06-029786-2(7)) HarperCollins Pubs.

Dennis, Jeanne Gowen & Seifert, Sheila. Attack! Hohn, David, tr. Hohn, David, illus. 2003. (Strive to Thrive Ser.). 96p. (J). pap., pap. 5.99 (978-0-7814-3894-0(2), 0781438942) Cook, David C. Publishing Co.

Eversole, Robyn. Red Berry Wool. 2002. (gr. k-3). lib. bdg. 15.25 (978-0-613-75727-0(0)) Tandem Library Bks.

Flinn, Lisa & Younger, Barbara. The Christmas Garland. Corvino, Lucy, tr. Corvino, Lucy, illus. 2003. 32p. (J). 14.95 (978-0-8249-5460-4(2), Ideals Children's Bks.) Ideals Pubns.

Fogle, Robin. The Shepherd Boy's Christmas. 2005. (J). pap. 1.79 (*978-1-59317-105-6(6)*) Warner Pr. Pubs.

Freed, Shirley Ann & Moon, Louise. Little Lamb & the Shepherd. Morelan, Bill, ed. Butler, Steven, illus. l.t. ed. 2002. 16p. (J). (gr. 6). pap. 3.99 (978-1-58938-033-2(9)) Concerned Communications.

Hamilton, Doris K. Daniel's Christmas Story. 2006. pap. 7.95 (978-0-533-15495-1(2)) Vantage Pr., Inc.

Howell, Trisha Adelena. The Stinky Shepherd. Marshall, Jamie, illus. 2005. 32p. (J). 15.95 (978-1-931210-25-6(X)) Howell Canyon Pr.

Jennings, Patrick. The Wolving Time. 2003. 208p. (J). pap. 15.95 (978-0-439-39555-7(0)) Scholastic, Inc.

Krenzer, Rolf. The Christmas Bell. Dusikova, Maja, illus. 2003. 32p. (J). 15.95 (978-1-57768-410-7(9), Gingham Dog Pr.) School Specialty Publishing.

Mackall, Dandi Daley, adapted by. El Pastorcito: Para ninos de 4-7 Anos.Tr. of Little Shepherd. (SPA.). 32p. 3.99 (978-0-7586-0362-3(2)) Concordia Publishing Hse.

Morpurgo, Michael. On Angel Wings. 2007. 48p. 8.99 (*978-0-7636-3466-7(2)*) Candlewick Pr.

Narvaez, Concha Lopez. Las Horas Largas. 2001. (SPA.). (gr. 7-12). lib. bdg. 15.70 (978-0-613-80554-4(2)) Tandem Library Bks.

Pearson, Tracey Campbell. Little Bo-Peep. 2004. (Mother Goose Board Bks.). (Illus.). 14p. (J). bds. 5.95 (978-0-374-30859-9(4), Farrar, Straus & Giroux (BYR)) Farrar, Straus & Giroux.

Spyri, Johanna. Moni, the Goat Boy: And Other Stories. 2000. (Illus.). 219p. (J). reprint ed. pap. 6.95 (978-1-883453-09-1(7)) Deutsche Buchhandlung-James Lowry.

That's What a Friend Is! 2003. 24p. (J). bds. 6.95 (978-0-8249-5468-0(8)) Ideals Pubns.

Thomas Nelson Publishing Staff. The Greatest Shepherd of All: A Really Woolly Christmas Story. 2006. (Illus.). 32p. (J). 7.99 (978-1-4003-0964-1(6)) Nelson, Thomas Inc.

SHERIDAN, PHILIP HENRY, 1831-1888

Balcavage, Dynise. Philip Sheridan. 2001. (Famous Figures of the Civil War Era Ser.). (Illus.). 80p. (J). pap. (978-0-7910-6407-8(7), Chelsea Hse.) Facts On File, Inc.

—Philip Sheridan: Union General. 2001. (Famous Figures of the Civil War Era Ser.). (Illus.). 80p. (J). (gr. 5 up). 25.00 (978-0-7910-6406-1(9), Chelsea Hse.) Facts On File, Inc.

SHERMAN, WILLIAM T. (WILLIAM TECUMSEH), 1820-1891

Hoogenboom, Lynn. William Tecumseh Sherman: The Fight to Preserve the Union. 2005. (Library of American Lives & Times). (Illus.). 112p. (J). (gr. 4-8). lib. bdg. 31.95 (978-0-8239-6625-7(9)) Rosen Publishing Group, Inc., The.

Kent, Zachary. William Tecumseh Sherman: Union General. 2002. (Historical American Biographies Ser.). (Illus.). 128p. (YA). (gr. 6-12). lib. bdg. 26.60 (978-0-7660-1621-7(8)) Enslow Pubs., Inc.

McLeese, Don. William Tecumseh Sherman. 2006. (Civil War Military Leaders Ser.). (Illus.). 32p. (gr. 3-6). 19.95 (978-1-59515-478-1(7)) Rourke Publishing, LLC.

Mcleese, Don. William Tecumseh Sherman. 2005. 32p. pap. 6.45 (978-1-59515-792-8(1)) Rourke Publishing, LLC.

Remstein, Henna. William Sherman. 2001. (gr. 5-8). lib. bdg. 17.60 (978-0-613-33253-8(9)) Tandem Library Bks.

—William Sherman: Union Military Leader. (Famous Figures of the Civil War Era Ser.). (Illus.). 80p. (J). 2001. (gr. 8-12). 25.00 (978-0-7910-6005-6(5)); 2000. (gr. 4-7). pap. 25.00 (978-0-7910-6143-5(4)) Facts On File, Inc. (Chelsea Hse.).

Whitelaw, Nancy. William Tecumseh Sherman: Defender & Destroyer. rev. exp. ed. 2004. (Illus.). 176p. (J). (gr. 6-12). 26.95 (978-1-931798-31-0(1)) Reynolds, Morgan Inc.

SHERMAN'S MARCH TO THE SEA

Hoogenboom, Lynn. William Tecumseh Sherman: The Fight to Preserve the Union. 2005. (Library of American Lives & Times). (Illus.). 112p. (J). (gr. 4-8). lib. bdg. 31.95 (978-0-8239-6625-7(9)) Rosen Publishing Group, Inc., The.

SHERMAN'S MARCH TO THE SEA—FICTION

Dahl, Candy. Emma & the Civil Warrior. 2001. 158p. (J). 12.95 (978-0-9706358-3-9(4)); per. 6.95 (978-0-9706358-4-6(2)) Carolina Moon Publishing.

SHIP BUILDING

see Shipbuilding

SHIPBUILDING

see also Boatbuilding; Naval Architecture; Ships; Steamboats

Tunis, Edwin. Oars, Sails & Steam: A Picture Book of Ships. 2002. (Illus.). 80p. pap. 25.00 (978-0-8018-6932-7(3)) Johns Hopkins Univ. Pr.

SHIPPING—FICTION

Bang, Molly Garrett. Dawn. 2002. (gr. k-3). lib. bdg. 14.10 (978-0-613-62742-9(3)) Tandem Library Bks.

Maurer, Tracy. Storm Codes. Rodriguez, Christina, illus. 2007. 40p. (J). pap. 8.95 (*978-0-89317-064-6(X)*, WW-064X); (gr. 1-7). lib. bdg. 17.95 (*978-0-89317-063-9(1)*, WW-0631) Finney Co., Inc. (Windward Publishing).

SHIPS

see also Boats and Boating; Navigation; Sailing; Steamboats; Submarines (Ships); Warships

Amato, William. Cruceros. 2004. (Vehiculos de Alta Tecnologia Ser.). (SPA & ENG., Illus.). 24p. (J). (gr. 3-6). lib. bdg. 17.25 (978-0-8239-6884-8(7), Buenas Letra) Rosen Publishing Group, Inc., The.

—Cruise Ships. 2002. (Reading Power Ser.). (Illus.). 24p. (J). (gr. 2). lib. bdg. 17.25 (978-0-8239-6010-1(2), PowerKids Pr.) Rosen Publishing Group, Inc., The.

Armentrout, David & Armentrout, Patricia. Ships. 2003. (Transportation Ser.). (Illus.). 24p. (J). 20.64 (978-1-58952-671-6(6)) Rourke Publishing, LLC.

Beech, Linda Ward. The Exxon Valdez's Deadly Oil Spill. 2007. (Code Red Ser.). (Illus.). 32p. (J). (gr. 3-7). lib. bdg. 25.27 (978-1-59716-366-8(X)) Bearport Publishing Co., Inc.

Bender, Lionel. Ships & Boats. 2006. (J). (978-1-59389-268-5(3)) Chrysalis Education.

Biesty, Stephen. Look Inside Cross-Sections: Ships. (Illus.). 32p. (J). mass mkt. 8.99 (978-0-590-24342-1(X)) Scholastic, Inc.

Birnbaum Travel Guides Staff. Birnbaum's Disney Cruise Line 2007. 2006. (Illus.). 224p. (ps-17). pap. 13.95 (978-1-4231-0052-2(2), Disney Editions) Disney Pr.

Bryan, Nichol. Exxon Valdez: Oil Spill. 2003. (Environmental Disasters Ser.). (Illus.). 48p. (gr. 5 up). (J). pap. 11.95 (978-0-8368-5513-5(2)); (YA). lib. bdg. 30.00 (978-0-8368-5506-7(X)) Stevens, Gareth Inc. (World Almanac Library).

Build Your Own Pirate Ship. Date not set. (Build Your Own Ser.). (Illus.). 16p. (J). 3.98 (978-0-7525-7658-9(5)) Parragon, Inc.

Calvert, Patricia. Sir Ernest Shackleton: By Endurance We Conquer. 2002. (Great Explorations Ser.). (Illus.). 80p. (J). 29.93 (978-0-7614-1485-8(1), Benchmark Bks.) Cavendish, Marshall Corp.

Collicutt, Paul. This Boat. Collicutt, Paul, illus. 2001. (Illus.). 32p. (J). (ps-1). 15.00 (978-0-374-37495-2(3), Farrar, Straus & Giroux (BYR)) Farrar, Straus & Giroux.

Cooper, Jason. Cargo Ships. 1999. (Boats & Ships Discovery Library). (Illus.). 24p. (J). (gr. 1-4). lib. bdg. 19.27 (978-0-86593-561-7(0)) Rourke Publishing, LLC.

—Cruise Ships. 1999. (Boats & Ships Discovery Library). (Illus.). 24p. (J). (gr. 1-4). lib. bdg. 19.27 (978-0-86593-563-1(7)) Rourke Publishing, LLC.

—Sail Boats. 1999. (Boats & Ships Discovery Library). (Illus.). 24p. (J). (gr. 1-4). lib. bdg. 19.27 (978-0-86593-559-4(9)) Rourke Publishing, LLC.

Coppendale, Jean. Ships & Pirates. 2005. (Explore Inside Ser.). 10p. (J). 9.98 (978-0-7624-2322-4(6), Courage Bks.) Running Pr. Bk. Pubs.

Cruise Ships: Individual Title Six-Packs. (On Deck Ser.). 24p. (gr. 4-5). 35.00 (978-0-7578-1056-5(X)) Rigby Education.

The Discoverer Enterprise: Individual Title Six-Packs. (On Deck Ser.). 24p. (gr. 4-5). 35.00 (978-0-7578-1074-9(8)) Rigby Education.

Duble, Kathleen Benner. The Story of the Samson. Farquharson, Alexander, illus. 2008. (J). (*978-1-58089-183-7(7)*) Charlesbridge Publishing, Inc.

Ellis, Catherine. Ships. 2007. (Mega Military Machines Ser.). (Illus.). 24p. (J). (gr. k-5). lib. bdg. 21.25 (978-1-4042-3668-4(6)) Rosen Publishing Group, Inc., The.

Graham, Ian. In the Water. 2006. (QEB Machines at Work Ser.). (Illus.). 36p. (J). lib. bdg. 16.95 (978-1-59566-190-6(5)) QEB Publishing Inc.

—Ships. 2006. (Mighty Machines Ser.). (J). (978-1-58340-921-3(1)) Smart Apple Media.

—Ships & Submarines. 2000. (Fast Forward Ser.). (Illus.). 32p. (J). (gr. 4-8). pap. 9.95 (978-0-531-16446-4(2), Watts, Franklin) Scholastic Library Publishing.

—Ships & Submarines. Antram, David, illus. 2000. (Fast Forward Ser.). 32p. (J). (gr. 4-8). 29.00 (978-0-531-11880-1(0), Watts, Franklin) Scholastic Library Publishing.

—Ships & Submarines. 2000. (gr. 3-6). lib. bdg. 18.75 (978-0-613-34945-1(8)) Tandem Library Bks.

Green, Michael. Amphibious Ships. 1998. (Illus.). 48p. (J). (gr. 3-7). lib. bdg. 19.93 (978-0-516-21452-8(7), Children's Pr.) Scholastic Library Publishing.

Hamilton, John. Pirate Ships & Weapons. 2007. (ENG., Illus.). 32p. (J). lib. bdg. 24.21 (*978-1-59928-763-8(3)*, ABDO & Daughters) ABDO Publishing Co.

Harcourt School Publishers Staff. A Place Called Home. 3rd ed. 2002. (Trophies English Language Learners Ser.). (Illus.). pap. 5.10 (978-0-15-327763-4(7)) Harcourt Schl. Pubs.

—Sail Like a Viking Advanced Level. 3rd ed. 2002. (Trophies Reading Program Ser.). (Illus.). pap. 5.10 (978-0-15-323129-2(7)) Harcourt Schl. Pubs.

—The Ship From... Take-Home Book. 1999. (Signatures Ser.). (Illus.). (J). pap. 1.70 (978-0-15-313851-5(3)) Harcourt Schl. Pubs.

Haslam, Andrew. Ships. 2004. (Make It Work! Science Ser.). (Illus.). 48p. (J). (gr. 3-6). 12.95 (978-1-58728-373-4(5), Two Can Publishing) T&N Children's Publishing.

Haslam, Andrew & Solway, Andrew. Ships. 2004. (Make It Work! Science Ser.). (Illus.). 48p. (J). (gr. 3-6). pap. 6.95 (978-1-58728-360-4(3), Two Can Publishing) T&N Children's Publishing.

A History of Powered Ships. 2005. (Moving People, Things, & Ideas Ser.). (Illus.). 48p. (J). (ps-7). lib. bdg. 24.95 (978-1-4103-0660-9(7), Blackbirch Pr., Inc.) Thomson Gale.

A History of Sailing Ships. 2005. (Moving People, Things, & Ideas Ser.). (Illus.). 48p. (J). (ps-7). lib. bdg. 24.95 (978-1-4103-0661-6(5), Blackbirch Pr., Inc.) Thomson Gale.

The History of Water Travel. 2005. (Moving People, Things, & Ideas Ser.). (Illus.). 48p. (J). (ps-7). lib. bdg. 24.95 (978-1-4103-0662-3(3), Blackbirch Pr., Inc.) Thomson Gale.

Hoena, B. A. Shackleton & the Lost Antarctic Expedition. Hoover, Dave & Barnett, Charles, illus. 2006. (Graphic Library). 32p. (J). (978-0-7368-5482-5(7)) Capstone Pr., Inc.

Key Porter Books Staff. Gymboree on a Pirate Ship. rev. ed. 2007. (Illus.). 1p. (J). 16.95 (*978-1-55263-921-4(5)*) Key Porter Bks. CAN. *Dist:* Perseus Distribution.

Klingel, Cynthia Fitterer & Noyed, Robert B. Ships. 2000. (Wonder Books Level 1: Transportation Ser.). (Illus.). 24p. (J). (ps-3). 22.79 (978-1-56766-809-4(7)) Child's World, Inc.

Kramer, Sydelle A. Submarines. 2005. (Illus.). 48p. (J). (gr. 2-4). lib. bdg. 11.99 (978-0-375-92574-0(0)); (Step into Reading Ser.: No. 4). pap. 3.99 (978-0-375-82574-3(6)) Random Hse. Children's Bks. (Random Hse. Bks. for Young Readers).

Leacock, Elspeth. Exxon Valdez Oil Spill. 2005. (Environmental Disasters Ser.). (Illus.). 112p. (J). (gr. 6-12). 35.00 (978-0-8160-5754-2(0)) Facts On File, Inc.

LeapFrog Staff, compiled by. Boats Afloat. 2001. (J). (ps-2). spiral bd. 14.95 (978-1-58605-061-0(3)) LeapFrog Enterprises, Inc.

Levy, Janey. At Sea on a Viking Ship. 2004. (PowerMath Ser.). (Illus.). 24p. (J). lib. bdg. 21.25 (978-0-8239-8977-5(1), PowerKids Pr.) Rosen Publishing Group, Inc., The.

—At Sea on a Viking Ship: Solving Problems of Length & Weight Using the Four Math Operations. 2004. (PowerMath Ser.). (Illus.). 24p. (J). pap. (978-0-8239-8922-5(4), PowerKids Pr.) Rosen Publishing Group, Inc., The.

Lindeen, Mary. Ships. 2007. (Blastoff! Readers Ser.). (Illus.). 24p. (J). (gr. k-3). lib. bdg. 16.95 (978-1-60014-060-0(2)) Bellwether Media.

—Ships. 2007. (Blastoff! Readers Ser.). 24p. (J). (gr. k-2). 18.50 (*978-0-531-17558-3(8)*, Children's Pr.) Scholastic Library Publishing.

Loves, June. Ships. 2001. (Database Transportation Ser.). (Illus.). 32p. (J). (gr. 4 up). 22.95 (978-0-7910-6590-7(1), 010504, Chelsea Hse.) Facts On File, Inc.

MacDonald, Fiona. You Wouldn't Want to Sail with Christopher Columbus! Uncharted Waters You'd Rather Not Cross. Antram, David, illus. 2004. (You Wouldn't Want to Ser.). 32p. (J). (gr. 2-5). pap. 9.95 (978-0-531-16060-2(2), Watts, Franklin) Scholastic Library Publishing.

Margulies, Phillip. The Exxon Valdez Oil Spill: When Disaster Strikes! 2005. (When Disaster Strikes! Ser.). (Illus.). 48p. (YA). (gr. 5-8). lib. bdg. 23.95 (978-0-8239-3675-5(9)) Rosen Publishing Group, Inc., The.

Markle, Sandra. After the Spill: The Exxon Valdez Disaster, Then & Now. 1999. (Illus.). 32p. (J). (gr. 3-7). lib. bdg. 17.85 (978-0-8027-8611-1(1)) Walker & Co.

—After the Spill: The Exxon Valdez Disaster Then & Now. 1999. (Illus.). 32p. (J). (gr. 3-7). 16.95 (978-0-8027-8610-4(3)) Walker & Co.

Martin, Jacqueline Briggs. The Lamp, the Ice, & the Boat Called Fish: Based on a True Story. Krommes, Beth, illus. 2005. 48p. (J). (gr. k-3). 6.95 (978-0-618-54895-8(5)) Houghton Mifflin Co. Trade & Reference Div.

Mayer, Cassie. By Boat. 2006. (Illus.). 24p. (J). (978-1-4034-8389-8(2)); pap. (978-1-4034-8396-6(5)) Heinemann Library.

—En Barco. 2006. (ENG & SPA., Illus.). 24p. (J). (978-1-4034-8630-1(1)); pap. (978-1-4034-8637-0(9)) Heinemann Library.

Maynard, Christopher. I Wonder Why Planes Have Wings: And Other Questions about Transportation. 2003. (I Wonder Why Ser.). (Illus.). 32p. (J). (gr. k-3). 6.95 (978-0-7534-5662-0(1) , Kingfisher) Houghton Mifflin Co. Trade & Reference Div.

Mitton, Tony. Busy Boats. Parker, Ant, illus. (Amazing Machines Ser.). 24p. (J). (ps-k). 2005. pap., pap. 3.95 (978-0-7534-5916-4(7)); 2002. tchr. ed. 9.95 (978-0-7534-5404-6(1)) Houghton Mifflin Co. Trade & Reference Div. (Kingfisher).

Molzahn, Arlene Bourgeois. Ships & Boats. 2003. (Transportation & Communication Ser.). (Illus.). 48p. (J). (gr. 1-4). lib. bdg. 23.93 (978-0-7660-2025-2(8)) Enslow Pubs., Inc.

Mravec, James. You Can Draw Planes, Trains & Boats. 2005. (Illus.). 96p. spiral bd. (978-0-7853-8303-1(4) , 3460900) Publications International, Ltd.

O'Brien, Patrick. Great Ships. O'Brien, Patrick, illus. 2005. (Illus.). 40p. (J). pap. 7.95 (978-0-8027-7716-4(3)) Walker & Co.

Oxlade, Chris. All about Ships: Amazing Maritime Facts. 2000. (All About...Ser.). (Illus.). 64p. (gr. 3-7). pap. 7.95 (978-1-84215-015-3(4) , Southwater) Anness Publishing GBR. *Dist:* National Bk. Network.

—Boats & Ships. 2000. (Transportation Around the World Ser.). (Illus.). 32p. (J). (gr. k-2). lib. bdg. 21.36 (978-1-57572-301-3(8)) Heinemann Library.

Parker, Steve. Boat-Mania! 2003. (Vehicle-Mania! Ser.). (Illus.). 32p. (J). (gr. 2 up). lib. bdg. 23.33 (978-0-8368-3782-7(7)) Stevens, Gareth Inc.

Pipe, Jim. Ships. 2007. (J). ***(*978-1-59604-166-0(8))*** Stargazer Bks.

Platt, Richard & Biesty, Stephen. Man-of-War. (Illus.). (J). pap. 21.95 (978-0-590-74610-6(3)) Scholastic, Inc.

Plisson, Philip. Ships. Pendray, John, illus. 2007. 71p. (J). (gr. 2-7). 18.95 ***(*978-0-8109-1624-1(X)*** , Abrams Bks. for Young Readers) Abrams, Harry N., Inc.

Richardson, Adele D. Cargo Ships. 2000. (Transportation Library). (Illus.). 24p. (J). (gr. 1-2). lib. bdg. 18.60 (978-0-7368-0606-0(7) , Bridgestone Bks.) Capstone Pr., Inc.

Richter, Abigail. Boats That Float: Learning the OA Sound. (PowerPhonics Ser.). (Illus.). (J). 2002. 24p. (gr. 1). lib. bdg. 18.50 (978-0-8239-5935-8(X)); 2001. 23p. pap. 26.40 (978-0-8239-8280-6(7)) Rosen Publishing Group, Inc., The. (PowerKids Pr.).

Ring, Susan. Boats, Boats, Boats. 2005. (Yellow Umbrella Ser.). (Illus.). 17p. (J). (978-0-7368-5273-9(5)); (978-0-7368-5309-5(X)) Capstone Pr., Inc.

Rotner, Shelley. Boats Afloat. 1998. (Illus.). 32p. (J). (ps-k). 16.99 (978-0-531-33112-5(1)); pap. 15.95 (978-0-531-30112-8(5)) Scholastic, Inc. (Orchard Bks.).

Saunders-Smith, Gail. Boats. 1998. (J). pap. 13.25 (978-0-516-21228-9(1) , Children's Pr.) Scholastic Library Publishing.

Schaefer, Lola M. Boats. 2003. (Wheels, Wings, & Water Ser.). (Illus.). 24p. (J). lib. bdg. 18.50 (978-1-4034-0879 2(3)); pap. (978-1-4034-3618-4(5)) Heinemann Library.

Schaefer, Lola M. & Cano, Patricia. Barcos. 2003. (Ruedas, Alas y Agua Ser.).Tr. of Boats. (SPA.). 24p. (J). pap. 5.25 (978-1-4034-3529-3(4)) Heinemann Library.

Scher, Linda. The Texas City Disaster. 2007. (Code Red Ser.). (Illus.). 32p. (J). (gr. 3-7). lib. bdg. 25.27 (978-1-59716-363-7(5)) Bearport Publishing Co., Inc.

Ships. (Make it Work Ser.). 42p. (J). (gr. 4-8). pap. (978-1-882210-50-3(6)) Action Publishing, Inc.

Ships: Level N, 6 vols. (Wonder Worldtm Ser.). 48p. 34.95 (978-0-7802-2030-0(7)) Wright Group, The.

Shuter. Making Waves. 2004. (Technology Through Time Ser.). (Illus.). pap. 7.50 (978-1-4109-0980-0(8)) Raintree.

Sloan, Peter. Ships & Boats. 1999. (gr. k-3). lib. bdg. 11.80 (978-0-613-30726-0(7)) Tandem Library Bks.

Stickland, Paul. Boats. Stickland, Paul, illus. 1998. (On the Move Ser.). (Illus.). 16p. (J). (ps up). lib. bdg. 19.93 (978-0-8368-2151-2(3)) Stevens, Gareth Inc.

Stille, Darlene R. Boats. 2002. (Illus.). 32p. (J). (gr. 1 up). lib. bdg. 19.93 (978-0-7565-0289-8(6)) Compass Point Bks.

—Ships. 2004. (Illus.). 32p. (J). (gr. 1 up). 21.26 (978-0-7565-0608-7(5)) Compass Point Bks.

Stone, Lynn M. Amphibious Assault Ships. 2006. (Fighting Forces Ser.). (Illus.). 32p. (gr. 4-8). 19.95 (978-1-59515-460-6(4)) Rourke Publishing, LLC.

Sutherland, Jonathan & Canwell, Diane. Container Ships & Oil Tankers. 2007. (Amazing Ships Ser.). 32p. (J). (gr. 3-5). lib. bdg. 23.93 ***(*978-0-8368-8377-0(2))*** Stevens, Gareth Inc.

Tatge, Cathy. Boats. 2007. (J). ***(*978-1-58341-526-9(2)*** , Creative Education) Creative Co., The.

Tiner, John Hudson. Ships & Boats. (Illus.). 32p. 2004. pap. 8.95 (978-0-89812-390-6(9) , Creative Paperbacks); 2003. (J). lib. bdg. 18.95 (978-1-58341-257-2(3) , Creative Education) Creative Co., The.

Townsend, John. When Disaster Struck: The Exxon Valdez 1989. 2006. (Illus.). 56p. (978-1-4109-2280-9(4)) Steck-Vaughn.

Tripp, Will. Water Adventures. 2005. (Real Deal - Green Plus Ser.). (Illus.). 32p. (gr. 4-8). 19.00 (978-0-7910-8904-0(5)) Facts On File, Inc.

—Water Adventures. 2005. (Real Deal Ser.). (Illus.). 32p. (J). pap. (978-0-7608-9636-5(4)) Sundance/Newbridge Educational Publishing.

Tunis, Edwin. Oars, Sails & Steam: A Picture Book of Ships. 2002. (Illus.). 80p. pap. 25.00 (978-0-8018-6932-7(3)) Johns Hopkins Univ. Pr.

White, Steve. Naval Warship: FSF-1 Sea Fighter. 2007. (High-Tech Military Weapons Ser.). (Illus.). 48p. (J). ***(*978-1-4287-3127-1(X))*** Children's Pr., Ltd.

Wilkinson, Philip. Ships. 1999. (Single Subject References Ser.). (Illus.). 64p. (J). (gr. 5-9). tchr. ed. 16.95 (978-0-7534-5280-6(4) , Kingfisher) Houghton Mifflin Co. Trade & Reference Div.

—The World of Ships. 2005. (World Of Ser.). (Illus.). 64p. (J). (gr. 4-6). pap., pap. 8.95 (978-0-7534-5836-5(5) , Kingfisher) Houghton Mifflin Co. Trade & Reference Div.

Williams, Brian. Ships & Other Sea Craft. 96p. (J). (gr. 4-7). pap. 3.50 (978-0-528-87858-9(1)) Checkerboard Pr., Inc.

Willis, Shirley. Dime Como Flotan los Barcos. 2000. (SPA.). (gr. k-3). lib. bdg. 14.10 (978-0-613-72667-2(7)) Tandem Library Bks.

—Tell Me How Ships Float. 2000. (Whiz Kids Ser.). (Illus.). 32p. (J). (gr. 1-3). pap. 5.95 (978-0-531-15978-1(7) , Watts, Franklin) Scholastic Library Publishing.

Wright, Nicola. Ships. 2004. 24p. (YA). (gr. 1 up). lib. bdg. 22.80 (978-1-931983-56-3(9)) Chrysalis Education.

SHIPS—FICTION

Adventures of Suzy Starfish: The Sunken Ship. 2000. 24p. (J). (978-1-931015-04-2(X)) Distant Waters Publishing & Designs.

Aiken, Joan. Nightbirds on Nantucket. 1999. (978-0-606-21728-6(2)) Tandem Library Bks.

Averill, Esther Holden. Jenny Goes to Sea. Averill, Esther Holden, illus. 2005. (New York Review Children's Collection). (Illus.). 140p. (J). (ps-17). reprint ed. pap. 17.95 (978-1-59017-155-4(1) , NYR Children's Collection) New York Review of Bks., Inc., The.

Avi. Abigail Takes the Wheel. Bolognese, Don, illus. 1999. (I Can Read Bks.). 64p. (J). (gr. 3 up). 14.95 (978-0-06-027662-1(2)); lib. bdg. 17.89 (978-0-06-027663-8(0)) HarperCollins Pubs.

—Abigail Takes the Wheel. 2000. (Illus.). (J). (978-0-606-18672-8(7)) Tandem Library Bks.

Bang, Molly Garrett. Dawn. Bang, Molly Garrett, illus. 2002. (Illus.). 32p. (J). (gr. k-3). reprint ed. pap. 5.95 (978-1-58717-188-6(0) , SeaStar Bks.) Chronicle Bks. LLC.

Blake, Quentin. Green Ship. 2000. (gr. 3-6). lib. bdg. 18.75 (978-0-613-71597-3(7)) Tandem Library Bks.

Bowman, Vicki. Julie Flies Back to the Past. 2005. 71p. pap. 14.95 (978-1-4137-7529-7(2)) PublishAmerica, Inc.

Caszatt-Allen, Wendy. Last Voyage of the Griffon. 2007. (Illus.). 140p. (J). pap. 6.95 ***(*978-1-934133-08-8(6))*** Mackinac Island Pr., Inc.

Christian, Mary Blount. If Not for the Calico Cat. Serra, Sebastia, illus. 2007. 32p. (J). 16.99 (978-0-525-47779-2(9) , Dutton Juvenile) Penguin Group (USA) Inc.

Chronicle Books LLC Staff. Castaway Pirates. 2008. (J). 19.99 (978-0-8118-5923-3(1)) Chronicle Bks. LLC.

Clark, Joyce. Katie. 2006. 196p. ***(*978-1-4122-0067-7(9))*** Trafford Publishing.

Coatsworth, Elizabeth Jane. The Fair American. Sewell, Helen, illus. 2005. 137p. (J). ***(*978-1-883937-85-0(X))*** Bethlehem Bks.

Cole, James. The Lost Island. 2005. 180p. pap. 19.95 (978-1-4137-7572-3(1)) PublishAmerica, Inc.

Courtauld, Sarah. On a Pirate Ship. 2007. (Picture Bks). 24p. (J). 9.99 ***(*978-0-7945-1712-0(9)*** , Usborne) EDC Publishing.

David, Christopher. Denholme & the Skeleton Mystery. 2006. 274p. pap. ***(*978-1-4120-8014-9(2))*** Trafford Publishing.

Deedy, Carmen Agra. The Secret of Old Zeb. White, Michael P., illus. 2002. 36p. (J). (gr. 1-5). pap. 8.95 (978-1-56145-280-4(7)) Peachtree Pubs., Ltd.

—The Secret of Old Zeb. 2002. (gr. 3-6). lib. bdg. 17.60 (978-0-613-82662-4(0)) Tandem Library Bks.

Dobson, Jill. The Last Ship. 2006. (J). pap. 19.95 (978-0-7022-3394-4(3)) Univ. of Queensland Pr. AUS. *Dist:* International Specialized Bk. Services.

Drake, David. Pirates. 2002. (Cricket of Dew Drop Dell Ser.). (Illus.). 32p. (J). 3.49 (978-1-885631-59-6(6) , Family Of Man Pr., The) Hutchison, G.F. Pr.

Dupasquier, Philippe. Tom's Pirate Ship. 2003. (Illus.). 32p. (J). pap. 9.99 (978-1-84270-316-8(1)) Andersen GBR. *Dist:* Independent Pubs. Group.

Edwards, Julie Andrews & Cole, Henry. Little Bo: The Story of Bonnie Boadicea. 2006. (Illus.). 89p. (J). (gr. k-4). reprint ed. 17.00 (978-1-4223-5481-0(4)) DIANE Publishing Co.

Gisbert, Joan Manuel. El Misterio de la Isla Tokland. 1998. (SPA.). 288p. (J). 8.95 (978-84-395-0817-5(4)) Lectorum Pubns., Inc.

Golden Books Staff. Little Boy with a Big Horn. Yaccarino, Dan, illus. 2008. (Golden Classic Ser.). 48p. (J). (gr. k-k). lib. bdg. 17.99 ***(*978-0-375-93903-7(2)*** , Golden Bks.) Random Hse., Inc.

Graham, Ian. Botes, Buques, Submarinos. 1999. (SPA.). lib. bdg. 11.65 (978-0-613-89814-0(1)) Tandem Library Bks.

Greene, Janice. The 75-Cent Son: Set 1. 2002. 32p. (YA). 2.95 (978-1-56254-413-3(6) , SP 4136) Saddleback Educational Publishing.

Hansen, Andra. The Quest: A Story of a Stow Away, Who Eventually Ends up Owning the Ship. For the Barton Reading & Spelling System. 2003. (J). pap. 7.95 (978-0-9744343-2-2(9) , SA-305) Bright Solutions for Dyslexia, LLC.

Harlow, Joan Hiatt. Star in the Storm. 2001. (gr. 3-6). lib. bdg. 13.00 (978-0-613-53446-8(8)) Tandem Library Bks.

Hofmeister, Alan, et al. The Ship. (Reading for All Learners Ser.). (Illus.). (J). pap. (978-1-56861-133-4(1)) Swift Learning Resources.

Hutchins, Hazel J. Beneath the Bridge. Ohi, Ruth, illus. 2004. 24p. (J). (ps-k). pap. 7.95 (978-1-55037-858-0(9)); lib. bdg. 19.95 (978-1-55037-859-7(7)) Annick Pr., Ltd. CAN. *Dist:* Firefly Bks., Ltd.

Kidd, Rob. The Quest for the Sword of Cortes, Set. 2006. (Pirates of the Caribbean Ser.). 528p. (gr. 3-7). pap. 15.99 (978-1-4231-0656-2(3)) Disney Pr.

Lakeshore Learning Materials Staff, contrib. by. Sheep on a Ship Packet. 2000. (J). pap. 19.95 (978-1-929255-18-4(7)) Lakeshore Learning Materials.

Lawrence, Iain. The Buccaneers. (Illus.). 256p. (gr. 5-9). 2003. 5.99 (978-0-440-41671-5(X) , Yearling); 2001. 16.95 (978-0-385-32736-7(6) , Delacorte Bks. for Young Readers) Random Hse. Children's Bks.

—The Buccaneers. l.t. ed. 2001. (Illus.). 320p. (J). 23.95 (978-0-7862-3464-6(4)) Thorndike Pr.

—Ghost Boy. 2002. 352p. (YA). (gr. 7). reprint ed. pap. 6.50 (978-0-440-41668-5(X) , Laurel Leaf) Random Hse. Children's Bks.

—Ghost Boy. 2002. (gr. 7-12). lib. bdg. 14.15 (978-0-613-58216-2(0)) Tandem Library Bks.

—The Smugglers. (Illus.). (J). (gr. 5-9). 2000. 208p. 5.99 (978-0-440-41596-1(9) , Yearling); 1999. 192p. 15.95 (978-0-385-32663-6(7) , Delacorte Bks. for Young Readers) Random Hse. Children's Bks.

—The Smugglers. 2000. 184p. (J). (ps-7). lib. bdg. 12.15 (978-0-606-19693-2(5)) Tandem Library Bks.

—Smugglers. 2000. (gr. 5-8). lib. bdg. 13.55 (978-0-613-30132-9(3)) Tandem Library Bks.

—The Smugglers. l.t. ed. 2001. (Illus.). 246p. (J). 22.95 (978-0-7862-3465-3(2)) Thorndike Pr.

Lee, Brian, illus. A Pirate Ship. 2005. (What's Inside? Ser.). ***(*978-0-7607-6809-9(9))*** backpackbook.

Lloyd-Jones, Robin. See Inside Pirate Ships. 2007. (See Inside Board Bks). 16p. (J). bds. 12.99 ***(*978-0-7945-1601-7(7)*** , Usborne) EDC Publishing.

Manuel, Lynn. The Summer of the Marco Polo. Charko, Kasia, illus. 2007. 32p. (J). (ps-3). ***(*978-1-55143-330-1(3))*** Orca Bk. Pubs.

Marsh, Carole. The Cruise Ship Mystery. 2006. 128p. (gr. 3-5). pap. 5.99 ***(*978-0-635-06226-0(7));*** (gr. 7-14). 14.95 ***(*978-0-635-06228-4(3))*** Gallopade International.

Mateboer, Hans. Peter the Cruise Ship. 2007. (J). 16.95 ***(*978-0-9759487-1-2(7))*** Mateboer, Johannes Aart.

McAlister, Hugh. The Flight of the Silver Ship: Around the World Aboard a Giant Dirigible. 2004. reprint ed. pap. 26.95 (978-1-4179-2616-9(3)) Kessinger Publishing, LLC.

McCullagh, Sheila. Griffin. 2007. (Three Pirates Ser.). (Illus.). 48p. 15.95 ***(*978-1-84560-044-0(4))*** Mercury Bks. Ltd. GBR. *Dist:* International Publishers Marketing.

McKernan, Victoria. Shackleton's Stowaway. 2005. 336p. (gr. 7). (J). lib. bdg. 17.99 (978-0-375-92691-4(7)); (YA). 15.95 (978-0-375-82691-7(2)) Random Hse. Children's Bks. (Knopf Bks. for Young Readers).

McMullan, Kate. I'm Mighty! McMullan, Jim, illus. 2003. (J). (978-0-06-056882-5(8)); 40p. 16.99 (978 0 06 009290-0(4)) HarperCollins Pubs.

Metaxas, Eric. The Fool & the Flying Ship. Drescher, Henrik, illus. 2007. (J). 25.65 (978-1-59961-308-6(5)) ABDO Publishing Co.

Minter, J. Take It Off: An Insiders Novel. 2005. (Insiders Ser.). 300p. (YA). pap. 8.95 (978-1-58234-994-7(0) , Bloomsbury Children) Bloomsbury Publishing.

Nixon, Joan Lowery. Playing for Keeps. 2003. 208p. (YA). (gr. 7). pap. 5.50 (978-0-440-22867-7(0) , Laurel Leaf) Random Hse. Children's Bks.

—Playing for Keeps. 2003. (gr. 7-12). lib. bdg. 13.55 (978-0-613-64782-3(3)) Tandem Library Bks.

Ocean Explorers: Individual Title Six-Packs. (Rigby Infoquest Ser.). 24p. (gr. 3 up). 34.00 (978-0-7578-5773-7(6)) Rigby Education.

Orr, Wendy. Nim at Sea. Millard, Kerry, illus. 2008. 192p. (J). (gr. 3-7). 12.99 ***(*978-0-440-42232-7(9)*** , Knopf Bks. for Young Readers) Random Hse. Children's Bks.

Other. Build Your Own Pirate Ship: A Push-Out-and-Play Book. 2008. 12p. (J). bds. 8.95 ***(*978-0-385-61114-5(5))*** Transworld Publishers Ltd. GBR. *Dist:* Independent Pubs. Group.

Pighin, Marcel. Tickles the Bear Goes on a Cruise, 1 bk. Mitchell, Hazel, illus. 2006. 48p. (J). per. 10.49 ***(*978-0-9776679-7-0(9))*** MP2ME Enterprise.

Priest, Robert. The Old Pirate of Central Park PB. 2008. 32p. (J). (ps-3). pap. 6.95 ***(*978-0-618-99769-5(5))*** Houghton Mifflin Co. Trade & Reference Div.

Rappaport, Doreen. The Freedom Ship. James, Curtis, illus. 2006. 40p. (gr. k-4). 15.99 (978-0-7868-0645-4(1)) Disney Pr.

Rassmus, Jens. Farmer Enno & His Cow. 1998. (Illus.). 32p. (J). (gr. k-4). pap. 14.95 (978-0-531-30081-7(1) , Orchard Bks.) Scholastic, Inc.

Reasoner, Charles. Inside Jolly Roger's Pirate Ship. Reasoner, Charles, illus. 2007. 12p. (J). (gr. k). bds. 9.99 ***(*978-1-84666-149-5(8)*** , Tide Mill Pr.) Top That! Publishing PLC GBR. *Dist:* Random Hse., Inc.

Reiche, Dietlof. Ghost Ship. 2006. 320p. (J). pap. 5.99 (978-0-439-59705-0(6)) Scholastic, Inc.

—Ghost Ship. Brownjohn, John, tr. from GER. 2005. 320p. (J). pap. 16.95 (978-0-439-59704-3(8)) Scholastic, Inc.

Riddell, Chris & Stewart, Paul. Far-Flung Adventures: Corby Flood. 2006. (Illus.). 256p. (J). (gr. 3-7). 14.95 (978-0-385-75090-5(0)); lib. bdg. 17.99 (978-0-385-75091-2(9)) Random Hse. Children's Bks. (Fickling, David Bks.).

Robertson, Barbara. Rosemary at Sea: Back to 1919. 2001. (Hourglass Adventures Ser.: Bk. 3). (Illus.). 128p. (J). (gr. 4-6). pap. 4.95 (978-1-890817-57-2(0)) Winslow Pr.

Rosen, Michael J. Shakespeare: His Work & His World. Ingpen, Robert R., illus. 2001. 104p. (J). (gr. 7-11). 19.99 (978-0-7636-1568-0(4)) Candlewick Pr.

Rundstrom, T. S. Sherman the Sheep: A Sheep Adventure Story about Dreams, Doing Stuff & Happiness. Miller, Bryan & Marshall, H. Keene, illus. l.t. ed. 2002. per. (978-1-932062-00-7(9) , 02-0232SH) Hability Solution Services, Inc.

Shaw, Nancy. Sheep on a Ship. Apple, Margot, illus. 2002. (J). 12.81 (978-0-7587-3611-6(8)) Book Wholesalers, Inc.

Shearer, Alex. Sea Legs. 2006. 320p. (J). pap. 5.99 (978-0-689-87144-3(9) , Aladdin) Simon & Schuster Children's Publishing.

The Ship in a Bottle, 6 vols. (Ragged Island Mysteriestm Ser.). 161p. (gr. 5-7). 42.50 (978-0-322-01648-4(7)) Wright Group, The.

Soto, Gary. Chato Goes Cruisin' Guevara, Susan, tr. Guevara, Susan, illus. 2005. 32p. (J). (ps-3). 16.99 (978-0-399-23974-8(X) , Putnam Juvenile) Penguin Group (USA) Inc.

Standish, Burt L. Frank Merriwell's Cruise. Rudman, Jack, ed. 2003. (Frank Merriwell Ser.). (YA). (gr. 9 up). 29.95 (978-0-8373-9326-1(4)); pap. 9.95 (978-0-8373-9026-0(5) , FM-026) Merriwell, Frank Inc.

Stanley, George Edward. Adam Sharp No. 3: Swimming with Sharks. 2003. (gr. k-3). lib. bdg. 11.80 (978-0-613-82722-5(8)) Tandem Library Bks.

—Swimming with Sharks. Francis, Guy, illus. 2003. (Adam Sharp Ser.: No. 3). 48p. (J). (gr. 2-4). pap. 3.99 (978-0-307-26418-3(1) , Random Hse. Bks. for Young Readers) Random Hse. Children's Bks.

Stewart, Paul & Riddell, Chris. Far-Flung Adventures: Fergus Crane. 2006. (Illus.). 240p. (J). (gr. 3-7). 14.95 (978-0-385-75088-2(9) , Fickling, David Bks.) Random Hse. Children's Bks.

Strickland, Brad. Guns of Tortuga. 2003. (gr. 3-6). lib. bdg. 13.00 (978-0-613-60418-5(0)) Tandem Library Bks.

Surrell, Jason. Pirates of the Caribbean: from the Magic Kingdom to the Movies. 2006. (Illus.). 148p. (ps-17). pap. 22.95 (978-1-4231-0709-5(8) , Disney Editions) Disney Pr.

Taylor, Theodore & Gonzalez, Tomas. El Cavo. 2000. (SPA., Illus.). 106p. (J). (gr. k-2). 9.50 (978-84-279-3250-0(2) , NG0873) Lectorum Pubns., Inc.

There's a Ship Outside My Window: Individual Chapter Book Title Six-Packs. Vol. 27. 32p. (gr. 4 up). 44.00 (978-0-7635-4497-3(3)) Rigby Education.

Thornton, Duncan. The Star-Glass: The Return of Kalifax & Captain Jenny. Noblet, Yves, illus. 2003. (Kalifax Trilogy Ser.). 432p. (J). (gr. 5-7). pap. 10.95 (978-1-55050-269-5(7)) Coteau Bks. CAN. *Dist:* Fitzhenry & Whiteside, Ltd.

Two Red Tugs: Individual Title Six-Packs. 16p. (gr. 2 up). 35.00 (978-0-7635-9241-7(2)) Rigby Education.

Umansky, Kaye. Solomon Snow & the Stolen Jewel. Nash, Scott, illus. 2007. 256p. (J). (gr. 2-7). 12.99 (978-0-7636-2793-5(3)) Candlewick Pr.

Vasey, Tony. The Adventures of Lily Lifeboat. Baines, Jacqueline, illus. 1999. 12p. (J). (ps-1). pap. 21.00 (978-1-85072-187-1(4)) Sessions, William Ltd. GBR. *Dist:* State Mutual Bk. & Periodical Service, Ltd.

Verne, Jules. Twenty Thousand Leagues under the Sea. 2005. (Illus.). 32p. (C). pap. 9.00 ***(*978-0-582-85494-9(6))*** Pearson ESL.

Wells, Helen. Cherry Ames, Cruise Nurse. 2007. (YA). ***(*978-0-8261-0411-3(8))*** Springer.

Williams, Anita. The Captain's Hat. Banks, Timothy, illus. 2000. 104p. (J). (gr. 1-5). pap. 7.95 (978-1-57924-330-2(4) , 119743) Jones, Bob Univ. Pr.

Wisler, G. Clifton. Run the Blockade. 2000. (Illus.). 122p. (J). (gr. 5-9). 15.95 (978-0-688-16538-3(9)) HarperCollins Pubs.

SHIPS—HISTORY

Aaseng, Nathan. The Titanic. 1999. (Building History Ser.). (Illus.). 96p. (YA). (gr. 6-9). 28.70 (978-1-56006-569-2(9) , Lucent Bks.) Thomson Gale.

Beyer, Mark. Boats of the Past. 2002. (Reading Power Ser.). (Illus.). 24p. (J). (gr. 1). lib. bdg. 17.25 (978-0-8239-5988-4(0) , PowerKids Pr.) Rosen Publishing Group, Inc., The.

Burns, Phyllis B. Iron Lady at Sea: From Shipyard to Voyage, A Story of the Great Iron-Hulled Sailing Ship, Star of India. 2nd ed. 2003. (Illus.). 112p. (J). pap. 21.95 (978-0-9620065-0-0(5)) Burns, Phillys.

Clifford, Barry. Expedition Whydah: The Story of the World's First Excavation of a Pirate Treasure Ship & the Man Who Found Her. 1999. (gr. 7-12). lib. bdg. 24.60 (978-0-613-28837-8(8)) Tandem Library Bks.

Graham, Ian. Ships & Submarines. 2000. (J). (978-0-606-19793-9(1)) Tandem Library Bks.

Ireland, Charles E. Toolbox. Dienno, Trish, illus. 2006. (J). (978-1-892142-30-6(9)) Cedar Tree Bks.

S

Janveau, Teri-Lynn & Thompson, Allister. Sailing for Glory: The Story of Angus Walters. Thompson, Samantha, illus. 2006. 72p. (J). 16.95 (978-1-894917-09-4(X)) Napoleon Publishing/Rendezvous Pr. CAN. *Dist:* Atlas-Books Distribution.

MacDonald, Fiona, et al. You Wouldn't Want to Sail with Christopher Columbus! Uncharted Waters You'd Rather Not Cross. 2004. (You Wouldn't Want To Ser.). (J). 28.50 (978-0-531-12355-3(3) , Watts, Franklin) Scholastic Library Publishing.

McCarty, Peter. The Lusitania. Date not set. (J). 16.95 (978-0-8050-6934-1(8) , Holt, Henry & Co. Bks. For Young Readers) Holt, Henry & Co.

Morris, Neil. Ships. (Past & Present Ser.). (Illus.). 32p. lib. bdg. 24.25 (978-1-931983-38-9(0)) Chrysalis Education.

Ships to Forts. Date not set. (Illus.). 32p. (YA). (gr. 6 up). pap. 4.00 (978-1-890541-16-3(8)) Americana Souvenirs & Gifts.

Shuter, Jane. Making Waves: Travel by Sea. 2004. (Technology Through Time Ser.). (Illus.). 32p. (J). lib. bdg. 25.70 (978-1-4109-0581-9(0)) Raintree.

SHIPS IN ART

see Marine Painting

SHIPWRECKS

see also Salvage; Survival after Airplane Accidents, Shipwrecks, etc.

also names of wrecked ships

Addario, Yvonne. Treasure Diving with Captain Dom: Special Archival Section. 2007. (Illus.). 56p. (YA). per. 15.99 (***978-0-9743414-1-5(X)***) Adventure in Discovery.

Aston, Claire. Shipwreck: Fast Forward. Dennis, Peter, illus. 2004. 31p. (J). (gr. k-4). reprint ed. 15.00 (978-0-7567-8006-7(3)) DIANE Publishing Co.

Caper, William. Nightmare on the Titanic. 2007. (Code Red Ser.). (Illus.). 32p. (J). (gr. 3-7). lib. bdg. 25.27 (978-1-59716-362-0(7)) Bearport Publishing Co., Inc.

Cefrey, Holly. Steven Callahan: Adrift at Sea. 2003. lib. bdg. 15.25 (978-0-613-67934-3(2)) Tandem Library Bks.

Claybourne, Anna & Daynes, Katie. Titanic. 2006. 64p. (J). 8.99 (978-0-7945-1269-9(0) , Usborne) EDC Publishing.

Cole, Michael D. The Titanic: Disaster at Sea. 2001. (American Disasters Ser.). (Illus.). 48p. (YA). (gr. 4-10). lib. bdg. 23.93 (978-0-7660-1557-9(2)) Enslow Pubs., Inc.

Cook, Peter. You Wouldn't Want to Sail on 19th Century Whaling Ship. Antram, David, illus. 2004. (You Wouldn't Want to Ser.). 32p. (J). (gr. 2-5). pap. 9.95 (978-0-531-16399-3(7) , Watts, Franklin) Scholastic Library Publishing.

Cook, Peter & Salariya, David. You Wouldn't Want to Sail on a 19th-Century Whaling Ship! Grisly Tasks You'd Rather Not Do. Antram, David, illus. 2004. (You Wouldn't Want To Ser.). (J). 28.50 (978-0-531-12356-0(1) , Watts, Franklin) Scholastic Library Publishing.

Crosbie, Duncan. Titanic: The Ship of Dreams. Geist, Ken, ed. Moulder, Bob et al, illus. 2007. 30p. (J). 18.99 (978-0-439-89995-6(8) , Orchard Bks.) Scholastic, Inc.

Deady, Kathleen W. The Titanic: The Tragedy at Sea. 2002. (Disaster! Ser.). (Illus.). 32p. (J). (gr. 3-4). lib. bdg. 21.26 (978-0-7368-1323-5(3) , Capstone High-Interest Bks.) Capstone Pr., Inc.

Delgado, James P. Native American Shipwrecks. 2000. (Watts Library). (Illus.). 64p. (J). (gr. 5-7). 25.50 (978-0-531-20379-8(4) , Watts, Franklin) Scholastic Library Publishing.

—Native American Shipwrecks. 2000. (Illus.). 63p. (J). (gr. 4-7). lib. bdg. 17.60 (978-0-613-54041-4(7)) Tandem Library Bks.

—Shipwrecks from the Westward Movement. 2000. (Watts Library). (Illus.). 64p. (J). (gr. 5-7). 25.50 (978-0-531-20380-4(8) , Watts, Franklin) Scholastic Library Publishing.

—Shipwrecks from the Westward Movement. 2000. (gr. 3-6). lib. bdg. 17.60 (978-0-613-54658-4(X)) Tandem Library Bks.

—Wrecks of American Warships. 2000. (Watts Library). (Illus.). 64p. (J). (gr. 5-7). 25.50 (978-0-531-20376-7(X) , Watts, Franklin) Scholastic Library Publishing.

—Wrecks of American Warships. 2000. (gr. 3-6). lib. bdg. 17.60 (978-0-613-54796-3(9)) Tandem Library Bks.

Doeden, Matt. The Sinking of the Titanic. Barnett, Charles, III, illus. 2005. (Graphic Library). 32p. (J). 22.60 (978-0-7368-3834-4(1)) Capstone Pr., Inc.

Donkin, Andrew. Disasters at Sea. Martin, Linda, ed. 2001. (Readers Ser.). (Illus.). 48p. (J). (ps-3). pap. 3.99 (978-0-7894-7381-3(X)) Dorling Kindersley Publishing, Inc.

—Disasters at Sea. 2001. (gr. k-3). lib. bdg. 11.80 (978-0-613-35102-7(9)); (Illus.). (J). 10.75 (978-0-606-21149-9(7)) Tandem Library Bks.

Donkin, Andrew & Dorling Kindersley Publishing Staff. Disasters at Sea. 2001. (Readers Ser.). (Illus.). 48p. (J). (ps-3). 12.95 (978-0-7894-7382-0(8)) Dorling Kindersley Publishing, Inc.

Dorling Kindersley Publishing Staff, ed. Titanic. 2004. (Dk Eyewitness Books Ser.). (Illus.). 72p. (J). (ps-12). 15.99 (978-0-7566-0732-6(9)) Dorling Kindersley Publishing, Inc.

Dunn, Joeming W. & Dunn, Ben. The Titanic. Dunn, Joeming W. & Dunn, Ben, illus. 2007. (Graphic History Ser.). (Illus.). 32p. (J). (gr. 3-6). lib. bdg. 27.07 (***978-1-60270-079-6(6)*** , Graphic Planet) Magic Wagon.

Griffith, Anita. The 10 Most Unforgettable Shipwrecks. 2008. (Tentrade; Ser.). 48p. (J). pap. 14.99 (***978-1-55448-458-4(8)*** , Watts, Franklin) Scholastic Library Publishing.

Hamilton, Sue L. Air & Sea Mysteries. 2007. (Unsolved Mysteries Ser.). 32p. (J). (gr. 4-8). lib. bdg. 25.65 (***978-1-59928-837-6(0)*** , ABDO & Daughters) ABDO Publishing Co.

Harcourt School Publishers Staff. Vietnamese Treasure Below Level. 3rd ed. 2002. (Trophies Reading Program Ser.). (Illus.). pap. 5.10 (978-0-15-323422-4(9)) Harcourt Schl. Pubs.

Harmon, Daniel E. The Titanic. 2000. (Great Disasters, Reforms & Ramifications Ser.). (Illus.). 112p. (J). (gr. 6-8). 30.00 (978-0-7910-5265-5(6) , Chelsea Hse.) Facts On File, Inc.

Hertel, Robert. The Edmund Fitzgerald: Lost with All Hands. 1998. (Illus.). 56p. (J). (gr. 3-8). pap. 9.95 (978-0-938682-49-3(0) , 682-49-0) River Road Pubns., Inc.

Hill, Christine M. Robert Ballard: Oceanographer Who Discovered the Titanic. 1999. (People to Know Ser.). (Illus.). 128p. (YA). (gr. 6-12). lib. bdg. 26.60 (978-0-7660-1147-2(X)) Enslow Pubs., Inc.

Hoh, Diane. Remembering the Titanic. 1998. 72p. (YA). (gr. 6-10). pap. 4.99 (978-0-590-87585-1(X)) Scholastic, Inc.

Hook. Shipwrecks. 2003. (Mysteries of the Past Ser.). (Illus.). 32p. pap. 7.95 (978-1-4109-0065-4(7)) Raintree.

—Shipwrecks - Mysteries of the Past. 2004. pap. 48.30 (978-1-4109-0284-9(6)) Harcourt Schl. Pubs.

Hook, Jason. Shipwrecks. 2001. (Young Library - Mysteries of the Past). (Illus.). 32p. (J). lib. bdg. 25.69 (978-0-7398-4340-6(0)) Raintree.

—Shipwrecks. 2003. (gr. 3-6). lib. bdg. 16.40 (978-0-613-78229-6(1)) Tandem Library Bks.

Houghton, Gillian. The Wreck of the Andrea Gail: Three Days of a Perfect Storm. 2005. (When Disaster Strikes! Ser.). (Illus.). 48p. (YA). (gr. 5-8). lib. bdg. 23.95 (978-0-8239-3677-9(5)) Rosen Publishing Group, Inc., The.

Jeffrey, Gary. Spectacular Shipwrecks. Saraceni, Claudia, illus. 2007. (Graphic Discoveries Ser.). (J). 48p. (gr. 3-7). lib. bdg. (***978-1-4042-1091-2(1)***); (***978-1-4042-9598-8(4)***); pap. (***978-1-4042-9597-1(6)***) Rosen Publishing Group, Inc., The.

Kantar, Andrew. 29 Missing: The True & Tragic Story of the Disappearance of the SS Edmund Fitzgerald. 1998. (Illus.). 70p. (J). (gr. 7 up). pap. 14.95 (978-0-87013-446-3(9)) Michigan State Univ. Pr.

Kentley, Eric. The Story of the Titanic. Thistlethwaite, Diane, ed. Noon, Steve, illus. 2001. 32p. (J). (gr. k-3). 17.99 (978-0-7894-7943-3(5)) Dorling Kindersley Publishing, Inc.

Kupperberg, Paul. The Tragedy of the Titanic: When Disaster Strikes! 2005. (When Disaster Strikes! Ser.). (Illus.). 48p. (YA). (gr. 5-8). lib. bdg. 23.95 (978-0-8239-3679-3(1)) Rosen Publishing Group, Inc., The.

Landau, Elaine. Maritime Disasters. 1999. (Watts Library). (Illus.). 64p. (J). (gr. 5-7). 25.50 (978-0-531-20344-6(1) , Watts, Franklin) Scholastic Library Publishing.

—Maritime Disasters. 1999. (gr. 3-6). lib. bdg. 17.60 (978-0-613-29471-3(8)) Tandem Library Bks.

Leroe, Ellen. Disaster! Three Real-Life Stories of Survival. 2000. (gr. 5-8). lib. bdg. 14.15 (978-0-613-36304-4(3)) Tandem Library Bks.

Locke, Ian. Deadly Deep. Rowe, Alan, illus. 17th ed. 2003. 60p. (J). pap. 3.99 (978-0-330-37500-9(8) , Pan) Pan Macmillan GBR. *Dist:* Trafalgar Square Publishing.

Matsen, Bradford. The Incredible Quest to Find the Titanic. 2003. (Incredible Deep-Sea Adventures Ser.). (Illus.). 48p. (J). lib. bdg. 23.93 (978-0-7660-2191-4(2)) Enslow Pubs., Inc.

—The Incredible Search for the Treasure Ship Atocha. 2003. (Incredible Deep-Sea Adventures Ser.). (Illus.). 48p. (J). lib. bdg. 23.93 (978-0-7660-2193-8(9)) Enslow Pubs., Inc.

Mayell, Hillary. Shipwrecks. 2003. (Manmade Disasters Ser.). (Illus.). 112p. (J). 29.95 (978-1-59018-058-7(5) , Lucent Bks.) Thomson Gale.

Mitchell, Mark. Raising la Belle. Mitchell, Mark, illus. (Professor Wigglestix & the Weather Ser.). (Illus.). 112p. 10.95 (978-1-57168-703-6(3)) Eakin Pr.

Molony, Senan. Titanic: A Primary Source History. 2005. (Illus.). 48p. 26.00 (978-0-8368-5980-5(4)) Stevens, Gareth Inc.

Nobleman, Marc Tyler. The Sinking of the USS Indianapolis. 2006. 48p. (J). (gr. 4-7). lib. bdg. (978-0-7565-2031-1(2)) Compass Point Bks.

Osborne, Mary Pope & Osborne, Will. Titanic: A Nonfiction Companion to Tonight on the Titanic. Murdocca, Sal, illus. 2002. (Magic Tree House Research Guide Ser.: No. 7). 144p. (J). (gr. k-3). lib. bdg. 11.99 (978-0-375-91357-0(2)); pap. 4.99 (978-0-375-81357-3(8)) Random Hse. Children's Bks. (Random Hse. Bks. for Young Readers).

O'Shei, Tim. Shipwreck! Debbie Kiley's Story of Survival. 2008. (J). (***978-1-4296-0089-7(6)***) Capstone Pr., Inc.

Parker, Victoria. The Titanic, 1912. 2006. (When Disaster Struck Ser.). (Illus.). 56p. (J). lib. bdg. (978-1-4109-2282-3(0)) Steck-Vaughn.

Philbrick, Nathaniel. Revenge of the Whale: The True Story of the Whaleship Essex. 176p. 2002. (Illus.). (YA). (gr. 4 up). 16.99 (978-0-399-23795-9(X) , Putnam Juvenile); 2004. (J). (gr. 5-9). reprint ed. pap. 7.99 (978-0-14-240068-5(8) , Puffin) Penguin Group (USA) Inc.

—Revenge of the Whale: The True Story of the Whaleship Essex. 2004. (Illus.). 164p. (J). (gr. k-9). per. 16.65 (978-0-613-97779-1(3)) Tandem Library Bks.

Phillips, Dee. Sunken Treasure. 2003. (History Hunters Ser.). (Illus.). 32p. (J). (gr. 3 up). lib. bdg. 24.67 (978-0-8368-3743-8(6)) Stevens, Gareth Inc.

Pipe, Jim. You Wouldn't Want to Sail on an Irish Famine Ship! A Trip Across the Atlantic You'd Rather Not Make. (You Wouldn't Want to... : History of the World Ser.). 32p. (J). 2008. pap. 9.95 (***978-0-531-14854-9(8)*** , Watts, Franklin); 2007. spiral bd. 29.00 (***978-0-531-13913-4(1)*** , Children's Pr.) Scholastic Library Publishing.

Platt, Richard. Shipwreck: Eyewitness Books. Wilson, Alex & Chambers, Tina, photos by. 2004. (Illus.). 61p. (YA). (gr. 4-8). reprint ed. 16.00 (978-0-7567-7288-8(5)) DIANE Publishing Co.

Porterfield, Jason. Shipwreck: True Stories of Survival. 2006. (Survivor Stories Ser.). (Illus.). 48p. (J). (gr. 5-8). lib. bdg. 26.50 (978-1-4042-1000-4(8)) Rosen Publishing Group, Inc., The.

Sloan, Frank. Titanic. 1998. (Illus.). 128p. (YA). (gr. 3-7). 19.98 (978-0-8172-4091-2(8)) Raintree.

Smith, K. C. Ancient Shipwrecks. 2000. (Shipwrecks Library). (Illus.). 64p. (J). (gr. 5-7). 25.50 (978-0-531-20381-1(6) , Watts, Franklin) Scholastic Library Publishing.

—Ancient Shipwrecks. 2000. (gr. 3-6). lib. bdg. 17.60 (978-0-613-53912-8(5)) Tandem Library Bks.

—Exploring for Shipwrecks. 2000. (Shipwrecks Library). (Illus.). 64p. (J). (gr. 5-7). 25.50 (978-0-531-20377-4(8) , Watts, Franklin) Scholastic Library Publishing.

—Exploring for Shipwrecks. 2000. (gr. 3-6). lib. bdg. 17.60 (978-0-613-54467-2(6)) Tandem Library Bks.

—Shipwrecks of the Explorers. 2000. (Watts Library). (Illus.). 64p. (J). (gr. 5-7). 25.50 (978-0-531-20378-1(6) , Watts, Franklin) Scholastic Library Publishing.

—Shipwrecks of the Explorers. 2000. (gr. 3-6). lib. bdg. 17.60 (978-0-613-36667-0(0)); (Illus.). (978-0-606-20915-1(8)) Tandem Library Bks.

Spence, David & Spence, Susan. A History of Shipwrecks. 2006. (From Past to Present Ser.). (Illus.). 36p. (J). lib. bdg. 24.67 (978-0-8368-6288-1(0)) Stevens, Gareth Inc.

—Shipwrecks. 1999. (History Ser.). (Illus.). 31p. (J). (gr. 5-9). pap. 5.95 (978-0-7641-0646-0(5)) Barron's Educational Series, Inc.

Stewart, David. You Wouldn't Want to Sail on the Titanic! 2001. (gr. 3-6). lib. bdg. 18.75 (978-0-613-44280-0(6)) Tandem Library Bks.

—You Wouldn't Want to Sail on the Titanic! One Voyage You'd Rather Not Make. Antram, David, illus. 2001. (You Wouldn't Want to Be Ser.). 32p. (J). (gr. 2-5). 28.50 (978-0-531-14604-0(9)); pap. 9.95 (978-0-531-16210-1(9)) Scholastic Library Publishing. (Watts, Franklin).

Stonehouse, Frederick. Final Passage: True Shipwreck Adventures. Meyer, Susan Alby, illus. 2002. (J). 17.95 (978-1-892384-16-4(7)) Avery Color Studios, Inc.

Temple, Bob. The Titanic: An Interactive History Adventure. 2008. (You Choose Bks.). 112p. (J). (gr. 3-7). lib. bdg. 27.23 (***978-1-4296-0163-4(9)***) Capstone Pr., Inc.

Thompson, Gare. Monitor: The Iron Warship That Changed the World. Day, Larry, illus. 2003. (All Aboard Reading Ser.). 48p. (J). (gr. 4-4). pap. 3.99 (978-0-448-43245-8(5) , Grosset & Dunlap) Penguin Group (USA) Inc.

—The Monitor: The Iron Warship That Changed the World. Day, Larry, illus. 2003. (All Aboard Reading Ser.). 48p. (J). 13.89 (978-0-448-43283-0(8) , Grosset & Dunlap) Penguin Group (USA) Inc.

Wargin, Kathy-Jo. The Edmund Fitzgerald: The Song of the Bell. van Frankenhuyzen, Gijsbert, illus. 2003. 40p. (J). 17.95 (978-1-58536-126-7(7)) Sleeping Bear Pr.

Weil, Ann. Sea Disasters. 2003. (Illus.). 64p. (YA). per. (978-1-56254-660-1(0) , SP6600) Saddleback Educational Publishing.

Woods, Michael & Woods, Mary B. Disasters at Sea. 2008. (Disasters up Close Ser.). (J). lib. bdg. 27.93 (***978-0-8225-6773-8(3)*** , Lerner Pubns.) Lerner Publishing Group.

SHIPWRECKS—FICTION

Alger, Horatio. Facing the World. 2006. pap. (***978-1-4250-2212-9(X)***) Assistedreadingbooks.com Inc.

—Facing the World. 2006. pap. (***978-1-4065-0704-1(0)***) Dodo Pr.

Ardizzone, Edward. Tim in Danger. 2000. (Tim Bks.). (J). (ps-3). (Illus.). 48p. 15.95 (978-0-688-17675-4(5)); 15.89 (978-0-06-029206-5(7)) HarperCollins Pubs.

Autio, Karen. Second Watch. 2006. (Illus.). 208p. (J). pap. 8.95 (978-1-55039-151-0(8)) Sono Nis Pr. CAN. *Dist:* Orca Bk. Pubs. USA.

Ballantyne, R. The Coral Island. 2006. pap. 14.95 (***978-1-55742-666-6(X)***) Wildside Pr.

Barnum, P. T. Dick Broadhead: A Story of Perilous Adve. 2006. pap. 30.95 (***978-1-4286-1959-3(3)***) Kessinger Publishing, LLC.

Bayle, B. J. Perilous Passage. 2007. 176p. (YA). pap. 11.99 (***978-1-55002-689-4(5)*** , Sandcastle Bks.) Dundurn Group, The CAN. *Dist:* Univ. of Toronto Pr.

Beck, Ana. Elliot's Shipwreck. 2000. (gr. 3-6). lib. bdg. 14.10 (978-0-613-36328-0(0)) Tandem Library Bks.

Beck, Andrea. Elliot's Shipwreck. Beck, Andrea, illus. 2004. (Elliot Moose Ser.). (Illus.). 32p. (J). (gr. k-3). (978-1-55074-700-3(2)); reprint ed. (978-1-55074-698-3(7)) Kids Can Pr., Ltd.

Bingley, Thomas. Tales of Shipwrecks & Other Disasters. 2006. pap. 26.95 (***978-1-4286-5637-6(5)***) Kessinger Publishing, LLC.

Bodkin, Odds. The Ghost of the Southern Belle: A Sea Tale. Fuchs, Bernie, illus. 1999. 32p. (J). (gr. 3-7). 15.95 (978-0-316-02608-6(5)) Little Brown & Co.

Bowler, Tim. Apocalypse. 2005. 352p. (YA). 16.95 (978-1-4169-0370-3(4) , McElderry, Margaret K.) Simon & Schuster Children's Publishing.

Caszatt-Allen, Wendy. Last Voyage of the Griffon. 2007. (Illus.). 140p. (J). pap. 6.95 (***978-1-934133-08-8(6)***) Mackinac Island Pr., Inc.

Cosby, Bill. Shipwreck Saturday. Honeywood, Varnette P., illus. 1998. (Little Bill Books for Beginning Readers Ser.). (J). (gr. k-3). (978-0-606-13773-7(4)) Tandem Library Bks.

Crew, Gary. Pig on the Titanic: A True Story. Whatley, Bruce, illus. 2005. (J). 32p. 15.99 (978-0-06-052305-3(0)); 40p. lib. bdg. 17.89 (978-0-06-052306-0(9)) HarperCollins Pubs.

Crisp, Marty. White Star: A Dog on the Titanic. 2006. 160p. (J). pap. 4.99 (978-0-439-71265-1(3) , Scholastic Paperbacks) Scholastic, Inc.

David, Erica. Quiero Ser Libre. 2005. (Madagascar Ser.).Tr. of Born to Be Wild. (SPA., Illus.). 32p. (J). 3.99 (978-0-439-71575-1(X) , Scholastic en Espanol) Scholastic, Inc.

Defoe, Daniel. The Adventures of Robinson Crusoe. 2002. (Great Illustrated Classics Ser.).Tr. of Robinson Crusoe. (Illus.). 240p. (J). (gr. 3-8). 21.35 (978-1-57765-677-7(6) , ABDO & Daughters) ABDO Publishing Co.

—The Farther Adventures of Robinson Crusoe. (Illus.). (J). reprint ed. 32.50 (978-0-404-07912-3(1)) AMS Pr., Inc.

—Robinson Crusoe. Heller, Julek, illus. 1998. (Eyewitness Classics Ser.).Tr. of Robinson Crusoe. 64p. (J). (gr. 3-6). 14.95 (978-0-7894-3625-2(6)) Dorling Kindersley Publishing, Inc.

—Robinson Crusoe. Akib, Jamel, illus. 2006. (Classic Starts Ser.).Tr. of Robinson Crusoe. 160p. (J). 4.95 (978-1-4027-2664-4(3)) Sterling Publishing Co., Inc.

—Robinson Crusoe. 2000. (Coleccion "Clasicos Juveniles" Ser.).Tr. of Robinson Crusoe. (SPA., Illus.). 288p. (YA). (gr. 4-7). pap. 13.95 (978-1-58348-782-2(4)) iUniverse, Inc.

—Robinson Crusoe: With a Discussion of Resourcefulness. Landgraf, Kenneth, illus. 2003. (Values in Action Illustrated Classics Ser.). 190p. (J). (978-1-59203-035-4(1)) Learning Challenge, Inc.

Defoe, Daniel, et al. Robinson Crusoe. (Classics Illustrated Ser.).Tr. of Robinson Crusoe. (Illus.). 52p. (YA). pap. 4.95 (978-1-57209-021-7(9)) Classics International Entertainment, Inc.

DiTerlizzi, Tony & Black, Holly. El Arbol Metalico. Abreu, Carlos, tr. 2005. (Escritura desatada Ser.). (SPA., Illus.). 128p. (J). (gr. 4-7). 12.95 (978-84-666-1658-4(6)) Ediciones B ESP. *Dist:* Independent Pubs. Group.

—Spiderwick Cronicas: El Mapa Perdido. Abreu Fetter, Carlos, tr. 2005. (Escritura desatada Ser.). (SPA.). 128p. (J). 12.95 (978-84-666-1513-6(X)) Ediciones B ESP. *Dist:* Independent Pubs. Group.

Dorling Kindersley Publishing Staff. Shipwreck. 2005. (Eyewitness Books). (Illus.). 72p. (J). 15.99 (978-0-7566-1089-0(3) , 1241925) Dorling Kindersley Publishing, Inc.

Fama, Elizabeth. Overboard. 2002. (Illus.). 192p. (YA). (gr. 6-9). 15.95 (978-0-8126-2652-0(4)) Cricket Bks.

—Overboard. 2005. 160p. (YA). (gr. 7). pap. 5.50 (978-0-553-49436-5(8) , Laurel Leaf) Random Hse. Children's Bks.

Farber, Erica. Octopus Island. Mayer, Mercer, illus. 2006. (Critter Kids Adventure Ser.). 32p. (J). (gr. 2-5). pap. 4.95 (978-0-7696-4766-1(9) , Gingham Dog Pr.) School Specialty Publishing.

Fletcher, E. B. The Last American Star. 2005. 10.95 (978-0-533-15338-1(7)) Vantage Pr., Inc.

Frankowski, Leo A. Fata Morgana. 2000. (gr. 7-12). lib. bdg. 15.30 (978-0-613-36343-3(4)) Tandem Library Bks.

Fripp, Jon, et al. Kinnakeet & the Lighthouse. Moussa, Karen M., illus. 2000. 33p. (J). 5.50 (978-0-9638258-4-1(4)) Bicast, Inc.

Gelsey, James. Scooby-Doo & the Sunken Ship. 1999. (Scooby-Doo Mysteries Ser.: No. 4). (Illus.). 64p. (J). (ps-3). pap. 3.99 (978-0-590-81917-6(8)) Scholastic, Inc.

—Scooby-Doo & the Sunken Ship. 1999. (gr. 3-6). lib. bdg. 11.80 (978-0-613-17004-8(0)) Tandem Library Bks.

—Sunken Ship: Scooby-Doo y el Barco Hundido. 2004. (Scooby-Doo Ser.). (ENG & SPA.). 64p. (J). mass mkt. 3.99 (978-0-439-55116-8(1) , Scholastic en Espanol) Scholastic, Inc.

Grove, Vicki. Rhiannon. 2007. 224p. (YA). (gr. 5). 18.99 (***978-0-399-23633-4(3)*** , Putnam Juvenile) Penguin Group (USA) Inc.

Harcourt School Publishers Staff. Shipwrecked! Take-Home Book. 2001. (Collections Ser.). (Illus.). (J). pap. 1.90 (978-0-15-319522-8(3)) Harcourt Schl. Pubs.

—Shipwrecked Below Level. 3rd ed. 2002. (Trophies Reading Program Ser.). (Illus.). pap. 5.10 (978-0-15-323320-3(6)) Harcourt Schl. Pubs.

Hathaway, Lucinda. Takashi's Voyage: The Wreck of the Sindia. DiPiazza, Ellen & Ganss, Leslee, illus. 2005. 107p. (gr. 4-7). (978-0-945582-24-3(2)) Down The Shore Publishing.

Hyland, Hilary. The Wreck of the Ethie. 1999. (978-0-606-22861-9(6)) Tandem Library Bks.

—Wreck of the Ethie. 1999. (gr. 3-6). lib. bdg. 16.40 (978-0-613-23823-6(0)) Tandem Library Bks.

Jenner, Caryn. Survivors: The Night the Titanic Sank. Martin, Linda, ed. 2001. (Readers Ser.). (Illus.). 32p. (J). (ps-3). pap. 3.99 (978-0-7894-7373-8(9)) Dorling Kindersley Publishing, Inc.

Jenner, Caryn & Dorling Kindersley Publishing Staff. Survivors: The Night the Titanic Sank. 2001. (Readers Ser.). (Illus.). 32p. (J). (ps-3). 14.99 (978-0-7894-7374-5(7)) Dorling Kindersley Publishing, Inc.

Johnson, Sandi. Lost Island. Johnson, Britt, ed. Sturgeon, Bobbi, illus. l.t. ed. 2001. 22p. (J). (gr. k-5). spiral bd. 5.99 (978-1-929063-69-7(5) , 168) Moons & Stars Publishing For Children.

Jordan, Apple. Fearless Foursome. Dever, Bob & Morris, Michael, illus. 2005. (Madagascar Ser.). (SPA.). 64p. (J). (ps-ps). 2.99 (978-0-439-71307-8(2) , Scholastic en Espanol) Scholastic, Inc.

Keene, Carolyn. Operation Titanic. 1998. (Nancy Drew & Hardy Boys Super Mystery Ser.: No. 35). (YA). (gr. 6 up). (978-0-606-13650-1(9)) Tandem Library Bks.

Kingston, William H. G., tr. The Swiss Family Robinson. Wyss, Johann David, illus. 2005. 188p. per. 6.95 (978-1-4209-2269-1(6)) Digireads.com.

Korman, Gordon. The Deep. 2003. (Dive Ser.: No. 2). 144p. (J). (gr. 3-6). pap. 4.99 (978-0-439-50723-3(5) , Scholastic Paperbacks) Scholastic, Inc.

—Island Trilogy: Shipwreck; Survival; Escape. 2005. 404p. (YA). pap. (978-0-681-15634-0(1)); 2006. 416p. (J). pap. 9.99 (978-0-439-80911-5(8) , Scholastic) Scholastic, Inc.

—Shipwreck. 2001. (Island Ser.: Bk. 1). 143p. (J). (gr. 3-7). pap. 4.99 (978-0-439-16456-6(7)) Scholastic, Inc.

—Shipwreck. 2001. (gr. 3-6). lib. bdg. 12.40 (978-0-613-36068-5(0)); (Illus.). (J). (978-0-606-21251-9(5)) Tandem Library Bks.

Lawlor, Laurie. American Sisters: A Titanic Journey Across the Sea. 2000. (J). (978-0-606-20220-6(X)) Tandem Library Bks.

Lawrence, Iain. The Wreckers. 1999. (978-0-606-17565-4(2)) Tandem Library Bks.

—Wreckers. 1999. (gr. 5-8). lib. bdg. 13.55 (978-0-613-22807-7(3)) Tandem Library Bks.

—The Wreckers. 1999. (Dell Yearling Book Ser.). 224p. (J). (gr. 5-9). reprint ed. 5.99 (978-0-440-41545-9(4) , Yearling) Random Hse. Children's Bks.

—The Wreckers. unabr. ed. 2000. (YA). (gr. 7). pap., stu. ed. 59.95 incl. audio (978-0-7887-4195-1(0) , 41097) Recorded Bks., LLC.

Leavitt, Caroline. Robinhound Crusoe. l.t. ed. 1999. (Adventures of Wishbone Ser.: No. 4). (Illus.). 144p. (J). (gr. 4 up). lib. bdg. 22.60 (978-0-8368-2300-4(1)) Stevens, Gareth Inc.

Lofting, Hugh. The Story of Doctor Dolittle No. 3: Doctor Dolittle's Great Adventure. Kanzler, John, illus. 2007. (Easy Reader Classics Ser.). 32p. (J). pap. 3.95 (978-1-4027-4122-7(7)) Sterling Publishing Co., Inc.

Manuel, Lynn. The Summer of the Marco Polo. Charko, Kasia, illus. 2007. 32p. (J). (ps-3). *(*978-1-55143-330-1(3))* Orca Bk. Pubs.

McCurry, Meryl Alyse. The Sea Monster's Darkest Night. McCurry, Meryl Alyse, illus. 1999. (Illus.). 34p. (J). (ps-3). pap. 7.99 (978-1-881524-67-0(1)) Milligan Bks., Inc.

McKenzie, Lyn. Lavinia's Shoes. 2007. (J). pap. 12.95 *(*978-0-9788628-5-5(6))* Just Write Bks.

McMullan, Kate. Revenge of the Dragon Lady. 2007. (Dragon Slayers' Academy Ser.: No. 2). 112p. (J). (gr. 1-6). 24.21 *(*978-1-59961-378-9(6))* Spotlight.

Meddaugh, Susan. Harry on the Rocks. 2007. (Illus.). 32p. (J). (gr. k-3). 6.95 *(*978-0-618-84068-7(0)* , Walter Lorraine) Houghton Mifflin Co. Trade & Reference Div.

—Harry on the Rocks. Meddaugh, Susan, illus. 2003. (Illus.). 32p. (J). (gr. k-3). tchr. ed. 15.00 (978-0-618-27603-5(3) , Walter Lorraine) Houghton Mifflin Co. Trade & Reference Div.

Morpurgo, Michael. The Wreck of the Zanzibar. l.t. ed. 2003. (J). 16.95 (978-0-7540-7846-3(9) , Galaxy Children's Large Print) BBC Audiobooks America.

Oppel, Kenneth. Airborn. l.t. ed. 2006. 525p. (YA). pap. 10.95 (978-0-7862-8367-5(X)) Thorndike Pr.

Osborne, Mary Pope. Tonight on the Titanic. unabr. ed. 2004. (Magic Tree House Ser. : No. 17). 71p. (J). (gr. k-3). pap. 17.00 incl. audio (978-0-8072-0926-4(0) , S FTR 249 SP, Listening Library) Random Hse. Audio Publishing Group.

—Tonight on the Titanic. Murdocca, Sal, illus. 1999. (Magic Tree House Ser.: No. 17). (J). (gr. k-3). 96p. lib. bdg. 11.99 (978-0-679-99063-5(1)); 71p. pap. 3.99 (978-0-679-89063-8(7)) Random Hse. Children's Bks. (Random Hse. Bks. for Young Readers).

—Tonight on the Titanic. Murdocca, Sal, illus. 1999. (Magic Tree House Ser. : No. 17). 70p. (J). (gr. k-3). lib. bdg. 11.19 (978-0-606-16894-6(X)) Tandem Library Bks.

—Tonight on the Titanic. 1999. (Magic Tree House Ser. : No. 17). (J). (gr. k-3). lib. bdg. 11.80 (978-0-613-16226-5(9)) Tandem Library Bks.

Perrow, Angeli. Captain's Castaway. Harris, Emily, illus. 1998. 32p. (J). (ps-3). 15.95 (978-0-89272-419-2(6)) Down East Bks.

Platt, Richard. Shipwreck Detective. Cameron, Duncan, illus. 2006. 96p. (J). 24.99 (978-0-7566-2218-3(2)) Dorling Kindersley Publishing, Inc.

Platt, Richard & Dorling Kindersley Publishing Staff. Shipwreck. Wilson, Alex & Chambers, Tina, photos by. 2005. (Eyewitness Books). (Illus.). 72p. (J). (ps-7). lib. bdg. 19.99 (978-0-7566-1090-6(7) , 1241925) Dorling Kindersley Publishing, Inc.

Prins, Piet. Stefan Derksen's Polar Adventure. 2004. (Illus.). 237p. (J). pap. (978-1-894666-67-1(4)) Inheritance Pubns.

Ransom, Candice. Rescue on the Outer Banks. Ritz, Karen, illus. 2002. 48p. (J). (gr. 1-3). lib. bdg. 14.10 (978-0-613-46163-4(0)) Tandem Library Bks.

Ransom, Candice F. Rescue on the Outer Banks. Ritz, Karen, illus. 2002. (On My Own History Ser.). 48p. (J). (gr. 1-3). lib. bdg. 23.93 (978-0-87614-460-2(1) , Carolrhoda Bks.) Lerner Publishing Group.

Romeu, Emma. Naufragio en las Filipinas. 2003. Tr. of Shipwrecked in the Philippines. (SPA., Illus.). 162p. (J). (gr. 5-8). pap. 9.95 (978-968-19-0555-2(5)) Santillana USA Publishing Co., Inc.

—Naufragio en las Filipinas. 2002. Tr. of Shipwrecked in the Philippines. (SPA.). (gr. 5-8). lib. bdg. 18.75 (978-0-613-71354-2(0)) Tandem Library Bks.

Shipwreck: Fourth Grade Guided Comprehension Level Q. (On Our Way to English Ser.). (gr. 4 up). 34.50 (978-0-7578-7179-5(8)) Rigby Education.

Shipwrecked!, 6 vols., Pack. (Bookweb Ser.). 32p. (gr. 4 up). 34.00 (978-0-7635-3736-4(5)) Rigby Education.

Simpson, Fiona, ed. Madagascar: Play-Along. 2005. (Madagascar Ser.). 16p. (J). pap. 4.99 (978-0-439-69994-5(0)) Scholastic, Inc.

Spedden, Daisy Corning Stone. Polar the Titanic Bear. 2001. (978-0-606-22559-5(5)) Tandem Library Bks.

Steele, Michael Anthony. Esto es un Zoologico! 2005. (Madagascar Ser.).Tr. of Zoosters on the Loose. (SPA., Illus.). 24p. (J). 3.99 (978-0-439-71308-5(0)) Scholastic, Inc.

Swift, Jonathan. Los Viajes de Gulliver. (SPA., Illus.). 144p. (YA). 14.95 (978-84-7281-080-8(1) , AF1080) Auriga, Ediciones S.A. ESP. *Dist:* Continental Bk. Co., Inc.

—Los Viajes de Gulliver. (Coleccion Clasicos de la Juventud). (SPA., Illus.). 204p. (J). 12.95 (978-84-7189-062-7(3) , ORT322) Ortells, Alfredo Editorial S.L. ESP. *Dist:* Continental Bk. Co., Inc.

Tanaka, Shelley. On Board the Titanic: What It Was Like When the Great Liner Sank. 1999. (Illus.). (J). (978-0-606-15659-2(3)) Tandem Library Bks.

Taylor, Theodore. The Cay. 2000. 171p. (J). 15.60 (978-0-03-054604-4(4)) Holt, Rinehart & Winston.

—The Cay. 144p. 2003. (J). (gr. 5). mass mkt. 5.99 (978-0-440-22912-4(X) , Laurel Leaf); 2002. (gr. 4-7). 5.99 (978-0-440-41663-0(9) , Yearling) Random Hse. Children's Bks.

—Cay. 2003. (gr. 5-8). lib. bdg. 13.55 (978-0-613-72282-7(5)); 2002. (gr. 3-6). lib. bdg. 13.55 (978-0-613-33748-9(4)) Tandem Library Bks.

—Teetoncey. 2004. (Illus.). 228p. (J). 17.00 (978-0-15-205298-0(4) , Harcourt Young Classics); pap. 5.95 (978-0-15-205294-2(1) , Odyssey Classics) Harcourt Children's Bks.

—Teetoncey & Ben O'Neal. 2004. (Illus.). 240p. (J). 17.00 (978-0-15-205296-6(8) , Harcourt Young Classics); (Cape Hatteras Trilogy: Bk. 2). pap. 5.95 (978-0-15-205297-3(6) , Odyssey Classics) Harcourt Children's Bks.

—Timothy of the Cay. 2007. (Illus.). 176p. (YA). pap. 5.95 (978-0-15-206320-7(X) , Harcourt Paperbacks) Harcourt Children's Bks.

Tekkel, Tatjana. Jessie & the Dolphins. 2001. (Illus.). 24p. bds. 12.95 (978-1-85149-711-9(0)) Antique Collectors' Club.

Thompson, Lisa. Diving for the Ghost Galleon. Cantell, Brenda, illus. 2005. (Treasure Trackers Ser.). 80p. (gr. 5-9). 19.00 (978-0-7910-8873-9(1)) Facts On File, Inc.

Trimper, Marty. Hermione: Shipwrecked! in Ocean City, Maryland. Amy, Holloway, illus. 2004. (J). (978-1-886068-28-5(3)) Fruitbearer Publishing.

Wade, Judith. The Mermaid's Gift. 2004. 140p. (J). per. 5.99 (978-0-9728958-1-1(7) , 750) Riley Pr.

Wallace, Jim. Terror on the Titanic. 2007. (Choose Your Own Adventure Ser.: No. 24). (Illus.). 144p. (J). (gr. 3-7). pap. 6.99 *(*978-1-933390-24-6(7))* Chooseco LLC.

Walsh, Alice. Heroes of Isle aux Morts. ed. 2004. (J). (gr. k-3). spiral bd. (978-0-616-11138-3(X)); spiral bd. (978-0-616-11139-0(8)) Canadian National Institute for the Blind/Institut National Canadien pour les Aveugles.

—Heroes of Isle aux Morts. Butler, Geoff, illus. 2001. 32p. (J). (gr. 3-7). 17.95 (978-0-88776-501-8(7)) Tundra Bks., Inc./Livres Toundra, Inc. CAN. *Dist:* Random Hse., Inc.

Walton, O. F. Saved at Sea. 2003. (gr. k-3). lib. bdg. 14.15 (978-0-613-80081-5(8)) Tandem Library Bks.

Wells, H. G. The Island of Dr Moreau. 2007. (Illus.). vii, 54p. (C). pap. 9.00 *(*978-1-4058-4999-9(1))* Pearson ESL.

Welsh, T. K. The Unresolved. 2006. 160p. (YA). (gr. 9). 16.99 (978-0-525-47731-0(4) , Dutton Juvenile) Penguin Group (USA) Inc.

Wilkes, Angela. Robinson Crusoe. 2003. (gr. 3-6). lib. bdg. 14.10 (978-0-613-90680-7(2)) Tandem Library Bks.

Wilkes, Angela & Rawson, Christopher. Robinson Crusoe. 2004. (Young Reading Ser.). (Illus.). 64p. (J). (gr. 2 up). pap. 5.95 (978-0-7945-0410-6(8) , Usborne) EDC Publishing.

Willson, Sarah. Castaways: The Rugrats Meet the Wild Thornberrys. 2003. (gr. k-3). lib. bdg. 14.15 (978-0-613-66354-0(3)) Tandem Library Bks.

Wyss, Johann David. Swiss Family Robinson. 1998. (Children's Classics). (ENG., Illus.). 192p. (J). (gr. 4-7). pap. (978-1-85326-111-4(4) , 1114WW) Wordsworth Editions, Ltd.

—The Swiss Family Robinson. 2007. (Aladdin Classics Ser.). 576p. (J). pap. 6.99 (978-1-4169-3490-5(1) , Aladdin) Simon & Schuster Children's Publishing.

SHIRLEY, ANNE (FICTITIOUS CHARACTER)—FICTION

Dussling, Jennifer & Montgomery, L. M. Anne of Green Gables. Halverson, Lydia, illus. 2001. (All Aboard Reading Ser.). 48p. (J). (gr. 4-7). pap. 3.99 (978-0-448-42459-0(2) , Grosset & Dunlap) Penguin Group (USA) Inc.

Helldorfer, Mary-Claire. Anne of Green Gables. Beier, Ellen, illus. 2003. 40p. (J). (gr. k-3). pap. 6.99 (978-0-440-41614-2(0) , Dragonfly Bks.) Random Hse. Children's Bks.

McHugh, Fiona, adapted by. Anne of Green Gables Storybook. 2007. (Illus.). 80p. (J). (gr. 2-7). pap. 9.95 (978-0-920668-42-9(9)) Firefly Bks., Ltd.

Montgomery, L. M. Ana y la Casa de Sus Suenos. 2000. (Coleccion "Ana, la de Tejas Verdes" Ser.). (SPA.). 256p. (J). 10.95 (978-84-7888-217-5(0)) Lectorum Pubns., Inc.

—Anne d'Avonlea. 1998. (Avonlea Ser.: No. 2). Tr. of Anne of Avonlea. (FRE.). 194p. (YA). (gr. 5-8). pap. 10.95 (978-0-920304-88-4(5)) Ragweed Pr. CAN. *Dist:* Univ. of Toronto Pr.

—Anne of Avonlea. unabr. ed. 2002. (Dover Juvenile Classics Ser.). 272p. (J). (gr. 4-7). pap. 3.00 (978-0-486-42239-8(9)) Dover Pubns., Inc.

—Anne of Avonlea. l.t. ed. 1998. (Avonlea Ser.: No. 2). 401p. (YA). (gr. 5-8). lib. bdg. 35.95 (978-1-58118-039-8(X) , 22507) LRS.

—Anne of Avonlea. 1998. 270p. (YA). (gr. 5-8). reprint ed. lib. bdg. 25.00 (978-1-58287-013-7(6)) North Bks.

—Anne of Avonlea. 2000. (Anne of Green Gables Ser.: Vol. No. 2). (gr. 5-8). 194p. pap. 12.99 (978-1-57646-304-8(4)); 194p. (YA). 24.95 (978-1-57646-305-5(2)); 366p. pap. 21.99 (978-1-57646-306-2(0)) Quiet Vision Publishing.

—Anne of Avonlea. 2004. 336p. (J). pap. 3.99 (978-0-439-43649-6(4) , Scholastic Paperbacks) Scholastic, Inc.

—Anne of Avonlea Book & Charm. 2002. (Charming Classics). 256p. (ps-1). pap. 6.99 (978-0-694-01584-9(9) , Harper Festival) HarperCollins Pubs.

—Anne of Green Gables. 2004. 400p. per. 16.95 (978-1-59540-110-6(5)) 1st World Publishing, Inc.

—Anne of Green Gables. 349p. (978-1-58726-053-7(0)) Ann Arbor Media Group, LLC.

—Anne of Green Gables. 2000. (Avonlea Ser.: No. 1). 280p. (YA). (gr. 5-8). pap. 15.00 (978-0-7881-9155-8(1)) DIANE Publishing Co.

—Anne of Green Gables. 2007. per. 6.99 *(*978-1-4209-2922-5(4))* Digireads.com.

—Anne of Green Gables. 2000. (Avonlea Ser.: No. 1). 320p. (J). (gr. 4-7). pap. 3.50 (978-0-486-41025-8(0)) Dover Pubns., Inc.

—Anne of Green Gables. 2005. (My First Classics Ser.). 112p. (J). (gr. k-3). pap. 4.99 (978-0-06-079147-6(0) , Harper Festival); 2000. (Avonlea Ser.: No. 1). (YA). (gr. 5-8). (978-0-06-028227-1(4)); 1999. (Charming Classics). 400p. (J). (ps up). pap. 6.99 (978-0-694-01251-0(3) , Harper Festival) HarperCollins Pubs.

—Anne of Green Gables. (Avonlea Ser.: No. 1). (YA). (gr. 5-8). pap. (978-0-340-71500-0(6) , Hodder & Stoughton) Hodder General Publishing Division.

—Anne of Green Gables. 2003. 276p. pap. 15.99 *(*978-1-4043-6066-2(2))* IndyPublish.com.

—Anne of Green Gables. Stemach, Jerry, ed. Ham, Jeff, illus. 2000. 65.00 incl. audio, cd-rom (978-1-58702-311-8(3)); 2002. 150.00 (978-1-58702-021-6(1)); 2000. 50.00 (978-1-58702-502-0(7)) Johnston, Don Inc.

—Anne of Green Gables. 1998. 352p. (J). pap. (978-1-55109-249-2(2)); 252p. (YA). (gr. 5-8). reprint ed. (978-1-55109-013-9(9)) Nimbus Publishing, Ltd.

—Anne of Green Gables. 1998. 310p. (YA). (gr. 5-8). reprint ed. lib. bdg. 25.00 (978-1-58287-014-4(4)) North Bks.

—Anne of Green Gables. (Oxford Children's Classics). 2007. 400p. (YA). 9.95 *(*978-0-19-272000-9(7));* 2004. 8.50 (978-0-19-423273-9(5)) Oxford Univ. Pr., Inc.

—Anne of Green Gables. 2003. 320p. (gr. 12). 4.95 (978-0-451-52882-7(4) , Signet Classics) Penguin Group (USA) Inc.

—Anne of Green Gables. 2000. (Anne of Green Gables Ser.: Vol. No. 1). (gr. 5-8). 220p. pap. 12.99 (978-1-57646-300-0(1)); 220p. 24.95 (978-1-57646-301-7(X)); 294p. pap. 17.95 (978-1-57646-302-4(8)) Quiet Vision Publishing.

—Anne of Green Gables. 1998. (Children's Classics Ser.: No. 1). (Illus.). 256p. (J). (gr. 4-7). 6.99 (978-0-517-18968-9(2) , Children's Classics) Random Hse. Value Publishing.

—Anne of Green Gables. rev. ed. 2002. (Scholastic Classic Ser.). 400p. (J). pap. 4.99 (978-0-439-29577-2(7)) Scholastic, Inc.

—Anne of Green Gables. 2001. (Aladdin Classics Ser.). (Illus.). 480p. (J). pap. 5.99 (978-0-689-84622-9(3) , Aladdin) Simon & Schuster Children's Publishing.

—Anne of Green Gables. 2001. (gr. 3-6). lib. bdg. 11.80 (978-0-613-63175-4(7)); (gr. 5-8). lib. bdg. 13.00 (978-0-613-66688-6(7)) Tandem Library Bks.

—Anne of Green Gables. 1999. (Avonlea Ser.: No. 1). (YA). (gr. 5-8). 23.95 (978-0-8057-8090-1(4) , Macmillan Reference USA) Thomson Gale.

—Anne of Green Gables. Fernandez, Laura & Jacobson, Rick, illus. 2000. (Avonlea Ser.: No. 1). 328p. (J). (gr. 5-8). 24.95 (978-0-88776-515-5(7)) Tundra Bks., Inc./ Livres Toundra, Inc. CAN. *Dist:* Random Hse., Inc.

—Anne of Green Gables. MQ Publications Staff, ed. 1998. (Little Brown Notebooks Ser.). (Illus.). 256p. (978-1-84072-063-1(8)) Watson-Guptill Pubns., Inc.

—Anne of Green Gables, 100th Anniversary Edition. 2008. 19.95 *(*978-0-399-15478-2(7)* , Putnam Adult) Penguin Group (USA) Inc.

—Anne of Green Gables Cookbook. 22.95 (978-0-8488-2657-4(4)) Amereon LTD.

—Anne of Green Gables Diary. 22.95 (978-0-8488-2654-3(X)) Amereon LTD.

—Anne of Ingleside. 2000. (Avonlea Ser.: No. 10). (YA). (gr. 5-8). 23.95 (978-0-8488-0890-7(8)) Amereon LTD.

—Anne of Ingleside, Vol. 6. 1999. 384p. (J). pap. 3.99 (978-0-14-036801-7(9) , Putnam Juvenile) Penguin Group (USA) Inc.

—Anne of the Island. Date not set. mass mkt. (978-0-8125-6563-8(0) , Tor Bks.) Doherty, Tom Assocs., LLC.

—Anne of the Island. 2006. (ENG.). pap. *(*978-1-4068-2171-0(3));* pap. *(*978-1-4068-3175-7(1))* Echo Library.

—Anne of the Island. 2006. (ENG.). 102.99 *(*978-1-4219-3295-8(4))* IndyPublish.com.

—Anne of the Island. 2004. reprint ed. pap. 1.99 (978-1-4192-0718-1(0)); pap. 30.95 (978-1-4179-0885-1(8)) Kessinger Publishing, LLC.

—Anne of the Island. (Twelve-Point Ser.). 2001. 240p. lib. bdg. 25.00 (978-1-58287-157-8(4)); 2004. 396p. 26.00 (978-1-58287-640-5(1)) North Bks.

—Anne of the Island. abr. ed. 1998. (Avonlea Ser.: No. 4). 304p. (J). (gr. 5-8). pap. 4.99 (978-0-14-036777-5(2) , Puffin) Penguin Group (USA) Inc.

—Anne of the Island. 2000. (Anne of Green Gables Ser.: Vol. No. 3). (gr. 5-8). 182p. 24.95 (978-1-57646-309-3(5)); 182p. pap. 14.99 (978-1-57646-308-6(7)); 336p. pap. 19.99 (978-1-57646-310-9(9)) Quiet Vision Publishing.

—Anne of the Island. 2001. (gr. 7-12). lib. bdg. 30.40 (978-0-613-79774-0(4)) Tandem Library Bks.

—Anne of the Island Book & Charm. 2005. (Charming Classics). 304p. (J). pap. 6.99 (978-0-06-075859-2(7) , Harper Festival) HarperCollins Pubs.

—Anne of Windy Willows, Vol. 4. 1999. 336p. (J). pap. 3.99 (978-0-14-036800-0(0) , Putnam Juvenile) Penguin Group (USA) Inc.

—Anne's House of Dreams. l.t. ed. 1999. (Avonlea Ser.: No. 5). 364p. (YA). (gr. 5-8). lib. bdg. 34.95 (978-1-58118-048-0(9) , 22517) LRS.

—Anne's House of Dreams, Vol. 5. 1999. 320p. (J). 3.99 (978-0-14-036799-7(3) , Putnam Juvenile) Penguin Group (USA) Inc.

—Anne's House of Dreams. 2000. (Anne of Green Gables Ser.: Vol. No. 5). (gr. 5-8). 182p. 24.95 (978-1-57646-313-0(3)); 182p. pap. 14.99 (978-1-57646-312-3(5)); 336p. pap. 19.99 (978-1-57646-314-7(1)) Quiet Vision Publishing.

—The Complete Anne of Green Gables: Anne of Green Gables; Anne of the Island; Anne of Avonlea; Anne of Windy Poplars; Anne's House of Dreams; Anne of Ingleside; Rainbow Valley; Rilla of Ingleside, 8 vols. gif. ed. 1998. (J). (gr. 4-7). mass mkt. 40.43 (978-0-553-60941-7(6) , Starfire) Random Hse. Children's Bks.

Montgomery, L. M. Rilla of Ingleside. 2002. (ENG.). 272p. 19.99 *(*978-1-4043-2710-8(X));* pap. 14.99 *(*978-1-4043-2711-5(8))* IndyPublish.com.

—Rilla of Ingleside. 2004. 224p. (YA). pap. 10.95 (978-1-57646-891-3(7)) Quiet Vision Publishing.

Montgomery, L. M. & Greenwood, Barbara. Anne of Green Gables. Wood, Muriel, illus. rev. ed. 2001. (Avonlea Ser.: No. 1). 94p. (J). (gr. 5-8). pap. 9.95 (978-1-55013-431-5(0)) Key Porter Bks. CAN. *Dist:* Firefly Bks., Ltd.

Montgomery, L. M. & Hedge, Tricia. Anne of Green Gables, Level 2. 2nd abr. ed. 2000. (Bookworms Ser.). (Illus.). 64p. 6.50 (978-0-19-422965-4(3)) Oxford Univ. Pr., Inc.

Morton, Elizabeth. Anne: Six Titles Based on Anne of Green Gables. 2001. (Illus.). 64p. (J). (ps-3). 6.99 (978-0-694-01587-0(3) , Harper Festival) HarperCollins Pubs.

—Anne: The Animated Series Storybook. 2001. (Illus.). (J). (ps-4). 119.75 (978-0-694-01542-9(3)) HarperCollins Pubs.

Peterson. Anne of Green Gables. 1999. (Avonlea Ser.: No. 1). 32p. (YA). (gr. 5-8). pap. 4.95 (978-0-06-443535-2(0)) HarperCollins Pubs.

Stewart, Pat. Anne of Green Gables. 2001. (Avonlea Ser.: No. 1). (Illus.). 4p. (J). (gr. 5-8). pap. 1.50 (978-0-486-41280-1(6)) Dover Pubns., Inc.

SHOES

Brill, Marlene Targ. Shoes Through the Ages. 2000. (Pair-It Books). (Illus.). 40p. (J). pap. (978-0-7398-0881-8(8)) Steck-Vaughn.

Chambers, Catherine. Sneaker. 1998. (Look Inside Ser.). (Illus.). 24p. 19.92 (978-1-57572-624-3(6)) Heinemann Library.

Cooper, Arin. Boots & Shoes. 2004. 12p. (J). pap. 4.95 (978-1-57874-044-4(4)) Kaeden Corp.

Frisch, Aaron. The Story of Nike. 2003. (Built for Success Ser.). (Illus.). 48p. (J). lib. bdg. 19.95 (978-1-58340-295-5(0)) Smart Apple Media.

Jackson, Abby. Fancy Feet. 2006. (Illus.). 16p. (J). (gr. k-2). 15.93 (978-0-7368-5847-2(4) , Yellow Umbrella Bks.) Capstone Pr., Inc.

Kahalewai, Marilyn. Whose Slippers Are Those? Kobayashi, Gavin, illus. 2005. 24p. (J). (ps-ps). 10.95 (978-1-57306-238-1(3)) Bess Pr., Inc.

Keenan, Elaine F. Travelin' Shoes for Infants & Toddlers: Ceremony. 1998. 14p. (J). (ps-1). 14.95 (978-0-9663273-1-1(4)) Heirloom Memories, Inc.

—Travelin' Shoes for Infants & Toddlers: Classic. 1998. 14p. (J). (ps-1). 14.95 (978-0-9663273-2-8(2)) Heirloom Memories, Inc.

McNeil, Niki, et al. HOCPP 1094 Red Clogs. 2006. spiral bd. 15.50 *(*978-1-60308-094-1(5))* In the Hands of a Child.

Morris, Ann. Shoes, Shoes, Shoes. 1998. (Illus.). 32p. (J). (ps-3). pap. 6.99 (978-0-688-16166-8(9) , Harper Trophy) HarperCollins Pubs.

Raintree Steck-Vaughn Staff. Shoes Through the Ages. 1999. (Illus.). (J). pap. 35.60 (978-0-7398-0912-9(1)) Steck-Vaughn.

Reynolds, Helen. The Shoe. 2003. (Fashionable History of Costume Ser.). (Illus.). 32p. (J). lib. bdg. 25.70 (978-1-4109-0027-2(4)) Raintree.

Sneaker Factory. (J). pap. 13.15 (978-0-8136-4301-4(5)) Modern Curriculum Pr.

Solovic, Linda & Ikids. Tie Your Shoes: Rocket Style/Bunny Ears. 2003. (Illus.). (J). (ps-2). 9.99 (978-1-58476-207-2(1)) Innovative Kids.

Woods, Samuel G. Sneakers: From Start to Finish. Zucker, Gale, photos by. 1999. (Made in the U. S. A. Ser.). (Illus.). 32p. (J). (gr. 3-6). 23.70 (978-1-56711-393-8(1) , Blackbirch Pr., Inc.) Thomson Gale.

Yue, Charlotte & Yue, David. Shoes: Their History in Words & Pictures. 2000. (Illus.). 92p. (J). (gr. 5-7). reprint ed. 15.00 (978-0-7881-9465-8(8)) DIANE Publishing Co.

SHOOTING

see also Hunting

DiVito, Anna. Annie Oakley Saves the Day. DiVito, Anna, illus. 2004. (Illus.). 29p. (J). (ps-7). lib. bdg. 10.79 (978-0-606-32656-8(1)) Tandem Library Bks.

Martin, Michael J. Pheasant Hunting. 2002. (Great Outdoors Ser.). (Illus.). 48p. (J). (gr. 3-4). lib. bdg. 21.26 (978-0-7368-1057-9(9) , Capstone High-Interest Bks.) Capstone Pr., Inc.

Shooter's Dictionary. 2003. cd-rom 0.00 (978-0-9747407-1-3(3)) Southwest guns & stuff.

SHOOTING STARS

see Meteors

SHOP COMMITTEES

see Management—Employee Participation

SHOPLIFTING—FICTION

Cosgrove, Stephen. The Bugglar Brothers: Consequences of Stealing. Arroyo, Fian, illus. 2007. (J). (978-1-58804-381-8(9)) PCI Educational Publishing.

Harcourt School Publishers Staff. Somewhere to Go: Take-Home Book. 2001. (Collections Ser.). (Illus.). (J). pap. 1.90 (978-0-15-319547-1(9)) Harcourt Schl. Pubs.

Hutchins, Hazel J. TJ & the Rockets. 2004. (Orca Young Readers Ser.). (Illus.). 144p. (J). (gr. 3-6). pap., tchr. ed. 4.99 (978-1-55143-300-4(1) , 1234543) Orca Bk. Pubs. USA.

Pollack, Jenny. Klepto. 288p. (gr. 7). 2008. (YA). pap. 7.99 (*978-0-14-241072-1(1) , Puffin); 2006. (J). 16.99 (978-0-670-06061-0(5) , Viking Juvenile) Penguin Group (USA) Inc.

Weber, Lori. Klepto. 2004. (SideStreets Ser.). 160p. (gr. 7-12). 7.95 (978-1-55028-836-0(9)); (*978-1-55028-837-7(7)) Lorimer, James & Co., Ltd., Pubs. CAN. *Dist:* Casemate Pubs. & Bk. Distributors, LLC.

SHOPPERS' GUIDES

see Consumer Education; Shopping

SHOPPING

see also Consumer Education

Adil, Janeen R. Goods & Services. 2006. (First Facts. Learning about Money Ser.). (Illus.). 24p. (J). (978-0-7368-5395-8(2)) Capstone Pr., Inc.

At the Toyshop: Individual Title Six-Packs. (ps-2). 23.00 (978-0-7635-9005-5(3)) Rigby Education.

Bailey, Gerry & Law, Felicia. Save, Spend, Share: Using Your Money. Phillips, Mike et al, illus. 2006. (My Money Ser.). 24p. (J). (gr. 4-6). 27.93 (978-0-7565-1672-7(2)) Compass Point Bks.

Brent, Lynnette R. Going Shopping: Long Ago & Today. 2003. (Times Change Ser.). (Illus.). 32p. (J). lib. bdg. 24.22 (978-1-4034-4535-3(4)) Heinemann Library.

—Shopping. 2003. (Times Change Ser.). (Illus.). 32p. (J). (978-1-4034-4541-4(9)) Heinemann Library.

Canizares, Susan & Chanko, Pamela. Store. 2000. (Scholastic Placebook Ser.). (Illus.). 16p. (J). pap. (978-0-439-15369-0(7)) Scholastic, Inc.

Christmas Shopping: Individual Title Six-Packs. (Literatura 2000 Ser.). (gr. 1-2). 28.00 (978-0-7635-0088-7(7)) Rigby Education.

Dorling Kindersley Publishing Staff. Let's Go Shopping! 2006. (Keep me Busy Ser.). (Illus.). 12p. (J). bds. 12.99 (978-0-7566-1514-7(3)) Dorling Kindersley Publishing, Inc.

Gillis, Jennifer Blizin. Comprando en el Vecindario/Jennifer B. Gillis. 2007. (SPA.). (J). (*978-1-60044-293-3(5)) Rourke Publishing, LLC.

Gillis, Jennifer Blizin. Neighborhood Shopping. (Illus.). 24p. 2007. (J). (978-1-60044-204-9(8)); 2005. pap. 18.00 (*978-1-59515-559-7(7)) Rourke Publishing, LLC.

Gorman, Jacqueline Laks. The Shopping Mall. 2005. (I Like to Visit Ser.). (Illus.). 24p. (J). pap. (978-0-8368-4462-7(9)); (YA). lib. bdg. 19.33 (978-0-8368-4455-9(6)) Stevens, Gareth Inc.

—The Shopping Mall: El Centro Comercial. 2005. (ENG & SPA., Illus.). 24p. (J). pap. (978-0-8368-4606-5(0)); lib. bdg. 19.33 (978-0-8368-4599-0(4)) Stevens, Gareth Inc.

Hately, David. Talkabout Shopping. (Talkabouts Ser.: No. 735-4). (Illus.). 48p. (J). (ps). 3.50 (978-0-7214-1120-0(7) , Dutton Juvenile) Penguin Group (USA) Inc.

Hill, Mary. Signs at the Store. 2003. (Welcome Bks.). (Illus.). 24p. (J). (ps-2). pap. 4.95 (978-0-516-24363-4(2) , Children's Pr.) Scholastic Library Publishing.

—Signs at the Store. 2003. (gr. k-3). lib. bdg. 12.95 (978-0-613-59723-4(0)) Tandem Library Bks.

Hughes, Sarah. My Aunt Works in a Cheese Shop. 2001. (Welcome Bks.). (Illus.). 24p. (J). (ps-2). pap. 4.95 (978-0-516-29573-2(X) , Children's Pr.) Scholastic Library Publishing.

—My Aunt Works in a Cheese Shop. 2001. (gr. k-3). lib. bdg. 12.95 (978-0-613-58856-0(8)) Tandem Library Bks.

Minden, Cecilia. Smart Shopping. 2008. (J). lib. bdg. 25.26 (*978-1-60279-005-6(1)) Cherry Lake Publishing.

Rettore, Kenny E. Going Shopping. Ferri, Francesca, illus. 2004. 10p. (J). 16.95 (978-0-7641-2811-0(6)) Barron's Educational Series, Inc.

Richardson, Adele. Manners at the Store. 2006. (First Facts Ser.). (J). (978-0-7368-4295-2(0)) Capstone Pr., Inc.

Ridgway, Tom. The Young Zillionaire's Guide to Buying Goods & Services. 2000. (Be a Zillionaire Ser.). (Illus.). 48p. (YA). (gr. 5-8). lib. bdg. 23.95 (978-0-8239-3263-4(X) , ZIBUYI, Rosen Central) Rosen Publishing Group, Inc., The.

Roy, Jennifer Rozines & Roy, Gregory. Money at the Store. 2006. (Math All Around Ser.). (Illus.). 32p. (J). lib. bdg. 28.50 (978-0-7614-2264-8(1) , Benchmark Bks.) Cavendish, Marshall Corp.

Santos, Edson. People Who Love to Buy Things. 2006. (Cool Careers Without College Ser.). (Illus.). 144p. (J). (gr. 5-8). lib. bdg. 33.25 (978-1-4042-0751-6(1)) Rosen Publishing Group, Inc., The.

Shopping. 2001. (P. B. Bear Sticker Books Ser.). (Illus.). 16p. (J). pap. 6.95 (978-0-7894-1564-6(X) , D K Ink) Dorling Kindersley Publishing, Inc.

Shopping. (Butterfly Bks.). (ARA., Illus.). 15p. (J). 11.95 (978-0-86685-619-5(6) , LDL360) International Bk. Ctr., Inc.

Weber, Valerie & Crawford, Beverly. Shopping in Grandma's Day. Lafford, Stuart, illus. 1999. (In Grandma's Day Ser.). 32p. (J). (ps-3). lib. bdg. 21.27 (978-1-57505-324-0(1) , Carolrhoda Bks.) Lerner Publishing Group.

Weiss, Ellen. Math at the Store. 2007. (Scholastic News Nonfiction Readers: Everyday Math—NEW SUBSET Ser.). 24p. (J). pap. 6.95 (*978-0-531-18781-4(0)); (Illus.). (gr. 1-2). lib. bdg. 20.00 (*978-0-531-18528-5(1)) Scholastic Library Publishing. (Children's Pr.).

SHOPPING—FICTION

Ahlberg, Allan. The Shopping Expedition. Amstutz, Andre, illus. 2005. 32p. (J). (ps-1). 16.99 (978-0-7636-2586-3(8)) Candlewick Pr.

Ashley, Bernard. A Present for Paul. Mitchell, David, illus. 2004. 28p. (J). (ARA, CHI, BEN, GUJ & ENG.). (978-1-85269-359-6(2)); (CHI, ARA, BEN, GUJ & ENG.). (978-1-85269-360-2(6)) Mantra Publishing, Ltd.

Ashley, Bernard. That's the One! 2007. (J). lib. bdg. 16.95 (*978-1-59566-370-2(3)) QEB Publishing Inc.

Axelrod, Amy. Pigs Go to Market: Fun with Math & Shopping. McGinley-Nally, Sharon, illus. 1999. 40p. (J). (ps-3). 6.99 (978-0-689-82553-8(6) , 076714005990, Aladdin) Simon & Schuster Children's Publishing.

—Pigs Go to Market: Halloween Fun with Math & Shopping. 1999. (978-0-606-16330-9(1)); lib. bdg. 14.15 (978-0-613-19419-8(5)) Tandem Library Bks.

Aylesworth, Jim. McGraw's Emporium. 1998. (ps-2). lib. bdg. 16.40 (978-0-613-90149-9(5)) Tandem Library Bks.

Baggette, Susan K. Jonathan Goes to the Grocery Store. Moriarty, William J., photos by. 1998. (Jonathan Adventures Ser.). (Illus.). 16p. (J). (ps-k). bds. 5.95 (978-0-9660172-2-9(6)) Brookfield Reader, Inc., The.

Benenfeld, Rikki. Let's Go Shopping. Benenfeld, Rikki, illus. 2005. (Illus.). 24p. (J). 10.95 (978-1-929628-20-9(X)) Hachai Publishing.

Billy Bunny's Shopping List. 2002. (My First Tab Story Ser.). (J). bds. 3.98 (978-0-7525-8953-4(9)) Parragon, Inc.

Blackaby, Susan. Groceries for Grandpa. Lee, Ji Sun, illus. 2007. (J). lib. bdg. (*978-1-4048-2334-1(4)) Picture Window Bks.

Blackaby, Susan. Shopping for Lunch. Demski, James, Jr., illus. 2006. (Read-It! Readers Ser.). 24p. (J). (ps-3). 18.60 (978-1-4048-1589-6(9)) Picture Window Bks.

Bloor, Edward. Crusader. 2007. (Illus.). 496p. (YA). pap. 6.95 (*978-0-15-206314-6(5) , Harcourt Paperbacks) Harcourt Children's Bks.

Brenner, Barbara. Annie's Pet. Ziegler, Jack, illus. 1999. (Bank Street Reader Collection). (J). (gr. 1-3). lib. bdg. 22.60 (978-0-8368-2419-3(9)) Stevens, Gareth Inc.

Christelow, Eileen. Five Little Monkeys Go Shopping. Christelow, Eileen, illus. 2007. (Illus.). 40p. (J). (ps-k). 16.00 (*978-0-618-82161-7(9) , Clarion Bks.) Houghton Mifflin Co. Trade & Reference Div.

CINAR Corporation Staff, illus. Caillou at the Market. 2002. (Caillou Ser.). 26p. (J). pap. (978-2-89450-294-5(X)) Chouette Publishing.

Coulton, Mia. Danny & Dad Go Shopping. Coulton, Mia, photos by. 2003. (J). 4.95 (978-0-9720295-4-4(0)) Maryruth Bks., Inc.

Cousins, Lucy. Maisy Goes Shopping. Cousins, Lucy, illus. 2001. (Maisy Bks.). (Illus.). 24p. (J). (gr. k-k). pap. 3.99 (978-0-7636-1503-1(X)) Candlewick Pr.

Cowley, Joy. Shopping with the Meanies. 2002. (Shared Reading with Joy Ser.). (Illus.). (gr. k-1). pap. 43.76 (978-0-322-09776-6(2)) Wright Group, The.

Curry, Peter. Millie Goes Shopping. 2004. (First Words with Millie Ser.). (Illus.). 12p. (J). bds. 3.99 (978-1-85854-505-9(6)) Brimax Books Ltd. GBR. *Dist:* Byeway Bks.

Daly, Niki. Not So Fast, Songololo. 1998. (J). pap. 4.95 (978-0-87628-975-4(8)) Ctr. for Applied Research in Education, The.

Dewdney, Anna. Llama Llama Mad at Mama. Dewdney, Anna, illus. 2007. (Illus.). 40p. (J). (ps-k). 15.99 (*978-0-670-06240-9(5) , Viking Juvenile) Penguin Group (USA) Inc.

DiSalvo-Ryan, DyAnne. Grandpa's Corner Store. DiSalvo-Ryan, DyAnne, illus. 2000. (Illus.). 40p. (J). (gr. k-3). 16.99 (978-0-688-16716-5(0)) HarperCollins Pubs.

—Grandpa's Corner Store. 2000. (Illus.). 40p. (J). (gr. k-3). 15.89 (978-0-688-16717-2(9)) HarperCollins Pubs.

Doyle, Charlotte. Supermarket! Westcott, Nadine Bernard, tr. Westcott, Nadine Bernard, illus. 2004. (Super Study Picture Book Ser.). 24p. (J). (gr. k-ps). 8.99 (978-0-7636-2218-3(4)) Candlewick Pr.

Elya, Susan Middleton. Bebe Goes Shopping. Salerno, Steven, illus. 2008. 36p. (J). pap. 6.00 (*978-0-15-206142-5(8) , Voyager Bks./Libros Viajeros) Harcourt Children's Bks.

Enderle, Dotti & Sansum, Vicki. Grandpa for Sale. Gentry, T. Kyle, illus. 2007. 32p. (J). 15.95 (*978-0-9729225-8-6(X)) Flashlight Pr.

Esckilsen, Erik E. The Last Mall Rat. 192p. (YA). (gr. 7). 2005. pap. 5.95 (978-0-618-60896-6(6)); 2003. tchr. ed. 15.00 (978-0-618-23417-2(9)) Houghton Mifflin Co. Trade & Reference Div. (Walter Lorraine).

Friedman, Aimee. Hollywood Hills. 2007. 352p. (J). pap. 8.99 (978-0-439-79282-0(7) , Scholastic Paperbacks) Scholastic, Inc.

Going Shopping: First Wave Satellite Individual Title Six-Packs. (Sails Literacy Ser.). 16p. (gr. k up). 27.00 (978-0-7578-6861-0(4)) Rigby Education.

Hammelef, Danielle S. Shopping with the Nicholas Family. 2006. (Early Explorers Ser.). (J). 34.00 (*978-1-4108-6117-7(1)) Benchmark Education Co.

Harris, Robie H. I'm So Mad! Hollander, Nicole, illus. 2005. (Just Being Me Ser.: Vol. 1). 32p. (J). (ps-1). 7.99 (978-0-316-10939-0(8)) Little Brown & Co.

Hoban, Russell. A Bargain for Frances. 2002. (Frances Ser.). (Illus.). (J). 12.30 (978-0-7587-5999-3(1)) Book Wholesalers, Inc.

Jenck, Heidi Shelton. Gabe's Grocery List. Trover, Zachary, illus. 2006. 32p. (J). (*978-1-4048-3140-7(1)) Picture Window Bks.

Jones, Christianne C. Back to School. Haugen, Ryan, illus. 2005. (Read-It! Readers Ser.). 24p. (J). (ps-ps). lib. bdg. 18.60 (978-1-4048-1166-9(4)) Picture Window Bks.

Kirk, David. Miss Spider's New Car. Kirk, David, illus. 1999. (Miss Spider Ser.). (Illus.). 32p. (J). (ps-2). bds. 8.95 (978-0-439-04675-6(0)) Scholastic, Inc.

Klein, Adria F. Max Goes Shopping. Gallagher-Cole, Mernie, illus. 2005. (Read-It! Readers Ser.). 24p. (J). (ps). lib. bdg. 18.60 (978-1-4048-1177-5(X)) Picture Window Bks.

—Max Goes to the Grocery Store. Gallagher-Cole, Mernie, illus. 2007. (J). lib. bdg. (*978-1-4048-3682-2(9)) Picture Window Bks.

—Max Va De Compras. Lozano, Clara, tr. Gallagher-Cole, Mernie, illus. 2006. (SPA.). 24p. 19.99 (*978-1-4048-2669-4(6)) Picture Window Bks.

Le, Ny Jeanine. Once upon A Prom #1 Dream. 2008. 240p. pap. 5.99 (*978-0-545-02815-8(9) , Scholastic Paperbacks) Scholastic, Inc.

LeapFrog Staff, compiled by. Tad Goes Shopping. 2001. (J). (ps-1). spiral bd. 14.99 (978-1-58605-086-3(9)) LeapFrog Enterprises, Inc.

—Tad Goes Shopping - U. K. 2003. spiral bd. 18.00 (978-1-58605-950-7(5)) LeapFrog Enterprises, Inc.

Leonard, Marcia. No New Pants! Handelman, Dorothy, photos by. 1999. (Real Kids Readers Ser.). (Illus.). 32p. (ps-1). lib. bdg. 18.90 (978-0-7613-2063-0(6)); (J). pap. 4.99 (978-0-7613-2088-3(1)) Lerner Publishing Group. (Millbrook Pr.).

—No New Pants! 1999. (J). (978-0-606-19166-1(6)); lib. bdg. 11.80 (978-0-613-18161-7(1)) Tandem Library Bks.

—Pantalones Nuevos, No! Handelman, Dorothy, photos by. 2005. Tr. of No New Pants!. (ENG & SPA., Illus.). 32p. (J). (ps-1). pap. 4.99 (978-0-8225-3297-2(2)) Lerner Publishing Group.

—Pantalones Nuevos, ¡No! Handelman, Dorothy, photos by. 2005. (Lecturas para Niños de Verdad (Real Kids Readers) Ser.). (SPA., Illus.). 32p. (J). (ps-1). pap. 4.99 (978-0-8225-3296-5(4) , Ediciones Lerner) Lerner Publishing Group.

Long, Kathy. The Runaway Shopping Cart. Kwas, Susan Estelle, illus. 2007. 32p. (J). (ps-2). 16.99 (978-0-525-47187-5(1) , Dutton Juvenile) Penguin Group (USA) Inc.

Low, Alice. Aunt Lucy Went to Buy a Hat. Huliska-Beith, Laura, illus. 2004. 32p. (J). (ps-3). lib. bdg. 16.89 (978-0-06-008972-6(5)) HarperCollins Pubs.

—Aunt Lucy Went to Buy a Hat. Huliska-Beith, Laura, tr. Huliska-Beith, Laura, illus. 2004. 32p. (J). (ps-3). 15.99 (978-0-06-008971-9(7)) HarperCollins Pubs.

Maccarone, Grace. I Shop with My Daddy. Brunkus, Denise, illus. 2004. 32p. (J). lib. bdg. 15.00 (978-1-59054-659-8(8)) Fitzgerald Bks.

—I Shop with My Daddy. Brunkus, Denise, illus. 1998. (Hello Reader! Ser.). 32p. (J). (ps-1). pap. 3.99 (978-0-590-50196-5(8)) Scholastic, Inc.

—I Shop with My Daddy. 1998. (Hello Reader! Ser.). (J). 10.79 (978-0-606-13510-8(3)) Tandem Library Bks.

Mass, Wendy. Heaven Looks a Lot Like the Mall. 2007. 256p. (YA). (gr. 7 up). 16.99 (*978-0-316-05851-3(3)) Little, Brown Bks. for Young Readers.

Mayer, Mercer. Just Shopping with Mom. Mayer, Mercer, illus. 1998. (Little Critter Ser.). (Illus.). 24p. (J). (gr. k-k). pap. 3.99 (978-0-307-11972-8(6) , 11972, Random Hse. Bks. for Young Readers) Random Hse. Children's Bks.

McKay, Sindy. We Both Read-Ben & Becky Get a Pet. Johnson, Meredith, illus. (We Both Read Ser.). 44p. (J). (gr. 2 up). 1999. pap. 3.99 (978-1-891327-10-0(0)); 1998. 7.99 (978-1-891327-06-3(2)) Treasure Bay, Inc.

Mom Goes Shopping. 2003. (J). (978-1-58453-251-4(3)) Pioneer Valley Educational Pr., Inc.

Morgan, Beverly. Gregory Likes Saturdays: A Little Story about Being Lost in Wal-Mart. Brady, Jeannette, ed. l.t. ed. 2005. (Illus.). 27p. (J). 4.99 (978-0-9772109-1-6(X)) Joyful Noise.

Munsch, Robert. Algo Bueno. Martchenko, Michael, illus. 2001. (Hablemos Ser.). (SPA.). 24p. (J). (gr. k). pap. 5.95 (978-1-55037-683-8(7)) Annick Pr., Ltd. CAN. *Dist:* Firefly Bks., Ltd.

—Algo Bueno. 2001. (SPA.). (gr. k-3). lib. bdg. 14.10 (978-0-613-78388-0(3)) Tandem Library Bks.

—I'm So Embarrassed! Martchenko, Michael, illus. 2006. 32p. (J). pap. 4.99 (978-0-439-83578-7(X) , Cartwheel Bks.) Scholastic, Inc.

Nelson, Carol Ann. Sammy Knows What to Do. Costain, illus. 2000. (J). (gr. 1-3). 11.95 (978-1-893886-02-5(6)) How I Learn & Grow.

Prince, Sarah. Going Shopping. 1999. (ps-2). lib. bdg. 11.80 (978-0-613-30437-5(3)) Tandem Library Bks.

Puttock, Simon. Goat & Donkey in Strawberry Sunglasses. Julian, Russell, illus. 2007. 28p. (J). (ps-2). 16.00 (*978-1-56148-572-7(1)) Good Bks.

Rallison, Janette. It's a Mall World after All. 2006. 240p. (YA). 16.95 (978-0-8027-8853-5(X)) Walker & Co.

Rau, Dana Meachen. My Favorite Foods, Level C. Lin, Grace, illus. 2001. (Early Reader Ser.). 32p. (J). (gr. k up). lib. bdg. 18.60 (978-0-7565-0076-4(1)) Compass Point Bks.

Rodgers, Frank. What Mr. Croc Forgets. 2006. (Read-It! Chapter Books). (J). 21.26 (978-1-4048-2731-8(5)) Picture Window Bks.

Rylant, Cynthia. A Little Shopping. 2000. (Cobble Street Cousins Ser.: Vol. 2). (Illus.). 64p. (J). (gr. 2-5). pap. 3.99 (978-0-689-81709-0(6) , Aladdin) Simon & Schuster Children's Publishing.

—A Little Shopping. Halperin, Wendy Anderson, illus. 2000. (Cobble Street Cousins Ser.). 55p. (J). (ps-7). lib. bdg. 10.79 (978-0-606-16210-4(0)) Tandem Library Bks.

—A Little Shopping. 2000. (gr. 3-6). lib. bdg. 11.80 (978-0-613-28560-5(3)) Tandem Library Bks.

Sadler, Marilyn & Bollen, Roger. Money, Money, Honey Bunny! 2006. (Bright & Early Bks.). (Illus.). 36p. (J). 8.99 (978-0-375-83370-0(6)); lib. bdg. 12.99 (978-0-375-93370-7(0)) Random Hse. Children's Bks. (Random Hse. Bks. for Young Readers).

Santillo, LuAnn. The Pig. Santillo, LuAnn, ed. 2003. (Half-Pint Kids Readers Ser.). (Illus.). 7p. (J). (ps-1). pap. (978-1-59256-064-6(4)) Half-Pint Kids, Inc.

Shaw, Nancy. Sheep in a Shop. Apple, Margot, illus. 2002. (J). 12.81 (978-0-7587-3609-3(6)) Book Wholesalers, Inc.

Shopping with Dad, 6 vols., Pack. (ps-2). 23.00 (978-0-7635-8991-2(8)) Rigby Education.

Smith, Mary Ann & Milway, Katie Smith. Cappuccina Goes to Town. Fernandes, Eugenie, illus. 2004. 32p. (J). (gr. k-3). (978-1-55337-686-6(2)) Kids Can Pr., Ltd.

Smith, Mary Ann, et al. Cappuccina Goes to Town. Fernandes, Eugenie, illus. unabr. ed. 2002. 32p. (J). (gr. k-3). (978-1-55074-807-9(6)) Kids Can Pr., Ltd.

Souvenirs, 6 vols., Pack. (Literatura 2000 Ser.). (gr. 2-3). 33.00 (978-0-7635-0186-0(7)) Rigby Education.

Stanley, Mandy. Shopping. 2003. (Illus.). 12p. (J). (ps-k). 3.95 (978-0-7534-5681-1(8) , Kingfisher) Houghton Mifflin Co. Trade & Reference Div.

Stiles, Ginny. Time for a Taxi. Myers, Darcy, illus. 2002. (Read-To-Me Ser.). 24p. (J). (978-0-7665-1220-7(7)) Abrams, Harry N. , Inc.

Sula, Sondra. The Expanders: Quest for the Flubulator. 2000. mass mkt. 8.95 (978-1-931179-11-9(5)) Long Hill Productions, Inc.

—The Expanders: Quest for the Flubulator. Johnson, Terri L., illus. 2000. 32p. (J). (gr. 1-3). pap. (978-0-9701450-2-4(0)) Long Hill Productions, Inc.

Taylor, Marshall, illus. & photos by. Adventures of Cow, Too. Taylor, Marshall, photos by. 2007. 32p. (J). (ps-1). 12.95 (978-1-58246-189-2(9) , Tricycle Pr.) Ten Speed Pr.

Vail, Rachel. Mama Rex & T: Run Out of Tape. Bjorkman, Steve, illus. 2001. (Mama Rex & T Ser.). (J). (978-0-439-19920-9(4)) Scholastic, Inc.

—The Prize. Bjorkman, Steve, illus. 2003. 32p. (J). (978-0-439-47191-6(5) , Orchard Bks.) Scholastic, Inc.

Volker, Kerstin. Emma Goes Shopping. 2003. (Funny Friends Lift-and-Learn Bks.). 14p. (J). 5.99 (978-1-59384-021-1(7)) Parklane Publishing.

Waite, Judy. Shopaholic. 224p. (YA). 2003. (Illus.). 16.95 (978-0-689-85138-4(3) , Atheneum); 2004. reprint ed. pap. 6.99 (978-0-689-85139-1(1) , Simon Pulse) Simon & Schuster Children's Publishing.

Warner, Gertrude Chandler. The Mystery in the Mall. Tang, Charles, illus. 1999. 115p. (J). (ps-7). per. 11.80 (978-0-613-22057-6(9)) Tandem Library Bks.

—The Mystery in the Mall. 1999. (Boxcar Children Ser.: No. 72). (J). (gr. 2-5). (978-0-606-18765-7(0)) Tandem Library Bks.

Warner, Gertrude Chandler, creator. The Mystery in the Mall, Vol. 72. 2004. (Boxcar Children Ser.: No. 72). (Illus.). 128p. (J). (gr. 2-5). 14.95 (978-0-8075-5456-2(1)); pap. 4.50 (978-0-8075-5457-9(X)) Whitman, Albert & Co.

Wells, Rosemary. Bunny Money. 2000. (gr. k-3). lib. bdg. 14.15 (978-0-613-33681-9(X)) Tandem Library Bks.

Wigand, Molly. Here Comes Santa. 2007. 24p. (J). 21.35 (*978-1-59961-357-4(3)) Spotlight.

SHORT STORIES

A Lady. Tales from Ariosto: Retold for Children. 2007. pap. 28.95 (*978-1-4304-5008-5(8)) Kessinger Publishing, LLC.

Abbate, Jason. Welcome to Xooxville. 2004. (YA). per. 12.95 (978-0-9760959-0-3(4)) Rarecity Pr.

Abbott, Hailey, et al. Mistletoe. 2006. 240p. (J). pap. 8.99 (978-0-439-86368-1(6) , Scholastic) Scholastic, Inc.

Abbott, Jacob. Stories Told to Rollo's Cousin Lucy. 2005. pap. 22.95 (978-1-4179-5651-7(8)) Kessinger Publishing, LLC.

Abeya, Elisabet. Hansel & Gretel/Hansel y Gretel. Losantos, Cristina, illus. 2005. (SPA & ENG.). 32p. (J). (ps-ps). 14.95 (978-0-8118-4793-3(4)) Chronicle Bks. LLC.

Able and Talented Program Resource Room Students Staff, Able and Talented Program Resource Room, et al. Westerville Kids Celebrate the Written Word Vol. 1: 2000-2001. 2001. 254p. pap. 14.95 (978-0-595-20772-5(3) , Writers Club Pr.) iUniverse, Inc.

Abnett, Dan. Eisenhorn. Gascoigne, Marc, ed. 2005. 768p. pap. 10.99 (978-1-84416-156-0(0) , Games Workshop) Simon & Schuster.

Ackerman, Artur. Somewhere Below the Great White Clouds. l.t. ed. 2002. (Orig.). (J). pap. 12.95 (978-1-59232-053-0(8)) Seaburn Pubs.

Action Adventures Theme Pack, 5 vols. 2001. (Illus.). (J). (gr. 8-9). 19.95 (978-1-56762-146-4(5)) Modern Learning Pr.

Ada, Alma Flor. Actividades para el Hogar. 2001. (SPA.). (J). (gr. k-3). pap. 7.65 (978-1-58105-356-2(8)) Santillana USA Publishing Co., Inc.

—After the Storm. 1998. (Stories the Year 'Round Ser.). (J). (gr. k-12). pap. 7.95 (978-1-56014-337-6(1)) Santillana USA Publishing Co., Inc.

—The Empty Pinata. 1998. (Stories the Year 'Round Ser.). (J). (gr. k-12). pap. 7.95 (978-1-56014-336-9(3)) Santillana USA Publishing Co., Inc.

—A Rose with Wings. 1998. (Stories the Year 'Round Ser.). (J). (gr. k-12). pap. 7.95 (978-1-56014-335-2(5)) Santillana USA Publishing Co., Inc.

—Teatro del Gato Garabato. Campoy, F. Isabel, illus. (Puertas al Sol Ser.). (SPA & ENG.). 32p. (J). (gr. k-6). pap. 13.95 (978-1-58105-652-5(4)) Santillana USA Publishing Co., Inc.

Ada, Alma Flor & Campoy, F. Isabel. Una Semilla de Luz. Davalos, Felipe, illus. 2003. (Coleccion Derechos Del Nino Ser.). (SPA.). 32p. (J). (gr. 3-5). pap. 7.95 (978-84-204-5818-2(X)) Santillana USA Publishing Co., Inc.

—Tablado de Dona Rosita. (Puertas al Sol Ser.). (SPA & ENG., Illus.). 32p. (J). (gr. k-6). pap. 13.95 (978-1-58105-655-6(9)) Santillana USA Publishing Co., Inc.

—Teatrin de Don Crispin. (Puertas al Sol Ser.). (SPA & ENG.). 32p. (J). (gr. k-6). pap. 13.95 (978-1-58105-653-2(2)) Santillana USA Publishing Co., Inc.

Ada, Alma Flor & Campoy, F. Isabel, contrib. by. En Alas del Condor. (Literature Collection of Puertas Al Sol Ser.). (SPA.). 48p. (J). (gr. k-6). pap. 13.95 (978-1-58105-812-3(8)) Santillana USA Publishing Co., Inc.

—The Quetzal's Journey. (Gateways to the Sun). 48p. (J). (gr. k-6). pap. 13.95 (978-1-58105-963-2(9)) Santillana USA Publishing Co., Inc.

Adams, H. J. Of Dragons, Kings, Sages & Little Folk. 1999. 120p. (J). 22.50 (978-0-923687-52-6(1)) Celo Valley Bks.

Adams, W. Royce. Teacher, Teacher, I Declare! & Other Little Tattle Tales. 2nd ed. 2001. 228p. pap. 14.95 (978-0-9712206-1-4(1)) Rairarubia Bks.

Ademola, Lady Kofo. Princess Corn. 1999. (Illus.). 10p. pap. (978-978-2601-95-7(0)) Malthouse Press Ltd, Nigeria.

The Adventures of Rowdy Raccoon. 2006. (J). per. 16.95 incl. audio compact disk (*978-0-9766823-8-7(9)) Sable Creek Pr. LLC.

Aesop. Aesop's Fables. Zwerger, Lisbeth, illus. ed. 2006. 32p. (J). pap. 6.95 (978-0-7358-2069-2(4)); (YA). 16.95 (978-0-7358-2068-5(6)) North-South Bks., Inc.

Agnew, Kate. Would You Believe It? Parsons, Gary, illus. 128p. (J) pap. 7.50 (978-1-4052-0520-7(2)) Egmont Bks., Ltd. GBR. *Dist:* Trafalgar Square Publishing.

Agnew, Kate, ed. Family Like Mine. Parsons, Gary, illus. 2003. 128p. (J). pap. 6.99 (978-1-4052-0519-1(9)) Egmont Bks., Ltd. GBR. *Dist:* Independent Pubs. Group.

—Give Me Some Space! Parsons, Garry, illus. 2003. 128p. (J). pap. 7.50 (978-1-4052-0599-3(7)) Egmont Bks., Ltd. GBR. *Dist:* Independent Pubs. Group.

Ahlberg, Allan. The Better Brown Stories. Wegner, Fritz, illus. l.t. ed. 1998. 272p. (J). pap. (978-0-7540-6006-2(3), CLP 224) BBC Audio.

—Grandma Fox. 6th ed. (Fast Fox, Slow Dog Ser.: Vol. 6). (Illus.). 32p. (J). pap. 9.95 (978-0-14-056402-0(0)) Penguin Bks., Ltd. GBR. *Dist:* Trafalgar Square Publishing.

Ahlberg, Allan & Wegner, Fritz. The Better Brown Stories. 1998. (Illus.). 112p. 3.99 (978-0-14-037369-1(1)) Penguin Group (USA) Inc.

Ahmed, Rehana. Walking a Tightrope: New Writing from Asian Britain. 2005. 272p. (YA). pap. (978-0-330-41579-8(4), Macmillan Children's Bks.) Pan Macmillan.

Aiken, Joan. Necklace of Raindrops: And Other Stories. Hawkes, Kevin, illus. 2003. 96p. (J). (gr. 1-5). 5.50 (978-0-440-41850-4(X), Yearling) Random Hse. Children's Bks.

Al-Musrati, Ali-Mustafa. The General in Victoria Station & Other Stories. Suayeh, Saadun Ismail, tr. 2001. (YA). per. 15.00 (978-1-58684-171-3(8)) Global Academic Publishing.

Alcott, Louisa May. A Garland for Girls. 2006. pap. (*978-1-4065-0587-0(0)) Dodo Pr.

—Kitty's Class Day. l.t. ed. 2005. 424p. pap. (978-1-84637-055-7(8)) Echo Library.

—Kitty's Class Day & Other Stories. 2006. 208p. pap. 12.99 (978-1-4264-0876-2(5)); 200p. pap. 15.99 (978-1-4264-0857-1(9)) BiblioBazaar.

—Kitty's Class Day & Other Stories. 2006. 96.99 (*978-1-4219-7445-3(2)); pap. 90.99 (*978-1-4219-7438-5(X)) IndyPublish.com.

—Kitty's Class Day & Other Stories (Dod. 2006. pap. (*978-1-4065-0588-7(9)) Dodo Pr.

Alcott, Louisa May. The Louisa Alcott Reader. l.t. ed. 2005. 228p. pap. (978-1-84637-058-8(2)) Echo Library.

Aldous, Kate, illus. The Kingfisher Treasury of Christmas Stories. 2003. (Kingfisher Treasury of Stories Ser.). 160p. (J). (gr. k-3). pap. 5.95 (978-0-7534-5670-5(2), Kingfisher) Houghton Mifflin Co. Trade & Reference Div.

Alexander, Lloyd. The Foundling: And Other Tales of Prydain. 6th rev. ed. 2006. (Chronicles of Prydain Ser.). 128p. (J). (gr. 3-7). pap. 5.99 (978-0-8050-8053-7(8), Holt, Henry & Co. Bks. For Young Readers) Holt, Henry & Co.

Alfreda. Story Time Stories Without Rhyme. 2003. 21.95 (978-0-913597-90-3(2)) Prosperity & Profits Unlimited, Distribution Services.

Ali Baba y Los Cuarenta Ladrones: Ali Baba & the Forty Thieves. 2004. (Troquelados Clasicos Ser.). (SPA.). 16p. (J). pap. 2.95 (978-84-7864-732-3(5)) Combel Editorial, S.A. ESP. *Dist:* Independent Pubs. Group.

Allen, David. The Collection of Short Stories. Loftiss, Gary, ed. 2000. 201p. (J). pap. 12.95 (978-0-9642120-1-5(3)) Chiffon Pubs.

Almendros, Herminio. Habia una Vez. 2000. (SPA., Illus.). 200p. (J). (gr. 2-4). pap. 13.00 (978-968-439-521-3(3), PA5131) Publicaciones Cultural, S.A. de C.V. MEX. *Dist:* Ediciones Universal, Lectorum Pubns., Inc.

Alonso, Fernando. El Hombrecito Vestido de Gris. Wendell, Ulises, illus. 2003. (SPA.). 94p. (J). (gr. 3-5). pap. 8.95 (978-968-19-0439-5(7)) Santillana USA Publishing Co., Inc.

Altan. Fairy Tale Timpa. Reynolds, Michael, tr. Altan, illus. 2007. 48p. pap. 14.95 (*978-1-933372-38-9(9)) Europa Editions, Inc.

—Timpa Goes to the Sea. 2007. 48p. (J). pap. 14.95 (*978-1-933372-32-7(X)) Europa Editions, Inc.

Amahal y Los Tres Reyes. 2004. (Troquelados Clasicos Ser.). (SPA.). 16p. (J). pap. 2.95 (978-84-7864-731-6(7)) Combel Editorial, S.A. ESP. *Dist:* Independent Pubs. Group.

The Amazing Tales of Mr. Tidwell. l.t. ed. 2001. (Amazing Tales of Mr. Tidwell: Vol. 1). 40p. (J). 18.95 (978-0-9711726-0-9(9)) PressMark Publishing.

Ambrus, Victor G., illus. The Kingfisher Treasury of Stories from Around the World. 2004. (Kingfisher Treasury of Stories Ser.). 160p. (J). (gr. k-3). pap. 5.95 (978-0-7534-5727-6(X), Kingfisher) Houghton Mifflin Co. Trade & Reference Div.

—More Horse & Pony Stories. 2004. (Red Hot Reads Ser.). 224p. (J). (gr. k-3). pap. 6.95 (978-0-7534-5734-4(2), Kingfisher) Houghton Mifflin Co. Trade & Reference Div.

Amelio-Ortiz, Osvaldo P. Anita Anota. 2005. (SPA., Illus.). 28p. (J). 14.95 (978-84-933955-5-1(2)) Hardenville SA URY. *Dist:* Independent Pubs. Group.

American Cowboy Songs. 1998. (J). pap. 9.95 incl. audio (978-1-887120-04-3(1)) Production Assocs., Inc.

Amery, H. Stories from Around the World. 2004. (Stories for Young Children Ser.). 128p. (J). 7.95 (978-0-7945-0110-5(9), Usborne) EDC Publishing.

Amery, Heather. Another little book of farmyard Tales. Cartwright, Stephen, illus. 2005. 128p. (J). 8.95 (978-0-7945-1033-6(7), Usborne) EDC Publishing.

—Little Book of First Stories. 2004. (Mini Storybooks Ser.). (Illus.). 96p. (J). 7.95 (978-0-7945-0269-0(5), Usborne) EDC Publishing.

Amery, Heather & Cartwright, Stephen. Rusty's Train Ride. rev. ed. 2004. (Treasury of Farmyard Tales Ser.). 16p. (J). pap. 4.95 (978-0-7945-0602-5(X)) EDC Publishing.

Anaya, Hector. Cuenta, Cuenta. Moreno, Sergio, illus. 2nd rev. ed. 2004. (Castillo de la Lectura Verde Ser.). (SPA.). 184p. (J). pap. 7.95 (978-970-20-0135-5(8)) Castillo, Ediciones, S. A. de C. V. MEX. *Dist:* Macmillan.

Anaya, Rudolfo A. My Land Sings: Stories from the Rio Grande. Cordova, Amy, illus. 1999. 144p. (J). (gr. 5 up). 17.00 (978-0-688-15078-5(0), Rayo) HarperCollins Pubs.

Andersen, Hans Christian. Cuentos de Andersen. 2nd ed. 2003. (SPA., Illus.). 64p. (978-84-392-8880-0(8), EV6475) Gaviota Ediciones ESP. *Dist:* Lectorum Pubns., Inc.

—Cuentos de Anderson. 2000. Tr. of Stories of Anderson. (SPA., Illus.). 240p. (J). 17.95 (978-84-261-0255-3(7)) Juventud, Editorial ESP. *Dist:* Distribooks, Inc.

—Tales of Hans Christian Andersen. Lewis, Naomi, tr. from DAN. Stewart, Joel, illus. 2004. 208p. (J). (gr. 3-7). 22.99 (978-0-7636-2515-3(9)) Candlewick Pr.

Andersen, Hans Christian & Clark, Emma Chichester. Elf Hill. 2004. (Illus.). 72p. (J). pap. 11.95 (978-1-84507-188-2(3)) Lincoln, Frances Ltd. GBR. *Dist:* Transition Vendor.

Anderson, Carolyn. Granny's Farm Friends. 2005. (J). per. 39.95 (978-1-59453-550-5(7), Airleaf Publishing) Airleaf Publishing & Bookselling.

Anderson, Carolyn D. Granny¿s Favorite Tales. Anderson, Carolyn D. et al, illus. 2006. 156p. (J). per. 39.95 (*978-1-60002-098-8(4), 3915, Airleaf Publishing) Airleaf Publishing & Bookselling.

Anderson, Laurie Halse. Wild at Heart, 10 bks. Incl. Fear of Falling. 105p. lib. bdg. 23.33 (978-0-8368-3255-6(8)); Fight for Life. 127p. lib. bdg. 23.33 (978-0-8368-3256-3(6)); Homeless. 130p. lib. bdg. 23.33 (978-0-8368-3257-0(4)); Manatee Blues. 114p. lib. bdg. 23.33 (978-0-8368-3258-7(2)); Say Good-Bye. 129p. lib. bdg. 23.33 (978-0-8368-3259-4(0)); Storm Rescue. 105p. lib. bdg. 23.33 (978-0-8368-3260-0(4)); Teacher's Pet. 132p. lib. bdg. 23.33 (978-0-8368-3261-7(2)); Time to Fly. 113p. lib. bdg. 23.33 (978-0-8368-3262-4(0)); Trapped. 113p. lib. bdg. 23.33 (978-0-8368-3263-1(9)); Trickster. 124p. lib. bdg. 23.33 (978-0-8368-3264-8(7)); (J). (gr. 4). 2003. (Illus.). 2002. Set lib. bdg. 233.30 (978-0-8368-3251-9(X)) Stevens, Gareth Inc.

Anderson, Marcella F. Reflections from a Mud Puddle: Helping Children Cope & Grow. Wray, Christopher, illus. 2003. 96p. (J). (gr. 4-6). pap. 14.95 (978-1-56397-606-3(4)) Boyds Mills Pr.

Anderson, Max Elliot. Terror at Wolf Lake. 2003. 136p. pap. 10.95 (978-0-9729256-6-2(X), Tweener Pr.) Baker Trittin Pr.

Anderson, Robert Gordon. HalfPast Seven Stories Illustrated Editi. 2006. pap. (*978-1-4065-0868-0(3)) Dodo Pr.

Andreasen, Dan. Just Like Me. 2000. 32p. (J). (ps-3). 14.95 (978-0-06-027811-3(0)) HarperCollins Pubs.

Andrews, Jan. Stories at the Door. Blake, Francis, illus. 2007. 80p. (J). (gr. 1-4). 18.95 (*978-0-88776-811-8(3)) Tundra Bks., Inc./Livres Toundra, Inc. CAN. *Dist:* Random Hse., Inc.

Andrews, Jane & Hopkins, Louisa Parsons. The Seven Little Sisters Who Live on the Round Ball that Floats in the Air. 2004. reprint ed. pap. 21.95 (978-1-4179-1646-7(X)) Kessinger Publishing, LLC.

Andrews, V. C. Orphans. 2000. (gr. 7-12). lib. bdg. 16.45 (978-0-613-33602-4(X)) Tandem Library Bks.

Anfousse, Ginette. Les Catastrophes de Rosalie. Sarrazin, Marisol, illus. 2002. (Roman Jeunesse Ser.). (FRE.). 96p. (YA). (gr. 4-7). pap. (978-2-89021-065-3(0)) Diffusion du livre Mirabel.

Angela's Bookshelf Publishing Staff. Choice Stories for Children. 1998. (Illus.). 144p. (J). (ps-3). pap. 6.95 (978-1-881545-99-6(7)) A B Publishing.

Angelchild, P. Erotic Memoirs Volume 1. 2007. pap. (*978-1-84747-127-7(7)) Chipmunkapublishing.

Anholt, Catherine & Anholt, Laurence. Big Book of Little Children. Anholt, Catherine & Anholt, Laurence, illus. 2003. (Illus.). 80p. (J). (ps). 15.99 (978-0-7636-2210-7(9)) Candlewick Pr.

Anning, Michael Boiyool. Jirrbal: Rainforest Dreamtime Stories. 2001. (Illus.). 64p. (J). 24.95 (978-1-875641-06-2(8)) Magabala Bks. AUS. *Dist:* International Specialized Bk. Services.

Anonymous. Las Doce Historias de la Tía Margarita. Greendyk, William, tr. from ENG. l.t. ed. 2004. Orig. Title: Aunt Margaret's Twelve Stories. (SPA.). 84p. (J). pap. 3.99 (978-1-932789-00-3(6), X001N) Editorial Sendas Antiguas, LLC.

Anthology. Atrapada en la Escuela. 2001. Tr. of Trapped in School. (SPA.). (J). pap. 8.95 (978-970-643-220-9(5)) Selector, S.A. de C.V. MEX. *Dist:* Bilingual Pubns. Co., The, Libros Sin Fronteras.

Antologia Staff. El Libro de Oro de los Abuelos. 2004. (SPA.). 128p. 9.99 (978-980-257-274-8(8)) Ekare, Ediciones VEN. *Dist:* Lectorum Pubns., Inc.

Anytime Stories. (Anytime Stories Ser.). 48p. (J). Vol 1. (Illus.). bds. (978-2-7643-0177-7(4)); Vol. 2. (978-2-7643-0178-4(2)); Vol. 3. (Illus.). bds. (978-2-7643-0203-3(7)) Phidal Publishing, Inc./Editions Phidal, Inc.

Appelt, Kathi. Kissing Tennessee: And Other Stories from the Stardust Dance. 2004. (gr. 7-12). lib. bdg. 14.10 (978-0-613-71639-0(6)) Tandem Library Bks.

Applin, Barbara, ed. Carib Anth Stories for Children 1. 2006. 68p. pap. 11.95 (978-1-4050-3094-6(1)) Macmillan Caribbean GBR. *Dist:* Interlink Publishing Group, Inc.

Armentrout, James & Macon, Steven, eds. Alien Alerts Journal Winter 2003, 2004. (Illus.). 64p. pap. 5.00 (978-1-57688-038-8(9), 80389, Otherworlds Sci-Fi) Branch & Vine Pubs., LLC.

Armstrong, Jennifer. Shattered: Stories of Children & War. 2003. 176p. (YA). (gr. 7). pap. 5.99 (978-0-440-23765-5(3), Laurel Leaf) Random Hse. Children's Bks.

—Shattered: Stories of Children & War. l.t. ed. 2004. 201p. (J). 22.95 (978-0-7862-6508-4(6)) Thorndike Pr.

—What a Song Can Do: 12 Riffs on the Power of Music. 2004. 208p. (J). (gr. 5). 15.95 (978-0-375-82499-9(5), Knopf Bks. for Young Readers) Random Hse. Children's Bks.

—What a Song Can Do: 12 Riffs on the Power of Music. 2006. 208p. (YA). (gr. 7-11). pap. 5.99 (978-0-440-23816-4(1), Laurel Leaf) Random Hse. Children's Bks.

Arnold, Katya R., illus. & retold by. Me Too! Two Small Stories about Small Animals. Arnold, Katya R., retold by. 2000. 32p. (J). (gr. k-3). tchr. ed. 15.95 (978-0-8234-1483-3(3)) Holiday Hse., Inc.

Arturo y la Carrera por la Lectura. 2004. Tr. of Arthur & the Race to Read. (SPA., Illus.). (J). pap. 4.95 (978-1-930332-60-7(2)) Lectorum Pubns., Inc.

Aryal, Aimee. Hello Colonel Rebel! Moore, Danny, illus. 2005. (J). 19.95 (978-1-932888-28-7(4)) Mascot Bks., Inc.

—Hello Hairy Dawg! Turnbull, Jesse, illus. 2004. (J). 19.95 (978-1-932888-04-1(7)) Mascot Bks., Inc.

—Hello Herky! Reynolds, Julie, illus. 2004. (J). 19.95 (978-1-932888-05-8(5)) Mascot Bks., Inc.

—Hello Hook 'Em! Craig, Megan, illus. 2004. (J). 19.95 (978-1-932888-10-2(1)) Mascot Bks., Inc.

—Hello Joe Bruin! Perez, Gerry, illus. 2004. (J). 19.95 (978-1-932888-15-7(2)) Mascot Bks., Inc.

—Hello Jonathan! Higgins, Krystal, illus. 2004. (J). 19.95 (978-1-932888-31-7(4)) Mascot Bks., Inc.

—Hello Mike! Moore, Danny, illus. 2004. (J). 19.95 (978-1-932888-00-3(4)) Mascot Bks., Inc.

—Hello Mr. Wuf! Cooper, Blair, illus. 2004. (J). 19.95 (978-1-932888-06-5(3)) Mascot Bks., Inc.

—Hello Purdue Pete! Reynolds, Julie, illus. 2004. (J). 19.95 (978-1-932888-30-0(6)) Mascot Bks., Inc.

—Hello Rameses! Cooper, Blair, illus. 2004. (J). 19.95 (978-1-932888-17-1(9)) Mascot Bks., Inc.

—Hello Reveille! Craig, Megan, illus. 2004. (J). 19.95 (978-1-932888-18-8(7)) Mascot Bks., Inc.

—Hello Scarlet Knight! Turnbull, Jesse, illus. 2004. (J). 19.95 (978-1-932888-02-7(0)) Mascot Bks., Inc.

—Hello Smokey! Higgins, Krystal, illus. 2004. (J). 19.95 (978-1-932888-09-6(8)) Mascot Bks., Inc.

—Hello Sparty! Reynolds, Julie, illus. 2004. (J). (978-1-932888-01-0(2)) Mascot Bks., Inc.

—Hello Tommy Trojan! Perez, Gerry, illus. 2004. (J). 19.95 (978-1-932888-08-9(X)) Mascot Bks., Inc.

Asefi, Christo. The Adventures of Charlz from Marz: Book I Going Home. 2007. (Illus.). (YA). 14.95 (978-0-9763250-0-0(4)) DreamerLand.

Asher, Sandy & Harrison, David L. Dude! Stories & Stuff for Boys. 2006. (Illus.). xi, 258p. (J). (*978-1-4156-8094-0(9), Dutton Juvenile) Penguin Group (USA) Inc.

Asimov, Isaac. Isaac Asimov Collected Short Stories. Court, Robert, illus. 2001. (Great Author Ser.). (J). (978-0-9709033-5-8(9)) Peterson Publishing Co., Inc.

Atkinson, Ruth & Atkinson, Brett. Christmas Cutouts. Atkinson, Ruth & Atkinson, Brett, illus. (Illus.). (J). (gr. k-2). pap. (978-1-876367-20-6(2)) Wizard Bks.

Attar, Farid Al-Din. Attar Stories for Young Adults. 2000. (Illus.). 202p. (J). (gr. 7-12). pap. 12.95 (978-1-930637-06-1(3), A B C International Group, Inc.) Kazi Pubns., Inc.

Auch, Mary Jane. Peeping Beauty. Auch, Mary Jane, illus. 2002. (Illus.). (J). 15.47 (978-0-7587-3385-6(2)) Book Wholesalers, Inc.

Avi. Strange Happenings: Five Tales of Transformation. 160p. (J). 2008. (Illus.). pap. 5.95 (*978-0-15-206461-7(3), Magic Carpet Bks.); 2006. 15.00 (978-0-15-205790-9(0)) Harcourt Children's Bks.

Avi. What Do Fish Have to Do with Anything? And Other Stories. 2004. 208p. (J). (gr. 5-9). reprint ed. pap. 6.99 (978-0-7636-2319-7(9)) Candlewick Pr.

Avi & Priceman, Marjorie. Things That Sometimes Happen. 2002. (Illus.). 40p. (J). (ps-2). 16.95 (978-0-689-83914-6(6), Atheneum/Anne Schwartz Bks.) Simon & Schuster Children's Publishing.

Awdry, Wilbert V. Cow On the Line Book & CD. 2005. (Illus.). 24p. (J). (ps-2). 9.95 (978-0-375-83499-8(0), Random Hse. Bks. for Young Readers) Random Hse. Children's Bks.

—Cranky Day & Other Thomas the Tank Engine Stories Book & CD. 2005. (Book & CD Ser.). (Illus.). 24p. (J). (ps-2). 9.95 (978-0-375-83504-9(0), Random Hse. Bks. for Young Readers) Random Hse. Children's Bks.

—Diesel's Devious Deed Book & CD. 2005. (Illus.). 24p. (J). (ps-2). 9.95 (978-0-375-83498-1(2), Random Hse. Bks. for Young Readers) Random Hse. Children's Bks.

—Thomas Gets Tricked Book & CD. 2005. (Illus.). 24p. (J). (ps-2). audio compact disk 9.95 (978-0-375-83503-2(2), Random Hse. Bks. for Young Readers) Random Hse. Children's Bks.

—Thomas the Tank Engine Story Collection. 2005. (Illus.). 508p. (J). (gr. k-2). 29.95 (978-0-375-83409-7(5), Random Hse. Bks. for Young Readers) Random Hse. Children's Bks.

—Track Stars! Three Thomas & Friends Stories. Courtney, Richard, photos by. 2006. (Thomas & Friends Ser.). (Illus.). 24p. (J). (ps-1). pap. 3.99 (978-0-375-83462-2(1), Random Hse. Bks. for Young Readers) Random Hse. Children's Bks.

—Track Stars! Three Thomas & Friends Stories. Permane, Terry, illus. Palone, Terry & Permane, Terry, photos by. 2006. (Thomas & Friends Ser.). (J). (*978-1-4156-5364-7(X)) Random Hse. Children's Bks.

Awdry, Wilbert V. Trouble for Thomas Book & CD. 2005. (Book & CD Ser.). (Illus.). 24p. (J). (ps-2). 9.95 (978-0-375-83502-5(4), Random Hse. Bks. for Young Readers) Random Hse. Children's Bks.

Ayres, Honor, illus. Story of Jesus Boxed Set. 2006. 10p. bds. 14.99 (978-0-7847-1977-0(2)) Standard Publishing.

Bach, Richard & Gardner, Sally. La nina mas pequena del Mundo. Tapia, Sonia, tr. 2005. (Ninos Magicos Ser.). (SPA., Illus.). 128p. (J). pap. 7.95 (978-84-666-1339-2(0)) Ediciones B ESP. *Dist:* Independent Pubs. Group.

Badger, Pearstina. Jessica's Journeys: Stories about Life's Lessons. 2006. 56p. pap. 12.95 (978-1-4241-1576-1(0)) PublishAmerica, Inc.

Badillo, Rosa Maria. Cuentos para Quererse Mas: Autoestima Para Ninos y Jovenes. 2002. (SPA & ENG., Illus.). 112p. pap. 12.95 (978-970-15-0699-8(5)) Alfaomega Grupo Editor MEX. *Dist:* Independent Pubs. Group.

Badoe, Adwoa A. The Pot of Wisdom: Ananse Stories. Diakite, Baba Wague, illus. 2001. 64p. (J). (gr. 2 up). 18.95 (978-0-88899-429-5(X)) Groundwood Bks. CAN. *Dist:* Perseus Distribution.

Bailey, Carolyn Sherwin. Stories of Great Adventures. Burd, Clara M., illus. 2005. reprint ed. pap. 24.95 (978-1-4179-0215-6(9)) Kessinger Publishing, LLC.

Bailey, Helen. Topaz in the Limelight. 2007. (Illus.). 144p. pap. 7.95 (*978-0-340-89348-7(6)) Hodder Children's Division GBR. *Dist:* Independent Pubs. Group.

—Topaz Steals the Show. 2007. (Illus.). 128p. pap. 7.95 (*978-0-340-89346-3(X)) Hodder Children's Division GBR. *Dist:* Independent Pubs. Group.

—Topaz Takes a Chance. 2007. (Illus.). 128p. pap. 7.95 (*978-0-340-89347-0(8)) Hodder Children's Division GBR. *Dist:* Independent Pubs. Group.

Bailey, Peter, illus. The Kingfisher Treasury of Magical Stories. 2003. (Kingfisher Treasury of Stories Ser.: Vol. 16). 160p. (J). (gr. k-3). pap. 5.95 (978-0-7534-5624-8(9), Kingfisher) Houghton Mifflin Co. Trade & Reference Div.

Bake a Cake & Other Stories: Individual Title Six-Pack. (Story Steps Ser.). (gr. k-2). 42.00 (978-0-7635-9574-6(8)) Rigby Education.

Baker, Barrie. The Village of a Hundred Smiles. Jorisch, Stephane, illus. 1998. 48p. (J). (gr. k-3). lib. bdg. 18.95 (978-1-55037-522-0(9)) Firefly Bks., Ltd.

Baker, Liza. Disney's 5 Minute Princess Stories. Cuddy, Robbin, illus. 2001. 48p. (J). (ps-2). 12.99 (978-0-7868-3300-9(9)) Disney Pr.

Balcells, Jacqueline. El Archipielago de las Puntuadas. 2003. (SPA.). pap. (978-956-13-1472-6(X), AB0859) Bello, Andres CHL. *Dist:* Lectorum Pubns., Inc.

Baldwin, James. Fifty Famous People. l.t. ed. 2006. 126p. pap. 13.99 (978-1-4264-1427-5(7)) BiblioBazaar.

Ballantyne, R. M. The Lighthouse. 2006. pap. (*978-1-4065-0531-3(5)) Dodo Pr.

Balouch, Kristin. Listen to the Storyteller. 2001. (Illus.). 32p. (J). pap. (978-0-14-056431-0(4), Puffin) Penguin Group (USA) Inc.

Bandala, Luis Rodriguez. El Libro, el Escritor y Otros Cuentos. 2003. (SPA., Illus.). 184p. (YA). (gr. 5-12). 15.95 (978-968-6966-18-3(8)) EDITER'S Publishing Hse. MEX. *Dist:* EDITER'S Publishing Hse.

Banghart, Tracy E. What the Sea Wants. Blum, Julia C., illus. 2006. 64p. (YA). kivar 16.00 (978-0-9779753-0-3(4)) LizStar Bks.

Bank Street Ready-to-Read Collection Levels 1, 2, 3: Getting Ready to Read; Reading Together; I Can Read It Myself, 49 bks. Incl. Animal Hide-and-Seek. Slater, Teddy. Braginetz, Donna, illus. 48p. (gr. 1-3). 1998. lib. bdg. 22.60 (978-0-8368-1760-7(5)); Annie's Pet. Brenner, Barbara. Ziegler, Jack, illus. (gr. 1-3). 1999. lib. bdg. 22.60 (978-0-8368-2419-3(9)); Beavers Beware! Brenner, Barbara. McCully, Emily Arnold, illus. 48p. (gr. 1-3). 1998. lib. bdg. 22.60 (978-0-8368-1769-0(9)); Boy Who Cried "Wolf!" Schecter, Ellen. Chalk, Gary, illus. 48p. (ps-2). 1997. lib. bdg. 22.60 (978-0-8368-1691-4(9)); Button Soup. Orgel, Doris. Estrada, Pam, illus. 48p. (gr. 1-3). 1998. lib. bdg. 22.60 (978-0-8368-1761-4(3)); Choco-Louie. Kindley, Jeff. Sasaki, Ellen J., illus. 48p. (gr. 1-3). 1996. lib. bdg. 22.60 (978-0-8368-1618-1(8)); Christmas Witch. Oppenheim, Joanne. Mitra, Annie, illus. 48p. (gr. 2-4). 1997. lib. bdg. 22.60 (978-0-8368-1697-6(8)); Could It Be? Oppenheim, Joanne. Schindler, S. D., illus. 48p. (gr. 1-3). 1998. lib. bdg. 22.60 (978-0-8368-1770-6(2)); Dia-

S

monds & Toads. Schecter, Ellen. Blackshear, Ami, illus. (gr. 2-4). 1999. lib. bdg. 22.60 (978-0-8368-1781-2(8)); Do You Like Cats? Oppenheim, Joanne. Newsom, Carol, illus. 48p. (ps-2). 1998. lib. bdg. 22.60 (978-0-8368-1757-7(5)); Dozen Dizzy Dogs. Hooks, William H. Baseman, Gary, illus. 48p. (ps-2). 1997. lib. bdg. 22.60 (978-0-8368-1748-5(6)); Eency Weency Spider. Oppenheim, Joanne. Schindler, S. D., illus. 48p. (ps-2). 1997. lib. bdg. 22.60 (978-0-8368-1690-7(0)); Feed Me! An Aesop Fable. Cushman, Doug, illus. 48p. (ps-2). 1996. lib. bdg. 22.60 (978-0-8368-1616-7(1)); Fight. Boegehold, Betty D. Oz, Robin, illus. (gr. 1-3). 1999. lib. bdg. 22.60 (978-0-8368-2420-9(2)); Good News. Brenner, Barbara. Duke, Kate, illus. 48p. (ps-2). 1999. lib. bdg. 22.60 (978-0-8368-1775-1(3)); Gruff Brothers. Hooks, William H. Cornuel, Pierre, illus. 48p. (ps-2). 1997. lib. bdg. 22.60 (978-0-8368-1749-2(4)); Hedgehog Bakes a Cake. MacDonald, Maryann. Munsinger, Lynn, illus. 48p. (gr. 1-3). 1996. lib. bdg. 22.60 (978-0-8368-1619-8(6)); Horse Called Starfire. Boegehold, Betty D. Waldman, Neil, illus. 48p. (gr. 2-4). 1998. lib. bdg. 22.60 (978-0-8368-1763-8(X)); Lion & Lamb. Brenner, Barbara. (gr. 2-4). 1999. lib. bdg. 22.60 (978-0-8368-2421-6(0)); Lion & Lamb Step Out. Brenner, Barbara & Hooks, William H. Degen, Bruce, illus. 48p. (gr. 2-4). 1998. lib. bdg. 22.60 (978-0-8368-1772-0(9)); Little Poss & Horrible Hound. Hooks, William H. Newsom, Carol, illus. 48p. (gr. 2-4). 1998. lib. bdg. 22.60 (978-0-8368-1773-7(7)); Lo-Jack & the Pirates. Hooks, William H. Tusa, Tricia, illus. 48p. (gr. 2-4). 1999. lib. bdg. 22.60 (978-0-8368-1782-9(6)); Magic Box. Brenner, Barbara. Boix, Manuel, illus. 48p. (gr. 2-4). 1998. lib. bdg. 22.60 (978-0-8368-1764-5(8)); Monster from the Sea. Hooks, William H. Thomas, Angela T., illus. 32p. (gr. 1-3). 1997. lib. bdg. 22.60 (978-0-8368-1694-5(3)); Mr. Baseball. Hooks, William H. Meisel, Paul, illus. 48p. (gr. 2-4). 1998. lib. bdg. 22.60 (978-0-8368-1765-2(6)); Mr. Big Brother. Hooks, William H. Duke, Kate, illus. (ps-2). 1999. lib. bdg. 22.60 (978-0-8368-2417-9(2)); Mr. Bubble Gum. Hooks, William H. Meisel, Paul, illus. 48p. (gr. 2-4). 1997. lib. bdg. 22.60 (978-0-8368-1754-6(0)); Mr. Dinosaur. Hooks, William H. Meisel, Paul, illus. 48p. (gr. 2-4). 1997. lib. bdg. 22.60 (978-0-8368-1755-3(9)); My First Day at Camp. Weiss, Ellen. Thornburgh, Rebecca McKillip, illus. (ps-2). 1999. lib. bdg. 22.60 (978-0-8368-2418-6(0)); My Worst Days Diary. Altman, Suzanne. Allison, Diane W., illus. 48p. (gr. 2-4). 1996. lib. bdg. 22.60 (978-0-8368-1623-5(4)); Mystery of the Missing Tooth. Hooks, William H. Poydar, Nancy, illus. 48p. (ps-2). 1998. lib. bdg. 22.60 (978-0-8368-1758-4(3)); Not Now! Said the Cow. Oppenheim, Joanne. Demarest, Chris L., illus. 48p. (gr. 1-3). 1997. lib. bdg. 22.60 (978-0-8368-1752-2(4)); Peach Boy. Hooks, William H. Otani, June, illus. 48p. (gr. 2-4). 1996. lib. bdg. 22.60 (978-0-8368-1662-4(5)); Rabbit's Birthday Kite. MacDonald, Maryann. Munsinger, Lynn, illus. 48p. (gr. 1-3). 1999. lib. bdg. 22.60 (978-0-8368-1779-9(6)); Real Live Monsters! Schecter, Ellen. Braginetz, Donna, illus. 32p. (gr. 1-3). 1996. lib. bdg. 22.60 (978-0-8368-1620-4(X)); Rebus Bears. Reit, Seymour. Smith, Kenneth, illus. 48p. (ps-2). 1997. lib. bdg. 22.60 (978-0-8368-1750-8(8)); Scamper's Year. Kindley, Jeff. Rader, Laura, illus. 48p. (ps-2). 1999. lib. bdg. 22.60 (978-0-8368-1777-5(X)); She'll Be Coming Round the Mountain. Coplon, Emily. Barnes-Murphy, Rowan, illus. 48p. (ps-2). 1997. lib. bdg. 22.60 (978-0-8368-1689-1(7)); Show-and-Tell Frog. Oppenheim, Joanne. Duke, Kate, illus. 32p. (gr. 1-3). 1998. lib. bdg. 22.60 (978-0-8368-1762-1(1)); Sing, Little Sack! (Canta, Saquito!) Cruz, Ray, illus. (gr. 2-4). 1996. lib. bdg. 22.60 (978-0-8368-1621-1(8)); Sleep Tight, Pete. Schecter, Ellen. Weissman, Bari, illus. 48p. (ps-2). 1998. lib. bdg. 22.60 (978-0-8368-1766-9(4)); Swim Like a Fish. Schecter, Ellen. Cymerman, John E., illus. 48p. (ps-2). 1998. lib. bdg. 22.60 (978-0-8368-1767-6(2)); Too Many Mice. Brenner, Barbara. Cymerman, John E., illus. 48p. (gr. 1-3). 1998. lib. bdg. 22.60 (978-0-8368-1771-3(0)); Town Mouse & the Country Mouse. Aesop. Hannon, Holly, illus. 32p. (gr. 2-4). 1996. lib. bdg. 22.60 (978-0-8368-1622-8(6)); Two Crows Counting. Orgel, Doris. Moffatt, Judith, illus. 32p. (ps-2). 1996. lib. bdg. 22.60 (978-0-8368-1617-4(X)); Uh-Oh! Said the Crow. Oppenheim, Joanne. Demarest, Chris L., illus. 48p. (gr. 1-3). 1997. lib. bdg. 22.60 (978-0-8368-1753-9(2)); Warrior Maiden. Schecter, Ellen. Otani, June & Kelly, Laura, illus. 48p. (gr. 2-4). 1997. lib. bdg. 22.60 (978-0-8368-1696-9(X)); Where's Lulu? Hooks, William H. Alley, R. W., illus. 48p. (ps-2). 1998. lib. bdg. 22.60 (978-0-8368-1768-3(0)); Who Goes Out on Halloween? Alexander, Sue. Karas, G. Brian, illus. 32p. (ps-2). 1998. lib. bdg. 22.60 (978-0-8368-1759-1(1)); (J). Set lib. bdg. 489.93 (978-0-8368-2477-3(6)) Stevens, Gareth Inc.

Barbauld, Anna. Little Stories for Children; Being Easy. 2004. reprint ed. pap. 20.95 (978-0-7661-9037-5(4)) Kessinger Publishing, LLC.

Barber, Rachel, et al. Nine Novels by Younger Americans. 2007. 864p. (J). pap. 18.00 (978-0-9770844-4-9(2)) 826 Valencia.

Barbour, Ralph Henry. The New Boy at Hilltop & Other Stories. 2006. pap. (***978-1-4065-0779-9(2)***) Dodo Pr.

—The New Boy at Hilltop & Other Stories. 2006. 62.99 (***978-1-4219-9700-1(2)***); pap. 56.99 (***978-1-4219-9701-8(0)***) IndyPublish.com.

Barker, Jane Valentine. Building Up. pap. 7.95 (978-1-878611-07-9(0)) Silver Rim Pr.

Barkley, Roger C. Johnny Grasshopper. 2006. 52p. pap. 12.95 (978-1-4241-0221-1(9)) PublishAmerica, Inc.

Barnes, Emma. Sam & the Griswalds. Archbold, Tim, illus. 2004. 320p. (YA). pap. 12.99 (978-0-7475-5906-1(6)) Bloomsbury Publishing Plc GBR. *Dist:* Independent Pubs. Group.

Barton, Bob. Little Book of Northern Tales: The Bear Says North. Marton, Jirina, illus. 2006. 72p. 9.95 (978-0-88899-747-0(7)) Groundwood Bks. CAN. *Dist:* Perseus Distribution.

Baum, L. Frank. Collected Short Stories of L. Frank Baum. 2006. (J). 29.95 (978-1-930764-14-9(6)) International Wizard of Oz Club, The.

Baum, L. Frank & Denslow, W. W. Oz-Story 5. Maxine, David, ed. Shanower, Eric & Denslow, W. W., illus. 1999. (Oz Ser.:). 128p. (Orig.). (YA). (gr. 5-8). pap. 14.95 (978-1-929527-00-7(4)) Hungry Tiger Pr.

Baxter, Nicola. Best Loved Magical Tales for Bedtime. 2000. (Illus.). 480p. (J). (gr. 3-4). pap. 20.00 (978-0-7881-6893-2(2)) DIANE Publishing Co.

—Old MacDonald's: Barnyard Tales. Davis, Caroline, illus. 256p. (J). (978-0-7525-8771-4(4)) Parragon Bk. Service Ltd.

Be Afraid! Tales of Horror. 2000. (gr. 7-12). lib. bdg. 15.25 (978-0-613-77316-4(0)) Tandem Library Bks.

Beaudoin, Beau. Boetry. Beaudoin, Beau, illus. 2007. (Illus.). 40p. (J). per. 15.95 (***978-0-9788401-1-2(9)***) Red Ink Pr.

Because We Are Friends. 2001. 60p. pap. 12.95 (978-0-9650787-4-0(4)) MIBS Publishing.

Becker, Bob. Grampa's Stories... For Little Kids. Harstad, Debra, illus. 1998. 46p. (J). pap. 8.95 (978-1-885548-00-9(1)) Boot Prints.

Beckett, Bernard. Lester. 160p. (YA). (gr. 8 up). pap. 13.00 (978-1-877135-21-7(6)) Longacre Pr. NZL. *Dist:* Pacific Island Bks.

—Red Cliff. 2000. 143p. pap. 13.00 (978-1-877135-42-2(9)) Longacre Pr. NZL. *Dist:* Pacific Island Bks.

Beckhorn, Susan. In the Morning of the World: Six Woodland Why Stories. Beckhorn, Susan, illus. 2000. (Illus.). 48p. (gr. 4-7). 15.95 (978-0-89272-503-8(6)) Down East Bks.

Bedford, William. The Stowaway. Fletcher, Claire, illus. 2001. 89p. (J). pap. 7.50 (978-0-7497-4273-7(9)) Egmont Bks., Ltd. GBR. *Dist:* Independent Pubs. Group.

Bedtime Stories for Boys. 2002. 192p. (J). 14.98 (978-0-7525-6622-1(9)) Parragon, Inc.

Bedtime Stories for Girls. 2002. 192p. (J). 14.98 (978-0-7525-6620-7(2)) Parragon, Inc.

The Bedtime Treasury. 2002. (Little Treasuries Ser.). 256p. (J). 11.95 (978-0-7525-7687-9(9)) Parragon, Inc.

Bedtime with Rollo. 2005. (J). (978-0-9677238-8-4(4) , Sweet Dreams Pr.) Bier Brothers, Inc.

Bell, Frank & Bowler, Colin. Panda Power. Seaman, Paul, illus. 2004. 24p. pap. 7.00 (978-1-84161-084-9(4)) Ravette Publishing, Ltd. GBR. *Dist:* Parkwest Pubns., Inc.

Bell, Krista. No Strings. 2005. (Illus.). 159p. (J). (ps-7). pap. (978-0-7344-0626-2(6) , Lothian Bks.) Hachette Livre Australia.

Bell, Shirley. Boys on the Make. 2007. 54p. 12.95 (***978-1-4241-6575-9(X)***) PublishAmerica, Inc.

Bell, Wade. No Place Fit for a Child. 2007. (Prose Ser.). 200p. pap. 18.00 (***978-1-55071-266-7(7)***) Guernica Editions, Inc. CAN. *Dist:* Independent Pubs. Group.

Bella & Rosie Beach Stories. 2007. (J). per. (***978-1-932570-83-0(7)***) Literacy Footprints Inc.

Bendix, Jane. The Secret Map. 2001. (J). pap. 9.95 (978-0-89992-153-2(1)) Council for Indian Education.

Benforado, Sally. Bring Me a Story. rev. ed. (J). (gr. 6-10). 14.95 (978-0-915745-08-1(9)) Floricanto Pr.

A Benji's Pup Set, 6 vols. 32p. (gr. 1-3). 37.50 (978-0-322-00338-5(5)); 31.50 incl. 5.25 hd (978-0-7802-8045-8(0)) Wright Group, The.

Bennet, Jill, et al. Cuentos de Terror, Vol. 2. (SPA.). (YA). 8.95 (978-958-04-3393-4(3)) Norma S.A. COL. *Dist:* Distribuidora Norma, Inc.

Bennett, David. Witch & Wizard Stories. Thomas, Jacqui, illus. 2004. 158p. (J). (ps-ps). per. 12.60 (978-0-606-33268-2(5)) Tandem Library Bks.

Bennett, Jack. Tell Me a Story: A Collection of Short Stories. 2003. 68p. pap. (978-1-894650-25-0(5)) Moose Enterprise.

Bentley, Bernard E. Little Ben's Bedtime Stories. 2004. pap. 8.95 (978-0-533-14380-1(2)) Vantage Pr., Inc.

Bercowetz, Cynthia. Grandpa Herman¿s Petting Zoo. 2007. (Illus.). 48p. (J). per. 14.95 (***978-0-9708430-9-8(7)***) Uitti, Daniel.

Berenstain, Jan & Berenstain, Michael. The Berenstain Bears' Big Bedtime Book. 2008. (Berenstain Bears Ser.). 48p. (J). 12.99 (***978-0-06-057434-5(8)***); lib. bdg. 13.89 (***978-0-06-057435-2(6)***) HarperCollins Pubs.

Beresford, Elisabeth. The Bigfoot Womble: Wombles. (Illus.). 16p. pap. (978-0-340-74673-8(4) , Hodder & Stoughton) Hodder General Publishing Division.

—The Great Cake Mystery. (Illus.). 16p. (J). (gr. k-6). pap. (978-0-340-74672-1(6) , Hodder & Stoughton) Hodder General Publishing Division.

—The Great Womble Explorer: Wombles. (Illus.). 16p. (J). (gr. k-6). pap. (978-0-340-74675-2(0) , Hodder & Stoughton) Hodder General Publishing Division.

Berger, Carin. All Mixed Up: A Mix-and-Match Book. 2006. (Illus.). 46p. (J). 8.95 (978-0-8118-4966-1(X)) Chronicle Bks. LLC.

Bergida, Joanna. Wisdom from the Spring: A Collection of Short Storiesfrom the Class of 2010Cold Spring Harbor High School. 2007. 124p. pap. 10.95 (***978-0-595-44281-2(1)***) iUniverse, Inc.

Berman, Steve, ed. Magic in the Mirrorstone: Tales of Fantasy. 2008. 304p. (J). (gr. 3-7). 14.95 (***978-0-7869-4732-4(2)*** , Mirrorstone) Wizards of the Coast.

Bernal, Ricardo, prologue by. Los Mejores Relatos de Ciencia Ficcion. 6th ed. 2003. (SPA., Illus.). 195p. (J). (gr. 8-12). pap. 11.95 (978-84-204-4494-9(4)) Santillana USA Publishing Co., Inc.

Berocay, Roy. Babu. (SPA., Illus.). 60p. (J). (gr. 3-5). pap. 8.95 (978-1-58105-634-1(6)) Santillana USA Publishing Co., Inc.

—Un Mundo Perfecto. Arismendi, Elbio, illus. 2003. (Coleccion Derechos Del Nino Ser.). (SPA.). 32p. (J). (gr. 3-5). pap. 7.95 (978-84-204-5827-4(9)) Santillana USA Publishing Co., Inc.

—Pateando Lunas. Soulier, Daniel, illus. 2003. (SPA.). 166p. (J). (gr. 3). pap. 12.95 (978-9974-590-63-2(9)) Santillana S. A. URY. *Dist:* Santillana USA Publishing Co., Inc.

Berry, Joy Wilt. From Humans to Superstars: The Human Race Club Gets a New Name. Pace, Don, illus. 1999. (Superstar Kids' Club Short Stories Ser.). 48p. (J). (gr. 1-7). pap. 3.95 (978-1-58634-251-7(7)) Goldstar Publishing, Inc.

—One Leg at a Time: A Short Story about Human Similarities. Pace, Don, illus. 1999. (Superstar Kids' Club Short Stories Ser.: Vol. 1). 48p. (J). (gr. 2-6). pap. 3.95 (978-1-58634-252-4(5)) Goldstar Publishing, Inc.

Bertagna, Julie. Dolphin Boy. 1999. (Illus.). 96p. (J). pap. 7.50 (978-0-7497-3730-6(1)) Egmont Bks., Ltd. GBR. *Dist:* Independent Pubs. Group.

Between the Lions - Set of 5 Early Literacy Kits: Includes; Help!, Huff & Puff, Oh, Yes I Can!, Shooting Star & Zoop! Zoop!, 5 cass., 5 vols. 2005. (Between the Lions Ser.). 120p. (J). VHS 139.95 (978-1-59375-295-8(4) , WG38713) WGBH Boston Video.

Bianchi, John. Young Author's Day at Pokeweed Public School. 1999. (gr. k-3). lib. bdg. 12.95 (978-0-613-29151-4(4)) Tandem Library Bks.

Bibel, Philip. Tales of the Shtetl. 2004. (Illus.). 215p. per. 14.95 (978-0-9634067-1-2(X)) Metchnikoff, Elie Memorial Library.

Bickel, Karla. Heart Petals on the Hearth: A Collection of Children's Stories. Bickel, Karla, illus. 2004. (Illus.). 64p. (J). (ps-6). 20.00 (978-1-891452-00-0(2)) Heart Arbor Bks.

—Heart Petals on the Hearth: A Collection of Children's Stories. 2004. (Illus.). 64p. (J). (ps-6). pap. 16.00 (978-1-891452-01-7(0)) Heart Arbor Bks.

Biers-Ariel, Matt. The Seven Species. Goodman, Tama, illus. 2003. 48p. 19.95 (978-0-8074-0852-0(2) , 161902) URJ Pr.

Biery, David. Childrens Books. 2004. 3p. pap. 7.09 (978-1-4116-1015-6(6)) Lulu.com.

Big Book of R Carry-over Stories. 2004. per. 34.99 (978-0-9760490-4-3(X)) Say It Right.

Billings. Bizarre Endings. 1998. (Wild Side Ser.). (Illus.). (YA). (gr. 6-12). 13.00 (978-0-89061-803-5(8) , R0803-8E) Jamestown.

Billings, Henry. Total Panic. 1998. (Wild Side Ser.). (Illus.). (YA). (gr. 6-12). 13.00 (978-0-89061-804-2(6) , R0804-6E) Jamestown.

Billings Stuart, Elizabeth. Delightful Stories for Children. 2005. (J). 26.95 (978-0-911845-70-9(4)) Neumann Pr., The.

Bingham, Deanne Lee. Just Imagine. Below, Halina, illus. 24p. (J). (ps-k). 2000. pap. (978-1-55041-544-5(1)); 1998. (978-1-55041-381-6(3)) Fitzhenry & Whiteside, Ltd.

Bird Song: The Little Stories of Manoosh & Baloosh. 2003. (J). mass mkt. (978-1-932233-02-5(4)) Aurora Libris Corp.

Blabster, Sneedy. Boon Tales. 2003. (J). per. 15.50 (978-1-931062-31-2(5)) Pivotal Bks.

Black, & Still Beautiful. 2005. (YA). per. 6.95 (978-0-9630951-3-8(7)) Karnak Co.

The Black Eyed Zinger: And Other Middle School Stories. 2000. 117p. (J). pap. 5.99 (978-0-9703444-0-3(6)) M&R Publishing.

Blackfield, Neil. Boat Ride & Other Stories. 1999. (gr. 7-12). lib. bdg. 11.60 (978-0-613-30282-1(6)) Tandem Library Bks.

—Music Store & Other Stories. 1999. (gr. 7-12). lib. bdg. 11.60 (978-0-613-30616-4(3)) Tandem Library Bks.

—New City & Other Stories. 1999. (gr. 7-12). lib. bdg. 11.60 (978-0-613-30622-5(8)) Tandem Library Bks.

—Up in the Clouds. 1999. (gr. 7-12). lib. bdg. 11.60 (978-0-613-30829-8(8)) Tandem Library Bks.

Blackington, Debbie. Mama's Wish/Daughter's Wish. Sommer, Xiaolan, tr. from CHI. 2004. (Illus.). 48p. (J). 17.95 (978-0-9760011-0-2(1)) Pebbleton Pr.

Blake, Jon. Stinky Finger's House of Fun. Roberts, David, illus. 2007. 128p. (J). pap. 6.95 (***978-0-340-88459-1(2)***) Hodder Children's Division GBR. *Dist:* Independent Pubs. Group.

Blake, Quentin, selected by. Puffin Book of Nonsense Stories. 2000. (Illus.). 288p. (YA). (gr. 2 up). 10.95 (978-0-14-038213-6(5)) Penguin Bks., Ltd. GBR. *Dist:* Trafalgar Square Publishing.

Blakeslee, Ann. Go Baby Go. Palma, Anna, illus. 2005. 8p. (J). bds. 8.99 (978-0-439-72592-7(5) , Cartwheel Bks.) Scholastic, Inc.

Bledsoe, Glen & Bledsoe, Karen, compiled by. Classic Sea Stories. 1999. (Roxbury Park Bks.). (Illus.). 123p. (J). (gr. 3-7). pap. 5.95 (978-0-7373-0041-3(8) , 00418W) McGraw-Hill/Contemporary.

Blitz, Shmuel. Bedtime Stories of Jewish Holidays. 1998. 48p. 14.99 (978-1-57819-174-1(2) , BEDJH) Mesorah Pubns., Ltd.

—My First Book of Jewish Stories. Katz, Tova, illus. 1999. (ArtScroll Youth Ser.). 48p. (J). 14.99 (978-1-57819-294-6(3) , MFJS) Mesorah Pubns., Ltd.

Block, Francesca Lia. Girl Goddess: Nine Stories. 1998. (YA). (gr. 7 up). (978-0-606-12944-2(8)) Tandem Library Bks.

—Nine Stories. Scott, Steve, illus. 1998. (Girl Goddess Ser.: No. 9). 192p. (J). (gr. 12 up). pap. 7.99 (978-0-06-447187-9(X) , Harper Trophy) HarperCollins Pubs.

—The Rose & the Beast: Fairy Tales Retold. 2001. 240p. (J). (gr. 8 up). pap. 7.99 (978-0-06-440745-8(4) , Cotler, Joanna Books) HarperCollins Pubs.

Bloomfield, Susanne George & Reed, Melvin, eds. Adventures in the West: Stories for Young Readers. 2007. (Illus.). 302p. (gr. 3 up). pap. 19.95 (***978-0-8032-5974-4(3)*** , Bison Bks.) Univ. of Nebraska Pr.

Blow, Wind, Blow! & Other Stories: Individual Title Six-Pack. (Story Steps Ser.). (gr. k-2). 42.00 (978-0-7635-9586-9(1)) Rigby Education.

Blue Wolf & Friends Learning Adventure Package, 2 bks. 2004. (Illus.). 100p. lib. bdg. (978-0-9758759-0-2(6)) Progressive Language, Inc.

Blume, Judy. It's Fine to Be Nine. 2000. (Illus.). (J). (978-0-606-18566-0(6)) Tandem Library Bks.

Blume, Judy & Dahl, Roald. It's Heaven to Be Seven. 2000. (Illus.). (J). (978-0-606-18569-1(0)) Tandem Library Bks.

Blume, Judy, et al. It's Fine to Be Nine. 2000. (Illus.). 144p. (J). (gr. 3-6). pap. 3.99 (978-0-590-38604-3(2) , Scholastic Paperbacks) Scholastic, Inc.

—It's Heaven to Be Seven. 2000. (Illus.). 128p. (J). (gr. 2-5). pap. 3.99 (978-0-439-11675-6(9) , Scholastic Paperbacks) Scholastic, Inc.

Blundell, Tony, illus. Funny Stories. 2004. (Red Hot Reads Ser.). 256p. (J). (gr. k-3). pap. 6.95 (978-0-7534-5733-7(4) , Kingfisher) Houghton Mifflin Co. Trade & Reference Div.

Blyton, Enid. The Adventure of the Secret Necklace. (Illus.). 84p. (J). pap. 7.99 (978-0-7475-3211-8(7)) Bloomsbury Publishing Plc GBR. *Dist:* Trafalgar Square Publishing.

—Best Stories for Five-Year-Olds. 2000. (Enid Blyton's Best Stories Ser.). (Illus.). 128p. (J). (gr. k up). pap. 7.99 (978-0-7475-3225-5(7)) Bloomsbury Publishing Plc GBR. *Dist:* Trafalgar Square Publishing.

—Best Stories for Seven Year Olds. 2000. (Enid Blyton's Best Stories Ser.). (Illus.). 128p. (J). (gr. 2). pap. 7.99 (978-0-7475-3227-9(3)) Bloomsbury Publishing Plc GBR. *Dist:* Trafalgar Square Publishing.

—Best Stories for Six Year Olds. 2000. (Enid Blyton's Best Stories Ser.). (Illus.). 128p. (J). (gr. 1 up). pap. 6.99 (978-0-7475-3226-2(5)) Bloomsbury Publishing Plc GBR. *Dist:* Trafalgar Square Publishing.

—The Boy Who Wanted a Dog. (Illus.). 91p. (J). pap. 7.99 (978-0-7475-3213-2(3)) Bloomsbury Publishing Plc GBR. *Dist:* Trafalgar Square Publishing.

—The Children of St. Kidillin. (Illus.). 110p. (J). pap. 7.99 (978-0-7475-3216-3(8)) Bloomsbury Publishing Plc GBR. *Dist:* Trafalgar Square Publishing.

—Enid Blyton Circus Stories. (Illus.). (J). 11.95 (978-0-09-914131-0(0)) Random Hse. GBR. *Dist:* Trafalgar Square Publishing.

—Mr Meddle Stories. (J). pap. 5.95 (978-0-09-965550-3(0)) Random Hse. GBR. *Dist:* Trafalgar Square Publishing.

—Mr Pink-Whistle's Party. 2nd ed. (Illus.). 111p. (J). pap. 7.99 (978-0-7475-3853-0(0)) Bloomsbury Publishing Plc GBR. *Dist:* Trafalgar Square Publishing.

—Mr Twiddle in Trouble Again. 2000. (Enid Blyton's Happy Days Ser.). (Illus.). 95p. (J). (ps-3). pap. 7.99 (978-0-7475-4355-8(0)) Bloomsbury Publishing Plc GBR. *Dist:* Trafalgar Square Publishing.

—Noddy Hardcover Storybook, No. 2. 2001. (J). 8.95 (978-0-06-107365-6(2) , Harper Entertainment) HarperCollins Pubs.

—The Secret of Cliff Castle. (Illus.). 117p. (J). pap. 7.99 (978-0-7475-3214-9(1)) Bloomsbury Publishing Plc GBR. *Dist:* Trafalgar Square Publishing.

Bobadilla, Selene. Cuentos de Estraterrestres para Ninos. 1999. (Stories for Children Ser.).Tr. of Alien Stories for Kids. (SPA.). 125p. (J). mass mkt. 9.95 (978-970-643-166-0(7)) Selector, S.A. de C.V. MEX. *Dist:* Libros Sin Fronteras.

Bodger, Joan. Tales of Court & Castle. Lang, Mark, illus. 2003. 96p. (J). (gr. 3-7). pap. 9.95 (978-0-88776-614-5(5)) Tundra Bks., Inc./Livres Toundra, Inc. CAN. *Dist:* Random Hse., Inc.

Boelter, Ashaki. Diaries of the Doomed. Boelter, Ashaki, illus. 2004. (Illus.). 88p. (YA). per. 6.95 (978-0-9721067-4-0(X) , Writing Wild & Crazy) Shakalot High Entertainment.

Boelter, Ashaki. Diaries of the Doomed 2: Fate of the Fatal. 2007. (Illus.). 114p. (J). per. 11.95 (***978-0-9796219-0-1(9)*** , Writing Wild & Crazy) Shakalot High Entertainment.

Bofill Suris, Francesc. Los Guisantes Maravillosos. (Coleccion Fabulas y Cuentos Populares). (SPA.). 24p. (J). (gr. 2-4). (978-84-246-1932-9(3) , GL1165) La Galera, S.A. Editorial ESP. *Dist:* Lectorum Pubns., Inc.

Bogacki, Tomek. Mi Primer Jardin. 2003. (Picture Bks.). (SPA., Illus.). (J). (978-970-690-649-6(5)) Planeta Mexicana Editorial S. A. de C. V.

Boie, Kirsten. King-Kong, Mi Mascota Secreta. (Torre de Papel Ser.). (SPA.). (J). (gr. 2). 7.95 (978-958-04-1310-3(X)) Norma S.A. COL. *Dist:* Distribuidora Norma, Inc.

Bojunga, Lygia. La Cama. (SPA.). (J). (978-958-04-6492-1(8)) Norma S.A. COL. *Dist:* Distribuidora Norma, Inc.

Boldt, Ron, illus. & des. Not Just a Fish. Boldt, Ron, des. 2000. 7.95 (978-1-56123-133-1(9) , NJFC) Centering Corp.

Bolle, Frank, illus. Great Stories about Horses. 2001. 160p. (J). (gr. 3-9). lib. bdg. (978-0-87460-203-6(3)) Lion Bks.

Bolt, Ranjit & La Fontaine, Jean De. The Hare & the Tortoise & Other Fables of la Fontaine. Potter, Giselle, illus. 2006. 64p. (J). 19.99 (978-1-905236-54-1(9)) Barefoot Bks., Inc.

Bono, Elena. El Sombrero de Ramito. Brignole, Giancarla, tr. Bono, Elena, illus. rev. ed. 2006. (Fabulas De Familia Ser.). (SPA., Illus.). 32p. (J). pap. 6.95 (978-970-20-0261-1(3)) Castillo, Ediciones, S. A. de C. V. MEX. *Dist:* Macmillan.

Booker, Carolyn. Mr. Green Squash Takes a Journey. 2005. (J). pap. 8.00 (978-0-8059-6638-1(2)) Dorrance Publishing Co., Inc.

Booth-Cartwright, Karan. A Helping Hand: A Book of Short Stories for Children. l.t. ed. 2001. (Illus.). 65p. (J). (gr. k-8). pap. 12.95 (978-1-929819-50-8(1) , 01950) A+ Bk. Publishing.

Borges, Jorge Luis. Breve Ant de Ctos Fantastico. (SPA.). pap. 11.95 (978-950-07-1350-4(0)) Editorial Sudamericana S.A. ARG. *Dist:* Distribooks, Inc.

Borges, Jorge Luis, et al. Cuentos Latinoamericanos: Antologia. 2nd ed. 2003. (SPA., Illus.). 134p. (J). (gr. 8-12). 14.95 (978-968-19-0319-0(6)) Aguilar, Altea, Taurus, Alfaguara, S.A. de C.V MEX. *Dist:* Santillana USA Publishing Co., Inc.

The Boring Day. 2001. (978-1-58453-159-3(2)) Pioneer Valley Educational Pr., Inc.

Bornemann, Elsa. Disparatario. O'Kif, illus. 2002. (SPA.). 120p. (J). (gr. 3-5). pap. 11.95 (978-950-511-624-9(1)) Santillana USA Publishing Co., Inc.

—El Espejo Distraido. Trillo, Matias, illus. 2002. (SPA.). 124p. (J). (gr. 3-5). pap. 10.95 (978-950-511-725-3(6)) Santillana USA Publishing Co., Inc.

—Los Grendelines. Pez, illus. 2003. Tr. of Grendelines. (SPA.). 70p. (J). (gr. 3-5). pap. 11.95 (978-950-511-244-9(0)) Alfaguara S.A. de Ediciones ARG. *Dist:* Santillana USA Publishing Co., Inc.

—Lisa de los Paraguas. 2002. (SPA., Illus.). 118p. (J). (gr. 5-8). pap. 12.95 (978-950-511-284-5(X)) Santillana USA Publishing Co., Inc.

—El Nino Envuelto. Duforu, Sebastian, illus. 2003. (SPA.). 176p. (YA). (gr. 5-8). pap. 13.95 (978-950-511-623-2(3)) Alfaguara S.A. de Ediciones ARG. *Dist:* Santillana USA Publishing Co., Inc.

—Socorro! 12 Cuentos para Caerse de Miedo. (SPA., Illus.). 192p. (J). (gr. 5-8). pap. 10.95 (978-968-19-0549-1(0)) Santillana USA Publishing Co., Inc.

—Socorro Diez y Otros Cuentos.Tr. of Socorro Diez & Other Stories. (SPA.). (YA). (gr. 5-8). pap. 7.95 (978-958-04-2776-6(3)) Norma S.A. COL. *Dist:* Distribuidora Norma, Inc., Lectorum Pubns., Inc.

—Sol de Noche. Nine, Carlos, illus. 2002. (SPA.). 106p. (J). (gr. 3-5). pap. 11.95 (978-950-511-625-6(X)) Santillana USA Publishing Co., Inc.

Botero, Carolina Barrera, ed. Cuentos Clasicos: Disney, Vol. 1. (ESP., Illus.). 80p. (J). (978-958-04-7551-4(2)) Norma S.A.

Bottino, Marlane. Pup Tales Stories for Beginning Readers, 9 vols., Set 2. Bottino, Marlane, illus. 2001. (Pup Tales Ser.: Vol. 2). (Illus.). (J). (gr. k-2). pap. 7.00 (978-1-893615-04-5(9)) Creative Enterprises.

Bourgeois, Paulette. Franklin Visita el Museo. 2003. (SPA.). lib. bdg. 12.35 (978-0-613-81427-0(4)) Tandem Library Bks.

Boyle, T. C. The Human Fly & Other Stories. 2005. 192p. (YA). (gr. 7). 17.99 (978-0-670-06054-2(2) , Viking Juvenile); pap. 9.99 (978-0-14-240363-1(6) , Puffin) Penguin Group (USA) Inc.

Boynton, Sandra. Snoozers: 7 Short Short Bedtime Stories for Lively Little Kids. 2001. (J). bds. 7.99 (978-0-689-83617-6(1) , Simon & Schuster Children's Publishing) Simon & Schuster Children's Publishing.

Brace, Jason, et al. A River of Hands: A Collection of Deaf Heritage Stories. Tager, Edward et al, illus. 2005. 47p. (YA). (gr. 2-6). pap. 6.95 (978-1-896764-36-8(3)) Second Story Pr. CAN. *Dist:* Orca Bk. Pubs. USA, Univ. of Toronto Pr.

Bradbury, Ray. Ray Bradbury Collected Short Stories. Court, Robert, illus. 2001. (Great Author Ser.). (J). (978-0-9709033-2-7(4)) Peterson Publishing Co., Inc.

Bradley, Rachel Victoria. Dillon & Daisy: Magical Mayhem & Other Stories. 2006. 9.00 (978-0-8059-9000-3(3)) Dorrance Publishing Co., Inc.

Bradman, Tony. Give Me Shelter. 2007. 127p. (YA). (gr. 4 up). 16.95 (978-1-84507-522-4(6)) Lincoln, Frances Ltd. GBR. *Dist:* Perseus Distribution.

Bradman, Tony, compiled by. My Dad's a Punk: 12 Stories about Boys & Their Fathers. 2006. 240p. (J). (gr. 5-9). pap. 7.95 (978-0-7534-5870-9(5) , Kingfisher) Houghton Mifflin Co. Trade & Reference Div.

Brady, Karen. God Is Great: A Collection of 13 Story Book Poems, 1. l.t. ed. 2004. (Illus.). 20p. (J). 12.50 (978-0-9754169-0-7(1)) Bradybooks.biz.

Brain, Helen. Fly Cemetery & Other Juicy Stories. 1999. (Illus.). 92p. (J). (978-0-7981-3987-8(0)) Human & Rousseau.

Brainard, Cecilia M., ed. Growing up Filipino: Stories for Young Adults. 2003. (Illus.). xv, 298p. (YA). per. 18.95 (978-0-9719458-0-7(2)) PALH.

Brainard, Cecilia Manguerra. Growing up Filipino: Stories for Young Adults. 2003. (gr. 7-12). lib. bdg. 29.20 (978-0-613-77876-3(6)) Tandem Library Bks.

Brandeis, Madeline. Shaun O'Day of Ireland. 2004. reprint ed. pap. 22.95 (978-1-4179-2725-8(9)) Kessinger Publishing, LLC.

Breckon, Brett, illus. Dragon Days. 2004. 80p. pap. 17.95 (978-1-84323-301-5(0)) Beekman Bks., Inc.

Breier, Christine A., et al. Goodles & Oodles: A Collection of Short Stories, Drawings & Poetry of Children. 1998. 70p. (J). (ps-12). pap. 25.95 (978-0-7392-0013-1(5)) Morris Publishing.

Brenner, Barbara. Good News. Duke, Kate, illus. 1999. (Bank Street Reader Collection). 48p. (J). (ps-2). lib. bdg. 22.60 (978-0-8368-1775-1(3)) Stevens, Gareth Inc.

Breslin, Theresa. Gladiator. 2004. (J). pap. 29.95 incl. audio (978-0-7540-6277-6(5) , Chivers Children's Audio Bks.) BBC Audiobooks America.

—Homecoming for Kezzie. 2002. 320p. (J). pap. 8.99 (978-1-4052-0111-7(8)) Egmont Bks., Ltd. GBR. *Dist:* Independent Pubs. Group.

—The Tartan Rainbow. 2003. (Illus.). 256p. (J). pap. 9.99 (978-0-330-39921-0(7)) Pan Macmillan GBR. *Dist:* Trafalgar Square Publishing.

Brewster, Betty. Stories That Rhyme: Reading Fun Time. Tolan, R., illus. 1998. 20p. (J). (ps-2). pap. (978-1-57579-120-3(X)) Pine Hill Pr., Inc.

Brindis, Laura. Cuentos Universales del Barroco a la Vanguardia. 2003. (SPA., Illus.). 224p. (YA). (gr. 7 up). (978-968-6966-05-3(6)) EDITER'S Publishing Hse. MEX. *Dist:* EDITER'S Publishing Hse.

Bromfield, Val. If You Can't Sleep... & Other Stories. 2005. (ENG., Illus.). 48p. pap. **(*978-1-84401-416-3(9)*)** Athena Pr.

Brooks, Felicity & Litchfield, Jo. Tales from Littletown. 2004. (Usborne Easy Reading Bks.). (Illus.). 48p. (J). (ps-3). 9.95 (978-0-7460-3474-3(1)) EDC Publishing.

Brouillet, Chrystine. Un Bonheur Terrifiant. Jorisch, Stephane, illus. 2002. (Roman + Ser.). (FRE.). 160p. (YA). (gr. 8 up). pap. (978-2-89021-273-2(4)) Diffusion du livre Mirabel.

—Chauve-Souris Qui Pleurait d'Etre Trop Belle. 2000. (Illus.). 24p. (YA). (ps up). pap. (978-2-89021-331-9(5)) Diffusion du livre Mirabel.

Brouwer, Sigmund. Blazer Drive. 2007. (Orca Sports Ser.). 176p. (YA). (gr. 5 up). pap. **(*978-1-55143-717-0(1)*)** Orca Bk. Pubs.

Brower, Douglas. Backyard Friends. 2006. pap. 8.95 (978-0-533-15454-8(5)) Vantage Pr., Inc.

Brown, Abbie Farwell. Tales of the Red Children. 2006. pap. 20.95 **(*978-1-4286-1602-8(0)*)** Kessinger Publishing, LLC.

Brown, Elizabeth. Collection of Children's Tales. 2006. 94p. pap. 16.95 (978-1-4116-8022-7(7)) Lulu.com.

Brown, Janet Allison. Hello, Mr. Snowman. Chaffey, Samantha, illus. 2005. (Holidays In 3D Ser.). 8p. (J). bds. 4.95 (978-0-7641-5832-2(5)) Barron's Educational Series, Inc.

Brown, Marc. Family Stories You Can Relate To. 2001. (gr. 3-6). lib. bdg. 11.80 (978-0-613-56364-2(6)) Tandem Library Bks.

Brown, Marcia. Stone Soup. Brown, Marcia, illus. 2005. (Illus.). (J). pap. 18.95 incl. audio compact disk (978-1-59112-735-2(1)) Live Oak Media.

Brown, Marcia, et al. Children's Classics II, 5 bks., Set. unabr. ed. 1999. (Illus.). (J). (ps-3). pap. 76.95 incl. audio (978-0-87499-495-7(0)) Live Oak Media.

Brown, Margaret Wise. Goodnight Moon, 2 vols. Hurd, Clement, illus. 2001. 16p. (J). (ps up). 15.99 (978-0-694-01638-9(1) , Harper Festival) HarperCollins Pubs.

Browne, Diane, et al. The Cat Woman & the Spinning Wheel & Other Stories. Haynes-Peart, Andrea et al, illus. 2002. (Doctor Bird Reading Ser.). 64p. (J). pap. (978-976-637-092-3(3)) Randle, Ian Pubs.

—Sweet, Sweet Mango Tree & Other Stories. Brown, Clovis et al, illus. 2002. (Doctor Bird Reading Ser.). 32p. (J). pap. (978-976-637-090-9(7)) Randle, Ian Pubs.

Bruchac, Joseph, et al. Sports Shorts: An Anthology of Short Stories. 2005. (Illus.). 127p. (J). (gr. 4-7). per. 15.99 (978-1-58196-040-2(9)) Darby Creek Publishing.

Bruchac, Joseph, et al. Sports Shorts: Eight Short Stories. 2007. (J). pap. 4.99 **(*978-1-58196-058-7(1)*)** Darby Creek Publishing.

Bryant, Sara Cone. New Stories to Tell to Children: Stories You Never Have Heard. 2005. pap. 21.95 (978-1-4179-9646-9(3)) Kessinger Publishing, LLC.

Budreau, Craig C. Your Move. 2002. 120p. per. 12.95 (978-0-9717868-2-0(8)) WordWright.biz, Inc.

Bugs & Other Stories: Individual Title Six-Pack. (Story Steps Ser.). (gr. k-2). 48.00 (978-0-7635-9616-3(7)) Rigby Education.

Bull, Emma, et al. Firebirds: An Anthology of Original Fantasy & Science Fiction. Vess, Charles, illus. 2003. (Firebird Ser.). 432p. (YA). (gr. 6-11). 19.99 (978-0-14-250142-9(5) , Puffin) Penguin Group (USA) Inc.

Bulow, Wayde. Mystical Land: Short Stories for Children. 2001. 112p. pap. 9.95 (978-0-595-18550-4(9) , Writers Club Pr.) iUniverse, Inc.

Bumpus, Tawanna. Tawanna's Children's Short Story Collections. 2005. (Illus.). 48p. (J). pap. 14.95 (978-1-59800-007-8(1)) Outskirts Press, Inc.

Burgess, Thornton W. Big Book of Animal Stories. 2001. (Illus.). 208p. (J). (gr. 4-7). pap. 7.95 (978-0-486-41980-0(0)) Dover Pubns., Inc.

—Old Mother West Wind. 2004. reprint ed. pap. 15.95 (978-1-4191-3812-6(X)); pap. 1.99 (978-1-4192-3812-3(4)) Kessinger Publishing, LLC.

—Tales from the Storyteller's House. (J). 19.95 (978-0-8488-0930-0(0)) Amereon LTD.

Burkhalter, Mary L. Active Children's Literature: Alphabet Story, Colors, Mister Prince. 1998. (Illus.). 50p. (J). (gr. k-4). pap. 20.00 (978-0-934284-09-7(1)) Jolean Publishing Co.

Burnett, Eric. 21st Century Voices. 2003. 210p. (YA). pap. 17.95 (978-0-595-29649-1(0)) iUniverse, Inc.

Burnett, Frances Hodgson. Little Saint Elizabeth & Other Stories. 2006. 40.99 **(*978-1-4280-0252-4(9)*)**; pap. 34.99 **(*978-1-4280-0256-2(1)*)** IndyPublish.com.

Burnett, Frances Hodgson. Racketty-Packetty House & Other Stories. 2002. (Dover Juvenile Classics Ser.). (Illus.). 128p. (J). (gr. 4-7). pap. 2.50 (978-0-486-41860-5(X)) Dover Pubns., Inc.

Burnett-Guyinn, Lois. Mrs. Townsend's Class: Journeys in History. 2005. 13p. per. (978-1-59453-523-9(X) , 2704) Airleaf Publishing & Bookselling.

Burnham, Niki, et al. Fireworks: Four Summer Stories. 2007. (Fireworks Ser.). (Illus.). 240p. (YA). (gr. 7 up). pap. 8.99 (978-0-439-90300-4(9) , Scholastic Paperbacks) Scholastic, Inc.

Burns, Dal. The Kookaburra & Other Stories. 2007. (ENG.). 76p. per. 14.95 **(*978-1-4241-1770-3(4)*)** PublishAmerica, Inc.

Burroughs, Jean M. Children of Destiny: True Adventures of Three Cultures. 2001. (Illus.). 108p. (J). pap. 12.95 (978-0-913270-75-2(X)) Sunstone Pr.

Burrows, Terry. ¡Oh, No! Es Hipo! (SPA.). 78p. (J). (gr. k-2). (978-968-5308-88-5(8) , Silver Dolphin en Español) Advanced Marketing, S. de R. L. de C. V.

Burt, Peg O'Connor. The Evolution of Merucia. 2002. 157p. pap. 11.95 (978-0-595-22605-4(1) , Writers Club Pr.) iUniverse, Inc.

Burt, Steve. Wicked Odd: Still More Stories to Chill the Heart. Hagerman, Jessica, illus. 2006. 144p. (gr. 5 up). pap. 14.95 (978-0-9741407-2-8(4)) Burt Creations.

Burton, Tim. Melancholy Death of Oyster Boy: The Holiday Edition & Other Stories. 2007. (Illus.). 128p. (YA). (gr. 7 up). 19.95 (978-0-06-052649-8(1)) HarperCollins Pubs.

Butler, Ellis Parker. Pigs Is Pigs & Other Favorites. 2004. reprint ed. pap. 20.95 (978-1-4179-2471-4(3)) Kessinger Publishing, LLC.

Butterworth, Nick. The Whisperer. 2004. (Illus.). 31p. (J). **(*978-0-00-712017-8(6)*)** HarperCollins Pubs.

Bybee, Faith. Stories for Brittany II. 2002. 48p. (J). per. 9.95 (978-1-56167-750-4(7)) American Literary Pr.

Byers, Brian, illus. Noah's Babies Opposites & Offerings. 2005. 22p. (J). bds. 6.95 (978-0-9746440-6-6(4)) Virtue Bks.

Byers, Carla Rae. Life Sucks! I'm Stuck! Vol. 9: The Stories of Isee. l.t. ed. 2000. (Illus.). 22p. (J). 7.95 (978-1-930910-06-5(1)) Heyokah Publishing Co.

Cabot, Meg, et al. Shining On: 11 Star Author's Illuminating Stories. 2007. 176p. (YA). (gr. 7 up). 8.99 (978-0-385-73472-1(7) , Delacorte Bks. for Young Readers) Random Hse. Children's Bks.

Cabrera, Jane. Creaky Noise. 2004. (Popcorn & Banana Bob Ser.). (Illus.). 32p. 15.99 **(*978-0-689-86057-7(9)*)** Simon & Schuster, Ltd. GBR. *Dist:* Independent Pubs. Group.

Cabrol, Lauent. L' Enfant de la Montagne Noire. l.t. ed. 2001. (French Ser.). (Illus.). 30.99 (978-2-84011-432-1(1)) Ulverscroft Large Print Bks. GBR. *Dist:* Ulverscroft Large Print Bks., Ltd.

Caeden Goes to Daycare. 2004. (Illus.). 32p. (J). 5.95 (978-0-9759321-1-7(X)) Rascal Treehouse Publishing.

Caffrey-Kira, Albina. The White Tiger, & Other Children's Stories. 2006. 21.00 (978-0-8059-9023-2(2)) Dorrance Publishing Co., Inc.

Cagle, Erica. My Little Book of Stories. 2003. 40p. per. (978-1-59196-418-6(0)) Instantpublisher.com.

Cam, Philip, ed. Thinking Stories 1. 1998. (Illus.). 80p. (J). pap. 13.00 (978-0-86806-482-6(3)) Hale & Iremonger Pty., Ltd. AUS. *Dist:* Empire Publishing Service.

—Thinking Stories 2. 1998. (Illus.). 80p. (J). pap. 13.00 (978-0-86806-509-0(9)) Hale & Iremonger Pty., Ltd. AUS. *Dist:* Empire Publishing Service.

—Thinking Stories 3. (Illus.). 64p. tchr. ed. 28.00 (978-0-86806-633-2(8)); 1998. 80p. (J). pap. 14.00 (978-0-86806-632-5(X)) Hale & Iremonger Pty., Ltd. AUS. *Dist:* Empire Publishing Service.

Cambridge Young Writers Staff. I'm Telling You!, 6 vols., Pack. 2001. (Cambridge Reading Ser.). (Illus.). 80p. pap. 46.00 (978-0-521-01353-6(4)) Cambridge Univ. Pr.

—Tell You What!! Cambridge Young Writers Award 2001, Pack of 6. 2001. (Cambridge Reading Ser.). (J). pap. 41.00 (978-0-521-89207-0(4)) Cambridge Univ. Pr.

A Camel Called Bump-Along, 6 vols., Set B. 32p. (gr. 1-3). 31.50 (978-0-7802-8049-6(0)) Wright Group, The.

Cameron, Ann. More Stories Huey Tells. Toft, Lis, illus. 1999. 128p. (J). (gr. k-4). pap. 4.99 (978-0-679-88363-0(0) , Random Hse. Bks. for Young Readers) Random Hse. Children's Bks.

—More Stories Huey Tells. 1998. (J). pap. 4.99 (978-0-679-88576-4(5) , Knopf Bks. for Young Readers) Random Hse. Children's Bks.

—More Stories Huey Tells. 1999. (J). (978-0-606-16567-9(3)) Tandem Library Bks.

—More Stories Huey Tells. Toft, Lis, illus. 1999. 117p. (J). (ps-ps). per. 13.00 (978-0-613-10978-9(3)) Tandem Library Bks.

Camp Sing-Along. 1998. (J). 9.95 incl. audio (978-1-887120-02-9(5)) Production Assocs., Inc.

Campbell, Bebe Moore. Stompin' at the Savoy. Yarde, Richard, illus. 2006. 40p. (J). (gr. 1-4). 16.99 (978-0-399-24197-0(3) , Philomel) Penguin Group (USA) Inc.

Campbell, Judith. Let's Talk about It: Stories about Sensitive Issues, Dilemmas & Ethical Decision Making. Howard, Joanne, ed. Buckman, Frimma, illus. l.t. ed. 1998. 64p. (J). (gr. 2-6). pap. 10.00 (978-1-891180-51-4(7)) Campbell & Lockwood Pubs.

Campbell, Peggy, et al. How Did We Get Here? & Other Stories. Brown, Clovis et al, illus. 2002. (Doctor Bird Reading Ser.). 39p. (J). pap. (978-976-637-093-0(1)) Randle, Ian Pubs.

Candle in the Attic. 2001. (Illus.). 90p. (J). per. 8.00 (978-0-9715069-0-9(6)) Writers' Group of the Triad.

Candlewick Press Staff. Original Stories about Growing Up. Erlich, Amy, ed. 2001. (When I Was Your Age Ser.: Vol. 1). (Illus.). 160p. (J). (gr. 4-9). pap. 7.99 (978-0-7636-1034-0(8)) Candlewick Pr.

Candlewick Press Staff & LeapFrog Staff, compiled by. Once upon a Time. 2002. (J). (ps-2). 14.95 (978-1-58605-907-1(6) , LeapFrog Schl. Hse.) LeapFrog Enterprises, Inc.

Cantillon, Eli A. Amadeus: Four Stories in One. Stanley, Mandy, photos by. 1998. (Illus.). 62p. (J). (ps-k). 12.98 (978-1-58048-056-7(X)) Sandvik Publishing.

Caple, Kathy. Termite Trouble: Brand New Readers. Caple, Kathy, illus. 2005. (Illus.). 32p. (J). (ps-2). pap. 5.99 (978-0-7636-2573-3(6)) Candlewick Pr.

Captain, Cliff. Fables by the Sea, 2 vols. 2005. 145p. (J). Vol. 1. pap. (978-0-9766401-0-3(4)); Vol. 2. pap. (978-0-9766401-1-0(2)) Aenor Trust, The.

Card, Orson Scott, ed. Future on Ice. rev. ed. 1998. 432p. (YA). (gr. 7 up). 24.95 (978-0-312-86694-5(1) , Tor Bks.) Doherty, Tom Assocs., LLC.

Cardano, Sheila. Tail of A Squirrel & Other Tales Stor. 2006. pap. 28.99 **(*978-1-4259-4760-6(3)*)** AuthorHouse.

Cardenoso, Concha, adapted by. Cuentame un Cuento, No. 3. (SPA.). 96p. (J). (gr. k-3). (978-84-480-1144-4(9) , TM3382) Timun Mas, Editorial S.A. ESP. *Dist:* Lectorum Pubns., Inc.

Cardoso, Onelio Jorge. Caballito Blanco. 2003. (SPA.). 78p. (978-84-85334-48-3(5) , LG0124) Loguez Ediciones ESP. *Dist:* Lectorum Pubns., Inc.

Carey, Graham. The Tails Book. 2002. (Illus.). 132p. (J). reprint ed. 18.00 (978-1-930873-63-6(8)) Neumann Pr., The.

Carle, Eric. Der Klein Kafer Immerfrech. Carle, Eric, illus. 2000. (GER., Illus.). (J). pap. 15.95 (978-3-423-07924-2(X)) Deutscher Taschenbuch Verlag GmbH & Co KG DEU. *Dist:* Distribooks, Inc.

—Stories for All Seasons. Carle, Eric, illus. 1998. (Illus.). 96p. (J). (ps-3). 21.99 (978-0-689-82225-4(1)) Simon & Schuster Children's Publishing.

Carlson, Lavelle. Can a Toucan Hoot Too? A Phonemic Awareness Tale, 10 vols. Adams, Lucas, illus. 2003. 32p. (J). (ps-1). per. 16.95 (978-0-9725803-0-4(1)) Children's Publishing.

Carlson, Lori Marie. Moccasin Thunder: American Indian Stories for Today. 176p. (J). (gr. 9 up). 2005. 16.99 (978-0-06-623957-6(5)); 2000. lib. bdg. 16.89 (978-0-06-623959-0(1)) HarperCollins Pubs.

Carlson, M. La Oveja Perdida. 2004. Tr. of Lost lamb, The. 8.99 (978-0-7899-1240-4(6)) Editorial Unilit.

Carlson, Nancy. Loudmouth George Series. 2000. (Illus.). (J). (gr. k-3). pap. 29.95 incl. audio (978-0-87499-475-9(6)) Live Oak Media.

Carlyle, Linda Porter. A Child's Steps to Jesus. 2007. (J). **(*978-0-8163-2205-3(8)*)** Pacific Pr. Publishing Assn.

Carmichael, Bruce. The Little Path by Shadow Mountain. 2003. (J). per. 10.95 (978-1-58597-198-5(7)) Leathers Publishing.

Carrera, Jaume. Santi No Quiere Levantarse. Vila, Jordi, illus. 2002. (Santi No Quiere... Ser.).Tr. of Santi Doesn't Want to Get Up. (SPA & ENG.). 12p. (gr. k-2). pap. 2.95 (978-84-7864-577-0(2)) Combel Editorial, S.A. ESP. *Dist:* Independent Pubs. Group.

—Santi no quiere Obedecer. Vila, Jordi, illus. 2002. (Santi No Quiere... Ser.).Tr. of Santi Doesn't Want to Obey His Parents. (SPA & ENG.). 12p. (gr. k-2). pap. 2.95 (978-84-7864-580-0(2)) Combel Editorial, S.A. ESP. *Dist:* Independent Pubs. Group.

Carrero, Jorge & Cody, William. Buffalo Bill. 2003. (Timeless Classics Ser.). (SPA., Illus.). 92p. (J). (gr. 5-8). pap. 12.95 (978-84-204-5778-9(7)) Santillana USA Publishing Co., Inc.

Cart, Michael. Necessary Noise: Stories about Our Families as They Really Are. Noruzi, Charlotte, illus. 256p. (J). 2003. (gr. 12 up). 15.99 (978-0-06-027499-3(9)); 2006. reprint ed. pap. 8.99 (978-0-06-051437-2(X) , HarperTeen) HarperCollins Pubs.

Cart, Michael, ed. Tomorrowland: Ten Stories about the Future. 1999. 198p. (YA). (gr. 6-12). pap. 15.95 (978-0-590-37678-5(0)) Scholastic, Inc.

Carter, Alden R. Love, Football, & Other Contact Sports. 2006. 192p. (J). 16.95 (978-0-8234-1975-3(4)) Holiday Hse., Inc.

Cartoon Network Staff. Bubbles. 1999. (PB & J Noodle Stories Ser.). 32p. (J). pap. 3.99 (978-0-7868-4326-8(8)) Disney Pr.

Carus, Marianne, ed. Fire & Wings: Dragon Tales from East & West. Mistry, Nilesh, illus. 2002. ix, 146p. (J). (gr. 4-7). 17.95 (978-0-8126-2664-3(8)) Cricket Bks.

—That's Ghosts for You: 13 Scary Stories. Xuan, YongSheng, illus. 2000. viii, 134p. (J). (gr. 4-7). 15.95 (978-0-8126-2675-9(3)) Cricket Bks.

Carvajal, Victor. Como un Salto de Campana. Guzman, Catalina Guevara, illus. 2003. (SPA.). 143p. pap. 10.95 (978-956-270-001-6(1)) Santillana USA Publishing Co., Inc.

—Cuentatrapos. (Barco de Vapor). (SPA.). 120p. (YA). (gr. 5-8). (978-84-348-1606-0(7) , SM0595) SM Ediciones.

—Mamire, el Ultimo Rino. Osorio, Eduardo, illus. 2003. (SPA.). 110p. (J). (gr. 5-8). pap. 10.95 (978-956-239-020-0(9)) Santillana USA Publishing Co., Inc.

Carver, Peter, ed. The Blue Jean Collection. 2004. 224p. mass mkt. (978-0-920633-94-6(3)) Thistledown Pr., Ltd.

—Close-Ups: Best Stories for Teens. 2000. 224p. (YA). (gr. 5 up). pap. (978-0-88995-200-3(0)) Red Deer Pr.

—Notes Across the Aisle: Young Adults Fiction Anthology. 2004. 188p. pap. (978-1-895449-45-7(6)) Thistledown Pr., Ltd.

—Opening Tricks. 2004. 177p. pap. (978-1-895449-78-5(2)) Thistledown Pr., Ltd.

Carville, Declan. The Fairy Glen. (Illus.). 36p. pap. 7.95 (978-0-9538222-3-2(0)) Discovery Pubns. GBR. *Dist:* Irish Bks. & Media, Inc.

Casalderrey, Fina. La Abuela No Quiere Comer. Lopez Dominguez, Xan, illus. 2003. (Caballo Alado Ser.). (SPA & ENG.). 24p. 6.95 (978-84-7864-662-3(0)) Combel Editorial, S.A. ESP. *Dist:* Independent Pubs. Group.

—La Abuela Tiene una Medicina. Lopez Dominguez, Xan, illus. 2003. (Caballo Alado Ser.). (SPA & ENG.). 24p. 6.95 (978-84-7864-661-6(2)) Combel Editorial, S.A. ESP. *Dist:* Independent Pubs. Group.

—El Abuelo es Sabio. Lopez Dominguez, Xan, illus. 2003. (Caballo Alado Ser.). (SPA & ENG.). 24p. 6.95 (978-84-7864-664-7(7)) Combel Editorial, S.A. ESP. *Dist:* Independent Pubs. Group.

—El Abuelo Sale de Paseo. Lopez Dominguez, Xan, illus. 2003. (Caballo Alado Ser.). (ENG & SPA.). 24p. 6.95 (978-84-7864-663-0(9)) Combel Editorial, S.A. ESP. *Dist:* Independent Pubs. Group.

S

Caster, Harriet. Fat Puss & Slimpup. (Illus.). 96p. (J). 7.95 (978-0-14-036631-0(8)) Penguin Bks., Ltd. GBR. *Dist:* Trafalgar Square Publishing.

Cather, Willa. Willa Cather. Balkovek, James, illus. 2004. (Great American Short Stories Ser.). 80p. (J). lib. bdg. 23.33 (978-0-8368-4251-7(0)) Stevens, Gareth Inc.

Cattell, James. Albuman's Quest. Davidson, Dorelle, illus. 2002. 32p. (J). (978-0-7344-0166-3(3) , Lothian Bks.) Hachette Livre Australia.

Catuncan, Cheryl & Bacani, Julienne. An Awesome, Amazing, Awe-Inspiring Anthology. 2002. 114p. (J). pap. 10.95 (978-0-595-21489-1(4) , Writers Club Pr.) iUniverse, Inc.

Cedarmont, Ninos. Cantemos y Juguemos. 1999. (SPA.). 7.99 (978-0-7601-2853-4(7)) Brentwood Music, Inc.

—Cantos Escolares. 1999. (SPA.). 7.99 (978-0-7601-2855-8(3)) Brentwood Music, Inc.

—Cantos Pre-Escolares. 1999. (SPA.). 7.99 (978-0-7601-2856-5(1)) Brentwood Music, Inc.

Celebrated A Staff. Story Parade: A Collection of Modern Stories for Boys & Girls. 2005. reprint ed. pap. 33.95 (978-1-4191-1378-9(X)) Kessinger Publishing, LLC.

Challenger, Robert James. Grizzly's Home: And Other Northwest Coast Children's Stories. 2005. (Illus.). 48p. pap. 9.95 (978-1-894384-94-0(6)) Heritage Hse. Publishing Co., Ltd. CAN. *Dist:* Midpoint Trade Bks., Inc.

—Nature's Circle: And Other Northwest Coast Children's Stories. 2004. (Illus.). 48p. pap. 9.95 (978-1-894384-77-3(6)) Heritage Hse. Publishing Co., Ltd. CAN. *Dist:* Midpoint Trade Bks., Inc.

—Salmon's Journey: And More Northwest Stories. 2001. (Illus.). 48p. pap. (978-1-894384-34-6(2)) Heritage Hse. Publishing Co., Ltd.

Chang, Adam & Reetz, Kurt. Kid Beamster: Trapped by Evil Dr. I. Q. 2000. mass mkt. 4.50 (978-1-931179-29-4(8)); mass mkt. 8.95 (978-1-931179-40-9(9)) Long Hill Productions, Inc.

Channing, Blanche Mary. Zodiac Stories. 2006. pap. 30.95 (*978-1-4286-3675-0(7)) Kessinger Publishing, LLC.

Chaucer, Geoffrey. The Pardoner's Tale. (Illus.). 48p. (978-0-7502-3670-6(1) , Hodder & Stoughton) Hodder General Publishing Division.

Chaudhuri, Sukanta, ed. The Oxford India Illustrated Children's Tagore. 2006. (Illus.). 130p. 13.95 (*978-0-19-568417-9(6)) Oxford Univ. Pr., Inc.

Cheyney, Arnold. Legends of Arts. 2007. 128p. pap. (*978-1-59647-137-5(9)) Good Year Bks.

A Chicago Winds Set, 6 vols. 32p. (gr. 1-3). 26.50 (978-0-7802-8047-2(4)) Wright Group, The.

Chidebelu-Eze, Obi. The Tales of Tortoise: Inspirtional Words of Wisdom. 2005. (Illus.). 76p. (J). 16.00 (978-0-9766578-0-4(5)) Dove Publishing, Inc.

Chidley, Howard J. FiftyTwo Story Talks to Boys & Girls D. 2007. pap. (*978-1-4065-1446-9(2)) Dodo Pr.

Child, L. Maria. The Magician's Show Box & Other Stories. 2007. (ENG.). 124p. per. (*978-1-4065-1354-7(7)) Dodo Pr.

Child, Lydia Maria. The Magician's Show Box & Other Stories. 2004. reprint ed. pap. 19.95 (978-1-4191-7122-2(4)); pap. 1.99 (978-1-4192-7122-9(9)) Kessinger Publishing, LLC.

The Children's Portion. 2006. 168p. pap. 11.99 (*978-1-4264-5116-4(4)); 184p. pap. 14.99 (*978-1-4264-5417-2(1)) BiblioBazaar.

Chodzin, Sherab. Wisdom of the Crows & Other Buddhist Tales. 1998. (gr. 3-6). lib. bdg. 30.35 (978-0-613-70736-7(2)) Tandem Library Bks.

Christ at the Coffee Shop. 2004. lib. bdg. (978-0-9747425-0-2(3) , 09747425) Tranquility Ranch Publishing.

Christmas Is Coming. 2003. (J). 6.99 (978-1-59384-012-9(8)) Parklane Publishing.

Christophersen, Jane. Kakadu Calling: Stories for Kids. 2007. 64p. pap. 11.95 (*978-1-921248-00-9(9)) Magabala Bks. AUS. *Dist:* International Specialized Bk. Services.

Chronicle Books. Adventure Stories That Will Thrill You. 2001. (Reading Rainbow Readers Ser.). (Illus.). 64p. (J). pap. 3.99 (978-1-58717-102-4(3) , SeaStar Bks.) Chronicle Bks. LLC.

Chronicle Books Staff, contrib. by. Christmas Miniclassics. 2005. (J). 95.40 (978-0-8118-9877-5(6)) Chronicle Bks. LLC.

Chung, Jenny. A Subtler Shade: Poems in Prose. 2007. 60p. per. 8.95 (*978-0-595-45997-1(8)) iUniverse, Inc.

Civardi, Anne. Cambiarse de Casa. (SPA.). 16p. (J). 4.50 (978-84-7655-125-7(8)) Plaza Joven, S.A. ESP. *Dist:* AIMS International Bks., Inc.

Civardi, Anne, et al. More Nightlights: Stories for You to Read to Your Child to Encourage Calm, Confidence & Creativity. 2007. (Illus.). 144p. pap. 14.95 (978-1-84483-407-5(7)) Duncan Baird Pubs. GBR. *Dist:* Sterling Publishing Co., Inc.

Clairmont, Patsy. 5 Cheesy Stories: About Friendship, Bravery, Bullying, & More. 2007. (Tails from the Pantry Ser.). 144p. (J). 14.99 (*978-1-4003-1042-5(3)) Nelson, Thomas Inc.

Clark, Emma Chichester. No mas Besos! (SPA.). (J). 8.95 (978-958-04-6884-4(2)) Norma S.A. COL. *Dist:* Distribuidora Norma, Inc.

Clarke, J. Erskine. Chatterbox for 1927. 2005. pap. 30.95 (978-1-4179-8685-9(9)) Kessinger Publishing, LLC.

—Chatterbox For 1928. 2005. reprint ed. pap. 30.95 (978-1-4179-8686-6(7)) Kessinger Publishing, LLC.

Clasicos Argentinos. (Clasicos Juveniles Coleccion). (SPA.). (YA). (gr. 5-8). pap. (978-950-11-1409-6(0) , SG7924) Sigmar ARG. *Dist:* Lectorum Pubns., Inc.

Clasicos de Amor. (Clasicos Juveniles Coleccion). (SPA.). (YA). (gr. 5-8). pap. (978-950-11-1278-8(0) , SG4719) Sigmar ARG. *Dist:* Lectorum Pubns., Inc.

Clasicos de Animales. (Coleccion Clasicos Juveniles). (YA). (gr. 5-8). pap. (978-950-11-1579-6(8) , SG1714) Sigmar ARG. *Dist:* Lectorum Pubns., Inc.

Clasicos de Humor. (Coleccion Clasicos Juveniles). (SPA.). (YA). (gr. 5-8). pap. (978-950-11-1549-9(6) , SG30754) Sigmar ARG. *Dist:* Lectorum Pubns., Inc.

Classic Children's Tales. 2005. (ENG.). 912p. pap. (*978-1-84022-063-6(5)) Wordsworth Editions, Ltd.

Clawson, Kimberly. Fun O' Licious. Bellomy, Gail, illus. 2007. (ENG.). 56p. per. 12.95 (*978-1-4241-5556-9(8)) PublishAmerica, Inc.

Clay, Beatrice. Stories from le Morte d'Arthur & the M. 2006. 78.99 (*978-1-4280-4717-4(4)); pap. 71.99 (*978-1-4280-4712-9(3)) IndyPublish.com.

Claybourne, Anna, retold by. Stories from Shakespeare. 2005. (Stories from Shakespeare Ser.). 192p. (J). 24.99 (978-0-7945-0912-5(6) , Usborne) EDC Publishing.

Cleary, Beverly. It's Fun to Be Five. 2000. (Illus.). (J). (978-0-606-18567-7(4)) Tandem Library Bks.

—It's Great to Be Eight. 2000. (Illus.). (J). (978-0-606-18568-4(2)) Tandem Library Bks.

—It's Super to Be Six! 2000. (Illus.). (J). (978-0-606-18570-7(4)) Tandem Library Bks.

—Ramona Empieza el Curso. 2003. (Ramona Collection). (SPA.). 144p. (J). 9.95 (978-84-239-8891-4(0)) Espasa Calpe, S.A. ESP. *Dist:* Planeta Publishing Corp.

—Ramona y Su Madre. 2003. (Ramona Collection). (SPA.). 108p. (J). 9.95 (978-84-239-9040-5(0)) Espasa Calpe, S.A. ESP. *Dist:* Planeta Publishing Corp.

Cleary, Beverly, et al. It's Super to Be Six! 2000. (Illus.). 64p. (J). (gr. 1-4). pap. 3.99 (978-0-590-97802-6(0) , Scholastic Paperbacks) Scholastic, Inc.

Clements, Andrew. Head of the Class: Frindle; the Landry News; the Janitor's Boy. Selznick, Brian, illus. 2007. 416p. (J). 17.99 (*978-1-4169-4974-9(7) , Aladdin) Simon & Schuster Children's Publishing.

Clugston-Major, Chynna. Inbetween Days, 3 vols. 2003. (Blue Monday Ser.: Vol. 3). (Illus.). 96p. (YA). pap. 9.95 (978-1-929998-66-1(X)) Oni Pr., Inc.

Clynes, Kate. Ali Baba. Anstey, David, illus. 2005. (ENG & SWA.). 32p. (J). pap. 12.95 (978-1-84444-429-8(5)) Mantra Lingua GBR. *Dist:* Mantra Publishing, Ltd.

Coates, Theresa. Imaginary Time of Life. 2007. 102p. pap. 10.95 (*978-0-7414-4067-9(9)) Infinity Publishing.

Codell, Esmé Raji. Sing a Song of Tuna Fish: Hard-to-Swallow Stories from Fifth Grade. Pham, LeUyen, illus. 2006. 304p. (gr. 3-7). reprint ed. pap. 5.99 (978-0-7868-3652-9(0)) Hyperion Pr.

Cofer, Judith Ortiz. Riding Low Through the Streets of Gold: Latino Literature for Young Adults. 2003. (gr. 7-12). lib. bdg. 24.55 (978-0-613-90253-3(X)) Tandem Library Bks.

Cohen, Leslie, et al. Jewish Love Stories for Kids: An Anthology of Short Stories. 2005. (Jewish Stories for Kids Ser.). 232p. (J). 16.95 (978-1-930143-45-6(1) , 3451); pap. 12.95 (978-1-930143-46-3(X) , 346X) Pitspopany Pr. (Devora Publishing).

Cohn, Don J., ed. Dawn of Wisdom: Selections from the Japanese Collection of the Cotsen Children's Library. 2000. (Illus.). 136p. 35.00 (978-0-9666084-4-1(5)) Cotsen Occasional Pr.

Cohn, Marvin. Tell Me A Story Gramps. 2007. 52p. pap. 12.95 (*978-1-4241-5075-5(2)) PublishAmerica, Inc.

Colbert, David. Los Mundos Magicos de Harry Potter: Mitos, Leyendas y Datos Fascinantes. Belaustegui, Ines et al, trs. 2005. (Escritura desatada Ser.). (SPA., Illus.). 232p. (J). (gr. 4-7). 17.95 (978-84-666-1034-6(0)) Ediciones B ESP. *Dist:* Independent Pubs. Group.

Colbert, Larry C. Insights from an Out-of-Sight Guy. 2005. 111p. per. 20.00 (978-0-9766329-0-0(X)) Driving Vision, Inc.

Colby, C. B., et al. Scary Stories for Halloween Nights. 2005. (Illus.). 96p. (J). (gr. k-17). pap. 5.95 (978-1-4027-2181-6(1)) Sterling Publishing Co., Inc.

Cole, Babette. El Libro de Etiqueta de Lady Lupina. 2003. (Babette Cole Ser.). (SPA.). (J). 18.95 (978-84-233-3337-0(X)) Ediciones Destino ESP. *Dist:* Planeta Publishing Corp.

Cole, Bob. Power Reading: Nail-Biters! 2. Morton, Vivian, illus. 2005. 94p. (J). (gr. 6 up). vinyl bd. 89.95 (978-1-883186-25-8(0) , PPNB2) National Reading Styles Institute, Inc.

Cole, Joanna & Calmenson, Stephanie. Stories, Poems, Jokes & Riddles about Dogs. 1999. (Give A Dog A Bone Ser.). (Illus.). 96p. (J). (gr. 2-5). pap. 7.99 (978-0-439-08708-7(2)) Scholastic, Inc.

Colfer, Eoin. The Eternity Code. 2005. (Artemis Fowl Ser.: Bk. 3). 446p. (YA). (gr. 5-17). mass mkt. 5.99 (978-0-7868-5628-2(9)) Hyperion Bks. for Children.

A Collection of Stories Inspired by My Grandchildren. 2005. (YA). per. (978-1-59872-111-9(9)) Instantpublisher.com.

Colman. Pearl Story Book A Collection of Tales O. 2006. pap. 87.99 (*978-1-4280-4925-3(8)) IndyPublish.com.

Comella, Maria Angeles & Seix, Merce. Una Tarde con Joan Oro. (SPA., Illus.). (J). (gr. 2-4). (978-84-261-3075-4(5) , JV8905) Juventud, Editorial ESP. *Dist:* Lectorum Pubns., Inc.

Coming of Age Vol. 1: Fiction about Youth & Adolescence. 2nd ed. Incl. 2nd ed. Emra, Bruce & McGraw-Hill Staff. 311p. (C). pap., stu. ed. 41.32 (978-0-8442-0361-4(0) , 9780844203614); Vol. 1. Coming of Age. Emra, Bruce, contrib. by. (J). (978-0-8442-0362-1(9) , C03629); 1999. Set stu. ed. 46.00 (978-0-8442-0360-7(2) , 9780844203607) Glencoe/McGraw-Hill.

Concha, Beatriz. Cuatro Milagros de Nochebuena. 1999. (YA). (978-956-240-286-6(X)) Arrayan Editores S.A.

Connelly, Peg & Kenniger, Harriet. Grannies' Shorts. 2003. per. 14.95 (978-0-9725229-0-8(5)) Schoolyard Pr.

Connolly, Brian A. Allegheny River Christmas & Other Stories. 2007. 56p. per. 20.95 (*978-1-58939-992-1(7)) Virtualbookworm.com Publishing, Inc.

Conrad, Pam. Our House. Selznick, Brian, illus. 10th anniv. ed. 2005. 160p. (J). (gr. 4-7). pap. 16.99 (978-0-439-74508-6(X) , Scholastic Pr.) Scholastic, Inc.

Conteh, Gerald. I Still Believe in Santa. 2007. 188p. per. 14.95 (*978-1-60264-014-6(9)) Virtualbookworm.com Publishing, Inc.

Cook, Gary W. Stories for Small Angels. 2007. (J). per. 10.99 (*978-1-59886-977-4(9)) Tate Publishing & Enterprises, L.L.C.

Cooke, Flora J. Nature Myths & Stories for Little Chil. 2006. pap. 19.95 (*978-1-4254-9629-6(6)) Kessinger Publishing, LLC.

Cooling, Wendy. The Puffin Book of Stories for Five-Year-Olds. (Illus.). 144p. (J). pap. 9.95 (978-0-14-037458-2(2)) Penguin Bks., Ltd. GBR. *Dist:* Trafalgar Square Publishing.

Cooper, Veronica E. It's Time for Nana's Stories. 2005. pap. 7.95 (978-0-533-14906-3(1)) Vantage Pr., Inc.

Corbett, Jim. The Second Illustrated Corbett. 2006. (Illus.). 220p. pap. 19.95 (978-0-19-568428-5(1)) Oxford Univ. Pr., Inc.

Corning, Spring Mary. Miss Elliot's Girls (Stories of Beasts. 2006. 32.99 (*978-1-4280-2822-7(6)) IndyPublish.com.

Cortazar, Julio. Todos los Fuegos, el Fuego. (SPA.). (J). 9.00 (978-958-04-6757-1(9)) Norma S.A. COL. *Dist:* Distribuidora Norma, Inc.

Coville, Bruce. A Glory of Unicorns. 1998. (J). pap. (978-0-590-95582-9(9)) Scholastic, Inc.

—Oddest of All. 2008. (Illus.). 176p. (YA). 16.00 (978-0-15-205808-1(7)) Harcourt Children's Bks.

—Odds Are Good: An Oddly Enough & Odder Than Ever Omnibus. 2006. (Illus.). 352p. (J). pap. 6.95 (978-0-15-205716-9(1) , Magic Carpet Bks.) Harcourt Children's Bks.

Cowley, Joy. Mrs. Wishy-Washy's Tub. (Story Box(R) Ser.). 8p. 20.95 (978-0-7802-9365-6(7)) Wright Group, The.

Cox, Judith. Daddy Bo Brown's Mysterious Village, Plus. 2005. 18.00 (978-0-8059-9869-6(1)) Dorrance Publishing Co., Inc.

Cox, Merry L. Death by Bookbag: A Collection of Middle School Stories. 1998. 64p. (J). (gr. 6 up). pap. 7.00 (978-1-884416-27-9(6)) A Press.

Coxon, Rachel. A Collection of Children's Stories. ed. 2005. (J). spiral bd. (978-0-9761675-3-2(0)) Storybook Acres.

Coy, Steven. Sandwich: Short Stories & Screenplays by Steven Coy. Saia, Karla, ed. Vaughan, Jeremy, illus. 2003. 229p. (YA). per. 10.00 (978-0-9743235-0-3(0)) Better Non Sequitur.

Craven, Georgina. Adventures & Rhymes with Grandmother. 2006. (Illus.). 76p. pap. (*978-1-84401-648-8(X)) Athena Pr.

Crews, Nina. A High, Low, Near, Far, Loud, Quiet Story. 1999. (Illus.). 24p. (J). (ps-3). 15.89 (978-0-688-16795-0(0)) HarperCollins Pubs.

Cribbs, Randy, narrated by. Tales from the Oldest City: Selected Readings Vol 1. 2005. (YA). cd-rom 8.95 (978-0-9725796-3-6(X)) OCRS, Inc.

Cross, Linda B. Lines from Linda. l.t. ed. 2003. 104p. (YA). per. 7.00 (978-0-9748591-2-5(5) , MSP) Main St Publishing, Inc.

Cross, Luther S. The Inside Out Porcupine: And Other Stories for Kids. 2001. (FaithBuilders for Kids Ser.: Vol. 5). Tr. of Fam039000. 96p. (J). (ps-3). reprint ed. pap. 4.99 (978-0-8010-6349-7(3) , Easy Object Sto) Baker Bks.

Croteau-Fleury, Marie-Danielle. Mais Qui Sont les Hoo? St. Aubin, Bruno, illus. 2002. (Premier Roman Ser.). (FRE.). 64p. (J). (gr. 1-4). pap. (978-2-89021-533-7(4)) Diffusion du livre Mirabel.

Crothers, Samuel McChord. The Children of Dickens. 1999. (J). pap. (978-0-689-83075-4(0) , Simon & Schuster Children's Publishing) Simon & Schuster Children's Publishing.

Crowe, Robert L. Children's Stories for ALmost Everyone. l.t. ed. 2006. Orig. Title: Children's Stories for Adults. 92p. (J). per. (*978-0-9707173-8-2(5)) Consortium Publishing Co.

Crowley, Catherine M. Apples, Ripe & Rosy, Sir & Other Sto. 2006. pap. 71.99 (*978-1-4280-1376-6(8)) IndyPublish.com.

Crutcher, Chris. Athletic Shorts: Six Short Stories. 2002. 208p. (J). pap. 6.99 (978-0-06-050783-1(7)) HarperCollins Pubs.

—Athletic Shorts: Six Short Stories. 2002. 194p. (J). (ps-7). per. 15.30 (978-0-613-58540-8(2)) Tandem Library Bks.

Cuentecitos: El Pajaro Azul.Tr. of Little Stories: The Blue Bird. (SPA.). 12p. (J). 3.98 (978-970-607-902-2(5)) Larousse, Ediciones, S. A. de C. V. MEX. *Dist:* Giron Bks.

Cuentos Egipcios. (SPA., Illus.). (YA). 11.95 (978-84-7281-068-6(2) , AF1068) Auriga, Ediciones S.A. ESP. *Dist:* Continental Bk. Co., Inc.

Cuentos, Mitos y Leyendas para Ninos de America Latina (Stories, Myths & Legends for Latin American Children) (SPA., Illus.). 72p. (J). 9.95 (978-958-04-0957-1(9) , NOR9609) Norma S.A. COL. *Dist:* Distribuidora Norma, Inc.

Cuentos Nicas. 2002. Tr. of Stories from Nicaragua. (SPA.). 96p. (YA). 7.95 (978-84-7884-068-7(0)) Popular, Editorial S.A. ESP. *Dist:* AIMS International Bks., Inc.

El Cuidado del Aire. (Coleccion Biblioteca Juvenil de Ecología). (SPA., Illus.). (YA). (gr. 5-8). pap. (978-958-04-2406-2(3) , 80424062) Norma S.A. COL. *Dist:* Lectorum Pubns., Inc.

Cunningham, Patricia M. & Hall, Dorothy, eds. True Stories from Four-Blocks Classrooms. 2001. (Four-Blocks Ser.). 256p. (gr. k-8). pap. 26.99 (978-0-88724-628-9(1) , CD-2411) Carson-Dellosa Publishing Co., Inc.

Currier Brileya, Elizabeth. Grandma B. 's Bedtime Stories. 2006. 68p. (J). pap. 8.39 (978-1-4116-9504-7(6)) Lulu.com.

Curry, Robert. Summer Melodies: A Trio of Stories for Middle-schoolers. 2005. 73p. pap. 14.95 (978-1-4137-5832-0(0)) PublishAmerica, Inc.

Curtiss, A. Phebe. Christmas Stories & Legends. 2006. 41.99 (*978-1-4280-1439-8(X)); pap. 34.99 (*978-1-4280-1437-4(3)) IndyPublish.com.

Cuxart, Bernardette, illus. Cuentame un Cuento, No. 4. (SPA.). 96p. (J). (gr. k-3). (978-84-480-1602-9(5) , TM8095) Timun Mas, Editorial S.A. ESP. *Dist:* Lectorum Pubns., Inc.

Cyr, Joe. Magical Trees & Crayons: Great Stories. 2006. (Illus.). pap. 9.95 (*978-0-9778525-6-7(3)) Peppertree Pr., The.

Czarnota, Lorna MacDonald. Medieval Tales: That Kids Can Read & Tell. 2000. (Illus.). 96p. (J). (gr. 3-7). 21.95 (978-0-87483-589-2(5)); pap. 12.95 (978-0-87483-588-5(7)) August Hse. Pubs., Inc.

D C Thomson Staff, ed. Animals & You Annual 2004. 2003. (Illus.). 128p. (J). 9.95 (978-0-85116-840-1(X)) Thomson, D.C. & Co., Ltd. GBR. *Dist:* APG Sales and Fulfillment.

—Bunty Annual for Girls 2004. 2003. (Illus.). 128p. (J). (ps-4). (978-0-85116-825-8(6)) Thomson, D.C. & Co., Ltd. GBR. *Dist:* APG Sales and Fulfillment.

Dahl, Felicity. Roald Dahl's Even More Revolting Recipes. Blake, Quentin, illus. Baldwin, Jan, photos by. 2001. 32p. (J). (gr. 3-5). 17.99 (978-0-670-03515-1(7) , Viking Juvenile) Penguin Group (USA) Inc.

Dahl, Roald. Charlie und die Schokoladenfabrik.Tr. of Charlie & the Chocolate Factory. (GER.). pap. 17.95 (978-3-499-21211-6(0)); 2000. (J). pap. 12.95 (978-3-499-20778-5(8)) Rowohlt Taschenbuch Verlag GmbH DEU. *Dist:* Distribooks, Inc.

—Los Cretinos, Level 4.4. Blake, Quentin, illus. 2001. (SPA.). 112p. (J). (gr. 3-5). 12.95 (978-84-204-4435-2(9)) Alfaguara, Ediciones, S.A.- Grupo Santillana ESP. *Dist:* Santillana USA Publishing Co., Inc.

—Los Cretinos. Blake, Quentin, illus. 2005. (SPA.). 103p. (J). (gr. 3-5). pap. 9.95 (978-968-19-0559-0(8)) Santillana USA Publishing Co., Inc.

—Skin & Other Stories. 2002. 224p. (YA). pap. 8.99 (978-0-14-131034-3(0) , Puffin) Penguin Group (USA) Inc.

—Skin & Other Stories. Dahl, Roald, illus. 2000. (Illus.). 224p. (YA). (gr. 7-12). 15.99 (978-0-670-89184-9(3) , Viking Juvenile) Penguin Group (USA) Inc.

—Skin & Other Stories. 2002. (gr. 7-12). lib. bdg. 17.60 (978-0-613-67122-4(8)) Tandem Library Bks.

—The Umbrella Man & Other Stories. 288p. 2004. (YA). pap. 7.99 (978-0-14-240087-6(4) , Puffin); 1998. (J). (gr. 7-12). 16.99 (978-0-670-87854-3(5) , Viking Juvenile) Penguin Group (USA) Inc.

—The Umbrella Man & Other Stories. 2000. (978-0-606-18461-8(9)) Tandem Library Bks.

—The Wonderful Story of Henry Sugar & Six More. 2000. 240p. (YA). (gr. 7-12). pap. 6.99 (978-0-14-130470-0(7) , Puffin) Penguin Group (USA) Inc.

—The Wonderful Story of Henry Sugar & Six More. Blake, Quentin, illus. 2001. 240p. (J). (gr. 4-8). 15.95 (978-0-375-81423-5(X) , Knopf Bks. for Young Readers) Random Hse. Children's Bks.

—The Wonderful Story of Henry Sugar & Six More. 2000. (978-0-606-18462-5(7)) Tandem Library Bks.

Daily, Don. Classic Children's Storybook Collection. 2006. (Illus.). 112p. 14.98 (978-0-7624-2727-7(2)) Running Pr. Bk. Pubs.

D'Allance, Mireille. What a Tantrum. 2005. (SPA., Illus.). 32p. (J). 15.99 (978-84-8470-115-6(8)) Corimbo, Editorial S.L. ESP. *Dist:* Iaconi, Mariuccia Bk. Imports.

Dalmatian Press Staff. Power Rangers Carry-along Stories: 6 Stoybooks in a Box! Spanish Edition. rev. ed. 2007. 144p. pap. 9.99 (*978-1-4037-3273-6(6)) Dalmatian Pr.

Dalmatian Press Staff, adapted by. A Little Princess. 2003. (Spot the Classics Ser.). 180p. (J). 4.99 (978-1-57759-559-5(9)) Dalmatian Pr.

Dalmatian Press Staff, creator. Strawberry Shortcake Berry Big Box of Coloring Fun! 2005. (J). (ps-7). 9.99 (978-1-4037-1262-2(X)) Dalmatian Pr.

Daly. Not So Fast, Songololo. (J). pap. 9.95 (978-0-14-056352-8(0)) Penguin Bks., Ltd. GBR. *Dist:* Trafalgar Square Publishing.

Dana, B. J. Tales of the Sugar Hollow Twins: And their very most favorite stories, Book #4. 2006. 100p. (J). per. 13.95 (*978-1-59453-870-4(0) , 3165, Airleaf Publishing) Airleaf Publishing & Bookselling.

Dance from the Heart & Other Stories. 2001. 44p. (J). 7.00 (978-0-9716704-1-9(2)) M & M Bk. Publishing Co.

Daniels, Susan & Vincent, Seth. Student Bylines Vol. 1: Anthology. 2003. 184p. (YA). pap. 13.95 (978-0-595-27133-7(2) , Writers Club Pr.) iUniverse, Inc.

Dann, Penny. Classic Treasury of Best-Loved Bedtime Stories. 2007. 56p. (J). 9.98 (978-0-7624-2425-2(7) , Courage Bks.) Running Pr. Bk. Pubs.

Darby, Joel, et al. Milestones. Grant, Lisa, ed. Day, Linda S., illus. l.t. ed. 2004. 32p. (J). 12.95 (978-0-9759579-0-5(2)) Denver Broncos.

Dasent, G. W. East o' the Sun & West o' the Moon. 2005. pap. 28.95 (978-1-4179-0435-8(6)) Kessinger Publishing, LLC.

D'Ath, Justin. Terrors of Nature. 2000. (gr. 7-12). lib. bdg. 10.95 (978-0-613-29095-1(X)) Tandem Library Bks.

Datlow, Ellen & Windling, Terri, eds. The Green Man: Tales from the Mythic Forest. Charles, Vess, illus. 2004. 400p. (YA). pap. 8.99 (978-0-14-240029-6(7) , Puffin) Penguin Group (USA) Inc.

Davies, Helen Emanuel & Maclean, Andrew. Siff a Saff: A Straeon Eraill. 2005. (WEL., Illus.). 63p. (978-0-86381-364-1(X)) Gwasg Carreg Gwalch.

Davies, Nicola. Stories from Abergelli Street. 2002. (Illus.). 48p. pap. 11.95 (978-1-84323-075-5(5)) Beekman Bks., Inc.

Davies, Robert, adapted by. Lit a Shuck for Texas: Adapted Louis l'Amour Short Stories Series. 2003. (Adapted Louis L'Amour Short Stories Ser.). (Illus.). 56p. (YA). (978-1-57035-983-5(0) , 233LIT) Sopris West Educational Services.

—Merrano of the Dry Country: Adapted Louis l'Amour Short Story Series. 2003. (Adapted Louis L'Amour Short Stories Ser.). (Illus.). 60p. (J). (978-1-57035-985-9(7) , 233MERRANO) Sopris West Educational Services.

Davis, Donald. Listening for the Crack of Dawn: A Master Storyteller Recalls the Appalachia. 2000. (gr. 7-12). lib. bdg. 21.05 (978-0-7857-2705-7(1)) Tandem Library Bks.

Davis, Guy. The Marquis Vol. 2: Intermezzo, 2 vols. 2003. (Illus.). 112p. pap. 11.95 (978-1-929998-74-6(0)) Oni Pr., Inc.

Davis, Raymond. Morals & Memories for Tomorrow. 2003. 55p. pap. 11.95 (978-1-59286-753-0(7)) PublishAmerica, Inc.

Davis, Richard Harding. The Red Cross Girl & Other Stories. 2004. reprint ed. pap. 1.99 (978-1-4192-7996-6(3)) Kessinger Publishing, LLC.

Davis, Verna. Little Troy. 2005. 25p. 16.95 (978-0-533-14366-5(7)) Vantage Pr., Inc.

Day, Ed D. Why Dogs Bark: And Other Tall Tales Told by Ted. Scott, Sarah Chamberlin, illus. 2006. (J). per. 12.95 (978-1-933002-20-0(4)) PublishingWorks.

A Day for JJ & Me Set B, 6 vols. 32p. (gr. 1-3). 31.50 (978-0-7802-8050-2(4)) Wright Group, The.

De Anda, Diane. Immortal Rooster & Other Stories. 1999. (gr. 3-6). lib. bdg. 18.75 (978-0-613-88762-5(X)) Tandem Library Bks.

de Fontaine, Jean. Fables. (FRE.). 482p. pap. 9.95 (978-2-266-12775-2(6)) Presses Pocket FRA. *Dist:* Distribooks, Inc.

De Lint, Charles. Waifs & Strays. 2004. 416p. (YA). (gr. 7 up). pap. 8.99 (978-0-14-240158-3(7) , Puffin) Penguin Group (USA) Inc.

De Lint, Charles, contrib. by. Waifs & Strays. 2004. 391p. (YA). (gr. 7-17). lib. bdg. 14.64 (978-0-606-30808-3(3)) Tandem Library Bks.

de Nihlsburgo, Igoriano. Cuentos de Mutantes para Ninos. 1999. (Stories for Children Ser.).Tr. of Mutant Stories for Kids. (SPA.). 125p. (J). 7.95 (978-970-643-195-0(0)) Selector, S.A. de C.V. MEX. *Dist:* Libros Sin Fronteras.

de Paola, Tomie. La Hermanita de Tommy. (Buenas Noches Coleccion).Tr. of Baby Sister. (SPA.). (J). (gr. 1-3). pap. 7.95 (978-958-04-4290-5(8)) Norma S.A. COL. *Dist:* Distribuidora Norma, Inc., Lectorum Pubns., Inc.

De Souza, Eunice. 101 Folktales from India. 2005. (Illus.). 350p. (YA). 14.00 (978-0-670-04967-7(0) , Penguin Global) Penguin Group (USA) Inc.

Dean, Jan. Harry & the Megabyte Brain. Blundell, Tony, illus. 1998. (Cambridge Reading Ser.). 32p. (gr. 2-6). pap. 9.00 (978-0-521-63742-8(2)) Cambridge Univ. Pr.

Deary, Terry. Read-It! Chapter Books: Historical Tales, 8 bks., Set. Flook, Helen, illus. Incl. Actor, the Rebel, & the Wrinkled Queen. 64p. lib. bdg. 19.95 (978-1-4048-1297-0(0)); Gold in the Grave. 64p. lib. bdg. 19.95 (978-1-4048-1270-3(9)); Magic & the Mummy. 64p. lib. bdg. 19.95 (978-1-4048-1271-0(7)); Maid, the Witch, & the Cruel Queen. 60p. lib. bdg. 19.95 (978-1-4048-1299-4(7)); Phantom & the Fisherman. 64p. lib. bdg. 19.95 (978-1-4048-1272-7(5)); Plot on the Pyramid. 64p. lib. bdg. 19.95 (978-1-4048-1273-4(3)); Prince, the Cook, & the Cunning King. 60p. lib. bdg. 19.95 (978-1-4048-1298-7(9)); Thief, the Fool, & the Big Fat King. 61p. lib. bdg. 19.95 (978-1-4048-1300-7(4)); (Illus.). (J). (ps-k). 2005. 159.60 (978-1-4048-1530-8(9)) Picture Window Bks.

—Top Ten Shakespeare Stories. Tickner, Michael, illus. 1999. (Top Ten Ser.). 192p. (J). (gr. 6-12). pap. 4.50 (978-0-439-08387-4(7)) Scholastic, Inc.

—Top Ten Shakespeare Stories. 1999. (gr. 5-8). lib. bdg. 12.40 (978-0-613-22508-3(2)) Tandem Library Bks.

Decary, Marie & Beshwaty, Steve. Un Vrai Chevalier n'A Peur de Rien. 2001. (Premier Roman Ser.). (FRE.). 64p. (J). (gr. 1-4). pap. (978-2-89021-432-3(X)) Diffusion du livre Mirabel.

Deighton, Jo, adapted by. Ali Baba & the Forty Thieves: Traditional Stories:Cinderella: The Elves & the Shoemaker. (Scheherezade Presents Ser.: No. 11). (Illus.). 48p. (J). pap. (978-1-85964-101-9(6) , Ithaca Pr.) Garnet Publishing, Ltd.

—Bacbouc the Lazy Tailor: Traditional Stories:Beauty & the Beast: The Red Shoes. (Scheherezade Presents Ser.: No. 12). (Illus.). 48p. (J). pap. (978-1-85964-102-6(4) , Ithaca Pr.) Garnet Publishing, Ltd.

—The Fisherman & the Wicked Genie: Traditional Stories-:The Shepherdess & the Chimney Sweep: Seven with One Blow. (Scheherezade Presents Ser.: No. 14). (Illus.). 48p. (J). pap. (978-1-85964-104-0(0) , Ithaca Pr.) Garnet Publishing, Ltd.

Del Amo, Montserrat. El Nudo. (SPA.). 94p. (YA). (gr. 5-8). (978-84-261-1691-8(4) , JV2941) Juventud, Editorial ESP. *Dist:* Lectorum Pubns., Inc.

Del Negro, Janice. Passion & Poison: Tales of Shape-Shifters, Ghosts, & Spirited Women. 2007. 64p. (YA). (gr. 6 up). 16.99 (***978-0-7614-5361-1(X)*** Cavendish, Marshall Corp.

del Rio, Ana Maria. La Historia de Manu (Manu's Story) Cardemil, Carmen, illus. 2003. (Coleccion Derechos Del Nino Ser.). (SPA.). 32p. (J). (gr. 3-5). pap. 7.95 (978-84-204-5845-8(7)) Santillana USA Publishing Co., Inc.

Delacre, Lulu. Cuentos Con Sazon. Delacre, Lulu, illus. 2001. Tr. of Stories with Season. (SPA.). 112p. (J). pap. 4.50 (978-0-439-22649-3(X) , SO0638, Scholastic en Espanol) Scholastic, Inc.

Delbanco, Andrew, ed. Edgar Allan Poe. DuBois, Gerard, illus. 2006. (Stories for Young People Ser.). 48p. (J). (gr. 6 up). 14.95 (978-1-4027-1515-0(3)) Sterling Publishing Co., Inc.

Deogratias Simba. The Mystery Door. 2005. (Illus.). 22p. pap. 9.95 (978-9987-417-21-6(3)) Mkuki na Nyoka Pubs. TZA. *Dist:* Michigan State Univ. Pr.

dePaola, Tomie. Tomie dePaola's Big Book of Favorite Legends. dePaola, Tomie, illus. 2007. 144p. (J). (ps). 14.99 (***978-0-399-25035-4(2)*** , Putnam Juvenile) Penguin Group (USA) Inc.

DeSantis, Debi. A Bunch of Giggles & Hugs. l.t. ed. 2005. (Illus.). 26p. (J). 12.95 (978-0-9770043-0-0(9)) New Global Publishing.

Deseret Book Company Staff, contrib. by. A Story to Tell: The Classic Book of Virtues for Children. 2nd ed. 2004. 508p. (J). 16.95 (978-1-59038-359-9(1)) Deseret Bk. Co.

Deskins, Charlotte H. Tales from Poplar Hollow. Allen, Dana K., illus. 2004. 104p. pap. (978-0-9753671-1-7(0)) Shamus B. Publishing.

DeSpain, Pleasant. The Emerald Lizard: Fifteen Latin American Tales to Tell in English & Spanish. Bell, Don, illus. 1999. (ENG & SPA.). 192p. (gr. 4-7). 21.95 (978-0-87483-551-9(8)) August Hse. Pubs., Inc.

Dev, Jenny Power. Gorby. 2001. (Illus.). 50p. (J). 13.90 (978-0-7541-1392-8(2)) Minerva Pr. GBR. *Dist:* Unity Distribution.

Dewey, Jennifer Owings. Family Ties: Raising Wild Babies. 1998. (Accelerated Reader Bks.). (Illus.). 80p. (J). (gr. 3-7). 15.95 (978-0-7614-5037-5(8) , Cavendish Children's Bks.) Cavendish, Marshall Corp.

Dexter, Anthony. The Adventures of Manny the Manatee. 2004. 45p. pap. 19.95 (978-1-4137-2751-7(4)) PublishAmerica, Inc.

Diamond Head High Series Pack, Nos. 1-3. 12.95 (978-1-57306-108-7(5)) Bess Pr., Inc.

Diaz, Gloria Cecilia. La Botella Azul. (SPA.). (J). 8.95 (978-958-04-6489-1(8)) Norma S.A. COL. *Dist:* Distribuidora Norma, Inc.

Diaz Granados, Jose Luiz. Cuentos y Leyendas de Colombia. (Torre de Papel Ser.). (SPA.). (J). (gr. 4 up). 8.95 (978-958-04-5127-3(3)) Norma S.A. COL. *Dist:* Distribuidora Norma, Inc.

Dickens, Charles. A Christmas Carol. 2001. (CliffsComplete Ser.). 192p. (J). pap. 9.99 (978-0-7645-8722-1(6)) Wiley, John & Sons, Inc.

—Cuento de Navidad. Innocenti, Roberto, illus. 2000. Tr. of Christmas Story. (SPA.). 152p. (J). 19.95 (978-84-264-3643-6(9)) Editorial Lumen ESP. *Dist:* Distribooks, Inc.

—La Pequena Dorrit. 2003. (Historias de Siempre Ser.). (SPA., Illus.). 92p. (J). pap. 10.95 (978-84-204-5725-3(6)) Santillana USA Publishing Co., Inc.

—La Pequena Dorrit. 2000. (SPA.). (gr. 5-8). lib. bdg. 19.90 (978-0-613-84234-1(0)) Tandem Library Bks.

Dickens, Charles, et al. Christmas Books & Stories. 2004. (YA). cd-rom, audio compact disk 25.00 (978-0-917466-15-1(2)) B & R Samizdat Express.

Dickinson, Asa Don. Good Cheer Stories Every Child Should Know. 2005. 339p. (J). (***978-1-59605-692-3(4)*** , Cosimo Classics) Cosimo, Inc.

Dickinson, Asa Don & Dickinson, Helen Winslow, eds. Patriotic Stories Every Child Should Know. 2005. reprint ed. pap. 30.95 (978-1-4179-0694-9(4)) Kessinger Publishing, LLC.

Dickinson, Asa Don & Skinner, Ada M. The Children's Book of Christmas Stories. 2004. reprint ed. pap. 24.95 (978-1-4191-5657-1(8)); pap. 1.99 (978-1-4192-5657-8(2)) Kessinger Publishing, LLC.

Dickinson, Peter. The Lion Tamer's Daughter & Other Stories. 1998. (978-0-606-13572-6(3)) Tandem Library Bks.

Dicks, Terrance. Star Quest. 2004. 256p. pap. 24.99 (978-1-84435-066-7(5)) Reynolds & Hearn GBR. *Dist:* Independent Pubs. Group.

Dines, Carol. Talk to Me: Stories & a Novella. 1999. (978-0-606-16451-1(0)) Tandem Library Bks.

Dingman, Vera. Aunt Vera's Bedtime Stories. Gittus, Mark, ed. Dingman, Rolland, illus. 2001. No. 6. 114p. per. 7.50 (978-0-9711814-6-5(2)); Vol. 1. 100p. (J). per. 7.50 (978-0-9711814-1-0(1)); Vol. 2. 93p. (J). per. 7.50 (978-0-9711814-2-7(X)); Vol. 3. 104p. (J). per. 7.50 (978-0-9711814-3-4(8)); Vol. 4. 129p. (J). per. 7.50 (978-0-9711814-4-1(6)); Vol. 5. 121p. (J). per. 7.50 (978-0-9711814-5-8(4)) Dingman, Vera.

—Aunt Vera's Bedtime Stories. 1999. 128p. (J). (gr. 1-6). 5.00 (978-0-7392-0325-5(8)) Morris Publishing.

Disney 365 Bedtime Stories. 2004. (Illus.). 368p. (ps-2). 19.99 (978-0-7868-3500-3(1)) Disney Pr.

Disney Book Block, 10 vols. 1999. (Illus.). (J). (978-0-7853-3646-4(X)) Publications International, Ltd.

Disney Press, ed. Happily Ever after Stories. rev. ed. 2007. (Disney Princess Ser.). 304p. (gr. k-17). 15.99 (***978-1-4231-0442-1(0)***) Disney Pr.

Disney Princess Super Activity Fun Storybook Collection. 2005. (J). (978-1-59487-168-9(X)) Artist Studios, Ltd.

Disney Staff. Stories to Tell a Three Year Old. 2005. (J). pap. (978-0-7868-4333-6(0)) Disney Pr.

Disney Storybook Collection. 2005. (J). (978-1-59487-135-1(3)) Artist Studios, Ltd.

Dixon, George. Pauses along the Trail. l.t. ed. 2002. (Illus.). 95p. pap. 9.95 (978-0-9721833-0-7(2)) Sleepy D Publishing.

Dobrin, Arthur. Love Your Neighbor: Stories of Values & Virtues. Rogers, Jacqueline, illus. 1999. 64p. (J). (ps-3). pap. 16.95 (978-0-590-04410-3(9)) Scholastic, Inc.

Don't Call Me Katie Rose. 2000. (Katie Rose/Stacy Belford Ser.). 304p. (YA). pap. 12.95 (978-1-930009-10-3(0)) Image Cascade Publishing.

Don't Cry Little Girl. 2000. (Tippy Parrish Story Ser.). (YA). (gr. 6-10). per. 12.95 (978-1-930009-21-9(6)) Image Cascade Publishing.

The Doomed & the Dead. 2006. (Ghost Stories Ser.). (Illus.). 128p. (J). (gr. 7-9). lib. bdg. 25.27 (978-0-8368-6822-7(6)) Stevens, Gareth Inc.

Dowley, T. El Viaje Maravilloso. 2003. Tr. of Amazing Escape. (SPA.). bds. 9.99 (978-0-7899-1117-9(5)) Editorial Unilit.

Doyle, Alfreda C. As Long As the Sun Do Shine. 1999. (Illus.). 20p. pap. 9.95 (978-1-56820-392-8(6)) Story Time Stories That Rhyme.

—Ideas Make People Great. 1999. (Illus.). 20p. pap. 12.95 (978-1-56820-393-5(4)) Story Time Stories That Rhyme.

Doyle, Malachy & Jones, Jac. Lake of the Shadows. 2002. (Illus.). 32p. pap. 12.95 (978-1-84323-076-2(3)) Beekman Bks., Inc.

Doyle, William. Tell Me A Story Please. 2006. pap. (***978-1-84426-387-5(8)***) Upfront Publishing Ltd.

Dozier, Kim. The Ear-Less Kingdom. Dozier, Ashlyn McCauley, illus. l.t. ed. 2003. (ENG.). 24p. (J). 7.50 (978-0-9745839-1-4(X) , Fun to Read Bks. with Royally Good Morals) MKADesigns.

—The Forgetful Princess. Dozier, Ashlyn McCauley, illus. 2nd l.t. ed. 2003. (ENG.). 24p. (J). 10.00 (978-0-9745839-0-7(1) , Fun to Read Bks. with Royally Good Morals) MKADesigns.

Drake, David. Cricket & the Flying Horse. 2002. (Cricket of Dew Drop Dell Ser.). (Illus.). 32p. (J). 3.49 (978-1-885631-67-1(7)) Hutchison, G.F. Pr.

—Tommy Powers & the Sage of the Calibrators. 2005. 236p. (J). pap. 14.99 (978-1-885631-89-3(8)) Hutchison, G.F. Pr.

—What Color Is Grass. 2002. (Cricket of Dew Drop Dell Ser.). (Illus.). 32p. (J). 3.49 (978-1-885631-68-8(5)) Hutchison, G.F. Pr.

Drake, Michael. The Wise Man in the Checkered Shirt. 2000. (J). pap. (978-1-929281-07-7(2)) Cornerstone Publishing & Distribution, Inc.

Die Drei Kleinen Schweinchen: The Family, The House, Verbs. 1999. (Lesen Leicht Germacht Ser.). (GER & ENG., Illus.). 24p. (J). (ps-5). pap. 7.95 (978-88-8148-245-0(2)) European Language Institute ITA. *Dist:* Distribooks, Inc., Midwest European Pubns.

Dreser, Elena. El Secreto del Sauce. Diez, Dalia Alvarado, illus. 2003. (SPA.). 44p. (J). (gr. 3-5). pap. 6.95 (978-968-19-0617-7(9)) Santillana USA Publishing Co., Inc.

Dube, Jasmine. Tu N'es Plus Seul, Nazaire. Daigle, Sylvie, illus. 2003. (Premier Roman Ser.). (FRE.). 64p. (J). (gr. 2-5). pap. (978-2-89021-286-2(6)) Diffusion du livre Mirabel.

Dubrovin, Barbara. Fantasy Fair: Bright Stories of Imagination. Dubrovin, Barbara, illus. 2007. (Illus.). 128p. (J). pap. 17.50 (978-0-9638339-6-9(0)) Storycraft Publishing.

Dubya, Jay. The Eighteen Story Gingerbread House. 2003. 172p. (J). 23.95 (978-1-58909-176-4(0)); pap. 15.95 (978-1-58909-177-1(9)) Bookstand Publishing.

Duchene-Marshall, Michele A. Charley Finds A Family. Marshall, Alan David, ed. Ousley, Clayton Gerard, photos by. l.t. ed. 2004. Orig. Title: Charley finds a Home. (Illus.). 20p. (J). spiral bd. 10.00 (978-0-9761675-2-5(2)) Storybook Acres.

Duey, K. & Bale, K. A. Salvados! Titanic. 2003. (Survival Ser.).Tr. of Survival! Titanic. (SPA.). (J). pap. 9.95 (978-0-9715256-4-1(1)) Planeta Publishing Corp.

Dugdale, John, concept. Jump at the Sun: An African American Picture Book Collection. 2001. (Illus.). 208p. (J). (ps-17). 16.99 (978-0-7868-0754-3(7) , Jump at the Sun) Hyperion Bks. for Children.

Dunbar, Joyce. Kingfisher Read-Aloud Storybook. 2000. (J). (978-0-606-19436-5(3)) Tandem Library Bks.

Duncan, Sharyn. The Mouse House & other Stories: You Are the Artist. 2004. 40p. (J). 9.95 (978-1-933002-04-0(2)) PublishingWorks.

Duncan Sings-Alone. Grandpa Sings-Alone Favorite Tales. 2000. (J). audio 11.95 (978-1-929590-03-2(2)) Two Canoes Pr.

Durant, Alan. Sports Stories. 2000. (Story Library). (Illus.). 221p. (J). pap. (978-0-7534-5192-2(1) , Kingfisher) Houghton Mifflin Co. Trade & Reference Div.

—Sports Stories. Kearney, David, illus. 2000. (Story Library). 224p. (J). (gr. 4-9). tchr. ed. 14.95 (978-0-7534-5322-3(3) , Kingfisher) Houghton Mifflin Co. Trade & Reference Div.

—Sports Stories. 2001. (978-0-606-21450-6(X)); 2000. (gr. 5-8). lib. bdg. 15.25 (978-0-613-67435-5(9)) Tandem Library Bks.

Earl, Guy. Good Times & Bad Times. 2001. 284p. (YA). pap. 15.95 (978-0-595-18721-8(8) , Writers Club Pr.) iUniverse, Inc.

East, Helen & Maddern, Eric. Espiritu del Bosque: Cuentos Sobre Arboles De Todo El Mundo. Marks, Alan, illus. 2003. (FRE & SPA.). 46p. 16.95 (978-84-89396-92-0(2)) Blume ESP. *Dist:* Independent Pubs. Group.

Eckhardt, Eleanor June. Elmer the First. 2d ed. 2001. (YA). 12.50 (978-0-9709986-0-6(0)) His Majesty's Pubns.

—Elmer the Hero. 2nd ed. 2001. 11.50 (978-0-9709986-2-0(7)) His Majesty's Pubns.

Edens, Cooper. Big Book of Little. 2006. (Illus.). 124p. (J). 19.95 (978-0-8118-5085-8(4)) Chronicle Bks. LLC.

Edgar Allan Poe Collection of Stories Student Packet, Gr. 9-12. 2004. (YA). (978-1-58130-510-4(9)) Novel Units, Inc.

Edgeworth, Maria. Barring Out, & Eton Montem: Stories for Children. fac. ed. 2002. 176p. pap. 15.95 (978-1-4021-9138-1(3) , Elibron Classics) Adamant Media.

Eggleton, Jill. The Hole in the Garden: Early Level Satellite Individual Title Six-Packs. (Sails Literacy Ser.). 16p. (gr. 1-2). 27.00 (978-0-7578-2932-1(5)) Rigby Education.

Egoak, Julia K. The Story Knife. Egoak, Julia K. & Nevak, Caroline, illus. l.t. ed. 1999. 8p. (J). (gr. k-3). pap. 14.50 (978-1-58084-076-7(0)) Lower Kuskokwim Schl. District.

—Yaaruissun. Egoak, Julia K. & Nevak, Caroline, illus. l.t. ed. 1999. Tr. of Story Knife. (ESK.). 8p. (J). (gr. k-3). pap. 14.50 (978-1-58084-077-4(9)); pap. 14.50 (978-1-58084-118-4(X)) Lower Kuskokwim Schl. District.

Elliott, Craig. Racer Buddies-Rematch at Richmond. Harper, William A, illus. 2005. (J). per. 12.95 (978-0-9746445-1-6(X) , 10000) Powerband, LLC.

Emmanuel, Francois. La Chambre Voisine. l.t. ed. 2002. (French Ser.). (FRE., Illus.). 223p. 30.99 (978-2-84011-467-3(4)) Ulverscroft Large Print Bks. GBR. *Dist:* Ulverscroft Large Print Bks., Ltd.

Emmy Takes a Census. 2000. 22p. (J). mass mkt. 14.95 (978-0-9706331-0-1(6)) Magician's Ink.

En la Corte del Rey Blas (In King Blas' Court) (SPA.). 24p. (J). 4.95 (978-84-246-1629-8(4)) La Galera, S.A. Editorial ESP. *Dist:* AIMS International Bks., Inc.

Ende, Michael. El Dragon y la Mariposa. De Horna, Luis, illus. 2003. (SPA.). 48p. (J). (gr. k-3). pap. 8.95 (978-84-204-3710-1(7)) Santillana USA Publishing Co., Inc.

English, D. N. Downtown Wanderings: Stories & Pictures of Downtown Jackson Tennessee. Galloway, Annette, ed. l.t. ed. 2002. (Illus.). 184p. per. 15.95 (978-0-9710470-0-6(6)) Main St Publishing, Inc.

Ennis, Scott. Ah Sunflower. 2004. 27p. (J). per. 7.99 (978-1-4116-0571-8(3)) Lulu.com.

Ensminger, Allan. A Storymaker's Dozen. 2001. 116p. (J). pap. 14.95 (978-1-886225-64-0(8)) Day of Grace Publishing Services.

The Entire World of SH & CH Book of Stories. 2004. per. 34.99 (978-0-9760490-2-9(3)) Say It Right.

Equipo Staff. Brebajes Magicos: Coleccion Tarantula. 1999. (SPA.). 14p. mass mkt. 6.95 (978-950-08-2084-4(6)) Atlantida ARG. *Dist:* Libros Sin Fronteras.

—Una Fabula para Cada Dia. 2001. Tr. of Fable for Each Day. (SPA.). 304p. (978-84-305-2255-2(7)) Lectorum Pubns., Inc.

—Libro de la Selva y Cuatro Cuentos Mas.Tr. of Jungle Book & Four Tales More. (SPA.). 48p. (J). 16.48 (978-84-305-9297-5(0)) Susaeta Ediciones, S.A. ESP. *Dist:* AIMS International Bks., Inc.

—Pinocho y Cuatro Cuentos Mas.Tr. of Piniccui & Four Tales More. (SPA.). 124p. (J). 16.48 (978-84-305-9296-8(2)) Susaeta Ediciones, S.A. ESP. *Dist:* AIMS International Bks., Inc.

—111 Refranes. 2001. Tr. of One Hundred Refrains. (SPA.). 132p. (978-84-305-8337-9(8)) Lectorum Pubns., Inc.

—365 Cuentos, uno para Cada Dia.Tr. of Three Hundred Sixty-Five Tales, One for Everyday. (SPA.). 304p. 29.98 (978-84-305-2252-1(2)) Susaeta Ediciones, S.A. ESP. *Dist:* AIMS International Bks., Inc.

Erdrich, Lise. Bears Make Rock Soup: And Other Stories. Fifield, Lisa, illus. 2002. 32p. (J). (gr. 1 up). 16.95 (978-0-89239-172-1(3)) Children's Bk. Pr.

Erickson, Arnold. Stories to Be Shared. 2006. 94p. (J). 40.00 (978-0-9700108-3-4(4)) Creative Well, The.

Erlwanger, Beatrice Bwalya. Tales from Kasama. 2001. (Illus.). 80p. pap. (978-9982-30-108-4(X)) Multimedia Pubns.

Eslava, Jorge. El Maromero. Shiroma, Aldo, illus. 2001. (Coleccion Derechos Del Nino Ser.). (SPA.). 32p. (J). (gr. 3-5). pap. 7.95 (978-84-204-5842-7(2)) Santillana USA Publishing Co., Inc.

Esopo. La Zorra Se Pasa de Lista. (Coleccion Fabulas y Cuentos Populares). (SPA.). 24p. (J). (gr. 2-4). (978-84-246-1566-6(2) , GL1066) La Galera, S.A. Editorial ESP. *Dist:* Lectorum Pubns., Inc.

Eudy, Ellen D. Mrs. Maxine Gorden. 2002. (J). per. 7.50 (978-0-9717574-0-0(2)) Eudy, Ellen.

Eureka! Stories of Amazing Discoveries. (Critical Reading Ser.). (YA). (gr. 6-12). pap. (978-0-8092-1249-1(8)) Jamestown.

The Evangeline Nicholas Collection: 1 Each of 16. (gr. 1-3). tchr. ed., stu. ed. 91.50 (978-0-322-00761-1(5)) Wright Group, The.

The Evangeline Nicholas Collection: 1 Each of 6. (gr. 1-3). 199.50 (978-0-7802-9517-9(X)) Wright Group, The.

The Evangeline Nicholas Collection Set A: 6 Each of 8. (gr. 1-3). 222.50 (978-0-7802-8056-4(3)) Wright Group, The.

The Evangeline Nicholas Collection Set A,B: 6 Each of 16. (gr. 1-3). tchr. ed., stu. ed. 456.50 (978-0-7802-9516-2(1)) Wright Group, The.

The Evangeline Nicholas Collection Set B: 6 Each of 8. (gr. 1-3). stu. ed. 235.50 (978-0-7802-8057-1(1)) Wright Group, The.

Evans, Alwyn, ed. Life Bytes. 2002. 152p. pap. 12.95 (978-1-86368-382-1(8)) Fremantle Pr. AUS. *Dist:* International Specialized Bk. Services.

Evans, Alwyn, et al. Monty's Tale. (Illus.). 16p. (J). pap. 7.49 (978-1-86368-139-1(6)) Fremantle Pr. AUS. *Dist:* International Specialized Bk. Services.

Evans, Douglas. Math Rashes & Other Classroom Tales. Di Fiori, Larry, illus. 2002. 112p. (J). pap. 4.50 (978-0-439-33902-5(2) , Scholastic Paperbacks) Scholastic, Inc.

—Math Rashes & Other Classroom Tales. 2001. (gr. 3-6). lib. bdg. 12.40 (978-0-613-53834-3(X)) Tandem Library Bks.

—Tales from W. T. Melon Elementary School. Di Fiori, Lawrence, illus. 1999. 144p. (J). (gr. 3-7). (978-1-886910-45-4(6) , Lemniscaat) Boyds Mills Pr.

S

Everglades Environmental Storybook: Coastal Creatures. l.t. ed. 1999. (Voices of the Earth Ser.: Vol. I). (Illus.). 48p. (J). (gr. k-4). pap. 6.95 (978-0-9666720-1-5(1)) Earthwing Pubns.

Ewart, Franzeska G. Shadowflight. 2001. (Illus.). 81p. (J). pap. 7.50 (978-0-7497-4380-2(8)) Egmont Bks., Ltd. GBR. *Dist:* Independent Pubs. Group.

A Expressway Jewels Set, 6 vols. 32p. (gr. 1-3). 26.50 (978-0-7802-8046-5(6)) Wright Group, The.

Fables & Tall Tales (Gr. 3-4) 2003. (J). (978-1-58232-072-4(1)) Bryan Hse. Pubs., Inc.

Fables of Bah Ya Bah. 2002. 40p. (J). pap., tchr. ed. 10.00 (978-1-932008-11-1(X)) Fine Media Group.

Fabra, Jordi Sierra. La Asombrosa Historia del Viajero de las Estrellas. (SPA.). (YA). 8.95 (978-958-04-6872-1(9)) Norma S.A. COL. *Dist:* Distribuidora Norma, Inc.

Fabregat, Antonio-Manuel. Los Cuentos de Mi Escuela. (SPA.). 128p. (J). (gr. 4-6). (978-84-216-1185-2(2), BU3866) Bruño, Editorial ESP. *Dist:* Lectorum Pubns., Inc.

Fabulas de Siempre. l.t. ed. Tr. of Traditional Fables. (SPA.). (J). 3.98 (978-84-7630-901-8(5)) Selector, S.A. de C.V. MEX. *Dist:* AIMS International Bks., Inc.

Faine, Edward Allan. More Little Ned Stories. 2003. 112p. (J). pap. 6.95 (978-0-9716911-2-4(6)) IM Pr.

Fairbairn, John. Green Slime. Allen, Rosemary, illus. 96p. pap. 9.95 (978-0-7022-2488-1(X)) Univ. of Queensland Pr. AUS. *Dist:* International Specialized Bk. Services.

Falco, Joanna. Diana, the Angel, & the Holy Grail. 2007. 52p. (J). per. 8.95 ***(978-0-595-45733-5(9))*** iUniverse, Inc.

Falconer, Ian. Olivia Salva el Circo. 2002. (Olivia Ser.). (SPA.). 36p. 9.99 (978-968-16-6550-0(3)) Fondo de Cultura Economica USA.

Falconi, Maria Ines. Hasta el Domingo. (Torre de Papel Ser.). (SPA.). (YA). (gr. 6 up). 8.95 (978-958-04-2902-9(2)) Norma S.A. COL. *Dist:* Distribuidora Norma, Inc.

Falletta, Bernadette & Lewis, Marla. We Love to Read Stories & Songs. 2005. 27p. (J). 14.95 (978-1-4116-4734-3(3)) Lulu.com.

Family Stories: Jumbo Packs. (gr. k-2). 157.08 (978-0-7362-0051-6(7)) Hampton-Brown Bks.

Fantasy Collection. (Fiction Collections). 184.69 (978-1-59889-040-2(9)) Stone Arch Bks.

Farina von Buchwald, Martin & Prado Farina, Gabriela. The Joy of Giving. Avendano, Dolores, illus. Testino, Mario et al, photos by. 2005. 89p. (J). 18.00 (978-0-9777266-0-8(6)) von Buchwald, Martin Farina.

Farjeon, Eleanor. The Little Bookroom. Ardizzone, Edward, illus. 2003. (New York Review Children's Collection). 336p. (J). 18.95 (978-1-59017-048-9(2), NYR Children's Collection) New York Review of Bks., Inc., The.

Farre, Lluis. Buenas Noches, Victor. 2002. (Caballo Alado Ser.).Tr. of Good Night, Victor. (SPA & ENG., Illus.). 24p. pap. 4.95 (978-84-7864-435-3(0)) Combel Editorial, S.A. ESP. *Dist:* Independent Pubs. Group, Libros Sin Fronteras.

Faundez, Anne, ed. Little Red Riding Hood. 2004. (QEB Start Writing Ser.). (Illus.). 24p. (J). lib. bdg. 15.95 (978-1-59566-020-6(8)) QEB Publishing Inc.

Fedele, Mario. Stories for a Stormy Night: Volume I. 2004. 168p. pap. 19.95 (978-1-4137-4744-7(2)) PublishAmerica, Inc.

—Stories for a Stormy Night II: Featuring Two Novellas: Bugs: Runaway. 2005. 165p. pap. 19.95 (978-1-4137-4745-4(0)) PublishAmerica, Inc.

Federici, Elaine. The Rose Tales for Children: Inspirational Collection of Stories for Childen. 2000. (J). pap. 10.95 (978-1-930574-03-8(7)) Rose International Publishing Hse., Inc.

Ferro, Beatriz. Arriba el Telon. (SPA.). (YA). 8.95 (978-958-04-7263-6(7)) Norma S.A. COL. *Dist:* Distribuidora Norma, Inc.

Fiedler, Christamaria. El Verano de los Animales. Kessler, Siglint, illus. 2003. (SPA.). 155p. (J). (gr. 5-8). 9.95 (978-968-19-0706-8(X)) Aguilar, Altea, Taurus, Alfaguara, S.A. de C.V MEX. *Dist:* Santillana USA Publishing Co., Inc.

—El Verano de los Animales. 2000. (SPA., Illus.). 160p. (J). 15.95 (978-84-204-4819-0(2)) Alfaguara, Ediciones, S.A.- Grupo Santillana ESP. *Dist:* Santillana USA Publishing Co., Inc.

Field, Eugene. Little Book of Profitable Tales. 2006. 25.99 ***(978-1-4280-2741-1(6))*** IndyPublish.com.

Fiesta de Cuentos. (Coleccion Estrella). (SPA., Illus.). 64p. (J). 14.95 (978-950-11-0016-7(2), SGM016) Sigmar ARG. *Dist:* Continental Bk. Co., Inc.

Figueroa, Acton. Can't Take a Joke. Rousseau, Craig, illus. 2005. (Teen Titans Ser.). 32p. (J). (ps-3). pap. 3.99 (978-0-439-75476-7(3), Scholastic Paperbacks) Scholastic, Inc.

First Stories (Gr. K-1) 2003. (J). (978-1-58232-035-9(7)) Bryan Hse. Pubs., Inc.

Fisher, Karin, adapted by. Fish, Fox, & Then Some: Seven Aesop's Fables Retold Using One-syllable Words for the Barton Reading & Spelling System. 2003. (J). pap. 7.95 (978-0-9744343-1-5(0), SA-302) Bright Solutions for Dyslexia, LLC.

Fisher, Lillian M. Feathers in the Wind. 155p. (YA). (gr. 4-8). 9.99 (978-0-88092-438-2(1)) Royal Fireworks Publishing Co.

Fisher-Price Hardcover Ready Reader Storybooks. 2004. (J). (978-0-7666-1185-6(X), 39250); (978-0-7666-1186-3(8), 39250); (978-0-7666-1187-0(6), 39250); (978-0-7666-1188-7(4), 39250); (978-0-7666-1189-4(2), 39250); (978-0-7666-1190-0(6), 39250); (978-0-7666-1191-7(4), 39250); (978-0-7666-1192-4(2), 39250); (978-0-7666-1193-1(0), 39250); (978-0-7666-1194-8(9), 39250) Modern Publishing.

Fisher-Price Ready Readers: Stage 1 Preschool-Grade 1. 2004. (Illus.). 304p. (J). pap. (978-0-7666-0823-8(9), 11830) Modern Publishing.

Fisher-Price Ready Readers: Stage 2 Grades 1-3. 2004. (Illus.). 304p. (J). pap. (978-0-7666-0824-5(7), 11830) Modern Publishing.

Flake, Sharon G. Who Am I Without Him? Short Stories about Girls & the Boys in Their Lives. 2004. 176p. (gr. 7-17). 15.99 (978-0-7868-0693-5(1), Jump at the Sun) Hyperion Bks. for Children.

Flanagan, Jim. The School of Scary Stories. 2006. (Illus.). 125p. (J). per. 12.95 (978-0-9766666-5-3(0)) Arcadian Hse.

Fleischman, Paul. Graven Images. Ibatoulline, Bagram, illus. 128p. (J). (gr. 6-9). 2005. 5.99 (978-0-7636-2984-7(7)); 2006. reprint ed. 16.99 (978-0-7636-2775-1(5)) Candlewick Pr.

Fleischman, Sid. Here Comes McBroom! Three More Tall Tales. 1999. (J). (gr. 2-5). 21.75 (978-0-8446-7029-4(4)) Smith, Peter Pub., Inc.

—Here Comes Mcbroom! Three More Tall Tales. 1998. (Illus.). 79p. (J). (ps-k). lib. bdg. 13.00 (978-0-613-11625-1(9)) Tandem Library Bks.

—Here Comes McBroom! Three More Tall Tales. Blake, Quentin, illus. 1998. 80p. (J). (gr. 2-5). reprint ed. pap. 4.99 (978-0-688-16364-8(5)) HarperCollins Pubs.

Fonseca, Migdalia. Quitate Esa Gorra! Martinez, Enrique, illus. 2001. (Coleccion Derechos Del Nino Ser.). (SPA.). 32p. (J). (gr. 3-5). pap. 7.95 (978-84-204-5830-4(9)) Santillana USA Publishing Co., Inc.

Forrestal, Elaine. Glass Full of Giggles. 2002. (Illus.). 72p. pap. 12.95 (978-1-86368-358-6(5)) Fremantle Pr. AUS. *Dist:* International Specialized Bk. Services.

Fort, Gloria. La Bruja Megacirio. 2000. (Dulces Suenos Collection). (SPA., Illus.). 10p. (J). 7.95 (978-84-348-6258-6(1)) SM Ediciones ESP. *Dist:* Distribooks, Inc.

Foster, Cassandra. Do You Know Us? A Collection of Short Stories. 2006. (Illus.). 48p. (YA). per. 8.00 (978-0-9778641-1-9(1)) Smith, Mildred C.

—A Good Story: A Collection of Short Short Stories. 2006. (Illus.). 37p. (YA). per. 8.00 (978-0-9778641-0-2(3)) Smith, Mildred C.

Four Year Olds. Date not set. 96p. 7.98 (978-0-7525-8710-3(2)) Parragon, Inc.

Frank, Jeffrey & Frank, Diana, trs. from DAN. The Stories of Hans Christian Andersen: A New Translation from the Danish. Frolich, Lorenz & Pederson, Vilhelm, illus. 2003. 304p. tchr. ed. 30.00 (978-0-618-22456-2(4)) Houghton Mifflin Co. Trade & Reference Div.

Freeman, Don. Corduroy & Company: A Don Freeman Treasury. 2001. (Corduroy Ser.). (Illus.). 128p. (J). (gr. k-1). 25.00 (978-0-670-03510-6(6), Viking Juvenile) Penguin Group (USA) Inc.

Freese, Thomas, reader. Fog Swirler & 11 Other Ghost Stories. 2006. (J). Pt. 1. cd-rom 13.95 ***(978-0-9789511-0-8(7));*** Pt. 2. cd-rom 13.95 ***(978-0-9789511-1-5(5));*** Pt. 3. cd-rom 13.95 ***(978-0-9789511-2-2(3))*** Illumination Pubns.

—Shaker Ghost Stories from Pleasant Hill, KY Audio Book/cd. 2006. (J). cd-rom 17.95 ***(978-0-9789511-3-9(1))*** Illumination Pubns.

Friederich, Uve. The World of Bridgett & Emily. Fitzpatrick, Meg & Ravenhill, John A., illus. 2004. 41p. (J). mass mkt. 8.95 (978-0-9747532-4-9(6)) Taylor-Dth Publishing.

Friend, R. Time Out at Home. 2005. (Down on Friendly Acres Ser.: 2). (J). lib. bdg. (978-0-9743627-4-8(3)); per. 5.95 (978-0-9743627-1-7(9)) Sunflower Seeds Pr.

Friend, Rachel, et al. The Yew Tree Collection. 2002. 276p. pap. 15.95 (978-0-595-21465-5(7), Writers Club Pr.) iUniverse, Inc.

Friesen, Bernice. The Seasons Are Horses. 2004. 151p. pap. (978-1-895449-40-2(5)) Thistledown Pr., Ltd.

Fruchter, Yaakov. Best of Olomeinu - Series 2: Stories for All Year 'Round. 2003. 136p. 13.99 (978-1-57819-398-1(2), BO1H); pap. 10.99 (978-1-57819-399-8(0), BO1P) Mesorah Pubns., Ltd.

Fu, Shelley. Hoyi the Archer & other Classic Chinese Tales. Abboreno, Joseph F. & Fu, Sherwin, illus. 2005. 144p. (J). (gr. 4-8). reprint ed. 22.00 (978-0-7567-9713-3(6)) DIANE Publishing Co.

Fuchs, Menucha. A Coat for Two & Other Stories. Miri, illus. 2000. (Children's Learning Ser.: Vol. 9). 48p. (J). (gr. k-5). pap. 4.95 (978-1-880582-58-9(9)) Judaica Pr., Inc., The.

—Efrayim Saves the Day & Other Stories. Miri, illus. 2000. (Children's Learning Ser.: Vol. 10). 48p. (J). (gr. k-5). pap. 4.95 (978-1-880582-59-6(7)) Judaica Pr., Inc., The.

—Hand in Hand: Stories about You & Me. Goldfield, Zelda, tr. from HEB. Gershtein, Yonathan, illus. 1999. (Children's Learning Ser.: Vol. 2). 48p. (J). (gr. 1-4). pap. 4.95 (978-1-880582-43-5(0)) Judaica Pr., Inc., The.

—Pesach with the Cohen Family. Greenberg, Chana, illus. 2000. (Children's Learning Ser.: Vol. 7). 48p. (J). (gr. k-5). pap. 4.95 (978-1-880582-55-8(4)) Judaica Pr., Inc., The.

—The Picky Eater & Other Stories. 2004. (Children's Learning Ser.: 20). (HEB., Illus.). 48p. (J). per. 4.95 (978-1-932443-24-0(X), TPES) Judaica Pr., Inc., The.

—Safety First: Having Fun & Staying Safe. Miri, illus. 2000. (Children's Learning Ser.: Vol. 8). 48p. (J). (gr. k-5). pap. 4.95 (978-1-880582-54-1(6)) Judaica Pr., Inc., The.

—The Shabbos Queen & Other Shabbos Stories. Miri, illus. 2000. (Children's Learning Ser.: Vol. 6). 48p. (J). (gr. k-3). pap. 4.95 (978-1-880582-50-3(3)) Judaica Pr., Inc., The.

Fuente de Cristal. 2001. (SPA., Illus.). 127p. (YA). pap. 10.00 (978-1-931481-45-8(8)) LiArt-Literature & Art.

Fuentes, Carlos. Aura. (SPA.). (YA). 8.00 (978-958-04-6971-1(7)) Norma S.A. COL. *Dist:* Distribuidora Norma, Inc.

Fuentes, Peggy Jo. My Name Is Isabella. 2004. pap. 7.95 (978-0-533-14894-3(4)) Vantage Pr., Inc.

Fuertes, Gloria. Cuentos Para 365 Dias. 2003. (SPA.). 210p. 17.56 (978-84-305-9282-1(2), SU2166) Susaeta Ediciones, S.A. ESP. *Dist:* Lectorum Pubns., Inc.

Fujikawa, Gyo. Sunny Books - Four-Favorite Tales, 4 bks., Set. Fujikawa, Gyo, illus. (Illus.). (J). (ps). reprint ed. (978-1-55987-042-9(7), Sunny Bks.) JB Communications, Inc.

Fun Short Stories on Values & Morals of Life. 2003. (Illus.). 90p. (YA). per. (978-0-9742122-0-3(2)) Aunty Ems Boutique.

Fun with Foster Kids, Basic Facts Level 1 - Green. 2005. (J). per. 15.95 (978-1-59649-406-0(9)); cd-rom 15.95 (978-1-59649-409-1(3)) Whispering Pine Pr., Inc.

Fun with Foster Kids, Basic Facts Level 1- Green. 2005. (J). 15.95 (978-1-59649-408-4(5)); spiral bd. 15.95 (978-1-59649-407-7(7)) Whispering Pine Pr., Inc.

Fun with Foster Kids Story Book. 2005. (J). 7.95 (978-1-59649-182-3(5)) Whispering Pine Pr., Inc.

Fun with Foster Kids Storybook. 2005. (J). 15.95 (978-1-59649-403-9(4)); spiral bd. 7.95 (978-1-59649-183-0(3)); per. 7.95 (978-1-59649-472-5(7)); cd-rom 7.95 (978-1-59649-184-7(1)) Whispering Pine Pr., Inc.

The Furry Friends. 2005. (J). per. (978-0-9764783-2-7(0)) Jacqueline Beverly Hills.

Gaiman, Neil. Smoke & Mirrors: Short Fictions & Illusions. 2001. (gr. 5-8). lib. bdg. 22.25 (978-0-613-49458-8(X)) Tandem Library Bks.

Gaines, Isabel & Disney Press Staff. Easy-to-Read Stories. 2000. (Winnie the Pooh Ser.). (Illus.). 192p. (ps-3). 9.99 (978-0-7868-3317-7(3)) Disney Pr.

Galeanoardo, H. Relatos Vertiginosos: Antologia de Cuentos Minimos. 2000. (SPA.). (gr. 7-12). lib. bdg. 17.60 (978-0-613-83767-5(3)) Tandem Library Bks.

Galjanic, Lisa. When Series 6 Volume Set, 6, 6. 2007. (Illus.). 100p. (J). 34.95 ***(978-1-933532-06-6(8))*** LSG Pubns.

Gallego García, Laura. El Valle de Los Lobos. 2004. (Ciclo el Valle de Los Lobos the Valley of the Wolves Cycle Ser.). (SPA., Illus.). 222p. (YA). 10.99 (978-84-348-7361-2(3)) SM Ediciones ESP. *Dist:* Lectorum Pubns., Inc.

Gallego, Laura. La Leyenda Del Rey Errante. 2004. (SPA.). 224p. (YA). 7.99 (978-84-348-8818-0(1)) SM Ediciones ESP. *Dist:* Lectorum Pubns., Inc.

Gallo, Donald. On the Fringe: Stories. Gallo, Donald, ed. 2003. (Illus.). 240p. (YA). (gr. 7). pap. 6.99 (978-0-14-250026-2(7), Puffin) Penguin Group (USA) Inc.

Gallo, Donald R. First Crossing: Stories about Teen Immigrants. 2004. (Illus.). 240p. (J). (gr. 7 up). 16.99 (978-0-7636-2249-7(4)) Candlewick Pr.

—No Easy Answers: Short Stories about Teenagers Making Tough Choices. 1999. (gr. 7-12). lib. bdg. 13.55 (978-0-613-13200-8(9)) Tandem Library Bks.

—On the Fringe. 2003. (gr. 7-12). lib. bdg. 15.30 (978-0-613-61650-8(2)) Tandem Library Bks.

—Sixteen: Short Stories by Outstanding Writers for Young Adults. 2000. 179p. (YA). (gr. 7 up). pap. 5.99 (978-0-8072-3177-7(0), Listening Library) Random Hse. Audio Publishing Group.

—Time Capsule: Short Stories about Teenagers Throughout the Twentieth Century. 2001. (gr. 7-12). lib. bdg. 14.15 (978-0-613-36886-5(X)) Tandem Library Bks.

Gallo, Donald R., compiled by. What Are You Afraid Of? Stories about Phobias. 2006. 208p. (J). (gr. 7). 16.99 (978-0-7636-2654-9(6)) Candlewick Pr.

Gallo, Donald R., ed. Destination Unexpected: Short Stories. 2006. 240p. (YA). (gr. 7). pap. 8.99 (978-0-7636-3119-2(1)) Candlewick Pr.

—First Crossing: Stories about Teen Immigrants. 2007. 240p. (YA). (gr. 7). pap. 8.99 (978-0-7636-3291-5(0)) Candlewick Pr.

Gallo, Donald R., ed. What Are You Afraid Of? Stories about Phobias. 2007. (Illus.). 208p. (YA). (gr. 7). pap. 8.99 ***(978-0-7636-3417-9(4))*** Candlewick Pr.

Galvan, Nelinda. Cuentos de la Tradicion Mexicana. 1999. (Stories for Children Ser.).Tr. of Traditional Mexican Stories. (SPA.). 125p. (J). 7.95 (978-970-643-187-5(X)) Selector, S.A. de C.V. MEX. *Dist:* Libros Sin Fronteras.

Galvin, Laura Gates & Luther, Jacqueline. Read-a-Picture Collection: First Stories for Family Reading. rev. ed. 2005. (Reading to Grow Ser.). (Illus.). 40p. (J). (ps-3). 12.99 incl. audio compact disk (978-1-59069-449-7(X), 1A700) Studio Mouse LLC.

Garborg, Kent. Treasury of Christian Classics for Children Gift Book. Hogan, Rhonda S. & Hogan, Mary, eds. Lundquist, Roger & Lundquist, Larry, illus. 1999. (Best Childrens Ser.). 224p. (J). (ps-5). 14.99 (978-1-58375-475-7(X)) Garborg's, Inc.

Garcia, Geronimo, illus. Tell Me a Cuento (Cuenta Me un Story) No Way Jose; Mariposa Mariposa; Monday, Tuesday, Wednesday, O!; the Terrible Tragadabas. 2004. (ENG & SPA.). 64p. (ps-3). pap. 11.95 (978-0-938317-43-2(1), CPP7431) Cinco Puntos Pr.

García Marquez, Gabriel. Maria dos Prazeres. 10.50 (978-958-04-5572-1(4)) Norma S.A. COL. *Dist:* AIMS International Bks., Inc., Distribuidora Norma, Inc.

Garis, Howard Roger. Curly & Floppy Twistytail (the Funny P. 2006. 25.99 ***(978-1-4280-1724-5(0))*** IndyPublish-.com.

Garn, Laura Aimee. Bella Basset Ballerina. Sokolova, Valerie, illus. 2006. 32p. (J). (ps-3). 15.95 (978-0-9759378-0-8(4)) Pretty Please Pr., Inc.

Gartner, Hans & Poppel, Hans. Osito ILmpio y Osito Sucio. (SPA.). (J). 8.95 (978-958-04-6257-6(7)) Norma S.A. COL. *Dist:* Distribuidora Norma, Inc.

Gauthier, Bertrand. Les Jumeaux Bulle Series. Dumont, Daniel, illus. 2004. (FRE.). 64p. (J). (gr. 1-4). pap. (978-2-89021-684-6(5)) Diffusion du livre Mirabel.

Gauthier, Gilles & Derome, Pierre-Andre. Petit Chausson, Grande Babouche. 2003. (Premier Roman Ser.). 64p. (J). (gr. 2-5). pap. (978-2-89021-308-1(0)) Diffusion du livre Mirabel.

Gbala, Deswin R. Rock University: A Collection of Short Stories & Poems. Gbala, Deswin R., illus. Date not set. (Illus.). 51p. (Orig.). (J). (gr. 3-10). pap. 8.50 (978-0-9650629-2-3(9)) Coulee Region Pubns., Inc.

Geary, Robert, illus. Top Teen Stories. 2004. (Red Hot Reads Ser.). 256p. (J). (gr. 4-8). pap. 6.95 (978-0-7534-5721-4(0), Kingfisher) Houghton Mifflin Co. Trade & Reference Div.

Gebhart, Adalgiza. Gotta Have Hearts: Three Picture Stories for Preschoolers. Gebhart, Adalgiza, illus. l.t. ed. 2005. (Illus.). 76p. (J). 27.95 (978-0-922993-38-3(6)); per. 19.95 (978-0-922993-37-6(8)) Marquette Bks., LLC.

Gébler, Carlo. August '44. 2003. 288p. (J). pap. 11.00 (978-1-4052-0237-4(8)) Egmont Bks., Ltd. GBR. *Dist:* Independent Pubs. Group.

Geis, Patricia. Nestor Tellini. 2004. (Mi Ciudad Series Ser.). (SPA., Illus.). 24p. 6.95 (978-84-7864-798-9(8)) Combel Editorial, S.A. ESP. *Dist:* Independent Pubs. Group.

—Paca Lamar. 2004. (Mi Ciudad Series Ser.). (SPA., Illus.). 24p. 6.95 (978-84-7864-797-2(X)) Combel Editorial, S.A. ESP. *Dist:* Independent Pubs. Group.

—Pascual Midon. 2004. (Mi Ciudad Series Ser.). (SPA., Illus.). 24p. 6.95 (978-84-7864-799-6(6)) Combel Editorial, S.A. ESP. *Dist:* Independent Pubs. Group.

—Pepa Pas. 2004. (Mi Ciudad Series Ser.). (SPA., Illus.). 24p. 6.95 (978-84-7864-796-5(1)) Combel Editorial, S.A. ESP. *Dist:* Independent Pubs. Group.

Gershator, Phillis. Rata Pata Scata Fata: A Caribbean Story. Meade, Holly, illus. 2005. 32p. (J). (ps-ps). pap. 5.95 (978-1-932065-95-4(4)) Star Bright Bks., Inc.

—Rata-Pata-Scata-Fata: A Caribbean Story. Meade, Holly, illus. 2005. 32p. (J). (ps-ps). 15.95 (978-1-932065-94-7(6)) Star Bright Bks., Inc.

Ghose, Sanjoy. Gang Tales from Ranthambhor. 1998. (Illus.). 68p. (J). pap. 50.00 (978-81-86982-24-2(8)) Business Pubns. Inc. IND. *Dist:* State Mutual Bk. & Periodical Service, Ltd.

Gifford, Clive. The Kingfisher Treasury of Stories for Beginning Readers. Kingfisher Editors, ed. 2001. (Story Collections). (Illus.). 192p. (J). (gr. k-3). tchr. ed. 18.95 (978-0-7534-5410-7(6), Kingfisher) Houghton Mifflin Co. Trade & Reference Div.

The Gift of the Magi & Other Stories. 2004. (Literature Units Ser.). (Illus.). 48p. (J). 7.99 (978-1-57690-634-7(5)) Teacher Created Materials, Inc.

Gillam, Norm. Adventures in the Grove: A Collection of Children's Short Stories. 2002. 136p. (J). pap. 10.95 (978-0-595-26335-6(6), Writers Club Pr.) iUniverse, Inc.

Gillis, Jennifer B., et al. Reader's Clubhouse Level 1 Short-Vowel Valu-Pak. 2006. (Illus.). 120p. (J). 15.96 (978-0-7641-7967-9(5)) Barron's Educational Series, Inc.

Gingras, Charlotte. La Fille de la Forêt: Collection. 2002. (Roman Ser.). (FRE.). 96p. (YA). (gr. 8). pap. (978-2-89021-501-6(6)) Diffusion du livre Mirabel.

Giovanni, Nikki, frwd. Paint Me Like I Am: Teen Poems from WritersCorps. 2003. (Illus.). 144p. (J). (gr. 7 up). pap. 7.99 (978-0-06-447264-7(7)) HarperCollins Pubs.

Girard, Geoffrey. Tales of the Atlantic Pirates. 2006. (Illus.). 150p. (YA). per. 13.95 (978-0-9754419-5-4(7)) Middle Atlantic Pr.

Giuliani, Alfred, des. The Magic of Disney Storybook Collection. 2004. (Illus.). 320p. (J). (gr. k-5). 15.99 (978-0-7868-3523-2(0)) Disney Pr.

Glaser, Shirley. The Alphazeds. Glaser, Milton, illus. 2005. 32p. (J). (gr. k-4). reprint ed. 20.00 (978-0-7567-9367-8(X)) DIANE Publishing Co.

Glicksman, Caroline. Eric on the Red Planet. 2005. (Illus.). 32p. 19.99 (978-0-370-32825-6(6)) Random Hse. GBR. *Dist:* Independent Pubs. Group.

Gloden, et al. Tales of the Slayer, Vol. 3. Simon and Schuster Children's Staff, ed. 2003. (Buffy the Vampire Slayer Ser.). (Illus.). 336p. (YA). pap. 9.99 (978-0-689-86436-0(1), Simon Pulse) Simon & Schuster Children's Publishing.

Glynn, Gower. Stories Told in the Wigwam. 2006. pap. 24.95 ***(978-1-4254-9966-2(X))*** Kessinger Publishing, LLC.

Gmeyner, Elizabeth. The Key of the Kingdom: A Book of Stories & Poems for Children. Russell, Joyce, illus. 2004. 100p. (J). pap. 15.00 (978-0-88010-549-1(6), Bell Pond Bks.) SteinerBooks, Inc.

Godwin, Parke. Disney's Main Street Storybook Collection. 2003. (Illus.). 320p. (J). 15.99 (978-0-7868-3431-0(5)) Disney Pr.

Golden Books Staff. Animal Tales. 2007. (Little Golden Book Treasury Ser.). (Illus.). 224p. (J). (ps-k). 10.99 (978-0-375-84178-1(4), Golden Bks.) Random Hse. Children's Bks.

—Eloise Wilkin Stories. Wilkin, Eloise, illus. 2005. (Little Golden Book Treasury Ser.). 224p. (J). (ps-3). 10.95 (978-0-375-82928-4(8), Golden Bks.) Random Hse. Children's Bks.

—Farm Tales. 2007. (Little Golden Book Ser.). (Illus.). 224p. (J). (ps-k). 10.99 (978-0-375-83942-9(9), Golden Bks.) Random Hse. Children's Bks.

—Nick Book & CD Gift Set. 2007. (Book & CD Ser.). (Illus.). 32p. (J). (ps-2). 10.99 ***(978-0-375-84221-4(7)***, Golden Bks.) Random Hse. Children's Bks.

—Poky & Friends Travel Case, 5 bks., Set. 2000. (Illus.). 24p. (J). (ps-3). 12.99 (978-0-307-15893-2(4), 15893, Golden Bks.) Random Hse. Children's Bks.

—Sleepytime Tales. 2006. (Little Golden Book Treasury Ser.). (Illus.). 224p. (J). (gr. k-k). 10.95 (978-0-375-83848-4(1), Golden Bks.) Random Hse. Children's Bks.

—Walt Disney's Classic Little Golden Book' Library: Bambi; Dumbo; Mother Goose; Pinocchio; Scamp; Three Little Pigs. 2004. (Illus.). 144p. (J). (gr. k-3). 17.94 (978-0-7364-2276-5(5) , Golden/Disney) Random Hse. Children's Bks.

Golden Books Staff, et al. Little Golden Book Collection: Inspirational Tales. Williams, Garth & Edge, Liz, illus. 2006. (Little Golden Book Ser.). 224p. (J). (gr. k-1). 10.95 (978-0-375-83233-8(5) , Golden Inspirational) Random Hse. Children's Bks.

Golden, Christopher & Gilmore, Ford Lytle. Mischief, Vol. 3. 2006. (Hollow Ser.: No. 3). 224p. (YA). (gr. 7-12). mass mkt. 6.99 (978-1-59514-026-5(3) , Razorbill) Penguin Group (USA) Inc.

Goldin, Barbara Diamond. While the Candles Burn: Eight Stories for Hanukkah. 1999. (978-0-606-17434-3(6)) Tandem Library Bks.

Golding, Jacqueline. Healing Stories: Picture Books for the Big & Small Changes in a Child's Life. 2006. 336p. pap. 17.95 (978-1-59077-097-9(8)) ; 26.95 (978-1-59077-104-4(4)) Evans, M. & Co., Inc.

Goldsworthy, J. L. Approaching the Crossroads: Four Stories of Adolescence. 2000. 76p. (YA). (gr. 7-12). pap. 9.95 (978-0-595-14911-7(1) , Writer's Showcase Pr.) iUniverse, Inc.

Gomi, Taro. Mira lo Que Tengo! (Los Especiales de A la Orilla Del Viento Ser.). (SPA.). 18p. (J). 6.99 (978-968-16-5414-6(5)) Fondo de Cultura Economica USA.

Goodhart, Pippa. Ginny's Egg. Brouwer, Aafke, illus. 142p. (J). pap. 7.50 (978-0-7497-4557-8(6)) Egmont Bks., Ltd. GBR. *Dist:* Trafalgar Square Publishing.

—Kind of Twins. Busby, Ailie, illus. 2001. 58p. (J). pap. 7.50 (978-0-7497-4526-4(6)) Egmont Bks., Ltd. GBR. *Dist:* Independent Pubs. Group.

Goodman, Burton. Discoveries. 2002. (Goodman's Five-Star Stories Ser.). (gr. 6-12). pap. 17.32 (978-0-07-827355-1(2) , 9780078273551) Jamestown.

—Goodman's Five-Star: Level F. 2001. (gr. 4-12). pap., act. bk. ed. 13.96 (978-0-8092-0350-5(2) , 9780809203505) Jamestown.

—Goodman's Five-Star: Level G. 2001. (gr. 4-12). pap., act. bk. ed. 13.96 (978-0-8092-0351-2(0) , 9780809203512) Jamestown.

—Goodman's Five-Star: Level H. 2001. (gr. 4-12). pap., act. bk. ed. 13.96 (978-0-8092-0352-9(9) , 9780809203529) Jamestown.

Goose, Mother. Puppy Dog Tails Travel Pack. 2005. (Illus.). (J). 12.95 (978-1-59249-474-3(9) , 1D101) Soundprints.

Gordon, Benjamin. Sea Monkeys & Other Disappointments. 2002. (Illus.). 68p. per. 10.00 net. (978-0-9722885-0-7(3)) Raise Giant Frogs Publishing.

Gordon, Marie Elaina. My Grand-Mom Told Me... Book 1. 2006. 48p. pap. 12.95 (978-1-4241-2655-2(X)) PublishAmerica, Inc.

Gorman, Thomas. The Old Neighborhood. 2003. 77p. pap. 11.95 (978-1-59286-514-7(3)) PublishAmerica, Inc.

Goscinny, R. & Uderzo, A. Obelix et Compagnie. (FRE.). 21.95 (978-2-01-210023-7(6)) Hachette Groupe Livre FRA. *Dist:* Distribooks, Inc.

Goscinny, René & Uderzo, Albert. Bouclier Arverne. 21.95 (978-2-01-210011-4(2)) Hachette Groupe Livre FRA. *Dist:* Distribooks, Inc.

Gossman, Dave. Tales from the Oak Hammock. 2001. 124p. (YA). pap. 10.95 (978-0-595-19703-3(5)) iUniverse, Inc.

The Gracious Mother Goose. 2004. 64p. (J). pap. 9.99 (978-0-88724-217-5(0) , CD-2038) Carson-Dellosa Publishing Co., Inc.

Graham, Bob. Tales from the Waterhole. 2004. (Illus.). 64p. (J). (978-0-7445-6593-5(6)) Walker Bks., Ltd.

Grahame, Kenneth. Dream Days. 2005. (ENG.). 32.99 (***978-1-4219-0459-7(4)***) IndyPublish.com.

—Dream Days. Shepard, Ernest H., illus. 2004. reprint ed. pap. 21.95 (978-1-4179-0979-7(X)) Kessinger Publishing, LLC.

Granowsky, Alvin. Making Friends with Books Series Collection 1: Preprimer, Primer, First Reader, 15 vols. Botel, Morton & Dawkins, John, eds. 2nd ed. 1998. Orig. Title: Bookshop A. (Illus.). (J). (gr. 1-3). reprint ed. pap. 60.00 (978-1-891564-09-3(9)) Botel, Morton Assocs.

—Making Friends with Books Series Collection 2: Beginning Second, High Second, 16 vols. Botel, Morton & Dawkins, John, eds. 2nd ed. 1998. Orig. Title: Bookshop B. (Illus.). (J). (gr. 2-5). reprint ed. pap. 70.00 (978-1-891564-10-9(2)) Botel, Morton Assocs.

—Making Friends with Books Series Collection 3: Beginning Third, High Third, 16 vols. Botel, Morton & Dawkins, John, eds. 2nd ed. 1998. Orig. Title: Bookshop C. (Illus.). (J). (gr. 3-8). reprint ed. pap. 70.00 (978-1-891564-11-6(0)) Botel, Morton Assocs.

Gray, Elizabeth J., et al. Newberry Award & Honor, abr. ed. 1999. (Illus.). (J). (gr. 4-7). audio 55.95 (978-0-87499-578-7(7)) Live Oak Media.

Gray, Juliette, ed. Cherubic Children's New Classic Story Book Vol. 2: Teaching & Healing Stories to Help Children Learn, Understand & Cope. 1998. (Illus.). 385p. (J). (gr. k-6). 24.95 (978-1-889590-07-3(X)) Cherubic Pr.

—Cherubic Children's Spiritual Storybook, Vol. 1. 1998. (Illus.). 275p. (J). (gr. k-6). 24.95 (978-1-889590-02-8(9)) Cherubic Pr.

Gray, Keith. Dead Trouble. Scruton, Clive, illus. 90p. (J). pap. 7.50 (978-0-7497-4556-1(8)) Egmont Bks., Ltd. GBR. *Dist:* Trafalgar Square Publishing.

—Oe10,000. Edwards, Mark, illus. 2001. 73p. (J). pap. 7.50 (978-0-7497-4351-2(4)) Egmont Bks., Ltd. GBR. *Dist:* Independent Pubs. Group.

Grayson, Barry/Scott. Twisted Yarns: Bedtime Stories for Hip Kids. 2007. (Illus.). 40p. (J). pap. (***978-0-9774357-1-5(7)***) Grayson, Kate.

Great American Short Stories, 6 Vols. 139.98 (978-0-8368-4250-0(2)) Stevens, Gareth Inc.

Great Children's Stories. 2002. (Illus.). 160p. (J). (gr. k-7). 9.99 (978-1-57759-423-9(1)) Dalmatian Pr.

Great Illustrated Classics, Set. Incl. Adventures of Huckleberry Finn. Twain, Mark. Pablo Marcos Studio Staff, illus. 21.35 (978-1-57765-676-0(8)); Adventures of Robinson Crusoe. Defoe, Daniel. 21.35 (978-1-57765-677-7(6)); Adventures of Sherlock Holmes. Doyle, Arthur Conan, ed. Lynch, Brendan, illus. 21.35 (978-1-57765-678-4(4)); Adventures of Tom Sawyer. Twain, Mark. Pablo Marcos Studio Staff, illus. 21.35 (978-1-57765-679-1(2)); Anne of Green Gables. Montgomery, L. M. Miralles, Joseph, illus. 21.35 (978-1-57765-816-0(7)); Around the World in Eighty Days. Verne, Jules. 21.35 (978-1-57765-680-7(6)); Black Beauty. Sewell, Anna. 21.35 (978-1-57765-681-4(4)); Call of the Wild. London, Jack. Pablo Marcos Studio Staff, illus. 21.35 (978-1-57765-682-1(2)); Captains Courageous. Kipling, Rudyard. Landgraf, Ken, illus. 21.35 (978-1-57765-683-8(0)); Count of Monte Cristo. Dumas, Alexandre. 21.35 (978-1-57765-684-5(9)); David Copperfield. Dickens, Charles. Marcos, Pablo, illus. 21.35 (978-1-57765-685-2(7)); Frankenstein. Shelley, Mary Wollstonecraft. Pablo Marcos Studio Staff, illus. 21.35 (978-1-57765-686-9(5)); Great Expectations. Dickens, Charles. Lynch, Brendan, illus. 21.35 (978-1-57765-687-6(3)); Gulliver's Travels. Swift, Jonathan. Marcos, Pablo, illus. 21.35 (978-1-57765-818-4(3)); Hans Brinker & the Silver Skates. Dodge, Mary Mapes. Freshman, Floris, illus. 21.35 (978-1-57765-814-6(0)); Heidi. Spyri, Johanna. 21.35 (978-1-57765-688-3(1)); Hunchback of Notre Dame. Hugo, Victor. 21.35 (978-1-57765-813-9(2)); Invisible Man. Wells, H. G. Marcos, Pablo, illus. 21.35 (978-1-57765-817-7(5)); Ivanhoe. Scott, Walter, Sr. Marcos, Pablo, illus. 21.35 (978-1-57765-811-5(6)); Journey to the Center of the Earth. Verne, Jules. 21.35 (978-1-57765-689-0(X)); Jungle Book. Kipling, Rudyard. Pablo Marcos Studio Staff, illus. 21.35 (978-1-57765-812-2(4)); Kidnapped. Stevenson, Robert Louis. 21.35 (978-1-57765-690-6(3)); Last of the Mohicans. Cooper, James Fenimore. 21.35 (978-1-57765-692-0(X)); Legend of Sleepy Hollow & Rip Van Winkle. Irving, Washington. Marcos, Pablo, illus. 21.35 (978-1-57765-819-1(1)); Little Women. Alcott, Louisa May. 21.35 (978-1-57765-693-7(8)); Merry Adventures of Robin Hood. Pyle, Howard. 21.35 (978-1-57765-694-4(6)); Moby Dick. Melville, Herman. 21.35 (978-1-57765-695-1(4)); Mutiny on Board HMS Bounty. Bligh, William. Lynch, Brendan, illus. 21.35 (978-1-57765-696-8(2)); Oliver Twist. Estrada, Ric, illus. 21.35 (978-1-57765-697-5(0)); Peter Pan. Barrie, J. M. Davis, Allen, illus. 21.35 (978-1-57765-820-7(5)); Picture of Dorian Gray. Wilde, Oscar. Marcos, Pablo, illus. 21.35 (978-1-57765-821-4(3)); Pollyanna. Porter, Eleanor H. Gual, illus. 21.35 (978-1-57765-822-1(1)); Prince & the Pauper. Twain, Mark. Lynch, Brendan, illus. 21.35 (978-1-57765-698-2(9)); Rebecca of Sunnybrook Farm. Wiggin, Kate Douglas. Tadiello, Ed, illus. 21.35 (978-1-57765-823-8(X)); Red Badge of Courage. Crane, Stephen. Cruz, Ernesto R, illus. 21.35 (978-1-57765-699-9(7)); Secret Garden : A Young Reader's Edition of the Classic Story. Burnett, Frances Hodgson. Kaster, Shelley Austin, illus. 21.35 (978-1-57765-809-2(4)); Story of King Arthur & His Knights. Pyle, Howard. 21.35 (978-1-57765-691-3(1)); Strange Case of Dr. Jekyll & Mr. Hyde. Stevenson, Robert Louis. 21.35 (978-1-57765-800-9(0)); Swiss Family Robinson : Critical Reading Series. Wyss, Johann David. 21.35 (978-1-57765-801-6(9)); Tale of Two Cities. Dickens, Charles. Lynch, Brendan, illus. 21.35 (978-1-57765-802-3(7)); Tales of Mystery & Terror. Poe, Edgar Allan. Pablo Marcos Studio Staff, illus. 21.35 (978-1-57765-815-3(9)); Three Musketeers. Dumas, Alexandre. 21.35 (978-1-57765-803-0(5)); Time Machine. Wells, H. G. Lynch, Brendan, illus. 21.35 (978-1-57765-804-7(3)); Treasure Island. Stevenson, Robert Louis. McAllister, A. J., illus. 21.35 (978-1-57765-805-4(1)); White Fang. London, Jack, Vera, Ross, illus. 21.35 (978-1-57765-810-8(8)); Wind in the Willows. Grahame, Kenneth. Tomei, Lorna, illus. 21.35 (978-1-57765-808-5(6)); Wizard of Oz. Baum, L. Frank. 21.35 (978-1-57765-807-8(8)); 20,000 Leagues under the Sea. Verne, Jules. Marcos, Pablo, illus. 21.35 (978-1-57765-806-1(X)); 240p. (J). (gr. 3-8). , ABDO & Daughters 2002. 1024.80 (978-1-56239-319-9(7)) Spotlight.

Great Novels of Jane Austin. 2000. (YA). 19.95 (978-0-7525-4559-2(0)) Parragon, Inc.

Greaves, Nick. When Bat Was a Bird: And Other Animal Tales from Africa. du Plessis, David, illus. 2005. 144p. pap. 12.95 (978-1-86872-998-2(2)) Struik Pubs. ZAF. *Dist:* International Publishers Marketing.

Green, Kristi-ly. Nits. 2000. (Darkhorse Ser.: No. 10). (Illus.). 56p. pap. 12.00 (978-1-55096-518-6(2)) Exile Editions, Ltd. CAN. *Dist:* Independent Pubs. Group.

Greenberg, Martin H. & Hoyt, Sarah, eds. Something Magic This Way Comes. 2008. 320p. (gr. 12). mass mkt. 7.99 (***978-0-7564-0472-7(X)*** , D A W Bks., Inc.) Penguin Group (USA) Inc.

Greenberg, Martin H. & Waugh, Charles. Adoniram & Other Selections. l.t. ed. 2001. (Newbery Authors Collection: No. 6). 176p. (J). (gr. 4 up). lib. bdg. 23.33 (978-0-8368-2860-3(7)) Stevens, Gareth Inc.

—Dancing Tom & Other Selections. l.t. ed. 2001. (Newbery Authors Collection: No. 5). 160p. (J). (gr. 4 up). lib. bdg. 23.33 (978-0-8368-2859-7(3)) Stevens, Gareth Inc.

—For the Sake of Freedom & Other Selections. l.t. ed. 2001. (Newbery Authors Collection: No. 1). 176p. (J). (gr. 4 up). lib. bdg. 23.33 (978-0-8368-2855-9(0)) Stevens, Gareth Inc.

—The Highest Hit & Other Selections. l.t. ed. 2001. (Newbery Authors Collection: No. 2). 160p. (J). (gr. 4 up). lib. bdg. 23.33 (978-0-8368-2856-6(9)) Stevens, Gareth Inc.

—The Horse of the War God & Other Selections. l.t. ed. 2001. (Newbery Authors Collection: No. 3). 176p. (J). (gr. 4 up). lib. bdg. 23.33 (978-0-8368-2857-3(7)) Stevens, Gareth Inc.

—Lighthouse Island & Other Selections. l.t. ed. 2001. (Newbery Authors Collection: No. 4). 160p. (J). (gr. 4 up). lib. bdg. 23.33 (978-0-8368-2858-0(5)) Stevens, Gareth Inc.

Greenberg, Martin H. & Waugh, Charles, eds. Christmas on the Prairie & Other Selections. l.t. ed. 2001. (Newbery Authors Collection: No. 8). 160p. (J). (gr. 4 up). lib. bdg. 23.33 (978-0-8368-2950-1(6)) Stevens, Gareth Inc.

—For a Horse & Other Selections. l.t. ed. 2001. (Newbery Authors Collection: No. 7). 176p. (J). (gr. 4 up). lib. bdg. 23.33 (978-0-8368-2949-5(2)) Stevens, Gareth Inc.

—A Knife for Tomaso & Other Selections. l.t. ed. 2001. (Newbery Authors Collection: No. 10). 176p. (J). (gr. 4 up). lib. bdg. 23.33 (978-0-8368-2952-5(2)) Stevens, Gareth Inc.

—Little Sioux Girl & Other Selections. l.t. ed. 2001. (Newbery Authors Collection: No. 12). 160p. (J). (gr. 4 up). lib. bdg. 23.33 (978-0-8368-2954-9(9)) Stevens, Gareth Inc.

—Lone Cowboy & Other Selections. l.t. ed. 2001. (Newbery Authors Collection: No. 11). 176p. (J). (gr. 4 up). lib. bdg. 23.33 (978-0-8368-2953-2(0)) Stevens, Gareth Inc.

—The Wise Soldier of Sellebak & Other Selections. l.t. ed. 2001. (Newbery Authors Collection: No. 9). 160p. (J). (gr. 4 up). lib. bdg. 23.33 (978-0-8368-2951-8(4)) Stevens, Gareth Inc.

Greenberg, Martin H. & Waugh, Charles G., eds. A Newbery Christmas: Fourteen Stories of Christmas by Newbery Award - Winning Authors. 2005. 191p. (J). (gr. 4-8). reprint ed. 20.00 (978-0-7567-8943-5(5)) DIANE Publishing Co.

Greenwood, Mark. The Legend of Lasseter's Reef. 2003. (Illus.). 32p. 22.50 (978-1-876268-99-2(9)) Univ. of Western Australia Pr. AUS. *Dist:* International Specialized Bk. Services.

Greenwood-Ryan, Robin. Mary-Jo Knows: A Series of Short Stories. 2002. 32p. pap. 9.00 (978-0-8059-5666-5(2)) Dorrance Publishing Co., Inc.

Greer, Anthony L. Small Talk: A Collection of Short Stories. Greer, Anthony L., ed. 2002. 179p. (YA). per. 10.00 (978-0-9720579-0-5(0)) Aspiring Arts Publishing.

Grentencord, Barbara A. Granny's Buttons. 2005. pap. 7.95 (978-0-533-15125-7(2)) Vantage Pr., Inc.

Gressett, William H., Jr. Nor all your Piety nor Wit... . 2005. (YA). per. 9.99 (978-0-9765467-9-5(5)) Creative Bk. Pubs.

Griffin, Claire Janosik. Imagine That! Foley, Timothy, illus. 2000. (Rollicking Rhymes Ser.). 20p. (J). (gr. k-1). 3.99 (978-1-56822-977-5(1) , IF40211-E4, Instructional Fair) Schaffer, Frank Pubns.

—Kidding Around. Wright, Jane Chambless, illus. 2000. (Rollicking Rhymes Ser.). 20p. (J). (gr. k-1). 3.99 (978-1-56822-978-2(X) , IF40212-E4, Instructional Fair) Schaffer, Frank Pubns.

Griffiths, Andy. The Cat on the Mat Is Flat. Denton, Terry, illus. 2007. 176p. (J). (ps-3). 9.95 (***978-0-312-36787-9(2)***) Feiwel & Friends.

—Just Annoying! Denton, Terry, illus. 2003. (Just Books Ser.). 144p. (J). (gr. 3-5). pap. 4.99 (978-0-439-42471-4(2)) Scholastic, Inc.

—Just Annoying. 2003. (gr. 3-6). lib. bdg. 13.00 (978-0-613-86024-6(1)) Tandem Library Bks.

—Just Joking! Denton, Terry, illus. 2003. (Just Books Ser.). 144p. (J). (gr. 3-5). 4.99 (978-0-439-42472-1(0)) Scholastic, Inc.

—Just Stupid! Denton, Terry, illus. 2004. 160p. (J). pap. 4.99 (978-0-439-42474-5(7)) Scholastic, Inc.

Grigorov, Yassen. Los Angeles de la Guarda. (Los Especiales de A la Orilla Del Viento Ser.). (SPA.). 102p. (J). (978-968-16-7053-5(1)) Fondo de Cultura Economica USA.

Grimly, Gris. Little Jordan Ray's Muddy Spud. Grimly, Gris, illus. 2005. (Illus.). 40p. (J). 19.95 (978-0-9729388-6-0(9)) Baby Tattoo Bks.

Grimm. Bola de cristal. 2005. 24p. incl. cd-rom (978-84-494-2897-5(1)) Oceano Grupo Editoria, S.A.

—Tres pelos diablio. 2005. 24p. incl. audio compact disk (978-84-494-2898-2(X)) Oceano Grupo Editoria, S.A.

Grimm, Hermanos. El M. P. B. Caperucita Roja.Tr. of My First Library: Little Red Riding Hood. (SPA.). (J). 2.49 (978-968-13-2470-4(6)) Editorial Diana, S.A. MEX. *Dist:* Continental Bk. Co., Inc., Giron Bks.

Grimm, Jacob W. Cuentos de Grimm. Rackham, Arthur, illus. (Coleccion Cuentos Universales). (SPA.). 144p. (YA). (gr. 4 up). (978-84-261-1098-5(3) , JV30116) Juventud, Editorial ESP. *Dist:* Lectorum Pubns., Inc.

Grimm, Jacob W. & Grimm, Wilhelm K. Cuentos de Grimm.Tr. of Stories by Grimm. (SPA.). 144p. (J). (978-84-261-0618-6(8)) Juventud, Editorial.

—Cuentos de Grimm. (Coleccion Estrella).Tr. of Stories by Grimm. (SPA., Illus.). 64p. (J). 14.95 (978-950-11-0015-0(4) , SGM015) Sigmar ARG. *Dist:* Continental Bk. Co., Inc.

Grindley, Sally. Christmas Cheer: A Collection of Holiday Tales. 2008. (Illus.). 96p. (J). 17.95 (***978-1-59990-188-6(9)*** , Bloomsbury Children) Bloomsbury Publishing.

Grindley, Sally. The Kingfisher Book of Magical Tales: Tales of Enchantment. Field, Susan Anna, illus. 2002. (Story Collections). 80p. (J). (gr. 3-5). pap. 10.95 (978-0-7534-5388-9(6) , Kingfisher) Houghton Mifflin Co. Trade & Reference Div.

Grizzell, Larry. The Star: A Christmas Song. 2006. (Illus.). 25p. (J). 19.95 (978-0-9759542-2-5(9)) Adventures Galore.

Grosch, Greta & Grosch, Heidi. I Can Tell That Story in Two Pages or Less: Some Silly Sisters' Short Stories. 1999. (Illus.). (J). (ps-6). pap. 8.95 (978-0-9668728-1-1(9)) Oh, You Girls!.

—What We Did Last Summer Bk. 1: Some Silly Sisters' Summer Stories. Grosch, Heidi, illus. 1998. (Illus.). 70p. (J). (ps-6). pap. 8.95 (978-0-9668728-0-4(0)) Oh, You Girls!.

Gross, Jen & Hoch, Jen. A Visit up & down Wall Street. Gross, Margaret, illus. 2005. 32p. (J). 14.95 (978-0-9760875-0-2(2)) Harry and Stephanie Books.

Grosset & Dunlap Inc. Staff, Inc. We Play. 2004. (gr. k-3). lib. bdg. 11.80 (978-0-613-72545-3(X)) Tandem Library Bks.

—We See. 2004. (gr. k-3). lib. bdg. 11.80 (978-0-613-72509-5(3)) Tandem Library Bks.

—We Work. 2004. (gr. k-3). lib. bdg. 11.80 (978-0-613-72574-3(3)) Tandem Library Bks.

Gruber, Michael. The Legend of the Brog. Gruber, Michael & Graves, Linda, illus. 2005. (J). per. 9.95 (978-0-9770413-0-5(1)) Gruber Enterprises.

Guerrero, Andrés. La Noche. Guerrero, Andrés, illus. 2003. (SPA., Illus.). 28p. (J). (gr. k-3). 7.95 (978-84-204-4321-8(2)) Santillana USA Publishing Co., Inc.

Gulliver's Travels. 2004. (Classic Retelling Ser.). (gr. 6-12). (978-0-618-03149-8(9) , 2-00143) McDougal Littell Inc.

Gulliver's Travels. 2000. (Illus.). 80p. (YA). per. 6.95 (978-1-56254-285-6(0) , SP2850) Saddleback Educational Publishing.

Gunn, Robin Jones. Christy Miller Collection: A Time to Cherish; Sweet Dreams; A Promise Is Forever, Vol. 4. 2006. (Christy Miller Ser.: Bks. 10-12). 496p. 14.99 (978-1-59052-587-6(6) , Multnomah Fiction) WaterBrook Pr.

—Christy Miller Collection: Surprise Endings; Island Dreamer; A Heart Full of Hope, Vol. 2. 2006. (Christy Miller Ser.: Bks. 4-6). 496p. (J). 14.99 (978-1-59052-585-2(X) , Multnomah Fiction) WaterBrook Pr.

—Christy Miller Collection: True Friends; Starry Night; Seventeen Wishes, Vol. 3. 2006. (Christy Miller Ser.: Bks. 7-9). 480p. (J). 14.99 (978-1-59052-586-9(8) , Multnomah Fiction) WaterBrook Pr.

—Departures. 1999. (Christy Miller Ser.). 272p. (YA). (gr. 7-12). pap. 9.99 (978-0-7642-2271-9(6)) Bethany Hse. Pubs.

Guo, Jinsong. Touching Stories by Dr. Guo. 2004. pap. 10.00 (978-0-8059-6606-0(4)) Dorrance Publishing Co., Inc.

Gustafson, Scott, illus. Cuentos y Cantos de Navidad. 2004. (ESP & SPA.). 98p. (YA). 12.98 (978-1-4127-0628-5(9) , 7137007) Publications International, Ltd.

Guzaldo, Jessica. Murder & Betrayal, DeFalco, Julie & Cowhey, Dennis R., eds. Cowhey, Dennis E., illus. 2003. 72p. (YA). (gr. 7-8). pap. 9.95 (978-0-9642823-2-2(1)) Key Answer Products, Inc.

Hague, Michael. The Book of Dragons. Hague, Michael, illus. 2005. (Illus.). 160p. (J). (ps-7). pap., pap. 9.99 (978-0-06-075968-1(2) , Harper Trophy) HarperCollins Pubs.

Hall. Here Comes Zelda Claus: And Other Holiday Disasters. 2001. (J). pap. (978-0-15-216468-3(5)) Harcourt Trade Pubs.

Hall, S.C. Turns of Fortune & Other Tales. 2007. (ENG.). 116p. per. (***978-1-4065-1586-2(8)***) Dodo Pr.

Hamilton, Leo. Leo Hamilton's Odd Collection of Animal & Insect Stories Vol. 1: No Crayons. l.t. ed. 2000. 36p. per. 5.99 net. (978-0-9671660-6-3(3)) Story Place, The.

Hamilton, Martha. Noodlehead Stories: World Tales Can Read & Tell. 2000. (gr. 3-6). lib. bdg. 22.20 (978-0-613-35861-3(9)) Tandem Library Bks.

Hanft, Joshua E. Christmas Stories. Zerner, Jesse, illus. 2005. (Great Illustrated Classics Ser.). 240p. (J). (gr. 3-8). 21.35 (978-1-59679-238-8(8) , ABDO & Daughters) ABDO Publishing Co.

Hapka, Catherine. Simba the Rainmaker. 2000. (Illus.). 32p. (J). (ps-2). 12.99 (978-0-7868-3256-9(8)) Disney Pr.

Happy Times with Emily's Clothespin Kids. 2001. 28p. spiral bd. 6.00 (978-0-9711241-0-3(8)) Speer Publishing.

Harcourt School Publishers Staff. Full Count Advanced Level. 3rd ed. 2002. (Trophies Reading Program Ser.). (Illus.). pap. 5.10 (978-0-15-323481-1(4)) Harcourt Schl. Pubs.

—The Graceful Bull & Other Stories Below Level. 3rd ed. 2002. (Trophies Reading Program Ser.). (Illus.). pap. 5.10 (978-0-15-323334-0(6)) Harcourt Schl. Pubs.

—Living History Day Advanced Level. 3rd ed. 2002. (Trophies Reading Program Ser.). (Illus.). pap. 5.10 (978-0-15-323397-5(4)) Harcourt Schl. Pubs.

—A Place to Dream Bk. 1: Standard Anthology. 95th ed. 1998. (Treasury of Literature Ser.). (Illus.). (gr. 3). 58.90 (978-0-15-301233-4(1)) Harcourt Schl. Pubs.

—A Riddle a Day On Level. 3rd ed. 2002. (Trophies Reading Program Ser.). (Illus.). pap. 5.10 (978-0-15-323270-1(6)) Harcourt Schl. Pubs.

—Stories That Grandfather Told On Level. 3rd ed. 2002. (Trophies Reading Program Ser.). (Illus.). pap. 5.10 (978-0-15-323278-7(1)) Harcourt Schl. Pubs.

—Timeless Tales: Intervention Reader. 2000. (Collections Ser.). (Illus.). (gr. 5). pap. 16.80 (978-0-15-312736-6(8)) Harcourt Schl. Pubs.

—Timeless Tales: Intervention Reader & Practice Book. 2001. (Collections Ser.). (Illus.). (gr. 5). pap. 6.00 (978-0-15-324948-8(X)) Harcourt Schl. Pubs.

Hardy, Thomas & West, Clare. The Three Strangers & Other Stories. Hedge, Tricia & Bassett, Jennifer, eds. 2004. (Oxford Bookworms Ser.). (Illus.). 72p. 6.50 (978-0-19-423025-4(2)) Oxford Univ. Pr., Inc.

The Hare & the Tortoise: Individual Title Six-Packs. 32p. (gr. 2 up). 37.00 (978-0-7635-9219-6(6)) Rigby Education.

Hare, Lorraine H. Make Room for the Hollyhocks & Where the Birds Don't Sing. Johnson, Shannon et al, eds. 1999. 160p. (YA). (gr. 4 up). pap. 12.99 (978-1-893053-00-7(8)) PaceSetter Direct, Inc.

S

Harmer, Jeremy. The Double Bass Mystery: Level 2. 1999. (Cambridge English Readers Ser.). (Illus.). 48p. pap. 6.00 (978-0-521-65613-9(3)) Cambridge Univ. Pr.

Harper, Donna A., ed. The Later Simple Stories, Vol. 8. 2005. (Collected Works of Langston Hughes: Vol. 8). (Illus.). 384p. 34.95 (978-0-8262-1409-6(0)) Univ. of Missouri Pr.

HarperCollins Treasury of Picture Book Classics: A Child's First Collection. 2002. (Illus.). 448p. (J). (ps-k). 27.99 (978-0-06-008094-5(9)) HarperCollins Pubs.

Harris, Joel Chandle. Told by Uncle Remus: New Stories of the. 2006. (Illus.). pap. 31.95 (*978-1-4254-9964-8(3)) Kessinger Publishing, LLC.

Harris, Michael. A Forest for Christmas. Orchard, Eric, illus. 2007. 48p. (J). (gr. 2-10). (*978-1-55109-589-9(0)) Nimbus Publishing, Ltd.

Harris, Robie H. Hola, Hermanito! Emberley, Michael, illus. 2000. (J). (gr. k-2). (CAT.). 26p. 14.95 (978-84-95040-51-0(4)); (SPA.). 38p. 14.95 (978-84-95040-50-3(6) , RR1144) Serres, Ediciones, S. L. ESP. Dist: Lectorum Pubns., Inc.

Harrison, Daniel Bernard. Air in the Fourth Column. 1999. 85p. (YA). pap. (978-0-9678139-0-5(5)) Harrison, Daniel B.

Harrison, Jack M. Alaskan Tails of the Trail: A Collection of Short Stories. 2003. 124p. (J). pap. 11.99 (978-1-57921-606-1(4)) Pleasant Word.

Harrison, Michael & Stuart-Clark, Christopher. The Oxford Treasury of World Stories. 2000. (Illus.). 144p. (YA). 17.95 (978-0-19-278181-9(2)) Oxford Univ. Pr., Inc.

Harrison, Randolph R. The Frog King of Lily Pond World: Children's Short Stories & Poems. 2002. 131p. (J). pap. 10.95 (978-0-595-22480-7(6) , Writers Club Pr) iUniverse, Inc.

Hartenstine, Kristina. Teen Storytellers. 2001. (gr. 7-12). lib. bdg. 17.60 (978-0-613-77901-2(0)) Tandem Library Bks.

Hartenstine, Kristina, ed. A Teen Writer's Dream - Storytellers. 2002. (Teen Writer's Dream Teen Storytellers Ser.). 150p. (J). per. 8.95 (978-0-9704868-4-4(7)) Be-Mused Pubns.

Hartman, Bob. More Bible Bad Guys...& Gals. Anderson, Jeff, illus. 2001. 94p. (gr. 3-7). 13.99 (978-0-8066-4099-0(5) , Augsburg Bks.) Augsburg Fortress, Pubs.

Hasling, Jack. The Little Rock: And Other Stories. Rogers, Denny, illus. 2003. 32p. (Orig.). (J). (gr. 1-6). pap. 9.95 (978-1-878044-51-8(6) , Wild Rose) Mayhaven Publishing.

Hasling, Jack. Salamander the Great! 2006. (J). per. 10.00 (*978-0-9786988-1-2(9)) Hazel Street Productions.

Hassall, Jill & Bolam, Emily. Along the Road. 1999. (Go Along Bks.). (Illus.). 24p. (J). (ps-k). 12.95 (978-1-86233-091-7(3)) Sterling Publishing Co., Inc.

Das Hassliche Entlein: Farm Animals, The Farm, Seasons, The Weather. 1999. (Lesen Leicht Germacht Ser.). (GER & ENG., Illus.). 24p. (J). (ps-5). pap. 7.95 (978-88-8148-246-7(0)) European Language Institute ITA. Dist: Distribooks, Inc., Midwest European Pubns.

Hasty, Shaudalon. My Body. 2003. pap. 12.00 (978-0-8059-5968-0(8)) Dorrance Publishing Co., Inc.

Hauff, Wilhelm & Pak, Boris. Little Mook & Dwarf Longnose. 2004. (Illus.). 124p. 19.95 (978-1-56792-222-6(8)) Godine, David R. Pub.

Hautman, Pete, ed. Full House: 10 Stories about Poker. 2007. (Illus.). 161p. (YA). (gr. 7-12). 17.99 (*978-0-399-24528-2(6) , Putnam Juvenile) Penguin Group (USA) Inc.

Hawkins, Colin. Foxy Doesn't Feel Well. (Illus.). 23p. (J). pap. 8.99 (978-0-00-664758-4(8) , HarperSport) HarperCollins Pubs. Ltd. GBR. Dist: Trafalgar Square Publishing.

Hawthorn, P. Little Book of Bedtime Stories. 2004. (Mini Storybooks Ser.). (Illus.). 96p. (J). 7.95 (978-0-7945-0268-3(7) , Usborne) EDC Publishing.

—Usborne Story Box. Cartwright, Stephen, illus. 2004. 24p. (J). (ps). 14.95 (978-0-7460-2145-3(3)) EDC Publishing.

Hawthorne, Nathaniel. Nathaniel Hawthorne. McConnell, James, illus. 2004. (Great American Short Stories Ser.). 71p. (J). lib. bdg. 23.33 (978-0-8368-4252-4(9)) Stevens, Gareth Inc.

Hayashi, Leslie Ann. Fables Beneath the Rainbow. Bishop, Kathleen Wong, illus. 2005. 32p. (J). 14.95 (978-1-56647-741-3(7) , 477417) Mutual Publishing LLC.

—Fables from the Sea. Bishop, Kathleen Wong, illus. 2000. (Kolowalu Bks.). 40p. (ps-5). 14.95 (978-0-8248-2224-8(2) , Kolowalu Bk.) Univ. of Hawaii Pr.

Hayes, Joe. La Llorona/the Weeping Woman: An Hispanic Legend Told in Spanish & English. Garcia, Geronimo, illus. 1998. (ENG & SPA.). 32p. (ps-3). pap. 7.95 (978-0-938317-39-5(3)) Consortium Bk. Sales & Distribution.

Hays, Helen Ashe. The Adventures of Prince Lazybones: And Other Stories. 2007. 152p. pap. 11.99 (*978-1-4264-8474-2(7)); 168p. pap. 14.99 (*978-1-4264-8532-9(8)) BiblioBazaar.

Health Communications Staff, et al. Chicken Soup for the Soul Family Storybook Collection. 1998. (Chicken Soup for the Soul Ser.). 98p. (J). (ps-3). pap., tchr. ed. 12.95 (978-1-55874-642-8(0)) Health Communications, Inc.

Hedley, Alistair, selected by. Read to Me Daddy. Date not set. (Read to Me Ser.). (Illus.). 192p. (J). 14.98 (978-0-7525-9485-9(0)) Parragon, Inc.

Heine, Helme. Cuentas de Elefante. 2003. (la Orilla Del Viento Ser.). (SPA.). 40p. (J). 3.99 (978-968-16-6423-7(X) , 151) Fondo de Cultura Economica USA.

Heller, Sarah E. Disney's Princess Storybook Collection: Love & Friendship Stories. 1999. (Disneys Ser.). (Illus.). 304p. (J). (gr. k-5). 15.99 (978-0-7868-3247-7(9) , Disney Editions) Disney Pr.

Hello My Love Goodbye. 2000. (Katie Rose/Stacy Belford Ser.). (YA). (gr. 5-9). per. 12.95 (978-1-930009-16-5(X)) Image Cascade Publishing.

Henderson, Kathy. Bedtime Book. Ives, Penny, illus. 2000. 48p. (J). (ps-2). pap. 12.99 (978-0-7112-1574-0(X)) Lincoln, Frances Ltd. GBR. Dist: Transition Vendor.

Henriquez, Cesar, illus. Jonathan's Colorful Campus Tour - University of Connecticut A-Z. 2004. (J). 9.99 (978-1-933069-06-7(6)) Odd Duck Ink, Inc.

—Sebastian's Colorful Campus Tour - University of Miami A-Z. 2004. (J). 9.99 (978-1-933069-05-0(8)) Odd Duck Ink, Inc.

Henry, O. Stories by O. Henry. 1999. (978-0-606-17457-2(5)) Tandem Library Bks.

—100 Selected Stories. unabr. ed. 1998. (Wordsworth Classics Ser.). (YA). (gr. 6-12). 5.27 (978-0-89061-241-5(2) , R2412WW) Jamestown.

Henry, O. & Gianni, Gary. The Gift of the Magi. (Classics Illustrated Ser.). (Illus.). 52p. (YA). pap. 4.95 (978-1-57209-013-2(8)) Classics International Entertainment, Inc.

Henty, G. A. G. A. Henty Short Story Collection: Featuring: Sole Survivors, the Frontier Girl, the Ranch in the Valley, & on the Track, Vol. 1. 2004. (YA). pap. (978-1-931587-34-1(5)) Preston-Speed Pubns.

—G. A. Henty Short Story Collecton: Featuring: Sole Survivors, the Frontier Girl, the Ranch in the Valley, & on the Track, Vol. 1. 2004. (YA). lib. bdg. (978-1-931587-33-4(7)) Preston-Speed Pubns.

Herbert, Denise. Mon Enfance Illoise Racontee a ma Fille: Recits D'Antan (1950 a 1955) Silver, Joanne S., ed. Bagatta, Sharon, illus. l.t. ed. 2007. (FRE.). 86p. (YA). pap. 18.95 (*978-0-9743158-9-8(3)) Beach Lloyd Pubs., LLC.

Here's Marny. 2000. (Tippy Parrish Story Ser.). (YA). (gr. 6-10). per. 12.95 (978-1-930009-25-7(9)) Image Cascade Publishing.

Herlihy, Matt & Clarke, Nzingha, selected by. Sweet Fancy Moses: Book 2. 2005. per. (978-0-9767048-0-5(3)) Literary License, Inc.

La Hermanita; El Diente Molesto, 2 bks., Set. (Coleccion Chiquilines - Imagen y Sonido). (SPA.). (J). 15.95 incl. audio (978-950-11-0627-5(6) , SGM276) Sigmar ARG. Dist: Continental Bk. Co., Inc.

Herriot, James. James Herriot's Treasury of Inspirational Stories for Children: Warm & Joyful Tales by the Author of All Creatures Great & Small. Brown, Ruth & Barrett, Peter, illus. 2005. 260p. (gr. 4-7). per. 14.95 (978-0-312-34972-1(6) , St. Martin's Griffin) St. Martin's Pr.

Hewitt, Richard. Children's Delights: Four in One. l.t. ed. 2002. 143p. (J). pap. 11.95 (978-0-595-21706-9(0) , Writers Club Pr.) iUniverse, Inc.

Heyman, Alissa. The Big Book of Adventure. Rodriguez, Pedro, illus. 2008. 112p. (J). 12.95 (*978-1-4027-5156-1(7)) Sterling Publishing Co., Inc.

Hickey, Jack. A Storyteller's Book of Tales. 2002. 114p. (J). pap. 9.95 (978-0-595-22333-6(8) , Writer's Showcase Pr.) iUniverse, Inc.

Hickox, Rebecca. Zorro & Quwi: Tales of a Trickster Guinea Pig. 1998. (J). (gr. 3-5). (978-0-606-13945-8(1)) Tandem Library Bks.

Hide-and-Seek Hippo. 2001. (ps-2). lib. bdg. 9.80 (978-0-613-32639-1(3)) Tandem Library Bks.

Highstreet, Harry. Read Aloud Series. 2006. pap. 28.95 (*978-1-84728-641-3(0)) Lulu.com.

Hildebrandt, Greg. Magical Storybook Treasury. 2006. (Illus.). 184p. 14.98 (978-0-7624-2837-3(6) , Running Pr.) Running Pr. Bk. Pubs.

Hill, Clare. Granddad's Circus & Other Stories. 2004. 41p. pap. 19.95 (978-1-4137-3647-2(5)) PublishAmerica, Inc.

Hill, David. Ghosts & Ghoulies. 2000. (gr. 7-12). lib. bdg. 12.10 (978-0-613-28851-4(3)) Tandem Library Bks.

Hill, Nancy J. Nestle's Bits & Bites. Roberts, Amylyn, illus. 1999. 32p. (J). (gr. 1-5). pap. 11.95 (978-0-9669436-1-0(9)) Serenity Pr.

Hillert, Margaret. The Funny Baby. 2002. (Illus.). (J). 15.00 (978-0-7587-8968-6(8)) Book Wholesalers, Inc.

Hinds, Bill. Buzz Beamer, No. 2. 1999. (J). pap. (978-0-316-36449-2(5)) Little Brown & Co.

Hinojosa, Francisco. Ana, Verdad? Gedovius, Juan, illus. 2003. (Coleccion Derechos Del Nino Ser.). (SPA.). 32p. (J). (gr. 3-5). pap. 7.95 (978-84-204-5824-3(4)) Santillana USA Publishing Co., Inc.

—Yanka, Yanka. Hinojosa, Francisco, illus. 2003. (SPA., Illus.). 44p. (J). (gr. k-3). pap. 10.95 (978-968-19-0440-1(0)) Santillana USA Publishing Co., Inc.

Hobby, Nathan. The Fur. 2004. 220p. (YA). pap. 16.50 (978-1-920731-01-4(6)) Fremantle Pr. AUS. Dist: International Specialized Bk. Services.

Hoberman, Mary Ann. You Read to Me, I'll Read to You: Very Short Stories to Read Together. Emberley, Michael, illus. 2001. 32p. (J). (ps-17). 16.99 (978-0-316-36350-1(2)) Little, Brown Bks. for Young Readers.

—You Read to Me, I'll Read to You: Very Short Stories to Read Together. Emberley, Michael, illus. 2006. 32p. (J). (ps-1). pap. 6.99 (978-0-316-01316-1(1) , Tingley, Megan Bks.) Little, Brown Bks. for Young Readers.

Hodgson, Julie. Miniature Horse Tales. 2005. 37p. (J). 15.00 (978-1-4116-4144-0(2)) Lulu.com.

Hofer, Charles. Dragon Tales: 10 Tales. DiCicco, Sue, illus. 2001. (J). 15.95 (978-0-7853-4808-5(5)) Publications International, Ltd.

Hoffman, Alice. Local Girls. 2000. 197p. (gr. 7-12). lib. bdg. 22.20 (978-0-613-23735-2(8)) Tandem Library Bks.

Hoffman, Mary. Parables & Miracles of Jesus. Morris, Jackie, illus. 2007. 64p. (J). 19.95 (*978-1-84507-786-0(5)) Lincoln, Frances Ltd. GBR. Dist: Perseus Distribution.

Hoffmann, E. T. A. El Cascanueces. 2000. (SPA., Illus.). 32p. (J). (gr. k-2). 4.95 (978-84-392-8305-8(9)) Lectorum Pubns., Inc.

Hoffmann, Heinrich. Shock-Headed Peter: In Latin English German. Wiesmann, Peter & Wild, Ann E., trs. 2002. (GER., Illus.). 72p. 18.00 (978-0-86516-548-9(3)) Bolchazy-Carducci Pubs.

Hogan, Robb Dragon. There Was a Time: A Journey into Black & White with Taz. 2003. (Illus.). 43p. 6.00 (978-0-9742178-0-2(8)) TazTales.

Holeman, Linda. Toxic Love. 2003. (gr. 5-8). lib. bdg. 17.60 (978-0-613-77315-7(2)) Tandem Library Bks.

—Toxic Love. 2003. 184p. (J). (gr. 6-9). pap. 8.95 (978-0-88776-647-3(1)) Tundra Bks., Inc./Livres Toundra, Inc. CAN. Dist: Random Hse., Inc.

Holland, Elizabeth, compiled by. Cool Christmas Stories. 2007. (Super Shorts Ser.). 160p. (J). pap. 6.95 (*978-0-7534-6073-3(4) , Kingfisher) Houghton Mifflin Co. Trade & Reference Div.

Hollaway, David. Quigley Mccormick & the Stuperton Conspiracy. 2006. (J). per. 15.95 (978-1-933211-56-5(3)) Quackenworth Publishing.

Holmes, Sally, illus. Ballet Stories. 2003. (Red Hot Reads Ser.). 224p. (J). (gr. 4-8). pap. 6.95 (978-0-7534-5674-3(5) , Kingfisher) Houghton Mifflin Co. Trade & Reference Div.

Hopper, Celia. Violets. 2004. (YA). per. 8.99 (978-0-9754818-7-5(8)) Creative Bk. Pubs.

Horowitz, Anthony. The Complete Horowitz Horror. 2008. 448p. (J). (gr. 4-6). pap. 7.99 (*978-0-14-241162-9(0) , Puffin) Penguin Group (USA) Inc.

—Horowitz Horror: Stories You'll Wish You Never Read. 2006. 208p. (J). (gr. 4). 11.99 (978-0-399-24489-6(1) , Philomel) Penguin Group (USA) Inc.

—El Horrible Sueno de Harriet. 2002. (SPA.). 158p. 4.99 (978-968-16-6397-1(7)) Fondo de Cultura Economica USA.

—More Horowitz Horror: More Stories You'll Wish You'd Never Read. 2007. 208p. (YA). (gr. 4 up). 11.99 (978-0-399-24519-0(7) , Philomel) Penguin Group (USA) Inc.

Horowitz, Anthony, retold by. Myths ans Legends. 2007. 304p. (J). pap. 6.95 (*978-0-7534-6146-4(3) , Kingfisher) Houghton Mifflin Co. Trade & Reference Div.

Horse, Harry. Last Cowboys. Horse, Harry, illus. (Illus.). 96p. (J). pap. 7.95 (978-0-14-130028-3(0)) Penguin Bks., Ltd. GBR. Dist: Trafalgar Square Publishing.

Horvath, Polly. Todo sobre un Waffle.Tr. of Everything on a Waffle. (SPA.). (YA). 8.95 (978-958-04-6495-2(2)) Norma S.A. COL. Dist: Distribuidora Norma, Inc.

Houselander, Caryll. Catholic Tales for Boys & Girls. 2003. Orig. Title: Terrible Farmer Timson (New York: Sheed & Ward, 1957). (Illus.). 160p. (J). pap. 11.95 (978-1-928832-74-4(1)) Sophia Institute Pr.

Houston, Pam. Waltzing the Cat. 1999. (gr. 7-12). lib. bdg. 23.45 (978-0-613-27451-7(2)) Tandem Library Bks.

How Long Is Always? 2000. (Katie Rose/Stacy Belford Ser.). (YA). (gr. 5-9). per. 12.95 (978-1-930009-15-8(1)) Image Cascade Publishing.

Howard, Jane R. When I'm Sleepy. Cherry, Lynne, illus. 2000. (Picture Puffin Ser.). 24p. (J). (ps-1). pap. 5.99 (978-0-14-056759-5(3) , Puffin) Penguin Group (USA) Inc.

Howe, David J. Doctor Who - A Book of Monsters: Meet the Monster & Their Makers. 1999. (Doctor Who Ser.). (Illus.). 118p. (J). (978-0-563-40562-7(7)) BBC Worldwide.

Howe, James. Color of Absence: 12 Stories about Loss & Hope. 2003. (gr. 7-12). lib. bdg. 15.30 (978-0-613-61755-0(X)) Tandem Library Bks.

—Harold & Chester Stories. Date not set. (Bunnicula & Friends Ser.). (J). (gr. k-3). (978-0-688-10298-2(0)); lib. bdg. (978-0-688-10299-9(9)) HarperCollins Pubs.

—Horace & Morris but Mostly Delores. Walrod, Amy, illus. 2002. (J). 25.11 (978-0-7587-2749-7(6)) Book Wholesalers, Inc.

—Horace & Morris but Mostly Delores. Walrod, Amy, illus. 1999. 32p. (J). (ps-3). 16.00 (978-0-689-31874-0(X) , Atheneum) Simon & Schuster Children's Publishing.

Howe, James, ed. The Color of Absence: 12 Stories about Loss & Hope. 2003. (Illus.). 256p. (YA). (gr. 7 up). pap. 6.99 (978-0-689-85667-9(9) , Simon Pulse) Simon & Schuster Children's Publishing.

—13: Thirteen Stories That Capture the Agony & Ecstasy of Being Thirteen. 2003. 288p. (YA). 16.95 (978-0-689-82863-8(2) , Atheneum) Simon & Schuster Children's Publishing.

—13: Thirteen Stories That Capture the Agony & Ectasy of Being Thirteen. 2006. 288p. (YA). pap. 7.99 (978-1-4169-2684-9(4) , Simon Pulse) Simon & Schuster Children's Publishing.

Howe, Kim, illus. American Life Series: Family, Teacher, Friend, 3 books. 2006. 80p. 19.95 (978-1-59971-554-4(6)) Aardvark Global Publishing.

Hronas, Georgia. Tell Us a Story, Grandma: More of Grandma's Orthodox Spiritual Stories. 2005. 130p. (J). (gr. 3-7). pap. 12.95 (978-1-880971-93-2(3)) Light & Life Publishing Co.

Hughes, Ted. How the Whale Became: And Other Stories. Morris, Jackie, illus. 2000. 94p. (J). (ps-3). pap. 25.00 (978-0-531-30303-0(9) , Orchard Bks.) Scholastic, Inc.

Hughes, Valerie. Short Stories for Children. 1999. (Illus.). 30p. (J). (gr. k-4). pap. 4.99 (978-1-893181-23-6(5) , Lagesse Stevens) Martell Publishing Co.

Hume, Margaret Anne, ed. Just Mary Reader: Mary Grannan Selected Stories. 2006. 176p. pap. 24.99 (*978-1-55002-598-9(8) , Dundurn Pr.) Dundurn Group, The CAN. Dist: Univ. of Toronto Pr.

Hunter, Michele. Scary Stories for Stormy Nights, Vol. 8. 1999. 96p. (J). (gr. 3-6). pap. 5.95 (978-0-7373-0045-1(0) , Roxbury Park) Lowell Hse.

Hurston, Zora Neale. The Skull Talks Back: And Other Haunting Tales. Jenkins, Leonard, illus. 2004. 64p. (J). (gr. 5 up). 15.99 (978-0-06-000631-0(5)) HarperCollins Pubs.

Hurston, Zora Neale & Thomas, Joyce Carol. The Skull Talks Back: And Other Haunting Tales. Jenkins, Leonard, illus. 2004. 64p. (J). (gr. 5 up). lib. bdg. 16.89 (978-0-06-000634-1(X)) HarperCollins Pubs.

Hurwitz, Johanna. Elisa Michaels, Bigger & Better. Tilley, Debbie, illus. 2003. (Riverside Kids Ser.). 128p. (J). 15.99 (978-0-06-009601-4(2)); lib. bdg. 16.89 (978-0-06-009602-1(0)) HarperCollins Pubs.

Hutchens, David. PageLand: A Story about Love & Sharing & Working Together. Gombert, Bobby, illus. 2004. (gr. 4-8). 14.99 (978-0-8054-2726-4(0)) B&H Publishing Grp.

Hutchins, Pat. Pat Hutchins Collection. Hutchins, Pat, illus. 1999. (Illus.). pap. 61.95 incl. audio (978-0-87499-887-0(5)) Live Oak Media.

A I am a Gypsy Pot Set, 6 vols. 32p. (gr. 1-3). 26.50 (978-0-7802-8041-0(5)); 31.50 (978-0-322-00336-1(9)) Wright Group, The.

I Can Read: Stories of History. 2005. (J). (978-1-59564-721-4(X)) Steps To Literacy, LLC.

I Never Want to go There Again. 2007. per. (*978-1-59916-217-1(2)) Printing Systems.

Ibañez, Vincente Blasco & Lorente, Mariano J. Last Lion & Other Stories. 73p. (J). pap. 5.95 (978-0-8283-1444-2(6)) Branden Bks.

Ibbotson, Eva. El Concurso de Brujas. 2002. (SPA.). 192p. (978-84-7888-801-6(2) , 1952) Emece Editores.

Ihebereme, Chidozie . N. Dad Says Write. 2007. per. (*978-1-59872-954-2(3)) Instantpublisher.com.

Ilgaz, Rifat. Fourth Company. 2001. (TUR.). (YA). 11.95 incl. audio (978-1-84059-304-4(0)) Milet Publishing.

—Fourth Company. Croft, Damian, tr. 2001. (Turkish - English Short Stories Ser.). (TUR & ENG.). 161p. pap. 9.95 (978-1-84059-298-6(2)) Milet Publishing.

Illanes, Anamaria. Amigos en el Bosque. Moya, Rene, illus. 2003. (SPA.). 43p. (J). (gr. k-3). pap. 8.95 (978-956-239-112-2(4)) Santillana USA Publishing Co., Inc.

Illustrated Classics. 2006. (Illus.). (gr. 5-8). 189.50 (978-0-7910-9111-1(2)) Facts On File, Inc.

Infante, Begona. Takao Yo Soy de Japon (I'm from Japan) (SPA.). 32p. (J). 12.95 (978-84-246-9402-9(3)) La Galera, S.A. Editorial ESP. Dist: AIMS International Bks., Inc.

The Invisible Cell: One Man's Story about Surviving in a Generation Lost in the Social Justice System. 2004. (YA). per. 12.95 (978-0-9745244-0-5(9)) William Works, Inc.

Ionescu, Angela C. Cuentos y Leyendas de Rumania. (Torre de Papel Ser.). (SPA.). (J). (gr. 4 up). 8.95 (978-958-04-0781-2(9)) Norma S.A. COL. Dist: Distribuidora Norma, Inc.

Irgens, Barbara. An Anthology for Children. 2005. 108p. pap. 16.95 (978-1-4137-8254-7(X)) PublishAmerica, Inc.

Irving, Washington. The Legend of Sleepy Hollow & Other Stories from the Sketch Book. 2006. 384p. (gr. 12). pap. 5.95 (978-0-451-53012-7(8) , Signet Classics) Penguin Group (USA) Inc.

—The Legend of Sleepy Hollow & Rip Van Winkle. Marcos, Pablo, illus. 2002. (Great Illustrated Classics Ser.). 240p. (J). (gr. 3-8). 21.35 (978-1-57765-819-1(0) , ABDO & Daughters) ABDO Publishing Co.

—Washington Irving. Hall, Tracy, illus. 2004. (Great American Short Stories Ser.). 80p. (J). lib. bdg. 23.33 (978-0-8368-4253-1(7)) Stevens, Gareth Inc.

—Washington Irving's the Legend of Sleepy Hollow: And Other Stories. 1999. (Illustrated Junior Library). (Illus.). 256p. (J). (gr. 4-7). 16.99 (978-0-448-42074-5(0) , Grosset & Dunlap) Penguin Group (USA) Inc.

Is There an Alligator at Kaipapa'u? / Aia Ka 'Alakeka Ma Kaipapa'u? The Ho'ulu Hou Project: Stories Told by Us. 2004. (J). per. (978-0-9760892-1-6(1)) Na Kamalei Koolauloa Early Education Program.

Isadora, Rachel, et al. Caldecott Honor Collection, 8 bks., Set. unabr. ed. 1999. (Illus.). (J). pap. 152.95 incl. audio (978-0-87499-706-4(2)) Live Oak Media.

ISOL Staff. Secreto de Familia. 2003. (Los Primerisimos Ser.). (SPA.). 88p. (J). 5.99 (978-968-16-7046-7(9)) Fondo de Cultura Economica USA.

Isom, Lori. The Winner. Wise, Noreen, ed. Favazza, Keith, illus. 2002. (Gold Mixed Collection). 50p. (YA). (ps up). pap. 6.95 (978-1-58584-393-0(8)) Huckleberry Pr.

It Came from the Lab. 2005. (Thrillogy Ser.). (Illus.). 48p. (gr. 4-8). 17.50 (978-0-7910-8867-8(7)) Facts On File, Inc.

It's Fun to Be Five. 2000. (gr. k-3). lib. bdg. 11.80 (978-0-613-21784-2(5)) Tandem Library Bks.

It's Heaven to Be Seven. 1999. (gr. 3-6). lib. bdg. 11.80 (978-0-613-21786-6(1)) Tandem Library Bks.

Itterman, Bert. Growing up with Grandpa. 2006. (Illus.). 112p. pap. (*978-1-57579-330-6(X)) Pine Hill Pr., Inc.

Iturrondo, Angeles Molina. Pepitina. Guevara, Dennis Villanueva, illus. 2004. (Green Ser.). 24p. (J). (978-1-57581-435-3(8)) Ediciones Santillana, Inc.

—Sapo Sapito Sapote. Umpierre, Migdalia, illus. 2004. (Green Ser.). 24p. (J). (978-1-57581-440-7(4)) Ediciones Santillana, Inc.

Iturrondo, Angeles Molina & Iguina, Adriana. The Lost Sock. Montanez, Nivea Ortiz, illus. 2004. (Green Ser.). 24p. (J). (978-1-57581-434-6(X)) Ediciones Santillana, Inc.

Izgu, Muzaffer. Radical Niyazi Bey. 2001. (YA). 11.95 incl. audio (978-1-84059-307-5(5)); (TUR & ENG.). 11.95 incl. audio (978-1-84059-306-8(7)) Milet Publishing.

—Radical Niyazi Bey. Croft, Damian, tr. 2001. (Turkish - English Short Stories Ser.). (TUR & ENG.). 119p. pap. 9.95 (978-1-84059-299-3(0)) Milet Publishing.

Jack In The Box Staff. Favorite Children's Stories by Jack in T. 2005. pap. 30.95 (978-1-4179-8943-0(2)) Kessinger Publishing, LLC.

Jackson, Bobby L. African Heritage Short Stories. Grays, Kevin, illus. 32p. (J). 2001. (gr. 1). pap. 10.95 (978-1-884242-78-6(2)); 1999. (gr. k-2). lib. bdg. 19.95 (978-1-884242-79-3(0)) Multicultural Pubns.

Jackson, Carolyn E. Tales from the Master. 2004. per. 12.95 (978-0-9745866-2-5(5)) Innate Foundation Publishing.

Jackson, Gail. Three Stories for Children. 2007. 44p. pap. 7.95 (*978-0-533-15644-3(0)) Vantage Pr., Inc.

Jackson, Shirley. Shirley Jackson Collected Short Stories. Court, Robert, illus. 2001. (Great Author Ser.). (YA). (978-0-9709033-3-4(2)) Peterson Publishing Co., Inc.

Jacobs, Don. The Boy Who Saw Snowy Owls. 2003. 89p. pap. 8.95 (978-0-533-14191-3(5)) Vantage Pr., Inc.

Jacques, Brian. The Ribbajack & Other Curious Yarns. 2006. 176p. (J). (gr. 3). pap. 6.99 (978-0-14-240378-5(4) , Puffin) Penguin Group (USA) Inc.

—Seven Strange & Ghostly Tales. 1999. (gr. 5-8). lib. bdg. 14.15 (978-0-613-64214-9(7)) Tandem Library Bks.

Jaffe, Nina & Zeitlin, Steve. The Cow of No Color: Riddle Stories & Justice Tales from Around the World. Sherman, Whitney, illus. rev. ed. 1998. 128p. (J). (gr. 5-9). 17.95 (978-0-8050-3736-4(5) , Holt, Henry & Co. Bks. For Young Readers) Holt, Henry & Co.

James, C. L. R. The Nobbie Stories for Children & Adults. Webb, Constance, ed. 2006. 120p. 17.95 (978-0-8032-2608-1(X)) Univ. of Nebraska Pr.

James, Henry. Henry James: Selected Tales. 2001. (gr. 7-12). lib. bdg. 22.25 (978-0-613-64285-9(6)) Tandem Library Bks.

James, Kathleen Lehigh. Feelings, A to Z. 2002. (J). 11.95 (978-1-930353-51-0(0)) Masthof Pr.

Jantti, Mariana. Cuanta gente! Quienes Son? Amelio-Ortiz, Osvaldo P. & Rodriguez Vidal, Andrea, illus. 2005. (SPA.). 28p. (J). 14.95 (978-9974-7799-2-1(8) , nicanitas) Hardenville SA URY. Dist: Independent Pubs. Group.

Jaroszko, Mike. Children's Classics. 2002. (Illus.). 96p. (J). 12.98 (978-0-7853-6910-3(4) , 7168400) Publications International, Ltd.

Jarvis, Carol & Flosi, Jeanne. Ellie Rose & the Terrible Stomach Ache. 2006. (ENG., Illus.). 40p. (J). per. 13.95 (*978-1-59800-760-2(2)) Outskirts Press, Inc.

Jelloun, Tahar Ben. Papa ?Que Es el Racismo? 2002. (SPA.). (gr. 5-8). lib. bdg. 17.60 (978-0-613-71259-0(5)) Tandem Library Bks.

—Papa, Que Es el Racismo? 2003. Tr. of Racism Explaine to My Daughter. (SPA.). 92p. (J). (gr. 3-5). pap. 8.95 (978-968-19-1014-3(1)) Santillana USA Publishing Co., Inc.

Jennings, Paul. Paul Jennings' Weirdest Stories. 2008. 400p. (J). pap. 20.00 (*978-0-670-07064-0(5) , Penguin Global) Penguin Group (USA) Inc.

—Thirteen Unpredictable Tales. l.t. ed. 2005. (Illus.). 264p. (J). pap. (978-0-7540-6169-4(8) , CLP 362) BBC Audio.

—Unbearable! More Bizarre Stories. l.t. ed. 2005. (Illus.). 184p. (J). pap. incl. audio (978-0-7540-7856-2(6) , CLP 445) BBC Audio.

—Unseen! l.t. ed. 2005. 192p. (J). pap. (978-0-7540-7921-7(X) , CLP 478) BBC Audio.

Jewel Cases: Five Classic Mysteries of Theft. 2002. (Fingerprint Classics Ser.). 112p. (J). (978-1-57924-841-3(1)) Jones, Bob Univ. Pr.

Jippes, Daan, et al. Walt Disney's Comics & Stories, Vol. 666. 2006. 64p. pap. 6.95 (978-1-888472-19-6(7)) Gemstone Publishing, Inc.

Jocelyn, Marthe, ed. First Times. 2007. 200p. (J). (gr. 5-8). pap. 9.95 (*978-0-88776-777-7(X)) Tundra Bks., Inc./ Livres Toundra, Inc. CAN. Dist: Random Hse., Inc.

Jocelyn, Marthe, selected by. Secrets. 2005. 184p. (J). (gr. 4-7). pap. 8.95 (978-0-88776-723-4(0)) Tundra Bks., Inc./Livres Toundra, Inc. CAN. Dist: Random Hse., Inc.

Johnson, Angela, et al. Tripping over the Lunch Lady. Mercado, Nancy, ed. 2006. 192p. (J). (gr. 5). pap. 5.99 (978-0-14-240624-3(4) , Puffin) Penguin Group (USA) Inc.

Johnson, Barbara & Johnson, Priscilla. The Bread of Life: A Collection of Orthodox Short Stories. 1999. (Illus.). vii, 110p. (YA). pap. 8.50 (978-0-913026-48-9(4)) St. Nectarios Pr.

Johnson, Devon. Amber's Children Stories. 2001. (J). pap. 9.00 (978-0-8059-5238-4(1)) Dorrance Publishing Co., Inc.

Johnson, Liliane & Dufton, Jo S. Children's Chillers & Thrillers. Bruhn, Joan Z., illus. 136p. (Orig.). (J). pap. 10.00 (978-0-930069-04-9(8)) Jasmine Pr.

Johnson, Sally. Alfabeto Animal.Tr. of Animal Alphabet. (SPA., Illus.). (J). pap. 10.95 (978-950-04-2009-9(0)) Emecé Editores S.A. ARG. Dist: Planeta Publishing Corp.

Johnson, Tammie D. Tammie's Tales: An ABC Cat Series Featuring Simon, the S Cat. 2004. (J). 14.95 (978-1-58597-288-3(6)) Leathers Publishing.

Jolly, Mike. I'll See You in the Morning. Mariuchi, Mique, illus. 2005. 32p. (J). (ps-7). bds. 12.95 (978-0-8118-5037-7(4)) Chronicle Bks. LLC.

Jonah & the Junkyard Sled. 2001. 52p. per. 5.95 (978-1-931319-48-5(0)) Max Media, Inc.

Jones, Carol. Lake of the Lost. 2005. (Illus.). 160p. pap. (978-0-7344-0646-0(0) , Lothian Bks.) Hachette Livre Australia.

Jones, Diana Wynne. Stopping for a Spell. 2004. (gr. 3-6). lib. bdg. 14.15 (978-0-613-81137-8(2)) Tandem Library Bks.

—Unexpected Magic: Collected Stories. (J). 2006. 608p. pap. 7.99 (978-0-06-055535-1(1)); 2004. 512p. (gr. 5 up). 16.99 (978-0-06-055533-7(5)); 2004. 512p. (gr. 5 up). lib. bdg. 17.89 (978-0-06-055534-4(3)) HarperCollins Pubs.

Jones, Karen. Stories from the Television Show Imagination Way. 2006. 10.00 (978-0-8059-8195-7(0)) Dorrance Publishing Co., Inc.

Jones, Laureen. Tales of the Wish Faries. 2002. 138p. pap. 10.95 (978-0-595-22929-1(8) , Writers Club Pr.) iUniverse, Inc.

Jones, Terry & Newman, Nanette. Bedtime Stories. Foreman, Michael, illus. 2007. 192p. (J). pap. 16.99 (*978-1-84458-477-2(1)) Anova Bks. GBR. Dist: Independent Pubs. Group.

Joseph, Lynn. El Color de Mis Palabras. 2004. (SPA., Illus.). (YA). pap. 5.99 (978-1-930332-75-1(0)) Lectorum Pubns., Inc.

Joy Cowley Novels: Novel Set. (Joy Cowley Novels Ser.). 181p. (gr. 3-6). 16.50 (978-0-7802-8509-5(3)) Wright Group, The.

Juliao, David S. El Pais Mas Hermoso del Mundo. (Torre de Papel Ser.). (SPA., Illus.). (J). (gr. 2). 7.95 (978-958-04-0747-8(9)) Norma S.A. COL. Dist: Distribuidora Norma, Inc.

Jungman, Ann. The Prince Who Thought He Was a Rooster. 2008. 96p. (J). 14.95 (*978-1-84507-793-8(8)); (Illus.). pap. 7.95 (*978-1-84507-794-5(6)) Lincoln, Frances Ltd. GBR. Dist: Perseus Distribution.

Juravel, Dovid. A Journey with Rabbi Juravel: Lost on the Train & Other Stories. Toron, Eli, illus. 2002. 287p. (J). 21.95 (978-1-931681-37-7(6)) Israel Bk. Shop.

Juravel, Rabbi. A Journey with Rabbi Juravel III: The Great Escape & Other Stories. 2004. (Illus.). 252p. (J). 21.95 (978-1-931681-63-6(5)) Israel Bk. Shop.

Kahl, Virginia. The Duchess Bakes a Cake. Kahl, Virginia, illus. 2002. 32p. 17.95 (978-1-930900-14-1(7)) Purple Hse. Pr.

Kahn, Michele. Un Ordenador Nada Ordinario. LaPointe, Claude, illus. 2003. (SPA.). 104p. (J). (gr. 3-5). 13.95 (978-84-204-4817-6(6)) Alfaguara, Ediciones, S.A.-Grupo Santillana ESP. Dist: Santillana USA Publishing Co., Inc.

Kahn, Sheryl. Disney's Family Story Collection. 1999. 192p. (J). 19.99 (978-0-7868-3255-2(X)) Disney Pr.

Kallevig, Christine P. Fold-Along Stories: Quick & Easy Origami Tales for Beginners. 2001. 80p. pap. 11.50 (978-0-9628769-9-8(2)) Storytime Ink International.

Kalpish Ratna. Nyagrodha. Pandya, Yamini, illus. 2006. 287p. (J). (*978-0-670-04969-1(7) , Puffin) Penguin Group (USA) Inc.

Kane, Andrea. La Mascara de la Traicion. 2000. Tr. of Treason Mask. (SPA.). 286p. (978-84-01-50950-6(5)) Plaza & Janes Editories, S.A.

Kangeroo Kazoo. 2001. (ps-2). lib. bdg. 9.80 (978-0-613-32735-0(7)) Tandem Library Bks.

Kangira, Jairos. Creatures Great & Small: A Collection of Short Stories. 2005. vi, 114p. (*978-0-86922-786-2(6)) Mambo Pr.

Kanter. Encuentros Maravillosos: Gramatica a Traves de la Literatura. 1999. (SPA.). (YA). (gr. 9-12). 371p. stu. ed. 57.29 (978-0-673-21595-6(4)); 140p. tchr. ed. 23.47 (978-0-673-21598-7(9)); 371p. stu. ed., spiral bd. 29.47 (978-0-673-21596-3(2)); 75p. stu. ed., suppl. ed. 18.47 (978-0-673-21597-0(0)) Addison Wesley Schl. (Scott Foresman).

Kanzler, Janine. Things Are Not As They Seem. 2004. 92p. (YA). 14.00 (978-0-9759363-0-6(1)) Fernhouse Pr.

Katsoris, Nick. Loukoumi. 2006. 30p. (J). (ps-3). 15.95 (978-0-9705100-1-3(2)) Katsoris, Nicholas C.

Katz, Alan. Hairy Henry. Motoyama, Keiko, illus. 2007. 12p. (J). bds. 6.99 (978-1-4169-1833-2(7) , Little Simon) Simon & Schuster Children's Publishing.

Kaufman, Ruth & Bianki. Del Otro Lado del Mundo. Bianki, illus. 2001. (SPA., Illus.). 40p. (J). 15.95 (978-950-511-516-7(4)) Alfaguara S.A. de Ediciones ARG. Dist: Santillana USA Publishing Co., Inc.

Kavanagh, Herminie Templeton. Darby O'Gill & the Crocks of Gold: And Other Irish Tales. Schluenderfritz, Ted, illus. 2003. ix, 155p. (J). pap. 14.95 (978-1-928832-85-0(7)) Sophia Institute Pr.

Kawahara, Yumiko. Dolls, Vol. 2. Kawahara, Yumiko, illus. 2005. (Dolls Ser.). (Illus.). 216p. (YA). pap. 9.99 (978-1-59116-670-2(5)) Viz Media.

Keary, Annie & Keary, Eliza. Tales of the Norse Warrior Gods: The Heroes of Asgard. Brock, C. E., illus. 2005. 256p. (gr. 3-7). pap. 9.95 (978-0-486-44053-8(2)) Dover Pubns., Inc.

Keeler, Kathleen. I Double Dare You! More Stories to Scare You! Doucet, Bob, illus. 2002. (Hello Reader! Ser.). 40p. (J). pap. 3.99 (978-0-439-32255-3(3) , Cartwheel Bks.) Scholastic, Inc.

Keep Calm! Individual Title Six-Packs. (Bookweb Ser.). 32p. (gr. 4 up). 34.00 (978-0-7635-3732-6(2)) Rigby Education.

Kehl, Mark. Tournament of Fear: And Other Martial Arts Stories. Artenstein, Michael, ed. 1999. (Sports Shorts Ser.). (Illus.). 96p. (J). (gr. 3-7). 12.95 (978-1-56565-889-9(2) , 08892W, Roxbury Park) Lowell Hse.

Kelley, Amy. Spooky Campfire Stories. 2000. (Spooky Ser.). (Illus.). 116p. (J). pap. 7.95 (978-1-56044-867-9(9) , Falcon) Globe Pequot Pr., The.

Kelsey, Avonelle. Grandma Says, 4 bks., Set. Kelsey, Avonelle, illus. (Series of Short Stories). (Illus.). 200p. (J). (978-0-9640610-1-9(5)) Cheval International.

Kemp, Anna. Happy Tales to You: A Mix of Six. 2006. (ENG.). 76p. per. 14.95 (*978-1-4241-4642-0(9)) PublishAmerica, Inc.

Kemp, Moira. Tell Me a Story, Daddy. 2006. (Illus.). 32p. (J). pap. (978-0-340-87560-5(7) , Hodder Children's Books) Hodder Children's Division.

Kempton, Linda. Who'll Catch the Nightmares? 2000. (Illus.). 188p. (J). pap. 8.99 (978-0-7497-4491-5(X)) Egmont Bks., Ltd. GBR. Dist: Independent Pubs. Group.

Kenney, Cindy. Bob & Larry's Favorite Stories. 2004. bds. 16.95 (978-0-310-70791-2(9)) Zonderkidz.

Kenrick, Joanna. Tears of a Friend. 2004. (Shades Ser.). 56p. (J). pap. 8.99 (978-0-237-52731-0(6) , Evans Brothers, Limited) Evans Publishing Group GBR. Dist: Independent Pubs. Group.

Kerr, Judith. Mog Collection, 6 vols. Kerr, Judith, illus. 2007. 1p. (J). (gr. k-2). pap., pap., pap. 35.00 (*978-0-00-725944-1(1)) HarperCollins Pubs. Ltd. GBR. Dist: Independent Pubs. Group.

Kerrin, Jessica Scott. Martin Bridge: On the Lookout! Kelly, Joseph, illus. 2005. 144p. (978-1-55337-773-3(7)) Kids Can Pr., Ltd.

Keystone Books. (Illus.). 40p. (YA). (gr. 2-3). lib. bdg. 259.09 (978-1-59889-020-4(4)) Stone Arch Bks.

Khing, T. T. Where Is the Cake? 2007. (Illus.). 28p. (J). (ps-3). 12.95 (*978-0-8109-1798-9(X) , Abrams Bks. for Young Readers) Abrams, Harry N. , Inc.

Kick, J. D. The Amazing Tale of Archie the Alligator. Just, John, illus. 2nd ed. 2003. (J). per. 12.95 (978-1-929424-16-6(0) , Owl Creek Farm Bks.) Owl Tree Pr.

Kids in the Kitchen Story Book. 2005. (J). 15.95 (978-1-59649-430-5(1)) Whispering Pine Pr., Inc.

Kids' Kindness Story Book. 2005. (J). 19.95 (978-1-59649-416-9(6)) Whispering Pine Pr., Inc.

Kimmel, Eric A. The Jar of Fools: Eight Hanukkah Stories from Chelm. Gerstein, Mordicai, illus. 64p. (J). (gr. 4-6). tchr. ed. 18.95 (978-0-8234-1463-5(9)) Holiday Hse., Inc.

—The Lady in the Blue Cloak: Legends from the Texas Missions. Guevera, Susan, illus. 2005. 40p. (J). 16.95 (978-0-8234-1738-4(7)) Holiday Hse., Inc.

—Sword of the Samurai: Adventure Stories from Japan. Evans, Michael, illus. 2000. (Trophy Chapter Bks.). 112p. (J). (gr. 2-5). pap. 4.99 (978-0-06-442131-7(7) , Harper Trophy) HarperCollins Pubs.

Kimmel, Eric A. & Kang, Setha. The Rolling Stone: And Other Read Aloud Stories. Kuon, Vuthy, illus. 2004. 36p. (J). (gr. k-6). 15.95 (978-0-9651661-2-6(0)) Providence Publishing.

Kincaid, Eric, adapted by. Fabulas Clasicas.Tr. of Classic Fables. (SPA.). 64p. (J). (gr. 3-5). 10.80 (978-84-241-5430-1(4)) Aguilar Editorial MEX. Dist: Lectorum Pubns., Inc.

Kindt, Matt. Super Spy. 2007. 304p. (YA). pap. 19.95 (*978-1-891830-96-9(1)) Top Shelf Productions.

Kingfisher Editors, ed. Marvelous Magical Stories. 2007. (Super Shorts Ser.). 160p. (J). (gr. k-3). pap. 6.95 (978-0-7534-6072-6(6) , Kingfisher) Houghton Mifflin Co. Trade & Reference Div.

—Seriously Spooky Stories. 2007. (Super Shorts Ser.). 160p. (J). (gr. k-3). pap. 6.95 (978-0-7534-6074-0(2) , Kingfisher) Houghton Mifflin Co. Trade & Reference Div.

—You're the Best! 2006. 224p. (J). (gr. 5-9). pap. 7.95 (978-0-7534-5997-3(3) , Kingfisher) Houghton Mifflin Co. Trade & Reference Div.

Kinney, Robert & Kinney, Donald. Stories for Young Readers. 2000. (Illus.). 100p. (YA). Vol. 1. (gr. 3-10). per. (978-0-9702889-0-5(5)); Vol. 2. (gr. 9 up). per. (978-0-9702889-1-2(3)) Kinney Brothers Publishing.

Kipling, Bozenka. Stories from the Inner World: Introducing My Best Friends. Sawatzky, Goranka, illus. 2002. 48p. pap. (978-7-80127-995-8(6)) Seed Children, Inc.

—Together We Are Stronger. Sawatzky, Goranka, illus. 2002. 48p. (YA). (ps up). pap. (978-0-9689096-2-1(0)) Seed Children, Inc.

Kipling, R. Complete Children's Stories. 2005. (ENG., Illus.). 864p. pap. (*978-1-84022-057-5(0)) Wordsworth Editions, Ltd.

Kipling, Rudyard. The Jungle Book: Mowgli's Story. Bayley, Nicola, illus. unabr. ed. 2005. 160p. (J). (gr. 4-7). 19.99 (978-0-7636-2317-3(2)) Candlewick Pr.

—The Jungle Books. (Borders Classics Ser.). 276p. 7.95 (978-1-58726-165-7(0)) Ann Arbor Media Group, LLC.

—The Jungle Books. 2004. (Barnes & Noble Classics Ser.). (Illus.). 432p. pap. 5.95 (978-1-59308-109-6(X)) Barnes & Noble, Inc.

—The Jungle Books. 2005. 336p. (gr. 12). pap. 4.95 (978-0-451-52975-6(8) , Signet Classics) Penguin Group (USA) Inc.

—Just So Stories. 2003. (Illus.). 224p. (J). (gr. 2-9). 7.99 (978-0-517-26655-7(5) , Gramercy) Random Hse. Value Publishing.

—Just So Stories. Kipling, Rudyard, illus. 2002. (Aladdin Classics Ser.). 208p. (J). pap. 4.99 (978-0-689-85125-4(1) , Aladdin) Simon & Schuster Children's Publishing.

—Just So Stories Set: For Little Children. Salter, Safaya, illus. 2003. (Chrysalis Children's Classics Ser.). 125p. (YA). pap. (978-1-84365-036-2(3)) Chrysalis Children's Bks.

—Just So Stories Set: For Little Children. 2001. (Dover Juvenile Classics Ser.). (Illus.). 112p. (J). (gr. 4-7). pap. 2.50 (978-0-486-41722-6(0)) Dover Pubns., Inc.

—Just So Stories Set: For Little Children. 2003. (Illus.). 146p. 8.95 (978-1-84232-944-3(8)) House of Stratus, Inc. GBR. Dist: Midpoint Trade Bks., Inc.

—Just So Stories Set: For Little Children. Date not set. (Illus.). 192p. (YA). (gr. 3 up). reprint ed. 7.95 (978-1-56852-137-4(5) , Konecky & Konecky) Konecky, William S. Assocs., Inc.

—Just So Stories Set: For Little Children. Lewis, Lisa, ed. Kipling, Rudyard, illus. 1998. (Oxford World's Classics Ser.). (Illus.). 304p. 5.95 (978-0-19-283436-2(3)) Oxford Univ. Pr., Inc.

—Just So Stories Set: For Little Children. 100th anniv. ed. 2002. (Illus.). 160p. mass mkt. 4.95 (978-0-451-52836-0(0) , Signet Classics) Penguin Group (USA) Inc.

—Just So Stories Set: For Little Children. 2002. (gr. 3-6). lib. bdg. 11.80 (978-0-613-63205-8(2)); (gr. 5-8). lib. bdg. 12.95 (978-0-613-52417-9(9)) Tandem Library Bks.

—Just So Stories Set: For Little Children. 1998. (Children's Classics). (ENG., Illus.). 144p. (J). pap. (978-1-85326-102-2(5) , 1025WW) Wordsworth Editions, Ltd.

—Land & Sea Tales. 2001. 194p. 8.95 (978-1-84232-946-7(4)) House of Stratus, Inc. GBR. Dist: Midpoint Trade Bks., Inc.

—Rudyard Kipling: The Complete Children's Short Stories. 2006. (Illus.). 854p. (J). (gr. 4-8). reprint ed. pap. 22.00 (978-0-7567-9857-4(4)) DIANE Publishing Co.

—Rudyard Kipling Collected Short Stories. Court, Robert, illus. 2001. (Great Author Ser.). (J). (978-0-9709033-6-5(7)) Peterson Publishing Co., Inc.

—Rudyard Kipling's Just So Stories. Sis, Peter, illus. 2004. 128p. (J). (ps up). 22.99 (978-0-7636-2629-7(5)) Candlewick Pr.

Kirk, Kathy. A Day in the Life of Children Around the World: A Collection of Short Stories. 2001. (Illus.). 108p. (J). (gr. 3-5). pap. 9.95 (978-0-595-15542-2(1)) iUniverse, Inc.

The Klondike Kid. 2005. (J). pap. (*978-1-60015-070-8(5)) Steps To Literacy, LLC.

Knapp, Toni. Ordinary Splendors: Tales of Virtues & Wisdom. Sohl, Kevin, illus. 2000. 43p. (YA). (gr. 5-7). reprint ed. 16.00 (978-0-7881-6845-1(2)) DIANE Publishing Co.

Knowles, Tizzie, illus. Stories for Six Year Olds. 2004. (Kingfisher Treasury of Stories Ser.). 160p. (J). (gr. k-3). pap. 5.95 (978-0-7534-5712-2(1) , Kingfisher) Houghton Mifflin Co. Trade & Reference Div.

Koch, Carl, ed. Friends: Stories by Teenagers. 2003. (Stories by Teenagers Ser.: Vol. 2). (Illus.). 128p. (J). pap. 6.95 (978-0-88489-492-6(4)) St. Mary's Pr.

—I Know Things Now: Stories by Teenagers. 2003. (Stories by Teenagers Ser.: Vol. 1). (Illus.). 128p. (YA). (gr. 7-12). pap. 6.95 (978-0-88489-384-4(7)) St. Mary's Pr.

Koda-Callan, Elizabeth. Good Luck Pony. Koda-Callan, Elizabeth, illus. 2005. (Illus.). 48p. (J). (ps-ps). 9.95 (978-0-7611-3828-0(5) , 13828) Workman Publishing Co., Inc.

Koenig, John H. Stories to Learn By. Huddleston, Christine, illus. rev. ed. 2000. 160p. (J). (gr. k-4). pap. 12.95 (978-0-8198-6993-7(7) , 332-329) Pauline Bks. & Media.

Konigsburg, E. L. Altogether, One at a Time. Konigsburg, E. L., illus. 2002. (Illus.). 13.40 (978-0-7587-9170-2(4)) Book Wholesalers, Inc.

—Altogether, One at a Time. Mayer, Mercer et al, illus. 2nd ed. 1998. 88p. (YA). (gr. 3-7). reprint ed. pap. 4.99 (978-0-689-71290-6(1) , Aladdin) Simon & Schuster Children's Publishing.

—Altogether, One at a Time. 1999. (J). (gr. 3-6). lib. bdg. 13.00 (978-0-613-07223-6(5)) Tandem Library Bks.

Kosteinshek, Roland Michael. Are We There Yet? 2001. 48p. (J). per. (978-1-55306-246-2(9) , Guardian Bks.) Essence Publishing.

Krahn, Fernando. Un Paseo al Campo. Krahn, Fernando, illus. 2003. (SPA., Illus.). 29p. (J). (gr. k-3). pap. 7.95 (978-956-239-066-8(7)) Santillana USA Publishing Co., Inc.

—Quien Ha Visto las Tijeras? 2004. Tr. of Who Hass Seen the Scissors?. (SPA., Illus.). (J). 20.99 (978-84-8464-149-0(X)) Kalandraka Editora, S.L. ESP. Dist: Lectorum Pubns., Inc.

Krailing, Tessa. La Cabrita Revoltosa. (Club de las Mascotas Coleccion). (SPA.). 96p. (J). (gr. 3-5). (978-84-88061-88-1(9)) Serres, Ediciones, S. L. ESP. Dist: Lectorum Pubns., Inc.

Kranzler, Gershon. Chanan & His Violin & Other Stories. Waldman, Bryna, illus. 1999. 114p. (gr. 4-8). 13.95 (978-0-8266-0349-4(1)) Merkos L'Inyonei Chinuch.

Krensky Stephen. John Henry. Oldroyd, Mark, illus. 2007. (On My Own Folklore Ser.). (J). pap. 6.95 (*978-0-8225-6477-5(7) , First Avenue Editions) Lerner Publishing Group.

—Mike Fink. Reeves, Jeni, illus. 2007. (On My Own Folklore Ser.). (J). pap. 6.95 (*978-0-8225-6478-2(5) , First Avenue Editions) Lerner Publishing Group.

—Paul Bunyan. Orback, Craig, illus. 2007. (On My Own Folklore Ser.). (J). pap. 6.95 (*978-0-8225-6479-9(3) , First Avenue Editions) Lerner Publishing Group.

—Pecos Bill. Tong, Paul, illus. 2007. (On My Own Folklore Ser.). (J). pap. 6.95 (*978-0-8225-6475-1(0) , First Avenue Editions) Lerner Publishing Group.

Krohn, Genendel. The Miracle of the Rock & other Stories: Timeless Tales from the Lives of Our Sages. Pelleg, Tirtsa, illus. 2003. 56p. (J). 14.99 (978-1-58330-650-5(1)) Feldheim Pubs.

Kropp, Paul. El Lunatico y su Hermana Libertad. (SPA.). (YA). 9.95 (978-958-04-4386-5(6)) Norma S.A. COL. Dist: Distribuidora Norma, Inc.

—Running the Bases: Definitely Not a Book about Baseball. 2005. 160p. (YA). pap. (978-0-385-66147-8(9) , Doubleday Can) Doubleday Canada, Ltd. CAN. Dist: Random Hse., Inc.

Krulik, Nancy E., adapted by. Lucy. ed. 2005. (Illus.). 32p. (J). lib. bdg. 15.00 (978-1-59054-950-6(3)) Fitzgerald Bks.

Kusugak, Michael Arvaarluk. Arctic Stories. Krykorka, Vladyana Langer, illus. 1998. 40p. (J). (gr. k-4). pap. 7.95 (978-1-55037-452-0(4)) Annick Pr., Ltd. CAN. Dist: Firefly Bks., Ltd.

—Arctic Stories. 1999. (J). (978-0-606-16482-5(0)) Tandem Library Bks.

Kvasnosky, Laura McGee. Zelda & Ivy & the Boy Next Door: Three Stories about the Fabulous Fox Sisters. Kvasnosky, Laura McGee, illus. 2003. (Illus.). 48p. (J). (gr. k-4). pap. 6.99 (978-0-7636-1053-1(4)) Candlewick Pr.

Kyber, Manifred. Fables & Fairytales to Delight All Ages Book Two: Gossamer Kingdoms. 2007. 140p. per. (***978-1-84401-985-4(3)***) Athena Pr.

Labrosse, Darcia. One Yak Called Jack. (Illus.). 32p. 14.95 (***978-0-224-04685-5(3)*** , Jonathan Cape) Random Hse. Children's Bks. GBR. *Dist:* Trafalgar Square Publishing.

Lacasse, Michael. George & His Special New Friends. 2005. 48p. pap. 12.95 (978-1-4137-8285-1(X)) PublishAmerica, Inc.

Lago, Angela. Juan Felizario Contento: El Rey de los Negocios. 2004. (Los Especials de A la Orilla Del Viento Ser.). (SPA., Illus.). 28p. (J). (ps-13). 11.99 (978-968-16-7047-4(7)) Fondo de Cultura Economica USA.

Laird, Elizabeth. Hot Rock Mountain. 2004. (Illus.). 160p. (J). pap. 8.99 (978-1-4052-0324-1(2)) Egmont Bks., Ltd. GBR. *Dist:* Independent Pubs. Group.

Lal, Ranjit. Caterpillar Who Went on a Diet & Other Stories. 2004. (Illus.). 188p. (J). pap. (978-0-14-333593-1(6) , Puffin) Penguin Group (USA) Inc.

LaMaster, Melissa. Appaloosa Tales with a Christmas Spirit. 2006. 48p. pap. 12.95 (978-1-4241-3153-2(7)) PublishAmerica, Inc.

Lamb, Charles & Lamb, Mary. Shakespeare's Plays in Story Form. unabr. ed. 2002. (YA). pap. incl. audio compact disk (978-1-58472-358-5(0) , In Audio) Sound Room Pubs., Inc.

Lambert, Janet. Just Jenifer. 2001. (Jordon Ser.: Vol. 1). (YA). pap. 12.95 (978-1-930009-32-5(1)) Image Cascade Publishing.

—Myself & I. 2001. (Jordon Ser.: Vol. 6). (YA). pap. 12.95 (978-1-930009-37-0(2)) Image Cascade Publishing.

—The Stars Hang High. 2001. (Jordon Ser.: Vol. 7). (YA). pap. 12.95 (978-1-930009-38-7(0)) Image Cascade Publishing.

Lambert, Thelma. Surprise Disguise. (Illus.). 32p. (J). 13.95 (978-0-241-00296-4(6) , Hamilton, Hamish) Penguin Bks., Ltd. GBR. *Dist:* Trafalgar Square Publishing.

Lamprecht, Edith Hertel. Little Star Stories. Lamprecht, Andrew Parker, illus. 2000. 60p. (J). (ps-6). pap. 7.50 (978-0-9704468-0-0(2)) Lamprecht, Edith Hertel.

Lampshire Hayden, Gwendolen. Really Truly Stories #5/9. 2006. (Illus.). 130p. (YA). per. 11.95 (978-1-57258-437-2(8) , 945-6298) TEACH Services, Inc.

—Really Truly Stories #6/9. 2006. (Illus.). 128p. (YA). per. 11.95 (***978-1-57258-438-9(6)*** , 945-6299) TEACH Services, Inc.

—Really Truly Stories #7/9. 2007. (Illus.). 126p. per. 11.95 (***978-1-57258-439-6(4)*** , 945-6300) TEACH Services, Inc.

—Really Truly Stories #8/9. 2007. (Illus.). 126p. pap. 11.95 (***978-1-57258-440-2(8)***) TEACH Services, Inc.

—Really Truly Stories #9/9. 2007. (Illus.). 125p. pap. 11.95 (***978-1-57258-441-9(6)***) TEACH Services, Inc.

Lanagan, Margo. Black Juice. 2005. 208p. (J). (gr. 7 up). 15.99 (978-0-06-074390-1(5)); lib. bdg. 16.89 (978-0-06-074391-8(3)) HarperCollins Pubs.

—White Time. 2006. 224p. (J). (gr. 7 up). 15.99 (978-0-06-074393-2(X) , Eos); lib. bdg. 16.89 (978-0-06-074394-9(8)) HarperCollins Pubs.

Landen, Cynthia & Phillips, Lorrie. The Elson Readers, Primer. 2005. pap. (***978-1-890623-24-1(5)***) Lost Classics Bk. Co.

Landon, Letitia Elizabeth. Traits & Trials of Early Life. 1999. (Scholars' Facsimiles & Reprints Ser.: Vol. 523). 342p. reprint ed. 75.00 (978-0-8201-1523-8(1)) Scholars' Facsimiles & Reprints.

Lane Gross, Ila. Uncommon Tales Around the World: Global Understanding/Cultural Literacy. 2004. (Illus.). (YA). pap. 6.95 (978-0-9713649-6-7(6)) L.E.A.P. (Learning through an Expanded Arts Program, Inc).

Lane, Nickel. Dream Able. 1999. 29p. 7.61 (978-1-4116-0376-9(1)) Lulu.com.

Lang. Strange Story Book. 2006. pap. 31.95 (***978-1-4304-4181-6(X)***) Kessinger Publishing, LLC.

Lang, Andrew. Prince Ricardo of Pantouflia: Being the. 2006. (Illus.). pap. 24.95 (***978-1-4286-0645-6(9)***) Kessinger Publishing, LLC.

Lang, Andrew, ed. The Chronicles of Pantouflia. (J). 20.95 (978-0-89190-088-7(8)) Amereon LTD.

—The Red Book of Animal Stories 1899. Ford, Henry J., illus. 2004. reprint ed. pap. 34.95 (978-1-4179-8249-3(7)) Kessinger Publishing, LLC.

Lankester-Brisley, Joyce. Milly-Molly-Mandy Storybook. 2001. (Milly-Molly-Mandy Ser.). (Illus.). 224p. (J). (gr. k-3). tchr. ed. 13.95 (978-0-7534-5332-2(0) , Kingfisher) Houghton Mifflin Co. Trade & Reference Div.

Lansky, Bruce. Girls to the Rescue, Bk. 7. 2000. (Illus.). 120p. (J). (gr. 3-7). pap. 3.95 (978-0-689-84079-1(9)) Meadowbrook Pr.

—Girls to the Rescue. No. 6. 1999. (978-0-606-17665-1(9)); No. 7. 2000. (gr. 3-6). lib. bdg. 11.80 (978-0-613-31245-5(7)) Tandem Library Bks.

Lansky, Bruce, ed. The Best of Girls to the Rescue. 2002. (Girls to the Rescue Ser.). 250p. (J). pap. 5.95 (978-0-689-02468-9(1)) Meadowbrook Pr.

Larousse Staff, ed. Una Navidad Inolvidable. 2003. (SPA., Illus.). 112p. (J). (gr. k-3). tchr. ed. 11.95 (978-970-22-0421-3(6)) Larousse, Ediciones, S. A. de C. V. MEX. *Dist:* Houghton Mifflin Co. Trade & Reference Div.

Larson, Jean R. The Fish Bride & Other Gypsy Tales. Larson, Michael C., illus. 2000. 90p. (J). (ps up). 22.50 (978-0-208-02474-9(3) , Linnet Bks.) Shoe String Pr., Inc.

Lasky, Kathryn. Iron Girl (W. T.) 2007. 228p. (J). pap. 8.99 (978-0-689-86855-9(3) , Atheneum) Simon & Schuster Children's Publishing.

—The Outcast. 2005. (Guardians of Ga'Hoole Ser.: Bk. 8). (Illus.). 224p. (J). (gr. 4-7). pap. 4.99 (978-0-439-73951-1(9) , Scholastic Paperbacks) Scholastic, Inc.

Lattimore, Deborah Nourse. Winged Cat: And Other Tales of Ancient Civilization. 2002. (Illus.). 80p. (J). pap. 4.25 (978-0-06-442154-6(6) , Harper Trophy) HarperCollins Pubs.

Lavarello, Jose Maria, illus. Cuentame un Cuento, No. 2. (SPA.). 366p. (J). (gr. k-3). (978-84-480-1124-6(4) , TM2346) Timun Mas, Editorial S.A. ESP. *Dist:* Lectorum Pubns., Inc.

Law, Diane. Come Out & Play. 2006. (ENG, SPA, CHI, FRE & GER., Illus.). 24p. (J). 9.95 (978-0-7358-2060-9(0)) North-South Bks., Inc.

Lawrence, John, illus. The Kingfisher Treasury of Five-Minute Stories. 2004. (Kingfisher Treasury of Stories Ser.). 160p. (J). (gr. k-3). pap. 5.95 (978-0-7534-5726-9(1) , Kingfisher) Houghton Mifflin Co. Trade & Reference Div.

Lawrinson, Julia. Loz & Al. 2004. 148p. (Orig.). (J). pap. 13.50 (978-1-920731-24-3(5)) Fremantle Pr. AUS. *Dist:* International Specialized Bk. Services.

Lawson, Robert, et al. Newberry Award & Honor, abr. ed. 2000. (Illus.). (J). (gr. 4-7). pap. 99.95 incl. audio (978-0-87499-491-9(8)) Live Oak Media.

Lazewnik, Libby. The Burglar & Other Stories. 16.99 (978-1-56871-307-6(X)) Targum Pr., Inc.

—The Lemonade Lesson: And Other Stories. 1999. (Illus.). 196p. (gr. 3-9). 16.99 (978-1-56871-181-2(6)) Targum Pr., Inc.

—On the Road & Other Stories. 2000. 248p. (gr. 3-9). 15.95 (978-1-56871-162-1(X)) Targum Pr., Inc.

—The Thank You Note. 2002. 248p. 15.95 (978-1-56871-212-3(X)) Targum Pr., Inc.

Leach, Janet. Animal Tales. 2001. 124p. (J). pap. 10.95 (978-0-595-17898-8(7) , Writers Club Pr.) iUniverse, Inc.

LeapFrog Staff. Disney Princess Stories - France. 2003. (Illus.). spiral bd. 14.99 (978-1-59319-005-7(0)) LeapFrog Enterprises, Inc.

Leatham, Alan D. Four Cats, Five Monkeys, Absurd Birds & Other Fanciful Stuff. 2006. 108p. pap. 16.95 (***978-1-4241-0692-9(3)***) PublishAmerica, Inc.

Leather, Sue. Desert, Mountain, Sea: Short Stories, Level 4. Hedge, Tricia, ed. 2000. (Bookworms Ser.). (Illus.). 6.50 (978-0-19-423031-5(7)) Oxford Univ. Pr., Inc.

Leblanc, Louise. Sophie Court Après la Fortune. Gay, Marie-Louise, illus. 2001. (Premier Roman Ser.). (FRE.). 64p. (J). (gr. 1-4). pap. (978-2-89021-458-3(3)) Diffusion du livre Mirabel.

Lee, Betsy B. A Funny Dolch Word Book No. 1: Stories, Poems, Word Search Puzzles. l.t. ed. 2001. 24p. (J). pap. 5.95 (978-0-9658853-5-5(6)) Learning Abilities Bks.

—A Funny Dolch Word Book No. 2: Stories, Poems, Word Search Puzzles. 2001. 24p. (J). pap., wbk. ed. 5.95 (978-0-9658853-8-6(0)) Learning Abilities Bks.

—A Funny Dolch Word Book No. 3: Stories, Fables, Word Searches. 2001. 24p. pap., wbk. ed. 5.95 (978-0-9658853-9-3(9)) Learning Abilities Bks.

Lee, J. Marie. 4Teen Jellybean. 2003. 165p. (J). per. 19.95 (978-1-59196-327-1(3)) Instantpublisher.com.

Lee, Robert Chi-Kwong & Ong, Doreen Lee. Selections from the "100 Best" Children's Stories from China Vol. 1. 2000. (Illus.). 52p. (J). (ps-3). pap. 12.95 (978-0-9706876-0-9(5)) One Hundred Best Co., LLC.

Lefevre, Lucy B. Kenyo Finds a Mission. 2002. 108p. (J). pap. 9.95 (978-0-595-22619-1(1) , Writers Club Pr.) iUniverse, Inc.

LeFrancois, Anabel. Poems & Stories for Our Children. 2005. (Illus.). 91p. (J). per. 11.95 (978-1-59453-896-4(4) , Airleaf Publishing) Airleaf Publishing & Bookselling.

Lefrancois, Viateur. Coureurs des Bois a Clark City. Arseneau, Philippe & Drouin, Julie Saint-Onge, illus. 2003. (Collection des 9 Ans : Vol. 32). (FRE.). 136p. 8.95 (978-2-922565-69-0(6)) Editions de la Paix CAN. *Dist:* World of Reading, Ltd.

LeGrand, Hank, 3rd. Paddle Tail. Merrison, Stacy, illus. l.t. ed. 2004. 63p. (J). per. 7.95 (978-1-59466-020-7(4) , Growing Years) Port Town Publishing.

Leicester, Mal. Early Years Stories. 2006. (Illus.). xii, 106p. 41.50 (978-0-415-37603-7(3)) Routledge.

Leithart, Peters. Wise Words: Family Stories That Bring the Proverbs to Life. 2006. cd-rom 20.00 (***978-1-59128-585-4(2)***) Canon Pr.

Lemieux, Jean. Les Conquerants de L'infini. Casson, Sophie, illus. 2001. (FRE.). 64p. (J). pap. (978-2-89021-532-0(6)) Diffusion du livre Mirabel.

Lemonde, Connie. Short Stories: For the Young & Young at Heart. 2003. (YA). pap. 10.95 (978-1-932303-81-0(2) , Llumina Pr.) Media Creations, Inc.

Lenam, Salva. El aseo de Kiko. 2005. (Kiko Ser.). (SPA., Illus.). 10p. (J). 3.95 (978-84-95761-73-6(4)) Ediciones Norte, Inc.

—Buenas Noches, Kiko! Roman, Santi, illus. 2005. (Kiko Ser.). (SPA.). 10p. (J). 3.95 (978-84-95761-74-3(2)) Ediciones Norte, Inc.

—Kiko Dibuja y Pinta. Roman, Santi, illus. 2005. (Kiko Ser.). (SPA.). 10p. (J). 3.95 (978-84-95761-78-1(5)) Ediciones Norte, Inc.

—Kiko en Casa de los Abuelos. Roman, Santi, illus. 2005. (Kiko Ser.). (SPA.). 10p. (J). 3.95 (978-84-95761-81-1(5)) Ediciones Norte, Inc.

—A Kiko le Gusta la Playa. Roman, Santi, illus. 2005. (Kiko Ser.). (SPA.). 10p. (J). 3.95 (978-84-95761-75-0(0)) Ediciones Norte, Inc.

—A Kiko le Pican los Ojitos. Roman, Santi, illus. 2005. (Kiko Ser.). (SPA.). 10p. (J). 3.95 (978-84-95761-82-8(3)) Ediciones Norte, Inc.

—Kiko No Quiere Comer. Roman, Santi, illus. 2005. (Kiko Ser.). (SPA.). 10p. (J). 3.95 (978-84-95761-77-4(7)) Ediciones Norte, Inc.

—Kiko Ya Se Viste Solo. Roman, Santi, illus. 2005. (Kiko Ser.). (SPA.). 10p. (J). 3.95 (978-84-95761-80-4(7)) Ediciones Norte, Inc.

Lenihan, Edmund. Humorous Irish Tales for Children. 1998. 128p. pap. (978-1-85635-238-3(2)) Irish American Bk. Co.

Leo Hamilton's Odd Collection of Animal & Insect Stories Vol. 2: No Colored Pencils. 2000. per. 6.99 (978-0-9671660-7-0(1)) Story Place, The.

Leone, Dan. The Meaning of Lunch. 2000. 257p. (YA). pap. 14.95 (978-0-9666028-7-6(0) , Mammoth Bks.) Mammoth Pr., Inc.

Leppard, Lois Gladys. Mandie, Vols. 31-35. 2002. (Mandie Ser.). (Illus.). 832p. (J). 29.99 (978-0-7642-8942-2(X)) Bethany Hse. Pubs.

Lester, Julius. Long Journey Home: Stories from Black History. 2000. (J). (gr. 6 up). 20.75 (978-0-8446-7148-2(7)) Smith, Peter Pub., Inc.

—This Strange New Feeling: Three Love Stories from Black History. 2006. 208p. (YA). 16.99 (978-0-8037-3172-1(8) , Dial) Penguin Group (USA) Inc.

Levithan, David. How They Met, & Other Stories. 2008. (YA). (***978-0-375-84886-5(X)***); lib. bdg. (***978-0-375-94886-2(4)***) Knopf, Alfred A. Inc.

Levithan, David. The Realm of Possibility. 2004. 224p. (gr. 7). (J). lib. bdg. 17.99 (978-0-375-92845-1(6)); (YA). 15.95 (978-0-375-82845-4(1)) Random Hse. Children's Bks. (Knopf Bks. for Young Readers).

Levithan, David, ed. This Is PUSH: New Stories from the Edge. 2007. 240p. (J). (gr. 9 up). pap. 6.99 (978-0-439-89028-1(4) , PUSH) Scholastic, Inc.

—Where We Are, What We See. 2005. (Illus.). 288p. (J). pap. 7.99 (978-0-439-73646-6(3) , PUSH) Scholastic, Inc.

Levy, Nathan. Stories with Holes. Gordon, Juli A., ed. 2000. (Illus.). (J). Vol. 1. 32p. pap., tchr. ed. 5.99 (978-1-889319-49-0(X)); Vol. 2. 32p. pap., tchr. ed. 5.99 (978-1-889319-50-6(3)); Vol. 3. pap., tchr. ed. 5.99 (978-1-889319-51-3(1)); Vol. 4. pap., tchr. ed. 5.99 (978-1-889319-52-0(X)); Vol. 5. pap., tchr. ed. 5.99 (978-1-889319-53-7(8)); Vol. 6. pap., tchr. ed. 5.99 (978-1-889319-54-4(6)); Vol. 7. pap., tchr. ed. 5.99 (978-1-889319-55-1(4)); Vol. 8. pap., tchr. ed. 5.99 (978-1-889319-56-8(2)); Vol. 9. pap., tchr. ed. 5.99 (978-1-889319-57-5(0)); Vol. 10. pap., tchr. ed. 5.99 (978-1-889319-58-2(9)); Vol. 11. pap., tchr. ed. 5.99 (978-1-889319-59-9(7)); Vol. 12. pap., tchr. ed. 5.99 (978-1-889319-60-5(0)) Trend Enterprises, Inc. (MindMotion).

Lewis, Anthony, illus. The Kingfisher Treasury of Pony Stories. 2003. (Kingfisher Treasury of Stories Ser.). 160p. (J). (gr. k-3). pap. 5.95 (978-0-7534-5666-8(4) , Kingfisher) Houghton Mifflin Co. Trade & Reference Div.

Lewis, Beverly. Girls Only (Go!) (Girls Only (Go!) Ser.: Vols. 5-8). 512p. (J). 2002. (Illus.). pap. 27.99 (978-0-7642-8943-9(8)); 1999. (gr. 3-8). pap. 27.99 (978-0-7642-8552-3(1)) Bethany Hse. Pubs.

Lewis, C. S. The Lion, the Witch & the Wardrobe: Read-Aloud Edition. Baynes, Pauline, illus. 2005. (Chronicles of Narnia Ser.). 208p. (J). 14.99 (978-0-06-084524-7(4)) HarperCollins Pubs.

Lewis, Jan & Amery, Heather. Jan Lewis' Bedtime Stories. Lewis, Jan, illus. 2000. (Illus.). 90p. (J). (ps-1). 12.95 (978-1-57145-406-5(3) , Silver Dolphin Bks.) Advantage Pubs. Group.

Lewman, David. Chuckle & Cringe: SpongeBob's Book of Embarrassing Stories. 2007. (SpongeBob SquarePants Ser.). 48p. (J). pap. 3.99 (***978-1-4169-4746-2(9)*** , Simon Spotlight) Simon & Schuster Children's Publishing.

Leyendas Americanas. (Coleccion Leyendas). (SPA., Illus.). 64p. (J). vinyl bd. 16.95 (978-950-11-0133-1(9) , SGM133) Sigmar ARG. *Dist:* Continental Bk. Co., Inc.

Leyendas Argentinas. (Coleccion Leyendas). (SPA., Illus.). 64p. (J). vinyl bd. 16.95 (978-950-11-0132-4(0) , SGM132) Sigmar ARG. *Dist:* Continental Bk. Co., Inc.

Leyendas Universales. (Coleccion Leyendas). (SPA., Illus.). 64p. (J). vinyl bd. 16.95 (978-950-11-0002-0(2) , SGM131) Sigmar ARG. *Dist:* Continental Bk. Co., Inc.

Lias, Joe. The Wood Rats Dragging Their Long Tales. 2005. 183p. pap. 19.95 (978-1-4137-5900-6(9)) PublishAmerica, Inc.

Lichfield, Walter C. Fanciful Bear Stories for Small Kids & Factual Bear Stories for Big Kids. 2003. (Illus.). 84p. per. (978-1-931456-47-0(X)) Athena Pr.

Lilacs, Lotuses, & Ladybugs Set B, 6 vols. 32p. (gr. 1-3). 31.50 (978-0-7802-8052-6(0)) Wright Group, The.

Lily, Aunt. The Mystical Garden Path. Dove, Auntie, illus. 2001. 30p. (J). pap. 12.95 (978-0-9701704-2-2(4) , Diversified Productions) Williams Publishing Co.

Lim, Charlotte. Attack of the Swordfish & Other Singapore Tales: Text by Charlotte Lim: Illustrations by Alicia Tan Yen Ping: Creative Directing by Ruby Lim-Yang. 2005. (Illus.). 48p. (978-981-05-3215-4(6)) National Heritage Board.

Lincoln, Kelly J. Let's Go Storyknifing. Nevak, Caroline, illus. l.t. ed. 1999. 12p. (J). (gr. k-3). pap. 17.00 (978-1-58084-066-8(3)) Lower Kuskokwim Schl. District.

—Yaaruiyarciqukug. Nevak, Caroline, illus. l.t. ed. 1999. Tr. of Let's Go Story Knifing. (ESK.). 12p. (J). (gr. k-3). pap. 17.00 (978-1-58084-108-5(2)) Lower Kuskokwim Schl. District.

—Yaaruiyarluk. Nevak, Caroline, illus. l.t. ed. 1999. Tr. of Let's Go Story Knifing. (ESK.). 12p. (J). (gr. k-3). pap. 17.00 (978-1-58084-067-5(1)) Lower Kuskokwim Schl. District.

Lindo, Elvira. Amigos del Alma. Urberuaga, Emilio, illus. 2003. (Coleccion Derechos Del Nino Ser.). (SPA.). 32p. (J). (gr. 3-5). pap. 7.95 (978-84-204-5833-5(3)) Santillana USA Publishing Co., Inc.

Lindskoog, Kathryn & Hunsicker, Ranelda Mack, eds. Faerie Gold: Treasures from the Lands of Enchantment. 2005. (Classics for Young Readers Ser.). 304p. (J). per. 11.99 (978-0-87552-738-3(8)) P & R Publishing.

Lindwall, Laurie. Wings. 2002. (Illus.). 10p. (J). bds. (978-0-615-12314-1(7)) Little Teacher Bks.

Lister, Robin. The Odyssey. Baker, Alan, illus. 2004. (Kingfisher Epics Ser.). 176p. (J). (gr. 4-6). pap. 7.95 (978-0-7534-5723-8(7) , Kingfisher) Houghton Mifflin Co. Trade & Reference Div.

Little House Magazine, No. 1. 2000. (J). (978-0-06-028850-1(7)) HarperCollins Pubs.

Little Miss Atlas. 2000. (Tippy Parrish Story Ser.). (YA). (gr. 6-10). per. 12.95 (978-1-930009-19-6(4)) Image Cascade Publishing.

Little Tales Library. 2001. (J). 19.95 (978-0-7525-4795-4(X)) Parragon, Inc.

Lobel, Arnold. Adventure Stories That Will Thrill You. 2001. (gr. 3-6). lib. bdg. 11.80 (978-0-613-56166-2(X)) Tandem Library Bks.

Locker, Thomas. Mountain Dance: And Other Stories. Locker, Thomas, illus. 2001. (Illus.). 32p. (J). (gr. k-4). 17.00 (978-0-15-202622-6(3) , Silver Whistle) Harcourt Trade Pubs.

Lombard, Ernest. Remember the Seagulls: A Modern Fable. 2004. (Illus.). 32p. (J). 3.95 (978-0-9740473-0-0(9)) Pivotal Force.

London, Jack. Jack London Collected Short Stories. Court, Robert, illus. 2001. (Great Author Ser.). (YA). (978-0-9709033-4-1(0)) Peterson Publishing Co., Inc.

—Narraciones. 2000. (Coleccion "Clasicos Juveniles" Ser.). (SPA.). 196p. (gr. 4-7). pap. 8.95 (978-1-58348-785-3(9)) iUniverse, Inc.

—Rumbo Oeste y Otros Cuentos. (Clasicos Juveniles Coleccion). (SPA.). (YA). (gr. 5-8). pap. (978-950-11-1331-0(0) , SG2441) Sigmar ARG. *Dist:* Lectorum Pubns., Inc.

—To Build a Fire. 2003. (gr. 3-6). lib. bdg. 13.00 (978-0-613-89665-8(3)) Tandem Library Bks.

Long, Debbie. Short Stories with Imagination: The Imagination Series. 2004. 48p. (J). per. (978-1-55306-820-4(3) , Epic Pr.) Essence Publishing.

Longo, Jason, illus. Otto's Colorful Campus Tour - Syracuse University A-Z. 2004. (J). 9.99 (978-1-933069-04-3(X)) Odd Duck Ink, Inc.

Loomis, Christine. Hattie Hippo. Neubecker, Robert, illus. 2006. 32p. (J). pap. 16.99 (978-0-439-54340-8(1) , Orchard Bks.) Scholastic, Inc.

Lou Weber Staff, ed. Treasury of Mother Goose Rhymes. 2004. (Illus.). 384p. (J). 15.98 (978-0-7853-7391-9(8) , 3081901) Publications International, Ltd.

Loupy, Christophe. Hugs & Kisses. 2002. (Baby Faces Ser.). (Illus.). (J). bds. (978-0-439-33944-5(8)) Scholastic, Inc.

Love & Sex: Ten Stories of Truth. 2003. 225p. (YA). (gr. 8-12). per. 16.45 (978-0-613-60696-7(5)) Tandem Library Bks.

Lowell House Juvenile Staff. Million Dollar Bucket: And Other Stories about Your Favorite Sports. 2000. (Sports Shorts Ser.). (Illus.). 160p. (J). (gr. 3-7). pap. 5.95 (978-0-7373-0433-6(2) , 04332W, Roxbury Park) Lowell Hse.

Lowry, Lois. Stay! Keeper's Story. 1999. (978-0-606-16584-6(3)) Tandem Library Bks.

—Stay Keeper's Story. annual Kelley, True, illus. 1999. 128p. (J). (gr. 4-7). 5.50 (978-0-440-41524-4(1) , Yearling) Random Hse. Children's Bks.

Lowry, Lois, frwd. Shining On: 11 Star Authors' Illuminating Stories. 2007. 176p. (YA). (gr. 7). lib. bdg. 11.99 (978-0-385-90470-4(3) , Delacorte Bks. for Young Readers) Random Hse. Children's Bks.

Luba Folk Tales. 2005. (YA). 10.00 (978-1-59872-207-9(7)) Instantpublisher.com.

Lubar, David. The Curse of the Campfire Weenies: And Other Warped & Creepy Tales. rev. ed. 2007. 207p. (J). (gr. 5 up). 15.95 (***978-0-7653-1807-7(5)*** , Starscape) Doherty, Tom Assocs., LLC.

Lubar, David. Invasion of the Road Weenies: And Other Warped & Creepy Tales. 192p. (J). 2006. 5.99 (978-0-7653-5325-2(3)); 2005. 16.95 (978-0-7653-1447-5(9)) Doherty, Tom Assocs., LLC. (Starscape).

Lucas, Edward Verall. Forgotten Tales of Long Ago. 2006. (Illus.). pap. 36.95 (***978-1-4254-9801-6(9)***) Kessinger Publishing, LLC.

Luke, Deanna. What Good Is... Audio Story Book. 2001. (J). cd-rom 6.95 (978-1-928777-24-3(4) , BOW Bks.) Blessing Our World, Inc.

Luke, Pauline. Amber Pash on Pink. 2004. (Illus.). 160p. (Orig.). pap. 17.95 (978-0-7022-3428-6(1)) Univ. of Queensland Pr. AUS. *Dist:* International Specialized Bk. Services.

Lungus the Fungus. l.t. ed. 2001. 20p. (J). mass mkt. 4.99 (978-0-9713075-0-6(4)) Canasta Pr.

Lupton, Hugh. Freaky Tales from Far & Wide. Berkshire, Lisa, illus. 2000. 48p. (J). (ps-3). 15.95 (978-1-902283-16-6(3)) Barefoot Bks., Inc.

Lupton Hugh. Tales of Wisdom & Wonder. Sharkey Niamh, illus. 2006. 0064p. 15.99 (978-1-905236-84-8(0)) Barefoot Bks., Inc.

Lynch, P. J. & Wild, Oscar. Oscar Wilde Stories for Children. 2nd ed. 2007. (Illus.). (J). pap. (***978-0-340-89436-1(9)*** , Hodder Children's Books) Hodder Children's Division.

Lyons, Kay & Loh, Martin. Malaysian Children's Favorite Stories. 2004. (Illus.). 64p. (J). 16.95 (978-0-8048-3590-9(X)) Tuttle Publishing.

Lyons, Sarah. Fairy stories about sally & Mignonette. 2007. pap. 9.99 (***978-1-60034-860-0(2)***) Xulon Pr., Inc.

Lyrick Studios Staff. Barney's Count to 10. 1999. (Barney Ser.). (Illus.). 24p. (J). (ps-k). 6.95 (978-1-57064-623-2(6)) Scholastic, Inc.

Maar, Paul. La Puerta Olvidada. (Torre de Papel Ser.). (SPA.). (J). (gr. 2). 7.95 (978-958-04-1489-6(0)) Norma S.A. COL. *Dist:* Distribuidora Norma, Inc.

Mac Iver, Kathi. Ghosts of the Mining District. 2003. (Illus.). 60p. 9.95 (978-0-9651272-1-9(4)) Columbine Pr.

MacDonald, Betty. Hello, Mrs. Piggle-Wiggle. Boiger, Alexandra, illus. 2007. 192p. (J). lib. bdg. 16.89 ***(*978-0-06-125124-5(0))*** HarperCollins Pubs.

MacDonald, Margaret Read. Five-Minute Tales: More Stories to Read & Tell When Time Is Short. 2007. 160p. 24.95 ***(*978-0-87483-781-0(2));*** pap. 14.95 ***(*978-0-87483-782-7(0))*** August Hse. Pubs., Inc.

MacDonald, Margaret Read. Three-Minute Tales: Stories from Around the World to Tell or Read When Time Is Short. 2004. 160p. 24.95 (978-0-87483-728-5(6)); pap. 17.95 (978-0-87483-729-2(4)) August Hse. Pubs., Inc.

MacDonald, Maryann. Rabbit's Birthday Kite. Munsinger, Lynn, illus. 1999. (Bank Street Reader Collection). 48p. (J). (gr. 1-3). lib. bdg. 22.60 (978-0-8368-1779-9(6)) Stevens, Gareth Inc.

MacGregor, Roy. Forever: The Annual Hockey Classic. Deines, Brian, illus. 2005. 64p. (J). 22.95 (978-0-88995-306-2(6)) Red Deer Pr. CAN. *Dist:* Fitzhenry & Whiteside, Ltd.

MacHado, Ana Maria. Ah, Pajarita Si Yo Pudiera. (Torre de Papel Ser.). (SPA., Illus.). (J). 7.95 (978-958-04-4526-5(5) , NR31207) Norma S.A. COL. *Dist:* Distribuidora Norma, Inc., Lectorum Pubns., Inc.

—Aunque Parezca Mentira. (SPA., Illus.). 64p. (J). 16.95 (978-84-207-4412-4(3)) Grupo Anaya, S.A. ESP. *Dist:* Distribooks, Inc., Lectorum Pubns., Inc.

—El Barbero y el Coronel. Coll, Ivar Da, illus. Tr. of Barber & the Colonel. (SPA.). (J). (gr. 2-3). 7.95 (978-958-04-5035-1(8) , NR1718) Norma S.A. COL. *Dist:* Distribuidora Norma, Inc., Lectorum Pubns., Inc.

MacIntyre, R. P., ed. Takes: Stories for Young Adults. 2004. 160p. pap. (978-1-895449-54-9(5)) Thistledown Pr., Ltd.

—Up All Night. 2004. 160p. pap. (978-1-894345-27-9(4)) Thistledown Pr., Ltd.

MacLachlan, Patricia. Five Writers. 1998. (J). (978-0-385-32136-5(8) , Dell Books for Young Readers) Random Hse. Children's Bks.

MacLean, Moira, illus. In My Garden. 1999. (Magic Lanterns Ser.). 8p. (J). bds. 7.95 (978-1-57717-115-7(2)) New Line Bks.

—In the Woods. 1999. (Magic Lanterns Ser.). 8p. (J). bds. 7.95 (978-1-57717-116-4(0)) New Line Bks.

—On the Farm. 1999. (Magic Lanterns Ser.). 8p. (J). bds. 7.95 (978-1-57717-114-0(4)) New Line Bks.

MacPhail, Catherine. Fighting Back. (Illus.). 128p. (J). 7.95 (978-0-14-038270-9(4)) Penguin Bks., Ltd. GBR. *Dist:* Trafalgar Square Publishing.

—Fugitive. 128p. (J). (gr. k-6). 7.95 (978-0-14-038271-6(2)) Penguin Bks., Ltd. GBR. *Dist:* Trafalgar Square Publishing.

Madden, Gloria. Grandmother's Bedtime Stories, Bk. 3. 2003. (J). per. 14.50 (978-1-932301-31-1(3) , 1124) Airleaf Publishing & Bookselling.

—Grandmother's Bedtime Stories. 2005. 57p. pap. 12.95 (978-1-4137-6489-5(4)) PublishAmerica, Inc.

Maguire, Gregory. Leaping Beauty: And Other Animal Fairy Tales. Demarest, Chris L., illus. 2006. 224p. (J). reprint ed. pap. 5.99 (978-0-06-056419-3(9) , Harper Trophy) HarperCollins Pubs.

Mahy, Margaret. The Great Piratical Rumbustification & the Librarian & the Robbers. Blake, Quentin, illus. 2000. 32p. (J). pap. 6.95 (978-1-56792-169-4(8)) Godine, David R. Pub.

—El Rescate con el Chicle y Otras Historias. (Torre de Papel Ser.). (SPA.). (YA). (gr. 6). 8.95 (978-958-04-4146-5(4)) Norma S.A. COL. *Dist:* Distribuidora Norma, Inc.

Mahy, Margaret, et al. Don't Read This! And Other Tales of the Unnatural. 2004. (Illus.). 208p. (J). (gr. 4-7). per. 15.00 (978-0-606-33200-2(6)) Tandem Library Bks.

Mains, Barbara, ed. I Touched the Moon! Stories & Crafts for Kids. Lewis, Robin Baird et al, illus. Chevrier, Tim, photos by. 2001. 48p. (J). (ps-k). pap. 12.95 (978-1-55037-674-6(8)); lib. bdg. 19.95 (978-1-55037-675-3(6)) Annick Pr., Ltd. CAN. *Dist:* Firefly Bks., Ltd.

Maisner, Heather. Time to See the Doctor. Stephenson, Kristina, illus. 2004. (First Time Stories Ser.). 24p. (J). (gr. k-ps). pap. 3.95 (978-0-7534-5737-5(7) , Kingfisher) Houghton Mifflin Co. Trade & Reference Div.

Majid, Ellisha. A Sausage Went for a Walk. Kendall, Peter, illus. 2001. 24p. (J). pap. 9.95 (978-1-86368-007-3(1)) Fremantle Pr. AUS. *Dist:* International Specialized Bk. Services.

Malak, Annabel, illus. Three Little Pigs. 2000. (Classic Stories Ser.). 48p. (J). (ps-2). incl. audio (978-2-921997-73-7(8)) Coffragants.

Maltby, Ethel H. My Animal Story Book: A Treasury of Sunshine Stories for Children. Richardson, Frederick, illus. 2004. reprint ed. pap. 15.95 (978-1-4191-7300-4(6)) Kessinger Publishing, LLC.

Man-Kong, Mary & Golden Books Staff. The Magic of Pegasus: A Storybook. 2005. (Random House Pictureback Book Ser.). (Illus.). 24p. (J). (ps-2). pap. 3.99 (978-0-375-83337-3(4) , Golden Bks.) Random Hse. Children's Bks.

Manary, Adria. More Mommy Magic: 506 Ways to Nurture Your Child. 2005. 257p. pap. 14.95 (978-1-931643-65-8(2)) Seven Locks Pr.

Manning, Mick. Yuck! 2005. (Illus.). 24p. (J). 14.95 (978-1-84507-088-5(7)) Lincoln, Frances Ltd. GBR. *Dist:* Perseus Distribution.

Mansfield, Katherine. The Doll's House & Other Stories, Level 4. 2003. 64p. (C). pap. 9.00 (978-0-582-41811-0(9)) Longman Publishing Group.

Mara, Ferent. Looking-Glass Kate. 1999. (J). pap. 21.00 (978-963-13-4780-7(X)) Corvina Books HUN. *Dist:* State Mutual Bk. & Periodical Service, Ltd.

Marcantonio, Patricia Santos, et al. Red Ridin' in the Hood: And Other Cuentos. Alarcao, Renato, illus. 2005. 192p. (J). 16.00 (978-0-374-36241-6(6) , Farrar, Straus & Giroux (BYR)) Farrar, Straus & Giroux.

Marchand, Lizanne. The Punkin Poo Parables. Marchand, Lizanne, illus. 2002. (Illus.). 32p. (978-0-9719896-0-3(5)) Punkin Poo Publishing.

Mark, Jan. Eyes Wide Open. 2003. (ENG., Illus.). 105p. ***(*978-0-7136-7648-8(5))*** A & C Black.

Marlow, Herb. Sisters, Wild Dogs & Catfish Bait. Caffee, Julie, illus. 2005. 122p. (J). lib. bdg. 24.95 (978-1-893595-45-3(5)); per. 16.95 (978-1-893595-48-4(X)) Four Seasons Bks., Inc.

Marshall, Anne, ed. Childrens Classic Stories. 2007. (Illus.). 512p. pap. 14.95 ***(*978-1-84236-384-3(0))*** Miles Kelly Publishing, Ltd. GBR. *Dist:* National Bk. Network.

Marshall, Gloria. Little Ones Volume Two. 2006. pap. 21.99 ***(*978-1-4259-5752-0(8))*** AuthorHouse.

Marston, Elsa. Figs & Fate: Stories about Growing up in the Arab World Today. 2005. 146p. (J). 22.50 (978-0-8076-1551-5(X)); pap. 15.95 (978-0-8076-1554-6(4)) Braziller, George Inc.

Martin. Art of the Short Story Plus Barton Contemporary Handbook of Literary Terms. 2nd ed. 2005. (YA). pap., pap. 74.36 (978-0-618-72320-1(X) , 397264) Houghton Mifflin College Div.

Martin, Ann M. Friends: Stories Abt New Friends, Old Friends. Levithan, David, ed. 2005. (Friends Ser.). 192p. (J). (ps-7). pap. 16.95 (978-0-439-72991-8(2) , Scholastic Pr.) Scholastic, Inc.

Martin, Les & Poe, Edgar Allan. Tales of Terror. 2007. (Stepping Stone Bks.). 96p. (J). (gr. 2-5). pap. 3.99 (978-0-375-84055-5(9) , Random Hse. Bks. for Young Readers) Random Hse. Children's Bks.

Martineau, Diane. The Wall on 7th Street. 2005. 264p. (ps-7). pap. 7.95 (978-0-7387-0715-0(5)) Llewellyn Pubns.

Marzollo, Dan. I Spy Pirates! 2003. (gr. k-3). lib. bdg. 11.25 (978-0-613-72166-0(7)) Tandem Library Bks.

Mason, Bobbie. Shiloh & Other Stories. 2001. (gr. 7-12). lib. bdg. 21.05 (978-0-613-56842-5(7)) Tandem Library Bks.

Masters, William. Love & Sex. Cart, Michael, ed. 2003. 240p. (YA). pap. 13.95 (978-0-689-85668-6(7) , Simon Pulse) Simon & Schuster Children's Publishing.

Matthews, Andrew & Barrett, Angela. The Random House Book of Shakespeare Stories. 2003. (Illus.). 128p. (J). (gr. 3-7). 20.95 (978-0-375-81610-9(0) , Random Hse. Bks. for Young Readers) Random Hse. Children's Bks.

Matthews, Annette. Mischievous Molly. 2006. (Illus.). x, 48p. pap. ***(*978-1-4120-9693-5(6))*** Trafford Publishing.

Matthews, Caitlin & Negrin, Fabian. Fireside Stories: Tales for a Winter's Eve. Cann, Helen, illus. 2007. 96p. (J). (ps-5). 19.99 ***(*978-1-84686-065-2(2))*** Barefoot Bks., Inc.

Matthews, John. The Barefoot Book of Giants, Ghosts & Goblins: Traditional Tales from Around the World. Manna, Giovanni, illus. 2000. 80p. (J). (gr. 1-5). 19.95 (978-1-902283-27-2(9)) Barefoot Bks., Inc.

Matthews, John & Matthews, Caitlin. Trick of the Tale: A Collection of Trickster Tales. Tomic, Tomislav, illus. 2007. 96p. (J). (gr. 5). 18.99 ***(*978-0-7636-3646-3(0))*** Candlewick Pr.

Maupassant, Guy de. Contes du Jour et de la Nuit, Level C. (FRE.). (YA). (gr. 7-12). 8.95 (978-0-88436-989-9(7) , 40303) EMC/Paradigm Publishing.

Mawter, J. A. So Grotty! Gordon, Gus, illus. 5th ed. 2004. (So... Ser.: Bk. 5). 176p. (Orig.). (J). (978-0-207-20007-6(6) , Angus & Robertson) HarperCollins Pubs. AUS. *Dist:* HarperCollins Pubs.

Maxey, Ann. Country Style Oklahoma. 2005. (Illus.). 71p. (YA). per. 15.95 (978-0-9771939-1-2(8) , 0001) New World Publishing.

May, Sophie. Dotty Dimples Flyaway. 2007. 94.99 ***(*978-1-4280-5295-6(X));*** pap. 88.99 ***(*978-1-4280-5304-5(2))*** IndyPublish.com.

May, Steve. Dazzer Plays On. 2000. 192p. (J). pap. 8.99 (978-0-7497-3431-2(0)) Egmont Bks., Ltd. GBR. *Dist:* Independent Pubs. Group.

Mayer, Mercer. Storybook Collection. Mayer, Mercer, illus. 2005. (Little Critter Ser.). (Illus.). 176p. (J). pap. 9.99 (978-0-06-082009-1(8) , Harper Festival) HarperCollins Pubs.

Mayes, Walter M. Walter the Giant Storyteller's Giant Book of Giant Stories. O'Malley, Kevin, illus. 2005. 48p. (J). (gr. 1-5). 18.95 (978-0-8027-8974-7(9)) Walker & Co.

Mayne, William. Bells on Her Toes. (Illus.). 48p. (J). 12.95 (978-0-241-00158-5(7) , Hamilton, Hamish) Penguin Bks., Ltd. GBR. *Dist:* Trafalgar Square Publishing.

Mazer, Anne. A Walk in My World: International Short Stories about Youth. 2000. 224p. (gr. 8-12). pap. 8.95 (978-0-89255-249-8(2)) Persea Bks., Inc.

Mazer, Anne, ed. A Walk in My World: International Short Stories about Youth. 2000. (gr. 7-12). lib. bdg. 17.60 (978-0-613-60630-1(2)) Tandem Library Bks.

Mazer, Anne, ed. & intro. A Walk in My World: International Short Stories about Youth. Mazer, Anne, intro. 1998. 224p. (gr. 7). 17.95 (978-0-89255-237-5(9)) Persea Bks., Inc.

Mazer, Harry. Twelve Shots: Outstanding Short Stories about Guns. 1998. (J). (978-0-606-13880-2(3)) Tandem Library Bks.

McCaughrean, Geraldine. Daredevils & Desperadoes. l.t. ed. 2005. (J). pap. (978-0-7540-7845-6(0) , CLP 435) BBC Audio.

—Ghosts, Rogues & Highwaymen. l.t. ed. 2006. pap. 16.95 (978-1-4056-6013-6(9)) BBC Audio GBR. *Dist:* BBC Audiobooks America.

—Knights, Kings & Conquerors: 20 Stories from British History. Brassey, Richard, illus. l.t. ed. 2005. 216p. (J). pap. (978-0-7540-7820-3(5) , CLP 410) BBC Audio.

—Knights, Kings & Conquerors: 20 Stories from British History. Brassey, Richard, illus. 2003. 115p. (J). pap. 11.00 (978-1-85881-851-1(6)) Orion Bks. Ltd. GBR. *Dist:* Trafalgar Square Publishing.

—Princess Stories. 2000. (Illus.). 92p. (J). pap. 22.95 (978-0-385-40783-0(1)) Transworld Publishers Ltd. GBR. *Dist:* Trafalgar Square Publishing.

—Rebels & Royals. l.t. ed. 2005. 200p. (J). pap. (978-0-7540-7924-8(4) , CLP 479) BBC Audio.

McCaughrean, Geraldine & Ray, Jane. Cuentos de Amor y Amistad. 2003. (FRE., Illus.). 110p. 24.95 (978-84-95939-09-8(6)) Blume ESP. *Dist:* Independent Pubs. Group.

McCaughrean, Geraldine & Ross, Tony. Atenea y el Olivo ; la Diosa Mas Bella ; Casandra, la Divina. Ross, Tony, tr. 2005. (Mythology Series Collection Mitos Ser.). (SPA., Illus.). 50p. (J). (gr. 2-3). 9.95 (978-84-348-9385-6(1)) SM Ediciones ESP. *Dist:* Iaconi, Mariuccia Bk. Imports.

—Zeus Vence a Los Titanes ; el Enfado de la Diosa Hera. Ross, Tony, tr. 2005. (Mythology Series Collection Mitos Ser.). (SPA., Illus.). 47p. (J). (gr. 2-3). 9.95 (978-84-348-9386-3(X)) SM Ediciones ESP. *Dist:* Iaconi, Mariuccia Bk. Imports.

McCloskey, Robert. Make Way for McCloskey: A Robert McCloskey Treasury. 2004. (Illus.). 64p. (J). (ps). 26.00 (978-0-670-05934-8(X) , Viking Juvenile) Penguin Group (USA) Inc.

—A Robert McCloskey Collection. 2003. 198p. (J). 19.99 (978-0-670-05901-0(3) , Viking Juvenile) Penguin Group (USA) Inc.

McCourt, Lisa. Chicken Soup for Little Souls. 2000. (gr. k-3). lib. bdg. 22.20 (978-0-613-30312-5(1)) Tandem Library Bks.

McCourt, Lisa, et al. Chicken Soup for the Little Souls: 3 Colorful Stories to Warm the Hearts of Children. Dodson, Bert et al, illus. 2000. 96p. (J). (ps-3). pap. 12.95 (978-1-55874-812-5(1)) Health Communications, Inc.

Mccullagh, Sheila. Magic Griffle & Other Stories. 2007. (Tales from Puddle Lane Ser.). (Illus.). 96p. 19.95 ***(*978-1-84560-041-9(X))*** Mercury Bks. Ltd. GBR. *Dist:* International Publishers Marketing.

—Magician of Puddle Lane & Other Stories. 2007. (Tales from Puddle Lane Ser.). (Illus.). 96p. 19.95 ***(*978-1-84560-040-2(1))*** Mercury Bks. Ltd. GBR. *Dist:* International Publishers Marketing.

McCullagh, Sheila. Pirate Gold. 2007. (Three Pirates Ser.). (Illus.). 48p. 15.95 ***(*978-1-84560-042-6(8))*** Mercury Bks. Ltd. GBR. *Dist:* International Publishers Marketing.

—Shipwrecked. 2007. (Three Pirates Ser.). (Illus.). 48p. 15.95 ***(*978-1-84560-043-3(6))*** Mercury Bks. Ltd. GBR. *Dist:* International Publishers Marketing.

Mccullagh, Sheila. Wideawake Mice & Other Stories. 2007. (Illus.). 96p. 19.95 ***(*978-1-84560-038-9(X))*** Mercury Bks. Ltd. GBR. *Dist:* International Publishers Marketing.

—Wideawake Mice in Danger & Other Stories. 2007. (Tales from Puddle Lane Ser.). (Illus.). 96p. 19.95 ***(*978-1-84560-039-6(8))*** Mercury Bks. Ltd. GBR. *Dist:* International Publishers Marketing.

McCullagh, Sheila. Wild Pirates Attack. 2007. (Illus.). 48p. 15.95 ***(*978-1-84560-045-7(2))*** Mercury Bks. Ltd. GBR. *Dist:* International Publishers Marketing.

McDaniel, Lurlene. How Do I Love Thee: Three Stories. 272p. (YA). (gr. 7). 2002. pap. 5.50 (978-0-553-57107-3(9) , Laurel Leaf); 2001. 9.95 (978-0-553-57154-7(0) , Starfire) Random Hse. Children's Bks.

—Starry, Starry Night: Three Holiday Stories. 2000. (Illus.). 272p. (YA). (gr. 7-12). mass mkt. 5.50 (978-0-553-57106-6(0) , Laurel Leaf) Random Hse. Children's Bks.

—Starry, Starry Night: Three Holiday Stories. 2000. (gr. 7-12). lib. bdg. 13.55 (978-0-613-28376 2(7)) Tandem Library Bks.

McDonald, Ray. Bookworm Briefs. 2003. 144p. pap. 12.99 (978-1-58832-075-9(8)) Unlimited Publishing LLC.

Mcduffee, William. Story Time with Grandpa Bill Collection. 2006. 50p. pap. 12.95 (978-1-4241-4001-5(3)) PublishAmerica, Inc.

McGookin', Peggy. Isabel's Whisker's. 2004. pap. 7.95 (978-0-533-14580-5(5)) Vantage Pr., Inc.

McGovern, Sheila. The Entire World of S & Z Book of Stories: 58 Targeted S & Z Pure Stories to Remediate Frontal & Lateral Lisps. l.t. ed. 2003. (Illus.). 148p. per. 34.99 (978-0-9723457-5-0(2)) Say It Right.

McGraw-Hill Staff & Goodman, Burton. Choices. 2002. (Goodman's Five-Star Stories Ser.). (gr. 6-12). pap. 17.32 (978-0-07-827354-4(4) , 9780078273544) Jamestown.

—Goodman's Five-Star, Level D. 2001. (gr. 4-12). pap., act. bk. ed. 13.96 (978-0-8092-0448-9(7) , 9780809204489) Jamestown.

McHugh, Fiona. The Anne of Green Gables Story Book: Based on the Kevin Sullivan Film of Lucy Maud Montgomery's Classic Novel. 2004. (Illus.). 80p. (J). (gr. 4-8). reprint ed. 20.00 (978-0-7567-8464-5(6)) DIANE Publishing Co.

McIntosh, Gavin. Hausaland Tales from the Nigerian Market Place. 2005. (Illus.). 98p. (J). (gr. 5-9). reprint ed. 22.00 (978-0-7567-9714-0(4)) DIANE Publishing Co.

McKay, Jane. Tess & the Star Traveller. 2004. (Illus.). 96p. (Orig.). (J). pap. 8.95 (978-1-920731-43-4(1)) Fremantle Pr. AUS. *Dist:* International Specialized Bk. Services.

McKee, David. Elmer Sobre Zancos. 2003. (SPA., Illus.). 32p. (J). (gr. k-3). 12.95 (978-84-372-2354-4(7)) Altea, Ediciones, S.A. - Grupo Santillana ESP. *Dist:* Santillana USA Publishing Co., Inc.

McKinley, Robin. Door in the Hedge. 2003. (gr. 7-12). lib. bdg. 15.30 (978-0-613-73478-3(5)) Tandem Library Bks.

McKinley, Robin & Dickinson, Peter. Water: Tales of Elemental Spirits. 2002. (Illus.). 272p. (YA). (gr. 4 up). 18.99 (978-0-399-23796-6(8) , Putnam Juvenile) Penguin Group (USA) Inc.

McKissack, Patricia C. Dark-Thirty Southern Tales of the Supernatural. 2001. (gr. 5-8). lib. bdg. 13.55 (978-0-613-33690-1(9)) Tandem Library Bks.

—Porch Lies: Tales of Slicksters, Tricksters, & Other Wily Characters. Carrilho, André, illus. 2006. (J). 160p. (gr. 3-7). 18.95 (978-0-375-83619-0(5)); xii, 146p. ***(*978-1-4156-9337-7(4))*** Random Hse. Children's Bks. (Schwartz & Wade Bks.).

McLaughlin, Marilyn. Fierce Milly. 1999. (Illus.). 96p. (J). pap. 6.99 (978-0-7497-3731-3(X) , Mammoth) Egmont Bks., Ltd. GBR. *Dist:* Independent Pubs. Group.

—Fierce Milly & the Amazing Dog. Shearing, Leonie, illus. 2001. 55p. (J). pap. 6.99 (978-0-7497-4239-3(9)) Egmont Bks., Ltd. GBR. *Dist:* Independent Pubs. Group.

—Fierce Milly & the Demon Saucepan. Shearing, Leonie, illus. 2002. 64p. (J). pap. 6.99 (978-1-4052-0064-6(2)) Egmont Bks., Ltd. GBR. *Dist:* Independent Pubs. Group.

McMurry, Brown Lida. Fifty Famous Fables. 2006. pap. 88.99 ***(*978-1-4280-2948-4(6))*** IndyPublish.com.

McNatt, Martha. Grandmother's Face in the Mirror. 2003. (YA). per. 14.00 (978-0-9741294-0-2(2)) Main St Publishing, Inc.

McTaggart, William R. Ten More Christmas Stories: Plus Two Christmas Classics: Yes, Virginia There Is a Santa Claus & Twas the Night Before Christmas. Hibbard, Eugene J., illus. 1999. (Companion Reader Ser.: Vol. 2). 144p. (J). (ps-5). 16.00 (978-0-9669285-0-1(4)) Gramma Bks. Publishing Co.

—A Treasury of Ten Summertime Children's Stories. Hibbard, Eugene J., illus. 1999. (Companion Reader Ser.: Vol. 3). 128p. (J). (ps-5). 16.00 (978-0-9669285-1-8(2)) Gramma Bks. Publishing Co.

Me, Myself, & I & Other Stories: Individual Title Six-Pack. (Story Steps Ser.). (gr. k-2). 48.00 (978-0-7635-9813-6(5)) Rigby Education.

Medearis, Michael & Medearis, Angela Shelf. Daisy & the Doll. Johnson, Larry, illus. 2005. (Vermont Folklife Center Children's Book Ser.). 32p. (J). reprint ed. pap. 7.95 (978-0-916718-23-7(9)) Vermont Folklife Ctr.

Medernach, T. K. On the High Seas. 2007. 104p. pap. 12.95 ***(*978-0-615-16040-5(9))*** Medernach, T.K.

Memories of Christmas in West Tennessee: Short Stories & Poems from Area Writers. 2nd ed. 2002. per. 10.00 (978-0-9710470-8-2(1) , 400, MSP) Main St Publishing, Inc.

Menon, Geeta. Classic Collection: 22 Short Stories. Suman, Surendra, illus. 2005. 143p. (J). (978-81-7011-970-8(7)) Children's Bk. Trust.

Mensing, Katja. Un Regalo para Bruno. (SPA., Illus.). 34p. (J). (gr. k-2). (978-968-16-6037-6(4) , FC6412) Fondo de Cultura Economica MEX. *Dist:* Lectorum Pubns., Inc.

Merani, Tiziana. El Gran Libro de los Cuentos. 2007. 292p. 14.95 ***(*978-0-307-39175-9(2))*** Random House Mondadori ESP. *Dist:* Random Hse., Inc.

Mercado, Nancy. Every Man for Himself: Ten Short Stories about Being a Guy. 2007. 176p. (J). (gr. 4-7). pap. 6.99 (978-0-14-240813-1(1) , Puffin) Penguin Group (USA) Inc.

Mercer, Christa Blum. German War Child: Growing Up in World War II. 2004. (Illus.). 176p. pap. 14.95 (978-1-893597-07-5(5)) A. Borough Bks.

Merrigold Press Staff, compiled by. First Reader. 1999. (Storybook Ser.). (Illus.). 288p. (J). pap. 12.99 (978-0-307-37500-1(5) , Golden Bks.) Random Hse. Children's Bks.

Merrill, Lee. Lover Boy/Juanito el Carinoso: A Bilingual Counting Book. Delgado, Francisco, illus. 1998. (ENG & SPA.). 32p. (J). (ps-3). 15.95 (978-0-938317-38-8(5)) Cinco Puntos Pr.

The Messy Rooms. 2002. (978-1-58453-195-1(9)) Pioneer Valley Educational Pr., Inc.

Meyers, Elizabeth Ann. The Adventures of Winky & Binky. 2003. (J). 16.95 (978-0-533-14170-8(2)) Vantage Pr., Inc.

Mhlophe, Gcina. Our Story Magic. 2006. 100p. 29.95 ***(*978-1-86914-111-0(3))*** Univ. of Natal Pr. ZAF. *Dist:* International Specialized Bk. Services.

Mice & Other Stories: Individual Title Six-Pack. (Story Steps Ser.). (gr. k-2). 48.00 (978-0-7635-9823-5(2)) Rigby Education.

Michael's Faith. 2004. (J). bds. 14.95 (978-0-9741406-2-9(7) , 0138) Cranberry Quill Publishing Co.

Michel, Pauline. Frissons D'enfants: Nouvelles. 2006. (ENG & FRE.). 94p. (J). (978-2-89261-460-2(0)); (978-1-894852-21-0(4)) X Y Z Publishing.

Milbourne, Anna Et Al & Amery, Heather. Myths & Legends. 2007. 192p. (J). 22.99 (978-0-7945-1451-8(0) , Usborne) EDC Publishing.

Miller, Heather. My People or Myself. 2001. (J). pap. 9.95 (978-0-89992-154-9(X)) Council for Indian Education.

Miller, Sara Swan. Three Stories You Can Read to Your Cat. Kelley, True, illus. 1999. 48p. (J). (gr. 4-6). pap., pap. 5.95 (978-0-395-95752-3(4)) Houghton Mifflin Co. Trade & Reference Div.

Mills, Charles. The Jackrabbit Safari & Other High Speed Tales. 2002. 143p. (YA). pap. 9.99 (978-0-8280-1621-6(6)) Review & Herald Publishing Assn.

Milne, A. A. The Complete Tales of Winnie the Pooh. 70th ed. 1999. (Illus.). 368p. (J). (gr. 4-7). 40.00 (978-0-525-45060-3(2) , Dutton Juvenile) Penguin Group (USA) Inc.

S

—A Gallery of Children. Le Mair, Henriette Willebeek, illus. 2006. 79p. (J). (gr. k-4). reprint ed. 20.00 (978-1-4223-5106-2(8)) DIANE Publishing Co.

Mindel, Rabbi Nissan. The Storyteller Volume 5, Vol. 5. Smechov, Zeli, illus. 1998. 324p. (gr. 4-7). 17.95 (978-0-8266-1313-4(6)) Merkos L'Inyonei Chinuch.

Mirhady, Irandought. Thorn-Bush Boy: Pesare Tigh. Mirhady, Irandought, illus. 2004. Orig. Title: Pesare Tigh. (PEO., Illus.). 63p. (YA). per. (978-0-9760323-0-4(9)) Mirhady, Farhad.

Mirkov, Nadia. Cuentos de Encuentros Cercanos para Ninos. 1999. (Stories for Children Ser.).Tr. of Stories of Close Encounters. (SPA.). 125p. (J). mass mkt. 7.95 (978-970-643-172-1(1)) Selector, S.A. de C.V. MEX. *Dist:* Libros Sin Fronteras.

Miss America. 2000. (Tippy Parrish Story Ser.). (YA). (gr. 6-10). per. 12.95 (978-1-930009-20-2(8)) Image Cascade Publishing.

Miss Tippy. 2000. (Tippy Parrish Story Ser.). (YA). (gr. 6-10). per. 12.95 (978-1-930009-18-9(6)) Image Cascade Publishing.

MJ Illustration Staff. Berry Patch Tea Party: Sticker Stories. 2006. (Strawberry Shortcake Ser.). 16p. (J). (ps-1). pap. 4.99 (978-0-448-44273-0(6) , Grosset & Dunlap) Penguin Group (USA) Inc.

Molina, Maria Isabel. El Senor del Cero. Sole, Francisco, illus. 2003. (SPA.). 153p. (J). (gr. 5-8). pap. 8.95 (978-968-19-0388-6(9)) Santillana USA Publishing Co., Inc.

Molina Temboury, Pedro. No Encontraras el Tibet en un Mapa. 2004. (SPA., Illus.). 160p. (J). (978-84-667-1418-1(9)) Grupo Anaya, S.A.

Molist, Pep. Arena en los Zapatos. 2002. (Caballo Alado Ser.). (SPA & ENG., Illus.). 24p. pap. 4.95 (978-84-7864-565-7(9)) Combel Editorial, S.A. ESP. *Dist:* Independent Pubs. Group.

Monesson, Harry S. Berry Patch Tales: A Collection of Stories. 2000. (gr. 3-6). lib. bdg. 28.45 (978-0-613-79688-0(8)) Tandem Library Bks.

Monkman, Olga. Dos Perros y una Abuela. Calderon, Marcela, illus. 2003. (SPA.). 31p. (J). (gr. k-3). pap. 9.95 (978-950-511-642-3(X)) Santillana USA Publishing Co., Inc.

—Lo Que Cuentan los Inuit. (SPA.). (YA). (gr. 4 up). pap. (978-950-07-1845-5(6) , SA30064) Editorial Sudamericana S.A. ARG. *Dist:* Lectorum Pubns., Inc.

—Un Rey sin Corona. Sanchez, Javier G., illus. 2003. (SPA.). 39p. (J). (gr. k-3). pap. 7.95 (978-950-511-368-2(4)) Santillana USA Publishing Co., Inc.

Montgomery, L. M. Akin to Anne: Tales of Other Orphans. (YA). 22.95 (978-0-8488-2656-7(6)) Amereon LTD.

—Along the Shore: Tales by the Sea. (YA). 22.95 (978-0-8488-2655-0(8)) Amereon LTD.

—Christmas with Anne: And Other Holiday Stories. 2001. (gr. 5-8). lib. bdg. 13.00 (978-0-613-90391-2(9)) Tandem Library Bks.

—Christmas with Anne & Other Holiday Stories. Wilmshurst, Rea, ed. 2001. (Illus.). 224p. (YA). (gr. 5 up). pap. 4.99 (978-0-553-57100-4(1) , Starfire) Random Hse. Children's Bks.

Montgomery, R. A. Choose Your Own Adventure Four Book Boxed Set #1: The Abominable Snowman, Journey under the Sea, Space & Beyond, the Lost Jewels of Nabooti. 2006. 576p. (J). per. 19.95 (*978-1-933390-94-9(8)) Chooseco LLC.

Mooney, Bel, selected by. You Never Did Learn to Knock: 14 Stories about Girls & Their Mothers. 2006. 256p. (J). (gr. 5-9). pap. 7.95 (978-0-7534-5877-8(2) , Kingfisher) Houghton Mifflin Co. Trade & Reference Div.

Moore, Inga, illus. Horse Tales. 2005. 152p. (J). (gr. 4-7). 18.99 (978-0-7636-2657-0(0)) Candlewick Pr.

Moore, Stephanie Perry. Golden Spirit. 2006. (Carmen Browne Ser.). 144p. (YA). pap. 5.99 (978-0-8024-8169-6(8)) Moody Pubs.

Morck, Irene. Apples & Angel Ladders: A Collection of Pioneer Christmas Stories. Wood, Muriel, illus. 2001. 32p. (J). (978-1-55041-671-8(5)) Fitzhenry & Whiteside, Ltd.

Morden, Daniel. Weird Tales from the Storyteller. Jones, Jac, tr. Jones, Jac, illus. 2003. 64p. pap. 12.95 (978-1-84323-210-0(3)) Beekman Bks., Inc.

More, Hannah. Stories for the Young or Cheap Repositor. 2006. 32.99 (*978-1-4280-3380-1(7)) IndyPublish.com.

Moreno, Fanny. Ensuenos: Cuentos Cortos. Moreno, Fanny, ed. 2001. (SPA.). 76p. (YA). pap. 10.00 (978-0-9718874-1-1(1)) Moreno, Fanny.

Morgan, Matthew & Barnes, Samantha. Children's Miscellany Too. Catlow, Niki, illus. 2005. 128p. (J). 12.95 (978-0-8118-5067-4(6)) Chronicle Bks. LLC.

Morgan, Shane. Look & See. 2000. (Illus.). 24p. pap. 4.95 (978-1-875641-46-8(7)) Magabala Bks. AUS. *Dist:* International Specialized Bk. Services.

Moro, Robin, et al, illus. Read Aloud Spooky Stories. 320p. 15.98 (978-0-7853-6338-5(6) , 7159100) Publications International, Ltd.

Morpurgo, Michael. The Kingfisher Book of Great Boy Stories: A Treasury of Classics from Children's Literature. 2006. (Illus.). 160p. (J). (gr. 4-8). reprint ed. 20.00 (978-1-4223-5207-6(2)) DIANE Publishing Co.

Morpurgo, Michael, ed. More Muck & Magic. Blake, Quentin, illus. 2001. 148p. (J). pap. 8.99 (978-0-7497-4094-8(9)) Egmont Bks., Ltd. GBR. *Dist:* Independent Pubs. Group.

Morris, Ann. Grandma Lai Goon Remembers: A Chinese-American Family Story. 2002. (Illus.). 32p. (J). (gr. 5 up). pap. 7.95 (978-0-7613-1730-2(9) , Millbrook Pr.) Lerner Publishing Group.

—Grandma Lois Remembers: An African-American Family Story. 2002. (Illus.). 32p. (J). (gr. 5 up). pap. 7.95 (978-0-7613-1729-6(5) , Millbrook Pr.) Lerner Publishing Group.

—Grandma Maxine Remembers: A Native American Family Story. 2002. (Illus.). 32p. (J). (gr. 5 up). pap. 7.95 (978-0-7613-1728-9(7) , Millbrook Pr.) Lerner Publishing Group.

—Grandma Susan Remembers: A British-American Family Story. 2002. (Illus.). 32p. (J). (gr. 5 up). pap. 7.95 (978-0-7613-1732-6(5) , Millbrook Pr.) Lerner Publishing Group.

Morris, April. Eldon the Elephant. 2004. (J). lib. bdg. 25.95 (978-1-893595-49-1(8)) Four Seasons Bks., Inc.

Morris, Deborah. Runaway Bus & other True Stories: Real Kids Real Adventures. 2003. (Juvenile Ser.). (Illus.). (J). 21.95 (978-0-7862-5095-0(X)) Thorndike Pr.

Morrison, Jennifer. Beware of the Bull: Stories for the Young & the Incurably Eccentric. 2004. 90p. (YA). pap. 9.95 (978-0-595-31054-8(0)) iUniverse, Inc.

Moser, Barry, illus. Cowboy Stories. 2007. 184p. (YA). (gr. 7 up). 16.95 (978-0-8118-5418-4(3) , SeaStar Bks.) Chronicle Bks. LLC.

Moser, Erwin. Vicente, el Elefantito. (Buenas Noches Coleccion). (SPA.). (J). (gr. k-3). 8.95 (978-958-04-4903-4(1)) Norma S.A. COL. *Dist:* Distribuidora Norma, Inc.

Mother Goose. Sugar & Spice, 6 Bks. 2005. (Illus.). (J). bds. 12.95 incl. audio compact disk (978-1-59249-471-2(4) , 1D100) Soundprints.

Mouse Works Staff. Disney's Easy to Read Stories: A Collection of 6 Favorite Tales. 1999. (Illus.). 192p. (gr. k-2). 9.99 (978-0-7868-3244-6(4)) Disney Pr.

—Standard Characters Friendly Tales: Pack Out Box Set. 1999. (J). 27.96 (978-0-7364-0042-8(7)) Mouse Works.

Mowry, Jess. Crusader Rabbit & Other Stories. 2007. 280p. (YA). pap. 14.99 (978-1-59092-231-6(X) , Blue Works) Windstorm Creative.

Mueller, Sylvia Price. Barnyard Stories. 2003. 40p. pap. 9.00 (978-0-8059-5939-0(4)) Dorrance Publishing Co., Inc.

Mullican, Judy & Carroll, Ken, Jr. Bedtime Stories. l.t. ed. 1999. (Cuddle Bks.). (Illus.). 6p. (J). (ps-k). pap. 10.95 (978-1-57332-147-1(8)) HighReach Learning, Inc.

Muneefa. My Tales for Children. 2006. 90p. (J). pap. 13.95 (978-1-58909-339-3(9)) Bookstand Publishing.

Munoz de Coronado, Martha, ed. Subidos de Tono: Cuentos de Amor. 2005. (SPA., Illus.). 253p. (J). pap. 14.95 (978-9972-40-251-7(7)) Promocion Editorial Inca S.A., PEISA PER. *Dist:* Iaconi, Mariuccia Bk. Imports.

Munsch, Robert. Les Fantaisies d'Adele. Martchenko, Michael, illus. 2002. (Droles D'Histories Ser.). (FRE.). 24p. (J). (ps). pap. (978-2-89021-284-8(X)) Diffusion du livre Mirabel.

—Munschworks: The First Munsch Collection. Martchenko, Michael, illus. 1998. (Munsch for Kids Ser.). 128p. (J). (ps-2). lib. bdg. 19.95 (978-1-55037-523-7(7)) Annick Pr., Ltd. CAN. *Dist:* Firefly Bks., Ltd.

—Munschworks 2: The Second Munsch Treasury. Desputeaux, Helene & Martchenko, Michael, illus. 1999. 136p. (J). (ps-2). 19.95 (978-1-55037-553-4(9)) Annick Pr., Ltd. CAN. *Dist:* Firefly Bks., Ltd.

—Munschworks 3: The Third Munsch Treasury. Krykorka, Vladyana Langer & Martchenko, Michael, illus. 2000. 144p. (J). (ps-2). 19.95 (978-1-55037-633-3(0)) Annick Pr., Ltd. CAN. *Dist:* Firefly Bks., Ltd.

Munsch, Robert & Askar, Saoussan. Munschworks 4: The Fourth Munsch Treasury. Duranceau, Suzanne & Martchenko, Michael, illus. 2002. 136p. (J). (ps-2). 19.95 (978-1-55037-766-8(3)) Annick Pr., Ltd. CAN. *Dist:* Firefly Bks., Ltd.

Munsch, Robert & Kusugak, Michael Arvaarluk. The Munschworks Grand Treasury. Desputeaux, Helene et al, illus. 2001. 392p. (J). (ps-2). 39.95 (978-1-55037-685-2(3)) Annick Pr., Ltd. CAN. *Dist:* Firefly Bks., Ltd.

Munsinger, Lewis. Spot the Plot. 2009. (J). 15.95 (978-0-8118-4668-4(7)) Chronicle Bks. LLC.

Muralidharan, Anuradha. The Coconut Cutter & Other Stories. 2000. 98p. (J). (978-81-87075-47-9(3)) Srishti Pubs. & Distributors IND. *Dist:* Nesma Bks. India.

Murphy, Mary. Let's Go! 2005. (Illus.). 16p. (J). bds. 14.99 (978-1-4052-1115-4(6)) Egmont Bks., Ltd. GBR. *Dist:* Trafalgar Square Publishing.

Murray, Brendan. Tev on Home Turf. 2004. 192p. (YA). pap. 13.50 (978-1-920731-33-5(4)) Fremantle Pr. AUS. *Dist:* International Specialized Bk. Services.

Muth, Jon J. Zen Shorts (Collector's Edition) 2008. 40p. (J). 25.00 (*978-0-545-04087-7(6) , Scholastic) Scholastic, Inc.

Muttini, Pablo. Monstruos en la Noche. 2005. (SPA., Illus.). 28p. (J). 14.95 (978-9974-7799-4-5(4) , nicanitas) Hardenville SA URY. *Dist:* Independent Pubs. Group.

My First Book of Christmas Stories. 2003. (J). 8.99 (978-1-59384-014-3(4)) Parklane Publishing.

My Look-it-Up Book. 2002. act. bk. ed. 15.00 (978-0-7166-7404-7(1)) World Bk., Inc.

Myers, Tamar. Angels, Angels Everywhere. 2004. pap. 7.95 (978-0-9747685-3-3(7)) Bella Rosa Bks.

Myers, Walter Dean. Every Man for Himself: 10 Short Stories about Being a Guy. Mercado, Nancy, ed. 2005. (Illus.). 176p. (YA). (gr. 9). 16.99 (978-0-8037-2896-7(4) , Dial) Penguin Group (USA) Inc.

—145th Street: Short Stories. 160p. (YA). (gr. 7 up). 2001. pap. 5.99 (978-0-440-22916-2(2) , Laurel Leaf); 2000. 15.99 (978-0-385-32137-2(6) , Delacorte Bks. for Young Readers) Random Hse. Children's Bks.

—145th Street: Short Stories. 2001. (978-0-606-22414-7(9)) Tandem Library Bks.

Myers, Walter Dean. 145th Street: Short Stories. 2007. 160p. (YA). (gr. 7). lib. bdg. 18.99 (*978-0-385-90538-1(6) , Delacorte Bks. for Young Readers) Random Hse. Children's Bks.

Myra, Harold Lawrence. Easter Bunny, Are You for Real? Kurisu, Jane, illus. 2006. 18p. (J). bds. 6.99 (978-1-4003-0632-9(9)) Nelson, Thomas Inc.

Mysterious Chills & Thrills: 10 creepy, strange, adventurous short stories for kids to tickle the Imagination. 2004. (J). per. 6.95 (978-0-9749013-0-5(X)) LH Pubns. & Productions.

Nahu. Dolphina's World: And Other Stories. 2006. 80p. pap. 12.95 (978-1-59800-178-5(7)) Outskirts Press, Inc.

Naidoo, Beverley. The Great Tug of War. Grobler, Piet, illus. 2006. 96p. (gr. 3). pap. 7.95 (978-1-84507-055-7(0)) Lincoln, Frances Ltd. GBR. *Dist:* Perseus Distribution.

—Out of Bounds: Seven Stories of Conflict & Hope. 2003. (Illus.). 192p. (J). (gr. 5 up). 16.99 (978-0-06-050799-2(3)); lib. bdg. 17.89 (978-0-06-050800-5(0)) HarperCollins Pubs.

Naifeh, Ted. Courtney Crumrin & the Night Things. Jones, James Lucas, ed. 2005. (Illus.). 120p. lib. bdg. 19.00 (978-0-606-33365-8(7)) Tandem Library Bks.

Narena, Tammy. This Great Love to Cherish. 1999. (Illus.). 64p. (J). pap. 12.50 (978-1-929319-00-8(2)) Sean & I Publishing.

Narvaez, Concha Lopez. El Fuego de los Pastores.Tr. of Shepherds' Fire. (SPA.). (YA). (gr. 5). pap. (978-84-395-0902-8(2)) Espasa Calpe, S.A. ESP. *Dist:* Lectorum Pubns., Inc.

—El Silencio del Asesino. Salmeron, R. A., illus. 1999. (Espasa Juvenil Ser.: Vol. 81). (SPA.). 144p. (J). (gr. 7-12). (978-84-239-9052-8(4) , EC5059) Espasa Calpe, S.A. ESP. *Dist:* Lectorum Pubns., Inc.

Nesbit, E. The Book of Dragons. Millar, H. R., illus. 2001. 180p. (J). (ps-7). per. 18.75 (978-0-613-37138-4(0)) Tandem Library Bks.

—Book of Dragons. Millar, H. R. & Zelinsky, Paul O., illus. 2001. (Peter Glassman Bk.). 256p. (J). (gr. 3-7). pap. 9.95 (978-1-58717-106-2(6) , SeaStar Bks.) Chronicle Bks. LLC.

—The Book of Dragons. Fell, H. Granville & Millar, H. R., illus. unabr. ed. 2004. (Thrift Edition Ser.). 176p. pap. 7.95 (978-0-486-43648-7(9)) Dover Pubns., Inc.

—The Rainbow & the Rose. l.t. ed. 2006. 124p. pap. (978-1-84637-280-3(1)) Echo Library.

Ness, Berthetta. Originals: Short Stories for Children. 2007. (YA). pap. (*978-1-57579-351-1(2)) Pine Hill Pr., Inc.

Newbery Authors, 12 bks. l.t. ed. Incl. Adoniram & Other Selections. Greenberg, Martin H. & Waugh, Charles. 176p. lib. bdg. 23.33 (978-0-8368-2860-3(7)); Christmas on the Prairie & Other Selections. Greenberg, Martin H. & Waugh, Charles, eds. 160p. lib. bdg. 23.33 (978-0-8368-2950-1(6)); Dancing Tom & Other Selections. Greenberg, Martin H. & Waugh, Charles. 160p. lib. bdg. 23.33 (978-0-8368-2859-7(3)); For a Horse & Other Selections. Greenberg, Martin H. & Waugh, Charles, eds. 176p. lib. bdg. 23.33 (978-0-8368-2949-5(2)); For the Sake of Freedom & Other Selections. Greenberg, Martin H. & Waugh, Charles. 176p. lib. bdg. 23.33 (978-0-8368-2855-9(0)); Highest Hit & Other Selections. Greenberg, Martin H. & Waugh, Charles. 160p. lib. bdg. 23.33 (978-0-8368-2856-6(9)); Horse of the War God & Other Selections. Greenberg, Martin H. & Waugh, Charles. 176p. lib. bdg. 23.33 (978-0-8368-2857-3(7)); Knife for Tomaso & Other Selections. Greenberg, Martin H. & Waugh, Charles, eds. 176p. lib. bdg. 23.33 (978-0-8368-2952-5(2)); Lighthouse Island & Other Selections. Greenberg, Martin H. & Waugh, Charles. 160p. lib. bdg. 23.33 (978-0-8368-2858-0(5)); Little Sioux Girl & Other Selections. Greenberg, Martin H. & Waugh, Charles, eds. 160p. lib. bdg. 23.33 (978-0-8368-2954-9(9)); Lone Cowboy & Other Selections. Greenberg, Martin H. & Waugh, Charles, eds. 176p. lib. bdg. 23.33 (978-0-8368-2953-2(0)); Wise Soldier of Sellebak & Other Selections. Greenberg, Martin H. & Waugh, Charles, eds. 160p. lib. bdg. 23.33 (978-0-8368-2951-8(4)); (J). (gr. 4 up). 2001. 2000. Set lib. bdg. 279.96 (978-0-8368-2986-0(7)) Stevens, Gareth Inc.

Newman, Leslea. Daddy's Song. Ritz, Karen, illus. 2007. 32p. (J). (ps-1). 16.95 (978-0-8050-6975-4(5) , Holt, Henry & Co. Bks. For Young Readers) Holt, Henry & Co.

Newman, Nanette. Bedtime Stories. Foreman, Michael, illus. 2002. 192p. (J). (ps up). (978-1-86205-276-5(X) , Pavilion Bks., Ltd.) Anova Bks.

Newsham, Ian, illus. The Kingfisher Treasury of Irish Stories. 2004. (Kingfisher Treasury of Stories Ser.). 160p. (J). (gr. k-3). pap. 5.95 (978-0-7534-5672-9(9) , Kingfisher) Houghton Mifflin Co. Trade & Reference Div.

Nicholson, Nancy. Devotional Stories for Little Folks Too. 2007. (J). per. (*978-0-9771236-1-2(8)) For Little Folks.

Nicholson, Nancy E. Devotional Stories for Little Folks. 2002. (J). per. (978-0-9771236-0-5(X)) For Little Folks.

Nicholson, William. Silvador del Viento, el el Viento en Llamas 1. 2003. (SPA.). lib. bdg. 22.25 (978-0-613-81071-5(6)) Tandem Library Bks.

Nikola-Lisa, W. La Alegriade Ser Tu Yo. ed. 2004. (SPA., Illus.). (J). (gr. k-3). spiral bd. (978-0-616-03093-6(2)) Canadian National Institute for the Blind/Institut National Canadien pour les Aveugles.

Nimh, Sonia & Shaw, Hannah. Ghaddar the ghould & other palestinian Tales. 2008. (Illus.). 96p. (J). 14.95 (*978-1-84507-771-6(7)) Lincoln, Frances Ltd. GBR. *Dist:* Perseus Distribution.

Niño, Jairo Aníbal. El Quinto Viaje y Otras Historias Del Nuevo Continente. 2003. (SPA.). 164p. (978-958-30-0573-2(8) , PV4381) Centro de Informacion y Desarrollo de la Comunicacion y la Literatura MEX. *Dist:* Lectorum Pubns., Inc.

Nix, Garth. Across the Wall: A Tale of the Abhorsen & Other Stories. 2006. 432p. (J). pap. 7.99 (978-0-06-074715-2(3)) HarperCollins Pubs.

No Matter What You Do. 2000. 48p. (J). (978-0-9674165-0-2(2)) Eveott Enterprises, Inc.

No Nope Never No Way. 2000. 40p. (J). (978-0-9674165-1-9(5)) Eveott Enterprises, Inc.

Noakes, Polly, illus. Stories for Five Year Olds. 2004. (Kingfisher Treasury of Stories Ser.). 160p. (J). (gr. k-3). pap. 5.95 (978-0-7534-5711-5(3) , Kingfisher) Houghton Mifflin Co. Trade & Reference Div.

Noel for Jeanne Marie. 2004. (Illus.). 34p. (J). mass mkt. 9.99 (978-0-9740599-5-2(1)) Omnibus Publishing.

Nohel, Andre & Back, Francis. Trafic Chez les Hurons. 2001. (Roman Jeunesse Ser.). 96p. (J). (gr. 4-7). pap. (978-2-89021-436-1(2)) Diffusion du livre Mirabel.

Nolan, Polly, ed. Giants of the Sun. 2003. (Illus.). 256p. (J). pap. 9.99 (978-0-330-39617-2(X)) Pan Macmillan GBR. *Dist:* Trafalgar Square Publishing.

Noonan, Diana. A Whistle from the Blunder. 2000. 124p. (YA). (gr. 5 up). pap. 13.00 (978-1-877135-40-8(2)) Longacre Pr. NZL. *Dist:* Pacific Island Bks.

Norac, Carl & Dubois, Claude K. Quiero un Beso! 2004. (SPA., Illus.). 16p. (J). bds. 15.95 (978-84-8470-104-0(2)) Corimbo, Editorial S.L. ESP. *Dist:* Distribooks, Inc., Lectorum Pubns., Inc., Iaconi, Mariuccia Bk. Imports.

—Soy un Cielo. 2004. (SPA., Illus.). 16p. (J). bds. 9.95 (978-84-8470-105-7(0)) Corimbo, Editorial S.L. ESP. *Dist:* Lectorum Pubns., Inc., Iaconi, Mariuccia Bk. Imports.

Norris, Jill. 50 Little Stories to Read. 1998. (Early Learning Ser.). (Illus.). 112p. (J). (gr. k-1). pap., tchr. ed. 14.95 (978-1-55799-668-8(7) , EMC 743) Evan-Moor Educational Pubs.

Nostlinger, Christine. De Por Que a Franz le Dolio el Estomago. (Torre de Papel Ser.). (SPA.). (J). (gr. 2). 7.95 (978-958-04-1143-7(3)) Norma S.A. COL. *Dist:* Distribuidora Norma, Inc.

—Juanito Habichuela y Otros Cuentos. (Torre de Papel Ser.). (SPA.). (J). (gr. 4 up). 8.95 (978-958-04-4533-3(8)) Norma S.A. COL. *Dist:* Distribuidora Norma, Inc.

—Mas Historias de Franz. (Torre de Papel Ser.). (SPA.). (J). (gr. 2). 7.95 (978-958-04-1014-0(3)) Norma S.A. COL. *Dist:* Distribuidora Norma, Inc.

—Nuevas Historias de Franz en la Escuela. (Torre de Papel Ser.). (SPA.). (J). (gr. 2). 7.95 (978-958-04-1013-3(5)) Norma S.A. COL. *Dist:* Distribuidora Norma, Inc.

Noyes, Deborah. Gothic! Ten Original Dark Tales. 2006. 256p. (YA). (gr. 9). pap. 7.99 (978-0-7636-2737-9(2)) Candlewick Pr.

Noyes, Deborah, ed. Gothic! Ten Original Dark Tales. 2004. (Illus.). 256p. (YA). (gr. 9 up). 15.99 (978-0-7636-2243-5(5)) Candlewick Pr.

Nuhern, G. A. Christmas List Learn & Have Fun in School & the Magic of Wisdom. 2002. (ENG.). 124p. 20.95 (*978-0-595-65095-8(3) , Writers Club Pr.) iUniverse, Inc.

Oates, Joyce Carol. Small Avalanches & Other Stories. 2003. 400p. (YA). 17.89 (978-0-06-001218-2(8) , HarperTeen) HarperCollins Pubs.

—Small Avalanches & Other Stories. 2004. lib. bdg. 16.45 (978-0-613-71362-7(1)) Tandem Library Bks.

O'Callaghan, Elena. Unos Ratones Insoportables. 2002. (Caballo Alado Ser.).Tr. of Unbearable Mice. (SPA & ENG., Illus.). 24p. pap. 4.95 (978-84-7864-436-0(9)) Combel Editorial, S.A. ESP. *Dist:* Independent Pubs. Group.

O'Donnell, John. Doggy Poo (Picture Book) 2004. (Illus.). 36p. (J). pap. 7.99 (978-1-58664-966-1(3) , CP 72801) Central Park Media Corp.

Okeke-Ibezim, Felicia. African Folk Tales: Obiageli & Other Stories. 2006. (YA). per. 9.95 (*978-0-9661598-7-5(X)) Ekwike Bks. & Publishing.

O'Kif, Alis. No Somos Irrompibles (12 Cuentos de Chicos Enamorados) 2003. (SPA.). 143p. (J). (gr. 8-12). pap. 9.95 (978-950-511-243-2(2)) Santillana USA Publishing Co., Inc.

Okubo, Margaret. The Story of Angelo. 2005. (YA). per. 12.95 (978-0-9763686-2-5(5)) Rapha Publishing.

La Ola Gigante; El Primer Dia de Clases, 2 bks., Set. unabr. ed. (Coleccion Chiquilines - Imagen y Sonido). (SPA., Illus.). (J). 15.95 incl. audio (978-950-11-0626-8(8) , SGM268) Sigmar ARG. *Dist:* Continental Bk. Co., Inc.

Olcott, Frances Jenkins. Good Stories for Great Holidays. l.t. ed. 2006. 324p. pap. 19.99 (978-1-4264-1125-0(1)) BiblioBazaar.

—Good Stories for Holidays. 2004. reprint ed. pap. 27.95 (978-1-4191-2211-8(8)); pap. 1.99 (978-1-4192-2211-5(2)) Kessinger Publishing, LLC.

Oldfield, Jenny. I'd Like a Little Word, Leonie! Child, Lauren, illus. 99p. (J). pap. 8.99 (978-0-340-78501-0(2)) Macmillan Publishers Ltd. GBR. *Dist:* Trafalgar Square Publishing.

—Keep the Noise down, Kingsley. Layton, Neal, illus. (J). mass mkt. 8.99 (978-0-340-85105-0(8) , Hodder & Stoughton) Hodder General Publishing Division GBR. *Dist:* Independent Pubs. Group.

—Not Now, Nathan! Child, Lauren, illus. 107p. (J). pap. 7.99 (978-0-340-78502-7(0)) Macmillan Publishers Ltd. GBR. *Dist:* Trafalgar Square Publishing.

—Silver Spur. 2001. (Illus.). 144p. (J). pap. 9.99 (978-0-340-79169-1(1)) Macmillan Publishers Ltd. GBR. *Dist:* Trafalgar Square Publishing.

—Steamboat Charlie. 2001. (Illus.). 160p. (J). pap. 9.99 (978-0-340-79172-1(1) , Hodder & Stoughton) Hodder General Publishing Division GBR. *Dist:* Independent Pubs. Group.

—When Dad Went on a Date. (Illus.). (J). mass mkt. 8.99 (978-0-340-85075-6(2) , Hodder & Stoughton) Hodder General Publishing Division GBR. *Dist:* Independent Pubs. Group.

—When Ellie Cheated. (Illus.). (YA). mass mkt. 8.99 (978-0-340-85072-5(8) , Hodder & Stoughton) Hodder General Publishing Division GBR. *Dist:* Independent Pubs. Group.

—When Geri & I Fell Out. (Illus.). (J). mass mkt. 8.99 (978-0-340-85074-9(4) , Hodder & Stoughton) Hodder General Publishing Division GBR. *Dist:* Independent Pubs. Group.

—When I Won a Prize. (Illus.). (J). mass mkt. 8.99 (978-0-340-85076-3(0) , Hodder & Stoughton) Hodder General Publishing Division GBR. *Dist:* Independent Pubs. Group.

—When Scott Got Lost No. 2. (Illus.). (J). mass mkt. 8.99 (978-0-340-85073-2(6)) Macmillan Publishers Ltd. GBR. *Dist:* Trafalgar Square Publishing.

—When Shah Went Weird. (Illus.). (J). mass mkt. 8.99 (978-0-340-85077-0(9) , Hodder & Stoughton) Hodder General Publishing Division GBR. *Dist:* Independent Pubs. Group.

—You Must Be Joking, Jimmy! Child, Lauren, illus. 64p. (J). pap. 8.99 (978-0-340-78500-3(4) , Hodder & Stoughton) Hodder General Publishing Division GBR. *Dist:* Independent Pubs. Group.

Oldfield, Jenny, compiled by. Horse & Pony Stories. 2007. (Illus.). 128p. (J). pap. 9.95 (***978-0-7534-6156-3(0)*** , Kingfisher) Houghton Mifflin Co. Trade & Reference Div.

Oldfield, Jenny, compiled by. The Kingfisher Book of Horse & Pony Stories. 2005. (Kingfisher Book of Ser.). (Illus.). 128p. (J). (gr. 4-6). 17.00 (978-0-7534-5850-1(0) , Kingfisher) Houghton Mifflin Co. Trade & Reference Div.

Oliver, Chad. Far from This Earth & Other Stories. Olson, Priscilla, ed. Dennis, Jane, illus. 2003. (NESFA's Choice Ser.: 25). 480p. 24.00 (978-1-886778-48-1(5) , NESFA Pr.) New England Science Fiction Assn., Inc.

—A Star Above It & Other Stories. Olson, Priscilla, ed. Dennis, Jane, illus. 2003. (NESFA's Choice Ser.: 24). 480p. 24.00 (978-1-886778-45-0(0) , NESFA Pr.) New England Science Fiction Assn., Inc.

Olson, Arielle North & Schwartz, Howard. More Bones. 2008. 176p. (J). (gr. 3). 15.99 (***978-0-670-06339-0(8)*** , Viking Juvenile) Penguin Group (USA) Inc.

One Woman, One Hustle: Short Stories & Poems Inspired by Sheri J. Booker. 2003. per. 10.00 (978-0-9727776-0-5(1) , Book Her Publications) Lyrically Korrect Publishing.

O'Neal, Shaquille. Shaq & the Beanstalk: And Other Very Tall Tales. Evans, Shane W., illus. 1999. 80p. (J). (gr. 1-4). pap. 15.95 (978-0-590-91823-7(0) , Cartwheel Bks.) Scholastic, Inc.

Oppenheim, Joanne. Ramon Recuerda. Munsinger, Lynn, illus. (Buenas Noches Coleccion). (SPA.). (J). (gr. 6-8). 8.95 (978-958-04-2391-1(1)) Norma S.A. COL. *Dist:* Distribuidora Norma, Inc., Lectorum Pubns., Inc.

Oram, Hiawyn. Counting Leopard's Spots & other Stories. Warnes, Tim, illus. 2005. 96p. (J). (gr. k-4). reprint ed. 17.00 (978-0-7567-9252-7(5)) DIANE Publishing Co.

Orme, David. Plague. 2004. (Shades Ser.). 58p. (J). pap. 7.99 (978-0-237-52729-7(4) , Evans Brothers, Limited) Evans Publishing Group GBR. *Dist:* Independent Pubs. Group.

Ormsby, Nathaniel Hosea. Timeless Tales of Anansi: Ancestral Realm of Africa. 2006. 108p. pap. 16.95 (978-1-4241-3396-3(3)) PublishAmerica, Inc.

Oswald, Michael J. Serious Stories for Childrean. 2002. 55p. pap. 11.95 (978-0-7414-1110-5(5)) Infinity Publishing.

Otis, James. District Messenger Boy & A Necktie Par. 2006. pap. (***978-1-4250-1843-6(2)***); pap. (***978-1-4250-2095-8(X)***); pap. (***978-1-4250-2386-7(X)***); pap. (***978-1-4250-1391-2(0)***) Assistedreadingbooks.com Inc.

Our Lady of the Winding Sheets: The Cher'azade Series. 2006. (Cher'azade Ser.). (YA). 7.95 (***978-0-9746669-2-1(0)***) Franklin, J.E.

Ouriou, Susan, tr. from SPA. Little Book of Nursery Tales. Salvador, Carmen, illus. 2005. (Little Book Ser.). 104p. (J). (ps-7). 8.95 (978-0-88899-673-2(X)) Groundwood Bks. CAN. *Dist:* Perseus Distribution.

Overell, J. J. The Dancing Flame. Lawrie, Robin, illus. 2004. 124p. pap. 15.00 (978-0-7188-3036-6(9)) Lutherworth Pr., The GBR. *Dist:* Parkwest Pubns., Inc.

Oxenbury, Helen. The Helen Oxenbury Nursery Collection. 2004. (Illus.). 96p. (J). (gr. k-1). 19.95 (978-0-375-82992-5(X)); lib. bdg. 21.99 (978-0-375-92992-2(4)) Random Hse. Children's Bks. (Knopf Bks. for Young Readers).

Packard, Mary. Fall Leaves. Regan, Dana, illus. 2000. (My First Hello Reader! Ser.). 32p. (J). (ps-1). pap. 3.99 (978-0-439-09911-0(0)) Scholastic, Inc.

—Fall Leaves. 2000. (Hello Reader! Ser.). (J). 10.79 (978-0-606-19560-7(2)) Tandem Library Bks.

& Packer, Knife & McCoshan, Duncan. Captain Fact's Creepy Crawly Adventure. 2004. (Illus.). 96p. (J). pap. (***978-1-4052-0834-5(1)***) Egmont Bks., Ltd.

Padilla, Rebecca. Cuentitos de Mami Amor. Padilla, Felix, ed. Padilla, Star, illus. 1999. 34p. (J). 16.00 (978-0-9675413-3-4(6)) Libros, Encouraging Cultural Literacy.

—Mami Amor's Little Stories. Padilla, Felix, ed. Padilla, Star, illus. 1999. 36p. (J). (gr. 3 up). 16.00 (978-0-9675413-2-7(8)) Libros, Encouraging Cultural Literacy.

Padma, T. V. The Forbidden Temple: Stories from the Past. Vyas, Bhavana, illus. 2004. 95p. (J). (***978-81-8146-041-7(3)***) Tulika Pubs.

Page, Josephine. Peekaboo Kitty. Beasley, Roberta, illus. 2005. 6p. (J). (gr. 3-3). 7.99 (978-0-439-72513-2(5) , Cartwheel Bks.) Scholastic, Inc.

Pagnucci, Gian. Don't Count Your Chickens: Stories for Kids to Tell. Pagnucci, Susan, illus. 2000. 64p. (J). (ps-5). pap. 8.99 (978-0-929326-17-7(2)) Bur Oak Pr., Inc.

Paint Me Like I Am: Teen Poems from Writerscorps. 2003. 128p. (YA). (gr. 8-12). lib. bdg. 15.30 (978-0-613-66791-3(3)) Tandem Library Bks.

Pajaroflor. 2003. (SPA.). pap. (978-956-13-1080-3(5) , AB8005) Bello, Andres CHL. *Dist:* Lectorum Pubns., Inc.

Palazzetti, Toulla. The Nick & Pete Stories. Wise, Noreen, ed. Bowman, Sharon, illus. 3rd ed. 2001. (Gold Mixed Collection). 52p. (J). (ps up). pap. 7.50 (978-1-58584-417-3(9)) Huckleberry Pr.

Palermo, Miguel Angel. Lo Que Cuentan los Onas. (SPA.). (YA). (gr. 4 up). pap. (978-950-07-1260-6(1) , SA30066) Editorial Sudamericana S.A. ARG. *Dist:* Lectorum Pubns., Inc.

Palmer, Slim. The Albert Tales. 2005. (Illus.). 240p. (J). per. (978-1-905363-35-3(4) , Exposure Publishing) Meadow Bks.

Paloma, David. Una Buena Costumbre. 2003. (Caballo Alado Ser.). (SPA & ENG., Illus.). 24p. pap. 4.95 (978-84-7864-671-5(X)) Combel Editorial, S.A. ESP. *Dist:* Independent Pubs. Group.

Panman, Sandra & Panman, Richard. Short Stories. Panman, Sandra, ed. 5th ed. 2004. (Illus.). 192p. (YA). (gr. 7-12). reprint ed. pap. 23.95 (978-0-912813-32-5(6)) Active Learning Corp.

Pants & the Bully. 2004. (J). per. 7.99 (978-0-9755959-1-6(1)) Girl Named Pants, Inc., A.

Pants Feeds the Poor. 2004. (J). per. 7.99 (978-0-9755959-3-0(8)) Girl Named Pants, Inc., A.

Papademitriou, Lisa. Sixth-Grade Glommers, Norks, & Me. 2005. 224p. (gr. 3-7). 14.99 (978-0-7868-5169-0(4)) Hyperion Bks. for Children.

Papineau, Lucie, et al. Bamboo in Bamboo Land. Jolin, Dominique, illus. 2001. (Little Wolf Bks.: Level 1). 32p. (J). (gr. 1 up). pap. (978-1-894363-67-9(1)) Dominique & Friends.

Parker, Ruth A. Peach Pear Plum: 12 Collections of Poems, Stories, & Writings. 2000. (Illus.). 88p. (YA). (gr. 9 up). pap. 24.95 (978-1-930002-20-3(3)) I & L Publishing.

Parness, Arlyne. Five children's stories by Grandma. 2006. pap. 8.95 (978-0-533-15269-8(0)) Vantage Pr., Inc.

Parry, Glynn. Last Gasps. 2000. (gr. 7-12). lib. bdg. 12.10 (978-0-613-28921-4(8)) Tandem Library Bks.

Pascal, Francine. Ambiente Hostil. Orig. Title: Out of Place. (SPA.). 128p. (J). 6.95 (978-84-272-3792-6(8)) Molino, Editorial ESP. *Dist:* AIMS International Bks., Inc.

—Cambios Oportunos.Tr. of Standing Out. (SPA.). 112p. (J). 6.95 (978-84-272-3795-7(2)) Molino, Editorial ESP. *Dist:* AIMS International Bks., Inc.

Paterson, Andrew Barton 'Banjo'. Three Elephant Power & Other Stories. 2004. reprint ed. pap. 15.95 (978-1-4191-8979-1(4)); pap. 1.99 (978-1-4192-8979-8(9)) Kessinger Publishing, LLC.

Patneaude, David. Dark Starry Morning: Stories of This World & Beyond. 1998. 10.60 (978-0-606-13315-9(1)) Tandem Library Bks.

Patten, William. Animal & Nature Stories Vol. 8: The Junior Classics. 2004. reprint ed. pap. 1.99 (978-1-4192-6805-2(8)) Kessinger Publishing, LLC.

—The Junior Classics, Volume 5: Stories T. 2006. 65.99 (***978-1-4280-1823-5(9)***) IndyPublish.com.

—The Junior Classics, Volume 7: Stories O. 2006. 29.99 (***978-1-4280-0585-3(4)***); pap. 22.99 (***978-1-4280-0561-7(7)***) IndyPublish.com.

—Junior Classics Volume 8 Animal & Natu. 2006. 67.99 (***978-1-4280-3505-8(2)***); pap. 60.99 (***978-1-4280-3456-3(0)***) IndyPublish.com.

Paulsen, Gary, ed. Shelf Life: Stories by the Book. 2003. (Illus.). 192p. (J). (gr. 5-9). 17.99 (978-0-689-84180-4(9)) Simon & Schuster Children's Publishing.

Paws & Claws & Other Stories: Individual Title Six-Pack. (Story Steps Ser.). (gr. k-2). 42.00 (978-0-7635-9580-7(2)) Rigby Education.

Payne, Jan & Payne, Tony. It's Only Annie!, Bk. 3. Reeve, Rosie, illus. 2005. (Annie Ser.). (J). pap. 11.00 (978-1-84255-159-2(0)) Dolphin Paperbacks GBR. *Dist:* Trafalgar Square Publishing.

—Not Again, Annie!, Vol. 2. Reeve, Rosie, illus. 2005. (Annie Ser.). (J). pap. 11.95 (978-1-84255-158-5(2)) Dolphin Paperbacks GBR. *Dist:* Trafalgar Square Publishing.

Payne, Tony & Payne, Jan. Oh No, Annie!, Vol. 1. 2005. (Annie Ser.). (Illus.). 80p. (J). pap. 9.99 (978-1-84255-157-8(4)) Dolphin Paperbacks GBR. *Dist:* Trafalgar Square Publishing.

Peck, Richard. Past Perfect, Present Tense: New & Collected Stories. 192p. (J). 2004. (Illus.). (gr. 5). 16.99 (978-0-8037-2998-8(7) , Dial); 2006. (gr. 3). reprint ed. pap. 6.99 (978-0-14-240537-6(X) , Puffin) Penguin Group (USA) Inc.

Peckham, Lori, ed. Guide's Greatest Animal Stories. 2006. 144p. (YA). pap. 10.99 (***978-0-8280-1944-6(4)***) Review & Herald Publishing Assn.

—Guide's Greatest Mystery Stories. 2007. 160p. (J). pap. 11.99 (***978-0-8280-2038-1(8)***) Review & Herald Publishing Assn.

Pelletier, Marthe & Sottolichio, Rafael. Chante Pour Moi, Charlotte. 2001. (Roman Jeunesse Ser.). (FRE., Illus.). 96p. (J). (gr. 4-7). pap. (978-2-89021-493-4(1)) Diffusion du livre Mirabel.

Pellicer, Carlos. Juan y Sus Zapatos. (Los Especials de A la Orilla Del Viento Ser.). (SPA.). 20p. (J). (978-968-16-7021-4(3)) Fondo de Cultura Economica USA.

Penick Phillips-Cermak, Mosetta. The Wishing Flower. 2007. 24p. 16.50 (***978-0-615-15573-9(1)***) PM Moon Pubs.

Pennell, Kathleen. Missing Money. Pennell, Lauren, illus. 2000. (Pony Investigators Ser.: Vol. 1). 88p. (J). (gr. 3-6). pap. 5.95 (978-1-930353-21-3(9)) Masthof Pr.

The People on the Corner. 2003. pap. 15.00 (978-0-9740269-0-9(5)) Cyclops Pr.

Pepper, Dennis. New Young Oxford Book of Ghost Stories. 2000. (gr. 7-12). lib. bdg. 22.20 (978-0-613-58672-6(7)) Tandem Library Bks.

Perera, Hilda. Cuentos Para Chicos Y Grandes. 2001. (SPA.). (gr. 3-6). lib. bdg. 16.40 (978-0-613-64478-5(6)) Tandem Library Bks.

—Podria Ser Que una Vez. Delacre, Lulu, illus. (SPA.). 84p. (J). (gr. 3-5). 7.95 (978-84-241-3274-3(2) , EV0925) Everest de Ediciones y Distribucion, S.L. ESP. *Dist:* Lectorum Pubns., Inc.

Perez, Vivian. Stolen Stories for My Nieces. 2007. (ENG.). 68p. per. 12.95 (***978-1-4241-6679-4(9)***) PublishAmerica, Inc.

Perrault, Charles. Cuentos de Antano. (SPA.). 336p. (YA). (978-84-7525-123-3(4)) Ediciones Generales Anaya SA.

—Cuentos de Perrault.Tr. of Stories by Perrault. (SPA.). 128p. (J). 19.98 (978-84-305-8325-6(4)) Susaeta Ediciones, S.A. ESP. *Dist:* AIMS International Bks., Inc., Giron Bks.

—Puffin Book of Five Minute Stories. (Illus.). 128p. (J). 24.95 (978-0-670-87680-8(1)) Penguin Group (USA) Inc.

Perry, Glyn & Parry, Glyn. Invisible Girl. 2003. 160p. (YA). pap. 15.25 (978-1-920731-48-9(2)) Fremantle Pr. AUS. *Dist:* International Specialized Bk. Services.

Pescetti, Luis Maria. La Tarea Segun Natacha. 2000. (SPA.). 32p. (J). (978-84-204-5837-3(6)) Alfaguara, Ediciones, S.A.- Grupo Santillana.

—La Tarea Segun Natacha. O'Kif, illus. 2003. (Coleccion Derechos Del Nino Ser.). (SPA.). 32p. (J). (gr. 3-5). pap. 7.95 (978-84-204-5836-6(8)) Santillana USA Publishing Co., Inc.

Pet Stories Set 2 800888, 3 vols. 2005. (J). pap. (978-1-59794-063-4(1)) Environments, Inc.

Pet Stories Set 800887, 3 vols. 2005. (J). pap. (978-1-59794-062-7(3)) Environments, Inc.

Petcoff, Desmond Onyx. The Gift of Silliness: A Collection of 20 Silly Stories. 2003. (J). (978-0-9701184-9-3(X)) Onoma Enterprises.

Peters, Julie Anne. Grl2Grl. 2007. 160p. (YA). (gr. 10 up). pap. 11.99 (***978-0-316-01343-7(9)***) Little, Brown Bks. for Young Readers.

Peterson, Jim. Kitten Tales. 2006. (ENG.). 76p. per. 14.95 (***978-1-4241-4448-8(5)***) PublishAmerica, Inc.

Petterson, Aline. El Papalote y el Nopal. Pacheco, Gabriel, illus. 2003. (SPA.). 34p. (J). (gr. 3-5). 15.95 (978-968-19-0750-1(7)) Santillana USA Publishing Co., Inc.

Petty, Kate. The Nightspinners. Smith, Mary Claire, illus. 2004. 32p. (J). pap. 8.99 (978-1-84255-105-9(1)) Dolphin Paperbacks GBR. *Dist:* Trafalgar Square Publishing.

Phillpotts, Karl, et al. In Jamaica Where I Live & Other Stories. Stennett, Errol et al, illus. 2002. (Doctor Bird Reading Ser.). 31p. (J). pap. (978-976-637-089-3(3)) Randle, Ian Pubs.

Phinn, Gervase. Royston Knapper: Return of the Rogue. Fisher, Chris, illus. 2002. 128p. (J). 9.99 (978-0-85953-024-8(8)) Child's Play-International.

Pickering, H. G. The Pickering Collection: Neighbors Have My Ducks, Merry Xmas, Mr. Williams Dog Days on Trout Waters & Angling of the Test. Timmins, Harry L. & Gardner, Donald, illus. 1999. (Fifty Greatest Bks.: Bk. 47). 288p. (gr. 10 up). reprint ed. 50.00 (978-1-56416-047-8(5)) Derrydale Pr., The.

Picking Apples. 2001. (978-1-58453-167-8(3)) Pioneer Valley Educational Pr., Inc.

Pierce, Tamora & Sherman, Josepha. Young Warriors: Stories of Strength. 2006. 336p. (J). (gr. 7-11). pap. 8.95 (978-0-375-82963-5(6) , Random Hse. Bks. for Young Readers) Random Hse. Children's Bks.

La Pierna Lastimada, 2 bks., Set. (Coleccion Chiquilines - Imagen y Sonido). (SPA.). (J). 15.95 incl. audio (978-950-11-0625-1(X) , SGM25X) Sigmar ARG. *Dist:* Continental Bk. Co., Inc.

Pinguilly, Yves. Contes et Legendes de Bretagne. pap. 14.95 (978-2-09-282237-1(3)) Nathan, Fernand FRA. *Dist:* Distribooks, Inc.

Pinkney, Jerry, illus. The Little Red Hen. 2006. 32p. (J). (ps-2). 16.99 (978-0-8037-2935-3(9) , Dial) Penguin Group (USA) Inc.

Piper, Sophie & Massey, Jane. Little Teddy's Christmas Book. 2000. (Illus.). 64p. (J). 6.99 (978-0-7459-4561-3(9) , Lion) Lion Hudson plc GBR. *Dist:* Independent Pubs. Group.

Pirotta, Saviour. Around the World in 80 Tales. Johnson, Richard, illus. 2007. 176p. (J). (ps-3). 19.95 (***978-0-7534-5999-7(X)*** , Kingfisher) Houghton Mifflin Co. Trade & Reference Div.

Plante, Raymond. Les Manigances de Marilou Polaire. Favreau, Marie-Claude, illus. 2002. (Premier Roman Ser.). (FRE.). 64p. (J). (gr. 2-5). pap. (978-2-89021-274-9(2)) Diffusion du livre Mirabel.

Play Time. 2002. (978-0-9720825-0-1(6)) Toy Box Pr., The.

Plourde, Josee & Barrette, Doris. Sur les Traces de Lou Adams. 2001. (Roman Jeunesse Ser.). (FRE., Illus.). 96p. (J). (gr. 4-7). pap. (978-2-89021-485-9(0)) Diffusion du livre Mirabel.

Poe, Edgar Allan. Cuentos. 2000. (Coleccion "Clasicos Juveniles" Ser.). (SPA., Illus.). 212p. (gr. 4-7). pap. 10.95 (978-1-58348-824-9(3)) iUniverse, Inc.

—Edgar Allan Poe. McConnell, James, illus. 2004. (Great American Short Stories Ser.). 73p. (J). lib. bdg. 23.33 (978-0-8368-4254-8(5)) Stevens, Gareth Inc.

—Edgar Allan Poe Collection. Stemach, Jerry, ed. Ham, Jeff, illus. l.t. ed. 104p. 2002. 150.00 (978-1-58702-015-5(7)); 2000. 50.00 (978-1-58702-439-9(X)); 2000. 65.00 incl. audio, cd-rom (978-1-893376-70-0(2)) Johnston, Don Inc.

—El Escarabajo de Oro y Otros Relatos. 2nd ed. 2002. (SPA., Illus.). 192p. 15.95 (978-84-392-8016-3(5) , EV0875) Gaviota Ediciones ESP. *Dist:* Lectorum Pubns., Inc.

—Tales of Terror from Edgar Allan Poe. McCurdy, Michael, illus. 2005. 96p. (J). (gr. 5-7). 15.95 (978-0-375-83305-2(6)); lib. bdg. 17.99 (978-0-375-93305-9(0)) Random Hse. Children's Bks. (Knopf Bks. for Young Readers).

Poe, Edgar Allan & Bierce, Ambrose. Tales of Mystery & Horror. 2005. 160p. (J). per. 6.99 (978-1-58049-362-8(9) , PWH3629) Prestwick Hse., Inc.

Poe, Edgar Allan & Delbanco, Andrew. Edgar Allan Poe. Dubois, Gérard, illus. 2006. (Stories for Young People Ser.). 80p. (J). (***978-1-4027-4233-0(9)***) Sterling Publishing Co., Inc.

Poet Ajax, The, The Poet, et al. Stories That Won't Make Your Parents Hurl. Rosen, Selina, ed. Scott, Matthew, illus. 2000. 186p. (J). pap. 18.00 (978-1-893687-12-7(0)) Yard Dog Pr.

Poggio, Alredo. El Nino Durazno. Maddonni, Karina, illus. 2001. (SPA.). 136p. (YA). (gr. 5-8). 9.95 (978-950-511-651-5(9)) Alfaguara S.A. de Ediciones ARG. *Dist:* Santillana USA Publishing Co., Inc.

Pombo, Rafael. Cuentos, Pombo Rafael. Acosta, Patricia, illus. (SPA.). 68p. (J). (gr. 2). (978-958-30-0355-4(7) , PV0862) Panamericana Editorial COL. *Dist:* Lectorum Pubns., Inc.

Ponti, Claude. Mi Valle. 2003. (SPA.). 46p. (978-84-95150-60-8(3)) Corimbo, Editorial S.L.

—La Tempestad. 2003. (SPA.). 32p. (978-84-95150-41-7(7)) Corimbo, Editorial S.L.

Porter, Connie. Addy's Short Story Collection. Dellosso, Gabriella & Graef, Renee, illus. 2006. 248p. (J). 12.95 (***978-1-59369-122-6(X)***) American Girl Publishing, Inc.

S

Posadas, Carmen. Dorilda. 2003. (SPA., Illus.). 127p. (J). (gr. 3-5). pap. 13.95 (978-84-204-5800-7(7)) Santillana USA Publishing Co., Inc.

Post, Janet Smith. Thirty Stories I Can Read! 2000. 300p. (J). (978-0-9702826-7-5(2)) Breaking The Sounds' Barrier, Reading By Ear.

Potok, Chaim. Zebra & Other Stories. 2000. 146p. (YA). (gr. 8-12). per. 11.64 (978-0-606-19830-1(X)) Tandem Library Bks.

—Zebra & Other Stories. l.t. ed. 2000. (Illus.). 200p. (J). (gr. 8-12). 20.95 (978-0-7862-2978-9(0)) Thorndike Pr.

Potter, Author Tina M. The Horse Story. 2005. 36p. (J). pap. 9.65 (978-1-4116-5761-8(6)) Lulu.com.

Potter, Beatrix. Beatrix Potter Favorite Tales: The Tales of Peter Rabbit & Jemimapuddle Duck Read along Book & CD. 2006. (Illus.). 64p. (J). 9.99 (978-0-7232-5879-7(1) , Warne) Penguin Group (USA) Inc.

—Collection of Beatrix Potter Stories Eas. 2006. pap. (***978-1-4250-0274-9(9)***) Assistedreadingbooks.com Inc.

—The Complete Adventures of Peter Rabbit R/I. 2007. 80p. (J). (ps). 14.99 (***978-0-7232-5916-9(X)*** , Warne) Penguin Group (USA) Inc.

—Selections from Beatrix Potter. 2002. (J). cd-rom (978-0-9746806-0-6(5)) Alcazar AudioWorks.

—Treasured Tales from Beatrix Potter. 2007. (Illus.). 128p. (J). 7.99 (978-0-7232-5860-5(0) , Warne) Penguin Group (USA) Inc.

—World of Peter Rabbit, 12 vols. 2006. (Potter Ser.). (Illus.). (J). pap. 84.00 (978-0-7232-5790-5(6) , Warne) Penguin Group (USA) Inc.

—World of Peter Rabbit Presentn 1-23, 23 vols. 2006. (Illus.). (J). pap. 160.00 (978-0-7232-5763-9(9) , Warne) Penguin Group (USA) Inc.

Potts, Ghillian. Diary Days. 2005. (Young Corgis Ser.). (Illus.). 69p. (J). (gr. 2-4). pap. 7.50 (978-0-552-54686-7(0) , Corgi) Transworld Publishers Ltd. GBR. *Dist:* Independent Pubs. Group.

Power Reading: Power PAK. 2005. (Illus.). 80p. (J). (gr. 2-4). vinyl bd. 129.95 (978-1-883186-73-9(0) , PPMX2-3); (gr. 4-5). vinyl bd. 129.95 (978-1-883186-72-2(2) , PPMX4-5) National Reading Styles Institute, Inc.

Power Reading: Power PAK 4C. 2005. (Illus.). 80p. (J). (gr. 4-5). vinyl bd. 129.95 (978-1-883186-70-8(6) , PPO4C) National Reading Styles Institute, Inc.

PowerMark Issue 10 Vol. 1, Issue 10: Fang Shaw Revealed, Vol. 110. 2001. 32p. (J). pap. 2.95 (978-0-9705669-9-7(9)) PowerMark Productions.

PowerMark Issue 5 Vol. 1, Issue 5: Face Off. 2001. 32p. (J). pap. 2.95 (978-0-9705669-1-2(8)) PowerMark Productions.

PowerMark Issue 6 Vol. 1, Issue 6: They All Fall Down. 2001. 32p. (J). pap. 2.95 (978-0-9705669-5-9(6)) PowerMark Productions.

PowerMark Issue 7 Vol. 1, Issue 7: High & Mighty. 2001. 32p. (J). pap. 2.95 (978-0-9705669-6-6(4)) PowerMark Productions.

PowerMark Issue 8 Vol. 1, Issue 8: Family Matter. 2001. 32p. (J). pap. 2.95 (978-0-9705669-7-3(2)) PowerMark Productions.

PowerMark Issue 9 Vol. 1, Issue 9: Cyborg Mayhem. 2001. 32p. (J). pap. 2.95 (978-0-9705669-8-0(0)) PowerMark Productions.

A Prairie Heart. 2007. (Illus.). (J). per. 19.95 (***978-0-9793668-0-2(1)***) Prairie Heart Publishing.

Preece, Mary Ellen Goble. The ABC Cousins & Fun from A to Z. 2007. (J). per. 12.00 (***978-1-60458-005-1(4)***) Instantpublisher.com.

Preece, Phil. Nightmare Park. 2004. (Shades Ser.). 52p. (J). pap. 7.99 (978-0-237-52730-3(8) , Evans Brothers, Limited) Evans Publishing Group GBR. *Dist:* Independent Pubs. Group.

Preller, James. Ghost Cat & Other Spooky Tales. 2007. (Illus.). 80p. (J). (gr. 2-5). pap. 3.99 (***978-0-439-79398-8(X)***) Scholastic, Inc.

Prentiss, Elizabeth. Little Susy Stories. 1999. (J). (gr. 4-7). pap. 7.99 (978-1-881545-70-5(9)) A B Publishing.

Prevert, Jacques. Contes pour enfants pas Sage. (FRE.). pap. 16.95 (978-2-07-053885-0(0)) Gallimard, Editions FRA. *Dist:* Distribooks, Inc.

Price & Wilkinson. The Saga of Aslak. 2004. (Illus.). 96p. bds. 8.95 (978-0-7136-4076-2(6)) A & C Black GBR. *Dist:* Consortium Bk. Sales & Distribution.

Price, Susan. Horror Stories. 2003. (gr. 5-8). lib. bdg. 15.25 (978-0-613-67414-0(6)) Tandem Library Bks.

Priest, Christopher. Omnibus, Pt. 1. 363p. pap. (978-0-671-03389-7(1) , Free Pr.) Simon & Schuster.

Priestley, Chris. Uncle Montague's Tales of Terror. Roberts, David, illus. 2007. 192p. (J). (gr. 3-7). 12.95 (***978-1-59990-118-3(8)*** , Bloomsbury Children) Bloomsbury Publishing.

Proysen, Alf. Little Old Mrs. Pepperpot. l.t. ed. 2005. (Illus.). (J). pap. (978-0-7540-6199-1(X) , CLP 391) BBC Audio.

Publications International Staff. Thomas Helps Out. 2004. (Illus.). (J). 15.98 (978-0-7853-8073-3(6) , 7180800) Publications International, Ltd.

Puddephatt, Neal, illus. Classic Horse & Pony Stories. 2000. (J). (978-0-7894-6364-7(4)) Dorling Kindersley Publishing, Inc.

The Puffin Book of Bedtime Stories. 2006. 184p. (J). pap. 16.00 (978-0-670-05841-9(6) , Penguin Global) Penguin Group (USA) Inc.

Pugliano-Martin, Carol & Gordh, Bill. Barbie Story Collection. Wolcott, Karen, illus. 2006. (Step into Reading Ser.). 192p. (J). (ps-3). pap. 8.99 (978-0-375-84124-8(5) , Random Hse. Bks. for Young Readers) Random Hse. Children's Bks.

Pullen, Janis Charlton. Grandma¿s Stories. 2004. 44p. (J). per. 9.95 (***978-1-59453-422-5(5)*** , 2513, Airleaf Publishing) Airleaf Publishing & Bookselling.

Puncel, Maria. Manana es Domingo y Otras Rimas Infantiles. Recio, Ricardo, illus. 2003. (SPA.). 32p. 4.95 (978-84-372-8021-9(4)) Altea, Ediciones, S.A. - Grupo Santillana ESP. *Dist:* Santillana USA Publishing Co., Inc.

—El Patio de Mi Casa y Otras Canciones Infantiles. Escriva, Vivi, illus. 2003. (SPA.). 32p. 4.95 (978-84-372-8018-9(4)) Altea, Ediciones, S.A. - Grupo Santillana ESP. *Dist:* Santillana USA Publishing Co., Inc.

—Yo Subia la Escalera y Otras Rimas Infantiles. Bayley, Nicola, illus. 2003. (SPA.). 24p. 4.95 (978-84-372-8015-8(X)) Altea, Ediciones, S.A. - Grupo Santillana ESP. *Dist:* Santillana USA Publishing Co., Inc.

Punter, Russell. Stories of Santa Claus. 2006. 48p. (J). 8.99 (978-0-7945-1476-1(6) , Usborne) EDC Publishing.

Pushkin, Alexandr, et al. Cuentos Clasicos Juveniles. 2003. (SPA., Illus.). 124p. (J). (gr. 8-12). pap. 12.95 (978-968-19-0320-6(X)) Santillana USA Publishing Co., Inc.

Puttock, Simon. Who's the Boss Rhinoceros? Busby, Ailie, illus. 32p. (J). pap. 8.99 (978-0-7497-4354-3(9)) Egmont Bks., Ltd. GBR. *Dist:* Trafalgar Square Publishing.

Pyle, Howard. The Garden Behind the Moon. 2005. (Illus.). 128p. pap. 7.95 (978-0-486-44073-6(7)) Dover Pubns., Inc.

Queen, Ivana. A Child's Pet Frizzes & Parent Tizzies: Short Story Collection. 2007. 236p. pap. 15.95 (***978-1-4327-0050-8(2)***) Outskirts Press, Inc.

Quiroga, Horacio. Cuentos de la Selva. Vallejo, Esperanza, illus. 2004. Tr. of Jungle Stories. (SPA.). 186p. (J). (ps-7). pap. (978-958-30-0458-2(8)) Panamericana Editorial.

—Cuentos de la Selva. (Young Classics Ser.).Tr. of Jungle Stories. (SPA.). (J). (gr. 6-8). 5.60 (978-950-11-1268-9(3) , SG8741) Sigmar ARG. *Dist:* Lectorum Pubns., Inc.

—Los Cuentos de Mis Hijos.Tr. of Stories of My Children. (SPA.). 104p. (YA). (gr. 5-8). 7.50 (978-84-204-4585-4(1)) Alfaguara, Ediciones, S.A.- Grupo Santillana ESP. *Dist:* Lectorum Pubns., Inc.

Rabelo-Cartagena, Jose A. Cuentos de la Fauna Puertorriquea. Rabelo-Cartagena, Jose A., ed. 2002. (Illus.). 64p. per. 19.99 (978-0-9726446-1-7(X)) Ediciones PayaLila.

Rach, W. Dennis. The Goofy Principal at Silly School. 2007. (J). per. (***978-0-9792579-0-2(5)***) Rach, W. Dennis.

Rackham, Arthur. A Fairy Book 1923. 2004. reprint ed. pap. 20.95 (978-1-4179-7656-0(X)) Kessinger Publishing, LLC.

Rai, Bali. Dominoes & Other Stories. 2005. 192p. (J). pap. 9.99 (978-0-340-87732-6(4) , Hodder & Stoughton) Hodder General Publishing Division GBR. *Dist:* Trafalgar Square Publishing.

Rainbow after Rain. 2000. (Tippy Parrish Story Ser.). (YA). (gr. 6-10). per. 12.95 (978-1-930009-22-6(4)) Image Cascade Publishing.

Rainy Day. 1999. (PB & J Noodle Stories Ser.). 32p. (J). pap. 3.99 (978-0-7868-4327-5(6)) Disney Pr.

Ramaswamy, Maya, illus. U Sier Lapalang: A Khasi Tale. 2005. (J). (***978-81-89020-31-6(5)***) Katha.

Ramee, De La Louise. Bimbi (Stories for Children) 2006. 62.99 (***978-1-4280-1006-2(8)***); pap. 55.99 (***978-1-4280-1036-9(X)***) IndyPublish.com.

Ramee, Louise de la. Bimbi. 2006. pap. (***978-1-4250-1542-8(5)***) Assistedreadingbooks.com Inc.

Ramsey, Kimberly. Stories from Somerville. 2002. Vol. 1. 56p. 12.95 (978-1-881929-17-8(5)); Vol. 2. 64p. 12.95 (978-1-881929-18-5(3)) Oxton Hse., Pubs.

—Stories from Somerville: Comprehension Workbook. 2002. Vol. 1. 32p. 5.00 (978-1-881929-24-6(8)); Vol. 2. 52p. 7.00 (978-1-881929-26-0(4)) Oxton Hse., Pubs.

Random House Disney Staff. 12 Princess Stories. 2006. (Illus.). 176p. (J). (ps-2). 10.99 (978-0-7364-2351-9(6) , RH/Disney) Random Hse. Children's Bks.

Random House Disney Staff & Lagonegro, Melissa. Beauties in Bloom. Emslie, Peter, illus. 2003. (Disney Princess Ser.). 24p. (J). (gr. k-3). pap. 3.25 (978-0-7364-2094-5(0) , RH/Disney) Random Hse. Children's Bks.

Random House Value Publishing Staff. A Child's Book of Stories. 1998. (Children's Classics Ser.). 480p. (J). 6.99 (978-0-517-18961-0(5) , Children's Classics) Random Hse. Value Publishing.

Random House Value Publishing Staff, ed. Shakespeare, Illustrated Stories for Children. 1999. 6.99 (978-0-517-20430-6(4)) Random Hse. Value Publishing.

Rao, Cheryl. Mixed Score: Ghost & Other Stories. 2004. 122p. 15.00 (978-81-291-0401-4(6)) Rupa & Co. IND. *Dist:* South Asia Bks.

Rao, Rama Pemmaraju. Nine Tales from the Heart: Stories with Unique, Inspiring Messages for School-Ag. 2001. (gr. 3-6). lib. bdg. 28.00 (978-0-613-74700-4(3)) Tandem Library Bks.

Ravishankar, Anushka. Wish You Were Here. 2005. (Illus.). 28p. 14.95 (978-81-86211-75-5(6)) Tara Publishing IND. *Dist:* Consortium Bk. Sales & Distribution.

Ray, Jane. Puedes Pescar Una Sirena? Pittau, Francesco, tr. Ray, Jane, illus. 2005. (SPA., Illus.). 32p. (J). 16.95 (978-84-95939-21-0(5)) Blume ESP. *Dist:* Independent Pubs. Group.

Ray, Satyajit. Unicorn Expedition & Other Stories: The Exploits of Professor Shonku. 2004. (Illus.). x, 237p. (J). pap. (978-0-14-333584-9(7) , Puffin) Penguin Group (USA) Inc.

Read Magazine Editorial Staff. Read into the Millennium: Stories of the Future. 1999. (Best of READ Ser.). 160p. (gr. 5 up). lib. bdg. 24.90 (978-0-7613-0962-8(4) , Millbrook Pr.) Lerner Publishing Group.

Read to Me Mommy. Date not set. (Read to Me Ser.). 192p. (J). 14.98 (978-0-7525-9486-6(9)) Parragon, Inc.

Ready Reader Staff. Rush Rush Rush: Digraphs, 6 bks., set, Level B. 2003. (J). (ps-3). 33.50 (978-0-8136-2075-6(9)) Modern Curriculum Pr.

Realistic Fiction Collection. (Fiction Collections). 326.86 (978-1-59889-042-6(5)) Stone Arch Bks.

Rebmann, Charles. Christmas Stories from the Jersey Cape. 2003. 94p. pap. 9.95 (978-0-595-29692-7(0)) iUniverse, Inc.

Reetz, Kurt. Danny: The Big Move. 2000. mass mkt. 4.50 (978-1-931179-23-2(9)); mass mkt. 8.95 incl. audio compact disk (978-1-931179-34-8(4)) Long Hill Productions, Inc.

—Rochester & Merle: A Day at the Carnival. 2000. mass mkt. 8.95 (978-1-931179-10-2(7)) Long Hill Productions, Inc.

—Silly Audrey: It's Only Make Believe. 2000. mass mkt. 4.50 (978-1-931179-25-6(5)); mass mkt. 8.95 (978-1-931179-36-2(0)) Long Hill Productions, Inc.

—The Tin Horn Man: Rude Tootin. 2000. mass mkt. 8.95 (978-1-931179-54-6(9)) Long Hill Productions, Inc.

—The Tin Horn Man: Rude Tootin. Volodka, Aras, illus. 2000. mass mkt. 4.50 (978-1-931179-02-7(6)) Long Hill Productions, Inc.

Reggie-Foster, Debbi. It's Cool to Be Me! Mini Stories about. 2006. 48p. pap. 12.95 (***978-1-4241-4613-0(5)***) PublishAmerica, Inc.

Reid, Michael, illus. The Kingfisher Treasury of Pet Stories. 2003. (Kingfisher Treasury of Stories Ser.). 160p. (J). (gr. k-3). pap. 5.95 (978-0-7534-5668-2(0) , Kingfisher) Houghton Mifflin Co. Trade & Reference Div.

Reid, Mick, illus. Stories for Eight Year Olds. 2004. (Kingfisher Treasury of Stories Ser.). 160p. (J). (gr. k-3). pap. 5.95 (978-0-7534-5714-6(8) , Kingfisher) Houghton Mifflin Co. Trade & Reference Div.

Reit, Seymour, et al. Great Stories of Courage/[adapted by Seymour Reit ; Art by Ernie Colon]. 2006. pap. (***978-0-8368-7933-9(3)***); lib. bdg. (***978-0-8368-7926-1(0)***) Stevens, Gareth Inc. (World Almanac Library).

Relatos Escalofriantes. (SPA.). (YA). (gr. 5-8). pap. (978-956-13-1353-8(7) , AB9026) Bello, Andres CHL. *Dist:* Lectorum Pubns., Inc.

Reviejo, Carlos. Dejame Que te Cuente: Cincuenta Cuentos de Animales para Ninos. 2003. (SPA., Illus.). 212p. (978-84-348-7166-3(1) , SM31147) SM Ediciones ESP. *Dist:* Lectorum Pubns., Inc.

Reyes, Yolanda. Los Agujeros Negros. Lopez, Cristina, illus. 2003. (Coleccion Derechos Del Nino Ser.). (SPA.). 32p. (J). (gr. 3-5). pap. 7.95 (978-84-204-5839-7(2)) Santillana USA Publishing Co., Inc.

—Los Anos Terribles. (SPA.). (YA). 9.95 (978-958-04-5633-9(X)) Norma S.A. COL. *Dist:* Distribuidora Norma, Inc.

—Maria de los Dinosaurios. (Torre de Papel Ser.). (SPA.). (J). (gr. 2). 7.95 (978-958-04-4277-6(0)) Norma S.A. COL. *Dist:* Distribuidora Norma, Inc.

Reynolds, Adrian, illus. Mystery Stories. 2003. (Red Hot Reads Ser.). 224p. (gr. 4-8). pap. 6.95 (978-0-7534-5640-8(0) , Kingfisher) Houghton Mifflin Co. Trade & Reference Div.

Reynolds, Larry A. & La Belle, Tim. The Bear in the Basement: Includes the Story "The Foggy Frog of Soggy Swamp" Anderson, Beth, ed. 1998. (Illus.). 48p. (J). pap. 10.00 (978-0-9639445-1-1(7)) Hoosier Cider Pr.

Rice, David. Crazy Loco. Clayton, Christian, illus. 2003. 144p. (YA). (gr. 6-11). pap. 5.99 (978-0-14-250056-9(9) , Puffin) Penguin Group (USA) Inc.

Rice, David Talbot. Crazy Loco: Stories about Growing up Chicano in Southern Texas. 2003. (gr. 7-12). lib. bdg. 14.15 (978-0-613-67142-2(2)) Tandem Library Bks.

Richard, Martine. Chapeau, Camomille! Begin, Jean-Guy, illus. 2004. (Des 6 Ans Ser.). (FRE.). 64p. 7.95 (978-2-922565-96-6(3)) Editions de la Paix CAN. *Dist:* World of Reading, Ltd.

Richardson, Arleta. Still More Stories from Grandma's Attic, 1. rev. ed. 2003. (Grandma's Attic Ser.). (Illus.). 144p. (J). (gr. 12-8). pap., pap. 6.99 (978-0-7814-3270-2(7) , 0781432707) Cook, David C. Publishing Co.

Richmond, Beulah. Anancy & Friends: A Grandmother's Anancy Stories for Her Grandchildren. Brown, Clovis, illus. 2004. 52p. 5.99 (978-976-8184-48-1(5)) Penguin Group (USA) Inc.

Riddell, Chris. Chris Riddell's Da Vinci Cod & Other Illustrations for Unwritten Books. Riddell, Chris, illus. 2006. (Illus.). 72p. (J). (gr. 7). 7.99 (978-0-7636-3053-9(5)) Candlewick Pr.

Ries, Lori. Aggie & Ben: Three Stories. Dormer, Frank W., illus. 2007. 48p. (J). (ps-2). pap. 5.95 (***978-1-57091-649-6(7)***) Charlesbridge Publishing, Inc.

Rieser, William. Don't Just Stand There: Do Something! 2003. 332p. pap. 21.95 (978-1-59286-342-6(6)) PublishAmerica, Inc.

Riggs-Mayfield, Nellie. A Collection of Short Stories for Children. 2006. (J). per. 19.95 (978-1-59872-640-4(4)) Instantpublisher.com.

Ristuccia, Christine & McGovern, Sheila. The Entire World of R Book of Stories: A Collection of 63 Stories for all 21 Variations of "R" l.t. ed. 2002. (Illus.). 170p. per. 34.99 (978-0-9723457-1-2(X)) Say It Right.

Rivas, Maite Suarez, et al, eds. An Illustrated Treasury of Latino Read-Aloud Stories: 40 of the Best-Loved Stories for Parents & Children to Share. Lopez, Ana, illus. 2004. (SPA & ENG.). 192p. (J). (gr. 2-6). 14.95 (978-1-57912-398-7(8) , 81398) Black Dog & Leventhal Pubs., Inc.

Robar, Serena. Braced2Bite. 2006. 224p. (YA). (gr. 12). pap. 9.99 (978-0-425-20976-9(8) , Berkley Trade) Penguin Group (USA) Inc.

Roberts, Emrys & Knipping, Rod. Dau Gymro Dewr: A Storiau Gwir Eraill. 2005. (WEL., Illus.). 65p. (978-0-903131-17-9(X)) Urdd Gobaith Cymru.

Roberts, Rachel. The Avalon Collection, 3 vols., Bks. 1 - 3. 2005. (Avalon Ser.). 656p. (J). (gr. 2-6). pap. 9.95 (978-1-59315-320-5(1)) Vanguard Pr.

Robinson, Hilary. Batty Betty's Spells. Worsley, Belinda, illus. 2005. (Lightning Readers Ser.). 32p. (J). (gr. k-k). pap., pap. 3.95 (978-0-7696-4019-8(2) , Gingham Dog Pr.) School Specialty Publishing.

—Los hechizos de Chela de Lela. Worsley, Belinda, illus. 2005. (Lightning Readers Ser.). 32p. (J). (gr. k-k). pap. 3.95 (978-0-7696-4059-4(1) , Gingham Dog Pr.) School Specialty Publishing.

Robinson, Ronnie D. Children Stories. 2nd ed. 2004. 112p. (YA). pap. 11.95 (978-0-7414-1439-7(2)) Infinity Publishing.

—Children's Stories. 2004. 134p. (YA). pap. 12.95 (978-0-7414-1438-0(4)) Infinity Publishing.

Rochman, Hazel & McCampbell, Darlene Z., eds. Who do you Think you Are? 2005. 176p. (YA). 23.00 (978-0-8446-7269-4(6) , 3585) Smith, Peter Pub., Inc.

Rodoreda, Mercé. La Plaza del Diamante. 2000. Tr. of Diamond Plaza. (SPA.). (978-950-07-0131-0(6)) Editorial Sudamericana S.A.

Rodriguez, Elizabeth. Hannah's Ayuna. 2007. per. (***978-1-59916-153-2(2)***) Printing Systems.

—Hannah's Fast. 2006. per. (***978-1-59916-144-0(3)***) Printing Systems.

Rodríguez, Pedro, illus. The Big Book of Horror: 21 Tales to Make You Tremble. 2006. 112p. (J). (gr. 4-6). 12.95 (978-1-4027-3860-9(9)) Sterling Publishing Co., Inc.

Rojas, Emilio. Libro Magico de los 101 Relatos para Niños: Fabulas, Cuentos y Leyendas. 2003. (SPA., Illus.). 224p. (YA). (gr. 5 up). 15.95 (978-968-6966-19-0(6)) EDITER'S Publishing Hse. MEX. *Dist:* EDITER'S Publishing Hse.

—Mitos, Leyendas, Cuentos, Fabulas, Apologos y Parabolas, 3 vols, Vol. 2. Rojas, Emilio, ed. Farshchian, Mahmoud et al, illus. Arcos, Bernardo & Alcaraz, Lorena, photos by. l.t. ed. 2001. (SPA.). 224p. (J). (gr. 2 up). per. 15.95 (978-0-9706814-3-0(7)) EDITER'S Publishing Hse.

—Mitos, Leyendas, Cuentos, Fabulas, Apologos y Parabolas, 3 vols., Vol. 3. Rojas, Emilio, ed. Rojas, Lauyumi Michelle et al, illus. Alcaraz, Lorena & Arcos, Bernardo, photos by. 2nd rev. l.t. ed. 2002. (SPA.). 224p. (YA). (gr. 4 up). reprint ed. per. 15.95 (978-0-9706814-0-9(2)) EDITER'S Publishing Hse.

—Mitos, Leyendas, Cuentos, Fabulas, Apologos y Parabolas I, 3 vols. Rojas, Emilio, ed. Gonzalez, Elva Nitzchiani et al, illus. Alcaraz, Lorena & Arcos, Bernardo, photos by. l.t. ed. 2001. (SPA.). 224p. (YA). per. 15.95 (978-0-9706814-4-7(5)) EDITER'S Publishing Hse.

Rojas, Emilio, ed. El Cuento y las Corrientes Literarias. Minguer, Edgar, illus. Alcaraz, Lorena & Arcos, Bernardo, photos by. l.t. ed. 2002. (SPA.). 224p. (YA). (gr. 8 up). per. 15.95 (978-0-9706814-7-8(X)) EDITER'S Publishing Hse.

—En Busca de Si Mismo: Apologos y Parabolas. Minguer, Edgar, illus. Alcaraz, Lorena & Arcos, Bernardo, photos by. l.t. ed. 2002. (SPA.). 168p. (YA). per. 15.95 (978-0-9706814-9-2(6)) EDITER'S Publishing Hse.

Rolt, Molly. The Chocci-Croc & Other Stories. 2006. 64p. pap. (***978-1-84401-890-1(3)***) Athena Pr.

Romance, Trisha. A Star for Christmas. 2007. 40p. (J). 21.95 (***978-0-88776-836-1(9)***) Tundra Bks. of Northern New York.

Romano, Elaine Ambrose. Gators & Taters: A Week of Bedtime Stories, 2003. (Illus.). 64p. (J). pap. 9.95 (978-0-9728225-0-3(X)) Mill Park Publishing.

Romero Gutierrez, Astrid. Cuentos de Hombres-Lobo Para Nios. 2000. Tr. of Werewolves Stories for Children. (SPA.). lib. bdg. 20.00 (978-0-613-81986-2(1)) Tandem Library Bks.

Ronnholm, Ursula O. Mi Libro de Palabras, Oraciones y Cuentos. Deliz, Osdila O., ed. Montero, Miguel, illus. (SPA.). 100p. (J). (gr. k-6). pap. 7.00 (978-0-941911-02-3(0)) Two Way Bilingual, Inc.

Rookie Reader, Set. 2004. (Rookie Reader Ser.). (J). (ps-2). 9.95 (978-0-516-25000-7(0)); 9.95 (978-0-516-25001-4(9)); 9.95 (978-0-516-25002-1(7)) Scholastic Library Publishing. (Watts, Franklin).

A Rookie Reader Espanol: Thes Attractively Illustrated Stories in Spanish Make Learning Fun & Exciting, 10 Bks. , Set. 2005. (J). 170.00 (978-0-516-25213-1(5)) Scholastic Library Publishing.

Rose, Lela. Truth in Stories for Children 4 Through 6. 2003. pap. 8.00 (978-0-8059-5923-9(8)) Dorrance Publishing Co., Inc.

Rosen, Barry. Do You Know What a Stranger Is? Rosen, Barry & Bell, Greg, illus. 2003. 34p. (J). pap. 7.25 (978-0-9625593-4-1(2)) B.R. Publishing Co.

Rosen, Michael & Rosen, Michael. Fantastically Funny Stories. Brown, Mik, illus. 2005. (Sidesplitters Ser.). 64p. (J). (gr. 3-5). pap. 3.95 (978-0-7534-5876-1(4) , Kingfisher) Houghton Mifflin Co. Trade & Reference Div.

Rosenthal, Paul. Yo, Aesop! Get a Load of These Fables. Rosenthal, Marc, illus. 2005. 51p. reprint ed. pap. 16.00 (978-0-7567-8761-5(0)) DIANE Publishing Co.

Rosero, Evelio. Teresita Cantaba. (SPA.). (J). (978-958-04-6491-4(X)) Norma S.A. COL. *Dist:* Distribuidora Norma, Inc.

Ross, David. How We Got Back into the Inter-Schools Football Competition. Thomas, Jacqui, illus. 96p. (J). 8.95 (978-0-14-130014-6(0)) Penguin Bks., Ltd. GBR. *Dist:* Penguin Group (USA) Inc.

Ross, Stewart. Dear Mum, I Miss You! Clark, Linda, illus. 54p. (J). (978-0-237-52318-3(3) , Evans Brothers, Limited) Evans Publishing Group.

Ross, Tony. Rizos de Oro y los Tres Osos: Little Books. 2003. (Nuevos Horizontes Ser.). (SPA., Illus.). 32p. (J). (gr. 3-5). pap. 5.95 (978-84-372-1575-4(7)) Santillana USA Publishing Co., Inc.

Ross, Tony, illus. Funny Stories for 7 Year Olds. 2003. 237p. (J). pap. 9.99 (978-0-330-34945-1(7) , Pan) Pan Macmillan GBR. *Dist:* Trafalgar Square Publishing.

—Funny Stories for 8 Year Olds. 2003. 235p. (J). 9.99 (978-0-330-34946-8(5) , Pan) Pan Macmillan GBR. *Dist:* Trafalgar Square Publishing.

Rosseter, Patrick W. Grampa Pat's Little Animal Tales. 2005. 10.00 (978-0-8059-9797-2(0)) Dorrance Publishing Co., Inc.

Rostrom, Laura Lee. My Book of Mormon Storybook: 90 Favorite Stories. Rostrom, Laura Lee, photos by. 1999. (Illus.). (J). (ps-6). 19.95 (978-1-55517-352-4(7)) Cedar Fort, Inc./CFI Distribution.

Rotkappchen: Clothing, Food, Nature, the Human Body. 1999. (Lesen Leicht Germacht Ser.). (GER & ENG., Illus.). 24p. (J). (ps-5). pap. 7.95 (978-88-8148-244-3(4)) European Language Institute ITA. *Dist:* Distribooks, Inc., Midwest European Pubns.

Rowan Masters, Susan. Libby Bloom. 2002. 110p. pap. 9.95 (978-0-595-24225-2(1) , Backinprint.com) iUniverse, Inc.

Rowlands, Avril. The Christmas Sheep: And Other Stories. Moran, Rosslyn, illus. 2001. 48p. (J). (ps-3). 16.00 (978-1-56148-336-5(2)) Good Bks.

Roxbee-Cox, Phil. Find the Teddy. Cartwright, Stephen, illus. 2004. (Rhyming Board Bks.). 10p. (J). (ps up). bds. 3.95 (978-0-7460-3825-3(9)) EDC Publishing.

—Ted's Shed. 2004. (Easy Words to Read Ser.). (Illus.). 16p. (J). (gr. 1 up). pap. 6.95 (978-0-7460-4210-6(8)) EDC Publishing.

Rubel, William. The Stone Soup Book of Friendship Stories. 2004. (Illus.). 128p. (gr. 3-8). pap., tchr. ed. 8.95 (978-1-883672-76-8(7) , Tricycle Pr.) Ten Speed Pr.

Ruben, Pamela J. Yenta the Chicken & Other Fowl Tales! Ruben, Anthony R., ed. 2004. (Illus.). 19p. (J). 12.95 (978-0-9764813-0-0(8)) Peppery Pr.

Ruffell, Ann. Treachery by Night. 2004. (Shades Ser.). 62p. (J). pap. 7.99 (978-0-237-52728-0(6) , Evans Brothers, Limited) Evans Publishing Group GBR. *Dist:* Independent Pubs. Group.

Ruffenach, Jessie E., et al. Learn along with Ashkii: First Grade Level 1. Whitethorne, Bahe, Jr., illus. 2003. (NAV & ENG.). 32p. (J). pap. 7.95 (978-1-893354-41-8(5)) Salina Bookshelf.

Ruiz, John. Tea Cup. 1999. (Illus.). 24p. (J). (gr. k-6). pap. 3.99 (978-0-9715245-4-5(8)) Teamwork Foundation, Inc.

Rumi, Jalal Al-Din. Kalilah & Dimnah Stories for Young Adults. 2000. (Illus.). 172p. (J). (gr. 7-12). pap. 12.95 (978-1-930637-07-8(1) , A B C International Group, Inc.) Kazi Pubns., Inc.

—Rumi Stories for Young Adults. 2000. (Illus.). 200p. (YA). (gr. 7-12). pap. 12.95 (978-1-930637-04-7(7) , A B C International Group, Inc.) Kazi Pubns., Inc.

The Runaway Engine & Other Stories: Individual Title Six-Pack. (Story Steps Ser.). (gr. k-2). 48.00 (978-0-7635-9803-7(8)) Rigby Education.

Rushford, Betty. Best Buddies: And the Fruit of the Spirit. 2003. 41p. pap. 16.95 (978-1-59286-746-2(4)) PublishAmerica, Inc.

Russell, Keith A. When Doves Cry. Francis, Faith, ed. 2000. 120p. (YA). pap. 13.00 (978-0-9672684-1-5(9)) LaVonKeish Pubs.

Ruurs, Margriet & Gooderham, Andrew. Ms. Bee's magical bookcase. 2004. (Illus.). 32p. (J). pap. 8.95 (978-1-894601-10-8(6)) Chestnut Publishing Group CAN. *Dist:* Hushion Hse. Publishing, Ltd.

Ryan, Emer & Newman, Clive, eds. From Two Islands: The Best of Irish-Australian Writers with New Fiction for Younger Readers. 2000. 180p. (J). pap. 12.95 (978-1-86368-282-4(1)) Fremantle Pr. AUS. *Dist:* International Specialized Bk. Services.

Ryan, Margaret. Puffling in a Pickle. (Illus.). 64p. (J). 7.95 (978-0-14-037062-1(5)) Penguin Bks., Ltd. GBR. *Dist:* Trafalgar Square Publishing.

Rylant, Cynthia. El Caso del Mono Extraviado. (SPA.). (J). 7.95 (978-958-04-6866-0(4)) Norma S.A. COL. *Dist:* Distribuidora Norma, Inc.

—Henry & Mudge & Annie's Good Move. Stevenson, Sucie, illus. 2002. (Henry & Mudge Ser.). (J). pap. 18.95 incl. audio compact disk (978-1-59112-646-1(0)); 25.95 incl. audio (978-0-87499-965-5(0)); pap. 16.95 incl. audio (978-0-87499-964-8(2)) Live Oak Media.

Saadi, Muslih Din. Saadi Stories for Young Adults. 2000. (Illus.), 216p. (YA). (gr. 7-12). pap. 12.95 (978-1-930637-05-4(5) , A B C International Group, Inc.) Kazi Pubns., Inc.

Saal, Clea. Tales to Be Told by Children. 2002. 136p. 18.95 (978-1-58939-279-3(5)); per. 12.95 (978-1-58939-243-4(4)) Virtualbookworm.com Publishing, Inc.

Sachar, Louis. Sideways Stories from Wayside School. McCauley, Adam, illus. 1998. 128p. (J). (gr. 3-7). reprint ed. 15.99 (978-0-688-16086-9(7)) HarperCollins Pubs.

Sadu, Itah & Condy, Roy. Christopher Changes His Name. (Tell Me a Story Ser.). (Illus.). 32p. (J). 12.99 (978-0-590-24670-5(4)) Scholastic, Inc.

Safari Stories. (My Animal Library). (Illus.). 10p. (J). (978-2-7643-0154-8(5)) Phidal Publishing, Inc./Editions Phidal, Inc.

Sakade, Florence. Japanese Children's Favorite Stories. Yoshi, Kurosake, illus. 2005. Bk. 1. 112p. 21.95 incl. audio compact disk (978-0-8048-3717-0(1)); Vol. 2. 96p. 21.95 incl. audio compact disk (978-0-8048-3718-7(X)) Tuttle Publishing.

Sakairi, Masao. Vietnamese Fables of Frogs & Toads. Kojima, Shoko, illus. 2006. (Asian Folktales Retold Ser.). 32p. (J). 16.95 (978-0-89346-947-4(5)) Heian International Publishing, Inc.

—Vietnamese Tales of Rabbits & Watermelons. Kojima, Shoko, illus. 2006. (Asian Folktales Retold Ser.). 32p. (J). 16.95 (978-0-89346-948-1(3)) Heian International Publishing, Inc.

Saki & Border, Rosemary. Tooth & Claw: Short Stories, Level 3. 2nd ed. 2000. (Bookworms Ser.). (Illus.). 80p. 6.25 (978-0-19-423020-9(1)) Oxford Univ. Pr., Inc.

Saldana, Rene, Jr. Finding Our Way. 2004. 128p. (YA). (gr. 7). pap. 5.99 (978-0-440-23790-7(4) , Laurel Leaf) Random Hse. Children's Bks.

—Finding Our Way: Stories. 2004. 117p. (YA). (gr. 7-12). per. 13.04 (978-0-606-32790-9(8)) Tandem Library Bks.

Salerno, Tony, et al. Tony Salerno's Good News Express. Thompson, Del et al, illus. 64p. (Orig.). (J). (gr. k-6). pap. (978-1-881597-00-1(8)) Magination.

Salisbury, Graham. Island Boyz: Short Stories. 2003. (gr. 5-8). lib. bdg. 14.15 (978-0-613-72335-0(X)) Tandem Library Bks.

The Salt Water Bath. 2004. (J). per. (978-1-57657-472-0(5)) Paradise Pr., Inc.

Sam, Sam & Other Stories: Individual Title Six-Pack. (Story Steps Ser.). (gr. k-2). 48.00 (978-0-7635-9610-1(8)) Rigby Education.

Same Idea, Different Year: Individual Title Six-Packs. (Bookweb Ser.). 32p. (gr. 3 up). 34.00 (978-0-7635-3942-9(2)) Rigby Education.

Samson, Don. Teenage Aviation Stories. 2005. reprint ed. pap. 26.95 (978-1-4191-1624-7(X)) Kessinger Publishing, LLC.

San Souci, Robert D. More Short & Shivery. Coville, Katherine, illus. 2002. 176p. (J). (gr. 5). pap. 5.50 (978-0-440-41857-3(7) , Yearling) Random Hse. Children's Bks.

San Souci, Robert D. & San Souci, Daniel, illus. Sister Tricksters: Southern Tales of Clever Females. 2006. 70p. (J). (gr. 4-6). 19.95 (978-0-87483-791-9(X)) August Hse. Pubs., Inc.

Sanchez, Gloria. Siete Casas, Siete Brujas y un Huevo. Lopez Domínguez, Xan, tr. Lopez Domínguez, Xan, illus. 5th ed. 2005. (SPA.). 64p. (J). (gr. k-1). 6.95 (978-84-348-6003-2(1)) SM Ediciones ESP. *Dist:* Iaconi, Mariuccia Bk. Imports.

Sand, Marc. Sheltered. 2003. (YA). per. 5.95 (978-0-9726764-0-3(6)) Sketch Publishing.

Sandage, Charley. I can tell you stories, if you gather round Big Book. 2005. (J). pap. ***978-0-9794044-3-6(6))*** Archeological Assessments, Inc.

Sandburg, Carl. Rootabaga Pigeons. Petersham, Miska & Petersham, Maud Fuller, illus. 2001. (Rootabaga Stories Ser.). 218p. (J). (gr. 1-3). per. 12.95 (978-1-55709-509-1(4)) Applewood Bks.

Sargent, Dave & Sargent, Pat. Lizzy Lightning Bug/Lizzy la Luciérnaga, 10 vols., Vol. 17. Robinson, Laura, illus. 2004. (Learn to Read Ser.: 10). Tr. of Lizzy la Luciernaga. (ENG & SPA.). 18p. (J). (gr. k-2). lib. bdg. 19.95 (978-1-56763-993-3(3)) Ozark Publishing.

Sargent, Dave, et al. The Bundle Keeper: (Pawnee) Be Responsible, 20, 18. Lenoir, Sue, illus. 2004. (Story Keeper Ser.: No. 18). 42p. (J). lib. bdg. 22.60 (978-1-56763-937-7(2)) Ozark Publishing.

Sargent, Pat L. Jaguar #8 (PB), 6 vols. 2007. (Barney the Bear Killer Ser.: 8). (YA). pap. 9.95 ***(*978-1-59381-425-0(9))*** Ozark Publishing.

Sastrias, Marta. Cuentos de Todo y de Nada. Martinez y Luis San Vicente, Enrique, illus. 2003. (SPA.). 82p. (J). (gr. 3-5). (978-968-19-0551-4(2)) Aguilar, Altea, Taurus, Alfaguara, S.A. de C.V.

A Saturday Sandwiches Set, 6 vols. 32p. (gr. 1-3). 26.50 (978-0-7802-8043-4(1)) Wright Group, The.

Saunders, Helen B. Sweet Faces Story Book. 2004. Orig. Title: Sweet Faces. (Illus.). 29p. (J). 14.95 (978-0-9763143-0-1(4)) Happy Heart Kids Publishing.

Saunders, Susan. Saunders 2. Date not set. (J). 15.99 (978-0-380-97785-7(0)) HarperCollins Pubs.

Sauvageau, Juan. Stories, Fables & Poems for You, Vol. 1. 1998. Tr. of Cuentos, Fabulas y Poemas para Ti. (ENG & SPA., Illus.). 100p. (J). (gr. 3-5). pap. 9.95 (978-1-893493-00-1(8)) National Educational Systems, Inc.

Sawyer, Debra D. Let Me Speak You A Secret. 2004. (YA). reprint ed. per. 16.00 (978-0-9761207-0-4(4)) DiaShah Pr., LLC.

Sawyer, Timothy L., Jr. Stories of Mexico's Independence Days & Other Bilingual Children's Fables. Torres, Eliseo, ed. Ramirez, Herman, illus. 2005. (ENG & SPA.). 70p. (J). (gr. 3-7). pap. 13.95 (978-0-8263-3886-0(0)) Univ. of New Mexico Pr.

Scaperrotta, Kirstyn. I Lost My Cracker to the Big Cheese: A Collection of Voices. 2003. 126p. (YA). pap. 10.95 (978-0-595-26478-0(6) , Writers Club Pr.) iUniverse, Inc.

Scarry, Richard. The Best Mistake Ever! Scarry, Richard, illus. 2003. (Step into Reading Step 2 Bks.). (Illus.). 48p. (J). (ps-3). lib. bdg. 11.99 (978-0-394-96816-2(6) , Random Hse. Bks. for Young Readers) Random Hse. Children's Bks.

—The Best Mistake Ever! And Other Stories. Scarry, Richard, illus. 2002. (Illus.). (J). 11.91 (978-0-7587-0980-6(3)) Book Wholesalers, Inc.

—Richard Scarry's Best Storybook Ever. Scarry, Richard, illus. 2000. (Richard Scarry's Ser.). (Illus.). 288p. (J). (ps-2). 15.99 (978-0-307-16548-0(5) , Golden Bks.) Random Hse. Children's Bks.

—Richard Scarry's Color Book. Scarry, Richard, illus. 1999. (Jellybean Bks.). (Illus.). 24p. (J). (ps-k). lib. bdg. 7.99 (978-0-375-90145-4(0) , Random Hse. Bks. for Young Readers) Random Hse. Children's Bks.

Scarry, Richard & Golden Books Staff. Richard Scarry's Favorite Storybook Ever. 2003. (Picture Book Ser.). (Illus.). 72p. (J). (ps-3). 14.99 (978-0-375-82549-1(5) , Golden Bks.) Random Hse. Children's Bks.

Schecter, Ellen. Diamonds & Toads. Blackshear, Ami, illus. 1999. (Bank Street Reader Collection). (J). (gr. 2-4). lib. bdg. 22.60 (978-0-8368-1781-2(8)) Stevens, Gareth Inc.

—Sleep Tight, Pete. Weissman, Bari, illus. 1998. (Bank Street Reader Collection). 48p. (J). (ps-2). lib. bdg. 22.60 (978-0-8368-1766-9(4)) Stevens, Gareth Inc.

Schkolnik, Saul. Cuentos Ecologicos. Cardemil, Carmen, illus. 2nd ed. 2003. Tr. of Ecological Tales. (SPA.). 54p. (J). (ps-7). pap. 7.50 (978-968-16-4757-5(2) , FC6400) Fondo de Cultura Economica MEX. *Dist:* Lectorum Pubns., Inc.

Schmidt, John. Two Stories for Children: Betty Blooper Is Super! & Hands Holding Heaven. Heflin, David et al, trs. Beckner, Joni & King, Rachael, illus. 1999. (ENG & SPA.). 42p. (J). (ps-3). pap. 9.00 (978-1-891774-09-6(3)) Path Publishing, Inc.

Scholastic, Inc. Staff. Bedtime Storybook Collection. 2007. (Sweet Dreams Ser.). 96p. (J). pap. 7.99 ***(*978-0-439-93403-9(6)*** , Cartwheel Bks.) Scholastic, Inc.

—Here Comes Diego!, Bks. 7-12. 2007. (Go, Diego, Go! Phonics Reading Program Ser.). 112p. (J). pap. 5.99 ***(*978-0-439-93228-8(9))*** Scholastic, Inc.

—Hop to It! A Scholastic Treasury of Easter Tales. Torres, Melissa, ed. McPhail, David M., illus. 2003. 224p. (J). (ps-3). pap. 10.99 (978-0-439-44267-1(2) , Cartwheel Bks.) Scholastic, Inc.

Scholastic, Inc. Staff. Let's Go Rescue! 2007. (Go, Diego, Go! Phonics Reading Program Ser.: Bks. 1-6). 112p. (J). pap. 5.99 ***(*978-0-439-93229-5(7))*** Scholastic, Inc.

Scholastic, Inc. Staff, ed. It's Terrific to Be Ten! 2000. 144p. (J). (gr. 3-6). pap. 4.50 (978-0-439-21628-9(1)) Scholastic, Inc.

Scholtz, Pieter. Tales of the Tokoloshe. Treweek, Cherie, illus. 2005. 144p. (J). pap. 12.95 (978-1-86872-970-8(2)) Struik Pubs. ZAF. *Dist:* International Publishers Marketing.

Schonzeit, Miriam. The Sweetest Song & other Stories. 2006. 304p. (YA). 16.95 (978-1-932443-42-4(8) , SWSH) Judaica Pr., Inc., The.

School, Waverly. Waverly Review: Spring 2003, Issue 1. 2003. 70p. (YA). pap. 8.95 (978-0-595-27691-2(1)) iUniverse, Inc.

Schulman, Janet. The 20th Century Children's Book Treasury: Celebrated Picture Books & Stories to Read Aloud. Boughton, Simon, ed. 1998. (Illus.). 320p. (J). (gr. k-3). 40.00 (978-0-679-88647-1(8) , Knopf Bks. for Young Readers) Random Hse. Children's Bks.

Schulman, Janet, intro. The Random House Book of Easy-to-Read Stories. 2000. (Random House Book of... Ser.). (Illus.). 256p. (J). (gr. k-3). 19.95 (978-0-679-83438-0(9) , Random Hse. Bks. for Young Readers) Random Hse. Children's Bks.

Schulman, Janet, selected by. You Read to Me & I'll Read to You: 20th-Century Stories to Share. 2001. (Illus.). 256p. (J). (gr. k up). 34.95 (978-0-375-81083-1(8) , Knopf Bks. for Young Readers) Random Hse. Children's Bks.

Schultz, Dave. Little Ditties. 64p. (Orig.). (YA). pap. 3.00 (978-0-937393-08-6(8)) Fred Pr.

—Little Ditties. Newkirk, Greg, illus. Lingelbach, Lee G., photos by. 2nd ed. 1999. (ENG.). 80p. (Orig.). pap. 5.00 (978-0-937393-11-6(8)) Fred Pr.

Science Fiction Collection. (Fiction Collections). 160.77 (978-1-59889-043-3(3)) Stone Arch Bks.

Scieszka, Jon. The Stinky Cheese Man & Other Fairly Stupid Tales. Smith, Lane, illus. 2004. 48p. (J). (gr. k-4). reprint ed. 22.00 (978-0-7567-7699-2(6)) DIANE Publishing Co.

—The Stinky Cheese Man & Other Fairly Stupid Tales. Smith, Lane, illus. 2007. 56p. (J). (ps). pap. 9.99 ***(*978-0-670-06300-0(2)*** , Viking Juvenile) Penguin Group (USA) Inc.

Scott, Robert. Shades of Monte Christo & Other Short Stories. 2004. (YA). per. 19.86 (978-1-4116-0484-1(9)) Lulu.com.

Sea Star Editors. Pet Stories You Don't Have to Walk. 2000. (Reading Rainbow Readers Ser.). (J). (978-0-606-19628-4(5)) Tandem Library Bks.

Seagull. 2004. (J). per. (978-1-57657-457-7(1)) Paradise Pr., Inc.

Searle-White, Joshua. Magic Wanda's Travel Emporium: Tales of Love, Hate & Things in Between. 2006. (Illus.). 144p. (J). pap. (978-1-55896-510-2(6) , Skinner Hse. Bks.) Unitarian Universalist Assn.

Seasons of the Witch, Vol. 1. 2003. (gr. 7-12). lib. bdg. 16.45 (978-0-613-73452-3(1)) Tandem Library Bks.

SeaStar Publishing Staff, ed. Pet Stories You Don't Have to Walk. 2000. (Reading Rainbow Bks.). (Illus.). 64p. (J). (ps-3). 15.50 (978-1-58717-032-4(9) , SeaStar Bks.) Chronicle Bks. LLC.

—Pet Stories You Don't Have to Walk. 2000. (gr. 3-6). lib. bdg. 11.80 (978-0-613-32943-9(0)) Tandem Library Bks.

—Scary Stories: To Read When It's Dark. 2000. (Reading Rainbow Ser.). (Illus.). 64p. (J). (gr. 1-3). pap. 3.99 (978-1-58717-035-5(3) , SeaStar Bks.) Chronicle Bks. LLC.

—School Stories Your Dog Didn't Eat. 2000. (gr. 3-6). lib. bdg. 11.80 (978-0-613-33027-5(7)) Tandem Library Bks.

Sebring Lowrey, Janette & Crampton, Gertrude. The Poky Little Puppy & Other Stories to Color. Tenggren, Gustaf & Gergely, Tibor, illus. 2007. 96p. (J). (ps-2). 2.99 (978-0-375-83536-0(9) , Golden Bks.) Random Hse. Children's Bks.

Sefton, Catherine. Pocket Elephant. (Illus.). 32p. (J). 13.95 (978-0-241-00197-4(8) , Hamilton, Hamish) Penguin Bks., Ltd. GBR. *Dist:* Trafalgar Square Publishing.

Segal, Lore. Tell Me a Mitzi. (Blue-Ribbon Listen-and-Read Ser.). (J). (ps-2). pap. 5.95 incl. audio (978-0-590-63063-4(6)) Scholastic, Inc.

Selena Who Speaks in Silence Set B, 6 vols. 32p. (gr. 1-3). 26.50 (978-0-7802-8051-9(2)); 31.50 (978-0-322-00939-4(1)) Wright Group, The.

Sequera, Armando Jose. La Calle del Espejo. Sorg, Walter, illus. 2001. (Coleccion Derechos Del Nino Ser.). (SPA.). 32p. (J). (gr. 3-5). pap. 7.95 (978-84-204-5821-2(X)) Santillana USA Publishing Co., Inc.

Serafin, Michael. 4 Seasons of Baghdad. 2007. (ENG.). 60p. per. 12.95 ***(*978-1-4241-2303-2(8))*** PublishAmerica, Inc.

Serafin, Mike. 7 Stories from Baghdad. 2005. 50p. pap. 12.95 (978-1-4137-8808-2(4)) PublishAmerica, Inc.

Serna, Ana. Cuentos y Recetas de la Abuela.Tr. of Tales & Recipes from Grandmother. (SPA.). 144p. (J). 24.95 (978-84-305-7732-3(7)) Susaeta Ediciones, S.A. ESP. *Dist:* AIMS International Bks., Inc., Giron Bks.

Seton, Ernest Thompson. Johnny Bear & Other Stories from Lives. 2006. 62.99 ***(*978-1-4280-3514-0(1));*** pap. 55.99 ***(*978-1-4280-3489-1(7))*** IndyPublish.com.

Seuss, Dr. Gli Snicci e Altre Storie. pap. 24.95 (978-88-09-02448-9(6)) Giunti, Gruppo Editoriale ITA. *Dist:* Distribooks, Inc.

Shadow, Nick & Graves, Damien. Midnight Library. 2006. (Apple Ser.: Vol. 2). (Illus.). 176p. (J). pap. 5.99 (978-0-439-87187-7(5) , Scholastic Paperbacks) Scholastic, Inc.

Shan, Darren, pseud. Cirque du Freak Boxed Set: A Living Nightmare; the Vampire's Assistant; Tunnels of Blood; Vampire Mountain, Set. 1. 2005. (Cirque du Freak: Bks. 1-4). (J). (gr. 5-17). pap., pap. 27.99 (978-0-316-15378-2(8)) Little Brown & Co.

Shanks Jr. A Father's Stories for His Children: A Christian Reader for Students Grades 5-9. 2006. pap. 9.99 ***(*978-1-59781-946-6(8))*** Xulon Pr., Inc.

Shannon, George. True Lies: 10 Tales for You to Judge. O'Brien, John, illus. 1998. 64p. (J). (gr. 3 up). reprint ed. pap. 4.99 (978-0-688-16371-6(8) , Harper Trophy) HarperCollins Pubs.

Shanower, Eric. The Salt Sorcerer of Oz & Other Stories. Shanower, Eric, illus. 2003. (Oz Ser.). (Illus.). 288p. (J). 24.95 (978-1-929527-06-9(3)) Hungry Tiger Pr.

Sharmat, Marjorie Weinman. Yo, el Gran Fercho. (Torre de Papel Ser.).Tr. of Nate the Great. (SPA.). (YA). 8.95 (978-958-04-2599-1(X)) Norma S.A. COL. *Dist:* Distribuidora Norma, Inc.

Shaw, Hannah. Palestinian Stories. 2008. (Illus.). 96p. (J). pap. 7.95 ***(*978-1-84507-523-1(4))*** Lincoln, Frances Ltd. GBR. *Dist:* Perseus Distribution.

Shaw, Janet Beeler. Kaya's Boxed Set. 2002. (American Girls Collection Ser.). (J). (gr. 2). 74.95 (978-1-58485-512-5(6)) American Girl Publishing, Inc.

Shearer, Alex. Child for the Afternoon (Pb) 2005. 282p. (J). pap. ***(*978-0-330-43190-3(0)*** , Macmillan Children's Bks.) Pan Macmillan.

Sheehan, Christy. Buzby. Richards, Betsa, illus. 1999. 13p. (J). 8.95 (978-0-7414-0097-0(9)) Infinity Publishing.

Sheffield, Sherry Overton. Children's Choices: What Would YOU Do? 2005. (Illus.). 112p. (J). per. (978-0-9772513-0-8(6) , 804-337-8915) Thumbs Up Pr.

Shephard, Esther. Paul Bunyan. Kent, Rockwell, illus. 2006. 256p. (J). pap. 5.95 (978-0-15-205857-9(5) , Odyssey Classics) Harcourt Children's Bks.

Sheppard, Benjamin. The Gardens of Sir Verity. Sappo, Joanne, ed. 1998. 272p. (YA). (gr. 7-12). pap. 14.00 (978-0-9667583-0-6(7)) Creative Heart Media.

Shepperson, Jacqueline. Martins of the Everglades. 2007. (ENG.). 152p. per. 19.95 ***(*978-1-4241-5446-3(4))*** PublishAmerica, Inc.

Shepperson, Jacqueline Ruth. The Blue Jay Tales. 2005. 89p. pap. 14.95 (978-1-4137-3884-1(2)) PublishAmerica, Inc.

Shewver, Margaret. Without a Trace & Other Stories. 2005. 91p. (YA). (gr. 6-12). pap. 17.95 (978-0-936389-59-2(1)) Tudor Pubs., Inc.

Shoo, Shoo, Shoo! & Other Stories, 6 Packs. (Story Steps Ser.). (gr. k-2). 48.00 (978-0-7635-9604-0(3)) Rigby Education.

Showstack, Richard. The Gift of the Magic: And Other Enchanting Character-Building Stories for Smart Teenage Girls Who Want to Grow up to Be Strong Women. Eric, Whitfield, illus. 2004. 156p. (YA). per. 14.95 (978-1-888725-64-3(8) , BeachHouse Bks.) Science & Humanities Pr.

—The Gift of the Magic: And Other Enchanting Character-Building Stories for Smart Teenage Girls Who Want to Grow up to Be Strong Women. Whitfield, Eric, illus. l.t. ed. 2004. 156p. (YA). per. 24.95 (978-1-888725-65-0(6) , MacroPrintBooks) Science & Humanities Pr.

Shulman, Mark. Louis & the Dodo. Nguyen, Vincent, illus. 2005. 36p. (J). (gr. k-2). 14.95 (978-1-4027-2872-3(7)) Sterling Publishing Co., Inc.

Shusterman, Neal. Red Rider's Hood. 2005. (Dark Fusion Ser.). 192p. (J). (gr. 5-7). 15.99 (978-0-525-47562-0(1) , Dutton Juvenile) Penguin Group (USA) Inc.

Siegal, Aranka. Memories of Babi. 2008. 128p. (J). 16.00 (978-0-374-39978-8(6) , Farrar, Straus & Giroux (BYR)) Farrar, Straus & Giroux.

Sierra i Fabra, Jordi. El Niño Que Vivía en Las Estrellas. 2003. (SPA., Illus.). 102p. (J). 8.95 (978-968-19-0557-6(1)) Aguilar, Altea, Taurus, Alfaguara, S.A. de C.V MEX. *Dist:* Santillana USA Publishing Co., Inc.

Siert, Kara Grace ManJian. Tales of Cunburra & Other Stories. 2006. 240p. pap. ***(*978-1-84549-114-7(9))*** arima publishing.

Silly Stories. 2002. 256p. (J). 12.98 (978-0-7525-5672-7(X)) Parragon, Inc.

Silva, Maria Luisa. El Gorila Razan. Saraniti, Marco, illus. 2003. (SPA.). 35p. (J). (gr. k-3). pap. 7.95 (978-956-239-117-7(5)) Santillana USA Publishing Co., Inc.

Silver Dolphin en Español Editors. Disney Tesoro de Libros de Calcomanias, Vol. 6. 2005. (Disney Calcomanias Ser.). (SPA., Illus.). 96p. (J). (ps). 14.95 (978-970-718-245-5(8)) Advanced Marketing, S. de R. L. de C. V. MEX. *Dist:* Perseus Distribution.

Silverman, A. O. Mirror, Mirror: Twisted Tales. 2002. (Illus.). 176p. (J). (gr. 5). pap. 15.95 (978-0-439-29593-2(9) , Chicken Hse., The) Scholastic, Inc.

Silvestre, R. Quique lo Salvo y Otras Historias. (Raton de Biblioteca Coleccion). (SPA.). 139p. (J). (gr. 3-5). 7.95 (978-84-88061-70-6(6)) Serres, Ediciones, S. L. ESP. *Dist:* Lectorum Pubns., Inc.

Simba's World: Disney's Easy to Read Stories, Bk. 3. 2000. 32p. (J). 6.99 (978-0-7364-0148-7(2)) Mouse Works.

Simmons, Steven J. Alicia & Greta. 1999. Tr. of Aice & Greta. (J). 14.75 (978-0-606-17213-4(0)) Tandem Library Bks.

Simms, Donna A. The Hillsborough Tales. (Children's Book). (Illus.). 76p. (J). (gr. 4-7). (978-0-942078-22-0(5)) Tanner, Ralph Assocs., Inc.

Simms, Susan Rose. 216 Artic Tickle Stories. DeShong, Molly & Spielvogle, Keri, eds. 2001. (Illus.). (J). (ps-6). spiral bd. 29.95 (978-1-58650-199-0(2)) Super Duper Pubns.

Simon & Schuster, eds. Millennium Madness. 2000. (gr. 3-6). lib. bdg. 14.15 (978-0-613-22002-6(1)) Tandem Library Bks.

Simon and Schuster Children's Staff, ed. Growing up with Blue: A 10th Anniversary Story Collection. 2006. (Blue's Clues Ser.). 192p. (J). 10.95 (978-1-4169-1332-0(7) , Simon Spotlight/Nickelodeon) Simon & Schuster Children's Publishing.

Simon, Francesca. Horrid Henry Gets Rich Quick. Ross, Tony, illus. l.t. ed. 2002. (J). 16.95 (978-0-7540-7829-6(9) , Galaxy Children's Large Print) BBC Audiobooks America.

—Horrid Henry Strikes it Rich. 2000. (Illus.). 68p. (J). lib. bdg. 14.49 (978-0-7868-2452-6(2)) Hyperion Bks. for Children.

Sims, Lesley. Stories of Princesses (Combined Volume) 2006. 144p. (J). 14.99 (978-0-7945-1385-6(9) , Usborne) EDC Publishing.

Sims, Lesley & Stowell, Louie. Illustrated Stories for Boys. 2007. 352p. (J). 19.99 (978-0-7945-1420-4(0) , Usborne) EDC Publishing.

—Illustrated Stories for Girls. 2007. 352p. (J). 19.99 (978-0-7945-1419-8(7) , Usborne) EDC Publishing.

Singer, Isaac Bashevis. Cuentos Judios de la Aldea de Chelm.Tr. of Zlateh the Goat & Other Stories. (SPA.). 62p. (J). 7.96 (978-84-264-3404-3(5) , LM2595) Editorial Lumen ESP. *Dist:* Lectorum Pubns., Inc.

—Zlateh the Goat & Other Stories. Sendak, Maurice, illus. 2001. (Sendak Reissues Ser.). 104p. (gr. 4-7). 17.95 (978-0-06-028477-0(3)) HarperCollins Pubs.

Singer, Marilyn. Stay True: Short Stories for Strong Girls. 1998. 208p. (J). (gr. 7-12). pap. 16.95 (978-0-590-36031-9(0)) Scholastic, Inc.

Singer, Marilyn, ed. Face Relations: 11 Stories about Seeing Beyond Color. 2004. (Illus.). 240p. (YA). (gr. 7-17). 17.95 (978-0-689-85637-2(7)) Simon & Schuster Children's Publishing.

Singh, Rina. Moon Tales: Myths of the Moon from Around the World. Lush, Debbie, illus. 2001. 80p. (J). (gr. 3-6). 25.00 (978-0-7475-4112-7(4)) Bloomsbury Publishing Plc GBR. *Dist:* Trafalgar Square Publishing.

Slade, Arthur G. Villainology: Fabulous Lives of the Big, the Bad, & the Wicked. Mah, Derek, illus. 2007. 96p. (J). (gr. 4-7). pap. 9.95 ***(*978-0-88776-809-5(1))*** Tundra Bks., Inc./Livres Toundra, Inc. CAN. *Dist:* Random Hse., Inc.

Smith, A. Nora. The Story Hour. 2006. 62.99 ***(*978-1-4219-9391-1(0));*** pap. 55.99 ***(*978-1-4219-9410-9(0))*** IndyPublish.com.

Smith, Alexander McCall. El Arbol del Chicle Hinchable. (Raton de Biblioteca Coleccion). (SPA.). 128p. (J). (gr. 3). 7.95 (978-84-88061-86-7(2)) Serres, Ediciones, S. L. ESP. *Dist:* Lectorum Pubns., Inc.

Smith, Alexander McCall. The Perfect Hamburger & Other Delicious Stories. Rankin, Laura, illus. 2007. 288p. (J). (gr. 2-4). 15.95 ***(*978-1-59990-134-3(X));*** pap. 7.95 ***(*978-1-59990-157-2(9))*** Bloomsbury Publishing. (Bloomsbury Children).

Smith, Cathy Jo. Seamus Mcseamus, an Irish Rover. 2005. (Illus.). 104p. per. 11.95 (978-0-9766666-0-8(X)) Arcadian Hse.

Smith, Geof. City Tales. Sorra, Kristin, illus. 2002. 16p. (J). (978-0-439-35145-4(6)) Scholastic, Inc.

Smith, Helene. Dreamstone. Guinard, Geraldine, illus. 2005. 80p. (YA). pap. 13.50 (978-1-920731-63-2(6)) Fremantle Pr. AUS. *Dist:* International Specialized Bk. Services.

Smith, Marie, et al. N Is for our Nation's Capital: A Washington, DC Alphabet. Gibson, Barbara Leonard, illus. 2005. (Discover America State by State Ser.). 40p. (J). 17.95 (978-1-58536-148-9(8)) Sleeping Bear Pr.

Smith, Pamela Colman. Annancy Stories. 2006. (YA). reprint ed. pap. 19.99 (978-0-9769612-2-9) , Pixiefire) Darker Intentiona Pr.

Smith, Philip, ed. Listen & Read Aladdin & Other Favorite Arabian Nights Stories. 1998. (gr. 3-6). pap. 7.95 (978-0-486-40108-9(1)) Dover Pubns., Inc.

Smith, Valerie H. The Spirit Stories: A Series of Short Stories for Children. 2007. 64p. per. 8.95 (*978-1-59824-450-2(7)) E-BookTime LLC.

Smoot, Madeline, compiled by. Summer Shorts: A Short Story Collection. 2006. (Illus.). 428p. (J). pap. 8.95 (978-0-9769417-5-0(9)) Blooming Tree Pr.

Snyder, Margaret. Sesame Street Elmo's Day. Kwiat, Ernie, illus. 2005. (Multi Wheel Ser.). 10p. (J). (ps-ps). bds. 12.99 (978-0-7944-0683-7(1)) Reader's Digest Assn., Inc., The.

So-Un, Kim & Kyoung-Sim, Jeong. Korean Children's Favorite Stories. 2004. (Illus.). 96p. 16.95 (978-0-8048-3591-6(8)) Tuttle Publishing.

Sobol, Donald J. Keeps the Peace. 2008. (Encyclopedia Brown Ser.: No. 6). 96p. (J). (gr. 2). 4.99 (*978-0-14-240950-3(2) , Puffin) Penguin Group (USA) Inc.

Sohaili, Monira. Stories from Earth & Beyond: Enchanting & Inspirational Stories. 2006. (Illus.). 94p. per. 9.95 (978-1-60002-044-5(5) , 2833, Airleaf Publishing) Airleaf Publishing & Bookselling.

Solotareff, Gregoire. Edu, El Pequeno Lobo. 2003. (SPA.). 32p. (978-84-95150-46-2(8)) Corimbo, Editorial S.L.

—Edu, El Pequeno Lobo. 2003. (SPA.). 32p. 17.95 (978-84-95150-44-8(1)) Corimbo, Editorial S.L. ESP. *Dist:* Distribooks, Inc.

Somaiah, Rosemarie. Indian Children's Favorite Stories. 2006. (Illus.). 80p. (J). 16.95 (978-0-8048-3687-6(6)) Tuttle Publishing.

Somoskey, Rebecca. Say What? Kool Kids Stories from Appalachia. 2004. (J). 4.00 (978-0-9768514-2-4(3)) Bearwallow Blessings Ministries.

A Song in Their Hearts. 2000. (Tippy Parrish Story Ser.). (YA). (gr. 6-10). per. 12.95 (978-1-930009-24-0(0)) Image Cascade Publishing.

Soto, G., et al. Multicultural Collection. Soto, G. et al, illus. 2003. pap. 91.95 incl. audio (978-0-87499-673-9(2)) Live Oak Media.

Soto, Gary. Baseball in April & Other Stories. 10th anniv. ed. 2000. 128p. (YA). (gr. 3-7). (SPA.). 17.00 (978-0-15-202573-1(1)); pap. 6.00 (978-0-15-202567-0(7) , Harcourt Paperbacks) Harcourt Children's Bks.

—Help Wanted: Stories. 2005. 224p. (YA). 17.00 (978-0-15-205201-0(1)) Harcourt Children's Bks.

—Help Wanted: Stories. 2007. (Illus.). 228p. (YA). pap. 6.95 (978-0-15-205663-6(7) , Harcourt Paperbacks) Harcourt Children's Bks.

—Local News: Stories. 2003. (Illus.). 156p. (YA). pap. 5.95 (978-0-15-204695-8(X) , Harcourt Paperbacks) Harcourt Children's Bks.

—Petty Crimes. 2006. (Illus.). 168p. (J). pap. 5.95 (978-0-15-205437-3(5) , Harcourt Paperbacks) Harcourt Children's Bks.

Spalding, Andrea. Bottled Sunshine. Ohi, Ruth, illus. 2005. 32p. (J). (gr. 1). (978-1-55041-703-6(7)) Fitzhenry & Whiteside, Ltd.

Sparks, Kerry. Dimples. 2002. 108p. pap. 9.95 (978-0-595-22461-6(X) , Writers Club Pr.) iUniverse, Inc.

Speceal, Edetha. The Lost Egg & Other Stories. 2006. 144p. pap. (*978-1-84401-644-0(7)) Athena Pr.

Spelman, Cornelia Maude. Mama & Daddy Bear's Divorce. 2001. (gr. k-3). lib. bdg. 15.25 (978-0-613-70954-5(3)) Tandem Library Bks.

Spencely, Annabel, illus. The Kingfisher Treasury of Bedtime Stories. 2003. (Kingfisher Treasury of Stories Ser.: Vol. 9). 160p. (J). (gr. k-3). pap. 5.95 (978-0-7534-5669-9(9) , Kingfisher) Houghton Mifflin Co. Trade & Reference Div.

—The Kingfisher Treasury of Monster Stories, Vol. 7. 2003. (Kingfisher Treasury of Stories Ser.). 164p. (J). (gr. k-3). pap. 5.95 (978-0-7534-5667-5(2) , Kingfisher) Houghton Mifflin Co. Trade & Reference Div.

A Spicy-Herby Day, 6 vols.; set. 32p. (gr. 1-3). 26.50 (978-0-7802-8044-1(X)) Wright Group, The.

Spiegel, Richard A. & Fisher, Barbara, eds. Streams. (YA). (gr. 7-12). No. 12. 1998. 134p. pap. 10.00 (978-0-934830-65-2(7)); No. 13. 1999. (Illus.). 150p. pap. 10.00 (978-0-934830-66-9(5)) Ten Penny Players, Inc.

Spiegelman, Art. Little Lit Three-Book Collection: Strange Stories for Strange Kids; Folklore & Fairytale Funnies; It Was a Dark & Silly Night. 2001. (Illus.). 176p. (J). (978-0-06-059826-6(3)) HarperCollins Pubs.

Spiegelman, Art & Mouly, Francoise. Strange Stories for Strange Kids. Spiegelman, Art, illus. 2001. (Little Lit Ser.). (Illus.). 64p. (J). (ps-3). 19.95 (978-0-06-028626-2(1) , Cotler, Joanna Books) HarperCollins Pubs.

Spiegle, Dan, et al. Historical Adventure. 2006. (Illus.). 56p. pap. (*978-0-8368-7934-6(1)); (YA). (gr. 4 up). lib. bdg. 29.27 (*978-0-8368-7927-8(9)) Stevens, Gareth Inc. (World Almanac Library).

Spirn, Michele. Wait till the Midnight Hour. 2001. (YA). pap. (978-1-56765-069-3(4) , R698P) AMSCO Schl. Pubns., Inc.

Spoon, Cynthia. The Can-Do Stories. 2005. (Illus.). 72p. (J). per. 12.95 (978-1-59453-912-1(X) , Airleaf Publishing) Airleaf Publishing & Bookselling.

Spoor, Trudy. Women of the Bible: Stories for 4 & 5 year Children. 2006. (ENG.). 68p. (J). per. 31.99 (*978-1-4141-0637-3(8)) Pleasant Word.

Springham, James. Earth-n-Bones: Blue Things. 2006. 54p. pap. 12.95 (978-1-4137-9738-1(5)) PublishAmerica, Inc.

Spyropulos, Diana. Cornelius y la Estrella Perro. 2004. (SPA.). 48p. (978-84-7720-790-0(9)) Obelisco, Ediciones S.A.

Squeaky. 2004. (J). per. (978-1-57657-352-5(4)) Paradise Pr., Inc.

St John Taylor, Jeannie & Idle, Molly Schaar. Le Fameux Arbre de Noël de Pingouin. 2007. (FRE., Illus.). 24p. (J). pap. 9.95 (*978-2-922435-16-0(4)) Lobster Pr. CAN. *Dist:* National Bk. Network.

Stadtler, Bea. Baked By Savta: A Collection of Childrens' Stories. 2002. 123p. (J). (gr. 4-7). pap. 10.95 (978-0-595-21389-4(8) , Writer's Showcase Pr.) iUniverse, Inc.

Staggs, Alvin DeWayne. Stories for Animal Lovers. 2000. 195p. (J). pap. 13.95 (978-0-7414-0553-1(9)) Infinity Publishing.

Stahl, R. James, ed. Merlyn's Pen: Fiction, Essays & Poems by America's Teenagers, Vol. IV. 2000. 100p. (YA). (gr. 6-12). per. (978-1-886427-50-1(X) , MP4A) Merlyn's Pen, Inc.

Stanek, Robert. Student's Classroom Handbook for Robert Stanek's Magic Lands. 2005. 116p. (Orig.). pap. 12.00 (978-1-57545-035-3(6) , Ruin Mist Pubns.) Reagent Pr.

Starbright Foundation Staff. Once upon a Fairy Tale: Four Favorite Stories Retold by the Stars. 2001. (Illus.). 80p. (J). 30.00 (978-0-670-03500-7(9) , Viking Juvenile) Penguin Group (USA) Inc.

Steadman, Pamela M. Hannah Savannah's Favorite Tales. 2005. 78p. (YA). per. 7.95 (978-1-59196-854-2(2)) Instantpublisher.com.

Steck, Nyle. Dream Time Friend. Polanco, Ian & Karrle, Mike, illus. 1999. (Tuck 'Em in Bedtime Stories Ser.). 28p. (J). (ps-3). 18.50 (978-0-9675277-0-3(8)) Dragon Tales Publishing.

Steck-Vaughn Staff. Legends & Fables: Sky Got It's Stars/ Tug of War. 1998. (Illus.). (J). pap. (978-0-8172-8642-2(X)) Steck-Vaughn.

—Old & New. 2000. (gr. k-3). lib. bdg. 12.95 (978-0-613-75916-8(8)) Tandem Library Bks.

Steig, William. The One & Only Shrek. Steig, William, illus. 2007. (Illus.). 32p. (J). (ps-3). 29.95 (*978-0-312-36713-8(9)) Farrar, Straus & Giroux.

Steiner, George, illus. The Candle & the Night: A Dreidel Spin Through The Calendar. 2002. 42p. (J). spiral bd. 10.95 (978-0-9643273-6-8(8)) AZURE/BMI.

Stephens, Sarah Hines. The Little Mermaid & Other Stories. 2002. (Scholastic Junior Classics Ser.). 96p. (J). pap. 3.99 (978-0-439-29145-3(3)) Scholastic, Inc.

Sternfeld, Nathan. Adventures with Rebbe Mendel. Pomerantz, Riva, tr. Bichman, David, illus. 230p. 21.99 (978-1-58330-550-8(5)) Feldheim Pubs.

Stevens, Tim, illus. More Ghost Stories. 2004. (Red Hot Reads Ser.). 224p. (J). (gr. k-3). pap. 6.95 (978-0-7534-5736-8(9) , Kingfisher) Houghton Mifflin Co. Trade & Reference Div.

Stevenson, Robert Louis. The Merry Men. 2004. 304p. pap. 14.95 (978-1-59540-514-2(3) , 1st World Library - Literary Society) 1st World Publishing, Inc.

Stickle, Beverly Graham. Slow down & Simplify: Busy People Share Tips for Rediscovering Peace in Your Life. Wade, Kenneth R., ed. 1998. 158p. pap. 10.99 (978-0-8163-1688-5(0)) Pacific Pr. Publishing Assn.

Stillerman, Robbie. Willie the Wizard: With 14 Stickers. 2001. 4p. (J). pap. 1.50 (978-0-486-41764-6(6)) Dover Pubns., Inc.

Stine, R. L. The Haunting Hour: Chills in the Dead of Night. (Illus.). 160p. (J). (gr. 3 up). 2002. pap. 5.99 (978-0-06-441045-8(5)); 2001. 15.99 (978-0-06-623604-9(5)); 2001. 14.89 (978-0-06-623605-6(3)) HarperCollins Pubs.

—Haunting Hour: Chills in the Dead of Night. 2002. (gr. 3-6). lib. bdg. 13.00 (978-0-613-54437-5(4)) Tandem Library Bks.

—La Hora de Las Pesadillas. Batlles Vinn, Camila, tr. 2005. (Escritura desatada Ser.). (SPA.). 192p. (YA). 10.95 (978-84-666-0020-0(5)) Ediciones B ESP. *Dist:* Independent Pubs. Group.

Stockton, Frank Richard. The Bee-Man of Orn: And Other Fanciful Tales. 2007. 140p. pap. 10.99 (*978-1-4264-5788-3(X)); 154p. pap. 14.99 (*978-1-4264-5848-4(7)) BiblioBazaar.

Stone, Megan & Hartenstine, Kristina, eds. Teen Storytellers: A Teen Writer's Dream, Vol. 2. 2003. (Teen Writer's Dream Teen Storytellers Ser.: 2). (YA). per. 8.95 (978-0-9740763-1-7(7)) Be-Mused Pubns.

Stop! & Other Stories: Individual Title Six-Pack. (Story Steps Ser.). (gr. k-2). 42.00 (978-0-7635-9592-0(6)) Rigby Education.

Stories for Girls. 2007. 512p. pap. 14.95 (*978-1-84236-586-1(X)) Miles Kelly Publishing, Ltd. GBR. *Dist:* National Bk. Network.

A Story, a Story. 2004. (J). 24.95 incl. audio (978-1-56008-211-8(9)); pap. 32.75 incl. audio (978-1-55592-315-0(1)); pap. 14.95 incl. audio (978-1-56008-212-5(7)) Weston Woods Studios, Inc.

Story Lady. Over the Fence Non-Sense Tales. 2001. 212p. pap. 14.95 (978-0-595-20611-7(5) , Writers Club Pr.) iUniverse, Inc.

The Story of Chase. 2001. lib. bdg. 25.00 net. (978-0-9701105-6-5(1)) Gulf War Pr.

Storytime for One Year Olds. 2002. 32p. (J). pap. 4.95 (978-0-7894-8495-6(1)) Dorling Kindersley Publishing, Inc.

Stover, Anne Long. Cloudy. Spears, Ashley E., illus. 2005. 20p. (J). (978-0-9762389-0-4(X)) Trent's Prints.

Stowe, Harriet Beecher. Bettys Bright Idea Deacon Pitkins Farm A. 2006. pap. (*978-1-4068-3093-4(3)) Echo Library.

Strahan, Jonathan. The Starry Rift. 2008. (J). (gr. 7). 19.99 (*978-0-670-06059-7(3) , Viking Juvenile) Penguin Group (USA) Inc.

Strauss, Jess. The Adventures of Little Willie & Little Wilma: Stories to Be Read to Young Children with Love. l.t. ed. 2002. 171p. (J). per. 12.95 (978-1-931934-05-3(3)) Back Yard Pub.

Strauss, Kevin. Loon & Moon: And Other Animal Stories. Scheibe, Nancy, illus. 2005. 48p. (J). pap. 12.95 (978-0-9766264-3-5(8)) Raven Productions, Inc.

Strawberry Laminated Book. 2005. (J). per. 15.95 (978-1-59649-309-4(7)) Whispering Pine Pr., Inc.

Students of Wallenberg High School. Exactly* Ten Beavers, Nine Fairies, Eight Dreams, Seven Knights, Six Princesses, Five Dogs, Four Otters, Three Old Men, Two Robots, One Traveling Shoe & Everything Else it Takes to Make a Great Children's Story Book. San Francisco Bay Area Illustrators, illus. 2007. 256p. (gr. 3 up). 28.00 (*978-0-9790073-2-3(1)) 826 Valencia.

Sturt, M. Canterbury Pilgrims. 2007. pap. (*978-1-4068-3599-1(4)) Echo Library.

Stuve-Bodeen, Stephanie. Mama Elizabeti. Hale, Christy, illus. 32p. (ps-2). 7.95 (978-1-58430-236-0(4)) Lee & Low Bks., Inc.

Suarez, Isabel. Cuentos de Amecameca. 2002. Tr. of Stories of Amecameca. (SPA.). (YA). 6.95 (978-968-7205-26-7(1)) Amaquemecan, Editorial MEX. *Dist:* AIMS International Bks., Inc.

Suarez, Maribel. Frutas. 1998. (ACE & SPA.). (J). (ps-3). pap. (978-970-05-0730-9(0)) Grijalbo, Editorial.

Sula, Sondra. Little Rosie & Trouble. 2000. mass mkt. 4.50 (978-1-931179-22-5(0)); mass mkt. 8.95 incl. audio compact disk (978-1-931179-33-1(6)) Long Hill Productions, Inc.

—The Mill Creek Kids: Stampede. 2000. mass mkt. 4.50 (978-1-931179-24-9(7)); mass mkt. 8.95 incl. audio compact disk (978-1-931179-35-5(2)) Long Hill Productions, Inc.

Sullivan, Jean. The Blakely Field Stories. 2005. 58p. pap. 12.95 (978-1-4137-8611-8(1)) PublishAmerica, Inc.

Sullivan, Pam. Young Adult Short Story Competition 2001-2002. 2002. 162p. (YA). pap. 12.95 (978-0-595-25078-3(5) , Writer's Showcase Pr.) iUniverse, Inc.

Sulzenko, J. C. Back to Back Stories for Lilli & Zach. 2000. (Illus.). 32p. (J). pap. (978-0-9685094-1-8(X)) Blue Poodle Bks.

Summer & Winter: Individual Title Six-Packs. (Story Steps Ser.). (gr. k-2). 32.00 (978-0-7635-9809-9(7)) Rigby Education.

Summer, Jane, ed. Not the Only One: Lesbian & Gay Fiction for Teens. 2004. 224p. pap. 13.95 (978-1-55583-834-8(0)) Alyson Pubns.

Summer Sands, 6 vols., Set B. 32p. (gr. 1-3). 31.50 (978-0-7802-8054-0(7)) Wright Group, The.

Summers, Everette. Grandaddy's Short Stories. 2006. 48p. pap. 12.95 (978-1-4241-2468-8(9)) PublishAmerica, Inc.

The Surf Trilogy. 2003. (YA). per. 39.95 (978-0-9640858-5-5(2)) Chubasco Publishing Co.

Surprise! Individual Title Six-Packs. (Story Steps Ser.). (gr. k-2). 32.00 (978-0-7635-9605-7(1)) Rigby Education.

Surprises & Other Stories: Individual Title Six-Pack. (Story Steps Ser.). (gr. k-2). 48.00 (978-0-7635-9818-1(6)) Rigby Education.

Sutherland, Casey. Not Quite So Stories. 2001. 32p. (J). (ps-7). 8.95 (978-0-9677274-2-4(1)) BlacKat Publishing.

Sweeney, Joan & Fain, Kathleen. Once upon a Lily Pad: Froggy Love in Monet's Garden. Fain, Kathleen, illus. 2005. (Illus.). 32p. (J). (ps-ps). 10.95 (978-0-8118-5079-7(X)) Chronicle Bks. LLC.

Swindells, Robert. Doodlebug Alley. (Illus.). 56p. (J). pap. 6.99 (978-0-7497-3860-0(X)) Egmont Bks., Ltd. GBR. *Dist:* Trafalgar Square Publishing.

Swindells, Robert, et al. Cuentos de Terror. (SPA.). (YA). 8.95 (978-958-04-3392-7(5)) Norma S.A. COL. *Dist:* Distribuidora Norma, Inc.

T/K. Read to Me Treasury, Vol. 2. 2001. (Illus.). 400p. (ps-2). 19.99 (978-0-7868-3301-6(7)) Disney Pr.

Taback, Simms. Kibitzers & Fools: Tales My Zayda Told Me. 2008. 48p. (J). (ps). pap. 6.99 (*978-0-14-241065-3(9) , Puffin) Penguin Group (USA) Inc.

Tabuas, Mireya. Cuentos para Leer a Escondidas. (SPA.). (J). pap. (978-980-01-1060-7(7)) Monte Avila Editores Latinoamericana CA VEN. *Dist:* Lectorum Pubns., Inc.

Tagore, Rabindranath. He (Shey) 2008. 154p. (gr. 12). pap. 10.00 (*978-0-14-310209-0(5) , Penguin Global) Penguin Group (USA) Inc.

Talbert, Marc. Doble o Nada. (Torre de Papel Ser.). (SPA.). (J). (gr. 4 up). 7.95 (978-958-04-2384-3(9)) Norma S.A. COL. *Dist:* Distribuidora Norma, Inc.

Talbott, Kerry, illus. Pirates! 2006. (Sticker Stories Ser.). 16p. (J). (ps-1). 4.99 (978-0-448-44342-3(2) , Grosset & Dunlap) Penguin Group (USA) Inc.

The Talent among Us: Trail of Tales. 2003. (YA). per. 13.00 (978-0-9741294-2-6(9) , MSP) Main St Publishing, Inc.

Talone, Augusto. The Adventures of Max & Sandy: Three Short Stories about a Yellow Labrador Retriever Named Max & a Simese House Cat Named Sandy, Who Solve Mysteries. 2006. 96p. (J). pap. 11.99 (978-1-59977-005-5(9)) Annotation Pr.

—The Boy Deputies: Six Short Stories about Two Young Boys Who Help Their Father, A Sheriff, Solve Crimes. 2006. 232p. (J). pap. 17.99 (978-1-59977-004-8(0)) Annotation Pr.

Tappan, Eva March. The Children's Hour: Stories from Seven Old Favorites, 5. l.t. ed. 2007. 338p. pap. 17.99 (*978-1-4264-7382-1(6)) BiblioBazaar.

—The Children's Hour, Volume V: Stories from Seven Old Favorites. 2007. 304p. pap. 14.99 (*978-1-4264-7309-8(5)) BiblioBazaar.

Tarkington, Booth. Beasley's Christmas Party. 2005. 76p. pap. 10.95 (978-1-4218-0407-1(7) , 1st World Library - Literary Society) 1st World Publishing, Inc.

—Beasley's Christmas Party. Clements, Ruth Sypherd, illus. 2004. reprint ed. pap. 15.95 (978-1-4179-0186-9(1)) Kessinger Publishing, LLC.

—Beasley's Christmas Party. 2004. reprint ed. pap. 1.99 (978-1-4192-0925-3(6)) Kessinger Publishing, LLC.

Tavares, Wendy. Stories for My Son. 2006. 40p. 8.29 (978-1-4116-7660-2(2)) Lulu.com.

Taylor, Catherine. Thirst. 2005. 224p. (J). (gr. k-8). pap. (978-1-55005-107-0(5)) Fitzhenry & Whiteside, Ltd.

Taylor-Gaines, Lonnetta. Fia & the Butterfly: 7 Stories for Character Education. 2005. 13.00 (978-0-8059-9848-1(9)) Dorrance Publishing Co., Inc.

Taylor, James Henry. Honeysuckle & Other Stories. 2001. 83p. per. 6.50 (978-0-9713497-0-4(5)) Cave Hollow Pr.

Taylor, Kenneth N. Family-Time Bible in Pictures. 2007. 320p. (J). 12.99 (*978-1-4143-1577-5(5) , Tyndale Kids) Tyndale Hse. Pubs.

Taylor, Vincent. Cornbread Runs for Class President, Griffin, Kasana & Griggs, Charles, eds. Latorre, Adolfo, illus. 2004. (Cornbread Ser.: 1). 96p. (J). per. 4.99 (978-0-9704512-4-8(5)) TriEclipse, Inc.

Taylor, William. At the Big Red Rooster. 160p. (YA). (gr. 8 up). pap. 13.00 (978-1-877135-20-0(8)) Longacre Pr. NZL. *Dist:* Pacific Island Bks.

Teitelbaum, Michael. The Scary States of America. 2007. 416p. (J). (gr. 4-7). pap. 7.99 (978-0-385-73331-1(3)); lib. bdg. 12.99 (*978-0-385-90348-6(0)) Random Hse. Children's Bks. (Delacorte Bks. for Young Readers).

Temperley, Alan. The Magician of Samarkand. l.t. ed. 2005. 216p. (J). pap. (978-0-7540-7883-8(3) , CLP 459) BBC Audio.

—The Magician of Samarkand. 2004. (J). pap. 29.95 incl. audio (978-0-7540-6279-0(1) , Chivers Children's Audio Bks.) BBC Audiobooks America.

Ten Little Ducks & Other Stories: Individual Title Six-Pack. (Story Steps Ser.). (gr. k-2). 48.00 (978-0-7635-9798-6(8)) Rigby Education.

Ten Short Tall Tales for Children. 2002. per. (978-1-930493-49-0(5)) Athena Pr.

Terhune, Albert Payson. The Way of a Dog. l.t. ed. 1999. (Perennial Bestsellers Ser.). 337p. (YA). (gr. 5-9). 26.95 (978-0-7838-8743-2(4)) Thorndike Pr.

Tezuka, Osamu. Phoenix. 2006. (Phoenix Ser.). 208p. (YA). Vol. 7. pap. 15.99 (978-1-4215-0517-6(7)); Vol. 8. pap. 15.99 (978-1-4215-0518-3(5)) Viz Media.

A These Old Rags Set, 6 vols. 32p. (gr. 1-3). 31.50 (978-0-7802-8040-3(7)) Wright Group, The.

Thomas, Jacqui, illus. The Kingfisher Treasury of Witch & Wizard Stories. 2004. (Kingfisher Treasury of Stories Ser.: Vol. 23). 160p. (J). (gr. k-3). pap. 5.95 (978-0-7534-5729-0(6) , Kingfisher) Houghton Mifflin Co. Trade & Reference Div.

Thomas, Jerry D. Danger on Seventh Street & Other Stories. Sox, Aileen Andres, ed. Justinen Creative Group Staff, illus. 1998. (Great Stories for Kids Ser.). 192p. (J). (gr. 3-6). pap. 14.99 (978-0-8163-1658-8(9)) Pacific Pr. Publishing Assn.

—Horse, a Hat & a Big Wet Splat & Other Stories A. 2000. (Great Stories for Kids Ser.: Vol. 5). (J). (ps-3). 14.99 (978-0-8163-1715-8(1)) Pacific Pr. Publishing Assn.

—My Friend Fang & Other Great Stories for Kids: Learning How to Be Someone Who Has Good Friends. 2001. (Illus.). 95p. (J). (978-0-8163-1822-3(0)) Pacific Pr. Publishing Assn.

Thomas, Marlo & Cerf, Christopher, eds. Thanks & Giving: All Year Long. 2005. 96p. (J). 17.95 (978-1-4169-1586-7(9)) Simon & Schuster Children's Publishing.

Thomas, Piri. Stories from el Barrio. 2nd rev. ed. 2005. 136p. pap. 19.95 (*978-0-915117-11-6(8)) Freedom Voices Pubns.

Thomas, Rob. Doing Time: Notes from the Underground. 1999. (J). (978-0-606-16336-1(0)) Tandem Library Bks.

Thompson, Joel. Critter Sitters: And Other Stories That Teach Christian Values. 2003. (ClubZone Kids Ser.). (Illus.). 80p. (J). pap. 5.99 (978-0-8010-4511-0(8)) Baker Bks.

—Shortcuts: And Other Stories That Teach Christian Values. 2003. (Clubzone Kids Ser.). (Illus.). 80p. (J). pap. 5.99 (978-0-8010-4510-3(X)) Baker Bks.

Thompson, Lisa. Read-It! Chapter Books: Wonder Wits, 8 bks., Set. Thompson, Lisa & Stapleton, Matthew, illus. Incl. Artrageous! lib. bdg. 19.95 (978-1-4048-1348-9(9)); Bony Puzzle. lib. bdg. 19.95 (978-1-4048-1345-8(4)); Gadget Hero. lib. bdg. 19.95 (978-1-4048-1349-6(7)); Game Plan. lib. bdg. 19.95 (978-1-4048-1344-1(6)); Look Out! lib. bdg. 19.95 (978-1-4048-1343-4(8)); What's Next? lib. bdg. 19.95 (978-1-4048-1350-2(0)); Wild Ideas. lib. bdg. 19.95 (978-1-4048-1346-5(2)); Wonder Worlds. lib. bdg. 19.95 (978-1-4048-1347-2(0)); (Illus.). 48p. (J). (ps-k). 2005. Set lib. bdg. 159.60 (978-1-4048-1524-7(4)) Picture Window Bks.

Thompson, Susan, et al. Mayan Folktales: Cuentos Folkloricos Mayas. 2007. (World Folklore Ser.). (SPA & ENG.). 236p. 35.00 (*978-1-59158-138-3(9) , LU1389) Libraries Unlimited, Inc.

Thompson, Ted & Horowitz, Eli, eds. Noisy Outlaws, Unfriendly Blobs, & Some Other Things ... That Aren't as Scary, Maybe, Depending on How You Feel about Lost Lands, Stray Cellphones, Creatures from the Sky, Parents Who Disappear in Peru, a Man Named Lars Farf, & One Other Story We Couldn't Quite Finish, So Maybe You Could Help Us Out. 2005. (Illus.). 208p. (YA). (gr. 3-17). 22.00 (978-1-932416-35-0(8)) McSweeney's Publishing.

Thompson, Tolya L. Ingrown Tyrone. Brian, Harrold, illus. 2004. (Smarties Ser.: 4). 33p. (J). 16.00 (978-0-9708296-2-7(0)) Savor Publishing Hse., Inc.

Thomson. Barrel of Stories. 2000. (Illus.). 163p. (J). 16.95 (978-0-385-40545-4(6)) Transworld Publishers Ltd. GBR. *Dist:* Trafalgar Square Publishing.

—Box of Stories for 6 Year-olds. 2000. (Illus.). 135p. (J). 16.95 (978-0-385-40726-7(2)) Transworld Publishers Ltd. GBR. *Dist:* Trafalgar Square Publishing.

—Crate of Stories for 8 Year Olds. 2000. (Illus.). 131p. (J). pap. 6.95 (978-0-552-52959-4(1)) Transworld Publishers Ltd. GBR. *Dist:* Trafalgar Square Publishing.

—Stocking Full of Christmas Stories. 2000. (Illus.). 165p. (J). pap. 4.95 (978-0-552-52739-2(4) , Corgi Bks. Ltd.) Random Hse. Children's Bks. GBR. *Dist:* Trafalgar Square Publishing.

Thomson, Pat. Band of Joining-in Stories. 2000. (Illus.). 143p. (J). 16.95 (978-0-385-40543-0(X)) Transworld Publishers Ltd. GBR. *Dist:* Trafalgar Square Publishing.

—Barrel of Stories for 7 Year Olds. 2000. (Illus.). 163p. (J). pap. 6.95 (978-0-552-52817-7(X)) Transworld Publishers Ltd. GBR. *Dist:* Trafalgar Square Publishing.

—A Basket of Stories for Seven Year Olds. 2000. (Illus.). 179p. (J). pap. 8.99 (978-0-552-52729-3(7)) Transworld Publishers Ltd. GBR. *Dist:* Independent Pubs. Group.

—A Bucketful of Stories for 6 Year-Olds. 2000. (Illus.). 177p. (J). pap. 9.99 (978-0-552-52757-6(2)) Transworld Publishers Ltd. GBR. *Dist:* Independent Pubs. Group.

—Cracker Full of Christmas Stories. 2000. (Illus.). 165p. (J). 15.95 (978-0-385-40483-9(2)) Transworld Publishers Ltd. GBR. *Dist:* Trafalgar Square Publishing.

—Sackful of Stories for Eight Year Olds. 2000. (Illus.). 208p. (J). pap. 9.99 (978-0-552-52730-9(0)) Transworld Publishers Ltd. GBR. *Dist:* Trafalgar Square Publishing.

—Satchel of School Stories. 2000. (Illus.). 240p. (J). pap. 8.99 (978-0-552-52738-5(6)) Transworld Publishers Ltd. GBR. *Dist:* Independent Pubs. Group.

—You Can't Bring That in Here! 2005. (Illus.). 192p. (J). 7.50 (978-0-09-948386-1(6) , Red Fox) Random Hse. Children's Bks. GBR. *Dist:* Trafalgar Square Publishing.

Three Witches & Other Stories. 2002. per. (978-1-931456-05-0(4)) Athena Pr.

Throwing Shadows. 2007. 150p. (J). (gr. 3-7). per. 5.99 (***978-1-4169-4959-6(3)*** , Aladdin) Simon & Schuster Children's Publishing.

Thury, Fredrick H. Hoshmakaka. van Kampen, Vlasta, illus. 2003. Tr. of Last Straw. (SPA.). (J). (gr. 2-4). 13.56 (978-84-8418-046-3(8)) Zendrera Zariquiey, Editorial ESP. *Dist:* Lectorum Pubns., Inc.

Tich, Jan. Caos en el Mercado. 2005. (SPA., Illus.). 28p. (J). 14.95 (978-84-933955-8-2(7)) Hardenville SA URY. *Dist:* Independent Pubs. Group.

Tiddle, Deanna Hessedal. Apartment Horse & Friends. 2003. 62p. (J). pap. 9.95 (978-0-7414-1724-4(3)) Infinity Publishing.

Tierno, Susan F. Piensa-Tu: Coleccion de Libros, 20 vols., Set. Alvarado, Ana María, tr. Ramirez, Michael, illus. 2000. Tr. of Think Kids Book Collection. (SPA.). (J). (gr. 1-4). pap. 2.95 (978-1-58237-059-0(1)) Creative Thinkers, Inc.

Tingle, Tim & Moore. Spooky Texas Tales. Miller, Gina, illus. 2005. x, 85p. (J). pap. (978-0-89672-566-9(9)) Texas Tech Univ. Pr.

To Kill the Truth. 2001. 152p. pap. 13.95 (978-1-57072-187-8(4)); 23.95 (978-1-57072-186-1(6)) Overmountain Pr. (Silver Dagger Mysteries).

Tobesman, Rachmiel. The Magic Glasses: Stories & Other Activities for Children of Separation & Divorce. 1998. (Illus.). 38p. (J). (ps-12). spiral bd. 12.95 (978-0-9677266-0-1(3)) Project Shalom.

Toler, Violet M. Churchmouse Tales: Puppet Plays, 10 vols., Vol. 2. Koefler, Leatha, illus. 2nd rev. ed. 2004. Orig. Title: "Puppet Plays, Adventures of Charlie & His Friends". (J). (ps-6). pap. 10.95 (978-0-9749749-1-0(9)) Wayside Pubns.

Tolstoy, Leo. Classic Tales & Fables for Children. 2001. (gr. 7-12). lib. bdg. 19.95 (978-0-613-83698-2(7)) Tandem Library Bks.

—Death of Ivan Ilych & Other Stories. 2003. (gr. 7-12). lib. bdg. 15.25 (978-0-613-67240-5(2)) Tandem Library Bks.

—Leo Tolstoy Collected Short Stories. Court, Robert, illus. 2001. (Great Author Ser.). (YA). (978-0-9709033-0-3(8)) Peterson Publishing Co., Inc.

Tomaselli, Mela. The Magic Pot: Folk Tales & Legends of the Giriama of Kenya. 2004. (Illus.). 80p. (978-9966-21-950-3(1)) Paulines Pubns., Africa.

Tomkinson, Raymond. Bravo the Donkey & Other Stories for Christmas. 2006. 72p. pap. (***978-1-84549-151-2(3)***) arima publishing.

Tomlinson, Jill. The Otter Who Wanted to Know. Howard, Paul, illus. 2005. 96p. (J). reprint ed. pap. 6.99 (978-1-4052-1082-9(6)) Egmont Bks., Ltd. GBR. *Dist:* Trafalgar Square Publishing.

A Tonka Tale. 2004. (J). (978-0-9767179-1-1(3)) ABC Development, Inc.

Too-Tight Shoes, 6 vols. 2004. 32p. (gr. 1-3). 31.50 (978-0-322-00337-8(7)) Wright Group, The.

A Too-Tight Shoes Set, 6 vols. 32p. (gr. 1-3). 26.50 (978-0-7802-8042-7(3)) Wright Group, The.

La Tormenta de Truenos; Aventura en la Oscuridad, 2 bks., Set. (Coleccion Chiquilines - Imagen y Sonido). (SPA., Illus.). (J). 15.95 incl. audio (978-950-11-0624-4(1) , SGM241) Sigmar ARG. *Dist:* Continental Bk. Co., Inc.

Tormont Publications Inc., des. Perfect Presents, 20 bks. (Illus.). 40p. (J). vinyl bd. (978-2-7641-1284-7(X)) Tormont Pubns.

Totemeyer, Andree-Jeanne. Under the Story Tree: Readathon Stories. 2005. (Illus.). 93p. (***978-99916-0-509-8(6)***) Namibian Children's Bk. Forum.

(Translator), George Fyler Townsend. Aesops Fables EasyRead Edition. 2006. pap. (***978-1-4250-3319-4(9)***) Assistedreadingbooks.com Inc.

—Aesops Fables EasyRead Large Edition. 2006. pap. (***978-1-4250-4175-5(2)***) Assistedreadingbooks.com Inc.

Travels with Annie. 2002. per. 27.50 (978-0-9726639-0-8(8)) Sacred Mountain Foundation, A California Non Profit Public Benefit.

Travesuras y Aventuras. 2003. (SPA.). pap. (978-956-13-1045-2(7) , AB8007) Bello, Andres CHL. *Dist:* Lectorum Pubns., Inc.

El Trencito de los Cuentos. (Coleccion Estrella). (SPA., Illus.). 64p. (YA). 14.95 (978-950-11-0018-1(9) , SGM018) Sigmar ARG. *Dist:* Continental Bk. Co., Inc.

Las Tres Naranjas de la Vida. (Coleccion Fabulas y Cuentos Populares). (SPA.). (J). (gr. 2-4). (978-84-246-1627-4(8) , GL1107) La Galera, S.A. Editorial ESP. *Dist:* Lectorum Pubns., Inc.

Triple Play. 2006. (Illus.). (gr. 4-8). 167.40 (978-0-7910-9072-5(8)) Facts On File, Inc.

Triple Play-Yellow. 2006. (Illus.). (gr. 4-8). 167.40 (978-0-7910-9077-0(9)) Facts On File, Inc.

Tripp, Valerie. Felicity's Short Story Collection. Andreasen, Dan & Hood, Philip, illus. 2006. 232p. (J). 12.95 (***978-1-59369-120-2(3)***) American Girl Publishing, Inc.

—Kit's Short Story Collection. Rane, Walter & Graef, Renee, illus. 2006. 256p. (J). 12.95 (***978-1-59369-126-4(2)***) American Girl Publishing, Inc.

—Molly's Short Story Collection. Bakces, Nick & Hood, Philip, illus. 2006. 232p. (J). 12.95 (***978-1-59369-123-3(8)***) American Girl Publishing, Inc.

Trocme, Andre. Angels & Donkeys: Tales for Christmas & Other Times. Hewett, Nelly Trocme, tr. from FRE. gif. ed. 2002. 170p. 12.95 (978-1-56148-263-4(3)) Good Bks.

Troughton, Joanna, et al. A Friend for the King & Other Stories: Chitonga Version. Chisengele, tr. 2001. (Illus.). 48p. pap. 0.45 (978-0-521-89004-5(7)) Cambridge Univ. Pr.

—A Friend for the King & Other Stories: Cinyanja Version. Tembo, tr. 2001. (Illus.). 48p. pap. 0.45 (978-0-521-89005-2(5)) Cambridge Univ. Pr.

—A Friend for the King & Other Stories: Icibemba Version. Mulilo, tr. 2001. (Illus.). 48p. pap. 0.45 (978-0-521-89007-6(1)) Cambridge Univ. Pr.

—A Friend for the King & Other Stories: Kiikaonde Version. Muyebaa, tr. 2001. (Illus.). 48p. pap. 0.45 (978-0-521-89008-3(X)) Cambridge Univ. Pr.

—A Friend for the King & Other Stories: Luvale Version. Sakapaji, tr. 2001. (Illus.). 48p. pap. 0.45 (978-0-521-89010-6(1)) Cambridge Univ. Pr.

—A Friend for the King & Other Stories: Silozi Version. Mwendende, tr. 2001. (Illus.). 48p. pap. 0.25 (978-0-521-89011-3(X)) Cambridge Univ. Pr.

Trudell, Devin, illus. 3 Stories. Trudell, Devin, . 2007. (YA). 10.00 (***978-0-9794004-0-7(6)***) Art Night Bks.

Truman, Dennay H. The Happy Endings. 2007. 65p. per. 8.95 (***978-1-59824-435-9(3)***) E-BookTime LLC.

Tsaliovich, Anatoly. Of Wolves & Lambs & Others. Burke, Daniel, illus. 2005. 73p. (YA). pap. 12.99 (978-0-9773816-0-9(9)) ATInternational Pubs.

Tucker, Bob. Grandpa Tucker's Rhymes & Tales. Newlund, Christine & Smith, Larry, illus. 1999. 192p. (J). (gr. 1-6). pap. 13.95 (978-1-929146-00-0(0)) Keep Smiling.

Tucker, Marlin D. The Main Rooster & Other Short Stories. Tucker, Marlin D., illus. 2000. (Illus.). 382p. (YA). pap. 14.95 (978-1-56883-077-3(7) , 1-56883-077-7) Colonial Pr.

Turin, Adela. Las Cajas de Cristal. Bosnia, Nella, illus. 2001. Tr. of Crystal Boxes. (SPA.). 40p. (J). 12.76 (978-84-264-3595-8(5)) Editorial Lumen ESP. *Dist:* Lectorum Pubns., Inc.

Turner, Megan Whalen. Instead of Three Wishes: Magical Short Stories. 2006. 160p. (J). pap. 5.99 (978-0-06-084231-4(8)) HarperCollins Pubs.

Turner, Will. Mix Tape: The Will Turner Collection. 2004. 77p. pap. 14.95 (978-1-4137-4066-0(9)) PublishAmerica, Inc.

Twain, Mark. Mark Twain. Hall, Tracy, illus. 2004. (Great American Short Stories Ser.). 80p. (J). lib. bdg. 23.33 (978-0-8368-4255-5(3)) Stevens, Gareth Inc.

—Mark Twain. Camfield, Gregg, ed. Comport, Sally Wern, illus. 2005. (Stories for Young People Ser.). 80p. (J). (gr. 7-9). 14.95 (978-1-4027-1178-7(6)) Sterling Publishing Co., Inc.

Under the Big Green Umbrella. 2008. (J). spiral bd. (***978-0-9793930-4-4(3)***) Dandelion Publishing.

Ungerer, Tomi. I Am Papa Snap & These Are My Favorite No Such Stories. Ungerer, Tomi, illus. 1999. (Illus.). 32p. (J). (ps-3). reprint ed. 17.95 (978-1-57098-279-8(1)) Rinehart, Roberts Pubs.

Upham, Linda. Bronze Dagger. Littlejohn, Anna, illus. 2004. 128p. pap. 16.00 (978-0-7188-2775-5(9)) Lutherworth Pr., The GBR. *Dist:* Parkwest Pubns., Inc.

Urdaneta, Josefina. Si Canto... Soy un Cantueso. (SPA.). (J). pap. (978-980-01-0916-8(1)) Monte Avila Editores Latinoamericana CA VEN. *Dist:* Lectorum Pubns., Inc.

Ure, Jean. Is Anybody There? Seeing Is Believing. 2004. (Diary Ser.). (Illus.). 192p. (J). pap. 8.99 (978-0-00-716136-2(0) , Collins) HarperCollins Pubs. Ltd. GBR. *Dist:* Independent Pubs. Group.

Ure, Jean. Tutti Frutti Collection. 2005. (Diary Ser.). (Illus.). 528p. (J). pap. 15.99 (***978-0-00-719862-7(0)***) HarperCollins Pubs. Ltd. GBR. *Dist:* Independent Pubs. Group.

Urrea, Lourdes. Huellas en la Escalera. rev. ed. 2006. (Ediciones Castillo Castillo Del Terror Ser.). (SPA.). 120p. (J). (gr. 2-6). pap. 6.95 (978-970-20-0243-7(5)) Castillo, Ediciones, S. A. de C. V. MEX. *Dist:* Macmillan.

—El Mago. rev. ed. 2003. (Ediciones Castillo Castillo Del Terror Ser.). (SPA.). 112p. (J). (gr. 2-6). pap. 6.95 (978-970-20-0189-8(7)) Castillo, Ediciones, S. A. de C. V. MEX. *Dist:* Macmillan.

—El Nino de la Ventana. rev. ed. 2004. (Castillo del Terror Ser.). (SPA.). 312p. (J). pap. 6.95 (978-970-20-0188-1(9)) Castillo, Ediciones, S. A. de C. V. MEX. *Dist:* Macmillan.

Urrea, Luis. Calle Numero 31. 2005. (Ediciones Castillo Castillo Del Terror Ser.). (SPA.). (J). (gr. 2-6). pap. 7.95 (978-970-20-0187-4(0)) Castillo, Ediciones, S. A. de C. V. MEX. *Dist:* Giron Bks., Iaconi, Mariuccia Bk. Imports.

—Gruta Encantada. 2005. (Ediciones Castillo Castillo Del Terror Ser.). (SPA.). (J). (gr. 2-6). pap. 7.95 (978-970-20-0244-4(3)) Castillo, Ediciones, S. A. de C. V. MEX. *Dist:* Giron Bks., Iaconi, Mariuccia Bk. Imports.

—La Sombra Vegetal. 2005. (Ediciones Castillo Castillo Del Terror Ser.). (SPA.). (J). (gr. 2-6). pap. 7.95 (978-970-20-0249-9(4)) Castillo, Ediciones, S. A. de C. V. MEX. *Dist:* Giron Bks., Iaconi, Mariuccia Bk. Imports.

Urrea, Luis & Urrea, Lourdes. Silencio en el Castillo. rev. ed. 2006. (Ediciones Castillo Castillo Del Terror Ser.). (SPA.). 116p. (J). (gr. 2-6). pap. 6.95 (978-970-20-0247-5(8)) Castillo, Ediciones, S. A. de C. V. MEX. *Dist:* Macmillan.

—Vacaciones Mortales. rev. ed. 2007. (Ediciones Castillo Castillo Del Terror Ser.). (SPA.). 120p. (J). (gr. 2-6). pap. 6.95 (978-970-20-0248-2(6)) Castillo, Ediciones, S. A. de C. V. MEX. *Dist:* Macmillan.

Ury, Allen B. Scary Stories for Sleep-Overs. Been, Dwight, illus. 1998. (Scary Stories for Sleep-Overs Ser.: Vol. 9). 96p. (J). (gr. 4-7). pap. 5.95 (978-1-56565-895-0(7) , 08957W) Lowell Hse.

Uzuner, Buket. A Cup of Turkish Coffee. 2001. (YA). 11.95 incl. audio (978-1-84059-309-9(1)); (TUR.). 11.95 incl. audio (978-1-84059-308-2(3)) Milet Publishing.

—A Cup of Turkish Coffee. Croft, Damian, tr. 2001. (Turkish - English Short Stories Ser.). (TUR & ENG., Illus.). 141p. pap. 9.95 (978-1-84059-300-6(8)) Milet Publishing.

V., Patti. My Na Na Stories. 2005. 18.00 (978-0-8059-9806-1(3)) Dorrance Publishing Co., Inc.

Valgardson, W. D. The Divorced Kids Club: And Other Stories. 2002. (Illus.). 184p. (J). (gr. 6-10). pap. 6.95 (978-0-88899-370-0(6)) Groundwood Bks. CAN. *Dist:* Perseus Distribution.

—Divorced Kids Club: And Other Stories. 2000. (gr. 5-8). lib. bdg. 15.25 (978-0-613-33888-2(X)) Tandem Library Bks.

—Garbage Creek: And Other Stories. 1998. (Illus.). 136p. (J). (gr. 3-7). 5.95 (978-0-88899-339-7(0)) Groundwood Bks. CAN. *Dist:* Perseus Distribution.

Vallejo-Nagera, Alejandra. Cuanto me Quieren! Guerrero, Andrés, illus. 2003. (SPA.). 23p. (J). (gr. k-1). 8.95 (978-84-204-4951-7(2)) Santillana USA Publishing Co., Inc.

Valriu Llinas, Caterina. El Traje Buevo del Emperador. (Coleccion Fabulas y Cuentos Populares).Tr. of Emperor's New Clothes. (SPA.). 24p. (J). (gr. 2-4). 10.36 (978-84-246-1940-4(4)) La Galera, S.A. Editorial ESP. *Dist:* Lectorum Pubns., Inc.

Van Belkom, Edo, ed. Be Afraid! Tales of Horror. 2000. 184p. (J). (gr. 6-9). pap. 6.95 (978-0-88776-496-7(7)) Tundra Bks., Inc./Livres Toundra, Inc. CAN. *Dist:* Random Hse., Inc.

Van Belkom, Edo, selected by. Be Very Afraid! More Tales of Horror. 2002. 200p. (J). (gr. 6 up). pap. 7.95 (978-0-88776-595-7(5)) Tundra Bks., Inc./Livres Toundra, Inc. CAN. *Dist:* Random Hse., Inc.

Van Horn, William, et al. Walt Disney's Comics & Stories. 64p. Vol. 664. 2006. pap. 6.95 (978-1-888472-17-2(0)); Vol. 665. 2006. pap. 6.95 (978-1-888472-18-9(9)); Vol. 667. 2005. pap. 6.95 (978-1-888472-20-2(0)) Gemstone Publishing, Inc.

van Kampen, Vlasta, illus. & retold by. Bear Tales: Three Treasured Stories. van Kampen, Vlasta, retold by. 2000. (Folk Tales Ser.). 40p. (J). (gr. k-3). pap. 6.95 (978-1-55037-618-0(7)); lib. bdg. 18.95 (978-1-55037-619-7(5)) Annick Pr., Ltd. CAN. *Dist:* Firefly Bks., Ltd.

Van Laan, Nancy & Rusch, Amy. Moose Tales. 2001. (Illus.). 48p. (J). (gr. k-3). pap. 5.95 (978-0-618-11128-2(X)) Houghton Mifflin Co. Trade & Reference Div.

Van Pelt, James. Strangers & Beggars: Stories. 2002. (gr. 7-12). lib. bdg. 28.05 (978-0-613-60619-6(1)) Tandem Library Bks.

Vance, Elsbet, ed. & illus. Mistletoe Madness: A Short Story Collection. Vance, Elsbet, illus. 2004. 400p. (J). (gr. 2-6). pap. (978-0-9718348-2-8(2)) Blooming Tree Pr.

Vande Velde, Vivian. All Hallow's Eve: 13 Stories. 2006. (Illus.). 240p. (YA). 17.00 (978-0-15-205576-9(2)) Harcourt Children's Bks.

—Being Dead: Stories. 2001. (gr. 7-12). lib. bdg. 15.25 (978-0-613-68194-0(0)) Tandem Library Bks.

Vande Velde, Vivian. Curses, Inc. & Other Stories. 2007. (Illus.). 240p. (J). pap. 6.95 (***978-0-15-206107-4(X)*** , Magic Carpet Bks.) Harcourt Children's Bks.

Varonka, Steve. Hard Coal Times: Pennsylvania Anthracite Stories, Vol. 1. 2003. (Illus.). 40p. (J). 4.72 (978-0-9709630-2-4(5)) Coal Hole Productions.

Vasco, Irene. El Dedo de Estefania y Otros Cuentos. 2003. Tr. of Estefania's Finger & Other Tales. (SPA., Illus.). 47p. (J). (gr. k-3). (978-958-8061-54-2(7)) Distribuidora y Editora Aguilar, Altea, Taurus en el Sello Alfaguara S.A.

Velthuijs, Max. Sapo y el Ancho Mundo. 1999. (Coleccion Sapo). (SPA., Illus.). 28p. (J). (ps-3). 14.99 (978-980-257-229-8(2) , KM2292) Ekare, Ediciones VEN. *Dist:* Kane/Miller Bk. Pubs., Inc., Lectorum Pubns., Inc.

Vergara, Ricardo Baquero, tr. Cuentos Clasicos II. (Illus.). 80p. (J). (978-958-04-7550-7(4)) Norma S.A.

Verhoeff, Carolyn. All about Johnnie Jones. 2006. 77.99 (***978-1-4280-3885-1(X)***); pap. 70.99 (***978-1-4280-3905-6(8)***) IndyPublish.com.

Vicente, Marta. La Cajita. 2004. (Los Especiales de A la Orilla Del Viento Ser.). (SPA., Illus.). 32p. (J). (ps-7). per. 12.95 (978-968-16-7181-5(3)) Fondo de Cultura Economica USA.

Vidal, Cesar. El Perro de Gudrum. 1999. (SPA.). 208p. 9.95 (978-84-239-9057-3(5)) Espasa Calpe, S.A. ESP. *Dist:* Libros Sin Fronteras.

Villarreal, Carlos C. The Light Beneath the Shadow: Sharing God's Love with Your Child as You Read Together: A Bedtime Story Intended to Awaken Your Parental Christian Spirit. 2006. 48p. pap. 12.95 (978-1-4241-1247-0(8)) PublishAmerica, Inc.

Villaseñor, Victor. Walking Stars: Stories of Magic & Power. 2003. (gr. 7-12). lib. bdg. 19.90 (978-0-613-89452-4(9)); 1998. 180p. (YA). (gr. 8-12). lib. bdg. 22.20 (978-0-613-59028-0(7)) Tandem Library Bks.

Villegas, Eduardo. El Baul de los Cuentos. (SPA.). (J). 7.98 (978-970-643-159-2(4)) Selector, S.A. de C.V. MEX. *Dist:* AIMS International Bks., Inc.

Villnerve, Janice C. Mama Cat's Adventures in Child Training Presents No Whining! 2004. (Illus.). 32p. (J). lib. bdg. 14.95 (978-0-9746013-0-4(6)) Paradigm Publishing.

Villoro, Carmen & Perez, Federico. Amarina y el Viejo Pesadilla y Otros Cuentos. (Torre de Papel Ser.). (SPA.). (J). (gr. 2). 7.95 (978-958-04-3650-8(9)) Norma S.A. COL. *Dist:* Distribuidora Norma, Inc.

Virtuous Short Stories of Fun & Prose. 2003. (Illus.). 90p. (YA). per. (978-0-9742122-2-7(9)) Aunty Ems Boutique.

Volke, Gordon. The Big Posh Yacht. Bowler, Colin, illus. 2004. 24p. pap. 7.00 (978-1-84161-116-7(6)) Ravette Publishing, Ltd. GBR. *Dist:* Parkwest Pubns., Inc.

—The Nasty Black Stuff. Bowler, Colin, illus. 2004. 24p. pap. 7.00 (978-1-84161-119-8(0)) Ravette Publishing, Ltd. GBR. *Dist:* Parkwest Pubns., Inc.

—Old Grumpus & Other Stories. 2004. (Illus.). 91p. 5.00 (978-1-84161-035-1(6)) Ravette Publishing, Ltd. GBR. *Dist:* Parkwest Pubns., Inc.

—The Pirate's Gold. Bowler, Colin, illus. 2004. 24p. pap. 7.00 (978-1-84161-117-4(4)) Ravette Publishing, Ltd. GBR. *Dist:* Parkwest Pubns., Inc.

—A Spider for Tea & Other Stories. 2004. (Illus.). 90p. 5.00 (978-1-84161-036-8(4)) Ravette Publishing, Ltd. GBR. *Dist:* Parkwest Pubns., Inc.

Von Drogas, Johann. Those Famous Fairy Tales, What Really Happened? 2000. (Illus.). 180p. (YA). (gr. 7-12). pap. 5.90 (978-0-9620016-6-6(X)) Great Lakes Publishing Co.

von Eggers, Jennie, et al, creators. Times Tales. 2003. (J). spiral bd. 13.95 (978-0-9762024-1-7(7)) Trigger Memory Systems.

von Konigslow, Andrea Wayne. Toilet Tales. von Konigslow, Andrea Wayne, illus. 2003. (Illus.). 24p. (J). (gr. k-ps). (Toddler Ser.). pap. 5.95 (978-0-920303-13-9(7)); (Toddler Ser.). lib. bdg. 15.95 (978-0-920303-14-6(5)); (Annikins Ser.: Vol. 6). pap. 1.25 (978-0-920303-81-8(1)) Annick Pr., Ltd. CAN. *Dist:* Firefly Bks., Ltd.

Voyles, Robert. The Golden Eclipse. 1999. 175p. (YA). (gr. 7-12). pap. 9.95 (978-0-9665055-1-1(4)) Hallmark Emporium.

Vv. Clasicos para Sonar: Bambi, Mago de Oz, Pulgarcita, Sirenita (Libro Rosa) 2003. (SPA.). 84p. 18.95 (978-84-305-9976-9(2)) Susaeta Ediciones, S.A. ESP. *Dist:* Giron Bks.

—Clasicos para Sonar: Blancanieves, Gato C/Botas, Caperucita (Libro Rojo) 2003. (SPA.). 86p. 18.95 (978-84-305-9975-2(4)) Susaeta Ediciones, S.A. ESP. *Dist:* Giron Bks.

—Clasicos Para Sonar: Libro de la Selva, Casita Chocolate, Mago Merlin. 2003. (SPA.). 96p. 18.95 (978-84-305-9974-5(6)) Susaeta Ediciones, S.A. ESP. *Dist:* Giron Bks.

—Clasicos para Sonar: Pinocho, Bella y la Bestia, Alicia (Libro Verde) 2003. (SPA.). 82p. 18.95 (978-84-305-9977-6(0)) Susaeta Ediciones, S.A. ESP. *Dist:* Giron Bks.

Wagner, Paul. Jock Jokes: And Other Stories. 2004. 236p. (YA). pap. 15.95 (978-0-595-30757-9(4)) iUniverse, Inc.

Wake Up! Individual Title Six-Packs. (Story Steps Ser.). (gr. k-2). 29.00 (978-0-7635-9581-4(0)) Rigby Education.

Walder, Chaim. Kids Speak, Vol. 4. 21.99 (978-1-58330-442-6(8)) Feldheim Pubs.

Walker, Brian, illus. Adventure Stories. 2004. (Red Hot Reads Ser.). 256p. (J). (gr. 5-9). pap. 6.95 (978-0-7534-5718-4(0) , Kingfisher) Houghton Mifflin Co. Trade & Reference Div.

Walker, Neva M. Grandma's Teddy Bear Tales. Coonce, Phillip, illus. 2002. 144p. (J). (gr. 2-7). pap. (978-0-9721303-0-1(6)) Neva's Arts & Crafts.

Walker, Richard. The Barefoot Book of Trickster Tales. Munoz, Claudio, illus. 1998. 80p. (J). (gr. 4-7). 18.95 (978-1-902283-08-1(2)) Barefoot Bks., Inc.

Walker, Sally M. The 18 Penny Goose. Beier, Ellen, illus. 2002. (J). 12.34 (978-0-7587-5964-1(9)) Book Wholesalers, Inc.

—The 18 Penny Goose. Beier, Ellen, illus. 1999. (I Can Read Bks.). 64p. (J). (gr. k-3). pap. 3.99 (978-0-06-444250-3(0) , Harper Trophy) HarperCollins Pubs.

—The 18 Penny Goose. 1999. (I Can Read Bks.). (J). lib. bdg. 10.79 (978-0-606-15517-5(1)) Tandem Library Bks.

Wallace, Karen. Freaky Families- Cousin Cedric Goes. (Illus.). 64p. (J). 7.95 (978-0-14-038500-7(2)) Penguin Bks., Ltd. GBR. *Dist:* Trafalgar Square Publishing.

Walls, P. Abby: En busca del Tesoro. 2003. (Abby Ser.).Tr. of Abby: In Search of Treasure. pap. 6.99 (978-0-7899-0968-8(5)) Editorial Unilit.

Walsh, Ann. Beginnings: Stories of Canada's Past. 2005. (Illus.). 228p. (J). pap. 12.95 (978-0-921870-87-6(6)) Ronsdale Pr. CAN. *Dist:* Literary Pr. Group of Canada.

Walsh, Joanna. Amos Jellybean Gets It Right. 2005. (Illus.). (J). pap., pap. 9.99 (978-0-340-88231-3(X)) Headway GBR. *Dist:* Trafalgar Square Publishing.

Walsh, Maria Elena. Chaucha y Palito. Ink, Lancman, illus. 2003. (SPA.). 134p. (J). (gr. 5-8). pap. 11.95 (978-950-511-615-7(2)) Santillana USA Publishing Co., Inc.

S

—El Diablo Ingles. 2002. (SPA., Illus.). 62p. (J). (gr. 3-5). pap. 12.95 (978-950-511-627-0(6)) Santillana USA Publishing Co., Inc.

Walther, William. A Collection of Fairy Tales: Volume One. 2007. (YA). per. 12.95 (***978-0-9795087-0-7(3))*** Ctr. Stage Puppets.

Walton, O. F. Little Faith. 2002. (Illus.). 95p. 14.00 (978-1-929241-52-1(6)) Vision Forum, Inc., The.

Walton, Rick. Mini Mysteries: 20 Tricky Tales to Untangle. 2004. (gr. 3-6). lib. bdg. 16.40 (978-0-613-85506-8(X)) Tandem Library Bks.

Ware, Shirley. Just Kids. 2006. 52p. pap. 12.95 (978-1-4241-3194-5(4)) PublishAmerica, Inc.

Warner, Rex. Men & Gods: Myths & Legends of the Ancient Greeks. Gorey, Ward, illus. 2008. 296p. (J). 16.95 (***978-1-59017-263-6(9)*** , NYR Children's Collection) New York Review of Bks., Inc., The.

Warren, Jean. Storytime Ideas for Circle Time. Cubley, Kathleen, ed. Burris, Priscilla, illus. 2001. (Circle Time Book Ser.). 96p. (J). (ps-k). pap. 10.99 (978-1-57029-241-5(8) , WPH04903, Totline Pubns.) Schaffer, Frank Pubns.

Washington State Story Book. 2005. (J). 15.95 (978-1-59649-435-0(2)) Whispering Pine Pr., Inc.

Waters, Fiona, retold by. Sisters with Glass Hearts. 2000. (Illus.). 93p. (J). pap. 10.99 (978-0-7475-4709-9(2)) Bloomsbury Publishing Plc GBR. *Dist:* Independent Pubs. Group.

—Three Princesses: And Other Classic Fairy Tales. 2000. (Illus.). 95p. (J). pap. 10.99 (978-0-7475-4714-3(9)) Bloomsbury Publishing Plc GBR. *Dist:* Independent Pubs. Group.

—Widow & Her Daughters. 2000. (Illus.). 95p. (J). pap. 9.99 (978-0-7475-4719-8(X)) Bloomsbury Publishing Plc GBR. *Dist:* Independent Pubs. Group.

Watson, Margery. Ruffles & Danny or the Responsibility. 2005. pap. 22.95 (978-1-4191-0387-2(3)) Kessinger Publishing, LLC.

Watson, Viola. A Selection of Children's Short Stories. 2007. per. (***978-1-59581-349-7(7)*** , Brentwood Christian Pr.) Brentwood Communications Group.

Watt, Fiona & Wells, Rachel. That's Not My Train: Its Wheels Are Too Slippery. 2004. (Touchy-Feely Board Bks.). (SPA., Illus.). 10p. (J). (ps up). bds. 7.95 (978-0-7460-3779-9(1)) EDC Publishing.

Weaver, Irene. Glued Together: Brady's Country Kids. 2002. pap. 6.95 (978-1-930353-66-4(9)) Masthof Pr.

Webb, Beth. Fleabag & the Ring's End. 2000. (Fleabag Ser.). 208p. (J). pap. 8.99 (978-0-7459-4411-1(6) , Lion) Lion Hudson plc GBR. *Dist:* Independent Pubs. Group.

Webb, Mack Henry, Jr. Webb's Wondrous Tales Book 1. Webb, Celia, illus. 2006. 184p. (YA). per. 14.95 (978-0-9779576-1-3(6)) Pilinut Pr., Inc.

Weber, Lou, ed. Spooky Stories. 2005. 24p. (J). bds. 10.98 (978-1-4127-3385-4(5) , 3911601) Publications International, Ltd.

—Stories That Go Carry Case. 2005. 48p. (J). bds. 7.98 (978-1-4127-3467-7(3) , 7251700) Publications International, Ltd.

—3 Minute Christmas Stories. 2004. (Illus.). 160p. (J). 9.98 (978-1-4127-3245-1(X) , 7235300) Publications International, Ltd.

Weed, Thurlow R. Camel Fables from the Sailors of the Sudan. 2004. 84p. pap. 15.95 (978-0-7414-2229-3(8)) Infinity Publishing.

Weinfeld, Chaya Baila. A Breath of Fresh Air. 2000. 186p. (YA). pap. 11.95 (978-0-9670705-4-4(6)) Israel Bk. Shop.

Weiss, Jerry M. From One Experience to Another: Stories about Turning Points. 1999. (J). 11.64 (978-0-606-15782-7(4)) Tandem Library Bks.

Weiss, M. Jerry. Big City Cool: Short Stories about Urban Youth. 2002. (gr. 7-12). lib. bdg. 17.60 (978-0-613-84993-7(0)) Tandem Library Bks.

Weiss, M. Jerry & Weiss, Helen S. Dreams & Visions. 256p. (J). 2007. 5.99 (978-0-7653-5107-4(2)); 2006. 19.95 (978-0-7653-1249-5(2)) Doherty, Tom Assocs., LLC. (Starscape).

Weiss, M. Jerry & Weiss, Helen S., eds. The Big City Cool: Short Stories about Urban Youth. 2002. 192p. pap. 8.95 (978-0-89255-278-8(6)) Persea Bks., Inc.

Wellander, J. D. Tales Written in a Forest. 2000. 108p. (J). pap. 9.95 (978-0-595-13336-9(3)) iUniverse, Inc.

Wenke, Christine. Willa's Secret. 2005. 160p. (Orig.). pap. (978-0-7344-0675-0(4) , Lothian Bks.) Hachette Livre Australia.

West, Colin. Long Tales, Short Tales & Tall Tales. 2000. (Illus.). 94p. (J). pap. 6.95 (978-0-552-52798-9(X)) Transworld Publishers Ltd. GBR. *Dist:* Trafalgar Square Publishing.

Westall, Robert. Voices in the Wind. 2003. 178p. (J). mass mkt. 8.99 (978-0-330-35218-5(0)) Pan Macmillan GBR. *Dist:* Trafalgar Square Publishing.

Wetherill, Steve. Shape up Goz. 2005. (Baby Goz Ser.). (Illus.). 16p. (J). (ps-7). 5.95 (978-1-84507-077-9(1)) Lincoln, Frances Ltd. GBR. *Dist:* Perseus Distribution.

Wharton, Edith. Edith Wharton. McConnell, James, illus. 2004. (Great American Short Stories Ser.). 74p. (J). lib. bdg. 23.33 (978-0-8368-4256-2(1)) Stevens, Gareth Inc.

What Do I Look Like? (Peek A Boo Pockets Ser.). 12p. (J). bds. (978-2-7643-0106-7(5)) Phidal Publishing, Inc./Editions Phidal, Inc.

Wheeler, Joe. The Candle in the Forest: And Other Christmas Stories Children Love. 2007. 96p. 16.99 (***978-1-4165-4219-3(1)*** , Howard Bks.) Simon & Schuster.

Wheeler, Joe L. The Candle in the Forest: And Other Christmas Stories Children Love. 2007. (J). (***978-1-58229-707-1(X)*** , Howard Bks.) Simon & Schuster.

Whitehouse, Patricia. Que Puede Saltar? Abello, Patricia, tr. 2004. (SPA.). 24p. (J). 12.95 (978-1-4034-4386-1(6)) Heinemann Library.

—Que Puede Volar? Abello, Patricia, tr. 2004. (SPA.). 24p. (J). 12.95 (978-1-4034-4385-4(8)) Heinemann Library.

Whitlock, Jennifer. The Principle Woods Book of Courage. 2000. 72p. (J). mass mkt. 14.95 (978-0-9700601-0-5(6)) Principle Woods, Inc.

—The Principle Woods Book of Honesty. Shore, Kevin, illus. 2001. 80p. (J). (gr. k-3). 14.95 (978-0-9700601-6-7(5)) Principle Woods, Inc.

—The Principle Woods Book of Work. 2000. 60p. (J). mass mkt. 14.95 (978-0-9700601-1-2(4)) Principle Woods, Inc.

Who Does That? (Peek A Boo Pockets Ser.). 12p. (J). bds. (978-2-89393-977-3(5)) Phidal Publishing, Inc./Editions Phidal, Inc.

Whybrow, Ian, compiled by. The Kingfisher Book of Classic Christmas Stories. 2004. (Illus.). 144p. (J). (gr. 3-5). 19.95 (978-0-7534-5732-0(6) , Kingfisher) Houghton Mifflin Co. Trade & Reference Div.

Wiggin, Kate Douglas. The Talking Beasts. 2006. 80.99 (***978-1-4280-1893-8(X))*** IndyPublish.com.

Wilbur's Wild Ride & Other Stories: Individual Title Six-Pack. (Story Steps Ser.). (gr. k-2). 42.00 (978-0-7635-9598-2(5)) Rigby Education.

Wilde, Oscar. Cuentos de Oscar Wilde. (SPA.). (YA). 8.95 (978-958-04-2378-2(4)) Norma S.A. COL. *Dist:* Distribuidora Norma, Inc.

—El Joven Rey y Otros Cuentos. 1998. (SPA.). 208p. (gr. 6-8). (978-84-239-2781-4(4)) Espasa Calpe, S.A.

—Oscar Wilde. Holland, Merlin, ed. Brierley, G. L., illus. 2005. (Stories for Young People Ser.). 48p. (J). (gr. 7-9). 14.95 (978-1-4027-1514-3(5)) Sterling Publishing Co., Inc.

Wilde, Oscar & Irving, Washington. Narraciones Fantasticas. 2000. (SPA.). (J). (gr. 9-12). pap. (978-968-19-0444-9(3)) Aguilar Editorial.

Willard, Eliza. Jackie Chan Super Special: Day of the Dragon. 2003. (gr. k-3). lib. bdg. 14.15 (978-0-613-72544-6(1)) Tandem Library Bks.

Williams, Ann. The Multifarious Adventures of Fred the Raindrop. 2005. 22p. (J). 8.00 (978-1-4116-4175-4(2)) Lulu.com.

Williams, Arlene L. Tales from the Dragon's Cave: Peacemaking Stories for Everyone. Williams, Arlene L., illus. 2nd ed. 2002. 160p. (J). pap. 12.95 (978-0-9605444-8-6(8)) Waking Light Pr., The.

Williams, Leslie. Que Hay Detras... Arbol? 2000. Tr. of What Is Behind the Tree?. (SPA.). (J). 13.50 (978-84-7183-342-6(5)) El Hogar y La Moda, S.A. ESP. *Dist:* AIMS International Bks., Inc.

Williams, Marcia, illus. & retold by. Charles Dickens & Friends: Five Lively Retellings. Williams, Marcia, retold by. 2006. 48p. (J). (gr. 3-7). pap. 7.99 (978-0-7636-3198-7(1)) Candlewick Pr.

Williams, Mary. Spellbound. 2001. 72p. (J). pap. 9.00 (978-0-8059-5470-8(8)) Dorrance Publishing Co., Inc.

Williford, Lex. Scribner Anthology of Contemporary Short Fiction. 1999. (978-0-606-18627-8(1)) Tandem Library Bks.

Wilson, Budge. The Leaving. 176p. (J). mass mkt. 6.95 (978-0-7736-7363-2(6)) Stoddart Kids CAN. *Dist:* Fitzhenry & Whiteside, Ltd.

Wilson, Greg. Three Sensible Adventures. Lytle, William S., illus. 1999. 56p. (J). (gr. k-3). lib. bdg. 18.95 (978-1-55037-599-2(7)) Annick Pr., Ltd. CAN. *Dist:* Firefly Bks., Ltd.

—Three Sensible Adventures. 1999. (gr. k-3). lib. bdg. 16.40 (978-0-613-27242-1(0)) Tandem Library Bks.

Wilson, Mary. Kopper "K" Kidds & Corky. 2003. per. (978-1-59196-169-7(6)) Instantpublisher.com.

Windham, Kathryn Tucker. It's Christmas! Crump, Buz, illus. 2002. 32p. 15.95 (978-1-57966-031-4(2)) River City Publishing.

The Winds of March: A Katie Rose Belford Story. 2000. (Katie Rose/Stacy Belford Ser.). (YA). pap. 12.95 (978-1-930009-11-0(9)) Image Cascade Publishing.

Winners: Poems & Stories, 2003 Spring Writing Contest. 2003. (J). 5.00 (978-0-9702646-2-6(3)); (YA). 5.00 (978-0-9702646-3-3(1)) New Sweden Pr.

Wishing Stars: Tales for Children. 5.95 (978-1-57054-560-3(X)) Klutz.

Wizard Academies I: The Heart of Darkness. 2006. 658p. pap. 23.72 (978-1-4116-7787-6(0)) Lulu.com.

Wolf, Ema. Silencio, Ninos! Y Otros Cuentos. Pez, illus. (Torre de Papel Ser.).Tr. of Quiet, Children! & Other Stories. (SPA.). 116p. (J). (gr. 4-6). 8.95 (978-958-04-3927-1(3)) Norma S.A. COL. *Dist:* Distribuidora Norma, Inc.

Wood, Kim Marie. Forelocks, Fetlocks & Horse Tales. Graham, Kimberly, illus. 1999. 110p. (J). per. 5.95 (978-0-9671978-2-1(1)) Syncopated Pr.

Wood, Steve. Courageous Cats' Club: "Sticks & Stones" & "The Beast in the Night" Fox, Woody, illus. 2004. 96p. (J). pap. 9.99 (978-0-7459-4832-4(4) , Lion) Lion Hudson plc GBR. *Dist:* Independent Pubs. Group.

Wooden Soldier. 2004. (J). per. (978-1-57657-383-9(4)) Paradise Pr., Inc.

Woods, Carol. Everybody Knows Rabbits Don't Like Mice. 2002. (Illus.). 32p. (J). 14.95 (978-0-9714356-9-8(3)) A-Brite Look Publishing.

Woods, Cindy Smith. Once Inside A Storybook... Good Morals in Short Stories to Encourage Correct Behavior in the Little Ones in Your Life. 2006. 59p. pap. 12.95 (978-1-4241-2905-8(2)) PublishAmerica, Inc.

Woody, Velma B. Branscum. Bandits, Bears & Backaches: A Collection of Short Stories Based on Arkansas History. 2004. (J). per. 12.50 (978-0-9708574-2-2(X)) Butler Ctr. for Arkansas Studies.

Wormell, Christopher. Dos Ramas. 2004. (SPA.). 32p. (J). 20.99 (978-84-261-3354-0(1)) Juventud, Editorial ESP. *Dist:* Lectorum Pubns., Inc.

Wrede, Patricia C. Book of Enchantments. 2005. 256p. (J). (gr. 5). pap. 5.95 (978-0-15-205508-0(8) , Magic Carpet Bks.) Harcourt Children's Bks.

Wright, Lloyd. Stories for Gramp's Little Friends. 2004. 158p. (J). 22.95 (978-0-595-66287-6(0)); pap. 12.95 (978-0-595-31266-5(7)) iUniverse, Inc.

Writers Corps Youth Staff, ed. Smart Mouth: Poetry & Prose. Sorrenzo, Joey et al, illus. 2000. 156p. (YA). pap. 12.95 (978-1-888048-05-6(0) , WritersCorps Bks.) San Francisco Art Commission, The.

Wynne-Jones, Tim. Some of the Kinder Planets. 2000. (Illus.). (J). (gr. 4-7). pap. 7.95 (978-0-88899-418-9(4)) Groundwood Bks. CAN. *Dist:* Transition Vendor.

Yaber, Armando. Mariana Sale el Sol. 2005. (SPA.). (YA). per. 9.99 (978-0-9765467-1-9(X)) Creative Bk. Pubs.

Yacowitz, Caryn. The Jade Stones. 2005. (Illus.). 32p. (J). 15.95 (978-1-58980-359-6(0)) Pelican Publishing Co., Inc.

Yamamoto, Lani. Alberto. Moreno Llort, Lluisa, tr. Yamamoto, Lani, illus. 2005. (SPA., Illus.). 28p. (J). 14.95 (978-84-9801-010-7(1)) Blume ESP. *Dist:* Independent Pubs. Group.

Yeahpau, Thomas M. X-Indian Chronicles: The Book of Mausape. 2006. 240p. (YA). (gr. 9). 16.99 (978-0-7636-2706-5(2)) Candlewick Pr.

Yellow Bananas, 11 bks. Incl. Amina's Blanket. Dunmore, Helen. Dainton, Paul, illus. 2002. lib. bdg. (978-0-7787-0938-1(8)); Break in the Chain. D'Lacey, Chris. Carey, Joanna, illus. 2002. lib. bdg. (978-0-7787-0931-2(0)); Colly's Barn. Morpurgo, Michael. Andrew, Ian P., illus. 2002. lib. bdg. (978-0-7787-0932-9(9)); Dragon Trouble. Lively, Penelope. Rowland, Andrew, illus. 2002. lib. bdg. (978-0-7787-0941-1(8)); Fine Feathered Friend. Gavin, Jamila. Williams, Dan, illus. 2002. lib. bdg. (978-0-7787-0939-8(6)); Jo-Jo the Melon Donkey. Morpurgo, Michael. Kerins, Tony, illus. 2002. lib. bdg. (978-0-7787-0942-8(6)); Monster from Underground. Cross, Gillian. Priestley, Chris, illus. 2002. lib. bdg. (978-0-7787-0935-0(3)); My Brother Bernadette. Wilson, Jacqueline. Roberts, David, illus. 2002. lib. bdg. (978-0-7787-0940-4(X)); Soccer Star. Hardcastle, Michael. Cox, Ken, illus. 2002. lib. bdg. (978-0-7787-0933-6(7)); Stranger from Somewhere in Time. McBratney, Sam. Chatterton, Martin & Chatterton, Ann, illus. 2003. lib. bdg. (978-0-7787-0937-4(X)); Who's a Clever Girl? Impey, Rose. Amstutz, Andre, illus. 2002. lib. bdg. (978-0-7787-0930-5(2)); 48p. (J). (gr. 3-4). 2003. (978-0-7787-0929-9(9)); Set pap. (978-0-7787-0975-6(2)) Crabtree Publishing Co.

Yes Yep Yea Hooray. 2000. 40p. (J). (978-0-9674165-2-6(3)) Eveott Enterprises, Inc.

Yip, Mingmei. Chinese Children's Favorite Stories. 2004. (Illus.). 96p. 16.95 (978-0-8048-3589-3(6)) Tuttle Publishing.

Yolen, Jane. Open Sesame. 1999. (Illus.). (J). 17.99 (978-0-7636-0627-5(8)) Candlewick Pr.

—Twelve Impossible Things Before Breakfast: Stories. 2001. (Illus.). 192p. (YA). (gr. 5 up). pap. 6.00 (978-0-15-216444-7(8) , Magic Carpet Bks.) Harcourt Children's Bks.

—Twelve Impossible Things Before Breakfast: Stories. 2001. (gr. 7-12). lib. bdg. 14.15 (978-0-613-35476-9(1)) Tandem Library Bks.

Yolen, Jane & Mannheim, Linda, eds. The Liars' Book. Hawkes, Kevin, illus. 1999. (J). 16.95 (978-0-590-48999-7(2) , Blue Sky Pr., The) Scholastic, Inc.

Yoon, Salina. Fire Truck. Yoon, Salina, illus. 2005. (Illus.). 10p. (J). (ps-1). bds. 5.99 (978-0-8431-1395-2(2) , Price Stern Sloan) Penguin Group (USA) Inc.

Yorinks, Arthur. The Floating Cow & Other Stories. 2000. (Illus.). (J). pap. (978-0-439-09256-2(6)) Scholastic, Inc.

Young Ray Hicks Learns the Jack Tales. 2004. 15.99 (978-0-9706527-5-1(5)); per. 8.00 (978-0-9706527-6-8(3)) Montville Pr.

Youngquist, D. M. Ghosts of Interstate 80. 2007. (Illus.). 180p. (YA). per. 9.95 (***978-1-57166-459-4(9))*** Quixote Pr.

You're Invited to a Halloween Party! 1998. (J). pap. 9.95 incl. audio (978-1-887120-03-6(3)) Production Assocs., Inc.

Yourgrau, Barry. Nasty Book. 2005. 192p. (J). (gr. k-9). 11.99 (978-0-06-057978-4(1) , Cotler, Joanna Books) HarperCollins Pubs.

—NASTYbook. 2005. 192p. (J). (gr. k-9). lib. bdg. 13.89 (978-0-06-057979-1(X)) HarperCollins Pubs.

Yourgrau, Barry. Yet Another NASTYbook: MiniNasties. Swaab, Neil, illus. 2007. 160p. (J). lib. bdg. 13.89 (***978-0-06-077677-0(3)*** , Cotler, Joanna Books) HarperCollins Pubs.

Yoyo Books Staff. At Home: One Minute Goodnight Stories. 2004. 40p. bds. 12.95 (978-90-5843-583-5(0)) YoYo Bks. BEL. *Dist:* National Bk. Network.

—At School: One Minute Goodnight Stories. 2004. 40p. bds. 12.95 (978-90-5843-582-8(2)) YoYo Bks. BEL. *Dist:* National Bk. Network.

Yuki, Kaori. Godchild, Vol. 4. 2007. (GodChild Ser.). 200p. (YA). pap. 8.99 (978-1-4215-0478-0(2)) Viz Media.

Zebrowski, Marianne. Babka's Serenade. Teis, Kyra, illus. 2002. 9.95 (978-1-56123-161-4(4) , BASC) Centering Corp.

Zeman, Ludmila. Sindbad in the Land of Giants. 2001. (FRE., Illus.). 32p. (J). (gr. 1 up). 17.95 (978-0-88776-461-5(4)) Tundra Bks., Inc./Livres Toundra, Inc. CAN. *Dist:* Random Hse., Inc.

Zevallos, Dorys, ed. Leyendas Americanas de la Tierra. 1999. (J). (978-956-240-271-2(1)) Arrayan Editores S.A.

Zimelman, Nathan. Little Red Baseball Stockings & Other Stories. 2005. 80p. pap. 11.95 (978-1-889658-22-3(7)) New Canaan Publishing Co. LLC.

Zoehfeld, Kathleen Weidner. My Very First Winnie the Pooh: Roo's New Babysitter. 2005. 32p. (J). No.13. 11.99 (978-0-7868-3160-9(X)); No.14. 11.99 (978-0-7868-3161-6(8)) Disney Pr.

Zurita, Fidel Gonzalez. El Nido de la Ciguena. Diego, Rapi, illus. 2003. (SPA.). 32p. (J). (gr. 3-5). pap. 9.95 (978-968-19-0609-2(8)) Santillana USA Publishing Co., Inc.

Zwemer, M. Samuel. Topsy-Turvy Land (Arabia Pictured for Ch. 2006. 77.99 (***978-1-4280-4803-4(0));*** pap. 70.99 (***978-1-4280-4810-2(3))*** IndyPublish.com.

3 Minutes Nursery Stories. (Illus.). 160p. (J). 9.98 (978-0-7853-7821-1(9) , 7177000) Publications International, Ltd.

5 Minute Bedtime Stories: Sleepy Time Stories. 2001. (SPA.). (J). (978-1-58805-137-0(4)) DS-Max USA, Inc.

7 Cuentos para antes de Dormir.Tr. of Seven Bedtime Stories. (SPA.). (J). (978-84-7773-016-3(4)); Vol. 2. (978-84-7773-302-7(3)); Vol. 4. (978-84-7773-017-0(2)) Grafalco, S.A.

12 Bedtime Stories. pap. 10.98 (978-0-7853-7921-8(5)) Publications International, Ltd.

16 Cuentos Latinoamericanos. 2002. (SPA.). 224p. (YA). pap. 15.95 (978-980-257-190-1(3) , EK5912) Ekare, Ediciones VEN. *Dist:* Lectorum Pubns., Inc.

101 Stories to Tell & Write. (Illus.). (J). (gr. 3-6). pap. (978-1-876367-67-1(9)) Wizard Bks.

365 Fabulas.Tr. of Three Hundred Sixty-Five Fables. (SPA.). 208p. (J). (978-84-7773-031-6(8)) Grafalco, S.A.

1000 Stories & Rhymes. 2002. 1024p. (J). 24.98 (978-0-7525-9096-7(0)) Parragon, Inc.

SHOWBOATS—FICTION

Sage, James. Showboat. 1999. (Illus.). 32p. (J). 16.00 (978-0-15-201398-1(9)) Harcourt Trade Pubs.

SHRIMPS

Coldiron, Deborah. Shrimp. 2007. (Underwater World Ser.). (ENG., Illus.). 32p. (J). (gr. k-4). lib. bdg. 24.21 (***978-1-59928-814-7(1)*** , Buddy Bks.) ABDO Publishing Co.

Harman, Amanda. Shrimp. 2004. (Nature's Children Ser.). (Illus.). 48p. (J). (978-0-7172-5972-4(2) , Grolier) Scholastic Library Publishing.

Nuzzolo, Deborah. Shrimp. 2008. (J). (***978-1-4296-0035-4(7)*** , Pebble Bks.) Capstone Pr., Inc.

Stone, Lynn M. Shrimp. 2003. (Science under the Sea Discovery Library Ser.). 24p. (gr. 2-5). 14.95 (978-1-58952-321-0(0)) Rourke Publishing, LLC.

SHRUBS

Aldrich, William & Williamson, Don. Tree & Shrub Gardening for Illinois, Vol. 1. rev. ed. 2004. (Illus.). 352p. (gr. 4). pap. 18.95 (978-1-55105-404-9(3)) Lone Pine Publishing USA.

Burine. Shrublands. 2003. (Illus.). 64p. pap. 9.50 (978-1-4109-0015-9(0)) Raintree.

De Medeiros, Michael. Chaparral. 2006. (J). (978-1-59036-439-0(2)); (Illus.). 32p. (gr. 4-6). lib. bdg. 26.00 (978-1-59036-438-3(4)) Weigl Pubs., Inc.

Hower, Fred & Beck, Alison. Tree & Shrub Gardening for Ohio, Vol. 1. rev. ed. 2004. (Illus.). 360p. (gr. 4). pap. 18.95 (978-1-55105-402-5(7)) Lone Pine Publishing USA.

Shrublands. 2003. (Biomes Atlas Ser.). (Illus.). pap. 48.30 (978-1-4109-0250-4(1)) Raintree.

Tanem, Bob & Williamson, Don. Tree & Shrub Gardening for Northern California. rev. ed. 2003. (Illus.). 360p. (gr. 4). pap. 18.95 (978-1-55105-275-5(X)) Lone Pine Publishing USA.

Wood, Timothy D. & Beck, Alison. Tree & Shrub Gardening for Michigan. rev. ed. 2003. (Illus.). 352p. (J). (gr. 4). pap. 18.95 (978-1-55105-347-9(0)) Lone Pine Publishing USA.

SIAM

see Thailand

SIBERIA (RUSSIA)

Buell, Janet. Ancient Horsemen of Siberia. 1998. (Time Travelers Ser.: 8). (Illus.). 64p. (gr. 5-8). lib. bdg. 25.90 (978-0-7613-3005-9(4) , Twenty-First Century Bks.) Lerner Publishing Group.

Holt, Rinehart and Winston Staff. The Endless Steppe. 3rd ed. 2002. pap., stu. ed. 13.20 (978-0-03-067528-7(6)) Holt, Rinehart & Winston.

—The Endless Steppe: With Connections. 3rd ed. 2002. 14.64 (978-0-03-067527-0(8)) Holt, Rinehart & Winston.

Lengyel, Emil. Siberia. 2004. reprint ed. pap. 36.95 (978-1-4191-0872-3(7)) Kessinger Publishing, LLC.

Stephanie, St Pierre. Siberian Tigers. 2001. (In the Wild Ser.). (Illus.). 24p. (J). (ps-3). lib. bdg. 21.36 (978-1-58810-110-5(X)) Heinemann Library.

SIBERIA (RUSSIA)—FICTION

Caffrey-Kira, Albina. The Bear Who Loves Apples. 2006. 25.00 (978-0-8059-9128-4(X)) Dorrance Publishing Co., Inc.

Cross, Gillian. Phoning a Dead Man. 2002. 256p. (J). (gr. 7 up). 16.95 (978-0-8234-1685-1(2)) Holiday Hse., Inc.

Halam, Ann. Siberia: A Novel. 2005. (J). (gr. 7). 272p. 16.95 (978-0-385-74650-2(4)); 262p. lib. bdg. 18.99 (978-0-385-90885-6(7)) Random Hse. Children's Bks. (Lamb, Wendy).

Ingram, W. J. Evelyn. Saint Crispin & Other Quaint Conceits. 2005. pap. 24.95 (978-1-4179-6255-6(0)) Kessinger Publishing, LLC.

Schuch, Steve. A Symphony of Whales. Sylvada, Peter, illus. 2002. 32p. (J). (gr. 1-4). pap. 7.00 (978-0-15-216548-2(7) , Voyager Bks./Libros Viajeros) Harcourt Children's Bks.

—Symphony of Whales. 2002. (gr. k-3). lib. bdg. 14.15 (978-0-613-56636-0(X)) Tandem Library Bks.

Whelan, Gloria. The Impossible Journey. 2004. 256p. (J). (gr. 5 up). reprint ed. pap. 5.99 (978-0-06-441083-0(8) , Harper Trophy) HarperCollins Pubs.
—The Impossible Journey. 2004. 248p. (J). (gr. k-9). per. 14.30 (978-0-613-99970-0(3)) Tandem Library Bks.

SIBLING RIVALRY

Godfrey, Jan. Sam's New Baby. Coulson, Jane, illus. 1998. 32p. (J). (ps-1). 2.99 (978-0-687-09570-4(0)) Abingdon Pr.
Vogel, Elizabeth. Dealing with Being the Oldest Child in Your Family. 2000. (Conflict Resolution Library). (Illus.). 24p. (J). (gr. 3). lib. bdg. 18.75 (978-0-8239-5409-4(9) , PowerKids Pr.) Rosen Publishing Group, Inc., The.

SIBLING RIVALRY—FICTION

Al Shaikh, Latifa. I'm Still Waiting for that Chocolate. 2007. 52p. (YA). per. 8.95 (***978-0-595-42982-0(3)***) iUniverse, Inc.
Alley, R. W. Bratty Brothers & Selfish Sisters: All about Sibling Rivalry. Alley, R. W., illus. 2007. (J). per. 7.95 (***978-0-87029-404-4(0)***) Abbey Pr.
Blackaby, Susan. One up for Brad. Epstein, Len, illus. 2006. (Read-It! Readers Ser.). (J). 19.93 (978-1-4048-2418-8(0)) Picture Window Bks.
Blume, Judy. Soupy Saturdays with the Pain & the Great One. Stevenson, James, illus. 2007. 128p. (J). (gr. k-4). lib. bdg. 16.99 (***978-0-385-90324-0(3));*** 12.99 (***978-0-385-73305-2(4)***) Random Hse. Children's Bks. (Delacorte Bks. for Young Readers).
Blume, Judy. Superfudge. 2007. (Fudge Ser.). 192p. (J). (gr. 2). 5.99 (978-0-14-240880-3(8) , Puffin) Penguin Group (USA) Inc.
Clark, Emma Chichester. Mimi's Book of Opposites. Clark, Emma Chichester, illus. 2004. (Illus.). 24p. (J). 9.95 (978-1-57091-574-1(1)) Charlesbridge Publishing, Inc.
De Groat, Diane. Mother, You're the Best! (but Sister, You're a Pest!) 2008. 32p. (J). 16.99 (***978-0-06-123899-4(6));*** lib. bdg. 17.89 (***978-0-06-123900-7(3)***) HarperCollins Pubs.
Duke, Kate. The Tale of Pip & Squeak. 2007. 32p. (J). (ps). 16.99 (978-0-525-47777-8(2) , Dutton Juvenile) Penguin Group (USA) Inc.
Enderle, Judith Ross & Gordon, Stephanie Jacob. Smile, Principessa! Litzinger, Rosanne & Curmi, Serena, illus. 2007. 40p. (J). (ps-3). 16.99 (978-1-4169-1004-6(2) , McElderry, Margaret K.) Simon & Schuster Children's Publishing.
Feeney, Josephine. Holy Terrors. 142p. 2001. pap. 7.99 (978-0-00-675533-3(X)); 2000. (Illus.). (YA). 19.99 (978-0-00-185745-2(2) , HarperSport) HarperCollins Pubs. Ltd. GBR. *Dist:* Trafalgar Square Publishing.
Figiel, Lisa. Another Bird in Our Nest. 2007. (J). per. 6.99 (***978-1-60247-356-0(0)***) Tate Publishing & Enterprises, L.L.C.
Forsyth, Christine. Two on One. 2005. (Sports Stories Ser.). 112p. (J). (gr. 3-8). (***978-1-55028-901-5(2));*** 7.95 (978-1-55028-900-8(4)) Lorimer, James & Co., Ltd., Pubs. CAN. *Dist:* Casemate Pubs. & Bk. Distributors, LLC.
Friedman, Laurie. Mallory vs. Max. Schmitz, Tamara, illus. 2006. (J). pap. 5.95 (978-1-57505-863-4(4) , First Avenue Editions) Lerner Publishing Group.
Friedman, Laurie B. Mallory vs. Max. Schmitz, Tamara, illus. 2005. 160p. (J). (ps-k). 15.95 (978-1-57505-795-8(6)) Lerner Publishing Group.
Gaetz, Dayle Campbell. Spoiled Rotten. 2005. (Orca Currents Ser.). 112p. (J). (gr. 4-10). pap. 7.95 (978-1-55143-474-2(1)) Orca Bk. Pubs. USA.
Gray, Keith. Oe10,000. Edwards, Mark, illus. 2001. 73p. (J). pap. 7.50 (978-0-7497-4351-2(4)) Egmont Bks., Ltd. GBR. *Dist:* Independent Pubs. Group.
Henbit & the Roly-Poly. 2007. (J). (***978-0-9791982-2-9(4)***) Donnellan, Martha.
Henbit & the Roly-Poly - Large Print Specially Formatted Edition. 2007. (J). (***978-0-9791982-3-6(2)***) Donnellan, Martha.
Henkes, Kevin. Julius, the Baby of the World. Henkes, Kevin, illus. 2003. (Illus.). (J). 25.95 incl. audio (978-1-59112-250-0(3)); 28.95 incl. audio compact disk (978-1-59112-518-1(9)); pap. 33.95 incl. audio (978-1-59112-251-7(1)); pap. 35.95 incl. audio compact disk (978-1-59112-523-5(5)) Live Oak Media.
Hughes, Mair Wynn & Davies, Tracy. Brawd Newydd. 2005. (WEL., Illus.). 15p. pap. (978-0-86243-453-3(X)) Y Lolfa.
Hughes, Mark Peter. I Am the Wallpaper. 2007. 256p. (YA). (gr. 7-11). pap. 7.99 (978-0-440-42046-0(6)); 2005. 240p. (J). (gr. 5). 15.95 (978-0-385-73241-3(4)); 2005. 240p. (J). (gr. 5). lib. bdg. 17.99 (978-0-385-90265-6(4)) Random Hse. Children's Bks. (Delacorte Bks. for Young Readers).
Jomo & Mata: Evaluation Guide. 2006. (J). (978-1-55942-411-0(7)) Marsh Media.
Koller, Jackie Fre. Horace the Horrible: A Knight Meets His Match. Urbanovic, Jackie, illus. 2003. 32p. (J). 16.95 (978-0-7614-5150-1(1)) Cavendish, Marshall Corp.
Li, Deborah, illus. Tricia & the Blue Cap. l.t. ed. 2003. 28p. (J). 7.95 net. (978-0-9706654-5-4(8)) Sprite Pr.
Mackel, Kathy. A Season of Comebacks. 1998. (J). (978-0-606-13767-6(X)) Tandem Library Bks.
Mario, Heidi S. I'd Rather Have an Iguana. 1999. (Illus.). 32p. (J). (ps-3). 14.95 (978-0-88106-357-8(6)) Charlesbridge Publishing, Inc.
Mazer, Anne. What Goes up Must Go Down. 2008. (Amazing Days of Abby Hayes Ser.: No. 18). 128p. (J). 4.99 (***978-0-439-82926-7(7)*** , Scholastic Paperbacks) Scholastic, Inc.
Michels-Gualtieri, Akaela S. I Was Born to Be a Sister. Ramsey, Marcy Dunn, illus. 2001. 32p. (ps-7). 16.95 (978-1-930775-03-9(2)) Platypus Media, L.L.C.
—I was Born to be a Sister. Ramsey, Marcy Dunn, illus. 2006. 32p. 18.95 (978-1-930775-11-4(3)) Platypus Media, L.L.C.
—I was Born to Be a Sister. 2005. 32p. pap. 9.95 incl. audio compact disk (978-1-930775-24-4(5)) Platypus Media, L.L.C.
Montanari, Eva. Tiff, Taff, & Lulu. 2004. (Illus.). 32p. (J). (gr. k-3). tchr. ed. 16.00 (978-0-618-40238-0(1)) Houghton Mifflin Co. Trade & Reference Div.
Ostrow, Vivian. My Brother Is from Outer Space: The Book of Proof. Brace, Eric, illus. 1999. 32p. (J). (gr. k-4). pap. 6.95 (978-0-8075-5326-8(3)) Whitman, Albert & Co.
Packard, Mary. The New Baby. Haley, Amanda, tr. Haley, Amanda, illus. 2004. (My First Reader Ser.). 31p. (J). 18.50 (978-0-516-24409-9(4) , Children's Pr.) Scholastic Library Publishing.
Palatini, Margie. Good As Goldie. Palatini, Margie, illus. 2000. (Illus.). 32p. (ps-k). 14.99 (978-0-7868-0502-0(1)) Hyperion Bks. for Children.
Phillips, Leigh Hope. Birthday Wishes. Fountain, John, illus. 2005. (J). pap. (978-1-933156-10-1(4)); per. (978-1-933156-03-3(1)) GSVQ Publishing. (VisionQuest Kids).
Phoenix, Woodrow & Price, Robin. Count Milkula: A Tale of Milk & Monsters! 2007. 32p. (J). 19.95 (***978-0-9546576-5-9(9)***) Mogzilla GBR. *Dist:* Independent Pubs. Group.
Polacco, Patricia. My Rotten, Redheaded Older Brother. Polacco, Patricia, illus. 2002. (Illus.). (J). 15.53 (978-0-7587-3229-3(5)) Book Wholesalers, Inc.
—My Rotten Redheaded Older Brother. Polacco, Patricia, illus. 1998. (Illus.). 32p. (J). (ps-3). pap. 7.99 (978-0-689-82036-6(4) , Aladdin) Simon & Schuster Children's Publishing.
Reynolds, Peter. The Best Kid in the World. 2006. (Illus.). (J). (***978-1-4156-9188-5(6)***) Simon & Schuster Children's Publishing.
Reynolds, Peter H. The Best Kid in the World: A SugarLoaf Book. Reynolds, Peter H., illus. 2006. (Illus.). 48p. (J). (ps-2). 15.95 (978-0-689-87624-0(6)) Simon & Schuster Children's Publishing.
Robinson, Susan. Edward's Magic Paintbox. Leach, Helen May Keedwell, illus. 2002. 32p. (J). (978-0-7344-0193-9(0) , Lothian Bks.) Hachette Livre Australia.
Rosenberry, Vera. Vera's Baby Sister. rev. ed. 2005. (Illus.). 32p. (J). 16.95 (978-0-8050-7126-9(1) , Holt, Henry & Co. Bks. For Young Readers) Holt, Henry & Co.
Schad, Kristine. Do You Love Me Best? Timmons, Gayle, illus. 2007. 40p. (J). lib. bdg. 23.95 (***978-1-58374-156-6(9)***) Chicago Spectrum Pr.
Scott, Ann Herbert. En Las Piernas de Mama: On Mother's Lap. Coalson, Glo, illus. 2007. 14p. (J). (gr. k-ps). bds. 5.95 (978-0-618-75247-8(1) , Clarion Bks.) Houghton Mifflin Co. Trade & Reference Div.
Seif, Adam, creator. Tacos, Beans & Rice... the Episodes: From the Beginning. l.t. ed. 2006. (Illus.). 32p. (J). (978-0-9719518-0-8(2)) Doodle Publishing.
Sheldon, Dyan. My Brother Is a Superhero. 1998. (gr. 3-6). lib. bdg. 13.00 (978-0-613-74681-6(3)) Tandem Library Bks.
Simmons, Celeste. The Adventures of Booger Malone: Busted in the Backseat. 2007. (J). per. 10.95 (***978-0-9777041-2-5(2)***) Third Dimension Publishing.
Simons, Joseph. Under a Living Sky. 2005. (Orca Young Readers Ser.). (Illus.). 144p. (J). (gr. 3-6). pap. 5.95 (978-1-55143-355-4(9)) Orca Bk. Pubs. USA.
Skinner, Daphne. Henry Keeps Score. O'Rourke, Page Eastburn, illus. 2001. (Math Matters Ser.). 32p. (J). (ps-2). pap. 4.95 (978-1-57565-102-6(5)) Kane Pr., The.
Speed, Nakesha. Yucky Brother. 2006. pap. 12.95 (978-1-4241-2040-6(3)) PublishAmerica, Inc.
Spinelli, Jerry. Who Put That Hair in My Toothbrush? 2000. 225p. (J). (gr. 4-7). pap. 6.99 (978-0-316-80687-9(0)) Little Brown & Co.
Stephen, Smith. Red Card. 2006. 128p. (J). pap. 5.99 (978-0-7847-1438-6(X) , 42143) Standard Publishing.
Teenick: Drake And Josh: Ch Bk #2, et al. Sibling Revelry. 2006. (Teenick Ser.. Vol. 2). 113p. (J). pap. 4.99 (978-0-439-83163-5(6) , Scholastic) Scholastic, Inc.
thomas, Dalandra, illus. Nooinimals: The New Baby. thomas, Dalandra, . rev. ed. 2007. 40p. (J). pap. 14.99 (***978-0-9796832-0-6(3)***) Nooni Publishing.
Wynne-Jones, Tim. The Boat in the Tree. Shelley, John, illus. 2007. 40p. (J). (ps-2). 17.95 (978-1-932425-49-9(7) , Front Street) Boyds Mills Pr.

SICILY (ITALY)—FICTION

Blasi, Kathleen McAlpin. A Name of Honor. Bowman, Leslie W., illus. 2006. (J). (978-1-59336-692-6(2)) Mondo Publishing.
Buzzati, Dino & Lobb, Frances. The Bears' Famous Invasion of Sicily. 2003. (New York Review Children's Collection). (Illus.). 152p. (J). 18.95 (978-1-59017-076-2(8) , NYR Children's Collection) New York Review of Bks., Inc., The.
Buzzati, Dino & Snicket, Lemony. The Bears' Famous Invasion of Sicily. Buzzati, Dino, illus. 2005. (Illus.). 192p. (J). pap. 5.99 (978-0-06-072608-9(3)) HarperCollins Pubs.
Coville, Bruce & Shakespeare, William. William Shakespeare's the Winter's Tale. Pham, LeUyen, illus. 2007. 40p. (J). (gr. 3 up). 16.99 (***978-0-8037-2709-0(7)*** , Dial) Penguin Group (USA) Inc.
Williams, Annie Morris. Marianne's Secret Cousins. Oldham, Cindi, illus. 2005. (Family History Adventures for Young Readers Ser.: 2). 240p. (J). per. 10.00 (978-0-9645272-8-7(6)) Field Stone Pubs.

SICK

see also Diseases; Mentally Ill

Edwards, Dianna. Meet Patou. 2006. (J). pap. 29.95 (978-0-9767756-0-7(3)) Patou Bks., LLC.
—When Niki Got Sick, Bk. 2. 2004. (J). (978-0-9767756-2-1(X)) Patou Bks., LLC.
Get Well Soon: A Record of Visitors & Good Wishes for Children in the Hospital. 1999. (Illus.). 32p. (J). 9.90 (978-1-929669-00-4(3)) Vinings Publishing.
Kittredge, Mary. Headaches. 2001. (Twenty-First Century Health & Wellness Ser.). 103p. (J). (gr. 7-12). 24.95 (978-0-7910-5981-4(2) , Chelsea Hse.) Facts On File, Inc.
Murphy, Patricia. Everything You Need to Know about Staying in the Hospital. 2005. (Need to Know Library). (Illus.). 64p. (YA). (gr. 7-12). 25.25 (978-0-8239-3325-9(3)) Rosen Publishing Group, Inc., The.
Wainwright, Tabitha. You & an Illness in Your Family. 2005. (Family Matters Ser.). (Illus.). 48p. (YA). (gr. 5-8). lib. bdg. 23.95 (978-0-8239-3352-5(0)) Rosen Publishing Group, Inc., The.

SICK—FICTION

Arrington, Aileen. Paper Heart. 2006. 113p. (J). 16.95 (978-1-932425-61-1(6) , Lemniscaat) Boyds Mills Pr.
Banks, Steven. Sick Day. 2003. (gr. k-3). lib. bdg. 11.25 (978-0-613-66382-3(9)) Tandem Library Bks.
Banks, Steven. Spongebob Goes to the Doctor. Saunders, Zina, illus. 2005. 22p. (J). lib. bdg. 15.00 (***978-1-4242-0976-7(5)***) Fitzgerald Bks.
Banks, Steven & Hillenburg, Stephen. SpongeBob Goes to the Doctor. Saunders, Zina, illus. 2005. (J). (***978-1-4156-3131-7(X)*** , Simon Spotlight/Nickelodeon) Simon & Schuster Children's Publishing.
Bartels, Alice. Grandmother Doll. 2001. (ps-2). lib. bdg. 15.25 (978-0-613-78378-1(6)) Tandem Library Bks.
Bemelmans, Ludwig. Madeline: Edicion en Espanol. Anasal, Arshes, ed. 2005. (SPA., Illus.). 44p. (J). (gr. k-4). reprint ed. 16.00 (978-0-7567-8842-1(0)) DIANE Publishing Co.
Bermiss, Aamir. I Hate to Be Sick! Wilson-Max, Ken, illus. 2004. 32p. (J). (gr. k-1). lib. bdg. 11.19 (978-0-606-33350-4(9)) Tandem Library Bks.
Bermiss, Aamir Lee. I Hate to Be Sick! Wilson-Max, Ken, illus. 2004. 32p. (J). lib. bdg. 15.00 (***978-1-4242-0220-1(5)***) Fitzgerald Bks.
Berry, Eileen M. Looking for Home. 2005. 75p. (J). (978-1-59166-493-2(4)) Jones, Bob Univ. Pr.
Bottner, Barbara. Marsha Makes Me Sick. 1999. (J). (978-0-606-16139-8(2)) Tandem Library Bks.
Bracken, Carolyn & Edwards, Ken, illus. The Big Bad Cold. 2002. (Big Red Reader Ser.). 32p. (J). (978-0-439-38989-1(5)) Scholastic, Inc.
Bridwell, Norman. Tummy Trouble. Bridwell, Norman, illus. 2002. (Big Red Readers Ser.). (Illus.). (J). 11.91 (978-0-7587-5218-5(0)) Book Wholesalers, Inc.
Cazet, Denys. Grandpa Spanielson's Chicken Pox Stories No. 1: The Octopus. Cazet, Denys, illus. 2005. (I Can Read Bks.). (Illus.). 48p. (J). (ps-3). lib. bdg. 16.89 (978-0-06-051089-3(7)) HarperCollins Pubs.
—Octopus. Cazet, Denys, illus. 2005. (I Can Read Bks.). (Illus.). 48p. (J). (ps-3). 15.99 (978-0-06-051088-6(9)) HarperCollins Pubs.
Chanda, J-P. Ah-Choo! Piluso, Piero, illus. 2003. (Oswald Pre-School Ready-to-Read Ser.: Vol. 2). 24p. (J). pap. 3.99 (978-0-689-85853-6(1) , Simon Spotlight/ Nickelodeon) Simon & Schuster Children's Publishing.
Charlip, Remy & Supree, Burton. Mother Mother I Feel Sick Send for the Doctor Quick Quick Quick. 2004. (Illus.). 46p. (J). (ps-2). 16.95 (978-1-58246-043-7(4) , Tricycle Pr.) Ten Speed Pr.
Child, Lauren. This is Actually My Party. 2007. (Charlie & Lola Ser.). 32p. (J). (ps-2). pap. 6.99 (978-0-448-44569-4(7) , Grosset & Dunlap) Penguin Group (USA) Inc.
Christopher, Matt. Slam Dunk. 2004. (Illus.). 128p. (J). (gr. 4-7). pap. 4.99 (978-0-316-60762-9(2)) Little Brown & Co.
Collins, Ross. Germs. 2004. (Illus.). 32p. (J). 16.95 (978-1-58234-926-8(6) , Bloomsbury Children) Bloomsbury Publishing.
Coolidge, Susan. What Katy Did. 2007. (ENG.). 148p. per (***978-1-4065-1527-5(2)***) Dodo Pr.
—What Katy Did. 2006. 160p. (J). pap. 6.95 (978-0-486-44760-5(X)) Dover Pubns., Inc.
—What Katy Did. 2005. (ENG.). pap. 71.99 (***978-1-4219-1393-3(3)***) IndyPublish.com.
Dealey, Erin. Goldie Locks Has Chicken Pox. ed. 2004. (Illus.). (J). (gr. k-3). spiral bd. (978-0-616-14572-2(1)); spiral bd. (978-0-616-14573-9(X)) Canadian National Institute for the Blind/Institut National Canadien pour les Aveugles.
—Goldie Locks Has Chicken Pox. Wakiyama, Hanako, illus. 40p. (J). 2002. 17.99 (978-0-689-82981-9(7) , Atheneum); 2005. reprint ed. 6.99 (978-0-689-87610-3(6) , Aladdin) Simon & Schuster Children's Publishing.
Deem, Saitofi Anne. Myrtle's Friend Is Very Sick. 1998. (Teachable Moments Ser.). (Illus.). 8p. (J). (ps-3). pap. 7.95 (978-1-930694-15-6(6)) Myrtle Learns.
Downham, Jenny. Before I Die. 2007. 326p. (YA). (gr. 9 up). lib. bdg. 18.99 (***978-0-385-75158-2(3)*** , Fickling, David Bks.) Random Hse. Children's Bks.
Droop, Constanza, illus. Felix's Cookbook. 2001. 72p. (J). pap. 24.95 (978-0-7892-0750-0(8) , Abbeville Kids) Abbeville Pr., Inc.
Duquennoy, Jacques. Operation Ghost. 1999. (J). (978-0-606-19002-2(3)) Tandem Library Bks.
Egan, Brigid. Blue's Sniffly Day. Miller, Victoria A., illus. 2002. (Blue's Clues Ser.). 24p. (J). pap. 3.99 (978-0-689-83874-3(3) , Simon Spotlight/Nickelodeon) Simon & Schuster Children's Publishing.
—Blue's Sniffly Day. 2002. (gr. k-3). lib. bdg. 11.25 (978-0-613-51293-0(6)) Tandem Library Bks.
Ehrenhaft, Daniel. 10 Things to Do Before I Die. 2006. 224p. (YA). (gr. 7). pap. 7.95 (978-0-385-73406-6(9) , Delacorte Bks. for Young Readers) Random Hse. Children's Bks.
Ehrlich, H. M., et al. Dr. Duck. Rader, Laura, illus. 2000. 36p. (J). (ps-1). pap. 14.95 (978-0-531-30254-5(7) , Orchard Bks.) Scholastic, Inc.
Estes, Don. Willy & Friends traveling through the Seasons: The continuing story of Willy the little fire Jeep. Glass, Eric, illus. 2006. (J). (978-1-883551-75-9(7) , Maple Corners Press) Attic Studio Publishing Hse.
Fairy-Tale Flowers: Individual Title, 6 pack. (Story Steps Ser.). (gr. k-2). 23.00 (978-0-7635-9842-6(9)) Rigby Education.
Finchler, Judy. Miss Malarkey Won't Be in Today. O'Malley, Kevin, illus. 2000. 32p. (J). (gr. k-4). reprint ed. pap. 6.95 (978-0-8027-7591-7(8)) Walker & Co.
Fine, Anne. Poor Monty. Evans, Kevin, illus. 2004. 32p. 18.00 (978-1-4052-0161-2(4)) Egmont Bks., Ltd. GBR. *Dist:* Trafalgar Square Publishing.
Finley, Martha. Elsie's Impossible Choice, Bk. 2. Williams, Scott, illus. 1999. (Elsie Dinsmore: Bk. 2). 238p. (YA). (gr. 5-9). 12.99 (978-1-928749-02-8(X)) Zonderkidz.
—Elsie's Impossible Choice, Vol. 2. 2006. (Life of Faith': Elsie Dinsmore Ser.). 224p. (J). pap. 7.99 (978-1-928749-81-3(X)) Zonderkidz.
Fleming, Denise. Buster Goes to Cowboy Camp. 2008. 40p. (J). 16.95 (***978-0-8050-7892-3(4)***) Holt, Henry & Co.
Fontes, Justine. Jordan's Silly Sick Day. Lee, Jared D., illus. 2005. (Rookie Reader Espanol Ser.). 32p. (J). (gr. k-2). pap. 4.95 (978-0-516-26821-7(X) , Children's Pr.) Scholastic Library Publishing.
—Jordan's Silly Sick Day. Lee, Jared D., tr. Lee, Jared D., illus. 2004. (Rookie Reader Ser.). 31p. (J). 19.50 (978-0-516-25897-3(4) , Children's Pr.) Scholastic Library Publishing.
Fuqua, Jonathon Scott. Willoughby Spit Wonder. 2004. (Illus.). 160p. (J). (gr. 5-8). 15.99 (978-0-7636-1776-9(8)) Candlewick Pr.
Garvin, Sharon. Alexandra's Rag-Time Band. 2006. 28p. (J). per. 12.95 (978-1-56167-926-3(7)) American Literary Pr.
Giblin, James Cross. The Boy Who Saved Cleveland: Based on a True Story. Dooling, Michael, illus. rev. ed. 2006. 80p. (J). 15.95 (978-0-8050-7355-3(8) , Holt, Henry & Co. Bks. For Young Readers) Holt, Henry & Co.
Gold, Becky. Centrum's Phil & Lil Go to the Doctor. Roper, Robert, illus. 2002. 24p. (J). mass mkt. 3.50 (978-0-689-85153-7(7) , Simon Spotlight/Nickelodeon) Simon & Schuster Children's Publishing.
Gray, Kes. The Get Well Soon Book. 2000. (Single Titles Ser.: 1). (Illus.). 32p. (J). (ps-3). (978-0-7613-1435-6(0) , Millbrook Pr.) Lerner Publishing Group.
—The Get Well Soon Book: Good Wishes for Bad Times. McQuillan, Mary, illus. 2000. 32p. (J). (ps-1). lib. bdg. 22.90 (978-0-7613-1922-1(0) , Millbrook Pr.) Lerner Publishing Group.
Gray, Libba Moore. Miss Tizzy. Rowland, Jada, illus. 1998. 40p. (J). (ps-3). 6.99 (978-0-689-81897-4(1) , Aladdin) Simon & Schuster Children's Publishing.
—Miss Tizzy. 1998. (978-0-606-13611-2(8)) Tandem Library Bks.
Greene, Rhonda Gowler. Barnyard Song. 2001. (ps-2). lib. bdg. 14.15 (978-0-613-34598-9(3)) Tandem Library Bks.
Greenfield, Eloise. William & the Good Old Days. Date not set. (Illus.). 32p. (J). (gr. k-3). pap. 4.99 (978-0-06-443453-9(2)) HarperCollins Pubs.
Grejniec, Michael. Mira. 1999. (978-0-606-17713-9(2)); (SPA.). lib. bdg. 15.25 (978-0-613-28961-0(7)) Tandem Library Bks.
Guest, Elissa Haden. Iris & Walter: The School Play. Davenier, Christine, illus. 2003. (Iris & Walter Ser.). 44p. (J). 15.00 (978-0-15-216481-2(2)) Harcourt Children's Bks.
—Iris & Walter: The School Play. Davenier, Christine, illus. 2004. 44p. (J). (gr. 1-4). lib. bdg. 13.15 (978-0-606-30392-7(8)) Tandem Library Bks.
—The School Play. Davenier, Christine, illus. 2006. (Iris & Walter Ser.). 44p. (J). pap. 5.95 (978-0-15-205668-1(8) , Harcourt Paperbacks) Harcourt Children's Bks.
Hannigan, Katherine. Ida B: ... And Her Plans to Maximize Fun, Avoid Disaster, & (Possibly) Save the World. 256p. 2004. (J). (gr. 4 up). 16.99 (978-0-06-073024-6(2)); 2004. (gr. 4 up). lib. bdg. 16.89 (978-0-06-073025-3(0)); 2007. reprint ed. pap. 5.99 (978-0-06-073026-0(9) , Harper Trophy) HarperCollins Pubs.
Hanson, Janell Marie. The Side-Effects Kid. 2001. (Illus.). 228p. (J). pap. 19.95 (978-0-9662608-0-9(5)) Partae Pr.
Harcourt School Publishers Staff. Rick Is Sick Advanced Level. 3rd ed. 2002. (Trophies Reading Program Ser.). (Illus.). (J). pap. 3.70 (978-0-15-323010-3(X)) Harcourt Schl. Pubs.
—Trofeos Advanced Level: Como Tose Bento! 3rd ed. 2002. (SPA., Illus.). pap. 5.50 (978-0-15-323921-2(2)) Harcourt Schl. Pubs.
Havill, Juanita. Brianna, Jamaica, & the Dance of Spring. O'Brien, Anne Sibley, illus. 2002. 32p. (J). (gr. 4-6). 16.00 (978-0-618-07700-7(6)) Houghton Mifflin Co. Trade & Reference Div.
Hawkins, Michelle Lee. What a Headache?! Wise, Noreen, ed. Porcaro, Susan Tait, illus. 2001. (Medical Mystery Ser.: Vol. 3). 54p. (J). (gr. 1-5). pap. 6.95 (978-1-58584-456-2(X)) Huckleberry Pr.
Hershenhorn, Esther. Chicken Soup by Heart. Litzinger, Rosanne, illus. 2002. 32p. (J). (gr. k-3). 16.95 (978-0-689-82665-8(6)) Simon & Schuster Children's Publishing.
Hest, Amy. Don't You Feel Well, Sam? Jeram, Anita, illus. 32p. (J). (ps). 2007. pap. 4.99 (978-0-7636-2408-8(X)); 2002. 15.99 (978-0-7636-1009-8(7)) Candlewick Pr.
—Guess Who, Baby Duck! Barton, Jill, illus. 2004. 32p. (J). (gr. k-k). 15.99 (978-0-7636-1981-7(7)) Candlewick Pr.
—No Te Sientes Bien, Sam? Jeram, Anita, illus. 2002. (SPA.). (J). (gr. k-2). 16.00 (978-1-930332-39-3(4) , LC8551) Lectorum Pubns., Inc.

S

Hudson, Charlotte & McQuillan, Mary. Get Well Soon. Hudson, Charlotte & McQuillan, Mary, illus. 2007. (Illus.). 32p. (J). pap. 10.95 (***978-0-09-943945-5(X)*** , Red Fox) Random Hse. Children's Bks. GBR. *Dist:* Independent Pubs. Group.

Hurd, Clement, illus. Johnny Lion's Bad Day. 2002. (Johnny Lion Ser.). (J). 12.34 (978-0-7587-5039-6(0)) Book Wholesalers, Inc.

Hurd, Edith Thacher. Johnny Lion's Bad Day. Hurd, Clement, illus. 2000. (I Can Read Bks.). 64p. (J). (gr. k-3). 14.95 (978-0-06-029335-2(7)) HarperCollins Pubs.

Inches, Alison. Wendy Helps Out. 2001. (978-0-606-22131-3(X)); lib. bdg. 11.80 (978-0-613-51329-6(0)) Tandem Library Bks.

The Internal Adventures of Marcus Snarkis Adventure Pack. 2001. (978-1-883772-32-1(X)) Flying Rhinoceros, Inc.

Jaredo's Day Off. 2002. (J). pap. 9.00 (978-0-8059-5394-7(9)) Dorrance Publishing Co., Inc.

Jaworski, Anna M. My Brother Needs an Operation. Ball, Linda, illus. 1998. 57p. (J). (ps-5). 20.00 (978-0-9652508-2-5(2)) Baby Hearts Pr.

Jeffs, Stephanie. Jenny: Coming to Terms with the Death of a Sibling. Thomas, Jacqui, illus. 2006. 32p. (ps-3). 14.00 (978-0-687-49709-6(4)) Abingdon Pr.

Jensen, Patricia. I Am Sick. Hantel, Johanna, illus. (J). (gr. k-1). 2006. 32p. pap. 3.95 (978-0-516-24970-4(3)); 2005. 31p. 18.50 (978-0-516-24878-3(2)) Scholastic Library Publishing. (Children's Pr.).

Jinkins, Jim. Pinky Dinky Doo: Polka Dot Pox. 2004. (Illus.). 48p. (J). (gr. 1-3). pap. 3.99 (978-0-375-82713-6(7) , Random Hse. Bks. for Young Readers) Random Hse. Children's Bks.

Karu, Tim, et al. Henry & the White Wolf. Karu, Tyler, illus. 2000. (Illus.). 32p. (J). (ps-3). 12.95 (978-0-7611-2135-0(8) , 12135) Workman Publishing Co., Inc.

Kay, Elizabeth. Divide. 2007. 320p. (J). pap. 6.99 (***978-0-439-54343-9(6)*** , Chicken Hse., The) Scholastic, Inc.

Keeling, Annie E. Andrew Golding A Tale of the Great Plague. 2004. reprint ed. pap. 15.95 (978-1-4191-0694-1(5)); pap. 1.99 (978-1-4192-0694-8(X)) Kessinger Publishing, LLC.

Keeling, E. Annie. Andrew Golding (a Tale of the Great Plag. 2006. 40.99 (***978-1-4280-0516-7(1));*** pap. 34.99 (***978-1-4280-0515-0(3)***) IndyPublish.com.

Kippling, Bozenka. Stories from the Inner World: Introducing My Best Friends. Sawatzky, Goranka, illus. l.t. ed. 2002. 48p. (J). per. (978-0-9689096-1-4(2)) Seed Children, Inc.

Kirk, David. The Bug Flu. 2007. 32p. (J). (ps-2). 6.99 (***978-0-448-44691-2(X)***) Callaway Editions, Inc.

Knappman, Timothy. Guess What I Found in Dragon Wood? Millward, Gwen, illus. 2007. 32p. (J). 16.95 (***978-1-59990-190-9(0)***) Bloomsbury Publishing.

Knights, Harry B. Angel's Star. 2006. (J). lib. bdg. 20.00 (978-0-9632248-8-0(3)) Synergetic Pubns., Inc.

Koertge, Ronald. Shakespeare Bats Clean-Up. 2003. 128p. (YA). (gr. 7). 15.99 (978-0-7636-2116-2(1)) Candlewick Pr.

Lancett, Peter. Dark Candle. 2007. (Dark Man Ser.). 36p. pap. 6.95 (***978-1-84167-603-6(9)***) Ransom Publishing Ltd. GBR. *Dist:* International Publishers Marketing.

Lesynski, Loris. Sopa de Niño o el Ogro con Gripe. Canetti, Yanitzia, tr. from ENG. Lesynski, Loris, illus. 2004. (ENG & SPA., Illus.). 32p. (J). (ps-3). pap. 5.95 (978-1-55037-855-9(4)) Annick Pr., Ltd. CAN. *Dist:* Firefly Bks., Ltd.

Lewison, Wendy Cheyette. Easter Bunny's Amazing Egg Machine. 2002. (ps-2). lib. bdg. 10.95 (978-0-613-83538-1(7)) Tandem Library Bks.

Louie, Therese On. Raymond's Perfect Present. Wang, Suling, illus. 2002. (J). (gr. 2-4). 16.95 (978-1-58430-055-7(8)) Lee & Low Bks., Inc.

Lubar, David. Dunk. (YA). (gr. 7-10). 2002. 256p. tchr. ed. 15.00 (978-0-618-19455-1(X) , Clarion Bks.); 2004. 272p. reprint ed. pap. 6.99 (978-0-618-43909-6(9) , Graphia) Houghton Mifflin Co. Trade & Reference Div.

Lutz, Norma Jean. Smallpox Strikes! Cotton Mather's Bold Experiment. 1999. (American Adventure Ser.: No. 7). (Illus.). 144p. (J). (gr. 3-7). lib. bdg. 15.95 (978-0-7910-5047-7(5) , Chelsea Hse.) Facts On File, Inc.

Maccarone, Grace. I Have a Cold. Lewin, Betsy, illus. 1999. (Hello Reader! Ser.: Level 1). 32p. (J). (ps-3). pap. 3.99 (978-0-590-39638-7(2) , Cartwheel Bks.) Scholastic, Inc.

McDaniel, Lurlene. How Do I Love Thee: Three Stories. 272p. (YA). (gr. 7). 2002. pap. 5.50 (978-0-553-57107-3(9) , Laurel Leaf); 2001. 9.95 (978-0-553-57154-7(0) , Starfire) Random Hse. Children's Bks.

—Reach for Tomorrow. 1999. (One Last Wish Ser.: No. 12). 208p. (J). (gr. 5-9). pap. 4.99 (978-0-553-57109-7(5) , Laurel Leaf) Random Hse. Children's Bks.

—Reach for Tomorrow. 1999. (One Last Wish Ser.: No. 12). (978-0-606-16375-0(1)); (gr. 5-8). lib. bdg. 12.40 (978-0-613-16186-2(6)) Tandem Library Bks.

McDonald, Megan. Doctor Is In! Reynolds, Peter H., illus. 2006. (Judy Moody Ser.: No. 5). 176p. (J). (gr. 1-5). pap. 5.99 (978-0-7636-2615-0(5)) Candlewick Pr.

—Doctor Is In! Reynolds, Peter H., tr. Reynolds, Peter H., illus. 2004. (Judy Moody Ser.: No. 5). 176p. (J). (gr. 1-5). 15.99 (978-0-7636-2024-0(6)) Candlewick Pr.

Mckeever Stacia & Beyer Ingrid. Why Is Keiko Sick? 2006. 32p. 12.99 (978-0-89051-463-4(1)) Master Bks.

McKissack, Patricia C. & Moss, Onawumi Jean. Precious & the Boo Hag. Brooker, Kyrsten, illus. 2005. 40p. (J). (ps-3). 17.99 (978-0-689-85194-0(4) , Atheneum/Anne Schwartz Bks.) Simon & Schuster Children's Publishing.

McPhail, David. Rick Is Sick. McPhail, David, illus. 2004. (Illus.). 24p. (J). lib. bdg. 10.00 (***978-1-4242-0183-9(7)***) Fitzgerald Bks.

McPhail, David M. Rick Is Sick. 2004. (Green Light Readers Level 1 Ser.). (Illus.). 24p. (J). 12.95 (978-0-15-205091-7(4)); pap. 3.95 (978-0-15-205092-4(2)) Harcourt Children's Bks. (Green Light Readers).

Mead, Alice & Weber James, Alice. Madame Squidley & Beanie. 2004. 144p. (J). 16.00 (978-0-374-34688-1(7) , Farrar, Straus & Giroux (BYR)) Farrar, Straus & Giroux.

Miller, Jennifer. Run, Rasputin, Run! Trials & Friendships (Book 2) 2006. (ENG., Illus.). 172p. per. (***978-1-4120-8494-9(6)***) Trafford Publishing.

Mills, Joyce C. Little Tree: A Story for Children with Serious Medical Illness. Sebern, Brian, illus. 2nd ed. 2003. 32p. (J). pap. 8.95 (978-1-59147-042-7(0)); 14.95 (978-1-59147-041-0(2)) American Psychological Assn. (Magination Pr.).

Moses, Shelia P. The Legend of Buddy Bush. unabr. ed. 2005. (J). (gr. 3-7). 55.70 incl. audio (978-1-4193-3575-4(8) , 42043) Recorded Bks., LLC.

—The Legend of Buddy Bush. (Illus.). 224p. 2005. (YA). pap. 5.99 (978-1-4169-0716-9(5) , Simon Pulse); 2003. (J). 15.95 (978-0-689-85839-0(6) , McElderry, Margaret K.) Simon & Schuster Children's Publishing.

—The Legend of Buddy Bush. l.t. ed. 2005. 179p. 22.95 (978-0-7862-7311-9(9)) Thorndike Pr.

Murphy, Jill. Mr. Large in Charge. Murphy, Jill, illus. 2007. (Illus.). 40p. (J). (ps-2). 16.99 (978-0-7636-3504-6(9)); pap. 6.99 (978-0-7636-2739-3(9)) Candlewick Pr.

My Doctor, My Friend. 2002. (Illus.). 24p. (J). (ps-3). 5.95 (978-0-8249-5389-8(4)) Ideals Pubns.

Neitzel, Shirley. I'm Not Feeling Well Today. Parker, Nancy Winslow, illus. 2001. 32p. (J). (gr. k-2). 15.95 (978-0-688-17380-7(2)) HarperCollins Pubs.

Nolan, Han. When We Were Saints. (YA). 2005. 312p. pap. 6.95 (978-0-15-205322-2(0) , Harcourt Paperbacks); 2003. (Illus.). 304p. 17.00 (978-0-15-216371-6(9) , 53586153) Harcourt Children's Bks.

O'Ryan, Ellie. Care Bears Christmas Wishes. Moore, Saxton, illus. 2005. (J). (***978-1-4156-8978-3(4)***) Scholastic, Inc.

Page, Josephine. Tummy Trouble. Edwards, Ken, illus. 2001. (Clifford, the Big Red Dog Ser.). 32p. (J). (gr. k-2). pap. 3.99 (978-0-439-21358-5(4)) Scholastic, Inc.

Park, Barbara. Junie B., First Grader: Shipwrecked. Brunkus, Denise, illus. 2004. 88p. (J). lib. bdg. 18.46 (***978-1-4242-0360-4(0)***) Fitzgerald Bks.

—Junie B., 1st Grader: Shipwrecked. Brunkus, Denise, illus. 2004. (Junie B. Jones Ser.: No. 23). 96p. (J). (gr. 1-4). 11.95 (978-0-375-82804-1(4) , Random Hse. Bks. for Young Readers) Random Hse. Children's Bks.

—Junie B., First Grader: Shipwrecked. Brunkus, Denise, illus. (Junie B. Jones Ser.: No. 23). 96p. (J). (gr. k-3). 2005. mass mkt. 3.99 (978-0-375-82805-8(2)); 2004. lib. bdg. 13.99 (978-0-375-92804-8(9)) Random Hse. Children's Bks. (Random Hse. Bks. for Young Readers).

Perrin, Randy, et al. Time Like a River. 2004. 144p. (gr. 5 up). 14.95 (978-1-57143-061-8(X)) RDR Bks.

Rader, Laura. Who'll Pull Santa's Sleigh Tonight? Rader, Laura, illus. 2006. 40p. (J). pap. 6.99 (978-0-06-008090-7(6) , Harper Trophy) HarperCollins Pubs.

Rakusin, Sudie. Dear Calla Roo..., Love, Savannah Blue No. 2: A Letter about Getting Sick & Feeling Better. Rakusin, Sudie, illus. 2003. (Illus.). 32p. (J). (ps-4). 16.95 (978-0-9664805-3-5(8)) Winged Willow Pr.

Rapp, Adam. 33 Snowfish. Ering, Timothy Basil, illus. 2006. 192p. (YA). (gr. 10). pap. 6.99 (978-0-7636-2917-5(0)) Candlewick Pr.

Raschka, Chris. The Purple Balloon. 2007. (Illus.). 32p. (J). (ps-2). 16.99 (978-0-375-84146-0(6) , Schwartz & Wade Bks.) Random Hse. Children's Bks.

Riggs, Sandy. Nick Is Sick. 2006. (Reader's Clubhouse Set A Ser.). (Illus.). 24p. (J). pap. 3.99 (978-0-7641-3284-1(9)) Barron's Educational Series, Inc.

Rosenberry, Vera. When Vera Was Sick. rev. ed. 2002. (Illus.). 32p. (J). (gr. k-2). pap. 6.95 (978-0-8050-6832-0(5) , Holt, Henry & Co. Bks. For Young Readers) Holt, Henry & Co.

—When Vera Was Sick. Rosenberry, Vera, illus. rev. ed. 1998. (Illus.). 32p. (J). (ps-2). 15.95 (978-0-8050-5405-7(7) , Holt, Henry & Co. Bks. For Young Readers) Holt, Henry & Co.

—When Vera Was Sick. Rosenberry, Vera, illus. unabr. ed. 2006. (Picture Book Readalong Ser.). (Illus.). (J). (ps-2). pap. 16.95 incl. audio (978-1-59519-650-7(1)); pap. 18.95 incl. audio compact disk (978-1-59519-651-4(X)); Set. pap. 37.95 incl. audio (978-1-59519-652-1(8)); Set. pap. 39.95 incl. audio compact disk (978-1-59519-653-8(6)) Live Oak Media.

Rosenfeld, Dina. Get Well Soon. Lyampe, Rina, illus. 2001. 32p. (J). (ps-k). 9.95 (978-1-929628-05-6(6)) Hachai Publishing.

Rostoker-Gruber, Karen. Rooster Can't Cock-a-Doodle-Doo. Ratz de Tagyos, Paul, illus. 32p. (J). (ps). 2006. pap. 5.99 (978-0-14-240646-5(5) , Puffin); 2004. 15.99 (978-0-8037-2877-6(8) , Dial) Penguin Group (USA) Inc.

Rylant, Cynthia. Henry & Mudge Get the Cold Shivers. Stevenson, Sucie, illus. (Henry & Mudge Ser.). 9.95 (978-1-59112-290-6(2)); 1999. 28.95 incl. audio compact disk (978-1-59112-573-0(1)); 1999. pap. 31.95 incl. audio compact disk (978-1-59112-572-3(3)) Live Oak Media.

—Mr. Putter & Tabby Catch the Cold. 2003. (Mr. Putter & Tabby Ser.). (gr. k-3). lib. bdg. 6.95 (978-0-613-70520-2(3)) Tandem Library Bks.

Scholastic, Inc. Staff & Bermiss, Aamir Lee. Just for You: I Hate to Be Sick. Wilson-Max, Ken, illus. 2004. (Just for You! Ser.). 32p. (gr. k-3). pap. 3.99 (978-0-439-56877-7(3) , Teaching Resources) Scholastic, Inc.

Selway, Martina, illus. Fred's Cold. 1999. (J). (978-0-7608-3192-2(0)) Sundance/Newbridge Educational Publishing.

Shulman, Dee. Hetty the Yeti. Shulman, Dee, illus. 2005. (Read-It! Chapter Bks.). (Illus.). 52p. (J). (ps-k). lib. bdg. 19.95 (978-1-4048-1276-5(8)) Picture Window Bks.

Simon, Charnan. The Good Bad Day. Handelman, Dorothy, photos by. 1998. (Real Kids Readers Ser.). (Illus.). 32p. (gr. k-2). (J). pap. 4.99 (978-0-7613-2042-5(3)); lib. bdg. 18.90 (978-0-7613-2017-3(2)) Lerner Publishing Group. (Millbrook Pr.).

Slate, Joseph. Miss Bindergarten Stays Home from Kindergarten. Wolff, Ashley, illus. (J). (ps-2). 2000. 1p. 16.99 (978-0-525-46396-2(8) , Dutton Juvenile); 2004. 48p. reprint ed. pap. 6.99 (978-0-14-230127-2(2) , Puffin) Penguin Group (USA) Inc.

Sleator, William. The Last Universe. (J). (gr. 7-11). 2006. 240p. pap. 6.95 (978-0-8109-9213-9(2)); 2005. 224p. 16.95 (978-0-8109-5858-6(9) , Amulet Bks.) Abrams, Harry N., Inc.

Sonnenblick, Jordan. Drums, Girls & Dangerous Pie. 2004. 208p. (J). 15.95 (978-0-9761030-1-1(X)) Scholastic, Inc.

Soto, Gary. Chato Goes Cruisin' Guevara, Susan, illus. 2007. 32p. (J). (ps). pap. 6.99 (978-0-14-240810-0(7) , Puffin) Penguin Group (USA) Inc.

Strong, Jeremy. Dinosaur Pox. l.t. ed. 2000. (Illus.). 112p. (J). pap. (978-0-7540-6122-9(1) , CLP 317) BBC Audio.

Taylor-Butler, Christine. Ah-Choo. Koeller, Carol, illus. 2005. (My First Reader Ser.). (J). (gr. k-1). 31p. pap. 3.95 (978-0-516-25275-9(5)); 32p. 18.50 (978-0-516-25175-2(9)) Scholastic Library Publishing. (Children's Pr.).

Thomas, Shelley Moore. Get Well, Good Knight. Plecas, Jennifer, illus. 48p. (J). 2004. pap. 3.99 (978-0-14-240050-0(5) , Puffin); 2002. 13.99 (978-0-525-46914-8(1) , Dutton Juvenile) Penguin Group (USA) Inc.

Thorpe, Kiki. Ah-Choo! 2003. (ps-2). lib. bdg. 11.80 (978-0-613-73405-9(X)) Tandem Library Bks.

Urdahl, Cathy Nelson. Emma's Question. Dawson, Janine, illus. 2008. (J). (***978-1-58089-145-5(4)***) Charlesbridge Publishing, Inc.

Waddell, Martin. The Toymaker. 1999. (J). (978-0-606-19322-1(7)) Tandem Library Bks.

Wax, Wendy. Watch Out, Otto! Pilar-Newton, Michelle, illus. 2002. (Rocket Power Ready-to-Read Ser.: Vol. 1). 32p. (J). pap. 3.99 (978-0-689-85008-0(5) , Simon Spotlight/Nickelodeon) Simon & Schuster Children's Publishing.

—Watch Out, Otto! 2002. lib. bdg. 11.80 (978-0-613-57588-1(1)) Tandem Library Bks.

Weber, Lori. Tattoo Heaven. 2005. (SideStreets Ser.). 168p. (YA). (gr. 7-12). (***978-1-55028-903-9(9));*** 7.95 (978-1-55028-902-2(0)) Lorimer, James & Co., Ltd., Pubs. CAN. *Dist:* Casemate Pubs. & Bk. Distributors, LLC.

Weiss, Ellen. Nose Knows. 2002. (gr. k-3). lib. bdg. 13.00 (978-0-613-53756-8(4)) Tandem Library Bks.

Weiss, Ellen & Lucas, Margeaux. The Nose Knows. 2002. (Science Solves It! Ser.). (Illus.). 32p. (J). 4.99 (978-1-57565-120-0(3)) Kane Pr., The.

Wells, Rosemary. Felix Feels Better. Wells, Rosemary, illus. 2000. (Illus.). 32p. (J). (ps-k). 12.99 (978-0-7636-0639-8(1)) Candlewick Pr.

—The Germ Busters. (ps-2). 2002. lib. bdg. 11.80 (978-0-613-53188-7(4)); 2001. (J). 10.79 (978-0-606-22551-9(X)) Tandem Library Bks.

Weninger, Brigitte. Stay in Bed Davy. Tharlet, Eve, illus. 2007. 0032p. pap. 6.95 (***978-0-7358-2154-5(2)***) North-South Bks., Inc.

When I Was Sick: Individual Title, 6 packs. (Literatura 2000 Ser.). (gr. 1-2). 28.00 (978-0-7635-0018-4(6)) Rigby Education.

Whybrow, Ian. Sammy & the Robots. Reynolds, Adrian, illus. 2001. 32p. (J). (ps-1). pap. 15.95 (978-0-531-30327-6(6) , Orchard Bks.) Scholastic, Inc.

Williams, Dar. Amalee. (J). 2006. 208p. pap. 5.99 (978-0-439-39564-9(X) , Scholastic Paperbacks); 2004. 192p. pap. 16.95 (978-0-439-39563-2(1)) Scholastic, Inc.

Wilson, Karma. Bear Feels Sick. Chapman, Jane, illus. 2007. 40p. (J). (ps-2). 16.99 (978-0-689-85985-4(6) , McElderry, Margaret K.) Simon & Schuster Children's Publishing.

Wilson, Rebekah. Grandmother's Hope Chest: Lucie's Snowflakes. l.t. ed. 2004. (Illus.). 80p. (J). 15.00 (978-1-59565-003-0(2)) Hope Chest Legacy, Inc.

Wolff, Ashley, illus. Miss Bindergarten Stays Home from Kindergarten. 2002. (Miss Bindergarten Ser.). (J). 25.45 (978-0-7587-3144-9(2)) Book Wholesalers, Inc.

Yolen, Jane. How Do Dinosaurs Get Well Soon? Teague, Mark, illus. 2003. 40p. (J). (ps-1). pap. 15.95 (978-0-439-24100-7(6) , Blue Sky Pr., The) Scholastic, Inc.

Youngberg, Norma R. Jungle Thorn. 2000. (Illus.). 112p. (J). reprint ed. per. 8.95 (978-1-57258-157-9(3) , 945-6024) TEACH Services, Inc.

Zaugg, Sandra L. A Prayer for Mother. 2005. (Illus.). 95p. (J). (978-0-8163-2056-1(X)) Pacific Pr. Pubns.

Zinnen, Linda. Holding at Third. 2006. 160p. (YA). (gr. 4). pap. 5.99 (978-0-14-240554-3(X) , Puffin) Penguin Group (USA) Inc.

SIDEREAL SYSTEM

see Stars

SIERRA LEONE

Brimson, Samuel. Sierra Leone-United Arab Emirates, 8 vols. 2003. (Nations of the World Ser.: Vol. 7). (Illus.). 64p. (J). (gr. 5 up). lib. bdg. 30.00 (978-0-8368-5491-6(8) , World Almanac Library) Stevens, Gareth Inc.

Hasday, Judy L. Sierra Leone. 2007. (J). (978-1-4222-0092-6(2)) Mason Crest Pubs.

LeVert, Suzanne. Sierra Leone. 2007. (Cultures of the World Ser.). (Illus.). 128p. (J). lib. bdg. 39.93 (978-0-7614-2334-8(6) , Benchmark Bks.) Cavendish, Marshall Corp.

SIERRA NEVADA (CALIF. AND NEV.)—FICTION

Roll, Renee. The Wolf Pups. 2006. (YA). pap. (***978-0-9727995-2-2(4)***) Roll, Renee.

Shahan, Sherry. Death Mountain. 2005. 176p. (J). 15.95 (978-1-56145-353-5(6)) Peachtree Pubs., Ltd.

Sierra Summer. 2003. (Illus.). pap. 15.99 (978-0-7868-4561-3(9)) Disney Pr.

Uncle Markie. Piglettè & Bobo Join the Manscouts. 2003. (YA). ring bd. 9.95 (978-1-933129-05-1(0)) Studio 403.

SIGHT

see Vision

SIGN BOARDS

see Signs and Signboards

SIGN LANGUAGE

see also Indian Sign Language

Ace Academics, ed. Sign Language Pt. 1: A Whole Course in a Box!, 3 vols. 2007. (Exambusters Ser.: Part 1 of 3). (Illus.). 192p. (gr. 7 up). 12.95 (978-1-881374-95-4(5) , Exambusters) Ace Academics, Inc.

Allen, Joy. Baby Signs: A Baby-Sized Guide to Speaking with Sign Language. 2008. 16p. (J). (ps). bds. 6.99 (***978-0-8037-3193-6(0)*** , Dial) Penguin Group (USA) Inc.

Audia, John P. The Creation Story: In Words & Sign Language. Spohn, David, illus. 2007. (J). (***978-0-8146-3174-4(6)***) Liturgical Pr.

Ault, Kelly. Let's Sign! Every Baby's Guide to Communicating with Grownups. Landry, Leo, illus. 2005. 80p. (J). (gr. k-ps). 17.00 (978-0-618-50774-0(4)) Houghton Mifflin Co. Trade & Reference Div.

Awareness & Caring - Sign Language, 10 bks. (J). lib. bdg. 175.50 (978-1-56674-912-1(3)) Forest Hse. Publishing Co., Inc.

Barfell, Judith A. Learn & Sign Funtime Beginnings. 2004. (Beginnings Ser.: Bk. 1). (Illus.). 40p. (J). per. 14.95 (978-0-9753717-1-8(1)) Learn and Sign Funtime Bks.

Barfell, Judy. Learn & Sign Funtime: The United States Presidents. 2005. (J). per. 29.90 (978-0-9753717-4-9(6)) Learn and Sign Funtime Bks.

Beginning Signs: Flip Charts. (J). spiral bd. 15.95 (978-1-930820-34-0(8)) Garlic Pr.

Board Book Vol. 1: My First Signs. 2005. (J). bds. (978-1-933543-00-0(0)) Two Little Hands Productions LLC.

Board Book Vol. 2: Playtime Signs. 2005. (J). bds. (978-1-933543-01-7(9)) Two Little Hands Productions LLC.

Board Book Vol. 3: Everyday Signs. 2005. (J). bds. (978-1-933543-02-4(7)) Two Little Hands Productions LLC.

Breindel, Tina Jo. Let's Eat. Carter, Michael, illus. 2006. (American Sign Language Babies Ser.). 16p. (J). bds. 5.95 (978-1-58121-152-8(X)) DawnSignPress.

Collins, S. Harold. Expanded Songs in Sign. Kifer, Kathy & Schneider, Jane, illus. 1998. (Beginning Sign Language Ser.). 32p. (J). (ps up). pap. 6.95 (978-0-931993-05-3(9)) Garlic Pr.

Collins, Stanley H., et al. Holidays & Celebrations. Schneider, Jane & Kifer, Kathy, illus. 1999. (Beginning Sign Language Ser.). 32p. (J). pap. 6.95 (978-0-931993-10-7(5)) Garlic Pr.

Cryan, Michelle. Where Is Baby? A Lift-the-Flap Sign Language Book. 2007. (Illus.). 24p. 10.95 (***978-1-56368-353-4(9)***) Gallaudet Univ. Pr.

Ehlke, Paul. Clouds: Science Information in American Sign Language: A Paws Science Adventure. 2003. (J). cd-rom 29.95 (978-0-9752933-2-4(X)) Institute for Disabilities Research & Training, Inc.

Flodin, Mickey. The Kids' Pocket Signing Guide. 2005. 192p. (gr. 12). pap. 12.95 (978-0-399-53207-8(2) , Perigee Trade) Penguin Group (USA) Inc.

—Signing for Kids. rev. ed. 2007. 160p. pap. 12.95 (978-0-399-53320-4(6) , Perigee Trade) Penguin Group (USA) Inc.

Gleason, Bruce, ed. Say, Sing & Sign Abc. 2001. (American Sign Language Ser.). 28p. (J). (gr. k-6). pap. 19.95 incl. VHS (978-1-887120-10-4(6)) Production Assocs., Inc.

Greene, Laura. Sign-Me-Fine: Experiencing American Sign Language. 2002. (gr. 7-12). lib. bdg. 21.05 (978-0-613-88924-7(X)) Tandem Library Bks.

Heelan, Jamee Riggio. Can You Hear a Rainbow? The Story of a Deaf Boy Named Chris. Simmonds, Nicola, illus. 2002. (Rehabilitation Institute of Chicago Learning Book Ser.). 32p. (J). (gr. 1-5). 14.95 (978-1-56145-268-2(8) , Q34265) Peachtree Pubs., Ltd.

Heller, Lora. Sign Language for Kids: A Fun & Easy Guide to American Sign Language. 2004. (Illus.). 96p. (J). 14.95 (978-1-4027-0672-1(3)) Sterling Publishing Co., Inc.

—Teaching Your Baby to Sign. 2004. (Baby Fingers Ser.). (Illus.). 24p. (J). bds. 4.95 (978-1-4027-1728-4(8)) Sterling Publishing Co., Inc.

Holub, Joan & Scholastic, Inc. Staff. My First Book of Sign Language. 2004. 32p. (J). pap. 3.50 (978-0-439-63582-0(9)) Scholastic, Inc.

Hossell, Karen Price. Sign Language. 2003. (Communicating Ser.). 48p. (J). (gr. 3-5). pap. 8.50 (978-1-58810-943-9(7) , 91582) Heinemann Library.

Hubler, Michael & Hubler, Lillian. Time to Sign with Children Infant/Toddler: Time to Sign with Music Infant/Toddler. 2003. Orig. Title: Time to Sign with Music Infant/Toddler. (Illus.). 42p. (J). per. 20.00 (978-0-9713666-0-2(8)) Time to Sign, Incorporated.

Hyperion Staff & Wow Worldwide Limited Staff. Wow Babies: First Words. 2007. 12p. (ps-ps). 6.99 (***978-1-4231-0247-2(9)***) Hyperion Pr.

Itsy, Bitsy Spider. 2005. (Sign & Signalong Ser.). (Illus.). 10p. (J). (ps). per. 4.99 (978-1-904550-43-3(6)) Child's Play-International.

Jensema, Marissa, illus. ASL Songs for Kids - 1: With Songs in American Sign Language. 2003. (J). cd-rom 29.95 (978-0-9752933-1-7(1)) Institute for Disabilities Research & Training, Inc.

Katschka, Gustav. Mr. Cue's Zoo: Phonics & Cued Speech. Katschka, Gustav, illus. 1998. (Illus.). 53p. (J). (gr. k-5). spiral bd. 30.00 (978-1-892917-05-8(X)) Cued Speech for Integrated Communication, Inc.

Kent, Deborah. American Sign Language. 2003. (Watts Library). (Illus.). 64p. (J). (gr. 5-7). pap. 8.95 (978-0-531-16662-8(7) , Watts, Franklin) Scholastic Library Publishing.

—American Sign Language. 2003. (gr. 5-8). lib. bdg. 17.60 (978-0-613-67596-3(7)) Tandem Library Bks.

Kramer, Jackie. You Can Learn Sign Language! 1999. (978-0-606-18671-1(9)) Tandem Library Bks.

Kubler, Annie, illus. Teddy Bear, Teddy Bear. 2004. (Sign & Signalong Ser.). 12p. (J). (ps). bds. 4.99 (978-1-904550-40-2(1)) Child's Play-International.

—Twinkle, Twinkle, Little Star. 2002. (Sign & Signalong Ser.). 12p. (J). (ps). bds. 4.99 (978-1-904550-42-6(8)) Child's Play-International.

Layton, Meredith. Baby's First Words: A Sign & Say Interactive Language Book. Anderson, Brad & Goodwin, Sharon, illus. David Nester Photography Staff, photos by. 1999. (Sign & Say Interactive Language Ser.). 32p. (J). 16.95 (978-0-9670821-0-3(2)) Peek-A-Boo Publishing.

Learn & Sign Funtime - Beginnings. 2007. (FRE.). (J). per. 14.95 (978-0-9753717-9-4(7)) Learn and Sign Funtime Bks.

Learn & Sign Funtime - Beginnings: British Edition. 2005. (J). per. (978-0-9753717-7-0(0)) Learn and Sign Funtime Bks.

Learn & Sign Funtime - Beginnings: Lakota Edition. 2007. Orig. Title: Learn & Sign Funtime. (SAI.). per. (978-0-9753717-8-7(9)) Learn and Sign Funtime Bks.

Learn & Sign Funtime - Haitian Edition: Beginnings. 2005. (CRP.). (J). per. 14.95 net. (978-0-9753717-6-3(2)) Learn and Sign Funtime Bks.

Learn & Sign Funtime: Beginnings. 4th ed. 2005. Orig. Title: Learn & Sign Funtime - Beginnings Third Edition. (J). per. 14.95 (978-0-9753717-5-6(4)) Learn and Sign Funtime Bks.

Learn & Sign Funtime: Beginnings - Auslan. 3rd ed. 2004. per. 14.95 (978-0-9753717-3-2(8)) Learn and Sign Funtime Bks.

Lewis, Anthony. Getting Ready Sign About. 2006. 12p. pap. 4.99 (978-1-84643-029-9(1)) Child's Play-International.

—Going Out Sign About. 2006. 12p. pap. 4.99 (978-1-84643-032-9(1)) Child's Play-International.

—Meal Time Sign About. 2006. 12p. pap. 4.99 (978-1-84643-030-5(5)) Child's Play-International.

—Play Time Sign About. 2006. 12p. pap. 4.99 (978-1-84643-031-2(3)) Child's Play-International.

Lowenstein, Felicia. All about Sign Language: Talking with Your Hands. 2004. (Transportation & Communication Ser.). (Illus.). 48p. (J). lib. bdg. 23.93 (978-0-7660-2028-3(2)) Enslow Pubs., Inc.

McIntosh, Anne. Sometimes I Talk, Sometimes I Sign: Algunas Veces Hablo, Algunas Veces Uso el Lenguaje Manual. Campagna, Jeff, ed. Kidd, Dawn, tr. Padbury, Scott, illus. 2000. 40p. (J). (ps-4). pap. 19.95 (978-0-9679353-0-0(X)) Communication Connection.

Millman, Isaac. Moses Goes to a Concert. Millman, Isaac, illus. (Moses Goes To Ser.). (Illus.). 40p. (J). 2002. pap. 6.95 (978-0-374-45366-4(7) , Sunburst); 1998. 17.00 (978-0-374-35067-3(1) , Farrar, Straus & Giroux (BYR)) Farrar, Straus & Giroux.

—Moses Goes to a Concert. 2002. (gr. k-3). lib. bdg. 14.10 (978-0-613-53841-1(2)) Tandem Library Bks.

Neal, Vonda & Herbold, Marvin, compiled by. British Sign Language American Sign Language Translator. 2004. (YA). cd-rom 19.95 (978-0-9752933-8-6(9)) Institute for Disabilities Research & Training, Inc.

Price Hossell, Karen. Sign Language. 2003. (Communicating Ser.). (Illus.). 48p. (J). (gr. 3-5). lib. bdg. 27.07 (978-1-58810-487-8(7)) Heinemann Library.

Primm & Petelinsek. Animals/Animales. 2004. (Talking Hands, Listening Eyes Ser.). (ENG & SPA., Illus.). 24p. (J). (ps-3). 21.36 (978-1-59296-018-7(9)) Child's World, Inc.

—Colors & Shapes/Colores y Formas. 2004. (Talking Hands, Listening Eyes Ser.). (ENG & SPA., Illus.). 24p. (J). (ps-3). 21.36 (978-1-59296-019-4(7)) Child's World, Inc.

—Food/Comida. 2004. (Talking Hands, Listening Eyes Ser.). (ENG & SPA., Illus.). 24p. (J). (ps-3). 21.36 (978-1-59296-020-0(0)) Child's World, Inc.

—Seasons/Estaciones. 2004. (Talking Hands, Listening Eyes Ser.). (ENG & SPA., Illus.). 24p. (J). (ps-3). 21.36 (978-1-59296-023-1(5)) Child's World, Inc.

Primm & Petelinsek, Kathleen. Feelings & Emotions. 2004. (Talking Hands, Listening Eyes Ser.).Tr. of Sentimientos. (ENG & SPA., Illus.). 24p. (J). (ps-3). 21.36 (978-1-59296-022-4(7)) Child's World, Inc.

—Home. 2004. (Talking Hands, Listening Eyes Ser.).Tr. of Casa. (ENG & SPA., Illus.). 24p. (J). (ps-3). 21.36 (978-1-59296-021-7(9)) Child's World, Inc.

Rosas, Heather J. My Very First Signs. 2007. (Little Signs Ser.). 10p. (J). (ps). bds. 5.99 (978-0-8431-2216-9(1) , Price Stern Sloan) Penguin Group (USA) Inc.

Sawyer, Louise. ABC & ASL. 2002. (YA). 6.95 (978-0-9719842-9-5(8)) Martin & Brothers.

—Jimmy. 2002. (YA). 6.95 (978-0-9719842-6-4(3)) Martin & Brothers.

—Jr @ the Cobbler Shop. 2001. (YA). spiral bd. 9.95 (978-0-9719842-7-1(1)) Martin & Brothers.

—Snakes & Hot Dogs. 2002. (YA). 7.95 (978-0-9719842-5-7(5)) Martin & Brothers.

Scholastic, Inc. Staff. Magnetic Journal. Im, Angela, ed. 2002. 160p. (J). 9.99 (978-0-439-28862-0(2) , Tangerine Pr.) Scholastic, Inc.

Sewell, James. Jesus Loves Me! Scriptures & Songs in Sign Language. 2003. 64p. (J). 7.99 (978-0-88724-874-0(8)) Carson-Dellosa Publishing Co., Inc.

Sign Language Conversations for Beginning Signers. 2001. 112p. (J). per. 12.95 (978-1-930820-12-8(7)) Garlic Pr.

Signs & Symbols: Lessons & activities for children Ages 5-10. 2005. (J). pap. 14.95 (978-1-58459-268-6(0)) World Library Pubns.

Vinopol, Corinne. Con-SIGN-tration 3: Computer Software Game in American Sign Language. 2003. (J). cd-rom 19.95 (978-0-9752933-6-2(2)) Institute for Disabilities Research & Training, Inc.

—Con-SIGN-tration 4: Computer Software Game in American Sign Language. 2003. (J). cd-rom 19.95 (978-0-9752933-7-9(0)) Institute for Disabilities Research & Training, Inc.

—Spell Well: CD-ROM American Sign Language Spelling Game. 2003. (YA). cd-rom 19.95 (978-0-9752933-0-0(3)) Institute for Disabilities Research & Training, Inc.

Vinopol, Corinne & Bednarczyk, Angela. American Sign Language Clip & Create: Clip Art Software. 2003. (YA). cd-rom 34.95 (978-0-9752933-4-8(6)) Institute for Disabilities Research & Training, Inc.

Vinopol, Corinne K. American Sign Language Clip & Create 2. 2nd ed. 2004. cd-rom 34.95 (978-0-9760818-0-7(6)) Institute for Disabilities Research & Training, Inc.

Vreeland, Kristine. I Can Talk with My Hands, Vol. 4408. Kupperstein, Joel, ed. Jarrett, Michael, photos by. 1998. (Learn to Read Social Studies). (Illus.). 16p. (J). (ps-2). pap. 2.75 (978-1-57471-331-2(0) , 4408) Creative Teaching Pr., Inc.

Warner, Penny. Signing Fun: American Sign Language Phrases, Vocabulary, Games, & Activities. Gray, Paula, illus. 2006. 192p. pap. 19.95 (978-1-56368-292-6(3)) Gallaudet Univ. Pr.

SIGN LANGUAGE—FICTION

Addabbo, Carole. Dina the Deaf Dinosaur. Valentine, illus. 1998. 32p. (J). (ps-5). 19.95 (978-1-889262-04-8(8)) Hannacroix Creek Bks., Inc.

Brightwood, Laura, illus. Debate in Sign Language. Brightwood, Laura, . 2006. (J). (978-0-9779290-6-1(X)) 3-C Institute for Social Development.

Ferris, Jean. Of Sound Mind. 224p. (YA). 2001. (gr. 8 up). 16.00 (978-0-374-35580-7(0) , Farrar, Straus & Giroux (BYR)); 2004. reprint ed. pap. 6.95 (978-0-374-45584-2(8) , Sunburst) Farrar, Straus & Giroux.

Guest, Jacqueline. Secret Signs. 2006. (Illus.). 144p. (J). pap. 5.95 (978-1-55143-599-2(3)) Orca Bk. Pubs. USA.

Jordan, Sherryl. The Raging Quiet. 2004. 368p. (YA). mass mkt. 5.99 (978-0-689-87004-0(3) , Simon Pulse) Simon & Schuster Children's Publishing.

—The Raging Quiet. 2000. (YA). (978-0-606-20093-6(2)) Tandem Library Bks.

—The Raging Quiet. l.t. ed. 2005. 416p. 22.95 (978-0-7862-7313-3(5) , Large Print Pr.) Thorndike Pr.

—The Raging Quiet. l.t. ed. 2000. (Illus.). 464p. (978-0-7089-9535-8(7)) Ulverscroft Large Print Bks.

Millman, Isaac. Moses Goes to School. Millman, Isaac, illus. 2000. (Moses Goes To Ser.). (Illus.). 32p. (J). (gr. k-3). 16.00 (978-0-374-35069-7(8) , Farrar, Straus & Giroux (BYR)) Farrar, Straus & Giroux.

—Moses Goes to the Circus. Millman, Isaac, illus. 2003. (Moses Goes To Ser.). (Illus.). 32p. (J). (ps-3). 16.00 (978-0-374-35064-2(7) , Farrar, Straus & Giroux (BYR)) Farrar, Straus & Giroux.

Sawyer, Louise. The Barking Baby. 2001. (YA). spiral bd. 9.95 (978-0-9719842-2-6(0)) Martin & Brothers.

—Mother's Storybook Signs. 2004. (YA). Vol. 1. spiral bd. 19.95 (978-0-9719842-0-2(4)); Vol. 2. spiral bd. 19.95 (978-0-9719842-8-8(X)) Martin & Brothers.

Uhlberg, Myron. The Printer. Sorensen, Henri, tr. Sorensen, Henri, illus. 2003. 32p. (J). (gr. 1-5). 16.95 (978-1-56145-221-7(1)) Peachtree Pubs., Ltd.

SIGNALS AND SIGNALING

see also Flags; Radio

Cefrey, Holly. The Inventions of Martha Coston: Signal Flares That Saved Sailors' Lives. 2003. (19th Century American Inventors Ser.). (Illus.). 24p. (J). lib. bdg. 17.25 (978-0-8239-6444-4(2) , PowerKids Pr.) Rosen Publishing Group, Inc., The.

SIGNERS OF THE DECLARATION OF INDEPENDENCE

see United States—Declaration of Independence

SIGNS (ADVERTISING)

see Signs and Signboards

SIGNS AND SIGNBOARDS

see also Posters

Bauer, David. Signs. 2006. (Illus.). 8,16p. (J). 6.50 (978-0-7368-1719-6(0)) Red Brick Learning.

Caviezel, Giovanni. Street Safety Hints. 2005. (Illus.). 10p. (J). bds. 10.99 (978-0-7641-5840-7(6)) Barron's Educational Series, Inc.

Dorling Kindersley Publishing Staff. Signs in Our World. 2006. (Illus.). 32p. (J). 15.99 (978-0-7566-1834-6(7)); pap. 5.99 (978-0-7566-1827-8(4)) Dorling Kindersley Publishing, Inc.

Green Means Go. 2006. (Yellow Umbrella Social Studies). 8,16p. (J). 6.50 (978-0-7368-1716-5(6)) Red Brick Learning.

Harcourt School Publishers Staff. I Read Signs. 3rd ed. 2002. (Trophies Reading Program Ser.). (Illus.). pap. 55.10 (978-0-15-326468-9(3)) Harcourt Schl. Pubs.

—I Read Signs Little Book. 3rd ed. 2002. (Trophies Reading Program Ser.). (Illus.). (J). pap. 10.20 (978-0-15-326504-4(3)) Harcourt Schl. Pubs.

Hill, Mary. Signs at School. 2003. (Signs in My World Ser.). (Illus.). 24p. (J). 18.00 (978-0-516-24274-3(1)); pap. 4.95 (978-0-516-24366-5(7)) Scholastic Library Publishing. (Children's Pr.).

—Signs at School. 2003. (gr. k-3). lib. bdg. 12.95 (978-0-613-59719-7(2)) Tandem Library Bks.

—Signs at the Airport. 2003. (Signs in My World Ser.). (Illus.). 24p. (J). 18.00 (978-0-516-24272-9(5)); pap. 4.95 (978-0-516-24364-1(0)) Scholastic Library Publishing. (Children's Pr.).

—Signs at the Airport. 2003. (gr. k-3). lib. bdg. 12.95 (978-0-613-59720-3(6)) Tandem Library Bks.

—Signs at the Park. 2003. (Welcome Bks.). (Illus.). 24p. (J). (ps-2). pap. 4.95 (978-0-516-24365-8(9) , Children's Pr.) Scholastic Library Publishing.

—Signs at the Park. 2003. (gr. k-3). lib. bdg. 12.95 (978-0-613-59721-0(4)) Tandem Library Bks.

—Signs at the Pool. 2003. (Welcome Bks.). (Illus.). 24p. (J). (ps-2). pap. 4.95 (978-0-516-24367-2(5) , Children's Pr.) Scholastic Library Publishing.

—Signs at the Store. 2003. (Welcome Bks.). (Illus.). 24p. (J). (ps-2). pap. 4.95 (978-0-516-24363-4(2) , Children's Pr.) Scholastic Library Publishing.

—Signs at the Store. 2003. (gr. k-3). lib. bdg. 12.95 (978-0-613-59723-4(0)) Tandem Library Bks.

—Signs on the Road. 2003. (Signs in My World Ser.). (Illus.). 24p. (J). 18.00 (978-0-516-24270-5(9)); pap. 4.95 (978-0-516-24362-7(4)) Scholastic Library Publishing. (Children's Pr.).

—Signs on the Road. 2003. (gr. k-3). lib. bdg. 12.95 (978-0-613-59724-1(9)) Tandem Library Bks.

Milich, Zoran. City signs. 2005. (Illus.). 32p. (J). (gr. k up). (978-1-55337-748-1(6)) Kids Can Pr., Ltd.

—City signs. Milich, Zoran, illus. 2002. (Illus.). 32p. (J). (ps-k). (978-1-55337-003-1(1)) Kids Can Pr., Ltd.

SIGNS AND SIGNBOARDS—FICTION

Armstrong, Jennifer. Once upon a Banana. Small, David, illus. 2006. 48p. (J). (ps-3). 16.95 (978-0-689-84251-1(1) , Simon & Schuster Children's Publishing) Simon & Schuster Children's Publishing.

Jordan, Taylor. Movin' on In. Wummer, Amy, illus. 2005. (Social Studies Connects). 32p. (J). pap. 4.99 (978-1-57565-159-0(9)) Kane Pr., The.

Road Signs. 2005. (J). per. 9.95 (978-1-59352-179-0(0)) Christian Services Publishing.

Say, Allen. The Sign Painter. Say, Allen, illus. 2000. (Illus.). 32p. (J). (gr. k-3). tchr. ed. 17.00 (978-0-395-97974-7(9) , Walter Lorraine) Houghton Mifflin Co. Trade & Reference Div.

SIGNS AND SYMBOLS

see also Ciphers; Cryptography; Heraldry; Signals and Signaling; Symbolism

Baa Baa, Black Sheep! 2005. (Sign & Signalong Ser.). (Illus.). 8p. (J). (ps). per. 4.99 (978-1-904550-41-9(X)) Child's Play-International.

Benchmark Education Staff. Symbols of the United States. 2005. 2.00 (***978-1-4108-4638-9(5)***) Benchmark Education Co.

Binns, Tristan Boyer. The Bald Eagle. 2001. (J). 13.79 (978-0-606-22573-1(0)) Tandem Library Bks.

Bodach, Vijaya. Pictographs. 2008. (J). (***978-1-4296-0041-5(1)***) Capstone Pr., Inc.

Bracken, Thomas. Good Luck Symbols & Talismans. 1999. (Looking Into the Past Ser.). (Illus.). 64p. (YA). lib. bdg. 19.75 (978-0-7910-4683-8(4) , Chelsea Hse.) Facts On File, Inc.

Brannon, Barbara. Discover Symbols of the United States. 2005. 39.00 (***978-1-4108-5144-4(3)***) Benchmark Education Co.

Breindel, Tina Jo. First Signs. Carter, Michael, illus. 2006. (American Sign Language Babies Ser.). 16p. (J). bds. 5.95 (978-1-58121-151-1(1)) DawnSignPress.

Campbell, Melvin D. Signs, Signs, Signs. 2007. (J). (978-1-59515-935-9(5)) Rourke Publishing, LLC.

Celebrate Freedom: Songs, Symbols, & Sayings of the United States. 2003. (Illus.). 32p. (gr. k-2). (978-0-328-03672-1(2)); 48p. (gr. 3-6). (978-0-328-03674-5(9)) Addison-Wesley Educational Pubs., Inc. (Scott Foresman).

Cipriano, Jeri. Symbols of Our Country. 2005. (Navigators Ser.). (J). pap. 38.00 (***978-1-4108-5096-6(X)***) Benchmark Education Co.

DeGezelle, Terri. The Great Seal of the United States. 2004. (Illus.). 24p. (J). 15.95 (978-0-7368-2528-3(2)) Capstone Pr., Inc.

Dell, Pamela. The Bald Eagle. 2004. (Let's See Library). (Illus.). 24p. (J). (gr. 1 up). lib. bdg. 19.93 (978-0-7565-0616-2(6)) Compass Point Bks.

Diaz-Cubero, Jose H. Practicas de Ortografia: 5 Grado. (SPA & ENG.). (J). (gr. 5). 9.95 (978-84-357-0125-9(5) , CPR92) Ediciones y Distribuciones Codice, S.A. ESP. *Dist:* Continental Bk. Co., Inc.

Douglas, Lloyd G. Welcome BooksTM: American Symbols. 2004. (Illus.). 87.00 (978-0-516-29783-5(X)) Scholastic Library Publishing.

French, Vivian. Write Around the World. Collins, Ross, illus. 1998. (J). (gr. k-4). (978-1-84089-025-9(8) , Zero to Ten, Limited) Evans Publishing Group.

Hancock, Maryann. The Bald Eagle. 2006. (Illus.). 32p. (J). pap. (978-1-4034-7010-2(3)); lib. bdg. (978-1-4034-7003-4(0)) Heinemann Library.

Harris, Nancy. The Bald Eagle. 2007. (J). (***978-1-4034-9380-4(4)***); pap. (***978-1-4034-9387-3(1)***) Heinemann Library.

—The Liberty Bell. 2007. (J). (***978-1-4034-9381-1(2)***); pap. (***978-1-4034-9388-0(X)***) Heinemann Library.

—The Pledge of Allegiance. 2007. (J). (***978-1-4034-9378-1(2)***); pap. (***978-1-4034-9385-9(5)***) Heinemann Library.

—The Statue of Liberty. 2007. (J). (***978-1-4034-9382-8(0)***); pap. (***978-1-4034-9389-7(8)***) Heinemann Library.

—The White House. 2007. (J). (***978-1-4034-9383-5(9)***); pap. (***978-1-4034-9390-3(1)***) Heinemann Library.

Hicks, Terry Allan. The Bald Eagle. 2006. (Symbols of America Ser.). (Illus.). 40p. (J). lib. bdg. 28.50 (978-0-7614-2133-7(5) , Benchmark Bks.) Cavendish, Marshall Corp.

Hicks, Terry Allan. Symbols of America Group 2, 6 bks., Set. Incl. Bald Eagle. lib. bdg. 28.50 (978-0-7614-2133-7(5)); Capitol. lib. bdg. 28.50 (978-0-7614-2132-0(7)); Declaration of Independence. lib. bdg. 28.50 (978-0-7614-2135-1(1)); Ellis Island. lib. bdg. 28.50 (978-0-7614-2134-4(3)); Pledge of Allegiance. lib. bdg. 28.50 (978-0-7614-2136-8(X)); Uncle Sam. lib. bdg. 28.50 (978-0-7614-2137-5(8)); (Illus.). 40p. (J). 2006. 2007. Set lib. bdg. 171.00 (***978-0-7614-2130-6(0)*** , Benchmark Bks.) Cavendish, Marshall Corp.

Johnson, Etta. Symbols of the United States. 2005. 39.00 (***978-1-4108-4590-0(7)***) Benchmark Education Co.

Keenan, Sheila. O, Say Can You See? America's Symbols, Landmarks, & Inspiring Words. Boyajian, Ann, illus. 2004. (Oh Say Can You See Ser.). 64p. (J). (ps-3). pap. 16.95 (978-0-439-42450-9(X) , Scholastic Reference) Scholastic, Inc.

Kishel, Ann-Marie. U.S. Symbols. 2007. (First Step Nonfiction Ser.). 24p. (J). (gr. k-2). 18.60 (978-0-8225-6394-5(0) , Lerner Pubns.) Lerner Publishing Group.

Kubler, Annie, illus. My First Signs. 2005. 12p. (J). (ps). per. 6.99 (978-1-904550-39-6(8)); bds. 6.99 (978-1-904550-04-4(5)) Child's Play-International.

Lomas, Sue. Maps & Symbols. 2004. (Geography First Ser.). (J). 23.70 (978-1-4103-0113-0(3) , Blackbirch Pr., Inc.) Thomson Gale.

Love, Mary A. The ABC's & Symbols. Flournoy, L. Diana, illus. 1998. 32p. (J). pap. 4.50 (978-1-929548-01-9(X)) Love's Creative Resources.

Marcovitz, Hal. The Bald Eagle. 2002. (American Symbols & Their Meanings Ser.). (Illus.). 48p. (YA). (gr. 4 up). lib. bdg. (978-1-59084-032-0(1)) Mason Crest Pubs.

—Uncle Sam. 2002. (American Symbols & Their Meanings Ser.). (Illus.). 48p. (YA). (gr. 4 up). lib. bdg. (978-1-59084-023-8(2)) Mason Crest Pubs.

Maurer, Tracy. License Plates. 1999. (Guide to State Symbols Ser.). (Illus.). 48p. (J). (gr. 3-8). lib. bdg. 29.93 (978-1-57103-298-0(3)) Rourke Publishing, LLC.

Moreno, Barry, intro. American Symbols & Their Meanings, 20 vols., Set. 2002. (Illus.). 48p. (YA). (gr. 4 up). lib. bdg. (978-1-59084-021-4(6)) Mason Crest Pubs.

Pearl, Norman. The Great Seal of the United States. Skeens, Matthew, illus. 2006. 24p. (J). (ps-2). lib. bdg. 23.93 (978-1-4048-2214-6(3)) Picture Window Bks.

Primary Sources of American Symbols. (J). (gr. k-6). 119.70 (978-1-4042-3300-3(8)) Rosen Publishing Group, Inc., The.

Running Press Staff. Spy School Kit, No. 1. 2008. 64p. (J). pap. 14.95 (978-0-7624-2049-0(9)) Running Pr. Bk. Pubs.

Saunders-Smith, Gail, ed. American Symbols. (First Facts Ser.). (Illus.). (J). (gr. 1-2). lib. bdg. 297.64 (978-0-7368-2569-6(X)) Capstone Pr., Inc.

Scholastic, Inc. Staff & Keenan, Sheila. O, Say Can You See? America's Symbols, Landmarks, & Important Words. 2007. 64p. (J). pap. 5.99 (***978-0-439-59360-1(3)*** , Scholastic Nonfiction) Scholastic, Inc.

Silate, Jennifer. The Bald Eagle. 2005. (Illus.). 24p. (J). lib. bdg. (978-1-4042-2697-5(4)) Rosen Publishing Group, Inc., The.

Thames, Susan. Nuestros Símbolos Americanos. 2007. (J). (***978-1-60044-304-6(4)***) Rourke Publishing, LLC.

—Our American Symbols. 2007. (Illus.). 24p. (J). (***978-1-59515-994-6(0)***) Rourke Publishing, LLC.

Yanuck, Debbie L. The Bald Eagle. 2003. (American Symbols Ser.). (Illus.). 24p. (J). (gr. 1-2). lib. bdg. 23.93 (978-0-7368-1629-8(1) , Bridgestone Bks.) Capstone Pr., Inc.

SIKHISM

Barrow, Joy. Sikhism. 2003. (Illus.). lib. bdg. 28.50 (978-1-59389-134-3(2)) Chrysalis Education.

—Sikhism. 2005. (World Religions Ser.). (Illus.). 58p. (J). (gr. 4-12). pap. 12.95 (978-1-55285-652-9(6) , Walrus Bks.) Whitecap Bks., Ltd. CAN. *Dist:* Firefly Bks., Ltd.

Bawa, Ujagar S. Vaara of Bhai Gurdaj Vol. II: A Part of Sikh Scriptures. 2001. (Books on Sikhism Ser.). (PAN & ENG.). 519p. (YA). (gr. 9 up). 35.00 (978-0-942245-12-7(1)) Washington Sikh Ctr./Sikh Youth Forum.

—Vaars of Bhai Gurdaj Vol. I: A Part of Sikh Scriptures. 2001. (Books on Sikhism Ser.). (ENG & PAN.). 519p. (YA). (gr. 9 up). 35.00 (978-0-942245-11-0(3)) Washington Sikh Ctr./Sikh Youth Forum.

Bingham, Jane. Sikh Gurdwaras. 2005. (Let's Find Out about Ser.). (Illus.). 32p. (J). (978-1-4034-7034-8(0)) Steck-Vaughn.

Bingham, Jane. Sikhism Around the World. 2007. (J). (***978-1-59920-059-0(7)***) Smart Apple Media.

Ganeri, Anita. The Guru Granth Sahib & Sikhism. 2003. 30p. (J). lib. bdg. 24.25 (978-1-58340-245-0(4)) Smart Apple Media.

—Sikh Festivals Throughout The Year. 2003. (Year of Festivals Ser.). (Illus.). 30p. lib. bdg. 24.25 (978-1-58340-374-7(4)) Smart Apple Media.

—Sikh Stories. Phillips, Rachael, illus. 2003. (Storyteller Ser.). 30p. (J). (978-0-237-52037-3(0) , Evans Brothers, Limited) Evans Publishing Group.

Ganeri, Anita & Dalton, David. Sikhism. 2006. (This Is My Faith Bks.). (Illus.). 32p. (J). (gr. 1-4). 11.99 (978-0-7641-5968-8(2)); pap. 4.99 (978-0-7641-3477-7(9)) Barron's Educational Series, Inc.

Kaur, Harliv & Kaur, Jasmine, compiled by. My Gurmukhi Khajana: A Gurmat Based Primer. 2007. (ENG & PAN., Illus.). 43p. (J). 13.00 (***978-1-60411-000-5(7)***) Sikh Research Institute.

Kaur-Singh, Kanwaljit. My Sikh Faith. 2006. (World Faiths Ser.). (Illus.). 32p. (J). (978-1-84234-387-6(4) , Cherrytree Books) Evans Publishing Group.

S

—My Sikh Faith. 1998. (My Faith Ser.). (Illus.). 32p. 9.99 (978-0-237-51980-3(1) , Evans Brothers, Limited) Evans Publishing Group GBR. *Dist:* Independent Pubs. Group.

—Sikhism. 2006. (QEB World of Faiths Ser.). (Illus.). 32p. (J). (gr. 3-6). lib. bdg. 27.10 (978-1-59566-211-8(1)) QEB Publishing Inc.

Kaur-Singh, Kanwaljit & Nason, Ruth. Visiting a Gurdwara. 2005. (Start up Religion Ser.). (Illus.). 24p. (J). (gr. 1-4). lib. bdg. (978-1-84234-345-6(9) , Cherrytree Books) Evans Publishing Group.

Kaus-Singh, Kanwaljit. Sikh Gurdwara. 1999. (Places of Worship Ser.). (Illus.). 32p. (J). (gr. 2 up). lib. bdg. 23.33 (978-0-8368-2610-4(8)) Stevens, Gareth Inc.

Mayled, Jon. Sikhism. 2003. (Living Religions Ser.). (Illus.). 62p. (J). 28.56 (978-0-7398-6387-9(8)) Raintree.

Panesar, Rajinder Singh & Ganeri, Anita. Sikh Prayer & Worship. 2007. (J). ***(978-1-59771-094-7(6))*** Sea-To-Sea Pubns.

Parker, Victoria. The Golden Temple. 2003. (Holy Places Ser.). (Illus.). 32p. (J). 24.28 (978-0-7398-6079-3(8)) Raintree.

Penney, Sue. Sikhism. (World Beliefs & Cultures Ser.). 48p. (J). 2000. (Illus.). (gr. 5-7). lib. bdg. 25.64 (978-1-57572-359-4(X)); 2nd ed. (gr. 6-9). 22.00 ***(978-1-4329-0317-6(9))*** Heinemann Library.

Senker, Cath. My Sikh Year. (Illus.). 2005. (J). pap. (978-0-7502-4055-0(5)); 2003. (978-0-7502-4054-3(7)) Hodder Children's Division. (Hodder Wayland).

—My Sikh Year. 2007. (J). lib. bdg. ***(978-1-4042-3733-9(X)*** , PowerKids Pr.) Rosen Publishing Group, Inc., The.

Singh, Nikky-Guninder Kaur. Sikhism. 2nd rev. ed. 2004. (World Religions Ser.). (Illus.). 128p. (J). (gr. 6-12). 30.00 (978-0-8160-5726-9(5)) Facts On File, Inc.

Teece, Geoff. Sikhism. 2004. (Religion in Focus Ser.). (J). lib. bdg. (978-1-58340-469-0(4)) Smart Apple Media.

SIKHS

Chambers, Catherine. Sikh. (Illus.). 32p. (YA). (gr. 3 up). lib. bdg. 27.10 (978-1-932889-14-7(0)) Sea-To-Sea Pubns.

The Sikhs. 2004. (Exploring World Beliefs Ser.). (Illus.). 48p. (J). 7.99 (978-0-7439-3682-8(5)) Teacher Created Materials, Inc.

SILK

see also Silkworms

Ballard, Carol. Silk. 2004. (J). pap. 7.50 (978-1-4109-0896-4(8)) Harcourt Schl. Pubs.

Franck, Irene M. & Brownstone, David M. Silk. 2003. (Illus.). 32p. (J). (978-0-7172-5723-2(1) , Grolier) Scholastic Library Publishing.

Gleason, Carrie. The Biography of Silk. 2006. (How Did That Get Here? Ser.). (Illus.). 32p. (J). (978-0-7787-2487-2(5)); (gr. 5). pap. (978-0-7787-2523-7(5)) Crabtree Publishing Co.

Levete, Sarah. Rubber. 2006. (Material Matters Ser.). (J). (978-1-59389-273-9(X)) Chrysalis Education.

Oxlade, Chris. How We Use Silk. 2004. (Illus.). (J). 25.70 (978-1-4109-0605-2(1)); Pack. pap. 40.50 (978-1-4109-0903-9(4)) Harcourt Schl. Pubs.

The Secret of Silk, 6 Packs. (Rigby Focus Ser.). 24p. (gr. 2 up). 30.00 (978-0-7578-5574-0(1)) Rigby Education.

The Secret of Silk: Individual Title Six-Packs. (Rigby Focus Ser.). 24p. (gr. 2 up). 28.00 (978-0-7578-5344-9(7)) Rigby Education.

Strathern, Paul, tr. Exploration by Land. 2002. (World Issues Ser.). (Illus.). 45p. (J). lib. bdg. 28.50 (978-1-931983-32-7(1)) Chrysalis Education.

SILKWORMS

Drits, Dina. Silkworm Moths. 2001. (Early Bird Nature Bks.). (Illus.). 48p. (J). (gr. 2-4). lib. bdg. 25.26 (978-0-8225-0069-8(8) , Lerner Pubns.) Lerner Publishing Group.

Fridell, Ron & Walsh, Patricia. Life Cycle of a Silkworm. 2001. (Heinemann First Library). (Illus.). 32p. (J). (gr. k-2). lib. bdg. 21.36 (978-1-58810-094-8(4)) Heinemann Library.

—Silkworm. 2002. (Life Cycle of a... Ser.). (Illus.). 32p. (J). (gr. k-2). pap. 6.95 (978-1-58810-396-3(X) , 91142) Heinemann Library.

Pfeffer, Wendy. Mysterious Spinners. Kim, Julie J., illus. 2005. 48p. (J). (978-1-59336-315-4(X)); pap. (978-1-59336-316-1(8)) Mondo Publishing.

SILVER

see also Coinage; Money

Franck, Irene M. & Brownstone, David M. Silver. 2003. (Illus.). 32p. (J). (978-0-7172-5724-9(X) , Grolier) Scholastic Library Publishing.

Morris, Neil. Gold & Silver. 2005. (Earth's Resources Ser.). (Illus.). 32p. (J). (gr. 4-7). lib. bdg. 27.10 (978-1-58340-630-4(1)) Smart Apple Media.

Murray, Peter. Silver. 2001. (From the Earth Ser.). (Illus.). 24p. (J). 21.35 (978-1-58340-109-5(1)) Smart Apple Media.

Tocci, Salvatore. Silver. 2005. (True Bks.). (Illus.). (J). (gr. 3-5). 47p. pap. 6.95 (978-0-516-25572-9(X)); 48p. 25.00 (978-0-516-23696-4(2)) Scholastic Library Publishing. (Children's Pr.).

Watt, Susan. Silver. 2002. (Elements Ser.). (Illus.). 32p. (J). 25.64 (978-0-7614-1464-3(9) , Benchmark Bks.) Cavendish, Marshall Corp.

SILVER MINES AND MINING

Hopkins, Ellen H. Tarnished Legacy: The Story of the Comstock Lode. 2001. (Cover-to-Cover Bks.). (Illus.). 64p. (J). (gr. 4-7). lib. bdg. 17.95 (978-0-7807-9702-4(7)) Perfection Learning Corp.

Spence, Clark C. For Wood River or Bust: Idaho's Silver Boom of the 1880s. 2004. (Idaho Legacy Ser.). (Illus.). 278p. 29.95 (978-0-89301-215-1(7)) Univ. of Idaho Pr.

SIMPLE (FICTITIOUS CHARACTER)—FICTION

Hughes, Langston. Simple Speaks His Mind. (J). (gr. 5-6). reprint ed. lib. bdg. 22.95 (978-0-88411-061-3(3)) Amereon LTD.

SINGAPORE

Baker, James Michael & Baker, Junia Marion. Singapore. 2002. (Countries of the World Ser.). (Illus.). 96p. (J). (gr. 6 up). lib. bdg. 30.00 (978-0-8368-2346-2(X)) Stevens, Gareth Inc.

Barber, Nicola. Singapore. 2005. (Great Cities of the World Ser.). (Illus.). 48p. (J). pap. (978-0-8368-5207-3(9)); lib. bdg. 30.00 (978-0-8368-5047-5(5)) Stevens, Gareth Inc. (World Almanac Library).

Guile, Melanie. Singapore. 2003. (Illus.). 32p. (J). lib. bdg. 25.70 (978-1-4109-0474-4(1)) Raintree.

Kummer, Patricia K. Singapore. 2003. (Enchantment of the World, Second Ser.). (Illus.). 144p. (YA). (gr. 5-9). 36.00 (978-0-516-22531-9(6) , Children's Pr.) Scholastic Library Publishing.

Layton, Lesley & Pang, G. K. Singapore. 2nd ed. 2001. (Cultures of the World Ser.). (Illus.). 144p. (gr. 5 up). lib. bdg. 37.07 (978-0-7614-1352-3(9) , Benchmark Bks.) Cavendish, Marshall Corp.

Wee, Jessie. Singapore. 1999. (Major World Nations Ser.). (Illus.). 104p. (J). (gr. 4-7). 19.95 (978-0-7910-5397-3(0) , Chelsea Hse.) Facts On File, Inc.

Yong, Jui Lin, et al. Welcome to Singapore. 2003. (Welcome to My Country Ser.). (Illus.). 48p. (J). (gr. 2 up). lib. bdg. 26.00 (978-0-8368-2546-6(2)) Stevens, Gareth Inc.

SINGAPORE—FICTION

Bidwell, Dafne. Danger Unlimited: Action, Mystery & Adventure. 2007. 181p. pap. 15.50 ***(978-1-921064-89-0(7))*** Fremantle Pr. AUS. *Dist:* International Specialized Bk. Services.

Heidell, Valerie. Mirika's Story. 2006. (YA). per. 10.95 (978-0-9774822-4-5(3)) Crosam Pr.

See, Ee Lin. My Kiasu Teenage Life in Singapore. 2005. (Illus.). 176p. pap. 12.95 (978-981-05-3016-7(1)) Monsoon Bks. Pte. Ltd. SGP. *Dist:* Biblio Distribution.

SINGERS

Acker, Kerry. Nina Simone. (Women in the Arts Ser.). (Illus.). 112p. 2004. pap. 30.00 (978-0-7910-7952-2(X)); 2003. (gr. 6-12). 30.00 (978-0-7910-7456-5(0)) Facts On File, Inc. (Chelsea Hse.).

Adebayo, Yinka. Boyz II Men. 1998. (Illus.). 144p. (J). (978-1-874509-29-5(8)) X Pr., The.

Adler, David A. & Adler, Michael S. A Picture Book of John Hancock. Himler, Ronald, illus. 2007. 32p. (J). (ps-3). 16.95 ***(978-0-8234-2005-6(1))*** Holiday Hse., Inc.

African-American Singers. 2000. (My Ancestors—My Heroes Ser.: Vol. 38). (J). (gr. 3-4). (978-1-893091-37-5(6)) Parker Publishing Co.

Alagna, Magdalena. Billie Holiday. 2006. (Rock & Roll Hall of Famers Ser.). (Illus.). 112p. (YA). (gr. 5-8). lib. bdg. 29.25 (978-0-8239-3640-3(6)) Rosen Publishing Group, Inc., The.

Alexander, Lauren. Mad for Miley: An Unauthorized Biography. 2007. 128p. (J). pap. 4.99 ***(978-0-8431-2684-6(1)*** , Price Stern Sloan) Penguin Group (USA) Inc.

Bankston, John. Alicia Keys. l.t. ed. 2002. (Real Life Reader Biography Ser.). (Illus.). 32p. (gr. 3-8). lib. bdg. 15.95 (978-1-58415-133-3(1)) Mitchell Lane Pubs., Inc.

—Christina Aguilera. 2004. (Blue Banner Biography Ser.). (Illus.). 32p. (J). lib. bdg. (978-1-58415-331-3(8)) Mitchell Lane Pubs., Inc.

—Jessica Simpson. 2001. (Real-Life Reader Biography Ser.). (Illus.). 32p. (J). (gr. 3-8). lib. bdg. 15.95 (978-1-58415-072-5(6)) Mitchell Lane Pubs., Inc.

—Mandy Moore. 2001. (Real-Life Reader Biography Ser.). (Illus.). 32p. (gr. 3-8). lib. bdg. 15.95 (978-1-58415-073-2(4)) Mitchell Lane Pubs., Inc.

—Missy Elliott: Hip-Hop Superstar. l.t. ed. 2004. (Blue Banner Biography Ser.). (Illus.). 32p. (J). (gr. 3-8). lib. bdg. 25.70 (978-1-58415-219-4(2)) Mitchell Lane Pubs., Inc.

Barnham, Kay. Jennifer Lopez. 2004. (Star Files Ser.). 29.93 (978-1-4109-1086-8(5)) Harcourt Schl. Pubs.

Benson, Michael. Gloria Estefan. (Biography Ser.). (Illus.). 112p. (gr. 6-12). 2005. lib. bdg. 27.93 (978-0-8225-4982-6(4)); 2003. (YA). pap. 7.95 (978-0-8225-9692-9(X) , Carolrhoda Bks.) Lerner Publishing Group.

Berman, Connie. Cher. 2001. (Women of Achievement Ser.). (Illus.). 112p. (J). (gr. 8-12). pap. 9.95 (978-0-7910-5908-1(1) , Chelsea Hse.) Facts On File, Inc.

Beyer, Mark. Ray Charles. 2006. (Rock & Roll Hall of Famers Ser.). (Illus.). 112p. (YA). (gr. 5-8). lib. bdg. 29.25 (978-0-8239-3642-7(2)) Rosen Publishing Group, Inc., The.

Boekhoff, P. M. & Kallen, Stuart A. Famous People - N'SYNC. 2002. (Famous People Ser.). (Illus.). 48p. (J). (gr. 3-5). 26.20 (978-0-7377-1460-9(3) , Kidhaven) Thomson Gale.

Boulais, Sue. Gloria Estefan. 1999. (Real-Life Reader Biographies Ser.). (Illus.). 32p. (gr. 3-8). lib. bdg. 15.95 (978-1-883845-62-9(9)) Mitchell Lane Pubs., Inc.

—Vanessa Williams. 1998. (Real-Life Reader Biographies Ser.). (Illus.). 32p. (gr. 3-8). lib. bdg. 15.95 (978-1-883845-75-9(0)) Mitchell Lane Pubs., Inc.

Britton, Tamara L. Britney Spears. 2000. (Young Profiles Ser.). (Illus.). 32p. (J). (gr. k-6). lib. bdg. 22.78 (978-1-57765-368-4(8) , Checkerboard Library) ABDO Publishing Co.

Broadwater, Andrea. Marian Anderson: Singer & Humanitarian. 2000. (African-American Biographies Ser.). (Illus.). 128p. (YA). (gr. 6-12). lib. bdg. 26.60 (978-0-7660-1211-0(5)) Enslow Pubs., Inc.

Brown, Monica. My Name Is Celia: The Life of Celia Cruz. Lopez, Rafael, illus. 2004. Tr. of Me Llamo Celia; la Vida de Celia Cruz. (ENG & SPA.). 32p. (gr. 2-4). 15.95 (978-0-87358-872-0(X) , Luna Rising) Northland Publishing.

B*Witched: Backstage Pass. 1999. (gr. 3-6). lib. bdg. 14.15 (978-0-613-21275-5(4)) Tandem Library Bks.

Carroll, Jillian. Aretha Franklin. 2003. (Illus.). 64p. (J). pap. 8.95 (978-1-4109-0314-3(1)); lib. bdg. 28.56 (978-0-7398-7029-7(7)) Raintree.

—Aretha Franklin. 2003. (gr. 3-6). lib. bdg. 18.20 (978-0-613-78176-3(7)) Tandem Library Bks.

Casapulla, Louise. Ashlee Simpson. 2005. (Pop People Ser.). (Illus.). 137p. (J). (978-0-439-76581-7(1)) Scholastic, Inc.

Chambers, Veronica. Celia Cruz, Queen of Salsa. Maren, Julie, illus. 40p. (J). 2007. (gr. k). pap. 6.99 (978-0-14-240779-0(8) , Puffin); 2005. (gr. 2). 15.99 (978-0-8037-2970-4(7) , Dial) Penguin Group (USA) Inc.

Chandler, Michael. The Littlest Cowboy's Christmas. Jacobson, Terry, illus. 2006. 32p. (J). 17.95 incl. audio compact disk (978-1-58980-381-7(7)) Pelican Publishing Co., Inc.

Christensen, Bonnie. Woody Guthrie: Poet of the People. 2001. (Illus.). 32p. (J). (gr. k-12). 16.95 (978-0-375-81113-5(3) , Knopf Bks. for Young Readers) Random Hse. Children's Bks.

Cole, Melanie. Celine Dion. 1998. (Real-Life Reader Biographies Ser.). (Illus.). 32p. (J). (gr. k-3). lib. bdg. 15.95 (978-1-883845-76-6(9)) Mitchell Lane Pubs., Inc.

Collins, Tracy Brown. Missy Elliott. 2007. (Hip-Hop Stars Ser.). 104p. (J). (gr. 6-12). 30.00 ***(978-0-7910-9569-0(X)*** , Chelsea Hse.) Facts On File, Inc.

The Confessions of Prima Donna. 2001. 300p. (YA). reprint ed. 98.00 (978-0-7222-6280-1(9)) Library Reprints, Inc.

Coombs, Karen Mueller. Woody Guthrie: America's Folksinger. (Illus.). 120p. (J). 2003. pap. 8.95 (978-0-8225-3750-2(8)); 2001. (gr. 4-7). lib. bdg. 27.93 (978-1-57505-464-3(7) , Carolrhoda Bks.) Lerner Publishing Group.

Dalmatian Press Staff, adapted by. Pollyanna. 2003. (Spot the Classics Ser.). 192p. (J). 4.99 (978-1-57759-561-8(0)) Dalmatian Pr.

Day, Holly. Shakira. 2007. (People in the News Ser.). 128p. (J). (gr. 7-10). 32.45 ***(978-1-59018-974-0(4)*** , Lucent Bks.) Thomson Gale.

Delmege, Sarah & Andrews McMeel Publishing Staff. Britney Spears. 2000. (Illus.). 47p. (YA). (gr. 8-12). pap., pap. 5.95 (978-1-84222-173-0(6)) Carlton Bks., Ltd. GBR. *Dist:* Ingram Pub. Services.

Dougherty, Terri. Beyonce. 2006. (Illus.). 112p. (J). (gr. 7-10). 32.45 (978-1-59018-929-0(9) , Lucent Bks.) Thomson Gale.

Dower, Laura. Britney Spears. 2000. (POP People Ser.). (Illus.). 112p. (gr. 3-7). pap. 4.50 (978-0-439-22222-8(2)) Scholastic, Inc.

Duggleby, John. Uh Huh! The Story of Ray Charles. 2005. (Modern Music Masters Ser.). (Illus.). 160p. (YA). (gr. 9-12). lib. bdg. 26.95 (978-1-931798-65-5(6)) Reynolds, Morgan Inc.

Dyson, Cindy. Janet Jackson: Singer. 2000. (Black Americans of Achievement Ser.). (Illus.). 144p. (J). (gr. 4-7). 32.00 (978-0-7910-5283-9(4)); (YA). (gr. 5 up). pap. 30.00 (978-0-7910-5284-6(2)) Facts On File, Inc. (Chelsea Hse.).

Edwards, Henry Sutherland. The Prima Donna, Her History & Surroundings from the Seventeenth to the Nineteenth Century, 2 vols., set. 2001. (YA). reprint ed. 250.00 (978-0-7222-6237-5(X)) Library Reprints, Inc.

Ella Fitzgerald: The Tale of a Vocal Virtuosa. 2004. 29.95 incl. cd-rom (978-1-55592-498-0(0)) Weston Woods Studios, Inc.

Fandel, Jennifer. James Brown. 2003. (Illus.). 64p. (J). pap. 9.50 (978-1-4109-0317-4(6)); lib. bdg. 28.56 (978-0-7398-7027-3(0)) Raintree.

Fisher, Doris. Kelly Clarkson. 2006. (Today's Superstars). 32p. (J). (gr. 5 up). lib. bdg. 23.93 ***(978-0-8368-7649-9(0))*** Stevens, Gareth Inc.

Fisher, Mary McMillan. Rosita's Bridge. Whitehead, Barbara Mathews, illus. 2001. 32p. (J). (gr. 2-4). 16.95 (978-1-893271-18-0(8)) Maverick Publishing Co.

Fitzgerald, Dawn. Destiny's Child. 2002. (Galaxy of Superstars Ser.). (Illus.). 64p. (J). 25.00 (978-0-7910-6770-3(X) , Chelsea Hse.) Facts On File, Inc.

Ford, Carin T. Paul Robeson: I Want to Make Freedom Ring. 2007. (African-American Biography Library). (Illus.). 128p. (J). (gr. 6 up). lib. bdg. 31.93 ***(978-0-7660-2703-9(1))*** Enslow Pubs., Inc.

Ford, Carin T. Ray Charles: I Was Born with Music Inside Me. 2007. (African-American Biography Library). (Illus.). 128p. (J). lib. bdg. 31.93 (978-0-7660-2701-5(5)) Enslow Pubs., Inc.

Freedman, Russell. The Voice That Challenged a Nation: Marian Anderson & the Struggle for Equal Rights. 2004. (Illus.). 128p. (J). (gr. 4-6). tchr. ed. 18.00 (978-0-618-15976-5(2) , Clarion Bks.) Houghton Mifflin Co. Trade & Reference Div.

Furman, Leah. Jennifer Lopez. (Latinos in the Limelight Ser.). (Illus.). 64p. (J). 2002. pap. (978-0-7910-6111-4(6)); 2001. (gr. 3 up). 27.50 (978-0-7910-6110-7(8)) Facts On File, Inc. (Chelsea Hse.).

Gabriel, Jan. Christina Aguilera. 2000. (gr. 3-6). lib. bdg. 14.15 (978-0-613-24580-7(6)) Tandem Library Bks.

Gaines, Ann Graham. Britney Spears. (Blue Banner Biography Ser.). (Illus.). 32p. 2004. (J). lib. bdg. (978-1-58415-329-0(6)); 1999. (gr. 3-8). lib. bdg. 15.95 (978-1-58415-060-2(2)) Mitchell Lane Pubs., Inc.

—Faith Hill. 2001. (Real-Life Reader Biography Ser.). (Illus.). 32p. (gr. 3-8). lib. bdg. 15.95 (978-1-58415-091-6(2)) Mitchell Lane Pubs., Inc.

Galaxy of Superstars. 2005. pap. 925.00 (978-0-7910-9145-6(7) , Chelsea Hse.) Facts On File, Inc.

Galaxy of Superstars, 6 bks., Set. Incl. Hanson. Powell, Phelan. (J). (gr. 3 up). pap. 25.00 (978-0-7910-5325-6(3)); Jonathan Taylor Thomas. Grabowski, John F. (YA). pap. 25.00 (978-0-7910-5330-0(X)); LeAnn Rimes. Zymet, Cathy Alter. (YA). (gr. 3). pap. 25.00 (978-0-7910-5327-0(X)); Leonardo DiCaprio. Stauffer, Stacey. (YA). pap. 25.00 (978-0-7910-5326-3(1)); Venus Williams. Aronson, Virginia. (J). pap. 25.00 (978-0-7910-5329-4(6)); 1999. (Illus.). 64p. 1999. Set pap. 59.70 (978-0-7910-5337-9(7) , Chelsea Hse.) Facts On File, Inc.

Gallagher, Jim. Shania Twain: Grammy Award-Winning Singer. 1999. (Real-Life Reader Biography Ser.). (Illus.). 32p. (gr. 3-8). lib. bdg. 15.95 (978-1-58415-000-8(9)) Mitchell Lane Pubs., Inc.

Garcia, Kimberly. Janet Jackson. 2002. (Real-Life Reader Biography Ser.). (Illus.). 32p. (J). (gr. 3-8). lib. bdg. 15.95 (978-1-58415-113-5(7)) Mitchell Lane Pubs., Inc.

Geoghegan, Bronwyn. Livewire Real Lives Kylie Minogue. 2000. (Livewires Ser.). (Illus.). 32p. pap. 7.00 (978-0-521-77617-2(1)) Cambridge Univ. Pr.

Glass, Eartha. Destiny's Child! 2001. (POP People Ser.). (Illus.). 112p. (J). (gr. 8). pap. 4.50 (978-0-439-32695-7(8)) Scholastic, Inc.

Gloria Estefan. 1999. (SmartReader Ser.). (J). Level 1. pap., tchr. ed. 19.95 incl. audio (978-0-7887-1032-2(X) , 79338T3); Level 2. pap., tchr. ed. 19.95 incl. audio (978-0-7887-1036-0(2) , 79339T3) Recorded Bks., LLC.

Gnojewski, Carol. Madonna: Express Yourself. 2007. (American Rebels Ser.). (Illus.). 160p. (J). (gr. 6 up). lib. bdg. 34.60 (978-0-7660-2442-7(3)) Enslow Pubs., Inc.

Gogerly, Liz. Elvis Presley. 2004. (Illus.). 48p. (J). lib. bdg. 28.56 (978-0-7398-6629-0(X)) Raintree.

Gonzales, Doreen. Gloria Estefan: Singer & Entertainer. 1998. (Hispanic Biographies Ser.). (Illus.). 128p. (YA). (gr. 6-12). lib. bdg. 26.60 (978-0-89490-890-3(1)) Enslow Pubs., Inc.

Goodall, Lian. Singing Towards the Future: The Story of Portia White. 2004. (Stories of Canada Ser.). (Illus.). 63p. (J). 16.95 (978-1-894917-08-7(1)) Napoleon Publishing/Rendezvous Pr. CAN. *Dist:* AtlasBooks Distribution.

Gourse, Leslie. Sophisticated Ladies: The Great Women of Jazz. French, Martin, illus. 2007. 64p. (J). 19.99 (978-0-525-47198-1(7) , Dutton Juvenile) Penguin Group (USA) Inc.

Grabowski, John F. 'N Sync. 1999. (Galaxy of Superstars Ser.). (Illus.). 64p. (YA). pap. 25.00 (978-0-7910-5494-9(2)); (J). (gr. 3 up). 25.00 (978-0-7910-5493-2(4)) Facts On File, Inc. (Chelsea Hse.).

Granados, Christine. Enrique Iglesias. 2000. (Real-Life Reader Biography Ser.). (Illus.). 32p. (J). (gr. 3-8). lib. bdg. 15.95 (978-1-58415-045-9(9)) Mitchell Lane Pubs., Inc.

Gray, Scott. Chicks Rule. 1999. (gr. 7-12). lib. bdg. 14.15 (978-0-613-21333-2(5)) Tandem Library Bks.

Greene, Meg. Lauryn Hill. 1999. (Galaxy of Superstars Ser.). (Illus.). 64p. (J). pap. 25.00 (978-0-7910-5496-3(9) , Chelsea Hse.) Facts On File, Inc.

—Lauryn Hill. 2000. (gr. 5-8). lib. bdg. 17.60 (978-0-613-21883-2(3)) Tandem Library Bks.

Hampton, Wilborn. Up Close: Elvis Presley. 2007. 192p. (YA). (gr. 7 up). 16.99 (978-0-670-06166-2(2) , Viking Juvenile) Penguin Group (USA) Inc.

Hand. Westlife. (Illus.). 128p. (J). (978-1-85227-995-0(8)) Virgin Bks. Ltd.

Hasday, Judy L. Tina Turner: Singer. 1999. (Black Americans of Achievement Ser.). (Illus.). (J). (gr. 4-7). 112p. 30.00 (978-0-7910-4967-9(1)); 104p. pap. 30.00 (978-0-7910-4968-6(X)) Facts On File, Inc. (Chelsea Hse.).

Hauk, Minnie. Memories of a Singer. 2001. 295p. (YA). reprint ed. 98.00 (978-0-7222-6282-5(5)) Library Reprints, Inc.

Hawes, Esme. Frank Sinatra. 1999. (Life & Times of Ser.). (Illus.). 48p. (YA). (gr. 5 up). 12.95 (978-0-7910-4639-5(7) , Chelsea Hse.) Facts On File, Inc.

Hayes, Donna. Brandy. 1999. (Real-Life Reader Biography Ser.). (Illus.). 32p. (J). (gr. 3-8). lib. bdg. 15.95 (978-1-883845-93-3(9)) Mitchell Lane Pubs., Inc.

Hill, Anne E. Celine Dion. 2004. (World Musicmakers Ser.). (Illus.). 64p. (J). 26.20 (978-1-56711-971-8(9) , Blackbirch Pr., Inc.) Thomson Gale.

Hillstrom, Laurie. Kelly Clarkson. 2007. (People in the News Ser.). (Illus.). 128p. (gr. 7-10). 31.20 ***(978-1-4205-0013-4(9)*** , Lucent Bks.) Thomson Gale.

Holland, Henry S. Jenny Lind the Artist, 1820-1851. 2001. 473p. (YA). reprint ed. 98.00 (978-0-7222-6225-2(6)) Library Reprints, Inc.

Holt, Julia. Beyonce. 2005. 32p. pap. 8.50 (978-0-340-90065-9(2)) Cambridge Univ. Pr.

—Cher. 2001. (Livewire Ser.). (Illus.). 28p. pap. (978-0-340-80093-5(3) , Hodder Arnold) Hodder Education.

—Geri Halliwell. 2001. (Livewire Real Lives Ser.). (Illus.). iv, 28p. pap. (978-0-340-80088-1(7) , Hodder Arnold) Hodder Education.

Horn, Geoffrey M. Alicia Keyes. 2005. (Today's Superstars). (Illus.). 32p. (J). (gr. 5 up). lib. bdg. 23.93 (978-0-8368-4233-3(2)) Stevens, Gareth Inc.

—Beyonce. 2005. (Today's Superstars). (Illus.). 32p. (J). (gr. 5 up). lib. bdg. 23.93 (978-0-8368-4230-2(8)) Stevens, Gareth Inc.

Howard, Kathleen. Confessions of an Opera Singer. 2001. 273p. (YA). reprint ed. 98.00 (978-0-7222-6283-2(3)) Library Reprints, Inc.

Hurst, Heidi. Britney Spears. 2003. (Illus.). 112p. (J). 32.45 (978-1-59018-224-6(3) , Lucent Bks.) Thomson Gale.

—Jennifer Lopez. 2003. (People in the News Ser.). (Illus.). 112p. (J). 32.45 (978-1-59018-325-0(8) , Lucent Bks.) Thomson Gale.

Jacobs, George & Stadiem, William. Mr S: My Life with Frank Sinatra. 2005. (Illus.). 260p. (YA). reprint ed. 25.00 (978-0-7567-9324-1(6)) DIANE Publishing Co.

Jeffrey, Gary. Bob Marley: The Life of a Reggae Superstar. Riley, Terry, illus. 2006. (Graphic Biographies Ser.). 48p. (J). lib. bdg. 29.95 (978-1-4042-0854-4(2)) Rosen Publishing Group, Inc., The.

Johns, Michael-Anne. Britney Spears: Backstage Pass. 1999. (Illus.). 48p. (J). (gr. 4-7). pap. 5.99 (978-0-439-13548-1(6)) Scholastic, Inc.

—Cool in School. 1999. (gr. 3-6). lib. bdg. 11.80 (978-0-613-24678-1(0)) Tandem Library Bks.

—Justin Timberlake. 2000. (POP People Ser.). (Illus.). 112p. (J). (gr. 4-7). pap. 4.50 (978-0-439-22224-2(9)) Scholastic, Inc.

—Justin Timberlake. 2000. (gr. 3-6). lib. bdg. 12.40 (978-0-613-83890-0(4)) Tandem Library Bks.

Johns, Michael-Anne & Gold, David. Ricky Martin. 1999. (Illus.). 48p. (gr. 6 up). pap. 5.99 (978-0-439-15329-4(8)) Scholastic, Inc.

Jones, Veda Boyd. Selena. (Latinos in the Limelight Ser.). (Illus.). 2002. 64p. (J). pap. 17.95 (978-0-7910-6113-8(2)); 2001. 64p. (J). (gr. 3 up). 31.00 (978-0-7910-6112-1(4)); 2000. 48p. (YA). 21.95 (978-0-7910-5230-3(3)) Facts On File, Inc. (Chelsea Hse.).

Jones, Victoria Garrett. Marian Anderson: A Voice Uplifted. 2008. (Sterling Biographies Ser.). (Illus.). 128p. (J). pap. 5.95 (***978-1-4027-4239-2(8)***) Sterling Publishing Co., Inc.

Joseph, Paul. Backstreet Boys. 1999. (Young Profiles Ser.). (Illus.). 32p. (J). (gr. k-6). lib. bdg. 22.78 (978-1-57765-350-9(5) , Checkerboard Library) ABDO Publishing Co.

—'N Sync. 2000. (Young Profiles Ser.). (Illus.). 32p. (J). (gr. k-6). lib. bdg. 22.78 (978-1-57765-430-8(7) , Checkerboard Library) ABDO Publishing Co.

—Ricky Martin. 2000. (Young Profiles Ser.). (Illus.). 32p. (J). (gr. k-6). lib. bdg. 22.78 (978-1-57765-370-7(X) , Checkerboard Library) ABDO Publishing Co.

Kaminsky, Kristy & Dombowski, Brian. Ashlee & Jessica Simpson. 2007. (J). (***978-1-4222-0208-1(9)***) Mason Crest Pubs.

Kenyatta, Kelly. Destiny's Child: The Complete Story. Rose, Tony, ed. Goshorn, Walik, photos by. 2001. (Illus.). 120p. pap. 12.95 (978-0-9702224-4-2(0)) Amber Bks.

Kinstad-Pupeza, Lori. Brandy. 1999. (Young Profiles Ser.). (Illus.). 32p. (J). (gr. k-6). lib. bdg. 22.78 (978-1-57765-323-3(8) , Checkerboard Library) ABDO Publishing Co.

Kjelle, Marylou Morano. Ashlee Simpson. 2005. (Blue Banner Biography Ser.). (Illus.). 32p. (J). (gr. 3-8). lib. bdg. 25.70 (978-1-58415-383-2(0)) Mitchell Lane Pubs., Inc.

—Jessie Mccartney. 2006. (Robbie Reader Ser.). (Illus.). 32p. (J). (gr. 1-4). lib. bdg. 25.70 (978-1-58415-500-3(0)) Mitchell Lane Pubs., Inc.

Klein, Hermann. The Reign of Patti. 2001. 470p. (YA). reprint ed. 98.00 (978-0-7222-6292-4(2)) Library Reprints, Inc.

Koopmans, Andy. Madonna. 2002. (People in the News Ser.). (Illus.). 112p. (YA). (gr. 6-9). 32.45 (978-1-59018-138-6(7) , Lucent Bks.) Thomson Gale.

Korman, Susan. Christina Aguilera. (Latinos in the Limelight Ser.). (Illus.). 64p. (J). 2002. pap. 27.50 (978-0-7910-6107-7(8)); 2001. (gr. 3 up). 31.00 (978-0-7910-6106-0(X) , Chelsea Hse.) Facts On File, Inc.

Kramer, Barbara. Gloria Estefan: Never Give Up. 2005. (Awesome Values in Famous Lives Ser.). (Illus.). 48p. (J). (gr. 3-4). lib. bdg. 23.93 (978-0-7660-2380-2(X) , Enslow Elementary) Enslow Pubs., Inc.

—Mahalia Jackson: The Voice of Gospel & Civil Rights. 2003. (African-American Biographies Ser.). (Illus.). 128p. (J). lib. bdg. 26.60 (978-0-7660-2115-0(7)) Enslow Pubs., Inc.

Krohn Katherine. Shakira. 2007. (Biography Ser.). (J). 30.60 (***978-0-8225-7159-9(5)*** , Twenty-First Century Bks.) Lerner Publishing Group.

Krohn, Katherine E. Gwen Stefani. 2007. (J). lib. bdg. (***978-0-8225-7157-5(9)***) Twenty First Century Bks.

Lahee, Henry Charles. The Grand Opera Singers of Today: An Account of the Leading Operatic Stars Who Have Sung During Recent Years, Together with a Sketch of the Chief Operatic Enterprises. 2001. 461p. (YA). reprint ed. 98.00 (978-0-7222-6271-9(X)) Library Reprints, Inc.

Laslo, Cynthia. Brandy. 2000. (High Interest Bks.). (Illus.). 48p. (YA). (gr. 7-12). pap. 6.95 (978-0-516-23520-2(6) , Children's Pr.); (J). pap. (978-0-531-17608-5(8) , Watts, Franklin) Scholastic Library Publishing.

—Lauryn Hill. 2000. (gr. 7-12). lib. bdg. 15.25 (978-0-613-58708-2(1)) Tandem Library Bks.

Laslo, Cynthia, contrib. by. Brandy. 2000. (J). (978-0-531-12108-5(9) , Watts, Franklin) Scholastic Library Publishing.

—Lauryn Hill. 2000. (J). (978-0-531-12110-8(0) , Orchard Bks.) Scholastic, Inc.

Lawlor, Michelle. Kelly Clarkson. 2007. (J). (***978-1-4222-0199-2(6)***) Mason Crest Pubs.

Lawlor, Michelle. Missy Elliott. 2006. (Hip-Hop Ser.). (Illus.). 64p. (J). (gr. 5 up). 22.95 (978-1-4222-0117-6(1)) Mason Crest Pubs.

Leavitt, Amie. Ciara. 2007. (Blue Banner Biography Ser.). (Illus.). 32p. (J). (gr. 4-8). lib. bdg. 25.70 (***978-1-58415-610-9(4)***) Mitchell Lane Pubs., Inc.

—Miley Cyrus. 2007. (Robbie Reader Ser.). (Illus.). 32p. (J). (gr. 1-4). lib. bdg. 25.70 (***978-1-58415-590-4(6)***) Mitchell Lane Pubs., Inc.

—Raven-Symone. 2007. (Robbie Reader Ser.). (Illus.). 32p. (J). (gr. 1-4). lib. bdg. 25.70 (***978-1-58415-593-5(0)***) Mitchell Lane Pubs., Inc.

Lee, Sally. Gloria Estefan: Superstar of Song. 2005. (Latino Biography Library). (Illus.). 128p. (J). (gr. 6-12). lib. bdg. 31.93 (978-0-7660-2490-8(3)) Enslow Pubs., Inc.

Lind, Jenny. Early Art-Life, 2 Vols. 2001. (YA). reprint ed. 250.00 (978-0-7222-6224-5(8)) Library Reprints, Inc.

Livorse, Kay. Let Freedom Sing. Copeland, Greg, illus. 2002. 16p. (J). (978-0-439-35159-1(6)) Scholastic, Inc.

Lorrain, Mora, et al. Mandy Moore. 2000. (Backstage Pass Ser.). (Illus.). 48p. (J). (gr. 4-7). pap. 5.99 (978-0-439-22223-5(0)) Scholastic, Inc.

Lutz, Norma Jean. Britney Spears. 2000. (Galaxy of Superstars Ser.). 64p. (J). (gr. 4-7). 25.00 (978-0-7910-5499-4(3) , Chelsea Hse.) Facts On File, Inc.

—Britney Spears. 2000. (gr. 5-8). lib. bdg. 17.60 (978-0-613-21252-6(5)); (Illus.). (J). (978-0-606-18033-7(8)) Tandem Library Bks.

—Celine Dion. 2000. (Galaxy of Superstars Ser.). (J). (Illus.). pap. 9.95 (978-0-7910-5778-0(X)); 64p. (gr. 4-7). 25.00 (978-0-7910-5777-3(1)) Facts On File, Inc. (Chelsea Hse.).

MacKinlay, Malcolm S. Garcia the Centenarian & His Times: A Memoir of Manuel Garcia's Life & Labours for the Advancement of Music & Science. 2001. 335p. (YA). reprint ed. 98.00 (978-0-7222-5411-0(3)) Library Reprints, Inc.

Manera, Alexandria. Bessie Smith. 2003. (African-American Biographies Ser.). (Illus.). 64p. pap. 8.95 (978-1-4109-0034-0(7)); (J). lib. bdg. 28.56 (978-0-7398-6875-1(6)) Raintree.

Marcovitz, Hal. Justin Timberlake. 2007. (J). (***978-1-4222-0209-8(7)***) Mason Crest Pubs.

Mariah Carey Backstage Pass. 2000. (Illus.). 48p. (J). 5.99 (978-0-439-19916-2(6)) Scholastic, Inc.

Marley, Bob. Bob Marley. 1999. (They Died Too Young Ser.). (Illus.). 48p. (YA). 27.00 (978-0-7910-5228-0(1) , Chelsea Hse.) Facts On File, Inc.

Marquez, Heron. Latin Sensations. (Biography Ser.). (Illus.). 112p. (gr. 6-12). 2005. lib. bdg. 27.93 (978-0-8225-4993-2(X)); 2003. (YA). pap. 7.95 (978-0-8225-9695-0(4) , Lerner Pubns.) Lerner Publishing Group.

Marron, Maggie. Britney Spears. 1999. (gr. 7-12). lib. bdg. 18.80 (978-0-613-21254-0(1)) Tandem Library Bks.

—The Ultimate Britney Spears Quiz Book. 2000. (Illus.). 96p. (YA). pap. 7.98 (978-1-58663-136-9(5)) Friedman, Michael Publishing Group, Inc.

Masar, Brendan. Usher. 2006. (Illus.). 112p. (J). (gr. 7-10). 32.45 (978-1-59018-724-1(5) , Lucent Bks.) Thomson Gale.

Mathis, Sharon Bell. Ray Charles. 2001. (ps-2). lib. bdg. 15.25 (978-0-613-45536-7(3)) Tandem Library Bks.

Mattern, Joanne. Celine Dion. 2002. (Illus.). 104p. (J). (gr. 4-12). 32.45 (978-1-59018-137-9(9) , Lucent Bks.) Thomson Gale.

Maughan, Teresa. Five on the Road. 1999. (Illus.). 60p. (YA). (gr. 4 up). pap. 13.99 (978-0-7522-1786-4(0) , Boxtree) Pan Macmillan GBR. *Dist:* Trafalgar Square Publishing.

McAvoy, Jim. Aretha Franklin. 2001. (Black Americans of Achievement Ser.). (Illus.). 112p. (J). pap. 30.00 (978-0-7910-5809-1(3)); (gr. 4-7). 30.00 (978-0-7910-5808-4(5)) Facts On File, Inc. (Chelsea Hse.).

McDonald, Elizabeth & Carlton Books Staff. Backstreet Boys. rev. ed. 2002. (Illus.). 48p. pap. 7.95 (978-1-84222-420-5(4)) Carlton Bks., Ltd. GBR. *Dist:* Ingram Pub. Services, Simon & Schuster, Inc.

McKissack, Lisa Beringer. Women of the Harlem Renaissance. 2006. 48p. (J). (978-0-7565-2034-2(7)) Compass Point Bks.

McVeigh, Mark. Julio & Enrique Iglesias. 2004. (Famous Families Ser.). (Illus.). 48p. (J). lib. bdg. 25.25 (978-1-4042-0260-3(9)) Rosen Publishing Group, Inc., The.

Medlock Adams, Michelle. Jessica Simpson. 2007. (Blue Banner Biography Ser.). (Illus.). 32p. (J). (gr. 4-8). lib. bdg. 25.70 (***978-1-58415-616-1(3)***) Mitchell Lane Pubs., Inc.

Menard, Valerie. Jennifer Lopez. 2000. (Real-Life Reader Biography Ser.). (Illus.). 32p. (J). (gr. 3-8). lib. bdg. 15.95 (978-1-58415-025-1(4)) Mitchell Lane Pubs., Inc.

—Ricky Martin. 1999. (Real Life Reader Biography Ser.). (Illus.). 32p. (gr. 3-8). lib. bdg. 15.95 (978-1-58415-059-6(9)) Mitchell Lane Pubs., Inc.

Miall, Bernard. Pierr Garat, Singer & Exquisite: His Life & His World. 2001. 364p. (YA). reprint ed. 98.00 (978-0-7222-6281-8(7)) Library Reprints, Inc.

Mitchell, Susan K. Jessica Simpson. 2007. (Today's Superstars). 32p. (J). (gr. 5 up). lib. bdg. 23.93 (***978-0-8368-8201-8(6)***) Stevens, Gareth Inc.

Morreale, Marie T. & Johns, Michael-Anne. Hanging with the Backstreet Boys: An Unauthorized Biography. rev. ed. 1998. 99p. (J). (gr. 4-7). pap. 3.99 (978-0-439-04532-2(0)) Scholastic, Inc.

Newman, Matthew. Brandy. 2000. (Galaxy of Superstars Ser.). (J). (Illus.). pap. 9.95 (978-0-7910-5782-7(8)); 64p. (gr. 4-7). 25.00 (978-0-7910-5781-0(X)) Facts On File, Inc. (Chelsea Hse.).

—Ricky Martin. 2000. (Galaxy of Superstars Ser.). (Illus.). 64p. (J). pap. 9.95 (978-0-7910-5772-8(0)); (gr. 4-7). 25.00 (978-0-7910-5771-1(2)) Facts On File, Inc. (Chelsea Hse.).

Nichols, Angie. Britney Spears: Special Edition. 2000. (Illus.). 32p. (J). pap. 7.95 (978-0-8230-7865-3(5) , Billboard Bks.) Watson-Guptill Pubns., Inc.

Norton, James R. Beyoncé. 2006. (Contemporary Musicians & Their Music Ser.). (Illus.). 48p. (J). lib. bdg. (978-1-4042-0712-7(0)) Hudson Hills Pr. LLC.

Norwich, Grace. Amped up Aly & Aj Official Biography. 2007. 128p. (J). (gr. 3). 5.99 (***978-0-448-44841-1(6)*** , Grosset & Dunlap) Penguin Group (USA) Inc.

—Vanessa Hudgens: Breaking Free: An Unauthorized Biography. 2007. (Illus.). 128p. (J). pap. 4.99 (***978-0-8431-2668-6(X)*** , Price Stern Sloan) Penguin Group (USA) Inc.

Orgill, Roxane. Mahalia: A Life in Gospel Music. 2004. (Illus.). 132p. (gr. 4-8). reprint ed. 20.00 (978-0-7567-7945-0(6)) DIANE Publishing Co.

—Shout Sister, Shout! Ten Girl Singers who Shaped a Century. 2001. (Illus.). 160p. (YA). (gr. 7 up). 19.95 (978-0-689-81991-9(9) , McElderry, Margaret K.) Simon & Schuster Children's Publishing.

Orr, Tamra. Jamie Foxx. 2006. (Blue Banner Biography Ser.). (Illus.). 32p. (J). (gr. 4-8). lib. bdg. 25.70 (978-1-58415-503-4(5)) Mitchell Lane Pubs., Inc.

O'Shei, Tim. Gloria Estefan: Singing Sensation. 2006. (Fact Finders Ser.). (Illus.). 32p. (J). (978-0-7368-5439-9(8)) Capstone Pr., Inc.

—98 Degrees. 2001. (Galaxy of Superstars Ser.). (Illus.). 64p. (J). 25.00 (978-0-7910-6467-2(0) , Chelsea Hse.) Facts On File, Inc.

Pappas, Rita. Barbra Streisand: Entertainer. 2000. (Women of Achievement Ser.). (Illus.). 112p. (J). (gr. 4-7). 30.00 (978-0-7910-5285-3(0) , Chelsea Hse.) Facts On File, Inc.

Parish, James Robert. Gloria Estefan: Singer. 2006. (Illus.). 128p. (gr. 6-12). 25.00 (978-0-8160-5833-4(4) , Ferguson Publishing Co.) Facts On File, Inc.

—Jennifer Lopez: Actor & Singer. 2005. (Ferguson Career Biographies Ser.). (Illus.). 144p. (gr. 6-12). 25.00 (978-0-8160-5832-7(6) , Ferguson Publishing Co.) Facts On File, Inc.

Parker, Judy. Ricky Martin. 2001. (gr. 7-12). lib. bdg. 15.25 (978-0-613-58726-6(X)) Tandem Library Bks.

Patrick, Chris. Beyoncé & Destiny's Child. 2005. (Illus.). 122p. (J). (978-0-439-80832-3(4)) Scholastic, Inc.

Pearce, Charles E. Polly Peachum: The Story of Lavinia Fenton. 2001. 382p. (YA). reprint ed. 98.00 (978-0-7222-6248-1(5)) Library Reprints, Inc.

Pearl, A. 'N Sync: Now & Forever. 2nd ed. 2000. (Backstage Pass Ser.). (Illus.). 48p. (J). (gr. 2-9). pap. 5.99 (978-0-439-22220-4(6)) Scholastic, Inc.

Philips, Jane H. Gloria Estefan. 2001. (Women of Achievement Ser.). (Illus.). (J). 111p. pap. 9.95 (978-0-7910-5884-8(0)); 112p. (gr. 4-7). 30.00 (978-0-7910-5883-1(2)) Facts On File, Inc. (Chelsea Hse.).

Pickels, Dwayne E. Shania Twain. 2001. (Overcoming Adversity Ser.). (Illus.). 112p. (J). 30.00 (978-0-7910-5901-2(4) , Chelsea Hse.) Facts On File, Inc.

Pierre Van Rensselaer Key Staff. Enrico Caruso: A Biography. 2001. 455p. (YA). reprint ed. 98.00 (978-0-7222-6221-4(3)) Library Reprints, Inc.

Pinkney, Andrea Davis. Ella Fitzgerald: The Tale of a Vocal Virtuosa. Pinkney, Brian, illus. 2007. 32p. (gr. k-4). pap. 5.99 (978-0-7868-1416-9(0)) Disney Pr.

—Ella Fitzgerald: The Tale of a Vocal Virtuosa. Pinkney, Brian, illus. 2002. 32p. (gr. k-4). 17.49 (978-0-7868-2493-9(X)); 16.99 (978-0-7868-0568-6(4)) Hyperion Bks. for Children. (Jump at the Sun).

Plantz, Connie. Elvis Presley: Music Legend, Movie Star, the King. 2004. (People to Know Ser.). (Illus.). 128p. (J). lib. bdg. 26.60 (978-0-7660-2103-7(3)) Enslow Pubs., Inc.

Pougin, Arthur. Marie Malibran: Histoire d' Une Cantatrice. 2001. 323p. (YA). reprint ed. 98.00 (978-0-7222-6286-3(8)) Library Reprints, Inc.

Ransom, Candice F. Maria von Trapp: Beyond The Sound of Music. 2003. 112p. (J). pap. 8.95 (978-0-8225-3749-6(4)) Lerner Publishing Group.

Reeves, Sims. Sims Reeves, His Life & Recollections. 2001. 279p. (YA). reprint ed. 98.00 (978-0-7222-6228-3(0)) Library Reprints, Inc.

Reid, Jamie. Diana Krall. 2004. 224p. pap. 17.95 (978-1-894997-07-2(7)) Kingston Pr. CAN. *Dist:* SCB Distributors.

Rivera, Ursula. Aretha Franklin. 2006. (Rock & Roll Hall of Famers Ser.). (Illus.). 112p. (YA). (gr. 5-8). lib. bdg. 29.25 (978-0-8239-3639-7(2)) Rosen Publishing Group, Inc., The.

—Shakira. 2003. (gr. 7-12). lib. bdg. 15.25 (978-0-613-67929-9(6)) Tandem Library Bks.

—The Supremes. 2006. (Rock & Roll Hall of Famers Ser.). (Illus.). 112p. (YA). (gr. 5-8). lib. bdg. 29.25 (978-0-8239-3527-7(2)) Rosen Publishing Group, Inc., The.

Robb, Jacqueline. Go, Girl! Young Women Superstars of Pop Music. 2000. (Illus.). 144p. (J). (gr. 6-12). lib. bdg. 19.95 (978-1-888105-45-2(3)) Avisson Pr., Inc.

Ruth, Amy. Queen Latifah. 2000. (Biography Ser.). (Illus.). 112p. (YA). (gr. 6-12). lib. bdg. 27.93 (978-0-8225-4988-8(3) , Lerner Pubns.) Lerner Publishing Group.

Ryan, Pam Muñoz. When Marian Sang: The True Recital of Marian Anderson. Selznick, Brian, illus. pap. 16.95 incl. audio (978-1-59112-943-1(5)); pap. incl. audio (978-1-59112-945-5(1)); pap. 18.95 incl. audio compact disk (978-1-59112-947-9(8)); pap. incl. audio compact disk (978-1-59112-949-3(4)); 2004. (J). 25.95 incl. audio (978-1-59112-944-8(3)); 2004. (J). 28.95 incl. audio compact disk (978-1-59112-948-6(6)) Live Oak Media.

—When Marian Sang: The True Recital of Marian Anderson. Selznick, Brian, illus. 2002. 40p. (J). (gr. 1-5). pap. 16.95 (978-0-439-26967-4(9) , Scholastic Pr.) Scholastic, Inc.

Santley, Charles. Student & Singer. 2001. 327p. (YA). reprint ed. 98.00 (978-0-7222-6232-0(9)) Library Reprints, Inc.

Scott, Celicia. Mariah Carey. 2007. (Hip-Hop Ser.). (Illus.). 64p. (YA). (gr. 5 up). 22.95 (978-1-4222-0114-5(7)) Mason Crest Pubs.

Shapiro, Marc. Mariah Carey. 2001. (Illus.). 220p. pap. 16.95 (978-1-55022-444-3(1)) ECW Pr. CAN. *Dist:* Independent Pubs. Group.

Shore, Nancy. Spice Girls. 1999. (Galaxy of Superstars Ser.). (Illus.). 64p. (J). (gr. 3 up). pap. 25.00 (978-0-7910-5328-7(8) , Chelsea Hse.) Facts On File, Inc.

—Spice Girls. 1999. (gr. 5-8). lib. bdg. 17.60 (978-0-613-17737-5(1)) Tandem Library Bks.

Simpkins, Daphne. Nat King Cole: An Unforgettable Life of Music. 2001. (J). (gr. 4-7). pap. 7.95 (978-1-58838-023-4(8) , Junebug Bks.) NewSouth, Inc.

Sloate, Susan. Ray Charles: Find Another Way! 2007. (Defining Moments Ser.). (Illus.). 32p. (J). lib. bdg. 25.27 (978-1-59716-267-8(1)) Bearport Publishing Co., Inc.

—Ray Charles: Young Musician. Henderson, Meryl, illus. 2007. (Childhood of Famous Americans Ser.). 176p. (J). pap. 5.99 (978-1-4169-1437-2(4) , Aladdin) Simon & Schuster Children's Publishing.

Speregen, Devra Newberger. The Backstreet Boys. 2000. (POP People Ser.). (Illus.). 112p. (J). (gr. 4-7). pap. 4.50 (978-0-439-22226-6(5)) Scholastic, Inc.

Stockdale, Tom. Marvin Gaye. 1999. (They Died Too Young Ser.). (Illus.). 48p. (YA). 27.00 (978-0-7910-5227-3(3) , Chelsea Hse.) Facts On File, Inc.

Stone, Tanya Lee. Up Close: Ella Fitzgerald: Ella Fitzgerald. 2008. 208p. (YA). (gr. 6). 16.99 (***978-0-670-06149-5(2)*** , Viking Juvenile) Penguin Group (USA) Inc.

Strauss, Alix. Britney Spears. 1999. (gr. 3-6). lib. bdg. 13.00 (978-0-613-21255-7(X)) Tandem Library Bks.

Talmadge, Morgan. Christina Aguilera. 2001. (Celebrity Bios Ser.). (Illus.). 48p. (J). (gr. 7-12). 23.00 (978-0-516-23422-9(6) , Children's Pr.) Scholastic Library Publishing.

—Enrique Iglesias. 2001. (High Interest Bks.). (Illus.). 48p. (J). (gr. 7-12). pap. 6.95 (978-0-516-23579-0(6) , Children's Pr.) Scholastic Library Publishing.

Taylor, Gail. Livewire Real Lives Dame Nellie Melba. 1999. (Livewire Real Lives Ser.). 32p. (gr. 6-9). pap. 6.00 (978-0-521-77636-3(8)) Cambridge Univ. Pr.

Thatcher Murcia, Rebecca. Shakira. 2007. (Blue Banner Biography Ser.). (Illus.). 32p. (J). (gr. 4-8). lib. bdg. 25.70 (***978-1-58415-609-3(0)***) Mitchell Lane Pubs., Inc.

Thompson, John. Jewel. 2001. (Overcoming Adversity Ser.). 102p. (J). 32.00 (978-0-7910-5895-4(6)); pap. 9.95 (978-0-7910-5896-1(4)) Facts On File, Inc. (Chelsea Hse.).

Tierney, Tom. Famous Country Singers Paper Dolls. 2006. 32p. (J). pap. 6.95 (978-0-486-44741-4(3)) Dover Pubns., Inc.

Tokunaga, Wendy. Christina Aguilera. 2002. (Famous People Ser.). (Illus.). 48p. (J). (gr. 3-5). 26.20 (978-0-7377-1385-5(2) , Kidhaven) Thomson Gale.

Torres, Jennifer. Ashanti. 2005. (Blue Banner Biography Ser.). (Illus.). 32p. (J). lib. bdg. 25.70 (978-1-58415-378-8(4)) Mitchell Lane Pubs., Inc.

Torres, Jennifer. JoJo. 2007. (Blue Banner Biography Ser.). (Illus.). 32p. (J). (gr. 4-8). lib. bdg. 25.70 (***978-1-58415-615-4(5)***) Mitchell Lane Pubs., Inc.

Torres, John. Usher. 2005. (Blue Banner Biography Ser.). (Illus.). 32p. (J). (ps-8). lib. bdg. 25.70 (978-1-58415-379-5(2)) Mitchell Lane Pubs., Inc.

Torres, John Albert. Marc Anthony. 2001. (Real-Life Reader Biography Ser.). (Illus.). 32p. (J). (gr. 3-8). lib. bdg. 15.95 (978-1-58415-069-5(6)) Mitchell Lane Pubs., Inc.

Tracy, Kathleen. Aly & AJ. 2007. (Robbie Reader Ser.). (Illus.). 32p. (J). (gr. 1-4). lib. bdg. 25.70 (***978-1-58415-595-9(7)***) Mitchell Lane Pubs., Inc.

—Avril Lavigne. 2004. (Uncharted, Unexplored & Unexplained Ser.). (Illus.). 32p. (J). (gr. 3-8). lib. bdg. 25.70 (978-1-58415-314-6(8)) Mitchell Lane Pubs., Inc.

—Beyonce. 2004. (Blue Banner Biography Ser.). (Illus.). 32p. (J). (gr. 3-8). lib. bdg. 25.70 (978-1-58415-312-2(1)) Mitchell Lane Pubs., Inc.

—Carrie Underwood. 2005. (Blue Banner Biography Ser.). (Illus.). 32p. (J). (gr. 3-8). lib. bdg. 25.70 (978-1-58415-425-9(X)) Mitchell Lane Pubs., Inc.

—Justin Timberlake. 2007. (Blue Banner Biography Ser.). (Illus.). 32p. (J). (gr. 4-8). lib. bdg. 25.70 (***978-1-58415-611-6(2)***) Mitchell Lane Pubs., Inc.

—Kelly Clarkson. 2006. (Blue Banner Biography Ser.). (Illus.). 32p. (J). (gr. 4-8). lib. bdg. (978-1-58415-518-8(3)) Mitchell Lane Pubs., Inc.

—Mariah Carey. 2006. (Blue Banner Biography Ser.). (Illus.). 32p. (J). (gr. 4-8). lib. bdg. (978-1-58415-516-4(7)) Mitchell Lane Pubs., Inc.

Trendsetters Publishing Staff, contrib. by. Backstreet Boys Larger Than Life. 2000. (J). 5.99 (978-1-894335-32-4(5)) Lone Wolf Enterprises, Ltd.

Troupe, Quincy. Little Stevie Wonder. Cohen, Lisa, illus. 2005. 32p. (J). (gr. k-3). 18.00 (978-0-618-34060-6(2)) Houghton Mifflin Co. Trade & Reference Div.

Ventresca, Yvonne. Avril Lavigne. 2006. (Illus.). 112p. (J). (gr. 7-10). 32.45 (978-1-59018-932-0(9) , Lucent Bks.) Thomson Gale.

Wagnalls, Mabel. The Stars of the Opera: A Description of Twelve Operas & a Series of Personal Sketches, with Interviews of Marcella Sembrich, Emma Eames, Emma Calve, Lillian Nordica, Lilli Lehmann & Nellie Melba. 2001. 368p. (YA). reprint ed. 98.00 (978-0-7222-6274-0(4)) Library Reprints, Inc.

Waters, Rosa. Ashanti. 2007. (Hip-Hop Ser.). (Illus.). 64p. (YA). (gr. 5 up). 22.95 (978-1-4222-0111-4(2)) Mason Crest Pubs.

—Beyoncé. 2007. (Hip-Hop Ser.). (Illus.). 64p. (J). (gr. 5 up). 22.95 (978-1-4222-0112-1(0)) Mason Crest Pubs.

Waters, Rosa. Bob Marley & the Wailers. 2008. (J). (***978-1-4222-0192-3(9)***) Mason Crest Pubs.

Weber, Terri. Alicia Keys. 2004. (J). pap. (978-1-932724-29-5(X)); lib. bdg. (978-1-932724-28-8(1)) Panda Publishing, L.L.C. (Bios for Kids).

Weber, Terri Smith. Dixie Chicks. 2004. (J). lib. bdg. (978-0-9740180-1-0(5) , Bios for Kids) Panda Publishing, L.L.C.

—Jennifer Lopez: Living the Dream. 2004. (J). pap. (978-1-932724-21-9(4)); lib. bdg. (978-1-932724-20-2(6)) Panda Publishing, L.L.C. (Bios for Kids).

—Jennifer Lopez: Realizando Los Suenos. 2003. (SPA.). (J). pap. (978-0-9740180-4-1(X)); lib. bdg. (978-0-9740180-3-4(1)) Panda Publishing, L.L.C. (Bios for Kids).

S

—Shakira: Following Her Heart. 2004. (SPA.). (J). pap. (978-1-932724-05-9(2)); lib. bdg. (978-1-932724-04-2(4)) Panda Publishing, L.L.C. (Bios for Kids).

Webster, Christine. Beyonce Knowles. 2005. (Great African American Women for Kids Ser.). (Illus.). 24p. (J). (ps-7). pap. 6.95 (978-1-59036-337-9(X)); lib. bdg. 26.00 (978-1-59036-331-7(0)) Weigl Pubs., Inc.

Wellman, Sam. Mariah Carey. 1999. (Galaxy of Superstars Ser.). (Illus.). 64p. (J). pap. 25.00 (978-0-7910-5333-1(4)); (YA). 25.00 (978-0-7910-5233-4(8)) Facts On File, Inc. (Chelsea Hse.).

Wells, Peggysue. Fergie. 2007. (Blue Banner Biography Ser.). (Illus.). 32p. (J). (gr. 4-8). lib. bdg. 25.70 (978-1-58415-521-8(3)) Mitchell Lane Pubs., Inc.

West, Betsy. Jennifer Hudson: American Dream Girl: American Dream Girl An Unauthorized Biography. 2007. 128p. (J). (gr. 3). pap. 4.99 (***978-0-8431-2687-7(6)***, Price Stern Sloan) Penguin Group (USA) Inc.

Wheeler, Jill C. Enrique Iglesias. 2003. (Young Profiles Ser.). (Illus.). 32p. (J). (gr. k-6). lib. bdg. 22.78 (978-1-57765-993-8(7)) ABDO Publishing Co.

—Jennifer Lopez. 2003. (Star Tracks Ser.). (Illus.). 64p. (J). (gr. 3-8). lib. bdg. 25.65 (978-1-57765-770-5(5)) ABDO Publishing Co.

—Jessica Simpson. 2004. (Young Profiles Ser.). (Illus.). 32p. (J). (gr. k-6). 22.78 (978-1-59197-879-4(3)) ABDO Publishing Co.

—Kelly Clarkson. 2003. (Young Profiles Ser.). (Illus.). 32p. (J). (gr. k-6). lib. bdg. 22.78 (978-1-57765-994-5(5)) ABDO Publishing Co.

—Madonna. 2003. (Star Tracks Ser.). (Illus.). 64p. (J). (gr. 3-8). lib. bdg. 25.65 (978-1-57765-768-2(3)) ABDO Publishing Co.

—Shania Twain. 2001. (Star Tracks Ser.). (Illus.). 64p. (J). (gr. 3-8). lib. bdg. 25.65 (978-1-57765-552-7(4) , ABDO & Daughters) ABDO Publishing Co.

—Star Tracks, Set. Incl. Jim Carrey. lib. bdg. 25.65 (978-1-57765-556-5(7)); Julia Roberts. lib. bdg. 25.65 (978-1-57765-555-8(9)); Michael J. Fox. lib. bdg. 25.65 (978-1-57765-551-0(6)); Shania Twain. lib. bdg. 25.65 (978-1-57765-552-7(4)); Tom Cruise. lib. bdg. 25.65 (978-1-57765-553-4(2)); Tom Hanks. lib. bdg. 25.65 (978-1-57765-554-1(0)); 64p. (J). (gr. 3-8). 2001. (Illus.). 2001. Set lib. bdg. 153.90 (978-1-57765-504-6(4) , ABDO & Daughters) ABDO Publishing Co.

Whitcombe, Dan. Justin Timberlake. 2004. (Star Files Ser.). (Illus.). 48p. 29.93 (978-1-4109-1087-5(3)) Harcourt Schl. Pubs.

Whiting, Jim. Mandy Moore. 2007. (J). (***978-1-4222-0207-4(0)***) Mason Crest Pubs.

Willett, Edward. Janis Joplin. 2008. (American Rebels Ser.). (Illus.). 152p. (J). (gr. 9-12). lib. bdg. 34.60 (***978-0-7660-2837-1(2)***) Enslow Pubs., Inc.

Wilson, Mike. Britney Spears. 2001. (Livewire Ser.). (Illus.). 27p. pap. (978-0-340-80084-3(4) , Hodder Arnold) Hodder Education.

—Destiny's Child. 2005. (Illus.). 32p. pap. (978-0-340-87647-3(6)) Cambridge Univ. Pr.

—Eminem. 2005. 32p. pap. 8.50 (978-0-340-90080-2(6)) Cambridge Univ. Pr.

Wilson, Wayne. Shakira. 2001. (Real-Life Reader Biography Ser.). (Illus.). 32p. (J). (gr. 3-8). lib. bdg. 15.95 (978-1-58415-071-8(8)) Mitchell Lane Pubs., Inc.

Woog, Adam. Frank Sinatra. 2000. (Importance of Ser.). (Illus.). 112p. (YA). (gr. 7-10). 32.45 (978-1-56006-749-8(7) , Lucent Bks.) Thomson Gale.

Woronoff, Kristen. Leontyne Price: Singing Star. 2002. (Famous Women Juniors Ser.). (Illus.). 32p. (J). (gr. 3-5). 23.70 (978-1-56711-589-5(6) , Blackbirch Pr., Inc.) Thomson Gale.

Young, Filson. Mastersingers: Appreciations of Music & Musicians. 2001. 201p. (YA). reprint ed. 98.00 (978-0-7222-5295-6(1)) Library Reprints, Inc.

Zannos, Susan. Paula Abdul. 1998. (Real-Life Reader Biographies Ser.). (Illus.). 32p. (J). (gr. 4-7). lib. bdg. 15.95 (978-1-883845-74-2(2)) Mitchell Lane Pubs., Inc.

Zier, Nina. 98 Degrees: Backstage Pass. 1999. (gr. 3-6). lib. bdg. 14.15 (978-0-613-16985-1(9)) Tandem Library Bks.

Zymet, Cathy Alter. Enrique Iglesias. 2001. (Latinos in the Limelight Ser.). (Illus.). 64p. (J). (gr. 4-7). 27.50 (978-0-7910-6478-8(6) , Chelsea Hse.) Facts On File, Inc.

—Ricky Martin. 2001. (Latinos in the Limelight Ser.). (Illus.). 64p. (J). (gr. 4-7). 27.50 (978-0-7910-6100-8(0) , Chelsea Hse.) Facts On File, Inc.

SINGING

see also Voice; Voice Culture

Breare, William H. Vocal Faults & Their Remedies. 2001. (YA). reprint ed. 150.00 (978-0-7222-6203-0(5)) Library Reprints, Inc.

—Vocal Technique: How It Feels to Sing. 2001. (YA). reprint ed. 150.00 (978-0-7222-6204-7(3)) Library Reprints, Inc.

Coward, Henry. A Choral Technique & Interpretaton. 2001. 333p. (YA). reprint ed. 98.00 (978-0-7222-6121-7(7)) Library Reprints, Inc.

Cranium Inc. Staff. Cranium: the Star Performer Book of Outrageous Fun! Sing it, Dance it, Act It! Baseman, illus. 2006. 38p. (J). (gr. 2-17). 14.99 (978-0-316-05759-2(2)) Little, Brown Bks. for Young Readers.

Croft, J. B. Practical Plainsong. 2001. (YA). reprint ed. 150.00 (978-0-7222-6153-8(5)) Library Reprints, Inc.

DeBandi, Yvonne. Affordable Singing Lessons: Featuring the Fast & Funky Singers' Warmup. 2001. 40p. audio compact disk 179.95 (978-0-9715793-2-3(6)) LOTI Publishing.

—Singing Is Easy, Basic Foundation Series: A Revolutionary Vocal Coaching System & Online Training Program. 2001. 180p. spiral bd. 49.99 incl. audio compact disk (978-0-9715793-0-9(X) , Singing Is Easy) LOTI Publishing.

Ellis, Alexander J. Pronunciation for Singers: Numerous Examples & Exercises for the Use of Teachers & Advanced Students. 2001. 246p. (YA). reprint ed. 98.00 (978-0-7222-6161-3(6)) Library Reprints, Inc.

Ellis, Alexander John. Speech in Song. 2001. 137p. (YA). reprint ed. 88.00 (978-0-7222-6162-0(4)) Library Reprints, Inc.

Emmer, Rae. Chorus. 2002. (Reading Power Ser.). (Illus.). 24p. (J). (gr. 1). lib. bdg. 17.25 (978-0-8239-5970-9(8) , PowerKids Pr.) Rosen Publishing Group, Inc., The.

Evans, Edwin. The Vocal Works. 2001. 599p. (YA). reprint ed. 98.00 (978-0-7222-5364-9(8)) Library Reprints, Inc.

Feierabend, John M. The Book of Pitch Exploration: Can Your Voice Do This? 2004. (First Steps in Music Ser.). 33p. (J). pap. 11.95 (978-1-57999-242-2(0)); (Illus.). pap. 11.95 (978-1-57999-265-1(X) , G-5276) GIA Pubns., Inc.

Fucito, Salvatore. Caruso & the Art of Singing. 2001. 219p. (YA). reprint ed. 98.00 (978-0-7222-6101-9(2)) Library Reprints, Inc.

Garcia-Castillas, G. A Guide to Solo Singing. 2001. (YA). reprint ed. 150.00 (978-0-7222-6080-7(6)) Library Reprints, Inc.

Gib, Charles. Art of Vocal Expression. 2001. (YA). reprint ed. 150.00 (978-0-7222-6133-0(0)) Library Reprints, Inc.

—Vocal Success: Thinking & Feeling in Speech & Song. 2001. (YA). reprint ed. 150.00 (978-0-7222-6081-4(4)) Library Reprints, Inc.

Greenwood, J. Lancashire Sol-Fa. 2001. (YA). reprint ed. 150.00 (978-0-7222-6168-2(3)) Library Reprints, Inc.

Harris & Brewe. Improve Sight-Singing Treble: Low to Medium Voice. 1998. 40p. (J). (gr. 1-5). 6.95 (978-0-571-51766-4(8)) Faber & Faber, Ltd. GBR. *Dist:* Leonard, Hal Corp.

Harris, P & Brewe. Improve Sight-Singing: High & Medium Voice. 1998. 40p. (J). (gr. 1-5). 6.95 (978-0-571-51733-6(1)) Faber & Faber, Ltd. GBR. *Dist:* Leonard, Hal Corp.

Henderson, William J. The Art of the Singer: Practical Hints about Vocal Technics & Style. 2001. 270p. (YA). reprint ed. 98.00 (978-0-7222-6084-5(9)) Library Reprints, Inc.

Howard, Elisabeth. ABCs of Vocal Harmony: Music Reading, Ear Training. rev. ed. 2004. (Illus.). 124p. per. 29.95 (978-0-934419-01-7(9)) Vocal Power Inc.

Kain, Roger. Xtreme Vocals. 2005. (Illus.). 80p. audio compact disk 14.95 (978-1-84492-034-1(8)) Sanctuary Publishing, Ltd. GBR. *Dist:* Warner Bros. Pubns.

Lehmann, Lilli. How to Sing. 2001. 323p. (YA). reprint ed. 98.00 (978-0-7222-6087-6(3)) Library Reprints, Inc.

Levitan, Diane Lima. 1,2,3 Let's Sing the Basics. Agrella, Donavan M., illus. 2002. (SPA.). 20p. (J). pap., act. bk. ed. 6.50 (978-1-930866-05-8(4)) I E S Language Foundation.

Mancini, Giambattista. Practical Reflections on the Figurative Art of Singing. 2001. 194p. (YA). reprint ed. 88.00 (978-0-7222-6089-0(X)) Library Reprints, Inc.

Marchesi, Mathilde. Marchesi & Music: Passages from the Life of a Famous Singing-Teacher. 2001. 301p. (YA). reprint ed. 98.00 (978-0-7222-6227-6(2)) Library Reprints, Inc.

Martin, G. C. The Art of Training Choir Boys. 2001. (YA). reprint ed. 150.00 (978-0-7222-6123-1(3)) Library Reprints, Inc.

McGraw-Hill Staff. Essential Elements for Choir: Level 3 Musicianship. 2001. stu. ed. 27.32 (978-0-07-826047-6(7) , 9780078260476) Glencoe/McGraw-Hill.

—Essential Elements for Choir: Level 4 Musicianship. 2001. (C). stu. ed. 27.32 (978-0-07-826055-1(8) , 9780078260551) Glencoe/McGraw-Hill.

McKerrow, Janet. The Vocal Movements & Some Others: A Study of Parallels. 2001. 368p. (YA). reprint ed. 98.00 (978-0-7222-6088-3(1)) Library Reprints, Inc.

McLellan, Eleanor. Voice Education. 2001. (YA). reprint ed. 150.00 (978-0-7222-6209-2(4)) Library Reprints, Inc.

Miller, Frank E. Vocal Art-Science & Its Application. 2001. 278p. (YA). reprint ed. 98.00 (978-0-7222-6091-3(1)) Library Reprints, Inc.

Mills, Wesley Joseph. Voice Production in Singing & Speaking, Based on Scientific Principles. 2001. 294p. (YA). reprint ed. 98.00 (978-0-7222-6210-8(8)) Library Reprints, Inc.

Randegger, Alberto. The Singing. 2001. (YA). reprint ed. 150.00 (978-0-7222-6092-0(X)) Library Reprints, Inc.

Ross & Guymon-King. Super Little Singers. 2004. pap. 12.95 (978-1-59156-163-7(9)); cd-rom 12.95 (978-1-59156-164-4(7)) Covenant Communications, Inc.

San Carlo, Irene. Commonsense of Voice Production. 2001. (YA). reprint ed. 150.00 (978-0-7222-6213-9(2)) Library Reprints, Inc.

Santley, Charles. The Art of Singing & Vocal Declamation. 2001. 143p. (YA). reprint ed. 88.00 (978-0-7222-6093-7(8)) Library Reprints, Inc.

—The Singing Master. 2001. (YA). reprint ed. 150.00 (978-0-7222-6094-4(6)) Library Reprints, Inc.

Shaw, William W. The Lost Vocal Art & Its Restoration. 2001. 219p. (YA). reprint ed. 98.00 (978-0-7222-6095-1(4)) Library Reprints, Inc.

Sieling, Peter. Folk Songs. 2002. (North American Folklore Ser.). (Illus.). 112p. (YA). (gr. 7 up). lib. bdg. (978-1-59084-344-4(4)) Mason Crest Pubs.

Stockhausen, J. Method of Singing. 2001. (YA). reprint ed. 150.00 (978-0-7222-6096-8(2)) Library Reprints, Inc.

Stultz, Marie. Innocent Sounds: Building Choral Tone & Artistry in Your Children's Choir. 1999. (Illus.). 180p. pap. 29.95 (978-0-944529-30-0(5)) Morning Star Music Pubs.

Stultz, Marie. Innocent Sounds: Building Choral Tone & Artistry with the Beginning Treble Voice. 2007. (***978-0-944529-44-7(5)***) Morning Star Music Pubs.

Sutro, Emil. Duality of Voice: An Outline of Original Research. 2001. 224p. (YA). reprint ed. 98.00 (978-0-7222-6214-6(0)) Library Reprints, Inc.

Thorp, G. E. Textbook on National Use of Voice. 2001. (YA). reprint ed. 150.00 (978-0-7222-6216-0(7)) Library Reprints, Inc.

Wronski, Thaddeus. The Singer & His Art. 2001. 265p. (YA). reprint ed. 98.00 (978-0-7222-6100-2(4)) Library Reprints, Inc.

SINGING—FICTION

Anaya, Rudolfo A. My Land Sings: Stories from the Rio Grande. Cordova, Amy, illus. 2001. (SPA.). 176p. (J). (gr. 5 up). pap. 5.99 (978-0-380-72902-9(4)) HarperCollins Pubs.

—My Land Sings: Stories from the Rio Grande. 2001. (gr. 5-8). lib. bdg. 12.95 (978-0-613-44405-7(1)) Tandem Library Bks.

Answer the Phone, Fiona! Individual Title Six-Pack Pouch - Level H. (Lighthouse Ser.). 16p. (gr. 1 up). 26.00 (978-0-7578-0844-9(1)) Rigby Education.

Arterburn, Stephen & Hunt, Angela Elwell. Shane. 2004. (Young Believer on Tour Ser.). (J). pap. 3.99 (978-0-8423-8339-4(5)) Tyndale Hse. Pubs.

Baker, Georgette. Cantemos Chiquitos, No. 2. (SPA., Illus.). (J). (gr. k-12). pap. 12.95 incl. audio (978-0-9623930-2-0(9) , TAL002) Cantemos-Bilingual Books and Music.

Beechwood, Beth. Face the Music. 9th rev. ed. 2007. (Hannah Montana Ser.: No. 9). 128p. (gr. 3-7). pap. 4.99 (***978-1-4231-0772-9(1)***) Disney Pr.

Blackaby, Susan. Sunny Bumps the Drums. Muehlenhardt, Amy Bailey, illus. 2004. (Read-It! Readers Classroom Tales Ser.). 32p. (C). (gr. k-3). 18.60 (978-1-4048-0587-3(7)) Picture Window Bks.

Bolliger, Max. The Happy Troll. Ignatowicz, Nina, tr. from GER. Sis, Peter, illus. 2005. 32p. (J). reprint ed. 16.95 (978-0-8050-6982-2(8) , Holt, Henry & Co. Bks. For Young Readers) Holt, Henry & Co.

Bradley, Kimberly Brubaker. For Freedom: The Story of a French Spy. 2005. 192p. (J). (gr. 5-9). pap. 5.50 (978-0-440-41831-3(3) , Laurel Leaf) Random Hse. Children's Bks.

Brightwood, Laura, illus. I Am A Frog. Brightwood, Laura, . 2007. (J). DVD (***978-1-934409-02-2(2)***) 3-C Institute for Social Development.

Brouillard, Anne. The Bathtub Prima Donna. Brouillard, Anne, illus. 2004. (Illus.). 24p. (J). (gr. k-4). reprint ed. 13.00 (978-0-7567-7755-5(0)) DIANE Publishing Co.

Carmichael, Leslie. Lyranel's Song. (Illus.). 288p. (J). 2007. pap. 10.95 (978-0-9718348-6-6(5)); 2005. 23.95 (978-0-9718348-5-9(7)) Blooming Tree Pr.

Carter, D. J. The Singing Lesson. 2007. (J). per. 6.99 (***978-1-59886-914-9(0)***) Tate Publishing & Enterprises, L.L.C.

Cave, Kathryn. Henry's Song. Hendra, Sue, illus. 2000. 32p. (J). (ps-3). 16.00 (978-0-8028-5198-7(3) , Eerdmans Bks For Young Readers) Eerdmans, William B. Publishing Co.

Cole, Babette. That's Why. 2008. (Illus.). 32p. (J). pap. 9.95 (***978-0-09-946399-3(7)***, Red Fox) Random Hse. Children's Bks. GBR. *Dist:* Independent Pubs. Group.

Conkling, Neil & Philip, Hilda. A Bird's Way of Singing. Date not set. (J). 12.95 (978-0-8050-4795-0(6) , Holt, Henry & Co. Bks. For Young Readers) Holt, Henry & Co.

Cow Wants to Sing. 2002. (J). 4.98 (978-0-7525-7220-8(2)) Parragon, Inc.

Cox, Tiffany. Amy, the Frog Who Loved to Sing. 2006. 9.00 (***978-0-8059-8806-2(8)***) Dorrance Publishing Co., Inc.

Crimi, Carolyn. Tessa's Tip-Tapping Toes. Carrington, Marsha Gray, illus. 2002. 32p. (J). (ps-2). pap. 16.95 (978-0-439-31768-9(1) , Orchard Bks.) Scholastic, Inc.

Curry, Jane Louise. The Black Canary. 2005. (Illus.). 288p. (J). (gr. 5 up). 17.99 (978-0-689-86478-0(7) , McElderry, Margaret K.) Simon & Schuster Children's Publishing.

D'Arcy, Karen Scourby. My Grandmother Is a Singing Yaya. Palmisciano, Diane, illus. 2001. (J). (978-0-531-30323-8(3)); lib. bdg. (978-0-531-33323-5(X)) Scholastic, Inc. (Orchard Bks.).

Davis, Joyce. Can't Stop the Shine. 2007. 256p. pap. 9.99 (***978-0-373-83078-7(5)***) Harlequin Enterprises, Ltd. CAN. *Dist:* Simon & Schuster, Inc.

De Gasztold, Carmen B. & Godden, Rumer. The Creatures' Choir. (FRE., Illus.). (J). (gr. 3-8). 29.95 (978-0-8288-9331-2(4) , F140841) French & European Pubns., Inc.

Denmead, Sally. Songs My Granda Sang. Archambault, Matthew, illus. 2002. 16p. (J). (978-0-439-35152-2(9)) Scholastic, Inc.

Disney Press Staff, creator. The Cheetah Girls Quiz Book. 2005. 80p. (gr. 3-7). pap. 3.99 (978-0-7868-4718-1(2) , Jump at the Sun) Hyperion Bks. for Children.

Disney Press Staff, ed. Best of Both Worlds Boxed Set: Keeping Secrets; Face-off; Super Sneak; Truth or Dare. rev. ed. 2007. (gr. 3-7). pap. 15.99 (***978-1-4231-1081-1(1)***) Disney Pr.

Dixon, Franklin W. Top Ten Ways to Die. 2006. 169p. (J). lib. bdg. 16.92 (***978-1-4242-0390-1(2)***) Fitzgerald Bks.

Dodds, Dayle Ann. Sing, Sophie! 1999. (J). (978-0-606-19321-4(9)) Tandem Library Bks.

Dubovoy, Silvia. Donde Canta el Mar. Peinador, Angeles, illus. 2004. (SPA.). 32p. (J). 14.99 (978-84-241-7988-5(9)) Everest de Ediciones y Distribucion, S.L. ESP. *Dist:* Lectorum Pubns., Inc.

Emond, Landis J. Caruso the Mouse. 2nd rev. ed. 2007. 44p. (J). pap. 9.99 (978-1-59092-204-0(2) , Little Blue Works) Windstorm Creative.

Flaxman, Jessica & Hall, Kirsten. Who Says? Becker, Wayne, illus. 2003. (My First Reader Ser.). 32p. (J). 18.50 (978-0-516-22958-4(3) , Children's Pr.) Scholastic Library Publishing.

Flinn, Alex. Diva. 2006. 272p. (YA). 16.99 (978-0-06-056843-6(7)); lib. bdg. 17.89 (978-0-06-056845-0(3)) HarperCollins Pubs. (HarperTeen).

Fullwood, Millie F. Crow Joins the Choir. Srba, Lynne, illus. l.t. ed. 1998. 32p. (J). (ps-3). mass mkt. 9.95 (978-0-9667672-0-9(9) , 3468998-00) Fullwood Marketing Communications Co.

Geras, Adele. Pictures of the Night. 2005. (Egerton Hall Novels: Vol. 3). 192p. (YA). (gr. 7-17). pap. 6.95 (978-0-15-205543-1(6) , Harcourt Paperbacks) Harcourt Children's Bks.

Golden Books Staff. Rising Stars. Duarte, Pamela, illus. 2004. (Barbie Ser.). 64p. (J). (ps-2). 2.99 (978-0-375-82649-8(1) , Golden Bks.) Random Hse. Children's Bks.

Gregory, Deborah. The Cheetah Girls, No. 2, Bks. 5-8. 2003. 624p. (J). (gr. 3-7). pap. 9.99 (978-0-7868-1790-0(9)) Hyperion Bks. for Children.

—Cheetah Girls No.13: OOPS, Doggy Dog! 2002. (gr. 3-6). lib. bdg. 11.80 (978-0-613-91004-0(4)) Tandem Library Bks.

—Cheetah Girls Bind Up No.1, Bks. 1-4: Livin' Large! 2003. lib. bdg. 18.80 (978-0-613-75036-3(5)) Tandem Library Bks.

—Cheetah Girls Bind Up No.2: Supa Dupa Sparkle! Book 5-8. 2003. (gr. 3-6). lib. bdg. 18.80 (978-0-613-74957-2(X)) Tandem Library Bks.

—The Cheetah Girls Livin' Large, No. 1, Bks. 1-4. 2003. 576p. (J). (gr. 3-7). pap. 9.99 (978-0-7868-1789-4(5)) Hyperion Bks. for Children.

—Showdown at the Okie Dokie. 2000. (Cheetah Girls Ser.: Bk. 9). 160p. (J). (gr. 3-7). pap. 3.99 (978-0-7868-1475-6(6) , Jump at the Sun) Hyperion Bks. for Children.

—Who's Bout to Bounce, Baby? 3rd rev. ed. 1999. (Cheetah Girls Ser.: No. 3). 160p. (gr. 3-7). pap. 3.99 (978-0-7868-1386-5(5)) Hyperion Bks. for Children.

Grekul, Lisa. Kalyna's Song. 2nd ed. 2007. 472p. (YA). (gr. 10 up). pap. 12.95 (***978-1-55050-355-5(3)***) Coteau Bks. CAN. *Dist:* Fitzhenry & Whiteside, Ltd.

Grigg, Carol. The Singing Snowbear. Grigg, Carol, illus. 1999. (Illus.). 32p. (J). (gr. k-3). tchr. ed. 15.00 (978-0-395-94223-9(3)) Houghton Mifflin Co. Trade & Reference Div.

Hannah, Montana. Hannah Montana Valentines. rev. ed. 2007. 32p. (gr. 2-7). pap. 5.99 (***978-1-4231-1061-3(7)***) Disney Pr.

Hanson, Anders. Whale Tale. Nobens, C. A., illus. 2007. (Fact & Fiction Ser.). 24p. (J). pap. (978-1-59928-477-4(4)); 21.35 (978-1-59928-476-7(6)) ABDO Publishing Co.

Harcourt School Publishers Staff. Mine for a Song: Take-Home Book. 2001. (Collections Ser.). (Illus.). (J). pap. 1.90 (978-0-15-319564-8(9)) Harcourt Schl. Pubs.

—Mine for a Song Below Level. 3rd ed. 2002. (Trophies Reading Program Ser.). (Illus.). pap. 5.10 (978-0-15-323417-0(2)) Harcourt Schl. Pubs.

Harrison, Emma. The Cheetah Girls Supa-Star Scrapbook. 2005. (Illus.). 48p. (J). (gr. 3-7). pap. 6.99 (978-0-7868-4717-4(4)) Disney Pr.

Holmes, Lynda. Spring Cleaning. 2006. 55p. pap. 12.95 (978-1-4241-4324-5(1)) PublishAmerica, Inc.

Hopkinson, Deborah. A Band of Angels: A Story Inspired by the Jubilee Singers. Colon, Raul, illus. 1999. (Anne Schwartz Bks.). 40p. (J). (gr. 1-4). 16.95 (978-0-689-81062-6(8) , Atheneum/Anne Schwartz Bks.) Simon & Schuster Children's Publishing.

Howe, James. Horace & Morris Join the Chorus. Waldrod, Amy, illus. pap. 16.95 incl. audio (978-1-59112-447-4(6)); pap. incl. audio (978-1-59112-449-8(2)); pap. 18.95 incl. audio compact disk (978-1-59112-907-3(9)); pap. incl. audio compact disk (978-1-59112-909-7(5)); 2005. (J). 25.95 incl. audio (978-1-59112-448-1(4)); 2005. (J). 28.95 incl. audio compact disk (978-1-59112-908-0(7)) Live Oak Media.

—Horace & Morris Join the Chorus: But What about Dolores? Walrod, Amy, illus. 2002. 32p. (J). (ps-2). 16.95 (978-0-689-83939-9(1) , Atheneum) Simon & Schuster Children's Publishing.

Hyperion Staff. First Singing ABC. 2007. 64p. (J). (ps-3). 16.99 (978-1-4231-0248-9(7)) Hyperion Pr.

Inman, Robert. Christmas Bus. Baskin, Lyle, illus. 2006. 84p. (J). 19.95 (978-0-9760963-6-8(6)) Novello Festival Pr.

Jackson, Chris. The Gaggle Sisters Sing Again. Jackson, Chris, illus. 2005. (Gaggle Sisters Trilogy Ser.). (Illus.). 32p. (J). 15.95 (978-1-894222-56-3(3)) Lobster Pr. CAN. *Dist:* Univ. of Toronto Pr.

Jefferies, Cindy. Rising Star. 2007. (Fame School Ser.: No. 2). 128p. (J). 4.99 (978-0-14-240716-5(X) , Puffin) Penguin Group (USA) Inc.

Joachimowski, Paula L. Swamp Band Lullaby. 2007. (J). per. 12.99 (***978-1-59879-211-9(3)***) Lifevest Publishing, Inc.

Jones, Jasmine. The Cheetah Girls Movie: Junior Novel. 2004. (Illus.). 128p. (gr. 3-7). pap. 4.99 (978-0-7868-4713-6(1)) Disney Pr.

King, M. C. Seeing Green. 8th rev. ed. 2007. (Hannah Montana Ser.: No. 8). (Illus.). 142p. (J). (gr. 3-7). per. 4.99 (***978-1-4231-0463-6(3)***) Disney Pr.

Lawston, Lisa. Can You Sing? Vere, Ed, illus. 1999. 10p. (J). (ps). pap. 5.95 (978-0-531-30132-6(X) , Orchard Bks.) Scholastic, Inc.

Levine, Gail Carson. Fairest. 2006. 336p. (J). (gr. 3-9). 16.99 (978-0-06-073408-4(6)); lib. bdg. 17.89 (978-0-06-073409-1(4)) HarperCollins Pubs.

—Fairest. l.t. rev. ed. 2007. 356p. (YA). 23.95 (***978-0-7862-9270-7(9)***) Thorndike Pr.

Little Tommy Tucker: 6 Small Books. (gr. k-2). 23.00 (978-0-7635-8502-0(5)) Rigby Education.

Martin, Jacqueline Briggs. Chicken Joy on Redbean Road: A Bayou Country Romp. Sweet, Melissa, illus. 2007. 32p. (J). (gr. 3-5). 17.00 (978-0-618-50759-7(0)) Houghton Mifflin Co.

McElroy, Laurie. Nightmare on Hannah Street. 7th rev. ed. 2007. (Hannah Montana Ser.: No. 7). 128p. (J). (gr. 3-7). pap. 4.99 (*978-1-4231-0462-9(5)) Disney Pr.

Mitchelhill, Barbara & MacKeith, Bridget. Eric & the Peculiar Pong. 2003. (Illus.). 80p. (J). pap. 8.99 (978-1-84270-288-8(2)) Andersen GBR. Dist: Independent Pubs. Group.

Morris, Jackie. The Snow Leopard. 2007. (Illus.). 32p. (J). (ps-3). 16.95 (*978-1-84507-600-9(1)) Lincoln, Frances Ltd. GBR. Dist: Perseus Distribution.

Newman, Barbara Johansen. Tex & Sugar: A Big City Kitty Ditty. Newman, Barbara Johansen, illus. 2007. (Illus.). 32p. (J). (gr. k-2). 14.95 (978-1-4027-3887-6(0)) Sterling Publishing Co., Inc.

Plante, Raymond & Jorisch, Stephane. Les Voyageurs Clandestins. 2001. (Roman Jeunesse Ser.). (FRE.). 96p. (J). (gr. 4-7). pap. (978-2-89021-435-4(4)) Diffusion du livre Mirabel.

Post, Jim & Post, Janet. Barnyard Boogie. Vasconsellos, Daniel, illus. gif. ed. 2003. 32p. (J). 15.99 (978-1-57939-130-0(3)) Accord Publishing, Ltd.

Poth, Karen. If I Sang a Silly Song. Hardin, Greg & Spadaford, Joe, illus. 2006. (VeggieTales Ser.). 16p. (J). bds. 7.99 (978-1-4169-4060-9(X) , Little Simon Inspirations) Simon & Schuster Children's Publishing.

Priddy, Roger. Sing-along Christmas Carols. 2007. 24p. (J). bds. 12.95 (*978-0-312-50019-1(X) , Priddy Bks.) St. Martin's Pr.

Santillo, LuAnn. The King. Santillo, LuAnn, ed. 2003. (Half-Pint Kids Readers Ser.). (Illus.). 7p. (J). (ps-1). pap. (978-1-59256-050-9(4)) Half-Pint Kids, Inc.

Sardon, Sonya. Young Warren Sings! 2004. pap. 7.95 (978-0-533-14852-3(9)) Vantage Pr., Inc.

Sing along Barney: Story Reader. 2004. 26p. (J). spiral bd. (978-1-4127-3229-1(8) , 7237200) Publications International, Ltd.

Sing-along Bob the Builder: Story Reader. 2004. 26p. (J). spiral bd. (978-1-4127-3238-3(7) , 7236900) Publications International, Ltd.

Sing-along Disney Princess: Story Reader. 2004. 26p. (J). spiral bd. (978-1-4127-3236-9(0) , 7236800) Publications International, Ltd.

Sing along Elmo: Story Reader. 2004. 26p. (J). spiral bd. (978-1-4127-3232-1(8) , 7237500) Publications International, Ltd.

Spears, Britney. Mother's Gift. 2003. (gr. 5-8). lib. bdg. 14.15 (978-0-613-72254-4(X)) Tandem Library Bks.

Steig, William. Roland the Minstrel Pig. 1999. 32p. (J). (ps-1). pap. 4.95 (978-0-06-443346-4(3)) HarperCollins Pubs.

Stenmark, Victoria. The Singing Chick. Cecil, Randy, illus. rev. ed. 1999. 32p. (J). (ps-1). 15.95 (978-0-8050-5255-8(0) , Holt, Henry & Co. Bks. For Young Readers) Holt, Henry & Co.

Sweeney, Jacqueline. Meadow Magic. 2001. (We Can Read! Ser.). (Illus.). 32p. (J). (gr. 1-2). lib. bdg. 21.36 (978-0-7614-1124-6(0) , Benchmark Bks.) Cavendish, Marshall Corp.

Tanemura, Arina. O Sagashite. Tanemura, Arina, illus. 2006. (Full Moon o Sagashite Ser.). 200p. (YA). pap. 8.99 (978-1-4215-0397-4(2)) Viz Media.

Taylor, Ann & HarperCollins Staff. Baby Dance. Van Heerden, Marjorie, illus. 1999. (Growing Tree Ser.). 16p. (J). (ps up). 6.99 (978-0-694-01206-0(8) , Harper Festival) HarperCollins Pubs.

Wallace, Karen. The Peanut Prankster. Brown, Judy, illus. 2007. (Read-It! Chapter Books). (J). 21.26 (978-1-4048-2724-0(2)) Picture Window Bks.

Wells, Rosemary. The Bear Went over the Mountain. Wells, Rosemary, illus. 2007. (Bruno & Boots Book Ser.). (Illus.). 18p. (J). bds. 5.99 (978-0-590-02910-0(X)) Scholastic, Inc.

Wright, Bil. When the Black Girl Sings. 2008. 272p. (YA). (gr. 7 up). 16.99 (*978-1-4169-3995-5(4) , Simon & Schuster Children's Publishing) Simon & Schuster Children's Publishing.

Zion, Gene. Harry & the Lady Next Door. Graham, Margaret Bloy, illus. 2002. (J). 12.34 (978-0-7587-6128-6(7)) Book Wholesalers, Inc.

SINGING GAMES

Adams, Pam, illus. The Farmer in the Dell. 2001. 16p. (J). 19.99 (978-0-85953-894-7(X)) Child's Play-International.

Cabrera, Jane, illus. If You're Happy & You Know It! 2005. 32p. (J). 16.95 (978-0-8234-1881-7(2)) Holiday Hse., Inc.

Kubler, Annie. The Farmer in the Dell. Adams, Pam & Freeman, Tina, illus. 2001. (Classic Books with Holes). 16p. (J). (ps-3). bds. 5.99 (978-0-85953-796-4(X)) Child's Play-International.

—Head, Shoulders, Knees & Toes. 2004. (Illus.). (J). (ALB & ENG.). (978-1-84444-144-0(X)); (ARA & ENG., (978-1-84444-145-7(8)); (BEN & ENG., 20p. (978-1-84444-146-4(6)); (CHI & ENG., (978-1-84444-147-1(4)); (978-1-84444-148-8(2)); (ENG & FRE., (978-1-84444-149-5(0)); (ENG & GUJ., (978-1-84444-150-1(4)); (ENG & PAN., (978-1-84444-151-8(2)); (ENG & POR., (978-1-84444-152-5(0)); (ENG & SOM., (978-1-84444-153-2(9)); (ENG & SPA., (978-1-84444-154-9(7)); (ENG & TAM., (978-1-84444-155-6(5)); (ENG & TUR., (978-1-84444-156-3(3)) Mantra Publishing, Ltd.

Kubler, Annie, et al, illus. Here We Go Round the Mulberry Bush. 2001. (Classic Books with Holes). 16p. (J). (ps-3). bds. 5.99 (978-0-85953-795-7(1)) Child's Play-International.

—The Wheels on the Bus Go Round & Round. 2001. (Classic Books with Holes). 16p. (J). (ps-3). bds. 5.99 (978-0-85953-797-1(8)) Child's Play-International.

Kubler, Annie, tr. & illus. The Wheels on the Bus Go Round & Round. Kubler, Annie, illus. 2003. (Classic Books with Holes). (J). 4.99 (978-0-85953-136-8(8)) Child's Play-International.

Mason, Jane B. & Hines Stephens, Sarah. Gymboree Music Play. rev. ed. 2007. (Illus.). 36p. (J). bds. 16.95 (*978-1-55263-964-1(9)) Key Porter Bks. CAN. Dist: Perseus Distribution.

Moore, Mary-Alice. The Wheels on the School Bus. Huliska-Beith, Laura, illus. 2006. 32p. (J). 15.99 (978-0-06-059427-5(6)) HarperCollins Pubs.

Plume, Ilse. The Farmer in the Dell: Pictures by Ilse Plume. 2004. (Illus.). 64p. (J). 17.95 (978-1-56792-270-7(8)) Godine, David R. Pub.

Sierra, Judy. Schoolyard Rhymes: Kids' Own Rhymes for Rope-Skipping, Hand Clapping, Ball Bouncing, & Just Plain Fun. Sweet, Melissa, illus. 2005. 40p. (J). (gr. 1-7). 15.95 (978-0-375-82516-3(9) , Knopf Bks. for Young Readers) Random Hse. Children's Bks.

—Schoolyard Rhymes: Kids' Own Rhymes for Rope Skipping, Hand Clapping, Ball Bouncing, & Just Plain Fun. Sweet, Melissa, illus. 2005. 40p. (J). (gr. 1-7). lib. bdg. 17.99 (978-0-375-92516-0(3) , Knopf Bks. for Young Readers) Random Hse. Children's Bks.

Warhola, James. If You're Happy & You Know It: Jungle Edition. Geist, Ken, ed. 2007. 32p. (J). (ps-k). pap. 14.99 (978-0-439-72766-2(9) , Orchard Bks.) Scholastic, Inc.

Yolen, Jane, ed. This Little Piggy & Other Rhymes to Sing & Play: Lap Songs, Finger Plays, Clapping Games & Pantomime Rhymes. Hillenbrand, Will, illus. 2006. 80p. (J). (gr. k-ps). 19.99 (978-0-7636-1348-8(7)) Candlewick Pr.

SINGLE-PARENT FAMILIES

Levins, Sandra. Was It the Chocolate Pudding? A Story for Little Kids about Divorce. Langdo, Bryan, illus. 2005. 40p. (J). pap. 8.95 (978-1-59147-309-1(8) , Magination Pr.) American Psychological Assn.

Levy, Janice. Totally Uncool. Monroe, Chris, illus. 1999. (Picture Bks.). 32p. (J). (ps-3). 15.95 (978-1-57505-306-6(3) , Carolrhoda Bks.) Lerner Publishing Group.

Lindsay, Jeanne Warren. Do I Have a Daddy? A Story about a Single-Parent Child with a Special Section for Single Mothers & Fathers. Moffett, Jamie, illus. rev. ed. 1999. 48p. (J). (ps-3). pap. 7.95 (978-1-885356-63-5(3)) Morning Glory Pr., Inc.

SINGLE-PARENT FAMILIES—FICTION

Ackerman, Karen. By the Dawn's Early Light: Al Amanecer. 1999. (J). (978-0-606-15924-1(X)) Tandem Library Bks.

Aldrich, Vickie. Dad Has a New Girlfriend, What about Me? Crow, Madge, illus. 2000. VI, 25p. (J). (ps-3). pap. 7.95 (978-0-9706093-0-4(2)) Aldrich/Crow.

Alice-by-Accident Bound Galley. 2000. (J). (978-0-06-029056-6(0)) HarperCollins Pubs.

Banks, Kate. Lenny's Space. 2007. 160p. (J). (gr. 3-7). 16.00 (*978-0-374-34575-4(9) , Farrar, Straus & Giroux (BYR)) Farrar, Straus & Giroux.

Banks, Lynne Reid. Alice-by-Accident. 2000. (Avon Camelot Bks.). 144p. (J). (gr. 4-7). 14.95 (978-0-380-97865-6(2)) HarperCollins Pubs.

Bateman, Colin. Running with the Reservoir Pups. 2005. 272p. (J). (gr. 5-9). lib. bdg. 17.99 (978-0-385-90268-7(9) , Delacorte Bks. for Young Readers) Random Hse. Children's Bks.

Bateson, Catherine. The Boyfriend Rules of Good Behavior. 2006. 192p. (YA). 16.95 (978-0-8234-2026-1(4)) Holiday Hse., Inc.

Birdsall, Jeanne. The Penderwicks. 2005. 272p. (J). (gr. 3-7). lib. bdg. 17.99 (978-0-375-93143-7(0) , Knopf Bks. for Young Readers) Random Hse. Children's Bks.

—The Penderwicks. 2006. 301p. (YA). 23.95 (978-0-7862-8897-7(3)) Thorndike Pr.

—The Penderwicks: A Summer Tale of Four Sisters, Two Rabbits, & a Very Interesting Boy. 272p. (J). 2007. (gr. 4-7). 6.50 (978-0-440-42047-7(4) , Yearling); 2005. (gr. 3-7). 15.95 (978-0-375-83143-0(6) , Knopf Bks. for Young Readers) Random Hse. Children's Bks.

Black, Holly & DiTerlizzi, Tony. Spiderwick Chronicles Set: The Field Guide, the Seeing Stone, Lucinda's Secret, the Ironwood Tree, the Wrath of Mulgarath. DiTerlizzi, Tony, illus. movie tie-in ed. 2008. (Spiderwick Chronicles). 672p. (J). 49.99 (*978-1-4169-5016-5(8)) Simon & Schuster Children's Publishing.

Bognomo, Joel Ebouerne. Madoulina: A Girl Who Wanted to Go to School. 2003. (Illus.). 32p. (J). (gr. 2-4). 14.95 (978-1-56397-769-5(9)); pap. 8.95 (978-1-56397-822-7(9)) Boyds Mills Pr.

—Madoulina: A Girl Who Wanted to Go to School. 1999. (978-0-606-17704-7(3)); lib. bdg. 17.60 (978-0-613-23339-2(5)) Tandem Library Bks.

Brugman, Alyssa. Being Bindy. 2006. 208p. (YA). (gr. 7). 15.95 (978-0-385-73294-9(5)); lib. bdg. 17.99 (978-0-385-90315-8(4)) Random Hse. Children's Bks. (Delacorte Bks. for Young Readers).

Caletti, Deb. The Fortunes of Indigo Skye. 2008. 304p. (YA). 15.99 (*978-1-4169-1007-7(7) , Simon & Schuster Children's Publishing) Simon & Schuster Children's Publishing.

Coles, William E., Jr. Another Kind of Monday. 1999. 246p. per. 14.64 (978-0-606-16357-6(3)) Tandem Library Bks.

Coolidge, Susan. What Katy Did. 2006. 62.99 (*978-1-4280-3108-1(1)) IndyPublish.com.

Cooper, Melrose. Gettin' Through Thursday. 2000. (Illus.). 32p. (J). (ps-5). 6.95 (978-1-58430-014-4(0)) Lee & Low Bks., Inc.

—Gettin' Through Thursday. Bennett, Nneka, illus. 1999. 32p. (J). (ps-5). 15.95 (978-1-880000-67-0(9)) Lee & Low Bks., Inc.

—Gettin' Through Thursday. Bennett, Nneka, illus. 2000. (J). 13.75 (978-0-606-19831-8(8)) Tandem Library Bks.

Corbett, Sue. Free Baseball. 2008. 160p. (J). (gr. 3). 5.99 (*978-0-14-241080-6(2) , Puffin) Penguin Group (USA) Inc.

Davis, Deborah. Not Like You. 2007. 272p. (YA). (gr. 7 up). 16.00 (*978-0-618-72093-4(6) , Clarion Bks.) Houghton Mifflin Co. Trade & Reference Div.

Dee, Barbara. Just Another Day in My Insanely Real Life. 2007. 256p. (J). pap. 5.99 (*978-1-4169-4739-4(6)) Kaplan Bks.

—Just Another Day in My Insanely Real Life. 2006. (Illus.). 256p. (J). 15.95 (978-1-4169-0861-6(7) , McElderry, Margaret K.) Simon & Schuster Children's Publishing.

Deuker, Carl. Runner. 224p. (YA). (gr. 7). 2007. pap. 7.99 (*978-0-618-73505-1(4) , Graphia); 2005. 16.00 (978-0-618-54298-7(1)) Houghton Mifflin Co. Trade & Reference Div.

DiTerlizzi, Tony & Black, Holly. The Field Guide. DiTerlizzi, Tony, illus. (Spiderwick Chronicles: Bk. 1). 128p. (J). 2003. (Illus.). 10.99 (978-0-689-85936-6(8) , 53409542); 2008. 10.99 (*978-1-4169-5017-2(6)) Simon & Schuster Children's Publishing.

—The Field Guide. l.t. ed. 2006. (Spiderwick Chronicles: Bk. 1). 120p. (J). 23.95 (978-0-7862-8284-5(3)) Thorndike Pr.

—The Seeing Stone. DiTerlizzi, Tony, illus. movie tie-in ed. (Spiderwick Chronicles: Bk. 2). 128p. (J). 2008. 10.99 (*978-1-4169-5018-9(4)); Bk. 2. 2003. (Illus.). 10.99 (978-0-689-85937-3(6) , 53409541) Simon & Schuster Children's Publishing.

—The Seeing Stone. l.t. ed. 2006. (Spiderwick Chronicles: No. 2). (YA). 23.95 (978-0-7862-8581-5(8)) Thorndike Pr.

Dudley, David L. The Bicycle Man. 2005. 256p. (J). (gr. 5-9). 16.00 (978-0-618-54233-8(7) , Clarion Bks.) Houghton Mifflin Co. Trade & Reference Div.

Edwards, Michelle. Papa's Latkes. Gustavson, Adam & Schuett, Stacey, illus. 2004. 32p. (J). (gr. k-2). 15.99 (978-0-7636-0779-1(7)) Candlewick Pr.

Edwards, Michelle. Papa's Latkes. Schuett, Stacey, illus. 2007. 32p. (J). (gr. k-2). pap. 6.99 (*978-0-7636-3563-3(4)) Candlewick Pr.

Ferguson, Alane. The Angel of Death. 2006. (Forensic Mystery Ser.). 272p. (YA). (gr. 7). 15.99 (978-0-670-06055-9(0) , Viking Adult) Penguin Group (USA) Inc.

Ferguson, Alane. Angel of Death. 2008. (Forensic Mystery Ser.). 272p. (YA). (gr. 7). pap. 6.99 (*978-0-14-241087-5(X) , Puffin) Penguin Group (USA) Inc.

Flake, Sharon G. Money Hungry. (J). 2003. 208p. (gr. 5-17). pap. 5.99 (978-0-7868-1503-6(5)); 2001. 192p. (gr. 3-7). 15.99 (978-0-7868-0548-8(X) , Jump at the Sun) Hyperion Bks. for Children.

Fletcher, Ralph. The One O'Clock Chop. 2007. 192p. (J). (gr. 5-11). 16.95 (*978-0-8050-8143-5(7) , Holt, Henry & Co. Bks. For Young Readers) Holt, Henry & Co.

Fogelin, Adrian. The Real Question. 2006. 240p. (YA). 15.95 (978-1-56145-383-2(8) , Peachtree Junior) Peachtree Pubs., Ltd.

Fogelin, Adrian. The Sorta Sisters. 2007. 240p. (J). (gr. 3-7). 14.95 (*978-1-56145-424-2(9) , Peachtree Junior) Peachtree Pubs., Ltd.

Frank, Lucy. Lucky Stars. (J). 2006. 240p. pap. 5.99 (978-0-689-85934-2(1) , Aladdin); 2005. (Illus.). 304p. 16.95 (978-0-689-85933-5(3) , Atheneum) Simon & Schuster Children's Publishing.

Freymann-Weyr, Garret. The Kings Are Already Here. 2003. 160p. (YA). (gr. 7). tchr. ed. 15.00 (978-0-618-26363-9(2)) Houghton Mifflin Co. Trade & Reference Div.

Fuqua, Jonathon Scott. Reappearance of Sam Webber. 1999. (Illus.). 232p. (YA). pap. 23.95 (978-1-890862-03-9(7)) Bancroft Pr.

—The Reappearance of Sam Webber. 2001. (Illus.). 288p. (J). (gr. 5). reprint ed. pap. 9.99 (978-0-7636-1424-9(6)) Candlewick Pr.

Gantos, Jack. Joey Pigza Swallowed the Key. 1998. (Joey Pigza Ser.). (Illus.). 196p. (J). (gr. 4-7). 16.00 (978-0-374-33664-6(4) , Farrar, Straus & Giroux (BYR)) Farrar, Straus & Giroux.

—Joey Pigza Swallowed the Key. 2000. (J). pap., tchr. ed. (978-0-06-449267-6(2)); 160p. (gr. 5 up). pap. 5.99 (978-0-06-440833-2(7)) HarperCollins Pubs. (Harper Trophy).

—Joey Pigza Swallowed the Key. unabr. ed. 2004. 154p. (J). (gr. 5-9). pap. 29.00 incl. audio (978-0-8072-8166-6(2) , YA120SP, Listening Library) Random Hse. Audio Publishing Group.

—Joey Pigza Swallowed the Key. 2000. (gr. 3-6). lib. bdg. 14.15 (978-0-613-28228-4(0)); (Illus.). (J). 12.64 (978-0-606-18904-0(1)) Tandem Library Bks.

—Joey Pigza Swallowed the Key. l.t. ed. 2000. 174p. (J). 21.95 (978-0-7862-2912-3(8)) Thorndike Pr.

Gauthier, Gilles. Life without Mooch. Cummins, Sarah, tr. from FRE. Derome, Pierre-Andre, illus. 2000. (First Novels Ser.). 64p. (gr. 1-5). 4.95 (978-0-88780-524-0(8)); (J). (978-0-88780-525-7(6)) Formac Publishing Co., Ltd. CAN. Dist: Casemate Pubs. & Bk. Distributors, LLC.

—Life without Mooch. 2001. (gr. k-3). lib. bdg. 11.80 (978-0-613-83144-4(6)) Tandem Library Bks.

Gauthier, Gilles & Derome, Pierre-Andre. Mon Cher Chausson. 2000. (Premier Roman Ser.). (FRE.). 64p. (J). (gr. 2-5). pap. (978-2-89021-416-3(8)) Diffusion du livre Mirabel.

Gibbons, Alan. The Lost Boys' Appreciation Society. 2006. 176p. (J). pap. 11.99 (*978-1-84255-095-3(0)) Orion Publishing Group, Ltd. GBR. Dist: Independent Pubs. Group.

Gorman, Carol & Findley, Ron. The Stumptown Kid. 2005. 224p. (J). (gr. 3-7). 14.95 (978-1-56145-337-5(4)) Peachtree Pubs., Ltd.

Green, Julia. Hunter's Heart. 2007. 264p. (YA). (gr. 7-12). 16.95 (*978-0-7613-9493-8(1) , Carolrhoda Bks.) Lerner Publishing Group.

Grindele, Jenny. Josh, the Jock of High School. 2005. 48p. pap. 12.95 (978-1-4137-6950-0(0)) PublishAmerica, Inc.

Grindley, Sally. Bravo, Max! Ross, Tony, illus. 2007. 160p. (J). (gr. 1-4). 15.99 (978-1-4169-0393-2(3) , McElderry, Margaret K.); pap. 4.99 (978-1-4169-3645-9(9) , Aladdin) Simon & Schuster Children's Publishing.

Hahn, Mary Downing. Witch Catcher. 2006. 240p. (J). (gr. 4-6). 16.00 (978-0-618-50457-2(5) , Clarion Bks.) Houghton Mifflin Co. Trade & Reference Div.

Halvorson, Marilyn. Let It Go. 2004. 224p. (YA). (gr. 7-9). (978-1-55005-105-6(9)) Fitzhenry & Whiteside, Ltd.

Hamilton, Virginia. Sweet Whispers, Brother Rush. 1999. (J). (gr. 4-7). pap. 12.25 (978-0-88103-610-7(2)) Tandem Library Bks.

Headley, Justina Chen. Nothing but the Truth (And a Few White Lies) 2006. 256p. (J). (gr. 5-9). 16.99 (978-0-316-01128-0(2)) Little Brown & Co.

—Nothing but the Truth (And a Few White Lies) 2007. 256p. (J). (gr. 7 up). pap. 7.99 (*978-0-316-01131-0(2)) Little, Brown Bks. for Young Readers.

Hemphill, Helen. Runaround. 2007. 117p. (YA). (gr. 8 up). 16.95 (978-1-932425-83-3(7) , Front Street) Boyds Mills Pr.

Herrick, Steven. By the River. 2006. 240p. (YA). 16.95 (978-1-932425-72-7(1) , Lemniscaat) Boyds Mills Pr.

Hicks, Betty. Busted ! rev. ed. 2004. 176p. (J). 15.95 (978-1-59643-004-4(4)) Roaring Brook Pr.

—Busted ! 2008. 192p. (J). pap. 6.99 (*978-0-312-38053-3(4)) Square Fish.

Hixson, Nancy E. Distorted Vision. 1999. 90p. (J). pap. 15.95 (978-0-936389-62-2(1)) Tudor Pubs., Inc.

Hopkins, Lee Bennett. Mama. Marchesi, Stephen, illus. 2003. 80p. (YA). (gr. 4-6). pap. 8.95 (978-1-56397-813-5(X)) Boyds Mills Pr.

—Mama. 2000. (gr. 3-6). lib. bdg. 17.60 (978-0-613-78895-3(8)) Tandem Library Bks.

—Mama & Her Boys. Marchesi, Stephen, illus. 2003. 80p. (YA). (gr. 4-6). pap. 8.95 (978-1-56397-814-2(8)) Boyds Mills Pr.

—Mama & Her Boys. 2000. 130p. (J). (gr. 4-7). per. 17.60 (978-0-613-78896-0(6)) Tandem Library Bks.

Jonsberg, Barry. Am I Right or Am I Right? 2007. 256p. (gr. 7). (J). lib. bdg. 18.99 (978-0-375-93637-1(8)); (YA). 15.99 (978-0-375-83637-4(3)) Random Hse. Children's Bks. (Knopf Bks. for Young Readers).

Kennedy, Marlane. Me & the Pumpkin Queen. 2007. 192p. (J). (gr. 3-7). 15.99 (978-0-06-114022-8(8)); lib. bdg. 16.89 (978-0-06-114023-5(6)) HarperCollins Pubs.

Kinsey-Warnock, Natalie. Lumber Camp Library. Bernardin, James, illus. 2003. 96p. (J). pap. 4.99 (978-0-06-444292-3(6)) HarperCollins Pubs.

—Lumber Camp Library. 2002. (gr. 3-6). lib. bdg. 13.00 (978-0-613-68447-7(8)) Tandem Library Bks.

Klam, Cheryl. Learning to Swim. 2007. 224p. (YA). (gr. 7). pap. 8.99 (978-0-385-73372-4(0)); lib. bdg. 13.99 (978-0-385-90387-5(1)) Random Hse. Children's Bks. (Delacorte Bks. for Young Readers).

Kurzweil, Allen. Leon & the Spitting Image. Bertholf, Bret, illus. 320p. (J). (gr. 3 up). 2005. pap. 6.99 (978-0-06-053932-0(1) , Harper Trophy); 2003. 16.99 (978-0-06-053930-6(5)); 2003. lib. bdg. 16.89 (978-0-06-053931-3(3)) HarperCollins Pubs.

Lachtman, Ofelia Dumas. The Summer of El Pintor. 2001. (Illus.). 240p. (J). (gr. 11 up). pap. 9.95 (978-1-55885-327-0(8) , Piñata Books) Arte Publico Pr.

—Summer of el Pintor. 2001. (gr. 5-8). lib. bdg. 18.75 (978-0-613-59023-5(6)) Tandem Library Bks.

Levy, Janice. Totally Uncool. Monroe, Chris, illus. (Picture Bks.). 32p. (J). (ps-3). 1999. 15.95 (978-1-57505-306-6(3)); 2003. reprint ed. 6.95 (978-1-57505-555-8(4)) Lerner Publishing Group. (Carolrhoda Bks.).

Lewis, Beverly. Star Status. 2002. (Girls Only (Go!) Ser.: Vol. 8). 128p. (J). reprint ed. pap. 6.99 (978-1-55661-643-3(0)) Bethany Hse. Pubs.

Lowry, Brigid. Things You Either Hate or Love. 2005. 179p. (YA). 16.95 (978-0-8234-2004-9(3)) Holiday Hse., Inc.

Mankell, Henning. A Bridge to the Stars. 2007. 176p. (YA). (gr. 7). 15.99 (*978-0-385-73495-0(6)); lib. bdg. 18.99 (*978-0-385-90489-6(4)) Random Hse. Children's Bks. (Delacorte Bks. for Young Readers).

Mankell, Henning & Thompson, Laurie. Shadows in the Twilight. 2008. 176p. (J). (*978-0-385-73496-7(4)); (YA). (gr. 7). lib. bdg. 18.99 (*978-0-385-90490-2(8)) Dell Publishing. (Delacorte Pr.).

McDaniel, Lurlene. Prey. 2008. 208p. (YA). (*978-0-385-73453-0(0) , Delacorte Pr.) Dell Publishing.

McDonald, Janet. Off-Color. 2007. 176p. (YA). (gr. 7 up). 16.00 (*978-0-374-37196-8(2)) Farrar, Straus & Giroux.

McKissack, Patricia C. Ma Dear's Aprons. 2002. (Illus.). (J). 14.47 (978-0-7587-5149-2(4)) Book Wholesalers, Inc.

—Ma Dear's Aprons. 2000. (gr. k-3). lib. bdg. 14.15 (978-0-613-23015-5(9)) Tandem Library Bks.

McNish, Cliff. Breathe: A Ghost Story. 2006. 264p. (J). 15.95 (978-0-8225-6443-0(2) , Carolrhoda Bks.) Lerner Publishing Group.

Mead, Alice. Junebug & the Reverend. 2002. (Illus.). (J). 13.40 (978-0-7587-6518-5(5)) Book Wholesalers, Inc.

—Junebug & the Reverend. 2000. (J). (ps-7). 186p. per. 13.00 (978-0-613-21831-3(0)); (Illus.). 11.64 (978-0-606-18785-5(5)) Tandem Library Bks.

—Junebug in Trouble. 2003. (Illus.). 144p. (J). (gr. 4-7). pap. 5.50 (978-0-440-41937-2(9) , Yearling) Random Hse. Children's Bks.

Mead, Alice & Weber James, Alice. Junebug in Trouble. 2002. 144p. (J). (gr. 4-7). 16.00 (978-0-374-33969-2(4) , Farrar, Straus & Giroux (BYR)) Farrar, Straus & Giroux.

S

Mills, Claudia. Being Teddy Roosevelt. Alley, R. W., illus. 2007. 96p. (J). (gr. 2-5). 16.00 (978-0-374-30657-1(5) , Farrar, Straus & Giroux (BYR)) Farrar, Straus & Giroux.

Mohr, L. C. Krumbuckets. 2008. (Illus.). 144p. (J). per. 8.95 (978-0-9769417-7-4(5)) Blooming Tree Pr.

—Krumbuckets. Musheno, Erica, illus. 2007. 144p. (J). (gr. 2-7). 13.95 (978-0-9769417-6-7(7)) Blooming Tree Pr.

Morpurgo, Michael. Private Peaceful. (J). 2006. 176p. pap. 5.99 (978-0-439-63653-7(1) , Scholastic Paperbacks); 2004. 208p. (gr. 7 up). 16.95 (978-0-439-63648-3(5) , Scholastic Pr.) Scholastic, Inc.

—Private Peaceful. l.t. ed. 2006. 225p. (J). 21.95 (978-0-7862-8946-2(5)) Thorndike Pr.

—Snakes & Ladders. Wilson, Anne, illus. 2006. 46p. (J). (978-0-7787-0952-7(3)) Crabtree Publishing Co.

Myers, Anna. Wart. 2007. 224p. (J). (gr. 5-9). 16.95 ***978-0-8027-8977-8(3))** Walker & Co.

Naylor, Phyllis Reynolds. Alice In-Between. Vaccaro, Nick, photos by. 2004. (Alice Ser.). (Illus.). 160p. (J). pap. 4.99 (978-0-689-81685-7(5) , Aladdin) Simon & Schuster Children's Publishing.

—Alice in Blunderland. 2003. (Alice Ser.). (Illus.). 208p. (J). 15.95 (978-0-689-84397-6(6) , Atheneum) Simon & Schuster Children's Publishing.

—Alice on the Outside. (Alice Ser.). 176p. (gr. 5-9). 2000. (YA). mass mkt. 5.99 (978-0-689-80594-3(2) , Simon Pulse); 1999. (J). 16.00 (978-0-689-80359-8(1) , Atheneum) Simon & Schuster Children's Publishing.

—Alice on the Outside. 2000. (Alice Ser.). (YA). (gr. 5-9). 11.64 (978-0-606-19706-9(0)) ; (gr. 7-12). lib. bdg. 13.00 (978-0-613-29866-7(7)) Tandem Library Bks.

—Lovingly Alice. (Alice Ser.). (J). 2006. 176p. pap. 5.99 (978-0-689-84400-3(X) , Aladdin); 2006. 166p. ***978-1-4156-5199-5(X)** , Aladdin); 2004. (Illus.). 176p. 15.95 (978-0-689-84399-0(2) , Atheneum) Simon & Schuster Children's Publishing.

—Outrageously Alice. 1998. (Alice Ser.). 144p. (J). (gr. 5-9). pap. 5.99 (978-0-689-80596-7(9) , Aladdin) Simon & Schuster Children's Publishing.

—Patiently Alice. (Alice Ser.). 256p. (YA). 2004. mass mkt. 5.99 (978-0-689-87073-6(6) , Simon Pulse); 2003. (Illus.). 15.95 (978-0-689-82636-8(2) , Atheneum) Simon & Schuster Children's Publishing.

—Starting with Alice. (Alice Ser.). 192p. (J). 2004. (Illus.). pap. 4.99 (978-0-689-84396-9(8) , Aladdin); 2002. 15.95 (978-0-689-84395-2(X) , Atheneum) Simon & Schuster Children's Publishing.

—Starting with Alice. 2004. (gr. 3-6). lib. bdg. 13.00 (978-0-613-87056-6(5)) Tandem Library Bks.

Naylor, Phyllis Reynolds & Vaccaro, Nick. Alice in Blunderland. 2005. (Alice Ser.). (Illus.). 208p. (J). reprint ed. pap. 4.99 (978-0-689-84398-3(4) , Aladdin) Simon & Schuster Children's Publishing.

Nelson, Theresa. Ruby Electric. 272p. (J). 2003. (Illus.). 16.95 (978-0-689-83852-1(2) , Atheneum/Richard Jackson Bks.); 2004. reprint ed. pap. 5.99 (978-0-689-87146-7(5) , Aladdin) Simon & Schuster Children's Publishing.

Patneaude, David. Deadly Drive. 184p. (J). 2007. pap. 6.95 ***978-0-8075-0845-9(4));** 2005. (gr. 6-8). 15.95 (978-0-8075-0844-2(6)) Whitman, Albert & Co.

Pearsall, Shelley. All Shook Up. 2008. (J). ***978-0-375-83698-5(5));** 256p. lib. bdg. ***978-0-375-93698-2(X))** Knopf, Alfred A. Inc.

Polacco, Patricia. Something about Hensley's. Polacco, Patricia, illus. 2006. (Illus.). 48p. (J). (ps-3). 16.99 (978-0-399-24538-1(3) , Philomel) Penguin Group (USA) Inc.

Quattlebaum, Mary. Jackson Jones & the Curse of the Outlaw Rose. 2006. 112p. (J). (gr. 3-7). 14.95 (978-0-385-73349-6(6)); lib. bdg. 16.99 (978-0-385-90365-3(0)) Random Hse. Children's Bks. (Delacorte Bks. for Young Readers).

Radford, Michelle. Almost Fabulous. 2008. 256p. (J). pap. 8.99 ***978-0-06-125235-8(2)** , HarperTeen) HarperCollins Pubs.

Rees, Gwyneth. The Mum Hunt. l.t. ed. 2006. pap. 16.95 (978-1-4056-6061-7(9)) BBC Audio GBR. *Dist:* BBC Audiobooks America.

Richardson, Regina. Maggie's Treasured Stone. 2006. (ENG.). 36p. per. 19.99 ***978-1-4259-3095-0(6))** AuthorHouse.

Rottman, S. L. Slalom. 2004. 256p. (YA). (gr. 7). 16.99 (978-0-670-05913-3(7) , Viking Juvenile) Penguin Group (USA) Inc.

Russo, Marisabina. A Portrait of Pia. 2007. (Illus.). 240p. (YA). (gr. 6-8). 17.00 (978-0-15-205577-6(0)) Harcourt Trade Pubs.

—When Mama Gets Home. Russo, Marisabina, illus. 1998. (Illus.). 24p. (J). (ps-3). 16.99 (978-0-688-14985-7(5)) HarperCollins Pubs.

Rylant, Cynthia. A Kindness. Date not set. (Sky Bks.). 104p. pap. 54.75 (978-0-582-08106-2(8)) Addison-Wesley Longman, Ltd. GBR. *Dist:* Trans-Atlantic Pubns., Inc.

Schotter, Roni. Mama, I'll Give You the World. Gallagher, Susan Saelig, illus. 2006. 40p. (J). (ps-3). lib. bdg. 18.99 (978-0-375-93612-8(2)); 16.95 (978-0-375-83612-1(8)) Random Hse. Children's Bks. (Schwartz & Wade Bks.).

—The World. Gallagher, Susan Saelig, illus. 2003. (J). 16.95 (978-0-689-84485-0(9) , Atheneum/Anne Schwartz Bks.) Simon & Schuster Children's Publishing.

Schwartz, Virginia Frances. Messenger. 2002. 290p. (J). (gr. 7 up). tchr. ed. 17.95 (978-0-8234-1716-2(6)) Holiday Hse., Inc.

Shands, Linda I. White Water. 2001. (Wakara of Eagle Lodge Ser.).Tr. of Juv033010. (Illus.). 176p. (YA). (gr. 7-9). pap. 5.99 (978-0-8007-5772-4(6) , Spire) Revell.

—Wild Fire. 2001. (Wakara of Eagle Lodge Ser.: Vol. 1). (Illus.). 176p. (J). (gr. 7-9). pap. 5.99 (978-0-8007-5746-5(7)) Revell.

Shearer, Alex. Sea Legs. 2006. 320p. (J). pap. 5.99 (978-0-689-87144-3(9) , Aladdin) Simon & Schuster Children's Publishing.

Sidney, Margaret. Five Little Peppers & How They Grew. 2006. (Dover Value Editions Ser.). (Illus.). 224p. (J). pap. 5.95 (978-0-486-45267-8(0)) Dover Pubns., Inc.

Slate, Joseph. Crossing the Trestle. 1999. (Accelerated Reader Bks.). 144p. (J). (gr. 3-7). 14.95 (978-0-7614-5053-5(X) , Cavendish Children's Bks.) Cavendish, Marshall Corp.

Steele, Michael Anthony. Movie Novel. Cecil, Lauren, ed. 2007. (Firehouse Dog Ser.). 160p. (J). pap. 4.99 (978-0-439-89642-9(8)) Scholastic, Inc.

Thomas, Eliza. The Red Blanket. Cepeda, Joe, tr. Cepeda, Joe, illus. 2004. 32p. (J). pap. 15.95 (978-0-439-32253-9(7)) Scholastic, Inc.

Thompson, Lauren. A Christmas Gift for Mama. Burke, Jim, illus. 2003. (J). 48p. pap. 16.95 (978-0-590-30725-3(8)); pap. 16.95 (978-0-590-30726-0(6)) Scholastic, Inc.

Tocher, Timothy. Long Shot. 2001. (J). 137p. (978-0-88166-395-2(6)); 144p. pap. 4.95 (978-0-689-84331-0(3)) Meadowbrook Pr.

Valentine, Jenny. Me, the Missing, & the Dead. 2008. 208p. (J). 16.99 ***978-0-06-085068-5(X));** lib. bdg. 17.89 ***978-0-06-085069-2(8))** HarperCollins Pubs.

Vaughn Zimmer, Tracie. Reaching for Sun. 2007. 144p. (J). (gr. 7 up). 14.95 (978-1-59990-037-7(8) , Bloomsbury Children) Bloomsbury Publishing.

Vrettos, A. M. Sight. 2007. 272p. (YA). (gr. 7 up). 16.99 ***978-1-4169-0657-5(6)** , McElderry, Margaret K.) Simon & Schuster Children's Publishing.

Warner, Sally. Only Emma. Harper, Jamie, illus. 2006. 144p. (J). (gr. 3). pap. 5.99 (978-0-14-240711-0(9) , Puffin) Penguin Group (USA) Inc.

Warner, Sally & Harper, Jamie. Only Emma. 2005. (Illus.). 128p. (J). (gr. 3-7). 14.99 (978-0-670-05979-9(X) , Viking Juvenile) Penguin Group (USA) Inc.

Whitmore, Benette. Shelter. 2006. 304p. (YA). 16.95 (978-0-8027-8884-9(X)) Walker & Co.

Williams, Dar. Amalee. (J). 2006. 208p. pap. 5.99 (978-0-439-39564-9(X) , Scholastic Paperbacks); 2004. 192p. pap. 16.95 (978-0-439-39563-2(1)) Scholastic, Inc.

Williams, Laura E. Up a Creek. l.t. ed. 2001. 121p. (J). 22.95 (978-0-7862-3728-9(7)) Thorndike Pr.

Williams, Lori Aurelia. Broken China. 2005. 272p. (YA). (gr. 7 up). 16.95 (978-0-689-86878-8(2) , Simon & Schuster Children's Publishing) Simon & Schuster Children's Publishing.

Wilson, Jacqueline. Double Act. Sharrat, Nick & Heap, Sue, illus. 1999. 192p. (gr. 3-7). 5.50 (978-0-440-41374-5(5) , Yearling) Random Hse. Children's Bks.

—The Illustrated Mum. 288p. 2005. (J). (gr. 5). lib. bdg. 17.99 (978-0-385-90263-2(8) , Delacorte Bks. for Young Readers); 2006. (gr. 4-7). reprint ed. 5.50 (978-0-440-42043-9(1) , Yearling) Random Hse. Children's Bks.

—The Lottie Project. 2000. (Illus.). 203p. (J). 17.95 (978-0-385-40703-8(3)) Transworld Publishers Ltd. GBR. *Dist:* Trafalgar Square Publishing.

—Lottie Project. 2001. (gr. 3-6). lib. bdg. 12.40 (978-0-613-33835-6(9)) Tandem Library Bks.

Wolff, Virginia Euwer. Make Lemonade. 2006. 208p. (YA). pap. 6.95 (978-0-8050-8070-4(8) , Holt, Henry & Co. Bks. For Young Readers) Holt, Henry & Co.

—Make Lemonade. unabr. ed. 2004. (Young Adult Cassette Librariestm Ser.). 200p. (J). (gr. 7 up). pap. 36.00 incl. audio (978-0-8072-0793-2(4) , S YA 348 SP, Listening Library) Random Hse. Audio Publishing Group.

—Make Lemonade. l.t. ed. 2004. 257p. pap. 10.95 (978-0-7862-6358-5(X)) Thorndike Pr.

—True Believer. 2004. (Make Lemonade Trilogy Ser.). 272p. (J). (gr. 7 up). pap. 38.00 incl. audio (978-0-8072-2283-6(6) , Listening Library) Random Hse. Audio Publishing Group.

—True Believer. Gordon, Russell, illus. 2002. 272p. (YA). pap. 8.99 (978-0-689-85288-6(6) , Simon Pulse) Simon & Schuster Children's Publishing.

—True Believer. 2001. (Make Lemonade Trilogy Ser.). 272p. (J). (gr. 7 up). 17.00 (978-0-689-82827-0(6) , Atheneum) Simon & Schuster Children's Publishing.

—True Believer. 2002. (gr. 7-12). lib. bdg. 16.45 (978-0-613-60942-5(5)) Tandem Library Bks.

Zisk, Mary. The Best Single Mom in the World: How I Was Adopted. Zisk, Mary, illus. 2001. (Illus.). 32p. (J). (ps-3). 15.95 (978-0-8075-0666-0(4)) Whitman, Albert & Co.

SISTERS

Auld, Mary. Mi Hermana. 2004. (Conoce la Familia Ser.). (SPA., Illus.). 24p. (J). (gr. 1 up). lib. bdg. 20.67 (978-0-8368-3930-2(7)) Stevens, Gareth Inc.

—My Sister. 2004. (Meet the Family Ser.). (Illus.). 24p. (J). (gr. 1 up). lib. bdg. 20.67 (978-0-8368-3928-9(5)) Stevens, Gareth Inc.

Hunter, Rebecca. My New Sister. Fairclough, Chris, photos by. 2007. (First Times Ser.). (Illus.). 24p. (J). pap. 10.95 ***978-0-237-52695-5(6)** , Evans Brothers, Limited) Evans Publishing Group GBR. *Dist:* Independent Pubs. Group.

Katschke, Judy & Pope, Liz. The Best Thing about Sisters. Pope, Kate, illus. 2007. 16p. (J). 14.99 (978-0-7944-1278-4(5)) Reader's Digest Assn., Inc., The.

Mauthner, Melanie L. Sistering: Power & Change in Female Relationships. 2005. (Illus.). 240p. pap. 31.95 (978-1-4039-4125-1(4)) Palgrave Macmillan.

Mqp, creator. Sisters Make the Best Friends. 2005. 96p. 9.95 (978-1-84601-014-9(4)) M Q Pubns. GBR. *Dist:* Ingram Pub. Services.

Richmond, Marianne R. So Glad We're Sisters. 2005. (Illus.). 40p. (J). 7.95 (978-0-9763101-4-3(7)) Marianne Richmond Studios, Inc.

Running Press Staff. Bear Hugs for Sisters. 2003. (Inspirio/Zondervan Miniature Editionstm Ser.). (Illus.). 128p. 4.95 (978-0-7624-1674-5(2) , Running Pr. Minature Editions) Running Pr. Bk. Pubs.

Ruth, Angie. My Sister: Early My Adventure. 2007. 44p. (J). 8.99 (978-1-59092-484-6(3) , Orchard Academy Pr.) Windstorm Creative.

Schaefer, Lola M. Sisters. Saunders-Smith, Gail, ed. 1999. (Families Ser.). (Illus.). 24p. (J). (gr. k-1). lib. bdg. 15.93 (978-0-7368-0260-4(6) , Pebble Bks.) Capstone Pr., Inc.

Sim, David. Cos You're My Sister. 2001. (Illus.). 32p. (J). pap. 6.99 (978-0-7459-4542-2(2) , Lion) Lion Hudson plc GBR. *Dist:* Independent Pubs. Group.

Wenzel, Doris, et al. Ten Little Sisters. Hill, Lana, illus. 1999. 32p. (J). (gr. 3-6). pap. 14.95 (978-1-878044-38-9(9) , Wild Rose) Mayhaven Publishing.

SISTERS—FICTION

Ahrens, Robin Isabel. Dee & Bee. Haley, Amanda, illus. 2000. 40p. (J). (ps-1). 14.95 (978-1-890817-26-8(0)) Winslow Pr.

Aitken, Susan. Anna's Scrapbook: Journal of a Sister's Love. Aitken, Sarah, illus. 2000. (J). (978-1-56123-134-8(7)) Centering Corp.

Alcott, Louisa May. Little Women. 2002. (Great Illustrated Classics Ser.). (Illus.). 240p. (J). (gr. 3-8). 21.35 (978-1-57765-693-7(8) , ABDO & Daughters) ABDO Publishing Co.

—Little Women. Dryhurst, Dinah, illus. 2000. 288p. (J). pap. 8.99 (978-1-86205-220-8(4) , Pavilion Bks., Ltd.) Anova Bks. GBR. *Dist:* Trafalgar Square Publishing.

—Little Women. 2002. (YA). 14.04 (978-0-7587-7589-4(X)) Book Wholesalers, Inc.

—Little Women. 2001. (Young Reader's Classics Ser.). 94p. (J). pap. 9.95 (978-1-55013-783-5(2) , Key Porter kids) Key Porter Bks. CAN. *Dist:* Firefly Bks., Ltd.

—Little Women. Lauter, Richard, illus. 192p. (J). 9.95 (978-1-56156-371-5(4)) Kidsbooks, Inc.

—Little Women. 2001. (Classics Ser.). (Illus.). 528p. pap. 7.95 (978-0-375-75672-6(8) , Modern Library) Random House Publishing Group.

—Little Women. 1998. (Children's Classics Ser.). (Illus.). 400p. (J). 6.99 (978-0-517-18954-2(2)) Random Hse. Value Publishing.

—Little Women. 2000. 576p. (J). (gr. 4-7). pap. 4.99 (978-0-439-10136-3(0)) Scholastic, Inc.

—Little Women. 2000. (Classics Ser.). 704p. (J). (gr. 4-7). pap. 5.99 (978-0-689-83531-5(0) , Aladdin) Simon & Schuster Children's Publishing.

—Little Women. 2001. (gr. k-3). lib. bdg. 14.15 (978-0-613-86261-5(9)); 2000. (gr. 3-6). lib. bdg. 10.65 (978-0-613-90409-4(5)); 2000. (gr. 3-6). lib. bdg. 14.15 (978-0-613-63211-9(7)); 2000. (gr. 5-8). lib. bdg. 13.00 (978-0-613-66717-3(4)) Tandem Library Bks.

—Little Women. 2001. (Signature Classics Ser.). (Illus.). 544p. (J). 12.95 (978-1-58279-069-5(8) , 64) Trident Pr. International.

—Little Women. Dryhurst, Dinah & Rust, Graham, illus. 2001. (Storytime Classics Ser.). 32p. (J). (ps-3). pap. 5.99 (978-0-14-131202-6(5) , Puffin) Penguin Group (USA) Inc.

—Little Women. Corvino, Lucy, illus. 2005. (Classic Starts Ser.). 160p. 4.95 (978-1-4027-1236-4(7)) Sterling Publishing Co., Inc.

—Little Women. unabr. ed. 2004. (Chrysalis Children's Classics Ser.). (Illus.). 190p. (YA). pap. (978-1-84365-049-2(5)) Chrysalis Children's Bks.

—Little Women. unabr. ed. 2000. (Dover Juvenile Classics Ser.). (Illus.). 608p. (J). (gr. 4-7). pap. 4.00 (978-0-486-41023-4(4)) Dover Pubns., Inc.

—Little Women. 1998. 559p. (J). reprint ed. lib. bdg. 25.00 (978-1-58287-046-5(2)) North Bks.

—Little Women, Bk. 1. 2003. (gr. 3-6). lib. bdg. 15.30 (978-0-613-70764-0(8)) Tandem Library Bks.

—Little Women. deluxe ed. 2000. (Signature Classics Ser.). (Illus.). 544p. (J). (978-1-58279-075-6(2)) Trident Pr. International.

—Little Women: Book & Charm. (Charming Classics). (Illus.). (J). 2003. 384p. 6.99 (978-0-06-051180-7(X)); 2000. 5.95 (978-0-694-01527-6(X)) HarperCollins Pubs. (Harper Festival).

—Little Women: Two Books in One. 2003. (gr. 3-6). lib. bdg. 22.25 (978-0-613-77101-6(X)) Tandem Library Bks.

—Little Women: With a Discussion of Family. Lauter, Richard, illus. 2003. (Values in Action Illustrated Classics Ser.). 191p. (J). (978-1-59203-032-3(7)) Learning Challenge, Inc.

—Little Women & Good Wives. 1998. (Children's Classics). (ENG.). 224p. (J). (gr. 4-7). pap. (978-1-85326-116-9(5) , 1165WW) Wordsworth Editions, Ltd.

—The Little Women Pop-Up Dollhouse. Krystanovich, Vesna, illus. 2000. 8p. (J). 21.95 (978-1-55263-290-1(3)) Key Porter Bks. CAN. *Dist:* Firefly Bks., Ltd.

—A Modern Cinderella. l.t. ed. 2005. 224p. pap. (978-1-84637-050-2(7)) Echo Library.

—Modern Cinderella or the Little Old Shoe. 2006. pap. 44.99 ***978-1-4219-8892-4(5))** IndyPublish.com.

Alcott, Louisa May. Mujercitas. (SPA., Illus.). 192p. (YA). 11.95 (978-84-7281-101-0(8) , AF1101) Auriga, Ediciones S.A. ESP. *Dist:* Continental Bk. Co., Inc.

—Mujercitas. 2002. (Classics for Young Readers Ser.). (SPA.). (YA). 14.95 (978-84-392-0901-0(0) , EV30608) Lectorum Pubns., Inc.

—Mujercitas. (YA). 7.95 (978-84-95311-16-0(X)) Mestas, Jorge A. Ediciones Escolares La Escuela Nueva y Alinorma, S.L. ESP. *Dist:* Continental Bk. Co., Inc.

—Mujercitas. 1998. (SPA., Illus.). 304p. (J). (978-84-01-46257-3(6)) Plaza & Janes Editories, S.A.

—Mujercitas. (Coleccion Estrella). (SPA., Illus.). 64p. (J). 14.95 (978-950-11-0010-5(3) , SGM010) Sigmar ARG. *Dist:* Continental Bk. Co., Inc.

—Mujercitas. 2000. (Coleccion "Clasicos Juveniles" Ser.). (SPA., Illus.). 292p. (gr. 4-7). pap. 12.95 (978-1-58348-784-6(0)) iUniverse, Inc.

Alcott, Louisa May & Dorling Kindersley Publishing Staff. Little Women. Gerver, Jane E., ed. Molan, Chris, illus. 1999. (Eyewitness Classics Ser.). 64p. (J). (gr. 2 up). 14.99 (978-0-7894-4767-8(3)) Dorling Kindersley Publishing, Inc.

Alcott, Louisa May & Eiselein, Gregory. Little Women. 2003. (Illus.). 352p. (YA). pap. 13.00 (978-0-393-97614-4(9)) Norton, W. W. & Co., Inc.

Alcott, Louisa May, et al. Mujercitas. Prunier, James, tr. 2002. (SPA., Illus.). 268p. (J). 29.95 (978-84-348-5324-9(8)) SM Ediciones ESP. *Dist:* AIMS International Bks., Inc.

Alexander, Goldie. Body & Soul. 2003. 236p. pap. 17.50 (978-0-9578735-9-9(X)) Indra Publishing AUS. *Dist:* International Specialized Bk. Services.

Alexander, Heather. The Case of the Unicorn Mystery. 2005. 82p. (J). (ps-7). lib. bdg. 11.64 (978-0-606-33342-9(8)) Tandem Library Bks.

Alexander, Martha. Nobody Asked ME If I Wanted a Baby Sister. Alexander, Martha, illus. 2006. (Illus.). 32p. (J). 9.95 (978-1-57091-679-3(9)) Charlesbridge Publishing, Inc.

Amadeo, Diana M. My Baby Sister Is a Preemie. Bladholm, Cheri, illus. 2005. (Helping Kids Heal Ser.). 32p. (J). 9.99 (978-0-310-70867-4(2)) Zonderkidz.

Amato, Mary. The Chicken of the Family. Durand, Delphine, illus. 2008. 32p. (J). (ps). 16.99 (978-0-399-24196-3(5) , Putnam Juvenile) Penguin Group (USA) Inc.

Amo, Montserrat del. Ring! Ring! 2000. (SPA., Illus.). 90p. 7.95 (978-84-239-7089-6(2)) Espasa Calpe, S.A. ESP. *Dist:* Libros Sin Fronteras.

Anderson, Paris. The Sisters Kennington. 2004. 140p. (J). per. 16.00 (978-1-58982-195-8(5) , Millennial Mind Publishing) American Bk. Publishing Group.

Anderson, Rachael. Los Mejores Amigos. McNicholas, Shelagh, illus. 2003. (SPA.). 120p. (J). (gr. 3-5). 9.95 (978-84-204-4377-5(8)) Alfaguara, Ediciones, S.A.-Grupo Santillana ESP. *Dist:* Santillana USA Publishing Co., Inc.

Andracki, Zenon. Dear Ashley: A Middle Grade Novel. 2006. (ENG.). 84p. per. 14.95 ***978-1-4241-6168-3(1))** PublishAmerica, Inc.

Andrews, Jane. The Seven Little Sisters Who Live on the. 2006. 32.99 ***978-1-4219-7737-9(0));** pap. 25.99 ***978-1-4219-7749-2(4))** IndyPublish.com.

—Seven Little Sisters Who Live on the Rou. 2006. (Illus.). pap. ***978-1-4065-0858-1(6))** Dodo Pr.

Andrews, Jane & Hopkins, Louisa Parsons. The Seven Little Sisters Who Live on the Round Ball that Floats in the Air. 2004. reprint ed. pap. 21.95 (978-1-4179-1646-7(X)) Kessinger Publishing, LLC.

Andrews-McKinney, Joyce. Jentle & Jewel Fix Things. Andrews-McKinney, Joyce, illus. l.t. ed. 2006. (Illus.). 17p. (J). im. lthr. 8.00 (978-0-9728975-4-9(2)) JA-M Pubs., LLC.

Anna, Jennifer. The Best Thing: An Almost True Story of Ladybugs & Sisters. 2007. (Illus.). 64p. (Orig.). (J). pap. 14.99 ***978-1-59092-154-8(2)** , Blue Works) Windstorm Creative.

Arenella, Betsy Bottino. Isabelle's Dream: A Story & Activity Book for a Child's Grief Journey. Henderson, Dana, illus. 2007. 48p. (J). per. 7.95 ***978-0-9675532-9-0(6))** Quality of Life Publishing Co.

Arnold, Marsha D. The Bravest of Us All. Sneed, Brad, illus. 2000. 32p. (J). (ps-3). 16.99 (978-0-8037-2409-9(8) , Dial) Penguin Group (USA) Inc.

Ashcraft, Shelly & Hunter, Cheryl. Mamaw & the Girls. 2007. per. 10.99 ***978-1-59886-846-3(2))** Tate Publishing & Enterprises, L.L.C.

Ballard, Robin. When I Am a Sister. 1998. (Illus.). 24p. (J). (ps-3). 15.00 (978-0-688-15397-7(6)) HarperCollins Pubs.

Banks, Lynne Reid. Angela & Diabola. 163p. (J). (gr. 4-6). pap. 4.50 (978-0-8072-1515-9(5) , Listening Library) Random Hse. Audio Publishing Group.

—Angela & Diabola. 1998. (J). (978-0-606-13124-7(8)) Tandem Library Bks.

Barasch, Lynne. The Reluctant Flower Girl. Barasch, Lynne, illus. 2001. (Illus.). 40p. (J). (gr. k-3). 14.95 (978-0-06-028809-9(4)) HarperCollins Pubs.

Barasui, illus. & creator. Strawberry Marshmallow: Ichigo Mashimaro. Barasui, creator. 2006. 192p. pap. 9.99 (978-1-59816-494-7(5) , Tokyopop Adult) TOKYOPOP, Inc.

Bart, Muriel. Sisters - Strangers. Wise, Noreen, ed. 2000. (Lemonade Collection). 208p. (J). (gr. k up). pap. 9.95 (978-1-58584-281-0(8)) Huckleberry Pr.

Bastedo, Jaya. The How 'Bout Sisters. Pacey, Janet, illus. 2000. 12p. (J). (ps-3). pap. (978-1-894303-26-2(1)) Raven Rock Publishing.

Batanda, Jackee Budesta. The Blue Marble. 2005. (Illus.). 44p. 12.95 (978-9988-550-89-9(8)) Sub-Saharan Pubs. & Traders GHA. *Dist:* Michigan State Univ. Pr.

Bauer, Marion Dane. The Red Ghost. Ferguson, Peter, illus. 2008. (J). ***978-0-375-84081-4(8));** pap. ***978-0-375-84082-1(6));** lib. bdg. ***978-0-375-94081-1(2))** Random Hse., Inc.

Beamish, Diane. Amy's Silent World. 2006. 24p. 10.25 (978-1-4116-5759-5(4)) Lulu.com.

Beard, Darleen Bailey. The Babbs Switch Story. 2002. 176p. (J). 16.00 (978-0-374-30475-1(0) , Farrar, Straus & Giroux (BYR)) Farrar, Straus & Giroux.

Benevenia, Rose. Dolly & Babe. Benevenia, Rose, illus. l.t. ed. 2004. (Illus.). 9p. (J). (gr. k-2). pap. 9.00 (978-0-9729044-0-7(9)) Cabbage Patch Pr.

Bennett, James W. Faith Wish. 2003. 160p. (J). (gr. 7 up). tchr. ed. 16.95 (978-0-8234-1778-0(6)) Holiday Hse., Inc.

Bennett, Veronica. Cassandra's Sister. 2007. (Illus.). 240p. (YA). (gr. 7). 15.99 (*978-0-7636-3464-3(6)) Candlewick Pr.

Bercun, Brenda. I'm Going to be a Big Sister. Gross, Sue, illus. 2007. 33p. (J). 15.95 (978-0-9767198-6-1(X)) Nurturing Your Children Pr.

Bernstein, Margery. My Brother, the Pest. Handelman, Dorothy, photos by. 1999. (Real Kids Readers Ser.). (Illus.). 32p. (gr. k-2). (J). pap. 4.99 (978-0-7613-2080-7(6)); lib. bdg. 18.90 (978-0-7613-2055-5(5)) Lerner Publishing Group. (Millbrook Pr.).

—My Brother, the Pest. 1999. (J). (978-0-606-19164-7(X)); lib. bdg. 11.80 (978-0-613-16773-4(2)) Tandem Library Bks.

Berten, Jinny Powers & Holt, Norah. Littsie of Cincinnati. 2003. (Illus.). 125p. (J). per. 9.95 (978-0-9724421-0-7(3)) Fountain Square Publishing.

Beskow, Elsa. Aunt Brown's Birthday. 2004. (Illus.). 32p. (J). 17.95 (978-0-86315-388-4(7)) Floris Bks. GBR. *Dist:* SteinerBooks, Inc.

—Aunt Green, Aunt Brown & Aunt Lavender. 2001. (Illus.). 32p. (J). 17.95 (978-0-86315-348-8(8)) Floris Bks. GBR. *Dist:* Gryphon Hse., Inc., SteinerBooks, Inc.

Bial, Raymond. Shadow Island: A Tale of Lake Superior. 2006. 176p. (J). (gr. 3-7). 18.95 (978-1-883953-37-9(5)); (gr. 4-7). pap. 12.95 (978-1-883953-36-2(7)) Midwest Traditions, Inc. (Blue Horse Bks.).

Big Little Sister. 2003. per. (978-0-9740182-1-8(X)) HuntForMo Creations.

Birdsall, Jeanne. The Penderwicks. 2005. 272p. (J). (gr. 3-7). lib. bdg. 17.99 (978-0-375-93143-7(0) , Knopf Bks. for Young Readers) Random Hse. Children's Bks.

—The Penderwicks. 2006. 301p. (YA). 23.95 (978-0-7862-8897-7(3)) Thorndike Pr.

—The Penderwicks: A Summer Tale of Four Sisters, Two Rabbits, & a Very Interesting Boy. 272p. (J). 2007. (gr. 4-7). 6.50 (978-0-440-42047-7(4) , Yearling); 2005. (gr. 3-7). 15.95 (978-0-375-83143-0(6) , Knopf Bks. for Young Readers) Random Hse. Children's Bks.

Black, Sonia W. Jumping the Broom. Wright and Hu, Cornelius Van and Ying-Hwa, illus. 2004. 32p. (J). lib. bdg. 15.00 (*978-1-4242-0234-8(5)) Fitzgerald Bks.

Blackman, S. A. A Smickamookum Drinks Belly. Gubitosi, Lillian, illus. 2003. 32p. (J). (ps-k). 16.95 incl. audio (978-1-929409-02-0(8)) Blade Publishing.

Blume, Lesley. Cornelia & the Audacious Escapades of the Somerset Sisters. 2006. 272p. (J). (gr. 3-7). 15.95 (978-0-375-83523-0(7) , Knopf Bks. for Young Readers) Random Hse. Children's Bks.

Blume, Lesley M. M. Cornelia & the Audacious Escapades of the Somerset Sisters. 2006. 272p. (J). (gr. 3-7). lib. bdg. 17.99 (978-0-375-93523-7(1) , Knopf Bks. for Young Readers) Random Hse. Children's Bks.

Boling, Katharine. January 1905. 2006. 192p. (YA). pap. 5.95 (978-0-15-205121-1(X) , Harcourt Paperbacks); 2004. 176p. (J). 16.00 (978-0-15-205119-8(8)) Harcourt Children's Bks.

Bondoux, Anne-Laure. Life As It Comes. 2007. 224p. (YA). (gr. 9). lib. bdg. 18.99 (978-0-385-90391-2(X) , Delacorte Bks. for Young Readers) Random Hse. Children's Bks.

—Life As It Comes. Maudet, Y., tr. from FRE. 2007. 224p. (YA). (gr. 9). 15.99 (978-0-385-90390-5(1) , Delacorte Bks. for Young Readers) Random Hse. Children's Bks.

Bonnett-Rampersaud, Louise. Bubble & Squeak. Banta, Susan, illus. 2006. 24p. (J). 14.99 (978-0-7614-5310-9(5)) Cavendish, Marshall Corp.

Bottner, Barbara. Marsha Makes Me Sick. 1999. (J). (978-0-606-16139-8(2)) Tandem Library Bks.

Bourgeois, Paulette. Benjamin et Sa Petite Soeur. ed. 2004. Tr. of Franklin's Baby Sister. (FRE., Illus.). (J). (gr. k-3). spiral bd. (978-0-616-14597-5(7)) Canadian National Institute for the Blind/Institut National Canadien pour les Aveugles.

Boza, Eduardo Robles. Mi Amigo Tiene Hermanita (My Friend Has a Little Sister) (SPA.). (J). 4.95 (978-968-419-844-9(2)) Grijalbo, Editorial MEX. *Dist:* AIMS International Bks., Inc.

Brisson, Pat. Little Sister, Big Sister. Bluthenthal, Diana Cain, illus. rev. ed. 1999. (Redfeather Chapter Book Ser.). 64p. (J). (gr. 1-3). 16.95 (978-0-8050-5887-1(7) , Holt, Henry & Co. Bks. For Young Readers) Holt, Henry & Co.

Bryant, Ann. She's No Angel. 2005. (Step-Chain Ser.). 190p. (J). pap. 4.95 (978-1-894222-75-4(X)) Lobster Pr. CAN. *Dist:* Univ. of Toronto Pr.

Buckley, Michael. The Fairy Tale Detectives. Ferguson, Peter, illus. 2007. (Sisters Grimm Ser.: Bk. 1). 312p. (J). (gr. 2-8). pap. 5.95 (*978-0-8109-9322-8(8) , Amulet Bks.) Abrams, Harry N. , Inc.

—Magic & Other Misdemeanors. Ferguson, Peter, illus. 2007. (Sisters Grimm Ser.: Bk. 5). 304p. (YA). (gr. 3-7). 14.95 (*978-0-8109-9358-7(9) , Amulet Bks.) Abrams, Harry N. , Inc.

—Once upon a Crime. Ferguson, Peter, illus. 2007. (Sisters Grimm Ser.: Bk. 4). 288p. (J). (gr. 2-8). 14.95 (*978-0-8109-1610-4(X) , Amulet Bks.) Abrams, Harry N. , Inc.

—The Problem Child. Ferguson, Peter, illus. (Sisters Grimm Ser.: Bk. 3). 320p. (gr. 3-7). 2007. (YA). pap. 5.95 (*978-0-8109-9359-4(7)); 2006. (J). 14.95 (978-0-8109-4914-0(8) , Amulet Bks.) Abrams, Harry N. , Inc.

—The Unusual Suspects. Ferguson, Peter, illus. 2007. (Sisters Grimm Ser.: Bk. 2). 320p. (J). (gr. 2-8). pap. 5.95 (*978-0-8109-9323-5(6) , Amulet Bks.) Abrams, Harry N. , Inc.

Buffie, Margaret. Seeker. 2002. (gr. 7-12). lib. bdg. 15.25 (978-0-613-70772-5(9)) Tandem Library Bks.

Bunce, Elizabeth. A Curse Dark As Gold. 2008. 400p. (J). pap. 17.99 (*978-0-439-89576-7(6) , Levine, Arthur A. Bks.) Scholastic, Inc.

Bunt, Barbara & Karram, Mona. Lulu. Chouan, Joe, illus. 2002. (J). (ps-1). 18.95 (978-0-9724929-0-4(9)) LuLu Bks Ltd.

Bunting, Eve. The Days of Summer. Low, William, illus. 2001. 40p. (J). (gr. k-3). 16.00 (978-0-15-201840-5(9)) Harcourt Children's Bks.

Butcher, Nancy. It's Snow Problem. 2001. (gr. 3-6). lib. bdg. 13.00 (978-0-613-43934-3(1)) Tandem Library Bks.

Buzzeo, Toni. The Sea Chest. GrandPré, Mary, illus. 2002. 32p. (J). (gr. k up). 16.99 (978-0-8037-2703-8(8) , Dial) Penguin Group (USA) Inc.

Byars, Betsy. The Golly Sisters Go West. 2002. (Illus.). (J). 12.30 (978-0-7587-6115-6(5)) Book Wholesalers, Inc.

—The Golly Sisters Go West. 2000. (YA). pap. 23.20 incl. audio (978-0-7887-4335-1(X) , 41130) Recorded Bks., LLC.

—Keeper of the Doves. (J). 2002. 96p. (gr. 3-7). 14.99 (978-0-670-03576-2(9) , Viking Juvenile); 2004. (Illus.). 128p. reprint ed. pap. 5.99 (978-0-14-240063-0(7) , Puffin) Penguin Group (USA) Inc.

—Keeper of the Doves. 2004. (gr. 3-6). lib. bdg. 14.15 (978-0-613-89805-8(2)) Tandem Library Bks.

Cabbage, Betty, text. Betty & the Devil's Bottle. 2005. (Illus.). 52p. (J). (978-1-59799-000-4(0)) Deaf Missions.

Cameron, Ann. The Secret Life of Amanda K. Woods. 1999. (Illus.). 208p. (J). (gr. 5-9). pap. 6.99 (978-0-14-130642-1(4) , Puffin) Penguin Group (USA) Inc.

—Secret Life of Amanda K Woods. 1999. (gr. 3-6). lib. bdg. 14.15 (978-0-613-23031-5(0)) Tandem Library Bks.

Capucilli, Alyssa Satin. Katy Duck, Big Sister. Cole, Henry, illus. 2007. 14p. (J). (ps-k). 7.99 (*978-1-4169-4209-2(2) , Little Simon) Simon & Schuster Children's Publishing.

Carvell, Marlene. Sweetgrass Basket. 2005. 256p. (J). (gr. 3-6). 16.99 (978-0-525-47547-7(8) , Dutton Juvenile) Penguin Group (USA) Inc.

Casad, Mary Brooke & Brooke Casad, Mary. Bluebonnet at the East Texas Oil Museum. Vincent, Benjamin, illus. 2005. 32p. (J). (gr. k-3). per. 15.95 (978-1-58980-358-9(2)) Pelican Publishing Co., Inc.

Caseley, Judith. Sisters. Caseley, Judith, illus. 2004. 32p. (J). 15.99 (978-0-06-051046-6(3)) HarperCollins Pubs.

Castillo, Carol. Me Too! Harrell, Rob, illus. l.t. ed. 2002. 16p. (J). (gr. 1-2). pap. 3.99 (978-1-58938-023-3(1)) Concerned Communications.

Chaconas, Dori. Dancing with Katya. Bergum, Constance Rummel, illus. 2006. 32p. (J). 16.95 (978-1-56145-376-4(5) , Peachtree Junior) Peachtree Pubs., Ltd.

Chan, Ching. Mystery of the Black Sun: Songs of the Unicorn. 2006. (Anime Sticker Stories Ser.). 16p. (J). (ps-1). 4.99 (978-0-448-44340-9(6) , Grosset & Dunlap) Penguin Group (USA) Inc.

Chapman, Brenda. Where Trouble Leads. 2007. (Illus.). 136p. (YA). (gr. 5 up). pap. 8.95 (*978-1-894917-44-5(8)) Napoleon Publishing/Rendezvous Pr. CAN. *Dist:* AtlasBooks Distribution.

Cheng, Andrea. The Lemon Sisters. Mai-Wyss, Tatjana, illus. 2006. 32p. (J). (ps). 16.99 (978-0-399-24023-2(3) , Putnam Juvenile) Penguin Group (USA) Inc.

Chetkowski, Emily. Sister Sluggers. 2007. per. 15.95 (*978-1-933002-35-4(2)) PublishingWorks.

Cleary, Beverly. Beezus & Ramona. (Ramona Quimby Ser.). 142p. (J). (gr. 3-5). pap. 4.99 (978-0-8072-1441-1(8) , Listening Library) Random Hse. Audio Publishing Group.

—The Ramona Collection, Volume 1. Dockray, Tracy, illus. 2006. (J). pap. 19.99 (978-0-06-124647-0(6) , Harper Trophy) HarperCollins Pubs.

—The Ramona Collection, Volume 2. Dockray, Tracy, illus. 2006. (J). pap. 19.99 (978-0-06-124648-7(4) , Harper Trophy) HarperCollins Pubs.

Climo, Shirley. Persian Cinderella. 2001. (gr. k-3). lib. bdg. 14.10 (978-0-613-44245-9(8)) Tandem Library Bks.

Cohen, Miriam. Mimmy & Sophie All Around the Town. Yezerski, Thomas F., illus. 2004. 80p. (J). 16.00 (978-0-374-34989-9(4) , Farrar, Straus & Giroux (BYR)) Farrar, Straus & Giroux.

Cole, Brock. Fair Monaco. 2004. (Illus.). 32p. (J). 16.95 (978-1-932425-07-9(1) , Lemniscaat) Boyds Mills Pr.

Cole, Joanna. I'm a Big Sister. Stevens-Marzo, Bridget, illus. 2008. 32p. (J). 6.99 (*978-0-06-134907-2(0)) HarperCollins Pubs.

—I'm a Big Sister Lap Edition. Chambliss, Maxie, illus. 2006. 28p. (J). 12.99 (978-0-06-085413-3(8) , Harper Festival) HarperCollins Pubs.

Cole, Joanna. I'm a Big Sister (Spanish Edition) Stevens-Marzo, Bridget, illus. 2008. (SPA.). 32p. (J). 6.99 (*978-0-06-134909-6(7) , Rayo) HarperCollins Pubs.

Coolidge, Susan. What Katy Did at School. 2004. reprint ed. pap. 20.95 (978-1-4191-9354-5(6)); pap. 1.99 (978-1-4192-9354-2(0)) Kessinger Publishing, LLC.

—What Katy Did at School. 2006. (ENG.). 180p. per. 12.45 (*978-1-59462-472-8(0) , 508, Book Jungle) Standard Pubns., Inc.

Cooney, Barbara. Lost Treasures Bk. 1: The Kellyhorns. 2001. 256p. (J). 13.49 (978-0-7868-2596-7(0)) Hyperion Pr.

Couloumbis, Audrey. Getting near to Baby. 2002. (Illus.). (J). 13.19 (978-0-7587-6515-4(0)) Book Wholesalers, Inc.

—Getting near to Baby. 224p. (J). (gr. 5-9). 2001. pap. 5.99 (978-0-698-11892-8(8)); 1999. 17.99 (978-0-399-23389-0(X)) Penguin Group (USA) Inc. (Putnam Juvenile).

—Getting near to Baby. unabr. ed. 2004. 211p. (J). (gr. 5-9). pap. 36.00 incl. audio (978-0-8072-8876-4(4) , LYA 287 SP, Listening Library) Random Hse. Audio Publishing Group.

—Getting near to Baby. 2001. (J). 12.64 (978-0-606-21210-6(8)); (gr. 5-8). lib. bdg. 14.15 (978-0-613-44208-4(3)) Tandem Library Bks.

—Getting near to Baby. l.t. ed. 2000. (Juvenile Ser.). (Illus.). 215p. (J). (gr. 4-7). 22.95 (978-0-7862-2705-1(2)) Thorndike Pr.

—Maude March on the Run! 2007. (Illus.). 320p. (J). (gr. 3-7). 15.99 (978-0-375-83246-8(7) , Random Hse. Bks. for Young Readers) Random Hse. Children's Bks.

—Maude March on the Run!, or Trouble Is Her Middle Name. 2007. (Illus.). 309p. (J). pap. (978-0-375-83248-2(3)) Random Hse., Inc.

—Maude March on the Run!, Or, Trouble Is Her Middle Name. 2007. (Illus.). 320p. (J). (gr. 3-7). lib. bdg. 17.99 (978-0-375-93246-5(1) , Random Hse. Bks. for Young Readers) Random Hse. Children's Bks.

Crispin, Paula. I'm Getting a Baby Sister? 2004. 23p. pap. 14.95 (978-1-4137-3380-8(8)) PublishAmerica, Inc.

Culbertson, Jan E. The Legend of Dunsmoor Manor. 2006. 88p. pap. 13.95 (978-1-58909-348-5(8)) Bookstand Publishing.

—The Legend of the Lost Tiki. 2006. 95p. (YA). pap. 13.95 (978-1-58909-315-7(1)) Bookstand Publishing.

Cuyler, Margery. The Bumpy Little Pumpkin. Hillenbrand, Will, illus. 2005. 32p. (J). pap. 15.95 (978-0-439-52835-1(6) , Scholastic Pr.) Scholastic, Inc.

Czernecki, Stefan & Peterson, Jeanne Whitehouse. Don't Forget Winona. Root, Kimberly B., illus. 2004. 32p. (J). (ps-3). 15.99 (978-0-06-027197-8(3)) HarperCollins Pubs.

Dalmatian Press Staff, adapted by. Little Women. 2003. (Spot the Classics Ser.). 180p. (J). 4.99 (978-1-57759-560-1(2)) Dalmatian Pr.

Davies, Nicola. Tangled Webs. 2000. 120p. (YA). pap. 12.95 (978-1-85902-847-6(0)) Beekman Bks., Inc.

Davis, Joyce. Can't Stop the Shine. 2007. 256p. pap. 9.99 (*978-0-373-83078-7(5)) Harlequin Enterprises, Ltd. CAN. *Dist:* Simon & Schuster, Inc.

Dean, Pamela. Juniper, Gentian, & Rosemary. 1998. 352p. (YA). (gr. 10 up). 24.95 (978-0-312-86004-2(8) , Tor Bks.) Doherty, Tom Assocs., LLC.

Dean, Zoey. Tall Cool One. 2005. (A-List Ser.: No. 4). 295p. (YA). (gr. 7-17). per. 16.64 (978-0-606-33462-4(9)) Tandem Library Bks.

Deiss, A. The Sullivan Girls & the Mystery of Moonhouse. 2003. 104p. (Orig.). pap. 9.95 (978-0-595-29580-7(0)) iUniverse, Inc.

Dent, Grace. LBD: Live & Fabulous! 2006. 288p. (YA). (gr. 5). pap. 6.99 (978-0-14-240662-5(7) , Puffin) Penguin Group (USA) Inc.

Despain, Kellene. A Certain Kind of Treasure. 2000. (Illus.). 215p. (J). (gr. 5-9). per. 7.95 (978-0-9679046-0-3(9)) Gray Hse. Bks.

Dessen, Sarah. Dreamland. 2000. (Illus.). 256p. (J). (gr. 7-12). 15.99 (978-0-670-89122-1(3) , Viking Juvenile) Penguin Group (USA) Inc.

—That Summer. 1998. (J). (978-0-606-13842-0(0)) Tandem Library Bks.

Dhami, Narinder. Bhangra Babes. 192p. (J). 2007. (gr. 4-7). 5.99 (*978-0-440-42106-1(3) , Yearling); 2006. (gr. 3-7). 14.95 (978-0-385-73318-2(6) , Delacorte Bks. for Young Readers); 2006. (gr. 3-7). lib. bdg. 16.99 (978-0-385-90337-0(5) , Delacorte Bks. for Young Readers) Random Hse. Children's Bks.

—Bindi Babes. 192p. (gr. 3-7). 2004. (J). 14.95 (978-0-385-73177-5(9) , Delacorte Bks. for Young Readers); 2005. reprint ed. pap. 5.99 (978-0-440-42019-4(9) , Yearling) Random Hse. Children's Bks.

—Bollywood Babes. 224p. (J). 2006. (gr. 4-7). pap. 5.50 (978-0-440-42020-0(2) , Yearling); 2005. (gr. 3). 14.95 (978-0-385-73178-2(7) , Delacorte Bks. for Young Readers) Random Hse. Children's Bks.

Dobkin, Bonnie. Dream Spinner. 2006. 288p. pap. 8.95 (978-0-7387-0919-2(0) , Flux) Llewellyn Pubns.

Driehaus, Cyndy Ann. The Royal Adventures of Princess Daisy & Princess Darcy. Huser, Jessie Ann, illus. 2007. (J). (*978-1-933197-31-9(5)) Orange Frazer Pr.

Driscoll, Laura. Lila the Fair. Sims, Blanche, illus. 2005. 32p. (J). lib. bdg. 20.00 (*978-1-4242-1106-7(9)) Fitzgerald Bks.

—Lila the Fair. Sims, Blanche, illus. 2005. (Social Studies Connects). 32p. (J). pap. 4.99 (978-1-57565-148-4(3)) Kane Pr., The.

Duble, Kathleen Benner. The Sacrifice. 2007. 224p. (J). pap. 5.99 (*978-0-689-87651-6(3) , Aladdin) Simon & Schuster Children's Publishing.

Duble, Kathleen Benner & Vojnar, Kamil. The Sacrifice. 2005. 224p. (J). (gr. 4-8). 16.99 (978-0-689-87650-9(5) , McElderry, Margaret K.) Simon & Schuster Children's Publishing.

Dubosarsky, Ursula. The Red Shoe. 2007. 192p. (J). (gr. 7 up). 16.95 (978-1-59643-265-9(9)) Roaring Brook Pr.

Duey, Kathleen. Margret & Flynn 1875. 2008. 160p. (J). (gr. 3). 5.99 (*978-0-14-241019-6(5) , Puffin) Penguin Group (USA) Inc.

DuJardin, Rosamond. Practically Seventeen: A Tobey Heydon Story. 2003. (YA). per. 12.95 (978-1-930009-68-4(2) , 800-691-7779) Image Cascade Publishing.

Dunkle, Clare B. The Hollow Kingdom. 2003. (Hollow Kingdom Trilogy Ser.). (Illus.). 240p. (YA). (gr. 7). 16.95 (978-0-8050-7390-4(6) , Holt, Henry & Co. Bks. For Young Readers) Holt, Henry & Co.

—Hollow Kingdom. 2006. (Hollow Kingdom Trilogy Ser.). 240p. (YA). reprint ed. pap. 6.95 (978-0-8050-8108-4(9) , Holt, Henry & Co. Bks. For Young Readers) Holt, Henry & Co.

—The Hollow Kingdom, Vol. 5. l.t. ed. 2004. 360p. 21.95 (978-0-7862-6769-9(0) , Large Print Pr.) Thorndike Pr.

East, Jacqueline. Ed the Pup Ed's New Baby Sister. 1999. (Ed the Pup Ser.). (ps-3). (978-1-894155-67-0(X)) Cethial & Bossche Co.

Edwards, Dorothy. More Naughty Little Sister Stories. Hughes, Shirley, illus. 2002. (My Naughty Little Sister Ser.). 128p. (J). pap. 7.50 (978-1-4052-0290-9(4)) Egmont Bks., Ltd. GBR. *Dist:* Independent Pubs. Group.

—My Naughty Little Sister. 2004. (J). 24.95 incl. audio (978-0-7540-6269-1(4) , Chivers Children's Audio Bks.) BBC Audiobooks America.

—My Naughty Little Sister. Hughes, Shirley, illus. l.t. ed. 2003. 120p. (J). 16.95 (978-0-7540-7843-2(4) , Gunsmoke) BBC Audiobooks America.

—My Naughty Little Sister's Friends. Hughes, Shirley, illus. 2002. (My Naughty Little Sister Ser.). 128p. (J). pap. 7.50 (978-1-4052-0291-6(2)) Egmont Bks., Ltd. GBR. *Dist:* Independent Pubs. Group.

Edwards, Dorothy, et al. My Naughty Little Sister. 2002. (My Naughty Little Sister Ser.). (Illus.). 128p. (J). pap. 7.50 (978-1-4052-0289-3(0)) Egmont Bks., Ltd. GBR. *Dist:* Independent Pubs. Group.

Ellis, Marvie. Keisha's Doors Bk. 1: An Autism Story. l.t. ed. 2005. Tr. of Las Puertas de Keisha. (SPA., Illus.). 32p. (J). per. 16.95 (978-1-933319-00-1(3)) Speech Kids Texas Pr.

Emerson, Charlotte. Amy's True Prize. 1999. (Little Women Journals Ser.). (J). (978-0-606-16348-4(4)) Tandem Library Bks.

—Beth's Snow Dancer. 1999. (Little Women Journals Ser.). (J). (978-0-606-16347-7(6)) Tandem Library Bks.

—Meg's Dearest Wish. 1999. (Little Women Journals). (J). (978-0-606-16350-7(6)) Tandem Library Bks.

Emerson, Charlotte & Alcott, Louisa May. Amy's True Prize. Wasden, Kevin, illus. 1999. (Little Women Journals). 128p. (J). (gr. 3-7). mass mkt. 3.99 (978-0-380-79706-6(2)) HarperCollins Pubs.

—Beth's Snow Dancer. Wasden, Kevin, illus. 1999. (Little Women Journals). 128p. (J). (gr. 3-7). pap. 3.99 (978-0-380-79704-2(6)) HarperCollins Pubs.

—Jo's Troubled Heart. Wasden, Kevin, illus. 1999. (Little Women Journals). 128p. (J). (gr. 3-7). pap. 3.99 (978-0-380-79669-4(4)) HarperCollins Pubs.

—Meg's Dearest Wish. Wasden, Kevin, illus. 1999. (Little Women Journals). 128p. (J). (gr. 3-7). pap. 3.99 (978-0-380-79705-9(4)) HarperCollins Pubs.

Ericsson, Jennifer A. She Did It! Westcott, Nadine Bernard, illus. 2002. 32p. (J). (ps-3). 16.00 (978-0-374-36776-3(0) , Farrar, Straus & Giroux (BYR)) Farrar, Straus & Giroux.

Fietzek, Petra. Trommeln, Trommeln. 2002. (GER.). 128p. pap. 15.00 (978-1-4000-3958-6(4) , New Media German Language) Random House Foreign Language Publishing.

Figley, Marty Rhodes. The Schoolchildren's Blizzard. Haas, Shelly O., illus. 2004. (On My Own History Ser.). 48p. (J). lib. bdg. 23.93 (978-1-57505-586-2(4) , Carolrhoda Bks.) Lerner Publishing Group.

Fisher, Valorie. My Big Sister. Fisher, Valorie, photos by. 2003. (Illus.). 40p. (J). 14.95 (978-0-689-85479-8(X) , Atheneum/Anne Schwartz Bks.) Simon & Schuster Children's Publishing.

Fitzpatrick, Marie-Louise. Silly Mommy, Silly Daddy. Fitzpatrick, Marie-Louise, illus. 2006. (Illus.). 32p. 15.95 (978-1-84507-547-7(1)) Lincoln, Frances Ltd. GBR. *Dist:* Perseus Distribution.

Foggo, Cheryl. I Have Been in Danger. Hotchkiss, Conrad & Graham, Heather, illus. 2005. (In the Same Boat Ser.: No. 3). 184p. (J). (gr. 4-6). pap. 7.95 (978-1-55050-185-8(2)) Coteau Bks. CAN. *Dist:* Fitzhenry & Whiteside, Ltd.

Foster, Kinsley. Wild Abandon Vol. 5: Mirror, Mirror. 2000. (YA). (gr. 6-12). pap. 10.95 (978-0-9667634-4-7(0)) What's Inside Pr.

Freedman, Deborah. Scribble. 2007. (Illus.). 40p. (J). (ps-1). 15.99 (978-0-375-83966-5(6)); lib. bdg. 18.99 (978-0-375-93966-2(0)) Random Hse. Children's Bks. (Knopf Bks. for Young Readers).

Freymann-Weyr, Garret. Stay with Me. 2006. 320p. (YA). (gr. 8). 16.00 (978-0-618-60571-2(1)) Houghton Mifflin Co.

—Stay with Me. 2007. 320p. (YA). (gr. 9 up). pap. 8.99 (*978-0-618-88404-9(1)) Houghton Mifflin Co. Trade & Reference Div.

Friedman, Aimee. Year My Sister Got Lucky. 2008. 384p. (J). pap. 16.99 (*978-0-439-92227-2(5)) Scholastic, Inc.

Friend, Natasha. Perfect. 2004. 232p. (J). 16.95 (978-1-57131-652-3(3)); pap. 6.95 (978-1-57131-651-6(5)) Milkweed Editions.

Frost, Helen. The Braid. 2006. (Illus.). 112p. (YA). (gr. 7 up). 16.00 (978-0-374-30962-6(0) , Frances Foster Bks.) Farrar, Straus & Giroux.

Fuller, Bob. Tea for Two. 2007. (Paddywhack Lane Ser.). 24p. (J). pap. 3.99 (978-0-448-44509-0(3) , Grosset & Dunlap) Penguin Group (USA) Inc.

Gabriel, Nat. Bubble Trouble. Nez, John, illus. 2004. 32p. (J). lib. bdg. 20.00 (*978-1-4242-1085-5(2)) Fitzgerald Bks.

—Bubble Trouble. Nez, John, tr. Nez, John, illus. 2004. (Science Solves It! Ser.). (J). pap. 4.99 (978-1-57565-133-0(5)) Kane Pr., The.

Gallagher, Diana G. & Burge, Constance M. Mystic Knoll. 2005. 217p. (J). (978-1-4155-8004-2(9) , Simon Spotlight) Simon & Schuster Children's Publishing.

Gardner, Lyn. Into the Woods. Grey, Mini, illus. 2007. 488p. (J). (gr. 3-7). 16.99 (978-0-385-75115-5(X)); lib. bdg. 19.99 (978-0-385-75116-2(8)) Random Hse. Children's Bks. (Fickling, David Bks.).

Gauch, Patricia Lee. Tanya & the Red Shoes. Ichikawa, Satomi, illus. 2002. 40p. (J). 16.99 (978-0-399-23314-2(8) , Philomel) Penguin Group (USA) Inc.

Gayle, Amber. On the Naive but Honorable Self-Determination of Teenage Girls: My Evil Twin Sister No. 5. 2004. 228p. (YA). pap. 6.00 (978-0-9712972-8-9(2)) Evil Twin Pubns.

S

Gerver, Jane E. Lucky. Rogers, Jacqueline, illus. 2007. (Stablemates Ser.). 48p. (J). 4.99 (978-0-439-72234-6(9)) Scholastic, Inc.

Gibbs, Lynne. Quiet as a Mouse. Mitchell, Melanie, illus. 2003. (Growing Pains Ser.). 32p. (J). pap. 4.95 (978-1-57768-928-7(3)) ; 12.95 (978-1-57768-481-7(8)) School Specialty Publishing. (Gingham Dog Pr.).

Giles, Gail. Dead Girls Don't Write Letters. rev. ed. 2003. 144p. (YA). (gr. 7 up). 16.95 (978-0-7613-1727-2(9)) Roaring Brook Pr.

—Dead Girls Don't Write Letters. 2004. 128p. (YA). reprint ed. pap. 6.99 (978-0-689-86624-1(0) , Simon Pulse) Simon & Schuster Children's Publishing.

Glencoe McGraw-Hill Staff & McGraw-Hill - Jamestown Education Staff. Topics from the Restless, Bk. 1. unabr. ed. 1999. (Wordsworth Classics Ser.). (gr. 10 up). pap. 24.64 (978-0-89061-116-6(5) , 9780890611166) Jamestown.

Godbersen, Anna. The Luxe. 2007. (Luxe Ser.). 448p. (J). lib. bdg. 18.89 (*978-0-06-134567-8(9)); (YA). (gr. 9 up). 17.99 (*978-0-06-134566-1(0)) HarperCollins Pubs. (HarperTeen).

Godwin, Jane. Falling from Grace. 2007. 204p. (YA). (gr. 6 up). 16.95 (*978-0-8234-2105-3(8)) Holiday Hse., Inc.

Golden Books Staff. Barbie in the Twelve Dancing Princesses: A Magical Tale. 2006. (Illus.). 32p. (J). (ps-2). pap. 3.99 (978-0-375-83765-4(5) , Golden Bks.) Random Hse. Children's Bks.

—A Perfect Fit. 2006. (Deluxe Coloring Book Ser.). (Illus.). 96p. (J). (ps-2). pap. 3.99 (978-0-375-84004-3(4) , Golden/Disney) Random Hse. Children's Bks.

—Sisters Forever. deluxe ed. 2006. (Deluxe Coloring Book Ser.). 64p. (J). (ps-2). pap. 3.99 (978-0-375-83766-1(3) , Golden Bks.) Random Hse. Children's Bks.

Good, Merle. Reuben & the Fire. Moss, P. Buckley, illus. 2003. (Bestselling Children's Book Ser.). 32p. (J). 7.95 (978-1-56148-388-4(5)) Good Bks.

—Reuben & the Fire. 2003. (gr. k-3). lib. bdg. 16.40 (978-0-613-84738-4(5)) Tandem Library Bks.

Gray, Dianne E. Tomorrow, the River. Cooper, Stephanie, illus. 2006. 240p. (J). (gr. 5-9). 16.00 (978-0-618-56329-6(6)) Houghton Mifflin Co.

Green, Holly. Don't Slam the Door! Scott, Sarah Chamberlin, illus. 2005. (J). 19.95 (978-0-9744803-7-4(1)) PublishingWorks.

Gregory, Deborah. Cheetah Girls No.13: OOPS, Doggy Dog! 2002. (gr. 3-6). lib. bdg. 11.80 (978-0-613-91004-0(4)) Tandem Library Bks.

—Oops, Doggy Dog! 2002. (Cheetah Girls Ser.: Bk. 13). 160p. (gr. 3-7). pap. 3.99 (978-0-7868-1484-8(5)) Hyperion Bks. for Children.

Griffin, Adele. The Other Shepards. 1999. (978-0-606-17144-1(4)) Tandem Library Bks.

—The Other Shepards. l.t. ed. 2000. (Illus.). 209p. (J). (gr. 4-7). 20.95 (978-0-7862-2914-7(4)) Thorndike Pr.

—Where I Want to Be. 160p. (gr. 7). 2007. (YA). 6.99 (*978-0-14-240948-0(0) , Puffin); 2005. (J). 15.99 (978-0-399-23783-6(6) , Putnam Juvenile) Penguin Group (USA) Inc.

—Witch Twins & the Ghost of Glenn Bly. Rogers, Jacqueline, illus. 2005. 128p. (gr. 2-6). pap. 5.99 (978-0-7868-5496-7(0)) Hyperion Bks. for Children.

—Witch Twins at Camp Bliss. Rogers, Jacqueline, illus. 2003. 144p. (gr. 2-6). pap. 5.99 (978-0-7868-1583-8(3)) Hyperion Bks. for Children.

—Witch Twins at Camp Bliss. 2003. (gr. 3-6). lib. bdg. 14.15 (978-0-613-63671-1(6)) Tandem Library Bks.

Grimes, Nikki. Jazmin's Notebook. 2002. (Illus.). (J). 12.34 (978-0-7587-0368-2(6)) Book Wholesalers, Inc.

—Jazmin's Notebook. 112p. (J). 1998. (gr. 8-12). 15.99 (978-0-8037-2224-8(9) , Dial); 2000. (gr. 5-9). reprint ed. pap. 5.99 (978-0-14-130702-2(1) , Puffin) Penguin Group (USA) Inc.

—Jazmin's Notebook. 2000. (gr. 7-12). lib. bdg. 14.15 (978-0-613-23623-2(8)) ; (Illus.). (J). 12.64 (978-0-606-18414-4(7)) Tandem Library Bks.

Grossman, Bill. My Little Sister Hugged an Ape. Hawkes, Kevin, illus. 2004. 40p. (J). (gr. k-3). 16.95 (978-0-517-80017-1(9)) ; lib. bdg. 18.99 (978-0-517-80018-8(7)) Random Hse. Children's Bks. (Knopf Bks. for Young Readers).

Guest, Elissa Haden. Iris & Walter, Lost & Found. Davenier, Christine, illus. (Iris & Walter Ser.). 44p. (J). 2006. pap. 5.95 (978-0-15-205662-9(9) , Harcourt Paperbacks); 2004. 15.00 (978-0-15-216701-1(3) , Gulliver Bks.) Harcourt Children's Bks.

Gunn, Robin Jones. Don't You Wish. 1998. (Sierra Jensen Ser.: Bk. 3). (Illus.). 144p. (YA). (gr. 7-11). pap. (978-1-56179-486-7(4)) Focus on the Family Publishing.

Gutman, Anne. Lisa's Baby Sister. Hallensleben, Georg, illus. 2003. (Misadventures of Gaspard & Lisa Ser.). 32p. (J). (ps-3). 9.95 (978-0-375-82251-3(8) , Knopf Bks. for Young Readers) Random Hse. Children's Bks.

H. Kraus, Joanna & Luisa, Anna. A Night of Tamales & Roses. 2007. 32p. (J). 15.95 (*978-0-9726614-4-7(1)) Shenanigan Bks.

Haas, Jessie. Scamper & the Horse Show. Apple, Margot, illus. 2004. 32p. (J). 15.99 (978-0-06-001338-7(9)) HarperCollins Pubs.

Hakala, Joann. A Baby Brother! Oh No! Shaw-Peterson, Kimberly, illus. 2006. 32p. (J). per. 10.95 (978-1-59298-152-6(6)) Beaver's Pond Pr., Inc.

Hale, Stephanie. Twisted Sisters. 2008. 224p. (gr. 12). pap. 9.99 (*978-0-425-21950-8(X) , Berkley Trade) Penguin Group (USA) Inc.

Half Baked Sistas-in the Beginning. 2004. 242p. (YA). lib. bdg. 12.99 (978-0-9761819-0-3(8) , 002) Smart Publishing.

Hall, Kirsten. Hide-and-Seek: All about Location. Luedecke, Bev, illus. 2005. (Beastieville Ser.). 32p. (J). (gr. k-1). pap. 3.95 (978-0-516-25519-4(3) , Children's Pr.) Scholastic Library Publishing.

Hallinan, P. K. We're Very Good Friends, My Sister & I. 2001. (Illus.). 24p. (J). (ps-3). 5.95 (978-0-8249-5386-7(X)) Ideals Pubns.

Halstead, Jayce N. The True Legend of White Crow: Adventures of the Fudge Sisters. Twomey-Lange, Marianna, photos by. 2004. (Illus.). 80p. (J). per. 7.95 (978-0-9749046-3-4(5)) Aarow Pr.

Hamilton, Richard & McCord, Patricia. Pictures in the Dark. 2004. (Illus.). 225p. (J). (gr. 5 up). 16.95 (978-1-58234-848-3(0) , Bloomsbury Children) Bloomsbury Publishing.

Harcourt School Publishers Staff. Girl Detectives: On Level. 3rd ed. 2002. (Trophies Reading Program Ser.). (Illus.). pap. 5.10 (978-0-15-323002-8(9)) Harcourt Schl. Pubs.

—Jenny's Wish: Take-Home Book. 1999. (Collections Ser.). (Illus.). (J). pap. 1.90 (978-0-15-317221-2(5)) Harcourt Schl. Pubs.

—Sister Rabbit: Take-Home Book. 1999. (Collections Ser.). (Illus.). (J). pap. 1.90 (978-0-15-317204-5(5)) Harcourt Schl. Pubs.

—We Are Big Now: Take-Home Book. rev. ed. 2001. (Collections Ser.: Vol. 3). (Illus.). (J). pap. 1.90 (978-0-15-317816-0(7)) Harcourt Schl. Pubs.

HarperCollins Staff, ed. How to Flunk Your First Date. 1999. (gr. 3-6). lib. bdg. 12.10 (978-0-613-16126-8(2)) Tandem Library Bks.

—One Twin Too Many. 1999. (gr. 3-6). lib. bdg. 12.10 (978-0-613-16172-5(6)) Tandem Library Bks.

—Two's a Crowd. 1999. (gr. 3-6). lib. bdg. 12.10 (978-0-613-22544-1(9)) Tandem Library Bks.

Harris, Ruth Elwin. Sarah's Story. 2002. (Quantock's Quartet Ser.). (Illus.). 288p. (YA). (gr. 7 up). pap. 5.99 (978-0-7636-1707-3(5)) Candlewick Pr.

—Sarah's Story. 2002. (gr. 7-12). lib. bdg. 14.15 (978-0-613-74779-0(8)) Tandem Library Bks.

Harrison, Mette. Mira, Mirror. 2006. 320p. (YA). (gr. 7). pap. 6.99 (978-0-14-240643-4(0) , Puffin) Penguin Group (USA) Inc.

Harrison, Troon. Bushel of Light. 2001. (gr. 5-8). lib. bdg. 16.40 (978-0-613-44633-4(X)) Tandem Library Bks.

Havill, Juanita. Brianna, Jamaica, & the Dance of Spring. O'Brien, Anne Sibley, illus. 2002. 32p. (J). (gr. 4-6). 16.00 (978-0-618-07700-7(6)) Houghton Mifflin Co. Trade & Reference Div.

Hayes, Joe. Little Gold Star: A Cinderella Cuento. 2002. (gr. k-3). lib. bdg. 16.40 (978-0-613-77773-5(5)) Tandem Library Bks.

Hearn, Julie. The Minister's Daughter. 2006. 272p. (YA). pap. 7.99 (978-0-689-87691-2(2) , Simon Pulse) Simon & Schuster Children's Publishing.

Hearn, Julie & Frost, Michael. The Minister's Daughter. 2005. 272p. (YA). (gr. 7 up). 17.99 (978-0-689-87690-5(4) , Atheneum) Simon & Schuster Children's Publishing.

Hemphill, Helen. Runaround. 2007. 117p. (YA). (gr. 8 up). 16.95 (978-1-932425-83-3(7) , Front Street) Boyds Mills Pr.

Henbit & the Roly-Poly. 2007. (J). (*978-0-9791982-2-9(4)) Donnellan, Martha.

Henbit & the Roly-Poly - Large Print Specially Formatted Edition. 2007. (J). (*978-0-9791982-3-6(2)) Donnellan, Martha.

Henkes, Kevin. Sheila Rae, the Brave. Henkes, Kevin, illus. (Illus.). 9.95 (978-1-59112-865-6(X)) ; 2002. 28.95 incl. audio compact disk (978-1-59112-550-1(2)) ; 2002. pap. 35.95 incl. audio compact disk (978-1-59112-549-5(9)) Live Oak Media.

—Sheila Rae, the Brave. 2002. (Illus.). (J). pap., tchr.'s planning gde. ed. 33.95 incl. audio (978-0-87499-954-9(5)) ; 25.95 incl. audio (978-0-87499-953-2(7)) Live Oak Media.

Henning, Ann. Cow Patty Patti. 2004. 47p. pap. 19.95 (978-1-4137-3456-0(1)) PublishAmerica, Inc.

Heredia, Maria Fernanda. Por Si No Te Lo He Dicho. 2003. (SPA., Illus.). 24p. (J). (gr. 3-5). 15.95 (978-9978-07-467-1(8)) Santillana USA Publishing Co., Inc.

Herman, Gail. Keep Your Distance! Smath, Jerry, illus. 2005. (Math Matters Ser.). 32p. (J). (gr. 2-3). pap. 4.95 (978-1-57565-107-1(6)) Kane Pr., The.

—Keep Your Distance! Smath, Jerry, illus. 2001. 32p. (J). (ps-3). lib. bdg. 12.95 (978-0-613-39333-1(3)) Tandem Library Bks.

Hershey, Mary. My Big Sister Is So Bossy She Says You Can't Read This Book. 2006. 176p. (gr. 4-7). 5.50 (978-0-553-48797-8(3) , Yearling) Random Hse. Children's Bks.

Hesse, Karen & Hesse, Hermann. A Time for Angels. rev. ed. 2000. 288p. (gr. 5-9). 16.99 (978-0-7868-0621-8(4)) ; 17.49 (978-0-7868-2534-9(0)) Hyperion Pr.

Hinojosa, Francisco. Mi Hermana Quiere Ser Una Sirena. El Fisgon, illus. 2003. (SPA.). 43p. (J). (gr. k-3). 14.95 (978-968-19-0546-0(6)) Santillana USA Publishing Co., Inc.

Hirano, Toshiki, illus. Shaolin Sisters Vol. 1: Reborn. 2005. 224p. pap. 9.99 (978-1-59532-507-5(7) , Tokyopop Kids) TOKYOPOP, Inc.

Ho, Minfong. The Stone Goddess. 2003. (First Person Fiction Ser.). 208p. (J). (gr. 4-7). pap. 16.95 (978-0-439-38197-0(5) , Orchard Bks.) Scholastic, Inc.

Hofmeister, Alan, et al. Sis in a Mess. (Reading for All Learners Ser.). (Illus.). (J). pap. (978-1-56861-091-7(2)) Swift Learning Resources.

—Sis in the Well. (Reading for All Learners Ser.). (Illus.). (J). pap. (978-1-56861-098-6(X)) Swift Learning Resources.

Hogan, Mary. Perfect Girl. 2008. 208p. (J). 7.99 (*978-0-06-084110-2(9) , HarperTeen) HarperCollins Pubs.

Holabird, Katharine. Angelina's Baby Sister. Craig, Helen, illus. 2006. (Angelina Ballerina Ser.). 32p. (J). (ps). 12.99 (978-0-670-06146-4(8) , Viking Juvenile) Penguin Group (USA) Inc.

—Angelina's Silly Little Sister: Station Stop 1. Craig, Helen, illus. 2007. (Angelina Ballerina Ser.). 32p. (J). pap. 3.99 (978-0-448-44468-0(2) , Grosset & Dunlap) Penguin Group (USA) Inc.

Holmes, Elizabeth. Pretty Is. 2007. 224p. (J). (gr. 4-6). 16.99 (978-0-525-47813-3(2) , Dutton Juvenile) Penguin Group (USA) Inc.

Holt, Kimberly Willis. Piper Reed, Navy Brat. Davenier, Christine, illus. 2007. 160p. (J). (gr. 3-6). 14.95 (*978-0-8050-8197-8(6) , Holt, Henry & Co. Bks. For Young Readers) Holt, Henry & Co.

—Piper Reed, Navy Brat. Davenier, Christine, illus. 2008. 176p. (J). pap. 6.99 (*978-0-312-38020-5(8)) Square Fish.

Hood, Susan. I Am Mad! Handelman, Dorothy, photos by. 1999. (Real Kids Readers Ser.). (Illus.). 32p. (gr. k-1). (J). pap. 4.99 (978-0-7613-2086-9(5)) ; lib. bdg. 18.90 (978-0-7613-2061-6(X)) Lerner Publishing Group. (Millbrook Pr.).

—I Am Mad! 1999. (J). 11.79 (978-0-606-19155-5(0)) ; lib. bdg. 13.00 (978-0-613-18156-3(5)) Tandem Library Bks.

Hooper, Mary. At the Sign of the Sugared Plum. (J). 2005. 176p. (gr. 4-7). pap. 6.95 (978-1-58234-695-3(X)); 2003. 200p. 16.95 (978-1-58234-849-0(9)) Bloomsbury Publishing. (Bloomsbury Children).

—Petals in the Ashes. (J). 2006. 192p. pap. 6.95 (978-1-58234-720-2(4)); 2004. 200p. (gr. 5 up). 16.95 (978-1-58234-936-7(3)) Bloomsbury Publishing. (Bloomsbury Children).

Hope, Laura Lee. Bunny Brown & His Sister Sue on Grandpa's Farm. 2007. (ENG.). 164p. 95.99 (*978-1-4280-7438-5(4)); per. 89.99 (*978-1-4280-7440-8(6)) IndyPublish.com.

Horrocks, Anita. What They Don't Know. braille ed. 2003. (J). (gr. 2). spiral bd. (978-0-616-15267-6(1)) Canadian National Institute for the Blind/Institut National Canadien pour les Aveugles.

—What They Don't Know. 1999. (Illus.). 240p. (YA). (gr. 7-10). pap. 8.95 (978-0-7737-6001-1(6)) Stoddart Kids CAN. *Dist:* Fitzhenry & Whiteside, Ltd.

—What They Don't Know. 1999. (J). (978-0-606-19101-2(1)) Tandem Library Bks.

Howard, Elizabeth Fitzgerald. The Train to Lulu's. 1998. (J). pap. 4.95 (978-0-87628-336-3(9)) Simon & Schuster.

—What's in Aunt Mary's Room? Lucas, Cedric, illus. 2002. 32p. (J). (gr. k-3). pap. 5.95 (978-0-618-24621-2(5) , Clarion Bks.) Houghton Mifflin Co. Trade & Reference Div.

—What's in Aunt Mary's Room? 2002. (gr. k-3). lib. bdg. 14.10 (978-0-613-72911-6(0)) Tandem Library Bks.

Hyde, E. A. Watson. Little Sisters to the Camp Fire Girls. 2004. reprint ed. pap. 15.95 (978-1-4179-9442-7(8)) Kessinger Publishing, LLC.

Jackson, Chris. The Gaggle Sisters River Tour. Pavanel, Jane, ed. Jackson, Chris, illus. 2002. (Illus.). 32p. (J). (ps-1). 15.95 (978-1-894222-58-7(X)) Lobster Pr. CAN. *Dist:* Univ. of Toronto Pr.

—The Gaggle Sisters Sing Again. Jackson, Chris, illus. 2005. (Gaggle Sisters Trilogy Ser.). (Illus.). 32p. (J). 15.95 (978-1-894222-56-3(3)) Lobster Pr. CAN. *Dist:* Univ. of Toronto Pr.

Jackson, Melanie. Spy in the Alley. 2002. (gr. 3-6). lib. bdg. 15.25 (978-0-613-88907-0(X)) Tandem Library Bks.

Jacobs, E. Caroline. The S. W. F. Club. 2006. 77.99 (*978-1-4280-4783-9(2)); pap. 71.99 (*978-1-4280-4779-2(4)) IndyPublish.com.

Jeffs, Stephanie. Jenny: Coming to Terms with the Death of a Sibling. Thomas, Jacqui, illus. 2006. 32p. (ps-3). 14.00 (978-0-687-49709-6(4)) Abingdon Pr.

Jenkins, Emily. Daffodil. Bogacki, Tomek, illus. 2004. 32p. (J). 16.00 (978-0-374-31676-1(7) , Farrar, Straus & Giroux (BYR)) Farrar, Straus & Giroux.

—Daffodil, Crocodile. Bogacki, Tomek, illus. 2007. 32p. (J). (ps-3). 16.00 (978-0-374-39944-3(1) , Farrar, Straus & Giroux (BYR)) Farrar, Straus & Giroux.

Jocelyn, Marthe. Mable Riley: A Reliable Record of Humdrum, Peril, & Romance. 288p. (J). (gr. 5). 2007. 6.99 (978-0-7636-3287-8(2)); 2004. (Illus.). 15.99 (978-0-7636-2120-9(X)) Candlewick Pr.

Jocelyn, Marthe. Would You? 2008. (YA). (*978-0-375-83703-6(5)); lib. bdg. (*978-0-375-93703-3(X)) Dell Publishing. (Delacorte Pr.).

Johnson, Angela. A Cool Moonlight. 2005. 144p. (J). (gr. 3-6). reprint ed. pap. 5.99 (978-0-14-240284-9(2) , Puffin) Penguin Group (USA) Inc.

—A Cool Moonlight. 2005. 133p. (J). (ps-7). per. 12.64 (978-0-606-33124-1(7)) Tandem Library Bks.

Johnson, Gillian. My Sister Gracie. 2005. (Illus.). 32p. (J). (ps-k). pap. 7.95 (978-0-88776-750-0(8)) Tundra Bks., Inc./Livres Toundra, Inc. CAN. *Dist:* Random Hse., Inc.

Johnson, Janie, compiled by. Up from the Cotton Fields. 2003. 114p. per. 29.95 net. (978-0-9718254-8-2(3)) Excel Digital Pr., Inc.

Johnson, Lindan Lee. The Dream Jar. Curmi, Serena, illus. 2005. 32p. (J). (gr. k-3). 16.00 (978-0-618-17698-4(5)) Houghton Mifflin Co. Trade & Reference Div.

Johnson, Maureen G. The Key to the Golden Firebird. 2005. 304p. (YA). reprint ed. pap. 7.99 (978-0-06-054140-8(7) , Harper Trophy) HarperCollins Pubs.

Johnston, Julie. In Spite of Killer Bees. 2002. (gr. 5-8). lib. bdg. 17.60 (978-0-613-77264-8(4)) Tandem Library Bks.

—In Spite of Killer Bees. 2002. 264p. (J). (gr. 6 up). pap. 9.95 (978-0-88776-601-5(3)) Tundra Bks., Inc./Livres Toundra, Inc. CAN. *Dist:* Random Hse., Inc.

—A Very Fine Line. 2006. 208p. (J). (gr. 6). 18.95 (978-0-88776-746-3(X)) Tundra Bks., Inc./Livres Toundra, Inc. CAN. *Dist:* Random Hse., Inc.

Jones, Diana Wynne. The Time of the Ghost. 2002. 304p. (J). (gr. 7 up). 16.99 (978-0-06-029887-6(1)) HarperCollins Pubs.

Jukes, Mavis. Expecting the Unexpected. 1999. (J). (978-0-606-15911-1(8)) Tandem Library Bks.

Kadohata, Cynthia. Kira-Kira. 2004. (Illus.). 256p. 16.95 (978-0-689-85639-6(3) , Atheneum); 2006. 272p. (J). reprint ed. pap. 6.99 (978-0-689-85640-2(7) , Aladdin) Simon & Schuster Children's Publishing.

—Kira-Kira. l.t. ed. 2005. 201p. 23.95 (978-0-7862-7616-5(9) , Large Print Pr.) Thorndike Pr.

Kakinouchi, Narumi. Juline, 5 vols. 168p. Vol. 1. 2001. (gr. 7-12). pap. 12.99 (978-1-892213-63-1(X)); Vol. 3. 3rd rev. ed. 2002. pap. 12.99 (978-1-931514-03-3(8)) TOKYOPOP, Inc.

Kanter, Angela. My Ballerina Sister. 2002. (Illus.). 64p. pap. 8.99 (978-0-09-941702-6(2)) Random Hse. GBR. *Dist:* Trafalgar Square Publishing.

Kaslik, Ibi. Skinny. 2006. (YA). 256p. 16.95 (978-0-8027-9608-0(7)) ; viii, 244p. (*978-1-4287-0474-9(4)) Walker & Co.

Kassirer, Sue. What's Next, Nina? O'Rourke, Page Eastburn, illus. 2005. (Math Matters Ser.). 32p. (gr. 1-3). pap. 4.95 (978-1-57565-106-4(8)) Kane Pr., The.

—What's Next, Nina? 2001. (gr. k-3). lib. bdg. 12.95 (978-0-613-39372-0(4)) Tandem Library Bks.

Katschke, Judy. Bye-Bye Boyfriend. 2000. (gr. 3-6). lib. bdg. 13.00 (978-0-613-31037-6(3)) Tandem Library Bks.

—The Case of the Weird Science Mystery. 2002. (New Adventures of Mary-Kate & Ashley Ser.: 29). (Illus.). 96p. (gr. 1-5). mass mkt. 4.50 (978-0-06-106651-1(6)) HarperCollins Pubs.

Katz, Bebe Weinberg. Princess Claudia & the Freckles. 2007. (ENG.). 48p. per. 12.95 (*978-1-4241-6446-2(X)) PublishAmerica, Inc.

Katz, Karen. Best-Ever Big Sister. 2006. (Illus.). 14p. (J). (ps-k). bds. 5.99 (978-0-448-43915-0(8) , Grosset & Dunlap) Penguin Group (USA) Inc.

Kawashita, Mizuki. Ichigo 100% Sweet Little Sister, Vol. 7. (JPN., Illus.). 180p. (YA). pap. (978-4-08-873518-4(8)) Shuei-Sha.

Kerry, Mary. Saving the Scrolls. 2003. 159p. (J). (gr. 4-7). 16.95 (978-1-888842-30-2(X)) Absey & Co.

Kiernan, Kristy. Catching Genius. 2007. 384p. pap. 14.00 (978-0-425-21435-0(4) , Berkley Trade) Penguin Group (USA) Inc.

Kinsey-Warnock, Natalie. If Wishes Were Horses. Kinsey-Warnock, Natalie, illus. 2002. (Illus.). 144p. (J). pap. 5.99 (978-0-14-230143-2(4) , Puffin) Penguin Group (USA) Inc.

—If Wishes Were Horses. 2002. (gr. 3-6). lib. bdg. 14.15 (978-0-613-45283-0(6)) Tandem Library Bks.

Klam, Cheryl. The Pretty One. 2008. 288p. (YA). (gr. 7). pap. 9.99 (*978-0-385-73373-1(9) , Delacorte Bks. for Young Readers) Random Hse. Children's Bks.

Knudson, Michelle. The Case of Vampire Vivian. Wummer, Amy, illus. 2003. (Science Solves It! Ser.). 32p. (J). 4.99 (978-1-57565-127-9(0)) Kane Pr., The.

Korba, Joanna. Cindy Eller Plays Ball: A Modern-Day Cinderella Tale. 2006. 42.00 (*978-1-4108-6164-1(3)) Benchmark Education Co.

Kroll, Virginia K. Faraway Drums. Cooper, Floyd, illus. 1998. 32p. (J). (ps-3). 14.95 (978-0-316-50449-2(1)) Little Brown & Co.

Kuhn, Betsy. Not Exactly Nashville. 1999. (978-0-606-16708-6(0)) Tandem Library Bks.

Kvasnosky, Laura McGee. Zelda & Ivy. Kvasnosky, Laura McGee, illus. 2007. (Candlewick Sparks Ser.). (Illus.). 40p. (J). (ps-3). pap. 4.99 (978-0-7636-3261-8(9)) Candlewick Pr.

—Zelda & Ivy. 2001. (J). (gr. k-4). 26.95 incl. audio (978-0-8045-6868-5(5) , 6868) Spoken Arts, Inc.

—Zelda & Ivy: One Christmas. Kvasnosky, Laura McGee, illus. 2004. (Illus.). 39p. (J). (gr. k-4). reprint ed. pap. 7.00 (978-0-7567-7997-9(9)) DIANE Publishing Co.

—Zelda & Ivy: The Runaways. Kvasnosky, Laura McGee, illus. (Candlewick Sparks Ser.). (Illus.). 48p. (J). 2007. (ps-3). pap. 4.99 (978-0-7636-3061-4(6)); 2006. (gr. 1-4). 14.99 (978-0-7636-2689-1(9)) Candlewick Pr.

—Zelda & Ivy & the Boy Next Door: Three Stories about the Fabulous Fox Sisters. Kvasnosky, Laura McGee, illus. 2003. (Illus.). 48p. (J). (gr. k-4). pap. 6.99 (978-0-7636-1053-1(4)) Candlewick Pr.

—Zelda & Ivy: One Christmas. Kvasnosky, Laura McGee, illus. 2006. 40p. (J). (gr. 1-4). pap. 4.99 (978-0-7636-3047-8(0)) Candlewick Pr.

—Zelda & Ivy One Christmas: A Story about the Fabulous Fox Sisters. Kvasnosky, Laura McGee, illus. 2002. (Illus.). 48p. (J). (gr. k-4). pap. 6.99 (978-0-7636-1344-0(4)) Candlewick Pr.

Lambert, Janet. Candy Kane. 2001. (Candy Kane Ser.: Vol. 1). (YA). pap. 12.95 (978-1-930009-45-5(3)) Image Cascade Publishing.

—For Each Other: A Campbell Story. 2002. (J). per. 9.95 (978-1-930009-57-8(7)) Image Cascade Publishing.

Lane, Dakota. Orpheus Obsession. 2005. (Illus.). 288p. (J). 16.99 (978-0-06-074173-0(2) , Tegen, Katherine Bks) ; lib. bdg. 17.89 (978-0-06-074174-7(0) , HarperTeen) HarperCollins Pubs.

Larsen, Kirsten. Tara Pays Up! Billin-Frye, Paige, illus. 2006. (Social Studies Connects). 32p. (J). (gr. k-3). pap. 4.99 (978-1-57565-187-3(4)) Kane Pr., The.

Las dos Hermanas: Lap Book. (Pebble Soup Exploraciones Ser.). (SPA.). 16p. (ps up). 21.00 (978-0-7578-1692-5(4)) Rigby Education.

Las dos Hermanas: Small Book. (Pebble Soup Exploraciones Ser.). (SPA.). 16p. (ps up). 5.00 (978-0-7578-1732-8(7)) Rigby Education.

Lavender, William. Aftershocks. 2006. (Illus.). 352p. (YA). 17.00 (978-0-15-205887-1(6)) Harcourt Children's Bks.

Lawlor, Laurie. American Sisters: A Titanic Journey Across the Sea. 2000. (J). (978-0-606-20220-6(X)) Tandem Library Bks.

—Down the Rio Grande, Eighteen Twenty-Nine. 2001. (gr. 3-6). lib. bdg. 12.40 (978-0-613-51210-7(3)) Tandem Library Bks.

—Exploring the Chicago World's Fair 1893. 2002. (gr. 3-6). lib. bdg. 13.00 (978-0-613-45036-2(1)) Tandem Library Bks.

Lears, Laurie. Becky the Brave: A Story about Epilepsy. Piazza, Gail, illus. 2002. 32p. (J). (gr. 1-4). 15.95 (978-0-8075-0601-1(X)) Whitman, Albert & Co.

Levine, Gail Carson. The Two Princesses of Bamarre. (J). 2003. 256p. (gr. 5 up). pap. 6.99 (978-0-06-440966-7(X)); 2001. 256p. (gr. 5 up). 17.99 (978-0-06-029315-4(2)); 2001. 256p. (gr. 5 up). lib. bdg. 17.89 (978-0-06-029316-1(0)); 2004. (Illus.). 304p. (gr. 7 up). reprint ed. pap. 6.99 (978-0-06-057580-9(8)) HarperCollins Pubs.

—The Two Princesses of Bamarre. 2003. (Illus.). (gr. 7-12). lib. bdg. 14.15 (978-0-613-67233-7(X)) Tandem Library Bks.

Levinson, Robin K. Miriam's Journey: Discovering a New World. 2006. (Illus.). 64p. (J). per. 12.00 (978-0-9773673-0-6(4)) Gali Girls, Inc.

Levy, Elizabeth. Big Trouble in Little Twinsville. Elliot, Mark, illus. 2001. 96p. (J). (gr. 2-5). 15.89 (978-0-06-028591-3(5)) HarperCollins Pubs.

Liebenthal, Jean Z. Curiosity. 1999. 133p. (J). (978-1-57008-707-3(5)) Scribbulations LLC.

Lieurance, Suzanne. The Locket: Surviving the Triangle Shirtwaist Fire. 2008. (Historical Fiction Adventures (HFA) Ser.). (Illus.). 160p. (J). (gr. 3-6). lib. bdg. 27.93 ***(978-0-7660-2928-6(X))*** Enslow Pubs., Inc.

Lilly-Lolly Little-Legs: Individual Title, 6 packs. (Literatura 2000 Ser.). (gr. 1-2). 28.00 (978-0-7635-0095-5(X)) Rigby Education.

Linklater, Eric. The Wind on the Moon. Bentley, Nicolas, illus. 2004. (New York Review Children's Collection). 376p. (J). 18.95 (978-1-59017-100-4(4) , NYR Children's Collection) New York Review of Bks., Inc., The.

Lisle, Janet Taylor. The Lost Flower Children. Ichikawa, Satomi, illus. 2001. 112p. (J). (ps-7). pap. 5.99 (978-0-698-11880-5(4) , Putnam Juvenile) Penguin Group (USA) Inc.

—Lost Flower Children. 2001. (gr. 3-6). lib. bdg. 14.15 (978-0-613-35975-7(5)) Tandem Library Bks.

—The Lost Flower Children. l.t. ed. 2000. (Illus.). 188p. (J). 21.95 (978-0-7862-2890-4(3)) Thorndike Pr.

—Sirens & Spies. 2002. (gr. 3-6). lib. bdg. 13.00 (978-0-613-45104-8(X)) Tandem Library Bks.

Lispi, Robert. Buddy Hawk: Story of Buddy Hawk. 2005. (J). pap. 8.00 (978-0-8059-6602-2(1)) Dorrance Publishing Co., Inc.

Little Farm down the Lane, Bk. III. 2005. pap. 10.99 (978-1-59781-702-8(3)) Xulon Pr., Inc.

Little Reader Digital Storybook: Cinderella. 2005. (J). cd-rom 8.99 (978-0-9767657-7-6(2)) Mullings Media.

Littlefield, William. The Circus in the Woods. 2001. 208p. (J). (gr. 4-6). tchr. ed. 15.00 (978-0-618-06642-1(X)) Houghton Mifflin Co. Trade & Reference Div.

Lloyd-Jones, Sally. How to Be a Baby—By Me, the Big Sister. Heap, Sue, illus. 2007. 40p. (J). (ps-3). 15.99 (978-0-375-83843-9(0) , Schwartz & Wade Bks.) Random Hse. Children's Bks.

—How to Be a Baby—by Me, the Big Sister. Heap, Sue, illus. 2007. 40p. (J). (ps-3). lib. bdg. 17.99 (978-0-375-93843-6(5) , Schwartz & Wade Bks.) Random Hse. Children's Bks.

Lopez, Loretta. The Birthday Swap. Lopez, Loretta, illus. 1999. (Illus.). 32p. (J). (gr. k-3). pap. 6.95 (978-1-880000-89-2(X)) Lee & Low Bks., Inc.

Lowrey, Becky. Chirps. 2004. 45p. pap. 19.95 (978-1-4137-2984-9(3)) PublishAmerica, Inc.

MacDonald, Maryann. The Costume Copycat. Wilsdorf, Anne, illus. 2006. 32p. (J). (ps). 10.99 (978-0-8037-2929-2(4) , Dial) Penguin Group (USA) Inc.

MacGregor, Doug. The Incredible Tongue Twister That Swallowed My Sister: Another Santa Story by Doug MacGregor. MacGregor, Doug, illus. ltd. ed. 2006. (J). per. (978-0-9654843-5-0(1)) MacGregor, Doug.

MacIntyre, R. P. Revved. 2005. 220p. pap. 11.95 (978-1-894345-46-0(0)) Thistledown Pr., Ltd. CAN. *Dist:* Literary Pr. Group of Canada.

Mackall, Dandi Daley. Please Reply! 2004. 128p. (J). pap. 5.99 (978-1-4003-0328-1(1)) Nelson, Thomas Inc.

Mackel, Kathy. A Season of Comebacks. 1998. (J). (978-0-606-13767-6(X)) Tandem Library Bks.

Madison, Alan. Velma Gratch & the Way Cool Butterfly. Hawkes, Kevin, illus. 2007. 40p. (J). (ps-3). 16.99 ***(978-0-375-83597-1(0));*** lib. bdg. 19.99 ***(978-0-375-93597-8(5))*** Random Hse. Children's Bks. (Schwartz & Wade Bks.).

—Velma Gratch & the Way Cool Butterfly. Hawkes, Kevin, illus. 2007. (J). (978-0-689-86921-1(5) , Atheneum) Simon & Schuster Children's Publishing.

Manten tu Distancia: Keep Your Distance Spanish Edition. 2006. (SPA.). 32p. (J). pap. 4.95 (978-1-57565-168-2(8)) Kane Pr., The.

Marillier, Juliet. Wildwood Dancing. 416p. (J). (gr. 7). 2008. pap. 9.99 ***(978-0-375-84474-4(0));*** 2007. 16.99 (978-0-375-83364-9(1)); 2007. lib. bdg. 19.99 (978-0-375-93364-6(6)) Random Hse. Children's Bks. (Knopf Bks. for Young Readers).

Marlow, Herb. Sisters, Wild Dogs & Catfish Bait. Caffee, Julie, illus. 2005. 122p. (J). lib. bdg. 24.95 (978-1-893595-45-3(5)); per. 16.95 (978-1-893595-48-4(X)) Four Seasons Bks., Inc.

Martin, Ann M. Adios, Stacey, Adios. 2000. (Baby-Sitters Club Ser.).Tr. of Goodbye, Stacey, Goodbye. (SPA.). 152p. (YA). 11.95 (978-84-272-3663-9(8)) Molino, Editorial ESP. *Dist:* AIMS International Bks., Inc.

—Mary Anne Salva la Situacion. 2000. (Baby-Sitters Club Ser.).Tr. of Mary Anne Saves the Day. (SPA.). 168p. (YA). 11.95 (978-84-272-3654-7(9)) Molino, Editorial ESP. *Dist:* AIMS International Bks., Inc.

Martin, Ann M. Welcome to Camden Falls. 2007. (Main Street Ser.: No. 1). 192p. (J). (gr. 4-7). pap. 6.99 ***(978-0-439-86879-2(3)*** , Scholastic Paperbacks) Scholastic, Inc.

Matute, Ana M. El Polizon de Ulises.Tr. of Stonaway of Ulises. (SPA.). 126p. (YA). (gr. 5 up). 10.36 (978-84-264-3022-9(8) , LM0588) Editorial Lumen ESP. *Dist:* Lectorum Pubns., Inc.

May, Sophie. Little Prudys Sister Susy. 2006. 77.99 ***(978-1-4280-2588-2(X))*** IndyPublish.com.

Mayfield, Marilee Joy. The Tiny Adventures of Big Sister & Little Sister: A Hearts-Beared Book. 2004. 48p. (J). lib. bdg. 19.95 (978-0-9659222-2-7(7)) Leaping Antelope Productions.

Mazer, Anne. Have Wheels, Will Travel. 2001. (Amazing Days of Abby Hayes Ser.: No. 4). (gr. 3-6). lib. bdg. 12.40 (978-0-613-43045-6(X)) Tandem Library Bks.

—Mabel Makes the Grade. 2007. (Sister Magic Ser.). 96p. (J). pap. 3.99 ***(978-0-439-87248-5(0)*** , Scholastic Paperbacks) Scholastic, Inc.

—Sister Magic. 2007. (Sister Magic Ser.: Bk. 2). 112p. (J). pap. 3.99 ***(978-0-439-87247-8(2))*** Scholastic, Inc.

—The Trouble with Violet. Brown, Bill, illus. 2007. (Sister Magic Ser.: Bk. 1). 112p. (J). (gr. 2-4). pap. 4.99 ***(978-0-439-87246-1(4))*** Scholastic, Inc.

Mazer, Norma Fox. The Missing Girl. 2008. 288p. (J). 16.99 ***(978-0-06-623776-3(9));*** lib. bdg. 17.89 ***(978-0-06-623777-0(7))*** HarperCollins Pubs. (HarperTeen).

—Ten Ways to Make My Sister Disappear. 2007. (J). ***(978-0-439-83984-6(X));*** 160p. (gr. 4-7). pap. 16.99 ***(978-0-439-83983-9(1))*** Scholastic, Inc. (Levine, Arthur A. Bks.).

Mazer, Norma Fox. When She Was Good. 2000. 240p. (J). (gr. 7-12). pap. 16.95 (978-0-590-13506-1(6)); (Illus.). pap. 5.99 (978-0-590-31990-4(6) , Scholastic Paperbacks) Scholastic, Inc.

—When She Was Good. 2003. 228p. (YA). (gr. 7-12). per. 14.15 (978-0-613-23050-6(7)); 2000. (978-0-606-18615-5(8)) Tandem Library Bks.

McCarthy, Meghan. Adventures of Patty & the Big Red Bus. 2005. (Illus.). 40p. (J). (ps-1). 12.95 (978-0-375-82939-0(3)); lib. bdg. 14.99 (978-0-375-92939-7(8)) Random Hse. Children's Bks. (Knopf Bks. for Young Readers).

McCombie, Karen. Marshmallow Magic & the Wild Rose Roug. l.t. ed. 2005. pap. 16.95 (978-1-4056-6036-5(8)) BBC Audio GBR. *Dist:* BBC Audiobooks America.

McDaniel, Lurlene. Angel of Hope. 2000. (Mercy Trilogy). 240p. (YA). (gr. 7-12). pap. 4.99 (978-0-553-57148-6(6) , Laurel Leaf) Random Hse. Children's Bks.

—Angel of Hope. 2000. (Mercy Trilogy). (gr. 7-12). lib. bdg. 13.00 (978-0-613-24184-7(3)); (Illus.). (J). 11.64 (978-0-606-17991-1(7)) Tandem Library Bks.

—Briana's Gift. 2006. 176p. (YA). (gr. 7). 10.95 (978-0-385-73160-7(4)); lib. bdg. 12.99 (978-0-385-90197-0(6)) Random Hse. Children's Bks. (Delacorte Bks. for Young Readers).

—The End of Forever. 2007. 320p. (YA). (gr. 7). pap. 7.99 ***(978-0-375-84170-5(9)*** , Laurel Leaf) Random Hse. Children's Bks.

McDaniel, Lurlene. Raina's Story. 2005. (Angels in Pink Ser.). 208p. (J). (gr. 7). lib. bdg. 12.99 (978-0-385-90194-9(1) , Delacorte Bks. for Young Readers) Random Hse. Children's Bks.

McDonald, Janet. Twists & Turns. 144p. (YA). 2006. pap. 6.95 (978-0-374-40006-4(7)); 2003. 16.00 (978-0-374-39955-9(7)) Farrar, Straus & Giroux. (Farrar, Straus & Giroux (BYR)).

—Twists & Turns, Vol. 5. l.t. ed. 2004. 147p. 21.95 (978-0-7862-6664-7(3) , Large Print Pr.) Thorndike Pr.

McDonough, Yona Zeldis. The Dollhouse Magic. Palmisciano, Diane, illus. rev. ed. 2000. 96p. (J). (gr. 2-4). 15.00 (978-0-8050-6464-3(8) , Holt, Henry & Co. Bks. For Young Readers) Holt, Henry & Co.

McGhee, Alison. All Rivers Flow to the Sea. 176p. (YA). (gr. 9 up). 2007. (Illus.). pap. 7.99 ***(978-0-7636-3372-1(0));*** 2005. 15.99 (978-0-7636-2591-7(4)) Candlewick Pr.

McKay, Hilary. The Exiles in Love. 1999. (J). 11.15 (978-0-606-17315-5(3)) Tandem Library Bks.

McKissack, Pat. The All-I'll-Ever-Want Christmas Doll. Pinkney, Jerry, illus. 2007. (J). ***(978-0-375-83615-2(2)*** , Schwartz & Wade Bks.) Random Hse. Children's Bks.

McKissack, Patricia. The All-I'll-Ever-Want Christmas Doll. Pinkney, Jerry, illus. 2007. 40p. (J). (ps-3). lib. bdg. 19.99 ***(978-0-375-93759-0(5));*** 16.99 ***(978-0-375-83759-3(0))*** Random Hse. Children's Bks. (Schwartz & Wade Bks.).

McKissack, Patricia C. Color Me Dark: The Diary of Nellie Lee Love, the Great Migration North, Chicago, Illinois, 1919. 2000. (Dear America Ser.). (J). 9.95 (978-0-439-26653-6(X)) Scholastic, Inc.

—Color Me Dark: The Diary of Nellie Lee Love, the Great Migration North, Chicago, Illinois, 1919. 2000. (Dear America Ser.). (Illus.). 224p. (J). (gr. 4-9). pap. 10.95 (978-0-590-51159-9(9)) Scholastic, Inc.

McKnight, Gillian. To Catch a Prince. 2006. 240p. (YA). mass mkt. 5.99 (978-0-689-87734-6(X) , Simon Pulse) Simon & Schuster Children's Publishing.

McMillon, LaToya. Bad News! 2006. (ENG.). 28p. per. 14.99 ***(978-1-4259-3563-4(X))*** AuthorHouse.

McTighe, Carolyn. The Sakura Tree. Brownlee, Karen, illus. 2008. 32p. (J). (ps-3). 17.95 ***(978-0-88995-354-3(6))*** Red Deer Pr. CAN. *Dist:* Fitzhenry & Whiteside, Ltd.

McVeity, Jen. On Different Shores. 1998. (Illus.). 167p. (YA). (gr. 5-9). 17.99 (978-0-531-33115-6(6)); pap. 16.95 (978-0-531-30115-9(X)) Scholastic, Inc. (Orchard Bks.).

Meadows, Daisy. Rainbow Magic: Heather the Violet Fairy. Ripper, Georgie, illus. 2006. 80p. (J). pap. 4.99 (978-0-439-74686-1(8) , Scholastic Paperbacks) Scholastic, Inc.

Meng, Cece. The Wonderful Thing about Hiccups. Pedersen, Janet, illus. 2007. 32p. (J). (gr. k-3). 16.00 (978-0-618-59544-0(9) , Clarion Bks.) Houghton Mifflin Co. Trade & Reference Div.

Mercer, Sienna. Fangtastic! 2007. (My Sister the Vampire Ser.: No. 2). 208p. (J). (gr. 3-7). pap. 5.99 ***(978-0-06-087115-4(6)*** , Harper Trophy) HarperCollins Pubs.

Messer, Celeste M. The Ghost of Piper's Landing. Hoeffner, Deb, illus. 2004. 82-92p. 4.95 (978-0-9702171-7-2(X)) AshleyAlan Enterprises.

Meyer, Carolyn. Beware, Princess Elizabeth. (Young Royals Ser.). 2002. (Illus.). 240p. (YA). pap. 5.95 (978-0-15-204556-2(2)); 2001. (J). 17.00 (978-0-15-202639-4(8)) Harcourt Children's Bks. (Gulliver Bks.).

Michels-Gualtieri, Akaela S. I Was Born to Be a Sister. Ramsey, Marcy Dunn, illus. 2001. 32p. (ps-7). 16.95 (978-1-930775-03-9(2)) Platypus Media, L.L.C.

—I was Born to be a Sister. Ramsey, Marcy Dunn, illus. 2006. 32p. 18.95 (978-1-930775-11-4(3)) Platypus Media, L.L.C.

—I was Born to Be a Sister. 2005. 32p. pap. 9.95 incl. audio compact disk (978-1-930775-24-4(5)) Platypus Media, L.L.C.

Mikaelsen, Ben. Tree Girl. 2005. 240p. (J). pap. 7.99 (978-0-06-009006-7(5) , HarperTeen) HarperCollins Pubs.

Miller, Mitzi & Millner, Denene. Hotlanta #1. 2008. 288p. (J). 8.99 ***(978-0-545-00308-7(3)*** , Scholastic Paperbacks) Scholastic, Inc.

Mlynowski, Sarah. Bras & Broomsticks. 2005. 320p. (YA). (gr. 7). 15.95 (978-0-385-73181-2(7) , Delacorte Bks. for Young Readers) Random Hse. Children's Bks.

Mooney, E. S. Snow-off. 2000. (gr. k-3). lib. bdg. 11.25 (978-0-613-33069-5(2)) Tandem Library Bks.

Moore, Liz. Zizi & Tish. Milkau, Liz, illus. 2003. 32p. (J). (ps-2). 7.95 (978-1-55143-254-0(4)) Orca Bk. Pubs. USA.

Mora, Pat. Uno, Dos, Tres: One, Two, Three. Lavallee, Barbara, illus. 2000. (SPA.). 43p. (ps-ps). lib. bdg. 15.25 (978-0-613-28687-9(1)) Tandem Library Bks.

Morris, Kim. Molly in the Middle. Handelman, Dorothy, photos by. 1999. (Real Kids Readers Ser.). (Illus.). 48p. (gr. 1-3). lib. bdg. 18.90 (978-0-7613-2059-3(8)); 32p. (J). (gr. 2-4). pap. 4.99 (978-0-7613-2084-5(9)) Lerner Publishing Group. (Millbrook Pr.).

—Molly in the Middle. 1999. (J). (978-0-606-19161-6(5)); lib. bdg. 13.00 (978-0-613-16764-2(3)) Tandem Library Bks.

Mortenson, R. K. Landon Snow & the Auctors Kingdom # 5. 2007. (Landon Snow Ser.). 224p. (J). 9.97 ***(978-1-59789-297-1(1))*** Barbour Publishing, Inc.

Mortenson, Randall Kent. Landon Snow & the Island of Arcanum. 2006. 224p. (J). 9.97 (978-1-59789-358-9(7) , Barbour Bks.) Barbour Publishing, Inc.

Moss, Marissa. Amelia Hits the Road. 1999. (Amelia's Notebooks). (J). (gr. 3-5). 12.75 (978-0-606-19867-7(9)) Tandem Library Bks.

—Amelia's 6th Grade Notebook. Moss, Marissa, illus. 2005. (Amelia's Notebooks). (Illus.). 80p. (J). (gr. k-8). 9.95 (978-0-689-87040-8(X) , Simon & Schuster Children's Publishing) Simon & Schuster Children's Publishing.

—Amelia's Are-We-There-yet Longest Ever Car Trip. Moss, Marissa, illus. 2006. (Amelia's Notebooks). (Illus.). 40p. (J). 9.95 (978-1-4169-0906-4(0) , Simon & Schuster/ Paula Wiseman Bks.) Simon & Schuster Children's Publishing.

—Amelia's Longest, Biggest, Most-Fights-Ever Family Reunion. Moss, Marissa, illus. 2006. (Amelia's Notebooks). (Illus.). 80p. (J). 9.95 (978-0-689-87447-5(2) , Simon & Schuster Children's Publishing) Simon & Schuster Children's Publishing.

—Amelia's Most Unforgettable Embarrassing Moments. Moss, Marissa, illus. 2005. (Amelia's Notebooks). (Illus.). 80p. (J). 9.95 (978-0-689-87041-5(8) , Simon & Schuster Children's Publishing) Simon & Schuster Children's Publishing.

—Amelia's Notebook. Moss, Marissa, illus. 2006. (Amelia's Notebooks). (Illus.). 40p. (J). 9.95 (978-1-4169-0905-7(2)) Simon & Schuster Children's Publishing.

—Amelia's Notebook. Moss, Marissa, illus. 2006. (Amelia's Notebooks). (J). 5.99 (978-1-4169-1286-6(X)) Simon & Schuster, Inc.

—Amelia's Notebook. 1999. (Amelia's Notebooks). (Illus.). (J). (gr. 3-5). 12.75 (978-0-606-18353-6(1)) Tandem Library Bks.

—Oh Boy, Amelia! 2001. (Amelia's Notebooks). (Illus.). (J). (978-0-606-21365-3(1)) Tandem Library Bks.

Mulford, Philippa Greene. The Holly Sisters on Their Own. 1998. (Accelerated Reader Bks.). 160p. (J). (gr. 5-9). lib. bdg. 14.95 (978-0-7614-5022-1(X) , Cavendish Children's Bks.) Cavendish, Marshall Corp.

Murphy, Barbara. Life! How I Love You! Baca, Elena, illus. 2004. (Museo Kids Ser.). 1p. 16.95 (978-0-89013-468-9(5)) Museum of New Mexico Pr.

Murphy, Claire Rudolf. Gold Star Sister. 2000. 176p. (YA). (gr. 5-11). pap. 6.99 (978-0-9704437-0-0(6)) North Star Publishing.

My Sister & I. 2003. (Illus.). 24p. (J). (ps-k). bds. 7.95 (978-0-8249-5456-7(4)) Ideals Pubns.

My Sister Jess: Set C Individual Title Six-Packs. (gr. k-3). 29.00 (978-0-7635-0546-2(3)) Rigby Education.

Na, An. Wait for Me. 2007. 192p. (YA). (gr. 7 up). 7.99 ***(978-0-14-240918-3(9)*** , Puffin) Penguin Group (USA) Inc.

Naylor, Phyllis Reynolds. The Boys Return. 2003. (gr. 3-6). lib. bdg. 13.00 (978-0-613-88332-0(2)) Tandem Library Bks.

—The Boys Start the War. 2002. (gr. 3-6). lib. bdg. 13.00 (978-0-613-86229-5(5)) Tandem Library Bks.

—The Girls Get Even. 2002. (gr. 3-6). lib. bdg. 13.00 (978-0-613-37145-2(3)) Tandem Library Bks.

—Girls Rule! 2004. 160p. (gr. 4-7). 15.95 (978-0-385-73139-3(6) , Delacorte Bks. for Young Readers) Random Hse. Children's Bks.

—The Girls Take Over. 2004. 160p. (gr. 4-7). pap. 5.99 (978-0-440-41678-4(7) , Yearling) Random Hse. Children's Bks.

—The Girls Take Over. l.t. ed. 2004. (Boys Girl Battle Ser.). 170p. (J). 22.95 (978-0-7862-5823-9(3)) Thorndike Pr.

—A Spy among the Girls. 2002. (gr. 3-6). lib. bdg. 13.00 (978-0-613-88330-6(6)) Tandem Library Bks.

—A Traitor among the Boys. 2001. (Boy/Girl Battle Ser.). 128p. (J). (gr. 3-7). pap. 5.50 (978-0-440-41386-8(9) , Random Hse. Bks. for Young Readers) Random Hse. Children's Bks.

—A Traitor among the Boys. 2001. (gr. 3-6). lib. bdg. 13.00 (978-0-613-33733-5(6)) Tandem Library Bks.

—Who Won the War? 2006. 160p. (J). (gr. 4-7). 15.95 (978-0-385-73141-6(8)); lib. bdg. 17.99 (978-0-385-90172-7(0)) Random Hse. Children's Bks. (Delacorte Bks. for Young Readers).

—Witch's Sister. 2002. 160p. (J). pap. 4.99 (978-0-689-85315-9(7) , Aladdin) Simon & Schuster Children's Publishing.

—Witch's Sister. 2002. (gr. 3-6). lib. bdg. 13.00 (978-0-613-90184-0(3)) Tandem Library Bks.

Neasi, Barbara J. Como Yo. 2002. Tr. of Just Like Me. (gr. k-3). lib. bdg. 12.95 (978-0-613-59462-2(2)) Tandem Library Bks.

—Just Like Me. Hantel, Johanna, illus. rev. ed. 2003. (Rookie Reader Espanol Ser.). 32p. (J). (gr. k-2). pap. 4.95 (978-0-516-27495-9(3) , Children's Pr.) Scholastic Library Publishing.

—Just Like Me. rev. ed. 2002. (Rookie Readers Ser.). (J). lib. bdg. 19.00 (978-0-516-22564-7(2) , Children's Pr.) Scholastic Library Publishing.

—Just Like Me. Hantel, Johanna, illus. rev. ed. 2002. (Rookie Readers Ser.). 31p. (J). (gr. 1-2). 19.50 (978-0-516-22669-9(X) , Children's Pr.) Scholastic Library Publishing.

—Just Like Me. rev. ed. 2002. (ps-2). lib. bdg. 12.95 (978-0-613-59651-0(X)) Tandem Library Bks.

Nesbit, E. In Homespun. 2006. pap. ***(978-1-4068-3502-1(1))*** Echo Library.

Noel, Alyson. Saving Zoe: A Novel. 2007. 240p. (YA). (gr. 8 up). pap. 8.95 ***(978-0-312-35510-4(6)*** , St. Martin's Griffin) St. Martin's Pr.

Noland, Charles. The Adventures of Drew & Ellie: The Magical Dress. Baker, Sherri, illus. 2006. (J). (978-0-9789297-1-8(3)); 2nd rev. ed. per. 7.95 (978-0-9789297-0-1(5)) TMD Enterprises.

Nolen, Jerdine. Pitching in for Eubie. Lewis, E. B., illus. 2007. 32p. (J). lib. bdg. 17.89 ***(978-0-06-056960-0(3));*** 16.99 ***(978-0-688-14917-8(0))*** HarperCollins Pubs. (Amistad).

Norling, Beth. Sister Night & Sister Day. Norling, Beth, illus. 2001. (Illus.). 32p. (J). (ps). 14.95 (978-1-86448-863-0(8)) Allen & Unwin AUS. *Dist:* Independent Pubs. Group.

Nostlinger, Christine. Por Favor, Vuelve a Casa (Please, Come Back Home) (SPA.). 176p. (YA). (gr. 7-9). 9.95 (978-958-04-2379-9(2) , 10266266) Norma S.A. COL. *Dist:* Distribuidora Norma, Inc.

Numeroff, Laura Joffe. The Chicken Sisters. Collicott, Sharleen, illus. 2002. 28.95 incl. audio compact disk (978-1-59112-533-4(2)); pap. 39.95 incl. audio compact disk (978-1-59112-532-7(4)) Live Oak Media.

—What Sisters Do Best: What Brothers Do Best. Munsinger, Lynn, illus. 2003. (J). 15.00 (978-0-689-82937-6(X) , Simon & Schuster Children's Publishing) Simon & Schuster Children's Publishing.

Nusom, Jacqueline. My Little Sister & Me. 2006. 12p. (J). 8.47 (978-1-4116-7352-6(2)) Lulu.com.

Nyikos, Stacy. Dragon Wishes. 2008. (J). 16.95 ***(978-1-933831-11-4(1))*** Blooming Tree Pr.

Oaks, Tina. Sister Trap Stepsisters, No. 2. 2003. (J). pap. 2.50 (978-0-590-40903-2(4)) Scholastic, Inc.

O'Brien, May. The Legend of the Seven Sisters. 1999. (Illus.). 29p. (J). pap. 16.50 (978-0-85575-216-3(5)) Aboriginal Studies Pr. AUS. *Dist:* International Specialized Bk. Services.

Olaizola, José Luis. Mi Hermana Gabriela. Alonso Díaz-Toledo, Juan Ramon, illus. (SPA.). 120p. (YA). (gr. 5-8). (978-84-207-3065-3(3) , GS4005) Grupo Anaya, S.A. ESP. *Dist:* Lectorum Pubns., Inc.

Olsen, Ashley. Dream Date Debate. 2003. (gr. 5-8). lib. bdg. 13.00 (978-0-613-64706-9(8)) Tandem Library Bks.

—Dream Team. 2002. (gr. k-3). lib. bdg. 12.40 (978-0-613-64707-6(6)) Tandem Library Bks.

—Getting There. 2002. (gr. 5-8). lib. bdg. 13.00 (978-0-613-64720-5(3)) Tandem Library Bks.

Olsen, Mary-Kate. My Best Friend's Boyfriend. 2002. (gr. 5-8). lib. bdg. 13.00 (978-0-613-64749-6(1)) Tandem Library Bks.

—Too Good to Be True. 2002. (gr. 5-8). lib. bdg. 13.00 (978-0-613-64774-8(2)) Tandem Library Bks.

Olsen, Mary-Kate & Olsen, Ashley. The Case of the Icy Igloo Inn. 2002. (Illus.). (J). pap. 18.00 (978-0-06-052114-1(7) , Harper Entertainment) HarperCollins Pubs.

—Forget Me Not, Set. 2002. (J). pap. 19.96 (978-0-06-052112-7(0) , Harper Entertainment) HarperCollins Pubs.

S

—Holiday Magic. Innelli, ed. 2004. (Two of a Kind Ser.: No. 38). (Illus.). 112p. 4.99 (978-0-06-059590-6(6) , Harper Entertainment) HarperCollins Pubs.

—Starring You & Me. 2002. (Mary-Kate & Ashley Sweet 16 Ser.: No. 5). (Illus.). 128p. 4.99 (978-0-06-052811-9(7) , Harper Entertainment) HarperCollins Pubs.

Orante, Ann-Jeanette P. Best Sisters for Life... 2007. (ENG., Illus.). 36p. (J). per. 11.95 (***978-1-59800-972-9(9)***) Outskirts Press, Inc.

Orgel, Doris. Sarah's Room. Sendak, Maurice, illus. 2005. 47p. (J). (gr. k-4). reprint ed. 15.00 (978-0-7567-9683-9(0)) DIANE Publishing Co.

Ormerod, Jan. Ballet Sisters No. 1: The Duckling & the Swan. 2007. (Scholastic Reader Ser.). 32p. (J). (gr. k-2). pap. 5.99 (978-0-439-82281-7(5)) Scholastic, Inc.

Ormerod, Jan. The Newest Dancer. 2008. (Ballet Sisters Ser.: No. 2). 32p. (J). pap. 5.99 (***978-0-439-82282-4(3)***) Scholastic, Inc.

Ostow, Micol & Burge, Constance M. Changeling Places: An Original Novel. 2005. 152p. (J). (978-1-4155-8183-4(5) , Simon Spotlight) Simon & Schuster Children's Publishing.

Otten, Charlotte. Home in a Wilderness Fort: Copper Harbor 1844. 2006. (J). pap. 14.95 (978-0-9766104-5-8(0)) Arbutus Pr.

Owens, Vivian W. I Met a Great Lady: Ivy Meets Mary McLeod Bethune. Maxwell, Carolyn, ed. Watson, Richard J., illus. unabr. ed. 1998. 80p. (J). (gr. 4-11). pap. 8.95 (978-0-9623839-5-3(3)) Eschar Pubns.

Pagliarulo, Antonio. The Celebutantes: In the Club. 2008. (YA). (***978-0-385-73473-8(5)***); 12.99 (***978-0-385-90472-8(X)***) Dell Publishing. (Delacorte Pr.).

Pagliarulo, Antonio. On the Avenue. 2007. (Celebutantes Ser.). 352p. (YA). (gr. 9 up). pap. 9.99 (978-0-385-73404-2(2)); lib. bdg. 12.99 (978-0-385-90415-5(0)) Random Hse. Children's Bks. (Delacorte Bks. for Young Readers).

Pagratis, Maggie. My Sister the Bee. 2004. 29p. (J). per. 11.38 (978-1-4116-1098-9(9)) Lulu.com.

The Paper Pup. 2004. 39p. pap. 17.95 (978-1-4137-3012-8(4)) PublishAmerica, Inc.

Pascal, Francine. One 2 Many. 1999. (Sweet Valley Jr. High Ser.: No. 27). (gr. 3-6). lib. bdg. 12.40 (978-0-613-16173-2(4)) Tandem Library Bks.

Paterson, Katherine. Jacob Have I Loved. l.t. ed. 2000. (LRS Large Print Cornerstone Ser.). 266p. (J). (gr. 5-12). lib. bdg. 29.95 (978-1-58118-073-2(X) , 23658) LRS.

Patz, Nancy & Roth, Susan L. Babies Can't Eat Kimchee! Patz, Nancy & Roth, Susan L., illus. 2006. (Illus.). 32p. (J). (ps-2). 16.95 (978-1-59990-017-9(3)) Bloomsbury Publishing.

Paul, Dominique. The Possibility of Fireflies. 224p. 2007. (YA). pap. 8.99 (***978-1-4169-1311-5(4)***, Simon Pulse); 2006. (J). 15.95 (978-1-4169-1310-8(6)) Simon & Schuster Children's Publishing.

Paulits, John. Philip & the Case of the Mistaken Identity & Philip & the Baby. 2007. (YA). pap. 7.50 (***978-1-59705-109-5(8)***); pap. 13.95 (***978-1-59705-897-1(1)***) Wings ePress, Inc.

Pearson, Mary E. Generous Me. Krejca, Gary, illus. (Rookie Reader Espanol Ser.). (J). 2003. 32p. (gr. k-2). pap. 4.95 (978-0-516-27819-3(3)); 2002. 31p. (gr. 1-2). 19.50 (978-0-516-22253-0(8)) Scholastic Library Publishing. (Children's Pr.).

—Generous Me. 2002. (gr. k-3). lib. bdg. 12.95 (978-0-613-59484-4(3)) Tandem Library Bks.

Perrault, Charles. Las Hadas. Trias, Margarida, tr. Dumas, Philippe, illus. 2002. (SPA.). 52p. (978-84-8470-058-6(5)) Corimbo, Editorial S.L.

Perry, Carol. One Sister Too Many. 1998. 144p. (J). (gr. 5-8). reprint ed. pap. 3.99 (978-0-87406-903-7(3) , Willowisp Pr.) Darby Creek Publishing.

Pershall, Mary K. Chomps: The Little Sister Makeover: Can Alex De-Geek Her Sister? 2nd rev. ed. 2008. (Nibbles, Bites, & Chomps: Ser.). 84p. (J). pap. 3.95 (***978-0-7624-3057-4(5)***, Running Pr. Kids) Running Pr. Bk. Pubs.

Peterson, Jeanne Whitehouse. Don't Forget Winona. Root, Kimberly B., illus. 2004. 32p. (J). (ps-3). lib. bdg. 15.89 (978-0-06-027198-5(1)) HarperCollins Pubs.

Pfeffer, Susan Beth. Ghostly Tales: Four Stories. 2002. (Portraits of Little Women Ser.). (gr. 3-6). lib. bdg. 12.40 (978-0-613-85700-0(3)) Tandem Library Bks.

Pfister, Marcus. El Dragon Marino. 2002. Tr. of Star of the Sea. (SPA.). (gr. k-3). lib. bdg. 11.80 (978-0-613-85242-5(7)) Tandem Library Bks.

—Star of the Sea. 2002. (ps-2). lib. bdg. 11.80 (978-0-613-82618-1(3)) Tandem Library Bks.

Pham, LeUyen. Big Sister, Little Sister. 2005. (Illus.). 40p. (ps-3). 15.99 (978-0-7868-5182-9(1)) Hyperion Bks. for Children.

Plourde, Lynn & Couch, Greg. Spring's Sprung. 2002. (Illus.). 32p. (J). (ps-3). 16.00 (978-0-689-84229-0(5)) Simon & Schuster Children's Publishing.

Powell, Pamela. La Patrulla de las Tortugas. 2003. (SPA., Illus.). 190p. (YA). (gr. 5-8). (978-84-236-3791-1(3) , ED1183) Edebé ESP. *Dist:* Lectorum Pubns., Inc.

Purdy, Betty Jane. Aunt Hattie, Aunt Mattie, & Aunt Pattie. 2005. (ENG., Illus.). 32p. (J). per. (978-1-4141-0365-5(4)) Pleasant Word.

Purtill, C. Leigh. Love, Meg. 2007. 304p. (YA). 16.99 (978-1-59514-116-3(2) , Razorbill) Penguin Group (USA) Inc.

Rainbow Magic Staff & Meadows, Daisy. Ruby the Red Fairy. 2007. (Rainbow Magic Ser.). 80p. (J). pap. 2.99 (***978-0-545-01037-5(3)***) Scholastic, Inc.

Rao, Sirish & Wolf, Gita. Tree Girl. Ramanathan, Rathna, illus. 2003. 64p. 9.99 (978-81-86211-32-8(2)) Penguin Group (USA) Inc.

Raven, Margot Theis. America's White Table. Ellison, Chris, illus. 2005. 32p. (J). 16.95 (978-1-58536-216-5(6)) Sleeping Bear Pr.

Reader's Digest Editors. Barbie & the Twelve Dancing Princess. 2006. 12p. (J). bds. 9.99 (978-0-7944-1108-4(8)) Reader's Digest Assn., Inc., The.

Reader's Digest Staff. Barbie & the Twelve Dancing Princess Panorama Sticker Storybook. 2006. (Barbie Movie Tie-in Ser.). 16p. (J). 7.99 (978-0-7944-1109-1(6)) Reader's Digest Assn., Inc., The.

Redmond, Zelie. The Adventures of Sister Regina Marie: Sister Finds a Friend. Redmond, Zelie, . 2005. (J). per. 6.95 (978-0-9774345-0-3(8)) Joy of my Youth Pubns., The.

Rees, Celia. Host Rides Out. 2002. (gr. 3-6). lib. bdg. 16.40 (978-0-613-71842-4(9)) Tandem Library Bks.

Reiss, Kathryn. Paperquake: A Puzzle. 2002. (gr. 5-8). lib. bdg. 14.15 (978-0-613-53851-0(X)) Tandem Library Bks.

Renninson, Lou. Frontalknutschen. pap. 17.95 (978-3-570-30008-4(0)) Bertelsman, Verlagsgruppe C. GmbH DEU. *Dist:* Distribooks, Inc.

Richardson, Regina. Maggie's Treasured Stone. 2006. (ENG.). 36p. per. 19.99 (***978-1-4259-3095-0(6)***) AuthorHouse.

Rivers, Camilla Reghelini. Off the Wall. 2001. (Sports Stories Ser.). 128p. (gr. 3-8). (J). (***978-1-55028-751-6(6)***); 7.95 (978-1-55028-750-9(8)) Lorimer, James & Co., Ltd., Pubs. CAN. *Dist:* Casemate Pubs. & Bk. Distributors, LLC.

Rizzo, Cynthia. Julie & the Unicorn 2. 2004. 55p. pap. 12.95 (978-1-4137-4841-3(4)) PublishAmerica, Inc.

Rizzo, Cynthia Marie. Angela & the Princess. 2006. 89p. pap. 14.95 (978-1-4241-2599-9(5)) PublishAmerica, Inc.

Roberts, Willo Davis. The One Left Behind. (J). 2007. 139p. (gr. 3-7). per. 5.99 (978-0-689-85083-7(2)); 2006. (Illus.). 144p. 16.95 (978-0-689-85075-2(1) , Atheneum) Simon & Schuster Children's Publishing.

Rocklin, Joanne & Burns, Marilyn. Not Enough Room! Ong, Cristina et al, illus. 1998. (Hello Reader! Math Ser.). 32p. (J). (gr. k-2). pap. 3.99 (978-0-590-39962-3(4)) Scholastic, Inc.

Rodda, Emily. The Sister of the South. McBride, Marc, illus. 2005. (Deltora Ser.: Vol. 4). 224p. (J). pap. 4.99 (978-0-439-63376-5(1) , Scholastic Paperbacks) Scholastic, Inc.

Rodriguez, Lauren. Finding Her Courage. 2005. 170p. pap. 19.95 (978-1-4137-7131-2(9)) PublishAmerica, Inc.

Roorda, Julie. Wings of a Bee: A Young Adult Novel. 2007. (Illus.). 232p. pap. 9.95 (***978-1-894549-68-4(6)***) Sumach Pr. CAN. *Dist:* Univ. of Toronto Pr.

Rothberg, Abraham. Pinocchio's Sister: A Feminist Fable. 2005. 159p. pap. 11.95 (978-1-4116-4347-5(X)) Lulu.com.

Rowe, Jamie. Moon Flower. 2002. 38p. pap. 9.95 (978-1-59129-835-9(0)) PublishAmerica, Inc.

Rowen, Amy. April's Trust. 2002. 160p. pap. 13.95 (978-0-595-22373-2(7) , Writers Club Pr.) iUniverse, Inc.

Rubel, Nicole. It's Hot & Cold in Miami. 2006. (Illus.). 208p. (J). 17.00 (978-0-374-33611-0(3)) Farrar, Straus & Giroux.

Ruditis, Paul & Burge, Constance M. As Puck Would Have It. 2006. (Charmed Ser.). 240p. (YA). pap. 6.99 (978-1-4169-1468-6(4) , Simon Spotlight Entertainment) Simon & Schuster.

Rushton, Rosie. The Dashwood Sisters' Secrets of Love. 2005. 336p. (gr. 7-17). 15.99 (978-0-7868-5136-2(8)) Hyperion Bks. for Children.

—The Dashwood Sisters' Secrets of Love. 2006. 336p. (gr. 7-17). reprint ed. pap. 8.99 (978-0-7868-5137-9(6)) Hyperion Pr.

Russo, Marisabina. Hannah's Baby Sister. Russo, Marisabina, illus. 1998. (Illus.). 32p. (J). (ps-3). 15.00 (978-0-688-15831-6(5)) HarperCollins Pubs.

Salerni, Dianne K. High Spirits: A Tale of Ghostly Rapping & Romance. 2007. 368p. per. 20.95 (***978-0-595-42350-7(7)***) iUniverse, Inc.

Salisbury, Linda G. No Sisters Sisters Club: A Bailey Fish Adventure. Grotke, Christopher A., illus. 2005. 188p. (J). per. 8.95 (978-0-881539-40-7(7)) Tabby Hse. Bks.

Samuels, Barbara. Dolores on Her Toes. Samuels, Barbara, illus. 2003. (Dolores Ser.). (Illus.). 40p. (J). 16.50 (978-0-374-31818-5(2) , Farrar, Straus & Giroux (BYR)) Farrar, Straus & Giroux.

—Happy Valentine's Day, Dolores. 2005. (Dolores Ser.). (Illus.). 32p. (J). 16.00 (978-0-374-32844-3(7) , Melanie Kroupa Bks.) Farrar, Straus & Giroux.

Santillo, LuAnn. Jane. Santillo, LuAnn, ed. 2003. (Half-Pint Kids Readers Ser.). (Illus.). 7p. (J). (ps-1). pap. (978-1-59256-099-8(7)) Half-Pint Kids, Inc.

Sasman, Irene D. H. Cinderella Around the World Children's Library, Set. 1998. (Illus.). (J). (ps-4). pap. 89.95 (978-1-56831-380-1(2)) Learning Connection, The.

Scholastic, Inc. Staff & Black, Sonia. Just for You! Jumping the Broom. 2004. (Just for You! Ser.). (Illus.). 32p. pap. 3.99 (978-0-439-56878-4(1) , Teaching Resources) Scholastic, Inc.

Scholastic, Inc. Staff & Daugherty, George. Princess Sheegwa. Schields, Gretchen, illus. 2002. (Sagwa, the Chinese Siamese Cat Ser.: No. 2). 32p. (J). pap. 3.99 (978-0-439-42880-4(7)) Scholastic, Inc.

Schwabach, Karen. The Hope Chest. 2008. 288p. (J). (gr. 4-7). 16.99 (***978-0-375-84095-1(8)***); lib. bdg. 19.99 (***978-0-375-94095-8(2)***) Random Hse., Inc.

Schwartz, Amy. Annabelle Swift, Kindergartner. Schwartz, Amy, illus. 2002. (Illus.). (J). 14.74 (978-0-7587-1954-6(X)) Book Wholesalers, Inc.

—Annabelle Swift, Kindergartner. 2000. (J). pap. 19.97 incl. audio (978-0-7366-9198-7(7)) Books on Tape, Inc.

Schwartz, Amy & Kaye, Randye. Annabelle Swift, Kindergartner. 2004. (Live Oak Readalong Ser.). (Illus.). (J). pap. 18.95 incl. audio compact disk (978-1-59112-687-4(8)) Live Oak Media.

Schwartz, Roslyn. Mole Sisters & the Fairy Ring. 2003. (ps-2). lib. bdg. 12.95 (978-0-613-78408-5(1)) Tandem Library Bks.

—The Mole Sisters & the Rainy Day. Schwartz, Roslyn, illus. 2001. (Mole Sisters Ser.). (Illus.). 32p. (J). (ps-k). lib. bdg. 14.95 (978-1-55037-611-1(X)) Annick Pr., Ltd. CAN. *Dist:* Firefly Bks., Ltd.

—Mole Sisters & the Rainy Day. 2001. (ps-2). lib. bdg. 12.95 (978-0-613-78347-7(6)) Tandem Library Bks.

Seewald, Jacqueline. Clair's Curse. 2004. 228p. (YA). per. 22.00 (978-1-58982-191-0(2) , Bedside Bks.) American Bk. Publishing Group.

Shaik, Fatima. Melitte. 2000. (978-0-606-18432-8(5)) Tandem Library Bks.

Shaw, Janet Beeler. Kaya Shows the Way. 2002. (gr. 3-6). lib. bdg. 14.10 (978-0-613-46222-8(X)) Tandem Library Bks.

—Kaya Shows the Way Bk. 5: A Sister Story. Farnsworth, Bill & McAliley, Susan, illus. 2002. (American Girls Collection: Bk. 5). 88p. (J). (gr. 2-7). 12.95 (978-1-58485-432-6(4)) American Girl Publishing, Inc.

Sheila Rae, the Brave. 2003. (Illus.). (J). (ps-2). 18.95 (978-1-59112-326-2(7)) Live Oak Media.

Shu, Sammy. There's a Season for All. Cone, Carl, illus. 2006. 54p. (J). per. 16.95 (978-0-9778211-0-5(2) , Raynestorm Bks.) Silver Rose Publishing.

Siegel, Bernie S. Smudge Bunny. Bryant, Laura J., illus. 2004. 32p. 15.95 (978-1-932073-03-4(5)) Kramer, H.J. Inc.

Simon, Charnan. The Sillies. Petelinsek, Kathleen, illus. 2006. (Magic Door to Learning Ser.). 24p. (J). 21.36 (978-1-59296-627-1(6)) Child's World, Inc.

Simpson, Carolie. Allie Applebee — Can't Wait for Eight. 2003. 40p. pap. 9.95 (978-1-4137-0104-3(3)) PublishAmerica, Inc.

Smallcomb, Pam. Trimoni Twins & the Changing Coin. 2004. 175p. (J). 15.95 (978-1-58234-939-8(8) , Bloomsbury Children) Bloomsbury Publishing.

Smith, Jane Denitz. Mary by Myself. 1999. (J). (978-0-606-16701-7(3)) Tandem Library Bks.

Smith, Sherwood. The Emerald Wand of Oz. Stout, William, illus. 2007. 262p. (J). 17.00 (***978-1-4223-6710-0(X)***) DIANE Publishing Co.

Smothers, Ethel Footman. Moriah's Pond. 2004. 96p. (J). pap. 7.00 (978-0-8028-5249-6(1)) Eerdmans, William B. Publishing Co.

—Moriah's Pond. 2003. (gr. 3-6). lib. bdg. 15.30 (978-0-613-67247-4(X)) Tandem Library Bks.

Spangler, Paula Jeanne. Abigail's Christmas ~ Christmas Morn Reveals A Newborn. 2004. 17p. (J). pap. 14.08 (978-1-4116-1045-3(8)) Lulu.com.

Spirn, Michele Sobel. The Bridges in Edinburgh. 2004. (Going to Ser.). 144p. pap. 6.95 (978-1-893577-11-4(2)) Four Corners Publishing Co., Inc.

—The Bridges in Paris. 2000. (Going to Ser.). (Illus.). 121p. (J). (gr. 4-8). pap. 6.95 (978-1-893577-04-6(X)) Four Corners Publishing Co., Inc.

Steck-Vaughn Staff. My Sister Is My Friend. 1999. (Illus.). pap. (978-0-8172-8723-8(X)) Steck-Vaughn.

—Special Friends: My Dog/Sister. 1998. (Illus.). (J). pap. (978-0-8172-8645-3(4)) Steck-Vaughn.

Stein, Meg. My Baby Sister. 1999. (ps-2). lib. bdg. 11.55 (978-0-613-30617-1(1)) Tandem Library Bks.

Stem, Jacqueline. Mystery of the Whispering Walls. 2004. (J). 148p. pap. (978-1-57168-844-6(7)); (Hollow Tree Mystery Ser.: Bk. 6). (Illus.). v, 142p. (978-1-57168-850-7(1) , Eakin Pr.) Eakin Pr.

Stilton, Geronimo. Shipwreck on the Pirate Islands. 2005. (Geronimo Stilton Ser.: No. 18). (Illus.). 128p. (J). 5.99 (978-0-439-69141-3(9) , Scholastic Paperbacks) Scholastic, Inc.

Stine, R. L. Dangerous Girls. 2003. (J). 256p. 111.92 (978-0-06-056909-9(3)); 256p. 111.92 (978-0-06-056910-5(7)); (Illus.). (gr. 7 up). 13.99 (978-0-06-053080-8(4)) HarperCollins Pubs.

Strickland, Brad. Mutiny. 2002. (gr. 3-6). lib. bdg. 13.00 (978-0-613-57578-2(4)) Tandem Library Bks.

—No-Rules Weekend! 2001. (gr. 3-6). lib. bdg. 11.80 (978-0-613-85082-7(3)) Tandem Library Bks.

Suarez, Natalie. Aieres' Mirror Bk. One: Finding Shelter. 2002. 120p. (YA). pap. 10.95 (978-0-595-24268-9(5) , Writers Club Pr.) iUniverse, Inc.

Sumner, Bea. Sisters Three: Scary's Not a Part of Me. 2007. (J). pap. (***978-0-9787375-0-4(4)***) Sisters Three Publishing Inc.

Swicord, Robin. Little Women: The Children's Picture Book. 2004. (Illus.). 96p. (gr. 2 up). 15.95 (978-1-55704-216-3(0)) Newmarket Pr.

Tada, Joni Eareckson. Mission Adventure. 2001. (gr. 3-6). lib. bdg. 14.15 (978-0-613-89086-1(8)) Tandem Library Bks.

Tada, Joni Eareckson & Jensen, Steve. The Mission Adventure. 2005. (Darcy & Friends Ser.). 143p. (gr. 3-6). pap. 5.99 (978-1-58134-257-4(8) , Crossway Bibles) Crossway Bks.

T'choupi a une Petite Soeur. 2000. (FRE.). (J). (978-2-09-202034-0(X)) Nathan, Fernand FRA. *Dist:* Distribooks, Inc.

Tetro, Marc. A Barbecue for Charlotte. 1999. (Illus.). 32p. 19.95 (978-1-55278-112-8(7)) McArthur & Co. CAN. *Dist:* National Bk. Network.

Thorpe, Kiki. Lilo & Stitch: The Junior Novelization. 2002. (ps-2). lib. bdg. 13.00 (978-0-613-50630-4(8)) Tandem Library Bks.

Tiernan, Cate. A Necklace of Water, Vol. 4. 2006. (Balefire Ser.). 240p. (YA). (gr. 7-12). mass mkt. 5.99 (978-1-59514-048-7(4) , Razorbill) Penguin Group (USA) Inc.

Tinstman, Gretchen. Meet the Silly Sisters. 2006. 28p. (J). per. 12.99 (***978-1-59886-683-4(4)***) Tate Publishing & Enterprises, L.L.C.

Torras, Meri. Mi Hermana Aixa. Valverde, Mikel, illus. (SPA.). 120p. (J). (gr. 3-5). (978-84-246-5915-8(5) , GL6491) La Galera, S.A. Editorial ESP. *Dist:* Lectorum Pubns., Inc.

Toten, Teresa. Game. 2001. (gr. 7-12). lib. bdg. 16.40 (978-0-613-60557-1(8)) Tandem Library Bks.

Tripp, Valerie. Changes for Josefina Bk. 6: A Winter Story. Tibbles, Jean-Paul & McAliley, Susan, illus. 1998. (American Girls Collection: Bk. 6). 80p. (J). (gr. 2 up). 12.95 (978-1-56247-592-5(4)); pap. 6.95 (978-1-56247-591-8(6)) American Girl Publishing, Inc.

—Changes for Josefina Bk. 6: A Winter Story. Tibbles, Jean-Paul, illus. 1998. (American Girls Collection: Bk. 6). (YA). (gr. 2 up). 12.75 (978-0-606-13264-0(3)) Tandem Library Bks.

—Nellie's Promise. 2004. (American Girl Ser.). (Illus.). 96p. (J). 12.95 (978-1-58485-893-5(1)) American Girl Publishing, Inc.

—Nellie's Promise. Andreasen, Dan, illus. 2004. (American Girl Ser.). 96p. (gr. 2 up). pap. 6.95 (978-1-58485-890-4(7)) American Girl Publishing, Inc.

Troulis, Jennifer. Penelope & Priscilla & the Enchanted House of Whispers. 2005. (Illus.). (J). pap. 13.95 (978-0-9768602-0-4(1)) Twin Monkeys Pr.

Tucker, Kathy. The Seven Chinese Sisters. Lin, Grace, illus. 2003. 32p. (J). (gr. k-3). 16.95 (978-0-8075-7309-9(4)) Whitman, Albert & Co.

The Two Sisters: Lap Book. (Pebble Soup Explorations Ser.). (SPA.). 16p. (ps up). 21.00 (978-0-7578-1668-0(1)) Rigby Education.

The Two Sisters: Small Book. (Pebble Soup Explorations Ser.). (SPA.). 16p. (ps up). 5.00 (978-0-7578-1708-3(4)) Rigby Education.

Ugawa, Hiroki. Shrine of the Morning Mist. Ukawa, Hiroki, illus. 2006. (YA). pap. 9.99 (978-1-59816-343-8(4) , Tokyopop Kids) TOKYOPOP, Inc.

Umansky, Kaye. Wilma's Wicked Revenge. unabr. l.t. ed. 2003. (Read-Along Ser.). (gr. 2). 29.95 incl. audio (978-0-7540-6235-6(X) , RAO36, Galaxy Children's Large Print) BBC Audiobooks America.

Underdahl, S. T. The Other Sister. 2007. 264p. (J). (gr. 7 up). pap. 8.95 (978-0-7387-0933-8(6) , Flux) Llewellyn Pubns.

Ure, Jean. Boys Beware. 2005. (Diary Ser.). (Illus.). 192p. (J). pap. 8.99 (***978-0-00-716138-6(7)***) HarperCollins Pubs. Ltd. GBR. *Dist:* Independent Pubs. Group.

Veit, Kimberly Michelle. To Be Thirteen. 2006. 57p. pap. 12.95 (978-1-4241-1392-7(X)) PublishAmerica, Inc.

Viguie, Debbie. Miss O & Friends: Trouble with a Capital O. Brindak, Hermine, illus. 2006. (Miss O & Friends Ser.). 128p. (J). pap. 5.99 (978-0-8230-2946-4(8)) Watson-Guptill Pubns., Inc.

Viorst, Judith. Super-Completely & Totally the Messiest! Glasser, Robin Preiss, illus. 2006. 32p. (J). 15.99 (978-1-4169-4200-9(9) , Atheneum) Simon & Schuster Children's Publishing.

Waboose, Jan Bourdeau. Sky Sisters. Deines, Brian, illus. 2000. 32p. (J). (gr. k-3). (978-1-55074-697-6(9)) Kids Can Pr., Ltd.

—Skysisters. Deines, Brian, illus. 2002. 32p. (J). (gr. k-3). (978-1-55074-699-0(5)) Kids Can Pr., Ltd.

Walker, Nan. Stressbusters. Wummer, Amy, illus. 2006. (Social Studies Connects). 32p. (J). (gr. k-3). pap. 4.99 (978-1-57565-185-9(8)) Kane Pr., The.

Wallace, Barbara Brooks. Can Do, Missy Charlie. 2000. (Illus.). 228p. (YA). (gr. 4-7). pap. 14.95 (978-0-595-09574-2(7) , Backinprint.com) iUniverse, Inc.

Walsh, Marissa. A Field Guide to High School. 2007. 144p. (YA). (gr. 7). lib. bdg. 18.99 (***978-0-385-90427-8(4)***); 15.99 (***978-0-385-73410-3(7)***) Random Hse. Children's Bks. (Delacorte Bks. for Young Readers).

Ward, Dan. Meet the Boomer Sisters. 2006. 131p. pap. 13.95 (978-1-4116-6927-7(4)) Lulu.com.

Warner, Sally. Sister Split. 2001. (gr. 3-6). lib. bdg. 14.10 (978-0-613-85509-9(4)) Tandem Library Bks.

Waters, Fiona, retold by. Faithful Sister. (Illus.). 94p. (J). pap. 10.99 (978-0-7475-4704-4(1)) Bloomsbury Publishing Plc GBR. *Dist:* Trafalgar Square Publishing.

—Sisters with Glass Hearts. 2000. (Illus.). 93p. (J). pap. 10.99 (978-0-7475-4709-9(2)) Bloomsbury Publishing Plc GBR. *Dist:* Independent Pubs. Group.

—Three Princesses: And Other Classic Fairy Tales. 2000. (Illus.). 95p. (J). pap. 10.99 (978-0-7475-4714-3(9)) Bloomsbury Publishing Plc GBR. *Dist:* Independent Pubs. Group.

—Widow & Her Daughters. 2000. (Illus.). 95p. (J). pap. 9.99 (978-0-7475-4719-8(X)) Bloomsbury Publishing Plc GBR. *Dist:* Independent Pubs. Group.

Weber, Lori. Klepto. 2004. (SideStreets Ser.). 160p. (gr. 7-12). 7.95 (978-1-55028-836-0(9)); (***978-1-55028-837-7(7)***) Lorimer, James & Co., Ltd., Pubs. CAN. *Dist:* Casemate Pubs. & Bk. Distributors, LLC.

Welch, Lester. Last Summer. 2004. 12.95 (978-1-930252-96-7(X)) PageFree Publishing, Inc.

Werner, Jane. Cinderella. Worcester, Retta Scott, illus. 2002. (Little Golden Book Ser.). 24p. (J). (gr. k-k). 2.99 (978-0-7364-2151-5(3) , Golden/Disney) Random Hse. Children's Bks.

Wesley, Valerie Wilson. How to (Almost) Ruin Your School Play. Roos, Maryn, illus. 2005. 105p. (J). (978-1-4155-7357-0(3) , Jump at the Sun) Hyperion Bks. for Children.

—How to Almost Ruin Your School Play. 2005. (Illus.). 105p. (J). lib. bdg. 15.00 (***978-1-4242-0645-2(6)***) Fitzgerald Bks.

—How to Lose Your Cookie Money. Roos, Maryn, illus. 2004. 105p. (J). lib. bdg. 15.00 (***978-1-4242-0644-5(8)***) Fitzgerald Bks.

—Willimena, Bk. 2. 2002. 368p. (J). 12.99 (978-0-7868-0466-5(1)) Hyperion Bks. for Children.
—Willimena Rules! Bk. 1: How to Lose Your Class Pet. Roos, Maryn, illus. 2003. 96p. (gr. 2-5). pap. 3.99 (978-0-7868-1322-3(9) , Jump at the Sun) Hyperion Bks. for Children.
Wesley, Valerie Wilson. Willimena Rules!: How to Have the Best Kwanzaa Ever - Book #7. 7th rev. ed. 2007. (Illus.). 96p. (J). (gr. 2-7). pap. 3.99 (***978-1-4231-0037-9(9)*** , Jump at the Sun) Hyperion Bks. for Children.
West, Tracey. Bubblevision. 2001. (gr. k-3). lib. bdg. 11.25 (978-0-613-43799-8(3)) Tandem Library Bks.
Weyn, Suzanne. The Night Dance. 2005. 193p. (YA). (978-1-4156-4311-2(3) , Simon Pulse) Simon & Schuster Children's Publishing.
White, Ruth. Memories of Summer. 2000. 144p. (J). (gr. 7-10). 17.00 (978-0-374-34945-5(2) , Farrar, Straus & Giroux (BYR)) Farrar, Straus & Giroux.
Whybrow, Ian. A Baby for Grace. Birmingham, Christian, illus. 1998. 32p. (J). (gr. k-ps). tchr. ed. 15.95 (978-0-7534-5142-7(5) , Kingfisher) Houghton Mifflin Co. Trade & Reference Div.
—Baby for Grace. 2001. (ps-2). lib. bdg. 19.90 (978-0-613-90362-2(5)) Tandem Library Bks.
Wiebe, Trina. Ants Don't Catch Flying Saucers. Sarrazin, Marisol, illus. 2004. (Abby & Tess Pet-Sitters Ser.: Vol. 5). 96p. (J). pap. 5.95 (978-1-894222-31-0(8)) Lobster Pr. CAN. *Dist:* Univ. of Toronto Pr.
—Ants Don't Catch Flying Saucers. 2001. (gr. 3-6). lib. bdg. 14.10 (978-0-613-62546-3(3)) Tandem Library Bks.
—Goats Don't Brush Their Teeth. Pavanel, Jane, ed. Sarrazin, Marisol, illus. 2004. (Abby & Tess Pet-Sitters Ser.). 96p. (J). (gr. 2-4). pap. 5.95 (978-1-894222-59-4(8)) Lobster Pr. CAN. *Dist:* Univ. of Toronto Pr.
—Goats Don't Brush Their Teeth. 2002. (gr. 3-6). lib. bdg. 14.10 (978-0-613-62554-8(4)) Tandem Library Bks.
Wiggin, Kate Douglas. Rebecca of Sunnybrook Farm. McClintock, Barbara, illus. anniv. ed. 2006. 290p. (J). (gr. 4-8). reprint ed. 22.00 (978-1-4223-5332-5(X)) DIANE Publishing Co.
Wilcox, Mary. Caught on Tape. 2007. (Hollywood Sisters Ser.). 208p. (J). (gr. 5). 7.99 (***978-0-385-73356-4(9)***); lib. bdg. 10.99 (***978-0-385-90371-4(5)***) Random Hse. Children's Bks. (Delacorte Bks. for Young Readers).
—The Hollywood Sisters: Backstage Pass. 2006. 256p. (J). (gr. 5). 7.95 (978-0-385-73354-0(2)); lib. bdg. 9.99 (978-0-385-90369-1(3)) Random Hse. Children's Bks. (Delacorte Bks. for Young Readers).
—On Location. 2007. (Hollywood Sisters Ser.). 240p. (J). (gr. 5). 7.99 (978-0-385-73355-7(0)); lib. bdg. 9.99 (978-0-385-90370-7(7)) Random Hse. Children's Bks. (Delacorte Bks. for Young Readers).
Wilcox, Mary. Truth or Dare. 2008. (J). (***978-0-385-90514-5(9)***); pap. (***978-0-385-73528-5(6)***) Dell Publishing. (Delacorte Pr.).
Wiley, Melissa. Beyond the Heather Hills. Graef, Renee, illus. 2003. (Little House Ser.). 208p. (J). pap. 6.99 (978-0-06-440715-1(2)) HarperCollins Pubs.
—Beyond the Heather Hills. 2003. (gr. 3-6). lib. bdg. 14.15 (978-0-613-62171-7(9)) Tandem Library Bks.
Wilkes, Maria D. Caroline & Her Sister. Ettlinger, Doris, illus. 2000. (Little House Chapter Bks.: No. 2). 80p. (J). (gr. 3-6). 14.89 (978-0-06-028155-7(3)) HarperCollins Pubs.
—Caroline & Her Sister. 2000. (Little House Chapter Bks.: No. 2). (J). (gr. 3-6). 11.05 (978-0-606-20285-5(4)) Tandem Library Bks.
Wilkinson, Dean. The Legend of Arthur King. l.t. ed. 2005. (J). pap. (978-1-4056-6022-8(8)) BBC Audio.
Williams, Vera B. Amber Was Brave, Essie Was Smart: The Story of Amber & Essie, Told Here in Poems & Pictures. Williams, Vera B., illus. 2001. (Illus.). 72p. (J). (gr. 2 up). 15.99 (978-0-06-029460-1(4)) HarperCollins Pubs.
Willis, Wren. Why Is My Name September? 2005. 155p. pap. 11.39 (978-1-4116-6534-7(1)) Lulu.com.
Wilson, Jacqueline. Double Act. Sharrat, Nick & Heap, Sue, illus. 1999. 192p. (gr. 3-7). 5.50 (978-0-440-41374-5(5) , Yearling) Random Hse. Children's Bks.
—The Illustrated Mum. 288p. 2005. (J). (gr. 5). lib. bdg. 17.99 (978-0-385-90263-2(8) , Delacorte Bks. for Young Readers); 2006. (gr. 4-7). reprint ed. 5.50 (978-0-440-42043-9(1) , Yearling) Random Hse. Children's Bks.
Winfrey, Elizabeth. Lets Put on a Show! 2000. (Full House Sisters Ser.: No. 7). 160p. (J). (gr. 4-6). pap. 3.99 (978-0-671-04088-8(X) , Simon Spotlight) Simon & Schuster Children's Publishing.
—Let's Put on a Show. 2000. (gr. 3-6). lib. bdg. 11.80 (978-0-613-27935-2(2)) Tandem Library Bks.
Winston, Sherri. Acting: A Novel. 2004. 256p. (YA). 15.95 (978-0-7614-5173-0(0)) Cavendish, Marshall Corp.
Winter, Jeanette. September Roses. 2004. (Illus.). 40p. (J). 14.00 (978-0-374-36736-7(1) , Farrar, Straus & Giroux (BYR)) Farrar, Straus & Giroux.
Winter, Susan. A Baby Just Like Me. (J). 2002. (TUR & ENG.). 13.95 (978-1-85269-295-7(2)); 2000. (ARA & ENG.). 13.99 (978-1-85269-297-1(9)); 2000. (BEN & ENG.). 13.95 (978-1-85269-248-3(0)); 2000. (CHI.). 13.99 (978-1-85269-259-9(6)); 2000. (GUJ & ENG.). 13.95 (978-1-85269-290-2(1)); 2000. (SOM & ENG.). 19.95 (978-1-85269-292-6(8)); 2000. (URD & ENG.). 13.95 (978-1-85269-296-4(0)) Mantra Publishing, Ltd. GBR. *Dist:* AIMS International Bks., Inc.
Woods, Brenda. The Red Rose Box. Woods, Brenda, illus. 2003. 144p. (J). (gr. 3-7). pap. 5.99 (978-0-14-250151-1(4) , Puffin) Penguin Group (USA) Inc.
—The Red Rose Box. 2002. 160p. (YA). (gr. 4-6). 16.99 (978-0-399-23702-7(X) , Putnam Juvenile) Penguin Group (USA) Inc.
—The Red Rose Box. 2003. (gr. 5-8). lib. bdg. 14.15 (978-0-613-87822-7(1)) Tandem Library Bks.
Woodson, Jacqueline. Lena. 2006. 144p. (YA). (gr. 4). 17.99 (978-0-399-24469-8(7) , Putnam Juvenile); (gr. 5). pap. 5.99 (978-0-14-240616-8(3) , Puffin) Penguin Group (USA) Inc.
—Lena, unabr. ed. 1999. (YA). pap., stu. ed. 42.95 incl. audio (978-0-7887-3646-9(9) , 41012X4) Recorded Bks., LLC.
—Lena. 2000. (978-0-606-17832-7(5)) Tandem Library Bks.
Wright, Betty Ren. The Dollhouse Murders. unabr. ed. 1999. (Illus.). (J). (gr. 4-6). 39.95 incl. audio (978-0-87499-521-3(3)); pap. 30.95 incl. audio (978-0-87499-520-6(5)) Live Oak Media.
—The Dollhouse Murders, Grades 4-6. unabr. ed. 1999. (Illus.). (J). pap., tchr. ed. 41.95 incl. audio (978-0-87499-522-0(1)) Live Oak Media.
YKids Staff. Little Women. 2007. (Manga Literary Classics Ser.). 148p. (J). (gr. 4-7). pap. 14.95 (***978-981-05-4943-5(1)***) Youngjin (Singapore) Pte Ltd. SGP. *Dist:* Independent Pubs. Group.
Yoemans, Ellen. Lost & Found: Remembering a Sister. Johnson, Joy, ed. DeRosa, Dee, illus. 2000. 32p. (J). (gr. k-4). pap. 8.95 (978-1-56123-129-4(0) , LAFC) Centering Corp.
Yokococo. Be Good Girls! 2005. (Illus.). 32p. (J). (gr. k-k). 15.95 (978-0-7696-4434-9(1) , Gingham Dog Pr.) School Specialty Publishing.
Young, Ed. My Mei Mei. Young, Ed, illus. 2006. (Illus.). 40p. (J). (gr. 1). 16.99 (978-0-399-24339-4(9) , Philomel) Penguin Group (USA) Inc.
Zemach, Kaethe & Zemach, Margot, illus. Eating up Gladys. 2005. 32p. (J). (ps-3). pap. 16.99 (978-0-439-66490-5(X) , Levine, Arthur A. Bks.) Scholastic, Inc.
Zemach, Margot & Zemach, Kaethe, illus. Eating up Gladys. 2005. (J). (978-0-439-66491-2(8) , Levine, Arthur A. Bks.) Scholastic, Inc.
Zimmer, Tracie Vaughn. Sketches from a Spy Tree. Glass, Andrew, illus. 2005. 64p. (J). (gr. 4-6). 16.00 (978-0-618-23479-0(9) , Clarion Bks.) Houghton Mifflin Co. Trade & Reference Div.
Zimmerman, Mary Joyce. Just Four. 2005. (Illus.). 32p. (ps-5). 2.70 (978-0-7399-2340-5(4) , 2779) Rod & Staff Pubs., Inc.

SISTERS (IN RELIGIOUS ORDERS, CONGREGATIONS, ETC.)

see Nuns

SITTING BULL, 1831-1890

Abnett, Dan. Sitting Bull & the Battle of the Little Bighorn. 2007. (Jr. Graphic Biographies Ser.). (Illus.). 24p. (J). (978-1-4042-2337-0(1)); pap. (978-1-4042-2147-5(6)); (gr. 2-6). lib. bdg. 21.25 (978-1-4042-3394-2(6)) Rosen Publishing Group, Inc., The. (PowerKids Pr.).
Bruchac, Joseph. A Boy Called Slow: The True Story of Sitting Bull. 1998. (Illus.). 32p. (J). (ps-3). pap. 6.99 (978-0-698-11616-0(X) , Putnam Juvenile) Penguin Group (USA) Inc.
—A Boy Called Slow: The True Story of Sitting Bull. 1998. (J). 13.79 (978-0-606-13223-7(6)) Tandem Library Bks.
Calvert, Patricia. Stand-off at Standing Rock. 2001. (Single Titles Ser.: up). (Illus.). 144p. (gr. 8-12). lib. bdg. (978-0-7613-1360-1(5) , Millbrook Pr.) Lerner Publishing Group.
Collier, James Lincoln. The Sitting Bull You Never Knew. (You Never Knew Ser.). (J). 2004. (gr. 4-6). pap. 6.95 (978-0-516-25836-2(2)); 2003. (Illus.). 80p. 25.50 (978-0-516-24344-3(6)) Scholastic Library Publishing. (Children's Pr.).
Davis, Kenneth C. Don't Know Much about Sitting Bull Sitting Bull, Vol. 2. 2003. (Don't Know Much About Ser.). (Illus.). 144p. (J). (gr. 3-7). 16.89 (978-0-06-028818-1(3)) HarperCollins Pubs.
Evento, Susan. Sitting Bull. 2005. (Rookie Biographies Ser.). (Illus.). 32p. (J). (gr. 1-2). pap. 4.95 (978-0-516-25829-4(X) , Children's Pr.) Scholastic Library Publishing.
Evento, Susan & Vargus, Nanci Reginelli. Sitting Bull. 2004. (Rookie Biographies Ser.). (J). 20.50 (978-0-516-21719-2(4) , Children's Pr.) Scholastic Library Publishing.
Gosda, Randy T. Sitting Bull. 2002. (First Biographies Ser.). (Illus.). 32p. (J). (gr. k-4). lib. bdg. 22.78 (978-1-57765-737-8(3) , Buddy Bks.) ABDO Publishing Co.
Iannone, Catherine. Sitting Bull: Lakota Leader. 1999. (Book Report Biographies Ser.). (Illus.). 112p. (YA). (gr. 6-8). pap. 6.95 (978-0-531-15934-7(5) , Watts, Franklin) Scholastic Library Publishing.
Isaacs, Sally Senzell. America in the Time of Sitting Bull: 1840 to 1890, 2 vols. 1999. (America in the Time of... Ser.). (Illus.). 48p. (gr. 4-7). lib. bdg. (978-1-57572-762-2(5)) Heinemann Library.
Isaacs, Sally Senzell, contrib. by. America in the Time of Sitting Bull: 1840 to 1890. 2000. 48p. (J). (gr. 4-8). pap. 8.50 (978-1-57572-940-4(7)) Heinemann Library.
Jeffrey, Gary & Petty, Kate. Sitting Bull: The Life of a Lakota Sioux Chief. 2005. (Graphic Nonfiction Ser.). (Illus.). 48p. (J). (gr. 4-6). lib. bdg. 26.50 (978-1-4042-0247-4(1)) Rosen Publishing Group, Inc., The.
Marcovitz, Hal. Sitting Bull. 2001. (Famous Figures of the American Frontier Ser.). (Illus.). 64p. (J). (gr. 5 up). pap. 8.95 (978-0-7910-6488-7(3)); 25.00 (978-0-7910-6487-0(5)) Facts On File, Inc. (Chelsea Hse.).
—Sitting Bull. 2001. (Illus.). 64p. (J). (gr. 4-7). lib. bdg. 17.60 (978-0-613-51001-1(1)) Tandem Library Bks.
McLeese, Don. Sitting Bull. 2003. (Native American Legends Ser.). (Illus.). 32p. (J). 28.50 (978-1-58952-730-0(5)) Rourke Publishing, LLC.
Roop, Connie. Sitting Bull. 2002. (gr. 3-6). lib. bdg. 12.40 (978-0-613-50833-9(5)) Tandem Library Bks.
Roop, Connie & Roop, Peter. Sitting Bull. 2002. (In Their Own Words Ser.). (Illus.). 128p. (J). pap. 4.99 (978-0-439-26322-1(0) , Scholastic Reference) Scholastic, Inc.
Rucker, Jeffrey A. La Historia de Toro Sentado. Gonzalez, Tomas, tr. 2002. (Buenas Letras Reading Room Ser.). (SPA., Illus.). 24p. (J). (gr. 4-7). lib. bdg. 18.75 (978-0-8239-6516-8(3) , Buenas Letra) Rosen Publishing Group, Inc., The.
—The Story of Sitting Bull. 2002. (Reading Room Collection). (J). pap. (978-0-8239-8169-4(X)); (Illus.). 24p. lib. bdg. 18.75 (978-0-8239-3732-5(1)) Rosen Publishing Group, Inc., The.
Todd, Anne M. Sitting Bull 1831-1890. 2002. (American Indian Biographies Ser.). (Illus.). 32p. (J). (gr. 3-4). lib. bdg. 23.93 (978-0-7368-1215-3(6) , Blue Earth Bks.) Capstone Pr., Inc.
Trumbauer, Lisa. Sitting Bull. (First Biographies Ser.). 24p. (J). pap. 5.95 (978-0-7368-5088-9(0)) Capstone Pr., Inc.
—Sitting Bull. Saunders-Smith, Gail, ed. 2004. (First Biographies Ser.). (Illus.). 24p. (J). (gr. k-1). lib. bdg. 15.93 (978-0-7368-2371-5(9) , Pebble Bks.) Capstone Pr., Inc.
Turner, Ann Warren. Sitting Bull Remembers. Date not set. 32p. (J). (ps-3). 15.99 (978-0-06-029153-2(2)); pap. 5.99 (978-0-06-443725-7(6)); lib. bdg. 16.89 (978-0-06-029154-9(0)) HarperCollins Pubs.

SIX DAY WAR, 1967

see Israel-Arab War, 1967

SIZE AND SHAPE

see also Mensuration

Accorsi, William. The 10 Color Book. 2007. (Illus.). 14p. bds. 15.95 (***978-0-7611-4739-8(X)***) Workman Publishing Co., Inc.
Ada, Alma Flor. Amigos, Level 3.9. (Libros Para Contar Ser.). (SPA., Illus.). 16p. (J). (gr. k-3). pap. 6.95 (978-1-58105-200-8(6)) Santillana USA Publishing Co., Inc.
—Friends. Escriva, Vivi, illus. (Stories for the Telling Ser.). 16p. (J). (gr. k-3). pap. 6.95 (978-1-58105-234-3(0)) Santillana USA Publishing Co., Inc.
Adler, David A. How Tall, How Short, How Far Away. Tobin, Nancy, illus. 1999. 32p. (J). (gr. k-3). tchr. ed. 16.95 (978-0-8234-1375-1(6)) Holiday Hse., Inc.
Aigner-Clark, Julie. Asomate y Ve Las Figuras. Zaidi, Nadeem, illus. 2004. (Baby Einstein Ser.). (SPA.). 16p. (J). bds. 5.95 (978-970-718-151-9(6) , Silver Dolphin en Español) Advanced Marketing, S. de R. L. de C. V. MEX. *Dist:* Perseus Distribution.
—Baby Einstein: Puzzling Shapes, Spanish-Language Edition. Zaidi, Nadeem, illus. 2005. (Baby Einstein: Libros de Carton Ser.). (SPA.). 12p. (J). bds. 6.95 (978-970-718-303-2(9) , Silver Dolphin en Español) Advanced Marketing, S. de R. L. de C. V. MEX. *Dist:* Perseus Distribution.
—Baby Einstein - Shape Sorted Set. Zaidi, Nadeem, illus. 2006. (Baby Einstein Ser.). 54p. (J). (ps-17). 18.99 (978-1-4231-0000-3(X)) Baby Einstein Co., LLC, The.
—Baby Einstein: Shapes Flip Flap Book. Zaidi, Nadeem, illus. 2006. 12p. (J). (ps-17). bds. 6.99 (978-0-7868-4952-9(5)) Baby Einstein Co., LLC, The.
—Baby Einstein: Wrist Books. Zaidi, Nadeem, illus. 2006. 6p. (J). (ps-17). bds. 7.99 (978-0-7868-4953-6(3)) Baby Einstein Co., LLC, The.
—Puzzling Shapes. Zaidi, Nadeem, illus. 2002. (Baby Einstein Ser.). 12p. (ps-ps). 6.99 (978-0-7868-0844-1(6)) Hyperion Bks. for Children.
—See & Spy Shapes. Zaidi, Nadeem, illus. 2001. (Baby Einstein Ser.). 16p. (J). (ps-ps). 5.99 (978-0-7868-0809-0(8)) Hyperion Bks. for Children.
Alvarez, Lourdes M. Shapes. Brooks, David, illus. 2005. (My First Book Ser.). 9p. (J). (ps-ps). bds. 3.95 (978-1-933050-11-9(X)) Sweetwater Pr.
American Education Publishing Staff. Colors & Shapes. 2003. (Brighter Child Preschool Flash Cards Ser.). (Illus.). 36p. (J). (ps). 2.99 (978-1-56189-460-4(5) , 31044, American Education Publishing) School Specialty Publishing.
Amery, Heather. On the Farm? rev. ed. 2006. 16p. (J). pap. 5.99 (978-0-7945-1288-0(7) , Usborne) EDC Publishing.
Anastasio, Dina. Pre-K: Shapes & Sizes. 2002. (Clifford, the Big Red Dog Ser.: No. 1). (Illus.). 32p. (J). (ps). pap. 2.99 (978-0-439-39849-7(5)) Scholastic, Inc.
Animal Shapes, 6 vols., Pack. (Rigby Focus Ser.). 16p. (gr. 1 up). 30.00 (978-0-7578-5542-9(3)) Rigby Education.
Animal Shapes: Individual Title Six-Packs. (Rigby Focus Ser.). 16p. (gr. 1 up). 28.00 (978-0-7578-5310-4(2)) Rigby Education.
Anness Publishing Staff & Lorenz Editors. Patterns. 2001. (Let's Look at Board Bks.). (Illus.). 12p. 5.00 (978-0-7548-0710-0(X)) Anness Publishing GBR. *Dist:* National Bk. Network.
Arnold, Caroline. Who Is Bigger? Who Is Smaller? Arnold, Caroline, illus. 2004. (Illus.). 18p. (J). bds. 5.95 (978-1-57091-495-9(8)) Charlesbridge Publishing, Inc.
Arps, Melissa. Shapes. 2006. (Illus.). (J). (***978-0-7364-2383-0(4)***) Random Hse., Inc.
Back to the Basics. 2000. (Learning Fun for Little Ones Ser.). (Illus.). 64p. (ps-1). pap. 8.99 (978-0-88724-568-8(4) , CD-6400) Carson-Dellosa Publishing Co., Inc.
Baker, Alan. Brown Rabbit's Shape Book. 1999. (Little Rabbit Bks.). (Illus.). 24p. (J). (gr. k-ps). 3.95 (978-0-7534-5255-4(3) , Kingfisher) Houghton Mifflin Co. Trade & Reference Div.
—Brown Rabbit's Shape Book. 1999. (ps-2). lib. bdg. 11.80 (978-0-613-90018-8(9)) Tandem Library Bks.
Barber, Patti. First Shape Book. Stanley, Mandy, illus. 2002. (First Bks.). 48p. (J). (gr. k-ps). tchr. ed. 12.95 (978-0-7534-5433-6(5) , Kingfisher) Houghton Mifflin Co. Trade & Reference Div.
Beers, Jack. Looking at Shapes. 2000. (Metro Math Readers Yellow Level Ser.). (J). (gr. 1-2). 49.95 (978-1-58830-105-5(2)) Metropolitan Teaching & Learning Co.
Benchmark Education Staff, compiled by. Insects Measure up! & ¡Vamos a medir Insectos! 2005. 52.00 (***978-1-4108-4496-5(X)***) Benchmark Education Co.
—Patterns & Shapes. 2006. spiral bd. 259.00 (***978-1-4108-7049-0(9)***); spiral bd. 249.00 (***978-1-4108-7075-9(8)***); spiral bd. 135.00 (***978-1-4108-7092-6(8)***) Benchmark Education Co.
Bennett, Madeline. The Silliest Shapes & Colors Book in the Wild West. Bennett, Gary, illus. 2001. 32p. (J). (ps-2). 14.95 (978-1-893860-60-5(4)) Arizona Highways.
Berger, Samantha. Big & Little. 1999. (gr. 3-6). lib. bdg. 10.10 (978-0-613-53959-3(1)) Tandem Library Bks.
Berger, Samantha & Chanko, Pamela. Big & Little. 1999. (Learning Center Emergent Readers Ser.). (J). 2.50 (978-0-439-04597-1(5)) Scholastic, Inc.
Big & Little. 2000. (J). 4.95 (978-0-439-15522-9(3)) Scholastic, Inc.
Big or Small? 2006. (Yellow Umbrella Math Ser.). 8,16p. (J). 6.50 (978-0-7368-1692-2(5)) Red Brick Learning.
Bippert, Judy & Vandling, Louise. A-maze-ing Shapes. 2000. (Illus.). (J). (gr. 4-8). 44.00 (978-1-57336-125-5(9) , 2023) Interaction Pubs., Inc.
A Book about Shapes: Jelly Belly. 2006. (Jelly Belly Ser.). 10p. (J). (ps-1). bds. 5.99 (978-0-448-44404-8(6) , Grosset & Dunlap) Penguin Group (USA) Inc.
Book Company Staff. Learn Your Shapes: Bee at the Park. 2005. (Illus.). 22p. (J). (gr. 2-4). bds. 5.95 (978-1-74047-607-0(1)) Book Co. Publishing Pty, Ltd., The AUS. *Dist:* Penton Overseas, Inc.
—My Cuddly Book of Shapes. 2002. (Novelty Bks.). 6p. (J). 12.95 (978-1-74047-253-1(5)) Book Co. Publishing Pty, Ltd., The AUS. *Dist:* Penton Overseas, Inc.
Boothroyd, Jennifer. Combining Shapes. 2007. (First Step Nonfiction Ser.). (J). pap. (978-0-8225-6831-5(4)) Lerner Publishing Group.
—Patterns. 2007. (First Step Nonfiction Ser.). (J). pap. (978-0-8225-6829-2(2)) Lerner Publishing Group.
Brighter Vision Publishing Staff. About Colors, Shapes & Sizes. 2000. (My Discovery Bks.). (Illus.). 20p. (J). (ps). pap. 2.95 (978-1-55254-208-8(4)) Brighter Vision Pubns.
—Color & Shapes. 2000. (Illus.). 32p. (J). (ps). pap. 1.39 (978-1-55254-148-7(7)) Brighter Vision Pubns.
Brooks, Felicity. First Shapes. Litchfield, Jo, illus. 2007. 12p. (J). bds. 14.99 (978-0-7945-1450-1(2) , Usborne) EDC Publishing.
Brown, Lisa. Baby Fix My Car. 2006. 12p. 6.95 (978-1-932416-56-5(0)) McSweeney's Publishing.
Brown, Margery W. Afro-Bets Book of Shapes. Blair, Culverson & Simpson, Howard, illus. 2nd ed. 2004. (Afro-Bets Ser.). 24p. (J). (ps-1). pap. 3.95 (978-0-940975-58-3(0) , Sankofa Bks.) Just Us Bks., Inc.
Bruce, Lisa. Patterns in the Park. 2003. (Raintree Sprouts Ser.). (Illus.). 24p. (J). lib. bdg. 18.56 (978-1-4109-0634-2(5)); pap. 5.50 (978-1-4109-0660-1(4)) Raintree.
—Patterns in the Park. 2003. (ps-2). lib. bdg. 13.55 (978-0-613-78201-2(1)) Tandem Library Bks.
—Shapes at Home. 2003. (Illus.). 24p. (J). pap. 5.50 (978-1-4109-0661-8(2)); lib. bdg. 18.56 (978-1-4109-0635-9(3)) Raintree.
—Shapes at Home. 2003. (ps-2). lib. bdg. 13.55 (978-0-613-78204-3(6)) Tandem Library Bks.
—Sizes at School. 2003. (Raintree Sprouts Ser.). (Illus.). 24p. (J). pap. 5.50 (978-1-4109-0659-5(0)); lib. bdg. 18.56 (978-1-4109-0633-5(7)) Raintree.
—Sizes at School. 2003. (ps-2). lib. bdg. 13.55 (978-0-613-78260-9(7)) Tandem Library Bks.
Bryant-Mole, Karen. Shapes. Mukhida, Zul, photos by. 1999. (Mortimer's Math Ser.). (Illus.). 24p. (J). (ps up). lib. bdg. 22.00 (978-0-8368-2619-7(1)) Stevens, Gareth Inc.
—Size. Mukhida, Zul, photos by. 1999. (Mortimer's Math Ser.). (Illus.). 24p. (J). (ps up). lib. bdg. 22.00 (978-0-8368-2620-3(5)) Stevens, Gareth Inc.
Bryant-Mole, Karen, et al. Sizes. rev. ed. 1999. (First Learning Ser.). (Illus.). 24p. (YA). (ps-3). pap., act. bk. ed. 4.95 (978-0-7460-3585-6(3)) EDC Publishing.
Buck, Joanna. My First Shapes & Colors Book. Church, Caroline Jayne, illus. 1999. (My First Bks.). 16p. (J). (ps-1). 16.95 (978-1-57145-361-7(X) , Silver Dolphin Bks.) Advantage Pubs. Group.
Bullard, Lisa. Long & Short: An Animal Opposites Book. Saunders-Smith, Gail, ed. 2005. (Illus.). 32p. (J). (ps-7). 22.60 (978-0-7368-4275-4(6)) Capstone Pr., Inc.
Bulloch, Ivan. Shapes. 2004. (Action Math Ser.). (SPA., Illus.). 32p. (ps-3). 9.95 (978-1-58728-283-6(6)); (J). pap. 5.95 (978-1-58728-054-2(X)) T&N Children's Publishing. (Two Can Publishing).
Burke, Jennifer S. Ovals. 2000. (gr. k-3). lib. bdg. 12.95 (978-0-613-58795-2(2)) Tandem Library Bks.
—Rectangles. 2000. (Welcome Bks.). (Illus.). 24p. (J). (ps-2). 18.00 (978-0-516-23077-1(8) , Children's Pr.) Scholastic Library Publishing.
—Rectangles. 2000. (gr. k-3). lib. bdg. 12.95 (978-0-613-58796-9(0)) Tandem Library Bks.
—Squares. 2000. (Welcome Bks.). (Illus.). 24p. (J). (ps-2). 18.00 (978-0-516-23078-8(6) , Children's Pr.) Scholastic Library Publishing.
—Squares. 2000. (gr. k-3). lib. bdg. 12.95 (978-0-613-58802-7(9)) Tandem Library Bks.
—Stars. 2000. (Welcome Bks.). (Illus.). 24p. (J). (ps-2). pap. 4.95 (978-0-516-23004-7(2) , Children's Pr.) Scholastic Library Publishing.
—Triangles. 2000. (Welcome Bks.). (Illus.). 24p. (J). (ps-2). 18.00 (978-0-516-23080-1(8) , Children's Pr.) Scholastic Library Publishing.
—Triangles. 2000. (gr. k-3). lib. bdg. 12.95 (978-0-613-58808-9(8)) Tandem Library Bks.

S

Burstein, John. Geometry: Looking Down on Monster Town. 2003. (Weekly Reader Early Learning Library). (Illus.). 24p. (J). (gr. 1 up). pap. 7.93 (978-0-8368-3824-4(6), Weekly Reader Early Learning Library) Stevens, Gareth Inc.

Burton, Margie & French, Tammy, Cathy - Jones. ¿Qué sigue? & What Comes Next? 2005. spiral bd. 66.00 (*978-1-4108-5628-9(3)) Benchmark Education Co.

Burton, Margie, et al. Bigger Than, Smaller Than. Evento, Susan, ed. 1998. (Early Connections Ser.). 16p. (J). (gr. k-2). pap. 4.25 (978-1-892393-38-8(7)) Benchmark Education Co.

—Looking for Patterns. Adams, Alison, ed. 1999. (Early Connections Ser.). 16p. (J). (gr. k-2). pap. 4.50 (978-1-58344-070-4(4)) Benchmark Education Co.

—Looking for Shapes. Adams, Alison, ed. 1999. (Early Connections Ser.). 16p. (J). (gr. k-2). pap. 4.50 (978-1-58344-071-1(2)) Benchmark Education Co.

—Shapes. Evento, Susan, ed. 1998. (Early Connections Ser.). 16p. (J). (gr. k-2). pap. 4.25 (978-1-892393-37-1(9)) Benchmark Education Co.

Butler, Roberta. Making Shapes. Moon, Jo, illus. 2006. 14p. (J). bds. 7.95 (978-1-57791-250-7(0)) Brighter Minds Children's Publishing.

Caillou: Colors & Shapes. 2003. 32p. pap., wbk. ed. 14.95 incl. cd-rom (978-1-57791-029-9(X)) Brighter Minds Children's Publishing.

Canizares, Susan & Berger, Samantha. Building Shapes. 1999. (J). pap. 3.25 (978-0-439-04585-8(1)) Scholastic, Inc.

Canning, Shelagh. Just Be Nice... And Get Ready for Bed. Yee, Josie, illus. 1999. (Super Shape Bks.). 24p. (J). (ps-k). pap. 3.29 (978-0-307-10062-7(6), 10062, Golden Bks.) Random Hse. Children's Bks.

Carle, Eric. My Very First Book of Shapes. Carle, Eric, illus. 2005. (Illus.). 20p. (J). (ps-1). bds. 5.99 (978-0-399-24387-5(9), Philomel) Penguin Group (USA) Inc.

Caroll, Danielle. Tiling with Shapes. 2006. 16p. (J). (gr. k-2). 15.93 (978-0-7368-5857-1(1), Yellow Umbrella Bks.) Capstone Pr., Inc.

Carroll, Danielle. Tiling with Shapes. 2005. (Illus.). 16p. (J). (978-0-7368-5287-6(5)); (978-0-7368-5323-1(5)) Capstone Pr., Inc.

Chappell, Rachel M. Geometry at Every Turn. 2007. (Illus.). 24p. (J). (978-1-59515-974-8(6)) Rourke Publishing, LLC.

Circles. (Shapes Ser.). 32p. (J). 7.95 (978-0-7368-5058-2(9)) Capstone Pr., Inc.

Clements, Andrew. Raggedy Andy's Christmas Shapes Snowden Board Book With Plush. 1998. (J). 4.99 (978-0-689-82365-7(7), Little Simon) Simon & Schuster Children's Publishing.

Color, Cut, Paste, & Trace: Colors & Shapes. (ps-k). 2.99 (978-0-7424-0169-3(3), IF0402) School Specialty Publishing.

Color Patterns, Set B. 2002. (J). (gr. k-2). act. bk. ed. 6.99 (978-1-56451-414-1(5)) School Specialty Publishing.

Colores, Formas y Opuestos. 2007. (Sesame Street Ser.). (SPA & ENG., Illus.). 50p. (J). 2.95 (*978-1-59545-059-3(9)) Learning Horizons, Inc.

Colors & Shapes. 2002. (First Steps Reading Ser.). 24p. (J). pap. 3.95 (978-0-7894-8489-5(7)) Dorling Kindersley Publishing, Inc.

Colors & Shapes. (My First Homework Booklets Ser.). 80p. 2.99 (978-1-56822-761-0(2), IF0311) School Specialty Publishing.

Colors & Shapes. 2007. (Illus.). 10p. bds. 14.95 (*978-1-59125-796-7(4), Penton Kids) Penton Overseas, Inc.

Colors & Shapes Booster. 2005. (J). per. 0.00 (978-1-59441-506-7(4), C04038) Carson-Dellosa Publishing Co., Inc.

Colors & Shapes Fun Wipe-Off Book. 2001. (Illus.). 16p. (J). (gr. k-2). mass mkt. 3.79 (978-1-889319-99-5(6)) Trend Enterprises, Inc.

Connelly, Neil O. Shapes. Thornburgh, Rebecca, illus. 10p. (J). (ps). bds. 3.95 (978-1-58989-002-2(7)) Thurman Hse., LLC.

Cooper, Cathie Hilterbran. Color & Shape Books for All Ages. 2000. (School Library Media Ser.: No. 18). (Illus.). 176p. pap. 42.00 (978-0-8108-3542-9(8)) Scarecrow Pr., Inc.

Counting, Numbers, & Shapes. 2004. (Beastieville Ser.). 198.80 (978-0-516-25145-5(7), Children's Pr.) Scholastic Library Publishing.

Cowder, Pansy. El Juego de las Formas: Metro Math Readers Yellow Level. 2000. (Metro Math Readers Yellow Level Ser.). (SPA.). (J). (gr. 1-2). 3.75 (978-1-58120-476-6(0)) Metropolitan Teaching & Learning Co.

—The Shape Game: Metro Math Readers Yellow Level. 2000. (Metro Math Readers Yellow Level Ser.). (J). (gr. 1-2). 3.75 (978-1-58120-413-1(2)) Metropolitan Teaching & Learning Co.

Coxe, Molly. 6 Sticks. 1999. (978-0-606-16889-2(3)) Tandem Library Bks.

Crowther, Robert. Shapes. Crowther, Robert, illus. 2002. (Illus.). 14p. (J). (ps-2). 12.99 (978-0-7636-1889-6(6)) Candlewick Pr.

Dalmatian Press Staff. Colors & Shapes. 2003. (Tools Ser.). (Illus.). 32p. (J). (ps up). pap. 2.29 (978-1-57759-191-7(7)) Dalmatian Pr.

—Little Builder: Board Book Set, 4 bks., Set. 2003. (Illus.). 10p. (J). bds. 7.99 (978-1-57759-714-8(1)) Dalmatian Pr.

—My Spanish Book of Shapes: Mi libro de las formas en ingles y Espanol. rev. ed. 2007. 12p. 7.99 (*978-1-4037-3051-0(2)) Dalmatian Pr.

Dalmatian Press Staff. Precious Moments Lowercase Colors & Shapes. 1999. (Precious Moments Ser.). (Illus.). 32p. (J). (ps-3). pap., wbk. ed. 2.99 (978-1-57759-207-5(7)) Dalmatian Pr.

D'Amelio, Dennis P. Shape Train Coming. D'Amelio, Dennis P., illus. 1998. (Right Track Bks.: Vol. 2). (Illus.). (J). (ps). pap. (978-1-891528-55-2(6)) Telescopic Pr.

DeGrie, Eve. Shapes. Rose, Drew, illus. 2005. 16p. (J). bds. 6.95 (978-0-8249-6581-5(7)) Ideals Pubns.

Delpech, Sylvie & Leclerc, Caroline, eds. Henri Matisse. 2006. (Sticker Art Shapes Ser.). (Illus.). 28p. 7.95 (978-1-84507-675-7(3)) Lincoln, Frances Ltd. GBR. *Dist:* Perseus Distribution.

Diehl, David. A Circle Here, A Square There: My Shapes Book. 2007. (Illus.). 22p. (J). bds. 4.95 (*978-1-60059-116-7(7)) Lark Bks.

Dingles, Molly. Crescent Kitchen. Brodie, Neale, illus. 2006. (Community of Shapes Ser.). (J). (*978-1-59646-049-2(0)) Dingles & Co.

—Diamond Downhill. Dobson, Len, illus. 2005. (Community of Shapes Ser.). 32p. (J). pap. 9.95 (978-1-59646-240-3(X)); lib. bdg. 20.65 (978-1-59646-043-0(1)); per. 9.95 (978-1-59646-241-0(8)) Dingles & Co.

—Diamond Downhill/Cuesta abajo en forma de Rombo. Dobson, Len, illus. 2005. (Community of Shapes Ser.).Tr. of Cuesta abajo en forma de Rombo. (ENG & SPA.). 32p. (J). pap. 9.95 (978-1-59646-242-7(6)); lib. bdg. 20.65 (978-1-59646-044-7(X)); per. 9.95 (978-1-59646-243-4(4)) Dingles & Co.

—Oval Opera. Brodie, Neale, illus. 2006. (Community of Shapes Ser.). 29p. (J). (*978-1-59646-047-8(4)) Dingles & Co.

—Rectangle Ranch. Dobson, Len, illus. 2005. (Community of Shapes Ser.). 32p. (J). pap. 9.95 (978-1-59646-244-1(2)); lib. bdg. 20.65 (978-1-59646-035-5(0)); per. 9.95 (978-1-59646-245-8(0)) Dingles & Co.

—Rectangle Ranch/Rancho Rectangular. Dobson, Len, illus. 2005. (Community of Shapes Ser.).Tr. of Rancho Rectangular. (ENG & SPA.). 32p. (J). pap. 9.95 (978-1-59646-246-5(9)); lib. bdg. 20.65 (978-1-59646-036-2(9)); per. 9.95 (978-1-59646-247-2(7)) Dingles & Co.

—Seaside Circles. Brodie, Neale, illus. 2006. (Community of Shapes Ser.). 32p. (J). pap. 9.95 (978-1-59646-256-4(6)); lib. bdg. 20.65 (978-1-59646-033-1(4)); per. 9.95 (978-1-59646-257-1(4)) Dingles & Co.

—Seaside Circles/Círculos a la orilla del Mar. Brodie, Neale, illus. 2006. (Community of Shapes Ser.).Tr. of Círculos a la orilla del Mar. (ENG & SPA.). 32p. (J). pap. 9.95 (978-1-59646-258-8(2)); lib. bdg. 20.60 (978-1-59646-034-8(2)) Dingles & Co.

—Seaside Circles/Círculos a la orilla del Mar. Brodie, Neal, illus. 2006. (Community of Shapes Ser.).Tr. of Círculos a la orilla del Mar. (ENG & SPA.). 32p. (J). per. 9.95 (978-1-59646-259-5(0)) Dingles & Co.

—Star Ship. Brodie, Neale, illus. 2006. (Community of Shapes Ser.). 29p. (J). (*978-1-59646-039-3(3)) Dingles & Co.

—Sweet Hearts. Brodie, Neale, illus. 2006. (Community of Shapes Ser.). (J). (*978-1-59646-037-9(7)) Dingles & Co.

—Town Squares. Brodie, Neale, illus. 2006. (Community of Shapes Ser.). 32p. (J). pap. 9.95 (978-1-59646-264-9(7)); lib. bdg. 20.65 (978-1-59646-041-6(5)); per. 9.95 (978-1-59646-265-6(5)) Dingles & Co.

—Town Squares/Cuadrados en la Plaza. Brodie, Neale, illus. 2006. (Community of Shapes Ser.).Tr. of Cuadrados en la Plaza. (ENG & SPA.). 32p. (J). pap. 9.95 (978-1-59646-266-3(3)); lib. bdg. 20.65 (978-1-59646-042-3(3)); per. 9.95 (978-1-59646-267-0(1)) Dingles & Co.

Disney Staff. Pooh's Colorful Shapes. Disney Staff, illus. 1999. (Pooh's Learn & Grow Ser.: Vol. 1). (Illus.). 12p. (J). 3.49 (978-1-57973-035-2(3)) Advance Pubs. LLC.

DK Publishing. Colors & Shapes. 2007. 26p. (J). (ps-k). 9.99 (*978-0-7566-3370-7(2)) Dorling Kindersley Publishing, Inc.

DK Publishing Staff. Colors & Shapes. 2007. (Let's Look Ser.). (Illus.). 36p. (J). 4.99 (978-0-7566-2594-8(7)) Dorling Kindersley Publishing, Inc.

Does It Belong? 2003. (Preschool Ser.). (J). 19.99 (978-1-58947-903-6(3)) School Zone Publishing Co.

Dora the Explorer Shapes & Patterns. 2004. (J). 3.95 (*978-1-58610-905-9(7)) Learning Horizons, Inc.

Dora the Explorer Sort & Compare. 2006. (J). pap. 2.95 (*978-1-58610-988-2(X)) Learning Horizons, Inc.

Dorling Kindersley Publishing Staff. Are Eggs Square? 2003. (My First World Ser.). (Illus.). 21p. (J). 6.99 (978-0-7894-9849-6(9)) Dorling Kindersley Publishing, Inc.

—Are Elephants Tiny? 2003. (DK See Through Ser.). (Illus.). 21p. (J). 6.99 (978-0-7894-9852-6(9)) Dorling Kindersley Publishing, Inc.

—Las Formas / Shapes. 2004. (My 1ST Board Books Ser.). 24p. (J). (ps-3). bds. 3.99 (978-0-7566-0441-7(9)) Dorling Kindersley Publishing, Inc.

—My First Touch & Feel Picture Cards: Colors & Shapes. 2005. (Baby Genius Ser.). 16p. (J). pap. 9.99 (978-0-7566-1516-1(X)) Dorling Kindersley Publishing, Inc.

—Shapes All Around. 2006. (Baby Fun Ser.). (Illus.). 20p. (J). (ps-3). bds. 4.99 (978-0-7566-2008-0(2)) Dorling Kindersley Publishing, Inc.

—Sizes. 2001. (Sticker Activity Books Ser.). (Illus.). 16p. (J). (ps-3). pap. 6.99 (978-0-7894-7664-7(9)) Dorling Kindersley Publishing, Inc.

Dorling Kindersley Publishing Staff, contrib. by. My First Look At: Shapes. 2001. (My First Look At... Ser.). (Illus.). 24p. (J). (ps-k). pap. 3.95 (978-0-7894-7660-9(6), D K Ink) Dorling Kindersley Publishing, Inc.

—My First Look At: Sizes. 2001. (My First Look At... Ser.). (Illus.). 24p. (J). (ps-k). pap. 3.95 (978-0-7894-7661-6(4), D K Ink) Dorling Kindersley Publishing, Inc.

Dotlich, Rebecca Kai. What Is Square? Ferrari, Maria, illus. 1999. (Growing Tree Ser.). 24p. (J). (ps up). 9.95 (978-0-694-01207-7(6), Harper Festival) HarperCollins Pubs.

Douglas, Lloyd G. What Is a Plane? 2002. (Wel-Simple MacHines Ser.). (Illus.). 24p. (J). (ps-2). 18.00 (978-0-516-23964-4(3)); pap. 4.95 (978-0-516-24023-7(4)) Scholastic Library Publishing. (Children's Pr.).

Douglas, Vincent. Shapes & Sizes. 2001. (Illus.). 32p. pap. 3.49 (978-1-56189-218-1(1), American Education Publishing) School Specialty Publishing.

Douglas, Vincent & School Specialty Publishing Staff. Alphabet, Colors, & Shapes. 2004. (My Little Heavenly Helpers Ser.). (Illus.). 64p. (J). (ps-k). pap. 3.99 (978-0-7696-3649-8(7), Brighter Child) School Specialty Publishing.

—Color, Shape, & Size. 2004. (Kindergarten Bound Ser.). (Illus.). 80p. (J). pap. 5.95 (978-0-7696-3520-0(2), American Education Publishing) School Specialty Publishing.

—Colors & Shapes Touch & Learn Board Book. Touch and Learn Staff, ed. 2003. (Padded Board Books with Textured Letters Ser.). (Illus.). 26p. (J). bds. 19.95 (978-1-58845-575-8(0), Brighter Child) School Specialty Publishing.

—Making & Baking Learn about Shapes Craft Kit. 2004. (Craft Kits Ser.). (Illus.). 52p. (J). pap. 16.95 (978-1-58845-624-3(2), Brighter Child) School Specialty Publishing.

Draze, Dianne. Attribute Block - Sequences: Thinking Activities. 2005. 32p. 9.95 (978-1-59363-053-9(0)) Prufrock Pr.

Eck, Kristin. Shapes in My House. 2004. (Look-And-Learn Books). (Illus.). (J). lib. bdg. 7.95 (978-1-4042-2699-9(0), PowerKids Pr.) Rosen Publishing Group, Inc., The.

Ekblad, Linda. Figuras. 2000. (Metro Math Readers Red Level Ser.). (J). (gr. k-1). 46.95 (978-1-58830-524-4(4)) Metropolitan Teaching & Learning Co.

—Mira Con Cuidado! 2000. (Metro Math Readers Red Level Ser.). (J). (gr. k-1). 46.95 (978-1-58830-525-1(2)) Metropolitan Teaching & Learning Co.

—Shapes. 2000. (Metro Math Readers Red Level Ser.). (J). (gr. k-1). 46.95 (978-1-58120-554-1(6)) Metropolitan Teaching & Learning Co.

Ellering, Joanie. Let's Learn Shapes. 1999. (J). (ps-3). (978-1-929343-01-0(9)) Stretching Charts, Inc.

Ellis, Belinda. Things That Go. 2005. (Baby-See-A Shape Ser.). (Illus.). 10p. (ps-ps). bds. 4.95 (978-1-84610-022-2(4)) Make Believe Ideas GBR. *Dist:* Ingram Pub. Services.

Emberley, Ed. The Wing on a Flea. Emberley, Ed, illus. 2001. (Illus.). 32p. (J). (gr. 1-3). 15.99 (978-0-316-23487-0(7)) Little, Brown Bks. for Young Readers.

Emberley, Rebecca. My Shapes/ Mis Formas. Emberley, Rebecca, illus. 2000. (ENG & SPA., Illus.). 10p. (J). (ps-ps). bds. 6.99 (978-0-316-23355-2(2)) Little Brown & Co.

Equipo Staff. El Libro de Bugui: Formas. 2000. Tr. of Shapes. (SPA., Illus.). 32p. (J). (ps-k). 8.95 (978-84-488-0857-0(6)) Beascoa, Ediciones S.A. ESP. *Dist:* Distribooks, Inc.

Ferarro, Bonita. Color & Shapes: Preschool. 2003. (Brighter Child Workbooks Ser.). (Illus.). 24p. (J). (ps). pap. 2.25 (978-1-56189-058-3(8), 41210) School Specialty Publishing.

Filipowich, Bob. Splashtime Book of Shapes. 2000. (God's Creation Ser.). (Illus.). (J). pap. 4.99 (978-0-310-98094-0(1)) Zonderkidz.

First Steps: Colors & Shapes. 2002. (First Steps Reading Ser.). 32p. (J). pap. 2.95 (978-0-7894-8482-6(X)) Dorling Kindersley Publishing, Inc.

Foil Book Colors & Numbers & Shapes, Oh My! (English) 2000. (J). (978-1-58805-033-5(5)) DS-Max USA, Inc.

Formas. (Coleccion Mi Primer Libro). (SPA., Illus.). (J). 13.95 (978-84-207-3781-2(X), ANY877) Grupo Anaya, S.A. ESP. *Dist:* Continental Bk. Co., Inc.

Formas. (Coleccion Libritos Acordeon). (SPA., Illus.). 10p. (J). pap. 5.50 (978-950-11-0793-7(0), SGM930) Sigmar ARG. *Dist:* Continental Bk. Co., Inc.

Formas (Shapes) (SPA.). (J). 6.95 (978-968-419-056-6(5)) Grijalbo, Editorial MEX. *Dist:* AIMS International Bks., Inc.

Formas y Colores. (Coleccion Picaros Peluchines). (SPA.). (J). 5.50 (978-950-11-0400-4(1), SGM400) Sigmar ARG. *Dist:* Continental Bk. Co., Inc.

Formas y Series. 2007. (Dora The Explorer Ser.). (SPA & ENG., Illus.). 48p. (J). 2.95 (*978-1-59545-058-6(0)) Learning Horizons, Inc.

Forte, Imogene. Ready to Learn Shapes & Colors. 2003. (Illus.). 64p. per. 7.95 (978-0-86530-593-9(5)) Incentive Pubns., Inc.

Freed, Shirley & Moon, Louise. Little Big. Morelan, Bill, ed. Harrell, Rob, illus. 2003. 8p. (J). (gr. k up). pap. 3.99 (978-1-58938-101-8(7)) Concerned Communications.

Freudentha. Grasp Sizes: Math/Context - Spanish Student Edition. 98th ed. 2002. 7.86 (978-0-85229-720-9(3)) Encyclopaedia Britannica, Inc.

Freudenthal. Math in Context: Grasping Sizes. 3rd ed. 2002. 8.33 (978-0-85229-848-0(X)) Encyclopaedia Britannica, Inc.

Freymann, Saxton, illus. Food for Thought: The Complete Book of Concepts for Growing Minds. 2005. 61p. (J). lib. bdg. (978-1-4155-7707-3(2), Levine, Arthur A. Bks.) Scholastic, Inc.

Freymann, Saxton, et al. Food for Thought: The Complete Book of Concepts for Growing Minds. Freymann, Saxton, illus. 2005. (Illus.). 64p. (J). pap. 14.95 (978-0-439-11018-1(1), Levine, Arthur A. Bks.) Scholastic, Inc.

Fried, Miriam. My Jelly Bean Book. 2005. (Illus.). (J). (978-1-57400-049-8(7)) Data Trace Publishing, Co.

Geddes, Anne. Shapes. 2005. (Illus.). 24p. (J). (ps-k). 12.95 (978-0-7407-5585-9(4)) Andrews McMeel Publishing.

—Shapes. Geddes, Anne, photos by. 2005. (Illus.). 24p. (J). (ps-k). bds. 6.95 (978-0-7407-5584-2(6)) Andrews McMeel Publishing.

Gerth, Melanie. Mi primer gran libro de las Formas. 2005. (Mi primer gran libro de ... Ser.). (SPA., Illus.). 10p. (J). 16.95 (978-84-7864-931-0(X)) Combel Editorial, S.A. ESP. *Dist:* Independent Pubs. Group.

Gibson, Leah. Nombra las Formas. 2007. (Sesame Street Ser.). (SPA & ENG.). 24p. (J). pap., wbk. ed. 4.99 (*978-1-59545-066-1(1)) Learning Horizons, Inc.

Gill, Janie S. Shapes, Shapes All over the Place. Morgan, Karen O. L., illus. 1999. 24p. 5.95 (978-0-89868-439-1(0)); pap. 3.95 (978-0-89868-438-4(2)); (J). lib. bdg. 10.95 (978-0-89868-437-7(4)) ARO Publishing Co.

Ginsburg, Herbert P., et al. Favorite Shapes. 2003. (Illus.). 9.95 (978-0-7690-3043-2(2)) Seymour, Dale Pubns.

Girard, Franck. Mi primer baul de Palabras. Jonniaux, Isabelle, illus. 2005. (Baul de Palabras Ser.). (SPA.). 120p. (J). 18.95 (978-84-7864-788-0(0)) Combel Editorial, S.A. ESP. *Dist:* Independent Pubs. Group.

Gobo Books Staff. Ready to Read & Write: Little Learners. 2007. (Magnix Little Learners Ser.). 40p. (J). (ps-1). bds. 14.95 (*978-1-932915-44-0(3)) Sandvik Innovations, LLC.

Gold, Kari Jenson. Solid Shapes! Date not set. (Early Math Big Bks.). (Illus.). 16p. (J). (ps-2). pap. 16.95 (978-1-58273-143-8(8)) Sundance/Newbridge Educational Publishing.

—Tiling Shapes. Date not set. (Early Math Big Bks.). (Illus.). 16p. (J). (ps-2). pap. 16.95 (978-1-58273-477-4(1)) Sundance/Newbridge Educational Publishing.

Golden Books Staff. No Matter How Small. 2008. (Deluxe Coloring Book Ser.). (Illus.). 96p. (J). (ps-2). pap. 3.99 (*978-0-375-83821-7(X), Golden Bks.) Random Hse. Children's Bks.

Gordon, Sharon. Big Small (Grande Pequeño) 2006. (Bookworms Ser.). (ENG & SPA.). 24p. (J). lib. bdg. 22.79 (*978-0-7614-2445-1(8)) Cavendish, Marshall Corp.

Graham, Noel. Circles: Activities for Children. 2001. (Illus.). 32p. (J). (gr. k-3). pap. 10.00 (978-1-871098-66-2(1)) Claire Pubns. GBR. *Dist:* Parkwest Pubns., Inc.

Granowsky, Alvin. Big & Small. 2001. 11.79 (978-0-606-22439-0(4)) Tandem Library Bks.

—Shapes. 2001. (978-0-606-22368-3(1)) Tandem Library Bks.

—Shapes. 2001. (ps-2). lib. bdg. 13.00 (978-0-613-45223-6(2)) Tandem Library Bks.

Gregorich, Barbara. Shapes & Colors. 2005. 32p. (J). (ps-k). pap. 2.49 (*978-0-88743-728-1(1)) School Zone Publishing Co.

Gunzi, Christiane. Las Formas. 2004. (Mi Primera Mirada. . . Ser.). (SPA., Illus.). 24p. (ps-k). (J). pap. 5.95 (978-1-58728-431-1(6)); 9.95 (978-1-58728-424-3(3)) Quayside. (Creative Publishing International).

—My Very First Look at Shapes. 2006. (Illus.). 22p. (J). bds. 6.95 (978-1-58728-576-9(2), Two Can Publishing) T&N Children's Publishing.

—Shapes. 2004. (My Very First Look at Ser.). (SPA., Illus.). 24p. (ps-k). (J). pap. 5.95 (978-1-58728-278-2(X)); 9.95 (978-1-58728-238-6(0)) T&N Children's Publishing. (Two Can Publishing).

—Sizes. 2004. (My Very First Look at Ser.). (SPA., Illus.). 24p. (ps-k). (J). pap. 5.95 (978-1-58728-279-9(8)); 9.95 (978-1-58728-239-3(9)) T&N Children's Publishing. (Two Can Publishing).

—Los Tamanos. 2004. (Mi Primera Mirada. . . Ser.).Tr. of MVFLA Sizes. (SPA., Illus.). 24p. (ps-k). (J). pap. 5.95 (978-1-58728-433-5(2)); 9.95 (978-1-58728-432-8(4)) Quayside. (Creative Publishing International).

Hall, Margaret. Day & Night. 2007. (Pebble Plus Ser.). (Illus.). 24p. (J). 19.93 (978-0-7368-6338-4(9)) Capstone Pr., Inc.

Hall, Pamela. Rectangles. Holm, Sharon Lane, illus. 2007. (Shapes Ser.). 24p. (J). (ps-2). lib. bdg. 25.65 (*978-1-60270-046-8(X), Looking Glass Library) Magic Wagon.

—Squares. Holm, Sharon Lane, illus. 2007. (Shapes Ser.). 24p. (J). (ps-2). lib. bdg. 25.65 (*978-1-60270-047-5(8), Looking Glass Library) Magic Wagon.

Hammersmith, Craig. Patterns. 2003. (Spyglass Books). (Illus.). 24p. (J). (gr. 1 up). lib. bdg. 18.60 (978-0-7565-0452-6(X)) Compass Point Bks.

Handberg, Irene. The World of Shapes & Colors: Learning Center, Set. rev. ed. 1998. (Illus.). (J). (ps-5). pap. 62.95 (978-1-56831-210-1(5)) Learning Connection, The.

—The World of Shapes & Colors, Grades Preschool-3: Learning Center. 1998. (Illus.). 8p. (J). (gr. k-6). tchr. ed. 24.95 (978-1-56831-212-5(1)) Learning Connection, The.

Harcourt School Publishers Staff. From Here to There: Take-Home Book. 1999. (Collections Ser.). (Illus.). (J). pap. 1.90 (978-0-15-317319-6(X)) Harcourt Schl. Pubs.

—The Shape of Things Big Book. 3rd ed. 2002. (Trophies Reading Program Ser.). (Illus.). pap. 52.60 (978-0-15-325446-8(7)) Harcourt Schl. Pubs.

—The Shape of Things Little Book. 3rd ed. 2002. (Trophies Reading Program Ser.). (Illus.). (J). pap. 10.20 (978-0-15-325451-2(3)) Harcourt Schl. Pubs.

—What Shape Is That? 3rd ed. 2002. (Trophies English Language Learners Ser.). (Illus.). pap. 5.10 (978-0-15-327719-1(X)) Harcourt Schl. Pubs.

Harder Tangvald, Christine. God Made Shapes...for Me! 1999. (for Me! Bks.). (Illus.). 16p. (J). (ps). pap. 4.99 (978-0-7642-2284-9(8)) Bethany Hse. Pubs.

Harper, Charise Mericle. The Little Book of Not So. 2005. (Illus.). 32p. (J). (ps-k). 9.95 (978-0-618-47319-9(X)) Houghton Mifflin Co. Trade & Reference Div.

Harris, Nancy. Shapes & Patterns We Know. 2008. (J). (*978-1-60044-636-8(1)) Rourke Publishing, LLC.

—What Is Big Compared to Me? A Book about Measurements. 2008. (J). (****978-1-60044-635-1(3)***) Rourke Publishing, LLC.

Harris, Nicholas. How Big? 2003. (How? Ser.). (Illus.). 30p. (J). 23.70 (978-1-4103-0068-3(4)); 11.20 (978-1-4103-0197-0(4)) Thomson Gale. (Blackbirch Pr., Inc.).

—How Long? 2003. (Illus.). 30p. (J). 23.70 (978-1-4103-0066-9(8)); 11.20 (978-1-4103-0195-6(8)) Thomson Gale. (Blackbirch Pr., Inc.).

Harvey, Jayne. Busy Bugs: A Book about Patterns. Adnet, Bernard, illus. 2003. (All Aboard Math Reader Station Stop Ser.: Level 1). 32p. (J). (gr. 1-3). pap. 3.99 (978-0-448-43159-8(9) , Grosset & Dunlap) Penguin Group (USA) Inc.

Head, Honor. Size & Shape. Stower, Adam, illus. 1998. (Ed Mouse Finds Out about Ser.). 32p. (J). (ps-2). pap. 5.95 (978-0-8172-8101-4(0)) Steck-Vaughn.

Heinze, Monica Bacon. A Day with Shapes. Dow, S. B., illus. 2004. (J). (****978-0-9761710-0-3(7)***) Paisley Publishing.

Hendler, Muncie. Shapes. 1998. (Illus.). 32p. (J). pap. 1.50 (978-0-486-40351-9(3)) Dover Pubns., Inc.

Heurtelou, Maude. Fom/Shape. 1999. (Big Book Ser.). (Illus.). 12p. (J). (gr. k-2). 19.50 (978-1-58432-068-5(0)) Educa Vision.

—Shapes: Fom. 2000. (CRP & ENG.). 12p. (J). (gr. k-2). pap. 4.50 (978-1-58432-022-7(2)) Educa Vision.

Hicks, Barbara Jean. I Like Colors. Prap, Lila, illus. 2006. 32p. (J). 9.95 (978-1-58925-057-4(5) , tiger tales) ME Media LLC.

Hill, Eric. Spot Looks at Shapes. Hill, Eric, illus. 2003. (Illus.). 8p. (J). (ps-1). bds. 3.99 (978-0-399-24042-3(X) , Putnam Juvenile) Penguin Group (USA) Inc.

Hillman, Ben. How Big Is It? A Big Book All about Bigness. 2007. 48p. (J). (gr. 2-5). pap. 14.99 (****978-0-439-91808-4(1)***) Scholastic, Inc.

Hoban, Tana. So Many Circles, So Many Squares. 1998. (Illus.). 40p. (J). (ps-3). 16.99 (978-0-688-15165-2(5)) HarperCollins Pubs.

Hoffman, Joan. Guess Who? A Book of Colors & Shapes. 1999. (Illus.). 16p. (J). (ps-3). bds. 4.99 (978-0-88743-602-4(1) , 06603) School Zone Publishing Co.

Holden, Arianne. Shapes. 2002. (Playschool Ser.). (Illus.). 32p. pap. 5.99 (978-1-84215-645-2(4) , Southwater) Anness Publishing GBR. *Dist:* National Bk. Network.

Holt, Rinehart and Winston Staff. Math in Context: Grasping Sizes. 3rd ed. 2002. tchr. ed. 33.53 (978-0-85229-858-9(7)) Encyclopaedia Britannica, Inc.

Hop, L. L. C. Hooked on Pre-K Super Workbook. 2006. 320p. 12.99 (978-1-931020-72-5(8)) HOP, LLC.

Horne, Jane. Shapes: First Concepts. 2007. (Busy Baby Ser.). (Illus.). 12p. (ps-k). per., bds. 6.95 (****978-1-84610-470-1(X)***) Make Believe Ideas GBR. *Dist:* Ingram Pub. Services.

Hunt, Darleen L. Samantha Visits Grandpa Geo: Shapes. Komarck, Michael, illus. 2003. (Sherman's Math Corner Ser.). (J). (ps-3). (978-1-929591-01-5(2)) Reading Rock, Inc.

Hunt, Janie. Shapes. Chrystall, Claire, illus. 2003. (Busy Finger Ser.). 10p. (J). bds. 10.95 (978-1-57145-938-1(3) , Silver Dolphin Bks.) Advantage Pubs. Group.

I Know My Shapes. 2005. (J). pap., stu. ed. 19.95 (978-1-58970-699-6(4)) Lakeshore Learning Materials.

I Know My Shapes! Big Book Series. 2005. (J). pap. 49.95 (978-1-58970-698-9(6)) Lakeshore Learning Materials.

Imperato, Teresa. Trick or Treat! A Halloween Shapes Book. Winston, Jeannie, illus. 2005. 12p. (J). 7.95 (978-1-58117-325-3(3) , Intervisual/Piggy Toes) Dalmatian Pr.

Innovative Kids Staff, et al. Bugs in the Garden. Filipowich, Bob, illus. 2003. (J). (ps). 8.99 (978-1-58476-171-6(7)) Innovative Kids.

Island, Sylvester, Jr. Li'l Rex Says, Let's Have Fun with Shapes. Island, Sylvester, Jr., illus. 1998. (Illus.). (J). (ps-6). pap. 3.95 (978-1-892089-51-9(3)) Our Kids Pubn., Inc.

Jacobs, Daniel. City Shapes. 2003. (Yellow Umbrella Books for Early Readers). (Illus.). 17p. (J). 15.93 (978-0-7368-2915-1(6)); pap. (978-0-7368-2874-1(5)) Yellow Umbrella Pr.

Jagoda, Susan, et al. Shapes, Loops & Images. Bergman, Lincoln & Fairwell, Kay, eds. Klofkorn, Lisa & Pepino, Nona, illus. Jagoda, Susan & Sneider, Cary, photos by. rev. ed. 1998. (Great Explorations in Math & Science Ser.). 80p. (ps-12). pap. 21.00 (978-0-924886-12-6(9) , GEMS) Univ. of California, Berkeley, Lawrence Hall of Science.

Jocelyn, Marthe. One, Some, Many. Slaughter, Tom, illus. 2006. 16p. (J). (gr. k-k). bds. 7.95 (978-0-88776-789-0(3)) Candlewick Pr.

—Over, Under. Slaughter, Tom, illus. 2005. 24p. (J). (gr. k-k). 15.95 (978-0-88776-708-1(7)) Tundra Bks., Inc./Livres Toundra, Inc. CAN. *Dist:* Random Hse., Inc.

Johnson, Jinny & Woods, Michael. How Big Is a Whale? (Illus.). (J). pap. 18.99 (978-0-590-24629-3(1)) Scholastic, Inc.

Johnson, Rebecca L. Sizing up Shapes. 2004. (Math Behind the Science Ser.). (Illus.). 24p. (J). pap. (978-0-7922-4589-6(X)) National Geographic Society.

Jones, Otis. Geonopolis, the Shapely City of Geometry. 2003. (Illus.). 21p. (J). (978-0-9744123-0-6(9)) Colorful Crayons For Kids Publishing, LLC.

Kai-Dotlich, Rebecca. What Is Round? Ferrari, Maria, photos by. 1999. (Growing Tree Ser.). (Illus.). 24p. (J). (ps up). pap. 9.95 (978-0-694-01208-4(4) , Harper Festival) HarperCollins Pubs.

Kalman, Bobbie. How Does It Look? 2007. (Looking at Nature Ser.). (Illus.). 24p. (J). (ps-2). pap. (****978-0-7787-3335-5(1)***) Crabtree Publishing Co.

—Is It Big or Small? 2007. (Looking at Nature Ser.). (Illus.). 24p. (J). (ps-2). (****978-0-7787-3316-4(5)***); pap. (****978-0-7787-3336-2(X)***) Crabtree Publishing Co.

—What Shape Is It? 2007. (Looking at Nature Ser.). (Illus.). 24p. (J). (ps-2). pap. (****978-0-7787-3340-9(8)***); lib. bdg. (****978-0-7787-3320-1(3)***) Crabtree Publishing Co.

Kelly, Lorraine. Mary Ellen & Cameron Play Party Games. 2000. (Illus.). 16p. (J). pap. 8.95 (978-0-233-99922-7(1)) Andre Deutsch GBR. *Dist:* Trafalgar Square Publishing.

Kirkby, David. Shapes. 1998. (Mini Math Ser.). (Illus.). 24p. (J). (978-1-57572-002-9(7)) Heinemann Library.

Klein, Adria. Which One is More? Metro Math Readers Yellow Level. 2000. (Metro Math Readers Yellow Level Ser.). (J). (gr. 1-2). 3.75 (978-1-58120-420-9(5)) Metropolitan Teaching & Learning Co.

Kompelien, Tracy. I See a Pattern, What Can I Learn? (Math Made Fun Ser.). (Illus.). 24p. (J). 2007. 19.93 (978-1-59928-533-7(9)); 2006. (978-1-59928-534-4(7)) ABDO Publishing Co.

—Let's Compare If You Dare. 2007. (Illus.). 24p. (J). 19.93 (978-1-59928-537-5(1) , SandCastle) ABDO Publishing Co.

—Let's Compare, If You Dare! 2006. (Illus.). 24p. (J). (978-1-59928-538-2(X)) ABDO Publishing Co.

—2-D Shapes Are Behind the Drapes! (Math Made Fun Ser.). (Illus.). 24p. (J). 2007. 19.93 (978-1-59928-507-8(X)); 2006. (978-1-59928-508-5(8)) ABDO Publishing Co.

—3-D Shapes are Like Green Grapes! 2007. (Math Made Fun Ser.). (Illus.). 24p. (J). 19.93 (978-1-59928-509-2(6) , SandCastle) ABDO Publishing Co.

—3-D Shapes Are Like Green Grapes! 2006. (Math Made Fun Ser.). (Illus.). 24p. (J). pap. (978-1-59928-510-8(X)) ABDO Publishing Co.

Koomen, Michele. Shapes: Discovering Flats & Solids. 2001. (Exploring Math Ser.). (Illus.). 24p. (J). (gr. 1-2). lib. bdg. 18.60 (978-0-7368-0820-0(5) , Bridgestone Bks.) Capstone Pr., Inc.

Kottke, Jan. City Shapes, 6 bks., Set. 2004. 24p. (J). (ps-2). 87.00 (978-0-516-23225-6(8) , Children's Pr.) Scholastic Library Publishing.

Kumon Publishing North America, creator. Let's Cut Paper! A Kumon First Steps Workbook, 4 vols. 2005. (Illus.). 40p. (J). (ps). per. 5.95 (978-1-933241-14-2(4)) Kumon Publishing North America, Inc.

Lacing Patterns, Set D. 2002. (J). (gr. k-2). act. bk. ed. 6.99 (978-1-56451-416-5(1)) School Specialty Publishing.

Lady Bird Johnson Wildflower Center Staff, Lady Bird Johnson, compiled by. Exploring the Native Plant World Pre-K-K: Patterns & Shapes. 2004. 44p. (J). pap. 14.95 (978-1-57168-680-0(0) , Eakin Pr.) Eakin Pr.

Lakeshore Learning Materials Staff, contrib. by. Shapes Activity Kit. 2000. (J). pap. 19.95 (978-1-929255-58-0(6)) Lakeshore Learning Materials.

Lamut, Sonja. Halloween Shapes. Lamut, Sonja, illus. 2000. (My Turn Bks.). (Illus.). 12p. (J). (ps). 4.99 (978-0-448-41992-3(0) , Grosset & Dunlap) Penguin Group (USA) Inc.

Land, Fiona. Shapes. 2007. (Little Scholastic Ser.). (J). bds. 4.99 (****978-0-439-02146-3(4)***) Scholastic, Inc.

Landoll Inc. Staff. Colors & Shapes Workbook. 2000. (Beginners Bible Ser.). (J). pap. 14.95 (978-0-56189-618-9(7) , American Education Publishing) School Specialty Publishing.

Law, Felicia. Patchwork First Poem Books - Shape. Knight, Paula, illus. (Patchwork First Poem Bks.). 24p. 8.95 (978-1-904668-85-5(2)) Mercury Bks. Ltd. GBR. *Dist:* International Publishers Marketing.

—Patchwork First Poem Books - Size. Knight, Paula, illus. (Patchwork First Poem Bks.). 24p. 8.95 (978-1-904668-81-7(X)) Mercury Bks. Ltd. GBR. *Dist:* International Publishers Marketing.

Leake, Diyan. Circulos. 2005. (SPA & ENG., Illus.). 24p. (J). (978-1-4034-7489-6(3)); pap. (978-1-4034-7494-0(X)) Heinemann Library.

—Rectangles. 2005. (Illus.). 24p. (J). (ps-1). pap. 6.00 (978-1-4034-7480-3(X)) Heinemann.

—Rectangulos. 2005. (SPA & ENG., Illus.). 24p. (J). (978-1-4034-7490-2(7)); pap. (978-1-4034-7496-4(6)) Heinemann Library.

—Squares. 2005. (Illus.). 24p. (J). (ps-1). pap. 6.00 (978-1-4034-7481-0(8)); lib. bdg. 21.36 (978-1-4034-7476-6(1)) Steck-Vaughn.

—Triangles. 2005. (Illus.). 24p. (J). (ps-1). lib. bdg. 21.36 (978-1-4034-7477-3(X)) Steck-Vaughn.

LeapFrog Shapes & Sizes Wipe Off. 2007. (J). 4.99 (****978-1-59545-135-4(8)***) Learning Horizons, Inc.

LeapFrog Staff, compiled by. Counting on Leap. 2001. (J). (ps-2). spiral bd. 14.99 (978-1-58605-028-3(1)) LeapFrog Enterprises, Inc.

Learning Company Books Staff, ed. Reader Rabbit Fun with Paint: Shapes. 2004. (Illus.). 32p. (J). pap. 4.99 (978-0-7630-7739-6(9)) Learning Co. Bks.

Learning to Match. 2003. (Kermit the Frog & Friends Ser.). (Illus.). 16p. (J). (ps-k). pap., act. bk. ed. 4.99 (978-1-57768-717-7(5)) School Specialty Publishing.

Learning to Order. 2003. (Kermit the Frog & Friends Ser.). (Illus.). 16p. (J). (ps-k). pap., act. bk. ed. 4.99 (978-1-57768-718-4(3)) School Specialty Publishing.

Learning Wrap-Ups Early Child. 2004. 29.99 (978-0-943343-18-1(6)) Learning Wrap-Ups.

Lee, Quinlan. Splish! Splash! Splosh! Scholastic, Inc. Staff, ed. Salter, Carlton, illus. 2004. (Rubbadubbers Ser.). 32p. (J). pap. 4.99 (978-0-439-51217-6(4)) Scholastic, Inc.

Leech, Bonnie Coulter. Circles & Spheres. 2007. (Library of Plane & Solid Geometric Shapes). (Illus.). 24p. (J). lib. bdg. (978-1-4042-3494-9(2) , PowerKids Pr.) Rosen Publishing Group, Inc., The.

—Triangles. 2007. (Library of Plane & Solid Geometric Shapes). (Illus.). 24p. (J). lib. bdg. (978-1-4042-3495-6(0) , PowerKids Pr.) Rosen Publishing Group, Inc., The.

Leonard, Barry, ed. Squishy Shapes: Dinosaurs. 2005. (Illus.). 10p. (J). (ps-2). reprint ed. 13.00 (978-0-7567-8529-1(4)) DIANE Publishing Co.

Let's Draw with Shapes: Set 2.Tr. of Vamos a dibujar con figuras Set 2. (Illus.). (J). (gr. k-1). 103.50 (978-1-4042-2947-1(7) , Powerstart Pr.); (ENG & SPA., 103.50 (978-1-4042-7560-7(6) , Buenas Letra) Rosen Publishing Group, Inc., The.

Lewis, J. Patrick. Big Is Big (And Little, Little) A Book of Contrasts. Barner, Bob, illus. 2007. 32p. (J). (ps-k). 16.95 (****978-0-8234-1909-8(6)***) Holiday Hse., Inc.

El Libro de Contar de los Chocolates M & M's Brand. 2004. 32p. (J). pap. 6.95 (978-1-57091-370-9(6)) Charlesbridge Publishing, Inc.

Line & Circle. 2004. (Illus.). 24p. (J). (CHI & ENG.). (978-1-84444-004-7(4)); (PER & ENG., (978-1-84444-006-1(0)); (ENG & POR., (978-1-84444-014-6(1)); (ENG & TUR., (978-1-84444-019-1(2)) Mantra Publishing, Ltd.

Lionni, Leo. Pezzettino. 2006. (Illus.). 40p. (J). (gr. k-3). lib. bdg. 17.99 (978-0-394-93156-2(4) , Pantheon) Knopf Publishing Group.

Llewellyn, Claire. Sizes. Anness Publishing Staff, ed. 1999. (Fun to Learn Ser.). (Illus.). 48p. (ps-1). 7.95 (978-0-7548-0209-9(4) , Lorenz Bks.) Anness Publishing GBR. *Dist:* National Bk. Network.

—Sizes. 2002. (Playschool Ser.). (Illus.). 32p. pap. 5.99 (978-1-84215-644-5(6) , Southwater) Anness Publishing GBR. *Dist:* National Bk. Network.

Lorbiecki, Marybeth. Triangles. Holm, Sharon Lane, illus. 2007. 24p. (J). (ps-2). lib. bdg. 25.65 (****978-1-60270-048-2(6)***, Looking Glass Library) Magic Wagon.

Lorenz Books Staff. Patterns. (Let's Look at...Ser.). (Illus.). 2002. 20p. 5.99 (978-0-7548-1051-3(8) , Lorenz Bks.); 2000. 16p. pap. 4.95 (978-0-7548-0437-6(2)) Anness Publishing GBR. *Dist:* National Bk. Network.

—Shapes. 1999. (Sticker Fun Ser.). (Illus.). 16p. (ps-k). pap. 4.95 (978-0-7548-0278-5(7) , Lorenz Bks.) Anness Publishing GBR. *Dist:* National Bk. Network.

—Sizes: With over 50 Reusable Stickers. 1998. (Sticker Fun Ser.). (Illus.). 16p. (ps-k). pap. 4.95 (978-1-85967-771-1(1)) Anness Publishing GBR. *Dist:* National Bk. Network.

Lorenz Books Staff & Lorenz, Joanna. Shapes. 1999. (Let's Look at Board Bks.). (Illus.). 12p. 4.95 (978-0-7548-0302-7(3) , Lorenz Bks.) Anness Publishing GBR. *Dist:* National Bk. Network.

Lorenz Editors. Shapes & Patterns, 4 vols., Set 4. 2001. (Mini Board Bks.). (Illus.). 12p. bds. 12.95 (978-0-7548-0873-2(4)) Anness Publishing GBR. *Dist:* National Bk. Network.

Lowery, Lawrence F. Look & See. 2nd ed. 2004. (J). per. (978-0-9762724-9-6(0)) Educational Research & Applications, LLC.

MacDonald, Suse. Sea Shapes. MacDonald, Suse, illus. 2002. (Illus.). (J). 19.96 (978-0-7587-3585-0(5)) Book Wholesalers, Inc.

—Sea Shapes. 1998. (Illus.). 32p. (J). pap. 7.00 (978-0-15-201700-2(3) , Harcourt Paperbacks) Harcourt Children's Bks.

—Sea Shapes. 1998. (978-0-606-13765-2(3)) Tandem Library Bks.

MacKall, Dandi Daley. The Shape of Things. Newton, Jill, illus. 2004. (Imagination Ser.). 12p. 6.99 (978-0-8066-4384-7(6) , Augsburg Bks.) Augsburg Fortress, Pubs.

MacKall, Dandi Daley & Kucharik, Elena. Blessings Come in Shapes. 2005. (Tyndale Kids Ser.). (Illus.). 32p. (J). bds. 6.99 (978-1-4143-0290-4(8)) Tyndale Hse. Pubs.

MacKinnon, Debbie. Eye Spy Shapes. Sieveking, Anthea, illus. 2000. 24p. (J). (ps-3). 6.95 (978-0-88106-135-2(2)) Charlesbridge Publishing, Inc.

Marks, Jenny L. Sorting by Size. 2007. (Sorting Ser.). (Illus.). 32p. (J). (gr. k-3). lib. bdg. 23.93 (978-0-7368-6740-5(6)) Capstone Pr., Inc.

Marqina, Mignon. Shapes & Me: A Flip & Learn Book. l.t. ed. 2006. (Illus.). 32p. (J). lib. bdg. (****978-1-934190-05-0(5)***) Ocean Front Bk. Publishing, Inc.

Marsh, Valerie. Storytelling with Shapes & Numbers. 1999. (Illus.). 86p. (J). (ps-1). pap. 15.95 (978-1-57950-024-5(2) , Upstart Bks.) Highsmith Inc.

Martin, Elena. So Many Circles. 2006. (Yellow Umbrella Books for Early Readers). (Illus.). 18p. (J). (978-0-7368-5979-0(9)); (ENG & SPA., (978-0-7368-6015-4(0)) Yellow Umbrella Pr.

Maruda, Trotsky. Line & Circle. 2004. (J). (ENG & RUS.). (978-1-84444-015-3(X)); (ARA & ENG., Illus.). 24p. (978-1-84444-002-3(8)); (BEN & ENG., Illus.). 24p. (978-1-84444-003-0(6)); (CZE & ENG., Illus.). 24p. (978-1-84444-005-4(2)); (ENG & FRE., Illus.). 24p. (978-1-84444-007-8(9)); (ENG & GER., Illus.). 24p. (978-1-84444-008-5(7)); (ENG & ITA., Illus.). 24p. (978-1-84444-010-8(9)); (ALB & ENG., Illus.). 24p. (978-1-84444-000-9(1)); (ENG & PAN., Illus.). 24p. (978-1-84444-012-2(5)); (ENG & POL., Illus.). 24p. (978-1-84444-013-9(3)); (ENG & KUR., Illus.). 24p. (978-1-84444-011-5(7)); (ENG & SER., Illus.). 24p. (978-1-84444-016-0(8)); (ENG & SOM., Illus.). 24p. (978-1-84444-017-7(6)); (ENG & URD., Illus.). 24p. (978-1-84444-020-7(6)); (ENG & VIE., Illus.). 24p. (978-1-84444-021-4(4)) Mantra Publishing, Ltd.

Marudu, Trotsky. Line & Circle. 2004. (ENG & GUJ., Illus.). 24p. (J). (978-1-84444-009-2(5)) Mantra Publishing, Ltd.

Mascall, Susan. Big Shapes for Little Kids: A Creative & Learning Discovery Toy. 1999. (Illus.). 16p. (J). pap. 9.99 (978-1-929992-10-2(6) , 054-002) Fundangles.

—Fundangles. 1999. (Illus.). 16p. (J). pap. (978-1-929992-00-3(9) , 054-001) Fundangles.

McCallister, Wendy. Shapes: 4 Friends Lost. 2004. (Illus.). 32p. (J). (ps up). 14.99 (978-1-59094-004-4(0) , Top Shelf) Jawbone Publishing Corp.

McCourt, Lisa. The Long & Short of It. Nathan, Cheryl, illus. 1999. (J). (978-0-606-16872-4(9)) Tandem Library Bks.

McGraw-Hill Staff & Taylor, Jody. Hidden Pictures. 2001. (Homework Helpers Activity Bks.). 56p. (J). (gr. k-1). pap., act. bk. ed. 2.99 (978-0-7682-0685-2(5) , FS109014, Schaffer, Frank) Schaffer, Frank Pubns.

McGuire, Leslie. Circles at the Circus: My First Book of Shapes. Haskamp, Steven, illus. 1999. (Gymboree Book Ser.). 16p. (J). reprint ed. 5.95 (978-1-892374-20-2(X)) Weldon Owen, Inc.

Meet the Shapes. 2005. (J). 7.99 (978-0-9770215-1-2(3)) KRO Publishing.

Meet the Shapes Lift the Flap Book. 2005. (J). bds. 9.99 (978-0-9770215-0-5(5)) KRO Publishing.

Menon, Radhika. Line & Circle. Marudu, Trotsky, illus. 2004. (ENG & SPA.). 24p. (J). (978-1-84444-018-4(4)) Mantra Publishing, Ltd.

Merrell, Patrick, illus. Colors & Shapes: Fun Color & Shape Activities! 2001. (My Wipe-Off Book Ser.). (J). (978-0-7853-5861-9(7)) Publications International, Ltd.

Metropolitan Museum of Art Staff, contrib. by. Museum Shapes. 2005. (Illus.). 48p. (J). (ps-1). 16.99 (978-0-316-05698-4(7)) Little Brown & Co.

Micklethwait, Lucy. I Spy Shapes in Art. 2004. (Illus.). 40p. (J). 19.99 (978-0-06-073193-9(1)) HarperCollins Pubs.

Miles Kelly Staff. Sizes: Let's Learn. Nilsen, Anna, ed. 2003. (Let's Learn Ser.). (Illus.). 20p. (J). 7.95 (978-1-84236-140-5(6)) Miles Kelly Publishing, Ltd. GBR. *Dist:* Independent Pubs. Group.

Miles Kelly Staff & Nilsen, Anna. Shapes: Let's Learn. 2003. (Let's Learn Ser.). (Illus.). 20p. (J). 7.95 (978-1-84236-016-3(7)) Miles Kelly Publishing, Ltd. GBR. *Dist:* Independent Pubs. Group.

Millard, Anne. Baby's Little Library. 2001. (Illus.). 1p. (J). 9.99 (978-0-7894-6798-0(4)) Dorling Kindersley Publishing, Inc.

A Mirror Image. 2002. (Illus.). (J). pap. (978-0-7398-5943-8(9)) Steck-Vaughn.

Montague-Smith, Ann. Mi Primer Libro de Figuras. Stanley, Mandy, illus. 2003. (Mi Primer Libro Ser.). (SPA.). 48p. (J). (gr. k-ps). pap. 6.95 (978-0-7534-5527-2(7) , Kingfisher) Houghton Mifflin Co. Trade & Reference Div.

—Sizes & Shapes. 2004. (QEB Start Math Ser.). (Illus.). 24p. (J). Vol. 1. lib. bdg. 15.95 (978-1-59566-026-8(7)); Vol. 2. lib. bdg. 15.95 (978-1-59566-030-5(5)) QEB Publishing Inc.

Moore, Cassandra. Shape/Color Master. 2007. (Illus.). 75p. (J). spiral bd. 12.95 (****978-1-886297-30-2(4)***) Omega Publishing Hse.

Moyer, Julia. Comparemos Tamaños. 2007. (Sesame Street Ser.). (SPA & ENG.). 24p. (J). pap., wbk. ed. 4.99 (****978-1-59545-068-5(8)***) Learning Horizons, Inc.

Muench-Williams, Heather, ed. Color, Shape, & Number Fun for Little Ones: Activities for Preschoolers. 2005. (J). pap. (978-1-57332-380-2(2)) HighReach Learning, Inc.

Murphy. Captain Invincible. 2002. (Illus.). pap. (978-0-7398-6791-4(1)) Steck-Vaughn.

Murphy, Chuck. Shapes. Murphy, Chuck, illus. 2001. (Slide 'n' Seek Ser.: Vol. 3). (Illus.). 12p. (J). bds. 5.99 (978-0-689-84477-5(8) , Little Simon) Simon & Schuster Children's Publishing.

Murphy, Stuart J. Bigger, Better, Best! Winborn, Marsha, illus. 2002. (MathStart Ser.). 40p. (J). (gr. 1 up). pap. 5.99 (978-0-06-446247-1(1)) HarperCollins Pubs.

—Captain Invincible & the Space Shapes. Simard, Remy, illus. 2001. (MathStart Ser.). 40p. (J). (gr. 1 up). 16.89 (978-0-06-028023-9(9)); pap. 5.99 (978-0-06-446731-5(7) , Harper Trophy) HarperCollins Pubs.

—Captain Invincible & the Space Shapes. 2001. (gr. k-3). lib. bdg. 12.95 (978-0-613-59231-4(X)) Tandem Library Bks.

—A House for Birdie. Miller, Edward, illus. 2004. (MathStart Ser.). 40p. (J). 15.99 (978-0-06-052351-0(4)); pap. 5.99 (978-0-06-052353-4(0)) HarperCollins Pubs.

My Big Box of Colors, Shapes, & Numbers: Contains Twenty Beautifully Illustrated Board Books. (Illus.). (J). bds. (978-1-904613-80-0(2)) O'Mara, Michael Bks., Ltd.

My First BK Of: Shapes. 2007. 12p. pap. 7.99 (****978-1-4037-3056-5(3)***) Dalmatian Pr.

My First Book of Shapes. 2003. (J). 41.70 (978-0-590-66408-0(5)) Scholastic, Inc.

My First Shapes. 2003. 12p. (J). bds. 6.99 (978-0-7894-9752-9(2)) Dorling Kindersley Publishing, Inc.

My House of Shapes. 2000. (Point & Peek Books Ser.). (Illus.). 6p. (J). (ps-1). bds. (978-1-57584-362-9(5)) Reader's Digest Children's Publishing, Inc.

Nieker, Diane. Big & Small. 2005. (Heinemann Read & Learn Ser.). (Illus.). 24p. (J). pap. (978-1-4034-7574-9(1)); lib. bdg. (978-1-4034-7569-5(5)) Steck-Vaughn.

—Tall & Short. 2005. (Heinemann Read & Learn Ser.). (Illus.). 24p. (J). pap. (978-1-4034-7576-3(8)); lib. bdg. (978-1-4034-7571-8(7)) Steck-Vaughn.

—Wide & Narrow. 2005. (Illus.). 24p. (J). pap. (978-1-4034-7577-0(6)); lib. bdg. (978-1-4034-7572-5(5)) Steck-Vaughn.

Norma Staff, ed. Formas. 2005. 14p. (978-958-04-8070-9(2)) Norma S.A.

Numbers, Shapes, & Colors. (Puppet & Flannelboard Stories Ser.). (Illus.). 2004. 96p. 11.99 (978-0-7439-3699-6(X)); 2003. 48p. (J). pap. 7.99 (978-0-7439-3230-1(7)) Teacher Created Materials, Inc.

Los Numeros (Touch & Feel 1, 2, 3) 2000. (SPA., Illus.). 10p. (J). (ps). pap. (978-950-11-1420-1(1)) Sigmar.

Olson, Nathan. Circles Around Town. 2007. (Illus.). 32p. (J). 23.93 (978-0-7368-6368-1(0)) Capstone Pr., Inc.

—Cones. 2008. (J). (****978-1-4296-0048-4(9)***) Capstone Pr., Inc.

—Cubes. 2008. (J). (****978-1-4296-0049-1(7)***) Capstone Pr., Inc.

—Cylinders. 2008. (J). (*978-1-4296-0050-7(0)) Capstone Pr., Inc.

—Pyramids. 2008. (J). (*978-1-4296-0051-4(9)) Capstone Pr., Inc.

—Rectangles Around Town. 2007. (Illus.). 32p. (J). 23.93 (978-0-7368-6370-4(2)) Capstone Pr., Inc.

—Squares Around Town. 2007. (Illus.). 32p. (J). (978-0-7368-6371-1(0)) Capstone Pr., Inc.

—Stars Around Town. 2007. (Illus.). 32p. (J). (978-0-7368-6372-8(9)) Capstone Pr., Inc.

Omary, Rachel, illus. Shapes & Colors in Dari. 2004. 5p. (J). spiral bd. 14.95 (978-0-9740535-7-8(0)) Knight Publishing.

—Shapes & Colors in Farsi. l.t. ed. 2004. 5p. (J). spiral bd. 14.95 (978-0-9740535-6-1(2)) Knight Publishing.

—Shapes & Colors in Pashto. l.t. ed. 2004. 5p. (J). spiral bd. 14.95 (978-0-9740535-8-5(9)) Knight Publishing.

O'Neal, Rachael. The Rabbit. 2002. (Animal Shapes Ser.). (Illus.). 10p. (J). bds. 2.95 (978-0-7641-5474-4(5)) Barron's Educational Series, Inc.

O'Neill, Cynthia, ed. My First Colors & Shapes. 2004. (SPA.). 16p. (J). (ps-12). bds. 6.99 (978-0-7566-0449-3(4)) Dorling Kindersley Publishing, Inc.

—My First Sizes & Opposites. 2004. (Barbie Sticker Books Ser.). (SPA.). 16p. (J). bds. 6.99 (978-0-7566-0450-9(8)) Dorling Kindersley Publishing, Inc.

Onyefulu, Ifeoma. Triangle for Adaora: An African Book of Shapes. 2007. (Illus.). 32p. (J). pap. 7.95 (978-1-84507-738-9(5)) Lincoln, Frances Ltd. GBR. *Dist:* Perseus Distribution.

Osofsky, Jill. Making Patterns. 2000. (Funtastic Frogs Ser.). 32p. (J). (gr. k-2). pap., act. bk. ed. 4.99 (978-1-56451-315-1(7) , ID43014) School Specialty Publishing.

—Matching & Sorting. 2000. (Funtastic Frogs Activity Bks.). 32p. (J). (gr. k-2). pap., act. bk. ed. 4.99 (978-1-56451-314-4(9) , ID43011) School Specialty Publishing.

Pallotta, Jerry. Icky Bug Shapes. Bersani, Shennen, illus. 2004. 32p. (J). pap. 5.99 (978-0-439-38918-1(6) , Cartwheel Bks.) Scholastic, Inc.

—Twizzlers: Shapes & Patterns. Bolster, Rob, illus. 2002. 32p. (J). (gr. k-3). pap. 14.95 (978-0-439-35796-8(9) , Cartwheel Bks.) Scholastic, Inc.

Parker, Ant. Shapes. 1999. (Touch & Feel Ser.). (Illus.). 12p. (J). (ps). pap. 4.95 (978-0-7373-0290-5(9) , 02909W, Roxbury Park) Lowell Hse.

Patilla, Peter. Fun with Sizes. McDonald, Brigitte, illus. 1998. (Fun with... Ser.). 32p. (ps-2). lib. bdg. 23.90 (978-0-7613-0959-8(4) , Millbrook Pr.) Lerner Publishing Group.

—Shapes. 1999. (Math Links Ser.). 32p. (J). (gr. k-2). lib. bdg. 21.36 (978-1-57572-968-8(7)) Heinemann Library.

—Starting off with Shapes. 2001. (Starting Off Ser.). (Illus.). (J). (978-0-606-21462-9(3)) Tandem Library Bks.

Patterns. 2007. (J). lib. bdg. 9.95 (*978-0-9768706-3-0(0)) Learning Props.

Patterns All Around. 2002. (Illus.). (J). pap. 3.74 (978-0-7398-5856-1(4)) Steck-Vaughn.

Patterns & Shapes. 2002. (J). pap. 8.95 (978-1-56911-047-8(6)) Learning Resources, Inc.

Peat, Ann. My World. 2005. (Heinemann Read & Learn Ser.). (Illus.). 24p. (J). lib. bdg. (978-1-4034-6467-5(7)) Heinemann Library.

—Shapes. 2005. (My World Ser.). (Illus.). 24p. (J). (gr. k-2). lib. bdg. 20.64 (978-1-4034-6462-0(6)) Heinemann Library.

Penton Overseas, Inc. Staff. Colors, Shapes & Sizes. abr. ed. 2003. (J). (ps-3). 12.99 incl. audio, cd-rom (978-1-894677-24-0(2)) Kidzup Productions.

Peterson, Ingela, illus. Ellie & Pinky's Pop-Up Shapes. 2003. (First Concepts Ser.). 10p. (J). 7.95 (978-1-58117-184-6(6) , Intervisual/Piggy Toes) Dalmatian Pr.

Petty, Colin. Shapes. 2006. (Concept Sliders Ser.). (Illus.). 10p. (J). 5.99 (978-0-7641-5944-2(5)) Barron's Educational Series, Inc.

Pfloog, Jan. Puppy Book: Shape Book. 1999. (gr. k-3). lib. bdg. 11.00 (978-0-613-81152-1(6)) Tandem Library Bks.

Phidal Publishing Staff, ed. Shapes. (Turn & Learn Ser.). 12p. (J). (978-2-7643-0078-7(6)) Phidal Publishing, Inc./Editions Phidal, Inc.

Phillips, Sarah. Wipe Clean: Shapes. 2007. (Trace, Stick & Learn Ser.). (Illus.). 12p. (J). (ps-3). pap. 4.99 (*978-1-84610-479-4(3)) Make Believe Ideas GBR. *Dist:* Ingram Pub. Services.

Phillips, Sarah & Tattam, Mark. Shapes. 2005. (Baby-See-A Shape Ser.). (Illus.). 12p. (ps-k). bds. 4.95 (978-1-905051-90-8(5)) Make Believe Ideas GBR. *Dist:* Ingram Pub. Services.

Pipe, Jim. Big Animals. 2007. (J). (*978-1-59604-161-5(7)) Stargazer Bks.

Pistoia, Sara. Patterns. 2006. (MathBooks Ser.). 24p. (J). 24.21 (978-1-59296-690-5(X)) Child's World, Inc.

Play & Learn Fo, ed. Shapes. 2007. (Play & Learn Foam Puzzle Bks.). 10p. (J). bds. 16.95 (*978-0-7696-5409-6(6) , Brighter Child) School Specialty Publishing.

Play Bac Edu-Team, creator. EyeLike Shapes. 2007. (Illus.). 64p. (J). 9.95 (*978-1-60214-020-2(0)) Play Bac Publishing, USA.

Pluckrose, Henry. Discovering Shapes. 2001. (Let's Explore Ser.). (Illus.). 32p. (J). (gr. 1 up). lib. bdg. 23.33 (978-0-8368-2959-4(X)) Stevens, Gareth Inc.

Pluckrose, Henry Arthur. What Shape Is It? 2006. (Illus.). 32p. (J). (978-1-59771-039-8(3)) Sea-To-Sea Pubns.

—What Size Is It? 2006. (Illus.). 32p. (J). (978-1-59771-040-4(7)) Sea-To-Sea Pubns.

Pocket Chart Math: Colors, Shapes & Patterns. 2002. (J). pap. 9.95 (978-1-56911-078-2(6)) Learning Resources, Inc.

Poitier, Antonine & School Zone Staff. Shapes Spin Wheel Board Books. 2006. (J). (ps-k). bds. 3.99 (*978-0-88743-618-5(8)) School Zone Publishing Co.

Potter, Tony & Kolanovic, Dubravka. Shapes with Albert & Amy: The Fun Way! Kolanovic, Dubravka, illus. 2005. (Illus.). 10p. (J). (gr. 2-5). bds. 5.95 (978-1-59125-569-7(4)) Penton Overseas, Inc.

Powers, Amelia. Giant Pop-Out Shapes. 2007. (Illus.). 26p. (J). (ps). 10.95 (978-0-8118-5921-9(5)) Chronicle Bks. LLC.

Practice Power Flip & Learn Shapes. 2000. (Illus.). 16p. (J). (ps-1). spiral bd. (978-1-930355-22-4(X)) Greenbrier/Scentex.

Practice Power Practice Book - Shapes. (Illus.). (J). (ps-1). 2001. 18p. spiral bd., wbk. ed. (978-1-930355-32-3(7)); 2000. 16p. spiral bd. (978-1-930355-18-7(1)) Greenbrier/Scentex.

Preller, James. NBA Book of Big & Little. 1998. 32p. (J). (ps-2). pap. 3.50 (978-0-590-37756-0(6)) Scholastic, Inc.

Priddy Books Staff & Priddy, Roger. Turn the Wheel Shapes & Sorting: Easy Learning Fun, for the Very You. rev. ed. 2004. (Play & Learn Ser.). (Illus.). 12p. (J). bds. 8.95 (978-0-312-49396-7(7) , Priddy Bks.) St. Martin's Pr.

Professor Q's Chinese-English Language Books: Xing Zhuang - Shapes. 2006. (J). (978-0-9743359-4-0(0)) Murdock Publishing Co.

Publishing Staff, Carson Dellosa. Shapes & Colors. 2005. 80p. pap. (978-1-59441-277-6(4) , RB-904010) Carson-Dellosa Publishing Co., Inc.

Pugliano-Martin, Carol. Building with Shapes. ed. 2004. (Shared Connections Ser.). (J). pap. 27.00 (978-1-4108-1637-5(0)); pap., instr.'s gde. ed. 27.00 (978-1-4108-1613-9(3)) Benchmark Education Co.

QEB Start Math Book Stores Edition: Sizes & Shapes - Book 1. 2006. (J). per. (978-1-59566-273-6(1)) QEB Publishing Inc.

QEB Start Math Book Stores Edition: Sizes & Shapes Book 2. 2006. (J). per. (978-1-59566-277-4(4)) QEB Publishing Inc.

Quadrillion Media Staff. Shapes. 1999. (J). pap. 1.99 (978-1-84100-283-5(6)) Quadrillion Media LLC.

—Shapes. 1999. (Let's Learn Ser.). (J). pap. 3.99 (978-1-84100-298-9(4)) Quadrillion Publishing.

—Toby Plays with Shapes. 1999. bds. 3.95 (978-1-58185-209-7(6)) Quadrillion Media LLC.

Rainbow Bridge Publishing Staff. Spanish Colors & Shapes: First Step Spanish, Level 1. 2002. (First Step Spanish Ser.). (SPA., Illus.). 64p. 5.95 (978-1-887923-83-5(7)) Rainbow Bridge Publishing.

Randolph, Joanne. Drawing Birds. 2005. (Let's Draw with Shapes Ser.). (Illus.). 24p. (J). 17.25 (978-1-4042-2792-7(X) , PowerKids Pr.) Rosen Publishing Group, Inc., The.

—Let's Draw a Bird with Shapes: Vamos a Dibujar un Ave Usando Figuras. Muschinske, Emily, illus. 2005. (Let's Draw with Shapes/ Vamos a dibujar con Figuras Ser.). (J). 17.25 (978-1-4042-7555-3(X) , PowerKids Pr.) Rosen Publishing Group, Inc., The.

Rau, Dana Meachen. Bookworms: The Shape of the World, 6 bks., Set. Incl. Circles. lib. bdg. 22.79 (*978-0-7614-2280-8(3)); Many-Sided Shapes. lib. bdg. 22.95 (*978-0-7614-2279-2(X)); Ovals. lib. bdg. 22.79 (*978-0-7614-2281-5(1)); Rectangles. lib. bdg. 22.79 (*978-0-7614-2282-2(X)); Squares. lib. bdg. 22.79 (*978-0-7614-2284-6(6)); Triangles. lib. bdg. 22.79 (*978-0-7614-2286-0(2)); (Illus.). 24p. (J). (ps-k). 2006. Set lib. bdg. 136.71 (*978-0-7614-2278-5(1) , Benchmark Bks.) Cavendish, Marshall Corp.

—Many-Sided Shapes. 2006. (Bookworms Ser.). (Illus.). 24p. (J). lib. bdg. 22.95 (*978-0-7614-2279-2(X) , Benchmark Bks.) Cavendish, Marshall Corp.

Rau, Dana Meachen. A Star in My Orange: Looking for Nature's Shapes. 2006. (Illus.). (J). pap. 6.95 (978-0-8225-5992-4(7) , First Avenue Editions) Lerner Publishing Group.

Read-Think-Do Math: Sizes & Shapes Book 1. 2006. pap. 4.49 (978-1-4206-8166-6(4)) Teacher Created Materials, Inc.

Read-Think-Do Math: Sizes & Shapes Book 2. 2006. pap. 4.49 (978-1-4206-8170-3(2)) Teacher Created Materials, Inc.

Ready Set Learn Staff. Peeps Shapes. 2005. (Illus.). 24p. (J). (ps-2). bds. 15.99 (978-1-59249-521-4(4) , 1C304) Soundprints.

Realtime Associates and Mazer Corporation Staff & LeapFrog Staff, compiled by. Compare & Name Plane & Solid Shapes. 2002. (J). (gr. 3). 66.75 (978-1-58605-404-5(X) , LeapFrog Schl. Hse.) LeapFrog Enterprises, Inc.

—Compare Plane & Solid Shapes. 2002. (J). (gr. 2). 66.75 (978-1-58605-345-1(0) , LeapFrog Schl. Hse.) LeapFrog Enterprises, Inc.

—Recognize a Shape That Has Changed Orientation. 2002. (J). (gr. 2). 66.75 (978-1-58605-343-7(4) , LeapFrog Schl. Hse.) LeapFrog Enterprises, Inc.

—Recognize Solid Figures (Cube, Cone, Cylinder, Sphere) 2002. (J). (gr. 2). 66.75 (978-1-58605-344-4(2) , LeapFrog Schl. Hse.) LeapFrog Enterprises, Inc.

—Understand & Extend Number or Shape Patterns. 2002. (J). (gr. 3). 66.75 (978-1-58605-405-2(8) , LeapFrog Schl. Hse.) LeapFrog Enterprises, Inc.

Reisberg, Joanne A. Zachary Zormer: Shape Transformer: A Math Adventure. Hohn, David, illus. 2006. (Math Adventures Ser.). (J). 16.95 (978-1-57091-875-9(9)); pap. 6.95 (978-1-57091-876-6(7)) Charlesbridge Publishing, Inc.

Ribke, Simone T. A Garden Full of Sizes. 2005. (Rookie Read-About Math Ser.). (Illus.). 32p. (J). (gr. 1-2). pap. 5.95 (978-0-516-25849-2(4) , Children's Pr.) Scholastic Library Publishing.

Ribke, Simone T. & Vargus, Nanci Reginelli. A Garden Full of Sizes. 2004. (Rookie Read-About Math Ser.). (Illus.). 31p. (J). 20.50 (978-0-516-24432-7(9) , Children's Pr.) Scholastic Library Publishing.

Rigby Education Staff. Discovery World Yel Sizes. (Discovery World Ser.). (Illus.). 12p. (gr. k-1). 23.00 (978-0-7635-2695-5(9)) Rigby Education.

—Little & Big. (Illus.). 8p. (J). bds. 3.95 (978-0-7635-6467-4(2) , 764672C99) Rigby Education.

Rigol, Francesc, illus. Los Contrarios. 2002. (Aprendo con Dan y Din Ser.).Tr. of Opposites. (SPA.). 10p. (ps). 5.95 (978-84-7864-524-4(1)) Combel Editorial, S.A. ESP. *Dist:* Independent Pubs. Group.

—Las Formas. 2002. (Aprendo con Dan y Din Ser.).Tr. of Shapes. (SPA.). 10p. (ps). 5.95 (978-84-7864-521-3(7)) Combel Editorial, S.A. ESP. *Dist:* Independent Pubs. Group.

Ring, Susan. Big or Small? 2006. (Illus.). (J). 16p. (978-0-7368-5983-5(7)); (SPA & ENG., 18p. (978-0-7368-6019-2(3)) Yellow Umbrella Pr.

—Haciendo Formas. 2005. Tr. of Making Shapes. (SPA., Illus.). 16p. (J). (gr. k-1). lib. bdg. 15.93 (978-0-7368-4155-9(5)) Capstone Pr., Inc.

—I See Patterns. 2006. (Yellow Umbrella Books for Early Readers). (Illus.). (J). 16p. (978-0-7368-5978-1(6)(3(0)); (ENG & SPA., 18p. (978-0-7368-6014-7(2)) Yellow Umbrella Pr.

Rivera, Sheila. Is It Big or Little? 2004. (First Step Nonfiction Ser.). (J). pap. (978-0-8225-5406-6(2) , Lerner Pubns.) Lerner Publishing Group.

Robinson, Alice. Shapes in Space: A Shapes Book. 2005. (Illus.). 16p. (J). (ps-k). per. 6.95 (978-1-58117-393-2(8) , Intervisual/Piggy Toes) Dalmatian Pr.

Rosenthal-Gazit, Roni. On Shapes & More. 2007. (J). per. 7.99 (*978-0-9792800-0-9(1)) StoryTime World Publishing Hse.

Ross, Kathy. Kathy Ross Crafts Triangles, Rectangles, Circles & Squares. Barger, Jan, illus. 2002. (Crafts from Kathy Ross Ser.). 48p. (J). (gr. k-2). pap. 7.95 (978-0-7613-1696-1(5) , Millbrook Pr.) Lerner Publishing Group.

Roy, Jennifer Rozines & Roy, Gregory. Shapes in Transportation. 2006. (Math All Around Ser.). (Illus.). 32p. (J). lib. bdg. 28.50 (978-0-7614-2265-5(X) , Benchmark Bks.) Cavendish, Marshall Corp.

Running Press Staff. Shapes: Fit-a-shape. 2000. (Fit-a-Shape Ser.). (Illus.). 10p. (J). (ps-k). pap. 6.95 (978-0-7624-0814-6(6) , Running Pr. Kids) Running Pr. Bk. Pubs.

Running Press Staff, et al. Shapes. 2003. (Magic Windows Ser.). (Illus.). 8p. (J). pap. 4.95 (978-0-7624-1508-3(8) , Running Pr. Kids) Running Pr. Bk. Pubs.

Salisbury, Kent. Circus of Shapes: Fun with All Your Exciting Friends at the Big Top. 1998. (Illus.). 13p. (J). (ps-k). 6.99 (978-0-7681-0083-9(6) , McClanahan Bk.) Learning Horizons, Inc.

Salzmann, Mary Elizabeth. Circles. l.t. ed. 1999. (What Shape Is It? Ser.). (Illus.). 24p. (J). (ps-3). lib. bdg. 19.93 (978-1-57765-163-5(4) , SandCastle) ABDO Publishing Co.

—Ovals. l.t. ed. 1999. (What Shape Is It? Ser.). (Illus.). 24p. (J). (ps-3). lib. bdg. 19.93 (978-1-57765-168-0(5) , SandCastle) ABDO Publishing Co.

—Rectangles. l.t. ed. 1999. (What Shape Is It? Ser.). (Illus.). 24p. (J). (ps-3). lib. bdg. 19.93 (978-1-57765-167-3(7) , SandCastle) ABDO Publishing Co.

—Squares. l.t. ed. 1999. (What Shape Is It? Ser.). (Illus.). 24p. (J). (ps-3). lib. bdg. 19.93 (978-1-57765-164-2(2) , SandCastle) ABDO Publishing Co.

—Triangles. l.t. ed. 1999. (What Shape Is It? Ser.). (Illus.). 24p. (J). (ps-3). lib. bdg. 19.93 (978-1-57765-165-9(0) , SandCastle) ABDO Publishing Co.

—What Color Is It?, Set. l.t. ed. Incl. Blue. lib. bdg. 19.93 (978-1-57765-161-1(8)); Green. lib. bdg. 19.93 (978-1-57765-162-8(6)); Orange. lib. bdg. 19.93 (978-1-57765-158-1(8)); Purple. lib. bdg. 19.93 (978-1-57765-160-4(X)); Red. lib. bdg. 19.93 (978-1-57765-159-8(6)); Yellow. lib. bdg. 19.93 (978-1-57765-157-4(X)); 24p. (J). (ps-3). 1999. Tr. of ¿de Qué Color Es?. (Illus.). 1999. Set lib. bdg. 119.58 (978-1-57765-264-9(9) , SandCastle) ABDO Publishing Co.

—What Shape Is It?, Set. l.t. ed. Incl. Circles. lib. bdg. 19.93 (978-1-57765-163-5(4)); Ovals. lib. bdg. 19.93 (978-1-57765-168-0(5)); Rectangles. lib. bdg. 19.93 (978-1-57765-167-3(7)); Squares. lib. bdg. 19.93 (978-1-57765-164-2(2)); Stars. lib. bdg. 19.93 (978-1-57765-166-6(9)); Triangles. lib. bdg. 19.93 (978-1-57765-165-9(0)); 24p. (J). (ps-3). 1999. (Illus.). 2000. Set lib. bdg. 119.58 (978-1-57765-280-9(0) , SandCastle) ABDO Publishing Co.

SAMi. Big Little. 2007. (Illus.). 24p. (J). bds. 8.95 (978-1-59354-164-4(3)) Handprint Bks.

Santillana & Dorling Kindersley Publishing Staff. Figuras. (Show Me Ser.). (SPA., Illus.). 16p. (J). (ps-k). bds. 6.95 (978-1-58986-327-5(9)) Santillana USA Publishing Co., Inc.

—Tamanos. (Show Me Ser.). (SPA., Illus.). 16p. (J). (ps-k). bds. 6.95 (978-1-58986-328-6(3)) Santillana USA Publishing Co., Inc.

Sarfatti, Esther. Figuras: Circulos/Shapes: Circles. 2008. (Conceptos (Bilingual) Ser.). (SPA & ENG., Illus.). 24p. (J). (ps-3). lib. bdg. (*978-1-60044-751-8(1)) Rourke Publishing, LLC.

—Figuras: Cuadrados/Shapes: Squares. 2008. (Conceptos (Bilingual) Ser.). (SPA & ENG., Illus.). 24p. (J). (ps-3). lib. bdg. (*978-1-60044-753-2(8)) Rourke Publishing, LLC.

—Figuras: Triangulos/Shapes: Triangles. 2008. (Conceptos (Bilingual) Ser.). (SPA & ENG., Illus.). 24p. (J). (ps-3). lib. bdg. (*978-1-60044-754-9(6)) Rourke Publishing, LLC.

—Shapes: Circles. 2008. (J). (*978-1-60044-525-5(X)) Rourke Publishing, LLC.

—Shapes: Rectangles. 2008. (J). (*978-1-60044-526-2(8)) Rourke Publishing, LLC.

—Shapes: Squares. 2008. (J). (*978-1-60044-527-9(6)) Rourke Publishing, LLC.

—Shapes: Triangles. 2008. (J). (*978-1-60044-528-6(4)) Rourke Publishing, LLC.

Sargent, Brian. Grandfather's Shape Story. 2006. (Rookie Read-About Math Ser.). (Illus.). 32p. (J). (gr. k-2). 20.50 (978-0-516-29919-8(0) , Children's Pr.) Scholastic Library Publishing.

Savary, Fabien. Caillou: Que Falta? Tipeo, illus. 2004. Tr. of What's Missing?. (SPA.). 12p. (J). bds. 4.95 (978-1-58728-349-9(2) , Creative Publishing International) Quayside.

Savary, Fabien & Vadeboncoeur, Isabelle. Caillou: Donde Esta? Tipeo, illus. 2004. Tr. of Where Is It?. (SPA.). 12p. (J). bds. 4.95 (978-1-58728-402-1(2) , Creative Publishing International) Quayside.

—Caillou: Sorpresa! Tipeo, illus. 2004. Tr. of What's Inside?. (SPA.). 12p. (J). bds. 4.95 (978-1-58728-390-1(5) , Creative Publishing International) Quayside.

Schaefer, Lola M. Fomas en Movimiento. (Ruedas, Alas y Agua Ser.). 24p. pap. 5.25 (978-1-4034-3533-0(2)) Heinemann Library.

—Shapes to Go. 2003. (Wheels, Wings, & Water Ser.). (Illus.). 24p. (J). lib. bdg. 18.50 (978-1-4034-0886-0(6)); pap. (978-1-4034-3622-1(3)) Heinemann Library.

—Shapes to Go. 2003. (gr. k-3). lib. bdg. 13.30 (978-0-613-67433-1(2)) Tandem Library Bks.

—What Is Big, Big, Big? 2007. (J). (978-1-59515-930-4(4)) Rourke Publishing, LLC.

Schneck, Susan J. Shapes & Colors. 1999. (Step Ahead Workbooks Ser.). (Illus.). 32p. (J). (ps). pap., wbk. ed. 2.99 (978-0-307-23556-5(4) , 03556, Golden Bks.) Random Hse. Children's Bks.

Scholastic, Inc. Staff. Fun Shapes: A Pull & Pop Book. 2007. (Let's Find Out Ser.). 12p. (J). pap. 6.99 (*978-0-439-85363-7(X)) Scholastic, Inc.

Scholastic, Inc. Staff. My First Shapes. 2006. (Leapfrog Ser.). 12p. (J). 9.99 (978-0-439-85358-3(3) , Cartwheel Bks.) Scholastic, Inc.

Scholastic, Inc. Staff, ed. Secret Shapes. (Changing Picture Bks.). (Illus.). (J). pap. 9.99 (978-0-590-24644-6(5)) Scholastic, Inc.

Scholastic, Inc. Staff & Gerth, Melanie. My First Jumbo Book of Shapes. Diaz, James, illus. 2004. (My First Jumbo Book Ser.). 10p. (J). pap. 9.95 (978-0-439-62377-3(4) , Cartwheel Bks.) Scholastic, Inc.

School Specialty Publishing. Colors & Shapes. 2006. (Brighter Child Flash Cards Ser.). 54p. (J). 2.99 (978-0-7696-4689-3(1) , Brighter Child) School Specialty Publishing.

—Colors & Shapes / Los Colores y las Formas. 2006. (Brighter Child Flash Cards Ser.). 54p. (J). 2.99 (978-0-7696-4769-2(3) , Brighter Child) School Specialty Publishing.

—Colors & Shapes, Preschool. 2006. (Skills for Scholars Ser.). 80p. (C). pap. 4.99 (*978-0-7696-5009-8(0) , Schaffer, Frank) Schaffer, Frank Pubns.

—Easy Alphabet, Colors, Numbers & Shapes. 2001. (Phonics Flash Cards Ser.). 104p. (C). 6.99 (978-0-86734-411-0(3) , Schaffer, Frank) Schaffer, Frank Pubns.

—Lacing Patterns. 2000. (Funtastic Frogs Activity Cards Ser.). 18p. (J). (gr. k-2). 8.99 (978-1-56451-347-2(5)) School Specialty Publishing.

—Photo Shapes. 2002. (Learning Cards Ser.). 9p. (J). (gr. k-2). 7.99 (978-0-7424-1495-2(7) , Instructional Fair) Schaffer, Frank Pubns.

—Shapes. 2004. (On-File Ser.). 4p. (J). (gr. k-k). ring bd. 4.99 (978-0-7424-2879-9(6) , Instructional Fair) Schaffer, Frank Pubns.

—Sizes. 2003. (Skills for Every Child Ser.). 32p. (J). pap. 5.99 (978-1-57029-458-7(5) , WPH99014, Totline Pubns.) Schaffer, Frank Pubns.

School Specialty Publishing. Starter sk Wbk-color/shape/sz. 2007. (English-Espanol Starter Skills Ser.). 80p. (J). (gr. k-2). pap. 8.99 (*978-0-7682-3439-8(5) , Schaffer, Frank) Schaffer, Frank Pubns.

School Zone Publishing. Same or Different. 2003. (Preschool Ser.). (J). cd-rom 19.99 (978-1-58947-902-9(5)) School Zone Publishing Co.

School Zone Publishing Company Staff. Guess Who? A Book of Colors & Shapes. 2000. (Illus.). 16p. (J). bds. 4.99 (978-0-88743-606-2(4) , 06607) School Zone Publishing Co.

—Preschool Basics. 2002. (Illus.). 128p. (J). (ps). pap., wbk. ed. 7.99 (978-1-58947-002-6(8) , 02453) School Zone Publishing Co.

—Shapes & Colors. 2005. 64p. (J). (ps-k). pap., wbk. ed. 3.79 (978-1-58947-357-7(4)) School Zone Publishing Co.

School Zone Staff. Colors, Shapes & More. 2004. (J). 2.79 (978-1-58947-988-3(2)) School Zone Publishing Co.

Schuette, Sarah L. Circles. 2002. (A+ Shape Books). (Illus.). 32p. (J). (gr. k-1). lib. bdg. 22.60 (978-0-7368-1460-7(4) , Aplus Bks.) Capstone Pr., Inc.

—Ovals. 2002. (A+ Shape Books). (Illus.). 32p. (J). (gr. k-1). lib. bdg. 22.60 (978-0-7368-1461-4(2) , Aplus Bks.) Capstone Pr., Inc.

—Rectangles. 2002. (A+ Shape Books). (Illus.). 32p. (J). (gr. k-1). lib. bdg. 22.60 (978-0-7368-1462-1(0) , Aplus Bks.) Capstone Pr., Inc.

—Shapes, 6 bks. Incl. Circles. lib. bdg. 22.60 (978-0-7368-1460-7(4)); Ovals. lib. bdg. 22.60 (978-0-7368-1461-4(2)); Rectangles. lib. bdg. 22.60 (978-0-7368-1462-1(0)); Squares. lib. bdg. 22.60 (978-0-7368-1463-8(9)); Stars. lib. bdg. 22.60 (978-0-7368-1464-5(7)); Triangles. lib. bdg. 22.60 (978-0-7368-1465-2(5)); 32p. (J). (gr. k-1). 2002. (Illus.). 2002. Set lib. bdg. 135.60 (978-0-7368-1466-9(3) , Aplus Bks.) Capstone Pr., Inc.

—Squares. 2002. (A+ Shape Books). (Illus.). 32p. (J). (gr. k-1). lib. bdg. 22.60 (978-0-7368-1463-8(9) , Aplus Bks.) Capstone Pr., Inc.

—Stars. 2002. (A+ Shape Books). (Illus.). 32p. (J). (gr. k-1). lib. bdg. 22.60 (978-0-7368-1464-5(7) , Aplus Bks.) Capstone Pr., Inc.

—Triangles. 2002. (A+ Shape Books). (Illus.). 32p. (J). (gr. k-1). lib. bdg. 22.60 (978-0-7368-1465-2(5) , Aplus Bks.) Capstone Pr., Inc.

Schulte, Jessica. Can You Find It Inside? Search & Discover for Young Art Lovers. 2005. (Illus.). 32p. (J). (gr. k-4). 10.95 (978-0-8109-5794-7(9) , Abrams Bks. for Young Readers) Abrams, Harry N. , Inc.

—Can You Find It Outside? Search & Discover for Young Art Lovers. 2005. (Illus.). 32p. (J). (gr. k-4). 10.95 (978-0-8109-5795-4(7) , Abrams Bks. for Young Readers) Abrams, Harry N. , Inc.

schumacher, Bev. Shape Land. 2004. (ENG.). 20p. (J). lib. bdg. 9.95 (978-0-9741549-8-5(9)) Learning Props.

Schwartz, Betty Ann. The Spinning Book of Colors, Shapes, & Numbers. Berg, Michelle, illus. 2007. 16p. (J). (ps-1). 9.99 (978-0-06-079974-8(9) , Harper Festival) HarperCollins Pubs.

Scott, Janine. The Shape of Things. 2003. (Spyglass Books). (Illus.). 24p. (J). (gr. 1 up). lib. bdg. 18.60 (978-0-7565-0453-3(8)) Compass Point Bks.

Senisi, Ellen B. A 3-D Birthday Party. 2006. (Rookie Read-About Math Ser.). (Illus.). 31p. (J). (978-0-516-29828-3(3)) Children's Pr., Ltd.

Sequencing Sizes Cards-Which Is Big? Bigger? Biggest? (ps-3). 7.99 (978-1-56451-634-3(2) , ID2686) School Specialty Publishing.

Sesame Building Blocks: Cube Books. 2002. (J). (978-1-931312-81-3(8)) SoftPlay, Inc.

Seuss, Dr. The Tooth Book. Jonaitis, Alice, ed. Mathieu, Joe, illus. 2000. (Bright & Early Bks.). 48p. (J). (gr. k-1). lib. bdg. 11.99 (978-0-375-91039-5(5) , Random Hse. Bks. for Young Readers) Random Hse. Children's Bks.

—The Tooth Book. Mathieu, Joe, illus. 2000. (Bright & Early Bks.: Vol. 25). 48p. (J). (gr. k-1). 8.99 (978-0-375-81039-8(0) , Random Hse. Bks. for Young Readers) Random Hse. Children's Bks.

Sevaly, Karen. Nothing But... Shape Books! Reproducible Shape Book Patterns for All Occasions! Sevaly, Karen, illus. 1999. (Illus.). 80p. (J). pap. 9.95 (978-1-57882-022-1(7) , TF-1654) Teacher's Friend Pubns., Inc.

Sevaly, Karen, ed. Hands on Learning: Color & Shape Dominoes. 2006. 12.99 (978-0-439-82402-6(8) , Teaching Resources) Scholastic, Inc.

Shapeland. 2004. Tr. of Figuralandia. (SPA.). lib. bdg. 9.95 net. (978-0-9741549-2-3(X)) Learning Props.

Shapes. (Sparkly Board Bks.). (Illus.). (J). bds. (978-1-84239-256-0(5)) Alligator Bks. Ltd.

Shapes. 2003. (Illus.). 12p. 5.95 (978-0-7548-0378-2(3) , Lorenz Bks.) Anness Publishing GBR. *Dist:* National Bk. Network.

Shapes. 2004. 12p. (J). bds. 3.99 (978-1-85997-814-6(2)) Byeway Bks.

Shapes. 2002. (Home Workbooks Ser.). 64p. (J). pap. 2.49 (978-0-88724-710-1(5) , CD-4512) Carson-Dellosa Publishing Co., Inc.

Shapes. 2002. (Puppy Steps Ser.). (Illus.). 10p. (J). (ps). bds. 3.99 (978-1-57759-636-3(6)) Dalmatian Pr.

Shapes. 2000. (Pajama Bedtime Bear Ser.). (Illus.). 14p. (J). (ps). bds. 3.95 (978-0-7894-1422-9(8) , D K Ink) Dorling Kindersley Publishing, Inc.

Shapes, Vol. 4. (Early Intervention Levels Ser.). 3.85 (978-1-56334-972-0(8)) Hampton-Brown Bks.

Shapes. 2003. (J). per. (978-1-57657-917-6(4)); per. (978-1-57657-915-2(8)) Paradise Pr., Inc.

Shapes. Date not set. (Illus.). 16p. (J). 2.98 (978-0-7525-9454-5(0)) Parragon, Inc.

Shapes. (Skills for Every Child Ser.). 32p. 5.99 (978-1-57029-457-0(7) , WPH99013, Totline Pubns.) Schaffer, Frank Pubns.

Shapes. 2003. (Preschool Ser.). (J). 19.99 (978-1-58947-904-3(1)) School Zone Publishing Co.

Shapes. 2001. (Early Learning Ser.). (J). (gr. k-12). vinyl bd. 4.95 (978-1-58845-047-0(3)) School Specialty Publishing.

Shapes. 2002. (Illus.). (J). pap. 3.74 (978-0-7398-5858-5(0)) Steck-Vaughn.

Shapes anc colors shaped layer Book. 2006. (J). bds. 4.99 (978-1-934004-08-1(1)) Byeway Bks.

Shapes & Opposites: Fun to Learn. 1999. (Illus.). 32p. (ps-2). 1.99 (978-1-58279-010-7(8) , 96) Trident Pr. International.

Shapes for Me. 1998. (Fisher-Price Bubble-Bath Bks.). (Illus.). 6p. (J). (ps). vinyl bd. (978-0-7666-0146-8(3) , Honey Bear Bks.) Modern Publishing.

Shapes in My World: Big Book: Level F. (Visionstm Ser.). 8p. 20.95 (978-0-322-00629-4(5)) Wright Group, The.

Shapes of Aloha. 2000. (J). 8.99 (978-0-89610-355-9(2)) Island Heritage Publishing.

Sharman, Lydia. The Amazing Book of Shapes. (Illus.). 40p. (J). pap. 18.95 (978-0-590-24306-3(3)) Scholastic, Inc.

Shaw, Charles Green. It Looked Like Spilt Milk: Nwg Zoo Le Mig Nyuj Nchuav/Nws Zoo Li Mis Nyuj Nchuav. 2000. (Illus.). 32p. (J). (ps-1). pap. 6.95 (978-1-931016-00-1(3)) Minnesota Humanities Commission.

Shepard, Daniel. Solid Shapes. 2005. (J). (978-0-7368-5319-4(7)); (Illus.). 17p. (978-0-7368-5283-8(2)) Capstone Pr., Inc.

Ship Shapes. 2000. (Pooh Learning Ser.). (J). (ps-3). pap. 6.98 incl. audio (978-0-7634-0471-0(3)) Walt Disney Records.

Shopping for Shapes & Colors. 1998. (Fisher-Price Little People Concept Bks.: Vol. 4). (Illus.). 24p. (J). (978-0-7666-0322-6(9) , 19615) Modern Publishing.

Shulman, Mark. My Square Breakfast. Miline, Bill, photos by. 2006. (Illus.). 10p. (J). (gr. k-4). reprint ed. 6.00 (978-1-4223-5710-1(4)) DIANE Publishing Co.

Siede, George & Press, Donna, photos by. Collections. 1998. (Active Minds Ser.). (Illus.). 40p. (J). bds. 12.98 (978-1-58048-032-1(2)) Sandvik Publishing.

—Shapes. 1998. (Active Minds Ser.). (Illus.). 10p. (J). bds. 3.99 (978-1-58048-029-1(2)) Sandvik Publishing.

Silver Dolphin en Español Editors. Caritas felices: Tigger: Happy Faces: Tigger, Spanish-Language Edition. 2007. (Illus.). 8p. (J). bds. 7.95 (***978-970-718-391-9(8)*** , Silver Dolphin en Español) Advanced Marketing, S. de R. L. de C. V. MEX. *Dist:* Perseus Distribution.

—Disney Learning: Formas: Disney Learning: Shapes, Spanish-Language Edition. 2006. (Illus.). 12p. (J). 3.99 (***978-970-718-429-9(9)*** , Silver Dolphin en Español) Advanced Marketing, S. de R. L. de C. V. MEX. *Dist:* Perseus Distribution.

Silver Dolphin en Español Staff, ed. Baby Einstein: Libro con ventanas: Formas: Baby Einstein Flip Flap Book: Shapes. 2007. (Baby Einstein. Libro con Ventanas Ser.). (Illus.). 5p. (J). 6.95 (***978-970-718-468-8(X)*** , Silver Dolphin en Español) Advanced Marketing, S. de R. L. de C. V. MEX. *Dist:* Perseus Distribution.

Simard, Remy. Captain Invincible & the Space Shapes: Three-Dimensional Shapes. 2001. 11.79 (978-0-606-22288-4(X)) Tandem Library Bks.

Sizes: Individual Title Six-Packs. (Discovery World Ser.). 12p. (gr. k-1). 28.00 (978-0-7635-8447-4(9)) Rigby Education.

Sizes & Shapes. 2005. (J). Bk. 1. per. 8.95 (978-1-59566-155-5(7)); Bk. 2. per. 8.95 (978-1-59566-159-3(X)) QEB Publishing Inc.

Slaughter, Tom. One, Two, Three. 2003. (Illus.). 24p. (J). (gr. k-k). 12.95 (978-0-88776-664-0(1)) Tundra Bks., Inc./ Livres Toundra, Inc. CAN. *Dist:* Random Hse., Inc.

Southwater Staff. Look & Learn: Shapes & Sizes. 2000. (Look & Learn Ser.). (Illus.). 32p. (ps). 7.95 (978-1-84215-047-4(2) , Southwater) Anness Publishing GBR. *Dist:* National Bk. Network.

—Look & Learn about Opposites. 2001. (Look & Learn Ser.). (Illus.). 32p. (ps). 7.95 (978-1-84215-285-0(8) , Southwater) Anness Publishing GBR. *Dist:* National Bk. Network.

—Look & Learn, Mix & Match. 2001. (Look & Learn Ser.). (Illus.). 32p. (ps). 7.95 (978-1-84215-286-7(6) , Southwater) Anness Publishing GBR. *Dist:* National Bk. Network.

Spots or Stripes. 2002. (Benchmark Bks.). (J). pap. 3.74 (978-0-7398-5852-3(1)) Steck-Vaughn.

Squares. (Shapes Ser.). 32p. (J). 7.95 (978-0-7368-5061-2(9)) Capstone Pr., Inc.

Steck-Vaughn Staff. Early Math: Shapes, 10 Pack. 2005. pap. 29.95 (978-1-4190-0344-8(5)) Steck-Vaughn.

—Early Math Set 1: Shapes. 2005. pap. 2.99 (978-1-4190-0320-2(8)) Steck-Vaughn.

—Head for Home: Colors & Shapes. 2004. (Illus.). pap. (978-0-7398-8554-3(5)) Steck-Vaughn.

—I'm Just the Right Size. 2000. (Illus.). (J). bds. (978-0-7398-4444-1(X)) Steck-Vaughn.

—Mathematics Level H-J: Shape Search. 2003. (Illus.). (J). bds. (978-0-7398-7664-0(3)) Steck-Vaughn.

—Super Sizes! 2003. pap. 4.10 (978-0-7398-7658-9(9)) Steck-Vaughn.

Sterling Publishing Co., Inc. & Arena Verlag. Kids' First Mandalas. 2005. (Illus.). 64p. pap. 4.95 (978-1-4027-1801-4(2)) Sterling Publishing Co., Inc.

—Kids' Flower Mandalas. 2005. (Illus.). 64p. pap. 4.95 (978-1-4027-1803-8(9)) Sterling Publishing Co., Inc.

Sterling Publishing Company Staff. Color by Shapes. 1999. (Balloon Ser.). (Illus.). 16p. (J). pap. 2.95 (978-0-8069-1941-6(8)) Sterling Publishing Co., Inc.

—Colors & Shapes. 1998. (Balloon Ser.). (Illus.). 16p. (ps-1). pap. 5.95 (978-0-8069-9607-3(2)) Sterling Publishing Co., Inc.

Sterling/Balloon. Color by Shapes. 1999. (Balloon Ser.). (Illus.). 16p. (J). (ps-k). pap. 2.95 (978-0-8069-1943-0(4)) Sterling Publishing Co., Inc.

Stockland, Patricia M. Pointy, Long, or Round: A Book about Animal Shapes. Ouren, Todd, illus. 2005. (Animal Wise Ser.). 24p. (J). (gr. k-2). 22.60 (978-1-4048-0935-2(X)) Picture Window Bks.

Stoppard, Miriam. Shapes. 2006. (Let's Play Ser.). (Illus.). 14p. (J). bds. 8.99 (978-0-7566-1699-1(9)) Dorling Kindersley Publishing, Inc.

Studio Mouse. Tracing Shapes. rev. ed. 2005. (Illus.). 28p. (J). 14.99 incl. cd-rom (978-1-59069-445-9(7) , 1A600) Studio Mouse LLC.

Studio Mouse, ed. Colors & Shapes. rev. ed. 2007. (Illus.). 28p. 16.99 incl. audio compact disk (978-1-59069-505-0(4) , 1C1000) Studio Mouse LLC.

Tagel, Peggy, illus. On the Go. 2003. (Squishy Shapes Ser.). 10p. (J). 12.95 (978-1-57145-739-4(9) , Silver Dolphin Bks.) Advantage Pubs. Group.

Taylor, Barbara. Mega & Micro. 2001. (Weird & Wonderful Ser.). (Illus.). 24p. (J). (gr. 1-5). 9.95 (978-0-87226-659-9(1) , Bedrick, Peter Bks.) School Specialty Publishing.

Taylor, Geraldine. Shapes. 2003. (Baby Genius Ser.). (Illus.). 16p. (J). bds. 6.99 (978-0-7894-9884-7(7)) Dorling Kindersley Publishing, Inc.

Teis, Kyra. Look! Teis, Kyra, illus. 2005. (Illus.). 20p. (J). (ps-ps). per. 6.95 (978-1-59572-022-1(7)) Star Bright Bks., Inc.

Top That Publishing Staff, ed. Shapes. 2004. (Magnetic Play & Learn Ser.). (Illus.). 12p. (J). (978-1-84510-048-3(4)) Top That! Publishing PLC.

Triangles. (Shapes Ser.). 32p. (J). 7.95 (978-0-7368-5063-6(5)) Capstone Pr., Inc.

Tucker, Shirley & Rambo, Jane. Looking at Shapes. 2002. (Yellow Umbrella Books). (Illus.). 16p. (J). (gr. 1). lib. bdg. 14.60 (978-0-7368-1284-9(9) , Pebble Bks.) Capstone Pr., Inc.

Tuxworth, Nicola. Learn-a-Word Picture Book: Patterns, 12 vols. 2006. (Learn-A-Word Picture Bks.). (Illus.). 12p. bds. 6.99 (978-0-7548-1460-3(2) , Lorenz Bks.) Anness Publishing GBR. *Dist:* National Bk. Network.

—Shapes. 2005. (Illus.). 12p. (gr. 2-13). bds. 6.99 (978-0-7548-1476-4(9) , Lorenz Bks.) Anness Publishing GBR. *Dist:* National Bk. Network.

—Sizes. 2005. (Illus.). 12p. (gr. 2-13). bds. 6.99 (978-0-7548-1412-2(2) , Lorenz Bks.) Anness Publishing GBR. *Dist:* National Bk. Network.

Tuxworth, Nicola & Lorenz Editors. Shapes. 2001. (Let's Look at... Ser.). (Illus.). 20p. 5.95 (978-0-7548-0947-0(1)) Anness Publishing GBR. *Dist:* National Bk. Network.

—Sizes. 2001. (Let's Look at...Ser.). (Illus.). 20p. 5.95 (978-0-7548-0952-4(8) , Lorenz Bks.) Anness Publishing GBR. *Dist:* National Bk. Network.

Valat, Pierre-Marie & Grant, Donald. Shapes. 2001. (First Discovery Look-Inside Board Bks.). (Illus.). 10p. (J). bds. 4.95 (978-0-439-29729-5(X) , Cartwheel Bks.) Scholastic, Inc.

VanVoorst, Jennifer. Making Shapes. 2003. (Yellow Umbrella Books for Early Readers). (Illus.). 17p. (J). 15.93 (978-0-7368-2933-5(4)); pap. (978-0-7368-2892-5(3)) Yellow Umbrella Pr.

Vogel, Julia. Crescents. Holm, Sharon Lane, illus. 2007. (Shapes Ser.). 24p. (J). (ps-2). lib. bdg. 25.65 (***978-1-60270-044-4(3)*** , Looking Glass Library) Magic Wagon.

—Ovals. Holm, Sharon Lane, illus. 2007. (Shapes Ser.). 24p. (J). (ps-2). lib. bdg. 25.65 (***978-1-60270-045-1(1)*** , Looking Glass Library) Magic Wagon.

Walsh, Melanie. Big & Little. Walsh, Melanie, illus. 2001. (Illus.). 14p. (J). (ps-k). bds. 4.99 (978-0-7636-1512-3(9)) Candlewick Pr.

Ward, Becki. Jumbo's Book of Shapes. Lambert, Jonathan, illus. 1998. 6p. (J). pap. 14.98 (978-1-58048-039-0(X)) Sandvik Publishing.

Watt, Melanie. Shapes. 2005. (Learning with Animals Board Bks.). (Illus.). 24p. (J). (gr. k up). (978-1-55337-833-4(4)) Kids Can Pr., Ltd.

Weatherill, Stephen. Shape up, Goz! 2003. (Baby Goz Ser.). (Illus.). 16p. (J). 12.95 (978-1-84507-005-2(4)) Lincoln, Frances Ltd. GBR. *Dist:* Perseus Distribution.

Weber, Lou, ed. Shapes & Colors. 2004. 1p. (J). 7.98 (978-1-4127-3300-7(6) , 5542200) Publications International, Ltd.

—Zoom Zoom Lace & Learn. 2004. 16p. (J). spiral bd., bds. 9.98 (978-1-4127-3153-9(4) , 7232200) Publications International, Ltd.

Weber, Rebecca. Building with Shapes. 2004. (Spyglass Books). 24p. (J). (gr. 1 up). lib. bdg. 19.93 (978-0-7565-0655-1(7)) Compass Point Bks.

Weekly Reader Early Learning Library (Firm) Staff, contrib. by. I Know Big & Small. 2006. (I'm Ready for Math Ser.). (Illus.). 16p. (J). pap. (978-0-8368-6479-3(4)); lib. bdg. 16.67 (978-0-8368-6474-8(3)) Stevens, Gareth Inc.

—I Know Big & Small: Grande y Pequeño. 2006. (ENG & SPA., Illus.). 16p. (J). pap. (978-0-8368-6489-2(1)); lib. bdg. 16.67 (978-0-8368-6484-7(0)) Stevens, Gareth Inc.

—I Know Shapes: Las Figuras. 2006. (ENG & SPA., Illus.). 16p. (J). pap. 4.50.(978-0-8368-6492-2(1)); lib. bdg. 16.67 (978-0-8368-6487-8(5)) Stevens, Gareth Inc.

What Belongs? 2003. (Bear in the Big Blue House Ser.). 16p. (J). pap., act. bk. ed. 4.99 (978-1-57768-713-9(2)) School Specialty Publishing.

What Color Is It? 2004. Tr. of ¿de Qué Color Es?. (SPA.). lib. bdg. 9.95 net. (978-0-9741549-0-9(3)) Learning Props.

What Color Is It? 2003. (Bear in the Big Blue House Ser.).Tr. of ¿de Qué Color Es?. (Illus.). 16p. (J). (ps-k). pap., act. bk. ed. 4.99 (978-1-57768-701-6(9)) School Specialty Publishing.

What Comes Next? 2000. (Illus.). 16p. (J). (ps-1). wbk. ed. 3.79 (978-1-889319-80-3(5)) Trend Enterprises, Inc.

What Goes Next? 2003. (Bear in the Big Blue House Ser.). (Illus.). 16p. (J). (ps-k). pap., act. bk. ed. 4.99 (978-1-57768-703-0(5)) School Specialty Publishing.

What Is Missing? 2003. (Bear in the Big Blue House Ser.). 16p. (J). (ps-k). pap., act. bk. ed. 4.99 (978-1-57768-714-6(0)) School Specialty Publishing.

Which Does Not Belong. 2002. (Illus.). (J). pap. 3.74 (978-0-7398-5861-5(0)) Steck-Vaughn.

Whitehouse, Patricia. Tamanos en el Zoologico. 2002. (Matematicas del Zoologico (Zoo Math) Ser.). (SPA.). 24p. (J). (ps-1). pap. 5.25 (978-1-58810-864-7(3) , 91630); lib. bdg. 18.50 (978-1-58810-805-0(8)) Heinemann Library.

—Zoo Sizes. 2002. 24p. (J). (ps-1). pap. (978-1-58810-759-6(0) , 91413); (Illus.). lib. bdg. 18.50 (978-1-58810-551-6(2)) Heinemann Library.

Wipe-Away Books: Colors & Shapes. 2003. (Illus.). 16p. (J). (ps up). pap. 3.99 (978-0-7682-0069-0(5)) School Specialty Publishing.

Wise the Turtle Counts to Tenb & Shapes. 2003. 3.99 (978-0-915960-05-7(2)) Ebon Research Systems Publishing, LLC.

The World of Eric Carle My Shapes Activity Kit. 2007. (J). 16.99 (***978-0-9794445-3-1(5)***) Loew-Cornell, Inc.

Yates, Irene. Shape. 2002. (All about Ser.). (Illus.). 32p. (J). lib. bdg. 24.25 (978-1-930643-98-7(5)) Chrysalis Education.

Yenawine, Philip. Shapes. 2nd ed. 2006. (Illus.). 32p. (gr. 13 up). 9.95 (978-0-87070-177-1(0)) D.A.P./Distributed Art Pubs.

Yolen, Jane. Animal Train: A Lift-the-Flap Concept Book. Cushman, Doug, illus. 2002. 14p. (J). (ps-1). bds. 8.99 (978-0-689-84838-4(2) , Little Simon) Simon & Schuster Children's Publishing.

Yoon, Salina, illus. Foil Fun Learning Books: Numbers, Colors, Opposites, Shapes, 4 bks. Incl. Foil Fun Colors. (J). bds. 4.95 (978-1-58117-061-0(0)); Foil Fun Numbers. bds. 4.95 (978-1-58117-062-7(9)); Foil Fun Opposites. (J). bds. 4.95 (978-1-58117-063-4(7)); Foil Fun Shapes. (J). bds. 4.95 (978-1-58117-064-1(5)); 10p. (ps). 2000. (Foil Fun Board Bks.). (Illus.). 2000. Set bds. 14.95 (978-1-58117-065-8(3) , Intervisual/Piggy Toes) Dalmatian Pr.

Your Baby Can Learn! Shapes, Vol. 1. 2007. (J). 7.95 (***978-1-931026-13-0(0)***) Infant Learning Co., The.

Zeifert, Harriet. Go! SAMi, illus. 2006. 24p. bds. 8.95 (978-1-59354-138-5(4)) Blue Apple Bks.

Zuckerman, Rory. Shapely Sleepy Sheep. Roos, Maryn, illus. 2004. (J). bds. 12.95 (978-0-9749305-2-7(0)) Castle Pacific Publishing.

Zuravicky, Orli. Exploring Pyramids Around the World: Making Models of Geometric Solids. 2004. (PowerMath Ser.). (Illus.). 32p. (J). lib. bdg. 22.50 (978-0-8239-8992-8(5) , PowerKids Pr.) Rosen Publishing Group, Inc., The.

S

SIZE AND SHAPE—FICTION

Aigner-Clark, Julie. What's Bigger Than Me? Zaidi, Nadeem, illus. 2006. 16p. (ps-17). 5.99 (978-0-7868-4974-1(6)) Hyperion Bks. for Children.

Albee, Sarah. Kidoozle Kids & the Great Shape Rescue! 2004. (Illus.). 12p. bds. 9.95 (978-1-932915-02-0(8)) Sandvik Publishing.

Alborough, Jez. Tall. Alborough, Jez, illus. 2005. (Illus.). 40p. (J). (ps up). 15.99 (978-0-7636-2784-3(4)) Candlewick Pr.

—Tall. Alborough, Jez, illus. 2007. (Illus.). 34p. (J). (gr. k-ps). bds. 6.99 (978-0-7636-3328-8(3)) Candlewick Pr.

—Watch Out! Big Bro's Coming! Alborough, Jez, illus. 1998. (Illus.). 32p. (J). (ps-3). pap. 6.99 (978-0-7636-0584-1(0)) Candlewick Pr.

Allcroft, Britt. Little Engines Can Do Big Things. Coatimundi Studios, illus. 2000. (Thomas & the Magic Railroad Ser.). 24p. (J). (ps-1). pap. 3.25 (978-0-375-80553-0(2) , Random Hse. Bks. for Young Readers) Random Hse. Children's Bks.

—Little Engines Can Do Big Things. 2000. (gr. k-3). lib. bdg. 10.95 (978-0-613-26025-1(2)) Tandem Library Bks.

Anderson, Doug. Too Big to Dance. Anderson, Sara, illus. 2004. 32p. (J). 15.95 (978-1-59354-046-3(9)) Handprint Bks.

Archer, Mike. Looking after Little Ellie. Archer, Dosh, illus. 2005. 300p. (J). 15.95 (978-1-58234-971-8(1)) Bloomsbury Publishing.

Aston, Dianna Hutts. Not So Tall for Six. Dormer, Frank W., illus. 2008. (J). (***978-1-57091-705-9(1)***) Charlesbridge Publishing, Inc.

Augarde, Steve. Hello, Moon. 2004. (Silly Monsters Ser.). (Illus.). 8p. (J). 5.95 (978-0-7696-3338-1(2) , Gingham Dog Pr.) School Specialty Publishing.

Auseon, Andrew. Funny Little Monkey. 2005. 304p. (YA). (gr. 9-12). 17.00 (978-0-15-205334-5(4)) Harcourt Children's Bks.

Barkly, Bob. A Puppy to Love. Kurtz, John, illus. 2001. (Clifford, the Big Red Dog Ser.). (J). (gr. k-2). pap. (978-0-439-22004-0(1)) Scholastic, Inc.

Barnes, Laura T. Teeny Tiny Ernest. Camburn, Carol A., illus. 2002. (Ernest Ser.: Vol. 2). 32p. (J). (ps-3). 15.95 (978-0-9674681-1-2(6)) Barnesyard Bks.

Bauer, Joan. Stand Tall. 192p. (YA). 2005. (gr. 5). pap. 7.99 (978-0-14-240427-0(6) , Puffin); 2002. (gr. 6-9). 16.99 (978-0-399-23473-6(X) , Putnam Juvenile) Penguin Group (USA) Inc.

Bedford, David. Big Bears Can! Hansen, Gaby, illus. 2007. 18p. (J). (ps-k). bds. 6.95 (***978-1-58925-826-6(6)*** , tiger tales) ME Media LLC.

Beetle Dan & the Big Purple Slide. 2006. 32p. pap. 14.99 (978-1-59185-921-5(2) , Creation Hse.) Strang Communications Co.

Benjamin, A. H. & Holstien, Elisabeth. A Duck So Small. 1998. (Illus.). 32p. (J). (ps-3). 14.95 (978-1-888444-30-8(4) , 21028) Little Tiger Pr.

Bentley, Dawn. Shapes. Rivoli Group Staff, illus. 2000. (Jay Jay the Jet Plane's Peek-a-Boo Board Bks.). 12p. (J). (ps-k). bds. 6.95 (978-1-58117-101-3(3) , Intervisual/ Piggy Toes) Dalmatian Pr.

Berenstain, Stan & Berenstain, Jan. The Berenstain Bears in the House of Mirrors. Berenstain, Stan & Berenstain, Jan, illus. 2002. (Berenstain Bears Ser.). (Illus.). (J). (gr. k-3). 11.91 (978-0-7587-0974-5(9)) Book Wholesalers, Inc.

—The Berenstain Bears in the House of Mirrors. 1999. (Berenstain Bears Ser.). (J). (ps-k). 10.79 (978-0-606-16837-3(0)) Tandem Library Bks.

Bergen, Lara. Thumper's Shapes. Disney Press Staff, ed. Naggi, Maria Elena et al, illus. 2007. 16p. (J). (ps-k). 5.99 (***978-1-4231-0438-4(2)***) Disney Pr.

Bernstein, Margery. That's Hard, That's Easy. Handelman, Dorothy, photos by. 1998. (Real Kids Readers Ser.). (Illus.). 32p. (gr. k-2). (J). pap. 4.99 (978-0-7613-2032-6(6)); lib. bdg. 18.90 (978-0-7613-2007-4(5)) Lerner Publishing Group. (Millbrook Pr.).

Berry, Matt. Up on Daddy's Shoulders. Corvino, Lucy, illus. 2006. 32p. (J). pap. 6.99 (978-0-439-67045-6(4) , Cartwheel Bks.) Scholastic, Inc.

Bessen, Luc. Arthur & the Minimoys. Sowchek, Ellen, tr. from FRE. 2005. 240p. (J). 15.99 (978-0-06-059623-1(6)) HarperCollins Pubs.

Besson, Luc. Arthur & the Forbidden City. (Illus.). 192p. (J). 2006. pap. 5.99 (978-0-06-059628-6(7) , Harper Trophy); 2005. 15.99 (978-0-06-059626-2(0)); 2005. lib. bdg. 16.89 (978-0-06-059627-9(9)) HarperCollins Pubs.

—Arthur & the Invisibles. movie tie-in ed. 2006. 416p. (J). pap. 7.99 (978-0-06-122726-4(9)) HarperCollins Pubs.

—Arthur & the Minimoys. (Illus.). (J). 2006. 256p. pap. 6.99 (978-0-06-059625-5(2) , Harper Trophy); 2005. 240p. lib. bdg. 16.89 (978-0-06-059624-8(4)) HarperCollins Pubs.

Big & Little. 2003. (J). pap. 12.95 (978-0-590-40698-7(1)) Scholastic, Inc.

Blackstone, Stella. Bear in a Square. 2000. (J). 12.79 (978-0-606-19702-1(8)) Tandem Library Bks.

—How Big Is a Pig? Beaton, Clare, illus. 24p. (J). (gr. k-2). 2002. bds. 6.99 (978-1-84148-959-9(X)); 2000. 14.99 (978-1-84148-077-0(0)) Barefoot Bks., Inc.

—Oso en un Cuadrado. 2003. (SPA.). (gr. k-3). lib. bdg. 14.15 (978-0-613-65708-2(X)) Tandem Library Bks.

Blackstone, Stella. Ship Shapes. Bell, Siobhan, illus. 2006. (J). (***978-1-4156-6474-2(9)***) Barefoot Bks., Inc.

Blades, Ann. Too Small. Blades, Ann, illus. 2000. (Illus.). 32p. (J). (ps-3). 15.95 (978-0-88899-400-4(1)) Groundwood Bks. CAN. *Dist:* Perseus Distribution.

Bonnell, Kris. Round Around Us. 2005. (J). 3.75 (978-1-933727-14-1(4)) Reading Reading Bks., LLC.

Boulden, Jim & Boulden, Joan. Tall Paul. Tate, Susan, ed. Drengenberg, Heiko, illus. 1999. 24p. (YA). (gr. 6-9). pap. 5.95 (978-1-892421-12-8(7) , 12-7ab) Boulden Publishing.

Boxes, 6 Pack. (Literatura 2000 Ser.). (gr. 1-2). 28.00 (978-0-7635-0122-8(0)) Rigby Education.

Bridges, Margaret Park. Am I Big or Little? Dockray, Tracy, illus. 2002. 32p. (J). (ps-2). pap. 5.95 (978-1-58717-147-5(3) , SeaStar Bks.) Chronicle Bks. LLC.

Bridges, Margaret Park & Dockray, Tracy. Am I Big or Little? 2000. (Illus.). 32p. (J). (ps-3). 16.50 (978-1-58717-020-1(5) , SeaStar Bks.) Chronicle Bks. LLC.

Bridwell, Norman. Clifford the Small Red Puppy. 2005. 40p. (J). pap. 3.99 (978-0-439-72526-2(7) , Cartwheel Bks.) Scholastic, Inc.

Brimner, Larry Dane. Bigger & Smaller. Girouard, Patrick, illus. 2005. (Magic Door to Learning Ser.). 24p. (J). (ps-3). 21.36 (978-1-59296-532-8(6)) Child's World, Inc.

Brown, Margaret. Bumble Bugs & Elephants: A Big & Little Book. Hurd, Clement, illus. 2006. 32p. (J). 14.99 (978-0-06-074512-7(6)); lib. bdg. 15.89 (978-0-06-074513-4(4)) HarperCollins Pubs.

Brown, Margaret Wise. Big & Little. 2002. 32p. (J). pap. 5.99 (978-0-7868-1450-3(0)) Hyperion Pr.

Bunting, Eve. Little Bear's Little Boat. Carpenter, Nancy, illus. 2003. 32p. (J). (gr. k-ps). tchr. ed. 12.00 (978-0-395-97462-9(3) , Clarion Bks.) Houghton Mifflin Co. Trade & Reference Div.

Campbell, Louisa. Biglet. 2002. (Illus.). 32p. (ps-1). 5.99 (978-0-7868-3363-4(7)) Disney Pr.

Carlson, Nancy. Piensa en Grande! 2005. (Libros Ilustrados (Picture Bks.)). (SPA., Illus.). 32p. (J). (ps-ps). lib. bdg. 15.95 (978-0-8225-3192-0(5) , Ediciones Lerner) Lerner Publishing Group.

—Think Big! 2005. (Illus.). 32p. (J). (ps-ps). 15.95 (978-1-57505-622-7(4) , Carolrhoda Bks.) Lerner Publishing Group.

Carter, David A. Whoo? Whoo? Carter, David A., illus. 2007. (Illus.). 32p. (J). (ps-1). 12.99 (***978-1-4169-3816-3(8)*** , Little Simon) Simon & Schuster Children's Publishing.

Chaconas, Dori. Cork & Fuzz: Short & Tall. McCue, Lisa, illus. 2006. (Viking Easy-To-Read Ser.). 32p. (J). (gr. k-3). 13.99 (978-0-670-05985-0(4) , Viking Adult) Penguin Group (USA) Inc.

Choldenko, Gennifer. How to Make Friends with a Giant. Walrod, Amy, illus. 2006. 32p. (J). (ps-3). 16.99 (978-0-399-23779-9(8)) Penguin Group (USA) Inc.

Christopher, Matt. Cool as Ice. 2001. 160p. (J). (gr. 3-7). pap. 4.99 (978-0-316-13520-7(8)) Little Brown & Co.

—Cool as Ice. 2001. (J). 11.15 (978-0-606-21121-5(7)) Tandem Library Bks.

Christopher, Matt & Mantell, Paul. Cool as Ice. 2001. 160p. (J). (gr. 4-7). 15.95 (978-0-316-13489-7(9)) Little Brown & Co.

Clements, Andrew. Big Al & Shrimpy. Kogo, Yoshi, illus. 2002. 40p. (J). (gr. k-3). 16.95 (978-0-689-84247-4(3)) Simon & Schuster Children's Publishing.

—Big Al & Shrimpy. Kogo, Yoshi, illus. 2005. 30p. (J). (ps-3). lib. bdg. 14.19 (978-0-606-33907-0(8)) Tandem Library Bks.

Colfer, Eoin. Half-Moon Investigations. 2007. 304p. (gr. 5-17). pap. 7.99 (***978-0-7868-4960-4(6)***) Miramax Bks.

Condon, Bill. A Waste of Space. Tulloch, Coral, illus. 1999. (Supa Doopers Ser.). 64p. (J). (978-0-7608-3294-3(3)) Sundance/Newbridge Educational Publishing.

—Waste of Space. 1999. (gr. 3-6). lib. bdg. 12.60 (978-0-613-30846-5(8)) Tandem Library Bks.

Coulton, Mia. Danny's Favorite Shapes. Coulton, Mia, photos by. 2004. (J). (978-0-9746475-4-8(3)) Maryruth Bks., Inc.

Coville, Bruce. Jeremy Thatcher, Dragon Hatcher: A Magic Shop Book. Lippincott, Gary A., illus. 2007. (Magic Shop Book Ser.). 168p. (J). (gr. 3-7). pap. 5.95 (***978-0-15-206252-1(1)*** , Magic Carpet Bks.) Harcourt Children's Bks.

A Crab Called Mouse. 2006. (J). pap. 9.50 (***978-0-9787995-2-6(6)***) High-Pitched Hum Inc.

Cross, Gillian. The Black Room: The Lost. 2006. (Dark Ground Ser.). 256p. (YA). (gr. 6). 16.99 (978-0-525-47487-6(0) , Dutton Juvenile) Penguin Group (USA) Inc.

Cross, Gillian. The Nightmare Game. 2007. 272p. (J). (gr. 7). 18.99 (***978-0-525-47923-9(6)*** , Dutton Juvenile) Penguin Group (USA) Inc.

Cuyler, Margery. Biggest, Best Snowman, Library Edition. 2007. (J). 18.95 (***978-0-545-01780-0(7)***) Scholastic, Inc.

—Biggest Best Snowman, The (Readalong) 2007. (J). 9.95 (***978-0-545-01484-7(0)***) Scholastic, Inc.

Cuyler, Margery. Bookshelf: Biggest, Best Snowman. Hillenbrand, Will, illus. 1998. (J). (ps-2). pap. 15.95 (978-0-590-13493-4(0)) Scholastic, Inc.

Cuyler, Margery & Hillenbrand, Will. Bookshelf: Biggest, Best Snowman. 1998. (Illus.). 32p. (J). (ps-2). pap. 15.95 (978-0-590-13922-9(3)) Scholastic, Inc.

Daniel, Chloe. Star Shapes. 1999. (Lamaze Ser.). (Illus.). 8p. (J). (ps). 6.99 (978-1-56799-890-0(9) , Friedman-Fairfax) Friedman, Michael Publishing Group, Inc.

Davis, Caroline, illus. My Friends. 2007. 12p. (J). (ps). bds. 6.95 (***978-1-58925-823-5(1)*** , tiger tales) ME Media LLC.

de Brunhoff, Laurent. Babar & the Circus Star. 2005. (J). (978-0-8109-5774-9(4)) Abrams, Harry N. , Inc.

Donnio, Sylviane. I'd Really Like to Eat a Child. De Monfreid, Dorothée, illus. 2007. (Picture Book Ser.). 32p. (J). (ps-1). lib. bdg. 17.99 (978-0-375-93761-3(7) , Random Hse. Bks. for Young Readers) Random Hse. Children's Bks.

—I'd Really Like to Eat a Child. Martin, Leslie, tr. from FRE. De Monfreid, Dorothée, illus. 2007. (Picture Book Ser.). 32p. (J). (ps-1). 14.99 (978-0-375-83761-6(2) , Random Hse. Bks. for Young Readers) Random Hse. Children's Bks.

The Dooples & the Shapes. l.t. ed. 2001. (Meet the Dooples). 32p. (J). lib. bdg. 19.95 (978-0-9656279-3-1(4)) Educational Media Enterprises, Inc.

Dr. Seuss Enterprises Staff & Perkins, Al. The Nose Book. Mathieu, Joe, illus. 2003. 24p. (J). (gr. k-ps). bds. 4.99 (978-0-375-82493-7(6) , Random Hse. Bks. for Young Readers) Random Hse. Children's Bks.

Dull, Dennis Stanley. Baby Basics & Beyond: ABC's, 123's & Shapes. Dull, Dennis Stanley, illus. 2nd ed. 2004. (J). (978-0-9717475-4-8(7)) Laurel Valley Graphics, Inc.

Dunbar, Joyce. Tell Me What It's Like to Be Big. Gliori, Debi, illus. 2005. 32p. (J). reprint ed. pap. 6.00 (978-0-15-205247-8(X) , Voyager Bks./Libros Viajeros) Harcourt Children's Bks.

Emmett, Jonathan. Dino Boulder Ball. Rutherford, Peter, illus. 2006. 32p. (J). (***978-1-4048-3116-2(9)***) Picture Window Bks.

Emmett, Jonathan. Someone Bigger. Reynolds, Adrian, illus. 2004. 32p. (J). (gr. k-3). 16.00 (978-0-618-44397-0(5) , Clarion Bks.) Houghton Mifflin Co. Trade & Reference Div.

Ensor, Barbara. Thumbelina: Tiny Little Runaway Bride. 2008. (J). (***978-0-375-83960-3(7)); (*978-0-375-93960-0(1)***) Random Hse. Children's Bks. (Schwartz & Wade Bks.).

Equipo Staff. El Libro de Bugui: Formas. 2000. Tr. of Shapes. (SPA., Illus.). 32p. (J). (ps-k). 8.95 (978-84-488-0857-0(6)) Beascoa, Ediciones S.A. ESP. *Dist:* Distribooks, Inc.

Falwell, Cathryn. Shape Capers. Falwell, Cathryn, illus. 2007. 32p. (J). (ps-k). 16.99 (***978-0-06-123699-0(3)*** , Greenwillow Bks.) HarperCollins Pubs.

—Shape Capers. 2007. 32p. (J). (ps-k). lib. bdg. 17.89 (***978-0-06-123700-3(0)*** , Greenwillow Bks.) HarperCollins Pubs.

Fernandes, Kim & Fernandes, Eugenie. Little Toby & the Big Hair. Fernandes, Kim & Fernandes, Eugenie, illus. 1998. (Illus.). 32p. (J). (gr. k-2). pap. 5.95 (978-1-55209-257-6(7)) Firefly Bks., Ltd.

Fisher, Doris. Happy Birthday to Whooo? Downey, Lisa, illus. (J). 2007. 1p. 8.95 (***978-1-934359-06-8(8));*** 2006. 32p. 15.95 (978-0-9768823-1-2(0)) Sylvan Dell Pubng.

Fontes, Justine. Black Meets White. Waring, Geoff, illus. 2005. 24p. (J). (gr. k-ps). 12.99 (978-0-7636-1933-6(7)) Candlewick Pr.

Freed, Shirley Ann & Moon, Louise. A Very Little Man. Morelan, Bill, ed. Butler, Steven, illus. 24th ed. 2002. 16p. (J). (gr. 1-2). pap. 3.99 (978-1-58938-024-0(X)) Concerned Communications.

Freschet, Gina. Feet Man & Mr. Tiny. 2006. (Illus.). 32p. (J). 16.00 (978-0-374-32294-6(5)) Farrar, Straus & Giroux.

Garfield, Valerie. So Big! Yaccarino, Dan, illus. 2001. (Playtime Rhymes Ser.). 12p. (J). (ps up). pap. 7.99 (978-0-694-01509-2(1) , Harper Festival) HarperCollins Pubs.

Garland, Michael. Hooray Jose! 2007. (Illus.). 32p. (J). 14.99 (***978-0-7614-5345-1(8)***) Cavendish, Marshall Corp.

Garland, Michael, illus. Hooray José! 2007. (J). (***978-1-4287-3591-0(7)*** , Cavendish Children's Bks.) Cavendish, Marshall Corp.

Gillespie, Jane. Diving for Shapes in Hawaii: An Identification Book for Keiki. Bosgra, Johann, illus. 2004. 20p. (J). bds. 6.95 (978-1-933067-04-9(7)) Beachhouse Publishing, LLC.

Golden Books Staff. Fun with Colors & Shapes. 2000. (Disney Ser.). (Illus.). 48p. (J). (ps-k). pap. 2.99 (978-0-307-20132-4(5) , 20132, Golden Bks.) Random Hse. Children's Bks.

Gorbachev, Valeri. Big Little Elephant. 2005. (Illus.). 32p. (J). (ps-ps). 16.00 (978-0-15-205195-2(3) , Harcourt Children's Bks.) Harcourt Children's Bks.

Graham, Elspeth. Sandwich that Jack Made. Mould, Chris, illus. 2004. 24p. (J). lib. bdg. (***978-1-59646-698-2(7)***) Dingles & Co.

Greban, Tanguy. Sarah So Small. Greban, Quentin, illus. 2004. 32p. (J). 16.95 (978-0-689-03594-4(2) , Milk & Cookies) ibooks, Inc.

Green-Armytage, Stephen. Dudley: The Little Terrier That Could. 1999. (Illus.). 32p. (gr. 8-17). 12.95 (978-0-8109-4098-7(1)) Abrams, Harry N. , Inc.

Greenburg, J. C. In the Bathroom. 2002. (Andrew Lost Ser.: Bk. 1). (Illus.). 96p. (J). (gr. 2-5). lib. bdg. 11.99 (978-0-375-91278-8(9) , Random Hse. Bks. for Young Readers) Random Hse. Children's Bks.

—In the Bathroom, No. 2. Palen, Debbie, illus. 2002. (Andrew Lost Ser.: Bk. 1). 96p. (J). (gr. 2-5). pap. 3.99 (978-0-375-81278-1(4) , Random Hse. Bks. for Young Readers) Random Hse. Children's Bks.

—In the Kitchen. 2002. (Andrew Lost Ser.: Bk. 3). (Illus.). 96p. (J). (gr. 2-5). lib. bdg. 11.99 (978-0-375-91279-5(7) , Random Hse. Bks. for Young Readers) Random Hse. Children's Bks.

—In the Kitchen. Palen, Debbie, illus. 2002. (Andrew Lost Ser.: Bk. 3). 96p. (J). (gr. 2-5). pap. 3.99 (978-0-375-81279-8(2) , Random Hse. Bks. for Young Readers) Random Hse. Children's Bks.

—In the Kitchen. 2002. (Andrew Lost Ser.: Bk. 3). (J). (gr. 3-6). lib. bdg. 11.80 (978-0-613-86248-6(1)) Tandem Library Bks.

—In Uncle Al. Gerardi, Jan, illus. 2007. (Andrew Lost Ser.: Bk. 16). 96p. (J). (gr. 2-4). 3.99 (***978-0-375-83565-0(2));*** lib. bdg. 11.99 (***978-0-375-93565-7(7)***) Random Hse. Children's Bks. (Random Hse. Bks. for Young Readers).

Greenburg, J. C. On the Dog. Palen, Debbie, illus. 2002. (Andrew Lost Ser.: Bk. 1). 96p. (J). (gr. 1-4). pap. 3.99 (978-0-375-81277-4(6) , Random Hse. Bks. for Young Readers) Random Hse. Children's Bks.

—On the Dog. 2002. (Andrew Lost Ser.: Bk. 1). (J). (ps-2). lib. bdg. 11.80 (978-0-613-50405-8(4)) Tandem Library Bks.

Hall, Kirsten. Tug-of-War: All about Balance. Luedecke, Bev, illus. (Beastieville Ser.). (J). (gr. k-1). 2005. 32p. pap. 3.95 (978-0-516-25523-1(1)); 2004. 31p. 19.50 (978-0-516-22899-0(4)) Scholastic Library Publishing. (Children's Pr.).

Hanson, Warren. Grandpa Has a Great Big Face. Elliott, Mark, illus. 2006. 32p. (J). 16.99 (978-0-06-078775-2(9)); lib. bdg. 17.89 (978-0-06-078776-9(7)) HarperCollins Pubs. (Geringer, Laura Book).

Hargreaves, Roger. Little Miss Tiny. 1999. (Mr. Men & Little Miss Ser.). (Illus.). 32p. (J). (gr. k up). pap. 3.99 (978-0-8431-7511-0(7) , Price Stern Sloan) Penguin Group (USA) Inc.

—Mr. Tall. Hargreaves, Roger, illus. 1999. (Mr. Men & Little Miss Ser.). (Illus.). 32p. (J). pap. 3.99 (978-0-8431-7510-3(9) , Price Stern Sloan) Penguin Group (USA) Inc.

Hartmann, Annabelle. As Big As a Mountain. 2003. (Illus.). 32p. (YA). (978-1-84365-001-0(0)) Chrysalis Children's Bks.

Harwood, Beth & Wood, Amanda. Amazing Baby Round, Square! Dodd, Emma, illus. 2006. (Amazing Baby Ser.). 18p. (J). bds. 3.95 (978-1-59223-584-1(0) , Silver Dolphin Bks.) Advantage Pubs. Group.

Have You Seen Joe?, Pk. 6. (ps-2). 23.00 (978-0-7635-8800-7(8)) Rigby Education.

Hawkes, Kevin. The Wicked Big Toddlah. 2007. 40p. (J). (ps-3). 16.99 (978-0-375-82427-2(8)); lib. bdg. 19.99 (978-0-375-92427-9(2)) Random Hse. Children's Bks. (Knopf Bks. for Young Readers).

Hays, Anna Jane. So Big! Moroney, Christopher, illus. 2003. (Sesame Beginnings Ser.). 14p. (J). bds. 7.99 (978-0-375-81537-9(6) , Random Hse. Bks. for Young Readers) Random Hse. Children's Bks.

Head, Honor. Size & Shape. Stower, Adam, illus. 1998. (Ed Mouse Finds Out about Ser.). 32p. (J). (ps-2). 19.98 (978-0-8172-5201-4(0)) Raintree.

Healy, Nick. Louie the Layabout. Erkocak, Sahin, illus. 2007. (Pfeffernut County Ser.). 32p. (J). (gr. k-2). lib. bdg. 23.93 (***978-1-4048-3697-6(7)***) Picture Window Bks.

Henkes, Kevin. The Biggest Boy. Tafuri, Nancy, illus. 1998. 24p. (J). (ps-3). pap. 5.99 (978-0-688-15841-5(2) , Harper Trophy) HarperCollins Pubs.

Herman, R. A. The Littlest Christmas Tree. Rogers, Jacqueline, illus. 2007. 32p. (J). pap. 3.99 (***978-0-439-54007-0(0)***) Scholastic, Inc.

Higginson, Sheila. Up, up, & Away! Disney Storybook Artists Staff, illus. 2007. 24p. (J). (ps-k). pap. 3.99 (***978-1-4231-0647-0(4)***) Disney Pr.

Hill, Eric. Spot's Colors, Shapes, & Numbers. Hill, Eric, illus. 2007. 18p. (J). (ps-k). bds. 12.99 (***978-0-399-24779-8(3)*** , Putnam Juvenile) Penguin Group (USA) Inc.

Hill, Susan. Stuart at the Fun House. Halverson, Lydia, illus. 2001. (I Can Read Bks.). 32p. (J). (ps-1). pap. 3.99 (978-0-06-444304-3(3) , Harper Trophy); Bk. 1. 15.89 (978-0-06-029635-3(6)); Bk. 1. 15.99 (978-0-06-029539-4(2)) HarperCollins Pubs.

Hillert, Margaret. I Like Things. (J). 4.95 (978-0-87895-683-8(2)) Modern Curriculum Pr.

—Tom Thumb. Hockerman, Dennis, illus. rev. ed. 2006. (Beginning to Read Ser.). 32p. (J). lib. bdg. 18.60 (978-1-59953-028-4(7)) Norwood Hse. Pr.

Hindley, Judy. Ten Bright Eyes. Bartlett, Alison, illus. 1998. 32p. (J). (ps-3). 14.95 (978-1-56145-173-9(8)) Peachtree Pubs., Ltd.

Hoban, Tana. Cubes, Cones, Cylinders, & Spheres. Hoban, Tana, illus. 2000. (Illus.). 24p. (J). (ps-3). 16.99 (978-0-688-15325-0(9)); lib. bdg. 17.89 (978-0-688-15326-7(7)) HarperCollins Pubs.

—So Many Circles, So Many Squares. 1998. (Illus.). 40p. (J). (ps-3). 15.89 (978-0-688-15166-9(3)) HarperCollins Pubs.

Hogan, Mary. Winnie the Pooh Shapes. 2002. (Illus.). 10p. (J). (978-0-7868-3395-5(5)); (978-0-7868-3396-2(3)); (978-0-7868-3397-9(1)); (978-0-7868-3398-6(X)); (978-0-7868-3399-3(8)) Disney Pr.

Hood, Susan. Too-Tall Paul, Too-Small Paul. Handelman, Dorothy, photos by. 1998. (Real Kids Readers Ser.). (Illus.). 32p. (gr. k-2). lib. bdg. 18.90 (978-0-7613-2021-0(0)); (J). pap. 4.99 (978-0-7613-2046-3(6)) Lerner Publishing Group. (Millbrook Pr.).

Houghton Mifflin Company Editors. Curious George Discovery Day. 2007. (Illus.). 14p. (J). (gr. k-ps). bds. 13.95 (***978-0-618-73761-1(8)***) Houghton Mifflin Co. Trade & Reference Div.

How to Get Dressed. 1998. (Illus.). 6p. (J). 10.99 (978-1-929174-13-3(6)) Oshkosh B'Gosh, Inc.

Hutchins, Hazel J. Two So Small. 2000. (gr. k-3). lib. bdg. 16.40 (978-0-613-50386-0(4)) Tandem Library Bks.

Hutchins, Pat. Titch. Hutchins, Pat, illus. 2002. (Illus.). (J). 14.47 (978-0-7587-3818-9(8)) Book Wholesalers, Inc.

Inches, Alison. In the Mushroom Meadow. 2002. (gr. k-3). lib. bdg. 10.95 (978-0-613-86241-7(4)) Tandem Library Bks.

Jonell, Lynne. Mommy Go Away! 2000. (Illus.). (J). (978-0-606-22033-0(X)) Tandem Library Bks.

Jones, Jennifer B. The Short Story of My Life. 2004. 160p. (J). 16.95 (978-0-8027-8905-1(6)) Walker & Co.

Joyce, William. Big Time Olie. Joyce, William, illus. 2006. (Rolie Polie Olie Ser.). 40p. (J). pap. 6.99 (978-0-06-008812-5(5) , Harper Trophy) HarperCollins Pubs.

—Rolie Polie Olie. 2003. 32p. (J). pap. 3.50 (978-0-7868-4533-0(3)); pap. 3.50 (978-0-7868-4534-7(1)); pap. 3.50 (978-0-7868-4535-4(X)) Disney Pr.

—Rolie Polie Olie. Joyce, William, illus. 1999. (Laura Geringer Bks.). (Illus.). 48p. (J). (ps-k). 16.99 (978-0-06-027163-9(5) , Geringer, Laura Book) HarperCollins Pubs.

—Rolie Polie Olie. 1999. (Laura Geringer Bks.). (Illus.). 48p. (J). (ps-3). 15.89 (978-0-06-027164-0(7)) HarperCollins Pubs.

—Rolie Polie Olie. Joyce, William, illus. 2003. (Rolie Polie Olie Ser.). (Illus.). 32p. (J). (ps-k). 6.99 (978-0-06-055716-4(8) , Harper Festival) HarperCollins Pubs.

—Rolie Polie Olie. Joyce, William, illus. 2006. (Rolie Polie Olie Ser.). (Illus.). 48p. (J). reprint ed. pap. 6.99 (978-0-06-053484-4(2) , Harper Trophy) HarperCollins Pubs.

Kahn, Peggy, et al. Welcome to Birdwell Island. 2001. (Clifford, the Big Red Dog Ser.). (Illus.). (J). pap. (978-0-439-22005-7(X)) Scholastic, Inc.

Kellogg, Steven. Much Bigger Than Martin. Kellogg, Steven, illus. 2002. (Illus.). (J). 14.04 (978-0-7587-3198-2(1)) Book Wholesalers, Inc.

Kimmel, Eric A. When Mindy Saved Hanukkah. McClintock, Barbara, illus. 1998. 32p. (J). (ps-2). pap. 15.95 (978-0-590-37136-0(3)) Scholastic, Inc.

Kirk, Daniel. Bigger. 2000. (Illus.). (J). (978-0-606-18390-1(6)) Tandem Library Bks.

Latimer, Miriam. Shrinking Sam. 2007. (Illus.). 32p. (J). (gr. 1-3). 16.99 (***978-1-84686-038-6(5)***) Barefoot Bks., Inc.

Leaf, Munro, ed. The Story of Ferdinand: El Cuento de Ferdinando, 2 bks., Set. Belpré, Pura, tr. Lawson, Robert, illus. unabr. ed. 1999. (ENG & SPA.). (J). (gr. 1-3). pap. 33.95 incl. audio (978-0-87499-567-1(1)) Live Oak Media.

Liberts, Jennifer. Piglet Feels Small. Yee, Josie, illus. 2002. (Early Step into Reading Ser.). 32p. (J). (ps-1). pap. 3.99 (978-0-7364-1226-1(3) , RH/Disney) Random Hse. Children's Bks.

Love, Pamela. Dos pies suben, dos pies Bajan: Two Feet up, Two Feet Down. Chapman, Lynne, illus. 2005. (Rookie Reader(R) Espanol Ser.). 32p. (gr. k-2). 19.50 (978-0-516-25252-0(6) , Children's Pr.) Scholastic Library Publishing.

Maar, Paul & Schulte, T. Gloria the Cow. 2006. (Illus.). 32p. (J). 16.95 (978-0-7358-2096-8(1)) North-South Bks., Inc.

Mangan, Anne. The Smallest Bear. Moss, Joanne, illus. 1998. 32p. (J). (ps-3). 14.95 (978-1-56656-266-9(X) , Crocodile Bks.) Interlink Publishing Group, Inc.

Marzollo, Jean & Marzollo, Dan. Basketball Buddies, Level 3. Kelley, True, illus. 1998. (Hello Reader! Ser.). 32p. (J). (gr. 1-3). pap. (978-0-590-38401-8(5)) Scholastic, Inc.

Masurel, Claire. Domino. Walker, David, illus. 2007. (Super Sturdy Picture Book Ser.). 24p. (J). (gr. k-ps). 8.99 (978-0-7636-2862-8(X)) Candlewick Pr.

May, Kara. Joe Lion's Big Boots. Allen, Jonathan, illus. 2005. (I Am Reading Ser.). 48p. (J). (gr. k-3). pap. 3.95 (978-0-7534-5856-3(X) , Kingfisher) Houghton Mifflin Co. Trade & Reference Div.

Mayer, Mercer. Just Big Enough. Mayer, Mercer, illus. 2004. (Little Critter Ser.). (Illus.). 40p. (J). (ps-2). 6.99 (978-0-06-053963-4(1) , Harper Festival) HarperCollins Pubs.

—When I Get Bigger. Mayer, Mercer, illus. 1999. (Little Critter Ser.). (Illus.). 24p. (J). (gr. k-3). reprint ed. pap. 3.99 (978-0-307-11943-8(2) , 11943, Random Hse. Bks. for Young Readers) Random Hse. Children's Bks.

McClure, Brian D. The Raindrop. 2006. (Illus.). 36p. (J). 14.95 (978-1-933426-01-3(2)) Universal Flag Publishing.

McDonald, Jill. Shapes: A Play-with-Me BK. 2007. 5p. bds. 6.95 (***978-1-58117-604-9(X)*** , Intervisual/Piggy Toes) Dalmatian Pr.

McDonald, Megan. Stink: The Incredible Shrinking Kid. Reynolds, Peter H., illus. (J). (gr. k-3). 2006. 128p. pap. 4.99 (978-0-7636-2891-8(3)); 2005. 112p. 12.99 (978-0-7636-2025-7(4)) Candlewick Pr.

McGrory, Anik. Kidogo. 2005. (Illus.). 32p. (J). 15.95 (978-1-58234-974-9(6)) Bloomsbury Publishing.

McNamara, Margaret. How Many Seeds in a Pumpkin? Karas, G. Brian, illus. 2007. 40p. (J). (ps-2). 14.99 (978-0-375-84014-2(1)); lib. bdg. 17.99 (***978-0-375-94014-9(6)***) Random Hse. Children's Bks. (Schwartz & Wade Bks.).

Mead, David. Noah's Babies Shapes & Sharing. Byers, Brian, illus. 2005. 22p. (J). bds. 6.95 (978-0-9746440-5-9(6)) Virtue Bks.

Meade, David. Shapes & Sharing. Byers, Brian, illus. 2005. 22p. (J). (gr. k-5). bds. 6.95 (978-1-59125-518-5(X) , Penton Kids) Penton Overseas, Inc.

Meddaugh, Susan. Just Teenie. 2006. (Illus.). 32p. (J). (gr. k-3). 16.00 (978-0-618-68565-3(0)) Houghton Mifflin Co.

Meister, Cari. When Tiny Was Tiny. Davis, Rich, illus. 1999. (Easy-to-Read Ser.). 32p. (J). (ps-2). pap. 3.99 (978-0-14-130419-9(7) , Puffin) Penguin Group (USA) Inc.

—When Tiny Was Tiny. Davis, Rich, illus. 1999. (J). (ps-ps). lib. bdg. 11.80 (978-0-613-22619-6(4)) Tandem Library Bks.

—When Tiny Was Tiny. 1999. (J). (978-0-606-19509-6(2)) Tandem Library Bks.

Meserve, Jessica. Small Sister. Meserve, Jessica, illus. 2007. (Illus.). 32p. (J). (ps-k). 16.00 (978-0-618-77658-0(3) , Clarion Bks.) Houghton Mifflin Co. Trade & Reference Div.

Miller, Margaret. Big & Little. Miller, Margaret, illus. 1998. (Illus.). 24p. (J). (ps-3). 16.99 (978-0-688-14748-8(8)) HarperCollins Pubs.

Mitchell, Adrian. Twice My Size. Pudles, Daniel, illus. 1999. (Fun Early Math Concepts Ser.). 32p. (ps-1). lib. bdg. 22.90 (978-0-7613-1423-3(7) , Millbrook Pr.) Lerner Publishing Group.

Mitchell, Rita Phillips. Hue Boy. Binch, Caroline, illus. 1999. 32p. (J). (gr. k-3). pap. 11.95 (978-0-14-056354-2(7)) Penguin Bks., Ltd. GBR. *Dist:* Trafalgar Square Publishing.

Moncure, Jane Belk. Word Bird's Shapes. 2002. (New Word Bird Library). (Illus.). 32p. (J). (ps-3). 22.79 (978-1-56766-998-5(0)) Child's World, Inc.

Mourlevat, Jean-Claude. The Pull of the Ocean. Maudet, Y., tr. from FRE. 2006. 208p. (gr. 7). (J). 13.95 (978-0-385-73348-9(8)); (YA). lib. bdg. 15.99 (978-0-385-90364-6(2)) Random Hse. Children's Bks. (Delacorte Bks. for Young Readers).

Mouse Works Staff. Peanut's Shapes. 1999. (P B & J Otter Noodle Stories Ser.). (Illus.). 16p. (J). (ps-k). 3.50 (978-0-7364-0183-8(0)) Mouse Works.

Mueller, Doris. Small One's Adventure. Guevara, Linda L., ed. Fulton, Parker, illus. 2004. 32p. (J). (gr. k-5). 16.95 (978-0-9710278-1-7(1)) All About Kids Publishing.

Mullican, Judy & Crowell, Knox. Caillou Finds Shapes. Gillen, Lisa P., illus. l.t. ed. 2005. (Hrl Board Book Ser.). (J). (ps-k). bds. 10.95 (978-1-57332-312-3(8)) HighReach Learning, Inc.

Munsch, Robert. Marilou Casse-Cou. ed. 2004. Tr. of Up, up, down. (FRE., Illus.). (J). (gr. k-3). spiral bd. (978-0-616-11144-4(4)) Canadian National Institute for the Blind/Institut National Canadien pour les Aveugles.

Murawski, Kevin, illus. Harold & the Purple Crayon: Under the Sea. 2004. 32p. (J). (ps-ps). lib. bdg. 10.79 (978-0-606-29924-4(6)) Tandem Library Bks.

Murphy. Best Bug Parade: Comparing Sizes Big Book. 2002. (Illus.). (J). pap. (978-0-7398-6775-4(X)) Steck-Vaughn.

—Circus Shapes: Recognizing Shapes Big Book. 2002. (Illus.). (J). pap. (978-0-7398-6779-2(2)) Steck-Vaughn.

Murphy, Frank. Ben Franklin & the Magic Squares. Walz, Richard, illus. 2001. (Step into Reading Ser.). 48p. (J). (gr. k-3). pap. 3.99 (978-0-375-80621-6(0)); lib. bdg. 11.99 (978-0-375-90621-3(5)) Random Hse. Children's Bks. (Random Hse. Bks. for Young Readers).

My Daddy Is a Giant. 2004. (J). (ALB & ENG.). (978-1-84444-499-1(6)); (ARA & ENG.). (978-1-84444-501-1(1)); (BEN & ENG.). (978-1-84444-502-8(X)); (CHI & ENG.). (978-1-84444-503-5(8)); (CHI & ENG.). (978-1-84444-504-2(6)); (CRO & ENG.). (978-1-84444-505-9(4)); (ENG & PER.). (978-1-84444-506-6(2)); (ENG & FRE.). (978-1-84444-507-3(0)); (ENG & GUJ.). (978-1-84444-509-7(7)); (ENG & HIN.). (978-1-84444-510-3(0)); (ENG & ITA.). (978-1-84444-511-0(9)); (ENG & JPN.). (978-1-84444-512-7(7)); (ENG & KOR.). (978-1-84444-513-4(5)); (ENG & KUR.). (978-1-84444-514-1(3)); (ENG & PAN.). (978-1-84444-515-8(1)); (ENG & POL.). (978-1-84444-516-5(X)); (ENG & POR.). (978-1-84444-517-2(8)); (ENG & RUS.). (978-1-84444-518-9(6)); (ENG & SOM.). (978-1-84444-519-6(4)); (ENG & SPA.). (978-1-84444-520-2(8)); (ENG & TAG.). (978-1-84444-508-0(9)); (ENG & TAM.). (978-1-84444-521-9(6)); (ENG & TUR.). (978-1-84444-522-6(4)); (ENG & URD.). (978-1-84444-523-3(2)); (ENG & VIE.). (978-1-84444-524-0(0)) Mantra Publishing, Ltd.

Nolen, Jerdine. Hewitt Anderson's Great Big Life. Nelson, Kadir A., illus. 2005. 40p. (J). 16.95 (978-0-689-86866-5(9) , Simon & Schuster/Paula Wiseman Bks.) Simon & Schuster Children's Publishing.

O'Leary, Sara. When You Were Small. Morstad, Julie, illus. 2006. 32p. (J). 16.95 (978-1-894965-36-1(1)) Simply Read Bks. CAN. *Dist:* Perseus Distribution.

Oliver, Lin. Attack of the Growling Eyeballs. 2008. (Who Shrunk Daniel Funk? Ser.). 112p. (J). 14.99 ***(978-1-4169-0951-4(6)** , Simon & Schuster Children's Publishing) Simon & Schuster Children's Publishing.

Papineau, Lucie. Gilda the Giraffe & Papaya the Panda. Sarrazin, Marisol, illus. 2005. (Gilda the Giraffe Ser.). 32p. (J). (ps-3). lib. bdg. 22.60 (978-1-4048-1293-2(8)) Picture Window Bks.

Parr, Todd. The Silly Book of Shapes. 2006. (Illus.). 10p. (J). (ps-3). bds., bds. 8.99 (978-0-316-05709-7(6)) Little, Brown Bks. for Young Readers.

Pass, Erica & Hot Animation Staff, Animation. A World of Shapes. 2005. (Rubbadubbers Ser.). 22p. (J). bds. 4.99 (978-0-689-87429-1(4) , Simon Spotlight) Simon & Schuster Children's Publishing.

Passen, Lisa. The Incredible Shrinking Teacher. 2008. (Illus.). 32p. (J). pap. 6.99 ***(978-0-312-38017-5(8))*** Square Fish.

Paton Walsh, Jill. A Parcel of Patterns. 137p. (YA). (gr. 7 up). pap. 3.95 (978-0-8072-1485-5(X) , Listening Library) Random Hse. Audio Publishing Group.

Patricelli, Leslie. Silencio Ruido. Rozarena, P., tr. Patricelli, Leslie, illus. 2003. (SPA., Illus.). 25p. (J). (ps-k). bds. 7.95 (978-970-29-0987-3(2)) Santillana USA Publishing Co., Inc.

Paul, Ann Whitford. Hop! Hop! Hop! Gerardi, Jan, illus. 2005. 32p. (J). (ps-1). pap. 3.99 (978-0-375-82857-7(5) , Random Hse. Bks. for Young Readers) Random Hse. Children's Bks.

Pinkwater, Daniel M. Big Bob & the Thanksgiving Potatoes. Pinkwater, Jill, illus. 1999. (Hello Reader! Ser.). 32p. (J). (gr. 1-3). pap. 3.99 (978-0-590-64095-4(X)) Scholastic, Inc.

Pinto, Sara. Apples & Oranges: Going Bananas with Pairs. 2007. (Illus.). 32p. (J). 17.85 ***(978-1-59990-235-7(4))*** Bloomsbury Publishing.

—Apples & Oranges: Going Bananas with Pairs. Pinto, Sara, illus. 2007. (Illus.). 32p. (J). 16.95 ***(978-1-59990-103-9(X)** , Bloomsbury Children) Bloomsbury Publishing.

Pitino, Donna Marie. Too-Tall Tina. Woodruff, Liza, illus. 2005. 32p. (J). lib. bdg. 13.00 ***(978-1-4242-1076-3(3))*** Fitzgerald Bks.

—Too-Tall Tina. Woodruff, Liza, illus. 2005. (Math Matters Ser.). 32p. (J). pap. 4.95 (978-1-57565-150-7(5)) Kane Pr., The.

Pollack, Pam & Belviso, Meg. Chickens on the Move. Adams, Lynn, illus. 2002. (Math Matters Ser.). 32p. (J). pap. 4.95 (978-1-57565-113-2(0)) Kane Pr., The.

Pollack, Pamela & Belviso, Meg. Chickens on the Move. Adams, Lynn, illus. 2002. 32p. (J). (ps-3). lib. bdg. 12.95 (978-0-613-53491-8(3)) Tandem Library Bks.

Potter, Beatrix. Peter Rabbit Lift-the-flap Shapes, Opposites & Sizes. 2007. (Potter Ser.). 12p. (J). (ps). 14.99 ***(978-0-7232-5961-9(5)** , Warne) Penguin Group (USA) Inc.

Powell, Jillian. Tall Tilly. Archbold, Tim, illus. 2005. 32p. (J). (gr. 1-2). lib. bdg. 11.15 (978-0-606-33587-4(0)) Tandem Library Bks.

Powell, Richard. What's in the Box? Martín Larrañaga, Ana, illus. 2004. (Ana's Mini Movers Ser.). 12p. (J). 5.95 (978-1-58925-742-9(1) , tiger tales) ME Media LLC.

Random House Disney Staff. Pooh Shapes. 2006. (Illus.). 12p. (J). (gr. k-k). bds. 8.99 (978-0-7364-2376-2(1) , RH/Disney) Random Hse. Children's Bks.

Reidy, Hannah. All Sorts of Shapes. Dodd, Emma, illus. 2005. (All Sort of Things Ser.). 24p. (J). (gr. k-3). 22.60 (978-1-4048-1061-7(7)) Picture Window Bks.

Rey, Margret & Rey, H. A. Curious George's Dream. 1998. (Curious George Ser.). (Illus.). 24p. (J). (gr. k-3). tchr. ed. 12.95 (978-0-395-91905-7(3)) Houghton Mifflin Co. Trade & Reference Div.

Rich, Francine Poppo. Small, Not Tall. Difilippi, Thomas, illus. 2001. 32p. (J). (ps-3). 16.00 (978-0-9674602-2-0(X)) Blue Marlin Pubns.

Rockliff, Mara. Al Lado de una Hormiga. Constantin, Pascale, illus. 2005. (Rookie Reader Espanol Ser.). (SPA & ESP.). 23p. (J). (gr. k-2). pap. 4.95 (978-0-516-25531-6(2)) Scholastic Library Publishing.

—Al lado de una Hormiga: Next to an Ant. Constantin, Pascale, illus. 2005. (Rookie Reader(R) Espanol Ser.). (ENG & SPA.). 24p. (J). (gr. k-2). 19.50 (978-0-516-25251-3(8) , Children's Pr.) Scholastic Library Publishing.

—Next to an Ant. Constantin, Pascale, illus. (Rookie Reader Espanol Ser.). (J). (gr. k-2). 2005. 24p. pap. 4.95 (978-0-516-26830-9(9)); 2004. 23p. 19.50 (978-0-516-25903-1(2)) Scholastic Library Publishing. (Children's Pr.).

Rocklin, Joanne & Burns, Marilyn. Not Enough Room! Ong, Cristina et al, illus. 1998. (Hello Reader! Math Ser.). 32p. (J). (gr. k-2). pap. 3.99 (978-0-590-39962-3(4)) Scholastic, Inc.

Roddie, Shen. You're Too Small! Lavis, Steve, illus. 2004. 32p. (J). 6.95 (978-1-58925-385-8(X)); tchr. ed. 15.95 (978-1-58925-038-3(9)) ME Media LLC. (tiger tales).

Rogers, Alan. Ship Shape. 2004. (Little Giants Ser.). (Illus.). 16p. (J). (ps-k). pap. 3.95 (978-1-58728-395-6(6) , Two Can Publishing) T&N Children's Publishing.

Rogers, Karen M. Como Hay Rayas! Alvarado, Ana María, tr. Vasquez, Perry, illus. 2000. (Think-Kids Book Collection).Tr. of Yipes! Stripes!. (SPA.). 16p. (J). pap. 2.95 (978-1-58237-043-9(5)) Creative Thinkers, Inc.

Rosen, Michael J. Three Feet Small. Gorbachev, Valeri, illus. 2005. 32p. (J). 16.00 (978-0-15-204938-6(X) , Gulliver Bks.) Harcourt Children's Bks.

Ross, Odette, illus. Shapes. 2007. 12p. (J). bds. 5.95 ***(978-1-894965-89-7(2))*** Simply Read Bks. CAN. *Dist:* Perseus Distribution.

Ross, Tony. Figuras. 2006. (Little Princess Ser.).Tr. of Shapes. (SPA.). (J). (ps-k). bds. 7.95 (978-968-19-1486-8(4) , AT33280) Lectorum Pubns., Inc.

Ruckman, Kathleen, told to. The Big Book: God Made Giant Things, Too! 2002. (Illus.). 24p. (J). pap. 5.99 (978-0-89051-358-3(9)) Master Bks.

Santomero, Angela C. Blue y tu, Detective de Formas! Craig, Karen, illus. 2004. (Blue's Clues Ser.). (SPA.). 14p. (J). bds. 5.99 (978-0-689-87323-2(9) , Libros Para Ninos) Simon & Schuster Children's Publishing.

Schafer, Milton. I'm Big! Lew-Vriethoff, Joanne, illus. 2006. (J). ***(978-1-4156-8150-3(3)** , Dial) Penguin Group (USA) Inc.

Shaskan, Trisha Speed. Princess Bella's Birthday Cake. Eroglu, Aysin D., illus. 2006. 24p. (J). ***(978-1-4048-3166-7(5))*** Picture Window Bks.

—Princess Bella_s Birthday Cake. 2007. (Illus.). 24p. (J). ***(978-1-4048-1240-6(7))*** Picture Window Bks.

Shavick, Andrea. You'll Grow Soon, Alex. Ayto, Russell, illus. 2000. 32p. (J). (ps-3). 15.95 (978-0-8027-8736-1(3)) Walker & Co.

Shaw, Charles Green. It Looked Like Spilt Milk. Shaw, Charles Green, illus. 2002. (Illus.). (J). 14.47 (978-0-7587-9763-6(X)) Book Wholesalers, Inc.

Sheena, Roberts. We All Go Traveling By. Siobhan, Bell, illus. 2004. 24p. pap. 5.99 (978-1-84148-595-9(0)) Barefoot Bks., Inc.

Shepherd, Jodie & Moroney, Christopher. Sesame Street Big, Bigger, Biggest. 2007. 10p. (J). bds. 14.99 (978-0-7944-1232-6(7)) Reader's Digest Assn., Inc., The.

Sherry, Kevin. I'm the Biggest Thing in the Ocean. 2007. (Illus.). 32p. (J). (ps). 16.99 (978-0-8037-3192-9(2) , Dial) Penguin Group (USA) Inc.

Shulman, Mark. Big Cat. Chambers, Sally, illus. 2004. 8p. (J). bds. 6.95 (978-1-58925-737-5(5) , tiger tales) ME Media LLC.

—El Gato Grande. Chambers, Sally, illus. 2004. (Todo cambia Ser.). (SPA.). 8p. 12.95 (978-84-7864-822-1(4)) Combel Editorial, S.A. ESP. *Dist:* Independent Pubs. Group.

Silver Dolphin en Español Editors. Caritas felices: Dumbo: Happy Faces: Dumbo, Spanish-Language Edition. 2007. (Illus.). 8p. (J). bds. 7.95 ***(978-970-718-394-0(2)** , Silver Dolphin en Español) Advanced Marketing, S. de R. L. de C. V. MEX. *Dist:* Perseus Distribution.

Simon, Charnan. Pumpkin Fever. Bryan-Hunt, Jan, illus. 2007. (Rookie Reader Ser.). 30p. (J). pap. ***(978-0-531-12488-8(6))*** Children's Pr., Ltd.

Simon, Charnan. Pumpkin Forever. Bryan-Hunt, Jan, illus. 2006. (Rookie Reader Skill Set Ser.). 32p. (J). (gr. k-2). 19.50 (978-0-531-12086-6(4) , Children's Pr.) Scholastic Library Publishing.

Simson, Dana. Shapes. 2003. (Dana Simson Chunky Books Ser.). 10p. (J). bds. 2.95 (978-1-74047-257-9(8)) Book Co. Publishing Pty, Ltd., The AUS. *Dist:* Penton Overseas, Inc.

Spafford, Suzy. Witzy's Shapes. 2002. (Little Suzy's Zoo Ser.). (Illus.). 12p. (J). bds. 4.99 (978-0-439-36632-8(1)) Scholastic, Inc.

Stadler, John. Big & Little. 2007. (Illus.). 32p. (J). (ps-1). 9.99 (978-0-375-84175-0(X) , Robin Corey Bks.) Random Hse. Children's Bks.

Stinson, Kathy. Big or Little? Lewis, Robin Baird, illus. 2003. (Toddler Ser.). 32p. (J). (ps-1). pap. 5.95 (978-0-920236-32-1(4)) Annick Pr., Ltd. CAN. *Dist:* Firefly Bks., Ltd.

Stohner, Anu. Santa's Littlest Helper Travels the World. Wilson, Henrike, illus. 2007. 32p. (J). (ps-3). 15.95 ***(978-1-59990-187-9(0)** , Bloomsbury Children) Bloomsbury Publishing.

Sundberg, Norma J. An Odd Fable. Leiper, Esther M., illus. 2007. (ENG.). 32p. (J). pap. 13.95 ***(978-0-9776958-5-0(9))*** CyPress Pubns.

Sutton, Scott E. Look at the Size of That Long-Legged Ploot! 2006. 44p. 14.95 (978-1-888045-16-1(7)) Action Publishing, LLC.

Tagel, Peggy, illus. Animal Safari. 2003. (Squishy Shapes Ser.). 10p. (J). 12.95 (978-1-57145-741-7(0) , Silver Dolphin Bks.) Advantage Pubs. Group.

—Dinosaurs. 2003. (Squishy Shapes Ser.). 10p. (J). 12.95 (978-1-57145-740-0(2) , Silver Dolphin Bks.) Advantage Pubs. Group.

Thompson, Lauren. Wee Little Chick. Butler, John, illus. 2008. (Wee Little Ser.). 32p. (J). 14.99 ***(978-1-4169-3468-4(5))*** Simon & Schuster Children's Publishing.

The Treehouse Shapes Up. 1998. (Fisher-Price Hideaway Hollow Padded Board Bks.). (Illus.). 16p. (J). (gr. 1). bds. (978-0-7666-0114-7(5) , Honey Bear Bks.) Modern Publishing.

Van Der Meer, Ron. How Many? ltd. ed. 2007. (Illus.). 12p. (J). (gr. 2). 250.00 ***(978-0-375-84239-9(X)** , Robin Corey Bks.) Random Hse. Children's Bks.

—How Many? Spectacular Paper Sculptures. 2007. (Illus.). 12p. (J). (gr. 2-7). 24.99 ***(978-0-375-84226-9(8)** , Robin Corey Bks.) Random Hse. Children's Bks.

Van Fleet, Matthew. Spotted Yellow Frogs: Fold-Out Fun with Patterns, Colors, 3-D Shapes, Animals. 1998. (Illus.). 24p. (J). (ps-k). 10.99 (978-0-8037-2350-4(4) , Dial) Penguin Group (USA) Inc.

Vaughan, Christina. The Fattest Pig. 2000. (Illus.). 32p. (J). (gr. 1-5). spiral bd. 18.95 (978-0-9641697-9-1(7) , You-Draw-It Bks.) Castlebrook Pubns.

Vere, Ed. Everyone's Little. 2003. (Illus.). 14p. (J). bds. 6.95 (978-0-333-78039-8(6)) Macmillan Publishers Ltd. GBR. *Dist:* Trafalgar Square Publishing.

—Everyone's Little. 2001. (Illus.). 12p. (J). (ps). 6.95 (978-0-531-30336-8(5) , Orchard Bks.) Scholastic, Inc.

Wallace, Rich. Fast Company. 2005. (Winning Season Ser.: Vol. 3). 128p. (J). (gr. 3-6). pap. 4.99 (978-0-14-240468-3(3) , Puffin) Penguin Group (USA) Inc.

—Fast Company No. 3. 2005. 128p. (J). (gr. 3-7). 14.99 (978-0-670-05942-3(0) , Viking Juvenile) Penguin Group (USA) Inc.

Wang, Margaret. Hungry Bunny. 2007. 16p. pap. 9.95 ***(978-1-58117-556-1(6))*** Dalmatian Pr.

Warrence, Michelle. Colors, Shapes & Sizes. del Sur, Duendes, illus. 2000. (Jumpstart Workbooks Ser.). 32p. (J). pap., wbk. ed. 3.99 (978-0-439-16421-4(4)) Scholastic, Inc.

Wheeler, Lisa. Avalanche Annie: A Not-So-Tall Tale. Cyrus, Kurt, illus. 2005. 30p. (J). (gr. k-4). reprint ed. 16.00 (978-0-7567-8536-9(7)) DIANE Publishing Co.

—Avalanche Annie: A Not-So-Tall Tale. Cyrus, Kurt, illus. 2003. 32p. (J). 16.00 (978-0-15-216735-6(8)) Harcourt Children's Bks.

Williams, Deborah Holt. Not Too Small at All. Hickman, Estella L., illus. 2000. 16p. (J). (gr. k-2). pap. 3.75 (978-1-58323-008-4(4) , Seedling Pubns.) Continental Pr., Inc.

Willis, Jeanne. Cottonball Colin. Ross, Tony, illus. 2008. (J). ***(978-0-8028-5331-8(5)** , Eerdmans Bks For Young Readers) Eerdmans, William B. Publishing Co.

Wilson, Zachary. A Circle in the Sky. Adinolfi, JoAnn, illus. 2007. (Rookie Reader Ser.). 31p. (J). pap. ***(978-0-531-12589-2(0))*** Children's Pr., Ltd.

—A Circle in the Sky. 2006. (Rookie Reader Skill Set Ser.). (Illus.). 32p. (J). (gr. k-2). 19.50 (978-0-531-12570-0(X) , Children's Pr.) Scholastic Library Publishing.

Winnie the Pooh Shapes. 2002. (Illus.). 10p. (J). (978-0-7868-3401-3(3)) Disney Pr.

Winters, Kay. The Teeny Tiny Ghost. Munsinger, Lynn, illus. 2002. (J). 14.43 (978-0-7587-3770-0(X)) Book Wholesalers, Inc.

—The Teeny Tiny Ghost. Munsinger, Lynn, illus. 1999. 32p. (J). (ps-3). pap. 6.99 (978-0-06-443590-1(3) , Harper Trophy) HarperCollins Pubs.

—The Teeny Tiny Ghost & the Monster, Vol. 3. Munsinger, Lynn, illus. 2004. 32p. (J). (ps-3). 14.99 (978-0-06-028884-6(1)); lib. bdg. 15.89 (978-0-06-028885-3(X)) HarperCollins Pubs.

Wurtz, K. D. Digby in Disguise. Carrier, Tracey Dahle, illus. 2001. (Digby in Disguise Ser.: Vol. 1). (J). (978-0-9712840-1-2(6)) Boyds Collection Ltd., The.

Wynne-Jones, Tim. I'll Make You Small. (J). pap. 15.95 (978-0-88899-045-7(6)); pap. 4.95 (978-0-88899-105-8(3)) Groundwood Bks. CAN. *Dist:* Transition Vendor.

Yeager, Nancy & Yeager, Doug. A Tiny Little Story. 1999. 32p. (J). (ps). pap. (978-1-879911-01-7(9)) Rams Horn Bks.

Young, Amy. Belinda the Ballerina. 2005. (Illus.). 30p. (J). (ps-ps). lib. bdg. 12.79 (978-0-606-33108-1(5)) Tandem Library Bks.

—Belinda, the Ballerina. 2005. (Illus.). 32p. (J). (gr. k-2). reprint ed. pap. 5.99 (978-0-14-240272-6(9) , Puffin) Penguin Group (USA) Inc.

YoYo. Forms, Colors, & Opposites. 2005. 40p. bds. 6.95 (978-90-5843-888-1(0)) YoYo Bks. BEL. *Dist:* National Bk. Network.

Zobel-Nolan, Allia. Look at Me! A Book about Differences. Terry, Michael, illus. 2003. 5p. (J). bds. 7.99 (978-0-7944-0254-9(2) , Reader's Digest Children's Bks.) Reader's Digest Children's Publishing, Inc.

SKATEBOARDING

Anderson, Jameson. A Day in the Life of a Skateboarder. 2006. (Illus.). 32p. (J). (978-1-4109-2482-7(3)); pap. (978-1-4109-2487-2(4)) Steck-Vaughn.

Bermudez, Ben. Go Skate: The Mongo's Guide to Skateboarding. 2001. (Illus.). 128p. pap. 19.95 (978-1-931497-42-8(7)) 17th Street Productions, An Alloy Online Inc. Co.

Bloomquist, Christopher. Skateboarding in the X Games. 2003. (Kids Guide to the X Games Ser.). (Illus.). 24p. (J). lib. bdg. 19.95 (978-0-8239-6300-3(4) , PowerKids Pr.) Rosen Publishing Group, Inc., The.

Bradley, Michael. Tony Hawk. 2004. (Illus.). 48p. (J). 27.07 (978-0-7614-1759-0(1) , Benchmark Bks.) Cavendish, Marshall Corp.

Braun, Eric. Tony Hawk. 2004. (Amazing Athletes Ser.). (Illus.). 32p. (J). (gr. 3-4). lib. bdg. 23.93 (978-0-8225-1367-4(6)) Lerner Publishing Group.

—Tony Hawk. 2003. (gr. 3-6). lib. bdg. 14.10 (978-0-613-81867-4(9)) Tandem Library Bks.

Buntrock, Susan. Finger Skateboard Tricks & Tips. 2000. (Illus.). 32p. (J). (gr. 4-7). 7.95 (978-0-439-19453-2(9)) Scholastic, Inc.

Burke, L. M. Skateboarding! Surf the Pavement. 2000. (Extreme Sports Collection). (Illus.). 64p. (J). (gr. 5-8). lib. bdg. 26.50 (978-0-8239-3014-2(9) , EXSKBO, Rosen Central) Rosen Publishing Group, Inc., The.

Burke, L. M., told to. Skateboarding! Surf the Pavement. 2000. (Illus.). 64p. (YA). per. 9.95 (978-1-56254-304-4(0) , SP 3040) Saddleback Educational Publishing.

Christopher, Matt. On the Halfpipe with... Tony Hawk. 2001. (Illus.). 96p. (J). (gr. 3-7). pap. 4.99 (978-0-316-14223-6(9)) Little, Brown Bks. for Young Readers.

—On the Halfpipe with... Tony Hawk. 2001. (978-0-606-22558-8(7)); (gr. 3-6). lib. bdg. 13.00 (978-0-613-44173-5(7)) Tandem Library Bks.

Christopher, Matt & Christopher, Matthew F. Matt Christopher Extreme Sports, 8 vols., Set. #1 Sports Writer for Kids Staff, illus. 2004. (J). (gr. 3-7). pap., pap. 6.50 (978-0-316-01143-3(6)) Little Brown & Co.

Craats, Rennay. For the Love of Skateboarding. 2003. (gr. 3-6). lib. bdg. 15.25 (978-0-613-79826-6(0)) Tandem Library Bks.

—Skateboarding. 2001. (For the Love of Sports Ser.). (Illus.). 24p. (J). lib. bdg. 15.95 (978-1-930954-27-4(1)) Weigl Pubs., Inc.

Crossingham, John. Extreme Skateboarding. 2003. (Extreme Sports - No Limits Ser.). (Illus.). 32p. (J). (gr. 3). pap. (978-0-7787-1714-0(3)) Crabtree Publishing Co.

—Extreme Skateboarding. 2003. (gr. 3-6). lib. bdg. 15.25 (978-0-613-87231-7(2)) Tandem Library Bks.

—Patinetas en Accion. Rouse, Bonna, illus. Crabtree, Marc, photos by. 2005. (Deportes en Accion Ser.). (SPA.). 32p. (J). (gr. 6-9). pap. (978-0-7787-8620-7(X)) Crabtree Publishing Co.

—Patinetas en Accion. 2005. (SPA., Illus.). 32p. (J). (978-0-7787-8574-3(2)) Crabtree Publishing Co.

Crossingham, John & Kalman, Bobbie. Extreme Skateboarding. 2003. (Extreme Sports - No Limits Ser.). (Illus.). 32p. (J). (gr. 3). (978-0-7787-1668-6(6)) Crabtree Publishing Co.

Curry, Don, ed. On the Edge Skateboarding/on the Edge Snowboarding. 2008. 48p. (J). pap. 6.99 ***(978-0-696-23980-9(9))*** Meredith Bks.

David, Jack. Big Air Skateboarding. 2007. (Illus.). 24p. (J). lib. bdg. 19.95 (978-1-60014-121-8(8)) Bellwether Media.

—Big Air Skateboarding. 2007. (Torque: Action Sports Ser.). (Illus.). 24p. (J). (gr. 3-7). lib. bdg. 20.00 (***978-0-531-18489-9(7)*** , Children's Pr.) Scholastic Library Publishing.

DeGezelle, Terri. Let's Skateboard! 2006. (Pebble Plus Ser.). (Illus.). 24p. (J). (978-0-7368-5365-1(0)) Capstone Pr., Inc.

Dieterich, Alice. Tony Hawk & Andy MacDonald Ride to the Top. 2003. (gr. 3-6). lib. bdg. 11.80 (978-0-613-72472-2(0)) Tandem Library Bks.

Dieterich, Alice & Chipponeri, Kelli. Tony Hawk & Andy MacDonald: Ride to the Top. 2003. (All Aboard Reading Ser.: Vol. 3). (Illus.). 48p. (J). (gr. 2-4). pap. 3.99 (978-0-448-43160-4(2) , Grosset & Dunlap) Penguin Group (USA) Inc.

Dietrich, Alice & Chipponeri, Kelli. Tony Hawk & Andy Macdonald: Ride to the Top. 2003. (All Aboard Science Reader Station Stop Ser.: Vol. 3). (Illus.). 48p. (J). (gr. 2-4). 13.89 (978-0-448-43231-1(5) , Grosset & Dunlap) Penguin Group (USA) Inc.

Doeden, Matt. Skateboarding. 2004. (To the Extreme Ser.). (Illus.). 32p. (J). lib. bdg. 19.93 (978-0-7368-2730-0(7)) Capstone Pr., Inc.

—Skateparks: Grab Your Skateboard. 2002. (Skateboarding Ser.). (Illus.). 32p. (J). (gr. 3-4). lib. bdg. 21.26 (978-0-7368-1072-2(2) , Capstone High-Interest Bks.) Capstone Pr., Inc.

Dorling Kindersley Publishing Staff. Skateboarding. 2006. (Illus.). 64p. (J). pap. 9.99 (978-0-7566-2074-5(0)); pap. 12.99 (978-0-7566-2075-2(9)) Dorling Kindersley Publishing, Inc.

Dougherty, Terri. Girls' Skateboarding. 2008. (J). (***978-1-4296-0134-4(5)***) Capstone Pr., Inc.

Eck, Kristin. Skateboarding: Check It Out. 2001. (Reading Power Ser.). (Illus.). 24p. (J). (gr. 1). lib. bdg. 17.25 (978-0-8239-5695-1(4) , PKSKBO, PowerKids Pr.) Rosen Publishing Group, Inc., The.

Eckart, Edana. I Can Skateboard. 2003. (gr. k-3). lib. bdg. 12.95 (978-0-613-59637-4(4)) Tandem Library Bks.

Fandel, Jennifer. Skateboarding. 2007. (J). (978-1-58341-469-9(X) , Creative Education) Creative Co., The.

Freimuth, Jeri. Extreme Skateboarding Moves. 2001. (Behind the Moves Ser.). (Illus.). 32p. (J). (gr. 3-4). lib. bdg. 21.26 (978-0-7368-0783-8(7) , Capstone High-Interest Bks.) Capstone Pr., Inc.

Galashan, Kathy. Skate Boarding. 2nd ed. 2005. (Illus.). 32p. pap. (978-0-340-81127-6(7)) Cambridge Univ. Pr.

Galens, Judy. Tony Hawk. 2007. (People in the News Ser.). (Illus.). 128p. (J). (gr. 7-10). 31.20 (***978-1-4205-0016-5(3)*** , Lucent Bks.) Thomson Gale.

Gifford, Clive. Skateboarding. 2005. (Adrenalin! Ser.). (Illus.). 32p. (J). (gr. 4 up). lib. bdg. 27.10 (978-1-59389-236-4(5)) Chrysalis Education.

Greene, Edgar. Tony Hawk. 2003. (Sports Heroes & Legends Ser.). (Illus.). 103p. (J). (978-0-7607-3216-8(7)) Barnes & Noble, Inc.

Harsley, Andy. Skateboarding. 2002. (Radical Sports Ser.). (Illus.). 32p. (J). (gr. 5-7). pap. 7.50 (978-1-4034-0106-9(3) , 91654) Heinemann Library.

Hawk, Tony. Tony Hawk: Professional Skateboarder. 2002. (gr. 7-12). lib. bdg. 15.30 (978-0-613-70951-4(9)) Tandem Library Bks.

Herran, Joe & Thomas, Ron. Skateboarding. 2002. (Action Sports Ser.). (Illus.). 32p. (gr. 4-8). 28.00 (978-0-7910-6998-1(2) , Chelsea Hse.) Facts On File, Inc.

Hinter, Parker C. & Rowland, Della. The Case of the Winning Skateboard. 1998. (Clue Jr. Ser.: No. 12). (J). (gr. 2-4). pap. 3.99 (978-0-590-13787-4(5)) Scholastic, Inc.

Hocking, Justin. Awesome Obstacles: How to Build Your Own Skateboard Ramps & Ledges. 2004. (World of Skateboard Parks Ser.). (Illus.). 48p. (J). lib. bdg. 26.50 (978-1-4042-0337-2(0)) Rosen Publishing Group, Inc., The.

—Famous Skateboarders. 2006. (Illus.). 24p. (J). (978-1-4042-3050-7(5) , PowerKids Pr.) Rosen Publishing Group, Inc., The.

—Half-Pipes, Ramps, & Other Obstacles. 2006. (Illus.). 24p. lib. bdg. (978-1-4042-3051-4(3) , PowerKids Pr.) Rosen Publishing Group, Inc., The.

—Off the Wall: A Skateboarder's Guide to Riding Bowls & Pools. 2004. (Illus.). 48p. (J). lib. bdg. 26.50 (978-1-4042-0339-6(7)) Rosen Publishing Group, Inc., The.

—Rippin' Ramps: A Skateboarder's Guide to Riding Half-pipes. 2004. (World of Skateboard Parks Ser.). (Illus.). 48p. (J). lib. bdg. 26.50 (978-1-4042-0340-2(0)) Rosen Publishing Group, Inc., The.

—Skate Parks. 2006. (Power Skateboarding Ser.). (Illus.). 24p. (J). lib. bdg. (978-1-4042-3047-7(5) , PowerKids Pr.) Rosen Publishing Group, Inc., The.

—Skateboarding Competitions. 2006. (Illus.). 24p. lib. bdg. (978-1-4042-3052-1(1) , PowerKids Pr.) Rosen Publishing Group, Inc., The.

—Skateboarding Design & Construction: How Your Board Gets Built. 2006. (Illus.). 24p. (J). (978-1-4042-3048-4(3) , PowerKids Pr.) Rosen Publishing Group, Inc., The.

—Skateboarding Tricks & Techniques. 2006. (Power Skateboarding Ser.). (Illus.). 24p. (J). lib. bdg. (978-1-4042-3049-1(1) , PowerKids Pr.) Rosen Publishing Group, Inc., The.

—Taking Action: How to Get Your City to Build a Public Skatepark. 2004. (World of Skateboard Parks Ser.). (Illus.). 48p. (J). lib. bdg. 26.50 (978-1-4042-0341-9(9)) Rosen Publishing Group, Inc., The.

—Technical Terrain: A Skateboarder's Guide to Riding Skate Park Street Courses. 2004. (Illus.). 48p. (J). lib. bdg. 26.50 (978-1-4042-0342-6(7)) Rosen Publishing Group, Inc., The.

Hoena, Blake A. Skateboards: Designs & Equipment. 2002. (Skateboarding Ser.). (Illus.). 32p. (J). (gr. 3-4). lib. bdg. 21.26 (978-0-7368-1073-9(0) , Capstone High-Interest Bks.) Capstone Pr., Inc.

Horsley, Andy. Skateboarding. 2002. (Radical Sports Ser.). (Illus.). 32p. (J). (gr. 5-7). lib. bdg. 25.64 (978-1-58810-625-4(X)) Heinemann Library.

—Skateboarding. 2001. (To the Limit Ser.). (Illus.). 32p. (J). (gr. 4-7). lib. bdg. 25.69 (978-0-7398-3163-2(1)) Raintree.

—Skateboarding. 2003. (gr. 5-8). lib. bdg. 15.25 (978-0-613-45832-0(X)) Tandem Library Bks.

Howard, Devon. Skateboards: From Start to Finish. Howard, Devon, photos by. 2005. (Made in the USA Ser.). (Illus.). 32p. (J). (gr. 3-7). lib. bdg. 23.70 (978-1-4103-0658-6(5) , Blackbirch Pr., Inc.) Thomson Gale.

Hughes, Morgan. Skateboarding. 2003. (Wheels in Motion Ser.). (Illus.). 24p. (J). 20.64 (978-1-58952-668-6(6)) Rourke Publishing, LLC.

Junor, Amy. Skate! 2008. (Dk Readers Ser.). 48p. (J). (gr. 2-3). 14.99 (***978-0-7566-3828-3(3)***); pap. 3.99 (***978-0-7566-3829-0(1)***) Dorling Kindersley Publishing, Inc.

Kaelberer, Angie Peterson. Skateboarding Greats: Champs of the Ramps. 2002. (Skateboarding Ser.). (Illus.). 32p. (J). (gr. 3-4). lib. bdg. 21.26 (978-0-7368-1074-6(9) , Capstone High-Interest Bks.) Capstone Pr., Inc.

Kalman, Bobbie. Figure Skating in Action. 2001. (gr. 3-6). lib. bdg. 14.10 (978-0-613-32551-6(6)) Tandem Library Bks.

Kalman, Bobbie & Crossingham, John. Skateboarding in Action. Rouse, Bonna, illus. 2002. (Sports in Action Ser.). 32p. (J). (gr. 3-4). (978-0-7787-0117-0(4)); pap. (978-0-7787-0123-1(9)) Crabtree Publishing Co.

Kelley, K. C. Skateboard Stars. 2007. (Boys Rock! Ser.). 32p. (J). (gr. 1-5). 24.21 (***978-1-59296-861-9(9)***) Child's World, Inc.

Kelley, K. C. Skateboarding. 2003. (Extreme Sports Ser.). (Illus.). 24p. (J). lib. bdg. 22.00 (978-0-8368-3724-7(X)) Stevens, Gareth Inc.

Kennedy, Mike. Skateboarding. (Watts Library). (Illus.). 64p. (J). (gr. 5-7). 2002. pap. 8.95 (978-0-531-16584-3(1)); 2001. 25.50 (978-0-531-13952-3(2)) Scholastic Library Publishing. (Watts, Franklin).

Kjelle, Marylou Morano. Tony Hawk. 2004. (Robbie Reader Ser.). (Illus.). 32p. (J). (gr. 1-4). lib. bdg. 25.70 (978-1-58415-285-9(0)) Mitchell Lane Pubs., Inc.

Loizos, Constance. Skateboard! Your Guide to Street, Vert, Downhill, & More. Dickason, Jack, illus. 2002. (Extreme Sports Ser.). 64p. (J). (gr. 4-7). pap. 8.95 (978-0-7922-8229-7(9) , National Geographic Children's Bks.) National Geographic Society.

Lowe, Diane. Skateboarding. 2004. 16p. (J). (gr. k-3). pap. 4.95 (978-1-57874-079-6(7)) Kaeden Corp.

Mahaney, Ian. Tony Hawk: Skateboarding Champ. 2005. (Extreme Sports Biographies Ser.). (Illus.). 24p. (J). 19.95 (978-1-4042-2747-7(4) , PowerKids Pr.) Rosen Publishing Group, Inc., The.

Marsh, James. Super.Activ Skateboarding. (Illus.). iv, 122p. (YA). pap. 8.99 (978-0-340-79160-8(8) , Hodder & Stoughton) Hodder General Publishing Division GBR. *Dist:* Trafalgar Square Publishing.

Martin, Michael. Skateboarding History: From the Backyard to the Big Time. 2002. (Skateboarding Ser.). (Illus.). 32p. (J). (gr. 3-4). lib. bdg. 21.26 (978-0-7368-1071-5(4) , Capstone High-Interest Bks.) Capstone Pr., Inc.

McAuliffe, Bill. Skateboarding. 2002. (Illus.). 32p. (J). lib. bdg. 24.25 (978-1-58340-162-0(8)) Smart Apple Media.

Miller, Connie Colwell. Skateboarding Big Air. 2008. (J). (***978-1-4296-0108-5(6)***) Capstone Pr., Inc.

—Skateboarding Vert. 2008. (J). (***978-1-4296-0109-2(4)***) Capstone Pr., Inc.

Miller, Raymond H. Tony Hawk. 2004. (Stars of Sport Ser.). (Illus.). 48p. (J). 26.20 (978-0-7377-1568-2(5) , Greenhaven Pr., Inc.) Thomson Gale.

Morgan, Jed. Skateboarding. 2006. (Illus.). 32p. (J). (978-1-58340-959-6(9)) Smart Apple Media.

Murdico, Suzanne J. Skateboarding in the X-Games. 2005. (World of Skateboarding Ser.). (Illus.). 48p. (YA). (gr. 5-8). lib. bdg. 26.50 (978-0-8239-3645-8(7)) Rosen Publishing Group, Inc., The.

—Street Luge & Dirtboarding. 2005. (World of Skateboarding Ser.). (Illus.). 48p. (YA). (gr. 5-8). lib. bdg. 26.50 (978-0-8239-3647-2(3)) Rosen Publishing Group, Inc., The.

Murray, Julie. Tony Hawk. 2004. (Awesome Athletes Ser.). (Illus.). 32p. (J). (gr. k-6). lib. bdg. 22.78 (978-1-59197-489-5(5)) ABDO Publishing Co.

Noll, Rhyn. Skateboarding: Past—Present—Future. 2003. (Illus.). 192p. (gr. 10-13). pap. 29.95 (978-0-7643-1845-0(4)) Schiffer Publishing, Ltd.

Perez, Marlene. Skateboarding. ed. 2004. (Shared Connections Ser.). (J). pap. 27.00 (978-1-4108-1636-8(2)); pap., instr.'s gde. ed. 27.00 (978-1-4108-1612-2(5)) Benchmark Education Co.

Powell, Ben. Skateboarding. 2004. (Extreme Sports Ser.). (Illus.). 32p. (J). (gr. 3-6). lib. bdg. 22.60 (978-0-8225-1241-7(6)) Lerner Publishing Group.

Powell, Ben, et al. Skateboarding. 1999. (Extreme Sports Ser.). (Illus.). 32p. (J). (gr. 5-9). pap. 7.95 (978-0-7641-0797-9(6)) Barron's Educational Series, Inc.

Preszler, Eric. Skateboarding. 2004. (Edge Books, X-Sports). (Illus.). 32p. (J). lib. bdg. 22.60 (978-0-7368-2712-6(9)) Capstone Pr., Inc.

Red Bird Press, creator. 3D Board Mania. 2005. (Mission Xtreme 3D Ser.). (Illus.). 18p. (J). pap. 4.95 (978-1-902626-81-9(8)) Red Bird Publishing GBR. *Dist:* Perseus Distribution.

Rosenberg, Aaron. Advanced Skateboarding: From Kick Turns to Catching Air. 2005. (World of Skateboarding Ser.). (Illus.). 48p. (YA). (gr. 5-8). lib. bdg. 26.50 (978-0-8239-3649-6(X)) Rosen Publishing Group, Inc., The.

—A Beginner's Guide to Very Cool Skateboarding Tricks. 2005. (World of Skateboarding Ser.). (Illus.). 48p. (YA). (gr. 5-8). lib. bdg. 26.50 (978-0-8239-3646-5(5)) Rosen Publishing Group, Inc., The.

Sadler, Wendy. Scooters & Skateboards. 2005. (Illus.). 32p. (J). (978-1-4034-6827-7(3)); pap. (978-1-4034-6833-8(8)) Heinemann Library.

Savage, Jeff. Street Skating: Grinds & Grabs. 2004. (Skateboarding Ser.). (Illus.). 32p. (J). lib. bdg. 22.60 (978-0-7368-2706-5(4)) Capstone Pr., Inc.

—Tony Hawk: Skateboarding Legend. 2004. (Skateboarding Ser.). (Illus.). 32p. (J). lib. bdg. 22.60 (978-0-7368-2704-1(8)) Capstone Pr., Inc.

—Vert Skating: Mastering the Ramp. 2004. (Skateboarding Ser.). (Illus.). 32p. (J). lib. bdg. 22.60 (978-0-7368-2705-8(6)) Capstone Pr., Inc.

—The X-Games: Skateboarding's Greatest Event. 2004. (Skateboarding Ser.). (Illus.). 32p. (J). lib. bdg. 22.60 (978-0-7368-2707-2(2)) Capstone Pr., Inc.

Segovia, Patty. Skate Girls. 2006. (Girls Rock! Ser.). (Illus.). 32p. (J). (gr. 1-5). 24.21 (978-1-59296-748-3(5)) Child's World, Inc.

Skateboarding. (To the Extreme Ser.). 32p. (YA). 7.95 (978-0-7368-5226-5(3)); (Illus.). (J). (gr. 3-4). lib. bdg. 180.80 (978-0-7368-2764-5(1)) Capstone Pr., Inc.

Skateboarding. 2000. (J). (978-1-58453-128-9(2)) Pioneer Valley Educational Pr., Inc.

Skateboarding, 4 bks. Incl. Skateboarding Greats : Champs of the Ramps. Kaelberer, Angie Peterson. lib. bdg. 21.26 (978-0-7368-1074-6(9)); Skateboarding History : From the Backyard to the Big Time. Martin, Michael. lib. bdg. 21.26 (978-0-7368-1071-5(4)); Skateboards : Designs & Equipment. Hoena, Blake A. lib. bdg. 21.26 (978-0-7368-1073-9(0)); Skateparks : Grab Your Skateboard. Doeden, Matt. lib. bdg. 21.26 (978-0-7368-1072-2(2)); 32p. (J). (gr. 3-4). 2002. (Illus.). Set lib. bdg. 85.04 (978-0-7368-1084-5(6) , Capstone High-Interest Bks.) Capstone Pr., Inc.

Skateboarding: Individual Nonfiction Title Six-Packs. 24p. (gr. 3-4). 44.00 (978-0-7635-4489-8(2)) Rigby Education.

Smalley, Carol. Exteme Skateboarding with Paul Rodriguez. 2006. (Extreme Sports Ser.). (Illus.). 32p. (J). (gr. 1-4). lib. bdg. (978-1-58415-489-1(6)) Mitchell Lane Pubs., Inc.

Smith, Terri Smith. Tony Hawk: Flying High. 2003. (J). pap. (978-1-932724-01-1(X) , Bios for Kids) Panda Publishing, L.L.C.

Sorensen, Lita. Tony Hawk & His Team: Skateboarding Superstars. 2005. (Illus.). 64p. (J). (gr. 5-8). lib. bdg. 26.50 (978-1-4042-0070-8(3)) Rosen Publishing Group, Inc., The.

Spencer, Russ. Skateboarding. 2005. (Kids' Guides Ser.). 32p. (J). (gr. 1-5). 25.64 (978-1-59296-210-5(6)) Child's World, Inc.

Stewart, Mark. One Wild Ride: The Life of Skateboarding Superstar Tony Hawk. (Illus.). 64p. (gr. 6 up). 2003. pap. (978-0-7613-1689-3(2)); 2002. lib. bdg. 24.90 (978-0-7613-2666-3(9)) Lerner Publishing Group. (Twenty-First Century Bks.).

Streissguth, Thomas. Skateboarding Street Style. 2008. (Illus.). 24p. (J). lib. bdg. 19.95 (***978-1-60014-142-3(0)***) Bellwether Media.

—Skateboarding Vert. 2008. (Illus.). 24p. (J). lib. bdg. 19.95 (***978-1-60014-141-6(2)***) Bellwether Media.

Studelska, Jana Voelke. Skateboarding for Fun! 2007. (J). lib. bdg. (***978-0-7565-3291-8(4)***) Compass Point Bks.

Thomas, Keltie. Blades, Boards & Scooters. Attoe, Steve & Moon, Allan, illus. 2005. (Popular Mechanics for Kids Ser.). 64p. (J). pap., pap. 9.95 (978-1-897066-34-8(1)) Maple Tree Pr. CAN. *Dist:* Perseus Distribution.

Thrasher: Insane Terrain. 2001. (gr. 5-8). lib. bdg. 39.10 (978-0-613-49378-9(8)) Tandem Library Bks.

Tony Hawk. 2001. 32p. (J). pap. 4.99 (978-0-439-34293-3(7)) Scholastic, Inc.

Vieregger, K. E. Skateboarding. 2003. (X-Treme Sports Ser.). (Illus.). 32p. (J). (gr. k-6). lib. bdg. 22.78 (978-1-57765-928-0(7)) ABDO Publishing Co.

Weber, Terri Smith. Tony Hawk: Flying High. 2003. (J). lib. bdg. (978-1-932724-00-4(1) , Bios for Kids) Panda Publishing, L.L.C.

Weigl Publishers Staff & Craats, Rennay. For the Love of Skateboarding. Nault, Jennifer & Turner, Kara, eds. 2003. (For the Love of Sports Ser.). (Illus.). 24p. (J). pap. 6.95 (978-1-59036-070-5(2)) Weigl Pubs., Inc.

Werner, Doug & Badillo, Steve. Skateboarder's Start-up: A Beginner's Guide to Skateboarding. 2000. (Start-Up Sports Ser.: Vol. 11). (Illus.). 144p. (gr. 4-8). pap. 11.95 (978-1-884654-13-8(4)) Tracks Publishing.

Willett, Edward. Skateboarding. 2005. (Rad Sports Techniques, Training, & Tricks Ser.). (Illus.). 48p. (YA). (gr. 5-8). lib. bdg. 26.50 (978-0-8239-3848-3(4)) Rosen Publishing Group, Inc., The.

Wingate, Brian. Tony Hawk: Skateboarding Champion. 2005. (World of Skateboarding Ser.). (Illus.). 48p. (YA). (gr. 5-8). lib. bdg. 26.50 (978-0-8239-3651-9(1)) Rosen Publishing Group, Inc., The.

The World of Skateboarding. 2005. (Illus.). 48p. (gr. 5-8). lib. bdg. 159.00 (978-0-8239-3891-9(3)) Rosen Publishing Group, Inc., The.

SKATEBOARDING—FICTION

Anderson, Gary H. Gameplayer: The Genesis Portal. 2006. (J). pap. (***978-0-9778205-5-9(6)***) Helm Publishing.

Burnett, Eric. Skateboarder Steve Stops Falling Down. 2002. 124p. pap. 9.95 (978-0-595-22197-4(1) , Writers Club Pr.) iUniverse, Inc.

Choyce, Lesley. Smoke & Mirrors. 2004. 200p. (YA). pap. 8.99 (978-1-55002-534-7(1)) Dundurn Group, The CAN. *Dist:* Univ. of Toronto Pr.

Christopher, Matt. Into the Danger Zone. Koelsch, Michael, illus. 6th ed. 2004. (Extreme Team Ser.: Vol. 6). 64p. (J). (gr. 2-4). pap. 4.99 (978-0-316-76267-0(9) , Tingley, Megan Bks.) Little, Brown Bks. for Young Readers.

—Skateboard Renegade. ed. 2000. (Sports Classics IV Ser.). 139p. (J). lib. bdg. 15.00 (978-1-59054-768-7(3)) Fitzgerald Bks.

—Skateboard Renegade. 2000. (J). (978-0-606-19843-1(1)); (gr. 3-6). lib. bdg. 12.40 (978-0-613-30735-2(6)) Tandem Library Bks.

Christopher, Matt. Skateboard Tough. 2007. (J). lib. bdg. (***978-1-59953-115-1(1)***) Norwood Hse. Pr.

Disney Press Staff. Head over Heels. 2001. (gr. 3-6). lib. bdg. 13.00 (978-0-613-74997-8(9)) Tandem Library Bks.

Doeden, Matt. Shaun White. 2006. (Illus.). 32p. (J). pap. 5.95 (978-0-8225-6841-4(1) , First Avenue Editions) Lerner Publishing Group.

Flynn, Pat. Alex Jackson: Swa. Scarff, Eileen, ed. 2002. 168p. (YA). pap. 14.95 (978-0-7022-3307-4(2)) Univ. of Queensland Pr. AUS. *Dist:* International Specialized Bk. Services.

Free Wheelin' Coloring/Activity Book (English) 2005. (Illus.). (J). (978-0-9770455-7-0(9)) Educational Adventures.

Graham, Rosemary. Thou Shalt Not Dump the Skater Dude & Other Commandments I Have Broken. 2005. 224p. (J). (gr. 7). 16.99 (978-0-670-06017-7(8) , Viking Juvenile) Penguin Group (USA) Inc.

—Thou Shalt Not Dump the Skater Dude (Splashproof Edition) 2007. 1p. (YA). (gr. 7). pap. 6.99 (978-0-14-240836-0(0) , Puffin) Penguin Group (USA) Inc.

Hornby, Nick. Slam. 2007. 304p. (J). (gr. 6). 19.99 (***978-0-399-25048-4(4)*** , Putnam Juvenile) Penguin Group (USA) Inc.

Lawrie, Robin & Lawrie, Christine, illus. Snow Bored. 2007. (J). 32p. pap. (***978-1-59889-444-8(7)***); 40p. (gr. 2-6). lib. bdg. 21.26 (***978-1-59889-349-6(1)***) Stone Arch Bks.

Little Dinosaur's Skateboard. 2005. (J). (978-1-932570-42-7(X)) Literacy Footprints Inc.

Lobdell, Scott. The Hardy Boys #8: Board to Death. Henrique, Paulo, illus. 8th rev. ed. 2007. (Hardy Boys: Undercover Brothers Ser.). 112p. (J). 12.95 (978-1-59707-054-6(8)); pap. 7.95 (978-1-59707-053-9(X)) Papercutz.

Maddox, Jake. Board Rebel. Tiffany, Sean, illus. 2007. (J). 72p. (***978-1-59889-319-9(X)***); 65p. pap. (***978-1-59889-414-1(5)***) Stone Arch Bks.

Moloney, James. Trapped. Tan, Shaun, illus. 2008. 80p. (J). pap. (***978-1-59889-919-1(8)***); (YA). (gr. 5-9). lib. bdg. 16.95 (***978-1-59889-863-7(9)***) Stone Arch Bks.

Nelson, Blake. Paranoid Park. 2006. 176p. (YA). (gr. 7). 15.99 (978-0-670-06118-1(2) , Viking Juvenile) Penguin Group (USA) Inc.

Simon, Francesca. Little Yellow Dog Says Look at Me. Lucas, James E., illus. 2004. (Little Yellow Dog Ser.). 32p. (J). pap. 7.99 (978-1-84255-244-5(9)) Orion Children's Bks. GBR. *Dist:* Independent Pubs. Group.

Vaughan, Garth. Tommy's New Block Skates. Smith, David Preston, illus. 2004. 32p. 16.95 (978-1-55109-499-1(1)) Nimbus Publishing, Ltd. CAN. *Dist:* National Bk. Network.

Zucker, Jonny. Skateboard Power. Savage, Paul, illus. 2006. 40p. (J). (gr. 2-3). lib. bdg. (978-1-59889-007-5(7)) Stone Arch Bks.

SKATING

Boo, Michael. The Story of Figure Skating. 1998. (Illus.). 240p. pap. 7.95 (978-0-688-15821-7(8)) HarperCollins Pubs.

Bray-Moffatt, Naia & Dorling Kindersley Publishing Staff. Ice Skating School. Hanley, David, photos by. 2004. (Illus.). 48p. (J). 12.99 (978-0-7566-0267-3(X)) Dorling Kindersley Publishing, Inc.

Brooks, Lou. Skate Crazy. 2003. (Illus.). 144p. pap. 16.95 (978-0-7624-1460-4(X) , Running Pr.) Running Pr. Bk. Pubs.

Browning, Kurt. A Is for Axel: An Ice Skating Alphabet. Rose, Melanie, illus. rev. ed. 2006. 40p. (J). 17.95 (978-1-58536-280-6(8)) Sleeping Bear Pr.

Buckley, James, Jr. & Dorling Kindersley Publishing Staff. Ice Skating Stars, Vol. 2. 2003. (DK Readers Ser.: Level. 2). (Illus.). 32p. (J). pap. 3.99 (978-0-7894-9898-4(7)) Dorling Kindersley Publishing, Inc.

Buckley, James & Dorling Kindersley Publishing Staff. Ice Skating Stars: Level 2. 2003. (Readers Ser.). (Illus.). 32p. (J). 12.99 (978-0-7894-9897-7(9)) Dorling Kindersley Publishing, Inc.

Calder, Kate. Figure Skating in Action. 2000. (Sports in Action Ser.). (Illus.). 32p. (J). (gr. 3-4). (978-0-7787-0165-1(4)); pap. (978-0-7787-0177-4(8)) Crabtree Publishing Co.

—Figure Skating in Action. 2000. 12.75 (978-0-606-22832-9(2)) Tandem Library Bks.

Carty, Michelle. Follow Your Dreams Vol. 4560: The Olympic Sport of Figure Skating. Samoiloff, Sheri, ed. Allsport Staff, photos by. 2002. (Illus.). 16p. (gr. 3-6). pap. 3.49 (978-1-57471-931-4(9)) Creative Teaching Pr., Inc.

Cohen, Sasha. Sasha Cohen: Autobiography of a Champion Figure Skater. Goedeken, Kathy, illus. 2005. (J). (gr. 3 up). pap. 9.99 (978-0-06-072489-4(7)) HarperCollins Pubs.

Cohen, Sasha & Maciel, Amanda. Sasha Cohen: Fire on Ice: Autobiography of a Champion Figure Skater. Goedeken, Kathy, illus. rev. ed. 2006. 224p. (J). pap. 9.99 (978-0-06-115385-3(0)) HarperCollins Pubs.

Cranston, Patty. The Best on Ice: The World's Top Figure Skaters. 1999. (Illus.). 100p. (J). (gr. 2-5). (978-1-55074-581-6(6)) Kids Can Pr., Ltd.

—Best on Ice: The World's Top Figure Skaters. 1999. (gr. 3-6). lib. bdg. 12.95 (978-0-613-21205-2(3)) Tandem Library Bks.

Dorling Kindersley Publishing Staff. DK Readers: Ice Skating Stars. 2004. (gr. k-3). lib. bdg. 11.80 (978-0-613-75241-1(4)) Tandem Library Bks.

Dougherty, Terri. Tara Lipinski. 1999. (Jam Session Ser.). (Illus.). 32p. (J). (gr. 3-8). lib. bdg. 24.21 (978-1-57765-312-7(2) , ABDO & Daughters) ABDO Publishing Co.

Eargle, Michele, illus. Ice Skating. 1998. 15p. (J). (ps-4). pap. 12.00 (978-1-890703-12-7(5) , Bookmates) Penny Laine Papers, Inc.

Eckart, Edana. I Can Ice Skate. 2002. (Welcome Bks.). (Illus.). 24p. (J). (ps-2). pap. 4.95 (978-0-516-24029-9(3) , Children's Pr.) Scholastic Library Publishing.

—I Can Ice Skate. 2002. (gr. k-3). lib. bdg. 12.95 (978-0-613-58840-9(1)) Tandem Library Bks.

Ellison, Nancy, photos by. Becoming a Figure Skater. 2004. (Illus.). 96p. (J). (gr. 2-7). 19.95 (978-0-7893-1189-4(5)) Universe Publishing.

Farbs, C. Olympic Ice Skating. 2007. (Great Moments in Olympic History Ser.). (Illus.). 48p. (J). (gr. 5-8). lib. bdg. 26.50 (*978-1-4042-0969-5(7)) Rosen Publishing Group, Inc., The.

Freese, Joan. Play-by-Play Figure Skating. King, Andy, illus. King, Andy, photos by. 2004. (Play-by-Play Ser.). 80p. (J). (gr. 4-8). lib. bdg. 23.93 (978-0-8225-3934-6(9)) Lerner Publishing Group.

Gatto, Kimberly. Michelle Kwan: Champion on Ice. 1998. (Sports Achievers Biographies Ser.). (Illus.). 64p. (J). (gr. 4-9). lib. bdg. (978-0-8225-3669-7(2)); pap. 5.95 (978-0-8225-9830-5(2)) Lerner Publishing Group. (LernerSports).

Goodridge, Catherine. Michelle Kwan. ed. 2004. (SPA.). (J). pap. 5.00 (978-1-4108-2428-8(4) , A24284) Benchmark Education Co.

Goodridge, Catherine. Michelle Kwan (Spanish) & Michelle Kwan. 2005. spiral bd. 70.00 (*978-1-4108-5659-3(3)) Benchmark Education Co.

Gutman, Bill. Queen of the Ice: Tara Lipinski. 1999. (978-0-606-17391-9(9)) Tandem Library Bks.

Harcourt School Publishers Staff. Lipinski Below Level: Olympic Champion. 3rd ed. 2002. (Trophies Reading Program Ser.). (Illus.). pap. 5.10 (978-0-15-323135-3(1)) Harcourt Schl. Pubs.

Helmer, Diana Star & Owens, Tom. The History of Figure Skating. 2000. (Sports Throughout History Ser.). 24p. (J). (gr. 2-4). lib. bdg. 18.75 (978-0-8239-5472-8(2) , PowerKids Pr.) Rosen Publishing Group, Inc., The.

Hill, Anne E. Sergei Grinkov. 2000. (They Died Too Young Ser.). (Illus.). 48p. (J). (gr. 4-7). 21.95 (978-0-7910-5855-8(7) , Chelsea Hse.) Facts On File, Inc.

La Historia del Patinaje Artistico, 6 Packs. (On Deck en Espanol Ser.).Tr. of Story of Figure Skating. (SPA.). 24p. (gr. 4-5). 35.00 (978-0-7578-6397-4(3)) Rigby Education.

Hughes, Morgan. Ice Skating. 2005. (Junior Sports Ser.). (Illus.). 32p. (gr. 2-4). 19.95 (978-1-59515-192-6(3)) Rourke Publishing, LLC.

Isadora, Rachel. Sophie Skates. 2001. (978-0-606-22521-2(8)) Tandem Library Bks.

Johnson, Marion. Caillou Learns to Skate. rev. ed. 2003. (Clubhouse Ser.). (Illus.). 24p. (J). pap. 2.50 (978-2-89450-420-8(9)) Chouette Publishing CAN. Dist: Independent Pubs. Group.

Jones, Jen. Figure Skating for Fun! 2006. (For Fun Ser.). (Illus.). 48p. (J). (gr. 3-5). 22.60 (978-0-7565-1679-6(X)) Compass Point Bks.

Jones, Veda Boyd. Nicole Bobek. 1999. (Female Figure Skating Legends Ser.). (Illus.). 64p. (YA). (ps up). lib. bdg. 18.65 (978-0-7910-5029-3(7) , Chelsea Hse.) Facts On File, Inc.

—Tara Lipinski. 1999. (Female Figure Skating Legends Ser.). (Illus.). 64p. (YA). (gr. 4-7). lib. bdg. 18.65 (978-0-7910-4876-4(4) , Chelsea Hse.) Facts On File, Inc.

Kehoe, Stasia Ward. Tara Lipinski, Superstar Ice Skater. 2001. (Great Record Breakers in Sports Ser.). (Illus.). 24p. (J). lib. bdg. 18.75 (978-0-8239-5634-0(2) , PowerKids Pr.) Rosen Publishing Group, Inc., The.

Kennedy, Mike & Stewart, Mark. Michelle Kwan: Quest for Gold. 2002. (Inspiring People Ser.). (Illus.). 64p. (gr. 4 up). lib. bdg. 24.90 (978-0-7613-2622-9(7) , Millbrook Pr.) Lerner Publishing Group.

Krawiec, Richard. Sudden Champion: The Sarah Hughes Story. 2002. (Illus.). 100p. (Orig.). (J). (gr. 6-12). pap. 19.95 (978-1-888105-53-7(4)) Avisson Pr., Inc.

Kule, Elaine A. Kristi Yamaguchi. 2005. (Asian-American Biographies Ser.). (Illus.). 64p. (J). (gr. 6-9). pap. 9.50 (978-1-4109-1130-8(6)) Raintree.

Kwan, Michelle. Michelle Kwan: My Book of Memories. 1998. (Illus.). (J). (gr. 4-7). pap. 5.99 (978-0-590-45890-0(6)) Scholastic, Inc.

—Michelle Kwan: My Special Moments. 2001. (Illus.). 48p. (gr. 3-17). pap. 6.99 (978-0-7868-1580-7(9)) Hyperion Bks. for Children.

—Michelle Kwan Chapterbook. 2000. 64p. (J). pap. 4.99 (978-0-7868-1383-4(0)) Disney Pr.

—Michelle Kwan, Heart of a Champion: An Autobiography. 1998. (978-0-606-13607-5(X)) Tandem Library Bks.

Lindeen, Carol K. Let's Ice-Skate. 2006. (Pebble Plus Ser.). (Illus.). 24p. (J). 19.93 (978-0-7368-5360-6(X)) Capstone Pr., Inc.

Mattox, Brenda Sneathen. Figure Skating Coloring Book. 2004. (Illus.). 32p. (J). pap. 3.95 (978-0-486-43046-1(4)) Dover Pubns., Inc.

Miller, Raymond H. Michelle Kwan. 2003. (Stars of Sports Ser.). (Illus.). 48p. (J). 26.20 (978-0-7377-1540-8(5) , Greenhaven Pr., Inc.) Thomson Gale.

Milton, Steve. Figure Skating Champions. 2002. (gr. 3-6). lib. bdg. 14.10 (978-0-613-56369-7(7)) Tandem Library Bks.

—Figure Skating Champions: Includes the 2002 Winter Olympics. Chataigneau, Gérard, photos by. 2002. (Illus.). 32p. (J). (gr. 2-7). pap. 5.95 (978-1-55297-658-6(0)) Firefly Bks., Ltd.

Moncrief, Kathryn. Competitive Figure Skating for Girls. 2005. (SportsGirl Ser.). (Illus.). 64p. (YA). (gr. 5-8). lib. bdg. 26.50 (978-0-8239-3403-4(9)) Rosen Publishing Group, Inc., The.

Olson, Kay Melchisedech. Frank Zamboni & the Ice-Resurfacing Machine. Dominguez, Richard & Barnett, Charles, III, illus. 2008. (J). (*978-1-4296-0147-4(7)) Capstone Pr., Inc.

Paprocki, Sherry. Michelle Kwan. 2000. (Women Who Win Ser.). (Illus.). 64p. (J). (gr. 4-7). pap. 25.00 (978-0-7910-6152-7(3)); 25.00 (978-0-7910-5792-6(5)) Facts On File, Inc. (Chelsea Hse.).

—Michelle Kwan. 2001. (gr. 3-6). lib. bdg. 17.60 (978-0-613-32832-6(9)) Tandem Library Bks.

Peterson, Todd. Michelle Kwan: Figure Skater. 2005. (Ferguson Career Biographies Ser.). (Illus.). 128p. (J). (gr. 6-12). 25.00 (978-0-8160-6104-4(1) , Ferguson Publishing Co.) Facts On File, Inc.

Poynter, Margaret. Top 10 American Women's Figure Skaters. 1998. (Sports Top 10 Ser.). (Illus.). 48p. (YA). (gr. 4-10). lib. bdg. 23.93 (978-0-7660-1075-8(9)) Enslow Pubs., Inc.

Preston, David Curtis. A World-Class Ice Skater. 2004. (Making of a Champion Ser.). (Illus.). 48p. (J). pap. 8.50 (978-1-4034-5551-2(1)); lib. bdg. 27.07 (978-1-4034-5367-9(5)) Heinemann Library.

Rambeck, Richard & Klingel, Cynthia Fitterer. Gymnastics. 2003. (Wonder Books Level 2: Sports Ser.). (Illus.). 24p. (J). (ps-2). 22.79 (978-1-56766-459-1(8)) Child's World, Inc.

—Ice Skating. 2003. (Nonfiction Readers: Level 2 Ser.). (Illus.). 24p. (J). (ps-2). 22.79 (978-1-56766-461-4(X)) Child's World, Inc.

Rosenberg, Aaron. Taig Khris:In-Line Skating. 2005. (Illus.). 64p. (J). (gr. 5-8). lib. bdg. 26.50 (978-1-4042-0069-2(X)) Rosen Publishing Group, Inc., The.

Rossiter, Sean & Carson, Paul. Skating for Power & Speed. 2003. (Hockey the NHL Way Ser.). (Illus.). 64p. (J). (gr. 3-7). pap. 9.95 (978-1-55054-916-4(2)) Douglas & McIntyre, Ltd. CAN. Dist: Transition Vendor.

Rutledge, Rachel. The Best of the Best in Figure Skating. 1998. (Women of Sports Ser.). (Illus.). 64p. (gr. 5 up). lib. bdg. 24.90 (978-0-7613-1302-1(8) , Twenty-First Century Bks.) Lerner Publishing Group.

Sandler, Michael. Ice Skating: The Incredible Michelle Kwan. 2006. (Upsets & Comebacks Ser.). (Illus.). 32p. (J). lib. bdg. 25.27 (978-1-59716-252-4(3)) Bearport Publishing Co., Inc.

Schwartz, Heather E. Girls' Figure Skating: Ruling the Rink. 2007. (Girls Got Game Ser.). 32p. (J). (gr. 3-6). 25.26 (978-0-7368-6822-8(4)) Capstone Pr., Inc.

Shea, Pegi Deitz. Ekatarina Gordeeva. 1999. (Female Figure Skating Legends Ser.). (Illus.). 64p. (YA). (gr. 2-7). 12.95 (978-0-7910-5027-9(0) , Chelsea Hse.) Facts On File, Inc.

Skating: Big Book: Level E. Group 2. (Story Box(R) Ser.). 16p. 20.95 (978-0-7802-9369-4(X)) Wright Group, The.

Smith, Pohla. Superstars of Men's Figure Skating. 1999. (Male Sports Stars Ser.). (Illus.). 64p. (YA). (gr. 4-7). 18.65 (978-0-7910-4586-2(2) , Chelsea Hse.) Facts On File, Inc.

The Story of Figure Skating: Individual Title Six-Packs. (On Deck Ser.). 24p. (gr. 4-5). 35.00 (978-0-7578-1014-5(4)) Rigby Education.

Streeter, Michael. Ice Skating. 2003. (Sports Injuries Ser.). (Illus.). 64p. (J). lib. bdg. (978-1-59084-635-3(4)) Mason Crest Pubs.

Suen, Anastasia. La Historia Del Patinaje Artistico. 2004. (Historia de los Deportes Ser.). (SPA & ENG., Illus.). 24p. (J). (gr. 3-6). lib. bdg. 17.25 (978-0-8239-6872-5(3) , Buenas Letra) Rosen Publishing Group, Inc., The.

—The Story of Figure Skating. 2002. (Reading Power Ser.). (Illus.). 24p. (J). (gr. 2). lib. bdg. 17.25 (978-0-8239-5999-0(6) , PowerKids Pr.) Rosen Publishing Group, Inc., The.

U. S. Olympic Committee. A Basic Guide to Figure Skating. 2002. (Olympic Guides). (Illus.). 160p. (J). (gr. 6 up). lib. bdg. 23.33 (978-0-8368-3102-3(0)) Stevens, Gareth Inc.

—A Basic Guide to Speed Skating. 2002. (Olympic Guides). (Illus.). 160p. (J). (gr. 6 up). lib. bdg. 23.33 (978-0-8368-3105-4(5)) Stevens, Gareth Inc.

Wallner, Rosemary. Michelle Kwan. 2001. (Sports Heroes Ser.). (Illus.). 48p. (J). (gr. 3-4). lib. bdg. 21.26 (978-0-7368-0779-1(9) , Capstone High-Interest Bks.) Capstone Pr., Inc.

Wellman, Sam. Kristi Yamaguchi. 1999. (Female Figure Skating Legends Ser.). (Illus.). 64p. (YA). (gr. 2-5). 12.95 (978-0-7910-5025-5(4) , Chelsea Hse.) Facts On File, Inc.

—Michelle Kwan. 1999. (Female Figure Skating Legends Ser.). (Illus.). 64p. (YA). (gr. 4-7). 12.95 (978-0-7910-4875-7(6) , Chelsea Hse.) Facts On File, Inc.

Weyn, Suzanne, adapted by. Ice Princess. 2005. (Illus.). 124p. (J). pap. (978-0-439-74552-9(7)) Scholastic, Inc.

Where Is Kate's Skate? KinderReaders Individual Title Six-Packs. (Kinderstarters Ser.). 8p. (ps-1). 21.00 (978-0-7635-8644-7(7)) Rigby Education.

Wilkes, Debbi. The Figure Skating Book: A Young Persons' Guide to Figure Skating. 1999. (Young Performer's Guide Ser.). (Illus.). 128p. (gr. 3-9). pap. 12.95 (978-1-55209-445-7(6)); lib. bdg. 19.95 (978-1-55209-444-0(8)) Firefly Bks., Ltd.

Wilner, Barry. Figure Skating. 2000. (Composite Guides Ser.). 64p. (YA). (gr. 8-12). 12.95 (978-0-7910-5864-0(6) , Chelsea Hse.) Facts On File, Inc.

—Michelle Kwan: Star Figure Skater. 2001. (Sports Reports). (Illus.). 104p. (YA). (gr. 4-10). lib. bdg. 26.60 (978-0-7660-1504-3(1)) Enslow Pubs., Inc.

—Scott Hamilton: Star Figure Skater. 1999. (Sports Reports). (Illus.). 104p. (YA). (gr. 4-10). lib. bdg. 26.60 (978-0-7660-1236-3(0)) Enslow Pubs., Inc.

—Tara Lipinski: Star Figure Skater. 2001. (Sports Reports). (Illus.). 104p. (J). (gr. 4-10). lib. bdg. 26.60 (978-0-7660-1505-0(X)) Enslow Pubs., Inc.

Yamaguchi, Kristi. Always Dream. 1998. 40p. 14.95 (978-0-87833-996-9(5)) Taylor Trade Publishing.

SKATING—FICTION

Abbott, Tony. The Great Ice Battle. Jessell, Tim, illus. 1999. (Secrets of Droon Ser.: No. 5). 96p. (J). (gr. 2-5). pap. 3.99 (978-0-590-10843-0(3) , Scholastic Paperbacks) Scholastic, Inc.

Adler, David A. Young Cam Jansen & the Ice Skate Mystery. 2000. (Young Cam Jansen Ser.: No. 4). (gr. k-3). lib. bdg. 11.80 (978-0-613-22667-7(4)) Tandem Library Bks.

Alma, Ann. Skateway to Freedom. 2008. 136p. (YA). pap. 11.99 (*978-1-55002-719-8(0) , Sandcastle Bks.) Dundurn Group, The CAN. Dist: Univ. of Toronto Pr.

Bailey, Linda. The Best Figure Skater in the Whole Wide World. ed. 2004. (Illus.). (J). (gr. k-3). spiral bd. (978-0-616-11093-5(6)); spiral bd. (978-0-616-11094-2(4)) Canadian National Institute for the Blind/Institut National Canadien pour les Aveugles.

—The Best Figure Skater in the Whole Wide World. Daniel, Alan & Daniel, Lea, illus. 2003. 32p. (J). (gr. k-3). (978-1-55074-881-9(5)) Kids Can Pr., Ltd.

—The Best Figure Skater in the Whole Wide World. Daniel, Alan et al, illus. 2001. 32p. (J). (gr. k-3). (978-1-55074-879-6(3)) Kids Can Pr., Ltd.

Bell, William. Death Wind. 2002. (Soundings Ser.). 96p. (J). (gr. 7-12). pap. 7.95 (978-1-55143-215-1(3)) Orca Bk. Pubs. USA.

—Death Wind. 2002. (gr. 7-12). lib. bdg. 16.40 (978-0-613-62940-9(X)) Tandem Library Bks.

Bossley, Michele Martin. Winning Edge. 1999. (gr. 7-12). lib. bdg. 13.55 (978-0-613-18223-2(5)) Tandem Library Bks.

Bunge, Daniela. The Scarves. Bishop, Kathryn, tr. from GER. Bunge, Daniela, illus. 2006. (Illus.). 32p. (J). (ps-3). 16.99 (978-0-698-40045-0(3) , Minedition) Penguin Group (USA) Inc.

Catching Air! Individual Chapter Book Title Six-Pack. Vol. 29. 32p. (gr. 5 up). 44.00 (978-0-7578-0974-3(X)) Rigby Education.

Christopher, Matt. Inline Skater. ed. 2005. (Sports Classics IV Ser.). 153p. (J). lib. bdg. 15.00 (978-1-59054-759-5(4)) Fitzgerald Bks.

—Snowboard Maverick. ed. 2005. (Sports Classics IV Ser.). 156p. (J). lib. bdg. 15.00 (978-1-59054-769-4(1)) Fitzgerald Bks.

Clark, Catherine. Frozen Rodeo. 2003. 304p. (J). (gr. 8 up). 15.99 (978-0-06-009070-8(7)) HarperCollins Pubs.

Cook, Lyn. The Bells on Finland Street. 2002. (Illus.). 183p. (YA). pap. (978-1-55041-794-4(0)) Fitzhenry & Whiteside, Ltd.

Danger on Ice. 2002. (Illus.). (J). pap. (978-0-7398-5068-8(7)) Steck-Vaughn.

Disney Staff. Head over Heels. 2001. (Jersey Ser.). (Illus.). (J). 11.64 (978-0-606-21264-9(7)) Tandem Library Bks.

Dodge, Mary. Hans Brinker, or the Silver Skates. 2005. (Illus.). 239p. (J). (*978-1-59605-666-4(5)); pap. (*978-1-59605-415-8(8)) Cosimo, Inc.

Dodge, Mary Mapes. Hans Brinker & the Silver Skates. Freshman, Floris, illus. 2002. (Great Illustrated Classics Ser.). 240p. (J). (gr. 3-8). 21.35 (978-1-57765-814-6(0) , ABDO & Daughters) ABDO Publishing Co.

—Hans Brinker or the Silver Skates. 2002. (Classics Ser.). (Illus.). 400p. (J). pap. 4.99 (978-0-689-84909-1(5) , Aladdin) Simon & Schuster Children's Publishing.

—Hans Brinker or the Silver Skates. 2002. 381p. (gr. 3-6). per. 13.00 (978-0-613-63199-0(4)) Tandem Library Bks.

—Hans Brinker or the Silver Skates A Story of Life in Holland. Doggett, Allen B., illus. 2004. reprint ed. pap. 34.95 (978-1-4179-4127-8(8)) Kessinger Publishing, LLC.

Dodge, Mary Mapes. Hans Brinker; or, the Silver Skates (Dod. 2006. pap. (*978-1-4065-0961-8(2)) Dodo Pr.

Fisch, Sarah. Skating with Friends. Durk, Jim, illus. 2007. (Little Red Reader Ser.). (J). pap. (*978-0-439-90898-6(1)) Scholastic, Inc.

Flanagan, Katie. Polar Bears on Ice. 2001. (Hello Reader! Ser.). (Illus.). (J). pap. (978-0-439-32360-4(6)) Scholastic, Inc.

Flynn, Pat. Alex Jackson: Closing Out. 2003. 168p. (J). pap. 15.50 (978-0-7022-3353-1(6)) Univ. of Queensland Pr. AUS. Dist: International Specialized Bk. Services.

Forrestal, Elaine. Graffiti on the Fence. 1999. 144p. (J). pap. (978-0-14-130519-6(3) , Puffin) Penguin Group (USA) Inc.

Garis, Howard Roger. Daddy Takes Us Skating. 2006. pap. 33.99 (*978-1-4219-7310-4(3)) IndyPublish.com.

—Daddy Takes Us Skating. 2004. reprint ed. pap. 15.95 (978-1-4191-1489-2(1)); pap. 1.99 (978-1-4192-1489-9(6)) Kessinger Publishing, LLC.

Graham, Wendy. High Jinx: Sloanes Beach, Skateboard Hero, Rock on, Bearded Toad. 2005. (Triple Play Ser.). (Illus.). 48p. (gr. 4-8). 41.85 (978-0-7910-9074-9(4)) Facts On File, Inc.

Grindley, Sally. Polar Skater. Hieta, Heli, illus. 2004. 32p. (J). (ps-2). 15.95 (978-1-894222-88-4(1)) Lobster Pr. CAN. Dist: Univ. of Toronto Pr.

Grindley, Sally. Reve de Glace et Patins Blancs. Duchesne, Christiane, tr. from ENG. Hieta, Heli, illus. (FRE.). 28p. (J). pap. 6.95 (*978-2-922435-06-1(7)) Editions Homard CAN. Dist: Univ. of Toronto Pr.

Hawley, Mabel C. Four Little Blossoms Through the Holidays. 2005. pap. 22.95 (978-1-4179-9003-0(1)) Kessinger Publishing, LLC.

Henke, Mary. The Magic Skates. Henke, Mary, illus. 1999. (Illus.). 32p. (Orig.). (J). pap. 6.95 (978-0-87012-602-4(4)) McClain Printing Co.

Herman, Gail. Slip! Slide! Skate! Billin-Frye, Paige, illus. 2004. 32p. (J). lib. bdg. 15.00 (978-1-59054-382-5(3)) Fitzgerald Bks.

—Slip! Slide! Skate! Billin-Frye, Paige, illus. 2000. (Hello Reader! Ser.). 32p. (J). (gr. k-2). pap. 3.99 (978-0-439-09907-3(2)) Scholastic, Inc.

—Slip! Slide! Skate! (Hello Reader! Ser.). 2000. (J). (978-0-606-19612-3(9)); 1999. lib. bdg. 11.80 (978-0-613-33064-0(1)) Tandem Library Bks.

Holabird, Katharine. Angelina Ice Skates. Craig, Helen, illus. 2007. 32p. (J), (ps). 13.99 (*978-0-670-06237-9(5) , Viking Juvenile) Penguin Group (USA) Inc.

Hutchins, Hazel. Skate, Robyn, Skate. Cathcart, Yvonne, illus. 2004. 57p. (J). lib. bdg. 12.00 (*978-1-4242-1244-6(8)) Fitzgerald Bks.

Hutchins, Hazel J. Skate, Robyn, Skate. Cathcart, Yvonne, illus. 2004. (First Novel Ser.). 64p. (J). (gr. 1). (*978-0-88780-627-8(9)); 4.95 (978-0-88780-626-1(0)) Formac Publishing Co., Ltd. CAN. Dist: Casemate Pubs. & Bk. Distributors, LLC.

Inkpen, Mick. Skates. 2001. (gr. k-3). lib. bdg. 12.95 (978-0-613-51326-5(6)) Tandem Library Bks.

Isadora, Rachel. Sophie Skates. Isadora, Rachel, illus. 2001. (Illus.). 40p. (J). pap. 6.99 (978-0-698-11905-5(3) , Putnam Juvenile) Penguin Group (USA) Inc.

—Sophie Skates. 2001. (gr. k-3). lib. bdg. 15.30 (978-0-613-44417-0(5)) Tandem Library Bks.

Jack's New Skates. 2000. (J). (978-1-58453-132-6(0)) Pioneer Valley Educational Pr., Inc.

Jewel, Judy. Sole Shoes: Nate the Skate in Search of His Mate. 2005. 19.95 (978-0-9767066-0-1(1)) Dunamis Development.

Johnson, Mildred D. Wait, Skates! Stromoski, Rick, illus. rev. ed. 2000. (Rookie Reader Skill Set Ser.). 32p. (J). (gr. k-2). pap. 4.95 (978-0-516-27002-9(8) , Children's Pr.) Scholastic Library Publishing.

Keller, Holly. Pearl's New Skates. Keller, Holly, illus. 2005. (Illus.). 24p. (J). 16.99 (978-0-06-056280-9(3)); lib. bdg. 16.89 (978-0-06-056281-6(1)) HarperCollins Pubs.

Kephart, Beth. Undercover. 2007. 288p. (gr. 7 up). (J). 16.99 (*978-0-06-123893-2(7)); (YA). lib. bdg. 17.89 (*978-0-06-123894-9(5)) HarperCollins Pubs. (HarperTeen).

King, Donna. Double Twist. 2007. 144p. (J). (gr. 4-6). pap. 5.95 (978-0-7534-6023-8(8) , Kingfisher) Houghton Mifflin Co. Trade & Reference Div.

Koda-Callan, Elizabeth, illus. The Shiny Skates. 2004. 48p. (J). 9.95 (978-0-7611-3639-2(8) , 13639) Workman Publishing Co., Inc.

Kovalski, Maryann. Omar on Ice. ed. 2004. (J). (gr. k-3). spiral bd. (978-0-616-01690-9(5)); spiral bd. (978-0-616-01691-6(3)) Canadian National Institute for the Blind/Institut National Canadien pour les Aveugles.

—Omar on Ice. Kovalski, Maryann, illus. (First Flight Ser.). (Illus.). (J). (gr. 1-3). 40p. lib. bdg. (978-1-55041-409-7(7)); 2002. 32p. pap. (978-1-55041-783-8(5)) Fitzhenry & Whiteside, Ltd.

—Omar on Ice. 1999. (First Flight Ser.). (Illus.). 32p. (J). (gr. k-3). (978-1-55041-507-0(7)) Fitzhenry & Whiteside, Ltd.

—Omar on Ice. Kovalski, Maryann, illus. 1999. (First Flight Ser.). (Illus.). 38p. (J). (gr. 1-3). pap. (978-1-55041-407-3(0)) Fitzhenry & Whiteside, Ltd.

Lawrence, Megan & Lawrence, Kevin. Sarah on Ice: A Skater's Story. 2002. 128p. pap. 10.95 (978-0-595-25379-1(2) , Writers Club Pr.) iUniverse, Inc.

Lewis, Beverly. Photo Perfect. 2001. (Girls Only (Go!) Ser.: Vol. 7). 128p. (J). (gr. 4-7). pap. 6.99 (978-1-55661-642-6(2)) Bethany Hse. Pubs.

Mayer, Mercer. Skating Day. 2003. (Little Critter Ser.). (Illus.). 24p. (J). (ps-k). pap. 3.95 (978-1-57768-588-3(1)) School Specialty Publishing.

—Skating Day. 2004. lib. bdg. 11.80 (978-0-613-88738-0(7)) Tandem Library Bks.

Mazer, Anne. Have Wheels, Will Travel. 2001. (Amazing Days of Abby Hayes Ser.: No. 4). (gr. 3-6). lib. bdg. 12.40 (978-0-613-43045-6(X)) Tandem Library Bks.

Muldrow, Diane. Ice Skating Dreams. 2000. (gr. k-3). lib. bdg. 11.00 (978-0-613-83883-2(1)) Tandem Library Bks.

Paulsen, Gary. Dancing Carl. 2007. 144p. (J). pap. 5.99 (*978-1-4169-3938-2(5) , Aladdin) Simon & Schuster Children's Publishing.

Polak, Monique. Scarred. 2007. (SideStreets Ser.). 168p. (YA). (gr. 7-12). 7.95 (*978-1-55028-964-0(0)) Lorimer, James & Co., Ltd., Pubs. CAN. Dist: Casemate Pubs. & Bk. Distributors, LLC.

Prats, Joan De Deu. Sebastian's Roller Skates. Rovira, Francesc, illus. 2005. 32p. (J). (gr. k-3). 15.95 (978-1-929132-81-2(6)) Kane/Miller Bk. Pubs., Inc.

Schade, Susan. Cat on Ice. 2001. (Road to Reading Ser.). (Illus.). (J). 10.79 (978-0-606-20596-2(9)) Tandem Library Bks.

Shaw, Mary. Brady Brady & the Super Skater, 11 vols. Temple, Chuck, illus. l.t. ed. 2005. 32p. (J). per. (978-1-897169-06-3(X)) Brady Brady, Inc.

Skating at Rainbow Lake: Individual Title Six-Packs. (gr. 3 up). 35.00 (978-0-7635-9663-7(9)) Rigby Education.

The Skating Trail: Individual Title Six-Packs. 16p. (gr. 2 up). 35.00 (978-0-7635-9226-4(9)) Rigby Education.

Spinelli, Eileen. Callie Cat, Ice Skater. Kennedy, Anne, illus. 2007. 32p. (J). (gr. 1-4). 16.95 (*978-0-8075-1042-1(4)) Whitman, Albert & Co.

Stevenson, James. Sam the Zamboni Man. Stevenson, Harvey, illus. 2000. 30p. (YA). (gr. 9-11). reprint ed. 15.00 (978-0-7881-6924-3(6)) DIANE Publishing Co.

Tétro, Marc. I Can Skate. 2005. (Illus.). (978-1-55278-542-3(4)) McArthur & Co. CAN. Dist: National Bk. Network.

Thacker, Nola. Champion's Luck. 2000. (gr. 3-6). lib. bdg. 13.00 (978-0-613-31054-3(3)) Tandem Library Bks.

S

—Coach's Choice. 2001. (Skating Dreams Ser.: Vol. 6). (Illus.). 128p. (gr. 3-5). pap. 4.99 (978-0-7868-1571-5(X), Volo) Hyperion Bks. for Children.

—Coach's Choice. 2001. (gr. 3-6). lib. bdg. 13.00 (978-0-613-74963-3(4)) Tandem Library Bks.

—Gold Medal Mystery. 2001. (Skating Dreams Ser.: Vol. 8). (Illus.). 176p. (J). (gr. 3-5). pap. 4.99 (978-0-7868-1647-7(3), Volo) Hyperion Bks. for Children.

—Skating Backward. 2000. (gr. 3-6). lib. bdg. 13.00 (978-0-613-31711-5(4)) Tandem Library Bks.

—Staying Balanced. 2000. (gr. 3-6). lib. bdg. 13.00 (978-0-613-31754-2(8)) Tandem Library Bks.

—Turning Point. 2000. (gr. 3-6). lib. bdg. 13.00 (978-0-613-31845-7(5)) Tandem Library Bks.

—Wishing for Gold. 2001. (Skating Dreams Ser.: Vol. 7). (Illus.). 144p. (J). (gr. 3-5). pap. 4.99 (978-0-7868-1646-0(5)) Hyperion Bks. for Children.

Thompson, Lisa, illus. New York City. 2006. (Read-It! Chapter Books). 80p. (J). (gr. 2-4). 19.95 (978-1-4048-1670-1(4)) Picture Window Bks.

van Stockum, Hilda. A Day on Skates: 2007 Commemorative Edition. van Stockum, Hilda, illus. 2007. (Illus.). 44p. (J). 19.95 (***978-1-932350-18-0(7)***) Bethlehem Bks.

Warner, Gertrude Chandler. Hockey Mystery. 2001. (gr. 3-6). lib. bdg. 11.80 (978-0-613-30474-0(8)) Tandem Library Bks.

Whybrow, Ian. Bella Gets Her Skates On. Reeve, Rosie, illus. 2007. 32p. (J). (ps-3). 15.95 (***978-0-8109-9416-4(X)***) Abrams, Harry N., Inc.

Withers, Pam. Skater Stuntboys. 2005. (Take it to the Extreme Ser.). 191p. (YA). (gr. 7-12). pap. 6.95 (978-1-55285-647-5(X), Walrus Bks.) Whitecap Bks., Ltd. CAN. *Dist:* Firefly Bks., Ltd.

SKELETON

Arnau, Eduard. Nuestra Arquitectura Osea. (Mundo Invisible Ser.). (SPA., Illus.). (YA). (gr. 5-8). pap. 8.00 (978-958-04-3227-2(9)) Norma S.A. COL. *Dist:* Distribuidora Norma, Inc., Lectorum Pubns., Inc.

—Nuestra Arquitectura Osea. (SPA.). 88p. (J). 10.00 (978-84-342-1739-3(2)) Parramon Ediciones S.A. ESP. *Dist:* Distribuidora Norma, Inc.

Arnold, Caroline. El Sistema Oseo. 2006. (Libros Sobre el Cuerpo Humano para Madrugadores Ser.). (ENG & SPA.). 48p. (J). 25.26 (978-0-8225-6257-3(X)) Lerner Publishing Group.

—The Skeletal System. 2005. (Early Bird Body Systems Ser.). (Illus.). 48p. (J). (gr. 2-4). lib. bdg. 25.26 (978-0-8225-5140-9(3)) Lerner Publishing Group.

—Skeletal System. 2005. (Illus.). 48p. (YA). pap. (978-0-8225-2523-3(2), Lerner Pubns.) Lerner Publishing Group.

Ballard, Carol. Bones. 2002. (Body Focus Ser.). (Illus.). 48p. (J). pap. (978-1-4034-0450-3(X)) Heinemann Library.

Benchmark Education Staff. Your Skeleton. 2005. 2.00 (***978-1-4108-4643-3(1)***) Benchmark Education Co.

Bend & Stretch. (Amazing Body Ser.). 24p. (J). 7.95 (978-1-4048-0507-1(9)) Picture Window Bks.

Bilgrami, Shaheen. Safari Animal Adventure. Kees, Chantal & Shields, Chris, illus. 2003. (Magic Color Bks.). 12p. (J). (gr. k-2). 9.95 (978-1-4027-0822-0(X)) Sterling Publishing Co., Inc.

Bounford, Trevor. The Skeleton. 2005. (Glow in the Dark Ser.). 24p. (J). 5.95 (978-1-902626-74-1(5)) Red Bird Publishing GBR. *Dist:* Perseus Distribution.

Brannon, Barbara. Discover Your Skeleton. 2005. 39.00 (***978-1-4108-5135-2(4)***) Benchmark Education Co.

Build a Skeleton. 2004. (J). per. 7.99 (978-1-932855-16-6(5)) becker&mayer! books.

Creative Media Applications Staff. The Human Body & Environment: Skeletal & Muscular Systems, 4 vols., Vol. 1. 2003. (Middle School Reference Ser.). (Illus.). (J). (gr. 4-8). 160.00 (978-0-313-32559-5(6)) Greenwood Publishing Group, Inc.

Domnauer, Teresa. The Skeletal System. 2003. (Illus.). 24p. (J). lib. bdg. 21.35 (978-1-58340-311-2(6)) Smart Apple Media.

Feely, Jenny. Animal Skeletons. 1999. (ps-2). lib. bdg. 11.80 (978-0-613-19334-4(2)) Tandem Library Bks.

Freeman, Marcia S. How Muscles & Bones Hold You Up: A Book about Models. 2008. (J). (***978-1-60044-539-2(X)***) Rourke Publishing, LLC.

Frost, Helen. The Skeletal System. Saunders-Smith, Gail, ed. 2000. (Human Body Systems Ser.). (Illus.). 24p. (J). (gr. k-1). lib. bdg. 15.93 (978-0-7368-0653-4(9), Pebble Bks.) Capstone Pr., Inc.

Ganeri, Anita. Your Muscles & Bones. Shott, Steve, photos by. 2003. (How Your Body Works). (Illus.). 32p. (J). (gr. 2 up). lib. bdg. 23.33 (978-0-8368-3635-6(9)) Stevens, Gareth Inc.

Gilbert, Laura. The Skeletal System. 2001. (Insider's Guide to the Body Ser.). (Illus.). 48p. (YA). (gr. 5-8). lib. bdg. 23.95 (978-0-8239-3338-9(5), Rosen Central) Rosen Publishing Group, Inc., The.

Glassman, Jackie. Skeletons. Degen, Bruce et al, illus. 2002. (Magic School Bus Fact Finder Ser.). 96p. (J). pap. 4.99 (978-0-439-31436-7(4)) Scholastic, Inc.

Gold, Susan Dudley. The Musculoskeletal System & the Skin. 2003. (Human Body Library Ser.). (Illus.). 48p. (YA). (gr. 4-10). lib. bdg. 23.93 (978-0-7660-2023-8(1)) Enslow Pubs., Inc.

Goode, Katherine. Skeleton & Muscles. 2000. (Bodyworks Ser.). (Illus.). 32p. (J). (gr. 3-6). 23.70 (978-1-56711-498-0(9), Blackbirch Pr., Inc.) Thomson Gale.

Gray, Susan Heinrichs. The Skeletal System. 2003. (Body Systems Ser.). (Illus.). 32p. (J). (gr. 2-6). 27.07 (978-1-59296-041-5(3)) Child's World, Inc.

Green, Jen. Skeleton. 2005. (Illus.). 32p. (J). (gr. 4-7). lib. bdg. 27.10 (978-1-59604-055-7(6)) Stargazer Bks.

Gross, Ruth B. Un Libro Sobre el Esqueleto. 2001. Tr. of Book about Your Skeleton. (978-0-606-22662-2(1)) Tandem Library Bks.

Gross, Ruth Belov & Bjorkman, Steve. A Book about Your Skeleton. (Hello Reader! Ser.). (FRE., Illus.). 42p. (J). pap. 5.99 (978-0-590-16005-6(2)) Scholastic, Inc.

Hall, Katy, pseud. Esqueletos! Esqueletos! Todo Acerca de los Huesos. Billin-Frye, Paige, illus. (SPA.). (J). pap. 3.16 net. (978-0-590-46873-2(1), SO30501, Scholastic en Espanol) Scholastic, Inc.

Hands-On Crafts for Kids. How Do You Move? 2002. (Balloon Ser.). (Illus.). 12p. (J). bds. 3.95 (978-1-4027-0176-4(4), Balloon Bks.) Sterling Publishing Co., Inc.

Harrison, James. Discover Amazing Earth. Smith, Jan & Bull, Peter, illus. 2005. (Magic Color Bks.). 12p. (J). 9.95 (978-1-4027-2626-2(0), Sterling/Pinwheel) Sterling Publishing Co., Inc.

Houghton, Gillian. The Skeletal System. 2007. (How Your Body Works). (Illus.). 24p. (J). lib. bdg. (978-1-4042-2372-1(X)); pap. (978-1-4042-2182-6(4)) Rosen Publishing Group, Inc., The. (PowerKids Pr.).

Johnson, Jinny. Skeletons: An Inside Look at Animals. Gray, Elizabeth, illus. 1999. 46p. (J). (gr. 5-7). reprint ed. 25.00 (978-0-7881-6810-9(X)) DIANE Publishing Co.

Krensky, Stephen. Bones. Jones, Davy, illus. 1999. (Step into Reading Step 1 Bks.). 32p. (J). (ps-2). pap. 3.99 (978-0-679-89036-2(X), Random Hse. Bks. for Young Readers) Random Hse. Children's Bks.

—Bones. 1999. (Step into Reading Ser.). (J). 10.79 (978-0-606-16976-9(8)) Tandem Library Bks.

LeVert, Suzanne. Bones & Muscles. 2001. (Kaleidoscope Ser.). (Illus.). 48p. (J). (gr. 3 up). lib. bdg. 25.64 (978-0-7614-1309-7(X), Benchmark Bks.) Cavendish, Marshall Corp.

Llamas, Andreu. Muscles & Bones. Rizo, Luis, illus. 1998. (Human Body Ser.). 32p. (J). (gr. 5 up). lib. bdg. 24.67 (978-0-8368-2112-3(2)) Stevens, Gareth Inc.

Maestro, Betsy. What Is a Skeleton. Date not set. 40p. (J). (ps-1). 15.99 (978-0-06-029006-1(4)); lib. bdg. 16.89 (978-0-06-029007-8(2)) HarperCollins Pubs.

—What Is a Skeleton? Date not set. 40p. (J). (ps-1). pap. 4.99 (978-0-06-445215-1(8)) HarperCollins Pubs.

My Skeleton Wallchart. 2004. (Wall Charts Ser.). (J). 4.99 (978-1-85997-268-7(3)) Byeway Bks.

Nettleton, Pamela Hill. Bend & Stretch: Learning about Your Bones & Muscles. Shipe, Becky, illus. 2004. (Amazing Body Ser.). 24p. (C). (gr. k-3). 22.60 (978-1-4048-0256-8(8)) Picture Window Bks.

Our Skeleton, 6 vols. (Sunshinetm Science Ser.). 24p. (gr. 1-2). 31.50 (978-0-7802-0299-3(6)) Wright Group, The.

Parker, Steve. Skin, Muscles, & Bones. 2004. (Understanding the Human Body Ser.). (Illus.). 32p. (J). lib. bdg. 24.67 (978-0-8368-4207-4(3)) Stevens, Gareth Inc.

Parker, Steve & Dorling Kindersley Publishing Staff. Skeleton: Discover the Evolution, Atructure, & Function of Bones. 2004. (Eyewitness Books). (Illus.). 72p. (J). (ps-7). lib. bdg. 19.99 (978-0-7566-0726-5(4)) Dorling Kindersley Publishing, Inc.

Parsons, Michelle Hyde. Your Skeleton. 2005. 39.00 (***978-1-4108-4595-5(8)***) Benchmark Education Co.

Petrie, Kristin. The Skeletal System. 2007. (Checkerboard Science Library). (Illus.). 32p. (J). 22.78 (978-1-59679-714-7(2)) ABDO Publishing Co.

Royston, Angela. Why Do Bones Break? And Other Questions about Bones & Muscles. 2003. (Body Matters Ser.). (Illus.). 32p. (J). (gr. 3-5). lib. bdg. 24.22 (978-1-4034-0201-1(9)); pap. 7.50 (978-1-4034-0456-5(9)) Heinemann Library.

Rushworth, Gary. Body Systems: Skeletal & Muscular. 2005. (Navigators Ser.). (J). pap. 42.00 (***978-1-4108-5085-0(4)***) Benchmark Education Co.

Sacks, Janet. Discover Ancient Greece: A Magic Skeleton Book. Smith, Jan & Bull, Peter, illus. 2005. (Magic Color Bks.). 12p. (J). 9.95 (978-1-4027-2625-5(2), Sterling/Pinwheel) Sterling Publishing Co., Inc.

School Specialty Publishing. The Skeleton. 2004. (On-File Ser.). 4p. (J). (gr. 4-6). ring bd. 4.99 (978-0-7424-2906-2(7), Instructional Fair) Schaffer, Frank Pubns.

Simon, Seymour. Bones: Our Skeletal System. 1998. (Human Body Ser.). (Illus.). 32p. (J). (gr. k-3). lib. bdg. 17.89 (978-0-688-14645-0(7)) HarperCollins Pubs.

El sistema oseo (the Skeletal System) 2007. (J). pap. 7.95 (978-0-8225-6648-9(6), Ediciones Lerner) Lerner Publishing Group.

The Skeletal System, 6 vols. (gr. k-2). 28.95 (978-0-7368-8805-9(5)) Red Brick Learning.

Skeleton Sticker Book. 2003. (Illus.). 16p. (J). 2.98 (978-1-84273-121-5(1), Exclusive Editions) Parragon, Inc.

Thames, Susan. Our Skeleton. 2008. (J). (***978-1-60044-514-9(4)***) Rourke Publishing, LLC.

Wood, Lily. Skeletons. 2001. (Scholastic Science Readers Ser.). (Illus.). 48p. (J). (gr. 2-3). pap. 3.99 (978-0-439-29586-4(6), Scholastic Reference); 3.99 (978-0-439-20547-4(6)) Scholastic, Inc.

—Skeletons. 2001. (gr. 3-6). lib. bdg. 11.80 (978-0-613-54663-8(6)); (Illus.). (J). (978-0-606-21416-2(X)) Tandem Library Bks.

World Book, Inc Staff, contrib. by. The Skeletal System/The Muscular System. 2006. (World Book's Human Body Works). (Illus.). 48p. (J). (978-0-7166-4426-2(6)) World Bk., Inc.

SKETCHING

see Drawing

SKIING

see Skis and Skiing

SKIING, WATER

see Water Skiing

SKIN

Angliss, Sarah. The Outer Shell: Skin. 1999. (Human Machine Ser.). (Illus.). 32p. (J). lib. bdg. 16.95 (978-1-929298-21-1(8)) Chrysalis Education.

Berger, Melvin & Berger, Gilda. Your Skin. 2005. (Illus.). pap. (978-0-439-77372-0(5)) Scholastic, Inc.

Bozzo, Linda. Amazing Animal Skin. 2008. (J). lib. bdg. (***978-1-4042-4168-8(X)***, PowerKids Pr.) Rosen Publishing Group, Inc., The.

Brown, Jonatha A. Animal Skin & Fur. 2006. (Illus.). 24p. (J). pap. (978-0-8368-6867-8(6)); lib. bdg. (978-0-8368-6862-3(5)) Stevens, Gareth Inc.

Brynie, Faith Hickman. 101 Questions about Your Skin That Got under Your Skin . . . until Now. Holm, Sharon Lane, illus. 1999. (One Hundred One Questions... Ser.). 176p. (gr. 7 up). lib. bdg. 27.90 (978-0-7613-1259-8(5), Twenty-First Century Bks.) Lerner Publishing Group.

Buckmaster, Marjorie L. Skin Cancer. 2007. (Health Alert Ser.). 64p. (J). lib. bdg. 31.36 (***978-0-7614-2703-2(1)***, Benchmark Bks.) Cavendish, Marshall Corp.

Ceaser, Jennifer. Everything You Need to Know about Acne. (Need to Know Library). (Illus.). 64p. (gr. 4-6). 2000. (J). lib. bdg. 25.25 (978-0-8239-3222-1(2), NTACNE); 2005. (YA). lib. bdg. 25.25 (978-0-8239-3769-1(0)) Rosen Publishing Group, Inc., The.

Dahl, Michael. Do Frogs Have Fur? A Book about Animal Coats & Coverings. Yesh, Jeff, illus. 2004. (Animals All Around Ser.). 24p. (J). (gr. k-2). 22.60 (978-1-4048-0292-6(4)) Picture Window Bks.

Degezelle, Terri. Taking Care of My Skin. 2005. (Keeping Healthy Ser.). (Illus.). 24p. (J). (ps-2). lib. bdg. 19.93 (978-0-7368-4263-1(2)) Capstone Pr., Inc.

Glaser, Jason. Head Lice. 2005. (First Facts Ser.). (Illus.). 24p. (J). (gr. 1-3). lib. bdg. 21.26 (978-0-7368-4291-4(8)) Capstone Pr., Inc.

Gold, Susan Dudley. The Musculoskeletal System & the Skin. 2003. (Human Body Library Ser.). (Illus.). 48p. (YA). (gr. 4-10). lib. bdg. 23.93 (978-0-7660-2023-8(1)) Enslow Pubs., Inc.

Goode, Katherine. Skin & Hair. 2000. (Bodyworks Ser.). (Illus.). 32p. (J). (gr. 3-6). 23.70 (978-1-56711-497-3(0), Blackbirch Pr., Inc.) Thomson Gale.

Gordon, Sharon. My Skin. 2004. (Bookworms Ser.). (ENG & SPA., Illus.). 31p. (J). 21.36 (978-0-7614-1778-1(8), Benchmark Bks.) Cavendish, Marshall Corp.

Gray, Susan Heinrichs. The Skin. 2005. (Human Body Ser.). (Illus.). 32p. (J). (gr. 2-6). 27.07 (978-1-59296-429-1(X)) Child's World, Inc.

Green, Jen. Skin, Hair & Hygiene. 2005. (Illus.). 32p. (J). (gr. 3-7). lib. bdg. 27.10 (978-1-59604-053-3(X)) Stargazer Bks.

Gregson, Susan R. Skin Care. 2000. (Perspectives on Physical Health Ser.). (Illus.). 64p. (J). (gr. 4-6). lib. bdg. 23.93 (978-0-7368-0419-6(6), LifeMatters Bks.) Capstone Pr., Inc.

Hall, Margaret. Skin Deep. 2006. (Illus.). 32p. (J). (978-1-4109-2582-4(X)); pap. (978-1-4109-2611-1(7)) Steck-Vaughn.

Harrison, Emma. From Head to Toe: The Girls' Life Guide to Taking Care of You. Montagna, Frank, illus. 2004. 124p. (J). (978-0-439-44983-0(9)) Scholastic, Inc.

Kee, Lisa Morris. Whose Skin Is This? A Look at Skin - Scaly, Furry & Prickly. Landmark, Ken, illus. 2004. (Whose Is It? Ser.). 24p. (C). (gr. k-2). 22.60 (978-1-4048-0010-6(7)) Picture Window Bks.

Kinch, Michael P. Warts. 2000. (gr. 3-6). lib. bdg. 15.25 (978-0-613-31878-5(1)) Tandem Library Bks.

Klingel, Cynthia Fitterer. Let's Read about Our Bodies-Skin. 2002. (gr. k-3). lib. bdg. 22.20 (978-0-613-76731-6(4)) Tandem Library Bks.

Klingel, Cynthia Fitterer & Noyed, Robert B. Skin. Andersen, Gregg, photos by. 2002. (Weekly Reader Early Learning Library). (Illus.). 24p. (J). (ps up). pap. 5.95 (978-0-8368-3158-0(6)); lib. bdg. 19.33 (978-0-8368-3069-9(5)) Stevens, Gareth Inc. (Weekly Reader Early Learning Library).

—Skin/Piel. Acosta, Tatiana & Gutiérrez, Guillermo, trs. Andersen, Gregg, photos by. 2002. (Weekly Reader Early Learning Library). (Illus.). 24p. (J). (ps up). (SPA & ENG.). pap. (978-0-8368-3327-0(9)); (ENG & SPA., lib. bdg. 19.33 (978-0-8368-3078-1(4)) Stevens, Gareth Inc. (Weekly Reader Early Learning Library).

Labella, Susan. Chameleons & Other Animals with Amazing Skin. 2005. (Scholastic News Nonfiction Readers Ser.). (Illus.). 24p. (J). (gr. 1-2). 19.00 (978-0-516-24925-4(8), Children's Pr.) Scholastic Library Publishing.

Light, Douglas W. Cells, Tissue, & Skin. 2003. (Your Body, How It Works). (Illus.). 112p. (J). (gr. 9-13). 31.95 (978-0-7910-7708-5(X), Chelsea Hse.) Facts On File, Inc.

Maurer, Tracy. Skin. 1999. (Illus.). 24p. (J). (gr. 1-4). lib. bdg. 19.27 (978-0-86593-582-2(3)) Rourke Publishing, LLC.

Mayer, Cassie. Skin. 2006. (Illus.). 24p. (J). (978-1-4034-8373-7(6)); pap. (978-1-4034-8379-9(5)) Heinemann Library.

Miles, Elizabeth. Skin, Scales, & Shells. 2003. (Animal Parts Ser.). (Illus.). 32p. (J). (gr. k-2). lib. bdg. 21.36 (978-1-4034-0021-5(0)); pap. 6.95 (978-1-4034-0430-5(5)) Heinemann Library.

Miller, Sara Swan. All Kinds of Skin. 2007. (All Kinds Of Ser.). (Illus.). 48p. (J). (ps-3). lib. bdg. 28.50 (***978-0-7614-2713-1(9)***) Cavendish, Marshall Corp.

My Skin: Big Book: Level E. (Wonder Worldtm Ser.). 16p. 26.50 (978-0-7802-3475-8(8)) Wright Group, The.

My Skin: Level E, 6 vols. (Wonder Worldtm Ser.). 16p. 29.95 (978-0-7802-1229-9(0)) Wright Group, The.

The Nervous System/The Senses/The Skin. 2006. (World Book's Human Body Works). (Illus.). 48p. (J). (978-0-7166-4430-9(4)) World Bk., Inc.

Novick, Nelson. Skin Care for Teens. 2000. (Illus.). 148p. (YA). (gr. 8-12). pap. 9.95 (978-0-595-14042-8(4)) iUniverse, Inc.

Novick, Nelson L. Skin Care for Teens. 2000. (gr. 7-12). lib. bdg. 18.75 (978-0-613-84095-8(X)) Tandem Library Bks.

Parker, Steve. Skin, Muscles, & Bones. 2004. (Understanding the Human Body Ser.). (Illus.). 32p. (J). lib. bdg. 24.67 (978-0-8368-4207-4(3)) Stevens, Gareth Inc.

Rau, Dana Meachen. My Skin (La Piel) 2006. (Bookworms Ser.). (ENG & SPA., Illus.). 32p. (J). lib. bdg. 22.79 (978-0-7614-2484-0(9)) Cavendish, Marshall Corp.

—La Piel. 2006. (Bookworms Ser.). (SPA & ENG., Illus.). 32p. (J). lib. bdg. 22.79 (978-0-7614-2406-2(7)) Cavendish, Marshall Corp.

Royston, Angela. Cuts & Grazes. 2004. (Illus.). 32p. (J). lib. bdg. (978-1-4034-4825-5(6)) Heinemann Library.

—Healthy Skin. 2003. (Heinemann First Library). (Illus.). 32p. (J). pap. 6.95 (978-1-4034-4453-0(6)); lib. bdg. (978-1-4034-4444-8(7)) Heinemann Library.

—Why Do I Get a Sunburn? And Other Questions about Skin. 2003. (Body Matters Ser.). (Illus.). 32p. (J). (gr. 3-5). lib. bdg. 24.22 (978-1-4034-0203-5(5)) Heinemann Library.

—Why Do I Get Sunburn? 2003. (Body Matters Ser.). 32p. pap. 7.50 (978-1-4034-0458-9(5)) Heinemann Library.

Sheen, Barbara. Acne. 2004. (Diseases & Disorders Ser.). (Illus.). 96p. (J). 32.45 (978-1-59018-345-8(2), Lucent Bks.) Thomson Gale.

Silverstein, Alvin. Burns & Blisters. 2002. (gr. 3-6). lib. bdg. 15.25 (978-0-613-53974-6(5)) Tandem Library Bks.

Silverstein, Alvin, et al. Burns & Blisters. 2002. (My Health Ser.). (Illus.). 48p. (J). (gr. 3-5). 25.50 (978-0-531-11871-9(1), Watts, Franklin) Scholastic Library Publishing.

Skin. 2001. (Human Anatomy Ser.). (J). (gr. k-12). vinyl bd. 4.95 (978-1-58845-085-2(6)) School Specialty Publishing.

Spilsbury, Louise. Why Should I Wash My Hair? And Other Questions about Healthy Skin & Hair. 2003. (Body Matters Ser.). (Illus.). 32p. (J). lib. bdg. 16.95 (978-1-4034-4685-5(7)) Heinemann Library.

Swanson, Diane. Skin That Slimes & Scares. 2001. (Up Close Ser.). (Illus.). (J). (ps-3). 9.95 (978-1-55054-817-4(4)) Sterling Publishing Co., Inc.

Thames, Susan. Our Skin. 2008. (J). (***978-1-60044-515-6(2)***) Rourke Publishing, LLC.

Williams, Julie. Skin & Nails: Care Tips for Girls. Banner, Shawn, illus. 2003. (American Girl Library). 64p. pap. 9.95 (978-1-58485-793-8(5)) American Girl Publishing, Inc.

SKIN, COLOR OF

see Human Skin Color

SKIN—DISEASES

Abramovitz, Melissa. Lupus. 2007. (Diseases & Disorders Ser.). (Illus.). 128p. (gr. 7-10). 31.20 (***978-1-59018-999-3(X)***, Lucent Bks.) Thomson Gale.

Crowe, Karen. Under My Skin: A Kid's Guide to Atopic Dermatitis. Bendell, Norm, illus. 2000. 48p. (J). (gr. 3-8). pap. 5.95 (978-0-9702446-2-8(2)) Astellas Pharma US, Inc.

Gordon, Sharon. Sunburn. 2002. (Rookie Read-About Health Ser.). (Illus.). 32p. (J). (gr. k-2). pap. 5.95 (978-0-516-26873-6(2), Children's Pr.) Scholastic Library Publishing.

—Sunburn. 2002. (gr. k-3). lib. bdg. 14.10 (978-0-613-50751-6(7)) Tandem Library Bks.

Hartley, Karen. Head Louse. 2000. (gr. k-3). lib. bdg. 14.75 (978-0-613-44361-6(6)) Tandem Library Bks.

Hartley, Karen, et al, contrib. by. Head Louse. 2000. (Bug Books Ser.). (Illus.). 32p. (J). (gr. k-2). lib. bdg. 21.36 (978-1-57572-549-9(5)) Heinemann Library.

Lamberg, Lynne. Skin Disorders. 2000. (Twenty-First Century Health & Wellness Ser.). (Illus.). (J). (gr. 7-12). 24.95 (978-0-7910-5983-8(9), Chelsea Hse.) Facts On File, Inc.

Long, Wendy. Coping with Melanoma & Other Skin Cancers. 1999. (Coping Ser.). (Illus.). 128-192p. (YA). (gr. 7-12). lib. bdg. 26.50 (978-0-8239-2852-1(7), COMELA) Rosen Publishing Group, Inc., The.

Royston, Angela. Head Lice. 2001. (It's Catching Ser.). (Illus.). 32p. (J). (gr. k-2). lib. bdg. 21.36 (978-1-58810-229-4(7)) Heinemann Library.

—Warts. 2001. (It's Catching Ser.). (Illus.). 32p. (J). (gr. k-2). lib. bdg. 21.36 (978-1-58810-231-7(9)) Heinemann Library.

San-Joyz, Naweko. Acne Messages: Crack the Code of Your Zits & Say Goodbye to Acne. 2004. (Illus.). 224p. (YA). per. 14.99 (978-0-9749122-0-2(4)) Noixia's Reading Circle.

Sheen, Barbara. Acne. 2004. (Diseases & Disorders Ser.). (Illus.). 96p. (J). 32.45 (978-1-59018-345-8(2), Lucent Bks.) Thomson Gale.

Silverstein, Alvin. Is That a Rash? 2000. (gr. 3-6). lib. bdg. 15.25 (978-0-613-31365-0(8)) Tandem Library Bks.

Silverstein, Alvin, et al. Head Lice. 2000. (My Health Ser.). (Illus.). 48p. (J). (gr. 3-5). 25.50 (978-0-531-11624-1(7), Watts, Franklin) Scholastic Library Publishing.

—Is That a Rash? 2000. (My Health Ser.). (Illus.). 48p. (J). (gr. 3-5). 25.50 (978-0-531-11637-1(9), Watts, Franklin) Scholastic Library Publishing.

Simons, Rae. For All to See: A Teen's Guide to Healthy Skin. 2004. (Science of Health Ser.). (Illus.). 128p. (J). (978-1-59084-849-4(7)) Mason Crest Pubs.

SKIN DIVING

Here are entered works on free diving with the use of mask, fins, and snorkel. Works on free diving with the use of a self-contained underwater breathing apparatus are entered under Scuba Diving.

see also Underwater Exploration

Covert, Kim. Extreme Diving. 2005. (X-Sports Ser.). (Illus.). 32p. (J). 22.60 (978-0-7368-3782-8(5)) Capstone Pr., Inc.

Earle, Sylvia A. Dive: My Adventures in the Deep Frontier. 1999. (My Adventures Ser.). (Illus.). 64p. (J). (gr. 3-7). 18.95 (978-0-7922-7144-4(0) , National Geographic Children's Bks.) National Geographic Society.

Harcourt School Publishers Staff. The World under the Water Below Level. 3rd ed. 2002. (Trophies Reading Program Ser.). (Illus.). pap. 5.10 (978-0-15-323058-5(4)) Harcourt Schl. Pubs.

Mason, Paul. Snorkeling & Diving. 2007. (J). ***(978-1-59920-128-3(3))*** Smart Apple Media.

Vander Hook, Sue. Scuba Diving. 2000. (World of Sports Ser.). (Illus.). 32p. (J). (gr. 4 up). lib. bdg. 16.95 (978-1-887068-59-8(7)) Smart Apple Media.

SKIN DIVING—FICTION

Baker, Jeannie. The Hidden Forest. 2000. (Illus.). 40p. (J). (gr. k up). 16.89 (978-0-688-15761-6(0)) HarperCollins Pubs.

Hillert, Margaret. The Yellow Boat. 2002. (Illus.). 15.00 (978-1-4046-2001-8(X)) Book Wholesalers, Inc.

Silverhardt, Lauryn, adapted by. Underwater Adventure. ed. 2005. (Rubbadubbers Ser.: 1). (Illus.). 24p. (J). lib. bdg. 15.00 (978-1-59054-823-3(X)) Fitzgerald Bks.

SKIS AND SKIING

see also Water Skiing

Cotter, Alison. Skiing. 2003. (History of Sports Ser.). (Illus.). 112p. (YA). (gr. 6-9). 29.95 (978-1-59018-072-3(0) , Lucent Bks.) Thomson Gale.

Crossingham, John & Kalman, Bobbie. Skiing in Action. 2004. (Sports in Action Ser.). (Illus.). 32p. (J). (978-0-7787-0337-2(1)); pap. (978-0-7787-0357-0(6)) Crabtree Publishing Co.

Dippold, Joel. Picabo Sreet: Downhill Dynamo. rev. ed. 1998. (J). 5.95 (978-0-8225-9839-8(6)) Lerner Publishing Group.

Eckart, Edana. I Can Ski. 2003. (gr. k-3). lib. bdg. 12.95 (978-0-613-59638-1(2)) Tandem Library Bks.

Firestone, Mary. Extreme Downhill Skiing Moves. 2003. (Behind the Moves Ser.). (Illus.). 32p. (J). lib. bdg. 22.60 (978-0-7368-2153-7(8)) Capstone Pr., Inc.

Hammerle, Susa. Let's Try Skiing. Grobekettler, Friederike, illus. 2007. 32p. (J). (ps). 12.95 ***(978-0-7358-2142-2(9))*** North-South Bks., Inc.

Herran, Joe & Thomas, Ron. Skiing. 2003. (Action Sports Ser.). (Illus.). 32p. (J). (gr. 4-8). 28.00 (978-0-7910-7537-1(0) , Chelsea Hse.) Facts On File, Inc.

Jefferis, David. Snow Sports. 2001. (Young Library - Super Sports). (Illus.). 32p. (J). lib. bdg. 25.69 (978-0-7398-4342-0(7)) Raintree.

Klingel, Cynthia Fitterer. Downhill Skiing. 2003. (Wonder Books Level 2: Sports Ser.). (Illus.). 24p. (J). (ps-2). 22.79 (978-1-56766-456-0(3)) Child's World, Inc.

Lindeen, Carol K. Let's Downhill Ski! 2007. (Sports & Activities Ser.). (Illus.). 24p. (J). (ps-1). lib. bdg. 19.93 (978-0-7368-6359-9(1) , Pebble Bks.) Capstone Pr., Inc.

MacAulay, Kelley & Kalman, Bobbie. Extreme Skiing. 2006. (Extreme Sports No Limits! Ser.). (Illus.). 32p. (J). (gr. 3-9). pap. (978-0-7787-1728-7(3) , 1253447); (978-0-7787-1682-2(1) , 1253447) Crabtree Publishing Co.

Mason, Paul. Skiing. 2002. (Radical Sports Ser.). (Illus.). 32p. (J). (gr. 5-7). lib. bdg. 25.64 (978-1-58810-628-5(4)); pap. 7.50 (978-1-4034-0107-6(1) , 91655) Heinemann Library.

—Skiing. 2003. (gr. 5-8). lib. bdg. 15.25 (978-0-613-45833-7(8)) Tandem Library Bks.

Maurer, Tracy. Snow Skiing. 2001. (Radsports Guides). (Illus.). 48p. (J). (gr. 4-7). lib. bdg. 29.93 (978-1-58952-105-6(6)) Rourke Publishing, LLC.

Morina, Barbara. Skiing/Snowboarding: A Skiers Journal. Morina, Barbara, ed. 2002. (Write It down Ser.). (Illus.). 202p. (YA). (gr. 2 up). 19.95 (978-1-892033-30-7(5)) Journals Unlimited, Inc.

Pollack, Pamela & Masoff, Joy. Extreme Sports: Ski. 2002. (Illus.). 64p. (J). (gr. 4-9). pap. 8.95 (978-0-7922-6738-6(9) , National Geographic Children's Bks.) National Geographic Society.

Sanger, Rick. Do Teddy Bears Ski? Russell, Carol, illus. 1998. 32p. (J). (ps-1). 14.95 (978-0-9653149-1-6(X)) Mountain Path Pr.

Schindler, John E. Extreme Skiing. 2005. (Illus.). 24p. (J). pap. (978-0-8368-4546-4(3)); lib. bdg. 22.00 (978-0-8368-4539-6(0)) Stevens, Gareth Inc.

Smalley, Carol. Bernie Mac. 2006. (Blue Banner Biography Ser.). (Illus.). 32p. (J). (gr. 4-8). lib. bdg. 25.70 (978-1-58415-488-4(8)) Mitchell Lane Pubs., Inc.

Stiefer, Sandy. Marathon Skiing. 2002. (Ultra Sports Ser.). (Illus.). 64p. (YA). (gr. 5-8). lib. bdg. 26.50 (978-0-8239-3554-3(X) , Rosen Central) Rosen Publishing Group, Inc., The.

Teitelbaum, Michael. Skiing. 2008. (J). pap. 7.95 ***(978-1-60279-091-9(4));*** lib. bdg. 25.26 ***(978-1-60279-015-5(9))*** Cherry Lake Publishing.

U. S. Olympic Committee. A Basic Guide to Skiing & Snowboarding. 2002. (Olympic Guides). (Illus.). 160p. (J). (gr. 6 up). lib. bdg. 23.33 (978-0-8368-3104-7(7)) Stevens, Gareth Inc.

SKIS AND SKIING—FICTION

Alba, Gene. Mutley Goes to Snow Mountain. 1999. (Mutley's True Life Adventures Ser.). (Illus.). 32p. (J). (ps-3). 14.95 (978-0-89346-877-4(0)) Heian International Publishing, Inc.

Bryant, Louella. Two Tracks in the Snow. Fargo, Todd, illus. l.t. ed. 2004. (Turtle Bks.). 32p. (J). lib. bdg. 15.95 (978-0-944727-46-1(8)); per. 9.95 (978-0-944727-45-4(X)) Jason & Nordic Pubs. (Turtle Bks.).

Busby, Cylin. The Ski Trip Trouble: A Choose Your Boyfriend Book. 2007. (Date Him or Dump Him? Ser.). 192p. (J). (gr. 5 up). pap. 6.95 ***(978-1-59990-106-0(4))*** Bloomsbury Publishing.

Butcher, Nancy. It's Snow Problem. 2001. (gr. 3-6). lib. bdg. 13.00 (978-0-613-43934-3(1)) Tandem Library Bks.

Cheshire, Simon. The Prince & the Snowgirl. 2007. 176p. (J). (gr. 7). pap. 8.99 (978-0-385-73342-7(9)); lib. bdg. 12.99 (978-0-385-90359-2(6)) Random Hse. Children's Bks. (Delacorte Bks. for Young Readers).

Crossingham, John & Kalman, Bobbie. Le Ski Alpin. 2007. (FRE.). 32p. pap. 7.95 ***(978-2-89579-167-6(8))*** Editions Banjo CAN. *Dist:* Crabtree Publishing Co.

Delaney, Kaz. My Life as a Snow Bunny. 2003. (YA). mass mkt. 5.99 (978-0-8439-5296-4(2)) Dorchester Publishing Co., Inc.

—My Life as a Snow Bunny. 2003. (gr. 7-12). lib. bdg. 14.15 (978-0-613-76908-2(2)) Tandem Library Bks.

Devries, Douglas. Matt Bugs Me. 2005. 132p. pap. 13.99 (978-1-4141-0451-5(0)) Pleasant Word.

Dower, Laura. Give Me a Break. 2004. 166p. (J). lib. bdg. 16.92 ***(978-1-4242-0649-0(9))*** Fitzgerald Bks.

—Give Me a Break. 2004. 166p. (J). (978-1-4155-7364-8(6)); 18th rev. ed. 2005. (From the Files of Madison Finn Ser.: Bk. 18). 176p. (gr. 3-7). pap. 4.99 (978-0-7868-0988-2(4)) Hyperion Bks. for Children. (Volo).

Franklin, Emily. Balancing Acts: Chalet Girls. 2007. 244p. (YA). (gr. 12 up). per. 9.99 ***(978-0-451-22219-0(9)*** , N A L Trade) Penguin Group (USA) Inc.

Gerber, Linda. The Finnish Line. 2007. (S. A. S. S. (Students Across the Seven Seas) Ser.). 224p. (YA). (gr. 7). pap. 6.99 ***(978-0-14-240916-9(2)*** , Puffin) Penguin Group (USA) Inc.

Gregory, Matt. Ski Tales. 2005. (Illus.). 36p. (J). 20.00 (978-0-9766442-0-0(7)) Gregory, Charles Matthew.

Gunn, Robin Jones. True Friends. rev. ed. 1999. (Christy Miller Ser.: Bk. 7). 160p. (YA). (gr. 7-12). pap. 6.99 (978-1-56179-720-2(0)) Bethany Hse. Pubs.

Herman, Gail. The Haunted Ski Lodge. del Sur, Duendes, illus. 2001. (Scooby-Doo Ser.: No. 9). 32p. (J). pap. 3.99 (978-0-439-33493-8(4)) Scholastic, Inc.

High Escape (Ski Racing) 64p. (YA). (gr. 6-12). pap. 10.95 (978-0-8224-6478-5(0)) Globe Fearon Educational Publishing.

Hood, Karen Jean Matsko. Joel's First Ski Trip. 2002. 24.95 (978-1-59210-080-4(5) , 1-59210-080-5); 24.95 (978-1-930948-47-1(6)) Whispering Pine Pr., Inc.

Horton, Randy. Big Sundae. 2001. (gr. 5-8). lib. bdg. 11.80 (978-0-613-51202-2(2)) Tandem Library Bks.

Imagine This, James Robert: Individual Title, 6 packs. (Action Packs Ser.). 120p. (gr. 3-5). 44.00 (978-0-7635-8418-4(5)) Rigby Education.

Jones, Melanie Davis. I Can Ski! 2004. (Rookie Reader Skill Set Ser.). (Illus.). 31p. (J). (gr. k-2). pap. 4.95 (978-0-516-27901-5(7) , Children's Pr.) Scholastic Library Publishing.

—I Can Ski! Boles, Terry, illus. 2003. (Rookie Reader - Level B Ser.). 32p. (J). 19.50 (978-0-516-22878-5(1) , Children's Pr.) Scholastic Library Publishing.

Keene, Carolyn. Ski School Sneak. Pamintuan, Macky, illus. 2007. (Nancy Drew & the Clue Crew Ser.: No. 11). 96p. (J). (gr. 1-4). pap. 3.99 ***(978-1-4169-4936-7(4)*** , Aladdin) Simon & Schuster Children's Publishing.

Knipe, Floyd P. Forest Goes Snow Skiing. Jackson, James K., illus. 2000. (Forest the Huggable Dog Ser.: Vol. 4). 23p. (J). (ps-3). pap. 4.95 (978-1-930130-10-4(4)) Nature's Nest Bks.

—Forest Goes Snow Skiing Coloring Book. Jackson, James K., illus. 2000. (Forest the Huggable Dog Ser.: Vol. 4). 23p. (J). (ps-3). pap. 2.00 (978-1-930130-11-1(2)) Nature's Nest Bks.

Krulik, Nancy E. It's Snow Joke, No. 22. John and Wendy Staff, illus. 2006. (Katie Kazoo, Switcheroo Ser.: No. 22). 80p. (J). (gr. 2-5). pap. 3.99 (978-0-448-44396-6(1) , Grosset & Dunlap) Penguin Group (USA) Inc.

Lewis, Beverly. Star Status. 2002. (Girls Only (Go!) Ser.: Vol. 8). 128p. (J). reprint ed. pap. 6.99 (978-1-55661-643-3(0)) Bethany Hse. Pubs.

Lewman, David. Blizzard Bluster! SpongeBob's Book of Frosty Funnies. 2008. (SpongeBob SquarePants Ser.). 48p. (J). pap. 3.99 ***(978-1-4169-4747-9(7)*** , Simon Spotlight) Simon & Schuster Children's Publishing.

Linko, G. J. Tess's Touchstone. 2004. (Seekers Ser.: No. 5). 108p. 5.99 (978-0-8066-4189-8(4) , Augsburg Bks.) Augsburg Fortress, Pubs.

Moscovich, Rotem & Saric, Lazar. Curious George Snowy Day. 2007. (Illus.). 24p. (J). (gr. k-ps). 3.99 ***(978-0-618-80043-8(3))*** Houghton Mifflin Co.

Muldrow, Diane. Deep Freeze. Pollack, Barbara, illus. 2007. (Dish Ser.: No. 12). 160p. (J). (gr. 4-7). pap. 4.99 ***(978-0-448-44693-6(6)*** , Grosset & Dunlap) Penguin Group (USA) Inc.

Nielsen, Gwyn English. Torey the Turkey Goes Skiing. 2003. (Illus.). 24p. (Orig.). (ps-4). pap. 5.99 (978-0-9660726-0-0(X)) C.G.S. Pr.

Osorio, Rick. The Great Adventure of Sally Rock & el Lobo. 2007. (ENG.). 96p. per. 14.95 ***(978-1-4241-5869-0(9))*** PublishAmerica, Inc.

Pendziwol, Jean E. Marja's Skis. Marton, Jirina, illus. 2007. 32p. (J). (ps-3). 17.95 ***(978-0-88899-674-9(8))*** Groundwood Bks. CAN. *Dist:* Perseus Distribution.

Pogo the Clown. The Great Blue Sky: Harley's Great Adventures. Miller, Richard D., illus. 2005. (J). 12.95 (978-0-9755253-6-4(0)) Chiliric Pubns.

Ribeiro, Nelson & Gorelick, Victor, Betty & Veronica in Trendsetter. 2007. (Illus.). 80p. (J). 24.21 (978-1-59961-268-3(2)) Spotlight.

Rottman, S. L. Slalom. 2004. 256p. (YA). (gr. 7). 16.99 (978-0-670-05913-3(7) , Viking Juvenile) Penguin Group (USA) Inc.

Seuling, Barbara. Robert & the Great Escape. Brewer, Paul, illus. 2003. (Robert Bks.). 120p. 15.95 (978-0-8126-2700-8(8)) Cricket Bks.

Sheeley, Jill. Rescue on Vail Mountain. 2000. (Adventures of Fraser the Yellow Dog Ser.). (Illus.). (J). 14.95 (978-0-9609108-5-4(9)) Courtney Pr.

Simon, Francesca. Camels Don't Ski. Busby, Ailie, illus. 1999. 32p. (ps-3). 14.95 (978-1-899607-59-4(5)) Sterling Publishing Co., Inc.

Skiing: KinderConcepts Individual Title Six-Packs. (Kinderstarters Ser.). 8p. (ps-1). 21.00 (978-0-7635-8718-5(4)) Rigby Education.

Stewart, Melanie. Hitting the Slopes. 1999. (gr. 3-6). lib. bdg. 11.80 (978-0-613-27877-5(1)) Tandem Library Bks.

Weinmann, Julianne. The Mis-Adventures of Frissue the Tissue. 2005. 48p. (J). pap. 15.69 (978-1-4116-5310-8(6)) Lulu.com.

Wilshire, Florence A. They're all from the Skies. 2005. 82p. pap. 24.95 (978-1-4116-3892-1(1)) Lulu.com.

Withers, Pam. Peak Survival. 2003. (Take It to the Extreme Ser.). 176p. (YA). (gr. 7-11). pap. 6.95 (978-1-55285-530-0(9)) Whitecap Bks., Ltd. CAN. *Dist:* Firefly Bks., Ltd.

SKULL

see Brain

SKUNKS

Bekkering, Annalise. Skunks. 2007. (J). ***(978-1-59036-685-1(9)); (978-1-59036-686-8(7))*** Weigl Pubs., Inc.

Biel, Timothy Levi. Skunks & Their Relatives. 2001. (Zoobooks Ser.). 24p. (J). (gr. 1-7). 15.95 (978-1-888153-03-3(2)) Wildlife Education, Ltd.

Campbell, Sam. Sweet Sue's Adventures. 2002. (Illus.). 119p. (J). reprint ed. pap. 8.95 (978-1-57258-210-1(3)) TEACH Services, Inc.

Hildebrand, Cody. How the Skunk Earned His Stripes: A Pet Parent's Guide to Having a Skunk in the Family. 2004. (YA). 14.95 (978-0-9753729-0-6(4)) Hildebrand, Betty.

Jacobs, Lee. Skunk. 2002. (Illus.). 24p. (J). 21.20 (978-1-56711-641-0(8) , Blackbirch Pr., Inc.) Thomson Gale.

Lockwood, Sophie. Skunks. 2008. (World of Mammals Ser.). 40p. (J). (gr. 2-6). 29.93 ***(978-1-59296-929-6(1))*** Child's World, Inc.

Markle, Sandra. Skunks. 2007. (Animal Prey Ser.). 40p. (J). (gr. 4-6). 25.26 (978-0-8225-6437-9(8) , Lerner Pubns.) Lerner Publishing Group.

Mason, Adrienne. Skunks. Ogle, Nancy Gray, illus. 2006. (Kids Can Press Wildlife Ser.). 32p. (J). ***(978-1-55337-733-7(8))*** Kids Can Pr., Ltd.

Mattern, Joanne. Skunks Are Night Animals. 2006. (Illus.). 24p. (J). pap. ***(978-0-8368-7857-8(4));*** lib. bdg. ***(978-0-8368-7850-9(7))*** Stevens, Gareth Inc. (Weekly Reader Early Learning Library).

—Skunks Are Night Animals: Los Zorrillos Son Animales Nocturnos. 2006. (SPA & ENG., Illus.). 24p. (J). pap. ***(978-0-8368-8054-0(4));*** lib. bdg. ***(978-0-8368-8047-2(1))*** Stevens, Gareth Inc. (Weekly Reader Early Learning Library).

Nelson, Kristin L. Spraying Skunks. 2003. (Pull Ahead Bks.). (Illus.). 32p. (J). 22.60 (978-0-8225-4670-2(1) , Lerner Pubns.) Lerner Publishing Group.

—Spraying Skunks. 2003. (gr. k-3). lib. bdg. 14.10 (978-0-613-58939-0(4)) Tandem Library Bks.

Otfinoski, Steven. Skunks. 2008. (J). ***(978-0-7614-2929-6(8))*** Cavendish, Marshall Bks., Ltd.

Skunks, 6 Pack. 16p. (gr. 2 up). 36.00 (978-0-7635-9396-4(6)) Rigby Education.

Souza, Dorothy M. Skunks Do More Than Stink! 2002. (All about Animals Ser.). (Illus.). 32p. (gr. k-3). lib. bdg. 21.90 (978-0-7613-2503-1(4) , Millbrook Pr.) Lerner Publishing Group.

Swanson, Diane. Skunks. 2002. (Welcome to the World of Animals Ser.). (Illus.). 32p. (J). (gr. 3 up). lib. bdg. 23.33 (978-0-8368-3317-1(1)) Stevens, Gareth Inc.

—Welcome to the World of Skunks. 2004. (Welcome to the World Ser.). (Illus.). 32p. (J). (ps-2). pap. 5.95 (978-1-55110-855-1(0)) Whitecap Bks., Ltd. CAN. *Dist:* Firefly Bks., Ltd.

Whitehouse, Patricia. Skunks. 2003. (What's Awake? Ser.). (Illus.). 24p. (J). lib. bdg. 17.08 (978-1-58810-883-8(X)); pap. (978-1-4034-0630-9(8)) Heinemann Library.

—El Zorrillo. 2003. (Que Esta Despierto? (What's Awake?) Ser.). (SPA.). 24p. (ps-1). (J). lib. bdg. 17.08 (978-1-4034-0398-8(8)); (Illus.). pap. 5.25 (978-1-4034-0639-2(1)) Heinemann Library.

SKUNKS—FICTION

Adams, Gloria. Five Little Skunks. Collier-Morales, Roberta, illus. 2006. (Sing-A-Story Ser.). 16p. (J). bds. 10.95 (978-0-7696-4916-0(5)) School Specialty Publishing.

Avi. Poppy's Return. Floca, Brian, illus. 2005. (Poppy Stories Ser.). 240p. (J). 15.99 (978-0-06-000012-7(0)) HarperCollins Pubs.

Bridwell, Norman. The Dog Who Cried "Woof!" Kurtz, John & Bridwell, Norman, illus. 2001. (Big Red Reader Ser.). 32p. (J). (ps-1). pap. 3.99 (978-0-439-28978-8(5) , Cartwheel Bks.) Scholastic, Inc.

—The Dog Who Cried "Woof!" Bridwell, Norman, illus. 2002. (Big Red Readers Ser.). (Illus.). (J). 11.91 (978-0-7587-6772-1(2)) Book Wholesalers, Inc.

Burgess, Thornton W. The Adventures of Jimmy Skunk. (J). 18.95 (978-0-8488-0384-1(1)) Amereon LTD.

Clegg, Helen. Tip's Day Out. Lenoir, Jane, illus. 2001. (J). (gr. k-5). lib. bdg. 14.95 (978-0-9705727-9-0(4)) Coastal Publishing Carolina, Inc.

Crum, Shutta. The Bravest of the Brave. Bowers, Tim, illus. 2005. 40p. (J). (ps-3). 15.95 (978-0-375-82637-5(8) , Knopf Bks. for Young Readers) Random Hse. Children's Bks.

Frog & Skunk. 1998. (Fisher-Price Phonics Storybooks Ser.: Vol. 2). (Illus.). (J). pap. (978-0-7666-0172-7(2) , Honey Bear Bks.) Modern Publishing.

Garside, Alice H. The Man, the Fox & the Skunk, Set 1. l.t. ed. 1999. (Illus.). 19p. (Orig.). (J). (gr. k-6). reprint ed. pap. 2.50 (978-1-893688-01-8(1)) Carroll Schl., The.

Hamilton, Elizabeth L. Stinky Skunk's Self-Control. 2004. (Character Critters Ser.: No. 4). (Illus.). 32p. (J). (ps-3). per. 5.95 (978-0-9713749-6-6(1) , Character-in-Action) Quiet Impact, Inc.

Hodgson, Mona Gansberg. Smelly Tales. Sharp, Chris, illus. 1998. (Desert Critter Friends Ser.: Vol. 4). 48p. (J). (ps-2). 4.99 (978-0-570-05071-1(5) , 56-1895) Concordia Publishing Hse.

—Smelly Tales. 1998. (ps-2). lib. bdg. 13.00 (978-0-613-72807-2(6)) Tandem Library Bks.

Jenkins, Emily. Skunkdog. Pratt, Pierre, illus. 2008. 32p. (J). 16.95 ***(978-0-374-37009-1(5)*** , Farrar, Straus & Giroux (BYR)) Farrar, Straus & Giroux.

Jennings, Dwayne G. The Strawberry Skunk. Jennings, Daren G., illus. 2000. 16p. (J). (gr. k-7). (978-0-9678111-0-9(4)) Strawberry Laine LLC.

Maccarone, Grace. Magic Matt & the Skunk in the Tub. 2003. (gr. k-3). lib. bdg. 11.80 (978-0-613-63556-1(6)) Tandem Library Bks.

Martin, Anne E. Midnight Kitties. 2007. (Illus.). 46p. (J). per. 13.99 ***(978-1-59879-245-4(8))*** Lifevest Publishing, Inc.

Nanette. Buddy & Muddy: The Twin Brown Skunks. 2004. (J). 12.95 (978-0-9741269-5-1(0)) St. Bernard Publishing, LLC.

Newman, Lesléa. Skunk's Spring Surprise. Gorbachev, Valeri, illus. 2007. 44p. (J). 16.00 (978-0-15-205683-4(1)) Harcourt Trade Pubs.

Oke, Janette. New Kid in Town. 2001. (Orig.). (gr. k-3). lib. bdg. 14.15 (978-0-613-82429-3(6)) Tandem Library Bks.

Penn, Audrey. A Kiss Goodbye. Gibson, Barbara Leonard, illus. 2007. 32p. (ps-3). 16.95 ***(978-1-933718-04-0(8))*** Tanglewood Pr.

—A Kiss Goodbye. Gibson, Barbara, illus. 2007. 32p. 16.95 ***(978-1-933718-03-3(X))*** Tanglewood Pr.

Pilkey, Dav. Big Dog & Little Dog Making a Mistake. 1999. (Big Dog & Little Dog Ser.). (Illus.). 14p. (J). (ps-1). bds. 5.95 (978-0-15-200354-8(1) , Red Wagon Bks.) Harcourt Children's Bks.

Pochocki, Ethel. The Blessing of the Beasts. Moser, Barry, illus. 2007. 40p. (J). (gr. k up). 18.95 (978-1-55725-502-0(4)) Paraclete Pr., Inc.

Reed, Lynn Rowe. Please Don't Upset P.U. Zorilla. 2006. (Illus.). 32p. (J). (ps-3). 15.95 (978-0-375-83654-1(3)); lib. bdg. 17.99 (978-0-375-93654-8(8)) Random Hse. Children's Bks. (Knopf Bks. for Young Readers).

Rhodes, C. J. The Rabbit, the Skunk & the Cuckoo. Spears-Stewart, Reta, ed. Secca, Phillip, illus. 1998. 36p. (J). pap. 12.00 (978-0-9638648-5-7(8)) Nottinghill Bks.

Sargent, Dave. Finding Sammy #1 (PB), 10 vols. 2007. (Little Stinker Ser.: 1). (J). pap. 9.95 ***(978-1-59381-274-4(4))*** Ozark Publishing.

—I Named Him Sammy #7, 10 vols. 2007. (Little Stinker Ser.: 7). (J). lib. bdg. 22.60 ***(978-1-59381-291-1(4))*** Ozark Publishing.

—I Named Him Sammy #7 (PB), 10 vols. 2007. (Little Stinker Ser.: 7). (J). pap. 9.95 ***(978-1-59381-292-8(2))*** Ozark Publishing.

Sargent, Dave & Sargent, Pat. Sammy Skunk: I'm a Little Stinker, 56 vols., 9. Huff, Jeane, illus. 2nd rev. ed. 2003. (Animal Pride Ser.: 9). 42p. (J). lib. bdg. 19.95 (978-1-56763-775-5(2)) Ozark Publishing.

Sheely, Barbara R. Lucky - A Skunk's Adventure in the Endless Mountains of Pennsylvania. 1999. (Illus.). 20p. (J). (gr. k-5). pap. 8.00 (978-0-9672077-0-4(3)) Sheeley, Barbara.

Staunton, Ted. Stinky. Gardos, Susan, illus. 2004. (Northern Lights Young Novels Ser.). 64p. (J). (gr. 2-5). pap. 4.95 (978-0-88995-263-8(9)) Red Deer Pr. CAN. *Dist:* Fitzhenry & Whiteside, Ltd.

—Stinky. 2003. (gr. 3-6). lib. bdg. 12.95 (978-0-613-84450-5(5)) Tandem Library Bks.

Stevens, Jan Romero. Carlos & the Skunk. 2001. Tr. of Carlos y el Zorrillo. (Illus.). (J). 14.75 (978-0-606-20590-0(X)) Tandem Library Bks.

—Carlos & the Skunk (Carlos y el Zorrilo) Arnold, Jeanne, illus. 2001. (SPA & ENG.). 32p. (J). (gr. 2-3). 7.95 (978-0-87358-779-2(0) , Rising Moon Bks. for Young Readers) Northland Publishing.

Thomas, Jerry D. Skunk by the Tail A. 1998. (J). (gr. 4-7). 14.99 (978-0-8163-1644-1(9)) Pacific Pr. Publishing Assn.

Wilson, Karma. Sweet Briar Goes to School. Pham, LeUyen, illus. 2003. 32p. (J). (ps). 16.99 (978-0-8037-2767-0(4) , Dial) Penguin Group (USA) Inc.

—Sweet Briar Goes to School. Pham, LeUyen, illus. 2005. 32p. (J). pap. 5.99 (978-0-14-240281-8(8) , Puffin) Penguin Group (USA) Inc.

Ziefert, Harriet. One Smart Skunk. Cohen, Santiago, illus. 2004. 40p. (gr. k-3). 15.95 (978-1-59354-064-7(7)) Blue Apple Bks.

SKY DIVING

see Skydiving

SKYDIVING

Braulick, Carrie A. The U.S. Army Golden Knights. 2006. (Blazers—The U.S. Armed Forces Ser.). (Illus.). 32p. (J). (978-0-7368-4393-5(0)) Capstone Pr., Inc.

Cefrey, Holly. Skysurfing. 2003. (High Interest Bks.). (Illus.). 48p. (YA). (gr. 7-12). pap. 6.95 (978-0-516-24380-1(2) , Watts, Franklin) Scholastic Library Publishing.

—Skysurfing. 2003. (gr. 7-12). lib. bdg. 15.25 (978-0-613-59727-2(3)) Tandem Library Bks.

George, Charles & George, Linda. Team Skydiving. 1998. (Sports Alive! Ser.). (Illus.). 48p. (J). (gr. 3-4). lib. bdg. 21.26 (978-0-7368-0054-9(9) , Capstone High-Interest Bks.) Capstone Pr., Inc.

Hopkins, Ellen H. The Golden Knights: The U. S. Army Parachute Team. 2001. (Serving Your Country Ser.). (Illus.). 48p. (J). (gr. 3-4). lib. bdg. 21.26 (978-0-7368-0775-3(6) , Capstone High-Interest Bks.) Capstone Pr., Inc.

Marx, Mandy. Skydiving. 2006. (Blazers—To the Extreme Ser.). (Illus.). 32p. (J). (978-0-7368-5464-1(9)) Capstone Pr., Inc.

Norman, Tony. Skydiving. 2006. (Illus.). 32p. (J). 24.67 (978-0-8368-6369-7(0)) Stevens, Gareth Inc.

Roberts, Jeremy. Skydiving! Take the Leap. 1999. (Extreme Sports Collection). (Illus.). 64p. (YA). (gr. 5-8). lib. bdg. 26.50 (978-0-8239-3015-9(7) , EXSKDI, Rosen Central) Rosen Publishing Group, Inc., The.

—Skydiving! Take the Leap. 2000. (Illus.). 64p. (YA). per. 9.95 (978-1-56254-305-1(9) , SP 3059) Saddleback Educational Publishing.

Schindler, John E. Skydiving. 2005. (Illus.). 24p. (J). pap. 5.95 (978-0-8368-4550-1(1)); (YA). lib. bdg. 22.00 (978-0-8368-4543-3(9)) Stevens, Gareth Inc.

SKYDIVING—FICTION

Marlow, Herb & Marlow, Lynn. Max the Skydiving Mouse. Newberry, Loretta, illus. l.t. ed. 2002. 28p. (J). lib. bdg. 14.95 (978-1-893595-19-4(6)) Four Seasons Bks., Inc.

Myers, Bill. My Life as a Screaming Skydiver, Vol. 14. 1998. (Incredible Worlds of Wally McDoogle Ser.: No. 14). (Illus.). 128p. (J). (gr. 3-7). pap. 6.99 (978-0-8499-4023-1(0)) Nelson, Thomas Inc.

Sky Ride. 2004. (Illus.). (J). (978-1-59577-008-0(9)) Starfall Education.

Stadler, John. Three Cheers for Hippo. Stadler, John, illus. 2006. (Illus.). 32p. (J). reprint ed. pap. (978-1-59572-046-7(4)) Star Bright Bks., Inc.

Stein, Tammar. High Dive. 2008. 240p. (YA). (gr. 7). lib. bdg. 18.99 (***978-0-375-93024-9(8)** , Knopf Bks. for Young Readers) Random Hse. Children's Bks.

SKYSCRAPERS

Britton, Tamara L. The World Trade Center. 2005. (Symbols, Landmarks & Monuments Ser.). (Illus.). 40p. (J). (gr. k-6). lib. bdg. 22.78 (978-1-57765-850-4(7)) ABDO Publishing Co.

Buildings That Go up Up Up. 2002. (Illus.). (J). pap. 5.43 (978-0-7398-5920-9(X)) Steck-Vaughn.

Corona, Laurel. The World Trade Center. 2002. (Building History Ser.). (Illus.). 104p. (J). (gr. 6-9). 32.45 (978-1-59018-214-7(6) , Lucent Bks.) Thomson Gale.

Curlee, Lynn. Skyscraper. Curlee, Lynn, illus. 2007. 48p. (J). (gr. 3-7). 17.99 (978-0-689-84489-8(1)) Simon & Schuster Children's Publishing.

Currie, Stephen. The Tallest Building. 2003. (Extreme Places Ser.). (Illus.). 48p. (J). (gr. 3-5). 26.20 (978-0-7377-1374-9(7) , Kidhaven) Thomson Gale.

Encarnacion, Elizabeth. Sky Scrapers. 2007. (J). lib. bdg. 19.95 (***978-1-59566-371-9(1))** QEB Publishing Inc.

Goodman, Susan E. Skyscraper. Doolittle, Michael J., photos by. 2004. (Illus.). 40p. (J). (gr. 1-5). 16.95 (978-0-375-81309-2(8) , Knopf Bks. for Young Readers) Random Hse. Children's Bks.

—Skyscraper: From the Ground Up. Doolittle, Michael J., photos by. 2004. (Illus.). 40p. (J). (gr. 1-5). 18.99 (978-0-375-91309-9(2) , Knopf Bks. for Young Readers) Random Hse. Children's Bks.

Halfmann, Janet. Skyscrapers. 2002. (Illus.). 23p. (J). 21.35 (978-1-58340-145-3(8)) Smart Apple Media.

Holland, Gini. The Empire State Building: How It Was Built & How It Is Used. 2004. (Illus.). 48p. (J). (gr. 4-8). reprint ed. 15.00 (978-0-7567-7718-0(6)) DIANE Publishing Co.

Johmann, Carol A. Skyscrapers! Super Structures to Design & Build. 2001. (Kaleidoscope Kids Bks.). (Illus.). 96p. (J). (gr. 2-8). pap. 12.95 (978-1-885593-50-4(3) , Williamson Bks.) Ideals Pubns.

Jomann, Carol. Skyscrapers! Super Structures to Design & Build. 2001. (gr. 3-6). lib. bdg. 19.90 (978-0-613-55900-3(2)) Tandem Library Bks.

Joseph, Leonard. Rascacielos: Por Dentro y por Fuera. 2002. (Tecnología Ser.). (SPA.). 48p. (YA). lib. bdg. 26.50 (978-0-8239-6151-1(6) , Buenas Letra) Rosen Publishing Group, Inc., The.

—Skyscrapers: Inside & Out. 2002. (Technology Ser.). (Illus.). 48p. (YA). (ps-3). lib. bdg. 26.50 (978-0-8239-6109-2(5) , PowerKids Pr.) Rosen Publishing Group, Inc., The.

Koll, Hilary, et al. Using Math to Build a Skyscraper. 2006. (Mathworks!). (Illus.). 32p. (J). pap. (978-0-8368-6771-8(8)); lib. bdg. (978-0-8368-6764-0(5)) Stevens, Gareth Inc.

Korman, Justine. Tonka Building the Skyscraper. 1999. (ps-2). lib. bdg. 11.25 (978-0-613-72020-5(2)) Tandem Library Bks.

Landau, Elaine. Skyscrapers. 2001. (True Bks.). (Illus.). 48p. (J). (gr. 3-5). pap. 6.95 (978-0-516-27324-2(8)); 25.00 (978-0-516-22184-7(1)) Scholastic Library Publishing. (Children's Pr.).

—Skyscrapers. 2001. (gr. 3-6). lib. bdg. 15.25 (978-0-613-53561-8(8)) Tandem Library Bks.

Levy, Debbie. The World Trade Center. 2005. (Great Structures in History Ser.). (Illus.). 48p. (J). (ps-8). lib. bdg. 26.20 (978-0-7377-2071-6(9) , Greenhaven Pr., Inc.) Thomson Gale.

Lusted, Marcia Amidon. The Empire State Building. 2004. (Building History Ser.). (Illus.). 112p. (YA). (gr. 7-10). lib. bdg. 32.45 (978-1-59018-546-9(3) , Lucent Bks.) Thomson Gale.

Macken, JoAnn Early. Building a Skyscraper. 2008. (J). (***978-1-4296-1233-3(9))** Capstone Pr., Inc.

Murray, Julie. Sears Tower. 2005. (Buddy Book Ser.). (Illus.). 24p. (J). (gr. k-4). lib. bdg. 21.35 (978-1-59197-508-3(5)) ABDO Publishing Co.

Oxlade, Chris. Skyscrapers. (Building Amazing Structures Ser.). (Illus.). 32p. (J). 2000. (gr. 4-7). lib. bdg. 22.79 (978-1-57572-278-8(X)); 2nd ed. 2005. (978-1-4034-7904-4(6)) Heinemann Library.

—Skyscrapers: Uncovering Technology. 2006. (Uncovering Ser.). (Illus.). 52p. (J). (gr. 3-12). 16.95 (978-1-55407-136-4(4)) Firefly Bks., Ltd.

Pascoe, Elaine, ed. Skyscrapers. 2003. (Super Structures of the World Ser.). (J). 11.20 (978-1-4103-0192-5(3) , Blackbirch Pr., Inc.) Thomson Gale.

The Petronas Twin Towers: Individual Title Six-Packs. (On Deck Ser.). 24p. (gr. 4-5). 35.00 (978-0-7578-1070-1(5)) Rigby Education.

Rau, Dana Meachen. Bookworms: The Inside Story, 6 bks., Set. Incl. Castle. 32p. lib. bdg. 22.79 (978-0-7614-2272-3(2)); Igloo. 24p. lib. bdg. 22.79 (978-0-7614-2273-0(0)); Log Cabin. 24p. lib. bdg. 22.79 (***978-0-7614-2274-7(9));** Pyramid. 32p. lib. bdg. 22.79 (***978-0-7614-2275-4(7));** Skyscraper. 32p. lib. bdg. 22.79 (978-0-7614-2276-1(5)); Tepee. 32p. lib. bdg. 22.79 (978-0-7614-2277-8(3)); (Illus.). (J). (gr. k-2). 2006. 2006. Set lib. bdg. 136.71 (***978-0-7614-2271-6(4)** , Benchmark Bks.) Cavendish, Marshall Corp.

Rau, Dana Meachen. Skyscraper. 2006. (Bookworms Ser.). (Illus.). 32p. (J). lib. bdg. 22.79 (978-0-7614-2276-1(5) , Benchmark Bks.) Cavendish, Marshall Corp.

Richards, Julie. Skyscrapers & Towers. 2003. 32p. (J). lib. bdg. 24.25 (978-1-58340-348-8(5)) Smart Apple Media.

Roza, Greg. The Incredible Story of Skyscrapers. 2004. (Kid's Guide to Incredible Technology Ser.). (Illus.). 24p. (J). lib. bdg. 19.95 (978-0-8239-6716-2(6)) Rosen Publishing Group, Inc., The.

Severance, John B. Skyscrapers: How America Grew Up. 2000. (Illus.). 112p. (J). (gr. 7 up). tchr. ed. 18.95 (978-0-8234-1492-5(2)) Holiday Hse., Inc.

Simon, Seymour. Seemore Skyscrapers. 2005. (Illus.). 32p. (J). 14.95 (978-1-58717-266-3(6) , SeaStar Bks.) Chronicle Bks. LLC.

Stone, Lynn M. Skyscrapers. 2001. (How are They Built? Ser.). (Illus.). 48p. (J). (gr. 4-8). lib. bdg. 29.93 (978-1-58952-139-1(0)) Rourke Publishing, LLC.

Thomas, Mark. The Petronas Twin Towers: World's Tallest Buildings. 2002. (Reading Power Ser.). (Illus.). 24p. (J). (gr. 1). lib. bdg. 17.25 (978-0-8239-5989-1(9) , PowerKids Pr.) Rosen Publishing Group, Inc., The.

—Record-Breaking Structures, 6 bks. Incl. Akashi-Kaikyo Bridge : World's Longest Bridge. lib. bdg. 17.25 (978-0-8239-5990-7(2)); Discoverer Enterprise : World's Largest Offshore Drilling Rig. (gr. 1). lib. bdg. 17.25 (978-0-8239-5994-5(5)); Itaipu Dam : World's Biggest Dam. (gr. 1). lib. bdg. 17.25 (978-0-8239-5993-8(7)); Maracanaa : World's Largest Stadium. (gr. 1). lib. bdg. 17.25 (978-0-8239-5992-1(9)); Petronas Twin Towers : World's Tallest Buildings. (gr. 1). lib. bdg. 17.25 (978-0-8239-5989-1(9)); Seikan Railroad Tunnel : World's Longest Tunnel. (gr. 1). lib. bdg. 17.25 (978-0-8239-5991-4(0)); 24p. (J). 2002. (Illus.). 2001. Set lib. bdg. 96.00 (978-0-8239-7123-7(6) , PowerKids Pr.) Rosen Publishing Group, Inc., The.

Willard, Keith. Skyscrapers. 1999. (Designing the Future Ser.). (Illus.). 32p. (J). (gr. 4-7). lib. bdg. (978-0-88682-719-9(1) , Creative Education) Creative Co., The.

SKYSCRAPERS—FICTION

Hopkinson, Deborah. Sky Boys: Building the Empire State Building. Ransome, James E., illus. 2006. 48p. (J). (ps-4). lib. bdg. 18.99 (978-0-375-93610-4(6) , Schwartz & Wade Bks.) Random Hse. Children's Bks.

—Sky Boys: How They Built the Empire State Building. Ransome, James E., illus. 2006. 48p. (J). (ps-4). 16.95 (978-0-375-83610-7(1) , Schwartz & Wade Bks.) Random Hse. Children's Bks.

Skyscrapers & Farms. 2005. (J). per. 5.00 (978-1-59872-020-4(1)) Instantpublisher.com.

Wax, Wendy. Empire Dreams. Doney, Todd, illus. 2000. (Adventures in America Ser.). 96p. (J). (gr. 4-7). lib. bdg. 14.95 (978-1-893110-19-2(9)) Silver Moon Pr.

SKYWALKER, ANAKIN (FICTITIOUS CHARACTER)—FICTION

Strasser, Todd. Anakin Skywalker. 1999. (Star Wars Episode 1 : Vol. 1). (Illus.). 112p. (J). (gr. 4-7). pap. 5.99 (978-0-590-52093-5(8)) Scholastic, Inc.

—Anakin Skywalker. 1999. (gr. 3-6). lib. bdg. 14.15 (978-0-613-16588-4(8)) Tandem Library Bks.

Watson, Jude. The Trail of the Jedi. 2002. (Star Wars Ser.: No. 2). (gr. 3-6). lib. bdg. 13.00 (978-0-613-50649-6(9)) Tandem Library Bks.

—The Way of the Apprentice. 2002. (Star Wars Ser.: No. 1). (gr. 3-6). lib. bdg. 13.00 (978-0-613-50655-7(3)) Tandem Library Bks.

SKYWALKER, LUKE (FICTITIOUS CHARACTER)—FICTION

Davids, Paul & Davids, Hollace. The Lost City of the Jedi. 1999. (Star Wars Ser.: Bk. 2). (Illus.). 94p. (J). (gr. 4-7). reprint ed. pap. 10.00 (978-0-7881-6480-4(5)) DIANE Publishing Co.

—Star Wars, 3 bks. l.t. ed. Incl. Prophets of the Dark Side. lib. bdg. 22.60 (978-0-8368-1994-6(2)); Queen of the Empire. lib. bdg. 22.60 (978-0-8368-1993-9(4)); Zorba the Hutt's Revenge. lib. bdg. 22.60 (978-0-8368-1991-5(8)); 112p. (J). (gr. 4 up). 1997. Set lib. bdg. 67.80 (978-0-8368-1988-5(8)) Stevens, Gareth Inc.

Lucas, George. Return of the Jedi. 1999. (Star Wars Manga Ser.: No. 4). 96p. (J). (gr. 3 up). pap. 9.95 (978-1-56971-397-6(9)); pap. 9.95 (978-1-56971-396-9(0)); pap. 9.95 (978-1-56971-395-2(2)); pap. 9.95 (978-1-56971-394-5(4)) Dark Horse Comics.

Macan, Darko, et al. Vader's Quest. (Star Wars Ser.). (Illus.). 96p. (YA). (gr. 7 up). pap. 11.95 (978-1-56971-415-7(0)) Dark Horse Comics.

Watson, Jude. The Desperate Mission. 2005. (Star Wars Ser.: No. 1). 168p. (J). lib. bdg. 20.00 (***978-1-4242-0774-9(6))** Fitzgerald Bks.

—The Desperate Mission. 2005. (Star Wars Ser.: No. 1). 168p. (J). (978-1-4155-9754-5(5)) Scholastic, Inc.

SLATER, SAMUEL, 1768-1835

Wooten, Sara McIntosh. The Industrial Revolution. 2003. (People at the Center of Ser.). (Illus.). 48p. (J). 24.95 (978-1-56711-766-0(X) , Blackbirch Pr., Inc.) Thomson Gale.

SLAVE TRADE

Capstone Press, contrib. by. Slave Trade in Early America. (Colonial America Ser.). 48p. (YA). pap. 7.95 (978-0-7368-4482-6(1)) Capstone Pr., Inc.

Haskins, James. Bound for America: The Forced Migration of Africans to the New World. Cooper, Floyd, illus. 1999. 48p. (J). (gr. 6 up). 17.89 (978-0-688-10259-3(X)) HarperCollins Pubs.

Haskins, James & Benson, Kathleen. Africa: A Look Back. 2006. (Drama of African-American History Ser.). (Illus.). 80p. (J). lib. bdg. 34.21 (978-0-7614-2148-1(3) , Benchmark Bks.) Cavendish, Marshall Corp.

Hatt, Christine. The African-American Slave Trade. 2003. (Questioning History Ser.). (J). lib. bdg. 28.50 (978-1-58340-265-8(9)) Smart Apple Media.

Kleinman, Joseph & Kurtis-Kleinman, Eileen. Life on an African Slave Ship. 2000. (Way People Live Ser.). (Illus.). 112p. (J). (gr. 7-10). 28.70 (978-1-56006-653-8(9) , LML00902-178007, Lucent Bks.) Thomson Gale.

McKissack, Patricia C. Amistad: Station Stop 3. Stanley, Sanna, illus. 2005. (All Aboard Reading Ser.). 48p. (J). (gr. 2-4). pap. 3.99 (978-0-448-43900-6(X) , Grosset & Dunlap) Penguin Group (USA) Inc.

Nardo, Don. The Atlantic Slave Trade. 2007. (Lucent Library of Black History Ser.). (Illus.). 128p. (J). (gr. 7-10). 28.70 (***978-1-4205-0007-3(4)** , Lucent Bks.) Thomson Gale.

Newman, Shirlee Petkin. The African Slave Trade. 2001. (Watts Library). (Illus.). 64p. (J). (gr. 5-7). pap. 8.95 (978-0-531-16537-9(X) , Watts, Franklin) Scholastic Library Publishing.

Sharp, S. Pearl & Schomp, Virginia. The Slave Trade & the Middle Passage. 2006. (Drama of African-American History Ser.). (Illus.). 80p. (J). lib. bdg. 34.21 (978-0-7614-2176-4(9) , Benchmark Bks.) Cavendish, Marshall Corp.

Slave Runners. 2000. (My Ancestors—My Heroes Ser.: Vol. 9). (J). (gr. 3-4). (978-1-893091-08-5(2)) Parker Publishing Co.

Theophile, Conneau. Captain Canot; or Twenty Years of an African Slaver. 2006. (Illus.). 448p. (YA). cd-rom 499.00 (978-1-892824-83-7(3)) AFCHRON.

Thoennes Keller, Kristin. The Slave Trade in Early America. 2004. (Let Freedom Ring Ser.). (Illus.). 48p. (J). 17.95 (978-0-7368-2465-1(0) , Bridgestone Bks.) Capstone Pr., Inc.

Thornton, Jeremy. Immigration & the Slave Trade: Africans Come to America (1607-1830) 2004. (Primary Sources of Immigration & Migration in America Ser.). (Illus.). 24p. (J). lib. bdg. 19.95 (978-0-8239-6829-9(4) , PowerKids Pr.) Rosen Publishing Group, Inc., The.

Worth, Richard. Africans in America. 2004. (Immigration to the United States Ser.). (Illus.). 96p. (J). (gr. 4-9). 35.00 (978-0-8160-5691-0(9)) Facts On File, Inc.

—The Slave Trade in America: Cruel Commerce. 2004. (Slavery in American History Ser.). (Illus.). 128p. (J). lib. bdg. 26.60 (978-0-7660-2151-8(3)) Enslow Pubs., Inc.

SLAVERY

Africans in America: America's Journey Through Slavery. 2004. (gr. 7 up). tchr. ed. 19.95 incl. VHS, cd-rom (978-1-57807-195-1(X) , WG665) WGBH Boston Video.

Anastasio, Dina. Harriet Tubman. Morgan, Jacqui, illus. 2002. 16p. (J). pap. (978-0-439-35163-8(4)) Scholastic, Inc.

Brownell, Richard. The Civil War: The Fall of the Confederacy & the End of Slavery. 2005. (History's Great Defeats Ser.). (Illus.). 109p. (YA). (gr. 7-10). lib. bdg. 29.95 (978-1-59018-429-5(7) , Lucent Bks.) Thomson Gale.

Cameron, Ann. Kidnapped Prince: The Life of Olaudah Equiano. 2000. (gr. 5-8). lib. bdg. 13.00 (978-0-613-23007-0(8)) Tandem Library Bks.

Currie, Stephen. A Peculiar Institution: Slavery in the Plantation South. 2005. (Lucent Library of Black History). (Illus.). 112p. (YA). (gr. 7-10). lib. bdg. 32.45 (978-1-59018-704-3(0) , Lucent Bks.) Thomson Gale.

Edwards, Judith. Abolitionists & Slave Resistance: Breaking the Chains of Slavery. 2004. (Slavery in American History Ser.). (Illus.). 128p. (J). lib. bdg. 26.60 (978-0-7660-2155-6(6)) Enslow Pubs., Inc.

Fradin, Dennis Brindell. My Family Shall Be Free! The Life of Peter Still. 2001. (gr. 5 up). (Illus.). 208p. (J). 17.89 (978-0-06-029328-4(4)); (YA). pap. 16.95 (978-0-06-447262-3(0)) HarperCollins Pubs.

Fradin, Dennis Brindell & Fradin, Judith Bloom. 5000 Miles to Freedom: Ellen & William Craft's Flight from Slavery. 2006. (National Geographic Ser.). (Illus.). 96p. (J). (gr. 5-9). 19.95 (978-0-7922-7885-6(2) , National Geographic Children's Bks.) National Geographic Society.

Fradin, Dennis Brindell & Fradin,Judy. 5000 Miles to Freedom: Ellen & William Craft's Flight from Slavery. 2006. (Illus.). 96p. (J). (gr. 5-9). 29.90 (978-0-7922-7886-3(0) , National Geographic Children's Bks.) National Geographic Society.

Greene, Jacqueline Dembar. Slavery in Ancient Egypt & Mesopotamia. 2000. (History of Slavery Library). (Illus.). 64p. (J). (gr. 5-7). 25.50 (978-0-531-11692-0(1) , Watts, Franklin) Scholastic Library Publishing.

—Slavery in Ancient Egypt & Mesopotamia. 2000. (gr. 3-6). lib. bdg. 17.60 (978-0-613-34472-2(3)) Tandem Library Bks.

—Slavery in Ancient Greece & Rome. 2000. (History of Slavery Library). (Illus.). 64p. (J). (gr. 5-7). 25.50 (978-0-531-11693-7(X) , Watts, Franklin) Scholastic Library Publishing.

—Slavery in Ancient Greece & Rome. 2000. (gr. 3-6). lib. bdg. 17.60 (978-0-613-34473-9(1)) Tandem Library Bks.

Haskins, James. Bound for America: The Forced Migration of Africans to the New World. Cooper, Floyd, illus. 1999. 48p. (J). (gr. 6 up). 17.89 (978-0-688-10259-3(X)) HarperCollins Pubs.

Howat, Irene. John Newton, a Slave Set Free. 144p. (J). mass mkt. 5.99 (978-1-85792-834-1(2) , Christian Focus) Christian Focus Pubns. GBR. *Dist:* Riverside.

King, Wilma. Children of the Emancipation. 2005. (Picture the American Past Ser.). (Illus.). 48p. (gr. 2-5). 22.60 (978-1-57505-396-7(9)) Lerner Publishing Group.

Kleinman, Joseph & Kurtis-Kleinman, Eileen. Life on an African Slave Ship. 2000. (Way People Live Ser.). (Illus.). 112p. (J). (gr. 7-10). 28.70 (978-1-56006-653-8(9) , LML00902-178007, Lucent Bks.) Thomson Gale.

MacDonald, Fiona. You Wouldn't Want to Be a Slave in Ancient Greece! 2000. (gr. 3-6). lib. bdg. 18.75 (978-0-613-44278-7(4)) Tandem Library Bks.

—You Wouldn't Want to Be a Slave in Ancient Greece! A Life You'd Rather Not Have. Antram, David, illus. 2001. (You Wouldn't Want to Ser.). 32p. (J). (gr. 2-5). 28.50 (978-0-531-14600-2(6)); pap. 9.95 (978-0-531-16203-3(6)) Scholastic Library Publishing. (Watts, Franklin).

Martin, Michael J. Emancipation Proclamation: Hope of Freedom for the Slaves. 2002. (Let Freedom Ring Ser.). (Illus.). 48p. (J). (gr. 3-4). lib. bdg. 22.60 (978-0-7368-1339-6(X) , Bridgestone Bks.) Capstone Pr., Inc.

Moore, Cathy. The Daring Escape of Ellen Craft. Young, Mary O'Keefe, illus. 2002. (On My Own History Ser.). 48p. (J). (gr. 1-3). lib. bdg. 23.93 (978-0-87614-462-6(8) , Carolrhoda Bks.) Lerner Publishing Group.

Morley, Jacqueline. You Wouldn't Want to Be a Sumerian Slave! A Life of Hard Labor You'd Rather Avoid. Antram, David, illus. 2007. (You Wouldn't Want to... Ser.). 32p. (J). (gr. 2-5). 28.50 (***978-0-531-18728-9(4)** , Watts, Franklin) Scholastic Library Publishing.

Newman, Shirlee Petkin. Child Slavery in Modern Times. 2000. (Watts Library). (Illus.). 64p. (J). (gr. 5-7). 25.50 (978-0-531-11696-8(4) , Watts, Franklin) Scholastic Library Publishing.

Prince, Mary. History of Mary Prince. 2000. (gr. 7-12). lib. bdg. 21.10 (978-0-613-64287-3(2)) Tandem Library Bks.

Rappaport, Doreen. No More! Songs & Stories of Slave Resistance. Evans, Shane W., illus. 2001. 64p. (J). (gr. 4-7). 17.99 (978-0-7636-0984-9(6)) Candlewick Pr.

Rausch, Monica. Harriet Tubman. 2006. 24p. (J). pap. (***978-0-8368-7693-2(8));** lib. bdg. (***978-0-8368-7686-4(5))** Stevens, Gareth Inc. (Weekly Reader Early Learning Library).

Rikson, Paule. Daily Life on a Southern Plantation 1853. 2004. (Illus.). 48p. (J). (gr. 4-8). reprint ed. 17.00 (978-0-7567-7709-8(7)) DIANE Publishing Co.

Schroeder, Alan. Minty: A Story of Young Harriet Tubman. Pinkney, Jerry, illus. 2000. (J). (ps-ps). lib. bdg. 15.30 (978-0-613-33712-0(3)) Tandem Library Bks.

Sharp, S. Pearl & Schomp, Virginia. The Slave Trade & the Middle Passage. 2006. (Drama of African-American History Ser.). (Illus.). 80p. (J). lib. bdg. 34.21 (978-0-7614-2176-4(9) , Benchmark Bks.) Cavendish, Marshall Corp.

Shone, Rob & Ganeri, Anita. Harriet Tubman: The Life of an African-American Abolitionist. 2005. (Graphic Nonfiction Ser.). (Illus.). 48p. (J). (gr. 4-6). lib. bdg. 26.50 (978-1-4042-0245-0(5)) Rosen Publishing Group, Inc., The.

Slavery DBA. 2002. spiral bd. 16.95 (978-1-56004-128-3(5)) Social Studies Schl. Service.

Slavery in the Nineteenth Century. (YA). (gr. 5-8). spiral bd., tchr.'s planning gde. ed. 13.00 (978-0-382-40935-6(3)) Cobblestone Publishing Co.

Stearman, Kaye. Slavery Today. 1999. (Talking Points Ser.). (Illus.). 64p. (J). (gr. 4-7). lib. bdg. 27.12 (978-0-8172-5320-2(3)) Raintree.

Stein, R. Conrad. Escaping Slavery on the Underground Railroad. 2008. (From Many Cultures, One History Ser.). (Illus.). 128p. (J). (gr. 5 up). lib. bdg. 31.93 (***978-0-7660-2799-2(6))** Enslow Pubs., Inc.

Sylvester, Theodore L. Slavery Throughout History: Almanac. Benson, Sonia, ed. 2000. (Slavery Throughout History Reference Library). (Illus.). xlvii, 263p. (J). (gr. 4-7). 67.00 (978-0-7876-3176-5(0) , GML00502-112777, UXL) Thomson Gale.

—Slavery Throughout History: Biographies. 2000. (Slavery Throughout History Reference Library). (Illus.). xxxviii, 235p. (J). (gr. 4-7). 67.00 (978-0-7876-3177-2(9) , GML00502-112778, UXL) Thomson Gale.

Tackach, James. Early Black Reformers. 2003. (gr. 7-12). lib. bdg. 33.25 (978-0-613-73930-6(0)) Tandem Library Bks.

—Early Black Reformers. 2003. (History Firsthand Ser.). (Illus.). (YA). 224p. pap. 24.95 (978-0-7377-1598-9(7)); 202p. lib. bdg. 36.20 (978-0-7377-1597-2(9)) Thomson Gale. (Greenhaven Pr., Inc.).

Taylor, Marian. Harriet Tubman. 2005. (Black Americans of Achievement Ser.). (Illus.). 112p. (J). (gr. 6-12). pap. 13.25 (978-0-7910-8340-6(3) , Chelsea Hse.) Facts On File, Inc.

Waldstreicher, David. The Struggle Against Slavery: A History in Documents. 2001. (Pages from History Ser.). (Illus.). 176p. (gr. 7 up). reprint ed. 36.95 (978-0-19-510850-7(7)) Oxford Univ. Pr., Inc.

Watkins, Richard. Slavery: Bondage throughout History. Watkins, Richard, photos by. 2006. (Illus.). 136p. (J). (gr. 4-8). reprint ed. 18.00 (978-1-4223-5333-2(8)) DIANE Publishing Co.

Williams, Jean Kinney. African-Americans in the Colonies. 2002. (We the People Ser.). (Illus.). 48p. (J). (gr. 4 up). lib. bdg. 22.60 (978-0-7565-0303-1(5)) Compass Point Bks.

Wilson, Camilla. Frederick Douglass: A Voice for Freedom in the 1800s. 2003. (Scholastic Biography Ser.). (Illus.). 90p. (J). pap. (978-0-439-38082-9(0)) Scholastic, Inc.

SLAVERY—FICTION

Altman, Linda Jacobs. The Legend of Freedom Hill. Van Wright, Cornelius, illus. 2003. 32p. (J). (978-1-58430-169-1(4)) Lee & Low Bks., Inc.

—The Legend of Freedom Hill. Van Wright, Cornelius & Hu, Ying-Hwa, illus. 2000. 32p. (J). (ps up). 15.95 (978-1-58430-003-8(5)) Lee & Low Bks., Inc.

—The Legend of Freedom Hill. Van Wright, Cornelius et al, illus. 2004. 32p. (J). (ps-k). lib. bdg. 13.75 (978-0-606-30127-5(5)) Tandem Library Bks.

American Tract Society Staff. Step by Step or Tidy's Way to Freedom. 2006. 50.99 (*978-1-4219-8162-8(9)); pap. 44.99 (*978-1-4219-8160-4(2)) IndyPublish.com.

Anderson, M. T. The Astonishing Life of Octavian Nothing, Traitor to the Nation. 2006. (Pox Party Ser.: Vol. 1). (Illus.). 368p. (YA). (gr. 9). 17.99 (978-0-7636-2402-6(0)) Candlewick Pr.

Anderson, M. T. Astonishing Life of Octavian Nothing, Traitor to the Nation: The Pox Party. rev. l.t. ed. 2007. (Astonishing Life of Octavian Nothing Ser.). 500p. (YA). 23.95 (*978-0-7862-9552-4(X)) Thorndike Pr.

Asim, Jabari. Road to Freedom: A Story of Reconstruction. 2000. (gr. 5-8). lib. bdg. 14.95 (978-0-613-36867-4(3)) Tandem Library Bks.

—The Road to Freedom: A Story of the Reconstruction. 2004. (Jamestown's American Portraits Ser.). (Illus.). 136p. (J). (gr. 5-7). pap. 4.95 (978-0-7696-3432-6(X), Waterbird Bks.) School Specialty Publishing.

Ayres, Katherine. Stealing South: A Story of the Underground Railroad. l.t. ed. 2002. 231p. (J). 22.95 (978-0-7862-4422-5(4)) Thorndike Pr.

Bauer Mueller, Pamela. Neptune's Honor: A Story of Loyalty & Love. 2005. 192p. 16.99 (978-0-9685097-6-0(2)); (Illus.). pap. 10.99 (978-0-9685097-5-3(4)) Pinata Publishing.

Bennerson, Denise. Daniel & the 150th Emancipation Celebration. Vega, Edwin, illus. 2001. 11p. (J). 4.00 (978-0-9646279-5-6(7)) Bennerson, Denise.

Bjerregaard, Marcia. First Heroes for Freedom. Jones, Marty, illus. 2000. (Adventures in America Ser.). 92p. (J). (gr. 3-7). lib. bdg. 14.95 (978-1-893110-17-5(6)) Silver Moon Pr.

Boeve, Eunice. A Window to the World. 2004. 110p. pap. 16.95 (978-1-4137-3212-2(7)) PublishAmerica, Inc.

Booth, Bradley. Plagues in the Palace. 2006. 159p. (J). (978-0-8163-2143-8(4)) Pacific Pr. Publishing Assn.

Brook, Harry, retold by. Kidnapped. 2004. (Paperback Classics Ser.). 144p. (J). lib. bdg. 12.95 (978-1-58086-640-8(9), Usborne) EDC Publishing.

Brown, Marc. D. W. the Big Boss. 2005. (Arthur's 8 x 8 Bks.). (Illus.). 24p. (J). (ps-3). pap. 3.99 (978-0-316-73395-3(4)) Little Brown & Co.

Broyles, Anne. Priscilla & the Hollyhocks. Alter, Anna, illus. 2008. (J). (*978-1-57091-675-5(6)) Charlesbridge Publishing, Inc.

Bugtime Adventures - Blessing in Disguise. 2005. (J). 3.95 (978-1-933262-26-0(5)) Lightning Bug Flix.

Burt, William D. The Greenstones: Book IV of the King of the Trees Series. 2003. 216p. (YA). pap. 14.95 (978-1-57921-671-9(4)) WinePress Publishing.

Carbone, Elisa. Night Running: How James Escaped with the Help of His Faithful Dog. Lewis, Earl, illus. 2007. (J). (978-0-375-82247-6(X)); lib. bdg. (978-0-375-92247-3(4)) Knopf, Alfred A. Inc.

—Stealing Freedom. 2002. (EMC Masterpiece Series Access Editions). (Illus.). xix, 284p. (J). 14.60 (978-0-8219-2507-2(5)) EMC/Paradigm Publishing.

—Stealing Freedom. 2001. (Illus.). 272p. (YA). (gr. 5-8). 5.99 (978-0-440-41707-1(4), Yearling) Random Hse. Children's Bks.

—Stealing Freedom. 2001. (J). (978-0-606-20926-7(3)); (gr. 5-8). lib. bdg. 13.55 (978-0-613-33729-8(1)) Tandem Library Bks.

—Stealing Freedom. l.t. ed. 2005. 346p. pap. 10.95 (978-0-7862-7314-0(3), Large Print Pr.) Thorndike Pr.

Cardenas, Teresa. Old Dog. Unger, David, tr. from SPA. 2007. 144p. (YA). (gr. 7 up). 16.95 (*978-0-88899-757-9(4)) Groundwood Bks. CAN. *Dist:* Perseus Distribution.

—Perro Viejo. Unger, David, tr. 2007. (SPA.). 144p. (gr. 7 up). 16.95 (*978-0-88899-758-6(2)) Groundwood Bks. CAN. *Dist:* Perseus Distribution.

Chambers, Veronica. Amistad Rising: A Story of Freedom. 1998. (Illus.). 40p. (J). (gr. 4-7). lib. bdg. (978-0-8172-5510-7(9)) Raintree.

Chbosky, Stacy. Who Owns the Sun? Chbosky, Stacy, illus. 2002. (Illus.). 32p. (J). (gr. 4-7). per. 19.95 (978-0-933849-82-2(6)) Landmark Editions, Inc.

Chimombo, S. Bird Boy's Song. 2004. 91p. 13.95 (978-99908-48-07-6(6)) Wasi Pubns. ZWE. *Dist:* Michigan State Univ. Pr.

Coatsworth, Elizabeth Jane. The White Horse. Sewell, Helen, illus. 2005. 169p. (J). pap. 11.95 (978-1-883937-86-7(8)) Bethlehem Bks.

Coleman, Evelyn. To Be a Drum. Robinson, Aminah B., illus. 1998. 32p. (YA). (gr. k-3). lib. bdg. 16.95 (978-0-8075-8006-6(6)) Whitman, Albert & Co.

—To Be a Drum. Robinson, Aminah B., illus. 2004. 32p. (J). (gr. k up). pap. 6.95 (978-0-8075-8007-3(4)) Whitman, Albert & Co.

Connelly, Bernardine. Follow the Drinking Gourd. Buchanan, Yvonne, illus. 2005. (Rabbit Ears-A Classic Tale Ser.). 40p. (J). (gr. k-5). 25.65 (978-1-59197-763-6(0)) Spotlight.

Curry, Kenneth. The Legend of the Dancing Trees: An African American Folk Tale. 2007. 111p. (J). per. 14.95 (*978-0-9798364-0-4(9)) Curry Brothers Publishing.

Curry, Kenneth, et al. The Legend of the Dancing Tees Teachers Resource: The Legend of the Dancing Trees. 2007. Tr. of Teachers Resource. per. 19.95 (*978-0-9798364-1-1(7)) Curry Brothers Publishing.

Curtis, Christopher Paul. Elijah of Buxton. 2007. (J). (*978-0-439-02345-0(9)); 352p. (gr. 4-7). 16.99 (*978-0-439-02344-3(0), Scholastic Pr.) Scholastic, Inc.

Dahlberg, Maurine F. The Spirit & Gilly Bucket. 2002. 240p. (J). (gr. 3-7). 18.00 (978-0-374-31677-8(5), Farrar, Straus & Giroux (BYR)) Farrar, Straus & Giroux.

—The Story of Jonas. 2007. (Illus.). 160p. (J). (gr. 4-7). 16.00 (978-0-374-37264-4(0), Farrar, Straus & Giroux (BYR)) Farrar, Straus & Giroux.

De Angeli, Marguerite. Thee, Hannah! De Angeli, Marguerite, illus. 2nd ed. 2000. (Illus.). 112p. (J). (gr. 3-7). pap. 15.99 (978-0-8361-9106-6(4)) Herald Pr.

Dell, Pamela. Aquila's Drinking Gourd: A Story of the Underground Railroad. 2002. (Scrapbooks of America Ser.). (Illus.). 48p. (J). (gr. 2-6). 28.50 (978-1-59187-013-5(5)) Child's World, Inc.

Denenberg, Barry. Atticus of Rome, 30 B. C. 2004. (Life & Times Ser.). 176p. (J). (gr. 4-7). pap. 10.95 (978-0-439-52453-7(9)) Scholastic, Inc.

Downey, Glen. Gladiators. 2007. (Illus.). 48p. (J). lib. bdg. 23.08 (*978-1-4242-1627-7(3)) Fitzgerald Bks.

Draper, Sharon M. Copper Sun. (YA). 2008. 336p. pap. 8.99 (*978-1-4169-5348-7(5), Simon Pulse); 2006. 320p. (gr. 8 up). 16.95 (978-0-689-82181-3(6), Atheneum) Simon & Schuster Children's Publishing.

—Copper Sun. l.t. ed. 2006. 358p. (YA). (gr. 8 up). 22.95 (978-0-7862-8948-6(1)) Thorndike Pr.

Duey, Kathleen. Silence & Lily: 1773. 2007. 176p. (J). (gr. 5). pap. 5.99 (*978-0-14-240909-1(X), Puffin) Penguin Group (USA) Inc.

Duey, Kathleen. Summer MacCleary: Virginia, 1749. 1998. (American Diaries Ser.: Vol. 10). (J). (gr. 3-7). (978-0-606-13120-9(5)) Tandem Library Bks.

Elliott, L. M. Annie, Between the States. 2006. 544p. (J). pap. 6.99 (978-0-06-001213-7(7), Harper Trophy) HarperCollins Pubs.

Elliott, Laura Malone. Annie, Between the States. 2004. (Illus.). 496p. (J). (gr. 7 up). 16.99 (978-0-06-001211-3(0)); lib. bdg. 16.89 (978-0-06-001212-0(9)) HarperCollins Pubs.

Endore, Guy. Babouk. rev. ed. (Voices of Resistance Ser.). 352p. (YA). (gr. 9-12). 35.00 (978-0-85345-759-6(X)) Monthly Review Pr.

Farhat-Holzman, Laina, tr. The Slave Who Lied but Once a Year & Other Persian Tales. 2001. (YA). per. 15.00 (978-1-58684-119-5(X)) Global Academic Publishing.

Ferris, Jean. Underground. 2007. (Illus.). 176p. (J). (gr. 7 up). 16.00 (*978-0-374-37243-9(8), Farrar, Straus & Giroux (BYR)) Farrar, Straus & Giroux.

Fleischman, Sid. The Whipping Boy. 2002. (Illus.). (J). 12.83 (978-0-7587-0225-8(6)) Book Wholesalers, Inc.

—The Whipping Boy. Sís, Peter, illus. 2003. (HarperClassics Ser.). 96p. (J). (gr. 3 up). pap. 5.99 (978-0-06-052122-6(8), Harper Trophy) HarperCollins Pubs.

Fleischner, Jennifer. Nobody's Boy. 2006. (Illus.). 96p. (J). pap. 12.95 (978-1-883982-58-4(8)) Missouri Historical Society Pr.

Fox, Paula. The Slave Dancer. Eros, Keith, illus. 2002. (J). 14.47 (978-0-7587-0214-2(0)) Book Wholesalers, Inc.

—The Slave Dancer. 1998. (Assessment Packs Ser.). 15p. pap., tchr.'s training gde. ed. 15.95 (978-1-58303-061-5(1)) Pathways Publishing.

—The Slave Dancer. unabr. ed. 2004. 152p. (J). (gr. 5-9). pap. 38.00 incl. audio (978-0-8072-0458-0(7), Listening Library) Random Hse. Audio Publishing Group.

—The Slave Dancer. Keith, Eros, illus. 2001. 192p. (YA). 18.99 (978-0-689-84505-5(7), Atheneum/Richard Jackson Bks.) Simon & Schuster Children's Publishing.

Freed, Shirley Ann & Moon, Louise. Joseph's Dream. Morelan, Bill, ed. Butler, Steven, illus. l.t. ed. 2002. 24p. (J). (gr. 7). pap. 3.99 (978-1-58938-043-1(6)) Concerned Communications.

Gavin, Jamila. Coram Boy. 336p. (YA). 2001. (Illus.). (gr. 7-9). 19.00 (978-0-374-31544-3(2), Farrar, Straus & Giroux (BYR)); 2005. reprint ed. pap. 7.95 (978-0-374-41374-3(6), Sunburst) Farrar, Straus & Giroux.

Gayle, Sharon Shavers. Emma's Escape: A Story of America's Underground Railroad. Velasquez, Eric, illus. 3rd ed. 2005. (Soundprints' Read-and-Discover Ser.). 48p. (J). (gr. 2-4). pap. 3.95 (978-1-59249-021-9(2), S2009) Soundprints.

—Escape! A Story of the Underground Railroad. Velasquez, Eric, illus. 1999. (Smithsonian Odyssey Ser.: Vol. 11). 32p. (J). (gr. 2-5). 14.95 (978-1-56899-622-6(5), B6009); (ps-3). pap. 5.95 (978-1-56899-623-3(3)) Soundprints.

—Harriet Tubman & the Freedom Train. 2003. (gr. 3-6). lib. bdg. 11.80 (978-0-613-61560-0(3)) Tandem Library Bks.

Geary, Judith. Getorix: The Eagle & the Bull. 2006. (Illus.). 278p. 24.95 (978-1-932158-74-8(X)) Ingalls Publishing Group, Inc.

Graafland, Monique Fijtje. 1774: Freedom Wanted. 2002. (ENG.). 96p. pap. (*978-1-55306-393-3(7)) Essence Publishing.

Grifalconi, Ann. The Village That Vanished. Nelson, Kadir A., illus. 2002. 40p. (J). (gr. k up). 16.99 (978-0-8037-2623-9(6), Dial) Penguin Group (USA) Inc.

Guzman, Lila. Lorenzo's Secret Mission. 2001. (gr. 3-6). lib. bdg. 18.75 (978-0-613-84747-6(4)) Tandem Library Bks.

Guzman, Lila & Guzman, Rick. Lorenzo's Secret Mission. 160p. (YA). pap. 9.95 (978-1-55885-341-6(3), Piñata Books) Arte Publico Pr.

Hahn, Mary Downing. Promises to the Dead. 2000. 208p. (J). (gr. 5-9). tchr. ed. 15.00 (978-0-395-96394-4(X), Clarion Bks.) Houghton Mifflin Co. Trade & Reference Div.

Haislip, Phyllis Hall. Lottie's Courage: A Contraband Slave's Story. 2003. (Illus.). 120p. (J). pap. 7.95 (978-1-57249-311-7(9), White Mane Kids) White Mane Publishing Co., Inc.

Hamilton, Virginia. The People Could Fly: The Picture Book. Dillon, Leo & Dillon, Diane, illus. 32p. (J). 2007. audio compact disk 20.99 (*978-0-375-94553-3(9)); 2004. 16.95 (978-0-375-82405-0(7)) Random Hse. Children's Bks. (Knopf Bks. for Young Readers).

—The People Could Fly Picture. Dillon, Leo & Dillon, Diane, illus. 2007. 32p. (J). 17.99 incl. audio compact disk (*978-0-375-84553-6(4), Knopf Bks. for Young Readers) Random Hse. Children's Bks.

Hart, Alison. Gabriel's Horses. 2007. 224p. (J). (gr. 3-7). 14.95 (*978-1-56145-398-6(6), Peachtree Junior) Peachtree Pubs., Ltd.

Hegamin, Tonya. Most Loved in All the World. Cohen, Lisa, illus. 2010. (J). (978-0-618-41903-6(9)) Houghton Mifflin Co.

Helmer, Diana Star. Give Me Liberty. Aspengren, Michael A. & Hatala, Dan, illus. 1999. (Cover-to-Cover Historical Moments Bks.). 56p. (J). (gr. 1-4). lib. bdg. 16.95 (978-0-7807-9042-1(1), Covercraft); (gr. 3-6). pap. 8.95 (978-0-7891-5078-3(6)) Perfection Learning Corp.

Hill, Pamela Smith. A Voice from the Border. 2000. (J). (978-0-606-20004-2(5)) Tandem Library Bks.

Hopkinson, Deborah. From Slave to Soldier: Based on a True Civil War Story. Floca, Brian, illus. (Ready-to-Reads Ser.). 48p. (J). 2007. pap. 3.99 (978-0-689-83966-5(9), Aladdin); 2005. 14.95 (978-0-689-83965-8(0), Atheneum) Simon & Schuster Children's Publishing.

—Sweet Clara & the Freedom Quilt. Ransome, James E., illus. 2003. 40p. (J). (gr. k-5). 15.95 (978-0-679-82311-7(5), Knopf Bks. for Young Readers) Random Hse. Children's Bks.

Houston, Gloria M. Bright Freedom's Song: A Story of the Underground Railroad. 1998. (Illus.). 160p. (YA). (gr. 5 up). 17.00 (978-0-15-201812-2(3), Silver Whistle) Harcourt Trade Pubs.

Hulme, Lucy V. Passages, 1 bk. Redpath, Dale, illus. 2005. 40p. (J). 7.95 (978-0-9769854-0-2(3), 001) Combs-Hulme Publishing.

Hurmence, Belinda. A Girl Called Boy. 2006. 176p. (J). (gr. 4-6). pap. 5.95 (978-0-618-68925-5(7), Clarion Bks.) Houghton Mifflin Co. Trade & Reference Div.

Jacques, Brian. Voyage of Slaves. (Castaways of the Flying Dutchman Ser.: No. 3). 2007. 320p. (gr. 12). mass mkt. 7.99 (*978-0-441-01528-3(X), Ace Bks.); 2006. (Illus.). 368p. (YA). (gr. 5). 23.99 (978-0-399-24549-7(9), Philomel) Penguin Group (USA) Inc.

Johnson, Dolores. Now Let Me Fly: The Story of a Slave Family. 1998. pap. 5.99 (978-0-87628-977-8(4)) Ctr. for Applied Research in Education, The.

Johnson, Lois Walfrid. Raider's Promise. 2006. (Raiders from the Sea Ser.). (Illus.). 304p. (J). pap. 8.99 (978-0-8024-3116-5(X)) Moody Pubs.

Johnson, Nancy. A Sweet-Sounding Place: A Civil War Story. 2007. 160p. (gr. 5-9). 14.95 (*978-0-89272-757-5(8)) Down East Bks.

Johnston, Tony. The Wagon. 1999. (Illus.). 40p. (J). (ps-3). pap. 5.95 (978-0-688-16694-6(6)) HarperCollins Pubs.

—Wagon. 1999. (978-0-606-16677-5(7)) Tandem Library Bks.

Jones, Joyce Elaine. For Such a Journey. 2005. (J). 5.99 (978-0-9766559-0-9(X)) Treorca Pr.

Kay, Alan N. Send 'Em South. 2001. (Young Heroes of History Ser.: Vol. 1). (Illus.). 145p. (J). (gr. 3-6). pap. 7.95 (978-1-57249-208-0(2), White Mane Kids) White Mane Publishing Co., Inc.

Kirby, Susan E. Hattie's Story. 2000. (American Quilts Ser.: Vol. 2). (J). 11.64 (978-0-606-20080-6(0)) Tandem Library Bks.

Kirkpatrick, Katherine. Escape Across the Wide Sea. 2004. (Illus.). 224p. (J). (gr. 4-6). tchr. ed. 17.95 (978-0-8234-1854-1(5)) Holiday Hse., Inc.

Lasky, Kathryn. The Last Girls of Pompeii. 2007. 160p. (J). (gr. 5 up). 15.99 (978-0-670-06196-9(4), Viking Juvenile) Penguin Group (USA) Inc.

—True North: A Novel of the Underground Railroad. 1998. (J). (978-0-606-13874-1(9)) Tandem Library Bks.

Lawrence, Caroline. The Colossus of Rhodes. 2006. (Roman Mysteries Ser.). (Illus.). 208p. (J). 16.95 (978-1-59643-082-2(6)) Roaring Brook Pr.

—Pirates of Pompeii, Vol. 3. 2004. (Roman Mysteries Ser.: No. 3). (Illus.). 176p. (J). (gr. 3). pap. 5.99 (978-0-14-240227-6(3), Puffin) Penguin Group (USA) Inc.

Lawrence, Iain. The Castaways. 2007. 256p. (YA). (gr. 7). lib. bdg. 18.99 (*978-0-385-90112-3(7), Delacorte Bks. for Young Readers) Random Hse. Children's Bks.

Lester, Julius. Day of Tears. 2007. 192p. (gr. 7 up). pap. 7.99 (*978-1-4231-0409-4(9), Jump at the Sun) Hyperion Bks. for Children.

—Day of Tears: A Novel in Dialogue. 2005. 192p. (gr. 4-8). 15.99 (978-0-7868-0490-0(4), Jump at the Sun) Hyperion Bks. for Children.

—The Old African. Pinkney, Jerry, illus. 2005. 80p. (J). (gr. 3). 19.99 (978-0-8037-2564-5(7), Dial) Penguin Group (USA) Inc.

—This Strange New Feeling: Three Love Stories from Black History. 2006. 208p. (YA). 16.99 (978-0-8037-3172-1(8), Dial) Penguin Group (USA) Inc.

—Time's Memory. 2006. (Illus.). 240p. (YA). 17.00 (978-0-374-37178-4(4), Farrar, Straus & Giroux (BYR)) Farrar, Straus & Giroux.

Levine, Ellen. Henry's Freedom Box: A True Story. Nelson, Kadir, illus. 2007. 40p. (J). (ps-3). pap. 16.99 (978-0-439-77733-9(X), Scholastic Pr.) Scholastic, Inc.

Levitin, Sonia. Clem's Chances. 2001. (Illus.). 208p. (J). (gr. 2-7). pap. 17.95 (978-0-439-29314-3(6), Orchard Bks.) Scholastic, Inc.

Literature Connections English: I, Juan de Pareja. 2004. (gr. 6-12). (978-0-395-77531-8(0), 2-80100) McDougal Littell Inc.

Literature Connections English: The Autobiography of Miss Jane Pittman. 2004. (gr. 6-12). (978-0-395-86993-2(5), 2-70829) McDougal Littell Inc.

Literature Connections English: The House of Dies Drear. 2004. (gr. 6-12). (978-0-395-77523-3(X), 2-80092) McDougal Littell Inc.

Lutz, Norma Jean. Escape from Slavery: A Family's Fight for Freedom. 1999. (American Adventure Ser.: No. 16). 144p. (J). (gr. 3-7). 11.95 (978-0-7910-5590-8(6), Chelsea Hse.) Facts On File, Inc.

Lynch, Marcia. United in Freedom. Cornelison, Sue F., illus. 2000. (Cover-to-Cover Bks.). 92p. (J). pap. (978-0-7891-5102-5(2)); (gr. 2-5). lib. bdg. 13.95 (978-0-7807-9068-1(5)) Perfection Learning Corp.

Lyons, Mary E. Letters from a Slave Boy: The Story of Joseph Jacobs. 2007. 208p. (YA). (gr. 4-8). 15.99 (978-0-689-87867-1(2), Atheneum) Simon & Schuster Children's Publishing.

—Letters from a Slave Girl: The Story of Harriet Jacobs. 2007. 192p. (YA). pap. 5.99 (978-1-4169-3637-4(8), Simon Pulse) Simon & Schuster Children's Publishing.

—Letters from Slave Girl. 1998. (J). pap. 3.95 (978-0-87628-518-3(3)) Ctr. for Applied Research in Education, The.

—Poison Place. 1999. (978-0-606-16334-7(4)) Tandem Library Bks.

Lyons, Mary E. & Branch, Muriel M. Dear Ellen Bee: A Civil War Scrapbook of Two Union Spies. Tauss, Marc, illus. 2000. 176p. (J). (gr. 4 up). 21.99 (978-0-689-82379-4(7), Atheneum) Simon & Schuster Children's Publishing.

MacHado, Ana Maria. Del Otro Lado Hay Secretos. (SPA.). pap. 11.95 (978-950-07-2221-6(6)) Editorial Sudamericana S.A. ARG. *Dist:* Distribooks, Inc.

—From Another World. Baeta, Luisa, tr. from POR. Brandao, Lucia, illus. 2005. 128p. (J). pap. 6.95 (978-0-88899-641-1(1)); 15.95 (978-0-88899-597-1(0)) Groundwood Bks. CAN. *Dist:* Perseus Distribution.

Masters, Anthony. The Desert Pirates. Buckley, Harriet, illus. 2008. (J). pap. (*978-1-59889-906-1(6)); lib. bdg. (*978-1-59889-870-5(1)) Stone Arch Bks.

Masters, Susan Rowan. Night Journey to Vicksburg. Killcoyne, Hope L., ed. Smith, Duane A., illus. 2003. (Adventures in America Ser.). 74p. (J). 14.95 (978-1-893110-30-4(3)) Silver Moon Pr.

Matas, Carol. The War Within: A Novel of the Civil War. l.t. ed. 2003. (J). 22.95 (978-0-7862-5499-6(8)) Thorndike Pr.

McCormick, Patricia. Sold. 2006. 272p. (gr. 7 up). 15.99 (978-0-7868-5171-3(6)) Hyperion Pr.

McCully, Emily Arnold. The Escape of Oney Judge: Martha Washington's Slave Finds Freedom. 2007. (Illus.). 32p. (J). (gr. 1). 16.00 (978-0-374-32225-0(2), Farrar, Straus & Giroux (BYR)) Farrar, Straus & Giroux.

McKissack, Patricia C. Look to the Hills: Diary of Lozette Moreau, a French Slave Girl, New York Colony 1763. 2004. (Dear America Ser.). (Illus.). 192p. (J). pap. 10.95 (978-0-439-21038-6(0)) Scholastic, Inc.

—A Picture of Freedom: The Diary of Clotee, a Slave Girl, Belmont Plantation, Virginia, 1859. 1999. (Dear America Ser.). (J). 9.95 (978-0-439-15599-1(1)) Scholastic, Inc.

McKissack, Patricia C. & McKissack, Fredrick L. Christmas in the Big House: Christmas in the Quarters. Thompson, John, illus. 2002. 80p. (J). pap. 6.99 (978-0-590-43028-9(9)) Scholastic, Inc.

McKissack, Patricia C. & McKissack, Fredrick L., Jr. Let My People Go: Bible Stories Told by a Freeman of Color. Ransome, James E., illus. 1998. 144p. (YA). (gr. 4-7). 21.99 (978-0-689-80856-2(9), Atheneum/Anne Schwartz Bks.) Simon & Schuster Children's Publishing.

McMullan, Margaret. How I Found the Strong. 2004. 144p. (J). (gr. 5-9). tchr. ed. 15.00 (978-0-618-35008-7(X)) Houghton Mifflin Co. Trade & Reference Div.

—How I Found the Strong. 2006. 144p. (YA). (gr. 7). reprint ed. mass mkt. 5.50 (978-0-553-49492-1(9), Laurel Leaf) Random Hse. Children's Bks.

Meltzer, Milton. Underground Man. 2006. 288p. (YA). pap. 5.95 (978-0-15-205524-0(X), Odyssey Classics); (Illus.). 17.00 (978-0-15-205518-9(5), Harcourt Young Classics) Harcourt Children's Bks.

Mitchell, Betsy. Journey to the Bottomless Pit: The Story of Stephen Bishop & Mammoth Cave. 2004. (Illus.). 128p. (J). (gr. 3-7). 15.99 (978-0-670-05908-9(0), Viking Juvenile) Penguin Group (USA) Inc.

Morrow, Barbara Olenyik. A Good Night for Freedom. Jenkins, Leonard, illus. 2003. 32p. (J). (gr. k-3). tchr. ed. 16.95 (978-0-8234-1709-4(3)) Holiday Hse., Inc.

S

Moses, Shelia P. The Baptism. 2007. 144p. (YA). (gr. 7 up). 15.99 (978-1-4169-0671-1(1) , McElderry, Margaret K.) Simon & Schuster Children's Publishing.

—I, Dred Scott: A Fictional Slave Narrative Based on the Life & Legal Precedent of Dred Scott. Christensen, Bonnie, illus. 2005. 112p. (YA). (gr. 7 up). 16.95 (978-0-689-85975-5(9) , McElderry, Margaret K.) Simon & Schuster Children's Publishing.

Mosley, Walter. 47. 240p. (gr. 7-17). 2005. (YA). 16.99 (978-0-316-11035-8(3)); 2006. (J). reprint ed. pap. 7.99 (978-0-316-01635-3(7)) Little Brown & Co.

Moss, Marissa. Galen: My Life in Imperial Rome. Moss, Marissa, illus. 2002. (Ancient World Journals). (Illus.). 48p. (YA). (gr. 3-7). 15.00 (978-0-15-216535-2(5) , Silver Whistle) Harcourt Trade Pubs.

Mussi, Sarah. The Door of No Return. 2008. (YA). (***978-1-4169-1550-8(8)** , McElderry, Margaret K.) Simon & Schuster Children's Publishing.

Myers, Walter Dean. The Glory Field. 1999. 420p. (J). 15.60 (978-0-03-054616-7(8)) Holt, Rinehart & Winston.

Napoli, Donna Jo. Hush: An Irish Princess' Tale. 2007. 320p. (YA). (gr. 7 up). 16.99 (***978-0-689-86176-5(1))** Simon & Schuster Children's Publishing.

Nelson, Vaunda Micheaux. Almost to Freedom. Bootman, Colin, illus. 2003. (Carolrhoda Picture Books Ser.). 40p. (J). (gr. 1-5). 15.95 (978-1-57505-342-4(X)) Lerner Publishing Group.

Nicholson, William. Slaves of the Mastery. Sis, Peter, illus. 2001. (Wind on Fire Trilogy: Bk. 2). 448p. (gr. 5-9). 17.99 (978-0-7868-0570-9(6)) Hyperion Bks. for Children.

Night of the Witches: The Beginnings, 8. 2002. 113p. (YA). mass mkt. 4.99 (978-0-9667232-1-2(X) , 152091) Rhapsody Branding, Inc.

Nixon, Joan Lowery. Caesar's Story, 1759. 2004. (J). (978-0-87935-199-1(3)) Colonial Williamsburg Foundation.

—Will's Story, 1771. 2004. (J). (978-0-87935-226-4(4)) Colonial Williamsburg Foundation.

Nolen, Jerdine. Big Jabe. Nelson, Kadir A., illus. 32p. (J). (gr. 1 up). 2004. pap. 6.99 (978-0-06-054061-6(3) , Amistad); 2000. 16.89 (978-0-688-13663-5(X)) HarperCollins Pubs.

—Big Jabe. 2004. (gr. k-3). lib. bdg. 15.30 (978-0-613-71462-4(8)) Tandem Library Bks.

Orzechowski, Shaween. Midnight Journey: Running for Freedom on the Underground Railroad. 2006. (J). pap. 8.95 (978-1-57249-379-7(8) , White Mane Kids) White Mane Publishing Co., Inc.

Pace, Lorenzo. Jalani & the Lock. 2001. (Jalani & the Lock Ser.). (Illus.). 24p. (J). lib. bdg. 23.95 (978-0-8239-9700-8(6) , PowerKids Pr.) Rosen Publishing Group, Inc., The.

Paterson, Katherine. Jip, His Story. (gr. 5-9). 2005. 192p. (YA). pap. 5.99 (978-0-14-240411-9(X)); 1998. 208p. (J). pap. 6.99 (978-0-14-038674-5(2)) Penguin Group (USA) Inc. (Puffin).

Paulsen, Gary. The Legend of Bass Reeves. 2006. 160p. (YA). (gr. 7). 15.95 (978-0-385-74661-8(X)); lib. bdg. 17.99 (978-0-385-90898-6(9)) Random Hse. Children's Bks. (Lamb, Wendy).

—Nightjohn: El Esclavo Que Me Enseno a Leer. 2003. (SPA., Illus.). 72p. (YA). (gr. 5-8). (978-84-8453-003-9(5) , PT2562) Ediciones del Bronce ESP. *Dist:* Lectorum Pubns., Inc.

—Sarny. 1999. 192p. (YA). (gr. 7-12). mass mkt. 5.99 (978-0-440-21973-6(6) , Laurel Leaf) Random Hse. Children's Bks.

—Sarny. 1999. (gr. 7-12). lib. bdg. 13.55 (978-0-613-19444-0(6)) Tandem Library Bks.

—Sarny: A Life Remembered. 1999. (978-0-606-16454-2(5)) Tandem Library Bks.

Pearsall, Shelley. Trouble Don't Last. 256p. (gr. 4-8). 2002. (Illus.). 14.95 (978-0-375-81490-7(6) , Knopf Bks. for Young Readers); 2002. (Illus.). lib. bdg. 16.99 (978-0-375-91490-4(0) , Knopf Bks. for Young Readers); 2003. (J). reprint ed. pap. 5.99 (978-0-440-41811-5(9) , Yearling) Random Hse. Children's Bks.

—Trouble Don't Last. 2003. (gr. 3-6). lib. bdg. 13.55 (978-0-613-85706-2(2)) Tandem Library Bks.

Pferdehirt, Julia, et al. David Livingstone: Escape from the Slave Traders. 2000. (Trailblazer Bks.). (Illus.). 24p. (J). pap., stu. ed. 4.99 (978-0-7642-2346-4(1)) Bethany Hse. Pubs.

Pinkney, Andrea Davis. Abraham Lincoln: Letters from a Young Slave Girl. 2001. (Dear Mr. President Ser.). (Illus.). 136p. (J). (gr. 4-7). 8.95 (978-1-890817-60-2(0)) Winslow Pr.

—Silent Thunder: A Civil War Story. 2001. (gr. 5-8). lib. bdg. 14.15 (978-0-613-62425-1(4)) Tandem Library Bks.

Polisar, Barry Louis. Stolen Man: The Story of the Amistad Rebellion. 2007. 32p. (J). (gr. 3-5). pap. 7.95 (***978-0-938663-50-8(X))** Rainbow Morning Music Alternatives.

Pryor, Bonnie. Joseph: 1861 - A Rumble of War. Dodson, Bert, illus. 1999. (American Adventures Ser.). 176p. (J). (gr. 3-7). 14.95 (978-0-688-15671-8(1)) HarperCollins Pubs.

—Joseph: 1861 - A Rumble of War. 2000. (Illus.). (J). (978-0-606-17975-1(5)) Tandem Library Bks.

—Joseph: 1861—A Rumble of War. 2000. (American Adventures Ser.). (Illus.). 176p. (J). (gr. 3-7). pap. 4.50 (978-0-380-73103-9(7) , Harper Trophy) HarperCollins Pubs.

—Joseph's Choice 1861. Dodson, Bert, illus. 2000. (American Adventures Ser.). 176p. (J). (gr. 3 up). 14.89 (978-0-06-029226-3(1)) HarperCollins Pubs.

Rappaport, Doreen. Freedom River. Collier, Bryan, illus. 2007. 23p. (J). 15.00 (***978-1-4223-6700-1(2))** DIANE Publishing Co.

Reed, Jennifer. Hadi's Journey. 2003. 110p. pap. 10.95 (978-0-595-29375-9(1)) iUniverse, Inc.

Reed, Stephanie. Across the Wide River: A Novel. 2004. 176p. (J). pap. 9.99 (978-0-8254-3576-8(5)) Kregel Pubns.

Reeder, Carolyn. Across the Lines. 1998. 224p. (J). (gr. 4-7). pap. 5.99 (978-0-380-73073-5(1) , Harper Trophy) HarperCollins Pubs.

Rees, Douglas. Lightning Time. 1999. (J). (978-0-606-19069-5(4)) Tandem Library Bks.

Riggio, Anita. Secret Signs: An Escape Through the Underground Railroad. Riggio, Anita, illus. 2003. (Illus.). 32p. (J). (gr. k-2). pap. 9.95 (978-1-59078-072-5(8)) Boyds Mills Pr.

—Secret Signs: An Escape Through the Underground Railroad. 2003. (gr. k-3). lib. bdg. 17.60 (978-0-613-59359-5(6)) Tandem Library Bks.

Riley, Lehman, et al. The Adventures of Papa Lemon's Little Wanderers Bk. 2: The Dangerous Escape from Slavery. 2005. 52p. pap. 5.99 (978-0-9760523-1-9(8)) Matter of Africa America Time.

Rinaldi, Ann. Come Juneteenth. 2007. (Great Episodes Ser.). (Illus.). 256p. (YA). 17.00 (978-0-15-205947-7(4)) Harcourt Children's Bks.

—Taking Liberty: The Story of Oney Judge, George Washington's Runaway Slave. Dudash, C. Michael, illus. 2004. 272p. (YA). mass mkt. 5.99 (978-0-689-85188-9(X) , Simon Pulse) Simon & Schuster Children's Publishing.

—Taking Liberty: The Story of Oney Judge, George Washington's Runaway Slave. 2002. 272p. (YA). (gr. 7 up). 16.95 (978-0-689-85187-2(1)) Simon & Schuster Children's Publishing.

—Taking Liberty: The Story of Oney Judge, George Washington's Runaway Slave. 2004. (gr. 7-12). lib. bdg. 14.15 (978-0-613-73369-4(X)) Tandem Library Bks.

—An Unlikely Friendship: A Novel of Mary Todd Lincoln & Elizabeth Keckley. 2007. (Harcourt Great Episodes Ser.). (Illus.). 256p. (YA). (gr. 6-9). 17.00 (978-0-15-205597-4(5)) Harcourt Children's Bks.

Ringgold, Faith. The Invisible Princess. 2001. 13.79 (978-0-606-20729-4(5)) Tandem Library Bks.

Riordan, James. Rebel Cargo. 2007. 300p. (gr. 4 up). (YA). pap. 7.95 (***978-1-84507-525-0(0));** (Illus.). (J). 16.95 (***978-1-84507-774-7(1))** Lincoln, Frances Ltd. GBR. *Dist:* Perseus Distribution.

Roberts, Judson. Viking Warrior. (Strongbow Saga Ser.: Bk. 1). 368p. 2007. (J). pap. 7.99 (***978-0-06-079999-1(4)** , HarperTeen); 2006. (Illus.). (YA). 16.99 (978-0-06-079996-0(X)); Bk. 1. 2006. (Illus.). (YA). lib. bdg. 17.89 (978-0-06-079997-7(8)) HarperCollins Pubs.

Robinet, Harriette Gillem. Forty Acres & Maybe a Mule. 2000. (gr. 3-6). lib. bdg. 13.00 (978-0-613-22986-9(X)) Tandem Library Bks.

Roddy, Lee. Risking the Dream. 2000. (Between Two Flags Ser.: Vol. 6). (Illus.). 176p. (J). (gr. 6-9). pap. 5.99 (978-0-7642-2030-2(6)) Bethany Hse. Pubs.

Ruby, Lois. Steal Away Home. 1999. 208p. (J). (gr. 3-7). pap. 5.99 (978-0-689-82435-7(1) , Aladdin) Simon & Schuster Children's Publishing.

—Steal Away Home. 1999. 192p. lib. bdg. 11.64 (978-0-606-15921-0(5)); (gr. 3-6). lib. bdg. 13.00 (978-0-613-12154-5(6)) Tandem Library Bks.

Rue, Nancy N. The Ally. 1998. (Christian Heritage Ser.). 192p. (J). (gr. 3-7). pap. (978-1-56179-561-1(5)) Focus on the Family Publishing.

—The Escape. 1998. (Christian Heritage Ser.). 192p. (J). (gr. 3-7). pap. 5.99 (978-1-56179-639-7(5)) Bethany Hse. Pubs.

—The Hostage. 1998. (Christian Heritage Ser.). 208p. (J). (gr. 3-7). pap. 5.99 (978-1-56179-638-0(7)) Bethany Hse. Pubs.

—The Misfit. 1998. (Christian Heritage Ser.). 192p. (J). (gr. 3-7). pap. (978-1-56179-560-4(7)) Focus on the Family Publishing.

—The Threat. 1998. (Christian Heritage Ser.). 208p. (J). (gr. 3-7). pap. (978-1-56179-566-6(6)) Focus on the Family Publishing.

—The Trap. 1998. (Christian Heritage Ser.). 208p. (J). (gr. 3-7). pap. (978-1-56179-567-3(4)) Focus on the Family Publishing.

Sargent, Dave & Sargent, Pat. Cassidy: (Dark Bucksin) Equal Rights for All, 30, 11. Lenoir, Jane, illus. 2001. (Saddle Up Ser.: 11). 36p. (J). lib. bdg. 22.60 (978-1-56763-669-7(1)) Ozark Publishing.

Schlabach, Janet. Riverboat Runaways. 1999. (Illus.). 138p. (J). (gr. 4-8). pap. 15.95 (978-0-936389-75-2(3)) Tudor Pubs., Inc.

Schotter, Roni & Dorling Kindersley Publishing Staff. F Is for Freedom. Mordan, C. B., illus. 2000. 96p. (J). (gr. 2-5). 15.99 (978-0-7894-2641-3(2)) Dorling Kindersley Publishing, Inc.

Schraff, Anne. Freedom Knows No Color. 2000. 118p. (J). pap. (978-0-7891-5136-0(7)); (gr. 5-12). lib. bdg. 13.95 (978-0-7807-9270-8(X)) Perfection Learning Corp.

Schwabach, Karen. A Pickpocket's Tale. 240p. (J). (gr. 3-7). 2008. 5.99 (***978-0-375-83380-9(3)** , Yearling); 2006. (Illus.). 15.95 (978-0-375-83379-3(X) , Random Hse. Bks. for Young Readers) Random Hse. Children's Bks.

Schwartz, Virginia Frances. If I Just Had Two Wings. (Illus.). 221p. pap. 9.95 (978-0-7737-6192-6(6)); 2001. (J). (gr. 5 up). 15.95 (978-0-7737-3302-2(7)) Stoddart Kids CAN. *Dist:* Fitzhenry & Whiteside, Ltd.

Shaik, Fatima. Melitte. 2000. (978-0-606-18432-8(5)) Tandem Library Bks.

Siegelson, Kim L. Escape South. Jackson, Shelley, illus. 2004. (Road to Reading Ser.). 80p. (J). (gr. k-3). pap. 3.99 (978-0-307-26504-3(8) , Random Hse. Bks. for Young Readers) Random Hse. Children's Bks.

—Escape South. 2000. (J). 10.79 (978-0-606-18931-6(9)) Tandem Library Bks.

—In the Time of the Drums. Pinkney, Brian, illus. 1999. (Jump at the Sun Bks.). 32p. (gr. 1-4). 15.99 (978-0-7868-0436-8(X)) Hyperion Bks. for Children.

Slave Dancer. 1999. (YA). 9.95 (978-1-56137-133-4(5)) Novel Units, Inc.

Smalls, Irene. A Strawbeater's Thanksgiving. Rosales, Meodye, illus. 1998. 32p. (J). (gr. 2-5). 15.95 (978-0-316-79866-2(5)) Little Brown & Co.

Smith, Grant Callie. Janie's Freedom: African-Americans in the Aftermath of the Civil War. 2006. 144p. (J). pap. 4.97 (978-1-59789-086-1(3)) Barbour Publishing, Inc.

Smucker, Barbara. Underground to Canada. 25th anniv. ed. 1999. (Illus.). 144p. (J). (gr. 3-9). (978-0-14-130686-5(6)) Penguin Group (USA) Inc.

Something Upstairs. 2002. (Avi Ser.). (Illus.). (J). 13.40 (978-0-7587-9129-0(1)) Book Wholesalers, Inc.

Steirnagle, Michael, illus. On the Wings of the West Wind. 2005. 14.99 (978-1-58134-372-4(8) , Crossway Bibles) Crossway Bks.

Sterne, Emma Gelders. The Story of the Amistad. unabr. ed. 2001. (Dover Juvenile Classics Ser.). (Illus.). 128p. (J). (gr. 4-7). pap. 2.00 (978-0-486-41537-6(6)) Dover Pubns., Inc.

Stolz, Mary. A Ballad of the Civil War. Martinez, Sergio, illus. 1998. (Trophy Chapter Bks.). 64p. (J). (gr. 2-5). pap. 4.99 (978-0-06-442088-4(4)) HarperCollins Pubs.

Stowe, Cynthia. The Second Escape of Arthur Cooper. 2000. (Illus.). 112p. (YA). (gr. 5-9). 14.95 (978-0-7614-5069-6(6) , Cavendish Children's Bks.) Cavendish, Marshall Corp.

Stowe, Harriet Beecher. La Cabaña del Tío Tom. 2002. (Classics for Young Readers Ser.). (SPA.). (YA). 14.95 (978-84-392-0905-8(3) , EV30595) Lectorum Pubns., Inc.

—La Cabaña del Tío Tom. 2000. (Coleccion "Clasicos Juveniles" Ser.). (SPA., Illus.). 480p. pap. 21.95 (978-1-58348-829-4(4)) iUniverse, Inc.

—Uncle Tom's Cabin. 2002. (gr. 3-6). lib. bdg. 14.15 (978-0-613-63239-3(7)) Tandem Library Bks.

Stowe, Harriet Beecher. Uncle Toms Cabin Young Folks Edition Ill. 2006. pap. (***978-1-4065-1077-5(7))** Dodo Pr.

Stowe, Harriet Beecher & Beecher, Harriet Elizabeth. La Cabaña del Tío Tom. 2001. (SPA.). 96p. (978-84-305-1436-6(8)) Lectorum Pubns., Inc.

Strohmeier, Lenice. Mingo. Farnsworth, Bill, illus. 2003. 32p. (J). 16.95 (978-0-7614-5111-2(0)) Cavendish, Marshall Corp.

Stroud, Bettye. The Patchwork Path: A Quilt Map to Freedom. Bennett, Erin Susanne, illus. 2007. 32p. (J). (gr. k-3). pap. 7.99 (***978-0-7636-3519-0(7))** Candlewick Pr.

Sutcliff, Rosemary. The Mark of the Horse Lord. 2006. 256p. (YA). pap. 10.95 (978-1-932425-62-8(4) , Lemniscaat) Boyds Mills Pr.

Switzer-Clarke, Eileen. Blossom: A Girl's Adventures in Revolutionary Rockland. Carney, Barbara J., illus. 1998. 108p. (J). (gr. 3-6). pap. 8.00 (978-0-911183-44-3(2)) Historical Society of Rockland County, The.

The Sword, the Ring, & the Parchment. 2006. (J). per. 7.99 (978-0-9785523-0-5(X)) Dunlop, Edward.

Tamura, Yumi. Basara, Vol. 15. 2005. (Basara Ser.). (Illus.). 200p. (YA). pap. 9.99 (978-1-4215-0135-2(X)) Viz Media.

Taylor, Mildred D. The Land. 2003. (gr. 7-12). lib. bdg. 15.30 (978-0-613-86520-3(0)) Tandem Library Bks.

Tingle, Tim. Crossing Bok Chitto: A Choctaw Tale of Friendship & Freedom. Bridges, Jeanne Rorex, illus. 2006. (SPA & ENG.). 40p. (J). 17.95 (978-0-938317-77-7(6)) Cinco Puntos Pr.

Torrey, Michele. Voyage of Midnight. 2006. 240p. (gr. 5). (J). 17.99 (978-0-375-92382-1(9)); (YA). 15.95 (978-0-375-82382-4(4)) Random Hse. Children's Bks. (Knopf Bks. for Young Readers).

Turner, Glennette Tilley. Running for Our Lives. 2004. (J). pap. 7.95 (978-0-938990-06-2(3)) Newman Educational Publishing Co.

Turtleback Books, creator. Evvy's Civil War. 2004. 209p. (YA). (gr. 8-12). per. 13.64 (978-0-606-30114-5(3)) Tandem Library Bks.

Twain, Mark. The Adventures of Huckleberry Finn. (Great Classics for Children Ser.). (Illus.). 192p. (J). 5.99 (978-1-4037-0594-5(1)) Dalmatian Pr.

—The Adventures of Huckleberry Finn. 2004. (Classic Retelling Ser.). (Illus.). 235p. (J). (gr. 6-12). (978-0-618-00374-7(6) , 2-00111) McDougal Littell Inc.

—The Adventures of Huckleberry Finn. (Coleccion Clasicos de la Juventud). (SPA., Illus.). 192p. (J). 12.95 (978-84-7189-027-6(5) , ORT313) Ortells, Alfredo Editorial S.L. ESP. *Dist:* Continental Bk. Co., Inc.

—The Adventures of Huckleberry Finn. 2003. (gr. 7-12). lib. bdg. 14.15 (978-0-613-64012-1(8)); 1999. (gr. 3-6). lib. bdg. 11.80 (978-0-613-63171-6(4)) Tandem Library Bks.

—The Adventures of Huckleberry Finn. Andreasen, Dan, illus. 2006. (Classic Starts Ser.). 160p. 4.95 (978-1-4027-2499-2(3)) Sterling Publishing Co., Inc.

—The Adventures of Huckleberry Finn. abr. ed. 1999. (gr. 7-12). lib. bdg. 15.25 (978-0-613-32245-4(2)) Tandem Library Bks.

—The Adventures of Huckleberry Finn: With a Discussion of Friendship. Lauter, Richard, tr. Lauter, Richard, illus. 2003. (Values in Action Illustrated Classics Ser.). (J). (978-1-59203-042-2(4)) Learning Challenge, Inc.

—The Adventures of Tom Sawyer. (J). (978-0-448-41455-3(4) , Putnam Juvenile) Penguin Group (USA) Inc.

—Mark Twain/the Adventures of Huckleberry Finn. Redondo, Frank, illus. 2005. 48p. (gr. 5-8). 25.50 (978-0-7910-9101-2(5)) Facts On File, Inc.

Vande Velde, Vivian. There's a Dead Person Following My Sister Around. 2001. 160p. (J). pap. 5.99 (978-0-14-131281-1(5) , Puffin) Penguin Group (USA) Inc.

—There's a Dead Person Following My Sister Around. 2001. (gr. 5-8). lib. bdg. 13.00 (978-0-613-43899-5(X)) Tandem Library Bks.

Vaughan, Marcia. The Secret to Freedom. Johnson, Larry, illus. 32p. (J). 2001. (gr. 1-4). 16.95 (978-1-58430-021-2(3)); 2nd ed. 2005. (ps-ps). pap. 7.95 (978-1-58430-251-3(8)) Lee & Low Bks., Inc.

—Up the Learning Tree. Blanks, Derek, illus. 2003. 32p. (J). 16.96 (978-1-58430-049-6(3)) Lee & Low Bks., Inc.

Verne, Jules. Dick Sands: The Boy Captain. ELLEN E. FREWER, tr. 2006. 298p. pap. 13.99 (978-1-4264-3403-7(0)) BiblioBazaar.

—Dick Sands: The Boy Captain. Frewer, Ellen E., tr. l.t. ed. 2006. 328p. pap. 18.99 (978-1-4264-3453-2(7)) BiblioBazaar.

Wait, Lea. Seaward Born. (Illus.). 160p. (J). 2004. pap. 5.99 (978-0-689-84860-5(9) , Aladdin); 2003. 16.95 (978-0-689-84719-6(X) , McElderry, Margaret K.) Simon & Schuster Children's Publishing.

Wallin, Luke. The Slavery Ghosts. 2001. 132p. (YA). pap. 11.95 (978-0-595-19277-9(7)) iUniverse, Inc.

Walter, Mildred Pitts. Alec's Primer. Johnson, Larry, illus. 2005. (Family Heritage Ser.). 36p. (J). 15.95 (978-0-916718-20-6(4)) Vermont Folklife Ctr.

Ware, Jim. Dangerous Dreams. 2001. (Kidwitness Tales Ser.). (Illus.). 128p. (J). (gr. 4-7). mass mkt. (978-1-56179-956-5(4)) Focus on the Family Publishing.

Warren, Bertie. Sammie's Journey to Freedom. 2006. (ENG.). 52p. per. 12.95 (***978-1-4241-5142-4(2))** PublishAmerica, Inc.

Whitmore, Arvella. Trapped Between the Lash & the Gun: A Boy's Journey. 2001. 184p. (YA). (gr. 7-12). lib. bdg. 14.15 (978-0-613-33734-2(4)) Tandem Library Bks.

Williams, Mark London. Trail of Bones. Koelsch, Michael, illus. 2005. (Danger Boy Ser.: No. 3). 320p. (J). (gr. 4-8). 12.99 (978-0-7636-2154-4(4)) Candlewick Pr.

Williams, Mark London. Trail of Bones: Danger Boy Episode 3. 2007. (Illus.). 320p. (J). (gr. 4-8). 5.99 (***978-0-7636-3410-0(7))** Candlewick Pr.

Williams, Sheron & Daly, Jude. Imani's Music. 2002. (Illus.). 40p. (J). (gr. 1-4). 17.00 (978-0-689-82254-4(5) , Atheneum) Simon & Schuster Children's Publishing.

Wilson, Diane Lee. Black Storm Comin' (J). 2006. 240p. pap. 5.99 (978-0-689-87138-2(4) , Aladdin); 2005. 304p. (gr. 5-9). 17.99 (978-0-689-87137-5(6) , McElderry, Margaret K.) Simon & Schuster Children's Publishing.

Winter, Jeanette. Follow the Drinking Gourd. Winter, Jeanette, illus. 2002. (Illus.). (J). 15.74 (978-0-7587-2527-1(2)) Book Wholesalers, Inc.

Wisehart, Randall. A Winding Road to Freedom. 1999. 184p. (J). (gr. 5-8). pap. 13.00 (978-0-944350-47-8(X)) Friends United Pr.

Woodruff, Elvira. Dear Austin: Letters from the Underground Railroad. 2000. (gr. 5-8). lib. bdg. 13.00 (978-0-613-28463-9(1)) Tandem Library Bks.

Woods, Brenda. My Name Is Sally Little Song. 192p. (J). 2007. (gr. 2). 5.99 (***978-0-14-240943-5(X)** , Puffin); 2006. (gr. 3-6). 15.99 (978-0-399-24312-7(7) , Putnam Juvenile) Penguin Group (USA) Inc.

Woodson, Jacqueline. Show Way. Talbott, Hudson, illus. 2005. 48p. (J). (ps). 16.99 (978-0-399-23749-2(6) , Putnam Juvenile) Penguin Group (USA) Inc.

Wyeth, Sharon Dennis. Freedom's Wings: Corey's Underground Railroad Diary. 2002. (gr. 3-6). lib. bdg. 13.00 (978-0-613-53813-8(7)) Tandem Library Bks.

—Message in the Sky Bk. 3: Corey's Underground Railroad Diary. 2003. (My America Ser.). 112p. (J). pap. 10.95 (978-0-439-37057-8(4) , Scholastic Pr.) Scholastic, Inc.

Zahn, Timothy. Dragon & Slave: The Third Dragonback Adventure. rev. ed. 2005. (Dragonback Ser.). 304p. (J). 17.95 (978-0-7653-0126-0(1) , Tor Bks.) Doherty, Tom Assocs., LLC.

SLAVERY—UNITED STATES

see also Abolitionists; Slave Trade; Southern States—History; Underground Railroad

Abnett, Dan. Harriet Tubman & the Underground Railroad. 2007. (Jr. Graphic Biographies Ser.). (Illus.). 24p. (J). (978-1-4042-2336-3(3)); pap. (978-1-4042-2146-8(8)); (gr. 2-6). lib. bdg. 21.25 (978-1-4042-3393-5(8)) Rosen Publishing Group, Inc., The. (PowerKids Pr.).

Adler, David A. Enemies of Slavery. Smith, Donald A., illus. 2004. 32p. (J). (gr. k-3). tchr. ed. 16.95 (978-0-8234-1596-0(1)) Holiday Hse., Inc.

Altman, Linda Jacobs. The Politics of Slavery: Fiery National Debates Fueled by the Slave Economy. 2004. (Slavery in American History Ser.). (Illus.). 128p. (J). lib. bdg. 26.60 (978-0-7660-2150-1(5)) Enslow Pubs., Inc.

—Slavery & Abolition in American History. 1999. (In American History Ser.). (Illus.). 128p. (YA). (gr. 5-12). lib. bdg. 26.60 (978-0-7660-1124-3(0)) Enslow Pubs., Inc.

Anderson, Dale. The Causes of the Civil War. 2004. (World Almanac Library of the Civil War). (Illus.). 48p. (J). (gr. 5 up). pap. 11.95 (978-0-8368-5590-6(6)); lib. bdg. 30.00 (978-0-8368-5581-4(7)) Stevens, Gareth Inc. (World Almanac Library).

Ashby, Ruth. The Underground Railroad. 2002. (Illus.). 48p. (J). lib. bdg. 28.50 (978-1-58340-181-1(4)) Smart Apple Media.

Asim, Jabari. The Road to Freedom. 2001. (American Portraits Ser.). 126p. (gr. 5-8). 15.32 (978-0-8092-0583-7(1) , 9780809205837) Jamestown.

Asim, Jabari & McGraw-Hill Staff. American Portraits: The Road to Freedom. 2001. (Jamestown Classics Ser.). (Illus.). 144p. (gr. 5-8). pap. 10.00 (978-0-8092-0625-4(0) , 9780809206254) Jamestown.

Barr, Gary. Slavery in the Civil War Era. 2004. (Illus.). 56p. (J). pap. 8.95 (978-1-4034-4578-0(8)); lib. bdg. (978-1-4034-4570-4(2)) Heinemann Library.

Bisson, Terry. Nat Turner: Slave Revolt Leader. 2005. (Black Americans of Achievement Ser.). (Illus.). 112p. (J). (gr. 6-12). pap. 13.25 (978-0-7910-8341-3(1) , Chelsea Hse.) Facts On File, Inc.

Bjornlund, Lydia D. Women in Colonial America. 2003. (Illus.). 112p. (J). 32.45 (978-1-59018-470-7(X) , Lucent Bks.) Thomson Gale.

Blue, Rose & Naden, Corinne J. Dred Scott: Person or Property? 2004. (Supreme Court Milestones Ser.). (Illus.). 128p. (J). 37.07 (978-0-7614-1841-2(5) , Benchmark Bks.) Cavendish, Marshall Corp.

Blumberg, Rhoda. York's Adventures with Lewis & Clark: An African-American's Part in the Great Expedition. 2007. 96p. (J). pap. 7.99 (978-0-06-009113-2(4)) HarperCollins Pubs.

Brill, Marlene Targ. Allen Jay & the Underground Railroad. 2007. (Readalongs for Beginning Readers Ser.). (J). (gr. 1-3). pap. 18.95 incl. audio compact disk (***978-1-59519-949-2(7)***) Live Oak Media.

Burgan, Michael. Escaping to Freedom: The Underground Railroad. 2006. (Slavery in the Americas Ser.). (Illus.). 112p. (J). (gr. 4-9). 35.00 (978-0-8160-6137-2(8)) Facts On File, Inc.

—The Missouri Compromise. 2006. (We the People Ser.). (Illus.). 48p. (J). (gr. 4-6). 23.93 (978-0-7565-1634-5(X)) Compass Point Bks.

—The Reconstruction Amendments. 2006. (Illus.). 48p. (J). (gr. 4-6). 23.93 (978-0-7565-1636-9(6)) Compass Point Bks.

Calkhoven, Laurie. Harriet Tubman: Leading the Way to Freedom. 2008. (Sterling Biographies Ser.). (Illus.). 128p. (J). pap. 5.95 (***978-1-4027-4117-3(0)***) Sterling Publishing Co., Inc.

Capstone Press, contrib. by. Underground Railroad: Bringing Slaves North to Freedom. (Civil War Ser.). 48p. (YA). pap. 7.95 (978-0-7368-4521-2(6)) Capstone Pr., Inc.

Cartlidge, Cherese. Reparations for Slavery. 2007. (Lucent Library of Black History Ser.). (Illus.). 128p. (J). (gr. 7-10). 28.70 (***978-1-59018-868-2(3)*** , Lucent Bks.) Thomson Gale.

Cary, Lorene. Free: Great Escapes from Slavery on the Underground Railroad. 2006. (Illus.). 86p. pap. 15.00 (978-0-88378-268-2(5)) Third World Press.

Child, L. Maria. The Duty of Disobedience to the Fugitive Slave Act. 2007. (ENG.). 48p. per. (***978-1-4065-1352-3(0)***) Dodo Pr.

Clare, John D. The Black Peoples of America. 2001. (Illus.). 48p. pap. 23.50 (***978-0-340-79033-5(4)*** , Hodder Murray) Hodder Education GBR. *Dist:* Trans-Atlantic Pubns., Inc.

Clinton, Catherine. Underground Railroad. 2007. 32p. (J). lib. bdg. 17.89 (978-0-06-050426-7(9)) HarperCollins Pubs.

—When Harriet Met Sojourner. Evans, Shane, illus. 2007. 32p. (J). (gr. k-2). 16.99 (978-0-06-050425-0(0)) HarperCollins Pubs.

Cloud Tapper, Suzanne. Voices from Slavery's Past: Yearning to Be Heard. 2004. (Slavery in American History Ser.). (Illus.). 128p. (J). lib. bdg. 26.60 (978-0-7660-2157-0(2)) Enslow Pubs., Inc.

Connell, Kate. Tales from the Underground Railroad. 2001. (Nonfiction Bookbag Ser.). (J). (gr. 4-5). per. 8.45 (978-1-58830-204-5(0)) Metropolitan Teaching & Learning Co.

Copeland, Peter F. The Story of the Underground Railroad. 2000. 48p. (J). pap. 3.95 (978-0-486-41158-3(3)) Dover Pubns., Inc.

Corrick, James. The Civil War & Emancipation. 2007. (Lucent Library of Black History Ser.). (Illus.). 128p. (J). (gr. 7-10). 28.70 (***978-1-4205-0008-0(2)*** , Lucent Bks.) Thomson Gale.

Creative Media Applications. Slavery in the Americas Set. 2006. (Slavery in the Americas Ser.). 672p. (gr. 4-9). 210.00 (978-0-8160-6133-4(5)) Facts On File, Inc.

Currie, Stephen. Escapes from Slavery. 2003. (Great Escapes Ser.). (Illus.). 112p. (J). 29.95 (978-1-59018-276-5(6) , Lucent Bks.) Thomson Gale.

—The Quest for Freedom: The Abolitionist Movement. 2005. (Lucent Library of Black History). (Illus.). 112p. (YA). (gr. 7-10). lib. bdg. 32.45 (978-1-59018-703-6(2) , Lucent Bks.) Thomson Gale.

—Slavery. 1998. (Opposing Viewpoints Digests Ser.). (Illus.). 112p. (YA). (gr. 6-9). lib. bdg. 31.20 (978-1-56510-881-3(7) , Greenhaven Pr., Inc.) Thomson Gale.

DeFord, Deborah H. Life under Slavery. 2006. (Slavery in the Americas Ser.). (Illus.). 112p. (YA). (gr. 4-9). 35.00 (978-0-8160-6135-8(1)) Facts On File, Inc.

Deiters, Erika & Deiters, Jim. The African Community in America. 2003. (J). lib. bdg. (978-1-58417-032-7(8)) Lake Street Pubs.

Diouf, Sylviane A. Growing up in Slavery. 2001. (Growing Up in... Ser.). (Illus.). 96p. (J). (gr. 5-8). lib. bdg. 25.90 (978-0-7613-1763-0(5) , Millbrook Pr.) Lerner Publishing Group.

Doak, Robin S. Slave Rebellions. 2006. (Slavery in the Americas Ser.). 112p. (YA). (gr. 4-9). 35.00 (978-0-8160-6136-5(X)) Facts On File, Inc.

Donlan, Leni. Following Freedom: The Underground Railroad. 2006. (American History Through Primary Sources Ser.). (Illus.). 32p. (J). (gr. 2-4). lib. bdg. 28.21 (978-1-4109-2418-6(1)) Raintree.

—Following Freedom: The Underground Railroad. 2006. (American History Through Primary Sources Ser.). (Illus.). 32p. (J). pap. 7.99 (978-1-4109-2429-2(7)) Steck-Vaughn.

Edwards, Judith. Abolitionists & Slave Resistance: Breaking the Chains of Slavery. 2004. (Slavery in American History Ser.). (Illus.). 128p. (J). lib. bdg. 26.60 (978-0-7660-2155-6(6)) Enslow Pubs., Inc.

Emancipation Proclamation: Hope of Freedom for the Slaves. (Civil War Ser.). 48p. (YA). 7.95 (978-0-7368-4517-5(8)) Capstone Pr., Inc.

Empak Publishing Company Staff. Historic Black Abolitionists: A Gift of Heritage. ("Black History" Publication Ser.). 2.50 (978-0-922162-80-2(8)) Empak Publishing Co.

Erickson, Paul. Daily Life on a Southern Plantation. Gabbey, Terry, illus. Slingsby, Miki, photos by. 2006. 48p. (J). (gr. 2-5). reprint ed. pap. 8.00 (978-1-4223-5727-9(9)) DIANE Publishing Co.

Eskridge, Ann E. Slave Uprisings & Runaways: Fighting for Freedom & the Underground Railroad. 2004. (Slavery in American History Ser.). (Illus.). 128p. (J). lib. bdg. 26.60 (978-0-7660-2154-9(8)) Enslow Pubs., Inc.

Espinosa, Rod. Underground Railroad. 2007. (Graphic History Ser.). (Illus.). 32p. (J). (gr. 3-6). lib. bdg. 27.07 (***978-1-60270-080-2(X)*** , Graphic Planet) Magic Wagon.

Fauchald, Nick. William Lloyd Garrison: Abolitionist & Journalist. 2004. (Signature Lives Ser.). (Illus.). 112p. (J). 30.60 (978-0-7565-0819-7(3) , 1240146) Compass Point Bks.

Featonby, Douglas & Whittock, Martyn. The Black Peoples of America. 2001. (Illus.). 48p. pap. 23.50 (***978-0-340-79034-2(2)*** , Hodder Murray) Hodder Education GBR. *Dist:* Trans-Atlantic Pubns., Inc.

Ferris, Jeri Chase. With Open Hands: A Story about Biddy Mason. 2003. (Creative Minds Biographies Ser.). (Illus.). 64p. (J). (gr. 3-6). pap. 6.95 (978-0-87614-845-7(3) , Carolrhoda Bks.) Lerner Publishing Group.

—With Open Hands: A Story about Biddy Mason. Ramstad, Ralph L., illus. 1999. (Creative Minds Biographies Ser.). 64p. (J). (gr. 3-6). lib. bdg. 22.60 (978-1-57505-330-1(6) , Carolrhoda Bks.) Lerner Publishing Group.

—With Open Hands: A Story about Biddy Mason. 1999. (gr. 3-6). lib. bdg. 15.25 (978-0-613-68482-8(6)) Tandem Library Bks.

Findley, Violet. Easy Reader Biographies: Harriet Tubman: Follow the North Star. 2007. 16p. pap. 2.99 (***978-0-439-92330-9(1)*** , Teaching Resources) Scholastic, Inc.

Fleischner, Jennifer. I Was Born A Slave: The Story of Harriet Jacobs. 2000. 6. (Illus.). 96p. (gr. 4-6). pap. (978-0-7613-0166-0(6) , Millbrook Pr.) Lerner Publishing Group.

Ford, Carin T. Lincoln, Slavery, & the Emancipation Proclamation. 2004. (Civil War Library Ser.). (Illus.). 48p. (J). lib. bdg. 23.93 (978-0-7660-2252-2(8)) Enslow Pubs., Inc.

—Slavery & the Underground Railroad: Bound for Freedom. 2004. (Civil War Library Ser.). (Illus.). 48p. (J). lib. bdg. 23.93 (978-0-7660-2251-5(X)) Enslow Pubs., Inc.

A Forgotten History: The Slave Trade & Slavery in New England, 2. 2005. (Illus.). 104p. (YA). pap. (978-1-891306-86-0(3)) Choices Education Program, Watson Institute, Brown Univ.

Fradin, Dennis B. The Emancipation Proclamation. 2007. (Turning Points in U. S. History Ser.). (J). lib. bdg. (978-0-7614-2038-5(X) , Benchmark Bks.) Cavendish, Marshall Corp.

Fradin, Dennis Brindell. Bound for the North Star: True Stories of Fugitive Slaves. 2000. (Illus.). 224p. (J). (gr. 7-12). tchr. ed. 20.00 (978-0-395-97017-1(2) , Clarion Bks.) Houghton Mifflin Co. Trade & Reference Div.

Freedman, Suzanne. United States vs. Amistad: Rebellion on a Slave Ship. 2000. (Landmark Supreme Court Cases Ser.). (Illus.). 112p. (J). (gr. 6-12). lib. bdg. 26.60 (978-0-7660-1337-7(5)) Enslow Pubs., Inc.

Garrison, Mary. Slaves Who Dared: The Stories of Ten African-American Heroes. 2002. (Illus.). 150p. (J). (gr. 4-6). lib. bdg. 19.95 (978-1-57249-272-1(4) , White Mane Kids) White Mane Publishing Co., Inc.

Gold, Susan Dudley. United States v. Amistad: Slave Ship Mutiny. 2006. (Supreme Court Milestones Ser.). (Illus.). 144p. (J). lib. bdg. 39.93 (978-0-7614-2143-6(2) , Benchmark Bks.) Cavendish, Marshall Corp.

Green, Jen. The Africans. 2000. 15.75 (978-0-606-22825-1(X)) Tandem Library Bks.

—Africans. 2000. (gr. 3-6). lib. bdg. 17.60 (978-0-613-27697-9(3)) Tandem Library Bks.

Greene, Meg. Slave Young, Slave Long: The American Slave Experience. 1999. (People's History Ser.). (Illus.). 88p. (YA). (gr. 6-12). (978-0-8225-1739-9(6) , Lerner Pubns.) Lerner Publishing Group.

Greenwood, Barbara. The Last Safe House: A Story of the Underground Railroad. Collins, Heather, illus. 1998. (History Comes Alive Ser.). 120p. (J). (gr. 4-6). (978-1-55074-509-2(3)); (978-1-55074-507-8(7)) Kids Can Pr., Ltd.

Gunderson, Cory Gideon. The Dred Scott Decision. 2005. (American Moments Ser.). (Illus.). 48p. (J). (gr. 4-8). lib. bdg. 25.65 (978-1-59197-283-9(3)) ABDO Publishing Co.

Hamilton, Virginia. Many Thousand Gone: African Americans from Slavery to Freedom. Dillon, Leo & Dillon, Diane, illus. 2002. 160p. (J). (gr. 3-9). lib. bdg. 18.99 (978-0-394-92873-9(3) , Knopf Bks. for Young Readers) Random Hse. Children's Bks.

Hansen, Joyce & McGowan, Gary. Freedom Roads: Searching for the Underground Railroad. Ransome, James E., illus. 2003. (Marcato Book Ser.). 166p. (J). (gr. 5-9). 18.95 (978-0-8126-2673-5(7)) Cricket Bks.

Haskins, James & Benson, Kathleen. Africa: A Look Back. 2006. (Drama of African-American History Ser.). (Illus.). 80p. (J). lib. bdg. 34.21 (978-0-7614-2148-1(3) , Benchmark Bks.) Cavendish, Marshall Corp.

—Building a New Land: African Americans in Colonial America. Ransome, James E., illus. 2001. (Amistad Ser.). 48p. (J). (gr. 2-5). 17.89 (978-0-06-029361-1(6)); 17.95 (978-0-688-10266-1(2)) HarperCollins Pubs.

Haskins, James, et al. Following Freedom's Star: The Story of the Underground Railroad. 2001. (Great Journeys Ser.). (Illus.). 112p. (J). (gr 5 up). lib. bdg. 32.79 (978-0-7614-1229-8(8) , Benchmark Bks.) Cavendish, Marshall Corp.

Hatt, Christine. The African-American Slave Trade. 2003. (Questioning History Ser.). (J). lib. bdg. 28.50 (978-1-58340-265-8(9)) Smart Apple Media.

Healy, Nick. Harriet Tubman. 2005. (Fact Finders Ser.). (Illus.). 32p. (J). 22.60 (978-0-7368-3743-9(4)) Capstone Pr., Inc.

Heinrichs, Ann. The Underground Railroad. 2001. (We the People Ser.). (Illus.). 48p. (J). (gr. 4 up). lib. bdg. 22.60 (978-0-7565-0102-0(4)) Compass Point Bks.

Hicks, Kyra E. Martha Ann's Quilt for Queen Victoria. 2006. (J). 16.95 (978-1-933285-59-7(1)) Brown Bks. Publishing Group.

Hudson, Wade. The Underground Railroad. 2005. (Cornerstones of Freedom Ser.). (Illus.). 48p. (J). (gr. 4-6). 26.00 (978-0-516-23630-8(X) , Children's Pr.) Scholastic Library Publishing.

Imbriaco, Alison. Causes of the Civil War: A MyReportLinks. com Book. 2004. (American Civil War Ser.). (Illus.). 48p. (J). lib. bdg. 25.26 (978-0-7660-5186-7(2) , MyReportLinks.com Bks.) Enslow Pubs., Inc.

Jacobs, Harriet A. Incidents in the Life of a Slave Girl. 2005. (Barnes & Noble Classics Ser.). 272p. pap. 5.95 (978-1-59308-283-3(5)) Barnes & Noble, Inc.

—Incidents in the Life of a Slave Girl. 2005. 78.99 (***978-1-4219-2600-1(8)***); pap. 72.99 (***978-1-4219-2601-8(6)***) IndyPublish.com.

—Incidents in the Life of a Slave Girl. 2000. (gr. 7-12). lib. bdg. 14.10 (978-0-613-21756-9(X)) Tandem Library Bks.

—Incidents in the Life of a Slave Girl. Barsky, Lisa, ed. 2004. 152p. mass mkt. 2.00 (978-1-59194-026-5(5)) Townsend Pr.

January, Brendan. The Dred Scott Decision. De Capua, Sarah, ed. 1998. (Cornerstones of Freedom Ser.). (Illus.). 32p. (J). (gr. 4-6). pap. 5.95 (978-0-516-26457-8(5) , Children's Pr.) Scholastic Library Publishing.

Jordan, Anne Devereaux & Schomp, Virginia. Slavery & Resistance. 2006. (Drama of African-American History Ser.). (Illus.). 80p. (J). lib. bdg. 34.21 (978-0-7614-2178-8(5) , Benchmark Bks.) Cavendish, Marshall Corp.

Jordan, Denise M. Juneteenth. 2003. (Holiday Histories Ser.). 32p. pap. 6.95 (978-1-4034-3690-0(8)) Heinemann Library.

Kallen, Stuart A. The Civil War & Reconstruction. 2001. (Black History Ser.). (Illus.). 48p. (J). (gr. 3-8). lib. bdg. 25.65 (978-1-57765-469-8(2) , ABDO & Daughters) ABDO Publishing Co.

Kamma, Anne. If You Lived When There Was Slavery in America. 2004. (Illus.). 80p. (J). pap. 5.99 (978-0-439-56706-0(8)) Scholastic, Inc.

Katz, William Loren. Breaking the Chains: African-American Slave Resistance, Class Set. unabr. ed. 1998. (YA). 155.80 incl. audio (978-0-7887-2556-2(4) , 46726) Recorded Bks., LLC.

—Breaking the Chains Homework Set: African-American Slave Resistance. unabr. ed. 1998. (YA). 53.25 incl. audio (978-0-7887-2252-3(2) , 40736) Recorded Bks., LLC.

Kent, Jacqueline C. Phillis Wheatley. 2003. (Women of the Revolution Ser.). (J). pap. (978-1-58417-089-1(1)); lib. bdg. (978-1-58417-026-6(3)) Lake Street Pubs.

Kiely Miller, Barbara. Frederick Douglass. 2007. (J). pap. (***978-0-8368-8322-0(5)*** , Weekly Reader Early Learning Library) Stevens, Gareth Inc.

Krass, Peter. Sojourner Truth: Antislavery Activist. 2005. (Black Americans of Achievement Ser.). (Illus.). 112p. (J). (gr. 6-12). pap. 13.25 (978-0-7910-8339-0(X) , Chelsea Hse.) Facts On File, Inc.

Kulling, Monica. Escape North! the Story of Harriet Tubman. 2000. (gr. k-3). lib. bdg. 11.80 (978-0-613-32507-3(9)) Tandem Library Bks.

Landau, Elaine. The Abolitionist Movement. 2004. (Cornerstones of Freedom Ser.). (Illus.). 48p. (J). 26.00 (978-0-516-24202-6(4) , Children's Pr.) Scholastic Library Publishing.

—The Emancipation Proclamation: Would You Do What Lincoln Did? 2008. (What Would You Do? Ser.). (Illus.). 48p. (J). (gr. 3-4). lib. bdg. 23.93 (***978-0-7660-2899-9(2)*** , Enslow Elementary) Enslow Pubs., Inc.

Landau, Elaine. Fleeing to Freedom on the Underground Railroad: The Courageous Slaves, Agents, & Conductors. 2006. (People's History Ser.). (Illus.). 88p. (J). 29.27 (978-0-8225-3490-7(8) , Twenty-First Century Bks.) Lerner Publishing Group.

Lassieur, Allison. The Underground Railroad: An Interactive History Adventure. 2008. (You Choose Bks.). 112p. (J). (gr. 3-7). lib. bdg. 27.23 (***978-1-4296-0164-1(7)***) Capstone Pr., Inc.

Leavitt, Amie. Harriet Tubman. 2007. (What's So Great About... ? Ser.). (J). lib. bdg. 25.70 (***978-1-58415-577-5(9)***) Mitchell Lane Pubs., Inc.

Lemke, Donald B. The Brave Escape of Ellen & William Craft. Barnett, Charles, III et al, illus. 2005. (Graphic Library). 32p. (J). (gr. 3-7). lib. bdg. 25.26 (978-0-7368-4973-9(4)) Capstone Pr., Inc.

Lester, Julius. From Slave Ship to Freedom Road. Brown, Rod, illus. 1999. 40p. (J). (gr. 5-8). pap. 6.99 (978-0-14-056669-7(4) , Puffin) Penguin Group (USA) Inc.

—From Slave Ship to Freedom Road. Brown, Rod, illus. 1999. 40p. (J). (gr. k-8). lib. bdg. 15.30 (978-0-613-22990-6(8)) Tandem Library Bks.

—To Be a Slave. Feelings, Tom, illus. 30th anniv. ed. (J). 2000. 176p. (gr. 5-9). pap. 6.99 (978-0-14-131001-5(4) , Puffin); 1998. 168p. (gr. 7-12). 20.00 (978-0-8037-2347-4(4) , Dial) Penguin Group (USA) Inc.

—To Be a Slave. 2000. (J). (978-0-606-20261-9(7)); (gr. 5-8). lib. bdg. 15.30 (978-0-613-33732-8(8)) Tandem Library Bks.

Lester, Julius & Feelings, Tom. To Be a Slave. 2005. 176p. (J). (gr. 5). pap. 5.99 (978-0-14-240386-0(5) , Puffin) Penguin Group (USA) Inc.

Levy, Debbie. Slaves on a Southern Plantation. 2004. (Daily Life Ser.). (Illus.). 48p. (J). 26.20 (978-0-7377-1827-0(7) , Greenhaven Pr., Inc.) Thomson Gale.

Mayer, Cassie. Frederick Douglass. 2007. (J). (***978-1-4034-9974-5(8)***); pap. (***978-1-4034-9983-7(7)***) Heinemann Library.

McArthur, Debra. The Kansas-Nebraska Act & Bleeding Kansas in American History. 2003. (In American History Ser.). (Illus.). 128p. (J). lib. bdg. 26.60 (978-0-7660-1988-1(8)) Enslow Pubs., Inc.

McDougal, Littell Staff, contrib. by. A Nation Dividing 1800-1860. 2004. (Stories in History Ser.). (Illus.). 176p. (gr. 6-12). 13.32 (978-0-618-14222-4(3) , 2-00242) McDougal Littell Inc.

McGill, Alice. Mile's Song. 2002. (978-0-606-22270-9(7)) Tandem Library Bks.

—Way up & over Everything. 2005. (J). (978-0-618-38796-0(X)) Houghton Mifflin Co.

McKissack, Patricia C. Rebels Against Slavery: American Slave Revolts. 1999. 176p. (YA). (gr. 5-9). pap. 5.99 (978-0-590-66259-8(7)); 1998. (J). (gr. 3-9). pap. 4.50 (978-0-590-45736-1(5)) Scholastic, Inc.

—Rebels Against Slavery: American Slave Revolts. 1998. (978-0-606-13731-7(9)) Tandem Library Bks.

McKissack, Patricia C. & McKissack, Fredrick L. End of Slavery in the United States. Dillon, Leo & Dillon, Dianne, illus. 2003. (Days of Jubilee Ser.). 144p. (J). (gr. 3-7). pap. 18.95 (978-0-590-10764-8(X) , Scholastic Pr.) Scholastic, Inc.

McLaurin, Melton A. Celia, a Slave. 1999. (J). (978-0-606-16086-5(8)) Tandem Library Bks.

McNeese, Tim. Dred Scott V. Sandford. 2006. (Great Supreme Court Decisions Ser.). (Illus.). 120p. (J). (gr. 5-8). 30.00 (978-0-7910-9236-1(4) , Chelsea Hse.) Facts On File, Inc.

—The Rise & Fall of American Slavery: Freedom Denied, Freedom Gained. 2004. (Slavery in American History Ser.). (Illus.). 128p. (J). lib. bdg. 26.60 (978-0-7660-2156-3(4)) Enslow Pubs., Inc.

McPherson, Stephanie Sammartino. Sisters Against Slavery: A Story about Sarah & Angelina Grimke. Ritz, Karen, illus. 64p. (J). pap. 22.60 (978-1-57505-815-3(4)); 1999. (gr. 3-6). lib. bdg. 21.27 (978-1-57505-361-5(6) , Carolrhoda Bks.) Lerner Publishing Group.

Miller, Barbara Kiely. Frederick Douglass. 2007. (Great Americans Ser.). 24p. (J). (gr. 2-4). lib. bdg. 19.93 (***978-0-8368-8315-2(2)*** , Weekly Reader Early Learning Library) Stevens, Gareth Inc.

Monroe, Judy. The Underground Railroad: Bringing Slaves North to Freedom. 2002. (Let Freedom Ring Ser.). (Illus.). 48p. (J). (gr. 3-4). lib. bdg. 22.60 (978-0-7368-1344-0(6) , Bridgestone Bks.) Capstone Pr., Inc.

Moore, Cathy. Daring Escape of Ellen Craft. 2002. (gr. 3-6). lib. bdg. 14.10 (978-0-613-46125-2(8)) Tandem Library Bks.

Mortensen, Lori. Harriet Tubman: Hero of the Underground Railroad. Moore, Frances, illus. 2006. (Biographies Ser.). 24p. (J). (gr. k-3). lib. bdg. 23.93 (***978-1-4048-3103-2(7)***) Picture Window Bks.

Naden, Corinne J. & Blue, Rose. Civil War Ends: Assassination, Reconstruction & the Aftermath. 1999. (House Divided Ser.). (Illus.). 112p. (J). (gr. 5-10). lib. bdg. 31.40 (978-0-8172-5583-1(4)) Raintree.

Nelson, Michael. Juneteenth. Schroder, Marc, illus. 2006. (On My Own Holidays Ser.). 48p. (J). pap. 5.95 (978-0-8225-5974-0(9) , First Avenue Editions) Lerner Publishing Group.

Newman, Shirlee P. Slavery in the United States. 2000. (978-0-606-20920-5(4)); (gr. 3-6). lib. bdg. 17.60 (978-0-613-34474-6(X)) Tandem Library Bks.

Newman, Shirlee Petkin. Slavery in the United States. 2000. (Watts Library). (Illus.). 64p. (J). (gr. 5-7). 25.50 (978-0-531-11695-1(6) , Watts, Franklin) Scholastic Library Publishing.

O'Connell, Kim A. Slavery, Emancipation, & the Civil War: A MyReportLinks. com Book. 2004. (American Civil War Ser.). (Illus.). 48p. (J). lib. bdg. 25.26 (978-0-7660-5190-4(0) , MyReportLinks.com Bks.) Enslow Pubs., Inc.

Olson, Kay Melchisedech. Africans in America, 1665-1865. 2002. (Blue Earth Books). (Illus.). 32p. (J). (gr. 4). lib. bdg. 22.60 (978-0-7368-1204-7(0) , Bridgestone Bks.) Capstone Pr., Inc.

Perrin, Pat, ed. Slavery. 2000. (Researching American History Ser.). (Illus.). 56p. (J). (978-1-57960-062-4(X)) History Compass, LLC.

Perrin, Pat & Coleman, Wim. The Mystery of the Vanishing Slaves. 2004. (Cover-To-Cover Books). (Illus.). 64p. (J). (gr. 4-7). lib. bdg. 17.95 (978-0-7569-1041-9(2)) Perfection Learning Corp.

Pringle, Laurence P. American Slave, American Hero: York of the Lewis & Clark Expedition. Van Wright, Cornelius & Hu, Ying-Hwa, illus. 2006. 40p. (J). (gr. 3-5). 17.95 (978-1-59078-282-8(8)) Boyds Mills Pr.

Rappaport, Doreen. Escape from Slavery. 1999. (J). 12.79 (978-0-606-15855-8(3)) Tandem Library Bks.

—Escape from Slavery: Five Journeys to Freedom. Lilly, Charles, illus. 1999. 128p. (J). (gr. 4-7). pap. 5.99 (978-0-06-446169-6(6) , Harper Trophy) HarperCollins Pubs.

—Escape from Slavery: Five Journeys to Freedom. 1999. (gr. 3-6). lib. bdg. 14.15 (978-0-613-11514-8(7)) Tandem Library Bks.

—Freedom River. Collier, Bryan, illus. 32p. (gr. k-4). 2000. 14.99 (978-0-7868-0350-7(9)); 2007. pap. 6.99 (***978-1-4231-0634-0(2)***) Hyperion Bks. for Children. (Jump at the Sun).

—No More! Stories & Songs of Slave Resistance. Evans, Shane W., illus. 2005. 64p. (J). (gr. 4-7). reprint ed. pap. 7.99 (978-0-7636-2876-5(X)) Candlewick Pr.

S

Rausch, Monica. Hariet Tubman. 2006. (ENG & SPA.). (J). pap. (***978-0-8368-7992-6(9)***); lib. bdg. (***978-0-8368-7985-8(6)***) Stevens, Gareth Inc. (Weekly Reader Early Learning Library).

Riehecky, Janet. The Emancipation Proclamation: The Abolition of Slavery. 2002. (Point of Impact Ser.). (Illus.). 32p. (J). (gr. 5-7). lib. bdg. 25.64 (978-1-58810-556-1(3)) Heinemann Library.

—The Emancipation Proclamation Set: The Abolition of Slavery. 2002. (Point of Impact Ser.). (Illus.). 32p. (J). (gr. 5-7). pap. (978-1-4034-0071-0(7) , 91552) Heinemann Library.

Rife, Douglas M. Emancipation Proclamation. Mitchell, Judy, ed. Smith, Bron, illus. 2002. 32p. (J). (gr. 4-8). pap. 5.95 (978-1-57310-349-7(7)) Teaching & Learning Co.

Robert Smalls Sails to Freedom. 2007. (J). pap. 5.95 (***978-0-8225-6051-7(8)*** , First Avenue Editions) Lerner Publishing Group.

Rosen, Daniel. Dred Scott & the Supreme Court. 2006. (Navigators Ser.). (J). pap. 42.00 (***978-1-4108-6258-7(5)***) Benchmark Education Co.

Rosinsky, Natalie M. Juneteenth. 2004. (Let's See Ser.). (Illus.). 24p. (J). (gr. 1). lib. bdg. 19.93 (978-0-7565-0770-1(7)) Compass Point Bks.

Ruffin, Frances E. Frederick Douglass: Rising up from Slavery. 2008. (Sterling Biographies Ser.). (Illus.). 128p. (J). pap. 5.95 (***978-1-4027-4118-0(9)***) Sterling Publishing Co., Inc.

Schleichert, Elizabeth. The Thirteenth Amendment: Ending Slavery. 1998. (Constitution Ser.). (Illus.). 128p. (YA). (gr. 6-12). lib. bdg. 26.60 (978-0-89490-923-8(1)) Enslow Pubs., Inc.

Schroeder, Alan. Minty: A Story of Young Harriet Tubman. Pinkney, Jerry, illus. 2002. (YA). 25.45 (978-0-7587-0382-8(1)) Book Wholesalers, Inc.

—Minty: A Story of Young Harriet Tubman. 2000. (978-0-606-20365-4(6)); (YA). (978-0-606-20246-6(3)) Tandem Library Bks.

Simms, Patsy Ford. Harriet's Freedom Train. 2000. (J). stu. ed. 12.50 (978-0-7692-9377-6(8)); tchr. ed. 24.95 (978-0-7692-9376-9(X)) Alfred Publishing Co., Inc. (Warner Bros. Pubns.).

Simon, Barbara Brooks. Escape to Freedom: The Underground Railroad Adventures of Callie & William. 2004. (I Am American Ser.). (Illus.). 40p. (J). (gr. 3-7). pap. 6.99 (978-0-7922-6551-1(3) , National Geographic Children's Bks.) National Geographic Society.

Sirimarco, Elizabeth. The Time of Slavery. 2006. (American Voices Ser.). (Illus.). xxiii, 114p. (J). lib. bdg. 37.07 (978-0-7614-2169-6(6) , Benchmark Bks.) Cavendish, Marshall Corp.

Slade, Suzanne. Frederick Douglass: Writer, Speaker, & Opponent of Slavery. McGuire, Robert, illus. 2006. (Biographies Ser.). 24p. (J). (gr. k-3). lib. bdg. 23.93 (***978-1-4048-3102-5(9)***) Picture Window Bks.

The Slave Trade in Early America, 6 vols. (gr. 2-5). 39.95 (978-0-7368-4571-7(2)) Red Brick Learning.

Slavery: Analyzing Visual Primary Sources. 2006. cd-rom 59.95 net. (978-1-56004-262-4(1)) Social Studies Schl. Service.

Slavery in America. 2004. (Historical Reader Ser.). (Illus.). 240p. (gr. 6-12). 13.32 (978-0-618-04822-9(7) , 2-00154) McDougal Littell Inc.

Slavicek, Louise Chipley. Harriet Tubman & the Underground Railroad. 2006. (Lucent Library of Black History). 112p. (J). (gr. 7-10). 32.45 (978-1-59018-927-6(2) , Lucent Bks.) Thomson Gale.

Spengler, Kremena. Frederick Douglass: Voice for Freedom. 2006. (Fact Finders Ser.). (Illus.). 32p. (J). 22.60 (978-0-7368-5434-4(7) , Fact Finders) Capstone Pr., Inc.

Stearns, Dan. Harriet Tubman & the Underground Railroad. 2006. (In the Footsteps of American Heroes Ser.). (Illus.). 64p. (J). pap. 11.95 (978-0-8368-6433-5(6)); lib. bdg. 32.67 (978-0-8368-6428-1(X)) Stevens, Gareth Inc. (World Almanac Library).

Steck-Vaughn Staff. Journeys of Courage on Underground Railroads. 2002. pap. (978-0-7398-6166-0(2)) Steck-Vaughn.

Strangis, Joel. Lewis Hayden & the War Against Slavery. 1999. (Illus.). xiv, 167p. (YA). (gr. 9 up). 25.00 (978-0-208-02430-5(1) , Linnet Bks.) Shoe String Pr., Inc.

Stroyer, Jacob. My Life in the South. 2001. 108p. (YA). reprint ed. (978-1-58218-719-8(3)) Digital Scanning, Inc.

Swain, Gwenyth. Dred & Harriet Scott: A Family's Struggle for Freedom. 2004. (Illus.). 102p. pap. 12.95 (978-0-87351-483-5(1) , Borealis Bk.) Minnesota Historical Society Pr.

—President of the Underground Railroad: A Story about Levi Coffin. Ramstad, Ralph L., illus. 2001. (Creative Minds Biographies Ser.). 64p. (J). (gr. 3-6). lib. bdg. 22.60 (978-1-57505-551-0(1) , Carolrhoda Bks.) Lerner Publishing Group.

—President of the Underground Railroad: A Story of Levi Coffin. 2001. (gr. 3-6). lib. bdg. 15.25 (978-0-613-68377-7(3)) Tandem Library Bks.

Tackach, James. The Abolition of American Slavery. 2002. (World History Ser.). (Illus.). 112p. (YA). (gr. 8-11). 32.45 (978-1-59018-002-0(X) , LML00902-178746, Lucent Bks.) Thomson Gale.

Taylor, Charles A. Juneteenth: A Celebration of Freedom. Taylor, Charles A., Jr., illus. 2002. 32p. (YA). (gr. 5-8). trans. 19.95 (978-0-940880-68-9(7)) Open Hand Publishing, LLC.

Taylor, Yuval, ed. Growing up in Slavery: Stories of Young Slaves as Told by Themselves. 2007. (Illus.). 256p. (J). pap. 9.95 (978-1-55652-635-0(0) , Hill, Lawrence Bks.) Chicago Review Pr., Inc.

Thoennes Keller, Kristin. The Slave Trade in Early America. 2004. (Let Freedom Ring Ser.). (Illus.). 48p. (J). 17.95 (978-0-7368-2465-1(0) , Bridgestone Bks.) Capstone Pr., Inc.

Turner, Glennette Tilley. An Apple for Harriet Tubman. Keeter, Susan, illus. 2006. 24p. (J). 15.95 (978-0-8075-0395-9(9)) Whitman, Albert & Co.

Underwood, Deborah. Nat Love. 2008. (History Maker Biographies Ser.). (J). lib. bdg. 26.60 (***978-0-8225-7171-1(4)*** , Lerner Pubns.) Lerner Publishing Group.

Washington Is Burning. 2007. (J). pap. 5.95 (***978-0-8225-6050-0(X)*** , First Avenue Editions) Lerner Publishing Group.

Wilkerson, J. L. From Slave to World-Class Horseman: Tom Bass. 2000. (Great Heartlanders Ser.). (Illus.). 135p. (YA). (gr. 5-9). pap. 9.95 (978-0-9664470-3-3(4)) Acorn Bks.

Williams, Jean Kinney. African-Americans in the Colonies. 2002. (We the People Ser.). (Illus.). 48p. (J). (gr. 4 up). lib. bdg. 22.60 (978-0-7565-0303-1(5)) Compass Point Bks.

Worth, Richard. Africans in America. 2004. (Immigration to the United States Ser.). (Illus.). 96p. (J). (gr. 4-9). 35.00 (978-0-8160-5691-0(9)) Facts On File, Inc.

—Cinque of the Amistad & the Slave Trade in World History. 2001. (In World History Ser.). (Illus.). 112p. (J). (gr. 5-12). lib. bdg. 26.60 (978-0-7660-1460-2(6)) Enslow Pubs., Inc.

—Slave Life on the Plantation: Prisons Beneath the Sun. 2004. (Slavery in American History Ser.). (Illus.). 128p. (J). lib. bdg. 26.60 (978-0-7660-2152-5(1)) Enslow Pubs., Inc.

SLAVERY—UNITED STATES—POETRY

McGill, Alice. In the Hollow of Your Hand: Slave Lullabies. Cummings, Michael, illus. 2000. 40p. (J). (gr. k-3). 18.00 (978-0-618-10445-1(3)); tchr. ed. 18.00 (978-0-395-85755-7(4)) Houghton Mifflin Co. Trade & Reference Div.

McLeese, Don. Phillis Wheatley. 2004. (Heroes of the American Revolution Ser.). (Illus.). 32p. (J). (ps-ps). pap. 5.95 (978-1-59515-320-3(9)) Rourke Publishing, LLC.

SLEEP

see also Dreams

Alda, Arlene. The Book of ZZZs. 2005. (Illus.). 24p. (J). (gr. k-k). 15.95 (978-0-88776-699-2(4)) Tundra Bks., Inc./ Livres Toundra, Inc. CAN. *Dist:* Random Hse., Inc.

Bayer, Linda N. Sleep Disorders. 2000. (Encyclopedia of Psychological Disorders Ser.). (Illus.). 88p. (J). (gr. 7 up). 35.00 (978-0-7910-5314-0(8) , Chelsea Hse.) Facts On File, Inc.

Beck, Isabel L., et al. Trophies Kindergarten: I Nap. 2003. (Trophies Ser.). (gr. k-6). 13.80 (978-0-15-329528-7(7)) Harcourt Schl. Pubs.

Bonnett-Rampersaud, Louise. How Do You Sleep? Kest, Kristin, illus. 2005. 32p. (J). (ps-1). per. 14.95 (978-0-7614-5231-7(1)) Cavendish, Marshall Corp.

Culbert, Timothy & Kajander, Rebecca. Be the Boss of Your Sleep: Self-Care for Kids. 2007. (Be the Boss of Your Body Ser.). (Illus.). 34p. (J). (gr. 4-7). 6.95 (***978-1-57542-255-8(7)***) Free Spirit Publishing, Inc.

DK Publishing, creator. Goodnight, Sleep Tight. 2007. (Kids Play (Paperback) Ser.). (Illus.). 8p. (J). (ps-2). per. 11.99 (***978-0-7566-3093-5(2)***) Dorling Kindersley Publishing, Inc.

Esherick, Joan, frwd. Drug Therapy & Sleep Disorders. 2003. (Encyclopedia of Psychiatric Drugs & Their Disorders Ser.). (Illus.). 128p. (J). lib. bdg. (978-1-59084-576-9(5)) Mason Crest Pubs.

Feeney, Kathy. Sleep Well: You Need to Rest. 2001. (Your Health Ser.). (Illus.). 24p. (J). (gr. 1-2). lib. bdg. 18.60 (978-0-7368-0970-2(8) , Bridgestone Bks.) Capstone Pr., Inc.

Feldman, Eve B. Animals Don't Wear Pajamas: A Book about Sleeping. 2004. (Illus.). 32p. (J). pap. 16.95 (978-0-9764957-0-3(8)) Saturn International.

Feldman, Heather. My Bedtime: A Book about Getting Ready for Bed. 2000. (PowerKids Readers Ser.). (Illus.). 24p. (J). (gr. 1). lib. bdg. 16.00 (978-0-8239-5522-0(2) , PKMYBE, PowerKids Pr.) Rosen Publishing Group, Inc., The.

Gaston, P. J. How Do You Know When It's Time to Go to Bed? Gaston, Carter J., illus. 1999. 24p. (J). (ps up). pap. 8.00 (978-0-9675574-0-3(2)) "How Do You Know".

Gelb, John. Power Nap Kit. 2003. (YA). 34.95 (978-0-9742002-0-0(4)) At Peace Media, LLC.

Gordon, Sharon. A Good Night's Sleep. (Rookie Read-About Health Ser.). (Illus.). 32p. (J). (gr. k-2). 2003. pap. 5.95 (978-0-516-26874-3(0)); 2002. pap. 20.50 (978-0-516-22570-8(7)) Scholastic Library Publishing. (Children's Pr.).

—Good Night's Sleep. 2002. (gr. k-3). lib. bdg. 14.10 (978-0-613-59491-2(6)) Tandem Library Bks.

Goulding, Sylvia. Sleeping Well. 2005. (Healthy Kids Ser.). (Illus.). 32p. (J). (gr. 3-6). 19.95 (978-1-59515-205-3(9)) Rourke Publishing, LLC.

Gray, Shirley W. Sleeping to Stay Healthy. 2003. (Living Well). (Illus.). 32p. (J). (gr. 2-6). 27.07 (978-1-59296-080-4(4)) Child's World, Inc.

La Hora de Dormir, 6 Packs. (Chiquilibros Ser.). (SPA.). (gr. k-1). 23.00 (978-0-7635-8597-6(1)) Rigby Education.

Johnson, Marion. Caillou, What's That Noise. CINAR Corporation staff, illus. 2004. (Clubhouse Usa Ser.). 24p. (J). pap. 3.95 (978-2-89450-489-5(6)) Chouette Publishing CAN. *Dist:* Perseus Distribution.

Kajikawa, Kimiko. Sweet Dreams: How Animals Sleep. rev. ed. 1999. (Illus.). 32p. (J). (ps-2). 16.95 (978-0-8050-5890-1(7) , Holt, Henry & Co. Bks. For Young Readers) Holt, Henry & Co.

Kent, Susan. Let's Talk about When You Have Trouble Going to Sleep. 2000. (Let's Talk Library). (Illus.). 24p. (J). (gr. 3). lib. bdg. 18.75 (978-0-8239-5424-7(2) , PowerKids Pr.) Rosen Publishing Group, Inc., The.

Kittler, Robert. Can't Sleep, Count Sheep. Jackson, Nick, illus. 1998. 123p. (gr. 4-7). pap. 9.95 (978-0-9668622-0-1(1)) Count Sheep Publishing.

Lamstein, Sarah. Sleepy Birds. Alter, Anna, illus. 2006. (J). (978-1-58089-305-3(8)) Charlesbridge Publishing, Inc.

L'Heureux, Christine, et al. Caillou: Good Night! 2006. (Hand in Hand Ser.). (Illus.). 24p. (J). pap. 5.95 (***978-2-89450-588-5(4)***) Chouette Publishing CAN. *Dist:* Independent Pubs. Group.

Magsamen, Susan. Nighty Night. 2007. 48p. 17.95 (***978-1-4027-4824-0(8)***) Sterling Publishing Co., Inc.

Matero, Robert. Animals Asleep. 2000. (Illus.). 80p. (gr. 3-6). lib. bdg. (978-0-7613-1652-7(3) , Millbrook Pr.) Lerner Publishing Group.

McPhee, Andrew T. Sleep & Dreams. 2001. (Single Title - Science Ser.). (Illus.). 112p. (J). (gr. 9-12). 26.00 (978-0-531-11735-4(9) , Watts, Franklin) Scholastic Library Publishing.

Nelson, Robin. Getting Rest. 2006. (Pull Ahead Bks.). (Illus.). 32p. (J). 22.60 (978-0-8225-3487-7(8) , Lerner Pubns.) Lerner Publishing Group.

Olive, M. Foster. Sleep AIDS. Triggle, David J., ed. 2005. (Drugs: the Straight Facts Ser.). (Illus.). 106p. (YA). (gr. 9-12). 30.00 (978-0-7910-8200-3(8) , Chelsea Hse.) Facts On File, Inc.

Perkins, Wendy. Animals Sleeping. 2004. (First Facts Ser.). (Illus.). 24p. (J). 15.95 (978-0-7368-2511-5(8) , Bridgestone Bks.) Capstone Pr., Inc.

Romanek, Trudee. Zzz... The Most Interesting Book You'll Ever Read about Sleep. Cowles, Rose, illus. 2004. (Mysterious You Ser.). 40p. (J). (gr. 4-6). (978-1-55074-946-5(3)) Kids Can Pr., Ltd.

—Zzz: The Most Interesting Book You'll Ever Read about Sleep. 2002. (gr. 3-6). lib. bdg. 15.25 (978-0-613-87157-0(X)) Tandem Library Bks.

—Zzz... The Most Interesting Book You'll Ever Read about Sleep. Cowles, Rose, illus. unabr. ed. 2004. (Mysterious You Ser.). 40p. (J). (gr. 4-6). (978-1-55074-944-1(7)) Kids Can Pr., Ltd.

Royston, Angela. Get Some Rest! 2003. (Look After Yourself Ser.). (Illus.). 32p. (J). lib. bdg. 22.79 (978-1-4034-4442-4(0)) Heinemann Library.

Salzmann, Mary Elizabeth. Getting Enough Sleep. 2004. (Healthy Habits Ser.). (Illus.). 23p. (J). (ps-3). lib. bdg. 19.93 (978-1-59197-552-6(2)) ABDO Publishing Co.

Silverstein, Alvin. Sleep. 2000. (gr. 3-6). lib. bdg. 15.25 (978-0-613-31714-6(9)) Tandem Library Bks.

Sleep Well. (Your Health Ser.). 24p. (J). 6.95 (978-0-7368-4452-9(X)) Capstone Pr., Inc.

Sleeping: Individual Title Six-Packs. (Literatura 2000 Ser.). (gr. 1-2). 28.00 (978-0-7635-0113-6(1)) Rigby Education.

Sleepyheads. 2002. (Baby Faces Ser.). (Illus.). (J). bds. 4.95 (978-0-439-33946-9(4)) Scholastic, Inc.

Stewart, Gail B. Sleep Disorders. 2002. (Diseases & Disorders Ser.). (Illus.). 112p. (YA). (gr. 6-9). 32.45 (978-1-56006-909-6(0) , Lucent Bks.) Thomson Gale.

Swain, Gwenyth. Bedtime! 2003. (Illus.). 24p. (J). (ps-2). pap. 6.95 (978-1-57505-162-8(1)) Lerner Publishing Group.

—Bedtime! 2002. (gr. k-3). lib. bdg. 15.25 (978-0-613-46049-1(9)) Tandem Library Bks.

Trueit, Trudi Strain, tr. Dreams & Sleep. 2004. (Life Balance Ser.). (Illus.). 80p. (J). 20.50 (978-0-531-12260-0(3) , Watts, Franklin) Scholastic Library Publishing.

Twinem, Neecy. Sleepy Beasties. 2006. (Illus.). 12p. (J). bds. 6.95 (978-1-55971-945-2(1) , 1259987, NorthWord Bks. for Young Readers) T&N Children's Publishing.

Vallejo-Nagera, Alejandra. No Tengo Sueno! Guerrero, Andrés, illus. (SPA.). 31p. (J). (gr. k-1). 8.95 (978-1-58986-546-4(4)) Santillana USA Publishing Co., Inc.

Windsor, Jo. At Night: Emergent Level Satellite Individual Title Six-Packs. (Sails Literacy Ser.). (gr. k-1). 27.00 (978-0-7578-7944-9(6)) Rigby Education.

—Time to Sleep: Emergent Level Satellite Individual Title Six-Packs. (Sails Literacy Ser.). (gr. k-1). 27.00 (978-0-7578-7948-7(9)) Rigby Education.

Zolotow, Charlotte. Sleepy Book. Date not set. 32p. (J). (ps-3). pap. 5.99 (978-0-06-443737-0(X)) HarperCollins Pubs.

—Sleepy Book. Vitale, Stefano, illus. 2001. 40p. (J). (ps-2). 15.95 (978-0-06-027873-1(0)) HarperCollins Pubs.

SLEEP—FICTION

Ackerley, Sarah. Patrick the Somnambulist. Ackerley, Sarah, illus. 2008. (Illus.). 32p. (J). (ps-3). 14.95 (***978-1-933831-07-7(3)***) Blooming Tree Pr.

Advantage Publishers Group & Rojany Buccieri, Lisa. Let's Make Noise Around the House. 2007. (Illus.). 10p. (J). 12.95 (978-1-59223-640-4(5) , Silver Dolphin Bks.) Advantage Pubs. Group.

Ambrosio, Michael. It Takes a Lot of Love. Awes, Jennifer, illus. 2007. 32p. (J). 14.95 (***978-0-9716085-4-2(7)***) LionX Publishing.

Asch, Frank. Good Night, Baby Bear. Asch, Frank, illus. 2001. (Illus.). 32p. (J). (ps-k). pap. 7.00 (978-0-15-216368-6(9) , Voyager Bks./Libros Viajeros) Harcourt Children's Bks.

—Good Night, Baby Bear. 2001. 12.80 (978-0-606-22600-4(1)); lib. bdg. 14.15 (978-0-613-53034-7(9)) Tandem Library Bks.

Ashworth, Camilla. La Cama de Horacio. (Picture Books Collection). (SPA., Illus.). 32p. (J). (gr. k-3). pap. 10.95 (978-1-56014-581-3(1)) Santillana USA Publishing Co., Inc.

Baggette, Susan K. The Night the Moon Slept. Saunders, Ward, illus. 2000. 32p. (J). (ps-3). (978-0-9660172-8-1(5)) Brookfield Reader, Inc., The.

Ballard, Robin. Tonight & Tomorrow. 2000. (Illus.). 24p. (J). (ps up). 15.95 (978-0-688-16790-5(X)) HarperCollins Pubs.

Balloon Books Staff. Go to Sleep: Book & Doll. 1999. (Balloon Ser.). (Illus.). 4p. (ps-k). 6.95 (978-0-8069-5925-2(8)) Sterling Publishing Co., Inc.

Bean, Jonathan. At Night. 2007. (Illus.). 32p. (J). (ps-3). 15.00 (***978-0-374-30446-1(7)***) Farrar, Straus & Giroux.

Bennett, John Roy. Jason Mason Middleton-Tapp. Pavanel, Jane, ed. Charbonneau, Isabelle, illus. 2000. 32p. (J). (ps-k). pap. 8.95 (978-1-894222-12-9(1)) Lobster Pr. CAN. *Dist:* Univ. of Toronto Pr.

Bernstein, Margery. That Cat! Handelman, Dorothy, photos by. 1998. (Real Kids Readers Ser.). (Illus.). 32p. (gr. k-2). (J). pap. 4.99 (978-0-7613-2044-9(X)); lib. bdg. 18.90 (978-0-7613-2019-7(9)) Lerner Publishing Group. (Millbrook Pr.).

Berry, Ron & Sharp, Chris. It's Bedtime. Sharp, Chris & Currant, Gary, illus. 2003. (It's Time to Ser.). 14p. (J). (ps-k). bds. 6.95 (978-1-891100-61-1(0)) Smart Kids Publishing.

Bishop, Gavin. Stay Awake, Bear! Bishop, Gavin, illus. 2000. (Illus.). 32p. (J). (ps-1). 16.99 (978-0-531-33249-8(7)); pap. 15.95 (978-0-531-30249-1(0)) Scholastic, Inc. (Orchard Bks.).

Bittner, Wolfgang. Despierta, Osogris! 1999. (gr. k-3). (SPA.). lib. bdg. 15.25 (978-0-613-73509-4(9)); 13.75 (978-0-606-17635-4(7)) Tandem Library Bks.

Blomgren, Jennifer. Where Do I Sleep? A Pacific Northwest Lullaby. Gabriel, Andrea, illus. 2002. 32p. (J). (ps-1). 16.95 (978-1-57061-258-9(7)) Sasquatch Bks.

Bock, Lee. Oh, Crumps!/¡Ay, Caramba! de la Vega, Eida, tr. Midgett, Morgan, illus. 2003. Tr. of ¡Ay, Caramba!. (SPA & ENG.). 32p. (J). (gr. k-3). 16.95 (978-0-9720192-4-8(3) , 626999) Raven Tree Pr.

Bonnell, Kris. Where Can Louis Sleep? 2007. (J). 3.95 (***978-1-933727-57-8(8)***) Reading Reading Bks., LLC.

Bourgeois, Paulette. Franklin's Blanket. 2000. (Franklin Ser.). (Illus.). 180p. (J). (ps-3). (978-1-55074-686-0(3)) Kids Can Pr., Ltd.

Boynton, Sandra. The Going to Bed Book. Boynton, Sandra, illus. 2006. 14p. (J). 12.95 (978-1-4169-2794-5(8) , Little Simon) Simon & Schuster Children's Publishing.

Boza, Eduardo Robles. Mi Amiga No Qiere Dormir.Tr. of My Friend Doesn't Want to Sleep. (SPA.). (J). 4.95 (978-970-05-0130-7(2)) Grijalbo, Editorial MEX. *Dist:* AIMS International Bks., Inc.

Brady, Kymberli W. The Sleepy Little Star. 2002. (Illus.). 32p. (J). 14.99 (978-0-9711758-0-8(2)) Get Graphic Publishing.

Branford, Henrietta. Little Pig Figwort Can't Get to Sleep. Munoz, Claudio, illus. 2002. 32p. (J). (gr. k-3). 14.00 (978-0-618-15968-0(1) , Clarion Bks.) Houghton Mifflin Co. Trade & Reference Div.

Brewer, Elly. Jerry & the Jannans. 2006. 320p. (J). pap. 11.99 (***978-0-7475-8213-7(0)***) Bloomsbury Publishing Plc GBR. *Dist:* Independent Pubs. Group.

Brooks, Stephen J. Sleep Peacefully, My Princess. Schrampfer, William M., II, illus. 2005. (J). 16.96 (978-0-9769017-0-9(6)) Purple Sky Publishing.

Brown, Jeff. The Flat Stanley Collection Box Set. Nash, Scott, illus. 2006. (Flat Stanley Ser.). (J). pap. 14.99 (978-0-06-083776-1(4) , Harper Trophy) HarperCollins Pubs.

Brown, Margaret Wise. Sheep Don't Count Sheep. Huang, Benrei, illus. 2003. 32p. (J). (ps). 14.95 (978-0-689-83346-5(6) , McElderry, Margaret K.) Simon & Schuster Children's Publishing.

Buchholz, Quint. Sleep Well, Little Bear. 2004. (Illus.). pap. (978-0-374-46709-8(9)) Farrar, Straus & Giroux.

Butler, John. While You Were Sleeping. 2001. 24p. (J). bds. 6.95 (978-1-56145-254-5(8) , Q24081) Peachtree Pubs., Ltd.

Capucilli, Alyssa Satin. Bizcocho. Mlawer, Teresa, tr. Schories, Pat, illus. 2nd ed. 2001. (Coleccion Ya Se Leer). (SPA.). 32p. (J). (ps up). pap. 4.99 (978-0-06-444310-4(8) , HC30732) HarperCollins Pubs.

—Bizcocho. 2001. (SPA.). (ps-2). lib. bdg. 12.95 (978-0-613-35909-2(7)) Tandem Library Bks.

—Little Spotted Cat. Andreasen, Dan, illus. 2005. 32p. (J). (ps-ps). 14.99 (978-0-8037-2692-5(9) , Dial) Penguin Group (USA) Inc.

Caviezel, Giovanni. Sleep Tight, Little Bear. Pagnoni, Roberta, illus. 2006. 12p. (J). bds. 6.99 (978-1-4169-1383-2(1) , Little Simon) Simon & Schuster Children's Publishing.

Chacon, Dulce. La Voz Dormida. 2005. (SPA., Illus.). 384p. pap. 22.95 (978-84-204-6438-1(4) , AF13909, Alfaguara) Santillana USA Publishing Co., Inc.

Chadha, Radhika & Kuriyan, Priya. I'm So Sleepy. 2004. (Illus.). 24p. (J). (978-81-8146-033-2(2)) Tulika Pubs.

Child, Lauren. La Cama de Tus Suenos. 2002. (Illus.). 16p. (J). (CAT.). 20.95 (978-84-8488-005-9(2)); (SPA., 20.95 (978-84-8488-004-2(4) , RR5225) Serres, Ediciones, S. L. ESP. *Dist:* Lectorum Pubns., Inc.

—No Tengo Sueno y No Quiero Irme a la Cama. 2002. (Illus.). (J). (gr. k-3). (CAT.). 25p. 17.95 (978-84-8488-014-1(1)); (SPA., 312p. 17.95 (978-84-8488-010-3(9) , RR0510) Serres, Ediciones, S. L. ESP. *Dist:* Lectorum Pubns., Inc.

Clements, Andrew. Naptime for Slippers. Bynum, Janie, illus. 2005. 32p. (J). (ps). 12.99 (978-0-525-47287-2(8) , Dutton Juvenile) Penguin Group (USA) Inc.

Coe, Frances. Sleepy Little Lamb: With Soft Cloth Blanket. Elgar, Rebecca, illus. 1999. (Little Blanket Bks.). 10p. (J). (ps). bds. 3.95 (978-0-7641-5176-7(2)) Barron's Educational Series, Inc.

Colbert, Norman. Norman Okay, Not Today. 2001. 109p. pap. 11.95 (978-0-7414-0674-3(8)) Infinity Publishing.

Cook, Sally. Good Night Pillow Fight. Date not set. (Illus.). (J). pap. 5.99 (978-0-06-205932-1(7)) HarperCollins Pubs.

—Good Night Pillow Fight. Cornell, Laura, illus. 2004. 32p. (J). 15.99 (978-0-06-205189-9(X)) HarperCollins Pubs.

Cooper, Helen. Boy Who Wouldn't Go to Bed. 2000. (gr. k-3). lib. bdg. 14.15 (978-0-613-33679-6(8)) Tandem Library Bks.

—The Boy Who Wouldn't Go to Bed: Pictures & Story. Cooper, Helen, illus. 2000. (Illus.). 32p. (J). (ps-2). pap. 5.99 (978-0-14-056771-7(2) , Puffin) Penguin Group (USA) Inc.

Cosgrove, Stephen. Wheedle on the Needle. James, Robin, illus. ed. 2002. (Serendipity Ser.). 32p. (J). reprint ed. pap. 4.99 (978-0-8431-4872-5(1) , Price Stern Sloan) Penguin Group (USA) Inc.

—Wheedle on the Needle. 2002. (gr. k-3). lib. bdg. 13.00 (978-0-613-64617-8(7)) Tandem Library Bks.

Cotten, Cynthia. Some Babies Sleep. Tong, Paul, illus. 2007. 32p. (J). 12.99 (978-0-399-24030-0(6) , Philomel) Penguin Group (USA) Inc.

Cousins, Lucy. Maisy's Bedtime. Cousins, Lucy, illus. 1999. (Maisy Bks.). (Illus.). 24p. (J). pap. 3.99 (978-0-7636-0908-5(0)) Candlewick Pr.

Cox, Judy. Go to Sleep, Groundhog! Meisel, Paul, illus. 32p. (gr. k-3). reprint ed. pap. 6.95 (978-0-8234-1874-9(X)) Holiday Hse., Inc.

Cox, Phil Roxbee. Sam Sheep Can't Sleep. Cartwright, Stephen, illus. rev. ed. 2006. 16p. (J). pap. 6.99 (978-0-7945-1508-9(8) , Usborne) EDC Publishing.

Dale, Penny. Princess, Princess. Dale, Penny, illus. 2003. (Illus.). 32p. (J). (ps-1). 14.99 (978-0-7636-2212-1(5)) Candlewick Pr.

Dale, Penny & Platt, Richard. Pirate Diary. Ridell, Chris, illus. 2003. 128p. (J). (gr. 4). pap. 6.99 (978-0-7636-2169-8(2)) Candlewick Pr.

De Lint, Charles. The Riddle of the Wren. 2002. (gr. 7-12). lib. bdg. 15.30 (978-0-613-56586-8(X)) Tandem Library Bks.

de Vries, Maggie. How Sleep Found Tabitha. Lott, Sheena, illus. 2002. 32p. (J). (ps-2). 16.95 (978-1-55143-193-2(9)) Orca Bk. Pubs. USA.

Deacon, Alexis. While You Are Sleeping. 2006. (Illus.). 36p. (J). 16.50 (978-0-374-38330-5(8) , Farrar, Straus & Giroux (BYR)) Farrar, Straus & Giroux.

Demers, Dominique. Every Single Night. Debon, Nicolas, illus. 2006. 32p. (J). 17.95 (978-0-88899-699-2(3)) Groundwood Bks. CAN. *Dist:* Perseus Distribution.

Dennis, Murray Marjorie. Dont Wake up Bear. Wittmann, Patricia, illus. 2006. 32p. 5.99 (978-0-7614-5330-7(X)) Cavendish, Marshall Corp.

Dillon, Jana. Upsie Downsie, Are You Asleep? Dillon, Jana, illus. 2002. (Illus.). 32p. (J). 15.95 (978-1-56554-941-8(4)) Pelican Publishing Co., Inc.

DiPucchio, Kelly S. Bed Hogs. Fine, Howard, illus. 2004. 32p. (ps-k). 15.99 (978-0-7868-1884-6(0)) Hyperion Bks. for Children.

Dodd, Lynley. Wake up, Bear. Dodd, Lynley, illus. 2001. (Gold Star First Readers Ser.). (Illus.). 32p. (J). (gr. 1 up). lib. bdg. 22.00 (978-0-8368-2786-6(4)) Stevens, Gareth Inc.

Downey, Lynn. The Flea's Sneeze. Firehammer, Karla, illus. rev. ed. 2000. 32p. (J). (ps-1). 17.95 (978-0-8050-6103-1(7) , Holt, Henry & Co. Bks. For Young Readers) Holt, Henry & Co.

Dube, Jasmine & Barrette, Doris. Grattelle au Bois Mordant. 1998. (Etait une Fois Ser.). (Illus.). 24p. (J). pap. (978-2-89021-332-6(3)) Diffusion du livre Mirabel.

Edwards, Frank B. & Bianchi, John. The Zookeeper's Sleepers. 1999. (New Reader Ser.). (Illus.). 24p. (J). (ps-1). pap. (978-1-894323-07-9(6)) Pokeweed Pr.

Elgar, Rebecca. Sshh! Everyone is Sleeping. 1999. (Illus.). 10p. 6.95 (978-1-899607-12-9(9)) Sterling Publishing Co., Inc.

Flam, Chanie. Good Night. (Goldie Gold Board Book Ser.: Vol. 6). (Illus.). (J). (ps-1). bds. 4.95 (978-1-58330-030-5(9)) Feldheim Pubs.

Fleming, Denise. Time to Sleep. rev. ed. 2001. (Illus.). 32p. (J). (ps-3). pap. 7.95 (978-0-8050-6767-5(1) , Holt, Henry & Co. Bks. For Young Readers) Holt, Henry & Co.

—Time to Sleep. 2001. (ps-2). lib. bdg. 15.25 (978-0-613-75372-2(0)) Tandem Library Bks.

Flether, Ralph. The Sand Man. rev. ed. 2008. (Illus.). 32p. (J). 16.95 (*978-0-8050-7726-1(X)) Holt, Henry & Co.

Fleuriel, Allison. Are You Done Sleeping? 2006. (J). pap. 16.00 (978-0-8059-7115-6(7)) Dorrance Publishing Co., Inc.

Fox, Mem. Where the Giant Sleeps. Radunsky, Vladimir, illus. 2007. 32p. (J). (ps-2). 16.00 (978-0-15-205785-5(4)) Harcourt Trade Pubs.

Fox, Mem & Horacek, Judy. Where Is the Green Sheep? 2004. (Illus.). 32p. (J). (ps-k). 16.00 (978-0-15-204907-2(X)) Harcourt Children's Bks.

Frampton, David. The Whole Night Through. Frampton, David, illus. Date not set. (Illus.). 32p. (J). (ps-1). pap. 5.99 (978-0-06-443652-6(7)) HarperCollins Pubs.

—The Whole Night Through: A Lullaby. Frampton, David, illus. 2004. (Illus.). 30p. (J). (gr. k-4). reprint ed. (978-0-7567-7723-4(2)) DIANE Publishing Co.

—The Whole Night Through: A Lullaby. Frampton, David, illus. 2001. (Illus.). 32p. (J). (ps-1). 15.89 (978-0-06-028826-6(4)) ; 15.95 (978-0-06-028825-9(6)) HarperCollins Pubs.

Freed, Shirley Ann & Moon, Louise. Baby Is Sleeping. Morelan, Bill, ed. l.t. ed. 2002. (Illus.). 16p. (J). (gr. 5). pap. 3.99 (978-1-58938-006-6(1)) Concerned Communications.

Furlong, Marguerite, text. Kim Goes to Camp. 2002. pap. 5.00 (978-1-882541-29-4(4)) Food Allergy & Anaphylaxis Network.

Gaines, Simon Ludvigsen. Good Night, Sleep Tight. 2007. (Little Scholastic Ser.). (Illus.). 24p. (J). (ps). bds. 9.99 (*978-0-439-86726-9(6) , Cartwheel Bks.) Scholastic, Inc.

Gikow, Louise. A Day with Daddy. Mazali, Gustavo, tr. Mazali, Gustavo, illus. 2004. (My First Reader Ser.). 31p. (J). 18.50 (978-0-516-24410-5(8) , Children's Pr.) Scholastic Library Publishing.

Gilbert, Frances. Sleepy Dog. Sterling Publishing Company Staff, ed. 2003. (Illus.). 16p. (J). bds. 4.95 (978-1-4027-0576-2(X)) Sterling Publishing Co., Inc.

Girard, Jeremy Marc. A Dreamer's Story: The Tales of Slumber. 2004. 207p. (J). pap. 19.95 (978-1-4137-1530-9(3)) PublishAmerica, Inc.

Glass, Julie. Counting Sheep. 2000. (Illus.). (J). 11.99 (978-0-375-90658-9(4)); 32p. pap. 3.99 Random Hse. Children's Bks.

—Counting Sheep. Wohnoutka, Mike, illus. 2000. (Step into Reading Ser.). (J). 10.79 (978-0-606-19890-5(3)) Tandem Library Bks.

Glass, Timothy. Sleepytown Beagles Penny's 4th of July. Mikle, Toby, illus. 2006. 24p. (J). per. 15.95 (*978-1-888461-10-7(1)); 16.95 (*978-1-888461-11-4(X)) Islewest Publishing.

Golden Books Staff. Journey to Fairytale Land. 2007. (Book & CD Ser.). (Illus.). 24p. (J). (ps-2). 9.99 (978-0-375-84025-8(7) , Golden Bks.) Random Hse. Children's Bks.

—Sleepy Bunny. 2003. (Cloth Book Ser.). (Illus.). 8p. (J). (gr. k-k). 12.95 (978-0-375-82531-6(2) , Golden Bks.) Random Hse. Children's Bks.

Goodman, Joan Elizabeth. Bernard's Nap. Catalano, Dominic, illus. 2003. 32p. (J). (ps up). 14.95 (978-1-56397-728-2(1)) Boyds Mills Pr.

Graham, Winston. The Sleeping Partner. 2002. 281p. pap. 9.99 (978-0-330-33905-6(2) , Pan) Pan Macmillan GBR. *Dist:* Trafalgar Square Publishing.

Grimes, Nikki. A Day with Daddy. Tadgell, Nicole, illus. 2004. 32p. (J). lib. bdg. 15.00 (*978-1-4242-0226-3(4)) Fitzgerald Bks.

Guy, Ginger Foglesong. Siesta. Moreno, Rene King, illus. 2005. (ENG & SPA.). 32p. (J). lib. bdg. 16.89 (978-0-06-056063-8(0)); 15.99 (978-0-06-056061-4(4)) HarperCollins Pubs.

Half a Moon & One Whole Star. 1998. (J). pap. 5.99 (978-0-87628-391-2(1)) Ctr. for Applied Research in Education, The.

Half a Moon & One Whole Star. 1999. (J). (gr. k-3). 16.00 (978-0-689-82667-2(2) , Atheneum) Simon & Schuster Children's Publishing.

Harcourt School Publishers Staff. An Afternoon Nap: Below Level. 3rd ed. 2002. (Trophies Reading Program Ser.). (J). pap. 4.10 (978-0-15-322971-8(3)) Harcourt Schl. Pubs.

—Picture a Kite: Below Level. 3rd ed. 2002. (Trophies Reading Program Ser.). (Illus.). (J). (gr. 1). pap. 4.10 (978-0-15-322960-2(8)) Harcourt Schl. Pubs.

—Picture a Kite 5-Pack, Below Level. 3rd ed. 2002. (Trophies Reading Program Ser.). (Illus.). (J). (gr. 1). pap. 20.10 (978-0-15-326810-6(7)) Harcourt Schl. Pubs.

—Ready, Set, Sleep: On Level. 3rd ed. 2002. (Trophies Reading Program Ser.). (Illus.). pap. 5.10 (978-0-15-323005-9(3)) Harcourt Schl. Pubs.

—Trofeos Below Level: La Cometa. 3rd ed. 2002. (SPA., Illus.). pap. 5.50 (978-0-15-323871-0(2)) Harcourt Schl. Pubs.

Harrison, David Lee. The Big Sleepover. Edwards, Ken, illus. 2001. (Clifford, the Big Red Dog Ser.). (J). pap. (978-0-439-22364-5(4)) Scholastic, Inc.

Harshman, Marc. All the Way to Morning. Davalos, Felipe, illus. 1999. (Accelerated Reader Bks.). 32p. (J). (ps-k). 15.95 (978-0-7614-5042-9(4) , Cavendish Children's Bks.) Cavendish, Marshall Corp.

—All the Way to Morning. Davalos, Felipe, illus. 2006. (J). per. 7.95 (978-1-891852-49-7(3)) Quarrier Pr.

Hazen, Barbara Shook. Where Do Bears Sleep? Van Royen, Mary Morgan, illus. 1998. (Growing Tree Ser.). 24p. (J). (ps up). 9.95 (978-0-694-01037-0(5) , Harper Festival) HarperCollins Pubs.

Heine, Helme. Wunderbare Reise Durch Die Na. 12.95 (978-3-7876-9528-7(1)) Middelhauve Verlags GmbH DEU. *Dist:* Distribooks, Inc.

Hertz, Grete Janus. Olie's Bedtime Walk. Rose, Tatin, tr. from DUT. Talsma, Nynke Mare, illus. 2002. 36p. (J). (ps-2). 12.95 (978-1-887734-90-5(2)) Star Bright Bks., Inc.

Heyer, Carol. The Sleeping Beauty in the Wood. 2001. (J). (gr. 4-7). 14.95 (978-0-8249-5401-7(7)) Ideals Pubns.

Higgins, Gladys. Goodnight, Charlie. 2005. 18.00 (978-0-8059-8116-2(0)) Dorrance Publishing Co., Inc.

Hillard, Shirley. Who's Not Asleep? 2004. (Illus.). 24p. (J). 13.95 (978-1-933014-31-9(8)) Mamoo Hse.

Hindley, Judy. Sleepy Places. Freeman, Tor, illus. 2006. 32p. (J). (ps-1). 15.99 (978-0-7636-2983-0(9)) Candlewick Pr.

Hinman, Bobbie. The Knot Fairy. 2007. 32p. 15.95 (*978-0-9786791-0-1(5)) Hinman, Bobbie E. Inc.

Hoellwarth, Cathryn Clinton. The Underbed. Gerig, Sibyl Graber, illus. 2001. 32p. (J). (ps-1). 6.95 (978-1-56148-331-0(1)) Good Bks.

Honeycutt, Scarlet. Quit Waking Us Up. We're Trying to Sleep! Aarvig, Cindy, illus. 2001. 28p. (J). 16.85 (978-1-55618-194-8(9)) Brunswick Publishing Corp.

Howard, Jane R. When I'm Sleepy. 2000. (978-0-606-20379-1(6)); lib. bdg. 14.15 (978-0-613-31909-6(5)) Tandem Library Bks.

Howarth, Daniel, illus. Somewhere to Sleep. 2006. 14p. (J). bds. 14.95 (978-1-4027-3170-9(1)) Sterling Publishing Co., Inc.

Hulme, John, et al. The Seems: The Glitch in Sleep. 2007. (Illus.). 288p. (J). (gr. 5 up). 16.95 (*978-1-59990-129-9(3) , Bloomsbury Children) Bloomsbury Publishing.

Hurd, Thacher. Sleepy Cadillac: A Bedtime Drive. Hurd, Thacher, illus. 2005. (Illus.). 32p. (J). 15.99 (978-0-06-073020-8(X)); lib. bdg. 16.89 (978-0-06-073021-5(8)) HarperCollins Pubs.

Inches, Alison. Run-Away Roley. Ellis, Art, illus. 2002. (Bob the Builder Ready-to-Read Ser.: Bk. 3). 32p. (J). (ps-1). pap. 3.99 (978-0-689-84753-0(X) , Simon Spotlight) Simon & Schuster Children's Publishing.

—Run-Away Roley. 2002. (gr. k-3). lib. bdg. 11.80 (978-0-613-51322-7(3)) Tandem Library Bks.

Intrater, Roberta Grobel. Sleep. 2002. (Baby Faces Ser.). (Illus.). 10p. (J). bds. 4.95 (978-0-439-42004-4(0) , Cartwheel Bks.) Scholastic, Inc.

Ira Sleeps Over. 2005. (J). (978-1-59564-973-7(5)) Steps To Literacy, LLC.

Irving, Washington & Busch, Jeffrey. Rip Van Winkle. (Classics Illustrated Ser.). (Illus.). 52p. (YA). pap. 4.95 (978-1-57209-009-5(X)) Classics International Entertainment, Inc.

Irving, Washington & Moses, Will. Rip Van Winkle. 1999. (Illus.). 1p. (J). (ps-3). 17.99 (978-0-399-23152-0(8) , Philomel) Penguin Group (USA) Inc.

Jam, Teddy. Night Cars. Beddows, Eric, illus. 2006. 32p. 9.95 (978-0-88899-748-7(5)) Groundwood Bks. CAN. *Dist:* Perseus Distribution.

Johnson, Linda & Hodges, Quae. 21st Century Parables: A Child's Book. 2006. 48p. pap. 14.95 (*978-1-60145-071-5(0)) Booklocker.com, Inc.

Jolin, Dominique. Washington Takes a Nap. Jolin, Dominique, illus. 2000. (Tickle Ser.). (Illus.). 16p. (YA). (ps up). bds. (978-1-894363-36-5(1)) Dominique & Friends.

Jones, Sylvie. Go Back to Sleep. Constantin, Pascale, illus. 2006. 32p. 15.95 (978-1-59354-171-2(6)) Blue Apple Bks.

Jossa, Isabelle. Ned Goes to Bed. 2005. (Illus.). 32p. (J). (ps-7). 16.95 (978-1-894965-17-0(5)) Simply Read Bks. CAN. *Dist:* Perseus Distribution.

Keller, Holly. Geraldine's Blanket. Keller, Holly, illus. 2002. (Illus.). (J). 14.43 (978-0-7587-2579-0(5)) Book Wholesalers, Inc.

Kelly, Mij. One More Sheep. Ayto, Russell, illus. 2006. 30p. (J). 16.95 (978-1-56145-378-8(1) , Peachtree Junior) Peachtree Pubs., Ltd.

Kenyon, Tony. Oops! It's Olly Bear. 2003. (Illus.). 32p. (J). 18.00 (978-1-85881-899-3(0)) Orion Bks. Ltd. GBR. *Dist:* Trafalgar Square Publishing.

Keselman, Gabriela. Marc Just Couldn't Sleep. Villamuza, Noemi, illus. 2004. 32p. (J). 15.95 (978-1-929132-68-3(9)) Kane/Miller Bk. Pubs., Inc.

Kienzle, Patricia Taylor. Good Morning! Good Morning? Individual Differences. Coffey, Peg, illus. 1999. 24p. (J). (ps-2). pap. 4.95 (978-1-890798-10-9(X)) Kienzle, Patricia Taylor.

Kim Learns How to Take Care of Herself. 2001. (J). pap. 5.00 (978-1-882541-28-7(6)) Food Allergy & Anaphylaxis Network.

Kitamura, Satoshi. When Sheep Can't Sleep (Cuando los Borregos no Pueden Dormir) (SPA.). (J). (gr. 1-6). 19.95 (978-84-372-6605-3(X)) Santillana USA Publishing Co., Inc.

Kleinberg, Naomi. Good Night, Tucked in Tight (All about Sleep) Goldberg, Barry, illus. 2007. 32p. (J). (gr. k-ps). 6.99 (978-0-375-83568-1(7) , Random Hse. Bks. for Young Readers) Random Hse. Children's Bks.

Kleinberg, Naomi. It's Naptime, Little One. Moroney, Christopher, illus. 2007. (Sesame Beginnings Ser.). 12p. (J). (gr. k-ps). bds. 6.99 (*978-0-375-84123-1(7) , Random Hse. Bks. for Young Readers) Random Hse. Children's Bks.

Krasner, Steven. Have a Nice Nap, Humphrey. Griffis, Sandy, illus. 1998. 36p. (J). (gr. k-5). pap. 12.95 (978-0-9642721-2-5(1)) Gorilla Productions.

Kraus, Robert. Milton the Early Riser. Aruego, Jose & Dewey, Ariane, illus. 2006. (Stories to Go! Ser.). 32p. (J). pap. 4.99 (978-1-4169-1856-1(6) , Aladdin) Simon & Schuster Children's Publishing.

Krauss, Ruth. Goodnight Goodnight Sleepyhead. Dyer, Jane, illus. 2004. 32p. (J). (ps-1). lib. bdg. 16.89 (978-0-06-028895-2(7)) HarperCollins Pubs.

—Goodnight Goodnight Sleepyhead Board. Dyer, Jane, illus. 2007. 32p. (J). (ps-1). 6.99 (978-0-694-01501-6(6) , Harper Festival) HarperCollins Pubs.

Kuskin, Karla. The Lullaway of Rockabye. 32p. (J). (ps up). Date not set. 14.89 (978-0-06-027716-1(5)); 1999. 13.95 (978-0-06-027715-4(7)) HarperCollins Pubs.

Labatt, Mary. Franklin Stays Up. 2003. (gr. k-3). lib. bdg. 11.80 (978-0-613-87146-4(4)) Tandem Library Bks.

Langford, Jane. Hero. Vince, Dawn, illus. 2005. 24p. (J). lib. bdg. 22.65 (*978-1-59646-720-0(7)) Dingles & Co.

Levine, Gail Carson. Princess Sonora & the Long Sleep. Elliott, Mark, illus. 1999. (Princess Tales Ser.). 112p. (J). (ps-3). 9.99 (978-0-06-028064-2(6)) HarperCollins Pubs.

Lewis, Anne Margaret. Sleeping Bear. Grant, Sarah, illus. 2007. 32p. (J). 16.95 (*978-1-934133-15-6(9)) Mackinac Island Pr., Inc.

Lewis, Kim. Good Night Harry. Lewis, Kim, illus. 2004. (Illus.). 32p. (J). (ps-1). 15.99 (978-0-7636-2206-0(0)) Candlewick Pr.

Lewis, Paeony. No More Yawning! Granstrom, Brita, illus. 2008. 32p. (J). pap. 16.99 (*978-0-545-02957-5(0) , Chicken Hse., The) Scholastic, Inc.

Maas, James B. Remmy & the Brain Train: Traveling Through the Land of Good Sleep. Danella, Guy, illus. 2001. 32p. (J). (ps-3). 16.95 (978-0-9712140-0-2(X)) Maas Presentations, LLC.

Magic Moon Dreams. 2003. (J). 8.99 (978-0-89610-767-0(1)) Island Heritage Publishing.

Mallat, Kathy. Seven Stars More! Mallat, Kathy, illus. 1998. (Illus.). 24p. (J). (ps-1). 14.95 (978-0-8027-8675-3(8)); lib. bdg. 15.85 (978-0-8027-8676-0(6)) Walker & Co.

Markes, Julie. Shhhhh! Everybody's Sleeping. Parkins, David, illus. 2005. 32p. (J). (ps-1). 14.99 (978-0-06-053790-6(6)); lib. bdg. 16.89 (978-0-06-053791-3(4)) HarperCollins Pubs.

Marx, Patricia. Now I Will Never Go to Sleep. Date not set. (Illus.). (J). 15.89 (978-0-06-027482-5(4)); 14.99 (978-0-06-027483-2(2)) HarperCollins Pubs.

Massie, Diane Redfield. The Baby Beebee Bird. Kellogg, Steven, illus. 32p. (J). (ps-1). 2003. pap. 6.99 (978-0-06-051784-7(0)); 2000. 16.99 (978-0-06-028083-3(2)) HarperCollins Pubs.

Matsutani, Miyoko. Sleepy Time. Segawa, Yasuo, illus. 2006. 20p. (J). 10.95 (978-1-74126-046-5(9)) R.I.C. Pubns. AUS. *Dist:* SCB Distributors.

Mayer, Mercer. Goodnight, Little Critter, Vol. 3. 2002. (Little Critter First Readers Ser.). (Illus.). 24p. (J). (gr. 1-2). pap. 3.95 (978-1-57768-834-1(1)) School Specialty Publishing.

McGee, Marni. Sleepy Me Proprietary Proprietary. Williams, illus. 2003. 32p. pap. 2.99 (978-0-689-86622-7(4) , Simon & Schuster Children's Publishing) Simon & Schuster Children's Publishing.

McOmber, Rachel B., ed. McOmber Phonics Storybooks: Snores & More. rev. ed. (Illus.). (J). (978-0-944991-59-6(9)) Swift Learning Resources.

Meade, Holly. A Place to Sleep. 2001. (Illus.). 32p. (J). (ps-1). 15.95 (978-0-7614-5096-2(3) , Cavendish Children's Bks.) Cavendish, Marshall Corp.

Merritt, Susan E. Sleep Little Centipede, Sleep. 1999. (Mudcat Kids Ser.). (Illus.). 58p. (J). (gr. 2-4). pap. (978-1-55125-021-2(7)) Vanwell Publishing, Ltd.

Michaels, Kat. Gentle Is the Night. 2008. (J). 15.95 (*978-0-9745052-7-5(7)) Tree Of Life Publishing.

Milgrim, David. See Santa Nap. Milgrim, David, illus. 2004. (Adventures of Otto Ser.). (Illus.). 32p. (J). 14.95 (978-0-689-85928-1(7) , Atheneum) Simon & Schuster Children's Publishing.

Morris, Kerry Nicole. The Baby Who Just... WON't Sleep! Parker's Story. 2004. 35p. pap. 17.95 (978-1-4137-3724-0(2)) PublishAmerica, Inc.

Moulton, Eugena. The Age of Merrik: The Anointing. 2007. 200p. 24.95 (*978-0-595-67899-0(8)); per. 14.95 (*978-0-595-41367-6(6)) iUniverse, Inc.

Munoz, Isabel. Eric & Julieta: It's Mine/Es Mio. Mazali, Gustavo, illus. 2006. (ENG & SPA.). 24p. (J). pap. 3.99 (978-0-439-78370-5(4)) Scholastic, Inc.

Munsch, Robert. Get Out of Bed! Daniel, Alan & Daniel, Lea, illus. 1998. 32p. (J). (ps-1). pap. 10.95 (978-0-590-76977-8(4) , Cartwheel Bks.) Scholastic, Inc.

—Get Out of Bed! (ps-2). 2002. lib. bdg. 11.80 (978-0-613-46072-9(3)); 1999. (Illus.). (J). 10.79 (978-0-606-18550-9(X)) Tandem Library Bks.

Murray, Marjorie Dennis. The Stars Are Waiting. Rogers, Jacqueline, illus. 1998. (Accelerated Reader Bks.). 32p. (J). (ps-k). lib. bdg. 15.95 (978-0-7614-5024-5(6) , Cavendish Children's Bks.) Cavendish, Marshall Corp.

Nadeau, Nicole & Brignaud, Pierre. Caillou Wakes up at Night. rev. ed. 2008. (Hand in Hand Ser.). (Illus.). 24p. (J). bds. 5.95 (*978-2-89450-643-1(0)) Chouette Publishing CAN. *Dist:* Independent Pubs. Group.

A Nap in Sand Land, Bk. 2. 1999. (McGraw-Hill Junior Academic Ser.). (Illus.). 16p. (J). (gr. 1). pap. 2.99 (978-1-57768-521-0(0)) School Specialty Publishing.

Német, Andreas. Five Little Sleepyheads. Schmidt, Hans-Christian, illus. 2007. 12p. (J). 8.95 (*978-0-7358-2138-5(0)) North-South Bks., Inc.

Nobisso, Josephine. The Yawn. Coalson, Glo, photos by. 2001. (Illus.). (J). 15.95 (978-0-531-30319-1(5) , Orchard Bks.) Scholastic, Inc.

Nobisso, Josephine & Coalson, Glo. The Yawn. 2001. (Illus.). (J). lib. bdg. (978-0-531-33319-8(1) , Orchard Bks.) Scholastic, Inc.

Nortung, Sandra. Watching over You. Wimmer, Greg, illus. 2000. 32p. (J). (gr. k-5). 11.95 (978-1-892885-51-7(4)) Daring Child Pr.

Novak, Matt. Rock-A-Bye Christmas. 2007. (Illus.). 16p. (J). (ps-1). 7.95 (*978 1 59643-187-4(3)) Roaring Brook Pr.

Numeroff, Laura Joffe. When Sheep Sleep. McPhail, David, illus. 2006. 24p. (J). (ps-3). 15.95 (978-0-8109-5469-4(9)) Abrams, Harry N. , Inc.

Owen, Dan. Ellen. 2006. 32p. (J). pap. 11.99 (978-1-4116-9069-1(9)) Lulu.com.

Packard, Mary. Don't Make a Sound. Yerkes, Lane, illus. 2004. 16p. (J). (gr. 1 up). lib. bdg. 19.33 (978-0-8368-4099-5(2)) Stevens, Gareth Inc.

Page, Nick & Page, Claire. Sleeping Beauty: Ready to Read Level 1. 2007. (Ready to Read: Level 1 (Make Believe Ideas) Ser.). (Illus.). 31p. (J). (gr. k-2). 3.99 (*978-1-84610-441-1(6)) Make Believe Ideas GBR. *Dist:* Ingram Pub. Services.

Peters, Lisa Westberg. Sleepyhead Bear. Schoenherr, Ian, illus. 2006. (J). 32p. 16.99 (978-0-06-059675-0(9)); 40p. lib. bdg. 17.89 (978-0-06-059676-7(7)) HarperCollins Pubs.

Piers, Helen. Who's in My Bed? Saunders, Dave, illus. 1999. (Accelerated Reader Bks.). 24p. (J). (ps-k). 15.95 (978-0-7614-5046-7(7) , Cavendish Children's Bks.) Cavendish, Marshall Corp.

Pinkney, Andrea Davis. Sleeping Cutie. Pinkney, Brian, illus. 2004. 32p. (J). 16.00 (978-0-15-202544-1(8) , Harcourt Children's Bks) Harcourt Children's Bks.

Prap, Lila. Animal Lullabies. 2006. (Illus.). 40p. (J). 14.95 (978-0-7358-2097-5(X)) North-South Bks., Inc.

Prater, John. I Love My Bed. 2007. (Illus.). 32p. (J). (*978-0-340-85535-5(5)) Hodder General Publishing Division.

—I Love My Bed. 2007. (Illus.). 32p. (J). pap. 9.99 (*978-0-340-85536-2(3)) Hodder General Publishing Division GBR. *Dist:* Independent Pubs. Group.

Puddlepot, Bing. Jimmy Jonny Brownie Stays up All Night. Schwartzrock, Sherwin G., illus. 2000. 32p. (J). (ps-3). 14.95 (978-0-9676148-1-6(3)) Bing Puddlepot.

S

Quintart, Natalie. Mama Bear. Blanchart, Stephanie, illus. 2005. 32p. (J). (ps-ps). 6.95 (978-1-58925-394-0(9) , tiger tales) ME Media LLC.

Raintree Steck-Vaughn Staff, contrib. by. The Napping House. 1999. (J). (ps-3). 16.00 (978-0-8172-9783-1(9)); pap. 22.00 (978-0-8172-9789-3(8)) Steck-Vaughn.

Raschka, Chris. Can't Sleep. Raschka, Chris, illus. 1999. (Illus.). (J). (ps-1). 32p. 15.99 (978-0-531-08779-4(4)); 16p. bds. 6.95 (978-0-531-30201-9(6)); 32p. pap. 14.95 (978-0-531-09479-2(0)) Scholastic, Inc. (Orchard Bks.).

Raye, Rebekah. The Very Best Bed. Raye, Rebekah, illus. 2006. (Illus.). 32p. (J). (ps-3). 16.95 (978-0-88448-284-0(7)) Tilbury Hse. Pubs.

Reyes, Yolanda. A Bed for Three. Coll, Ivar Da, illus. 2004. (SPA.). 36p. (J). (gr. k-3). 14.95 (978-958-704-055-5(4)) Santillana USA Publishing Co., Inc.

Robbins, Maria Polushkin. Mother, Mother, I Want Another. Goodell, Jon, illus. 2005. 32p. (J). (ps-1). 14.95 (978-0-375-82588-0(6)); lib. bdg. 16.99 (978-0-375-92588-7(0)) Random Hse. Children's Bks. (Knopf Bks. for Young Readers).

Rock, Michelle L. Nighttime Adventures Counting Sheep. Longmore, Nickolai, illus. 2006. 32p. (J). 3.99 net. (978-0-9771700-1-2(2)) Mystic Arts, LLC.

Rodgers, Phillip W. When Does God Sleep? 2007. 12.99 ***(978-0-8254-3631-4(1))*** Kregel Pubns.

Root, Phyllis. Ten Sleepy Sheep. Gaber, Susan, illus. 2004. 32p. (J). (gr. k-k). 15.99 (978-0-7636-1545-1(5)) Candlewick Pr.

Roth, Carol. Little Bunny's Sleepless Night. Gorbachev, Valeri, illus. 32p. (J). (ps-2). 2002. pap. 6.95 (978-0-7358-1804-0(5)); 1999. 15.95 (978-0-7358-1069-3(9)); 1999. 16.50 (978-0-7358-1070-9(2)) North-South Bks., Inc.

Rothstein, Nancy. My Daddy Snores. 2007. 32p. (J). pap. 5.99 ***(978-0-545-02834-9(5))*** Scholastic, Inc.

Samarrippas, Gloria. In Search for Lucky's Lost Toys. 2006. 17.00 ***(978-0-8059-7329-7(X))*** Dorrance Publishing Co., Inc.

Sanroman, Susana. Senora Reganona: A Mexican Bedtime Story. 2000. (Illus.). 32p. (J). (ps-k). pap. 5.95 (978-0-88899-389-2(7) , Libros Tigrillo) Groundwood Bks. CAN. *Dist:* Perseus Distribution.

—Senora Reganona: A Mexican Bedtime Story. 2000. (978-0-606-18344-4(2)); lib. bdg. 14.10 (978-0-613-28059-4(8)) Tandem Library Bks.

Schecter, Ellen. Sleep Tight, Pete. Weissman, Bari, illus. 1998. (Bank Street Reader Collection). 48p. (J). (ps-2). lib. bdg. 22.60 (978-0-8368-1766-9(4)) Stevens, Gareth Inc.

Scheving, Magnus & Artful Doodlers Limited Staff. Sleepless in LazyTown. 2006. (LazyTown Ser.). (Illus.). 24p. (J). pap. 3.99 (978-1-4169-0077-1(2) , Simon Spotlight/Nickelodeon) Simon & Schuster Children's Publishing.

Scholastic, Inc. Staff. Diaper David Plush Diaper David. 2005. (Diaper David Plush Ser.). (J). 9.99 (978-0-439-72696-2(4) , Sidekicks TM) Scholastic, Inc.

Schroeder, Lisa. Baby Can't Sleep. Garofoli, Viviana, illus. 2007. 24p. (J). bds. 5.95 (978-1-4027-4323-8(8)) Sterling Publishing Co., Inc.

Scott, Janine. The Rowdy Rooster. Forss, Ian, illus. 2006. 32p. (J). (gr. k-2). 22.60 (978-1-4048-1699-2(2)) Picture Window Bks.

Scotton, Rob. Go to Sleep, Russell the Sheep. Scotton, Rob, illus. 2007. 16p. (J). 9.99 ***(978-0-06-128434-2(3))*** HarperCollins Pubs.

Scotton, Rob. Russell the Sheep. 2005. (Illus.). 40p. (J). (ps-2). 15.99 (978-0-06-059848-8(4)) HarperCollins Pubs.

—Russell the Sheep. Scotton, Rob, illus. 2005. (Illus.). 40p. (J). (ps-ps). lib. bdg. 17.89 (978-0-06-059849-5(2)) HarperCollins Pubs.

Shapely Sleepy Sheep. ed. 2005. (J). bds. 7.95 (978-0-9749305-6-5(3)) Castle Pacific Publishing.

Shields, Gillian. Angel Baby. 2006. (Illus.). 24p. (J). (ps). pap. 9.99 (978-0-00-718006-6(3) , HarperCollins Children's Bks.) HarperCollins Pubs. Ltd. GBR. *Dist:* Independent Pubs. Group.

Shulevitz, Uri. So Sleepy Story. 2006. (Illus.). 32p. (J). (ps-1). 16.00 (978-0-374-37031-2(1)) Farrar, Straus & Giroux.

Simmons, Jane. Go to Sleep, Daisy. Simmons, Jane, illus. 1999. (Illus.). 8p. (J). (ps). bds. 5.95 (978-0-316-79761-0(8)) Little Brown & Co.

Sites, Terry A. While You're Asleep. Huddleston, Christine, illus. 1998. 32p. (J). (ps-2). pap. 4.95 (978-0-8198-8292-9(5) , 332-403) Pauline Bks. & Media.

—While You're Asleep. 1998. (ps-2). lib. bdg. 12.95 (978-0-613-76562-6(1)) Tandem Library Bks.

Sleep Tight Spaceboy. 2003. (J). (978-1-932570-02-1(0)) Literacy Footprints Inc.

Sotelo, Roberto. Anacleto el Esqueleto Inquieto (Anacleto the Restless Skeleton) Un Paseo en el Parque (A Walk in the Park) Wright, Douglas, illus. 2001. (SPA.). (J). (ps). pap. (978-950-08-2553-5(8)) Atlantida.

—Anacleto el Esqueleto Inquieto (Anacleto the Restless Skeleton) Una Noche de Insomnia (A Sleepless Night) Wright, Douglas, illus. 2001. (SPA.). (J). (ps). pap. (978-950-08-2554-2(6)) Atlantida.

Star, Nancy. Mystery of the Snow Day Bigfoot. Bernardin, James, illus. 2005. (Calendar Club Mysteries Ser.: Vol. 3). 77p. (J). pap. ***(978-0-439-67262-7(7))*** Scholastic, Inc.

Stewart, Amber. How Many Sleeps? (Illus.). 32p. (978-0-19-279189-4(3)) Oxford Univ. Pr., Inc.

Stewart, Amber & Marlow, Layn. How Many Sleeps? (Illus.). 32p. (978-0-19-279188-7(5)) Oxford Univ. Pr., Inc.

Ted in a Red Bed Kid Kit. (Kid Kits Ser.). (Illus.). 10p. (J). 11.95 (978-1-58086-416-9(3)); 2004. bds. 9.95 (978-1-58086-404-6(X)) EDC Publishing.

Torrel, Wendy. Guardian of Dreams: A Bedtime Story, Klingbeil, Kendall, illus. l.t. ed. 2004. 32p. (J). 14.95 (978-0-9746890-0-5(9)); pap. 10.95 (978-0-9746890-1-2(7)) White Tulip Publishing.

U'Ren, Andrea. Mary Smith. U'Ren, Andrea, illus. 2003. (Illus.). 32p. (J). 16.00 (978-0-374-34842-7(1) , Farrar, Straus & Giroux (BYR)) Farrar, Straus & Giroux.

Vagnozzi, Barbara. Sleepy Baby. 2002. (Baby's Day Ser.). (Illus.). 16p. (J). (ps up). 3.95 (978-1-84089-239-0(0) , Zero to Ten, Limited) Evans Publishing Group GBR. *Dist:* Independent Pubs. Group.

Vagnozzi, Barbara, illus. Sleeping Beauty. 2007. (First Fairy Tales Ser.). 31p. (J). ***(*978-1-59771-073-2(3))*** Sea-To-Sea Pubns.

Van Patter, Bruce. Farley Found It. (Illus.). (J). 16.95 (978-1-59078-351-1(4)) Boyds Mills Pr.

Vere, Ed. Everyone's Sleepy. 2003. (Illus.). 14p. (J). 8.99 (978-0-333-78038-1(8)) Macmillan Publishers Ltd. GBR. *Dist:* Trafalgar Square Publishing.

Volker, Kerstin. Suzie Goes to Sleep. 2003. (Funny Friends Lift-and-Learn Bks.). (Illus.). 14p. (J). 5.99 (978-1-59384-024-2(1)) Parklane Publishing.

Walker, Nan. The Midnight Kid. Gott, Barry, illus. 2007. (Science Solves It! Ser.). 32p. (J). ***(*978-1-57565-238-2(2)); (*978-1-4287-1923-1(7))*** Kane Pr., The.

Walsh, Joanna. All Asleep. rev. ed. 2008. 24p. (J). (ps). bds. 6.99 ***(*978-0-316-11871-2(0))*** Little, Brown Bks. for Young Readers.

Walsh, Melanie. Hide & Sleep. 1999. (978-0-7894-4842-2(4)); (J). pap. (978-0-7894-4819-4(X)) Dorling Kindersley Publishing, Inc.

Walton, Rick. Herd of Cows! Flock of Sheep! Olson, Julie Hansen, illus. 2002. 32p. (J). 15.95 (978-1-58685-153-8(5)) Gibbs Smith, Publisher.

Warnes, Tim. Por Que no Duermes, Motas? 2002. Tr. of Can't You Sleep, Dotty?. (SPA.). 124p. (J). 15.95 (978-84-488-1160-0(7) , BS31492) Beascoa, Ediciones S.A. ESP. *Dist:* Distribooks, Inc., Lectorum Pubns., Inc.

Watt, F. Felices Suenos! 2004. (Mundo del Pequenin Ser.).Tr. of Baby's Bedtime. (SPA., Illus.). 16p. (YA). (ps up). pap. 4.95 (978-0-7460-3869-7(0)) EDC Publishing.

Wells, Rosemary. Max's Bedtime. 2003. 12p. (J). pap. 5.99 (978-0-670-88710-1(2) , Viking Juvenile) Penguin Group (USA) Inc.

Willson, Sarah. The Rugrats & the Zombies. Goldberg, Barry, illus. 1998. (Rugrats Ser.). 24p. (J). (ps-2). pap. 3.50 (978-0-689-82125-7(5) , Simon Spotlight/Nickelodeon) Simon & Schuster Children's Publishing.

Wilson-Max, Ken. Wake up, Sleep Tight. 1998. (Illus.). 16p. (J). (ps-k). pap. 11.95 (978-0-590-76779-8(8) , Cartwheel Bks.) Scholastic, Inc.

Wood, Audrey. The Napping House. Wood, Audrey, illus. 2002. (Illus.). (J). 21.70 (978-0-7587-3238-5(4)) Book Wholesalers, Inc.

—The Napping House. Wood, Don, illus. (J). 2004. 32p. 17.95 (978-0-15-205080-1(9)); 2000. 16p. bds. 6.95 (978-0-15-202632-5(0) , Red Wagon Bks.) Harcourt Children's Bks.

Wood, David. Bedtime Story: A Slip-in-the-Slot Book. 2000. (Illus.). 20p. (J). 10.95 (978-0-385-40648-2(7)) Transworld Publishers Ltd. GBR. *Dist:* Trafalgar Square Publishing.

—Under the Bed. Fowler, Richard, illus. 2006. 18p. (J). 9.99 (978-0-7641-5926-8(7)) Barron's Educational Series, Inc.

Wright, Michael. Jake Stays Awake. 2007. (Illus.). 40p. (J). (ps-2). 16.95 ***(*978-0-312-36797-8(X))*** Feiwel & Friends.

Yisrael, A'mon. Mr. Jerry's Nap. 2005. (Illus.). 9p. (J). 8.99 (978-0-9772424-0-5(4)) Yisrael, Sean Publishing Co.

Ziefert, Harriet. Mommy, I Want to Sleep in Your Bed! Kreloff, Elliot, illus. 2005. 40p. 15.95 (978-1-59354-103-3(1)) Handprint Bks.

SLEEPING BEAUTY (FICTITIOUS CHARACTER)—FICTION

Amery, H. & Cartwright, S. Sleeping Beauty. 2004. (First Stories Ser.). 16p. (J). pap. 4.95 (978-0-7945-0604-9(6)) EDC Publishing.

Amery, H. & Cartwright, Stephen. Sleeping Beauty. 16p. (J). lib. bdg. 12.95 (978-1-58086-622-4(0) , Usborne) EDC Publishing.

Amery, Heather & Howell, Laura. Sleeping Beauty Sticker Bk. 2006. 16p. (J). pap. 6.99 (978-0-7945-1313-9(1) , Usborne) EDC Publishing.

Cartwheel Books Staff. Sleeping Beauty. Stevenson, Peter, illus. 2000. (Finger Puppet Theater Bks.). 16p. (J). (ps-1). bds. 14.95 (978-0-439-17680-4(8)) Scholastic, Inc.

Disney Staff. The Sleeping Beauty. (FRE.). 96p. (J). (gr. k-5). pap. 9.95 (978-0-7859-8854-0(8)) French & European Pubns., Inc.

Fairy Tales- Sleeping Beauty. 2005. (J). bds. (978-1-4194-0042-1(8)) Paradise Pr., Inc.

Grimm. Sleeping Beauty. Mantovani, Maria & Barsotti, Renzo, illus. 32p. (J). (ps). 7.95 (978-1-904668-60-2(7)) Mercury Bks. Ltd. GBR. *Dist:* International Publishers Marketing.

Heyer, Carol. The Sleeping Beauty in the Wood. 2001. (J). (gr. 4-7). 14.95 (978-0-8249-5401-7(7)) Ideals Pubns.

Lagonegro, Melissa. The Fairest of the Fall. Emslie, Peter, illus. 2003. (Disney Princess Ser.). 24p. (J). (gr. k-3). pap. 3.25 (978-0-7364-2148-5(3) , RH/Disney) Random Hse. Children's Bks.

Leonard, Barry, ed. Sleeping Beauty. 2003. (Illus.). 12p. (J). (gr. k-4). reprint ed. 17.00 (978-0-7567-6865-2(9)) DIANE Publishing Co.

Mueller, Martina, illus. Sleeping Beauty: A Grimm's Fairy Tale. 2001. 28p. (J). 16.95 (978-0-86315-342-6(9)) Floris Bks. GBR. *Dist:* Gryphon Hse., Inc., SteinerBooks, Inc.

Sleeping Beauty. (Read-Along Ser.). (J). 7.99 incl. audio (978-1-55723-010-2(2)) Walt Disney Records.

Teitelbaum, Michael. Sleeping Beauty. DiCicco, Sue, illus. 2004. (Little Golden Book Ser.). 24p. (J). (gr. k-k). 2.99 (978-0-7364-2198-0(X) , Golden/Disney) Random Hse. Children's Bks.

Umansky, Kaye. Sleeping Beauty. Crossland, Caroline, illus. 2003. (Plays & Play Collections). 48p. (J). pap. 15.00 (978-0-7136-5371-7(X)) A & C Black GBR. *Dist:* Players Pr., Inc.

SLEEPOVERS

American Girl Editorial Staff, ed. Snooze-A-Palooza! More Than 100 Slumber Party Ideas. Yoshizumi, Carol, illus. 2005. (American Girl Library). 80p. (J). pap. 9.95 (978-1-58485-978-9(4)) American Girl Publishing, Inc.

Foxx, Kylie & Ledesma, Sophie. Pajama Parties: Truth or Dare. 2001. (Illus.). 16p. (gr. 3-6). tchr. ed. 7.95 (978-0-7611-2388-0(1) , 12388) Workman Publishing Co., Inc.

Girlfriends' Get-Together Craft Book. 2007. 48p. (J). (gr. 2-6). pap. 7.95 ***(*978-0-7613-9465-5(6)*** , First Avenue Editions) Lerner Publishing Group.

Goldsack, Gaby. The Ultimate Sleepover Pack. Reeves, Sue, illus. 24p. (J). 79.60 (978-0-7641-7662-3(5)) Barron's Educational Series, Inc.

Griffin, Margot. The Sleepover Book. Kurisu, Jane, illus. 2001. 144p. (J). (gr. 4-6). (978-1-55074-522-1(0)) Kids Can Pr., Ltd.

—The Sleepover Book. Kurisu, Jane, illus. 2001. 144p. (J). (978-0-439-35642-8(3)) Scholastic, Inc.

Kauffmann, Jon. The Sleepover Journal. Douglass, Ali, illus. 2002. 144p. (gr. 2-8). 15.95 (978-0-8118-3334-9(8)) Chronicle Bks. LLC.

Nicholson, Sue. Sleepover. 2003. (Wicked Wallets Ser.). (Illus.). 96p. (YA). pap. (978-1-84347-061-8(6)) Chrysalis Children's Bks.

Pillow Talk. 2001. (gr. 3-6). lib. bdg. 11.80 (978-0-613-32949-1(X)) Tandem Library Bks.

Radabaugh, Melinda Beth. Sleeping Over. 2003. (First Time Ser.). (Illus.). 24p. (J). pap. 5.25 (978-1-4034-0470-1(4)) Heinemann Library.

—Sleeping Over. 2003. (ps-2). lib. bdg. 13.30 (978-0-613-60929-6(8)) Tandem Library Bks.

Ross, Kathy. Girlfriends' Get-Together Craft Book. Bosch, Nicole in den, illus. 2007. (Girl Crafts Ser.). 48p. (J). (gr. 2-5). lib. bdg. 25.26 (978-0-7613-3408-8(4) , Millbrook Pr.) Lerner Publishing Group.

Warner, Penny. Slumber Parties. 2000. (Illus.). 107p. (J). (978-0-88166-365-5(4)) Meadowbrook Pr.

—Slumber Parties. Bradley, Amanda, illus. 2000. 112p. (J). (gr. 3-9). pap. 8.00 (978-0-689-84077-7(2)) Meadowbrook Pr.

Willson, Sarah. The Ultimate Sleepover Book. 2003. (Nick Reference Ser.). (Illus.). 48p. (J). pap. 5.99 (978-0-689-84559-8(6) , Simon Spotlight/Nickelodeon) Simon & Schuster Children's Publishing.

SLEEPOVERS—FICTION

Baker, Roberta. Olive's First Sleepover. Tilley, Debbie, illus. 2007. 36p. (J). (ps-3). 16.99 (978-0-316-73418-9(7)) Little Brown & Co.

Barker, Henry. It Came from Outer Space. 2003. (gr. k-3). lib. bdg. 13.00 (978-0-613-79228-8(9)) Tandem Library Bks.

Benenfeld, Rikki. I Go Visiting. 2007. (Illus.). 32p. (J). 10.95 (978-1-929628-33-9(1)) Hachai Publishing.

Benjamin, Ruth. My Little Pony: Sleepover Surprise. Yee, Josie, illus. 2006. 24p. (J). lib. bdg. 13.85 ***(*978-1-4242-0812-8(2))*** Fitzgerald Bks.

Bergen, Lara. Dora's Sleepover. Miller, Victoria, illus. 2006. (Dora the Explorer Ser.). 24p. (J). pap. 3.99 (978-1-4169-1508-9(7) , Simon Spotlight/Nickelodeon) Simon & Schuster Children's Publishing.

Bottner, Barbara. Two Messy Friends. 1999. (Hello Reader! Ser.). (Illus.). 32p. (J). (gr. k-2). pap. 3.99 (978-0-590-63285-0(X)) Scholastic, Inc.

Bourgeois, Paulette & Clark, Brenda. Franklin Has a Sleepover. 1999. (Franklin Ser.). (Illus.). 168p. (J). (ps-3). (978-1-55074-664-8(2)) Kids Can Pr., Ltd.

Brown, Marc. Arthur's First Sleepover. Brown, Marc, illus. 2002. (Arthur Adventure Ser.). (Illus.). (J). 13.15 (978-0-7587-1982-9(5)) Book Wholesalers, Inc.

—Arthur's First Sleepover. Brown, Marc, illus. 2005. (Arthur Adventure Ser.). 32p. (J). (ps-1). pap. 10.99 (978-0-316-05956-5(0)) Little Brown & Co.

—Arthur's First Sleepover. Brown, Marc, illus. 1999. (Arthur Adventure Ser.). (Illus.). 30p. (J). (ps-k). bds. 5.95 (978-0-316-10560-6(0)) Little, Brown Bks. for Young Readers.

—Arthur's First Sleepover. 1998. (Arthur Adventure Ser.). (J). (gr. k-3). pap. 5.95 (978-0-316-11974-0(1)); 32p. 9.95 (978-0-316-11948-1(2)) Little, Brown Bks. for Young Readers.

Clark, Brenda, illus. Franklin Has a Sleepover. 2002. (Franklin Ser.). (J). 12.40 (978-1-4046-0313-4(1)) Book Wholesalers, Inc.

Clarke, Jane. Dippy's Sleepover: A Reassuring Story for Kids Who Have a Bedwetting Problem. McQuillan, Mary, illus. 2006. 32p. (J). pap. 6.99 (978-0-7641-3425-8(6)) Barron's Educational Series, Inc.

Colby, C. B., et al. Scary Stories for Sleepovers. 2006. (Illus.). 96p. pap. 5.95 (978-1-4027-2182-3(X)) Sterling Publishing Co., Inc.

Dahl, Michael. Frog Pajama Party. Schultz, Sara, illus. 2005. (Read-It! Readers Ser.). 32p. (J). (ps). lib. bdg. 18.60 (978-1-4048-1170-6(2)) Picture Window Bks.

Davis, Lee. Spooky Game: Bear Read Alone. 2001. (Pajama Bedtime Bear Ser.). (Illus.). 24p. (J). (ps-1). pap. 6.95 (978-0-7894-4945-0(5) , D K Ink) Dorling Kindersley Publishing, Inc.

Edwards, Helen L. Clara's Imagination. Doggett, Al, illus. 2005. 19.95 (978-0-9765414-0-6(8)) Bad Publishing.

Ellis, Sarah. Ben Over Night. LaFave, Kim, illus. 2005. 32p. (J). (978-1-55041-807-1(6)) Fitzhenry & Whiteside, Ltd.

Epstein, Robin. Choose or Lose: How to Pick a Winner. 2005. (Groovy Girls Sleepover Club Ser.: Vol. 5). 60p. (J). (978-0-439-65793-8(8)) Scholastic, Inc.

Epstein, Robin. Pranks a Lot: The Girls vs. the Boys. 2005. (Groovy Girls Sleepover Club Ser.: Vol. 2). (Illus.). 58p. (J). pap. ***(*978-0-439-65790-7(3))*** Scholastic, Inc.

Freeman, Don & Hennessy, B. G. Corduroy's Sleepover. 2007. 20p. (J). 11.99 (978-0-670-06185-3(9) , Viking Juvenile) Penguin Group (USA) Inc.

Gaydos, Nora & Girouard, Patrick. The Sleepover. 2007. 24p. (J). (gr. k-17). pap. 6.99 ***(*978-1-58476-611-7(5)*** , IKIDS) Innovative Kids.

Giglio, Judy. The Tapping Tale. Cepeda, Joe, illus. 2003. (Green Light Readers Level 1 Ser.). 24p. (J). 11.95 (978-0-15-204812-9(X)); pap. 3.95 (978-0-15-204852-5(9)) Harcourt Children's Bks. (Green Light Readers).

Girls Club. Slumber Party: Fun Stuff to Unlock & Share. 2001. (Girls Club Ser.). (Illus.). 32p. (J). (gr. 4-7). pap. 9.95 (978-0-7624-0951-8(7) , Courage Bks.) Running Pr. Bk. Pubs.

Greene, Rhonda Gowler. At Grandma's. Firehammer, Karla, illus. rev. ed. 2003. 32p. (J). (ps-k). 15.95 (978-0-8050-6336-3(6) , Holt, Henry & Co. Bks. For Young Readers) Holt, Henry & Co.

Guest, Elissa Haden. Sleepover. Davenier, Christine, illus. 2002. (Iris & Walter Ser.). 44p. (J). (gr. 1-4). 14.00 (978-0-15-216487-4(1) , Gulliver Bks.) Harcourt Children's Bks.

—The Sleepover. Davenier, Christine, illus. 2006. (Iris & Walter Ser.). 44p. (J). pap. 5.95 (978-0-15-205674-2(2) , Harcourt Paperbacks) Harcourt Children's Bks.

Harper, Charise Mericle. When Randolph Turned Rotten. 2007. 40p. (J). (gr. k-3). 16.99 ***(*978-0-375-84071-5(0)); lib. bdg. 19.99 (*978-0-375-94071-2(5))*** Random Hse. Children's Bks. (Knopf Bks. for Young Readers).

Hartley, Susan. Jake's Sleepover. 2003. (Early Connections Ser.). (J). pap. 33.00 (978-1-4108-1090-8(9)) Benchmark Education Co.

Hearson, Ruth. Cinnamon's Fairy Sleepover. Hearson, Ruth, illus. 2006. (Illus.). 14p. (J). 5.99 (978-1-4169-1401-3(3) , Little Simon) Simon & Schuster Children's Publishing.

Held, Elissa. My Sleepover Bag: More than 45 Play Pieces Inside! Smith, Tammy, illus. 2004. 14p. (J). pap. 14.95 (978-0-689-87337-9(9) , Little Simon) Simon & Schuster Children's Publishing.

Hill, Eric. Spot Sleeps Over. Hill, Eric, illus. 2004. (Spot Ser.). (Illus.). 24p. (J). (ps-1). pap. 6.99 (978-0-14-240168-2(4) , Puffin) Penguin Group (USA) Inc.

—Spot's First Words. Hill, Eric, illus. 2006. 12p. (J). (ps-k). bds. 12.99 (978-0-399-24616-6(9) , Putnam Juvenile) Penguin Group (USA) Inc.

Hoberman, Mary Ann. I'm Going to Grandma's. Beeke, Tiphanie, illus. 2007. 32p. (J). (ps-2). 16.00 (978-0-15-216592-5(4)) Harcourt Trade Pubs.

Holabird, Katharine. Angelina's Diary. Craig, Helen, illus. 2006. (Angelina Ballerina Ser.). 80p. (J). (gr. 1-3). 3.99 (978-0-448-44016-3(4) , Grosset & Dunlap) Penguin Group (USA) Inc.

Holub, Joan. Pajama Party. Durrell, Julie, illus. 1998. (All Aboard Reading Ser.). 32p. (J). (gr. k-2). pap. 3.99 (978-0-448-41739-4(1) , Grosset & Dunlap) Penguin Group (USA) Inc.

Hopkins, Cathy. Mates, Dates & Sleepover Secrets. 2003. (Mates, Dates Ser.). 208p. (YA). mass mkt. 5.99 (978-0-689-85991-5(0) , Simon Pulse) Simon & Schuster Children's Publishing.

—Mates, Dates & Sleepover Secrets. 2003. (gr. 7-12). lib. bdg. 13.00 (978-0-613-73417-2(3)) Tandem Library Bks.

Jordan, Apple & S. I. International Staff. Slumberrific Sleepover Party. Yee, Josie, illus. 2007. (Groovy Girls Ser.). 48p. (J). 3.99 ***(*978-1-4169-3880-4(X)*** , Simon Scribbles) Simon & Schuster Children's Publishing.

Keene, Carolyn. Sleepover Sleuths. Pamintuan, Macky, illus. 2006. (Nancy Drew & the Clue Crew Ser.: No. 1). 96p. (J). (gr. 1-4). pap. 3.99 (978-1-4169-1255-2(X) , Aladdin) Simon & Schuster Children's Publishing.

—Sleepover Sleuths. 2007. (Nancy Drew & the Clue Crew Ser.). 96p. (J). (gr. 2-4). 24.21 ***(*978-1-59961-348-2(4))*** Spotlight.

Klein, Adria F. Max Stays Overnight. 2007. (Read-It! Readers Ser.). (Illus.). 24p. (J). ***(*978-1-4048-3547-4(4)*** , 1265796) Picture Window Bks.

—Max Stays Overnight. Gallagher-Cole, Mernie, illus. 2006. (Read-It! Readers Ser.). 24p. (J). ***(*978-1-4048-3149-0(5)*** , 1265796) Picture Window Bks.

Life, Kay, illus. Benny's Boxcar Sleepover, Vol. 12. 2004. (Adventures of Benny & Watch: 12). 32p. (J). (gr. 1-3). pap. 3.95 (978-0-8075-0636-3(2)) Whitman, Albert & Co.

London, Jonathan. Froggy's Sleepover. Remkiewicz, Frank, illus. 2007. (Froggy Ser.). 32p. (J). pap. 5.99 (978-0-14-240750-9(X) , Puffin) Penguin Group (USA) Inc.

Lozano, Neal. Can God See Me in the Dark? Hatke, Ben, illus. 2007. (J). ***(*978-1-883551-45-2(5)*** , Maple Corners Press) Attic Studio Publishing Hse.

Lynne, Rustyna. Janel's Shampoo. Lynne, Rustyna, illus. 2002. (Illus.). 17p. (J). (gr. k-2). spiral bd. 11.95 (978-0-9722829-0-1(4)) Red Carpet Publishing.

Maccarone, Grace. Sleepover. Lewin, Betsy, illus. 2005. (Hello Reader! Ser.). 32p. (J). pap. 3.99 (978-0-439-38575-6(X) , Cartwheel Bks.) Scholastic, Inc.

MacDonald, Anne Louise. The Memory Stone. Ouellet, Joanne, illus. 1998. 72p. (J). pap. (978-0-921556-71-8(3)) Nimbus Publishing, Ltd.

—The Memory Stone. Ouellet, Joanne, illus. 2003. 24p. (J). 7.95 (978-1-55109-442-7(8)) Nimbus Publishing, Ltd. CAN. *Dist:* National Bk. Network.

Masurel, Claire. Emily's First Sleepover. 2003. (gr. k-3). lib. bdg. 11.25 (978-0-613-72542-2(5)) Tandem Library Bks.

Mc Auley, Rowan. Go Girl! #5 - Sleepover! Oswald, Ash, illus. 2008. (Go Girl! Ser.). 96p. (J). pap. 3.99 (*978-0-312-34641-6(7)) Feiwel & Friends.

McKissack, Patricia C. & McKissack, Fredrick L. Messy Bessey & the Birthday Overnight. Regan, Dana, illus. 1998. (Rookie Readers Ser.). 32p. (J). (gr. 1-2). 19.50 (978-0-516-20828-2(4) , Children's Pr.) Scholastic Library Publishing.

Morrissey, Dean. The Monster Trap. Morrissey, Dean, illus. 2006. (Illus.). 40p. (J). reprint ed. pap. 6.99 (978-0-06-052500-2(2) , Harper Trophy) HarperCollins Pubs.

Morrissey, Dean & Krensky, Stephen. The Monster Trap. Morrissey, Dean, illus. 2004. (Illus.). 40p. (J). lib. bdg. 17.89 (978-0-06-052499-9(5)) HarperCollins Pubs.

Mullins, Julie. The Sleepover. Foye, Lloyd, illus. 2005. (Girlz Rock! Ser.). (J). pap. (978-1-59336-707-7(4)) Mondo Publishing.

Pachela, Czes, illus. The Sleepover. 2001. 24p. (J). pap. 3.50 (978-1-58925-364-3(7) , tiger tales) ME Media LLC.

The Pajama Party. 1998. (P. B. Bear Ser.). (Illus.). 24p. (J). (ps). 6.95 (978-0-7894-3107-3(6)) Dorling Kindersley Publishing, Inc.

Papademetriou, Lisa. Really? 1999. (Real Kids Readers Ser.: 3). (Illus.). 32p. (J). (gr. 2-4). pap. 4.99 (978-0-7613-2097-5(0) , Millbrook Pr.) Lerner Publishing Group.

—Really? Handelman, Dorothy, photos by. 1999. (Real Kids Readers Ser.). (Illus.). 48p. (gr. 1-3). lib. bdg. 18.90 (978-0-7613-2072-2(5) , Millbrook Pr.) Lerner Publishing Group.

—Really? 1999. (J). (978-0-606-19171-5(2)); (gr. 3-6). lib. bdg. 11.80 (978-0-613-18163-1(8)) Tandem Library Bks.

Paul, Ann Whitford. Everything to Spend the Night: From A to Z. 2001. (978-0-606-22366-9(5)) Tandem Library Bks.

Peltzman, Adam. Blue's Sleepover Party. Pontillo, Jenine, illus. 2005. (Blue's Clues Ser.). 36p. (J). bds. 8.99 (978-1-4169-0627-8(4) , Simon Spotlight/Nickelodeon) Simon & Schuster Children's Publishing.

Peterson, Doug. The Mess Detectives: The Big Sleepover. 2004. (Mess Detectives Ser.). (Illus.). 40p. 6.99 (978-0-310-70736-3(6)) Zonderkidz.

Petty, Kate. Staying Overnight. 2007. (J). (*978-1-59604-156-1(0)) Stargazer Bks.

Pinkwater, Daniel M. Sleepover Larry. 2007. (Illus.). 32p. 16.99 (*978-0-7614-5335-2(0)) Cavendish, Marshall Corp.

—Sleepover Larry. Pinkwater, Jill, illus. 2006. 32p. (J). (ps-3). 16.99 (978-0-7614-5314-7(8)) Cavendish, Marshall Corp.

Preller, James. The Case of the Spooky Sleepover. Alley, R. W., illus. 2001. (Jigsaw Jones Mystery Ser.: No. 4). 80p. (J). (gr. 1-4). pap. 3.99 (978-0-590-69129-1(5)) Scholastic, Inc.

—The Case of the Spooky Sleepover. 1999. (Jigsaw Jones Mystery Ser.: No. 4). (Illus.). (J). (gr. 1-4). 10.79 (978-0-606-16586-0(X)) Tandem Library Bks.

Pulley, Kelly. The Beginner's Bible Lion's Big Sleepover Daniel's Scary Night. 2007. (Beginner's Bible' Ser.). 20p. (J). 6.99 (978-0-310-71387-6(0)) Zondervan.

Rogers, Jacqueline. Best Friends Sleep Over. 2000. (Illus.). 32p. (YA). (ps-4). pap. 5.99 (978-0-439-19994-0(8)) Scholastic, Inc.

Rose, Maddy. The Midnight Feast. 2007. (Illus.). 24p. (J). pap. 9.95 (*978-1-86230-340-9(1)) Transworld Publishers Ltd. GBR. *Dist:* Independent Pubs. Group.

Ruelle, Karen Gray. Easy As Apple Pie: A Harry & Emily Adventure. (Holiday House Readers Ser.). (Illus.). 32p. (J). (gr. k-3). 4.95 (978-0-8234-1800-8(6)) Holiday Hse., Inc.

—Easy As Apple Pie: A Harry & Emily Adventure. Ruelle, Karen Gray, illus. (Holiday House Reader Ser.). (Illus.). 32p. (J). (gr. k-3). tchr. ed. 14.95 (978-0-8234-1759-9(X)) Holiday Hse., Inc.

Rylant, Cynthia. Henry & Mudge & the Big Sleepover. Stevenson, Sucie, illus. (Henry & Mudge Ser.). 40p. (J). 2007. pap. 3.99 (978-0-689-83451-6(9) , Aladdin); 2006. 14.95 (978-0-689-81171-5(3) , Simon & Schuster Children's Publishing) Simon & Schuster Children's Publishing.

Siamon, Sharon. Haunted Hotel Sleepover. Bk. 3. (Illus.). 152p. (J). pap. 8.99 (978-0-340-67278-5(1) , Hodder & Stoughton) Hodder General Publishing Division GBR. *Dist:* Trafalgar Square Publishing.

—Lost Attic, Bk. 6. (Illus.). 137p. (J). pap. 8.99 (978-0-340-70905-4(7) , Hodder & Stoughton) Hodder General Publishing Division GBR. *Dist:* Trafalgar Square Publishing.

—Sleepover: Secret Room. (Illus.). 137p. (J). pap. (978-0-340-67276-1(5) , Hodder & Stoughton) Hodder General Publishing Division.

Spinner, Stephanie. It Came from Outer Space. Gott, Barry, illus. 2003. (Science Solves It! Ser.). 32p. (J). 4.99 (978-1-57565-122-4(X)) Kane Pr., The.

Syatt, Steve. Sleepover Surprise. Caruso, Frank, illus. 2008. 32p. (J). 10.95 (*978-0-312-37853-0(X)) St. Martin's Pr.

Sykes, Julie. Sleepover. 2001. (gr. k-3). lib. bdg. 11.25 (978-0-613-53562-5(6)) Tandem Library Bks.

Van Leeuwen, Jean. Amanda Pig & Her Best Friend Lollipop. Schweninger, Ann, illus. 2000. (Puffin-Easy-to-Read Ser.). 48p. (J). (ps-3). pap. 3.99 (978-0-14-037999-0(1) , Puffin) Penguin Group (USA) Inc.

—Amanda Pig & Her Best Friend Lollipop. 2000. (gr. k-3). lib. bdg. 11.80 (978-0-613-28401-1(1)); (Illus.). (J). 10.79 (978-0-606-18832-6(0)) Tandem Library Bks.

Viselman, Kenn. The Surprise. 2003. 32p. pap. 3.99 (978-0-06-054839-1(8) , Harper Entertainment) HarperCollins Pubs.

Vulliamy, Clara. Small. 2002. (Illus.). 32p. (J). (gr. k-ps). 15.00 (978-0-618-19459-9(2) , Clarion Bks.) Houghton Mifflin Co. Trade & Reference Div.

Waber, Bernard. Bearsie Bear & the Surprise Sleepover Party. 2002. (Illus.). 40p. (J). (gr. k-3). pap. 4.95 (978-0-618-12541-8(8) , Walter Lorraine) Houghton Mifflin Co. Trade & Reference Div.

—Quique Duerme Fuera de Casa. Mlawer, Teresa, tr. 2003. (SPA., Illus.). (J). (gr. k-2). pap. (978-968-6579-15-4(X) , SI6510) Sistemas Tecnicos de Edicion, S.A. de C.V. MEX. *Dist:* Lectorum Pubns., Inc.

Walters, Jennie. Lauren's Spooky Sleepover. 2003. (Illus.). 128p. (J). pap. 7.99 (978-0-340-79591-0(3) , Hodder & Stoughton) Hodder General Publishing Division GBR. *Dist:* Trafalgar Square Publishing.

Warner, Sally. Accidental Lily. 2000. (J). (978-0-606-17112-0(6)) Tandem Library Bks.

Wilson, Gina. Grandma's Bears. Howard, Paul, illus. 2004. 40p. (J). (ps-1). 15.99 (978-0-7636-2518-4(3)) Candlewick Pr.

Winthrop, Elizabeth. Squashed in the Middle. Cummings, Pat, illus. 2005. 32p. (J). 16.95 (978-0-8050-6497-1(4) , Holt, Henry & Co. Bks. For Young Readers) Holt, Henry & Co.

SLEIGHT OF HAND

see Magic

SLESSOR, MARY MITCHELL, 1848-1915

Meloche, Renee. Mary Slessor: Courage in Africa. 2002. (Illus.). 32p. 8.99 (978-1-57658-237-4(X)) YWAM Publishing.

Robinson, Virgil E. Mighty Mary: The Story of Mary Slessor. 2000. (Illus.). 121p. (YA). (gr. 8 up). reprint ed. per. 8.95 (978-1-57258-159-3(X) , 945-6019) TEACH Services, Inc.

SLOTHS

Goecke, Michael P. Giant Ground Sloth. 2003. (Prehistoric Animals Ser.). (Illus.). 24p. (J). (gr. k-4). lib. bdg. 21.35 (978-1-57765-968-6(6)) ABDO Publishing Co.

Lynch, Wayne, photos by. Baby Sloth. (Illus.). 36p. (J). 2004. pap. (978-1-55041-827-9(0)); 2003. (978-1-55041-825-5(4)) Fitzhenry & Whiteside, Ltd.

Miller, Sara Swan. Sloths. 2008. (J). lib. bdg. (*978-1-4042-4166-4(3) , PowerKids Pr.) Rosen Publishing Group, Inc., The.

Paige, Joy. El Perezoso: El Mamifero Mas Lento Del Mundo. 2004. (Campeones Del Mundo Animal Ser.). (SPA & ENG., Illus.). 24p. (J). (gr. 3-6). lib. bdg. 17.25 (978-0-8239-6893-0(6) , Buenas Letra) Rosen Publishing Group, Inc., The.

—The Sloth: The World's Slowest Mammal. 2002. (Reading Power Ser.). (Illus.). 24p. (J). (gr. 1). lib. bdg. 17.25 (978-0-8239-5961-7(9) , PowerKids Pr.) Rosen Publishing Group, Inc., The.

Riehecky, Janet. Giant Ground Sloths. 2008. (J). (*978-1-4296-0036-1(5) , Pebble Bks.) Capstone Pr., Inc.

The Sloth: Individual Title Six-Packs. (On Deck Ser.). 24p. (gr. 4-5). 35.00 (978-0-7578-1067-1(5)) Rigby Education.

Steele, Christy. Sloths. 2001. (Animals of the Rain Forest Ser.). (Illus.). 32p. (J). lib. bdg. 22.83 (978-0-7398-4683-4(3)) Raintree.

Stewart, Melissa. Sloths. 2005. (Nature Watch Ser.). (Illus.). 48p. (J). 25.26 (978-1-57505-577-0(5) , Carolrhoda Bks.) Lerner Publishing Group.

Windsor, Jo. An Upside down Life: Early Level Satellite Individual Title Six-Packs. (Sails Literacy Ser.). 16p. (gr. 1-2). 27.00 (978-0-7578-2937-6(5)) Rigby Education.

SLOTHS—FICTION

Brooks, Erik, illus. Slow Days, Fast Friends. 2005. 32p. (J). (ps-ps). 16.95 (978-0-8075-7437-9(6)) Whitman, Albert & Co.

Carle, Eric. Slowly, Slowly Said the Sloth. Carle, Eric, illus. 2007. 32p. (J). (ps). pap. 7.99 (978-0-14-240847-6(6) , Puffin) Penguin Group (USA) Inc.

—"Slowly, Slowly, Slowly," Said the Sloth. 2002. (Illus.). 32p. 16.99 (978-0-241-14193-9(1) , Putnam Juvenile) Penguin Group (USA) Inc.

Clarke, Jane & Gale, Cathy. Plodney Creeper, Supersloth. 2006. (Blue Bananas Ser.). (Illus.). 47p. (J). (978-0-7787-0850-6(0)) Crabtree Publishing Co.

Emerson, Carl. Speed up, Sammy the Tree Sloth! Trover, Zachary, illus. 2007. (Animal Underdogs Ser.). 32p. (J). (ps-4). lib. bdg. 27.07 (*978-1-60270-019-2(2) , Looking Glass Library) Magic Wagon.

Lazy Sloth: Individual Title Six-Packs. (Sails Literacy Ser.). (gr. 1-2). 36.00 (978-0-7578-4013-5(2)) Rigby Education.

Murray, Andrew. The Very Sleepy Sloth. Tickle, Jack, tr. Tickle, Jack, illus. 2003. 32p. (J). tchr. ed. 15.95 (978-1-58925-033-8(8) , tiger tales) ME Media LLC.

SLUMBER SONGS

see Lullabies

SLUMS

see Housing

SMALL ARMS

see Firearms

SMALL BUSINESS

Allen, Kathleen. Entrepreneurship & Small Business Management. 2nd ed. 1999. (C). stu. ed. 69.32 (978-0-02-644068-4(7) , 9780026440684) Glencoe/McGraw-Hill.

Bochner, Arthur & Bochner, Rose. The New Totally Awesome Business Book for Kids. 3rd rev. ed. 2007. 160p. (J). pap. 9.95 (*978-1-55704-757-1(X)) Newmarket Pr.

Erlbach, Arlene. The Kids' Business Book. 1998. (Kids' Ventures Ser.). (Illus.). 64p. (J). (gr. 3-6). (978-0-8225-2413-7(9)); pap. (978-0-8225-9821-3(3)) Lerner Publishing Group. (Lerner Pubns.).

Giesecke, Ernestine. Be Your Own Boss: Small Businesses. (Everyday Economics Ser.). (Illus.). 48p. (J). 2003. (gr. 3-5). lib. bdg. (978-1-58810-493-9(1)); 2002. pap. 8.50 (978-1-58810-956-9(9)) Heinemann Library.

Mariotti, Steve. How to Start & Operate a Small Business. 2005. (YA). pap., stu. ed. 15.00 (978-1-890859-19-0(2)); (gr. 9-12). 49.95 (978-1-890859-18-3(4)); (gr. 9-12). tchr. ed. 46.95 (978-1-890859-21-3(4)); (gr. 9-12). pap. 79.95 (978-1-890859-20-6(6)); (gr. 9-12). trans. 15.00 (978-1-890859-23-7(0)) National Foundation for Teaching Entrepreneurship, The.

—How to Start & Operate a Small Business: A Guide for the Young Entrepreneur. Towle, Tony, ed. Wilder, Maija, illus. Krasner, Bob, photos by. rev. ed. 2001. xv, 513p. (YA). (gr. 9-12). 65.00 (978-1-890859-00-8(1)) National Foundation for Teaching Entrepreneurship, The.

—How to Start & Operate a Small Business: A Guide for the Young Entrepreneur. Towle, Tony, ed. 9th ed. 2001. (Illus.). 297p. (YA). pap., wbk. ed. 15.00 (978-1-890859-01-5(X)) National Foundation for Teaching Entrepreneurship, The.

—How to Start & Operate a Small Business: Exam View Text Bank - CD. 2005. (YA). (gr. 9-12). pap. incl. cd-rom (978-1-890859-24-4(9)) National Foundation for Teaching Entrepreneurship, The.

McGraw-Hill Staff. Entrepreneurship & Small Business Management. 2nd ed. 1999. (C). pap., stu. ed., wbk. ed. 17.32 (978-0-02-644070-7(9) , 9780026440707) Glencoe/McGraw-Hill.

Meyer, Earl C. & Allen, Kathleen R. Entrepreneurship & Small Business Management. 1999. (Illus.). 192p. (YA). (gr. 6-12). stu. ed., wbk. ed. 8.10 (978-0-02-675122-3(4)) Glencoe/McGraw-Hill.

Mohr, Angie. Bookkeepers' Boot Camp: Get a Grip on Accounting Basics. 2004. (Numbers 101 for Small Business Ser.). (Illus.). 208p. per. (978-1-55180-449-1(2)) Self-Counsel Pr., Inc.

Ruffin, Frances E. Let's Have a Bake Sale: Calculating Profit & Unit Cost. 2004. (PowerMath Ser.). (Illus.). 24p. (J). lib. bdg. (978-0-8239-8893-8(7) , PowerKids Pr.) Rosen Publishing Group, Inc., The.

SMALLS, ROBERT, 1839-1915

Brown, Susan Taylor. Robert Smalls Sails to Freedom. Marshall, Felicia, illus. 2006. (On My Own History Ser.). 48p. (J). 25.26 (978-1-57505-872-6(3)) Lerner Publishing Group.

Robert Smalls Sails to Freedom. 2007. (J). pap. 5.95 (*978-0-8225-6051-7(8) , First Avenue Editions) Lerner Publishing Group.

SMELL

Barraclough, Sue. What Can I Smell? 2005. (Illus.). 24p. (J). (978-1-4109-2164-2(6)); pap. (978-1-4109-2170-3(0)) Heinemann Library.

—What Can I Smell? 2005. (J). (978-1-4034-7079-9(0)); pap. (978-1-4034-7085-0(5)) Steck-Vaughn.

Beaumont, Susanna & Baby Senses Staff. Smell. 2005. (Baby Senses Ser.). (Illus.). 12p. (ps-k). bds. 5.95 (978-1-905051-49-6(2)) Make Believe Ideas GBR. *Dist:* Ingram Pub. Services.

Beck, Esther. Cool Odor Decoders: Fun Science Projects about Smells. 2007. (Cool Science Ser.). (Illus.). 32p. (J). (gr. k-6). lib. bdg. 24.21 (*978-1-59928-909-0(1) , Checkerboard Library) ABDO Publishing Co.

Casado, Dami & Casado, Alicia. El Olfato. 2005. (Sentidos y Algo Mas). (SPA & ESP.). 16p. 8.99 (978-84-272-6413-7(5)) Molino, Editorial ESP. *Dist:* Santillana USA Publishing Co., Inc.

Cobb, Vicki. Follow Your Nose: Discover Your Sense of Smell. 2000. (Five Senses Ser.: 4). (Illus.). 32p. (gr. 2-4). lib. bdg. 22.90 (978-0-7613-1521-6(7) , Millbrook Pr.) Lerner Publishing Group.

Douglas, Lloyd G. My Nose. 2004. (Wel-My Body Ser.). (J). 18.00 (978-0-516-24063-3(3) , Children's Pr.) Scholastic Library Publishing.

Equipo Staff. El Olfato. (Coleccion Mundo Maravilloso). (SPA., Illus.). 38p. (J). (gr. 2-4). (978-84-348-1778 1(7) , OL2004) SM Ediciones ESP. *Dist:* Lectorum Pubns., Inc.

Frost, Helen. Smelling. Saunders-Smith, Gail, ed. 1999. (Senses Ser.). (Illus.). 24p. (J). (gr. k-1). lib. bdg. 15.93 (978-0-7368-0384-7(X) , Pebble Bks.) Capstone Pr., Inc.

—Smelling. 1999. pap. 13.25 (978-0-516-21911-0(1) , Children's Pr.) Scholastic Library Publishing.

Gordon, Sharon. Smelling. 2002. (Rookie Read-About Health Ser.). (Illus.). 32p. (J). (gr. k-2). pap. 5.95 (978-0-516-25991-8(1) , Children's Pr.) Scholastic Library Publishing.

—Smelling. 2001. (gr. k-3). lib. bdg. 14.10 (978-0-613-50745-5(2)) Tandem Library Bks.

Hall, Kirsten. Animal Smell. 2005. (Illus.). 24p. (J). pap. (978-0-8368-4810-6(1)); lib. bdg. 19.33 (978-0-8368-4804-5(7)) Stevens, Gareth Inc.

—Animal Smell: El Olfato en Los Animales. 2005. (ENG & SPA., Illus.). 23p. (J). pap. (978-0-8368-4822-9(5)); lib. bdg. 19.33 (978-0-8368-4816-8(0)) Stevens, Gareth Inc.

Hanel, Rachael. Smell. 2003. 24p. (J). lib. bdg. 21.35 (978-1-58340-306-8(X)) Smart Apple Media.

Klingel, Cynthia Fitterer & Noyed, Robert B. Nose. Andersen, Gregg, photos by. 2002. (Weekly Reader Early Learning Library). (Illus.). 24p. (J). (ps up). pap. 5.95 (978-0-8368-3157-3(8)); lib. bdg. 19.33 (978-0-8368-3068-2(7)) Stevens, Gareth Inc. (Weekly Reader Early Learning Library).

—Nose/Nariz. Acosta, Tatiana & Gutiérrez, Guillermo, trs. Andersen, Gregg, photos by. 2002. (Weekly Reader Early Learning Library). (Illus.). 24p. (J). (ps up). (SPA & ENG.). pap. (978-0-8368-3326-3(0)); (ENG & SPA., lib. bdg. 19.33 (978-0-8368-3077-4(6)) Stevens, Gareth Inc. (Weekly Reader Early Learning Library).

Llewellyn, Claire. Smelling & Tasting. 2005. (Illus.). 24p. (J). (gr. 1-4). lib. bdg. 22.80 (978-1-932889-49-9(3)) Sea-To-Sea Pubns.

Mackill, Mary. Smelling. 2006. (Heinemann Read & Learn Ser.). (Illus.). 24p. (J). (978-1-4034-7377-6(3)); pap. (978-1-4034-7384-4(6)) Steck-Vaughn.

Match Game Staff. Smelly Scented Memory Game. 2005. pap. 19.95 (978-0-9762524-3-6(0)) Gimme Gimme Toys & Games Inc.

Molter, Carey. Sense of Smell. l.t. ed. 2001. (Senses Ser.). (Illus.). 24p. (J). (ps-3). lib. bdg. 19.93 (978-1-57765-628-9(8) , SandCastle) ABDO Publishing Co.

Murphy, Patricia J. Smell. 2003. (True Bks.). (gr. 3-5). pap. 6.95 (978-0-516-26969-6(0) , Children's Pr.) Scholastic Library Publishing.

—Smell. 2003. (gr. 3-6). lib. bdg. 15.25 (978-0-613-67984-8(9)) Tandem Library Bks.

Nelson, Robin. Smelling. 2005. (Senses Ser.). (Illus.). 24p. (gr. k-2). lib. bdg. 17.27 (978-0-8225-1263-9(7)) Lerner Publishing Group.

El Olfato (Smelling) (J). 2007. pap. 4.25 (978-0-8225-6546-8(3)); 2006. (SPA.). 18.60 (978-0-8225-6223-8(5)) Lerner Publishing Group. (Ediciones Lerner).

Olien, Rebecca. Smelling. 2005. (Illus.). 24p. (J). (ps-7). lib. bdg. 21.26 (978-0-7368-4303-4(5) , 1243930) Capstone Pr., Inc.

Pringle, Laurence P. Smell. 2000. (Explore Your Senses Ser.). (Illus.). 32p. (J). (gr. 4-8). lib. bdg. 25.64 (978-0-7614-0737-9(5) , Benchmark Bks.) Cavendish, Marshall Corp.

Pryor, Kimberley Jane. Smelling. 2003. (Senses Ser.). (Illus.). 32p. (gr. 2-4). 23.00 (978-0-7910-7556-2(7) , Chelsea Hse.) Facts On File, Inc.

Rau, Dana Meachen. Sniff, Sniff: A Book about Your Sense of Smell. Peterson, Rick, illus. 2005. (Amazing Body Ser.). 24p. (C). (gr. k-3). 22.60 (978-1-4048-1020-4(X)) Picture Window Bks.

Royston, Angela. Smell. 2005. (Illus.). 32p. (J). (gr. 1 up). lib. bdg. 27.10 (978-1-59389-201-2(2)) Chrysalis Education.

Rybolt, Thomas R. & Rybolt, Leah M. Science Fair Success with Scents, Aromas, & Smells. 2002. (Science Fair Success Ser.). (Illus.). 112p. (YA). (gr. 6-12). lib. bdg. 26.60 (978-0-7660-1625-5(0)) Enslow Pubs., Inc.

Sarkisian, Kevin. You Need Your Nose: Learning the N Sound. 2002. (PowerPhonics Ser.). (Illus.). (J). 23p. lib. bdg. (978-0-8239-8255-4(6)); 24p. (gr. 1). lib. bdg. 18.50 (978-0-8239-5910-5(4) , PowerKids Pr.) Rosen Publishing Group, Inc., The.

Schuh, Mari. The Sense of Smell. 2007. (Illus.). 24p. (J). lib. bdg. 19.95 (978-1-60014-072-3(6)) Bellwether Media.

Silverstein, Alvin, et al. Smell, the Subtle Sense. Neumann, Ann, illus. 2000. 90p. (J). (gr. 6-7). reprint ed. 22.00 (978-0-7881-9064-3(4)) DIANE Publishing Co.

—Smelling & Tasting. 2002. (Senses & Sensors Ser.). (Illus.). 64p. (gr. 5-8). lib. bdg. 25.90 (978-0-7613-1667-1(1) , Millbrook Pr.) Lerner Publishing Group.

Singer, Marilyn. What Stinks? 2006. (Illus.). 64p. (J). 17.95 (978-1-58196-035-8(2)) Darby Creek Publishing.

Smelling, 6 vols. (gr. k-2). 28.95 (978-0-7368-8585-0(4)) Red Brick Learning.

Tyler, Jenny & Hawthorn, P. Who's Making That Smell? rev. ed. 2004. (Illus.). 16p. (J). (gr. 1 up). pap. 7.95 (978-0-7945-0523-3(6)) EDC Publishing.

Viegas, Jennifer. The Mouth & Nose: Learning How We Taste & Smell. 2002. (3-D Library of the Human Body). (Illus.). 48p. (YA). (gr. 5-8). lib. bdg. 26.50 (978-0-8239-3535-2(3) , Rosen Central) Rosen Publishing Group, Inc., The.

Windsor, Jo. Smelling! Early Level Satellite Individual Title Six-Packs. (Sails Literacy Ser.). 16p. (gr. 1-2). 27.00 (978-0-7578-6511-4(9)) Rigby Education.

Woodward, John. Stinkers. 2005. (Planet's Most Extreme Ser.). (Illus.). 48p. (J). (gr. 3-7). 24.95 (978-1-4103-0397-4(7) , Blackbirch Pr., Inc.) Thomson Gale.

Woodward, Kay. Smell. 2005. (Illus.). 24p. (J). lib. bdg. 22.00 (978-0-8368-4408-5(4)) Stevens, Gareth Inc.

SMELL—FICTION

Anson-Weber, Joan. Snuffles Goes to Scotland Yard. Russell, Judith, illus. 2001. (J). 16.95 (978-0-87797-293-8(1)) Cherokee Publishing Co.

Clarke, Gus. Scratch N' Sniff. 1998. (Illus.). 27p. (J). pap. 9.95 (978-0-86264-810-7(6)) Andersen GBR. *Dist:* Trafalgar Square Publishing.

Cook, Sherry & Johnson, Terri. Nosey Nina, 26 vols. Kuhn, Jesse, illus. l.t. ed. 2006. (Quirkles—Exploring Phonics through Science Ser.: 14). 32p. (J). 7.99 (978-1-933815-13-8(2) , Quirkles, The) Creative 3, LLC.

Hernandez, Richard J. Smelly Cheese. 2001. (J). (ps-3). pap. (978-0-9708489-1-8(9)) Storitime Publishing.

Palatini, Margie. Stinky Smelly Feet: A Love Story. Long, Ethan, illus. 2004. 32p. (J). (ps). 15.99 (978-0-525-47201-8(0) , Dutton Juvenile) Penguin Group (USA) Inc.

Peep and Big Wide World & Galvin, Laura. Very Good Smell. 2006. 32p. pap. 2.99 (978-1-59249-552-8(4)) Soundprints.

Postgate, Daniel. Smelly Bill. 2007. (Illus.). 24p. (J). (ps-2). 16.95 (*978-0-7358-2135-4(6)) North-South Bks., Inc.

Taylor, Alastair. Mr. Blewitt's Nose. 2005. (J). (gr. k-3). 16.00 (978-0-618-58111-5(1)); (Illus.). 32p. 16.00 (978-0-618-42353-8(2)) Houghton Mifflin Co. Trade & Reference Div.

Tekavec, Heather. What's That Awful Smell? Margaret, Spengler, illus. 2006. 32p. (J). pap. 5.99 (978-0-14-240586-4(8) , Puffin) Penguin Group (USA) Inc.

—What's That Awful Smell? Spengler, Margaret, illus. 2004. 32p. (J). (gr. k-3). 15.99 (978-0-8037-2660-4(0) , Dial) Penguin Group (USA) Inc.

S

Tyler, Jenny & Hawthorn, Phillip. Who's Making that Smell? 2007. (Luxury Flap Bks). 16p. (J). 9.99 (*978-0-7945-1696-3(3)*, Usborne) EDC Publishing.

Weiss, Ellen. Nose Knows. 2002. (gr. k-3). lib. bdg. 13.00 (978-0-613-53756-8(4)) Tandem Library Bks.

Weiss, Ellen & Lucas, Margeaux. The Nose Knows. 2002. (Science Solves It! Ser.). (Illus.). 32p. (J). 4.99 (978-1-57565-120-0(3)) Kane Pr., The.

Wright, Lynn F. Grandma, Tell Me a Story. Pagliughi, Debbie, illus. 1999. (J). 13.95 (978-1-881519-10-2(4)); pap. 6.95 (978-1-881519-11-9(2)) WorryWart Publishing Co.

SMITH, BESSIE, 1898-1937

Manera, Alexandria. Bessie Smith. 2003. (African-American Biographies Ser.). (Illus.). 64p. pap. 8.95 (978-1-4109-0034-0(7)); (J). lib. bdg. 28.56 (978-0-7398-6875-1(6)) Raintree.

SMITH, CASEY (FICTITIOUS CHARACTER)—FICTION

Ellerbee, Linda. Ghoul Reporter Digs up Zombies! 2000. (Get Real Ser.: No. 5). 208p. (J). (gr. 3-7). 14.89 (978-0-06-028249-3(5)); No. 5. pap. 4.99 (978-0-06-440759-5(4), Avon) HarperCollins Pubs.

—Girl Reporter Blows Lid off Town! 2000. (Get Real Ser.: No. 1). (Illus.). 208p. (J). (gr. 3-7). 14.89 (978-0-06-028245-5(2)) HarperCollins Pubs.

—Girl Reporter Bytes Back! 2001. (Get Real Ser.: No. 8). 176p. (J). (gr. 3-7). 14.89 (978-0-06-029258-4(X)) HarperCollins Pubs.

—Girl Reporter Gets the Skinny! 2001. (Get Real Ser.: No. 7). (Illus.). 192p. (J). (gr. 3-7). 14.89 (978-0-06-029257-7(1)) HarperCollins Pubs.

—Girl Reporter Gets the Skinny! 2001. (gr. 3-6). lib. bdg. 13.00 (978-0-613-31242-4(2)) Tandem Library Bks.

—Girl Reporter Rocks Polls! 2000. (Get Real Ser.: No. 6). 224p. (J). (gr. 3-7). 14.89 (978-0-06-028250-9(9)) HarperCollins Pubs.

—Girl Reporter Sinks School! 2000. (Get Real Ser.: No. 2). (Illus.). 176p. (J). (gr. 3-7). 14.89 (978-0-06-028246-2(0)) HarperCollins Pubs.

—Girl Reporter Snags Crush! 2000. (Get Real Ser.: No. 4). (Illus.). 229p. (J). (gr. 3-7). 14.89 (978-0-06-028248-6(7)) HarperCollins Pubs.

—Girl Reporter Stuck in Jam! 2000. (Get Real Ser.: No. 3). (Illus.). 224p. (J). (gr. 3-7). 14.89 (978-0-06-028247-9(9)) HarperCollins Pubs.

SMITH, JEDEDIAH STRONG, 1799-1831

Maynard, Charles W. Jedediah Smith: Mountain Man of the American West. 2003. (Famous Explorers of the American West Ser.). (Illus.). 24p. (J). lib. bdg. 18.75 (978-0-8239-6287-7(3), PowerKids Pr.) Rosen Publishing Group, Inc., The.

Nelson, Sharlene P. & Nelson, Ted W. Jedediah Smith. 2004. (Watts Library). (Illus.). 64p. (J). 25.50 (978-0-531-12287-7(5), Watts, Franklin) Scholastic Library Publishing.

SMITH, JOHN, 1580-1631

Adams, Colleen. Pocahontas: The Life on an Indian Princess. 2006. (Rosen Publishing Group's Reading Room Collection). (Illus.). 16p. (J). lib. bdg. (978-1-4042-3348-5(2), PowerKids Pr.) Rosen Publishing Group, Inc., The.

Benge, Janet & Benge, Geoff. John Smith: A Foothold in the New World. 2006. (Illus.). 192p. (J). pap. (978-1-932096-36-1(1)) Emerald Bks.

Bruchac, Joseph. Pocahontas. 2003. (Illus.). 192p. (J). (gr. 6-8). 17.00 (978-0-15-216737-0(4), Silver Whistle) Harcourt Trade Pubs.

Compass Point Books, contrib. by. Smith. (Exploring the World Ser.). 48p. (YA). pap. 8.95 (978-0-7565-1149-4(6)) Compass Point Bks.

Doak, Robin S. Smith: John Smith & the Settlement of Jamestown. 2003. (Exploring the World Ser.). (Illus.). 48p. (J). (gr. 4 up). lib. bdg. 22.60 (978-0-7565-0423-6(6)) Compass Point Bks.

Doherty, Kieran. To Conquer Is to Live: The Life of Captain John Smith of Jamestown. 2001. (Single Titles Ser.). (Illus.). 144p. (J). (gr. 6-8). lib. bdg. 23.90 (978-0-7613-1820-0(8), Twenty-First Century Bks.) Lerner Publishing Group.

Edwards, Judith. Jamestown, John Smith, & Pocahontas in American History. 2002. (In American History Ser.). (Illus.). 128p. (YA). (gr. 5-12). lib. bdg. 26.60 (978-0-7660-1842-6(3)) Enslow Pubs., Inc.

Kline, Trish. Captain John Smith. 2001. (Discover the Life of an Explorer Ser.). (Illus.). 24p. (J). (gr. 1-4). lib. bdg. 20.64 (978-1-58952-065-3(3)) Rourke Publishing, LLC.

Krull, Kathleen. Pocahontas: Princess of the New World. Diaz, David, illus. 2007. 40p. (J). (gr. 1-6). 17.85 (978-0-8027-9555-7(2)); 16.95 (978-0-8027-9554-0(4)) Walker & Co.

Loker, Aleck. Fearless Captain: The Adventures of John Smith. 2006. (Founders of the Republic Ser.). 176p. (J). lib. bdg. 26.95 (978-1-931798-83-9(4)) Reynolds, Morgan Inc.

Marcovitz, Hal. John Smith, Explorer & Colonial Leader. 2001. (Explorers of New Worlds Ser.). (Illus.). (J). 63p. pap. (978-0-7910-6433-7(6)); 64p. (gr. 4-6). 25.00 (978-0-7910-6432-0(8)) Facts On File, Inc. (Chelsea Hse.).

Marsh, Carole. Captain John Smith. 2002. (One Thousand Readers Ser.). (Illus.). 12p. (J). (gr. k-4). 2.95 (978-0-635-01559-4(5), 15595) Gallopade International.

—The Virginia Reader: Captain John Smith. 2001. (Virginia Experience! Ser.). (Illus.). 12p. (J). (gr. k-4). pap. 2.95 (978-0-635-00378-2(3)) Gallopade International.

Mello, Tara Baukus. John Smith. 1999. (Colonial Leaders Ser.). (Illus.). 80p. (J). (gr. 3 up). pap. 27.50 (978-0-7910-5688-2(0), Chelsea Hse.) Facts On File, Inc.

—John Smith: English Explorer & Colonist. 2000. (Colonial Leaders Ser.). (Illus.). 80p. (J). (gr. 4-5). lib. bdg. 27.50 (978-0-7910-5345-4(8), Chelsea Hse.) Facts On File, Inc.

Petrie, Kristin. John Smith. 2007. (Illus.). 32p. (J). 22.78 (978-1-59679-751-2(7)) ABDO Publishing Co.

Schaefer, Lola M. Pocahontas. Saunders-Smith, Gail, ed. 2002. (First Biographies Ser.). (Illus.). 24p. (J). (gr. k-1). lib. bdg. 15.93 (978-0-7368-1175-0(3), Pebble Bks.) Capstone Pr., Inc.

Schanzer, Rosalyn. John Smith Escapes Again! Schanzer, Rosalyn, illus. 2006. (Illus.). 64p. (J). (gr. 4-9). 16.95 (978-0-7922-5930-5(0)); lib. bdg. 25.90 (978-0-7922-5931-2(9)) National Geographic Society. (National Geographic Children's Bks.).

Sullivan, George E. Pocahontas. 2002. (In Their Own Words Ser.). (Illus.). 128p. (J). (gr. 3-7). 4.99 (978-0-439-16585-3(7)); pap. 12.95 (978-0-439-32668-1(0)) Scholastic, Inc. (Scholastic Reference).

Zemlicka, Shannon. Pocahontas. Reeves, Jeni, illus. 2002. (On My Own Biographies Ser.). 47p. (J). lib. bdg. 23.93 (978-0-87614-598-2(5), Carolrhoda Bks.) Lerner Publishing Group.

—Pocahontas. 2002. (gr. 3-6). lib. bdg. 14.10 (978-0-613-52481-0(0)) Tandem Library Bks.

SMITH, JOHN, 1580-1631—FICTION

Foster, Genevieve. World of Captain John Smith. Foster, Genevieve, illus. 1999. (Illus.). 416p. (J). (gr. 5-8). pap. 15.95 (978-1-893103-00-9(5)) Beautiful Feet Bks.

Karwoski, Gail Langer. Surviving Jamestown: The Adventures of Young Sam Collier. Casale, Paul, illus. 2001. 192p. (J). (gr. 3-7). 14.95 (978-1-56145-239-2(4)); pap. 8.95 (978-1-56145-245-3(9)) Peachtree Pubs., Ltd.

—Surviving Jamestown: The Adventures of Young Sam Collier. 2001. (gr. 3-6). lib. bdg. 17.60 (978-0-613-51595-5(1)) Tandem Library Bks.

Massie, Elizabeth. 1609: Winter of the Dead: A Novel of the Founding of Jamestown. 2007. (Young Founders Ser.). 192p. (YA). 5.99 (978-0-7653-5604-8(X), Tor Kids) Doherty, Tom Assocs., LLC.

Ransom, Candice F. Sam Collier & the Founding of Jamestown. Archambault, Matthew, illus. 2006. (On My Own History Ser.). 48p. (J). (gr. 1-2). 25.26 (978-1-57505-874-0(X), Millbrook Pr.) Lerner Publishing Group.

SMITH, JOSEPH, 1805-1844

Bagley, Val Chadwick. Joseph's First Vision. 2005. (Illus.). (J). (978-1-59156-996-1(6)) Covenant Communications.

Lasater, Amy. This Is the Hill. Gerber, Patric, illus. 2005. (J). (978-1-59156-720-2(3)) Covenant Communications.

Passey, Marion. My Tiny Book of Joseph Smith. 2004. (Illus.). (J). 5.95 (978-1-59038-243-1(9)) Deseret Bk. Co.

Perry, David Earl, retold by. Joseph Smith, a Sacred Story. 2005. (Illus.). 149p. (J). per. (978-0-941518-51-2(5)) Perry Enterprises.

Turley, Richard E. & Littke, Lael. Stories from the Life of Joseph Smith. 2003. (Illus.). viii, 184p. (J). (978-1-57008-915-2(9)) Deseret Bk. Co.

SMITH, MARGARET CHASE, 1897-1995

Plourde, Lynn. What a President She Would Have Been: Margaret Chase Smith. 2008. (J). (*978-1-58089-234-6(5)*) Charlesbridge Publishing, Inc.

SMITHSONIAN INSTITUTION

Britton, Tamara L. The Smithsonian Institution. 2005. (Symbols, Landmarks, & Monuments Set Ii Ser.). (Illus.). 32p. (J). (gr. k-6). lib. bdg. 22.78 (978-1-59197-521-2(2)) ABDO Publishing Co.

SMOKING

see also Tobacco Habit

Amos, Janine. Kate Smokes Cigarettes. 2002. (Body Matters Ser.). (Illus.). 32p. (YA). 19.99 (978-1-84234-108-7(1), Cherrytree Books) Evans Publishing Group GBR. *Dist:* Independent Pubs. Group.

Anderson, Judith. Smoking. 2005. (It's Your Health Ser.). (Illus.). 45p. (J). (gr. 6-9). lib. bdg. 29.95 (978-1-58340-587-1(9)) Smart Apple Media.

Bingham, Jane. Smoking. 2005. (What's the Deal? Ser.). (Illus.). 56p. (J). (978-1-4034-7021-8(9)) Heinemann Library.

Connelly, Elizabeth Russell. Nicotine = Busted! 2006. (Busted! Ser.). (Illus.). 112p. (J). lib. bdg. 31.93 (978-0-7660-2473-1(3)) Enslow Pubs., Inc.

Connolly, Sean. Tobacco. 2000. (Just the Facts Ser.). (Illus.). 56p. (YA). (gr. 6-8). lib. bdg. 24.22 (978-1-57572-260-3(7)) Heinemann Library.

Deboo, Ana. Tobacco. 2007. (J). (*978-1-4034-9738-3(9)*); pap. (*978-1-4034-9743-7(5)*) Heinemann Library.

Egendorf, Laura. Smoking. 2007. (Issues that Concern You Ser.). 144p. (gr. 7-10). 33.70 (*978-0-7377-2420-2(X)*, Greenhaven Pr., Inc.) Thomson Gale.

Esherick, Joan. Clearing the Haze: A Teen's Guide to Smoking-Related Health Issues. 2005. (Science of Health Ser.). (Illus.). 128p. (J). lib. bdg. 24.95 (978-1-59084-844-9(6)) Mason Crest Pubs.

Green, Carl R. Nicotine & Tobacco: A Myreportlinks. com Book. 2005. (Drugs Ser.). (Illus.). 48p. (J). (ps-10). lib. bdg. 25.26 (978-0-7660-5283-3(4), MyReportLinks.com Bks.) Enslow Pubs., Inc.

Haughton, Emma. The Right to Smoke? 2005. (Illus.). 32p. (J). (gr. 5-8). lib. bdg. 27.10 (978-1-932889-62-8(0)) Sea-To-Sea Pubns.

Hirschfelder, Arlene B. Kick Butts! A Kid's Action Guide to a Tobacco-Free America. 2001. 160p. pap. 29.95 (978-0-8108-3913-7(X)) Scarecrow Pr., Inc.

Holt, Rinehart and Winston Staff. Decisions for Health Blue, Chptr. 14: Tobacco. 4th ed. 2004. (YA). pap. 11.20 (978-0-03-068048-9(4)) Holt, Rinehart & Winston.

Hudson, David. Smoking Bans. 2004. (Point/Counterpoint Ser.). (Illus.). 120p. (gr. 9-13). 32.95 (978-0-7910-7974-4(0), Chelsea Hse.) Facts On File, Inc.

Jaffe, Steven L., ed. Nicotine & Cigarettes. 1999. (Junior Drug Awareness Ser.). (Illus.). 80p. (J). (gr. 4-8). 32.00 (978-0-7910-5175-7(7), Chelsea Hse.) Facts On File, Inc.

Jones, David C. One Person to Another: Smoking, Chewing Tobacco & Young Peopole. l.t. ed. 2003. 20p. (YA). 4.00 (978-1-878400-17-8(7)) Dolphin Publishing.

Kaplan, Sheldon A. Cold Turkey Before You Become One! Stop Smoking, Drinking, Gambling & or Abusing Drugs. Resseguie, Douglas, ed. deluxe ed. 1999. (YA). 5.95 (978-0-9677993-1-5(7)) Kaplan, Sheldon A. & Assocs.,.

Keyishan, Elizabeth. Everything You Need to Know about Smoking. rev. ed. 2000. (Need to Know Library). (Illus.). 64p. (J). (gr. 4-6). lib. bdg. 25.25 (978-0-8239-3221-4(4), NTSMOK) Rosen Publishing Group, Inc., The.

Keyishan, Elizabeth. Smoking. rev. ed. 2005. (Need to Know Library). (Illus.). 64p. (J). (gr. 7-12). lib. bdg. 25.25 (978-0-8239-4092-9(6)) Rosen Publishing Group, Inc., The.

Kranz, Rachel. Straight Talk about Smoking. 1999. (Straight Talk Ser.). 160p. (YA). (gr. 6-12). lib. bdg. 27.45 (978-0-8160-3976-0(3)) Facts On File, Inc.

Landau, Elaine. Cigarettes. 2003. (Watts Library). 64p. (J). (gr. 5-7). pap. 8.95 (978-0-531-16666-6(X), Watts, Franklin) Scholastic Library Publishing.

—Cigarettes. 2003. (gr. 5-8). lib. bdg. 17.60 (978-0-613-67603-8(3)) Tandem Library Bks.

LeVert, Suzanne. The Facts about Nicotine. 2006. (Drugs Ser.). (Illus.). 112p. (J). lib. bdg. 39.93 (978-0-7614-2244-0(7), Benchmark Bks.) Cavendish, Marshall Corp.

Lobster Press Staff, ed. Let's Clear the Air: 10 Reasons Not to Start Smoking. Staffo, Deanna, illus. 2007. 192p. (YA). (gr. 4-10). pap. 14.95 (*978-1-897073-66-7(6)*) Lobster Pr. CAN. *Dist:* National Bk. Network.

Lynette, Rachel. Tobacco. 2007. (J). (*978-1-4034-9696-6(X)*); pap. (*978-1-4034-9703-1(6)*) Heinemann Library.

Marcom Group Ltd, prod. Smoke Screen Win Labpak. (YA). cd-rom 222.50 (978-0-7365-4344-6(9)) Films Media Group.

McGraw-Hill Staff. Teen Health Course 2, Modules, Tobacco, Alcohol, & Other Drugs. 5th ed. 2002. (Three-Level Middle School Health Ser.). (C). (gr. 7 up). 15.32 (978-0-07-826183-1(X), 9780078261831) Glencoe/McGraw-Hill.

McMillan, Daniel. Teen Smoking: Understanding the Risk. 1998. (Issues in Focus Ser.). (Illus.). 128p. (YA). (gr. 6-12). lib. bdg. 20.95 (978-0-89490-722-7(0)) Enslow Pubs., Inc.

Miller, Michelle. Aggie & Rowdy Say No Way to Cigarettes: Dog Tales, Cancer Stories for Kids. 2007. 53p. pap. 12.99 (*978-1-58752-258-1(6)*) Timberwolf Pr., Inc.

Moe, Barbara. Teen Smoking & Tobacco Use. 2000. (Hot Issues Ser.). (Illus.). 64p. (YA). (gr. 6-12). lib. bdg. 27.93 (978-0-7660-1359-9(6)) Enslow Pubs., Inc.

Monroe, Judy. Nicotine. 2001. (Drug Library). (Illus.). 128p. (YA). (gr. 6-12). pap. 13.26 (978-0-7660-1926-3(8)) Enslow Pubs., Inc.

Morgan, Sally. Smoking. 2002. (Health Issues Ser.). (Illus.). 64p. (YA). (gr. 6-8). lib. bdg. 28.54 (978-0-7398-4774-9(0)) Raintree.

Powell, Jillian. Why Do People Smoke? 2001. (Exploring Tough Issues Ser.). (Illus.). 48p. (J). (gr. 4-7). lib. bdg. 25.69 (978-0-7398-3234-9(4)) Raintree.

Price, Sean. Nicotine. 2008. (Junior Drug Awareness Ser.). 112p. (J). (gr. 5-8). 30.00 (*978-0-7910-9696-3(3)*, Chelsea Hse.) Facts On File, Inc.

Royston, Angela. Tobacco. 2000. (Learn to Say No! Ser.). (Illus.). 32p. (J). (gr. 4-6). lib. bdg. 22.79 (978-1-57572-239-9(9)) Heinemann Library.

Sanders, Bruce. Smoking. 2005. (Illus.). 32p. (J). (gr. 3-7). lib. bdg. 27.10 (978-1-59604-047-2(5)) Stargazer Bks.

Sanders, Pete & Myers, Steve. Smoking. 2006. (Choices & Decisions Ser.). (Illus.). 32p. (J). (978-1-59604-098-4(X)) Stargazer Bks.

Silverstein, Alvin, et al. Smoking. 2003. (My Health Ser.). 48p. (YA). 25.50 (978-0-531-12193-1(3), Watts, Franklin) Scholastic Library Publishing.

—Smoking. 2003. (Illus.). 47p. (J). (ps-3). lib. bdg. 15.25 (978-0-613-67930-5(X)) Tandem Library Bks.

Smoking 2007. 2007. 140p. (gr. 10-12). pap. 19.95 (*978-0-7377-2421-9(8)*, Greenhaven Pr., Inc.) Thomson Gale.

Stewart, Gail B. Ripped from the Headlines: Smoking. 2007. (J). (*978-1-60217-017-9(7)*) Erickson Pr.

Stewart, Gail B. Smoking. 2002. (Understanding Issues Ser.). (Illus.). 48p. (J). (gr. 3-5). 26.20 (978-0-7377-1026-7(8), Kidhaven) Thomson Gale.

Wagner, Heather Lehr. Nicotine. 2003. (Drugs, the Straight Facts Ser.). (Illus.). 112p. (J). (gr. 9-13). 30.00 (978-0-7910-7264-6(9), Chelsea Hse.) Facts On File, Inc.

Weitzman, Elizabeth. Let's Talk about Smoking. 1998. (PowerKids Ser.). 24p. (J). (ps-3). reprint ed. pap. 6.95 (978-1-56838-220-3(0)) Hazelden Publishing & Educational Services.

Williams, Mary E. Teen Smoking. 2000. (Contemporary Issues Companion Ser.). 144p. (YA). (gr. 9-12). lib. bdg. 36.20 (978-0-7377-0169-2(2)); (Illus.). (gr. 10 up). lib. bdg. 24.95 (978-0-7377-0168-5(4)) Thomson Gale. (Greenhaven Pr., Inc.).

SMOKING—FICTION

Brenneman, Tim. Jimmie Boogie Learns about Smoking. Hedrick, Bonnie & Canning, Robert, eds. 3rd ed. 2002. (Illus.). 12p. (J). 5.99 (978-0-9700453-2-4(8)) Grand Unification Pr., Inc.

Koss, Amy Goldman. Smoke Screen. 2000. (978-0-606-21791-0(6)) Tandem Library Bks.

Palmer, Raenette. Santa Quits. Cook, Dylan, illus. 1998. 32p. (J). (gr. k-5). 15.95 (978-1-890394-08-0(4), Sage Creek Pr.) Rhodes & Easton.

Proctor, Darrell. The Cigarette Monster. 2006. (J). pap. 8.00 (978-0-8059-6790-6(7)) Dorrance Publishing Co., Inc.

The Tobacco Temptation. (J). 39.50 (978-1-56230-082-1(2)) Syndistar, Inc.

Wert, Debra L. Eglin Long-Horn of Nightshade County: A Story about Tobacco Use & Choosing to Be Tobacco-Free. Wheeler, Penny et al, eds. 1998. (Illus.). 71p. (J). (gr. 4-6). pap. 12.95 (978-0-944576-25-0(7), 420) Rocky River Pubs., LLC.

SMUGGLING

Butterfield, Moira. Pirates & Smugglers. 2005. (Kingfisher Knowledge Ser.). (Illus.). 64p. (J). (gr. 5-9). 12.95 (978-0-7534-5864-8(0), Kingfisher) Houghton Mifflin Co. Trade & Reference Div.

Green, Michael. Customs Service. 2000. (Law Enforcement Ser.). (Illus.). 48p. (J). (gr. 3-4). lib. bdg. 21.26 (978-1-56065-756-9(1), Capstone High-Interest Bks.) Capstone Pr., Inc.

SMUGGLING—FICTION

Aldridge, Janet. The Meadow-Brook Girls by the Sea, or Th. 2006. pap. (*978-1-4065-0693-8(1)*) Dodo Pr.

Benjamin, Ruth. The Mysterious Lighthouse of Chelton. 2006. (ENG.). 160p. (J). 14.95 (*978-1-932443-57-8(6)*) Judaica Pr., Inc., The.

Broome, Errol. Nightwatch. (Illus.). 143p. (YA). pap. 9.95 (978-1-86368-110-0(8)) Fremantle Pr. AUS. *Dist:* International Specialized Bk. Services.

Buckey, Sarah Masters. The Smuggler's Treasure. 1999. (American Girl Collection Ser.). (978-0-606-17520-3(2)) Tandem Library Bks.

Decary, Marie. Adam et le Raton Dessinateur. Beshwaty, Steve, illus. 2004. (Premier Roman Ser.). (FRE.). 64p. (J). (gr. 1-4). pap. (978-2-89021-643-3(8)) Diffusion du livre Mirabel.

Decary, Marie. Adam's Tropical Adventure. Beshwaty, Steve, illus. 2005. 54p. (J). lib. bdg. 12.00 (*978-1-4242-1202-6(2)*) Fitzgerald Bks.

Deuker, Carl. Runner. 224p. (YA). (gr. 7). 2007. pap. 7.99 (*978-0-618-73505-1(4)*, Graphia); 2005. 16.00 (978-0-618-54298-7(1)) Houghton Mifflin Co. Trade & Reference Div.

Evarts, Hal G. Smuggler's Road. 2000. (J). pap. 1.95 (978-0-590-04503-2(2)) Scholastic, Inc.

Furtney, Charles S. Tryconnel: An Antebellum Adventure along the C & O Canal. 2004. (Illus.). iii, 156p. (J). pap. (978-0-9711835-3-7(8)) Local History Co., The.

Harvey, M. A. The Scorpion Secret: Dare to Take the Test. 2004. (Illus.). 128p. (J). pap. (978-1-84458-050-7(4)) Chrysalis Children's Bks.

Holmes, Victoria. Rider in the Dark: An Epic Horse Story. 2004. (Illus.). 320p. (J). (gr. 5 up). 15.99 (978-0-06-052025-0(6)); lib. bdg. 16.89 (978-0-06-052026-7(4)) HarperCollins Pubs.

Inspector Grub & the Fizzer-X Spy: Individual Title Six-Packs. (Bookweb Ser.). 32p. (gr. 5 up). 34.00 (978-0-7635-3786-9(1)) Rigby Education.

Lawrence, Iain. The Smugglers. (Illus.). (J). (gr. 5-9). 2000. 208p. 5.99 (978-0-440-41596-1(9), Yearling); 1999. 192p. 15.95 (978-0-385-32663-6(7), Delacorte Bks. for Young Readers) Random Hse. Children's Bks.

—The Smugglers. 2000. 184p. (J). (ps-7). lib. bdg. 12.15 (978-0-606-19693-2(5)) Tandem Library Bks.

—Smugglers. 2000. (gr. 5-8). lib. bdg. 13.55 (978-0-613-30132-9(3)) Tandem Library Bks.

—The Smugglers. l.t. ed. 2001. (Illus.). 246p. (J). 22.95 (978-0-7862-3465-3(2)) Thorndike Pr.

Lloyd-Jones, Robin. Moonfleet. 2007. (Young Reading Series 3 Gift Bks). 64p. (J). 8.99 (*978-0-7945-1906-3(7)*, Usborne) EDC Publishing.

Prins, Piet. The Haunted Castle. 2006. (Illus.). 139p. (J). pap. (978-1-894666-44-2(5)) Inheritance Pubns.

Pyle, Jack R. The Gold Bug of Farrow Point. 2003. 130p. (J). (978-1-887905-78-7(2)) Parkway Pubs., Inc.

Shaler, Robert. The Boy Scouts on Picket Duty. 2006. pap. 33.99 (*978-1-4219-7290-9(5)*) IndyPublish.com.

Stem, Jacqueline. The Ghosts of Goliad. 2003. iii, 165p. (J). 17.95 (978-1-57168-785-2(8), Eakin Pr.) Eakin Pr.

Striker, Fran. Lone Ranger Traps Smugglers. (J). 21.95 (978-0-8488-1183-9(6)) Amereon LTD.

Taylor, Cora. Murder in Mexico. 2007. (Spy Who Wasn't There Ser.). (Illus.). 360p. (J). (gr. 4-7). pap. 7.95 (*978-1-55050-353-1(7)*) Coteau Bks. CAN. *Dist:* Fitzhenry & Whiteside, Ltd.

Ungerer, Tomi. The Mellops Go Spelunking. Ungerer, Tomi, illus. 1998. (Illus.). 32p. (J). (gr. k-4). pap. 5.95 (978-1-57098-228-6(7)) Rinehart, Roberts Pubs.

SNAILS

Adams, Pam. Snail. 1999. (Pocket Pals Ser.). (Illus.). 12p. (J). (ps-1). bds. 1.99 (978-0-85953-860-2(5)) Child's Play-International.

Allen, Judy. Are You a Snail? Humphries, Tudor, illus. 2000. (Backyard Bks.). 32p. (J). (gr. k-3). tchr. ed. 9.95 (978-0-7534-5242-4(1), Kingfisher) Houghton Mifflin Co. Trade & Reference Div.

—Are You a Snail? 2003. (ps-2). lib. bdg. 12.95 (978-0-613-90774-3(4)) Tandem Library Bks.

—Are You a Snail? Humphries, Tudor, illus. 2003. (Backyard Bks.). 32p. (J). (ps up). pap. 5.95 (978-0-7534-5604-0(4), Kingfisher) Houghton Mifflin Co. Trade & Reference Div.

Chanell, Jim & Greenaway, Theresa. Slugs & Snails. 1999. (Minipets Ser.). (Illus.). 32p. (J). (gr. 1-5). lib. bdg. 25.69 (978-0-8172-5587-9(7)) Raintree.

Fowler, Allan. A Snail's Pace. 1999. (gr. k-3). lib. bdg. 12.95 (978-0-613-54667-6(9)) Tandem Library Bks.

Fredericks, Anthony D. In One Tidepool: Crabs, Snails, & Salty Tails. DiRubbio, Jennifer, illus. 2004. (Sharing Nature with Children Book Ser.). 32p. (J). (ps-2). 16.95 (978-1-58469-039-9(9)); pap. 7.95 (978-1-58469-038-2(0)) Dawn Pubns.

Gilpin, Daniel. Snails, Shellfish & Other Mollusks. 2006. (Animal Kingdom Classification Ser.). (Illus.). 48p. (J). (gr. 4-6). 26.60 (978-0-7565-1613-0(7) , 1253127) Compass Point Bks.

Green, Jen. Snails. 2004. (Nature's Children Ser.). (Illus.). 48p. (J). (978-0-7172-5973-1(0) , Grolier) Scholastic Library Publishing.

Greenaway, Theresa. Slugs & Snails. 1999. (Minipets Ser.). (Illus.). 32p. (gr. 1-5). pap. 7.95 (978-0-8172-4207-7(4)) Steck-Vaughn.

Hartley, Karen. Snail. 2002. (Bug Bks.). (Illus.). 32p. (J). (gr. k-2). pap. 6.95 (978-1-57572-460-7(X) , 90450) Heinemann Library.

Hartley, Karen & Macro, Chris. Snail. 2006. (Illus.). 32p. (J). (***978-1-4034-8301-0(9)***); 2nd ed. pap. (***978-1-4034-8314-0(0)***) Heinemann Library.

Hipp, Andrew. The Life Cycle of a Snail. Kuhn, Dwight, illus. Kuhn, Dwight, photos by. 2002. (Life Cycles Library). 24p. (J). lib. bdg. 18.75 (978-0-8239-5871-9(X) , PowerKids Pr.) Rosen Publishing Group, Inc., The.

Houbre, Gilbert & Gallimard Jeunesse Publishing Staff. Turtles & Snails. 1998. (First Discovery Book Ser.). (Illus.). 24p. (J). (ps-2). 12.95 (978-0-590-11764-7(5) , Scholastic Reference) Scholastic, Inc.

How Snails Live: 6 Each of 1 Student Book, 6 vols. (Sunshinetm Science Ser.). 24p. (gr. 1-2). 41.95 (978-0-7802-2702-6(6)) Wright Group, The.

How Snails Live: Big Book. (Sunshinetm Science Ser.). 24p. (gr. 1-2). 37.50 (978-0-7802-2785-9(9)) Wright Group, The.

How Snails Protect Themselves: 6 Each of 1 Student Book, 6 vols. (Sunshinetm Science Ser.). 24p. (gr. 1-2). 41.95 (978-0-7802-2704-0(2)) Wright Group, The.

How Snails Protect Themselves: Big Book. (Sunshinetm Science Ser.). 24p. (gr. 1-2). 37.50 (978-0-7802-2786-6(7)) Wright Group, The.

Hughes, Monica. Snails. 2003. (Raintree Sprouts Ser.). (Illus.). 24p. (J). 5.50 (978-1-4109-0651-9(5)); lib. bdg. 18.56 (978-1-4109-0625-0(6)) Raintree.

—Snails. 2003. (ps-2). lib. bdg. 13.55 (978-0-613-78261-6(5)) Tandem Library Bks.

Jacobs, Liza. Snails. 2003. (Wild Wild World Ser.). (Illus.). 24p. (J). 22.45 (978-1-4103-0034-8(X) , Blackbirch Pr., Inc.) Thomson Gale.

The Life Cycle of a Snail. (Sunshinetm Science Ser.). 24p. (gr. 1-2). 37.50 (978-0-7802-2784-2(0)) Wright Group, The.

The Life Cycle of a Snail: 6 Each of 1 Student Book, 6 vols. (Sunshinetm Science Ser.). 24p. (gr. 1-2). 41.95 (978-0-7802-2700-2(X)) Wright Group, The.

Llewellyn, Claire. Slugs & Snails. 2001. (gr. k-3). lib. bdg. 12.95 (978-0-613-54357-6(2)) Tandem Library Bks.

Murray, Peter. Snails. 2006. (New Naturebooks). (Illus.). 32p. (J). (gr. 1-5). 27.07 (978-1-59296-650-9(0)) Child's World, Inc.

Ofinoski, Steven A. Snails & Other Mollusks. World Book, Inc. Staff, ed. 2002. (World Book's Animals of the World Ser.: Set 3). (Illus.). 64p. (J). (978-0-7166-1232-2(1)) World Bk., Inc.

Pascoe, Elaine. Snails & Slugs. Kuhn, Dwight, photos by. 1998. (Nature Close-Up Ser.). (Illus.). 48p. (J). (gr. 4-8). 23.70 (978-1-56711-181-1(5) , Blackbirch Pr., Inc.) Thomson Gale.

Pyers. Snails, 6 packs. 2004. (Minibeasts up Close Ser.). pap. 40.50 (978-1-4109-1546-7(8)) Harcourt Schl. Pubs.

Pyers, Greg. Snails up Close. (Minibeasts up Close Ser.). (Illus.). 32p. (J). (ps-ps). 2005. lib. bdg. 26.36 (978-1-4109-1532-0(8)); 2004. pap. (978-1-4109-1539-9(5)) Harcourt Schl. Pubs.

Ross, Michael Elsohn. Snailology. Erickson, Darren, illus. Grogan, Brian, photos by. 2003. (Backyard Buddies Ser.). 48p. (YA). (gr. 3-5). 6.95 (978-1-57505-437-7(X) , Carolrhoda Bks.) Lerner Publishing Group.

Schaefer, Lola M. La Babosa. 2002. (Animales Resbalosos (Ooey-Gooey Animals) Ser.). (SPA.). 24p. (J). (ps-1). lib. bdg. 18.50 (978-1-58810-768-8(X)); (Illus.). pap. 5.25 (978-1-58810-812-8(0) , 91517) Heinemann Library.

The Snail Trail. 2004. 10p. (J). bds. 5.99 (978-1-85997-875-7(4)) Byeway Bks.

Snails. (Animals Ser.). 32p. (J). 6.95 (978-0-7368-8066-4(6)) Capstone Pr., Inc.

Snails, 6 vols. (gr. 2-5). 36.95 (978-0-7368-8176-0(X)) Red Brick Learning.

Snails Sets: 1 Each of 3 Big Books. (Sunshinetm Science Ser.). (gr. 1-2). 111.50 (978-0-7802-2822-1(7)) Wright Group, The.

Snails Sets: 1 Each of 3 Student Books. (Sunshinetm Science Ser.). (gr. 1-2). 20.95 (978-0-7802-2823-8(5)) Wright Group, The.

Steck-Vaughn Staff. Animal Facts: Slowpoke Snail. 1998. (Illus.). (J). pap. (978-0-8172-8643-9(8)) Steck-Vaughn.

Stone, Lynn M. Sea Snails. 2003. (Rourke Discovery Library). (Illus.). 24p. (gr. 2-5). 14.95 (978-1-58952-320-3(2)) Rourke Publishing, LLC.

Watts, Barrie. Snail. 2002. (Illus.). 32p. (J). lib. bdg. 24.25 (978-1-58340-198-9(9)) Smart Apple Media.

—Snails & Slugs. (Illus.). 32p. (YA). (gr. 2 up). lib. bdg. 27.10 (978-1-932889-21-5(3)) Sea-To-Sea Pubns.

Weber, Rebecca. Tricky Insects: And Other Fun Creatures. 2002. (Spyglass Books). (Illus.). 24p. (J). (gr. 1 up). lib. bdg. 18.60 (978-0-7565-0388-8(4)) Compass Point Bks.

Wingfield, Al. The Little Snail That Lives near a Pail. Ramey, Lisa L., illus. Ramey, Lisa L., photos by. 1999. 14p. (J). (ps-3). pap. 7.95 (978-1-930260-00-9(8)) CTS Family Pr.

SNAILS—FICTION

Abrams, Harry N., Staff, contrib. by. Snail. 2001. (Portable Pets Ser.). (Illus.). 12p. (J). (ps-ps). bds. 6.95 (978-0-8109-5672-8(1)) Abrams, Harry N. , Inc.

Almond the Snail. 2001. (J). pap. 9.00 (978-0-8059-5122-6(9)) Dorrance Publishing Co., Inc.

Andersen, Hans Christian. IceMaiden & Other Tales. 2006. pap. (***978-1-4068-0421-8(5)***) Echo Library.

Avi. A Beginning, a Muddle, & an End: The Return of the End of the Beginning. Tusa, Tricia, illus. 2008. 176p. (J). 14.95 (***978-0-15-205555-4(X)***) Harcourt Trade Pubs.

—The End of the Beginning: Being the Adventures of a Small Snail (and an Even Smaller Ant) Tusa, Tricia, illus. 144p. (J). 2008. pap. 6.95 (***978-0-15-205532-5(0)*** , Harcourt Paperbacks); 2004. 14.95 (978-0-15-204968-3(1)) Harcourt Children's Bks.

Bronson, Tammy Carter. Tiny Snail. Bronson, Tammy Carter, illus. (Illus.). 32p. (J). (ps-3). 2000. pap. 10.95 (978-0-9678167-0-8(X)); 2002. pap. 7.99 (978-0-9678167-2-2(6)); 2002. lib. bdg. 14.99 (978-0-9678167-1-5(8)) Bookaroos Publishing, Inc.

Cave. The Snail That Snored. 1998. (Illus.). pap. (978-0-8172-5670-8(9)) Steck-Vaughn.

Chojnowski, Bryan. Muffin Time: Origins. 2005. 98p. pap. 25.01 (978-1-4116-4440-3(9)) Lulu.com.

Dijs, Carla. Snail's Big Surprise. 1999. (Illus.). 12p. (J). 8.99 (978-0-85953-718-6(8)) Child's Play-International.

Discovery Snail: A Play & Discover Book. 2002. (J). (978-1-931312-55-4(9)) SoftPlay, Inc.

D'Lacey, Chris. The Snail Patrol. Reeve, Philip, tr. Reeve, Philip, illus. 2005. 123p. (J). pap. 5.95 (978-1-903015-30-8(8)) Barn Owl Bks, London GBR. *Dist:* Independent Pubs. Group.

Donaldson, Julia. The Snail & the Whale. Scheffler, Axel, tr. Scheffler, Axel, illus. 2004. 32p. (J). (gr. k-3). 16.99 (978-0-8037-2922-3(7) , Dial) Penguin Group (USA) Inc.

—The Snail & the Whale. Scheffler, Axel, illus. 2006. 32p. (J). reprint ed. pap. 6.99 (978-0-14-240580-2(9) , Puffin) Penguin Group (USA) Inc.

Dorros, Arthur. When the Pigs Took Over. Greenseid, Diane, illus. 2002. (SPA.). 32p. (J). (ps-2). 15.99 (978-0-525-42030-9(4) , Dutton Juvenile) Penguin Group (USA) Inc.

Dubovoy, Silvia. Donde Canta el Mar. Peinador, Angeles, illus. 2004. (SPA.). 32p. (J). 14.99 (978-84-241-7988-5(9)) Everest de Ediciones y Distribucion, S.L. ESP. *Dist:* Lectorum Pubns., Inc.

Fermin, Alice. The Snail & the Rose Tree: Adaptation of a Hans Christian Andersen Story. Barrera, Sandra A., tr. 1999. Tr. of Caracol y el Rosal. (ENG & SPA.). 36p. (J). (ps-3). 14.95 (978-0-931722-16-5(0)) Corona Publishing, Co.

Fleming, Maria. Word Family Tales: Snail Mail. Fletcher, Rusty, illus. 2002. (Word Family Tales Ser.). 16p. (ps-2). pap. 2.95 (978-0-439-26262-0(3)) Scholastic, Inc.

Flowers, Natasha. Sammy the Snail. 2006. 10.00 (978-0-8059-9158-1(1)) Dorrance Publishing Co., Inc.

George, Lindsay Barrett. The Secret. George, Lindsay Barrett, illus. 2005. (Illus.). 32p. (J). 15.99 (978-0-06-029598-1(8)); 16.89 (978-0-06-029600-1(3)) HarperCollins Pubs.

Greenfield Educational Center Staff. Small Snail Goes to School. 2000. (I Can Read Ser.: Bk. 7). (CHI & ENG., Illus.). 8p. (J). pap. 2.99 (978-962-563-076-2(7)) Greenfield Enterprises, Ltd. HKG. *Dist:* Cheng & Tsui Co.

—Small Snail Goes to School: Simplified Edition. 2000. (I Can Read Ser.: Bk. 7). (CHI & ENG., Illus.). 8p. (J). pap. 2.99 (978-962-563-212-4(3)) Greenfield Enterprises, Ltd. HKG. *Dist:* Cheng & Tsui Co.

Harcourt School Publishers Staff. Two Snails: On Level. 3rd ed. 2002. (Trophies Reading Program Ser.). (Illus.). pap. 5.10 (978-0-15-323000-4(2)) Harcourt Schl. Pubs.

Harvey, Damian. Snail's Legs. Paul, Korky, illus. 2006. 32p. (J). 15.95 (***978-1-84507-112-7(3)***) Lincoln, Frances Ltd. GBR. *Dist:* Perseus Distribution.

Hilario. Stephanie's Dream. 2006. (Stories for Smaller Kids Ser.). (Illus.). 16p. (J). bds. 5.95 (978-9974-7925-5-5(X)) Hardenville SA URY. *Dist:* Independent Pubs. Group.

Hill, Franklin. Wings of Change. Cheung, Aries, illus. l.t. ed. 2001. 32p. (J). (ps-3). 15.95 (978-0-935699-18-0(X) , 093569918x) Illumination Arts Publishing Co., Inc.

Howe, Tina Field. Snailsworth, a Slow Little Story. Howe, Tina Field, illus. l.t. ed. 2005. (Illus.). 24p. (J). 12.95 (978-0-9768585-0-8(9) , 001) Howe, Tina Field.

Hyde, Margaret E. DreddieLocks & the Three Slugs. Parker, Curtis, illus. 2003. 36p. (J). lib. bdg. 16.95 (978-1-888108-07-1(X)) Budding Artists, Inc.

—Dreddielocks & the Three Slugs. Parker, Curtis, illus. 2004. 36p. (J). 16.95 (978-1-58980-231-5(4)) Pelican Publishing Co., Inc.

Janovitz, Marilyn. Look Out Bird. 2007. (Illus.). 32p. (J). 9.95 (978-0-7358-2078-4(3)) North-South Bks., Inc.

Karre, Nancy. On Herman's Pond. 2005. 8.00 (978-1-933281-00-1(6) , 2267) Battle Creek Area Mathematics & Science Ctr.

Less, Emma. Snail's Journey Through the Jungle. Moon, Jo, illus. 2006. (Snail#39;s Adventures Ser.). 10p. (J). bds. 15.95 (978-0-7696-4608-4(5) , Brighter Child) School Specialty Publishing.

—Snail's Race Around the World. Moon, Jo, illus. 2006. (Snail#39;s Adventures Ser.). 10p. (J). bds. 15.95 (978-0-7696-4607-7(7) , Brighter Child) School Specialty Publishing.

Loomis, Christine. The Best Father's Day Present Ever. Paparone, Pam, illus. 2007. 32p. (J). (gr. k-3). 15.99 (978-0-399-24253-3(8) , Putnam Juvenile) Penguin Group (USA) Inc.

Marshall, James. The Guest. 2001. (gr. k-3). lib. bdg. 12.95 (978-0-613-35523-0(7)) Tandem Library Bks.

McGuirk, Leslie. Snail Boy: An Adventure in Slow Motion. McGuirk, Leslie, illus. 2003. (Illus.). 32p. (J). (ps-2). 15.99 (978-0-7636-1259-7(6)) Candlewick Pr.

McKirdy, Mark. The Garden Party. 2004. 19p. (J). pap. 13.95 (978-1-4116-1847-3(5)) Lulu.com.

Nath, D. Smith. She, the Tale of a Sail. 30p. (J). (gr. k-2). pap. 5.95 (978-1-886134-03-4(0)) Miraculous Fingerprints Pubs.

New Home for Snail. 2003. (Daisy Board Books Ser.). 10p. (J). bds. 9.95 (978-0-7525-8299-3(2)) Parragon, Inc.

Nordahl, Danielle. How the Snail Got Her Shell. 2006. (ENG.). 28p. per. 13.95 (***978-1-4259-7339-1(6)***) AuthorHouse.

O'Connor, Jane. Snail City. 2001. (gr. k-3). lib. bdg. 11.80 (978-0-613-35622-0(5)) Tandem Library Bks.

Ostrow, Kim. The Great Snail Race. Bond, Clint & Clark, Andy, illus. ed. 2005. (SpongeBob Squarepants Ser.: No. 6). 22p. (J). lib. bdg. 15.00 (978-1-59054-830-1(2)) Fitzgerald Bks.

Palmer, Slim. Albert & the Dragon's Egg. 2005. (Illus.). 76p. pap. 11.05 (978-1-4116-4139-6(6)) Lulu.com.

—Albert the Third. 2008. (Illus.). 240p. (J). pap. 15.99 (978-1-84685-115-5(7) , Exposure Publishing) Meadow Bks. GBR. *Dist:* Ingram Bk. Co.

Paul, Ann Whitford. Snail's Good Night. Litzinger, Rosanne, illus. 2008. (J). (***978-0-8234-1912-8(6)***) Holiday Hse., Inc.

Porter, Marylyn Kight. Speedy the Snail & His New Family. 2006. 10.00 (978-0-8059-9134-5(4)) Dorrance Publishing Co., Inc.

Rempt, Fiona. Snail's Birthday Wish. Smit, Noelle, illus. 2007. 32p. (J). (ps-1). 14.95 (***978-1-905417-52-0(7)***) Boxer Bks., Ltd. GBR. *Dist:* Sterling Publishing Co., Inc.

Rigby Education Staff. Animals Say... (Sails Literacy Ser.). (Illus.). 16p. (gr. 2-3). 27.00 (978-0-7635-9943-0(3) , 699433C99) Rigby Education.

Rosoff, Meg. Jumpy Jack & Googily. Blackall, Sophie, illus. 2008. 32p. (J). 16.95 (***978-0-8050-8066-7(X)***) Holt, Henry & Co.

Santillo, LuAnn. Bee. Santillo, LuAnn, ed. 2003. (Half-Pint Kids Readers Ser.). (Illus.). 7p. (J). (ps-1). pap. (978-1-59256-108-7(X)) Half-Pint Kids, Inc.

—Snail. Santillo, LuAnn, ed. 2003. (Half-Pint Kids Readers Ser.). (Illus.). 7p. (J). (ps-1). pap. (978-1-59256-106-3(3)) Half-Pint Kids, Inc.

The Shy Snail. 2003. (J). per. (978-1-57657-937-4(9)) Paradise Pr., Inc.

So-Slow Snail. 2004. (Plush Pals Board Bks.). (Illus.). (J). (gr. k-1). bds. (978-0-7666-0559-6(0) , 39395) Modern Publishing.

Sollinger, Emily, ed. Snail City. O'Connor, Jane & Brown, Rick, illus. 2001. (All Aboard Reading Ser.). 32p. (J). (ps-3). pap. 3.99 (978-0-448-42418-7(5) , Grosset & Dunlap) Penguin Group (USA) Inc.

Stadler, John. Snail Saves the Day. Stadler, John, illus. 2006. (Illus.). 32p. (J). reprint ed. pap. 5.95 (978-1-59572-045-0(6)) Star Bright Bks., Inc.

Those Slowpoke Snails. 2002. per. (978-1-930493-24-7(X)) Athena Pr.

Ungerer, Tomi. Snail, Where Are You? 2005. (Illus.). 24p. (ps-3). 12.95 (978-1-59354-096-8(5)) Blue Apple Bks.

Waddell, Martin. Hi, Harry! The Moving Story of How One Slow Tortoise Slowly Made a Friend. Firth, Barbara, illus. 2003. 56p. (J). (ps-1). 14.99 (978-0-7636-1802-5(0)) Candlewick Pr.

Walsh, Vivian & Seibold, J. Otto. Gluey: A Snail Tale. 2002. (Illus.). 48p. (J). 15.00 (978-0-15-216620-5(3)) Harcourt Children's Bks.

Wenger, Shaunda. Caterpillar Can't Wait! 2006. (Early Explorers Ser.). (J). 34.00 (***978-1-4108-6101-6(5)***) Benchmark Education Co.

SNAKES

Allman, Toney. Vipers. 2004. (Animals Attack! Ser.). (Illus.). 48p. (J). 26.20 (978-0-7377-3006-7(4) , 1238322, Greenhaven Pr., Inc.) Thomson Gale.

Animal Lives: Snakes. 2006. pap. 4.99 (978-1-4206-8156-7(7)) Teacher Created Materials, Inc.

Animals & the Environment: Incl. Lizards (4 bks.), Sharks (4 bks.), Snakes (12 bks.), 20 bks. (Illus.). (J). (gr. 3-4). lib. bdg. (978-1-56065-810-8(X) , Capstone High-Interest Bks.) Capstone Pr., Inc.

Arnosky, Jim. All about Rattlesnakes. 2002. (All About Ser.). 32p. (J). pap. 5.99 (978-0-439-37617-4(3)) Scholastic, Inc.

Bargar, Sherie & Johnson, Linda. Mambas (Mambas) Date not set. (Culebras Ser.). (SPA., Illus.). 24p. (J). (gr. 1-4). lib. bdg. 18.60 (978-0-86593-331-6(6)) Rourke Publishing, LLC.

Barnes, Julia. 101 Facts about Snakes. 2004. (One Hundred One Facts about Predators Ser.). (Illus.). 32p. (J). (gr. 3 up). lib. bdg. 23.33 (978-0-8368-4040-7(2)) Stevens, Gareth Inc.

Barth, Kelly L. Snakes. 2000. (Endangered Animals & Habitats Ser.). (Illus.). 96p. (YA). (gr. 4-12). 27.45 (978-1-56006-696-5(2) , Lucent Bks.) Thomson Gale.

Behler, Deborah A. & Behler, John L. Snakes. 2001. (Animalways Ser.). (Illus.). 112p. (J). (gr. 5 up). lib. bdg. 31.36 (978-0-7614-1265-6(4) , Benchmark Bks.) Cavendish, Marshall Corp.

Berger, Melvin & Berger, Gilda. Snakes Live in Grass. 2003. (Scholastic Time-To-Discover Readers Ser.). (Illus.). (J). (978-0-439-47177-0(X)) Scholastic, Inc.

Berkowitz, Henry. Snakes: An Educational Coloring Book. Berkowitz, Henry, illus. 2001. (Illus.). 32p. (J). (ps-3). pap. 4.95 (978-0-932855-63-3(6)) Winner Enterprises.

Berman, Ruth & Nature's Images Staff. Buzzing Rattlesnakes. 1998. (Pull Ahead Bks.). (Illus.). 32p. (gr. k-2). (J). pap. 5.95 (978-0-8225-3609-3(9)); lib. bdg. 22.60 (978-0-8225-3603-1(X)) Lerner Publishing Group.

Books Are Fun 8 Title Animal Lives Set: Snakes. 2006. (J). (978-1-59566-306-1(1)) QEB Publishing Inc.

Bredeson, Carmen. Fun Facts about Snakes! 2007. (I Like Reptiles & Amphibians! Ser.). (Illus.). 24p. (J). (gr. 1-3). lib. bdg. 21.26 (***978-0-7660-2787-9(2)*** , Enslow Elementary) Enslow Pubs., Inc.

Burns, Diane L. Snakes, Salamanders & Lizards. Garrow, Linda, illus. 1998. 47p. (J). (gr. 2-5). lib. bdg. 16.40 (978-0-613-26969-8(1)) Tandem Library Bks.

Campbell, Jonathan A., et al, trs. The Venomous Reptiles of the Western Hemisphere, 2 vols. 2005. (Comstock Books in Herpetology). (Illus.). 1032p. 149.95 (978-0-8014-4141-7(2)) Cornell Univ. Pr.

Catala, Ellen. Snakes & Lizards. 2003. (J). 15.93 (978-0-7368-2940-3(7)); pap. (978-0-7368-2899-4(0)) Yellow Umbrella Pr.

—Venomous Snakes. 2003. (Science Links Ser.). (Illus.). 32p. (gr. 3-5). 23.00 (978-0-7910-7430-5(7) , Chelsea Hse.) Facts On File, Inc.

Clarke, Penny. Snakes Alive. 2002. (gr. 3-6). lib. bdg. 15.25 (978-0-613-53648-6(7)) Tandem Library Bks.

Clarke, Penny & Bergin, Mark. Snakes Alive. Scrace, Carolyn, illus. 2002. (Scary Creatures Ser.). 32p. (J). (gr. 2-4). pap. 22.50 (978-0-531-14673-6(1) , Watts, Franklin) Scholastic Library Publishing.

Corwin, Jeff. Snake-Tacular. Pascoe, Elaine, ed. 2003. (Jeff Corwin Experience Ser.). (J). 23.70 (978-1-4103-0205-2(9)); 9.95 (978-1-4103-0206-9(7)) Thomson Gale. (Blackbirch Pr., Inc.).

Craats, Rennay. Caring for Your Snake. 2004. (Caring for Your Pet Ser.). (Illus.). (J). pap. (978-1-59036-216-7(0)); 32p. lib. bdg. 16.95 (978-1-59036-196-2(2)) Weigl Pubs., Inc.

Crawford, Tracey. Snakes. 2006. (Illus.). 24p. (J). (978-1-4034-8452-9(X)); pap. (978-1-4034-8459-8(7)) Heinemann Library.

Crossingham, John & Kalman, Bobbie. The Life Cycle of a Snake. 2003. (Life Cycle Ser.). (Illus.). 32p. (J). (gr. 3-4). (978-0-7787-0660-1(5)); pap. (978-0-7787-0690-8(7)) Crabtree Publishing Co.

Las Culebras, 6 vols., Vol. 2. (Explorers. Exploradores Nonfiction Sets Ser.). (SPA.). 32p. (gr. 3-6). 44.95 (978-0-7699-0639-3(7)) Shortland Pubns. (U. S. A.) Inc.

Dalgleish, Sharon. Snakes. 2002. (Junior Adventure Ser.). (Illus.). 32p. (J). (gr. 3 up). lib. bdg. 19.95 (978-1-59084-179-2(4)) Mason Crest Pubs.

—Snakes. 1999. (Explorers Ser.). (Illus.). 32p. (J). (978-0-7699-0479-5(3)) Shortland Pubns. (U. S. A.) Inc.

Dennard, Deborah. Snakes. Dewey, Jennifer Owings, illus. 2004. (Our Wild World Ser.). 48p. (J). (gr. 2-5). ring bd. 10.95 (978-1-55971-856-1(0)); pap. 7.95 (978-1-55971-855-4(2)) T&N Children's Publishing. (NorthWord Bks. for Young Readers).

Dewey, Jennifer Owings. Rattlesnake Dance: True Tales, Mysteries, & Rattlesnake Ceremonies. Dewey, Jennifer Owings, illus. 2003. (Illus.). 48p. (YA). (gr. 4-6). pap. 10.95 (978-1-56397-877-7(6)) Boyds Mills Pr.

DK Publishing. Snakes Slither & Hiss. 2008. (Dk Readers Ser.). 32p. (J). (ps-1). 14.99 (***978-0-7566-3748-4(1)***); pap. 3.99 (***978-0-7566-3749-1(X)***) Dorling Kindersley Publishing, Inc.

Doeden, Matt. Boa Constrictors. 2005. (Reptiles Ser.). (Illus.). 24p. (J). 21.26 (978-0-7368-3729-3(9)) Capstone Pr., Inc.

—Copperheads. 2005. (World of Reptiles Ser.). (Illus.). 24p. (J). 21.26 (978-0-7368-3731-6(0)) Capstone Pr., Inc.

—Cottonmouths. 2005. (Illus.). 24p. (J). 21.26 (978-0-7368-3730-9(2)) Capstone Pr., Inc.

—Garter Snakes. 2005. (World of Reptiles Ser.). (Illus.). 24p. (J). 21.26 (978-0-7368-3732-3(9)) Capstone Pr., Inc.

—Pythons. 2005. (World of Reptiles Ser.). (Illus.). 24p. (J). 21.26 (978 0 7368-3733-0(7)) Capstone Pr., Inc.

—Rattlesnakes. 2005. (Illus.). (J). (gr. 3 up). lib. bdg. 21.26 (978-0-7368-3734-7(5)); 24p. (ps-7). lib. bdg. 21.26 (978-0-7368-3675-3(6)) Capstone Pr., Inc.

Dollar, Sam. Boa Constrictors. Sloan, Frank, ed. 2001. (Animals of the Rain Forest Ser.). (Illus.). 32p. (J). (gr. 4-7). lib. bdg. 22.83 (978-0-7398-3553-1(X)) Raintree.

Domnauer, Teresa. Warning: Snakes!, Level 1: Snakes!, Level 1. 2007. (Extreme Readers Ser.). 32p. (J). pap. 3.95 (***978-0-7696-5249-8(2)***) School Specialty Publishing.

Donovan, Sandy. A Snake in Its Burrow. 2003. (Where Do Animals Live? Ser.). (J). pap. (978-1-58417-193-5(6)); lib. bdg. (978-1-58417-192-8(8)) Lake Street Pubs.

Dorling Kindersley Publishing Staff. The Snake. 2000. (Ultimate Sticker Bks.). (Illus.). 16p. (J). (gr. k-3). pap. 6.99 (978-0-7894-5239-9(1)) Dorling Kindersley Publishing, Inc.

—The Snake Book. 2000. (Illus.). 32p. (J). (gr. 1-5). pap. 8.99 (978-0-7894-6068-4(8)) Dorling Kindersley Publishing, Inc.

Durrett, Deanne. Rattlesnake. 2003. (Nature's Predators Ser.). (Illus.). 48p. (J). 26.20 (978-0-7377-1889-8(7) , Greenhaven Pr., Inc.) Thomson Gale.

Dussling, Jennifer & Dorling Kindersley Publishing Staff. Slinky, Scaly Snakes! 1998. (Eyewitness Readers). (Illus.). 32p. (J). (ps-3). 12.99 (978-0-7894-3766-2(X)) Dorling Kindersley Publishing, Inc.

Dussling, Jennifer & Royston, Angela. Bugs! Bugs! Bugs! & Slinky, Scaly Snakes! 2007. (Read & Listen Bks.). 64p. (J). 9.99 (978-0-7566-2669-3(2)) Dorling Kindersley Publishing, Inc.

—Slinky, Scaly Snakes! 1998. (Dk Readers Ser.). (Illus.). 32p. (J). (gr. 1-3). pap. 3.99 (978-0-7894-3439-5(3)) Dorling Kindersley Publishing, Inc.

S

Eckart, Edana. California Condor. 2003. (Welcome Bks.). (Illus.). 24p. (J). (ps-2). pap. 4.95 (978-0-516-27883-4(5) , Children's Pr.) Scholastic Library Publishing.

—King Cobra. 2003. (Welcome Book Ser.). (Illus.). 24p. (J). 17.00 (978-0-516-24305-4(5)); pap. 4.95 (978-0-516-27892-6(4)) Scholastic Library Publishing. (Children's Pr.).

—King Cobra. 2003. (gr. k-3). lib. bdg. 12.95 (978-0-613-67735-6(8)) Tandem Library Bks.

Feldman, Heather. Copperheads. 2004. (Really Wild Life of Snakes Ser.). (Illus.). 24p. (J). lib. bdg. 18.75 (978-0-8239-6721-6(2) , PowerKids Pr.) Rosen Publishing Group, Inc., The.

—Coral Snakes. 2004. (Really Wild Life of Snakes Ser.). (Illus.). 24p. (J). lib. bdg. 18.75 (978-0-8239-6719-3(0) , PowerKids Pr.) Rosen Publishing Group, Inc., The.

—Cottonmouths. 2004. (Really Wild Life of Snakes Ser.). (Illus.). 24p. (J). lib. bdg. 18.75 (978-0-8239-6722-3(0) , PowerKids Pr.) Rosen Publishing Group, Inc., The.

—Diamondbacks. 2004. (Really Wild Life of Snakes Ser.). 24p. (J). lib. bdg. 18.75 (978-0-8239-6718-6(2)) Rosen Publishing Group, Inc., The.

—King Snakes. 2004. (Really Wild Life of Snakes Ser.). (Illus.). 24p. (J). lib. bdg. 18.75 (978-0-8239-6723-0(9) , PowerKids Pr.) Rosen Publishing Group, Inc., The.

—Milk Snakes. 2004. (Really Wild Life of Snakes Ser.). 24p. (J). lib. bdg. 18.75 (978-0-8239-6720-9(4) , PowerKids Pr.) Rosen Publishing Group, Inc., The.

Fiedler, Julie. Cobras. 2008. (J). lib. bdg. (***978-1-4042-3837-4(9)** , PowerKids Pr.) Rosen Publishing Group, Inc., The.

—Mambas. 2007. (J). lib. bdg. (***978-1-4042-3838-1(7)** , PowerKids Pr.) Rosen Publishing Group, Inc., The.

Foley, Cate. Find the Snake. 2000. (Welcome Bks.). (Illus.). 24p. (J). (ps-2). 17.00 (978-0-516-23097-9(2) , Children's Pr.) Scholastic Library Publishing.

Frost, Helen. Boa Constrictors. Saunders-Smith, Gail, ed. 2002. (Rain Forest Animals Ser.). (Illus.). 24p. (J). (gr. k-1). lib. bdg. 15.93 (978-0-7368-1191-0(5) , Pebble Bks.) Capstone Pr., Inc.

George, Linda. Anacondas. 2001. (Snakes Ser.). (Illus.). 48p. (J). (gr. 3-4). lib. bdg. 21.26 (978-0-7368-0907-8(4) , Capstone High-Interest Bks.) Capstone Pr., Inc.

—King Snakes. 2001. (Snakes Ser.). (Illus.). 48p. (J). (gr. 3-4). lib. bdg. 21.26 (978-0-7368-0908-5(2) , Capstone High-Interest Bks.) Capstone Pr., Inc.

—Rat Snakes. 2001. (Snakes Ser.). (Illus.). 48p. (J). (gr. 3-4). lib. bdg. 21.26 (978-0-7368-0909-2(0) , Capstone High-Interest Bks.) Capstone Pr., Inc.

—Vipers. 2001. (Snakes Ser.). (Illus.). 48p. (J). (gr. 3-4). lib. bdg. 21.26 (978-0-7368-0910-8(4) , Capstone High-Interest Bks.) Capstone Pr., Inc.

Gibbons, Gail. Snakes. Gibbons, Gail, illus. 2007. (Illus.). 32p. (J). (ps-3). 16.95 (***978-0-8234-2122-0(8))** Holiday Hse., Inc.

Gibson, Deborah C. Snakes & Their Homes. 1999. (Animal Habitats Ser.). (Illus.). 24p. (J). (gr. k-4). lib. bdg. 18.75 (978-0-8239-5310-3(6) , PowerKids Pr.) Rosen Publishing Group, Inc., The.

Gish, Melissa. Snakes. (Let's Investigate Ser.). (Illus.). 32p. (J). 2000. pap. 10.60 (978-0-89812-009-7(8) , Creative Paperbacks); 1998. lib. bdg. (978-0-88682-967-4(4) , Creative Education) Creative Co., The.

Gordon, Sharon. Guess Who Hisses. 2004. (SPA & ENG., Illus.). 31p. (J). 21.36 (978-0-7614-1767-5(2) , Benchmark Bks.) Cavendish, Marshall Corp.

Gordon, Sharon. Guess Who Hisses: Adivina Quién Silba. 2007. (SPA & ENG.). (J). (***978-0-7614-2883-1(6)); (*978-0-7614-2866-4(6))** Cavendish, Marshall Bks., Ltd.

Gray, Maurice. Constrictors. 2005. (Animals Attack Ser.). (Illus.). 48p. (J). (gr. 4-8). lib. bdg. 26.20 (978-0-7377-3005-0(6) , Greenhaven Pr., Inc.) Thomson Gale.

Greenaway, Theresa. Snakes. 2001. (Secret World Of... Ser.). (Illus.). 48p. (J). (gr. 4-7). lib. bdg. 27.12 (978-0-7398-3510-4(6)) Raintree.

Grolier Educational Staff, contrib. by. Rattlesnakes. 2001. (Nature's Children Ser.). (Illus.). 48p. (J). (978-0-7172-5545-0(X) , Grolier) Scholastic Library Publishing.

Gunzi, Christiane. The Best Book of Snakes. (Best Book of... Ser.). 32p. (J). (gr. k-3). 2006. 6.95 (978-0-7534-5937-9(X)); 2003. (Illus.). tchr. ed. 12.95 (978-0-7534-5578-4(1) , Kingfisher) Houghton Mifflin Co. Trade & Reference Div.

Gutman, Bill. Becoming Best Friends with Your Iguana, Snake or Turtle. Green, Anne Canevari, illus. 2001. (Pet Friends Ser.). 64p. (gr. 4-6). lib. bdg. 24.90 (978-0-7613-1862-0(3) , Millbrook Pr.) Lerner Publishing Group.

Hansen, Paul. When Snakes Attack! 2006. (When Wild Animals Attack! Ser.). (Illus.). 48p. (J). (gr. 4-10). lib. bdg. 23.93 (978-0-7660-2667-4(1)) Enslow Pubs., Inc.

Harcourt School Publishers Staff. All about Snakes Advanced level. 3rd ed. 2002. (Trophies Reading Program Ser.). (Illus.). pap. 5.10 (978-0-15-323116-2(5)) Harcourt Schl. Pubs.

Harrison, Paul. Snakes. 2007. (Up Close Ser.). (Illus.). 24p. (J). (gr. 3-5). lib. bdg. 23.95 (***978-1-4042-3764-3(X)** , PowerKids Pr.) Rosen Publishing Group, Inc., The.

Hedrick, Helen Groves. Rattlesnake Riddle. 48p. 10.00 (978-0-87012-687-1(3)) McClain Printing Co.

Hill, LaTanya. The Snakes. 2004. 89p. pap. 14.95 (978-1-4137-4442-2(7)) PublishAmerica, Inc.

Hirschmann, Kris. Snakes. 2002. (Nature's Predators Ser.). (Illus.). 48p. (J). (gr. 3-5). 23.70 (978-0-7377-1006-9(3) , Kidhaven) Thomson Gale.

Hoff, Mary King. Snakes. 2006. (Wild World of Animals Ser.). (Illus.). 32p. (gr. 3-5). 18.95 (978-1-58341-436-1(3) , Creative Education) Creative Co., The.

Holub, Joan. Why Do Snakes Hiss? And Other Questions about Snakes, Lizards & Turtles. Divito, Anna, illus. 2004. (Easy-to-Read, Puffin Ser.). 48p. (J). (gr. k-2). pap. 3.99 (978-0-14-240105-7(6) , Puffin) Penguin Group (USA) Inc.

—Why Do Snakes Hiss? And Other Questions about Snakes, Lizards, & Turtles. 2004. (Easy-to-Read, Dial Ser.). (Illus.). 48p. (J). (gr. k). 14.99 (978-0-8037-3000-7(4) , Dial) Penguin Group (USA) Inc.

—Why Do Snakes Hiss? And Other Questions about Snakes, Lizards, & Turtles. DiVito, Anna, illus. 2004. 48p. (J). (ps-ps). lib. bdg. 11.19 (978-0-606-32712-1(6)) Tandem Library Bks.

Houghton, Sarah. Snakes! Deadly Predators or Harmless Pets? 2001. (High Five Reading Ser.). (Illus.). 64p. (J). pap. (978-0-7368-9503-3(5)); (gr. 4-5). lib. bdg. 22.60 (978-0-7368-4003-3(6) , Capstone High-Interest Bks.) Capstone Pr., Inc.

Huggins-Cooper, Lynn. Slithering Snakes. 2006. (Killer Nature! Ser.). (Illus.). 32p. (J). (gr. 3-5). lib. bdg. 28.50 (978-1-58340-934-3(3) , 1262609) Smart Apple Media.

Hughes, Monica. Scary Snakes. 2006. (I Love Reading Ser.). (Illus.). 24p. (J). lib. bdg. 19.96 (978-1-59716-154-1(3)) Bearport Publishing Co., Inc.

Johnson, Jinny. Snake. Rosewarne, Graham, illus. 2005. 32p. (J). (gr. 2-5). lib. bdg. 27.10 (978-1-58340-644-1(1)) Smart Apple Media.

Johnson, Sylvia A. Cobras. 2007. (Nature Watch Ser.). (Illus.). 48p. (J). 25.26 (978-1-57505-871-9(5) , Lerner Pubns.) Lerner Publishing Group.

Kalman, Bobbie. Life Cycle of a Snake. 2003. (gr. 3-6). lib. bdg. 15.25 (978-0-613-59130-0(5)) Tandem Library Bks.

Klein, Adam G. Black Mambas. 2006. (Checkerboard Animal Library). (Illus.). 24p. (J). (gr. k-6). 21.35 (978-1-59679-278-4(7) , Checkerboard Library) ABDO Publishing Co.

—Common Adders. 2006. (Checkerboard Animal Library). (Illus.). 24p. (J). (gr. k-6). 21.35 (978-1-59679-279-1(5) , Checkerboard Library) ABDO Publishing Co.

—Coral Snakes. 2006. (Checkerboard Animal Library). (Illus.). 24p. (J). (gr. k-6). 21.35 (978-1-59679-280-7(9) , Checkerboard Library) ABDO Publishing Co.

—Pit Vipers. 2006. (Checkerboard Animal Library). (Illus.). 24p. (J). (gr. k-6). 21.35 (978-1-59679-282-1(5) , Checkerboard Library) ABDO Publishing Co.

—Snakes Set II. 2006. 128.10 (978-1-59679-277-7(9) , Checkerboard Library) ABDO Publishing Co.

—Water Moccasins. 2006. (J). (gr. k-6). 21.35 (978-1-59679-283-8(3) , Checkerboard Library) ABDO Publishing Co.

—Yellow-Bellied Sea Snakes. 2006. (Checkerboard Animal Library). (Illus.). 24p. (J). (gr. k-6). 21.35 (978-1-59679-281-4(7) , Checkerboard Library) ABDO Publishing Co.

Landau, Elaine. Big Snakes: Hunters of the Night. 2007. (Animals after Dark Ser.). (Illus.). 32p. (J). (gr. 2-4). lib. bdg. 22.60 (978-0-7660-2769-5(4) , Enslow Elementary) Enslow Pubs., Inc.

—Sinister Snakes. 2003. (Fearsome, Scary, & Creepy Animals Ser.). (Illus.). 48p. (J). (gr. 1-4). lib. bdg. 23.93 (978-0-7660-2057-3(6)) Enslow Pubs., Inc.

Lewis, David, contrib. by. Snakes. 1999. (Junior Pet Care Ser.). (Illus.). 48p. (gr. 4-7). 18.65 (978-0-7910-4910-5(8) , Chelsea Hse.) Facts On File, Inc.

Ling, Mary. Snake Book: A Breathtaking Close-up Look at Splendid, Scaly, Slithery Snake. 2000. (gr. 3-6). lib. bdg. 17.60 (978-0-613-75114-8(0)) Tandem Library Bks.

Lockwood, Sophie. Cobras. 2006. (World of Reptiles Ser.). (Illus.). 40p. (J). (gr. 2-6). 29.93 (978-1-59296-544-1(X)) Child's World, Inc.

—Rattlesnakes. 2006. (World of Reptiles Ser.). (Illus.). 40p. (J). (gr. 2-6). 29.93 (978-1-59296-549-6(0)) Child's World, Inc.

Macken, JoAnn Early. Rattlesnakes. 2005. (Illus.). 24p. (J). pap. (978-0-8368-4836-6(5)); lib. bdg. 19.33 (978-0-8368-4829-8(2)) Stevens, Gareth Inc.

—Rattlesnakes: Serpientes de Cascabel. 2005. (ENG & SPA., Illus.). 24p. (J). pap. (978-0-8368-4850-2(0)); lib. bdg. 19.33 (978-0-8368-4843-4(8)) Stevens, Gareth Inc.

—Snakes. 2002. (Weekly Reader Early Learning Library). (Illus.). 24p. (J). (ps up). pap. 5.95 (978-0-8368-3288-4(4)); lib. bdg. 19.33 (978-0-8368-3275-4(2)) Stevens, Gareth Inc. (Weekly Reader Early Learning Library).

—Snakes: Las Serpientes. 2004. (ENG & SPA., Illus.). 24p. (J). pap. (978-0-8368-4390-3(8)); lib. bdg. 19.33 (978-0-8368-4385-9(1)) Stevens, Gareth Inc.

Male, Alan. Can Snakes Crawl Backwards? 2001. (gr. 3-6). lib. bdg. 14.10 (978-0-613-45359-2(X)) Tandem Library Bks.

Manning, David. Keeping Snakes. 2001. (Unusual Pets Ser.). (Illus.). 64p. (J). (gr. 3-7). 5.95 (978-0-7641-1758-9(0)) Barron's Educational Series, Inc.

Markle, Sandra. Outside & Inside Snakes. 1998. (Outside & Inside Ser.). (978-0-606-13691-4(6)) Tandem Library Bks.

—Snakes: Biggest! Littlest! 2004. (Illus.). 32p. (J). 15.95 (978-1-59078-189-0(9)) Boyds Mills Pr.

Martin, Michael. The World's Deadliest Snakes. 2006. (Illus.). 32p. (J). (978-0-7368-5454-2(1)) Capstone Pr., Inc.

Mason, Adrienne. Snakes. Ogle, Nancy Gray, illus. 2005. (Kids Can Press Wildlife Ser.). 32p. (J). (gr. k-5). (978-1-55337-628-6(5)); (978-1-55337-627-9(7)) Kids Can Pr., Ltd.

McDonald, Mary Ann. Garter Snakes. 2006. (New Naturebooks). (Illus.). 32p. (J). (gr. 1-5). 27.07 (978-1-59296-633-2(0)) Child's World, Inc.

McNab, Chris & Lewis, Brenda Ralph. Poisonous Snakes. 2006. (Nature's Monsters Ser.). (Illus.). 32p. (J). 23.33 (978-0-8368-6174-7(4)) Stevens, Gareth Inc.

Miller, Sara Swan. Snakes & Lizards: What They Have in Common. 2000. (Animals in Order Ser.). (Illus.). 48p. (J). (gr. 4-6). 26.50 (978-0-531-11594-7(1) , Watts, Franklin) Scholastic Library Publishing.

—Snakes & Lizards: What They Have in Common. 2000. (gr. 3-6). lib. bdg. 15.25 (978-0-613-37542-9(4)) Tandem Library Bks.

Mitchell, Melanie S. Snakes. (First Step Nonfiction Ser.). (Illus.). (J). (gr. k-2). 2005. 24p. lib. bdg. 17.27 (978-0-8225-4606-1(X)); 2003. 23p. (J). pap. 5.95 (978-0-8225-4607-8(8) , Lerner Pubns.) Lerner Publishing Group.

Montgomery, Sy. The Snake Scientist. Bishop, Nic, photos by. (Scientists in the Field Ser.). (Illus.). 48p. (J). (gr. 3-5). 2001. pap., pap. 6.95 (978-0-618-11119-0(0)); 1999. tchr. ed. 16.00 (978-0-395-87169-0(7)) Houghton Mifflin Co. Trade & Reference Div.

—The Snake Scientist. 2001. (Illus.). (J). (978-0-606-21437-7(2)); 1999. (gr. 3-6). lib. bdg. 12.95 (978-0-613-35570-4(9)) Tandem Library Bks.

Moreton, Daniel & Chanko, Pamela. Snakes & Lizards. annual 1998. (Science Emergent Readers Ser.). (J). 3.25 (978-0-590-63900-2(5)) Scholastic, Inc.

—Snakes & Lizards: Serpientes y Lagartos. 2002. (Science Emergent Readers Ser.). (ENG & SPA., Illus.). (J). pap. (978-0-439-41163-9(7)) Scholastic, Inc.

Mudd-Ruth, Maria. Snakes. 2001. (Animals Animals Ser.). (Illus.). 48p. (J). (gr. 3-5). lib. bdg. 25.64 (978-0-7614-1262-5(X)) Cavendish, Marshall Corp.

Mulks, Mitchell. Zonata: The California Mountain Kingsnake. Merker, Gerold, photos by. 2004. (Illus.). 64p. pap. 15.95 (978-0-9760770-0-8(0)) LM Digital.

Murray, Julie. Copperheads. 2005. (Animal Kingdom Set Ii Ser.). (Illus.). 24p. (J). (gr. k-4). lib. bdg. 21.35 (978-1-59197-309-6(0)) ABDO Publishing Co.

—King Cobras. 2002. (Buddy Book Ser.). (Illus.). 24p. (J). (gr. k-4). lib. bdg. 21.35 (978-1-57765-731-6(4)) ABDO Publishing Co.

—Pythons. 2002. (Animal Kingdom Ser.). (Illus.). 24p. (J). (gr. k-4). lib. bdg. 21.35 (978-1-57765-730-9(6)) ABDO Publishing Co.

—Rattlesnakes. 2005. (Animal Kingdom Set Ii Ser.). (Illus.). 24p. (J). (gr. k-4). lib. bdg. 21.35 (978-1-59197-333-1(3)) ABDO Publishing Co.

National Wildlife Federation Staff. Let's Hear It for Herps! All about Reptiles & Amphibians. 1999. (Ranger Rick's Naturescope Ser.). (Illus.). 96p. (J). (gr. 1-7). 32.00 (978-0-7910-4835-1(7) , Chelsea Hse.) Facts On File, Inc.

O'Hare, Ted. Boa Constrictors. 2005. (Amazing Snakes Discovery Library). 24p. (gr. 1-4). 5.45 (978-1-59515-306-7(3)); (Illus.). 14.95 (978-1-59515-143-8(5)) Rourke Publishing, LLC.

—Cobras. 2005. (Amazing Snakes Discovery Library). 24p. (gr. 1-4). 5.45 (978-1-59515-307-4(1)); (Illus.). 14.95 (978-1-59515-144-5(3)) Rourke Publishing, LLC.

—Copperheads. 2005. (Amazing Snakes Discovery Library). 24p. (gr. 1-4). 5.45 (978-1-59515-308-1(X)); (Illus.). 14.95 (978-1-59515-145-2(1)) Rourke Publishing, LLC.

—Coral Snakes. 2005. (Amazing Snakes Discovery Library). 24p. (gr. 1-4). 5.45 (978-1-59515-309-8(8)); (Illus.). 14.95 (978-1-59515-142-1(7)) Rourke Publishing, LLC.

—Cottonmouths. (Rourke Discovery Library). 24p. 2005. (Illus.). (gr. 1-4). 14.95 (978-1-59515-146-9(X)); 2004. pap. 4.95 (978-1-59515-310-4(1)) Rourke Publishing, LLC.

—Mambas. 2005. (Amazing Snakes Discovery Library). 24p. (gr. 1-4). 5.45 (978-1-59515-311-1(X)); (Illus.). 14.95 (978-1-59515-147-6(8)) Rourke Publishing, LLC.

—Pythons. 2005. (Amazing Snakes Discovery Library). 24p. (gr. 1-4). 5.45 (978-1-59515-312-8(8)); (Illus.). 14.95 (978-1-59515-148-3(6)) Rourke Publishing, LLC.

—Rattlesnakes. 2005. (Amazing Snakes Discovery Library). 24p. (gr. 1-4). 5.45 (978-1-59515-313-5(6)); (Illus.). 14.95 (978-1-59515-149-0(4)) Rourke Publishing, LLC.

Olien, Becky. Snakes: Cold-Blooded Crawlers. 2002. (Wild World of Animals Ser.). (Illus.). 24p. (J). (gr. 1-2). lib. bdg. 18.60 (978-0-7368-1138-5(9) , Bridgestone Bks.) Capstone Pr., Inc.

O'Neill, Amanda. I Wonder Why Snakes Shed Their Skin: And Other Questions about Reptiles. 2003. (I Wonder Why Ser.). 32p. (J). (gr. k-3). pap. 6.95 (978-0-7534-5612-5(5) , Kingfisher) Houghton Mifflin Co. Trade & Reference Div.

—I Wonder Why Snakes Shed Their Skins: And Other Questions about Reptiles. 2003. (gr. k-3). lib. bdg. 14.10 (978-0-613-63161-7(7)) Tandem Library Bks.

Patent, Dorothy Hinshaw. Slinky, Scaly, Slithery Snakes. Jubb, Kendahl Jan, illus. 32p. (J). 2003. (gr. 1-5). pap. 6.95 (978-0-8027-7652-5(3)); 2000. (gr. 1-5). 16.95 (978-0-8027-8743-9(6)); 2000. (gr. 2-5). 17.85 (978-0-8027-8744-6(4)) Walker & Co.

—Slinky Scaly Slithery Snakes. 2003. (gr. 3-6). lib. bdg. 15.25 (978-0-613-75345-6(3)) Tandem Library Bks.

Pringle, Laurence P. Snakes! Strange & Wonderful. Henderson, Meryl, illus. 2004. (Strange & Wonderful Ser.). 32p. (J). (gr. 2-4). 15.95 (978-1-59078-003-9(5)) Boyds Mills Pr.

Rake, Jody Sullivan. Sea Snakes. 2007. (Illus.). 24p. (J). (978-0-7368-6725-2(2)) Capstone Pr., Inc.

Randolph, Joanne. Snakes. 2007. (Classroom Pets Ser.). (Illus.). 24p. (J). (gr. k-5). lib. bdg. 21.25 (***978-1-4042-3679-0(1)** , PowerKids Pr.) Rosen Publishing Group, Inc., The.

Resnick, Jane Parker. Snakes. 2001. (Nature's Wild Ser.). (J). lib. bdg. (978-1-58952-204-6(4)) Rourke Publishing, LLC.

Richardson, Adele D. Hognose Snakes. 2003. (Snakes Ser.). (Illus.). 48p. (J). lib. bdg. 22.60 (978-0-7368-2136-0(8)) Capstone Pr., Inc.

—Mambas. 2003. (Snakes Ser.). (Illus.). 48p. (J). lib. bdg. 22.60 (978-0-7368-2137-7(6)) Capstone Pr., Inc.

—North American Racer Snakes. 2003. (Snakes Ser.). (Illus.). 48p. (J). lib. bdg. 22.60 (978-0-7368-2139-1(2) , Capstone High/Low Bks.) Capstone Pr., Inc.

—Pit Vipers. 2003. (Snakes Ser.). (Illus.). 48p. (J). lib. bdg. 22.60 (978-0-7368-2138-4(4) , Capstone High/Low Bks.) Capstone Pr., Inc.

—Rattlesnakes. 2002. (Predators in the Wild Ser.). (Illus.). 32p. (J). (gr. 3-4). lib. bdg. 21.26 (978-0-7368-1317-4(9) , Capstone High-Interest Bks.) Capstone Pr., Inc.

Ring. Anacondas. 2003. (Untamed World Ser.). (Illus.). 64p. (J). lib. bdg. 28.56 (978-0-7398-6842-3(X)) Raintree.

Ring, Susan. Serpientes y Lagartos. 2005. Tr. of Snakes & Lizards. (SPA., Illus.). 16p. (J). (gr. 1 up). lib. bdg. 15.93 (978-0-7368-4166-5(0)) Capstone Pr., Inc.

Robinson, Claire. Snake. 1999. (In the Wild Ser.). (Illus.). 24p. (J). (gr. k-2). lib. bdg. 21.36 (978-1-57572-864-3(8)) Heinemann Library.

—Snakes. 2002. (In the Wild Ser.). (Illus.). 24p. (J). (gr. k-2). pap. 6.95 (978-1-58810-324-6(2) , 91049) Heinemann Library.

Rothaus, Don P. Pythons. 2006. (New Naturebooks). (Illus.). 32p. (J). (gr. 1-5). 27.07 (978-1-59296-646-2(2)) Child's World, Inc.

Rudy, Lisa Jo. Snakes! 2005. 32p. (J). lib. bdg. 13.85 (***978-1-4242-0861-6(0))** Fitzgerald Bks.

Rudy, Lisa Jo & Time for Kids Editors. Snakes! 2005. (Time for Kids Science Scoops Ser.). (Illus.). 32p. (J). 14.99 (978-0-06-057637-0(5)) HarperCollins Pubs.

Rustad, Martha E. Sea Snakes, Vol. 2. 2005. (Ocean Life Ser.). 24p. (YA). (gr. k-3). pap. (978-0-7368-3415-5(X) , Pebble Bks.) Capstone Pr., Inc.

Rustad, Martha E. H. Sea Snakes. 2003. (Ocean Life Ser.). (Illus.). 24p. (J). (gr. k-1). lib. bdg. 15.93 (978-0-7368-1658-8(5) , Pebble Bks.) Capstone Pr., Inc.

—Snakes. 2001. (All about Pets Ser.). (Illus.). 24p. (J). (gr. k-1). lib. bdg. 15.93 (978-0-7368-0977-1(5) , Pebble Bks.) Capstone Pr., Inc.

Savage, Candace Sherk, et al. Pelicans. 1999. (Getting to Know ... Nature's Children Ser.). (Illus.). 47p. (J). (978-0-7172-8840-3(4) , Grolier) Scholastic Library Publishing.

Savage, Stephen. Snake. 2005. (Illus.). 32p. (J). (978-0-7502-4663-7(4) , Hodder Wayland) Hodder Children's Division.

Schafer, Susan. Snakes. 2002. (Perfect Pets Ser.). (Illus.). 32p. (J). 25.64 (978-0-7614-1396-7(0) , Benchmark Bks.) Cavendish, Marshall Corp.

Schlaepfer, Gloria G. & Samuelson, Mary Lou. Pythons & Boas: Squeezing Snakes. 2003. (Watts Library Ser.). (Illus.). 64p. (J). (gr. 5-7). pap. 8.95 (978-0-531-16599-7(X) , Watts, Franklin) Scholastic Library Publishing.

Schwartz, David M. La Culebra Verde. Kuhn, Dwight, photos by. 2001. (Springboards into Science Ser.). (SPA., Illus.). 24p. (J). (gr. 1 up). lib. bdg. 20.67 (978-0-8368-2994-5(8)) Stevens, Gareth Inc.

—Green Snake. Kuhn, Dwight, photos by. 2001. (Springboards into Science Ser.). (Illus.). 24p. (J). (gr. 1 up). lib. bdg. 20.67 (978-0-8368-2973-0(5)) Stevens, Gareth Inc.

Serpentacular! 2005. (Jeff Corwin Experience Ser.). (ENG & SPA., Illus.). 48p. (J). (ps-7). lib. bdg. 24.95 (978-1-4103-0676-0(3) , Blackbirch Pr., Inc.) Thomson Gale.

Sheikh-Miller, Jonathan. Snakes. 2004. (Discovery Program Ser.). (SPA., Illus.). 64p. (J). (gr. 2 up). pap. 8.95 (978-0-7945-0004-7(8) , Usborne); lib. bdg. 16.95 (978-1-58086-344-5(2)) EDC Publishing.

Silverman, Buffy. Gliding Garter Snakes. (Pull Ahead Books). (Illus.). 32p. (J). 2007. 22.60 (978-0-8225-6043-2(7) , Lerner Pubns.); 2006. pap. 5.95 (978-0-8225-6509-3(9) , First Avenue Editions) Lerner Publishing Group.

Simon, Seymour. Seemore Giant Snakes. 2006. (Illus.). 32p. (J). 14.50 (978-0-8118-5410-8(8)); pap. 3.95 (978-0-8118-5411-5(6)) Chronicle Bks. LLC.

—Snakes. 2007. 32p. (J). 16.99 (978-0-06-114096-9(1)); pap. 6.99 (978-0-06-114095-2(3)) HarperCollins Pubs.

Smith, Molly. Green Anaconda: The World's Heaviest Snake. 2007. (SuperSized! Ser.). (Illus.). 24p. (J). (gr. k-2). lib. bdg. 21.28 (978-1-59716-391-0(0) , 1265936) Bearport Publishing Co., Inc.

The Snake: Individual Title Six-Packs. (Sails Literacy Ser.). 16p. (gr. k up). 27.00 (978-0-7635-4429-4(9)) Rigby Education.

Snake & the Birds: Individual Title Six-Packs. (Sails Literacy Ser.). (gr. 1-2). 36.00 (978-0-7578-4012-8(4)) Rigby Education.

Snake Animals in Wild Series. 2003. (J). pap. 2.50 (978-0-590-44625-9(8)) Scholastic, Inc.

Snakes. (Eyes on Nature Ser.). 32p. (J). (gr. 1). pap. (978-1-882210-58-9(1)) Action Publishing, Inc.

Snakes! (Creatures Corner Ser.). 16p. (J). (978-2-7643-0124-1(3)) Phidal Publishing, Inc./Editions Phidal, Inc.

Snakes, 12 bks., Set. Incl. Anacondas. George, Linda. 2001. lib. bdg. 21.26 (978-0-7368-0907-8(4)); Boa Constrictors. McDonald, Mary Ann. 1995. lib. bdg. 21.26 (978-1-56065-297-7(7)); Cobras. George, Linda. 1998. lib. bdg. 21.26 (978-1-56065-691-3(3)); Copperheads. George, Linda. 1998. lib. bdg. 21.26 (978-1-56065-693-7(X)); Coral Snakes. George, Linda. 1998. lib. bdg. 21.26 (978-1-56065-692-0(1)); Cottonmouths. George, Linda. 1998. lib. bdg. 21.26 (978-1-56065-694-4(8)); Garter Snakes. McDonald, Mary Ann. 1995. lib. bdg. 21.26 (978-1-56065-295-3(0)); King Snakes. George, Linda. 2001. lib. bdg. 21.26 (978-0-7368-0908-5(2)); Pythons. McDonald, Mary Ann. 1995. lib. bdg. 21.26 (978-1-56065-296-0(9)); Rat Snakes. George, Linda. 2001. lib. bdg. 21.26 (978-0-7368-0909-2(0)); Rattlesnakes. McDonald, Mary Ann. 1995. lib. bdg. 21.26 (978-1-56065-294-6(2)); Vipers. George, Linda. 2001. lib. bdg. 21.26 (978-0-7368-0910-8(4)); 48p. (J). (gr. 3-4). (Illus.). Set lib. bdg. 255.12 (978-0-7368-1002-9(1) , Capstone High-Interest Bks.) Capstone Pr., Inc.

Snakes: Level N, 6 vols. (Wonder Worldtm Ser.). 48p. 34.95 (978-0-7802-4601-0(2)) Wright Group, The.

Snakes: Level P, 6 vols., Vol. 2. (Explorers Ser.). 32p. (gr. 3-6). 44.95 (978-0-7699-0603-4(6)) Shortland Pubns. (U. S. A.) Inc.

Snakes & Other Reptiles. 2002. (Wild, Wild World Ser.). 32p. (J). 9.95 (978-0-7525-4684-1(8)) Parragon, Inc.

Snakes! Deadly Predators or Harmless Pets?, 6 vols. (gr. 4 up). 49.95 (978-0-7368-9513-2(2) , High Five) Red Brick Learning.

Snakes that Rattle: Individual Title Six-Packs. (Sails Literacy Ser.). (gr. 1-2). 36.00 (978-0-7578-4029-6(9)) Rigby Education.

So Many Snakes. (Rosen Real Readers Big Bookstm Ser.). 12p. (J). (gr. 1-2). 31.95 (978-1-4042-6214-0(8)) Rosen Publishing Group, Inc., The.

Solway, Andrew. Deadly Snakes. 2004. (J). 29.93 (978-1-4034-5766-0(2)); pap. 8.50 (978-1-4034-5772-1(7)) Heinemann Library.

—Snakes & Other Reptiles. 2006. (Illus.). 48p. (J). (978-1-4034-8224-2(1)); pap. (978-1-4034-8231-0(4)) Heinemann Library.

Souza, Dorothy M. Sea Snakes. 1998. (Creatures All Around Us Ser.). (Illus.). 40p. (J). (gr. 2-4). lib. bdg. (978-1-57505-263-2(6) , Carolrhoda Bks.) Lerner Publishing Group.

Sovak, Jan. Learning about Snakes. 1998. (Learning about Ser.). (Illus.). 16p. (J). (gr. 3-5). pap. 1.50 (978-0-486-40335-9(1) , 40335-1) Dover Pubns., Inc.

Spilsbury, Louise & Spilsbury, Richard. Watching Cobras in Asia. 2006. (Illus.). 32p. (J). (978-1-4034-7224-3(6)); pap. (978-1-4034-7237-3(8)) Heinemann Library.

Steele. Anacondas. 2001. (Animals of the Rain Forest Ser.). (SPA., Illus.). pap. (978-0-7398-3359-9(6)) Steck-Vaughn.

Steele, Christy. Anacondas. 2000. (Animals of the Rain Forest Ser.). (Illus.). 32p. (J). (gr. 4-7). lib. bdg. 22.83 (978-0-7398-3099-4(6)) Raintree.

Stille, Darlene R. Snakes. 2001. (First Reports). (Illus.). 48p. (J). (gr. 3 up). lib. bdg. 21.26 (978-0-7565-0057-3(5)) Compass Point Bks.

Stone, L. Cuando las Serpientes Van a Cazar. Marcuse, Aida E., tr. 2002. (Cara a Cara Con las Serpientes (Eye to Eye with Snakes) Ser.).Tr. of Snakes on the Hunt. (SPA., Illus.). 24p. mass mkt. 5.95 (978-1-58952-072-1(6) , RK31444) Rourke Publishing, LLC.

—El Interesante Mundo de las Serpientes. Marcuse, Aida E., tr. (Cara a Cara Con las Serpientes (Eye to Eye with Snakes) Ser.).Tr. of Wild World of Snakes. (SPA., Illus.). 24p. 2002. mass mkt. 5.95 (978-1-58952-073-8(4) , RK31445); 2001. (J). (gr. 1-3). lib. bdg. 19.27 (978-1-55916-335-4(6) , RK0410) Rourke Publishing, LLC.

—Las Serpientes y Nosotros. 2002. Tr. of Living with Snakes. (SPA.). (gr. k-3). lib. bdg. 14.10 (978-0-613-79401-5(X)) Tandem Library Bks.

—Serpientes Que Atrapan y Estrujan. Marcuse, Aida E., tr. 2002. (Cara a Cara Con las Serpientes (Eye to Eye with Snakes) Ser.).Tr. of Snakes That Squeeze & Snatch. (SPA., Illus.). 24p. mass mkt. 5.95 (978-1-58952-097-4(1) , RK31448) Rourke Publishing, LLC.

—Las Serpientes y Nosotros. Marcuse, Aida E., tr. 2002. (Cara a Cara Con las Serpientes (Eye to Eye with Snakes) Ser.).Tr. of Living with Snakes. (SPA., Illus.). 24p. mass mkt. 5.95 (978-1-58952-074-5(2) , RK31446) Rourke Publishing, LLC.

—La Vida Secreta de las Serpientes. Marcuse, Aida E., tr. 2002. (Cara a Cara Con las Serpientes (Eye to Eye with Snakes) Ser.).Tr. of Secret Lives of Snakes. (SPA., Illus.). 24p. mass mkt. 5.95 (978-1-58952-096-7(3) , RK31447) Rourke Publishing, LLC.

Stone, Lynn M. Boa Constrictors. 2001. (Illus.). 24p. (J). (gr. 1-4). lib. bdg. 20.64 (978-1-58952-036-3(X)) Rourke Publishing, LLC.

—Living with Snakes. 2000. (Eye to Eye with Snakes Ser.). (Illus.). 24p. (J). (gr. 1-4). lib. bdg. 20.64 (978-1-55916-264-7(3)) Rourke Publishing, LLC.

—Secret Lives of Snakes. 2000. (Eye to Eye with Snakes Ser.). (Illus.). 24p. (J). (gr. 1-4). lib. bdg. 20.64 (978-1-55916-262-3(7)) Rourke Publishing, LLC.

—Snakes on the Hunt. 2000. (Eye to Eye with Snakes Ser.). (Illus.). 24p. (J). (gr. 1-4). lib. bdg. 20.64 (978-1-55916-263-0(5)) Rourke Publishing, LLC.

—Snakes That Squeeze & Snatch. 2000. (Eye to Eye with Snakes Ser.). (Illus.). 24p. (J). (gr. 1-4). lib. bdg. 20.64 (978-1-55916-260-9(0)) Rourke Publishing, LLC.

—Snakes with Venom. 2000. (Eye to Eye with Snakes Ser.). (Illus.). 24p. (J). (gr. 1-4). lib. bdg. 20.64 (978-1-55916-259-3(7)) Rourke Publishing, LLC.

—The Wild World of Snakes. 2000. (Eye to Eye with Snakes Ser.). (Illus.). 24p. (J). (gr. 1-4). lib. bdg. 20.64 (978-1-55916-261-6(9)) Rourke Publishing, LLC.

Stone, Tanya Lee. Snakes. 2003. (Wild Wild World Ser.). 24p. (YA). 24.94 (978-1-56711-823-0(2) , Blackbirch Pr., Inc.) Thomson Gale.

Swanson, Diane. Snakes. 2002. (Welcome to the World of Animals Ser.). (Illus.). 32p. (J). (gr. 3 up). lib. bdg. 23.33 (978-0-8368-3318-8(X)) Stevens, Gareth Inc.

—Snakes. 2001. (gr. k-3). lib. bdg. 14.10 (978-0-613-78508-2(8)) Tandem Library Bks.

—Snakes. 2001. (Welcome to the World Ser.). (Illus.). 32p. (J). (ps-2). pap. 5.95 (978-1-55285-171-5(0)) Whitecap Bks., Ltd. CAN. *Dist:* Firefly Bks., Ltd.

Taylor, Barbara. Cobras. 2003. (Predators Ser.). (Illus.). 32p. (J). 25.70 (978-0-7398-6599-6(4)) Raintree.

—Snakes. 2000. (Nature Factfile Ser.). (Illus.). 64p. pap. 7.95 (978-1-84215-018-4(9) , Southwater) Anness Publishing GBR. *Dist:* National Bk. Network.

Thomson, Sarah L. Amazing Snakes! (I Can Read Bks.). 32p. (J). 2007. pap. 3.99 (978-0-06-054464-5(3) , Harper Trophy); 2006. (Illus.). 15.99 (978-0-06-054462-1(7)); 2006. (Illus.). lib. bdg. 16.89 (978-0-06-054463-8(5)) HarperCollins Pubs.

Time for Kids Editors. Snakes! 2005. (Time for Kids Science Scoops Ser.). (Illus.). 32p. (J). pap. 3.99 (978-0-06-057636-3(7)) HarperCollins Pubs.

Townsend, Emily Rose. Rattlesnakes. Saunders-Smith, Gail, ed. 2003. (Desert Animals Ser.). (Illus.). 24p. (J). (gr. k-1). lib. bdg. 15.93 (978-0-7368-2078-3(7) , Pebble Bks.) Capstone Pr., Inc.

Trueit, Trudi Strain. Snakes. 2003. (True Bks.). (gr. 3-5). pap. 6.95 (978-0-516-29350-9(8) , Children's Pr.) Scholastic Library Publishing.

—Snakes. 2003. (gr. 3-6). lib. bdg. 15.25 (978-0-613-67985-5(7)) Tandem Library Bks.

Twist, Clint. Snake Dictionary: An a to Z of Amazing Snakes. 2003. (Illus.). 64p. (J). (978-0-439-54425-2(4)) Scholastic, Inc.

—Snakes A-Z. 2003. (Illus.). 64p. 26.20 (978-1-4103-0074-4(9) , Blackbirch Pr., Inc.) Thomson Gale.

Ury, Allen B. Dangerous Encounters No. 2: Real-Life Animal Attacks. 2000. (Roxbury Park Bks.). (Illus.). 96p. (J). (gr. 3-7). pap. 5.95 (978-0-7373-0119-9(8) , 01198W) McGraw-Hill/Contemporary.

Venn, Cecilia. Rattlers & Other Snakes, Vol. 9. World Book, Inc. Staff, ed. 2002. (World Book's Animals of the World Ser.: Set 1). 64p. (J). (978-0-7166-1246-9(1)) World Bk., Inc.

Wallach, Van. Al descubierto: una Cobra: Uncover a Snake. 2007. (Al Descubierto Ser.). (Illus.). 16p. 18.95 (***978-970-718-497-8(3)*** , Silver Dolphin en Español) Advanced Marketing, S. de R. L. de C. V. MEX. *Dist:* Perseus Distribution.

Wallach, Van. Uncover a Cobra: Take a Three-Dimensional Look Inside a Cobra! 2005. (Uncover Bks.). (Illus.). 16p. (J). (gr. 4-7). 18.95 (978-1-59223-376-2(7) , Silver Dolphin Bks.) Advantage Pubs. Group.

Waters, Jo. The Wild Side of Snakes. 2004. (Raintree Perspectives Ser.). (Illus.). 32p. (J). (978-1-4109-1407-1(0)); pap. (978-1-4109-1413-2(5)) Harcourt Schl. Pubs.

Watts, Barrie. Snake. 2002. 32p. (J). lib. bdg. 24.25 (978-1-58340-200-9(4)) Smart Apple Media.

Weber, Valerie J. African Rock Pythons. 2003. (World's Largest Snakes Ser.). (Illus.). 24p. (J). (gr. 2 up). lib. bdg. 22.00 (978-0-8368-3652-3(9)) Stevens, Gareth Inc.

—Anacondas. 2003. (World's Largest Snakes Ser.). (Illus.). 24p. (J). (gr. 2 up). lib. bdg. 22.00 (978-0-8368-3653-0(7)) Stevens, Gareth Inc.

—Asian Rock Pythons. 2003. (World's Largest Snakes Ser.). (Illus.). 24p. (J). (gr. 2 up). lib. bdg. 22.00 (978-0-8368-3655-4(3)) Stevens, Gareth Inc.

—Boa Constrictors. 2003. (World's Largest Snakes Ser.). (Illus.). 24p. (J). (gr. 2 up). lib. bdg. 22.00 (978-0-8368-3654-7(5)) Stevens, Gareth Inc.

—Reticulated Pythons. 2003. (World's Largest Snakes Ser.). (Illus.). 24p. (J). (gr. 2 up). lib. bdg. 22.00 (978-0-8368-3656-1(1)) Stevens, Gareth Inc.

—Scrub Pythons. 2003. (World's Largest Snakes Ser.). (Illus.). 24p. (J). (gr. 2 up). lib. bdg. 22.00 (978-0-8368-3657-8(X)) Stevens, Gareth Inc.

—World's Largest Snakes, 6 bks. Incl. African Rock Pythons. lib. bdg. 22.00 (978-0-8368-3652-3(9)); Anacondas. lib. bdg. 22.00 (978-0-8368-3653-0(7)); Asian Rock Pythons. lib. bdg. 22.00 (978-0-8368-3655-4(3)); Boa Constrictors. lib. bdg. 22.00 (978-0-8368-3654-7(5)); Reticulated Pythons. lib. bdg. 22.00 (978-0-8368-3656-1(1)); Scrub Pythons. lib. bdg. 22.00 (978-0-8368-3657-8(X)); 24p. (J). (gr. 2 up). 2003. (Illus.). 2002. Set lib. bdg. 132.00 (978-0-8368-3651-6(0)) Stevens, Gareth Inc.

Wechsler, Doug. Boas. 2001. (Really Wild Life of Snakes Ser.). (Illus.). 24p. (J). lib. bdg. 18.75 (978-0-8239-5603-6(2) , PowerKids Pr.) Rosen Publishing Group, Inc., The.

—Garter Snakes. 2001. (Really Wild Life of Snakes Ser.). (Illus.). 24p. (J). lib. bdg. 18.75 (978-0-8239-5601-2(6) , PowerKids Pr.) Rosen Publishing Group, Inc., The.

—Pit Vipers. 2001. (Really Wild Life of Snakes Ser.). (Illus.). 24p. (J). lib. bdg. 18.75 (978-0-8239-5605-0(9) , PowerKids Pr.) Rosen Publishing Group, Inc., The.

—Pythons. 2001. (Really Wild Life of Snakes Ser.). (Illus.). 24p. (J). lib. bdg. 18.75 (978-0-8239-5604-3(0) , PowerKids Pr.) Rosen Publishing Group, Inc., The.

—Really Wild Life of Snakes, Vol. 1. (Illus.). 80.70 (978-0-8239-7078-0(7)) Rosen Publishing Group, Inc., The.

—Taipans. 2001. (Really Wild Life of Snakes Ser.). (Illus.). 24p. (J). lib. bdg. 18.75 (978-0-8239-5602-9(4) , PowerKids Pr.) Rosen Publishing Group, Inc., The.

Welsbacher, Anne. Anacondas. 2001. (Predators in the Wild Ser.). (Illus.). 48p. (J). (gr. 3-4). lib. bdg. 21.26 (978-0-7368-0785-2(3) , Capstone High-Interest Bks.) Capstone Pr., Inc.

Wexo, John Bonnett. Serpientes. Rountree, Monica, tr. 2003. (Zoobooks). Orig. Title: Snakes. (SPA., Illus.). 24p. (J). (gr. 1-7). lib. bdg. 15.95 (978-1-888153-83-5(0)) Wildlife Education, Ltd.

—Snakes. (Zoobooks Ser.). (Illus.). 24p. 2001. (J). (gr. 1-6). 15.95 (978-1-888153-46-0(6)); 2003. 10.95 (978-1-888153-96-5(2) , Zoo Bks.) Wildlife Education, Ltd.

Wheeler, Donald G. Tales from the Golden Age of Rattlesnake Hunting. 2001. (Illus.). 169p. 28.00 (978-0-9713197-3-8(1)); pap. 12.95 (978-0-9713197-0-7(7)) ECO Herpetological Pub. & Dist.

Where Do Snakes Live? Individual Title Six-Packs. (Sails Literacy Ser.). (gr. 1-2). 36.00 (978-0-7578-6745-3(6)) Rigby Education.

Whitecap Books Staff. Snakes. 2000. (Investigate Ser.). (Illus.). 64p. (J). (gr. 1-7). pap. 3.95 (978-1-55285-069-5(2)) Whitecap Bks., Ltd. CAN. *Dist:* Firefly Bks., Ltd.

Whitehouse, Patricia. Snakes. 2003. (Heinemann Read & Learn Ser.). (Illus.). 24p. (J). pap. 5.25 (978-1-4034-4329-8(7)); lib. bdg. 18.50 (978-1-4034-4320-5(3)) Heinemann Library.

Whiting, Jim. Care for a Pet Snake. 2007. (How to Convince Your Parents You Can ... Ser.). (Illus.). 32p. (J). (gr. 1-4). lib. bdg. 25.70 (***978-1-58415-604-8(X)***) Mitchell Lane Pubs., Inc.

Wildlife Education, Ltd. Staff. Rattlesnakes. Hayward, Tim & Stuart, Walter, illus. (Zoobooks Ser.). (J). 2001. 24p. 15.95 (978-0-937934-86-9(0)); 1998. 18p. pap. 2.95 (978-0-937934-56-2(9)) Wildlife Education, Ltd.

—Snakes. Hoopes, Barbara & Oden, Dick, illus. 2001. (Zoobooks Ser.). 18p. (Orig.). (YA). (gr. 5 up). pap. 2.95 (978-0-937934-05-0(4)) Wildlife Education, Ltd.

Wilsdon, Christina. Snakes. 2007. (J). (***978-1-59939-137-3(6)*** , Reader's Digest Young Families, Inc.) Reader's Digest Children's Publishing, Inc.

Woodward, John. Boas. 2004. (Nature's Children Ser.). (J). (978-0-7172-5959-5(5) , Grolier) Scholastic Library Publishing.

15 Facts about Snakes, 6 Packs. (Rigby Focus Ser.). 24p. (gr. 2 up). 30.00 (978-0-7578-5576-4(8)) Rigby Education.

15 Facts about Snakes: Individual Title Six-Packs. (Rigby Focus Ser.). 24p. (gr. 2 up). 28.00 (978-0-7578-5346-3(3)) Rigby Education.

SNAKES—FICTION

Adler, David A. Cam Jansen & the Scary Snake Mystery. Natti, Susanna, illus. 2005. (Cam Jansen Ser.: No. 17). 64p. (J). (gr. 2-4). pap. 3.99 (978-0-14-240288-7(5) , Puffin) Penguin Group (USA) Inc.

Aidinoff, Elsie V. The Garden. 2004. (Illus.). 416p. (J). 17.99 (978-0-06-055605-1(6)); lib. bdg. 17.89 (978-0-06-055606-8(4)) HarperCollins Pubs. (HarperTeen).

Alston, Emerson. Moccasins. 2000. 128p. (gr. 7-12). 11.95 (978-1-56315-220-7(7)) SterlingHouse Pubs., Inc.

—Moccasins. 2000. (gr. 7-12). lib. bdg. 16.40 (978-0-613-88171-5(0)) Tandem Library Bks.

Anaya, Rudolfo A. Roadrunner's Dance. Diaz, David, illus. 2000. 32p. (gr. k-4). 16.49 (978-0-7868-2209-6(0)) Disney Pr.

—Roadrunner's Dance. Diaz, David, illus. 2000. 32p. (gr. k-4). 15.99 (978-0-7868-0254-8(5)) Hyperion Bks. for Children.

Arnosky, Jim. Crinkleroot's Visit to Crinkle Cove. 1999. (J). (978-0-606-18948-4(3)) Tandem Library Bks.

Ata, Te. Baby Rattlesnake. Reisberg, Mira, illus. 2006. 32p. (J). pap. 7.95 (978-0-89239-216-2(9)) Children's Bk. Pr.

—Baby Rattlesnake / Viborita de Cascabel. Alarcon, Francisco X., tr. Reisberg, Mira, illus. 2003. Tr. of Viborita de Cascabel. (SPA & ENG.). 32p. (J). pap. 7.95 (978-0-89239-188-2(X)) Children's Bk. Pr.

Atwater-Rhodes, Amelia. Falcondance. 2005. 192p. (YA). (gr. 7-12). lib. bdg. 16.99 (978-0-385-90334-9(0) , Delacorte Bks. for Young Readers) Random Hse. Children's Bks.

—Falcondance Vol. III: The Kiesha'ra. 2007. 208p. (YA). (gr. 7). pap. 7.99 (978-0-440-23885-0(4) , Delacorte Bks. for Young Readers) Random Hse. Children's Bks.

—Falcondance Vol. 3: The Kiesha'ra. 2005. 192p. (YA). (gr. 7-12). 14.95 (978-0-385-73194-2(9) , Delacorte Bks. for Young Readers) Random Hse. Children's Bks.

—Snakecharm Vol. 2: The Kiesha'ra. 2007. 176p. (YA). (gr. 7). pap. 7.99 (978-0-385-73493-6(X) , Delacorte Bks. for Young Readers) Random Hse. Children's Bks.

—Wolfcry. 2008. 208p. (YA). (gr. 9). pap. 7.99 (***978-0-440-23886-7(2)*** , Delacorte Bks. for Young Readers) Random Hse. Children's Bks.

Atwater-Rhodes, Amelia. Wolfcry Vol. 4: The Kiesha'ra. 2006. (Illus.). 208p. (YA). (gr. 7). 14.95 (978-0-385-73195-9(7)); lib. bdg. 16.99 (978-0-385-90354-7(5)) Random Hse. Children's Bks. (Delacorte Bks. for Young Readers).

Bagley, Conor. Ziggy McFinster's Nantucket Adventure. Westcott, Nadine Bernard, illus. 2008. 40p. (***978-1-56625-315-4(2)*** , Volt Pr.) Bonus Bks., Inc.

Bellingham, Brenda. Lilly & the Snakes. MacDonald, Clarke, illus. 2007. (First Novel Ser.). 64p. (J). (gr. 2-5). (***978-0-88780-727-5(5)***); 4.95 (***978-0-88780-723-7(2)***) Formac Publishing Co., Ltd. CAN. *Dist:* Casemate Pubs. & Bk. Distributors, LLC.

Brouillet, Chrystine. Le Ventre du Serpent. Gagnon, Nathalie, illus. 2002. (Roman Jeunesse Ser.). (FRE.). 96p. (YA). (gr. 4-7). pap. (978-2-89021-262-6(9)) Diffusion du livre Mirabel.

Callaway, Phil. Jake & the Scrambled Snake. 2002. (Illus.). 36p. (J). pap. 3.99 (978-1-55305-029-2(0)) Cygnet Publishing Group, Inc./Coolreading.com CAN. *Dist:* Orca Bk. Pubs. USA.

Cannon, Janell. Verdi. Cannon, Janell, illus. 2002. (Illus.). (J). 23.40 (978-0-7587-3898-1(6)) Book Wholesalers, Inc.

—Verdi. (SPA., Illus.). 48p. (J). 2003. (gr. 1-3). (978-84-261-3042-6(9) , JV7591); 2000. 22.50 (978-84-261-2949-9(8) , JV9498) Juventud, Editorial ESP. *Dist:* Lectorum Pubns., Inc., AIMS International Bks., Inc., Continental Bk. Co., Inc., Distribooks, Inc.

—Verdi. pap. 24.95 (978-85-325-1343-4(3)) Rocco, Editora, Ltda BRA. *Dist:* Distribooks, Inc.

Capaul, Roxanne. Snakey Jake to the Rescue! Whiting, Anne, illus. 2002. 40p. (J). (ps-6). 17.00 (978-0-9719222-0-4(9)) Rotire, Inc.

Carter, Candace. Sid's Surprise. Un Kim, Joung, illus. 2005. 32p. (J). lib. bdg. 10.00 (***978-1-4242-0185-3(3)***) Fitzgerald Bks.

—Sid's Surprise. Kim, Joung Un, illus. 2005. (Green Light Readers Level 1 Ser.). 32p. (J). 12.95 (978-0-15-205183-9(X)); pap. 3.95 (978-0-15-205182-2(1)) Harcourt Children's Bks. (Green Light Readers).

Chidvilasananda, Swami. The Great Hiss. Cornelis, Susan, illus. 2002. 32p. (J). 18.95 (978-0-911307-90-0(7) , 205221, Siddha Yoga Pubn.) SYDA Foundation.

Clark, Clara Gillow. Willie & the Rattlesnake King. 2003. (Illus.). 168p. (YA). (gr. 4-6). pap. 7.95 (978-1-56397-763-3(X)) Boyds Mills Pr.

Condi-Babich, Kris. 4Cam. us. 2004. 71p. pap. 14.95 (978-1-4137-2241-3(5)) PublishAmerica, Inc.

Cook, Sherry & Johnson, Terri. Susie Sound, 26. Kuhn, Jesse, illus. l.t. ed. 2006. 32p. (J). 7.99 (978-1-933815-18-3(3) , Quirkles, The) Creative 3, LLC.

de Brunhoff, Laurent. Babar the King. de Brunhoff, Laurent, illus. 2002. (Babar Ser.). (Illus.). (J). 23.36 (978-0-7587-2011-5(4)) Book Wholesalers, Inc.

Dewey, Ariane & Aruego, Jose. The Last Laugh. 2006. (Illus.). 32p. (J). (ps). 12.99 (978-0-8037-3093-9(4) , Dial) Penguin Group (USA) Inc.

Doudna, Kelly. Snake Charmer. Nobens, C. A., illus. (Fact & Fiction Ser.). 24p. (J). 2007. 21.35 (978-1-59928-470-5(7)); 2006. (978-1-59928-471-2(5)) ABDO Publishing Co.

Eagle, Golden. It's Good to Shed Your Skin (Snake Medicine) l.t. ed. 2004. (Illus.). 20p. (J). per. 9.95 (978-1-932338-38-6(1)) Lifevest Publishing, Inc.

Eckert, Allan W. The King Snake. Altschuler, Franz, illus. 2001. 156p. (gr. 4-7). pap. 11.95 (978-0-595-18006-6(X)) iUniverse, Inc.

Estes-Hill, Katrina. My Imagination. Kwong, Alvina, illus. 2007. 32p. (J). (ps-2). 15.95 (***978-0-9745715-6-0(3)***) KRBY Creations, LLC.

S

Frazier, Craig. Stanley Mows the Lawn. 2005. (Illus.). 40p. (J). 15.95 (978-0-8118-4846-6(9)) Chronicle Bks. LLC.

Giff, Patricia Reilly. Watch Out! Man-Eating Snake. 79p. (J). (gr. 1-2). pap. 3.99 (978-0-8072-1281-3(4) , Listening Library) Random Hse. Audio Publishing Group.

Gollub, Matthew. Tio Culebra. Martinez, Leovigildo, illus. 2002. Tr. of Uncle Snake. (SPA.). 32p. pap. 6.95 (978-1-889910-24-6(4)) Tortuga Pr.

—Tio Culebra. Guzman, Martin Luis, tr. Martinez, Leovigildo, illus. 2002. Tr. of Uncle Snake. (SPA.). 32p. 15.95 (978-1-889910-23-9(6)) Tortuga Pr.

Greenburg, Dan. When Bad Snakes Attack Good Children. Fischer, Scott M., illus. 2007. (Secrets of Dripping Fang Ser.: Bk. 8). 144p. (J). 9.95 (978-0-15-206056-5(1)) Harcourt Children's Bks.

Harcourt School Publishers Staff. Rikki-Tikki-Tavi Level D Library. 2001. (Vamos de Fiesta Ser.). (SPA., Illus.). 79p. (gr. 8-12). 28.10 (978-84-03-60277-9(4)) Harcourt Schl. Pubs.

Haussinger, D. Susanna the Snake. Date not set. 144p. (YA). (gr. 7 up). 5.99 (978-0-06-447212-8(4)) HarperCollins Pubs.

Hayes, Joe. The Gum-Chewing Rattler. 2006. (Illus.). 32p. (J). (gr. k-3). 16.95 (978-0-938317-99-9(7)) Cinco Puntos Pr.

—Soft Child: How Rattlesnake Got Its Fangs. Sather, Kay, illus. 2000. 32p. (ps-3). pap. 8.95 (978-0-943173-89-4(2)) Rinehart, Roberts Pubs.

Huxley, Aldous. The Crows of Pearblossom. (J). 15.95 (978-0-89190-167-9(1)) Amereon LTD.

Jackson, Barry. Danny Diamondback. 2008. 40p. (J). 17.89 (***978-0-06-113185-1(7)***); 16.99 (***978-0-06-113184-4(9)***) HarperCollins Pubs.

Jake the Snake: Set D Individual Title, 6 Packs. (gr. k-3). 29.00 (978-0-7635-0550-9(1)) Rigby Education.

Jarman, Julia. Class Two at the Zoo. Chapman, Lynne, illus. 2007. (Carolrhoda Picture Bks.). 32p. (J). (gr. k-3). 16.95 (***978-0-8225-7132-2(3)*** , Carolrhoda Bks.) Lerner Publishing Group.

Johansen, K. V. Torrie & the Snake-Prince. Delezenne, Christine, illus. 2007. (Torrie Quests Ser.). 192p. (J). (gr. 4-6). 18.95 (***978-1-55451-070-2(8)***) Annick Pr., Ltd. CAN. *Dist:* Firefly Bks., Ltd.

Jonell, Lynne. I Need a Snake. 2000. (J). (978-0-606-20240-4(4)) Tandem Library Bks.

Kaaberbol, Lene. The Serpent Gift. 3rd rev. ed. 2006. (Shamer Chronicles Ser.). Orig. Title: Slangens Gave. (Illus.). 384p. (J). 18.95 (978-0-8050-7770-4(7)) Holt, Henry & Co.

Kellogg, Steven, illus. The Day Jimmy's Boa Ate the Wash. 2002. (Jimmy's Boa Constrictor Ser.). (J). 14.04 (978-0-7587-2356-7(3)) Book Wholesalers, Inc.

—Jimmy's Boa & the Big Splash Birthday Bash. 2002. (Jimmy's Boa Constrictor Ser.). (J). 25.45 (978-0-7587-2902-6(2)) Book Wholesalers, Inc.

—Jimmy's Boa Bounces Back. 2002. (Jimmy's Boa Constrictor Ser.). (J). 14.04 (978-0-7587-2903-3(0)) Book Wholesalers, Inc.

Kimmel, Eric A. Why the Snake Crawls on Its Belly. Davis, Allen, illus. 2005. 32p. (J). (gr. 1-4). 14.95 (978-1-930143-20-3(6) , Devora Publishing) Pitspopany Pr.

Klemer, Amy Wade. The Scary Snake Monster. 2003. (Illus.). 16p. (J). pap. 8.00 (978-0-9729216-1-9(3)) AB-CDMoon Publishing.

Krensky, Stephen. Sacagawea & the Bravest Deed. Magnuson, illus. 2002. (Ready-to-Read Cofa Ser.). 32p. (J). pap. 3.99 (978-0-689-84803-2(X) , Aladdin) Simon & Schuster Children's Publishing.

—Sacagawea & the Bravest Deed. 2002. (gr. k-3). lib. bdg. 11.80 (978-0-613-57582-9(2)) Tandem Library Bks.

Krulik, Nancy E. Free the Worms!, No. 28. John and Wendy Staff, illus. 2008. (Katie Kazoo, Switcheroo Ser.: No. 28). 80p. (J). (gr. 2-5). pap. 3.99 (***978-0-448-44675-2(8)*** , Grosset & Dunlap) Penguin Group (USA) Inc.

Lasher, Sylvia E. The Little Garden Snake's First Adventure. 2000. (J). pap. 7.00 (978-0-8059-4699-4(3)) Dorrance Publishing Co., Inc.

Law, Felicia. Rumble Meets Vikki Viper. Pak, Yoon Mi, illus. 2006. (Read-It! Readers Ser.). 32p. (J). (gr. 2-4). 18.60 (978-1-4048-1342-7(X)) Picture Window Bks.

Lawrence, Cherry. David & the Blue Racer. 2006. 53p. pap. 12.95 (978-1-4241-3339-0(4)) PublishAmerica, Inc.

Layden, Joseph Lyon. The Other Side of Yore. 2007. 156p. pap. 14.95 (*978-1-60145-122-4(9)) Booklocker.com, Inc.

Lester, Julius. Why Heaven Is Far Away. Cepeda, Joe, illus. 2002. 40p. (J). (gr. 1-3). pap. 16.95 (978-0-439-17871-6(1) , Scholastic Pr.) Scholastic, Inc.

Littte, Lorna. The Mark of the Wagarl. Lyndon, Janice, illus. 2004. 28p. (J). 20.75 (978-1-875641-97-0(1)) Magabala Bks. AUS. Dist: International Specialized Bk. Services.

Lorenzen, Margaret. Slinky Slithertail. Habalou, Matthew, illus. 2001. 112p. (J). (gr. 2-6). per. 15.00 (978-0-9708053-4-8(9)) Authors & Artists Publishers of New York, Inc.

Lorenzen, Margartet. Slinky Slithertail & the Talent Show. Sawyer, Jocelyn, illus. 2004. 96p. (J). per. 12.50 (978-0-9708053-9-3(X)) Authors & Artists Publishers of New York, Inc.

Lumpkin, Jimmy. Rattlesnake Ranch. 2003. 128 p. pap. 17.95 (978-1-4137-0530-0(8)) PublishAmerica, Inc.

MacGill-Callahan, Sheila. The Last Snake in Ireland: A Story about St. Patrick. Hillenbrand, Will, illus. 1999. 32p. (J). (gr. k-3). 6.95 (978-0-8234-1555-7(4)) Holiday Hse., Inc.

Madonna. Las Aventuras de Abdi. 2005. (SPA.). 32p. (J). 19.95 (978-0-439-74072-2(X)) Scholastic, Inc.

Maelor, Gwawr, et al. Neli Neidr. 2005. (WEL., Illus.). 12p. (978-1-85644-839-0(8)) Univ. of Wales, Aberystwyth, Centre for Educational Studies.

Marshall, James. Snake: His Story. 2000. (Illus.). 32p. (J). (gr. k-3). tchr. ed. 5.95 (978-0-618-07320-7(5)) Houghton Mifflin Co. Trade & Reference Div.

McCardie, Amanda. Davy & the Snake. 2000. (Illus.). 64p. (J). pap. 5.99 (978-0-09-940179-7(7)) Random Hse. GBR. Dist: Independent Pubs. Group.

McKay, Sindy. We Both Read-Ben & Becky Get a Pet. Johnson, Meredith, illus. (We Both Read Ser.). 44p. (J). (gr. 2 up). 1999. pap. 3.99 (978-1-891327-10-0(0)); 1998. 7.99 (978-1-891327-06-3(2)) Treasure Bay, Inc.

McKee, David. Elmer & Snake. 2004. (Illus.). 32p. (978-1-84270-303-8(X)) Andersen.

McPhail, David. Sylvie & True. 2007. (Illus.). 32p. (J). (ps). 15.00 (978-0-374-37364-1(7)) Farrar, Straus & Giroux.

Miller, Scott. Prairie Whispers. 2006. 99p. pap. 14.95 (*978-1-4241-4790-8(5)) PublishAmerica, Inc.

Montgomery Gibson, Jane. Jake the Fake Snake. Montgomery Gibson, Jane, illus. 2005. (J). bds. 8.99 (978-1-4183-0026-5(8)) Christ Inspired, Inc.

Morpurgo, Michael. Snakes & Ladders. Wilson, Anne, illus. 2006. 46p. (J). (978-0-7787-0952-7(3)) Crabtree Publishing Co.

Moses, Brian. The Playground Snake. Mostyn, David, illus. 2004. (Read-It! Readers Ser.). 32p. (C). (gr. k-3). 18.60 (978-1-4048-0556-9(7)) Picture Window Bks.

Naidu, Vayu. Hiss, Don't Bite. 1998. (Under the Banyan Ser.). (Illus.). 22p. (YA). (gr. 2 up). 11.99 incl. audio (978-81-86838-31-0(7)) APG Sales and Fulfillment.

Noble, Trinka Hakes. Jimmy's Boa & the Bungee Jump Slam Dunk. Kellogg, Steven, illus. 2003. 32p. (J). (ps). 16.99 (978-0-8037-2600-0(7) , Dial) Penguin Group (USA) Inc.

—Jimmy's Boa & the Bungee Jump Slam Dunk. Kellogg, Steven, illus. 2005. 32p. (J). pap. 5.99 (978-0-14-240453-9(5) , Puffin) Penguin Group (USA) Inc.

Nygaard, Elizabeth. Snake Alley Band. 1999. (978-0-606-16731-4(5)) Tandem Library Bks.

Paul, Ann Whitford. Count on Culebra. Long, Ethan, illus. 2008. (J). (*978-0-8234-2124-4(4)) Holiday Hse., Inc.

Perry, Marie/Fritz. Cecil's New Year's Eve Tail. Perry, Marie/Fritz, illus. 2007. (Illus.). 32p. (J). lib. bdg. (*978-0-9755675-2-4(7)) Buttonweed Pr., L.L.C.

Pickup, Michael. The Adventures of Bhakta Musika & the Terrible Snake. 1998. (Illus.). 38p. (J). (ps-5). pap. 4.95 (978-81-87216-08-7(5)) Torchlight Publishing.

Poindexter, Sidney. Mongoose-Girl vs. the Black Mamba. 2004. 50p. per. 8.95 (978-1-59453-501-7(9) , 2656) Airleaf Publishing & Bookselling.

Polisar, Barry Louis. The Snake Who Was Afraid of People. Clark, David, illus. 2003. (Rainbow Morning Music Picture Bks.). 32p. (J). (ps-2). reprint ed. 14.95 (978-0-938663-16-4(X)) Rainbow Morning Music Alternatives.

—Snakes & the Boy Who Was Afraid of Them. Clark, David, illus. 2003. (Rainbow Morning Music Picture Bks.). 32p. (J). (ps-3). reprint ed. 14.95 (978-0-938663-15-7(1)) Rainbow Morning Music Alternatives.

Powers, Paul. Tales of the Swamp Creatures. 2003. 71p. pap. 11.95 (978-1-4137-0160-9(4)) PublishAmerica, Inc.

Provencher, Rose-Marie. Slithery Jake. Carter, Abby, illus. 2004. 32p. (J). 15.99 (978-0-06-623820-3(X)) HarperCollins Pubs.

—Slithery Jake. Provencher, Rose-Marie & Carter, Abby, illus. 2004. 32p. (J). lib. bdg. 17.89 (978-0-06-623821-0(8)) HarperCollins Pubs.

Redeker, Kent. The Bidding War. Brandt, Elizabeth, illus. 2001. (Angela Anaconda Ser.: Vol. 5). 64p. (J). pap. 3.99 (978-0-689-84183-5(3) , Simon Spotlight) Simon & Schuster Children's Publishing.

Renaud, Philip Francis. The Adventures of Sonny the Snow Snake. Wohlers, Lori, illus. l.t. ed. 2002. 22p. (J). bds. 10.95 (978-0-9711805-0-5(4)) Renaud & Co.

Roberts, Kerry Daniel. Mark of the Yuan-Ti, Bk. 12. 2006. (Knights of the Silver Dragon Ser.: Bk. 12). (Illus.). 192p. (J). pap. 5.99 (978-0-7869-4033-2(6) , Mirrorstone) Wizards of the Coast.

Sargent, Dave & Sargent, Pat. Young Redi: Friendship!, 3. Woodward, Elaine, illus. 2003. (Young Animal Pride Ser.: 3). 24p. (J). pap. 6.95 (978-1-56763-868-4(6)); lib. bdg. 19.95 (978-1-56763-867-7(8)) Ozark Publishing.

Schraff, Anne. Something Dreadful down Below: Set 3. 2002. 32p. (YA). 2.95 (978-1-56254-432-4(2) , SP 4322) Saddleback Educational Publishing.

Seuling, Barbara. Robert & the Great Escape. Brewer, Paul, illus. 2003. (Robert Bks.). 120p. 15.95 (978-0-8126-2700-8(8)) Cricket Bks.

Smiley, Mark. A Journey Far Away. 2005. pap. 13.95 (*978-1-59526-494-7(9)) Media Creations, Inc.

Smith, Alexander McCall. Akimbo & the Snakes. Pham, LeUyen, illus. (Akimbo Ser.). 80p. (J). 2007. pap. 4.95 (*978-1-59990-034-6(3)); 2006. 9.95 (978-1-58234-705-9(0)) Bloomsbury Publishing. (Bloomsbury Children).

Smith, Mavis. Snake Mistake: Level 2. 1998. (Puffin Easy-to-Read Ser.). (J). (978-0-606-13780-5(7)) Tandem Library Bks.

Smith, Mavis & Ziefert, Harriet. A Snake Mistake. 1998. (Puffin Easy-to-Read Program Ser.). (Illus.). 32p. (J). (gr. k-3). pap. 3.99 (978-0-14-038813-8(3) , Puffin) Penguin Group (USA) Inc.

Snake's Reward: Individual Title Six-Packs. (Story Steps Ser.). (gr. k-2). 32.00 (978-0-7635-9821-1(6)) Rigby Education.

Snicket, Lemony, pseud. Le Laboratoire aux Serpents. 24.95 (978-2-09-211034-8(9)) Nathan, Fernand FRA. Dist: Distribooks, Inc.

Snyder, Susan E. Shivers & Shakes. 2007. (Illus.). 24p. (J). 9.95 (978-0-9767163-5-8(6)) Kotzig Publishing, Inc.

Spohn. Turtle & Snake & the Christmas Tree. 2000. (Easy-to-Read Ser.). (J). (978-0-606-20262-6(5)) Tandem Library Bks.

Spohn, Kate. Turtle & Snake & the Christmas Tree. 2000. (Puffin Easy-to-Read Ser.). (978-0-606-20378-4(8)) Tandem Library Bks.

—Turtle & Snake at Work. 1999. (Puffin Easy-to-Read Ser.). (978-0-606-16823-6(0)) Tandem Library Bks.

—Turtle & Snake Go Camping. 2000. (Easy-to-Read Ser.). (Illus.). 32p. (J). (ps-2). pap. 3.99 (978-0-14-130670-4(X) , Puffin) Penguin Group (USA) Inc.

—Turtle & Snake Go Camping. 2000. (Puffin Easy-to-Read Ser.). (978-0-606-18460-1(0)); lib. bdg. 11.80 (978-0-613-27346-6(X)) Tandem Library Bks.

—Turtle & Snake's Day at the Beach. Spohn, Kate, illus. 2004. (Easy-to-Read, Puffin Ser.). (Illus.). 32p. (J). (ps up). pap. 3.99 (978-0-14-240157-6(9) , Puffin) Penguin Group (USA) Inc.

—Turtle & Snake's Happy-Spooky Halloween. 2003. (gr. k-3). lib. bdg. 11.80 (978-0-613-87830-2(2)) Tandem Library Bks.

—Turtle & Snake's Spooky Halloween. Spohn, Kate, illus. 2003. (Easy-to-Read Ser.). (Illus.). 32p. (J). (gr. k-1). pap. 3.99 (978-0-14-250078-1(X) , Puffin) Penguin Group (USA) Inc.

—Turtle & Snake's Spooky Halloween. 2002. (Viking Easy-to-Read Ser.). (Illus.). 32p. (J). 13.99 (978-0-670-03560-1(2) , Viking Juvenile) Penguin Group (USA) Inc.

—Turtle & Snake's Valentine's Day. 2003. (Viking Easy-To-Read Ser.). (Illus.). 32p. (J). (ps-3). 13.99 (978-0-670-03613-4(7) , Viking Juvenile) Penguin Group (USA) Inc.

Springer, Nancy. Dusssie. 2007. 176p. (J). (gr. 5-9). 16.95 (*978-0-8027-9649-3(4)) Walker & Co.

Stanley, George Edward. Snake Camp. Lee, Jared D., illus. 2000. (Road to Reading Ser.). 48p. (J). (gr. 2-5). pap. 3.99 (978-0-307-26406-0(8) , Random Hse. Bks. for Young Readers) Random Hse. Children's Bks.

—Snake Camp. 2000. (J). (978-0-606-18927-9(0)); (gr. 3-6). lib. bdg. 11.80 (978-0-613-33066-4(8)) Tandem Library Bks.

Stone, Jeff. Snake. 2006. (Five Ancestors Ser.: Bk. 3). 208p. (J). (gr. 5). 15.95 (978-0-375-83075-4(8)); lib. bdg. 17.99 (978-0-375-93075-1(2)) Random Hse. Children's Bks. (Random Hse. Bks. for Young Readers).

Stoodt, Jeffrey. How the Rattlesnake Got Its Rattle. 1998. (Illus.). 24p. (ps-3). pap. 4.95 (978-0-8172-7978-3(4)) Steck-Vaughn.

Stroud, Bettye. Dance Y'All. Van Wright, Cornelius & Hu, Ying-Hwa, illus. 2001. 32p. (J). (gr. k-3). 15.95 (978-0-7614-5065-8(3) , Cavendish Children's Bks.) Cavendish, Marshall Corp.

Sula, Sondra. Gopher World: The Sleazy Snakes. 2000. mass mkt. 8.95 (978-1-931179-14-0(X)) Long Hill Productions, Inc.

—Gopher World: The Sleazy Snakes. Johnson, Terri L., illus. 2000. 32p. (J). (gr. 1-3). pap. (978-0-9701450-7-9(1)) Long Hill Productions, Inc.

Sweeney, Jacqueline. Hester. Hart, G. K. & Empey, Mark, illus. 1999. (We Can Read! Ser.). 32p. (J). (gr. 1-2). lib. bdg. 21.36 (978-0-7614-0923-6(8) , Benchmark Bks.) Cavendish, Marshall Corp.

Takerer, Sharon R. Seamus: The Patron Snake of Ireland (A Wee Bit of Nonsense) 2001. (Illus.). 32p. (J). (gr. k-8). pap. 9.95 (978-1-893757-28-8(5) , 28-5) Needer, E.T. Publishing.

Thompson, Lisa, illus. Incredible India. 2006. (Read-It! Chapter Books). 80p. (J). (gr. 2-4). 19.95 (978-1-4048-1676-3(3)) Picture Window Bks.

Townson, Hazel. Snakes Alive & Other Stories. 2005. (Illus.). 192p. (J). pap. 8.99 (*978-1-84270-508-7(3)) Transworld Publishers Ltd. GBR. Dist: Independent Pubs. Group.

Twinem, Neecy. Baby Snake's Shapes. 2004. (New Board Book Ser.).Tr. of Las formas de Bebe Serpiente. (Illus.). (J). 12p. bds. 5.95 (978-0-87358-850-8(9)); (ENG & SPA., bds. 5.95 (978-0-87358-866-9(5)) Northland Publishing. (Rising Moon Bks. for Young Readers).

Vera Viper's Valentine. 2001. (ps-2). lib. bdg. 9.80 (978-0-613-33181-4(8)) Tandem Library Bks.

Walker, Cheryl. Black Snake, King Snake. 2003. 7p. (J). pap. 1.50 (978-0-9726326-2-1(X)) TechArts International LLC.

Wallace, Carol. Flying Flea, Callie & Me. 1999. (gr. 3-6). lib. bdg. 13.00 (978-0-613-84533-5(1)) Tandem Library Bks.

Walsh, Ellen Stoll. Mouse Count: Lap-Sized Board Book. 2006. (Illus.). 30p. (J). bds. 10.95 (978-0-15-205699-5(8) , Red Wagon Bks.) Harcourt Children's Bks.

Welling, Peter J. Shawn O'Hisser, the Last Snake in Ireland. Welling, Peter J., illus. 2002. (Illus.). 32p. (J). (gr. k-3). 15.95 (978-1-58980-014-4(1)) Pelican Publishing Co., Inc.

Weston, Anne. My Brother Needs a Boa. Nathan, Cheryl, illus. 2005. 32p. (J). (gr. 2-4). 15.95 (978-1-932065-96-1(2)) Star Bright Bks., Inc.

Whitaker, Zai. Kali & the Rat Snake. Natarajan, Srividya, illus. 2006. 32p. (J). 15.95 (978-1-933605-10-4(3)) Kane/Miller Bk. Pubs., Inc.

Wildsmith, Brian. Jungle Party. Wildsmith, Brian, illus. 2006. (Illus.). 32p. (J). 16.95 (978-1-59572-052-8(9)); pap. 6.95 (978-1-59572-053-5(7)) Star Bright Bks., Inc.

Williams, Jacklyn. Pick a Pet, Gus! Cushman, Doug, illus. 2006. (Read-It! Readers Ser.). (J). 19.93 (978-1-4048-2712-7(9)) Picture Window Bks.

Willis, Jeanne. Be Gentle, Python! Birchall, Mark, illus. 2005. (Picture Bks.). 28p. (J). (gr. k-2). 7.95 (978-1-57505-508-4(2)) Lerner Publishing Group.

SNOOPY (FICTITIOUS CHARACTER)—FICTION

Katschke, Judy, adapted by. Take A Hike, Snoopy! ed. 2005. (Illus.). 32p. (J). lib. bdg. 15.00 (978-1-59054-955-1(4)) Fitzgerald Bks.

Schulz, C. Snoopy: Flying Ace to the Rescue. LoBianco, Peter & LoBianco, Nick, illus. 2002. 31p. (gr. k-3). lib. bdg. 11.80 (978-0-613-57583-6(0)) Tandem Library Bks.

Schulz, Charles M. Alles Peanuts. Herbst, Gabriele & Rolle, Ekkehard, trs. from ENG. (Snoopy & die Peanuts Ser.: Vol. 26). (GER., Illus.). 96p. (J). pap. (978-3-8105-1871-2(9)) Kruger, Wolfgang Verlag, GmbH DEU. Dist: International Bk. Import Service, Inc.

—Allzeit Bereit. Herbst, Gabriele & Rolle, Ekkehard, trs. from ENG. (Snoopy & die Peanuts Ser.: Vol. 35). (GER., Illus.). 96p. (J). pap. (978-3-8105-1891-0(3)) Kruger, Wolfgang Verlag, GmbH DEU. Dist: International Bk. Import Service, Inc.

— An der Langen Leine. Herbst, Gabriele & Rolle, Ekkehard, trs. from ENG. (Snoopy & die Peanuts Ser.: Vol. 30). (GER., Illus.). 96p. (J). pap. (978-3-8105-1880-4(8)) Kruger, Wolfgang Verlag, GmbH DEU. Dist: International Bk. Import Service, Inc.

—Auf den Hund Gekommen. Herbst, Gabriele & Rolle, Ekkehard, trs. from ENG. (Snoopy & die Peanuts Ser.: Vol. 34). (GER., Illus.). 96p. (J). pap. (978-3-8105-1888-0(3)) Kruger, Wolfgang Verlag, GmbH DEU. Dist: International Bk. Import Service, Inc.

—Baby Snoopy's Valentine. Schulz, Charles M., illus. 2003. (Baby Snoopy Ser.). (Illus.). 12p. (J). bds. 5.99 (978-0-689-85781-2(0) , Little Simon) Simon & Schuster Children's Publishing.

—Beagle Scout Snoopy. Schulz, Charles M., illus. 2003. (Peanuts Ser.). (Illus.). 14p. (J). pap. 6.99 (978-0-689-85855-0(8) , Little Simon) Simon & Schuster Children's Publishing.

—Den Wind im Ruecken. Herbst, Gabriele & Rolle, Ekkehard, trs. from ENG. (Snoopy & die Peanuts Ser.: Vol. 6). (GER., Illus.). 96p. (J). pap. (978-3-8105-1819-4(0)) Kruger, Wolfgang Verlag, GmbH DEU. Dist: International Bk. Import Service, Inc.

—Einfach Genial. Herbst, Gabriele & Rolle, Ekkehard, trs. from ENG. (Snoopy & die Peanuts Ser.: Vol. 31). (GER., Illus.). 96p. (J). pap. (978-3-8105-1881-1(6)) Kruger, Wolfgang Verlag, GmbH DEU. Dist: International Bk. Import Service, Inc.

—Einfach Unschlagbar. Herbst, Gabriele & Rolle, Ekkehard, trs. from ENG. (Snoopy & die Peanuts Ser.: Vol. 1). (GER., Illus.). 96p. (J). pap. (978-3-8105-1811-8(5)) Kruger, Wolfgang Verlag, GmbH DEU. Dist: International Bk. Import Service, Inc.

—Friends Forever, Snoopy. 2001. (gr. k-3). lib. bdg. 11.80 (978-0-613-61768-0(1)) Tandem Library Bks.

—Grundlos Gluecklich. Herbst, Gabriele & Rolle, Ekkehard, trs. from ENG. (Snoopy & die Peanuts Ser.: Vol. 37). (GER., Illus.). 96p. (J). pap. (978-3-8105-1893-4(X)) Kruger, Wolfgang Verlag, GmbH DEU. Dist: International Bk. Import Service, Inc.

—Gut Aufgelegt. Herbst, Gabriele & Rolle, Ekkehard, trs. from ENG. (Snoopy & die Peanuts Ser.: Vol. 12). (GER., Illus.). 96p. (J). pap. (978-3-8105-1828-6(X)) Kruger, Wolfgang Verlag, GmbH DEU. Dist: International Bk. Import Service, Inc.

—Herzlich Unverschaemt. Herbst, Gabriele & Rolle, Ekkehard, trs. from ENG. (Snoopy & die Peanuts Ser.: Vol. 9). (GER., Illus.). 128p. (J). pap. (978-3-8105-1823-1(9)) Kruger, Wolfgang Verlag, GmbH DEU. Dist: International Bk. Import Service, Inc.

—Himmel & Hoelle. Herbst, Gabriele & Rolle, Ekkehard, trs. from ENG. (Snoopy & die Peanuts Ser.: Vol. 23). (GER., Illus.). 96p. (J). pap. (978-3-8105-1867-5(0)) Kruger, Wolfgang Verlag, GmbH DEU. Dist: International Bk. Import Service, Inc.

—Hoch die Tassen. Herbst, Gabriele & Rolle, Ekkehard, trs. from ENG. (Snoopy & die Peanuts Ser.: Vol. 36). (GER., Illus.). 96p. (J). pap. (978-3-8105-1892-7(1)) Kruger, Wolfgang Verlag, GmbH DEU. Dist: International Bk. Import Service, Inc.

—Immer Dabei. Herbst, Gabriele & Rolle, Ekkehard, trs. from ENG. (Snoopy & die Peanuts Ser.: Vol. 27). (GER., Illus.). 96p. (J). pap. (978-3-8105-1872-9(7)) Kruger, Wolfgang Verlag, GmbH DEU. Dist: International Bk. Import Service, Inc.

—"It Was a Dark & Stormy Night, Snoopy" 2004. (Illus.). 160p. pap. 11.95 (978-0-345-44272-7(5) , Ballantine Bks.) Random House Publishing Group.

—It's Time for School, Charlie Brown. 2002. (gr. k-3). lib. bdg. 11.80 (978-0-613-61782-6(7)) Tandem Library Bks.

—Kaum zu Bremsen. Rolle, Ekkehard, tr. from ENG. (Snoopy & die Peanuts Ser.: Vol. 11). (GER., Illus.). 128p. (J). pap. (978-3-8105-1827-9(1)) Kruger, Wolfgang Verlag, GmbH DEU. Dist: International Bk. Import Service, Inc.

—The Many Faces of Snoopy. 2006. (Illus.). 352p. pap. 16.95 (978-0-345-47983-9(1) , Ballantine Bks.) Random House Publishing Group.

—Peanuts: Snoopy at Bat. 2008. 10p. (J). pap. 7.95 (*978-0-7624-3235-6(7) , Running Pr.) Running Pr. Bk. Pubs.

—Pfoten Hoch! Herbst, Gabriele & Rolle, Ekkehard, trs. from ENG. (Snoopy & die Peanuts Ser.: Vol. 33). (GER., Illus.). 96p. (J). pap. (978-3-8105-1887-3(5)) Kruger, Wolfgang Verlag, GmbH DEU. Dist: International Bk. Import Service, Inc.

—Schwer in Fahrt. Herbst, Gabriele & Rolle, Ekkehard, trs. from ENG. (Snoopy & die Peanuts Ser.: Vol. 7). (GER., Illus.). 128p. (J). pap. (978-3-8105-1820-0(4)) Kruger, Wolfgang Verlag, GmbH DEU. Dist: International Bk. Import Service, Inc.

—Snoopy, Flying Ace to the Rescue! Schulz, Charles M., illus. 2002. (Peanuts Ser.). 32p. (J). pap. 3.99 (978-0-689-85148-3(0) , Little Simon) Simon & Schuster Children's Publishing.

—Voll auf die Schnauze. Herbst, Gabriele & Rolle, Ekkehard, trs. from ENG. (Snoopy & die Peanuts Ser.: Vol. 32). (GER., Illus.). 96p. (J). pap. (978-3-8105-1886-6(7)) Kruger, Wolfgang Verlag, GmbH DEU. Dist: International Bk. Import Service, Inc.

—Voll im Griff. Herbst, Gabriele & Rolle, Ekkehard, trs. from ENG. (Snoopy & die Peanuts Ser.: Vol. 13). (GER., Illus.). 128p. (J). pap. (978-3-8105-1829-3(8)) Kruger, Wolfgang Verlag, GmbH DEU. Dist: International Bk. Import Service, Inc.

Schulz, Charles M., illus. Friends Forever, Snoopy. 2001. (Ready-to-Read Ser.). 32p. (J). pap. 3.99 (978-0-689-84597-0(9) , Little Simon) Simon & Schuster Children's Publishing.

SNORKELLING

see Skin Diving

SNOW

Ball, Jacqueline A. Blizzard! The 1888 Whiteout. 2005. (X-Treme Disasters That Changed America Ser.). (Illus.). 32p. (J). lib. bdg. 25.27 (978-1-59716-006-3(7)) Bearport Publishing Co., Inc.

Bauer, Marion Dane. Snow. Wallace, John, illus. 2003. (Ready-to-Read Ser.). 32p. (J). pap. 3.99 (978-0-689-85437-8(4) , Aladdin); lib. bdg. 11.89 (978-0-689-85436-1(6) , Aladdin Library) Simon & Schuster Children's Publishing.

Berger, Melvin & Berger, Gilda. A Snowy Day. 2003. (Scholastic Readers Ser.). (Illus.). (J). (978-0-439-56695-7(9)) Scholastic, Inc.

Boyett, Suzi. Let's Read about Snow. 2006. (J). lib. bdg. (*978-0-8368-7806-6(X)); (Illus.). 12p. pap. (*978-0-8368-7811-0(6)) Stevens, Gareth Inc. (Weekly Reader Early Learning Library).

—Nieva. 2006. (J). lib. bdg. (*978-0-8368-8114-1(1) , Weekly Reader Early Learning Library) Stevens, Gareth Inc.

—Que Tiempo Hace? Nieva. 2006. (Que Tiempo Hace? (Let's Read about Weather) Ser.). (SPA., Illus.). 12p. (J). pap. (*978-0-8368-8119-6(2) , Weekly Reader Early Learning Library) Stevens, Gareth Inc.

Branley, Franklyn M. Snow Is Falling. rev. ed. 2000. (Let's-Read-and-Find-Out Science Ser.). (Illus.). 40p. (J). (ps-1). 15.95 (978-0-06-027990-5(7)) HarperCollins Pubs.

—Snow Is Falling. Keller, Holly, illus. rev. ed. 2000. (Let's-Read-and-Find-Out Science Ser.). 40p. (J). (ps-1). pap. 5.99 (978-0-06-445186-4(0) , Harper Trophy) HarperCollins Pubs.

—Snow Is Falling. 2000. (gr. k-3). lib. bdg. 13.00 (978-0-8085-8584-8(3)) Tandem Library Bks.

Bundey, Nikki. Snow & People. 2005. (Science of Weather Ser.). (Illus.). 32p. (gr. 4-6). lib. bdg. 21.27 (978-1-57505-496-4(5)) Lerner Publishing Group.

—Snow & the Earth. 2005. (Science of Weather Ser.). (Illus.). 32p. (gr. 4-6). lib. bdg. 21.27 (978-1-57505-471-1(X)) Lerner Publishing Group.

Carpino, Nancy. What Makes a Snowflake Grow? McNeilis, Jessica, illus. 1999. 48p. (Orig.). (J). (gr. k-7). pap. 6.95 (978-1-928675-00-6(X)) Carpino Bks.

Clements, Andrew. Snowden Activity Book: Snow Time Fun Sticker Book. 1998. (Illus.). 16p. (J). mass mkt. 1.99 (978-0-689-82362-6(2) , Little Simon) Simon & Schuster Children's Publishing.

D'Aubuisson, Elisabeth. Snowy Days. 2007. (What's the Weather? Ser.). (Illus.). 24p. (J). (gr. k-3). lib. bdg. 21.25 (*978-1-4042-3684-4(8) , PowerKids Pr.) Rosen Publishing Group, Inc., The.

DeGezelle, Terri. Snowplows. 2006. (Pebble Plus Ser.). (Illus.). 24p. (978-0-7368-5357-6(X)) Capstone Pr., Inc.

Un día nevado (A Snowy Day) 2006. (J). 18.60 (978-0-8225-6212-2(X) , Ediciones Lerner) Lerner Publishing Group.

Un Día nevado (A Snowy Day) 2007. (J). pap. 4.25 (978-0-8225-6551-2(X) , Ediciones Lerner) Lerner Publishing Group.

Doubleday Entertainment USA - Weather Watch: Snow. 2006. (J). per. 7.95 (978-1-59566-232-3(4)) QEB Publishing Inc.

Doudna, Kelly. It Is Snowing. 2003. (Weather Ser.). (Illus.). 23p. (J). (ps-3). lib. bdg. 19.93 (978-1-57765-775-0(6)) ABDO Publishing Co.

Drake, Jane & Love, Ann. Snow Amazing: Cool Facts & Warm Tales. Thurman, Mark, illus. 2004. 80p. (J). (gr. 4). 19.95 (978-0-88776-670-1(6)) Tundra Bks., Inc./Livres Toundra, Inc. CAN. Dist: Random Hse., Inc.

Filella, Nacho & Garcia, Gloria. La Nieve. 2005. (SPA.). 6p. 9.95 (978-84-272-6681-0(2)) Molino, Editorial ESP. *Dist:* Distribooks, Inc., Santillana USA Publishing Co., Inc.

Flanagan, Alice K. Snow. 2003. (Wonder Books Level 1: Weather Ser.). (Illus.). 24p. (J). (ps-2). 22.79 (978-1-56766-453-9(9)) Child's World, Inc.

Frost, Helen. Snow. Saunders-Smith, Gail, ed. 2004. (Weather Ser.). (Illus.). 24p. (J). (gr. k-1). lib. bdg. 15.93 (978-0-7368-2095-0(7) , Pebble Bks.) Capstone Pr., Inc.

—Water As a Solid. 1999. pap. 13.25 (978-0-516-21917-2(0) , Children's Pr.) Scholastic Library Publishing.

Galiano, Dean. Clouds, Rain & Snow. rev. ed. 2005. (Weather Watcher's Library). (Illus.). 48p. (gr. 5-8). lib. bdg. 23.95 (978-0-8239-3771-4(2)) Rosen Publishing Group, Inc., The.

Gallup, Tracy. Snow Crazy. Gallup, Tracy, illus. 2007. (Crazy Little Ser.). (Illus.). (J). 9.95 (***978-1-934133-26-2(4)***) Mackinac Island Pr., Inc.

Ganeri, Anita. Snow. 2004. (Illus.). 24p. (J). pap. (978-0-8368-4305-7(3)); lib. bdg. 19.33 (978-0-8368-4300-2(2)) Stevens, Gareth Inc.

Golden Books Staff. Snowy Surprise! 2005. (Hologramatic Sticker Book Ser.). (Illus.). 32p. (J). (ps-2). pap. 3.99 (978-0-375-83182-9(7) , Golden Bks.) Random Hse. Children's Bks.

Grossnickle, Anna H. What Can You Do in the Snow? Kliros, Thea, illus. 1999. 10p. (J). (ps-k). pap. 5.95 (978-0-688-16078-4(6)) HarperCollins Pubs.

Head, Honor. Snow. 2006. (QEB Weather Watch Ser.). (Illus.). 24p. (J). lib. bdg. 16.95 (978-1-59566-184-5(0)) QEB Publishing Inc.

Helget, Nicole Lea. Snow. 2006. (My First Look at Weather Ser.). 24p. 15.95 (***978-1-58341-451-4(7)*** , Creative Education) Creative Co., The.

Heller, Ruth. Snowflakes. 1998. (Ruth Heller's Stained Glass Designs for Coloring Ser.). (Illus.). 32p. (J). (ps-3). pap. 6.99 (978-0-448-41854-4(1) , Grosset & Dunlap) Penguin Group (USA) Inc.

Herriges, Ann. Snow. 2006. (Blastoff! Readers Ser.). (Illus.). 24p. (J). lib. bdg. 16.95 (978-1-60014-029-7(7)) Bellwether Media.

Howard, Pam. See the Snow. Crowell, Knox, illus. l.t. ed. 2004. (HRL Board Book Ser.). 10p. (J). (ps-k). bds. 10.95 (978-1-57332-265-2(2)) HighReach Learning, Inc.

Jennings, Terry J. The Weather: Snow. 2004. (J). lib. bdg. 27.10 (978-1-59389-145-9(8)) Chrysalis Education.

Kalz, Jill. Snow. 2002. (Illus.). 23p. (J). 21.35 (978-1-58340-155-2(5)) Smart Apple Media.

Kaner, Etta. Who Likes the Snow? Lafrance, Marie, illus. 2006. 32p. (978-1-55337-842-6(3)) Kids Can Pr., Ltd.

Lakeshore Learning Materials Staff, contrib. by. I Love Snow Packet. 2000. (J). pap. 36.95 (978-1-929255-52-8(7)) Lakeshore Learning Materials.

Lands of Ice & Snow: Individual Title Six-Packs. (Rigby Infoquest Ser.). 32p. (gr. 4 up). 37.00 (978-0-7578-5732-4(9)) Rigby Education.

Martin, Jacqueline Briggs. Snowflake Bentley. ed. 2004. (Illus.). (J). (ps-3). spiral bd. (978-0-616-01714-2(6)) Canadian National Institute for the Blind/Institut National Canadien pour les Aveugles.

—Snowflake Bentley. Azarian, Mary, illus. 1998. 32p. (J). (gr. k-3). lib. bdg., tchr. ed. 16.00 (978-0-395-86162-2(4)) Houghton Mifflin Co. Trade & Reference Div.

Marzollo, Jean. I Am Snow. 2000. (Hello Reader! Ser.). (J). 10.79 (978-0-606-19567-6(X)) Tandem Library Bks.

Mayer, Cassie. Nieve. 2006. (ENG & SPA.). (J). (***978-1-4034-8656-1(5)***) Heinemann Library.

—Nieve (Snow) 2006. (ENG & SPA.). 24p. (J). pap. (***978-1-4034-8664-6(6)***) Heinemann Library.

Mayer, Cassie. Snow. 2006. (Illus.). 24p. (J). (978-1-4034-8415-4(5)); pap. 5.99 (978-1-4034-8423-9(6)) Heinemann Library.

McNeil, Niki, et al. HOCPP 1136 Let it Snow. 2006. spiral bd. 14.00 (***978-1-60308-136-8(4)***) In the Hands of a Child.

Merk, A. Rain, Snow & Ice. 2003. (Weather Report Discovery Library). (Illus.). 24p. (gr. 1-4). 14.95 (978-1-58952-571-9(X)) Rourke Publishing, LLC.

Miles, Elizabeth. Snow. 2005. (Illus.). 32p. (J). (gr. k-2). lib. bdg. 25.36 (978-1-4034-6551-1(7)); pap. (978-1-4034-6556-6(8)) Heinemann Library.

Nelson, Robin. Snowy. 2004. (First Step Nonfiction Ser.). (J). pap. (978-0-8225-5366-3(X) , Lerner Pubns.) Lerner Publishing Group.

—A Snowy Day. (First Step Nonfiction Ser.). (Illus.). 24p. (gr. k-2). 2005. lib. bdg. 17.27 (978-0-8225-0175-6(9)); 2003. (J). pap. 4.25 (978-0-8225-1964-5(X)) Lerner Publishing Group.

—Snowy Day. 2001. (gr. k-3). lib. bdg. 11.80 (978-0-613-76619-7(9)) Tandem Library Bks.

Rain, Snow, & Hail: Individual Title Six-Packs. (Discovery World Ser.). 16p. (gr. 1-2). 28.00 (978-0-7635-8466-5(5)) Rigby Education.

Richards, Julie. It's Snowing! 2004. (J). lib. bdg. 27.10 (978-1-58340-539-0(9)) Smart Apple Media.

Ring, Susan. Snow. (Illus.). (J). (gr. k-2). 2006. 16p. 15.93 (978-0-7368-5831-1(8) , Yellow Umbrella Bks.); 2005. 17p. (978-0-7368-5297-5(2)); 2005. 17p. (978-0-7368-5261-6(1)) Capstone Pr., Inc.

Rockwell, Anne F. The First Snowfall. Rockwell, Anne F., illus. 2002. (Illus.). (J). 14.47 (978-0-7587-2505-9(1)) Book Wholesalers, Inc.

Rustad, Martha E. H. Today Is Snowy. 2006. (Illus.). 24p. (J). 19.93 (978-0-7368-5345-3(6)) Capstone Pr., Inc.

Ruth, Angie. My Adventure in the Snow. 2006. 44p. (J). 8.99 (978-1-59092-435-8(5) , Orchard Academy Pr.) Windstorm Creative.

Schaefer, Lola M. A Snowy Day. Saunders-Smith, Gail, ed. 1999. (What Kind of Day is It? Ser.). (Illus.). 24p. (J). (gr. k-1). lib. bdg. 15.93 (978-0-7368-0405-9(6) , Pebble Bks.) Capstone Pr., Inc.

—A Snowy Day. 1999. pap. 13.25 (978-0-516-21930-1(8) , Children's Pr.) Scholastic Library Publishing.

Sherman, Joseph. Flakes & Flurries: A Book about Snow. Wesley, Omarr, illus. 2004. (Amazing Science Ser.). 24p. (J). (gr. k-3). 22.60 (978-1-4048-0098-4(0)) Picture Window Bks.

Sievert, Terri. Precipitation. 2005. (Weather Update Ser.). (Illus.). 24p. (J). 21.26 (978-0-7368-3737-8(X)) Capstone Pr., Inc.

Silverman, Maida. Snow Search Dogs. 2005. (Dog Heroes Ser.). 32p. (J). lib. bdg. 25.27 (978-1-59716-017-9(2)) Bearport Publishing Co., Inc.

The Snow: First Wave Satellite Individual Title Six-Packs. (Sails Literacy Ser.). 16p. (gr. k up). 27.00 (978-0-7578-6858-0(4)) Rigby Education.

Snow & Ice: Individual Title Six-Packs. (Sails Literacy Ser.). (gr. 1-2). 36.00 (978-0-7578-6738-5(3)) Rigby Education.

Snow Weather. 2006. (Illus.). 24p. (J). (gr. k-2). 18.50 (***978-0-531-17881-2(1)***) Scholastic Library Publishing.

A Snowy Day, Vol. 2. 2005. (Our Seasons & Weather Ser.). (YA). (gr. k-3). (978-0-7368-8623-9(0) , Pebble Bks.) Capstone Pr., Inc.

A Snowy Day, 6 vols. (gr. k-2). 28.95 (978-0-7368-8629-1(X)) Red Brick Learning.

Steele, Philip. Snow & Ice. 1998. (Living with the Weather Ser.). (Illus.). 48p. (J). (gr. 4-7). lib. bdg. 18.98 (978-0-8172-5052-2(2)) Raintree.

Thomas, Rick. Whiteout! A Book about Blizzards. Shea, Denise, illus. 2005. (Amazing Science Ser.). 24p. (C). (gr. k-3). 22.60 (978-1-4048-0925-3(2)) Picture Window Bks.

Waldman, Neil. The Snowflake: A Water Cycle Story. Waldman, Neil, illus. 2003. 32p. (J). 14.95 (978-0-7613-2347-1(3) , Millbrook Pr.) Lerner Publishing Group.

Ward, Kristin. Snow. 2000. (PowerKids Readers Ser.). (Illus.). 24p. (J). (gr. 1). lib. bdg. 16.00 (978-0-8239-5529-9(X) , PKNASN, PowerKids Pr.) Rosen Publishing Group, Inc., The.

Williams, Judith. Why Is It Snowing? 2005. (I Like Weather! Ser.). (Illus.). 24p. (J). lib. bdg. 21.26 (978-0-7660-2319-2(2) , Enslow Elementary) Enslow Pubs., Inc.

Yarnelle, Darlene. Snow Sheets, L. K., illus. 1998. (J). (ps-3). 8.50 (978-1-891883-00-2(3)) Make Pretend, Inc.

Zuehlke, Jeffrey. Snowplows. (Pull Ahead Books). (Illus.). 32p. (J). 2007. 22.60 (978-0-8225-6009-8(7) , Lerner Pubns.); 2006. pap. 5.95 (978-0-8225-5897-2(1) , First Avenue Editions) Lerner Publishing Group.

SNOW—FICTION

Ada, Alma Flor. I Don't Want to Melt! (Stories the Year 'Round Ser.). (Illus.). 16p. (J). (gr. k-3). pap. 8.95 (978-1-58105-204-6(9)) Santillana USA Publishing Co., Inc.

Aigner-Clark, Julie. What Does Violet See? Snowflakes & Icicles. Zaidi, Nadeem, illus. 2002. (Baby Einstein Ser.). 16p. (ps-ps). 5.99 (978-0-7868-0872-4(1)) Disney Pr.

Aikins, Dave, illus. The Secret of Snow. 2006. (Backyardigans Ser.). 24p. (J). pap. 3.99 (978-1-4169-1510-2(9) , Simon Spotlight/Nickelodeon) Simon & Schuster Children's Publishing.

Allen, J. J. Hello Kitty's Fun Friend Day! 2003. (Illus.). 32p. (J). pap. (978-0-439-44917-5(0)) Scholastic, Inc.

Allen, Janet. Best Little Wingman. Postier, Jim, illus. 2004. 32p. (J). 15.95 (978-1-59078-197-5(X)) Boyds Mills Pr.

Anderson, H.C. La Reine des Neiges. (FRE.). pap. 16.95 (978-2-07-051630-8(X)) Gallimard, Editions FRA. *Dist:* Distribooks, Inc.

Bahr, Mary. My Brother Loved Snowflakes: The Story of Wilson A. Bentley, the Snowflake Man. Jacobsen, Laura, illus. 2003. 32p. (J). (gr. k-2). 15.95 (978-1-56397-689-6(7)) Boyds Mills Pr.

Baker, Courtney. Surprise! Snow Day! Goodnow, Patti, illus. 2003. (Hello Reader! Ser.). (J). pap. (978-0-439-47113-8(3)) Scholastic, Inc.

Barner. Snow. (J). 16.95 (978-0-8118-4171-9(5)) Chronicle Bks. LLC.

Bauer, Dane. Snow. Wallace, John, illus. ed. 2005. 32p. (J). lib. bdg. 15.00 (978-1-59054-934-6(1)) Fitzgerald Bks.

Beck, Ian. Lost in the Snow. 2000. (Illus.). (J). pap. (978-0-439-17521-0(6)) Scholastic, Inc.

—Perdido en la Nieve. 2001. (SPA., Illus.). 32p. (J). (gr. k-2). (978-84-261-3103-4(4) , JV4196) Juventud, Editorial ESP. *Dist:* Lectorum Pubns., Inc.

—Teddy's Snowy Day. Beck, Ian, illus. 2002. (Illus.). 32p. (J). (ps-1). pap. 15.95 (978-0-439-17520-3(8) , Scholastic Pr.) Scholastic, Inc.

Bedford, David. Bedtime for Little Bears! Pedler, Caroline, illus. 2007. 28p. (J). (ps-2). 16.95 (***978-1-56148-587-1(X)***) Good Bks.

Beeke, Joel & Kleyn, Diana. How God Used a Snowdrift. Anderson, Jeff, illus. (Building on the Rock Ser.). 176p. (J). pap. (978-1-85792-817-4(2) , Christian Focus) Christian Focus Pubns. GBR. *Dist:* Riverside.

Bianchi, John. Snowed in at Pokeweed Public School. (Illus.). (J). (gr. 1-5). (978-1-894323-34-5(3)) Pokeweed Pr.

—Snowed in at Pokeweed Public School. 1999. (Illus.). 24p. (J). (gr. 1-5). pap. 4.95 (978-1-894323-12-3(2)) Pokeweed Pr. CAN. *Dist:* Fitzhenry & Whiteside, Ltd.

The Big Snow. 2000. (J). (978-1-58453-129-6(0)) Pioneer Valley Educational Pr., Inc.

Bildner, Phil. Turkey Bowl. Payne, C. F., illus. 2006. (J). 16.99 (978-0-689-87896-1(6) , Simon & Schuster Children's Publishing) Simon & Schuster Children's Publishing.

Blackstone, Stella. Cleo in the Snow. Mockford, Caroline, illus. 2002. 24p. (J). (gr. k-2). 14.99 (978-1-84148-951-3(4)) Barefoot Bks., Inc.

Blanca Nieves - (Estrella de Mar) 2003. (SPA., Illus.). 16p. 2.95 (978-968-855-185-1(6)) Suromex, Ediciones, S.A. MEX. *Dist:* Giron Bks.

Bledsoe, Lucy Jane. Tracks in the Snow. 2000. (978-0-606-17830-3(9)) Tandem Library Bks.

Bogacki, Tomek. Cat & Mouse in the Snow. Bogacki, Tomek, illus. 1999. (Illus.). 26p. (J). (gr. 2-4). reprint ed. 16.00 (978-0-7567-6125-7(5)) DIANE Publishing Co.

Bonnell, Kris. The White, White Snow. 2007. (J). 3.95 (***978-1-933727-44-8(6)***) Reading Reading Bks., LLC.

Books, Fernleigh. Snow Bear. 2007. 32p. (J). pap. 4.99 (***978-0-439-92533-4(9)*** , Cartwheel Bks.) Scholastic, Inc.

Brennan, Linda Crotta. Flannel Kisses. Takabayashi, Mari, illus. 2006. 32p. (J). (gr. k-3). 6.95 (978-0-618-73752-9(9)) Houghton Mifflin Co. Trade & Reference Div.

Brett, Jan. The Mitten. Brett, Jan, illus. 2002. (Illus.). (J). 23.64 (978-0-7587-3151-7(5)) Book Wholesalers, Inc.

—The Mitten. 2001. (J). (gr. k-3). 27.95 incl. audio (978-0-8045-6862-3(6) , 6862) Spoken Arts, Inc.

Bridwell, Norman. Clifford's First Snow Day. Bridwell, Norman, illus. 1998. (Clifford, the Big Red Dog Ser.). (Illus.). 32p. (J). (gr. k-2). 3.99 (978-0-590-03480-7(4) , Cartwheel Bks.) Scholastic, Inc.

Briggs, Raymond. The Snowman. Briggs, Raymond, illus. 2002. (Illus.). (J). 16.60 (978-0-7587-3649-9(5)) Book Wholesalers, Inc.

—The Snowman. Labrack, Joy, ed. 2000. (Bright & Early Board Bks.). (Illus.). 24p. (J). (gr. k-ps). bds. 4.99 (978-0-375-81067-1(6) , Random Hse. Bks. for Young Readers) Random Hse. Children's Bks.

—The Snowman, 1 vol. Downer, Maggie, illus. 1999. (Early Step into Reading Ser.). 32p. (J). (gr. k-ps). pap. 3.99 (978-0-679-89443-8(8) , Random Hse. Bks. for Young Readers) Random Hse. Children's Bks.

—The Snowman. Briggs, Raymond, illus. 1998. (Nifty Lift-and-Look Bks.). (Illus.). 12p. (J). (gr. k-1). bds. 5.99 (978-0-679-88896-3(9) , Random Hse. Bks. for Young Readers) Random Hse. Children's Bks.

Briggs, Raymond & Knudsen, Michelle. The Snowman. Downer, Maggie, illus. 1999. (Step into Reading Ser.). 32p. (J). (ps-2). lib. bdg. 11.99 (978-0-679-99443-5(2) , Random Hse. Bks. for Young Readers) Random Hse. Children's Bks.

Brown, Marc. Arthur & the Big Snow. Brown, Marc, illus. 2005. (Illus.). 24p. (J). (ps-1). pap. 3.99 (978-0-316-05770-7(3)) Little Brown & Co.

Brown, Richard. Snow in the Kitchen. 2005. (Cambridge Storybooks Ser.). 32p. pap. 7.00 (978-0-521-67480-5(8)) Cambridge Univ. Pr.

Brunelle, Nicholas. Snow Moon. 2005. (Illus.). 36p. (J). 15.99 (978-0-670-06024-5(0) , Viking Juvenile) Penguin Group (USA) Inc.

Buehner, Caralyn. Snowmen at Night. Buehner, Mark, illus. (J). (ps). 2004. 26p. bds. 6.99 (978-0-8037-3041-0(1)); 2002. 32p. 15.99 (978-0-8037-2550-8(7)); Set. 2003. 26p. 16.99 (978-0-8037-2975-9(8)) Penguin Group (USA) Inc. (Dial).

—The Snowmen Pop-up Book. Buehner, Mark, illus. 2006. 14p. (J). (ps). 21.99 (978-0-8037-3180-6(9) , Dial) Penguin Group (USA) Inc.

Butler, M. Christina. One Snowy Night. Macnaughton, Tina, illus. 2005. 26p. (J). (ps-3). 16.00 (978-1-56148-452-2(0)) Good Bks.

Butterworth, Nick. One Snowy Night. Butterworth, Nick, illus. 2008. (Percy the Park Keeper Ser.). (Illus.). 32p. (J). 12.95 (***978-0-00-726024-9(5)***) HarperCollins Pubs. Ltd. GBR. *Dist:* Independent Pubs. Group.

—One Snowy Night. 2003. (Percy the Park Keeper Ser.). (Illus.). 32p. (J). pap. 11.00 (978-0-00-714693-2(0) , HarperSport) HarperCollins Pubs. Ltd. GBR. *Dist:* Independent Pubs. Group.

Butterworth, Nick. One Snowy Night: Hardback plus DVD. Butterworth, Nick, illus. 2007. (Illus.). 32p. (J). 24.00 (***978-0-00-725942-7(5)***) HarperCollins Pubs. Ltd. GBR. *Dist:* Independent Pubs. Group.

Carle, Eric. Dream Snow. Gauch, Patricia Lee, ed. Carle, Eric, illus. 2000. (Illus.). 32p. (J). (ps-1). 21.99 (978-0-399-23579-5(5) , Philomel) Penguin Group (USA) Inc.

Carlson, Nancy. Harriet & Walt. rev. ed. (Carolrhoda Picture Books Ser.). (Illus.). 32p. (J). (gr. k-2). 2005. 15.95 (978-1-57505-672-2(0)); 2004. pap. (978-1-57505-723-1(9)) Lerner Publishing Group.

Chardiet, Bernice & Maccarone, Grace. The Snowball War. Karas, G. Brian, illus. 1999. (J). (978-0-439-10803-4(9)) Scholastic, Inc.

Charman, Andy. The Snowman They Tried to Ban. Silcock, Sara, illus. 2001. 16p. (ps-k). pap. 5.00 (978-0-7548-0235-8(3)) Anness Publishing, Inc.

Cheng, Andrea. The Lemon Sisters. Mai-Wyss, Tatjana, illus. 2006. 32p. (J). (ps). 16.99 (978-0-399-24023-2(3) , Putnam Juvenile) Penguin Group (USA) Inc.

Child, Lauren. An Extremely Wintery Winter Activity Kit. 2007. 32p. (J). (ps-k). 19.99 (***978-0-8037-3242-1(2)*** , Dial) Penguin Group (USA) Inc.

Christopher, Matt. Snowboard Showdown. 2007. (J). lib. bdg. (***978-1-59953-116-8(X)***) Norwood Hse. Pr.

Clark, Joan. Snow. Denton, Kady MacDonald, illus. 2006. 32p. 16.95 (978-0-88899-712-8(4)) Groundwood Bks. CAN. *Dist:* Perseus Distribution.

Colandro, Lucille. There Was a Cold Lady Who Swallowed Some Snow. Lee, Jared D., illus. 2003. 32p. (J). pap. 5.95 (978-0-439-56703-9(3)); pap. 5.95 (978-0-439-47109-1(5)) Scholastic, Inc. (Cartwheel Bks.).

—There Was a Cold Lady Who Swallowed Some Snow. unabr. ed. 2006. (J). (gr. k-2). pap. 9.95 incl. audio compact disk (978-0-439-89556-9(1)) Scholastic, Inc.

—There Was A Cold Lady Who Swallowed Some Snow -library. 2006. (J). 18.95 (978-0-439-89841-6(2)) Scholastic, Inc.

Cook, Lisa Broadie. Martin MacGregor's Snowman. McCauley, Adam, illus. 2003. 32p. (J). 16.95 (978-0-8027-8858-0(0)) Walker & Co.

Courtin, Thierry. T choupi fait un bonhomme De. 13.95 (978-2-09-202037-1(4)) Nathan, Fernand FRA. *Dist:* Distribooks, Inc.

Courtney, Richard, illus. Thomas Gets a Snowplow. 2004. 24p. (J). (ps-2). 3.99 (978-0-375-82783-9(8) , Random Hse. Bks. for Young Readers) Random Hse. Children's Bks.

Cuyler, Margery. Biggest, Best Snowman, Library Edition. 2007. (J). 18.95 (***978-0-545-01780-0(7)***) Scholastic, Inc.

—Biggest Best Snowman, The (Readalong) 2007. (J). 9.95 (***978-0-545-01484-7(0)***) Scholastic, Inc.

Cuyler, Margery. Bookshelf: Biggest, Best Snowman. Hillenbrand, Will, illus. 1998. (J). (ps-2). pap. 15.95 (978-0-590-13493-4(0)) Scholastic, Inc.

Cuyler, Margery & Hillenbrand, Will. Bookshelf: Biggest, Best Snowman. 1998. (Illus.). 32p. (J). (ps-2). pap. 15.95 (978-0-590-13922-9(3)) Scholastic, Inc.

Dadey, Debbie & Jones, Marcia Thornton. Dragons Don't Throw Snowballs. 2006. (Little Apple Ser.). (Illus.). 80p. (J). pap. 3.99 (978-0-439-79337-7(8) , Scholastic Paperbacks) Scholastic, Inc.

de Beer, Hans. Lars & His Friends: Board Book & Doll. 2004. (Little Polar Bear Story Ser.). (Illus.). 22p. 9.95 (978-1-4027-1341-5(X)) Sterling Publishing Co., Inc.

De La Cour, Gary, illus. & creator. Counting in the Snow. De La Cour, Gary, creator. gif. ed. 2005. 10p. (J). bds. 9.99 (978-1-57791-186-9(5)) Brighter Minds Children's Publishing.

deGroat, Diane. Jingle Bells, Homework Smells. 2000. (gr. k-3). lib. bdg. 14.15 (978-0-613-68435-4(4)) Tandem Library Bks.

Denslow, Sharon Phillips. In the Snow. Tafuri, Nancy, illus. 2005. 40p. (J). 15.99 (978-0-06-059683-5(X)); lib. bdg. 16.89 (978-0-06-059684-2(8)) HarperCollins Pubs.

DePrisco, Dorothea. Snowbear's Winter Day: A Winter Wonder Book. Fehlau, Dagmar, illus. 2005. 18p. (J). (ps). 9.95 (978-1-58117-133-4(1) , Intervisual/Piggy Toes) Dalmatian Pr.

Diviny, Sean. Snow Inside the House. Rocco, Joe, illus. 1998. 32p. (J). (ps-3). 14.95 (978-0-06-027354-5(2)) HarperCollins Pubs.

DiVito, Anna. Annie Oakley Saves the Day. DiVito, Anna, illus. ed. 2005. (Illus.). 32p. (J). lib. bdg. 15.00 (978-1-59054-939-1(2)) Fitzgerald Bks.

Dooley, Norah. Everybody Serves Soup. Thornton, Peter J., illus. 2004. (Picture Bks.). 40p. (J). (ps-3). 15.95 (978-1-57505-422-3(1)); pap. 6.95 (978-1-57505-791-0(3)) Lerner Publishing Group.

Downey, Glen. Ice Journey. Brucker, Glenn, illus. 2007. 48p. (J). lib. bdg. 23.08 (***978-1-4242-1618-5(4)***) Fitzgerald Bks.

Downey, Lynn. Papa's Birthday Gift. Schuett, Stacey, tr. Schuett, Stacey, illus. 2004. 32p. (J). 16.99 (978-0-8066-4557-5(1) , Augsburg Bks.) Augsburg Fortress, Pubs.

Earhart, Kristin, ed. Lost in the Snow. 2006. (Magic School Bus Science Reader Ser.). 32p. (J). pap. 3.99 (978-0-439-56990-3(7) , Cartwheel Bks.) Scholastic, Inc.

Eastman, P. D. & McKee, R. Snow. 1998. 4.99 (978-0-679-89246-5(X) , Random Hse. Bks. for Young Readers) Random Hse. Children's Bks.

Ehlert, Lois. Snowballs. Ehlert, Lois, illus. 2002. (Illus.). (J). 14.04 (978-0-7587-3648-2(7)) Book Wholesalers, Inc.

—Snowballs. Ehlert, Lois, illus. 2001. (Illus.). 26p. (J). (ps up). bds. 6.95 (978-0-15-216275-7(5) , Red Wagon Bks.) Harcourt Children's Bks.

—Snowballs. 1999. (Illus.). 36p. (J). (ps-3). pap. 7.00 (978-0-15-202095-8(0) , Voyager Bks./Libros Viajeros) Harcourt Children's Bks.

—Snowballs. 1999. (gr. k-3). lib. bdg. 15.30 (978-0-613-22939-5(8)) Tandem Library Bks.

Emerson, Alice B. Ruth Fielding at Snow Camp: Or, Lost in the Backwoods. 2006. 134p. pap. 10.99 (***978-1-4264-5024-2(9)***), 144p. pap. 13.99 (***978-1-4264-5325-0(6)***) BiblioBazaar.

Emmett, Jonathan. Diamond in the Snow. Cabban, Vanessa, illus. 2006. 32p. (J). (ps-1). 15.99 (978-0-7636-3117-8(5)) Candlewick Pr.

Erickson, Betty. Where's the Snow? Power, Kate Eason, illus. 1999. 12p. (J). (ps-2). pap. 3.75 (978-1-880612-87-3(9) , Seedling Pubns.) Continental Pr., Inc.

Fallon, Jimmy. Snowball Fight! Stower, Adam, illus. 2005. 32p. (J). (ps). 15.99 (978-0-525-47456-2(0) , Dutton Juvenile) Penguin Group (USA) Inc.

Farnes, Catherine. Snow. 1999. (YA). (gr. 9 up). 6.49 (978-1-57924-199-5(9) , 117275) Jones, Bob Univ. Pr.

Feldman, Estelle. Snowy Winter Day. Demarest, Chris L., illus. 2002. (Rhyme Time Readers Ser.). 32p. (J). 3.99 (978-0-439-33401-3(2)) Scholastic, Inc.

Fenner, Carol. Snowed in with Grandmother Silk. Harvey, Amanda, illus. 2005. 80p. (J). (gr. 2). pap. 6.99 (978-0-14-240472-0(1) , Puffin) Penguin Group (USA) Inc.

Figueredo, D. H. Un Mundo Nuevo. de la Vega, Eida, tr. from ENG. Sanchez, Enrique O., illus. 2000. (SPA & ENG.). 32p. (J). (gr. k-2). 15.95 (978-1-58430-006-9(X) , LW2987); pap. 6.95 (978-1-58430-007-6(8) , LW3110) Lee & Low Bks., Inc.

—Un Mundo Nuevo. Sanchez, Enrique O., illus. 2000. (SPA.). (J). (978-0-606-19833-2(4)); (978-0-606-19834-9(2)) Tandem Library Bks.

—When This World Was New. Sanchez, Enrique O., illus. 2003. (J). pap. 6.95 (978-1-58430-173-8(2)); 1999. 32p. (YA). 12.76 (978-1-880000-86-1(5)) Lee & Low Bks., Inc.

—When This World Was New. 2003. (gr. k-3). lib. bdg. 15.25 (978-0-613-83688-3(X)) Tandem Library Bks.

Ford, Bernette G. First Snow. Braun, Sebastien, illus. 2005. 32p. (J). (***978-0-9547373-3-7(4)***) Boxer Bks., Ltd.

S

—First Snow. Braun, Sebastien, illus. 2005. 32p. (J). (ps-ps). 16.95 (978-0-8234-1937-1(1)) Holiday Hse., Inc.

Ford, Christine. Snow! Whitman, Candace, illus. 1999. (Growing Tree Ser.). 24p. (J). (ps up). 9.95 (978-0-694-01199-5(1) , Harper Festival) HarperCollins Pubs.

Freeman, Don. Corduroy's Snow Day. McCue, Lisa, illus. 2005. 16p. (J). pap. 5.99 (978-0-670-06046-7(1) , Viking Juvenile) Penguin Group (USA) Inc.

French, Vivian. The Snow Dragon. 2003. (Illus.). 32p. (J). pap. 11.99 (978-0-552-54595-2(3)) Transworld Publishers Ltd. GBR. *Dist:* Trafalgar Square Publishing.

Fun in the Snow. 2003. (J). (978-1-932570-13-7(6)) Literacy Footprints Inc.

Gaffney, Sean. Larryboy & the Sinister Snow Day. 2003. (Illus.). 96p. pap. 4.99 (978-0-310-70561-1(4)) Zonderkidz.

Garland, Michael. Christmas Magic. 2003. (Illus.). 32p. (J). (ps-k). pap. 7.99 (978-0-14-250140-5(9) , Puffin) Penguin Group (USA) Inc.

—Christmas Magic. Garland, Michael, illus. 2001. (Illus.). 32p. (J). (ps-2). 16.99 (978-0-525-46797-7(1) , Dutton Juvenile) Penguin Group (USA) Inc.

Gay, Marie-Louise. Estela, Reina de la Nieve. 2002. (SPA.). 32p. (J). pap. (978-980-257-275-5(6)) Ekare, Ediciones.

—Stella, Queen of the Snow. ed. 2004. (J). (ps-1). spiral bd. (978-0-616-08493-9(5)) Canadian National Institute for the Blind/Institut National Canadien pour les Aveugles.

—Stella, Queen of the Snow. Gay, Marie-Louise, illus. 2000. (Stella Ser.). (Illus.). 32p. (J). (ps-k). 15.95 (978-0-88899-404-2(4)) Groundwood Bks. CAN. *Dist:* Perseus Distribution.

—Stella, Reine des Neiges. ed. 2004. (FRE., Illus.). (J). (gr. k-3). spiral bd. (978-0-616-14596-8(9)) Canadian National Institute for the Blind/Institut National Canadien pour les Aveugles.

Gay, Marie-Louise, illus. Stella, Queen of the Snow. braille ed. 2004. (J). (ps-1). spiral bd. (978-0-616-08492-2(7)) Canadian National Institute for the Blind/Institut National Canadien pour les Aveugles.

Gelsey, James. Chill-Out Scooby-Doo. 2007. (Scooby-Doo Video Tie-In Novelization Ser.). 64p. (J). pap. 3.99 ***(978-0-439-91595-3(3))** Scholastic, Inc.

Gelsey, James, et al. Chill-Out Scooby-Doo. 2007. (Scooby-Doo 8x8 Video Tie-In Ser.). 24p. (J). pap. 3.99 ***(978-0-439-91597-7(X))** Scholastic, Inc.

George, Jean Craighead. Snowboard Twist. Minor, Wendell, illus. 2004. (Outdoor Adventures Ser.). 32p. (J). 15.99 (978-0-06-050595-0(8)) HarperCollins Pubs.

George, Lindsay B. In the Snow: Who's Been Here? George, Lindsay B., illus. 1999. (Illus.). 48p. (J). (ps-3). pap. 7.99 (978-0-688-17056-1(0) , Harper Trophy) HarperCollins Pubs.

—In the Snow: Who's Been Here? 1999. (ps-2). lib. bdg. 15.30 (978-0-613-22874-9(X)) Tandem Library Bks.

Gerber, Carole. Baa Baa Black Sheep. Husted, Marty, illus. 2004. 26p. (J). bds. 6.95 (978-1-58089-089-2(X)) Charlesbridge Publishing, Inc.

—Blizzard. Husted, Marty, illus. 2001. (J). pap. (978-1-58089-065-6(2)); 15.95 (978-1-58089-064-9(4)) Charlesbridge Publishing, Inc.

Gershator, Phillis. When It Starts to Snow. Matje, Martin, illus. rev. ed. 2001. 32p. (J). (ps-2). pap. 7.95 (978-0-8050-6765-1(5) , Holt, Henry & Co. Bks. For Young Readers) Holt, Henry & Co.

—When It Starts to Snow. 2001. (ps-2). lib. bdg. 15.25 (978-0-613-51425-5(4)) Tandem Library Bks.

Gilbert in the Snow. 2005. (J). (978-1-58453-297-2(1)) Pioneer Valley Educational Pr., Inc.

Gilman, Phoebe. Jillian Jiggs & the Great Big Snow. ed. 2004. (Illus.). (J). (gr. k-3). spiral bd. (978-0-616-14582-1(9)); spiral bd. (978-0-616-14583-8(7)) Canadian National Institute for the Blind/Institut National Canadien pour les Aveugles.

Ginolfi, Arthur. Tiny Snowflake Picture Book. Max, Louise Reinoehl, illus. 2003. 32p. (J). 7.99 (978-1-4003-0205-5(0)) Nelson, Thomas Inc.

Golden Books Staff. Frosty the Snowman. 2001. bds. 3.99 (978-0-307-16614-2(7) , Golden Bks.) Random Hse. Children's Bks.

—It's Snow Place Like Home. 2001. 32p. (J). (ps-3). pap. 4.99 (978-0-307-27621-6(X) , Golden Bks.) Random Hse. Children's Bks.

Good, Merle. Reuben & the Blizzard. Moss, P. Buckley, illus. 2003. (Reuben Ser.). 32p. (J). (gr. k-3). 7.95 (978-1-56148-375-4(3)) Good Bks.

Gore, Leonid. Danny's First Snow. Gore, Leonid, illus. 2007. 40p. (J). (ps-2). 16.99 (978-1-4169-1330-6(0)) Simon & Schuster Children's Publishing.

Gott, Barry, illus. Please Let It Snow! 2006. (I'm Going to Read Ser.). 32p. (J). pap. 3.95 (978-1-4027-3090-0(X)) Sterling Publishing Co., Inc.

Grizzell, Larry. What Would You Like to Do Today? Fun in the Snow. 2006. (Illus.). 30p. (J). 16.95 (978-0-9759542-1-8(0)) Adventures Galore.

Haddon, Mark. The Ice Bear's Cave. Axtell, David, illus. 2002. 30p. (J). (gr. k-2). pap. 9.99 (978-0-00-664628-0(X)) HarperCollins Pubs. Ltd. GBR. *Dist:* Trafalgar Square Publishing.

Hader, Berta H. The Big Snow. Hader, Berta H., illus. 2002. (Illus.). (J). 15.49 (978-0-7587-0041-4(5)) Book Wholesalers, Inc.

Hader, Berta H. & Hader, Elmer. The Big Snow. Hader, Berta H. & Hader, Elmer, illus. 3rd ed. 2005. (Stories to Go! Ser.). (Illus.). 48p. (J). 4.99 (978-0-689-87826-8(5) , Aladdin) Simon & Schuster Children's Publishing.

Hall, Kirsten. The Big Sled Race. Burnett, Lindy, illus. 2003. (Hello Reader! Ser.). (J). pap. 3.99 (978-0-439-32104-4(2)) Scholastic, Inc.

Halpern, Julie. Toby & the Snowflakes. Cordell, Matthew R., illus. 2004. 32p. (J). (gr. k-3). tchr. ed. 15.00 (978-0-618-42004-9(5)) Houghton Mifflin Co. Trade & Reference Div.

Hanson, Bonnie Compton. Lost on Monster Mountain. 2004. (Ponytail Girls Ser.). (Illus.). 208p. (J). pap. 7.99 (978-1-58411-031-6(7) , Legacy Pr.) Rainbow Pubs. & Legacy Pr.

Harcourt School Publishers Staff. The Path: On Level. 3rd ed. 2002. (Trophies Reading Program Ser.). (Illus.). (J). pap. 4.10 (978-0-15-322980-0(2)) Harcourt Schl. Pubs.

Hargreaves, Roger. Mr. Snow. 1999. (Mr. Men & Little Miss Ser.). 32p. (J). (gr. k). pap. 3.99 (978-0-8431-7502-8(8) , Price Stern Sloan) Penguin Group (USA) Inc.

—Mr Snow. 1999. (ps-2). lib. bdg. 10.65 (978-0-613-22022-4(6)) Tandem Library Bks.

Harper, Piers, illus. Snow Bear's Surprise. 2004. 32p. (J). (978-1-4050-4883-5(2)) Macmillan Publishers Ltd.

Harshman, Marc. Snow Company. Bowman, Leslie, illus. 2002. 32p. (J). per. 6.95 (978-1-891852-22-0(1)) Quarrier Pr.

Hedrick, Georgia. Cloud Woman: The Story of Snow. 2002. 26p. (J). cd-rom 10.95 (978-0-9706612-6-5(6)) JetKor.

Heigh, Stephen. The Snowman in the Moon. Burton, Kevin, ed. Heigh, Stephen, illus. 2005. (Illus.). 32p. (J). 16.95 (978-0-9745715-5-3(5)) KRBY Creations, LLC.

Heller, Ruth. Snowflakes. 1998. (Ruth Heller's Stained Glass Designs for Coloring Ser.). (Illus.). 32p. (J). (ps-3). pap. 6.99 (978-0-448-41854-4(1) , Grosset & Dunlap) Penguin Group (USA) Inc.

Hendry, Diana. The Very Snowy Christmas. Chapman, Jane, illus. 32p. (J). 2007. pap. 6.95 ***(978-1-58925-406-0(6));** 2005. 15.95 (978-1-58925-051-2(6)) ME Media LLC. (tiger tales).

Henkes, Kevin. Oh! Dronzek, Laura, illus. 1999. 24p. (J). (ps-k). 16.99 (978-0-688-17053-0(6)) HarperCollins Pubs.

Herman, Gail. The Icicle Forest. 2000. (Fairy School Ser.). (Illus.). (J). 10.79 (978-0-606-21633-3(2)) Tandem Library Bks.

High, Linda Oatman. City of Snow: The Great Blizzard Of 1888. Filippucci, Laura Francesca, illus. 2004. 32p. (J). 17.85 (978-0-8027-8911-2(0)); 16.95 (978-0-8027-8910-5(2)) Walker & Co.

Hillert, Margaret. The Snow Baby. Dauber, Liz, illus. rev. exp. ed. 2007. (J). lib. bdg. (978-1-59953-045-1(7)) Norwood Hse. Pr.

El Hombrecito de las Nieves 8: Leveled Books. 2001. (McGraw-Hill. Lectura Ser.). (ENG & SPA.). (gr. 2 up). (978-0-02-188033-1(6)) Macmillan/McGraw-Hill Schl. Div.

Howell, Gill. Snow King. Cann, Helen, illus. 2005. 24p. (J). lib. bdg. 22.65 ***(978-1-59646-742-2(8))** Dingles & Co.

Hubbell, Will. Snow Day Dance. Hubbell, Will, illus. 2005. (Illus.). 32p. (J). (gr. 5-8). 16.95 (978-0-8075-7523-9(2)) Whitman, Albert & Co.

Hudson, Cheryl Willis. What Do You Know? Snow! Walker, Sylvia, illus. 2004. 32p. (J). (ps-ps). lib. bdg. 10.79 (978-0-606-30031-5(7)) Tandem Library Bks.

Hudson, Cheryl Willis. What Do You Know? SNOW! Walker, Sylvia, illus. 2004. 32p. (J). lib. bdg. 15.00 ***(978-1-4242-0233-1(7))** Fitzgerald Bks.

Huneck, Stephen. Sally's Snow Adventure. 2006. (Illus.). 32p. (J). (ps-3). 15.95 (978-0-8109-7061-8(9)) Abrams, Harry N., Inc.

Hutchins, Hazel J. Ben's Snow Song: A Winter Picnic. ed. 2004. (Illus.). (J). (gr. k-3). spiral bd. (978-0-616-01677-0(8)) Canadian National Institute for the Blind/Institut National Canadien pour les Aveugles.

—Norman's Snowball. Ohi, Ruth, illus. 2003. 24p. (J). (ps-k). (Toddler Ser.). 12.95 (978-1-55037-053-9(7)); (Toddler Ser.). pap. 4.95 (978-1-55037-050-8(2)); (Annikins Ser.: Vol. 15). pap. 1.25 (978-1-55037-494-0(X)) Annick Pr., Ltd. CAN. *Dist:* Firefly Bks., Ltd.

Inkpen, Mick. Kipper's Snowy Day. Inkpen, Mick, illus. 2002. (Kipper Ser.). (Illus.). (J). 13.15 (978-0-7587-2935-4(9)) Book Wholesalers, Inc.

—Kipper's Snowy Day. 1999. (978-0-606-17488-6(5)) Tandem Library Bks.

Isadora, Rachel. Mr. Moon. Date not set. (J). 15.99 (978-0-06-029821-0(9)); lib. bdg. 16.89 (978-0-06-029822-7(7)) HarperCollins Pubs.

Jenkins, Barbie. The Legend of Christmas Kiss. 2005. 32p. 13.99 (978-1-4165-3382-5(6) , Howard Bks.) Simon & Schuster.

Johnson, Andi. Hailey Snowstorm. 2004. (Illus.). 16p. 9.00 (978-1-84161-113-6(1)) Ravette Publishing, Ltd. GBR. *Dist:* Parkwest Pubns., Inc.

Johnson, David. Snow Sounds: An Onomatopoeic Story. 2006. (Illus.). 32p. (J). (gr. k-3). 16.00 (978-0-618-47310-6(6)) Houghton Mifflin Co.

Johnson, Tiffany Kira. Why Snow Falls in Winter. 2006. pap. 8.95 (978-0-533-15149-3(X)) Vantage Pr., Inc.

Jones, Jennifer Berry. Who Lives in the Snow? Powell, Consie, illus. 2001. 32p. (ps-5). 16.95 (978-1-57098-287-3(2)) Rinehart, Roberts Pubs.

Joosse, Barbara M. Snow Day! Plecas, Jennifer, illus. 1999. 32p. (J). (gr. k-3). pap. 5.95 (978-0-395-96890-1(9) , Clarion Bks.) Houghton Mifflin Co. Trade & Reference Div.

Joyce, William. Snowie Rolie. Joyce, William, illus. (Rolie Polie Olie Ser.). (Illus.). 40p. (J). 2005. pap. 5.99 (978-0-06-443742-4(6) , Harper Trophy); 2000. 15.95 (978-0-06-029285-0(7) , Geringer, Laura Book); 2000. 15.89 (978-0-06-029286-7(5) , Geringer, Laura Book) HarperCollins Pubs.

Kasischke, Laura. White Bird in a Blizzard. 1999. 249p. 22.95 (978-0-7868-6366-2(8)) Hyperion Pr.

Kauflin, Chris. Smiletown's Big Snow Day. 2006. (J). per. 14.95 (978-0-9785132-0-7(7) , Smiletown Bks.) Smile-a-Lot, LLP.

Keats, Ezra Jack. The Snowy Day. Keats, Ezra Jack, illus. 2002. (Illus.). (J). 12.40 (978-0-7587-0027-8(X)) Book Wholesalers, Inc.

—The Snowy Day. 2000. (J). pap. 19.97 incl. audio (978-0-7366-9215-1(0)) Books on Tape, Inc.

—The Snowy Day; Un Dia de Nieve, 2 bks. Keats, Ezra Jack, illus. unabr. ed. 1999. (ENG & SPA., Illus.). (J). (gr. k-3). pap. 33.95 incl. audio (978-0-87499-563-3(9)) Live Oak Media.

Keats, Ezra Jack. The Snowy Day/Whistle for Willie DVD & Book Gift Set. 2007. 64p. (J). (gr. 12). 19.99 ***(978-0-670-06253-9(7)** , Viking Juvenile) Penguin Group (USA) Inc.

Kirk, Daniel. Snow Dude. 2004. (Illus.). 32p. (ps-3). 16.99 (978-0-7868-1942-3(1)) Hyperion Bks. for Children.

Kneen, Maggie. The Christmas Surprise. Kneen, Maggie, illus. 2006. (Illus.). 32p. (J). (gr. k-4). reprint ed. 16.00 (978-0-7567-9837-6(X)) DIANE Publishing Co.

Kroll, Virginia L. Good Citizen Sarah. Cote, Nancy, illus. 2007. (Way I ACT Books). 24p. (J). (gr. 1-4). 15.95 ***(978-0-8075-2992-8(3))** Whitman, Albert & Co.

Labatt, Mary. Sam's Snowy Day. Sarrazin, Marisol, illus. 2005. 32p. (J). lib. bdg. 10.00 ***(978-1-4242-1155-5(7))** Fitzgerald Bks.

—Sam's Snowy Day. Sarrazin, Marisol, illus. 2005. (Kids Can Start to Read Ser.). 32p. (J). (ps-ps). (978-1-55337-790-0(7)) Kids Can Pr., Ltd.

Lakin, Patricia. Max & Mo Make a Snowman. Floca, Brian, illus. 2007. (Ready-to-Reads Ser.). 32p. (J). lib. bdg. 13.89 ***(978-1-4169-2538-5(4));** pap. 3.99 ***(978-1-4169-2537-8(6))** Simon & Schuster Children's Publishing. (Aladdin).

Lakin, Patricia. Snow Day! Nash, Scott, illus. 2002. 32p. (J). (ps-2). 15.99 (978-0-8037-2642-0(2) , Dial) Penguin Group (USA) Inc.

Laminack, Lester L. Snow Day! 2007. 32p. (J). (ps-3). 16.95 ***(978-1-56145-418-1(4)** , Peachtree Junior) Peachtree Pubs., Ltd.

Landry, Leo. The Snow Ghosts. Landry, Leo, illus. 2003. (Illus.). 32p. (J). (ps-3). tchr. ed. 9.95 (978-0-618-19655-5(2)) Houghton Mifflin Co. Trade & Reference Div.

Law, Felicia. The Snowflakes. Philpott, Claire & Radford, Karen, illus. 2007. (J). (978-1-4048-2597-0(5)) Picture Window Bks.

LeBlanc, Anne & Sterling Publishing Company Staff. Benjamin in the Snow. 1999. (Adventures with Benjamin Bear Ser.). (Illus.). 20p. (ps-k). 4.95 (978-0-8069-1931-7(0)) Sterling Publishing Co., Inc.

Lee, Huy Voun, ed. In the Snow. rev. ed. 2000. (Illus.). 32p. (J). (ps). pap. 7.95 (978-0-8050-6579-4(2) , Holt, Henry & Co. Bks. For Young Readers) Holt, Henry & Co.

Lee, Huy Voun, ed. In the Snow. 2000. (Illus.). (J). (ps-ps). lib. bdg. 15.25 (978-0-613-30516-7(7)) Tandem Library Bks.

Legacy, Esther. Where the Snowman Lives. Legacy, Esther, illus. 1998. (Illus.). 15p. (J). (ps). pap. 3.95 (978-0-9667332-0-4(7)) Legacy, Esther.

Lemieux, Jean & Casson, Sophie. Le Bonheur Est une Tempête Avec un Chien. 2002. (Premier Roman Ser.). (FRE., Illus.). 64p. pap. (978-2-89021-568-9(7)) Diffusion du livre Mirabel.

Lewis, Anthony, illus. Little Snow Explorers. 2007. 14p. bds. 7.99 ***(978-1-84643-037-4(2))** Child's Play International Ltd. GBR. *Dist:* Child's Play-International.

Lewison, Wendy Cheyette. Big Snowball. 2000. (All Aboard Reading Ser.). 10.79 (978-0-606-20402-6(4)); (J). (978-0-606-20266-4(8)) Tandem Library Bks.

—The Big Snowball. Cocca-Leffler, Maryann, illus. 2000. (All Aboard Reading Ser.). 32p. (J). (ps-3). pap. 3.99 (978-0-448-42184-1(4) , Grosset & Dunlap) Penguin Group (USA) Inc.

Lin, Grace. Robert's Snow. 2004. (Illus.). 40p. (J). (ps). 15.99 (978-0-670-05911-9(0) , Viking Juvenile) Penguin Group (USA) Inc.

London, Jonathan. Froggy Gets Dressed. 2007. (Puffin Storytime Ser.). 32p. (J). (ps). pap. 9.99 (978-0-14-240870-4(0) , Puffin) Penguin Group (USA) Inc.

Louise, Martha. Why Kings & Queens Don't Wear Crowns. Sevig-Fajardo, Mari Elise, tr. from NOR. Nyhus, Svein, illus. 2005. Orig. Title: Hvorfor de kongelige ikke har krone pa Hodet. 32p. (J). 17.95 (978-1-57534-037-1(2) , CSC 100) Skandisk, Inc.

Lynn, Tracy. Snow. Craft, Kinuko Y., illus. 2005. 224p. (YA). mass mkt. 3.99 (978-1-4169-0518-9(9) , Simon Pulse) Simon & Schuster Children's Publishing.

MacArthur, Nancy. Adventure of the Big Snow. 1998. (J). (gr. 2-4). pap. 3.99 (978-0-590-37209-1(2)) Scholastic, Inc.

—Adventure of the Big Snow. 1998. (J). (978-0-606-12868-1(9)) Tandem Library Bks.

Mahoney, Daniel J. A Really Good Snowman. 2005. (Illus.). 32p. (J). (gr. k-3). 15.00 (978-0-618-47554-4(0) , Clarion Bks.) Houghton Mifflin Co. Trade & Reference Div.

Majestic's Search. 2004. (J). (978-0-615-12544-2(1)) Jadenaila Publishing.

Mantell, Paul. Snow Board Showdown. 2007. 143p. (J). lib. bdg. ***(978-1-59953-109-0(7))** Norwood Hse. Pr.

Mariposa Publishing Inc. Staff. Me Gusta el Invierno! 2003. Tr. of Winter Ice is Nice!. (SPA.). (ps-2). lib. bdg. 11.80 (978-0-613-85121-3(8)) Tandem Library Bks.

Mayer, Mercer. Just a Snowy Vacation. 2001. (ps-2). lib. bdg. 11.00 (978-0-613-53269-3(4)) Tandem Library Bks.

—Little Critter: Just a Snowman. Mayer, Mercer, illus. 2004. (Little Critter Ser.). (Illus.). 24p. (J). (ps-2). pap. 3.99 (978-0-06-053947-4(X) , Harper Festival) HarperCollins Pubs.

—Snow Day. 2002. (Little Critter Ser.). (Illus.). 24p. (J). (ps-k). pap. 3.95 (978-1-57768-805-1(8)) School Specialty Publishing.

—Snow Day. 2002. (gr. k-3). lib. bdg. 11.80 (978-0-613-65135-6(9)) Tandem Library Bks.

Mazer, Harry. Snow Bound. 144p. (YA). (gr. 7 up). pap. 4.99 (978-0-8072-1367-4(5) , Listening Library) Random Hse. Audio Publishing Group.

McClatchy, Lisa & Thompson, Kay. Eloise & the Snowman. Lyon, Tammie, illus. 2006. (Eloise Ser.). 32p. (J). pap. 3.99 (978-0-689-87451-2(0) , Aladdin) Simon & Schuster Children's Publishing.

McCully, Emily Arnold. First Snow. McCully, Emily Arnold, illus. 2004. (Illus.). 32p. (J). (ps-k). 16.99 (978-0-06-623852-4(8)); lib. bdg. 17.89 (978-0-06-623853-1(6)) HarperCollins Pubs.

McDaniels, Preston. A Perfect Snowman. McDaniels, Preston, illus. 2007. 40p. (J). (ps-3). 15.99 ***(978-1-4169-1026-8(3))** Simon & Schuster Children's Publishing.

McGeorge, Constance W. Snow Riders. Whyte, Mary, illus. 1999. 32p. (J). (ps-1). pap. 6.95 (978-0-8118-2464-4(0)) Chronicle Bks. LLC.

McKee, David. Elmer in the Snow. McKee, David, illus. 2004. (Elmer Bks.). (Illus.). 32p. (J). 9.99 (978-0-06-075240-8(8)) HarperCollins Pubs.

McSwigan, Marie. Snow Treasure. 2005. 208p. (J). (gr. 3-6). 10.99 (978-0-525-47626-9(1) , Dutton Juvenile) Penguin Group (USA) Inc.

Medearis, Angela Shelf. Best Friends in the Snow. Wilson-Max, Ken, illus. 2002. (My First Hello Reader! Ser.). 32p. (J). (ps-k). pap. 3.99 (978-0-590-52284-7(1) , Cartwheel Bks.); pap. 3.99 (978-0-439-61912-7(2) , Scholastic, Inc.) Scholastic, Inc.

Meister, Cari. Tiny the Snow Dog. 2001. (gr. k-3). lib. bdg. 11.80 (978-0-613-64426-6(3)) Tandem Library Bks.

Melling, David. The Tale of Jack Frost. 2003. (Illus.). 32p. (J). 14.95 (978-0-7641-5675-5(6)) Barron's Educational Series, Inc.

Mercer, Lynn. Schubert's Snowflakes. 2002. (Illus.). 32p. (J). (gr. k-3). pap. 12.95 (978-0-9535413-6-2(3)) iynx publishing GBR. *Dist:* Dufour Editions, Inc.

Metzger, Steve. Let's Go Sledding! Wilhelm, Hans, illus. 2002. (Dinofours Ser.). (J). (ps-1). pap. 3.25 (978-0-439-29571-0(8)) Scholastic, Inc.

Meyer, Marianne. Snow Problem: The Case of the Mushing Madness. 1998. (Kinetic City Super Crew: No. 9). (Illus.). 160p. (gr. 4-7). pap. 4.25 (978-0-07-006693-9(0) , 9780070066939) McGraw-Hill Cos., The.

Milbourne, Anna. The Snowy Day. Temporin, Elena, illus. 2007. (J). ***(978-0-439-88988-9(X))** Scholastic, Inc.

Mills, Charles. Storm on Shadow Mountain. 2003. 127p. (J). (978-0-8163-1993-0(6)) Pacific Pr. Publishing Assn.

Mitchell, Robin & Steedman, Judith, illus. Snowy & Chinook. 2005. 32p. (J). 15.95 (978-0-9688768-9-3(7)) Simply Read Bks. CAN. *Dist:* Perseus Distribution.

Mitra, Annie. Chloe the Cat Snowy Day. 1998. (Chloe Weather Board Bks.). (Illus.). 16p. pap. 5.95 (978-1-86233-046-7(8)) Sterling Publishing Co., Inc.

MJ Illustrations Staff, illus. Snow Princess. 2006. (Strawberry Shortcake Ser.). 16p. (J). (ps-1). pap. 4.99 (978-0-448-44410-9(0) , Grosset & Dunlap) Penguin Group (USA) Inc.

Monks, Lydia. Ooo, Ooo, Ooo, Gorilla! 2008. (Illus.). 32p. (J). pap. 9.95 ***(978-1-4052-2754-4(0))** Egmont Bks., Ltd. GBR. *Dist:* Independent Pubs. Group.

Moscovich, Rotem & Saric, Lazar. Curious George Snowy Day. 2007. (Illus.). 24p. (J). (gr. k-ps). 3.99 ***(978-0-618-80043-8(3))** Houghton Mifflin Co.

Moskin, Marietta D. Day of the Blizzard. 1999. (J). 1.50 (978-0-590-30092-6(X)) Scholastic, Inc.

Moulton, Mark Kimball. A Snowman Named Just Bob. Crouch, Karen Hillard, illus. 2003. 36p. (J). 14.95 (978-0-8249-5860-2(8) , 53876801) Ideals Pubns.

—A Snowman Named Just Bob. Crouch, Karen Hillard, illus. 1999. 32p. (J). pap. 18.00 (978-0-7412-0283-3(2)) Lang Graphics, Ltd.

Nagel, Karen B. Snow? Let's Go! Croll, Carolyn, illus. 2000. (My First Hello Reader! Ser.). 32p. (J). (ps-1). pap. 3.99 (978-0-439-09906-6(4)) Scholastic, Inc.

—Snow? Let's Go! 2000. (Hello Reader! Ser.). (J). (978-0-606-19613-0(7)) Tandem Library Bks.

Nash, Margaret. The Best Snowman. Saupe, Jorg, illus. 2004. (Read-It! Readers Ser.). 32p. (C). (gr. k-3). 18.60 (978-1-4048-0048-9(4)) Picture Window Bks.

Natti, Susanna, illus. Cam Jansen & the Snowy Day Mystery. 2004. (Cam Jansen Ser.: No. 24). 64p. (J). (gr. 3-7). 13.99 (978-0-670-05922-5(6) , Viking Juvenile) Penguin Group (USA) Inc.

Obed, Ellen B. A Letter from the Snow. Hammond, Gordon, illus. 1999. 36p. (J). (gr. 1-4). pap. 10.00 (978-0-9618592-8-2(8)) Maine Writers & Pubs. Alliance.

O'Connell, Matthew J. The Adventures of Rick Cliff: The Almost Great Penguin Race. 2004. 80p. (J). pap. 6.95 ***(978-1-932560-66-4(1)** , Llumina Pr.) Media Creations, Inc.

O'Connor, Jane & Schindler, S. D. The Snow Globe Family. 2006. (Illus.). 40p. (J). (ps-3). 16.99 (978-0-399-24242-7(2)) Penguin Group (USA) Inc.

O'Day, Joseph E. I Like Snow! Foster, Ron, illus. 2006. 28p. (J). pap. ***(978-1-929039-37-1(9))** Ambassador Bks., Inc.

O'Malley, Kevin. Straight to the Pole. (Illus.). 32p. (J). (gr. k-2). 2004. 15.95 (978-0-8027-8866-5(1)); 2004. 16.85 (978-0-8027-8868-9(8)); 2006. reprint ed. pap. 6.95 (978-0-8027-9570-0(6)) Walker & Co.

Orleans, Daniel Elliot. Snow Buddies. 2007. (Illus.). 14p. (ps). bds. 9.95 ***(978-1-59354-605-2(X))** Blue Apple Bks.

Paradise, Susan. Snow Princess. 2005. (Illus.). 32p. (J). (ps-3). 16.95 (978-1-932425-31-4(4) , Lemniscaat) Boyds Mills Pr.

Parvensky Barwell, Catherine A. Tommi's First Snowfall, 4 vols. 2006. (Illus.). 32p. (J). (978-0-9774409-1-7(5) , TL002) ILT Publishing.

Pearson, Mary E. Puedo Hacer de Todo. Shelly, Jeff, illus. rev. ed. 2002. (Rookie Readers - Spanish Ser.).Tr. of I Can Do It All. (SPA.). 32p. (J). (gr. k-2). 19.50 (978-0-516-22683-5(5) , Children's Pr.) Scholastic Library Publishing.

—Puedo Hacer de Todo. 2002. Tr. of I Can Do It All. (gr. k-3). lib. bdg. 12.95 (978-0-613-59542-1(4)) Tandem Library Bks.

—Yo, la Generosa. Krejca, Gary, illus. 2002. (Rookie Espanol Ser.).Tr. of Generous Me. (SPA.). 32p. (J). (gr. k-2). 19.50 (978-0-516-22682-8(7) , Children's Pr.) Scholastic Library Publishing.

—Yo, la Generosa. 2002. Tr. of Generous Me. (gr. k-3). lib. bdg. 12.95 (978-0-613-59557-5(2)) Tandem Library Bks.

Peck, M. Scott & Ariel Books. The Friendly Snowflake: A Fable of Faith, Love & Family. 2001. (Illus.). 64p. 9.95 (978-0-7407-1882-3(7)) Andrews McMeel Publishing.

Perkins, Lynne Rae. Snow Music. Perkins, Lynne Rae, illus. 2003. (Illus.). 40p. (J). 15.99 (978-0-06-623956-9(7)); lib. bdg. 16.89 (978-0-06-623958-3(3)) HarperCollins Pubs.

—Snow Music. 2000. pap. 4.95 (978-0-06-443875-9(9)) HarperCollins Pubs.

Perkins, Nicole D. I Wish for Snow. Ogene, Chuma C., illus. 2005. (J). per. 19.95 (978-0-9755566-0-3(6)) Azreal Publishing Co.

Plourde, Lynn & Takahashi, Hideko. Snow Day. 2001. (Illus.). 32p. (J). 16.00 (978-0-689-82600-9(1)) Simon & Schuster Children's Publishing.

Poydar, Nancy. Snip, Snip...Snow! Poydar, Nancy, illus. 2002. (Illus.). (J). 15.47 (978-0-7587-3644-4(4)) Book Wholesalers, Inc.

Preller, James. The Case of the Snowboarding Superstar. 2006. (Jigsaw Jones Ser.: No. 29). (Illus.). 80p. (J). pap. 3.99 (978-0-439-79395-7(5) , Scholastic Paperbacks) Scholastic, Inc.

Pulver, Robin. Axle Annie. Kane, Cindy, ed. 1999. (Illus.). 32p. (J). (ps-3). 15.99 (978-0-8037-2096-1(3) , Dial) Penguin Group (USA) Inc.

Rader, Laura, illus. I Hate Boots! 2005. (I'm Going to Read Ser.). 24p. (J). (ps-ps). pap. 3.95 (978-1-4027-2093-2(9)) Sterling Publishing Co., Inc.

Regan, Dana. Penguin's Big Hill. 2002. (Rhyme Time Readers Ser.). (Illus.). 32p. (J). (978-0-439-44161-2(7)) Scholastic, Inc.

Remkiewicz, Frank, illus. Froggy Gets Dressed. 2002. (Froggy Ser.). (J). 13.19 (978-0-7587-2550-9(7)) Book Wholesalers, Inc.

Rey, Margret & Rey, H. A. Curious George in the Snow. 1998. (Curious George Ser.). (Illus.). 24p. (J). (gr. k-3). tchr. ed. 12.00 (978-0-395-91902-6(9)) Houghton Mifflin Co. Trade & Reference Div.

Roche, Hannah. Su's Snowgirl. 1998. (My First Weather Bks.). (Illus.). 24p. (J). (ps-3). (978-1-84089-034-1(7) , Zero to Ten, Limited) Evans Publishing Group.

Rockhill, Dennis. Polar Slumber. Rockhill, Dennis, illus. 2006. 32p. (J). (gr. k-3). pap. 16.95 (978-0-9741992-8-3(1)) Raven Tree Pr.

Rogan, John. The Biggest Snowball Ever. 1999. (978-0-606-22306-5(1)) Tandem Library Bks.

Rohmann, Eric. A Kitten Tale. 2008. (J). ***(978-0-517-70915-3(5));*** lib. bdg. ***(978-0-517-70916-0(3))*** Knopf, Alfred A. Inc.

Root, Phyllis. Grandmother Winter. Krommes, Beth, illus. 32p. (J). (gr. k-3). 1999. tchr. ed. 16.00 (978-0-395-88399-0(7)); 2004. reprint ed. pap. 5.95 (978-0-618-49485-9(5)) Houghton Mifflin Co. Trade & Reference Div.

Ross, Christine Johanson. A Snowflake Dream. 2001. (gr. k-3). lib. bdg. 28.00 (978-0-613-74534-5(5)) Tandem Library Bks.

Ruelle, Karen Gray. The Crunchy, Munchy Christmas Tree. Ruelle, Karen Gray, illus. (Holiday House Readers Ser.). (Illus.). 32p. (J). (gr. k-3). tchr. ed. 14.95 (978-0-8234-1787-2(5)) Holiday Hse., Inc.

—Crunchy, Munchy Christmas Tree. (Illus.). 32p. (J). (gr k-3). pap. 4.95 (978-0-8234-1799-5(9)) Holiday Hse., Inc.

—Snow Valentines. (Holiday House Readers Ser.). (Illus.). 48p. (J). (gr. k-3). 4.95 (978-0-8234-1782-7(4)) Holiday Hse., Inc.

Rylant, Cynthia. Snow. Stringer, Lauren, illus. 2007. (J). (978-0-15-205303-1(4)) Harcourt Trade Pubs.

Sabuda, Robert. Winter in White: A Mini Pop-up Treat. Sabuda, Robert, illus. 2007. 18p. (J). 12.99 ***(978-0-689-85365-4(3)*** , Little Simon) Simon & Schuster Children's Publishing.

Sams, Carl R., II & Stoick, Jean. Stranger in the Woods: A Photographic Fantasy. 2002. (gr. 2-5). 12.95 (978-0-9671748-2-2(1)) Sams, II, Carl R. Photography, Inc.

—Stranger in the Woods: A Photographic Fantasy. Sams, Carl R., II & Stoick, Jean, photos by. 1999. (Illus.). 48p. (J). (gr. 2-4). pap. 19.95 (978-0-9671748-0-8(5)) Sams, II, Carl R. Photography, Inc.

Schertle, Alice. All You Need for a Snowman. Lavallee, Barbara, illus. 2007. 32p. (J). pap. 6.00 ***(978-0-15-206115-9(0)*** , Voyager Bks./Libros Viajeros) Harcourt Children's Bks.

—All You Need for a Snowman. Lavallee, Barbara, illus. 2002. 32p. (J). 16.00 (978-0-15-200789-8(X) , Silver Whistle) Harcourt Trade Pubs.

Scholastic, Inc. Staff. Me Gusta el Invierno! Winter Ice Is Nice. Salas, Macarena, ed. 2003. (Clifford Big Red Readers Ser.). (SPA., Illus.). 32p. (J). (ps-k). pap. 3.99 (978-0-439-39523-6(2) , Scholastic en Espanol) Scholastic, Inc.

Scholastic, Inc. Staff. Snow Fun. 2007. (Care Bears Ser.). 24p. (J). pap. 3.99 ***(978-0-545-01310-9(0))*** Scholastic, Inc.

Scholastic, Inc. Staff & Hudson, Cheryl. Just for You! What Do You Know? Snow! Walker, Sylvia, illus. 2004. (Just for You! Ser.). 32p. pap. 3.99 (978-0-439-56851-7(X) , Teaching Resources) Scholastic, Inc.

Scraper, Katherine. Max's Job. 2006. (Early Explorers Ser.). (J). 30.00 ***(978-1-4108-6035-4(3))*** Benchmark Education Co.

Sheeley, Jill. Rescue on Star Mountain. 2000. (Adventures of Fraser the Yellow Dog Ser.). (Illus.). (J). 15.95 (978-0-9609108-6-1(7)) Courtney Pr.

—Rescue on Vail Mountain. 2000. (Adventures of Fraser the Yellow Dog Ser.). (Illus.). (J). 14.95 (978-0-9609108-5-4(9)) Courtney Pr.

Shopping for Snowflakes. (J). pap. 13.75 (978-0-8136-3403-6(2)) Modern Curriculum Pr.

Shulevitz, Uri. Snow. Shulevitz, Uri, illus. 2002. (Illus.). (J). 25.45 (978-0-7587-0144-2(6)) Book Wholesalers, Inc.

—Snow. ed. 2004. (J). (gr. k-3). spiral bd. (978-0-616-01781-4(2)) Canadian National Institute for the Blind/Institut National Canadien pour les Aveugles.

—Snow. Shulevitz, Uri, illus. 1998. (Illus.). 32p. (J). (ps-3). 16.00 (978-0-374-37092-3(3) , Farrar, Straus & Giroux (BYR)) Farrar, Straus & Giroux.

—Snow. 2004. (Illus.). 32p. (J). reprint ed. pap. 5.95 (978-0-374-46862-0(1) , Sunburst) Farrar, Straus & Giroux.

—Snow. Shulevitz, Uri, illus. 2000. (Illus.). 28.95 incl. audio (978-1-59112-354-5(2)) Live Oak Media.

—Snow. 2000. (Illus.). (J). (gr. k-3). 25.95 incl. audio (978-0-87499-627-2(9)) Live Oak Media.

Siddals, Mary McKenna. Millions of Snowflakes. Sayles, Elizabeth, illus. 1998. 32p. (J). (gr. k-ps). tchr. ed. 13.00 (978-0-395-71531-4(8) , Clarion Bks.) Houghton Mifflin Co. Trade & Reference Div.

Sinclair, Michelle Colman. Winter Babies Wear Layers. Dion, Nathalie, illus. 2007. 20p. (J). bds. 6.95 ***(978-1-58246-209-7(7)*** , Tricycle Pr.) Ten Speed Pr.

Slater, Jean M. Wonderful Snow! Slater, Jean M., illus. 2003. (Illus.). 9p. (J). bds. 16.00 (978-0-9743149-1-4(9)) Slater Software. Inc.

Slusser, Janet S. Smokey & the Big Snow. 2003. (Illus.). 32p. (J). per. 15.95 (978-0-9745171-0-0(0)) RiverCreek Bks., Inc.

Snow Treasure. 1999. (J). 9.95 (978-1-56137-285-0(4)) Novel Units, Inc.

Snow Treasure. 1998. (J). (gr. 4). pap. 3.95 (978-0-439-04461-5(8)) Scholastic, Inc.

Snow X-mas. 2004. (J). per. (978-1-57657-384-6(2)) Paradise Pr., Inc.

The Snowy Day. 2001. (J). pap., wbk. ed. (978-1-56137-476-2(8)) Novel Units, Inc.

The Snowy Day. 2004. 29.95 incl. cd-rom (978-1-55592-853-7(6)) Weston Woods Studios, Inc.

Solomon, Harry. The Day Silver Snowed. Solomon, Harry, illus. 2000. (Illus.). 112p. (J). 39.00 (978-0-9630376-1-9(7)) Figure 8 Pr.

Speregen, Devra Newberger. Snow Day! Vincent, Benjamin & DePew, Robert, illus. 2005. (John Deere Lift the Flap Bks.: No. 4). 10p. (J). (ps-1). pap. 11.95 (978-0-7624-2371-2(4) , Running Pr. Kids) Running Pr. Bk. Pubs.

Stainton, Sue. Santa's Snow Kitten. Mortimer, Anne, illus. 2008. (J). ***(978-0-06-082714-4(9));*** lib. bdg. ***(978-0-06-082715-1(7))*** HarperCollins Pubs.

Steinberg, David. The Snow Ball. Conrad, Liz, illus. 2007. 10p. (J). (ps-k). bds. 6.99 ***(978-0-8431-2680-8(9)*** , Price Stern Sloan) Penguin Group (USA) Inc.

Sycamore, Beth. Plow with Airport Plow. Youssi, John, illus. 2003. (Matchbox Ser.). 16p. (J). 6.99 (978-0-689-86200-7(8) , Little Simon) Simon & Schuster Children's Publishing.

Thomas, Peggy. Snow Dance. Facklam, Paul, illus. 2007. 32p. (J). 15.95 ***(978-1-58980-478-4(3))*** Pelican Publishing Co., Inc.

Thompson, Lauren & Erdogan, Buket. Mouse's First Snow. 2005. (Illus.). 32p. (J). 12.95 (978-0-689-85836-9(1)) Simon & Schuster Children's Publishing.

Thomson, Sarah L. Imagine a Night. Gonsalves, Rob, illus. 2003. 40p. (J). 18.99 (978-0-689-85218-3(5) , Atheneum) Simon & Schuster Children's Publishing.

Tibo, Gilles. Simon & the Snowflakes. Tibo, Gilles, illus. 1999. (Simon Ser.). (Illus.). 24p. (J). (ps-1). pap. 4.95 (978-0-88776-274-1(3)) Tundra Bks., Inc./Livres Toundra, Inc. CAN. *Dist:* Random Hse., Inc.

Toast, Sarah & Milne, A. A. Piglet's Not So Small Snowball. Williams, Don, illus. 2002. (Disney's Winnie the Pooh Ser.). (J). (978-0-7853-7617-0(8)) Publications International, Ltd.

Townsend, John. The Omen & the Ghost. Cunningham, Kelley, illus. 2007. (J). 80p. ***(978-1-59889-353-3(X));*** 71p. pap. ***(978-1-59889-448-6(X))*** Stone Arch Bks.

Turner, Barbara F. Charles T. Bear & the Christmas Snow. Turner, Barbara F., illus. 1998. (Illus.). (J). (ps-3). pap. 6.00 (978-1-892614-07-0(3) , SC-CTB-2) Briarwood Pubns.

Tyrell, Melissa. Hurray for Snow! Patrick, Tom, illus. enl. ed. 2005. (Holiday Sparkler Bks.). 10p. (J). (ps-3). 4.95 (978-1-58117-118-1(8) , Intervisual/Piggy Toes) Dalmatian Pr.

Tyrrell, Melissa. Hurray for Snow! A Little Foil Book. 1998. (Merry Little Foil Bks.). (Illus.). 10p. (YA). (ps up). 3.95 (978-1-58117-008-5(4) , Intervisual/Piggy Toes) Dalmatian Pr.

Uhlberg, Myron. Flying over Brooklyn. 2003. (Illus.). 32p. (J). (gr. k-3). pap. 6.95 (978-1-56145-294-1(7)) Peachtree Pubs., Ltd.

—Flying over Brooklyn. Fitzgerald, Gerald, illus. 1999. 32p. (J). (ps-3). 15.95 (978-1-56145-194-4(0)) Peachtree Pubs., Ltd.

Umansky, Kaye. Never Meddle with Magic Mirrors! Voce, Stella, illus. 1998. (Cambridge Reading Ser.). 64p. (gr. 2-6). pap. 12.00 (978-0-521-47627-0(5)) Cambridge Univ. Pr.

Van Leeuwen, Jean. Oliver & Amanda & the Big Snow. Schweninger, Ann, illus. 1998. (Puffin-Easy-to-Read Ser.). 48p. (J). (gr. k-3). pap. 3.99 (978-0-14-038250-1(X) , Puffin) Penguin Group (USA) Inc.

Ventruella, D. J. First Snow: Jeremiah's Christmas. 1999. 118p. (J). pap. 4.95 (978-1-929804-01-6(6) , Compass Special Editions) Compass Publishing Corp.,The.

Vestergaard, Hope. Hello, Snow! Westcott, Nadine Bernard, illus. 2004. 32p. (J). 16.00 (978-0-374-32949-5(4) , Farrar, Straus & Giroux (BYR)) Farrar, Straus & Giroux.

Waddell, Martin. Snow Bears. Fox-Davies, Sarah, illus. 2002. 32p. (J). (ps-1). 14.99 (978-0-7636-1906-0(X)) Candlewick Pr.

Wallace, Nancy Elizabeth, illus. Snow. 2007. 24p. (J). (ps-3). bds. 6.99 ***(978-0-7614-5362-8(8))*** Cavendish, Marshall Corp.

Warner, Gertrude Chandler. Boxcar Children Winter Special. 2007. 376p. (J). pap. 7.95 ***(978-0-8075-0886-2(1))*** Whitman, Albert & Co.

Watt, Fiona. That's Not My Snowman. 2006. 10p. (J). bds. 9.99 (978-0-7945-1414-3(6) , Usborne) EDC Publishing.

Wetterer, Margaret K. & Wetterer, Charles M. The Snow Walker. 2005. (On My Own History Ser.). (Illus.). (J). pap. 18.95 incl. audio compact disk (978-1-59112-669-0(X)) Live Oak Media.

—The Snow Walker. O'Keefe-Young, Mary, illus. unabr. ed. (Historical Fiction Ser.). (J). (gr. 1-6). 24.95 incl. audio (978-0-87499-394-3(6)); 2005. pap. 16.95 incl. audio (978-0-87499-393-6(8)) Live Oak Media.

White Snow, Bright Snow. 2004. pap. 14.95 incl. audio (978-0-7882-0599-6(4)); (J). 24.95 incl. audio (978-1-56008-232-3(1)) Weston Woods Studios, Inc.

Whybrow, Ian. Harry & the Snow King Book & Plush Set. Reynolds, Adrian, illus. 1999. 32p. (J). (ps-2). pap. 19.95 (978-1-86233-132-7(4)) Sterling Publishing Co., Inc.

Wilder, Laura Ingalls. Sugar Snow. Ettlinger, Doris, illus. 1999. (My First Little House Bks.). 32p. (J). (ps-3). pap. 6.99 (978-0-06-443571-0(7) , Harper Trophy) HarperCollins Pubs.

—Sugar Snow. 1999. (gr. k-3). lib. bdg. 14.15 (978-0-613-22459-8(0)) Tandem Library Bks.

Wilhelm, Hans. I Love Snow! 2007. (Scholastic Reader Level 1 Ser.). 32p. (J). pap. 3.99 ***(978-0-439-79594-4(X)*** , Cartwheel Bks.) Scholastic, Inc.

Williams, Rozanne Lanczak. Tess Builds a Snowman. Maio, Barbara & Faulkner, Stacey, eds. Harris, Jenny B., illus. 2006. (J). per. 4.99 ***(978-1-59198-337-8(1))*** Creative Teaching Pr., Inc.

Wood, David. The Toy Cupboard. Fowler, Richard, illus. 2005. 14p. (J). (ps-3). 14.95 (978-1-58117-103-7(X) , Intervisual/Piggy Toes) Dalmatian Pr.

Wood, Francis. The SnowPeople. Larsen, Dan, illus. 2003. 96p. (YA). per. 14.95 (978-0-9746372-0-4(3)) Tip-Of-The-Moon Publishing Co.

Yee, Wong Herbert. Tracks in the Snow. Yee, Wong Herbert, illus. rev. ed. 2003. (Illus.). 32p. (J). 15.95 (978-0-8050-6771-2(X) , Holt, Henry & Co. Bks. For Young Readers) Holt, Henry & Co.

—Tracks in the Snow. 2007. (Illus.). 32p. (J). pap. 6.99 ***(978-0-312-37134-0(9))*** Square Fish.

Yerxa, Leo. Last Leaf First Snowflake fo Fall. Yerxa, Leo, illus. (Illus.). (J). 16.95 (978-0-88899-183-6(5)) Groundwood Bks. CAN. *Dist:* Transition Vendor.

Yoon, Salina. Snowman's Snow Day. 2006. 10p. (J). (ps-k). bds. 5.99 (978-0-8431-2123-0(8) , Price Stern Sloan) Penguin Group (USA) Inc.

Yuji, Iwahara. Chikyu Misaki, Vol. 1. Yuji, Iwahara, illus. 2005. (Illus.). 196p. (YA). pap. 9.99 (978-1-4012-0799-1(5)) DC Comics.

SNOWBOARDING

Barr, Matt & Moran, Chris. Snowboarding. 2004. (Extreme Sports Ser.). (Illus.). 32p. (J). (gr. 3-6). lib. bdg. 22.60 (978-0-8225-1242-4(4)) Lerner Publishing Group.

Brimner, Larry Dane. Snowboarding. 1998. (First Bks.). (Illus.). 64p. (J). (gr. 5-7). pap. 6.95 (978-0-531-15890-6(X) , Watts, Franklin) Scholastic Library Publishing.

—Snowboarding. 1998. (Illus.). 63p. (J). (gr. 5-7). lib. bdg. 15.25 (978-0-613-15167-2(4)) Tandem Library Bks.

Brouwer, Sigmund. Snowboarding . . . to the Extreme: Rippin' 2004. (Illus.). 60p. (YA). pap. 3.99 (978-1-55305-011-7(8)) Cygnet Publishing Group, Inc./Coolreading.com CAN. *Dist:* Orca Bk. Pubs. USA.

Brown, Gillian. Snowboarding. 2003. (gr. 7-12). lib. bdg. 15.25 (978-0-613-59731-9(1)) Tandem Library Bks.

Brown, Gillian C. P. Snowboarding. 2003. (High Interest Bks.). (Illus.). 48p. (J). 24.00 (978-0-516-24322-1(5) , Children's Pr.); (YA). (gr. 7-12). pap. 6.95 (978-0-516-24383-2(7) , Watts, Franklin) Scholastic Library Publishing.

Craats, Rennay. Snowboarding. (J). 2007. ***(978-1-59036-687-5(5));*** 2007. ***(978-1-59036-688-2(3));*** 2001. (Illus.). 24p. lib. bdg. 15.95 (978-1-930954-37-3(9)) Weigl Pubs., Inc.

Curry, Don, ed. On the Edge Skateboarding/on the Edge Snowboarding. 2008. 48p. (J). pap. 6.99 ***(978-0-696-23980-9(9))*** Meredith Bks.

DeGezelle, Terri. Let's Snowboard. 2006. (Pebble Plus Ser.). (Illus.). 24p. (J). 19.93 (978-0-7368-5366-8(9)) Capstone Pr., Inc.

Doeden, Matt. Shaun White. 2007. (Amazing Athletes Ser.). (Illus.). 32p. (J). (gr. 2-4). 23.93 (978-0-8225-6840-7(3) , Lerner Pubns.) Lerner Publishing Group.

—Snowboarding. 2004. (To the Extreme Ser.). (Illus.). 149p. (J). 19.93 (978-0-7368-2731-7(5)) Capstone Pr., Inc.

Eck, Kristin. Snowboarding: Check It Out. 2001. (Reading Power Ser.). (Illus.). 24p. (J). (gr. 1). lib. bdg. 17.25 (978-0-8239-5694-4(6) , PKSNBO, PowerKids Pr.) Rosen Publishing Group, Inc., The.

Eckart, Edana. I Can Snowboard. 2003. (gr. k-3). lib. bdg. 12.95 (978-0-613-59639-8(0)) Tandem Library Bks.

Endres, Hollie. Snowboarding. 2007. (Illus.). 24p. (J). lib. bdg. 19.95 (978-1-60014-128-7(5)) Bellwether Media.

—Snowboarding. 2007. (Torque: Action Sports Ser.). (Illus.). 24p. (J). (gr. 3-7). lib. bdg. 20.00 ***(978-0-531-18495-0(1)*** , Children's Pr.) Scholastic Library Publishing.

Fandel, Jennifer. Snowboarding. 2007. (J). (978-1-58341-470-5(3) , Creative Education) Creative Co., The.

Firestone, Mary. Extreme Snowboard Halfpipe Moves. 2003. (Behind the Moves Ser.). (Illus.). 32p. (J). lib. bdg. 22.60 (978-0-7368-2154-4(6) , Capstone High/Low Bks.) Capstone Pr., Inc.

Fitzpatrick, Jim. Snowboarding. 2008. (J). pap. 7.95 ***(978-1-60279-092-6(2));*** lib. bdg. ***(978-1-60279-018-6(3))*** Cherry Lake Publishing.

Fraser, Andy. Snowboarding. 2002. (Radical Sports Ser.). 32p. (J). (gr. 5-7). pap. 7.50 (978-1-4034-0108-3(X) , 91656) Heinemann Library.

Fraser, Andy, contrib. by. Snowboarding. 1999. (Radical Sports Ser.). (Illus.). 32p. (J). (gr. 5-7). lib. bdg. 24.22 (978-1-57572-946-6(6)) Heinemann Library.

Freimuth, Jeri. Extreme Snowboarding Moves. 2001. (Behind the Moves Ser.). (Illus.). 32p. (J). (gr. 3-4). lib. bdg. 21.26 (978-0-7368-0784-5(5) , Capstone High-Interest Bks.) Capstone Pr., Inc.

Gifford, Clive. Snow Boarding. 2005. (Adrenalin! Ser.). (Illus.). 32p. (J). (gr. 4 up). lib. bdg. 27.10 (978-1-59389-238-8(1)) Chrysalis Education.

—Snowboarding. 2006. (Illus.). 64p. (J). 12.99 (978-0-7566-2559-7(9)) Dorling Kindersley Publishing, Inc.

Gifford, Clive & Dorling Kindersley Publishing Staff. Snowboarding. 2006. (Illus.). 64p. (J). pap. 9.99 (978-0-7566-2560-3(2)) Dorling Kindersley Publishing, Inc.

Gigliotti, Jim. LaDainian Tomlinson. 2008. (World's Greatest Athletes Ser.). 32p. (J). (gr. 1-5). 27.07 ***(978-1-59296-881-7(3))*** Child's World, Inc.

Hayhurst, Chris. Snowboarding! Shred the Powder. 1999. (Extreme Sports Collection). (Illus.). 64p. (YA). (gr. 5-8). lib. bdg. 26.50 (978-0-8239-3010-4(6) , EXSNBO, Rosen Central) Rosen Publishing Group, Inc., The.

—Snowboarding! Shred the Powder. 2000. (Illus.). 64p. (YA). per. 9.95 (978-1-56254-306-8(7) , SP 3067) Saddleback Educational Publishing.

Hedlund, Stephanie F. Snowboarding. 2003. (X-Treme Sports Ser.). (Illus.). 32p. (J). (gr. k-6). lib. bdg. 22.78 (978-1-57765-929-7(5)) ABDO Publishing Co.

Herran, Joe & Thomas, Ron. Snowboarding. 2002. (Action Sports Ser.). (Illus.). 32p. (J). (gr. 4-8). 28.00 (978-0-7910-7003-1(4) , Chelsea Hse.) Facts On File, Inc.

Hughes, Morgan. Snowboarding. 2005. (Junior Sports Ser.). (Illus.). 32p. (gr. 2-4). 19.95 (978-1-59515-190-2(7)) Rourke Publishing, LLC.

Iguchi, Bryan. Jovenes Aficionados al Snowboard (The Young Snowboarder) (SPA.). 38p. (YA). (gr. 2 up). 18.36 (978-84-272-4970-7(5)) Molino, Editorial ESP. *Dist:* Lectorum Pubns., Inc.

Kalman, Bobbie & Crossingham, John. Snowboarding in Action. Rouse, Bonna, illus. 2002. (Sports in Action Ser.). 32p. (J). (gr. 3-4). (978-0-7787-0119-4(0)); pap. (978-0-7787-0125-5(5)) Crabtree Publishing Co.

Kalman, Bobbie & MacAulay, Kelley. Extreme Snowboarding. 2003. (Extreme Sports - No Limits Ser.). (Illus.). 32p. (J). (978-0-7787-1672-3(4)); pap. (978-0-7787-1718-8(6)) Crabtree Publishing Co.

King, Ron S. Rad Boards: Snowboarding & Bodyboarding: The Total Guide to the Cutting Edge. 1999. (J). (978-0-316-49354-3(6)) Little Brown & Co.

Layden, Joe. No Limits: Burton Snowboards' Pro Riders. 2001. (Burton Ser.). 32p. (J). pap. 5.99 (978-0-439-34277-3(5)) Scholastic, Inc.

—No Limits: Burton Snowboards' Pro Riders. 2001. (gr. 3-6). lib. bdg. 14.15 (978-0-613-87084-9(0)) Tandem Library Bks.

Lurie, Jon. Play-by-Play Snowboarding. 2004. (Play-by-Play Ser.). (Illus.). 80p. (J). (gr. 4-8). lib. bdg. 23.93 (978-0-8225-3937-7(3)) Lerner Publishing Group.

—Play-by-Play Snowboarding. Clarke, Jimmy, photos by. 2003. (Play-By-Play Ser.). (Illus.). 80p. (J). (gr. 5 up). pap. 7.95 (978-0-8225-9881-7(7)) Lerner Publishing Group.

—Play-by-Play Snowboarding. 2001. (gr. 3-6). lib. bdg. 16.40 (978-0-613-82393-7(1)) Tandem Library Bks.

Mahaney, Ian F. Kevin Jones: Snowboarding Champion. 2005. (Extreme Sports Biographies Ser.). (Illus.). 24p. (J). 19.95 (978-1-4042-2745-3(8) , PowerKids Pr.) Rosen Publishing Group, Inc., The.

Masoff, Joy. Extreme Sports: Snowboard. 2002. (Illus.). 64p. (J). (gr. 4-9). pap. 8.95 (978-0-7922-6740-9(0) , National Geographic Children's Bks.) National Geographic Society.

—Snowboard! Your Guide to Freeriding, Pipe & Park, Jibbing, Backcountry, Alpine, 2002. (gr. 5-8). lib. bdg. 17.60 (978-0-613-60611-0(6)) Tandem Library Bks.

Mason, Paul. Snowboarding. 2001. (To the Limit Ser.). (Illus.). 32p. (J). (gr. 4-7). lib. bdg. 25.69 (978-0-7398-3164-9(X)) Raintree.

Maurer, Tracy. Snowboarding. 2001. (Radsports Guides). (Illus.). 48p. (J). (gr. 4-8). lib. bdg. 29.93 (978-1-58952-106-3(4)) Rourke Publishing, LLC.

McAuliffe, Bill. Snowboarding. 2002. (Illus.). 32p. (J). lib. bdg. 24.25 (978-1-58340-163-7(6)) Smart Apple Media.

McKenna, Anne T. Big-Air Snowboarding. 1999. (Extreme Sports Ser.). (Illus.). 48p. (J). (gr. 3-4). lib. bdg. 21.26 (978-0-7368-0166-9(9) , Capstone High-Interest Bks.) Capstone Pr., Inc.

S

Miller, Chuck. Snowboarding. 2001. (Extreme Sports Ser.). (Illus.). 48p. (J). lib. bdg. 24.26 (978-0-7398-4690-2(6)) Raintree.

Miller, Connie Colwell. Snowboard Superpipe. 2008. (J). (*978-1-4296-0110-8(8)) Capstone Pr., Inc.

—Snowboarder X. 2008. (J). (*978-1-4296-0111-5(6)) Capstone Pr., Inc.

Morgan, Jed. Snowboarding. 2006. (Illus.). 32p. (J). (978-1-58340-960-2(2)) Smart Apple Media.

Morina, Barbara. Skiing/Snowboarding: A Skiers Journal. Morina, Barbara, ed. 2002. (Write It down Ser.). (Illus.). 202p. (YA). (gr. 2 up). 19.95 (978-1-892033-30-7(5)) Journals Unlimited, Inc.

Murdico, Suzanne J. Snowboarding. 2005. (Rad Sports Techniques & Tricks Ser.). (Illus.). 48p. (YA). (gr. 5-8). lib. bdg. 26.50 (978-0-8239-3849-0(2)) Rosen Publishing Group, Inc., The.

O'Hearn, Michael. Jake Burton Carpenter & the Snowboard. Frenz, Ron & Barnett, Charles, illus. 2007. (Graphic Library). 32p. (J). 25.26 (978-0-7368-6481-7(4)); (*978-0-7368-7516-5(6)) Capstone Pr., Inc.

O'Neal, Claire. Extreme Snowboarding with Lindsey Jacobellis. 2007. (J). lib. bdg. (*978-1-58415-598-0(1)) Mitchell Lane Pubs., Inc.

O'Shei, Tim. Stranded in the Snow! Eric LeMarque's Story of Survival. 2007. (Illus.). 32p. (J). (*978-0-7368-6777-1(5)) Capstone Pr., Inc.

Preszler, Eric. Snowboarding. 2004. (Edge Books, X-Sports). (Illus.). 32p. (J). lib. bdg. 22.60 (978-0-7368-2713-3(7)) Capstone Pr., Inc.

Schwartz, Heather E. Girls' Snowboarding. 2008. (J). (*978-1-4296-0135-1(3)) Capstone Pr., Inc.

Slade, Suzanne. Let's Go Snowboarding. 2007. (Adventures Outdoors Ser.). (Illus.). 32p. (J). (gr. 4-6). lib. bdg. 23.95 (978-1-4042-3648-6(1), PowerKids Pr.) Rosen Publishing Group, Inc., The.

Snowboarding Diary, 6 vols., Pack. 24p. (gr. 3-4). 44.00 (978-0-7635-4487-4(6)) Rigby Education.

Snowboarding for Fun! (For Fun Ser.). 48p. (YA). 8.95 (978-0-7565-1160-9(7)) Compass Point Bks.

Sullivan, Sean. Lines: The Snowboard Photography of Sean Sullivan. 2003. (Illus.). 176p. (YA). pap. 19.95 (978-0-7603-1678-8(3)) MBI Publishing Co. LLC.

Thomas, Keltie. Blades, Boards & Scooters. Attoe, Steve & Moon, Allan, illus. 2005. (Popular Mechanics for Kids Ser.). 64p. (J). pap., pap. 9.95 (978-1-897066-34-8(1)) Maple Tree Pr. CAN. *Dist:* Perseus Distribution.

U. S. Olympic Committee. A Basic Guide to Skiing & Snowboarding. 2002. (Olympic Guides). (Illus.). 160p. (J). (gr. 6 up). lib. bdg. 23.33 (978-0-8368-3104-7(7)) Stevens, Gareth Inc.

Weinstein, Anna. Kevin Jones, Snowboarding Superstar. 2005. (Extreme Sports Ser.). (Illus.). 64p. (J). (gr. 5-8). lib. bdg. 26.50 (978-1-4042-0068-5(1)) Rosen Publishing Group, Inc., The.

Woods, Bob. Snowboarding. 2005. (Kids' Guides Ser.). (Illus.). 32p. (J). (gr. 1-5). 25.64 (978-1-59296-211-2(4)) Child's World, Inc.

—Snowboarding. 2003. (Extreme Sports Ser.). (Illus.). 24p. (J). (gr. 2 up). lib. bdg. 22.00 (978-0-8368-3725-4(8)) Stevens, Gareth Inc.

SNOWMOBILES

Doeden, Matt. Snowmobiles. 2005. (Blazers—Horsepower Ser.). (Illus.). 32p. (J). 19.33 (978-0-7368-3791-0(4)) Capstone Pr., Inc.

Dubois, Muriel L. Snowmobiles. 2001. (Wild Rides! Ser.). (Illus.). 32p. (J). (gr. 3-4). lib. bdg. 21.26 (978-0-7368-0932-0(5), Capstone High-Interest Bks.) Capstone Pr., Inc.

Mara, W. P. Snowmobile Racing. 1998. (MotorSports Ser.). (Illus.). 48p. (J). (gr. 3-4). lib. bdg. 21.26 (978-0-7368-0027-3(1), Capstone High-Interest Bks.) Capstone Pr., Inc.

Marx, Mandy. Extreme Snowmobiling. 2006. (Blazers—To the Extreme Ser.). (Illus.). 32p. (978-0-7368-5465-8(7)) Capstone Pr., Inc.

Maurer, Tracy. Snocross. 2003. (Radsports Guides Ser.). (Illus.). 48p. (gr. 4-8). 20.95 (978-1-58952-279-4(6)) Rourke Publishing, LLC.

Payan, Gregory. Essential Snowmobiling for Teens. 2000. (High Interest Bks.). (Illus.). 48p. (YA). (gr. 7-12). pap. 6.95 (978-0-516-23558-5(3), Children's Pr.); (J). (978-0-531-17646-7(0), Watts, Franklin) Scholastic Library Publishing.

—Essential Snowmobiling for Teens. 2000. (gr. 7-12). lib. bdg. 15.25 (978-0-613-52035-5(1)) Tandem Library Bks.

Payan, Gregory, contrib. by. Essential Snowmobiling for Teens. 2000. (YA). (978-0-531-12146-7(1), Watts, Franklin) Scholastic Library Publishing.

Salas, Laura Purdie. Snowmobiling. 2008. (*978-1-4296-0825-1(0)); 2002. (Illus.). 48p. (J). (gr. 3-4). lib. bdg. 21.26 (978-0-7368-1058-6(7), Capstone High-Interest Bks.) Capstone Pr., Inc.

Snowmobile Racing, 6 vols. (gr. 4 up). 39.95 (978-0-7368-8961-2(2)) Red Brick Learning.

Snowmobiles. (Horsepower Ser.). 32p. (YA). 7.95 (978-0-7368-5214-2(X)) Capstone Pr., Inc.

Snowmobiles, 6 vols. (gr. 4 up). 39.95 (978-0-7368-9295-7(8)) Red Brick Learning.

Sommers, Michael A. Snowmobiling: Have Fun, Be Smart. (Explore the Outdoors Ser.). (Illus.). 64p. 2005. (YA). (gr. 7-12). lib. bdg. 26.50 (978-0-8239-3761-5(5)); 2000. (J). (gr. 4-6). lib. bdg. 26.50 (978-0-8239-3171-2(4), EOSNOW) Rosen Publishing Group, Inc., The.

SOAP

Bradley, Kimberly Brubaker. Pop! A Book about Bubbles. Miller, Margaret, illus. 2001. (Let's-Read-and-Find-Out Science Ser.). 40p. (J). (ps-1). pap. 5.99 (978-0-06-445208-3(5), Harper Trophy) HarperCollins Pubs.

Browning, Marie. Totally Cool Soapmaking for Kids. 2005. (Illus.). 96p. pap. 9.95 (978-1-4027-2242-4(7)) Sterling Publishing Co., Inc.

Madden, Priscilla. Bubble Bubble Toil AndFun. 2006. pap. 29.40 (*978-1-4259-7654-5(9)) AuthorHouse.

Tocci, Salvatore. Experiments with Soap. 2003. (True Bks.). (gr. 3-5). pap. 6.95 (978-0-516-27466-9(X), Children's Pr.) Scholastic Library Publishing.

—Experiments with Soap. 2003. (gr. 3-6). lib. bdg. 15.25 (978-0-613-67891-9(5)) Tandem Library Bks.

Wagner, Lisa. Cool Melt N Pour Soaps. 2005. (Cool Crafts Ser.). (Illus.). 32p. (J). (gr. k-6). lib. bdg. 22.78 (978-1-59197-741-4(X)) ABDO Publishing Co.

SOARING FLIGHT

see Gliding and Soaring

SOCCER

Adams, Michelle Medlock. Brandi Chastain. 2005. (No Hands Allowed Ser.). (Illus.). 32p. (J). (gr. 1-4). lib. bdg. 25.70 (978-1-58415-390-0(3)) Mitchell Lane Pubs., Inc.

Adamson, Heather. Let's Play Soccer. 2006. (Pebble Plus Ser.). (Illus.). 24p. (J). (978-0-7368-5363-7(4)) Capstone Pr., Inc.

Armentrout, David & Armentrout, Patricia, trs. Mia Hamm. 2003. (Discover the Life of a Sports Star Ser.). (Illus.). 24p. (J). 20.64 (978-1-58952-652-5(X)) Rourke Publishing, LLC.

Arnold. Fifa Latin America. 2005. (J). pap. 2.50 (978-0-00-638306-2(8)) HarperCollins Pubs.

Axelrod-Contrada, Joan. MIA Hamm: Soccer Player. 2005. (Ferguson Career Biographies Ser.). (Illus.). 144p. (J). (gr. 6-12). 25.00 (978-0-8160-5887-7(3), Ferguson Publishing Co.) Facts On File, Inc.

Aylmore, Angela. I Like Soccer. 2007. 24p. (J). (978-1-4034-9275-3(1)); pap. (978-1-4034-9284-5(0)) Heinemann Library.

Barth, Katrin & Zempel, Ullrich, trs. from GER. Learning Soccer. 2004. (Illus.). 136p. pap. 14.95 (978-1-84126-130-0(0)) Meyer & Meyer Sport, Ltd. GBR. *Dist:* Lewis International, Inc.

—Training Soccer. 2004. (Illus.). 152p. pap. 14.95 (978-1-84126-131-7(9)) Meyer & Meyer Sport, Ltd. GBR. *Dist:* Lewis International, Inc.

Basic Skills Agency Staff, contrib. by. Livewire Real Lives: Pack 9, 6 vols. 2nd rev. ed. 2000. (Illus.). pap. (978-0-340-84870-8(7)) Cambridge Univ. Pr.

Beckham, David. David Beckham's Soccer Skills. 2007. (Illus.). 160p. (J). (gr. 2-9). pap. 19.99 (978-0-06-115475-1(X)) HarperCollins Pubs.

Blackstone, Margaret. This Is Soccer. O'Brien, John, illus. rev. ed. 1999. (This is Soccer Ser.). 32p. (J). (ps-2). 15.95 (978-0-8050-2801-0(3), Holt, Henry & Co. Bks. For Young Readers) Holt, Henry & Co.

Bonilla, Daniel and David. The Making of a Champion: An Inspiring Story of Courage & Determination, Illustrating the Rules of the Game of Soccer. 2004. 45p. pap. 19.95 (978-1-4137-2729-6(8)) PublishAmerica, Inc.

Bonney, Barbara. Futbol: Las Reglas del Juego. 2002. (Juega Como un Profesional Ser.). (SPA.). (J). 23.93 (978-1-58952-445-3(4)) Rourke Publishing, LLC.

—Futbol: Los Fundamentos. 2002. (Juega Como un Profesional Ser.). (SPA.). (J). 23.93 (978-1-58952-444-6(6)) Rourke Publishing, LLC.

Brassey, Richard. David Beckham, Vol. 4. (Illus.). 24p. (J). pap. 8.99 (978-1-84255-230-8(9)) Dolphin Paperbacks GBR. *Dist:* Trafalgar Square Publishing.

Bratton, Deboral B. & Bratton, Ashley D. Record-a-Sport Soccer Sport Organizer. Bratton, Deboral B. & Bratton, Ashley D., eds. 2003. (Illus.). (gr. 1 up). 18.95 (978-1-931746-04-5(4)) Sport Your Stuff Corp.

Brill, Marlene Targ. Soccer. 2001. (Winning Women in Sports Ser.). (Illus.). 104p. (YA). (gr. 4 up). lib. bdg. 14.95 (978-1-56674-309-9(5)) Forest Hse. Publishing Co., Inc.

—Winning Women in Soccer. 1999. (Sport Success Ser.). 90p. (YA). (gr. 5 up). pap. 6.95 (978-0-7641-1116-7(7)) Barron's Educational Series, Inc.

—Winning Women in Soccer. 1999. (978-0-606-18006-1(0)) Tandem Library Bks.

Brown, Jonatha A. Soccer. 2004. (J). pap. (978-0-8368-4348-4(7)); lib. bdg. 19.33 (978-0-8368-4341-5(X)) Stevens, Gareth Inc.

Buckley, James. Landon Donovan. 2006. (World's Greatest Athletes Ser.). (Illus.). 32p. (J). (gr. 1-5). 27.07 (978-1-59296-754-4(X)) Child's World, Inc.

—Soccer Superstars. 2006. (Boys Rock! Ser.). (Illus.). 32p. (J). (gr. 1-5). 24.21 (978-1-59296-736-0(1)) Child's World, Inc.

—Soccer Superwomen. 2006. (Girls Rock! Ser.). 32p. (J). (gr. 1-5). 24.21 (978-1-59296-750-6(7)) Child's World, Inc.

Burke, Rick. Mia Hamm. 2001. (Sports Files Ser.). (Illus.). 32p. (J). lib. bdg. (978-1-58810-112-9(6)) Heinemann Library.

Burleigh, Robert. Goal. Johnson, Stephen T., illus. 2001. 32p. (J). (gr. 1-4). 16.00 (978-0-15-201789-7(5), Silver Whistle) Harcourt Trade Pubs.

Buxton, Ted. Soccer Skills: For Young Players. 2000. (gr. 3-6). lib. bdg. 24.55 (978-0-613-78530-3(4)) Tandem Library Bks.

Caviezel, Giovanni. Soccer. 2006. (Illus.). 10p. (J). bds. 10.99 (978-0-7641-6009-7(5)) Barron's Educational Series, Inc.

Chatelier, Ed. Can You Spot the Ball? 2002. (Illus.). 24p. (J). pap. 13.99 (978-0-233-05075-1(2)) Andre Deutsch GBR. *Dist:* Independent Pubs. Group.

Childs, Rob. All Goalies Are Crazy. 2000. (Yearling Soccer Ser.: No. 1). (Illus.). 118p. (J). pap. 6.95 (978-0-440-86350-2(3)) Transworld Publishers Ltd. GBR. *Dist:* Trafalgar Square Publishing.

—Football Flukes. l.t. ed. 2000. (Illus.). 120p. (978-0-7089-9515-0(2)) Ulverscroft Large Print Bks.

Christopher, Matt. Goalkeeper in Charge: Will Tina's Shyness Ruin Her Chances to Play Keeper? 2002. (gr. 3-6). lib. bdg. 12.40 (978-0-613-50613-7(8)) Tandem Library Bks.

—In the Goal with... Brianna Scurry. 2000. (YA). 11.60 (978-0-606-19839-4(3)) Tandem Library Bks.

—Mia Hamm. 1998. (Illus.). 131p. (J). (ps-7). per. 13.00 (978-0-613-11941-2(X)) Tandem Library Bks.

—On the Field with... Mia Hamm. 1998. (Matt Christopher Sports Biographies Ser.). (978-0-606-13678-5(9)) Tandem Library Bks.

Clark, Brooks. Kids' Book of Soccer: Skills, Strategies & the Rules of the Game. 2000. (Illus.). 1p. (gr. 2-7). pap. 9.95 (978-0-8065-1916-6(9), Citadel Pr.) Kensington Publishing Corp.

Cline-Ransome, Lesa. Young Pele: Soccer's First Star. Ransome, James, illus. 2007. 40p. (J). (ps-3). lib. bdg. 19.99 (*978-0-375-93599-2(1), Schwartz & Wade Bks.) Random Hse. Children's Bks.

Coffey, Wayne. Meet the Women of American Soccer: An Inside Look at America's Team. 1999. (Illus.). 48p. (J). (gr. 2-7). pap. 5.99 (978-0-439-08654-7(X)) Scholastic, Inc.

Coleman, Lori. Girls' Soccer: Going for the Goal. 2007. (Girls Got Game Ser.). (Illus.). 32p. (J). (gr. 3-6). 25.26 (*978-0-7368-6823-5(2)) Capstone Pr., Inc.

Coleman, Lori. Soccer. King, Andy, photos by. 2005. (Play-by-Play Ser.). (Illus.). 80p. (gr. 4-8). pap., lib. bdg. 23.93 (978-0-8225-9876-3(0)) Lerner Publishing Group.

Collie, Ashley. The World of Soccer. Rolfe, John, ed. 2000. (Sports Illustrated for Kids Bks.). 96p. (J). (gr. 4-8). pap. 3.99 (978-1-886749-87-0(6)) Sports Illustrated For Kids.

Collie, Ashley Jude. World of Soccer: A Complete Guide to the World's Most Popular Sport. 2005. (Sports Illustrated for Kids Bks.). (Illus.). 176p. (YA). (gr. 7-12). lib. bdg. 27.95 (978-0-8239-3698-4(8)) Rosen Publishing Group, Inc., The.

Cook, Malcolm. 101 Youth Soccer Drills: Ages 7-11. 1999. (Illus.). 128p. (J). pap. 14.95 (978-1-890946-22-7(2)) Reedswain, Inc.

—101 Youth Soccer Drills for 12 to 16 Year Olds. 2003. (Illus.). 128p. (YA). pap. 14.95 (978-1-890946-23-4(0)) Reedswain, Inc.

Cope, Suzanne. Great Soccer: Team Defense. 2001. (High Interest Bks.). (Illus.). 48p. (YA). (gr. 7-12). pap. 6.95 (978-0-516-29562-6(4), Children's Pr.) Scholastic Library Publishing.

—Great Soccer: Team Offense. 2001. (Sports Clinic Ser.). (Illus.). 48p. (YA). (gr. 7-12). 23.00 (978-0-516-23167-9(7)); pap. 6.95 (978-0-516-29563-3(2)) Scholastic Library Publishing. (Children's Pr.).

Craats, Rennay. For the Love of Soccer. Craats, Rennay, illus. 2001. (For the Love of Sports Ser.). (Illus.). 24p. (J). (gr. 1-3). lib. bdg. 15.95 (978-1-930954-10-6(7)) Weigl Pubs., Inc.

Crats, Rennay & Rediger, Pat. For the Love of Soccer. Kissock, Heather, ed. 2003. (For the Love of Sports Ser.). (Illus.). 24p. (J). pap. 6.95 (978-1-59036-069-9(9)) Weigl Pubs., Inc.

Crisfield, Deborah. The Everything Kids' Soccer Book: Rules, Techniques, & More about Your Favorite Sport! 2002. (Illus.). 144p. 7.95 (978-1-58062-642-2(4)) Adams Media Corp.

—Everything Kids' Soccer Books: Rules, Techniques, & More about Your Favorite S. 2002. (gr. 3-6). lib. bdg. 15.25 (978-0-613-51250-3(2)) Tandem Library Bks.

Cross, Mandy. Goal Power: A Real-Life Girls' Soccer Story. 1999. (Illus.). 128p. (J). (gr. 3-9). pap. 4.95 (978-1-902618-46-3(7)) Element Children's Bks.

Crowther, Robert. Soccer: Facts & Stats & the World Cup & Superstars: A Pop-up Book. Crowther, Robert, illus. 2004. (Illus.). 14p. (J). (gr. 2-8). reprint ed. 18.00 (978-0-7567-7368-7(7)) DIANE Publishing Co.

Currie, Stephen. Mia Hamm. 2002. (Stars of Sports Ser.). (Illus.). 48p. (J). 26.20 (978-0-7377-1394-7(1), Greenhaven Pr., Inc.) Thomson Gale.

de Leon, Mauricio Velazquez, tr. Alexi Lalas, Sensacion del Futbol Soccer. 2002. (Coleccion Power Kids). (SPA & ENG., Illus.). 24p. (J). (gr. k-2). lib. bdg. 17.25 (978-0-8239-6137-5(0), RN31305, Buenas Letra) Rosen Publishing Group, Inc., The.

—Cobi Jones, Estrella del Futbol Soccer. 2002. (Coleccion Power Kids). (SPA & ENG., Illus.). 24p. (J). (gr. k-2). lib. bdg. 17.25 (978-0-8239-6135-1(4), RN31307, PowerKids Pr.) Rosen Publishing Group, Inc., The.

DK Publishing. Soccer: The Ultimate Guide. 2008. (J). 152p. 17.99 (*978-0-7566-3434-6(2)); 144p. pap. 12.99 (*978-0-7566-3441-4(5)) Dorling Kindersley Publishing, Inc.

Dorling Kindersley Publishing Staff. Play Soccer. 2006. (Illus.). 64p. (J). (gr. 5). 12.99 (978-0-7566-2032-5(5)) Dorling Kindersley Publishing, Inc.

Dougherty, Terri. Mia Hamm. 2000. (Jam Session Ser.). (Illus.). 32p. (J). (gr. 3-8). lib. bdg. 24.21 (978-1-57765-364-6(5), ABDO & Daughters) ABDO Publishing Co.

Drewett, Jim. How to Improve at Soccer. 2007. 48p. (J). (gr. 3-9). pap. (*978-0-7787-3591-5(5)) Crabtree Publishing Co.

Eckart, Edana. I Can Play Soccer. 2002. (Wel-Sports Ser.). (Illus.). 24p. (J). (ps-2). 18.00 (978-0-516-23969-9(4)); pap. 4.95 (978-0-516-24031-2(5)) Scholastic Library Publishing. (Children's Pr.).

—I Can Play Soccer. 2002. (gr. k-3). lib. bdg. 12.95 (978-0-613-58842-3(8)) Tandem Library Bks.

Edom, Helen & Osborne, Mike. Starting Soccer - Internet Linked. rev. ed. 2006. 32p. (J). pap. 4.99 (978-0-7945-0671-1(2)) EDC Publishing.

Farrow, Peter. Soccer. 2003. (Sports Injuries Ser.). (Illus.). 64p. (J). lib. bdg. (978-1-59084-637-7(0)) Mason Crest Pubs.

Fauchald, Nick. Score! You Can Play Soccer. Dickson, Bill, illus. 2004. (Game Day Ser.). 24p. (J). (gr. k-3). 22.60 (978-1-4048-0262-9(2), 1229517) Picture Window Bks.

Feldman, Heather. Mia Hamm, 6 Packs. (On Deck Ser.). 24p. (gr. 4-5). 35.00 (978-0-7578-0998-9(7)) Rigby Education.

—Mia Hamm: Soccer Superstar. 2001. (Reading Power Ser.). (Illus.). 24p. (J). (gr. 1). lib. bdg. 17.25 (978-0-8239-5716-3(0), PKHAMM, PowerKids Pr.) Rosen Publishing Group, Inc., The.

—Mia Hamm, Super-Estrella del Futbol Soccer. 2002. (Coleccion Power Kids). (SPA., Illus.). 24p. (J). (gr. k-2). lib. bdg. 17.25 (978-0-8239-6136-8(2), RN31306, Buenas Letra) Rosen Publishing Group, Inc., The.

—Mia Hamm, Superestrella del Futbol Soccer. 2002. (Superestrellas del Deporte Ser.). (SPA & ENG., Illus.). 24p. (J). lib. bdg. 17.25 (978-0-8239-6118-4(4), Buenas Letra) Rosen Publishing Group, Inc., The.

Fischer, George. The Illustrated Laws of Soccer. McRae, Patrick T., illus. 2001. 32p. (J). (gr. 4-7). pap. 5.95 (978-0-8249-5423-9(8), Ideals Children's Bks.) Ideals Pubns.

Futbol, 6 Pack. (On Deck en Espanol Ser.). (SPA.). 24p. (gr. 4-5). 35.00 (978-0-7578-6390-5(6)) Rigby Education.

Futbol en el Parque: Individual Title Six-Packs. (Coleccion Pm Ser.).Tr. of Soccer at the park. (SPA.). 16p. (gr. 1 up). 26.00 (978-0-7578-2999-4(6)) Rigby Education.

Gibbons, Gail. My Soccer Book. Gibbons, Gail, illus. 2000. (Illus.). 24p. (J). (ps-2). 5.99 (978-0-688-17138-4(9)) HarperCollins Pubs.

Gibbs, Lynne. A Word about Soccer. Smith, Jan, illus. 2005. (Word About Ser.). 24p. (J). (ps-3). pap., pap. 3.95 (978-0-7696-3386-2(2), Brighter Child) School Specialty Publishing.

Gifford, Clive. Goalkeeper. 2007. (J). (*978-1-59771-084-8(9)) Sea-To-Sea Pubns.

—The Kingfisher Soccer Encyclopedia. 2006. (Illus.). 144p. (J). (gr. 5-9). 19.95 (978-0-7534-5928-7(0), Kingfisher) Houghton Mifflin Co. Trade & Reference Div.

—So You Think You Know David Beckham? 2003. 128p. (J). pap. 9.99 (978-0-340-87765-4(0), Hodder & Stoughton) Hodder General Publishing Division GBR. *Dist:* Trafalgar Square Publishing.

—So You Think You Know Premier League Football? 2004. mass mkt. 8.95 (978-0-340-88190-3(9), Hodder & Stoughton) Hodder General Publishing Division GBR. *Dist:* Trafalgar Square Publishing.

—Soccer: The Ultimate Guide to the Beautiful Game. (Illus.). 96p. (J). (gr. 4-6). 2004. pap. 8.95 (978-0-7534-5752-8(0)); 2002. tchr. ed. 18.95 (978-0-7534-5416-9(5)) Houghton Mifflin Co. Trade & Reference Div. (Kingfisher).

—Soccer Skills. 2005. (Illus.). 48p. (J). (gr. 3-5). vinyl bd. 4.95 (978-0-7534-5932-4(9), Kingfisher) Houghton Mifflin Co. Trade & Reference Div.

—Striker. 2007. (J). (*978-1-59771-085-5(7)) Sea-To-Sea Pubns.

Gifford, Clive. Tactics. 1998. (Soccer School Ser.). (Illus.). 32p. (J). (gr. 3 up). lib. bdg. 13.95 (978-1-58086-013-0(3)) EDC Publishing.

Glaser, Jason. David Beckham. 2008. (J). (*978-1-4042-4182-4(5), PowerKids Pr.) Rosen Publishing Group, Inc., The.

Godsall, Ben. A World Soccer Star. 2004. (Making of a Champion Ser.). (J). pap. 8.50 (978-1-4034-5549-9(X)); lib. bdg. 27.07 (978-1-4034-5365-5(9)) Heinemann Library.

Goin, Kenn. Soccer for Fun. 2003. (Sports for Fun Ser.). (Illus.). 48p. (J). (gr. 3 up). lib. bdg. 21.26 (978-0-7565-0431-1(7)) Compass Point Bks.

Group/McGraw-Hill, Wright. SoCer: Level I, 6 vols. (Take Twostm Ser.). 16p. 29.95 (978-0-322-08970-9(0)) Wright Group, The.

Hamm, Mia. WUSA Girl's Guide to Soccer Life. 2003. (Illus.). 192p. (J). (gr. 3-11). per. 19.99 (978-1-59186-040-2(7)) Cool Springs Pr.

HarperCollins UK. England, the Facts: Sticker Book. 2006. (Illus.). 32p. pap. 8.99 (978-0-00-721695-6(5), HarperCollins Children's Bks.) HarperCollins Pubs. Ltd. GBR. *Dist:* Independent Pubs. Group.

—England World Cup Dream Team: Sticker Scene Book. 2006. (Illus.). 6p. pap. 8.99 (978-0-00-721696-3(3), HarperCollins Children's Bks.) HarperCollins Pubs. Ltd. GBR. *Dist:* Independent Pubs. Group.

—England World Cup Junior Companion. 2006. (Illus.). 48p. pap. 8.99 (978-0-00-721698-7(X), HarperCollins Children's Bks.) HarperCollins Pubs. Ltd. GBR. *Dist:* Independent Pubs. Group.

—England_s Road to the World Cup. 2006. (Illus.). 32p. (ps). pap., act. bk. ed. 6.99 (978-0-00-721693-2(9), HarperCollins Children's Bks.) HarperCollins Pubs. Ltd. GBR. *Dist:* Independent Pubs. Group.

Harrison, Paul. David Beckham. 2005. (Star Files Ser.). (Illus.). 48p. (J). (gr. 6-8). lib. bdg. 29.93 (978-1-4109-1664-8(2)) Harcourt Schl. Pubs.

Harvey, Gill, et al. Complete Soccer School. 2001. (Soccer School Ser.). (Illus.). 256p. (YA). (gr. 3 up). 29.95 (978-0-7460-2918-3(7)) EDC Publishing.

Helmer, Diana Star & Owens, Tom. The History of Soccer. 2000. (Sports Throughout History Ser.). (Illus.). 24p. (J). (gr. 2-4). lib. bdg. 18.75 (978-0-8239-5467-4(6), PowerKids Pr.) Rosen Publishing Group, Inc., The.

Herman, Hank. Sudden Death! And Other Soccer Stories. 2000. (Sports Shorts Ser.). (Illus.). 64p. (J). (gr. 3-7). pap. 5.95 (978-0-7373-0398-8(0), 03980W, Roxbury Park Juvenile) Lowell Hse. Juvenile.

Herran, Joe & Thomas, Ron. Getting into Soccer. Porcellato, Nives & Craig, Andy, illus. 2005. (Getting into Sports Ser.). 32p. (J). (ps-8). lib. bdg. 28.00 (978-0-7910-8806-7(5) , Chelsea Clubhouse) Facts On File, Inc.

Herzog, Brad. K Is for Kick: A Soccer Alphabet. Rose, Melanie, illus. rev. ed. 2003. 40p. (J). 16.95 (978-1-58536-130-4(5)) Sleeping Bear Pr.

Herzog, Brad. A Soccer Alphabet. rev. ed. 2007. 40p. pap. 7.95 (***978-1-58536-339-1(1)***) Sleeping Bear Pr.

Hiebert, Elfrieda H. & Juel, Connie. Silvia's Soccer Game. (Little Book Practice Reader). (J). (978-0-8136-2064-0(3)) Modern Curriculum Pr.

Hornby, Hugh. Soccer. 2008. (DK Eyewitness Bks.). 72p. (J). (gr. 3-8). 15.99 (***978-0-7566-3779-8(1)***) Dorling Kindersley Publishing, Inc.

Hornby, Hugh & Dorling Kindersley Publishing Staff. Soccer. Crawford, Andy, photos by. 2005. (Eyewitness Books). (Illus.). 72p. (J). (ps-7). 15.99 (978-0-7566-1091-3(5)); lib. bdg. 19.99 (978-0-7566-1092-0(3)) Dorling Kindersley Publishing, Inc.

Housel, Debra J. Soccer: Easy Olympic Sports Reader. 2004. (U. S. Olympic Committee Easy Olympic Sports Readers Ser.). (Illus.). 16p. (J). pap. 2.99 (978-1-58000-113-7(0)) Griffin Publishing Group.

Hughes, Morgan. Soccer. 2005. (Junior Sports Ser.). (Illus.). 32p. (gr. 2-4). 19.95 (978-1-59515-187-2(7)) Rourke Publishing, LLC.

Humber, William. The Kid's Soccer Book: For Kids & Coaches. 1998. (Illus.). 64p. reprint ed. pap. 10.00 (978-0-7881-5166-8(5)) DIANE Publishing Co.

Jacobs, Elisabeth & Smith, Benjamin Eli. Soccer Kicks: A Play-by-Play Soccer Journal. 2001. (Illus.). 132p. (YA). (gr. 7-9). reprint ed. ring bd. 22.00 (978-0-7567-6289-6(8)) DIANE Publishing Co.

Kalman, Bobbie. Soccer in Action. 2000. (gr. 3-6). lib. bdg. 14.10 (978-0-613-22400-0(0)) Tandem Library Bks.

Kalman, Bobbie & Crossingham, John. Kick It Soccer. 2007. (Illus.). 32p. (J). (gr. 1-5). (***978-0-7787-3138-2(3));*** pap. (***978-0-7787-3170-2(7)***) Crabtree Publishing Co.

Kennedy, Mike. Soccer. 2001. (Sports Ser.). (Illus.). 64p. (J). (gr. 5-7). 25.50 (978-0-531-12022-4(8) , Watts, Franklin) Scholastic Library Publishing.

—Soccer. 2002. (Illus.). 63p. (J). (gr. 4-7). lib. bdg. 17.60 (978-0-613-51677-8(X)); (gr. 3-6). lib. bdg. 15.25 (978-0-613-59732-6(X)) Tandem Library Bks.

Kirkpatrick, Rob. Alexia Lalas: Soccer Sensation. 2000. (Reading Power Ser.). (Illus.). 24p. (J). (gr. 1). lib. bdg. 17.25 (978-0-8239-5541-1(9) , PowerKids Pr.) Rosen Publishing Group, Inc., The.

—Cobi Jones: Soccer Star. 2000. (Reading Power Ser.). (Illus.). 24p. (J). (gr. 1). lib. bdg. 17.25 (978-0-8239-5540-4(0) , PowerKids Pr.) Rosen Publishing Group, Inc., The.

Kjelle, Marylou Morano. Josh Wolff. 2005. (No Hands Allowed Ser.). (Illus.). 32p. (J). (gr. 1-4). lib. bdg. 25.70 (978-1-58415-388-7(1)) Mitchell Lane Pubs., Inc.

Kramer, Sydelle A. U. S. Soccer Superstars. 2000. (All Aboard Reading Ser.). (978-0-606-18474-8(0)) Tandem Library Bks.

Lineker, Gary. Soccer. 2000. (Young Enthusiast Ser.). (Illus.). 1p. (J). (gr. 4-7). 9.99 (978-0-7894-5425-6(4)) Dorling Kindersley Publishing, Inc.

Lishak, Antony. Defender. 2007. (J). (***978-1-59771-083-1(0)***) Sea-To-Sea Pubns.

Mackin, Bob. Soccer the Winning Way: Play Like the Pros. 2004. (Illus.). 64p. (YA). (gr. 3 up). pap. 10.95 (978-1-55054-825-9(5)) Douglas & McIntyre, Ltd. CAN. *Dist:* Transition Vendor.

The Maracana: Individual Title Six-Packs. (On Deck Ser.). 24p. (gr. 4-5). 35.00 (978-0-7578-1075-6(6)) Rigby Education.

Marshall, David. Soccer. 1998. (Successful Sports Ser.). 32p. (J). lib. bdg. 21.36 (978-1-57572-069-2(8)) Heinemann Library.

Mattern, Joanne. Brian McBride. 2005. (No Hands Allowed Ser.). (Illus.). 32p. (J). (gr. 1-4). lib. bdg. 25.70 (978-1-58415-389-4(X)) Mitchell Lane Pubs., Inc.

McGrath, Barbara Barbieri & Alderman, Peter. Soccer Counts! Estrada, Pau, illus. 2004. 32p. (J). 16.95 (978-1-57091-553-6(9)); pap. 6.95 (978-1-57091-554-3(7)) Charlesbridge Publishing, Inc.

Mead, Richard. The England Team Quiz & Joke Book. 2006. (Illus.). 144p. pap. 6.99 (978-0-00-721697-0(1)) HarperCollins Pubs. Ltd. GBR. *Dist:* Independent Pubs. Group.

Miller, Jonathan. Goalkeeping. 1998. (Soccer School Ser.). (Illus.). 32p. (YA). (gr. 3 up). lib. bdg. 13.95 (978-1-58086-131-1(8)) EDC Publishing.

—Goalkeeping. Bond, Bob, illus. 1998. (Soccer School Ser.). 256p. (YA). (gr. 3 up). pap. 5.95 (978-0-7460-2907-7(1)) EDC Publishing.

Miller, Marla. All-American Girls: The U. S. Women's National Soccer Team. 1999. (YA). pap. 40.24 incl. audio (978-0-7887-3653-7(1) , 41019) Recorded Bks., LLC.

—All-American Girls: The U. S. Women's National Soccer Team. 1999. (J). (978-0-606-19045-9(7)) Tandem Library Bks.

Mitchell Lane Publishers. A Robbie Reader-No Hands Allowed. 2007. (No Hands Allowed Ser.). (J). lib. bdg. 334.10 (***978-1-58415-602-4(3)***) Mitchell Lane Pubs., Inc.

Mugford, Simon. Official Manchester United Activity. 2001. (Illus.). 20p. (J). pap. 7.99 (978-0-233-99973-9(6)) Andre Deutsch GBR. *Dist:* Independent Pubs. Group.

Murcia, Rebecca Thatcher. David Beckham. 2005. (No Hands Allowed Ser.). (Illus.). 32p. (J). (gr. 1-4). lib. bdg. 25.70 (978-1-58415-384-9(9)) Mitchell Lane Pubs., Inc.

—Freddy Adu. 2005. (No Hands Allowed Ser.). (Illus.). 32p. (J). (gr. 1-4). lib. bdg. 25.70 (978-1-58415-385-6(7)) Mitchell Lane Pubs., Inc.

—Landon Donovan. 2005. (No Hands Allowed Ser.). (Illus.). 32p. (J). (gr. 1-4). lib. bdg. 25.70 (978-1-58415-386-3(5)) Mitchell Lane Pubs., Inc.

—Robbie & Ryan Play Indoor Soccer. 2006. (No Hands Allowed Ser.). (Illus.). 32p. (J). (gr. 1-4). lib. bdg. 25.70 (978-1-58415-414-3(4)) Mitchell Lane Pubs., Inc.

Murphy, Patricia J. DK Readers Level 1: Let¿s Play Soccer. 2008. (Dk Readers Ser.). 32p. (J). (gr. k-2). 14.99 (***978-0-7566-3459-9(8));*** pap. 3.99 (***978-0-7566-3458-2(X)***) Dorling Kindersley Publishing, Inc.

No Hands Allowed: Stories for Kids Who Love Soccer, 7 bks., Set. Incl. Brandi Chastain. Adams, Michelle Medlock. lib. bdg. 25.70 (978-1-58415-390-0(3)); Brian McBride. Mattern, Joanne. lib. bdg. 25.70 (978-1-58415-389-4(X)); DaMarcus Beasley. Smalley, Carol Parenzan. 25.70 (978-1-58415-387-0(3)); David Beckham. Murcia, Rebecca Thatcher. lib. bdg. 25.70 (978-1-58415-384-9(9)); Freddy Adu. Murcia, Rebecca Thatcher. lib. bdg. 25.70 (978-1-58415-385-6(7)); Josh Wolff. Kjelle, Marylou Morano. lib. bdg. 25.70 (978-1-58415-388-7(1)); Landon Donovan. Murcia, Rebecca Thatcher. lib. bdg. 25.70 (978-1-58415-386-3(5)); 32p. (J). (gr. 1-4). 2005. (Robbie Reader Ser.). (Illus.). 2005. Set lib. bdg. 118.65 (978-1-58415-413-6(6)) Mitchell Lane Pubs., Inc.

Orme, David. Football. 2007. (Trailblazers Ser.). (Illus.). 36p. pap. 7.95 (***978-1-84167-425-4(7)***) Ransom Publishing Ltd. GBR. *Dist:* International Publishers Marketing.

Otten, Jack. Futbol. 2004. (Entrenamiento Deportivo Ser.). (SPA & ENG., Illus.). 24p. (J). lib. bdg. 17.25 (978-0-8239-6850-3(2) , Buenas Letra) Rosen Publishing Group, Inc., The.

—Soccer. 2002. (Reading Power Ser.). (Illus.). 24p. (J). (gr. 1). lib. bdg. 17.25 (978-0-8239-5972-3(4) , PowerKids Pr.) Rosen Publishing Group, Inc., The.

Owens, Tom. Soccer. 1999. (Game Plan Ser.). 64p. (gr. 5-8). lib. bdg. 26.90 (978-0-7613-1400-4(8) , Twenty-First Century Bks.) Lerner Publishing Group.

Page, Jason. El Futbol. 2004. (Club Deportivo Ser.).Tr. of Soccer. (SPA., Illus.). 32p. (J). (gr. 3-6). 9.95 (978-1-58728-398-7(0)); pap. 5.95 (978-1-58728-397-0(2)) T&N Children's Publishing. (Two Can Publishing).

—El Futbol. 2001. Tr. of Soccer. 12.75 (978-0-606-22729-2(6)) Tandem Library Bks.

—Soccer. rev. ed. 2004. (Sports Club Ser.). (SPA., Illus.). 32p. (gr. 3-6). (J). pap. 5.95 (978-1-58728-003-0(5)); 9.95 (978-1-58728-001-6(9)) T&N Children's Publishing. (Two Can Publishing).

Palmer, Edward. Getting Started Sports Books: Soccer Instructional Coloring Book. Howard, Robert & Flynn Sabatino and Day Staff, photos by. rev. ed. 1998. (Illus.). 24p. (J). (ps-4). pap. 4.95 (978-1-890527-02-0(5)) Nuway Youth Sports.

Pendleton, Ken. David Beckham. 2007. (J). lib. bdg. (***978-0-8225-7161-2(7)***) Twenty First Century Bks.

Pilger, Sam. The Future Is United into 2000 & Beyond with Manchester United. 1999. (Illus.). 48p. (J). pap. 11.99 (978-0-233-99829-9(2)) Andre Deutsch GBR. *Dist:* Independent Pubs. Group.

Preston, Roy & Preston, Sue. He Shoots, He Scores: 30 Fact-Filled Crosswords. 2003. (Illus.). 94p. (J). 5.99 (978-0-330-34106-6(5) , Pan) Pan Macmillan GBR. *Dist:* Trafalgar Square Publishing.

Priddy, Roger. Sticker Activity Fun Pirate. 2007. 48p. (J). bds. 3.95 (978-0-312-49920-4(5) , Priddy Bks.) St. Martin's Pr.

Robinson, Tom. David Beckham: Soccer's Superstar. 2008. (People to Know Today Ser.). 128p. (J). (gr. 6 up). lib. bdg. 31.93 (***978-0-7660-3110-4(1)***) Enslow Pubs., Inc.

Ross, David & Cattell, Bob. World Cup. 2000. (Strikers Ser.). (Illus.). 128p. pap. 7.99 (978-0-233-99693-6(1)) Andre Deutsch GBR. *Dist:* Independent Pubs. Group.

Roth, B. A. David Beckham: Born to Play. 2008. (All Aboard Reading Ser.). 48p. (J). (gr. 1-3). pap. 3.99 (***978-0-448-44788-9(6)*** , Grosset & Dunlap) Penguin Group (USA) Inc.

Roza, Greg. David Beckham: Soccer Superstar. 2006. (Tony Stead Nonfiction Independent Reading Collection). (J). pap. (978-1-4042-5539-5(7)) Rosen Publishing Group, Inc., The.

Rumaner, Marc. Let's Play Soccer! Incl. 2 1/2 " Soccer Ball. (Illus.). 12p. (J). (ps-1). bds. (978-1-56021-373-4(6) , 220) W.J. Fantasy, Inc.

Rutledge, Rachel. The Best of the Best in Soccer. 1998. (Women of Sports Ser.: up). (Illus.). 64p. (gr. 5 up). lib. bdg. 24.90 (978-0-7613-1315-1(X) , Twenty-First Century Bks.) Lerner Publishing Group.

—The Best of the Best in Soccer. 1999. (J). (978-0-606-19848-6(2)) Tandem Library Bks.

—Best of the Best in Soccer. 1999. (gr. 5-8). lib. bdg. 16.40 (978-0-613-28419-6(4)) Tandem Library Bks.

—The Best of the Best in Soccer. rev. ed. 2000. (Women of Sports Ser.: up). (Illus.). 64p. (gr. 5-11). pap. (978-0-7613-1392-2(3) , Twenty-First Century Bks.) Lerner Publishing Group.

—Mia Hamm: Striking Superstar. 2000. (Soccer's New Wave Ser.: up). (Illus.). 48p. (gr. 4-8). pap. (978-0-7613-1381-6(8) , Millbrook Pr.) Lerner Publishing Group.

—Mia Hamm: Striking Superstar. 2000. (YA). (978-0-606-20196-4(3)); (gr. 3-6). lib. bdg. 15.25 (978-0-613-26200-2(X)) Tandem Library Bks.

Sampler, Robert. Mind Mastery for Soccer. 2000. 115p. (YA). (gr. 6 up). pap. 29.95 (978-0-9653920-6-8(6) , 12119) Aries International (U.B.T.O.).

Sandler, Michael. Soccer: The Amazing U. S. World Cup Team. 2006. (Upsets & Comebacks Ser.). (Illus.). 32p. (J). lib. bdg. 25.27 (978-1-59716-169-5(1)) Bearport Publishing Co., Inc.

Savage, Jeff. Freddy Adu. 2006. (Amazing Athletes Ser.). (Illus.). (J). 32p. 22.60 (978-0-8225-3430-3(4) , Lerner Pubns.); pap. 5.95 (978-0-8225-3595-9(5) , First Avenue Editions) Lerner Publishing Group.

—Julie Foudy: Soccer Superstar. 1999. (Sports Achievers Biographies Ser.). (Illus.). 80p. (gr. 7-12). lib. bdg. 22.60 (978-0-8225-3662-8(5)) Lerner Publishing Group.

—Julie Foudy: Soccer Superstar. 1999. (gr. 3-6). lib. bdg. 14.10 (978-0-613-81863-6(6)) Tandem Library Bks.

Schnakenberg, Robert. Mia Hamm. 2001. (gr. 3-6). lib. bdg. 17.60 (978-0-613-32830-2(2)) Tandem Library Bks.

Schnakenberg, Robert E. Mia Hamm. 2000. (Women Who Win Ser.). (Illus.). 64p. (J). (gr. 4-7). pap. 25.00 (978-0-7910-6151-0(5)); (YA). (gr. 8 up). 25.00 (978-0-7910-5791-9(7)) Facts On File, Inc. (Chelsea Hse.).

—Mia Hamm. 2001. (Women Who Win Ser.). (Illus.). (J). (978-0-606-20798-0(8)) Tandem Library Bks.

Scott, Nina Savin. Smart Soccer: How to Use Your Mind to Play Your Best. 1999. (Single Titles Ser.: up). (Illus.). 96p. (gr. 5-9). pap. 8.95 (978-0-7613-1294-9(3) , Millbrook Pr.) Lerner Publishing Group.

—The Thinking Kid's Guide to Successful Soccer. Green, Anne Canevari, illus. 1999. (Sports Palaces Ser.). 96p. (gr. 5 up). lib. bdg. 21.90 (978-0-7613-0324-4(3) , Millbrook Pr.) Lerner Publishing Group.

Shea, Therese. Soccer Stars. 2007. (Sports Stars Ser.). (Illus.). 48p. (J). pap. (978-0-531-18705-0(5)) Children's Pr., Ltd.

—Soccer Stars. 2006. (Sports Stars Ser.). (Illus.). 48p. (J). (978-0-531-12588-5(2) , Children's Pr.) Scholastic Library Publishing.

Sherman, Josepha. Competitive Soccer for Girls. 2005. (SportsGirl Ser.). (Illus.). 64p. (YA). (gr. 5-8). lib. bdg. 26.50 (978-0-8239-3405-8(5)) Rosen Publishing Group, Inc., The.

Smalley, Carol Parenzan. DaMarcus Beasley. 2005. (No Hands Allowed Ser.). (Illus.). 32p. (J). (gr. 1-4). 25.70 (978-1-58415-387-0(3)) Mitchell Lane Pubs., Inc.

Smith, Dave, et al. Step-by-Step Soccer Skills: Techniques, Tactics, Skills, Fitness. Hamlyn, ed. 2000. (Illus.). 160p. pap. (978-0-600-60114-2(5) , Hamlyn) Octopus Publishing Group.

Soccer, 6 vols., Pack. (On Deck Ser.). 24p. (gr. 4-5). 35.00 (978-0-7578-1007-7(1)) Rigby Education.

Soccer: Level 30. 2003. 31.95 (978-0-673-57967-6(0)) Celebration Pr.

Soccer Crazy. 2002. 64p. (J). pap., act. bk. ed. 3.98 (978-0-7525-7997-9(5)) Parragon, Inc.

Soccer for Fun! (For Fun Ser.). 48p. (YA). 8.95 (978-0-7565-1161-6(5)) Compass Point Bks.

Soccer Fun. 2002. 64p. (J). pap., act. bk. ed. 3.98 (978-0-7525-7998-6(3)) Parragon, Inc.

Stewart, Gail B. Soccer. 2000. (History of Sports Ser.). (Illus.). 96p. (YA). (gr. 6-9). 29.95 (978-1-56006-712-2(8) , Lucent Bks.) Thomson Gale.

Stewart, Mark. Mia Hamm: Good As Gold. 1999. (gr. 3-6). lib. bdg. 14.10 (978-0-613-62302-5(9)) Tandem Library Bks.

—Mia Hamm: Striking Superstar. 2000. (New Wave Ser.). (Illus.). 48p. (gr. 4 up). lib. bdg. 22.90 (978-0-7613-1802-6(X) , Millbrook Pr.) Lerner Publishing Group.

—The World Cup. Kennedy, Mike, ed. 2003. (Watts History of Sports Ser.). (Illus.). 112p. (J). 34.50 (978-0-531-11957-0(2) , Watts, Franklin) Scholastic Library Publishing.

Stewart, Mark Alan. Briana Scurry: Super Saver. 2000. (Sports Stars Ser.). (Illus.). 48p. (J). (gr. 3-4). pap. 5.95 (978-0-516-27070-8(2) , Children's Pr.) Scholastic Library Publishing.

—Soccer: An Intimate History of the World's Most Popular Game. 1998. (Watts History of Sports Ser.). (Illus.). 128p. (YA). (gr. 5-8). 34.50 (978-0-531-11456-8(2) , Watts, Franklin) Scholastic Library Publishing.

Stone, Lynn M. Goalies. 2008. (J). (***978-1-60044-593-4(4)***) Rourke Publishing, LLC.

—Strikers. 2008. (J). (***978-1-60044-598-9(5)***) Rourke Publishing, LLC.

The Story of Soccer: Individual Title Six-Packs. (On Deck Ser.). 24p. (gr. 4-5). 35.00 (978-0-7578-1013-8(6)) Rigby Education.

Stout, Glenn & Christopher, Matt. Mia Hamm: On the Field With... 1998. (Matt Christopher Sports Biographies Ser.). (Illus.). 128p. (J). (gr. 3-7). pap. 4.99 (978-0-316-14217-5(4)) Little, Brown Bks. for Young Readers.

Suen, Anastasia. The Story of Soccer. 2002. (Reading Power Ser.). (Illus.). 24p. (J). (gr. 2). lib. bdg. 17.25 (978-0-8239-5998-3(8) , PowerKids Pr.) Rosen Publishing Group, Inc., The.

Sullivan, George. All about Soccer. 2005. (Illus.). 122p. (J). (gr. 4-8). reprint ed. pap. 10.00 (978-0-7567-9750-8(0)) DIANE Publishing Co.

Tamra, Orr. Abby Wambach. 2007. (No Hands Allowed Ser.). (Illus.). 32p. (J). lib. bdg. 25.70 (***978-1-58415-601-7(5)***) Mitchell Lane Pubs., Inc.

Thatcher, Rebecca. Ronaldinho. 2007. (No Hands Allowed Ser.). (Illus.). 32p. (J). lib. bdg. 25.70 (***978-1-58415-600-0(7)***) Mitchell Lane Pubs., Inc.

Thomas, Keltie. How Soccer Works. MacEachern, Stephen, illus. 2007. (How Sports Work Ser.). 64p. (J). (gr. 3-7). 21.95 (***978-1-897349-00-7(9));*** pap. 10.95 (***978-1-897349-01-4(7)***) Maple Tree Pr. CAN. *Dist:* Perseus Distribution.

Thompson, Howard. Youth Soccer: A Complete Guide for Coaches, Players & Parents. 2001. 120p. (J). pap. 16.95 (978-1-58518-328-9(8)) Coaches Choice.

Tow, Rebecca. Manchester United Official Superstars 2. 2002. (Illus.). 32p. pap. 11.95 (978-0-233-05022-5(1)) Andre Deutsch GBR. *Dist:* Independent Pubs. Group.

Urigs, Timothy. Superstars of Men's Soccer. 1999. (Male Sports Stars Ser.). (Illus.). 64p. (YA). (gr. 4-7). 12.95 (978-0-7910-4588-6(9) , Chelsea Hse.) Facts On File, Inc.

Velazquez, Mauricio, tr. Alexi Lalas, Sensacion del Futbol Soccer. 2002. (Power Kids Coleccion). (SPA.). 24p. (J). (gr. 2-3). lib. bdg. 17.25 (978-0-8239-6119-1(2) , RN30776, Buenas Letra) Rosen Publishing Group, Inc., The.

Venturini, Tisha & Cohen, Judith Love. You Can Be a Woman Soccer Player. 2000. (Illus.). 88p. (J). (gr. 4-9). 13.95 (978-1-880599-49-5(X)); pap. 7.00 (978-1-880599-48-8(1)) Cascade Pass, Inc.

Waite, Elsie, et al. Following Rules. Sparck, Carole C., illus. l.t. ed. 2001. 8p. (J). pap. 6.00 (978-1-58084-169-6(4)) Lower Kuskokwim Schl. District.

Walker, Niki. Soccer in Action. 2000. (978-0-606-18067-2(2)) Tandem Library Bks.

Walker, Niki & Dann, Sara. Le Soccer. rev. ed. 2007. (FRE., Illus.). 32p. (J). (gr. 3-4). pap. (***978-2-89579-124-9(4)***) Editions Banjo.

Walker, Niki & Dann, Sarah. Futbol en Accion. 2005. (FRE & SPA., Illus.). 32p. (J). (978-0-7787-8570-5(X)) Crabtree Publishing Co.

—Soccer in Action. 1999. (Sports in Action Ser.). (Illus.). 32p. (J). (gr. 3-4). (978-0-7787-0161-3(1)); pap. (978-0-7787-0173-6(5)) Crabtree Publishing Co.

Walker, Niki, et al. Futbol en Accion. 2005. (Deportes en Accion Ser.). (SPA., Illus.). 32p. (J). (gr. 6-9). pap. (978-0-7787-8616-0(1)) Crabtree Publishing Co.

Ward, Adam. Motson's National Obsession: The Greatest Football Trivia Book Ever. 2004. (Illus.). 200p. (978-1-86074-601-7(2)) Sanctuary Publishing, Ltd.

Watson, Galadriel Findlay. David Beckham. 2007. (J). (***978-1-59036-641-7(7)); (978-1-59036-642-4(5))*** Weigl Pubs., Inc.

Wheeler, Jill C. David Beckham. 2007. (Awesome Athletes Ser.). (Illus.). 32p. (J). 22.78 (978-1-59928-304-3(2)) ABDO Publishing Co.

Whitfield, David. World Cup. 2007. (J). (***978-1-59036-695-0(6)); (978-1-59036-696-7(4))*** Weigl Pubs., Inc.

Williams, Cinthia Louise. The Flippin' Soccer Guide. 2003. (Illus.). 40p. (YA). 14.95 (978-0-9742500-0-7(7)) Flippin' Bks. LLC.

Wingate, Brian. Soccer: Rules, Tips, Strategy, & Safety. 2006. (Sports from Coast to Coast Ser.). (Illus.). 48p. (J). (gr. 5-8). lib. bdg. 26.50 (978-1-4042-0995-4(6)) Rosen Publishing Group, Inc., The.

Woods, P. Improve Your Soccer Skills. 2004. (Superskills Ser.). (Illus.). 48p. (YA). (gr. 6-10). lib. bdg. 13.95 (978-0-88110-296-3(2)) EDC Publishing.

Woog, Dan. The Ultimate Soccer Almanac. 1998. (Illus.). 144p. (J). (gr. 2-7). 12.95 (978-1-56565-951-3(1) , 09511W); pap. 8.95 (978-1-56565-891-2(4) , 08914W) Lowell Hse. Juvenile. (Roxbury Park Juvenile).

—The Ultimate Soccer Almanac: Newly Updated! rev. ed. 2000. (Illus.). 144p. (J). (gr. 3-7). pap. 8.95 (978-0-7373-0430-5(8) , 04308W, Roxbury Park) Lowell Hse.

—The Ultimate Soccer Encyclopedia. 2000. (Sports Shorts Ser.). (Illus.). 144p. (J). (gr. 3-7). pap. 9.95 (978-0-7373-0399-5(9) , 03999W, Roxbury Park Juvenile) Lowell Hse. Juvenile.

Wukovits, John F. Soccer. 1999. (Composite Guide Ser.). (Illus.). 64p. (YA). (gr. 4-7). 28.00 (978-0-7910-4718-7(0) , Chelsea Hse.) Facts On File, Inc.

YMCA of the USA Staff. Playing YMCA Soccer: Bronze Edition. 2000. (Illus.). 48p. (J). pap. 6.00 (978-0-7360-3046-5(8) , YMCA of the U.S.A.) Human Kinetics Pubs.

—Playing YMCA Soccer: Gold Edition. 2000. (Illus.). 48p. (J). pap. 6.00 (978-0-7360-3048-9(4) , YMCA of the U.S.A.) Human Kinetics Pubs.

—Playing YMCA Soccer: Silver Edition. 2000. (Illus.). 48p. (J). pap. 6.00 (978-0-7360-3047-2(6) , YMCA of the U.S.A.) Human Kinetics Pubs.

Zarzycki, Daryl. Mia Hamm. 2004. (Robbie Reader Ser.). (Illus.). 32p. (J). (gr. 1-4). lib. bdg. 25.70 (978-1-58415-286-6(9)) Mitchell Lane Pubs., Inc.

SOCCER—FICTION

Anderson, Scoular. The Mean Team from Mars. Anderson, Scoular, illus. 2005. (Read-It! Chapter Bks.). (Illus.). 52p. (J). (ps-k). lib. bdg. 19.95 (978-1-4048-1274-1(1)) Picture Window Bks.

—Stan the Dog & the Golden Goals. 2006. (Read-It! Chapter Books). (J). 21.26 (978-1-4048-2740-0(4)) Picture Window Bks.

Andrews, Phil. Own Goals. (J). 278p. pap. 16.95 (978-0-340-74821-3(4)); 320p. pap. 13.99 (978-0-340-74822-0(2)) Hodder General Publishing Division GBR. (Hodder & Stoughton). *Dist:* Trafalgar Square Publishing.

Arena, Felice & Kettle, Phil. Park Soccer. Gordon, Gus, illus. 2004. (J). (978-1-59336-366-6(4)) Mondo Publishing.

Artful Doodlers Limited Staff. The Soccer Game. 2006. (LazyTown Ser.). 24p. (J). pap. 3.99 (978-1-4169-0796-1(3) , Simon Spotlight/Nickelodeon) Simon & Schuster Children's Publishing.

Ashley, Chris. Wasim the Wanderer. 2007. (Illus.). 80p. (J). 15.95 (***978-1-84507-776-1(8)***) Lincoln, Frances Ltd. GBR. *Dist:* Perseus Distribution.

—Wasim the Wanderer. Pankhurst, Kate, illus. 2007. 80p. (J). pap. 7.95 (***978-1-84507-745-7(8)***) Lincoln, Frances Ltd. GBR. *Dist:* Perseus Distribution.

Averbuch, Gloria. Turn for Lucas. Guterman, Yaacov, illus. 2006. 32p. (J). 17.95 (978-1-58726-291-3(6) , Mitten Pr.) Ann Arbor Media Group, LLC.

Bedford, David. Soccer Camp. Brumpton, Keith, illus. 2006. (Team Ser.: 3). 76p. (J). pap. 4.95 (978-1-933605-07-4(3)) Kane/Miller Bk. Pubs., Inc.

S

—The Soccer Machine. Brumpton, Keith, illus. 2006. (Team Ser.: 1). 72p. (J). pap. 4.95 (978-1-933605-00-5(6)) Kane/Miller Bk. Pubs., Inc.

—Superteam. Brumpton, Keith, illus. 2006. (Team Ser.). 76p. (J). pap. 4.95 (978-1-933605-06-7(5)) Kane/Miller Bk. Pubs., Inc.

—Top of the League. Brumpton, Keith, illus. 2006. (Team Ser.: 2). 84p. (J). pap. 4.95 (978-1-933605-01-2(4)) Kane/Miller Bk. Pubs., Inc.

Beinstein, Phoebe. The Soccer Ball Mystery. Saunders, Zina, illus. 2005. (Backyardigans Ser.). 10p. (J). bds. 7.99 (978-1-4169-0972-9(9) , Simon Spotlight/Nickelodeon) Simon & Schuster Children's Publishing.

Berenstain, Stan & Berenstain, Jan. The Berenstain Bears Get Their Kicks. 1998. (Berenstain Bears First Time Bks.). (Illus.). 32p. (J). (gr. k-3). pap. 3.25 (978-0-679-88955-7(8) , Random Hse. Bks. for Young Readers) Random Hse. Children's Bks.

—The Berenstain Bears Get Their Kicks. 1998. (Berenstain Bears First Time Bks.). (J). (gr. k-2). 10.05 (978-0-606-13955-7(9)) Tandem Library Bks.

Berry, Andrea. Goalie: The Dynamite Diaries. 2003. 144p. (YA). pap. 11.95 (978-0-595-27678-3(4)) iUniverse, Inc.

Black, Denise & Schwartz, Janet. Around Atlanta with Children: A Guide to Family Activities. 7th ed. 2004. 334p. pap. 15.95 (978-1-56145-202-6(5)) Peachtree Pubs., Ltd.

Blackaby, Susan. The Best Soccer Player. Haugen, Ryan, illus. 2005. (Read-It! Readers Ser.). 32p. (J). (gr. k-3). 18.60 (978-1-4048-1055-6(2)) Picture Window Bks.

—El Mejor Futbolista. Haugen, Ryan, illus. 2006. (Read-It! Readers en Espanol Ser.).Tr. of Best Soccer Player. (SPA.). 32p. (J). (ps-3). 19.95 (978-1-4048-1690-9(9)) Picture Window Bks.

Blacker, Terence. Dream Team. 2003. 138p. (J). pap. 6.99 (978-0-330-32915-6(4) , Pan) Pan Macmillan GBR. *Dist:* Trafalgar Square Publishing.

Bloor, Edward. Tangerine. 2006. (Illus.). 324p. (YA). pap. 6.95 (978-0-15-205780-0(3) , Harcourt Paperbacks) Harcourt Children's Bks.

—Tangerine. 1998. (Apple Signature Edition Ser.). 304p. (YA). (gr. 6 up). pap. 4.99 (978-0-590-43277-1(X) , Scholastic Paperbacks) Scholastic, Inc.

—Tangerine. 2001. (J). (978-0-606-21480-3(1)) Tandem Library Bks.

Borchard, Therese Johnson. Whitney Climbs the Tower of Babel & Learns What Happens to Snobs. VanNest, Wendy, illus. 2001. (Emerald Bible Collection). 80p. (J). (gr. 3-7). 5.95 (978-0-8091-6675-6(5) , 6675-5) Paulist Pr.

Bossley, Michele Martin. Kicker. 2007. (Orca Sports Ser.). 160p. (YA). (gr. 5 up). pap. (***978-1-55143-706-4(6)***) Orca Bk. Pubs.

Bourgeois, Paulette. Franklin Juega al Futbol. Lopez Varela, Alejandra, tr. from ENG. Clark, Brenda, illus. 1998. (Franklin Ser.). (SPA.). 32p. (J). (ps-3). pap. 5.95 (978-1-880507-44-5(7) , LC7851) Lectorum Pubns., Inc.

Bradman, Tony. Bad Boys. 2003. 169p. (YA). (gr. 7). pap. 9.99 (978-0-552-54761-1(1) , Corgi) Transworld Publishers Ltd. GBR. *Dist:* Independent Pubs. Group.

Brown, Marc. Arthur & the Best Coach Ever. Brown, Marc, illus. 4th ed. 2001. (Arthur Good Sports Ser.: Bk. 4). (Illus.). 64p. (J). (gr. 2-4). 13.95 (978-0-316-11965-8(2)); pap. 4.25 (978-0-316-12117-0(7)) Little, Brown Bks. for Young Readers.

—Arthur & the Best Coach Ever. 2001. (Arthur Good Sports Ser.: Bk. 4). (gr. 3-6). lib. bdg. 11.80 (978-0-613-35627-5(6)); (Illus.). (J). 10.75 (978-0-606-21910-5(2)) Tandem Library Bks.

Browne, Anthony. Willy the Wizard. 2003. (gr. k-3). lib. bdg. 14.15 (978-0-613-63757-2(7)) Tandem Library Bks.

Burkett, Kathy. Foul Play! 2003. (Mad Science Ser.). 112p. (J). pap. 4.50 (978-0-439-44259-6(1) , Scholastic Paperbacks) Scholastic, Inc.

—Foul Play! 2003. (gr. 3-6). lib. bdg. 12.40 (978-0-613-72195-0(0)) Tandem Library Bks.

Chambers, Sally, et al. Waldo'n Ennill y Dydd. 2005. (WEL., Illus.). 32p. pap. (978-1-85596-658-1(1)) Dref Wen.

Chatelier, Ed. What's the Time, Ref? Tell the Time with Manchester United. 2002. (Illus.). 24p. (J). pap. 11.99 (978-0-233-05076-8(0)) Andre Deutsch GBR. *Dist:* Independent Pubs. Group.

Childs, Rob. Big Chance. 2000. (Illus.). 77p. (J). pap. 7.95 (978-0-552-52824-5(2)) Transworld Publishers Ltd. GBR. *Dist:* Trafalgar Square Publishing.

—Big Football Feast. 2000. (Illus.). 89p. (J). pap. 9.95 (978-0-552-54596-9(1)) Transworld Publishers Ltd. GBR. *Dist:* Trafalgar Square Publishing.

—The Big Game. 2000. (Illus.). 78p. (J). pap. 7.95 (978-0-552-52804-7(8)) Transworld Publishers Ltd. GBR. *Dist:* Trafalgar Square Publishing.

—The Big Star. 2000. (Illus.). 76p. (J). pap. 7.99 (978-0-552-52825-2(0)) Transworld Publishers Ltd. GBR. *Dist:* Trafalgar Square Publishing.

—Keeper's Ball. 2005. (Corgi Pups Ser.). (Illus.). 64p. pap. 7.50 (978-0-552-55030-7(2) , Corgi) Transworld Publishers Ltd. GBR. *Dist:* Independent Pubs. Group.

—Soccer Mad, No. 4. 2000. (Yearling Book Ser.). (Illus.). 120p. (J). pap. 8.95 (978-0-440-86344-1(9)) Transworld Publishers Ltd. GBR. *Dist:* Trafalgar Square Publishing.

—Soccer Stars. l.t. ed. 2000. (Illus.). 112p. (978-0-7089-9523-5(3)) Ulverscroft Large Print Bks.

Choyce, Lesley. Sudden Impact. 2005. (Orca Currents Ser.). 112p. (J). (gr. 4-10). pap. 7.95 (978-1-55143-476-6(8)) Orca Bk. Pubs. USA.

Christopher, Matt. Top Wing. ed. 2005. (Sports Classics III Ser.). 154p. (J). lib. bdg. 15.00 (978-1-59054-776-2(4)) Fitzgerald Bks.

Christopher, Matt. The Captain Contest. 2001. 11.79 (978-0-606-22565-6(X)) Tandem Library Bks.

—The Comeback Challenge. 2005. (Sports Classics III Ser.). 147p. (J). lib. bdg. 15.00 (978-1-59054-774-8(8)) Fitzgerald Bks.

—Goalkeeper in Charge: Will Tina's Shyness Ruin Her Chances to Play Keeper? ed. 2005. (Sports Classics III Ser.). 139p. (J). lib. bdg. 15.00 (978-1-59054-758-8(6)) Fitzgerald Bks.

—Goalkeeper in Charge: Will Tina's Shyness Ruin Her Chances to Play Keeper? 2002. 144p. (J). (gr. 3-7). pap. 4.99 (978-0-316-07548-0(5)) Little, Brown Bks. for Young Readers.

—Heads Up! 2000. (J). (978-0-316-13730-0(8)) Little Brown & Co.

—Heads Up! Vasconcellos, Daniel, illus. 6th ed. 2003. (Soccer 'Cats Ser.: No. 6). 64p. (J). (gr. 1-4). pap. 4.99 (978-0-316-16497-9(6)) Little, Brown Bks. for Young Readers.

—El Mediocampista, Soccer Halfback. 2005. (SPA.). 176p. (J). 15.95 (978-0-316-73758-6(5)) Little Brown & Co.

—On the Court with... Kobe Bryant. 2001. (Illus.). 128p. (J). (gr. 3-7). pap. 4.99 (978-0-316-13732-4(4)) Little, Brown Bks. for Young Readers.

—Operation Baby-Sitter. 2001. (978-0-606-22564-9(1)) Tandem Library Bks.

—Soccer 'Cats: Switch Play! 2003. (gr. k-3). lib. bdg. 13.00 (978-0-613-71889-9(5)) Tandem Library Bks.

—Soccer Duel. 2000. (Illus.). 148p. (J). (gr. 3-7). 15.95 (978-0-316-13474-3(0)) Little Brown & Co.

—Soccer Duel. 2000. (ps-7). 148p. (J). per. 12.40 (978-0-613-26983-4(7)); (978-0-606-18265-2(9)) Tandem Library Bks.

—Soccer Duel: There Are Two Sides to Every Story... 2000. 160p. (J). (gr. 3-7). pap. 4.99 (978-0-316-13406-4(6)) Little Brown & Co.

—Soccer Halfback. 2007. 144p. (J). lib. bdg. (***978-1-59953-110-6(0)***) Norwood Hse. Pr.

—Soccer Hero. rev. ed. 2007. 74p. (J). (gr. 3-7). pap. 4.99 (***978-0-316-11345-8(X)***) Little, Brown Bks. for Young Readers.

—Soccer Scoop. ed. 2005. (Sports Classics III Ser.). 137p. (J). lib. bdg. 15.00 (978-1-59054-772-4(1)) Fitzgerald Bks.

—Soccer Scoop. 2007. (J). lib. bdg. (***978-1-59953-117-5(8)***) Norwood Hse. Pr.

—Switch Play! Vasconcellos, Daniel, illus. 9th ed. 2003. (Soccer 'Cats Ser.: No. 9). 64p. (J). (gr. 2-4). pap. 4.99 (978-0-316-73807-1(7)) Little, Brown Bks. for Young Readers.

—You Lucky Dog. Vasconcellos, Daniel, illus. 8th ed. 2003. (Soccer 'Cats Ser.: No. 8). 64p. (J). (gr. 1-4). pap. 4.99 (978-0-316-73805-7(0)) Little, Brown Bks. for Young Readers.

—You Lucky Dog. 2003. (gr. k-3). lib. bdg. 13.00 (978-0-613-71888-2(7)) Tandem Library Bks.

Clark, Brenda, illus. Franklin Plays the Game. 2002. (Franklin Ser.). 12.40 (978-1-4046-0317-2(4)) Book Wholesalers, Inc.

Colgan, Trevor. The Stretford Enders - Square One. 2003. 256p. pap. 9.99 (978-0-09-943219-7(6) , Red Fox) Random Hse. Children's Bks. GBR. *Dist:* Independent Pubs. Group.

Costello, Emily. Calling the Shots. 1999. (Soccer Stars Ser.: No. 7). (J). (gr. 3-7). (978-0-606-17152-6(5)) Tandem Library Bks.

—Foul Play, 1. 1998. (Soccer Stars Ser.: No. 1). (J). (gr. 3-7). (978-0-606-13785-0(8)) Tandem Library Bks.

—On the Sidelines. 1998. (Soccer Stars Ser.: No. 2). (J). (gr. 3-7). (978-0-606-13786-7(6)) Tandem Library Bks.

—Teaming Up. 1999. (Soccer Stars Ser.: No. 8). (J). (gr. 3-7). (978-0-606-17749-8(3)) Tandem Library Bks.

Couric, Katie. The Blue Ribbon Day. Priceman, Marjorie, illus. 2004. 32p. (gr. k-2). 15.95 (978-0-385-50142-2(0)); (gr. 3-6). 17.95 (978-0-385-51292-3(9)) Doubleday Publishing. (Doubleday).

Culver, Dan. My Little Everest: A Story about Dealing with Fear. 2000. (Illus.). 48p. (J). (gr. 3-7). 11.95 (978-1-55039-105-3(4)) Sono Nis Pr. CAN. *Dist:* Orca Bk. Pubs. USA.

Dabbs, Douglas, illus. The Legend's Granddaughter: Not Quite Super, Book 1. 2007. 281p. (J). pap. (***978-0-9793168-0-7(4)***) NQSBks.

Davies, Elgan Philip. Cic o'r Smotyn. 2005. (WEL., Illus.). 56p. (978-1-902416-18-2(X)) Cymdeithas Lyfrau Ceredigion.

Deem, Saitofi Anne. Myrtle Makes a Choice. 1998. (Teachable Moments Ser.). (Illus.). 8p. (J). (ps-3). pap. 7.95 (978-1-930694-02-6(4)) Myrtle Learns.

Diersch, Sandra. Alecia's Challenge. 1999. (gr. 3-6). lib. bdg. 13.55 (978-0-613-29543-7(9)) Tandem Library Bks.

—Great Lengths. 1999. 12.30 (978-0-606-17668-2(3)) Tandem Library Bks.

—Offside! 2001. (gr. 5-8). lib. bdg. 13.55 (978-0-613-78317-0(4)) Tandem Library Bks.

Diersch, Sandra. Play On. 2004. (Sports Stories Ser.). 96p. (gr. 4-8). (***978-1-55028-857-5(1)***); (J). 7.95 (978-1-55028-856-8(3)) Lorimer, James & Co., Ltd., Pubs. CAN. *Dist:* Casemate Pubs. & Bk. Distributors, LLC.

Downes, Alice. Soccer Season. 2002. (ps-2). lib. bdg. 10.95 (978-0-613-50501-7(8)) Tandem Library Bks.

The Dream Team: Individual Title Six-Pack Pouch - Level J. (Lighthouse Ser.). 16p. (gr. 2 up). 28.00 (978-0-7578-0865-4(4)) Rigby Education.

Durant. Super Sub. 2003. (Illus.). 80p. (J). pap. 5.99 (978-0-330-37450-7(8) , Pan) Pan Macmillan GBR. *Dist:* Trafalgar Square Publishing.

—Team on Tour. 2003. (Illus.). 86p. (J). pap. 6.99 (978-0-330-35131-7(1) , Pan) Pan Macmillan GBR. *Dist:* Trafalgar Square Publishing.

Elliott, Laura. Hunter & Stripe & the Soccer Showdown. Munsinger, Lynn, illus. 2005. 32p. (J). (ps-2). lib. bdg. 16.89 (978-0-06-052760-0(9)) HarperCollins Pubs.

Elliott, Laura Malone. Hunter & Stripe & the Soccer Showdown. Munsinger, Lynn, illus. 2005. 32p. (J). (ps-2). 15.99 (978-0-06-052759-4(5)) HarperCollins Pubs.

Esckilsen, Erik E. Offsides. 2004. 176p. (YA). (gr. 5-9). tchr. ed. 15.00 (978-0-618-46284-1(8) , Walter Lorraine) Houghton Mifflin Co. Trade & Reference Div.

Farrell, John. It's Just a Game. Cymerman, John E., illus. 2003. 32p. (J). (gr. k-2). 15.95 (978-1-56397-785-5(0)); pap. 9.95 (978-1-56397-824-1(5)) Boyds Mills Pr.

—It's Just a Game. 1999. (gr. k-3). lib. bdg. 16.40 (978-0-613-78899-1(0)) Tandem Library Bks.

Finchler, Judy. You're a Good Sport, Miss Malarkey. O'Malley, Kevin, illus. 2002. 32p. (J). 2004. pap. 6.95 (978-0-8027-7700-3(7)); 2002. 15.95 (978-0-8027-8815-3(7)) Walker & Co.

Fitzgerald, Dawn. Soccer Chick Rules. 2006. 160p. (J). 16.95 (978-1-59643-137-9(7)) Roaring Brook Pr.

FitzGerald, Dawn. Soccer Chick Rules. 2007. 160p. (J). pap. 6.99 (***978-0-312-37662-8(6)***) Square Fish.

A Fufu on the Soccer Team. 2001. 65p. (J). 14.95 (978-0-9709119-6-4(3)) Limpid Butterfly Productions, The.

Furgang, Kathy. Chaparro se une al equipo & Shrimp Joins the Team. 2005. spiral bd. 66.00 (***978-1-4108-5651-7(8)***) Benchmark Education Co.

Gibbons, Alan. Julie & Me: Treble Trouble. 2006. 176p. (J). pap. 11.99 (***978-1-84255-077-9(2)***) Orion Publishing Group, Ltd. GBR. *Dist:* Independent Pubs. Group.

—Julie & Me & Michael Owen Makes Three. 2006. 208p. (J). pap. 11.99 (***978-1-84255-048-9(9)***) Orion Publishing Group, Ltd. GBR. *Dist:* Independent Pubs. Group.

Gikow, Louise. The Big Game. Garner, Phil, illus. 2004. (My First Reader Pb Ser.). 32p. (J). (gr. k-1). pap. 3.95 (978-0-516-25500-2(2) , Children's Pr.) Scholastic Library Publishing.

—The Big Game. Garner, Phil, tr. Garner, Phil, illus. 2004. (My First Reader Ser.). 31p. (J). 18.50 (978-0-516-24408-2(6) , Children's Pr.) Scholastic Library Publishing.

Golden Books Staff. Go, Go, Goal! 2008. (Book & CD Ser.). (Illus.). 24p. (J). (ps-2). pap. 5.99 (***978-0-375-84297-9(7)*** , Golden Bks.) Random Hse. Children's Bks.

The Green Dragons: Individual Title Six-Packs. 16p. (gr. 2 up). 35.00 (978-0-7635-9232-5(3)) Rigby Education.

Greene, Stephanie. Owen Foote, Soccer Star. Weston, Martha, illus. 96p. (J). 2001. (gr. 4-6). pap. 5.95 (978-0-618-13055-9(1)); 1998. (gr. k-3). tchr. ed. 14.00 (978-0-395-86143-1(8)) Houghton Mifflin Co. Trade & Reference Div. (Clarion Bks.).

—Owen Foote, Soccer Star. 2001. (978-0-606-22276-1(6)) Tandem Library Bks.

Guest, Jacqueline. Soccer Star! 2003. (Sports Stories Ser.). 104p. (J). (gr. 3-8). 7.95 (978-1-55028-788-2(5)); (***978-1-55028-789-9(3)***) Lorimer, James & Co., Ltd., Pubs. CAN. *Dist:* Casemate Pubs. & Bk. Distributors, LLC.

Guillain, Adam. Bella's Brazilian Football. Erkocak, Sahin, illus. 2007. (Bella Balistica Ser.). 32p. (J). pap. 8.95 (978-1-84059-488-1(8)) Milet Publishing.

Gutman, Dan. The Million Dollar Kick. rev. ed. 2003. 208p. (gr. 3-7). pap. 5.99 (978-0-7868-1584-5(1)) Hyperion Bks. for Children.

—The Million Dollar Kick. 2nd ed. 2006. (Illus.). 208p. (gr. 3-7). pap. 5.99 (978-1-4231-0082-9(4)) Hyperion Pr.

—The Million Dollar Kick. 2003. (gr. 3-6). lib. bdg. 14.15 (978-0-613-74962-6(6)) Tandem Library Bks.

Hamm, Mia. Winners Never Quit! Thompson, Carol, illus. 32p. (J). 2006. pap. 6.99 (978-0-06-074052-8(3) , Harper Trophy); 2004. lib. bdg. 16.89 (978-0-06-074051-1(5)); 2004. 16.99 (978-0-06-074050-4(7)) HarperCollins Pubs.

Hammerle, S. & Trapp, K. Let's Try Soccer. 2006. (Illus.). 24p. (J). 12.95 (978-0-7358-2092-0(9)) North-South Bks., Inc.

Harcourt School Publishers Staff. My School Year. 3rd ed. 2002. (Trophies English Language Learners Ser.). (Illus.). pap. 5.10 (978-0-15-327715-3(7)) Harcourt Schl. Pubs.

—1, 2, 3, Kick! Take-Home Book. rev. ed. 2001. (Collections Ser.: Vol. 6). (Illus.). (J). pap. 1.90 (978-0-15-317819-1(1)) Harcourt Schl. Pubs.

Hardcastle, Michael. My Brother's a Keeper. Moulder, Bob, illus. 2007. (Graphic Quest Ser.). 32p. (J). (***978-1-59889-212-3(6)*** , 1256168) Stone Arch Bks.

Hardcastle, Michael. Soccer Star. Cox, Ken, illus. 2002. (Yellow Bananas Ser.). 48p. (J). (gr. 3-4). pap. (978-0-7787-0979-4(5)); lib. bdg. (978-0-7787-0933-6(7)) Crabtree Publishing Co.

—Soccer Star. 2002. (gr. 3-6). lib. bdg. 12.95 (978-0-613-52909-9(X)) Tandem Library Bks.

Harrison, Paul. Billy's Big Game, Level P. RAGA, Silvia, illus. 2006. (Lightning Readers Ser.). 32p. (J). pap. 3.95 (978-0-7696-4177-5(6) , Gingham Dog Pr.) School Specialty Publishing.

—El gran partido de Guille, Level P. RAGA, Silvia, illus. 2006. (Lightning Readers Ser.). 32p. (J). pap. 3.95 (978-0-7696-4207-9(1) , Gingham Dog Pr.) School Specialty Publishing.

Harrison/Raga, Paul/Silvia. Billy's Big Game. 2005. (Illus.). 32p. (J). lib. bdg. 9.00 (***978-1-4242-0878-4(5)***) Fitzgerald Bks.

Hicks, Betty. Goof-Off Goalie. McCauley, Adam, illus. 2008. (J). (***978-1-59643-244-4(6)***) Roaring Brook Pr.

Hunter, Dawn. Heads Up! 2001. (gr. 5-8). lib. bdg. 13.55 (978-0-613-78315-6(8)) Tandem Library Bks.

Hunter, Dawn & Hunter, Karen. Heads Up! 2001. (Sports Stories Ser.). 85p. (gr. 3-8). (J). (***978-1-55028-719-6(2)***); 7.95 (978-1-55028-718-9(4)) Lorimer, James & Co., Ltd., Pubs. CAN. *Dist:* Casemate Pubs. & Bk. Distributors, LLC.

Isaac, Christine Verney. Faith's Journey. Vaughn, Patrika, ed. Donato, Angela, illus. 2001. 112p. (J). (gr. 2-7). 17.95 (978-0-9706576-3-3(3) , Advocate Hse.) A Cappela Publishing.

Jones, Miranda. Little Genie: A Puff of Pink. Calver, David, tr. Calver, David, illus. 2004. 128p. (gr. 1-3). lib. bdg. 10.99 (978-0-385-90188-8(7) , Delacorte Bks. for Young Readers) Random Hse. Children's Bks.

—Puff of Pink. 2006. (Little Genie Ser.). (Illus.). 128p. (J). (gr. 1-3). pap. 4.99 (978-0-440-41975-4(1) , Yearling) Random Hse. Children's Bks.

King, Donna. Kick Off. 2007. 168p. (J). (gr. 3-5). pap. 5.95 (***978-0-7534-6082-5(3)*** , Kingfisher) Houghton Mifflin Co. Trade & Reference Div.

Knowlton, Laurie. N 2 Deep. 2004. 128p. (J). pap. 5.99 (978-1-4003-0327-4(3)) Nelson, Thomas Inc.

Korman, Gordon. No Girly-Girls Allowed! 2000. (gr. 3-6). lib. bdg. 13.00 (978-0-613-31529-6(4)) Tandem Library Bks.

Krensky, Stephen. Louise, Soccer Star? Natti, Susanna, illus. 2002. (Chapters Ser.). 80p. (J). pap. 4.99 (978-0-14-230139-5(6) , Puffin) Penguin Group (USA) Inc.

—Louise, Soccer Star? 2002. (gr. 3-6). lib. bdg. 13.00 (978-0-613-50342-6(2)) Tandem Library Bks.

Leon McCann, Jesse. Scooby-Doo & the Soccer Monster. del Sur, Duendes, illus. 2004. (Scooby Doo Ser.). 24p. (J). pap. 5.99 (978-0-439-54602-7(8)) Scholastic, Inc.

Lineker, Gary. More of Gary Lineker's Favourite Football Stories. 2003. 211p. (J). 19.99 (978-0-333-73782-8(2)) Macmillan Publishers Ltd. GBR. *Dist:* Trafalgar Square Publishing.

London, Jonathan. Froggy Juega al Futbol. 2003. (Froggy Ser.). (SPA., Illus.). (J). (gr. k-2). pap. 3.16 net. (978-0-439-24321-6(1) , SO30406) Scholastic, Inc.

—Froggy Plays Soccer. Remkiewicz, Frank, illus. 32p. (J). (ps-3). 2001. pap. 5.99 (978-0-14-056809-7(3) , Puffin); 1999. 15.99 (978-0-670-88257-1(7) , Viking Juvenile) Penguin Group (USA) Inc.

—Froggy Plays Soccer. 2001. (gr. k-3). lib. bdg. 14.15 (978-0-613-35949-8(6)); (Illus.). (J). 12.79 (978-0-606-21204-5(3)) Tandem Library Bks.

Maccarone, Grace. Un Partido de Futbol. Johnson, Meredith, illus. 1998. (Coleccion "Hola, Lector" Ser.). (SPA.). 32p. (J). (ps-1). pap. 3.99 (978-0-590-27499-9(6) , SO7596, Cartwheel Bks.) Scholastic, Inc.

—Un Partido de Futbol. 1998. (Mariposa Scholastica en Espanol Ser.). (J). (978-0-606-13882-6(X)) Tandem Library Bks.

MacDonald, Alan. Trolls United! Beech, Mark, illus. 2007. 128p. (J). (gr. 1-5). 14.95 (***978-1-59990-125-1(0)***); pap. 5.95 (***978-1-59990-126-8(9)***) Bloomsbury Publishing.

Maddox, Jake. Soccer Shootout. Tiffany, Sean, illus. 2008. (J). pap. (***978-1-59889-896-5(5)***); lib. bdg. (***978-1-59889-844-6(2)***) Stone Arch Bks.

Mammano, Julie. Rhinos Who Play Soccer. 2001. (Illus.). 32p. (J). (ps-1). 12.95 (978-0-8118-2779-9(8)) Chronicle Bks. LLC.

Mantell, Paul. Soccer Dual. ed. 2005. (Sports Classics III Ser.). 153p. (J). lib. bdg. 15.00 (978-1-59054-771-7(3)) Fitzgerald Bks.

Marsh, Carole. The Secret Soccer Ball. 2006. 64p. (gr. 2-4). 14.95 (***978-0-635-06219-2(4)***); pap. 3.99 (***978-0-635-06213-0(5)***) Gallopade International.

Marzollo, Jean. Companeros en el Futbol. Trivas, Irene, illus. 1999. (Coleccion "Hola, Lector" Ser.). (SPA.). 48p. (J). (gr. 2-4). pap. 3.99 (978-0-439-08056-9(8) , SO8904, Scholastic en Espanol) Scholastic, Inc.

—Companeros en el Futbol. 1999. (J). lib. bdg. 10.79 (978-0-606-17055-0(3)); (SPA.). (gr. 3-6). lib. bdg. 11.80 (978-0-613-16916-5(6)) Tandem Library Bks.

May, Eleanor. The Great Shape-Up. Gott, Barry, illus. 2007. (Science Solves It! Ser.). 32p. (J). (gr. 1-3). 4.99 (***978-1-57565-248-1(X)***) Kane Pr., The.

May, Steve. Dazzer Plays On. 2000. 192p. (J). pap. 8.99 (978-0-7497-3431-2(0)) Egmont Bks., Ltd. GBR. *Dist:* Independent Pubs. Group.

Mayfield, Sue. Shoot! Cox, Ken, illus. 2001. (Blue Bananas Ser.). 48p. (J). (gr. 1-2). (978-0-7787-0847-6(0)); pap. (978-0-7787-0893-3(4)) Crabtree Publishing Co.

—Shoot! 2002. lib. bdg. 12.95 (978-0-613-52906-8(5)) Tandem Library Bks.

McGinley, Jerry. Joaquin Strikes Back. 1998. 158p. (YA). (gr. 5-10). 18.95 (978-0-936389-58-5(3)) Tudor Pubs., Inc.

McLoughlin, Tom. My First Soccer Book: A Story, Coloring & Parent-Child Activity Book. McLoughlin, Damien & Albrecht, Jan, illus. 1998. (Soccer Kids Ser.). 16p. (J). (ps-k). pap. 4.95 (978-0-9666681-8-6(9)) United Publishing.

McNamara, Margaret. The Playground Problem. Gordon, Mike, illus. 2005. (Ready-to-Read Ser. Level 1). 32p. (J). lib. bdg. 15.00 (978-1-59054-931-5(7)) Fitzgerald Bks.

McNamara, Margaret & Gordon, Mike. The Playground Problem. 2004. (Robin Hill School Ser.). (Illus.). 32p. (J). pap. 3.99 (978-0-689-85876-5(0) , Aladdin) Simon & Schuster Children's Publishing.

McNaughton, Colin. Preston's Goal! 2001. (978-0-606-22599-1(4)) Tandem Library Bks.

Moeyaert, Bart & Boeke, Wanda. Dani Bennoni. 2008. (YA). (***978-1-932425-97-0(7)*** , Front Street) Boyds Mills Pr.

Morningstar, Jeremy. Penalty Kick. 2005. 56p. pap. 9.00 (978-1-4116-6572-9(4)) Lulu.com.

Morpurgo, Michael. Billy the Kid. Foreman, Michael, illus. 2000. 80p. (J). 22.99 (978-1-86205-361-8(8) , Pavilion Bks., Ltd.) Anova Bks. GBR. *Dist:* Trafalgar Square Publishing.

Mueller, Ross. The Big Ball of String. Smith, Craig, illus. 2005. 32p. (J). (ps-ps). 14.95 (978-1-74114-044-6(7)) Allen & Unwin AUS. *Dist:* Independent Pubs. Group.

Murphy, Stuart J. Game Time! Jabar, Cynthia, illus. 2000. (Mathstart Ser.). (J). 11.79 (978-0-606-19984-1(5)) Tandem Library Bks.

Myers, Bill. My Life As a Stupendously Stomped Soccer Star. 2006. (Incredible Worlds of Wally McDoogle Ser.). 128p. (J). pap. 6.99 (978-1-4003-0635-0(3)) Nelson, Thomas Inc.

Olsen, Sylvia. Murphy & Mousetrap. 2005. (Orca Young Readers Ser.). (Illus.). 128p. (J). (gr. 3-6). pap. 5.95 (978-1-55143-344-8(3)) Orca Bk. Pubs. USA.

Orme, David. Space Games. Savage, Paul, illus. 2007. 40p. (J). (*978-1-59889-246-8(0)) Stone Arch Bks.

Orr, Tamra. No Hands Allowed, Plus Robbie & Ryan Play Indoor Soccer, 11 vols., Set. 2006. (Robbie Reader, Weekend Soccer Ser.). (J). (gr. 1-4). lib. bdg. (978-1-58415-490-7(X)) Mitchell Lane Pubs., Inc.

Pee-Wee Soccer. 2003. (J). per. (978-1-57657-941-1(7)) Paradise Pr., Inc.

Peet, Mal. Alf Saves the Day. Hammond, Andy, illus. 2004. 24p. (J). lib. bdg. 22.65 (*978-1-59646-692-0(8)) Dingles & Co.

Peet, Mal. Keeper. 240p. (J). (gr. 5). 2007. pap. 6.99 (978-0-7636-3286-1(4)); 2005. 15.99 (978-0-7636-2749-2(6)) Candlewick Pr.

Popescu, Petru. Weregirls: Birth of the Pack. rev. ed. 2007. 352p. (YA). (gr. 8 up). pap. 9.95 (*978-0-7653-1641-7(2) , Tor Teen) Doherty, Tom Assocs., LLC.

Portratz, Wendy. Agnes Plays Soccer: A Young Cow's Lesson in Sportsmanship. 2006. 90p. (J). per. 9.95 (978-1-59886-326-0(6)) Tate Publishing & Enterprises, L.L.C.

Posner, Pat. Princess Fidgety Feet. Norman, Philip, illus. 2003. 32p. (J). 15.95 (978-1-57768-447-3(8) , Gingham Dog Pr.) School Specialty Publishing.

Price, Mathew. Me Encanta el Futbol. (SPA.). pap. 11.95 (978-950-07-2081-6(7)) Editorial Sudamericana S.A. ARG. *Dist:* Distribooks, Inc.

Priddy, Roger. Sticker Activity Fun Soccer. 2007. 24p. (J). pap. 3.95 (*978-0-312-50009-2(2) , Priddy Bks.) St. Martin's Pr.

Rayner, Robert. Falling Star. 2007. (Sports Stories Ser.). 136p. (J). (gr. 3-8). 7.95 (*978-1-55028-970-1(5)) Lorimer, James & Co., Ltd., Pubs. CAN. *Dist:* Casemate Pubs. & Bk. Distributors, LLC.

—Out of Sight. 2006. (Sports Stories Ser.). 112p. (J). (gr. 3-8). (*978-1-55028-919-0(5)); 7.95 (978-1-55028-918-3(7)) Lorimer, James & Co., Ltd., Pubs. CAN. *Dist:* Casemate Pubs. & Bk. Distributors, LLC.

—Suspended. 2004. (Sports Stories Ser.). 112p. (J). (gr. 4-8). (*978-1-55028-861-2(X)); 7.95 (978-1-55028-860-5(1)) Lorimer, James & Co., Ltd., Pubs. CAN. *Dist:* Casemate Pubs. & Bk. Distributors, LLC.

Rayner, Shoo. Ginger Ninja 5: World Cup Winners. (Illus.). 63p. (J). (gr. k-6). pap. 8.99 (978-0-340-69379-7(7) , Hodder & Stoughton) Hodder General Publishing Division GBR. *Dist:* Trafalgar Square Publishing.

Redmond, Diane. Wendy's Big Game. Hot Animation Staff, Animation, illus. 2003. (Bob the Builder Ser.: Vol. 6). 24p. (J). pap. 3.50 (978-0-689-85460-6(9) , Simon Spotlight) Simon & Schuster Children's Publishing.

—Wendy's Big Game. 2003. (Illus.). 32p. (gr. k-3). lib. bdg. 11.25 (978-0-613-58170-7(9)) Tandem Library Bks.

Regan, Peter. Dynamo Rouge. 2000. (Riverside Ser.: Vol. 6). (Illus.). 112p. (J). (gr. 3-7). pap. 7.95 (978-1-901737-21-9(7)) Anvil Bks., Ltd. IRL. *Dist:* Dufour Editions, Inc.

—Riverside: The Curse. Myler, Terry, illus. 2004. 127p. (J). pap. 9.95 (978-1-901737-46-2(2)) Anvil Bks., Ltd. IRL. *Dist:* Dufour Editions, Inc.

—Riverside Loot! 2000. (Riverside Ser.: Vol. 5). (Illus.). 112p. (J). (gr. 3-7). pap. 7.95 (978-1-901737-19-6(5)) Anvil Bks., Ltd. IRL. *Dist:* Dufour Editions, Inc.

—Scout! Myler, Terry, illus. 2001. 112p. (J). pap. 7.95 (978-1-901737-22-6(5)) Anvil Bks., Ltd. IRL. *Dist:* Dufour Editions, Inc.

Remkiewicz, Frank, illus. Froggy Plays Soccer. 2002. (Froggy Ser.). (J). 13.19 (978-0-7587-5111-9(7)) Book Wholesalers, Inc.

Riding, John. Sean's World Cup Final Day Out - Wembley 1966. 2006. 97p. (YA). pap. (978-1-84685-059-2(2) , Exposure Publishing) Meadow Bks.

Rigby, Robert. Goal! 2: Living the Dream. 2007. (Illus.). 224p. (YA). pap. 6.95 (978-0-15-205881-4(8) , Harcourt Paperbacks) Harcourt Children's Bks.

Rigby, Robert. Goal III. 2008. (Illus.). 240p. (YA). pap. 6.95 (*978-0-15-205921-7(0) , Harcourt Paperbacks) Harcourt Children's Bks.

Rigby, Robert & Random House U. K. Ltd. Staff. Goal! The Dream Begins. 2006. (Illus.). 240p. (YA). pap. 6.95 (978-0-15-205798-5(6) , Harcourt Paperbacks) Harcourt Children's Bks.

Rivers, Camilla Reghelini. Off the Wall. 2001. (Sports Stories Ser.). 128p. (gr. 3-8). (J). (*978-1-55028-751-6(6)); 7.95 (978-1-55028-750-9(8)) Lorimer, James & Co., Ltd., Pubs. CAN. *Dist:* Casemate Pubs. & Bk. Distributors, LLC.

Robinson, Amy. Sam's Soccer Problem. Carrozza, Kyle A., illus. 2001. 32p. (J). 9.95 (978-1-58284-006-2(7) , SSP001, Thoughtful Education Pr., The) Silver Strong & Assocs.

Rockwell, Anne F. Morgan Plays Soccer. Meisel, Paul, illus. 1999. 32p. (J). (ps-1). pap. 5.95 (978-0-06-446739-1(2)) HarperCollins Pubs.

Ross, David. How We Got Back into the Inter-Schools Football Competition. Thomas, Jacqui, illus. 96p. (J). 8.95 (978-0-14-130014-6(0)) Penguin Bks., Ltd. GBR. *Dist:* Penguin Group (USA) Inc.

Rosseau, Paul. Docteur Soccer. Mongeau, Marc, illus. 2002. (Roman Jeunesse Ser.). (FRE.). 96p. (J). (gr. 4-7). pap. (978-2-89021-582-5(2)) Diffusion du livre Mirabel.

Rushby, Pamela. Shadows in the Garden. 2000. (gr. 7-12). lib. bdg. 12.25 (978-0-613-29063-0(1)) Tandem Library Bks.

Schraff, Anne. Phantom Falcon. 2000. (gr. 7-12). lib. bdg. 11.80 (978-0-613-51054-7(2)) Tandem Library Bks.

Scroggs, Kirk Brandon. Super Soccer Freak Show. 4th ed. 2007. (Wiley & Grampa's Creature Features Ser.: No. 4). (Illus.). 112p. (J). (gr. 3-7). 12.99 (978-0-316-05946-6(3)); pap. 3.99 (978-0-316-05947-3(1)) Little Brown & Co.

Scudamore, Beverly. Foul Play. 2005. (Sports Stories Ser.). 112p. (J). (gr. 3-8). (*978-1-55028-875-9(X)); 7.95 (978-1-55028-874-2(1)) Lorimer, James & Co., Ltd., Pubs. CAN. *Dist:* Casemate Pubs. & Bk. Distributors, LLC.

Seto, Andy. Shaolin Soccer. 2005. (Illus.). 128p. (YA). Vol. 1. pap. 13.95 (978-1-58899-318-2(3)); Vol. 2. pap. 13.95 (978-1-58899-319-9(1)) ComicsOne Corp./Dr. Masters.

Shahan, Sherry. That's Not How You Play Soccer, Daddy! Mai-Wyss, Tatjana, illus. 2007. 32p. (J). (ps-3). 15.95 (*978-1-56145-416-7(8) , Peachtree Junior) Peachtree Pubs., Ltd.

Sheldon, Tom. Big Match Manager 2. Burton, Nathaniel, illus. 2006. 288p. (J). pap. 11.99 (*978-0-7475-8205-2(X)) Bloomsbury Publishing Plc GBR. *Dist:* Independent Pubs. Group.

Sinclair, Jay. No Girly-Girls Allowed! 2000. (Jersey Ser.). (Illus.). (J). (978-0-606-20737-9(6)) Tandem Library Bks.

Sis, Peter. Madlenka's Soccer Ball. 2005. (J). (978-0-375-82852-2(4)); lib. bdg. (978-0-375-92852-9(9)) Random Hse., Inc.

Skead, Robert. Elves Can't Kick. 2005. 84p. per. 7.99 (978-1-929478-66-8(6)) Cross Training Publishing.

Sloan, Holly Goldberg. Keeper. 2003. 146p. 9.95 (978-0-9708992-3-1(8)) Scobre Pr. Corp.

Smiley, Sophie. Bobby, Charlton & the Mountain. 2003. (Illus.). 64p. (J). pap. 7.99 (978-1-84270-178-2(9)) Andersen GBR. *Dist:* Independent Pubs. Group.

Stamper, Judith Bauer. Go, Fractions! Demarest, Chris L., illus. 2003. (All Aboard Math Reader Station Stop Ser.). 48p. (J). (gr. 2-3). pap. 3.99 (978-0-448-43113-0(0) , Grosset & Dunlap) Penguin Group (USA) Inc.

—Go, Fractions! 2003. lib. bdg. 11.80 (978-0-613-64044-2(6)) Tandem Library Bks.

Staunton, Ted. Great Play, Morgan. Slavin, Bill, illus. 2001. (First Novels Ser.: Vol. 19). 61p. (gr. 1-5). (978-0-88780-537-0(X)); 4.95 (978-0-88780-536-3(1)) Formac Publishing Co., Ltd. CAN. *Dist:* Casemate Pubs. & Bk. Distributors, LLC.

Stephen, Smith. Red Card. 2006. 128p. (J). pap. 5.99 (978-0-7847-1438-6(X) , 42143) Standard Publishing.

Stern, Ricki & Worcester, Heidi P. Beryl E. Bean Book 1: Mighty Adventurer of the Planet. Bates, Amy June, illus. 2002. (Beryl E. Bean Ser.). 64p. (J). (gr. 2-4). pap. 5.95 (978-0-06-442120-1(1)) HarperCollins Pubs.

Stuve-Bodeen, Stephanie. Babu's Song. Boyd, Aaron, illus. 2003. 32p. (J). 16.95 (978-1-58430-058-8(2)) Lee & Low Bks., Inc.

Swanson, Julie A. Going for the Record. 2004. 223p. (J). pap. 8.00 (978-0-8028-5273-1(4)) Eerdmans, William B. Publishing Co.

Tamar, Erika. Venus & the Comets. 2004. (Junior Library Guild Selection Ser.). 96p. (J). (gr. 2 up). 14.95 (978-1-58196-007-5(7)); pap. 4.99 (978-1-58196-018-1(2)) Darby Creek Publishing.

Teamwork Works. 2005. 39p. (J). 3.99 (978-0-9763213-3-0(5)) OHC Group LLC.

Tigelaar, Liz. Pretty Tough. 2007. 256p. (YA). (gr. 5-12). 8.99 (978-1-59514-112-5(X) , Razorbill) Penguin Group (USA) Inc.

Torrey, Richard. Beans Baker's Best Shot. 2006. (Illus.). 48p. (J). (gr. 1-3). lib. bdg. 11.99 (978-0-375-92839-0(1)); (Step into Reading Ser.: Vol. 3). 3.99 (978-0-375-82839-3(7)) Random Hse. Children's Bks. (Random Hse. Bks. for Young Readers).

Tulloch, Richard. Weird Stuff. 2006. (Illus.). 208p. (J). 16.95 (978-0-8027-8058-4(X)) Walker & Co.

Wallace, Rich. Double Fake. 2005. (Winning Season Ser.: No. 4). 128p. (J). (gr. 3-7). 14.99 (978-0-670-05943-0(9) , Viking Juvenile) Penguin Group (USA) Inc.

—Shots on Goal. 1998. 160p. (YA). (gr. 7-11). pap. 5.99 (978-0-679-88671-6(0) , Laurel Leaf) Random Hse. Children's Bks.

Wallace, Rich & Warner, Sally. Not-So-Weird Emma: Double Fake. Harper, Jamie, illus. 2005. 128p. (J). (gr. 3-7). 14.99 (978-0-670-06005-4(4) , Viking Adult) Penguin Group (USA) Inc.

Walsh, Sheila. The Purple Ponies. Johnson, Meredith, illus. 2008. (Gigi, God's Little Princess Ser.). 32p. (J). 12.99 (*978-1-4003-1124-8(1)) Nelson, Thomas Inc.

Weeks, Jan. Let Toby Lane Play Goalie. Dickson, David, illus. 2006. 64p. (J). (gr. 2-4). 19.95 (978-1-4048-1668-8(2)) Picture Window Bks.

West, Tracey. El Futbol en Todo el Mundo. Albrecht, Jeff, illus. 2005. (Maya & Miguel Ser.). (SPA.). 32p. (J). (ps-ps). pap. 3.99 (978-0-439-78348-4(8) , Scholastic en Espanol) Scholastic, Inc.

—Sporty Sprite. 2001. (gr. 3-6). lib. bdg. 11.80 (978-0-613-33086-2(2)) Tandem Library Bks.

Weyn, Suzanne. Gracie. 2007. 160p. (YA). (gr. 4-7). pap. 6.95 (*978-1-55704-779-3(0)) Newmarket Pr.

Wilson, Bob. Stanley Bagshaw & the Short-Sighted Football Trainer. 2006. (Stanley Bagshaw Ser.). (Illus.). 32p. (J). pap. 6.95 (978-1-903015-26-1(X)) Barn Owl Bks, London GBR. *Dist:* Independent Pubs. Group.

Zucker, Jonny. The Phantom Striker. Tavares, Victor, illus. 2008. (J). pap. (*978-1-59889-901-6(5)); 33p. (YA). (gr. 5-9). lib. bdg. 21.26 (*978-1-59889-849-1(3)) Stone Arch Bks.

—Soccer Showdown. Troiano, Enzo, illus. 2007. 33p. (J). pap. (*978-1-59889-430-1(7)); 40p. (YA). (gr. 5-9). lib. bdg. 21.26 (*978-1-59889-334-2(3)) Stone Arch Bks.

SOCIAL ADJUSTMENT

Perfection Learning Staff, contrib. by. And Justice for All. 2000. (Literature & Thought Ser.). (Illus.). 144p. (J). (978-0-7807-9665-2(9)); pap. (978-0-7891-5228-2(2)) Perfection Learning Corp.

Rogers, George L. The Seven C's of Thinking Clearly Grades 5-9: Character Based Learning Activities for Developing Emotional. Social & Thinking Skills. Rogers, Gerald R., illus. 2002. 192p. (YA). (gr. 5-9). 24.95 (978-0-938399-13-1(6)) ChoiceSkills, Inc.

SOCIAL CHANGE

Bowden, Rob. Globalization. 2004. (21st Century Debates Ser.). (Illus.). 64p. (J). lib. bdg. 28.56 (978-0-7398-6466-1(1)) Raintree.

Goodier, Steve. Lessons of the Turtle: Living Right Side Up. 2002. 136p. pap. 14.95 (978-1-929664-15-3(X)) Life Support System Publishing, Inc.

Heinz, Brian J. Nathan of Yesteryear & Michael of Today. Friar, Joanne H., illus. 2006. (Exceptional Social Studies Titles for Intermediate Grades). 32p. (J). lib. bdg. 22.60 (978-0-7613-2893-3(9) , Millbrook Pr.) Lerner Publishing Group.

Hill, Laban Carrick. America Dreaming. 2007. (Illus.). 176p. (YA). (gr. 7-17). 19.99 (*978-0-316-00904-1(0)) Little Brown & Co.

Kent, Deborah. Dorothy Day: Friend to the Forgotten. 2004. (Illus.). 187p. (J). pap. 12.00 (978-0-8028-5265-6(3)) Eerdmans, William B. Publishing Co.

Masilela, Johnny. We Shall Not Weep. 2003. 132p. pap. 17.00 (978-0-7957-0147-4(0)) Kwela Bks. ZAF. *Dist:* Independent Pubs. Group.

McNeese, Tim. The Progressive Movement: Advocating Social Change. 2007. (Reform Movements in American History Ser.). 136p. (J). (gr. 6-12). 30.00 (*978-0-7910-9501-0(0) , Chelsea Hse.) Facts On File, Inc.

SOCIAL CLASSES

Hinds, Kathryn. The Patricians. 2004. (Illus.). 72p. (J). 29.93 (978-0-7614-1654-8(4) , Benchmark Bks.) Cavendish, Marshall Corp.

Nardo, Don. Lords, Ladies, Peasants & Knights: Class in the Middle Ages. 2006. (Lucent Library of Historical Eras). 112p. (YA). (gr. 7-10). lib. bdg. 32.45 (978-1-59018-928-3(0) , Lucent Bks.) Thomson Gale.

SOCIAL CONDITIONS

see Social History

SOCIAL CONFLICT

Albright, Jim & Albright, Kim Y. Fight Right! A Christian Approach to Conflict. 1998. (Generation Why Ser.: Vol. 3:7). 36p. (J). (gr. 9-12). pap. 12.95 (978-0-87303-279-7(9)) Faith & Life Pr.

Casey, Carolyn. Conflict Resolution: The Win-Win Situation. 2001. (Teen Issues Ser.). (Illus.). 64p. (YA). (gr. 6-12). lib. bdg. 22.60 (978-0-7660-1584-5(X)) Enslow Pubs., Inc.

Doak, Robin S. Conflict Resolution. 2003. (Illus.). 32p. (J). pap. 7.50 (978-1-4109-0322-8(2)); lib. bdg. 24.28 (978-0-7398-7004-4(1)) Raintree.

Gallagher, Jim & Cavenaugh, Dorothy. A Guys' Guide to Conflict; A Girls' Guide to Conflict. 2008. (Flip-It-over Guides to Teen Emotions Ser.). (Illus.). 128p. (J). (gr. 5 up). lib. bdg. 31.93 (*978-0-7660-2852-4(6)) Enslow Pubs., Inc.

Holt, Rinehart and Winston Staff. Decisions for Health Blue, Chptr. 12: Conflict Management. 4th ed. 2004. pap. 11.20 (978-0-03-068046-5(8)) Holt, Rinehart & Winston.

Judson, Karen. Resolving Conflicts: How to Get along When You Don't Get Along. 2005. (Issues in Focus Today). (Illus.). 112p. (J). (gr. 6-12). lib. bdg. 31.93 (978-0-7660-2359-8(1)) Enslow Pubs., Inc.

Polland, Barbara Kay. We Can Work It Out: Conflict Resolution for Children. 2004. (Illus.). 64p. (J). (ps-5). 13.95 (978-1-58246-031-4(0) , Tricycle Pr.) Ten Speed Pr.

Polland, Barbara Kay & DeRoy, Craig. We Can Work It Out: Conflict Resolution for Children. 2004. (Illus.). 64p. (J). (ps-5). 9.95 (978-1-58246-029-1(9) , Tricycle Pr.) Ten Speed Pr.

Rue, Nancy N. Everything You Need to Know about Peer Mediation. rev. ed. 2001. (Need to Know Library). (Illus.). 64p. (YA). (gr. 4-6). lib. bdg. 25.25 (978-0-8239-3464-5(0)) Rosen Publishing Group, Inc., The.

Sande, Corlette. The Young Peacemaker, 13 vols., Set. 2nd ed. 2002. (J). (gr. 4-6). reprint ed. 29.95 (978-0-9663786-9-6(5)) Shepherd Pr, Inc.

Schmidt, Fran. Mediation for Kids. 3rd ed. 2001. pap., stu. ed. 16.95 (978-1-878227-67-6(X)) Peace Education Foundation.

Slavens, Elaine. Fighting: Without Coming to Blows. Murray, Steven, illus. 2004. (Deal with It Ser.). 32p. (J). (gr. 4-8). 12.95 (978-1-55028-791-2(5)) Lorimer, James & Co., Ltd., Pubs. CAN. *Dist:* Casemate Pubs. & Bk. Distributors, LLC.

Thomas, Pat. Is It Right to Fight? A First Look at Anger. Harker, Lesley, illus. 2003. (First Look at Bks.). 32p. (J). pap. 6.99 (978-0-7641-2458-7(7)) Barron's Educational Series, Inc.

SOCIAL CUSTOMS

see Manners and Customs

SOCIAL DEMOCRACY

see Socialism

SOCIAL DISTINCTIONS

see Social Classes

SOCIAL EQUALITY

see Equality

SOCIAL HISTORY

see also Economic History; Labor and Laboring Classes; Social Problems

Faith-based Initiatives: Solution toTerrorism, Poverty, & Despair. 2004. (978-0-9755927-0-0(X)) Church Without Walls Pubns., Inc.

Hills, Ken & Barber, Nicola. Headlines of World War II. 2005. (Illus.). 46p. (J). pap. 13.95 (978-0-237-52908-6(4) , Evans Brothers, Limited) Evans Publishing Group GBR. *Dist:* Independent Pubs. Group.

Hughes, Shirley. A Brush with the Past 1900-1950: The Years That Changed Our Lives. 2005. (Illus.). 112p. 24.99 (*978-0-370-32839-3(6)) Transworld Publishers Ltd. GBR. *Dist:* Independent Pubs. Group.

Martell, Hazel Mary. Everyday Life in Viking Times. 2005. (Clues to the Past Ser.). (Illus.). 32p. (J). (gr. 4-7). lib. bdg. 27.10 (978-1-932889-80-2(9)) Sea-To-Sea Pubns.

McFall, Sally, ed. Pro/Con, 12 vols. 2002. (Illus.). (YA). (978-0-7172-5928-1(5)); (978-0-7172-5929-8(3)); (978-0-7172-5930-4(7)); (978-0-7172-5931-1(5)); (978-0-7172-5932-8(3)); (978-0-7172-5933-5(1)); (978-0-7172-5754-6(1)); (978-0-7172-5755-3(X)); (978-0-7172-5756-0(8)); (978-0-7172-5757-7(6)); (978-0-7172-5758-4(4)); (978-0-7172-5759-1(2)) Scholastic Library Publishing. (Grolier).

—Pro/Con 3, 12 vols. 2004. (Illus.). (YA). 339.00 (978-0-7172-5927-4(7) , Grolier) Scholastic Library Publishing.

Sharman, Margaret, et al. Headlines of World War I. 2005. (Illus.). 46p. (J). pap. 13.95 (978-0-237-52907-9(6) , Evans Brothers, Limited) Evans Publishing Group GBR. *Dist:* Independent Pubs. Group.

Sonneborn, Liz. The Environmental Movement: Protecting Our Natural Resources. 2007. (Reform Movements in American History Ser.). 128p. (J). (gr. 6-12). 30.00 (*978-0-7910-9537-9(1) , Chelsea Hse.) Facts On File, Inc.

Stearman, Kaye. Homelessness. 1999. (Talking Points Ser.). (Illus.). 64p. (YA). (gr. 4-7). lib. bdg. 27.12 (978-0-8172-5312-7(2)) Raintree.

Townsend, John. Crime Through Time. 2005. (Raintree Freestyle Ser.). (Illus.). 48p. (J). (978-1-4109-2051-5(8)); pap. (978-1-4109-2056-0(9)) Steck-Vaughn.

SOCIAL HYGIENE

see Health; Public Health

SOCIAL LIFE AND CUSTOMS

see Manners and Customs

SOCIAL POLICY

see also Multiculturalism

Marzilli, Alan. Affirmative Action. 2004. (Point/Counterpoint Ser.). (Illus.). 120p. (gr. 9-13). 32.95 (978-0-7910-7918-8(X) , Chelsea Hse.) Facts On File, Inc.

Open for Debate, 6 bks., Group 2. Incl. Animal Testing. Judson, Karen. 144p. (978-0-7614-1882-5(2)); Censorship. Gottfried, Ted. 143p. (978-0-7614-1883-2(0)); Civil Liberties. Spangenburg, Ray & Moser, Diane. 143p. (978-0-7614-1886-3(5)); Environmental Issues. Fridell, Ron. 144p. (978-0-7614-1885-6(7)); Taxes. Kowalski, Kathiann M. 139p. (978-0-7614-1887-0(3)); (Illus.). (J). 2005. 2005. (978-0-7614-1881-8(4) , Benchmark Bks.) Cavendish, Marshall Corp.

SOCIAL PROBLEMS

see also Children—Employment; Crime and Criminals; Discrimination; Divorce; Emigration and Immigration; Ethnic Relations; Housing; Juvenile Delinquency; Migrant Labor; Public Health; Race Relations

Alter, Judy. Cissie Palmer: Putting Wealth to Work. 1999. (Community Builders Ser.). (Illus.). 48p. (J). (gr. 3-5). pap. 6.95 (978-0-516-26345-8(5) , Children's Pr.) Scholastic Library Publishing.

Bausum, Ann. Muckrakers: How Writers Exposed Scandal, Inspired Reform, & Invented Investigative Journalism. 2007. (Illus.). 112p. (YA). (gr. 5 up). 21.95 (*978-1-4263-0137-7(5)); lib. bdg. 32.90 (*978-1-4263-0138-4(3)) National Geographic Society. (National Geographic Children's Bks.).

Dudley, William. Opposing Viewpoints in Social Issues. 2000. (Opposing Viewpoints Ser.). 360p. (YA). (gr. 9-12). 36.20 (978-0-7377-0123-4(4) , Greenhaven Pr., Inc.) Thomson Gale.

Edwards, Nicola. Bullying. (Illus.). 32p. 18.95 (978-1-932333-07-7(X)) Chrysalis Education.

Engelbert, Phillis. Activists, Rebels & Reformers, 3 vols. Sawinski, Diane M., ed. (Illus.). (J). 2001. 600p. (gr. 6 up). lib. bdg. 181.00 net. (978-0-7876-4847-3(7) , GML00502-114891); 2000. xxx, 596p. (978-0-7876-4848-0(5)); 2000. xxx, 596p. (978-0-7876-4849-7(3)) Thomson Gale. (UXL).

Engelbert, Phillis & Sawinski, Diane M. Activists, Rebels & Reformers, 3 vols., Set. 2000. (Illus.). xxx, 596p. (J). (978-0-7876-4850-3(7)) Visible Ink Pr.

Gellman, Marc. Bad Stuff in the News: A Guide to Handling the Headlines. 2002. (gr. 5-8). lib. bdg. 12.95 (978-0-613-87927-9(9)) Tandem Library Bks.

Gellman, Marc & Hartman, Tom. Bad Stuff in the News: A Guide to Handling the Headlines. 2002. 128p. (J). (gr. 4-9). reprint ed. pap. 4.95 (978-1-58717-232-8(1) , SeaStar Bks.) Chronicle Bks. LLC.

Global Issues, 9 bks., Set. Incl. Closing the Borders. Davies, Wendy. 1995. lib. bdg. 19.98 (978-1-56847-335-2(4) , AS335-4); Exploitation of Children. Ennew, Judith. 1996. lib. bdg. 19.98 (978-0-8172-4546-7(4)); Gender Issues. Stearman, Kaye & Vander Gaag, Nikki. 1996.

S

lib. bdg. 19.98 (978-0-8172-4545-0(6)); Genetic Engineering. Bryan, Jenny. 1997. lib. bdg. 19.98 (978-0-8172-4860-4(9)); Racism. Garg, Samidha & Hardy, Jan. 1997. lib. bdg. 19.98 (978-0-8172-4548-1(0)); Refugees. Warner, Rachel. 1997. lib. bdg. 19.98 (978-0-8172-4547-4(2)); Rich-Poor Divide. Garlake, Teresa. 1995. lib. bdg. 19.98 (978-1-56847-336-9(2) , AS336-2); Terrorism. Raintree Steck-Vaughn Staff. 2000. lib. bdg. 19.98 (978-0-8172-4862-8(5)); United Nations - Peacekeeper? Johnson, Edward. 1995. lib. bdg. 19.98 (978-1-56847-267-6(6) , AS267-6); (Illus.). 64p. (YA). (gr. 5-10). Set lib. bdg. 179.82 (978-0-7398-1534-2(2)) Raintree.

Gourley, Catherine. Society's Sisters: Stories of Women Who Fought for Social Justice in America. 2003. (Single Titles Ser.). (Illus.). 96p. (gr. 7 up). lib. bdg. 25.90 (978-0-7613-2865-0(3) , Twenty-First Century Bks.) Lerner Publishing Group.

Harmony Island: ATropical Adventure in Conflict Resolutuion. 2005. (YA). cd-rom (978-0-9754754-4-7(4)) Academic Edge, Inc.

Harvey, Bonnie Carman. Jane Addams: Nobel Prize Winner & Founder of Hull House. 1999. (Historical American Biographies Ser.). (Illus.). 128p. (YA). (gr. 6-12). lib. bdg. 26.60 (978-0-7660-1094-5(5)) Enslow Pubs., Inc.

Haughton, Emma & Clarke, Penny. Rights in the Home. 2005. (What Do We Mean by Human Rights? Ser.). (Illus.). 46p. (J). (gr. 5-9). lib. bdg. 29.95 (978-1-932889-65-9(5)) Sea-To-Sea Pubns.

Hazen, Walter A. Everyday Life: Reform in America. 2004. (Illus.). iv, 100p. pap. (978-0-673-58898-2(X)) Good Year Bks.

Herstek, Amy Paulson. Dorothea Dix: Crusader for the Mentally Ill. 2001. (Historical American Biographies Ser.). (Illus.). 128p. (YA). (gr. 6-12). lib. bdg. 26.60 (978-0-7660-1258-5(1)) Enslow Pubs., Inc.

January, Brendan. De Witt & Lila Wallace: Charity for All. De Capua, Sarah, ed. 1998. (Community Builders Ser.). (Illus.). 48p. (J). (gr. 3-5). pap. 6.95 (978-0-516-26329-8(3) , Children's Pr.) Scholastic Library Publishing.

Kallen, Stuart A. Does Equality Exist in America? 2006. (Illus.). 128p. (gr. 10-12). 21.20 (978-0-7377-3434-8(5)); pap. 29.95 (978-0-7377-3433-1(7)) Thomson Gale. (Greenhaven Pr., Inc.).

Kent, Deborah. Dorothy Day: Friend to the Forgotten. 2004. (Illus.). 187p. (J). pap. 12.00 (978-0-8028-5265-6(3)) Eerdmans, William B. Publishing Co.

Kravetz, Jonathan. Let's Work It Out, 6 bks., Set. Incl. How to Deal with Anger. Fiedler, Julie. lib. bdg. 21.25 (978-1-4042-3671-4(6)); How to Deal with Bullies. lib. bdg. 21.25 (978-1-4042-3670-7(8)); How to Deal with Fighting. lib. bdg. 21.25 (978-1-4042-3672-1(4)); How to Deal with Insults. Fiedler, Julie. lib. bdg. 21.25 (***978-1-4042-3673-8(2)** , PowerKids Pr.); How to Deal with Jealousy. lib. bdg. 21.25 (***978-1-4042-3674-5(0)** , PowerKids Pr.); How to Deal with Teasing. Fiedler, Julie. lib. bdg. 21.25 (***978-1-4042-3675-2(9)** , PowerKids Pr.); (Illus.). 24p. (J). (gr. 2-5). 2007. 2007. Set lib. bdg. 127.50 (***978-1-4042-3607-3(4)** , PowerKids Pr.) Rosen Publishing Group, Inc., The.

Lewis, Barbara A. Kid's Guide to Social Action: How to Solve the Social Problems You Choose-A. 1998. (gr. 7-12). lib. bdg. 29.20 (978-0-613-89622-1(X)) Tandem Library Bks.

McFall, Sally, ed. Pro/Con, 12 vols. 2002. (Illus.). (YA). (978-0-7172-5928-1(5)); (978-0-7172-5929-8(3)); (978-0-7172-5930-4(7)); (978-0-7172-5931-1(5)); (978-0-7172-5932-8(3)); (978-0-7172-5933-5(1)); (978-0-7172-5754-6(1)); (978-0-7172-5755-3(X)); (978-0-7172-5756-0(8)); (978-0-7172-5757-7(6)); (978-0-7172-5758-4(4)); (978-0-7172-5759-1(2)) Scholastic Library Publishing. (Grolier).

—Pro/Con 3, 12 vols. 2004. (Illus.). (YA). 339.00 (978-0-7172-5927-4(7) , Grolier) Scholastic Library Publishing.

Parrot, Andrea. Coping with Date Rape & Acquaintance Rape. 1999. (Coping Ser.). (Illus.). 173p. (YA). (gr. 7-12). lib. bdg. 26.50 (978-0-8239-2861-3(6) , CODARA) Rosen Publishing Group, Inc., The.

Raintree Steck-Vaughn Staff. World Issues: Arkansas Edition. 2003. (Illus.). 1151.04 (978-1-4109-0167-5(X)) Raintree.

Riley, John B. Jane Addams: A Photo Biography. l.t. ed. 2004. (First Biographies Ser.). (Illus.). 24p. (YA). (gr. 5 up). 16.95 (978-1-883846-61-9(7) , First Biographies) Reynolds, Morgan Inc.

Sakany, Lois. The Platforms & Policies of America's Reform Politicians. 2004. (Progressive Movement, 1900-1920 Ser.). (Illus.). 32p. (J). lib. bdg. (978-1-4042-0193-4(9)) Rosen Publishing Group, Inc., The.

Vogel, Elizabeth. The Conflict Resolution Library: Set 4: Facing Changes, 6 bks. Incl. Dealing with Being the Middle Child in Your Family. lib. bdg. 18.75 (978-0-8239-5408-7(0)); Dealing with Being the Oldest Child in Your Family. lib. bdg. 18.75 (978-0-8239-5409-4(9)); Dealing with Being the Youngest Child in Your Family. lib. bdg. 18.75 (978-0-8239-5407-0(2)); Dealing with Choices. lib. bdg. 18.75 (978-0-8239-5410-0(2)); Dealing with Rules at Home. lib. bdg. 18.75 (978-0-8239-5411-7(0)); Dealing with Showoffs. lib. bdg. 18.75 (978-0-8239-5412-4(9)); 24p. (J). (gr. 3). 2000. (Illus.). Set lib. bdg. 95.58 (978-0-8239-7007-0(8) , PowerKids Pr.) Rosen Publishing Group, Inc., The.

Williams, Horace Randall. Johnnie Carr: A Life of Quiet Activism. 2001. (J). (gr. 4-7). pap. 7.95 (978-1-58838-025-8(4) , Junebug Bks.) NewSouth, Inc.

Williams, Mary, ed. Culture Wars. 1998. (Opposing Viewpoints Ser.). (Illus.). 208p. (YA). (gr. 8-12). lib. bdg. 32.45 (978-1-56510-939-1(2) , LML00501-177490, Greenhaven Pr., Inc.) Thomson Gale.

21st Century Debates, 24 vols. (Twenty-First Century Debates Ser.). 2004. (Illus.). (YA). (gr. 6-8). 479.76 (978-0-7398-6471-5(8)); 2003. 433.92 (978-0-7398-5510-2(7)); 2000. (J). 216.96 (978-0-7398-3182-3(8)) Raintree.

21st Century Debates, 12 bks., Set. Incl. Air Pollution : Our Impact on the Planet. Chapman, Matthew & Bowden, Rob. (YA). 2002. lib. bdg. 19.99 (978-0-7398-4874-6(7)); Climate Change : Our Impact on the Planet. Scoones, Simon. (YA). 2001. lib. bdg. 27.12 (978-0-7398-3177-9(1)); Endangered Species : Our Impact on the Planet. Penny, Malcolm. (YA). 2002. lib. bdg. 27.12 (978-0-7398-4873-9(9)); Energy Resources : Our Impact on the Planet. McLeish, Ewan. (YA). 2001. lib. bdg. 27.12 (978-0-7398-3178-6(X)); Food Supply : Our Impact on the Planet. Bowden, Rob. (YA). 2002. lib. bdg. 27.12 (978-0-7398-4871-5(2)); Genetics : The Impact on Our Lives. Dowswell, Paul. (YA). 2001. lib. bdg. 27.12 (978-0-7398-3174-8(7)); Internet : The Impact on Our Lives. Graham, Ian. (J). 2001. lib. bdg. 27.12 (978-0-7398-3173-1(9)); Media : The Impact on Our Lives. Petley, Julian. (YA). 2001. lib. bdg. 27.12 (978-0-7398-3175-5(5)); Overcrowded World? Our Impact on the Planet. Bowden, Rob. (YA). 2002. lib. bdg. 27.12 (978-0-7398-4872-2(0)); Rain Forests : Our Impact on the Planet. McLeish, Ewan. (YA). 2001. lib. bdg. 27.12 (978-0-7398-3179-3(8)); Surveillance : The Impact on Our Lives. McGwire, Scarlett. (YA). 2001. lib. bdg. 27.12 (978-0-7398-3172-4(0)); Waste, Recycling & Reuse : Our Impact on the Planet. Bowden, Rob. (YA). 2001. lib. bdg. 27.12 (978-0-7398-3180-9(1)); 64p. (gr. 6-8). (Illus.). Set lib. bdg. 325.44 (978-0-7398-4876-0(3)) Raintree.

SOCIAL PROBLEMS—FICTION

Animal Farm. 1999. (YA). 11.95 (978-1-56137-306-2(0)) Novel Units, Inc.

Blume, Judy. Then Again, Maybe I Won't. (J). 125p. pap. 3.99 (978-0-8072-1445-9(0)); 2004. 164p. (gr. 5-9). pap. 29.00 incl. audio (978-0-8072-0796-3(9) , LYA 354 SP) Random Hse. Audio Publishing Group. (Listening Library).

Calhoun, Dia. White Midnight. 2003. 304p. (YA). 18.00 (978-0-374-38389-3(8) , Farrar, Straus & Giroux (BYR)) Farrar, Straus & Giroux.

Dower, Laura & Powers, Stephanie. Off the Wall. 15th rev. ed. 2004. (From the Files of Madison Finn Ser.: No. 15). (Illus.). 176p. (gr. 3-7). pap. 4.99 (978-0-7868-1737-5(2)) Hyperion Pr.

Fuchshuber, Annegert. Carly. Howe, Florence & Kirk, Heidi, trs. from ENG. 2004. (Illus.). 28p. (ps-3). 16.95 (978-1-55861-177-1(0)) Feminist Pr. at The City Univ. of New York.

Hinton, S. E. Esto Ya Es Otra Historia. (SPA.). (J). 6.95 (978-84-204-4121-4(X)) Santillana USA Publishing Co., Inc.

—Rumble Fish. 2006. 21.50 (978-0-8446-7283-0(1)) Smith, Peter Pub., Inc.

—That Was Then, This Is Now. 1998. 160p. (YA). (gr. 7-12). pap. 7.99 (978-0-14-038966-1(0) , Puffin) Penguin Group (USA) Inc.

—That Was Then, This Is Now. 1998. (Puffin Book Ser.). (YA). (978-0-606-12861-2(1)) Tandem Library Bks.

Holburn, Sandra. The Angel & the Bear. 2006. (ENG.). 28p. per. 15.30 (***978-1-4259-4994-5(0))** AuthorHouse.

James, Sara & Ruckdeschel, Liz. What If... Everyone Was Doing It. 2007. (What If... Ser.). (YA). (gr. 7). 272p. pap. 8.99 (***978-0-385-73502-5(2))**; 240p. lib. bdg. 11.99 (***978-0-385-90496-4(7))** Random Hse. Children's Bks. (Delacorte Bks. for Young Readers).

Jonsberg, Barry. Dreamrider. 2008. 256p. (J). (gr. 9). lib. bdg. 18.99 (***978-0-375-94457-4(5)** , Knopf Bks. for Young Readers) Random Hse. Children's Bks.

Leedom, Tim C. The Light Side. l.t. ed. 2002. 80p. (J). per. 21.95 (978-0-9646885-1-3(4)) Manoa Valley Publishing Co., The.

Morrison, Toni, et al. The Book of Mean People. 2002. (Illus.). 48p. (ps-3). 17.49 (978-0-7868-2471-7(9)) Disney Pr.

Pascal, Francine. My Mother Was Never a Kid. 2003. 256p. (YA). mass mkt. 5.99 (978-0-689-85988-5(0) , Simon Pulse) Simon & Schuster Children's Publishing.

—My Mother Was Never a Kid. 2003. (Victoria Martin Trilogy: No. 1). (gr. 7-12). lib. bdg. 13.00 (978-0-613-66464-6(7)) Tandem Library Bks.

Ramos, Ricardo. Searching for the Key: A Novel. 2002. 196p. pap. 13.95 (978-0-595-22812-6(7) , Writers Club Pr.) iUniverse, Inc.

Rubio, Carlos. Bullwhip. 2003. 200p. pap. 19.95 (978-1-4137-0202-6(3)) PublishAmerica, Inc.

Sullivan, Therese M. & Bitner, Pamela. A Gift from Valentine. 2007. 24p. (J). per. 12.95 (***978-1-58939-981-5(1))** Virtualbookworm.com Publishing, Inc.

Thomas, Joyce Carol. Linda Brown, You Are Not Alone: The Brown V. Board of Education Decision. 2003. (Illus.). 128p. (J). 16.49 (978-0-7868-2640-7(1)) Hyperion Pr.

Wagner, Jane. J. T. 125p. (J). (gr. 3-5). pap. 3.00 (978-0-8072-1403-9(5) , Listening Library) Random Hse. Audio Publishing Group.

Yansky, Brian. Wonders of the World. 2007. 240p. (J). 16.95 (978-0-7387-1084-6(9) , Flux) Llewellyn Pubns.

Zindel, Lizabeth. The Secret Rites of Social Butterflies. 2008. 224p. (YA). (gr. 7). 16.99 (***978-0-670-06217-1(0)** , Viking Juvenile) Penguin Group (USA) Inc.

SOCIAL PROBLEMS AND THE CHURCH

see Church and Social Problems

SOCIAL PSYCHOLOGY

see also Attitude (Psychology); Interpersonal Relations; Social Adjustment; Violence

Brehm. Social Psychology. 6th ed. 2004. (Illus.). xxvi, 551p. (YA). 125.96 (978-0-618-40337-0(X) , 305050) Houghton Mifflin College Div.

—Study Guide: Used with ... Brehm-Social Psychology. 6th ed. 2004. (YA). stu. ed. 35.16 (978-0-618-40340-0(X) , 305053) Houghton Mifflin College Div.

Donahue, Jill L. Being Cooperative. Previn, Stacey, illus. 2007. (J). lib. bdg. (***978-1-4048-3779-9(5))** Picture Window Bks.

Gordon, Sharon. Somos un Equipo. 2006. (Bookworms Ser.). (SPA & ENG., Illus.). 24p. (J). lib. bdg. 22.79 (978-0-7614-2357-7(5) , Benchmark Bks.) Cavendish, Marshall Corp.

—We Are a Team (Somos un Equipo) 2006. (Bookworms Ser.). (ENG & SPA., Illus.). 24p. (J). lib. bdg. 22.79 (978-0-7614-2436-9(9)) Cavendish, Marshall Corp.

Hotchner, Beverly. Do I Really Love You? 1999. (Illus.). 62p. (YA). (gr. 8-12). pap. 12.95 (978-0-9677406-0-7(6)) Selwyn & Ross Pubs.

Souder, Patti. On the Edge of Disaster: Youth in the Juvenile Court System, 15 vols. 2004. (Youth with Special Needs Ser.). (Illus.). 128p. (J). lib. bdg. (978-1-59084-727-5(X)) Mason Crest Pubs.

SOCIAL REFORM

see Social Problems

SOCIAL SCIENCES

see also Economics; Political Science; Social Change; Sociology

Accelerated Curriculum for Social Studies Grade 11 Exit TAKS Student Edition. 2005. (Region IV ESC Resources for Social Studies Ser.). spiral bd. (978-1-932797-29-9(7)) Region IV Education Service Ctr.

Acoma: la ciudad del Cielo: Libros Aventuras (Adventure Books) 2000. (MacMillan/McGraw-Hill. Estudios Sociales Ser.). (ENG & SPA.). (gr. 3 up). (978-0-02-148688-5(3)) Macmillan/McGraw-Hill Schl. Div.

Adams, Alison. Somos Iguales. 2003. (Primeras Conexiones Ser.). (SPA.). (J). pap. 35.00 (978-1-4108-0324-5(4)) Benchmark Education Co.

Al rescate de Ballenas: Libros Aventuras (Adventure Books) 2003. (MacMillan/McGraw-Hill. Estudios Sociales Ser.). (ENG & SPA.). (gr. 4 up). (978-0-02-150115-1(7)) Macmillan/McGraw-Hill Schl. Div.

La alegria de ser tu y yo, Unidad 3: Superlibros (Big Books) 2000. (Aventuras A Traves Del Tiempo Ser.). (ENG & SPA.). (gr. 3 up). (978-0-02-147875-0(9)) Macmillan/McGraw-Hill Schl. Div.

All Kinds of Clothes Social Studies, 6 vols. (gr. k-2). 28.95 (978-0-7368-1758-5(1) , Yellow Umbrella Bks.) Capstone Pr., Inc.

All Kinds of Farms Social Studies, 6 vols. (gr. k-2). 28.95 (978-0-7368-2989-2(X) , Yellow Umbrella Bks.) Capstone Pr., Inc.

Allen, Tony & Ross, Stewart. Point of Impact Series, 12 bks. (Illus.). (J). (gr. 5-7). Set. lib. bdg. 290.64 (978-1-58810-187-7(8)); Set 2. 2001. lib. bdg. 121.10 (978-1-58810-180-8(0)) Heinemann Library.

The Allyn & Bacon Atlas for Elementary Social Studies. 2005. (J). (978-1-930194-19-9(6)) Maps.com.

Ambulances, 6 vols. (gr. k-2). 28.95 (978-0-7368-8125-8(5)) Red Brick Learning.

Amelia Earhart, 6 vols. (gr. k-2). 28.95 (978-0-7368-9409-8(8)); (gr. 2-5). 36.95 (978-0-7368-8432-7(7)) Red Brick Learning.

America Goes to War Classroom Library. (gr. 2-5). lib. bdg. 24.95 (978-0-7368-8933-9(7)) Red Brick Learning.

America Goes to War Complete Unit. (gr. 2-5). 142.95 (978-0-7368-8934-6(5)) Red Brick Learning.

American Civics Complete Unit. (gr. 2-5). 142.95 (978-0-7368-8928-5(0)) Red Brick Learning.

American Girl Editorial Staff, ed. Licorice Book & Plush Set. Casey, Lukatz, illus. 2005. (American Girl Today Ser.). 80p. (J). 21.95 (978-1-58485-970-3(9) , American Girl) American Girl Publishing, Inc.

Los amigos Cuenta-cuentos: Libros Aventuras (Adventure Books) 2000. (MacMillan/McGraw-Hill. Estudios Sociales Ser.). (ENG & SPA.). (gr. 3 up). (978-0-02-148691-5(3)) Macmillan/McGraw-Hill Schl. Div.

Los amigos Panda: Aventuras (Adventure Books) 2000. (Aventuras A Traves Del Tiempo Ser.). (ENG & SPA.). (gr. 1 up). (978-0-02-148667-0(0)) Macmillan/McGraw-Hill Schl. Div.

Amigos por Correspondencia: Libros Aventuras (Adventure Books) 2000. (MacMillan/McGraw-Hill. Estudios Sociales Ser.). (ENG & SPA.). (gr. 2 up). (978-0-02-148685-4(9)) Macmillan/McGraw-Hill Schl. Div.

Andersen, W. H. Hooray for the Red, White, & Blue: A Content Area Reader-Social Studies. 2005. (Emergent/Early (Prek-2) Social Studies Package Ser.). 16p. (YA). (ps-2). 25.20 (978-0-8215-7819-3(7)) Sadlier, William H. Inc.

Anderson, Wendy. Livewire Investigates Uluru (Ayers Rock) 2003. (Livewires Ser.). 32p. pap. 4.60 (978-0-521-53836-7(X)) Cambridge Univ. Pr.

—Livewire Real Lives Fred Hollows. 2003. (Livewires Ser.). 32p. pap. 4.75 (978-0-521-53837-4(8)) Cambridge Univ. Pr.

Anibal: Aventuras (Adventure Books) 2000. (Aventuras A Traves Del Tiempo Ser.). (ENG & SPA.). (gr. 6 up). (978-0-02-148752-3(9)) Macmillan/McGraw-Hill Schl. Div.

Anne Hutchinson, 6 vols. (gr. 2-5). 39.95 (978-0-7368-4572-4(0)) Red Brick Learning.

Un ano en la ciudad, Unidad 1: Superlibros (Big Books) 2000. (Aventuras A Traves Del Tiempo Ser.). (ENG & SPA.). (gr. 3 up). (978-0-02-147873-6(2)) Macmillan/McGraw-Hill Schl. Div.

Antarctica. (Early Intervention Levels Ser.). 31.86 (978-0-7362-0664-8(7)) Hampton-Brown Bks.

La Antartida. 2000. (McGraw-Hill Ciencias Ser.). (ENG & SPA.). (gr. 5 up). (978-0-02-279687-7(8)) Macmillan/McGraw-Hill Schl. Div.

Antologia: Aqui Estoy! 2000. (Aventuras A Traves Del Tiempo Ser.). (ENG & SPA.). (gr. 1 up). (978-0-02-147934-4(8)) Macmillan/McGraw-Hill Schl. Div.

Antologia: Comunidades. 2000. (Aventuras A Traves Del Tiempo Ser.). (ENG & SPA.). (gr. 3 up). (978-0-02-147936-8(4)) Macmillan/McGraw-Hill Schl. Div.

Antologia: Gente. 2000. (Aventuras A Traves Del Tiempo Ser.). (ENG & SPA.). (gr. 2 up). (978-0-02-147935-1(6)) Macmillan/McGraw-Hill Schl. Div.

Aprenda Preparacion y Practica: Assessment. 2003. (MacMillan/McGraw-Hill. Estudios Sociales Ser.). (ENG & SPA.). (gr. 1 up). (978-0-02-149775-1(3)); (gr. 4 up). (978-0-02-149778-2(8)) Macmillan/McGraw-Hill Schl. Div.

Aprenda preparacion y practica, Guia del Maestro: Assessment. 2003. (MacMillan/McGraw-Hill. Estudios Sociales Ser.). (ENG & SPA.). (gr. 2 up). (978-0-02-150016-1(9)) Macmillan/McGraw-Hill Schl. Div.

Aprenda preparacion y practica, Libro del Estudiante: Assessment. 2003. (MacMillan/McGraw-Hill. Estudios Sociales Ser.). (ENG & SPA.). (gr. 2 up). (978-0-02-149776-8(1)) Macmillan/McGraw-Hill Schl. Div.

Aprenda preparacion y practica, Pupil Edition: Assessment. 2003. (MacMillan/McGraw-Hill. Estudios Sociales Ser.). (ENG & SPA.). (gr. 3 up). (978-0-02-149777-5(X)); (gr. 5 up). (978-0-02-149779-9(6)) Macmillan/McGraw-Hill Schl. Div.

Aprender de nuestras Madres: Libros Aventuras (Adventure Books) 2000. (MacMillan/McGraw-Hill. Estudios Sociales Ser.). (ENG & SPA.). (gr. 1 up). (978-0-02-148663-2(8)) Macmillan/McGraw-Hill Schl. Div.

Aqui estoy! Guia del Maestro: Aqui Estoy! 2000. (Aventuras A Traves Del Tiempo Ser.). (ENG & SPA.). (gr. k up). (978-0-02-147817-0(1)) Macmillan/McGraw-Hill Schl. Div.

Archer, Anita, et al. REWARDS Plus: Application to Social Studies: Reading Excellence: Word Attack & Rate Development Strategies: Student Book. 2003. (Illus.). 154p. per. (978-1-57035-803-6(6) , 136SOCSE) Sopris West Educational Services.

Archibald, Donna, et al. NETS*S Curriculum Series: Social Studies Units for Grades 9-12. McKenzie, Walter, ed. 2004. (Nets-S Curriculum Ser.). (Illus.). 195p. pap. 38.95 (978-1-56484-212-1(6)) International Society for Technology in Education.

Arriba, arriba!Al espacio! la historia de Mae Jemison: Libros Aventuras (Adventure Books) 2000. (MacMillan/McGraw-Hill. Estudios Sociales Ser.). (ENG & SPA.). (gr. 3 up). (978-0-02-148694-6(8)) Macmillan/McGraw-Hill Schl. Div.

Ashbe, Jeanne. Es hora de Recoger: Traduccion Anna Coll-Vinent. 2004. (SPA.). 16p. (978-84-8470-163-7(8)) Corimbo, Editorial S.L.

—La hora del Bano. 2004. (SPA.). 16p. (978-84-8470-165-1(4)) Corimbo, Editorial S.L.

—Oh!, esta Oscuro. 2004. (SPA.). 16p. (978-84-8470-164-4(6)) Corimbo, Editorial S.L.

Asi es la escuela, Unidad 1: Superlibros (Big Books) 2000. (Aventuras A Traves Del Tiempo Ser.). (ENG & SPA.). (gr. k up). (978-0-02-147833-0(3)) Macmillan/McGraw-Hill Schl. Div.

At Play in the USA, 6 vols. (Book2WebTM Ser.). (gr. 4-8). 36.50 (978-0-322-02983-5(X)) Wright Group, The.

At the Park Social Studies, 6 vols. (gr. k-2). 28.95 (978-0-7368-2984-7(9) , Yellow Umbrella Bks.) Capstone Pr., Inc.

Auch, Allison. Electrifying Personalities. 2004. (Navigators Ser.). (J). pap. 42.00 (978-1-4108-0440-2(2)) Benchmark Education Co.

Auld, Mary. Conoce la Familia, 6 bks. Incl. Mi Hermana. lib. bdg. 20.67 (978-0-8368-3930-2(7)); Mi Hermano. lib. bdg. 20.67 (978-0-8368-3931-9(5)); Mi Mama. lib. bdg. 20.67 (978-0-8368-3932-6(3)); Mi Papa. lib. bdg. 20.67 (978-0-8368-3933-3(1)); Mis Abuelos. lib. bdg. 20.67 (978-0-8368-3934-0(X)); Mis Tios. lib. bdg. 20.67 (978-0-8368-3935-7(8)); 24p. (J). (gr. 1 up). (SPA., Illus.). 2004. 124.02 (978-0-8368-3929-6(3)) Stevens, Gareth Inc.

Autoadhesivos: Libros de la Biblioteca (Classroom Library) 2000. (Aventuras A Traves Del Tiempo Ser.). (ENG & SPA.). (gr. 1 up). (978-0-02-147829-3(5)) Macmillan/McGraw-Hill Schl. Div.

Autoadhesivos: Superlibros (Big Books) 2000. (Aventuras A Traves Del Tiempo Ser.). (ENG & SPA.). (gr. k up). (978-0-02-147828-6(7)); (gr. 2 up). (978-0-02-147831-6(0)) Macmillan/McGraw-Hill Schl. Div.

Aventuras Books Classroom Set: Aventuras (Adventure Books) 2000. (Aventuras A Traves Del Tiempo Ser.). (ENG & SPA.). (gr. 1 up). (978-0-02-148754-7(5)); (gr. 2 up). (978-0-02-148755-4(3)); (gr. 3 up). (978-0-02-148756-1(1)); (gr. 4 up). (978-0-02-148761-5(8)); (gr. 5 up). (978-0-02-148762-2(6)); (gr. 6 up). (978-0-02-148763-9(4)) Macmillan/McGraw-Hill Schl. Div.

Aventuras Books Deluxe Classroom Set: Aventuras (Adventure Books) 2000. (Aventuras A Traves Del Tiempo Ser.). (ENG & SPA.). (gr. k up). (978-0-02-149048-6(1)); (gr. 1 up). (978-0-02-149049-3(X)); (gr. 2 up). (978-0-02-149051-6(1)); (gr. 3 up). (978-0-02-149052-3(X)); (gr. 4 up). (978-0-02-149053-0(8)); (gr. 5 up). (978-0-02-149054-7(6)); (gr. 6 up). (978-0-02-149055-4(4)) Macmillan/McGraw-Hill Schl. Div.

Avey, F. M. My Legacy Book. 2000. (Illus.). 50p. (YA). (gr. 5-10). pap., stu. ed., wbk. ed. 12.95 (978-1-930758-60-5(X) , Legacy Kids) Yeva Corp.

Axiom Press, ed. CultureGrams Kids Edition. 2003. spiral bd. 69.99 (978-1-931694-63-6(X)); ring bd. 69.99 incl. cd-rom (978-1-931694-64-3(8)) ProQuest CSA.

S

—CultureGrams States Edition. 2003. spiral bd. 59.99 incl. cd-rom (978-1-931694-65-0(6)); ring bd. 59.99 incl. cd-rom (978-1-931694-66-7(4)) ProQuest CSA.

Aylesworth, Jim. Folks in the Valley. 1999. 32p. (J). (ps-3). pap. 19.95 (978-0-06-443394-5(3)) HarperCollins Pubs.

The Battle of Gettysburg, 6 vols. (gr. 2-5). 39.95 (978-0-7368-4596-0(8)) Red Brick Learning.

The Battles of Lexington & Concord, 6 vols. (gr. 2-5). 39.95 (978-0-7368-4577-9(1)) Red Brick Learning.

Beare, Emma. Tell Me about History. 2006. (Tell Me About Ser.). 224p. (J). 18.95 (978-0-7696-4287-1(X)) School Specialty Publishing.

Bednarz, Robert, et al. About My Community. 3rd ed. 2003. (Horizons Ser.). (gr. 2 up). pupil's gde. ed. 46.80 (978-0-15-320179-0(7)) Harcourt Schl. Pubs.

Benchmark Education Staff, compiled by. Being a Good Citizen. 2006. spiral bd. 125.00 (***978-1-4108-7065-0(0)***) Benchmark Education Co.

—Civic Ideals & Practices. 2005. spiral bd. 90.00 (***978-1-4108-3937-4(0)***); spiral bd. 65.00 (***978-1-4108-4504-7(4)***); spiral bd. 110.00 (***978-1-4108-5427-8(2)***); spiral bd. 60.00 (***978-1-4108-5428-5(0)***) Benchmark Education Co.

—Community Counts & Community Change. 2005. spiral bd. 225.00 (***978-1-4108-5803-0(0)***) Benchmark Education Co.

—Community Counts & Local GOVT. 2005. spiral bd. 225.00 (***978-1-4108-5802-3(2)***) Benchmark Education Co.

—Individual Development & Identity. 2005. spiral bd. 1100.00 (***978-1-4108-3746-2(7)***); spiral bd. 400.00 (***978-1-4108-3938-1(9)***); spiral bd. 245.00 (***978-1-4108-3939-8(7)***); spiral bd. 585.00 (***978-1-4108-3963-3(X)***); spiral bd. 360.00 (***978-1-4108-3964-0(8)***); spiral bd. 75.00 (***978-1-4108-3973-2(7)***); spiral bd. 35.00 (***978-1-4108-3981-7(8)***); spiral bd. 685.00 (***978-1-4108-4505-4(2)***); spiral bd. 1050.00 (***978-1-4108-5424-7(8)***); spiral bd. 715.00 (***978-1-4108-5840-5(5)***) Benchmark Education Co.

—Individuals, Groups & Institutions. 2005. spiral bd. 25.00 (***978-1-4108-4500-9(1)***) Benchmark Education Co.

—Individuals, Groups, & Institutions. 2005. spiral bd. 55.00 (***978-1-4108-3969-5(9)***); spiral bd. 80.00 (***978-1-4108-5431-5(0)***) Benchmark Education Co.

—Neighborhoods & Communities. 2006. spiral bd. 219.00 (***978-1-4108-7040-7(5)***); spiral bd. 235.00 (***978-1-4108-7085-8(5)***) Benchmark Education Co.

—People, Places & Environments. 2005. spiral bd. 575.00 (***978-1-4108-3748-6(3)***); spiral bd. 55.00 (***978-1-4108-3968-8(0)***); spiral bd. 235.00 (***978-1-4108-5836-8(7)***); spiral bd. 150.00 (***978-1-4108-5837-5(5)***) Benchmark Education Co.

—People, Places, & Environments. 2005. spiral bd. 245.00 (***978-1-4108-3944-2(3)***); spiral bd. 185.00 (***978-1-4108-3945-9(1)***); spiral bd. 145.00 (***978-1-4108-3955-8(9)***); spiral bd. 75.00 (***978-1-4108-3956-5(7)***); spiral bd. 110.00 (***978-1-4108-3967-1(2)***); spiral bd. 50.00 (***978-1-4108-3975-6(3)***); spiral bd. 315.00 (***978-1-4108-4503-0(6)***); spiral bd. 450.00 (***978-1-4108-5420-9(5)***); spiral bd. 315.00 (***978-1-4108-5421-6(3)***) Benchmark Education Co.

—Read & Achieve Social Studies Small Group Set. 2005. spiral bd. 3500.00 (***978-1-4108-3816-2(1)***); spiral bd. 500.00 (***978-1-4108-4179-7(0)***) Benchmark Education Co.

—Read & Achieve Social Studies Small-Group Set W/PD. 2005. spiral bd. 3500.00 (***978-1-4108-4180-3(4)***) Benchmark Education Co.

—Read & Achieve Social Studies Whole Group Set. 2005. spiral bd. 2275.00 (***978-1-4108-4177-3(4)***); spiral bd. 5275.00 (***978-1-4108-4178-0(2)***) Benchmark Education Co.

—Regions of the U. S. 2006. spiral bd. 330.00 (***978-1-4108-7006-3(5)***); 2006. spiral bd. 239.00 (***978-1-4108-7111-4(8)***); 2005. (J). spiral bd. 265.00 (***978-1-4108-5769-9(7)***) Benchmark Education Co.

—Social Studies Theme: People, Places & Environments. 2005. spiral bd. 220.00 (***978-1-4108-5328-8(4)***) Benchmark Education Co.

—Social Studies Theme: Time, Continuity & Change. 2005. spiral bd. 560.00 (***978-1-4108-5322-6(5)***) Benchmark Education Co.

—Spanish Social Studies Standard Set. 2005. spiral bd. 3225.00 (***978-1-4108-5845-0(6)***) Benchmark Education Co.

—Time, Continuity, & Change. 2005. spiral bd. 1250.00 (***978-1-4108-3745-5(9)***); spiral bd. 340.00 (***978-1-4108-3942-8(7)***); spiral bd. 120.00 (***978-1-4108-3943-5(5)***); spiral bd. 640.00 (***978-1-4108-3952-7(4)***); spiral bd. 75.00 (***978-1-4108-3953-4(2)***); spiral bd. 55.00 (***978-1-4108-3970-1(2)***); spiral bd. 55.00 (***978-1-4108-3971-8(0)***); spiral bd. 190.00 (***978-1-4108-3977-0(X)***); spiral bd. 110.00 (***978-1-4108-3978-7(8)***); spiral bd. 365.00 (***978-1-4108-4502-3(8)***); spiral bd. 265.00 (***978-1-4108-5834-4(0)***); spiral bd. 715.00 (***978-1-4108-5835-1(9)***) Benchmark Education Co.

—Time, Continuity & Change. 2005. spiral bd. 550.00 (***978-1-4108-5417-9(5)***); spiral bd. 1050.00 (***978-1-4108-5418-6(3)***) Benchmark Education Co.

—World Communities. 2006. spiral bd. 109.00 (***978-1-4108-7098-8(7)***) Benchmark Education Co.

Biddy Mason Una mujer Generosa: Libros Aventuras (Adventure Books) 2000. (MacMillan/McGraw-Hill. Estudios Sociales Ser.). (ENG & SPA.). (gr. 4 up). (978-0-02-148699-1(9)) Macmillan/McGraw-Hill Schl. Div.

Billings. How: People, Places, & Ideas. 2003. (Illus.). Vol. 1. (J). pap. 21.50 (978-0-7398-7948-1(0)); Vol. 2. pap. (978-0-7398-7949-8(9)) Steck-Vaughn.

Binns, Tristan Boyer. Government Agencies, 6 vols., Set. 2003. (J). (gr. 3-5). lib. bdg. 135.35 (978-1-58810-460-1(5)) Heinemann Library.

Bittinger, Gayle. 1-2-3 Community. 2003. (1-2-3 Ser.). 80p. (J). pap. 10.99 (978-1-57029-467-9(4) , WPH99017, Totline Pubns.) Schaffer, Frank Pubns.

BJU Staff. Geography Activity Student Gr9. 2004. 14.50 (978-1-57924-300-5(2)) Jones, Bob Univ. Pr.

—World Studies Activity St Grd7. 2004. pap. 14.50 (978-1-57924-302-9(9)) Jones, Bob Univ. Pr.

Blue Earth Books: Diaries, Letters, & Memoirs, 12 bks. Incl. Boyhood Diary of Charles Lindbergh, 1913-1916 : Early Adventures of the Famous Aviator. O'Hara, Megan, ed. lib. bdg. 22.60 (978-0-7368-0600-8(8)); Boyhood Diary of Theodore Roosevelt, 1869-1870 : Early Travels of the 26th U. S. President. Roosevelt, Theodore. Saterern, Shelley Swanson, ed. lib. bdg. 22.60 (978-0-7368-0601-5(6)); Civil War Drummer Boy : The Diary of William Bircher, 1861-1865. Bircher, William. Sateren, Shelley Swanson. ed. lib. bdg. 22.60 (978-0-7368-0348-9(3)); Colonial Quaker Girl : The Diary of Sally Wister, 1777-1778. Wister, Sally. O'Hara, Megan, ed. lib. bdg. 22.60 (978-0-7368-0349-6(1)); Confederate Girl : The Diary of Carrie Berry, 1864. Bunkers, Suzanne L. & Berry, Carrie. Steele, Christy & Todd, Ann, eds. lib. bdg. 22.60 (978-0-7368-0343-4(2)); Covered-Wagon Girl : The Diary of Sallie Hester, 1849-1850. Hester, Sallie. Steele, Christy & Hodgeson, Ann, eds. lib. bdg. 22.60 (978-0-7368-0344-1(0)); Free Black Girl Before the Civil War : The Diary of Charlotte Forten, 1854. Forten, Charlotte L. Steele, Christy & Graves, Kerry, eds. lib. bdg. 22.60 (978-0-7368-0345-8(9)); Girlhood Diary of Louisa May Alcott, 1843-1846 : Writings of a Young Author. Alcott, Louisa May. Graves, Kerry A., ed. lib. bdg. 22.60 (978-0-7368-0599-5(0)); Girlhood Diary of Wanda Gag, 1908-1909 : Portrait of a Young Artist. O'Hara, Megan, ed. lib. bdg. 22.60 (978-0-7368-0598-8(2)); Nineteenth-Century Schoolgirl : The Diary of Caroline Cowles Richards, 1852-1855. Richards, Caroline Cowles. Graves, Kerry A., ed. lib. bdg. 22.60 (978-0-7368-0342-7(4)); Pioneer Farm Girl : The Diary of Sarah Gillespie, 1877-1878. Gillespie, Sarah. Bunkers, Suzanne L. & Hodgson, Ann, eds. lib. bdg. 22.60 (978-0-7368-0347-2(5)); Whaling Captain's Daughter : The Diary of Laura Jernegan, 1868-1871. Jernegan, Laura. O'Hara, Megan, ed. lib. bdg. 22.60 (978-0-7368-0346-5(7)); 32p. (J). (gr. 3-4). 2000. (Illus.). Set lib. bdg. 271.20 (978-0-7368-0679-4(2) , Bridgestone Bks.) Capstone Pr., Inc.

Blue Earth Books: Going to School in History, 6 bks. Incl. Going to School During the Civil Rights Movement. Koestler-Grack, Rachel A. lib. bdg. 22.60 (978-0-7368-0799-9(3)); Going to School During the Civil War : The Confederacy. Graves, Kerry A. lib. bdg. 22.60 (978-0-7368-0802-6(7)); Going to School During the Civil War : The Union. Graves, Kerry A. lib. bdg. 22.60 (978-0-7368-0801-9(9)); Going to School During the Great Depression. Graves, Kerry A. lib. bdg. 22.60 (978-0-7368-0800-2(0)); Going to School in Colonial America. Sateren, Shelley Swanson. lib. bdg. 22.60 (978-0-7368-0803-3(5)); Going to School in Pioneer Times. Graves, Kerry A. lib. bdg. 22.60 (978-0-7368-0804-0(3)); 32p. (J). (gr. 3-4). 2001. (Illus.). Set lib. bdg. 135.60 (978-0-7368-0878-1(7) , Bridgestone Bks.) Capstone Pr., Inc.

Boehm, Richard G. & Armstrong, David M. Our World Today: People Places, & Issues. 2002. 738p. (C). stu. ed. 82.00 (978-0-07-827382-7(X) , 9780078273827) Glencoe/McGraw-Hill.

Boehm, Richard G., et al. Activity Books: A Child's Place. 1998. (Harcourt Brace Social Studies). (gr. k-7). pap., act. bk. ed. 7.80 (978-0-15-310304-9(3)) Harcourt Schl. Pubs.

—Activity Books: Communities. 2003. (Harcourt Brace Social Studies). (gr. k-7). act. bk. ed. 7.70 (978-0-15-310306-3(X)) Harcourt Schl. Pubs.

—Activity Books: Making a Difference. 2003. (Harcourt Brace Social Studies). (gr. k-7). act. bk. ed. 5.80 (978-0-15-310305-6(1)) Harcourt Schl. Pubs.

—Assessment Programs: A Child's Place. 2003. (Harcourt Brace Social Studies). (gr. k-7). 44.60 (978-0-15-310297-4(7)) Harcourt Schl. Pubs.

—Assessment Programs: Early United States. 1999. (Harcourt Brace Social Studies). (gr. k-7). pap. 95.10 (978-0-15-310301-8(9)) Harcourt Schl. Pubs.

—Assessment Programs: Making a Difference. 2003. (Harcourt Brace Social Studies). (gr. k-7). 44.60 (978-0-15-310298-1(5)) Harcourt Schl. Pubs.

—Assessment Programs: United States in Modern Times. 1998. (Harcourt Brace Social Studies). (gr. k-7). pap. 69.80 (978-0-15-311402-1(9)) Harcourt Schl. Pubs.

—Big Book Libraries. 2003. (Harcourt Brace Social Studies). (gr. 1 up). 317.70 (978-0-15-310448-0(1)); (gr. 2 up). 317.70 (978-0-15-310455-8(4)) Harcourt Schl. Pubs.

—Game Time! A Child's Place. 2003. (Harcourt Brace Social Studies). (gr. k-7). 7.30 (978-0-15-312349-8(4)) Harcourt Schl. Pubs.

—Game Time! Making a Difference. 2003. (Harcourt Brace Social Studies). (gr. k-7). 7.30 (978-0-15-312351-1(6)) Harcourt Schl. Pubs.

—Libros Del Alumno: Descubro Al Mundo. 2000. (Harcourt Brace Estudios Sociales Ser.). (SPA.). (gr. k-7). pap., pupil's gde. ed. 56.70 (978-0-15-310486-2(4)) Harcourt Schl. Pubs.

—My World & Me: A Kindergarten Program. 2003. (Harcourt Brace Social Studies). (gr. k-7). act. bk. ed. 5.30 (978-0-15-310303-2(5)); 124.30 (978-0-15-310441-1(4)) Harcourt Schl. Pubs.

—Reading Support & Test Preparation: Communities. 2003. (Harcourt Brace Social Studies). (gr. k-7). 27.00 (978-0-15-312379-5(6)) Harcourt Schl. Pubs.

—Reading Support & Test Preparation: Making a Difference. 2003. (Harcourt Brace Social Studies). (gr. k-7). 27.00 (978-0-15-312376-4(1)) Harcourt Schl. Pubs.

—Reading Support & Test Preparation: The World. 1999. (Harcourt Brace Social Studies). (gr. k-7). pap. 32.70 (978-0-15-312396-2(6)) Harcourt Schl. Pubs.

—Social Studies Libraries: A Child's Place. 2003. (Harcourt Brace Social Studies). (gr. k-7). 90.00 (978-0-15-310442-8(2)) Harcourt Schl. Pubs.

—Social Studies Libraries: Communities. 2003. (Harcourt Brace Social Studies). (gr. k-7). 117.60 (978-0-15-310444-2(9)) Harcourt Schl. Pubs.

—Social Studies Libraries: Making a Difference. 2003. (Harcourt Brace Social Studies). (gr. k-7). 95.70 (978-0-15-310443-5(0)) Harcourt Schl. Pubs.

—Vocabulary Picture Cards. 2003. (Harcourt Brace Social Studies). (SPA.). (gr. 1 up). 61.90 (978-0-15-310295-0(0)); (gr. 2 up). 69.30 (978-0-15-310296-7(9)) Harcourt Schl. Pubs.

—Write-on Charts. 2003. (Harcourt Brace Social Studies). (SPA.). (gr. 3 up). 216.40 (978-0-15-310292-9(6)) Harcourt Schl. Pubs.

The Boston Tea Party, 6 vols. (gr. 2-5). 39.95 (978-0-7368-4579-3(8)) Red Brick Learning.

Breaud, Odile, et al. Cultures of the World. 1998. (Creative Discoveries Ser.: Vol. 8). Orig. Title: Living Around the World. (Illus.). 75p. (J). (gr. 2-8). lib. bdg. 23.95 (978-0-88682-957-5(7) , Creative Education) Creative Co., The.

Brimson, Samuel. Nations of the World, 8 bks. Incl. Afghanistan-Botswana. lib. bdg. 30.00 (978-0-8368-5485-5(3)); Brazil-East Timor. lib. bdg. 30.00 (978-0-8368-5486-2(1)); Ecuador-Honduras. lib. bdg. 30.00 (978-0-8368-5487-9(X)); Hungary-Kiribati. lib. bdg. 30.00 (978-0-8368-5488-6(8)); Korea, North-Nicaragua. lib. bdg. 30.00 (978-0-8368-5489-3(6)); Niger-Seychelles. lib. bdg. 30.00 (978-0-8368-5490-9(X)); Sierra Leone-United Arab Emirates. lib. bdg. 30.00 (978-0-8368-5491-6(8)); United Kingdom-Zimbabwe. lib. bdg. 30.00 (978-0-8368-5492-3(6)); 64p. (J). (gr. 5 up). (Illus.). 2003. Set lib. bdg. 240.00 (978-0-8368-5484-8(5) , World Almanac Library) Stevens, Gareth Inc.

Brocker, Susan. Voices from the Civil War. 2004. (Navigators Ser.). (J). pap. 42.00 (978-1-4108-0434-1(8)) Benchmark Education Co.

Bunker, Barbara Benedict, et al. A Student's Guide to Conducting Social Science Research. 1999. 120p. (YA). (gr. 6-12). 16.95 (978-0-936386-78-2(9)) Creative Learning Pr., Inc.

Burnett, Eric. Middle Ages for the Classroom: Plays, Fairy Tales & Resources for the Classroom Teacher. 2002. 153p. pap. 11.95 (978-0-595-23430-1(5) , Writers Club Pr.) iUniverse, Inc.

Butrymowicz, Sarah. World So Different. 1999. (Publish-a-Book Ser.). (Illus.). 24p. (J). (gr. 1-6). pap. 8.50 (978-0-7398-0053-9(1)) Steck-Vaughn.

El Caballo de Troya: Aventuras (Adventure Books) 2000. (Aventuras A Traves Del Tiempo Ser.). (ENG & SPA.). (gr. 6 up). (978-0-02-148743-1(X)) Macmillan/McGraw-Hill Schl. Div.

El calendario Chino: Aventuras (Adventure Books) 2000. (Aventuras A Traves Del Tiempo Ser.). (ENG & SPA.). (gr. 6 up). (978-0-02-148744-8(8)) Macmillan/McGraw-Hill Schl. Div.

Callella, Trisha. Integrating Growth of a Nation with Reading Instruction. Walter, LaDawn, ed. Campbell, Jenny, illus. 2002. 72p. (J). (gr. 3-4). pap. 10.99 (978-1-57471-904-8(1) , 2829) Creative Teaching Pr., Inc.

—Integrating Our Community with Reading Instruction. Walter, LaDawn, ed. Campbell, Jenny, illus. 2002. 72p. (J). (gr. 1-2). pap. 10.99 (978-1-57471-902-4(5) , 2827) Creative Teaching Pr., Inc.

—Integrating Our Country & World with Reading Instruction. Walter, LaDawn, ed. Campbell, Jenny, illus. 2002. 72p. (J). (gr. 1-2). pap. 10.99 (978-1-57471-903-1(3) , 2828) Creative Teaching Pr., Inc.

El camino de Oregon el diario de Callie Stokes: Libros Aventuras (Adventure Books) 2000. (MacMillan/McGraw-Hill. Estudios Sociales Ser.). (ENG & SPA.). (gr. 5 up). (978-0-02-148736-3(7)) Macmillan/McGraw-Hill Schl. Div.

El campamento de Lewis y Clark: Libros Aventuras (Adventure Books) 2003. (MacMillan/McGraw-Hill. Estudios Sociales Ser.). (ENG & SPA.). (gr. 4 up). (978-0-02-150121-2(1)) Macmillan/McGraw-Hill Schl. Div.

Carder, Ken, et al. Songs That Teach States & Capitals. 2006. (Songs That Teach Ser.). 72p. (J). pap. 14.95 (978-0-7696-7713-2(4) , American Education Publishing) School Specialty Publishing.

La casa de la Guera 24: Leveled Books. 2001. (McGraw-Hill. Lectura Ser.). (ENG & SPA.). (gr. 2 up). (978-0-02-188025-6(5)) Macmillan/McGraw-Hill Schl. Div.

Una casa muy Grande: Aventuras (Adventure Books) 2000. (Aventuras A Traves Del Tiempo Ser.). (ENG & SPA.). (gr. 1 up). (978-0-02-148666-3(2)) Macmillan/McGraw-Hill Schl. Div.

Celebraciones Social Studies, 6 vols.Tr. of Celebrations Social Studies. (SPA.). (gr. k-2). 28.95 (978-0-7368-3038-6(3) , Yellow Umbrella Bks.) Capstone Pr., Inc.

Celebrations Social Studies, 6 vols. (gr. k-2). 28.95 (978-0-7368-3002-7(2) , Yellow Umbrella Bks.) Capstone Pr., Inc.

La ceramica de los indigenas Pueblo: Libros Aventuras (Adventure Books) 2003. (MacMillan/McGraw-Hill. Estudios Sociales Ser.). (ENG & SPA.). (gr. 5 up). (978-0-02-150124-3(6)) Macmillan/McGraw-Hill Schl. Div.

Cervantes, Carmen María, ed. Activos en la Historia. 2003. (Builders of Hope Ser.). (SPA., Illus.). 216p. (YA). pap. 11.95 (978-0-88489-442-1(8)) St. Mary's Pr.

Cesar Chavez, 6 vols. (gr. k-2). 28.95 (978-0-7368-8134-0(4)); (gr. 2-5). 36.95 (978-0-7368-8436-5(X)) Red Brick Learning.

Changing Face Of..., 22 vols. 2003. (Illus.). (978-0-7398-6046-5(1)) Raintree.

The Changing Face Of..., 4 vols., Set. 2002. 48p. (J). (gr. 5-6). 108.48 (978-0-7398-4969-9(7)) Raintree.

Cheney, Glen. Trapped! 2004. 64p. (YA). per. 3.95 (978-1-56254-832-2(8) , SP8328) Saddleback Educational Publishing.

Cheyney, Arnold. History Challenge Level 1: 190 Brainteasers about the United States. 2005. (Illus.). 192p. (J). (ps-k). pap. (978-1-59647-065-1(8) , EAS002) Good Year Bks.

—History Challenge Level 2: 190 Brainteasers about the World. 2005. 192p. (J). (ps-7). pap. (978-1-59647-066-8(6) , EAS002) Good Year Bks.

Chief Joseph of the Nez Perce, 6 vols. (gr. 2-5). 36.95 (978-0-7368-8437-2(8)) Red Brick Learning.

A Child's Day Series, 5 bks., Set. 79.75 (978-0-7614-1406-3(1) , Benchmark Bks.) Cavendish, Marshall Corp.

Cinco de Mayo, 6 vols. (gr. k-2). 28.95 (978-0-7368-9431-9(4)) Red Brick Learning.

La ciudad antigua de Tebas: Aventuras (Adventure Books) 2000. (Aventuras A Traves Del Tiempo Ser.). (ENG & SPA.). (gr. 6 up). (978-0-02-148738-7(3)) Macmillan/McGraw-Hill Schl. Div.

Clases de ropa Social Studies, 6 vols.Tr. of All Kinds of Clothes Social Studies. (SPA.). (gr. k-2). 28.95 (978-0-7368-3131-4(2) , Yellow Umbrella Bks.) Capstone Pr., Inc.

S

Clearly Social Studies. 2002. (J). 59p. (gr. 5-5). pap. 15.99 (978-0-7682-0633-3(2) , J332005); 56p. (gr. 6-6). pap. 15.99 (978-0-7682-0634-0(0) , J332006) School Specialty Publishing.

Coetzee, Eirka, et al. Social Science Matters: Grade 8 Learner's Book. 2000. 144p. (gr. 8). pap. 10.60 (978-0-521-78869-4(2)) Cambridge Univ. Pr.

—Social Science Matters Grade 8 Learner's Book. 2nd rev. ed. 2006. 192p. pap. 13.00 (978-0-521-67888-9(9)) Cambridge Univ. Pr.

—Social Science Matters Grade 8 Learner's Book Afrikaans Translation. 2nd ed. 2006. 192p. pap., stu. ed. 14.00 (978-0-521-67890-2(0)) Cambridge Univ. Pr.

Coetzee, Erika, et al. Social Science Matters: Grade 8. 2000. 80p. (gr. 8). pap., tchr. ed. 11.05 (978-0-521-78870-0(6)) Cambridge Univ. Pr.

—Social Science Matters: Grade 9. 2001. (gr. 9). pap., tchr. ed. 9.70 (978-0-521-78872-4(2)) Cambridge Univ. Pr.

—Social Science Matters: Grade 9 Learner's Book. 2001. 152p. (gr. 9). pap. 8.75 (978-0-521-78871-7(4)) Cambridge Univ. Pr.

—Social Sciences Matters Grade 7 Learner's Book. 2005. 160p. pap. 12.95 (978-0-521-67066-1(7)) Cambridge Univ. Pr.

Coletti, Sharon. The Power of One: A Guide to Service-Learning & Social Science Research. 2005. (YA). ring bd. 99.95 (978-1-933558-07-3(5)) InspirEd Educators.

Collett, Jo & Smith, Lee. Social Science Matters: Grade 4 Learner's Book. 2nd ed. 2004. 96p. pap., stu. ed. 8.85 (978-0-521-54438-2(6)) Cambridge Univ. Pr.

—Social Science Matters Grade 4 Afrikaans Translation. 2004. (AFR.). 96p. pap., stu. ed. 8.85 (978-0-521-54440-5(8)) Cambridge Univ. Pr.

Collett, Jo, et al. Social Sciences Matters: Grade 5 Learner's Book. 2nd rev. ed. 2004. 112p. pap. 9.95 (978-0-521-54601-0(X)) Cambridge Univ. Pr.

—Social Sciences Matters: Grade 5 Learners Book Afrikaans Translation. 2nd rev. ed. 2004. (AFR.). 112p. pap. 9.95 (978-0-521-54603-4(6)) Cambridge Univ. Pr.

Colonial America Classroom Library. (gr. 2-5). lib. bdg. 49.95 (978-0-7368-4488-8(0)) Red Brick Learning.

Communities at Work: Set 1. (Illus.). (J). (gr. k-5). 119.70 (978-1-4042-2949-5(3)) Rosen Publishing Group, Inc., The.

Communities at Work: Set 2. (Illus.). (J). (gr. k-5). 119.70 (978-1-4042-2948-8(5)) Rosen Publishing Group, Inc., The.

Community Helpers Classroom Library. (gr. 2-5). lib. bdg. 116.95 (978-0-7368-7074-0(1)) Red Brick Learning.

Community Helpers Complete Unit (gr. 2-5). 664.95 (978-0-7368-7075-7(X)) Red Brick Learning.

Community Helpers/Careers Classroom Library. (gr. k-2). lib. bdg. 91.95 (978-0-7368-1830-8(8)) Red Brick Learning.

Community Helpers/Careers Complete Unit. (gr. k-2). 433.95 (978-0-7368-1831-5(6)) Red Brick Learning.

A Community of Helpers. 2000. (Illus.). (J). lib. bdg. 3.21 (978-0-7398-4493-9(8)) Steck-Vaughn.

Complete Set: (8 Titles) (Many Cultures, One World Ser.). (gr. 3-5). 191.44 (978-0-7368-2338-8(7) , Blue Earth Bks.) Capstone Pr., Inc.

Comunidades Guia del Maestro: Comunidades. 2000. (Aventuras A Traves Del Tiempo Ser.). (ENG & SPA.). (gr. 3 up). (978-0-02-147821-7(X)) Macmillan/McGraw-Hill Schl. Div.

Comunidades libro del Estudiante: Comunidades. 2000. (Aventuras A Traves Del Tiempo Ser.). (ENG & SPA.). (gr. 3 up). (978-0-02-147806-4(6)) Macmillan/McGraw-Hill Schl. Div.

Comunidades libro del estudiante en Audiocasete: Comunidades. 2000. (Aventuras A Traves Del Tiempo Ser.). (ENG & SPA.). (gr. 3 up). (978-0-02-147813-2(9)) Macmillan/McGraw-Hill Schl. Div.

Concept Summaries: Language Support Cantonese: Teacher Resources. 2000. (McGraw-Hill Science Ser.). (gr. 6 up). (978-0-02-279462-0(X)) Macmillan/McGraw-Hill Schl. Div.

Conexion con el Hogar: Aqui Estoy! 2000. (Aventuras A Traves Del Tiempo Ser.). (ENG & SPA.). (gr. k up). (978-0-02-148434-8(1)) Macmillan/McGraw-Hill Schl. Div.

Conexion con el Hogar: Comunidades. 2000. (Aventuras A Traves Del Tiempo Ser.). (ENG & SPA.). (gr. 3 up). (978-0-02-148437-9(6)) Macmillan/McGraw-Hill Schl. Div.

Conexion con el Hogar: Gente. 2000. (Aventuras A Traves Del Tiempo Ser.). (ENG & SPA.). (gr. 2 up). (978-0-02-148436-2(8)) Macmillan/McGraw-Hill Schl. Div.

Conexion con el Hogar: Mi Mundo. 2000. (Aventuras A Traves Del Tiempo Ser.). (ENG & SPA.). (gr. 1 up). (978-0-02-148435-5(X)) Macmillan/McGraw-Hill Schl. Div.

Conozcamos a las familias, Unidad 2: Superlibros (Big Books) 2000. (Aventuras A Traves Del Tiempo Ser.). (ENG & SPA.). (gr. k up). (978-0-02-147834-7(1)) Macmillan/McGraw-Hill Schl. Div.

Consideration, 6 vols. (gr. 2-5). 36.95 (978-0-7368-9252-0(4)) Red Brick Learning.

Construction Workers, 6 vols. (gr. 2-5). 36.95 (978-0-7368-8049-7(6)) Red Brick Learning.

The Continents Collection. 2005. (J). pap. (***978-1-60015-012-8(8)**) Steps To Literacy, LLC.

Cornerstones of Freedom Accelerated Reader Series, Vol. 1. 2002. pap. 672.00 (978-0-516-29704-0(X) , Children's Pr.) Scholastic Library Publishing.

La cosecha Social Studies, 6 vols.Tr. of Harvest Time Social Studies. (SPA.). (gr. k-2). 28.95 (978-0-7368-3039-3(1) , Yellow Umbrella Bks.) Capstone Pr., Inc.

Costain, Meredith & Collins, Paul. Countries of the World Series, 12 bks. Incl. Welcome to Brazil. 32p. 28.00 (978-0-7910-6547-1(2) , 010201); Welcome to China. 32p. 28.00 (978-0-7910-6548-8(0) , 010202); Welcome to France. 32p. 28.00 (978-0-7910-6551-8(0) , 010203); Welcome to Germany. 32p. 28.00 (978-0-7910-6546-4(4) , 010204); Welcome to Greece. 32p. 28.00 (978-0-7910-6545-7(6) , 010204); Welcome to Indonesia. 32p. 28.00 (978-0-7910-6543-3(X) , 010206); Welcome to Italy. 32p. 28.00 (978-0-7910-6550-1(2) , 010207); Welcome to Japan. 32p. 28.00 (978-0-7910-6541-9(3) , 010208); Welcome to Russia. 32p. 28.00 (978-0-7910-6549-5(9) , 010209); Welcome to South Africa. 28.00 (978-0-7910-6540-2(5) , 010210); Welcome to the United Kingdom. 32p. 28.00 (978-0-7910-6544-0(8) , 010211); Welcome to the United States of America. 32p. 28.00 (978-0-7910-6542-6(1) , 010212); (J). (gr. 4 up). 2001. (Illus.). 203.40 (978-0-7910-6539-6(1) , 010200S, Chelsea Hse.) Facts On File, Inc.

The Cotton Tale. abr. ed. 2004. (Thrilling Tales in Time Ser.: Vol. 41). (J). 19.95 (978-1-58123-372-8(8)) Larson Learning, Inc.

Countries & Cultures, 12 bks. Incl. Australia. Boraas, Tracey. (gr. 3-4). 2002. lib. bdg. 23.93 (978-0-7368-1075-3(7)); Brazil. Boraas, Tracey. (gr. 3-4). 2001. lib. bdg. 23.93 (978-0-7368-0765-4(9)); Canada. Boraas, Tracey. (gr. 3-4). 2001. lib. bdg. 23.93 (978-0-7368-0766-1(7)); China. Salas, Laura Purdie. (gr. 3-4). 2001. lib. bdg. 23.93 (978-0-7368-0767-8(5)); Colombia. Boraas, Tracey. (gr. 3-4). 2002. lib. bdg. 23.93 (978-0-7368-1076-0(5)); Egypt. Boraas, Tracey. (gr. 3-4). 2001. lib. bdg. 23.93 (978-0-7368-0768-5(3)); England. Boraas, Tracey. (gr. 4). 2002. lib. bdg. 23.93 (978-0-7368-0937-5(6)); France. Knoell, Donna L. (gr. 3-4). 2002. lib. bdg. 23.93 (978-0-7368-1077-7(3)); Germany. Salas, Laura Purdie. (gr. 3-4). 2001. lib. bdg. 23.93 (978-0-7368-0769-2(1)); Greece. Nobleman, Marc Tyler. (gr. 3-4). 2003. lib. bdg. 23.95 (978-0-7368-1547-5(3)); Haiti. Graves, Kerry A. (gr. 3-4). 2002. lib. bdg. 23.93 (978-0-7368-1078-4(1)); India. Mattern, Joanne. (gr. 3-4). 2003. lib. bdg. 23.95 (978-0-7368-1548-2(1)); Ireland. Mattern, Joanne. (gr. 3-4). 2003. lib. bdg. 23.95 (978-0-7368-1549-9(X)); Israel. Boraas, Tracey. (gr. 4). 2002. lib. bdg. 23.93 (978-0-7368-0938-2(4)); Japan. Boraas, Tracey. (gr. 3-4). 2001. lib. bdg. 23.93 (978-0-7368-0770-8(5)); Kenya. Saffer, Barbara. (gr. 3-4). 2001. lib. bdg. 23.93 (978-0-7368-0771-5(3)); Mexico. Saffer, Barbara. (gr. 3-4). 2001. lib. bdg. 23.93 (978-0-7368-0772-2(1)); Pakistan. Nobleman, Marc Tyler. (gr. 3-4). 2003. lib. bdg. 18.60 (978-0-7368-1550-5(3)); Sweden. Boraas, Tracey. (gr. 4). 2002. lib. bdg. 23.93 (978-0-7368-0939-9(2)); Thailand. Boraas, Tracey. (gr. 3-4). 2002. lib. bdg. 23.93 (978-0-7368-0940-5(6)); 64p. (J). (Illus.). 2001. Set lib. bdg. 478.60 (978-0-7368-1599-4(6) , Bridgestone Bks.) Capstone Pr., Inc.

Countries of the World Classroom Library. (gr. 2-5). lib. bdg. 139.95 (978-0-7368-7072-6(5)) Red Brick Learning.

Countries of the World Complete Unit. (gr. 2-5). 797.95 (978-0-7368-7073-3(3)) Red Brick Learning.

Country Fact Files, 28 bks., Set. Incl. Argentina, Chile, Paraguay, Uruguay. Selby, Anna. 1999. lib. bdg. 27.12 (978-0-8172-5408-7(0)); Australia. Allison, Robert J. 1996. lib. bdg. 27.12 (978-0-8114-5642-5(0)); Bangladesh. Cumming, David. 1999. lib. bdg. 27.12 (978-0-8172-5405-6(6)); Brazil. Morrison, Marion. 1994. lib. bdg. 27.12 (978-0-8114-1842-3(1)); Canada. Sylvester, John. 1996. lib. bdg. 27.12 (978-0-8114-6197-9(1)); Central America. Parker, Edward. 1999. lib. bdg. 27.12 (978-0-8172-5406-3(4)); China. Charley, Catherine. 1998. lib. bdg. 27.12 (978-0-8172-5410-0(2)); East Africa. Binns, Tony & Bowden, Rob. 1998. lib. bdg. 27.12 (978-0-8172-5401-8(3)); Eastern Europe. Burke, Patrick. 1997. lib. bdg. 27.12 (978-0-8172-4628-0(2)); Egypt. Loveridge, Emma W. Marffy, Janos, illus. 1997. lib. bdg. 27.12 (978-0-8172-4626-6(6)); France. Bussolin, Veronique. 1995. lib. bdg. 27.12 (978-0-8114-2784-5(6)); Germany. Flint, David. 1994. lib. bdg. 27.12 (978-0-8114-1845-4(6)); India. Ganeri, Anita & Ganeri, Jonardon. 1995. lib. bdg. 27.12 (978-0-8114-2787-6(0)); Israel. Patterson, Jose. 1997. lib. bdg. 27.12 (978-0-8172-4627-3(4)); Italy. Allen, Derek. 1996. lib. bdg. 27.12 (978-0-8114-6196-2(3)); Japan. Baines, John. 1994. lib. bdg. 27.12 (978-0-8114-1847-8(2)); Mexico. Parker, Edward. 1996. lib. bdg. 27.12 (978-0-8114-6198-6(X)); Russia. Sallnow, John & Saiko, Tatyana. 1997. lib. bdg. 27.12 (978-0-8172-4625-9(8)); Saudi Arabia. Honeyman, Susannah. 1995. lib. bdg. 27.12 (978-0-8114-2786-9(2)); Southeast Asia. Rigg, Jonathan. 1995. lib. bdg. 27.12 (978-0-8114-2788-3(9)); Southern Africa. Middleton, Nick. 1995. lib. bdg. 27.12 (978-0-8114-2785-2(4)); Spain. Selby, Anna. 1994. lib. bdg. 27.12 (978-0-8114-1848-5(0)); Sweden. Carlson, Bo Kage. 1999. lib. bdg. 27.12 (978-0-8172-5407-0(2)); United Kingdom. Flint, David. 1994. lib. bdg. 27.12 (978-0-8114-1849-2(9)); United States. Baines, John D. 1994. lib. bdg. 27.12 (978-0-8114-1857-7(X)); West Africa. Binns, Tony & Bowden, Rob. 1998. lib. bdg. 27.12 (978-0-8172-5400-1(5)); West Indies. Hodge, Alison. 1998. lib. bdg. 27.12 (978-0-8172-5402-5(1)); (Illus.). 48p. (J). (gr. 4-8). 2000. Set lib. bdg. 759.36 (978-0-7398-4371-0(0)) Raintree.

Cousins, 6 vols. (gr. k-2). 28.95 (978-0-7368-8265-1(0)) Red Brick Learning.

Cronin, Sarah, contrib. by. Book of Knowledge: The Usborne Internet-Linked. 2005. (Illus.). 208p. (J). (ps-7). 14.95 (978-0-7945-1080-0(9) , Usborne) EDC Publishing.

Cuaderno de Evaluacion: Comunidades. 2000. (Aventuras A Traves Del Tiempo Ser.). (ENG & SPA.). (gr. 3 up). (978-0-02-147997-9(6)) Macmillan/McGraw-Hill Schl. Div.

Cuaderno de Evaluacion: Gente. 2000. (Aventuras A Traves Del Tiempo Ser.). (ENG & SPA.). (gr. 2 up). (978-0-02-147996-2(8)) Macmillan/McGraw-Hill Schl. Div.

Cuaderno de Evaluacion: Mi Mundo. 2000. (Aventuras A Traves Del Tiempo Ser.). (ENG & SPA.). (gr. 1 up). (978-0-02-147995-5(X)) Macmillan/McGraw-Hill Schl. Div.

Cuaderno de Evaluacion: Student & Teacher Support Resources. 2003. (MacMillan/McGraw-Hill. Estudios Sociales Ser.). (ENG & SPA.). (gr. 1 up). (978-0-02-149458-3(4)); (gr. 2 up). (978-0-02-149459-0(2)); (gr. 3 up). (978-0-02-149461-3(4)); (gr. 4 up). (978-0-02-149971-7(3)); (gr. 5 up). (978-0-02-149463-7(0)) Macmillan/McGraw-Hill Schl. Div.

Cuaderno de Practica: Comunidades. 2000. (Aventuras A Traves Del Tiempo Ser.). (ENG & SPA.). (gr. 3 up). (978-0-02-147885-9(6)) Macmillan/McGraw-Hill Schl. Div.

Cuaderno de Practica: Gente. 2000. (Aventuras A Traves Del Tiempo Ser.). (ENG & SPA.). (gr. 2 up). (978-0-02-147884-2(8)) Macmillan/McGraw-Hill Schl. Div.

Cuaderno de Practica: Mi Mundo. 2000. (Aventuras A Traves Del Tiempo Ser.). (ENG & SPA.). (gr. 1 up). (978-0-02-147883-5(X)) Macmillan/McGraw-Hill Schl. Div.

Cuaderno de practica y Actividades: Student & Teacher Support Resources. 2003. (MacMillan/McGraw-Hill. Estudios Sociales Ser.). (ENG & SPA.). (gr. 1 up). (978-0-02-150009-3(6)); (gr. 1 up). (978-0-02-149453-8(3)); (gr. 2 up). (978-0-02-150010-9(X)); (gr. 2 up). (978-0-02-149454-5(1)); (gr. 3 up). (978-0-02-150011-6(8)); (gr. 3 up). (978-0-02-149455-2(X)); (gr. 4 up). (978-0-02-149970-0(5)); (gr. 5 up). (978-0-02-150014-7(2)); (gr. 5 up). (978-0-02-149457-6(6)) Macmillan/McGraw-Hill Schl. Div.

Cuaderno de Proyectos: Aqui Estoy! 2000. (Aventuras A Traves Del Tiempo Ser.). (ENG & SPA.). (gr. k up). (978-0-02-147889-7(9)) Macmillan/McGraw-Hill Schl. Div.

Cuaderno de Proyectos: Comunidades. 2000. (Aventuras A Traves Del Tiempo Ser.). (ENG & SPA.). (gr. 3 up). (978-0-02-147893-4(7)) Macmillan/McGraw-Hill Schl. Div.

Cuaderno de Proyectos: Gente. 2000. (Aventuras A Traves Del Tiempo Ser.). (ENG & SPA.). (gr. 2 up). (978-0-02-147892-7(9)) Macmillan/McGraw-Hill Schl. Div.

Cuaderno de Proyectos: Mi Mundo. 2000. (Aventuras A Traves Del Tiempo Ser.). (ENG & SPA.). (gr. 1 up). (978-0-02-147891-0(0)) Macmillan/McGraw-Hill Schl. Div.

Cuando el sol se cayo del Cielo: Libros Aventuras (Adventure Books) 2000. (MacMillan/McGraw-Hill. Estudios Sociales Ser.). (ENG & SPA.). (gr. 2 up). (978-0-02-148679-3(4)) Macmillan/McGraw-Hill Schl. Div.

Cuatro de Julio en las llanuras, Unidad 4: Superlibros (Big Books) 2000. (Aventuras A Traves Del Tiempo Ser.). (ENG & SPA.). (gr. 3 up). (978-0-02-147876-7(7)) Macmillan/McGraw-Hill Schl. Div.

El cuento de Abuelo: Aventuras (Adventure Books) 2000. (Aventuras A Traves Del Tiempo Ser.). (ENG & SPA.). (gr. 1 up). (978-0-02-148673-1(5)) Macmillan/McGraw-Hill Schl. Div.

Cuidando a las mascotas Social Studies, 6 vols.Tr. of Taking Care of Pets Social Studies. (SPA.). (gr. k-2). 28.95 (978-0-7368-3115-4(0) , Yellow Umbrella Bks.) Capstone Pr., Inc.

CultureGrams 2001. 2000. 177 p. (J). pap. 139.00 (978-0-9702937-0-1(4)); 2001st ed. 177p. pap. 149.00 incl. cd-rom (978-0-9702937-1-8(2)) ProQuest CSA.

CultureGrams 2001: PDF Format. 2000. 6.00 (978-0-9702937-8-7(X)) ProQuest CSA.

CultureGrams 2001: Server Edition. 2000. 177p. (978-0-9702937-9-4(8)) ProQuest CSA.

CultureGrams 2001: The Nations Around Us, set; 2 vols. 2000. 720p. per. 139.00 (978-0-9702937-5-6(5)); 720p. per. 149.00 incl. cd-rom (978-0-9702937-6-3(3)); Vol. 1. 316p. per. 55.95 (978-0-9702937-3-2(9)); Vol. 2. 404p. per. 85.95 (978-0-9702937-4-9(7)) ProQuest CSA.

CultureGrams 2002 Standard Edition. 2001. 177 p. ring bd. 141.99 (978-1-931694-00-1(1)) ProQuest CSA.

CultureGrams 2002 Vol. I & II: The Nations Around Us, , 2002nd ed. 2001. 720p. per. 141.99 (978-1-931694-01-8(X)) ProQuest CSA.

CultureGrams 2003 Kids Edition. 2002. (J). per. 69.99 incl. cd-rom (978-1-931694-38-4(9)); ring bd. 69.99 incl. cd-rom (978-1-931694-39-1(7)) ProQuest CSA.

CultureGrams 2003 World Edition. 2002. (J). per. 129.99 incl. cd-rom (978-1-931694-32-2(X)) ProQuest CSA.

CultureGrams 2005 World Edition. 2004. (YA). per. 129.99 (978-1-931694-87-2(7)); ring bd. 139.99 (978-1-931694-88-9(5)) ProQuest CSA.

CultureGrams Kids Edition. 2001. (J). spiral bd. 71.99 (978-1-931694-13-1(3)); ring bd. 71.99 (978-1-931694-12-4(5)) ProQuest CSA.

Cultures of the World - Group 22, 6 vols. Incl. Belize. Jermyn, Leslie. lib. bdg. 37.07 (978-0-7614-1190-1(9)); Bhutan. Cooper, Robert. lib. bdg. 37.07 (978-0-7614-1191-8(7)); Eritrea. NgCheong-Lum, Roseline. (J). lib. bdg. 37.07 (978-0-7614-1192-5(5)); Kazakhstan. Cheng, Pang Guek. (J). lib. bdg. 37.07 (978-0-7614-1193-2(3)); Trinidad & Tobago. Sheehan, Sean. (J). lib. bdg. 37.07 (978-0-7614-1194-9(1)); Wales. Hestler, Anna. (J). lib. bdg. 37.07 (978-0-7614-1195-6(X)); (gr. 5-12). 2001. (Illus.). 128p. 2001. 222.43 (978-0-7614-1189-5(5) , Benchmark Bks.) Cavendish, Marshall Corp.

Daronco, Mickey & Ohanesian, Diane. Am I Sad? 2nd rev. ed. 2003. (BuildUp Ser.). (J). pap. 22.00 (978-1-4108-0740-3(1)) Benchmark Education Co.

—At the Mat. 2nd rev. ed. 2003. (BuildUp Ser.). (J). pap. 22.00 (978-1-4108-0735-9(5)) Benchmark Education Co.

—A Cake for Nate. 2nd rev. ed. 2003. (BuildUp Ser.). (J). pap. 22.00 (978-1-4108-0752-6(5)) Benchmark Education Co.

Days That Changed the World, 6 bks. Incl. D-Day. Hynson, Colin. pap. 11.95 (978-0-8368-5575-3(2)); Fall of the Berlin Wall. Smith, Jeremy. pap. 11.95 (978-0-8368-5576-0(0)); First Man in Space. Cullen, David. pap. 11.95 (978-0-8368-5577-7(9)); First "Test-Tube Baby" MacDonald, Fiona. pap. 11.95 (978-0-8368-5574-6(4)); Release of Nelson Mandela. Beecroft, Simon. pap. 11.95 (978-0-8368-5578-4(7)); September 11th Terrorist Attacks. Beecroft, Simon. pap. 11.95 (978-0-8368-5579-1(5)); 48p. (J). (gr. 5 up). (Illus.). 2004. Set pap. 71.70 (978-0-8368-5573-9(6)); Set lib. bdg. 180.00 (978-0-8368-5566-1(3)) Stevens, Gareth Inc. (World Almanac Library).

De aqui a alla Social Studies, 6 vols.Tr. of From Here to There Social Studies. (SPA.). (gr. k-2). 28.95 (978-0-7368-3021-8(9) , Yellow Umbrella Bks.) Capstone Pr., Inc.

De Compras: Libros Aventuras (Adventure Books) 2000. (MacMillan/McGraw-Hill. Estudios Sociales Ser.). (ENG & SPA.). (gr. 1 up). (978-0-02-148668-7(9)) Macmillan/McGraw-Hill Schl. Div.

The Declaration of Independence, 6 vols. (gr. 2-5). 39.95 (978-0-7368-4580-9(1)) Red Brick Learning.

Del arbol a la mesa Social Studies, 6 vols.Tr. of From Tree to Table Social Studies. (SPA.). (gr. k-2). 28.95 (978-0-7368-3132-1(0) , Yellow Umbrella Bks.) Capstone Pr., Inc.

Desert Day: Level B, 6 vols. 8p. 24.95 (978-0-7802-8916-1(1)) Wright Group, The.

El dia del Rodeo: Aventuras (Adventure Books) 2000. (Aventuras A Traves Del Tiempo Ser.). (ENG & SPA.). (gr. 4 up). (978-0-02-148712-7(X)) Macmillan/McGraw-Hill Schl. Div.

Un dia en el Ciclotaxi: Libros Aventuras (Adventure Books) 2000. (MacMillan/McGraw-Hill. Estudios Sociales Ser.). (ENG & SPA.). (gr. 2 up). (978-0-02-148675-5(1)) Macmillan/McGraw-Hill Schl. Div.

Un dia tranquilo para Mia: Libros Aventuras (Adventure Books) 2000. (MacMillan/McGraw-Hill. Estudios Sociales Ser.). (ENG & SPA.). (gr. 2 up). (978-0-02-148687-8(5)) Macmillan/McGraw-Hill Schl. Div.

Diario de la Frontera: Libros Aventuras (Adventure Books) 2003. (MacMillan/McGraw-Hill. Estudios Sociales Ser.). (ENG & SPA.). (gr. 4 up). (978-0-02-150118-2(1)) Macmillan/McGraw-Hill Schl. Div.

El diario de una nina Inmigrante: Libros Aventuras (Adventure Books) 2003. (MacMillan/McGraw-Hill. Estudios Sociales Ser.). (ENG & SPA.). (gr. 5 up). (978-0-02-150126-7(2)) Macmillan/McGraw-Hill Schl. Div.

Un Dibujo: Aventuras (Adventure Books) 2000. (Aventuras A Traves Del Tiempo Ser.). (ENG & SPA.). (gr. k up). (978-0-02-148654-0(9)) Macmillan/McGraw-Hill Schl. Div.

Diferentes clases de granjas Social Studies, 6 vols.Tr. of All Kinds of Farms Social Studies. (SPA.). (gr. k-2). 28.95 (978-0-7368-3025-6(1) , Yellow Umbrella Bks.) Capstone Pr., Inc.

Diffily, Deborah & Sassman, Charlotte. Service Learning Projects for Elementary Students. Weaver-Spencer, Jennifer, ed. 2005. 96p. (J). per. 10.99 (978-1-59441-058-1(5) , CD-104032) Carson-Dellosa Publishing Co., Inc.

Discos compactos: Libro del Estudiante: Technology. 2003. (MacMillan/McGraw-Hill. Estudios Sociales Ser.). (ENG & SPA.). (gr. 2 up). (978-0-02-150052-9(5)); (gr. 3 up). (978-0-02-150053-6(3)); (gr. 4 up). (978-0-02-150055-0(X)); (gr. 5 up). (978-0-02-150056-7(8)) Macmillan/McGraw-Hill Schl. Div.

Discovering Cultures Series - Group 1, 6 bks., Set. 158.86 (978-0-7614-1181-9(X) , Benchmark Bks.) Cavendish, Marshall Corp.

Dnistrian, Steve. Partnership Attitude Tracking Study (Spring 2000) 2001. (Illus.). 69p. (YA). (gr. 7-12). pap. 20.00 (978-0-7567-1361-4(7)) DIANE Publishing Co.

The Doctor's Office, 6 vols. (gr. k-2). 28.95 (978-0-7368-8004-6(6)) Red Brick Learning.

Donde va el correo? Social Studies, 6 vols.Tr. of Where Does the Mail Go? Social Studies. (SPA.). (gr. k-2). 28.95 (978-0-7368-3136-9(3) , Yellow Umbrella Bks.) Capstone Pr., Inc.

Donde vives tu? Social Studies. (SPA.). (gr. k-2). 19.95 (978-0-7368-3108-6(8)) Red Brick Learning.

Dorling Kindersley Publishing Staff. My Favorite Things. 2005. (Barbie sticker Bks.). 20p. (J). pap. 6.99 (978-0-7566-1178-1(4)) Dorling Kindersley Publishing, Inc.

Douglas, Vincent. Daily Learning Drills: Grade 4. 2003. (Daily Learning Drills Ser.). (Illus.). 416p. (J). (gr. 4-4). pap., wbk. ed. 10.95 (978-0-7696-3094-6(4) , American Education Publishing) School Specialty Publishing.

—Daily Learning Drills: Grade 5. 2003. (Daily Learning Drills Ser.). (Illus.). 416p. (J). (gr. 5-5). pap., wbk. ed. 10.95 (978-0-7696-3095-3(2) , American Education Publishing) School Specialty Publishing.

—Daily Learning Drills: Grade 6. 2003. (Daily Learning Drills Ser.). (Illus.). 416p. (J). (gr. 6-6). pap. 10.95 (978-0-7696-3096-0(0) , Brighter Child) School Specialty Publishing.

Downing, David & Tames, Richard. Political & Economic Systems, 6 vols., Set. 2003. (YA). (gr. 6-8). lib. bdg. 171.00 (978-1-4034-0321-6(X)) Heinemann Library.

DynaNotes Grade 8 Social Studies Review Guide Transparency Set. 2006. (YA). trans. (978-1-933854-35-9(9)) DynaStudy, Inc.

DynaNotes Grade 8 Social Studies TAKS Review Guide. 2006. pap. (978-1-933854-31-1(6)) DynaStudy, Inc.

Early Social Studies Package. 2005. (Emergent/Early (Prek-2) Social Studies Package Ser.). (YA). (gr. k-2). 126.00 (978-0-8215-7862-9(6)) Sadlier, William H. Inc.

Edificios: Libros Aventuras (Adventure Books) 2000. (MacMillan/McGraw-Hill. Estudios Sociales Ser.). (ENG & SPA.). (gr. 1 up). (978-0-02-148665-6(4)) Macmillan/McGraw-Hill Schl. Div.

Los elefantes tienen Casa: Aventuras (Adventure Books) 2000. (Aventuras A Traves Del Tiempo Ser.). (ENG & SPA.). (gr. k up). (978-0-02-148655-7(7)) Macmillan/McGraw-Hill Schl. Div.

Emancipation Proclamation, 6 vols. (gr. 2-5). 39.95 (978-0-7368-4597-7(6)) Red Brick Learning.

Emergent Social Studies Package. 2005. (Emergent/Early (Prek-2) Social Studies Package Ser.). (YA). (gr. k-1). 135.00 (978-0-8215-7876-6(6)) Sadlier, William H. Inc.

Emergent/Early Social Studies Package. 2005. (Social Studies). (YA). (gr. k-2). 243.00 (978-0-8215-7886-5(3)) Sadlier, William H. Inc.

En el parque Social Studies, 6 vols.Tr. of At the Park Social Studies. (SPA.). (gr. k-2). 28.95 (978-0-7368-3020-1(0) , Yellow Umbrella Bks.) Capstone Pr., Inc.

Enciende la vela! Toca el Tambor! Superlibros (Big Books) 2000. (Aventuras A Traves Del Tiempo Ser.). (ENG & SPA.). (gr. k up). (978-0-02-147858-3(9)) Macmillan/McGraw-Hill Schl. Div.

Eri busca de un Hogar: Libros Aventuras (Adventure Books) 2003. (MacMillan/McGraw-Hill. Estudios Sociales Ser.). (ENG & SPA.). (gr. 5 up). (978-0-02-150123-6(8)) Macmillan/McGraw-Hill Schl. Div.

Es una regla Social Studies, 6 vols.Tr. of It's a Rule Social Studies. (SPA.). (gr. k-2). 28.95 (978-0-7368-3133-8(9) , Yellow Umbrella Bks.) Capstone Pr., Inc.

Esta granja Social Studies, 6 vols.Tr. of This Farm Social Studies. (SPA.). (gr. k-2). 28.95 (978-0-7368-3116-1(9) , Yellow Umbrella Bks.) Capstone Pr., Inc.

Estudios sociales Scott Foresman. 2003. (SPA.). (gr. k up). stu. ed. (978-0-328-05613-2(8)); (gr. 1 up). stu. ed. (978-0-328-01920-5(8)); (gr. 1 up). stu. ed. (978-0-328-05499-2(2)); (gr. 2 up). (978-0-328-01921-2(6)); (gr. 2 up). stu. ed. (978-0-328-05500-5(X)); (gr. 3 up). stu. ed. (978-0-328-01922-9(4)); (gr. 4 up). stu. ed. (978-0-328-05001-7(6)); (gr. 5 up). stu. ed. (978-0-328-01923-6(2)) Addison-Wesley Educational Pubs., Inc. (Scott Foresman).

Estudios sociales Scott Foresman: Additional Resources. 2003. (SPA.). (gr. k-2). (978-0-328-03696-7(X)); (gr. k-2). (978-0-328-03874-9(1)); (gr. k-2). (978-0-328-08332-9(1)); (gr. k-2). tchr. ed. (978-0-328-04213-5(7)); (gr. k-5). (978-0-328-03873-2(3)); (gr. k up). (978-0-328-05503-6(4)); (gr. k up). (978-0-328-03860-2(1)); (gr. 1 up). (978-0-328-05504-3(2)); (gr. 1 up). (978-0-328-03867-1(9)); (gr. 1 up). (978-0-328-04202-9(1)); (gr. 1 up). (978-0-328-03861-9(X)); (gr. 1 up). (978-0-328-05737-5(1)); (gr. 2 up). (978-0-328-05505-0(0)); (gr. 2 up). (978-0-328-03862-6(8)); (gr. 2 up). (978-0-328-04203-6(X)); (gr. 2 up). (978-0-328-05738-2(X)); (gr. 2 up). (978-0-328-03868-8(7)); (gr. 3-5). (978-0-328-03698-1(6)); (gr. 3-5). (978-0-328-03872-5(5)); (gr. 3-5). (978-0-328-04182-4(3)); (gr. 3-5). tchr. ed. (978-0-328-04214-2(5)); (gr. 3 up). (978-0-328-03869-5(5)); (gr. 3 up). (978-0-328-05509-8(3)); (gr. 3 up). (978-0-328-05506-7(9)); (gr. 3 up). (978-0-328-04204-3(8)); (gr. 3 up). (978-0-328-03863-3(6)); (gr. 4 up). (978-0-328-05779-5(7)); (gr. 4 up). (978-0-328-05776-4(2)); (gr. 4 up). (978-0-328-05780-1(0)); (gr. 4 up). (978-0-328-05784-9(3)); (gr. 4 up). (978-0-328-05777-1(0)); (gr. 5 up). (978-0-328-05508-1(5)); (gr. 5 up). (978-0-328-04206-7(4)); (gr. 5 up). (978-0-328-03865-7(2)); (gr. 5 up). (978-0-328-05511-1(5)); (gr. 5 up). (978-0-328-03871-8(7)) Addison-Wesley Educational Pubs., Inc. (Scott Foresman).

Estudios sociales Scott Foresman: Practice/Assessment. 2003. (Test Talk Practice Book Ser.). (SPA.). (gr. 1 up). (978-0-328-03855-8(5)); (gr. 1 up). (978-0-328-03463-5(0)); (gr. 1 up). wbk. ed. (978-0-328-01932-8(1)); (gr. 2 up). (978-0-328-03856-5(3)); (gr. 2 up). (978-0-328-03464-2(9)); (gr. 2 up). wbk. ed. (978-0-328-01933-5(X)); (gr. 3 up). (978-0-328-03465-9(7)); (gr. 3 up). (978-0-328-03857-2(1)); (gr. 3 up). wbk. ed. (978-0-328-01934-2(8)); (gr. 4 up). (978-0-328-05687-3(1)); (gr. 4 up). (978-0-328-05781-8(9)); (gr. 4 up). wbk. ed. (978-0-328-05686-6(3)); (gr. 5 up). (978-0-328-03467-3(3)); (gr. 5 up). (978-0-328-03859-6(8)); (gr. 5 up). wbk. ed. (978-0-328-01936-6(4)) Addison-Wesley Educational Pubs., Inc. (Scott Foresman).

Estudios sociales Scott Foresman: Technology. 2003. (SPA.). (gr. k-5). cd-rom (978-0-328-05749-8(5)); (gr. 1 up). (978-0-328-09220-8(7)); (gr. 1 up). (978-0-328-05726-9(6)); (gr. 1 up). cd-rom (978-0-328-05932-4(3)); (gr. 1 up). cd-rom (978-0-328-05744-3(4)); (gr. 2 up). (978-0-328-09221-5(5)); (gr. 2 up). (978-0-328-05727-6(4)); (gr. 2 up). cd-rom (978-0-328-05745-0(2)); (gr. 2 up).

cd-rom (978-0-328-05933-1(1)); (gr. 3 up). (978-0-328-05728-3(2)); (gr. 3 up). (978-0-328-09222-2(3)); (gr. 3 up). cd-rom (978-0-328-05934-8(X)); (gr. 3 up). cd-rom (978-0-328-05746-7(0)); (gr. 4 up). (978-0-328-09223-9(1)); (gr. 4 up). (978-0-328-05800-6(9)); (gr. 4 up). cd-rom (978-0-328-05936-2(6)); (gr. 4 up). cd-rom (978-0-328-05786-3(X)); (gr. 5 up). (978-0-328-05730-6(4)); (gr. 5 up). (978-0-328-09224-6(X)); (gr. 5 up). cd-rom (978-0-328-05937-9(4)); (gr. 5 up). cd-rom (978-0-328-05748-1(7)) Addison-Wesley Educational Pubs., Inc. (Scott Foresman).

The Events to Independence. 2004. (Thrilling Tales in Time Ser.: Vol. 3). (J). (978-1-58123-369-8(8)) Larson Learning, Inc.

Everyone Eats Bread! Social Studies, 6 vols. (gr. k-2). 28.95 (978-0-7368-2986-1(5) , Yellow Umbrella Bks.) Capstone Pr., Inc.

Everything Has a Story Social Studies. (gr. k-2). 19.95 (978-0-7368-2902-1(4)) Red Brick Learning.

Explora el Mundo. 288p. (J). (gr. 3-8). (978-0-7166-7096-4(8)) World Bk., Inc.

Exploremos, Unidad 3: Superlibros (Big Books) 2000. (Aventuras A Traves Del Tiempo Ser.). (ENG & SPA.). (gr. k up). (978-0-02-147835-4(X)) Macmillan/McGraw-Hill Schl. Div.

Exploring Tough Issues, 16 vols., Set. 2004. 478.88 (978-1-4109-1367-8(8)) Harcourt Schl. Pubs.

Exploring Tough Issues, 6 bks., Set. Incl. Why Do People Drink Alcohol? Johnson, Julie. Sloan, Frank, ed. lib. bdg. 25.69 (978-0-7398-3235-6(2)); Why Do People Gamble? Stearman, Kaye. lib. bdg. 25.69 (978-0-7398-3233-2(6)); Why Do People Join Gangs? Johnson, Julie. Sloan, Frank, ed. lib. bdg. 25.69 (978-0-7398-3236-3(0)); Why Do People Live on the Streets? Stearman, Kaye. lib. bdg. 25.69 (978-0-7398-3232-5(8)); Why Do People Smoke? Powell, Jillian. lib. bdg. 25.69 (978-0-7398-3234-9(4)); Why Do People Take Drugs? Westcott, Patsy. lib. bdg. 25.69 (978-0-7398-3231-8(X)); (Illus.). 48p. (J). (gr. 4-7). 2001. Set lib. bdg. 154.14 (978-0-7398-3237-0(9)) Raintree.

Exploring Tough Issues S02. 2002. 102.76 (978-0-7398-4963-7(8)) Raintree.

Face the Facts, 7 bks. 2003. 199.92 (978-0-7398-6437-1(8)); Set. 2004. (Illus.). pap. 338.30 (978-1-4109-1253-4(1)); Set 3. 2004. (Illus.). 171.36 (978-1-4109-1073-8(3)); Sets 1&2. 2003. (Illus.). pap. 56.35 (978-1-4109-0433-1(4)) Raintree.

Faherty, Sara. Welfare Reform. 2004. (Point/Counterpoint Ser.). (Illus.). 170p. (YA). (gr. 9-14). bds. 32.95 (978-0-7910-8093-1(5) , Chelsea Hse.) Facts On File, Inc.

Family Fun. 2005. (Social Studies). (YA). (gr. k-1). 25.20 (978-0-8215-7835-3(9)) Sadlier, William H. Inc.

Feliz cumpleanos, Estados Unidos! Aventuras (Adventure Books) 2000. (Aventuras A Traves Del Tiempo Ser.). (ENG & SPA.). (gr. k up). (978-0-02-148653-3(0)) Macmillan/McGraw-Hill Schl. Div.

La feria de Artesanias: Aventuras (Adventure Books) 2000. (Aventuras A Traves Del Tiempo Ser.). (ENG & SPA.). (gr. 2 up). (978-0-02-148686-1(7)) Macmillan/McGraw-Hill Schl. Div.

Ferraro, Bonita. Be a Good Citizen: A Content Area Reader-Social Studies. 2005. (Sadlier-Oxford Content Area Readers Ser.). 12p. (YA). (ps-2). 25.20 (978-0-8215-7820-9(0)) Sadlier, William H. Inc.

Un ferrocarril en la montana Dorado: Libros Aventuras (Adventure Books) 2000. (MacMillan/McGraw-Hill. Estudios Sociales Ser.). (ENG & SPA.). (gr. 5 up). (978-0-02-148727-1(8)) Macmillan/McGraw-Hill Schl. Div.

Field Trips: Out & about the Apple Orchard; Out & about at the Bakery; Out & about at the Dairy Farm; Out & about at the Fire Station; Out & about at the Orchestra; Out & about at the Zoo. 2003. (Illus.). (J). (ps-3). lib. bdg. 135.60 (978-1-4048-0078-6(6)) Picture Window Bks.

Field Trips Set. (gr. k-2). 114.95 (978-0-7368-9063-2(7)) Red Brick Learning.

Una Fiesta: Aventuras (Adventure Books) 2000. (Aventuras A Traves Del Tiempo Ser.). (ENG & SPA.). (gr. k up). (978-0-02-148661-8(1)) Macmillan/McGraw Hill Schl. Div.

Firth, Rachel. Los Caballeros - Internet Linked. Gaudenzi, Giacinto, illus. 2004. (Titles in Spanish Ser.). (SPA.). 48p. (J). pap. 8.95 (978-0-7460-5083-5(6) , Usborne) EDC Publishing.

Floor Map: Gente. 2000. (Aventuras A Traves Del Tiempo Ser.). (ENG & SPA.). (gr. 2-3). (978-0-02-147569-8(5)) Macmillan/McGraw-Hill Schl. Div.

Fontes, Justine & Fontes, Ron. Communities & Cultures: A to Z. 2004. (Illus.). 235.00 (978-0-516-29661-6(2)) Scholastic Library Publishing.

For a Better Life. 2003. (Illus.). pap. 5.60 (978-0-7398-7508-7(6)) Steck-Vaughn.

Forte, Imogene & Schurr, Sandra. Standards-Based Social Studies Graphic Organizers & Rubrics. 2004. 128p. (J). per. 13.95 (978-0-86530-630-1(3)) Incentive Pubns., Inc.

Foster, Ruth. Nonfiction Reading Comprehension: Social Studies. 2006. 144p. pap. 15.99 (978-1-4206-8023-2(4)); pap. 15.99 (978-1-4206-8024-9(2)); pap. 15.99 (978-1-4206-8027-0(7)) Austin & Company, Inc.

Friendliness, 6 vols. (gr. 2-5). 36.95 (978-0-7368-9253-7(2)) Red Brick Learning.

From Here to There Social Studies, 6 vols. (gr. k-2). 28.95 (978-0-7368-2985-4(7) , Yellow Umbrella Bks.) Capstone Pr., Inc.

From Tree to Table Social Studies, 6 vols. (gr. k-2). 28.95 (978-0-7368-1759-2(X) , Yellow Umbrella Bks.) Capstone Pr., Inc.

Frontline Coverage of Current Events, 6 Bks., Set. 2005. (J). 159.00 (978-1-4042-0378-5(8)) Rosen Publishing Group, Inc., The.

Frost, Helen. Our World, 12 bks. Saunders-Smith, Gail, ed. Incl. Look at Australia. 2002. lib. bdg. 15.93 (978-0-7368-1165-1(6)); Look at Canada. 2002. lib. bdg. 15.93 (978-0-7368-1166-8(4)); Look at China. 2001. lib. bdg. 15.93 (978-0-7368-0983-2(X)); Look at Cuba. 2002. lib. bdg. 15.93 (978-0-7368-1428-7(0)); Look at Egypt. 2002. lib. bdg. 15.93 (978-0-7368-1429-4(9)); Look at France. 2002. lib. bdg. 15.93 (978-0-7368-1167-5(2)); Look at Germany. 2002. lib. bdg. 15.93 (978-0-7368-1430-0(2)); Look at Japan. 2002. lib. bdg. 15.93 (978-0-7368-1168-2(0)); Look at Kenya. 2001. lib. bdg. 15.93 (978-0-7368-0984-9(8)); Look at Mexico. 2001. lib. bdg. 15.93 (978-0-7368-0985-6(6)); Look at Russia. 2001. lib. bdg. 15.93 (978-0-7368-0986-3(4)); Look at Vietnam. 2002. lib. bdg. 15.93 (978-0-7368-1431-7(0)); 24p. (J). (gr. k-1). (Illus.). 2001. Set lib. bdg. 191.16 (978-0-7368-1432-4(9) , Pebble Bks.) Capstone Pr., Inc.

Una Fuerza Especial: Aventuras (Adventure Books) 2000. (Aventuras A Traves Del Tiempo Ser.). (ENG & SPA.). (gr. 5 up). (978-0-02-148728-8(6)) Macmillan/McGraw-Hill Schl. Div.

Gakken Co. Ltd. Editors. World We Live In. Time-Life Books Editors, tr. 1999. (Illus.). 88p. (J). (gr. 1-4). 14.95 (978-0-8094-4885-2(8)) Time-Life, Inc.

Garbage Collectors, 6 vols. (gr. 2-5). 36.95 (978-0-7368-8050-3(X)) Red Brick Learning.

Garza, Carmen Lomas. Family Pictures. 15th anniv. ed. 2005. (ENG & SPA., Illus.). 32p. (J). (ps-17). 16.95 (978-0-89239-206-3(1)) Children's Bk. Pr.

Gay, Kathlyn. Cultural Diversity: Conflicts & Challenges: The Ultimate Teen Guide. 2003. (It Happened to Me Ser.: No. 6). (Illus.). 144p. pap. 30.95 (978-0-8108-4805-4(8)) Scarecrow Pr., Inc.

Genialidades 14: Leveled Books. 2001. (McGraw-Hill. Lectura Ser.). (ENG & SPA.). (gr. 2 up). (978-0-02-188039-3(5)) Macmillan/McGraw-Hill Schl. Div.

La gente cambia la tierra Social Studies, 6 vols.Tr. of People Change the Land Social Studies. (SPA.). (gr. k-2). 28.95 (978-0-7368-3042-3(1) , Yellow Umbrella Bks.) Capstone Pr., Inc.

Gente de Maiz 16: Leveled Books. 2001. (McGraw-Hill. Lectura Ser.). (ENG & SPA.). (gr. 2 up). (978-0-02-188041-6(7)) Macmillan/McGraw-Hill Schl. Div.

Gente Guia del Maestro: Gente. 2000. (Aventuras A Traves Del Tiempo Ser.). (ENG & SPA.). (gr. 2 up). (978-0-02-147819-4(8)) Macmillan/McGraw-Hill Schl. Div.

Gente libro del Estudiante: Gente. 2000. (Aventuras A Traves Del Tiempo Ser.). (ENG & SPA.). (gr. 2 up). (978-0-02-147805-7(8)) Macmillan/McGraw-Hill Schl. Div.

Gente libro del estudiante en Audiocasete: Gente. 2000. (Aventuras A Traves Del Tiempo Ser.). (ENG & SPA.). (gr. 2 up). (978-0-02-147812-5(0)) Macmillan/McGraw-Hill Schl. Div.

La Gente y el Trabajo, Unidad 3: Libros de la Biblioteca (Classroom Library) 2000. (Aventuras A Traves Del Tiempo Ser.). (ENG & SPA.). (gr. 1 up). (978-0-02-147841-5(4)) Macmillan/McGraw-Hill Schl. Div.

Geo Aventuras: Comunidades. 2000. (Aventuras A Traves Del Tiempo Ser.). (ENG & SPA.). (gr. 3 up). (978-0-02-147899-6(6)) Macmillan/McGraw-Hill Schl. Div.

Geo Aventuras: Gente. 2000. (Aventuras A Traves Del Tiempo Ser.). (ENG & SPA.). (gr. 2 up). (978-0-02-147898-9(8)) Macmillan/McGraw-Hill Schl. Div.

Geo Aventuras: Mi Mundo. 2000. (Aventuras A Traves Del Tiempo Ser.). (ENG & SPA.). (gr. 1 up). (978-0-02-147897-2(X)) Macmillan/McGraw-Hill Schl. Div.

Geschichte. (Duden-Schuelerduden Ser.). (GER., Illus.). 540p. (YA). (978-3-411-05413-8(1)) Bibliographisches Institut & F. A. Brockhaus AG DEU. *Dist:* International Bk. Import Service, Inc.

Geschichte I. (Duden Abiturhilfen Ser.). (GER.). 86p. (YA). (gr. 12-13). (978-3-411-02640-1(5)) Bibliographisches Institut & F. A. Brockhaus AG DEU. *Dist:* International Bk. Import Service, Inc.

Get a Clue: An Introduction to Primary Sources. 2005. (J). pap. (978-1-932663-09-9(6)) History Compass, LLC.

Giesecke, Ernestine. Kids' Guide, 4 bks., Set. Incl. Governments Around the World. lib. bdg. 22.79 (978-1-57572-511-6(8)); Local Government. lib. bdg. 22.79 (978-1-57572-512-3(6)); National Government. lib. bdg. 22.79 (978-1-57572-510-9(X)); State Government. lib. bdg. 22.79 (978-1-57572-513-0(4)); 32p. (J). (gr. 4-6). (Illus.). 2000. Set lib. bdg. 91.16 (978-1-57572-509-3(6)) Heinemann Library.

Gifford, Clive. Racism. (Illus.). 64p. (YA). (gr. 5 up). lib. bdg. 29.95 (978-1-931983-83-9(6)) Chrysalis Education.

—Racism. 2006. (Global Issues Ser.). (Illus.). 64p. (J). (gr. 4-12). pap. 12.95 (978-1-55285-745-8(X) , Walrus Bks.) Whitecap Bks., Ltd. CAN. *Dist:* Firefly Bks., Ltd.

Globos en el Cielo 9: Leveled Books. 2001. (McGraw-Hill. Lectura Ser.). (ENG & SPA.). (gr. 3 up). (978-0-02-188106-2(5)) Macmillan/McGraw-Hill Schl. Div.

Goldenstern, Joyce. American Women Against Violence. 1998. (Collective Biographies Ser.). (Illus.). 128p. (YA). (gr. 6-12). lib. bdg. 26.60 (978-0-7660-1025-3(2)) Enslow Pubs., Inc.

Goodwin, Evelyn. Meet the Children from the Fifty States in Poetry. 2007. 106p. pap. 37.50 (***978-0-615-16145-7(6))** Goodwin, Evelyn.

Gorman, Jacqueline Laks. El Bombero. 2003. Tr. of Firefighter. (SPA.). (gr. k-3). lib. bdg. 14.10 (978-0-613-88101-2(X)) Tandem Library Bks.

El gran Tecumseh: Libros Aventuras (Adventure Books) 2000. (MacMillan/McGraw-Hill. Estudios Sociales Ser.). (ENG & SPA.). (gr. 5 up). (978-0-02-148725-7(1)) Macmillan/McGraw-Hill Schl. Div.

Granowsky, Alvin, et al. Take-Home Books, Blackline Masters: Content Area Readers-Social Studies. 2002. (J). pap. (978-0-8215-7857-5(X) , Sadlier-Oxford) Sadlier, William H. Inc.

Gravois, Michael. Country Report Projects for Any Country: Ready-to-Go Templates & Easy Instructions for 26 Engaging Projects That Showcase Students' Learning. 2004. 64p. (gr. 5 up). pap. 11.99 (978-0-439-51887-1(3)) Scholastic, Inc.

Green Means Go Social Studies, 6 vols. (gr. k-2). 28.95 (978-0-7368-1752-3(2) , Yellow Umbrella Bks.) Capstone Pr., Inc.

Griese, Arnold A. The Way of Our People. Coalson, Glo, illus. 2003. 96p. (J). (gr. 4-6). pap. 10.95 (978-1-56397-648-3(X)) Boyds Mills Pr.

Grossmann, Peggy & Jet, Betty. Current Capers: A Handbook of Techniques for Current Events Activities. 2003. 104p. (J). pap. 19.95 (978-0-945984-92-4(8) , Zephyr Pr.) Chicago Review Pr., Inc.

Group/McGraw-Hill, Wright. Amazing Asia, 6 vols. (Book2WebTM Ser.). (gr. 4-8). 36.50 (978-0-322-04437-1(5)) Wright Group, The.

—Ancient Egypt: The Realm of Pharaohs, 6 vols. (Book2WebTM Ser.). (gr. 4-8). 36.50 (978-0-322-04451-7(0)) Wright Group, The.

—Las Aranas, 6 vols., Vol. 2. (First Explorers. Primeros Exploradores Nonfiction Sets Ser.). (SPA.). (gr. 1-2). 34.95 (978-0-7699-1489-3(6)) Shortland Pubns. (U. S. A.) Inc.

—Cold Facts about Ice Ages, 6 vols. (Book2WebTM Ser.). (gr. 4-8). 36.50 (978-0-322-04434-0(0)) Wright Group, The.

—Como nos Transportamos, 6 vols. (First Explorers. Primeros Exploradores Nonfiction Sets Ser.). (SPA.). (gr. 1-2). 29.95 (978-0-7699-1470-1(5)) Shortland Pubns. (U. S. A.) Inc.

—D-Man & Beans: Classroom Library Set. (D-Man Beans Ser.). (gr. 4-6). 150.95 (978-0-322-09210-5(8)) Wright Group, The.

—D-Man & Beans: Complete Set. (D-Man Beans Ser.). (gr. 4-6). 479.95 (978-0-322-09211-2(6)) Wright Group, The.

—D-Man's Escape, 6 vols. (D-Man Beans Ser.). 47p. (gr. 4-6). 42.50 (978-0-322-06267-2(5)) Wright Group, The.

—Donde Vive la Gente, 6 vols., Vol. 2. (First Explorers. Primeros Exploradores Nonfiction Sets Ser.). (SPA.). (gr. 1-2). 29.95 (978-0-7699-1486-2(1)) Shortland Pubns. (U. S. A.) Inc.

—Fuerzas de la Naturaleza, 6 vols., Vol. 2. (First Explorers. Primeros Exploradores Nonfiction Sets Ser.). (SPA.). (gr. 1-2). 34.95 (978-0-7699-1482-4(9)) Shortland Pubns. (U. S. A.) Inc.

—Going Places: Level I, 6 vols. (First Explorers Ser.). 24p. (gr. 1-2). 29.95 (978-0-7699-1446-6(2)) Shortland Pubns. (U. S. A.) Inc.

—Lagunas y Rios, 6 vols. (First Explorers. Primeros Exploradores Nonfiction Sets Ser.). (SPA.). (gr. 1-2). 29.95 (978-0-7699-1475-6(6)) Shortland Pubns. (U. S. A.) Inc.

—Making Sense of Sound & Music, 6 vols. (Book2WebTM Ser.). (gr. 4-8). 36.50 (978-0-322-04430-2(8)) Wright Group, The.

—Mountain Majesty, 6 vols. (Book2WebTM Ser.). (gr. 4-8). 36.50 (978-0-322-04440-1(5)) Wright Group, The.

—Para Que Construye el Hombre, 6 vols., Vol. 2. (First Explorers. Primeros Exploradores Nonfiction Sets Ser.). (SPA.). (gr. 1-2). 34.95 (978-0-7699-1480-0(2)) Shortland Pubns. (U. S. A.) Inc.

—People on the Path Toward Human Rights, 6 vols. (Book2WebTM Ser.). (gr. 4-8). 36.50 (978-0-322-04466-1(9)) Wright Group, The.

—Por Que se Mueven Las Cosas, 6 vols., Vol. 2. (First Explorers. Primeros Exploradores Nonfiction Sets Ser.). (SPA.). (gr. 1-2). 34.95 (978-0-7699-1490-9(X)) Shortland Pubns. (U. S. A.) Inc.

—El Sonido, 6 vols., Vol. 2. (First Explorers. Primeros Exploradores Nonfiction Sets Ser.). (SPA.). (gr. 1-2). 34.95 (978-0-7699-1488-6(8)) Shortland Pubns. (U. S. A.) Inc.

—Take-Twos Social Studies Vol. 2: Fluency - Complete Kit. (gr. 3-4). 483.50 (978-0-322-09177-1(2)) Wright Group, The.

—Take-Twos Social Studies Vol. 2: Fluency - Student Book Set - 1 Each of 12 Titles. (gr. 3-4). 81.95 (978-0-322-09305-8(8)) Wright Group, The.

—Why Things Move: Level K, 6 vols., Vol. 2. (First Explorers Ser.). 24p. (gr. 1-2). 34.95 (978-0-7699-1466-4(7)) Shortland Pubns. (U. S. A.) Inc.

—Wonder World Complete Sets: Social Studies Set - 1 Each of 73 Titles. (Wonder Worldtm Ser.). (gr. k-6). 398.95 (978-0-322-06713-4(8)) Wright Group, The.

—Wonder World Early & Upper Emergent Sets: Social Studies Set - 1 Each of 43 Titles. (Wonder Worldtm Ser.). (gr. k-6). 204.95 (978-0-322-06719-6(7)) Wright Group, The.

—Wonder World Early Fluency & Fluency: Social Studies Set - 1 Each of 30 Titles. (Wonder Worldtm Ser.). (gr. k-6). 194.50 (978-0-322-06716-5(2)) Wright Group, The.

—World Leaders Through the Ages, 6 vols. (Book2WebTM Ser.). (gr. 4-8). 36.50 (978-0-322-04471-5(5)) Wright Group, The.

Guatemala, 6 vols. (gr. 2-5). 36.95 (978-0-7368-8394-8(0)) Red Brick Learning.

Gustando. (Coleccion Mil Preguntas). (SPA., Illus.). 24p. (J). pap. 5.50 (978-950-11-0660-2(8) , SGM627) Sigmar ARG. *Dist:* Continental Bk. Co., Inc.

Haciendo dinero Social Studies, 6 vols.Tr. of Making Money Social Studies. (SPA.). (gr. k-2). 28.95 (978-0-7368-3041-6(3) , Yellow Umbrella Bks.) Capstone Pr., Inc.

Hands: Level B, 6 vols. 8p. 24.95 (978-0-7802-8915-4(3)) Wright Group, The.

Hansen, Merrily P. Homes Around the World: A Content Area Reader-Social Studies. 2005. (Emergent/Early (Prek-2) Social Studies Package Ser.). 12p. (YA). (ps-2). 25.20 (978-0-8215-7817-9(0)) Sadlier, William H. Inc.

Hanukkah, 6 vols. (gr. k-2). 28.95 (978-0-7368-9435-7(7)) Red Brick Learning.

Harcourt School Publishers Staff. Activity Book States/Regions. 3rd ed. 2001. (Horizons Ser.). (Illus.). (gr. k-7). pap. 9.30 (978-0-15-322597-0(1)) Harcourt Schl. Pubs.

—All about People, Unit 4. 3rd ed. 2003. (Horizons Ser.). (Illus.). pap. 166.70 (978-0-15-340223-4(7)) Harcourt Schl. Pubs.

—All the People, No. 4. 2nd ed. 2003. (Illus.). (gr. 1). pap. 139.70 (978-0-15-337559-0(0)) Harcourt Schl. Pubs.

—Assortment Program States & Regions. 3rd ed. 2002. (Horizons Ser.). (gr. k-7). pap. 102.00 (978-0-15-322585-7(8)) Harcourt Schl. Pubs.

—At Home with the Family, Unit 2. 3rd ed. 2003. (Harcourt Brace Social Studies). pap. 76.00 (978-0-15-341059-8(0)) Harcourt Schl. Pubs.

—Beginnings. 3rd ed. 2003. (Horizons Ser.). stu. ed. 69.60 (978-0-15-339620-5(2)) Harcourt Schl. Pubs.

—Beginnings to 1877. 3rd ed. 2001. (Horizons Ser.). (Illus.). (gr. k-7). pap., tchr. ed., act. bk. ed. 23.10 (978-0-15-322613-7(7)) Harcourt Schl. Pubs.

—Being a Citizen, Unit 5. 3rd ed. 2003. (Harcourt Brace Social Studies). pap. 76.00 (978-0-15-341070-3(1)) Harcourt Schl. Pubs.

—Catch a Dream Level 1-2. 3rd ed. 2003. (Trophies Reading Program Ser.). (Illus.). (gr. 1 up). pupil's gde. ed. 29.90 (978-0-15-322470-6(3)) Harcourt Schl. Pubs.

—Civil War/Present. 3rd ed. 2001. (Horizons Ser.). (Illus.). (gr. k-7). pap., act. bk. ed. 10.40 (978-0-15-322604-5(8)) Harcourt Schl. Pubs.

—Civil War/Present Horizons. 3rd ed. 2001. (Harcourt Horizons Ser.). (Illus.). (gr. k-7). pap., tchr. ed., act. bk. ed. 23.10 (978-0-15-322614-4(5)) Harcourt Schl. Pubs.

—Daily Geography: North Carolina Edition. 97th ed. 1998. (Stories in Time Ser.). (Illus.). (gr. 4). pap. 9.60 (978-0-15-311397-0(9)) Harcourt Schl. Pubs.

—The Declaration of Independence. 3rd ed. 2002. (Horizons Ser.). (Illus.). (J). pap. 7.30 (978-0-15-333571-6(8)) Harcourt Schl. Pubs.

—Distant Voyages. 3rd ed. 2003. (Trophies Reading Program Ser.). (Illus.). (gr. 5 up). pupil's gde. ed. 64.60 (978-0-15-322479-9(7)) Harcourt Schl. Pubs.

—A Fisher's Life. 3rd ed. 2002. (Horizons Ser.). (Illus.). (J). pap. 5.50 (978-0-15-333392-7(8)) Harcourt Schl. Pubs.

—Going to School Big Book No. 1. 2nd ed. 2003. (Illus.). (gr. 1). pap. 139.70 (978-0-15-337556-9(6)) Harcourt Schl. Pubs.

—Here & There Level 1-3. 3rd ed. 2003. (Trophies Reading Program Ser.). (Illus.). (gr. 1 up). pupil's gde. ed. 31.40 (978-0-15-322471-3(1)) Harcourt Schl. Pubs.

—Horizons. 3rd ed. (Harcourt Horizons Ser.). (Illus.). 2003. (gr. 1 up). act. bk. ed. 6.80 (978-0-15-322594-9(7)); 2003. (gr. 2 up). act. bk. ed. 6.80 (978-0-15-322595-6(5)); 2003. (gr. 4-7). pupil's gde. ed. 75.00 (978-0-15-320183-7(5)); 2001. (gr. k-7). pap., act. bk. ed. 7.00 (978-0-15-324842-9(4)); 2001. (gr. 3 up). pap., tchr. ed., act. bk. ed. 21.40 (978-0-15-322606-9(4)); 2001. (gr. 3 up). pap., act. bk. ed. 9.30 (978-0-15-322596-3(3)) Harcourt Schl. Pubs.

—Horizons: "All About Me" Unit. 3rd ed. 2003. (Harcourt Horizons Ser.). (Illus.). (gr. k-7). pap. 254.10 (978-0-15-320943-7(7)) Harcourt Schl. Pubs.

—Horizons: Assessment Program. 3rd ed. (Horizons Ser.). 2003. (gr. 1). pap. 51.70 (978-0-15-340284-5(9)); 2003. (gr. 2). pap. 51.70 (978-0-15-340285-2(7)); 2002. (Illus.). (gr. 1 up). pap. 53.20 (978-0-15-322582-6(3)); 2002. (Illus.). (gr. 2 up). pap. 53.20 (978-0-15-322583-3(1)); 2002. (Illus.). (gr. 3 up). pap. 70.50 (978-0-15-322584-0(X)) Harcourt Schl. Pubs.

—Horizons: Conner Prairie. 3rd ed. 2002. (Illus.). pap. 5.60 (978-0-15-333533-4(5)) Harcourt Schl. Pubs.

—Horizons: Deadly Funnels. 3rd ed. 2002. (Illus.). pap. 5.60 (978-0-15-333501-3(7)) Harcourt Schl. Pubs.

—Horizons: Indiana. 3rd ed. 2001. (Illus.). pap. 10.10 (978-0-15-322600-7(5)) Harcourt Schl. Pubs.

—Horizons: Indiana: Assessment Program. 3rd ed. 2001. (Illus.). pap. 103.90 (978-0-15-322588-8(2)) Harcourt Schl. Pubs.

—Horizons: Mountain Builders. 3rd ed. 2002. (Illus.). pap. 5.60 (978-0-15-333494-8(0)) Harcourt Schl. Pubs.

—Horizons: Museum Miracle. 3rd ed. 2002. (Illus.). pap. 5.60 (978-0-15-333543-3(2)) Harcourt Schl. Pubs.

—Horizons: North Carolina. 3rd ed. 2001. (Illus.). pap. 10.70 (978-0-15-322599-4(8)) Harcourt Schl. Pubs.

—Horizons: North Carolina: Assessment Program. 3rd ed. 2001. (Illus.). pap. 105.80 (978-0-15-322587-1(4)) Harcourt Schl. Pubs.

—Horizons: Tecumseh. 3rd ed. 2002. (Illus.). pap. 5.60 (978-0-15-333509-9(2)) Harcourt Schl. Pubs.

—Horizons: Texas. 3rd ed. 2001. (Illus.). (J). pap. 8.30 (978-0-15-322598-7(X)) Harcourt Schl. Pubs.

—Horizons: Texas: Assessment Program. 3rd ed. 2002. (Illus.). (gr. 4). pap. 105.80 (978-0-15-322586-4(6)) Harcourt Schl. Pubs.

—Horizons: The World. 2nd ed. 2002. (Harcourt Horizons Ser.). (gr. 4-7). (Illus.). pupil's gde. ed. 75.00 (978-0-15-335786-2(X)); Vol. I. tchr. ed. 143.40 (978-0-15-335787-9(8)); Vol. II. tchr. ed. 143.40 (978-0-15-335788-6(6)) Harcourt Schl. Pubs.

—Horizons: Time for Kids Collections. 18th ed. 2002. (J). (gr. 2). 63.70 (978-0-15-333185-5(2)); (gr. 1). 63.70 (978-0-15-333139-8(9)) Harcourt Trade Pubs.

—Horizons: Time for Kids Collections: Civil Present. 3rd ed. 2002. (Harcourt Horizons Ser.). (gr. k-7). pap. 159.90 (978-0-15-333598-3(X)) Harcourt Schl. Pubs.

—Horizons: Time for Kids: Postsale 18 Packages, 5 Collections. 2nd ed. 2003. (Harcourt Horizons Ser.). (gr. 1 up). 272.50 (978-0-15-336041-1(0)); (gr. 2 up). 272.50 (978-0-15-336042-8(9)) Harcourt Schl. Pubs.

—Horizons: Time for Kids Readers Grade 3. 3rd ed. 2002. (Harcourt Horizons Ser.). (gr. 3 up). pap., tchr. ed. 56.30 (978-0-15-334648-4(5)) Harcourt Schl. Pubs.

S

—Horizons: Time for Kids Readers: World Regions. 3rd ed. 2002. (Harcourt Horizons Ser.). (gr. k-7). pap., tchr. ed. 69.40 (978-0-15-334657-6(4)) Harcourt Schl. Pubs.
—Horizons: Trappers & Traders. 3rd ed. 2002. (Illus.). pap. 5.60 (978-0-15-333527-3(0)) Harcourt Schl. Pubs.
—Horizons: Virginia. 3rd ed. 2001. (Illus.). pap. 11.00 (978-0-15-322601-4(3)) Harcourt Schl. Pubs.
—Horizons: Virginia: Assessment Program. 3rd ed. 2001. (Illus.). pap. 107.80 (978-0-15-322589-5(0)) Harcourt Schl. Pubs.
—Horizons: World Regions. 3rd ed. 2003. (Harcourt Horizons Ser.). (Illus.). (gr. k-7). 9.80 (978-0-15-322605-2(6)) Harcourt Schl. Pubs.
—Horizons: World Regions Assessment Program. 3rd ed. 2002. (Harcourt Horizons Ser.). (gr. k-7). pap. 131.40 (978-0-15-322593-2(9)) Harcourt Schl. Pubs.
—Horizons Bk. 2: World Regions. 3rd ed. 2003. (Illus.). pap. 9.30 (978-0-15-333944-8(6)) Harcourt Schl. Pubs.
—Horizons Unit 1: Going to School. 3rd ed. 2001. (Illus.). (gr. 1). pap. 169.80 (978-0-15-322569-7(6)) Harcourt Schl. Pubs.
—Horizons Unit 2: Good Citizens. 3rd ed. 2001. (Illus.). pap. 169.80 (978-0-15-322570-3(X)) Harcourt Schl. Pubs.
—Horizons Unit 5: Past & Present. 3rd ed. 2001. (Illus.). pap. 169.80 (978-0-15-322580-2(7)) Harcourt Schl. Pubs.
—Horizons Unit 6: People at Work. 3rd ed. 2001. pap. 169.80 (978-0-15-322581-9(5)) Harcourt Schl. Pubs.
—Horizons ESL Summary. 4th ed. 2004. (gr. 3). pap. 10.80 (978-0-15-343720-5(0)) Harcourt Schl. Pubs.
—Horizons, Grade 1. 2nd ed. 2002. (Harcourt Horizons Ser.). (gr. 1 up). Vol. 1. tchr. ed. 104.20 (978-0-15-328511-0(7)); Vol. 2. tchr. ed. 104.20 (978-0-15-328512-7(5)) Harcourt Schl. Pubs.
—Horizons, Grade 2. 2nd ed. 2002. (Harcourt Horizons Ser.). (gr. 2 up). Vol. 1. tchr. ed. 110.60 (978-0-15-328513-4(3)); Vol. 2. tchr. ed. 110.60 (978-0-15-328514-1(1)) Harcourt Schl. Pubs.
—Horizons, Grade 2: Time for Kids Readers. 3rd ed. 2003. (Harcourt Horizons Ser.). pap., tchr. ed. 51.20 (978-0-15-334647-7(7)) Harcourt Schl. Pubs.
—Horizons, Grade 3. 2nd ed. 2002. (Harcourt Horizons Ser.). (gr. 3 up). Vol. 1. tchr. ed. 110.60 (978-0-15-328515-8(X)); Vol. 2. tchr. ed. 110.60 (978-0-15-328516-5(8)) Harcourt Schl. Pubs.
—Horizons, Grade K. 3rd ed. 2002. (Harcourt Horizons Ser.). (gr. k-7). tchr. ed. 113.40 (978-0-15-321954-2(8)) Harcourt Schl. Pubs.
—Horizons with Ancient Civilizations. 4th ed. 2004. (gr. 3). 53.20 (978-0-15-344221-6(2)) Harcourt Schl. Pubs.
—Horizontes: Unit Big Book Collection. 3rd ed. 2003. (Harcourt Horizontes Ser.). (SPA., Illus.). (gr. k-6). 1112.80 (978-0-15-325844-2(6)); 1112.80 (978-0-15-325845-9(4)) Harcourt Schl. Pubs.
—Horizontes: World Regions: Time for Kids Readers. 3rd ed. 2002. (Harcourt Horizontes Ser.). (SPA.). (gr. 3 up). pap., tchr. ed. 81.10 (978-0-15-334665-1(5)) Harcourt Schl. Pubs.
—Horizontes Bk. 10: Time for Kids 5 Pack. 3rd ed. 2002. (Harcourt Horizontes Ser.). (SPA., Illus.). (gr. 2 up). pap. 24.00 (978-0-15-333764-2(8)) Harcourt Schl. Pubs.
—Horizontes Bk. 11: Time for Kids 5 Pack. 3rd ed. 2002. (Harcourt Horizontes Ser.). (SPA., Illus.). (gr. 2 up). pap. 24.00 (978-0-15-333766-6(4)) Harcourt Schl. Pubs.
—Horizontes Bk. 22: Time for Kids: World Regions 5 Pack. 3rd ed. 2002. (Harcourt Horizontes Ser.). (SPA., Illus.). (gr. 3 up). pap. 46.20 (978-0-15-333985-1(3)) Harcourt Schl. Pubs.
—Horizontes, Grade 1. 2nd ed. 2003. (Harcourt Horizontes Ser.). (SPA.). (gr. k-6). Vol. 1. tchr. ed. 114.40 (978-0-15-328413-7(7)); Vol. 2. tchr. ed. 114.40 (978-0-15-328414-4(5)) Harcourt Schl. Pubs.
—Horizontes, Grade 1: Time for Kids Readers. 3rd ed. 2002. (Harcourt Horizontes Ser.). (SPA.). (gr. 1 up). pap., tchr. ed. 65.80 (978-0-15-334659-0(0)) Harcourt Schl. Pubs.
—Horizontes, Grade 2, Vol. 1. 2nd ed. 2003. (Harcourt Horizontes Ser.). (SPA.). (gr. k-6). tchr. ed. 121.50 (978-0-15-328415-1(3)) Harcourt Schl. Pubs.
—Horizontes, Grade 2: Time for Kids Readers. 3rd ed. 2002. (Harcourt Horizontes Ser.). (SPA.). (gr. 2 up). pap., tchr. ed. 65.80 (978-0-15-334660-6(4)) Harcourt Schl. Pubs.
—Horizontes, Grade 3. 2nd ed. 2003. (Harcourt Horizontes Ser.). (SPA.). (gr. k-6). Vol. 1. tchr. ed. 121.50 (978-0-15-328509-7(5)); Vol. 2. tchr. ed. 121.50 (978-0-15-328510-3(9)) Harcourt Schl. Pubs.
—Horizontes, Grade 3: Time for Kids Readers. 3rd ed. 2002. (Harcourt Horizontes Ser.). (SPA.). (gr. 3 up). pap., tchr. ed. 65.80 (978-0-15-334661-3(2)) Harcourt Schl. Pubs.
—In & Around the Land, Unit 4. 3rd ed. 2003. (Harcourt Brace Social Studies). pap. 76.00 (978-0-15-341061-1(2)) Harcourt Schl. Pubs.
—John & Abigail Adams. 3rd ed. 2002. (Horizons Ser.). (Illus.). (J). pap. 7.30 (978-0-15-333567-9(X)) Harcourt Schl. Pubs.
—Land Around, No. 3. 2nd ed. 2003. (Illus.). (gr. 1). pap. 139.70 (978-0-15-337558-3(2)) Harcourt Schl. Pubs.
—Learn about People, Unit 4. 3rd ed. 2003. (Horizons Ser.). (Illus.). pap. 166.70 (978-0-15-340230-2(X)) Harcourt Schl. Pubs.
—Learn about the People No. 4. 2nd ed. 2003. (Illus.). pap. 139.70 (978-0-15-337569-9(8)) Harcourt Schl. Pubs.
—Living in a Community, Unit 1. 3rd ed. 2003. (Horizons Ser.). (Illus.). (gr. 2). pap. 166.70 (978-0-15-340227-2(X)) Harcourt Schl. Pubs.
—Looking Back Big Book No. 5. 2nd ed. 2003. (Illus.). pap. 139.70 (978-0-15-337560-6(4)) Harcourt Schl. Pubs.
—My Heros, Unit 5. 3rd ed. 2003. (Harcourt Brace Social Studies). pap. 76.00 (978-0-15-341062-8(0)) Harcourt Schl. Pubs.
—Our Government, Unit 2. 3rd ed. 2003. (Horizons Ser.). (Illus.). pap. 166.70 (978-0-15-340228-9(8)) Harcourt Schl. Pubs.
—Past & Present, Unit 5. 3rd ed. 2003. (Horizons Ser.). (Illus.). (gr. 2). pap. 166.70 (978-0-15-340231-9(8)) Harcourt Schl. Pubs.
—Past & Present Big Book No. 5. 2nd ed. 2003. (Illus.). pap. 139.70 (978-0-15-337570-5(1)) Harcourt Schl. Pubs.
—People at Work, Unit 6. 3rd ed. 2003. (Horizons Ser.). (Illus.). pap. 166.70 (978-0-15-340232-6(6)) Harcourt Schl. Pubs.
—People in History, Unit 4. 3rd ed. 2003. (Harcourt Brace Social Studies). pap. 76.00 (978-0-15-341069-7(8)) Harcourt Schl. Pubs.
—People in Time, Unit 6. 3rd ed. 2003. (Harcourt Brace Social Studies). pap. 76.00 (978-0-15-341071-0(X)) Harcourt Schl. Pubs.
—Preparation Book of TAKS. 2nd ed. 2002. (Horizons Ser.). pap. 12.00 (978-0-15-336576-8(5)); (gr. 1). pap. 10.00 (978-0-15-336571-3(4)); (gr. 2). pap. 10.00 (978-0-15-336572-0(2)); (gr. 3). pap. 11.20 (978-0-15-336573-7(0)) Harcourt Schl. Pubs.
—Preparation Book of TAKS: Answer Key. 2nd ed. 2002. pap. 14.40 (978-0-15-336587-4(0)); pap. 14.40 (978-0-15-336588-1(9)); (gr. 1). pap. 14.40 (978-0-15-336582-9(X)); (gr. 2). pap. 14.40 (978-0-15-336583-6(8)); (gr. 3). pap. 14.40 (978-0-15-336584-3(6)); (gr. 4). pap. 14.40 (978-0-15-336586-7(2)) Harcourt Schl. Pubs.
—Preparation Book of TAKS: Texas Edition. 2nd ed. 2002. (Horizons Ser.). (gr. 4). pap. 11.20 (978-0-15-336574-4(9)) Harcourt Schl. Pubs.
—Primary Black Line Master Harcourt Braise Social Studies: Tennessee Edition. 2nd ed. 2002. (gr. 1). pap. 19.40 (978-0-15-335862-3(9)); (gr. 2). pap. 19.40 (978-0-15-335863-0(7)); pap. 19.40 (978-0-15-329066-4(8)) Harcourt Schl. Pubs.
—School Days, Unit 1. 3rd ed. 2003. (Harcourt Brace Social Studies). (gr. 1). pap. 76.00 (978-0-15-341058-1(2)) Harcourt Schl. Pubs.
—Social Science: United States: FL Edition. 2nd ed. 2002. (Illus.). (gr. 5). 60.70 (978-0-15-320106-6(1)) Harcourt Schl. Pubs.
—Social Studies. 2000. (Harcourt Brace Estudios Sociales Ser.). (SPA., Illus.). (gr. k-7). pap., act. bk. ed. 8.50 (978-0-15-310535-7(6)) Harcourt Schl. Pubs.
—Social Studies: A Child's Place. 1999. (Harcourt Brace Social Studies). (Illus.). (gr. k-7). pap., pupil's gde. ed. 48.20 (978-0-15-309783-6(3)) Harcourt Schl. Pubs.
—Social Studies: Activity Book. (Harcourt Brace Estudios Sociales Ser.). (SPA., Illus.). (gr. k-7). 2000. pap., act. bk. ed. 8.50 (978-0-15-310536-4(4)); 2000. pap., act. bk. ed. 8.50 (978-0-15-310537-1(2)); 1999. pap., act. bk. ed. 12.70 (978-0-15-310541-8(0)); 1999. pap., act. bk. ed. 12.70 (978-0-15-310542-5(9)); 1998. pap., act. bk. ed. 10.20 (978-0-15-310538-8(0)) Harcourt Schl. Pubs.
—Social Studies: Assessment Program. 2000. (SPA., Illus.). (gr. 4). pap. 96.70 (978-0-15-310531-9(3)) Harcourt Schl. Pubs.
—Social Studies: FCAT Test Preparation. 2nd ed. 2002. (Illus.). (J). (gr. 3). pap. 6.40 (978-0-15-320365-7(X)); (gr. 4). pap. 6.40 (978-0-15-320366-4(8)); (gr. 5). pap. 7.10 (978-0-15-320367-1(6)) Harcourt Schl. Pubs.
—Social Studies: FCAT Test Preparation Answer Key. 2nd ed. 2002. (Illus.). (J). (gr. 3). pap. 10.80 (978-0-15-320368-8(4)); (gr. 4). pap. 10.80 (978-0-15-320369-5(2)); (gr. 5). pap. 11.50 (978-0-15-320370-1(6)) Harcourt Schl. Pubs.
—Social Studies: FL Activity Book. 2nd ed. 2002. (Illus.). (J). (gr. 4). pap. 8.90 (978-0-15-319591-4(6)) Harcourt Schl. Pubs.
—Social Studies: FL Assessment. 2nd ed. 2002. (Illus.). pap. 64.00 (978-0-15-319593-8(2)) Harcourt Schl. Pubs.
—Social Studies: FL Game Time. 2nd ed. 2002. (Illus.). (J). (gr. 4). pap. 7.90 (978-0-15-319431-3(6)) Harcourt Schl. Pubs.
—Social Studies: FL Reading Support. 2nd ed. 2002. (Illus.). (J). (gr. 4). pap. 14.60 (978-0-15-319432-0(4)) Harcourt Schl. Pubs.
—Social Studies: Florida Big Book Collection. 2nd ed. 2002. (Illus.). (gr. 1). pap. 1083.80 (978-0-15-320166-0(5)); (gr. 2). pap. 1040.60 (978-0-15-320454-8(0)) Harcourt Schl. Pubs.
—Social Studies: Florida Library Collection. 2nd ed. 2002. (Illus.). (J). (gr. 4). pap. 122.30 (978-0-15-320473-9(7)) Harcourt Schl. Pubs.
—Social Studies: KY State Activity Book with Answer Key. 2000. (Illus.). (gr. 4). pap. 10.40 (978-0-15-319762-8(5)) Harcourt Schl. Pubs.
—Social Studies: Making a Difference. 2001. (Harcourt Brace Social Studies). (Illus.). (gr. k-7). pap., pupil's gde. ed. 48.20 (978-0-15-309784-3(1)) Harcourt Schl. Pubs.
—Social Studies: Mississippi Assessment Program. 1999. (Illus.). (gr. 4). pap. 30.50 (978-0-15-316041-7(1)) Harcourt Schl. Pubs.
—Social Studies: New York State Activity Book. 2001. (Illus.). (gr. 4). pap. 11.50 (978-0-15-321559-9(3)) Harcourt Schl. Pubs.
—Social Studies: New York State Activity Book & Answer Key. 2001. (Illus.). pap. 11.90 (978-0-15-321560-5(7)) Harcourt Schl. Pubs.
—Social Studies: States & Regions: Activity Book. 2003. (Harcourt Brace Social Studies). (Illus.). (gr. k-7). act. bk. ed. 9.40 (978-0-15-312124-1(6)) Harcourt Schl. Pubs.
—Social Studies: States & Regions: Library Book Collection. 2003. (Harcourt Brace Social Studies). (Illus.). (gr. k-7). 76.00 (978-0-15-308392-1(1)) Harcourt Schl. Pubs.
—Social Studies: Tennessee State Activity Book. 2001. (Illus.). pap. 11.50 (978-0-15-321562-9(3)) Harcourt Schl. Pubs.
—Social Studies: Tennessee State Activity Book & Answer Key. 2001. (Illus.). pap. 11.90 (978-0-15-321563-6(1)) Harcourt Schl. Pubs.
—Social Studies: The World. (Harcourt Brace Social Studies). (Illus.). (gr. k-7). 2003. tchr. ed., act. bk. ed. 9.80 (978-0-15-312127-2(0)); 1999. pupil's gde. ed. 77.30 (978-0-15-312102-9(5)) Harcourt Schl. Pubs.
—Social Studies: United States: Activity Book. 2003. (Harcourt Brace Social Studies). (Illus.). (gr. k-7). act. bk. ed. 9.80 (978-0-15-312126-5(2)) Harcourt Schl. Pubs.
—Social Studies: Washington DC Activities Book Answer Key. 2000. (Illus.). pap. 14.40 (978-0-15-320657-3(8)) Harcourt Schl. Pubs.
—Social Studies: Washington, DC Activity Book. 2000. (Illus.). (gr. 3). pap. 11.20 (978-0-15-320656-6(X)) Harcourt Schl. Pubs.
—Social Studies Bk. 1: Save the Everglades: Florida Library Book. 2nd ed. 2002. (Illus.). (J). pap. 24.50 (978-0-15-320474-6(5)) Harcourt Schl. Pubs.
—Social Studies Bk. 2: Florida: Florida Library Book. 2nd ed. 2002. (Illus.). (J). pap. 24.50 (978-0-15-320475-3(3)) Harcourt Schl. Pubs.
—Social Studies Bk. 3: Osceola: Florida Library Book. 2nd ed. 2002. (Illus.). (J). pap. 24.50 (978-0-15-320476-0(1)) Harcourt Schl. Pubs.
—Social Studies Bk. 4: Building a Dream: Florida Library Book. 2nd ed. 2002. (Illus.). (J). (gr. 4). pap. 24.50 (978-0-15-320477-0(X)) Harcourt Schl. Pubs.
—Social Studies Bk. 5: Rockets & Spacecraft: Florida Library Book. 2nd ed. 2002. (Illus.). (J). pap. 24.50 (978-0-15-320478-4(8)) Harcourt Schl. Pubs.
—Social Studies Unit 1: Florida Big Book. 2nd ed. 2002. (Illus.). (J). pap. 155.20 (978-0-15-320167-7(3)) Harcourt Schl. Pubs.
—Social Studies Unit 2: Florida Big Book. 2nd ed. 2002. (Illus.). (J). pap. 155.20 (978-0-15-320168-4(1)) Harcourt Schl. Pubs.
—Social Studies Unit 3: Florida Big Book. 2nd ed. 2002. (Illus.). (J). pap. 155.20 (978-0-15-320169-1(X)) Harcourt Schl. Pubs.
—Social Studies, Grade 1: FL Lesson Planner. 2nd ed. 2002. pap. 15.60 (978-0-15-320138-7(X)) Harcourt Schl. Pubs.
—Social Studies, Grade 2: FL Lesson Planner. 2nd ed. 2002. pap. 15.60 (978-0-15-320139-4(8)) Harcourt Schl. Pubs.
—Social Studies, Grade 3. 1998. (Harcourt Brace Estudios Sociales Ser.). (SPA.). (gr. 3-7). pap., tchr. ed., act. bk. ed. 20.00 (978-0-15-310543-2(7)) Harcourt Schl. Pubs.
—Social Studies, Grade 3: FL Lesson Planner. 2nd ed. 2002. pap. 18.40 (978-0-15-320140-0(1)) Harcourt Schl. Pubs.
—Social Studies, Grade 4: FL Activity Book. 2nd ed. 2002. pap., tchr. ed. 15.10 (978-0-15-319592-1(4)) Harcourt Schl. Pubs.
—Social Studies, Grade 4: FL Lesson Planner. 2nd ed. 2002. pap. 18.40 (978-0-15-320141-7(X)) Harcourt Schl. Pubs.
—Social Studies, Grade 5: Activity Book. 1999. (Harcourt Brace Estudios Sociales Ser.). (SPA.). (gr. 3-7). pap., tchr. ed., act. bk. ed. 23.00 (978-0-15-310546-3(1)) Harcourt Schl. Pubs.
—Social Studies, Grade 5: FL Lesson Planner. 2nd ed. 2002. pap. 18.40 (978-0-15-320142-4(8)) Harcourt Schl. Pubs.
—Social Studies, Grade 5 Vol. 1: United States: FL Edition. 2nd ed. 2002. tchr. ed. 108.00 (978-0-15-320107-3(X)) Harcourt Schl. Pubs.
—Social Studies, Grade 6. 1999. (Harcourt Brace Estudios Sociales Ser.). (SPA.). (gr. 3-7). pap., tchr. ed., act. bk. ed. 23.00 (978-0-15-310547-0(X)) Harcourt Schl. Pubs.
—Social Studies Library. 2003. (Harcourt Brace Estudios Sociales Ser.). (SPA., Illus.). (gr. k up). 37.60 (978-0-15-310599-9(2)) Harcourt Schl. Pubs.
—States/Regions Horizons. 3rd ed. 2001. (Harcourt Horizons Ser.). (Illus.). (gr. k-7). pap., tchr. ed., act. bk. ed. 21.80 (978-0-15-322607-6(2)) Harcourt Schl. Pubs.
—TIME for Kids. 3rd ed. (Horizontes (Social Studies) Ser.). Bk. 1. 2003. (SPA.). (gr. 3). pap. 7.00 (978-0-15-333782-6(6)); Bk. 2. 2003. (SPA.). pap. 7.00 (978-0-15-333784-0(2)); Bk. 2. 2002. (SPA.). (J). pap. 4.50 (978-0-15-333710-9(9)); Bk. 3. 2003. (SPA.). pap. 7.00 (978-0-15-333786-4(9)); Bk. 3. 2002. (SPA.). (J). pap. 4.50 (978-0-15-333712-3(5)); Bk. 4. 2003. (SPA.). pap. 7.00 (978-0-15-333788-8(5)); Bk. 4. 2002. (SPA., Illus.). (J). (gr. 1). pap. 4.00 (978-0-15-333714-7(1)); Bk. 5. 2003. (SPA.). pap. 7.00 (978-0-15-333790-1(7)); Bk. 5. 2002. (SPA., Illus.). (J). pap. 4.00 (978-0-15-333716-1(8)); Bk. 6. 2003. (SPA.). pap. 7.00 (978-0-15-333792-5(3)); Bk. 6. 2002. (SPA., Illus.). (J). pap. 4.00 (978-0-15-333718-5(4)); Bk. 7. 2003. pap. 7.00 (978-0-15-333794-9(X)); Bk. 7. 2002. (SPA.). (J). pap. 4.50 (978-0-15-333720-8(6)); Bk. 8. 2003. (SPA.). pap. 7.00 (978-0-15-333796-3(6)); Bk. 8. 2002. (SPA.). (J). pap. 4.50 (978-0-15-333722-2(2)); Bk. 9. 2003. (SPA.). pap. 7.00 (978-0-15-333798-7(2)); Bk. 9. 2002. (SPA.). (J). pap. 4.50 (978-0-15-333724-6(9)); Bk. 10. 2002. (SPA.). (J). pap. 4.50 (978-0-15-333726-0(5)); Bk. 11. 2002. (SPA.). (J). pap. 4.50 (978-0-15-333728-4(1)) Harcourt Schl. Pubs.
—Time for Kids, Bk. 12. 3rd ed. 2002. (Horizontes (Social Studies) Ser.). (SPA., Illus.). (J). pap. 4.00 (978-0-15-333730-7(3)) Harcourt Schl. Pubs.
—TIME for Kids. 3rd ed. (Horizontes (Social Studies) Ser.). (SPA.). Bk. 13. 2003. pap. 7.00 (978-0-15-333806-9(7)); Bk. 13. 2002. (J). pap. 4.50 (978-0-15-333732-1(X)); Bk. 14. 2003. pap. 7.00 (978-0-15-333808-3(3)); Bk. 14. 2002. (J). pap. 4.50 (978-0-15-333734-5(6)); Bk. 15. 2003. pap. 7.00 (978-0-15-333810-6(5)); Bk. 15. 2002. (J). pap. 4.50 (978-0-15-333736-9(2)); Bk. 16. 2003. pap. 7.00 (978-0-15-333812-0(1)); Bk. 16. 2002. (J). pap. 4.50 (978-0-15-333738-3(9)); Bk. 17. 2003. pap. 7.00 (978-0-15-333814-4(8)); Bk. 17. 2002. (J). pap. 4.50 (978-0-15-333740-6(0)); Bk. 18. 2003. pap. 7.00 (978-0-15-333816-8(4)); Bk. 18. 2002. (J). pap. 4.50 (978-0-15-333742-0(7)) Harcourt Schl. Pubs.
—TIME for Kids: Texas. 3rd ed. 2002. (Horizontes (Social Studies) Ser.). (SPA., Illus.). Bk. 8. pap. 7.00 (978-0-15-333833-5(4)); Bk. 9. pap. 7.00 (978-0-15-333835-9(0)); Bk. 10. pap. 7.00 (978-0-15-333837-3(7)); Bk. 11. pap. 7.00 (978-0-15-333839-7(3)); Bk. 12. pap. 7.00 (978-0-15-333841-0(5)); Bk. 13. pap. 7.00 (978-0-15-333843-4(1)); Bk. 14. pap. 7.00 (978-0-15-333845-8(8)); Bk. 15. pap. 7.00 (978-0-15-333847-2(4)); Bk. 16. pap. 7.00 (978-0-15-333849-6(0)); Bk. 17. pap. 7.00 (978-0-15-333851-9(2)); Bk. 18. pap. 7.00 (978-0-15-333853-3(9)) Harcourt Schl. Pubs.
—Time for Kids: TIK-TAKS Reading Intervention Pack. 2nd ed. 2002. (Horizontes (Social Studies) Ser.). (SPA.). (gr. 6). pap. 620.50 (978-0-15-336282-8(0)) Harcourt Schl. Pubs.
—TIME for Kids: TIK-TAKS Reading Intervention Pack. 2nd ed. 2002. (Horizontes (Social Studies) Ser.). (SPA., Illus.). (gr. 5). pap. 1064.70 (978-0-15-336281-1(2)) Harcourt Schl. Pubs.
—TIME for Kids: World Regions. 3rd ed. (Horizontes (Social Studies) Ser.). (SPA., Illus.). Bk. 1. 2003. pap. 9.30 (978-0-15-333942-4(X)); Bk. 3. 2003. pap. 9.30 (978-0-15-333946-2(2)); Bk. 4. 2003. pap. 9.30 (978-0-15-333948-6(9)); Bk. 5. 2003. pap. 9.30 (978-0-15-333950-9(0)); Bk. 6. 2003. pap. 9.30 (978-0-15-333952-3(7)); Bk. 7. 2003. pap. 9.30 (978-0-15-333954-7(3)); Bk. 8. 2003. pap. 9.30 (978-0-15-333956-1(X)); Bk. 9. 2003. pap. 9.30 (978-0-15-333958-5(6)); Bk. 10. 2003. pap. 9.30 (978-0-15-333960-8(8)); Bk. 11. 2003. pap. 9.30 (978-0-15-333962-2(4)); Bk. 12. 2003. pap. 9.30 (978-0-15-333964-6(0)); Bk. 13. 2003. pap. 9.30 (978-0-15-333966-0(7)); Bk. 14. 2003. pap. 9.30 (978-0-15-333968-4(3)); Bk. 16. 2003. pap. 9.30 (978-0-15-333972-1(1)); Bk. 17. 2003. pap. 9.30 (978-0-15-333974-5(8)); Bk. 18. 2003. pap. 9.30 (978-0-15-333976-9(4)); Bk. 19. 2003. pap. 9.30 (978-0-15-333978-3(0)); Bk. 20. 2003. pap. 9.30 (978-0-15-333980-6(2)); Bk. 21. 2003. pap. 9.30 (978-0-15-333982-0(9)); Bk. 22. 2002. pap. 9.30 (978-0-15-333984-4(5)); Bk. 23. 2002. pap. 9.30 (978-0-15-333986-8(1)); Bk. 24. 2002. pap. 9.30 (978-0-15-333988-2(8)); Bk.15. 2003. pap. 9.30 (978-0-15-333970-7(5)) Harcourt Schl. Pubs.
—TIME for Kids Bk. 11: World Region, 5 Packs. 3rd ed. 2003. (Horizontes (Social Studies) Ser.). (SPA.). (gr. 3 up). pap. 46.20 (978-0-15-333963-9(2)) Harcourt Schl. Pubs.
—TIME for Kids Bk. 12: State & Region, 5 Packs. 3rd ed. 2002. (Horizontes (Social Studies) Ser.). (SPA.). (gr. 3 up). pap. 34.90 (978-0-15-333879-3(2)) Harcourt Schl. Pubs.
—TIME for Kids 5 Pack. 3rd ed. 2003. (Horizontes (Social Studies) Ser.). (SPA.). (gr. 3 up). Bk. 2. pap. 34.90 (978-0-15-333785-7(0)); Bk. 3. pap. 34.90 (978-0-15-333787-1(7)) Harcourt Schl. Pubs.
—Time for Kids Collections: US History. 3rd ed. 2002. (Horizons Ser.). Bk. 2. pap. 9.30 (978-0-15-333895-3(4)); Bk. 3. pap. 9.30 (978-0-15-333897-7(0)); Bk. 5. pap. 9.30 (978-0-15-333901-1(2)); Bk. 6. pap. 9.30 (978-0-15-333903-5(9)); Bk. 9. pap. 9.30 (978-0-15-333909-7(8)) Harcourt Schl. Pubs.
—Time/Kids Readers: Texas Edition. 3rd ed. 2002. (Horizontes (Social Studies) Ser.). pap., tchr. ed. 65.80 (978-0-15-334662-0(0)) Harcourt Schl. Pubs.
—Timeless Treasure. 3rd ed. 2003. (Trophies Reading Program Ser.). (Illus.). (gr. 6 up). pupil's gde. ed. 64.60 (978-0-15-322480-5(0)) Harcourt Schl. Pubs.
—U. S. History Horizons: Activity Book. 3rd ed. 2001. (Harcourt Horizons Ser.). (gr. k-7). pap., tchr. ed. 23.10 (978-0-15-322612-0(9)) Harcourt Schl. Pubs.
—US History: The Civil War to the Present. 3rd ed. 2003. (Horizons Ser.). Vol. 1. tchr. ed. 139.50 (978-0-15-339636-6(9)); Vol. 2. tchr. ed. 139.50 (978-0-15-339637-3(7)) Harcourt Schl. Pubs.
—US History, Grade 5: Beginnings. 3rd ed. 2003. (Horizons Ser.). Vol. 1. tchr. ed. 139.50 (978-0-15-339634-2(2)); Vol. 2. tchr. ed. 139.50 (978-0-15-339635-9(0)) Harcourt Schl. Pubs.
—Victory at Yorktown. 3rd ed. 2002. (Horizons Ser.). (Illus.). (J). pap. 7.30 (978-0-15-333569-3(6)) Harcourt Schl. Pubs.
—A Village Celebrates. 3rd ed. 2002. (Horizons Ser.). (Illus.). (J). pap. 7.30 (978-0-15-333634-8(X)) Harcourt Schl. Pubs.
—We Belong in Groups, Unit 1. 3rd ed. 2003. (Harcourt Brace Social Studies). (gr. 2). pap. 76.00 (978-0-15-341066-6(3)) Harcourt Schl. Pubs.
—We Work Together, Unit 3. 3rd ed. 2003. (Harcourt Brace Social Studies). pap. 76.00 (978-0-15-341068-0(X)) Harcourt Schl. Pubs.
—The World. 2nd ed. (Horizons Ser.). (gr. k-7). 2003. (Illus.). act. bk. ed. 9.80 (978-0-15-335789-3(4)); 2002. pap., tchr. ed., act. bk. ed. 23.30 (978-0-15-335790-9(8)) Harcourt Schl. Pubs.
—World History: States & Regions. 3rd ed. 2003. (Horizons Ser.). (Illus.). 63.30 (978-0-15-339618-2(0)) Harcourt Schl. Pubs.
—World History - Grade 6. 2nd ed. 2002. (Horizons Ser.). tchr. ed. 139.50 (978-0-15-338041-9(1)); Vol. 2. tchr. ed. 139.50 (978-0-15-338042-6(X)) Harcourt Schl. Pubs.
—World History, Grade 4: States & Regions. 3rd ed. 2004. (Horizons Ser.). Vol. 1. tchr. ed. 114.90 (978-0-15-339630-4(X)); Vol. 2. tchr. ed. 114.90 (978-0-15-339631-1(8)) Harcourt Schl. Pubs.

Lucharon por la libertad Los ninos en el Movimiento por los derechos Civiles: Libros Aventuras (Adventure Books) 2000. (MacMillan/McGraw-Hill. Estudios Sociales Ser.). (ENG & SPA.). (gr. 5 up). (978-0-02-148726-4(X)) Macmillan/McGraw-Hill Schl. Div.

El lugar donde vivimos, Unidad 1: Libros de la Biblioteca (Classroom Library) 2000. (Aventuras A Traves Del Tiempo Ser.). (ENG & SPA.). (gr. 1 up). (978-0-02-147838-5(4)) Macmillan/McGraw-Hill Schl. Div.

Lund, Bill. The Apache Indians, 6 vols. (gr. 2-5). 36.95 (978-0-7368-8446-4(7)) Red Brick Learning.

Macmillan/Mcgraw. Alternative Learning Strategies: Staff Development Videotapes. (Staff Development Ser.). (gr. k-8). (978-0-02-178701-2(8)) Macmillan/McGraw-Hill Schl. Div.

—Cooperative Learning: Staff Development Videotapes. (Staff Development Ser.). (gr. k-8). (978-0-02-178702-9(6)) Macmillan/McGraw-Hill Schl. Div.

Making Money Social Studies, 6 vols. (gr. k-2). 28.95 (978-0-7368-3005-8(7) , Yellow Umbrella Bks.) Capstone Pr., Inc.

Making Patterns: Level C. 8p. 20.95 (978-0-322-00361-3(X)) Wright Group, The.

Maneras de comunicar Social Studies, 6 vols.Tr. of Ways We Communicate Social Studies. (SPA.). (gr. k-2). 28.95 (978-0-7368-3135-2(5) , Yellow Umbrella Bks.) Capstone Pr., Inc.

Los manuscritos del mar Muerto: Aventuras (Adventure Books) 2000. (Aventuras A Traves Del Tiempo Ser.). (ENG & SPA.). (gr. 6 up). (978-0-02-148742-4(1)) Macmillan/McGraw-Hill Schl. Div.

Many Cultures, One World, 14 bks. Incl. Afghanistan. Knox, Barbara. 2004. lib. bdg. 23.93 (978-0-7368-2448-4(0)); Canada. Olson, Kay Melchisedech. 2003. lib. bdg. 23.93 (978-0-7368-2166-7(X)); China. Olson, Kay Melchisedech. 2003. lib. bdg. 23.93 (978-0-7368-1531-4(7)); Dominican Republic. Englar, Mary. 2004. lib. bdg. 23.93 (978-0-7368-2453-8(7)); England. Olson, Kay Melchisedech. 2003. lib. bdg. 23.93 (978-0-7368-1532-1(5)); Ethiopia. Delzio, Suzanne. 2004. lib. bdg. 23.93 (978-0-7368-2449-1(9)); Greece. DeAngelis, Gina. 2003. lib. bdg. 23.93 (978-0-7368-2167-4(8)); Ireland. Olson, Kay Melchisedech. 2003. lib. bdg. 23.93 (978-0-7368-2168-1(6)); Japan. DeAngelis, Gina. 2003. lib. bdg. 23.93 (978-0-7368-1533-8(3)); Mexico. DeAngelis, Gina. 2003. lib. bdg. 23.93 (978-0-7368-1534-5(1)); Pakistan. DeAngelis, Gina. 2003. lib. bdg. 23.93 (978-0-7368-2169-8(4)); Peru. Knox, Barbara. 2004. lib. bdg. 23.93 (978-0-7368-2450-7(2)); Spain. Yanuck, Debbie L. 2004. lib. bdg. 23.93 (978-0-7368-2451-4(0)); Sweden. Yanuck, Debbie L. 2004. lib. bdg. 23.93 (978-0-7368-2452-1(9)); 32p. (J). (gr. 2-3). (Illus.). 2003. Set lib. bdg. 335.02 (978-0-7368-2553-5(3) , Bridgestone Bks.) Capstone Pr., Inc.

Map Skills for Today. (J). Bk. 1. (978-0-8374-2214-5(0) , 321); Bk. 2. (978-0-8374-0224-6(7) , 322); Bk. 6. (978-0-8374-0261-1(1) , 326) Weekly Reader Corp.

Mapas en Blanco: Comunidades. 2000. (Aventuras A Traves Del Tiempo Ser.). (ENG & SPA.). (gr. 3 up). (978-0-02-147922-1(4)) Macmillan/McGraw-Hill Schl. Div.

Mapas en Blanco: Gente. 2000. (Aventuras A Traves Del Tiempo Ser.). (ENG & SPA.). (gr. 2 up). (978-0-02-147921-4(6)) Macmillan/McGraw-Hill Schl. Div.

Mapas en Blanco: Mi Mundo. 2000. (Aventuras A Traves Del Tiempo Ser.). (ENG & SPA.). (gr. 1 up). (978-0-02-147919-1(4)) Macmillan/McGraw-Hill Schl. Div.

Mapas Laminadas: Aqui Estoy! 2000. (Aventuras A Traves Del Tiempo Ser.). (ENG & SPA.). (gr. k-1). (978-0-02-147913-9(5)) Macmillan/McGraw-Hill Schl. Div.

Mapas Laminadas: Comunidades. 2000. (Aventuras A Traves Del Tiempo Ser.). (ENG & SPA.). (gr. 3 up). (978-0-02-147915-3(1)) Macmillan/McGraw-Hill Schl. Div.

Mapas Laminadas: Gente. 2000. (Aventuras A Traves Del Tiempo Ser.). (ENG & SPA.). (gr. 2 up). (978-0-02-147914-6(3)) Macmillan/McGraw-Hill Schl. Div.

Mara, Wil. Rookie Biographies, 10 bks., Set. 2004. (Illus.). 32p. (J). (gr. 1-2). 494.00 (978-0-516-29791-0(0)) Scholastic Library Publishing.

Mattern, Joanne. Katharine Graham: American Publisher: Individual Title Six-Packs. (On Deck Ser.: Vol. 2). 24p. (gr. 4-5). 35.00 (978-0-7578-5845-1(7)) Rigby Education.

McEwan, Rebecca. Lost Cities. 2004. (Navigators Ser.). (J). pap. 42.00 (978-1-4108-0419-8(4)) Benchmark Education Co.

McGraw-Hill - Jamestown Education Staff. The Outer Edge: Friend or Foe. 2005. pap. 16.64 (978-0-07-869054-9(4) , 9780078690549) Glencoe/McGraw-Hill.

McGraw-Hill Staff. Civics Today. 2002. stu. ed. 85.33 incl. cd-rom (978-0-07-829629-1(3) , 9780078296291) Glencoe/McGraw-Hill.

—Civics Today: Citizenship, Economics, & You. 2nd ed. 2004. (C). stu. ed. 82.64 (978-0-07-860970-1(4) , 9780078609701) Glencoe/McGraw-Hill.

—Civics Today: Citizenship, Economics & You. 2nd ed. 2005. cd-rom 106.64 (978-0-07-866528-8(0) , 9780078665288) Glencoe/McGraw-Hill.

—Civics Today: Citizenship, Economics & You, Spanish Reading Essentials. 2nd ed. 2004. (SPA.). stu. ed., wbk. ed. 18.00 (978-0-07-865613-2(3) , 9780078656132) Glencoe/McGraw-Hill.

—Economics: Principles & Practices. 2001. (gr. 6-12). stu. ed. 91.33 (978-0-07-828093-1(1) , 9780078280931) Glencoe/McGraw-Hill.

—Journey Across Time: Early Ages. 2004. (C). pap., stu. ed., act. bk. ed. 10.00 (978-0-07-868197-4(9) , 9780078681974) Glencoe/McGraw-Hill.

—Our World Today: People, Places, & Issues. 2002. stu. ed. 83.11 incl. cd-rom (978-0-07-829599-7(8) , 9780078295997) Glencoe/McGraw-Hill.

—Sociology & You. 2002. stu. ed. 90.00 (978-0-07-829301-6(4) , 9780078293016); (C). stu. ed. 90.00 (978-0-07-828576-9(3) , 9780078285769) Glencoe/McGraw-Hill.

—The World & Its People. 2005. (SPA.). (C). stu. ed. 84.64 (978-0-07-867382-5(8) , 9780078673825) Glencoe/McGraw-Hill.

—The World & Its People: Active Reading Note-Taking Guide. 2004. pap., stu. ed. 18.00 (978-0-07-868140-0(5) , 9780078681400) Glencoe/McGraw-Hill.

—The World & Its People: Eastern Hemisphere. 2004. stu. ed., wbk. ed. 18.00 (978-0-07-868055-7(7) , 9780078680557) Glencoe/McGraw-Hill.

—The World & Its People: Eastern Hemisphere, Active Reading Note-Taking Guide. 2004. (C). pap., stu. ed. 18.00 (978-0-07-868058-8(1) , 9780078680588) Glencoe/McGraw-Hill.

—The World & Its People: Eastern Hemisphere, Spanish Reading. 2004. (SPA.). (C). pap., stu. ed. 18.00 (978-0-07-868076-2(X) , 9780078680762) Glencoe/McGraw-Hill.

—The World & Its People: Reading Essentials. 2004. (C). pap., stu. ed., wbk. ed. 18.00 (978-0-07-865513-5(7) , 9780078655135) Glencoe/McGraw-Hill.

—The World & Its People: Spanish Essentials & Study Guide. 2004. (SPA.). pap., stu. ed., wbk. ed. 18.00 (978-0-07-865518-0(8) , 9780078655180) Glencoe/McGraw-Hill.

—The World & Its People: Western Hemisphere, Europe & Russia. 2004. (C). pap., stu. ed., wbk. ed. 10.00 (978-0-07-868026-7(3) , 9780078680267) Glencoe/McGraw-Hill.

—The World & Its People: Western Hemisphere, Europe & Russia, Active Reading Note-Taking Guide. 2004. (C). pap., stu. ed. 18.00 (978-0-07-868033-5(6) , 9780078680335) Glencoe/McGraw-Hill.

—The World & Its People: Western Hemisphere, Europe & Russia, Reading Essentials. 2004. pap., stu. ed., wbk. ed. 18.00 (978-0-07-868030-4(1) , 9780078680304) Glencoe/McGraw-Hill.

—The World & Its People: Western Hemisphere, Europe & Russia, Spanish Reading Essentials. 2004. (SPA.). pap., stu. ed., wbk. ed. 18.00 (978-0-07-868050-2(6) , 9780078680502) Glencoe/McGraw-Hill.

—The World & Its People, Eastern Hemisphere. 2005. (SPA.). (C). stu. ed. 69.32 (978-0-07-868376-3(9) , 9780078683763); 2004. pap., wbk. ed. 10.00 (978-0-07-868120-2(0) , 9780078681202) Glencoe/McGraw-Hill.

—The World & Its People, Eastern Hemisphere, Student-Works Plus CD-ROM. 2005. 93.32 (978-0-07-866303-1(2) , 9780078663031) Glencoe/McGraw-Hill.

—The World & Its People, StudentWorks Plus CD-ROM. 2005. (C). 108.00 (978-0-07-866345-1(8) , 9780078663451) Glencoe/McGraw-Hill.

—The World & Its People, Western Hemisphere, Europe, & Russia, Spanish Student Edition. 2005. 60.00 (978-0-07-868380-0(7)) Glencoe/McGraw-Hill.

—The World & Its People, Western Hemisphere, Europe, & Russia, StudentWorks Plus CD-ROM. 2005. 93.32 (978-0-07-866322-2(9) , 9780078663222) Glencoe/McGraw-Hill.

Measure It: Big Book: Level D. 8p. 20.95 (978-0-322-00362-0(8)) Wright Group, The.

El mejor Precio: Libros Aventuras (Adventure Books) 2003. (MacMillan/McGraw-Hill. Estudios Sociales Ser.). (ENG & SPA.). (gr. 3 up). (978-0-02-150113-7(0)) Macmillan/McGraw-Hill Schl. Div.

Meunier, A., et al. Sam Generations. 2000. (C). pap. 47.50 (978-0-03-030941-0(7)) Harcourt Trade Pubs.

Meyers Schlaglichter des 20 Jahrhunderts. (978-3-411-07411-2(6)) Bibliographisches Institut & F. A. Brockhaus AG DEU. *Dist:* i.b.d., Ltd.

Meyers Taschenlexikon in einem Band. (978-3-411-10134-4(2)) Bibliographisches Institut & F. A. Brockhaus AG DEU. *Dist:* i.b.d., Ltd.

Middle Grades History. 2004. 556.00 (978-0-531-14700-9(2)) Scholastic Library Publishing.

Milenio 1: Serie de Estudies Sociales para la Escuela Elemental. (SPA.). 25.00 (978-958-04-5593-6(7)) Norma S.A. COL. *Dist:* Distribuidora Norma, Inc.

Milenio 2: Serie de Estudies Sociales para la Escuela Elemental. (SPA.). 25.00 (978-958-04-5594-3(5)) Norma S.A. COL. *Dist:* Distribuidora Norma, Inc.

Milenio 3: Serie de Estudies Sociales para la Escuela Elemental. (SPA.). 30.00 (978-958-04-5595-0(3)) Norma S.A. COL. *Dist:* Distribuidora Norma, Inc.

Milenio 4: Serie de Estudies Sociales para la Escuela Elemental. (SPA.). 40.00 (978-958-04-5596-7(1)) Norma S.A. COL. *Dist:* Distribuidora Norma, Inc.

Milenio 5: Serie de Estudies Sociales para la Escuela Elemental. (SPA.). 45.00 (978-958-04-5597-4(X)) Norma S.A. COL. *Dist:* Distribuidora Norma, Inc.

Milenio 6: Serie de Estudies Sociales para la Escuela Elemental. (SPA.). 45.00 (978-958-04-5598-1(8)) Norma S.A. COL. *Dist:* Distribuidora Norma, Inc.

Milenio K: Serie de Estudies Sociales para la Escuela Elemental. (SPA.). 25.00 (978-958-04-5592-9(9)) Norma S.A. COL. *Dist:* Distribuidora Norma, Inc.

Miller, Amy. Pony Express. 2002. (Instant Social Studies Activities Folders Ser.). (Illus.). 6p. (gr. 4-8). 3.95 (978-0-439-37092-9(2)) Scholastic, Inc.

El misterio de la colonia Perdida: Libros Aventuras (Adventure Books) 2000. (MacMillan/McGraw-Hill. Estudios Sociales Ser.). (ENG & SPA.). (gr. 5 up). (978-0-02-148717-2(0)) Macmillan/McGraw-Hill Schl. Div.

Mix It Up: Big Book: Level E. 8p. 20.95 (978-0-322-00363-7(6)) Wright Group, The.

MoCasins: Level A, 6 vols. 8p. 24.95 (978-0-7802-9109-6(3)) Wright Group, The.

Moger, Susan. Pilgrims. 2003. (Learn All About Ser.). (Illus.). 64p. pap. 10.95 (978-0-439-51886-4(5)) Scholastic, Inc.

Mono y Camaleon: Aventuras (Adventure Books) 2000. (Aventuras A Traves Del Tiempo Ser.). (ENG & SPA.). (gr. 5 up). (978-0-02-148735-6(9)) Macmillan/McGraw-Hill Schl. Div.

Moore, Willamarie. StarFestival Grades 3-6 Tanabata Festival Team: Exploring Cultural Heritage. Miyagawa, Shigeru, ed. 2000. (Illus.). 50p. (J). (gr. 3). pap., stu. ed., wbk. ed. 10.00 (978-1-929724-05-5(5)) StarFestival, Inc.

—StarFestival Grades 7-9 Fishing Industry Teams: Exploring Cultural Heritage. Miyagawa, Shigeru, ed. 2000. (Illus.). 47p. (YA). (gr. 7-11). pap., stu. ed., wbk. ed. 10.00 (978-1-929724-11-6(X)) StarFestival, Inc.

—StarFestival Grades 7-9 Home Hobbies Team: Exploring Cultural Heritage. Miyagawa, Shigeru, ed. 2000. (Illus.). 47p. (YA). (gr. 7-11). pap., stu. ed., wbk. ed. 10.00 (978-1-929724-09-3(8)) StarFestival, Inc.

—StarFestival Grades 7-9 World War II Team: Exploring Cultural Heritage. Miyagawa, Shigeru, ed. 2000. (Illus.). 47p. (YA). (gr. 7-11). pap., wbk. ed. 10.00 (978-1-929724-12-3(8)) StarFestival, Inc.

—StarFestival Student Workbook: Grades 2-6 Food & Clothing Team: Exploring Cultural Heritage. Miyagawa, Shigeru, ed. 2000. (Illus.). 50p. (J). (gr. 3-6). pap., wbk. ed. 10.00 (978-1-929724-03-1(9)) StarFestival, Inc.

—StarFestival Student Workbook: Grades 3-6 Home & Hobbies Team: Exploring Cultural Heritage. Miyagawa, Shigeru, ed. 2000. (Illus.). 50p. (J). (gr. 3). pap., wbk. ed. 10.00 (978-1-929724-04-8(7)) StarFestival, Inc.

Moran, Margaret. Cowhands & Cattle Trails. 2004. (Navigators Ser.). (J). pap. 42.00 (978-1-4108-0426-6(7)) Benchmark Education Co.

Morris, Ann. Teamwork. 1999. (Illus.). 32p. (J). (ps up). 16.00 (978-0-688-16551-2(6)) HarperCollins Pubs.

Mountford, Peter, et al. Cambridge Checkpoints VCE Legal Studies 2004. 2003. (Cambridge Checkpoints Ser.). pap. 11.00 (978-0-521-54286-9(3)) Cambridge Univ. Pr.

Mulvihill, Naomi. Inventions! Multicultural Social Studies & Technology Curriculum. Zuman, John, ed. Rooney, Veronica, illus. 2002. 60p. (J). stu. ed., spiral bd. 36.00 (978-1-58332-040-2(7)) Intercultural Center for Research in Education (I N C R E).

Un Mundo de Communidades.Tr. of World of Communities. (SPA., Illus.). 32p. pap., act. bk. ed. 12.45 (978-1-56711-531-4(4)); 80p. (J). (gr. 3-5). 28.70 (978-1-56711-529-1(2)) Thomson Gale. (Blackbirch Pr., Inc.).

Un mundo que trajaba, Unidad 3: Superlibros (Big Books) 2000. (Aventuras A Traves Del Tiempo Ser.). (ENG & SPA.). (gr. 2 up). (978-0-02-147847-7(3)) Macmillan/McGraw-Hill Schl. Div.

Museums: Collections to Share, 6 vols. (Book2WebTM Ser.). (gr. 4-8). 36.50 (978-0-322-02986-6(4)) Wright Group, The.

My Favorite Things. (Totally Girls Ser.). 16p. (J). (978-2-7643-0189-0(8)) Phidal Publishing, Inc./Editions Phidal, Inc.

My Favorite Things. 2005. (Emergent/Early (Prek-2) Social Studies Package Ser.). 12p. (YA). (ps-2). 25.20 (978-0-8215-7831-5(6)) Sadlier, William H. Inc.

My World: E-Journals. (Technology: Social Studies). (SPA.). (gr. k-1). (978-0-02-147228-4(9)) Macmillan/McGraw-Hill Schl. Div.

Nations of the World Series, 4 vols., Set. 2003. pap. 137.12 (978-0-7398-7002-0(5)); 2000. (Illus.). 342.60 (978-0-7398-4182-2(3)) Steck-Vaughn.

Native Peoples Complete Unit. (gr. 2-5). 265.95 (978-0-7368-7079-5(2)) Red Brick Learning.

Needs & Wants Social Studies, 6 vols. (gr. k-2). 28.95 (978-0-7368-1761-5(1) , Yellow Umbrella Bks.) Capstone Pr., Inc.

The New World. 2004. (Thrilling Tales in Time Ser.: Vol. 2). (J). 19.95 (978-1-58123-371-1(X)) Larson Learning, Inc.

Un nino visita Williamsburg Colonial: Libros Aventuras (Adventure Books) 2000. (MacMillan/McGraw-Hill. Estudios Sociales Ser.). (ENG & SPA.). (gr. 5 up). (978-0-02-148718-9(9)) Macmillan/McGraw-Hill Schl. Div.

Nitert, Deb. Exploring Change, Grades 3-4 Vol. 1: Social & Cultural Progress, 3 vols. 2000. 48p. (J). (gr. 3-4). pap. 6.95 (978-1-58324-073-1(X) , World Teachers Pr.) Didax Educational Resources, Inc.

—Exploring Change, Grades 5-6 Vol. 2: Social & Cultural Progress, 3 vols. 2000. 48p. (J). (gr. 5-6). pap. 6.95 (978-1-58324-074-8(8) , World Teachers Pr.) Didax Educational Resources, Inc.

—Exploring Change, Grades 7-8 Vol. 3: Social & Cultural Progress, 3 vols. 2000. 48p. (YA). (gr. 7-8). pap. 6.95 (978-1-58324-075-5(6) , World Teachers Pr.) Didax Educational Resources, Inc.

No, Daniel, No! Libros Aventuras (Adventure Books) 2000. (MacMillan/McGraw-Hill. Estudios Sociales Ser.). (ENG & SPA.). (gr. 1 up). (978-0-02-148662-5(X)) Macmillan/McGraw-Hill Schl. Div.

El nombre de mis Companeros: Superlibros (Big Books) 2000. (Aventuras A Traves Del Tiempo Ser.). (ENG & SPA.). (gr. k up). (978-0-02-147854-5(6)) Macmillan/McGraw-Hill Schl. Div.

Nosotros, el pueblo, Unidad 4: Superlibros. 2000. (Aventuras A Traves Del Tiempo Ser.). (ENG & SPA.). (gr. 2 up). (978-0-02-147848-4(1)) Macmillan/McGraw-Hill Schl. Div.

Nuestra primera Bandera: Libros Aventuras (Adventure Books) 2003. (MacMillan/McGraw-Hill. Estudios Sociales Ser.). (ENG & SPA.). (gr. 1 up). (978-0-02-150110-6(6)) Macmillan/McGraw-Hill Schl. Div.

Nuestro mundo, Unidad 4: Libros de la Biblioteca (Classroom Library) 2000. (Aventuras A Traves Del Tiempo Ser.). (ENG & SPA.). (gr. 1 up). (978-0-02-147842-2(2)) Macmillan/McGraw-Hill Schl. Div.

Nuestro Pais, Neustro mundo, Unidad 4: Superlibros (Big Books) 2000. (Aventuras A Traves Del Tiempo Ser.). (ENG & SPA.). (gr. k up). (978-0-02-147836-1(8)) Macmillan/McGraw-Hill Schl. Div.

Nuestro pasado, Unidad 5: Superlibros (Big Books) 2000. (Aventuras A Traves Del Tiempo Ser.). (ENG & SPA.). (gr. 2 up). (978-0-02-147849-1(X)) Macmillan/McGraw-Hill Schl. Div.

Nuestro primer Presidente: Aventuras (Adventure Books) 2000. (Aventuras A Traves Del Tiempo Ser.). (ENG & SPA.). (gr. 1 up). (978-0-02-148664-9(6)) Macmillan/McGraw-Hill Schl. Div.

Una ocasion de Compartir: Libros Aventuras (Adventure Books) 2000. (MacMillan/McGraw-Hill. Estudios Sociales Ser.). (ENG & SPA.). (gr. 1 up). (978-0-02-148674-8(3)) Macmillan/McGraw-Hill Schl. Div.

Oceans of the World, 6 Packs. (Rigby Infoquest Ser.). 32p. (gr. 4 up). 37.00 (978-0-7578-5736-2(1)) Rigby Education.

La Oficina de Libertos: Libros Aventuras (Adventure Books) 2003. (MacMillan/McGraw-Hill. Estudios Sociales Ser.). (ENG & SPA.). (gr. 4 up). (978-0-02-150117-5(3)) Macmillan/McGraw-Hill Schl. Div.

O'Hara, Megan. Blue Earth Books: Living History, 4 bks. Incl. Frontier Fort : Fort Life on the Upper Mississippi, 1826. lib. bdg. 22.60 (978-1-56065-724-8(3)); General Store : A Village Store in 1902. lib. bdg. 22.60 (978-1-56065-723-1(5)); Lighthouse : Living in a Great Lakes Lighthouse, 1910 to 1940. lib. bdg. 22.60 (978-1-56065-725-5(1)); Pioneer Farm : Living on a Farm in the 1880s. lib. bdg. 22.60 (978-1-56065-726-2(X)); 32p. (J). (gr. 3-4). 1998. (Illus.). Set lib. bdg. 90.40 (978-1-56065-823-8(1) , Bridgestone Bks.) Capstone Pr., Inc.

O'Keefe, Cynthia A. Exploring the Real World: Middle School Edition. Date not set. 200p. (Orig.). (J). pap. 85.00 (978-0-913956-89-2(9)) EBSCO Industries, Inc.

—Exploring the Real World: Primary School Edition. Date not set. 200p. (Orig.). (J). (gr. 4-6). pap. 65.00 (978-0-913956-88-5(0)) EBSCO Industries, Inc.

—Exploring the Real World: Secondary Edition. Date not set. 366p. (Orig.). (YA). (gr. 7-12). pap. 283.00 (978-0-913956-87-8(2)) EBSCO Industries, Inc.

O'Kelley, Jeff. Mapping the Way. 2006. (Early Explorers Ser.). (J). 34.00 (***978-1-4108-6106-1(6)***) Benchmark Education Co.

Our Country. 2005. (Emergent/Early (Prek-2) Social Studies Package Ser.). 12p. (YA). (ps-2). 25.20 (978-0-8215-7832-2(4)) Sadlier, William H. Inc.

El paraiso del Panqueque: Aventuras (Adventure Books) 2000. (Aventuras A Traves Del Tiempo Ser.). (ENG & SPA.). (gr. k up). (978-0-02-148652-6(2)) Macmillan/McGraw-Hill Schl. Div.

Paul Cezanne. 2002. 32p. (J). (gr. k-2). pap. 6.50 (978-1-4034-0498-5(4) , 91807) Heinemann Library.

Peacefulness, 6 vols. (gr. 2-5). 36.95 (978-0-7368-9254-4(0)) Red Brick Learning.

Pebble Books: One World, Many Cultures. 2005. (YA). (gr. k-3). 712.80 (978-0-7368-4217-4(9) , Pebble Bks.) Capstone Pr., Inc.

Penchina, Sharon R. Bend at Your Knees ... If You Please! 2006. 28p. 12.95 (978-0-9740684-7-3(0)) 2 Imagine.

People at Odds, sets. 2005. 112p. (YA). (gr. 5 up). pap. 180.00 (978-0-7910-6704-8(1) , Chelsea Hse.) Facts On File, Inc.

People Change the Land Social Studies, 6 vols. (gr. k-2). 28.95 (978-0-7368-3006-5(5) , Yellow Umbrella Bks.) Capstone Pr., Inc.

People in the Past Series, 15 bks., Set 1-3. 2003. (J). (gr. 4-6). lib. bdg. 406.05 (978-1-4034-0308-7(2)) Heinemann Library.

People Set. (gr. k-2). 114.95 (978-0-7368-9065-6(3)) Red Brick Learning.

People to Know, 55 bks., Set. (Illus.). (YA). (gr. 6-12). lib. bdg. 1152.25 (978-0-89490-450-9(7)) Enslow Pubs., Inc.

El Pescador: Libros Aventuras (Adventure Books) 2003. (MacMillan/McGraw-Hill. Estudios Sociales Ser.). (ENG & SPA.). (gr. 3 up). (978-0-02-150112-0(2)) Macmillan/McGraw-Hill Schl. Div.

Phillis Wheatly, 6 vols. (gr. 2-5). 39.95 (978-0-7368-4584-7(4)) Red Brick Learning.

Photo-Illustrated Biographies Classroom Library. (gr. 2-5). lib. bdg. 81.95 (978-0-7368-7070-2(9)) Red Brick Learning.

Photo-Illustrated Biographies Complete Unit. (gr. 2-5). 464.95 (978-0-7368-7071-9(7)) Red Brick Learning.

Photo-Illustrated Biographies II Classroom Library. (gr. 2-5). lib. bdg. 81.95 (978-0-7368-4477-2(5)) Red Brick Learning.

Photo-Illustrated Biographies II Complete Unit. (gr. 2-5). 464.95 (978-0-7368-4476-5(7)) Red Brick Learning.

El placer de vivir al borde: Lavida de Yakima Canutt: Aventuras (Adventure Books) 2000. (Aventuras A Traves Del Tiempo Ser.). (ENG & SPA.). (gr. 4 up). (978-0-02-148702-8(2)) Macmillan/McGraw-Hill Schl. Div.

Plantemos Semillas: Aventuras (Adventure Books) 2000. (Aventuras A Traves Del Tiempo Ser.). (ENG & SPA.). (gr. k up). (978-0-02-148658-8(1)) Macmillan/McGraw-Hill Schl. Div.

The Playground: Level A. 8p. 20.95 (978-0-322-00367-5(9)); 24.95 (978-0-7802-8913-0(7)) Wright Group, The.

The Plymouth Colony, 6 vols. (gr. 2-5). 39.95 (978-0-7368-4569-4(0)) Red Brick Learning.

Poear, Allan. El Escarabajo de Oro. 2000. (SPA.). (gr. 3-6). lib. bdg. 26.45 (978-0-613-80853-8(3)) Tandem Library Bks.

Pompeya: Los ultimos dias de una ciudad Romana: Aventuras (Adventure Books) 2000. (Aventuras A Traves Del Tiempo Ser.). (ENG & SPA.). (gr. 6 up). (978-0-02-148751-6(0)) Macmillan/McGraw-Hill Schl. Div.

El Pony Express: Libros Aventuras (Adventure Books) 2000. (MacMillan/McGraw-Hill. Estudios Sociales Ser.). (ENG & SPA.). (gr. 4 up). (978-0-02-148713-4(8)) Macmillan/McGraw-Hill Schl. Div.

Postcards from... Series, Set. 2001. (Postcards from...Ser.). (Illus.). 436.95 (978-0-7398-5048-0(2)) Steck-Vaughn.

Practica: Resources & Ancillaries. 2001. (McGraw-Hill. Lectura Ser.). (ENG & SPA.). (gr. k up). (978-0-02-186168-2(4)); (gr. 1 up). (978-0-02-186537-6(X)); (gr. 2 up). (978-0-02-186538-3(8)); (gr. 3 up). (978-0-02-186539-0(6)); (gr. 4 up). (978-0-02-186417-1(9)); (gr. 5 up). (978-0-02-186418-8(7)); (gr. 6 up). (978-0-02-186419-5(5)) Macmillan/McGraw-Hill Schl. Div.

Practica: Edicion del Maestro: Resources & Ancillaries. 2001. (McGraw-Hill. Lectura Ser.). (ENG & SPA.). (gr. k up). (978-0-02-186559-8(0)); (gr. 1 up). (978-0-02-186544-4(2)); (gr. 2 up). (978-0-02-186545-1(0)); (gr. 3 up). (978-0-02-186546-8(9)); (gr. 4 up). (978-0-02-186420-1(9)); (gr. 5 up). (978-0-02-186421-8(7)); (gr. 6 up). (978-0-02-186422-5(5)) Macmillan/McGraw-Hill Schl. Div.

Prentiss, Timothy. What Is a Good Citizen? 2006. (Early Explorers Ser.). (J). 34.00 ***(978-1-4108-6110-8(4))*** Benchmark Education Co.

Presidents' Day, 6 vols. (gr. k-2). 28.95 (978-0-7368-8753-3(9)) Red Brick Learning.

Proyecto Raices: un sueno hecho Realidad: Libros Aventuras (Adventure Books) 2003. (MacMillan/McGraw-Hill. Estudios Sociales Ser.). (ENG & SPA.). (gr. 5 up). (978-0-02-150127-4(0)) Macmillan/McGraw-Hill Schl. Div.

Un punado de semillas, Unidad 5: Superlibros (Big Books) 2000. (Aventuras A Traves Del Tiempo Ser.). (ENG & SPA.). (gr. 3 up). (978-0-02-147877-4(5)) Macmillan/McGraw-Hill Schl. Div.

Quasha, Jennifer. Great Social Studies Projects, 6 bks. Incl. Birth & Growth of a Nation : Hands-On Projects about Symbols of American Liberty. lib. bdg. 19.95 (978-0-8239-5703-3(9)); Covered Wagons : Hands-On Projects about America's Westward Expansion. lib. bdg. 19.95 (978-0-8239-5704-0(7)); Gold Rush : Hands-On Projects about Mining the Riches of California. lib. bdg. 19.95 (978-0-8239-5705-7(5)); Jamestown : Hands-On Projects about One of America's First Communities. lib. bdg. 19.95 (978-0-8239-5701-9(2)); Pilgrims & Native Americans : Hands-on Projects about Life in Early America. lib. bdg. 19.95 (978-0-8239-5700-2(4)); Pony Express : Hands-On Projects about Early Communication. lib. bdg. 19.95 (978-0-8239-5702-6(0)); 24p. (J). (gr. 3). (Illus.). 2001. Set lib. bdg. 117.00 (978-0-8239-7067-4(1) , PowerKids Pr.) Rosen Publishing Group, Inc., The.

Que hace un bombero? Social Studies, 6 vols.Tr. of What Does a Firefighter Do? Social Studies. (SPA.). (gr. k-2). 28.95 (978-0-7368-3024-9(3) , Yellow Umbrella Bks.) Capstone Pr., Inc.

Que Hacemos? Aventuras (Adventure Books) 2000. (Aventuras A Traves Del Tiempo Ser.). (ENG & SPA.). (gr. 1 up). (978-0-02-148669-4(7)) Macmillan/McGraw-Hill Schl. Div.

Que hay de Nuevo? Aventuras (Adventure Books) 2000. (Aventuras A Traves Del Tiempo Ser.). (ENG & SPA.). (gr. 2 up). (978-0-02-148684-7(0)) Macmillan/McGraw-Hill Schl. Div.

Que hay de Nuevo? Libros Aventuras (Adventure Books) 2003. (MacMillan/McGraw-Hill. Estudios Sociales Ser.). (ENG & SPA.). (gr. 1 up). (978-0-02-150109-0(2)) Macmillan/McGraw-Hill Schl. Div.

Quienes nos protegen? Social Studies, 6 vols.Tr. of Who Keeps Us Safe? Social Studies. (SPA.). (gr. k-2). 28.95 (978-0-7368-3118-5(5) , Yellow Umbrella Bks.) Capstone Pr., Inc.

Raintree. Itlp 2004 Grade 4 Soc Stud Sta. 2004. pap. (978-1-4109-1575-7(1)); pap. (978-1-4109-1577-1(8)) Harcourt Schl. Pubs.

—Itlp 2004 Grades 2-4 Soc Stud. 2004. pap. (978-1-4109-1573-3(5)); pap. (978-1-4109-1578-8(6)) Harcourt Schl. Pubs.

—Itlp 2004 Grades 3-4 Soc Stud. 2004. pap. (978-1-4109-1574-0(3)); pap. (978-1-4109-1576-4(X)) Harcourt Schl. Pubs.

—Itlp 2004 Grades K-1 Soc Stud. 2004. pap. (978-1-4109-1572-6(7)) Harcourt Schl. Pubs.

—Itlp 2004 Grades K-2 Science S. 2004. pap. (978-1-4109-1568-9(9)) Harcourt Schl. Pubs.

Raintree Steck-Vaughn Staff. Foods from Friends & Neighbors: Level B. 2000. (Read All about It Ser.). (Illus.). (J). pap. 4.95 (978-0-8114-3802-5(3)) Steck-Vaughn.

—Lemonade Stand. 2000. (Read All about It Ser.). (Illus.). (J). pap. 4.95 (978-0-8114-3800-1(7)) Steck-Vaughn.

—Let's Work Together. 2000. (Read All about It Ser.). (Illus.). (J). pap. 4.95 (978-0-8114-3797-4(3)) Steck-Vaughn.

—Look Out on the Road. 2000. (Read All about It Ser.). (Illus.). (J). (ps-3). pap. 4.95 (978-0-8114-3736-3(1)) Steck-Vaughn.

—Looking Around. 2000. (Read All about It Ser.). (Illus.). (J). (ps-3). pap. 4.95 (978-0-8114-3721-9(3)) Steck-Vaughn.

—Our Family Tree: Level B. 2000. (Read All about It Ser.). (Illus.). (J). pap. 4.95 (978-0-8114-3803-2(1)) Steck-Vaughn.

La rata Cambalachera: Libros Aventuras (Adventure Books) 2003. (MacMillan/McGraw-Hill. Estudios Sociales Ser.). (ENG & SPA.). (gr. 4 up). (978-0-02-150114-4(9)) Macmillan/McGraw-Hill Schl. Div.

Reading to Learn in Social Studies for Grades 6-8. 2006. spiral bd. (978-1-933049-56-4(1)) Region IV Education Service Ctr.

Reading to Learn in Social Studies for Grades 9-12. 2006. spiral bd. (978-1-933049-57-1(X)) Region IV Education Service Ctr.

Ready for Take-off: Individual Title Six-Packs. (Bookweb Ser.). 32p. (gr. 3 up). 34.00 (978-0-7635-3952-8(X)) Rigby Education.

Regional Social Studies Variety Pack. 1999. (Illus.). (J). pap. (978-0-7398-2771-0(5)) Steck-Vaughn.

Reid, Struan. The Science & History Project Book. 2004. (Illus.). 512p. 45.00 (978-0-7548-1445-0(9) , Lorenz Bks.) Anness Publishing GBR. *Dist:* National Bk. Network.

Responsibility, 6 vols. (gr. 2-5). 36.95 (978-0-7368-9256-8(7)) Red Brick Learning.

Resumenes de las Lecciones: Student & Teacher Support Resources. 2003. (MacMillan/McGraw-Hill. Estudios Sociales Ser.). (ENG & SPA.). (gr. 3 up). (978-0-02-149901-4(2)); (gr. 5 up). (978-0-02-149903-8(9)) Macmillan/McGraw-Hill Schl. Div.

Resumes de las Lecciones: Student & Teacher Support Resources. 2003. (MacMillan/McGraw-Hill. Estudios Sociales Ser.). (ENG & SPA.). (gr. 4 up). (978-0-02-150075-8(4)) Macmillan/McGraw-Hill Schl. Div.

Revision de Ensenanza: Resources & Ancillaries. 2001. (McGraw-Hill. Lectura Ser.). (ENG & SPA.). (gr. 1 up). (978-0-02-186411-9(X)); (gr. 2 up). (978-0-02-186412-6(8)); (gr. 3 up). (978-0-02-186413-3(6)); (gr. 4 up). (978-0-02-186414-0(4)); (gr. 5 up). (978-0-02-186415-7(2)); (gr. 6 up). (978-0-02-186416-4(0)) Macmillan/McGraw-Hill Schl. Div.

The Revolutionary War, 6 vols. (gr. 2-5). 39.95 (978-0-7368-8931-5(0)) Red Brick Learning.

Robinson-Masters, Nancy. Wings of War, 4 bks. Incl. Airplanes of World War II. lib. bdg. 21.26 (978-1-56065-531-2(3)); Bombers of World War II. lib. bdg. 21.26 (978-1-56065-532-9(1)); Fighter Planes of World War II. lib. bdg. 21.26 (978-1-56065-533-6(X)); Training Planes of World War II. lib. bdg. 21.26 (978-1-56065-534-3(8)); 48p. (J). (gr. 3-4). 1998. (Illus.). Set lib. bdg. 85.04 (978-1-56065-816-0(9) , Capstone High-Interest Bks.) Capstone Pr., Inc.

Rogers, Kathy. Color & Learn - Medieval Times. Adams, Elizabeth, illus. 1999. 32p. (J). (gr. 2-6). pap., wbk. ed. 3.99 (978-1-56472-201-0(5) , EP201) Edupress, Inc.

Rookie Espanol: Geografia: Nonfiction Spanish for Beginning Readers., 5 Bks, Set. 2004. (SPA., Illus.). (J). 85.00 (978-0-516-25105-9(8) , Watts, Franklin) Scholastic Library Publishing.

Rossberg, Ellin M. & Rossberg, Amy. Need to Know: A Guide for the Middle Grades. 2002. (YA). pap. 34.95 (978-1-57960-090-7(5)) History Compass, LLC.

Rotsky, Leslie A. At Work in the Neighborhood: A Content Area Reader-Social Stuides. 2005. (Emergent/Early (Prek-2) Social Studies Package Ser.). 16p. (YA). (ps-2). 25.20 (978-0-8215-7818-6(9)) Sadlier, William H. Inc.

Sager. People, Places & Change: An Introduction to World Studies - Western World. 3rd ed. 2003. (Illus.). (gr. 6-8). 58.00 (978-0-03-053607-6(3)) Holt, Rinehart & Winston.

Saunders-Smith, Gail. Community Helpers Social Studies. (gr. k-2). 19.95 (978-0-7368-9217-9(6)) Red Brick Learning.

—Families Social Studies. (gr. k-2). 19.95 (978-0-7368-9218-6(4)) Red Brick Learning.

—Transportation Social Studies. (gr. k-2). 19.95 (978-0-7368-9216-2(8)) Red Brick Learning.

Saunders-Smith, Gail, ed. A Visit To. (Pebble Plus Ser.). (Illus.). (J). (gr. k-1). lib. bdg. 199.30 (978-0-7368-2743-0(9)) Capstone Pr., Inc.

Schaub, Michelle. Where Are We? 2006. (Early Explorers Ser.). (J). 34.00 ***(978-1-4108-6108-5(2))*** Benchmark Education Co.

Schofield, Tracey Ann. 101 Social Studies Activities for Curious Kids. Mitchell, Judy, ed. Glikin, Alex, illus. 2000. 96p. (J). (gr. 3-6). pap., tchr. ed. 10.95 (978-1-57310-262-9(8)) Teaching & Learning Co.

Scholastic, Inc. Staff. Colonial Life. 2002. pap. 8.95 (978-0-439-39592-2(5)) Scholastic, Inc.

—Pioneer. 2002. (Super Social Studies Bulletin Board Set Ser.). lthr. 8.95 (978-0-439-39607-3(7) , Teaching Resources) Scholastic, Inc.

Scholastic Library Publishing Staff, ed. Rookie Choices. 2004. 342.00 (978-0-516-24704-5(2)) Scholastic Library Publishing.

School Principals, 6 vols. (gr. 2-5). 36.95 (978-0-7368-8477-8(7)) Red Brick Learning.

School Specialty Publishing. Make Your Own Emergent Readers: Social Studies. 2006. (Make Your Own Emergent Readers Ser.). 64p. (J). (gr. k-2). pap. 8.99 (978-0-7682-3381-0(X) , Schaffer, Frank) Schaffer, Frank Pubns.

School Zone Publishing Company Staff & Giglio, Judith. Summer Scholar Grade 1. deluxe ed. 2000. (Deluxe Wkbks.). (Illus.). 64p. (J). (gr. 1). pap., wbk. ed. 3.79 (978-0-88743-832-5(6) , 02232) School Zone Publishing Co.

School Zone Publishing Company Staff & Hall, M. C. Summer Scholar Grade 3. deluxe ed. 2000. (Deluxe Wkbks.). (Illus.). 64p. (J). (gr. 3). pap., wbk. ed. 3.79 (978-0-88743-834-9(2) , 02234) School Zone Publishing Co.

School Zone Publishing Company Staff & Kupecky, Jere M. Summer Scholar Grade 2. Carmona, Lisa, ed. Sandford, John, illus. deluxe ed. 2000. (Deluxe Wkbks.). 64p. (J). (gr. 2). pap., wbk. ed. 3.79 (978-0-88743-833-2(4) , 02233) School Zone Publishing Co.

Schwartz, Linda. Social Studies & Science Quiz Whiz 3-5, Vol. 432. VanBlaricum, Pam, ed. Armstrong, Beverly, illus. 2004. 128p. (J). (gr. 3-5). pap. 10.99 (978-0-88160-375-0(9) , LW-432) Creative Teaching Pr., Inc.

Scott Foresman Social Studies. 2003. stu. ed. (978-0-328-04348-4(6) , Scott Foresman) Addison-Wesley Educational Pubs., Inc.

Scott Foresman Social Studies: Additional Resources. 2003. (gr. k-2). (978-0-328-08331-2(3)); (gr. k-2). (978-0-328-04105-3(X)); (gr. k-2). tchr. ed. (978-0-328-04180-0(7)); (SPA.). (gr. k-5). (978-0-328-04089-6(4)); (gr. k-6). (978-0-328-04094-0(0)); (gr. k up). (978-0-328-03591-5(2)); (gr. k up). (978-0-328-05706-1(1)); (gr. k up). (978-0-328-05716-0(9)); (gr. k up). (978-0-328-03918-0(7)); (gr. k up). (978-0-328-03775-9(3)); (gr. k up). (978-0-328-06262-1(6)); (gr. k up). tchr. ed. (978-0-328-03608-0(0)); (gr. 1 up). (978-0-328-06263-8(4)); (gr. 1 up). (978-0-328-03776-6(1)); (gr. 1 up). (978-0-328-05717-7(7)); (gr. 1 up). (978-0-328-03919-7(5)); (gr. 1 up). (978-0-328-05707-8(X)); (gr. 1 up). (978-0-328-03592-2(0)); (gr. 1 up). (978-0-328-04095-7(9)); (SPA.). (gr. 1 up). tchr. ed. (978-0-328-03609-7(9)); (gr. 2 up). (978-0-328-03777-3(X)); (gr. 2 up). (978-0-328-06264-5(2)); (gr. 2 up). (978-0-328-03920-3(9)); (gr. 2 up). (978-0-328-03593-9(9)); (gr. 2 up). (978-0-328-04096-4(7)); (gr. 2 up). (978-0-328-05708-5(8)); (gr. 2 up). (978-0-328-05718-4(5)); (SPA.). (gr. 2 up). tchr. ed. (978-0-328-03610-3(2)); (gr. 3-6). (978-0-328-04106-0(8)); (gr. 3-6). tchr. ed. (978-0-328-04181-7(5)); (gr. 3 up). (978-0-328-04097-1(5)); (gr. 3 up). (978-0-328-03594-6(7)); (gr. 3 up). (978-0-328-03601-1(3)); (gr. 3 up). (978-0-328-03778-0(8)); (gr. 3 up). (978-0-328-05709-2(6)); (gr. 3 up). (978-0-328-06265-2(0)); (gr. 3 up). (978-0-328-03921-0(7)); (SPA.). (gr. 3 up). tchr. ed. (978-0-328-03611-0(0)); (gr. 4 up). (978-0-328-05710-8(X)); (gr. 4 up). (978-0-328-03602-8(1)); (gr. 4 up). (978-0-328-03595-3(5)); (gr. 4 up). (978-0-328-03922-7(5)); (gr. 4 up). (978-0-328-06266-9(9)); (gr. 4 up). (978-0-328-04098-8(3)); (gr. 4 up). (978-0-328-03779-7(6)); (SPA.). (gr. 4 up). tchr. ed. (978-0-328-03612-7(9)); (gr. 5 up). (978-0-328-06267-6(7)); (gr. 5 up). (978-0-328-04099-5(1)); (gr. 5 up). (978-0-328-03603-5(X)); (gr. 5 up). (978-0-328-05711-5(8)); (gr. 5 up). (978-0-328-03926-5(8)); (gr. 5 up). (978-0-328-03780-3(X)); (gr. 5 up). (978-0-328-03596-0(3)); (SPA.). (gr. 5 up). tchr. ed. (978-0-328-03613-4(7)); (gr. 6 up). (978-0-328-05712-2(6)); (gr. 6 up). (978-0-328-03781-0(8)); (gr. 6 up). (978-0-328-03927-2(6)); (gr. 6 up). (978-0-328-06268-3(5)); (gr. 6 up). (978-0-328-03597-7(1)); (gr. 6 up). (978-0-328-04100-8(9)); (gr. 6 up). (978-0-328-03604-2(8)); (gr. 6 up). tchr. ed. (978-0-328-03614-1(5)) Addison-Wesley Educational Pubs., Inc. (Scott Foresman).

Scott Foresman Social Studies: Practice/Assessment. 2003. (gr. k up). (978-0-328-03090-3(2)); (gr. k up). wbk. ed. (978-0-328-01937-3(2)); (gr. 1 up). (978-0-328-03091-0(0)); (gr. 1 up). (978-0-328-04107-7(6)); (gr. 1 up). wbk. ed. (978-0-328-01938-0(0)); (gr. 2 up). (978-0-328-03092-7(9)); (gr. 2 up). (978-0-328-04108-4(4)); (gr. 2 up). wbk. ed. (978-0-328-01939-7(9)); (gr. 3 up). (978-0-328-03093-4(7)); (gr. 3 up). (978-0-328-04109-1(2)); (gr. 3 up). wbk. ed. (978-0-328-01940-3(2)); (gr. 4 up). (978-0-328-04110-7(6)); (gr. 4 up). (978-0-328-03094-1(5)); (gr. 4 up). wbk. ed. (978-0-328-01941-0(0)); (gr. 5 up). (978-0-328-04111-4(4)); (gr. 5 up). (978-0-328-03095-8(3)); (gr. 5 up). (978-0-328-03100-9(3)); (gr. 5 up). wbk. ed. (978-0-328-01943-4(7)); (gr. 5 up). wbk. ed. (978-0-328-01942-7(9)); (gr. 6 up). (978-0-328-04112-1(2)); (gr. 6 up). (978-0-328-03096-5(1)); (gr. 6 up). wbk. ed. (978-0-328-01945-8(3)) Addison-Wesley Educational Pubs., Inc. (Scott Foresman).

Scott Foresman Social Studies: Pupil Edition. 2003. (gr. k up). (978-0-328-04344-6(3)); (gr. 1 up). (978-0-328-01759-1(0)); (gr. 1 up). (978-0-328-04345-3(1)); (gr. 2 up). (978-0-328-04346-0(X)); (gr. 2 up). (978-0-328-01760-7(4)); (gr. 3 up). (978-0-328-01761-4(2)); (gr. 4 up). (978-0-328-01762-1(0)); (gr. 5 up). (978-0-328-01763-8(9)); (gr. 6 up). (978-0-328-01766-9(3)) Addison-Wesley Educational Pubs., Inc. (Scott Foresman).

Scott Foresman Social Studies: Technology. 2003. (gr. k-6). cd-rom (978-0-328-04347-7(8)); (gr. k up). (978-0-328-05696-5(0)); (gr. k up). cd-rom (978-0-328-03875-6(X)); (SPA.). (gr. k up). cd-rom (978-0-328-05663-7(4)); (gr. 1 up). (978-0-328-05697-2(9)); (SPA.). (gr. 1 up). cd-rom (978-0-328-05664-4(2)); (gr. 1 up). cd-rom (978-0-328-05878-5(5)); (gr. 1 up). cd-rom (978-0-328-03876-3(8)); (gr. 2 up). (978-0-328-05698-9(7)); (gr. 2 up). cd-rom (978-0-328-03877-0(6)); (SPA.). (gr. 2 up). cd-rom (978-0-328-05665-1(0)); (gr. 2 up). cd-rom (978-0-328-05879-2(3)); (gr. 3 up). (978-0-328-05699-6(5)); (gr. 3 up). cd-rom (978-0-328-05880-8(7)); (gr. 3 up). cd-rom (978-0-328-03878-7(4)); (SPA.). (gr. 3 up). cd-rom (978-0-328-05666-8(9)); (gr. 4 up). (978-0-328-05700-9(2)); (gr. 4 up). cd-rom (978-0-328-06259-1(6)); (gr. 4 up). cd-rom (978-0-328-03879-4(2)); (SPA.). (gr. 4 up). cd-rom (978-0-328-05667-5(7)); (gr. 5 up). (978-0-328-05701-6(0)); (gr. 5 up). cd-rom (978-0-328-05882-2(3)); (gr. 5 up). cd-rom (978-0-328-03880-0(6)); (SPA.). (gr. 5 up). cd-rom (978-0-328-05668-2(5)); (gr. 6 up). (978-0-328-05702-3(9)); (gr. 6 up). cd-rom (978-0-328-03881-7(4)); (gr. 6 up). cd-rom (978-0-328-05669-9(3)) Addison-Wesley Educational Pubs., Inc. (Scott Foresman).

Scott, James. The Old Man & the Sea: Activity Pack. 2002. 135p. (YA). (gr. 7-12). pap., act. bk. ed. 34.95 (978-1-58049-610-0(5) , PA0115) Prestwick Hse., Inc.

Secession, 6 vols. (gr. 2-5). 39.95 (978-0-7368-4600-4(X)) Red Brick Learning.

Secretos del alfabeto Perdido: Aventuras (Adventure Books) 2000. (Aventuras A Traves Del Tiempo Ser.). (ENG & SPA.). (gr. 6 up). (978-0-02-148749-3(9)) Macmillan/McGraw-Hill Schl. Div.

Senales y rotulos Social Studies, 6 vols.Tr. of Signs Social Studies. (SPA.). (gr. k-2). 28.95 (978-0-7368-3114-7(2) , Yellow Umbrella Bks.) Capstone Pr., Inc.

Serving Your Country, 16 bks. Incl. Air Assault Teams. Stapleton, Gerard. 1996. lib. bdg. 21.26 (978-1-56065-285-4(3)); Air Rescue Teams. Green, Michael. 2000. lib. bdg. 21.26 (978-0-7368-0470-7(6)); Blue Angels : The U. S. Navy Flight Demonstration Squadron. Bledsoe, Karen & Bledsoe, Glen. 2001. lib. bdg. 21.26 (978-0-7368-0773-9(X)); Canadian Forces Snowbirds : 431 Air Demonstration Squadron. Oberle, Lora Polack. 2001. lib. bdg. 21.26 (978-0-7368-0774-6(8)); Golden Knights : The U. S. Army Parachute Team. Hopkins, Ellen H. 2001. lib. bdg. 21.26 (978-0-7368-0775-3(6)); Green Berets. Streissguth, Thomas. 1996. lib. bdg. 21.26 (978-1-56065-283-0(7)); Military Police. Green, Michael. 2000. lib. bdg. 21.26 (978-0-7368-0473-8(0)); Thunderbirds : The U. S. Air Force Aerial Demonstration Squadron. Hopkins, Ellen H. 2001. lib. bdg. 21.26 (978-0-7368-0776-0(4)); U. S. Army Rangers. Koons, James. 1996. lib. bdg. 21.26 (978-1-56065-284-7(5)); U. S. Army Special Operations. Green, Michael. 2000. lib. bdg. 21.26 (978-0-7368-0471-4(4)); U. S. Navy SEALs. Streissguth, Thomas. 1996. lib. bdg. 21.26 (978-1-56065-282-3(9)); United States Air Force. Green, Michael. 1998. lib. bdg. 21.26 (978-1-56065-687-6(5)); United States Army. Green, Michael. 1998. lib. bdg. 21.26 (978-1-56065-688-3(3)); United States Coast Guard. Green, Michael. 2000. lib. bdg. 21.26 (978-0-7368-0472-1(2)); United States Marine Corps. Green, Michael. 1998. lib. bdg. 21.26 (978-1-56065-689-0(1)); United States Navy. Green, Michael. 1998. lib. bdg. 21.26 (978-1-56065-690-6(5)); 48p. (J). (gr. 3-4). (Illus.). 2001. Set lib. bdg. 340.16 (978-0-7368-0872-9(8) , Capstone High-Interest Bks.) Capstone Pr., Inc.

Shabaka, Dahia. Africa & You: Little Book #3. 1999. (Living & Working Together Ser.). (J). (gr. k). 4.95 (978-1-58120-828-3(6)); 26.95 (978-1-58830-303-5(9)) Metropolitan Teaching & Learning Co.

—Africa & You: Social Studies Big Book #3. 1999. (Living & Working Together Ser.). (J). (gr. k). 41.95 (978-1-58120-802-3(2)) Metropolitan Teaching & Learning Co.

—All about You: Little Book #1. 2000. (Living & Working Together Ser.). (J). (gr. k). 4.95 (978-1-58120-826-9(X)); 26.95 (978-1-58830-301-1(2)) Metropolitan Teaching & Learning Co.

—All about You: Social Studies Big Book #1. 2000. (Living & Working Together Ser.). (J). (gr. k). 41.95 (978-1-58120-800-9(6)) Metropolitan Teaching & Learning Co.

—Families. (Living & Working Together Ser.). (J). (gr. 1). Bk. 1. 1999. stu. ed. 16.95 (978-1-58120-820-7(0)); Bk. 2. 2000. stu. ed. 16.95 (978-1-58120-821-4(9)) Metropolitan Teaching & Learning Co.

—Families Blackline Masters. (Living & Working Together Ser.). (gr. 1). Bk. 1. 1999. 14.95 (978-1-58120-824-5(3)); Bk. 2. 2000. 14.95 (978-1-58120-825-2(1)) Metropolitan Teaching & Learning Co.

—Neighborhoods. (Living & Working Together Ser.). (J). (gr. 2). Bk. 1. 1999. stu. ed. 16.95 incl. 5.25 hd (978-1-58120-830-6(8)); Bk. 2. 2000. stu. ed. 16.95 (978-1-58120-831-3(6)) Metropolitan Teaching & Learning Co.

—Neighborhoods Blackline Masters. (Living & Working Together Ser.). (gr. 2). Bk. 1. 1999. 14.95 (978-1-58120-834-4(0)); Bk. 2. 2000. 14.95 (978-1-58120-835-1(9)) Metropolitan Teaching & Learning Co.

—People Around You: Little Book #2. 1999. (Living & Working Together Ser.). (J). (gr. k). 4.95 (978-1-58120-827-6(8)); 26.95 (978-1-58830-302-8(0)) Metropolitan Teaching & Learning Co.

—People Around You: Social Studies Big Book #2. 1999. (Living & Working Together Ser.). (J). (gr. k). 41.95 (978-1-58120-801-6(4)) Metropolitan Teaching & Learning Co.

—Social Studies Blms: Big Books 1-3. 1999. (Living & Working Together Ser.). (gr. k). 14.95 (978-1-58120-809-2(X)) Metropolitan Teaching & Learning Co.

—Social Studies Blms: Big Books 4-6. 2000. (Living & Working Together Ser.). (gr. k). 14.95 (978-1-58120-810-8(3)) Metropolitan Teaching & Learning Co.

—The Tools We Use: Little Book #6. 2000. (Living & Working Together Ser.). (J). (gr. k). 4.95 (978-1-58120-978-5(9)); 26.95 (978-1-58830-306-6(3)) Metropolitan Teaching & Learning Co.

—The Tools We Use: Social Studies Big Book #6. 2000. (Living & Working Together Ser.). (J). (gr. k). 41.95 (978-1-58120-805-4(7)) Metropolitan Teaching & Learning Co.

—We Have Needs & Wants: Little Book #4. 2000. (Living & Working Together Ser.). (J). (gr. k). 26.95 (978-1-58830-304-2(7)) Metropolitan Teaching & Learning Co.

—We Have Needs & Wants Bk. 4: Little Book. 2000. (Living & Working Together Ser.). (J). (gr. k). 4.95 (978-1-58120-977-8(0)) Metropolitan Teaching & Learning Co.

—We Have Needs & Wants Bk. 4: Social Studies. 2000. (Living & Working Together Ser.). (J). (gr. k). 41.95 (978-1-58120-803-0(0)) Metropolitan Teaching & Learning Co.

—We Learn about the World: Little Book #5. 2000. (Living & Working Together Ser.). (J). (gr. k). 4.95 (978-1-58120-829-0(4)); 26.95 (978-1-58830-305-9(5)) Metropolitan Teaching & Learning Co.

—We Learn about the World: Social Studies Big Book #5. 2000. (Living & Working Together Ser.). (J). (gr. k). 41.95 (978-1-58120-804-7(9)) Metropolitan Teaching & Learning Co.

Shades of Gray. (J). pap., stu. ed. (978-0-13-620188-5(1)) Prentice Hall (Schl. Div.).

Shafer, Jean. Learning from Charts & Graphs: Lessons in History, Civics, Geography, & Economics. 2003. (Illus.). 48p. (J). 15.95 (978-0-938682-76-9(8)) River Road Pubns., Inc.

Shields, Charles J. Standardized Test Practice for 6th Grade. 1999. 96p. (J). (gr. 6). pap., tchr. ed. 11.99 (978-1-57690-681-1(7) , TCA2681) Teacher Created Materials, Inc.

Shireman, Myrl. Social Studies Skills Made Easy. 1999. (Illus.). 96p. (YA). (gr. 5-8). pap. 10.95 (978-1-58037-097-4(7)) Twain, Mark Media, Inc. Pubs.

S

Show What You Know on the OAT for Grade 8, Social Studies, Student Self Study Workbook. 2006. (YA). per. 16.95 (978-1-59230-176-8(2)) Englefield & Assocs., Inc.

Shulman, Mark. Flip-O-Matic: Instant History for Ages 9-12. 2006. 256p. pap. 10.00 (978-1-4195-4178-0(1)) Kaplan Publishing.

Shuter, Jane. History Opens Windows, 4 bks. (J). Set 2. 2002. lib. bdg. 91.16 (978-1-58810-459-5(1)); Set 3. 2003. (gr. 2-4). lib. bdg. 68.37 (978-1-4034-0257-8(4)) Heinemann Library.

Signs Social Studies, 6 vols. (gr. k-2). 28.95 (978-0-7368-1755-4(7) , Yellow Umbrella Bks.) Capstone Pr., Inc.

Sims, Kathy C., illus. & text. Louisiana Potpourri from A to Z. Sims, Kathy C., text. 2004. Tr. of Pot-pourri louisianais d' A a Z. (FRE.). 64p. (YA). lib. bdg. 24.95 (978-0-9753435-0-0(5)) Louisiana Ladybug Pr.

SIRS Enduring Issues 2006, 8 vols., Set. 2005. (Illus.). (YA). ring bd. 849.00 (978-0-89777-554-0(6)) SIRS Publishing, Inc.

Snakes are Not Slimy, 6 vols. (Book2WebTM Ser.). (gr. 4-8). 36.50 (978-0-322-02976-7(7)) Wright Group, The.

Social Studies Add-on Set, Early Level. (gr. k-2). 57.95 (978-0-7368-3061-4(8) , Yellow Umbrella Bks.) Capstone Pr., Inc.

Social Studies Add-on Set, Emergent Level. (gr. k-2). 57.95 (978-0-7368-1789-9(1) , Yellow Umbrella Bks.) Capstone Pr., Inc.

Social Studies at Work, High School, 6 vols., Vol. 4. 2001. (At Work High School Ser.: Vol. 4). (YA). cd-rom 69.95 (978-1-929879-20-5(2)) Career Kids.

Social Studies Big Books, English. (gr. k-2). 112.95 (978-0-7368-3248-9(3)) Red Brick Learning.

Social Studies Big Books, Spanish. (SPA.). (gr. k-2). 37.95 (978-0-7368-3249-6(1)) Red Brick Learning.

Social Studies Program, Early Level. (gr. k-2). 348.95 (978-0-7368-3060-7(X) , Yellow Umbrella Bks.) Capstone Pr., Inc.

Social Studies Program, Emergent Level. (gr. k-2). 348.95 (978-0-7368-1790-5(5) , Yellow Umbrella Bks.) Capstone Pr., Inc.

Social Studies Projects for the Gifted Student. 48p. (gr. 5-9). 8.99 (978-0-7682-0012-6(1) , GA1672) School Specialty Publishing.

The Social Studies Reading Room Collection. (J). (gr. k-5). 79.50 (978-1-4042-3381-2(4)) Rosen Publishing Group, Inc., The.

Social Studies Set, 8 vols. (Content Collections). (gr. k-2). 265.66 (978-0-7362-2270-9(7)) Hampton-Brown Bks.

Social Studies University-Tapestry Collage, Story Towers, Country Collage, Listen Transfer & Problem Solve. 2002. (J). spiral bd. 29.95 (978-1-56820-042-2(0)) Story Time Stories That Rhyme.

Los sombreros de la Tia Flossie , Unidad 1: Superlibros (Big Books) 2000. (Aventuras A Traves Del Tiempo Ser.). (ENG & SPA.). (gr. 2 up). (978-0-02-147866-8(X)) Macmillan/McGraw-Hill Schl. Div.

Spanish Social Studies Add-on Set, Early Level. (SPA.). (gr. k-2). 57.95 (978-0-7368-3063-8(4) , Yellow Umbrella Bks.) Capstone Pr., Inc.

Spanish Social Studies Add-on Set, Emergent Level. (SPA.). (gr. k-2). 57.95 (978-0-7368-3152-9(5) , Yellow Umbrella Bks.) Capstone Pr., Inc.

Spanish Social Studies Program, Early Level. (SPA.). (gr. k-2). 348.95 (978-0-7368-3062-1(6) , Yellow Umbrella Bks.) Capstone Pr., Inc.

Spanish Social Studies Program, Emergent Level. (SPA.). (gr. k-2). 348.95 (978-0-7368-3151-2(7) , Yellow Umbrella Bks.) Capstone Pr., Inc.

Spies! Real People, Real Stories, 6 vols. (gr. 4 up). 49.95 (978-0-7368-2840-6(0) , High Five) Red Brick Learning.

Spilsbury, Louise. Moving People. 2004. (Illus.). 48p. (J). 28.56 (978-1-4109-1115-5(2)) Raintree.

Spyglass Books - Around the World, 7 bks. Incl. Be a Good Friend! Waters, Jennifer. lib. bdg. 18.60 (978-0-7565-0376-5(0)); Be a Good Sport! Waters, Jennifer. lib. bdg. 18.60 (978-0-7565-0375-8(2)); Cool Customs. Scott, Janine. lib. bdg. 18.60 (978-0-7565-0364-2(7)); Let's Eat : Foods of Our World. Scott, Janine. lib. bdg. 18.60 (978-0-7565-0365-9(5)); Let's Get Dressed : What People Wear. Scott, Janine. lib. bdg. 18.60 (978-0-7565-0366-6(3)); Right at Home. Waters, Jennifer. lib. bdg. 18.60 (978-0-7565-0380-2(9)); Stick to It! The Story of Wilma Rudolph. Conrad, David. lib. bdg. 18.60 (978-0-7565-0384-0(1)); 24p. (J). (gr. 1 up). 2002. (Illus.). 2003. Set lib. bdg. 130.20 (978-0-7565-0780-0(4)) Compass Point Bks.

Spyglass Books - People & Cultures, 8 bks. Incl. All Kinds of People : What Makes Us Different. Waters, Jennifer. lib. bdg. 18.60 (978-0-7565-0377-2(9)); Law & Order. Conrad, David. lib. bdg. 18.60 (978-0-7565-0383-3(3)); Let's Talk : How We Communicate. Waters, Jennifer. lib. bdg. 18.60 (978-0-7565-0381-9(7)); Life Long Ago. Scott, Janine. lib. bdg. 18.60 (978-0-7565-0361-1(2)); Make It! Ship It! Scott, Janine. lib. bdg. 18.60 (978-0-7565-0363-5(9)); Money. Waters, Jennifer. lib. bdg. 18.60 (978-0-7565-0374-1(4)); What Is a Family? Hammersmith, Craig & Stewart, Joan. lib. bdg. 18.60 (978-0-7565-0367-3(1)); Work We Do. Conrad, David. lib. bdg. 18.60 (978-0-7565-0382-6(5)); 24p. (J). (gr. 1 up). 2002. (Illus.). 2003. Set lib. bdg. 148.80 (978-0-7565-0781-7(2)) Compass Point Bks.

Spyglass Books-People & Cultures Complete Set. (Spyglass Books-People & Cultures Ser.). (gr. 1-2). 259.09 (978-0-7565-0802-9(9)) Compass Point Bks.

St Patrick's Day, 6 vols. (gr. k-2). 28.95 (978-0-7368-9405-0(5)) Red Brick Learning.

StateGrams. 2001. (J). spiral bd. 71.99 (978-1-931694-15-5(X)); 51 four-page rep. ring bd. 71.99 (978-1-931694-14-8(1)) ProQuest CSA.

StateGrams 2003 Kids Edition. 2002. (J). per. 59.99 incl. cd-rom (978-1-931694-40-7(0)); ring bd. 59.99 incl. cd-rom (978-1-931694-41-4(9)) ProQuest CSA.

The States & Their Symbols, 52 bks. Incl. Alabama Facts & Symbols. McAuliffe, Emily. 2000. lib. bdg. 18.60 (978-0-7368-0374-8(2)); Alaska Facts & Symbols. Dubois, Muriel L. 2000. lib. bdg. 13.95 (978-0-7368-0522-3(2)); Arizona Facts & Symbols. McAuliffe, Emily. 1998. lib. bdg. 18.60 (978-0-7368-0080-8(8)); Arkansas Facts & Symbols. Kule, Elaine A. 2000. lib. bdg. 18.60 (978-0-7368-0634-3(2)); California Facts & Symbols. McAuliffe, Emily. 1998. lib. bdg. 18.60 (978-1-56065-763-7(4)); Colorado Facts & Symbols. McAuliffe, Emily. 1998. lib. bdg. 18.60 (978-1-56065-764-4(2)); Connecticut Facts & Symbols. McAuliffe, Emily. 1999. lib. bdg. 18.60 (978-0-7368-0214-7(2)); Delaware Facts & Symbols. Kule, Elaine A. 2000. lib. bdg. 18.60 (978-0-7368-0635-0(0)); Florida Facts & Symbols. McAuliffe, Emily. 1998. lib. bdg. 18.60 (978-1-56065-765-1(0)); Georgia Facts & Symbols. McAuliffe, Emily. 1999. lib. bdg. 18.60 (978-0-7368-0215-4(0)); Hawaii Facts & Symbols. McAuliffe, Emily. 2000. lib. bdg. 13.95 (978-0-7368-0375-5(0)); Idaho Facts & Symbols. Kule, Elaine A. 2000. lib. bdg. 18.60 (978-0-7368-0636-7(9)); Illinois Facts & Symbols. McAuliffe, Emily. 1998. lib. bdg. 18.60 (978-1-56065-766-8(9)); Indiana Facts & Symbols. McAuliffe, Bill. 1999. lib. bdg. 18.60 (978-0-7368-0218-5(5)); Iowa Facts & Symbols. Kule, Elaine A. 2000. lib. bdg. 18.60 (978-0-7368-0637-4(7)); Kansas Facts & Symbols. Deady, Kathleen W. 2000. lib. bdg. 18.60 (978-0-7368-0638-1(5)); Kentucky Facts & Symbols. Deady, Kathleen W. 2000. lib. bdg. 18.60 (978-0-7368-0639-8(3)); Louisiana Facts & Symbols. McAuliffe, Emily. 1998. lib. bdg. 18.60 (978-0-7368-0081-5(6)); Maine Facts & Symbols. McAuliffe, Emily. 2000. lib. bdg. 18.60 (978-0-7368-0376-2(9)); Maryland Facts & Symbols. Dubois, Muriel L. 2000. lib. bdg. 18.60 (978-0-7368-0523-0(0)); Massachusetts Facts & Symbols. McAuliffe, Emily. 1998. lib. bdg. 18.60 (978-0-7368-0082-2(4)); Michigan Facts & Symbols. McAuliffe, Emily. 1998. lib. bdg. 18.60 (978-0-7368-0083-9(2)); Minnesota Facts & Symbols. McAuliffe, Bill. 1999. lib. bdg. 18.60 (978-0-7368-0219-2(3)); Mississippi Facts & Symbols. Gibson, Karen Bush. 2000. lib. bdg. 18.60 (978-0-7368-0640-4(7)); Missouri Facts & Symbols. McAuliffe, Emily. 2000. lib. bdg. 18.60 (978-0-7368-0377-9(7)); Montana Facts & Symbols. Sateren, Shelley Swanson. 2000. lib. bdg. 18.60 (978-0-7368-0378-6(5)); Nebraska Facts & Symbols. McAuliffe, Emily. 1998. lib. bdg. 18.60 (978-0-7368-0084-6(0)); Nevada Facts & Symbols. Gibson, Karen Bush. 2000. lib. bdg. 18.60 (978-0-7368-0641-1(5)); New Hampshire Facts & Symbols. Dubois, Muriel L. 2000. lib. bdg. 13.95 (978-0-7368-0524-7(9)); New Jersey Facts & Symbols. Sateren, Shelley Swanson. 2000. lib. bdg. 18.60 (978-0-7368-0379-3(3)); New Mexico Facts & Symbols. Sateren, Shelley Swanson. 2000. lib. bdg. 18.60 (978-0-7368-0380-9(7)); New York Facts & Symbols. McAuliffe, Emily. 1998. lib. bdg. 18.60 (978-1-56065-767-5(7)); North Carolina Facts & Symbols. Sateren, Shelley Swanson. 2000. lib. bdg. 18.60 (978-0-7368-0381-6(5)); North Dakota Facts & Symbols. Gibson, Karen Bush. 2000. lib. bdg. 18.60 (978-0-7368-0642-8(3)); Ohio Facts & Symbols. McAuliffe, Emily. 1998. lib. bdg. 18.60 (978-0-7368-0085-3(9)); Oklahoma Facts & Symbols. Gibson, Karen Bush. 2000. lib. bdg. 18.60 (978-0-7368-0643-5(1)); Oregon Facts & Symbols. McAuliffe, Emily. 1999. lib. bdg. 18.60 (978-0-7368-0216-1(9)); Pennsylvania Facts & Symbols. McAuliffe, Emily. 1998. lib. bdg. 18.60 (978-0-7368-0086-0(7)); Puerto Rico Facts & Symbols. Feeney, Kathy. 2000. lib. bdg. 18.60 (978-0-7368-0644-2(X)); Rhode Island Facts & Symbols. Feeney, Kathy. 2000. lib. bdg. 18.60 (978-0-7368-0645-9(8)); South Carolina Facts & Symbols. McAuliffe, Bill. 1999. lib. bdg. 18.60 (978-0-7368-0220-8(7)); South Dakota Facts & Symbols. Feeney, Kathy. 2000. lib. bdg. 18.60 (978-0-7368-0646-6(6)); Tennessee Facts & Symbols. Feeney, Kathy. 2000. lib. bdg. 13.95 (978-0-7368-0525-4(7)); Texas Facts & Symbols. McAuliffe, Emily. 1998. lib. bdg. 18.60 (978-1-56065-768-2(5)); Utah Facts & Symbols. Feeney, Kathy. 2000. lib. bdg. 13.95 (978-0-7368-0526-1(5)); Vermont Facts & Symbols. Feeney, Kathy. 2000. lib. bdg. 18.60 (978-0-7368-0647-3(4)); Virginia Facts & Symbols. McAuliffe, Bill. 1999. lib. bdg. 18.60 (978-0-7368-0221-5(5)); Washington, D. C. Facts & Symbols. Feeney, Kathy. 2000. lib. bdg. 18.60 (978-0-7368-0527-8(3)); Washington Facts & Symbols. McAuliffe, Emily. 1998. lib. bdg. 18.60 (978-0-7368-0087-7(5)); West Virginia Facts & Symbols. Feeney, Kathy. 2000. lib. bdg. 18.60 (978-0-7368-0528-5(1)); Wisconsin Facts & Symbols. McAuliffe, Emily. 1999. lib. bdg. 18.60 (978-0-7368-0217-8(7)); Wyoming Facts & Symbols. Dubois, Muriel L. 2000. lib. bdg. 18.60 (978-0-7368-0529-2(X)); 24p. (J). (gr. 2-3). (Illus.). Set lib. bdg. 967.20 (978-0-7368-0687-9(3) , Bridgestone Bks.) Capstone Pr., Inc.

Steck-Vaughn Staff. Access Social Studies. 2004. (Illus.). pap. 14.96 (978-0-7398-8931-2(1)) Steck-Vaughn.

—Arctic People. 2003. pap. 4.10 (978-0-7398-7650-3(3)) Steck-Vaughn.

—A Bird's-Eye View. 2003. pap. 4.10 (978-0-7398-7649-7(X)) Steck-Vaughn.

—Events in My World: Windows & Macintosh Version. 1998. pap. 83.10 incl. cd-rom (978-0-8172-8554-8(7)) Steck-Vaughn.

—Events in My World: Windows/Macintosh Labs. 1998. pap. 249.40 incl. cd-rom (978-0-8172-8555-5(5)) Steck-Vaughn.

—GED Exercises: Social Studies. 2000. pap. 11.67 (978-0-7398-3605-7(6)) Steck-Vaughn.

—Higher Scores on Social Studies Standard Tests. 2000. (Illus.). (J). (gr. 2). pap. (978-0-7398-3441-1(X)); (gr. 3). pap. (978-0-7398-3442-8(8)); (gr. 4). pap. (978-0-7398-3443-5(6)); (gr. 5). pap. (978-0-7398-3444-2(4)); (gr. 6). pap. (978-0-7398-3445-9(2)) Steck-Vaughn.

—History of Our Country: Level E. 2000. tchr. ed., ring bd. 132.20 (978-0-7398-2963-9(7)) Steck-Vaughn.

—Homes Everywhere. 2002. (Illus.). pap. (978-0-7398-5981-0(1)) Steck-Vaughn.

—Lady Liberty. 2003. pap. 4.10 (978-0-7398-7646-6(5)) Steck-Vaughn.

—Life on the Tallest Tree. 2003. pap. 4.10 (978-0-7398-7636-7(8)) Steck-Vaughn.

—Many Places. 2000. (Illus.). (J). bds. (978-0-7398-4453-3(9)) Steck-Vaughn.

—Many Places, Friendly Faces: 10 Lab Classroom. 1998. pap. 748.30 (978-0-8172-8148-9(7)) Steck-Vaughn.

—Many Places, Friendly Faces: 3 Lab Classroom. 1998. pap. 415.70 (978-0-8172-8146-5(0)) Steck-Vaughn.

—Many Places, Friendly Faces: 5 Lab Classroom. 1998. pap. 582.00 (978-0-8172-8147-2(9)) Steck-Vaughn.

—Map Room of American History. 1998. pap. 665.20 (978-0-8172-8567-8(9)) Steck-Vaughn.

—Map Room of American History: Windows & Macintosh Version. 1998. pap. 83.10 incl. cd-rom (978-0-8172-8562-3(8)) Steck-Vaughn.

—Map Room of American History: Windows/Macintosh Labs. 1998. pap. 249.40 incl. cd-rom (978-0-8172-8563-0(6)) Steck-Vaughn.

—Map Room of American History Pack: Windows/Macintosh Labs, 3. 1998. pap. 415.70 incl. cd-rom (978-0-8172-8564-7(4)); pap. 582.00 incl. cd-rom (978-0-8172-8565-4(2)); pap. 748.30 incl. cd-rom (978-0-8172-8566-1(0)) Steck-Vaughn.

—Matter All Around Us. 2003. pap. 4.10 (978-0-7398-7639-8(2)) Steck-Vaughn.

—Mosaica Powerup Complete Package, Levels 1-4. 2004. pap. 241.00 (978-1-4190-0443-8(3)) Steck-Vaughn.

—Mosaica Powerup Pack. 2004. Level 1. pap. 47.00 (978-1-4190-0439-1(5)); Level 2. pap. 60.00 (978-1-4190-0440-7(9)); Level 3. pap. 60.00 (978-1-4190-0441-4(7)); Level 4. pap. 74.00 (978-1-4190-0442-1(5)) Steck-Vaughn.

—Social Studies: Economics, Civics, Government. 2002. (Illus.). pap. (978-0-7398-5427-3(5)) Steck-Vaughn.

—Social Studies: Key Historical Document. 2002. (Illus.). (J). pap. (978-0-7398-6396-1(7)) Steck-Vaughn.

—Social Studies Level C: Living in Communities. 2005. pap. 15.50 (978-0-7398-9220-6(7)); pap. 112.30 (978-0-7398-9226-8(6)); pap., tchr. ed. 15.10 (978-0-7398-9232-9(0)) Steck-Vaughn.

—Social Studies Level D: Regions of the Country. 2005. pap. 15.50 (978-0-7398-9221-3(5)); pap. 137.30 (978-0-7398-9227-5(4)) Steck-Vaughn.

—Social Studies Level A: Homes & Families. 2005. pap. 13.50 (978-0-7398-9218-3(5)); pap. 112.30 (978-0-7398-9224-4(X)); pap., tchr. ed. 15.10 (978-0-7398-9230-5(4)) Steck-Vaughn.

—Social Studies Level B: People & Places. 2005. pap. 112.30 (978-0-7398-9225-1(8)); pap., tchr. ed. 15.10 (978-0-7398-9231-2(2)) Steck-Vaughn.

—Social Studies Level B: People & Places Nearby. 2005. pap. 13.50 (978-0-7398-9219-0(3)) Steck-Vaughn.

—Social Studies Level E: History of the Country. 2005. pap. 137.30 (978-0-7398-9228-2(2)); pap., tchr. ed. 15.10 (978-0-7398-9234-3(7)) Steck-Vaughn.

—Social Studies Level F: World Cultures. 2005. pap. 17.30 (978-0-7398-9223-7(1)); pap. 96.70 (978-0-7398-9229-9(0)); pap., tchr. ed. 15.10 (978-0-7398-9235-0(5)) Steck-Vaughn.

—Social Studies Level J-M: Communities Around the World. 2003. (Illus.). pap. (978-0-7398-7688-6(0)) Steck-Vaughn.

—Thank You! Thanksgiving Day, 6 Pack. 2002. pap. (978-0-7398-6241-4(3)) Steck-Vaughn.

—What Did People Use Back Then. 2003. pap. 4.10 (978-0-7398-7643-5(0)) Steck-Vaughn.

—What's the Question? 2003. pap. 4.10 (978-0-7398-7663-3(5)) Steck-Vaughn.

Stradling, Jan. People & Places: Level I, 6 vols., Vol. 2. (First Explorers Ser.). 24p. (gr. 1-2). 29.95 (978-0-7699-1462-6(4)) Shortland Pubns. (U. S. A.) Inc.

—Under Attack: Level I, 6 vols. (First Explorers Ser.). 24p. (gr. 1-2). 29.95 (978-0-7699-1453-4(5)) Shortland Pubns. (U. S. A.) Inc.

—You are Special: Level I, 6 vols. (First Explorers Ser.). 24p. (gr. 1-2). 29.95 (978-0-7699-1454-1(3)) Shortland Pubns. (U. S. A.) Inc.

Sucedio en America, Unidad 5: Libros de la Biblioteca (Classroom Library) 2000. (Aventuras A Traves Del Tiempo Ser.). (ENG & SPA.). (gr. 1 up). (978-0-02-147843-9(0)) Macmillan/McGraw-Hill Schl. Div.

Sullivan, Erin Ash. Communities Helping Communities. 2006. (Navigators Ser.). (J). pap. 38.00 (***978-1-4108-6246-4(1)***) Benchmark Education Co.

Superlibro de la vida en las Rocas: Unit 5: la vida en las rocas (Rocky Homes) 2000. (McGraw-Hill Ciencias Ser.). (ENG & SPA.). (gr. 2 up). (978-0-02-277175-1(1)) Macmillan/McGraw-Hill Schl. Div.

Superlibro Recursos: Superlibros. 2003. (MacMillan/McGraw-Hill. Estudios Sociales Ser.). (ENG & SPA.). (gr. 1 up). (978-0-02-149977-9(2)) Macmillan/McGraw-Hill Schl. Div.

Superlibro Recursos: Vivimos Juntos: Superlibros. 2003. (MacMillan/McGraw-Hill. Estudios Sociales Ser.). (ENG & SPA.). (gr. 2 up). (978-0-02-149978-6(0)) Macmillan/McGraw-Hill Schl. Div.

Superlibros de Literatura: Libros de la Biblioteca (Classroom Library) 2000. (Aventuras A Traves Del Tiempo Ser.). (ENG & SPA.). (gr. 1 up). (978-0-02-148513-0(5)) Macmillan/McGraw-Hill Schl. Div.

Susan B Anthony, 6 vols. (gr. k-2). 28.95 (978-0-7368-9449-4(7)); (gr. 2-5). 36.95 (978-0-7368-8433-4(5)) Red Brick Learning.

Swain, Gwenyth. Carrying. 1999. (Small World Ser.). (Illus.). 24p. (J). (ps-2). lib. bdg. 19.93 (978-1-57505-259-5(8) , Carolrhoda Bks.) Lerner Publishing Group.

—Smiling. 1999. (Small World Ser.). (Illus.). 24p. (J). (ps-2). lib. bdg. 19.93 (978-1-57505-256-4(3) , Carolrhoda Bks.) Lerner Publishing Group.

TAKS Social Studies Preparation for Grade 5. 2004. stu. ed., spiral bd. (978-1-933049-08-3(1)) Region IV Education Service Ctr.

TAKS Social Studies Preparation Grade 10. 2004. (Region IV ESC Resources for Social Studies Ser.). stu. ed., per., wbk. ed. (978-1-932524-66-6(5)) Region IV Education Service Ctr.

TAKS Social Studies Preparation Grade 11 Exit - Student Workbook. 2003. (Region IV ESC Resources for Social Studies Ser.). stu. ed., per. (978-1-932524-67-3(3)) Region IV Education Service Ctr.

TAKS Social Studies Preparation Grade 8. 2004. (Region IV ESC Resources for Social Studies Ser.). stu. ed., per., wbk. ed. (978-1-932524-65-9(7)) Region IV Education Service Ctr.

Talmadge Salle, Katherine. Daily Life Around the World. 2006. (Navigators Ser.). (J). pap. 38.00 (***978-1-4108-6245-7(3)***) Benchmark Education Co.

Tarjetas de Vocabulario: Aqui Estoy! 2000. (Aventuras A Traves Del Tiempo Ser.). (ENG & SPA.). (gr. k up). (978-0-02-148888-9(6)) Macmillan/McGraw-Hill Schl. Div.

Tarjetas de Vocabulario: Comunidades. 2000. (Aventuras A Traves Del Tiempo Ser.). (ENG & SPA.). (gr. 3 up). (978-0-02-148538-3(0)) Macmillan/McGraw-Hill Schl. Div.

Tarjetas de Vocabulario: Gente. 2000. (Aventuras A Traves Del Tiempo Ser.). (ENG & SPA.). (gr. 2 up). (978-0-02-148537-6(2)) Macmillan/McGraw-Hill Schl. Div.

Tarjetas de Vocabulario: Mi Mundo. 2000. (Aventuras A Traves Del Tiempo Ser.). (ENG & SPA.). (gr. 1 up). (978-0-02-148536-9(4)) Macmillan/McGraw-Hill Schl. Div.

Tarjetas de Vocabulario: Student & Teacher Support Resources. (McGraw-Hill Ciencias Ser.). (ENG & SPA.). 2000. (gr. k up). (978-0-02-279142-1(6)); 1999. (gr. k up). (978-0-02-110737-7(8)); 1999. (gr. 1 up). (978-0-02-110671-4(1)); 1999. (gr. 2 up). (978-0-02-110672-1(X)); 1999. (gr. 3 up). (978-0-02-110673-8(8)); 1999. (gr. 5 up). (978-0-02-110675-2(4)); 1999. (gr. 6 up). (978-0-02-110676-9(2)) Macmillan/McGraw-Hill Schl. Div.

Teacher's Resource Package: Aqui Estoy! 2000. (Aventuras A Traves Del Tiempo Ser.). (ENG & SPA.). (gr. k up). (978-0-02-148528-4(3)) Macmillan/McGraw-Hill Schl. Div.

Teacher's Resource Package: Gente. 2000. (Aventuras A Traves Del Tiempo Ser.). (ENG & SPA.). (gr. 2 up). (978-0-02-148531-4(3)) Macmillan/McGraw-Hill Schl. Div.

Teacher's Resource Package: Mi Mundo. 2000. (Aventuras A Traves Del Tiempo Ser.). (ENG & SPA.). (gr. 1 up). (978-0-02-148529-1(1)) Macmillan/McGraw-Hill Schl. Div.

La tercera Compana: Libros Aventuras (Adventure Books) 2000. (MacMillan/McGraw-Hill. Estudios Sociales Ser.). (ENG & SPA.). (gr. 2 up). (978-0-02-148682-3(4)) Macmillan/McGraw-Hill Schl. Div.

Test Generator: Technology. 2003. (MacMillan/McGraw-Hill. Estudios Sociales Ser.). (ENG & SPA.). (gr. 5 up). incl. audio compact disk (978-0-02-150074-1(6)) Macmillan/McGraw-Hill Schl. Div.

Thanksgiving, 6 vols. (gr. k-2). 28.95 (978-0-7368-9439-5(X)) Red Brick Learning.

This Farm Social Studies, 6 vols. (gr. k-2). 28.95 (978-0-7368-1753-0(0) , Yellow Umbrella Bks.) Capstone Pr., Inc.

La Tierra, nuestro hogar, Unidad 2: Superlibros (Big Books) 2000. (Aventuras A Traves Del Tiempo Ser.). (ENG & SPA.). (gr. 2 up). (978-0-02-147846-0(5)) Macmillan/McGraw-Hill Schl. Div.

La Tierra y Yo: Superlibros (Big Books) 2001. (Aventuras A Traves Del Tiempo Ser.). (ENG & SPA.). (gr. k up). (978-0-02-147857-6(0)) Macmillan/McGraw-Hill Schl. Div.

Timed Readings Plus in Social Studies Book 6, Bk. 6. 2003. (gr. 7-12). lib. bdg. 24.20 (978-0-613-81059-3(7)) Tandem Library Bks.

Todos comen pan! Social Studies, 6 vols.Tr. of Everyone Eats Bread! Social Studies. (SPA.). (gr. k-2). 28.95 (978-0-7368-3022-5(7) , Yellow Umbrella Bks.) Capstone Pr., Inc.

Toys Long Ago Social Studies, 6 vols. (gr. k-2). 28.95 (978-0-7368-1757-8(3) , Yellow Umbrella Bks.) Capstone Pr., Inc.

Trabajando juntos Social Studies, 6 vols.Tr. of Working Together Social Studies. (SPA.). (gr. k-2). 28.95 (978-0-7368-3043-0(X) , Yellow Umbrella Bks.) Capstone Pr., Inc.

Trabajando Social Studies, 6 vols.Tr. of Working Social Studies. (SPA.). (gr. k-2). 28.95 (978-0-7368-3023-2(5) , Yellow Umbrella Bks.) Capstone Pr., Inc.

Transparencias: Ayudas Graficas: Comunidades. 2000. (Aventuras A Traves Del Tiempo Ser.). (ENG & SPA.). (gr. 3 up). (978-0-02-148495-9(3)) Macmillan/McGraw-Hill Schl. Div.

Transparencias: Mapas: Comunidades. 2000. (Aventuras A Traves Del Tiempo Ser.). (ENG & SPA.). (gr. 3 up). (978-0-02-148005-0(2)) Macmillan/McGraw-Hill Schl. Div.

Transparencias: Mapas: Gente. 2000. (Aventuras A Traves Del Tiempo Ser.). (ENG & SPA.). (gr. 2 up). (978-0-02-148004-3(4)) Macmillan/McGraw-Hill Schl. Div.

Transparencias: Mapas: Mi Mundo. 2000. (Aventuras A Traves Del Tiempo Ser.). (ENG & SPA.). (gr. 1 up). (978-0-02-148003-6(6)) Macmillan/McGraw-Hill Schl. Div.

Traugh, Steven. Voices of American History: United & Divided: A Young Nation Through the Civil War, 4 vols., 2542. Jennett, Pam, ed. Keely, John & Grayson, Rick, illus. rev. ed. 2002. (Voices of American History Ser.). 48p. (YA). (gr. 4-8). pap. 17.99 (978-1-57471-843-0(6) , CTP 2542) Creative Teaching Pr., Inc.

—Voices of American History: Westward Expansion: America Moves West, 4 vols., 2543. Jennett, Pam, ed. rev. ed. 2001. (Voices of American History Ser.). (Illus.). 48p. (Orig.). (YA). (gr. 4-8). pap. 17.99 (978-1-57471-844-7(4) , CTP 2543) Creative Teaching Pr., Inc.

Trowell, Cynthia. Out of the Mist: A Survival Guide for Young Adults. 2004. (Illus.). 104p. (YA). per. 16.95 (978-1-59094-045-7(8) , Top Shelf) Jawbone Publishing Corp.

True Book of the Continents Collection. 2005. (J). pap. **(*978-1-60015-013-5(6))** Steps To Literacy, LLC.

True Books: Assorted Themes, Vol. 3. 2004. 517.00 (978-0-516-24713-7(1)) Scholastic Library Publishing.

True Books: Social Studies - Assorted Themes, 32 bks., Set. 2004. pap. 799.00 (978-0-516-29709-5(0) , Children's Pr.) Scholastic Library Publishing.

Trumbauer, Lisa. Computer Fun Social Studies. 2000. (J). (978-0-606-19151-7(8)) Tandem Library Bks.

—Teamwork. 2000. (Yellow Umbrella Books). (Illus.). 16p. (J). (gr. 1). lib. bdg. 14.60 (978-0-7368-0733-3(0) , Pebble Bks.) Capstone Pr., Inc.

Tutankamon: el diario de un joven Principe: Aventuras (Adventure Books) 2000. (Aventuras A Traves Del Tiempo Ser.). (ENG & SPA.). (gr. 6 up). (978-0-02-148748-6(0)) Macmillan/McGraw-Hill Schl. Div.

TV Reporters, 6 vols. (gr. 2-5). 36.95 (978-0-7368-8478-5(5)) Red Brick Learning.

Uncles, 6 vols. (gr. k-2). 28.95 (978-0-7368-8272-9(3)) Red Brick Learning.

Under Water: Big Book: Level C. 8p. 20.95 (978-0-322-00625-6(2)) Wright Group, The.

Underground: Big Book: Level D. 8p. 20.95 (978-0-322-00345-3(8)) Wright Group, The.

Understanding People in the Past, 4 bks., Set 2. 2002. (J). (gr. 4-6). lib. bdg. 114.00 (978-1-58810-426-7(5)) Heinemann Library.

UNICEF Staff, contrib. by. A Life Like Mine: How Children Live Around the World. 2002. (Illus.). 128p. pap. 24.95 (978-0-7513-3982-6(2)) Dorling Kindersley Publishing, Inc.

Unidad 1 Superlibro: Familias: Superlibros. 2003. (MacMillan/McGraw-Hill. Estudios Sociales Ser.). (ENG & SPA.). (gr. 1 up). (978-0-02-149434-7(7)) Macmillan/McGraw-Hill Schl. Div.

Unidad 3 Superlibro: Civismo: Superlibros. 2003. (MacMillan/McGraw-Hill. Estudios Sociales Ser.). (ENG & SPA.). (gr. 1 up). (978-0-02-149436-1(3)) Macmillan/McGraw-Hill Schl. Div.

Unidad 3 Superlibro: Historia: Vivimos Juntos: Superlibros (Big Books) 2003. (MacMillan/McGraw-Hill. Estudios Sociales Ser.). (ENG & SPA.). (gr. 2 up). (978-0-02-149443-9(6)) Macmillan/McGraw-Hill Schl. Div.

Unidad 5 Superlibro: Gobierno: Vivimos Juntos: Superlibros (Big Books) 2003. (MacMillan/McGraw-Hill. Estudios Sociales Ser.). (ENG & SPA.). (gr. 2 up). (978-0-02-149445-3(2)) Macmillan/McGraw-Hill Schl. Div.

Unidad 5 Superlibro: Historia: Superlibros. 2003. (MacMillan/McGraw-Hill. Estudios Sociales Ser.). (ENG & SPA.). (gr. 1 up). (978-0-02-149438-5(X)) Macmillan/McGraw-Hill Schl. Div.

University of Cambridge Local Examinations Syndication Staff. IGCSE Development Studies. 1998. (Cambridge Open Learning Project in South Africa Ser.). Module 3. 76p. pap. 9.30 (978-0-521-65848-5(9)); Module 4. 108p. pap. 9.30 (978-0-521-65847-8(0)) Cambridge Univ. Pr.

—IGCSE Development Studies Module 2. 1998. (Cambridge Open Learning Project in South Africa Ser.). 116p. pap. 9.30 (978-0-521-65849-2(7)) Cambridge Univ. Pr.

Unlocking Social Studies Skills. 2001. (YA). (gr. 6-12). pap. 16.50 (978-1-55675-681-8(X)) Globe Fearon Educational Publishing.

van de Lagemaat, Richard. Theory of Knowledge for the IB Diploma. 2005. (Illus.). 480p. pap. 31.00 (978-0-521-54298-2(7)) Cambridge Univ. Pr.

VanVoorst, Jennifer. Todo tiene una historia Social Studies. (SPA.). (gr. k-2). 19.95 (978-0-7368-2979-3(2)) Red Brick Learning.

VanVoorst, Jenny. The Letter Zz: How Things Move, 6 vols. (gr. k-2). 17.50 (978-0-7368-4125-2(3)) Red Brick Learning.

Verde dice adelante Social Studies, 6 vols.Tr. of Green Means Go Social Studies. (SPA.). (gr. k-2). 28.95 (978-0-7368-3113-0(4) , Yellow Umbrella Bks.) Capstone Pr., Inc.

Viaje a la selva Tropical: Libros Aventuras (Adventure Books) 2003. (MacMillan/McGraw-Hill. Estudios Sociales Ser.). (ENG & SPA.). (gr. 5 up). (978-0-02-150128-1(9)) Macmillan/McGraw-Hill Schl. Div.

El viaje de Maria: Libros Aventuras (Adventure Books) 2000. (MacMillan/McGraw-Hill. Estudios Sociales Ser.). (ENG & SPA.). (gr. 4 up). (978-0-02-148711-0(1)) Macmillan/McGraw-Hill Schl. Div.

Viaje por la Historia: Libros Aventuras (Adventure Books) 2003. (MacMillan/McGraw-Hill. Estudios Sociales Ser.). (ENG & SPA.). (gr. 4 up). (978-0-02-150120-5(3)) Macmillan/McGraw-Hill Schl. Div.

Videotape Set: Comunidades. 2000. (Aventuras A Traves Del Tiempo Ser.). (ENG & SPA.). (gr. 3 up). (978-0-02-147231-4(9)) Macmillan/McGraw-Hill Schl. Div.

El viejo MacDonald tenia una Granja: Aventuras (Adventure Books) 2000. (Aventuras A Traves Del Tiempo Ser.). (ENG & SPA.). (gr. k up). (978-0-02-148656-4(5)) Macmillan/McGraw-Hill Schl. Div.

The Viking Saga. 2004. (Thrilling Tales in Time Ser.: Vol. 1). (J). (978-1-58123-370-4(1)) Larson Learning, Inc.

Una visita a los arboles Gigantes: Libros Aventuras (Adventure Books) 2000. (MacMillan/McGraw-Hill. Estudios Sociales Ser.). (ENG & SPA.). (gr. 4 up). (978-0-02-148701-1(4)) Macmillan/McGraw-Hill Schl. Div.

Vivan los dias de fiesta, Unidad 5: Superlibros (Big Books) 2000. (Aventuras A Traves Del Tiempo Ser.). (ENG & SPA.). (gr. k up). (978-0-02-147837-8(6)) Macmillan/McGraw-Hill Schl. Div.

Vivimos en grupos, Unidad 2: Libros de la Biblioteca (Classroom Library) 2000. (Aventuras A Traves Del Tiempo Ser.). (ENG & SPA.). (gr. 1 up). (978-0-02-147839-2(2)) Macmillan/McGraw-Hill Schl. Div.

Voy con mi familia a ver a la Abuelita: Superlibros (Big Books) 1999. (Aventuras A Traves Del Tiempo Ser.). (ENG & SPA.). (gr. 1 up). (978-0-02-110164-1(7)) Macmillan/McGraw-Hill Schl. Div.

Walker, Pamela. Real People, 6 bks., Set. 2004. (Welcome Books Ser.). (Illus.). 24p. (J). (ps-2). 261.00 (978-0-516-22997-3(4) , Children's Pr.) Scholastic Library Publishing.

War Planes, 12 bks. Incl. Attack Helicopters : The AH-64 Apaches. Sweetman, Bill. 2001. lib. bdg. 17.08 (978-0-7368-0789-0(6)); Combat Rescue Helicopters : The MH-53 Pave Lows. Sweetman, Bill. 2002. lib. bdg. 21.26 (978-0-7368-1067-8(6)); High-Altitude Spy Planes : The U-2s. Sweetman, Bill. 2001. lib. bdg. 17.01 (978-0-7368-0790-6(X)); Jump Jets : The AV-8B Harriers. Sweetman, Bill. 2002. lib. bdg. 21.26 (978-0-7368-1068-5(4)); Long-Range Bombers : The B-1B Lancers. Green, Michael & Green, Gladys. 2003. lib. bdg. 21.26 (978-0-7368-1508-6(2)); Night Attack Gunships : The AC-130H Spectres. Green, Michael & Green, Gladys. 2003. lib. bdg. 21.26 (978-0-7368-1509-3(0)); Radar Jammers : The EA-6B Prowlers. Sweetman, Bill. 2002. lib. bdg. 21.26 (978-0-7368-1069-2(2)); Stealth Attack Fighters : The F-117A Nighthawks. Green, Michael & Green, Gladys. 2003. lib. bdg. 21.26 (978-0-7368-1510-9(4)); Stealth Bombers : The B-2 Spirits. Sweetman, Bill. 2001. lib. bdg. 21.26 (978-0-7368-0791-3(8)); Strike Fighters : The F/A-18E/F Super Hornets. Sweetman, Bill. 2002. lib. bdg. 21.26 (978-0-7368-1070-8(6)); Supersonic Fighters : The F-16 Fighting Falcons. Sweetman, Bill. 2001. lib. bdg. 17.01 (978-0-7368-0792-0(6)); Tactical Fighters : The F-15 Eagles. Green, Michael & Green, Gladys. 2003. lib. bdg. 21.26 (978-0-7368-1511-6(2)); 32p. (J). (gr. 3-4). (Illus.). Set lib. bdg. 255.12 (978-0-7368-1522-2(8) , Capstone High-Interest Bks.) Capstone Pr., Inc.

Warm up to Social Studies for Grade 11. 2005. spiral bd. (978-1-933049-17-5(0)) Region IV Education Service Ctr.

Waters, Carrie. A Look Back in Time: A Content Area Reader-Social Studies. 2005. (Emergent/Early (Prek-2) Social Studies Package Ser.). 20p. (YA). (ps-2). 25.20 (978-0-8215-7816-2(2)) Sadlier, William H. Inc.

Ways We Communicate Social Studies, 6 vols. (gr. k-2). 28.95 (978-0-7368-1762-2(X) , Yellow Umbrella Bks.) Capstone Pr., Inc.

We Need Custodians, 6 vols. (gr. k-2). 28.95 (978-0-7368-8738-0(5)) Red Brick Learning.

We Need Mail Carriers, 6 vols. (gr. k-2). 28.95 (978-0-7368-8602-4(8)) Red Brick Learning.

We Need Principals, 6 vols. (gr. k-2). 28.95 (978-0-7368-8740-3(7)) Red Brick Learning.

Welcome to My Country New Releases: Afghanistan, Chile, Iraq, Malaysia, Morocco, Norway, 6 bks. 2004. (Illus.). (J). (gr. 2 up). lib. bdg. 151.60 (978-0-8368-2556-5(X)) Stevens, Gareth Inc.

What Does a Firefighter Do? Social Studies, 6 vols. (gr. k-2). 28.95 (978-0-7368-2988-5(1) , Yellow Umbrella Bks.) Capstone Pr., Inc.

What Kind of Dog Am I? Level C. 8p. 20.95 (978-0-322-00371-2(7)) Wright Group, The.

What's Black & White & Moos? Level F. 16p. 31.50 (978-0-7802-9741-8(5)) Wright Group, The.

Where Do You Live? Social Studies. (gr. k-2). 19.95 (978-0-7368-1797-4(2)) Red Brick Learning.

Where Does the Mail Go? Social Studies, 6 vols. (gr. k-2). 28.95 (978-0-7368-1763-9(8) , Yellow Umbrella Bks.) Capstone Pr., Inc.

Who Keeps Us Safe? Social Studies, 6 vols. (gr. k-2). 28.95 (978-0-7368-1756-1(5) , Yellow Umbrella Bks.) Capstone Pr., Inc.

Who Says? Big Book: Level F. 16p. 31.50 (978-0-322-00377-4(6)) Wright Group, The.

Whose Shoes? Level F. 16p. 31.50 (978-0-322-00351-4(2)) Wright Group, The.

Why? Big Book: Level F. 16p. 31.50 (978-0-322-00352-1(0)) Wright Group, The.

Williams, Bernard. The A-Z of PSE. 1999. (Illus.). 144p. (J). (gr. 6-11). pap. 24.00 (978-0-7487-3892-2(4)) Nelson Thornes Ltd. GBR. *Dist:* Trans-Atlantic Pubns., Inc.

Williams, Brian. Way We Live: Biggest & Best. 2004. (Biggest & Best Ser.). (Illus.). 40p. (J). pap. 7.95 (978-1-84236-064-4(7)) Miles Kelly Publishing, Ltd. GBR. *Dist:* Independent Pubs. Group.

Wise, William. The Two Reigns of Tutankhamen. Burton, Harry, photos by. 2001. (Illus.). 188p. (YA). (gr. 4-7). pap. 12.95 (978-0-595-16864-4(7)) iUniverse, Inc.

Wood: Big Book: Level D. 8p. 20.95 (978-0-7802-9743-2(1)) Wright Group, The.

Working Social Studies, 6 vols. (gr. k-2). 28.95 (978-0-7368-3007-2(3) , Yellow Umbrella Bks.) Capstone Pr., Inc.

Working Together Social Studies, 6 vols. (gr. k-2). 28.95 (978-0-7368-2987-8(3) , Yellow Umbrella Bks.) Capstone Pr., Inc.

World Book, Inc. Staff, ed. The World Book Blackline Masters: Indians. 2001. 80p. (J). (gr. 2 up). (978-0-7166-7406-1(8) , 60048) World Bk., Inc.

World Cultures Classroom Library. (gr. k-2). lib. bdg. 109.95 (978-0-7368-9454-8(3)) Red Brick Learning.

World Cultures Complete Unit. (gr. k-2). 624.95 (978-0-7368-9455-5(1)) Red Brick Learning.

World Today: Heath Social Studies. Incl. The World Today. tchr. ed. (978-0-669-11400-3(6)); The World Today. suppl. ed. (978-0-669-11426-3(X)); The World Today. pap., wbk. ed. (978-0-669-11406-5(5)); The World Today. pap., wbk. ed. (978-0-669-11412-6(X)); The World Today. suppl. ed. (978-0-669-11432-4(4)); The World Today. suppl. ed. (978-0-669-11728-8(5)); The World Today. suppl. ed. (J). (gr. 6-7). (978-0-669-11392-1(1)) Houghton Mifflin Co. (Schl. Div.).

World Watch, 6 vols., Set 1. 2003. (World Watch Ser.). (Illus.). (YA). (gr. 6-8). 113.94 (978-0-7398-6618-4(4)) Raintree.

WrightGroup/McGraw-Hill. Social Studies: A How to Skills Resource. 2002. (Science/Social Studies). Level 1. (gr. 1 up). pap. 96.99 (978-0-07-572398-1(0)); Level 2. (gr. 2 up). pap. 96.99 (978-0-07-572399-8(9)); Level 3. (gr. 3 up). pap., wbk. ed. 93.99 (978-0-07-572402-5(2)); Level 6. (gr. 6 up). pap., stu. ed. 13.95 (978-0-07-569254-6(6)) SRA/McGraw-Hill.

Yellow Umbrella Books - Social Studies: About 100 Years Ago; At School; Communities; Earth's Land & Water; Families; On the Go!; Our Favorite Things to Do; People & Places; People Work; Teamwork; What Is a Map?; Who Is a Friend?, 12 bks. 2001. (Illus.). (J). (gr. 1). lib. bdg. 175.20 (978-0-7368-0756-2(X) , Pebble Bks.) Capstone Pr., Inc.

Yellow Umbrella Books: Social Studies, 12 bks. Incl. About 100 Years Ago. Trumbauer, Lisa. 2000. lib. bdg. 14.60 (978-0-7368-0736-4(5)); All Kinds of Clothes. Cipriano, Jeri S. 2003. lib. bdg. 14.60 (978-0-7368-2025-7(6)); At School. Trumbauer, Lisa. 2000. lib. bdg. 14.60 (978-0-7368-0741-8(1)); Communities. Trumbauer, Lisa. 2000. lib. bdg. 14.60 (978-0-7368-0744-9(6)); Earth's Land & Water. Beers, Bonnie. 2000. lib. bdg. 14.60 (978-0-7368-0737-1(3)); Families. Trumbauer, Lisa. 2000. lib. bdg. 14.60 (978-0-7368-0734-0(9)); From Tree to Table. Ring, Susan. 2003. lib. bdg. 14.60 (978-0-7368-2026-4(4)); It's a Rule. Cipriano, Jeri S. 2003. lib. bdg. 14.60 (978-0-7368-2027-1(2)); Needs & Wants. Ring, Susan. 2003. lib. bdg. 14.60 (978-0-7368-2028-8(0)); On the Go! Trumbauer, Lisa. 2000. lib. bdg. 14.60 (978-0-7368-0735-7(7)); Our Favorite Things to Do. Trumbauer, Lisa. 2000. lib. bdg. 14.60 (978-0-7368-0739-5(X)); People & Places. Weidenman, Lauren. 2000. lib. bdg. 14.60 (978-0-7368-0743-2(8)); People Work. Ecker, Debbie. 2000. lib. bdg. 14.60 (978-0-7368-0740-1(3)); Teamwork. Trumbauer, Lisa. 2000. lib. bdg. 14.60 (978-0-7368-0733-3(0)); Ways We Communicate. Catala, Ellen. 2003. lib. bdg. 14.60 (978-0-7368-2029-5(9)); What Is a Map? Weidenman, Lauren. 2000. lib. bdg. 14.60 (978-0-7368-0742-5(X)); Where Does the Mail Go? Shepard, Daniel. 2003. lib. bdg. 14.60 (978-0-7368-2030-1(2)); Who Is a Friend? Trumbauer, Lisa. 2000. lib. bdg. 14.60 (978-0-7368-0738-8(1)); 16p. (J). (gr. 1). (Illus.). Set lib. bdg. 262.80 (978-0-7368-2034-9(5) , Pebble Bks.) Capstone Pr., Inc.

Yellowstone: Libros Aventuras (Adventure Books) 2003. (MacMillan/McGraw-Hill. Estudios Sociales Ser.). (ENG & SPA.). (gr. 4 up). (978-0-02-150122-9(X)) Macmillan/McGraw-Hill Schl. Div.

Young, Ian. Amazing Journeys: Following in History's Footsteps, 6 vols. (gr. 4 up). 49.95 (978-0-7368-2841-3(9) , High Five) Red Brick Learning.

Zike, Dinah. Big Book of Social Studies - Elementary K-6. 2002. 136p. per. 19.95 (978-1-882796-45-8(4) , CCC 103) Dinah-Might Adventures, LP.

SOCIAL SCIENCES—STUDY AND TEACHING

Boehm, Richard G., et al. Carteles de la Unidad: La Historia de Nuestro Mundo: Relatos de la Historia. 97th ed. 2003. (Harcourt Brace Estudios Sociales Ser.). (SPA.). (gr. k-7). pap. 84.30 (978-0-15-309146-9(0)) Harcourt Schl. Pubs.

—Desk Maps: Intermediate (3-7) Package Of 10. 2003. (Harcourt Brace Social Studies). (SPA.). (gr. 3-7). 27.00 (978-0-15-310432-9(5)) Harcourt Schl. Pubs.

—Desk Maps: Primary (K-2) Package Of 10. 2003. (Harcourt Brace Social Studies). (SPA.). (gr. k-2). 27.00 (978-0-15-310431-2(7)) Harcourt Schl. Pubs.

—Ediciones Del Maestro: Comunidades. 1998. (Harcourt Brace Estudios Sociales Ser.). (SPA.). (gr. k-7). tchr. ed. 189.40 (978-0-15-310494-7(5)) Harcourt Schl. Pubs.

—Ediciones Del Maestro: Descubro Al Mundo. 2000. (Harcourt Brace Estudios Sociales Ser.). (SPA.). (gr. k-7). tchr. ed. 172.80 (978-0-15-310493-0(7)) Harcourt Schl. Pubs.

—Ediciones Del Maestro: Las Antiguas Civilizaciones. 1999. (Harcourt Brace Estudios Sociales Ser.). (SPA.). (gr. k-7). tchr. ed. 249.50 (978-0-15-310498-5(8)) Harcourt Schl. Pubs.

—Ediciones Del Maestro: Los Comienzos de Estados Unidos Volumes 1 And 2, 2 vols. 2000. (Harcourt Brace Estudios Sociales Ser.). (SPA.). (gr. k-7). tchr. ed. 249.50 (978-0-15-310496-1(1)) Harcourt Schl. Pubs.

—Ediciones Del Maestro: Un Lugar Para Mi. 2000. (Harcourt Brace Estudios Sociales Ser.). (SPA.). (gr. k-7). tchr. ed. 172.80 (978-0-15-310492-3(9)) Harcourt Schl. Pubs.

—Libros Del Alumno: Comunidades. 2000. (Harcourt Brace Estudios Sociales Ser.). (SPA.). (gr. k-7). pupil's gde. ed. 65.30 (978-0-15-310487-9(2)) Harcourt Schl. Pubs.

—Libros Del Alumno: Las Antiguas Civilizaciones. 1998. (Harcourt Brace Estudios Sociales Ser.). (SPA.). (gr. k-7). pupil's gde. ed. 88.40 (978-0-15-310490-9(2)) Harcourt Schl. Pubs.

—Libros Del Alumno: Los Comienzos de Estados Unidos. 1998. (Harcourt Brace Estudios Sociales Ser.). (SPA.). (gr. k-7). pupil's gde. ed. 88.40 (978-0-15-310489-3(9)) Harcourt Schl. Pubs.

—Libros Del Alumno: Un Lugar Para Mi. 2000. (Harcourt Brace Estudios Sociales Ser.). (SPA.). (gr. k-7). pap., pupil's gde. ed. 56.70 (978-0-15-310485-5(6)) Harcourt Schl. Pubs.

—Mi Mundo y Yo: A Kindergarten Program. 1998. (Harcourt Brace Estudios Sociales Ser.). (SPA.). (gr. k-7). tchr. ed. 146.20 (978-0-15-310491-6(0)) Harcourt Schl. Pubs.

—Superlibros de la Unidad. 1999. (Harcourt Brace Estudios Sociales Ser.). (SPA.). (gr. 1 up). pap. 1246.90 (978-0-15-312968-1(9)); (gr. 2 up). pap. 1246.90 (978-0-15-312969-8(7)) Harcourt Schl. Pubs.

—Superlibros de Literatura: Kindergarten. 2000. (Harcourt Brace Estudios Sociales Ser.). (SPA.). (gr. k-7). pap. 361.30 (978-0-15-310515-9(1)) Harcourt Schl. Pubs.

—Transparencias: La Historia de Nuestro Mundo: Relatos de la Historia. 97th ed. 2003. (Harcourt Brace Estudios Sociales Ser.). (SPA.). (gr. k-7). pap. 138.70 (978-0-15-309147-6(9)) Harcourt Schl. Pubs.

—Write-on Charts. 2003. (Harcourt Brace Estudios Sociales Ser.). (SPA.). (gr. 1 up). 248.40 (978-0-15-313132-5(2)); (gr. 2 up). 248.40 (978-0-15-313133-2(0)) Harcourt Schl. Pubs.

Butrymowicz, Sarah. World So Different. 1999. (Publish-a-Book Ser.). (Illus.). 24p. (J). (gr. 1-6). pap. 8.50 (978-0-7398-0053-9(1)) Steck-Vaughn.

Harcourt School Publishers Staff. Harcourt Social Studies: Literature Anthology Big Book. 1999. (Illus.). Vol. 1. (J). pap. 59.20 (978-0-15-312116-6(5)); Vol. 1. (SPA., pap. 122.50 (978-0-15-312409-9(1)); Vol. 2. (J). pap. 59.20 (978-0-15-312117-3(3)); Vol. 2. (SPA., pap. 122.50 (978-0-15-312410-5(5)); Vol. 3. (J). pap. 59.20 (978-0-15-312119-7(X)); Vol. 3. (SPA., pap. 122.50 (978-0-15-312411-2(3)) Harcourt Schl. Pubs.

—Horizons: US History: Canada, Mexico & Central America. 3rd ed. 2001. (Harcourt Horizons Ser.). (gr. 4-7). (Illus.). pap., pupil's gde. ed. 82.50 (978-0-15-324809-2(2)); Vol. 1. pap., tchr. ed. 157.30 (978-0-15-324810-8(6)); Vol. 2. pap., tchr. ed. 157.30 (978-0-15-324811-5(4)) Harcourt Schl. Pubs.

—Horizontes. 3rd ed. 2003. (Harcourt Horizontes Ser.). (SPA., Illus.). (gr. k-6). 7.00 (978-0-15-324549-7(2)); act. bk. ed. 8.40 (978-0-15-324550-3(6)); act. bk. ed. 8.40 (978-0-15-324551-0(4)); act. bk. ed. 10.20 (978-0-15-324552-7(2)); pupil's gde. ed. 47.30 (978-0-15-324532-9(8)); pupil's gde. ed. 54.10 (978-0-15-324533-6(6)); pupil's gde. ed. 47.30 (978-0-15-324531-2(X)) Harcourt Schl. Pubs.

—Horizontes: Assessment Program. 3rd ed. 2002. (Harcourt Horizontes Ser.). (SPA., Illus.). (gr. k-6). pap. 66.20 (978-0-15-324542-8(5)); pap. 66.20 (978-0-15-324543-5(3)); pap. 87.80 (978-0-15-324544-2(1)) Harcourt Schl. Pubs.

—Horizontes: Big Book. 3rd ed. 2003. (Harcourt Horizontes Ser.). (SPA., Illus.). (gr. k-6). tchr. ed. 268.00 (978-0-15-324832-0(7)) Harcourt Schl. Pubs.

—Horizontes: States & Regions. 3rd ed. 2003. (Harcourt Horizontes Ser.). (SPA., Illus.). (gr. k-6). act. bk. ed. 10.50 (978-0-15-324553-4(0)); pupil's gde. ed. 64.60 (978-0-15-324534-3(4)) Harcourt Schl. Pubs.

—Horizontes: States & Regions: Assessment Program. 3rd ed. 2002. (Harcourt Horizontes Ser.). (SPA., Illus.). (gr. k-6). pap. 127.00 (978-0-15-324545-9(X)) Harcourt Schl. Pubs.

—Horizontes: Unit 1. 3rd ed. 2002. (SPA., Illus.). (J). (gr. 2). 176.20 (978-0-15-324570-1(0)) Harcourt Schl. Pubs.

—Horizontes: Unit 2. 3rd ed. 2002. (SPA., Illus.). (J). 176.20 (978-0-15-324571-8(9)) Harcourt Schl. Pubs.

—Horizontes: Unit 3. 3rd ed. 2002. (SPA., Illus.). (J). 176.20 (978-0-15-324572-5(7)) Harcourt Schl. Pubs.

—Horizontes: Unit 4. 3rd ed. 2002. (SPA., Illus.). (J). 176.20 (978-0-15-324573-2(5)) Harcourt Schl. Pubs.

—Horizontes: Unit 5. 3rd ed. 2002. (SPA., Illus.). (J). 176.20 (978-0-15-324574-9(3)) Harcourt Schl. Pubs.

—Horizontes: Unit 6. 3rd ed. 2002. (SPA., Illus.). (J). 176.20 (978-0-15-324575-6(1)) Harcourt Schl. Pubs.

—Horizontes: US History: Assessment Program. 3rd ed. 2002. (Harcourt Horizontes Ser.). (SPA.). (gr. k-6). pap., tchr. ed. 163.60 (978-0-15-324547-3(6)) Harcourt Schl. Pubs.

—Horizontes: World Regions. 3rd ed. (Harcourt Horizontes Ser.). (SPA., (gr. k-6). 2003. Illus.). act. bk. ed. 11.80 (978-0-15-324556-5(5)); 2002. pap., tchr. ed., act. bk. ed. 27.90 (978-0-15-324561-9(1)) Harcourt Schl. Pubs.

—Horizontes: World Regions: Assessment Program. 3rd ed. 2002. (Harcourt Horizontes Ser.). (SPA.). (gr. k-6). pap., tchr. ed. 163.60 (978-0-15-324548-0(4)) Harcourt Schl. Pubs.

—Horizontes Bk. 5: Time for Kids 5 Pack. 3rd ed. 2002. (Harcourt Horizontes Ser.). (SPA., Illus.). (gr. 2 up). pap. 24.00 (978-0-15-333754-3(0)) Harcourt Schl. Pubs.

—Horizontes Bk. 9: Timre for Kids 5 Pack. 3rd ed. 2002. (Harcourt Horizontes Ser.). (SPA., Illus.). (gr. 2 up). pap. 24.00 (978-0-15-333762-8(1)) Harcourt Schl. Pubs.

—Horizontes Bk. 12: Time for Kids 5 Pack. 3rd ed. 2002. (Harcourt Horizontes Ser.). (SPA., Illus.). (gr. 2 up). pap. 24.00 (978-0-15-333768-0(0)) Harcourt Schl. Pubs.

—Horizontes, Grade 2, Vol. 2. 2nd ed. 2003. (Harcourt Horizontes Ser.). (SPA.). (gr. k-6). tchr. ed. 121.50 (978-0-15-328508-0(7)) Harcourt Schl. Pubs.

—Horizontes, Grade 3. 3rd ed. 2002. (Harcourt Horizontes Ser.). (SPA.). (gr. k-6). pap., tchr. ed., act. bk. ed. 25.70 (978-0-15-324557-2(3)) Harcourt Schl. Pubs.

—Horizontes, Grade 4: States & Regions. 3rd ed. 2003. (Harcourt Horizontes Ser.). (SPA.). (gr. k-6). Vol. 1. tchr. ed. 133.80 (978-0-15-321975-7(0)); Vol. 2. tchr. ed. 133.80 (978-0-15-321976-4(9)) Harcourt Schl. Pubs.

—Horizontes, Grade 4: States & Regions: Activity Book. 3rd ed. 2002. (Harcourt Horizontes Ser.). (SPA.). (gr. k-6). pap., tchr. ed., act. bk. ed. 26.10 (978-0-15-324558-9(1)) Harcourt Schl. Pubs.

—Horizontes, Grade K. 3rd ed. 2002. (Harcourt Horizontes Ser.). (SPA.). (gr. k-6). tchr. ed., act. bk. ed. 127.90 (978-0-15-321971-9(8)) Harcourt Schl. Pubs.

—Signatures Big Book Collection, 11 vols. 99th ed. 1998. (Illus.). (gr. 1). pap. 662.30 (978-0-15-310863-1(0)) Harcourt Schl. Pubs.

—Social Studies: Activity Book. 1999. (SPA., Illus.). (gr. 4). pap. 11.30 (978-0-15-310539-5(9)) Harcourt Schl. Pubs.

—Social Studies: Alabama State Activity Book. 1999. (Illus.). (gr. 4). pap., act. bk. ed. 11.50 (978-0-15-313485-2(2)) Harcourt Schl. Pubs.

—Social Studies: Ancient Civilizations. 1998. (Harcourt Brace Social Studies). (Illus.). (gr. k-7). pupil's gde. ed. 77.30 (978-0-15-309789-8(2)) Harcourt Schl. Pubs.

—Social Studies: Big Book Library: California Edition. 1999. (Illus.). (gr. 1). pap. 391.50 (978-0-15-314925-2(6)); (gr. 2). pap. 391.50 (978-0-15-314926-9(4)) Harcourt Schl. Pubs.

—Social Studies: California. 1998. (Illus.). (gr. 4). 71.10 (978-0-15-309787-4(6)) Harcourt Schl. Pubs.

—Social Studies: Communities. 1998. (Harcourt Brace Social Studies). (Illus.). (gr. k-7). pupil's gde. ed. 55.10 (978-0-15-309785-0(X)) Harcourt Schl. Pubs.

—Social Studies: Early United States. 1998. (Harcourt Brace Social Studies). (Illus.). (gr. k-7). pupil's gde. ed. 71.20 (978-0-15-309788-1(4)) Harcourt Schl. Pubs.

—Social Studies: South Carolina Assessment. 1999. (Illus.). pap. 76.10 (978-0-15-314190-4(5)) Harcourt Schl. Pubs.

—Social Studies: South Carolina Program. 1999. (Illus.). pap., act. bk. ed. 9.60 (978-0-15-314188-1(3)); (gr. 3). 70.10 (978-0-15-314186-7(7)) Harcourt Schl. Pubs.

—Social Studies Level 2: Somewhere Right Now. 1998. (Illus.). (gr. 1). pap. 68.00 (978-0-15-310454-1(6)) Harcourt Schl. Pubs.

—Social Studies Unit 4: Florida Big Book. 2nd ed. 2002. (Illus.). (gr. 1). pap. 155.20 (978-0-15-320170-7(3)) Harcourt Schl. Pubs.

—Social Studies Unit 5: Florida Big Book. 2nd ed. 2002. (Illus.). (J). pap. 155.20 (978-0-15-320171-4(1)) Harcourt Schl. Pubs.

—Social Studies Unit 6: Florida Big Book. 2nd ed. 2002. (Illus.). (J). pap. 155.20 (978-0-15-320172-1(X)) Harcourt Schl. Pubs.

—Social Studies Unit 7: Florida Big Book. 2nd ed. 2002. (Illus.). (J). pap. 162.00 (978-0-15-320174-5(6)); (gr. 2). pap. 185.80 (978-0-15-320175-2(4)) Harcourt Schl. Pubs.

—Social Studies, Grade 5: Canada/Latin America. 1999. (Harcourt Brace Social Studies). (gr. k-7). tchr. ed. 81.50 (978-0-15-316094-3(2)) Harcourt Schl. Pubs.

—Teacher Edition Package: Texas Edition. 3rd ed. 2002. (Horizons Ser.). (J). (gr. 1). tchr. ed. 228.80 (978-0-15-321972-6(6)); (J). (gr. 2). tchr. ed. 242.90 (978-0-15-321973-3(4)); (J). (gr. 3). tchr. ed. 242.90 (978-0-15-321974-0(2)); (gr. 4). tchr. ed. 333.30 (978-0-15-321985-6(8)); (J). (gr. 5). 267.60 (978-0-15-334253-0(6)); (gr. 5). 312.30 (978-0-15-334245-5(5)); (J). (gr. 6). 267.60 (978-0-15-334254-7(4)) Harcourt Schl. Pubs.

—World Regions. 3rd ed. (Horizontes (Social Studies) Ser.). 2003. (SPA., Illus.). (gr. k-6). pupil's gde. ed. 75.50 (978-0-15-324537-4(9)); Vol. 1. 2001. (gr. 4-7). pap., tchr. ed. 143.40 (978-0-15-322565-9(3)); Vol. 2. 2001. (gr. 4-7). pap., tchr. ed. 143.40 (978-0-15-322566-6(1)) Harcourt Schl. Pubs.

Heese, Susan & Heese, Sue. Social Science Matters: Grade 4 Learner's Book. 2000. 96p. (gr. 4). pap. 7.35 (978-0-521-78853-3(6)) Cambridge Univ. Pr.

Heese, Susan & Smith, Lee. Social Science Matters: Grade 4. 2000. 96p. (gr. 4). pap., tchr. ed. 9.20 (978-0-521-78856-4(0)) Cambridge Univ. Pr.

—Social Science Matters: Grade 5. 2001. (gr. 5). pap., tchr. ed. 9.20 (978-0-521-78857-1(9)) Cambridge Univ. Pr.

Heese, Susan, et al. Social Science Matters: Grade 5 Learner's Book. 2001. (gr. 5). pap. 6.90 (978-0-521-78854-0(4)) Cambridge Univ. Pr.

Holt, Rinehart and Winston Staff. People, Places & Change: North Carolina Edition - Standard Test Preparation Workbook. 3rd ed. 2002. pap. 11.13 (978-0-03-069911-5(8)) Holt, Rinehart & Winston.

—People, Places & Change: Preparation Workbook. 3rd ed. 2002. (J). pap. 14.00 (978-0-03-069054-9(4)) Holt, Rinehart & Winston.

Wells, Rosemary. The World Around Us: Based on Timothy Goes to School & Other Stories. Koelsch, Michael, illus. 2001. (Get Set for Kindergarten Ser.). 24p. (J). pap. 5.99 (978-0-14-056844-8(1) , Puffin) Penguin Group (USA) Inc.

—The World Around Us: Based on Timothy Goes to School & Other Stories. 2001. (ps-2). lib. bdg. 14.15 (978-0-613-35709-8(4)) Tandem Library Bks.

SOCIAL SERVICE

see also Social Settlements

Armentrout, David & Armentrout, Patricia. Jane Addams. 2002. (People Who Made a Difference Ser.). (Illus.). 24p. (gr. 2-5). 14.95 (978-1-58952-054-7(8)) Rourke Publishing, LLC.

—Jane Addams. Sarfatti, Esther & de la Vega, Eida, trs. 2001. (Personas que Cambiaron la Historia Ser.). (SPA., Illus.). 24p. (J). (gr. 1-4). lib. bdg. 19.27 (978-1-58952-065-0(X) , RK7297) Rourke Publishing, LLC.

Catalano, Angela. Community Resources: Human, Capital, & Natural Resources in Communities. 2005. (Communities at Work Ser.). (Illus.). 24p. (J). 19.95 (978-1-4042-2781-1(4) , PowerKids Pr.) Rosen Publishing Group, Inc., The.

—Community Resources: The Land & the People in Communities. 2005. (Communities at Work Ser.). (Illus.). 24p. (J). pap. (978-1-4042-5016-1(6) , PowerKids Pr.) Rosen Publishing Group, Inc., The.

Center for Learning Staff. Doing My Part: Curriculum Unit. 2003. (Cross-Curriculum Ser.). 42p. (YA). tchr. ed., spiral bd. 19.95 (978-1-56077-740-3(0)) Ctr. for Learning, The.

—Doing My Part Student Edition: Curriculum Unit. 2003. (Cross-Curriculum Ser.). 96p. (YA). stu. ed., per. 8.95 (978-1-56077-741-0(9)) Ctr. for Learning, The.

Clarke, Liam. Health & Social Care for Foundation GNVQ. 2nd ed. 2000. (Illus.). 368p. (J). pap. 42.50 (978-0-7487-3509-9(7)) Nelson Thornes Ltd. GBR. *Dist:* Trans-Atlantic Pubns., Inc.

—Health & Social Care for Intermediate GNVQ. 2nd ed. 2000. (Illus.). 224p. (J). pap. 42.50 (978-0-7487-3508-2(9)) Nelson Thornes Ltd. GBR. *Dist:* Trans-Atlantic Pubns., Inc.

Clarke, Liam, et al. Health & Social Care for Advanced GNVQ. 3rd ed. 2000. (Illus.). 344p. (J). pap. 59.50 (978-0-7487-3510-5(0)) Nelson Thornes Ltd. GBR. *Dist:* Trans-Atlantic Pubns., Inc.

Community Helpers, 42 bks. (Illus.). (J). (gr. 1-2). lib. bdg. 781.20 (978-0-7368-1161-3(3) , Bridgestone Bks.) Capstone Pr., Inc.

Community Helpers, 42 bks. Incl. Astronauts. Deedrick, Tami. 24p. (gr. 1-2). 1998. lib. bdg. 18.60 (978-1-56065-727-9(8)); Auto Mechanics. Boraas, Tracey. 24p. 1999. lib. bdg. 18.60 (978-0-7368-0072-3(7)); Bakers. Deedrick, Tami. 92p. (gr. 1-2). 1998. 18.60 (978-1-56065-728-6(6)); Bank Tellers. Bagley, Katie. 92p. (gr. 1-2). 2001. 18.60 (978-0-7368-0805-7(1)); Carpenters. Yanuck, Debbie L. 24p. (gr. 1-2). 2002. lib. bdg. 18.60 (978-0-7368-1126-2(5)); Cashiers. Bagley, Katie. 92p. (gr. 1-2). 2001. 18.60 (978-0-7368-0806-4(X)); Chefs & Cooks. Snow, Panky. 24p. (gr. 1-2). 2001. lib. bdg. 18.60 (978-0-7368-0955-9(4)); Child Care Workers. Gibson, Karen Bush. 92p. (gr. 1-2). 2000. 18.60 (978-0-7368-0622-0(9)); Coaches. Bagley, Katie. 24p. (gr. 1-2). 2001. lib. bdg. 18.60 (978-0-7368-0807-1(8)); Construction Workers. Deedrick, Tami. 92p. (gr. 1-2). 1998. 18.60 (978-1-56065-729-3(4)); Couriers. DeGezelle, Terri. 24p. (gr. 1-2). 2001. lib. bdg. 18.60 (978-0-7368-0957-3(0)); Custodians. Yanuck, Debbie L. 24p. (gr. 1-2). 2002. lib. bdg. 18.60 (978-0-7368-1127-9(3)); Dental Hygienists. Hodgkins, Fran. 24p. (gr. 1-2). 2001. lib. bdg. 18.60 (978-0-7368-0808-8(6)); Dentists. Ready, Dee. 24p. (gr. 1-2). 1997. lib. bdg. 18.60 (978-1-56065-558-9(5)); Doctors. Ready, Dee. 92p. (gr. 1-2). 1997. 18.60 (978-1-56065-509-1(7)); Electricians. Firestone, Mary. 24p. (gr. 1-2). 2001. lib. bdg. 18.60 (978-0-7368-0956-6(2)); Emergency Medical Technicians. Gibson, Karen Bush. 92p. (gr. 1-2). 2000. 18.60 (978-0-7368-0623-7(7)); Farmers. Ready, Dee. 24p. (gr. 1-2). 1997. lib. bdg. 18.60 (978-1-56065-511-4(9)); Fire Fighters. Ready, Dee. 24p. (gr. 1-2). 1997. lib. bdg. 18.60 (978-1-56065-510-7(0)); Food Service Workers. Yanuck, Debbie L. 24p. (gr. 1-2). 2002. lib. bdg. 18.60 (978-0-7368-1128-6(1)); Garbage Collectors. Deedrick, Tami. 92p. (gr. 1-2). 1998. 18.60 (978-1-56065-730-9(8)); Librarians. Ready, Dee. 92p. (gr. 1-2). 1997. 18.60 (978-1-56065-559-6(3)); Lifeguards. Christian, Sandra J. 92p. (gr. 1-2). 2002. 18.60 (978-0-7368-1129-3(X)); Mail Carriers. Ready, Dee. 92p. (gr. 1-2). 1997. 18.60 (978-1-56065-557-2(7)); Meteorologists. Christian, Sandra J. 24p. (gr. 1-2). 2002. lib. bdg. 18.60 (978-0-7368-1130-9(3)); Newspaper Carriers. Christian, Sandra J. 92p. (gr. 1-2). 2002. 18.60 (978-0-7368-1131-6(1)); Nurses. Ready, Dee. 92p. (gr. 1-2). 1997. 18.60 (978-1-56065-512-1(7)); Park Rangers. Firestone, Mary. 24p. (gr. 1-2). 2003. lib. bdg. 19.93 (978-0-7368-1615-1(1)); Pharmacists. Gibson, Karen Bush. 92p. (gr. 1-2). 2000. 18.60 (978-0-7368-0624-4(5)); Photographers. Hodgkins, Fran. 92p. (gr. 1-2). 2001. 18.60 (978-0-7368-0809-5(4)); Pilots. Hodgkins, Fran. 24p. (gr. 1-2). 2001. lib. bdg. 18.60 (978-0-7368-0810-1(8)); Plumbers. Boraas, Tracey. 24p. (gr. 1-2). 1999. lib. bdg. 18.60 (978-0-7368-0073-0(5)); Police Officers. Ready, Dee. 24p. (gr. 1-2). 1997. lib. bdg. 18.60 (978-1-56065-513-8(5)); Radio Announcers. Snow, Panky. 24p. (gr. 1-2). 2001. lib. bdg. 18.60 (978-0-7368-0958-0(9)); School Bus Drivers. Ready, Dee. 92p. (gr. 1-2). 1997. 18.60 (978-1-56065-560-2(7)); School Crossing Guards. DeGezelle, Terri. 24p. (gr. 1-2). 2001. lib. bdg. 18.60 (978-0-7368-0959-7(7)); School Principals. Boraas, Tracey. 92p. (gr. 1-2). 1999. 18.60 (978-0-7368-0074-7(3)); School Secretaries. Firestone, Mary. 24p. (gr. 1-2). 2003. lib. bdg. 19.93 (978-0-7368-1617-5(8)); Security Guards. Firestone, Mary. 92p. (gr. 1-2). 2003. 19.93 (978-0-7368-1616-8(X)); Social Workers. Firestone, Mary. 24p. (gr. 1-2). 2001. lib. bdg. 18.60 (978-0-7368-0960-3(0)); Supermarket Managers. Firestone, Mary. 24p. (gr. 1-2). 2003. lib. bdg. (978-0-7368-1614-4(3)); Teachers. Deedrick, Tami. 92p. (gr. 1-2). 1998. 18.60 (978-1-56065-731-6(6)); Truck Drivers. Gibson, Karen Bush. 92p. (gr. 1-2). 2000. 18.60 (978-0-7368-0625-1(3)); TV Reporters. Boraas, Tracey. 92p. (gr. 1-2). 1999. 18.60 (978-0-7368-0075-4(1)); Veterinarians. Ready, Dee. 92p. (gr. 1-2). 1997. 18.60 (978-1-56065-514-5(3)); Zoo Keepers. Deedrick, Tami. 24p. (gr. 1-2). 1998. lib. bdg. 18.60 (978-1-56065-732-3(4)); (J). (Illus.). Set lib. bdg. 855.60 (978-0-7368-1636-6(4) , Bridgestone Bks.) Capstone Pr., Inc.

Community Service: Individual Title Six-Packs. (On Deck Ser.). 24p. (gr. 4-5). 35.00 (978-0-7578-1024-4(1)) Rigby Education.

Davies, Elaine, et al. Dysgu Gofalu / Learning to Care. 2005. (978-0-9543372-0-9(4)) Cofal Cymru.

Emmer, Rae. Servicio Comunitario. 2004. (Actividades Escolares Ser.). (SPA & ENG., Illus.). 24p. (J). lib. bdg. 17.25 (978-0-8239-6900-5(2) , Buenas Letra) Rosen Publishing Group, Inc., The.

Facts on File, Inc. Staff. Social Work. 2nd rev. ed. 2005. (Careers in Focus Ser.). (Illus.). 204p. (J). (gr. 6-12). 22.95 (978-0-8160-5869-3(5) , Ferguson Publishing Co.) Facts On File, Inc.

Haley, James, ed. Welfare. 2002. (Opposing Viewpoints Ser.). (Illus.). 200p. (J). lib. bdg. 36.20 (978-0-7377-1246-9(5)); 2nd ed. (gr. 10-12). pap. 24.95 (978-0-7377-1245-2(7)) Thomson Gale. (Greenhaven Pr., Inc.).

Houle, Michelle. Lindsey Williams: Gardening for Impoverished Families. 2007. (Young Heroes Ser.). (Illus.). 64p. (J). (gr. 4-8). 24.95 (***978-0-7377-3867-4(7)*** , Kidhaven) Thomson Gale.

Kaye, Cathryn Berger. A Kids' Guide to Helping Others Read & Succeed: How to Take Action. 2007. (Illus.). 48p. (J). pap. (***978-1-57542-241-1(7)***) Free Spirit Publishing, Inc.

Kaye, Cathryn Berger. The Service Learning Bookshelf: A Bibliography of Fiction & Nonfiction to Inspire Student Learning. 1999. 50p. (J). pap. 7.95 (978-0-9678072-0-1(4)) ABCD Bks.

Kramer, Barbara. Jimmy Carter: A Life of Service. 2005. (Awesome Values in Famous Lives Ser.). (Illus.). 48p. (J). (ps-7). lib. bdg. 23.93 (978-0-7660-2379-6(6) , Enslow Elementary) Enslow Pubs., Inc.

Lewis, Barbara A. The Kid's Guide to Service Projects: Over 500 Service Ideas for Young People Who Want to Make a Difference. 2004. (Self-Help for Kids Ser.). 184p. (YA). (gr. 5 up). pap. 12.95 (978-0-915793-82-2(2) , FS323) Free Spirit Publishing, Inc.

The Library of Social Activism. 2005. (Illus.). (gr. 7-12). lib. bdg. 212.00 (978-0-8239-9330-7(2)) Rosen Publishing Group, Inc., The.

Make the World a Better Place. 2006. spiral bd. 19.95 (978-0-9774155-0-2(3)) Learning to Give.

Moore, Stephen. Social Welfare Alive! An Introduction to Issues & Policies in Health & Welfare. 3rd rev. ed. 2002. (Illus.). 464p. pap. 37.00 (978-0-7487-6561-4(1)) Nelson Thornes Ltd. GBR. *Dist:* International Specialized Bk. Services.

Prentiss, Timothy. A Volunteer Helps. 2006. (Early Explorers Ser.). (J). 34.00 (***978-1-4108-6112-2(0)***) Benchmark Education Co.

Thomas, Eric, illus. Community Workers, 8 bks. Incl. Caring for Your Pets : A Book about Veterinarians. Owen, Ann. 22.60 (978-1-4048-0087-8(5)); Delivering Your Mail : A Book about Mail Carriers. Owen, Ann. 22.60 (978-1-4048-0091-5(3)); Helping You Heal : A Book about Nurses. Wohlrabe, Sarah. 22.60 (978-1-4048-0086-1(7)); Helping You Learn : A Book about Teachers. Wohlrabe, Sarah. 22.60 (978-1-4048-0084-7(0)); Keeping You Healthy : A Book about Doctors. Owen, Ann. 22.60 (978-1-4048-0085-4(9)); Keeping You Safe : A Book about Police Officers. Owen, Ann. 22.60 (978-1-4048-0089-2(1)); Protecting Your Home : A Book about Firefighters. Owen, Ann. 22.60 (978-1-4048-0088-5(3)); Taking You Places : A Book about Bus Drivers. Owen, Ann. 22.60 (978-1-4048-0090-8(5)); 24p. (C). (gr. k-3). 2004. (Illus.). 2003. 170.08 (978-1-4048-0083-0(2)) Picture Window Bks.

Wagner, Viqi. Poverty. 2007. (Opposing Viewpoints Ser.). (Illus.). 224p. (gr. 10-12). 36.20 (***978-0-7377-3747-9(6)***); pap. 24.95 (***978-0-7377-3748-6(4)***) Thomson Gale. (Greenhaven Pr., Inc.).

SOCIAL SERVICE—FICTION

Guest, Jacqueline. Goal in Sight. 2003. (gr. 3-6). lib. bdg. 13.55 (978-0-613-78325-5(5)) Tandem Library Bks.

Lupica, Mike. Heat. 2007. 240p. (J). pap. 6.99 (978-0-14-240757-8(7) , Puffin); 2006. 220p. (YA). (gr. 5). 16.99 (978-0-399-24301-1(1) , Philomel) Penguin Group (USA) Inc.

McDaniel, Lurlene. Journey of Hope: Two Novels: Angel of Mercy & Angel of Hope. 2004. (Mercy Trilogy). 448p. (YA). (gr. 7). mass mkt. 7.99 (978-0-553-49451-8(1) , Laurel Leaf) Random Hse. Children's Bks.

Monninger, Joseph. Baby. 2007. 204p. (YA). (gr. 8 up). 16.95 (***978-1-59078-502-7(9)*** , Front Street) Boyds Mills Pr.

Peterseil, Tehila. The Secret Files of Lisa Weiss. 1998. 208p. (J). (gr. 4-7). pap. 8.95 (978-0-943706-39-9(4) , Devora Publishing) Pitspopany Pr.

—Secret Files of Lisa Weiss. rev. ed. 1998. 208p. (J). (gr. 4-7). 14.95 (978-0-943706-30-6(0) , Devora Publishing) Pitspopany Pr.

Wakefield, Janet. What If Everybody Gave? Julie, Woehead, illus. 2002. 36p. (J). lib. bdg. 15.00 net. (978-0-9717497-0-2(1)) Community Partnership with Youth, Inc.

SOCIAL SERVICE—VOCATIONAL GUIDANCE

Brinkerhoff, Shirley. Social Worker. 2002. (Careers with Character Ser.). (Illus.). 96p. (YA). (gr. 7 up). (978-1-59084-324-6(X)) Mason Crest Pubs.

Firestone, Mary. Social Workers. 2001. (Community Helpers Ser.). (Illus.). 24p. (J). (gr. 1-2). lib. bdg. 18.60 (978-0-7368-0960-3(0) , Bridgestone Bks.) Capstone Pr., Inc.

Simpson, Carolyn & Simpson, Dwain. Exploring Careers in Social Work. rev. ed. 1999. (Careers). (Illus.). 192p. (YA). (gr. 7-12). lib. bdg. 26.50 (978-0-8239-2879-8(9) , CASOWO) Rosen Publishing Group, Inc., The.

Tretout, Pat. Choosing a Career in the Helping Professions. rev. ed. 1999. (World of Work Ser.). (Illus.). 64p. (YA). (gr. 7-12). lib. bdg. 25.25 (978-0-8239-3003-6(3) , WWHEPR) Rosen Publishing Group, Inc., The.

SOCIAL SETTLEMENTS

see also Playgrounds

also names of settlements, e.g. Hull House, Chicago; etc.

Arnold, Caroline. Children of the Settlement Houses. 1998. (Picture the American Past Ser.). (Illus.). 48p. (gr. 2-5). lib. bdg. 22.60 (978-1-57505-242-7(3)) Lerner Publishing Group.

Friedman, Michael & Friedman, Brett. Settlement Houses: Improving the Social Welfare of America's Immigrants. (Progressive Movement, 1900-1920—Efforts to Reform America's New Industrial Society Ser.). (Illus.). 32p. (J). 2006. (978-1-4042-0859-9(3)); 2004. lib. bdg. (978-1-4042-0194-1(7)) Rosen Publishing Group, Inc., The.

SOCIAL SETTLEMENTS—FICTION

Ayres, Katherine. Under Copp's Hill. 2000. (American Girl Collection). (Illus.). (J). (978-0-606-20963-2(8)) Tandem Library Bks.

Faigen, Anne G. New World Waiting. 2006. iii, 188p. (J). pap. (978-0-9744715-5-6(0)) Local History Co., The.

SOCIAL STUDIES

see Geography; Social Sciences

SOCIAL WELFARE

see Social Problems; Social Service

SOCIAL WORK

see Social Service

SOCIALISM

see also Capitalism; Communism; Labor and Laboring Classes; Labor Unions; National Socialism; Utopias

Jarnow, Jesse. Socialism: A Primary Source Analysis. 2003. (Primary Sources of Political Systems Ser.). (Illus.). 64p. (J). lib. bdg. 29.25 (978-0-8239-4521-4(9)) Rosen Publishing Group, Inc., The.

Ritchie, Nigel. Communism. 2001. (Ideas of the Modern World Ser.). (Illus.). 64p. (YA). (gr. 7-9). lib. bdg. 25.69 (978-0-7398-3158-8(5)) Raintree.

SOCIALISM—UNITED STATES—HISTORY

Skahill, Carolyn M. The Socialist Party: Eugene V. Debs & the Radical Politics of the American Working Class. 2004. (Progressive Movement, 1900-1920 Ser.). (Illus.). 32p. (J). lib. bdg. (978-1-4042-0198-9(X)) Rosen Publishing Group, Inc., The.

SOCIETY, PRIMITIVE

see Primitive Societies

SOCIETY OF FRIENDS

Blanc, Felice. I Am a Quaker. 1999. (Religions of the World Ser.). 24p. (J). (gr. k-4). lib. bdg. 18.75 (978-0-8239-5264-9(9) , PowerKids Pr.) Rosen Publishing Group, Inc., The.

Brill, Marlene Targ. Allen Jay & the Underground Railroad. 2007. (Readalongs for Beginning Readers Ser.). (J). (gr. 1-3). pap. 18.95 incl. audio compact disk (***978-1-59519-949-2(7)***) Live Oak Media.

Kroll, Steven. William Penn: Founder of Pennsylvania. Himler, Ronald, illus. 2000. 32p. (J). (gr. 4-6). tchr. ed. 16.95 (978-0-8234-1439-0(6)) Holiday Hse., Inc.

Woog, Adam. What Makes Me a Quaker? 2004. (What Makes Me A—? Ser.). (Illus.). 48p. (J). (gr. 3-7). lib. bdg. 26.20 (978-0-7377-3082-1(X) , Greenhaven Pr., Inc.) Thomson Gale.

SOCIETY OF FRIENDS—FICTION

Avi. Night Journeys. 2000. (Illus.). 160p. (J). (gr. 3-7). pap. 5.99 (978-0-380-73242-5(4) , Harper Trophy) HarperCollins Pubs.

—Night Journeys. 2000. (978-0-606-17978-2(X)); (gr. 5-8). lib. bdg. 14.15 (978-0-613-22094-1(3)) Tandem Library Bks.

Bruchac, Joseph. The Arrow over the Door. Watling, James, illus. 2002. 96p. (J). pap. 4.99 (978-0-14-130571-4(1) , Puffin) Penguin Group (USA) Inc.

—The Arrow over the Door. 1998. (Illus.). 96p. (J). (gr. 2-4). 15.99 (978-0-8037-2078-7(5) , Dial) Penguin Group (USA) Inc.

De Angeli, Marguerite. Thee, Hannah! De Angeli, Marguerite, illus. 2nd ed. 2000. (Illus.). 112p. (J). (gr. 3-7). pap. 15.99 (978-0-8361-9106-6(4)) Herald Pr.

Rinaldi, Ann. Finishing Becca: A Story about Peggy Shippen & Benedict Arnold. 2004. (Great Episodes Ser.). 384p. (YA). pap. 6.95 (978-0-15-205079-5(5) , Gulliver Bks.) Harcourt Children's Bks.

Ruby, Lois. Steal Away Home. 1999. 208p. (J). (gr. 3-7). pap. 5.99 (978-0-689-82435-7(1) , Aladdin) Simon & Schuster Children's Publishing.

—Steal Away Home. 1999. 192p. lib. bdg. 11.64 (978-0-606-15921-0(5)); (gr. 3-6). lib. bdg. 13.00 (978-0-613-12154-5(6)) Tandem Library Bks.

Vernon, Louise A. Key to the Prison. Eitzen, Allan, illus. 2nd ed. 2002. (Louise A. Vernon's Religious Heritage Ser.). 144p. (YA). (gr. 4-9). 7.99 (978-0-8361-1813-1(8)) Herald Pr.

SOCIOLOGY

see also Cities and Towns; Civilization; Communism; Emigration and Immigration; Equality; Ethnic Relations; Labor and Laboring Classes; Population; Primitive Societies; Psychology; Race Relations; Social Change; Social Classes; Social History; Social Problems; Socialism

Arantowicz, Gerard. Differences. 2002. (Illus.). (J). pap. 11.95 (978-1-58597-155-8(3)) Leathers Publishing.

Austin and Nelson Publishers Staff. Social Studies Mind Stretches. 1998. 96p. (gr. 6-8). 9.99 (978-1-56822-746-7(9) , IF2499) School Specialty Publishing.

Berendes, Mary. People. 2007. (WordBooks/Libros de Palabras Ser.). (SPA & ENG.). 24p. (J). 19.93 (***978-1-59296-800-8(7)***) Child's World, Inc., The.

Berry, Joy Wilt. Being Good: A Social Skills Book About. Bartholomew, illus. rev. ed. 2000. (Living Skills Ser.: Vol. 6). 48p. (J). (gr. 1-7). pap. 4.95 (978-1-58634-115-2(4)) Goldstar Publishing, Inc.

Blundell, Jonathan, et al. Sociology AS: The Complete Companion AQA. 2003. (Illus.). 176p. pap. 35.00 (978-0-7487-7212-4(X)) Nelson Thornes Ltd. GBR. *Dist:* Trans-Atlantic Pubns., Inc.

Boehm, Richard G., et al. Game Time! The World. 1999. (Harcourt Brace Social Studies). (gr. k-7). pap. 9.40 (978-0-15-312372-6(9)) Harcourt Schl. Pubs.

Borgenicht, David & Epstein, Robin. The Worst-Case Scenario Survival Handbook: Junior Edition. Gonzales, Chuck, illus. 2007. 128p. (J). (gr. 4-7). pap. 9.95 (***978-0-8118-6065-9(5)***) Chronicle Bks. LLC.

Cook, Diane. Mohandas K. Gandi: Spiritual Leader. 2002. (Great Names Ser.). (Illus.). 32p. (J). (gr. 3 up). lib. bdg. (978-1-59084-143-3(3)) Mason Crest Pubs.

Cook, Diane & Gauguin, Paul. Great Names, 27 vols., Set. 2002. (Great Names Ser.). (Illus.). 32p. (J). (gr. 3 up). lib. bdg. (978-1-59084-133-4(6)) Mason Crest Pubs.

Coupe, Robert. People from the Past. 2002. (Junior Adventure Ser.). (Illus.). 32p. (J). (gr. 3 up). lib. bdg. (978-1-59084-194-5(8)) Mason Crest Pubs.

Days That Changed the World, 6 bks. Incl. D-Day. Hynson, Colin. lib. bdg. 30.00 (978-0-8368-5568-5(X)); Fall of the Berlin Wall. Smith, Jeremy. lib. bdg. 30.00 (978-0-8368-5569-2(8)); First Man in Space. Cullen, David. lib. bdg. 30.00 (978-0-8368-5570-8(1)); First "Test-Tube Baby" MacDonald, Fiona. lib. bdg. 30.00 (978-0-8368-5567-8(1)); Release of Nelson Mandela. Beecroft, Simon. lib. bdg. 30.00 (978-0-8368-5571-5(X)); September 11th Terrorist Attacks. MacDonald, Fiona. lib. bdg. 30.00 (978-0-8368-5572-2(8)); (J). (gr. 5 up). (Illus.). 48p. 2004. Set lib. bdg. 180.00 (978-0-8368-5566-1(3), World Almanac Library) Stevens, Gareth Inc.

Dingles, Molly. Oval Opera. Brodie, Neale, illus. 2006. (Community of Shapes Ser.). 29p. (J). (***978-1-59646-047-8(4)***) Dingles & Co.

—Star Ship. Brodie, Neale, illus. 2006. (Community of Shapes Ser.). 29p. (J). (***978-1-59646-039-3(3)***) Dingles & Co.

—Sweet Hearts. Brodie, Neale, illus. 2006. (Community of Shapes Ser.). (J). (***978-1-59646-037-9(7)***) Dingles & Co.

Gerdes, Louise. What are the Causes of Prostitution? 2007. (At Issue Ser.). 128p. (J). (gr. 10-12). 29.95 (***978-0-7377-2737-1(3)***, Greenhaven Pr., Inc.) Thomson Gale.

Gottfried, Ted. Homelessness: Whose Problem Is It? 1999. (Issue & Debate Ser.: up). 128p. (gr. 7-12). lib. bdg. 25.90 (978-0-7613-0953-6(5), Twenty-First Century Bks.) Lerner Publishing Group.

Hall, M. C. Polish Americans. 2003. (We Are America Ser.). 32p. pap. 6.95 (978-1-4034-3137-0(X)) Heinemann Library.

Holt, Rinehart and Winston Staff. Psychology & Sociology: Study Skills with Reading Guide. 3rd ed. 2002. pap. 23.80 (978-0-03-064652-2(9)) Holt, Rinehart & Winston.

—Taks Every Day! Activities for People, Places & Change. 3rd ed. 2002. (Illus.). pap. 45.60 (978-0-03-066702-2(X)) Holt, Rinehart & Winston.

Hovanec, Erin M. Get Involved! A Girl's Guide to Volunteering. 1999. (Girls' Guides). (Illus.). 48p. (YA). (gr. 5-8). lib. bdg. 23.95 (978-0-8239-2985-6(X), GGGEIN) Rosen Publishing Group, Inc., The.

Ideas of the Modern World, 4 bks., Set. 2001. (Illus.). lib. bdg. 71.92 (978-0-7398-3162-5(3)) Raintree.

Kalman, Bobbie. What Is a Community? From A to Z. 2000. (978-0-606-18070-2(2)) Tandem Library Bks.

—What Is a Community? from A to Z. 1999. (AlphaBasiCs Ser.). (Illus.). 32p. (J). (gr. 2-3). pap. (978-0-86505-414-1(2)); lib. bdg. (978-0-86505-384-7(7)) Crabtree Publishing Co.

Marx, Trish. One Boy from Kosovo. 2000. (Illus.). (YA). (gr. 2-5). 24p. 15.95 (978-0-688-17732-4(8)); 32p. 15.89 (978-0-688-17733-1(6)) HarperCollins Pubs.

McFall, Sally, ed. Pro/Con, 12 vols. 2002. (Illus.). (YA). (978-0-7172-5928-1(5)); (978-0-7172-5929-8(3)); (978-0-7172-5930-4(7)); (978-0-7172-5931-1(5)); (978-0-7172-5932-8(3)); (978-0-7172-5933-5(1)); (978-0-7172-5754-6(1)); (978-0-7172-5755-3(X)); (978-0-7172-5756-0(8)); (978-0-7172-5757-7(6)); (978-0-7172-5758-4(4)); (978-0-7172-5759-1(2)) Scholastic Library Publishing. (Grolier).

—Pro/Con 3, 12 vols. 2004. (Illus.). (YA). 339.00 (978-0-7172-5927-4(7), Grolier) Scholastic Library Publishing.

McGraw-Hill Staff. Sociology & You. 2002. stu. ed. 90.00 (978-0-07-829301-6(4), 9780078293016); (C). stu. ed. 90.00 (978-0-07-828576-9(3), 9780078285769) Glencoe/McGraw-Hill.

—Sociology & You, Student Edition. 2006. 90.00 (***978-0-07-874519-5(5)***, 9780078745195) Glencoe/McGraw-Hill.

—Sociology & You, StudentWorks. 2007. (C). cd-rom 102.00 (***978-0-07-878105-6(1)***, 9780078781056) Glencoe/McGraw-Hill.

McGraw-Hill Staff. Understanding Sociology. 2nd ed. 2000. (C). stu. ed. 86.00 (978-0-07-823684-6(3), 9780078236846) Glencoe/McGraw-Hill.

Milet Limited Publishing Staff & Swain, Gwenyth. Carrying. 2000. (Small World Ser.). (Illus.). 24p. (J). (BEN & ENG.). pap. 9.95 (978-1-84059-123-1(4)); (CHI & ENG., pap. 9.95 (978-1-84059-124-8(2)); (GUJ & ENG., pap. 9.95 (978-1-84059-125-5(0)); (PAN & ENG., pap. 9.95 (978-1-84059-126-2(9)); (TUR, URD & ENG., pap. 9.95 (978-1-84059-127-9(7)); (ENG & URD., pap. 9.95 (978-1-84059-128-6(5)); (VIE & ENG., pap. 9.95 (978-1-84059-129-3(3)) Milet Publishing.

—Carrying. Al-Hamdi, Ahmed, tr. from ENG. 2nd ed. 2000. (Small World Ser.). (ARA & ENG., Illus.). 24p. (J). pap. 9.95 (978-1-84059-122-4(6)) Milet Publishing.

—Celebrating. 2000. (Small World Ser.). (Illus.). 24p. (J). (BEN & ENG.). pap. 9.95 (978-1-84059-131-6(5)); (CHI & ENG., pap. 9.95 (978-1-84059-132-3(3)); (GUJ & ENG., pap. 9.95 (978-1-84059-133-0(1)); (PAN & ENG., pap. 9.95 (978-1-84059-134-7(X)); (URD & ENG., pap. 9.95 (978-1-84059-136-1(6)) Milet Publishing.

—Celebrating. Wood, Kim Marie, tr. from ENG. 2000. (Small World Ser.). (VIE & ENG., Illus.). 24p. (J). pap. 9.95 (978-1-84059-137-8(4)) Milet Publishing.

—Celebrating. 2nd ed. 2000. (Small World Ser.). (TUR & ENG., Illus.). 24p. (J). pap. 9.95 (978-1-84059-135-4(8)) Milet Publishing.

—Celebrating. Al-Hamdi, Ahmed, tr. from ENG. 2nd ed. 2000. (Small World Ser.). (ARA & ENG., Illus.). 24p. (J). pap. 9.95 (978-1-84059-130-9(7)) Milet Publishing.

Morrow, Carol. Forgiveness Is Smart for the Heart. Alley, R. W., illus. 2003. (Elf-Help Books for Kids). 32p. (J). per. 6.95 (978-0-87029-370-2(2)) Abbey Pr.

The Need to Know Library: Making Informed Choices, 8 bks. Incl. Everything You Need to Know about Abusive Relationships. Rue, Nancy N. (J). 1998. lib. bdg. 25.25 (978-0-8239-2832-3(2), NTABRE); Everything You Need to Know about AIDS. Taylor, Barbara. Rosen, Ruth C., ed. (J). 1998. lib. bdg. 25.25 (978-0-8239-2833-0(0), NTAIDS); Everything You Need to Know about an Alcoholic Parent. Shuker, Nancy. (YA). 1998. lib. bdg. 25.25 (978-0-8239-2869-9(1), NTALPA); Everything You Need to Know about Birth Control. Mucciolo, Gary. (YA). 2000. lib. bdg. 25.25 (978-0-8239-3301-3(6)); Everything You Need to Know about Decision-Making. Parker, Julie F. (YA). 1998. lib. bdg. 25.25 (978-0-8239-2746-3(6), NTDEMA); Everything You Need to Know about Living with Your Baby & Your Parents under One Roof. Simpson, Carolyn. (YA). 1998. lib. bdg. 25.25 (978-0-8239-2840-8(3), NTLIBA); Everything You Need to Know about Self-Mutilation : A Helping Book for Teens Who Hurt Themselves. Ng, Gina. (YA). 1998. lib. bdg. 25.25 (978-0-8239-2758-6(X), NTSEMU); Everything You Need to Know When You Are the Victim of a Violent Crime. Palmer, Jed. (YA). 1998. lib. bdg. 25.25 (978-0-8239-2622-0(2), NTVICR); 64p. (gr. 4-6). (Illus.). Set lib. bdg. 176.75 (978-0-8239-9439-7(2)) Rosen Publishing Group, Inc., The.

O'Connell, Diane. People Person: The Story of Sociologist Marta Tienda. 2006. (Women's Adventures in Science Ser.). 128p. pap. 9.95 (978-0-309-09557-0(3), Joseph Henry Pr.) National Academies Pr.

—People Person: The Story of Sociologist Marta Tienda. 2005. (Women's Adventures in Science Ser.). (Illus.). 108p. (YA). (gr. 5-8). 31.00 (978-0-531-16781-6(X), Watts, Franklin) Scholastic Library Publishing.

Powell, Phelan. Major Unsolved Crimes. Sarat, Austin, ed. 1999. (Crime, Justice & Punishment Ser.). (Illus.). 80p. (J). (gr. 7-12). 30.00 (978-0-7910-4277-9(4), Chelsea Hse.) Facts On File, Inc.

Raintree Steck-Vaughn Staff. Along the Beach: Level B. 2000. (Read All about It Ser.). (Illus.). (J). pap. 4.95 (978-0-8114-3792-9(2)) Steck-Vaughn.

Raintree Steck-Vaughn Staff, ed. Talking Points. 2000. (J). pap. 271.20 (978-0-8172-5323-3(8)) Raintree.

—We Come From... 1999. (Illus.). (J). 63.92 (978-0-7398-2685-0(9)) Raintree.

Return of the Native. (ARA., Illus.). 48p. (J). 12.00 (978-0-86685-625-6(0)) International Bk. Ctr., Inc.

Riera, Mike. Surviving High School: Making the Most of the High School Years. 2004. (Illus.). 160p. (gr. 8-12). pap. 12.95 (978-0-89087-825-5(0), Celestial Arts Publishing Company) Ten Speed Pr.

Ring, Susan. Helping Hands. 2005. (J). (978-0-7368-5306-4(5)); (Illus.). 17p. (978-0-7368-5270-8(0)) Capstone Pr., Inc.

Simmons, Rachel. Odd Girl Speaks Out. 2004. (gr. 7-12). lib. bdg. 15.10 (978-0-613-70533-2(5)) Tandem Library Bks.

Slattery, Martin. Key Ideas in Sociology. 2003. (Illus.). 304p. pap. 20.75 (978-0-7487-6565-2(4)) Nelson Thornes Ltd. GBR. *Dist:* International Specialized Bk. Services.

Suen, Anastasia. Medicos Sin Fronteras. 2004. (Organizaciones de Ayuda Ser.). (SPA & ENG., Illus.). 24p. (J). (gr. 3-6). lib. bdg. 17.25 (978-0-8239-6860-2(X), Buenas Letra) Rosen Publishing Group, Inc., The.

Talking About, 6 vols. 1999. (Illus.). (J). 154.14 (978-0-7398-1507-6(5)) Raintree.

Weitzman, Elizabeth. Staying in a Shelter. 2004. (Lets Talk Library). (Illus.). 24p. (J). lib. bdg. 18.75 (978-0-8239-6812-1(X), PowerKids Pr.) Rosen Publishing Group, Inc., The.

21st Century Debates: Genetics, Internet, Media, Surveillance, 4 bks., Set. 2001. (Illus.). 64p. (YA). (gr. 6-8). 108.48 (978-0-7398-3176-2(3)) Raintree.

SOCIOLOGY, RURAL

see also Country Life; Peasantry

Pancella, Peggy. Comunidades Agrícolas. 2005. (SPA & ENG., Illus.). 32p. (J). (978-1-4034-6233-6(X)); pap. (978-1-4034-6239-8(9)) Heinemann Library.

—Farm Community. 2005. (Illus.). 32p. (J). pap. (978-1-4034-6222-0(4)); lib. bdg. 25.36 (978-1-4034-6216-9(X)) Heinemann Library.

Sterling, Kristin. Rural Communities. 2008. (First Step Nonfiction - Communities Ser.). (J). lib. bdg. 18.60 (***978-0-8225-8599-2(5)***, Lerner Pubns.) Lerner Publishing Group.

SOCIOLOGY, URBAN

see also Cities and Towns

Hopkinson, Deborah. Shutting Out the Sky: Life in the Tenements of New York, 1880-1924. 2003. (Illus.). 144p. (J). pap. 17.95 (978-0-439-37590-0(8), Orchard Bks.) Scholastic, Inc.

MacAulay, Kelley. Habitats de Jardín. 2007. (SPA.). 32p. (J). (gr. 1-2). (***978-0-7787-8335-0(9)***) Crabtree Publishing Co.

MacAulay, Kelley & Kalman, Bobbie. Habitats de Jardín. rev. ed. 2007. (SPA.). 32p. (J). (gr. 1-2). pap. (***978-0-7787-8359-6(6)***) Crabtree Publishing Co.

SOCRATES

Bowen, Richard. Socrates: Greek Philosopher. 2002. (Great Names Ser.). (Illus.). 32p. (J). (gr. 3 up). lib. bdg. (978-1-59084-150-1(6)) Mason Crest Pubs.

Usher, Mark David. Wise Guy: The Life & Philosophy of Socrates. Bramhall, William, illus. 2005. 40p. (J). 16.00 (978-0-374-31249-7(4), Farrar, Straus & Giroux (BYR)) Farrar, Straus & Giroux.

Zannos, Susan. The Life & Times of Socrates. 2004. (Biography from Ancient Civilizations Ser.). (Illus.). 48p. (J). (gr. 4-8). lib. bdg. 29.95 (978-1-58415-282-8(6)) Mitchell Lane Pubs., Inc.

SOFTBALL

Adelson, Bruce. The Composite Guide to Softball. 2000. (Composite Guide Ser.). (J). (gr. 8-12). 28.00 (978-0-7910-5867-1(0), Chelsea Hse.) Facts On File, Inc.

Barron's Educational Editorial Staff. Winning Women in Baseball & Softball. 2000. (Sport Success Ser.). 112p. (J). (gr. 5-9). pap. 6.95 (978-0-7641-1231-7(7)) Barron's Educational Series, Inc.

Blackall, Bernie. Softball. 1998. (Top Sport Ser.). (Illus.). 32p. (J). (978-1-57572-634-2(3)) Heinemann Library.

Bonney, Barbara. Softball: Pitching. 1998. (Softball Ser.). (Illus.). (J). lib. bdg. 23.93 (978-0-86593-478-8(9)) Rourke Publishing, LLC.

Bratton, Deborah B. & Bratton, Ashley D. Record-a-Sport Baseball & Softball Organizer. Bratton, Deborah B. & Bratton, Ashley D., eds. Bratton, Deborah B. & Bratton, Ashley D., illus. 2003. (Illus.). (J). (gr. 1 up). 18.95 (978-1-931746-03-8(6)) Sport Your Stuff Corp.

Brill, Marlene Targ. Baseball & Softball. 2001. (Winning Women in Sports Ser.). (Illus.). 104p. (YA). (gr. 4 up). lib. bdg. 14.95 (978-1-56674-306-8(0)) Forest Hse. Publishing Co., Inc.

Douty, Sheila Cornell & Cohen, Judith Love. You Can Be a Woman Softball Player. 2000. (Illus.). 40p. (YA). (gr. 4-9). 13.95 (978-1-880599-47-1(3)); 7.00 (978-1-880599-46-4(5)) Cascade Pass, Inc.

Fauchald, Nick. Batter Up! You Can Play Softball. Rooney, Ronnie, illus. 2005. (Game Day Ser.). 24p. (J). (ps). lib. bdg. 22.60 (978-1-4048-1152-2(4)) Picture Window Bks.

Forkos, Heather. Dorothy "Dot" Richardson. 2001. (J). pap. (978-0-7910-6536-5(7)); (Illus.). 64p. (gr. 3 up). 25.00 (978-0-7910-6535-8(9)) Facts On File, Inc. (Chelsea Hse.).

Gregory, Paul. Baseball & Softball. 3rd ed. 1999. (Play the Game Ser.). (Illus.). 80p. (J). (gr. 3-7). pap. 10.95 (978-0-7063-7713-2(3)) Ward Lock GBR. *Dist:* Sterling Publishing Co., Inc.

Hofstetter, Adam B. Softball: Rules, Tips, Strategy, & Safety. 2006. (Sports from Coast to Coast Ser.). (Illus.). 48p. (J). (gr. 5-8). lib. bdg. 26.50 (978-1-4042-0996-1(4)) Rosen Publishing Group, Inc., The.

Lockman, Darcy. Softball for Fun! 2006. (Sports for Fun! Ser.). (Illus.). 48p. (J). (gr. 3-5). 22.60 (978-0-7565-1682-6(X)) Compass Point Bks.

Migliaccio, Eric. Baseball & Softball Easy Olympic Sports Reader. 2004. (U. S. Olympic Committee Easy Olympic Sports Readers Ser.). (Illus.). 16p. (J). pap. 2.99 (978-1-58000-110-6(6)) Griffin Publishing Group.

Nitz, Kristin Wolden. Softball. King, Andy, photos by. 2005. (Play-by-Play Ser.). (Illus.). 80p. (gr. 4-8). pap., lib. bdg. 23.93 (978-0-8225-9875-6(2)) Lerner Publishing Group.

Schwartz, Heather E. Girls' Softball: Winning on the Diamond. 2007. (Illus.). 32p. (J). (978-0-7368-6824-2(0)) Capstone Pr., Inc.

U. S. Olympic Committee. A Basic Guide to Softball. 2001. (Olympic Guides). (Illus.). 160p. (J). (gr. 6 up). lib. bdg. 23.33 (978-0-8368-2798-9(8)) Stevens, Gareth Inc.

Wesley, Ann. Competitive Fastpitch Softball for Girls. 2005. (SportsGirl Ser.). (Illus.). 64p. (YA). (gr. 5-8). lib. bdg. 26.50 (978-0-8239-3409-6(8)) Rosen Publishing Group, Inc., The.

YMCA of the USA Staff. Playing YMCA Baseball & Softball: Bronze Edition. 2000. (Illus.). 48p. (J). pap. 6.00 (978-0-7360-3040-3(9), YMCA of the U.S.A.) Human Kinetics Pubs.

—Playing YMCA Baseball & Softball: Gold Edition. 2000. (Illus.). 48p. (J). pap. 6.00 (978-0-7360-3042-7(5), YMCA of the U.S.A.) Human Kinetics Pubs.

—Playing YMCA Baseball & Softball: Silver Edition. 2000. (Illus.). 48p. (J). pap. 6.00 (978-0-7360-3041-0(7), YMCA of the U.S.A.) Human Kinetics Pubs.

SOFTBALL—FICTION

Chetkowski, Emily. Sister Sluggers. 2007. per. 15.95 (***978-1-933002-35-4(2)***) PublishingWorks.

Christopher, Matt. Windmill Windup: Windmill Windup: the #1 Sports Series for Kids. ed. 2005. (Sports Classics I Ser.). 139p. (J). lib. bdg. 15.00 (978-1-59054-778-6(0)) Fitzgerald Bks.

Cross, Steve. Walt Michaels Is A Wienie. 2007. (YA). pap. 13.95 (***978-1-59705-808-7(4)***) Wings ePress, Inc.

The Grumpy Millionaire: Individual Title Six-Packs. (Bookweb Ser.). 32p. (gr. 5 up). 34.00 (978-0-7635-3777-7(2)) Rigby Education.

Johnson, Maureen G. The Key to the Golden Firebird. 2005. 304p. (YA). reprint ed. pap. 7.99 (978-0-06-054140-8(7), Harper Trophy) HarperCollins Pubs.

Mackel, Kathy. MadCat. 2005. (Illus.). 192p. (J). 15.99 (978-0-06-054869-8(X)); lib. bdg. 16.89 (978-0-06-054870-4(3)) HarperCollins Pubs.

Mackey, Weezie Kerr. Throwing a Like Girl. 2007. 272p. (J). (gr. 7 up). 16.99 (***978-0-7614-5342-0(3)***) Cavendish, Marshall Corp.

RealBuzz Studios Staff. Hits & Misses. 2007. 128p. (YA). No. 1. pap. 4.97 (978-1-59789-569-9(5)); No. 2. pap. 4.97 (978-1-59789-570-5(9)); No. 3. pap. 4.97 (978-1-59789-571-2(7)); No. 4. pap. 4.97 (978-1-59789-572-9(5)) Barbour Publishing, Inc. (Barbour Bks.).

Ritter, John H. Under the Baseball Moon. 2008. 320p. (J). (gr. 6). 6.99 (***978-0-14-241090-5(X)***, Puffin); 2006. (Illus.). 224p. (YA). (gr. 5). 16.99 (978-0-399-23623-5(6), Philomel) Penguin Group (USA) Inc.

Smith, Stephen & Caldwell, Lise. Strike Three. 2006. (Game on for Girls Ser.). 128p. (J). pap. 5.99 (978-0-7847-1729-5(X), 42146) Standard Publishing.

Tocher, Timothy. Playing for Pride. 2002. (J). 110p. (978-0-88166-424-9(3)); 120p. pap. 4.95 (978-0-689-02453-5(3)) Meadowbrook Pr.

Van Draanen, Wendelin. Sammy Keyes & the Search for Snake Eyes. VanDraanen, Wendelin, illus. 2003. (Sammy Keyes Ser.: Bk. 7). pap. 36.95 incl. audio (978-1-59112-273-9(2)); pap. 54.95 incl. audio compact disk (978-1-59112-281-4(3)) Live Oak Media.

—Sammy Keyes & the Search for Snake Eyes. (Sammy Keyes Ser.: Bk. 7). (gr. 5). 2003. 320p. (J). pap. 5.99 (978-0-440-41900-6(X), Yearling); 2002. 272p. lib. bdg. 17.99 (978-0-375-91175-0(8), Knopf Bks. for Young Readers) Random Hse. Children's Bks.

—Sammy Keyes & the Sisters of Mercy. VanDraanen, Wendelin, illus. 2001. (Sammy Keyes Ser.: Bk. 3). pap. 49.95 incl. audio compact disk (978-0-87499-838-2(7)) Live Oak Media.

—Sammy Keyes & the Sisters of Mercy. 1999. (Sammy Keyes Ser.: Bk. 3). (gr. 5-8). lib. bdg. 13.00 (978-0-613-22298-3(9)) Tandem Library Bks.

Winkler, Henry & Oliver, Lin. The Zippity Zinger. 2004. (Hank Zipzer Ser.: No. 4). 160p. (J). (gr. 2-6). pap. 29.00 incl. audio (978-1-4000-9009-9(1), Listening Library) Random Hse. Audio Publishing Group.

—The Zippity Zinger. 2006. (Hank Zipzer Ser.: No. 4). (J). (gr. 3-8). 24.21 (978-1-59961-103-7(1)) Spotlight.

Wolff, Virginia Euwer. Bat 6. 256p. (J). (gr. 4-6). pap. 4.99 (978-0-8072-8223-6(5)); 2004. (gr. 5-9). pap. 36.00 incl. audio (978-0-8072-8222-9(7), YYA144SP) Random Hse. Audio Publishing Group. (Listening Library).

—Bat 6. 240p. (gr. 5-9). 2000. (Illus.). (J). pap. 4.99 (978-0-590-89800-3(0), Scholastic Reference); 1998. (YA). pap. 16.95 (978-0-590-89799-0(3)) Scholastic, Inc.

—Bat 6. 2000. (Illus.). (J). 11.64 (978-0-606-18516-5(X)); 1999. (gr. 5-8). lib. bdg. 13.00 (978-0-613-28413-4(5)) Tandem Library Bks.

SOIL EROSION

see Erosion

SOIL FERTILITY

see Soils

SOILS

see also Clay

also headings beginning with the word Soil

Ballard, Carol. Soil. 2004. (Using Materials Ser.). (Illus.). 32p. (J). pap. 7.50 (978-1-4109-0897-1(6)) Harcourt Schl. Pubs.

Bocknek, Jonathan. The Science of Soil. 1999. (Living Science Ser.). (Illus.). 32p. (J). (gr. 2 up). lib. bdg. 23.93 (978-0-8368-2468-1(7)) Stevens, Gareth Inc.

Bourgeois, Paulette. The Dirt on Dirt. Newbigging, Martha, illus. 2008. 48p. pap. (***978-1-55453-102-8(0)***) Kids Can Pr., Ltd.

Burton, Jane & Taylor, Kim. The Nature & Science of Mud. Bingxin, Wang et al, trs. 2000. (Nature & Science Ser.). (CHI & ENG., Illus.). 32p. (J). 8.95 (978-7-5600-1748-8(7)) Foreign Languages Teaching & Research Pr. CHN. *Dist:* Cheng & Tsui Co.

Chappell, Rachel M. So What about Soil? A Book about Form & Function. 2008. (J). (***978-1-60044-540-8(3)***) Rourke Publishing, LLC.

Cooper, Sharon Katz. Using Soil. 2007. (Illus.). 24p. (J). (***978-1-4034-9321-7(9)***); lib. bdg. 21.36 (***978-1-4034-9313-2(8)***) Heinemann.

Dewey, Jennifer Owings. Mud Matters: Stories from a Mud Lover. Dewey, Jennifer Owings, illus. Trimble, Stephen, photos by. 1998. (Accelerated Reader Bks.). (Illus.). 72p. (J). (gr. 2-5). 15.95 (978-0-7614-5014-6(9), Cavendish Children's Bks.) Cavendish, Marshall Corp.

Dirt. (Amazing Science Ser.). 24p. (J). 7.95 (978-1-4048-0331-2(9)) Picture Window Bks.

Ditchfield, Christin. Soil. (True Bks.). (Illus.). 48p. (J). (gr. 3-5). 2003. pap. 6.95 (978-0-516-29368-4(0)); 2002. pap. 25.00 (978-0-516-22344-5(5)) Scholastic Library Publishing. (Children's Pr.).

—Soil. 2002. (gr. 3-6). lib. bdg. 15.25 (978-0-613-59549-0(1)) Tandem Library Bks.

Faulkner, Rebecca. Soil. 2007. (J). (***978-1-4109-2753-8(9)***); pap. (***978-1-4109-2761-3(X)***) Steck-Vaughn.

Flanagan, Alice K. Soil. 2000. (Simply Science Ser.). (Illus.). 32p. (J). (gr. 3 up). lib. bdg. 19.93 (978-0-7565-0035-1(4)) Compass Point Bks.

Gardner, Robert. Super Science Projects about Earth's Soil & Water. LaBaff, Tom, illus. 2007. (Rockin' Earth Science Experiments Ser.). 48p. (J). (gr. 4-6). lib. bdg. 23.93 (978-0-7660-2735-0(X), Enslow Elementary) Enslow Pubs., Inc.

Glaser, Jason. Soil. 2006. (First Facts Ser.). (J). (978-0-7368-4299-0(3)) Capstone Pr., Inc.

Graham, Ian. Soil: A Resource Our World Depends On. 2004. (Heinemann Infosearch Ser.). (Illus.). 32p. (J). (ps-k). lib. bdg. 27.07 (978-1-4034-5618-2(6)); pap. 7.50 (978-1-4034-5626-7(7)) Heinemann Library.

Gurney, Beth. Sand & Soil. 2004. (Rocks, Minerals, & Resources Ser.). (Illus.). 32p. (J). (978-0-7787-1417-0(9)); pap. (978-0-7787-1449-1(7)) Crabtree Publishing Co.

Hewitt, Sally. Rocks & Soil. 2007. (J). (***978-1-59604-138-7(2)***) Stargazer Bks.

S

Hodge, Judith. Las riquezas de la tierra & Riches from Earth. 2005. spiral bd. 84.00 (*978-1-4108-5716-3(6)) Benchmark Education Co.

Holt, Rinehart and Winston Staff. Holt Science & Technology Chapter 10: Earth Science: Weathering of Soil. 5th ed. 2004. (Illus.). pap. 12.86 (978-0-03-030311-1(7)) Holt, Rinehart & Winston.

Investigating Earth Systems Soil. 2002. stu. ed., bds. (978-1-58591-108-0(9)); 2001. stu. ed. (978-1-58591-073-1(2)) It's About Time, Herff Jones Education Diiv.

Jennings, Terry. Rocas y Suelos (Rocks & Soils) (SPA.). 32p. (J). 6.95 (978-84-348-1912-2(0)) SM Ediciones ESP. *Dist:* AIMS International Bks., Inc.

John Farndon. Life in the Soil. 2004. (J). 23.70 (978-1-4103-0124-6(9) , Blackbirch Pr., Inc.) Thomson Gale.

Korb, Rena B. Digging on Dirt. Reibeling, Brandon, illus. 2007. (Science Rocks Ser.). 32p. (J). (ps-4). lib. bdg. 27.07 (*978-1-60270-038-3(9) , Looking Glass Library) Magic Wagon.

Lindeen, Carol. Soil Basics. 2008. (J). (*978-1-4296-0003-3(9) , Pebble Bks.) Capstone Pr., Inc.

—Solids, Liquids, & Gases. 2008. (J). (*978-1-4296-0002-6(0)) Capstone Pr., Inc.

Lunis, Natalie. Rocks & Soil. Ellis, Linette, ed. 1998. (Early Science Ser.). 16p. (J). (ps-2). pap., stu. ed. 3.33 (978-1-56784-384-2(0)); (Illus.). pap. 16.95 (978-1-56784-383-5(2)) Sundance/Newbridge Educational Publishing.

Martin, Michael. Earth Evidence. 2007. 32p. (J). (978-0-7368-6787-0(2)) Capstone Pr., Inc.

Morris, Neil. Rocks & Soil. 2002. (Our World Ser.). (Illus.). 32p. (J). lib. bdg. 24.25 (978-1-930643-79-6(9)) Chrysalis Education.

Nelson, Robin. Soil. 2005. (First Step Nonfiction Ser.). (Illus.). 23p. (J). (ps-7). 18.60 (978-0-8225-2612-4(3) , Lerner Pubns.) Lerner Publishing Group.

Newson, Lesley & Wadsworth, Pamela. Rhagor Am Greigiau, Pridd a Thywydd. 2005. (WEL., Illus.). 24p. pap. (978-1-85596-238-5(1)) Dref Wen.

Oxlade, Chris. How We Use Soil, 6, Pack. 2004. (Using Materials Ser.). (Illus.). (J). pap. 40.50 (978-1-4109-0904-6(2)) Harcourt Schl. Pubs.

—How We Use Soils. 2004. (Using Materials Ser.). (Illus.). 32p. (J). 25.70 (978-1-4109-0606-9(X)) Harcourt Schl. Pubs.

—Soil. 2002. (Materials, Materials, Materials Ser.). (Illus.). 32p. (J). (gr. k-2). lib. bdg. 22.79 (978-1-58810-587-5(3)); pap. 6.95 (978-1-4034-0088-8(1) , 91529) Heinemann Library.

Parker, Steve. Microlife That Lives in Soil. 2005. (J). (978-1-4109-1846-8(7)); pap. (978-1-4109-1851-2(3)) Steck-Vaughn.

Pascoe, Elaine. Soil. 2004. (Illus.). 24p. (J). (gr. 2-4). 22.45 (978-1-4103-0311-0(X) , Blackbirch Pr., Inc.) Thomson Gale.

Redlin, Janice L. Land Abuse & Soil Erosion. 2004. (Understanding Global Issues Ser.). (J). lib. bdg. (978-1-59036-237-2(3)) Weigl Pubs., Inc.

Richardson, Adele D. Soil. (Exploring the Earth Ser.). 24p. (J). pap. 6.95 (978-0-7368-3367-7(6)) Capstone Pr., Inc.

Richardson, Adele G. Soil. 2001. (Bridgestone Science Library). (Illus.). 24p. (J). (gr. 2-3). lib. bdg. 18.60 (978-0-7368-0954-2(6) , Bridgestone Bks.) Capstone Pr., Inc.

Rosinsky, Natalie M. Dirt: The Scoop on Soil. Boyd, Sheree, illus. 2004. (Amazing Science Ser.). 24p. (C). (gr. k-4). 22.60 (978-1-4048-0012-0(3)) Picture Window Bks.

Royston, Angela. Soil: Let's Look at a Garden. 2005. (Heinemann Read & Learn Ser.). (Illus.). 24p. (J). (978-1-4034-7674-6(8)); pap. (978-1-4034-7683-8(7)) Heinemann Library.

—Soil: Let's Look at a Garden. 2005. (J). (978-1-4109-1821-5(1)); pap. (978-1-4109-1830-7(0)) Steck-Vaughn.

Schmid, Eleonore. Living Earth. 2000. (Illus.). 32p. (J). (gr. k-3). pap. 6.95 (978-0-7358-1315-1(9)) North-South Bks., Inc.

Sian Revision Soil Studies. 2004. (J). (978-1-59242-071-1(0)) Delta Education, LLC.

Soil. 2007. 48p. (gr. 3-8). 26.20 (*978-0-7377-3638-0(0) , Kidhaven) Thomson Gale.

Stewart, Melissa. Down to Earth. 2004. (Investigate Science Ser.). (Illus.). 32p. (J). (gr. 1 up). lib. bdg. 21.26 (978-0-7565-0595-0(X)) Compass Point Bks.

—Soil. 2002. (Rocks & Minerals Ser.). (Illus.). 32p. (J). (gr. 4-6). lib. bdg. 24.22 (978-1-58810-260-7(2)); pap. 7.50 (978-1-4034-0096-3(2) , 91663) Heinemann Library.

Stille, Darlene R. Soil: Digging into Earth's Vital Resource. 2004. (Exploring Science Ser.). (Illus.). 48p. (J). 25.27 (978-0-7565-0857-9(6)) Compass Point Bks.

Tomecek, Steve. Dirt. Woodman, Nancy, illus. 2007. (Jump into Science Ser.). 32p. (J). (ps-3). 6.95 (978-1-4263-0089-9(1) , National Geographic Children's Bks.) National Geographic Society.

—Dirt: Jump into Science. Woodman, Nancy, illus. 2002. (Jump into Science Ser.). 32p. (J). (ps-3). 16.95 (978-0-7922-8204-4(3) , National Geographic Children's Bks.) National Geographic Society.

Wade, Mary Dodson. Tiny Life on the Ground. (Rookie Read-About Science Ser.). (Illus.). (J). 2006. 32p. (gr. 1-2). pap. 4.95 (978-0-516-25479-1(0)); 2005. 31p. (ps-ps). 20.50 (978-0-516-25298-8(4)) Scholastic Library Publishing. (Children's Pr.).

Wadsworth, Pamela. Creigiau, Pridd a Thywydd. 2005. (WEL., Illus.). 24p. pap. (978-1-85596-237-8(3)) Dref Wen.

Wadsworth, Pamela & Tate, Sylvia. Golwg Gyntaf Ar Greigiau, Pridd a Thywydd. 2005. (WEL., Illus.). 24p. pap. (978-1-85596-253-8(5)) Dref Wen.

Walker, Sally M. Soil. 2007. (Early Bird Earth Science Ser.). (Illus.). 48p. (J). 25.26 (978-0-8225-5948-1(X) , Lerner Pubns.) Lerner Publishing Group.

SOLAR ENERGY

Costain, Meredith. Power from the Sun. 2000. (gr. k-3). lib. bdg. 11.80 (978-0-613-30682-9(1)) Tandem Library Bks.

Gibson, Diane. Solar Power. 2001. (Sources of Energy Ser.). (Illus.). 24p. (J). (gr. 2-7). lib. bdg. 21.30 (978-1-887068-78-9(3)) Smart Apple Media.

Gould, Alan. Hot Water & Warm Homes from Sunlight. Gould, Alan et al, illus. Sneider, Cary I., photos by. rev. ed. 2005. (Great Explorations in Math & Science Ser.). 80p. 13.50 (978-1-931542-04-3(X) , GEMS) Univ. of California, Berkeley, Lawrence Hall of Science.

Graham, Ian. Solar Power. 1999. (Energy Forever? Ser.). (Illus.). 48p. (J). (gr. 3-7). lib. bdg. 27.12 (978-0-8172-5362-2(9)) Raintree.

Hirschmann, Kris. Solar Energy. 2005. (Our Environment Ser.). (Illus.). 48p. (J). (gr. 4-8). lib. bdg. 26.20 (978-0-7377-3049-4(8) , Greenhaven Pr., Inc.) Thomson Gale.

Jones, Susan. Solar Power of the Future: New Ways of Turning Sunlight into Energy. 2005. (Library of Future Energy). (Illus.). 64p. (YA). (gr. 7-12). lib. bdg. 26.50 (978-0-8239-3663-2(5)) Rosen Publishing Group, Inc., The.

Klutz Press Staff. The Solar Car Book. 2001. (Illus.). 48p. (J). spiral bd. 21.95 (978-1-57054-646-4(0)) Klutz.

Levete, Sarah. Solar Power. 2007. (Illus.). 32p. lib. bdg. (*978-1-59604-104-2(8) , 1262725) Stargazer Bks.

The Library of Future Energy. 2005. (Illus.). (gr. 7-12). lib. bdg. 212.00 (978-0-8239-3901-5(4)) Rosen Publishing Group, Inc., The.

Mahaney, Ian F. Solar Energy. 2007. (Illus.). 24p. pap. (978-1-4042-2188-8(3)); (J). (gr. 4-6). lib. bdg. 21.25 (978-1-4042-3479-6(9)) Rosen Publishing Group, Inc., The. (PowerKids Pr.).

Morris, Neil. Solar Power. 2006. (Energy Sources Ser.). (Illus.). 32p. (J). (978-1-58340-908-4(4)) Smart Apple Media.

Muschal, Frank. Energy from Wind, Sun, & Tides. 2008. (J). pap. 7.95 (*978-1-60279-096-4(5)) Cherry Lake Publishing.

—Energy fromWind, Sun, & Tides. 2008. (J). lib. bdg. 25.26 (*978-1-60279-046-9(9)) Cherry Lake Publishing.

Naff, Clay Farris. Solar Power. 2006. (Illus.). 244p. (gr. 10-12). 34.95 (978-0-7377-3565-9(1) , Greenhaven Pr., Inc.) Thomson Gale.

Parker, Steve. Solar Power. 2004. (Science Files Ser.). (Illus.). 32p. (J). (gr. 3 up). lib. bdg. 24.67 (978-0-8368-4032-2(1)) Stevens, Gareth Inc.

Petersen, Christine. Solar Power. 2004. (True Bks.). (Illus.). 48p. (J). 25.00 (978-0-516-22807-5(2) , Watts, Franklin) Scholastic Library Publishing.

Richards, Julie. Solar Power. 2003. 32p. (J). lib. bdg. 24.25 (978-1-58340-332-7(9)) Smart Apple Media.

Rooney, Anne. Solar Power. 2007. (J). pap. (*978-0-8368-8412-8(4)); 24p. (gr. 3-5). lib. bdg. 26.60 (*978-0-8368-8403-6(5)) Stevens, Gareth Inc.

Science stories foss spanish solar energy ea Cr05. 2005. (J). (978-1-59242-595-2(X)) Delta Education, LLC.

Sherman, Josepha. Solar Energy. 2004. (Fact Finders Ser.). (Illus.). 32p. (J). 16.95 (978-0-7368-2474-3(X)) Capstone Pr., Inc.

Solar Power. (Energy at Work Ser.). 32p. (J). 7.95 (978-0-7368-5194-7(1)) Capstone Pr., Inc.

Thomas, Isabel. Solar Power: The Pros & Cons. 2007. (J). lib. bdg. (*978-1-4042-3741-4(0) , Rosen Central) Rosen Publishing Group, Inc., The.

Walker, Niki. Harnessing Power from the Sun. 2006. (Energy Revolution Ser.). (Illus.). 32p. (J). (gr. 3-9). pap. (978-0-7787-2926-6(5)); lib. bdg. (978-0-7787-2912-9(5)) Crabtree Publishing Co.

SOLAR HEATING

see Solar Energy; Sun

SOLAR PHYSICS

see Sun

SOLAR POWER

see Solar Energy

SOLAR RADIATION

see also Solar Energy

Ring, Susan. El Sol. Ramos, Gloria, tr. 2005. (Illus.). 20p. (J). 15.93 (978-0-7368-4139-9(3) , Yellow Umbrella Bks.) Capstone Pr., Inc.

—The Sun. 2003. (Yellow Umbrella Books). (Illus.). 16p. (J). (gr. 1). lib. bdg. 14.60 (978-0-7368-2022-6(1) , Pebble Bks.) Capstone Pr., Inc.

—The Sun. 2003. (J). (978-0-7368-1714-1(X)) Yellow Umbrella Pr.

Stewart, Tobi Stanton. Solar Storms. 2003. (Reading Room Collection). (Illus.). 24p. (J). lib. bdg. 18.75 (978-0-8239-3709-7(7)) Rosen Publishing Group, Inc., The.

SOLAR SYSTEM

Ashby, Ruth. How the Solar System Was Formed. 2003. (New Solar System Ser.). (J). lib. bdg. 28.50 (978-1-58340-285-6(3)) Smart Apple Media.

Asimov, Isaac & Hantula, Richard. Isaac Asimov's 21st Century Library of the Universe: Set 1: The Solar System, 12 bks. rev. ed. Incl. Asteroids. 2003. lib. bdg. 24.67 (978-0-8368-3233-4(7)); Earth. 2002. lib. bdg. 24.67 (978-0-8368-3234-1(5)); Jupiter. 2002. lib. bdg. 24.67 (978-0-8368-3235-8(3)); Mars. 2003. lib. bdg. 24.67 (978-0-8368-3236-5(1)); Mercury. 2003. lib. bdg. 24.67 (978-0-8368-3237-2(X)); Moon. 2003. lib. bdg. 24.67 (978-0-8368-3238-9(8)); Neptune. 2003. lib. bdg. 24.67 (978-0-8368-3239-6(6)); Pluto & Charon. 2003. lib. bdg. 24.67 (978-0-8368-3240-2(X)); Saturn. 2003. lib. bdg. 24.67 (978-0-8368-3241-9(8)); Sun. 2003. lib. bdg. 24.67 (978-0-8368-3242-6(6)); Uranus. 2003. lib. bdg. 24.67 (978-0-8368-3243-3(4)); Venus. 2003. lib. bdg. 24.67 (978-0-8368-3244-0(2)); 32p. (YA). (gr. 3 up). (Illus.). 2003. Set lib. bdg. 296.04 (978-0-8368-3232-7(9)) Stevens, Gareth Inc.

—Our Planetary System. 2005. (Isaac Asimov's 21st Century Library of the Universe). (Illus.). 32p. (J). lib. bdg. 24.67 (978-0-8368-3969-2(2)) Stevens, Gareth Inc.

Barnes-Svarney, Patricia L. A Traveler's Guide to the Solar System. 2008. (Illus.). 96p. (J). pap. 6.95 (*978-1-4027-2628-6(7)) Sterling Publishing Co., Inc.

Becklake, John. Solar System. (Collectafact Ser.). (J). 2002. 14.95 (978-1-58728-698-8(X)); 2000. (Illus.). 48p. (gr. 1-5). 4.95 (978-1-58728-752-7(8)) T&N Children's Publishing. (Two Can Publishing).

Becklake, Sue. Space. 2004. (Picture Reference Ser.). (SPA., Illus.). 48p. (gr. 3-6). (J). pap. 7.95 (978-1-58728-660-5(2)); 13.95 (978-1-58728-653-7(X)) T&N Children's Publishing. (Two Can Publishing).

—Space: The Book & Disk That Work Together. 2000. (Interfact Reference Ser.). (Illus.). 48p. (J). (gr. 3-6). 19.95 incl. cd-rom (978-1-58728-473-1(1) , Two Can Publishing) T&N Children's Publishing.

Bell, Trudy E. Comets, Meteors, Asteroids, & the Outer Reaches. 2003. (New Solar System Ser.). (J). lib. bdg. 28.50 (978-1-58340-289-4(6)) Smart Apple Media.

Benchmark Education Staff, compiled by. Earth & Space. 2006. spiral bd. 215.00 (*978-1-4108-7106-0(1)); 2006. spiral bd. 239.00 (*978-1-4108-7120-6(7)); 2005. spiral bd. 110.00 (*978-1-4108-3873-5(0)) Benchmark Education Co.

—Our Solar System. 2006. spiral bd. 95.00 (*978-1-4108-7062-9(6)) Benchmark Education Co.

Berger, Melvin. Do Stars Have Points? 1999. (Question & Answer Ser.). (J). 12.75 (978-0-606-20054-7(1)) Tandem Library Bks.

Berger, Melvin & Berger, Gilda. Do Stars Have Points? Questions & Answers about Stars & Planets. Di Fate, Vincent, illus. 1999. (Scholastic Question & Answer Ser.). 48p. (J). (gr. 2-4). pap. 12.95 (978-0-590-13080-6(3) , Scholastic Reference) Scholastic, Inc.

Berger, Melvin & Berger, Gilda. Think Factory: Solar System. 2005. (Illus.). 47p. (J). (*978-0-439-51155-1(0)) Scholastic, Inc.

Birch, Robin. The Solar System. 2002. (Space Ser.). (Illus.). 32p. (J). (gr. k-2). 23.00 (978-0-7910-6969-1(9) , Chelsea Hse.) Facts On File, Inc.

Bond, Peter. Guide to Space: A Photographic Journey Through the Universe. 1999. (DK Guides Ser.). (Illus.). 64p. (J). (gr. 4-7). 19.99 (978-0-7894-3946-8(8)) Dorling Kindersley Publishing, Inc.

Branley, Franklyn M. The Planets in Our Solar System. O'Malley, Kevin, illus. 1998. (Let's-Read-and-Find-Out Science Ser.). 32p. (J). (gr. k-4). pap. 5.99 (978-0-06-445178-9(X)); Stage 2. 15.95 (978-0-06-027769-7(6)); Stage 2. 15.89 (978-0-06-027770-3(X)) HarperCollins Pubs.

Bredeson, Carmen. El Sistema Solar. 2004. (Rookie Readers - Spanish Ser.). (J). 19.50 (978-0-516-24446-4(9) , Watts, Franklin) Scholastic Library Publishing.

—El Sistema Solar: The Solar System. 2005. (Rookie Espanol: Ciencias Ser.). (SPA., Illus.). 32p. (J). (gr. k-2). pap. 5.95 (978-0-516-24695-6(X) , Children's Pr.) Scholastic Library Publishing.

—Solar System. 2003. (gr. k-3). lib. bdg. 12.95 (978-0-613-67931-2(8)) Tandem Library Bks.

Bredeson, Carmen. What Is the Solar System? 2008. (I Like Space! Ser.). (Illus.). 32p. (J). (gr. 1-3). lib. bdg. 22.60 (*978-0-7660-2944-6(1) , Enslow Elementary) Enslow Pubs., Inc.

Brudnak, Karen, ed. Investigating Science - Solar System. 2000. 48p. 9.95 (978-1-56234-390-3(4) , Mailbox Bks., The) Education Ctr., Inc.

Carroll, Jillian. Zoom Around a Moon. 2003. (J). pap. (978-1-58417-241-3(X)); lib. bdg. (978-1-58417-240-6(1)) Lake Street Pubs.

Carson, Jana. We Both Read-about Space. 2001. (We Both Read Ser.). (Illus.). 44p. (J). (gr. 1-2). 7.99 (978-1-891327-39-1(9)); pap. 3.99 (978-1-891327-40-7(2)) Treasure Bay, Inc.

Carson, Mary Kay. Exploring the Solar System: A History with 22 Activities. 2006. (For Kids Ser.). (Illus.). 176p. (J). pap. 17.95 (978-1-55652-593-3(1)) Chicago Review Pr., Inc.

Carson, Mary Kay. Extreme Planets! QandA. 2008. 48p. (J). 16.99 (*978-0-06-089975-2(1)); pap. 7.99 (*978-0-06-089974-5(3)) HarperCollins Pubs.

Cheshire, Gerard. The Solar System & Beyond. 2006. (Fundamental Physics Ser.). (Illus.). 48p. (978-1-58340-998-5(X)) Smart Apple Media.

Children of the Sun. 2000. (Illus.). 12p. (J). (ps up). pap. 7.99 (978-0-85953-002-6(7)) Child's Play-International.

Claybourne, Anna. The Solar System. 2006. (Science in Focus Ser.). (Illus.). 48p. (J). 27.00 (978-0-7910-8862-3(6) , Chelsea Hse.) Facts On File, Inc.

Cohn, Arlen. Solar System SOS. Sullivan, Don, illus. 1998. Vol. 6. 32p. (J). (ps up). 15.99 (978-0-939251-98-8(1)) Accord Publishing, Ltd.

Cole, Michael D. The Sun: The Center of the Solar System. 2001. (Countdown to Space Ser.). (Illus.). 48p. (J). (gr. 4-10). lib. bdg. 23.93 (978-0-7660-1508-1(4)) Enslow Pubs., Inc.

Cooper, Christopher. The Solar System. 2000. (Science Fact Files Ser.). (Illus.). 48p. (J). (gr. 4-7). lib. bdg. 27.12 (978-0-7398-1006-4(5)) Raintree.

Croswell, Ken. Ten Worlds: Everything That Orbits the Sun. (Illus.). 2007. 56p. (*978-1-59078-531-7(2)); 2006. 60p. (J). 19.95 (978-1-59078-423-5(5)) Boyds Mills Pr.

Davis, Kenneth C. Don't Know Much about the Solar System. Martin, Pedro, illus. (Don't Know Much About Ser.). 48p. (gr. 1-4). 2004. pap. 6.99 (978-0-06-446230-3(7)); 2001. (J). 16.99 (978-0-06-028613-2(X)) HarperCollins Pubs.

Deboo, Ana. Mapping the Planets & Space. 2006. (Map Readers Ser.). (Illus.). 32p. (J). (978-1-4034-6791-1(9)); pap. (978-1-4034-6798-0(6)) Heinemann Library.

Dicks, Ian & Watton, Nick, illus. God's Solar System. 1999. (Zoomers Ser.). 4p. (J). (gr. 3-7). 2.99 (978-0-7847-1121-7(6) , 03531, Bean Sprouts) Standard Publishing.

Dillon, Christine J., ed. The Solar System & Space. 1998. (My First Report Ser.). (Illus.). 58p. (J). (gr. 1-4). ring bd. 5.95 (978-1-57896-019-4(3) , 2472) Hewitt Research Foundation, Inc.

Dobeck, Maryann. Circling the Sun. 2004. (Illus.). 16p. (J). (978-0-7608-8917-6(1)) Sundance/Newbridge Educational Publishing.

Douglas, Vincent & School Specialty Publishing Staff. The Complete Book of Our Solar System. 2003. (Complete Book Ser.). (Illus.). 352p. (J). (gr. 1-3). pap. 14.95 (978-1-57768-605-7(5) , American Education Publishing) School Specialty Publishing.

—Solar System. 2006. (Just the Facts Ser.). (Illus.). 64p. (J). (gr. 5-8). pap. 9.95 (978-0-7696-4259-8(4)) School Specialty Publishing.

Dyer, Alan. Space. 2007. (Insiders Ser.). 64p. (J). 16.99 (*978-1-4169-3860-6(5)) Simon & Schuster Children's Publishing.

Elkins-Tanton, Linda T. The Solar System Set. 2006. (Solar System Ser.). 864p. (gr. 6-12). 225.00 (978-0-8160-5192-2(5)) Facts On File, Inc.

Farrington, Karen. Make Your Own Solar System. 1998. (Illus.). 24p. (J). (gr. 1 up). pap. 7.95 (978-0-688-16330-3(0)) HarperCollins Pubs.

Fredette, Nathalie & Lafleur, Claude. The Solar System & the Stars. 2001. (Twenty-First Century Science Ser.). (Illus.). 64p. (J). (gr. 5 up). lib. bdg. 32.67 (978-0-8368-5004-8(1) , World Almanac Library) Stevens, Gareth Inc.

Furniss. Spinning Through Space, 4 bks., Set. 2000. (Illus.). (J). (978-0-7398-4258-4(7)) Raintree.

Furniss, Tim. Solar System. 2000. (gr. k-3). lib. bdg. 19.20 (978-0-613-74108-8(0)) Tandem Library Bks.

—The Solar System. 2000. (Spinning Through Space Ser.). (Illus.). 32p. (J). (gr. 2-4). pap. 10.34 (978-0-7398-3092-5(9)) Steck-Vaughn.

Furniss, Tim, et al. The Solar System. 2000. (Spinning Through Space Ser.). (Illus.). 32p. (J). (gr. 2-4). lib. bdg. 25.69 (978-0-7398-2740-6(5)) Raintree.

Goldsmith, Mike. Solar System. 2004. (Kingfisher Young Knowledge Ser.). (Illus.). 48p. (J). (gr. k-3). 9.95 (978-0-7534-5773-3(3) , Kingfisher) Houghton Mifflin Co. Trade & Reference Div.

Goldstein, Margaret J. The Solar System. 2005. (Pull Ahead Bks.). (Illus.). 32p. (gr. 2-4). lib. bdg. 22.60 (978-0-8225-4657-3(4)) Lerner Publishing Group.

—The Sun. 2005. (Pull Ahead Bks.). (Illus.). 32p. (gr. 2-4). lib. bdg. 22.60 (978-0-8225-4647-4(7)) Lerner Publishing Group.

Gore, Bryson. Astronomy: Every Galaxy Has a Black Hole. 2005. (Wow Science Ser.). (Illus.). 32p. (J). (gr. 4). lib. bdg. 27.10 (978-1-59604-068-7(8)) Stargazer Bks.

Graham, Ian. El Sistema Solar. 2004. (Interfact Ser.). (SPA., Illus.). 48p. (J). (gr. 3-6). 14.95 incl. cd-rom (978-1-58728-976-7(8) , Two Can Publishing) T&N Children's Publishing.

Graun, Ken. Our Earth & the Solar System. Niwa, Debra K., illus. 2001. (Twenty-First Century Astronomy Ser.: Vol. 1). 36p. (J). (gr. 4-6). 15.95 (978-1-928771-02-9(5)) Ken Pr.

Group/McGraw-Hill, Wright. Earth & Physical Science: Our Solar System, 6 vols. (Book2WebTM Ser.). (gr. 4-8). 36.50 (978-0-322-04427-2(8)) Wright Group, The.

Harcourt School Publishers Staff. Harcourt Science Unit D: The Solar System & Beyond. 2000. (Illus.). pap. 17.10 (978-0-15-315701-1(1)) Harcourt Schl. Pubs.

Heather Zschock. Solar System Scratch & Sketch. 2006. (Activity Book Ser.). 64p. (J). 12.99 (978-1-59359-917-1(X)) Peter Pauper Pr. Inc.

Hirschmann, Kris. The Solar System. 2004. (World Discovery Science Readers Ser.). (Illus.). 32p. (J). pap. (978-0-439-67649-6(5)) Scholastic, Inc.

Hoffmann, Sara. The Little Book of Space. 2005. (Illus.). 24p. (J). (978-1-58728-517-2(7)); (978-1-58728-485-4(5)) T&N Children's Publishing. (Two Can Publishing).

Holt, Rinehart and Winston Staff. Beyond the Solar System Resources: Texas Edition. 2nd ed. 2001. (Holt Science & Technology Ser.). (Illus.). pap. 26.00 (978-0-03-064876-2(9)) Holt, Rinehart & Winston.

—Holt Science & Technology Chapter 20: Earth Science: Formation of the Solar System. 5th ed. 2004. (Illus.). pap. 12.86 (978-0-03-030341-8(9)) Holt, Rinehart & Winston.

—Holt Science & Technology Chptr. 8: Formation of the Solar System: Chapter Resources - Tennessee Edition. 3rd ed. 2003. (J). pap. 11.40 (978-0-03-069114-0(1)) Holt, Rinehart & Winston.

—Holt Science Spectrum Chptr. 19: The Solar System. 4th ed. Date not set. pap. 11.20 (978-0-03-068058-8(1)) Holt, Rinehart & Winston.

In Our Solar System: Third Grade Newcomer Books. (On Our Way to English Ser.). (gr. 3 up). 29.50 (978-0-7578-7252-5(2)) Rigby Education.

Inquiry Investigations: Solar System. 2004. 48p. (J). pap. 6.99 (978-0-88724-267-0(7) , CD-2364) Carson-Dellosa Publishing Co., Inc.

Jackson, Ellen B. The World Around Us: A Space Voyage. Miller, Ron, illus. 2006. (Exceptional Science Title for Intermediate Grades). 40p. (J). lib. bdg. 23.93 (978-0-7613-3405-7(X) , Millbrook Pr.) Lerner Publishing Group.

Jenkins, Alvin. Next Stop Neptune: Experiencing the Solar System. Jenkins, Steve, illus. 2004. 40p. (J). (gr. 3-5). tchr. ed. 16.00 (978-0-618-41603-5(X)) Houghton Mifflin Co. Trade & Reference Div.

Kerrod, Robin. Our Solar System, 6 vols., Set. Incl. Comets & Meteors. 32p. lib. bdg. 16.95 (978-1-929298-63-1(3)); Earth & Moon. 48p. lib. bdg. 16.95 (978-1-929298-64-8(1)); Far Planets. 32p. lib. bdg. 16.95 (978-1-929298-65-5(X)); Giant Planets. 48p. lib. bdg. 16.95 (978-1-929298-66-2(8)); Near Planets. 48p. lib. bdg. 16.95 (978-1-929298-67-9(6)); Sun. 48p. lib. bdg. 16.95 (978-1-929298-68-6(4)); (J). (gr. 2-6). (Illus.). 48p. 2000. Set lib. bdg. 101.70 (978-1-929298-69-3(2)) Chrysalis Education.

—Planets. 2001. (Illus.). 32p. (J). lib. bdg. 24.25 (978-1-930643-27-7(6)) Chrysalis Education.

—The Solar System. 2001. (Exploring the Universe Ser.). (Illus.). 48p. (J). lib. bdg. 27.12 (978-0-7398-2817-5(7)) Raintree.

—The Sun's Family. 1999. (J). (978-1-57505-363-9(2) , Carolrhoda Bks.) Lerner Publishing Group.

Knocke, Melanie Melton. Astronomy. Garbot, Dave, illus. 2008. (Little Giant Bks.). 352p. (J). pap. 6.95 (***978-1-4027-3234-8(1)***) Sterling Publishing Co., Inc.

Kortenkamp, Steve. Why Isn't Pluto a Planet? A Book about Planets. 2007. 32p. (J). (978-0-7368-6753-5(8)) Capstone Pr., Inc.

Kranz, Rachel. Our Solar System/el sistema Solar: English/Spanish Pair, 12 texts, 2 titles, Vol. 2. ed. 2004. (Navigators Ser.). (J). pap., instr.'s gde. ed. 84.00 (978-1-4108-1766-2(0) , 17660) Benchmark Education Co.

LaFontaine, Bruce. Learning about the Solar System. 2000. (Learning about Ser.). (Illus.). 16p. (J). (gr. 3-5). pap. 1.50 (978-0-486-41009-8(9)) Dover Pubns., Inc.

—Solar System. 1998. (Illus.). 4p. (J). (ps-5). 1.50 (978-0-486-40308-3(4)) Dover Pubns., Inc.

Lambert, David & Redfern, Martin. The Kingfisher Young People's Book of the Universe. 2001. (Kingfisher Book of Ser.). (Illus.). 224p. (J). (gr. 5-8). tchr. ed. 24.95 (978-0-7534-5327-8(4) , Kingfisher) Houghton Mifflin Co. Trade & Reference Div.

Larousse Mexico Staff, ed. El Universo. 2005. (Mi Pequena Enciclopedia Ser.). (SPA.). 38p. (ps-k). pap. 3.95 (978-970-22-0858-7(0)) Larousse, Ediciones, S. A. de C. V. MEX. *Dist:* Houghton Mifflin Co. Trade & Reference Div.

Lauw, Darlene. Earth & the Solar System. 2003. (gr. 3-6). lib. bdg. 16.40 (978-0-613-52834-4(4)) Tandem Library Bks.

Lauw, Darlene & Puay, Lim Cheng. Earth & the Solar System. 2002. (Science Alive! Ser.). (Illus.). 32p. (J). (gr. 4-5). lib. bdg. (978-0-7787-0569-7(2)) Crabtree Publishing Co.

—The Earth & the Solar System. 2002. (Science Alive! Ser.). (Illus.). 32p. (J). (gr. 4-5). pap. (978-0-7787-0615-1(X)) Crabtree Publishing Co.

Lawrence, Debbie & Lawrence, Richard. Our Universe. 2004. (Illus.). vi, 134p. (gr. 1-6). pap. 18.00 (978-0-9725365-4-7(X)) R & D Educational Ctr.

Leigh, Autumn. A Trip Through Our Solar System. 2006. (Rosen Publishing Group's Reading Room Collection). (J). lib. bdg. (978-1-4042-3345-4(8) , PowerKids Pr.) Rosen Publishing Group, Inc., The.

L'Hommedieu, Arthur John. Children of the Sun. L'Hommedieu, Arthur John, illus. (J). (gr. k-11). (GER.). 10.99 (978-0-85953-939-5(3)); 1999. (FRE.). 10.99 (978-0-85953-938-8(5)) Child's Play International Ltd. GBR. *Dist:* Child's Play-International.

Linde, Barbara M. Math in Our Solar System: Applying Problem-Solving Strategies. 2005. (PowerMath Ser.). (J). 22.50 (978-1-4042-2936-5(1) , PowerKids Pr.); pap. (978-1-4042-5135-9(9)) Rosen Publishing Group, Inc., The.

Lopez, Delano. Amazing Solar System Projects You Can Build Yourself. 2008. (Build It Yourself Ser.). 128p. (J). pap. 14.95 (***978-0-9792268-1-6(3)***) Nomad Pr.

Low, Robert S., ed. My Guide to Our Solar System. 2002. 40p. (J). (gr. 3-4). wbk. ed. 2.75 (978-1-56762-166-2(X)) Modern Learning Pr.

Malloy, Christine. The Solar System: Flip Out & Learn. Leighton, Aaron, illus. 2003. (Pull-Out Book Ser.). 8p. (J). 12.95 (978 0 8118 3488-9(3)) Chronicle Bks. LLC.

Miller, Ron. Stars & Galaxies. 2006. (Worlds Beyond Ser.). (Illus.). 96p. (J). (gr. 5-9). 27.93 (978-0-7613-3466-8(1) , Twenty-First Century Bks.) Lerner Publishing Group.

—Worlds Beyond, 10 vols. 2004. (Illus.). (YA). (gr. 7 up). (978-0-7613-3174-2(3) , Twenty-First Century Bks.) Lerner Publishing Group.

Mist, Rosalind. Is There Life on Other Planets? The Planets of Our Solar System. 2006. (Stargazers Guides Ser.). (Illus.). 48p. (J). (978-1-4034-7708-8(6)); pap. (978-1-4034-7715-6(9)) Heinemann Library.

Mitton, S. Kingdom of the Sun: A Book about the Planets. Mitton, Jacqueline & Balit, Christina, illus. 2001. 32p. (J). (ps-3). 16.95 (978-0-7922-7220-5(X) , National Geographic Children's Bks.) National Geographic Society.

Mullican, Judy. The Solar System Dance. Coates, Jennifer, illus. l.t. ed. 2001. (Little Bks.). (J). (ps-1). pap. 10.95 (978-1-57332-190-7(7)); 8p. pap. 10.95 (978-1-57332-189-1(3)) HighReach Learning, Inc.

O'Donnell, Kerri. Space Circles: Learning about Radius & Diameter. 2004. (PowerMath Ser.). (Illus.). 32p. (J). lib. bdg. (978-0-8239-8878-5(3)); lib. bdg. 22.50 (978-0-8239-8985-0(2)) Rosen Publishing Group, Inc., The. (PowerKids Pr.).

Olien, Rebecca. Exploring the Planets in Our Solar System. 2007. (Objects in the Sky Ser.). (Illus.). 24p. (J). (978-1-4042-2366-0(5)); pap. (978-1-4042-2175-8(1)); (gr. 4-6). lib. bdg. 21.25 (978-1-4042-3467-3(5)) Rosen Publishing Group, Inc., The. (PowerKids Pr.).

Orme, Helen. Why Is the Sun So Bright? 2003. (What? Where? Why? Ser.). (Illus.). 24p. (J). (gr. 1 up). lib. bdg. 20.67 (978-0-8368-3792-6(4)) Stevens, Gareth Inc.

Our Solar System. (Jump Ser.). 36p. (J). (gr. 2-7). pap. (978-1-882210-23-7(9)) Action Publishing, Inc.

Our Solar System, 13 bks., Set. 2003. (J). (gr. 2-4). 276.38 (978-0-7565-0461-8(9)) Compass Point Bks.

Our Solar System. 48p. (gr. 4-6). 8.99 (978-1-56417-961-6(3) , GA1604) Schaffer, Frank Pubns.

Our Solar System: Level Q, 6 vols. (Wonder Worldtm Ser.). 48p. 39.95 (978-0-7802-2952-5(5)) Wright Group, The.

Parker, Steve. Beyond the Solar System. 2007. (J). lib. bdg. (***978-1-4042-3739-1(9)*** , Rosen Central) Rosen Publishing Group, Inc., The.

Peddicord, Jane Ann. Night Wonders. Peddicord, Jane Ann, illus. 2005. (Illus.). 32p. (J). 16.95 (978-1-57091-877-3(5)) Charlesbridge Publishing, Inc.

—Night Wonders. 2005. (Illus.). 32p. (J). pap. 6.95 (978-1-57091-878-0(3)) Charlesbridge Publishing, Inc.

Perez, Miguel. El Sistema Solar. Rius, María, illus. 1998. (Universe Ser.).Tr. of Solar System. (SPA.). 36p. (J). pap. 5.95 (978-0-7641-0759-7(3)) Barron's Educational Series, Inc.

—The Solar System. Rius, María, illus. 1998. (Universe Ser.). 36p. (J). pap. 6.95 (978-0-7641-0685-9(6)) Barron's Educational Series, Inc.

—The Universe: The Solar System; Stars & Galaxies; The Earth & the Universe, 3 bks., Set. Rius, María, illus. 1998. 36p. (J). (ps-2). pap. 17.95 (978-0-7641-7203-8(4)) Barron's Educational Series, Inc.

Pitluga, Phyllis, ed. Our Solar System & It's Planets. TNT Stone and Associates Staff & Petertil Design Partners Staff, illus. 1998. (Powertools for Kids Ser.: No. 12). 4p. (J). (gr. 3-7). pap., wbk. ed. 4.95 (978-1-58220-011-8(4) , 32502, PowerTools for Kids) Navigator Systems, Inc.

Planets of Our Solar System, 6 Packs. (Rigby Focus Ser.). 24p. (gr. 2 up). 28.00 (978-0-7578-5360-9(9)) Rigby Education.

Planets of Our Solar System: Individual Title Six-Packs. (Rigby Focus Ser.). 24p. (gr. 2 up). 30.00 (978-0-7578-5590-0(3)) Rigby Education.

Pop-Out Play Pak: Solar System. Orig. Title: Child's Play. (Illus.). 24p. (J). (ps-4). reprint ed. (978-1-881469-77-3(8)) Safari, Ltd.

Rau, Dana Meachen. The Solar System. 2000. (Simply Science Ser.). (Illus.). 32p. (J). (gr. 3 up). lib. bdg. 21.26 (978-0-7565-0036-8(2)) Compass Point Bks.

—Space Leftovers: A Book about Comets, Asteroids, & Meteoroids. Shea, Denise, illus. 2005. (Amazing Science Ser.). 24p. (J). (ps-k). lib. bdg. 22.60 (978-1-4048-1137-9(0)) Picture Window Bks.

—Spinning in Space: A Book about the Planets. Shea, Denise, illus. 2005. (Amazing Science Ser.). 24p. (J). (ps-k). lib. bdg. 22.60 (978-1-4048-1138-6(9)) Picture Window Bks.

Rau, Dana Meachen & Shea, Denise. Sobras Del Espacio: Un Libro Sobre Cometas, Asteroides y Meteoroides. Shea, Denise, illus. 2006. (SPA.). (J). lib. bdg. (***978-1-4048-3230-5(0)***) Picture Window Bks.

Ride, Sally & O'Shaughnessy, Tam. Exploring Our Solar System. 2003. 112p. (J). (gr. 5). lib. bdg. 21.99 (978-0-375-91204-7(5)); (Illus.). 19.95 (978-0-375-81204-0(0)) Random Hse. Children's Bks. (Crown Books For Young Readers).

Ride, Sally K. & O'Shaughnessy, Tam E. Voyager: An Adventure to the Edge of the Solar System. 2nd rev. ed. 2005. (J). per. 20.00 (978-0-9753920-5-8(0)) Sally Ride Science.

Riley, Peter D. Earth in Space. 1999. (gr. 3-6). lib. bdg. 15.25 (978-0-613-31148-9(5)) Tandem Library Bks.

Riley, Peter D. Earth, Moon & Sun. 2007. (J). (***978-1-59920-025-5(2)***) Smart Apple Media.

Royston, Angela. Alien Neighbors? 2005. (Illus.). 32p. (J). lib. bdg. (978-1-4109-1931-1(5)) Steck-Vaughn.

—Alien Neighbors? The Solar System. 2005. (Illus.). 32p. (J). (gr. 3-5). 7.85 (978-1-4109-1962-5(5)) Steck-Vaughn.

Rudy, Lisa Jo. Planets! 2005. 32p. (J). lib. bdg. 15.00 (***978-1-4242-0859-3(9)***) Fitzgerald Bks.

Rustad, Martha E. H. The Planets. Saunders-Smith, Gail, ed. 2002. (Out in Space Ser.). (Illus.). 24p. (J). (gr. k-1). lib. bdg. 15.93 (978-0-7368-1178-1(8) , Pebble Bks.) Capstone Pr., Inc.

Scholastic, Inc. Staff. The Universe. 2007. (Scholastic First Discovery Ser.). 24p. (J). (ps-k). pap. 5.99 (***978-0-545-00146-5(3)*** , Scholastic Reference) Scholastic, Inc.

School Specialty Publishing. Our Solar System. 2003. (Brighter Child Activity Bks.). 32p. (J). (ps-4). pap. 2.99 (978-0-7696-3232-2(7) , Brighter Child) School Specialty Publishing.

Scott, Elaine. Close Encounters: Exploring the Universe with the Hubble Space Telescope. 1998. (Illus.). 64p. (J). (gr. 3-7). 16.95 (978-0-7868-0147-3(6)) Hyperion Bks. for Children.

Sian revision Earth-sun. 2004. (J). (978-1-59242-020-9(6)) Delta Education, LLC.

Simon, Seymour. Our Solar System (revised Edition) 2007. (J). 64p. 19.99 (***978-0-06-114008-2(2));*** 72p. lib. bdg. 20.89 (***978-0-06-114009-9(0)***) HarperCollins Pubs.

El Sistema Solar. (Coleccion Ventana Transparente). (SPA.). (978-950-11-1135-4(0) , SG5232) Sigmar ARG. *Dist:* Lectorum Pubns., Inc.

El Sol y su Familia: Cuaderno de Evaluacion: Unit 4: El Sol y su Familia (The Sun & Its Family) 2000. (McGraw-Hill Ciencias Ser.). (ENG & SPA.). (gr. 3 up). (978-0-02-278652-6(X)) Macmillan/McGraw-Hill Schl. Div.

El Sol y su Familia: Recursos para el Maestro con clave de Respuestas: Unit 4: El Sol y su Familia (The Sun & Its Family) 2000. (McGraw-Hill Ciencias Ser.). (ENG & SPA.). (gr. 3 up). (978-0-02-278695-3(3)) Macmillan/McGraw-Hill Schl. Div.

The Solar System. (First Facts about Ser.). 24p. (J). (gr. 3-7). pap. (978-1-882210-16-9(6)) Action Publishing, Inc.

The Solar System. 2003. (First Facts Ser.). (Illus.). (J). (gr. 1-2). lib. bdg. 233.86 (978-0-7368-3810-8(4)) Capstone Pr., Inc.

The Solar System. 2005. (Illus.). 32p. (gr. 3-5). pap. 276.00 (978-0-7910-7924-9(4) , Chelsea Hse.) Facts On File, Inc.

The Solar System. (Preschool Projects Ser.). 32p. (ps-k). 4.99 (978-1-57029-329-0(5) , WPH39009, Totline Pubns.) Schaffer, Frank Pubns.

Solar System Wall Chart. 2004. (Wall Charts Ser.). (J). 4.99 (978-1-85997-257-1(8)) Byeway Bks.

Space Quest: Exploring Our Solar System: Individual Title Six-Packs. (Discovery World Ser.). 24p. (gr. 1-2). 33.00 (978-0-7635-8481-8(9)) Rigby Education.

Sparrow, Giles. Exploring the Solar System: Journey Through Outer Space, 9 bks., Set. 2001. (Illus.). (J). (gr. 4-6). lib. bdg. 217.98 (978-1-57572-398-3(0)) Heinemann Library.

Spinning Through Space: Includes: The Earth; The Moon; The Solar System; The Sun, 4 bks., Set. 2000. (Illus.). (J). (gr. 2-4). 71.92 (978-0-7398-2741-3(3)) Raintree.

Steck-Vaughn Staff. Science Level J-M: Our Solar System. 2003. (Illus.). bds. (978-0-7398-7676-3(7)) Steck-Vaughn.

Sterling, Mary E. Solar System Photo Fun Activities. Rogers, Kathy, ed. Carrozza, John, illus. 1998. (Science Photo Fun Activities Ser.). 8p. (J). pap. 6.95 (978-1-56472-088-7(8)) Edupress, Inc.

Sun & Its Family. 2000. (McGraw-Hill Science Ser.). (gr. 3 up). (978-0-02-278211-5(7)) Macmillan/McGraw-Hill Schl. Div.

Sweeney, Joan. Me & My Place in Space. 1999. (Dragonfly Bks.). (Illus.). 32p. (J). (gr. k-3). pap. 6.99 (978-0-517-88590-1(5) , Dragonfly Bks.) Random Hse. Children's Bks.

Telford & Theodorou, Rod. Across the Solar System. 2002. (Amazing Journeys Ser.). (Illus.). 32p. (J). (gr. 2-6). pap. 7.50 (978-1-58810-305-5(6) , 91071) Heinemann Library.

Theodorou, Rod. Across the Solar System. 2000. (Amazing Journeys Ser.). 32p. (J). (gr. 3-5). lib. bdg. 22.79 (978-1-57572-486-7(3)) Heinemann Library.

Time for Kids Editors. Planets! 2005. (Time for Kids Ser.). (Illus.). 32p. (J). 14.99 (978-0-06-078203-0(X)); pap. 3.99 (978-0-06-078202-3(1) , Harper Trophy) HarperCollins Pubs.

A Trip Through Our Solar System. (Rosen Real Readers Big Bookstm Ser.). 16p. (J). (gr. 2-3). 38.75 (978-1-4042-6219-5(9)) Rosen Publishing Group, Inc., The.

Turiel, Isaac. How Do We Know the Size of the Solar System? 2001. (Great Scientific Questions & the Scientists Who Answered Them Ser.). (Illus.). 112p. (YA). (gr. 4-6). lib. bdg. 26.50 (978-0-8239-3386-0(5)) Rosen Publishing Group, Inc., The.

Twist, Clint. The Search for Life in Space. 2005. (Science Quest Ser.). (Illus.). 32p. (J). lib. bdg. 24.67 (978-0-8368-4557-0(9)) Stevens, Gareth Inc.

Two-Can Publishing Ltd. Staff, contrib. by. Solarsystem. 2004. (Interfact Reference Ser.). (Illus.). 48p. (J). (gr. 3-6). 19.95 incl. cd-rom (978-1-58728-422-9(7) , Two Can Publishing) T&N Children's Publishing.

VanCleave, Janice Pratt. Janice VanCleave's Solar System. 2000. (gr. 3-6). lib. bdg. 19.90 (978-0-613-25782-4(0)) Tandem Library Bks.

—Janice VanCleave's Solar System: Mind-Boggling Experiments You Can Turn into Science Fair Projects. 1999. (Spectacular Science Project Ser.: Vol. 14). (Illus.). 96p. (gr. 3-7). pap. 10.95 (978-0-471-32204-7(0) , Wiley-Interscience) Wiley, John & Sons, Inc.

Vogt, Gregory L. The Milky Way. 2002. (Galaxy Ser.). (Illus.). 24p. (J). (gr. 2-3). lib. bdg. 18.60 (978-0-7368-1384-6(5) , Bridgestone Bks.) Capstone Pr., Inc.

—Solar System. (Science Readers Level 2 Ser.). (Illus.). 48p. (J). 2002. pap. 3.99 (978-0-439-38247-2(5) , Scholastic Reference); 2001. (978-0-439-26991-9(1)) Scholastic, Inc.

—Solar System. 2002. (gr. 3-6). lib. bdg. 11.80 (978-0-613-57133-3(9)) Tandem Library Bks.

—The Solar System. 2002. (Galaxy Ser.). (Illus.). 24p. (J). (gr. 2-3). lib. bdg. 18.60 (978-0-7368-1385-3(3) , Bridgestone Bks.) Capstone Pr., Inc.

Walker, Jane. El Sistema Solar. 2001. (SPA., Illus.). 1053p. (J). (ps-3). 10.95 (978-84-263-3172-4(6)) Lectorum Pubns., Inc.

Whyman, Kathryn. The Solar System. 2004. (J). lib. bdg. (978-1-932799-29-3(X)) Stargazer Bks.

World Book, contrib. by. Galaxies & the Universe. 2nd ed. 2006. (World Book's Solar System & Space Exploration Library). (Illus.). 64p. (J). (***978-0-7166-9513-4(8)***) World Bk., Inc.

SOLDIERS

Here are entered works dealing with members of the armed forces in general, including the Navy, Marine Corps, etc. as well as the Army.

see also Armies; Generals; Military Art and Science; Military Service—Vocational Guidance; Scouts and Scouting

also names of countries with the subdivision Army—Military Life, e.g. United States—Army—Military life; etc.

Alter, Judy. Audie Murphy: War Hero & Movie Star. 2007. 72p. (YA). 14.95 (***978-1-933337-19-7(2)***) State Hse. Pr.

Anderson, Dale. Soldiers & Sailors in the American Revolution. 2005. (World Almanac Library of the American Revolution). (J). pap. (978-0-8368-5938-6(3)); lib. bdg. 30.00 (978-0-8368-5929-4(4)) Stevens, Gareth Inc. (World Almanac Library).

Beller, Susan Provost. Yankee Doodle & the Redcoats: Soldiering in the Revolutionary War. Day, Larry, illus. 2003. (Single Titles Ser.). 96p. (gr. 5 up). lib. bdg. 26.90 (978-0-7613-2612-0(X) , Twenty-First Century Bks.) Lerner Publishing Group.

Black, Wallace B. Slaves to Soldiers: African-American Fighting Men in the Civil War. 1998. (First Bks.). (Illus.). 64p. (J). (gr. 5-7). 22.00 (978-0-531-20252-4(6) , Watts, Franklin) Scholastic Library Publishing.

Boraas, Tracey. Kit Carson: Mountain Man. 2002. (Let Freedom Ring Ser.). (Illus.). 48p. (J). (gr. 3-4). lib. bdg. 22.60 (978-0-7368-1349-5(7) , Bridgestone Bks.) Capstone Pr., Inc.

Calvert, Patricia. Kit Carson: He Led the Way. 2006. (Great Explorations Ser.). (Illus.). 80p. (J). lib. bdg. 32.79 (978-0-7614-2223-5(4) , Benchmark Bks.) Cavendish, Marshall Corp.

Casad, Dede W. Texans of Valor: Military Heroes of the Twentieth Century. 1998. (Illus.). 152p. pap. 17.95 (978-1-57168-113-3(2)) Eakin Pr.

Crew, Hilary. Women Engaged in War in Literature for Youth: A Guide to Resources for Children & Young Adults. 2007. 324p. pap. 51.00 (***978-0-8108-4929-7(1)***) Scarecrow Pr., Inc.

Crompton, Samuel Willard. 100 Military Leaders Who Shaped World History. 1999. (gr. 7-12). lib. bdg. 16.40 (978-0-613-67577-2(0)) Tandem Library Bks.

Doak, Robin S. Zebulon Pike: Explorer & Soldier. 2005. (Signature Lives Ser.). (Illus.). 112p. (J). (gr. 5-7). (978-0-7565-0998-9(X)) Compass Point Bks.

Fortin, Noonie. Dad Wears Combat Boots. 2000. (Illus.). v, 77p. (J). (ps-6). pap. 15.95 (978-0-9700176-2-8(6)) Tales & Whales Publishing.

—Mom Wears Combat Boots. 2000. (Illus.). v, 77p. (J). (ps-6). pap. 15.95 (978-0-9700176-1-1(8)) Tales & Whales Publishing.

Gillis, Jennifer Blizin. The Confederate Soldier. 2006. 48p. (J). (gr. 4-6). lib. bdg. (978-0-7565-2025-0(8)) Compass Point Bks.

Gwilliam, Heather. Livewire Real Lives Sir John Monash. 1999. (Livewires Real Lives Ser.). 32p. (gr. 6-9). pap. 6.00 (978-0-521-77629-5(5)) Cambridge Univ. Pr.

Harmon, Daniel E. Fighting Units of the American Revolution. 1998. (Costume, Tradition & Culture). (Illus.). 64p. (J). 19.75 (978-0-7910-5162-7(5) , Chelsea Hse.) Facts On File, Inc.

Hooker, Forrestine C. Child of the Fighting Tenth: On the Frontier with the Buffalo Soldiers. Wilson, Steve, ed. 2003. (Illus.). 280p. (YA). 26.00 (978-0-19-516158-8(0)) Oxford Univ. Pr., Inc.

Koestler-Grack, Rachel A. Nathan Hale: Courageous Spy. 2005. (Leaders of the American Revolution Ser.). (Illus.). 124p. (J). (gr. 4-8). lib. bdg. 30.00 (978-0-7910-8623-0(2) , Chelsea Hse.) Facts On File, Inc.

Lough, Loree. Nathan Hale: Revolutionary Hero. 2000. (Illus.). 80p. (J). (gr. 3-17). lib. bdg. 17.60 (978-0-613-43357-0(2)) Tandem Library Bks.

MacDonald, Fiona. So You Want to Be a Roman Soldier. Hewetson, Nicholas, illus. 1999. (So You Want to Be... Ser.). 32p. (gr. 3-6). lib. bdg. 21.90 (978-0-7613-1421-9(0) , Twenty-First Century Bks.) Lerner Publishing Group.

MacLean, Alistair. Lawrence of Arabia. 2006. (Sterling Point Bks.). (Illus.). 176p. (J). pap. 6.95 (978-1-4027-3613-1(4)) Sterling Publishing Co., Inc.

Manning, Mick & Granstorm, Brita. Roman Fort. 2005. (Illus.). 40p. (J). 15.95 (978-1-84507-050-2(X)) Lincoln, Frances Ltd. GBR. *Dist:* Perseus Distribution.

Matthews, Rupert. You Wouldn't Want to Be an Assyrian Soldier! An Ancient Army You'd Rather Not Join. Antram, David, illus. 2007. (You Wouldn't Want to Ser.). 32p. (J). (gr. 2-5). 28.50 (***978-0-531-18727-2(6)*** , Watts, Franklin) Scholastic Library Publishing.

McDonnell, Peter. A Soldier in Disguise. Tormey, Carlotta, illus. 2005. 16p. (J). pap. (***978-0-7367-2909-3(7)***) Zaner-Bloser, Inc.

Military Personnel. 2000. (My Ancestors—My Heroes Ser.: Vol. 49). (J). (gr. 3-4). (978-1-893091-48-1(1)) Parker Publishing Co.

Nardo, Don. Life of a Roman Soldier. 2000. (Way People Live Ser.). (Illus.). 112p. (J). (gr. 7-10). 27.45 (978-1-56006-679-8(2) , LML00902-178031, Lucent Bks.) Thomson Gale.

O'Brien, Tim. If I Die in a Combat Zone: Box Me up & Ship Me Home. 1999. (gr. 7-12). lib. bdg. 21.10 (978-0-613-08043-9(2)) Tandem Library Bks.

Olson, Nathan. Nathan Hale: Revolutionary Spy. Martin, Cynthia & Schoonover, Brent, illus. 2005. (Graphic Library). 32p. (J). (gr. 3-7). lib. bdg. 25.26 (978-0-7368-4968-5(8)) Capstone Pr., Inc.

Pullen, John J. Something Abides: The Story of Joshua Chamberlain. 2003. (Illus.). 67p. (J). per. 7.95 (978-0-9704408-1-5(2)) 20th Maine, Inc.

Schomp, Virginia. World War II. 2001. (Letters from the Home Front Ser.). (Illus.). 96p. (J). (gr. 6 up). lib. bdg. 29.93 (978-0-7614-1098-0(8) , Benchmark Bks.) Cavendish, Marshall Corp.

Sims, Lesley. Roman Soldier's Handbook. 2006. 96p. (J). 12.99 (978-0-7945-0837-1(5) , Usborne) EDC Publishing.

Smith, A. G. Billy the Union Soldier: With 24 Stickers. 2000. 4p. (J). pap. 1.50 (978-0-486-40993-1(7)) Dover Pubns., Inc.

Sordu, John R. & Dean, Robert. Big Battles for Little Hands: Wargaming Source Book for Children. Palmer, Chris, photos by. 2002. (Illus.). 141p. (YA). 25.00 (978-1-889584-10-2(X) , 071102) LMW Works.

Williams, Brian. Ancient Roman War & Weapons. (People in the Past Ser.). (Illus.). 48p. (J). 2003. (gr. 4-6). lib. bdg. 27.07 (978-1-58810-630-8(6)); 2002. pap. 8.50 (978-1-4034-0521-0(2)) Heinemann Library.

S

Williams, Jack S. & Davis, Thomas L. Soldiers & Their Families of the California Mission Frontier. 2004. (People of the California Missions Ser.). (Illus.). 64p. (J). lib. bdg. 25.50 (978-0-8239-6285-3(7)) Rosen Publishing Group, Inc., The.

SOLDIERS—FICTION

Algeo, Kristie. When Daddy Comes Home. 2006. (ENG., Illus.). 36p. per. 21.99 (978-1-4141-0667-0(X)) Pleasant Word.

—When Daddy Goes Away. 2006. (ENG., Illus.). 36p. (J). per. 21.99 (978-1-4141-0643-4(2)) Pleasant Word.

Andersen, Hans Christian. The Tinderbox. Ibatoulline, Bagram, illus. 2007. 48p. (J). (gr. 1-5). 17.99 (978-0-7636-2078-3(5)) Candlewick Pr.

Barrett, Judi. Stone Soup. 2000. (J). pap. 19.97 incl. audio (978-0-7366-9217-5(7)) Books on Tape, Inc.

Barry, Rick. Gunner's Run. 2007. (YA). (***978-1-59166-761-2(5)***) Jones, Bob Univ. Pr.

Bates, Gordon. The Khaki Boys over the Top: Doing & Daring for Uncle Sam. 2007. 140p. pap. 10.99 (***978-1-4264-6542-0(4)***) BiblioBazaar.

Borden, Louise. Across the Blue Pacific: A World War II Story. Parker, Robert Andrew, illus. 2006. 48p. (J). (gr. k-3). 17.00 (978-0-618-33922-8(1)) Houghton Mifflin Co.

Breslin, Theresa. Death or Glory Boys. 2002. 182p. (J). pap. 8.99 (978-1-4052-0109-4(6)) Egmont Bks., Ltd. GBR. *Dist:* Independent Pubs. Group.

Brown, Marcia. Sopa de Piedras. Mlawer, Teresa, tr. 2001. (SPA., Illus.). (J). (gr. k-3). 7.96 net. (978-1-56137-559-2(4) , NU5657) Novel Units, Inc.

—Stone Soup; Sopa de Piedras, 2 bks., Set. Mlawer, Teresa, tr. Brown, Marcia, illus. unabr. ed. 1999. (ENG & SPA., Illus.). (J). (gr. 1-3). pap. 33.95 incl. audio (978-0-87499-571-8(X)) Live Oak Media.

Chetkowski, Emily. Gooseman. 2001. (J). 11.95 (978-1-880158-32-6(9)) Townsend, J.N. Publishing.

Cohen, Miriam. My Big Brother. Himler, Ronald, illus. 2005. 40p. (J). 15.95 (978-1-59572-007-8(3)) Star Bright Bks., Inc.

Connell, Kate. Yankee Blue or Rebel Grey: A Family Divided by the Civil War. 2003. (I Am American Ser.). (Illus.). 40p. (J). (gr. 3-7). pap. 6.99 (978-0-7922-5179-8(2) , National Geographic Children's Bks.) National Geographic Society.

Crump, Fred, Jr. Brave Toy Soldier. 2006. (Illus.). 32p. (J). pap. 9.95 (978-1-932715-82-8(7)) UMI (Urban Ministries, Inc.).

Crump, Fred. Brave Toy Soldier. 2007. 32p. (J). 12.95 (***978-1-934056-20-2(0)***) UMI (Urban Ministries, Inc.).

Denslow, Sharon Phillips. All Their Names Were Courage. 2003. 144p. (J). (gr. 2 up). 15.99 (978-0-06-623810-4(2)) HarperCollins Pubs.

DePalma, Johnny & Crabapple, Molly. Once upon a Christmas Tree - A Holiday Fairy Tale. 2007. 88p. pap. 10.50 (***978-0-615-15448-0(4)***) Umbrelly Bks.

Dixon, Franklin W. The Secret of the Soldier's Gold. 2003. (gr. 3-6). lib. bdg. 13.00 (978-0-613-90468-1(0)) Tandem Library Bks.

Dixon, Franklin W. & Walker, Jeff. The Secret of the Soldier's Gold. 2003. (Hardy Boys Ser.). (Illus.). 160p. (J). pap. 4.99 (978-0-689-85885-7(X) , Aladdin) Simon & Schuster Children's Publishing.

Dowell, Frances O'Roark. Shooting the Moon. 2008. 176p. (J). 16.99 (***978-1-4169-2690-0(9)***) Simon & Schuster Children's Publishing.

Duey, Kathleen. Pony Express: Time Soldiers Book #7. 2007. (Time Soldiers Ser.). (Illus.). (J). 48p. 15.95 (978-1-929945-68-9(X)); 96p. pap. 5.95 (978-1-929945-69-6(8)) Big Guy Bks., Inc.

Durbin, William. The Winter War. 2008. (J). (***978-0-385-90889-4(X)***); 240p. (gr. 7). 15.99 (***978-0-385-74652-6(0)***) Dell Publishing. (Delacorte Pr.).

Durrant, Lynda. My Last Skirt: The Story of Jennie Hodgers, Union Soldier. 2006. 245p. (YA). 21.95 (978-0-7862-8880-9(9)) Thorndike Pr.

Endoh, Minari. Dazzle, Vol. 1. 2006. (Illus.). (YA). (gr. 8 up). pap. 9.99 (978-1-59816-092-5(3) , Tokyopop Kids) TOKYOPOP, Inc.

Everett-Green, Evelyn. A Heroine of France. 2007. 188p. pap. 14.99 (***978-1-4264-7060-8(6)***); 206p. pap. 15.99 (***978-1-4264-7136-0(X)***) BiblioBazaar.

Fedor, Janis M. Girl Lieutenant in Blue, Vol. 2. 2002. 166p. (YA). (gr. 5-6). pap. 9.95 (978-0-936369-38-9(8)) Son-Rise Pubns. & Distribution Co.

Furtney, Charles S. Tryconnel: An Antebellum Adventure along the C & O Canal. 2004. (Illus.). iii, 156p. (J). pap. (978-0-9711835-3-7(8)) Local History Co., The.

Garland, Sherry. The Buffalo Soldier. Himler, Ronald, illus. 2006. 32p. (J). (gr. 3-6). 15.95 (978-1-58980-391-6(4)) Pelican Publishing Co., Inc.

—In the Shadow of the Alamo. 2001. (Great Episodes Ser.). 288p. (YA). (gr. 5-8). 18.00 (978-0-15-201744-6(5) , Gulliver Bks.) Harcourt Children's Bks.

Gilberstadt, Debra Pack. Unmarked Grave: Remembering an American Patriot. 2005. (YA). lib. bdg. 29.95 (978-0-9763033-0-5(2)) Eslinger Hse. Publishing.

Greene, Bette. Summer of My German Soldier. l.t. ed. 2000. (LRS Large Print Cornerstone Ser.). 305p. (YA). (gr. 6-12). lib. bdg. 29.95 (978-1-58118-059-6(4) , 23473) LRS.

—Summer of My German Soldier. 1999. (Illus.). 208p. (J). (gr. 5-9). pap. 6.99 (978-0-14-130636-0(X) , Puffin) Penguin Group (USA) Inc.

—Summer of My German Soldier. 2000. (J). (gr. 6 up). 20.50 (978-0-8446-7144-4(4)) Smith, Peter Pub., Inc.

—Summer of My German Soldier. 1999. (978-0-606-17432-9(X)) Tandem Library Bks.

Greene, Bette & Hunt, Robert, illus. Summer of My German Soldier. 2003. 256p. (J). (gr. 5). 18.99 (978-0-8037-2869-1(7) , Dial) Penguin Group (USA) Inc.

Hahn, Stephen. Pike McCallister. 1998. 253p. (YA). (gr. 6 up). per. 14.95 (978-1-888125-29-0(2)) Publication Consultants.

Harcourt School Publishers Staff. The Root Cellar: Take-Home Book. 2001. (Collections Ser.). (Illus.). (J). pap. 1.90 (978-0-15-319548-8(7)) Harcourt Schl. Pubs.

Hartnett, Sonya. The Silver Donkey. Powers, Don, illus. 272p. (J). (gr. 5). 2007. pap. 7.99 (***978-0-7636-3681-4(9)***); 2006. 15.99 (978-0-7636-2937-3(5)) Candlewick Pr.

—The Silver Donkey. Spudvilas, Anne, illus. 2004. viii, 193p. (J). (978-0-670-04240-1(4) , Viking Adult) Penguin Group (USA) Inc.

Harvey, Matthea. The Little General & the Giant Snowflake. Zechel, Elizabeth, illus. 2007. 64p. (J). 12.95 (***978-1-933368-83-2(7)***) Counterpoint.

Henderson, Jason & Salvaggio, Tony. Psy-Comm. 2007. (Kaplan SAT/ACT Score-Raising Manga Ser.). 192p. pap. 9.99 (***978-1-4277-5496-7(9)***) Kaplan Publishing.

Hilbrecht, Kirk & Hilbrecht, Sharron. My Daddy Is a Soldier. Hilbrecht, Kirk & Hilbrecht, Sharron, illus. 2000. (Illus.). 32p. (ps-3). reprint ed. pap. 6.95 (978-1-889658-01-8(4)) New Canaan Publishing Co. LLC.

Hopkinson, Deborah. Billy & the Rebel. Floca, Brian, illus. 2005. 44p. (J). lib. bdg. 15.00 (***978-1-4242-1148-7(4)***) Fitzgerald Bks.

—Billy & the Rebel: Based on a True Civil War Story. Floca, Brian, illus. 2006. (Ready-to-Reads Ser.). 48p. (J). pap. 3.99 (978-0-689-83396-0(2) , Aladdin) Simon & Schuster Children's Publishing.

—Billy & the Rebel: Based on a True Civil War Story. Anderson, Bethanne & Floca, Brian, illus. 2005. (Ready-to-Read Ser.). 48p. (J). 14.95 (978-0-689-83964-1(2) , Atheneum) Simon & Schuster Children's Publishing.

—From Slave to Soldier: Based on a True Civil War Story. Floca, Brian, illus. (Ready-to-Reads Ser.). 48p. (J). 2007. pap. 3.99 (978-0-689-83966-5(9) , Aladdin); 2005. 14.95 (978-0-689-83965-8(0) , Atheneum) Simon & Schuster Children's Publishing.

Hughes, Pat. Seeing the Elephant: A Story of the Civil War. Stark, Ken, illus. 2007. 40p. (J). (gr. 3 up). 16.00 (978-0-374-38024-3(4)) Farrar, Straus & Giroux.

Jorgensen, Norman. In Flanders Fields. Gray, Peter, ed. 2002. (Illus.). 40p. 22.95 (978-1-86368-369-2(0)) Fremantle Pr. AUS. *Dist:* International Specialized Bk. Services.

—In Flanders Fields. Harrison-Lever, Brian, illus. 2003. 32p. 16.95 (978-1-894965-01-9(9)) Simply Read Bks. CAN. *Dist:* Perseus Distribution.

Jorgensen, Norman & Harrison-Lever, Brian. In Flanders Fields. 2004. (Illus.). 32p. pap. 13.50 (978-1-920731-03-8(2)) Fremantle Pr. AUS. *Dist:* International Specialized Bk. Services.

Karesh, Tracy Ann. Brave Little Soldier. 2005. (J). pap. 15.00 (978-0-8059-6742-5(7)) Dorrance Publishing Co., Inc.

Kimmel, Eric. Sopa de Cactus. Huling, Phil, illus. 2007. 32p. (J). 16.99 (***978-0-7614-5344-4(X)***) Cavendish, Marshall Corp.

Krensky, Stephen. Davy Crockett A Life on the Frontier. Dacey, Bob & Bandelin, Debra, illus. ed. 2005. (Ready-to-Read Ser. Level 3). 48p. (J). lib. bdg. 15.00 (978-1-59054-959-9(7)) Fitzgerald Bks.

Le Feuvre, Amy. Teddy's Button. 2002. (Golden Inheritance Ser.: Vol. 6). (Illus.). 93p. (J). (978-0-921100-83-6(3)) Inheritance Pubns.

—Teddy's Button. 2004. reprint ed. pap. 15.95 (978-1-4191-5094-4(4)); pap. 1.99 (978-1-4192-5094-1(9)) Kessinger Publishing, LLC.

Lee, Mary. My Air Force Mom. 2007. (J). per. 6.99 (***978-1-60247-341-6(2)***) Tate Publishing & Enterprises, L.L.C.

Lewis, Floyd. The Foundered Mule. 2006. (YA). (***978-0-9788283-2-5(1)***) Acacia Publishing, Inc.

Linhart, Sandra Miller. Daddy's Boots. 2007. 44p. (J). 16.99 (978-1-59092-575-1(0) , Little Blue Works) Windstorm Creative.

Lynch, Keven R. What's a Buffalo Soldier? The Historical Adventures of Amber & Trevor. 2005. (J). pap. 12.00 (978-0-8059-6750-0(8)) Dorrance Publishing Co., Inc.

Maddox, Joseph & Maddox, Diana. See You in Hell. 2004. 215p. (YA). pap. 14.95 (978-0-7414-1872-2(X)) Infinity Publishing.

Marsh, Carole. The Adventure Diaries of Jack, the U. S. Army Special Forces Solider!, 4 vols. 48p. (J). 2003. (gr. 1-4). pap. 5.95 (978-0-635-01147-3(6)); 2002. (Illus.). lib. bdg. 9.95 (978-0-635-01273-9(1)) Gallopade International.

Martins, Miller Susan. Lizzie & the Redcoat: Stirrings of Revolution in the American Colonies. 2006. (Sisters in Time Ser.). 144p. (J). pap. 4.97 (978-1-59789-101-1(0)) Barbour Publishing, Inc.

McCaughrean, Geraldine. Cyrano. 2006. (Illus.). 128p. (J). (gr. 7 up). 16.00 (978-0-15-205805-0(2)) Harcourt Children's Bks.

McElroy, Lisa Tucker. Love, Lizzie: Letters to a Military Mom. Paterson, Diane, illus. 2005. 32p. (J). (gr. k-3). lib. bdg. 15.95 (978-0-8075-4777-9(8)) Whitman, Albert & Co.

Mercer, Peggy. There Come a Soldier. Mazellan, Ron, illus. 2007. 40p. (J). (gr. k up). 17.95 (***978-1-59354-192-7(9)***) Handprint Bks.

Millhouse, Jackie. The Tiger & the General. Girouard, Patrick, illus. 2007. (J). (***978-1-932911-32-9(4)***) World Tribune Pr.

Morpurgo, Michael. Private Peaceful. (J). 2006. 176p. pap. 5.99 (978-0-439-63653-7(1) , Scholastic Paperbacks); 2004. 208p. (gr. 7 up). 16.95 (978-0-439-63648-3(5) , Scholastic Pr.) Scholastic, Inc.

—Private Peaceful. l.t. ed. 2006. 225p. (J). 21.95 (978-0-7862-8946-2(5)) Thorndike Pr.

Morris, Jackie. The Snow Leopard. 2007. (Illus.). 32p. (J). (ps-3). 16.95 (***978-1-84507-600-9(1)***) Lincoln, Frances Ltd. GBR. *Dist:* Perseus Distribution.

Moverley, Richard. The Reluctant Rajput. Dean, David, illus. 2005. (Yellow Go Bananas Ser.). 48p. (J). lib. bdg. (978-0-7787-2723-1(8)) Crabtree Publishing Co.

Myers, Walter Dean. Patrol: An American Soldier in Vietnam. Grifalconi, Ann, illus. 2002. 40p. (J). lib. bdg. 17.89 (978-0-06-028364-3(5)); 16.99 (978-0-06-028363-6(7)) HarperCollins Pubs.

Nix, Garth. Sir Thursday. (Keys to the Kingdom Ser.: No. 4). 352p. (J). 2007. pap. 6.99 (***978-0-439-43657-1(5)*** , Scholastic Paperbacks); 2006. (gr. 4-7). pap. 16.99 (978-0-439-70087-0(6) , Scholastic Pr.) Scholastic, Inc.

Olasky, Susan. Will Northaway & the Gathering Storm. 2005. (Young American Patriots Ser.: No. 4). 96p. (J). (ps-7). pap. 5.99 (978-1-58134-478-3(3) , Crossway Bibles) Crossway Bks.

Paulsen, Gary. A Soldier's Heart. 2004. 128p. (J). (gr. 7 up). pap. 29.00 incl. audio (978-0-8072-8301-1(0) , Listening Library) Random Hse. Audio Publishing Group.

—Soldier's Heart. 2000. (Illus.). 106p. (YA). (gr. 8-12). per. 12.15 (978-0-606-19222-4(0)) Tandem Library Bks.

—Soldier's Heart: eing the Story of the Enlistment & Due Service of the Boy Charley Goddard in the First Minnesota Volunteers. 1998. 128p. (YA). (gr. 7-12). 15.95 (978-0-385-32498-4(7) , Delacorte Bks. for Young Readers) Random Hse. Children's Bks.

Pierce, Tamora & Sherman, Josepha. Young Warriors: Stories of Strength. 2006. 336p. (J). (gr. 7-11). pap. 8.95 (978-0-375-82963-5(6) , Random Hse. Bks. for Young Readers) Random Hse. Children's Bks.

Pinczes, Elinor J. Remainder of One. 2002. (gr. k-3). lib. bdg. 14.10 (978-0-613-90724-8(8)) Tandem Library Bks.

Reit, Seymour V. Guns for General Washington: A Story of the American Revolution. 2001. (Great Episodes Ser.). 160p. (YA). (gr. 5-9). pap. 6.00 (978-0-15-216435-5(9) , Gulliver Bks.) Harcourt Children's Bks.

Remarque, Erich Maria. All Quiet on the Western Front: With Related Readings. Wheen, A. W., tr. from GER. 2002. (EMC Masterpiece Series Access Editions). (Illus.). xxv, 249p. (YA). 14.60 (978-0-8219-2420-4(6)) EMC/Paradigm Publishing.

Rodman, Mary Ann. Jimmy's Stars. 2008. 272p. (J). 16.95 (***978-0-374-33703-2(9)***) Farrar, Straus & Giroux.

Schlitz, Laura Amy. The Bearskinner: A Tale of the Brothers Grimm. Grafe, Max, illus. 2007. 40p. (J). (gr. 3-6). 16.99 (***978-0-7636-2730-0(5)***) Candlewick Pr.

Scott, Gavin. Small Soldiers, Level 2. abr. ed. 1999. (C). pap. 9.00 (978-0-582-38099-8(5)) Longman Publishing Group.

Shinn, Sharon. General WInston's Daughter. 2007. 352p. (YA). (gr. 7 up). 17.99 (***978-0-670-06248-5(0)*** , Viking Juvenile) Penguin Group (USA) Inc.

Smith, Annie Laura. Saving da Vinci. 2005. (YA). mass mkt. 6.99 (***978-0-9753367-6-2(2)***) Onstage Publishing, LLC.

Styles, Showell. The Flying Ensign: Greencoats Against Napoleon. 2003. (Budget Bks., Illus.). Orig. Title: Greencoat Against Napoleon. 340p. (J). pap. 14.95 (978-1-883937-70-6(1)) Bethlehem Bks.

Sullivan, Jaqueline Levering. Annie's War. 2007. 190p. (J). (gr. 3-7). 15.00 (***978-0-8028-5325-7(0)*** , Eerdmans Bks For Young Readers) Eerdmans, William B. Publishing Co.

Summer of My German Soldier. 1999. (YA). 9.95 (978-1-56137-113-6(0)) Novel Units, Inc.

Sykes, Shelley & Szymanski, Lois. The Ghost Comes Out. 2001. (Gettysburg Ghost Gang Ser.: Vol. 1). 96p. (J). pap. 5.95 (978-1-57249-266-0(X) , White Mane Kids) White Mane Publishing Co., Inc.

—The Soldier in the Cellar. 2004. (Gettysburg Ghost Gang Ser.: Vol. 5). 96p. (J). pap. 5.95 (978-1-57249-299-8(6) , White Mane Kids) White Mane Publishing Co., Inc.

To Keep Me SAFE! A Story for Children Affected by Military Deployments. 2003. (J). 12.00 (978-0-9740289-0-3(8)) State of Growth Publishing Co.

Turner, Megan Whalen. The King of Attolia. 400p. (J). 2007. (gr. 5 up). pap. 7.99 (***978-0-06-083579-8(6)*** , Eos); 2006. 16.99 (978-0-06-083577-4(X)); 2006. lib. bdg. 17.89 (978-0-06-083578-1(8)) HarperCollins Pubs.

Walton, Jo. King's Peace. 2000. (gr. 5-8). lib. bdg. 16.45 (978-0-613-62634-7(6)) Tandem Library Bks.

Wilson, John. Flames of the Tiger. 2004. 176p. (YA). (gr. 13 up). (978-1-55337-618-7(8)); (Illus.). (978-1-55337-619-4(6)) Kids Can Pr., Ltd.

Wisler, G. Clifton. Red Cap. unabr. ed. 2000. (YA). pap., stu. ed. 41.24 incl. audio (978-0-7887-3629-2(9) , 41018X4) Recorded Bks., LLC.

—Red Cap. 2001. (YA). 20.25 (978-0-8446-7196-3(7)) Smith, Peter Pub., Inc.

Wolder, Dianne & Harrison-Lever, Brian. Photographs in the Mud. 2005. (Illus.). 32p. (J). 24.25 (978-1-920731-20-5(2)) Fremantle Pr. AUS. *Dist:* International Specialized Bk. Services.

Wolf, Joan M. Someone Named Eva. 2007. 208p. (J). (gr. 5-9). 16.00 (978-0-618-53579-8(9) , Clarion Bks.) Houghton Mifflin Co. Trade & Reference Div.

Wright, Caleb E. Marcus Blair A Story of Provincial Times. 2006. pap. 22.95 (***978-1-4286-6303-9(7)***) Kessinger Publishing, LLC.

Wulffson, Don L. Soldier X. 2003. 240p. (YA). pap. 6.99 (978-0-14-250073-6(9) , Puffin) Penguin Group (USA) Inc.

—Soldier X. 2003. (gr. 7-12). lib. bdg. 15.30 (978-0-613-67163-7(5)) Tandem Library Bks.

Young, Miriam. Miss Suzy. Lobel, Arnold, illus. 40th anniv. ed. 2004. 44p. (J). 17.95 (978-1-930900-28-8(7)) Purple Hse. Pr.

Zahn, Timothy. Dragon & Herdsman. 2007. (Dragonback Ser.). 304p. (J). mass mkt. 5.99 (***978-0-7653-5276-7(1)*** , Starscape) Doherty, Tom Assocs., LLC.

—Dragon & Slave: The Third Dragonback Adventure. rev. ed. 2005. (Dragonback Ser.). 304p. (J). 17.95 (978-0-7653-0126-0(1) , Tor Bks.) Doherty, Tom Assocs., LLC.

—Dragon & Soldier. 2005. (Dragonback Ser.). 304p. (J). 5.99 (978-0-7653-5017-6(3) , Starscape) Doherty, Tom Assocs., LLC.

SOLDIERS—UNITED STATES

see also African American Soldiers

Anderson, Dale. A Soldier's Life in the Civil War. 2004. (World Almanac Library of the Civil War). (Illus.). 48p. (J). (gr. 5 up). pap. 11.95 (978-0-8368-5595-1(7)); lib. bdg. 30.00 (978-0-8368-5586-9(8)) Stevens, Gareth Inc. (World Almanac Library).

Ashabranner, Brent. Their Names to Live: What the Vietnam Veterans Memorial Means to America. Ashabranner, Jennifer, photos by. 1998. (Great American Memorials Ser.). (Illus.). 64p. (gr. 4-8). lib. bdg. 24.90 (978-0-7613-3235-0(9) , Twenty-First Century Bks.) Lerner Publishing Group.

Beller, Susan Provost. Billy Yank & Johnny Reb: Soldiering in the Civil War. (Soldiers on the Battlefront Ser.). (Illus.). 2007. 112p. (YA). (gr. 6-8). lib. bdg. 33.26 (978-0-8225-6803-2(9)); 2000. 96p. (gr. 5 up). lib. bdg. (978-0-7613-1869-9(0) , Millbrook Pr.) Lerner Publishing Group.

—The Doughboys over There: Soldiering in World War I. 2007. (Soldiers on the Battlefront Ser.). (Illus.). 112p. (YA). (gr. 6-8). lib. bdg. 33.26 (978-0-8225-6295-5(2)) Lerner Publishing Group.

—Yankee Doodle & the Redcoats: Soldiering in the Revolutionary War. rev. ed. 2007. (Soldiers on the Battlefront Ser.). (Illus.). 112p. (YA). (gr. 6-8). lib. bdg. 33.26 (978-0-8225-6655-7(9) , Twenty-First Century Bks.) Lerner Publishing Group.

Castrovilla, Selene. By the Sword: A Young Man Meets War. 2007. (Illus.). 40p. (J). (gr. 4-6). 17.95 (978-1-59078-427-3(8)) Boyds Mills Pr.

Connell, Kate. Yankee Blue or Rebel Gray? The Civil War Adventures of Sam Shaw. 2003. (gr. 3-6). lib. bdg. 15.30 (978-0-613-67133-0(3)) Tandem Library Bks.

The G. I. Series: The Illustrated History of the American Soldier, His Uniform, & His Equipment, 21. 2005. 76 - 84p. pap. 577.50 (978-0-7910-8077-1(3) , Chelsea Hse.) Facts On File, Inc.

Gauch, Patricia Lee. The Impossible Major Rogers. Parker, Robert Andrew, illus. 2008. (J). (978-1-59078-334-4(4)) Boyds Mills Pr.

Haugen, Brenda & Santella, Andrew. Ethan Allen: Green Mountain Rebel. 2004. (Signature Lives Ser.). (Illus.). 112p. (J). 30.60 (978-0-7565-0824-1(X) , 1240131) Compass Point Bks.

Lerch, Kathryn W., ed. Words of War: Wartime Memories from the Civil War Through the Gulf War. 2002. (Illus.). xii, 177p. (YA). pap. 24.95 (978-1-57860-108-0(8)) Emmis Bks.

Lewis, Noah & Graham, Loretta. Edward Ned Hector. 2005. (ENG., Illus.). 36p. (J). per. 19.99 (***978-1-4208-6817-3(9)***) AuthorHouse.

Marsh, Carole. Old Abe. 2002. (One Thousand Readers Ser.). (Illus.). 12p. (J). (gr. k-4). 2.95 (978-0-635-01552-5(8) , 15528) Gallopade International.

Nathan, Amy. Count on US: American Women in the Military. 2004. (Illus.). 96p. (J). (gr. 5). 21.95 (978-0-7922-6330-2(8) , National Geographic Children's Bks.) National Geographic Society.

Price Hossell, Karen. Ethan Allen. 2004. (American War Biographies Ser.). (J). lib. bdg. 29.93 (978-1-4034-5077-7(3)); (Illus.). pap. 8.50 (978-1-4034-5084-5(6)) Heinemann Library.

Ratliff, Thomas. You Wouldn't Want to Be a Civil War Soldier! 2004. (You Wouldn't Want to Ser.). (Illus.). 32p. (J). (gr. 2-5). pap. 9.95 (978-0-531-16393-1(8) , Watts, Franklin) Scholastic Library Publishing.

Ratliff, Thomas M. & Salariya, David. You Wouldn't Want to Be a Civil War Soldier! A War You'd Rather Not Fight. Antram, David, illus. 2004. (You Wouldn't Want To Ser.). 32p. (J). 28.50 (978-0-531-12350-8(2) , Watts, Franklin) Scholastic Library Publishing.

Rebman, Renée C. The Union Soldier. 2006. 48p. (J). (gr. 4-6). lib. bdg. (978-0-7565-2030-4(4)) Compass Point Bks.

Savage, Douglas J. Soldier's Life During the Civil War. 2000. (Untold History of the Civil War Ser.). (Illus.). 64p. (J). (gr. 3 up). 25.00 (978-0-7910-5710-0(0) , Chelsea Hse.) Facts On File, Inc.

Smolinski, Diane. Revolutionary War Soldiers. (Americans at War Ser.). (Illus.). 32p. (J). (gr. 4-6). 2002. pap. 6.95 (978-1-58810-562-2(8) , 91694); 2001. lib. bdg. (978-1-58810-276-8(9)) Heinemann Library.

—Soldiers of the Civil War. 2002. (Americans at War Ser.). (Illus.). 32p. (J). (gr. 4-6). lib. bdg. (978-1-58810-098-6(7)); pap. 6.95 (978-1-58810-392-5(7) , 91132) Heinemann Library.

—Soldiers of the French & Indian War. 2003. (Americans at War Ser.). (Illus.). 32p. (J). (gr. 4-6). lib. bdg. 25.64 (978-1-4034-0172-4(1)) Heinemann Library.

—Soldiers of the French & Indian War. 2003. (gr. 3-6). lib. bdg. 15.25 (978-0-613-89119-6(8)) Tandem Library Bks.

—Soldiers of the Spanish-American War. 2003. (Americans at War Ser.). (Illus.). 32p. (J). (gr. 4-6). lib. bdg. 25.64 (978-1-4034-0173-1(X)) Heinemann Library.

—Soldiers of the War of 1812. 2003. (Americans at War Ser.). (Illus.). 32p. (J). (gr. 4-6). lib. bdg. 25.64 (978-1-4034-0174-8(8)) Heinemann Library.

Smolinski, Diane & Smolinski, Henry. Soldiers of the French & Indian War. (Americans at War Ser.). 32p. pap. 6.95 (978-1-4034-3154-7(X)) Heinemann Library.

S

—Soldiers of the Spanish-American War. (Americans at War Ser.). 32p. pap. 6.95 (978-1-4034-3156-1(6)) Heinemann Library.

—Soldiers of the War of 1812. (Americans at War Ser.). 32p. pap. 6.95 (978-1-4034-3158-5(2)) Heinemann Library.

A Soldier's Life Series, 6 vols., Set. 2003. (Illus.). (J). 188.52 (978-1-4109-0124-8(6)) Raintree.

Souza, Dorothy M. John Wesley Powell. 2004. (Watts Library). (Illus.). 64p. (J). (gr. 5-7). pap. 8.95 (978-0-531-16653-6(8)); 25.50 (978-0-531-12289-1(1)) Scholastic Library Publishing. (Watts, Franklin).

Stein, R. Conrad. Ethan Allen & the Green Mountain Boys. 2003. (Cornerstones of Freedom). (Illus.). 48p. (J). (gr. 4-6). 26.00 (978-0-516-24206-4(7) , Children's Pr.) Scholastic Library Publishing.

Stewart, Gail B. Life of a Soldier in Washington's Army. 2002. (Illus.). 112p. (J). 29.95 (978-1-59018-215-4(4) , Lucent Bks.) Thomson Gale.

Thornton, Jeremy. Foreign-Born Champions of the American Revolution. 2003. (Building Americas Democracy Ser.). (Illus.). 24p. (J). lib. bdg. 19.95 (978-0-8239-6277-8(6) , PowerKids Pr.) Rosen Publishing Group, Inc., The.

Witteman, Barbara. Miles Standish: Colonial Leader. 2004. (Let Freedom Ring Ser.). (Illus.). 48p. (J). 17.95 (978-0-7368-2457-6(X) , Bridgestone Bks.) Capstone Pr., Inc.

—Zebulon Pike: Soldier & Explorer. 2002. (Let Freedom Ring Ser.). (Illus.). 48p. (J). (gr. 3-4). lib. bdg. 22.60 (978-0-7368-1351-8(9) , Bridgestone Bks.) Capstone Pr., Inc.

SOLDIERS, AFRICAN AMERICAN

see African American Soldiers

SOLDIERS' LIFE

see Soldiers

SOLID GEOMETRY

see Geometry

SOLO, ANAKIN (FICTITIOUS CHARACTER)—FICTION

Moesta, Rebecca. Vader's Fortress. 1999. (Star Wars Ser.: No. 5). (978-0-606-14362-2(9)) Tandem Library Bks.

SOLO, HAN (FICTITIOUS CHARACTER)—FICTION

Crispin, A. C. The Paradise Snare. 1998. (Star Wars: Vol. 1). (gr. 7-12). lib. bdg. 15.30 (978-0-613-70932-3(2)) Tandem Library Bks.

Davids, Paul & Davids, Hollace. The Lost City of the Jedi. 1999. (Star Wars Ser.: Bk. 2). (Illus.). 94p. (J). (gr. 4-7). reprint ed. pap. 10.00 (978-0-7881-6480-4(5)) DIANE Publishing Co.

—Star Wars, 3 bks. l.t. ed. Incl. Prophets of the Dark Side. lib. bdg. 22.60 (978-0-8368-1994-6(2)); Queen of the Empire. lib. bdg. 22.60 (978-0-8368-1993-9(4)); Zorba the Hutt's Revenge. lib. bdg. 22.60 (978-0-8368-1991-5(8)); 112p. (J). (gr. 4 up). 1997. Set lib. bdg. 67.80 (978-0-8368-1988-5(8)) Stevens, Gareth Inc.

SOLO, JACEN (FICTITIOUS CHARACTER)—FICTION

Anderson, Kevin J. The Shards of Alderaan. 1999. (Star Wars Ser.: No. 7). (978-0-606-14313-4(0)) Tandem Library Bks.

SOLO, JAINA (FICTITIOUS CHARACTER)—FICTION

Anderson, Kevin J. The Shards of Alderaan. 1999. (Star Wars Ser.: No. 7). (978-0-606-14313-4(0)) Tandem Library Bks.

SOLOMON, KING OF ISRAEL

Burgdorf, Larry. Zerubbabel Rebuilds the Temple: Ezra 3-6 for Children. Eitzen, Allan, illus. 2006. (Arch Books). (ENG.). (J). 1.99 (978-0-7586-0870-3(5)) Concordia Publishing Hse.

De Graaf, Anne. Solomon. Montero, Jose Perez, illus. 2001. 38p. (J). (ps-1). 5.99 (978-0-8054-2191-0(2)) B&H Publishing Grp.

Ham, Ken. Solomon: A Man of Wisdom. 2000. (Awesome Adventure Bible Stories Ser.). (Illus.). (J). (gr. 2-7). pap. 5.99 (978-0-89051-332-3(5)) Master Bks.

Myers, Glenn, illus. Solomon Builds the Temple: 1 Kings 5:1-8:66. 2005. (Little Learner Bible Story Books). 16p. (J). pap. (***978-0-7586-0944-1(2)***) Concordia Publishing Hse.

SOLOMON, KING OF ISRAEL—FICTION

Biers-Ariel, Matt. Solomon & the Trees. Silverberg-Kiss, Esti, illus. 2004. (J). (gr. k-3). 13.95 (978-0-8074-0749-3(6) , 101055) URJ Pr.

Borchard, Therese Johnson. Whitney Solves a Dilemma with Solomon: And Learns the Importance of Honesty. 2000. (Emerald Bible Collection). (Illus.). 80p. (gr. 3-7). 5.95 (978-0-8091-6668-8(2) , 6668-2) Paulist Pr.

Haggard, H. Rider. Las Minas del Rey Salomon.Tr. of King Solomon's Mines. (SPA., Illus.). 184p. (YA). 11.95 (978-84-7281-094-5(1) , AF1094) Auriga, Ediciones S.A. ESP. *Dist:* Continental Bk. Co., Inc.

—Las Minas del Rey Salomon. 5th ed. (Coleccion Clasicos en Accion).Tr. of King Solomon's Mines. (SPA., Illus.). 80p. (YA). (gr. 5-8). 12.76 (978-84-241-5779-1(6)) Everest de Ediciones y Distribucion, S.L. ESP. *Dist:* Lectorum Pubns., Inc.

Oberman, Sheldon. The Wisdom Bird: A Tale of Solomon & Sheba. Waldman, Neil, illus. 2003. 32p. (YA). (gr. 2-4). 15.95 (978-1-56397-816-6(4)) Boyds Mills Pr.

SOMME, BATTLES OF THE, 1916, 1918

Ross, Stewart. The Battle of the Somme. 2003. (World Wars Ser.). (Illus.). 64p. (J). lib. bdg. 28.56 (978-0-7398-5479-2(8)) Raintree.

SONG BOOKS

see Songbooks

SONGBOOKS

see also School Songbooks

Amery, Heather. The Usborne Children's Songbook. Cartwright, Stephen, illus. 2nd rev. ed. 1998. (Songbooks Ser.). 64p. (J). (ps-3). pap. 10.95 (978-0-7460-2981-7(0)) EDC Publishing.

Barretta, Gene, illus. On Top of Spaghetti: A Silly Song Book. 2005. 12p. (J). 12.95 (978-1-58117-331-4(8) , Intervisual/Piggy Toes) Dalmatian Pr.

Beall, Pamela Conn & Nipp, Susan Hagen. The Wee Sing for Halloween. Klein, Nancy Spence, illus. 2002. (Wee Sing Ser.). 64p. (J). pap. 2.99 (978-0-8431-4909-8(4) , Price Stern Sloan) Penguin Group (USA) Inc.

Big's Big Baby. (Looney Tunes Song & Sound Bks.). (Illus.). 16p. (J). (ps-k). 7.98 (978-0-7853-1608-4(6) , PI10) Publications International, Ltd.

Bousman, Cindy. Pete & P. J. Sing, Dance & Read with Me, Read-Along with Big Book, CD & Instrument. 2000. 14p. (J). (ps-3). pap. 29.95 incl. audio compact disk (978-1-931127-38-7(7) , 986-006) Kindermusik International.

—Watch Me! Sing, Dance & Read with Me, Read-Along with Big Book. 2000. 12p. (J). (ps-3). pap. 29.95 incl. audio compact disk (978-1-931127-42-4(5) , 986-015) Kindermusik International.

Boytim, Joan Frey. Daffodils, Violets & Snowflakes: 24 Classical Songs for Young Women, Ages 10 to Mid-Teens. 2003. 88p. (gr. 5 up). pap. 14.95 incl. audio compact disk (978-0-634-06181-3(X) , 063406181X) Leonard, Hal Corp.

—Daffodils, Violets & Snowflakes: 24 Classical Songs for Young Women, Ages Ten to Mid-Teens. 2003. 88p. pap. 14.95 incl. audio compact disk (978-0-634-06212-4(3) , 0634062123) Leonard, Hal Corp.

Chenille. Teaching Hippopotomi to Fly Songbook. Dawdy, Cheryl, illus. 1998. 84p. (J). (ps-3). spiral bd. 17.98 (978-0-9659936-9-2(8) , CTR03) Cantoo Records.

Coates, Dan. The Kid's Music Collection. 1998. 156p. (J). (ps-3). 14.95 (978-0-7692-1859-5(8) , Warner Bros. Pubns.) Alfred Publishing Co., Inc.

—My First Book of Christmas. 2000. (J). 6.95 (978-0-7692-8971-7(1) , Warner Bros. Pubns.) Alfred Publishing Co., Inc.

Debussy, Claude. Oeuvres Complete Serie 1 Vol. 2: Images, pour le Piano, Children's Corner. 2001. 152p. pap. 89.95 (978-0-634-08211-5(6) , 0634082116) Leonard, Hal Corp.

Diaper Days Songs. (Baby Looney Tunes Song Bks.). (Illus.). 16p. (J). (ps). 7.98 (978-0-7853-1612-1(4) , PI112) Publications International, Ltd.

Flatau, Carole, ed. Sylvester's Snappy Songs: Primer Level for Early Elementary Students. 1999. (Looney Tunes Piano Library). (J). 59.95 (978-0-7692-8433-0(7) , Warner Bros. Pubns.) Alfred Publishing Co., Inc.

—Taz's Terrific Songs: Level Two for Late Elementary Students. 2000. (Looney Tunes Piano Library). 24p. (J). 5.95 (978-0-7692-8434-7(5) , Warner Bros. Pubns.) Alfred Publishing Co., Inc.

—Tweety's Easy Listening Songs: Level One for Elementary Students. 1999. (Looney Tunes Piano Library). (J). 5.95 (978-0-7692-8435-4(3) , Warner Bros. Pubns.) Alfred Publishing Co., Inc.

Fox, Dan, ed. A Treasury of Children's Songs: Forty Favorites to Sing & Play. rev. ed. 2003. (Illus.). 96p. (J). 19.95 (978-0-8050-7445-1(7) , Holt, Henry & Co. Bks. For Young Readers) Holt, Henry & Co.

Friedman, Randee & Jordan, Cecile. The Alef Bet: Hebrew Activity Kit & Songbook. Friedman, Randee & Lander, Donna, eds. 2001. (HEB.). 80p. (J). 21.95 (978-1-890161-46-0(2) , 0606261616365) Sounds Write Productions, Inc.

Frosty the Snowman: Songs of the Season: 5-Button Song Book. (Illus.). 10p. (J). (ps-2). 7.98 (978-0-7853-2067-8(9) , PI27) Publications International, Ltd.

Glazer, Tom. Tom Glazer's Treasury of Songs for Children. Seiden, Art, illus. 2nd ed. 2003. 256p. (J). (gr. 3-6). pap. 20.00 (978-1-58690-003-8(X)) Empire Publishing Service.

Goldstein, Rose B. Songs to Share. Schloss, E., illus. (ENG & HEB.). 64p. (J). (ps-5). 2.95 (978-0-8381-0720-1(6) , 10-720) United Synagogue of America Bk. Service.

Graham, Carolyn. Let's Chant, Let's Sing, Bk.6. 1999. (Illus.). 48p. 8.25 (978-0-19-435889-7(5)) Oxford Univ. Pr., Inc.

Hal Leonard Corp., creator. The Charlie Brown Songbook: Recorder Fun. 2003. (Style Collections). (Illus.). 32p. (J). pap. 9.95 (978-0-634-05598-0(4) , 0634055984) Leonard, Hal Corp.

—Children's TV Songs. 2003. 48p. pap. 10.95 (978-0-634-06695-5(1) , 0634066951) Leonard, Hal Corp.

Hal Leonard Corporation Staff, ed. Baby Boomer's Songbook. 1999. (Style Collections). (Illus.). 248p. pap. 19.95 (978-0-634-00547-3(2) , 0634005472) Leonard, Hal Corp.

Halfmann, Janet, et al. Barney's Favorite Songs. Davis, Guy, ed. Valentine-Ruppe, June, illus. 1999. (Barney Ser.). 112p. (J). (ps-k). act. bk. ed. 2.99 (978-1-57064-457-3(8)) Scholastic, Inc.

Harcourt School Publishers Staff. Rhymes & Songs Big Book. 3rd ed. 2002. (Trophies Reading Program Ser.). (Illus.). (gr. k-6). pap. 58.20 (978-0-15-325401-7(7)) Harcourt Schl. Pubs.

Hop! Hop! Hop! (J). 15.95 (978-0-8126-0086-5(X)) Open Court Publishing Co.

Horn, Patty. Patty Horn's Desert Dwellers Fiesta! Cude, Dana, illus. 1998. 46p. (J). (gr. k-8). spiral bd. 15.95 incl. audio (978-0-9644105-9-6(1)) Two Geckos Music & Publishing.

James, Susan. Shiny Dinah: Sing, Dance & Read with Me. 2000. 12p. (J). (ps-3). pap. 9.95 incl. audio (978-1-931127-49-3(2) , 986-007); pap. 14.95 incl. audio (978-1-931127-48-6(4) , 986-008) Kindermusik International.

—Shiny Dinah: Sing, Dance & Read with Me, Read-Along with Big Book. 2000. 12p. (J). (ps-3). pap. 29.95 incl. audio compact disk (978-1-931127-50-9(6) , 986-009) Kindermusik International.

—This Is My Dance: Sing, Dance & Read with Me, Read-Along with Big Book & Cassette. 2000. 16p. (J). (ps-3). pap. 14.95 incl. audio (978-1-931127-32-5(8) , 986-011) Kindermusik International.

LeapFrog Staff, compiled by. Mother Goose Songbook. 2001. (J). spiral bd. 14.99 (978-1-58605-050-4(8)) LeapFrog Enterprises, Inc.

Lewelling, Kim, et al. New Songs for New Singers Bk. 1: 30 Settings of Classic & New Texts. 2001. (Illus.). 96p. (YA). 25.95 incl. audio compact disk (978-1-889079-35-6(9)) Darcey Pr.

MacDonald, Margaret Read & Jaeger, Winifred. The Round Book: Rounds Kids Love to Sing. Davis, Yvonne L., illus. 1999. (J). (ps up). 128p. 22.50 (978-0-208-02441-1(7)); xiv, 128p. pap. 16.50 (978-0-208-02472-5(7)) Shoe String Pr., Inc. (Linnet Bks.).

Matters, Kris, et al. New Songs for New Singers Bk. 2: 26 Settings for Classic & New Texts. 2001. (Illus.). 96p. 25.95 incl. audio compact disk (978-1-889079-36-3(7)) Darcey Pr.

Merrill, Bob. How Much Is That Doggie in the Window? Trapani, Iza, illus. 2004. (J). (ps-2). 24p. bds. 6.95 (978-1-58089-031-1(8)); 32p. pap. 6.95 (978-1-58089-030-4(X)) Charlesbridge Publishing, Inc.

—How Much Is That Doggie in the Window? 1999. (Extended Nursery Rhymes Ser.). (Illus.). 32p. (J). (ps up). lib. bdg. 23.33 (978-0-8368-2486-5(5)) Stevens, Gareth Inc.

Meyer, Edward H. Samm: Accompaniment Songbook, Level 3. 1999. (J). (gr. 3-4). 25.00 (978-0-8100-0898-4(X)) Northwestern Publishing Hse.

—Samm: Student Songbook, Level 3. 1999. (J). (gr. 3-4). 7.50 (978-0-8100-0901-1(3)) Northwestern Publishing Hse.

Mickey's Favorites. (Sing-Along Ser.). (J). 11.99 incl. audio (978-1-55723-962-4(2)) Walt Disney Records.

Negus, Jacque. Welcome to Our House: Sing, Dance & Read with Me Activity Book with Cassette & Instrument. 2000. 36p. (J). (ps-3). pap. 15.95 incl. audio (978-1-931127-05-9(0) , 986-016) Kindermusik International.

—Welcome to Our House: Sing, Dance & Read with Me Activity Book with CD & Instrument. 2000. 36p. (J). (ps-3). pap. 18.95 incl. audio compact disk (978-1-931127-06-6(9) , 986-017) Kindermusik International.

Okun, Milton, ed. Cliff Eberhardt Songbook. Date not set. 56p. (YA). pap. 15.95 (978-0-89524-957-9(X)) Cherry Lane Music Co.

—Just for Kids. 32p. (YA). pap. 7.95 (978-0-89524-950-0(2) , 02505506) Cherry Lane Music Co.

Pingry, Patricia. O Little Town of Bethlehem. 2005. (Illus.). 16p. (J). bds. 12.99 (978-0-8249-6566-2(3)) Ideals Pubns.

Sdoia-Satz, Phyllis & Leon, Alfredo, Jr. Husky Gang: My Song & Story Book. 2001. (Illus.). 120p. (J). (ps-3). pap. 16.95 incl. audio compact disk (978-0-7579-7889-0(4) , Warner Bros. Pubns.) Alfred Publishing Co., Inc.

Seuss, Dr. The Cat in the Hat Songbook. Seuss, Dr., illus. 2002. (Illus.). (J). 19.57 (978-0-7587-2202-7(8)) Book Wholesalers, Inc.

Shake It up! Songbook. 120p. (J). 16.99 (978-0-8307-2769-8(8) , Gospel Light) Gospel Light Pubns.

Sweet Dreams Lullabies. (Baby Looney Tunes Song Bks.). (Illus.). 16p. (J). (ps). 7.98 (978-0-7853-1613-8(2) , PI13) Publications International, Ltd.

Tabby, Abigail. Cookie Rhyme, Cookie Time. Goldberg, Barry, illus. 2003. (Sesame Beginnings Ser.: Vol. 4). 14p. (J). (gr. k). bds. 7.99 (978-0-375-82342-8(5) , Random Hse. Bks. for Young Readers) Random Hse. Children's Bks.

—Hello! Good-Bye! Brannon, Tom, illus. 2003. (Sesame Beginnings Ser.). 14p. (J). (gr. k). bds. 7.99 (978-0-375-82343-5(3) , Random Hse. Bks. for Young Readers) Random Hse. Children's Bks.

Taz TV. (Looney Tunes Song & Sound Bks.). (Illus.). 16p. (J). (ps-k). 7.98 (978-0-7853-1609-1(4) , PI9) Publications International, Ltd.

Wells, Rosemary. The Bear Went over the Mountain. Wells, Rosemary, illus. 2007. (Bruno & Boots Book Ser.). (Illus.). 18p. (J). bds. 5.99 (978-0-590-02910-0(X)) Scholastic, Inc.

—The Itsy-Bitsy Spider. Wells, Rosemary, illus. 1998. (Bruno & Boots Book Ser.). (Illus.). 18p. (J). (ps). bds. 5.99 (978-0-590-02911-7(8)) Scholastic, Inc.

SONGS

see also Ballads; Carols; Folk Songs; Hymns; Lullabies; National Songs; Popular Music; School Songbooks; Sea Songs; Songbooks

Ada, Alma Flor, et al. Mama Goose: A Latino Nursery Treasury. Suarez, Maribel, illus. 2005. 128p. (ps-k). 19.99 (978-0-7868-1953-9(7)) Hyperion Bks. for Children.

Adams, Pam. Sing a Song of Sixpence. 1998. (Books with Holes Ser.). (Illus.). 16p. (J). (ps-3). 6.99 (978-0-85953-627-1(0)) Child's Play International Ltd. GBR. *Dist:* Child's Play-International.

Agnes & Aubrey. Art Songs: Ten Songs about Artists. 2006. (Illus.). 24p. (gr. k-4). 14.95 (978-1-85437-683-1(7)) Tate Gallery Publishing, Ltd. GBR. *Dist:* Hachette Bk. Group.

Aigner-Clark, Julie. Nighttime Lullaby. Zaidi, Nadeem, illus. 2005. (Baby Einstein Ser.). 10p. (J). (ps-17). bds. 12.99 (978-0-7868-5535-3(5)) Baby Einstein Co., LLC, The.

—Peek-a-Boo Bard. Zaidi, Nadeem, illus. 2005. 10p. (J). (ps-17). bds. 10.99 (978-0-7868-5534-6(7)) Baby Einstein Co., LLC, The.

Albee, Sarah. Elmo's 12 Days of Christmas. Swanson, Maggie, illus. 2003. 24p. (J). (gr. k-ps). bds. 4.99 (978-0-375-82506-4(1) , Random Hse. Bks. for Young Readers) Random Hse. Children's Bks.

All about Me. 2005. 128p. (J). per. 19.99 (978-1-59441-191-5(3) , DJ-604010) Carson-Dellosa Publishing Co., Inc.

Allen, Dennis. How the Grouch Found Christmas. 1999. 6.95 (978-0-7673-9631-8(6)) LifeWay Christian Resources.

Amery, Heather. Children's Songbook. 1998. (Songbook Ser.). 64p. (J). (ps-3). 18.95 (978-1-58086-151-9(2)) EDC Publishing.

Archambault, John & Plummer, David. Chicka Chicka Boom Boom, No. 2360. 1999. (Happy Song Sing-Alongs Ser.). (Illus.). 64p. (J). (ps-3). pap. 12.98 incl. audio (978-1-57471-549-1(6)) Creative Teaching Pr., Inc.

Ardis, Marcia M. Sing Alongs: Helping Children Learn to Read. Johnson, Linda, illus. l.t. ed. 1999. 96p. (J). (ps-2). pap. 9.95 (978-0-9667936-0-4(9) , 122) Literacy Links.

Armstrong, June Fischer. More Worship Songs for Children: A Collection of 22 Scripture Songs. 1999. (Children's Music Ser.). 32p. 12.95 (978-1-56212-476-2(5) , 001830, Faith Alive Christian Resources) CRC Pubns.

Arnold, Tedd. Catalina Magdalina Hoopensteiner Wallendiner Hogan Logan Bogan Was Her Name. Arnold, Tedd, illus. 2004. (Illus.). 40p. (J). pap. 10.95 (978-0-590-10994-9(4) , Cartwheel Bks.) Scholastic, Inc.

Arnosky, Jim. Big Jim & the White-Legged Moose. 1999. (Illus.). 32p. (J). (ps-3). 16.00 (978-0-688-10864-9(4)) HarperCollins Pubs.

Arrullos. (SPA & ENG.). (J). (ps-3). 10.00 net. (978-1-57417-032-0(5) , AC30087) Arcoiris Records, Inc.

Asch, Frank. Barnyard Lullaby. 2001. (Illus.). (J). (978-0-606-21610-4(3)) Tandem Library Bks.

Audio & Kidzup Productions Staff. Best Toddler Songbook. 2003. (Toddler Ser.). (J). pap. 12.99 incl. audio (978-1-894281-76-8(4)) Kidzup Productions.

—Sunday School Songbook. 2001. (Kidzup Ser.). (J). pap. 12.99 incl. audio (978-1-894281-77-5(2)) Kidzup Entertainment CAN. *Dist:* Penton Overseas, Inc.

Axford, Elizabeth C., compiled by. The Music Box & Other Delights. 2003. (Illus.). 72p. (J). spiral bd. 14.95 (978-1-931844-03-1(8) , PP1015) Piano Pr.

Axford, Elizabeth C., compiled by & des. Kidtunes Songbook & Activity Guide, Axford, Elizabeth C., des. 2003. (Illus.). 52p. (J). 14.95 (978-1-931844-01-7(1) , PP1013) Piano Pr.

The B-I-B-L-E Online Children Song. 2.00 (978-0-687-07975-9(6)) Abingdon Pr.

Baby Einstein, creator. Baby Einstein Discover & Play. 2005. (Pop-up Songbook Ser.). (Illus.). 14p. (J). (ps-ps). per. 15.98 (978-1-4127-0578-3(9) , 7223100) Publications International, Ltd.

Baby Signing Time. 2005. (J). Bk. 1. bds. (978-1-933543-06-2(X)); Bk. 2. bds. (978-1-933543-07-9(8)) Two Little Hands Productions LLC.

Bach, Albert B. The Art Ballad, Loewe & Schubert. 3rd ed. 2001. 215p. (YA). reprint ed. 98.00 (978-0-7222-5454-7(7)) Library Reprints, Inc.

Bair, Linda & Andrews, Jill. Fiddle-Dee-Dee: Songs, Stories & Activities. 2000. (Illus.). 120p. (J). (ps-2). pap. 16.95 (978-1-57950-037-5(4) , Upstart Bks.) Highsmith Inc.

Baker, Clara Belle & Kohlsaat, Caroline. Songs for the Little Child. 2005. reprint ed. pap. 19.95 (978-1-4179-3304-4(0)) Kessinger Publishing, LLC.

Barchas, Sarah. Bridges Across the World: A Multicultural Songfest. Gething, Elizabeth, illus. 1999. 60p. (J). (gr. k-6). pap. 16.98 incl. audio compact disk (978-1-889686-14-1(X)); pap. 14.98 incl. audio (978-1-889686-13-4(1)); pap. 5.95 (978-1-889686-16-5(6)) High Haven Music.

Barker, Dan. Mary Had a Little Lamb Songbook. 2003. 44p. (J). 5.00 (978-1-58302-239-9(2)) One Way St., Inc.

Baron, Andrew, illus. The Adventures of Octopus Rex. 2003. (J). per. 17.95 (978-0-9760348-0-3(8)) BaHart Pubns. / Eight Legs Publishing.

Barrett, William A. English Glees & Part-Songs: An Inquiry into Their Historical Development. 2001. 358p. (YA). reprint ed. 98.00 (978-0-7222-6135-4(7)) Library Reprints, Inc.

Baum, Maxie. I Have a Little Dreidel. Paschkis, Julie, illus. 2006. 32p. (J). pap. 9.99 (978-0-439-64997-1(8) , Cartwheel Bks.) Scholastic, Inc.

Beaky, Suzanne, illus. She'll Be Comin' Round the Mountain. 2007. 32p. 14.95 (***978-1-59249-687-7(3)***) Soundprints.

—She'll Be Comin' Round the Mountain: Paperback with CD. 2007. 32p. 8.95 (***978-1-59249-688-4(1)***) Soundprints.

Beall, Pamela Conn & Nipp, Susan Hagen. Around the World. Chauncey, G., illus. 2006. (Wee Sing Ser.). 64p. (J). 9.99 (978-0-8431-2005-9(3) , Price Stern Sloan) Penguin Group (USA) Inc.

—The Best of Wee Sing. 2007. (Wee Sing Ser.). 60p. (J). (ps-2). 9.99 (978-0-8431-2184-1(X) , Price Stern Sloan) Penguin Group (USA) Inc.

—For Baby. ed. 2002. (Wee Sing Ser.). (Illus.). 24p. (J). pap. 2.99 (978-0-8431-7775-6(6) , Price Stern Sloan) Penguin Group (USA) Inc.

—The Hokey Pokey. Wittwer, Hala, illus. 2002. (Wee Sing Ser.). 24p. (J). bds. 4.99 (978-0-8431-7706-0(3) , Price Stern Sloan) Penguin Group (USA) Inc.

—If You're Happy & You Know It. Wittwer, Hala, illus. 2002. (Wee Sing Ser.). 32p. (J). (ps-1). bds. 4.99 (978-0-8431-7759-6(4) , Price Stern Sloan) Penguin Group (USA) Inc.

S

—Old MacDonald. Wittwer, Hala, illus. 2002. (Wee Sing Ser.). 24p. (J). (ps-1). bds. 4.99 (978-0-8431-7758-9(6) , Price Stern Sloan) Penguin Group (USA) Inc.

—Wee Sing & Learn Colors. 2005. (Wee Sing & Learn Ser.). 20p. (J). (ps). 9.99 (978-0-8431-1663-2(3) , Price Stern Sloan) Penguin Group (USA) Inc.

—Wee Sing & Play. 2006. (Wee Sing Ser.). 64p. (J). (ps-3). 9.99 (978-0-8431-2003-5(7) , Price Stern Sloan) Penguin Group (USA) Inc.

—Wee Sing Bible Songs. 2005. (Wee Sing Ser.). 64p. (J). (ps-4). 9.99 (978-0-8431-1300-6(6) , Price Stern Sloan) Penguin Group (USA) Inc.

—Wee Sing Children's Songs & Fingerplays. 2005. (Wee Sing Ser.). 64p. (J). (ps-1). 9.99 (978-0-8431-1362-4(6) , Price Stern Sloan) Penguin Group (USA) Inc.

—Wee Sing Dinosaurs. 2006. (Wee Sing Ser.). 60p. (J). (ps-2). 9.99 (978-0-8431-2097-4(5) , Price Stern Sloan) Penguin Group (USA) Inc.

—Wee Sing for Baby. 2005. (Wee Sing Ser.). 60p. (J). (ps). 9.99 (978-0-8431-1338-9(3) , Price Stern Sloan) Penguin Group (USA) Inc.

—Wee Sing for Christmas. Guida, Liisa & Klein, Nancy, illus. ed. 2002. (Wee Sing Ser.). 64p. (J). pap. 9.99 (978-0-8431-4961-6(2) , Price Stern Sloan) Penguin Group (USA) Inc.

—Wee Sing in the Car. 2005. (Wee Sing Ser.). 60p. (J). (gr. 1). 9.99 (978-0-8431-1339-6(1) , Price Stern Sloan) Penguin Group (USA) Inc.

—Wee Sing More Bible Songs. ed. 2002. (Wee Sing Ser.). (Illus.). (J). 11.99 (978-0-8431-4927-2(2)); 64p. pap. 9.99 (978-0-8431-4926-5(4)) Penguin Group (USA) Inc. (Price Stern Sloan).

—Wee Sing Silly Songs. 2006. (Wee Sing Ser.). 64p. (J). 9.99 (978-0-8431-2004-2(5) , Price Stern Sloan) Penguin Group (USA) Inc.

—Wee Sing Sing-Alongs. 2005. (Wee Sing Ser.). Orig. Title: Wee Sing Around the Campfire. 64p. (J). (gr. 1). 9.99 (978-0-8431-1361-7(8) , Price Stern Sloan) Penguin Group (USA) Inc.

Beaumont. Miss Polly Wolly Doodle from T. (J). 15.95 (978-0-8118-4825-1(6)) Chronicle Bks. LLC.

Bee, Kati. Mrs. Flutterbee & the Funny Farm. 2007. (Illus.). 32p. (J). 15.99 (***978-0-9793760-0-9(9))** Kati Bee & Friends Publishing.

Berkner, Laurie. Laurie Berkner Songbook. 2007. 56p. pap. 16.95 incl. audio compact disk (***978-0-8256-3544-1(6)** , Amsco Music) Music Sales Corp.

Berkner, Laurie. Victor Vito & Freddie Vasco: Two Polar Bears on a Mission to Save Klondike Cafe! Cole, Henry, tr. Cole, Henry, illus. 2004. 40p. (J). pap. 16.95 (978-0-439-42914-6(5) , Orchard Bks.) Scholastic, Inc.

Berlin, Irving. Easter Parade. McCue, Lisa, illus. 32p. (J). 2006. pap. 6.99 (978-0-06-443720-2(5) , Harper Trophy); 2003. 16.89 (978-0-06-029126-6(5)); 2003. 15.99 (978-0-06-029125-9(7)) HarperCollins Pubs.

—God Bless America. Munsinger, Lynn, illus. 2002. (J). (ps-2). 24p. 15.99 incl. audio compact disk (978-0-06-009788-2(4)); 32p. 17.89 (978-0-06-009789-9(2)) HarperCollins Pubs.

—White Christmas. 2002. 32p. (J). 16.95 (978-0-06-029123-5(0)) HarperCollins Pubs.

Bernardez, Manucia. Space Songs for Children: Fun Songs & Activities about Outer Space. 1999. (Illus.). 100p. (J). pap. 17.95 (978-0-936823-19-5(4)) Pearce-Evetts Publishing.

Bernhard, Durga. In the Fiddle Is a Song: A Lift-the-Flap Book of Hidden Potential. 2006. (Illus.). 24p. (J). 10.95 (978-0-8118-4951-7(1)) Chronicle Bks. LLC.

Bernstein, Lee. Barney's Sing-Along Stories: I Love You. Valentine-Ruppe, June, illus. 2003. (Barney Ser.). 24p. (J). (ps-1). pap. 3.50 (978-1-58668-299-6(7)) Scholastic, Inc.

Bible Songs. 2001. (Illus.). pap., tchr. ed. 9.95 incl. audio Audio Memory Publishing.

Bible Songs. 2000. (Illus.). (J). 15.98 (978-0-7853-4853-5(0)) Publications International, Ltd.

Big Keep Books, Rhymes & Songs, 2002. (Illus.). 8p. (J). 20.00 net. (978-1-893986-23-7(3)) Keep Bks.

Birchard, C. C. Boy Scout Song Book. 2004. reprint ed. pap. 20.95 (978-1-4179-5741-5(7)) Kessinger Publishing, LLC.

Bleck, Linda, illus. A Children's Treasury of Lullabies. 2006. 24p. (J). bds. 12.95 (978-1-4027-2979-9(0)) Sterling Publishing Co., Inc.

Blevins, Wiley. Songs & Rhymes: Live Audio Tape, Reproducible Song & Rhyme Sheets & Easy Lessons That Prepare Kids for Phonics Instructions. 1999. (Phonemic Awareness Ser.). (Illus.). 72p. (J). 15.95 (978-0-590-64409-9(2)) Scholastic, Inc.

Bliss, Phil, et al, illus. Silly Songs Sing-Along. 2002. (J). (978-0-7853-7500-5(7)) Publications International, Ltd.

Bollinger, Max & Capek, Jindra. La Cancion Mas Bonita. 2001. (SPA.). 32p. (J). (gr. 3-5). (978-84-348-0942-0(7)) SM Ediciones.

Bolton, Bill & Smith, Jane, illus. If You're Happy & You Know It! 2002. (Nursery Rhymes Ser.). 10p. (J). bds. (978-1-59069-288-2(8) , MB1011) Studio Mouse LLC.

Bond, Denny, illus. Mary, Did You Know? 2005. 24p. (J). (ps-k). bds. 9.99 incl. audio compact disk (978-1-57791-176-0(8)) Brighter Minds Children's Publishing.

Boynton, Sandra. Blue Moo: 17 Jukebox Hits from Way Back Never. 2007. (Illus.). 64p. (J). (ps-3). pap. 16.95 (***978-0-7611-4775-6(6))** Workman Publishing Co., Inc.

Boynton, Sandra. Rhinoceros Tap. Boynton, Sandra, illus. 2004. (Illus.). 64p. (J). 16.95 (978-0-7611-3323-0(2) , 13323) Workman Publishing Co., Inc.

Bracken, Carolyn. Music Maker. Durk, Jim, illus. 2002. (Fisher-Price Little People Ser.). (J). 15.98 (978-0-7853-6476-4(5)) Publications International, Ltd.

Brady, Janeen. I Have a Song for You Vol. 1: About People & Nature. rev. ed. (Illus.). (J). (ps-4). pap., stu. ed. 9.95 incl. audio (978-0-944803-01-1(6)) Brite Music, Inc.

Brannon, Tom, illus. Elmo's Rock Star Guitar. 2002. (Sesame Street Ser.). (J). 16.98 (978-0-7853-7006-2(4)) Publications International, Ltd.

Bricusse, Leslie & Newley, Anthony. Willy Wonka & the Chocolate Factory. 2001. (Movies & Tv Collections). 32p. pap. 8.95 (978-0-634-03153-3(8) , 0634031538) Leonard, Hal Corp.

Bridgman, Herb. Songs for School: With the Bandimals, Vol. 1. Hanson, Travis, illus. 2002. 44p. (J). (gr. 2-6). pap. 12.95 (978-0-9700757-0-3(7)) Stirling, H. Publishing.

Brighter Minds. In My Daughter's Eyes. 2006. (Illus.). 24p. (J). bds. 9.99 incl. audio compact disk (978-1-57791-218-7(7)) Brighter Minds Children's Publishing.

Brighter Minds, creator. My Little Pony Sing & Play: Follow-Th-Lights Paino Songbook. gif. ed. 2005. (Illus.). 24p. (J). (ps-4). bds. 13.99 (978-1-57791-192-0(X)) Brighter Minds Children's Publishing.

Brimhall, John. My Favorite Classics: Level One. 120p. (J). (gr. 3-6). 13.95 (978-0-8494-2180-8(2) , 0114) Hansen, Charles Educational Music & Bks., Inc.

Brokering, Herbert F. Earth & All Stars. McDaniels, Preston, illus. 2002. (Hymns for Children Ser.). 32p. (ps-2). 4.95 (978-0-8192-1867-4(7)) Morehouse Publishing.

Bromberg, Brian J. Blue's Song Game: Play-a-Song. Cardillo, Brent, illus. 2001. (Blue's Clues). (J). 16.98 (978-0-7853-5237-2(6)) Publications International, Ltd.

Brooks, Amy. Home Songs for Little Darlings: Children. 2005. pap. 24.95 (978-1-4179-9169-3(0)) Kessinger Publishing, LLC.

Brower, Howard, illus. Barney Songs. 2001. (J). 16.95 (978-0-7853-4799-6(2)) Publications International, Ltd.

Brown, Greg. Down at the Sea Hotel: A Greg Brown Song. Levert, Mireille, illus. 2007. 36p. (J). 16.95 (***978-2-923163-34-5(6))** La Montagne Secrete CAN. *Dist:* National Bk. Network.

Brown, Linda Kayse. Jerboth Weaves a Song. Noble, Penny, illus. 2007. 20p. (J). pap. 9.95 (***978-0-9769742-0-8(7))** Bay Villager, The.

Browne, David. Dream Brother: The Lives & Music of Jeff & Tim Buckley. 2002. 400p. pap. 14.95 (978-0-380-80624-9(X) , Harper Entertainment) HarperCollins Pubs.

Bryan, Ashley. All Night, All Day: A Child's First Book of African-American Spirituals. 2004. (gr. k-3). lib. bdg. 15.30 (978-0-613-88070-1(6)) Tandem Library Bks.

Bryan, Ashley, illus. & selected by. All Night, All Day: A Child's First Book of African-American Spirituals. Bryan, Ashley, selected by. 2003. 48p. (J). 6.99 (978-0-689-86786-6(7) , Aladdin) Simon & Schuster Children's Publishing.

Bucchino, John. Grateful: A Song of Giving Thanks. Hakkarainen, Anna-Liisa, illus. 40p. (J). 2006. pap. 6.99 (978-0-06-051635-2(6)); 2003. 16.99 (978-0-06-051633-8(X)) HarperCollins Pubs. (Julie Andrews Collection).

Buchman, Rachel. Jewish Holiday Songs for Children. 2001. (ENG, HEB & YID.). 104p. (J). pap. 14.95 (978-0-7866-1346-5(7) , MB95623) Mel Bay Pubns., Inc.

Burke, Bobbye & Gerlach, Horace. Daddy's Little Girl. Kneen, Maggie, illus. 2004. 32p. (J). (ps-3). 14.99 (978-0-06-028722-1(5)) HarperCollins Pubs.

Burlin, Natalie C. Songs & Tales from the Dark Continent. 2001. 170p. (YA). reprint ed. 88.00 (978-0-7222-5068-6(1)) Library Reprints, Inc.

Burns, Robert. Notes on Scottish Song. 2001. 134p. (YA). reprint ed. 88.00 (978-0-7222-6198-9(5)) Library Reprints, Inc.

Burton, Virginia Lee, illus. The Song of Robin Hood. 2000. 128p. (J). (gr. 4-6). tchr. ed. 20.00 (978-0-618-07186-9(5)) Houghton Mifflin Co. Trade & Reference Div.

Busy Bees; Cassette. (Song Box(R) Ser.). (J). (gr. 1-2). 8.50 incl. audio (978-0-7802-2269-4(5)) Wright Group, The.

Buzick, Joan & Judd, Lindy. Wwrt: What Went Right Today. Sullivan, James Kevin, illus. 2006. 32p. 19.99 (978-0-9766990-0-2(1)) Buz-Land Presentations, Inc.

Cabrera, Jane. Ten in the Bed. 2006. (Illus.). 32p. (J). 16.95 (978-0-8234-2027-8(2)) Holiday Hse., Inc.

Cabrera, Jane, illus. If You're Happy & You Know It! 2005. 32p. (J). 16.95 (978-0-8234-1881-7(2)) Holiday Hse., Inc.

La cancion de Omar: Individual Title Six-Packs. (Coleccion Pm Ser.). (SPA.). 16p. (gr. 1 up). 26.00 (978-0-7578-3040-2(4)) Rigby Education.

La Cancion del Rey. (SPA.). (J). 3.99 (978-0-7899-0482-9(9) , 495652) Editorial Unilit.

Canciones de Mi Tierra Española: Songs of My Spanish Land: Canary Islands. 2005. 32p. (978-0-9766568-0-7(9)) ERPublishing, LLC.

Cantos al maiz: un poeta hopi habla del Maiz: 6 Softcover Books. (Saludos Ser.: Vol. 2). (SPA.). (gr. 3-5). 31.00 (978-0-7635-1813-4(1)) Rigby Education.

Canyon, Christopher, illus. & adapted by. John Denver's Take Me Home, Country Roads. Canyon, Christopher, adapted by. 2005. 32p. (J). (ps-3). 19.95 (978-1-58469-072-6(0)) Dawn Pubns.

Carder, Ken & Laroy, Sue. Songs That Teach Alphabet & Counting. 2006. (Songs That Teach Ser.). 72p. (J). pap. 14.95 (978-0-7696-6459-0(8) , American Education Publishing) School Specialty Publishing.

—Songs That Teach Preschool Skills. 2006. (Songs That Teach Ser.). 72p. (J). pap. 14.95 (978-0-7696-6439-2(3) , American Education Publishing) School Specialty Publishing.

Carder, Ken, et al. Songs That Teach Multiplication. 2006. (Songs That Teach Ser.). 72p. (J). pap. 14.95 (978-0-7696-7693-7(6) , American Education Publishing) School Specialty Publishing.

—Songs That Teach States & Capitals. 2006. (Songs That Teach Ser.). 72p. (J). pap. 14.95 (978-0-7696-7713-2(4) , American Education Publishing) School Specialty Publishing.

Carle, Eric. Today Is Monday. Carle, Eric, illus. 2002. (Illus.). (J). 14.04 (978-0-7587-3823-3(4)) Book Wholesalers, Inc.

—Today Is Monday. Carle, Eric, illus. 2001. (Illus.). 1p. (J). (ps-k). bds. 6.99 (978-0-399-23605-1(8) , Philomel) Penguin Group (USA) Inc.

Carpenter, Stephen, illus. Dreidel, Dreidel, Dreidel Board Book. 1998. 12p. (J). (ps up). 6.99 (978-0-694-01217-6(3) , Harper Festival) HarperCollins Pubs.

Carter, Nancy & Julien, Terry, illus. Jesus Loves Me. 2006. 16p. (J). pap. 1.99 (978-0-7847-1804-9(0) , 04186) Standard Publishing.

Cartwright, Stephen, illus. Children's Songbook - Internet Referenced. 2004. (Songbooks Ser.). 32p. (J). pap. 6.95 (978-0-7945-0710-7(7) , Usborne) EDC Publishing.

Carus, Marianne. Higgley Piggledy Pop! Or There Must Be More to Life. (J). 19.95 incl. audio (978-0-8126-0057-5(6)); 2002. (Illus.). 34p. 15.95 (978-0-8126-0056-8(8)) Open Court Publishing Co.

—Sing, Clap, & Dance with Ladybug. (J). 19.95 incl. audio (978-0-8126-0053-7(3)); 2002. 10.95 (978-0-8126-0083-4(5)) Open Court Publishing Co.

—Sing Together with Ladybug. (J). 19.95 incl. audio (978-0-8126-0081-0(9)); 2002. (Illus.). 34p. 15.95 (978-0-8126-0079-7(7)) Open Court Publishing Co.

Cassidy, Nancy & Cassidy, John, eds. Nancy Cassidy's Kids Songs, 2 vols. 2004. (Illus.). 96p. (J). (ps). 21.95 (978-1-57054-858-1(7)) Klutz.

Castiglione, Janice, illus. The Musical Twinkle, Twinkle, Little Star. 2000. (Rub-a-Dub-Tub Musical Bks.). (J). vinyl bd. 7.00 (978-1-883043-18-6(2)) Straight Edge Pr., The.

—The Musical Wheels on the Bus. 1999. (J). (ps-k). vinyl bd. 7.00 (978-1-883043-14-8(X)) Straight Edge Pr., The.

Celebration Song 1999. 1999. (978-0-689-00793-4(0) , Simon & Schuster Children's Publishing) Simon & Schuster Children's Publishing.

Cethial and Bossche Publishing Staff. Fairy Tale Garden Song Book. 2000. (Illus.). (J). (978-1-55274-054-5(4)) Cethial & Bossche Co.

Chamberlin-Calamar, Pat & Kogl, Sandy. Ballad of the Wild Bear. Hatton, Libby, illus. 2004. (J). 14.95 (978-0-930931-61-2(0)) Alaska Natural History Assn.

Chancellor, Carl C. Soul Songs. 2001. 142p. (YA). (gr. 10 up). pap. 13.95 (978-1-884242-76-2(6)); (Illus.). lib. bdg. 21.95 (978-1-884242-72-4(3)) Multicultural Pubns.

Chapela, Luz Maria. La Casa del Caracol. Vargas, Rodrigo, illus. (SPA.). 31p. (J). (gr. k-3). pap. 7.95 (978-968-19-0613-9(6)) Santillana USA Publishing Co., Inc.

Cherry Lane Music Staff. Pokemon 2 B. A. Master: E-Z Play Songbook. 2000. (Piano-Fun! Ser.). (Illus.). 64p. (ps-3). pap. 12.95 (978-1-57560-289-9(X) , 157560289X) Cherry Lane Music Co.

Child, Lydia Marie. Over the River & Through the Wood. Catrow, David, illus. rev. ed. 1999. 32p. (J). (ps-3). pap. 7.95 (978-0-8050-6311-0(0) , Holt, Henry & Co. Bks. For Young Readers) Holt, Henry & Co.

—Over the River & Through the Wood. Manson, Christopher, illus. 1998. 32p. (J). (ps-3). pap. 6.95 (978-1-55858-959-9(7)) North-South Bks., Inc.

Christmas Tree. 2002. (Little Pups Board Bks.). (Illus.). 11p. (J). (ps). bds. 2.99 (978-1-57759-998-2(5)) Dalmatian Pr.

Church, Ellen B. Great Big Book of Classroom Songs, Rhymes & Cheers: 200 Easy, Playful Language Experiences That Build Literacy & Community in Your Classroom. 2000. (Illus.). 248p. pap. 21.95 (978-0-590-37607-5(1)) Scholastic, Inc.

Chusid, Nancy. Favorite Nursery Songs. 1998. (Sing along for Little Ones Ser.). (Illus.). 32p. (J). (ps-2). pap. 6.95 incl. audio (978-1-878624-05-5(9) , McClanahan Bk.) Learning Horizons, Inc.

Coasas Rojas. 2002. (SPA.). 16p. (J). bds. 6.95 (978-980-6437-27-2(6)) Playco Editores, C.A.

Colandro, Lucille. There Was an Old Lady Who Swallowed A Shell! 2008. 32p. (J). pap. 5.99 (***978-0-439-87380-2(0)** , Cartwheel Bks.) Scholastic, Inc.

Cole, Joanna. Jump Rope Rhymes. 2000. (978-0-688-17708-9(5)) HarperCollins Pubs.

A Collection of Songs & Madrigals. 2001. 31p. (YA). reprint ed. 88.00 (978-0-7222-6142-2(X)) Library Reprints, Inc.

Collins, Billy & Gerlach, Horace. Daddy's Little Boy. Kneen, Maggie, illus. 2004. 32p. (J). (ps-3). 14.99 (978-0-06-029003-0(X)) HarperCollins Pubs.

Collins, Phil, contrib. by. Brother Bear. 2004. (Illus.). 48p. pap. 12.95 (978-0-634-07754-8(6) , 0634077546) Leonard, Hal Corp.

Collins, S. Harold. Expanded Songs in Sign. Kifer, Kathy & Schneider, Jane, illus. 1998. (Beginning Sign Language Ser.). 32p. (J). (ps up). pap. 6.95 (978-0-931993-05-3(9)) Garlic Pr.

Compact Disc Staff. Traditional Lullabies. 1998. (Growing Minds with Music Ser.). (J). audio compact disk 12.99 (978-1-57583-068-1(X)) Twin Sisters Productions, LLC.

Conrad, Jeffrey & Stein, David, illus. CareBears: Songs from Care-A-Lot. 2002. (J). (978-0-7853-7222-6(9)) Publications International, Ltd.

Cooper, Kay. Too Many Rabbits & Other Fingerplays. 2001. (Illus.). (J). (978-0-606-20949-6(2)) Tandem Library Bks.

Cooper, Melrose. The SEVEN DAYS of KWANZAA. 2007. 24p. (J). pap. 4.99 (***978-0-439-56746-6(7)** , Cartwheel Bks.) Scholastic, Inc.

Coots, J. Fred. Santa Claus Is Comin' to Town. Kellogg, Steven, illus. 2004. 40p. (J). (ps-3). 16.89 (978-0-06-623849-4(8)) HarperCollins Pubs.

Cosas Azules. 2002. (SPA.). 16p. (J). bds. 6.95 (978-980-6437-28-9(4)) Playco Editores, C.A.

Cosas Verdes. 2002. (SPA.). 16p. (J). bds. 6.95 (978-980-6437-26-5(8)) Playco Editores, C.A.

Cravath, Lynne W. Over the River & Through the Woods. 1998. (Illus.). 12p. (J). (ps up). 6.95 (978-0-694-01218-3(1) , Harper Festival) HarperCollins Pubs.

Creech, Sharon. Who's That Baby? New-Baby Songs. Diaz, David, tr. Diaz, David, illus. 2005. 32p. (J). 15.99 (978-0-06-052939-0(3)); lib. bdg. 16.89 (978-0-06-052940-6(7)) HarperCollins Pubs. (Cotler, Joanna Books).

Crisp, Dan, illus. Five Little Men in a Flying Saucer. 2005. 16p. (J). pap. (978-1-904550-30-3(4)) Child's Play-International.

Daffy Duck's Spectacular Songs: Primer Level for Early Elementary Students. 2000. (Looney Tunes Piano Library). 24p. (J). 12.95 incl. audio compact disk (978-0-7692-9606-7(8) , Warner Bros. Pubns.) Alfred Publishing Co., Inc.

Dahl, Michael. Bring Us Water, Molly Pitcher! A Fun Song about the Battle of Monmouth. D'Antonio, Sandra, illus. 2004. (Fun Songs Ser.). 24p. (gr. k-3). 22.60 (978-1-4048-0130-1(8)) Picture Window Bks.

—Fun Songs, 6 bks. D'Antonio, Sandra, illus. Incl. Bring Us Water, Molly Pitcher! A Fun Song about the Battle of Monmouth. 22.60 (978-1-4048-0130-1(8)); Keep on Sewing Betsy Ross! A Fun Song about the First American Flag. 22.60 (978-1-4048-0127-1(8)); Midnight Riders : A Fun Song about the Ride of Paul Revere. 22.60 (978-1-4048-0129-5(4)); Pass the Buck! A Fun Song about the Famous Faces & Places on American Money. 22.60 (978-1-4048-0132-5(4)); Row, Row, Row the Boats : A Fun Song about George Washington Crossing the Delaware. 22.60 (978-1-4048-0128-8(6)); Trouble Brewing! A Fun Song about the Boston Tea Party. 22.60 (978-1-4048-0131-8(6)); 24p. (gr. k-3). 2004. (Illus.). 2003. 127.56 (978-1-4048-0182-0(0)) Picture Window Bks.

—Keep on Sewing Betsy Ross! A Fun Song about the First American Flag. D'Antonio, Sandra, illus. 2004. (Fun Songs Ser.). 24p. (gr. k-3). 22.60 (978-1-4048-0127-1(8)) Picture Window Bks.

—Midnight Riders: A Fun Song about the Ride of Paul Revere. D'Antonio, Sandra, illus. 2004. (Fun Songs Ser.). 24p. (gr. k-3). 22.60 (978-1-4048-0129-5(4)) Picture Window Bks.

—Pass the Buck! A Fun Song about the Famous Faces & Places on American Money. D'Antonio, Sandra, illus. 2004. (Fun Songs Ser.). 24p. (gr. k-3). 22.60 (978-1-4048-0132-5(4)) Picture Window Bks.

—Row, Row, Row the Boats: A Fun Song about George Washington Crossing the Delaware. D'Antonio, Sandra, illus. 2004. (Fun Songs Ser.). 24p. (gr. k-3). 22.60 (978-1-4048-0128-8(6)) Picture Window Bks.

—Trouble Brewing! A Fun Song about the Boston Tea Party. D'Antonio, Sandra, illus. 2004. (Fun Songs Ser.). 24p. (gr. k-3). 22.60 (978-1-4048-0131-8(6)) Picture Window Bks.

Daizovi, Lonnie G. Francais Joyeux: Simple Songs That Teach French. 1999. (FRE., Illus.). 32p. (J). pap. 13.95 (978-0-935301-78-6(X)) Vibrante Pr.

Dalmatian Press Staff. Jesus Loves Me: Musical Book to Color. 2004. (Musical Book to Color Ser.). (Illus.). 32p. (J). pap. 3.99 (978-1-4037-0714-7(6)) Dalmatian Pr.

Dalmatian Press Staff. Walt Disney's the Tortoise & the Hare. rev. ed. 2007. 10p. 5.99 (***978-1-4037-3230-9(2))** Dalmatian Pr.

Dann, Penny. Eensy Weensy Spider. (Illus.). (J). 2003. 16p. bds. 4.99 (978-0-7641-5662-5(4)); 1999. 20p. pap. 4.95 (978-0-7641-0857-0(3)) Barron's Educational Series, Inc.

—Old MacDonald Had a Farm. 2002. (Illus.). 16p. (J). bds. 3.95 (978-0-7641-5445-4(1)) Barron's Educational Series, Inc.

—Row, Row, Row Your Boat. 2001. (Little Barron's Toddler Bks.). (Illus.). 20p. (J). (ps). 4.95 (978-0-7641-1832-6(3)) Barron's Educational Series, Inc.

Davidge, Bud. The Mummer's Song. Wallace, Ian, illus. 2002. (J). (978-0-88899-178-2(9)) Groundwood Bks.

Davies, Niki. Everything's Growing. 2000. (Illus.). 48p. 17.95 incl. audio compact disk (978-1-85909-607-9(7) , Warner Bros. Pubns.) Alfred Publishing Co., Inc.

Delman, Elliott. Songs That Go. Carroll, Michael, illus. 2003. (Take-Along Songs Ser.). 16p. (J). bds. incl. audio compact disk (978-0-7853-8608-7(4) , 7189500) Publications International, Ltd.

—Take-Along Songs: Bedtime Songs. Maday, Jane, illus. 2003. (Take-Along Songs Ser.). 16p. (J). bds. 9.98 incl. audio compact disk (978-0-7853-8599-8(1) , 7189400) Publications International, Ltd.

—Take-Along Songs: Farm Songs. Lyon, Tammie, illus. 2003. (Take-Along Songs Ser.). 16p. (J). bds. 9.98 incl. audio compact disk (978-0-7853-8601-8(7) , 7189300) Publications International, Ltd.

Demarest, Chris L. She'll Be Coming Around Mountain. 2005. (Sing-and-Read Ser.). 24p. (J). pap. 4.99 (978-0-439-72213-1(6)) Scholastic, Inc.

Denver, John. Ancient Rhymes, a Dolphin Lullaby. Canyon, Christopher, illus. 2004. (Sharing Nature with Children Book Ser.). 36p. (J). (ps-6). 8.95 (978-1-58469-065-8(8)) Dawn Pubns.

—Grandma's Feather Bed. Canyon, Christopher, illus. 2007. 36p. (J). (ps up). pap. 8.95 incl. audio compact disk (***978-1-58469-096-2(8));** 19.95 incl. audio compact disk (***978-1-58469-095-5(X))** Dawn Pubns.

—Sunshine on My Shoulders. Canyon, Christopher, tr. Canyon, Christopher, illus. 2004. 32p. 19.95 incl. audio compact disk (978-1-58469-048-1(8)) Dawn Pubns.

—Take Me Home, Country Roads. Canyon, Christopher, illus. 2005. 32p. (J). (ps-6). pap. 8.95 (978-1-58469-073-3(9)) Dawn Pubns.

Desert Praise: Ironwood's Collection of Camp Songs. 2002. 180p. (YA). spiral bd. 12.95 (978-1-931787-03-1(4)) Fundamental Christian Endeavors.

DiCicco, Gil, illus. Pooh's Piano Book. 2002. (Disney's Winnie the Pooh Ser.). (J). 16.98 (978-0-7853-5233-4(3)) Publications International, Ltd.

Dickens, Charles & Sims, Lesley. A Christmas Carol. gif. ed. 2004. 64p. (J). (gr. 2 up). 8.95 (978-0-7945-0584-4(8), Usborne) EDC Publishing.

Diliberto, Rosella. Welcome to Mussomeli: Children's Songs from an Italian Country Town, Vol. 1. 2000. 40p. (J). pap. 20.95 incl. audio compact disk (978-0-937203-90-3(4)) World Music Pr.

Disney Staff & Kipling, Rudyard. Walt Disney's the Jungle Book: Piano/Vocal-Easy Piano. 1999. 24p. pap. 9.95 (978-0-634-00380-6(1), 0634003801) Leonard, Hal Corp.

Dodd, Emma. Amazing Baby: Clap & Sing! 2007. (Amazing Baby Ser.). (Illus.). 12p. (J). bds. 12.95 (***978-1-59223-725-8(8)***, Silver Dolphin Bks.) Advantage Pubs. Group.

Donovan, Mary Lee. Won't You Come & Play with Me? Jabar, Cynthia, illus. 1998. 32p. (J). (gr. k-ps). 16.00 (978-0-395-84630-8(7)) Houghton Mifflin Co. Trade & Reference Div.

Dorn, Susy. Cantemos en Español Song-Book: Spanish Learning Song-Book for Children. Carbajal, Diego, illus. 2006. (SPA.). (J). (978-0-9764010-6-3(1)) Susy Dorn Productions, LLC.

—Sal y Pimienta Song-Book: Spanish Learning Song-Book for Children. Carbajal, Diego, illus. 2006. (SPA.). (J). (978-0-9764010-7-0(X)) Susy Dorn Productions, LLC.

Douglas, Vincent & School Specialty Publishing Staff. Rhymes, Songs, & Games. 2004. (Playful Learning Ser.). (Illus.). 128p. (J). (gr. k-k). pap. 10.95 (978-0-7696-3301-5(3), American Education Publishing) School Specialty Publishing.

Downes, Belinda. Baby Days: A Quilt of Rhymes & Pictures. Downes, Belinda, illus. 2006. (Illus.). 32p. (J). (gr. k-ps). 14.99 (978-0-7636-2786-7(0)) Candlewick Pr.

Duder, Tessa, ed. A Book of Pacific Lullabies. Hagin, Sally, illus. 2003. 32p. (J). pap. 16.95 (978-1-86950-393-2(7)) HarperCollins Pubs. New Zealand NZL. *Dist:* Consortium Bk. Sales & Distribution.

Dyer, Laura C. Little Language for Little Ones Book & Little Language Songs for Little Ones. 2002. mass mkt. 19.95 incl. audio (978-0-9718409-1-1(1)); 2001. mass mkt. 24.95 incl. audio compact disk (978-0-9718409-0-4(3)) Language for Little Ones.

Eagle, Kin. Humpty Dumpty. Gilbert, Rob, illus. 2000. (Extended Nursery Rhymes Ser.). 32p. (J). (ps up). lib. bdg. 23.33 (978-0-8368-2667-8(1)) Stevens, Gareth Inc.

—It's Raining, It's Pouring. Eagle, Kin, illus. 1998. (Nursery Rhyme Ser.). (Illus.). 26p. (J). (ps-k). bds. 6.95 (978-1-58089-017-5(2)) Charlesbridge Publishing, Inc.

—Rub a Dub Dub. Gilbert, Rob, illus. 2000. (Extended Nursery Rhymes Ser.). 32p. (J). (ps up). lib. bdg. 23.33 (978-0-8368-2669-2(8)) Stevens, Gareth Inc.

Eakle, Kit. In My Grandmother's Garden. Eakle, Laura Jean, illus. l.t. ed. 2001. 32p. (J). (gr. k-5). 21.95 (978-0-9713194-0-0(5), MusicTales) MusicKit.COM.

Edens, Cooper, compiled by. The Glorious American Songbook. 2005. (Illus.). 80p. (J). (ps-ps). 19.95 (978-0-8118-4552-6(4)) Chronicle Bks. LLC.

Edwards, Dic. The Shakespeare Factory - David - Moon River. 1998. (Seren Drama Ser.). 180p. (J). pap. (978-1-85411-224-8(4)) Seren Bks.

Elementary Piggyback Song Book. 2003. (J). (978-0-9745630-4-6(8)) F & S Music KS Publishing Co.

Elkins, Stephen. Little Dongs for Little Souls: Sharing God's Love. Davis, Lynne, illus. 2005. 32p. (J). 9.99 incl. audio compact disk (978-0-8054-2673-1(6)) B&H Publishing Grp.

—Little Songs for Little Souls: God Cares for Me. Davis, Lynne, illus. 2005. 32p. (J). 9.99 incl. audio compact disk (978-0-8054-2675-5(2)) B&H Publishing Grp.

—Little Songs for Little Souls: I Can Be Happy in Jesus. Davis, Lynne, illus. 2005. 32p. (J). 9.99 incl. audio compact disk (978-0-8054-2676-2(0)) B&H Publishing Grp.

—Little Songs for Little Souls: I Can Praise the Lord. Davis, Lynne, illus. 2005. 32p. (J). 9.99 incl. audio compact disk (978-0-8054-2677-9(9)) B&H Publishing Grp.

—LullaBible: A Musical Treasury for Mother & Baby. 2004. (Illus.). 224p. (J). 21.99 incl. audio compact disk (978-0-8054-2390-7(7)) B&H Publishing Grp.

—The LullaBible: A Musical Treasury for Mother & Baby. 2004. (Illus.). (J). 9.99 (978-0-8054-2391-4(5)) B&H Publishing Grp.

—The LullaBible: A Musical Treasury for Mother & Baby. Colton, Ellie, illus. 2004. (J). (ps). 223p. 14.99 (978-0-8054-2388-4(5)); 224p. 19.99 incl. audio (978-0-8054-2389-1(3)) B&H Publishing Grp.

—Lullabies for Babies. Colton, Ellie, illus. 2005. (Jesus Loves Me Ser.). 32p. (J). (ps-2). 6.99 (978-1-4169-0843-2(9), Little Simon Inspirations) Simon & Schuster Children's Publishing.

—Word & Song Christmas Storybook. 2000. (Illus.). 32p. (J). (gr. 5). 14.99 incl. audio compact disk (978-0-8054-2196-5(3)) B&H Publishing Grp.

Elkins, Stephen. 100 Bible Heroes, 100 Bible Songs. 2007. 208p. (J). 19.99 (***978-1-4003-1078-4(4)***) Nelson, Thomas Inc.

Elliott, James W. Mother Goose's Nursery Rhymes & Nursery Songs. 2001. 110p. (YA). reprint ed. 88.00 (978-0-7222-6146-0(2)) Library Reprints, Inc.

Elliott, Rebecca, et al, illus. Five Little Monkeys: And Other Counting Rhymes. 2004. (Mother Goose Ser.). 36p. (J). bds. 15.95 incl. audio compact disk (978-1-59249-523-8(0), 1D026) Soundprints.

Engvick, William. Lullabies & Night Songs. Sendak, Maurice, illus. 2004. (Sendak Reissues Ser.). 80p. (J). 40.00 (978-0-06-029733-6(6)) HarperCollins Pubs.

Episcopal Youth Event Song Book. 1999. 48p. (gr. 9-12). pap. 5.00 (978-0-88028-211-6(8), 1542) Forward Movement Pubns.

Essential Audition Songs for Kids. (J). 21.95 incl. audio compact disk (978-1-85909-867-7(3), Warner Bros. Pubns.) Alfred Publishing Co., Inc.

The Everyday Song Book. 2001. 115p. (ps-2). 16.99 incl. audio (978-0-513-02175-4(2), TSD21752) Denison, T. S. & Co., Inc.

Fallon, Kathy Reilly & Pellegrino, Frank. Heavenly Skies & Lullables: Illustrated Songbook & CD. Kelly, Becky, illus. 2006. (J). (ps-3). 29.95 incl. audio compact disk (***978-1-933626-06-2(2)***, Llumina Pr.) Media Creations, Inc.

Fatus, Sophie. Here We Go Round the Mulberry Bush. 2007. (J). (***978-1-84686-036-2(9)***) Barefoot Bks., Inc.

Fatus, Sophie, illus. Here We Go Round the Mulberry Bush. 2007. 32p. (J). (ps-k). 16.99 (***978-1-84686-035-5(0)***) Barefoot Bks., Inc.

Feierabend, John M. The Book of Bounces. 2000. (First Steps in Music Ser.). (Illus.). 112p. (J). (ps). pap. 12.95 (978-1-57999-055-8(X)) GIA Pubns., Inc.

—The Book of Finger Plays & Action Songs. 2003. (First Steps in Music Ser.). (Illus.). 88p. (J). pap. 11.95 (978-1-57999-212-5(9)) GIA Pubns., Inc.

—The Book of Simple Songs & Circles. 2000. (First Steps in Music Ser.). (Illus.). 72p. (J). (ps). pap. 9.95 (978-1-57999-057-2(6)) GIA Pubns., Inc.

—The Book of Songs & Rhymes with Beat Motions: Let's Clap Our Hands Together. 2004. (First Steps in Music Ser.). (Illus.). 142p. (J). pap. 14.95 (978-1-57999-267-5(6), G-5879) GIA Pubns., Inc.

Feis Ceoil Collection of Irish Airs Hitherto Unpublished. 2001. (YA). reprint ed. 150.00 (978-0-7222-6193-4(4)) Library Reprints, Inc.

Fettke, Tom, ed. & compiled by. Great Big Praise for a Great Big God Bk. 2: 100 Fun, Exciting, Singable Songs for Older Kids. Fettke, Tom, compiled by. 2001. 184p. 12.99 (978-0-8341-7110-7(4), MB-854) Lillenas Publishing Co.

Field, Eugene. New Songs for New Singers Bk. 1: 30 Settings of Classic & New Texts. 2001. 96p. (YA). (gr. 6-12). per. 12.95 (978-1-889079-29-5(4)) Darcey Pr.

Finck, Henry Theophilus. Fifty Songs by Nineteenth-Century Masters: For High Voice. 2001. 186p. (YA). reprint ed. 88.00 (978-0-7222-6345-7(7)) Library Reprints, Inc.

—Songs & Song Writers. 2001. 254p. (YA). reprint ed. 98.00 (978-0-7222-6169-9(1)) Library Reprints, Inc.

Findlay, Jessie Patrick. The Spindle-Side of Scottish Song. 2001. 200p. (YA). reprint ed. 98.00 (978-0-7222-6220-7(5)) Library Reprints, Inc.

First Animal Stories. 2002. (J). bds. 19.95 (978-0-7525-6554-5(0)) Parragon, Inc.

First Songs. 2002. (J). bds. 4.98 (978-0-7525-3993-5(0)) Parragon, Inc.

Fitzgerald, Ella & Alexander, Van. A Tisket, A Tasket. Eitan, Ora, illus. 2003. 32p. (J). (ps-1). 15.99 (978-0-399-23206-0(0), Philomel) Penguin Group (USA) Inc.

Flatau, Carole, ed. Daffy Duck's Spectacular Songs: Primer Level for Early Elementary Students. 2000. (Looney Tunes Piano Library). 24p. (J). 5.95 (978-0-7692-8432-3(9), Warner Bros. Pubns.) Alfred Publishing Co., Inc.

Flegal, Daphna. More Bible Songs to Tunes You Know. 2004. (Illus.). 48p. 10.00 (978-0-687-05840-2(6)) Abingdon Pr.

Fletcher, Terri. Scrumpy's Educational Kid Songs. 2003. (Illus.). 16p. (J). (ps-1). pap. 12.95 incl. audio compact disk (978-0-9672279-1-7(7)) Scrumps Entertainment, Inc.

Freedman, Claire. A Kiss Goodnight: A Collection of Lullabies. Williams, Sophy et al, illus. 2007. 28p. (J). (ps-1). 16.95 (***978-1-56148-564-2(0)***) Good Bks.

Friedman, Randee & Lander, Donna, eds. The New Rabbi Joe Black Songbook: Selected Songs from Aleph Bet Boogie, Everybody's Got A Little Music, Leave A Little Bit Undone, Sabbatical. 2004. (ENG & HEB.). 111p. (YA). per. 25.95 (978-1-890161-52-1(7)) Sounds Write Productions, Inc.

—The Water in the Well. 2001. (HEB.). 34p. 12.95 (978-1-890161-48-4(9), 0606261617362) Sounds Write Productions, Inc.

Frosty the Snowman. 2003. (Illus.). 24p. (J). bds. 6.95 (978-0-8249-6500-6(0)) Ideals Pubns.

Gaither, Gloria. I Am a Promise: I Can Be Anything God Wants Me to Be. Stephenson, Kristina, illus. 2002. 40p. (J). 14.99 (978-0-310-70075-3(2)) Zonderkidz.

Gaither, Gloria & Hranilovich, Barbara. My Father's Angels. Hranilovich, Barbara, illus. 1999. (Illus.). 32p. (J). (ps-3). 14.99 (978-0-310-23104-2(3)) Zonderkidz.

Ganeri, Anita. Day & Night. 2004. (Nature's Patterns Ser.). (Illus.). 32p. (J). pap. 7.25 (978-1-4034-5883-4(9)); lib. bdg. 24.21 (978-1-4034-5877-3(4)) Heinemann Library.

Garcia, Jerry. The Teddy Bears' Picnic. 2000. (Illus.). 32p. (J). (ps-3). pap. 5.95 (978-0-06-443655-7(1), Harper Trophy) HarperCollins Pubs.

García Lorca, Federico. Canciones (1921-1924) (SPA.). 96p. (J). 13.25 (978-84-206-6106-3(6), AZ6106) Alianza Editorial, S. A. ESP. *Dist:* Continental Bk. Co., Inc.

—Canciones y Poemas para Ninos. (Coleccion Poemas Juvenil). (SPA., Illus.). 96p. (J). 9.50 (978-84-335-8401-4(4), DD4014) Labor, Editorial S. A. ESP. *Dist:* Continental Bk. Co., Inc.

—Canciones y Poemas para Ninos. (SPA., Illus.). 64p. (J). (gr. 4-6). pap. 5.95 (978-1-887578-59-2(5), SQ0128) SpanPr., Inc.

Geist, Ken, ed. If You're Happy & You Know It. McDonald, Jill, illus. 2006. (My First Taggies Book Ser.). 10p. (J). bds. 6.99 (978-0-439-85372-9(9), Cartwheel Bks.) Scholastic, Inc.

Gershwin, George, et al. Summertime. Wimmer, Mike, illus. 2002. 32p. (J). (gr. k up). pap. 6.99 (978-0-689-85047-9(6), Aladdin) Simon & Schuster Children's Publishing.

Gillespie, Haven & Coots, J. Fred. Santa Claus Is Comin' to Town. Kellogg, Steven, tr. Kellogg, Steven, illus. 2004. 40p. (J). (ps-3). 15.99 (978-0-688-14938-3(3)) HarperCollins Pubs.

Gitarren Songs. 2004. (YA). cd-rom (978-1-891155-20-8(2)) EMedia Corp.

Gobo Books Staff. Sleepytime Songs. 2007. (Baby Sing & Play Ser.). 8p. (J). (ps). bds. 12.95 incl. audio compact disk (***978-1-932915-42-6(7)***) Sandvik Innovations, LLC.

God Is with You in Sleep. Date not set. 44p. (J). (ps-5). 16.99 incl. audio compact disk (978-0-9702219-0-2(8)) Bowden Music Co.

Goldish, Meish. Content-Building Learning Songs: Dozens & Dozens of Songs-Set to Favorite Tunes-That Help Children Build Background Knowledge & Vocabulary. 2007. 96p. pap. 14.99 (***978-0-439-60964-7(X)***, Teaching Resources) Scholastic, Inc.

—50 Learning Songs Sung to Your Favorite Tunes: Teach & Delight Every Child with Skill-Building Songs That Are Fun to Sing & a Snap to Learn! 2001. 64p. (ps). pap. 10.95 (978-0-439-24878-5(7)) Scholastic, Inc.

—50 Thematic Piggyback Songs: Teach & Delight Every Child with Playful Learning Songs Sung to the Music. 2000. (Illus.). 56p. (gr. k-2). pap. 10.95 (978-0-439-06162-9(8)) Scholastic, Inc.

Goodhart, Pippa. Row Row Row Your Boat. 1999. (978-0-606-17344-5(7)) Tandem Library Bks.

Goodman, Steve. The Train They Call New Orleans. McCurdy, Michael, illus. pap. 16.95 incl. audio (978-1-59112-899-1(4)); pap. incl. audio (978-1-59112-901-1(X)); pap. 18.95 incl. audio compact disk (978-1-59112-903-5(6)); pap. incl. audio compact disk (978-1-59112-905-9(2)) Live Oak Media.

—The Train They Call the City of New Orleans. McCurdy, Michael, illus. 2003. 32p. (J). (ps-3). 16.99 (978-0-399-23853-6(0), Putnam Juvenile) Penguin Group (USA) Inc.

Goose, Mother. Itsy Bitsy Spider & Other Clap Along Rhymes. 2005. (Illus.). 36p. (J). 12.95 incl. cd-rom (978-1-59249-522-1(2), 1D025) Soundprints.

—Lets Play. 2005. (Illus.). 36p. (J). bds. 7.95 (978-1-59249-535-1(4), 1D205) Soundprints.

—Old MacDonald & Other Sing Along Rhymes. 2005. (Illus.). 36p. (J). 12.95 incl. cd-rom (978-1-59249-525-2(7), 1D028) Soundprints.

Gospel Vision Staff, Gospel, creator. A Beatitude Attitude: Songbook 2002. 2002. (J). 6.95 (978-0-910683-81-4(6)) Townsend Pr. - Sunday Schl. Publishing Board.

—Songs Exalting Our Maker (Songbook) 2001. (YA). 6.95 (978-0-910683-78-4(6)) Townsend Pr. - Sunday Schl. Publishing Board.

Gott, Barry, illus. Head, Shoulders, Knees, & Toes. 2006. (J). (978-1-58987-056-7(5)) Kindermusik International.

Graham, Pat, et al. A Children's Songbook Companion. Grover, Nina, illus. 2005. (J). per. 23.99 (978-0-88290-795-6(6), Horizon Pubs.) Cedar Fort, Inc./CFI Distribution.

Grammar Songs. 2001. (Illus.). 72p. (YA). (gr. 2 up). pap., tchr. ed. 22.95 incl. audio compact disk Audio Memory Publishing.

Grammer, Red & Grammer, Kathy. Teaching Peace Song Book: Performance & Accompainiment. 2000. (J). (ps-6). 35.00 incl. cd-rom (978-1-886146-18-1(7)) Red Note Records.

Green, Steve. Hide 'em in Your Heart: Bible Memory Melodies for Kids. 2003. (Recorder Fun! Ser.). 24p. (J). pap. 9.95 (978-0-634-05228-6(4), 0634052284) Leonard, Hal Corp.

Group Publishing Staff. Sing & Shout Songs for Children's Ministry. 2000. (Illus.). (J). pap. 15.99 (978-0-7644-3071-8(8)); pap. 15.99 (978-0-7644-3072-5(6)); Vol. 1 pap. 15.99 (978-0-7644-3064-0(5)); Vol. 2. pap. 15.99 (978-0-7644-3068-8(8)); Vol. 3. pap. 15.99 (978-0-7644-3073-2(4)); Vol. 3. pap. 15.99 (978-0-7644-3069-5(6)); Vol. 4. pap. 15.99 (978-0-7644-3074-9(2)); Vol. 4. pap. 15.99 (978-0-7644-3070-1(X)) Group Publishing, Inc.

Group/McGraw-Hill, Wright. The Song Box Social Studies Songs: 1 Each of 4 Big Books. (Song Box(R) Ser.). (gr. 1-2). 124.95 (978-0-322-03797-7(2)) Wright Group, The.

—The Song Box Social Studies Songs: 1 Each of 4 Cassettes. (Song Box(R) Ser.). (gr. 1-2). 33.95 (978-0-322-03795-3(6)) Wright Group, The.

—The Song Box Social Studies Songs: 1 Each of 4 Student Books. (Song Box(R) Ser.). (gr. 1-2). 18.95 (978-0-322-03961-2(4)) Wright Group, The.

—The Song Box Social Studies Songs: 6 Each of 4 Student Books. (Song Box(R) Ser.). (gr. 1-2). 116.50 (978-0-322-03796-0(4)) Wright Group, The.

Guthrie, Woody. Bling Blang. Radunsky, Vladimir, illus. 2002. 18p. (J). (gr. 1-3). reprint ed. 17.00 (978-0-7567-5410-5(0)) DIANE Publishing Co.

—Enviarme a Ti, Level 2. Ada, Alma Flor, tr. Rosenberry, Vera, illus. 2003. (Dejame Leer Ser.). (SPA.). 8p. (J). (ps-1). 6.50 (978-0-673-36301-5(5), Good Year Bks.) Celebration Pr.

—New Baby Train. Frazee, Marla, illus. 2004. 32p. (J). 15.99 (978-0-316-07020-1(3), Tingley, Megan Bks.) Little, Brown Bks. for Young Readers.

Gutmann, Bessie P. Nursery Songs & Lullabies. 2007. 32p. (J). (ps-3). 6.99 (978-0-448-44502-1(6), Grosset & Dunlap) Penguin Group (USA) Inc.

Haidle, Helen. Sing Me to Sleep, Wake Me with a Song. 2001. 96p. (J). 6.99 (978-0-310-70133-0(3)) Zondervan.

Hal Leonard Corp., creator. The Barney Songbook. 2001. (Movies & Tv Collections). 68p. pap. 14.95 (978-0-634-02825-0(1), 0634028251) Leonard, Hal Corp.

—Barney Songs. 2001. 32p. pap. 7.95 (978-0-634-02827-4(8), 0634028278) Leonard, Hal Corp.

—Big Idea's Jonah: A Veggietales Movie (Recorder Fun) 2002. (Recorder Fun! Ser.). (Illus.). 24p. (J). pap. 9.95 (978-0-634-05040-4(0), 0634050400) Leonard, Hal Corp.

—Big Idea's Jonah - A VeggieTales Movie. 2002. (Illus.). 40p. pap. 7.95 (978-0-634-05394-8(9), 0634053949) Leonard, Hal Corp.

—Broadway Songs for Kids. 2000. 64p. pap. 7.95 (978-0-634-01679-0(2), 0634016792) Leonard, Hal Corp.

—The Cartoon Songbook: Themes from 11 Hit Shows. 2004. 32p. pap. 9.95 (978-0-634-07773-9(2), 0634077732) Leonard, Hal Corp.

—Children's Songs. 2000. (Paperback Songs Ser.). 256p. pap. 7.95 (978-0-634-01226-6(6), 0634012266) Leonard, Hal Corp.

—Christian Songs for Children. 2000. 72p. pap. 10.95 (978-0-634-01278-5(9), 0634012789) Leonard, Hal Corp.

—Disney Classics. 2000. (Easy Guitar Ser.). 64p. pap. 12.95 (978-0-634-00038-6(1), 0634000381) Leonard, Hal Corp.

—Disney Favorites. 1999. 64p. pap. 10.95 (978-0-634-00180-2(9), 0634001809); 2nd rev. ed. 2000. 136p. pap. 19.95 (978-0-634-01577-9(X), 063401577X) Leonard, Hal Corp.

—The Disney Greats. 1999. 64p. pap. 10.95 (978-0-634-00181-9(7), 0634001817) Leonard, Hal Corp.

—Disney Solos. 2000. 24p. pap. 12.95 incl. audio compact disk (978-0-634-00067-6(5), 0634000675); 24p. pap. 12.95 incl. audio compact disk (978-0-634-00068-3(3), 0634000683); 24p. pap. 12.95 incl. audio compact disk (978-0-634-00069-0(1), 0634000691); 23p. pap. 12.95 incl. audio compact disk (978-0-634-00071-3(3), 0634000713); 24p. pap. 12.95 incl. audio compact disk (978-0-634-00072-0(1), 0634000721); 24p. pap. 12.95 incl. audio compact disk (978-0-634-00073-7(X), 063400073X); 24p. pap. 12.95 incl. audio compact disk (978-0-634-00074-4(8), 0634000748); 24p. pap. 12.95 incl. audio compact disk (978-0-634-00075-1(6), 0634000756); 24p. pap. 12.95 incl. audio compact disk (978-0-634-00076-8(4), 0634000764) Leonard, Hal Corp.

S

—Disney Solos for Kids. 2002. 40p. pap. 19.95 incl. audio compact disk (978-0-634-04800-5(7), 0634048007) Leonard, Hal Corp.

—Disney's My First Songbook. 1998. (Style Collections). 96p. pap. 14.95 (978-0-7935-8356-0(X), 079358356X) Leonard, Hal Corp.

—Disney's My First Songbook: A Treasury of Favorite Songs to Sing & Play, Vol. 2. 2003. (Easy Piano Songbook Ser.). (Illus.). 87p. pap. 14.95 (978-0-634-04792-3(2), 0634047922) Leonard, Hal Corp.

—Easy Disney Favorites. 2000. 16p. pap. 12.95 incl. audio compact disk (978-0-634-00607-4(X), 063400607X); pap. 12.95 incl. audio compact disk (978-0-634-00608-1(8), 0634006088); pap. 12.95 incl. audio compact disk (978-0-634-00609-8(6), 0634006096); pap. 12.95 incl. audio compact disk (978-0-634-00610-4(X), 063400610X); pap. 12.95 incl. audio compact disk (978-0-634-00611-1(8), 0634006118) Leonard, Hal Corp.

—Fantasia 2000. 2001. (Easy Piano Ser.). (Illus.). 48p. pap. 16.95 (978-0-634-01610-3(5), 0634016105) Leonard, Hal Corp.

—Fantasia 2000: Piano Solo. 2001. (Illus.). 50p. pap. 16.95 (978-0-634-01609-7(1), 0634016091) Leonard, Hal Corp.

—The Fantastic Big Book of Children's Songs. 2004. (Illus.). 240p. pap. 16.95 (978-0-634-06820-1(2), 0634068202) Leonard, Hal Corp.

—Kids' Holiday Solos. 2002. 40p. pap. 19.95 incl. audio compact disk (978-0-634-04920-0(8), 0634049208) Leonard, Hal Corp.

—The Little Book of Children's Songs: 38 Fun Songs for Singing, Playing & Listening. 2004. 80p. pap. 12.95 incl. audio compact disk (978-0-634-05879-0(7), 0634058797) Leonard, Hal Corp.

—The Mighty Big Book of Children's Songs. 1999. 208p. pap. 14.95 (978-0-634-00084-3(5), 0634000845); 192p. pap. 14.95 (978-0-634-00102-4(7), 0634001027) Leonard, Hal Corp.

—My First Hymnal: Recorder Fun. 2003. (Recorder Fun! Ser.). 16p. (J). pap. 9.95 (978-0-634-05672-7(7), 0634056727) Leonard, Hal Corp.

—Selections from Disney's Princess Collection. 2002. (Piano Fun! Ser.). (Illus.). 16p. (J). pap. 19.95 (978-0-634-04437-3(0), 0634044370); pap. 9.95 (978-0-634-04436-6(2), 0634044362) Leonard, Hal Corp.

—Songs for Christian Kids. 2000. 72p. pap. 9.95 (978-0-634-01279-2(7), 0634012797) Leonard, Hal Corp.

—Songs for Kids: 28 Fun Favorites. 2003. (Illus.). 32p. pap. 9.95 (978-0-634-06631-3(5), 0634066315) Leonard, Hal Corp.

—Today's Kids' Favorites. 2002. 32p. pap. 7.95 (978-0-634-04949-1(6), 0634049496) Leonard, Hal Corp.

—The Ultimate Children's Songbook. 2000. (Style Collections). 216p. (gr. 4-7). pap. 18.95 (978-0-634-02181-7(8), 0634021818) Leonard, Hal Corp.

Hal Leonard Corp., creator. Worship Together Favorites for Kids. 2007. 72p. pap. 12.95 (***978-1-4234-2541-0(3)***, 1423425413) Leonard, Hal Corp.

Hal Leonard Corporation Staff. Best Children's Songs Ever. 1998. 304p. (ps-3). pap. 19.95 (978-0-7935-8966-1(5), 0793589665) Leonard, Hal Corp.

—Christian Children's Songbook. 2000. (Style Collections). (Illus.). 256p. pap. 19.95 (978-0-634-00336-3(4), 0634003364) Leonard, Hal Corp.

—Disney Big-Note Collection. 2001. (Big Note Piano Ser.). 192p. (gr. 4-7). pap. 19.95 (978-0-634-01761-2(6) , 0634017616) Leonard, Hal Corp.

—Tigger Movie Recorder Fun! 2000. (Recorder Fun! Ser.). (Illus.). 20p. (J). (gr. 4-7). pap. 9.95 (978-0-634-01657-8(1) , 0634016571) Leonard, Hal Corp.

—100 Kid's Songs. 2000. (Style Collections). 186p. pap. 14.95 (978-0-634-01494-9(3) , 0634014943) Leonard, Hal Corp.

Hal Leonard Corporation Staff, creator. The Kids' Collection: Recorder Fun! 3-Book Bonus Pack. 2006. 96p. (J). pap. 12.95 (*978-1-4234-1843-6(3) , 1423418433) Leonard, Hal Corp.

Hal Leonard Music Books Staff, creator. The Disney Heroes Collection: Recorder Fun! 3-Book Bonus Pack. 2006. 64p. (J). pap. 12.95 (*978-1-4234-1845-0(X) , 142341845X) Leonard, Hal Corp.

—The Disney Princess Collection: Recorder Fun! 3-Book Bonus Pack. 2007. 72p. (J). pap. 12.95 (*978-1-4234-1844-3(1) , 1423418441) Leonard, Hal Corp.

Hal Leonard Publications Staff. Children's Songs. 2004. (Piano Play-Along Ser.: Vol. 9). 32p. pap. 14.95 incl. audio compact disk (978-0-634-06909-3(8) , 0634069098) Leonard, Hal Corp.

Halfmann, Janet, et al. Barney's Favorite Songs. Davis, Guy, ed. Valentine-Ruppe, June, illus. 1999. (Barney Ser.). 112p. (J). (ps-k). act. bk. ed. 2.99 (978-1-57064-457-3(8)) Scholastic, Inc.

Harburg, E. Y. & Arlen, Harold. Over the Rainbow. Noonan, Julia, illus. 2004. 24p. (J). (gr. 4-8). reprint ed. 16.00 (978-0-7567-7340-3(7)) DIANE Publishing Co.

—Over the Rainbow. Noonan, Julia, illus. 2002. 32p. (J). 15.95 (978-0-06-028949-2(X)); (gr. 7 up). 15.89 (978-0-06-029500-4(7)) HarperCollins Pubs.

Harcourt School Publishers Staff. The Big Yellow Bus Big Book. 3rd ed. 2002. (Trophies Reading Program Ser.). (Illus.). pap. 52.60 (978-0-15-325447-5(5)) Harcourt Schl. Pubs.

—The Big Yellow Bus Little Book. 3rd ed. 2002. (Trophies Reading Program Ser.). (Illus.). (J). pap. 10.20 (978-0-15-325452-9(1)) Harcourt Schl. Pubs.

Harnick, Sheldon. Sunrise, Sunset. Schoenherr, Ian, illus. 2005. 32p. (J). (ps-1). lib. bdg. 16.89 (978-0-06-051527-0(9)) HarperCollins Pubs.

Harnick, Sheldon & Bock, Jerry. Sunrise, Sunset. Schoenherr, Ian, illus. 2005. 32p. (J). 15.99 (978-0-06-051525-6(2)) HarperCollins Pubs.

HarperCollins Children's Books. Silly Songs. 2007. (Word Play Ser.). 208p. (J). pap. 5.95 (*978-0-00-724340-2(5)) HarperCollins Pubs. Ltd. GBR. *Dist:* Independent Pubs. Group.

Harriott, M. S. Chants & Chuckles. Spoor, Mike, illus. 2001. 32p. (J). pap. 45.00 (978-1-871098-65-5(3)) Claire Pubns. GBR. *Dist:* Parkwest Pubns., Inc.

Hawn, C. Michael. Halle, Halle We Sing the World Round: Songs from the World Church for Children & Youth - Singer's Edition, 2 vols. 1999. (Illus.). 48p. (YA). (gr. 1-12). pap. 5.95 (978-1-929187-16-4(5) , CGC42) Choristers Guild.

Hayes, Larry E. My Name Starts with A (Library Version) 2004. (My Name Starts With Ser.). (Illus.). 32p. (J). lib. bdg. 12.95 (978-0-9725292-7-3(6)) Inspire Pubns.

Helldorfer, Mary-Claire. Hog Music. Schindler, S. D., illus. 2000. 32p. (J). (ps-3). 15.99 (978-0-670-87182-7(6) , Viking Juvenile) Penguin Group (USA) Inc.

Heras, Theo. What Will We Do with the Baby-O? Herbert, Jennifer, illus. 2004. 32p. (J). (gr. k-k). 12.95 (978-0-88776-689-3(7)) Tundra Bks., Inc./Livres Toundra, Inc. CAN. *Dist:* Random Hse., Inc.

Hinnant, Henry. Showdown at Dry Gulch: Value Pak: Leader'S/Accompanist Editions, Singer's Edition & Listening Cassette. 2004. (Illus.). (gr. 3-8). 25.00 (978-0-687-09681-7(2)) Abingdon Pr.

Hinojasa, Tish. Cada Nino/Every Child: A Bilingual Songbook for Kids. Perez, Lucia Angela, illus. 2002. (ENG & SPA.). 48p. (J). (gr. 4-7). 18.95 (978-0-938317-60-9(1)) Cinco Puntos Pr.

Hinojosa, Tish. Cada Nino: A Bilingual Songbook for Kids. Perez, Lucia Angela, illus. 2004. Tr. of Every Child. (ENG & SPA.). 56p. (J). pap. 9.95 (978-0-938317-79-1(2)) Cinco Puntos Pr.

His Fleece Was White As Snow: Songbook. 2003. 66p. (YA). 5.00 (978-1-58302-243-6(0)) One Way St., Inc.

Hoberman, Mary Ann. Bill Grogan's Goat. Westcott, Nadine Bernard, illus. 2002. 32p. (J). (ps-3). 14.95 (978-0-316-36232-0(8)) Little, Brown Bks. for Young Readers.

—The Eensy-Weensy Spider. Westcott, Nadine Bernard, illus. 2004. 32p. (J). (ps-1). pap. 6.99 (978-0-316-73412-7(8)) Little, Brown Bks. for Young Readers.

—The Eensy-Wensy Spider. Bernard, Nadine, illus. 2002. (J). 20.60 (978-0-7587-2438-0(1)) Book Wholesalers, Inc.

Hoberman, Mary Ann, ed. The Eensy-Weensy Spider. Westcott, Nadine Bernard, illus. 2004. 32p. (J). (ps-3). lib. bdg. 14.19 (978-0-606-32822-7(X)) Tandem Library Bks.

Hoberman, Mary Ann & Westcott, Nadine Bernard. The Eensy-Weensy Spider. Westcott, Nadine Bernard, illus. rev. ed. 2002. (Illus.). 11p. (J). (ps-ps). bds. 6.99 (978-0-316-22979-1(2) , Tingley, Megan Bks.) Little, Brown Bks. for Young Readers.

—Mary Had a Little Lamb. Westcott, Nadine Bernard, illus. 2003. (Sing-Along Stories Ser.). (Illus.). 32p. (J). (ps-3). 15.95 (978-0-316-60687-5(1)) Little Brown & Co.

Holiday, Billie. God Bless the Child. Pinkney, Jerry, illus. (J). 2008. 40p. 7.99 (978-0-06-443646-5(2)); 2004. 32p. lib. bdg. 17.89 (978-0-06-029487-8(6) , Amistad) HarperCollins Pubs.

Holiday, Billie & Herzog, Arthur. God Bless the Child. Pinkney, Jerry, illus. 2004. 32p. (J). 16.99 incl. audio compact disk (978-0-06-028797-9(7)) HarperCollins Pubs.

Hood, Karen Jean Matsko. Hood & Matsko Family Favorite Christmas Songs & Carols: Annual Edition 2002. 2002. 15.95 (978-1-59210-649-3(8)); cd-rom 13.95 (978-1-59210-651-6(X)) Whispering Pine Pr., Inc.

Hoopes, Marva, ed. In the Beginning: Songs from the Book of Genesis. Advision Associates Staff, illus. 1999. (Sing Through the Bible Ser.: Vol. 1). 208p. (J). (ps-5). pap. 19.99 (978-1-929617-02-9(X)) LIM Productions, LLC.

Hop! Hop! Hop! (J). 19.95 incl. audio (978-0-8126-0088-9(6)) Open Court Publishing Co.

Hop, Hop, Hop! Sing-and-Dance Songs from Ladybug. 2002. (Illus.). 34p. (J). (ps-1). 15.95 (978-0-8126-0072-8(X)) Cricket Bks.

Horn, Patty. Patty Horn's Desert Dwellers Fiesta! Cude, Dana, illus. 1998. 46p. (J). (gr. k-8). spiral bd. 15.95 incl. audio (978-0-9644105-9-6(1)) Two Geckos Music & Publishing.

Hort, Lenny. The Seals on the Bus. Karas, G. Brian, illus. 2002. (J). 26.47 (978-0-7587-3587-4(1)) Book Wholesalers, Inc.

—The Seals on the Bus. Karas, G. Brian, illus. rev. ed. 32p. (J). 2003. pap. 7.95 (978-0-8050-7263-1(2)); 2000. 16.95 (978-0-8050-5952-6(0)) Holt, Henry & Co. (Holt, Henry & Co. Bks. For Young Readers).

Houssin, Frédéric & Ramadier, Cédric. The Big Book of Car Games. 2003. (Illus.). 120p. spiral bd. 12.95 (978-1-57912-276-8(0) , 81276) Black Dog & Leventhal Pubs., Inc.

Houston, Scott. Play Piano in a Flash Fake Book for Kids! A song book for kids in lead sheet Format, 1. l.t. ed. 2006. 88p. (J). spiral bd. 24.95 (*978-0-9712861-2-2(4) , 75) Houston Enterprises.

Houston, Scott & Sowash, Bradley. Play Piano in a Flash! the Next Step: The Next Step. l.t. ed. 2006. 100p. spiral bd. 24.95 (*978-0-9712861-3-9(2)) Houston Enterprises.

Hubler, Michael & Hubler, Lillian. Time to Sign with Children Infant/Toddler: Time to Sign with Music Infant/Toddler. 2003. Orig. Title: Time to Sign with Music Infant/Toddler. (Illus.). 42p. (J). per. 20.00 (978-0-9713666-0-2(8)) Time to Sign, Incorporated.

Hull, Bunny. Happy, Happy Kwanzaa: Kwanzaa for the World. Saint-James, Synthia, illus. 2003. 24p. (J). (gr. k-5). pap. 16.95 incl. audio compact disk (978-0-9721478-1-1(0) , KCC/HHKCD810, Kid's Creative Classics) BrassHeart Music.

If You're Happy: Individual Title Six-Packs. (Literatura 2000 Ser.). (gr. 1-2). 28.00 (978-0-7635-0137-2(9)) Rigby Education.

Ingram, Scott. The Writing of "The Star-Spangled Banner" 2004. (Landmark Events in American History Ser.). (Illus.). 48p. (J). (gr. 5 up). pap. 11.95 (978-0-8368-5418-3(7)); lib. bdg. 30.00 (978-0-8368-5390-2(3)) Stevens, Gareth Inc. (World Almanac Library).

Inui, Tazuko & Yoon, Selina. Sing 'n Learn Japanese Two: More Japanese Through Favorite Songs, Vol. 2. 1998. (Sing 'n Learn Ser.). (ENG & JPN., Illus.). 32p. (J). (ps-6). pap. 14.95 incl. audio (978-1-888194-23-4(5)) Master Communications, Inc.

—Sing 'n Learn Japanese Two Vol. 2: More Japanese Through Favorite Songs. 1998. (Sing 'n Learn Ser.). (ENG & JPN., Illus.). 32p. (J). (ps-6). pap. 17.95 incl. audio compact disk (978-1-888194-24-1(3)) Master Communications, Inc.

Itsy Bitsy Spider. 2004. (J). per. (978-1-57657-427-0(X)) Paradise Pr., Inc.

Itsy Bitsy Spider. 2002. (Illus.). (J). bds. (978-1-59069-261-5(6) , MS1002) Studio Mouse LLC.

I've Been Working on the Railroad. (Song Box(R) Ser.). (gr. 1-2). 31.50 (978-0-7802-0936-7(2)); 8.50 incl. audio (978-0-7802-0938-1(9)) Wright Group, The.

I've Been Working on the Railroad: 1 Big Book, 6 Each of 1 Student Book, & 1 Cassette. (Song Box(R) Ser.). (gr. 1-2). 68.95 (978-0-7802-0939-8(7)) Wright Group, The.

I've Been Working on the Railroad: 6 Each of 1 Student Book, 6 vols. (Song Box(R) Ser.). (gr. 1-2). 29.50 (978-0-7802-0937-4(0)) Wright Group, The.

Jacobs, Paul DuBois & Swender, Jennifer. Children's Songbag. 2005. (Illus.). 112p. spiral bd. 12.95 (978-1-58685-356-3(2)) Gibbs Smith, Publisher.

Jensema, Marissa, illus. ASL Songs for Kids - 1: With Songs in American Sign Language. 2003. (J). cd-rom 29.95 (978-0-9752933-1-7(1)) Institute for Disabilities Research & Training, Inc.

Jesus Loves Me. 1999. (Play-a-Song Ser.). (Illus.). 16p. (J). (ps-k). bds. 10.99 (978-0-7847-0967-2(X) , 03629, Bean Sprouts) Standard Publishing.

Jesus Loves Me. (Illus.). 16p. (J). pap. 1.50 (978-0-87162-970-8(4) , E4983) Warner Pr. Pubs.

Jesus Songs. 2000. (Illus.). (J). 15.98 (978-0-7853-4874-0(3)) Publications International, Ltd.

Jimenez, Olga Lucia. Ronda que Ronda la Ronda. 2003. (SPA.). 144p. (978-958-30-0673-9(4) , PV30130) Panamericana Editorial COL. *Dist:* Lectorum Pubns., Inc.

Joel, Billy. New York State of Mind. Zenou, Izak, illus. 2005. 32p. (J). (ps-3). pap. 16.99 (978-0-439-55382-7(2) , Scholastic Pr.) Scholastic, Inc.

Jolly Songs (in print letters US) 2005. (J). cd-rom 14.95 (978-1-84414-079-4(2)) Jolly Learning, Ltd. GBR. *Dist:* American International Distribution Corp.

Jones, Betty M. A Child's Seasonal Treasury. Jones, Betty M. & Crowther, Catherine R., illus. 2004. 154p. (J). (ps-2). 24.95 (978-1-883672-30-0(9) , Tricycle Pr.) Ten Speed Pr.

Jordan, Sara. Celebrate Seasons. Howard, Joan, ed. Filipov, Alex, illus. 1999. 50p. (J). (gr. k-4). pap. 14.95 incl. audio (978-1-894262-02-6(6) , JMP118K) Jordan Music Productions, Inc.

Kaiser, Cecily. On the First Night of Chanukah. 2007. 24p. (J). pap. 3.99 (*978-0-439-75802-4(5) , Cartwheel Bks.) Scholastic, Inc.

Kanzler, John, tr. & illus. The Big Rock Candy Mountain. Kanzler, John, illus. 2004. 24p. (J). 15.95 (978-1-59336-062-7(2)); pap. (978-1-59336-063-4(0)) Mondo Publishing.

Kaplan, Shelley. Songs for Scratching Mosquito Bites & Petting the Cat. Hutchison, Robert W., illus. 1998. 32p. (J). (ps-8). 16.00 (978-0-9631833-1-6(1)) Kaplan Pr.

Katz, Alan. Are You Quite Polite? Silly Dilly Manners Songs. Catrow, David, illus. 2006. 32p. (J). (ps-3). 15.95 (978-0-689-86970-9(3) , McElderry, Margaret K.) Simon & Schuster Children's Publishing.

—I'm Still Here in the Bathtub: Brand New Silly Dilly Songs. Catrow, David, illus. 2003. 32p. (J). 16.99 (978-0-689-84551-2(0) , McElderry, Margaret K.) Simon & Schuster Children's Publishing.

—On Top of the Potty & Other Get-Up-And-Go Songs. Catrow, David, illus. 2008. 32p. (J). 16.99 (*978-0-689-86215-1(6) , McElderry, Margaret K.) Simon & Schuster Children's Publishing.

—Stinky Locker: Silly Dilly School Songs. Catrow, David, illus. 2008. (J). (*978-1-4169-0695-7(9) , McElderry, Margaret K.) Simon & Schuster Children's Publishing.

Katz, Alan. Take Me Out of the Bathtub & Other Silly Dilly Songs. Catrow, David, illus. 2001. 32p. (J). (ps-1). 16.99 (978-0-689-82903-1(5) , McElderry, Margaret K.) Simon & Schuster Children's Publishing.

Kauffman, Ron, illus. Rise & Shine. 2006. (Sing-A-Story Ser.). 16p. (J). bds. 10.95 (978-0-7696-5058-6(9)) School Specialty Publishing.

Keep Books Organization Staff. Mini-Sets 1 & 2. (Illus.). (ps-5). pap. (978-1-893986-01-5(2)) Keep Bks.

—Mini-Sets 3 & 4. (Illus.). 8p. (ps-5). pap. (978-1-893986-14-5(4)) Keep Bks.

Keillor, Garrison. Daddy's Girl. Glasser, Robin Preiss, illus. 2005. 40p. (J). (ps-ps). 16.99 incl. audio compact disk (978-0-7868-1986-7(3)) Hyperion Bks. for Children.

Kellogg, Steven. Yankee Doodle Proprietary. 2002. 40p. 5.95 (978-0-689-85567-2(2) , Simon & Schuster Children's Publishing) Simon & Schuster Children's Publishing.

Kennedy, Jimmy. Teddy Bear's Picnic. 2000. (Illus.). (J). (978-0-606-21621-0(9)) Tandem Library Bks.

—Teddy Bears' Picnic. 2000. (gr. k-3). lib. bdg. 14.15 (978-0-613-88163-0(X)) Tandem Library Bks.

Key, Francis Scott. The Star Spangled Banner. 2002. (Random House Pictureback Book Ser.). (Illus.). 24p. (J). (ps-3). pap. 3.25 (978-0-375-81596-6(1) , Random Hse. Bks. for Young Readers) Random Hse. Children's Bks.

Kidzup Productions Staff. Grammar & Punctuation Songs. 2002. (Learning Beat Ser.). (J). pap., wbk. ed. 13.99 (978-1-894677-31-8(5)) Kidzup Productions.

—Phonics Songs: Short Vowels. 2002. (Learning Beat Ser.). (J). pap., wbk. ed. 13.99 (978-1-894677-33-2(1)) Kidzup Productions.

—Spelling Songs: Language Arts Skills. 2002. (Learning Beat Ser.). (J). wbk. ed. 13.99 incl. audio, audio compact disk (978-1-894677-32-5(3)) Kidzup Productions.

Kirk, Daniel. Hush, Little Alien. 2001. (Illus.). 24p. (ps-k). 6.99 (978-0-7868-0759-8(8)) Hyperion Bks. for Children.

Knight, Paula & Smith, Jane, illus. I'm a Little Teapot. 2002. (Nursery Rhymes Ser.). 10p. (J). bds. (978-1-59069-287-5(X) , MB1010) Studio Mouse LLC.

Knoche, Keith & Wood, Jeff. WWJD? Radio. 2000. 12p. (gr. k-7). 14.99 (978-5-550-01681-7(8)) Faith Factory.

Kozlina, Yvonne. Fingerplays & Action Chants, Vols. 1 & 2. 1999. (Illus.). 128p. (J). reprint ed. pap. 29.95 (978-0-936823-18-8(6)) Pearce-Evetts Publishing.

Kraft, Tamera & Colkmire, Lance. Kid Konnection: Kids Entering the Presence of God, Vol. 5. 2003. (Illus.). 112p. ring bd. 69.99 (978-0-87148-383-6(1)) Pathway Pr.

Kragen, Emma. The Twelve Dogs of Christmas Board Book. (J). 2001. 16p. bds. 9.99 (978-0-8499-7946-0(3)); 1998. (Illus.). 32p. 12.99 incl. cd-rom Nelson, Thomas Inc.

Krauss, Gene, adapted by. Awesome Performance Music & Tracks. Krauss, Gene, . 2nd ed. 2005. (YA). spiral bd. 20.00 (978-0-9785992-0-1(9)) GuitarVoyager Inc.

Kriegman, Mitchell. Bear in the Big Blue House Good Night Songs. Rillo, Cary, illus. 2003. (Musical Nightlight Bks.). (J). bds. 15.98 (978-0-7853-7962-1(2)) Publications International, Ltd.

Kubler, Annie, illus. If You're Happy & You Know It. 2001. 12p. (J). (ps). bds. 4.99 (978-0-85953-846-6(X)) Child's Play-International.

Kurtz, John. What Belongs? Baby Looney Tunes. Shively, Julie, illus. 2004. 12p. bds. 6.95 (978-0-8249-6560-0(4)) Ideals Pubns.

Kwasi: a Storysong: Six-Pack. (Greetings Ser.: Vol. 2). 24p. (gr. 2-3). 31.00 (978-0-7635-9415-2(6)) Rigby Education.

Laing, Robin. The Whisky Muse: Collected & Introduced by Robin Laing. Dewar, Bob, illus. 2nd ed. 2004. (ENG.). 224p. per. 14.95 (978-1-84282-041-4(9)) Luath Pr. Ltd. GBR. *Dist:* Ingram Pub. Services.

Lakeshore Learning Materials, contrib. by. Big Book of Learning Songs. 2007. (J). 19.95 (*978-1-59746-016-3(8)) Lakeshore Learning Materials.

Lange, Nikki Bataille. Care Bears: Sing & Play Piano Songbook. Deters, Kevin, illus. 2006. (Care Bears Ser.). 24p. (YA). bds. 13.99 (*978-1-57791-300-9(0)) Brighter Minds Children's Publishing.

Langstaff, John. Over in the Meadow. Rojankovsky, Feodor, illus. 2002. (J). 14.04 (978-0-7587-3352-8(6)) Book Wholesalers, Inc.

Lansky, Bruce, ed. I've Been Burping in the Classroom: And Other Silly Sing-along Songs. Carpenter, Stephen, illus. 2007. 32p. (J). (978-0-88166-521-5(5)) Meadowbrook Pr.

Lansky, Bruce & Carpenter, Stephen. I've Been Burping in the Classroom. 2007. 32p. (J). 9.95 (978-1-4169-2946-8(0)) Meadowbrook Pr.

Larsen Chang, Tara, illus. The Friendly Beasts. 2006. (Sing-A-Story Ser.). 16p. (J). (ps-k). bds. 10.95 (978-0-7696-4914-6(9)) School Specialty Publishing.

—Up on the Housetop. 2006. (Sing-A-Story Ser.). 16p. (J). (ps-k). bds. 10.95 (978-0-7696-4912-2(2)) School Specialty Publishing.

Lawton, Toni-Mckay. BrainPower: Cd Extra. 2007. (Just in Rhyme Ser.). (Illus.). 12p. 6.95 (*978-1-84167-028-7(6)) Ransom Publishing Ltd. GBR. *Dist:* International Publishers Marketing.

—BrainPower: Jewel Case. 2007. (Just in Rhyme Ser.). (Illus.). 12p. 6.95 (*978-1-84167-027-0(8)) Ransom Publishing Ltd. GBR. *Dist:* International Publishers Marketing.

Le Lait, Alain. C'est si Bon: Easy-to-Learn French Songs for Children. Le Lait, Alain, . 2002. (FRE & ENG., Illus.). 28p. (J). (ps-7). audio compact disk 15.95 (978-0-9747122-3-9(X) , FRCD200) Yadeeda.com.

—It's So Good: Fun English Songs for Children, 1 bk & 1 CD. Le Lait, Alain, . 2003. (Illus.). 28p. (J). audio compact disk 15.95 (978-0-9747122-0-8(5) , ENG100) Yadeeda.com.

—Parapluie: Fabulous French Songs for Children. Le Lait, Alain, . 2006. (FRE.). (J). pap. 15.95 incl. audio compact disk (978-0-9747122-5-3(6)) Yadeeda.com.

—Soyons Amis: Easy to Learn French Songs for Children, 1 Book and 1 CD. Le Lait, Alain, . 1999. (FRE., Illus.). 34p. (J). pap. 15.95 incl. audio compact disk (978-0-9747122-1-5(3) , FRCD100) Yadeeda.com.

Learning Songs: Take along Songs. 2004. (Illus.). 16p. (J). bds. incl. audio compact disk (978-1-4127-0465-6(0) , 7220000) Publications International, Ltd.

Lee Bates, Katharine. America the Beautiful. Waldman, Neil, illus. 2004. 27p. (J). reprint ed. 17.00 (978-0-7567-8236-8(8)) DIANE Publishing Co.

Lemberg, Stephen H. Singin' Steve's Learning Land & Rainbow Village. Baker, Darrell, illus. 1999. (Singin' Steve's SmartSongs Ser.). (J). (ps-1). 14.95 incl. audio (978-1-882500-17-8(2)) SmartSong, Inc.

Lembey, Stephen H. & Bavid, Maria Elean. Singin' Steve's Smart Class: An Early Childhood Supplementary Curriculum Kit, 3 vols. 1999. 300p. (J). (ps-3). pap. 139.95 (978-1-882500-20-8(2)) SmartSong, Inc.

Lessac, Frane. Camp Granada: Sing-Along Camp Songs. rev. ed. 2003. (Illus.). 48p. (J). (gr. k-7). 18.95 (978-0-8050-6683-8(7) , Holt, Henry & Co. Bks. For Young Readers) Holt, Henry & Co.

Levine, David. Dance of a Child's Dreams - Songs for Home & School: Beginning-Intermediate Level. 1998. 32p. (J). pap. 8.95 (978-0-7866-3048-6(5) , 96790) Mel Bay Pubns., Inc.

Lewis, Stephen. Action Rhymes for You & Your Friends. 2000. ([DK Read & Listen] Ser.). (Illus.). 29p. (J). pap. (978-0-7894-4873-6(4)) Dorling Kindersley Publishing, Inc.

Lichfield, Wilma B. Pocketful of Melodies. 2007. (J). per. 17.95 (*978-1-60002-236-4(7) , Airleaf Publishing) Airleaf Publishing & Bookselling.

Lieurance, Thurlow. Songs of the North American Indian. 2001. 38p. (YA). reprint ed. 88.00 (978-0-7222-5074-7(6)) Library Reprints, Inc.

Light, John. Are These Rhymes Nonsense? 2005. (Illus.). 60p. 12.00 (978-0-907759-71-3(8)) KT Pubns. GBR. *Dist:* Photon Pr.

Limona, Mercedes. Juegos/Canciones. 2000. Tr. of Games & Songs. (SPA.). (J). 18.95 incl. audio (978-84-85546-04-6(0)) Servicios Editoriales, S.A. ESP. *Dist:* AIMS International Bks., Inc.

Linn, Jennifer. The Hungry Spider. 2003. 4p. pap. 2.50 (978-0-634-05819-6(3)) Leonard, Hal Corp.

Liszt, Franz. Thirty Songs, for High Voice. 2001. 144p. (YA). reprint ed. 88.00 (978-0-7222-6353-2(8)) Library Reprints, Inc.

Little Song Book. (De Canciones A Cuentos Ser.). (SPA.). (gr. k up). 8.91 (978-1-56334-800-6(4)); (gr. 1 up). 8.91 (978-1-56334-892-1(6)); (gr. 2 up). 8.91 (978-0-7362-0070-7(3)) Hampton-Brown Bks.

Loesser, Frank. I Love You! A Bushel & a Peck. Wells, Rosemary, illus. 2004. 32p. (J). (ps-1). 15.99 (978-0-06-028549-4(4)) HarperCollins Pubs.

Long, Lorraine & Roberts, Mary Lou. The Sing to Read Adventure, 7 bks. 1998. (J). (ps-1). pap. 16.95 incl. audio compact disk (978-1-893919-08-2(0) , 009, Sing to Read Adventure, The) Periwinkle Park Educational Productions.

Longo, Alejandra. Aserrin, Aserran Grandmother's Songs: Spanish. Harrington Villaverde, Clara, illus. 2004. (SPA.). 32p. (J). pap. 3.50 (978-0-439-63776-3(7) , Scholastic en Espanol) Scholastic, Inc.

Lou Weber Staff, ed. Dora Adventure Drum Song Book. 2004. 14p. (J). bds. 15.98 (978-1-4127-3199-7(2) , 7235200) Publications International, Ltd.

Lowenfield, Tricia. S Is for Shepherd. 2004. (Illus.). 32p. (J). per. 17.99 incl. audio compact disk (978-0-9747367-0-9(8)) Pumpkins Pansies Bunnies & Bears.

Lund, John, illus. Sing-Along Songs. 2002. (J). 16.98 (978-0-7853-6403-0(X)) Publications International, Ltd.

Luz, Ivan. Fire Truck! Dubin, Jill, illus. 2005. (Sing-and-Read Ser.). 32p. (J). pap. 4.99 (978-0-439-72212-4(8) , Cartwheel Bks.) Scholastic, Inc.

MacDonald, Margaret. The Round Book: Rounds Kids Love to Sing. 2006. 136p. (J). pap. 17.95 (978-0-87483-786-5(3)) August Hse. Pubs., Inc.

Mach, Steven, illus. The Wheels on the Bus: A Three-Dimensional Playset with Wind-Up Bus & Sound! 2001. (ps-3). act. bk. ed. 16.95 (978-1-58117-144-0(7) , Intervisual/Piggy Toes) Dalmatian Pr.

Macken, JoAnn Early & Pham, LeUyen. Sing along Song. 2004. (Illus.). 32p. (J). (ps-ps). 15.99 (978-0-670-05890-7(4) , Viking Juvenile) Penguin Group (USA) Inc.

MacMannis, Don, et al. A Pocket of Tunes: Songs & Activities for Social & Emotional Learning. Briles, Patty, illus. 2002. 48p. (J). (ps-3). pap. 16.95 (978-0-9724298-0-1(8)) Dr. Mac Productions.

Mad Monsters. 2002. (Tap My Nose Ser.). (J). (ps-k). 4.98 (978-0-7525-8728-8(5)) Parragon, Inc.

Mahoney, Anne Marie. Feliz Navidad: Learning Songs & Traditions in Spanish. Bjornson, Barb, illus. 2006. (SPA.). 32p. (J). (gr. k-6). lib. bdg. 19.95 incl. audio compact disk (978-1-59972-060-9(4) , Teach Me...) Teach Me Tapes, Inc.

Mahoney, Judy. Joyeux Noel: Learning Songs & Traditions in French. Bjornson, Barb, illus. 2006. (FRE.). (J). (gr. k-4). lib. bdg. 19.95 incl. audio compact disk (978-1-59972-061-6(2) , Teach Me...) Teach Me Tapes, Inc.

Mahoney, Judy & Mahoney, Anne. Teach Me... French Spiritual Songs. 2005. (FRE., Illus.). 24p. (J). audio compact disk 15.95 (978-0-934633-50-5(9)) Teach Me Tapes, Inc.

Maillard, Carol. Still the Same Me. Evans, Shane, illus. 2006. (J). 16.95 (978-0-689-86666-1(6) , Simon & Schuster Children's Publishing) Simon & Schuster Children's Publishing.

Marks, Anthony. The Usborne Farmyard Tales Songbook. Tyler, Jenny, ed. Cartwright, Stephen, illus. 2005. 31p. (J). (ps-7). per. 6.95 (978-0-7945-0918-7(5) , Usborne) EDC Publishing.

Martin Ramos, Juan Carlos. Las Palabras Que Se Lleva el Viento. 2004. (SPA.). 72p. (J). 9.50 (978-84-241-8666-1(4)) Everest de Ediciones y Distribucion, S.L. ESP. *Dist:* Lectorum Pubns., Inc.

Marvin the Martian's Modern Songs: Level Four for Intermediate Students. 2000. (Looney Tunes Piano Library). 24p. (J). 12.95 (978-0-7692-9608-1(4) , Warner Bros. Pubns.) Alfred Publishing Co., Inc.

Mass, Wendy, compiled by. Summer: Poems, Songs, Prayers. 2001. (Illus.). 10p. (J). (ps-2). 6.99 (978-0-570-07165-5(8)) Concordia Publishing Hse.

Master Index & Correlations. 2000. (gr. k-8). suppl. ed. 15.00 (978-0-382-34888-4(5)) Silver, Burdett & Ginn, Inc.

McCabe, Larry. Easiest Mandolin Tunes for Children. 2007. 32p. 14.95 (***978-0-7866-7535-7(7)***) Mel Bay Pubns., Inc.

McCutcheon, John. Happy Adoption Day! Paschkis, Julie, illus. 2001. 32p. (J). (ps-1). pap. 6.99 (978-0-316-60323-2(6)) Little, Brown Bks. for Young Readers.

—Happy Adoption Day! 2001. (J). 13.54 (978-0-606-21224-3(8)); lib. bdg. 14.10 (978-0-613-35640-4(3)) Tandem Library Bks.

McFarland-Johnson, Jeffrey. The Perfect ABC Songbook. Corel Gallery Magic 200,000 Staff, illus. 1998. 55p. (J). (ps-1). spiral bd. 24.95 incl. audio compact disk (978-1-892397-03-4(X)); spiral bd. 19.95 incl. audio (978-1-892397-04-1(8)) JohnSong Music.

McFarland-Johnson, Jeffrey, ed. The Perfect ABC Songbook. Corel Gallery Magic 200,000 Staff, illus. 1998. 55p. (J). (ps-1). spiral bd. 10.00 (978-1-892397-00-3(5)) JohnSong Music.

McGill, Alice. In the Hollow of Your Hand: Slave Lullabies. Cummings, Michael, illus. 2000. 40p. (J). (gr. k-3). 18.00 (978-0-618-10445-1(3)); tchr. ed. 18.00 (978-0-395-85755-7(4)) Houghton Mifflin Co. Trade & Reference Div.

McGraw-Hill Staff. Essential Elements for Choir: Musicianship, Level 1. 2001. (C). pap., stu. ed. 27.96 (978-0-07-826085-8(X) , 9780078260858) Glencoe/McGraw-Hill.

McInturff, Linda, illus. Take My Life & Let It Be. 2002. 13p. (J). pap. (978-1-932381-16-0(3) , 6420) Bible Visuals International, Inc.

McKee, Darren, illus. Barney's Dreamtime Songs. 2003. (Musical Nightlight Bks.). (J). bds. (978-0-7853-7983-6(5)) Publications International, Ltd.

McNeil, Keith & McNeil, Rusty. Civil War Songbook: With Historical Commentary. 1999. 104p. (YA). (gr. 4 up). pap. 15.95 (978-1-878360-24-3(8)) WEM Records.

Meadowbrook Press Staff. Oh My Darling, Porcupine. 2006. (Illus.). 32p. (J). 15.95 (978-0-689-05230-9(8)) Meadowbrook Pr.

Michels-Boyce, Steven, illus. When Jesus Was A Kid Like Me: A Counting Song about Jesus When He Was a Kid Like You & Me. 2005. (J). 15.95 (978-0-9761477-0-1(X)) SoJam Pr.

Miller. Rockin' Rainstricks: And Other Music Activities. 2004. 20.00 (978-0-687-03059-0(5)) Abingdon Pr.

Miller, J. Philip & Greene, Sheppard M. We All Sing with the Same Voice. Meisel, Paul, illus. (J). (ps-2). 2001. 32p. 16.99 (978-0-06-027475-7(1)); 2005. 40p. reprint ed. pap. 6.99 (978-0-06-073900-3(2) , Harper Trophy) HarperCollins Pubs.

Milne, A. A. Pooh's Playful Songs. 2004. (Deluxe Jukebox Ser.). (Illus.). 24p. (J). bds. (978-0-7853-9956-8(9) , 7209100) Publications International, Ltd.

Minster, C. J. We're All Peas in a Pod, 1. Willoughby, Jeanne, illus. 2002. 18p. (J). spiral bd. (978-0-9727714-0-5(9)) Protecting Our Diversity (POD).

Mitchell, Loretta. One, Two, Three... Echo Me! Ready-to-Use Songs, Games & Activities to Help Children Sing in Tune. 2003. (Illus.). 203p. pap. 29.95 (978-0-89328-157-1(3) , 30/1800H) Heritage Music Pr.

Mitzo Thompson, Kim. Bible Songs. 2006. (Sing along Activity Books with CDs Ser.). 32p. (J). pap. 4.99 (978-0-7696-4576-6(3)) School Specialty Publishing.

—Children's Favorite Songs. 2006. (Read, Sing, & Play Along! Ser.). 320p. (J). pap. 24.95 (978-0-7696-4314-4(0)) School Specialty Publishing.

—Traveling Songs. 2006. (Sing along Activity Books with CDs Ser.). 32p. (J). pap. 4.99 (978-0-7696-4579-7(8)) School Specialty Publishing.

Mitzo Thompson, Kim & Carder, Ken. Songs That Teach Phonics. 2006. (Songs That Teach Ser.). 72p. (J). pap. 14.95 (978-0-7696-6460-6(1) , American Education Publishing) School Specialty Publishing.

Mitzo Thompson, Kim & Mitzo Hilderbrand, Karen. Down Through the Chimney. Riley, R. W., illus. 2006. (Read & Sing along Board Books with CDs Ser.). 18p. (J). bds. 7.49 (978-0-7696-4937-5(8)) School Specialty Publishing.

—Songs That Teach Kindergarten Skills. 2006. (Songs That Teach Ser.). 72p. (J). pap. 14.95 (978-0-7696-6440-8(7) , American Education Publishing) School Specialty Publishing.

Mitzo Thompson, Kim, et al. Songs That Teach Addition. 2006. (Songs That Teach Ser.). 72p. (J). pap. 14.95 (978-0-7696-7691-3(X) , American Education Publishing) School Specialty Publishing.

—Songs That Teach Division. 2006. (Songs That Teach Ser.). 72p. (J). pap. 14.95 (978-0-7696-7703-3(7) , American Education Publishing) School Specialty Publishing.

—Songs That Teach Subtraction. 2006. (Songs That Teach Ser.). 72p. (J). pap. 14.95 (978-0-7696-7701-9(0) , American Education Publishing) School Specialty Publishing.

Moerbeek, Kees. Old MacDonald. 2000. (Illus.). 24p. (J). (ps-1). 10.99 (978-0-85953-649-3(1)) Child's Play-International.

Montoney, Jeanette, et al, illus. Rhymes & Songs: To Market, to Market; Hey! Diddle, Diddle; Fuzzy Wuzzy; Hickory, Dickory, Dock!; Teddy Bear, Teddy Bear; Five Little Ducks; Five Little Monkeys; This Little Pig, Set. 2000. 8p. (J). (ps-1). pap. (978-1-893986-21-3(7) , RS1) Keep Bks.

Moore, Mary-Alice. The Wheels on the School Bus. Huliska-Beith, Laura, illus. 2006. 32p. (J). 15.99 (978-0-06-059427-5(6)); lib. bdg. 16.89 (978-0-06-059428-2(4)) HarperCollins Pubs.

Mouse Works Staff. First Lullabye. 1998. (J). 4.98 (978-1-57082-714-3(1)) Mouse Works.

Muggli, Glorianne. Complete Primary Song Visual Aids Book. 2005. (J). pap. 12.95 (978-1-57665-122-3(3)) Muggli Graphics.

Music Sales, ed. Wiggles Party Song & Activity. 2007. 44p. pap. 9.95 (978-1-921029-01-1(3)) Music Sales Corp.

My Good Night Bible Songs. 2000. (My Good Night Bible Collection). (Illus.). 24p. (J). (ps up). bds. 16.99 (978-0-7847-1149-1(6) , 04008) Standard Publishing.

My TakeAlong Li, ed. Bible Stories. 2007. (My Take-along Library). 120p. (J). (ps-k). bds. 14.95 (***978-0-7696-5529-1(7)***) School Specialty Publishing.

Naji, Jamilla. Musical Storyland: A Sing-A-Long Book with Musical Disc. l.t. ed. 2004. (Illus.). 32p. (J). per. 19.99 (978-0-9745568-0-2(7)) Worlds In Ink Publishing, Inc.

Nelson, Steve & Rollins, Jack. Here Comes Peter Cottontail! Levy, Pamela R., illus. 26p. (J). 2007. bds. 12.99 (***978-0-8249-6701-7(1));*** 2003. bds. 6.95 (978-0-8249-4149-9(7) , Candy Cane Pr.) Ideals Pubns.

Newman, Ernest. Modern Russian Songs, 2 vols., set. 2001. (YA). reprint ed. 250.00 (978-0-7222-6188-0(8)) Library Reprints, Inc.

Newman, Gloria. My Mommy's Having a Baby. 2nd rev. ed. 2000. (Illus.). 20p. (J). (gr. k-3). pap. 12.95 (978-0-9659094-1-9(7)) Growing Up Great Productions.

Ng, Henry, illus. Rock'n'roll Guitar. 2002. 10p. (J). bds. (978-0-7853-7150-2(8)) Publications International, Ltd.

Northeast Foundation for Children Staff, compiled by. 16 Songs Kids Love to Sing. 1998. 37p. (J). (gr. k-8). 24.00 (978-0-9618636-9-2(2)) Northeast Foundation for Children, Inc.

Northlight Communications Sign Me Staff, creator. Pick Me Up! Fun Songs for Learning Signs. 2003. (Illus.). 64p. act. bk. ed. 36.95 incl. audio compact disk (978-0-9668367-8-3(2) , Sign2Me) Northlight Communications.

Norworth, Jack. Take Me Out to the Ballgame. Gillman, Alec, illus. 1999. 40p. (J). (ps-3). 6.99 (978-0-689-82433-3(5) , Aladdin) Simon & Schuster Children's Publishing.

—Take Me Out to the Ballgame. Gillman, Alec, illus. 1999. 30p. (J). (ps-3). lib. bdg. 15.30 (978-0-613-73244-4(8)) Tandem Library Bks.

Numeroff, Laura Joffe. Mouse Stroller Songs. Date not set. (J). 9.99 (978-0-694-01420-0(6)) HarperCollins Pubs.

O'Brien, John. The Farmer in the Dell. O'Brien, John, illus. 2003. (Illus.). 32p. (YA). (gr. k-2). 14.95 (978-1-56397-775-6(3)) Boyds Mills Pr.

Okun, Milton, ed. All My Life - Karla Bonoff (Piano - Vocal) (Illus.). 64p. (Orig.). (YA). pap. 14.95 (978-0-89524-707-0(0)) Cherry Lane Music Co.

—From the Heart - 30 Love Songs. 117p. (Orig.). (YA). pap. 14.95 (978-0-89524-864-0(6) , 02502146) Cherry Lane Music Co.

Omoto, Garrett, illus. Na Waiho'olu'u - The Colors. 2005. Tr. of (the Colors). (HAW & ENG.). (J). (978-1-933835-00-6(1)) Partners in Development.

On with the Beat: Children's Movement Songs for Praise & Worship. 2002. 135p. (J). pap. 59.99 (978-0-8341-7293-7(3)) Lillenas Publishing Co.

One Baby Jesus/Un Nino Dios. 2003. (ENG & SPA., Illus.). 30p. (J). 3.95 (978-0-8249-5472-7(6)) Ideals Pubns.

Orozco, Jose. Diez Deditos & Other Play Rhymes & Action Songs from Latin America. Orozco, Jose, tr. Kleven, Elisa, illus. 2002. (SPA.). 56p. (J). pap. 7.99 (978-0-14-230087-9(X) , Puffin) Penguin Group (USA) Inc.

Orozco, Jose-Luis. De Colores & Other Latin-American Folk Songs for Children. Kleven, Elisa, illus. abr. ed. 1999. (SPA.). 48p. (J). (ps-3). pap. 7.99 (978-0-14-056548-5(5) , Puffin) Penguin Group (USA) Inc.

—Diez Deditos & Other Play Rhymes & Action Songs from Latin America. 2002. (SPA.). (gr. k-3). lib. bdg. 16.45 (978-0-613-64434-1(4)) Tandem Library Bks.

—Fiestas: A Year of Latin American Songs of Celebration. Kleven, Elisa, illus. 2002. (SPA.). 56p. (J). (ps-2). 17.99 (978-0-525-45937-8(5) , Dutton Juvenile) Penguin Group (USA) Inc.

Ouren, Todd, illus. Yankee Doodle. 2004. (Patriotic Songs Ser.). 24p. (J). (ps-4). 22.60 (978-1-4048-0176-9(6)) Picture Window Bks.

Over in the Meadow. 2004. 29.95 incl. cd-rom (978-1-55592-852-0(8)); 24.95 incl. audio (978-1-56008-213-2(5)); pap. 18.95 incl. audio compact disk (978-1-55592-809-4(9)); pap. 38.75 incl. audio compact disk (978-1-55592-759-2(9)); pap. 32.75 incl. audio (978-1-55592-290-0(2)); pap. 14.95 incl. audio (978-1-56008-088-6(4)) Weston Woods Studios, Inc.

The Oxford Song Book. 2001. 211p. (YA). reprint ed. 98.00 (978-0-7222-6180-4(2)) Library Reprints, Inc.

Pancho Claus con Jose-Luis Orozco - Christmas with Jose-Luis Orozco. (SPA & ENG.). (J). (gr. k-3). 10.00 (978-1-57417-031-3(7)) Arcoiris Records, Inc.

Partin, Judith E. Songs in the Night: (A Collection of Hymns, Choruses, & Songs...) 2004. 211p. (YA). 25.00 (978-0-9748494-1-6(3)) Omega Publishing.

Pax Lodge Songbook. 2005. (J). (978-0-88441-690-6(9)) Girl Scouts of the USA.

Paxton, Tom. The Jungle Baseball Game. Schmidt, Karenlee, illus. 2005. 30p. (J). (ps-2). reprint ed. 16.00 (978-0-7567-8932-9(X)) DIANE Publishing Co.

Peek, Merle. Roll Over! A Counting Song. 1999. (Illus.). 12p. (J). (gr. k-ps). bds. 5.95 (978-0-395-98037-8(2) , Clarion Bks.) Houghton Mifflin Co. Trade & Reference Div.

Perkins, Jill E. Cherubs Chatter: A Collection of Original Songs & Poems. 2004. (Illus.). 88p. (J). per. 7.95 (978-0-9749862-2-7(4)) Theragogy.com.

Perry, Rex, illus. Over the River & Through the Woods. 2004. 24p. (J). lib. bdg. 8.00 (***978-1-4242-0640-7(5)***) Fitzgerald Bks.

Petersen, George & Jenkins, J. J. Crazy Campsongs. Davis, Jack, illus. 2003. 64p. (J). bds. 9.99 (978-0-9726794-9-7(9)) Jenpet Publishing.

Pitts, Christy, illus. Seamos Amigos: Easy-to-learn Children's Songs in Spanish, 1 Bk & 1CD. 1999. (SPA.). 28p. (J). pap. 15.95 incl. audio compact disk (978-0-9747122-2-2(1) , SPCD100) Yadeeda.com.

Pooh Songs. (Play-A-Song Ser.). (Illus.). 20p. (J). pap. 15.98 (978-0-7853-1326-7(5)) Publications International, Ltd.

Porky Pig's Christmas Songs: Level Four for Intermediate Students. 1999. (Looney Tunes Piano Library). (J). 12.95 (978-0-7692-8987-8(8) , Warner Bros. Pubns.) Alfred Publishing Co., Inc.

Potter, Beatrix. Peter Rabbit & Friends Classic Nursery Songs. 2003. (Illus.). (J). bds. (978-0-7853-8531-8(2)) Publications International, Ltd.

—Peter Rabbit's Songs & Rhymes. 2002. (Illus.). 10p. (J). (ps-ps). bds. 5.99 (978-0-7232-4846-0(X) , Warne) Penguin Group (USA) Inc.

Prater, John. Oh Where, Oh Where? 1998. (Illus.). 24p. (J). bds. 6.95 (978-0-7641-5109-5(6)) Barron's Educational Series, Inc.

Pratt, Susan, et al. Celebrate Holidays. Howard, Joan, ed. Filipov, Alex & Wyand, Glenn, illus. 1999. 48p. (J). (gr. k-3). pap. 14.95 incl. audio (978-1-894262-23-1(9) , JMP119K) Jordan Music Productions, Inc.

Precious Moments Starlight Songs. 2003. (Musical Nightlight Bks.). bds. (978-0-7853-7963-8(0)) Publications International, Ltd.

The Predator. (Song Box(R) Ser.). (gr. 1-2). 8.50 incl. audio (978-0-7802-2261-8(X)) Wright Group, The.

The Predator: 1 Big Book, 6 Each of 1 Student Book, & 1 Cassette. (Song Box(R) Ser.). (gr. 1-2). 68.95 (978-0-7802-3205-1(4)) Wright Group, The.

The Predator: 6 Each of 1 Student Book, 6 vols. (Song Box(R) Ser.). (gr. 1-2). 29.50 (978-0-7802-2259-5(8)) Wright Group, The.

The Predator: Big Book. (Song Box(R) Ser.). (gr. 1-2). 31.50 (978-0-7802-2260-1(1)) Wright Group, The.

Press Abingdon. Happylujah. 2007. 144p. pap. 35.00 (***978-0-687-64312-7(0)***) Abingdon Pr.

Prevert, Jacques. Chanson des Escargotsqui Vont l'Enterrement. ed. 2004. (Illus.). (J). (gr. 1-6). spiral bd. (978-0-616-07265-3(1)) Canadian National Institute for the Blind/Institut National Canadien pour les Aveugles.

Price, David & Ursell, Martin, illus. Birds & Beasts: Animal songs, games & Activities. 2006. (Classroom Music Ser.). 80p. (J). (gr. 1-6). spiral bd. 12.95 (978-0-7136-5653-4(0)) A & C Black GBR. *Dist:* Lubrecht & Cramer, Ltd.

Primary Song Visual Aids. 1999. (Illus.). 100p. (J). Vol. 1. pap. 8.95 (978-1-57665-057-8(X)); Vol. 2. pap. 8.95 (978-1-57665-058-5(8)); Vol. 3. pap. 8.95 (978-1-57665-059-2(6)) Muggli Graphics.

Primary Song Visual Aids Books, 3 vols. Incl. Vol. 1. Primary Song Visual Aids. pap. 8.95 (978-1-57665-057-8(X)); Vol. 2. Primary Song Visual Aids. pap. 8.95 (978-1-57665-058-5(8)); Vol. 3. Primary Song Visual Aids. pap. 8.95 (978-1-57665-059-2(6)); 100p. (J). (Illus.). 1999. Set pap. 23.95 (978-1-57665-063-9(4)) Muggli Graphics.

Print Music, contrib. by. The Definitive AC/DC Songbook. 2004. (Illus.). 800p. pap. 39.95 (978-0-8256-2783-5(4) , AM977119, Schirmer Trade Bks.) Music Sales Corp.

Publications International Staff. Enchanted Songs. (Disney Princess Ser.). (Illus.). 10p. (J). bds. 9.98 (978-0-7853-8279-9(8) , 7182300) Publications International, Ltd.

Qualey, Marsha, ed. The Ants Go Marching. D'Antonio, Sandra, illus. 2004. (Traditional Songs Ser.). 24p. (J). (gr. k-2). 22.60 (978-1-4048-0148-6(0)) Picture Window Bks.

—Clementine. D'Antonio, Sandra, illus. 2004. (Traditional Songs Ser.). 24p. (C). (gr. k-2). 22.60 (978-1-4048-0155-4(3)) Picture Window Bks.

—I Know an Old Lady Who Swallowed a Fly. D'Antonio, Sandra, illus. 2004. (Traditional Songs Ser.). 24p. (ps-2). 22.60 (978-1-4048-0150-9(2)) Picture Window Bks.

—Old MacDonald Had a Farm. D'Antonio, Sandra, illus. 2004. (Traditional Songs Ser.). 24p. (ps-2). 22.60 (978-1-4048-0152-3(9)) Picture Window Bks.

—Traditional Songs, 8 bks. D'Antonio, Sandra, illus. Incl. Ants Go Marching. (J). 22.60 (978-1-4048-0148-6(0)); Clementine. (C). 22.60 (978-1-4048-0155-4(3)); Farmer in the Dell. 22.60 (978-1-4048-0149-3(9)); I Know an Old Lady Who Swallowed a Fly. 22.60 (978-1-4048-0150-9(2)); I've Been Working on the Railroad. 22.60 (978-1-4048-0151-6(0)); Old MacDonald Had a Farm. 22.60 (978-1-4048-0152-3(9)); She'll Be Coming 'Round the Mountain. 22.60 (978-1-4048-0153-0(7)); Wheels on the Bus. 22.60 (978-1-4048-0154-7(5)); 24p. (ps-2). 2004. (Illus.). 2003. 170.08 (978-1-4048-0147-9(2)) Picture Window Bks.

—The Wheels on the Bus. D'Antonio, Sandra, illus. 2004. (Traditional Songs Ser.). 24p. (ps-2). 22.60 (978-1-4048-0154-7(5)) Picture Window Bks.

Radin, Isabel. Spanish Childrens Songs (Solo) Elementary Solo Piano, 12 Favorites to Play & Sing. 1998. (J). 5.95 (978-0-7692-5450-0(0) , Warner Bros. Pubns.) Alfred Publishing Co., Inc.

Raffi. If You're Happy & You Know It. Moore, Cyd, illus. 2005. 32p. (J). (gr. k-k). 15.95 (978-0-375-82917-8(2) , Knopf Bks. for Young Readers) Random Hse. Children's Bks.

—This Little Light of Mine. Schuett, Stacey, illus. 2004. 32p. (J). (gr. k-k). 15.95 (978-0-375-82871-3(0) , Knopf Bks. for Young Readers) Random Hse. Children's Bks.

Random House Staff. Clap Your Hands. Ewers, Joseph, illus. 2002. (Puppet Book Ser.). 10p. (J). (gr. k-ps). bds. 9.95 (978-0-375-82226-1(7) , Random Hse. Bks. for Young Readers) Random Hse. Children's Bks.

Rappin' Heart Rhyme. (Song Box(R) Ser.). (gr. 1-2). 8.50 incl. audio (978-0-322-00248-7(6)) Wright Group, The.

Rappin' Heart Rhyme: 1 Big Book, 6 Each of 1 Student Book, & 1 Cassette. (Song Box(R) Ser.). (gr. 1-2). 68.95 (978-0-322-00274-6(5)) Wright Group, The.

Rappin' Heart Rhyme: 6 Each of 1 Student Book, 6 vols. (Song Box(R) Ser.). (gr. 1-2). 29.50 (978-0-322-00270-8(2)) Wright Group, The.

Rappin' Heart Rhyme: Big Book. (Song Box(R) Ser.). (gr. 1-2). 31.50 (978-0-322-00265-4(6)) Wright Group, The.

Regan, Dana, illus. Old MacDonald Had a Farm. 2006. (Sing-A-Story Ser.). 16p. (J). bds. 10.95 (978-0-7696-4913-9(0)) School Specialty Publishing.

Rhodes, Phyllis. A Big Backyard: Nature's Musical Verse for Children. Moffett, David, illus. 1998. iv, 76p. (J). (ps-1). 30.00 incl. audio (978-0-9661359-0-9(3)) Curio Pr.

Ring, Laura, ed. Sing Praises! Marlin, Kathy, illus. 1999. (Happy Day Bks.). 24p. (J). (ps-2). 2.49 (978-0-7847-1047-0(3) , 04277, Bean Sprouts) Standard Publishing.

Rivers, Susan. Tiny Talk Songbook. 1999. (Illus.). 88p. 15.95 (978-0-19-435358-8(3)) Oxford Univ. Pr., Inc.

Rivers, Susan & Graham, Carolyn. Tiny Talk ABC Songbook, 2 vols. 1999. cd-rom, audio compact disk 35.95 (978-0-19-435360-1(5)) Oxford Univ. Pr., Inc.

Road Runner's Adventure Songs: For Intermediate Students, Level 4. 1999. (Looney Tunes Piano Library). (J). 12.95 incl. audio compact disk (978-0-7692-8984-7(3) , Warner Bros. Pubns.) Alfred Publishing Co., Inc.

Rock-a-Bye Songbook. 2001. (Kidzup Ser.). (J). pap. 12.99 incl. audio (978-1-894281-79-9(9)) Kidzup Entertainment CAN. *Dist:* Penton Overseas, Inc.

Rock, Lois. Lord Is My Shepherd: Psalm 23 for Children. Rivers, Ruth, illus. 2004. 32p. (J). pap. 9.99 (978-0-7459-4859-1(6) , Lion) Lion Hudson plc GBR. *Dist:* Independent Pubs. Group.

Rodgers, Richard & Hammerstein, Oscar, II. Getting to Know You! Rodgers & Hammerstein Favorites. Wells, Rosemary, illus. 2002. 64p. (J). (ps-3). 20.89 (978-0-06-623845-6(5)) HarperCollins Pubs.

Rojo, Andrea Szekasy & Bardsley, Maggie. I Love Spanish. Songs. 2003. (SPA., Illus.). 30p. (J). (ps-2). pap. 5.00 (978-0-9671053-7-6(4)) Language Adventure Pubns.

Romendik, Irena, illus. If You're Happy & You Know It Musical Book. 2001. (J). (ps-k). vinyl bd. 6.49 (978-1-883043-23-0(9)) Straight Edge Pr., The.

—I'm a Little Musical Teapot. 2001. (Rub-a-Dub-Tub Musical Bks.). 8p. (J). vinyl bd. 7.00 (978-1-883043-34-6(4)) Straight Edge Pr., The.

—The Musical Mary Had a Little Lamb. 2002. (Rub-a-Dub-Tub Musical Bks.). 8p. (J). vinyl bd. 7.00 (978-1-883043-39-1(5)) Straight Edge Pr., The.

—The Musical Muffin Man. 2003. (Rub a Dub Books Ser.). 8p. (J). (ps-k). vinyl bd. 7.00 (978-1-883043-45-2(X)) Straight Edge Pr., The.

Romendik, Irene, illus. I've Been Working on the Railroad: Musical Book. 2003. (J). 6.49 (978-1-883043-48-3(4)) Straight Edge Pr., The.

Ross, Kate. Help Yourself! Safety & Self-Esteem Songs for Young Children. 2001. (ps-2). lib. bdg. 33.80 (978-0-613-80427-1(9)) Tandem Library Bks.

Ross, Kathy. Crafts from Your Favorite Children's Songs. Enright, Vicky, illus. 2001. (Crafts from Kathy Ross Ser.). 48p. (gr. k-3). lib. bdg. (978-0-7613-1912-2(3)); pap. 8.95 (978-0-7613-1438-7(5)) Lerner Publishing Group. (Millbrook Pr.).

Roth, Susan L. Hanukkah, Oh Hanukkah. 2004. (Illus.). 24p. (J). (ps). 10.99 (978-0-8037-2843-1(3) , Dial) Penguin Group (USA) Inc.

Rothero, Chris, illus. Strawberry Fair. 2004. 96p. (gr. 1-6). 14.95 (978-0-7136-2676-6(3)) A & C Black GBR. *Dist:* Consortium Bk. Sales & Distribution.

Running Press Staff & Tharp, Jason. The Family Car Song Book: Hundreds of Miles of Fun. Goldberg, Howard A., ed. rev. ed. 2004. (Illus.). 80p. (J). pap. 12.95 (978-0-7624-1559-5(2) , Running Pr. Kids) Running Pr. Bk. Pubs.

S

Rupprecht, Karen & Minor, Pamela. Months of Music & More. 2005. (Illus.). 28p. (J). per. 18.95 (978-0-9704184-3-2(4)) Pennypack Productions, Inc.

Sabol, Elizabeth, illus. Day Is Done: A Lullaby. l.t. ed. 2004. 26p. (J). pap. incl. audio compact disk (978-0-9747382-0-8(4)) LeDor Publishing.

Sadlier We Believe Program Songbook. 2003. (J). per. (978-0-8215-5448-7(4) , Sadlier) Sadlier, William H. Inc.

Salgado. Nuevas Canciones Infantiles.Tr. of New Children's Songs. (SPA.). (J). 7.98 (978-968-403-664-2(7)) Selector, S.A. de C.V. MEX. *Dist:* AIMS International Bks., Inc., Giron Bks.

Sangam Songbook (Revised) 2005. (J). (978-0-88441-689-0(5)) Girl Scouts of the USA.

Saport, Linda. All the Pretty Little Horses: A Traditional Lullaby. Saport, Linda, illus. 2005. (Illus.). 32p. (J). (gr. k-ps). 5.95 (978-0-618-55162-0(X) , Clarion Bks.) Houghton Mifflin Co. Trade & Reference Div.

Save a Tree for Me: 1 Big Book, 6 Each of 1 Student Book, & 1 Cassette. (Song Box(R) Ser.). (gr. 1-2). 68.95 (978-0-7802-3206-8(2)) Wright Group, The.

Save a Tree for Me: 6 Each of 1 Student Book, 6 vols. (Song Box(R) Ser.). (gr. 1-2). 29.50 (978-0-7802-2263-2(6)) Wright Group, The.

Sawyer, Louise. The Phantom. 2003. (YA). 12.95 (978-0-9719842-1-9(2)) Martin & Brothers.

Sawyer, Shelley. Jesus Loves Me. 1998. (Sing-Along Bible Songs Ser.). (Illus.). 10p. (J). (ps). 6.99 (978-0-310-97557-1(3)) Zonderkidz.

S

Schiller, David. All American Car-I-Oke. 2003. (Illus.). 64p. (J). 14.95 (978-0-7611-3068-0(3) , 13068) Workman Publishing Co., Inc.

Schmicker, Michael. Old McDonald-San's Farm. Kenyon, Tony, illus. 2004. 16p. (J). (ps-5). pap. 13.95 incl. audio compact disk (978-0-9631154-4-7(8)) Watermark Publishing, LLC.

Schnetzler, Pattie. Earth Day Birthday. Wallace, Chad, illus. 2004. (Sharing Nature with Children Book Ser.). 32p. (J). 16.95 (978-1-58469-053-5(4)); 8.95 (978-1-58469-054-2(2)) Dawn Pubns.

Schoenberg, Jane. My Bodyworks: Songs about Your Bones, Muscles, Heart, & More! Fisher, Cynthia, illus. 2004. 28p. (J). 16.95 incl. audio compact disk (978-1-56656-583-7(9)) Interlink Publishing Group, Inc.

Scholastic Editorial Staff. My First Sing-along Book. 2007. (Barney Ser.). (J). bds. 9.99 (978-0-439-89460-9(3)) Scholastic, Inc.

School Specialty Publishing, et al. Happy Birthday, Jesus. Larsen Chang, Tara, illus. 2006. (Sing-A-Story Ser.). 16p. (J). (ps-k). bds. 10.95 (978-0-7696-4906-1(8)) School Specialty Publishing.

Schwartz, Stephen. Through Heaven's Eyes: Prince of Egypt. 1998. (Illus.). 32p. (J). (gr. k-3). 14.99 (978-0-8499-5897-7(0)) Nelson, Thomas Inc.

Schwortz, Anna M. A B C Rhymetime. Schwortz, Anna M., ed. Schwortz, Anna M., illus. 2005. (Illus.). 48p. (J). (gr. k-3). pap. (978-0-9769719-0-0(9)) AnnArt Pr.

Scruggs, Kathy. Espanol Con Senora Scruggs! 2003. (Illus.). 46p. (J). spiral bd. (978-0-9747272-0-2(2)) Permiso Por Favor Publishing Co.

Seasons & Celebrations. 2003. (Toddler Ser.). (Illus.). 36p. (J). pap. 12.99 (978-1-894677-48-6(X)) Kidzup Productions.

Seeger, Pete & Jacobs, Paul DuBois. Some Friends to Feed: The Story of Stone Soup. Hays, Michael, illus. 2005. 40p. (J). (ps-3). 16.99 incl. audio compact disk (978-0-399-24017-1(9) , Putnam Juvenile) Penguin Group (USA) Inc.

Selkirk, Blaine. The Presidents' Rap: Washington to George W. Bush. Stratton, Sara, ed. 2001. (Illus.). 56p. (J). (gr. 3-7). pap. 14.95 incl. audio (978-1-894262-51-4(4) , JMP121K) Jordan Music Productions, Inc.

Sharp, Chris, illus. Noah's Park Songs. 2001. (Noahs Park Ser.). (J). (978-0-7853-5426-0(3) , 0785354263) Cook, David C. Publishing Co.

Silly Kids. 2002. (Tap My Nose Ser.). (J). (ps-k). 4.98 (978-0-7525-8729-5(3)) Parragon, Inc.

Silly Songs. 2000. (Learning Fun for Little Ones Ser.). (Illus.). 64p. (ps-1). pap. 8.99 (978-0-88724-575-6(7) , CD-6407) Carson-Dellosa Publishing Co., Inc.

Silly Songs: Take along Songs. 2004. (Illus.). 16p. (J). bds. incl. audio compact disk (978-1-4127-0464-9(2) , 7219900) Publications International, Ltd.

Sing & Learn, ed. Bedtime Songs. 2007. (Sing & Learn Padded Board Bks.). 53p. (J). bds. 16.95 ***(978-0-7696-5439-3(8))*** School Specialty Publishing.

—Stories. 2007. (Sing & Learn Padded Board Bks.). 53p. (J). bds. 16.95 ***(978-0-7696-5449-2(5))*** School Specialty Publishing.

Sing-Along Collection: My Box of Songs, 4 bks. 2002. 32p. (J). bds. 15.95 (978-0-7525-8655-7(6)) Parragon, Inc.

Sing & Swing: With Ladybug. 2002. (J). (ps-1). 10.95 (978-0-8126-0256-2(0)) Cricket Bks.

Sing, Clap, & Dance with Ladybug. 2002. (J). (ps-1). 15.95 (978-0-8126-0054-4(1)) Cricket Bks.

Siomades, Lorianne. The Itsy Bitsy Spider. 2003. (Illus.). 12p. (J). (ps up). bds. 7.95 (978-1-56397-969-9(1)) Boyds Mills Pr.

—The Itsy Bitsy Spider. Siomades, Lorianne, illus. 2003. (Illus.). 24p. (J). (ps up). reprint ed. 9.95 (978-1-56397-727-5(3)) Boyds Mills Pr.

Slater, Teddy. ABC Sing-along. Chauncy Guida, Lisa, illus. 2006. 24p. (J). pap. 12.99 (978-0-439-85357-6(5) , Cartwheel Bks.) Scholastic, Inc.

Smith, Janet Kay. Sing A Song of Science: Lyrics for Kids From 1-99. 2005. (Illus.). 27p. (J). spiral bd. (978-0-9768786-0-5(7)) Kay, Janet Consulting.

Smith, Will. Just the Two of Us. Cooper, Floyd & Muth, Jon J., illus. 2001. 32p. (J). (ps-2). pap. 16.95 (978-0-439-08792-6(9)) Scholastic, Inc.

—Just the Two of Us. Nelson, Kadir A., illus. 2005. (Bookshelf Ser.). 32p. (J). pap. 5.99 (978-0-439-66943-6(X)) Scholastic, Inc.

Snyder, Joel, illus. Sing a Story the Wheels on the Bus. 2006. (Sing-A-Story Ser.). 16p. (J). bds. 10.95 (978-0-7696-4915-3(7)) School Specialty Publishing.

Soden, Alyce Bartholomew. Sing with the Angels. Hill, Sharon Elizabeth, illus. 2000. 40p. (J). (ps-3). pap. 22.95 (978-0-9705329-0-9(3)) Fish Rock Publishing Co.

The Song Box Science Songs: 1 Each of 12 Big Books. (Song Box(R) Ser.). (gr. 1-2). 375.50 (978-0-322-02962-0(7)) Wright Group, The.

The Song Box Science Songs: 1 Each of 12 Cassettes. (Song Box(R) Ser.). (gr. 1-2). 101.95 (978-0-322-02963-7(5)) Wright Group, The.

The Song Box Science Songs: 1 Each of 12 Student Books. (Song Box(R) Ser.). (gr. 1-2). 57.95 (978-0-322-02959-0(7)) Wright Group, The.

The Song Box Science Songs: 6 Each of 12 Student Books. (Song Box(R) Ser.). (gr. 1-2). 349.95 (978-0-322-02960-6(0)) Wright Group, The.

Songplay: A Collection of Playful Songs for Children. 1999. 844p. (J). pap. 24.95 (978-0-634-01157-3(X)) Leonard, Hal Corp.

Songs of Faith. 2002. (Illus.). (J). 12.99 (978-0-7853-6399-6(8)) Publications International, Ltd.

Songs to the Corn: A Hopi Poet Writes about Corn, 6 packs. (Greetings Ser.: Vol. 2). (gr. 3-5). 31.00 (978-0-7635-1808-0(5)) Rigby Education.

Sono, Janet Jensen, tr. from JPN. Let's Sing! Japanese Songs for Kids. Okada, Midori, illus. 1998. 38p. (J). (ps-12). pap. 24.00 incl. audio compact disk (978-1-893533-00-4(X)) Kamishibai for Kids.

Soundtracks. 2003. (J). (ps-1). pap., act. bk. ed. 15.99 (978-0-7424-1527-0(9)) School Specialty Publishing.

Spier, Peter, illus. The Fox Went Out on a Chilly Night. unabr. ed. 2006. (J). (ps-3). pap. 16.95 incl. audio ***(978-1-59112-440-5(9))*** ; pap. 18.95 incl. audio compact disk ***(978-1-59112-441-2(7))*** ; Set. pap. 39.95 incl. audio compact disk ***(978-1-59112-443-6(3))*** Live Oak Media.

Stannard, Kevin. 33 Songs for Children. 2003. (Illus.). 136p. 34.95 (978-0-19-343551-3(9)) Oxford Univ. Pr., Inc.

States & Capitals Songs. 2001. (Illus.). pap., tchr. ed. 12.95 incl. audio compact disk Audio Memory Publishing.

Steck-Vaughn Staff. Songs: Green Grass Grows. 1998. (Illus.). (J). pap. (978-0-8172-8639-2(X)) Steck-Vaughn.

Steele, Michael Anthony. Poster Song Book. 2007. (Naked Brothers Band Ser.). 32p. (J). pap. 4.99 ***(978-0-545-02072-5(7))*** Scholastic, Inc.

Stohs, Anita R. Sing-Along Praise. 2000. 64p. (ps-2). 9.99 (978-0-570-05245-6(9)) Concordia Publishing Hse.

Stott, Dorothy, illus. B-I-n-G-O. 2006. (Sing-A-Story). 16p. (J). bds. 10.95 (978-0-7696-4903-0(3)) School Specialty Publishing.

Strang Communications Company Staff, ed. Ages 2-3 Take-Home Papers Spring 2002: Discovering Together. 2002. (J). pap. 14.99 (978-1-57405-920-5(3)) CharismaLife Pubs.

—Stereo Boom Box Song Book. 1998. (J). pap. 9.99 (978-1-57405-874-1(6)) CharismaLife Pubs.

Strauss, Kurt & Strauss, Kim. Little Boy's Lullaby: A Songbook. 2005. (J). 35.00 (978-0-9760929-0-2(5)); DVD, audio compact disk 35.00 (978-0-9760929-3-3(X)) Blanket Street Publishing.

Stravinsky, Igor. The Firebird: Original 1910 Version. unabr. ed. 2000. (Illus.). 176p. pap. 7.95 (978-0-486-41403-4(5)) Dover Pubns., Inc.

—Fireworks & Song of the Nightingale in Full Score. 2000. 128p. pap. 12.95 (978-0-486-41392-1(6)) Dover Pubns., Inc.

Stroniarz, Christina V., illus. Let's Sing & Celebrate! 105 Original Songs for Seasons & Festivals. 2003. 224p. pap. 24.95 (978-0-9720913-9-8(4)) Songbird Pr.

Studio Mouse. Mother Goose Wheels on the Bus: Book & CD. rev. ed. 2007. 24p. 4.99 ***(978-1-59069-562-3(3))*** Studio Mouse LLC.

Sturges, Philemon. She'll Be Comin' 'Round the Mountain. Wolff, Ashley, illus. 2004. 32p. (J). (ps-3). 15.99 (978-0-316-82256-5(6)) Little Brown & Co.

Sullivan, Carolyn Rose, illus. The Music Box: Songs, Rhymes, & Games for Young Children, 1 box. 2006. 200p. (J). 49.95 (978-0-9772717-1-9(4)) ELZ Publishing.

Sullivan, James Kevin, illus. What Went RIght Today? Journal: WWRT Journal. 2007. 72p. (J). spiral bd. 12.95 ***(978-0-9766990-1-9(X))*** Buz-Land Presentations, Inc.

Taylor, Michelle. Singing Across the Old North State: Story-Songs of North Carolina. 2004. 44p. (J). pap. (978-1-880970-89-8(9)) Aerial Photography Services, Inc.

Taz's Terrific Songs: Level Two for Late Elementary Students. 2000. (Looney Tunes Piano Library). 24p. (J). 12.95 (978-0-7692-9714-9(5) , Warner Bros. Pubns.) Alfred Publishing Co., Inc.

Teletubbies Favorite Songs. 2001. (Illus.). (J). 7.95 (978-0-7853-4783-5(6)) Publications International, Ltd.

Thayer, Eva. The MeLand 3: Songs & Raps for 3-4-5 Year Olds. 2001. (J). 12.95 incl. audio compact disk (978-1-931228-02-2(7)) Tes Publishing Co.

Thomas & Friedns: Songs from the Station. 2005. (Play-A-Song Ser.). (Illus.). 8p. (J). bds. 15.98 (978-1-4127-3549-0(1) , 7263800) Publications International, Ltd.

Thomas, Joyce Carol. Singing Mama's Songs. Date not set. 32p. (J). 16.00 (978-0-06-025379-0(7)); lib. bdg. 15.89 (978-0-06-025382-0(7)) HarperCollins Pubs.

Thompson, Karen, selected by. Children's Bible Songs. 2006. (Read, Sing, & Play Along! Ser.). 320p. (J). pap. 24.95 (978-0-7696-4315-1(9)) School Specialty Publishing.

—Gross & Annoying Songs Kids Lo. 2006. (Read, Sing, & Play Along! Ser.). 320p. (J). pap. 24.95 (978-0-7696-4317-5(5)) School Specialty Publishing.

Tindall, Adrienne, et al. New Songs for New Singers Bk. 2: 26 Settings of Classic & New Texts - Accompaniment Formant. 2001. 96p. (YA). (gr. 7-12). pap. 32.95 (978-1-889079-34-9(0)) Darcey Pr.

Title-Movie Hits. 2000. 13.95 incl. audio compact disk (978-1-85909-705-2(7) , Warner Bros. Pubns.) Alfred Publishing Co., Inc.

Tocalli-Beller, Agustina. Bilingual Songs Vol. 1: English-Spanish. Ramirez, Gloria & Howard, Joan, eds. Brough-Jordan, Jessica & El-Shinnawy, Ihab, illus. 2002. (SPA & ENG.). 48p. (J). pap. 14.95 incl. audio (978-1-894262-66-8(2) , JMP S23K) Jordan Music Productions, Inc.

—Bilingual Songs Vol. 2: English-Spanish. Ranirez, Gloria & Howard, Joan, eds. El-Shinnawy, Ihab, illus. 2002. (ENG & SPA.). 48p. (J). pap. 14.95 incl. audio (978-1-894262-71-2(9) , JMP S24K) Jordan Music Productions, Inc.

Todd, Cynthia & Ziemann, Debbie. ABC Rappin' Zebra/ Garden Party. Johnston, Cassie, illus. l.t. ed. 1999. (Sing Me a Song Ser.). 48p. (J). (ps-3). 15.95 (978-1-879056-12-1(7)) Alpenhorn Pr.

—David David. Woessner, Circe, illus. 1998. (Sing Me a Song Ser.). 23p. (J). (gr. k-6). lib. bdg. 15.95 (978-1-879056-01-5(1)) Alpenhorn Pr.

—Heidelberg Castle/David David. Woessner, Circe, illus. 1999. (Sing Me a Song Ser.). 48p. (J). (ps-3). 15.95 incl. audio (978-1-879056-00-8(3)) Alpenhorn Pr.

—Mother Earth. Woessner, Circe, illus. 1998. (Sing Me a Song Ser.). 24p. (J). pap. 15.95 (978-1-879056-03-9(8)) Alpenhorn Pr.

—Nessie. Woessner, Circe, illus. 2nd ed. 1998. (Sing Me a Song Ser.). 9p. (J). (gr. k-6). lib. bdg. 15.95 (978-1-879056-02-2(X)) Alpenhorn Pr.

—Take One Hand. Woessner, Circe, illus. 1998. (Sing Me a Song Ser.). 25p. (J). (gr. k-6). lib. bdg. 15.95 (978-1-879056-05-3(4)) Alpenhorn Pr.

Todd, Cynthia A. Christmas Is Coming/Angel Food Cake. 1999. (Sing Me a Song Ser.). (Illus.). 48p. (J). (ps-3). 12.95 (978-1-879056-13-8(5)) Alpenhorn Pr.

Torribio, Penelope. Dinosaur Dance, Fun Songs on Serious Subjects: Includes Lyric Coloring Book. Ross, Suzanne, illus. 2000. 24p. (J). (gr. k-5). pap. 16.95 incl. cd-rom (978-0-9704516-2-0(8) , 003) One World Publishing.

—Monkey Dance: Fun Songs to Sing & Dance with CD. 2001. (Illus.). 22p. (J). (ps-4). 16.95 incl. audio compact disk (978-0-9704516-4-4(4)) One World Publishing.

—The Rain Is Coming - Songs & Poems of the Rainforest: Includes Lyric Coloring Book. Ross, Suzanne, illus. 2000. 32p. (J). (gr. k-6). pap. 16.95 incl. cd-rom (978-0-9704516-0-6(1) , 001) One World Publishing.

—Sing the Calendars Songs: Lyric Coloring Book. 2001. (J). (gr. k-3). spiral bd. 16.95 incl. audio compact disk (978-0-9704516-5-1(2)) One World Publishing.

Toy Story 2 Sing Along. 1999. (J). (ps-3). pap. 10.98 incl. audio (978-0-7634-0587-8(6)) Walt Disney Records.

Transcontinental Music Publications Staff. Complete Jewish Songbook for Children. 2002. 308p. (gr. k-3). pap. 39.95 (978-0-8074-0820-9(4) , 991700) URJ Pr.

Trapani, Iza. I'm a Little Teapot. Trapani, Iza, illus. 2004. (Illus.). 24p. (J). (ps-2). bds. 6.95 (978-1-58089-055-7(5)) Charlesbridge Publishing, Inc.

—I'm a Little Teapot. 1999. (Extended Nursery Rhymes Ser.). (Illus.). 32p. (J). (ps up). lib. bdg. 22.60 (978-0-8368-2487-2(3)) Stevens, Gareth Inc.

—The Itsy Bitsy Spider. Trapani, Iza, illus. 1998. (Illus.). 26p. (J). (ps-1). bds. 6.95 (978-1-58089-014-4(8)) Charlesbridge Publishing, Inc.

—Mary Had a Little Lamb. 2004. (Illus.). 32p. (J). pap. 6.95 (978-1-58089-090-8(3)) Charlesbridge Publishing, Inc.

—Oh Where, Oh Where Has My Little Dog Gone? Trapani, Iza, illus. 1998. (Illus.). 28p. (J). (ps-k). bds. 6.95 (978-1-58089-016-8(4)) Charlesbridge Publishing, Inc.

—Row, Row, Row Your Boat. 2004. (Illus.). 32p. (J). (ps-3). 15.95 (978-1-58089-022-9(9)) Charlesbridge Publishing, Inc.

—Row Row Row Your Boat. Trapani, Iza, illus. 2000. (Extended Nursery Rhymes Ser.). (Illus.). 32p. (J). (ps up). lib. bdg. 23.33 (978-0-8368-2668-5(X)) Stevens, Gareth Inc.

—Shoo Fly! 2004. (Illus.). 26p. (J). bds. 6.95 (978-1-58089-080-9(6)) Charlesbridge Publishing, Inc.

—Shoo Fly! Trapani, Iza, illus. 2004. (Illus.). 32p. (J). (ps-3). 15.95 (978-1-58089-052-6(0)) Charlesbridge Publishing, Inc.

—Shoo Fly! Trapani, Iza, illus. 2000. (Extended Nursery Rhymes Ser.). (Illus.). 32p. (J). (ps up). lib. bdg. 23.33 (978-0-8368-2670-8(1)) Stevens, Gareth Inc.

—Sing along with Iza & Friends: Row Row Row Your Boat. Trapani, Iza, illus. 2004. (Illus.). 32p. (J). pap. 9.95 incl. audio compact disk (978-1-58089-102-8(0)) Charlesbridge Publishing, Inc.

—Sing along with Iza & Friends: The Itsy Bitsy Spider. Trapani, Iza, illus. 2004. (Illus.). 32p. (J). pap. 9.95 incl. audio compact disk (978-1-58089-100-4(4)) Charlesbridge Publishing, Inc.

Trapani, Iza, illus. & as told by. Here We Go 'Round the Mulberry Bush. Trapani, Iza, as told by. 2006. 32p. (J). pap. 6.95 (978-1-57091-699-1(3)) Charlesbridge Publishing, Inc.

Trapani, Iza, illus. & as told by. Shoo Fly! Trapani, Iza, as told by. 2007. (J). pap. 6.95 ***(978-1-58089-076-2(8))*** Charlesbridge Publishing, Inc.

Trapani, Iza, illus. & retold by. Mary Had a Little Lamb. Trapani, Iza, retold by. 1998. 32p. (J). (ps-2). 16.95 (978-1-58089-009-0(1)) Charlesbridge Publishing, Inc.

Travis, George. State Songs. 1999. (Guide to State Symbols Ser.). (Illus.). 48p. (J). (gr. 3-8). lib. bdg. 29.93 (978-1-57103-299-7(1)) Rourke Publishing, LLC.

Tunes That Teach: A Collection of Language Arts, Health, Science & Math Songs. 2002. 80p. (gr. 1-3). 9.99 (978-0-7424-0120-4(0) , IF19211) School Specialty Publishing.

Tweety's Easy Listening Songs: Level One for Elementary Students. 1999. (Looney Tunes Piano Library). (J). 12.95 incl. audio compact disk (978-0-7692-8985-4(1) , Warner Bros. Pubns.) Alfred Publishing Co., Inc.

Twin Sisters IP, LLC., adapted by. Down by the Bay. 2006. (Sing-A-Story Ser.). 16p. (J). bds. 10.95 (978-0-7696-4904-7(1)) School Specialty Publishing.

—Five Little Monkeys Jumping on the Bed. 2006. (Sing-A-Story Ser.). 16p. (J). bds. 10.95 (978-0-7696-4902-3(5)) School Specialty Publishing.

Up on the Housetop - Musical Book. 2007. 26p. (J). bds. 12.99 ***(978-0-8249-6714-7(3)*** , Candy Cane Pr.) Ideals Pubns.

Vasylenko, Veronica, illus. Jingle Bells. 2007. 22p. (J). (ps-k). bds. 7.95 ***(978-1-58925-821-1(5)*** , tiger tales) ME Media LLC.

VBS Ready, Set, Gold! Music Guide. 2003. (J). pap. (978-0-8100-1528-9(5)) Northwestern Publishing Hse.

Velasquez, Crystal. Valentine Machine. 2006. (Maya & Miguel Ser.). (Illus.). 96p. (J). pap. 4.99 (978-0-439-78957-8(5)) Scholastic, Inc.

Vilsaint, Fequiere. Children Songs from Haiti: Chante Timoun Ayiti. Date not set. 28p. (J). (gr. 1-5). wbk. ed. 25.00 (978-1-881839-55-2(9)) Educa Vision.

Wade, Connie Morgan. Bible Songs & Action Rhymes: Ages 3-6. 2005. (Illus.). 224p. (J). (ps-3). pap. 15.99 (978-0-7847-1781-3(8) , 24190) Standard Publishing.

Walsh, Maria Elena. Canciones para Mirar. Jacoboni, Silvia, illus. 2002. (SPA.). 136p. (J). (gr. k-6). pap. 11.95 (978-950-511-640-9(3)) Santillana USA Publishing Co., Inc.

Walty, Margaret T., illus. Rock-a-Bye Baby: Lullabies for Bedtime. 2005. 40p. (J). (gr. k-4). reprint ed. 15.00 (978-0-7567-8555-0(3)) DIANE Publishing Co.

Wang, Margaret. Eency Weency Spider. Rueda, Claudia, illus. 2005. 22p. (J). (ps-ps). 10.95 (978-1-58117-418-2(7) , Intervisual/Piggy Toes) Dalmatian Pr.

Warhola, James. If You're Happy & You Know It: Jungle Edition. Geist, Ken, ed. 2007. 32p. (J). (ps-k). pap. 14.99 (978-0-439-72766-2(9) , Orchard Bks.) Scholastic, Inc.

Watt, Fiona. Christmas Lullabies With. 2006. 12p. (J). bds. 14.99 (978-0-7945-1469-3(3) , Usborne) EDC Publishing.

Watt, Fiona. Happy Baby Board Book with Cd. 2007. (Baby Board Books with CD Ser.). 12p. (J). bds. 15.99 ***(978-0-7945-1607-9(6)*** , Usborne) EDC Publishing.

Watts, Isaac. Divine & Moral Songs for Children. 1998. (Illus.). 120p. (J). (gr. k-7). reprint ed. 14.95 (978-1-57358-073-1(2)) Soli Deo Gloria Pubns.

Weber, Lou, ed. Barney Imagination Songs. 2005. 14p. (J). bds. 15.98 (978-1-4127-3372-4(3) , 7251200) Publications International, Ltd.

—Dora Princess Fairytale Songs Music Note. 2004. (Illus.). 10p. (J). bds. 9.98 (978-1-4127-3345-8(6) , 7249400) Publications International, Ltd.

—Dora Star Catcher Songs Night Light Book. 2004. 14p. (J). bds. 15.98 (978-1-4127-3292-5(1) , 7243900) Publications International, Ltd.

—Elmos Garden Little Sound Book. 2005. (Play-a-Sound Ser.). (Illus.). 10p. (J). bds. 9.98 (978-1-4127-3291-8(3) , 7244300) Publications International, Ltd.

—Little People Farm Songs. 2005. 14p. (J). bds. 15.98 (978-1-4127-3328-1(6) , 7246600) Publications International, Ltd.

—Old Macdonald. 2005. 24p. (J). bds. 10.98 (978-1-4127-3445-5(2) , 3923201) Publications International, Ltd.

—Peter Rabbit Songs Music Note Sound Book. 2004. 10p. (J). bds. 9.98 (978-1-4127-3121-8(6) , 7231300) Publications International, Ltd.

—Scooby Doo Monster Songs. 2004. 10p. (J). bds. 9.98 (978-1-4127-3336-6(7) , 7247100) Publications International, Ltd.

Weber, Louise. Songs of Joy. 2002. (Illus.). (J). 7.95 (978-0-7853-6421-4(8)) Publications International, Ltd.

Weeks, Sarah. Crocodile Smile: 10 Songs of the Earth As the Animals See It! Ehlert, Lois, illus. 2003. 48p. (J). (ps-2). 16.99 incl. audio compact disk (978-0-06-055745-4(1) , Geringer, Laura Book) HarperCollins Pubs.

—Don't Discover Me. Date not set. (J). (ps-3). 15.99 (978-0-06-028139-7(1)) HarperCollins Pubs.

Welch, Willy. Playing Right Field. 2000. (978-0-606-18883-8(5)) Tandem Library Bks.

Welfing, Melanie Rook. Sing for Joy. 2005. (J). pap. 1.69 (978-1-59317-119-3(6)) Warner Pr. Pubs.

Wells, Rosemary. The Bear Went over the Mountain. Wells, Rosemary, illus. 2007. (Bruno & Boots Book Ser.). (Illus.). 18p. (J). bds. 5.99 (978-0-590-02910-0(X)) Scholastic, Inc.

—Bingo! Wells, Rosemary, illus. 1999. (Bruno & Boots Book Ser.). (Illus.). 18p. (J). (ps-k). bds. 5.99 (978-0-590-02913-1(4)) Scholastic, Inc.

Westcott, Nadine Bernard. Skip to My Lou. Westcott, Nadine Bernard, illus. 2000. (Illus.). 24p. (J). (ps-k). 5.95 (978-0-316-93091-8(1)) Little Brown & Co.

Westcott, Nadine Bernard & Hoberman, Mary Ann. Sing-Along Songs Set: The Lady with the Alligator Purse, Skip to My Lou, & Miss Mary Mack, 3 bks., 1 tape. Westcott, Nadine Bernard, illus. 2002. (Illus.). 11p. (J). (ps-k). bds. 14.99 (978-0-316-93021-5(0)) Little, Brown Bks. for Young Readers.

Whatley, Bruce, illus. The Teddy Bear's Picnic. unabr. ed. 2000. (J). 15.98 incl. audio Random Hse. Audio Publishing Group.

Wilcox, Ella Wheeler. Historical Mother Goose: A Jingle Book O. 2006. pap. 15.95 (***978-1-4179-7078-0(2)***) Kessinger Publishing, LLC.

Wilhelm, Hans, illus. Sing-and-Read: B I N G O. 2005. (Sing-and-Read Ser.). 24p. (J). pap. 4.99 (978-0-439-68360-9(2)) Scholastic, Inc.

Winter's Gift. (Song Box(R) Ser.). (gr. 1-2). 31.50 (978-0-322-00267-8(2)) Wright Group, The.

Winter's Gift: 6 Each of 1 Student Book. (Song Box(R) Ser.). (gr. 1-2). 68.95 (978-0-322-00277-7(X)); 29.50 (978-0-322-00272-2(9)) Wright Group, The.

Winter's Gift: Cassette. (Song Box(R) Ser.). (gr. 1-2). 8.50 incl. audio (978-0-322-00251-7(6)) Wright Group, The.

Wolf, Hugo. Fifty Songs, 2 Vols., Set. 2001. (YA). reprint ed. 250.00 (978-0-7222-6362-4(7)) Library Reprints, Inc.

Word Music, Inc. Staff. Shining Lights & Shaky Nights. 2001. (Kidz Tunz Bible Songs Ser.: No. 6). 32p. (J). 6.99 (978-0-8423-5320-5(8)) Tyndale Hse. Pubs.

Word Music, Inc. Staff, prod. Marchin' Feet & a Groovin' Beat. unabr. ed. 2002. (Kidz Tunz Bible Songs Ser.: No. 9). (J). 6.99 (978-0-8423-5715-9(7)) Tyndale Hse. Pubs.

Yarrow, Peter & Lipton, Lenny. Puff, the Magic Dragon. Puybaret, Eric, illus. 2007. 24p. (J). (ps-2). 16.95 (***978-1-4027-4782-3(9)***) Sterling Publishing Co., Inc.

Yee, Josie, illus. Friendly Songs. 2001. (Fisher-Price Little People Ser.). (J). (978-0-7853-4792-7(5)) Publications International, Ltd.

Yolen, Jane. Apple for the Teacher: Thirty Songs for Singing While You Work. 2005. (Illus.). 120p. (J). (gr. 5-17). 24.95 (978-0-8109-4825-9(7)) Abrams, Harry N. , Inc.

Zaritzky, Bernard & Whippo, Walt. Little White Duck. Paley, Joan, illus. 2000. 32p. (J). (ps-3). 15.99 (978-0-316-03227-8(1)) Little Brown & Co.

Zawadsky, Pat. The Boy Who Stole the Fourth of July - Piano/Vocal Score. 1998. 18p. (YA). (gr. 5-12). pap. 15.00 (978-0-88680-451-0(5)) Clark, I. E. Pubns.

Zemach, Margot. Some from the Moon, Some from the Sun: Poems & Songs for Everyone. Zemach, Margot, illus. 2001. (Illus.). 48p. (J). (ps-2). 17.00 (978-0-374-39960-3(3) , Farrar, Straus & Giroux (BYR)) Farrar, Straus & Giroux.

Zimmerman, Dottie, creator. Interactive Sing-along Big Books Five Little Ducks. 2007. (J). spiral bd. 12.95 (***978-1-58650-713-8(3)***) Super Duper Pubns.

—Interactive Sing-along Big Books Here Come the Bugs! 2007. (J). spiral bd. 12.95 (***978-1-58650-714-5(1)***) Super Duper Pubns.

—Interactive Sing-along Big Books Where Are My Crayons? 2007. (J). spiral bd. 12.95 (***978-1-58650-712-1(5)***) Super Duper Pubns.

Zimmermann, Dotte, creator. Interactive Sing-along Big Books Little Bo Peep. 2007. (J). spiral bd. 12.95 (***978-1-58650-718-3(4)***) Super Duper Pubns.

Zimmermann, Dottie, creator. Interactive Sing-along Big Books Cool Camping Fun. 2007. (J). spiral bd. 12.95 (***978-1-58650-721-3(4)***) Super Duper Pubns.

—Interactive Sing-along Big Books Dress Me Bear. 2007. (J). spiral bd. (***978-1-58650-716-9(8)***) Super Duper Pubns.

—Interactive Sing-along Big Books Funny Face. 2007. (J). spiral bd. 12.95 (***978-1-58650-715-2(X)***) Super Duper Pubns.

—Interactive Sing-along Big Books Old MacDonald. 2007. (J). spiral bd. 12.95 (***978-1-58650-722-0(2)***) Super Duper Pubns.

—Interactive Sing-along Big Books This Old Man. 2007. (J). spiral bd. 12.95 (***978-1-58650-720-6(6)***) Super Duper Pubns.

Zondervan. Oh, Be Careful. 1998. (Sing-Along Bible Songs Ser.). (Illus.). 10p. (J). (ps). 5.99 (978-0-310-97558-8(1)) Zondervan.

2005 VBS SongBook. 2005. (J). (978-1-58942-262-9(7)) R.H. Boyd Publishing Corp.

SONGS, AFRICAN AMERICAN

see African Americans—Music

SONGS, NATIONAL

see National Songs

SONGS, POPULAR

see Popular Music

SOOTHSAYING

see Divination

SOPORIFICS

see Narcotics

SORCERY

see Occultism; Witchcraft

SOSA, SAMMY, 1968-

Barrymore, Drew. Sammy Sosa. 1999. (Overcoming Adversity Ser.). (Illus.). 128p. (YA). (gr. 5 up). pap. 9.95 (978-0-7910-5301-0(6) , Chelsea Hse.) Facts On File, Inc.

Brenner, Richard J. Sammy Sosa. 1999. (Illus.). 32p. (J). (gr. 1-4). pap. 4.50 (978-0-688-17084-4(6)) HarperCollins Pubs.

—Sammy Sosa. 1999. (978-0-606-17082-6(0)) Tandem Library Bks.

Burke, Rick. Sammy Sosa. 2001. (Sports Files Ser.). (Illus.). 32p. (J). (gr. 1-3). lib. bdg. (978-1-58810-113-6(4)) Heinemann Library.

Castle, George. Sammy Sosa: Slammin' Sammy. Rains, Rob, ed. 2003. (Superstar Ser.). (Illus.). 96p. (J). (gr. 4-7). pap. 4.95 (978-1-58261-029-0(0)) Sports Publishing, LLC.

—Sammy Sosa: Slammin' Sammy. 1999. (gr. 3-6). lib. bdg. 12.95 (978-0-613-17732-0(0)) Tandem Library Bks.

Christopher, Matt. At the Plate with... Sammy Sosa. 1999. 11.64 (978-0-606-17502-9(4)); (gr. 3-6). lib. bdg. 12.95 (978-0-613-21143-7(X)) Tandem Library Bks.

Christopher, Matt & Stout, Glenn. At the Plate with... Sammy Sosa. 1999. (Illus.). 128p. (J). (gr. 3-7). pap. 4.99 (978-0-316-13477-4(5)) Little Brown & Co.

Dougherty, Terri. Sammy Sosa. 1999. (Jam Session Ser.). (Illus.). 32p. (J). (gr. 3-8). lib. bdg. 24.21 (978-1-57765-348-6(3) , ABDO & Daughters) ABDO Publishing Co.

Driscoll, Laura. Sammy Sosa: Home Run Hero. Call, Ken, illus. 1999. (All Aboard Reading Ser.). 48p. (J). (gr. 2-3). pap. 3.99 (978-0-448-42067-7(8) , Grosset & Dunlap) Penguin Group (USA) Inc.

—Sammy Sosa: Home-Run Hero. 1999. (gr. k-3). lib. bdg. 11.80 (978-0-613-15129-0(1)) Tandem Library Bks.

Kirkpatrick, Rob. Sammy Sosa: Home Run Hitter. 2002. (Reading Power Ser.). (Illus.). 24p. (J). (gr. 1). lib. bdg. 17.25 (978-0-8239-5534-3(6) , PowerKids Pr.) Rosen Publishing Group, Inc., The.

—Sammy Sosa, Bateador de Home Runs. 2002. (Coleccion Power Kids). (SPA & ENG., Illus.). 24p. (J). (gr. k-2). lib. bdg. 17.25 (978-0-8239-6132-0(X) , RN31299, Buenas Letra) Rosen Publishing Group, Inc., The.

—Sammy Sosa, Batedor de Home Runs. 2002. (Deportistas de Poder Ser.). (SPA & ENG., Illus.). 24p. (J). lib. bdg. 17.25 (978-0-8239-6114-6(1) , Buenas Letra) Rosen Publishing Group, Inc., The.

Korman, Susan. Sammy Sosa. 2001. (Latinos in the Limelight Ser.). (Illus.). 64p. (J). (gr. 4-7). 27.50 (978-0-7910-6474-0(3) , Chelsea Hse.) Facts On File, Inc.

MacLean, Caleb. Sammy Sosa: Cubs Clubber. 1999. (gr. 3-6). lib. bdg. 14.10 (978-0-613-62314-8(2)) Tandem Library Bks.

Malone, Julio. Sammy Sosa en 9 Innings. 2nd exp. ed. 2004. (SPA.). (YA). pap. 12.95 net. (978-0-9671705-0-3(8)) Editorial Miglo.

—Sammy Sosa in 9 Innings. 2004. (YA). pap. 12.95 (978-0-9671705-1-0(6)) Editorial Miglo.

Molzahn, Arlene Bourgeois. Sammy Sosa. 2000. (Sports Heroes Ser.). (Illus.). 48p. (J). (gr. 3-4). lib. bdg. 21.26 (978-0-7368-0580-3(X) , Capstone High-Interest Bks.) Capstone Pr., Inc.

Morrison, John. Sammy Sosa. 2006. (Great Hispanic Heritage Ser.). (Illus.). 112p. (J). 30.00 (978-0-7910-8845-6(6) , Chelsea Hse.) Facts On File, Inc.

Muskat, Carrie. Sammy Sosa. 2000. (Overcoming Adversity Ser.). (Illus.). 112p. (YA). 30.00 (978-0-7910-5300-3(8) , Chelsea Hse.) Facts On File, Inc.

—Sammy Sosa. 1999. (Latinos in Baseball Ser.). (Illus.). 72p. (gr. 4-10). lib. bdg. 18.95 (978-1-883845-92-6(0)); 32p. (gr. 3-8). lib. bdg. 15.95 (978-1-883845-96-4(3)) Mitchell Lane Pubs., Inc.

Preller, James. McGwire & Sosa: A Season to Remember. 1998. (Illus.). 32p. (J). (ps up). pap. 5.99 (978-0-689-82871-3(3) , Simon Pulse) Simon & Schuster Children's Publishing.

Sammy Sosa. (Sports Heroes Ser.). 48p. (YA). 7.95 (978-0-7368-9183-7(8)) Capstone Pr., Inc.

Sammy Sosa. pap. 27.50 (978-0-7910-6921-9(4) , Chelsea Hse.) Facts On File, Inc.

Sammy Sosa, 6 vols. (gr. 4 up). 39.95 (978-0-7368-9277-3(X)) Red Brick Learning.

Sammy Sosa - Sports Action Flipp Book. 2003. (J). mass mkt. 4.99 (978-0-9744443-3-8(2)) Flipp Sports.

Sammy Sosa: Individual Title Six-Packs. (On Deck Ser.). 24p. (gr. 4-5). 35.00 (978-0-7578-1003-9(9)); (SPA.). 35.00 (978-0-7578-6386-8(8)) Rigby Education.

Savage, Jeff. Sammy Sosa. (Amazing Athletes Ser.). (J). 2006. (Illus.). (gr. 3-4). 23.93 (978-0-8225-3672-7(2)); 2005. 32p. (gr. 2-5). pap. 5.95 (978-0-8225-2041-2(9)) Lerner Publishing Group.

—Sammy Sosa: Heroe del Jonron. 2000. Tr. of Sammy Sosa: Home Run Hero. (978-0-606-18825-8(8)) Tandem Library Bks.

—Sammy Sosa: Home Run Hero. (Sports Achievers Biographies Ser.). (Illus.). 2005. (SPA.). 80p. (gr. 7-12). lib. bdg. 22.60 (978-0-8225-3681-9(1)); 2003. 64p. (J). (gr. 4-9). 5.95 (978-0-8225-9858-9(2) , Carolrhoda Bks.); 2000. (SPA., 64p. (YA). (gr. 4-9). pap. 5.95 (978-0-8225-9861-9(2) , LernerSports) Lerner Publishing Group.

—Sammy Sosa: Home Run Hero. 2000. (SPA.). (gr. 5-8). lib. bdg. 14.10 (978-0-613-84488-8(2)) Tandem Library Bks.

Stewart, Mark. Sammy Sosa: Touching All the Bases. 2004. (American Literary Greats Ser.). (Illus.). 64p. (J). (gr. 5 up). lib. bdg. 26.90 (978-0-7613-2778-3(9) , Millbrook Pr.) Lerner Publishing Group.

Torres, John Albert. Sports Great Sammy Sosa. 2003. (Sports Great Books). (Illus.). 64p. (J). (gr. 4-10). lib. bdg. 22.60 (978-0-7660-2065-8(7)) Enslow Pubs., Inc.

SOTO, HERNANDO DE, CA. 1500-1542

Brown, Janet Hubbard. Hernando de Soto: And His Expeditions Across the Americas. Goetzmann, William H., ed. 2005. (Explorers of New Lands Ser.). (Illus.). 138p. (J). (gr. 4-8). lib. bdg. 30.00 (978-0-7910-8610-0(0) , Chelsea Hse.) Facts On File, Inc.

De Soto. (Exploring the World Ser.). 48p. (YA). 8.95 (978-0-7565-1143-2(7)) Compass Point Bks.

Gaines, Ann Graham. Hernando de Soto & the Spanish Search for Gold in World History. 2002. (In World History Ser.). (Illus.). 112p. (YA). (gr. 5-12). lib. bdg. 26.60 (978-0-7660-1821-1(0)) Enslow Pubs., Inc.

Gallagher, Jim. Hernando de Soto & the Exploration of Florida. 1999. (Explorers of the New World Ser.). (Illus.). 63p. (J). (gr. 4 up). 31.00 (978-0-7910-5512-0(4) , Chelsea Hse.) Facts On File, Inc.

Garcia, Kimberly. Hernando de Soto. 2002. (Latinos in American History). (Illus.). 56p. (gr. 4-8). lib. bdg. 29.95 (978-1-58415-147-0(1)) Mitchell Lane Pubs., Inc.

Heinrichs, Ann. De Soto: Hernando de Soto Explores the Southeast. 2002. (Exploring the World Ser.). (Illus.). 48p. (J). (gr. 4 up). lib. bdg. 22.60 (978-0-7565-0179-2(2)) Compass Point Bks.

Larkin, Tanya. Hernando de Soto. 2001. (Famous Explorers Ser.). (Illus.). 24p. (J). (gr. 3). lib. bdg. 18.75 (978-0-8239-5557-2(5) , PowerKids Pr.) Rosen Publishing Group, Inc., The.

Manning, Ruth. Hernando De Soto. 2003. (Groundbreakers Ser.). (Illus.). 48p. pap. 8.50 (978-1-58810-343-7(9)) Heinemann Library.

—Hernando de Soto. 2000. (Groundbreakers Ser.). (Illus.). 48p. (J). (gr. 5-7). lib. bdg. 25.64 (978-1-57572-388-4(3)) Heinemann Library.

Pancella, Peggy. Hernando de Soto. 2003. (Historical Biographies Ser.). (Illus.). 32p. (J). pap. 6.95 (978-1-4034-3710-5(6)); lib. bdg. 22.79 (978-1-4034-3702-0(5)) Heinemann Library.

—Hernando de Soto. 2003. (gr. k-3). lib. bdg. 15.90 (978-0-613-82822-2(4)) Tandem Library Bks.

Petrie, Kristin. Hernando de Soto. 2004. (Explorers Set I Ser.). (J). (gr. k-6). lib. bdg. 22.78 (978-1-59197-600-4(6)) ABDO Publishing Co.

Stein, R. Conrad. Hernando de Soto: A Life of Adventure. 2005. (Proud Heritage: the Hispanic Library Ser.). (Illus.). 40p. (J). (gr. 3-7). 28.50 (978-1-59296-385-0(4)) Child's World, Inc.

SOUND

Arnold, Caroline. Did You Hear That? Animals with Super Hearing. Trachok, Cathy, illus. 2001. (J). pap. 6.95 (978-1-57091-405-8(2)); 32p. 16.95 (978-1-57091-404-1(4)) Charlesbridge Publishing, Inc.

—Did You Hear That? Animals with Super Hearing. 2001. (978-0-606-22634-9(6)) Tandem Library Bks.

At My Grandfather's, 6 Pcks. (ps-2). 27.00 (978-0-7635-9435-0(0)) Rigby Education.

Baker, Wendy, et al. Sound. (Make It Work! (Eureka!) Ser.). (FRE., Illus.). (J). pap. 9.99 (978-0-590-24631-6(3)) Scholastic, Inc.

Barlex, David & Wadsworth, Pamela. Rhagor Am Sain a Cherddoriaeth. 2005. (WEL., Illus.). 24p. pap. (978-1-85596-240-8(3)) Dref Wen.

—Sain a Cherddoriaeth. 2005. (WEL., Illus.). 24p. pap. (978-1-85596-239-2(X)) Dref Wen.

Bayrock, Fiona. Sound: A Question & Answer Book. 2006. (Fact Finders Ser.). (Illus.). 32p. (J). (978-0-7368-5449-8(5)) Capstone Pr., Inc.

Beech, Linda Ward. The Magic School Bus in the Haunted Museum: A Book about Sound. Duchesne, Lucie, tr. Schick, Joel, illus. (Magic School Bus Ser.). (FRE.). 32p. (J). (gr. 1-4). pap. 5.99 (978-0-590-24657-6(7)) Scholastic, Inc.

Benchmark Education Staff, compiled by. Light & Sound. 2006. spiral bd. 199.00 (***978-1-4108-7121-3(5)***) Benchmark Education Co.

The Bridgestone Science Library: Our Physical World, 4 bks. Incl. Electricity. Olien, Rebecca. lib. bdg. 18.60 (978-0-7368-1404-1(3)); Light. Olien, Rebecca. lib. bdg. 18.60 (978-0-7368-1405-8(1)); Magnets. Olien, Rebecca. lib. bdg. 18.60 (978-0-7368-1406-5(X)); Sound. Olien, Becky. lib. bdg. 18.60 (978-0-7368-1407-2(8)); 24p. (J). (gr. 1-2). 2002. (Illus.). 2002. Set lib. bdg. 74.40 (978-0-7368-1408-9(6) , Bridgestone Bks.) Capstone Pr., Inc.

Brudnak, Karen, ed. Investigating Science - Energy, Light, & Sound. 2000. 48p. 9.95 (978-1-56234-429-0(3) , Mailbox Bks., The) Education Ctr., Inc.

Bryant-Mole, Karen & Ansary, Mir Tamim. Sound & Light. 2002. (Science All Around Me Ser.). (Illus.). 24p. (J). (gr. 1-3). pap. 6.95 (978-1-4034-0055-0(5) , 91499) Heinemann Library.

Buck, Percy C. Acoustics for Musicians. 2001. 152p. (YA). reprint ed. 88.00 (978-0-7222-5627-5(2)) Library Reprints, Inc.

Burton, Margie, et al. Sounds. Adams, Alison, ed. 1999. (Early Connections Ser.). 16p. (J). (gr. k-2). pap. 4.50 (978-1-58344-082-7(8)) Benchmark Education Co.

Casado, Dami & Casado, Alicia. El Sueño. 2005. (Sentidos y Algo Mas). (SPA & ESP.). 16p. 8.99 (978-84-272-6417-5(8)) Molino, Editorial ESP. *Dist:* Santillana USA Publishing Co., Inc.

Challoner, Jack. Sound & Light. 2001. (Hands-On Science Ser.). (Illus.). (J). (978-0-606-21442-1(9)) Tandem Library Bks.

Cheshire, Gerard. Sound & Vibrations. 2006. (Illus.). 48p. (J). (978-1-58340-997-8(1)) Smart Apple Media.

Clemmet, Mike. Light & Sound. 1998. (Fact Finders Ser.). (Illus.). 48p. (J). (gr. 3-7). pap. (978-0-563-37505-0(1)) BBC Worldwide.

Cobb, Vicki. Bangs & Twangs: Science Fun with Sound. Haefele, Steve, illus. 2000. (Science Fun with Vicki Cobb Ser.). 48p. (gr. 3-6). lib. bdg. 24.90 (978-0-7613-1571-1(3) , Millbrook Pr.) Lerner Publishing Group.

Cooper, Christopher. Sound: From Doppler to Sonar. 2003. (Science Answers Ser.). (Illus.). 32p. (J). pap. 7.50 (978-1-4034-3553-8(7)); lib. bdg. 22.79 (978-1-4034-0956-0(0)) Heinemann Library.

Cooper, Jason. Sound. 2003. (Science Secrets Discovery Library). (Illus.). 24p. (gr. 1-4). 14.95 (978-1-58952-413-2(6)) Rourke Publishing, LLC.

Craats, Rennay. The Science of Sound. 2000. (Living Science Ser.). (Illus.). 32p. (J). (gr. 2 up). lib. bdg. 24.67 (978-0-8368-2682-1(5)) Stevens, Gareth Inc.

Dalton, Cindy Devine. Sound. 2001. (How Can I Experiment With? Ser.). (Illus.). 32p. (gr. 1-4). 19.95 (978-1-58952-015-8(7)) Rourke Publishing, LLC.

Diehl, David. Boom Boom, Beep Beep, Roar! My Sounds Book. 2007. (Illus.). 22p. (J). (ps), bds. 4.95 (***978-1-60059-114-3(0)***) Lark Bks.

Dixon, Malcolm & Smith, Karen. Sound & Music. 1998. (Young Scientists Ser.). (Illus.). 32p. (J). (ps-3). lib. bdg. 16.95 (978-1-887068-72-7(4)) Smart Apple Media.

Elmo Count along Music Note Sound Book. 2004. (Illus.). 10p. (J). bds. 9.98 (978-1-4127-3346-5(4) , 7249500) Publications International, Ltd.

La energia de la luz y el sonido: Cuaderno de Evaluacion: Unit 3: la energia de la luz y el sonido (the Energy of Sound & Light) 2000. (McGraw-Hill Ciencias Ser.). (ENG & SPA.). (gr. 5 up). (978-0-02-278673-1(2)) Macmillan/McGraw-Hill Schl. Div.

La energia de la luz y el sonido: Recursos para el maestro con clave de Respuestas: Unit 3: la energia de la luz y el sonido (the Energy of Sound & Light) 2000. (McGraw-Hill Ciencias Ser.). (ENG & SPA.). (gr. 5 up). (978-0-02-278709-7(7)) Macmillan/McGraw-Hill Schl. Div.

Frank, Marjorie Slavick, et al. Science Instant Readers Bk. 12: How Does Sound Travel? 1999. (Harcourt Science Ser.). (gr. 2 up). pap. 15.50 (978-0-15-316222-0(8)) Harcourt Schl. Pubs.

Frenkel, Karen A. Light & Sound Technology. 2006. (Navigators Ser.). (J). pap. 42.00 (***978-1-4108-6228-0(3)***) Benchmark Education Co.

—Listening to Sound. 2006. (Navigators Ser.). (J). pap. 42.00 (***978-1-4108-6227-3(5)***) Benchmark Education Co.

Garber, Linda. Sound Is Bound to Be Around. Garber, Linda, illus. l.t. ed. 1999. (Illus.). (J). (gr. 1-4). spiral bd. 9.95 (978-1-892218-06-3(2)) Murlin Pubns.

Gareth Stevens Publishing Staff, contrib. by. Sound. 2003. (Discovery Channel School Science Ser.). (Illus.). 32p. (J). (gr. 5 up). lib. bdg. 24.67 (978-0-8368-3363-8(5)) Stevens, Gareth Inc.

Gish, Melissa. Sound. 2005. (My First Look at Science Ser.). (Illus.). 24p. (gr. k-3). 15.95 (978-1-58341-374-6(X) , Creative Education) Creative Co., The.

Goldsmith, Mike. Light & Sound. 2007. (Kingfisher Young Knowledge Ser.). (Illus.). 48p. (J). (gr. k-3). 9.95 (978-0-7534-6036-8(X)) Houghton Mifflin Co.

Granowsky, Alvin. Sounds. 2001. (978-0-606-22436-9(X)) Tandem Library Bks.

—Sounds. 2001. (ps-2). lib. bdg. 13.00 (978-0-613-45225-0(9)) Tandem Library Bks.

Grimshaw, Caroline. Sound: A Journey That Changes Silence to Sound. 2000. (Invisible Journeys Ser.). (Illus.). 32p. (J). (gr. 3-6). 10.95 (978-1-58728-335-2(2)); pap. 5.95 (978-1-58728-328-4(X)) T&N Children's Publishing. (Two Can Publishing).

Harcourt School Publishers Staff. Harcourt Science: How Does Sound Travel Reader. 1999. (Illus.). pap. 3.10 (978-0-15-314875-0(6)) Harcourt Schl. Pubs.

—How Does Sound Travel: Science Reader. 1999. (SPA., Illus.). (J). pap. 3.70 (978-0-15-316127-8(2)) Harcourt Schl. Pubs.

Harwood, Beth. Amazing Baby Baby, Boo! 2006. (Amazing Baby Ser.). (Illus.). 16p. (J). bds. 5.95 (978-1-59223-585-8(9) , Silver Dolphin Bks.) Advantage Pubs. Group.

Haslam, Andrew, et al. Sound. (Make It Work! Ser.). (Illus.). 48p. (J). pap. 7.99 (978-0-590-24615-6(1)) Scholastic, Inc.

Herold, Vickey. Breaking the Sound Barrier. 2006. pap. 39.00 (***978-1-4108-6487-1(1)***) Benchmark Education Co.

—Discover Sound. 2006. pap. 39.00 (***978-1-4108-6489-5(8)***) Benchmark Education Co.

—Sound Is Energy. 2006. pap. 39.00 (***978-1-4108-6486-4(3)***) Benchmark Education Co.

Hewitt, Sally. Amazing Sound. 2007. (J). 32p. pap. (***978-0-7787-3629-5(6)); (978-0-7787-3615-8(6))*** Crabtree Publishing Co.

Hewitt, Sally. Roar Like a Lion: (Sound) 2002. (Why Can't I Ser.). (Illus.). 32p. (J). lib. bdg. 24.25 (978-1-930643-69-7(1)) Chrysalis Education.

Holt, Rinehart and Winston Staff. Holt Science & Technology: Sound & Light, Pt. O. 3rd ed. 2003. (SPA.). 18.60 (978-0-03-069363-2(2)) Holt, Rinehart & Winston.

—Holt Science & Technology Chapter 21: Physical Science: The Nature of Sound. 5th ed. 2004. (Illus.). pap. 12.86 (978-0-03-030436-1(9)) Holt, Rinehart & Winston.

—Holt Science & Technology Chptr. 16: The Nature of Sound: Chapter Resources - Tennessee Edition. 3rd ed. 2003. (J). pap. 11.40 (978-0-03-069124-9(9)) Holt, Rinehart & Winston.

—Holt Science & Technology 2002 Pt. O: Sound & Light. 2nd ed. 2002. 18.60 (978-0-03-064807-6(6)); 46.66 (978-0-03-064808-3(4)) Holt, Rinehart & Winston.

Horne, Jane. Busy Baby: Noisy Book. 2007. (Busy Baby Ser.). (Illus.). 12p. (ps). per., bds. 9.99 (978-0-84610-434-3(3)) Make Believe Ideas GBR. *Dist:* Ingram Pub. Services.

Hunter, Rebecca M. Sound. 2000. (Discovering Science Ser.). (Illus.). 32p. (J). (gr. 3-5). lib. bdg. 25.69 (978-0-7398-2974-5(2)) Raintree.

—Sound. 2000. (Discovering Science Ser.). (Illus.). 32p. (J). (gr. 3-5). pap. 8.95 (978-0-7398-3018-5(X)) Steck-Vaughn.

Jiménez, Vita. What Kind of Sound. 2006. (Yellow Umbrella Books for Early Readers). (Illus.). 18p. (J). (978-0-7368-5973-8(X)) Yellow Umbrella Pr.

—What Kind of Sound? 2006. (Yellow Umbrella Books for Early Readers). (SPA & ENG., Illus.). 18p. (J). (978-0-7368-6009-3(6)) Yellow Umbrella Pr.

Johnson, Rebecca L. The Magic of Light & Sound. 2003. (National Geographic Reading Expeditions Ser.). (Illus.). 32p. (J). pap. (978-0-7922-8886-2(6)) National Geographic Society.

Kelly, Lynne. Simple Concepts in Physics: Sound & Light. (Illus.). 88p. (J). (gr. 5-6). pap. (978-1-875739-69-1(6)) Wizard Bks.

Kids Publishing Science Staff. Catch a Wave: The Story of Sound & Light. 1999. (J). (gr. 2-6). pap. 6.95 (978-1-891418-16-7(5)) Science Kids.

Lakeshore Learning Materials Staff. Edward the Emu Packet. 2000. (J). pap. 19.95 (978-1-929255-25-2(X)) Lakeshore Learning Materials.

S

Lakeshore Learning Materials Staff, contrib. by. Henny Penny Packet. 2000. (J). pap. 19.95 (978-1-929255-21-4(7)) Lakeshore Learning Materials.

Llewellyn, Claire. Sound. 2005. (Illus.). 24p. (YA). (gr. 1 up). lib. bdg. 22.80 (978-1-932889-37-6(X)) Sea-To-Sea Pubns.

—Sound & Hearing. 2005. (Illus.). 24p. (J). (gr. 1-4). lib. bdg. (978-1-84234-332-6(7) , Cherrytree Books) Evans Publishing Group.

MacDonald, Ross. Achoo! Bang! Crash! The Noisy Alphabet. MacDonald, Ross, illus. rev. ed. 2003. (Illus.). 32p. (J). (ps-3). 23.90 (978-0-7613-2900-8(5)) Roaring Brook Pr.

Manolis, Kay. Sound. 2007. (Illus.). 24p. (J). lib. bdg. 19.95 (978-1-60014-099-0(8)) Bellwether Media.

Mason, Adrienne. Sound Off. Cupples, Pat, illus. 2002. (Lu & Clancy Ser.). 40p. (J). (gr. k-3). (978-1-55337-059-8(7)); (978-1-55337-058-1(9)) Kids Can Pr., Ltd.

Merrick, Patrick. Ticks. 2006. (New Naturebooks). (Illus.). 32p. (J). (gr. 1-5). 27.07 (978-1-59296-651-6(9)) Child's World, Inc.

Mondello, Cindy, ed. Investigating Science - Light & Sound. 2000. 48p. 9.95 (978-1-56234-437-5(4) , Mailbox Bks., The) Education Ctr., Inc.

Morgan, Sally. Sound. 2007. (J). (***978-1-4034-9928-8(4)***); pap. (***978-1-4034-9936-3(5)***) Heinemann Library.

Murray, Julie. Sound & Hearing. 2007. (First Science Ser.). (Illus.). 24p. (J). 21.35 (978-1-59679-831-1(9) , Buddy Bks.) ABDO Publishing Co.

My TakeAlong Li, ed. Farm Animals. 2007. (My Take-along Library). 120p. (J). (ps-k). bds. 14.95 (***978-0-7696-5559-8(9)***) School Specialty Publishing.

Olien, Becky. Sound. 2002. (Bridgestone Science Library). (Illus.). 24p. (J). (gr. 1-2). lib. bdg. 18.60 (978-0-7368-1407-2(8) , Bridgestone Bks.) Capstone Pr., Inc.

Parker, Steve. Light & Sound. 2000. (Science Fact Files Ser.). (Illus.). 48p. (J). (gr. 4-7). lib. bdg. 27.12 (978-0-7398-1011-8(1)) Raintree.

—Making Waves: Sound. 2004. (Illus.). 56p. (J). lib. bdg. (978-1-4034-4814-9(0)) Heinemann Library.

—Making Waves: Sound. 2004. (Illus.). 56p. (J). (gr. 6-8). pap. 8.90 (978-1-4034-6420-0(0)) Heinemann Library.

—Sound. 2004. (Science View Ser.). (Illus.). 32p. (J). (gr. 4-8). 28.00 (978-0-7910-8210-2(5) , Chelsea Hse.) Facts On File, Inc.

Pettigrew, Mark. Music & Sound. 2004. (J). lib. bdg. (978-1-932799-25-5(7)) Stargazer Bks.

Pfeffer, Wendy. Sounds All Around. Keller, Holly, illus. 1999. (Let's-Read-&-Find-Out Science Bks.). 32p. (J). (ps-1). pap. 5.99 (978-0-06-445177-2(1) , Harper Trophy) HarperCollins Pubs.

Pipe, Jim. Noisy Animals. 2007. (J). (***978-1-59604-160-8(9)***) Stargazer Bks.

Pipe, Jim. Sound & Hearing: Make a Noise! 2005. (Science Starters Ser.). (Illus.). 32p. (J). (gr. 1-4). lib. bdg. 27.10 (978-1-59604-016-8(5)) Stargazer Bks.

Prentice Hall Science Explorer: Sound & Light. stu. ed. 14.97 (978-0-13-115101-7(0)) Prentice Hall (Schl. Div.).

Prentice-Hall Staff. Sound & Light. 2nd ed. (J). stu. ed. 7.97 (978-0-13-400565-2(1)); pap., act. bk. ed. (978-0-13-400581-2(3)) Prentice Hall (Schl. Div.).

Que sonidos hay? Science, 6 vols.Tr. of What Kind of Sound? Science. (SPA.). (gr. k-2). 28.95 (978-0-7368-3130-7(4) , Yellow Umbrella Bks.) Capstone Pr., Inc.

Randolph, Joanne. Sounds in My World. 2006. (My World of Science Ser.). (J). 16.00 (978-1-4042-3287-7(7) , PowerKids Pr.) Rosen Publishing Group, Inc., The.

—Sounds in My World: Los Sonidos en Mi Mundo. 2006. (My World of Science/ Mi mundo y la Ciencia Ser.). (ENG & SPA.). (J). 16.00 (978-1-4042-3318-8(0) , PowerKids Pr.) Rosen Publishing Group, Inc., The.

Rau, Dana Meachen. So Many Sounds. Sorra, Kristin, illus. 2001. (Rookie Reader Skill Set Ser.). 24p. (J). (gr. k-2). pap. 4.95 (978-0-516-27290-0(X) , Children's Pr.) Scholastic Library Publishing.

—So Many Sounds. 2001. (gr. k-3). lib. bdg. 12.95 (978-0-613-54672-0(5)) Tandem Library Bks.

Riley, Peter D. Changing Sounds. 2007. (J). (***978-1-59920-023-1(6)***) Smart Apple Media.

—Sound. Moller, Ray, photos by. 2002. (Everyday Science Ser.). (Illus.). 32p. (J). (gr. 1 up). lib. bdg. 23.33 (978-0-8368-3253-2(1)) Stevens, Gareth Inc.

—Sound & Vibrations. 2005. (Making Sense of Science Ser.). (Illus.). 32p. (J). (gr. 4-7). lib. bdg. 27.10 (978-1-58340-718-9(9)) Smart Apple Media.

Rogers, K. Light, Sound & Electricity. 2004. (Library of Science Ser.). 64p. (J). lib. bdg. 17.95 (978-1-58086-376-6(0)) EDC Publishing.

Rosinsky, Natalie M. Sound: Loud, Soft, High, & Low. John, Matthew, illus. 2004. (Amazing Science Ser.). 24p. (C). (gr. k-4). 22.60 (978-1-4048-0016-8(6)) Picture Window Bks.

Rosinsky, Natalie M. & John, Matthew. El Sonido: Fuerte, Suave, Alto y Bajo. John, Matthew, illus. 2007. (ENG & SPA.). (J). lib. bdg. (***978-1-4048-3229-9(7)***) Picture Window Bks.

Ross, Katharine. The Little Quiet Book. Hirashima, Jean, illus. 2002. (Chunky Book(R) Ser.). 12p. (J). (gr. k-ps). bds. 4.99 (978-0-375-82398-5(0) , Random Hse. Bks. for Young Readers) Random Hse. Children's Bks.

Rothstein, Ruth S., et al. ARIES Exploring Waves: Ripple Tanks, Vibrations & Sound: Science Journal. 2000. (Aries Ser.). (Illus.). (J). pap. 3.80 (978-1-57091-254-2(8)) Charlesbridge Publishing, Inc.

Royston, Angela. Sound & Hearing. (Illus.). 32p. (J). (gr. k-2). 2002. pap. 6.95 (978-1-4034-0045-1(8) , 91489); 2001. lib. bdg. 21.36 (978-1-58810-246-1(7)) Heinemann Library.

—Sound & Hearing. 2002. (gr. k-3). lib. bdg. 15.25 (978-0-613-90102-4(9)) Tandem Library Bks.

Sadler, Wendy. Sound: Listen Up! 2005. (Raintree Perspectives Ser.). (Illus.). 32p. (J). (978-1-4109-1552-8(2)); pap. (978-1-4109-1560-3(3)) Steck-Vaughn.

Schaefer, Lola M. The Way Things Move Series, 6 bks., Set. 1999. (Illus.). (J). (ps-2). pap. 79.50 (978-0-516-29665-4(5) , Children's Pr.) Scholastic Library Publishing.

Science & Technology for Children BOOKS: Sound. 2007. (J). (***978-1-933008-42-4(3)***) National Science Resources Ctr.

Science & Technology for Children BOOKS: Sound Set. 2007. (J). 127.60 (***978-1-933008-46-2(6)***) National Science Resources Ctr.

Science Stories Foss Spanish Physics of Sound EA CR05. 2005. (J). (978-1-59242-587-7(9)) Delta Education, LLC.

Sian Revision Sound Vibrations. 2004. (J). (978-1-59242-075-9(3)) Delta Education, LLC.

Snedden, Robert. Light & Sound. 1999. (Smart Science Ser.). (Illus.). 32p. (J). (gr. 3-5). lib. bdg. 22.79 (978-1-57572-870-4(2)) Heinemann Library.

Somervill, Barbara A. Ticks: Digging for Blood. 2008. (J). lib. bdg. (***978-1-4042-3800-8(X)*** , PowerKids Pr.) Rosen Publishing Group, Inc., The.

Sound. (Make it Work! Ser.). 42p. (J). (gr. 4-8). pap. (978-1-882210-46-6(8)) Action Publishing, Inc.

Sound. 2001. (Physical Science Ser.). (J). (gr. k-12). vinyl bd. 4.95 (978-1-58845-114-9(3)); 32p. (gr. 4-5). 4.99 (978-1-56822-952-2(6) , IF20859) School Specialty Publishing.

Steck-Vaughn Staff. Light & Sound: Classroom Edition. 1999. (Illus.). (J). pap. (978-0-7398-1925-8(9)) Steck-Vaughn.

—Light & Sound: Ontario MOE Hybrid Version. 1999. (Illus.). (J). pap. 9.33 incl. cd-rom (978-0-7398-1271-6(8)) Raintree.

Stiegemeyer, Julie. Things I Hear in Church. Mitter, Kathy, illus. 2003. (ENG.). 20p. (J). bds. 4.99 (978-0-7586-0125-4(5)) Concordia Publishing Hse.

Stille, Darlene R. Sound. 2001. (Simply Science Ser.). (Illus.). 32p. (J). (gr. 3 up). lib. bdg. 19.93 (978-0-7565-0092-4(3)) Compass Point Bks.

Stradling, Jan. Sounds all Around: Level K, 6 vols., Vol. 2. (First Explorers Ser.). 24p. (gr. 1-2). 34.95 (978-0-7699-1464-0(0)) Shortland Pubns. (U. S. A.) Inc.

Tocci, Salvatore. Experiments with Sound. 2002. 13.75 (978-0-606-22878-7(0)) Tandem Library Bks.

Trumbauer, Lisa. All about Sound. 2004. (Rookie Read-About Science Ser.). 32p. (J). (gr. 1-2). pap. 4.95 (978-0-516-25847-8(8) , Children's Pr.) Scholastic Library Publishing.

Wadsworth, Pamela. Golwg Gyntaf Ar Sain a Cherddoriaeth. 2005. (WEL., Illus.). 24p. pap. (978-1-85596-247-7(0)) Dref Wen.

Walker, Sally M. El Sonido (Sound) 2007. (Libros de Energía para madrugadores (Early Bird Energy) Ser.). (SPA.). 48p. (J). (gr. 2-5). lib. bdg. 26.60 (***978-0-8225-7722-5(4)*** , Ediciones Lerner) Lerner Publishing Group.

Weber, Lou, ed. Baby Einstein Music Note Sound Book. 2004. 10p. (J). bds. 9.98 (978-1-4127-3495-0(9) , 7262600) Publications International, Ltd.

—Blues Room Little Sound Book. 2004. 10p. (J). bds. 9.98 (978-1-4127-3366-3(9) , 7251400) Publications International, Ltd.

—Clifford Baby Duck Day Little Sound Book. 2005. 10p. (J). bds. 9.98 (978-1-4127-3351-9(0) , 7249900) Publications International, Ltd.

What Is Noisy?, 6 Packs. (gr. 1-2). 22.00 (978-0-7635-9095-6(9)) Rigby Education.

What Is the Sound? 2003. (Bear in the Big Blue House Ser.). (Illus.). 16p. (J). (ps-k). pap., act. bk. ed. 4.99 (978-1-57768-711-5(6)) School Specialty Publishing.

What Kind of Sound? 2006. (Yellow Umbrella Science Ser.). 8,16p. (J). 6.50 (978-0-7368-1706-6(9)) Red Brick Learning.

Whitehouse, Patricia. Loud Sounds, Soft Sounds. 2007. (J). (978-1-60044-191-2(2)) Rourke Publishing, LLC.

Wood, Robert W. Sound Fundamentals. 1999. (Funtastic Science Activities for Kids Ser.). (Illus.). 160p. (YA). (gr. 4-7). 16.95 (978-0-7910-4840-5(3) , Chelsea Hse.) Facts On File, Inc.

Wright, Lynne. The Science of Noise. 1999. (Science World Ser.). (Illus.). 32p. (J). (gr. 2-5). lib. bdg. 25.69 (978-0-7398-1324-9(2)) Raintree.

SOUND—EXPERIMENTS

Baker, Wendy, et al. Sound. (Make It Work! Ser.). (Illus.). 48p. (J). pap. 15.95 (978-0-590-74522-2(0)) Scholastic, Inc.

—Sound. 2004. (Make It Work! Science Ser.). (Illus.). 48p. (gr. 3-6). (J). pap. 6.95 (978-1-58728-361-1(1)); 12.95 (978-1-58728-374-1(3)) T&N Children's Publishing. (Two Can Publishing).

Bangs & Twangs: Science Fun with Sound. 2007. (J). pap. 7.95 (***978-0-8225-7022-6(X)*** , First Avenue Editions) Lerner Publishing Group.

Challoner, Jack & Angliss, Sarah. Sound & Light. Le Jars, David, illus. 2001. (Hands-On Science Ser.). 40p. (J). (gr. 3-5). pap. 6.95 (978-0-7534-5347-6(9) , Kingfisher) Houghton Mifflin Co. Trade & Reference Div.

Clark, John Owen Edward. Light & Sound. 2006. (Real World Science Ser.). (Illus.). 32p. (J). 24.67 (978-0-8368-6306-2(2)) Stevens, Gareth Inc.

Cobb, Allan B. Super Science Projects about Sound. 2005. (Psyched for Science Ser.). (Illus.). 48p. (YA). (gr. 5-8). lib. bdg. 23.95 (978-0-8239-3176-7(5) , SCSOUN) Rosen Publishing Group, Inc., The.

Cobb, Vicki. Bangs & Twangs: Science Fun with Sound. Haefele, Steve, illus. 2000. (Science Fun with Vicki Cobb Ser.). 48p. (gr. 3-6). lib. bdg. 24.90 (978-0-7613-1571-1(3) , Millbrook Pr.) Lerner Publishing Group.

Dalton, Cindy Devine. Sound. 2001. (How Can I Experiment With? Ser.). (Illus.). 32p. (gr. 1-4). 19.95 (978-1-58952-015-8(7)) Rourke Publishing, LLC.

DiSpezio, Michael A. Awesome Experiments in Light & Sound. 2006. (Illus.). 160p. (J). pap. 6.95 (978-1-4027-2372-8(5)) Sterling Publishing Co., Inc.

Dixon, Malcolm & Smith, Karen. Sound & Music. 1998. (Young Scientists Ser.). (Illus.). 32p. (J). (ps-3). lib. bdg. 16.95 (978-1-887068-72-7(4)) Smart Apple Media.

Gardner, Robert. Jazzy Science Projects with Sound & Music. LaBaff, Tom, illus. 2006. (Fantastic Physical Science Experiments Ser.). 48p. (J). lib. bdg. 23.93 (978-0-7660-2588-2(8) , Enslow Elementary) Enslow Pubs., Inc.

—Light, Sound, & Waves Science Fair Projects Using Sunglasses, Guitars, & Other Stuff. 2004. (Physics! Best Science Projects Ser.). (Illus.). 128p. (J). lib. bdg. 26.60 (978-0-7660-2126-6(2)) Enslow Pubs., Inc.

—Science Projects about Sound. 2000. (Science Projects Ser.). (Illus.). 112p. (YA). (gr. 6-12). lib. bdg. 26.60 (978-0-7660-1166-3(6)) Enslow Pubs., Inc.

Gardner, Robert. Sound Projects with a Music Lab You Can Build. 2008. (Build-a-Lab! Science Experiments Ser.). (Illus.). 104p. (J). (gr. 5 up). lib. bdg. 31.93 (***978-0-7660-2809-8(7)***) Enslow Pubs., Inc.

Glover, David. Sound & Light: Science Facts & Experiments. 2002. (Young Discoverers Ser.). (Illus.). 32p. (J). (gr. k-3). pap. 7.95 (978-0-7534-5512-8(9) , Kingfisher) Houghton Mifflin Co. Trade & Reference Div.

—Sound & Music. 2001. (Experiments in Science Ser.). (Illus.). (J). (978-0-7894-7461-2(1)) Dorling Kindersley Publishing, Inc.

Lauw, Darlene. Sound. 2002. (gr. 3-6). lib. bdg. 16.40 (978-0-613-52910-5(3)) Tandem Library Bks.

Lauw, Darlene & Puay, Lim Cheng. Sound. 2002. (Science Alive! Ser.). (Illus.). 32p. (J). (gr. 4-5). pap. (978-0-7787-0608-3(7)); lib. bdg. (978-0-7787-0562-8(5)) Crabtree Publishing Co.

Merrill, Amy French. Everyday Physical Science Experiments with Light. 2006. (Tony Stead Nonfiction Independent Reading Collection). pap. (978-1-4042-5679-8(2)) Rosen Publishing Group, Inc., The.

—Everyday Physical Science Experiments with Light & Sound. 2002. (Science Surprises Ser.). (Illus.). 24p. (J). lib. bdg. 19.95 (978-0-8239-5804-7(3) , PowerKids Pr.) Rosen Publishing Group, Inc., The.

Parker, Steve. The Science of Sound: Projects & Experiments with Music & Sound Waves. 2005. (Tabletop Scientist Ser.). (Illus.). 32p. (J). (gr. 4-7). lib. bdg. 29.29 (978-1-4034-7281-6(5)) Heinemann Library.

—The Science of Sound: Projects with Experiments with Music & Sound Waves. 2005. (Illus.). 32p. (J). pap. (978-1-4034-7288-5(2)) Heinemann Library.

—Sound. 2004. (Science View Ser.). (Illus.). 32p. (J). (gr. 4-8). 28.00 (978-0-7910-8210-2(5) , Chelsea Hse.) Facts On File, Inc.

Searle, Bobbi. Sound. 2002. (gr. 3-6). lib. bdg. 17.60 (978-0-613-55903-4(7)) Tandem Library Bks.

Spilsbury, Richard & Spilsbury, Louise. What Is Sound? Exploring Science with Hands-On Activities. 2008. (In Touch with Basic Science Ser.). 32p. (J). (gr. 3-4). lib. bdg. 22.60 (***978-0-7660-3098-5(9)***) Enslow Pubs., Inc.

SOUND—FICTION

Ackroyd, Dorothea. What Can You Do? 1999. (Teach Me Bks.). (Illus.). 12p. (ps-k). bds. 3.95 (978-1-58185-206-6(1)) Quadrillion Media LLC.

—What Do You Hear? 1999. 3.95 (978-1-58185-204-2(5)) Quadrillion Media LLC.

Anastasio, Dina. So Scary! McCreary, Jane, illus. 2002. 16p. (J). (978-0-439-35189-8(8)) Scholastic, Inc.

Apperley, Dawn. Crash Bang, Thud! 2002. (Illus.). 25p. (J). (978-0-340-78800-4(3) , Hodder & Stoughton) Hodder General Publishing Division.

—Crash Bang, Thud! 2002. (Illus.). 32p. (J). pap. 9.99 (978-0-340-78801-1(1) , Hodder & Stoughton) Hodder General Publishing Division GBR. *Dist:* Trafalgar Square Publishing.

Arthur, Clint. Bleep Blop Bloop, 1. Schedeen, Minnie, illus. 2006. 24p. (J). per. 8.99 net. (978-1-4276-0218-3(2)) Aardvark Global Publishing.

Ashman, Linda. Starry Safari. Mack, Jeff, illus. 2005. 40p. (J). 16.00 (978-0-15-204766-5(2)) Harcourt Children's Bks.

Bedford, David & Worthington, Leonie. Who's Laughing. 2007. (Illus.). 16p. (J). (ps-k). 9.95 (***978-1-921049-40-8(5)***) Little Hare Bks. AUS. *Dist:* Independent Pubs. Group.

Bee, William. And the Train Goes... Bee, William, illus. 2007. (Illus.). 32p. (J). (ps-1). 15.99 (978-0-7636-3248-9(1)) Candlewick Pr.

Beil, Karen Magnuson. Mooove Over! A Book about Counting by Twos. Meisel, Paul, tr. Meisel, Paul, illus. 2004. 32p. (J). (gr. k-3). tchr. ed. 16.95 (978-0-8234-1736-0(0)) Holiday Hse., Inc.

Bentley, Dawn. Buzz-Buzz, Busy Bees: An Animal Sounds Book. Cahoon, Heather, illus. 2004. 24p. (J). 10.95 (978-0-689-86848-1(0) , Little Simon) Simon & Schuster Children's Publishing.

Blanchett, Marie. Ella Nepa-llu. Smart, B. George & Horesh, David, illus. 1998. Tr. of Air a Sound. (ESK.). 20p. (J). (gr. k-3). pap. 8.00 (978-1-58084-043-9(4)) Lower Kuskokwim Schl. District.

Bock, Lee. Oh Crumps/ Ay, Caramba. de la Vega, Eida, tr. Midgett, Morgan, illus. 2006. (SPA.). (J). 4.99 (978-0-9770906-3-1(9)) Raven Tree Pr.

Boynton, Sandra. Sandra Boynton's Moo, Baa, la la La! Book & Rattle. Boynton, Sandra, illus. 2009. 16p. (J). bds. 16.99 (***978-1-4169-5035-6(4)*** , Little Simon) Simon & Schuster Children's Publishing.

Carlson, Lavelle. EEK! I Hear A Squeak & the Scurrying of Little Feet. Loehr, Jenny, illus. 2006. 28p. (J). 19.95 (978-0-9725803-8-0(7)) Children's Publishing.

Choo Choo. (Dora the Explorer). (Illus.). 10p. (J). bds. 9.98 (978-0-7853-8278-2(X) , 7182700) Publications International, Ltd.

Cook, Sherry & Johnson, Terri. Susie Sound, 26. Kuhn, Jesse, illus. l.t. ed. 2006. 32p. (J). 7.99 (978-1-933815-18-3(3) , Quirkles, The) Creative 3, LLC.

Cowley, Rich. BRRRM! Woosh. Cowley, Rich, illus. 2001. (Snappy Sounds Ser.: No. 4). (Illus.). 24p. (J). (gr. k-ps). reprint ed. bds. 3.95 (978-1-55209-038-1(8)) Annick Pr., Ltd. CAN. *Dist:* Firefly Bks., Ltd.

—Ring! Tick Tock. Cowley, Rich, illus. 2001. (Snappy Sounds Ser.). (Illus.). 24p. (J). (gr. k-ps). reprint ed. bds. 3.95 (978-1-55209-036-7(1)) Firefly Bks., Ltd.

—Snap! Snap! Buzz Buzz. Cowley, Rich, illus. 2001. (Snappy Sounds Ser.). (Illus.). 24p. (J). (gr. k-ps). reprint ed. bds. 3.95 (978-1-55209-032-9(9)) Annick Pr., Ltd. CAN. *Dist:* Firefly Bks., Ltd.

Crazy Animals. 2002. (Tap My Nose Ser.). (J). (ps-k). 4.98 (978-0-7525-8726-4(9)) Parragon, Inc.

Crum, Shutta. All on a Sleepy Night. Daigneault, Sylvie, illus. 2002. 28p. (J). (ps-3). 15.95 (978-0-7737-3315-2(9)) Stoddart Kids CAN. *Dist:* Fitzhenry & Whiteside, Ltd.

Cumberbatch, Judy. Can You Hear the Sea? Wilson-Max, Ken, illus. 2006. 32p. (J). (gr. k-3). 15.95 (978-1-58234-703-5(4) , Bloomsbury Children) Bloomsbury Publishing.

Dalmatian Press Staff. Old Macdonald Had a Farm: Musical Book to Color. (Musical Book to Color Ser.). 32p. (J). pap. 3.99 (978-1-4037-0715-4(4)) Dalmatian Pr.

Davies, Jacqueline. The Night Is Singing Lullabies. Brooker, Kyrsten, illus. 2006. 40p. (J). (ps). 16.99 (978-0-8037-3004-5(7) , Dial) Penguin Group (USA) Inc.

DiPucchio, Kelly. Dinosnores. Goembel, Ponder, illus. 2005. 32p. (J). (ps-1). lib. bdg. 16.89 (978-0-06-051578-2(3)); 15.99 (978-0-06-051577-5(5)) HarperCollins Pubs.

Disney Publishing Staff. What's That Sound?, 15 vols. 2003. (It's Fun to Learn Ser.). (Illus.). 32p. (J). (ps-3). 3.99 (978-1-57973-132-8(5)) Advance Pubs. LLC.

Dorling Kindersley Publishing Staff. My Big Noisy Book: Use 8 Fun Sounds to Complete the Story! 2001. (DK Early Learners Ser.). (Illus.). 12p. (J). pap. (978-0-7513-1419-9(6)) Dorling Kindersley Publishing, Inc.

Dorling Kindersley Publishing Staff, ed. Old MacDonald Had a Farm. 2004. (Baby Fun Ser.). (Illus.). 16p. (J). bds. 5.99 (978-0-7566-0591-9(1)) Dorling Kindersley Publishing, Inc.

Doyle, Malachy. Rory's Lost His Voice. Semple, David, illus. 2005. 24p. (J). lib. bdg. 22.65 (***978-1-59646-714-9(2)***) Dingles & Co.

Edwards, Pamela Duncan & Cole, Henry. Slop Goes the Soup: A Noisy Warthog Word Book. 2001. (Illus.). 32p. (ps-1). 14.99 (978-0-7868-0469-6(6)); 15.49 (978-0-7868-2411-3(5)) Hyperion Bks. for Children.

Engineering is Elementary Team. Kwame's Sound: An Acoustical Engineering Story. 2005. (J). lib. bdg. 15.99 (***978-0-9774084-2-9(6)***) Museum of Science.

Fajerman, Deborah. How to Speak Moo! 2002. (gr. k-3). lib. bdg. 14.10 (978-0-613-87756-5(X)) Tandem Library Bks.

Fernandes, Eugenie. Busy Little Mouse. Fernandes, Kim, illus. 2006. 24p. 6.95 (978-1-55453-027-4(X)) Kids Can Pr., Ltd. CAN. *Dist:* Wybel Marketing Group.

Field, Elaine. Sounds (Cuddly Cuffs with Hang Tag) (Cuddly Cuffs Ser.). (Illus.). 12p. (J). tchr. ed. 5.95 (978-1-58925-708-5(1) , tiger tales) ME Media LLC.

Fleming, Denise. The Cow Who Clucked. 2006. (Illus.). (J). (***978-1-4156-9208-0(4)***) Holt, Henry & Co.

Forhan, Mary C. & Forhan, Mary C. Introduction to Letter Sounds: Fun, Active, Multisensory. 2003. (Illus.). 88p. spiral bd. 59.95 (978-0-9744575-0-5(7)) Butterfly Park Educational Materials, Inc.

Gershator, Phillis. Listen, Listen. Jay, Alison, illus. 2008. 32p. (J). (ps-4). 16.99 (***978-1-84686-084-3(9)***) Barefoot Bks., Inc.

Good Morning, Who's Snoring? Individual Title Six-Packs. (Story Steps Ser.). (gr. k-2). 32.00 (978-0-7635-9619-4(1)) Rigby Education.

Harder Tangvald, Christine. Whoo! Moo! Cock-a-Doodle-Doo! Conteh-Morgan, Jane, illus. 2000. 24p. (J). (ps-k). bds. 7.99 (978-0-570-07096-2(1)) Concordia Publishing Hse.

Harry, Rebecca, illus. Little Chimp. 2007. (Noisy Jungle Babies Ser.). 8p. (J). bds. 5.99 (978-0-7641-6034-9(6)) Barron's Educational Series, Inc.

—Little Elephant. 2007. (Noisy Jungle Babies Ser.). 8p. (J). bds. 5.99 (978-0-7641-6035-6(4)) Barron's Educational Series, Inc.

—Little Lion. 2007. (Noisy Jungle Babies Ser.). 8p. (J). bds. 5.99 (978-0-7641-6036-3(2)) Barron's Educational Series, Inc.

—Little Zebra. 2007. (Noisy Jungle Babies Ser.). 8p. (J). bds. 5.99 (978-0-7641-6037-0(0)) Barron's Educational Series, Inc.

Harshman, Marc. All the Way to Morning. Davalos, Felipe, illus. 1999. (Accelerated Reader Bks.). 32p. (J). (ps-k). 15.95 (978-0-7614-5042-9(4) , Cavendish Children's Bks.) Cavendish, Marshall Corp.

—All the Way to Morning. Davalos, Felipe, illus. 2006. (J). per. 7.95 (978-1-891852-49-7(3)) Quarrier Pr.

Hays, Anna Jane. The Pup Speaks Up: A Phonics Reader. Petrone, Valeria, illus. 2003. (Early Step into Reading Ser.). 32p. (J). (ps-1). pap. 3.99 (978-0-375-81232-3(6) , Random Hse. Bks. for Young Readers) Random Hse. Children's Bks.

Hearn, Emily. Woosh, I Hear a Sound. Collins, Heather, illus. 2003. (Annikins Ser.: Vol. 4). 24p. (J). (ps-2). pap. 0.99 (978-0-920303-21-4(8)) Annick Pr., Ltd. CAN. *Dist:* Firefly Bks., Ltd.

Hendry, Diana. Very Noisy Night. 2001. (gr. k-3). lib. bdg. 14.15 (978-0-613-44427-9(2)) Tandem Library Bks.

Heo, Yumi. One Afternoon. 2000. (Metro Reading Program Ser.). (J). (gr. k). 7.98 (978-1-58120-971-6(1)); 45.95 (978-1-58830-029-4(3)) Metropolitan Teaching & Learning Co.

Hofer, Charles. Construction Zone! Little People. Durk, Jim, illus. 10p. (J). bds. 7.98 (978-0-7853-4791-0(7)) Publications International, Ltd.

Jennings, Sharon. Don't Wake the Baby. Zaman, Farida, illus. 2002. 24p. (J). (ps-k). bds. (978-1-55041-687-9(1)) Fitzhenry & Whiteside, Ltd.

Ka Hulu Kohukohu. 2003. (J). 5.99 (978-0-89610-463-1(X)) Island Heritage Publishing.

Kidd, Ron. Bookee Presents Colors, Shapes & Sounds. Nord, Mary, illus. (Talking Book Adventures Ser.). 12p. (J). (ps up). 16.95 (978-0-9627001-1-8(8)) Futech Educational Products, Inc.

Krensky, Stephen. Noah's Bark. Rogé, illus. 2008. (J). lib. bdg. (***978-0-8225-7645-7(7)*** , Carolrhoda Bks.) Lerner Publishing Group.

Lane, Leonie. The Bushtails & other Stories. 2007. 228p. per. (***978-1-84685-592-4(6)*** , Exposure Publishing) Meadow Bks.

Losordo, Stephen. Cow Moo Me. Conteh-Morgan, Jane, illus. 1998. (Growing Tree Ser.). 16p. (J). (ps up). 5.95 (978-0-694-01108-7(8) , Harper Festival) HarperCollins Pubs.

MacDonald, Amy. Little Beaver & the Echo. Fox-Davies, Sarah, illus. 1998. 32p. (J). (ps-3). pap. 6.99 (978-0-698-11628-3(3) , Putnam Juvenile) Penguin Group (USA) Inc.

MacLennan, Cathy. Chicky Chicky Chook Chook. MacLennan, Cathy, illus. 2007. (Illus.). 32p. (J). (ps-1). 12.95 (978-1-905417-40-7(3)) Boxer Bks., Ltd. GBR. *Dist:* Sterling Publishing Co., Inc.

Matthews, Derek. Moo! Noisy Pop-Up Fun, 5 Fun Animal Sounds. 2004. (Snappy Ser.). (Illus.). 10p. (ps-k). 12.95 (978-1-59223-214-7(0)) Advantage Pubs. Group.

—Noisy Pop-Up Fun: Snappy Sounds, Roar. 2004. (Snappy Sounds Ser.). (Illus.). 10p. 12.95 (978-1-59223-213-0(2)) Advantage Pubs. Group.

Matthews, Derek. Once upon a Time: Noisy Pop-up Fun with Fun Fairy-Tale Sounds. 2007. (Snappy Sounds Ser.). (Illus.). 10p. (J). 12.95 (***978-1-59223-716-6(9)*** , Silver Dolphin Bks.) Advantage Pubs. Group.

Mayer, Mercer. Camping Out. 2002. (Little Critter Ser.). (Illus.). 24p. (J). (ps-k). pap. 3.95 (978-1-57768-806-8(6)) School Specialty Publishing.

—Camping Out. 2001. (ps-2). lib. bdg. 11.80 (978-0-613-79359-9(5)) Tandem Library Bks.

McGee, Marni. The Noisy Farm. Shearing, Leonie, tr. Shearing, Leonie, illus. 2004. 32p. (J). (ps-1). 15.95 (978-1-58234-879-7(0) , Bloomsbury Children) Bloomsbury Publishing.

McTaggart, Stephen & McTaggart, Debra. Bookee's Sounds Around. Nord, Mary, illus. (Talking Book Adventures Ser.). 12p. (J). (ps up). 16.95 (978-0-9627001-0-1(X)) Futech Educational Products, Inc.

Mysak, Mary. Little Train! Stickley, Kelly, illus. 2004. 16p. (J). 7.50 (978-0-9762274-0-3(1)) Helping Hands Children's Bks.

O'Connell, Rebecca. The Baby Goes Beep. Wilson-Max, Ken, illus. rev. ed. 2003. 32p. (J). (ps up). 22.90 (978-0-7613-2867-4(X)); 14.95 (978-0-7613-1789-0(9)) Roaring Brook Pr.

Oppenheim, Joanne. Could It Be? Schindler, S. D., illus. 1998. (Bank Street Reader Collection). 48p. (J). (gr. 1-3). lib. bdg. 22.60 (978-0-8368-1770-6(2)) Stevens, Gareth Inc.

Palatini, Margie. Moo Who? Graves, Keith, illus. 40p. (J). (ps-2). 2007. pap. 6.99 (***978-0-06-000107-0(0)*** , Harper Trophy); 2004. 15.99 (978-0-06-000105-6(4) , Tegen, Katherine Bks); 2004. lib. bdg 16.89 (978-0-06-000106-3(2)) HarperCollins Pubs.

Pearson, Debora. Big City Song! Reed, Lynn Rowe, illus. 2006. 32p. (J). 16.95 (978-0-8234-1988-3(6)) Holiday Hse., Inc.

Pearson, Tracey Campbell. Bob. Pearson, Tracey Campbell, illus. 2002. (Illus.). 32p. (J). (ps-1). 16.00 (978-0-374-39957-3(3) , Farrar, Straus & Giroux (BYR)) Farrar, Straus & Giroux.

—Bob. Pearson, Tracey Campbell, illus. 2006. (Illus.). 32p. (J). reprint ed. pap. 6.95 (978-0-374-40871-8(8)) Macmillan.

Peep and Big Wide World & Galvin, Laura. Quacks Masterpiece. 2006. 28p. pap. 2.99 (978-1-59249-550-4(8)) Soundprints.

—Whats That Sound. 2006. 28p. pap. 2.99 (978-1-59249-553-5(2)) Soundprints.

Perkins, Al. The Ear Book. Payne, Henry, illus. 2007. 36p. (J). (gr. k-1). 8.99 (978-0-375-84251-1(9)); lib. bdg. 12.99 (978-0-375-94251-8(3)) Random Hse. Children's Bks. (Random Hse. Bks. for Young Readers).

Perkins, Lynne Rae. Snow Music. Perkins, Lynne Rae, illus. 2003. (Illus.). 40p. (J). 15.99 (978-0-06-623956-9(7)); lib. bdg. 16.89 (978-0-06-623958-3(3)) HarperCollins Pubs.

—Snow Music. 2000. pap. 4.95 (978-0-06-443875-9(9)) HarperCollins Pubs.

Peters, Polly. The Ding-Dong Bag. Stockham, Jess, illus. 2006. 32p. pap. 7.99 (978-1-84643-015-2(1)) Child's Play-International.

Piglet's Big Movie: Interactive Play-a-Sound. 2003. per. (978-0-7853-8913-2(X)) Publications International, Ltd.

Pocahontas: Who's Making that Sound? (My First Read Along Ser.). (Illus.). (J). 7.99 incl. audio (978-1-55723-961-7(4)) Walt Disney Records.

Powers, John. The Lion Who Couldn't Roar. Colavecchio, Alan, illus. 2002. 32p. (J). 13.95 (978-1-929039-10-4(7)) Ambassador Bks., Inc.

Reidy, Hannah. All Sorts of Noises. Dodd, Emma, illus. 2005. (All Sort of Things Ser.). 24p. (C). (gr. k-3). 22.60 (978-1-4048-1064-8(1)) Picture Window Bks.

Rozen, Anna. The Merchant of Noises. Scarbrough, Carl W., tr. from FRE. Avril, Francois, illus. 2006. 28p. (J). (gr. k-5). 18.95 (***978-1-56792-321-6(6)***) Godine, David R. Pub.

Rundstrom, T. S. Cherry the Sheep Finds Her Sheep Sound. Miller, Bryan & Marshall, H. Keene, illus. 2002. (J). per. 16.00 (978-1-932062-10-6(6)) Hability Solution Services, Inc.

Scarry, Richard. Splish-Splash.Tr. of Splish-Splash. (SPA., Illus.). (J). pap. 6.95 (978-950-04-0676-5(4)) Emecé Editores S.A. ARG. *Dist:* Planeta Publishing Corp.

Seuss, Dr. Gerald McBoing Boing. Seuss, Dr., illus. 2004. (Little Golden Book Ser.). (Illus.). 24p. (J). (gr. k-k). 2.99 (978-0-375-82721-1(8) , Golden Bks.) Random Hse. Children's Bks.

—Gerald McBoing Boing. Crawford, Mel, illus. 2000. 32p. (J). (gr. k-3). 12.95 (978-0-679-89140-6(4) , Random Hse. Bks. for Young Readers) Random Hse. Children's Bks.

Shapiro, Arnold. Mice Squeak, We Speak. 2000. (ps-2). lib. bdg. 14.15 (978-0-613-30029-2(7)) Tandem Library Bks.

—Mice Squeak, We Speak. de Paola, Tomie, illus. 2000. (978-0-606-20364-7(8)) Tandem Library Bks.

Showers, Paul. The Listening Walk Big Book. 1999. 32p. (J). (ps-2). pap. 19.95 (978-0-06-443324-2(2)) HarperCollins Pubs.

Singer, Marilyn. Quiet Night. Manders, John, illus. 2002. 32p. (J). (gr. k-ps). 15.00 (978-0-618-12044-4(0) , Clarion Bks.) Houghton Mifflin Co. Trade & Reference Div.

Sohn, Emily. Adventures in Sound with Max Axiom, Super Scientist. Martin, Cynthia & Timmons, Anne, illus. 2007. (J). (***978-0-7368-6836-5(4)***) Capstone Pr., Inc.

Super-tuned!, 6 Packs. Vol. 26. 32p. (gr. 3-4). 44.00 (978-0-7635-4480-5(9)) Rigby Education.

Walsh, Melanie. Trinan los Monos? Walsh, Melanie, illus. 2002. Tr. of Do Monkeys Tweet?. (SPA., Illus.). 14p. (J). (gr. k-ps). bds. 5.95 (978-0-618-20318-5(4)) Houghton Mifflin Co. Trade & Reference Div.

Walton, Rick. Herd of Cows! Flock of Sheep! Olson, Julie Hansen, illus. 2002. 32p. (J). 15.95 (978-1-58685-153-8(5)) Gibbs Smith, Publisher.

Weber, Lou, ed. The Incredibles Little Sound Book. 2004. 10p. (J). bds. 9.98 (978-1-4127-3171-3(2) , 7232800) Publications International, Ltd.

Weinstein, Ellen. Everywhere the Cow Says "Moo!" Anderson, Kenneth, illus. 2008. (J). (***978-1-59078-458-7(8)***) Boyds Mills Pr.

Wells, Rosemary. Letters & Sounds. 2001. (ps-2). lib. bdg. 14.15 (978-0-613-31413-8(1)) Tandem Library Bks.

Whybrow, Ian. Noisy Way to Bed. Beeke, Tiphanie, tr. Beeke, Tiphanie, illus. 2004. 32p. (J). 16.95 (978-0-439-55689-7(9) , Levine, Arthur A. Bks.) Scholastic, Inc.

Whybrow, Ian. Say Hello to the Snowy Animals! Touch & Feel Animals on Every Page. Eaves, Edward, illus. rev. ed. 2007. 20p. 22.95 (***978-0-230-01391-9(0)*** , Macmillan Children's Bks.) Pan Macmillan GBR. *Dist:* Trans-Atlantic Pubns., Inc.

Witting, David. The Goul of the Garden. 2001. 48p. pap. 9.95 (978-0-7414-0789-4(2)) Infinity Publishing.

Woodward, Kay. Squish, Crunch, Splash! Colnaghi, Stefania, illus. 2006. (Lightning Readers Ser.). 32p. (J). pap. 3.95 (978-0-7696-4197-3(0) , Gingham Dog Pr.) School Specialty Publishing.

Wundrow, Deanna. Jungle Drum. Swan, Susan E., illus. 1999. (Our World Ser.). 24p. (gr. k-2). lib. bdg. 22.90 (978-0-7613-1270-3(6) , Millbrook Pr.) Lerner Publishing Group.

Zimmermann, Erik. Booga-Boo. 2002. (Illus.). 32p. per. 8.95 (978-0-9724680-0-8(5)) Lifevest Publishing, Inc.

SOUND—POETRY

O'Neill, Mary L. The Sound of Day: The Sound of Night. Jabar, Cynthia, illus. 1999. (J). (978-0-7894-2567-6(X)) Dorling Kindersley Publishing, Inc.

SOUND—RECORDING AND REPRODUCING

Ambrosek, Renee. Shawn Fanning: The Founder of Napster. 2006. (Internet Career Biographies Ser.). (Illus.). 112p. (YA). (gr. 7-12). lib. bdg. 31.95 (978-1-4042-0720-2(1)) Rosen Publishing Group, Inc., The.

Aronson, Virginia. The History of Motown. 2001. (African American Achievers Ser.). (Illus.). 112p. (gr. 6-12). 30.00 (978-0-7910-5814-5(X) , Chelsea Hse.) Facts On File, Inc.

Golus, Carrie. Russell Simmons. 2007. (J). lib. bdg. (***978-0-8225-7158-2(7)***) Twenty First Century Bks.

Graham, Amy. Thomas Edison: Wizard of Light & Sound. 2007. (Inventors Who Changed the World Ser.). (Illus.). 128p. (J). lib. bdg. 33.27 (978-1-59845-052-1(2) , MyReportLinks.com Bks.) Enslow Pubs., Inc.

Lommel, Cookie. Russell Simmons. 2007. (Hip-Hop Stars Ser.). 104p. (J). (gr. 6-12). 30.00 (***978-0-7910-9467-9(7)*** , Chelsea Hse.) Facts On File, Inc.

Schaefer, A. R. Making a First Recording. 2003. (Rock Music Library). (Illus.). 32p. (J). lib. bdg. 22.60 (978-0-7368-2147-6(3) , Capstone High/Low Bks.) Capstone Pr., Inc.

SOUND EFFECTS

see Sounds

SOUND WAVES

Lilly, Melinda. Sound up & Down. Thompson, Scott M., illus. 2003. 24p. (J). 20.64 (978-1-58952-644-0(9)) Rourke Publishing, LLC.

Mahaney, Ian F. Sound Waves. 2007. (Illus.). 24p. (J). (978-1-4042-2379-0(7)); pap. (978-1-4042-2189-5(1)); (gr. 4-6). lib. bdg. 21.25 (978-1-4042-3480-2(2)) Rosen Publishing Group, Inc., The. (PowerKids Pr.).

Parker, Steve. The Science of Sound: Projects & Experiments with Music & Sound Waves. 2005. (Tabletop Scientist Ser.). (Illus.). 32p. (J). (gr. 4-7). lib. bdg. 29.29 (978-1-4034-7281-6(5)) Heinemann Library.

—The Science of Sound: Projects with Experiments with Music & Sound Waves. 2005. (Illus.). 32p. (J). pap. (978-1-4034-7288-5(2)) Heinemann Library.

Riley, Peter D. Changing Sounds. 2007. (J). (***978-1-59920-023-1(6)***) Smart Apple Media.

SOUNDS

Adivina Lo Que Es: Individual 6-packs, Level 4. 2003. 23.95 (978-0-673-57868-6(2)) Celebration Pr.

Allen, Nancy Kelly. Whose Sound Is This? A Look at Animal Noises - Chirps, Clicks, & Hoots. Alderman, Derrick & Shea, Denise, illus. 2004. (Whose Is It? Ser.). 24p. (C). (gr. k-2). 22.60 (978-1-4048-0610-8(5)) Picture Window Bks.

Alphabet Soundtracks. 2003. (YA). (ps up). pap. 15.99 (978-0-7424-1538-6(4)) School Specialty Publishing.

Animal Soundtracks. 2003. (YA). (ps up). pap. 15.99 (978-0-7424-1528-7(7)) School Specialty Publishing.

Arnold, Caroline. Noisytime for Zoo Animals. 1999. (Zoo Animals Ser.). (Illus.). 32p. (J). (ps-2). 9.95 (978-1-57505-392-9(6) , Carolrhoda Bks.) Lerner Publishing Group.

—Noisytime for Zoo Animals. Hewett, Richard, illus. 1999. (Zoo Animals Ser.). 32p. (J). (ps-2). lib. bdg. 21.27 (978-1-57505-289-2(X) , Carolrhoda Bks.) Lerner Publishing Group.

Claybourne, Anna. Feel the Noise! 2005. (Illus.). 32p. (J). (978-1-4109-1948-9(X)); lib. bdg. (978-1-4109-1917-5(X)) Steck-Vaughn.

Cricket Magazine Group. Oink-Oink & Other Animal Sounds. Conteh-Morgan, Jane, illus. 2007. 20p. (J). bds. 7.95 (978-0-8126-7934-2(2)) Cricket Bks.

Dahl, Michael. Do Bears Buzz? A Book about Animal Noise. D'Antonio, Sandra, illus. 2004. (Animals All Around Ser.). 24p. (C). (gr. k-2). 22.60 (978-1-4048-0100-4(6)) Picture Window Bks.

Doudna, Kelly. Bow Wow. 2004. (Sound Words Ser.). (Illus.). 23p. (J). (ps-3). lib. bdg. 19.93 (978-1-59197-450-5(X)) ABDO Publishing Co.

—Clink Clank. 2004. (Sound Words Ser.). (Illus.). 23p. (J). (ps-3). lib. bdg. 19.93 (978-1-59197-451-2(8)) ABDO Publishing Co.

—Swish Swoosh. 2004. (Sound Words Ser.). (Illus.). 23p. (J). (ps-3). lib. bdg. 19.93 (978-1-59197-454-3(2)) ABDO Publishing Co.

—Tee Hee. 2004. (Sound Words Ser.). (Illus.). 23p. (J). (ps-3). lib. bdg. 19.93 (978-1-59197-452-9(6)) ABDO Publishing Co.

—Tick Tock. 2004. (Sound Words Ser.). (Illus.). 23p. (J). (ps-3). lib. bdg. 19.93 (978-1-59197-455-0(0) , SandCastle) ABDO Publishing Co.

Douglas, Vincent. Beginning Sounds. 2001. (Illus.). 32p. pap. 3.49 (978-1-56189-318-8(8) , American Education Publishing) School Specialty Publishing.

Gold-Vukson, Marji. The Sounds of My Jewish Year. Urban, Suzanne, illus. 2003. 12p. (J). (ps-1). 4.95 (978-1-58013-047-9(X)) Kar-Ben Publishing.

Golden Books Staff. Animal Sounds. Battaglia, Aurelius, illus. 2005. (Golden Sturdy Book Ser.). 24p. (J). (gr. k-k). 5.99 (978-0-375-83278-9(5) , Golden Bks.) Random Hse. Children's Bks.

Harcourt School Publishers Staff. A to Zoom: Letters & Sounds. 1999. (Collections Ser.). (Illus.). (gr. k-1). 8.60 (978-0-15-314980-1(9)) Harcourt Schl. Pubs.

—Mice Squeak, We Speak: Little Book. 2000. (Collections Ser.). (Illus.). (J). pap. 10.20 (978-0-15-314495-0(5)) Harcourt Schl. Pubs.

—Moo Moo Brown Cow: Little Book. 2000. (Collections Ser.). (Illus.). (J). pap. 10.20 (978-0-15-314507-0(2)) Harcourt Schl. Pubs.

Harder Tangvald, Christine. Ribbit! Roar! Quack, Quack, Quack! Conteh-Morgan, Jane, illus. 2000. (God's Noisy 1, 2, 3s Ser.). 24p. (J). (ps-k). bds. 7.99 (978-0-570-07097-9(X)) Concordia Publishing Hse.

Kimpton, Diana. Sounds: Individual Title Six-Pack Pouch - Level L. (Lighthouse Ser.). 16p. (gr. 2 up). 28.00 (978-0-7578-0884-5(0)) Rigby Education.

Lakeshore Learning Materials Staff, contrib. by. Buzz Said the Bee Packet. 2000. (J). pap. 19.95 (978-1-929255-22-1(5)) Lakeshore Learning Materials.

—Each Peach, Pear, Plum Packet. 2000. (J). pap. 19.95 (978-1-929255-24-5(1)) Lakeshore Learning Materials.

Leber, Nancy. Sounds All Around Us. 2003. (Compass Point Phonics Readers Ser.). (Illus.). 16p. (J). (gr. 1 up). 13.26 (978-0-7565-0524-0(0)) Compass Point Bks.

Letters & Their Sounds. 2002. (Home Workbooks Ser.). 64p. pap. 2.49 (978-0-88724-725-5(3) , CD-4527) Carson-Dellosa Publishing Co., Inc.

Matthews, Derek. Snappy Sounds Vroom! 2005. (Snappy Sounds Ser.). (Illus.). 10p. (J). 12.95 (978-1-59223-356-4(2) , Silver Dolphin Bks.) Advantage Pubs. Group.

Matthews, Derek, illus. Animales de la Selva. 2005. (Escucha y Aprende Ser.). (SPA.). 10p. (J). (ps-7). 12.95 (978-970-718-298-1(9) , Silver Dolphin en Español) Advanced Marketing, S. de R. L. de C. V. MEX. *Dist:* Perseus Distribution.

—Escucha y Aprende: Animales de la Granja. 2005. (Escucha y Aprende Ser.). (SPA.). 10p. (J). (ps-7). 12.95 (978-970-718-300-1(4) , Silver Dolphin en Español) Advanced Marketing, S. de R. L. de C. V. MEX. *Dist:* Perseus Distribution.

—Escucha y Aprende: Mascotas. 2005. (Escucha y Aprende Ser.). (SPA.). 10p. (J). (ps-7). 12.95 (978-970-718-299-8(7) , Silver Dolphin en Español) Advanced Marketing, S. de R. L. de C. V. MEX. *Dist:* Perseus Distribution.

—Escucha y Aprende: Trafico. 2005. (Escucha y Aprende Ser.). (SPA.). 10p. (J). (ps-7). 12.95 (978-970-718-297-4(0) , Silver Dolphin en Español) Advanced Marketing, S. de R. L. de C. V. MEX. *Dist:* Perseus Distribution.

—Snappy Sounds: Woof! Five Fun Animal Sounds. 2005. (Snappy Sounds Ser.). 10p. (J). 12.95 (978-1-59223-215-4(9) , Silver Dolphin Bks.) Advantage Pubs. Group.

McFarlane, Sheryl. What's That Sound? at the Circus. LaFave, Kim, illus. 2006. 20p. (J). bds. 7.95 (978-1-55041-959-7(5)) Fitzhenry & Whiteside, Ltd. CAN. *Dist:* F & W Pubns., Inc.

—What's That Sound by Sea. LaFave, Kim, illus. 2006. 20p. (J). bds. 7.95 (978-1-55041-957-3(9)) Fitzhenry & Whiteside, Ltd. CAN. *Dist:* F & W Pubns., Inc.

Newman, Fred. Mouthsounds: How to Whistle, Pop, Boing & Honk for All Occasions...and Then Some. 2004. (Illus.). 160p. pap. 13.95 (978-0-7611-3422-0(0) , 13422) Workman Publishing Co., Inc.

Perkins, Al. The Ear Book. Payne, Henry, illus. 2008. (Bright & Early Board Bks.). 24p. (J). (gr. k-ps). bds. 4.99 (***978-0-375-84279-5(9)*** , Random Hse. Bks. for Young Readers) Random Hse. Children's Bks.

Pfeffer, Wendy. Sounds All Around. Keller, Holly, illus. 1999. (Let's-Read-&-Find-Out Science Bks.). 32p. (J). (ps-1). 15.89 (978-0-06-027712-3(2)) HarperCollins Pubs.

—Sounds All Around. 1999. (978-0-606-16682-9(3)); lib. bdg. 13.00 (978-0-613-12129-3(5)) Tandem Library Bks.

Powell, Richard. Animal Noises. Martin Larrañaga, Ana, illus. 2001. (Copy Cats Ser.). 8p. (J). 6.95 (978-1-58925-665-1(4) , tiger tales) ME Media LLC.

Publications International, Ltd Staff, contrib. by. Bob the Builder: Baby's First Sound Book. 2002. (Illus.). (J). 7.95 (978-0-7853-6641-6(5)) Publications International, Ltd.

Rau, Dana Meachen. So Many Sounds, Level A. Sorra, Kristin, illus. 2001. (Rookie Readers Ser.). 24p. (J). (gr. k-1). 19.50 (978-0-516-22209-7(0) , Children's Pr.) Scholastic Library Publishing.

Richter, Dana. Baby Einstein: A Busy Box Book. Zaidi, Nadeem, illus. 2003. 14p. (J). bds. 15.98 (978-0-7853-7964-5(9) , 7174900) Publications International, Ltd.

Ring! Ring! 2002. (Little Board Books Ser.). 24p. (J). bds. 3.95 (978-0-7894-8466-6(8)) Dorling Kindersley Publishing, Inc.

Sayre, April Pulley. Secrets of Sound: Studying the Calls of Whales, Elephants, & Birds. 2006. (Scientists in the Field Ser.). (Illus.). 64p. (J). (gr. 3-5). pap. 6.95 (978-0-618-58546-5(X)) Houghton Mifflin Co.

—Secrets of Sound: Studying the Calls of Whales, Elephants, & Birds. Sayre, April Pulley, photos by. 2002. (Scientists in the Field Ser.). (Illus.). 64p. (J). (gr. 3-5). tchr. ed. 17.00 (978-0-618-01514-6(0)) Houghton Mifflin Co. Trade & Reference Div.

Sounds All Around: Fifth Grade Newcomer Books. (On Our Way to English Ser.). (gr. 5 up). 34.50 (978-0-7578-7275-4(1)) Rigby Education.

Stanley, Mandy. Quack! Quack! 1999. (Illus.). 12p. (J). 4.99 (978-0-7214-2734-8(0) , Dutton Juvenile) Penguin Group (USA) Inc.

Stone, Lynn M. How Do Animals Use Their Voices & Sound? 2008. (J). (***978-1-60044-507-1(1)***) Rourke Publishing, LLC.

Twin Sisters Productions Staff. Nature Sounds. 1998. (Growing Minds with Music Ser.). (J). audio compact disk 12.99 (978-1-57583-062-9(0)) Twin Sisters Productions, LLC.

Verplancke, Klass & Sanctobin, Veroniek. Que Hace el Bebe? 2002. (Que Hace? Ser.). (SPA & ENG., Illus.). 16p. 4.95 (978-84-7864-388-2(5)) Combel Editorial, S.A. ESP. *Dist:* Independent Pubs. Group.

—Que Hace la Gallina? 2002. (Que Hace? Ser.). (SPA & ENG., Illus.). 16p. 4.95 (978-84-7864-389-9(3)) Combel Editorial, S.A. ESP. *Dist:* Independent Pubs. Group.

—Que Me Pongo? 2002. (Que Hace? Ser.). (SPA & ENG., Illus.). 16p. 4.95 (978-84-7864-386-8(9)) Combel Editorial, S.A. ESP. *Dist:* Independent Pubs. Group.

—Que Veo? 2002. (Que Hace? Ser.). (SPA & ENG., Illus.). 16p. 4.95 (978-84-7864-387-5(7)) Combel Editorial, S.A. ESP. *Dist:* Independent Pubs. Group.

What's That Sound? (Peek A Boo Pockets Ser.). (Illus.). 12p. (J). bds. (978-2-89393-877-6(9)) Phidal Publishing, Inc./ Editions Phidal, Inc.

Wood, Jakki. Animal Hullabaloo. Wood, Jakki, illus. 1999. (Illus.). 32p. (J). (ps). pap. (978-0-7112-0946-6(4)) Lincoln, Frances Ltd. GBR. *Dist:* Transition Vendor.

SOUPS

Fishman, Cathy Goldberg. La Sopa. Rooney, Ronnie, illus. (Rookie Reader Espanol Ser.).Tr. of Soup. (SPA.). 32p. (J). (gr. k-2). 2003. pap. 4.95 (978-0-516-27799-8(5)); 2002. 19.50 (978-0-516-22687-3(8)) Scholastic Library Publishing. (Children's Pr.).

Fitros, Pamela. Chicken Soup. 2005. 16p. (J). pap. 4.95 (978-1-57874-084-0(3)) Kaeden Corp.

Hershenhorn, Esther. Chicken Soup by Heart. Litzinger, Rosanne, illus. 2002. 32p. (J). 16.95 (978-0-689-82665-8(6)) Simon & Schuster Children's Publishing.

S

SOUSA, JOHN PHILIP, 1854-1932

Gillis, Jennifer Blizin. John Philip Sousa: The King of March Music. 2005. (J). pap. (978-1-4034-6759-1(5)); (Illus.). 32p. 24.21 (978-1-4034-6751-5(X)) Heinemann Library.

Venezia, Mike. John Philip Sousa. Venezia, Mike, illus. (Getting to Know the World's Greatest Composers Ser.). (Illus.). 32p. (J). (gr. 3-4). 1999. pap. 6.95 (978-0-516-26401-1(X)); 1998. 27.00 (978-0-516-20761-2(X)) Scholastic Library Publishing. (Children's Pr.).

SOUTH, THE

see Southern States

SOUTH AFRICA

Here are entered works on the Republic of South Africa. Works on the area south of the countries of Zaire and Tanzania are entered under Africa, Southern.

Angelou, Maya. My Painted House, My Friendly Chicken & Me. Courtney-Clarke, Margaret, illus. 2003. 48p. (J). (gr. 1-4). pap. 7.99 (978-0-375-82567-5(3)); lib. bdg. 17.99 (978-0-375-92567-2(8)) Random Hse. Children's Bks. (Crown Books For Young Readers).

—My Painted House, My Friendly Chicken & Me. 2003. (gr. k-3). lib. bdg. 16.45 (978-0-613-71911-7(5)) Tandem Library Bks.

Blauer, Ettagale & Lauré, Jason. South Africa. rev. ed. 2006. (Enchantment of the World, Second Ser.). (Illus.). 144p. (J). (gr. 5-9). 36.00 (978-0-516-24853-0(7) , Children's Pr.) Scholastic Library Publishing.

Bowden, Rob. Cape Town. 2006. (Global Cities Ser.). 64p. (J). (gr. 5-8). 30.00 (978-0-7910-8856-2(1) , Chelsea Hse.) Facts On File, Inc.

Cave, Kathryn. One Child, One Seed: A South African Counting Book. Wulfsohn, Gisele, photos by. 2003. (Illus.). 32p. (J). (ps-2). 17.95 (978-0-8050-7204-4(7) , Holt, Henry & Co. Bks. For Young Readers) Holt, Henry & Co.

Clark, Domini. South Africa the Culture. 2000. (gr. 3-6). lib. bdg. 16.40 (978-0-613-22407-9(8)) Tandem Library Bks.

—South Africa the Land. 2000. (gr. 3-6). lib. bdg. 16.40 (978-0-613-22408-6(6)) Tandem Library Bks.

—South Africa the People. 2000. (gr. 3-6). lib. bdg. 16.40 (978-0-613-22409-3(4)) Tandem Library Bks.

Cottrell, Robert C. South Africa: A State of Apartheid. Matray, James I., ed. 2005. (Arbitrary Borders Ser.). (Illus.). 112p. (J). (gr. 9-13). 35.00 (978-0-7910-8257-7(1) , Chelsea Hse.) Facts On File, Inc.

Domingo, Vernon. South Africa. 2003. (Modern World Nations Ser.). (Illus.). 150p. (gr. 6-12). 30.00 (978-0-7910-7610-1(5) , Chelsea Hse.) Facts On File, Inc.

Downing, David. Apartheid in South Africa. 2004. (Illus.). 56p. (J). 27.07 (978-1-4034-4870-5(1)) Heinemann Library.

Gallagher, Michael. South Africa. 2007. (J). (*978-1-59920-020-0(1)) Smart Apple Media.

Graham, Ian. South Africa. 2004. (Country File Ser.). (Illus.). 32p. (J). lib. bdg. (978-1-58340-499-7(6)) Smart Apple Media.

Green, Jen. Focus on South Africa. 2006. (Illus.). 64p. (J). pap. (978-0-8368-6745-9(9)); (gr. 5-7). lib. bdg. 33.27 (978-0-8368-6738-1(6)) Stevens, Gareth Inc. (World Almanac Library).

Haskins, James & Benson, Kathleen. Count Your Way Through South Africa. Neibert, Alissa, illus. 2007. (Count Your Way Ser.). 24p. (J). 19.93 (978-1-57505-883-2(9) , Millbrook Pr.) Lerner Publishing Group.

Heinemann Staff. South Africa. (World Focus Ser.). (Illus.). 31p. (Orig.). (J). (gr. 3-7). pap. 3.99 (978-0-431-07268-5(X)) Oxfam Publishing GBR. *Dist:* Stylus Publishing, LLC.

Human Sciences Research Council Staff. Every Step of the Way: The Journey to Freedom in South Africa. 2004. pap. 18.25 (978-0-521-60791-9(4)) Cambridge Univ. Pr.

Kalman, Bobbie. South Africa: The Culture. 2000. (978-0-606-18068-9(0)) Tandem Library Bks.

Kizilos, Peter. South Africa: Nation in Transition. 1998. (World in Conflict Ser.). (Illus.). 96p. (J). (gr. 7-12). 25.26 (978-0-8225-3558-4(0) , Lerner Pubns.) Lerner Publishing Group.

Langley, Andrew. Cape Town. 2005. (Great Cities of the World Ser.). (Illus.). 48p. (J). pap. (978-0-8368-5205-9(2)); (YA). lib. bdg. 30.00 (978-0-8368-5045-1(9)) Stevens, Gareth Inc. (World Almanac Library).

Noonan, Sheila Smith. South Africa. 2004. (Africa Ser.). (Illus.). 80p. (J). lib. bdg. (978-1-59084-819-7(5)) Mason Crest Pubs.

Park. Taking Your Camera To..., 6 vols., Set 3. 2000. pap. (978-0-7398-4136-5(X)) Steck-Vaughn.

Park, Ted. Taking Your Camera To..., Set 3. 2000. pap., tchr. ed. (978-0-7398-4135-8(1)) Steck-Vaughn.

—Taking Your Camera to South Africa. 2000. (Illus.). pap. (978-0-7398-4133-4(5)) Steck-Vaughn.

Pogrund, Benjamin. Nelson Mandela. (Pacificadores Mundiales Ser.). 64p. (gr. 5-8). 28.70 (978-1-4103-0543-5(0) , Blackbirch Pr., Inc.) Thomson Gale.

Pugliano-Martin, Carol. Cape Town, South Africa. 2006. pap. 42.00 (*978-1-4108-6422-2(7)) Benchmark Education Co.

—Discover Cape Town. 2006. pap. 39.00 (*978-1-4108-6425-3(1)) Benchmark Education Co.

Ryan, Patrick. Welcome to South Africa. 2008. (Welcome to the World Ser.). 32p. (J). (gr. 1-5). 27.07 (*978-1-59296-977-7(1)) Child's World, Inc.

Senker, Cath. South Africa. Bennett, Peter, photos by. 2005. (Letters from Around the World Ser.). (Illus.). 32p. (J). (gr. 3-7). lib. bdg. (978-1-84234-354-8(8) , Cherrytree Books) Evans Publishing Group.

Spengler, Kremena. South Africa: A Question & Answer Book. 2007. (Fact Finders Ser.). (Illus.). 32p. (J). 22.60 (978-0-7368-6411-4(3)) Capstone Pr., Inc.

Stein, R. Conrad. Cape Town. 1998. (Cities of the World Ser.). (Illus.). 64p. (J). (gr. 4-9). 27.00 (978-0-516-20781-0(4) , Children's Pr.) Scholastic Library Publishing.

Taking Your Camera To... Includes: Argentina, China, Germany, India, South Africa, Vietnam, 6 bks., Set. 2001. (Taking Your Camera to Ser.). (Illus.). (J). (gr. 4-7). 136.98 (978-0-7398-3573-9(4)) Raintree.

Tames, Richard. End of Apartheid: A New South Africa. 2000. (Point of Impact Ser.). (Illus.). 32p. (J). (gr. 5-7). lib. bdg. 24.22 (978-1-57572-412-6(X)) Heinemann Library.

Venter, Sahm. Youth Day: June 16. 2007. (Exploring our National Days Ser.). 72p. pap. 20.00 (*978-1-77009-235-8(8)) Jacana Media ZAF. *Dist:* Independent Pubs. Group.

SOUTH AFRICA—BIOGRAPHY

Abrams, Dennis. Thabo Mbeki. 2007. (Modern World Leaders Ser.). 128p. (J). (gr. 6-12). 30.00 (*978-0-7910-9443-3(X) , Chelsea Hse.) Facts On File, Inc.

Boothroyd, Jennifer. Nelson Mandela: A Life of Persistence. 2007. (Pull Ahead Books). (Illus.). 32p. (J). 22.60 (978-0-8225-6385-3(1) , Lerner Pubns.) Lerner Publishing Group.

Cooper, Floyd. Mandela: From the Life of the South African Statesman. Cooper, Floyd, illus. 2000. (Illus.). 40p. (J). (gr. k-5). pap. 6.99 (978-0-698-11816-4(2) , Putnam Juvenile) Penguin Group (USA) Inc.

—Mandela: From the Life of the South African Statesman. 2000. (978-0-606-18430-4(9)); lib. bdg. 15.30 (978-0-613-23016-2(7)) Tandem Library Bks.

Literature Connections English: Kaffir Boy. 2004. (gr. 6-12). (978-0-395-85804-2(6) , 2-70804) McDougal Littell Inc.

Stamper, G. C. Nelson Mandela. 2005. (Illus.). 32p. (J). pap. (*978-0-7367-2922-2(4)) Zaner-Bloser, Inc.

Vandegrift, Tom. 24 New Moons. 2003. 429p. (YA). pap. 20.95 (978-0-7414-1503-5(8)) Infinity Publishing.

Wheeler, Jill C. Nelson Mandela. 2002. (Breaking Barriers Ser.). (Illus.). 64p. (J). (gr. 3-8). lib. bdg. 25.65 (978-1-57765-639-5(3) , ABDO & Daughters) ABDO Publishing Co.

SOUTH AFRICA—FICTION

Benjamin, Ruth. Yesterday's Child. Cohen, Deene, illus. (YA). 16.95 (978-1-56062-176-8(1) , CFR122H); pap. 13.95 (978-1-56062-177-5(X) , CFR122S) CIS Communications, Inc.

Brain, Helen. Fly Cemetery & Other Juicy Stories. 1999. (Illus.). 92p. (J). (978-0-7981-3987-8(0)) Human & Rousseau.

Clanahan, Mary. Nama Kwa's Garden. Taylor, Jacqui, illus. 2005. 72p. (J). (ps-7). 12.95 (978-1-77007-025-7(7)) Struik Pubs. ZAF. *Dist:* International Publishers Marketing.

Coman, Carolyn. Many Stones. 2002. 160p. (YA). pap. 5.99 (978-0-14-230148-7(5) , Puffin) Penguin Group (USA) Inc.

—Many Stones. 2002. 157p. (YA). (gr. 7-9). lib. bdg. 14.15 (978-0-613-45291-5(7)) Tandem Library Bks.

—Many Stones. l.t. ed. 2001. 24.95 (978-0-7862-3399-1(0)) Thorndike Pr.

Courtenay, Bryce. The Power of One. 2005. 304p. (J). (gr. 5-12). lib. bdg. 17.99 (978-0-385-90274-8(3) , Delacorte Bks. for Young Readers) Random Hse. Children's Bks.

Craig, Colleen. Afrika. 2008. 192p. pap. 9.95 (*978-0-88776-807-1(5)) Tundra Bks., Inc./Livres Toundra, Inc. CAN. *Dist:* Random Hse. of Canada, Ltd.

Daly, Niki. Happy Birthday, Jamela! Daly, Niki, illus. 2006. (Jamela Ser.). (Illus.). 32p. (J). (gr. k-2). 16.00 (978-0-374-32842-9(0) , Farrar, Straus & Giroux (BYR)) Farrar, Straus & Giroux.

—Jamela's Dress. Daly, Niki, illus. 2004. (Jamela Ser.). (Illus.). 32p. (J). reprint ed. pap. 6.95 (978-0-374-43720-6(3) , Sunburst) Farrar, Straus & Giroux.

—Jamela's Dress. 2001. (J). (ps-2). 26.95 incl. audio (978-0-8045-6878-4(2) , 6878) Spoken Arts, Inc.

—Not So Fast, Songololo. 1998. (J). pap. 4.95 (978-0-87628-975-4(8)) Ctr. for Applied Research in Education, The.

—Once upon a Time. Daly, Niki, illus. 2003. (Illus.). 32p. (J). (gr. k-3). 16.00 (978-0-374-35633-0(5) , Farrar, Straus & Giroux (BYR)) Farrar, Straus & Giroux.

—What's Cooking, Jamela? Daly, Niki, illus. 2001. (Jamela Ser.). (Illus.). 32p. (J). (ps-2). 16.95 (978-0-374-35602-6(5) , Farrar, Straus & Giroux (BYR)) Farrar, Straus & Giroux.

—Where's Jamela? 2004. (Jamela Ser.). (Illus.). 36p. (J). 16.00 (978-0-374-38324-4(3) , Farrar, Straus & Giroux (BYR)) Farrar, Straus & Giroux.

Erskine, Kathryn. Ibhubesi: The Lion. 2004. (Illus.). 194p. pap. 19.95 (978-1-4137-0364-1(X)) PublishAmerica, Inc.

Ferreira, Anton. Zulu Dog. 2002. (Illus.). 208p. (J). (gr. 5 up). 16.00 (978-0-374-39223-9(4) , Farrar, Straus & Giroux (BYR)) Farrar, Straus & Giroux.

Garisch, Dawn. Babyshoes. 2004. 288p. pap. 9.99 (978-0-689-83778-4(X)) Simon & Schuster, Ltd. GBR. *Dist:* Independent Pubs. Group.

Glass, Linzi Alex. The Year the Gypsies Came. 2006. (YA). 272p. 16.95 (978-0-8050-7999-9(8)); 260p. (*978-1-4156-7350-8(0)) Holt, Henry & Co.

Hart, Sue. Tales of the Full Moon. Harvey, Chris, illus. 2006. 96p. (J). pap. 16.95 (978-1-55591-582-7(5) , 800.992.2908) Fulcrum Publishing.

Heale, Jay. African Animal Tales. 2004. (Illus.). 96p. 10.00 (978-1-86872-704-9(1)) Struik Pubs. ZAF. *Dist:* Continental Enterprises Group, Inc. (CEG).

Hodson, Christopher. Little Library Literacy: Lizo's Song Ndebele. Pulles, Elizabeth, illus. 2007. pap. (*978-0-521-70282-9(8)) Cambridge Univ. Pr.

—Little Library Literacy: Lizo's Song Siswati. Pulles, Elizabeth, illus. 2007. pap. (*978-0-521-70286-7(0)) Cambridge Univ. Pr.

—Little Library Literacy: Lizo's Song Xhosa. Pulles, Elizabeth, illus. 2007. pap. (*978-0-521-70283-6(6)) Cambridge Univ. Pr.

Isadora, Rachel. A South African Night. Isadora, Rachel, illus. 1998. (Illus.). (J). (ps-3). 32p. 16.99 (978-0-688-11389-6(3)); 24p. 14.89 (978-0-688-11390-2(7)) HarperCollins Pubs.

Jessop, Sherry. The Great BooDinie Bird: Faith, 5 vols., Vol. 1. Staples, Deb, ed. Sketchit, Elly, illus. 2000. cd-rom 6.50 (978-1-931540-25-4(X)) SynergEbks.

Kramer, Berri, photos by & text. Mbali: A story from South Africa. Kramer, Berri, text. 2nd ed. 2006. (J). per. (*978-0-9706901-1-1(8)) Rotaplast Pr.

Mhlophe, Gcina. Our Story Magic. 2006. 100p. 29.95 (*978-1-86914-111-0(3)) Univ. of Natal Pr. ZAF. *Dist:* International Specialized Bk. Services.

Naidoo, Beverley. No Turning Back: A Novel of South Africa. 1999. 208p. (J). (gr. 3-7). pap. 5.99 (978-0-06-440749-6(7) , Harper Trophy) HarperCollins Pubs.

—No Turning Back: A Novel of South Africa. 1999. 189p. lib. bdg. 12.64 (978-0-606-15856-5(1)); (J). per. 14.10 (978-0-613-11922-1(3)) Tandem Library Bks.

—Out of Bounds: Seven Stories of Conflict & Hope. 2003. (Illus.). 192p. (J). (gr. 5 up). 16.99 (978-0-06-050799-2(3)); lib. bdg. 17.89 (978-0-06-050800-5(0)) HarperCollins Pubs.

The Other Side of the Invisible Fence. 2006. (YA). per. 9.95 (*978-0-9787783-8-5(3)) Trevor Romain Co., The.

Paton, Alan. Cry, the Beloved Country. 2003. (gr. 7-12). lib. bdg. 23.45 (978-0-613-70981-1(0)) Tandem Library Bks.

Penning, L. & Nelson, Marietjie. The Hero of Spionkop. 2006. (Illus.). 166p. (YA). pap. (978-1-894666-92-3(5)) Inheritance Pubns.

—The Lion of Modderspruit. 2004. (Illus.). 142p. (YA). pap. (978-1-894666-91-6(7)) Inheritance Pubns.

Reid, Mayne. Young Yagers or A Narrative of Hunting A. 2006. (Illus.). pap. 31.95 (*978-1-4286-2205-0(5)) Kessinger Publishing, LLC.

Schermbrucker, Reviva. An African Christmas Cloth. 2007. 36p. 27.95 (978-1-77009-081-1(9)); (Illus.). 40p. pap. 19.95 (978-1-77009-151-1(3)) Jacana Media ZAF. *Dist:* Independent Pubs. Group.

Seeger, Pete & Jacobs, Paul DuBois. Abiyoyo Returns. Hays, Michael, illus. 2004. (J). (ps-3). lib. bdg. 14.19 (978-0-606-32677-3(4)) Tandem Library Bks.

Sisulu, Eleanor Batezat. The Day Gogo Went to Vote. Wilson, Sharon, illus. 1999. 32p. (J). (ps-3). pap. 6.99 (978-0-316-70271-3(4)) Little, Brown Bks. for Young Readers.

Sisulu, Elinor Batezat. The Day Gogo Went to Vote. Wilson, Sharon, illus. 1999. (J). (ps-ps). lib. bdg. 14.10 (978-0-613-22837-4(5)) Tandem Library Bks.

St. John, Lauren. The White Giraffe. Dean, David, illus. 2007. 192p. (J). (gr. 3 up). 16.99 (978-0-8037-3211-7(2) , Dial) Penguin Group (USA) Inc.

Stewart, Diane. The Gift of the Sun. Daly, Jude, illus. 2007. 32p. (J). pap. 7.95 (*978-1-84507-787-7(3)) Lincoln, Frances Ltd. GBR. *Dist:* Perseus Distribution.

Stewart, Dianne. El Regalo del Sol. Daly, Jude, illus. 2000. (SPA.). 28p. (J). (ps-3). pap. 6.99 (978-980-257-258-8(6) , EK(1977)) Ekare, Ediciones VEN. *Dist:* Kane/Miller Bk. Pubs., Inc., Lectorum Pubns., Inc.

Tellem, Sundiata. Chaka Goes to S. Africa. 2005. (Illus.). 24p. (J). per. 8.99 (978-1-932338-74-4(8)) Lifevest Publishing, Inc.

Tlali, Miriam. Between Two Worlds. 2004. 222p. reprint ed. pap. (978-1-55111-605-1(7)) Broadview Pr.

Uncle Markie. Piglettè & Bobo in Sud Africa. 2003. (YA). ring bd. 9.95 (978-1-933129-15-0(8)) Studio 403.

—Piglettè & Bobo on Safari. 2003. (YA). ring bd. 9.95 (978-1-933129-16-7(6)) Studio 403.

van de Ruit, John. Spud. 2007. 352p. (YA). (gr. 7 up). 16.99 (*978-1-59514-170-5(7) , Razorbill) Penguin Group (USA) Inc.

YKids Staff. Nelson Mandela. 2008. (Great Figures in History Ser.). 144p. (J). (gr. 4-7). pap. 14.95 (*978-981-05-7551-9(3)) Youngjin (Singapore) Pte Ltd. SGP. *Dist:* Independent Pubs. Group.

SOUTH AFRICA—RACE RELATIONS

Connolly. Apartheid in South Africa. 2002. (Troubled World Ser.). (Illus.). 64p. (J). (gr. 6 up). lib. bdg. 28.54 (978-0-7398-6339-8(8)) Raintree.

Downing, David. Apartheid in South Africa. 2004. (Illus.). 56p. (J). 27.07 (978-1-4034-4870-5(1)); pap. (978-1-4034-6258-9(5)) Heinemann Library.

Finlayson, Reggie. Nelson Mandela. (Just the Facts Biographies Ser.). 2006. (Illus.). 112p. (J). (gr. 3-7). 27.93 (978-0-8225-2644-5(1)); 2004. (J). pap. (978-0-8225-5360-1(0)); 1998. (Illus.). 112p. (YA). (gr. 6-12). 27.93 (978-0-8225-4936-9(0)) Lerner Publishing Group. (Lerner Pubns.).

Hughes, Libby. Nelson Mandela: Voice of Freedom. 2000. (Illus.). 152p. (gr. 4-7). pap. 12.95 (978-0-595-00733-2(3) , Backinprint.com) iUniverse, Inc.

Martin, Michael. Apartheid in South Africa. 2006. (World History Ser.). 112p. (J). (gr. 7-10). 32.45 (978-1-59018-696-1(6) , Lucent Bks.) Thomson Gale.

SOUTH AMERICA

Aloian, Molly & Kalman, Bobbie. Explore South America. 2007. (Explore the Continents Ser.). (Illus.). 32p. (J). (gr. 1-7). (*978-0-7787-3076-7(X)); pap. (*978-0-7787-3090-3(5)) Crabtree Publishing Co.

Anita Ganeri. Exploring South America. 2007. (Illus.). 32p. (J). pap. (*978-1-4034-8255-6(1)) Heinemann Library.

Banting, Erinn. South America. 2005. (Illus.). 32p. (J). (ps-6). lib. bdg. 26.00 (978-1-59036-322-5(1)); pap. 7.95 (978-1-59036-329-4(9)) Weigl Pubs., Inc.

Bianchi, John-Paul. World Through Words: Central & South America. 2000. (gr. 5-8). lib. bdg. 24.50 (978-0-613-45700-2(5)) Tandem Library Bks.

Bianchi, John-Paul, ed. Central & South America. 2001. (World in Focus Ser.). (YA). (gr. 5 up). 64p. pap., suppl. ed. 16.20 (978-1-56711-349-5(4) , Blackbirch Pr., Inc.); 32p. pap., act. bk. ed. 11.20 (978-1-56711-351-8(6)) Thomson Gale.

Carr, Joaquin. Habitats of South America. 2005. (Navigators Ser.). (J). pap. 38.00 (*978-1-4108-5073-7(0)) Benchmark Education Co.

Chin-Lee, Cynthia, et al. A Is for the Americas. 1999. (Illus.). 32p. (J). (gr. k-4). 16.99 (978-0-531-33194-1(6) , Orchard Bks.) Scholastic, Inc.

Donaldson, Madeline. South America. 2005. (Pull Ahead Bks.). (Illus.). 32p. (J). (gr. k-3). lib. bdg. 22.60 (978-0-8225-4723-5(6)) Lerner Publishing Group.

Encyclopaedia Britannica Publishers, Inc. Staff. Views of the Americas. 2004. (Britannica Learning Library). (Illus.). (J). lib. bdg. 14.95 (978-1-59339-012-9(2)) Encyclopaedia Britannica, Inc.

Fowler, Allan. South America. 2001. (Rookie Read-About Geography Ser.). (Illus.). 32p. (J). (gr. 1-2). pap. 5.95 (978-0-516-27300-6(0)); 20.50 (978-0-516-21672-0(4)) Scholastic Library Publishing. (Children's Pr.).

—South America. 2001. (gr. k-3). lib. bdg. 14.10 (978-0-613-54678-2(4)) Tandem Library Bks.

Ganeri, Anita. South America. 2007. (Illus.). 32p. (J). (*978-1-4034-8247-1(0)) Heinemann Library.

Gibson, Karen Bush. South America. 2006. (Illus.). 24p. (J). (978-0-7368-5431-3(2)) Capstone Pr., Inc.

Goodnough, David. Simon Bolivar: South American Liberator. 1998. (Hispanic Biographies Ser.). (Illus.). 112p. (YA). (gr. 6-12). lib. bdg. 26.60 (978-0-7660-1044-4(9)) Enslow Pubs., Inc.

Gorrell, Gena K. In the Land of the Jaguar: South America & Its People. Krystoforski, Andrej, illus. 2007. 160p. (J). (gr. 4). 22.95 (*978-0-88776-756-2(7)) Tundra Bks., Inc./Livres Toundra, Inc. CAN. *Dist:* Random Hse., Inc.

Graf, Mike. South America. 2002. (Continents Ser.). (Illus.). 79p. (J). (gr. 1-2). 18.60 (978-0-7368-1421-8(3) , Bridgestone Bks.) Capstone Pr., Inc.

Henderson, James D., ed. Discovering South America, 13 vols., Set. (Illus.). 64p. (YA). (gr. 5 up). lib. bdg. (978-1-59084-284-3(7)) Mason Crest Pubs.

Hernandez, Roger E. South America: Facts & Figures. 2003. (Discovering South America Ser.). (Illus.). 64p. (YA). (gr. 5 up). lib. bdg. (978-1-59084-299-7(5)) Mason Crest Pubs.

Hirschmann, Kristine. Geography of South America. 2006. (Navigators Ser.). (J). pap. 44.00 (*978-1-4108-6264-8(X)) Benchmark Education Co.

Hovanec, Erin M. An Online Visit to South America. (Internet Field Trips Ser.). 24p. (J). 2002. lib. bdg. 18.75 (978-0-8239-6418-5(3)); 2001. (Illus.). (gr. 3). lib. bdg. 18.75 (978-0-8239-5655-5(5)) Rosen Publishing Group, Inc., The. (PowerKids Pr.).

The Library of the Western Hemisphere Set 2. (J). (gr. 5 up). 119.70 (978-1-4042-2964-8(7)) Rosen Publishing Group, Inc., The.

The Library of the Western Hemisphere Set 1. (J). (gr. 5 up). 119.70 (978-1-4042-2963-1(9)) Rosen Publishing Group, Inc., The.

McClish, Bruce. Land Bridges & New World Continents. 2003. (Continents Ser.). (Illus.). 32p. pap. 7.50 (978-1-4034-4246-8(0)) Heinemann Library.

McIntosh, Kenneth & McIntosh, Marsha. The Flight from Turmoil. 2005. (Illus.). 112p. (J). lib. bdg. (978-1-59084-930-9(2)) Mason Crest Pubs.

McLeish, Ewan & Weatherly, Myra. South America. 2003. (Continents Ser.). (Illus.). 32p. (J). (gr. 2-6). 27.07 (978-1-59296-062-0(6)) Child's World, Inc.

McLeish, Ewan & Whitecap Books Staff. South America. 2000. (Investigate Ser.). (Illus.). 64p. (J). (gr. 1-7). pap. 3.95 (978-1-55285-156-2(7)) Whitecap Bks., Ltd. CAN. *Dist:* Firefly Bks., Ltd.

Pelusey, Michael & Pelusey, Jane. South America. 2004. (Continents Ser.). (Illus.). 32p. (J). (gr. 2-4). 23.00 (978-0-7910-8277-5(6) , Chelsea Hse.) Facts On File, Inc.

Petersen, David. South America. 1999. (True Bks.). (Illus.). 48p. (J). (gr. 3-5). pap. 6.95 (978-0-516-26440-0(0) , Children's Pr.) Scholastic Library Publishing.

Sammis, Fran. South America. 1999. (Mapping Our World Ser.). (Illus.). 64p. (J). (gr. 4-8). lib. bdg. 27.07 (978-0-7614-0369-2(8) , Benchmark Bks.) Cavendish, Marshall Corp.

Sayre, April Pulley. South America. 1999. (Seven Continents Ser.). (Illus.). 64p. (gr. 5-8). lib. bdg. 25.90 (978-0-7613-1366-3(4) , Millbrook Pr.) Lerner Publishing Group.

—South America, Surprise! 2003. 32p. (J). (gr. 2-5). pap. 7.95 (978-0-7613-1989-4(1)); (Illus.). lib. bdg. 21.90 (978-0-7613-2123-1(3)) Lerner Publishing Group. (Millbrook Pr.).

Scoones, Simon. South America. 2005. (Illus.). 64p. (J). pap. (978-0-8368-5922-5(7)); lib. bdg. 32.67 (978-0-8368-5915-7(4)) Stevens, Gareth Inc. (World Almanac Library).

Shireman, Myrl. South America. 1998. (Illus.). 96p. (YA). (gr. 5-8). pap. 10.95 (978-1-58037-068-4(3)) Twain, Mark Media, Inc. Pubs.

Vierow, Wendy. South America. 2004. (Atlas of the Seven Continents Ser.). (Illus.). 24p. (J). lib. bdg. 21.25 (978-0-8239-6693-6(3) , PowerKids Pr.) Rosen Publishing Group, Inc., The.

SOUTH AMERICA—DESCRIPTION AND TRAVEL

Bateman, Helen & Denshire, Jayne. South America. 2006. (Illus.). 32p. (J). (978-1-58340-801-8(0) , 1262719) Smart Apple Media.

Bramwell, Martyn. Central & South America. 2000. (World in Maps Ser.). (Illus.). 40p. (YA). (gr. 5-12). lib. bdg. 23.93 (978-0-8225-2912-5(2) , Lerner Pubns.) Lerner Publishing Group.

Cunningham, Patrick. Brazil. Cunningham, Susan M., photos by. 2005. (Letters from Around the World Ser.). (Illus.). 32p. (J). (gr. 3-7). lib. bdg. (978-1-84234-253-4(3) , Cherrytree Books) Evans Publishing Group.

Fox, Mary Virginia. South America. 2001. (Continents Ser.). (Illus.). 32p. (J). (gr. k-2). lib. bdg. 21.36 (978-1-58810-002-3(2)) Heinemann Library.

Fox, Mary Virginia & Foster, Leila. South America. 2002. (Continents Ser.). (Illus.). 32p. (J). (gr. k-2). pap. 6.95 (978-1-58810-951-4(8) , 91441) Heinemann Library.

Lee, James, ed. South America in Charts & Graphs. 2004. (YA). cd-rom 25.00 (978-0-9749905-0-7(7)) JLM CD-ROM Publishing Co.

Lourie, Peter. Tierra Del Fuego: A Journey to the End of the Earth. Lourie, Peter, photos by. 2003. (Illus.). 48p. (YA). (gr. 4-6). pap. 19.95 (978-1-56397-973-6(X)) Boyds Mills Pr.

Southeastern States Grades 4-6. 2000. (J). pap. 8.94 (978-1-889369-43-3(8)) Teaching Ink, Inc.

Striveildi, Cheryl. South America. 2003. (Continents Ser.). (Illus.). 32p. (J). (gr. k-4). lib. bdg. 22.78 (978-1-57765-964-8(3)) ABDO Publishing Co.

Zronik, John Paul. Francisco Pizarro: Journeys Through Peru & South America. 2005. (In the Footsteps of Explorers Ser.). (Illus.). 32p. (J). (ps-9). (978-0-7787-2411-7(5)); pap. (978-0-7787-2447-6(6)) Crabtree Publishing Co.

SOUTH AMERICA—DISCOVERY AND EXPLORATION

see America—Discovery and Exploration

SOUTH AMERICA—FICTION

Appleton, Victor. Tom Swift in Captivity or A Daring Escap. 2006. pap. (***978-1-4065-0914-4(0)***) Dodo Pr.

Baglio, Ben M. Racing the Wind. 2003. (Dolphin Diaries: No. 6). 160p. (J). pap. 4.99 (978-0-439-31952-2(8)) Scholastic, Inc.

—Racing the Wind. 2003. (gr. 3-6). lib. bdg. 12.40 (978-0-613-72053-3(9)) Tandem Library Bks.

Ballantyne, R. M. The Lighthouse. 2006. pap. (***978-1-4065-0531-3(5)***) Dodo Pr.

Blase, Dean. There's an Octopus under My Bed. Ross, D., illus. 2007. 32p. (J). 16.99 (***978-0-9777651-1-9(3)***) Shake It.

Cabal, Graciela Beatriz. Jacinto. 2000. (SPA., Illus.). 64p. per. 7.95 (978-950-07-1190-6(7)) Editorial Sudamericana S.A. ARG. *Dist:* Libros Sin Fronteras.

Campoy, F. Isabel. Rosa Raposa. Aruego, Jose & Dewey, Ariane, illus. 2002. 32p. (J). (gr. k-2). 16.00 (978-0-15-202161-0(2) , Gulliver Bks.) Harcourt Children's Bks.

Carothers, Daniella. Over the Valley. 2007. 148p. pap. 17.95 (***978-1-59299-291-1(9)***) Inkwater Pr.

De Matos, Isabel Freire. Una Carta de Monica. Saez, Sofia, illus. 2004. (SPA.). 32p. pap. 6.95 (978-1-57581-574-9(5)) Santillana USA Publishing Co., Inc.

Doyle, Arthur Conan. The Lost World & Other Thrilling Tales. 2001. (gr. 7-12). lib. bdg. 17.65 (978-0-613-64299-6(6)) Tandem Library Bks.

Fraggalosch, Audrey. Land of the Wild Llama: A Story of the Patagonian Andes. Denman, Michael & Huiett, William J., illus. 2005. (Wild Habitats Ser.). 32p. (J). (gr. 1-4). 15.95 (978-1-931465-81-6(9) , B7022); 19.95 incl. reel tape (978-1-931465-83-0(5) , BC7022); pap. 6.95 (978-1-931465-82-3(7) , S7022) Soundprints.

—Land of the Wild Llama: A Story of the Patagonian Andes, Including 10" Toy. Denman, Michael & Huiett, William J., illus. 2002. (Wild Habitats Ser.). 36p. (J). (gr. 1-4). 26.95 (978-1-931465-85-4(1) , PB7022) Soundprints.

Hergé. The Broken Ear. (Illus.). 62p. (J). 24.95 (978-0-8288-5086-5(0)) French & European Pubns., Inc.

—L' Oreille Cassee.Tr. of Broken Ear. (FRE., Illus.). 62p. (J). 19.95 (978-0-8288-5054-4(2)) French & European Pubns., Inc.

Jones, Allan Frewin. Legend of the Anaconda King. 2006. 186p. (J). pap. (***978-0-439-85670-6(1)***) Scholastic, Inc.

Kavanagh, Shannon & McKay, Jeffrey. Safari Jeff & Shannon Visit South America. 2005. (Great Green Adventure Ser.). (Illus.). 46p. 14.95 (978-0-9734409-1-1(0)) Croctalk Publishing CAN. *Dist:* Hushion Hse. Publishing, Ltd.

Muller, Birte. Felipa & the Day of the Dead. 2005. (Illus.). 36p. (J). (ps up). reprint ed. pap. 6.95 (978-0-7358-2011-1(2)) North-South Bks., Inc.

—Felipa y el Dia de Los Muertos. 2005. (SPA., Illus.). 36p. (J). (ps up). 15.95 (978-0-7358-2009-8(0)) North-South Bks., Inc.

Rockwood, Roy. Jack North's Treasure Hunt: Or, Daring Adventures in South America. 2006. 142p. pap. 10.99 (978-1-4264-2654-4(2)); 146p. pap. 13.99 (978-1-4264-2711-4(5)) BiblioBazaar.

Schmidt, C. A. Useful Fools. 2007. 272p. (YA). (gr. 8 up). 18.99 (***978-0-525-47814-0(0)*** , Dutton Juvenile) Penguin Group (USA) Inc.

Torres, Leyla. Sancocho del Sabado. 1999. Tr. of Saturday Sancocho. (978-0-606-16478-8(2)) Tandem Library Bks.

—Sancocho Del Sabado. 1999. (SPA.). (gr. k-3). lib. bdg. 14.10 (978-0-613-17852-5(1)) Tandem Library Bks.

SOUTH AMERICA—HISTORY

Ackroyd, Peter. Cities of Blood. 2005. (Voyages through Time Ser.). (Illus.). 144p. (J). (gr. 4-7). pap. 9.99 (978-0-7566-1367-9(1)) Dorling Kindersley Publishing, Inc.

Allman, Barbara. Central & South America. Bianchi, John-Paul, ed. 2001. (World in Focus Ser.). (Illus.). 80p. (J). (gr. 5 up). pap. 17.45 (978-1-56711-347-1(8) , Blackbirch Pr., Inc.) Thomson Gale.

—World in Focus: Central & South America. 2000. (gr. 5-8). lib. bdg. 26.00 (978-0-613-45649-4(1)) Tandem Library Bks.

Aloian, Molly & Kalman, Bobbie. Explora América del Sur. 2007. (SPA.). 32p. (gr. 6-10). pap. (***978-0-7787-8301-5(4)***) Crabtree Publishing Co.

Barnett, Tracy. Immigration from South America. 2004. (Changing Face of North America Ser.). (Illus.). 112p. (J). lib. bdg. (978-1-59084-687-2(7)) Mason Crest Pubs.

Chin-Lee, Cynthia. A Es para Decir Americas. 1999. (978-0-606-17568-5(7)) Tandem Library Bks.

Chin-Lee, Cynthia & De la Pena, Terri. A Es para Decir America's. Sanchez, Enrique O., illus. 1999. (SPA.). 32p. (J). (gr. k-4). pap. 6.95 (978-0-531-07134-2(0) , Orchard Bks.) Scholastic, Inc.

Dixon, Dougal. Agustinia & Other Dinosaurs of Central & South America. 2007. (Illus.). 24p. (J). (***978-1-4048-2269-6(0)*** , 1265746) Picture Window Bks.

Goodnough, David. Simon Bolivar: South American Liberator. 1998. (Hispanic Biographies Ser.). (Illus.). 112p. (YA). (gr. 6-12). lib. bdg. 26.60 (978-0-7660-1044-4(9)) Enslow Pubs., Inc.

In North & South America. (J). (gr. 5). 3.80 (978-0-8374-1454-6(7) , 405) Weekly Reader Corp.

McAlarney, Kathryn, et al. Amazon Connections: The People, the Forest & the River. McAlarney, Kathryn, illus. 2002. (Illus.). 56p. (J). (gr. 3-5). pap. 12.00 (978-0-9701035-4-3(9)) Shedd Aquarium Society.

Schaffer, David. Discovering South America's Land, People, & Wildlife: A MyReportLinks. com Book. 2004. (Continents of the World Ser.). (Illus.). 48p. (J). lib. bdg. 25.26 (978-0-7660-5208-6(7) , MyReportLinks.com Bks.) Enslow Pubs., Inc.

South America: Regions of the World. 2003. spiral bd. 16.95 (978-1-56004-158-0(7)) Social Studies Schl. Service.

Tunica, Nicky. South & Central America. 2001. (Cambridge Junior History Ser.). (Illus.). 48p. pap. 7.00 (978-0-521-77645-5(7)) Cambridge Univ. Pr.

SOUTH ATLANTIC STATES

see Atlantic States

SOUTH CAROLINA

Berri, Victoria L. South Carolina: A MyReportLinks. Com Book. 2003. (States Ser.). (Illus.). 48p. (J). lib. bdg. 25.26 (978-0-7660-5139-3(0) , MyReportLinks.com Bks.) Enslow Pubs., Inc.

Bodie, Idella. Carolina Girl: A Writer's Beginning. 1998. (Illus.). 225p. (J). pap. 12.95 (978-0-87844-140-2(9)) Sandlapper Publishing Co., Inc.

Capstone Press Staff, contrib. by. South Carolina. rev. ed. 2002. (One Nation Ser.). (Illus.). 48p. (J). (gr. 3-4). lib. bdg. 22.60 (978-0-7368-1265-8(2) , Bridgestone Bks.) Capstone Pr., Inc.

Cherrington, Janelle. South Carolina. (Rookie Read-About Geography Ser.). (Illus.). (J). 2004. 31p. (gr. 1-2). pap. 5.95 (978-0-516-27329-7(9)); 2003. 32p. 20.50 (978-0-516-22743-6(2)) Scholastic Library Publishing. (Children's Pr.).

Christian, Sandra J. South Carolina. 2003. (Land of Liberty Ser.). (Illus.). 64p. (J). lib. bdg. 25.26 (978-0-7368-2197-1(X)) Capstone Pr., Inc.

Columbia in Pictures. 2004. (Illus.). lib. bdg. 27.93 (978-0-8225-1996-6(8)) Lerner Publishing Group.

Crane, Carol. Net Numbers: A South Carolina Number Book. Palmer, Gary, illus. 2006. 40p. (J). (gr. k-5). 17.95 (978-1-58536-202-8(6)) Sleeping Bear Pr.

—P Is for Palmetto: A South Carolina Alphabet. Whyte, Mary, illus. 2002. 40p. (J). 17.95 (978-1-58536-047-5(3)) Sleeping Bear Pr.

Dykstra, Mary. South Carolina. 2006. (Portraits of the States Ser.). (Illus.). 32p. (J). pap. 8.95 (978-0-8368-4694-2(X)); lib. bdg. 17.50 (978-0-8368-4675-1(3)) Stevens, Gareth Inc.

Fredeen, Charles. South Carolina. 2nd rev. exp. ed. 2002. (Hello U. S. A. Ser.). (Illus.). 84p. (J). (gr. 3-6). 25.26 (978-0-8225-4087-8(8) , Lerner Pubns.) Lerner Publishing Group.

—South Carolina. rev. ed. 2002. (gr. 3-6). lib. bdg. 15.25 (978-0-613-46103-0(7)) Tandem Library Bks.

Heinrichs, Ann. South Carolina. 2005. (Welcome to the USA Ser.). 40p. (J). (gr. 1-5). 27.07 (978-1-59296-482-6(6)) Child's World, Inc.

—South Carolina. 2003. (This Land Is Your Land Ser.). (Illus.). 48p. (J). (gr. 3 up). lib. bdg. 22.60 (978-0-7565-0326-0(4)) Compass Point Bks.

Hoffman, Nancy. South Carolina. 2001. (Celebrate the States Ser.). (Illus.). 144p. (gr. 4-8). lib. bdg. 37.07 (978-0-7614-1065-2(1) , Benchmark Bks.) Cavendish, Marshall Corp.

Klein, Patricia H. & Horne, Paul A. South Carolina: Its History & Geography. 2000. (Illus.). ix, 262p. (J). (978-1-56733-962-8(X)) Clairmont Pr., Inc.

Kovacik, Charles F. & Steinke, Theodore R., eds. South Carolina: An Atlas. 2005. (Illus.). 40p. (YA). 9.95 (978-0-9768247-0-1(1)) South Carolina Geographic Alliance.

Marsh, Carole. The Big South Carolina Reproducible Activity Book! 2001. (Carole Marsh South Carolina Bks.). (Illus.). 96p. (J). (gr. 2-6). pap., act. bk. ed. 9.95 (978-0-7933-9955-0(6)) Gallopade International.

—My First Book about South Carolina. 2001. (Carole Marsh South Carolina Bks.). (Illus.). 32p. (J). (gr. k-4). pap. 7.95 (978-0-7933-9897-3(5)) Gallopade International.

—South Carolina Classic Christmas Trivia. 2002. (Carole Marsh South Carolina Bks.). (Illus.). 32p. pap. 6.95 (978-0-635-01445-0(9) , 14459); lib. bdg. 21.95 (978-0-635-01446-7(7) , 14467) Gallopade International. (Marsh, Carole Bks.).

—South Carolina Current Events Projects: 30 Cool, Activities, Crafts, Experiments & More for Kids to Do to Learn about Your State! 2003. (South Carolina Experience Ser.). 32p. (gr. k-8). pap. 5.95 (978-0-635-02059-8(9) , Marsh, Carole Bks.) Gallopade International.

—The South Carolina Experience Pocket Guide. 2001. (Carole Marsh South Carolina Bks.). (Illus.). 96p. (J). (gr. 3-8). pap. 6.95 (978-0-7933-9926-0(2)) Gallopade International.

—South Carolina Geography Projects: 30 Cool, Activities, Crafts, Experiments & More for Kids to Do to Learn about Your State! 2003. (South Carolina Experience Ser.). 32p. (gr. k-5). pap. 5.95 (978-0-635-01859-5(4) , Marsh, Carole Bks.) Gallopade International.

—South Carolina Government Projects: 30 Cool, Activities, Crafts, Experiments & More for Kids to Do to Learn about Your State! 2003. (South Carolina Experience Ser.). 32p. (gr. k-5). pap. 5.95 (978-0-635-01959-2(0) , Marsh, Carole Bks.) Gallopade International.

—South Carolina Hot Zone! Viruses, Diseases, & Epidemics in Our State's History. 1998. (Hot Zones! Ser.). (Illus.). (J). (gr. 3-12). pap. 19.95 (978-0-7933-8949-0(6)) Gallopade International.

—South Carolina Jeopardy! Answers & Questions about Our State! Line Art Staff, illus. 2001. 32p. (J). (gr. 3-8). pap. 7.95 (978-0-7933-9810-2(X)) Gallopade International.

—South Carolina "Jography" A Fun Run Through the Palmetto State! 2001. (Carole Marsh South Carolina Bks.). (Illus.). 32p. (Orig.). (J). (gr. 3-8). pap. 7.95 (978-0-7933-9839-3(8)) Gallopade International.

—South Carolina People Projects: 30 Cool, Activities, Crafts, Experiments & More for Kids to Do to Learn about Your State! 2003. (South Carolina Experience Ser.). 32p. (gr. k-5). pap. 5.95 (978-0-635-02009-3(2) , Marsh, Carole Bks.) Gallopade International.

—South Carolina Symbols & Facts Projects: 30 Cool, Activities, Crafts, Experiments & More for Kids to Do to Learn about Your State! 2003. (South Carolina Experience Ser.). 32p. (gr. k-5). pap. 5.95 (978-0-635-01909-7(4) , Marsh, Carole Bks.) Gallopade International.

McAuliffe, Bill. South Carolina: Facts & Symbols. 1999. (J). lib. bdg. 14.00 (978-0-531-11805-4(3)) Capstone Pr., Inc.

—South Carolina Facts & Symbols. (States & Their Symbols Ser.). 24p. (J). 1999. (Illus.). (gr. 2-3). lib. bdg. 18.60 (978-0-7368-0220-8(7) , Bridgestone Bks.); 2003. lib. bdg. 19.93 (978-0-7368-2271-8(2)) Capstone Pr., Inc.

Murray, Julie. South Carolina. 2006. (Illus.). 32p. (J). (gr. k-4). lib. bdg. 22.78 (978-1-59197-699-8(5) , Buddy Bks.) ABDO Publishing Co.

O'Neill, Elizabeth. Alfred Visits South Carolina. 2007. 24p. (J). pap. 12.00 (***978-0-9790240-5-4(6)***) Funny Bone Bks.

Parker, Janice. A Guide to South Carolina. 2001. (American States Ser.). (Illus.). 32p. (J). lib. bdg. 16.95 (978-1-930954-59-5(X)) Weigl Pubs., Inc.

Paterson Chappell, Ruth. All 'Bout Charleston. Wroth, Dean, illus. 1998. 54p. (J). 14.95 (978-0-87844-144-0(1)) Sandlapper Publishing Co., Inc.

S. C. Department of Archives and History Staff. South Carolina State Symbols Coloring Book. Andrews, Judith M., ed. 1998. 20p. (J). reprint ed. 2.00 (978-1-880067-49-9(8)) South Carolina Dept. of Archives & History.

Sherrow, Victoria. Uniquely South Carolina. (Heinemann State Studies). (Illus.). 48p. (J). 2006. lib. bdg. 31.36 (978-1-4034-4661-9(X)); 2004. pap. 332.10 (978-1-4034-4737-1(3)) Heinemann Library.

South Carolina. (Switched on Schoolhouse Ser.). 2003. cd-rom 24.95 (978-0-7403-0664-8(2)); 2000. (Illus.). (YA). (gr. 7-12). pap. 24.95 incl. cd-rom (978-0-7403-0292-3(2) , SOSSC) Alpha Omega Pubns., Inc.

Stroud, Cynthia. Carolina Children: The Sandhills. 2007. (Illus.). 30p. pap. 17.99 (***978-0-9794580-0-2(5)***) Carolina Children.

Volkwein, Ann. South Carolina: The Palmetto State. 2002. (World Almanac Library of the States). (Illus.). 48p. (J) (gr. 5 up). lib. bdg. 30.00 (978-0-8368-5144-1(7)); pap. 14.95 (978-0-8368-5314-8(8)) Stevens, Gareth Inc. (World Almanac Library).

Way, Jennifer. South Carolina (Carolina del Sur) 2006. (Bilingual Library of the United States of America: Set 2). (ENG & SPA., Illus.). 32p. (J). (gr. 3-6). lib. bdg. 22.50 (978-1-4042-3106-1(4) , Buenas Letra) Rosen Publishing Group, Inc., The.

Weatherly, Myra S. South Carolina. 2002. (From Sea to Shining Sea Ser.: 2). (Illus.). 80p. (J). (gr. 3-5). 30.50 (978-0-516-22317-9(8) , Children's Pr.) Scholastic Library Publishing.

Worth, Richard. South Carolina. 2004. (Life in the Thirteen Colonies Ser.). (Illus.). 124p. (J). 36.00 (978-0-516-24579-9(1) , Children's Pr.) Scholastic Library Publishing.

SOUTH CAROLINA—FICTION

Arrington, Aileen. Camp of the Angel. 2003. 154p. (YA). (gr. 5). 16.99 (978-0-399-23882-6(4) , Philomel) Penguin Group (USA) Inc.

Asim, Jabari. The Road to Freedom. 2004. 131p. (J). lib. bdg. 16.92 (***978-1-4242-0765-7(7)***) Fitzgerald Bks.

Behrens, Andy. All the Way (Splashproof Edition) 2007. 224p. (YA). (gr. 9). pap. 7.99 (978-0-14-240833-9(6) , Puffin) Penguin Group (USA) Inc.

Charley's Columbia Backyard. 2006. (J). 14.95 (***978-0-9793808-0-8(4)***) Backyard Ambassador Reader Publishing Co.

Clinton, Cathryn. The Calling. 2007. (Illus.). 176p. (YA). (gr. 5 up). pap. 5.99 (***978-0-7636-3373-8(9)***) Candlewick Pr.

Crouse, Donna J. The Ruby Ring: The Whispering Cove Kids Club. 2005. 114p. pap. 12.99 (978-0-9765339-0-0(1)) Crouse, Donna J.

Draper, Sharon M. Copper Sun. (YA). 2008. 336p. pap. 8.99 (***978-1-4169-5348-7(5)*** , Simon Pulse); 2006. 320p. (gr. 8 up). 16.95 (978-0-689-82181-3(6) , Atheneum) Simon & Schuster Children's Publishing.

—Copper Sun. l.t. ed. 2006. 358p. (YA). (gr. 8 up). 22.95 (978-0-7862-8948-6(1)) Thorndike Pr.

Flood, Pansie Hart. Secret Holes. Marshall, Felicia, illus. 2004. 128p. (J). (gr. 3-6). 15.95 (978-0-87614-923-2(9) , Carolrhoda Bks.) Lerner Publishing Group.

—Sometimey Friend. Marshall, Felicia, illus. 2005. 128p. (J). (gr. 4-6). 15.95 (978-1-57505-866-5(9)) Lerner Publishing Group.

—Sylvia & Miz Lula Maye. Marshall, Felicia, illus. 2003. (Middle Grade Fiction Ser.). 120p. (J). (gr. 3-6). 15.95 (978-0-87614-204-2(8) , Carolrhoda Bks.) Lerner Publishing Group.

Fountain, Edwin. Whispers from the Past. 2004. 145p. pap. 19.95 (978-1-4137-3256-6(9)) PublishAmerica, Inc.

Fuqua, Jonathan Scott. Darby. 2002. 256p. (J). (gr. 5 up). 16.99 (978-0-7636-1417-1(3)) Candlewick Pr.

Fuqua, Jonathon Scott. Darby. 2006. 256p. (J). (gr. 5). 5.99 (978-0-7636-2290-9(7)) Candlewick Pr.

Hansen, Joyce. The Heart Calls Home. 1999. viii, 175p. (J). (gr. 7-12). 16.95 (978-0-8027-8636-4(7)) Walker & Co.

Harrison, Marie Joseph. Mosanna & Me. 2003. 160p. pap. 12.95 (978-0-916251-62-8(4)) Sunbelt Pubns., Inc.

—Mosanna & Me. 2003. (gr. 7-12). lib. bdg. 22.20 (978-0-613-89684-9(X)) Tandem Library Bks.

Haskins, James. The March on Washington. 2004. (Illus.). 192p. (J). (gr. 5 up). pap. 10.95 (978-0-940975-93-4(9) , Sankofa Bks.) Just Us Bks., Inc.

Ingle, Sheila C. Courageous Kate: A Daughter of the American Revolution. 2006. (J). (***978-1-891885-52-5(9)***) Hub City Writers Project.

Jones, Joyce Elaine. For Such a Journey. 2005. (J). 5.99 (978-0-9766559-0-9(X)) Treorca Pr.

Karr, Kathleen. Worlds Apart. 2005. 208p. (J). 15.95 (978-0-7614-5195-2(1)) Cavendish, Marshall Corp.

Luddy, Karon. Spelldown: The Big-Time Dreams of a Small-Town Word Whiz. 2007. 224p. (YA). 15.99 (978-1-4169-1610-9(5)) Simon & Schuster Children's Publishing.

Monte, Emily C. The Lost Sword of the Confederate Ghost: A Mystery in Two Centuries. 1999. 116p. (J). (gr. 4-7). 5.99 (978-1-57249-132-8(9)) White Mane Publishing Co., Inc.

Myers, Anna. The Keeping Room. 1999. (Illus.). 128p. (J). (gr. 3-7). pap. 5.99 (978-0-14-130468-7(5) , Puffin) Penguin Group (USA) Inc.

—The Keeping Room. 1999. (J). (978-0-606-16786-4(2)) Tandem Library Bks.

—Keeping Room. 1999. (gr. 3-6). lib. bdg. 14.15 (978-0-613-19519-5(1)) Tandem Library Bks.

Myers, Walter Dean. The Glory Field. 1999. 420p. (J). 15.60 (978-0-03-054616-7(8)) Holt, Rinehart & Winston.

O'Connor, Barbara. Beethoven in Paradise. 1999. (Illus.). 160p. (J). (gr. 5-8). pap. 7.95 (978-0-374-40588-5(3) , Sunburst) Farrar, Straus & Giroux.

—Beethoven in Paradise. 1999. (gr. 3-6). lib. bdg. 12.95 (978-0-613-29559-8(5)) Tandem Library Bks.

Plowden, Sally H. Turtle Tracks. Plowden, Tee, illus. 2002. 32p. (J). (gr. 4-6). 14.95 (978-0-9679016-6-4(9)) Palmetto Conservation Foundation.

Rinaldi, Ann. Cast Two Shadows: The American Revolution in the South. 2004. (Great Episodes Ser.). (Illus.). 304p. (YA). pap. 6.95 (978-0-15-205077-1(9) , Gulliver Bks.) Harcourt Children's Bks.

—Cast Two Shadows: The American Revolution in the South. 2000. (Illus.). (J). 12.65 (978-0-606-18805-0(3)) Tandem Library Bks.

Rizner, Staci. Last Chance Out. 2002. (gr. 7-12). lib. bdg. 24.55 (978-0-613-81754-7(0)) Tandem Library Bks.

Rue, Nancy N. The Ally. 1998. (Christian Heritage Ser.). 192p. (J). (gr. 3-7). pap. (978-1-56179-561-1(5)) Focus on the Family Publishing.

—The Escape. 1998. (Christian Heritage Ser.). 192p. (J). (gr. 3-7). pap. 5.99 (978-1-56179-639-7(5)) Bethany Hse. Pubs.

—The Hostage. 1998. (Christian Heritage Ser.). 208p. (J). (gr. 3-7). pap. 5.99 (978-1-56179-638-0(7)) Bethany Hse. Pubs.

—The Misfit. 1998. (Christian Heritage Ser.). 192p. (J). (gr. 3-7). pap. (978-1-56179-560-4(7)) Focus on the Family Publishing.

—The Trap. 1998. (Christian Heritage Ser.). 208p. (J). (gr. 3-7). pap. (978-1-56179-567-3(4)) Focus on the Family Publishing.

Swager, Christine R. Black Crows & White Cockades. 1999. (gr. 7-12). lib. bdg. 22.20 (978-0-613-89131-8(7)) Tandem Library Bks.

Teaster, Gerald Fred. Spirit up the People: Four Days to the Cowpens. 2006. (Illus.). 236p. per. 12.95 (978-0-9744556-2-4(8)) Junior History Pr.

Thomas, Earl W. Mystery of the Pirates' Treasure. 1999. (Illus.). 44p. (J). (ps-7). lib. bdg. 11.60 (978-0-613-29174-3(3)) Tandem Library Bks.

Victoria & the Baby Tree. 2005. pap. 14.95 (***978-1-59526-525-8(2)***) Media Creations, Inc.

Weatherford, Carole Boston. Champions on the Bench: The Cannon Street YMCA All-Stars. Jenkins, Leonard, illus. 2007. 32p. (J). (gr. 1-4). 16.99 (978-0-8037-2987-2(1) , Dial) Penguin Group (USA) Inc.

Williams, G. Walton. Of Mice & Bells. Kollock, John, illus. unabr. ed. 1999. 674p. (J). (gr. k-3). pap. 6.95 (978-0-9703570-1-4(X)) Barksdale Hse. Pr.

SOUTH CAROLINA—HISTORY

Blashfield, Jean F. The South Carolina Colony. 2003. (Spirit of America). (Illus.). 40p. (J). (gr. 2-6). 28.50 (978-1-56766-710-3(4)) Child's World, Inc.

S

Bodie, Idella. The Secret Message. 1998. (Heroes & Heroines of the American Revolution Ser.: Vol. 2). (Illus.). 45p. (J). (ps-3). pap. 5.95 (978-0-87844-145-7(X)) Sandlapper Publishing Co., Inc.

—The Wizard Owl. 2003. (Illus.). 86p. (J). pap. 6.95 (978-0-87844-167-9(0)) Sandlapper Publishing Co., Inc.

Born, Mark Alan. TIDELOG 2003 Graphic Almanac for Southeastern States: Covering the Entire South Carolina Coast, North to Wilmington NC, & South to Brunswick, Ga. Escher, M. C., illus. 2004. 144p. spiral bd. 14.95 (978-1-933120-05-8(3)) Pacific Pubs.

Britton, Tamara L. The South Carolina Colony. 2001. (Colonies Ser.). (Illus.). 32p. (J). (gr. k-6). lib. bdg. 22.78 (978-1-57765-581-7(8) , Checkerboard Library) ABDO Publishing Co.

Cornelius, Kay. Francis Marion: The Swamp Fox. 2001. (gr. 5-8). lib. bdg. 17.60 (978-0-613-32583-7(4)) Tandem Library Bks.

Doak, Robin. South Carolina, 1540-1776. 2007. (Voices from Colonial America Ser.). (Illus.). 112p. (YA). (gr. 5-9). 21.95 (***978-1-4263-0066-0(2)**); lib. bdg. 32.90 (***978-1-4263-0067-7(0)**) National Geographic Society. (National Geographic Children's Bks.).

Doherty, Craig A. & Doherty, Katherine M. South Carolina. 2005. (Thirteen Colonies Ser.). (Illus.). 144p. (J). (gr. 4-9). 35.00 (978-0-8160-5409-1(6)) Facts On File, Inc.

Girod, Christina M. South Carolina. 2001. (Thirteen Colonies Ser.). (Illus.). 104p. (YA). (gr. 4-12). lib. bdg. 27.45 (978-1-56006-994-2(5) , LML00902-178232, Lucent Bks.) Thomson Gale.

Haberle, Susan E. The South Carolina Colony. 2005. (Fact Finders Ser.). (Illus.). 32p. (J). (gr. 2-4). lib. bdg. 22.60 (978-0-7368-2683-9(1) , Fact Finders) Capstone Pr., Inc.

Hasan, Heather. A Primary Source History of the Colony of South Carolina. 2005. (Primary Sources of the Thirteen Colonies & the Lost Colony Ser.). (Illus.). 64p. (gr. 5-8). (J). pap. 14.60 (978-1-4042-0667-0(1)); (YA). lib. bdg. 29.25 (978-1-4042-0436-2(9)) Rosen Publishing Group, Inc., The.

Hawk, Frank. The Story of the H. L. Hunley & Queenie's Coin. Nance, Dan, illus. 2004. 40p. (J). 16.95 (978-1-58536-218-9(2)) Sleeping Bear Pr.

Huff, Archie V., Jr. The History of South Carolina in the Building of the Nation. rev. ed. 2000. (Illus.). (J). (978-1-57003-336-0(6)) Univ. of South Carolina Pr.

Kauffman, Scott. Francis Marion: Swamp Fox of South Carolina. 2006. (Forgotten Heroes of the American Revolution Ser.). (Illus.). 88p. (YA). (gr. 5-11). lib. bdg. 23.95 (978-1-59556-014-8(9)) OTTN Publishing.

Krebs, Laurie. A Day in the Life of a Colonial Indigo Planter. 2004. (Library of Living & Working in Colonial Times). (Illus.). 24p. (J). lib. bdg. 18.75 (978-0-8239-6229-7(6)) Rosen Publishing Group, Inc., The.

Marsh, Carole. The Lost Colony Storybook. 2002. (Carole Marsh Bks.). (Illus.). (J). 32p. (gr. k-4). pap. 7.95 (978-0-635-01353-8(3) , 13533); 36p. (gr. 3-9). lib. bdg. 21.95 (978-0-635-01354-5(1) , 13541) Gallopade International. (Marsh, Carole Bks.).

—My First Pocket Guide South Carolina. 2000. (South Carolina Experience! Ser.). (Illus.). 96p. (J). (gr. 3-8). 12.95 (978-0-635-01330-9(4) , 13304) Gallopade International.

—South Carolina History Projects: 30 Cool, Activities, Crafts, Experiments & More for Kids to Do to Learn about Your State! 2003. (South Carolina Experience Ser.). 32p. (gr. k-5). pap. 5.95 (978-0-635-01809-0(8) , Marsh, Carole Bks.) Gallopade International.

—South Carolina Millionaire. 2001. (GameBook Ser.). 32p. (J). (gr. 3-8). pap., act. bk. ed. 9.95 (978-0-635-00096-5(2)) Gallopade International.

—South Carolina Survivor. 2001. (GameBook Ser.). 32p. (J). (gr. 3-8). pap., act. bk. ed. 9.95 (978-0-635-00561-8(1)) Gallopade International.

—South Carolina Wheel of Fortune. 2001. (GameBook Ser.). 32p. (J). (gr. 3-8). pap., act. bk. ed. 9.95 (978-0-7933-9696-2(4)) Gallopade International.

—Wheel of Fortune. 2001. (South Carolina Experience! Ser.). (J). lib. bdg. 29.95 (978-0-7933-9697-9(2)) Gallopade International.

—Who Wants to Be a Millionaire? 2001. (Carole Marsh South Carolina Bks.). (J). lib. bdg. 29.95 (978-0-635-00097-2(0)) Gallopade International.

McDaniel, Suzanne H., et al. At Home in South Carolina. 2nd rev. ed. 2000. (Illus.). 378p. (J). (gr. 3-4). 32.85 (978-1-928930-00-6(X)) Educational Developmental Laboratories, Inc.

Mis, Melody S. The Colony of South Carolina: A Primary Source History. 2007. (Primary Source Library of the Thirteen Colonies & the Lost Colony). (Illus.). 24p. (J). lib. bdg. (978-1-4042-3438-3(1) , PowerKids Pr.) Rosen Publishing Group, Inc., The.

Peters Aheron, Piper. Pickens County, South Carolina. 2000. (Images of America Ser.). (Illus.). 128p. (gr. 5 up). pap. 19.99 (978-0-7385-0606-7(0)) Arcadia Publishing.

Shipwreck Search: Discovery of the H. L. Hunley. 2007. (J). pap. 5.95 (***978-0-8225-6449-2(1)** , First Avenue Editions) Lerner Publishing Group.

Strauch, Katina & Strauch, Ileana. College of Charlestion. 2000. (College History Ser.). (Illus.). 128p. pap. 19.99 (978-0-7385-0636-4(2)) Arcadia Publishing.

Walker, Sally M. Shipwreck Search: Discovery of the H. L. Hunley. Verstraete, Elaine, illus. 2006. (On My Own Science Ser.). 48p. (J). (gr. 2-4). lib. bdg. 25.26 (978-1-57505-878-8(2) , Millbrook Pr.) Lerner Publishing Group.

Weintraub, A. How to Draw South Carolinas Sights & Symbols. 2002. (Kids Guide to Drawing America Ser.). 32p. (J). lib. bdg. 25.25 (978-0-8239-6097-2(8) , PowerKids Pr.) Rosen Publishing Group, Inc., The.

Whitehurst, Susan. The Colony of South Carolina. 2000. (Library of the Thirteen Colonies & the Lost Colony). (Illus.), 24p. (J). (gr. 3). lib. bdg. 19.95 (978-0-8239-5486-5(2) , PowerKids Pr.) Rosen Publishing Group, Inc., The.

Wiener. South Carolina, 6 pack. 2004. (13 Colonies Ser.). (Illus.). 51.30 (978-1-4109-0375-4(3)) Harcourt Schl. Pubs.

Wiener, Roberta & Arnold, James R. South Carolina. 2004. (Illus.). 64p. (J). 28.56 (978-0-7398-6888-1(8)) Harcourt Schl. Pubs.

—The 13 Colonies: South Carolina. 2004. (Illus.). 64p. (J). 8.95 (978-1-4109-0312-9(5)) Harcourt Schl. Pubs.

SOUTH DAKOTA

Ackman, Geneva & Turnipseed, Susan. South Dakota: A Journey Through Time. 3rd ed. 2001. (Illus.). 48p. (YA). (gr. 3 up). pap., act. bk. ed. 9.00 (978-1-57579-131-9(5)) Pine Hill Pr., Inc.

Adamson, Thomas K. South Dakota. 2003. (Land of Liberty Ser.). (Illus.). 64p. (J). lib. bdg. 25.26 (978-0-7368-2198-8(8)) Capstone Pr., Inc.

Anderson, J. Christopher. Uniquely South Dakota. 2004. (Heinemann State Studies). (Illus.). 48p. (J). 31.36 (978-1-4034-4662-6(8)) Heinemann Library.

Anderson, Reuben. Uniquely South Dakota. 2004. (Heinemann State Studies). (Illus.). 48p. (J). (ps-7). pap. 9.00 (978-1-4034-4731-9(4)) Heinemann Library.

Brown, Jonatha A. South Dakota. 2006. (Portraits of the States Ser.). (J). pap. (978-0-8368-4725-3(3)); lib. bdg. (978-0-8368-4708-6(3)) Stevens, Gareth Inc.

Brown, Vanessa. South Dakota (Dakota del Sur) 2006. (Bilingual Library of the United States of America: Set 2). (ENG & SPA., Illus.). 32p. (J). (gr. 3-6). lib. bdg. 22.50 (978-1-4042-3107-8(2) , Buenas Letra) Rosen Publishing Group, Inc., The.

Bryan, Dale-Marie. South Dakota. 2006. (Rookie Read-About Geography Ser.). (Illus.). 32p. (J). (gr. 1-2). 20.50 (***978-0-516-25444-9(8)**) Scholastic Library Publishing.

Diekman, Diane. A Farm in the Hidewood: My South Dakota Home. 2001. 84p. pap. 6.00 (978-0-9708201-0-5(0)) Altruria Publishing Co.

Feeney, Kathy. South Dakota Facts & Symbols. (States & Their Symbols Ser.). 24p. (J). 2000. (Illus.). (gr. 2-3). lib. bdg. 18.60 (978-0-7368-0646-6(6) , Bridgestone Bks.); 2003. lib. bdg. 19.93 (978-0-7368-2272-5(0)) Capstone Pr., Inc.

Heinrichs, Ann. South Dakota. Kania, Matt, illus. 2005. (Welcome to the USA Ser.). 40p. (J). (gr. 1-5). 27.07 (978-1-59296-483-3(4)) Child's World, Inc.

—South Dakota. 2003. (This Land Is Your Land Ser.). (Illus.). 48p. (J). (gr. 3 up). lib. bdg. 22.60 (978-0-7565-0286-7(1)) Compass Point Bks.

Hirschmann, Kris. South Dakota: The Mount Rushmore State. 2003. (World Almanac Library of the States). (Illus.). 48p. (J). (gr. 5 up). pap. 14.95 (978-0-8368-5331-5(8)); lib. bdg. 30.00 (978-0-8368-5160-1(9)) Stevens, Gareth Inc. (World Almanac Library).

Kummer, Patricia K. South Dakota. rev. ed. 2002. (One Nation Ser.). (Illus.). 48p. (J). (gr. 3-4). lib. bdg. 22.60 (978-0-7368-1266-5(0) , Bridgestone Bks.) Capstone Pr., Inc.

Latza, Jodi Holley & Latza, Greg, photos by. South Dakota: An Alphabetical Scrapbook. 2000. (Illus.). (J). 11.95 (978-0-9673485-2-0(8)) PeopleScapes.

Marsh, Carole. The Big South Dakota Reproducible Activity Book. 2001. (Carole Marsh South Dakota Bks.). (Illus.). 96p. (J). (gr. 2-6). pap. 9.95 (978-0-7933-9956-7(4)) Gallopade International.

—My First Book about South Dakota. 2001. (Carole Marsh South Dakota Bks.). 32p. (J). (gr. k-4). pap. 7.95 (978-0-7933-9898-0(3)) Gallopade International.

—South Dakota Classic Christmas Trivia. 2002. (Carole Marsh South Dakota Bks.). (Illus.). 32p. pap. 14.95 (978-0-635-01447-4(5) , 14475); lib. bdg. 21.95 (978-0-635-01448-1(3) , 14483) Gallopade International. (Marsh, Carole Bks.).

—South Dakota Current Events Projects: 30 Cool, Activities, Crafts, Experiments & More for Kids to Do to Learn about Your State! 2003. (South Dakota Experience Ser.). 32p. (gr. k-8). pap. 5.95 (978-0-635-02060-4(2) , Marsh, Carole Bks.) Gallopade International.

—The South Dakota Experience Pocket Guide. 2001. (Carole Marsh South Dakota Bks.). (Illus.). 96p. (J). (gr. 3-8). pap. 6.95 (978-0-7933-9927-7(0)) Gallopade International.

—South Dakota Geography Projects: 30 Cool, Activities, Crafts, Experiments & More for Kids to Do to Learn about Your State! 2003. (South Dakota Experience Ser.). 32p. (gr. k-5). pap. 5.95 (978-0-635-01875-5(6) , Marsh, Carole Bks.) Gallopade International.

—South Dakota Government Projects: 30 Cool, Activities, Crafts, Experiments & More for Kids to Do to Learn about Your State! 2003. (South Dakota Experience Ser.). 32p. (gr. k-5). pap. 5.95 (978-0-635-01960-8(4) , Marsh, Carole Bks.) Gallopade International.

—South Dakota Jeopardy! Answers & Questions about Our State! Line Art Staff, illus. 2001. 32p. (J). (gr. 3-8). pap. 7.95 (978-0-7933-9811-9(8)) Gallopade International.

—South Dakota "Jography" A Fun Run Thru Our State! 2001. (Carole Marsh South Dakota Bks.). (Illus.). 32p. (J). (gr. 3-8). pap. 7.95 (978-0-7933-9840-9(1)) Gallopade International.

—South Dakota People Projects: 30 Cool, Activities, Crafts, Experiments & More for Kids to Do to Learn about Your State! 2003. (South Dakota Experience Ser.). 32p. (gr. k-5). pap. 5.95 (978-0-635-02010-9(6) , Marsh, Carole Bks.) Gallopade International.

—South Dakota Symbols & Facts Projects: 30 Cool, Activities, Crafts, Experiments & More for Kids to Do to Learn about Your State! 2003. (South Dakota Experience Ser.). 32p. (gr. k-5). pap. 5.95 (978-0-635-01910-3(8) , Marsh, Carole Bks.) Gallopade International.

—South Dakota Wheel of Fortune. 2001. (GameBook Ser.). 32p. (J). (gr. 3-8). pap., act. bk. ed. 9.95 (978-0-7933-9698-6(0)) Gallopade International.

—Wheel of Fortune. 2001. (South Dakota Experience! Ser.). (J). lib. bdg. 29.95 (978-0-7933-9699-3(9)) Gallopade International.

McDaniel, Melissa. South Dakota. 2nd ed. 2006. (Celebrate the States Ser.). (J). lib. bdg. 39.93 (978-0-7614-2156-6(4) , Benchmark Bks.) Cavendish, Marshall Corp.

Murray, Julie. South Dakota. 2006. (Illus.). 32p. (J). (gr. k-4). lib. bdg. 22.78 (978-1-59197-700-1(2) , Buddy Bks.) ABDO Publishing Co.

Savage, Jeff. South Dakota: A MyReportLinks. Com Book. 2003. (States Ser.). (Illus.). 48p. (J). lib. bdg. 25.26 (978-0-7660-5116-4(1) , MyReportLinks.com Bks.) Enslow Pubs., Inc.

Shepherd, Donna Walsh. South Dakota. 2001. (America the Beautiful Ser.). (Illus.). 144p. (J). (gr. 5-8). 36.00 (978-0-516-21093-3(9) , Children's Pr.) Scholastic Library Publishing.

Sirvaitis, Karen. South Dakota. 2nd exp. rev. ed. (Hello U. S. A. Ser.). (Illus.). 84p. (J). (gr. 3-6). 2003. pap. 6.95 (978-0-8225-4139-4(4)); 2002. 25.26 (978-0-8225-4070-0(3) , Lerner Pubns.) Lerner Publishing Group.

South Dakota. 2000. (Switched on Schoolhouse Ser.). (Illus.). (YA). (gr. 7-12). pap. 24.95 incl. cd-rom (978-0-7403-0293-0(0) , SOSSD) Alpha Omega Pubns., Inc.

South Dakota. 1999. pap. 19.93 (978-0-516-21798-7(4) , Children's Pr.) Scholastic Library Publishing.

Strudwick, Leslie. A Guide to South Dakota. 2001. (American States Ser.). 32p. (J). lib. bdg. 16.95 (978-1-930954-13-7(1)) Weigl Pubs., Inc.

Townsley, Janet Howe. Dakota Dreams: Fannie Sabra Howe's Own Story, 1881-1884. 2003. (Illus.). 77p. (J). 19.95 (978-0-9715171-4-1(2)) South Dakota State Historical Society.

Turnipseed, Susan. South Dakota: A Journey Through Time Student Workbook. Heers, Matt & Heers, Nate, illus. 2003. 28p. (J). pap. (978-1-57579-268-2(0)) Pine Hill Pr., Inc.

—South Dakota: A Journey Through Time Student Workbook Answer Key. Heers, Matt & Heers, Nate, illus. 2003. 28p. (J). pap. (978-1-57579-269-9(9)) Pine Hill Pr., Inc.

Yacowitz, Caryn Huberman. South Dakota. 2003. (From Sea to Shining Sea Ser.: 2). (Illus.). 80p. (J). 30.50 (978-0-516-22394-0(1) , Children's Pr.) Scholastic Library Publishing.

SOUTH DAKOTA—FICTION

Anderson, William. M Is for Mount Rushmore: A South Dakota Alphabet. Harness, Cheryl, illus. 2005. (Discover America State by State Ser.). 40p. (J). 17.95 (978-1-58536-141-0(0)) Sleeping Bear Pr.

Arrington, Frances. Prairie Whispers. 2005. 192p. (J). (gr. 5). pap. 6.99 (978-0-14-240306-8(7) , Puffin) Penguin Group (USA) Inc.

Baum, L. Frank. The Discontented Gopher. Conahan, Carolyn, illus. 2006. vii, 31p. (J). (978-0-9749195-9-1(4) , South Dakota State Historical Society Pr.) South Dakota State Historical Society.

Bensimon, Gladys. Paha Sapa: Black Hills. 2005. 81p. pap. 14.95 (978-1-4137-6972-2(1)) PublishAmerica, Inc.

Black Hills Summer. 2003. (YA). per. (978-0-9740718-0-0(3)) Strathmoor Pr.

Brouwer, Sigmund. Tyrant of the Badlands. 2002. (Accidental Detectives Ser.: Bk. 4). 144p. (J). (gr. 3-8). pap. 5.99 (978-0-7642-2567-3(7)) Bethany Hse. Pubs.

—Tyrant of the Badlands. 2002. (gr. 3-6). lib. bdg. 14.15 (978-0-613-82924-3(7)) Tandem Library Bks.

Brown, Marc. Buster Hits the Trail. 2005. (Postcards from Buster Ser.). (Illus.). 48p. (J). (gr. 1-4). 14.99 (978-0-316-15900-5(X)); pap., pap. 3.99 (978-0-316-00121-2(X)) Little, Brown Bks. for Young Readers.

Golden Books Staff. Westward, Ho! 2007. (Illus.). 48p. (J). (ps-2). pap. 3.99 (978-0-375-83471-4(0) , Golden Bks.) Random Hse. Children's Bks.

Harcourt School Publishers Staff. Button Time Advanced Level. 3rd ed. 2002. (Trophies Reading Program Ser.). (Illus.). pap. 5.10 (978-0-15-323291-6(9)) Harcourt Schl. Pubs.

Hill, Pamela Smith. Ghost Horses. 1999. 224p. (J). (gr. 4-7). pap. 4.50 (978-0-380-72942-5(3)) HarperCollins Pubs.

—Ghost Horses. 1999. (J). (978-0-606-16340-8(9)) Tandem Library Bks.

Hobbs, Will. Go Big or Go Home. 2008. 192p. (J). 15.99 (***978-0-06-074141-9(4)**); lib. bdg. 16.89 (***978-0-06-074142-6(2)**) HarperCollins Pubs.

Kotzwinkle, William. The Return of Crazy Horse. 2001. (Illus.). 32p. (J). (ps-3). 16.95 (978-1-58394-047-1(2) , Frog Ltd.) North Atlantic Bks.

Kropp, Joseph P. Hickok's Gold. 2006. (J). (***978-1-890905-25-5(9)**) Day to Day Enterprises.

Love, D. Anne. A Year Without Rain. 2000. (Illus.). 128p. (J). (gr. 4-6). tchr. ed. 15.95 (978-0-8234-1488-8(4)) Holiday Hse., Inc.

Raintree Steck-Vaughn Staff. Simon's Big Challenge. 1999. (Illus.). (J). pap. 35.60 (978-0-7398-0909-9(1)) Steck-Vaughn.

Schurch, Maylan Henry. The Meatless Mayhem Mystery. 2003. (Justin Case Adventures Ser.: 5). 121p. (J). pap. 7.99 (978-0-8280-1615-5(1) , 133-650) Review & Herald Publishing Assn.

Steck-Vaughn Staff. Simon's Big Challenge/Over-Comming Challenges: The Life of Charles F. Bolden Jr. 1999. (Take Me Home Ser.). (J). pap. 11.30 (978-0-7398-0944-0(X)) Steck-Vaughn.

Turner, Ann Warren. Grasshopper Summer. Meltzer, Erika, illus. 2000. 176p. (J). (gr. 4-7). pap. 4.99 (978-0-689-83522-3(1) , Aladdin) Simon & Schuster Children's Publishing.

—Grasshopper Summer. 2000. (Illus.). (J). (978-0-606-17921-8(6)) Tandem Library Bks.

Wilder, Laura Ingalls. The First Four Years. 2007. (Little House Ser.). 160p. (J). pap. 6.99 (978-0-06-088545-8(9) , Harper Trophy) HarperCollins Pubs.

—The First Four Years. Williams, Garth, illus. (Little House Ser.). (J). 2004. 160p. pap. 8.99 (978-0-06-058188-6(3) , Harper Trophy); 2003. 144p. pap. 5.99 (978-0-06-052243-8(7)) HarperCollins Pubs.

—The First Four Years. Williams, Garth, illus. l.t. ed. 2002. (LRS Large Print Cornerstone Ser.). (J). lib. bdg. 27.95 (978-1-58118-103-6(5) , 25535) LRS.

—The First Four Years. 2003. (gr. 3-6). lib. bdg. 14.15 (978-0-613-71430-3(X)) Tandem Library Bks.

—Little Town on the Prairie. Williams, Garth, illus. (Little House Ser.). 320p. (J). 2004. pap. 8.99 (978-0-06-058186-2(7) , Harper Trophy); 2003. pap. 5.99 (978-0-06-052242-1(9)) HarperCollins Pubs.

—Little Town on the Prairie. 2000. (Little House Ser.). (J). (gr. 3-6). pap. 9.90 (978-0-06-449101-3(3) , Harper Trophy) HarperCollins Pubs.

—Little Town on the Prairie. Williams, Garth, illus. l.t. ed. 2002. (LRS Large Print Cornerstone Ser.). (J). lib. bdg. 35.95 (978-1-58118-101-2(9) , 25533) LRS.

—Little Town on the Prairie. 2003. (gr. 3-6). lib. bdg. 14.15 (978-0-613-71425-9(3)) Tandem Library Bks.

—The Long Winter. Williams, Garth, illus. 2004. (Little House Ser.). 352p. (J). pap. 8.99 (978-0-06-058185-5(9) , Harper Trophy) HarperCollins Pubs.

—The Long Winter. Williams, Garth, illus. l.t. ed. 2002. (LRS Large Print Cornerstone Ser.). (J). lib. bdg. 35.95 (978-1-58118-100-5(0)) LRS.

—These Happy Golden Years. 2007. (Little House Ser.). 304p. (J). pap. 6.99 (978-0-06-088544-1(0) , Harper Trophy) HarperCollins Pubs.

—These Happy Golden Years. Williams, Garth, illus. (Little House Ser.). (J). 2004. 304p. pap. 8.99 (978-0-06-058187-9(5) , Harper Trophy); 2003. 336p. pap. 5.99 (978-0-06-052315-2(8)) HarperCollins Pubs.

—These Happy Golden Years. l.t. ed. (J). (gr. 3-6). 35.95 (978-1-58118-102-9(7)) LRS.

—These Happy Golden Years. 2003. (gr. 3-6). lib. bdg. 14.15 (978-0-613-71434-1(2)) Tandem Library Bks.

SOUTH DAKOTA—HISTORY

Bodden, Valerie. Mount Rushmore. 2006. (Modern Wonders of the World Ser.). (Illus.). 32p. 18.95 (978-1-58341-440-8(1) , Creative Education) Creative Co., The.

A Guide to South Dakota. 2001. (American States Ser.). 32p. (J). per. (978-1-930954-04-5(2)) Weigl Pubs., Inc.

Marsh, Carole. My First Pocket Guide South Dakota. 2000. (South Dakota Experience! Ser.). (Illus.). 96p. (J). (gr. 3-8). 12.95 (978-0-635-01331-6(2) , 13312) Gallopade International.

—South Dakota History Projects: 30 Cool, Activities, Crafts, Experiments & More for Kids to Do to Learn about Your State! 2003. (South Dakota Experience Ser.). 32p. (gr. k-5). pap. 5.95 (978-0-635-01810-6(1) , Marsh, Carole Bks.) Gallopade International.

—South Dakota Millionaire. 2001. (GameBook Ser.). 32p. (J). (gr. 3-8). pap., act. bk. ed. 9.95 (978-0-635-00098-9(9)) Gallopade International.

—South Dakota Survivor. 2001. (GameBook Ser.). 32p. (J). (gr. 3-8). pap., act. bk. ed. 9.95 (978-0-635-00562-5(X)) Gallopade International.

—The Survivor: A Class Challenge. 2001. (Carole Marsh South Dakota Bks.). (J). lib. bdg. 29.95 (978-0-635-00687-5(1)) Gallopade International.

—Who Wants to Be a Millionaire? 2001. (Carole Marsh South Dakota Bks.). (J). lib. bdg. 29.95 (978-0-635-00099-6(7)) Gallopade International.

Peters, S. True. How to Draw South Dakotas Sights & Symbols. 2002. (Kids Guide to Drawing America Ser.). 32p. (J). lib. bdg. 25.25 (978-0-8239-6098-9(6) , PowerKids Pr.) Rosen Publishing Group, Inc., The.

Waldman, Nomi J. Deadwood, South Dakota: A Frontier Community. 2006. (Navigators Ser.). (J). pap. 38.00 (***978-1-4108-6247-1(X)**) Benchmark Education Co.

Webb, Matt. Mount Rushmore. 2006. (Great Structures in History Ser.). (J). (978-0-7377-3155-2(9) , Greenhaven Pr., Inc.) Thomson Gale.

SOUTH POLE

Adil, Janeen R. Why Is the South Pole So Cold? A Book about Antarctica. 2007. (First Facts Ser.). (Illus.). 24p. (J). 21.26 (978-0-7368-6383-4(4)) Capstone Pr., Inc.

Gogerly, Liz. Amundsen & Scott's Race to the South Pole. 2007. (J). (***978-1-4034-9761-1(3)**) Heinemann Library.

Markle, Sandra. Super Cool Science: South Pole Stations, Past, Present, & Future. 1998. (Illus.). 32p. (J). (gr. 3-7). 16.95 (978-0-8027-8470-4(4)); lib. bdg. 17.85 (978-0-8027-8471-1(2)) Walker & Co.

Patton, Geoff. Poles Apart. 2005. (X-Zone Ser.). (Illus.). 30p. (gr. 4-8). 23.00 (978-0-7910-8988-0(6)) Facts On File, Inc.

Philips, Eric. Icetrek: A Journey to the South Pole. 2000. (YA). pap. 34.95 (978-1-86950-360-4(0)) HarperCollins Pubs. New Zealand NZL. *Dist:* Antipodes Bks. & Beyond.

Pipe, Jim. The Race to the South Pole. 2006. (Stories from History Ser.). 48p. (J). 14.95 (***978-0-7696-4722-7(7)**); pap. 6.95 (***978-0-7696-4702-9(2)**) School Specialty Publishing.

Ryan, Zoe Alderfer. Ann & Liv Cross Antarctica: A Dream Come True! 2001. (J). (gr. 1-6). pap. 10.95 (978-0-9711527-0-0(5)) yourexpedition.

S

Glasscock, Sarah. The Southwest. 2005. (Navigators Ser.). (J). pap. 42.00 (*978-1-4108-5104-8(4)) Benchmark Education Co.

Goodman, Michael E. Wyatt Earp. 2005. (Legends of the West Ser.). (Illus.). 48p. (gr. 5-9). 21.95 (978-1-58341-339-5(1) , Creative Education) Creative Co., The.

Hall, Margaret. Venom & Visions. 2007. (Shockwave: Arts & Culture Ser.). (Illus.). 36p. (J). (gr. 4-6). lib. bdg. 25.00 (*978-0-531-17788-4(2) , Children's Pr.) Scholastic Library Publishing.

Healy, Nick. Billy the Kid. 2005. (Illus.). 48p. (gr. 5-9). 21.95 (978-1-58341-335-7(9) , Creative Education) Creative Co., The.

Katchur, Matthew & Sterngass, Jon. Spanish Settlement in North America. 2006. (Latino American History Ser.). (Illus.). 112p. (J). (gr. 5-8). 35.00 (978-0-8160-6442-7(3) , Chelsea Hse.) Facts On File, Inc.

King, David C. Projects about the Spanish West. 2005. (Hands-On History Ser.). (Illus.). 47p. (J). (978-0-7614-1982-2(9) , Benchmark Bks.) Cavendish, Marshall Corp.

Lavender, David. Mother Earth, Father Sky: The Pueblo Indians of the American Southwest. 1998. (Illus.). 96p. (J). (gr. 4-7). tchr. ed. 16.95 (978-0-8234-1365-2(9)) Holiday Hse., Inc.

Lilly, Melinda. Spanish Missions. 2003. (Rourke Discovery Library). (Illus.). 24p. (gr. 1-4). 14.95 (978-1-58952-369-2(5)) Rourke Publishing, LLC.

Marcovitz, Hal. Coronado to Escalate: Francisco Coronado & the Exploration of the American Southwest. 1999. (Explorers of the New World Ser.). (Illus.). 64p. (J). (gr. 4 up). 31.00 (978-0-7910-5515-1(9) , Chelsea Hse.) Facts On File, Inc.

Marrin, Albert. Empires Lost & Won: The Spanish Heritage in the Southwest. 2004. (Illus.). 216p. (J). (gr. 4-8). reprint ed. 19.00 (978-0-7567-7800-2(X)) DIANE Publishing Co.

Martin, Carol O. Exploring the Southwest: Activity Cards. Margolin, Malcolm, ed. Miller, Carol S., illus. Carrow, Gene, photos by. 1998. (Explorers Ser.: Vol. 1). 110p. (J). (gr. 4-6). pap. 10.00 (978-0-9615635-1-6(6)) Bay Area Explorers.

McNeese, Tim. Santa Fe. 2007. (Colonial Settlements in America Ser.). 120p. (J). (gr. 5-8). 30.00 (*978-0-7910-9332-0(8) , Chelsea Hse.) Facts On File, Inc.

Mountjoy, Shane. Francisco Coronado & the Seven Cities of Gold. Goetzmann, William H., ed. 2005. (Explorers of New Lands Ser.). (Illus.). 142p. (J). (gr. 4-8). lib. bdg. 30.00 (978-0-7910-8631-5(3) , Chelsea Hse.) Facts On File, Inc.

National Geographic Society Staff, contrib. by. The Southwest Today. 2004. (Illus.). 32p. (J). (978-0-7922-4535-3(0)) National Geographic Society.

Sanford, William R. The Santa Fe Trail in American History. 2000. (In American History Ser.). (Illus.). 112p. (YA). (gr. 5-12). lib. bdg. 26.60 (978-0-7660-1348-3(0)) Enslow Pubs., Inc.

The Santa Fe Trail, 6 Packs. (On Deck Ser.: Vol. 2). 24p. (gr. 4-5). 35.00 (978-0-7578-5815-4(5)) Rigby Education.

Steele, Christy. California & the Southwest Join the United States. 2005. (Illus.). 48p. (J). pap. (978-0-8368-5793-1(3)); lib. bdg. 30.00 (978-0-8368-5786-3(0)) Stevens, Gareth Inc. (World Almanac Library).

Stefoff, Rebecca. Texas & the Far West. 2002. (North American Historical Atlases Ser.). (Illus.). 48p. (J). 27.07 (978-0-7614-1345-5(6) , Benchmark Bks.) Cavendish, Marshall Corp.

Stein, R. Conrad. In the Spanish West. 1999. (How We Lived Ser.). (Illus.). 72p. (J). (gr. 4-8). lib. bdg. 27.07 (978-0-7614-0906-9(8) , Benchmark Bks.) Cavendish, Marshall Corp.

—Spanish Missionaries: Bringing Spanish Culture to the Americas. 2005. (Proud Heritage: the Hispanic Library Ser.). (Illus.). 40p. (J). (gr. 3-7). 28.50 (978-1-59296-387-4(0)) Child's World, Inc.

Stone, Lynn M. Texas Longhorn. 2003. (Animals in U.S. History Ser.). (Illus.). 24p. (J). 25.64 (978-1-58952-702-7(X)) Rourke Publishing, LLC.

Worth, Richard. Independence for Latino America. 2006. (Latino-American History Ser.). 112p. (J). (gr. 5-8). 35.00 (978-0-8160-6441-0(5) , Chelsea Hse.) Facts On File, Inc.

SOUTHWEST, NEW—FICTION

Anaya, Rudolfo A. Roadrunner's Dance. Diaz, David, illus. 2000. 32p. (gr. k-4). 16.49 (978-0-7868-2209-6(0)) Disney Pr.

—Roadrunner's Dance. Diaz, David, illus. 2000. 32p. (gr. k-4). 15.99 (978-0-7868-0254-8(5)) Hyperion Bks. for Children.

Browne, Vee. The Stone Cutter & the Navajo Maiden. Bryceleа, Clifford, illus. 2008. (NAV.). 32p. (*978-1-893354-92-0(X)) Salina Bookshelf.

Cook, Jean Thor. Los Amiguitos' Fiesta. Wilson, Lincoln, ed. Shade, Judith Donoho, illus. l.t. ed. 2001. Tr. of Little Friends' Fiesta. (SPA.). 28p. (J). (ps-3). 17.00 (978-0-9708940-0-7(7)) Gently Worded Bks., LLC.

Curry, Jane Louise. The Egyptian Box. 2002. (Illus.). 192p. (J). (gr. 4-7). 16.95 (978-0-689-84273-3(2) , McElderry, Margaret K.) Simon & Schuster Children's Publishing.

—The Egyptian Box. l.t. ed. 2002. 216p. (J). 21.95 (978-0-7862-4896-4(3)) Thorndike Pr.

Hip Hip Hooray, It's Monsoon Day! 2007. (ENG & SPA.). (YA). pap. 15.95 (*978-1-886679-36-8(3)) Arizona Sonora Desert Museum Pr.

McMurtry, Larry. Anything for Billy: A Novel. 2001. (gr. 7-12). lib. bdg. 23.45 (978-0-613-57619-2(5)) Tandem Library Bks.

Parpan, Justin. Gwango's Lonesome Trail. Parpan, Justin, illus. 2006. (Illus.). 32p. (J). 15.95 (978-1-60108-004-2(2)) Red Cygnet Pr.

Polette, Keith. Isabel & the Hungry Coyote/Isabel y el Coyote Hambriento. Raven Tree Press Staff, ed. Szegedy, Esther, illus. 2004. Tr. of Isabel y el coyote Hambriento. (SPA.). 32p. (J). 16.95 (978-0-9724973-0-5(7) , 626999) Raven Tree Pr.

Roach, Joyce Gibson. Horned Toad Canyon. 2004. (Illus.). 48p. 17.95 (978-1-931721-01-1(7)) Bright Sky Pr.

Stein, R. Conrad. On the Old Western Frontier. 1999. (How We Lived Ser.). (Illus.). 72p. (J). (gr. 4-8). lib. bdg. 28.50 (978-0-7614-0909-0(2) , Benchmark Bks.) Cavendish, Marshall Corp.

Taylor, Bonnie Highsmith. Kodi's Mare. Marks, Dea, illus. 2000. (Cover-to-Cover Novel Ser.). 82p. (J). pap. (978-0-7891-2929-1(9)); (gr. 2-5). lib. bdg. 13.95 (978-0-7807-8962-3(8)) Perfection Learning Corp.

Travels with Annie. 2002. per. 27.50 (978-0-9726639-0-8(8)) Sacred Mountain Foundation, A California Non Profit Public Benefit.

Van Draanen, Wendelin. Sammy Keyes & the Wild Things. 2007. (Sammy Keyes Ser.: Bk. 11). 304p. (J). (gr. 5-8). 15.99 (978-0-375-83525-4(3) , Knopf Bks. for Young Readers) Random Hse. Children's Bks.

—Sammy Keyes & the Wild Things. Biggs, Brian, illus. 2007. (Sammy Keyes Ser.: Bk. 11). 304p. (J). (gr. 5-8). lib. bdg. 18.99 (978-0-375-93525-1(8) , Knopf Bks. for Young Readers) Random Hse. Children's Bks.

SOUTHWEST, OLD

Here are entered works on the section which comprised the southwestern part of the United States before the cessions of land from Mexico following the Mexican War. It includes Louisiana, Texas, Arkansas, Tennessee, Kentucky and Missouri.

Arnold, James R. & Wiener, Roberta. River to Victory: The Civil War in the West, 1861-1863. 2005. (Civil War Ser.). (Illus.). 72p. (J). (gr. 5-12). lib. bdg. 25.26 (978-0-8225-2314-7(0)) Lerner Publishing Group.

Doherty, Kieran. Ranchers, Homesteaders & Traders: Frontiersmen of the South-Central States. Johnson, Sylvia A. & Anderson, Jenna, eds. 2001. (Shaping America Ser.: Vol. No. 4). (Illus.). 176p. (J). (gr. 7 up). lib. bdg. 22.95 (978-1-881508-53-3(6)) Oliver Pr., Inc.

Gallagher, Derek, text. Ancient Dwellings of the Southwest. 2004. (Illus.). 10p. (J). 16.95 (978-1-58369-048-2(4)) Western National Parks Assn.

Wilson, Leonore. The Spanish Exploration of the Southwest. 2002. (Exploration & Discovery Ser.). (Illus.). 64p. (YA). (gr. 5 up). lib. bdg. (978-1-59084-055-9(0)) Mason Crest Pubs.

SOVEREIGNS

see Kings, Queens, Rulers, etc.; Queens

SOVIET UNION

Baker, Lawrence W. Cold War Reference Library Cumulative Index. 2003. (U-X-L Cold War Reference Library). 85p. (J). 5.00 (978-0-7876-7667-4(5) , UXL) Thomson Gale.

—Immigration & Migration Reference. 2003. (U-X-L Cold War Reference Library). (J). 5.00 (978-0-7876-7734-3(5)) Zagat Survey.

Boast, Clare. Russia. 1998. (Next Stop! Ser.). 32p. (J). (gr. 2-4). lib. bdg. 19.92 (978-1-57572-569-7(X)) Heinemann Library.

Conboy, Fiona & Rice, Terence M. G. Welcome to Russia. 1999. (Welcome to My Country Ser.). (Illus.). 48p. (J). (gr. 2 up). lib. bdg. 26.00 (978-0-8368-2498-8(9)) Stevens, Gareth Inc.

Hanes, Sharon M., et al. Cold War: Almanac, 2 vols. 2003. (U-X-L Cold War Reference Library). (Illus.). (J). (978-0-7876-9087-8(2) , UXL) Thomson Gale.

Harvey, Miles. Look What Came from Russia. 1999. (Look What Came from Ser.). 32p. (gr. 2-4). pap. 6.95 (978-0-531-15967-5(1) , Watts, Franklin) Scholastic Library Publishing.

—Look What Came from Russia. 1999. (J). (gr. 3-6). lib. bdg. 15.25 (978-0-8085-8424-7(3)); (Illus.). (J). (978-0-606-18154-9(7)) Tandem Library Bks.

Kallen, Stuart A. Primary Sources. 2003. (Illus.). 112p. (J). 29.95 (978-1-59018-243-7(X) , Lucent Bks.) Thomson Gale.

Kort, Michael G. Russia. rev. ed. 1998. (Nations in Transition Ser.). (Illus.). 208p. (J). (gr. 7-12). 25.00 (978-0-8160-3776-6(0)) Facts On File, Inc.

Marquez, Heron. Russia in Pictures. 2nd ed. 2004. (Visual Geography Series, Second Ser.). (Illus.). 80p. (J). (gr. 5-12). 27.93 (978-0-8225-0937-0(7)) Lerner Publishing Group.

Murrell, Kathleen Berton. Russia. 2000. (Eyewitness Bks.). (Illus.). 64p. (J). (gr. 4-7). 15.99 (978-0-7894-5880-3(2)) Dorling Kindersley Publishing, Inc.

Murrell, Kathleen Berton & Dorling Kindersley Publishing Staff. Russia. 2000. (Eyewitness Bks.). (Illus.). 64p. (J). (gr. 4-7). lib. bdg. 19.99 (978-0-7894-6623-5(6)) Dorling Kindersley Publishing, Inc.

Popescu, Julian. Russia. 1999. (Major World Nations Ser.). (Illus.). 144p. (YA). (gr. 4-7). 29.95 (978-0-7910-4750-7(4) , Chelsea Hse.) Facts On File, Inc.

Rice, Terence M. G. Russia. 1999. (Countries of the World Ser.). (Illus.). 96p. (J). (gr. 6 up). lib. bdg. 30.00 (978-0-8368-2263-2(3)) Stevens, Gareth Inc.

Richardson, Adele D. Russia. (Let's Investigate Ser.). (Illus.). 32p. (J). 2000. pap. 10.60 (978-0-89812-007-3(1) , Creative Paperbacks); 1998. lib. bdg. 19.95 (978-0-88682-986-5(0) , Creative Education) Creative Co., The.

Streissguth, Thomas. Life in Communist Russia. 2000. (Way People Live Ser.). (Illus.). 96p. (J). (gr. 7-10). 29.95 (978-1-56006-378-0(5) , LML00902-177763, Lucent Bks.) Thomson Gale.

Thoennes, Kristin. Russia. 1999. (Countries of the World Ser.). (Illus.). 126p. (J). (gr. 2-3). 18.60 (978-0-7368-0156-0(1) , Bridgestone Bks.) Capstone Pr., Inc.

SOVIET UNION—BIOGRAPHY

Downing, David. Vladimir Ilyich Lenin. 2002. (Leading Lives Ser.). 64p. (J). (gr. 5-7). (Illus.). lib. bdg. 28.50 (978-1-58810-582-0(2)); pap. 8.95 (978-1-4034-0137-3(3) , 91616) Heinemann Library.

Glaser, Jason. Maria Sharapova. 2008. (J). lib. bdg. (*978-1-4042-4181-7(7) , PowerKids Pr.) Rosen Publishing Group, Inc., The.

Goldstein, Margaret J. V. I. Lenin. 2007. (Biography Ser.). 112p. (J). (gr. 6-12). 29.27 (978-0-8225-5977-1(3) , Twenty-First Century Bks.) Lerner Publishing Group.

Langley, Andrew. Mikhail Gorbachev. 2003. (Leading Lives Ser.). 64p. (J). lib. bdg. 28.50 (978-1-4034-0831-0(9)) Heinemann Library.

Naden, Corinne J. & Blue, Rose. Lenin. 2003. (Importance of Ser.). (Illus.). 112p. (J). 32.45 (978-1-59018-233-8(2) , Lucent Bks.) Thomson Gale.

Resnick, Abraham. Lenin: Founder of the Soviet Union. 2004. 132p. (YA). pap. 13.95 (978-0-595-30701-2(9) , Authors Choice Pr.) iUniverse, Inc.

SOVIET UNION—FICTION

Brewster, Hugh. Anastasia's Album: The Last Tsar's Youngest Daughter. 1999. 64p. (J). pap. 7.99 (978-0-7868-1395-7(4)) Disney Pr.

Currier, Alvin Alexsi. Old Maria: A Grandfather's Tale of Spiritual Warfare Once upon a Time in Old Russia. Glazunova, Nadexda, illus. 2002. 28p. (J). (gr. 2-6). 14.95 (978-0-9723411-0-3(2)) Currier, Alvin Alexsi.

Dillon, Jana. Sasha's Matrioshka Dolls. Lattimore, Deborah Nourse, illus. 2007. 28p. (J). reprint ed. 16.00 (*978-1-4223-6684-4(7)) DIANE Publishing Co.

Grant, Myrna. Ivan & the Moscow Circus. (Illus.). 160p. (YA). mass mkt. 5.99 (978-1-85792-619-4(6) , Christian Focus) Christian Focus Pubns. GBR. *Dist:* Riverside.

Hergé. L' Affaire Tournesol. 1999. (Tintin Ser.).Tr. of Calculus Affair. (FRE.). (J). (gr. 4-7). 21.95 (978-2-203-00117-6(8)) Casterman, Editions FRA. *Dist:* Distribooks, Inc.

—The Calculus Affair. (Illus.). 62p. (J). 19.95 (978-0-8288-5014-8(3)) French & European Pubns., Inc.

—Tintin au Pays des Soviets. 1999. (Tintin Ser.). (FRE.). (J). (gr. 4-7). pap. 29.95 (978-2-203-01101-4(7)) Casterman, Editions FRA. *Dist:* Distribooks, Inc.

Herge. Tintin in the Land of the Soviets. 2007. (Adventures of Tintin Ser.). 144p. pap. 10.99 (*978-0-316-00374-2(3)) Little, Brown Bks. for Young Readers.

Hergé. Tintin in the Land of the Soviets: Reporter for Le Petit Vingtieme. fac. ed. 2004. (Adventures of Tintin Ser.). (Illus.). 138p. (J). reprint ed. 24.95 (978-0-86719-903-1(2)) Last Gasp of San Francisco.

Howell, Gill. Snow King. Cann, Helen, illus. 2005. 24p. (J). lib. bdg. 22.65 (*978-1-59646-742-2(8)) Dingles & Co.

Johnson, Vargie. Catherine the Great the Victorious: What Made Them Famous? 2006. 156p. (J). per. 15.00 (978-1-931195-96-6(X)) KiwE Publishing, Ltd.

Ludmila's Way - Teaching Guide. 2003. (J). 17.95 (978-1-55942-192-8(4)) Marsh Media.

Mazzeo Zocchi, Judy. Paulie & Sasha: Circus or Not. Vannozzi, Don, illus. 2001. (Adventures of Paulie & Sasha Ser.). 32p. (J). (gr. k-4). 15.95 (978-1-891997-00-6(9) , Treehouse Court) Dingles & Co.

Pirotta, Saviour & Marks, Alan. The Giant Oak Tree. 2007. (J). (*978-1-59771-080-0(6)) Sea-To-Sea Pubns.

Polacco, Patricia. Babushka Baba Yaga. 1999. (Illus.). 32p. (J). (ps-3). pap. 6.99 (978-0-698-11633-7(X) , Putnam Juvenile) Penguin Group (USA) Inc.

—Babushka Baba Yaga. 1999. (J). lib. bdg. 13.79 (978-0-606-16844-1(3)); lib. bdg. 15.30 (978-0-613-11296-3(2)) Tandem Library Bks.

—Rechenka's Eggs. Polacco, Patricia, illus. 2002. (Illus.). (J). 14.04 (978-0-7587-3502-7(2)) Book Wholesalers, Inc.

Ramblin' Rose: The Porcelain Mines in Russia. 2007. 196p. (YA). pap. 8.99 (*978-0-9776043-7-1(3)) Aspirations Media, Inc.

Sandman, Rochel. Perfect Porridge: A Story about Kindness. Zakashansky-Zverev, Chana, illus. 2000. 32p. (J). (ps-2). 9.95 (978-0-922613-92-2(3)) Hachai Publishing.

Scieszka, Jon. What's So Great about Peter? 2007. (Time Warp Trio). 96p. (J). pap. 6.99 (*978-0-06-111651-3(3) , Harper Trophy) HarperCollins Pubs.

Thompson, Kay & Knight, Hilary. Eloise in Moscow. 40th ed. 2000. (Illus.). 80p. (J). (ps-3). 17.00 (978-0-689-83211-6(7)) Simon & Schuster Children's Publishing.

Townsend, Tom. Nadia of the Night Witches. Kemnitz, Myrna, ed. 1998. 158p. (YA). (gr. 8 up). 9.99 (978-0-88092-273-9(7) , 2737) Royal Fireworks Publishing Co.

Whelan, Gloria. The Impossible Journey. 2004. 256p. (J). (gr. 5 up). reprint ed. pap. 5.99 (978-0-06-441083-0(8) , Harper Trophy) HarperCollins Pubs.

—The Turning. 2006. 224p. (J). 15.99 (978-0-06-075593-5(8)) HarperCollins Pubs.

SOVIET UNION—HISTORY

Blomquist, Christopher. Russia, a Primary Source Guide. 2005. (Countries of the World, a Primary Source Journey Ser.). (Illus.). 24p. (J). 19.95 (978-1-4042-2756-9(3) , PowerKids Pr.) Rosen Publishing Group, Inc., The.

Chrisp, Peter. Cuban Missile Crisis. 2002. (gr. 7-12). lib. bdg. 24.15 (978-0-613-52355-4(5)) Tandem Library Bks.

Downing, David. Vladimir Ilyich Lenin. 2002. (Leading Lives Ser.). 64p. (J). (gr. 5-7). (Illus.). lib. bdg. 28.50 (978-1-58810-582-0(2)); pap. 8.95 (978-1-4034-0137-3(3) , 91616) Heinemann Library.

Feldman, Heather. Valentina Tereshkova: The First Woman in Space. 2003. (Space Firsts Ser.). (Illus.). 24p. (J). lib. bdg. 19.95 (978-0-8239-6246-4(6) , PowerKids Pr.) Rosen Publishing Group, Inc., The.

Gottfried, Ted. The Road to Communism. Reim, Melanie K., illus. 2002. (Rise & Fall of the Soviet Union Ser.). 144p. (gr. 7 up). lib. bdg. 28.90 (978-0-7613-2557-4(3) , Twenty-First Century Bks.) Lerner Publishing Group.

Harkins, Susan and William. The Fall of the Soviet Union 1991. 2007. (Monumental Milestones Ser.). (Illus.). 48p. (YA). lib. bdg. 29.95 (*978-1-58415-539-3(6)) Mitchell Lane Pubs., Inc.

Haugen, Brenda. Joseph Stalin: Dictator of the Soviet Union. 2006. (Signature Lives Ser.). (Illus.). 112p. (J). (gr. 5-7). 30.60 (978-0-7565-1597-3(1)) Compass Point Bks.

Langley, Andrew. The Collapse of the Soviet Union: The End of an Empire. 2006. 96p. (J). (gr. 7 up). lib. bdg. (978-0-7565-2009-0(6)) Compass Point Bks.

Massie, Robert K. Nicholas & Alexandra. 2000. (gr. 7-12). lib. bdg. 28.05 (978-0-613-37162-9(3)) Tandem Library Bks.

Olszewski, Zbigniew. They Will Break Their Teeth on Us: The Heroic Russian Army-The Biggest of Napoleon's Enemies. 2000. (Illus.). 140p. (YA). per. 18.00 (978-0-9708198-1-9(1)) Olszewski, Zbigniew & Janis.

Russian Colonies in the Americas, 6 Packs. (On Deck Ser.: Vol. 2). 24p. (gr. 4-5). 35.00 (978-0-7578-5803-1(1)) Rigby Education.

Streissguth, Thomas. Rise of the Soviet Union. 2001. (gr. 7-12). lib. bdg. 33.25 (978-0-613-73853-8(5)) Tandem Library Bks.

Suib, Stella. Inside Russia's SVR: The Foreign Intelligence Service. 2005. (Illus.). 63p. (YA). reprint ed. 26.00 (978-0-7567-8668-7(1)) DIANE Publishing Co.

Theisen, Gordon. The Mystery of Anastasia Romanov. 2001. (History Channel History Guides Ser.). (Illus.). 40p. (J). pap. 9.99 (978-0-86730-846-4(X)) Lebhar-Friedman Bks.

SOVIET UNION—HISTORY—FICTION

Dueck, Adele. Nettie's Journey. 2006. (Illus.). 224p. (J). pap. 7.95 (978-1-55050-322-7(7)) Coteau Bks. CAN. *Dist:* F & W Pubns., Inc.

Fine, Anne. The Road of Bones. 2008. 224p. (YA). 16.95 (*978-0-374-36316-1(1)) Farrar, Straus & Giroux.

Gloria Whelan. The Turning. l.t. ed. 2006. 190p. (YA). 21.95 (978-0-7862-9035-2(8)) Thorndike Pr.

Holub, Josef. An Innocent Soldier. Hofmann, Michael, tr. from GER. 2005. (Illus.). 240p. (J). (gr. 8 up). pap. 16.99 (978-0-439-62771-9(0) , Levine, Arthur A. Bks.) Scholastic, Inc.

Holub, Josef & Hofmann, Michael. An Innocent Soldier. 2007. (Illus.). 256p. (J). pap. 6.99 (978-0-439-62772-6(9) , Levine, Arthur A. Bks.) Scholastic, Inc.

Lasky, Kathryn. Broken Song. 160p. (J). 2007. pap. 6.99 (978-0-14-240741-7(0) , Puffin); 2005. (gr. 7). 15.99 (978-0-670-05931-7(5) , Viking Juvenile) Penguin Group (USA) Inc.

—The Night Journey. 2005. 160p. (J). (gr. 3-7). 15.99 (978-0-670-05963-8(3) , Viking Juvenile); (Illus.). (YA). pap. 5.99 (978-0-14-240322-8(9) , Puffin) Penguin Group (USA) Inc.

—The Night Journey. 2002. (J). (gr. 6 up). 20.25 (978-0-8446-7210-6(6)) Smith, Peter Pub., Inc.

Meyer, Carolyn. Anastasia: The Last Grand Duchess: Russia 1914. 2000. (Royal Diaries Ser.). (Illus.). 224p. (J). (gr. 4-8). pap. 10.95 (978-0-439-12908-4(7)) Scholastic, Inc.

Pushkin, Alexandr. The Daughter of the Commandant. 2006. 77.99 (*978-1-4280-0068-1(2)); pap. 71.99 (*978-1-4280-0080-3(1)) IndyPublish.com.

Rabin, Staton. The Curse of the Romanovs. 2007. 288p. (J). (gr. 7 up). 17.99 (978-1-4169-0208-9(2) , McElderry, Margaret K.) Simon & Schuster Children's Publishing.

Verne, Jules. Michael Strogoff. 2002. (gr. 3-6). lib. bdg. 31.55 (978-0-613-83365-3(1)) Tandem Library Bks.

—Miguel Strogoff. (SPA., Illus.). 176p. (YA). 11.95 (978-84-7281-109-6(3) , AF1109) Auriga, Ediciones S.A. ESP. *Dist:* Continental Bk. Co., Inc.

—Miguel Strogoff. 2002. (SPA.). 14.95 (978-84-392-0915-7(0) , EV30597); 2001. (978-84-305-2204-0(2)) Lectorum Pubns., Inc.

—Miguel Strogoff. (Coleccion Clasicos de la Juventud). (SPA., Illus.). 236p. (J). 12.95 (978-84-7189-106-8(9) , ORT305) Ortells, Alfredo Editorial S.L. ESP. *Dist:* Continental Bk. Co., Inc.

Whelan, Gloria. Burying the Sun. 224p. (J). 2007. pap. 6.99 (*978-0-06-054114-9(8) , Harper Trophy); 2004. (gr. 5 up). 15.99 (978-0-06-054112-5(1)); 2004. (gr. 5 up). lib. bdg. 16.89 (978-0-06-054113-2(X)) HarperCollins Pubs.

Whelan, Gloria. The Impossible Journey. 2004. 248p. (J). (gr. k-9). per. 14.30 (978-0-613-99970-0(3)) Tandem Library Bks.

Wulffson, Don L. Soldier X. 2003. 240p. (YA). pap. 6.99 (978-0-14-250073-6(9) , Puffin); 2001. 244p. (J). (gr. 5-9). 16.99 (978-0-670-88863-4(X) , Viking Juvenile) Penguin Group (USA) Inc.

—Soldier X. 2003. (gr. 7-12). lib. bdg. 15.30 (978-0-613-67163-7(5)) Tandem Library Bks.

SOVIET UNION—HISTORY—1689-1800

Gibson, Karen Bush. The Life & Times of Catherine the Great. 2005. (Biography from Ancient Civilizations Ser.). (Illus.). 48p. (J). (gr. 4-7). lib. bdg. 29.95 (978-1-58415-347-4(4)) Mitchell Lane Pubs., Inc.

Hatt, Christine. Catherine the Great. 2003. (Judge for Yourself Ser.). (J). (Illus.). 64p. (gr. 5 up). lib. bdg. 30.00 (978-0-8368-5535-7(3)); pap. (978-0-8368-5538-8(8)) Stevens, Gareth Inc. (World Almanac Library).

Whitelaw, Nancy. Catherine the Great & the Enlightenment in Russia. 2004. (World Leaders Ser.). (Illus.). 160p. (YA). (gr. 6-12). lib. bdg. 26.95 (978-1-931798-27-3(3)) Reynolds, Morgan Inc.

SOVIET UNION—HISTORY—REVOLUTION OF 1905

Dowswell, Paul. The Russian Revolution. 2004. (Days That Shook the World Ser.). (Illus.). 47p. (J). lib. bdg. 28.56 (978-0-7398-6647-4(8)) Raintree.

Vail, John J. Peace, Land, Bread! A History of the Russian Revolution. 2006. (Illus.). 148p. (YA). (gr. 6-10). reprint ed. 22.00 (978-1-4223-5676-0(0)) DIANE Publishing Co.

SOVIET UNION—HISTORY—1917-

Hite, John, et al. Communist Russia under Lenin & Stalin. 2002. (Illus.). 336p. pap. 54.00 (***978-0-7195-7488-7(9)*** , Hodder Murray) Hodder Education GBR. *Dist:* Trans-Atlantic Pubns., Inc.

Joihnson, Robert, compiled by. Lenin, Stalin & Communist Russia: The Myth & Reality of Communism. 2003. (Studymates Ser.). (Illus.). 132p. (C). pap. 27.50 (978-1-84285-039-8(3)) Studymates Ltd. GBR. *Dist:* Trans-Atlantic Pubns., Inc.

Naden, Corinne J. & Blue, Rose. Lenin. 2003. (Importance of Ser.). (Illus.). 112p. (J). 32.45 (978-1-59018-233-8(2) , Lucent Bks.) Thomson Gale.

The Russian Revolution, 2. 2005. (Illus.). 124p. (YA). pap., lab manual ed. (978-1-891306-79-2(0)) Choices Education Program, Watson Institute, Brown Univ.

The Russian Revolution. 2003. (Eye on History Ser.). 32p. (gr. 5-12). 5.99 (978-1-56822-941-6(0) , IF2674) School Specialty Publishing.

Sherman, Josepha. The Cold War. 2004. (Chronicle of America's Wars Ser.). (Illus.). 96p. (J). (gr. 5-12). 27.93 (978-0-8225-0150-3(3)) Lerner Publishing Group.

SOVIET UNION—HISTORY—REVOLUTION, 1917-1921

Allan, Tony. The Russian Revolution. 2003. (20th-Century Perspectives Ser.). (Illus.). 48p. (J). (gr. 5-7). lib. bdg. 27.07 (978-1-4034-0151-9(9)) Heinemann Library.

Edwards, Judith. Lenin & the Russian Revolution in World History. 2001. (In World History Ser.). (Illus.). 128p. (J). (gr. 5-12). lib. bdg. 26.60 (978-0-7660-1464-0(9)) Enslow Pubs., Inc.

Ross, Stewart. The Russian Revolution. 2002. (Events & Outcomes Ser.). (Illus.). 80p. (J). lib. bdg. (978-0-7398-5801-1(7)) Raintree.

Whiting, Jim. The Russian Revolution 1917. 2007. (Monumental Milestones Ser.). (Illus.). 48p. (YA). lib. bdg. 29.95 (***978-1-58415-537-9(X)***) Mitchell Lane Pubs., Inc.

SOVIET UNION—HISTORY—1925-1953

Downing, David. Joseph Stalin. 2001. (Leading Lives Ser.). (Illus.). 64p. (J). (gr. 5-7). lib. bdg. 27.86 (978-1-58810-165-5(7)) Heinemann Library.

Ewing, E. Thomas. The Teachers of Stalinism: Policy, Practice, & Power in Soviet Schools of the 1930s. 2002. (History of Schools & Schooling Ser.). (Illus.). 352p. (C). pap. 29.95 (978-0-8204-5233-3(5)) Lang, Peter Publishing, Inc.

Gottfried, Ted. The Stalinist Empire. Reim, Melanie K., illus. 2002. (Rise & Fall of the Soviet Union Ser.). 128p. (gr. 7 up). lib. bdg. 28.90 (978-0-7613-2558-1(1) , Twenty-First Century Bks.) Lerner Publishing Group.

Joihnson, Robert, compiled by. Lenin, Stalin & Communist Russia: The Myth & Reality of Communism. 2003. (Studymates Ser.). (Illus.). 132p. (C). pap. 27.50 (978-1-84285-039-8(3)) Studymates Ltd. GBR. *Dist:* Trans-Atlantic Pubns., Inc.

Kenworthy, Joyce. Joseph Stalin. 2002. (History's Villains Ser.). (Illus.). 112p. (J). 29.94 (978-1-56711-626-7(4) , Blackbirch Pr., Inc.) Thomson Gale.

Marrin, Albert. Stalin. 2002. 244p. (J). 13.95 (978-1-893103-09-2(9)) Beautiful Feet Bks.

Zuehlke, Jeffrey. Joseph Stalin. 2006. (Illus.). 112p. (J). 27.93 (978-0-8225-3421-1(5) , Twenty-First Century Bks.) Lerner Publishing Group.

SOVIET UNION—POLITICS AND GOVERNMENT

Lugovskaya, Nina. I Want to Live: The Diary of a Young Girl in Stalin's Russia. Bromfield, Andrew, tr. from RUS. 2007. (Illus.). 304p. (YA). (gr. 7 up). 17.00 (***978-0-618-60575-0(4)***) Houghton Mifflin Co. Trade & Reference Div.

SPACE, OUTER

see Outer Space

SPACE AND TIME

see also Cyberspace; Relativity (Physics); Time Travel

Asimov, Isaac & Hantula, Richard. Space Junk. 2005. (Isaac Asimov's 21st Century Library of the Universe). (Illus.). 32p. (J). lib. bdg. 24.67 (978-0-8368-3983-8(8)) Stevens, Gareth Inc.

Butterfield, Moira. Space. Biggin, Gary & Lipscombe, Nick, illus. 32p. (J). mass mkt. 8.99 (978-0-590-24424-4(8)) Scholastic, Inc.

Carroll, Michael W., et al. Space & Time. 2005. (God's Creation Ser.). (Illus.). 40p. (J). 7.99 (978-0-310-70578-9(9)) Zonderkidz.

Gribbin, John R. Time & Space. 2000. (Eyewitness Bks.). (Illus.). 64p. (J). (gr. 3-7). 15.99 (978-0-7894-5578-9(1)) Dorling Kindersley Publishing, Inc.

Jacklin, Karl. A Space in Time. (Illus.). (J). (gr. 3-6). pap. (978-1-876367-04-6(0)) Wizard Bks.

Richardson, Hazel. How to Build a Time Machine. Rowe, Alan, illus. 2001. (How to Ser.). 96p. (J). (gr. 5-7). 16.00 (978-0-531-14644-6(8) , Watts, Franklin) Scholastic Library Publishing.

—How to Build a Time Machine. 2001. (gr. 5-8). lib. bdg. 12.95 (978-0-613-54545-7(1)) Tandem Library Bks.

Wadsworth, Pamela. Amser a Gofod. 2005. (WEL., Illus.). 24p. pap. (978-1-85596-247-1(0)) Dref Wen.

—Golwg Gyntaf Ar Amser a Gofod. 2005. (WEL., Illus.). 24p. pap. (978-1-85596-248-4(9)) Dref Wen.

—Rhagor Am Amser a Gofod. 2005. (WEL., Illus.). 24p. pap. (978-1-85596-242-2(X)) Dref Wen.

SPACE AND TIME—FICTION

Abela, Deborah. Mission: Hollywood. O'Connor, George, illus. 2006. (Spy Force Ser.). 240p. (J). 9.95 (978-0-689-87360-7(3)) Simon & Schuster Children's Publishing.

Abela, Deborah. Mission: Hollywood. O'Connor, George, illus. 2007. (Spy Force Ser.). 240p. (J). pap. 5.99 (***978-1-4169-3969-6(5)*** , Aladdin) Simon & Schuster Children's Publishing.

Ali, Khayyam Esab. The Wormhole Kids Visit President Kennedy. 2004. (ENG., Illus.). 56p. (J). per. 7.95 (978-1-59526-231-8(8)) Media Creations, Inc.

Alton, Steve. The Firehills. 2005. 192p. (J). (gr. 7-13). 15.95 (978-1-57505-798-9(0) , Carolrhoda Bks.) Lerner Publishing Group.

—The Malifex. 2003. (Middle Readers Ser.). (Illus.). 182p. (J). (gr. 3-7). 14.95 (978-0-8225-0959-2(8)) Lerner Publishing Group.

Amoss, Berthe. The Chalk Cross. 2007. 160p. (J). (gr. 5). pap. 6.95 (***978-0-618-82997-2(0)*** , Clarion Bks.) Houghton Mifflin Co. Trade & Reference Div.

Anacker, John. The Raven's Ring Pin. Hill, Connie, ed. 2004. (Illus.). 336p. pap. 12.95 (978-0-7387-0433-3(4)) Llewellyn Pubns.

Anthony, Joseph. Innerworld. 2002. 114p. (YA). pap. 9.95 (978-1-55517-574-0(0) , Bonneville Bks.) Cedar Fort, Inc./CFI Distribution.

—Innerworld. 2002. (gr. 7-12). lib. bdg. 18.75 (978-0-613-89648-1(3)) Tandem Library Bks.

Applegate, Katherine. In the Time of Dinosaurs. 1998. (Animorphs Ser.: No. 2). 229p. (J). (gr. 3-7). pap. 4.99 (978-0-590-95615-4(9) , Scholastic Paperbacks) Scholastic, Inc.

Appleton, Victor. Tom Swift & His Space Solatron. (Tom Swift Ser.). (J). (gr. 5-6). 20.95 (978-0-88411-457-4(0)) Amereon LTD.

Ardagh, Philip. The Rise of the House of McNally. Roberts, David, illus. 2005. (Unlikely Exploits Ser.: Vol. 3). 160p. (J). 9.95 (978-0-8050-7478-9(3) , Holt, Henry & Co. Bks. For Young Readers) Holt, Henry & Co.

Banks, Lynne Reid. The Indian in the Cupboard. 1999. (Indian in the Cupboard Ser.: No. 1). (J). (gr. 4-7). pap. 4.95 (978-5-553-81211-9(9)) HarperCollins Pubs.

—The Indian in the Cupboard. 181p. (J). (Indian in the Cupboard Ser.: No. 1). (gr. 4-7). pap. 4.99 (978-0-8072-1433-6(7)); 2004. (Indian in the Cupboard Ser.). (gr. 3-7). pap. 36.00 incl. audio (978-0-8072-7308-1(2) , YA809SP) Random Hse. Audio Publishing Group. (Listening Library).

—The Key to the Indian. 1999. (gr. 3-6). lib. bdg. 13.00 (978-0-613-23006-3(X)) Tandem Library Bks.

Barker, Clive. Abarat. 119.90 (978-0-06-056894-8(1)) HarperCollins Pubs.

—Abarat. Barker, Clive, illus. (Abarat Ser.). (Illus.). (J). 2002. 432p. 24.99 (978-0-06-028092-5(1) , Cotler, Joanna Books); 2002. 432p. lib. bdg. 26.89 (978-0-06-051084-8(6) , Cotler, Joanna Books); 2004. 496p. reprint ed. pap. 6.99 (978-0-06-059637-8(6)) HarperCollins Pubs.

—Abarat. 2002. (gr. 7-12). lib. bdg. 21.10 (978-0-613-68396-8(X)) Tandem Library Bks.

Batson, Wayne Thomas. The Door Within: The Door Within Trilogy - Book One. 2007. 336p. (J). pap. 9.99 (***978-1-4003-1011-1(3)***) Nelson, Thomas Inc.

—The Final Storm. 2006. (Door Within Trilogy: Bk. 3). (Illus.). 320p. (J). 16.99 (978-1-4003-0783-8(X)) Nelson, Thomas Inc.

Batson, Wayne Thomas. The Rise of the Wyrm Lord: The Door Within Trilogy - Book Two. 2007. 336p. (J). pap. 9.99 (***978-1-4003-1012-8(1)***) Nelson, Thomas Inc.

Bernstein, Nina. Magic by the Book. Kulikov, Boris, illus. 2005. 240p. (J). 17.00 (978-0-374-34718-5(2) , Farrar, Straus & Giroux (BYR)) Farrar, Straus & Giroux.

—Magic by the Book. unabr. ed. 2005. (J). 63.75 incl. audio (978-1-4193-3607-2(X) , 42048) Recorded Bks., LLC.

—Magic by the Book. l.t. ed. 2006. 248p. (J). 22.95 (978-0-7862-8382-8(3)) Thorndike Pr.

Dirney, Betty G. The Princess & the Peabodys. 2007. 256p. (J). lib. bdg. 16.89 (***978-0-06-084721-0(2));*** (gr. 5 up). 15.99 (***978-0-06-084720-3(4)***) HarperCollins Pubs.

Boston, Lucy M. Children of Green Knowe. 2002. (gr. 3-6). lib. bdg. 14.15 (978-0-613-54457-3(9)) Tandem Library Bks.

—The Children of Green Knowe. Boston, Peter, illus. 2002. (Green Knowe Ser.). 192p. (YA). reprint ed. (gr. 3 up). 17.00 (978-0-15-202462-8(X) , Harcourt Young Classics); (gr. 4-7). pap. 6.95 (978-0-15-202468-0(9) , Odyssey Classics) Harcourt Children's Bks.

—Treasure of Green Knowe. 2002. (gr. 3-6). lib. bdg. 14.15 (978-0-613-54447-4(1)) Tandem Library Bks.

—The Treasure of Green Knowe. Boston, Peter, illus. 2002. (Green Knowe Ser.). 224p. (YA). (gr. 4-7). reprint ed. pap. 7.00 (978-0-15-202601-1(0) , Odyssey Classics) Harcourt Children's Bks.

Browne, N. M. Warriors of Alavna. (J). 2004. 312p. (gr. 5-10). pap. 7.95 (978-1-58234-916-9(9)); 2002. 319p. 16.95 (978-1-58234-775-2(1)) Bloomsbury Publishing. (Bloomsbury Children).

Butler, Ted D. Menace Beyond the Moon: Book Two of the Belt Republic Series. 2005. 280p. (YA). pap. 14.99 (978-1-59092-235-4(2) , Blue Works) Windstorm Creative.

—2176: The Birth of the Belt Republic. 2005. 280p. (YA). pap. 14.99 (978-1-59092-234-7(4) , Blue Works) Windstorm Creative.

Carter, Mike. Access to the Universe. 2005. (Illus.). 160p. (Orig.). pap. (978-0-7344-0696-5(7) , Lothian Bks.) Hachette Livre Australia.

Cooper, Susan. Silver on the Tree. 2002. (Dark Is Rising Sequence Ser.). (Illus.). (J). 13.40 (978-0-7587-5639-8(9)) Book Wholesalers, Inc.

—Silver on the Tree. (Dark Is Rising Sequence Ser.). 288p. 2007. (YA). pap. 8.99 (***978-1-4169-4968-8(2)*** , Simon Pulse); 2000. (J). (gr. 4-7). pap. 5.99 (978-0-689-84033-3(0) , Aladdin) Simon & Schuster Children's Publishing.

—Silver on the Tree. 2000. (Dark Is Rising Sequence Ser.). (gr. 5-8). lib. bdg. 13.00 (978-0-613-30127-5(7)) Tandem Library Bks.

—Silver on the Tree. l.t. ed. 2002. (Dark Is Rising Sequence Ser.). (Illus.). 430p. (J). 23.95 (978-0-7862-2921-5(7)) Thomson Gale.

Cross, Gillian. The Nightmare Game. 2007. 272p. (J). (gr. 7). 18.99 (***978-0-525-47923-9(6)*** , Dutton Juvenile) Penguin Group (USA) Inc.

Curley, Marianne. The Key. (J). 2006. 416p. pap. 8.95 (978-1-59990-001-8(7)); 2005. 250p. 16.95 (978-1-58234-953-4(3)) Bloomsbury Publishing. (Bloomsbury Children).

—The Named. (J). 2002. 332p. (gr. 5 up). 16.95 (978-1-58234-779-0(4)); 2005. 336p. reprint ed. pap. 8.95 (978-1-58234-913-8(4)) Bloomsbury Publishing. (Bloomsbury Children).

David, Peter. Survival. 1999. 11.10 (978-0-7857-2419-3(2)) CRC Pr. LLC.

DK Publishing. Star Wars Ultimate Blueprints Collections. 2008. 10p. (J). (gr. 5-12). 19.99 (***978-0-7566-3869-6(0)***) Dorling Kindersley Publishing, Inc.

Duey, Kathleen. Arthur. 2007. (Illus.). 96p. (J). 24.21 (978-1-59961-224-9(0)) Spotlight.

—Mummy. 2007. (Illus.). 96p. (J). 24.21 (978-1-59961-225-6(9)) Spotlight.

—Patch. 2007. (Illus.). 96p. (J). 24.21 (978-1-59961-226-3(7)) Spotlight.

Dunn, Ben & Dunn, Ben, illus. The Time Machine. 2007. (Graphic Classics). 32p. (J). (gr. 3-6). lib. bdg. 27.07 (***978-1-60270-054-3(0)*** , Graphic Planet) Magic Wagon.

Eager, Edward. Half Magic. Bodecker, N. M., illus. 50th anniv. ed. 2004. 240p. (J). 18.95 (978-0-15-205302-4(6)) Harcourt Children's Bks.

—Seven-Day Magic. 1999. (gr. 3-6). lib. bdg. 14.15 (978-0-613-22363-8(2)) Tandem Library Bks.

—The Time Garden. 1999. (gr. 5-8). lib. bdg. 14.15 (978-0-613-70941-5(1)) Tandem Library Bks.

Ellis, Sarah. Back of Beyond: Stories of the Supernatural. 1998. 160p. (J). (gr. 7-10). pap. (978-0-88899-345-8(5) , Libros Tigrillo) Groundwood Bks. CAN. *Dist:* Transition Vendor.

Engdahl, Sylvia. Enchantress from the Stars. 2003. (Firebird Ser.). 304p. (YA). (gr. 6). pap. 6.99 (978-0-14-250037-8(2) , Puffin) Penguin Group (USA) Inc.

—Enchantress from the Stars. 2003. (gr. 7-12). lib. bdg. 15.30 (978-0-613-61619-5(7)) Tandem Library Bks.

Engdahl, Sylvia Louise. Enchantress from the Stars. Dillon, Leo & Dillon, Diane, illus. 2001. 288p. (YA). (gr. 6-11). reprint ed. 18.95 (978-0-8027-8764-4(9)) Walker & Co.

Ephron, Delia. Frannie in Pieces. 2007. 384p. (YA). (gr. 7 up). 16.99 (***978-0-06-074716-9(1)*** , HarperTeen) HarperCollins Pubs.

—Frannie in Pieces. Beckerman, Chad, illus. 2007. 384p. (YA). (gr. 7 up). lib. bdg. 17.89 (***978-0-06-074717-6(X)*** , HarperTeen) HarperCollins Pubs.

Etchison, Craig. The World Weaver: A Novel. 2001. 144p. (J). (gr. 4-7). pap. 8.95 (978-1-56474-359-6(4)) Fithian Pr.

Farshtey, Greg. Time Trap. 2005. 137p. (J). (***978-1-4156-3150-8(6)***) Scholastic, Inc.

Fine, Edith Hope. Cryptomania! Teleporting into Greek & Latin with the Cryptokids. Doner, Kim, illus. 2004. 48p. (J). tchr. ed. 15.95 (978-1-58246-062-8(0) , Tricycle Pr.) Ten Speed Pr.

Fisher, Catherine. Darkhenge. (J). 2007. 432p. pap. 7.99 (978-0-06-078584-0(5)); 2006. 352p. 15.99 (978-0-06-078582-6(9)) HarperCollins Pubs.

Garner, Alan. The Owl Service. 2006. (Illus.). 240p. (J). pap. 6.95 (978-0-15-205618-6(1) , Magic Carpet Bks.) Harcourt Children's Bks.

Glicksman, Caroline. Eric & the Red Planet: A Space Adventure with Numbers. 2004. (Illus.). 32p. (J). pap. 8.99 (978-0-09-945640-7(0) , Arrow Bks., Ltd.) Random Hse. GBR. *Dist:* Independent Pubs. Group.

Goodman-Pollack, Suzy. Life on a Lucky Star. 2000. 32p. (J). (ps-3). 19.90 incl. cd-rom (978-0-9672063-0-1(8)) Dandy Productions.

Haldeman, Joe. The Forever War. 2003. (gr. 7-12). lib. bdg. 23.40 (978-0-613-68423-1(0)) Tandem Library Bks.

Hamel, Mike. The Sword & the Flute: Matterhorn, the Brave Series. 2007. 176p. (J). pap. 12.99 (978-0-89957-833-0(0)) AMG Pubs.

—Talis Hunters: Matterhorn, the Brave Series, Vol. 2. 2007. 176p. (J). pap. 12.99 (978-0-89957-834-7(9)) AMG Pubs.

Hamilton, Virginia. Dustland. 1998. (Justice Cycle Ser.: Bk. 2). 214p. (YA). (gr. 6-12). pap. 4.50 (978-0-590-36217-7(8)) Scholastic, Inc.

—Dustland. 1998. (Justice Cycle Ser.). (978-0-606-12927-5(8)) Tandem Library Bks.

—The Gathering. 1998. (Justice Cycle Ser.: Bk. 3). 214p. (J). (gr. 6-12). mass mkt. 4.50 (978-0-590-36216-0(X)) Scholastic, Inc.

—The Gathering. 1998. (Justice Cycle Ser.). (978-0-606-13414-9(X)) Tandem Library Bks.

Harcourt School Publishers Staff. In Space: On Level. 3rd ed. 2002. (Trophies Reading Program Ser.). (Illus.). (J). pap. 4.10 (978-0-15-322981-7(0)) Harcourt Schl. Pubs.

—In Space 5 Pack. On Level. 3rd ed. 2002. (Trophies Reading Program Ser.). (Illus.). (J). (gr. 1). pap. 20.10 (978-0-15-326831-1(X)) Harcourt Schl. Pubs.

Hartinger, Brent. Grand & Humble. 2006. 224p. (J). lib. bdg. 16.89 (978-0-06-056728-6(7) , HarperTeen) HarperCollins Pubs.

Hennelly, Nilsson. Keeper of the River. 1999. (Rafters Ser.: Vol. 2). 144p. (J). (gr. 3-7). 12.95 (978-0-7373-0317-9(4) , 03174W); pap. 4.95 (978-0-7373-0299-8(2) , 02992W) Lowell Hse. (Roxbury Park).

Hickman, Janet. Ravine. 2002. 224p. (J). (gr. 3 up). 15.89 (978-0-06-029367-3(5)) HarperCollins Pubs.

Hill, Pamela Smith. The Last Grail Keeper. 2001. 240p. (J). (gr. 7 up). tchr. ed. 17.95 (978-0-8234-1574-8(0)) Holiday Hse., Inc.

Hoffman, Mary. City of Flowers. 2006. (Stravaganza Ser.). 496p. (YA). pap. 7.95 (978-1-58234-749-3(2) , Bloomsbury Children) Bloomsbury Publishing.

—City of Masks. 2002. (Illus.). 256p. (J). (gr. 7-12). 17.95 (978-1-58234-791-2(3) , Bloomsbury Children) Bloomsbury Publishing.

—City of Stars. 2003. (Stravaganza Ser.: Vol. 2). (Illus.). 300p. (J). 17.95 (978-1-58234-839-1(1) , Bloomsbury Children) Bloomsbury Publishing.

House, David James. The Key to Space. 2006. (ENM.). 364p. (YA). 24.95 (978-0-9777086-0-4(8)) House, David.

Hubert, Jerry. They Were Not Gods: A Space-Age Fairytale. 2003. 170p. (YA). 23.95 (978-0-595-66091-9(6)); pap. 13.95 (978-0-595-29970-6(9)) iUniverse, Inc.

S

Hulme, John, et al. The Seems: The Glitch in Sleep. 2007. (Illus.). 288p. (J). (gr. 5 up). 16.95 (***978-1-59990-129-9(3)*** , Bloomsbury Children) Bloomsbury Publishing.

Jacobs, Deborah Lynn. Choices. 2007. 208p. (YA). (gr. 7 up). 16.95 (***978-1-59643-217-8(9)***) Roaring Brook Pr.

Jacques, Brian. Voyage of Slaves. (Castaways of the Flying Dutchman Ser.: No. 3). 2007. 320p. (gr. 12). mass mkt. 7.99 (***978-0-441-01528-3(X)*** , Ace Bks.); 2006. (Illus.). 368p. (YA). (gr. 5). 23.99 (978-0-399-24549-7(9) , Philomel) Penguin Group (USA) Inc.

Jaffe, Charlotte & Doherty, Barbara. The Space Race. 2003. (Illus.). (J). (gr. 2-3). 60.00 (978-1-57336-395-2(2) , I5077) Interaction Pubs., Inc.

Jantti, Mariana. Lejos, Cerca. Donde Estan? 2006. (SPA., Illus.). 28p. (J). 14.95 (978-84-933955-6-8(0)) Hardenville SA URY. *Dist:* Independent Pubs. Group.

Jeapes, Ben. New World Order. 2006. 448p. (YA). (gr. 7). mass mkt. 6.50 (978-0-553-49491-4(0) , Laurel Leaf) Random Hse. Children's Bks.

Johnson, Jane. The Secret Country. Stower, Adam, illus. 336p. (J). 2007. (Eidolon Chronicles Ser.). pap. 5.99 (***978-1-4169-3815-6(X)*** , Aladdin); 2006. (Chronicles of Eidolon Ser.: Bk. 1). (gr. 3-7). 14.95 (978-1-4169-0712-1(2)) Simon & Schuster Children's Publishing.

Kenney, Cindy. Cool Hand Cuke: A Lesson in Giving. Big Idea Design Staff, illus. 2006. (VeggieTown Values Ser.: Bk. 5). 32p. (J). pap. 3.99 (978-0-310-70738-7(2)) Zonderkidz.

Kenney, Peterson, et al. The Snooze Brothers: A Lesson in Responsibility. Big Idea Design Staff, illus. 2006. (VeggieTown Values Ser.: Bk. 6). 32p. (J). pap. 3.99 (978-0-310-70739-4(0)) Zonderkidz.

King, Ron S. The Quantum July. 2007. 256p. (YA). (gr. 5). 15.99 (***978-0-385-73418-9(2));*** lib. bdg. 18.99 (***978-0-385-90432-2(0)***) Random Hse. Children's Bks. (Delacorte Bks. for Young Readers).

Kladstrup, Kristin. The Book of Story Beginnings. 2006. 368p. (J). (gr. 5-8). 15.99 (978-0-7636-2609-9(0)) Candlewick Pr.

Klass, David. Firestorm. 2006. (Caretaker Trilogy Ser.: Bk. 1). 304p. (YA). 17.00 (978-0-374-32307-3(0) , Frances Foster Bks.) Farrar, Straus & Giroux.

—Firestorm: The Caretaker Trilogy: Book 1. 2008. (Caretaker Trilogy Ser.). 320p. (YA). pap. 8.99 (***978-0-312-38018-2(6)***) Square Fish.

—Whirlwind. 2008. (Caretaker Trilogy Ser.). 304p. (YA). 17.95 (***978-0-374-32308-0(9)***) Farrar, Straus & Giroux.

Kurjian, Judi. In My Own Backyard. Wagner, David R., illus. 2000. 32p. (J). (ps-3). reprint ed. pap. 6.95 (978-0-88106-444-5(0)) Charlesbridge Publishing, Inc.

—In My Own Backyard. 2000. (J). 14.75 (978-0-606-19329-0(4)); lib. bdg. 15.25 (978-0-613-29988-6(4)) Tandem Library Bks.

Larbalestier, Justine. Magic Lessons. 2007. 304p. (YA). pap. 7.99 (978-1-59514-124-8(3) , Razorbill) Penguin Group (USA) Inc.

—Magic or Madness. (gr. 7-12). 2006. 304p. (YA). pap. 7.99 (978-1-59514-070-8(0)); 2005. 288p. (J). 16.99 (978-1-59514-022-7(0)) Penguin Group (USA) Inc. (Razorbill).

Lawrence, Michael. A Crack in the Line. (Withern Rise Ser.). 2005. 352p. (J). pap. 7.99 (978-0-06-072479-5(X) , HarperTeen); 2004. 336p. (J). lib. bdg. 16.89 (978-0-06-072478-8(1)); 2004. 336p. (YA). 15.99 (978-0-06-072477-1(3)) HarperCollins Pubs.

—Small Eternities. (Withern Rise Ser.). 336p. 2006. (J). pap. 7.99 (978-0-06-072482-5(X) , HarperTeen); 2005. (J). 15.99 (978-0-06-072480-1(3)); 2005. (YA). 16.89 (978-0-06-072481-8(1)) HarperCollins Pubs.

Lawrence, Michael. The Underwood See. 2007. (Withern Rise Ser.). 384p. (J). pap. 7.99 (***978-0-06-072485-6(4)*** , HarperTeen); 16.99 (978-0-06-072483-2(8)) ; lib. bdg. 17.89 (978-0-06-072484-9(6)) HarperCollins Pubs.

L'Engle, Madeleine. An Acceptable Time. 2007. 224p. (J). 6.99 (978-0-312-36862-3(3)); pap. 6.99 (978-0-312-36858-6(5)) Square Fish.

—A Wrinkle in Time: With Related Readings. 2002. (EMC Masterpiece Series Access Editions). (Illus.). xx, 250p. (J). 14.60 (978-0-8219-2532-4(6)) EMC/Paradigm Publishing.

Lennon, Joan. Questors. 2007. 368p. (J). (gr. 5-9). 16.99 (***978-1-4169-3658-9(0)*** , McElderry, Margaret K.) Simon & Schuster Children's Publishing.

Lindbergh, Anne M. The People in Pineapple Place. 2003. (Illus.). 192p. (J). (gr. 3-7). pap. 5.99 (978-0-7636-1739-4(3)) Candlewick Pr.

—People in Pineapple Place. Frazee, Marla, illus. 2003. 192p. (J). (gr. 3-7). 16.99 (978-0-7636-2131-5(5)) Candlewick Pr.

—Prisoner of Pineapple Place. 2003. (gr. 3-6). lib. bdg. 14.15 (978-0-613-70999-6(3)) Tandem Library Bks.

Matthews, L. S. The Outcasts. 2007. 272p. (YA). (gr. 7). 15.99 (*978-0-385-73367-0(4)); lib. bdg. 18.99 (*978-0-385-90382-0(0)) Random Hse. Children's Bks. (Delacorte Bks. for Young Readers).

McCaughrean, Geraldine. My Grandmother's Clock. Lambert, Stephen, illus. 2002. 32p. (J). (gr. k-3). 15.00 (978-0-618-21695-6(2), Clarion Bks.) Houghton Mifflin Co. Trade & Reference Div.

McCusker, Paul. Draven's Defiance. 2006. (Adventures in Odyssey Passages Ser.). 192p. (J). pap. 7.99 (978-1-58997-177-6(9)) Focus on the Family Publishing.

—Fendar's Legacy. 2006. (Adventures in Odyssey Passages Ser.). 192p. (J). pap. 7.99 (978-1-58997-178-3(7)) Focus on the Family Publishing.

—Glennall's Betrayal. 2006. (Adventures in Odyssey Passages Ser.). 224p. (J). pap. 7.99 (978-1-58997-170-7(1)) Focus on the Family Publishing.

McDonald, Joyce. Shades of Simon Gray. (YA). (gr. 7). 2003. 272p. pap. 6.50 (978-0-440-22804-2(2), Laurel Leaf); 2001. 256p. lib. bdg. 17.99 (978-0-385-90026-3(0), Delacorte Bks. for Young Readers) Random Hse. Children's Bks.

—Shades of Simon Gray. 2003. (gr. 7-12). lib. bdg. 13.55 (978-0-613-60396-6(6)) Tandem Library Bks.

McKinty, Adrian. The Lighthouse War. 2007. 403p. (J). (gr. 7-17). 16.95 (*978-0-8109-9354-9(6)) Abrams, Harry N., Inc.

McOmber, Rachel B., ed. McOmber Phonics Storybooks: The Time Box. rev. ed. (Illus.). (J). (978-0-944991-52-7(1)) Swift Learning Resources.

Montgomery, R. A. Prisoner of the Ant People. 1999. (Illus.). 115p. mass mkt. (978-0-553-23661-3(X)) Random Hse., Inc.

Moreau, Chris. The Professor's Telescope. Marek, Jane, illus. 2006. (YA). 10.95 (978-0-9785399-0-0(7)); cd-rom 7.95 (978-0-9785399-2-4(3)) Windows of Discovery.

Morrissey, Dean & Krensky, Stephen. The Moon Robber. 2001. (Magic Door Ser.). (Illus.). 64p. (J). (gr. 2-5). pap. 5.95 (978-0-06-442113-3(9), Harper Trophy) HarperCollins Pubs.

Naylor, Phyllis Reynolds. Footprints at the Window. 2002. (York Trilogy Ser.: Vol. 3). (Illus.). 173p. (J). pap. 4.99 (978-0-689-84963-3(X), Aladdin) Simon & Schuster Children's Publishing.

—Footprints at the Window. 2002. (gr. 7-12). lib. bdg. 13.00 (978-0-613-45042-3(6)) Tandem Library Bks.

Nix, Garth. Sir Thursday. (Keys to the Kingdom Ser.: No. 4). 352p. (J). 2007. pap. 6.99 (*978-0-439-43657-1(5), Scholastic Paperbacks); 2006. (gr. 4-7). pap. 16.99 (978-0-439-70087-0(6), Scholastic Pr.) Scholastic, Inc.

Norton, Andre. Lavender-Green Magic. 2006. (Magic Books: No. 5). 272p. (J). 5.99 (978-0-7653-5301-6(6), Starscape) Doherty, Tom Assocs., LLC.

Norton, Mary. Bedknob & Broomstick. 2000. 12.65 (978-0-606-20322-7(2)); (J). (978-0-606-20159-9(9)); (gr. 3-6). lib. bdg. 14.15 (978-0-613-29886-5(1)) Tandem Library Bks.

Osborne, Mary Pope. Tigers at Twilight, Vol. 19. unabr. ed. 2004. (Magic Tree House Ser.: No. 19). 72p. (J). (gr. k-3). pap. 17.00 incl. audio (978-0-8072-0928-8(7), S FTR 251 SP, Listening Library) Random Hse. Audio Publishing Group.

—Tigers at Twilight. Murdocca, Sal, illus. 1999. (Magic Tree House Ser.: No. 19). 96p. (J). (gr. k-3). lib. bdg. 11.99 (978-0-679-99065-9(8)); mass mkt. 3.99 (978-0-679-89065-2(3)) Random Hse. Children's Bks. (Random Hse. Bks. for Young Readers).

—Tigers at Twilight. 1999. (Magic Tree House Ser.: No. 19). (J). (gr. k-3). (Illus.). 71p. lib. bdg. 10.79 (978-0-606-16957-8(1)); lib. bdg. 11.80 (978-0-613-16224-1(2)) Tandem Library Bks.

—Vacation under the Volcano, Vol. 13. unabr. ed. 2004. (Magic Tree House Ser.: No. 13). 74p. (J). (gr. k-3). pap. 17.00 incl. audio (978-0-8072-0782-6(9), LFTR 241 SP, Listening Library) Random Hse. Audio Publishing Group.

—Vacation under the Volcano. Murdocca, Sal, illus. 1998. (Magic Tree House Ser.: No. 13). 80p. (J). (gr. k-3). mass mkt. 3.99 (978-0-679-89050-8(5), Random Hse. Bks. for Young Readers) Random Hse. Children's Bks.

—Vacation under the Volcano, nO. 13. Murdocca, Sal, illus. 1998. (Magic Tree House Ser.: No. 13). (J). (gr. k-3). (978-0-606-13972-4(9)) Tandem Library Bks.

Paulsen, Gary. The Time Hackers. 2005. 96p. (J). (gr. 4-7). lib. bdg. 17.99 (978-0-385-90896-2(2)); (gr. 5). 13.95 (978-0-385-74659-5(8)) Random Hse. Children's Bks. (Lamb, Wendy).

Peterson, Doug. Ben Hurry: Lesson in Patience. Big Idea Design Staff, illus. 2006. (VeggieTown Values Ser.: Bk. 8). 32p. (J). pap. 3.99 (978-0-310-70743-1(9)) Zonderkidz.

Prince, Maggie. The House on Hound Hill. 256p. (YA). 2003. (gr. 5). pap. 6.95 (978-0-618-33124-6(7)); 1998. (gr. 7-9). tchr. ed. 16.00 (978-0-395-90702-3(0)) Houghton Mifflin Co. Trade & Reference Div.

Rodda, Emily. The Key to Rondo. 2008. (J). (*978-0-545-03536-1(8)); 224p. pap. 16.99 (*978-0-545-03535-4(X)) Scholastic, Inc. (Scholastic Pr.).

Schmatz, Pat. Circle the Truth. 2007. (Exceptional Reading & Language Arts Titles for Upper Grades Ser.). 192p. (YA). (gr. 8-12). 16.95 (*978-0-8225-7268-8(0), Carolrhoda Bks.) Lerner Publishing Group.

Scholastic, Inc. Staff. Long-lost Map. 2007. (Ulysses Moore Ser.). 272p. (J). pap. 5.99 (*978-0-439-77673-8(2)) Scholastic, Inc.

Schwartz, Ellen. Jesse's Star. 2000. (Young Reader Ser.). (J). 11.64 (978-0-606-19476-1(2)) Tandem Library Bks.

Scott, Mavis. Magic Palace. Spoor, Mike, illus. 96p. pap. 8.95 (978-0-7022-2528-4(2)) Univ. of Queensland Pr. AUS. *Dist:* International Specialized Bk. Services.

Selfors, Suzanne. Saving Juliet. 2008. 256p. (YA). 16.95 (*978-0-8027-9740-7(7)) Walker & Co.

Shire, Poppy. Magic Pony Carousel #4: Jewel the Midnight Pony. Berg, Ron, illus. 2008. (Magic Pony Carousel Ser.). 96p. (J). pap. 3.99 (*978-0-06-083788-4(8), Harper Trophy) HarperCollins Pubs.

—Sparkle the Circus Pony. Berg, Ron, illus. 2007. (Magic Pony Carousel Ser.: No. 1). 96p. (J). pap. 3.99 (978-0-06-083779-2(9)); 14.99 (978-0-06-083777-8(2)) HarperCollins Pubs. (Harper Trophy).

Shire, Poppy. Star the Western Pony. Berg, Ron, illus. 2007. (J). (*978-0-06-083783-9(7)); (Magic Pony Carousel Ser.: No.3). 96p. (gr. 2-5). pap. 3.99 (*978-0-06-083785-3(3)) HarperCollins Pubs. (Harper Trophy).

Sleator, William. The Last Universe. (J). (gr. 7-11). 2006. 240p. pap. 6.95 (978-0-8109-9213-9(2)); 2005. 224p. 16.95 (978-0-8109-5858-6(9), Amulet Bks.) Abrams, Harry N., Inc.

Stories Beyond Time & Space. (J). pap. 15.50 (978-0-8359-0158-1(0)) Globe Fearon Educational Publishing.

Strickland, Brad. Grimoire: Curse of the Midions. 2006. 240p. (J). (gr. 4). 11.99 (978-0-8037-3060-1(8), Dial) Penguin Group (USA) Inc.

Thompson, Lisa. Saving Atlantis. Cantell, Brenda, illus. 2005. (Treasure Trackers Ser.). 80p. (J). (gr. 5-9). 19.00 (978-0-7910-8878-4(2)) Facts On File, Inc.

Valentine, James. The Past Is Gone. 2007. (Timejumpers Ser.). 288p. (J). pap. 5.99 (978-1-4169-3955-9(5), Aladdin) Simon & Schuster Children's Publishing.

Voake, Steve. The Dreamwalker's Child. (Illus.). 320p. (YA). 2007. pap. 7.95 (978-1-59990-038-4(6)); 2006. 16.95 (978-1-58234-661-8(5)) Bloomsbury Publishing. (Bloomsbury Children).

Voake, Steve & Voake, Steven. The Web of Fire. Watkinson, Mark, illus. 2007. 336p. (YA). (gr. 5-8). 17.95 (978-1-58234-737-0(9), Bloomsbury Children) Bloomsbury Publishing.

Wallace, Barbara Brooks. The Trouble with Miss Switch. 2002. 144p. (J). (gr. 5 up). reprint ed. pap. 4.99 (978-0-689-85177-3(4), Aladdin) Simon & Schuster Children's Publishing.

Warner, Mike. The Titanic Game. Ordaz, Frank, illus. 2007. 201p. (J). pap. 9.95 (978-0-9744446-2-8(6)) All About Kids Publishing.

Weyn, Suzanne. Reincarnation. 2008. 416p. (J). pap. 17.99 (*978-0-545-01323-9(2), Scholastic Pr.) Scholastic, Inc.

Wheatley, Marylou. Calypso & Strange Lands. 2004. 119p. pap. 16.95 (978-1-4137-1012-0(3)) PublishAmerica, Inc.

Williams, Maiya. The Hour of the Cobra. (YA). 2007. 320p. (gr. 2-7). pap. 5.95 (*978-0-8109-9362-4(7)); 2006. 312p. (gr. 4-9). 16.95 (978-0-8109-5970-5(4), Amulet Bks.) Abrams, Harry N., Inc.

—The Hour of the Outlaw. 2007. 360p. (YA). (gr. 4-9). 16.95 (*978-0-8109-9355-6(4)) Abrams, Harry N., Inc.

Wilson, N. D. 100 Cupboards. 2007. (J). pap. (*978-0-375-83882-8(1)); 304p. lib. bdg. (*978-0-375-93881-8(8)); 304p. (gr. 3-7). 16.99 (*978-0-375-83881-1(3)) Random Hse., Inc.

Winters, Jeffrey. Mystic Uncle & the Magical Bridge. 2005. (J). pap. (978-1-59526-167-0(2), Llumina Pr.) Media Creations, Inc.

Winterson, Jeanette. Tanglewreck. (J). 2007. 416p. (gr. 3-7). pap. 6.95 (*978-1-59990-081-0(5)); 2006. 250p. 16.95 (978-1-58234-919-0(3)) Bloomsbury Publishing. (Bloomsbury Children).

Yolen, Jane & Stemple, Adam. Pay the Piper: A Rock 'n' Roll Fairy Tale. 2006. 192p. (J). 5.99 (978-0-7653-5041-1(6), Starscape) Doherty, Tom Assocs., LLC.

SPACE EXPLORATION (ASTRONAUTICS)

see Outer Space—Exploration

SPACE FLIGHT

see also Interplanetary Voyages; Outer Space—Exploration; Space Stations

Adair, Amy. Space Adventure: Ligt-A-Flap Fun. Birmingham, Lloyd, tr. Birmingham, Lloyd, illus. 2002. (Leap Frog Ser.). 12p. (J). bds. 7.98 (978-0-7853-6347-7(5), 7159300) Publications International, Ltd.

All about Space: The Universe, Our Solar System, & Space Travel. 2002. (Illus.). 77p. (J). (ps-ps). lib. bdg. 16.40 (978-0-613-45355-4(7)) Tandem Library Bks.

Bailey, Gerry. Journey into Space. Boulter, Steve & Smith, Jan, illus. 2005. (Crafty Inventions Ser.). 48p. (C). (gr. 4-6). 26.60 (978-1-4048-1042-6(0)) Picture Window Bks.

Becklake, Sue. All about Space. 2002. (First Encyclopedia Ser.). (Illus.). 80p. (J). (gr. k-3). 7.95 (978-0-439-33020-6(3), Scholastic Reference) Scholastic, Inc.

Bergin, Mark. Exploration of Mars. 2001. (Fast Forward Ser.). (Illus.). 32p. (J). (gr. 4-8). 29.00 (978-0-531-14615-6(4), Watts, Franklin) Scholastic Library Publishing.

Biesty, Stephen. Stephen Biesty's Incredible Pop-up Cross-Sections. Biesty, Stephen, illus. 2004. (Illus.). 6p. (gr. 4-8). reprint ed. 17.00 (978-0-7567-7292-5(3)) DIANE Publishing Co.

Blast off with Ellen Ochoa! (Greetings Ser.: Vol. 3). 24p. (gr. 2-3). 31.00 (978-0-7635-5861-1(3)) Rigby Education.

Blast off with Ellen Ochoa! 6 Small Books. (Greetings Ser.: Vol. 3). 24p. (gr. 2-3). 31.00 (978-0-7635-9432-9(6)) Rigby Education.

Bondar, Barbara & Bondar, Roberta. On the Shuttle: Eight Days in Space. 2003. (Illus.). 64p. (J). (gr. 4-7). 16.95 (978-1-895688-12-2(4), Owl Bks.) Maple Tree Pr. CAN. *Dist:* Firefly Bks., Ltd.

Bown, Deni & Becklake, Sue. Space, Stars, Planets, & Spacecraft: See & Explore Library. 1998. (See & Explore Library Ser.). (Illus.). 64p. (J). (gr. 4-7). pap. 7.99 (978-0-7894-2966-7(7)) Dorling Kindersley Publishing, Inc.

Branley, Franklyn M. Is There Life in Outer Space? Miller, Edward, illus. 1999. (Let's-Read-and-Find-Out Science Ser.). 40p. (J). (ps-1). 15.89 (978-0-06-028145-8(6)); pap. 5.99 (978-0-06-445192-5(5), Harper Trophy) HarperCollins Pubs.

Branley, Franklyn Mansfield. Is There Life in Outer Space? Miller, Edward, illus. 1999. 31p. (J). (ps-ps). lib. bdg. 13.00 (978-0-613-22877-0(4)) Tandem Library Bks.

Bredeson, Carmen. The Challenger Disaster: Tragic Space Flight. 1999. (American Disasters Ser.). (Illus.). 48p. (YA). (gr. 4-10). lib. bdg. 23.93 (978-0-7660-1222-6(0)) Enslow Pubs., Inc.

—Liftoff! 2003. (gr. k-3). lib. bdg. 12.95 (978-0-613-67908-4(3)) Tandem Library Bks.

Canizares, Susan & Berger, Samantha. Voyage of Mae Jemison. 1999. (ps-2). lib. bdg. 10.10 (978-0-613-22577-9(5)) Tandem Library Bks.

Carroll, Jillian. Where to Stay. 2003. (J). pap. (978-1-58417-233-8(9)) Lake Street Pubs.

Dubbs, Chris. Space Dogs: Pioneers of Space Travel. 2003. 102p. (YA). pap. 11.95 (978-0-595-26735-4(1), Writer's Showcase Pr.) iUniverse, Inc.

Dunn, Herb. John Glenn: Young Astronaut. Brown, Robert S., illus. 2000. (Childhood of Famous Americans Ser.). (J). 11.64 (978-0-606-19714-4(1)) Tandem Library Bks.

Farbman, Melinda & Gaillard, Frye. Spacechimp: NASA's Ape in Space. 2000. (Countdown to Space Ser.). (Illus.). 48p. (YA). (gr. 4-10). lib. bdg. 23.93 (978-0-7660-1478-7(9)) Enslow Pubs., Inc.

Feldman, Heather. Dennis Tito, the First Space Tourist. 2003. (Space Firsts Ser.). (Illus.). 24p. (J). lib. bdg. 19.95 (978-0-8239-6249-5(0), PowerKids Pr.) Rosen Publishing Group, Inc., The.

Goodman, Susan E. Blasting off to Space Academy. 2002. (gr. 3-6). lib. bdg. 15.30 (978-0-613-45013-3(2)) Tandem Library Bks.

Graham, Ian. Space Travel. 2006. (Google E Guides). (Illus.). 96p. (J). pap. 9.99 (978-0-7566-2227-5(1)) Dorling Kindersley Publishing, Inc.

—You Wouldn't Want to Be on Apollo 13! 2003. lib. bdg. 18.75 (978-0-613-59560-5(2)) Tandem Library Bks.

The Great Space Race. (Color & Learn Ser.). 36p. (J). (gr. 1-5). pap. (978-1-882210-15-2(8)) Action Publishing, Inc.

Hansen, Ole Steen. Space Flight. 2003. (Story of Flight Ser.). (Illus.). 32p. (J). (gr. 2-9). lib. bdg. (978-0-7787-1207-7(9)); (gr. 4). pap. (978-0-7787-1223-7(0)) Crabtree Publishing Co.

Loeschnig, Louis V. No-Sweat Science: Space & Flight Experiments. Gallagher, Jack, illus. 2006. (No Sweat Science Ser.). 128p. (J). pap. 5.95 (978-1-4027-2334-6(2), 1262283) Sterling Publishing Co., Inc.

Lubka, S. Ruth. Pupniks: The Story of Two Space Dogs. 2003. (Illus.). 32p. (J). 16.95 (978-0-7614-5137-2(4)) Cavendish, Marshall Corp.

Miles, Lisa & Smith, Alastair. Astronomy & Space. 1998. (Complete Bks.). (Illus.). 96p. (YA). (gr. 3 up). lib. bdg. 22.95 (978-1-58086-130-4(X)) EDC Publishing.

Osborne, Mary Pope & Osborne, Will. Space: A Nonfiction Companion to Midnight on the Moon. Murdocca, Sal, illus. 2002. (Magic Tree House Research Guide Ser.: No. 6). 144p. (J). (gr. k-3). pap. 4.99 (978-0-375-81356-6(X)); lib. bdg. 11.99 (978-0-375-91356-3(4)) Random Hse. Children's Bks. (Random Hse. Bks. for Young Readers).

—Space: A Nonfiction Companion to Midnight on the Moon. 2002. (Magic Tree House Research Guide Ser.: No. 6). (J). (gr. k-3). lib. bdg. 13.00 (978-0-613-62996-6(5)) Tandem Library Bks.

Radevsky, Anton. The Pop-up Book of Space Craft. Radevsky, Anton, illus. 2004. (Illus.). 12p. (J). (gr. 4-8). reprint ed. 27.00 (978-0-7567-7761-6(5)) DIANE Publishing Co.

Randolph, Joanne. Dennis Tito, First Space Tourist. 2003. (Reading Room Collection). (Illus.). 24p. (J). lib. bdg. 18.75 (978-0-8239-3699-1(6)) Rosen Publishing Group, Inc., The.

Rau, Dana Meachen. Space Exploration. 2003. (Our Solar System Ser.). (Illus.). 32p. (J). (gr. 3 up). lib. bdg. 21.26 (978-0-7565-0439-7(2)) Compass Point Bks.

Richie, Jason. Space Flight: Crossing the Last Frontier. 2001. (Innovators Ser.: Vol. 10). (Illus.). 144p. (gr. 5 up). lib. bdg. 21.95 (978-1-881508-77-9(3)) Oliver Pr., Inc.

School Specialty Publishing. Space Travel. 2004. (Brighter Child Activity Bks.). 32p. (J). (gr. 1-3). pap. 2.99 (978-0-7696-3580-4(6), Brighter Child) School Specialty Publishing.

Schorer, Lonnie Jones. Kids to Space: A Space Traveler's Guide. 2006. (Illus.). 312p. (J). pap. 29.95 (978-1-894959-42-1(6)) Collector's Guide Publishing, Inc. CAN. *Dist:* Independent Pubs. Group.

Shuter. Flying High. 2004. (Technology Through Time Ser.). (Illus.). pap. 7.50 (978-1-4109-0978-7(6)) Raintree.

Shuter, Jane. Flying High: Travel by Air. 2004. (Technology Through Time Ser.). (Illus.). 32p. (J). lib. bdg. 25.70 (978-1-4109-0579-6(9)) Raintree.

Sibila, Tom. SpaceShipOne: Making History in Outer Space. 2005. (High Five Reading Ser.). (Illus.). 48p. (J). (978-0-7368-5744-4(3)); (978-0-7368-5734-5(6)) Capstone Pr., Inc.

Somervill, Barbara A. The History of Space Travel. 2004. (Timeline Library Ser.). 32p. (J). (gr. 2-6). 27.07 (978-1-59296-345-4(5)) Child's World, Inc.

Spangenburg, Ray & Moser, Kit. The History of NASA. 2001. (Out of This World Ser.). (Illus.). 128p. (YA). (gr. 7-9). pap. 14.95 (978-0-531-16511-9(6), Watts, Franklin) Scholastic Library Publishing.

—Project Gemini. 2001. (Out of This World Ser.). (Illus.). 112p. (YA). (gr. 7-9). pap. 14.95 (978-0-531-13973-8(5), Watts, Franklin) Scholastic Library Publishing.

—Project Gemini. 2001. (Illus.). 112p. (YA). (gr. 8-12). lib. bdg. 24.55 (978-0-613-54304-0(1)) Tandem Library Bks.

Steck-Vaughn Staff. The Moon & Beyond. 2002. (Illus.). pap. 41.60 incl. audio compact disk (978-0-7398-6978-9(7)) Steck-Vaughn.

Tesar, Jenny. Space Travel. 1998. (Space Observer Ser.). (Illus.). 24p. (ps-3). pap. (978-1-57572-581-9(9)) Heinemann Library.

Top That Publishing Staff, ed. Lets Explore Space. 2004. (Fun Kits Ser.). (Illus.). 48p. (J). (978-1-84510-244-9(4)) Top That! Publishing PLC.

A Trip into Space: Individual Title Six-Pack. (Story Steps Ser.). (gr. k-2). 23.00 (978-0-7635-9614-9(0)) Rigby Education.

Walker, Niki. The Life of an Astronaut. 2000. (Eye on the Universe Ser.). (Illus.). 32p. (J). (gr. 3-4). (978-0-86505-683-1(8)); pap. (978-0-86505-693-0(5)) Crabtree Publishing Co.

—Life of an Astronaut. 2001. (gr. 3-6). lib. bdg. 14.10 (978-0-613-32783-1(7)) Tandem Library Bks.

Weil, Ann. The Moon & Beyond. 2003. (Illus.). 60p. (J). (978-0-7398-5173-9(X)) Steck-Vaughn.

Whitehouse, Patricia. Space Travel. 2004. (Heinemann First Library). (Illus.). 32p. (J). 24.21 (978-1-4034-5155-2(9)); pap. 7.25 (978-1-4034-5659-5(3)) Heinemann Library.

SPACE FLIGHT—FICTION

Alexander, Martha. You're a Genius, Blackboard Bear. Alexander, Martha, illus. 2002. (Blackboard Bear Ser.). (Illus.). (J). 11.91 (978-0-7587-4064-9(6)) Book Wholesalers, Inc.

Appleton, Victor. The Alien Probe. (Tom Swift Ser.). (J). (gr. 3-7). 20.95 (978-0-88411-464-2(3)) Amereon LTD.

—The Rescue Mission. (Tom Swift Ser.). (J). (gr. 3-7). 20.95 (978-0-88411-458-1(9)) Amereon LTD.

—Terror on the Moons of Jupiter. (Tom Swift Ser.). (J). (gr. 3-7). 20.95 (978-0-88411-460-4(0)) Amereon LTD.

Baldry, Cherith. Surfers Mutiny in Space. (Illus.). 128p. (J). 7.95 (978-0-14-038489-5(8)) Penguin Bks., Ltd. GBR. *Dist:* Trafalgar Square Publishing.

Bell, David. Pyjamas in Space. 2007. (Dawn Gray Trilogy Ser.). 260p. pap. 11.95 (*978-1-84167-580-0(6)) Ransom Publishing Ltd. GBR. *Dist:* International Publishers Marketing.

Bergman, Mara. Oliver Who Would Not Sleep! Maland, Nick, illus. 2007. (J). (*978-0-439-92827-4(3)); 40p. pap. 16.99 (*978-0-439-92826-7(5)) Scholastic, Inc. (Levine, Arthur A. Bks.).

Brooks, Walter R. Freddy & the Space Ship. Wiese, Kurt, illus. 2001. 262p. (J). (gr. 3). 23.95 (978-1-58567-105-2(3)) Overlook Pr., The.

Brown, Jeff. Stanley in Space. Nash, Scott, illus. 2003. (Stanley Lambchop Adventure Ser.). 112p. (J). pap. 4.99 (978-0-06-442174-4(0)); lib. bdg. 15.89 (978-0-06-029827-2(8)) HarperCollins Pubs. (Harper Trophy).

Buckeridge, Anthony. According to Jennings. 2002. 177p. pap. 8.95 (978-0-7551-0165-8(0)) House of Stratus, Inc. GBR. *Dist:* Midpoint Trade Bks., Inc.

Burns, Dal. The Adventures of Phoo. 2006. 148p. pap. 19.95 (978-1-4241-1773-4(9)) PublishAmerica, Inc.

Byford, Sally. Thunderbirds Bumper Picture Storybook: Four Exciting Thunderbird Adventures! 2002. (Illus.). 96p. (J). pap. 11.00 (978-1-84222-732-9(7)) Carlton Bks., Ltd. GBR. *Dist:* Independent Pubs. Group.

Cameron, Eleanor. Stowaway to the Mushroom Planet. 2003. (J). (gr. 4-8). 21.50 (978-0-8446-7237-3(8)) Smith, Peter Pub., Inc.

Casad, Mary Brooke. Bluebonnet at Johnson Space Center. Vincent, Benjamin, illus. 2003. 32p. pap. 7.95 (978-1-58980-101-1(6)) Pelican Publishing Co., Inc.

Daley, Michael. Shanghaied to the Moon. 2007. 256p. (YA). 16.99 (978-0-399-24619-7(3), Putnam Juvenile) Penguin Group (USA) Inc.

Degen, Bruce, illus. Commander Toad & the Big Black Hole. 2002. (Commander Toad Ser.). (J). 13.19 (978-0-7587-4110-3(3)) Book Wholesalers, Inc.

DiTerlizzi, Tony. Jimmy Zangwow's Out-of-This-World Moon-Pie Adventure. 2003. (gr. k-3). lib. bdg. 15.30 (978-0-613-61784-0(3)) Tandem Library Bks.

Dwiggins, John H. True Power. unabr. ed. 1998. 311p. mass mkt. 5.99 (978-0-9658455-6-4(7), BBSF1) Basswood Bks.

Elliott, David. Hazel Nutt, Alien Hunter. Kelley, True, illus. 2005. 32p. (J). tchr. ed. 16.95 (978-0-8234-1843-5(X)) Holiday Hse., Inc.

Gehrt, Linda. My Trip, My Spaceship. 2004. 26p. pap. 14.95 (978-1-4137-3392-1(5)) PublishAmerica, Inc.

Golding, Sally. Foley & Jem. Mark, Oliver, illus. 2004. 32p. (J). 14.95 (978-1-4027-1364-4(9)) Sterling Publishing Co., Inc.

Guzzo, Anthony V. & Guzzo, Sandra E. Jason & the Time Modem: The Archimedes Challenge. 2001. (Illus.). 150p. (J). (gr. 4-7). pap. 9.95 (978-0-9643692-1-4(4)) Dandelion Pr.

Handford, Martin. Where's Waldo? Spaer Adventure: The Great Space Adventure. (Illus.). 24p. (J). (gr. k up). 19.95 (978-0-9627001-4-9(2)) Futech Educational Products, Inc.

Hergé. Destination Moon.Tr. of Objectif Lune. (J). (gr. 3-8). ring bd. 19.95 (978-0-8288-5026-1(7)); (Illus.). 62p. 19.95 (978-0-8288-5027-8(5)) French & European Pubns., Inc.

—Objectif Lune.Tr. of Destination Moon. (FRE., Illus.). (J). (gr. 7-9). ring bd. 19.95 (978-0-8288-5051-3(8)) French & European Pubns., Inc.

—On a Marche sur la Lune. (Tintin Ser.).Tr. of Explorers on the Moon. (FRE.). (J). pap. 21.95 (978-2-203-00116-9(X)) Casterman, Editions FRA. *Dist:* Distribooks, Inc.

—On a Marche sur la Lune.Tr. of Explorers on the Moon. (FRE., Illus.). (J). (gr. 7-9). ring bd. 19.95 (978-0-8288-5053-7(4)) French & European Pubns., Inc.

Herman, Gail. Friend for E T. 2002. (gr. k-3). lib. bdg. 11.25 (978-0-613-87767-1(5)) Tandem Library Bks.

Hobbs, Leigh. Old Tom Goes to Mars. Hobbs, Leigh, illus. 2005. (Illus.). 112p. (gr. 1-3). pap. 3.99 (978-0-7868-5514-8(2)) Hyperion Pr.

Hodges, Susan. Up in Space. Barr, Marilynn G., illus. 1999. (Rhyme & Reason Workbook Ser.). 32p. (J). (ps-k). pap. 3.95 (978-1-57029-254-5(X) , WPH 01106, Totline Pubns.) Schaffer, Frank Pubns.

Jeffers, Oliver. The Way Back Home. Jeffers, Oliver, illus. 2008. 32p. (J). (ps). 16.99 (***978-0-399-25074-3(3)*** , Philomel) Penguin Group (USA) Inc.

Jones, A. Starship. (Hunter & Moon Mystery Ser.: Vol. 5). 169p. (J). pap. 8.99 (978-0-340-70964-1(2) , Hodder & Stoughton) Hodder General Publishing Division GBR. *Dist:* Trafalgar Square Publishing.

Knife & Packer. Captain Fact: Space Adventure. 2004. (Illus.). 103p. (J). (***978-1-4156-0561-5(0)***) Hyperion Bks. for Children.

Kuper, Peter. Theo & the Blue Note. Kuper, Peter, illus. 2006. (Illus.). 32p. (J). (ps). 15.99 (978-0-670-06137-2(9) , Viking Juvenile) Penguin Group (USA) Inc.

Lavoie, Rejean. Des Legumes Pour Frank Einstein. Begin, Jean-Guy, illus. 2004. (Des 9 Ans. Ser.: Vol. 44). (FRE.). 120p. (J). 8.95 (978-2-89599-006-2(9)) Editions de la Paix CAN. *Dist:* World of Reading, Ltd.

Layne, Steven L. Thomas's Sheep & the Spectacular Science Project. Board, Perry, illus. 2004. 32p. (J). pap. 15.95 (978-1-58980-210-0(1)) Pelican Publishing Co., Inc.

Lego Staff. Rock Raiders Lego Game Books. 2000. (Illus.). 48p. 4.99 (978-1-903276-05-1(5)) Lego Media International, Inc.

Littler, Keith. Merlin & the Big Top. 2002. (Illus.). 24p. (J). (ps-3). pap. 7.99 (978-1-84222-618-6(5)) Carlton Bks., Ltd. GBR. *Dist:* Independent Pubs. Group.

Montgomery, R. A. War with the Evil Power Master. 2006. (Choose Your Own Adventure Ser.: No. 12). (Illus.). 144p. (J). mass mkt. 5.99 (978-1-933390-12-3(3) , CHCL12) Chooseco LLC.

—War with the Evil Power Master. 2005. (Illus.). 123p. (J). pap. (***978-0-7608-9700-3(X)***) Sundance/Newbridge Educational Publishing.

Munzel, Alexander. Where the Holy Thistle Blooms. 2003. (Illus.). 98p. (J). per. (978-0-9672566-1-0(5)) Technical Software, Inc.

Nash, Scott, illus. Stanley in Space. 2003. (gr. k-3). lib. bdg. 13.00 (978-0-613-66735-7(2)) Tandem Library Bks.

Nastasic, Susan. The Galaxy Diner. Bryant, Laura J., tr. Bryant, Laura J., illus. 2001. (Cover-To-Cover Novel Ser.). 72p. (J). (gr. 2-5). lib. bdg. 13.95 (978-0-7807-9716-1(7)) Perfection Learning Corp.

Norriss, Andrew. Aquila. Lt. ed. 2005. 232p. (J). pap. (978-0-7540-6052-9(7) , CLP 259) BBC Audio.

Oliver, Oliver J. Hare & Tortoise Race to the Moon. Oliver, Oliver J., illus. 2002. (Illus.). 40p. (J). (ps-3). 14.95 (978-0-8109-0566-5(3)) Abrams, Harry N. , Inc.

Orme, David. Space Games. Savage, Paul, illus. 2007. 40p. (J). (***978-1-59889-246-8(0)***) Stone Arch Bks.

Pati, Geeta. The Animals' Journey to the Moon. Dageforde, Linda, ed. 1999. (Illus.). 104p. (J). pap. 15.95 (978-1-886225-39-8(7) , 2000) Day of Grace Publishing Services.

Puttock, Simon. Earth to Stella! Hopman, Philip, illus. 2006. 32p. (J). (ps-k). 16.00 (978-0-618-58535-9(4) , Clarion Bks.) Houghton Mifflin Co. Trade & Reference Div.

Ragnar. Izzy's Very Important Job. Ragnar, illus. 2005. (Illus.). 32p. 9.00 (978-0-9729388-2-2(6)) Baby Tattoo Bks.

Rau, Dana Meachen. Moon Walk. Buchs, Thomas, illus. 3rd ed. 2005. (Soundprints' Read-and-Discover Ser.). 48p. (J). (gr. 2-4). pap. 3.95 (978-1-59249-015-8(8) , S2006) Soundprints.

Robinson, Alice. Shining Stars: A Colors Book. 2005. (Illus.). 16p. (J). (ps-k). per. 6.95 (978-1-58117-392-5(X) , Intervisual/Piggy Toes) Dalmatian Pr.

Robinson, Alise. Blast Off! A Numbers Books. 2005. (Illus.). 16p. (J). (ps-k). per. 6.95 (978-1-58117-394-9(6) , Intervisual/Piggy Toes) Dalmatian Pr.

Rockwell, Carey. The Space Pioneers. 2006. 95.99 (***978-1-4280-4341-1(1)***); pap. 89.99 (***978-1-4280-4388-6(8)***) IndyPublish.com.

Sargent, Pamela. Earthseed. 2007. (Seed Trilogy Ser.). (Illus.). 304p. (YA). (gr. 7 up). 6.99 (978-0-7653-5287-3(7) , Tor Teen) Doherty, Tom Assocs., LLC.

Scieszka, Jon. Baloney (Henry P.) Smith, Lane, illus. 2001. 32p. (J). (gr. k-3). 15.99 (978-0-670-89248-8(3) , Viking Juvenile) Penguin Group (USA) Inc.

The Secret Life of Jack O' Lanterns. 2004. 32p. 15.00 (978-1-883211-35-6(2)) Laughing Elephant.

Seltzer, Eric. Doodle Dog in Space. Seltzer, Eric, illus. 2005. (Ready-to-Reads Ser.). (Illus.). 32p. (J). (ps-3). pap. 3.99 (978-0-689-85912-0(0) , Aladdin) Simon & Schuster Children's Publishing.

Sendak, Maurice. Monsters in Space. 2003. (gr. k-3). lib. bdg. 11.80 (978-0-613-68264-0(5)) Tandem Library Bks.

Smith, Stu. Goldilocks & the Three Martians. Garland, Michael, tr. Garland, Michael, illus. 2004. 32p. (J). (ps). 15.99 (978-0-525-46972-8(9) , Dutton Juvenile) Penguin Group (USA) Inc.

Snyder, Lavinia Branca. Mission in Space: Softi's Adventures. 2003. (Illus.). (J). mass mkt. (978-1-932233-35-3(0)) Aurora Libris Corp.

Strasshofer, Craig. Picture Me in the Future. Thompson, Jennifer, photos by. 2000. (Picture Me Ser.). (Illus.). 10p. (J). (ps-2). bds. 6.99 (978-1-57151-585-8(2)) Playhouse Publishing.

Tan, Sheri. Handshake in Space: The Apollo-Soyuz Test Project. Bond, Higgins, illus. 1998. (Smithsonian Odyssey Ser.). 32p. (J). (gr. 2-5). 19.95 incl. audio (978-1-56899-536-6(9) , BC6010); Incl. toy. 29.95 (978-1-56899-538-0(5)); Incl. toy. pap. 17.95 (978-1-56899-539-7(3)) Soundprints.

Thomas, Lynne N. Sneak Force: Mission 1 the Legend. 2003. 148p. pap. 9.95 (***978-1-932303-18-6(9)*** , Llumina Pr.) Media Creations, Inc.

Townley, Roderick. The Constellation of Sylvie. 2006. (Illus.). 208p. (J). (gr. 5 up). 16.95 (978-0-689-85713-3(6) , Atheneum) Simon & Schuster Children's Publishing.

Walker, Peter Lancaster. Space Travelers Land at Buckingham Palace. Dixit, Rama, illus. 2007. (YA). per. 19.95 (***978-1-934138-12-0(6)***) Bouncing Ball Bks., Inc.

Wax, Wendy. Mission to Mars. 2007. 24p. (J). 21.35 (***978-1-59961-157-0(0)***) Spotlight.

Wilson-Max, Ken. Big Silver Space Shuttle. Wilson-Max, Ken, illus. 1998. (Illus.). 14p. (J). (ps-1). pap. 14.95 (978-0-590-10081-6(5) , Cartwheel Bks.) Scholastic, Inc.

Young, Selina. Big Dog & Little Dog Visit the Moon. Young, Selina, illus. 2001. (Blue Bananas Ser.). (Illus.). 48p. (J). (gr. 1-2). pap. (978-0-7787-0895-7(0)) Crabtree Publishing Co.

SPACE FLIGHT, MANNED

see Manned Space Flight

SPACE FLIGHT TO MARS

Bergin, Mark. Exploration of Mars. Bergin, Mark, illus. 2001. (Fast Forward Ser.). (Illus.). 32p. (J). (gr. 4-8). pap. 9.95 (978-0-531-14807-5(6) , Watts, Franklin) Scholastic Library Publishing.

—Exploration of Mars. 2001. (gr. 3-6). lib. bdg. 18.75 (978-0-613-54466-5(8)) Tandem Library Bks.

Branley, Franklyn M. Mission to Mars. Kelley, True, illus. 2002. (Let's-Read-&-Find-Out Science Bks.). 40p. (J). (gr. k-4). pap. 5.99 (978-0-06-445233-5(6)) HarperCollins Pubs.

—Mission to Mars. 2002. (gr. k-3). lib. bdg. 13.00 (978-0-613-59380-9(4)) Tandem Library Bks.

Cole, Michael D. Living on Mars: Mission to the Red Planet. 1999. (Countdown to Space Ser.). (Illus.). 48p. (J). (gr. 4-10). lib. bdg. 23.93 (978-0-7660-1121-2(6)) Enslow Pubs., Inc.

Gifford, Clive. How to Live on Mars. Anderson, Scoular, illus. 2001. (How to Ser.). 96p. (J). (gr. 5-7). 16.00 (978-0-531-14647-7(2) , Watts, Franklin) Scholastic Library Publishing.

Leedy, Loreen & Schuerger, Andrew. Messages from Mars. Leedy, Loreen, illus. 2006. (Illus.). 40p. (J). 16.95 (978-0-8234-1954-8(1)) Holiday Hse., Inc.

Quigley, Sebastian, illus. Mars Mission Masterbuilders. 2000. (LEGO Masterbuilders Ser.). (J). (ps-3). 19.99 (978-1-903276-16-7(0)) Lego Media International, Inc.

Trautmann Wunsch, Susi. The Adventures of Sojourner: The Mission to Mars That Thrilled the World. JPL Staff, illus. 1998. 64p. (J). (gr. 4-7). pap. 9.95 (978-0-9650493-6-8(1)); lib. bdg. 22.95 (978-0-9650493-5-1(3)) Mikaya Pr.

Wethered, Peggy & Edgett, Ken. Touchdown Mars! An ABC Adventure. Chesworth, Michael, illus. 2000. 1p. (J). (ps-3). 15.99 (978-0-399-23214-5(1) , Putnam Juvenile) Penguin Group (USA) Inc.

SPACE FLIGHT TO THE MOON

see also Moon—Exploration; Project Apollo

Aldrin, Buzz, Jr. Reaching for the Moon. Minor, Wendell, illus. 2005. 40p. (J). 16.99 (978-0-06-055445-3(2)); lib. bdg. 17.89 (978-0-06-055446-0(0)) HarperCollins Pubs.

—Reaching for the Moon. Minor, Wendell, illus. unabr. ed. 2006. (Picture Book Readalong Ser.). (J). (gr. k-4). 25.95 incl. audio (978-1-59519-581-4(5)); 28.95 incl. audio compact disk (978-1-59519-582-1(3)) Live Oak Media.

Anderson, Dale. The First Moon Landing. 2003. (Landmark Events in American History Ser.). (Illus.). 48p. (J). (gr. 5 up). pap. 14.95 (978-0-8368-5406-0(3)); lib. bdg. 30.00 (978-0-8368-5378-0(4)) Stevens, Gareth Inc. (World Almanac Library).

Crewe, Sabrina & Anderson, Dale. The First Moon Landing. 2004. (Events That Shaped America Ser.). (Illus.). 32p. (J). (gr. 3 up). lib. bdg. 24.67 (978-0-8368-3397-3(X)) Stevens, Gareth Inc.

Dunn, Joeming W. Moon Landing. Wight, Joseph et al, illus. 2007. (Graphic History Ser.). 32p. (J). (gr. 3-6). lib. bdg. 27.07 (***978-1-60270-078-9(8)*** , Graphic Planet) Magic Wagon.

Feinstein, Stephen. Read about Neil Armstrong. 2005. (I Like Biographies! Ser.). (Illus.). 24p. (J). lib. bdg. 21.26 (978-0-7660-2593-6(4) , Enslow Elementary) Enslow Pubs., Inc.

Getz, David. Moonwalkers. 2003. (Science Links Ser.). (Illus.). 32p. (gr. 3-5). 23.00 (978-0-7910-7417-6(X) , Chelsea Hse.) Facts On File, Inc.

Goldsmith, Mike. Neil Armstrong: The First Man in the Moon. 2001. (Famous Lives Ser.). (Illus.). 48p. (J). (gr. 4-6). lib. bdg. 27.12 (978-0-7398-4431-1(8)) Raintree.

Graham, Ian. You Wouldn't Want to Be on Apollo 13! 2003. lib. bdg. 18.75 (978-0-613-59560-5(2)) Tandem Library Bks.

—You Wouldn't Want to Be on Apollo 13! A Mission You'd Rather Not Go On. Antram, David, illus. 2003. (You Wouldn't Want to Ser.). 32p. (J). 28.50 (978-0-531-12311-9(1)); (gr. 2-5). pap. 9.95 (978-0-531-16650-5(3)) Scholastic Library Publishing. (Watts, Franklin).

Green, Carl R. Apollo 11 Rockets to First Moon Landing: A MyReportLinks. com Book. 2004. (Space Flight Adventures & Disasters Ser.). (Illus.). 48p. (J). lib. bdg. 25.26 (978-0-7660-5164-5(1) , MyReportLinks.com Bks.) Enslow Pubs., Inc.

Green, Jen & MacDonald, Fiona. Race to the Moon: The Story of Apollo 11. Bergin, Mark, illus. enl. ed. 1999. (Expedition Ser.). 32p. (J). (gr. 5-7). pap. 7.95 (978-0-531-15343-7(6) , Watts, Franklin) Scholastic Library Publishing.

Hehner, Barbara. First on the Moon: What It Was Like When Man Landed on the Moon. 2001. (I Was There Bk.). (Illus.). (J). 14.79 (978-0-606-20659-4(0)) Tandem Library Bks.

Higgins, Nadia. Moon Landing. 2007. (Essential Events Ser.). (ENG., Illus.). 112p. (YA). (gr. 8-12). lib. bdg. 32.79 (***978-1-59928-854-3(0)*** , Essential Library) ABDO Publishing Co.

Hilliard, Richard. Neil, Buzz, & Mike Go to the Moon. 2005. (Illus.). 32p. (J). (ps-7). 16.95 (978-1-59078-293-4(3)) Boyds Mills Pr.

Holden, Henry M. Triumph over Disaster Aboard Apollo 13: A MyReportLinks. com Book. 2004. (Space Flight Adventures & Disasters Ser.). (Illus.). 48p. (J). lib. bdg. 25.26 (978-0-7660-5167-6(6) , MyReportLinks.com Bks.) Enslow Pubs., Inc.

Hudson-Goff, Elizabeth & Anderson, Dale. The First Moon Landing. 2006. (Graphic Histories Ser.). (Illus.). pap. 8.95 (978-0-8368-6255-3(4)); 32p. (J). lib. bdg. 26.00 (978-0-8368-6203-4(1)) Stevens, Gareth Inc. (World Almanac Library).

Irwin, James. Destination Moon. 15th anniv. ed. 2004. 52p. 16.00 (978-1-929241-98-9(4)) STL Distribution North America.

Kelly, Nigel. The Moon Landing: The Race into Space. (Illus.). 32p. (J). 2006. (***978-1-4034-9145-9(3)***); 2000. (gr. 5-7). lib. bdg. 24.22 (978-1-57572-415-7(4)) Heinemann Library.

—Moon Landing: The Race into Space. 2001. (gr. 5-8). lib. bdg. 15.25 (978-0-613-36110-1(5)) Tandem Library Bks.

—The Moon Landing: The Race into Space, Set 1. 2002. (Point of Impact Ser.). (Illus.). 32p. (J). (gr. 5-7). pap. 7.50 (978-1-58810-356-7(0) , 91115) Heinemann Library.

Kelly, Nigel & Tames, Richard. Point of Impact Series, 7 bks., Set 1. (Illus.). (J). (gr. 5-7). lib. bdg. 169.54 (978-1-57572-419-5(7)) Heinemann Library.

Koestler-Grack, Rachel A. Moon Landing. 2005. (American Moments Ser.). (Illus.). 48p. (J). (gr. 4-8). lib. bdg. 25.65 (978-1-59197-932-6(3)) ABDO Publishing Co.

Kortenkamp, Steve. The First Moon Landing. 2008. (J). (***978-1-4296-0060-6(8)***) Capstone Pr., Inc.

Malam, John. Man Walks on the Moon. 2003. (Dates with History Ser.). 45p. (J). lib. bdg. 28.50 (978-1-58340-407-2(4)) Smart Apple Media.

Mason, Paul. The Moon Landing. 2002. (Days That Shook the World Ser.). (Illus.). 48p. (J). lib. bdg. 27.12 (978-0-7398-5236-1(1)) Raintree.

McNulty, Faith. If You Decide to Go to the Moon. Kellogg, Steven, illus. 2005. 48p. (J). (ps-3). pap. 16.99 (978-0-590-48359-9(5) , Scholastic Pr.) Scholastic, Inc.

Merchant, Peter. The Eagle Has Landed. 2002. (Illus.). 16p. (J). pap. (978-0-439-35140-9(5)) Scholastic, Inc.

Raum, Elizabeth. Edwin "Buzz" Aldrin. 2005. (American Lives Ser.). (Illus.). 32p. (978-1-4034-6939-7(3)); pap. (978-1-4034-6946-5(6)) Heinemann Library.

—Neil Armstrong. 2005. (American Lives Ser.). (Illus.). 32p. (J). (978-1-4034-6938-0(5)); pap. (978-1-4034-6945-8(8)) Heinemann Library.

Richardson, Hazel. How to Build a Rocket. Anderson, Scoular, illus. 2001. (How to Ser.). 96p. (J). (gr. 5-7). 16.00 (978-0-531-14643-9(X) , Watts, Franklin) Scholastic Library Publishing.

Siy, Alexandra. Footprints on the Moon. 2001. (Illus.). (J). 32p. (gr. 1-7). 16.95 (978-1-57091-408-9(7)); (gr. 4-7). pap. 7.95 (978-1-57091-409-6(5)) Charlesbridge Publishing, Inc.

—Footprints on the Moon. 2001. (J). 14.75 (978-0-606-20662-4(0)); (gr. 3-6). lib. bdg. 16.40 (978-0-613-49316-1(8)) Tandem Library Bks.

Tan, Sheri. Handshake in Space: The Apollo-Soyuz Test Project. Bond, Higgins, illus. 1998. (Smithsonian Odyssey Ser.). 32p. (J). (gr. 2-5). 14.95 (978-1-56899-534-2(2) , B6010); pap. 6.95 (978-1-56899-535-9(0) , S6010) Soundprints.

Thimmesh, Catherine. Team Moon: How 400,000 People Landed Apollo 11 on the Moon. 2006. (Illus.). 80p. (J). (gr. 5). 19.95 (978-0-618-50757-3(4)) Houghton Mifflin Co.

Vogt, Gregory L. Apollo Moonwalks: The Amazing Lunar Missions. 2000. (Countdown to Space Ser.). (Illus.). 48p. (YA). (gr. 4-10). lib. bdg. 23.93 (978-0-7660-1306-3(5)) Enslow Pubs., Inc.

Wilkinson, Philip. Spacebusters: The Race to the Moon, Vol. 3. 1998. (Eyewitness Readers). (Illus.). 48p. (J). (gr. 5-3). pap. 3.99 (978-0-7894-2961-2(6)) Dorling Kindersley Publishing, Inc.

Zelon, Helen. Apollo 11 Mission: The First Man to Walk on the Moon. 2002. (Space Missions Ser.). (Illus.). 24p. (J). (gr. 2-4). lib. bdg. 19.95 (978-0-8239-5772-9(1) , PowerKids Pr.) Rosen Publishing Group, Inc., The.

Zemlicka, Shannon. Neil Armstrong. (History Maker Bios Ser.). (Illus.). 48p. (J). 2003. (gr. 2-4). 26.60 (978-0-8225-0395-8(6)); 2002. pap. 6.95 (978-0-8225-1563-0(6)) Lerner Publishing Group. (Lerner Pubns.).

SPACE PROBES

see also Lunar Probes

also names of space vehicles and space projects, e.g. Mariner project; etc.

Angelo, Joseph A. Robot Spacecraft. 2006. (Frontiers in Space Ser.). (Illus.). 320p. (J). (gr. 9). 39.50 (978-0-8160-5773-3(7)) Facts On File, Inc.

—Spacecraft for Astronomy. 2006. (Frontiers in Space Ser.). 304p. (YA). (gr. 9). 39.50 (978-0-8160-5774-0(5)) Facts On File, Inc.

Asimov, Isaac & Hantula, Richard. Exploring Outer Space. 2005. (Isaac Asimov's 21st Century Library of the Universe). (Illus.). 32p. (J). (gr. 3-7). lib. bdg. 24.67 (978-0-8368-3981-4(1)) Stevens, Gareth Inc.

Bredeson, Carmen. NASA Planetary Spacecraft: Galileo, Magellan, Pathfinder & Voyager. 2000. (Countdown to Space Ser.). (Illus.). 48p. (YA). (gr. 4-10). lib. bdg. 23.93 (978-0-7660-1303-2(0)) Enslow Pubs., Inc.

Kerrod, Robin. Space Probes. 2004. (History of Space Exploration Ser.). (Illus.). 48p. (J). pap. (978-0-8368-5715-3(1)); (YA). lib. bdg. 30.00 (978-0-8368-5708-5(9)) Stevens, Gareth Inc. (World Almanac Library).

Kortenkamp, Steve. Space Probes. 2008. (J). (***978-1-4296-0063-7(2)***) Capstone Pr., Inc.

Miller Ron. Robot Explorers. 2007. (Space Innovations Ser.). (Illus.). 112p. (YA). (gr. 6-8). lib. bdg. 31.93 (***978-0-8225-7152-0(8)*** , Twenty-First Century Bks.) Lerner Publishing Group.

Sherman, Josepha. Deep Space Observation Satellites. 2003. (Library of Satellites). (Illus.). 64p. (YA). (gr. 5-8). lib. bdg. 26.50 (978-0-8239-3852-0(2) , Rosen Central) Rosen Publishing Group, Inc., The.

Telescopes & Space Probes. 2006. (World Book's Solar System & Space Exploration Library). (Illus.). (J). 63p. (978-0-7166-9510-3(3)); 2nd ed. 64p. (***978-0-7166-9520-2(0)***) World Bk., Inc.

SPACE RESEARCH

see Outer Space—Exploration; Space Sciences

SPACE SCIENCES

see also Astronautics; Astronomy; Geophysics; Outer Space

Asimov, Isaac & Hantula, Richard. Global Space Programs. 2005. (Isaac Asimov's 21st Century Library of the Universe). (Illus.). 32p. (J). lib. bdg. 24.67 (978-0-8368-3982-1(X)) Stevens, Gareth Inc.

Becklake, Sue, et al. All about Space. 1998. (Scholastic First Encyclopedia Ser.). (Illus.). 80p. (J). (gr. k-3). pap. 14.95 (978-0-590-10471-5(3)) Scholastic, Inc.

Benchmark Education Staff, compiled by. Earth & Space Science. 2006. spiral bd. 365.00 (***978-1-4108-6946-3(6)); 2006. spiral bd. 695.00 (978-1-4108-6942-5(3));*** 2006. spiral bd. 365.00 (***978-1-4108-6939-5(3));*** 2006. spiral bd. 365.00 (***978-1-4108-6925-8(3));*** 2006. spiral bd. 80.00 (***978-1-4108-6927-2(X));*** 2006. spiral bd. 235.00 (***978-1-4108-6934-0(2));*** 2005. spiral bd. 220.00 (***978-1-4108-3851-3(X));*** 2005. spiral bd. 370.00 (***978-1-4108-3858-2(7));*** 2005. spiral bd. 220.00 (***978-1-4108-3859-9(5));*** 2005. spiral bd. 75.00 (***978-1-4108-3870-4(6));*** 2005. spiral bd. 55.00 (***978-1-4108-3874-2(9));*** 2005. spiral bd. 870.00 (***978-1-4108-4518-4(4));*** 2005. spiral bd. 305.00 (***978-1-4108-3850-6(1));*** 2005. spiral bd. 950.00 (***978-1-4108-5441-4(8));*** 2005. spiral bd. 675.00 (***978-1-4108-5851-1(0));*** 2005. spiral bd. 405.00 (***978-1-4108-5852-8(9));*** 2005. spiral bd. 335.00 (***978-1-4108-3829-2(3));*** 2005. spiral bd. 580.00 (***978-1-4108-3826-1(9));*** 2005. spiral bd. 1025.00 (***978-1-4108-5440-7(X)***) Benchmark Education Co.

—Science Theme: Earth & Space Science. 2005. spiral bd. 340.00 (***978-1-4108-5314-1(4)***) Benchmark Education Co.

Bortz, Alfred B. Astrobiology. 2007. (Cool Science Ser.). 48p. (J). (gr. 4-8). lib. bdg. 26.60 (***978-0-8225-6771-4(7)*** , Lerner Pubns.) Lerner Publishing Group.

Cientificos! 9: Ciencias Terrestres y del Espacio. (SPA.). (J). 60.00 (978-958-04-6348-1(4)) Norma S.A. COL. *Dist:* Distribuidora Norma, Inc.

Clark, Stuart. Discovering the Universe. 2000. (Inside Look Ser.). (Illus.). 48p. (J). (gr. 4 up). lib. bdg. 26.00 (978-0-8368-2724-8(4)) Stevens, Gareth Inc.

Dasch, Patricia, ed. Space Business, 4 vols. 2000. (Science Library for Students). (Illus.). 192p. (J). 85.00 (978-0-02-865547-5(8) , Macmillan Reference USA) Thomson Gale.

DK Publishing Staff. Space. 2007. (Eye Know Ser.). 24p. (J). (ps-2). 8.99 (***978-0-7566-3083-6(5)***) Dorling Kindersley Publishing, Inc.

Dorling Kindersley Publishing Staff. Visual Encyclopedia of Space. 2006. (Illus.). 400p. (J). (gr. 8). pap. 12.99 (978-0-7566-1474-4(0)) Dorling Kindersley Publishing, Inc.

—Voyage to the Planets & Beyond: 3-D Space Adventures. 2005. (Illus.). 24p. (J). (ps-7). pap. 8.99 (978-0-7566-1294-8(2)) Dorling Kindersley Publishing, Inc.

Dowswell, Paul. First Encyclopedia of Space. 2004. (First Encyclopedia Ser.). (SPA., Illus.). 64p. (J). (gr. 3 up). pap. 9.99 (978-0-7945-0035-1(8) , Usborne); lib. bdg. 17.95 (978-1-58086-357-5(4)) EDC Publishing.

Elish, Dan. Kaleidoscope Space Gorup 2, 4 bks., Set. Incl. Galaxies. lib. bdg. 28.50 (978-0-7614-2047-7(9)); Nasa. lib. bdg. 28.50 (***978-0-7614-2046-0(0));*** Satellites. lib. bdg. 28.50 (978-0-7614-2098-9(3)); Sun. lib. bdg. 28.50 (978-0-7614-2048-4(7)); (Illus.). 48p. (J). 2006. 2007. Set lib. bdg. 114.00 (***978-0-7614-2045-3(2)*** , Benchmark Bks.) Cavendish, Marshall Corp.

Exploracion del Espacio, 6 vols., Vol. 3. (Explorers. Exploradores Nonfiction Sets Ser.). (SPA.). (gr. 3-6). (978-0-7699-0653-9(2)) Shortland Pubns. (U. S. A.) Inc.

Explore Space! Classroom Library. (gr. 2-5). lib. bdg. 22.95 (978-0-7368-9250-6(8)) Red Brick Learning.

Explore Space Collection. 2005. (J). pap. (***978-1-60015-016-6(0)***) Steps To Literacy, LLC.

Explore Space! Complete Unit. (gr. 2-5). 132.95 (978-0-7368-9251-3(6)) Red Brick Learning.

Explore Space! II Classroom Library. (gr. 2-5). lib. bdg. 22.95 (978-0-7368-4536-6(4)) Red Brick Learning.

Explore Space! II Complete Unit. (gr. 2-5). 132.95 (978-0-7368-4535-9(6)) Red Brick Learning.

Exploring Space: Level Q, 6 vols., Vol. 3. (Explorers Ser.). 32p. (gr. 3-6). 44.95 (978-0-7699-0617-1(6)) Shortland Pubns. (U. S. A.) Inc.

Feldman, Heather. Skylab: The First American Space Station. 2003. (Space Firsts Ser.). (Illus.). 24p. (J). lib. bdg. 19.95 (978-0-8239-6248-8(2) , PowerKids Pr.) Rosen Publishing Group, Inc., The.

Gardner, Robert. Science Project Ideas about Space Science. rev. ed. 2002. (Science Project Ideas Ser.). (Illus.). 128p. (J). (gr. 4-9). lib. bdg. 26.60 (978-0-7660-1707-8(9)) Enslow Pubs., Inc.

Grolier Educational Staff, contrib. by. Space Science, 8 vols. 2004. (Illus.). (J). 289.00 (978-0-7172-5825-3(4)); (978-0-7172-5826-0(2)); (978-0-7172-5827-7(0)); (978-0-7172-5828-4(9)); (978-0-7172-5829-1(7)); (978-0-7172-5830-7(0)); (978-0-7172-5831-4(9)); (978-0-7172-5832-1(7)); (978-0-7172-5833-8(5)) Scholastic Library Publishing. (Grolier).

Harcourt School Publishers Staff. The Moon: Science Reader. 1999. (SPA., Illus.). (J). pap. 3.70 (978-0-15-316122-3(1)) Harcourt Schl. Pubs.

Hewitt, Sally. Earth & Space. (Illus.). 32p. (YA). (gr. 2 up). lib. bdg. 27.10 (978-1-932333-31-2(2)) Chrysalis Education.

Hodges, Susan. Up in Space. Barr, Marilynn G., illus. 1999. (Rhyme & Reason Workbook Ser.). 32p. (J). (ps-k). pap. 3.95 (978-1-57029-254-5(X) , WPH 01106, Totline Pubns.) Schaffer, Frank Pubns.

Holt, Rinehart and Winston Staff. Holt Science & Technology Chapter 19: Earth Science: Stars, the Galaxy, & the Universe. 5th ed. 2004. (Illus.). pap. 12.86 (978-0-03-030336-4(2)) Holt, Rinehart & Winston.

—Holt Science & Technology Chapter 22: Earth Science: Exploring Space. 5th ed. 2004. (Illus.). pap. 12.86 (978-0-03-030351-7(6)) Holt, Rinehart & Winston.

Hutson, Matt. What Do You Want to Be? Explore Aerospace. 2005. (J). 6.00 (978-0-9753920-7-2(7)) Sally Ride Science.

Ivey, Catherine. Totally Amazing Careers in Space Sciences. 2006. (J). 7.80 (978-1-933798-00-4(9)) Sally Ride Science.

Jayawardhana, Ray. Star Factories: Stars & Planets. 1999. (Illus.). (J). pap. (978-0-7398-2494-8(5)) Steck-Vaughn.

Khan, Hena & Dyson, Marianne J. The Space Explorer's Guide to Out-Of-This-World Science. 2004. (Space University Ser.). (Illus.). 48p. (J). ***(978-0-439-55747-4(X))*** Scholastic, Inc.

MacDonald, Fiona. Space. 2000. (J). (978-0-606-19794-6(X)) Tandem Library Bks.

McCutcheon, Scott & McCutcheon, Bobbi. Space & Astronomy. 2006. (Science News for Kids Ser.). (Illus.). 64p. 30.00 (978-0-7910-9125-8(2) , Chelsea Clubhouse) Facts On File, Inc.

Milbourne, Anna. On the Moon. 2004. (On the Moon Ser.). 24p. (J). 9.95 (978-0-7945-0617-9(8) , Usborne) EDC Publishing.

Mobberley, Martin. Space. 2007. (Illus.). 48p. (J). ***(978-1-60044-262-9(5))*** Rourke Publishing, LLC.

Modules: Earth Science; Space Science TE. 2005. (gr. 6-12). (978-0-618-33422-3(X) , 2-01012) McDougal Littell Inc.

Modules: Physical Science; Space Science PE. 2005. (gr. 6-12). lab manual ed. (978-0-618-43734-4(7) , 2-01227) McDougal Littell Inc.

Mondello, Cindy, ed. Investigating Science - Space. 2000. 48p. 9.95 (978-1-56234-373-6(4) , Mailbox Bks., The) Education Ctr., Inc.

Newton, David E. Chemistry of Space. 2007. (New Chemistry Ser.). 256p. (gr. 6-12). 35.00 (978-0-8160-5274-5(3)) Facts On File, Inc.

Out in Space. 2005. (Earth & Outer Space Ser.). (YA). (gr. k-3). 118.80 (978-0-7368-4211-2(X) , Pebble Bks.) Capstone Pr., Inc.

Out in Space Set. (gr. k-2). 114.95 (978-0-7368-3264-9(5)) Red Brick Learning.

Parker. Space Mysteries - Space Busters. 2004. (YA). pap. 48.30 (978-1-4109-0293-1(5)) Harcourt Schl. Pubs.

Pebble Books: Earth & Outer Space. 2005. (YA). (gr. k-3). 594.00 (978-0-7368-4222-8(5) , Pebble Bks.) Capstone Pr., Inc.

Pentland, Peter & Stoyles, Pennie. Space Science. 2002. (Science & Scientists Ser.). (Illus.). 32p. (gr. 4-8). 28.00 (978-0-7910-7011-6(5) , Chelsea Hse.) Facts On File, Inc.

Pinna, Lorenzo. La Conquista del Espacio. (SPA.). 88p. (YA). (gr. 5-8). (978-84-7131-926-5(8)) Editex, Editorial S.A. ESP. *Dist:* Lectorum Pubns., Inc.

El Planeta Tierra.Tr. of Planet Earth. (SPA.). 96p. (YA). (gr. 5-8). 18.36 (978-84-241-1994-2(0)) Everest de Ediciones y Distribucion, S.L. ESP. *Dist:* Lectorum Pubns., Inc.

Pocket Chart Science: Space. 2001. (J). pap. 9.95 (978-1-56911-716-3(0)) Learning Resources, Inc.

Quigley, Sebastian & Pickering, Mel, illus. All about Space. 1998. (Scholastic First Encyclopedia Ser.). (J). pap. (978-0-590-10472-2(1)) Scholastic, Inc.

Rudy, Lisa Jo. Eyes in the Sky: Satellite Spies Are Watching You! 2007. (24/7 - Science Behind the Scenes Ser.). 64p. (YA). (gr. 8-12). 26.00 (978-0-531-12082-8(1) , Watts, Franklin) Scholastic Library Publishing.

Science & Nature. (Britannica Learning Library). (Illus.). (gr. 2-5). 14.95 (978-1-59339-002-0(5) , 049903-EN-REF) Encyclopaedia Britannica, Inc.

Science, Rookie Read-About Science: Space Science. 2004. (Illus.). (YA). 209.00 (978-0-516-29322-6(2)) Scholastic Library Publishing.

Sharp, Katie John. Science & Nature. Barrett, Tom, illus. 2005. (Look, Find & Learn Ser.). 32p. (J). per. (978-1-4127-1046-6(4) , 7234600) Publications International, Ltd.

Simon, Seymour. Destination: Mars. 2000. (Illus.). 32p. (J). (ps-3). 15.95 (978-0-688-15770-8(X)) HarperCollins Pubs.

Space, 4 bks., Set. Incl. Comets, Asteroids & Meteorites. Gallant, Roy A. 2001. lib. bdg. 25.64 (978-0-7614-1034-8(1)); Planets. Gallant, Roy A. 2000. lib. bdg. 25.64 (978-0-7614-1033-1(3)); Space Stations. Gallant, Roy A., ed. 2000. lib. bdg. 25.64 (978-0-7614-1035-5(X)); Stars. Gallant, Roy A. 2000. lib. bdg. 25.64 (978-0-7614-1036-2(8)); (J). (gr. 3 up). (Kaleidoscope Ser.). (Illus.). 48p. 2001. Set lib. bdg. 102.57 (978-0-7614-1032-4(5) , Benchmark Bks.) Cavendish, Marshall Corp.

Space Junk: 6 Each of 1 Anthology, 6 vols. (Wildcats Ser.). 32p. (gr. 2-8). (978-0-322-00576-1(0)) Wright Group, The.

Space Mail: Fifth Grade Guided Comprehension Level S. (On Our Way to English Ser.). (gr. 5 up). 34.50 (978-0-7578-6626-5(3)) Rigby Education.

Space Pack. 2000. (Step Ahead Workbooks Ser.). (J). 15.99 (978-0-307-19560-9(0) , Golden Bks.) Random Hse. Children's Bks.

Space Sailors: First Grade Guided Reading Level H. (On Our Way to English Ser.). (gr. 1 up). 27.75 (978-0-7578-7064-4(3)) Rigby Education.

Space, Stars, & Planets, 6 vols., Pack. (Sails Literacy Ser.). (gr. 1-2). 36.00 (978-0-7578-6739-2(1)) Rigby Education.

Steck-Vaughn Staff. Earth & Space Science. 1999. (J). (gr. 3). pap. (978-0-8172-3768-4(2)); (gr. 5). pap. (978-0-8172-3770-7(4)); (Illus.). (gr. 6). pap. (978-0-8172-3771-4(2)) Steck-Vaughn.

—Science: Earth & Space Science, Physical Science. 2002. (Illus.). pap. (978-0-7398-5425-9(9)) Steck-Vaughn.

—What's up...in Space? 2000. (J). pap. 57.11 incl. VHS (978-0-7398-3218-9(2)) Raintree.

Stott, Carole. I Wonder Why Stars Twinkle: And Other Questions about Space. 2003. (J). lib. bdg. 14.10 (978-0-613-63164-8(1)) Tandem Library Bks.

Stott, Carole. Space. 2008. 128p. (J). (gr. 3-6). 19.99 ***(978-0-7566-3842-9(9))*** Dorling Kindersley Publishing, Inc.

Technology & Inventions. (Britannica Learning Library). (Illus.). (gr. 2-5). 14.95 (978-1-59339-003-7(3) , 049904-EN-REF) Encyclopaedia Britannica, Inc.

Top That Publishing Staff, ed. Space. 2004. (Know How Know Why Ser.). (Illus.). (J). 48p. pap. (978-1-84510-026-1(3)); 24p. pap. (978-1-84510-114-5(6)); 48p. per. (978-1-84510-012-4(3)) Top That! Publishing PLC.

Turnbull, Stephanie. Living in Space (Level 2) - Internet Referenced. 2006. (Illus.). 32p. (J). 4.99 (978-0-7945-1339-9(5) , Usborne) EDC Publishing.

Vogt, Gregory L. The Milky Way & Other Galaxies. 2000. (Our Universe Ser.). (Illus.). 48p. (YA). (gr. 5-12). lib. bdg. 22.83 (978-0-7398-3107-6(0)) Raintree.

—The Milky Way & Other Galaxies. 2000. (Our Universe Ser.). (Illus.). (J). pap. (978-0-7398-3346-9(4)) Steck-Vaughn.

Wadsworth, Pamela. Golwg Gyntaf Ar Amser a Gofod. 2005. (WEL., Illus.). 24p. pap. (978-1-85596-248-4(9)) Dref Wen.

What Is in Space?, 6 vols. (Sunshinetm Science Ser.). 24p. (gr. 1-2). 31.50 (978-0-7802-0292-4(9)); 36.95 (978-0-7802-0543-7(X)) Wright Group, The.

What Is in the Sky? Set C, 6 vols. (Phonics Readers Ser.). (gr. k-2). 17.50 (978-0-7368-3202-1(5)) Red Brick Learning.

Whitehouse, Patricia. Working in Space. 2004. (J). 24.21 (978-1-4034-5158-3(3)); pap. 6.95 (978-1-4034-5662-5(3)) Heinemann Library.

Wilkinson, Philip. Al Espacio: La Carrera a la Luna. 2006. (Dk Readers Ser.). 48p. (J). 14.99 (978-0-7566-2128-5(3)); (gr. 5). pap. 3.99 (978-0-7566-2127-8(5)) Dorling Kindersley Publishing, Inc.

Windsor, Jo. Space Junk, 6 vols., Pack. (Sails Literacy Ser.). 20p. (gr. 4 up). 27.00 (978-0-7578-0787-9(9)) Rigby Education.

SPACE SHIPS—PILOTS

see Astronauts

SPACE SHUTTLES

Adamson, Heather. The Challenger Explosion. Bascle, Brian, illus. 2006. (Graphic Library). 32p. (J). (978-0-7368-5478-8(9) , 1252837) Capstone Pr., Inc.

Amato, William. The Space Shuttle. 2002. (Reading Power Ser.). (Illus.). 24p. (J). (gr. 2). lib. bdg. 17.25 (978-0-8239-6007-1(2) , PowerKids Pr.) Rosen Publishing Group, Inc., The.

—Transbordadores Espaciales. 2004. (Vehiculos de Alta Tecnologia Ser.). (SPA & ENG., Illus.). 24p. (J). (gr. 3-6). lib. bdg. 17.25 (978-0-8239-6885-5(5) , Buenas Letra) Rosen Publishing Group, Inc., The.

Biesty, Stephen. Stephen Biesty's Incredible Pop-up Cross-Sections. Biesty, Stephen, illus. 2004. (Illus.). 6p. (gr. 4-8). reprint ed. 17.00 (978-0-7567-7292-5(3)) DIANE Publishing Co.

Branley, Franklyn M. Floating in Space. Kelley, True, illus. 1998. (Let's-Read-and-Find-Out Science Ser.). 32p. (J). (gr. k-4). 15.89 (978-0-06-025433-9(5)); pap. 5.99 (978-0-06-445142-0(9)) HarperCollins Pubs.

Bredeson, Carmen. John Glenn Returns to Orbit: Life on the Space Shuttle. 2000. (Countdown to Space Ser.). (Illus.). 48p. (YA). (gr. 4-10). lib. bdg. 23.93 (978-0-7660-1304-9(9)) Enslow Pubs., Inc.

—Nave Espacial: Living on a Space Shuttle. 2005. (Rookie Espanol: Ciencias Ser.). (SPA., Illus.). 32p. (J). (gr. k-2). pap. 5.95 (978-0-516-25511-8(8) , Children's Pr.) Scholastic Library Publishing.

Bricker, Sandra D. Challenger. 2000. (gr. 5-8). lib. bdg. 11.80 (978-0-613-51203-9(0)) Tandem Library Bks.

Chandler, Gil. The Challenger: The Explosion on Liftoff. 2002. (Disaster! Ser.). (Illus.). 32p. (J). (gr. 3-4). lib. bdg. 21.26 (978-0-7368-1322-8(5) , Capstone High-Interest Bks.) Capstone Pr., Inc.

Cole, Michael D. The Columbia Space Shuttle Disaster: From First Liftoff to Tragic Final Flight. 2003. (Countdown to Space Ser.). (Illus.). 48p. (J). lib. bdg. 23.93 (978-0-7660-2295-9(1)) Enslow Pubs., Inc.

Dahl, Michael. On the Launch Pad: A Counting Book about Rockets. Aldermand, Derrick & Shea, Denise, illus. 2004. (Know Your Numbers Ser.). 24p. (J). (gr. k-3). 22.60 (978-1-4048-0581-1(8)) Picture Window Bks.

Dunn, Herb. John Glenn: Young Astronaut. Brown, Robert S., illus. 2000. (Childhood of Famous Americans Ser.). (J). 11.64 (978-0-606-19714-4(1)) Tandem Library Bks.

Fahey, Kathleen. Challenger & Columbia. 2005. (Illus.). 32p. (J). lib. bdg. 24.67 (978-0-8368-4496-2(3)) Stevens, Gareth Inc.

Feldman, Heather. Columbia: The First Space Shuttle. 2003. (Space Firsts Ser.). (Illus.). 24p. (J). lib. bdg. 19.95 (978-0-8239-6247-1(4) , PowerKids Pr.) Rosen Publishing Group, Inc., The.

Fly a Spaceship. 2003. 12p. (J). bds. 6.99 (978-0-7894-9526-6(0)) Dorling Kindersley Publishing, Inc.

Herrod, Robin. Space Shuttles. 2004. (History of Space Exploration Ser.). (Illus.). 48p. (J). pap. 22.50 (978-0-8368-5716-0(X)); (YA). 30.00 (978-0-8368-5709-2(7)) Stevens, Gareth Inc. (World Almanac Library).

Holden, Henry M. The Supersonic X-15 & High-Tech NASA Aircraft. 2002. (Aircraft Ser.). (Illus.). 48p. (J). (gr. 4-10). lib. bdg. 23.93 (978-0-7660-1717-7(6)) Enslow Pubs., Inc.

—The Tragedy of the Space Shuttle Challenger: A MyReportLinks. com Book. 2004. (Space Flight Adventures & Disasters Ser.). (Illus.). 48p. (J). lib. bdg. 25.26 (978-0-7660-5165-2(X) , MyReportLinks.com Bks.) Enslow Pubs., Inc.

Koestler-Grack, Rachel A. Space Shuttle Columbia Disaster. 2005. (American Moments Ser.). (Illus.). 48p. (J). (gr. 4-8). lib. bdg. 25.65 (978-1-59197-659-2(6) , ABDO & Daughters) ABDO Publishing Co.

Kortenkamp, Steve. Space Shuttles. 2008. (J). ***(978-1-4296-1259-3(2))*** Capstone Pr., Inc.

Lassieur, Allison. The Space Shuttle. 2000. (True Bks.). (Illus.). 48p. (J). (gr. 3-5). 25.00 (978-0-516-22003-1(9) , Children's Pr.) Scholastic Library Publishing.

—Space Shuttle. 2000. (gr. 3-6). lib. bdg. 15.25 (978-0-613-54681-2(4)) Tandem Library Bks.

Lieurance, Suzanne. The Space Shuttle Challenger Disaster in American History. 2001. (In American History Ser.). (Illus.). 128p. (J). (gr. 5-12). lib. bdg. 26.60 (978-0-7660-1419-0(3)) Enslow Pubs., Inc.

McNeese, Tim. The Challenger Disaster. 2003. (Cornerstones of Freedom, 2ND Ser.). lib. bdg. 24.00 (978-0-516-22840-2(4)); (Illus.). 48p. (J). 26.00 (978-0-516-24222-4(9)) Scholastic Library Publishing. (Children's Pr.).

On the Launch Pad. (Know Your Numbers Ser.). 24p. (J). 7.95 (978-1-4048-1119-5(2)) Picture Window Bks.

Oxlade, Chris. Space Shuttle. (Take It Apart Ser.). (Illus.). 32p. lib. bdg. 24.25 (978-1-930643-97-0(7)) Chrysalis Education.

—Space Shuttle. Grey, Mike, illus. 1999. (Take It Apart Ser.). (J). lib. bdg. 22.00 (978-0-382-42071-9(3)) Silver, Burdett & Ginn, Inc.

Rees, Peter. Secrets of the Space Shuttle. 2007. (Shockwave: Technology & Manufacturing Ser.). (Illus.). 36p. (J). (gr. 4-6). lib. bdg. 25.00 ***(978-0-531-17590-3(1)*** , Children's Pr.) Scholastic Library Publishing.

Richardson, Adele D. Space Shuttle. 1999. (Above & Beyond Ser.). (Illus.). 32p. (J). (gr. 4-7). lib. bdg. 16.95 (978-1-58340-052-4(4)) Smart Apple Media.

Roza, Greg. The Hubble Space Telescope: Understanding & Representing Numbers up to 1 Billion. 2005. (PowerMath Ser.). (Illus.). 32p. (J). 22.50 (978-1-4042-2931-0(0) , PowerKids Pr.); pap. (978-1-4042-5129-8(4)) Rosen Publishing Group, Inc., The.

Schafer, Christopher. The Space Shuttle Columbia Explosion. 2004. (American Moments Ser.). (J). (978-1-59197-288-4(4)) ABDO Publishing Co.

Shearer, Deborah A. Mission Control. 2002. (Explore Space! Ser.). (Illus.). 24p. (J). (gr. 1-2). lib. bdg. 18.60 (978-0-7368-1143-9(5) , Bridgestone Bks.) Capstone Pr., Inc.

Sofer, Barbara. Ilan Ramon: Israel's Space Hero. 2003. (Illus.). 64p. (J). (gr. 3-6). 16.95 (978-1-58013-115-5(8)); pap. (978-1-58013-116-2(6)) Kar-Ben Publishing.

The Space Shuttle: Individual Title Six-Packs. (On Deck Ser.). 24p. (gr. 4-5). 35.00 (978-0-7578-1055-8(1)) Rigby Education.

Space Shuttles. (Explore Space! Ser.). 24p. (J). 6.95 (978-0-7368-9170-7(6)) Capstone Pr., Inc.

Spangenburg, Ray. Onboard the Space Shuttle. 2002. (gr. 5-8). lib. bdg. 24.55 (978-0-613-53847-3(1)) Tandem Library Bks.

Stille, Darlene R. Space Shuttle. 2004. (Illus.). 32p. (J). (gr. 1 up). lib. bdg. 21.26 (978-0-7565-0609-4(3)) Compass Point Bks.

Sundance, ed. Space Shuttle. 2000. (ps-2). lib. bdg. 11.80 (978-0-613-37629-7(3)) Tandem Library Bks.

Taylor, Robert. Life Aboard the Space Shuttle. 2002. (Way People Live Ser.). (Illus.). 112p. (J). (gr. 7-10). 29.95 (978-1-59018-154-6(9) , LML00902-181109, Lucent Bks.) Thomson Gale.

Transbordadores Espaciales: Individual Title Six-Packs. (On Deck en Espanol Ser.).Tr. of Space Shuttle. (SPA.). 24p. (gr. 4-5). 35.00 (978-0-7578-6430-8(9)) Rigby Education.

A Trip into Space: Individual Title Six-Pack. (Story Steps Ser.). (gr. k-2). 23.00 (978-0-7635-9614-9(0)) Rigby Education.

Vogt, Greg. John Glenn's Return to Space. 2000. (Illus.). 72p. (gr. 5-8). lib. bdg. 24.90 (978-0-7613-1614-5(0) , Millbrook Pr.) Lerner Publishing Group.

Vogt, Gregory L. Space Shuttles. 1999. (Explore Space! Ser.). (Illus.). 24p. (J). (gr. 1-2). lib. bdg. 18.60 (978-0-7368-0200-0(2) , Bridgestone Bks.) Capstone Pr., Inc.

—Space Shuttles, 6 vols. (gr. 2-5). 36.95 (978-0-7368-9248-3(6)) Red Brick Learning.

Whitehouse, Patricia. Living in Space. 2004. (J). 24.21 (978-1-4034-5151-4(6)); pap. 6.95 (978-1-4034-5655-7(0)) Heinemann Library.

—Working in Space. 2004. (J). 24.21 (978-1-4034-5158-3(3)); pap. 6.95 (978-1-4034-5662-5(3)) Heinemann Library.

Zelon, Helen. The Endeavour Mission STS-61: Fixing the Hubble Space Telescope. 2002. (Space Missions Ser.). (Illus.). 24p. (J). (gr. 2-4). lib. bdg. 19.95 (978-0-8239-5774-3(8) , PowerKids Pr.) Rosen Publishing Group, Inc., The.

—The Endeavour SRTM: Mapping the Earth. 2002. (Space Missions Ser.). 24p. (J). lib. bdg. 19.95 (978-0-8239-5775-0(6) , PowerKids Pr.) Rosen Publishing Group, Inc., The.

Zuehlke, Jeffrey. The Space Shuttle. 2007. (J). (Illus.). 32p. pap. 5.95 ***(978-0-8225-6426-3(2)*** , First Avenue Editions); 22.60 (978-0-8225-6420-1(3) , Lerner Pubns.) Lerner Publishing Group.

SPACE SHUTTLES—FICTION

Bannister, Bram. Rupert, the Alien & the Bank Robbery. 2007. 56p. per. 8.95 ***(978-0-595-44839-5(9))*** iUniverse, Inc.

Collins, Dennis. Spinley's Spaceship. 2007. (Illus.). (J). per. 8.99 ***(978-1-60247-100-9(2))*** Tate Publishing & Enterprises, L.L.C.

Edick, Grant. Space Station. 2004. (Two Boys Adventure Story Ser.). 98p. (J). (gr. 3-6). 15.95 (978-0-9677839-9-4(2)) Wysteria Publishing.

Gentry, Stephen. Journey to the Stars & Back. 2005. 52p. (J). pap. 16.49 (978-1-4116-5985-8(6)) Lulu.com.

Greenburg, Dan. Dude, Where's My Spaceship? Pamintuan, Macky, illus. 2006. 96p. (J). (gr. 2-5). lib. bdg. 11.99 (978-0-375-93344-8(1) , Random Hse. Bks. for Young Readers) Random Hse. Children's Bks.

—Dude, Where's My Spaceship? Pamintuan, Macky, illus. 2006. 81p. (J). ***(978-1-4156-6704-0(7))*** Random Hse., Inc.

—Dude Where's My Spaceship. Calver, Dave & Pamintuan, Macky, illus. 2006. (Weird Planet Ser.: No. 1). 96p. (J). (gr. 2-5). pap. 3.99 (978-0-375-83344-1(7) , Random Hse. Bks. for Young Readers) Random Hse. Children's Bks.

—Lost in Las Vegas. Pamintuan, Macky, illus. 2006. 96p. (J). (gr. 2-5). pap. 3.99 (978-0-375-83345-8(5)); lib. bdg. 11.99 (978-0-375-93345-5(X)) Random Hse. Children's Bks. (Random Hse. Bks. for Young Readers).

Griffin, W. Marooned on Earth: The Adventures of O-Boo & U-Boo. 2005. 109p. pap. 16.95 (978-1-4137-6814-5(8)) PublishAmerica, Inc.

Lewis, Anthony, illus. Little Space Explorers. 2007. 14p. bds. 7.99 ***(978-1-84643-038-1(0))*** Child's Play International Ltd. GBR. *Dist:* Child's Play-International.

Reilly, Matthew. Ice Station. 2000. (gr. 7-12). lib. bdg. 15.30 (978-0-613-36423-2(6)) Tandem Library Bks.

Rex, Adam. The True Meaning of Smekday. Rex, Adam, illus. rev. ed. 2007. 432p. (gr. 2-7). 16.99 ***(978-0-7868-4900-0(2))*** Hyperion Pr.

Rigby Education Staff. The Space Cat. (Sails Literacy Ser.). (Illus.). 16p. (gr. 2-3). 27.00 (978-0-7635-9949-2(2) , 699492C99) Rigby Education.

Wilson-Max, Ken, illus. Big Silver Space Shuttle. ed. 2000. 14p. (J). (ps-k). bds. 7.95 (978-0-439-13656-3(3) , Cartwheel Bks.) Scholastic, Inc.

Wyre, Yvonne. The Further Adventures of Cuthbert the Coal Lorry & all His Friends. 2007. (Illus.). 204p. pap. ***(978-1-84401-801-7(6))*** Athena Pr.

SPACE STATIONS

Here are entered works dealing with manned installations existing for specific functions, such as servicing space ships, etc., in orbit around the earth or other natural extraterrestrial bodies.

Arnold, Eric. Race into Space. Torrisi, Gary, illus. 2004. 48p. (J). (gr. 1-3). lib. bdg. 11.19 (978-0-606-32797-8(5)) Tandem Library Bks.

Belfiore, Michael P. Life Aboard a Space Station. 2004. (Way People Live Ser.). (Illus.). 112p. (J). (gr. 7-10). 29.95 (978-1-59018-460-8(2) , Lucent Bks.) Thomson Gale.

Branley, Franklyn M. The International Space Station. Kelley, True, illus. 2000. (Let's-Read-and-Find-Out Science Ser.). 40p. (J). (gr. k-4). pap. 5.99 (978-0-06-445209-0(3) , Harper Trophy) HarperCollins Pubs.

—The International Space Station. Kelley, True, illus. 2000. (Let's-Read-and-Find-Out Ser.). (J). 12.79 (978-0-606-19978-0(0)) Tandem Library Bks.

—International Space Station. 2000. (gr. k-3). lib. bdg. 14.15 (978-0-613-31360-5(7)) Tandem Library Bks.

Carroll, Jillian. Where to Stay. 2003. (J). lib. bdg. (978-1-58417-232-1(0)) Lake Street Pubs.

Cole, Michael D. International Space Station: A Space Mission. 1999. (Countdown to Space Ser.). (Illus.). 48p. (YA). (gr. 4-10). lib. bdg. 23.93 (978-0-7660-1117-5(8)) Enslow Pubs., Inc.

Cowles, Rose, illus. The Amazing International Space Station. 2004. 48p. (J). (gr. 4-6). (978-1-55337-523-4(8)); (978-1-55337-380-3(4)) Kids Can Pr., Ltd.

Dyson, Marianne J. Space Station Science. Klug, Dave, illus. 2nd ed. 2004. 128p. (J). pap. 11.95 (978-0-89317-059-2(3) , WW-0593, Windward Publishing) Finney Co., Inc.

Dyson, Marianne J. & Klug, Dave. Space Station Science: Life in Free Fall. 1999. (Illus.). 128p. (J). (gr. 4-9). pap. 16.95 (978-0-590-05889-6(4) , Scholastic Reference) Scholastic, Inc.

Feldman, Heather. Skylab: The First American Space Station. 2003. (Space Firsts Ser.). (Illus.). 24p. (J). lib. bdg. 19.95 (978-0-8239-6248-8(2) , PowerKids Pr.) Rosen Publishing Group, Inc., The.

Gallant, Roy A., ed. Space Stations. 2000. (Kaleidoscope Ser.). (Illus.). 48p. (J). (gr. 3 up). lib. bdg. 25.64 (978-0-7614-1035-5(X) , Benchmark Bks.) Cavendish, Marshall Corp.

Harcourt School Publishers Staff. The International Space Station. 3rd ed. 2002. (Horizons Ser.). (Illus.). (J). pap. 5.50 (978-0-15-333248-7(4)) Harcourt Schl. Pubs.

Holden, Henry M. Living & Working Aboard the International Space Station: A MyReportLinks. com Book. 2004. (Space Flight Adventures & Disasters Ser.). (Illus.). 48p. (J). lib. bdg. 25.26 (978-0-7660-5168-3(4) , MyReportLinks.com Bks.) Enslow Pubs., Inc.

—The Supersonic X-15 & High-Tech NASA Aircraft. 2002. (Aircraft Ser.). (Illus.). 48p. (J). (gr. 4-10). lib. bdg. 23.93 (978-0-7660-1717-7(6)) Enslow Pubs., Inc.

Jefferis, David. Future Space: Beyond Earth. Quigley, Sebastian, illus. 2001. 48p. (J). 6.95 (978-0-439-31460-2(7)) Scholastic, Inc.

Kerrod, Robin. Space Stations. 2004. (History of Space Exploration Ser.). (Illus.). 48p. (J). pap. (978-0-8368-5717-7(8)); lib. bdg. 30.00 (978-0-8368-5710-8(0)) Stevens, Gareth Inc. (World Almanac Library).

Kortenkamp, Steve. Space Stations. 2008. (J). (***978-1-4296-0064-4(0)***) Capstone Pr., Inc.

Lusted, Marcia Amidon, et al. The International Space Station. 2005. (Building History Ser.). (Illus.). 112p. (YA). (gr. 7-10). lib. bdg. 32.45 (978-1-59018-666-4(4) , Lucent Bks.) Thomson Gale.

Nipaul, Devi. The International Space Station: An Orbiting Laboratory. 2004. (High Interest Bks.). (Illus.). 48p. (J). (gr. 7-12). pap. 6.95 (978-0-516-25908-6(3) , Children's Pr.) Scholastic Library Publishing.

Pascoe, Elaine, ed. International Space Station. 2003. (Super Structures of the World Ser.). (Illus.). 48p. (J). 24.95 (978-1-56711-865-0(8)); 11.20 (978-1-4103-0189-5(3)) Thomson Gale. (Blackbirch Pr., Inc.).

Rau, Dana Meachen. The International Space Station. 2005. (Our Solar System Ser.). (YA). (978-0-7565-0882-1(7)) Compass Point Bks.

Space Stations. (Explore Space! Ser.). 24p. (J). 6.95 (978-0-7368-9171-4(4)) Capstone Pr., Inc.

Space Stations, 6 vols. (gr. 2-5). 36.95 (978-0-7368-9249-0(4)) Red Brick Learning.

Spangenburg, Ray. Onboard the Space Shuttle. 2002. (gr. 5-8). lib. bdg. 24.55 (978-0-613-53847-3(1)) Tandem Library Bks.

Taylor, Robert. Space Stations. 2004. (Lucent Library of Science). (Illus.). 112p. (J). 29.95 (978-1-59018-106-5(9)) Thomson Gale.

Vogt, Gregory L. Living on Other Worlds. 2000. (Our Universe Ser.). (Illus.). 48p. (YA). (gr. 5-12). lib. bdg. 22.83 (978-0-7398-3114-4(3)) Raintree.

—Living on Other Worlds. 2000. (Illus.). (J). pap. (978-0-7398-3353-7(7)) Steck-Vaughn.

—Space Stations. 1999. (Explore Space! Ser.). (Illus.). 24p. (J). (gr. 1-2). lib. bdg. 18.60 (978-0-7368-0201-7(0) , Bridgestone Bks.) Capstone Pr., Inc.

Whitehouse, Patricia. Living in Space. 2004. (J). 24.21 (978-1-4034-5151-4(6)); pap. 6.95 (978-1-4034-5655-7(0)) Heinemann Library.

—Working in Space. 2004. (J). 24.21 (978-1-4034-5158-3(3)); pap. 6.95 (978-1-4034-5662-5(3)) Heinemann Library.

SPACE STATIONS—FICTION

Appleton, Victor. The Space Hotel. 2007. (Tom Swift, Young Inventor Ser.). 160p. (J). (gr. 4-7). 27.07 (***978-1-59961-353-6(0)***) Spotlight.

Cahill, Byron. Space Pox. 2005. 40.00 (***978-1-4108-4220-6(7)***) Benchmark Education Co.

Daley, Michael J. Space Station Rat. 2005. 144p. (J). 15.95 (978-0-8234-1866-4(9)) Holiday Hse., Inc.

Edick, Grant. Space Station. 2004. (Two Boys Adventure Story Ser.). 98p. (J). (gr. 3-6). 15.95 (978-0-9677839-9-4(2)) Wysteria Publishing.

Elmer, Robert. About-Face Space Race. 2001. (AstroKids Ser.). (Illus.). 112p. (J). (gr. 2-6). pap. 4.99 (978-0-7642-2360-0(7)) Bethany Hse. Pubs.

—The Great Galaxy Goof. 2000. (Astrokids Ser.: Vol. 1). (Illus.). 112p. (J). (gr. 2-6). pap. 5.99 (978-0-7642-2356-3(9)) Bethany Hse. Pubs.

—Miko's Muzzy Mess. 2001. (SpaceKids Ser.: Vol. 4). (Illus.). 112p. (J). (gr. 2-6). pap. 4.99 (978-0-7642-2359-4(3)) Bethany Hse. Pubs.

—Miko's Muzzy Mess. 2001. (gr. 3-6). lib. bdg. 13.00 (978-0-613-85064-3(5)) Tandem Library Bks.

—Wired Wonder Woof. 2001. (SpaceKids Ser.: Vol. 3). (Illus.). 112p. (J). (gr. 2-6). pap. 4.99 (978-0-7642-2358-7(5)) Bethany Hse. Pubs.

—Wired Wonder Woof. 2001. (gr. 3-6). lib. bdg. 13.00 (978-0-613-82426-2(1)) Tandem Library Bks.

—The Zero-G Headache. 2000. (Astrokids Ser.: Vol. 2). (Illus.). 112p. (J). (gr. 2-6). pap. 4.99 (978-0-7642-2357-0(7)) Bethany Hse. Pubs.

Geiger, Beth & Fuerst, Jeffrey B. Return to Earth: Reader's Theater Levels N-U (30-50) Wolk-Stanley, Jessica, illus. ed. 2004. (Reader's Theater Ser.). 16p. (J). pap. 22.00 (978-1-4108-2306-9(7) , A23067) Benchmark Education Co.

Haarsma, P. J. The Softwire: Virus on Orbis 1. 2008. (Illus.). 288p. (J). (gr. 5). 6.99 (***978-0-7636-3638-8(X)***) Candlewick Pr.

Rue, Nancy N. Sophie & the Scoundrels, Bk. 3. Chen, Grace, illus. 2005. (Faithgirlz Ser.). 128p. (J). pap. 6.99 (978-0-310-70758-5(7)) Zonderkidz.

SPACE SUITS

see Astronauts—Clothing

SPACE TELECOMMUNICATION

see Interstellar Communication

SPACE TRAVEL

see Interplanetary Voyages; Manned Space Flight; Space Flight

SPACE VEHICLES

see also Artificial Satellites; Space Probes; Space Stations

Adamson, Heather. The Challenger Explosion. Bascle, Brian, illus. 2006. (Graphic Library). 32p. (J). (978-0-7368-5478-8(9) , 1252837) Capstone Pr., Inc.

Avera, Randy. The Truth about Challenger. 2003. (Illus.). 344p. 34.00 (978-1-932258-00-4(0) , SAN # 254-9522) Randolph Publishing.

Beyer, Mark. Crisis in Space: Apollo 13. 2002. (Survivors Ser.). (Illus.). 48p. (YA). (gr. 7-12). 24.00 (978-0-516-23903-3(1)); pap. 6.95 (978-0-516-23485-4(4)) Scholastic Library Publishing. (Children's Pr.).

—Crisis in Space: Apollo Thirteen. 2002. (gr. 7-12). lib. bdg. 15.25 (978-0-613-58756-3(1)) Tandem Library Bks.

BHB International Staff. Spacecraft. 1998. (Our World in Pictures Ser.). (J). (978-2-215-06174-8(X)) Editions Fleurus.

Bricker, Sandra D. Challenger. Taylor, Marjorie, illus. rev. ed. 1999. (Take Ten Ser.). 47p. (YA). (gr. 4 up). pap. 3.95 (978-1-58659-021-5(9)) Artesian Pr.

—Challenger. 2000. (gr. 5-8). lib. bdg. 11.80 (978-0-613-51203-9(0)) Tandem Library Bks.

Brubaker, Paul E. Apollo 1 Tragedy: Fire in the Capsule. 2002. (American Disasters Ser.). (Illus.). 48p. (J). (gr. 4-10). lib. bdg. 23.93 (978-0-7660-1787-0(7)) Enslow Pubs., Inc.

Bruce, Linda. Space Technology. 2006. (How Does It Work? Ser.). (Illus.). 32p. (J). (978-1-58340-795-0(2)) Smart Apple Media.

Caper, William. The Challenger Space Shuttle Explosion. 2007. (Code Red Ser.). (Illus.). 32p. (J). (gr. 3-7). lib. bdg. 25.27 (978-1-59716-367-5(8)) Bearport Publishing Co., Inc.

Chippendale, Lisa. Apollo One/Challenger. 2000. (Great Disasters, Reforms & Ramifications Ser.). (Illus.). 120p. (J). (gr. 4-7). 21.95 (978-0-7910-5783-4(6) , Chelsea Hse.) Facts On File, Inc.

Cole, Michael D. NASA Space Vehicles: Capsules, Shuttles & Space Stations. 2000. (Countdown to Space Ser.). (Illus.). 48p. (YA). (gr. 4-10). lib. bdg. 23.93 (978-0-7660-1308-7(1)) Enslow Pubs., Inc.

—Space Emergency: Astronauts in Danger. 2000. (Countdown to Space Ser.). (Illus.). 48p. (YA). (gr. 4-10). lib. bdg. 23.93 (978-0-7660-1307-0(3)) Enslow Pubs., Inc.

Dorling Kindersley Publishing Staff. Rockets & Spaceships. 2001. (Readers Ser.). (Illus.). 32p. (J). (ps-3). 14.99 (978-0-7894-7360-8(7)) Dorling Kindersley Publishing, Inc.

Draw 50 Airplanes, Aircraft & Spacecraft. 2002. (Draw 50 Ser.). (Illus.). (J). 17.60 (978-0-7587-4700-6(4)) Book Wholesalers, Inc.

Fahey, Kathleen. Challenger & Columbia. 2005. (Illus.). 32p. (J). lib. bdg. 24.67 (978-0-8368-4496-2(3)) Stevens, Gareth Inc.

Furniss. Spacecraft. 2004. (Mean Machines Ser.). (Illus.). 64p. (J). pap. 8.95 (978-1-4109-1198-8(5)) Harcourt Schl. Pubs.

—Spacecraft 6 Pack. 2004. (Illus.). (J). pap. 48.30 (978-1-4109-1203-9(5)) Harcourt Schl. Pubs.

Furniss, Tim. Spacecraft. 2004. (Mean Machines Ser.). (Illus.). 64p. (J). 32.79 (978-1-4109-1083-7(0)) Harcourt Schl. Pubs.

Gogerly, Liz. When Disaster Struck: The Challenger 1986. 2006. (Illus.). 56p. (J). (978-1-4109-2279-3(0)) Steck-Vaughn.

Graham, Ian. The Best Book of Spaceships. 1998. (Best Book of... Ser.). (Illus.). 32p. (J). (gr. k-3). tchr. ed. 12.95 (978-0-7534-5133-5(6) , Kingfisher) Houghton Mifflin Co. Trade & Reference Div.

—In Space: Machines at Work. 2007. (J). lib. bdg. 19.95 (978-1-59566-318-4(5)) QEB Publishing Inc.

—Space Vehicles. 2005. (World's Greatest Ser.). (Illus.). 32p. (J). (978-1-4109-2086-7(0)); pap. (978-1-4109-2093-5(3)) Steck-Vaughn.

Graham, Ian. The Spaceships. 2008. (Best Book of... Ser.). (Illus.). 32p. (J). pap. 6.95 (***978-0-7534-6167-9(6)*** , Kingfisher) Houghton Mifflin Co. Trade & Reference Div.

Hamilton, John. Spaceships. 2007. (World of Science Fiction Ser.). (Illus.). 32p. (J). 24.21 (978-1-59679-995-0(1)) ABDO Publishing Co.

Hibbert, Clare. The Inside & Out Guide to Spacecraft. 2006. (Illus.). 32p. (J). (***978-1-4034-9088-9(0)***) Heinemann Library.

Holden, Henry M. Triumph over Disaster Aboard Apollo 13: A MyReportLinks. com Book. 2004. (Space Flight Adventures & Disasters Ser.). (Illus.). 48p. (J). lib. bdg. 25.26 (978-0-7660-5167-6(6) , MyReportLinks.com Bks.) Enslow Pubs., Inc.

Jefferis. Spacecraft - Monster Machines. 2003. pap. 48.30 (978-1-4109-0277-1(3)) Raintree.

Jefferis, David. Spacecraft. 2001. (Monster Machines Ser.). (Illus.). 32p. (J). (ps-3). lib. bdg. 25.69 (978-0-7398-2881-6(9)) Raintree.

—Spacecraft. 2003. (gr. 3-6). lib. bdg. 16.40 (978-0-613-78221-0(6)) Tandem Library Bks.

Jeffries. Spacecraft. 2003. (Monster Machines Ser.). (Illus.). 32p. (J). pap. 7.95 (978-1-4109-0058-6(4)) Raintree.

Landau, Elaine. Space Disasters. 1999. (Watts Library). (Illus.). 64p. (J). (gr. 5-7). 25.50 (978-0-531-20345-3(X) , Watts, Franklin) Scholastic Library Publishing.

Lemke, Donald B. The Apollo 13 Mission. Tucker, Keith, illus. 2006. (Graphic Library). 32p. (978-0-7368-5476-4(2)) Capstone Pr., Inc.

Loves, June. Spacecraft. 2001. (Database Transportation Ser.). (Illus.). 32p. (J). (gr. 4 up). 22.95 (978-0-7910-6588-4(X) , 010505, Chelsea Hse.) Facts On File, Inc.

McNeese, Tim. The Challenger Disaster. 2003. (Cornerstones of Freedom, 2ND Ser.). lib. bdg. 24.00 (978-0-516-22840-2(4)); (Illus.). 48p. (J). 26.00 (978-0-516-24222-4(9)) Scholastic Library Publishing. (Children's Pr.).

Miller, Heather. Naves Espaciales. 2003. (Ruedas, Alas y Agua Ser.).Tr. of Spacecraft. (SPA., 24p. (J). (ps-1). Illus.). lib. bdg. 18.50 (978-1-4034-0919-5(6)); pap. 5.25 (978-1-4034-3535-4(9)) Heinemann Library.

—Spacecraft. 2003. (Wheels, Wings, & Water Ser.). (Illus.). 24p. (J). lib. bdg. 18.50 (978-1-4034-0882-2(3)); pap. (978-1-4034-3623-8(1)) Heinemann Library.

—Spacecraft. 2003. (gr. k-3). lib. bdg. 13.30 (978-0-613-67434-8(0)) Tandem Library Bks.

Pierce, Alan. Apollo. 2005. (American Moments Set Ii Ser.). (J). (gr. 4-8). lib. bdg. 25.65 (978-1-59197-726-1(6) , ABDO & Daughters) ABDO Publishing Co.

Quigley, Sebastian, illus. Mars Mission Masterbuilders. 2000. (LEGO Masterbuilders Ser.). (J). (ps-3). 19.99 (978-1-903276-16-7(0)) Lego Media International, Inc.

Radevsky, Anton. The Pop-Up Book of Space Craft. 2000. (J). pap. 19.95 (978-3-8290-4864-4(5)) Konemann.

Royston, Angela. Space Station: Accident on Mir. 2000. (Eyewitness Readers Ser.). (J). (978-0-606-20125-4(4)) Tandem Library Bks.

Sautter, Aaron. How to Draw Unreal Spaceships. Bascle, Brian, illus. 2008. (J). (***978-1-4296-1302-6(5)***) Capstone Pr., Inc.

Saxton, Curtis & Jenssen, Hans. Star Wars: Complete Cross-Sections. 2007. (Star Wars Ser.). (Illus.). 136p. (J). (ps-12). 35.00 (978-0-7566-2704-1(4)) Dorling Kindersley Publishing, Inc.

Simon, Seymour. Destination: Space. 32p. (J). 2006. 16.99 (978-0-06-087722-4(7)); 2006. (Illus.). pap. 6.99 (978-0-06-087723-1(5)); 2002. (Illus.). (gr. 4-7). 15.99 (978-0-688-16289-4(4)) HarperCollins Pubs.

Sparrow, Giles. Exploring the Universe. 2006. (Illus.). 48p. (J). pap. (978-0-8368-7283-5(5)); lib. bdg. (978-0-8368-7276-7(2)) Stevens, Gareth Inc. (World Almanac Library).

Spizzirri, Linda, ed. Space Craft. Spizzirri, Peter M., illus. 32p. (J). (gr. 1-8). pap. 4.98 incl. audio (978-0-86545-036-3(6)) Spizzirri Pr., Inc.

Sundance, ed. In Space. 2000. (ps-2). lib. bdg. 11.65 (978-0-613-37623-5(4)) Tandem Library Bks.

Thimmesh, Catherine. Team Moon: How 400,000 People Landed Apollo 11 on the Moon. 2006. (Illus.). 80p. (J). (gr. 5). 19.95 (978-0-618-50757-3(4)) Houghton Mifflin Co.

Visca, Curt & Visca, Kelley. How to Draw Cartoon Spacecraft & Astronauts in Action. 2004. (Kid's Guide to Drawing Ser.). (Illus.). 24p. (J). lib. bdg. 21.25 (978-0-8239-6729-2(8) , PowerKids Pr.) Rosen Publishing Group, Inc., The.

Vogt, Gregory L. Disasters in Space Exploration. (Enthusiastic Astronomy Ser.). (Illus.). (gr. 5-8). 2001. 72p. lib. bdg. (978-0-7613-1920-7(4) , Millbrook Pr.); 2003. 80p. lib. bdg. 25.90 (978-0-7613-2895-7(5) , Twenty-First Century Bks.) Lerner Publishing Group.

Wallace, Karen. Rockets & Spaceships. 2001. (Readers Ser.). (Illus.). 32p. (J). (ps-3). pap. 3.99 (978-0-7894-7359-2(3)) Dorling Kindersley Publishing, Inc.

Walsh, Patricia. Space Vehicles. 2002. (Draw It! Ser.). (Illus.). 32p. (J). (gr. 3-6). pap. 7.50 (978-1-58810-294-2(7) , 91044) Heinemann Library.

Walsh, Patricia & Adamic, Marc. Space Vehicles. 2000. (Draw It! Ser.). (Illus.). 32p. (J). (gr. 3-5). lib. bdg. 22.79 (978-1-57572-350-1(6)) Heinemann Library.

Weil, Ann. Space Disasters. 2003. (Illus.). 64p. (YA). per. 3.95 (978-1-56254-662-5(7) , SP6627) Saddleback Educational Publishing.

—Space Play. Cressy, Mike, tr. Cressy, Mike, illus. 2003. 59p. (978-0-7398-5172-2(1)) Steck-Vaughn.

Whitehouse, Patricia. Space Equipment. 2004. (J). 24.21 (978-1-4034-5154-5(0)); pap. 7.25 (978-1-4034-5658-8(5)) Heinemann Library.

Woodford. Space Dramas. 2003. (Space Busters Ser.). (Illus.). 32p. (J). pap. 7.95 (978-1-4109-0073-9(8)) Raintree.

Woodford, Chris. Space Dramas. 2002. (Young Library - Space Busters Ser.). (Illus.). 32p. (J). (gr. 3-5). lib. bdg. 25.69 (978-0-7398-4850-0(X)) Raintree.

SPACE VEHICLES—MODELS

Boekhoff, P. M. Nifty Thrifty Space Crafts. 2007. (Nifty Thrifty Crafts for Kids Ser.). (Illus.). 32p. (J). lib. bdg. 22.60 (978-0-7660-2783-1(X) , Enslow Elementary) Enslow Pubs., Inc.

Farrington, Karen. Make Your Own Space Machines. 1998. (Illus.). 24p. (J). (gr. 1 up). pap. 7.95 (978-0-688-16329-7(7)) HarperCollins Pubs.

SPAIN

Armentrout, David & Armentrout, Patricia. Treasures from Spain. 2000. (Treasures from the Past Ser.). (Illus.). 48p. (J). (gr. 4-8). lib. bdg. 29.93 (978-1-55916-293-7(7)) Rourke Publishing, LLC.

Berendes, Mary. Welcome to Spain. 2008. (Welcome to the World Ser.). 32p. (J). (gr. 1-5). 27.07 (***978-1-59296-979-1(8)***) Child's World, Inc.

Blomquist, Christopher. Spain, a Primary Source Guide. 2005. (Countries of the World, a Primary Source Journey Ser.). (Illus.). 24p. (J). 19.95 (978-1-4042-2757-6(1) , PowerKids Pr.) Rosen Publishing Group, Inc., The.

Boast, Clare. Spain. 1998. (Next Stop! Ser.). 32p. (J). lib. bdg. 19.92 (978-1-57572-570-3(3)) Heinemann Library.

Campbell, Polly, et al. Focus on Spain. 2006. (Illus.). 64p. pap. (978-0-8368-6730-5(0)); lib. bdg. (978-0-8368-6723-7(8)) Stevens, Gareth Inc. (World Almanac Library).

Costain, Meredith & Collins, Paul, eds. Welcome to Spain. 2001. (Countries of the World Ser.). (Illus.). 32p. (J). 28.00 (978-0-7910-6878-6(1) , Chelsea Hse.) Facts On File, Inc.

Deady, Kathleen W. Spain. 2001. (Countries of the World Ser.). (Illus.). 126p. (J). (gr. 2-3). 18.60 (978-0-7368-0816-3(7) , Bridgestone Bks.) Capstone Pr., Inc.

Ellis, Royston. Trinidad. 1999. (Festivals of the World Ser.). (Illus.). 32p. (J). (gr. 3 up). lib. bdg. 24.67 (978-0-8368-2036-2(3)) Stevens, Gareth Inc.

Furlong, Kate A. Spain. 2000. (Countries Ser.). (Illus.). 40p. (J). (gr. k-6). lib. bdg. 22.78 (978-1-57765-388-2(2) , Checkerboard Library) ABDO Publishing Co.

Graham, Ian. Spain. 2003. (Country Files Ser.). 32p. (J). lib. bdg. 24.25 (978-1-58340-240-5(3)) Smart Apple Media.

Grinsted, Katherine. Spain. 1999. (Countries of the World Ser.). (Illus.). 96p. (J). (gr. 6 up). lib. bdg. 30.00 (978-0-8368-2312-7(5)) Stevens, Gareth Inc.

Harris, Nathaniel. Spain. 2003. (Nations of the World Ser.). (Illus.). 128p. (J). pap. 34.28 (978-0-7398-7001-3(7)) Steck-Vaughn.

Hintz, Martin. Spain. (True Bks.). (J). 2005. (Illus.). 48p. (gr. 3-5). pap. 6.95 (978-0-516-27930-5(0)); 2004. 25.00 (978-0-516-22815-0(3)) Scholastic Library Publishing. (Children's Pr.).

Kent, Deborah. Madrid. 1999. (Cities of the World Ser.). (Illus.). 64p. (J). (gr. 4-9). pap. 9.95 (978-0-516-26462-2(1)); (YA). 27.00 (978-0-516-20783-4(0)) Scholastic Library Publishing. (Children's Pr.).

—Madrid. 1999. (gr. 5-8). lib. bdg. 18.75 (978-0-613-51087-5(9)) Tandem Library Bks.

Kent, Su. Spain. 2006. (Living In- Ser.). (Illus.). 32p. (J). (978-1-59771-048-0(2)) Sea-To-Sea Pubns.

Kenyon, John. Spain. 2004. (QEB Travel Through Ser.). (Illus.). 32p. (J). lib. bdg. 18.95 (978-1-59566-061-9(5)) QEB Publishing Inc.

Kohen, Elizabeth & Graff, Marie Louise. Spain. 2nd ed. 2003. (Illus.). 144p. (gr. 5 up). lib. bdg. 37.07 (978-0-7614-1501-5(7) , Cavendish, Marshall Reference Bks.) Cavendish, Marshall Corp.

Lior, Noa. Spain: The Culture. 2002. (gr. 3-6). lib. bdg. 16.40 (978-0-613-52994-5(4)) Tandem Library Bks.

—Spain: The People. 2002. (gr. 3-6). lib. bdg. 16.40 (978-0-613-52996-9(0)) Tandem Library Bks.

Lior, Noa & Steele, Tara. Spain - The Culture. 2002. (Lands, Peoples & Cultures Ser.). (Illus.). 32p. (J). (gr. 4-5). pap. (978-0-7787-9734-0(1)); (978-0-7787-9366-3(4)) Crabtree Publishing Co.

—Spain - The Land. 2002. (Lands, Peoples & Cultures Ser.). (Illus.). 32p. (J). (gr. 4-5). (978-0-7787-9364-9(8)); pap. (978-0-7787-9732-6(5)) Crabtree Publishing Co.

—Spain - The People. 2002. (Lands, Peoples & Cultures Ser.). (Illus.). 32p. (J). (gr. 4-5). (978-0-7787-9365-6(6)); pap. (978-0-7787-9733-3(3)) Crabtree Publishing Co.

Mason, Paul. Spain. (Illus.). 48p. (J). 2006. lib. bdg. (***978-1-4109-2464-3(5));*** 2005. (978-1-4109-1863-5(7)) Steck-Vaughn.

Mathews, Sally Schofer. The Sad Night: The Story of an Aztec Victory & a Spanish Loss. Mathews, Sally Schofer, illus. 1999. (Illus.). 36p. (J). (gr. 4-6). 17.00 (978-0-7881-6762-1(6)) DIANE Publishing Co.

McKay, Susan. Spain. 1999. (Festivals of the World Ser.). (Illus.). 32p. (J). (gr. 3 up). lib. bdg. 24.67 (978-0-8368-2035-5(5)) Stevens, Gareth Inc.

Mesenas, Geraldine & Ginsted, Katherine. Welcome to Spain. 2000. (Welcome to My Country Ser.). (Illus.). 48p. (J). (gr. 2 up). lib. bdg. 26.00 (978-0-8368-2512-1(8)) Stevens, Gareth Inc.

Moritz, Patricia M. Spain. 2000. (Dropping in on Ser.). (Illus.). 32p. (J). (gr. 2-5). lib. bdg. 28.50 (978-1-55916-282-1(1)) Rourke Publishing, LLC.

Needham, Ed. Spain & the Spanish. 2004. (Focus on Europe Ser.). lib. bdg. 28.50 (978-1-932799-15-6(X)) Stargazer Bks.

Park, Ted. Spain. 2000. (Taking Your Camera to Ser.). (Illus.). 32p. (J). (gr. 4-7). lib. bdg. 22.83 (978-0-7398-1809-1(0)) Raintree.

—Taking Your Camera to Spain. 2001. (Illus.). pap. (978-0-7398-3330-8(8)) Steck-Vaughn.

Parker, Lewis K. Spain. 2003. (Discovering Cultures Ser.). (Illus.). 48p. (J). 25.64 (978-0-7614-1520-6(3)) Cavendish, Marshall Corp.

Paul Mason. Spain. 2006. (Illus.). 48p. (J). pap. (***978-1-4109-2471-1(8)***) Steck-Vaughn.

Pavlovic, Zoran & Hanks, Reuel. Spain. 2006. (Modern World Nations Ser.). (Illus.). 104p. (J). (gr. 6-12). 30.00 (978-0-7910-6697-3(5) , Chelsea Hse.) Facts On File, Inc.

Powell, Jillian. Looking at Spain. 2006. (Illus.). 32p. (J). pap. (***978-0-8368-7679-6(2)***); lib. bdg. (***978-0-8368-7672-7(5)***) Stevens, Gareth Inc.

Rogers, Lura. Spain. 2001. (Enchantment of the World, Second Ser.). (Illus.). 144p. (J). (gr. 5-9). 36.00 (978-0-516-21123-7(4) , Children's Pr.) Scholastic Library Publishing.

S

Schon, Isabel. The Best of Latino Heritage, 1996-2002: A Guide to the Best Juvenile Books about Latino People. 2003. (Illus.). 272p. 42.50 (978-0-8108-4669-2(1)) Scarecrow Pr., Inc.

Simons, Rae. Spain. 2006. (European Union Ser.). (Illus.). 88p. (J). (gr. 5 up). lib. bdg. (978-1-4222-0062-9(0)) Mason Crest Pubs.

Skog, Jason & Compass Point Books Staff. Teens in Spain. 2006. (Global Connections Ser.). (Illus.). 96p. (J). (gr. 5-7). 31.93 (978-0-7565-2446-3(6)) Compass Point Bks.

Spengler, Kremena. Spain: A Question & Answer Book. 2006. (Fact Finders Ser.). (Illus.). 32p. (J). (978-0-7368-4357-7(4)) Capstone Pr., Inc.

Taus-Bolstad, Stacy. Spain in Pictures. 2nd rev. expurg. ed. 2004. (Visual Geography Ser.). (Illus.). 80p. (J). (gr. 5-12). 27.93 (978-0-8225-1993-5(3)) Lerner Publishing Group.

Thompson, Linda. The Spanish in America. 2006. (Expansion of America II Ser.). (Illus.). 48p. (gr. 4-8). 20.95 (978-1-59515-514-6(7)) Rourke Publishing, LLC.

Welby, Rebecca. Hola Spain! 2006. (Young Traveler's Club Ser.). (ENG & SPA., Illus.). 60p. pap. 16.95 (978-0-9549476-2-0(2)) Beautiful Bks. GBR. *Dist:* International Publishers Marketing.

Wright, Nicola & De Saulles, Janet. Getting to Know Spain & Spanish. Wooley, Kim, illus. 2000. (Getting to Know Ser.). 32p. (J). (gr. 3-7). pap. 7.95 (978-0-8120-1535-5(5) , BA5355) Barron's Educational Series, Inc.

Wright, Rachel & Campbell, Catherine. Spain. 2005. (Illus.). 32p. (J). (gr. 4-7). lib. bdg. 27.10 (978-1-932889-98-7(1)) Sea-To-Sea Pubns.

Yanuck, Debbie L. Spain. 2004. (Many Cultures, One World Ser.). (Illus.). 32p. (J). (gr. 2-3). lib. bdg. 23.93 (978-0-7368-2451-4(0) , Bridgestone Bks.) Capstone Pr., Inc.

SPAIN—FICTION

Alonso, Manuel L. Tiempo de Nubes Negras. Gaban, Jesus, illus. Tr. of Time for Black Clouds. (SPA.). 176p. (J). pap. (978-84-667-0289-8(X)); 4th ed. 88p. (YA). (gr. 5-8). 7.16 (978-84-207-7770-2(6)) Grupo Anaya, S.A. ESP. *Dist:* Lectorum Pubns., Inc.

Aska, Warabe. Tapicero Tap Tap. 2006. (Illus.). 24p. (J). (gr. 1-3). 16.95 (978-0-88776-760-9(5)) Tundra Bks., Inc./Livres Toundra, Inc. CAN. *Dist:* Random Hse., Inc.

Blasco Ibañez, Vicente. Sangre y Arena Level 4. 1998. (SPA.). (gr. 7-12). lib. bdg. 15.25 (978-0-613-80710-4(3)) Tandem Library Bks.

Cann, Kate. Spanish Holiday: Or, How I Transformed the Worst Vacation Ever into the Best Sum. 2004. (gr. 7-12). lib. bdg. 14.15 (978-0-613-71954-4(9)) Tandem Library Bks.

—Spanish Holiday: Or, How I Transformed the Worst Vacation Ever into the Best Summer of My Life. 2004. (Illus.). 352p. pap. 5.99 (978-0-06-056160-4(2)) HarperCollins Pubs.

Carrero, Luis Maria. La Ciudad de los Dioses. 1998. (SPA.). (gr. 3-6). lib. bdg. 14.10 (978-0-613-80708-1(1)) Tandem Library Bks.

Cervantes Saavedra, Miguel de. Don Quixote. Marshall, Michael J., ed. abr. ed. 1999. (Core Classics Ser.: Vol. 6). (Illus.). 264p. (J). (gr. 4-6). pap. 7.95 (978-1-890517-10-6(0)) Core Knowledge Foundation.

—Don Quixote of the Mancha. 1999. (Everyman's Library Children's Classics). (Illus.). 256p. (gr. 8-12). 14.95 (978-0-375-40659-1(X) , Everyman's Library) Knopf Publishing Group.

—Tales of Don Quixote, Bk. 2. 2006. 224p. (J). (gr. 5). 18.95 (978-0-88776-744-9(3)) Tundra Bks., Inc./Livres Toundra, Inc. CAN. *Dist:* Random Hse., Inc.

El Cid. (SPA., Illus.). 128p. (J). 11.95 (978-84-7281-098-3(4) , AF1098) Auriga, Ediciones S.A. ESP. *Dist:* Continental Bk. Co., Inc.

Cillero Goiriastuena, Javi. The Girl Who Swam to Euskadi: Euskadiraino Igerian Joan Zen Neska. Kurlansky, Mark, illus. 2005. (ENG & BAQ.). 32p. (J). pap. 18.95 (978-1-877802-54-6(9)) Univ. of Nevada, Reno-Center for Basque Studies.

Comella, Maria Angeles, et al. Buenos Dias, Senor Tapies! 2001. Tr. of Good Day, Mr. Tapies!. (Illus.). 32p. (J). (CAT.). (gr. k-2). 14.95 (978-84-95040-97-8(2)); (SPA., (gr. 2-5). 14.95 (978-84-95040-96-1(4)) Serres, Ediciones, S. L. ESP. *Dist:* Lectorum Pubns., Inc.

Following Isabella - Evaluation Guide: Evaluation Guide. 2006. (J). (978-1-55942-406-6(0)) Marsh Media.

Following Isabella - Teaching Guide. 2000. 17.95 (978-1-55942-169-0(X)) Marsh Media.

Goscinny, René & Uderzo, Albert. Asterix in Spain. Uderzo, Albert, illus. 2004. (Illus.). 48p. pap. 9.95 (978-0-7528-6631-4(1)) Orion Bks. Ltd. GBR. *Dist:* Sterling Publishing Co., Inc.

Guardiola, Pepa. Los Ojos de la Nereida. 2000. Tr. of Eyes of the Sea Nymph. (SPA.). 92p. (J). (gr. 3-5). 9.95 (978-84-236-5503-8(2)) Baker & Taylor Bks.

Gutteridge, Alex. Oven Chips for Tea. l.t. ed. 2005. 198p. (J). (gr. 4-7). pap. (978-1-4056-6029-7(5)) BBC Audio.

Harcourt School Publishers Staff. An Afternoon Nap: Below Level. 3rd ed. 2002. (Trophies Reading Program Ser.). (J). pap. 4.10 (978-0-15-322971-8(3)) Harcourt Schl. Pubs.

Holub, Joan. Isabel Saves the Prince: Based on a True Story of Isabel I of Spain. Aleshina, Nonna, illus. 2007. (Young Princesses Around the World Ser.). 48p. (J). lib. bdg. 13.89 (*978-0-689-87198-6(8)* , Aladdin Library) Simon & Schuster Children's Publishing.

I, Juan de Pareja. 3rd ed. (J). pap., stu. ed. (978-0-13-667452-8(6)) Prentice Hall (Schl. Div.).

Jellen, Michelle. Spain or Shine. 2005. (S. A. S. S. (Students Across the Seven Seas) Ser.). (Illus.). 224p. (YA). (gr. 7). pap. 6.99 (978-0-14-240368-6(7) , Puffin) Penguin Group (USA) Inc.

Jessup, Jack. A Donkey Named Rico. 2001. 497p. lib. bdg. (978-0-7541-1539-7(9)) Minerva Pr.

Jiménez, Juan Ramon. Platero & I. 2000. (Illus.). 196p. (YA). pap. 12.95 (978-0-595-00345-7(1)) iUniverse, Inc.

—Platero y Yo. (SPA.). 192p. (J). 13.95 (978-84-206-1851-7(9) , AZ1851); (Illus.). 159p. 15.95 (978-84-206-3408-1(5)) Alianza Editorial, S. A. ESP. *Dist:* Continental Bk. Co., Inc., Distribooks, Inc., Distribooks, Inc.

—Platero y Yo. (SPA.). (J). pap. 9.95 (978-968-432-357-5(3) , PM223) Editorial Porrua MEX. *Dist:* Continental Bk. Co., Inc.

—Platero y Yo. annot. ed. (SPA., Illus.). 232p. (J). 15.95 (978-84-207-2636-6(2) , ANY010) Grupo Anaya, S.A. ESP. *Dist:* Continental Bk. Co., Inc.

—Platero y Yo. (SPA.). 240p. (YA). (gr. 5-8). (978-958-30-0744-6(7) , PV0560) Panamericana Editorial COL. *Dist:* Lectorum Pubns., Inc.

—Platero y Yo (Platero & I) (SPA.). (J). pap. 9.95 (978-968-416-022-4(4) , AOR01) Fernandez USA Publishing.

—Platero y Yo/Platero & I. Frasconi, Antonio, illus. 2003. 64p. (J). (gr. 4-6). pap. 5.95 (978-0-618-37838-8(3) , Clarion Bks.) Houghton Mifflin Co. Trade & Reference Div.

Johnson, Jane. La Princesa y el Pintor. Johnson, Jane, illus. 2003. Tr. of Princess & the Painter. (SPA., Illus.). 32p. (J). (ps-3). pap. 14.95 (978-1-56014-618-6(4) , SAN6184) Santillana USA Publishing Co., Inc.

—La Princesa y el Pintor. 1999. Tr. of Princess & the Painter. (Illus.). (J). (gr. 4-7). (CAT.). 38p. 14.95 (978-84-95040-23-7(9)); (SPA., 12p. 14.95 (978-84-88061-30-0(7)) Serres, Ediciones, S. L. ESP. *Dist:* Lectorum Pubns., Inc.

Kaserman, James F. & Kaserman, Sarah Jane. The Legend of Gasparilla: A Tale for All Ages. 2000. (Illus.). 304p. (J). pap. 14.95 (978-0-9674081-1-8(3)) Pirate Publishing International.

Kimmel, Eric A. Don Quixote & the Windmills. Fisher, Leonard Everett, illus. 2004. 32p. (J). 16.00 (978-0-374-31825-3(5) , Farrar, Straus & Giroux (BYR)) Farrar, Straus & Giroux.

Lewin, Waldtraut. Freedom Beyond the Sea. 2003. (gr. 7-12). lib. bdg. 13.55 (978-0-613-72276-6(0)) Tandem Library Bks.

Lewin, Waldtraut & Crawford, Elizabeth. Freedom Beyond the Sea. 2003. 272p. (YA). (gr. 9-12). pap. 5.50 (978-0-440-22868-4(9) , Laurel Leaf) Random Hse. Children's Bks.

Literature Connections Spanish: Yo, Juan de Pareja (I, Juan de Pareja) 2004. (gr. 6-12). (978-0-395-84375-8(8) , 2-70788) McDougal Littell Inc.

Mason, Simon. The Quigleys in a Spin. Stephens, Helen, illus. 2006. 192p. (J). (gr. k-7). 14.95 (978-0-385-75098-1(6) , Fickling, David Bks.) Random Hse. Children's Bks.

McNab, Andy & Rigby, Robert. Payback. 2007. 288p. (YA). (gr. 7). 7.99 (*978-0-14-240914-5(6)* , Puffin) Penguin Group (USA) Inc.

Moreno, Elena. El Misterio de la Llave. 1998. (SPA.). (gr. 7-12). lib. bdg. 14.10 (978-0-613-80728-9(6)) Tandem Library Bks.

Morningstar, Jeremy. Penalty Kick. 2005. 56p. pap. 9.00 (978-1-4116-6572-9(4)) Lulu.com.

Narvaez, Concha Lopez. El Fuego de los Pastores.Tr. of Shepherds' Fire. (SPA.). (YA). (gr. 5). pap. (978-84-395-0902-8(2)) Espasa Calpe, S.A. ESP. *Dist:* Lectorum Pubns., Inc.

Palacios, Argentina. Adventures of Don Quixote. abr. ed. 1999. (Dover Children's Thrift Classics Ser.). (Illus.). 64p. (J). (gr. 3-6). pap. 2.00 (978-0-486-40791-3(8)) Dover Pubns., Inc.

Parfitt, Tim. Spanish Vogue Book. 2006. 254p. pap. 22.00 (*978-1-4050-4619-0(8)*) Macmillan Publishers Ltd. GBR. *Dist:* Independent Pubs. Group.

Percy, Graham, illus. La Bella Durmiente del Bosque. l.t. ed. 2001. (SPA.). 28p. (ps-3). incl. audio compact disk (978-84-8214-049-0(3) , 1620) Peralt Montagut.

Pérez Galdos, Benito. Marianela. 2nd ed. (SPA.). 264p. 15.95 (978-84-206-9985-1(3)) Alianza Editorial, S. A. ESP. *Dist:* Continental Bk. Co., Inc., Lectorum Pubns., Inc.

—Marianela. 2003. (SPA.). 159p. (YA). 12.95 (978-968-6966-08-4(0)) EDITER'S Publishing Hse. MEX. *Dist:* EDITER'S Publishing Hse.

—Marianela. 9th ed. (SPA., Illus.). 240p. 18.50 (978-84-376-0380-3(3) , CT1174) Ediciones Catedra ESP. *Dist:* Continental Bk. Co., Inc.

—Marianela. 10th ed. 2003. (SPA., Illus.). 208p. (978-84-207-3415-6(2) , GS1219) Grupo Anaya, S.A. ESP. *Dist:* Lectorum Pubns., Inc.

—Marianela. 2000. (SPA.). 244p. pap. 11.95 (978-1-58348-812-6(X)) iUniverse, Inc.

Rabley, Stephen. The Barcelona Game. 2002. (Illus.). 16p. pap. (978-0-582-42771-6(1) , Putnam Juvenile) Penguin Group (USA) Inc.

Ratti, Marta. Madrid: Tell Us about Yourself. (SPA., Illus.). 80p. (978-84-96137-56-1(2)) Asppan, A., S.L. Distribuidora Internacional de Libros y Revistas.

Robertson, Barbara. Rosemary Rocks Spain. 2002. (Illus.). 128p. (J). (gr. 4-6). pap. 4.95 (978-1-890817-63-3(5)) Winslow Pr.

Servi Machlin, Edda. My Puppy Marrano. 2007. (YA). 19.95 (*978-1-878857-13-2(4)*) Giro Pr.

Sierra, Judy. The Beautiful Butterfly: A Folktale from Spain. Chess, Victoria, illus. 2005. 32p. (J). (gr. k-4). reprint ed. 19.00 (978-0-7567-9593-1(1)) DIANE Publishing Co.

Talley, Linda. Following Isabella - Kit. Chase, Andra, illus. 2001. (Key Concepts in Personal Development Ser.). 32p. (J). pap., tchr. ed. 89.95 incl. VHS (978-1-55942-170-6(3) , 9388K3) Marsh Media.

Thompson, Lisa. Spectacular Spain. Jones, Helen, illus. 2006. 80p. (J). (gr. 2-4). 19.95 (978-1-4048-1675-6(5)) Picture Window Bks.

Ventura, Antonio. El Tren. Delicado, Federico, illus. 2002. (Rosa y Manzana Ser.). (SPA.). 48p. (J). (gr. 1-3). 17.95 (978-84-89804-31-9(1)) Loguez Ediciones ESP. *Dist:* Baker & Taylor Bks.

Wojciechowska, Maia. Shadow of a Bull. Smith, Alvin, illus. 2007. 160p. (J). pap. 2.99 (*978-1-4169-4830-8(9)* , Aladdin) Simon & Schuster Children's Publishing.

—Shadow of a Bull, Vol. 5. l.t. ed. 2004. 150p. 20.95 (978-0-7862-6900-6(6) , Large Print Pr.) Thorndike Pr.

SPAIN—HISTORY

Anderson, Wayne. The ETA: Spain's Basque Terrorists. 2005. (Inside the World's Most Infamous Terrorist Organizations Ser.). (Illus.). 64p. (YA). (gr. 7-12). lib. bdg. 26.50 (978-0-8239-3818-6(2)) Rosen Publishing Group, Inc., The.

Ansary, Mir Tamim. El Día de la Independencia. 2003. (Historias de Fiestas Ser.).Tr. of Independance Day. (SPA & ENG., 32p. (J). Illus.). lib. bdg. 22.79 (978-1-4034-3003-8(9)); pap. 6.95 (978-1-4034-3026-7(8)) Heinemann Library.

—El Día de la Independencia. 2003. Tr. of Independance Day. (SPA.). (gr. k-3). lib. bdg. 14.75 (978-0-613-86891-4(9)) Tandem Library Bks.

Behar, Yvonne. Out of Spain Vol. 1: Our Spanish Heritage. Brooks, Andree Aelion, ed. 2000. (Illus.). 36p. (J). (gr. 5-7). pap. 4.95 (978-0-9702700-0-9(3)) Brooks, Andree Aelion.

—Out of Spain Vol. 2: Off to Other Lands - Sephardi Jews from 1492 to the Present. Brooks, Andree Aelion, ed. 2000. (Illus.). 65p. (J). (gr. 5-7). pap. 4.95 (978-0-9702700-1-6(1)) Brooks, Andree Aelion.

—Out of Spain Vol. 3: Celebrating Sephardi Culture. Brooks, Andree Aelion, ed. (Illus.). 58p. (J). (gr. 5-7). pap. 4.95 (978-0-9702700-3-0(8)) Brooks, Andree Aelion.

Benson, Sonia, et al, eds. UXL Hispanic American Chronology. 2nd ed. 2002. 200p. (J). 67.00 (978-0-7876-6600-2(9) , UXL) Thomson Gale.

Burgan, Michael & Overmyer-Velazquez, Mark. The Spanish Conquest of America: Prehistory - 1775. 2006. (Latino American History Ser.). (Illus.). 112p. (J). (gr. 5-8). 35.00 (978-0-8160-6440-3(7) , Chelsea Hse.) Facts On File, Inc.

Busby, Barbara Sheen. Foods of Spain. 2007. (Taste of Culture Ser.). 64p. (J). (gr. 3-6). 24.95 (*978-0-7377-3539-0(2)* , Kidhaven) Thomson Gale.

Champion, Neil. Spain. 2006. (Countries of the World Ser.). 64p. (J). (gr. 6-12). 30.00 (978-0-8160-6015-3(0)) Facts On File, Inc.

Cultures of the Past - Group 6, 4 bks. 119.71 (978-0-7614-1491-9(6) , Benchmark Bks.) Cavendish, Marshall Corp.

Davis, Kevin A. Look What Came from Spain. 2002. (gr. 3-6). lib. bdg. 15.25 (978-0-613-59509-4(2)) Tandem Library Bks.

Finkelstein, Norman H. Other 1492: Jewish Settlement in the New World. 2001. (gr. 7-12). lib. bdg. 18.75 (978-0-613-81390-7(1)) Tandem Library Bks.

Glot, Claudine. Rey Arturo. Gonzalez Batlle, Jorge, tr. Munch, Philippe, illus. 2004. (Tras los pasos de ... Ser.). (SPA.). 128p. (gr. 2-13). pap. 14.95 (978-84-95939-64-7(9)) Blume ESP. *Dist:* Independent Pubs. Group.

Greene, Meg. The Transcontinental Treaty, 1819: A Primary Source Examination of the Treaty Between the United States & Spain Over the American West. 2005. (Primary Sources of American Treaties Ser.). (J). lib. bdg. (978-1-4042-0439-3(3)) Rosen Publishing Group, Inc., The.

Lior, Noa. Spain: The Land. 2002. (gr. 3-6). lib. bdg. 16.40 (978-0-613-52995-2(2)) Tandem Library Bks.

MacGregor, Cynthia. Kids During the Age of Exploration. 1999. (Kids Throughout History Ser.). (Illus.). 24p. (J). (gr. 3). lib. bdg. 18.75 (978-0-8239-5257-1(6) , PowerKids Pr.) Rosen Publishing Group, Inc., The.

Malam, John. You wouldn't/sail in spanish Armada. 2006. (Illus.). 32p. (J). (gr. 2-5). 28.50 (*978-0-531-14974-4(9)*) Scholastic Library Publishing.

Mann, Kenny. Isabel, Ferdinand & Fifteenth-Century Spain. 2001. (Rulers & Their Times Ser.). (Illus.). 80p. (J). (gr. 6 up). lib. bdg. 29.93 (978-0-7614-1030-0(9) , Benchmark Bks.) Cavendish, Marshall Corp.

McGraw-Hill Staff. Journey Across Time, Spanish. 2005. (SPA.). (C). stu. ed. 78.00 (978-0-07-868152-3(9) , 9780078681523) Glencoe/McGraw-Hill.

McIntosh, Kenneth. First Encounters Between Spain & the Americas: Two Worlds Meet. 2005. (Illus.). 112p. (J). (ps-7). lib. bdg. (978-1-59084-925-5(6)) Mason Crest Pubs.

Melchiore, Susan McCarthy. The Spanish Inquisition. 2001. (Great Disasters, Reforms & Ramifications Ser.). (Illus.). 114p. (YA). (gr. 6-10). 32.00 (978-0-7910-6327-9(5) , Chelsea Hse.) Facts On File, Inc.

Millar, Heather. Spain in the Age of Exploration. 1998. (Cultures of the Past Ser.). (Illus.). 80p. (J). (gr. 5 up). lib. bdg. 29.93 (978-0-7614-0303-6(5) , Benchmark Bks.) Cavendish, Marshall Corp.

Parker, Lewis K. Spanish Colonies in the Americas. 2003. (Reading Power Ser.). (Illus.). 24p. (J). lib. bdg. 17.25 (978-0-8239-6471-0(X) , PowerKids Pr.) Rosen Publishing Group, Inc., The.

Stuart, Keith. Spain & Portugal. 2002. (Cultures & Costumes Ser.). (Illus.). 64p. (J). (gr. 7 up). lib. bdg. (978-1-59084-440-3(8)) Mason Crest Pubs.

Thompson, Linda. Los Españoles en América. 2005. (ENG & SPA., Illus.). 48p. (J). (978-1-59515-657-0(7)) Rourke Publishing, LLC.

Urrutia, Maria Christina & Libura, Krystyna. Ecos de la Conquista. 2005. (SPA.). (J). pap. 14.25 (978-968-7381-21-3(3)) Tecolote, Ediciones, S.A. de C.V. MEX. *Dist:* Iaconi, Mariuccia Bk. Imports.

Usborne Books Staff & Doherty, Gillian. 1001 Cosas Que Buscar en el Pasado. 2004. (SPA., Illus.). 32p. (J). (ps up). lib. bdg. 14.95 (978-1-58086-286-8(1) , EU1375) EDC Publishing.

Wade, Mary Dodson. Christopher Columbus. 2003. (Rookie Biographies Ser.). (Illus.). 32p. (J). (gr. 1-2). 20.50 (978-0-516-22851-8(X) , Children's Pr.) Scholastic Library Publishing.

Worth, Richard. Independence for Latino America. 2006. (Latino-American History Ser.). 112p. (J). (gr. 5-8). 35.00 (978-0-8160-6441-0(5) , Chelsea Hse.) Facts On File, Inc.

SPAIN—HISTORY—FICTION

Aiken, Joan. Go Saddle the Sea. 2007. (Illus.). 384p. (YA). pap. 6.95 (978-0-15-206064-0(2)) Harcourt Trade Pubs.

—The Teeth of the Gale. 2007. 352p. (YA). pap. 6.95 (978-0-15-206070-1(7)) Harcourt Trade Pubs.

Blatt, Evelyn. More Precious Than Gold: A Story of Inquisition Spain in the 1490's. Gardner, Eve-Lynn J., ed. Toron, Eli, illus. 2002. 200p. (J). (gr. 2-5). pap. 8.95 (978-1-929628-10-0(2)) Hachai Publishing.

Henty, G. A. With Moore at Corunna: A Tale of the Peninsular War. 2006. 334p. pap. 14.99 (978-1-4264-3149-4(X)); 372p. pap. 20.99 (978-1-4264-3242-2(9)) BiblioBazaar.

—With Moore at Corunna: A Tale of the Peninsular War. 2004. reprint ed. pap. 30.95 (978-1-4191-9445-0(3)); pap. 1.99 (978-1-4192-9445-7(8)) Kessinger Publishing, LLC.

Hoffman, Alice. Incantation. 2006. 176p. (J). (gr. 7 up). 16.99 (978-0-316-01019-1(7)) Little Brown & Co.

—Incantation. rev. ed. 2007. (Illus.). 166p. (YA). (gr. 7-17). per. 8.99 (*978-0-316-15428-4(8)*) Little, Brown Bks. for Young Readers.

Holub, Joan. Isabel Saves the Prince: Based on a True Story of Isabel I of Spain. Aleshina, Nonna, illus. 2007. (Young Princesses Around the World Ser.). 48p. (J). pap. 3.99 (*978-0-689-87197-9(X)* , Aladdin) Simon & Schuster Children's Publishing.

Lasky, Kathryn. Blood Secret. 2006. 304p. (J). pap. 5.99 (978-0-06-000063-9(5) , Harper Trophy) HarperCollins Pubs.

Meyer, Carolyn. Isabel: Jewel of Castilla, Spain 1466. 2000. (Royal Diaries Ser.). (Illus.). 208p. (J). (gr. 4-8). pap. 10.95 (978-0-439-07805-4(9)) Scholastic, Inc.

Miklowitz, Gloria. Secrets in the House of Delgado. 2001. (gr. 5-8). lib. bdg. 15.30 (978-0-613-55662-0(3)) Tandem Library Bks.

Miklowitz, Gloria D. Secrets in the House of Delgado. 2004. 192p. (J). (gr. 4 up). pap. 8.00 (978-0-8028-5210-6(6)) Eerdmans, William B. Publishing Co.

Myers, Walter Dean. Three Swords for Granada. Speirs, John, illus. 2002. 112p. (J). (gr. 4-6). tchr. ed. 15.95 (978-0-8234-1676-9(3)) Holiday Hse., Inc.

Narvaez, Concha Lopez. La Colina de Edeta. (SPA.). 124p. (YA). (gr. 5-8). (978-84-239-9050-4(8) , EC3401) Espasa Calpe, S.A. ESP. *Dist:* Lectorum Pubns., Inc.

Narvaez, Concha Lopez. El Tiempo y la Promesa.Tr. of Time & the Promise. (SPA.). (YA). (gr. 5-8). 164p. (978-84-216-2558-3(6) , BU7323); 9th ed. (Illus.). 208p. (978-84-216-1538-6(6) , BU6188) Bruño, Editorial ESP. *Dist:* Lectorum Pubns., Inc.

Orgad, Dorit & Silverston, Sondra. The Boy from Seville. 2007. (Kar-Ben for Older Readers Ser.). (J). (gr. 5-7). 16.95 (978-1-58013-253-4(7)) Kar-Ben Publishing.

Scholastic, Inc. Staff. Isabel: Jewel of Castilla, Spain 1466. 2000. (Royal Diaries Ser.). (J). lthr. 9.95 (978-0-439-26656-7(4)) Scholastic, Inc.

Styles, Showell. The Flying Ensign: Greencoats Against Napoleon. 2003. (Budget Bks.). Orig. Title: Greencoat Against Napoleon. 340p. (J). pap. 14.95 (978-1-883937-70-6(1)) Bethlehem Bks.

Wilson, John. Lost in Spain. (Illus.). 174p. 2000. (YA). (gr. 8-12). (978-1-55041-550-6(6)); 1999. (gr. 7-10). (978-1-55041-523-0(9)) Fitzhenry & Whiteside, Ltd.

—Lost in Spain. 2001. (gr. 7-12). lib. bdg. 18.75 (978-0-613-43694-6(6)) Tandem Library Bks.

SPAIN—HISTORY—CIVIL WAR, 1936-1939

Katz, William Loren & Crawford, Marc. The Lincoln Brigade: A Picture History. 2nd ed. 2001. (Illus.). 95p. pap. 18.95 (978-1-891843-07-5(9)) Apex Pr., The.

SPANISH AMERICA

see Latin America

SPANISH-AMERICAN WAR, 1898

Brannen, Daniel E. Spanish American War. McNeill, Allison, ed. 2003. (Illus.). 200p. (J). 67.00 (978-0-7876-6561-6(4) , UXL) Thomson Gale.

Collins, Mary. The Spanish-American War. De Capua, Sarah, ed. 1998. (Cornerstones of Freedom Ser.). (Illus.). 32p. (J). (gr. 4-6). pap. 5.95 (978-0-516-26337-3(4) , Children's Pr.) Scholastic Library Publishing.

Dolan, Edward F., Jr. The Spanish-American War. 2001. (Women at War Ser.). (Illus.). 112p. (gr. 5-8). lib. bdg. 28.90 (978-0-7613-1453-0(9) , Twenty-First Century Bks.) Lerner Publishing Group.

Golay, Michael. Spanish-American War. 2nd ed. 2003. (America at War Ser.). (Illus.). 176p. (J). (gr. 6-12). 35.00 (978-0-8160-4935-6(1)) Facts On File, Inc.

Graves, Kerry A. The Spanish-American War. 2000. (America Goes to War Ser.). (Illus.). 48p. (J). (gr. 3-4). lib. bdg. 22.60 (978-0-7368-0583-4(4) , Bridgestone Bks.) Capstone Pr., Inc.

—The Spanish-American War, 6 vols. (gr. 2-5). 39.95 (978-0-7368-8930-8(2)) Red Brick Learning.

Green, Carl R. The Spanish-American War: A MyReportLinks.com Book. 2002. (U. S. Wars Ser.). (Illus.). 48p. (J). (gr. 4-10). lib. bdg. 25.26 (978-0-7660-5091-4(2)) Enslow Pubs., Inc.

Hendrickson, Kenneth E. Primary Source Accounts of the Spanish-American War. 2006. (America's Wars Through Primary Sources Ser.). (Illus.). 128p. (J). lib. bdg. 33.27 (978-1-59845-007-1(7) , MyReportLinks.com Bks.) Enslow Pubs., Inc.

Langellier, John P. Uncle Sam's Little Wars: The Spanish-American War, Philippine Insurrection & Boxer Rebellion. 2001. (G. I. Ser.). (Illus.). 80p. (J). 27.50 (978-0-7910-6674-4(6) , Chelsea Hse.) Facts On File, Inc.

McGowen, Tom. The Spanish-American War & Teddy Roosevelt in American History. 2003. (In American History Ser.). (Illus.). 128p. (J). lib. bdg. 26.60 (978-0-7660-1987-4(X)) Enslow Pubs., Inc.

McNeese, Tim. Remember the Maine! The Spanish-American War Begins. 2004. (First Battles Ser.). (Illus.). 112p. (YA). (gr. 6-12). 23.95 (978-1-883846-79-4(X) , First Biographies) Reynolds, Morgan Inc.

Poulakidas, Georgene. The Spanish-American War. 2005. (Primary Sources of American Wars Ser.). (Illus.). 24p. (J). lib. bdg. (978-1-4042-2685-2(0)) Rosen Publishing Group, Inc., The.

Santella, Andrew. Roosevelt's Rough Riders. 2005. (We the People Ser.). (Illus.). 48p. (J). (gr. 4-6). 23.93 (978-0-7565-1268-2(9)) Compass Point Bks.

Smolinski, Diane. Battles of the Spanish-American War. 2003. (Americans at War Ser.). (Illus.). 32p. (J). (gr. 4-6). lib. bdg. 25.64 (978-1-4034-0170-0(5)) Heinemann Library.

—Soldiers of the Spanish-American War. 2003. (Americans at War Ser.). (Illus.). 32p. (J). (gr. 4-6). lib. bdg. 25.64 (978-1-4034-0173-1(X)) Heinemann Library.

Smolinski, Diane & Smolinski, Henry. Battles of the Spanish-American War. (Americans at War Ser.). 32p. pap. 6.95 (978-1-4034-3152-3(3)) Heinemann Library.

—Soldiers of the Spanish-American War. (Americans at War Ser.). 32p. pap. 6.95 (978-1-4034-3156-1(6)) Heinemann Library.

Somerlott, Robert. The Spanish-American War: Remember the Maine! 2002. (American War Ser.). (Illus.). 128p. (YA). (gr. 5-12). lib. bdg. 26.60 (978-0-7660-1855-6(5)) Enslow Pubs., Inc.

Spanish-American War. (America Goes to War Ser.). 48p. (YA). 6.95 (978-0-7368-8859-2(4)) Capstone Pr., Inc.

Thomson Gale Staff. Age of Reform & Industrialization: 1896-1920. 2002. (gr. 7-12). lib. bdg. 39.05 (978-0-613-73612-1(5)) Tandem Library Bks.

SPANISH-AMERICAN WAR, 1898—FICTION

Loughrey, Eithne. Annie Moore: New York City Girl. 2006. (YA). ***978-0-8368-7737-3(3))** Stevens, Gareth Inc.

Loughrey, Eithne. Annie Moore New York City Girl. l.t. ed. 2006. (Dales Ser.). 208p. 23.99 (978-1-84262-448-7(2)) Dales Large Print Bks. GBR. *Dist:* Ulverscroft Large Print Bks., Ltd.

Morrison, Harry Steele. The Adventures of A Boy Reporter. 2004. reprint ed. pap. 20.95 (978-1-4191-5137-8(1)); pap. 1.99 (978-1-4192-5137-5(6)) Kessinger Publishing, LLC.

Sargent, Dave & Sargent, Pat. Buckshot: (Blue Eyed Chestnut) Mind Your Manners, 25, 8. Lenoir, Jane, illus. 2001. (Saddle Up Ser.: 8). 36p. (J). pap. 6.95 (978-1-56763-674-1(8)); lib. bdg. 22.60 (978-1-56763-673-4(X)) Ozark Publishing.

SPANISH LANGUAGE

La Abeja Trabajadora. 2003. (J). 23.95 (978-0-673-77796-6(0)) Celebration Pr.

Abriendo Puertas. 2003. (Spanish Readers Ser.). (SPA.). Tomo 1. (J). (978-0-618-22206-3(5)); Tomo 1-2. (978-0-618-27260-0(7)); Tomo 2. (978-0-618-22207-0(3)) McDougal Littell Inc.

Ace Academics, ed. Spanish: A Whole Course in a Box! 2007. (Exambusters Ser.). 384p. (gr. 7 up). 12.95 (978-1-881374-97-8(1) , Exambusters) Ace Academics, Inc.

Actividades en Espanol. 2003. (Homework Booklets Ser.). (SPA., Illus.). 80p. (gr. 2-3). 2.99 (978-0-7424-0118-1(9) , IF0391) School Specialty Publishing.

Ada, Alma Flor. Guia del Maestro. 2001. (SPA) (J). (gr. k-3). pap. 43.95 (978-1-58105-237-4(5)) Santillana USA Publishing Co., Inc.

—Strange Visitors. (Stories for the Telling Ser.). (Illus.). 16p. (J). (gr. k-3). pap. 6.95 (978-1-58105-226-8(X)) Santillana USA Publishing Co., Inc.

Ada, Alma Flor & Campoy, F. Isabel, contrib. by. Smiles. (Literature Collection of Gateways to the Sun Ser.). 32p. (J). (gr. k-6). pap. 13.95 (978-1-59437-713-6(8)) Santillana USA Publishing Co., Inc.

—Steps. (Literature Collection of Gateways to the Sun Ser.). 32p. (J). (gr. k-6). pap. 13.95 (978-1-59437-716-7(2)) Santillana USA Publishing Co., Inc.

Aigner-Clark, Julie. La Guarderia de Idiomas (The Guarderia Language) 2004. (Baby Einstein Ser.). (SPA., Illus.). 16p. (J). bds. 5.95 (978-970-718-153-3(2) , Silver Dolphin en Español) Advanced Marketing, S. de R. L. de C. V. MEX. *Dist:* Perseus Distribution.

—Wordsworth's Book of Words: A Bilingual Book of Words. Zaidi, Nadeem, illus. 2002. (Baby Einstein Ser.). 64p. (ps-ps). 15.99 (978-0-7868-0883-0(7)) Disney Pr.

Alarcon, Francisco X, et al. Mundo 21. 3rd ed. 2004. 556p. (YA). pap., stu. ed. 89.56 incl. cd-rom (978-0-618-41312-6(X) , 351029) Houghton Mifflin College Div.

Amery, H. First Thousand Words. 2004. (SPA.). 70p. (J). pap. 9.95 (978-0-7945-0463-2(9)) EDC Publishing.

—First Thousand Words in Spanish IL. rev. ed. 2004. (First Thousand Words Ser.). (SPA.). 64p. (J). 12.99 (978-0-7945-0284-3(9)); lib. bdg. 20.99 (978-1-58086-564-7(X)) EDC Publishing.

Amery, H. & Cartwright, S. First Spanish Word Book. 2004. (Treasury of Farmyard Tales Ser.). (SPA.). 48p. (J). 10.95 (978-0-7945-0476-2(0)) EDC Publishing.

Amery, Heather. First Thousand Words in Spanish. Cartwright, Stephen, illus. 2004. (First Thousand Words Ser.). (ENG & SPA.). 64p. (J). pap. 5.95 (978-0-7945-0278-2(4) , Usborne) EDC Publishing.

Amos, Jamie. ¡Es Mio! Coffey, Colleen & Carrillo, Consuelo, trs. Spenceley, Annabel, illus. 2003. (Weekly Reader Early Learning Library). (SPA.). 32p. (J). (ps up). pap. 7.93 (978-0-8368-3692-9(8) , Weekly Reader Early Learning Library) Stevens, Gareth Inc.

Amos, Janine. ¡No Digas! Coffey, Colleen & Carrillo, Consuelo, trs. Spenceley, Annabel, illus. 2003. (Weekly Reader Early Learning Library). (SPA.). 32p. (J). (ps up). pap. 7.93 (978-0-8368-3693-6(6) , Weekly Reader Early Learning Library) Stevens, Gareth Inc.

—¡No Funciona! Coffey, Colleen & Carrillo, Consuelo, trs. Spenceley, Annabel, illus. 2003. (Weekly Reader Early Learning Library). (SPA.). 32p. (J). (ps up). pap. 7.93 (978-0-8368-3694-3(4) , Weekly Reader Early Learning Library) Stevens, Gareth Inc.

—¡No Funciona! Coffee, Carol & Carrillo, Consuelo, trs. Spenceley, Annabel, illus. 2002. (Weekly Reader Early Learning Library). (SPA.). 32p. (J). (ps up). lib. bdg. 23.33 (978-0-8368-3680-6(4)) Stevens, Gareth Inc.

—¡No Hagas Eso! Coffey, Colleen & Carrillo, Consuelo, trs. Spenceley, Annabel, illus. 2003. (Weekly Reader Early Learning Library). (SPA.). 32p. (J). (ps up). pap. 7.93 (978-0-8368-3695-0(2) , Weekly Reader Early Learning Library) Stevens, Gareth Inc.

—¡No Hagas Eso! Coffee, Carol & Carrillo, Consuelo, trs. Spenceley, Annabel, illus. 2002. (Weekly Reader Early Learning Library). (SPA.). 32p. (J). (ps up). lib. bdg. 23.33 (978-0-8368-3681-3(2)) Stevens, Gareth Inc.

—¡Quitate de Aqui! Coffey, Colleen & Carrillo, Consuelo, trs. Spenceley, Annabel, illus. 2003. (Weekly Reader Early Learning Library). (SPA.). 32p. (J). (ps up). pap. 7.93 (978-0-8368-3696-7(0) , Weekly Reader Early Learning Library) Stevens, Gareth Inc.

—¡Vete! Coffee, Carol & Carrillo, Consuelo, trs. Spenceley, Annabel, illus. (Weekly Reader Early Learning Library). (SPA.). 32p. (J). (ps up). lib. bdg. 23.33 (978-0-8368-3683-7(9)) Stevens, Gareth Inc.

—¡Vete! Coffey, Colleen & Carrillo, Consuelo, trs. Spenceley, Annabel, illus. 2003. (Weekly Reader Early Learning Library). (SPA.). 32p. (J). (ps up). pap. 7.93 (978-0-8368-3697-4(9) , Weekly Reader Early Learning Library) Stevens, Gareth Inc.

Ana Maria Matute. 2003. (Spanish Readers Ser.). (SPA.). (978-0-618-04826-7(X)) McDougal Littell Inc.

Anderson, Jill, ed. Let's Go on Safari!/Vamos de Safari! Utton, Peter, illus. 2005. (ENG & SPA.). 20p. (J). (ps-k). bds. 6.95 (978-1-58728-522-6(3) , Two Can Publishing) T&N Children's Publishing.

—Let's Visit the Jungle! !Vamos a la Selva!, 5. Holmes, Steve, illus. 2005. (ENG & SPA.). 20p. (J). (gr. 3-7). bds. 6.95 (978-1-58728-523-3(1) , Two Can Publishing) T&N Children's Publishing.

La Arana. 2003. 23.95 (978-0-673-77156-8(3)) Celebration Pr.

Asimov, Isaac & Hantula, Richard. Neptuno: El Gigante Mas Lejano. Porras, Carlos & D'Andrea, Patricia, trs. from ENG. 2003. (Isaac Asimov's Biblioteca del Universo del Siglo XXI). (SPA & ENG., Illus.). 32p. (J). (gr. 3 up). pap. 8.95 (978-0-8368-3871-8(8) , Weekly Reader Early Learning Library) Stevens, Gareth Inc.

Avery, Heather & Cartwright, Stephen. First Hundred Words in Spanish Sticker Book. 2004. (First Hundred Words Ser.). (SPA., Illus.). 40p. (J). pap. 8.99 (978-0-7945-0192-1(3) , Usborne) EDC Publishing.

Baker, Alan. Los conejitos aprenden Las Primeras Palabras. 2003. (SPA.). (gr. k-3). lib. bdg. 12.95 (978-0-613-65718-1(7)) Tandem Library Bks.

Barfell, Judith A. Learn & Sign Funtime-Beginnings-Spanish. 2005. (Beginnings Ser.: Bk. 1). (SPA.). (J). per. 14.95 (978-0-9753717-2-5(X)) Learn and Sign Funtime Bks.

Beaton, Clare, illus. English-Spanish Bilingual First Books, 6 bks. (J). lib. bdg. 86.70 (978-1-56674-944-2(1)) Forest Hse. Publishing Co., Inc.

—Opposites: Los Contrarios. l.t. ed. 1998. (English-Spanish Bilingual First Bks.). (ENG & SPA.). 24p. (J). (ps up). lib. bdg. 14.45 (978-1-56674-252-8(8)) Forest Hse. Publishing Co., Inc.

Beck, Jeanine. Los Animales, Mis Amigos. 2003. (ENG & SPA., Illus.). 64p. 14.99 (978-0-7548-1195-4(6)) Anness Publishing GBR. *Dist:* National Bk. Network.

—Mi Casa. 2003. (ENG & SPA., Illus.). 64p. 14.99 (978-0-7548-1194-7(8) , Lorenz Bks.) Anness Publishing GBR. *Dist:* National Bk. Network.

Benedetti, Mario. La Muerte y Otras Sorpresas. 1998. (SPA.). (gr. 7-12). lib. bdg. 15.25 (978-0-613-80713-5(8)) Tandem Library Bks.

Berlitz Publishing Staff. Spanish. rev. ed. 2003. (Berlitz Kids Language Pack Ser.). (SPA & ENG., Illus.). 26.95 (978-981-246-369-2(0) , 463690) Berlitz Publishing.

Berlitz Publishing Staff, ed. French. 2007. (FRE & ENG., Illus.). 12p. bds. 7.95 ***978-981-268-037-2(3))** APA Publications Services SGP. *Dist:* Langenscheidt Pubs Inc.

—Spanish. 2007. (Lift the Flap Ser.). (SPA & ENG., Illus.). 12p. bds. 7.95 ***978-981-268-038-9(1))** APA Publications Services SGP. *Dist:* Langenscheidt Pubs Inc.

—Spanish. 2nd rev. ed. 2005. (Berlitz 1,000 Words Ser.). (SPA & ENG., Illus.). 64p. pap. 9.95 (978-981-246-528-3(6) , 465286) Berlitz Publishing.

Blair, Robert W., creator. Power-Glide Spanish Junior Adventure Guide, 3 vols. 2002. (Illus.). 346p. (gr. 8-12). pap. 39.95 incl. audio compact disk (978-1-58204-219-0(5)) Power-Glide Foreign Language Courses.

Blake, Robert J. & Blasco, Javier. Tesoros. 2001. (SPA.). (C). (gr. 6-12). stu. ed. 89.69 incl. cd-rom (978-0-07-233996-3(9) , 9780072339963) Glencoe/McGraw-Hill.

Brandenberg, Aliki. La Fiesta Medieval. (SPA.). 32p. 15.95 (978-84-261-2696-2(0)) Juventud, Editorial ESP. *Dist:* Distribooks, Inc.

Bredeson, Carmen. Despegue. 2004. (Rookie Readers - Spanish Ser.). (J). 19.50 (978-0-516-25100-4(7) , Watts, Franklin) Scholastic Library Publishing.

Brimner, Larry Dane. Gatitos! Cordova, Jacqueline, tr. from ENG. Payne, Tom, illus. 2000. (Rookie Espanol Ser.). (SPA.). 24p. (J). (gr. k-2). 19.50 (978-0-516-22024-6(1) , Children's Pr.) Scholastic Library Publishing.

—Gatitos! 2000. (SPA.). (gr. k-3). lib. bdg. 12.95 (978-0-613-54228-9(2)) Tandem Library Bks.

Brooks, Felicity. Everyday Words in Spanish. Litchfield, Jo, illus. rev. ed. 2004. (Everyday Words Ser.). 48p. (J). pap. 9.95 (978-0-7945-0881-4(2) , Usborne) EDC Publishing.

Bruzzone, Catherine & Morton, Lone. Spanish Fun Audio Package. 2000. (SPA., Illus.). 16p. (gr. k-5). 12.95 (978-0-658-00426-1(3)) McGraw-Hill Cos., The.

Bryant-Mole, Karen. Veo, Veo! Series, 12 bks., Set. Incl. Alimentos. lib. bdg. 18.50 (978-1-57572-915-2(6)); En el Campo. lib. bdg. 18.50 (978-1-57572-905-3(9)); En la Ciudad. lib. bdg. 18.50 (978-1-57572-906-0(7)); En la Granja. lib. bdg. 18.50 (978-1-57572-907-7(5)); En la Playa. lib. bdg. 18.50 (978-1-57572-904-6(0)); Invierno. lib. bdg. 12.95 net. (978-1-57572-912-1(1)); Juegos. lib. bdg. 18.50 (978-1-57572-916-9(4)); Jueguetes. lib. bdg. 18.50 (978-1-57572-917-6(2)); Otono. lib. bdg. 18.50 (978-1-57572-909-1(1)); Primavera. lib. bdg. 18.50 (978-1-57572-910-7(5)); Ropa. lib. bdg. 18.50 (978-1-57572-914-5(8)); Verano. lib. bdg. 18.50 (978-1-57572-911-4(3)); (J). (ps-1). 1999. (SPA., Illus.). 24p. 1999. Set lib. bdg. 222.00 (978-1-57572-919-0(9)) Heinemann Library.

Bunnell, Deb T. My First Spanish ABC Picture Coloring Book. 1998. (Illus.). 32p. (J). (gr. k-5). pap. 2.95 (978-0-486-40358-8(0)) Dover Pubns., Inc.

Burke, David. GOLDILOCKS (Spanish to English - Level 2) Learn ENGLISH Through Fairy Tales. 2007. (SPA & ENG.). (J). per. 14.95 incl. audio compact disk ***978-1-891888-96-0(X))** Slangman Publishing.

Camarena, Cathy & Ruff, Gloria B. Valeria y Víctor. 2006. (Primeros Sonidos Ser.). (J). 21.35 (978-1-59679-907-3(2) , SandCastle); pap. (978-1-59679-908-0(0)) ABDO Publishing Co.

Carole Marsh. Uh,Oh,Amigo! 2004. (Little Linguist Ser.). 32p. 29.95 (978-0-635-02436-7(5)) Gallopade International.

—Uh,Oh,Amigo! Spanish for Kids. 2004. (Little Linguist Ser.). 32p. (gr. 2-6). pap. 5.95 (978-0-635-02428-2(4)) Gallopade International.

Chano: Individual Title Six-Packs. (Literatura 2000 Ser.). (gr. 2-3). 33.00 (978-0-7635-0194-5(8)) Rigby Education.

Chappell, Jackie. Our School Is Like a Family. 2007. (ENG & SPA.). (J). (978-1-59515-954-0(1)) Rourke Publishing, LLC.

Charlie: Individual Title Six-Packs. (Literatura 2000 Ser.). (gr. 2-3). 33.00 (978-0-7635-0221-8(9)) Rigby Education.

La Charreada. 2003. 23.95 (978-0-673-77782-9(0)) Celebration Pr.

Chessen, Betsey. Sharks: Tiburones. 2002. (Science Emergent Readers Ser.). (Illus.). (J). pap. (978-0-439-41162-2(9)) Scholastic, Inc.

Chiquilibros: Activity Masters. (SPA.). (ps-1). 26.00 (978-0-7635-2366-4(6)); 31.00 (978-0-7635-2578-1(2)); 21.00 (978-0-7635-2557-6(X)) Rigby Education.

Chiquilibros: Add-to Packs. (SPA.). (gr. k-1). 30.00 (978-0-7635-8585-3(8)); 30.00 (978-0-7635-8586-0(6)); 61.00 (978-0-7635-8587-7(4)); 30.00 (978-0-7635-8584-6(X)) Rigby Education.

Chiquilibros: Chiquicuentos Complete Package. (SPA.). (ps-1). 250.00 (978-0-7635-8571-6(8)) Rigby Education.

Chiquilibros: Chiquicuentos Grupo A Add-to Pack. (SPA.). (ps-1). 125.00 (978-0-7635-8568-6(8)) Rigby Education.

Chiquilibros: Chiquicuentos Grupo B Add-to Pack. (SPA.). (ps-1). 125.00 (978-0-7635-8569-3(6)) Rigby Education.

Chiquilibros: Cuentos listos Complete Packages. (SPA.). (gr. k-1). 114.00 (978-0-7635-8580-8(7)); 114.00 (978-0-7635-8581-5(5)); 114.00 (978-0-7635-8582-2(3)); 203.00 (978-0-7635-8583-9(1)) Rigby Education.

Chiquilibros: Grupo A Activity Guide. (SPA.). (gr. k-1). 18.00 (978-0-7635-2400-5(X)) Rigby Education.

Chiquilibros: Grupo B Activity Guide. (SPA.). (gr. k-1). 18.00 (978-0-7635-2401-2(8)) Rigby Education.

Chiquilibros: Grupo C Activity Guide. (SPA.). (gr. k-1). 18.00 (978-0-7635-2402-9(6)) Rigby Education.

Chiquilibros: Grupo D Activity Guide. (SPA.). (gr. k-1). 18.00 (978-0-7635-2403-6(4)) Rigby Education.

Chiquilibros: Grupos consonanticos Add-to Pack. (SPA.). (ps-1). 38.00 (978-0-7635-8579-2(3)) Rigby Education.

Chiquilibros: Grupos consonanticos Complete Package. (SPA.). (ps-1). 166.00 (978-0-7635-8578-5(5)) Rigby Education.

Chiquilibros: Silabas Add-to Pack. (SPA.). (ps-1). 78.00 (978-0-7635-8576-1(9)) Rigby Education.

Chiquilibros: Silabas Complete Package. (SPA.). (ps-1). 307.00 (978-0-7635-8577-8(7)) Rigby Education.

Coll, Ivar Da. Que Cumpleanos! 2001. (Torre de Carton Coleccion). (SPA.). (J). bds. (978-958-04-4907-2(4)) Norma S.A. COL. *Dist:* Lectorum Pubns., Inc.

Copeland, Mindy. Spanish for Young Children. 2005. 107p. pap. 41.11 (978-1-4116-3594-4(9)) Lulu.com.

El Coqui. 2003. 23.95 (978-0-673-77382-1(5)) Celebration Pr.

El Coqui: Poems, Rhymes, & Songs Listening Packs. 2003. 34.50 (978-0-673-58630-8(8)) Celebration Pr.

Coy, John, et al. Directo Al Aro. Jean-Bart, Leslie, illus. 2002. (SPA & ENG.). (J). 16.95 (978-1-58430-082-3(5)) Lee & Low Bks., Inc.

Creation House Staff, ed. Iglesia para Ninos: Canas de Pescar y Vides Fructiteras, Vol. 2. 1999. (SPA.). 160p. (J). (gr. 1-6). 129.99 (978-1-57405-445-3(7)) CharismaLife Pubs.

Cuaderno Suenos y Palabras. (SPA.). (J). (gr. k-6). wbk. ed. 18.00 (978-958-04-7094-6(4)); Vol. 2. (gr. k-6). wbk. ed. 18.00 (978-958-04-7095-3(2)); Vol. 3. (gr. k-6). wbk. ed. 18.00 (978-958-04-7096-0(0)); Vol. 4. (gr. k-6). wbk. ed. 18.00 (978-958-04-7737-2(X)); Vol. 5. (gr. k-6). wbk. ed. 18.00 (978-958-04-7738-9(8)); Vol. 6. (gr. k-6). wbk. ed. 18.00 (978-958-04-7739-6(6)); Vol. 7. (gr. 7-12). wbk. ed. 18.00 (978-958-04-5653-7(4)); Vol. 8. (gr. 7-12). wbk. ed. 18.00 (978-958-04-5654-4(2)); Vol. 9. (gr. 7-12). wbk. ed. 18.00 (978-958-04-5655-1(0)); Vol. 10. (gr. 7-12). wbk. ed. 18.00 (978-958-04-5956-9(8)); Vol. 11. (gr. 7-12). wbk. ed. 18.00 (978-958-04-5958-3(4)); Vol. 12. (gr. 7-12). wbk. ed. 18.00 (978-958-04-5960-6(6)) Norma S.A. COL. *Dist:* Distribuidora Norma, Inc.

Cuando el senor Rey ronco/When Mr Quinn Snored. 2005. (Take-Home Bks.). (SPA.). (YA). (ps-3). 15.75 (978-0-8215-1207-4(2)) Sadlier, William H. Inc.

Una cucarachita muy Rara 16: Leveled Books. 2001. (McGraw-Hill. Lectura Ser.). (ENG & SPA.). (gr. 1 up). (978-0-02-187945-8(1)) Macmillan/McGraw-Hill Schl. Div.

Cuidando a los animales/Keeping Baby Animals Safe. 2005. (Libros en Espanol Para Ninos Ser.). (SPA.). (YA). (ps-1). 11.97 (978-0-8215-0996-8(9)) Sadlier, William H. Inc.

S

Dalmatian Press Staff. My Spanish Book of Animals: Mi libro de los animales en espanol e Ingles. rev. ed. 2007. 12p. 7.99 ***978-1-4037-3054-1(7))** Dalmatian Pr.

—My Spanish Book of Colors: Mi libro de los colores en ingles y Espanol. rev. ed. 2007. 12p. 7.99 ***978-1-4037-3052-7(0))** Dalmatian Pr.

Davis, Carla Norman. Spanish Made Fun. 1999. (J). Vol. 1, Bk. 1. (gr. 1-3). wbk. ed. 15.00 (978-1-930272-00-2(6)); Vol. 1, Bk. 2. (gr. 4-5). wbk. ed. 15.00 (978-1-930272-01-9(4)) Queen Enterprises, Inc.

Deacon, Carol. Manualidades Divertidas. 2003. (SPA.). 64p. 12.98 (978-1-4054-1483-8(9)) Parragon, Inc.

DeCesare, Ruth. Songs for the Spanish Class. 2001. (J). 9.95 (978-0-8442-7610-6(3) , National Textbook Co.) McGraw-Hill/Contemporary.

Denne, Ben. Easy Spanish. 2002. (gr. 3-6). lib. bdg. 22.20 (978-0-613-75322-7(4)) Tandem Library Bks.

Dickey, Laurel. Early Emergent Set 1 Spanish. Dufresne, Michele, photos by. 2000. (SPA.). (J). 26.00 (978-1-58453-100-5(2)) Pioneer Valley Educational Pr., Inc.

Dingles, Molly. Blue as a Blueberry/Azul como un Arandano. Velez, Walter, illus. 2003. (SPA.). 32p. (J). lib. bdg. 20.65 (978-1-891997-28-0(9)) Dingles & Co.

—Brown as an Acorn. Velez, Walter, illus. 2004. (Community of Color Ser.). 32p. (J). pap. 9.95 (978-1-59646-346-2(5)) Dingles & Co.

—Brown as an Acorn/Marron como una Bellota. Velez, Walter, illus. 2004. (Community of Color Ser.).Tr. of Marron como una Bellota. (ENG & SPA.). 32p. (J). pap. 9.95 (978-1-59646-093-5(8)); lib. bdg. 20.65 (978-1-891997-37-2(8)) Dingles & Co.

—Gray as a Dolphin. Velez, Walter, illus. 2004. (Community of Color Ser.). 32p. (J). pap. 9.95 (978-1-59646-342-4(2)) Dingles & Co.

—Gray as a Dolphin/Gris como un Delfín. Velez, Walter, illus. 2004. (Community of Color Ser.).Tr. of Gris como un Delfín. (ENG & SPA.). 32p. (J). pap. 9.95 (978-1-59646-092-8(X)); lib. bdg. 20.65 (978-1-891997-58-7(0)) Dingles & Co.

—Green as a Frog/Verde como una Rana. Velez, Walter, illus. 2003. (Community of Color Ser.). (SPA.). 32p. (J). lib. bdg. 20.65 (978-1-891997-29-7(7)) Dingles & Co.

—Green as a Frog/Vert comme une Grenouille. Velez, Walter, illus. 2004. (Community of Color Ser.).Tr. of Vert comme une Grenouille. (ENG & FRE.). 32p. (J). lib. bdg. 20.65 (978-1-891997-71-6(8)) Dingles & Co.

—Red as a Fire Truck/Rojo como un camion de Bomberos. Velez, Walter, illus. 2003. (Community of Color Ser.).Tr. of Rojo Como un Camion de Bomberos. (SPA.). 32p. (J). lib. bdg. 20.65 (978-1-891997-27-3(0)) Dingles & Co.

—Yellow as a Lemon/Amarillo como un Limon. Velez, Walter, illus. 2003. (Community of Color Ser.). (SPA.). 32p. (J). lib. bdg. 20.65 (978-1-891997-30-3(0)) Dingles & Co.

Domínguez, Marcela, et al. Claro Que Si! An Integrated Skills Approach. 5th ed. 2004. 469p. (YA). 118.76 incl. cd-rom, cd-rom (978-0-618-55652-6(4) , 309783) Houghton Mifflin College Div.

Dorling Kindersley Publishing Staff. El Espacio. 2004. (Eyewitness Books). 72p. (J). lib. bdg. 19.99 (978-0-7566-0794-4(9)) Dorling Kindersley Publishing, Inc.

Dorling Kindersley Publishing Staff, ed. Barbie Word Book / Libro Barbie de Las Palabras. 2004. (J). 12.99 (978-0-7566-0492-9(3)) Dorling Kindersley Publishing, Inc.

Dorling Kindersley Smart Steps CD-Roms: DK Smart Steps Complete Package. 2003. 123.95 (978-0-673-61614-2(2)) Celebration Pr.

Dorn, Susy. Cantemos en Español Song-Book: Spanish Learning Song-Book for Children. Carbajal, Diego, illus. 2006. (SPA.). (J). (978-0-9764010-6-3(1)) Susy Dorn Productions, LLC.

—Sal y Pimienta Song-Book: Spanish Learning Song-Book for Children. Carbajal, Diego, illus. 2006. (SPA.). (J). (978-0-9764010-7-0(X)) Susy Dorn Productions, LLC.

Dorwick, Thalia, et al. Que Tal? 6th ed. 2002. (SPA.). 512p. (C). (gr. 6-12). stu. ed. 103.75 incl. cd-rom (978-0-07-253846-5(5) , 9780072538465) Glencoe/McGraw-Hill.

Douglas, Vincent & School Specialty Publishing Staff. Spanish-English Picture Dictionary. 2004. (ENG & SPA., Illus.). 48p. (J). 9.95 (978-0-7696-3526-2(1) , Waterbird Bks.) School Specialty Publishing.

Dover. Spanish Fun Books. 1998. (SPA., Illus.). 192p. (J). pap. 7.00 (978-0-486-28661-7(4)) Dover Pubns., Inc.

Downing, Julie, illus. All the Ways I Love You (bilingual Edition) 2005. (SPA & ENG.). 10p. (J). 8.95 (978-1-58117-335-2(0) , Intervisual/Piggy Toes) Dalmatian Pr.

Drawing Conclusions & Inferences Spanish Version, Gr. 1-3. 2005. (J). per. (978-1-58232-148-6(5)) Bryan Hse. Pubs., Inc.

Drawing Conclusions & Inferences Spanish Version, Gr. 4-5. 2005. (J). per. (978-1-58232-143-1(4)) Bryan Hse. Pubs., Inc.

Dunn, Opal. El Gato Leo Goes to School: A First Spanish Story. Gale, Cathy, illus. 2006. (ENG & SPA.). 24p. (J). 15.95 (***978-1-84507-552-1(8)***) Lincoln, Frances Ltd. GBR. *Dist:* Perseus Distribution.

Egan, Tracie. Cynthia Ann Parker: Cautiva de los Comanches. Gonzalez, Tomas, tr. 2003. (Grandes Personajes en la Historia de Los Estados Unidos Ser.). (ENG & SPA.). (J). pap. (978-0-8239-4225-1(2)) Rosen Publishing Group, Inc., The.

Ellis, Libby. Buenos Dias Baby. 2004. (ENG & SPA., Illus.). 20p. (J). bds. 3.95 (978-0-8118-4270-9(3)) Chronicle Bks. LLC.

Elya, Susan Middleton. Bebé Goes to the Beach. Salerno, Steven, illus. 2008. (ENG & SPA.). (J). (***978-0-15-206000-8(6)***) Harcourt Trade Pubs.

—Say Hola to Spanish at the Circus. Lopez, Loretta, illus. 32p. (J). 2003. pap. 6.95 (978-1-58430-042-7(6)); 2000. (ENG & SPA.). 15.95 (978-1-880000-92-2(X)) Lee & Low Bks., Inc.

—Say Hola to Spanish, Otra Vez (Again!) Lopez, Loretta, illus. (SPA.). 32p. (J). 1999. (gr. 1-4). ring bd. 15.95 (978-1-880000-59-5(8)); 1999. (ps-5). pap. 5.56 net. (978-1-880000-83-0(0)); 1998. (ps-5). pap. 6.95 (978-1-880000-64-9(4)) Lee & Low Bks., Inc.

Emberley, Rebecca. My Day. 2000. Tr. of Mi Dia. (SPA.). (ps-2). lib. bdg. 14.95 (978-0-613-26312-2(X)) Tandem Library Bks.

En el Bosque. 2003. 23.95 (978-0-673-77175-9(X)) Celebration Pr.

En el Bosque. (Coleccion Pequeno Simon). (SPA., Illus.). 32p. (J). 7.95 (978-84-7189-166-2(2) , ORT347) Ortells, Alfredo Editorial S.L. ESP. *Dist:* Continental Bk. Co., Inc.

En el Mercado. 2003. 23.95 (978-0-673-77790-4(1)) Celebration Pr.

En Mi Jardin. 2003. 23.95 (978-0-673-77131-5(8)) Celebration Pr.

El Enanito Maloigoloso. 2003. (J). (ps-2). 28.95 (978-0-673-77377-7(9)) Celebration Pr.

Escribir para Leer: Grade 1, Class Set C. 2001. Tr. of Writing to Read. (SPA., Illus.). (J). (gr. 1). stu. ed., wbk. ed. 159.00 (978-1-56014-987-3(6)) Santillana USA Publishing Co., Inc.

Escribir para Leer: Grade 2, Class Set E. 2001. Tr. of Writing to Read. (SPA., Illus.). (J). (gr. 2). stu. ed., wbk. ed. 159.00 (978-1-56014-989-7(2)) Santillana USA Publishing Co., Inc.

Escribir para Leer: Grade 3, Class Set G. 2001. Tr. of Writing to Read. (SPA., Illus.). (J). (gr. 3). stu. ed., wbk. ed. 159.00 (978-1-56014-991-0(4)) Santillana USA Publishing Co., Inc.

Escribir para Leer: Grade K, Class Set A. 2001. Tr. of Writing to Read. (SPA., Illus.). (J). stu. ed., wbk. ed. 159.00 (978-1-56014-985-9(X)) Santillana USA Publishing Co., Inc.

Escribir para Leer: Grades 1-2, Class Set D. 2001. Tr. of Writing to Read. (SPA., Illus.). (J). (gr. 1-2). stu. ed., wbk. ed. 159.00 (978-1-56014-988-0(4)) Santillana USA Publishing Co., Inc.

Escribir para Leer: Grades 2-3, Class Set F. 2001. Tr. of Writing to Read. (SPA., Illus.). (J). (gr. 2-3). stu. ed., wbk. ed. 159.00 (978-1-56014-990-3(6)) Santillana USA Publishing Co., Inc.

Escribir para Leer: Grades 3-4, Class Set H. 2001. Tr. of Writing to Read. (SPA., Illus.). (J). (gr. 3-4). stu. ed., wbk. ed. 159.00 (978-1-56014-992-7(2)) Santillana USA Publishing Co., Inc.

Escribir para Leer: Grades K-1, Class Set B. 2001. Tr. of Writing to Read. (SPA., Illus.). (J). (gr. k-1). stu. ed., wbk. ed. 159.00 (978-1-56014-986-6(8)) Santillana USA Publishing Co., Inc.

Escritura y Comunicacion. 2001. (Serie Siglo XXI). (SPA., Illus.). (J). (gr. 1). stu. ed., wbk. ed. 12.95 (978-1-57581-144-4(8)); (gr. 2). stu. ed., wbk. ed. 12.95 (978-1-57581-156-7(1)); (gr. 3). stu. ed., wbk. ed. 12.95 (978-1-57581-167-3(7)); (gr. 4). stu. ed., wbk. ed. 12.95 (978-1-57581-145-1(6)); (gr. 5). stu. ed., wbk. ed. 12.95 (978-1-57581-159-8(6)); (gr. 6). stu. ed., wbk. ed. 12.95 (978-1-57581-168-0(5)) Santillana USA Publishing Co., Inc.

Espanol: Grades 1-2, Class Set A. 2001. (Espanol Serie 2000). (SPA.). (J). (gr. 1-2). tchr. ed., wbk. ed. 230.00 (978-1-58105-859-8(4)) Santillana USA Publishing Co., Inc.

Espanol: Grades 3-4, Class Set B. 2001. (Espanol Serie 2000). (SPA., Illus.). (J). (gr. 3-4). stu. ed., wbk. ed. 230.00 (978-1-58105-860-4(8)) Santillana USA Publishing Co., Inc.

Espanol: Grades 4-5, Class Set C. 2001. (Espanol Serie 2000). (SPA., Illus.). (J). (gr. 4-5). tchr. ed., stu. ed. 230.00 (978-1-58105-861-1(6)) Santillana USA Publishing Co., Inc.

Espanol: Grades 5-6, Class Set D. 2001. (Espanol Serie 2000). (SPA., Illus.). (J). (gr. 5-6). 230.00 (978-1-58105-862-8(4)) Santillana USA Publishing Co., Inc.

Espanol: Grades 6-7, Class Set E. 2001. (Espanol Serie 2000). (SPA., Illus.). (YA). (gr. 6-7). tchr. ed., wbk. ed. 230.00 (978-1-58105-863-5(2)) Santillana USA Publishing Co., Inc.

Estoy Enojado. 2003. (J). (ps-2). 23.95 (978-0-673-77391-3(4)) Celebration Pr.

Estrada, Altamira Perea. Un Abecedario Muy Sabroso. (SPA.). (J). pap. 4.76 net. (978-0-590-93319-3(1)) Scholastic, Inc.

Fabra, Jordi Sierra. Aydin. 97th ed. 2003. (SPA., Illus.). 144p. pap. 23.40 (978-84-236-3708-9(5) , ED6264) Harcourt Schl. Pubs.

Fact & Opinion Spanish Version, Gr. 1-3. 2005. (J). per. (978-1-58232-149-3(3)) Bryan Hse. Pubs., Inc.

Fact & Opinion Spanish Version, Gr. 4-5. 2005. (J). per. (978-1-58232-144-8(2)) Bryan Hse. Pubs., Inc.

First Explorers Primeros Exploradores Set 1: Spanish - 1 Each of 12 Student Books. (First Explorers. Primeros Exploradores Nonfiction Sets Ser.). (gr. 1-2). 59.95 (978-0-7699-1370-4(9)) Shortland Pubns. (U. S. A.) Inc.

First Explorers Primeros Exploradores Set 1: Spanish - 1 Each of 12 Student Books, 1 Each of 12 Lesson Plans. (First Explorers. Primeros Exploradores Nonfiction Sets Ser.). (gr. 1-2). 107.95 (978-0-7699-1368-1(7)) Shortland Pubns. (U. S. A.) Inc.

First Explorers Primeros Exploradores Set 1: Spanish - 6 Each of 12 Student Books, 1 Each of 12 Lesson Plans. (First Explorers. Primeros Exploradores Nonfiction Sets Ser.). (SPA.). (gr. 1-2). 407.50 (978-0-7699-1372-8(5)) Shortland Pubns. (U. S. A.) Inc.

First Explorers Primeros Exploradores Set 2: Spanish - 1 Each of 12 Student Books. (First Explorers. Primeros Exploradores Nonfiction Sets Ser.). (gr. 1-2). 67.50 (978-0-7699-1371-1(7)) Shortland Pubns. (U. S. A.) Inc.

First Explorers Primeros Exploradores Set 2: Spanish - 1 Each of 12 Student Books, 1 Each of 12 Lesson Plans. (First Explorers. Primeros Exploradores Nonfiction Sets Ser.). (gr. 1-2). 115.50 (978-0-7699-1369-8(5)) Shortland Pubns. (U. S. A.) Inc.

First Explorers Primeros Exploradores Set 2: Spanish - 6 Each of 12 Student Books, 1 Each of 12 Lesson Plans. (First Explorers. Primeros Exploradores Nonfiction Sets Ser.). (SPA.). (gr. 1-2). 452.50 (978-0-7699-1373-5(3)) Shortland Pubns. (U. S. A.) Inc.

First Explorers Primeros Exploradores Sets 1-2: Spanish - 1 Each of 24 Student Books, 1 Each of 24 Lesson Plans. (First Explorers. Primeros Exploradores Nonfiction Sets Ser.). (gr. 1-2). 223.50 (978-0-7699-1358-2(X)) Shortland Pubns. (U. S. A.) Inc.

First Explorers Primeros Exploradores Sets 1-2: Spanish - 6 Each of 24 Student Books, 1 Each of 24 Lesson Plans. (First Explorers. Primeros Exploradores Nonfiction Sets Ser.). (SPA.). (gr. 1-2). 816.95 (978-0-7699-1367-4(9)) Shortland Pubns. (U. S. A.) Inc.

Friends Are Forever: Individual Title Six-Packs. (Literatura 2000 Ser.). (gr. 2-3). 33.00 (978-0-7635-0169-3(7)) Rigby Education.

Fui Al Mar. 2003. 23.95 (978-0-673-77162-9(8)) Celebration Pr.

Gallaher, Miriam Alvarez. Learn Spanish with Grace! The Catholic Approach to Learning Spanish. Ritchie, Diane, illus. 2nd ed. 2002. (SPA.). 194p. (J). per. 65.00 (978-0-9721392-1-2(4)) Quiet Waters Productions.

Garcia, Yolanda Pacheco. Spanish in a Taco Shell. Garcia, Veronica J., illus. 2000. (ENG & SPA.). (Orig.). (J). (gr. 4-9). pap. 10.95 (978-0-935303-04-9(9)) Victory Publishing.

Gardeski, Christina Mia. Toda Clase de Ninos. McMahon, Bob, illus. 2002. (Rookie Readers - Spanish Ser.).Tr. of All Kinds of Kids. (SPA.). 24p. (J). (gr. k-2). 19.50 (978-0-516-22681-1(9) , Children's Pr.) Scholastic Library Publishing.

Gardner, Dee. Bridge Books: Series A, 25 vols. 2000. (Language Development Ser.). (SPA & ENG., Illus.). (J). (gr. k-2). pap. 118.00 incl. audio compact disk (978-0-615-11585-6(3)) Language Literacy Links, L. C.

—Bridge Books: Series B, 25 vols. 2001. (Language Development Ser.). (SPA & ENG., Illus.). (J). (gr. k up). pap. 119.00 incl. audio compact disk (978-0-9711372-0-2(X)) Language Literacy Links, L. C.

Gareth Stevens Publishing Staff. Es Mio! 2003. (SPA.). (gr. k-3). lib. bdg. 14.10 (978-0-613-76725-5(X)) Tandem Library Bks.

—No Funciona! 2003. (SPA.). (gr. k-3). lib. bdg. 14.10 (978-0-613-76726-2(8)) Tandem Library Bks.

—Vete! 2003. (SPA.). (gr. k-3). lib. bdg. 14.10 (978-0-613-76727-9(6)) Tandem Library Bks.

Getting the Sequence Spanish Version, Gr. 1-3. 2005. (J). per. (978-1-58232-146-2(9)) Bryan Hse. Pubs., Inc.

Getting the Sequence Spanish Version, Gr. 4-5. 2005. (J). per. (978-1-58232-141-7(8)) Bryan Hse. Pubs., Inc.

Gibbons, Gail. De Sol a Sol. (SPA., Illus.). (J). (gr. 1-3). pap. 3.96 net. (978-0-590-46903-6(7) , SO30343, Scholastic en Espanol) Scholastic, Inc.

Gomez, Carlos Humberto. Workbook 1. (Coleccion Nos Comunicamos). (SPA & ENG.). (J). (gr. 1). pap., wbk. ed. 11.50 (978-958-04-2074-3(2) , 01021255) Norma S.A. COL. *Dist:* Continental Bk. Co., Inc.

—Workbook 2. (Coleccion Nos Comunicamos). (SPA & ENG.). (J). (gr. 2). pap., wbk. ed. 11.50 (978-958-04-2075-0(0) , 01021256) Norma S.A. COL. *Dist:* Continental Bk. Co., Inc.

—Workbook 3. (Coleccion Nos Comunicamos). (SPA & ENG.). (J). (gr. 3). pap., wbk. ed. 11.50 (978-958-04-2076-7(9) , 01021257) Norma S.A. COL. *Dist:* Continental Bk. Co., Inc.

—Workbook 4. (Coleccion Nos Comunicamos). (SPA & ENG.). (J). (gr. 4). pap., wbk. ed. 11.50 (978-958-04-1784-2(9) , 01021258) Norma S.A. COL. *Dist:* Continental Bk. Co., Inc.

—Workbook 6. (Coleccion Nos Comunicamos). (SPA & ENG.). (J). (gr. 6). pap., wbk. ed. 11.50 (978-958-04-1791-0(1) , 01021260) Norma S.A. COL. *Dist:* Continental Bk. Co., Inc.

—Workbook Kindergarten. (Coleccion Nos Comunicamos). (SPA & ENG.). (J). pap., wbk. ed. 11.50 (978-958-04-2035-4(1) , 01021254) Norma S.A. COL. *Dist:* Continental Bk. Co., Inc.

Gorbachev, Valeri. Ricitos de Oro y los Tres Osos. 2003. Tr. of Goldilocks & the Three Bears. (SPA.). (gr. 7-12). lib. bdg. 15.25 (978-0-613-81368-6(5)) Tandem Library Bks.

Gordon, et al. Repaso: A Review for Grammar, Communication, & Culture 2004. 2nd ed. 2004. (SPA.). (C). (gr. 6-12). pap., wbk. ed. 25.96 (978-0-07-846050-0(6) , 9780078460500) Glencoe/McGraw-Hill.

Grades 1-2 Complete Pinata/Mas Pinata Package. 2003. 1943.95 (978-0-673-58717-6(7)) Celebration Pr.

Grammar Basics Plus: Level B. 2003. 128p. (C). pap. 13.99 (978-0-7424-1857-8(X) , LL90015) School Specialty Publishing.

Grisewood, John. Fun to Learn Spanish. 2000. (ENG & SPA., Illus.). 40p. (J). (gr. 3-5). pap. 7.95 (978-0-7534-5302-5(9) , Kingfisher) Houghton Mifflin Co. Trade & Reference Div.

Guia para el Maestro: Grade 1. 2001. (SPA., Illus.). (J). (gr. 1). tchr.'s training gde. ed. 14.95 (978-1-57581-146-8(4)) Santillana USA Publishing Co., Inc.

Guia para el Maestro: Grade 2. 2001. (Serie Siglo XXI). (SPA., Illus.). (J). (gr. 2). tchr.'s training gde. ed. 14.95 (978-1-57581-169-7(3)) Santillana USA Publishing Co., Inc.

Guia para el Maestro: Grade 3. 2001. (Serie Siglo XXI). (SPA., Illus.). (J). (gr. 3). tchr.'s training gde. ed. 14.95 (978-1-57581-170-3(7)) Santillana USA Publishing Co., Inc.

Guia para el Maestro: Grade 4. 2001. (Serie Siglo XXI). (SPA., Illus.). (J). (gr. 4). tchr.'s training gde. ed. 14.95 (978-1-57581-147-5(2)) Santillana USA Publishing Co., Inc.

Guia para el Maestro: Grade 5. 2001. (Serie Siglo XXI). (SPA., Illus.). (J). (gr. 5). tchr.'s training gde. ed. 14.95 (978-1-57581-171-0(5)) Santillana USA Publishing Co., Inc.

Guy, Ginger Foglesong. ¡Perros! Perros!/Dogs! Dogs! A Story in English & Spanish. Glick, Sharon, illus. 2006. (ENG & SPA.). 32p. (J). (gr. k-2). 15.99 (978-0-06-083574-3(5)); lib. bdg. 16.89 (978-0-06-083575-0(3)) HarperCollins Pubs.

Harcourt School Publishers Staff. Acercate y Mira: Little Book. 1999. (Vamos Ser.). (SPA., Illus.). pap. 16.80 (978-0-15-315841-4(7)) Harcourt Schl. Pubs.

—Adios, Hola. 1999. (Vamos Ser.). (SPA., Illus.). pap. 19.10 (978-0-15-315874-2(3)) Harcourt Schl. Pubs.

—Adonde Gusta Ir: Get Ready Book. 1999. (Vamos Ser.). (SPA., Illus.). (J). pap. 3.00 (978-0-15-315903-9(0)) Harcourt Schl. Pubs.

—Al Zoologico: Get Ready Book. 1999. (Vamos Ser.). (SPA., Illus.). (J). pap. 3.00 (978-0-15-315901-5(4)) Harcourt Schl. Pubs.

—Amigas/Lombrices: Library Edition. 1999. (SPA., Illus.). pap. 19.10 (978-0-15-315877-3(8)) Harcourt Schl. Pubs.

—Animal Esta y Granja: Get Ready Book. 1999. (Vamos Ser.). (SPA., Illus.). (J). pap. 3.00 (978-0-15-315904-6(9)) Harcourt Schl. Pubs.

—Animales Favoritos. 1999. (Vamos Ser.: Theme Bk. 2). (SPA., Illus.). (J). pap. 3.60 (978-0-15-315844-5(1)) Harcourt Schl. Pubs.

—Un Aniversario: Get Ready Book. 1999. (Vamos Ser.). (SPA., Illus.). (J). pap. 3.00 (978-0-15-315891-9(3)) Harcourt Schl. Pubs.

—Aventuras/Animales Theme, Bk. 8. 1999. (Vamos Ser.). (SPA., Illus.). (J). pap. 3.60 (978-0-15-315850-6(6)) Harcourt Schl. Pubs.

—Bajo el Oceano Bk. 12: Theme. 1999. (Vamos Ser.). (SPA., Illus.). (J). pap. 3.60 (978-0-15-315854-4(9)) Harcourt Schl. Pubs.

—El Bano: Get Ready Book. 1999. (Vamos Ser.). (SPA., Illus.). (J). pap. 3.00 (978-0-15-315889-6(1)) Harcourt Schl. Pubs.

—Caida del Cielo On Level. 3rd ed. 2002. (Trofeos Ser.). (SPA., Illus.). pap. 6.80 (978-0-15-324011-9(3)) Harcourt Schl. Pubs.

—Caiman Debajo Mi Cama: Library Edition. 1999. (Vamos Ser.). (SPA., Illus.). pap. 19.10 (978-0-15-315871-1(9)) Harcourt Schl. Pubs.

—Cambios Advanced Level. 3rd ed. 2002. (Trofeos Ser.). (SPA., Illus.). pap. 6.80 (978-0-15-324115-4(2)) Harcourt Schl. Pubs.

—Camila Se Muda: Take-Home Book. 1999. (Vamos Ser.). (SPA., Illus.). (J). pap. 2.50 (978-0-15-318841-1(3)) Harcourt Schl. Pubs.

—Campamento y Verano: Take-Home Book. 1999. (Vamos Ser.). (SPA., Illus.). (J). pap. 2.50 (978-0-15-318843-5(X)) Harcourt Schl. Pubs.

—Catalina/Sabia Below Level. 3rd ed. 2002. (Trofeos Ser.). (SPA., Illus.). pap. 6.80 (978-0-15-324137-6(3)) Harcourt Schl. Pubs.

—Celebraciones/Ciudad On Level. 3rd ed. 2002. (Trofeos Ser.). (SPA., Illus.). (gr. 3). pap. 6.80 (978-0-15-324097-3(0)) Harcourt Schl. Pubs.

—Cerditos Gracsos On Level. 3rd ed. 2002. (Trofeos Ser.). (SPA., Illus.). pap. 6.80 (978-0-15-324072-0(5)) Harcourt Schl. Pubs.

—Los Cinco Patitos: Little Book. 1999. (Vamos Ser.). (SPA., Illus.). pap. 16.80 (978-0-15-315820-9(4)) Harcourt Schl. Pubs.

—Ciudadania Advanced Level. 3rd ed. 2002. (Trofeos Ser.). (SPA., Illus.). pap. 6.80 (978-0-15-324212-0(4)) Harcourt Schl. Pubs.

—Cosas Que Crecen Theme Bk. 10. 1999. (Vamos Ser.). (SPA., Illus.). (J). pap. 3.60 (978-0-15-315852-0(2)) Harcourt Schl. Pubs.

—Cosecha/Sandia: Get Ready Book. 1999. (Vamos Ser.). (SPA., Illus.). (J). pap. 3.00 (978-0-15-315895-7(6)) Harcourt Schl. Pubs.

—Cumpleanos/Tia: Library Edition. 1999. (SPA., Illus.). pap. 19.10 (978-0-15-315866-7(2)) Harcourt Schl. Pubs.

—Donde/Osito: Get Ready Book. 1999. (Vamos Ser.). (SPA., Illus.). (J). pap. 3.00 (978-0-15-315887-2(5)) Harcourt Schl. Pubs.

—Emparedado. 1999. (Vamos Ser.). (SPA., Illus.). (J). pap. 3.00 (978-0-15-315890-2(5)) Harcourt Schl. Pubs.

—En el Agua: Little Book. 1999. (Vamos Ser.). (SPA., Illus.). pap. 16.80 (978-0-15-315842-1(5)) Harcourt Schl. Pubs.

—En la Playa. 1999. (Vamos Ser.). (SPA., Illus.). pap. 16.80 (978-0-15-315808-7(5)) Harcourt Schl. Pubs.

—En Mi Auto: Get Ready Book. 1999. (Vamos Ser.). (SPA., Illus.). (J). pap. 3.00 (978-0-15-315898-8(0)) Harcourt Schl. Pubs.

—Es Hora: Little Book. 1999. (Vamos Ser.). (SPA., Illus.). pap. 16.80 (978-0-15-315809-4(3)) Harcourt Schl. Pubs.

—Escapada/Marvin: Little Book. 1999. (Vamos Ser.). (SPA., Illus.). pap. 16.80 (978-0-15-315838-4(7)) Harcourt Schl. Pubs.

—Espera y Veras: Library Edition. 1999. (Vamos Ser.). (SPA., Illus.). pap. 19.10 (978-0-15-315868-1(9)) Harcourt Schl. Pubs.

—Familia/Los Amigos, Theme Bk. 4. 1999. (Vamos Ser.). (SPA., Illus.). (J). pap. 3.60 (978-0-15-315846-9(8)) Harcourt Schl. Pubs.

—Familias de Animales, Theme Bk. 6. 1999. (Vamos Ser.). (SPA., Illus.). (J). pap. 3.60 (978-0-15-315848-3(4)) Harcourt Schl. Pubs.

—Fantastica Fiesta: Little Book. 1999. (Vamos Ser.). (SPA., Illus.). pap. 16.80 (978-0-15-315794-3(1)) Harcourt Schl. Pubs.

—La Fiesta Celestial: Take-Home Book. 1999. (Vamos Ser.). (SPA., Illus.). (J). (gr. 1). pap. 2.50 (978-0-15-318814-5(6)) Harcourt Schl. Pubs.

—Final de la Rama: Take-Home Book. 1999. (Vamos Ser.). (SPA., Illus.). (J). pap. 2.50 (978-0-15-318802-2(2)) Harcourt Schl. Pubs.

—Fondo Del Mar: Get Ready Book. 1999. (Vamos Ser.). (SPA., Illus.). (J). pap. 3.00 (978-0-15-315909-1(X)) Harcourt Schl. Pubs.

—El Frijo de Benito: Little Book. 1999. (Vamos Ser.). (SPA., Illus.). pap. 16.80 (978-0-15-315840-7(9)) Harcourt Schl. Pubs.

—La Gallinita Roja: Library Edition. 1999. (SPA., Illus.). pap. 19.10 (978-0-15-315882-7(4)) Harcourt Schl. Pubs.

—La Gente Trabaja: Little Book. 1999. (Vamos Ser.). (SPA., Illus.). pap. 16.80 (978-0-15-315839-1(5)) Harcourt Schl. Pubs.

—Un Gran Paseo: Get Ready Book. 1999. (Vamos Ser.). (SPA., Illus.). (J). pap. 3.00 (978-0-15-315897-1(2)) Harcourt Schl. Pubs.

—Iguanas y Azucar: Take-Home Book. 1999. (Vamos Ser.). (SPA., Illus.). (J). pap. 2.50 (978-0-15-318853-4(7)) Harcourt Schl. Pubs.

—Increible Armadillo: Take-Home Book. 1999. (Vamos Ser.). (SPA., Illus.). (J). pap. 2.50 (978-0-15-318836-7(7)) Harcourt Schl. Pubs.

—A la Mesa Theme, Bk. 3. 1999. (Vamos Ser.). (SPA., Illus.). (J). pap. 3.60 (978-0-15-315845-2(X)) Harcourt Schl. Pubs.

—Lazos de Amistad: Take-Home Book. 1999. (Vamos Ser.). (SPA., Illus.). (J). pap. 2.50 (978-0-15-318806-0(5)) Harcourt Schl. Pubs.

—Llaman/Puerta: Little Book. 1999. (Vamos Ser.). (SPA., Illus.). pap. 16.80 (978-0-15-315810-0(7)) Harcourt Schl. Pubs.

—Mi Amiga: Get Ready Book. 1999. (Vamos Ser.). (SPA., Illus.). (J). pap. 3.00 (978-0-15-315893-3(X)) Harcourt Schl. Pubs.

—Mi Mundo: Get Ready Book. 1999. (Vamos Ser.). (SPA., Illus.). (J). pap. 3.00 (978-0-15-315892-6(1)) Harcourt Schl. Pubs.

—Mira Como He Crecido, Theme Bk. 5. 1999. (SPA., Illus.). (J). pap. 3.60 (978-0-15-315847-6(6)) Harcourt Schl. Pubs.

—Nuestra Comunidad Theme Bk. 9. 1999. (Vamos Ser.). (SPA., Illus.). (J). pap. 3.60 (978-0-15-315851-3(4)) Harcourt Schl. Pubs.

—Nuestros Amigos: Take-Home Book. 1999. (Vamos Ser.). (SPA., Illus.). (J). (gr. 1). pap. 2.50 (978-0-15-318803-9(0)) Harcourt Schl. Pubs.

—Oruga/Hambrienta: Library Edition. 1999. (Vamos Ser.). (SPA., Illus.). pap. 19.10 (978-0-15-315883-4(2)) Harcourt Schl. Pubs.

—Paco Vamos de Fiesta: Library Edition. 1999. (Vamos Ser.). (SPA., Illus.). pap. 19.10 (978-0-15-315859-9(X)) Harcourt Schl. Pubs.

—Papaya Excribio: Take-Home Book. 1999. (Vamos Ser.). (SPA., Illus.). (J). pap. 2.50 (978-0-15-318822-0(7)) Harcourt Schl. Pubs.

—Paso a Pasito: Library Edition. 1999. (Vamos Ser.). (SPA., Illus.). pap. 19.10 (978-0-15-315884-1(0)) Harcourt Schl. Pubs.

—Pasteles/Conejitos: Library Edition. 1999. (SPA., Illus.). pap. 19.10 (978-0-15-315864-3(6)) Harcourt Schl. Pubs.

—Pin-Pin y Parlanchines: Take-Home Book. 1999. (Vamos Ser.). (SPA., Illus.). (J). pap. 2.50 (978-0-15-318823-7(5)) Harcourt Schl. Pubs.

—Primer/Escuela: Get Ready Book. 1999. (Vamos Ser.). (SPA., Illus.). (J). pap. 3.00 (978-0-15-315886-5(7)) Harcourt Schl. Pubs.

—Pueblito en Alaska: Take-Home Book. 1999. (Vamos Ser.). (SPA., Illus.). (J). pap. 2.50 (978-0-15-318830-5(8)) Harcourt Schl. Pubs.

—Que Divertido Theme Bk. 7. 1999. (Vamos Ser.). (SPA., Illus.). (J). pap. 3.60 (978-0-15-315849-0(2)) Harcourt Schl. Pubs.

—Que Soy: Get Ready Book. 1999. (Vamos Ser.). (SPA., Illus.). (J). pap. 3.00 (978-0-15-315906-0(5)) Harcourt Schl. Pubs.

—Quiero una Lonchera: Library Edition. 1999. (Vamos Ser.). (SPA., Illus.). pap. 19.10 (978-0-15-315857-5(3)) Harcourt Schl. Pubs.

—Quiero y Mariposa: Take-Home Book. 1999. (Vamos Ser.). (SPA., Illus.). (J). pap. 2.50 (978-0-15-318811-4(1)) Harcourt Schl. Pubs.

—El Raton Gloton: Get Ready Book. 1999. (SPA., Illus.). (J). pap. 3.00 (978-0-15-315905-3(7)) Harcourt Schl. Pubs.

—Salvemos a Este Oso: Take-Home Book. 1999. (Vamos Ser.). (SPA., Illus.). (J). (gr. 1). pap. 2.50 (978-0-15-318809-1(X)) Harcourt Schl. Pubs.

—La Selva Tropical: Take-Home Book. 1999. (Vamos Ser.). (SPA., Illus.). (J). pap. 2.50 (978-0-15-318825-1(1)) Harcourt Schl. Pubs.

—Soy Especial. 1999. (Vamos Ser.: Theme Bk. 1). (SPA., Illus.). (J). pap. 3.60 (978-0-15-315843-8(3)) Harcourt Schl. Pubs.

—Student Journal. 93rd ed. 1998. (Estrellas de Literatura Ser.). (gr. 1). 20.30 (978-0-15-304452-6(7)); (gr. 2). 20.30 (978-0-15-304453-3(5)) Harcourt Schl. Pubs.

—El Sueno y Beatriz: Get Ready Book. 1999. (Vamos Ser.). (SPA., Illus.). (J). pap. 3.00 (978-0-15-315900-8(6)) Harcourt Schl. Pubs.

—Teatro y Marionetas: Get Ready Book. 1999. (Vamos Ser.). (SPA., Illus.). (J). pap. 3.00 (978-0-15-315896-4(4)) Harcourt Schl. Pubs.

—Tengo una Mascota: Library Edition. 1999. (Vamos Ser.). (SPA., Illus.). pap. 19.10 (978-0-15-315858-2(1)) Harcourt Schl. Pubs.

—Teresa y Traviesa: Take-Home Book. 1999. (Vamos Ser.). (SPA., Illus.). (J). (gr. 2). pap. 2.50 (978-0-15-318819-0(7)) Harcourt Schl. Pubs.

—Tito y Dina: Library Edition. 1999. (SPA., Illus.). pap. 19.10 (978-0-15-315863-6(8)) Harcourt Schl. Pubs.

—Toc, Toc: Get Ready Book. 1999. (Vamos Ser.). (SPA., Illus.). (J). pap. 3.00 (978-0-15-315907-7(3)) Harcourt Schl. Pubs.

—Trofeos: Aventuras con Animales: Practice Book. 3rd ed. 2002. (SPA., Illus.). (J). pap. 2.20 (978-0-15-332075-0(3)) Harcourt Schl. Pubs.

—Trofeos: Explorems Nuestras: Practice Book. 3rd ed. 2002. (SPA., Illus.). (J). pap. 2.20 (978-0-15-332078-1(8)) Harcourt Schl. Pubs.

—Trofeos: Por la Ciudad: Practice Book. 3rd ed. 2002. (SPA., Illus.). (J). pap. 2.20 (978-0-15-332076-7(1)) Harcourt Schl. Pubs.

—Trofeos On Level: La Oruga. 3rd ed. 2002. (SPA., Illus.). pap. 5.50 (978-0-15-323896-3(8)) Harcourt Schl. Pubs.

—Trofeos, Grade 6. 3rd ed. 2002. (SPA.). Theme 1. tchr. ed. 110.60 (978-0-15-335083-2(0)); Theme 2. tchr. ed. 110.60 (978-0-15-335084-9(9)); Theme 3. tchr. ed. 110.60 (978-0-15-335085-6(7)); Theme 4. tchr. ed. 110.60 (978-0-15-335086-3(5)); Theme 5. tchr. ed. 110.60 (978-0-15-335087-0(3)); Theme 6. tchr. ed. 110.60 (978-0-15-335088-7(1)) Harcourt Schl. Pubs.

—Uno, Dos, Tres: Little Book. 1999. (SPA., Illus.). pap. 16.80 (978-0-15-315807-0(7)) Harcourt Schl. Pubs.

—Vamos de Fiesta: Bailes y Fiestas. 2000. (SPA., Illus.). (gr. 4). 96.80 (978-0-15-313298-8(1)) Harcourt Schl. Pubs.

—Vamos de Fiesta: Ritmos y Fiestas. 2000. (SPA., Illus.). (gr. 5). 98.20 (978-0-15-313299-5(X)) Harcourt Schl. Pubs.

—Vamos de Fiesta: Student Materials Package: Texas Edition. 1999. (SPA., Illus.). (gr. 1). pap. 186.30 (978-0-15-315020-3(3)); (gr. 2). pap. 103.50 (978-0-15-315021-0(1)); (gr. 3). pap. 103.50 (978-0-15-315022-7(X)) Harcourt Schl. Pubs.

—Vamos de Fiesta: Student Materials Package with Translation: Texas Edition. 1999. (SPA & ENG., Illus.). pap. 128.30 (978-0-15-315050-0(5)) Harcourt Schl. Pubs.

—Vamos de Fiesta Bk. 1: Dulces y Fiestas. 1999. (Vamos Ser.). (SPA., Illus.). (gr. 1). 35.00 (978-0-15-313295-7(7)) Harcourt Schl. Pubs.

—Vamos de Fiesta Bk. 1: Pasteles y Fiestas. 1999. (SPA., Illus.). (gr. 3). 59.60 (978-0-15-313297-1(3)) Harcourt Schl. Pubs.

—Vamos de Fiesta Bk. 1: Regalos y Fiestas. 1999. (SPA., Illus.). (gr. 2). 59.60 (978-0-15-313296-4(5)) Harcourt Schl. Pubs.

—Vamos de Fiesta Bk. 2: Risas y Fiestas. 1999. (SPA., Illus.). (gr. 1). 36.30 (978-0-15-314681-7(6)) Harcourt Schl. Pubs.

—Vamos de Fiesta Bk. 2: Sorpresas y Fiestas. 1999. (SPA., Illus.). (gr. 2). 59.60 (978-0-15-314685-5(0)) Harcourt Schl. Pubs.

—Vamos de Fiesta Bk. 2: Velitas y Fiestas. 1999. (SPA., Illus.). (gr. 3). 59.60 (978-0-15-314686-2(9)) Harcourt Schl. Pubs.

—Vamos de Fiesta Bk. 3: Cantos y Fiestas. 1999. (SPA., Illus.). 37.30 (978-0-15-314682-4(6)) Harcourt Schl. Pubs.

—Vamos de Fiesta Bk. 4: Juegas y Fiestas. 1999. (SPA., Illus.). (gr. 1). 37.30 (978-0-15-314683-1(4)) Harcourt Schl. Pubs.

—Vamos de Fiesta Bk. 5: Disfraces y Fiestas. 1999. (SPA., Illus.). (gr. 1). 37.90 (978-0-15-314684-8(2)) Harcourt Schl. Pubs.

—Vamos de Fiesta Level 1-a: Tito. 1999. (SPA., Illus.). (gr. 1). 7.00 (978-0-15-315118-7(8)) Harcourt Schl. Pubs.

—Vamos de Fiesta Level 1-b: Tu y Yo. 1999. (SPA., Illus.). 7.00 (978-0-15-315119-4(6)) Harcourt Schl. Pubs.

—Vamos de Fiesta Level 1-c: En el Circo. 1999. (SPA., Illus.). 7.00 (978-0-15-315120-0(X)) Harcourt Schl. Pubs.

—Vamos de Fiesta Level 1-d: Amigos. 1999. (SPA., Illus.). 7.00 (978-0-15-315121-7(8)) Harcourt Schl. Pubs.

—Vamos de Fiesta Level 1-e: Sorpresas. 1999. (SPA., Illus.). 7.00 (978-0-15-315122-4(6)) Harcourt Schl. Pubs.

—Vamos de Fiesta, Grade 4 Theme 2. 2001. (SPA.). pap., tchr. ed. 84.70 (978-0-15-320048-9(0)) Harcourt Schl. Pubs.

—Vamos de Fiesta, Grade 4 Theme 6: TX Edition. 2nd ed. 2001. (SPA.). pap., tchr. ed. 91.20 (978-0-15-320058-8(8)) Harcourt Schl. Pubs.

—Vamos de Fiesta, Grade 5: Leveled Library. 2001. (SPA.). pap., tchr. ed. 125.50 (978-0-15-319896-0(6)) Harcourt Schl. Pubs.

—Vamos Take-Home Book Collection. 1999. (Illus.). (gr. 1). pap. 63.40 (978-0-15-318910-4(X)); (gr. 2). pap. 63.40 (978-0-15-318911-1(8)); (gr. 3). pap. 63.40 (978-0-15-318912-8(6)) Harcourt Schl. Pubs.

—Veo, Veo: Get Ready Book. 1999. (Vamos Ser.). (SPA., Illus.). (J). pap. 3.00 (978-0-15-315899-5(9)) Harcourt Schl. Pubs.

—Zanahoria Gigante: Library Edition. 1999. (SPA., Illus.). pap. 19.10 (978-0-15-315861-2(1)) Harcourt Schl. Pubs.

—Zapatos de Amalia: Take-Home Book. 1999. (Vamos Ser.). (SPA., Illus.). (J). pap. 2.50 (978-0-15-318846-6(4)) Harcourt Schl. Pubs.

—Zoologico Fabulosa: Take-Home Book. 1999. (Vamos Ser.). (SPA., Illus.). (J). pap. 2.50 (978-0-15-318828-2(6)) Harcourt Schl. Pubs.

Harvey, William C. Ingles para Latinos Bk. 2: Level 2. 2000. (Barron's Ser.). (SPA.). 336p. 21.95 (978-0-7641-7297-7(2)) Barron's Educational Series, Inc.

Haughom, Lisa, illus. & text. Juegos de Vocabulario: Vocabulary & Verb Games for Learning Spanish. Haughom, Lisa, text. 1999. 74p. per. 21.95 (978-0-9723849-3-3(6)) Languages For Kids.

—Juegos para la Clase de Espanol: Board Games for Learning Basic Spanish. Haughom, Lisa, text. 1999. Tr. of Games for Learning Spanish. (SPA.). 54p. per. 21.95 (978-0-9723849-2-6(8)) Languages For Kids.

Hayhurst, Chris. Toro Sentado: Jefe Sioux. 2003. (ENG & SPA.). (J). pap. (978-0-8239-4238-1(4)) Rosen Publishing Group, Inc., The.

Hazan, Maurice, creator. El Camino: Practicing Everyday Vocabulary. 2000. (SPA.). (J). 90.00 (978-1-932770-44-5(5) , SG5) Symtalk, Inc.

—Clothes & Colors Game in Spanish. 2000. (SPA.). (J). 99.00 (978-1-932770-52-0(6) , SG13) Symtalk, Inc.

—The Conversation Game for Spanish. 2000. (SPA.). (YA). 90.00 (978-1-932770-47-6(X) , SG8) Symtalk, Inc.

—Dime quien Es: Spanish Dialogues Level 1. 2000. (SPA.). (J). 99.00 (978-1-932770-43-8(7) , SG4) Symtalk, Inc.

—Dime quien Es: Spanish Dialogues Level 2. 2000. (SPA.). (J). 99.00 (978-1-932770-45-2(3) , SG6) Symtalk, Inc.

—Dime quien Es: Spanish Dialogues Level 3. 2000. (SPA.). (YA). 199.00 (978-1-932770-55-1(0) , SG16) Symtalk, Inc.

—Escribamos: The Spanish Writing Game. 2000. (SPA.). (J). 175.00 (978-1-932770-50-6(X) , SG11) Symtalk, Inc.

—Frases y Fotos: Long Sentence Bingo. 2000. (SPA.). (YA). 90.00 (978-1-932770-46-9(1) , SG7) Symtalk, Inc.

—Los Perdidos: Directions in the City. 2000. (SPA.). (YA). 199.00 (978-1-932770-54-4(2) , SG15) Symtalk, Inc.

—Object, Color & Number Bingo. 2000. (SPA.). (J). 90.00 (978-1-932770-41-4(0) , SG2) Symtalk, Inc.

—The Prom Game for Spanish. 2000. (YA). 99.00 (978-1-932770-51-3(8) , SG12) Symtalk, Inc.

—Resto Presto. 2000. (SPA.). (J). 120.00 (978-1-932770-42-1(9) , SG3) Symtalk, Inc.

—Unusual Suspects: The Past Tense Game in Spanish. 2000. (SPA.). (YA). 99.00 (978-1-932770-53-7(4) , SG14) Symtalk, Inc.

Heinle. Avenidas: Sample Chapter. 2001. (978-0-8384-5095-6(4)) Thomson Heinle.

Holland, Gini. Alive & Not Alive: Vivo y No Vivo. 2007. (SPA & ENG.). (J). pap. (*978-0-8368-8308-4(X)* , Weekly Reader Early Learning Library) Stevens, Gareth Inc.

—Alive & Not Alive/Vivo y No Vivo. 2007. (I Know Opposites/Conceptos Contrarios Ser.). (SPA & ENG.). 24p. (J). (gr. k-2). lib. bdg. 17.27 (*978-0-8368-8303-9(9)* , Weekly Reader Early Learning Library) Stevens, Gareth Inc.

—Hot & Cold: Caliente y Frío. 2007. (SPA & ENG.). (J). pap. (*978-0-8368-8309-1(8)* , Weekly Reader Early Learning Library) Stevens, Gareth Inc.

—Hot & Cold/Caliente y Frio. 2007. (I Know Opposites/Conceptos Contrarios Ser.). (SPA & ENG.). 24p. (J). (gr. k-2). lib. bdg. 17.27 (*978-0-8368-8304-6(7)* , Weekly Reader Early Learning Library) Stevens, Gareth Inc.

Holt, Rinehart and Winston Staff. Adelante & En Camino: Correlations Guide to Video Program. 1999. pap. 6.20 (978-0-03-054427-9(0)) Holt, Rinehart & Winston.

—En Camino: Activities for Communication. 3rd ed. 2002. pap. 20.00 (978-0-03-065963-8(9)) Holt, Rinehart & Winston.

—En Camino: Listening Activities. 3rd ed. 2002. pap. 20.00 (978-0-03-065966-9(3)) Holt, Rinehart & Winston.

—En Camino: Practice. 3rd ed. 2002. pap., act. bk. ed. 13.20 (978-0-03-065961-4(2)) Holt, Rinehart & Winston.

—En Camino: Practice & Activity Book. 3rd ed. 2002. pap., tchr. ed. 20.00 (978-0-03-065962-1(0)) Holt, Rinehart & Winston.

—En Camino: Video Guide. 3rd ed. 2002. pap. 20.00 (978-0-03-065973-7(6)) Holt, Rinehart & Winston.

—Expresate: Premier Online Edition. 6th ed. Date not set. (SPA.). 76.80 (978-0-03-074564-5(0)); Level 1. 75.13 (978-0-03-074563-8(2)) Holt, Rinehart & Winston.

—Oraciones y Parrafos Elementos. 2003. (Elementos Del Lenguaje Ser.). (SPA.). (gr. 6 up). 11.00 (978-0-03-064587-7(5)) Holt, Rinehart & Winston.

—Spanish 2: Grammar & Vocabulary Reteaching & Practice Workbook. 1998. pap., wbk. ed. 15.33 (978-0-03-051382-4(0)) Holt, Rinehart & Winston.

—Spanish 3: Grammar & Vocabulary Reteaching & Practice Workbook. 1998. pap., wbk. ed. 16.20 (978-0-03-051383-1(9)) Holt, Rinehart & Winston.

—Ven Conmigo! Level 1: Indiana Edition. 3rd annot. ed. 2001. tchr. ed. 88.40 (978-0-03-067127-2(2)) Holt, Rinehart & Winston.

—Ven Conmigo! Level 1: Test Practice Story Book: Middle School. 1999. pap. 14.73 (978-0-03-054842-0(X)) Holt, Rinehart & Winston.

—Ven Conmigo! Level 1: Videodisc Guide. 1998. pap. 36.33 (978-0-03-052692-3(2)) Holt, Rinehart & Winston.

—Ven Conmigo! Level 1: With Lesson Planner: Georgia Edition. 3rd annot. ed. 2003. (SPA.). (J). tchr. ed. 85.00 (978-0-03-074088-6(6)) Holt, Rinehart & Winston.

—Ven Conmigo! Level 1: With Lesson Planner:Tennessee Edition. 3rd annot. ed. 2003. (SPA.). (J). tchr. ed. 85.00 (978-0-03-074084-8(3)) Holt, Rinehart & Winston.

—Ven Conmigo! Level 1a: Adelante: Middle School. 1999. 55.26 (978-0-03-051237-7(9)) Holt, Rinehart & Winston.

—Ven Conmigo! Level 2: Activities for Communication. 1999. pap. 21.86 (978-0-03-052699-2(X)) Holt, Rinehart & Winston.

—Ven Conmigo! Level 2: Indiana Version. 3rd annot. ed. 2002. tchr. ed. 90.26 (978-0-03-067128-9(0)) Holt, Rinehart & Winston.

—Ven Conmigo! Level 2: Video Guide. 1999. pap. 21.26 (978-0-03-052718-0(X)) Holt, Rinehart & Winston.

—Ven Conmigo! Level 2: Videodisc Guide. 1999. pap. 36.33 (978-0-03-052722-7(8)) Holt, Rinehart & Winston.

—Ven Conmigo! Level 2: With Lesson Planner: Georgia Edition. 3rd annot. ed. 2003. (SPA.). (J). tchr. ed. 86.80 (978-0-03-074089-3(4)) Holt, Rinehart & Winston.

—Ven Conmigo! Level 2: With Lesson Planner: Tennessee Edition. 3rd ed. 2003. (SPA.). (J). tchr. ed. 86.80 (978-0-03-074086-2(X)) Holt, Rinehart & Winston.

—Ven Conmigo! Level 3: Activities for Communication. 1999. pap. 21.86 (978-0-03-053953-4(6)); 3rd ed. 2002. pap. 21.66 (978-0-03-065549-4(8)) Holt, Rinehart & Winston.

—Ven Conmigo! Level 3: Alternative Assessment Guide. 1999. pap. 20.80 (978-0-03-053954-1(4)) Holt, Rinehart & Winston.

—Ven Conmigo! Level 3: Indiana Version. 3rd annot. ed. 2002. tchr. ed. 90.26 (978-0-03-067129-6(9)) Holt, Rinehart & Winston.

—Ven Conmigo! Level 3: Listening Activities. 1999. 43.73 (978-0-03-054431-6(9)); 3rd ed. 2001. pap. 37.86 (978-0-03-065556-2(0)) Holt, Rinehart & Winston.

—Ven Conmigo! Level 3: Practice & Activities Book. 1999. pap., tchr. ed. 28.13 (978-0-03-053952-7(8)) Holt, Rinehart & Winston.

—Ven Conmigo! Level 3: Reading Strategies. 3rd ed. 2002. 22.06 (978-0-03-065624-8(9)) Holt, Rinehart & Winston.

—Ven Conmigo! Level 3: Testing Program. 1999. pap. 53.33 (978-0-03-053807-0(6)) Holt, Rinehart & Winston.

—Ven Conmigo! Level 3: With Lesson Planner: Georgia Edition. 3rd annot. ed. 2003. (SPA.). (J). tchr. ed. 86.80 (978-0-03-074091-6(6)) Holt, Rinehart & Winston.

—Ven Conmigo! Level 3: With Lesson Planner: Tennessee Edition. 3rd ed. 2003. (SPA.). (J). tchr. ed. 86.80 (978-0-03-074087-9(8)) Holt, Rinehart & Winston.

Homework Student Spanish: RUA Homework Student Spanish. 2005. 150p. per. 4.25 (978-1-932976-78-6(7)) National Ctr. on Education & The Economy.

Homework Student Spanish: RUPA Homework Student Spanish. 2005. 152p. per. 4.25 (978-1-932976-55-7(8)) National Ctr. on Education & The Economy.

HOP, LLC. Hooked on Spanish. 2006. 99.99 (978-1-931020-75-6(2)); 64.99 (978-1-931020-92-3(2)) HOP, LLC.

—Hooked on Spanish Beginning Spanish. 2006. 24.99 (978-1-933863-14-6(5)) HOP, LLC.

Howard, Linda & Dockray, Tracy Arah, illus. Mi Gran Libro de Palabras Play-Doh. 2006. (SPA.). 10p. (J). (ps-4). reprint ed. 10.00 (978-1-4223-5586-2(1)) DIANE Publishing Co.

Humbach. Expresate: Premier Online Edition. 6th ed. Date not set. (SPA.). Level 1. stu. ed. 19.93 (978-0-03-040457-3(6)); Level 1a. stu. ed. 14.60 (978-0-03-040449-8(5)); Level 1b. 14.60 (978-0-03-040453-5(3)); Level 2. stu. ed. 19.93 (978-0-03-040459-7(2)); Level 3. stu. ed. 19.93 (978-0-03-040463-4(0)) Holt, Rinehart & Winston.

—Ven Conmigo: Online Edition, Level 3. 3rd ed. 2003. (SPA.). 71.40 (978-0-03-036149-4(4)) Holt, Rinehart & Winston.

I'm Learning Spanish, Vol. 3. 2005. (J). 12.99 (978-1-894677-77-6(3)) Kidzup Productions.

Jarvis, Ana & Lebredo, Raquel. Text: Basic Spanish for Law Enforcement. 2006. (ENG & SPA., Illus.). 288p. (YA). 57.96 (978-0-618-56785-0(2) , 328512) Houghton Mifflin College Div.

Jarvis, Ana C. & Lebredo, Raquel. Getting along in Spanish. 5th ed. 1999. (SPA & ENG., Illus.). 338p. (YA). 58.36 (978-0-395-96299-2(4) , 328074) Houghton Mifflin College Div.

Johnson, J. Bradley. Surround Yourself with Essential Vacation Spanish. 2005. per. 49.99 (978-0-9765236-2-8(0)) Innovative Language, LLC.

—Surround Yourself with Spanish: Beginner Level. 2005. (ENG & SPA.). 156p. (C). per. 99.99 (978-0-9765236-0-4(4)) Innovative Language, LLC.

—Surround Yourself with Spanish Conversations, Vol. 1. 2005. (ENG & SPA.). 92p. (C). per. 39.99 (978-0-9765236-1-1(2)) Innovative Language, LLC.

Jordan, Sara. Bilingual Kids Vol. 2: English - Spanish. 2005. 64p. (J). pap. (978-1-55386-025-9(X)) Crabtree Publishing Co.

—Espanol para Principiantes. 2005. 64p. (J). pap. (978-1-55386-043-3(8)) Crabtree Publishing Co.

—Spanish for Kids. 2005. 64p. (J). pap. (978-1-55386-044-0(6)) Crabtree Publishing Co.

Keep Books Organization Staff. Mini-Sets Spanish Caption Books & Spanish Nursery Rhymes. (SPA., Illus.). 8p. (ps-5). pap. (978-1-893986-16-9(0)) Keep Bks.

Kelley, Michelle. The Places I Go. 2007. (ENG & SPA.). (J). (978-1-59515-956-4(8)) Rourke Publishing, LLC.

—Rules, Rules, Rules! 2007. (ENG & SPA.). (J). (978-1-59515-957-1(6)) Rourke Publishing, LLC.

Kenny, Chantral Lacourciere. The Kids Can Press Spanish & English Phrase Book. Hendry, Linda, illus. 1999. (SPA & ENG.). 40p. (J). (gr. 4-6). (978-1-55074-541-2(7)) Kids Can Pr., Ltd.

Kest, Kristin, illus. 500 Words to Grow On. 2005. 24p. (J). (ps-2). pap. 3.99 (978-0-375-83307-6(2) , Random Hse. Bks. for Young Readers) Random Hse. Children's Bks.

Kidzup Productions Staff. I'm Learning Spanish. 2005. (J). Vol. 1. 12.99 (978-1-894677-75-2(7)); Vol. 2. 12.99 (978-1-894677-76-9(5)) Kidzup Productions.

Kim, Wood, ed. Visual Link Spanish. 9th exp. rev. ed. 2002. (SPA.). pap. 149.95 incl. cd-rom, audio compact disk (978-0-9719067-0-9(X)) U. S. Institute of Languages, Inc.

Larousse Staff, ed. Enciclopedia Mega: Naturaleza y Ecologia. 2003. (SPA., Illus.). 192p. (J). (gr. 4-6). pap. 11.95 (978-970-607-939-8(4)) Larousse, Ediciones, S. A. de C. V. MEX. *Dist:* Houghton Mifflin Co. Trade & Reference Div.

Lawless, Laura. The Everything Kids' Learning Spanish Book: Fun exercises to help you learn Español. 2006. (SPA., Illus.). 144p. pap. 7.95 (978-1-59337-716-8(9)) Adams Media Corp.

Le Jars, David. Dans Ma Maison. 2000. (Talk Together Ser.). (SPA., Illus.). 24p. (J). (ps-k). pap. 5.95 (978-1-58728-184-6(8) , Two Can Publishing) T&N Children's Publishing.

Learning Wrap-Ups Spanish. 2004. (ENG & SPA.). 34.99 (978-0-943343-76-1(3)) Learning Wrap-Ups.

Lectura y Comunicacion. 2001. (Serie Siglo XXI). (SPA., Illus.). (J). (gr. 1). 17.95 (978-1-57581-142-0(1)); (gr. 2). 17.95 (978-1-57581-157-4(X)); (gr. 3). 17.95 (978-1-57581-165-9(0)); (gr. 4). 17.95 (978-1-57581-143-7(X)); (gr. 5). 17.95 (978-1-57581-160-4(X)); (gr. 6). 17.95 (978-1-57581-166-6(9)) Santillana USA Publishing Co., Inc.

Lenguaje y Comunicacion. 2001. (Serie Siglo XXI). (SPA., Illus.). (J). (gr. 1). stu. ed. 20.95 (978-1-57581-140-6(5)); (gr. 2). stu. ed. 20.95 (978-1-57581-155-0(3)); (gr. 3). stu. ed. 20.95 (978-1-57581-163-5(4)); (gr. 4). stu. ed. 20.95 (978-1-57581-141-3(3)); (gr. 5). stu. ed. 20.95 (978-1-57581-158-1(8)); (gr. 6). stu. ed. 20.95 (978-1-57581-164-2(2)) Santillana USA Publishing Co., Inc.

Litchfield, J. Everyday Words Spanish Sticker Book. 2004. (Spot the Differences Ser.). (SPA.). 32p. (J). pap. 8.95 (978-0-7945-0478-6(7)) EDC Publishing.

Litchfield, Jo. Primeras Palabras. 2007. 18p. (J). bds. 14.99 (*978-0-7460-8570-7(2)* , Usborne) EDC Publishing.

Literature: Timeless Voices, Timeless Themes, Copper Level 2001. (SPA.). (J). (gr. 6). pap., tchr.'s training gde. ed. 5.47 (978-0-13-052380-8(1)) Prentice Hall PTR.

Literature: Timeless Voices, Timeless Themes, Copper Level 2001. (SPA.). (J). (gr. 6). pap. 29.97 (978-0-13-052387-7(9)) Prentice-Hall.

Long. nexos Multimedia: Used with ... Long-Nexos: Introductory Spanish. 2004. cd-rom 2.76 (978-0-618-06865-4(1) , 334239) Houghton Mifflin College Div.

The Lost Feet. 2003. 28.95 (978-0-673-78113-0(5)) Celebration Pr.

Una Luna 4: Leveled Books. 2001. (McGraw-Hill. Lectura Ser.). (ENG & SPA.). (gr. 1 up). (978-0-02-187981-6(8)) Macmillan/McGraw-Hill Schl. Div.

Macken, JoAnn Early. Mail Carrier/El Cartero. Coffey, Colleen & Carrillo, Consuelo, trs. 2003. (Weekly Reader Early Learning Library). (ENG & SPA., Illus.). 24p. (J). (ps up). lib. bdg. 19.33 (978-0-8368-3672-1(3) , Weekly Reader Early Learning Library) Stevens, Gareth Inc.

—Nurse/El Enfermero. Coffey, Colleen & Carrillo, Consuelo, trs. 2003. (Weekly Reader Early Learning Library). (ENG & SPA., Illus.). 24p. (J). (ps up). lib. bdg. 19.33 (978-0-8368-3673-8(1) , Weekly Reader Early Learning Library) Stevens, Gareth Inc.

—Penguins/Los Pinguinos. 2003. (Weekly Reader Early Learning Library). (ENG & SPA., Illus.). 24p. (J). (ps up). pap. 5.95 (978-0-8368-4006-3(2) , Weekly Reader Early Learning Library) Stevens, Gareth Inc.

—Sanitation Worker/El Recogedor de Basura. Coffey, Colleen & Carrillo, Consuelo, trs. 2003. (Weekly Reader Early Learning Library). (ENG & SPA., Illus.). 24p. (J). (ps up). lib. bdg. 19.33 (978-0-8368-3674-5(X) , Weekly Reader Early Learning Library) Stevens, Gareth Inc.

—Teacher/El Maestro. Coffey, Colleen & Carrillo, Consuelo, trs. 2003. (Weekly Reader Early Learning Library). (ENG & SPA., Illus.). 24p. (J). (ps up). lib. bdg. 19.33 (978-0-8368-3675-2(8) , Weekly Reader Early Learning Library) Stevens, Gareth Inc.

—Veterinarian/El Veterinario. Coffey, Colleen & Carrillo, Consuelo, trs. 2003. (Weekly Reader Early Learning Library). (ENG & SPA., Illus.). 24p. (J). (ps up). lib. bdg. 19.33 (978-0-8368-3676-9(6) , Weekly Reader Early Learning Library) Stevens, Gareth Inc.

Macken, JoAnn Early & Gorman, Jacqueline Laks. Mail Carrier/El Cartero. Coffey, Colleen & Carrillo, Consuelo, trs. Andersen, Gregg, photos by. 2003. (Weekly Reader Early Learning Library). (ENG & SPA., Illus.). 24p. (J). (ps up). pap. 5.95 (978-0-8368-3686-8(3) , Weekly Reader Early Learning Library) Stevens, Gareth Inc.

—Nurse/El Enfermero. Coffey, Colleen & Carrillo, Consuelo, trs. Andersen, Gregg, photos by. 2003. (Weekly Reader Early Learning Library). (ENG & SPA., Illus.). 24p. (J). (ps up). pap. (978-0-8368-3687-5(1) , Weekly Reader Early Learning Library) Stevens, Gareth Inc.

S

—Sanitation Worker/El Recogedor de Basura. Coffey, Colleen & Carrillo, Consuelo, trs. Andersen, Gregg, photos by. 2003. (Weekly Reader Early Learning Library). (ENG & SPA., Illus.). 24p. (J). (ps up). pap. 5.95 (978-0-8368-3688-2(X) , Weekly Reader Early Learning Library) Stevens, Gareth Inc.

—Teacher/El Maestro. Coffey, Colleen & Carrillo, Consuelo, trs. Andersen, Gregg, photos by. 2003. (Weekly Reader Early Learning Library). (ENG & SPA., Illus.). 24p. (J). (ps up). pap. 5.95 (978-0-8368-3689-9(8) , Weekly Reader Early Learning Library) Stevens, Gareth Inc.

—Veterinarian/El Veterinario. Carrillo, Consuelo & Coffey, Colleen, trs. Andersen, Gregg, photos by. 2003. (Weekly Reader Early Learning Library). (ENG & SPA., Illus.). 24p. (J). (ps up). pap. (978-0-8368-3690-5(1)) Stevens, Gareth Inc.

Mahoney, Anne Marie. Feliz Navidad: Learning Songs & Traditions in Spanish. Bjornson, Barb, illus. 2006. (SPA.). 32p. (J). (gr. k-6). lib. bdg. 19.95 incl. audio compact disk (978-1-59972-060-9(4) , Teach Me...) Teach Me Tapes, Inc.

Main Idea & Details Spanish Version, Gr. 4-5. 2005. (J). per. (978-1-58232-142-4(6)) Bryan Hse. Pubs., Inc.

El Maiz De Quetzalcoatl. 2003. 28.95 (978-0-673-78095-9(3)) Celebration Pr.

Una mano con Vocacion 17: Leveled Books. 2001. (McGraw-Hill. Lectura Ser.). (ENG & SPA.). (gr. 4 up). (978-0-02-188193-2(6)) Macmillan/McGraw-Hill Schl. Div.

Una mano tendida al Mundo 4: Leveled Books. 2001. (McGraw-Hill. Lectura Ser.). (ENG & SPA.). (gr. 5 up). (978-0-02-188252-6(5)) Macmillan/McGraw-Hill Schl. Div.

Manual Para Ensenar el Idioma Kreyol. 2001. (SPA.). 308p. (YA). (gr. 9 up). 29.50 (978-1-58432-046-3(X)) Educa Vision.

Marcela descubre el Secreto 1: Leveled Books. 2001. (McGraw-Hill. Lectura Ser.). (ENG & SPA.). (gr. 3 up). (978-0-02-188074-4(3)) Macmillan/McGraw-Hill Schl. Div.

Maremoto 13: Leveled Books. 2001. (McGraw-Hill. Lectura Ser.). (ENG & SPA.). (gr. 4 up). (978-0-02-188158-1(8)) Macmillan/McGraw-Hill Schl. Div.

El Mariachi. 2003. 23.95 (978-0-673-77788-1(X)) Celebration Pr.

Mariachi Tradition Videotape: Videotape Packages. 2003. (Share the Music Ser.). (gr. 1-8). (978-0-02-295488-8(0)) Macmillan/McGraw-Hill Schl. Div.

Marinelli, Patti J. & Oramas, Mirta. Avenidas. 2002. 3.00 net. incl. cd-rom (978-0-8384-2318-9(3)) Thomson Heinle.

—Avenidas: Answer Key. 2002. (C). wbk. ed., lab manual ed. 8.95 (978-0-8384-2315-8(9)); 352p. pap., wbk. ed., lab manual ed. 71.95 (978-0-8384-2314-1(0)) Thomson Heinle.

—Avenidas: Instructors Resource Manual. 2002. (C). 26.25 net. (978-0-8384-2384-4(1)) Thomson Heinle.

Mariposas monarca: las mensajeras Mayas 11: Leveled Books. 2001. (McGraw-Hill. Lectura Ser.). (ENG & SPA.). (gr. 5 up). (978-0-02-188235-9(5)) Macmillan/McGraw-Hill Schl. Div.

Marquez, Alister Ramirez. Quien Se Robo los Colores? Ruiz, Martha, illus. 2000. (SPA.). 96p. (YA). (gr. 7-12). 8.00 (978-1-877653-72-8(1)) Wayside Publishing.

Martin, Bill, Jr. Oso Polar, Oso Polar, Que Es Ese Ruido? Carle, Eric, illus. rev. ed. 2000. (SPA.). 32p. (J). (ps-k). 15.95 (978-0-8050-6427-8(3) , Holt, Henry & Co. Bks. For Young Readers) Holt, Henry & Co.

Martin, Jane. Spanish. Trotter, Stuart, illus. 3rd rev. unabr. ed. (ENG & SPA.). 9999p. (J). pap. (978-0-330-32871-5(9) , Pan) Pan Macmillan.

Maru-Fa 1: Leveled Books. 2001. (McGraw-Hill. Lectura Ser.). (ENG & SPA.). (gr. 2 up). (978-0-02-188026-3(3)) Macmillan/McGraw-Hill Schl. Div.

Marx, David F. Hola, Doctor. Hicks, Mark A., illus. 2000. (Rookie Espanol Ser.). (SPA.). 24p. (J). (gr. k-2). 19.50 (978-0-516-22274-5(0) , Children's Pr.) Scholastic Library Publishing.

—Hola, Doctor. 2000. (gr. k-3). lib. bdg. 12.95 (978-0-613-54243-2(6)) Tandem Library Bks.

—Que Esta Arriba Cuando Estas Abajo? Miller, Susan, illus. 2000. (Rookie Espanol Ser.). (SPA.). 24p. (J). (gr. k-2). 19.50 (978-0-516-22022-2(5) , Children's Pr.) Scholastic Library Publishing.

Mas respeto, por Favor 18: Leveled Books. 2001. (McGraw-Hill. Lectura Ser.). (ENG & SPA.). (gr. 3 up). (978-0-02-188115-4(4)) Macmillan/McGraw-Hill Schl. Div.

Mascotas al Rescate! 23: Leveled Books. 2001. (McGraw-Hill. Lectura Ser.). (ENG & SPA.). (gr. 3 up). (978-0-02-188144-4(8)) Macmillan/McGraw-Hill Schl. Div.

Mascotas Ideales 2: Leveled Books. 2001. (McGraw-Hill. Lectura Ser.). (ENG & SPA.). (gr. 2 up). (978-0-02-188027-0(1)) Macmillan/McGraw-Hill Schl. Div.

Matsunaga, Judd, illus. King's Kids Coloring Book. Fleming, Jesse, photos by. Date not set. (SPA.). 32p. (J). (978-0-9703880-4-9(7)) King's Kids Trading Cards, Inc.

Maurice, creator. The Spanish Question Game. 2000. (SPA.). (YA). 99.00 (978-1-932770-48-3(8) , SG9) Symtalk, Inc.

Mazxzeo, J. L. Xavia's X Book (BL) el libro X de Xavia (PB), 24 vols. 2007. (My Letter Library Ser.: 24). (SPA.). (J). pap. 9.95 ***978-1-59646-558-9(1))** Dingles & Co.

Mazzeo, J. L. Bebe¿s B Book (BL) el libro B de Bebé, 2 vols. 2007. (My Letter Library Ser.: 2). (SPA.). (J). lib. bdg. 22.60 ***978-1-59646-425-4(9))** Dingles & Co.

—Bebe¿s B Book (BL) el libro B de Bebé (PB), 2 vols. 2007. (My Letter Library Ser.: 2). (SPA.). (J). pap. 9.95 ***978-1-59646-426-1(7))** Dingles & Co.

—Delia¿s D Book (BL) el libro D de Delia, 4 vols. 2007. (My Letter Library Ser.: 4). (SPA.). (J). lib. bdg. 22.60 ***978-1-59646-437-7(2))** Dingles & Co.

—Delia¿s D Book (BL) el libro D de Delia (PB), 4 vols. 2007. (My Letter Library Ser.: 4). (SPA.). (J). pap. 9.95 ***978-1-59646-438-4(0))** Dingles & Co.

—Emma¿s E Book (BL) el libro E de Emma, 5 vols. 2007. (My Letter Library Ser.: 5). (J). lib. bdg. 22.60 ***978-1-59646-443-8(7))** Dingles & Co.

—Emma¿s E Book (BL) el libro E de Emma (PB), 5 vols. 2007. (My Letter Library Ser.: 5). (SPA.). (J). pap. 9.95 ***978-1-59646-444-5(5))** Dingles & Co.

—Faye¿s F Book (BL) el libro F de Faye, 5 vols. 2007. (My Letter Library Ser.: 6). (SPA.). (J). lib. bdg. 22.60 ***978-1-59646-449-0(6))** Dingles & Co.

—Faye's F Book (BL) el libro F de Faye (PB), 6 vols. 2007. (My Letter Library Ser.: 6). (SPA.). (J). pap. 9.95 ***978-1-59646-450-6(X))** Dingles & Co.

—George's G Book (BL) el libro G de George, 7 vols. 2007. (My Letter Library Ser.: 7). (J). lib. bdg. 22.60 ***978-1-59646-455-1(0))** Dingles & Co.

—George's G Book (BL) el libro G de George (PB), 7 vols. 2007. (My Letter Library Ser.: 7). (SPA.). (J). pap. 9.95 ***978-1-59646-456-8(9))** Dingles & Co.

—Henry's H Book (BL) el libro H de Henry, 8 vols. 2007. (My Letter Library Ser.: 8). (J). lib. bdg. 22.60 ***978-1-59646-461-2(5))** Dingles & Co.

—Henry's H Book (BL) el libro H de Henry (PB), 8 vols. 2007. (My Letter Library Ser.: 8). (SPA.). (J). pap. 9.95 ***978-1-59646-462-9(3))** Dingles & Co.

—Izzy's I Book (BL) el libro I de Izzy, 9 vols. 2007. (My Letter Library Ser.: 9). (SPA.). (J). lib. bdg. 22.60 ***978-1-59646-467-4(4))** Dingles & Co.

—Izzy's I Book (BL) el libro I de Izzy (PB), 9 vols. 2007. (My Letter Library Ser.: 9). (SPA.). (J). pap. 9.95 ***978-1-59646-468-1(2))** Dingles & Co.

—Jade's J Book (BL) el libro J de Jade, 10 vols. 2007. (My Letter Library Ser.: 10). (SPA.). (J). lib. bdg. 22.60 ***978-1-59646-473-5(9))** Dingles & Co.

—Jade's J Book (BL) el libro J de Jade (PB), 10 vols. 2007. (My Letter Library Ser.: 10). (SPA.). (J). pap. 9.95 ***978-1-59646-474-2(7))** Dingles & Co.

—Jade's J Book (PB), 10 vols. 2007. (My Letter Library Ser.: 10). (J). pap. 9.95 ***978-1-59646-471-1(2))** Dingles & Co.

—Kelsey's K Book (BL) el libro K de Kelsey, 11 vols. 2007. (My Letter Library Ser.: 11). (SPA.). (J). lib. bdg. 22.60 ***978-1-59646-479-7(8))** Dingles & Co.

—Kelsey's K Book (BL) el libro K de Kelsey (PB), 11 vols. 2007. (My Letter Library Ser.: 11). (SPA.). (J). pap. 9.95 ***978-1-59646-480-3(1))** Dingles & Co.

—Logan's L Book (BL) el libro L de Logan, 12 vols. 2007. (My Letter Library Ser.: 12). (SPA.). (J). lib. bdg. 22.60 ***978-1-59646-485-8(2))** Dingles & Co.

—Logan's L Book (BL) el libro L de Logan (PB), 12 vols. 2007. (My Letter Library Ser.: 12). (SPA.). (J). pap. 9.95 ***978-1-59646-486-5(0))** Dingles & Co.

—Mia's M Book (BL) el libro M de Mia, 13 vols. 2007. (My Letter Library Ser.: 13). (SPA.). (J). lib. bdg. 22.60 ***978-1-59646-491-9(7))** Dingles & Co.

—Mia's M Book (BL) el libro M de Mia (PB), 13 vols. 2007. (My Letter Library Ser.: 13). (SPA.). (J). pap. 9.95 ***978-1-59646-492-6(5))** Dingles & Co.

—Nate's N Book (BL) el libro N de Nate, 14 vols. 2007. (My Letter Library Ser.: 14). (SPA.). (J). lib. bdg. 22.60 ***978-1-59646-497-1(6))** Dingles & Co.

—Nate's N Book (BL) el libro N de Nate (PB), 14 vols. 2007. (My Letter Library Ser.: 14). (SPA.). (J). pap. 9.95 ***978-1-59646-498-8(4))** Dingles & Co.

—Owen's O Book (BL) el libro O de Owen, 15 vols. 2007. (My Letter Library Ser.: 15). (SPA.). (J). lib. bdg. 22.60 ***978-1-59646-503-9(4))** Dingles & Co.

—Owen's O Book (BL) el libro O de Owen (PB), 15 vols. 2007. (My Letter Library Ser.: 15). (SPA.). (J). pap. 9.95 ***978-1-59646-504-6(2))** Dingles & Co.

—Owen's O Book (PB). 15 vols. 2007. (My Letter Library Ser.: 15). (J). pap. 9.95 ***978-1-59646-501-5(8))** Dingles & Co.

—Peter's P Book (BL) el libro P de Peter, 16 vols. 2007. (My Letter Library Ser.: 16). (SPA.). (J). lib. bdg. 22.60 ***978-1-59646-509-1(3))** Dingles & Co.

—Peter's P Book (BL) el libro P de Peter (PB), 16 vols. 2007. (My Letter Library Ser.: 16). (SPA.). (J). pap. 9.95 ***978-1-59646-510-7(7))** Dingles & Co.

—Quinn's Q Book (BL) el libro Q de Quinn, 17 vols. 2007. (My Letter Library Ser.: 17). (SPA.). (J). lib. bdg. 22.60 ***978-1-59646-515-2(8))** Dingles & Co.

—Quinn's Q Book (BL) el libro Q de Quinn (PB), 17 vols. 2007. (My Letter Library Ser.: 17). (SPA.). (J). pap. 9.95 ***978-1-59646-516-9(6))** Dingles & Co.

—Rosie's R Book (BL) el libro R de Rosie, 18 vols. 2007. (My Letter Library Ser.: 18). (SPA.). (J). lib. bdg. 22.60 ***978-1-59646-521-3(2))** Dingles & Co.

—Rosie's R Book (BL) el libro R de Rosie (PB), 18 vols. 2007. (My Letter Library Ser.: 18). (SPA.). (J). pap. 9.95 ***978-1-59646-522-0(0))** Dingles & Co.

—Sofie's S Book (BL) el libro S de Sofie, 19 vols. 2007. (My Letter Library Ser.: 19). (SPA.). (J). lib. bdg. 22.60 ***978-1-59646-527-5(1))** Dingles & Co.

—Sofie's S Book (BL) el libro S de Sofie (PB), 19 vols. 2007. (My Letter Library Ser.: 19). (SPA.). (J). pap. 9.95 ***978-1-59646-528-2(X))** Dingles & Co.

—Tad's T Book (BL) el libro T de Tad, 20 vols. 2007. (My Letter Library Ser.: 20). (SPA.). (J). lib. bdg. 22.60 ***978-1-59646-533-6(6))** Dingles & Co.

—Tad's T Book (BL) el libro T de Tad (PB), 20 vols. 2007. (My Letter Library Ser.: 20). (SPA.). (J). pap. 9.95 ***978-1-59646-534-3(4))** Dingles & Co.

—Uri's U Book (BL) el libro U de Uri, 21 vols. 2007. (My Letter Library Ser.: 21). (SPA.). (J). lib. bdg. 22.60 ***978-1-59646-539-8(5))** Dingles & Co.

—Uri's U Book (BL) el libro U de Uri (PB), 21 vols. 2007. (My Letter Library Ser.: 21). (SPA.). (J). pap. 9.95 ***978-1-59646-540-4(9))** Dingles & Co.

—Vera's V Book (BL) el libro V de Vera, 22 vols. 2007. (My Letter Library Ser.: 22). (SPA.). (J). lib. bdg. 22.60 ***978-1-59646-545-9(X))** Dingles & Co.

—Vera's V Book (BL) el libro V de Vera (PB), 22 vols. 2007. (My Letter Library Ser.: 22). (SPA.). (J). pap. 9.95 ***978-1-59646-546-6(8))** Dingles & Co.

—Will's W Book (BL) el libro W de Will, 23 vols. 2007. (My Letter Library Ser.: 23). (SPA.). (J). lib. bdg. 22.60 ***978-1-59646-551-0(4))** Dingles & Co.

—Will's W Book (BL) el libro W de Will (PB), 23 vols. 2007. (My Letter Library Ser.: 23). (SPA.). (J). pap. 9.95 ***978-1-59646-552-7(2))** Dingles & Co.

—Xavia's X Book (BL) el libro X de Xavia, 24 vols. 2007. (My Letter Library Ser.: 24). (SPA.). (J). lib. bdg. 22.60 ***978-1-59646-557-2(3))** Dingles & Co.

—Yola's Y Book (BL) el libro Y de Yola, 25 vols. 2007. (My Letter Library Ser.: 25). (SPA.). (J). lib. bdg. 22.60 ***978-1-59646-563-3(8))** Dingles & Co.

—Yola's Y Book (BL) el libro Y de Yola (PB), 25 vols. 2007. (My Letter Library Ser.: 25). (SPA.). (J). pap. 9.95 ***978-1-59646-564-0(6))** Dingles & Co.

McGraw-Hill Staff. Buen Viaje! Writing Activities. 3rd ed. 1999. (SPA & ENG.). (gr. 6-12). pap., wbk. ed. 14.64 (978-0-02-641261-2(6) , 9780026412612); pap., wbk. ed. 15.96 (978-0-02-641834-8(7) , 9780026418348); Level 2. (C). pap., wbk. ed. 14.64 (978-0-02-641546-0(1) , 9780026415460) Glencoe/McGraw-Hill.

—Glencoe Middle School Spanish: Como te va? B Nivel azul. 2005. (C). stu. ed. 87.96 incl. cd-rom (978-0-07-874279-8(X) , 9780078742798) Glencoe/McGraw-Hill.

—NTC Language Masters: Listening. 1999. (SPA.). 48p. (C). (gr. 6-12). wbk. ed. 39.32 (978-0-8442-2744-3(7) , 9780844227443) Glencoe/McGraw-Hill.

Meister, Cari. Detenlo a Ese Gato! 2000. (SPA.). (gr. k-3). lib. bdg. 12.95 (978-0-613-54162-6(6)) Tandem Library Bks.

Mi Amigo. 2003. stu. ed. 35.50 (978-0-8136-8135-1(9)) Modern Curriculum Pr.

Millas, Juan Jose. El Desorden de Tu Nombre: Nivel 3. 1998. (SPA.). (gr. 7-12). lib. bdg. 14.10 (978-0-613-80714-2(6)) Tandem Library Bks.

Miller, Heather. Esto es lo Que Quiero Ser, 14 bks., Set. 2003. Tr. of This Is What I Want to Be. (SPA & ENG., Illus.). (J). (ps-1). lib. bdg. 259.00 (978-1-4034-0987-4(0)) Heinemann Library.

Mis Primeras Palabras (My First Words) (SPA.). (J). 6.95 (978-970-05-0284-7(8)) Grijalbo, Editorial MEX. *Dist:* AIMS International Bks., Inc.

Monckeberg, Paulina. Artilugia Spanish 2008. 2007. (Pascualina Family of Products Ser.). 114p. (J). spiral bd. 14.95 ***978-956-8222-58-1(8))** Pascualina Producciones S.A.

Montague-Smith, Ann. Mi Primer Libro de Figuras. 2003. (SPA.). (ps-2). lib. bdg. 15.25 (978-0-613-90581-7(4)) Tandem Library Bks.

Moreton, Daniel & Chanko, Pamela. Snakes & Lizards: Serpientes y Lagartos. 2002. (Science Emergent Readers Ser.). (ENG & SPA., Illus.). (J). pap. (978-0-439-41163-9(7)) Scholastic, Inc.

Morton, Lone & Martin, Rosa Maria. George, the Goldfish/ Jorge el Pez Dorado: English-Spanish Edition. Noyes, Leighton, illus. 2005. (I Can Read Spanish Ser.). (SPA & ENG.). 28p. (J). (ps). 7.99 (978-0-7641-5873-5(2)) Barron's Educational Series, Inc.

Munoz, Rosana Acquaroni. La Sombra de un Fotografo. 1998. (SPA.). (gr. 7-12). lib. bdg. 14.10 (978-0-613-80703-6(0)) Tandem Library Bks.

My Español Book level I. 2005. pap. (978-0-9767837-0-1(3)) Linguatechnics Publishing.

My Español Book, Level II. 2005. pap. (978-0-9767837-1-8(1)); pap., tchr. ed. (978-0-9767837-3-2(8)) Linguatechnics Publishing.

My First Coloring Book of Spansih Words. 1000th ed. 2003. (ENG & SPA., Illus.). 34p. (J). 5.95 (978-0-9722999-0-9(4)) Three Sisters Pr.

Nance, Kimberly A. & Rivera, Isidro J. Aprendizaje: Tecnicas de Composicion. 2nd ed. 2003. (SPA., Illus.). 196p. tchr. ed. (978-0-618-23127-0(7)) McDougal Littell Inc.

Ninos Aprenden Ingles Corp, Children Learning Spanish. 2005. (Illus.). 119p. (J). pap. 19.95 ***978-1-934665-04-6(5))** Ninos Aprenden Ingles Corp.

No Diga Si Cuando Quiera Decir No (Don't Say Yes When You Mean No) (SPA.). pap. (978-968-419-347-5(5)) Grijalbo, Editorial.

Nostlinger, Christine. Intercambio con un Ingles. 1999. Tr. of Foreign Language Student. (978-0-606-17672-9(1)) Tandem Library Bks.

NTC Publishing Group Staff. Drive-In Spanish for Kids: Songs & Games for On-the-Go Children. 2000. (Drive-In Ser.). (ENG & ENM., Illus.). 32p. (ps-2). pap. 9.95 incl. audio (978-0-658-00862-7(5) , 9780658008627) McGraw-Hill Cos., The.

Nuevo Bravo, Bravo! Student Kit, 15 bks. 2001. (SPA & ENG., Illus.). (J). stu. ed., wbk. ed. 336.00 (978-1-58105-865-9(9)) Santillana USA Publishing Co., Inc.

Nuevo Bravo, Bravo! Student Kit - Canciones, 15 bks. 2001. (SPA & ENG., Illus.). (J). (gr. 1). stu. ed., wbk. ed. 834.95 (978-1-58105-866-6(7)) Santillana USA Publishing Co., Inc.

Nuevo Bravo, Bravo! Student Kit - Personas, Grade 3, 15 bks. 2001. (SPA & ENG., Illus.). (J). (gr. 3). stu. ed., wbk. ed. 753.95 (978-1-58105-868-0(3)) Santillana USA Publishing Co., Inc.

Nuevo Bravo, Bravo! Student Kit, Animales, 15 bks. 2001. (SPA & ENG., Illus.). (J). (gr. 2). stu. ed., wbk. ed. 753.95 (978-1-58105-867-3(5)) Santillana USA Publishing Co., Inc.

Nuevo Bravo, Bravo! Classroom Library, Set. 2001. (SPA., Illus.). (J). (gr. k-3). 130.95 (978-1-58105-919-9(1)); 784.95 (978-1-58105-941-0(8)) Santillana USA Publishing Co., Inc.

Nuevo Siglo de Espanol: Student Kit, 15 bks., Set. 2001. (SPA & ENG., Illus.). (J). stu. ed. 445.00 (978-1-58105-873-4(X)); (gr. 1). stu. ed., wbk. ed. 565.95 (978-1-58105-874-1(8)); (gr. 2). stu. ed., wbk. ed. 511.95 (978-1-58105-875-8(6)); (gr. 3). stu. ed., wbk. ed. 538.95 (978-1-58105-876-5(4)); (gr. 5). stu. ed., wbk. ed. (978-1-58105-878-9(0)); (gr. 6). stu. ed., wbk. ed. (978-1-58105-879-6(9)) Santillana USA Publishing Co., Inc.

Nuevo Siglo de Espanol: Teacher's Resource Kit, Grade K. 2001. (SPA & ENG., Illus.). (J). 54.00 incl. trans. (978-1-58105-880-2(2)) Santillana USA Publishing Co., Inc.

Nunoz, Pilar. Campo Libre Vol. 2: La Vida Initima - Students Books. Thacker, Mike, ed. Munoz, Marta Perez, illus. Munoz, Marta Perez, photos by. 2000. (Campo Libre Ser.). (SPA & ENG.). 82p. (C). pap., stu. ed. 20.00 (978-0-85668-688-7(3)) Aris & Phillips GBR. *Dist:* Brown, David Bk. Co., The.

Oliver, Stephen, photos by. Formas. 2005. (Coleccion Primeras Imagenes). (SPA.). 86p. (J). (ps up). pap. 7.95 (978-950-11-0905-4(4) , SGM9054) Sigmar ARG. *Dist:* Continental Bk. Co., Inc., Lectorum Pubns., Inc., Iaconi, Mariuccia Bk. Imports.

—Tamanos. 2005. (Coleccion Primeras Imagenes).Tr. of My First Look at Sizes. (SPA., Illus.). (J). (ps up). pap. 7.95 (978-950-11-0907-8(0) , SGM9070) Sigmar ARG. *Dist:* Continental Bk. Co., Inc., Lectorum Pubns., Inc., Iaconi, Mariuccia Bk. Imports.

Olsen, Jan Z. Escribiendo Cursiva. Olsen, Jan Z., illus. 2005. Tr. of Cursive Handwriting. (SPA., Illus.). 92p. (J). 5.95 (978-1-891627-53-8(8)) Handwriting Without Tears, Inc.

—Exito con Cursiva. Olsen, Jan Z., illus. 2005. Tr. of Cursive Success. (SPA., Illus.). 92p. (J). 5.95 (978-1-891627-54-5(6)) Handwriting Without Tears, Inc.

—Letras y Numeros para Mi. Olsen, Jan Z., illus. 2006. Tr. of Letters & Numbers for Me. (SPA., Illus.). 96p. (J). 5.95 (978-1-891627-50-7(3)) Handwriting Without Tears, Inc.

—Mi Libro de Escribir Imprenta. Olsen, Jan Z., illus. 2005. Tr. of My Printing Book. (SPA., Illus.). 88p. (J). 5.95 (978-1-891627-51-4(1)) Handwriting Without Tears, Inc.

—El Poder de la Imprenta. Olsen, Jan Z., illus. 2004. Tr. of Printing Power. (SPA., Illus.). 80p. (J). (978-1-891627-52-1(X)) Handwriting Without Tears, Inc.

Orero, Maria Jesus. Nico y Sus Trajes. 2005. (SPA & ESP., Illus.). 12p. (ps-ps). per. 6.99 (978-84-272-6152-5(7)) Molino, Editorial ESP. *Dist:* Santillana USA Publishing Co., Inc.

Un Pajarito. 2003. 23.95 (978-0-673-77778-2(2)) Celebration Pr.

Pardo Bazan, Emilia. Los Pazos de Ulloa Level 6. 1998. (SPA.). (gr. 7-12). lib. bdg. 15.25 (978-0-613-80725-8(1)) Tandem Library Bks.

Parish, Ellen. Spanish: Level 1. 2003. (Skill Builders Ser.). 80p. 2.95 (978-1-932210-14-9(8)) Rainbow Bridge Publishing.

—Spanish: Level 2. 2003. (Skill Builders Ser.). 80p. 2.95 (978-1-932210-15-6(6)) Rainbow Bridge Publishing.

—Spanish Numbers & Alphabet: First Step Spanish, Level 1. 2002. (First Step Spanish Ser.). 5.95 (978-1-887923-84-2(5)) Rainbow Bridge Publishing.

El parque de Juegos, 2 Packs. (Chiquilibros Ser.). (SPA.). (ps-1). 12.00 (978-0-7635-8548-8(3)) Rigby Education.

El paseo en Trineo: Individual Title Two-Packs. (Chiquilibros Ser.). (SPA.). (ps-1). 12.00 (978-0-7635-8546-4(7)) Rigby Education.

El Payaso, 6 Packs. (Chiquilibros Ser.). (SPA.). (gr. k-1). 23.00 (978-0-7635-8785-7(0)) Rigby Education.

Pebble Soup Exploraciones: Pebble Soup Exploraciones Extra Ingredients. 239.00 (978-0-7578-3342-7(X)) Rigby Education.

El Pequenito Tonito. 2003. 23.95 (978-0-673-77368-5(X)) Celebration Pr.

Perez-Mercado, Mary Margaret. Zas! Torrey, Richard L., illus. 2001. (Rookie Reader Espanol Ser.). (SPA.). 24p. (J). (gr. k-2). pap. 4.95 (978-0-516-26797-5(3) , Children's Pr.) Scholastic Library Publishing.

El Perezoso: Individual Title Six-Packs. (On Deck en Espanol Ser.).Tr. of Sloth. (SPA.). 24p. (gr. 4-5). 35.00 (978-0-7578-6438-4(4)) Rigby Education.

Petelinsek, Kathleen & Primm, E. Russell. Actions/Acciones. 2006. (Talking Hands Ser.). (ENG & SPA., Illus.). 24p. (J). 21.36 (978-1-59296-679-0(9)) Child's World, Inc.

—At Play/En el Juego. 2006. (Talking Hands Ser.). (ENG & SPA., Illus.). 24p. (J). 21.36 (978-1-59296-683-7(7)) Child's World, Inc.

—Clothes/Ropa. 2006. (Talking Hands Ser.). (ENG & SPA., Illus.). 24p. (J). 21.36 (978-1-59296-680-6(2)) Child's World, Inc.

—Days & Times: Días y Horas. 2006. (Talking Hands Ser.). (ENG & SPA., Illus.). 24p. (J). 21.36 (978-1-59296-681-3(0)) Child's World, Inc.

—Weather. 2006. (Talking Hands Ser.).Tr. of El Tiempo. (ENG & SPA., Illus.). 24p. (J). 21.36 (978-1-59296-684-4(5)) Child's World, Inc.

Petrie, Catherine. A Jaime Josue le Gustan los Camiones. Snyder, Joel, illus. 2001. (Rookie Reader Espanol Ser.). (SPA.). 24p. (J). (gr. k-2). pap. 4.95 (978-0-516-26796-8(5) , Children's Pr.) Scholastic Library Publishing.

Phillips, Larissa. Cochise: Jefe Apache. de la Vega, Eida, tr. from ENG. 2003. (Grandes Personajes en la Historia de Los Estados Unidos Ser.). (ENG & SPA., Illus.). 32p. (J). pap. (978-0-8239-4223-7(6)) Rosen Publishing Group, Inc., The.

Pingry, Patricia A. The Story of Easter. Wells, Lorraine Schreiner, illus. 2002. (ENG & SPA.). 32p. (J). 3.95 (978-0-8249-4204-5(3)) Ideals Pubns.

Pirz, Therese S. Kids' Stuff Spanish: Easy Spanish Phrases to Teach your Kids (and Yourself) 1999. (Bilingual Kids Ser.: Vol. 2). (SPA., Illus.). 168p. (J). (gr. k-8). pap. 18.95 (978-0-9606140-2-8(8)) Chou-Chou Pr.

Pisonero, Isidoro, et al. Pasacalle 2: Curso de Espanol para Ninos. (SPA & ENG.). (J). (gr. 3-7). 96p. tchr. ed. (978-84-7143-715-0(5)); 96p. stu. ed. (978-84-7143-708-2(2)); 64p. wbk. ed. (978-84-7143-709-9(0)) Sociedad General Espanola de Libreria.

Price. La Luna Adormecedora. 1999. pap. 5.18 (978-0-7398-0726-2(9)) Steck-Vaughn.

Que Sigue? 2003. 23.95 (978-0-673-77129-2(6)) Celebration Pr.

Que Soy? 2003. Tr. of What Am I?. (J). (ps-2). 23.95 (978-0-673-77408-8(2)) Celebration Pr.

Que Soy? Big Book Packages. 2003. 64.95 (978-0-673-58600-1(6)) Celebration Pr.

Que Susto Me Dio! 2003. (J). (ps-2). 23.95 (978-0-673-77397-5(3)) Celebration Pr.

Quetzalcoatl's Corn. 2003. 28.95 (978-0-673-78116-1(X)) Celebration Pr.

Quien Vive Aqui? 2003. (J). (ps-2). 23.95 (978-0-673-77396-8(5)) Celebration Pr.

Quien Vive Aqui? Big Book Packages. 2003. 64.95 (978-0-673-58601-8(4)) Celebration Pr.

Raintree Steck-Vaughn Staff. En Parejas Emergent: Stage 2. 2002. (SPA.). pap. 49.90 (978-0-7398-6985-7(X)) Harcourt Trade Pubs.

Ramirez, Granados. Te Canto un Cuento? 2000. Tr. of Shall I Sing You a Story?. (SPA.). (J). 7.95 (978-968-29-0877-4(9)) Direccion General de Publicaciones del Consejo Nacional para la Cultura y las Artes MEX. *Dist:* AIMS International Bks., Inc.

Random House Staff. 500 Palabras Nuevas para Ti. Kest, Kristin, illus. 2005. 32p. (J). (ps-2). pap. 3.99 (978-0-375-83308-3(0) , RH Para Ninos) Random Hse. Children's Bks.

Rau, Dana Meachen. Las Manos. Stromoski, Rick, illus. 2000. (Rookie Espanol Ser.). (SPA.). 24p. (J). (gr. k-2). 19.50 (978-0-516-22021-5(7) , Children's Pr.) Scholastic Library Publishing.

—Los Pies. Stromoski, Rick, illus. 2000. (Rookie Espanol Ser.). (SPA.). 24p. (J). (gr. k-2). 19.50 (978-0-516-22020-8(9) , Children's Pr.) Scholastic Library Publishing.

Ray, Blaine. El Viaje de Su Vida: Level 1. 1999. (TPRS First-Year Spanish Novels Ser.). (SPA.). ii, 45p. (YA). (gr. 7-12). pap. 5.95 (978-0-929724-49-2(6) , BR002) Command Performance Language Institute.

Un rayo de Esperanza 4: Leveled Books. 2001. (McGraw-Hill. Lectura Ser.). (ENG & SPA.). (gr. 5 up). (978-0-02-188228-1(2)) Macmillan/McGraw-Hill Schl. Div.

El Rebozo: Big Book Packages. 2003. 64.95 (978-0-673-58595-0(6)) Celebration Pr.

El Recreo. 2003. 23.95 (978-0-673-77180-3(6)) Celebration Pr.

El Renacuajo. 2003. 23.95 (978-0-673-77169-8(5)) Celebration Pr.

Rin Tin Tin: el mejor perro del Cine 10: Leveled Books. 2001. (McGraw-Hill. Lectura Ser.). (ENG & SPA.). (gr. 2 up). (978-0-02-188059-1(X)) Macmillan/McGraw-Hill Schl. Div.

Robleda, Margarita. Jugando con las Vocales. Suarez, Maribel, illus. 2006. (SPA.). 10p. (J). 7.95 (978-1-59820-210-6(3) , Alfaguara) Santillana USA Publishing Co., Inc.

Roca, Nuria. Las tres erres; reutilizar, reducir, Reciclar: The Three R's: Reuse, Reduce, Recycle (Spanish Edition) Curto, Rosa M., illus. 2007. (What Do You Know about? Bks.). 36p. (J). (gr. k-1). pap. 6.99 (978-0-7641-3582-8(1)) Barron's Educational Series, Inc.

Rojo, Andrea Szekasy. Arcoiris. 2003. (SPA., Illus.). 48p. (Orig.). (J). (gr. 1-6). pap., act. bk. ed. 12.00 (978-0-9671053-5-2(8) , 0510) Language Adventure Pubns.

—Arcoiris: Spanish for Children. Porter, Susana, illus. 2nd rev. ed. 2001. (SPA.). 64p. (J). (gr. k-6). pap. (978-0-9671053-4-5(X) , 0410) Language Adventure Pubns.

—Arcoiris: Spanish for Elementary Students. Porter, Susana, illus. 1999. (SPA.). 64p. (Orig.). (J). (gr. 1-5). pap. (978-0-9671053-0-7(7) , 0101) Language Adventure Pubns.

—Arcoiris Level 2: Spanish for Elementary Students. Porter, Susana, illus. 2000. (SPA.). 64p. (J). (gr. k-5). pap. 24.00 (978-0-9671053-3-8(1) , 0310) Language Adventure Pubns.

Rookie Espanol: Ciencias: Nonfiction Spanics for Beginning Readers, 5 Bks, Set. 2004. (SPA.). (J). 85.00 (978-0-516-25103-5(1) , Children's Pr.) Scholastic Library Publishing.

Rosa-Mendoza, Gladys. English-Spanish Foundations Series: The Alphabet; Numbers; Colors & Shapes. Cifuentes, Carolina, ed. Noiset, Michele, illus. 2004. (Spanish Foundations Ser.). (ENG & SPA.). (J). bds. 19.95 (978-0-9679748-1-1(X)) Me+Mi Publishing.

Rosa tiene una casa Nueva 10: Leveled Books. 2001. (McGraw-Hill. Lectura Ser.). (ENG & SPA.). (gr. 3 up). (978-0-02-188107-9(3)) Macmillan/McGraw-Hill Schl. Div.

Rosa y Sus Amigos. 2003. 23.95 (978-0-673-77793-5(6)) Celebration Pr.

Rosenberg, Mary. Learning Sight Words Is Easy-Spanish. 2002. (Illus.). 96p. (J). (gr. 4-6). 10.95 (978-0-439-35533-9(8)) Scholastic, Inc.

Rosier, Michelle. Elementary Spanish - Worktext Step 1. 2006. 72p. per. 15.00 (978-1-59166-276-1(1)) Jones, Bob Univ. Pr.

—Elementary Spanish—Worktext Step 2. 2006. 72p. per. 15.00 (978-1-59166-277-8(X)) Jones, Bob Univ. Pr.

—Elementary Spanish—Worktext Step 3. 2006. 72p. per. 15.00 (978-1-59166-278-5(8)) Jones, Bob Univ. Pr.

Ruido o Musica? 13: Leveled Books. 2001. (McGraw-Hill. Lectura Ser.). (ENG & SPA.). (gr. 2 up). (978-0-02-188038-6(7)) Macmillan/McGraw-Hill Schl. Div.

Ryan, Pam Muñoz & Lopez, Rafael. Nuestra California. Lopez, Rafael, illus. 2008. (SPA & ENG.). ***(978-1-58089-226-1(4))*** Charlesbridge Publishing, Inc.

Saludos! Complete Blue Level Packages. 697.00 (978-0-7635-9510-4(1)) Rigby Education.

Salvemos los arboles de nuestro Parque 14: Leveled Books. 2001. (McGraw-Hill. Lectura Ser.). (ENG & SPA.). (gr. 2 up). (978-0-02-188063-8(8)) Macmillan/McGraw-Hill Schl. Div.

Samaniego, Fabian A., et al. Dimelo Tu! Intensive Accelerated Course. 2001. (SPA.). 462p. (C). pap. 98.95 incl. audio compact disk (978-0-03-033834-2(4)) Thomson Heinle.

Santiago, Carmen. Fun & Easy Spanish for You, Vol. 2. 2003. 48p. (J). per. 29.95 (978-1-56167-794-8(9)) American Literary Pr.

Santiago, Carmen Angelica. Fun & Easy Spanish for You. 2003. (SPA.). 50p. (J). Vol. 1. per. 29.95 (978-1-56167-793-1(0)); Vol. 3. (Illus.). per. 29.95 (978-1-56167-795-5(7)) American Literary Pr.

Sapo en Invierno 13: Leveled Books. 2001. (McGraw-Hill. Lectura Ser.). (ENG & SPA.). (gr. 1 up). (978-0-02-187990-8(7)) Macmillan/McGraw-Hill Schl. Div.

Un sapo en la Sopa 5: Leveled Books. 2001. (McGraw-Hill. Lectura Ser.). (ENG & SPA.). (gr. 1 up). (978-0-02-187934-2(6)) Macmillan/McGraw-Hill Schl. Div.

Sara, Sarita. 2003. (SPA.). 23.95 (978-0-673-77366-1(3)) Celebration Pr.

Scarry, Richard. Richard Scarry's Best Word Book Ever. 2004. (SPA & ENG., Illus.). 64p. 16.95 (978-0-87358-873-7(8) , Luna Rising) Northland Publishing.

—Richard Scarry's Best Word Book Ever. Scarry, Richard, illus. 2004. (SPA & ENG., Illus.). 64p. (J). pap. 10.95 (978-0-87358-874-4(6) , Luna Rising) Northland Publishing.

Schaefer, Ted. Machines Large & Small. 2007. (ENG & SPA.). (J). (978-1-59515-953-3(3)) Rourke Publishing, LLC.

—Ready for School. 2007. (ENG & SPA.). (J). (978-1-59515-952-6(5)) Rourke Publishing, LLC.

Schmitt, et al. Glencoe Middle School Spanish: Como te va? B Nivel Azul. 2003. (SPA.). (gr. 6-12). pap., wbk. ed. 11.32 (978-0-07-860556-7(3) , 9780078605567) Glencoe/McGraw-Hill.

—Glencoe Middle School Spanish: Como te va? Intro Nivel Rojo. 2003. (SPA.). (gr. 6-12). stu. ed. 46.00 incl. cd-rom (978-0-07-861026-4(5) , 9780078610264) Glencoe/McGraw-Hill.

Schmitt, Conrad J. & McGraw-Hill Staff. Bon Voyage, Level 1 A. 3rd ed. 2001. (FRE & ENG.). (C). stu. ed. 62.00 (978-0-07-824265-6(7) , 9780078242656) Glencoe/McGraw-Hill.

—Glencoe French Level 1 Bon Voyage!, Pt. B. 3rd ed. 2001. (FRE & ENG.). stu. ed. 62.00 (978-0-07-824266-3(5) , 9780078242663) Glencoe/McGraw-Hill.

Schmitt, Conrad J. & Woodford. Como te va? B Nivel Azul. 2003. (SPA.). (gr. 6-12). stu. ed. 63.96 incl. cd-rom (978-0-07-861025-7(7) , 9780078610257) Glencoe/McGraw-Hill.

Schmitt, Conrad J., et al. Como te va? Intro Nivel Rojo. 2003. (SPA.). (gr. 6-8). stu. ed. 46.00 (978-0-07-860350-1(0) , 9780078603501); pap., wbk. ed. 7.96 (978-0-07-860542-0(3) , 9780078605420) Glencoe/McGraw-Hill.

—Glencoe Middle School Spanish: ¿Como Te Va? A Nivel Verde. 2003. (SPA.). (gr. 6-12). stu. ed. 63.96 incl. cd-rom (978-0-07-861024-0(9) , 9780078610240) Glencoe/McGraw-Hill.

School Specialty Publishing. The Complete Book of Starter Spanish. 2007. (Complete Book Ser.). 352p. (J). pap. 14.95 ***(978-0-7696-5279-5(4)*** , American Education Publishing) School Specialty Publishing.

—Flip-FlashTM Spanish Flash Cards: Level I. 2002. (SPA.). 160p. (J). (gr. 1-12). pap. 7.99 (978-1-56451-387-8(4) , ID2441) School Specialty Publishing.

—Flip-FlashTM Spanish Flash Cards: Level II. 2002. (SPA.). 160p. (J). (gr. 1-12). pap. 7.99 (978-1-56451-388-5(2) , ID2442) School Specialty Publishing.

—Hablo Ingles! Level 1 - Pictures & Words. 1999. (Homework Booklets Ser.). (SPA.). 80p. (C). pap. 2.99 (978-0-88012-921-3(2) , IF0200, Instructional Fair) Schaffer, Frank Pubns.

—I Can Learn Spanish & English. 2006. (Brighter Child I Can... Ser.). 128p. (J). pap. 3.95 (978-0-7696-4897-2(5) , Brighter Child) School Specialty Publishing.

—Spanish, Grade 1. 2006. (Skills for Scholars Ser.). 80p. (C). pap. 4.99 ***(978-0-7696-8241-9(3)*** , Schaffer, Frank) Schaffer, Frank Pubns.

—Spanish, Grade 2. 2006. (Skills for Scholars Ser.). 80p. (C). pap. 4.99 ***(978-0-7696-8242-6(1)*** , Schaffer, Frank) Schaffer, Frank Pubns.

—Spanish, Grade 3. 2006. (Skills for Scholars Ser.). 80p. (C). pap. 4.99 ***(978-0-7696-8243-3(X)*** , Schaffer, Frank) Schaffer, Frank Pubns.

—Spanish, Grade 4. 2006. (Skills for Scholars Ser.). 80p. (C). pap. 4.99 ***(978-0-7696-8244-0(8)*** , Schaffer, Frank) Schaffer, Frank Pubns.

—Total English Spanish Learning Kit. 2007. (Total Learning Kits Ser.). 563p. (J). pap. 49.95 ***(978-0-7696-5489-8(4))*** School Specialty Publishing.

School Specialty Publishing Staff. English-Spanish Everything for Early Learning Kindergarten. American Education Publishing Staff, ed. 2006. (Everything for Early Learning English/Spanish Ser.). 320p. (J). pap. 7.95 (978-0-7696-6490-3(3) , American Education Publishing) School Specialty Publishing.

—English-Spanish Everything for Early Learning Preschool. American Education Publishing Staff, ed. 2006. (Everything for Early Learning English/Spanish Ser.). 320p. (J). pap. 7.95 (978-0-7696-6489-7(X) , American Education Publishing) School Specialty Publishing.

School Zone Publishing Company Staff. Bilingual Preschool Big Get Ready! 2005. 320p. (J). (gr. k). pap. 9.99 (978-1-58947-493-2(7)) School Zone Publishing Co.

Seidletz, Marcia. Easy Spanish Word Power Games: Early Intermediate to Advanced. 2003. (Easy... Word Puzzles Ser.). (SPA & ENG., Illus.). 80p. pap. 5.95 (978-0-8442-7246-7(9) , 9780844272467, Contemporary Bks.) McGraw-Hill Trade.

Una semana Dificil 2: Leveled Books. 2001. (McGraw-Hill. Lectura Ser.). (ENG & SPA.). (gr. 4 up). (978-0-02-188178-9(2)) Macmillan/McGraw-Hill Schl. Div.

Senor Cascaron. 2003. (SPA.). 23.95 (978-0-673-77170-4(9)) Celebration Pr.

Senor Cascaron: Poems, Rhymes, & Songs Listening Packs. 2003. (SPA.). 34.50 (978-0-673-58623-0(5)) Celebration Pr.

Shott, Stephen, photos by. El Mundo del Bebe: Mi Primer Libro de Palabras e Imagenes. 2002. (SPA., Illus.). 40p. (J). (gr. k-3). reprint ed. 20.00 (978-0-7567-5579-9(4)) DIANE Publishing Co.

Sombreros. 2003. (SPA.). 23.95 (978-0-673-77798-0(7)) Celebration Pr.

Sosa, Carlos. Celebrations. 2007. (Familia Banderas Ser.). (Illus.). 48p. (J). (gr. 3-7). per. 9.95 ***(978-1-933669-11-3(X))*** Literary Architects, LLC.

—Cultures. 2007. (Familia Banderas Ser.). (Illus.). 48p. (J). (gr. 3-7). per. 9.95 ***(978-1-933669-12-0(8))*** Literary Architects, LLC.

Soy la Cafetera. 2003. 23.95 (978-0-673-77386-9(8)) Celebration Pr.

Soy La Cafetera: Poems, Rhymes, & Songs Listening Packs. 2003. 34.50 (978-0-673-58634-6(0)) Celebration Pr.

Spanish II, Set. 2004. (YA). (gr. 9-12). 99.95 (978-0-7403-0241-1(8) , ES9915, Lifepac) Alpha Omega Pubns., Inc.

Spanish School Thesaurus: Sinonimos, Antonimos, Paronimos. 2004th ed. 2004. 380p. pap. 9.95 (978-950-11-1158-3(X)) Los Andes Publishing Co.

Spanish/English Desk Cards. 2004. (J). 8.95 (978-1-56911-177-2(4)) Learning Resources, Inc.

Spann, Mary Beth. Sight Words in Spanish: 20 Interactive Mini-Books That Help Every Child Get a Great Start in Reading: Grades PreK-2. 2000. (Reading Success Mini-Bks.). 48p. pap. 9.95 (978-0-439-14115-4(X)) Scholastic, Inc.

—29 Spanish Alphabet Mini-Books: Easy-to-Make Reproducible Books That Promote Literacy. 2001. (SPA.). 72p. pap. 9.95 (978-0-439-24442-8(0)) Scholastic, Inc.

Stanley, Mandy. My First Spanish Book: A Bilingual Introduction to Words, Numbers, Shapes, & Colours. 2007. (Illus.). 48p. (J). pap. 7.95 ***(978-0-7534-6148-8(X)*** , Kingfisher) Houghton Mifflin Co. Trade & Reference Div.

Steck-Vaughn Staff. Spanish Primary Collection, 7 vols. 2000. (SPA.). (J). pap. (978-0-7398-2358-3(2)) Steck-Vaughn.

Stein, Gail. CliffsStudySolver Spanish II. 2004. (ENG & SPA.). 512p. pap. 14.99 (978-0-7645-4112-4(9) , Cliff Notes) Wiley, John & Sons, Inc.

Stillman, David. Repaso: Answer Key. 2004. (SPA & ENG.). 416p. (gr. 6-12). pap. 8.95 (978-0-8442-7422-5(4) , NTC4224) Glencoe/McGraw-Hill.

Stokes, Jeffery D. !qué Bien Suena! Text. 2004. 201p. (YA). 94.36 incl. cd-rom (978-0-618-23502-5(7) , 354274) Houghton Mifflin College Div.

Stone, Tom B. Algo Raro en Mi Plato. 2002. (Graveyard School Ser.). (SPA.). (J). pap. 5.95 (978-950-24-0769-2(5) , AL30654) Albatros ARG. *Dist:* Lectorum Pubns., Inc.

The Story of the Ten Commandments/la Historia de Los Diez Mandamientos. 2002. (SPA & ENG., Illus.). 28p. (J). pap. 3.95 (978-0-8249-4205-2(1)) Ideals Pubns.

Suenos y Palabras. (SPA.). (J). (gr. k-6). 30.00 (978-958-04-7090-8(1)); 30.00 (978-958-04-7091-5(X)); Vol. 2. 30.00 (978-958-04-7092-2(8)); Vol. 3. 30.00 (978-958-04-7093-9(6)); Vol. 4. (978-958-04-7734-1(5)); Vol. 5. (978-958-04-7735-8(3)); Vol. 6. (978-958-04-7736-5(1)) Norma S.A. COL. *Dist:* Distribuidora Norma, Inc.

Suenos y Palabras 1. (J). 26.50 (978-958-04-4036-9(0)) Norma S.A. COL. *Dist:* Distribuidora Norma, Inc.

Suenos y Palabras 10. (SPA.). (J). (gr. 7-12). 40.00 (978-958-04-5955-2(X)) Norma S.A. COL. *Dist:* Distribuidora Norma, Inc.

Suenos y Palabras 11. (SPA.). (J). (gr. 7-12). 45.00 (978-958-04-5957-6(6)) Norma S.A. COL. *Dist:* Distribuidora Norma, Inc.

Suenos y Palabras 12. (SPA.). (J). (gr. 7-12). 50.00 (978-958-04-5959-0(2)) Norma S.A. COL. *Dist:* Distribuidora Norma, Inc.

Suenos y Palabras 2. (SPA.). (J). 26.50 (978-958-04-4037-6(9)) Norma S.A. COL. *Dist:* Distribuidora Norma, Inc.

Suenos y Palabras 3. (SPA.). (J). 26.50 (978-958-04-4038-3(7)) Norma S.A. COL. *Dist:* Distribuidora Norma, Inc.

Suenos y Palabras 4. (SPA.). (J). 26.50 (978-958-04-4039-0(5)) Norma S.A. COL. *Dist:* Distribuidora Norma, Inc.

Suenos y Palabras 5. (SPA.). (J). 26.50 (978-958-04-4040-6(9)) Norma S.A. COL. *Dist:* Distribuidora Norma, Inc.

Suenos y Palabras 6. (SPA.). (J). 26.50 (978-958-04-4041-3(7)) Norma S.A. COL. *Dist:* Distribuidora Norma, Inc.

Suenos y Palabras 7, Vol. 7. (SPA.). (J). (gr. 7-12). 35.00 (978-958-04-5650-6(X)) Norma S.A. COL. *Dist:* Distribuidora Norma, Inc.

Suenos y Palabras 8. (SPA.). (J). (gr. 7-12). 35.00 (978-958-04-5651-3(8)) Norma S.A. COL. *Dist:* Distribuidora Norma, Inc.

Suenos y Palabras 9. (SPA.). (J). (gr. 7-12). 40.00 (978-958-04-5652-0(6)) Norma S.A. COL. *Dist:* Distribuidora Norma, Inc.

Suenos y Palabras K. (SPA.). (J). 26.50 (978-958-04-4355-1(6)) Norma S.A. COL. *Dist:* Distribuidora Norma, Inc.

Ten Important Sentences. 2000. (SPA.). (gr. 1 up). 22.60 (978-0-673-63335-4(7)); (gr. 2 up). 22.60 (978-0-673-63336-1(5)); (gr. 3 up). 22.60 (978-0-673-63337-8(3)); (gr. 4 up). 22.60 (978-0-673-63338-5(1)); (gr. 5 up). 22.60 (978-0-673-63339-2(X)) Addison-Wesley Educational Pubs., Inc.

TestWorks. 2004. (gr. k up). cd-rom 99.00 (978-0-328-02541-1(0)); 2004. (gr. 1 up). tchr. ed. 99.00 incl. cd-rom (978-0-673-62281-5(9)); 2004. (gr. 2 up). cd-rom 99.00 (978-0-673-62282-2(7)); 2004. (gr. 3 up). cd-rom 99.00 (978-0-673-62283-9(5)); 2004. (gr. 4 up). tchr. ed. 99.00 incl. cd-rom (978-0-673-62284-6(3)); 2004. (gr. 5 up). tchr. ed. 99.00 incl. cd-rom (978-0-673-62285-3(1)); 2004. (gr. 6 up). tchr. ed. 99.00 incl. cd-rom (978-0-673-62286-0(X)); 2000. (SPA.). (gr. k up). cd-rom 110.88 (978-0-673-64887-7(7)); 2000. (SPA.). (gr. 1 up). cd-rom 110.88 (978-0-673-64888-4(5)); 2000. (SPA.). (gr. 2 up). cd-rom 110.88 (978-0-673-64889-1(3)); 2000. (SPA.). (gr. 3 up). cd-rom 110.88 (978-0-673-64890-7(7)); 2000. (SPA.). (gr. 4 up). cd-rom 110.88 (978-0-673-64891-4(5)); 2000. (SPA.). (gr. 5 up). cd-rom 110.88 (978-0-673-64892-1(3)) Addison-Wesley Educational Pubs., Inc.

Thomas, Rose. Spanish, Elementary, Level 2. 1999. (Homework Booklets Ser.). (SPA., Illus.). 80p. (J). (gr. 1-5). pap. 2.99 (978-0-88012-986-2(7) , IF0206, Instructional Fair) Schaffer, Frank Pubns.

—Spanish, Middle School/High School, Level 1. 1999. (Homework Booklets Ser.). (SPA., Illus.). 80p. (J). (gr. 6-12). pap. 2.99 (978-0-88012-987-9(5) , IF0207, Instructional Fair) Schaffer, Frank Pubns.

Tipton, Stacey. The Complete Musical Spanish: With New Bonus Verbs Learning CD, 1. 2nd ed. 2005. (SPA., Illus.). 112p. 49.99 (978-0-9706829-7-0(2)) Musical Linguist, The.

Todos Somos Amigos. 2003. 23.50 (978-0-673-77190-2(3)) Celebration Pr.

Un trabajo Airoso 18: Leveled Books. 2001. (McGraw-Hill. Lectura Ser.). (ENG & SPA.). (gr. 5 up). (978-0-02-188242-7(8)) Macmillan/McGraw-Hill Schl. Div.

Travis, Joelle & Figueras, Ligaya, eds. Los Animales y los Verbos. Hazan, Maurice, illus. 2003. (SPA.). 89p. (J). per. 20.00 (978-1-932770-16-2(X) , SWLB1) Symtalk, Inc.

Tu Amigo, Jorge. 2003. 28.95 (978-0-673-78106-2(2)) Celebration Pr.

Uno, Dos, Tres: Beginning Spanish for Young Children PK-1. 2004. 64p. (J). pap. 8.99 (978-0-88724-246-5(4) , CD-0058) Carson-Dellosa Publishing Co., Inc.

Uriz, Francisco J. & Harling, Birgit. En el Mundo Hispanico. 2002. stu. ed. 19.95 (978-0-8219-2324-5(2) , 70376); pap., tchr.'s training gde. ed. 5.50 (978-0-8219-2325-2(0) , 70865) EMC/Paradigm Publishing.

Vargo, Sharon Hawkins. Senor Felipes Alphabet Adventure: El Alfabeto Espanol. 2003. (Single Titles Ser.: Vol. 3). 32p. (J). (ps). 7.95 (978-0-7613-1897-2(6) , Millbrook Pr.) Lerner Publishing Group.

—Sensor Felipe's Alphabet Adventure: El Alfabeto Espanol. 2001. (Around the World Ser.). (SPA & ENG., Illus.). 32p. (ps-3). lib. bdg. 22.90 (978-0-7613-1860-6(7) , Millbrook Pr.) Lerner Publishing Group.

El Viaje de Carlos y Ceci. 2003. (Illus.). (J). 28.95 (978-0-673-78103-1(8)) Celebration Pr.

Un viaje en una tarde de Domingo 6: Leveled Books. 2001. (McGraw-Hill. Lectura Ser.). (ENG & SPA.). (gr. 2 up). (978-0-02-188031-7(X)) Macmillan/McGraw-Hill Schl. Div.

Villafane-Leon, Ines. A Story for All Seasons: Un Cuento Para Cada Estacion: Immigration of One. 2004. (ENG & SPA.). xiii, 367p. (YA). pap. 22.95 (978-1-882897-78-0(1)) Lost Coast Pr.

Whitehouse, Patricia. Partes Iguales en el Zoologico. 2002. (Matematicas del Zoologico (Zoo Math) Ser.). (SPA.). 24p. (J). (ps-1). 18.50 (978-1-58810-801-2(5)); pap. 5.25 (978-1-58810-860-9(0) , 91628) Heinemann Library.

Who Is Michael Ramirez? 2003. (J). 28.95 (978-0-673-78107-9(0)) Celebration Pr.

Wilkes, Angela, contrib. by. Spanish for Beginners. 1999. (Passport's Languages for Beginners Ser.). (SPA.). 48p. (J). 12.95 incl. audio (978-0-8442-1607-2(0) , 16070, Passport Bks.) McGraw-Hill Trade.

Ya Llego el Mariachi! 2003. (J). 28.95 (978-0-673-78104-8(6)) Celebration Pr.

Ya Mero Llegamos, Mami? 2003. 23.95 (978-0-673-78081-2(3)) Celebration Pr.

Yo Bailo! 2003. (J). 23.95 (978-0-673-77781-2(2)) Celebration Pr.

Yo Tengo una Tia. 2003. (J). 23.95 (978-0-673-78059-1(7)) Celebration Pr.

Yo Vivo Aqui. 2003. (J). 23.95 (978-0-673-77792-8(8)) Celebration Pr.

Zaz! 2003. 23.95 (978-0-673-77367-8(1)) Celebration Pr.

The 5 W's & H Spanish Version, Gr. 4-5. 2005. (J). per. (978-1-58232-140-0(X)) Bryan Hse. Pubs., Inc.

The 5 W's Spanish Version, Gr. 1-3. 2005. (J). per. (978-1-58232-145-5(0)) Bryan Hse. Pubs., Inc.

6+1 Traits Book. 2001. (Artes Del Lenguaje Ser.). (ENG & SPA.). (gr. 6 up). (978-0-02-245395-4(4)) Macmillan/McGraw-Hill Schl. Div.

SPANISH LANGUAGE—CONVERSATION AND PHRASE BOOKS

Berlitz Publishing Staff, creator. Animals (Spanish) 2006. (Berlitz Sticker Bks.). (ENG & SPA.). 28p. (J). pap. 4.95 (978-981-246-982-3(6)) Berlitz Publishing.

—Basic Words (Spanish Berlitz) 2006. (Berlitz Sticker Bks.). (ENG & SPA.). 28p. (J). pap. 4.95 (978-981-246-983-0(4)) Berlitz Publishing.

—Spanish. 2006. (Berlitz Flash Cards Ser.). (ENG & SPA.). 50p. 8.95 (978-981-246-971-7(0)) Berlitz Publishing.

S

Bruzzone, Catherine. Spanish Fun. 3rd ed. 2004. (Illus.). 20p. 12.95 (978-0-07-142816-3(X) , 9780071428163) McGraw-Hill Cos., The.

Bruzzone, Catherine & Martineau, Susan. Hide & Speak Spanish. Comfort, Louise, illus. 2003. (Hide & Speak Ser.). (SPA & ENG.). 32p. (J). pap. 7.95 (978-0-7641-2589-8(3)) Barron's Educational Series, Inc.

Bruzzone, Catherine, et al. Action Spanish! A Lively Activity Starter Pack for Adults & Children. 2000. (ENG & SPA., Illus.). 12p. (J). (ps-5). pap. 14.95 incl. audio (978-0-658-00443-8(3) , 004433) McGraw-Hill/Contemporary.

Calvert, Michael & Gonzalez Florido, Helena. ¡Así!, Bk. 1. 2004. (SPA., Illus.). 160p. (J). pap., stu. ed. 32.50 (978-0-7487-7811-9(X)) Nelson Thornes Ltd. GBR. *Dist:* Trans-Atlantic Pubns., Inc.

Crosbie, Duncan. Find Out about Spain: Learn Spanish Words & Phrases & about Life in Spain. Hutchinson, Tim, illus. 2006. (Find Out about Ser.). (ENG & SPA.). 64p. (J). (gr. 3 up). spiral bd. 12.99 (978-0-7641-5955-8(0)) Barron's Educational Series, Inc.

Emberley, Rebecca. My Day/Mi Día: A Book in Two Languages/Un Libro en Dos Lenguas. Emberley, Rebecca, illus. 2000. (ENG & SPA., Illus.). 28p. (J). (ps-3). pap. 6.99 (978-0-316-22983-8(0)) Little Brown & Co.

Espana, Graciela. En Espanol: Rapid Success in Spanish for Beginners. 2003. (Language Immersion Institute Ser.). (ENG & SPA., Illus.). 192p. pap. 32.95 incl. cd-rom (978-0-07-140642-0(5) , 9780071406420) McGraw-Hill Cos., The.

Finnie, Sue & Bourdais, Daniele. Sophie Learns Spanish. Tempest, Annabel, illus. 2003. (Language Learners Ser.). (SPA & ENG.). 32p. (J). (gr. 2-5). 11.99 (978-0-7641-7631-9(5)) Barron's Educational Series, Inc.

Jarvis. Spanish for Business & Finance & Audio CD-ROM Program Sixth Edition. 6th ed. 2002. (YA). pap. 78.36 incl. cd-rom (978-0-618-28396-5(X) , 385264) Houghton Mifflin College Div.

McGraw-Hill Staff. ¡Buen Viaje!, Level 2. 2nd ed. 2002. (SPA.). (C). (gr. 6-12). stu. ed. 82.00 (978-0-07-829180-7(1) , 9780078291807) Glencoe/McGraw-Hill.

—Buen Viaje! Level 1. 3rd ed. 1999. (SPA.). (gr. 6-12). pap., stu. ed. 8.48 (978-0-07-820999-4(4) , 9780078209994) Glencoe/McGraw-Hill.

—Buen Viaje! Level 2. 3rd ed. 1999. (SPA.). (C). (gr. 6-12). pap., stu. ed. 9.32 (978-0-07-821005-1(4) , 9780078210051) Glencoe/McGraw-Hill.

—Buen Viaje! Vol. 3: Level 3, 3rd ed. 1999. (SPA.). (gr. 6-12). pap., stu. ed. 9.32 (978-0-07-821006-8(2) , 9780078210068) Glencoe/McGraw-Hill.

Morton, Lone & Risk, Mary. Feliz Cumpleanos. 1998. (I Can Read Bks.).Tr. of Happy Birthday. (ENG & SPA., Illus.). 28p. (J). (ps up). audio 9.95 (978-0-7641-7192-5(5)) Barron's Educational Series, Inc.

—Get Dressed, Roberto. 1998. (Language Learning Story Bks.).Tr. of Vistete, Roberto. (ENG & SPA., Illus.). 28p. (J). (ps-3). 7.99 (978-0-7641-5129-3(0) , BA290) Barron's Educational Series, Inc.

—I'm Too Big. 1998. (I Can Read Bks.).Tr. of Je Suis Mucho Grande. (ENG & SPA., Illus.). 28p. (J). (ps up). audio 9.95 (978-0-7641-7193-2(3)) Barron's Educational Series, Inc.

Petelinsek, Kathleen & Primm, E. Russell. Greetings & Phrases: Saludos y Frases. 2006. (Talking Hands Ser.). (ENG & SPA., Illus.). 24p. (J). 21.36 (978-1-59296-682-0(9)) Child's World, Inc.

Pirz, Therese Slevin. Language Helper Spanish: Helping You Speak More Spanish. 2006. (Language Helper Ser.). (Illus.). 218p. (J). pap. 20.00 (978-0-9716605-8-8(1)) Chou-Chou Pr.

Renjilian/Burgy. Renjilian/burgy Caminos with Audio Cd Plus CD-ROM Three Point Zero Plus Workbook Webcard with Smarthinking Second Edition. 2nd ed. 2004. (YA). 147.16 incl. cd-rom, cd-rom (978-0-618-53935-2(2) , 389655) Houghton Mifflin College Div.

Reyes, Raquel, et al. I May Bien! Level E. 2005. (I May Bien! Ser.).Tr. of Very Good. (SPA.). 130p. (J). 22.95 (978-0-9718696-9-1(3)) Double R Publishing, LLC.

Risk, Mary & Morton, Lone. What's for Supper? Que Hay Para Cenar? 1998. (Language Learning Story Bks.). (ENG & SPA., Illus.). 28p. (J). (ps up). 8.99 (978-0-7641-5127-9(4) , BA274) Barron's Educational Series, Inc.

Roca, Nuria. La Primavera. 2004. (Cuatro Estaciones Ser.).Tr. of Spring. (SPA., Illus.). 36p. (J). pap. 7.99 (978-0-7641-2734-2(9)) Barron's Educational Series, Inc.

—El Verano. 2004. (Cuatro Estaciones Ser.).Tr. of Summer. (SPA., Illus.). 36p. (J). pap. 6.95 (978-0-7641-2736-6(5)) Barron's Educational Series, Inc.

Schmitt, et al. Como te va? a Nivel Verde: Audio Activities. 2003. (SPA.). (gr. 6-12). pap. 7.00 (978-0-07-860550-5(4)) Glencoe/McGraw-Hill.

—Como te va? B Nivel Azul: Audio Activities. 2003. (SPA.). (gr. 6-12). pap. 7.00 (978-0-07-860557-4(1)) Glencoe/McGraw-Hill.

School Specialty Publishing. Hablo Ingles! Level 2 - Words & Phrases. 1999. (Homework Booklets Ser.). (SPA.). 80p. (C). pap. 2.99 (978-0-88012-922-0(0) , IF0201, Instructional Fair) Schaffer, Frank Pubns.

Thompson. Quia Online: Used with ... Thompson-Mais Oui! 3rd ed. 2004. (YA). wbk. ed., lab manual ed. 63.96 incl. cd-rom (978-0-618-33824-5(1) , 355772) Houghton Mifflin College Div.

Tulip, Jenny. My First Spanish Word Book. 2004. (ENG & SPA., Illus.). 48p. (J). 5.99 (978-1-85854-394-9(0)) Brimax Books Ltd. GBR. *Dist:* Byeway Bks.

Vaamonde, Conchita, tr. My First Spanish Words. Tulip, Jenny, illus. 2004. (SPA.). 12p. (J). bds. 7.99 (978-1-85854-512-7(9)) Brimax Books Ltd. GBR. *Dist:* Byeway Bks.

Watson, Carol. Let's Learn Spanish. 2003. (gr. 3-6). lib. bdg. 18.75 (978-0-613-74956-5(1)) Tandem Library Bks.

Watson, Carol & De Saulles, Janet. Let's Learn Spanish. McNicholas, Shelagh, illus. 2003. (Let's Learn Ser.). 32p. pap. 9.95 (978-0-7818-1013-5(2)) Hippocrene Bks., Inc.

Whitehouse, Patricia. Quien Esta Despierto? 1 2 3. 2003. (Que Esta Despierto? (What's Awake?) Ser.). (SPA.). 24p. (J). (ps-1). lib. bdg. 17.08 (978-1-4034-0399-5(6)) Heinemann.

Wightwick, Jane. Way Cool Spanish Phrase Book. 2001. (Way Cool Ser.). (ENG & SPA., Illus.). 96p. (YA). (gr. 3-9). pap. 6.95 (978-0-658-01691-2(1) , 9780658016912) McGraw-Hill Cos., The.

—Way Cool Spanish Phrasebook. 2005. (ENG & SPA., Illus.). 96p. pap. 12.95 (978-0-07-144837-6(3) , 9780071448376) McGraw-Hill Cos., The.

SPANISH LANGUAGE—DICTIONARIES

Beaton, Clare, illus. Animals: Los Animales. l.t. ed. 1998. (English-Spanish Bilingual First Bks.). (ENG & SPA.). 24p. (J). (ps up). lib. bdg. 14.45 (978-1-56674-247-4(1)) Forest Hse. Publishing Co., Inc.

—Clothes: La Ropa. l.t. ed. 1998. (English-Spanish Bilingual First Bks.). (ENG & SPA.). 24p. (J). (ps up). lib. bdg. 14.45 (978-1-56674-248-1(X)) Forest Hse. Publishing Co., Inc.

—Colors: Los Colores. l.t. ed. 1998. (English-Spanish Bilingual First Bks.). (ENG & SPA.). 24p. (J). (ps up). lib. bdg. 14.45 (978-1-56674-249-8(8)) Forest Hse. Publishing Co., Inc.

—Numbers/Los Numeros. l.t. ed. 1998. (English-Spanish Bilingual First Bks.). (ENG & SPA.). 24p. (J). (ps up). lib. bdg. 14.45 (978-1-56674-251-1(X)) Forest Hse. Publishing Co., Inc.

Berlitz Publishing Staff. Spanish. 2nd ed. 2004. (Berlitz Kids Ser.). (SPA., Illus.). 128p. (ps-4). pap. 12.95 (978-981-246-431-6(X) , 46431X) Berlitz Publishing.

Davies, H. Spanish Dictionary for Beginners. 2004. (Beginner's Dictionaries Ser.). (SPA.). 128p. (J). pap. 12.99 (978-0-7945-0288-1(1)); lib. bdg. 20.99 (978-1-58086-488-6(0)) EDC Publishing.

Diaz-Cubero, Jose H. Practicas de Ortografia: 3 Grado. (SPA & ENG.). (J). (gr. 3). 9.95 (978-84-357-0127-3(1) , CPR88) Ediciones y Distribuciones Codice, S.A. ESP. *Dist:* Continental Bk. Co., Inc.

Diccionario de la Lengua Espanola Basico. (SPA., Illus.). (J). 5.95 (978-958-04-4116-8(2)) Norma S.A. COL. *Dist:* Distribuidora Norma, Inc.

Diccionario de la Lengua Espanola Mini. (SPA.). (J). 2.50 (978-958-04-4584-5(2)) Norma S.A. COL. *Dist:* Distribuidora Norma, Inc.

Diccionario Didactico de Espanol Elemental (Didactic Dictionary of Elementary Spanish) Edicion Mexicana (Mexican Edition) (SPA., Illus.). 880p. (978-84-348-4715-6(9) , SM1932) SM Ediciones ESP. *Dist:* i.b.d., Ltd.

Diccionario Enciclopedico 2001 (Encyclopedic Dicitonary 2001), 4 vols., Set. 2001. (ENG & SPA.). 1838p. (YA). (gr. 7 up). (978-970-22-0140-3(3)) Larousse.

Diccionario Usual Larousse.Tr. of Handy Larousse Spanish Dictionary. (SPA.). 782p. pap. (978-970-22-0126-7(8)) Larousse, Ediciones, S. A. de C. V.

Dorling Kindersley Publishing Staff. DK Spanish Dictionary. 1999. (Illus.). (J). (978-0-606-18116-7(4)) Tandem Library Bks.

Dorling Kindersley Publishing Staff, contrib. by. Spanish Dictionary. 2nd ed. 2003. (Pockets Ser.). (SPA & ENG.). 512p. (J). (gr. 3). pap. 6.99 (978-0-7894-9599-0(6)) Dorling Kindersley Publishing, Inc.

Douglas, Vincent & School Specialty Publishing Staff. Spanish Dictionary. 2002. (Notebook Reference Ser.). (Illus.). 128p. (J). (gr. 4-8). pap. 4.95 (978-1-57768-341-4(2)) School Specialty Publishing.

—Spanish Dictionary. Notebk Referenc, ed. 2nd rev. ed. 2006. (Notebook Reference Ser.). 144p. (J). pap. 3.95 (978-0-7696-4342-7(6) , American Education Publishing) School Specialty Publishing.

Enciclopedia Juvenil, 4 vols., Set. (J). 59.00 (978-84-272-5995-9(6) , MO501) Molino, Editorial ESP. *Dist:* Continental Bk. Co., Inc.

Equipo Staff. Diccionario Escolar de la Lengua Espanola (Student Dictionary of the Spanish Language) 1999. (ENG & SPA.). 674p. (J). (gr. 4-8). 10.95 (978-84-239-9070-2(2)) Espasa Calpe, S.A. ESP. *Dist:* Continental Bk. Co., Inc., Libros Sin Fronteras.

—Dicionario Inicial Everest. (SPA.). 336p. (978-84-241-1013-0(7)) Everest de Ediciones y Distribucion, S.L. ESP. *Dist:* Lectorum Pubns., Inc.

—Everest Diccionario Cima de la Lengua Espanola.Tr. of Everest Cima Dictionary of the Spanish Language. (SPA.). 566p. 19.95 (978-84-241-1027-7(7) , EV6705); 868p. 22.95 (978-84-241-1036-9(6) , EV7041) Everest de Ediciones y Distribucion, S.L. ESP. *Dist:* Lectorum Pubns., Inc.

—Everest Diccionario Practico de Sinonimos y Antonimos.Tr. of Everest Practical Thesaurus. (SPA.). 576p. 12.99 (978-84-241-1508-1(2) , EV7151) Everest de Ediciones y Distribucion, S.L. ESP. *Dist:* Lectorum Pubns., Inc.

Gareth Stevens Publishing Staff, contrib. by. My First Visual Dictionary/Mi Primer Diccionario Visual. 2001. (ENG & SPA., Illus.). 48p. (J). (gr. 3 up). lib. bdg. 26.00 (978-0-8368-2897-9(6)) Stevens, Gareth Inc.

Goodman, Marlene. Let's Learn Spanish Picture Dictionary. 2004. 80p. 9.95 (978-0-07-140828-8(2)) McGraw-Hill/Contemporary.

Hippocrene Books Staff. Hippocrene Children's Illustrated Spanish Dictionary. 2001. (gr. 3-6). lib. bdg. 21.05 (978-0-613-74951-0(0)) Tandem Library Bks.

Hippocrene Books Staff, compiled by. Hippocrene Children's Illustrated Spanish Dictionary: Spanish-English - English-Spanish. 1999. (Hippocrene Children's Illustrated Foreign Language Dictionaries Ser.). (ENG & SPA., Illus.). 96p. (YA). (gr. k-5). 16.95 (978-0-7818-0733-3(6)) Hippocrene Bks., Inc.

King, Alyson L. Joyful Jumping. 2007. (ENG & SPA.). (J). (978-1-59515-955-7(X)) Rourke Publishing, LLC.

Larousse Enciclopedico Universal (Larousse Universal Encyclopedia), 6 vols., Set. 2000. (ENG & SPA.). 1816p. (YA). (gr. 7 up). (978-970-22-0071-0(7)) Larousse.

Larousse Mexico Staff. Diccionario Educativo Juvenil. 2002. Tr. of Youthful Educative Dictionary. (SPA.). 734p. (gr. 5). pap. 8.95 (978-970-22-0055-0(5)) Larousse, Ediciones, S. A. de C. V. MEX. *Dist:* Houghton Mifflin Co. Trade & Reference Div.

McGraw-Hill Staff. El Español para Nosotros: Curso para Hispanohablantes, Level 2. 2005. (SPA.). pap., stu. ed., wbk. ed. 20.64 (978-0-07-867656-7(8) , 9780078676567) Glencoe/McGraw-Hill.

—McGraw-Hill's Spanish Picture Dictionary. 2004. (Language Dictionaries Ser.). (SPA & ENG., Illus.). 96p. 10.95 (978-0-07-142812-5(7) , 9780071428125) McGraw-Hill Cos., The.

National Educational Systems Inc. Staff. Diccionario Escolar, Sinonimos y Antonimos. 1998. (SPA., Illus.). 128p. (J). (gr. 3-12). pap. (978-1-893493-02-5(4)) National Educational Systems, Inc.

Norma Staff. Mi Primer Vocabulario (My First Vocabulary Dict.), 2 vols., Set. (SPA.). (J). 50.00 (978-958-04-3093-3(4)) Norma S.A. COL. *Dist:* AIMS International Bks., Inc.

NTC Publishing Group Editors & School Specialty Publishing Staff. Just Look 'n Learn Spanish: Picture Dictionary. 2000. (Just Look 'n Learn Picture Dictionary Ser.). (SPA & ENG., Illus.). 96p. (J). (gr. 4-7). 11.95 (978-0-8442-7052-4(0) , 70520, Bedrick, Peter Bks.) School Specialty Publishing.

Random House Staff. Random House Easy Learning Spanish Dictionary. 1999. pap. (978-0-375-70597-7(X) , spa) Random Hse. Information Group.

Random House Webster's Dictionary. 2001. (SPA.). (gr. 7-12). lib. bdg. 14.15 (978-0-613-36626-7(3)) Tandem Library Bks.

Random House Webster's School & Office Thesaurus Revised & Updated. 2002. (gr. 7-12). lib. bdg. 21.05 (978-0-613-53546-5(4)) Tandem Library Bks.

Renjilian/Burgy. Renjilian/burgy Caminos with Audio Cd Plus CD-ROM Three Point Zero Plus Workbook Webcard with Smarthinking Second Edition. 2nd ed. 2004. (YA). 147.16 incl. cd-rom, cd-rom (978-0-618-53935-2(2) , 389655) Houghton Mifflin College Div.

Rey, Alain. Robert junior Poche. pap. 29.95 (978-2-85036-687-1(0)) Le Robert FRA. *Dist:* Distribooks, Inc.

Richmond Concise Dictionary. (SPA.). 716p. (J). (gr. 3-8). pap. 30.95 (978-970-29-0661-2(X)) Santillana USA Publishing Co., Inc.

Salvador, Gregorio, prologue by. Nuevo Diccionario Esencial Santillana. (SPA., Illus.). 1414p. (J). (gr. 6-12). 29.95 (978-84-294-5935-7(9)) Santillana USA Publishing Co., Inc.

Sangregorio, Fernando, et al, illus. Pictodiccionario: Diccionario en Im Genes. (SPA.). 144p. (J). (gr. k-3). 25.95 (978-1-58105-973-1(6)) Santillana USA Publishing Co., Inc.

Schaefer, A. R. Food Around the World. 2007. (ENG & SPA.). (J). (978-1-59515-959-5(2)) Rourke Publishing, LLC.

—Help Me Find Something. 2007. (ENG & SPA.). (J). (978-1-59515-958-8(4)) Rourke Publishing, LLC.

Van Gool, A, illus. Mi Primer Libro de Palabras. 2002. (SPA & ENG.). 64p. (J). per. 12.95 (978-1-58087-063-4(5)) Stampley, C.D. Enterprises, Inc.

Varios. Diccionario de Primaria de la Lengua Española. 2nd ed. 2003. (SPA., Illus.). 1006p. (J). (gr. 3-7). (978-84-8332-061-7(4)) Bibliograf, S.A.

Vv. Diccionario Esencial. (SPA.). 1376p. 19.95 (978-84-294-3415-6(1)) Santillana USA Publishing Co., Inc.

—Diccionario Ilustrado. 2001. Tr. of Illustrated Dictionary. (SPA.). 202p. (978-84-305-1724-4(3)) Lectorum Pubns., Inc.

—Diccionario SM Basico. 3rd ed. 2002. Tr. of Basic School Dictionary. (SPA., Illus.). 504p. (J). 27.95 (978-84-348-6535-8(1)) SM Ediciones ESP. *Dist:* AIMS International Bks., Inc.

—Diccionario SM Intermedio. 2002. Tr. of Intermediate School Dictionary. (SPA.). 1312p. (J). 39.95 (978-84-348-7205-9(6)) SM Ediciones ESP. *Dist:* AIMS International Bks., Inc., Distribooks, Inc.

Wilson, Hannah & Ferris, Julie, eds. DK First Spanish Picture Dictionary. 2005. (SPA & ENG., Illus.). 128p. (J). 14.99 (978-0-7566-1370-9(1)) Dorling Kindersley Publishing, Inc.

Wittels, Harriet & Greisman, Joan. Spanish Thesaurus for Children: Libro de Sinonimos y Antonimos. 2nd ed. 2004. (SPA & ENG., Illus.). 160p. (J). pap. 8.95 (978-0-7641-2437-2(4)) Barron's Educational Series, Inc.

1091 Diccionario Escolar Junior. 2001. (SPA.). (978-970-607-313-6(2)) Larousse, Ediciones, S. A. de C. V.

SPANISH LANGUAGE—DICTIONARIES—ENGLISH

American Heritage Spanish Dictionary. 2000. (SPA.). (gr. 7-12). lib. bdg. 15.30 (978-0-8085-9469-7(9)) Tandem Library Bks.

Castillo, Carlos. University of Chicago Spanish & English Dictionary. 2003. (gr. 7-12). lib. bdg. 14.15 (978-0-613-66473-8(6)) Tandem Library Bks.

Corbeil, Jean-Claude & Archambault, Ariane. The Firefly Spanish/English Junior Visual Dictionary. 2006. (SPA & ENG., Illus.). 368p. (J). (gr. 5-12). 19.95 (978-1-55407-190-6(9)) Firefly Bks., Ltd.

—My First Spanish/English Visual Dictionary. 2006. (ENG & SPA., Illus.). 80p. (J). (gr. k-4). 14.95 (978-1-55407-194-4(1)) Firefly Bks., Ltd.

Dalmatian Press Staff. My First Spanish Word Book: Mis primeras palabras en espanol e Ingles. 2007. 12p. bds. 7.99 (***978-1-4037-3055-8(5)**) Dalmatian Pr.

Demarest, Chris L. & Berlitz Publishing Staff. Ingles Diccionario Ilustrado. 2nd ed. 2004. (Berlitz Kids Ser.). (SPA., Illus.). 128p. (ps-4). pap. 12.95 (978-981-246-389-0(5) , 463895) Berlitz Publishing.

Diccionario Basico Ingles/Espanol (1540) 2003. (SPA & ENG.). 528p. pap. 5.98 (978-970-22-0480-0(1)) Larousse, Ediciones, S. A. de C. V. MEX. *Dist:* Giron Bks.

Diccionario Bilingue Basico. (SPA & ENG.). (J). 5.95 (978-958-04-4118-2(9)) Norma S.A. COL. *Dist:* Distribuidora Norma, Inc.

Diccionario Espanol-Ingles, Merriam-Webster. 2001. (SPA.). (gr. 7-12). lib. bdg. 14.15 (978-0-613-51208-4(1)) Tandem Library Bks.

Faulkner, Keith. My First 100 Words in Spanish & English. Johnson, Paul, illus. 1998. (Simon & Schuster Books for Young Readers).Tr. of Mis Primeras 100 Palabras en Espanol e Ingles. (SPA & ENG.). 16p. (J). (ps-3). 12.95 (978-0-671-74965-1(X) , Libros Para Ninos) Simon & Schuster Children's Publishing.

Hippocrene Books, ed. Spanish Childrens Picture Dict: English-Spanish/Spanish-English. 2006. (ENG & SPA.). 104p. (J). pap. 14.95 (978-0-7818-1130-9(9)) Hippocrene Bks., Inc.

Hochstatter, Daniel J. Just Look 'n Learn Spanish Picture Dictionary. 2004. 96p. 11.95 (978-0-07-140829-5(0)) McGraw-Hill/Contemporary.

Jordan, Sara. Bilingual Kids Vol. I: English - Spanish. 2005. 64p. (J). pap. (978-1-55386-024-2(1)) Crabtree Publishing Co.

—English - Spanish. 2005. 64p. (J). (978-1-55386-036-5(5)); 4. pap. (978-1-55386-041-9(1)) Crabtree Publishing Co.

Larousse Diccionario School Plus Espanol (Larousse School Plus Dictionary) 1999. (ENG & SPA.). 526p. (YA). (gr. 8 up). (978-970-22-0001-7(6)) Larousse.

Laud, Valerie. The Picture Book Dictionary: The Essential Source for Bilingual Families, English-Spanish Edition. Latushkin, Valentin, illus. l.t. ed. 2005. (ENG & SPA.). 96p. (J). (978-0-9747387-0-3(0)) EKADOO Publishing Group.

Lea, Christine. Oxford New Spanish Dictionary. 1999. (SPA.). (gr. 7-12). lib. bdg. 14.15 (978-0-613-16407-8(5)) Tandem Library Bks.

Lipton, Gladys C. & Munoz, Olivia. Spanish Bilingual Dictionary: A Beginner's Guide in Words & Pictures. 3rd ed. 1998. (Beginning Dictionaries in Foreign Languages Ser.). (ENG & SPA., Illus.). 180p. (gr. 4-7). pap. 8.95 (978-0-7641-0281-3(8) , BA2743) Barron's Educational Series, Inc.

Longman. Longman Diccionario Pocket, Ingles-Espanol, Espanol-Ingles:Para Estudiantes Mexicanos. 2004. (ENG & SPA.). 832p. (C). pap. 19.93 (978-0-582-51157-6(7)) Pearson ESL.

Mabileau, Christine, et al. My First Spanish Picture Dictionary. 2001. (Children's First Picture Dictionaries Ser.). (ENG & SPA., Illus.). 48p. (J). 16.99 (978-0-7641-5437-9(0)) Barron's Educational Series, Inc.

Merriam-Webster, contrib. by. Merriam-Webster's Notebook Spanish-English Dictionary. 2004. (SPA & ENG.). 112p. (gr. 5). pap. 4.95 (978-0-87779-672-5(6) , MER-672) Merriam-Webster, Inc.

Salas, Macarena, ed. My First Spanish-english Dictionary with 190 Stickers (Mi Primer Diccionario Espanol-ingles con 190 Pegatinas) 2006. 32p. (J). pap. 5.99 (978-0-439-87314-7(2) , Scholastic en Espanol) Scholastic, Inc.

Spanish-English Picture Dictionary. 2003. (SPA & ENG.). (J). per. (978-1-884907-30-2(X)) Paradise Pr., Inc.

Vv. Richmond Advanced Dictionary: Spanish/English, English/Spanish. (ENG & SPA.). 720p. (J). (gr. 9-12). 30.95 (978-84-294-9861-5(3) , Richmond) Santillana USA Publishing Co., Inc.

—Richmond Pocket Dictionary: Spanish-English, English-Spanish. (SPA & ENG.). 806p. (J). (gr. 6-12). pap. 10.95 (978-84-294-9860-8(5)) Santillana USA Publishing Co., Inc.

Webster's Spanish-English Dictionary for Students. 2003. (gr. 3-6). lib. bdg. 10.65 (978-0-613-68550-4(4)) Tandem Library Bks.

Williams, Edwin B. The New College Spanish & English Dictionary. 3rd ed. 2003. (SPA & ENG.). 720p. (YA). (gr. 7-12). pap. (978-0-87720-538-8(8) , R760P) AMSCO Schl. Pubns., Inc.

SPANISH LANGUAGE—GRAMMAR

ABC. 2003. (J). per. (978-1-884907-44-9(X)); per. (978-1-884907-40-1(7)) Paradise Pr., Inc.

ABC. 2003. (First Concepts Book Ser.). 32p. (J). 3.98 (978-0-7525-8892-6(3)) Parragon, Inc.

ABC. 2001. (SPA.). 40p. (J). 15.95 (978-980-6437-20-3(9)) Playco Editores, C.A.

ABC. (Coleccion Picaros Peluchines). (SPA.). (J). 5.50 (978-950-11-0398-4(6) , SGM398) Sigmar ARG. *Dist:* Continental Bk. Co., Inc.

La Abeja Trabajadora. 2003. (J). 23.95 (978-0-673-77796-6(0)) Celebration Pr.

Acento 8: Cuaderno de Ortografia. (SPA.). (J). (gr. 1-9). 16.00 (978-958-04-3831-1(5)) Norma S.A. COL. *Dist:* Distribuidora Norma, Inc.

Acento 9: Cuaderno de Ortografia. (SPA., Illus.). (J). (gr. 1-9). 16.00 (978-958-04-3832-8(3)) Norma S.A. COL. *Dist:* Distribuidora Norma, Inc.

Advina Quien Soy? 2003. 23.95 (978-0-673-77182-7(2)) Celebration Pr.

Al Juego! 2003. 23.95 (978-0-673-77777-5(4)) Celebration Pr.
Albright, Thomas B. Simple Spanish. 2nd l.t. ed. 2001. (Languages). (SPA.). 48p. (978-1-888264-16-6(0)) Twenty-First Century Co., The.
Ana Y Tito. 2003. 23.95 (978-0-673-77783-6(9)) Celebration Pr.
Los Animales Nos Ayudan. 2003. 23.95 (978-0-673-77393-7(0)) Celebration Pr.
Antonio Y Su Poncho. 2003. 28.95 (978-0-673-78086-7(4)) Celebration Pr.
El Apartamento. 2003. 23.95 (978-0-673-77183-4(0)) Celebration Pr.
La Arana. 2003. 23.95 (978-0-673-77156-8(3)) Celebration Pr.
El Arco Iris. 2003. 23.95 (978-0-673-77128-5(8)) Celebration Pr.
Ay, Caramba! 2003. 28.95 (978-0-673-78097-3(X)) Celebration Pr.
Los Ayudantes. 2003. 23.95 (978-0-673-77164-3(4)) Celebration Pr.
Borreguita Negra: Poems, Rhymes, & Songs Listening Packs. 2003. 34.50 (978-0-673-58629-2(4)) Celebration Pr.
Brilla, Brilla, Estrellita. 2003. 23.95 (978-0-673-77365-4(5)) Celebration Pr.
Brinca La Tablita: Big Book Packages. 2003. 64.95 (978-0-673-58603-2(0)) Celebration Pr.
Bryant-Mole, Karen. Alimentos. 1999. (Veo, veo! Ser.). (SPA., Illus.). 24p. (J). (ps-1). lib. bdg. 18.50 (978-1-57572-915-2(6)) Heinemann Library.
—En el Campo. 1999. (Veo, veo! Ser.). (SPA., Illus.). 24p. (J). (ps-1). lib. bdg. 18.50 (978-1-57572-905-3(9)) Heinemann Library.
—En la Ciudad. 1999. (Veo, veo! Ser.). (SPA., Illus.). 24p. (J). (ps-1). lib. bdg. 18.50 (978-1-57572-906-0(7)) Heinemann Library.
—En la Granja. 1999. (Veo, veo! Ser.). (SPA., Illus.). 24p. (J). (ps-1). lib. bdg. 18.50 (978-1-57572-907-7(5)) Heinemann Library.
—En la Playa. 1999. (Veo, veo! Ser.). (SPA., Illus.). 24p. (J). (ps-1). lib. bdg. 18.50 (978-1-57572-904-6(0)) Heinemann Library.
—Invierno. 1999. (Veo, veo! Ser.). (SPA., Illus.). 24p. (J). (ps-1). lib. bdg. 12.95 net. (978-1-57572-912-1(1)) Heinemann Library.
—Juegos. 1999. (Veo, veo! Ser.). (SPA., Illus.). 24p. (J). (ps-1). lib. bdg. 18.50 (978-1-57572-916-9(4)) Heinemann Library.
—Juguetes. 1999. (Veo, veo! Ser.). (SPA., Illus.). 24p. (J). (ps-1). lib. bdg. 18.50 (978-1-57572-917-6(2)) Heinemann Library.
—Otono. 1999. (Veo, veo! Ser.). (SPA., Illus.). 24p. (J). (ps-1). lib. bdg. 18.50 (978-1-57572-909-1(1)) Heinemann Library.
—Primavera. 1999. (Veo, veo! Ser.). (SPA., Illus.). 24p. (J). (ps-1). lib. bdg. 18.50 (978-1-57572-910-7(5)) Heinemann Library.
—Ropa. 1999. (Veo, veo! Ser.). (SPA., Illus.). 24p. (J). (ps-1). lib. bdg. 18.50 (978-1-57572-914-5(8)) Heinemann Library.
—Verano. 1999. (Veo, veo! Ser.).Tr. of Summer. (SPA., Illus.). 24p. (J). (ps-1). lib. bdg. 18.50 (978-1-57572-911-4(3)) Heinemann Library.
Las Buenas Noches. 2003. 23.95 (978-0-673-77392-0(2)) Celebration Pr.
El Caldo. 2003. 23.95 (978-0-673-77773-7(1)) Celebration Pr.
Camarena, Cathy & Ruff, Gloria B. Ema y Eduardo. 2006. (Primeros Sonidos Ser.). (J). 21.35 (978-1-59679-857-1(2), SandCastle); pap. (978-1-59679-858-8(0)) ABDO Publishing Co.
—Olivia y Oscar. 2006. (Primeros Sonidos Ser.). (J). 21.35 (978-1-59679-889-2(0), SandCastle); pap. (978-1-59679-890-8(4)) ABDO Publishing Co.
Celebramos las Fiestas. 2003. 23.95 (978-0-673-77389-0(2)) Celebration Pr.
La Charreada. 2003. 23.95 (978-0-673-77782-9(0)) Celebration Pr.
Chisholm, Virginia. After School Spanish Primary. 2003. (100+ Seriestm Ser.). (SPA.). 128p. (C). pap. 12.99 (978-0-7424-1779-3(4), IFG99027) School Specialty Publishing.
Chisolm, Virginia. After School Spanish Intermediate. 2003. (100+ Seriestm Ser.). (SPA.). 128p. (C). pap. 12.99 (978-0-7424-1778-6(6), IFG99026) School Specialty Publishing.
Los Cinco Hermanos. 2003. 23.95 (978-0-673-77192-6(X)) Celebration Pr.
Los Cinco Sentidos. 2003. 23.95 (978-0-673-77126-1(1)) Celebration Pr.
El Conejo Magico. 2003. 23.95 (978-0-673-77191-9(1)) Celebration Pr.
Conozco una Viejita. 2003. 23.95 (978-0-673-77364-7(7)) Celebration Pr.
Los Contrarios (Opposites) (SPA.). (J). 6.95 (978-968-419-087-0(5)) Grijalbo, Editorial MEX. *Dist:* AIMS International Bks., Inc.
El Coqui: Big Book Packages. 2003. 64.95 (978-0-673-58596-7(4)) Celebration Pr.
El Correo: Individual Title Two-Packs. (Chiquilibros Ser.). (SPA.). (ps-1). 12.00 (978-0-7635-8561-7(0)) Rigby Education.
Cual Contiene Mas? 2003. 23.95 (978-0-673-77400-2(7)) Celebration Pr.
Cuando Me Bano. 2003. 23.95 (978-0-673-77160-5(1)) Celebration Pr.
Cuando Sea Grande. 2003. 23.95 (978-0-673-77388-3(4)) Celebration Pr.
Cuantos Hay? 2003. 23.95 (978-0-673-77159-9(8)) Celebration Pr.
La Cucaracha: Big Book Packages. 2003. 64.95 (978-0-673-58594-3(8)) Celebration Pr.
De Colores: Big Book Packages. 2003. 64.95 (978-0-673-58602-5(2)) Celebration Pr.
De Viaje! Bien Dicho! 2002. (SPA.). (gr. 2 up). stu. ed. 42.84 (978-0-7362-1106-2(3)) Hampton-Brown Bks.
Denne, B. & Irving, N. Easy Spanish. 2004. (Easy Languages Ser.). (SPA., Illus.). 128p. (J). (gr. 6 up). pap. 12.95 (978-0-7945-0142-6(7), Usborne); lib. bdg. 20.95 (978-1-58086-431-2(7)) EDC Publishing.
Diaz-Cubero, Jose H. Practicas de Ortografia: 2 Grado. (SPA & ENG.). (J). (gr. 2). 9.95 (978-84-357-0128-0(X), CPR86) Ediciones y Distribuciones Codice, S.A. ESP. *Dist:* Continental Bk. Co., Inc.
Diez Ositos. 2003. 23.95 (978-0-673-77362-3(0)) Celebration Pr.
Los Dinosaurios. 2003. Tr. of Great Dinosaur Search. 28.95 (978-0-673-77403-3(1)) Celebration Pr.
Donde Aprendo Yo. 2003. (J). (ps-2). 23.95 (978-0-673-77390-6(6)) Celebration Pr.
Donde Juego Yo. 2003. 23.95 (978-0-673-77185-8(7)) Celebration Pr.
En el Mercado. 2003. 23.95 (978-0-673-77790-4(1)) Celebration Pr.
En Mi Jardin. 2003. 23.95 (978-0-673-77131-5(8)) Celebration Pr.
Las Estaciones. 2003. 23.95 (978-0-673-77127-8(X)) Celebration Pr.
Estoy Enojado. 2003. (J). (ps-2). 23.95 (978-0-673-77391-3(4)) Celebration Pr.
Figueras, Ligaya, ed. En Plena Vista Level 1. Hazan, Maurice, illus. 5th ed. 2003. (SPA.). 140p. per. 22.00 (978-1-932770-98-8(4), SHB-SM) Symtalk, Inc.
Las Figuras Geometricas. 2003. 23.95 (978-0-673-77123-0(7)) Celebration Pr.
Fui Al Mar. 2003. 23.95 (978-0-673-77162-9(8)) Celebration Pr.
Funston, James F. & Bonilla, Alejandro Vargas. Somos Asi en Sus Marcas A. 1999. (SPA.). (YA). (gr. 7). 36.95 (978-0-8219-1954-5(7), 70506) EMC/Paradigm Publishing.
—Somos Asi Ya!, Level 3. 2nd ed. 1999. (SPA., Illus.). (YA). (gr. 10-12). pap., stu. ed. 51.95 (978-0-8219-1936-1(9), 70504); pap., wbk. ed. 11.95 (978-0-8219-1939-2(3), 70707) EMC/Paradigm Publishing.
Funston, James F., et al. Somos Asi Listos, Level 2. 2nd ed. 1999. (SPA.). (J). (gr. 10-12). pap., stu. ed. 50.95 (978-0-8219-1913-2(X), 70502); pap., wbk. ed. 10.95 (978-0-8219-1916-3(4), 70704) EMC/Paradigm Publishing.
Funston, James H., et al. Somos Asi en Sus Marcas B. 1999. (SPA.). (YA). (gr. 8). pap., wbk. ed. 9.95 (978-0-8219-1961-3(X), 70711) EMC/Paradigm Publishing.
Grades 1-2 Complete Pinata/Mas Pinata Package. 2003. 1943.95 (978-0-673-58717-6(7)) Celebration Pr.
Harcourt School Publishers Staff. Vamos de Fiesta, Grade 3: Grammar Practice. 1999. (SPA.). pap., tchr. ed. 19.30 (978-0-15-316145-2(0)) Harcourt Schl. Pubs.
—Vamos de Fiesta, Grade 4: Grammar Practice. 2001. (SPA.). pap., tchr. ed. 19.30 (978-0-15-316154-4(X)) Harcourt Schl. Pubs.
—Vamos de Fiesta, Grade 4: Spelling Practice. 2001. (SPA.). pap., tchr. ed. 18.80 (978-0-15-316156-8(6)) Harcourt Schl. Pubs.
—Vamos de Fiesta, Grade 5: Grammar Practice. 2001. (SPA.). pap., tchr. ed. 19.30 (978-0-15-316164-3(7)) Harcourt Schl. Pubs.
—Vamos de Fiesta, Grade 5: Spelling Practice. 2001. (SPA.). pap., tchr. ed. 18.80 (978-0-15-316166-7(3)) Harcourt Schl. Pubs.
Haughom, Lisa, illus. & text. Juegos de Gramatica: Games for Learning Spanish Grammar. Haughom, Lisa, text. 2001. 79p. per. 21.95 (978-0-9723849-6-4(0)) Languages For Kids.
—Juegos de Gramatica Vol. 2: Games for Learning Spanish Grammar. Haughom, Lisa, text. 2001. 79p. per. 21.95 (978-0-9723849-5-7(2)) Languages For Kids.
Hazan, Maurice. Saber, Deber, Querer, Poder: Symtalk Verb + Verb Infinitive Game for Spanish. 2000. (SPA.). (YA). 99.00 (978-1-932770-49-0(6), SG10) Symtalk, Inc.
Hazan, Maurice, creator. Los Verbos: Symtalk Verb Bingo. 2000. (SPA.). (J). 90.00 (978-1-932770-40-7(2), SG1) Symtalk, Inc.
—Spanish Conjugating Cards. 2004. (SPA.). 195.00 (978-1-932770-86-5(0), SCC) Symtalk, Inc.
Holt, Rinehart and Winston Staff. Adelante: Grammar & Vocabulary Workbook. 3rd ed. 2003. (SPA.). pap., tchr. ed. 16.00 (978-0-03-065941-6(8)) Holt, Rinehart & Winston.
—Adelante: Practice & Activity Book. 3rd ed. 2003. (SPA.). pap., tchr. ed. 20.00 (978-0-03-065943-0(4)) Holt, Rinehart & Winston.
—En Camino: Grammar & Vocabulary Quizzes. 3rd ed. 2002. pap. 27.00 (978-0-03-066484-7(5)) Holt, Rinehart & Winston.
—En Camino: Grammar & Vocabulary Workbook. 3rd ed. 2002. (SPA.). pap. 13.20 (978-0-03-065958-4(2)) Holt, Rinehart & Winston.
—Ven Conmigo! Level 1: Cuaderno de Grammar. 3rd ed. 2003. (SPA.). pap. 14.20 (978-0-03-064982-0(X)) Holt, Rinehart & Winston.
—Ven Conmigo! Level 1: Cuaderno/Act. 3rd ed. 2003. (SPA.). pap., tchr. ed. 22.93 (978-0-03-064981-3(1)) Holt, Rinehart & Winston.
—Ven Conmigo! Level 1: Cuaderno/Grammar. 3rd ed. 2003. (SPA.). pap., tchr. ed. 21.46 (978-0-03-064978-3(1)) Holt, Rinehart & Winston.
—Ven Conmigo! Level 1: Cuadero/Hispanic. 3rd ed. 2003. (SPA.). pap. 14.60 (978-0-03-065538-8(2)); pap., tchr. ed. 18.73 (978-0-03-065539-5(0)) Holt, Rinehart & Winston.
—Ven Conmigo! Level 2: Cuaderno de Act. 3rd ed. 2003. (SPA.). pap. 18.60 (978-0-03-064986-8(2)); pap., tchr. ed. 22.93 (978-0-03-064987-5(0)) Holt, Rinehart & Winston.
—Ven Conmigo! Level 2: Cuaderno de Grammar. 3rd ed. 2003. (SPA.). pap. 15.00 (978-0-03-064983-7(8)); pap., tchr. ed. 21.66 (978-0-03-064984-4(6)) Holt, Rinehart & Winston.
—Ven Conmigo! Level 2: Cuadero/Hispanic. 3rd ed. 2003. (SPA.). pap. 14.60 (978-0-03-065546-3(3)); pap., tchr. ed. 18.73 (978-0-03-065547-0(1)) Holt, Rinehart & Winston.
—Ven Conmigo! Level 3: Cuaderno de Act. 3rd ed. 2003. (SPA.). pap., tchr. ed. 25.33 (978-0-03-064992-9(7)) Holt, Rinehart & Winston.
—Ven Conmigo! Level 3: Grammar & Vocabulary. 1999. pap., tchr. ed., wbk. ed. 21.86 (978-0-03-053958-9(7)) Holt, Rinehart & Winston.
A La Cama! 2003. 23.95 (978-0-673-77399-9(X)) Celebration Pr.
Lakeshore Learning Materials, contrib. by. Spanish Alphabet Big Book. 2006. (SPA.). (J). pap. 19.95 ***(978-1-59746-000-2(1))*** Lakeshore Learning Materials.
Lasetras. 2003. 23.95 (978-0-673-77167-4(9)) Celebration Pr.
Leeme un Cuento. 2003. 23.95 (978-0-673-77189-6(X)) Celebration Pr.
Lengua Espanola: Cuarto Grado. (SPA & ENG.). (J). (gr. 4). 21.95 (978-84-357-0027-6(5), CPR76) Ediciones y Distribuciones Codice, S.A. ESP. *Dist:* Continental Bk. Co., Inc.
Lengua Espanola: Quinto Grado. (SPA & ENG.). (J). (gr. 5). 22.00 (978-84-357-0171-6(9), CPR78) Ediciones y Distribuciones Codice, S.A. ESP. *Dist:* Continental Bk. Co., Inc.
Lengua Espanola: Segundo Grado. (SPA & ENG.). (J). (gr. 2). 17.95 (978-84-357-0137-2(9), CPR72) Ediciones y Distribuciones Codice, S.A. ESP. *Dist:* Continental Bk. Co., Inc.
Lengua Espanola: Sexto Grado. (SPA & ENG.). (J). (gr. 6). 22.00 (978-84-357-0170-9(0), CPR80) Ediciones y Distribuciones Codice, S.A. ESP. *Dist:* Continental Bk. Co., Inc.
Lengua Espanola: Tercer Grado. (SPA & ENG.). (J). (gr. 3). 17.95 (978-84-357-0028-3(3), CPR74) Ediciones y Distribuciones Codice, S.A. ESP. *Dist:* Continental Bk. Co., Inc.
Lo Que Sale De un Huevo. 2003. 23.95 (978-0-673-77161-2(X)) Celebration Pr.
Looking for Insects. 2003. (J). 28.95 (978-0-673-78112-3(7)) Celebration Pr.
Los Tres Deseos. 2003. 23.95 (978-0-673-77193-3(8)) Celebration Pr.
Lupita Y David. 2003. (J). (ps-2). 28.95 (978-0-673-77380-7(9)) Celebration Pr.
Las Maquinas. 2003. (J). (ps-2). 28.95 (978-0-673-77401-9(5)) Celebration Pr.
La Mariposa. 2003. Tr. of Butterfly. 23.95 (978-0-673-77125-4(3)) Celebration Pr.
Las Mariposas de Alicia. 2003. 28.95 (978-0-673-78105-5(4)) Celebration Pr.
La Mariquita Triste. 2003. 23.95 (978-0-673-77795-9(2)) Celebration Pr.
Mazzeo, J. L. Aimee¿s A Book (BL) el libro A de Aimée, 1. 2007. (My Letter Library Ser.: 1). (SPA., Illus.). (J). lib. bdg. 22.60 ***(978-1-59646-419-3(4))*** Dingles & Co.
—Aimee¿s A Book (BL) el libro A de Aimée (PB), 1. 2007. (My Letter Library Ser.: 1). (SPA., Illus.). (J). pap. 9.95 ***(978-1-59646-420-9(8))*** Dingles & Co.
—Cassie's C Book (BL) el libro C de Cassie: S, 3 vols. 2007. (My Letter Library Ser.: 3). (SPA & ENG., Illus.). (J). lib. bdg. 22.60 ***(978-1-59646-431-5(3))*** Dingles & Co.
—Cassie's C Book (BL) el libro C de Cassie (PB), 3 vols. 2007. (My Letter Library Ser.: 3). (SPA & ENG., Illus.). (J). pap. 9.95 ***(978-1-59646-432-2(1))*** Dingles & Co.
—Zach's Z Book (BL) el libro Z de Zach, 26 vols. 2007. (My Letter Library Ser.: 26). (SPA & ENG., Illus.). (J). lib. bdg. 22.60 ***(978-1-59646-569-5(7))*** Dingles & Co.
—Zach's Z Book (BL) el libro Z de Zach (PB), 26 vols. 2007. (My Letter Library Ser.: 26). (SPA & ENG., Illus.). (J). pap. 9.95 ***(978-1-59646-570-1(0))*** Dingles & Co.
Me Encontre una Piedra. 2003. 23.95 (978-0-673-77158-2(X)) Celebration Pr.
Me Siento Feliz. 2003. (J). (ps-2). 23.95 (978-0-673-77394-4(9)) Celebration Pr.
Mi Bicicleta. 2003. 23.95 (978-0-673-77775-1(8)) Celebration Pr.
Mi Camion. 2003. 23.95 (978-0-673-77780-5(4)) Celebration Pr.
Mi Casa Nueva. 2003. 23.95 (978-0-673-77172-8(5)) Celebration Pr.
Mi Cuerpo. 2003. 23.95 (978-0-673-77124-7(5)) Celebration Pr.
Mi Dia. 2003. 23.95 (978-0-673-77165-0(2)) Celebration Pr.
Mi Gatito Fachoso. 2003. 23.95 (978-0-673-77176-6(8)) Celebration Pr.
Mi Libro de Cocina. 2003. (Illus.). 28.95 (978-0-673-78085-0(6)) Celebration Pr.
Mi Mama Trabaja. 2003. 23.95 (978-0-673-77184-1(9)) Celebration Pr.
A Mi Me Gusta. 2003. 23.95 (978-0-673-77387-6(6)) Celebration Pr.
Mi Mejor Amigo. 2003. 23.95 (978-0-673-77181-0(4)) Celebration Pr.
Mi Mundo. 2003. (J). (ps-2). 23.95 (978-0-673-77406-4(6)) Celebration Pr.
Mi Muneco De Nieve. 2003. 23.95 (978-0-673-77779-9(0)) Celebration Pr.
Mi Nana Chalita. 2003. 23.95 (978-0-673-77171-1(7)) Celebration Pr.
Mis Cinco Perritos. 2003. 23.95 (978-0-673-77363-0(9)) Celebration Pr.
Mis Comidas Favoritas. 2003. (SPA.). 23.95 (978-0-673-77799-7(5)) Celebration Pr.
Mis Mascotas. 2003. 23.95 (978-0-673-77177-3(6)) Celebration Pr.
Mis Zapatos Ruevos. 2003. 23.95 (978-0-673-77188-9(1)) Celebration Pr.
More Pizza. 2003. 28.95 (978-0-673-78111-6(9)) Celebration Pr.
Muchos Frijoles. 2003. 23.95 (978-0-673-77774-4(X)) Celebration Pr.
La Muneca Azul. 2003. (J). (ps-2). 23.95 (978-0-673-77383-8(3)) Celebration Pr.
La Muneca Azul: Poems, Rhymes, & Songs Listening Packs. 2003. 34.50 (978-0-673-58631-5(6)) Celebration Pr.
My Grandma's Memory Trunk. 2003. 28.95 (978-0-673-78110-9(0)) Celebration Pr.
Nacher, Patricia, illus. Comic Mnemonics: A Fun, Easy Way to Remember Spanish Verbs. 2004. (YA). per. 16.95 (978-0-9749096-3-9(7)) Alacan Publishing.
A Navegar! Bien Dicho! 2002. (SPA.). (gr. 5 up). stu. ed. 47.83 (978-0-7362-1109-3(8)); (gr. 6 up). stu. ed. 48.59 (978-0-7362-1110-9(1)) Hampton-Brown Bks.
Necesito Mi Desayuno. 2003. 23.95 (978-0-673-77178-0(4)) Celebration Pr.
No Les Tengo Miedo. 2003. 23.95 (978-0-673-77130-8(X)) Celebration Pr.
No Me Quiero Banar. 2003. (J). (ps-2). 23.95 (978-0-673-77395-1(7)) Celebration Pr.
No Quiero Ir Al Dentista. 2003. 23.95 (978-0-673-77174-2(1)) Celebration Pr.
Oscar. 2003. 23.95 (978-0-673-77369-2(8)) Celebration Pr.
A Paco. 2003. 23.95 (978-0-673-77797-3(9)) Celebration Pr.
Palencia, Ramon. Uso de la Gramatica Junior Avanzado. (SPA.). 128p. 24.95 (978-84-7711-555-7(9)) Edelsa Grupo Didascalia, S.A. ESP. *Dist:* Distribooks, Inc.
Las Partes De una Planta. 2003. (J). (ps-2). 23.95 (978-0-673-77402-6(3)) Celebration Pr.
Pattis, Anne-Francoise. Let's Learn Spanish Coloring Book. 2003. (SPA., Illus.). 64p. pap. 4.95 (978-0-07-142142-3(4), 9780071421423) McGraw-Hill Cos., The.
Pedro, Pedrito. 2003. (J). (ps-2). 23.95 (978-0-673-77384-5(1)) Celebration Pr.
Pedro, Pedrito: Big Book Packages. 2003. 64.95 (978-0-673-58598-1(0)) Celebration Pr.
Pedro, Pedrito: Poems, Rhymes, & Songs Listening Packs. 2003. 34.50 (978-0-673-58632-2(4)) Celebration Pr.
La Primavera. 2003. (J). (ps-2). 23.95 (978-0-673-77385-2(X)) Celebration Pr.
La Primavera: Poems, Rhymes, & Songs Listening Packs. 2003. 34.50 (978-0-673-58633-9(2)) Celebration Pr.
Primer Dia de Clases. 2003. 23.95 (978-0-673-77187-2(3)) Celebration Pr.
Que Alegria! 2003. 23.95 (978-0-673-77173-5(3)) Celebration Pr.
Que Comes Tu? 2003. 23.95 (978-0-673-77186-5(5)) Celebration Pr.
Que Dia Es Hoy? 2003. 23.95 (978-0-673-77157-5(1)) Celebration Pr.
Que Mala Suerte! 2003. (J). (ps-2). 23.95 (978-0-673-77398-2(1)) Celebration Pr.
Que Me Pongo? 2003. (J). (ps-2). 23.95 (978-0-673-77407-1(4)) Celebration Pr.
Que Me Pongo? Big Book Packages. 2003. 64.95 (978-0-673-58599-8(9)) Celebration Pr.
Que Miedo! 2003. 23.95 (978-0-673-77794-2(4)) Celebration Pr.
Ramon, David de. Ortografia Espaola - Como Escribir Correctamente. 2001. (SPA.). (gr. 3-6). lib. bdg. 15.45 (978-0-613-84669-1(9)) Tandem Library Bks.
Saber Es Poder: A Basic Grammar Book, Easy, Fun & Practical. (ENG & SPA.). 45.00 (978-0-944356-08-1(7)) Alegria Hispana Pubns.
Samaniego. mundo 21: Used With ... Samaniego-Mundo 21. 3rd ed. 2004. (YA). cd-rom 3.96 (978-0-618-27582-3(7), 351022) Houghton Mifflin College Div.
Sigmar Staff. Sinonimos - Ant - Paraonimos (Synonyms - Ant - Homonyms) (SPA.). (J). 9.95 (978-950-11-0639-8(X)) Sigmar ARG. *Dist:* AIMS International Bks., Inc.
La Sirenita. 2003. (SPA.). 28.95 (978-0-673-77379-1(5)) Celebration Pr.
Sweeney, Alyse. All about Me Spanish Write & Read Books: 15 Fun-Shaped Book Patterns with Motivating Prompts to Get Kids Excited about Writing! 2003. (SPA., Illus.). 64p. pap., tchr. ed. 11.95 (978-0-439-49870-8(8), Teaching Resources) Scholastic, Inc.
Tabor, Nancy. See What You Say. 2000. Tr. of Ve Lo Que Dices. (ENG & SPA., Illus.). (J). (978-1-57091-375-4(7)) Charlesbridge Publishing, Inc.
—See What You Say. 2000. Tr. of Ve Lo Que Dices. (SPA.). (gr. k-3). lib. bdg. 15.25 (978-0-613-28312-0(0)) Tandem Library Bks.
Tamayo, Reve. Lenguaje: Reference & Practice for Advanced Students of Spanish ., 1 vol., Vol. 1. 2001. (SPA.). 451p. (gr. 7-12). pap. 35.00 (978-1-883514-03-7(7)) Bastos Bk. Co.
—Lenguaje: Reference & Practice for Advanced Students of Spanish T. G. 2001. (SPA.). 51p. (YA). (gr. 7-12). instr.'s gde. ed. 6.00 (978-1-883514-04-4(5)) Bastos Bk. Co.
Thayer, Tanya. La Primavera. 2005. Tr. of Spring. (SPA.). (J). 24p. (gr. k-2). pap. 4.25 (978-0-8225-3158-6(5)); (Illus.). 23p. (gr. 3-7). lib. bdg. 17.27 (978-0-8225-3165-4(8), Ediciones Lerner) Lerner Publishing Group.
Thomas, Keith A. The Idioms. Thomas, Keith A., illus. (ENG & SPA., Illus.). 44p. (J). (gr. 3 up). pap. (978-0-9617451-4-1(2)) KALEXT Productions, LLC.

Thomas, Rose. Spanish - Elementary. 1999. (100+ Seriestm Ser.). (SPA.). 128p. (J). (gr. k-12). pap. 12.99 (978-1-56822-197-7(5) , IF8790) School Specialty Publishing.
—Spanish - Middle/High School. 1999. (100+ Seriestm Ser.). (SPA.). 128p. (J). (gr. k-12). pap. 12.99 (978-1-56822-198-4(3) , IF8791) School Specialty Publishing.
La Tostada. 2003. 23.95 (978-0-673-77800-0(2)) Celebration Pr.
Travis, Joelle & Figueras, Ligaya, eds. Numeros, Colores, Verbos y Frases. Hazan, Maurice, illus. 2003. (SPA.). 112p. (J). per. 20.00 (978-1-932770-17-9(8) , SWLB2) Symtalk, Inc.
Tulip, Jenny. My First Spanish Word Book. 2004. (ENG & SPA., Illus.). 48p. (J). 5.99 (978-1-85854-394-9(0)) Brimax Books Ltd. GBR. *Dist:* Byeway Bks.
Vaamonde, Conchita, tr. My First Spanish Words. Tulip, Jenny, illus. 2004. (SPA.). 12p. (J). bds. 7.99 (978-1-85854-512-7(9)) Brimax Books Ltd. GBR. *Dist:* Byeway Bks.
Via Libre! Bien Dicho! 2002. (SPA.). (gr. 3 up). stu. ed. 45.05 (978-0-7362-1107-9(1)); (gr. 4 up). stu. ed. 46.12 (978-0-7362-1108-6(X)) Hampton-Brown Bks.
Wise, Sue. How Do I Say That? Como Se Dice? Coirault, Christine, illus. 2006. (ENG & SPA.). 32p. (J). pap. 8.95 (978-0-8368-6583-7(9)); lib. bdg. 23.33 (978-0-8368-6259-1(7)) Stevens, Gareth Inc.
With addition of Elefonetica Phonics Storybooks Green & Orange Collections. (De Canciones A Cuentos Ser.). (SPA.). (gr. 1 up). 987.10 (978-0-7362-0703-4(1)) Hampton-Brown Bks.
Zocchi, Judith Mazzeo, et al. Aimee's a Book: El Libro a de Aimee. Revutsky, Helen Ross, illus. 2005. (J). ***978-1-59646-421-6(6))*** Dingles & Co.
Zocchi, Judy. Cassie's "C" Book: El Libro "C" de Cassie. 2005. (SPA & ENG., Illus.). (J). ***978-1-59646-433-9(X))*** Dingles & Co.

S

SPANISH LANGUAGE—READERS

Abrapalabra! (SPA.). (ps-1). 161.67 (978-0-7362-2592-2(7)) Hampton-Brown Bks.
Abuelita y Yo. (Spanish Early Intervention Levels Ser.). (SPA.). 23.10 (978-1-56334-777-1(6)); Vol. 3. 3.85 (978-1-56334-450-3(5)) Hampton-Brown Bks.
El abuelo Cascarrabias 17: Leveled Books. 2001. (McGraw-Hill. Lectura Ser.). (ENG & SPA.). (gr. 4 up). (978-0-02-188162-8(6)) Macmillan/McGraw-Hill Schl. Div.
Accame, Jorge. Quien Pidio un Vaso de Agua? 2002. (SPA.). 64p. (J). pap. 6.95 (978-1-4000-0007-4(6)) Random House Publishing Group.
Acento 1: Cuaderno de Ortografia. (SPA.). (J). (gr. 1-9). 16.00 (978-958-04-3823-6(4)) Norma S.A. COL. *Dist:* Distribuidora Norma, Inc.
Acento 2: Cuaderno de Ortografia. (SPA.). (J). 16.00 (978-958-04-3822-9(6)) Norma S.A. COL. *Dist:* Distribuidora Norma, Inc.
Acento 3: Cuaderno de Ortografia. (SPA.). (J). (gr. 1-9). 16.00 (978-958-04-3821-2(8)) Norma S.A. COL. *Dist:* Distribuidora Norma, Inc.
Acento 4: Cuaderno de Ortografia. (SPA.). (J). (gr. 1-9). 16.00 (978-958-04-3820-5(X)) Norma S.A. COL. *Dist:* Distribuidora Norma, Inc.
Acento 5: Cuaderno de Ortografia. (SPA.). (J). (gr. 1-9). 16.00 (978-958-04-3819-9(6)) Norma S.A. COL. *Dist:* Distribuidora Norma, Inc.
Acento 6: Cuaderno de Ortografia. (SPA.). (J). (gr. 1-9). 16.00 (978-958-04-3829-8(3)) Norma S.A. COL. *Dist:* Distribuidora Norma, Inc.
Acento 7: Cuaderno de Ortografia. (SPA.). (J). (gr. 1-9). 16.00 (978-958-04-3830-4(7)) Norma S.A. COL. *Dist:* Distribuidora Norma, Inc.
Adita se Escapo 12: Leveled Books. 2001. (McGraw-Hill. Lectura Ser.). (ENG & SPA.). (gr. 2 up). (978-0-02-188037-9(9)) Macmillan/McGraw-Hill Schl. Div.
Adivina cuanto te Quiero 6: Leveled Books. 2001. (McGraw-Hill. Lectura Ser.). (ENG & SPA.). (gr. 1 up). (978-0-02-187983-0(4)) Macmillan/McGraw-Hill Schl. Div.
Adivinalo!, 6, Pack. (Literatura 2000 Ser.). (SPA.). (gr. k-1). 28.00 (978-0-7635-1009-1(2)) Rigby Education.
El Aeropuerto, 2, Pack. (Chiquilibros Ser.). (SPA.). (ps-1). 12.00 (978-0-7635-8557-0(2)) Rigby Education.
Aguirre, Sergio. La Venganza de la Vaca. (SPA.). 9.95 (978-958-04-4380-3(7)) Norma S.A. COL. *Dist:* Distribuidora Norma, Inc.
Ahumada. Juguemos a Leer-Texto.Tr. of Lets Play to Read. (SPA.). (J). 8.98 (978-968-24-5631-2(2)) Trillas Editorial, S. A. MEX. *Dist:* Continental Bk. Co., Inc., Giron Bks.
El album de Fotos: Individual Title Six-Packs. (Coleccion Pm Ser.).Tr. of Photo Book. (SPA.). 16p. (gr. 1 up). 26.00 (978-0-7578-2955-0(4)) Rigby Education.
El album de las Familias 10: Leveled Books. 2001. (McGraw-Hill. Lectura Ser.). (ENG & SPA.). (gr. 1 up). (978-0-02-187963-2(X)) Macmillan/McGraw-Hill Schl. Div.
Alcantara, Ricardo. Cuenta Estrellas.Tr. of Counting Stars. (SPA.). 64p. (J). (gr. 3-5). 6.36 (978-84-261-2146-2(2)) Juventud, Editorial ESP. *Dist:* Lectorum Pubns., Inc.
Alfaro Sifontes, Manuel Guillermo. Alboroto en un Lugar Remoto. 2005. (Illus.). 32p. (J). (978-1-58018-052-8(3)) Versal Editorial Group.
Allan, Nicholas. El Cielo. 2000. Tr. of Heaven. (SPA.). (J). (ps-k). 9.20 (978-980-257-194-9(6)) Ekare, Ediciones VEN. *Dist:* Lectorum Pubns., Inc.
Alphabet Sorting Box. (ps-12). 22.40 (978-0-7362-1095-9(4)) Hampton-Brown Bks.
Alto! Vol. 2: Individual Title Six-Packs. (Coleccion Pm Ser.: Vol. 2). Tr. of Stop!. (SPA.). 16p. (gr. k-1). 26.00 (978-0-7578-0680-3(5)) Rigby Education.
Amanecer Grade K: Student Anthology. (Nuevos Horizontes Ser.). (SPA.). (J). 9.95 (978-1-56014-499-1(8)) Santillana USA Publishing Co., Inc.
Ambrus, Victor G. Busca a Dracula (Search for Dracula) (J). 5.95 (978-950-08-1288-7(6)) Atlantida ARG. *Dist:* AIMS International Bks., Inc.
—Cuenta con Dracula (Count with Dracula) (J). 5.95 (978-950-08-1286-3(X)) Atlantida ARG. *Dist:* AIMS International Bks., Inc.
—Lee Con Dracula (Read with Dracula) (J). 5.95 (978-950-08-1287-0(8)) Atlantida ARG. *Dist:* AIMS International Bks., Inc.
—Que Hora Es, Dracula? (What Time Is It, Dracula?) (J). 5.95 (978-950-08-1285-6(1)) Atlantida ARG. *Dist:* AIMS International Bks., Inc.
Un Amigo para el Conejito Blanco, 6 vols., Pack. (Coleccion Pm Ser.).Tr. of Friend for Little White Rabbit. (SPA.). 16p. (gr. 1 up). 26.00 (978-0-7578-2986-4(4)) Rigby Education.
Amigos, 6 vols., Pack. (Literatura 2000 Ser.). (SPA.). (gr. k-1). 28.00 (978-0-7635-1010-7(6)) Rigby Education.
Los amigos del Mono, 6 Pack. (Literatura 2000 Ser.). (SPA.). (gr. 1-2). 28.00 (978-0-7635-1033-6(5)) Rigby Education.
Amigos para Siempre: Individual Title Six-Packs. (Literatura 2000 Ser.). (SPA.). (gr. 2-3). 33.00 (978-0-7635-1081-7(5)) Rigby Education.
Amor de Beatriz. (SPA.). pap. 11.95 (978-88-8148-806-3(X)) European Language Institute ITA. *Dist:* Distribooks, Inc.
Amos, Janine. Admitir Nuestros Errores. Coffey, Colleen & Carrillo, Consuelo, trs. from ENG. 2002. (Weekly Reader Early Learning Library). (SPA., Illus.). 32p. (J). (ps up). lib. bdg. 23.33 (978-0-8368-3203-7(5)) Stevens, Gareth Inc.
—Ayudar a los Demas. Coffey, Colleen & Carrillo, Consuelo, trs. 2002. (Weekly Reader Early Learning Library). (SPA., Illus.). 32p. (J). (ps up). lib. bdg. 23.33 (978-0-8368-3204-4(3)) Stevens, Gareth Inc.
—Compartir. Coffey, Colleen & Carrillo, Consuelo, trs. from ENG. 2002. (Weekly Reader Early Learning Library). (SPA., Illus.). 32p. (J). (ps up). lib. bdg. 23.33 (978-0-8368-3205-1(1)) Stevens, Gareth Inc.
—Esperar Nuestro Turno. Coffey, Colleen & Carrillo, Consuelo, trs. 2002. (Weekly Reader Early Learning Library). (SPA., Illus.). 32p. (J). (ps up). lib. bdg. 23.33 (978-0-8368-3206-8(X)) Stevens, Gareth Inc.
—Hacer Amigos. Coffey, Colleen & Carrillo, Consuelo, trs. from ENG. 2002. (Weekly Reader Early Learning Library). (SPA., Illus.). 32p. (J). (ps up). lib. bdg. 23.33 (978-0-8368-3207-5(8)) Stevens, Gareth Inc.
—Ser Amables. Coffey, Colleen & Carrillo, Consuelo, trs. 2002. (Weekly Reader Early Learning Library). (SPA., Illus.). 32p. (J). (ps up). lib. bdg. 23.33 (978-0-8368-3208-2(6)) Stevens, Gareth Inc.
Anastasio, Dina. Por qué el cuervo es negro y el buho tiene manchitas & How Raven Became Black & Owl Got Its Spots. 2005. spiral bd. 66.00 ***978-1-4108-5626-5(7))*** Benchmark Education Co.
Anaya Publishers Staff. Aprender a Vivir 1. (SPA.). 56p. (J). (978-84-207-7136-6(8)) Grupo Anaya, S.A.
—Aprender a Vivir 2. (SPA.). (J). (978-84-207-7190-8(2)) Grupo Anaya, S.A.
—Aprender a Vivir 3. (SPA.). 88p. (J). (978-84-207-6555-6(4)) Grupo Anaya, S.A.
—Aprender a Vivir 3: Propuesta Didactica. (SPA.). 128p. (J). (978-84-207-6556-3(2)) Grupo Anaya, S.A.
—Aprender a Vivir 4. (SPA.). 88p. (J). (978-84-207-6557-0(0)) Grupo Anaya, S.A.
—Aprender a Vivir 4: Propuesta Didactica. (SPA.). 128p. (J). (978-84-207-6558-7(9)) Grupo Anaya, S.A.
—Aprender a Vivir 5. (SPA.). 88p. (J). (978-84-207-6559-4(7)) Grupo Anaya, S.A.
—Aprender a Vivir 5: Propuesta Didactica. (SPA.). 128p. (J). (978-84-207-6560-0(0)) Grupo Anaya, S.A.
—Aprender a Vivir 6. (SPA.). 88p. (J). (978-84-207-6561-7(9)) Grupo Anaya, S.A.
—Aprender a Vivir 6: Propuesta Didactica. (SPA.). 128p. (J). (978-84-207-6562-4(7)) Grupo Anaya, S.A.
Antartida, 6 vols., Pack. (On Deck en Espanol Ser.).Tr. of Antarctica. (SPA.). 24p. (gr. 4-5). 35.00 (978-0-7578-6450-6(3)) Rigby Education.
El Apicultor, 6 vols., Pack. (Literatura 2000 Ser.). (SPA.). (gr. 2-3). 33.00 (978-0-7635-1083-1(1)) Rigby Education.
La aplanadora Chiquita: Individual Title Six-Packs. (Coleccion Pm Ser.).Tr. of Little Bulldozer. (SPA.). 16p. (gr. 1 up). 26.00 (978-0-7578-2994-9(5)) Rigby Education.
La aplanadora chiquita ayuda otra Vez, 6 vols., Pack. (Coleccion Pm Ser.).Tr. of Little bulldozer helps again. (SPA.). 16p. (gr. 1 up). 26.00 (978-0-7578-3024-2(2)) Rigby Education.
Aquel que Escucha: Individual Title Six-Packs. (Literatura 2000 Ser.). (SPA.). (gr. 2-3). 33.00 (978-0-7635-1084-8(X)) Rigby Education.
Aquellos Dias de Dinosaurios: Little Book, Level 14, Vol. 14. 2003. (Fonolibros Ser.). 35.50 (978-0-7652-0124-9(0)) Modern Curriculum Pr.
El arbol de Diego: Individual Title Six-Packs. (Literatura 2000 Ser.). (SPA.). (gr. 1-2). 28.00 (978-0-7635-1034-3(3)) Rigby Education.
El arbol de la Miel: Individual Title Six-Packs. (Literatura 2000 Ser.). (SPA.). (gr. 2-3). 33.00 (978-0-7635-1254-5(0)) Rigby Education.
Are We There Yet, Mama? 2003. 23.95 (978-0-673-78136-9(4)) Celebration Pr.
Arnold, George. Los Gatos of the CIA. 2005. (SPA & ENG., Illus.). 225p. pap. 22.95 (978-1-57168-861-3(7) , Nortex Pr.) Eakin Pr.
Arrugas: Individual Title Six-Packs. (Literatura 2000 Ser.). (SPA.). (gr. 1-2). 28.00 (978-0-7635-1035-0(1)) Rigby Education.
Asi 2 (Lower) 2006. (Illus.). 160p. (YA). pap., stu. ed. 32.50 (978-0-7487-9173-6(6)) Nelson Thornes Ltd. GBR. *Dist:* Trans-Atlantic Pubns., Inc.
El Autobus Rojo, 6 Pcks. (Coleccion Pm Ser.).Tr. of Little Red Bus. (SPA.). 16p. (gr. 1 up). 26.00 (978-0-7578-3037-2(4)) Rigby Education.
La Aventura de Pimienta, 6 Pcks. (Coleccion Pm Ser.).Tr. of Pepper's adventure. (SPA.). 16p. (gr. 1 up). 26.00 (978-0-7578-3051-8(X)) Rigby Education.
Aventuras Infantiles/Adventures for Kids. (ENG & SPA.). 80p. (J). 17.00 (978-0-944356-04-3(4)) Alegria Hispana Pubns.
Aviones del Pasado: Individual Title, 6 pack. (On Deck en Espanol Ser.).Tr. of Planes of the Past. (SPA.). 24p. (gr. 4-5). 35.00 (978-0-7578-6424-7(4)) Rigby Education.
Aviones Supersonicos: Individual Title, 6 packs. (On Deck en Espanol Ser.).Tr. of Supersonic Jets. (SPA.). 24p. (gr. 4-5). 35.00 (978-0-7578-6434-6(1)) Rigby Education.
Ayer Vino Santa Clos: Individual, 6-packs. 2003. 23.95 (978-0-673-77137-7(7)) Celebration Pr.
La ballena Azul: Individual Title Six-Packs. (On Deck en Espanol Ser.).Tr. of Blue Whale. (SPA.). 24p. (gr. 4 5). 35.00 (978-0-7578-6437-7(6)) Rigby Education.
La banda del Sabihondo 8: Leveled Books. 2001. (McGraw-Hill. Lectura Ser.). (ENG & SPA.). (gr. 4 up). (978-0-02-188153-6(7)) Macmillan/McGraw-Hill Schl. Div.
Banegas, Candela. Una Rayuela Bk. A: Level 1. (SPA & ENG.). 96p. (J). (gr. 3-7). wbk. ed. 12.95 (978-84-7143-810-2(0) , SGS8100) Sociedad General Espanola de Libreria ESP. *Dist:* Continental Bk. Co., Inc.
—Una Rayuela Bk. B: Level 1. (SPA & ENG.). 98p. (J). (gr. 3-7). wbk. ed. 12.95 (978-84-7143-811-9(9) , SGS8119) Sociedad General Espanola de Libreria ESP. *Dist:* Continental Bk. Co., Inc.
El bano de Benito. (Spanish Early Intervention Levels Ser.). (SPA.). 21.30 (978-0-7362-0824-6(0)) Hampton-Brown Bks.
El Bano de Benito, Vol. 8. (Spanish Early Intervention Levels Ser.). (SPA.). 3.55 (978-0-7362-0770-6(8)) Hampton-Brown Bks.
El Bano de Papa, 6, Pack. (Literatura 2000 Ser.). (SPA.). (gr. 1-2). 28.00 (978-0-7635-1058-9(0)) Rigby Education.
Barredo, Jose Eduardo. Mundo Azul. (Torre de Papel Ser.). (SPA.). (YA). (gr. 7 up). 7.95 (978-958-04-4522-7(2)) Norma S.A. COL. *Dist:* Distribuidora Norma, Inc.
Un Barrio Muy Especial. (Coleccion Leo Con Figuras). (SPA., Illus.). 14p. (J). pap. 4.50 (978-950-11-0928-3(3) , SGM293) Sigmar ARG. *Dist:* Continental Bk. Co., Inc.
Beaude, Pierre Marie. Flora, la Desconocida del Espacio. (Torre de Papel Ser.). (SPA.). (YA). (gr. 6 up). 7.95 (978-958-04-1033-1(X)) Norma S.A. COL. *Dist:* Distribuidora Norma, Inc.
Beck, Paul. Disney Light up: el cuerpo Humano: Disney Light up: Human Body, Spanish-Language Edition. 2007. (Illus.). 48p. (J). 15.99 ***978-970-718-436-7(1)*** , Silver Dolphin en Español) Advanced Marketing, S. de R. L. de C. V. MEX. *Dist:* Perseus Distribution.
Benchmark Education Staff. Spanish Emergent Supplement. 2005. 130.00 ***978-1-4108-5615-9(1));*** (J). spiral bd. 880.00 ***978-1-4108-5613-5(5))*** Benchmark Education Co.
Benchmark Education Staff, compiled by. Spanish Early/ Fluent Supplement. 2005. spiral bd. 1350.00 ***978-1-4108-5661-6(5))*** Benchmark Education Co.
—Spanish Grade 3 Small Group Set. 2005. spiral bd. 4000.00 ***978-1-4108-5667-8(4));*** spiral bd. 1000.00 ***978-1-4108-5668-5(2))*** Benchmark Education Co.
—Spanish Grade 4 Small Group Set. 2005. spiral bd. 4000.00 ***978-1-4108-5669-2(0));*** spiral bd. 1000.00 ***978-1-4108-5670-8(4))*** Benchmark Education Co.
—Spanish Grade 5 Small Group Set. 2005. spiral bd. 1000.00 ***978-1-4108-4960-1(0))*** Benchmark Education Co.
Benegas, Candela. Una Rayuela: Level 1. (SPA & ENG.). 128p. (J). (gr. 3-7). stu. ed. 21.95 (978-84-7143-804-1(6) , SGS8046) Sociedad General Espanola de Libreria ESP. *Dist:* Continental Bk. Co., Inc.
Biblioteca Saltamontes Spanish Chapter Books Coleccion Viva Chivito! Classroom Set & Manipulatives. (SPA.). (gr. 1-2). 517.82 incl. audio compact disk (978-0-7362-1591-6(3)); 521.25 incl. reel tape (978-0-7362-1589-3(1)) Hampton-Brown Bks.
La Bicicross de Alex: Individual Title Six-Packs. (Literatura 2000 Ser.). (SPA.). (gr. 1-2). 28.00 (978-0-7635-1036-7(X)) Rigby Education.
Bienvenidos! (Illus.). 96p. (J). (gr. k-5). Level 1. (ENG & SPA.). pap., wbk. ed. 18.95 (978-88-8148-038-8(7)); Level 2. (SPA & ENG., pap., wbk. ed. 18.95 (978-88-8148-045-6(X)) European Language Institute ITA. *Dist:* Distribooks, Inc.
Blackaby, Susan. El Cuadro de Mary. Haugen, Ryan, illus. 2006. (Read-It! Readers en Espanol Ser.).Tr. of Mary's Art. (SPA.). 32p. (J). (ps-3). 19.95 (978-1-4048-1649-7(6)) Picture Window Bks.
—El Lugar de Luis. Gallagher-Cole, Mernie, illus. 2006. (Read-It! Readers en Espanol Ser.).Tr. of Place for Mike. (SPA.). 32p. (J). (ps-3). 19.95 (978-1-4048-1688-6(7)) Picture Window Bks.
—El Mejor Futbolista. Haugen, Ryan, illus. 2006. (Read-It! Readers en Espanol Ser.).Tr. of Best Soccer Player. (SPA.). 32p. (J). (ps-3). 19.95 (978-1-4048-1690-9(9)) Picture Window Bks.
—El Patito Feo: Version del Cuento de Hans Christian Andersen. Delage, Charlene, illus. 2006. (Read-It! Readers en Espanol Ser.).Tr. of Ugly Duckling: A Retelling of the Hans Christian Andersen Fairy Tale. (SPA.). 32p. (J). (ps-3). 19.95 (978-1-4048-1644-2(5)) Picture Window Bks.
—El Soldadito de Plomo: Version del Cuento de Hans Christian Andersen. Delage, Charlene, illus. 2006. (Read-It! Readers en Espanol Ser.).Tr. of Steadfast Tin Soldier: A Retelling of the Hans Christian Andersen Fairy Tale. (SPA.). 32p. (J). (ps-3). 19.95 (978-1-4048-1641-1(0)) Picture Window Bks.
—El Traje Nuevo del Emperador: Version del Cuento de los Hermanos Grimm. Delage, Charlene, illus. 2006. (Read-It! Readers en Espanol Ser.).Tr. of Emperor's New Clothes: A Retelling of the Grimm's Fairy Tale. (SPA.). 32p. (J). (ps-3). 19.95 (978-1-4048-1629-9(1)) Picture Window Bks.
Blair, Eric. El Cascabel del Gato: Version de la Fabula de Esopo. Silverman, Dianne, illus. 2006. (Read-It! Readers en Espanol Ser.).Tr. of Belling the Cat: A Retelling of Aesop's Fable. (SPA.). 32p. (J). (ps-3). 19.95 (978-1-4048-1615-2(1)) Picture Window Bks.
—El Cuervo y la Jarra: Version de la Fabula de Esopo. Silverman, Dianne, illus. 2006. (Read-It! Readers en Espanol Ser.).Tr. of Crow & the Pitcher: A Retelling of Aesop's Fable. (SPA.). 32p. (J). (ps-3). 19.95 (978-1-4048-1618-3(6)) Picture Window Bks.
—El Flautista de Hamelin. Peterson, Ben, illus. 2006. (Read-It! Readers en Espanol Ser.).Tr. of Pied Piper. (SPA.). 32p. (J). (ps-3). 19.95 (978-1-4048-1651-0(8)) Picture Window Bks.
—El Gato con Botas: Version del Cuento de los Hermanos Grimm. Ouren, Todd, illus. 2006. (Read-It! Readers en Espanol Ser.).Tr. of Puss in Boots: A Retelling of the Grimm's Fairy Tale. (SPA.). 32p. (J). (ps-3). 19.95 (978-1-4048-1635-0(6)) Picture Window Bks.
—El Lobo y los Siete Cabritos: Version del Cuento de los Hermanos Grimm. Petrusek, Brett, illus. 2006. (Read-It! Readers en Espanol Ser.).Tr. of Wolf & the Seven Little Kids: A Retelling of the Grimm's Fairy Tale. (SPA.). 32p. (J). (ps-3). 19.95 (978-1-4048-1645-9(3)) Picture Window Bks.
—El Ninito de Jengibre. Peterson, Ben, illus. 2006. (Read-It! Readers en Espanol Ser.).Tr. of Gingerbread Man. (SPA.). 32p. (J). (ps-3). 19.95 (978-1-4048-1647-3(X)) Picture Window Bks.
—El Pastorcito Mentiroso: Version de la Fabula de Esopo. Silverman, Dianne, illus. 2006. (Read-It! Readers en Espanol Ser.).Tr. of Boy Who Cried Wolf: A Retelling of Aesop's Fable. (SPA.). 32p. (J). (ps-3). 19.95 (978-1-4048-1616-9(X)) Picture Window Bks.
—El Pescador y su Mujer: Version del Cuento de los Hermanos Grimm. Ouren, Todd, illus. 2006. (Read-It! Readers en Espanol Ser.).Tr. of Fisherman & His Wife: A Retelling of the Grimm's Fairy Tale. (SPA.). 32p. (J). (ps-3). 19.95 (978-1-4048-1630-5(5)) Picture Window Bks.
—El Principe Encantado: Version del Cuento de los Hermanos Grimm. Ouren, Todd, illus. 2006. (Read-It! Readers en Espanol Ser.).Tr. of Frog Prince: A Retelling of the Grimm's Fairy Tale. (SPA.). 32p. (J). (ps-3). 19.95 (978-1-4048-1631-2(3)) Picture Window Bks.
—El Raton de Campo y el Raton de Ciudad: Version de la Fabula de Esopo. Silverman, Dianne, illus. 2006. (Read-It! Readers en Espanol Ser.).Tr. of Country Mouse & the City Mouse: A Retelling of Aesop's Fable. (SPA.). 32p. (J). (ps-3). 19.95 (978-1-4048-1617-6(8)) Picture Window Bks.
Blair, Robert. Power-Glide Spanish Children's Course Upgrade, 2 bks. l.t. ed. 2001. (Illus.). 204p. (J). pap. 59.95 incl. audio compact disk (978-1-58204-210-7(1)) Power-Glide Foreign Language Courses.
Blair, Robert W. Power-Glide Spanish Children's Course Workbook Upgrade, 2 bks. rev. ed. 2001. (SPA., Illus.). 204p. (J). pap., wbk. ed. 29.95 (978-1-58204-223-7(3)) Power-Glide Foreign Language Courses.
—Power-Glide Spanish Ultimate Adventure Course, 2 l.t. ed. 2002. (Illus.). 375p. (YA). pap. 149.95 incl. cd-rom, audio compact disk (978-1-58204-200-8(4)) Power-Glide Foreign Language Courses.
Blanco & Revah, Patricia. ABC. 2000. (SPA.). (J). 11.50 (978-970-629-152-3(0)) Sistemas Tecnicos de Edicion, S.A. de C.V. MEX. *Dist:* AIMS International Bks., Inc.
Blue Collection. (Elefonetica Ser.). (SPA.). (gr. 1-2). 373.22 (978-0-7362-0795-9(3)) Hampton-Brown Bks.
La Boda, 6, Pack. 2003. 23.95 (978-0-673-77138-4(5)) Celebration Pr.
La Boda, 6 pack. (Literatura 2000 Ser.). (SPA.). (gr. k-1). 28.00 (978-0-7635-1011-4(4)) Rigby Education.
La Boda de Trazo y Rayita. (SPA.). (J). 12.00 (978-958-02-1364-2(X)) Editorial Voluntad S.A. COL. *Dist:* Distribuidora Norma, Inc.
Boie, Kirsten. King-Kong, el Conejillo de Indias Viajeros. (Torre de Papel Ser.). (SPA.). (J). (gr. 2). 7.95 (978-958-04-1311-0(8)) Norma S.A. COL. *Dist:* Distribuidora Norma, Inc.
Bojunga, Lygia. La Casa de la Madrina. (Torre de Papel Ser.). (SPA.). (J). (gr. 4 up). 8.95 (978-958-04-3396-5(8) , NR30562) Norma S.A. COL. *Dist:* Distribuidora Norma, Inc., Lectorum Pubns., Inc.
—La Cuerda Floja. (Torre de Papel Ser.).Tr. of Tightrope. (SPA.). (J). (gr. 4 up). 8.95 (978-958-04-4527-2(3)) Norma S.A. COL. *Dist:* Distribuidora Norma, Inc.
Boo! Matching English, 6 Pack. 2003. 23.95 (978-0-673-76188-0(6)) Celebration Pr.
Bornemann, Elsa. El Libro de los Chicos Enamorados. (SPA.). (J). (gr. 5-8). 8.95 (978-958-04-3454-2(9) , NR7681) Norma S.A. COL. *Dist:* Distribuidora Norma, Inc., Lectorum Pubns., Inc.
—El Ultimo Mago de Bilembambudin. (Torre de Papel Ser.). (SPA.). (J). (gr. 4 up). 8.95 (978-958-04-3455-9(7)) Norma S.A. COL. *Dist:* Distribuidora Norma, Inc.
Borreguita Negra. 2003. 23.95 (978-0-673-77381-4(7)) Celebration Pr.
El bosque de Miel. (Saludos Ser.: Vol. 1). (SPA.). (gr. 2-3). 31.00 (978-0-7635-5731-7(5)) Rigby Education.

El bosque de Miel: 6 Small Books. (Saludos Ser.: Vol. 1). (SPA.). (gr. 2-3). 31.00 (978-0-7635-9538-8(1)) Rigby Education.

Brad el de la Mala Suerte: Bad Luck Brad in Spanish. 2006. (SPA.). 32p. (J). pap. 4.95 (978-1-57565-169-9(6)) Kane Pr., The.

Brady, Peter. Camiones de Bomberos. Schon, Isabel, ed. Ferrer, Martín Luis Guzman, tr. 1998. (Coleccion Primeros Lectores). (SPA., Illus.). 24p. (J). (gr. k-3). lib. bdg. 18.60 (978-1-56065-791-0(X) , CAP1078, Bridgestone Bks.) Capstone Pr., Inc.

—Cerdos. Schon, Isabel, ed. Ferrer, Martín Luis Guzman, tr. from ENG. Munoz, William, illus. 1998. (Coleccion Primeros Lectores). (SPA.). 24p. (J). (gr. k-3). lib. bdg. 18.60 (978-1-56065-789-7(8) , Bridgestone Bks.) Capstone Pr., Inc.

—Ovejas. Schon, Isabel, ed. Ferrer, Martín Luis Guzman, tr. from ENG. Munoz, William, illus. 1998. (Coleccion Primeros Lectores). (SPA.). 24p. (J). (gr. k-3). lib. bdg. 18.60 (978-1-56065-790-3(1) , CAP2405, Bridgestone Bks.) Capstone Pr., Inc.

—Vacas. Schon, Isabel, ed. Ferrer, Martín Luis Guzman, tr. from ENG. Munoz, William, illus. 1998. (Coleccion Primeros Lectores). (SPA.). 24p. (J). (gr. k-3). lib. bdg. 18.60 (978-1-56065-788-0(X) , Bridgestone Bks.) Capstone Pr., Inc.

Bravo, Queta!, 6 pack. 2003. 23.95 (978-0-673-78072-0(4)) Celebration Pr.

Bridwell, Norman. Clifford y el Monton de Hoyas. Salas, Macarena, ed. 2002. (Clifford Big Red Readers Ser.). (SPA., Illus.). 32p. (J). pap. 3.99 (978-0-439-25040-5(4) , SO30514, Scholastic en Espanol) Scholastic, Inc.

Brinca la Tablita. 2003. 28.95 (978-0-673-78091-1(0)) Celebration Pr.

Brooks, Felicity & Mackinnon, Mairi. First Picture Spanish - Internet Referenced. 2006. 18p. (J). bds. 14.99 (978-0-7945-1384-9(0) , Usborne) EDC Publishing.

Brownrigg, Sheri. Todos los Tutus Deberian Ser Rosas. Johnson, Meredith, illus. 2002. (Coleccion "Hola, Lector" Ser.). (SPA.). 32p. (J). (gr. k-2). pap. 3.99 (978-0-439-25985-9(1) , SO30499, Scholastic en Espanol) Scholastic, Inc.

Bruzzone, Catherine. First Spanish with Supergato. 2007. 13.95 (978-0-07-147931-8(7) , 9780071479318) McGraw-Hill Cos., The.

—Lucy the Cat at the Party/La Gatita Lucia en la Fiesta. Beaton, Claire, illus. 2006. (Bilingual Picture Strip Bks.). (SPA & ENG.). 24p. (J). pap. 4.99 (978-0-7641-3408-1(6)) Barron's Educational Series, Inc.

—Spanish on the Move for Kids. 2nd rev. ed. 2005. (ENG & SPA., Illus.). 24p. pap. 11.95 incl. cd-rom (978-0-07-145689-0(9) , 9780071456890) McGraw-Hill Cos., The.

Buceando en el Misterio. 2000. (SPA., Illus.). 70p. (YA). (gr. 8-10). pap. 11.95 (978-88-8148-333-4(5)) European Language Institute ITA. *Dist:* Distribooks, Inc., Midwest European Pubns.

Un buen Lugar. (Spanish Early Intervention Levels Ser.). (SPA.). 31.14 (978-0-7362-0326-5(5)) Hampton-Brown Bks.

Un Buen Lugar (E), Vol. 12. (Spanish Early Intervention Levels Ser.). (SPA.). 5.19 (978-0-7362-0301-2(X)) Hampton-Brown Bks.

Buen Viaje Pinguinos! (Coleccion Leo Con Figuras). (SPA., Illus.). 14p. (J). pap. 4.50 (978-950-11-0929-0(1) , SGM291) Sigmar ARG. *Dist:* Continental Bk. Co., Inc.

Buenas noches, Hermanito: Individual Title Six-Packs. (Literatura 2000 Ser.). (SPA.). (gr. 1-2). 28.00 (978-0-7635-1037-4(8)) Rigby Education.

Bulloch, Ivan & James, Diane. A Toi de Jouer. 2000. (My Turn Ser.). (Illus.). 12p. (J). (ps-k). bds. 6.95 (978-1-58728-166-2(X) , Two Can Publishing) T&N Children's Publishing.

A Bully Named Laura Sue: Social/Emotional Lap Book. (Pebble Soup Explorations Ser.). (SPA.). (ps up). 16.00 (978-0-7635-7568-7(2)) Rigby Education.

Burke, David. Cinderella (English to Spanish - Level 1) Learn SPANISH Through Fairy Tales. 2007. (Learn Spanish Through Fairy Tales Ser.). (ENG & SPA., Illus.). (J). per. 14.95 incl. audio compact disk ***(*978-1-891888-74-8(9))*** Slangman Publishing.

—Goldilocks (English to Spanish - Level 2) Learn SPANISH Through Fairy Tales. 2007. (Learn Spanish Through Fairy Tales Ser.). (ENG & SPA., Illus.). (J). per. 14.95 incl. audio compact disk ***(*978-1-891888-80-9(3))*** Slangman Publishing.

Burton, Margie & French, Tammy, Cathy - Jones. Playas limpias & Clean Beaches. 2005. spiral bd. 66.00 ***(*978-1-4108-5625-8(9))*** Benchmark Education Co.

Busquets, Jordi. Leo y Veo, las Brujas.Tr. of I Read & See, the Witches. (SPA.). (J). 3.48 (978-84-305-9406-1(X)) Susaeta Ediciones, S.A. ESP. *Dist:* AIMS International Bks., Inc., Giron Bks.

—Leo y Veo, las Hadas.Tr. of I Read & See, the Fairies. (SPA.). 24p. (J). 3.48 (978-84-305-9408-5(6)) Susaeta Ediciones, S.A. ESP. *Dist:* AIMS International Bks., Inc.

—Leo y Veo, los Gigantes.Tr. of I Read & See, the Giants. (SPA.). 24p. (J). 3.48 (978-84-305-9409-2(4)) Susaeta Ediciones, S.A. ESP. *Dist:* AIMS International Bks., Inc., Giron Bks.

—Leo y Veo, los Gnomos.Tr. of I Read & See, the Elves. (SPA.). 24p. (J). 3.48 (978-84-305-9407-8(8)) Susaeta Ediciones, S.A. ESP. *Dist:* AIMS International Bks., Inc.

Cabal, Graciela Beatriz. Toby. (Torre de Papel Ser.). (SPA., Illus.). (J). (gr. 4 up). 8.95 (978-958-04-4222-6(3)) Norma S.A. COL. *Dist:* Distribuidora Norma, Inc.

El Caballo Blanco, 6 Pack. (Literatura 2000 Ser.). (SPA.). (gr. 2-3). 33.00 (978-0-7635-1255-2(9)) Rigby Education.

El Caballo Comilon, 6 Pack. (Literatura 2000 Ser.). (SPA.). (gr. 1-2). 28.00 (978-0-7635-1038-1(6)) Rigby Education.

El caballo Mecanico, 6 Pack. (Chiquilibros Ser.). (SPA.). (gr. k-1). 23.00 (978-0-7635-8613-3(7)) Rigby Education.

Cae una Nuez. (Spanish Early Intervention Levels Ser.). (SPA.). 28.38 (978-0-7362-0838-3(0)) Hampton-Brown Bks.

Cae una Nuez (M), Vol. 20. (Spanish Early Intervention Levels Ser.). (SPA.). 4.73 (978-0-7362-0814-7(3)) Hampton-Brown Bks.

Caicedo, Maria Victoria. En la Casa con la Abuelita. (SPA.). (J). 8.95 (978-958-04-7445-6(1)) Norma S.A. COL. *Dist:* Distribuidora Norma, Inc.

Cajas: Individual Title Six-Packs. (Literatura 2000 Ser.). (SPA.). (gr. 1-2). 28.00 (978-0-7635-1059-6(9)) Rigby Education.

El Calcetin. (Spanish Early Intervention Levels Ser.). (SPA.). 23.10 (978-0-7362-0324-1(9)) Hampton-Brown Bks.

El Calcetin (E), Vol. 8. (Spanish Early Intervention Levels Ser.). (SPA.). 3.85 (978-0-7362-0299-2(4)) Hampton-Brown Bks.

Calderon, Eduardo Caballero. La Piedra Filosofal. (Torre de Papel Ser.). (SPA.). (J). (gr. 4 up). 8.95 (978-958-04-5043-6(9)) Norma S.A. COL. *Dist:* Distribuidora Norma, Inc.

Calvert, Mike & Gonzalez Florido, Helena. Asi 2 (Higher) 2006. (Illus.). (J). pap., stu. ed. 32.50 (978-0-7487-9172-9(8)) Nelson Thornes Ltd. GBR. *Dist:* Trans-Atlantic Pubns., Inc.

Camila y la Anciana-del-Barro: 6 Softcover Books. (Saludos Ser.: Vol. 1). (SPA.). (gr. 3-5). 31.00 (978-0-7635-1752-6(6)) Rigby Education.

Caminando: Individual Title Six-Packs. (Literatura 2000 Ser.). (SPA.). (gr. 2-3). 33.00 (978-0-7635-1085-5(8)) Rigby Education.

Caminata en la Ciudad, 6 Packs. (Chiquilibros Ser.). (SPA.). (ps-1). 12.00 (978-0-7635-8553-2(X)) Rigby Education.

Una Caminata Por el Bosque, 2 pack. (Chiquilibros Ser.). (SPA.). (ps-1). 12.00 (978-0-7635-8547-1(5)) Rigby Education.

La Camisa de Guerrero, 6 Pack. (Saludos Ser.: Vol. 2). (SPA.). (gr. 2-3). 31.00 (978-0-7635-9523-4(3)) Rigby Education.

Campbell, Eric. El Lugar de los Leones. (Torre de Papel Ser.).Tr. of Where Lions Wild. (SPA.). (YA). (gr. 6 up). 8.95 (978-958-04-3150-3(7)) Norma S.A. COL. *Dist:* Distribuidora Norma, Inc.

Campoy, F. Isabel, et al. Celebra el Ano Nuevo Chino con la Familia Fong. Castro, Mima, illus. 2006. (J). (978-1-59820-114-7(X) , Alfaguara) Santillana USA Publishing Co., Inc.

—Celebra Kwanzaa con Botitas y Sus Gatitos. Docampo, Valeria, illus. 2006. (J). (978-1-59820-123-9(9)) Santillana USA Publishing Co., Inc.

El cangrejo al fondo del Mar: Individual Title Six-Packs. (Literatura 2000 Ser.). (SPA.). (gr. 1-2). 28.00 (978-0-7635-1060-2(2)) Rigby Education.

El Cangurito: Individual Title Six-Packs. (Coleccion Pm Ser.).Tr. of Joey. (SPA.). 16p. (gr. 1 up). 26.00 (978-0-7578-3043-3(9)) Rigby Education.

Canizares, Susan & Chessen, Betsey. Storms: Tormentas. 2004. (Science Emergent Readers Ser.). (ENG & SPA., Illus.). (J). (978-0-439-66392-2(X)) Scholastic, Inc.

Cann, Kate. Viviendo Juntos. (SPA.). (YA). 9.95 (978-958-04-6873-8(7)) Norma S.A. COL. *Dist:* Distribuidora Norma, Inc.

Cano, Carles. El Arbol de las Hojas Din A-4. (SPA., Illus.). 28p. (J). (gr. k-2). (978-84-8464-027-1(2) , KA30310) Kalandraka Editora, S.L. ESP. *Dist:* Lectorum Pubns., Inc.

Caperucita Esquimal 9: Leveled Books. 2001. (McGraw-Hill. Lectura Ser.). (ENG & SPA.). (gr. 2 up). (978-0-02-188034-8(4)) Macmillan/McGraw-Hill Schl. Div.

Caperucita Tropical 9: Leveled Books. 2001. (McGraw-Hill. Lectura Ser.). (ENG & SPA.). (gr. 2 up). (978-0-02-188010-2(7)) Macmillan/McGraw-Hill Schl. Div.

La Cara del Oeste 4: Leveled Books. 2001. (McGraw-Hill. Lectura Ser.). (ENG & SPA.). (gr. 2 up). (978-0-02-188053-9(0)) Macmillan/McGraw-Hill Schl. Div.

Caritas. (Spanish Early Intervention Levels Ser.). (SPA.). 23.10 (978-1-56334-785-6(7)); Vol. 2. 3.85 (978-1-56334-458-9(0)) Hampton-Brown Bks.

Carlitos: Individual Title Six-Packs. (Literatura 2000 Ser.). (SPA.). (gr. 2-3). 33.00 (978-0-7635-1256-9(7)) Rigby Education.

El carnaval de Miami: Individual Title Six-Packs. (Coleccion Pm Ser.). (SPA.). 16p. (gr. 1 up). 26.00 (978-0-7578-3050-1(1)) Rigby Education.

La Carrera: Individual Title Six-Packs. (Coleccion Pm Ser.).Tr. of Cross-country Race. (SPA.). 16p. (gr. 1 up). 26.00 (978-0-7578-3052-5(8)) Rigby Education.

La Carrera 5: Leveled Books. 2001. (McGraw-Hill. Lectura Ser.). (ENG & SPA.). (gr. 5 up). (978-0-02-188229-8(0)) Macmillan/McGraw-Hill Schl. Div.

El Carrusel: Individual Title Six-Packs. (Coleccion Pm Ser.).Tr. of Merry-go-round. (SPA.). 16p. (gr. 1 up). 26.00 (978-0-7578-2957-4(0)) Rigby Education.

Carteles de Rimas y Canciones de Fonética (Phonics Songs & Rhymes Flip Chart) 2000. (SPA.). (gr. 1 up). suppl. ed. 116.50 (978-0-673-60598-6(1)) Addison-Wesley Educational Pubs., Inc.

Cartelones de Ensenanza: Resources & Ancillaries. 2001. (McGraw-Hill. Lectura Ser.). (ENG & SPA.). (gr. 1 up). (978-0-02-186586-4(8)); (gr. 2 up). (978-0-02-186587-1(6)); (gr. 3 up). (978-0-02-186588-8(4)); (gr. 4 up). (978-0-02-186589-5(2)); (gr. 5 up). (978-0-02-186590-1(6)) Macmillan/McGraw-Hill Schl. Div.

Una Casa: Individual Title Six-Packs. (Coleccion Pm Ser.: Vol. 1). Tr. of House. (SPA.). 16p. (gr. k-1). 26.00 (978-0-7578-0661-2(9)) Rigby Education.

La casa de Calabaza: Individual Title Six-Packs. (Literatura 2000 Ser.). (SPA.). (gr. 2-3). 33.00 (978-0-7635-1086-2(6)) Rigby Education.

La casa de Tita: Individual Title Six-Packs. (Literatura 2000 Ser.). (SPA.). (gr. 2-3). 33.00 (978-0-7635-1257-6(5)) Rigby Education.

La casa nueva de los Ortega: Individual Title Six-Packs. (Literatura 2000 Ser.). (SPA.). (gr. 1-2). 28.00 (978-0-7635-1061-9(0)) Rigby Education.

Una casa para Sergin: Six-Pack. (Saludos Ser.: Vol. 2). (SPA.). (gr. 2-3). 31.00 (978-0-7635-9542-5(X)) Rigby Education.

Casado, Dami & Casado, Alicia. La Nieve. 2005. (SPA., Illus.). 14p. (J). per. 8.99 (978-84-272-7297-2(9)) Molino, Editorial ESP. *Dist:* Santillana USA Publishing Co., Inc.

Casas. (Spanish Early Intervention Levels Ser.). (SPA.). 23.10 (978-1-56334-774-0(1)) Hampton-Brown Bks.

Cela. Y en el Planeta un Punto Tuy Cela Le, Level B. 2002. (SPA., Illus.). (J). pap. 8.95 (978-0-8219-1206-5(2) , 70354) EMC/Paradigm Publishing.

Chaktoura, Julia. El Baul de los Oficios: Un Libro Sobre las Vocales. Ink, Lancman, illus. (Coleccion el Baul Ser.). (SPA.). 10p. (J). (gr. k-1). (978-950-46-1158-5(3)) Santillana USA Publishing Co., Inc.

Chano: Individual Title Six-Packs. (Literatura 2000 Ser.). (SPA.). (gr. 2-3). 33.00 (978-0-7635-1087-9(4)) Rigby Education.

Charlesworth, Liza. My First Bilingual Little Readers. 2007. 64p. Level C. pap. 11.99 ***(*978-0-439-02425-9(0));*** Level B. pap. 11.99 ***(*978-0-439-02424-2(2))*** Scholastic, Inc.

Chico se Esconde: Individual Title Six-Packs. (Coleccion Pm Ser.).Tr. of Chico hides. (SPA.). 16p. (gr. 1 up). 26.00 (978-0-7578-2978-9(3)) Rigby Education.

Chiles. (Spanish Early Intervention Levels Ser.). (SPA.). 23.10 (978-1-56334-778-8(4)); Vol. 3. 3.85 (978-1-56334-451-0(3)) Hampton-Brown Bks.

Chiquilibros: Letras Add-to Pack. (SPA.). (ps-1). 103.00 (978-0-7635-8575-4(0)) Rigby Education.

Chiquilibros: Letras Complete Package. (SPA.). (ps-1). 374.00 (978-0-7635-8574-7(2)) Rigby Education.

Chirridos!, 6, Pack. (Literatura 2000 Ser.). (SPA.). (gr. 1-2). 28.00 (978-0-7635-1039-8(4)) Rigby Education.

El chivo Comilon. (Spanish Early Intervention Levels Ser.). (SPA.). 23.10 (978-1-56334-767-2(9)) Hampton-Brown Bks.

El Chivo Comilon, Vol. 2. (Spanish Early Intervention Levels Ser.). (SPA.). 3.85 (978-1-56334-438-1(6)) Hampton-Brown Bks.

Ciclo de la Vida de... Series, 5 bks., Set. 2003. Tr. of Life Cycle of a... Series. (SPA., Illus.). (J). lib. bdg. 113.95 (978-1-4034-3013-7(6)) Heinemann Library.

Cinetto, Liliana. El Baul de Mis Paseos: Un Libro Sobre las Posiciones. Clocchiatti, Constanza, illus. (Coleccion el Baul Ser.). (SPA.). 10p. (J). (gr. k-1). (978-950-46-1176-9(1)) Santillana USA Publishing Co., Inc.

El Circo: Individual Title Six-Packs. (Literatura 2000 Ser.). (SPA.). (ps-1). 28.00 (978-0-7635-1188-3(9)) Rigby Education.

Cirilo, el gallo Desafinado. (Spanish Early Intervention Levels Ser.). (SPA.). 28.38 (978-0-7362-0840-6(2)) Hampton-Brown Bks.

Cirilo, el Gallo Desafinado (L), Vol. 20. (Spanish Early Intervention Levels Ser.). (SPA.). 4.73 (978-0-7362-0816-1(X)) Hampton-Brown Bks.

The City Walk: Individual Title Two-Packs. (Chiquilibros Ser.). (ps-1). 12.00 (978-0-7635-8533-4(5)) Rigby Education.

Una ciudad, una escuela, muchas Comidas: 6 Small Books. (Saludos Ser.: Vol. 1). (SPA.). (gr. 3-5). 31.00 (978-0-7635-1805-9(0)) Rigby Education.

Claro que Si! (Spanish Early Intervention Levels Ser.). (SPA.). 28.38 (978-0-7362-0844-4(5)) Hampton-Brown Bks.

Claro Que Si! (K), Vol. 26. (Spanish Early Intervention Levels Ser.). (SPA.) 4.73 (978-0-7362-0820-8(8)) Hampton-Brown Bks.

La clase de Mascaras 11: Leveled Books. 2001. (McGraw-Hill. Lectura Ser.). (ENG & SPA.). (gr. 2 up). (978-0-02-188012-6(3)) Macmillan/McGraw-Hill Schl. Div.

Clavel, Bernard. Leyendas de Montanas. (Torre de Papel Ser.). (SPA.). (YA). (gr. 6 up). 7.95 (978-958-04-1529-9(3)) Norma S.A. COL. *Dist:* Distribuidora Norma, Inc.

—Leyendas del Mar. (Torre de Papel Ser.). (SPA.). (YA). (gr. 6 up). 8.95 (978-958-04-1387-5(8)) Norma S.A. COL. *Dist:* Distribuidora Norma, Inc.

Club de Teatro: Individual Title Six-Packs. (On Deck en Espanol Ser.).Tr. of Drama Club. (SPA.). 24p. (gr. 4-5). 35.00 (978-0-7578-6401-8(5)) Rigby Education.

Cochinita bien Vestida. (Spanish Early Intervention Levels Ser.). (SPA.). 21.30 (978-0-7362-0830-7(5)) Hampton-Brown Bks.

Cochinita Bien Vestida (E), Vol. 6. (Spanish Early Intervention Levels Ser.). (SPA.). 3.55 (978-0-7362-0776-8(7)) Hampton-Brown Bks.

La Cocina: Individual Title Two-Packs. (Chiquilibros Ser.). (SPA.). (ps-1). 12.00 (978-0-7635-8560-0(2)) Rigby Education.

El cocinero Feroz: Individual Title Six-Packs. (Literatura 2000 Ser.). (SPA.). (gr. 2-3). 33.00 (978-0-7635-1258-3(3)) Rigby Education.

La cola de Lagartija: Individual Title Six-Packs. (Coleccion Pm Ser.).Tr. of Lizard lost his tail. (SPA.). 16p. (gr. 1 up). 26.00 (978-0-7578-2969-7(4)) Rigby Education.

Colasanti, Marina. Lejos Como Mi Querer y Otros Cuentos. (SPA.). (YA). 8.95 (978-958-04-3651-5(7)) Norma S.A. COL. *Dist:* Distribuidora Norma, Inc.

Cole, Babette. El Principe Ceniciento.Tr. of Prince Cinders. (SPA.). 32p. (J). 12.95 (978-84-233-1687-8(4)) Ediciones Destino ESP. *Dist:* Planeta Publishing Corp.

El Colibri: Individual Title Six-Packs. (On Deck en Espanol Ser.).Tr. of Hummingbird. (SPA.). 24p. (gr. 4-5). 35.00 (978-0-7578-6436-0(8)) Rigby Education.

Los Collaros. 2003. 23.95 (978-0-673-77776-8(6)) Celebration Pr.

Come See My Farm. 2003. 23.95 (978-0-673-78129-1(1)) Celebration Pr.

Comida Magica: Individual Title-Six Packs. (Chiquilibros Ser.). (SPA.). (gr. k-1). 23.00 (978-0-7635-8615-7(3)) Rigby Education.

Una Comida Tradicional. 2003. 28.95 (978-0-673-78092-8(9)) Celebration Pr.

Como Criar un renacuajo Feliz 15: Leveled Books. 2001. (McGraw-Hill. Lectura Ser.). (ENG & SPA.). (gr. 3 up). (978-0-02-188088-1(3)) Macmillan/McGraw-Hill Schl. Div.

Como funciona? Interactive Packages: A rodar, a Rodar. (Pebble Soup Exploraciones Ser.). (SPA.). (ps up). 52.00 (978-0-7578-5268-8(8)) Rigby Education.

Como funciona? Interactive Packages: Mirandolo Bien. (Pebble Soup Exploraciones Ser.). (SPA.). (ps up). 52.00 (978-0-7578-5270-1(X)) Rigby Education.

Compartiendo: Individual Title Six-Packs. (Literatura 2000 Ser.). (SPA.). (gr. k-1). 28.00 (978-0-7635-1013-8(0)) Rigby Education.

Complete Big Books Set. (ENG & SPA.). (gr. k-2). 334.95 (978-0-7368-3184-0(3)) Red Brick Learning.

Complete Spanish Big Books Set. (gr. k-2). 106.95 (978-0-7368-3244-1(0)) Red Brick Learning.

Complete Spanish DRA Pack, 96 vols. (Spanish Dra Levels Ser.). (SPA.). 353.75 (978-0-7362-0993-9(X)) Hampton-Brown Bks.

Complete Spanish Guided Reading Pack, 96 vols. (Spanish Guided Reading Levels Ser.). (SPA.). 353.75 (978-0-7362-0991-5(3)) Hampton-Brown Bks.

Complete Spanish Lexile Pack, 92 vols. (Spanish Lexile Levels Ser.). (SPA.). 339.89 (978-0-7362-1512-1(3)) Hampton-Brown Bks.

Complete Yellow Umbrella Big Books Set. (ENG & SPA.). (gr. k-2). 269.95 (978-0-7368-3245-8(9)) Red Brick Learning.

Cooper, Patrick. El Tesoro de los Reyes de Irlanda. (SPA.). (J). 8.95 (978-958-04-7070-0(7)) Norma S.A. COL. *Dist:* Distribuidora Norma, Inc.

Cooper-Pete, Beverly. Tootie Fruity Bear's Sing-A-Long Tunes. 4th l.t. ed. 2001. Tr. of Para que cantes junto con el oso Tootie Fruity. (SPA & ENG.). 32p. pap. (978-0-9714093-2-3(3)) Trey-Ish & Co.

El corderito mas Chiquito: Lap Book. (Pebble Soup Exploraciones Ser.). (SPA.). 16p. (ps up). 21.00 (978-0-7578-1678-9(9)) Rigby Education.

El corderito mas Chiquito: Small Book. (Pebble Soup Exploraciones Ser.). (SPA.). 16p. (ps up). 5.00 (978-0-7578-1718-2(1)) Rigby Education.

Coro: Individual Title Six-Packs. (On Deck en Espanol Ser.).Tr. of Chours. (SPA.). 24p. (gr. 4-5). 35.00 (978-0-7578-6404-9(X)) Rigby Education.

El coro de Gatos: Individual Title Six-Packs. (Literatura 2000 Ser.). (SPA.). (gr. 2-3). 33.00 (978-0-7635-1088-6(2)) Rigby Education.

El Correo: Individual Title Two-Packs. (Chiquilibros Ser.). (SPA.). (ps-1). 12.00 (978-0-7635-8561-7(0)) Rigby Education.

Cosas Grandes, 6 vols., Pack. (Coleccion Pm Ser.: Vol. 1). Tr. of Big things. (SPA.). 16p. (gr. k-1). 26.00 (978-0-7578-0662-9(7)) Rigby Education.

Costales, A. Lupe Vargas & Her Super Best Friend: Lupe Vargas y su super mejor Amiga. 2006. (ENG & SPA., Illus.). 32p. (J). 15.95 (978-0-87358-888-1(6) , Luna Rising) Northland Publishing.

Cowan, Catherine & Buehner, Mark. Mi Vida con la Ola. Rubio, Esther, tr. Buehner, Mark, illus. 2004. (SPA., Illus.). 29p. (J). 19.99 (978-84-88342-45-4(4)) S.A. Kokinos ESP. *Dist:* Lectorum Pubns., Inc.

Cowen-Fletcher, Jane. Se Necesita Todo un Pueblo. 2003. (SPA., Illus.). (J). pap. 4.76 net. (978-0-590-29394-5(X) , SO30915) Scholastic, Inc.

Creador de Libros. 2000. (SPA.). (gr. k up). cd-rom 29.97 (978-0-673-64091-8(4)); (gr. 1 up). cd-rom 29.97 (978-0-673-64092-5(2)); (gr. 2 up). cd-rom 29.97 (978-0-673-64093-2(0)); (gr. 3 up). cd-rom 29.97 (978-0-673-64094-9(9)) Addison-Wesley Educational Pubs., Inc.

Creo que Si! (Spanish Early Intervention Levels Ser.). (SPA.). 31.14 (978-0-7362-0332-6(X)) Hampton-Brown Bks.

Creo Que Si! (G), Vol. 16. (Spanish Early Intervention Levels Ser.). (SPA.). 5.19 (978-0-7362-0307-4(9)) Hampton-Brown Bks.

Cruceros: Individual Title Six-Packs. (On Deck en Espanol Ser.).Tr. of Cruise Ships. (SPA.). 24p. (gr. 4-5). 35.00 (978-0-7578-6431-5(7)) Rigby Education.

La Cruz Roja: Individual Title Six-Packs. (On Deck en Espanol Ser.).Tr. of Red Cross. (SPA.). 24p. (gr. 4-5). 35.00 (978-0-7578-6413-1(9)) Rigby Education.

Cual es el Mio? (Spanish Early Intervention Levels Ser.). (SPA.). 23.10 (978-1-56334-791-7(1)); Vol. 6. 3.85 (978-1-56334-463-3(7)) Hampton-Brown Bks.

Cuando estaba Enferma: Individual Title Six-Packs. (Literatura 2000 Ser.). (SPA.). (gr. 1-2). 28.00 (978-0-7635-1040-4(8)) Rigby Education.

Cuando sea mas Grande: Individual Title Six-Packs. (Literatura 2000 Ser.). (SPA.). (gr. 1-2). 28.00 (978-0-7635-1063-3(7)) Rigby Education.

Cuando tienes Susto: Social/Emotional Lap Book. (Pebble Soup Exploraciones Ser.). (SPA.). (ps up). 16.00 (978-0-7578-1792-2(0)) Rigby Education.

Cuatro Ardillitas. (Spanish Early Intervention Levels Ser.). (SPA.). 31.14 (978-0-7362-0336-4(2)) Hampton-Brown Bks.

S

Cuatro Ardillitas (I), Vol. 18. (Spanish Early Intervention Levels Ser.). (SPA.). 5.19 (978-0-7362-0311-1(7)) Hampton-Brown Bks.

La Cucaracha: Individual 6-packs. 2003. 23.95 (978-0-673-78071-3(6)) Celebration Pr.

Cuenta con la Familia. (Spanish Early Intervention Levels Ser.). (SPA.). 3.85 (978-1-56334-429-9(7)); 23.10 (978-1-56334-758-0(X)) Hampton-Brown Bks.

Cuentitos mios Classroom Set: Green Series. (Rimas Y Risas Ser.). (SPA.). (ps-2). 352.70 (978-0-7362-0057-8(6)) Hampton-Brown Bks.

Cuentitos Mios Classroom Set: Green Series with addition of Manipulatives. (Rimas Y Risas Ser.). (SPA.). (ps-2). 477.31 (978-0-917837-96-8(7)) Hampton-Brown Bks.

El cuento de Dona Chila: 6 Softcover Books. (Saludos Ser.: Vol. 3). (SPA.). (gr. 3-5). 31.00 (978-0-7635-1780-9(1)) Rigby Education.

Cuentos de Muchos Mundos/Stories of Many Worlds. (ENG & SPA.). 160p. 20.00 (978-0-944356-19-7(2)) Alegria Hispana Pubns.

Cuentos Favoritos/Favorite Tales. (ENG & SPA.). 80p. 15.00 (978-0-944356-01-2(X)) Alegria Hispana Pubns.

Cuentos Matematicos/Math Tales. (ENG & SPA.). 80p. 17.00 (978-0-944356-05-0(2)) Alegria Hispana Pubns.

El Cuerpo de Paz: Individual Title Six-Packs. (On Deck en Espanol Ser.).Tr. of Peace Corps. (SPA.). 24p. (gr. 4-5). 35.00 (978-0-7578-6411-7(2)) Rigby Education.

Cuidado! Individual Title Six-Packs. (Literatura 2000 Ser.). (SPA.). (ps-1). 28.00 (978-0-7635-1189-0(7)) Rigby Education.

El cumpleanos de Alisa: Individual Title Six-Packs. (Literatura 2000 Ser.). (SPA.). (gr. k-1). 28.00 (978-0-7635-1014-5(9)) Rigby Education.

El cumpleanos de Bruno: Individual Title Six-Packs. (Literatura 2000 Ser.). (SPA.). (gr. 1-2). 28.00 (978-0-7635-1041-1(6)) Rigby Education.

El Cumpleanos de Julio: Individual Title Six-Packs. (Coleccion Pm Ser.).Tr. of Birthday Cake for Ben. (SPA.). 16p. (gr. 1 up). 26.00 (978-0-7578-2972-7(4)) Rigby Education.

El cumpleanos de mi Abuelito: Individual Title Six-Packs. (Literatura 2000 Ser.). (SPA.). (gr. 2-3). 33.00 (978-0-7635-1089-3(0)) Rigby Education.

Cuno, Sabine. Abre, cierra y Aprende: Open, Close, & Learn, Spanish-Lanaguage Edition. 2007. (Illus.). 12p. (J). 14.95 ***(978-970-718-489-3(2)*** , Silver Dolphin en Español) Advanced Marketing, S. de R. L. de C. V. MEX. *Dist:* Perseus Distribution.

Da Vacaciones. (SPA.). pap. 7.95 (978-88-8148-844-5(2)) European Language Institute ITA. *Dist:* Distribooks, Inc.

Dahl, Michael. Fito y el Pito. Lee, Ji Sun, illus. 2006. (Read-It! Readers en Espanol Ser.).Tr. of Fables Whistle. (SPA.). 32p. (J). (ps-3). 19.95 (978-1-4048-1691-6(7)) Picture Window Bks.

—Palancas. Schon, Isabel, ed. Ferrer, Martín Luis Guzman, tr. from ENG. 1998. (Coleccion Primeros Lectores). (SPA., Illus.). 24p. (J). (gr. k-3). lib. bdg. 18.60 (978-1-56065-793-4(6) , CAP1100, Bridgestone Bks.) Capstone Pr., Inc.

—Poleas. Schon, Isabel, ed. Ferrer, Martín Luis Guzman, tr. from ENG. 1998. (Maquinas Simples Ser.). (SPA., Illus.). 24p. (J). (gr. k-3). lib. bdg. 18.60 (978-1-56065-794-1(4) , CAP1155, Bridgestone Bks.) Capstone Pr., Inc.

Daniel: Individual Title Six-Packs. (Literatura 2000 Ser.). (SPA.). (gr. 1-2). 28.00 (978-0-7635-1064-0(5)) Rigby Education.

De Compras. (Spanish Early Intervention Levels Ser.). (SPA.). 23.10 (978-1-56334-784-9(9)); Vol. 2. 3.85 (978-1-56334-457-2(2)) Hampton-Brown Bks.

de Lambana, Martha Lucia Martinez. Grafias 4 4: Escritura Asociativa Script: Ejercitacion. (SPA.). (J). (gr. k-6). 12.00 (978-958-04-5329-1(2)) Norma S.A. COL. *Dist:* Distribuidora Norma, Inc.

—Grafias 5 5: Escritura Asociativa Script: Intermedio. (SPA.). (J). (gr. k-6). 12.00 (978-958-04-5330-7(6)) Norma S.A. COL. *Dist:* Distribuidora Norma, Inc.

—Grafias 6 6: Escritura Asociativa Script: Avanzada. (SPA.). (J). (gr. k-6). 12.00 (978-958-04-5331-4(4)) Norma S.A. COL. *Dist:* Distribuidora Norma, Inc.

—Grafias K: Escritura Asociativa Script: Apestamiento. (SPA.). (J). (gr. k-6). 12.00 (978-958-04-5316-1(0)) Norma S.A. COL. *Dist:* Distribuidora Norma, Inc.

De lo Que Contaron - Fraile (What They Told the Friar (XVI)) 2005. (SPA.). (J). pap. 9.95 (978-968-7381-04-6(3)) Tecolote, Ediciones, S.A. de C.V. MEX. *Dist:* Iaconi, Mariuccia Bk. Imports.

De padre a Hijo. (Saludos Ser.: Vol. 1). (SPA.). (gr. 3-5). 31.00 (978-0-7635-3134-8(0)) Rigby Education.

De padre a Hijo: 6 Small Books. (Saludos Ser.: Vol. 1). (SPA.). (gr. 3-5). 31.00 (978-0-7635-1755-7(0)) Rigby Education.

De Safari: Individual Title-Six Packs. (Chiquilibros Ser.). (SPA.). (gr. k-1). 23.00 (978-0-7635-8605-8(6)) Rigby Education.

De Valdenebro, Eladio. Tono y el Bosque. (Torre de Papel Ser.). (SPA.). (J). (gr. 4 up). 8.95 (978-958-04-3397-2(6)) Norma S.A. COL. *Dist:* Distribuidora Norma, Inc.

Debajo de la Cama, 6 Packs. (Chiquilibros Ser.). (SPA.). (gr. k-1). 23.00 (978-0-7635-8619-5(6)) Rigby Education.

del Moral, Susana. Baby Einstein: Baby da Vinci, mi Cuerpo: Baby Einstein: Baby da Vinci, My Body, Spanish-Language Edition. Zaidi, Nadeem, illus. 2006. 6p. (J). bds. 7.95 ***(978-970-718-455-8(8)*** , Silver Dolphin en Español) Advanced Marketing, S. de R. L. de C. V. MEX. *Dist:* Perseus Distribution.

del Moral, Susana & Zaidi, Nadeem. Baby Einstein: el Concurso: Baby Einstein: Mirror Me, Spanish-Lanuage Edition. 2006. (Illus.). 5p. (J). bds. 6.95 ***(978-970-718-458-9(2)*** , Silver Dolphin en Español) Advanced Marketing, S. de R. L. de C. V. MEX. *Dist:* Perseus Distribution.

Demado. En Avant: Enhanced Online Edition. 4th ed. 2003. (SPA.). cd-rom 54.80 (978-0-03-031974-7(9)) Holt, Rinehart & Winston.

Demasiada Ropa, 6 Pack. (Literatura 2000 Ser.). (SPA.). (gr. k-1). 28.00 (978-0-7635-1015-2(7)) Rigby Education.

Den Vueltas, 6 Packs. (Literatura 2000 Ser.). (SPA.). (gr. 1-2). 28.00 (978-0-7635-1065-7(3)) Rigby Education.

El Dentista, 2 Packs. (Chiquilibros Ser.). (SPA.). (ps-1). 12.00 (978-0-7635-8565-5(3)) Rigby Education.

Derek Jeter, 6 Packs. (On Deck en Espanol Ser.). (SPA.). 24p. (gr. 4-5). 35.00 (978-0-7578-6382-0(5)) Rigby Education.

DeRubertis, Barbara. Cuenta con Pablo: Math Matters en Espanol. Thornburgh, Rebecca, illus. 2005. 32p. pap. 4.95 (978-1-57565-151-4(3)) Kane Pr., The.

Despegue con Ellen Ochoa! 6 Small Books. (Saludos Ser.: Vol. 3). (SPA.). (gr. 2-3). 31.00 (978-0-7635-9548-7(9)) Rigby Education.

Despegue con Ellen Ochoa! Big Book. (Saludos Ser.: Vol. 3). (SPA.). (gr. 2-3). 31.00 (978-0-7635-5863-5(X)) Rigby Education.

Despierta, Papa, 6 Pack. (Coleccion Pm Ser.).Tr. of Wake up, Dad. (SPA.). 16p. (gr. 1 up). 26.00 (978-0-7578-2962-8(7)) Rigby Education.

Despues de la Inundacion: Individual Title Six-Packs. (Coleccion Pm Ser.).Tr. of After the flood. (SPA.). 16p. (gr. 1 up). 26.00 (978-0-7578-3045-7(5)) Rigby Education.

El dia de Escuela, 2 packs. (Chiquilibros Ser.). (SPA.). (ps-1). 12.00 (978-0-7635-8562-4(9)) Rigby Education.

Dia de la Mascota 20: Leveled Books. 2001. (McGraw-Hill. Lectura Ser.). (ENG & SPA.). (gr. 1 up). (978-0-02-187997-7(4)) Macmillan/McGraw-Hill Schl. Div.

El Dia de los Muertos: 6 Small Books. (Saludos Ser.: Vol. 1). (SPA.). 24p. (gr. 2-3). 31.00 (978-0-7635-9520-3(9)) Rigby Education.

Dia de Nieve, 6 packs. (Coleccion Pm Ser.).Tr. of Snow on the Hill. (SPA.). 16p. (gr. 1 up). 26.00 (978-0-7578-3048-8(X)) Rigby Education.

El Dia lluvioso, 2 packs. (Chiquilibros Ser.). (SPA.). (ps-1). 12.00 (978-0-7635-8552-5(1)) Rigby Education.

Diario de una Marquesa (Diary of a Marchioness) 2005. (SPA.). (J). pap. 9.95 (978-968-7381-05-3(1)) Tecolote, Ediciones, S.A. de C.V. MEX. *Dist:* Iaconi, Mariuccia Bk. Imports.

El Diario de Val. 2000. (SPA., Illus.). 70p. (YA). (gr. 7-9). pap. 11.95 (978-88-8148-328-0(9)) European Language Institute ITA. *Dist:* Distribooks, Inc., Midwest European Pubns.

Dias de Alegria. (Spanish Early Intervention Levels Ser.). (SPA.). 23.10 (978-1-56334-781-8(4)); Vol. 3. 3.85 (978-1-56334-454-1(8)) Hampton-Brown Bks.

Diaz Granados, Jose Luiz. Juegos y Versos Diversos. (Torre de Papel Ser.). (SPA.). (J). (gr. 4 up). 8.95 (978-958-04-4524-1(9)) Norma S.A. COL. *Dist:* Distribuidora Norma, Inc.

Dickens, Charles. Las Campanas.Tr. of Chimes. (SPA.). 7.75 (978-958-04-2124-5(2)) Norma S.A. COL. *Dist:* Distribuidora Norma, Inc.

Diez Ositos: Big Book Packages. 2003. 64.95 (978-0-673-58578-3(6)) Celebration Pr.

Dime como te Sientes: Big Book. (Pebble Soup Exploraciones Ser.). (SPA.). 16p. (ps up). 31.00 (978-0-7578-1685-7(1)) Rigby Education.

Dime como te Sientes: Small Book. (Pebble Soup Exploraciones Ser.). (SPA.). 16p. (ps up). 5.00 (978-0-7578-1725-0(4)) Rigby Education.

Los Dinosaurios: Big Book Packages. 2003. 64.95 (978-0-673-58597-4(2)) Celebration Pr.

La diosa del Volcan: 6 Small Books. (Saludos Ser.: Vol. 1). (SPA.). (gr. 3-5). 31.00 (978-0-7635-2055-7(1)) Rigby Education.

Discoverer Enterprise: Individual Title Six-Packs. (On Deck en Espanol Ser.).Tr. of Discoverer Enterprise. (SPA.). 24p. (gr. 4-5). 35.00 (978-0-7578-6445-2(7)) Rigby Education.

Disfraces, 6 Pack. (Chiquilibros Ser.). (SPA.). (gr. k-1). 23.00 (978-0-7635-8601-0(3)) Rigby Education.

Disher, Garry. Flaminio, el Piano. (Torre de Papel Ser.). (SPA.). (J). (gr. 4 up). 8.95 (978-958-04-4139-7(1)) Norma S.A. COL. *Dist:* Distribuidora Norma, Inc.

El Doctor, 6 Pack. (Coleccion Pm Ser.).Tr. of Doctor. (SPA.). 16p. (gr. 1 up). 26.00 (978-0-7578-3029-7(3)) Rigby Education.

El doctor Buscapistas: Social/Emotional Lap Book. (Pebble Soup Exploraciones Ser.). (SPA.). (ps up). 16.00 (978-0-7578-1790-8(4)) Rigby Education.

Dominguez, Ramon Garcia. El Grillo del Tercer Milenium. (SPA.). (J). 8.95 (978-958-04-6266-8(6)) Norma S.A. COL. *Dist:* Distribuidora Norma, Inc.

Dona Coneja. (Spanish Early Intervention Levels Ser.). (SPA.). 21.30 (978-0-7362-0826-0(7)) Hampton-Brown Bks.

Dona Coneja (E), Vol. 6. (Spanish Early Intervention Levels Ser.). (SPA.). 3.55 (978-0-7362-0772-0(4)) Hampton-Brown Bks.

Dona Flora's Flowers. 2003. 23.95 (978-0-673-78133-8(X)) Celebration Pr.

Donde esta Claudia? Individual Title Six-Packs. (Literatura 2000 Ser.). (SPA.). (gr. k-1). 28.00 (978-0-7635-1017-6(3)) Rigby Education.

Donde esta mi Mascota? Individual Title-Six Packs. (Chiquilibros Ser.). (SPA.). (gr. k-1). 23.00 (978-0-7635-8624-9(2)) Rigby Education.

Donde estan los Bebes? Individual Title Six-Packs. (Coleccion Pm Ser.: Vol. 2). Tr. of Where are the babies?. (SPA.). 16p. (gr. k-1). 26.00 (978-0-7578-0678-0(3)) Rigby Education.

Donde vivimos Interactive Packages: En mi Vecindario. (Pebble Soup Exploraciones Ser.). (SPA.). (ps up). 52.00 (978-0-7578-5258-9(0)) Rigby Education.

Donde vivimos Interactive Packages: Los Trabajos. (Pebble Soup Exploraciones Ser.). (SPA.). (ps up). 52.00 (978-0-7578-5256-5(4)) Rigby Education.

Donde Vivo Yo: Individual 6-packs. 2003. 23.95 (978-0-673-77136-0(9)) Celebration Pr.

Doro, el Potrillo. (Coleccion Leo Con Figuras). (SPA., Illus.). 14p. (J). pap. 5.50 (978-950-11-0841-5(4) , SGM414) Sigmar ARG. *Dist:* Continental Bk. Co., Inc.

Dos gatos Tontos, 6 Packs. (Literatura 2000 Ser.). (SPA.). (gr. 2-3). 33.00 (978-0-7635-1090-9(4)) Rigby Education.

Los Dos Volcanes. 2003. 28.95 (978-0-673-78100-0(3)) Celebration Pr.

El dragon Grunon. (Spanish Early Intervention Levels Ser.). (SPA.). 31.14 (978-0-7362-0338-8(9)) Hampton-Brown Bks.

El Dragon Grunon (H), Vol. 20. (Spanish Early Intervention Levels Ser.). (SPA.). 5.19 (978-0-7362-0313-5(3)) Hampton-Brown Bks.

Droop, Constanza. Que? Como? Por que?: Las estaciones del Ano: What? How? Why?: the Seasons of the Year, Spanish-Lanuage Edition. 2007. (Illus.). 16p. (J). 9.95 ***(978-970-718-492-3(2)*** , Silver Dolphin en Español) Advanced Marketing, S. de R. L. de C. V. MEX. *Dist:* Perseus Distribution.

Dual Language Flip Chart. 1999. (SPA.). (gr. k-2). suppl. ed. 187.00 (978-0-201-36992-2(3)); (gr. 3-6). suppl. ed. 187.00 (978-0-201-36993-9(1)) Addison-Wesley Educational Pubs., Inc.

El Duende Distraido. (Coleccion Leo Con Figuras). (SPA., Illus.). 14p. (J). pap. 4.50 (978-950-11-0930-6(5) , SGM305) Sigmar ARG. *Dist:* Continental Bk. Co., Inc.

Los Dulces. 2003. 23.95 (978-0-673-77163-6(6)) Celebration Pr.

Dulces Recuerdos. 2003. 28.95 (978-0-673-78102-4(X)) Celebration Pr.

Durmiendo: Individual Title Six-Packs. (Literatura 2000 Ser.). (SPA.). (gr. 1-2). 28.00 (978-0-7635-1043-5(2)) Rigby Education.

Dussling, Jennifer. El Problema de 100 Libras: Math Matters en Espanol. Thornburgh, Rebecca, illus. 2005. 32p. pap. 4.95 (978-1-57565-154-5(8)) Kane Pr., The.

Each Big Book Set: Green Series. (Rimas y Risas Ser.). (SPA.). (ps-2). 212.23 (978-1-56334-004-8(6)) Hampton-Brown Bks.

Each Big Book Set: Green Series with addition of Manipulatives. (Rimas Y Risas Ser.). (SPA.). (ps-2). 344.62 (978-0-7362-0054-7(1)) Hampton-Brown Bks.

Early Level Spanish & English. (ENG & SPA.). (gr. k-2). 1923.95 (978-0-7368-3182-6(7) , Yellow Umbrella Bks.) Capstone Pr., Inc.

Early Level Spanish & English Add-on Set. (ENG & SPA.). (gr. k-2). 346.95 (978-0-7368-3183-3(5) , Yellow Umbrella Bks.) Capstone Pr., Inc.

East, Jacqueline. No Quiero comer Eso! (SPA.). (J). 8.95 (978-958-04-7345-9(5)) Norma S.A. COL. *Dist:* Distribuidora Norma, Inc.

Ehlert, Lois. A Sembrar Sopa de Verduras. Campoy, F. Isabel & Ada, Alma Flor, trs. 2005. (SPA., Illus.). 32p. (J). (gr. 17-ps). bds. 6.95 (978-0-15-205608-7(4) , Red Wagon Bks.) Harcourt Children's Bks.

El/Dibujo de Maria: Individual Title, 6 packs. (Literatura 2000 Ser.). (SPA.). (gr. 1-2). 28.00 (978-0-7635-1042-8(4)) Rigby Education.

Elena y el Monito. (Spanish Early Intervention Levels Ser.). (SPA.). 21.30 (978-0-7362-0807-9(0)); Vol. 3. 3.55 (978-0-7362-0765-2(1)) Hampton-Brown Bks.

Elote, choclo, maiz Nuevo 16: Leveled Books. 2001. (McGraw-Hill. Lectura Ser.). (ENG & SPA.). (gr. 2 up). (978-0-02-188017-1(4)) Macmillan/McGraw-Hill Schl. Div.

Elsa's Shawl. 2003. 23.95 (978-0-673-78130-7(5)) Celebration Pr.

Elya, Susan Middleton. Say Hola to Spanish, Otra Vez. Lopez, Loretta, illus. 1999. (SPA.). (J). (ps-k). lib. bdg. 15.25 (978-0-613-19445-7(4)) Tandem Library Bks.

Emergent Level Spanish & English. (ENG & SPA.). (gr. k-2). 1923.95 (978-0-7368-3180-2(0) , Yellow Umbrella Bks.) Capstone Pr., Inc.

Emergent Level Spanish & English Add-on Set. (ENG & SPA.). (gr. k-2). 346.95 (978-0-7368-3181-9(9) , Yellow Umbrella Bks.) Capstone Pr., Inc.

En buenas Manos 14: Leveled Books. 2001. (McGraw-Hill. Lectura Ser.). (ENG & SPA.). (gr. 4 up). (978-0-02-188159-8(6)) Macmillan/McGraw-Hill Schl. Div.

En Busca De Insectos. 2003. 28.95 (978-0-673-78096-6(1)) Celebration Pr.

En Busca del Amigo Desaparecido. 2000. (SPA., Illus.). 70p. (YA). (gr. 6-8). 11.95 (978-88-8148-323-5(8)) European Language Institute ITA. *Dist:* Distribooks, Inc., Midwest European Pubns.

En casa de mis Padrinos. (Spanish Early Intervention Levels Ser.). (SPA.). 28.38 (978-0-7362-0847-5(X)) Hampton-Brown Bks.

En Casa de Mis Padrinos (K), Vol. 24. (Spanish Early Intervention Levels Ser.). (SPA.). 4.73 (978-0-7362-0823-9(2)) Hampton-Brown Bks.

En Donde Marchan los Elefantes? (Pebble Soup Exploraciones Ser.). (SPA.). 16p. (ps up). 31.00 (978-0-7578-1679-6(7)) Rigby Education.

En donde marchan los Elefantes? Small Book. (Pebble Soup Exploraciones Ser.). (SPA.). 16p. (ps up). 5.00 (978-0-7578-1719-9(X)) Rigby Education.

En el cielo de Medianoche: Big Book. (Pebble Soup Exploraciones Ser.). (SPA.). 16p. (ps up). 31.00 (978-0-7578-1693-2(2)) Rigby Education.

En el cielo de Medianoche: Small Book. (Pebble Soup Exploraciones Ser.). (SPA.). 16p. (ps up). 5.00 (978-0-7578-1733-5(5)) Rigby Education.

En el fondo del Mar 13: Leveled Books. 2001. (McGraw-Hill. Lectura Ser.). (ENG & SPA.). (gr. 4 up). (978-0-02-188213-7(4)) Macmillan/McGraw-Hill Schl. Div.

En el Jardin: Individual Title Six-Packs. (Literatura 2000 Ser.). (SPA.). (gr. 1-2). 28.00 (978-0-7635-1067-1(X)) Rigby Education.

En el Mundo. (Spanish Early Intervention Levels Ser.). (SPA.). 23.10 (978-1-56334-794-8(6)); Vol. 4. 3.85 (978-1-56334-467-1(X)) Hampton-Brown Bks.

En el Museo 20: Leveled Books. 2001. (McGraw-Hill. Lectura Ser.). (ENG & SPA.). (gr. 2 up). (978-0-02-188069-0(7)) Macmillan/McGraw-Hill Schl. Div.

En el Otono, 6 Pks. (Coleccion Pm Ser.).Tr. of Walking in the autumn. (SPA.). 16p. (gr. 1 up). 26.00 (978-0-7578-3055-6(2)) Rigby Education.

En el Rancho, 6, Pack. (Literatura 2000 Ser.). (SPA.). (gr. k-1). 28.00 (978-0-7635-1018-3(1)) Rigby Education.

En el restaurante de mis Tios. (Spanish Early Intervention Levels Ser.). (SPA.). 23.10 (978-1-56334-780-1(6)) Hampton-Brown Bks.

En el Restaurante de Mis Tios, Vol. 2. (Spanish Early Intervention Levels Ser.). (SPA.). 3.85 (978-1-56334-453-4(X)) Hampton-Brown Bks.

En el Supermercado, 6, Pack. (Chiquilibros Ser.). (SPA.). (gr. k-1). 23.00 (978-0-7635-8617-1(X)) Rigby Education.

En el Zoologico, 6, Pack. 2003. 23.95 (978-0-673-77146-9(6)) Celebration Pr.

En la Biblioteca, 6 Pks. (Coleccion Pm Ser.: Vol. 2). Tr. of At the library. (SPA.). 16p. (gr. k-1). 26.00 (978-0-7578-0686-5(4)) Rigby Education.

En la Ciudad. (Spanish Early Intervention Levels Ser.). (SPA.). 23.10 (978-1-56334-776-4(8)); Vol. 3. 3.85 (978-1-56334-447-3(5)) Hampton-Brown Bks.

En la ciudad de Roma: Individual Title Six-Packs. (Literatura 2000 Ser.). (SPA.). (gr. 2-3). 33.00 (978-0-7635-1091-6(2)) Rigby Education.

En la ciudad de San Antonio: Lap Book. (Pebble Soup Exploraciones Ser.). (SPA.). 16p. (ps up). 21.00 (978-0-7578-1680-2(0)) Rigby Education.

En la ciudad de San Antonio: Small Book. (Pebble Soup Exploraciones Ser.). (SPA.). 16p. (ps up). 5.00 (978-0-7578-1720-5(3)) Rigby Education.

En la Mananita. (Spanish Early Intervention Levels Ser.). (SPA.). 23.10 (978-1-56334-796-2(2)); Vol. 3. 3.85 (978-1-56334-469-5(6)) Hampton-Brown Bks.

En la oscuridad Interactive Packages: Duermete, mi Amor. (Pebble Soup Exploraciones Ser.). (SPA.). (ps up). 52.00 (978-0-7578-5271-8(8)) Rigby Education.

En la oscuridad Interactive Packages: Trabajos de Noche. (Pebble Soup Exploraciones Ser.). (SPA.). (ps up). 52.00 (978-0-7578-5274-9(2)) Rigby Education.

En La Playa, 6 Pks. 2003. 23.95 (978-0-673-77135-3(0)) Celebration Pr.

En la Playa, 6, Pack. (Chiquilibros Ser.). (SPA.). (gr. k-1). 23.00 (978-0-7635-8618-8(8)) Rigby Education.

En la Primavera, 6, Pack. (Coleccion Pm Ser.).Tr. of Walking in the spring. (SPA.). 16p. (gr. 1 up). 26.00 (978-0-7578-3053-2(6)) Rigby Education.

En la Verna, 6, Pack. (Coleccion Pm Ser.).Tr. of Walking in the summer. (SPA.). 16p. (gr. 1 up). 26.00 (978-0-7578-3054-9(4)) Rigby Education.

En mi Cama, 6 Pks. (Literatura 2000 Ser.). (SPA.). (gr. k-1). 28.00 (978-0-7635-1019-0(X)) Rigby Education.

En mi Cuarto: Individual Title Six-Packs. (Literatura 2000 Ser.). (SPA.). (gr. k-1). 28.00 (978-0-7635-1020-6(3)) Rigby Education.

En Mi Escuela. (Spanish Early Intervention Levels Ser.). (SPA.). 3.85 (978-1-56334-428-2(9)) Hampton-Brown Bks.

En mi Escuela. (Spanish Early Intervention Levels Ser.). (SPA.). 23.10 (978-1-56334-757-3(1)) Hampton-Brown Bks.

En Mi Jardin: Big Book Packages. 2003. 64.95 (978-0-673-58579-0(4)) Celebration Pr.

Encuentros. (Nuevos Horizontes Ser.). (SPA.). (J). (gr. 5). wbk. ed. 9.95 (978-1-56014-523-3(4)) Santillana USA Publishing Co., Inc.

Encuentros: Evaluations, Grade 5. (Nuevos Horizontes Ser.). (SPA.). (J). 22.50 (978-1-56014-524-0(2)) Santillana USA Publishing Co., Inc.

Encuentros: Student Anthology. (Nuevos Horizontes Ser.). (SPA.). (J). (gr. 5). 19.95 (978-1-56014-522-6(6)) Santillana USA Publishing Co., Inc.

English-Spanish Book Set 800937, 4 vols. 2005. (J). bds. (978-1-59794-096-2(8)) Environments, Inc.

Enriques, Graciela, et al. Formando Palabras Es Espanol. 2002. (Four-Blocks Ser.). 144p. (J). per. 19.99 (978-0-88724-816-0(0) , CD-2421) Carson-Dellosa Publishing Co., Inc.

La Ensalada, 6 Packs. 2003. 23.95 (978-0-673-77147-6(4)) Celebration Pr.

Erne, Andrea. Que? Como? Por que?: Autos y Camiones: What? How? Why?: Cars & Trucks, Spanish-Language Edition. 2007. (Illus.). 16p. (J). 9.95 ***(978-970-718-490-9(6)*** , Silver Dolphin en Español) Advanced Marketing, S. de R. L. de C. V. MEX. *Dist:* Perseus Distribution.

Es Mejor Dar Que Recibir. 2003. 28.95 (978-0-673-78099-7(6)) Celebration Pr.

Es Mia! Social/Emotional Lap Book. (Pebble Soup Exploraciones Ser.). (SPA.). (ps up). 16.00 (978-0-7578-1786-1(6)) Rigby Education.

Es tu Turno. 2004. (Tu y Yo). (SPA.). (J). 14.45 (978-1-4034-4422-6(6)) Heinemann Library.

Es un Elefante? (Spanish Early Intervention Levels Ser.). (SPA.). 21.30 (978-0-7362-0800-0(3)); Vol. 2. 3.55 (978-0-7362-0758-4(9)) Hampton-Brown Bks.

Escalando: Individual Title Six-Packs. (Literatura 2000 Ser.). (SPA.). (gr. k-1). 28.00 (978-0-7635-1021-3(1)) Rigby Education.

Las Escondidas (J), Vol. 16. (Spanish Early Intervention Levels Ser.). (SPA.). 5.19 (978-0-7362-0312-8(5)) Hampton-Brown Bks.

El Escondite: Individual Title, 6 pack. (Chiquilibros Ser.). (SPA.). (gr. k-1). 23.00 (978-0-7635-8625-6(0)) Rigby Education.

Escudos Rotos (Broken Shields (XVI Century)) 2005. (SPA.). (J). pap. 9.95 (978-968-7381-00-8(0)) Tecolote, Ediciones, S.A. de C.V. MEX. *Dist:* Iaconi, Mariuccia Bk. Imports.

Espanol Correcto. (SPA.). (J). 29.00 (978-958-04-5925-5(8)) Norma S.A. COL. *Dist:* Distribuidora Norma, Inc.

Estados Unidos: Formacion, Desarrollo y Transformacion. (SPA.). (J). (978-958-04-7743-3(4)) Norma S.A. COL. *Dist:* Distribuidora Norma, Inc.

Expertas en Terremotos. (Saludos Ser.: Vol. 2). (SPA.). (gr. 3-5). 31.00 (978-0-7635-3235-2(5)) Rigby Education.

Expertas en Terremotos: 6 Small Books. (Saludos Ser.: Vol. 2). (SPA.). (gr. 3-5). 31.00 (978-0-7635-2066-3(7)) Rigby Education.

Fabra, Jordi Sierra. El Disco Magico. (SPA.). (YA). 8.95 (978-958-04-6264-4(X)) Norma S.A. COL. *Dist:* Distribuidora Norma, Inc.

—Martes XXIII. (SPA.). (YA). 9.95 (978-958-04-6025-1(6)) Norma S.A. COL. *Dist:* Distribuidora Norma, Inc.

A Fair Is Fun, 6 vols.; Set. (Phonics Readers Ser.). (gr. k-2). 17.50 (978-0-7368-3203-8(3)) Red Brick Learning.

La Familia Ruidosa: Lap Book. (Pebble Soup Exploraciones Ser.). 16p. (ps up). 21.00 (978-0-7578-1671-0(1)) Rigby Education.

La Familia Ruidosa: Small Book. (Pebble Soup Exploraciones Ser.). 16p. (ps up). 5.00 (978-0-7578-1711-3(4)) Rigby Education.

Fantasia Bilingue/Bilingual Fantasy. (ENG & SPA.). 80p. 15.00 (978-0-944356-02-9(8)) Alegria Hispana Pubns.

Feeling Scared: Social/Emotional Lap Book. (Pebble Soup Explorations Ser.). (SPA.). (ps up). 16.00 (978-0-7635-7573-1(9)) Rigby Education.

Felipa y el Dragon: Individual Title Six-Packs. (Literatura 2000 Ser.). (SPA.). (gr. 1-2). 28.00 (978-0-7635-1069-5(6)) Rigby Education.

Feliz Ano Nuevo. 2003. 23.95 (978-0-673-78079-9(1)) Celebration Pr.

Fente, et al. Curso Intensivo de Espanol: Ejercicios Practicos: Nivel de Iniciacion y Elemental. (SPA.). 288p. stu. ed. 26.95 (978-84-85786-43-5(2) , SGS694) Edelsa Grupo Didascalia, S.A. ESP. *Dist:* Continental Bk. Co., Inc.

La Feria. (Spanish Early Intervention Levels Ser.). (SPA.). 23.10 (978-1-56334-770-2(9)); Vol. 2. 3.85 (978-1-56334-441-1(6)) Hampton-Brown Bks.

Fernandez de Lizardi, José Joaquín. El Periquillo Sarniento. 2003. (SPA.). 351p. (YA). 12.95 (978-968-6966-10-7(2)) EDITER'S Publishing Hse. MEX. *Dist:* EDITER'S Publishing Hse.

Fernandez, Jesus, et al. Curso Intensivo de Espanol: Niveles Elemental e Intermedio: Clave. (SPA.). 32p. (978-84-7143-416-6(4)) Sociedad General Espanola de Libreria.

—Curso Intensivo de Espanol: Niveles Intermedio y Superior: Clave. (SPA.). 64p. (978-84-7143-418-0(0)) Sociedad General Espanola de Libreria.

Fernandez, Mayra. Los Colores de Mi Mundo (Rainbow Kids) (SPA & ENG., Illus.). 20p. (J). pap. 6.95 (978-1-887578-01-1(3) , STK1SP) SpanPr., Inc.

Ferré, Rosario. Pico Rico Mandorico y Otros Cuentos. 2000. (SPA., Illus.). 60p. (J). (gr. 3-5). pap. 10.95 (978-968-19-0376-3(5)) Aguilar Editorial MEX. *Dist:* Santillana USA Publishing Co., Inc.

Ferri, Francesca, illus. Cucu-Tras: Peek-a-Boo, Spanish Edition. 2007. 10p. (J). 7.99 (978-0-7641-6039-4(7)) Barron's Educational Series, Inc.

—Cucu-Tras de las Selva: Peek-a-Boo Jungle, Spanish Edition. 2007. 10p. (J). 7.99 (978-0-7641-6040-0(0)) Barron's Educational Series, Inc.

Fiction & Nonfiction Packs: Combo Packs. (SPA.). (gr. k-2). 85.92 (978-1-56334-403-9(3)) Hampton-Brown Bks.

Fiction & Nonfiction Packs: Jumbo Packs. (SPA.). (gr. k-2). 438.19 (978-1-56334-400-8(9)) Hampton-Brown Bks.

La fiesta de Cumpleanos. (Spanish Early Intervention Levels Ser.). (SPA.). 23.10 (978-1-56334-759-7(8)) Hampton-Brown Bks.

La Fiesta de Cumpleanos, Vol. 2. (Spanish Early Intervention Levels Ser.). (SPA.). 3.85 (978-1-56334-430-5(0)) Hampton-Brown Bks.

Fiesta de Dinosaurios, 6 Pks. (Chiquilibros Ser.). (SPA.). (gr. k-1). 23.00 (978-0-7635-8786-4(9)) Rigby Education.

La Fiesta Monstruosa, 6 Pks. (Chiquilibros Ser.). (SPA.). (gr. k-1). 23.00 (978-0-7635-8600-3(5)) Rigby Education.

Fiestas con Velas, 8 bks., Set. 2002. (SPA.). (J). (ps-1). 129.50 (978-1-58810-788-6(4)) Heinemann Library.

Fito, el Perro. (Coleccion Leo Con Figuras). (SPA., Illus.). 14p. (J). pap. 5.50 (978-950-11-0840-8(6) , SGM410) Sigmar ARG. *Dist:* Continental Bk. Co., Inc.

Fleming, Maria. Hojas Vienen, Hojas Van. Fabiancic, Miriam, tr. Sweet, Melissa, illus. 2002. (Coleccion "Hola, Lector" Ser.).Tr. of Autumn Leaves Are Falling. (SPA.). 30p. (J). (gr. k-2). pap. 4.00 (978-0-439-21667-8(2) , SO5401) Scholastic, Inc.

Flip Chart. 2003. (gr. k up). suppl. ed. 294.00 (978-0-673-59350-4(9)); 2003. (gr. 1 up). suppl. ed. 435.75 (978-0-673-59351-1(7)); 2003. (gr. 2 up). suppl. ed. 435.75 (978-0-673-59352-8(5)); 2000. (SPA.). (gr. k up). suppl. ed. 308.70 (978-0-673-59486-0(6)); 2000. (SPA.). (gr. 1 up). suppl. ed. 457.50 (978-0-673-59487-7(4)); 2000. (SPA.). (gr. 2 up). suppl. ed. 457.50 (978-0-673-59488-4(2)); 2000. (SPA.). (gr. 3 up). suppl. ed. 275.60 (978-0-673-59489-1(0)) Addison-Wesley Educational Pubs., Inc.

Las Flores De Dona Flora: Individual 6-packs. 2003. 23.95 (978-0-673-78073-7(2)) Celebration Pr.

Focas. (Spanish Early Intervention Levels Ser.). (SPA.). 21.30 (978-0-7362-0827-7(5)) Hampton-Brown Bks.

Focas (G), Vol. 8. (Spanish Early Intervention Levels Ser.). (SPA.). 3.55 (978-0-7362-0773-7(2)) Hampton-Brown Bks.

Fonolibros Series: Complete Stage One. 2003. (SPA.). 1230.95 (978-0-7652-1052-4(5)) Modern Curriculum Pr.

Fonolibros Series: Complete Stage Two. 2003. (SPA.). 895.50 (978-0-7652-1053-1(3)) Modern Curriculum Pr.

Fontes, Justine. Daniel el Descortes: Rude Ralph. Jordan, Charles, illus. 2005. (Rookie Reader(R) Espanol Ser.). 32p. (gr. k-2). 19.50 (978-0-516-24444-0(2) , Children's Pr.) Scholastic Library Publishing.

Fox, Mem & Staub, Leslie. Quienquiera Que Seas. Ada, Alma Flor & Campoy, F. Isabel, trs. Staub, Leslie, illus. 2002. (ENG & SPA., Illus.). 32p. (J). pap. 7.00 (978-0-15-216460-7(X) , HB31513, Voyager Bks./Libros Viajeros) Harcourt Children's Bks.

Franklin en Paris 19: Leveled Books. 2001. (McGraw-Hill. Lectura Ser.). (ENG & SPA.). (gr. 3 up). (978-0-02-188140-6(5)) Macmillan/McGraw-Hill Schl. Div.

Fraser, Janine M. La Mariposa de Abdullah. (Torre de Papel Ser.). (SPA., Illus.). (J). (gr. 2). 7.95 (978-958-04-4917-1(1)) Norma S.A. COL. *Dist:* Distribuidora Norma, Inc.

Freddy the Fish. 2003. 23.95 (978-0-673-78128-4(3)) Celebration Pr.

Freed, Herb. Sing & Learn Spanish. 2004. 271p. (J). pap. 18.99 (978-0-9760472-0-9(9)) Global Village Kids, LLC.

French, Cathy. Haz un movil de animales & Make an Animal Mobile. 2005. spiral bd. 66.00 (***978-1-4108-5619-7(4)***) Benchmark Education Co.

—Haz una isla & Make an Island. 2005. spiral bd. 66.00 (***978-1-4108-5632-6(1)***) Benchmark Education Co.

La Fruta. (Spanish Early Intervention Levels Ser.). (SPA.). 3.85 (978-1-56334-437-4(8)); 23.10 (978-1-56334-762-7(8)) Hampton-Brown Bks.

Funston, James F., et al. Somos Asi en Sus Marcas B. 1999. (SPA.). (YA). (gr. 8). 36.95 (978-0-8219-1958-3(X) , 70508) EMC/Paradigm Publishing.

La Gallinita Roja: Lap Book. (Pebble Soup Exploraciones Ser.). (SPA.). 16p. (ps up). 21.00 (978-0-7578-1684-0(3)) Rigby Education.

La Gallinita Roja: Small Book. (Pebble Soup Exploraciones Ser.). (SPA.). 16p. (ps up). 5.00 (978-0-7578-1724-3(6)) Rigby Education.

La Gallinita Roja: Video Tape. (ENG & SPA.). (gr. k-1). 26.00 (978-0-7635-6276-2(9)) Rigby Education.

Game Time: Matching English 6-packs. 2003. 23.95 (978-0-673-57558-6(6)) Celebration Pr.

García Marquez, Gabriel. La Siesta del Martes.Tr. of Tuesday's Siesta. (SPA.). 10.50 (978-958-04-5574-5(0)) Norma S.A. COL. *Dist:* AIMS International Bks., Inc., Distribuidora Norma, Inc.

La gatita Presumida. (Spanish Early Intervention Levels Ser.). (SPA.). 28.38 (978-0-7362-0846-8(1)) Hampton-Brown Bks.

La Gatita Presumida (K), Vol. 18. (Spanish Early Intervention Levels Ser.). (SPA.). 4.73 (978-0-7362-0822-2(4)) Hampton-Brown Bks.

El Gatito Hambriento: Individual Title Six-Packs. (Coleccion Pm Ser.).Tr. of Hungry Kitten. (SPA.). 16p. (gr. 1 up). 26.00 (978-0-7578-2981-9(3)) Rigby Education.

Gatitos: Individual Title Six-Packs. (Literatura 2000 Ser.). (SPA.). (ps-1). 28.00 (978-0-7635-1195-1(1)) Rigby Education.

El Gato y el Raton: Individual Title Six-Packs. (Coleccion Pm Ser.: Vol. 2). Tr. of Cat & mouse. (SPA.). 16p. (gr. k-1). 26.00 (978-0-7578-0677-3(5)) Rigby Education.

Gaviota es Lista: Individual Title Six-Packs. (Coleccion Pm Ser.).Tr. of Seagull is clever. (SPA.). 16p. (gr. 1 up). 26.00 (978-0-7578-2995-6(3)) Rigby Education.

Gedovius, Juan. Purple Cubed. Gedovius, Juan, illus. (Illus.). 32p. (J). (gr. k-6). 13.95 (978-968-19-0751-8(5)) Santillana USA Publishing Co., Inc.

Gidwitz. Story in the Stone. 1999. (Illus.). (J). pap. (978-0-7398-2484-9(8)) Steck-Vaughn.

El gigante Solitario: Individual Title Six-Packs. (Literatura 2000 Ser.). (SPA.). (gr. 2-3). 33.00 (978-0-7635-1092-3(0)) Rigby Education.

Globos de Cumpleanos: Individual Title Six-Packs. (Coleccion Pm Ser.).Tr. of Birthday balloons. (SPA.). 16p. (gr. 1 up). 26.00 (978-0-7578-3017-4(X)) Rigby Education.

Gol!, 6 Pack. 2003. 23.95 (978-0-673-78064-5(3)) Celebration Pr.

Gol! (Spanish Early Intervention Levels Ser.). (SPA.). 23.10 (978-0-7362-0323-4(0)) Hampton-Brown Bks.

Gol! (E), Vol. 8. (Spanish Early Intervention Levels Ser.). (SPA.). 3.85 (978-0-7362-0298-5(6)) Hampton-Brown Bks.

Gomez, Carlos Humberto. Nos Comunicamos 1. (Coleccion Nos Comunicamos). (SPA & ENG.). (J). (gr. 1). pap. 23.50 (978-958-04-1580-0(3) , 15017309) Norma S.A. COL. *Dist:* Continental Bk. Co., Inc.

—Nos Comunicamos 2. (Coleccion Nos Comunicamos). (SPA & ENG.). (J). (gr. 2). pap. 23.50 (978-958-04-1581-7(1) , 15017310) Norma S.A. COL. *Dist:* Continental Bk. Co., Inc.

—Nos Comunicamos 4. (Coleccion Nos Comunicamos). (SPA & ENG.). (J). (gr. 4). pap. 23.50 (978-958-04-1583-1(8) , 1021251) Norma S.A. COL. *Dist:* Continental Bk. Co., Inc.

—Nos Comunicamos 6. (Coleccion Nos Comunicamos). (SPA & ENG.). (J). (gr. 6). pap. 23.50 (978-958-04-1585-5(4) , 1021253) Norma S.A. COL. *Dist:* Continental Bk. Co., Inc.

—Nos Comunicamos Kindergarten. (Coleccion Nos Comunicamos). (SPA & ENG.). (J). 23.50 (978-958-04-1579-4(X) , NOR5794) Norma S.A. COL. *Dist:* Continental Bk. Co., Inc.

Good Apple. Spanish - English Little Books to Make & Read. 2001. 128p. (J). (gr. k-2). pap. 14.99 (978-1-56417-659-2(2) , GA1569) Schaffer, Frank Pubns.

La Granja. 2005. 100p. (J). spiral bd. 14.99 (978-1-59441-455-8(6) , K04006) Carson-Dellosa Publishing Co., Inc.

La Granja. 2004. (¡Excursiones!). (J). 14.45 (978-1-4034-5638-0(0)) Heinemann Library.

La Granja De Don Manuel: Individual 6-packs. 2003. 23.95 (978-0-673-77151-3(2)) Celebration Pr.

Graphic Organizer Flip Chart. 2000. (SPA.). (gr. k up). suppl. ed. 98.75 (978-0-673-63152-7(4)) Addison-Wesley Educational Pubs., Inc.

Green Collection. (Elefonetica Ser.). (SPA.). (gr. 1-2). 324.85 (978-0-7362-0784-3(8)) Hampton-Brown Bks.

Greene, Inez. Adonde Esta Me Topito?, Level 1. Ada, Alma Flor, tr. 2003. (Dejame Leer Ser.). (SPA., Illus.). (J). (ps-3). 6.50 (978-0-673-36328-2(7) , Good Year Bks.) Celebration Pr.

Gregorio El Gallo, 6 Pack. 2003. 23.95 (978-0-673-78078-2(3)) Celebration Pr.

The Grocery Store: Individual Title Two-Packs. (Chiquilibros Ser.). (ps-1). 12.00 (978-0-7635-8539-6(4)) Rigby Education.

Groenlandia: Individual Title Six-Packs. (On Deck en Espanol Ser.).Tr. of Greenland. (SPA.). 24p. (gr. 4-5). 35.00 (978-0-7578-6452-0(X)) Rigby Education.

El grupo musical Lac Hong: 6 Small Books. (Saludos Ser.: Vol. 1). (SPA.). (gr. 3-5). 31.00 (978-0-7635-1757-1(7)) Rigby Education.

El Guerito Travieso, 6 Packs. 2003. 23.95 (978-0-673-77154-4(7)) Celebration Pr.

Guy, Ginger Foglesong. Fiesta. Moreno, Rene King, illus. 2007. 32p. (J). pap. 6.99 (***978-0-06-088226-6(3)*** , Rayo) HarperCollins Pubs.

Habitat para la Humanida: Individual Title Six-Packs. (On Deck en Espanol Ser.).Tr. of Habitat for Humanity. (SPA.). 24p. (gr. 4-5). 35.00 (978-0-7578-6416-2(3)) Rigby Education.

Hall, Zoe. It's Pumpkin Time! Halpern, Sheri, illus. 2002. (SPA.). 40p. (J). (gr. k-1). pap. 5.99 (978-0-439-18731-2(1) , SO30069, Scholastic en Espanol) Scholastic, Inc.

Harcourt School Publishers Staff. Alamo Cruza Texas: Library Edition. 1999. (SPA., Illus.). pap. 19.10 (978-0-15-315872-8(7)) Harcourt Schl. Pubs.

—Alerta Roja: Take-Home Book. 1999. (Vamos Ser.). (SPA., Illus.). (J). pap. 2.50 (978-0-15-318854-1(5)) Harcourt Schl. Pubs.

—Amigas/Lombrices: Library Edition. 1999. (SPA., Illus.). pap. 19.10 (978-0-15-315877-3(8)) Harcourt Schl. Pubs.

—Como Cuidar Vivero: Take-Home Book. 2001. (Vamos Ser.). (SPA., Illus.). (J). pap. 2.80 (978-0-15-319961-5(X)) Harcourt Schl. Pubs.

—El Elefantito: Little Book. 1999. (Vamos Ser.). (Illus.). pap. 16.80 (978-0-15-315821-6(2)) Harcourt Schl. Pubs.

—Fernando En la Fotografo: Phonics Practice Reader. 1999. (Vamos Ser.). (SPA., Illus.). pap. 5.00 (978-0-15-318963-0(0)) Harcourt Schl. Pubs.

—La Gatita Rosita: Phonics Practice Reader. 1999. (SPA., Illus.). pap. 5.00 (978-0-15-318989-0(4)) Harcourt Schl. Pubs.

—Gergorio y el Ogro: Phonics Practice Reader. 1999. (Vamos Ser.). (SPA., Illus.). pap. 5.00 (978-0-15-319002-5(7)) Harcourt Schl. Pubs.

—Golosito el Gatito: Phonics Practice Reader. 1999. (Vamos Ser.). (SPA., Illus.). pap. 5.00 (978-0-15-318952-4(5)) Harcourt Schl. Pubs.

—La Jugar! Phonics Practice Reader. 1999. (Vamos Ser.). (SPA., Illus.). pap. 5.00 (978-0-15-318960-9(6)) Harcourt Schl. Pubs.

—Lalo y Lupe: Phonics Practice Reader. 1999. (Vamos Ser.). (SPA., Illus.). (gr. 2). pap. 5.00 (978-0-15-318961-6(4)) Harcourt Schl. Pubs.

—La Lluvia: Phonics Practice Reader. 1999. (Vamos Ser.). (SPA., Illus.). pap. 5.00 (978-0-15-318990-6(8)) Harcourt Schl. Pubs.

—Mupi y Mama: Phonics Practice Reader. 1999. (Vamos Ser.). (SPA., Illus.). pap. 5.00 (978-0-15-318948-7(7)) Harcourt Schl. Pubs.

—Nina y Natan: Phonics Practice Reader. 1999. (Vamos Ser.). (SPA., Illus.). pap. 5.00 (978-0-15-318957-9(6)) Harcourt Schl. Pubs.

—Las Quesadilla: Phonics Practice Reader. 1999. (Vamos Ser.). (SPA., Illus.). pap. 5.00 (978-0-15-318992-0(4)) Harcourt Schl. Pubs.

Harvey, William C. Spanish Every Day: A Learning Adventure for Your Readers. 2001. (Illus.). 180p. (gr. 2-7). (SPA & ENG.). 16.99 (978-0-7641-7445-2(2)); pap. 11.99 (978-0-7641-1694-0(0)) Barron's Educational Series, Inc.

Has visto al jabali que anda por Aqui? Individual Title Six-Packs. (Literatura 2000 Ser.). (SPA.). (gr. 2-3). 33.00 (978-0-7635-1093-0(9)) Rigby Education.

Hay un esqueleto en el Autobus: Individual Title Six-Packs. (Literatura 2000 Ser.). (SPA.). (gr. 2-3). 33.00 (978-0-7635-1094-7(7)) Rigby Education.

Hecho en Corea: 6 Small Books. (Saludos Ser.: Vol. 3). (SPA.). (gr. 3-5). 31.00 (978-0-7635-1830-1(1)) Rigby Education.

Hector tiene Hipo. (Spanish Early Intervention Levels Ser.). (SPA.). 21.30 (978-0-7362-0833-8(X)) Hampton-Brown Bks.

Hector Tiene Hipo (G), Vol. 10. (Spanish Early Intervention Levels Ser.). (SPA.). 3.55 (978-0-7362-0779-9(1)) Hampton-Brown Bks.

Hercules y las Manzanas de Oro 17: Leveled Books. 2001. (McGraw-Hill. Lectura Ser.). (ENG & SPA.). (gr. 4 up). (978-0-02-188217-5(7)) Macmillan/McGraw-Hill Schl. Div.

La Hermanita, 6 Packs. (Coleccion Pm Ser.).Tr. of New Baby. (SPA.). 16p. (gr. 1 up). 26.00 (978-0-7578-3000-6(5)) Rigby Education.

Hermoso, A. S., et al. Curso Practico de la Gramatica de Espanol Lengua Extranjera: Curso Practico I. 2nd ed. (SPA.). 116p. wbk. ed. 18.95 (978-84-7711-073-6(5) , EDI0735) Edelsa Grupo Didascalia, S.A. ESP. *Dist:* Continental Bk. Co., Inc.

—Curso Practico de la Gramatica de Espanol Lengua Extranjera: Curso Practico II. (SPA.). 116p. wbk. ed. 18.95 (978-84-7711-074-3(3) , EDI0743) Edelsa Grupo Didascalia, S.A. ESP. *Dist:* Continental Bk. Co., Inc.

—Curso Practico de la Gramatica de Espanol Lengua Extranjera: Curso Practico III. (SPA., Illus.). 128p. wbk. ed. 24.95 (978-84-7711-075-0(1) , EDI0751) Edelsa Grupo Didascalia, S.A. ESP. *Dist:* Continental Bk. Co., Inc.

Herrera, Juan Felipe. The Upside down Boy. Gomez, Elizabeth, illus. 2006. Tr. of Nino de Cabeza. 32p. (J). pap. 7.95 (978-0-89239-217-9(7)) Children's Bk. Pr.

Herzig, Alison Cragin. El Gran Dilema. (Torre de Papel Ser.). (SPA.). (J). (gr. 2). 7.95 (978-958-04-3391-0(7)) Norma S.A. COL. *Dist:* Distribuidora Norma, Inc.

Hill, Eric. Donde Esta Spot. (SPA.). pap. 10.95 (978-950-07-1960-5(6)) Editorial Sudamericana S.A. ARG. *Dist:* Distribooks, Inc.

Hirigoyen, Maria. Guia para los Estudios del Espanol: Advanced Placement. 2001. (Coleccion Textos Ser.). (SPA.). 112p. (gr. 11-12). 12.00 (978-0-89729-692-2(3)) Ediciones Universal.

Hola! (Spanish Early Intervention Levels Ser.). (SPA.). 3.85 (978-1-56334-432-9(7)); 23.10 (978-1-56334-761-0(X)) Hampton-Brown Bks.

Hola y Adios, 6 Packs. (Literatura 2000 Ser.). (SPA.). (gr. k-1). 28.00 (978-0-7635-1023-7(8)) Rigby Education.

Holt, Rinehart and Winston Staff. En Avant: Online Edition. 4th ed. 2003. 43.86 (978-0-03-031718-7(5)) Holt, Rinehart & Winston.

—Ven Conmigo! Level 1: Storytelling Book. 3rd ed. 2003. (SPA.). pap. 14.60 (978-0-03-065474-9(2)) Holt, Rinehart & Winston.

El Hombrecito de pan de Jengibre. (ENG & SPA.). (gr. k-1). 26.00 incl. VHS (978-0-7635-6277-9(7)) Rigby Education.

Hongos para la Cena, 6 packs, . (Coleccion Pm Ser.).Tr. of Mushrooms for dinner. (SPA.). 16p. (gr. 1 up). 26.00 (978-0-7578-3026-6(9)) Rigby Education.

Hooked on Phonics Staff. Learn to Read: Localized Spanish for U. S. 2007. (J). (gr. k). 64.99 (***978-1-60143-890-4(7)***); (gr. k-1). 139.99 (***978-1-60143-889-8(3)***); (gr. 1). 64.99 (***978-1-60143-891-1(5)***) HOP, LLC.

Hopping, Lorraine Jean. Huracanes!, Level 4. Wheeler, Jody, illus. 2002. (Hello Reader! Ser.). (SPA.). 48p. (J). pap. 3.99 (978-0-439-41134-9(3) , Scholastic en Espanol) Scholastic, Inc.

—Wild Weather: Lightning! Salas, Macarena A., tr. Wheeler, Jody, illus. 2002. (Hello Reader! Science Ser.). (SPA.). 48p. (J). (gr. 2-4). pap. 3.99 (978-0-439-16165-7(7) , SO0343, Scholastic en Espanol) Scholastic, Inc.

Las Horas. (Coleccion Libritos Acordeon). (SPA., Illus.). 10p. (J). pap. 5.50 (978-950-11-0827-9(9) , SGM279) Sigmar ARG. *Dist:* Continental Bk. Co., Inc.

La Hormiga. 2004. (Bajo Mis Pies). (SPA.). 24p. (J). 14.45 (978-1-4034-4342-7(4)) Heinemann Library.

La Hormiga y el Saltamontes: Lap Book. (Pebble Soup Exploraciones Ser.). (SPA.). 16p. (ps up). 21.00 (978-0-7578-1682-6(7)) Rigby Education.

La hormiga y el Saltamontes: Small Book. (Pebble Soup Exploraciones Ser.). (SPA.). 16p. (ps up). 5.00 (978-0-7578-1722-9(X)) Rigby Education.

Huevo rojo y Jengibre: Six-Pack. (Saludos Ser.: Vol. 1). (SPA.). (gr. 2-3). 31.00 (978-0-7635-9518-0(7)) Rigby Education.

Huevos para el Desayuno: Individual Title Six-Packs. (Coleccion Pm Ser.).Tr. of Eggs for breakfast. (SPA.). 16p. (gr. 1 up). 26.00 (978-0-7578-2974-1(0)) Rigby Education.

Huracan a la Vista! 6 Small Books. (Saludos Ser.: Vol. 2). (SPA.). (gr. 3-5). 31.00 (978-0-7635-2069-4(1)) Rigby Education.

Hurt-Newton, Tania. Vamos de Paseo. (SPA.). pap. 7.95 (978-950-07-2027-4(2)) Editorial Sudamericana S.A. ARG. *Dist:* Distribooks, Inc.

Hutchings, Amy & Hutchings, Richard. Vamos a Rocoger Manzanas y Calabazas. Hutchings, Richard, illus. 2002. (SPA., Illus.). 32p. (J). (gr. 1-3). pap. 3.50 (978-0-439-31739-9(8) , Scholastic en Espanol) Scholastic, Inc.

I Dance 6 Packs: Matching English. 2003. 23.95 (978-0-673-57559-3(4)) Celebration Pr.

I Live Here: Matching English, 6 Packs. 2003. 23.95 (978-0-673-57560-9(8)) Celebration Pr.

The Ice Cream Shop: Individual Title, 2 Packs. (Chiquilibros Ser.). (ps-1). 12.00 (978-0-7635-8534-1(3)) Rigby Education.

Igual a mi Abuelo: Individual Title, 6 Packs. (Literatura 2000 Ser.). (SPA.). (gr. 1-2). 28.00 (978-0-7635-1045-9(9)) Rigby Education.

In the Dark Interactive Packages: Bedtime. (Pebble Soup Explorations Ser.). (SPA.). (ps up). 52.00 (978-0-7578-5247-3(5)) Rigby Education.

In the Dark Interactive Packages: Nighttime Jobs. (Pebble Soup Explorations Ser.). (SPA.). (ps up). 52.00 (978-0-7578-5250-3(5)) Rigby Education.

S

In the Midnight Sky. (Pebble Soup Explorations Ser.). (SPA.). 16p. (ps up). 31.00 (978-0-7578-1669-7(X)) Rigby Education.

In the Midnight Sky: Small Book. (Pebble Soup Explorations Ser.). (SPA.). 16p. (ps up). 5.00 (978-0-7578-1709-0(2)) Rigby Education.

Infante, Begona. Fatima Yo Soy de El Salvador.Tr. of I'm from El Salvador. (SPA.). 48p. (J). 12.95 (978-84-246-9403-6(1)) La Galera, S.A. Editorial ESP. *Dist:* AIMS International Bks., Inc.

El Ingles Animado por Walt Disney.Tr. of Animated English by Walt Disney. (SPA.). (978-970-22-0098-7(9)) Larousse, Ediciones, S. A. de C. V.

Inkiow, Dimiter. Yo, Clara y el Papagayo Pipo. (Torre de Papel Ser.). (SPA.). (J). (gr. 2). 7.95 (978-958-04-2072-9(6)) Norma S.A. COL. *Dist:* Distribuidora Norma, Inc.

—Yo, Clara y el Poni Miguelin. (SPA., Illus.). 7.95 (978-958-04-2389-8(X)) Norma S.A. COL. *Dist:* Distribuidora Norma, Inc.

Insectos, Insectos, 6 Packs. 2003. 23.95 (978-0-673-78070-6(8)) Celebration Pr.

Insects, Insects. 2003. 23.95 (978-0-673-78132-1(1)) Celebration Pr.

The Iron Horse, 6 Packs. (Chiquilibros Ser.). (gr. k-1). 23.00 (978-0-7635-0443-4(2)) Rigby Education.

Jackson, Garnet N. El Primer Dia de Accion de Gracias. Croll, Carolyn, illus. 2002. (Coleccion "Hola, Lector" Ser.). (SPA.). 40p. (J). (gr. 1-3). pap. 3.99 (978-0-439-31733-7(9) , SO30895, Scholastic en Espanol) Scholastic, Inc.

Jason y los Argonautas 1: Leveled Books. 2001. (McGraw-Hill. Lectura Ser.). (ENG & SPA.). (gr. 3 up). (978-0-02-188122-2(7)) Macmillan/McGraw-Hill Schl. Div.

Joanna la Magnifica 6: Leveled Books. 2001. (McGraw-Hill. Lectura Ser.). (ENG & SPA.). (gr. 5 up). (978-0-02-188254-0(1)) Macmillan/McGraw-Hill Schl. Div.

Jones, Christianne C. Cuantas Manchas Tiene el Leopardo? Zhurkina, Svetlana, illus. 2006. (Read-It! Readers en Espanol Ser.).Tr. of How Many Spots Does a Leopard Have?. (SPA.). 32p. (J). (ps-3). 19.95 (978-1-4048-1648-0(8)) Picture Window Bks.

—Un Cuarto para Dos. Trover, Zachary, illus. 2006. (Read-It! Readers en Espanol Ser.).Tr. of Room to Share. (SPA.). 32p. (J). (ps-3). 19.95 (978-1-4048-1694-7(1)) Picture Window Bks.

—Eric No Juega. Demski, James, Jr., illus. 2006. (Read-It! Readers en Espanol Ser.).Tr. of Eric Won't Do It. (SPA.). 32p. (J). (ps-3). 19.95 (978-1-4048-1683-1(6)) Picture Window Bks.

—Pollita Pequenita. Hermanson, Kyle, illus. 2006. (Read-It! Readers en Espanol Ser.).Tr. of Chicken Little. (SPA.). 32p. (J). (ps-3). 19.95 (978-1-4048-1646-6(1)) Picture Window Bks.

—El Primer Dia. Demski, James, Jr., illus. 2006. (Read-It! Readers en Espanol Ser.).Tr. of Joey's First Day. (SPA.). 32p. (J). (ps-3). 19.95 (978-1-4048-1627-5(5)) Picture Window Bks.

—Pruebalo. Yi, Hye Won, illus. 2006. (Read-It! Readers en Espanol Ser.).Tr. of Just Try it. (SPA.). 32p. (J). (ps-3). 19.95 (978-1-4048-1692-3(5)) Picture Window Bks.

Jordan, Denise M. Animales de Circo. 2002. (SPA.). 24p. (J). (ps-1). pap. 5.25 (978-1-58810-844-9(9) , 91569); lib. bdg. 17.08 (978-1-58810-797-8(3)) Heinemann Library.

—El Circo, 5 bks., Set. 2002. (SPA.). (J). (ps-1). 92.50 (978-1-58810-800-5(7)) Heinemann Library.

—El Circo 123. 2002. (SPA.). 24p. (J). (ps-1). pap. 5.25 (978-1-58810-846-3(5) , 91570) Heinemann Library.

—Payasos de Circo. 2002. 24p. (J). (ps-1). pap. 5.25 (978-1-58810-845-6(7) , 91571); (SPA.). lib. bdg. 17.08 (978-1-58810-798-5(1)) Heinemann Library.

Juan y Paula en la Granja. (Coleccion Leo Con Figuras). (SPA.). 14p. (J). pap. 4.50 (978-950-11-0837-8(6) , SGM376) Sigmar ARG. *Dist:* Continental Bk. Co., Inc.

Juego de Dedos. (Spanish Early Intervention Levels Ser.). (SPA.). 21.30 (978-0-7362-0805-5(4)); Vol. 3. 3.55 (978-0-7362-0763-8(5)) Hampton-Brown Bks.

Juez por un Dia: 6 Small Books. (Saludos Ser.: Vol. 1). (SPA.). (gr. 3-5). 31.00 (978-0-7635-1802-8(6)) Rigby Education.

Juez por un Dia: Big Book. (Saludos Ser.: Vol. 1). (SPA.). (gr. 3-5). 31.00 (978-0-7635-3172-0(3)) Rigby Education.

Juguemos con la Musica.Tr. of Let's Play with Music. (SPA.). (J). (gr. k-2). pap., stu. ed. 11.16 (978-968-24-3081-7(X)) Trillas Editorial, S. A. MEX. *Dist:* Lectorum Pubns., Inc.

Julia y el tronco de Maiz 22: Leveled Books. 2001. (McGraw-Hill. Lectura Ser.). (ENG & SPA.). (gr. 3 up). (978-0-02-188119-2(7)) Macmillan/McGraw-Hill Schl. Div.

Julian y el libro Magico 12: Leveled Books. 2001. (McGraw-Hill. Lectura Ser.). (ENG & SPA.). (gr. 3 up). (978-0-02-188109-3(X)) Macmillan/McGraw-Hill Schl. Div.

Julio busca el Tesoro: Individual Title Six-Packs. (Coleccion Pm Ser.).Tr. of Ben's treasure hunt. (SPA.). 16p. (gr. 1 up). 26.00 (978-0-7578-2967-3(8)) Rigby Education.

Just Bunny & Me: Big Book. (Pebble Soup Explorations Ser.). (SPA.). 16p. (ps up). 31.00 (978-0-7578-1666-6(5)) Rigby Education.

Just Bunny & Me: Small Book. (Pebble Soup Explorations Ser.). (SPA.). 16p. (ps up). 5.00 (978-0-7578-1706-9(8)) Rigby Education.

Kassirer, Sue. La Feria Musical de Matematicas: Math Matters en Espanol. Smath, Jerry, illus. 2005. 32p. pap. 4.95 (978-1-57565-153-8(X)) Kane Pr., The.

—Que Sigue, Nina? Math Matters en Espanol. O'Rourke, Page Eastburn, illus. 2005. 32p. pap. 4.95 (978-1-57565-152-1(1)) Kane Pr., The.

Kasza, Keiko. El Mas Poderoso. (SPA.). (J). 8.95 (978-958-04-6490-7(1)) Norma S.A. COL. *Dist:* Distribuidora Norma, Inc.

Kaut, Ellis. El Duende del Carpintero. (Torre de Papel Ser.). (SPA.). (J). (gr. 4 up). 7.95 (978-958-04-2889-3(1)) Norma S.A. COL. *Dist:* Distribuidora Norma, Inc.

Keep Books at The Ohio State University Staff. Spanish Emergent Reader 1, Set. 2005. (SPA.). (J). pap. (978-1-893986-42-8(X)) Keep Bks.

Keller. Como Eran l os Dinosaurios. 1999. (SPA.). pap. 5.18 (978-0-7398-0729-3(3)) Steck-Vaughn.

—Muestra Y Cuenta Entre Dinosau. 1999. pap. 5.18 (978-0-7398-0728-6(5)) Steck-Vaughn.

Kente: una tradicion Especial 14: Leveled Books. 2001. (McGraw-Hill. Lectura Ser.). (ENG & SPA.). (gr. 3 up). (978-0-02-188135-2(9)) Macmillan/McGraw-Hill Schl. Div.

Kique el Taxista. (Spanish Early Intervention Levels Ser.). (SPA.). 21.30 (978-0-7362-0835-2(6)) Hampton-Brown Bks.

Kique el Taxista (F), Vol. 12. (Spanish Early Intervention Levels Ser.). (SPA.). 3.55 (978-0-7362-0781-2(3)) Hampton-Brown Bks.

The Kitchen: Individual Title Two-Packs. (Chiquilibros Ser.). (ps-1). 12.00 (978-0-7635-8540-2(8)) Rigby Education.

Kittinger, Jo S. Cuando sea Grande: When I Grow Up. Lucas, Margeaux, illus. 2005. (Rookie Reader(R) Espanol Ser.). 24p. (gr. k-2). 19.50 (978-0-516-24443-3(4) , Children's Pr.) Scholastic Library Publishing.

Kline, Trish & Donev, Mary. Celebration of Letters A & B: Busy Preschoolers. 2007. (Illus.). 16p. (J). per. 20.00 ***(978-1-934307-04-5(1))*** Ghost Hunter Productions.

—Celebration of Letters C & D: Busy Preschoolers. 2007. (Illus.). 16p. (J). per. 20.00 ***(978-1-934307-05-2(X))*** Ghost Hunter Productions.

—Celebration of Letters E & F: Busy Preschoolers. 2007. (Illus.). 16p. (J). per. 20.00 ***(978-1-934307-06-9(8))*** Ghost Hunter Productions.

—Celebration of Letters G & H: Busy Preschoolers. 2007. (Illus.). 16p. (J). per. 20.00 ***(978-1-934307-07-6(6))*** Ghost Hunter Productions.

—Celebration of Letters I & J: Busy Preschoolers. 2007. (Illus.). 16p. (J). per. 20.00 ***(978-1-934307-08-3(4))*** Ghost Hunter Productions.

—Celebration of Letters K & L: Busy Preschoolers. 2007. (Illus.). 16p. (J). per. 20.00 ***(978-1-934307-09-0(2))*** Ghost Hunter Productions.

—Celebration of Letters M & N: Busy Preschoolers. 2007. (Illus.). 16p. (J). per. 20.00 ***(978-1-934307-10-6(6))*** Ghost Hunter Productions.

—Celebration of Letters O & Q: Busy Preschoolers. 2007. (Illus.). 16p. (J). per. 20.00 ***(978-1-934307-11-3(4))*** Ghost Hunter Productions.

—Celebration of Letters P & R: Busy Preschoolers. 2007. (Illus.). 16p. (J). per. 20.00 ***(978-1-934307-12-0(2))*** Ghost Hunter Productions.

—Celebration of Letters S & T: Busy Preschoolers. 2007. (Illus.). 16p. (J). per. 20.00 ***(978-1-934307-13-7(0))*** Ghost Hunter Productions.

—Celebration of Letters U & V: Busy Preschoolers. 2007. (Illus.). 16p. (J). per. 20.00 ***(978-1-934307-14-4(9))*** Ghost Hunter Productions.

—Celebration of Letters W & X: Busy Preschoolers. 2007. (Illus.). 16p. (J). per. 20.00 ***(978-1-934307-15-1(7))*** Ghost Hunter Productions.

—Celebration of Letters Y & Z: Busy Preschoolers. 2007. (Illus.). 16p. (J). per. 20.00 ***(978-1-934307-16-8(5))*** Ghost Hunter Productions.

Klopp, JoAnne Robinson. Actionlogues: Live Action TPR Spanish. Clark, Laura & Klopp, Stephen, illus. Klopp, Stephen, photos by. unabr. ed. 2000. (SPA.). 41p. (YA). (gr. 7-12). pap. 12.00 (978-0-940296-51-0(9) , 230) Sky Oaks Productions, Inc.

Kwasi: un cuento Cancion: 6 Small Books. (Saludos Ser.: Vol. 2). (SPA.). 24p. (gr. 2-3). 31.00 (978-0-7635-9525-8(X)) Rigby Education.

A la luz de una Vela: Individual Title Six-Packs. (Coleccion Pm Ser.).Tr. of Candlelight. (SPA.). 16p. (gr. 1 up). 26.00 (978-0-7578-3034-1(X)) Rigby Education.

Lab Manual. 2003. (gr. 1 up). tchr. ed., lab manual ed. 13.25 (978-0-673-59344-3(4)); 2003. (gr. 2 up). tchr. ed., lab manual ed. 13.25 (978-0-673-59345-0(2)); 2003. (gr. 3 up). tchr. ed., lab manual ed. 13.25 (978-0-673-59346-7(0)); 2003. (gr. 4 up). tchr. ed., lab manual ed. 13.25 (978-0-673-59347-4(9)); 2003. (gr. 4 up). stu. ed., lab manual ed. 5.95 (978-0-673-59341-2(X)); 2003. (gr. 5 up). tchr. ed., lab manual ed. 13.25 (978-0-673-59348-1(7)); 2003. (gr. 5 up). stu. ed., lab manual ed. 5.95 (978-0-673-59342-9(8)); 2003. (gr. 6 up). stu. ed., lab manual ed. 5.95 (978-0-673-59343-6(6)); 2000. (SPA.). (gr. 1 up). stu. ed., lab manual ed. 7.40 (978-0-673-59474-7(2)); 2000. (SPA.). (gr. 2 up). stu. ed., lab manual ed. 7.40 (978-0-673-59475-4(0)); 2000. (SPA.). (gr. 3 up). stu. ed., lab manual ed. 6.75 (978-0-673-59476-1(9)); 2000. (SPA.). (gr. 4 up). stu. ed., lab manual ed. 6.75 (978-0-673-59477-8(7)); 2000. (SPA.). (gr. 5 up). stu. ed., lab manual ed. 6.75 (978-0-673-59478-5(5)); 2000. (SPA.). (gr. 6 up). stu. ed., lab manual ed. 6.75 (978-0-673-59479-2(3)) Addison-Wesley Educational Pubs., Inc.

El Ladron: Individual Title-Six Packs. (Chiquilibros Ser.). (SPA.). (gr. k-1). 23.00 (978-0-7635-8606-5(4)) Rigby Education.

Lakeshore Learning Materials, contrib. by. Spanish Emergent Readers: Set of 8 Books. 2007. (SPA.). (J). 44.95 ***(978-1-59746-020-0(6))*** Lakeshore Learning Materials.

El Lapiz: Individual Title Six-Packs. (Coleccion Pm Ser.: Vol. 2). Tr. of Pencil. (SPA.). 16p. (gr. k-1). 26.00 (978-0-7578-0681-0(3)) Rigby Education.

Larousse Mexico Staff, ed. Buenas Noche. 2006. (Mi Pequena Enciclopedia Ser.). (Illus.). 38p. (ps-k). pap. 3.95 (978-970-22-1190-7(5)) Larousse, Ediciones, S. A. de C. V. MEX. *Dist:* Houghton Mifflin Co. Trade & Reference Div.

—Los Insectos (Insects) 2006. (Mi Pequena Enciclopedia Ser.). (Illus.). 38p. (ps-k). pap. 3.95 (978-970-22-1188-4(3)) Larousse, Ediciones, S. A. de C. V. MEX. *Dist:* Houghton Mifflin Co. Trade & Reference Div.

—Mi Pequena Enciclopedia Larousse Los Bomberos. 2006. (Mi Pequena Enciclopedia Ser.). 38p. (ps-k). pap. 3.95 (978-970-22-1191-4(3)) Larousse, Ediciones, S. A. de C. V. MEX. *Dist:* Houghton Mifflin Co. Trade & Reference Div.

—Mi Pequena Encicopedia Larousse el Zoologico. 2006. (Mi Pequena Enciclopedia Ser.). 38p. (ps-k). pap. 3.95 (978-970-22-1193-8(X)) Larousse, Ediciones, S. A. de C. V. MEX. *Dist:* Houghton Mifflin Co. Trade & Reference Div.

—Mi Pequena Larousse Enciclopedia Los Piratas. 2006. (Mi Pequena Enciclopedia Ser.). (Illus.). 38p. (ps-k). pap. 3.95 (978-970-22-1192-1(1)) Larousse, Ediciones, S. A. de C. V. MEX. *Dist:* Houghton Mifflin Co. Trade & Reference Div.

—Mi Primer Larousse de Animales. 2006. (Mi Primer Larousse Ser.). (Illus.). 160p. (gr. k-3). 19.95 (978-970-22-1086-3(0)) Larousse, Ediciones, S. A. de C. V. MEX. *Dist:* Houghton Mifflin Co. Trade & Reference Div.

—Mi Primer Larousse de las Ciencias de la vida y de las Tierra. 2006. (Mi Primer Larousse Ser.). 160p. (gr. k-3). 19.95 (978-970-22-1231-7(6)) Larousse, Ediciones, S. A. de C. V. MEX. *Dist:* Houghton Mifflin Co. Trade & Reference Div.

—Los Vehiculos (Vehicles) 2006. (Mi Pequena Enciclopedia Ser.). (Illus.). 38p. (ps-k). pap. 3.95 (978-970-22-1189-1(1)) Larousse, Ediciones, S. A. de C. V. MEX. *Dist:* Houghton Mifflin Co. Trade & Reference Div.

Las amigas de Mari: Individual Title Six-Packs. (Coleccion Pm Ser.).Tr. of Sally's friends. (SPA.). 16p. (gr. 1 up). 26.00 (978-0-7578-3010-5(2)) Rigby Education.

Las dos Hermanas: Lap Book. (Pebble Soup Exploraciones Ser.). (SPA.). 16p. (ps up). 21.00 (978-0-7578-1692-5(4)) Rigby Education.

Las dos Hermanas: Small Book. (Pebble Soup Exploraciones Ser.). (SPA.). 16p. (ps up). 5.00 (978-0-7578-1732-8(7)) Rigby Education.

Las Escondidas. (Spanish Early Intervention Levels Ser.). (SPA.). 31.14 (978-0-7362-0337-1(0)) Hampton-Brown Bks.

Las Escondidas: Individual Title Six-Packs. (Coleccion Pm Ser.).Tr. of Hide & seek. (SPA.). 16p. (gr. 1 up). 26.00 (978-0-7578-2971-0(6)) Rigby Education.

Las huellas Verdes: Individual Title Six-Packs. (Literatura 2000 Ser.). (SPA.). (gr. 1-2). 28.00 (978-0-7635-1044-2(0)) Rigby Education.

Las Lagartijas. 2004. (Mi Gran Jardín). (SPA.). (J). 14.45 (978-1-4034-5748-6(4)) Heinemann Library.

Las Moras: Individual Title Six-Packs. (Coleccion Pm Ser.).Tr. of Blackberries. (SPA.). 16p. (gr. 1 up). 26.00 (978-0-7578-2983-3(X)) Rigby Education.

Las Ovejitas. (Spanish Early Intervention Levels Ser.). (SPA.). 21.30 (978-0-7362-0825-3(9)) Hampton-Brown Bks.

Las Pinatas. (Spanish Early Intervention Levels Ser.). (SPA.). 21.30 (978-0-7362-0808-6(9)) Hampton-Brown Bks.

Las Visitas: Individual Title Six-Packs. (Literatura 2000 Ser.). (SPA.). (gr. k-1). 28.00 (978-0-7635-1032-9(7)) Rigby Education.

Laun D'Nealian Alphabet: Capital Letters. 1999. 13.45 (978-0-673-28591-1(X)) Addison-Wesley Educational Pubs., Inc.

Laun D'Nealian Alphabet: Lower-case Letters. 1999. 13.45 (978-0-673-28590-4(1)) Addison-Wesley Educational Pubs., Inc.

Lavaca BLANCA de botas NEGRAS. (SPA.). (J). 12.00 (978-958-02-1235-5(X)) Editorial Voluntad S.A. COL. *Dist:* Distribuidora Norma, Inc.

Lebscky, Ibi. Albert. Cardoni, Paolo, illus. (Coleccion Seran Famosos).Tr. of Little Albert Einstein. (SPA.). 28p. (J). (gr. 2-4). 10.36 (978-84-233-1400-3(6)) Ediciones Destino ESP. *Dist:* Lectorum Pubns., Inc.

Leche para Ovejita: Individual Title Six-Packs. (Coleccion Pm Ser.).Tr. of Baby lamb's first drink. (SPA.). 16p. (gr. 1 up). 26.00 (978-0-7578-2960-4(0)) Rigby Education.

Las Lechucitas: Individual Title Six-Packs. (Coleccion Pm Ser.).Tr. of Baby Owls. (SPA.). 16p. (gr. 1 up). 26.00 (978-0-7578-2975-8(9)) Rigby Education.

Lectura en Familia: Spanish Easy Reading Combo. (SPA.). (ps-2). 122.04 (978-1-56334-402-2(5)) Hampton-Brown Bks.

Lectura en Familia: Spanish Phonics Grade 1 Combo. (SPA.). (gr. 1 up). 200.04 (978-0-7362-1490-2(9)) Hampton-Brown Bks.

Lectura en Familia: Spanish Phonics Grade 2 Combo. (SPA.). (gr. 2 up). 114.18 (978-0-7362-1491-9(7)) Hampton-Brown Bks.

Leo 1. (SPA.). (J). 16.00 (978-958-04-5657-5(7)) Norma S.A. COL. *Dist:* Distribuidora Norma, Inc.

Leo 2. (SPA.). (J). 16.00 (978-958-04-5658-2(5)) Norma S.A. COL. *Dist:* Distribuidora Norma, Inc.

Leo 3. (SPA.). (J). 16.00 (978-958-04-5659-9(3)) Norma S.A. COL. *Dist:* Distribuidora Norma, Inc.

Leo 4. (SPA.). (J). 16.00 (978-958-04-5660-5(7)) Norma S.A. COL. *Dist:* Distribuidora Norma, Inc.

Leo 5. (SPA.). (J). 16.00 (978-958-04-5661-2(5)) Norma S.A. COL. *Dist:* Distribuidora Norma, Inc.

Leo 6. (SPA.). (J). 16.00 (978-958-04-5662-9(3)) Norma S.A. COL. *Dist:* Distribuidora Norma, Inc.

Leonard, Marcia & Handelman, Dorothy. The Pet Vet. Handelman, Dorothy, illus. Leonard, Marcia, photos by. 2005. (ENG & SPA., Illus.). 32p. (J). (ps-1). pap. 4.99 (978-0-8225-3299-6(9)) Lerner Publishing Group.

La Leyenda del Dorado. (SPA.). (J). 12.00 (978-958-02-1355-0(0)) Editorial Voluntad S.A. COL. *Dist:* Distribuidora Norma, Inc.

Libritos para Mi: Blue Set. (SPA.). (gr. k-2). 129.00 (978-0-7362-0711-9(2)) Hampton-Brown Bks.

Libritos para Mi: Green Set. (SPA.). (gr. k-2). 129.00 (978-0-7362-0709-6(0)) Hampton-Brown Bks.

Libritos para Mi: Orange Set. (SPA.). (gr. k-2). 129.00 (978-0-7362-0710-2(4)) Hampton-Brown Bks.

Libritos para Mi: Purple Set. (SPA.). (gr. k-2). 129.00 (978-0-7362-0708-9(2)) Hampton-Brown Bks.

Libritos para Mi: Red Set. (SPA.). (gr. k-2). 129.00 (978-0-7362-0707-2(4)) Hampton-Brown Bks.

Lillegard, Dee. Papas el Martes, Level 1. 2003. (Dejame Leer Ser.). (SPA., Illus.). (J). (ps-3). 6.50 (978-0-673-36327-5(9) , Good Year Bks.) Celebration Pr.

Linari, Adrian. Los Cuentos de Aguara. (SPA.). (J). 8.95 (978-958-04-5031-3(5)) Norma S.A. COL. *Dist:* Distribuidora Norma, Inc.

La linda Telarano: Individual Title Six-Packs. (Coleccion Pm Ser.).Tr. of Mrs. Spider's beautiful web. (SPA.). 16p. (gr. 1 up). 26.00 (978-0-7578-3042-6(0)) Rigby Education.

El Liston. (Spanish Early Intervention Levels Ser.). (SPA.). 23.10 (978-1-56334-773-3(3)); Vol. 3. 3.85 (978-1-56334-444-2(0)) Hampton-Brown Bks.

Litchfield, Jo. First Picture Word Bk in Spanish. Litchfield, Jo, illus. 2006. (SPA., Illus.). 16p. (J). bds. 11.99 (978-0-7945-1417-4(0) , Usborne) EDC Publishing.

Literature Library Package. 1999. (Literature Libraries Ser.). (SPA.). (gr. 6 up). 74.75 (978-0-201-37247-2(9)); Set. (gr. k up). 74.75 (978-0-201-37241-0(X)); Set. (gr. 2 up). 74.75 (978-0-201-37243-4(6)); Set. (gr. 3 up). 74.75 (978-0-201-37244-1(4)); Set. (gr. 4 up). 74.75 (978-0-201-37245-8(2)); Set. (gr. 5 up). 74.75 (978-0-201-37246-5(0)) Addison-Wesley Educational Pubs., Inc.

Little Books Collection: Includes 18 Little Books. 2003. 83.50 (978-0-7652-0130-0(5)) Modern Curriculum Pr.

Llamazares, Julio. Mi Tio Mario, Level D. 2nd ed. 2000. (Spanish Easy Reader Library: Level D). (SPA., Illus.). (YA). (gr. 10-12). pap. 9.50 (978-0-8219-1473-1(1) , 70350) EMC/Paradigm Publishing.

Llega la Abuelita: 6 Small Books. (Saludos Ser.: Vol. 2). (SPA.). (gr. 2-3). 31.00 (978-0-7635-9544-9(6)) Rigby Education.

La Llegada del Virrey (Arrival of the Viceroy) 2005. (SPA.). (J). pap. 9.95 (978-968-7381-01-5(9)) Tecolote, Ediciones, S.A. de C.V. MEX. *Dist:* Iaconi, Mariuccia Bk. Imports.

Llego la Banda, Vol. 4. (Spanish Early Intervention Levels Ser.). (SPA.). 3.55 (978-0-7362-0777-5(5)) Hampton-Brown Bks.

Llego la Banda (E) (Spanish Early Intervention Levels Ser.). (SPA.). 21.30 (978-0-7362-0831-4(3)) Hampton-Brown Bks.

Llorente, Maria Isabel Molina. El Misterio del Hombre Que Desaparecio. (Torre de Papel Ser.). (SPA.). (J). (gr. 4 up). 7.95 (978-958-04-0729-4(0)) Norma S.A. COL. *Dist:* Distribuidora Norma, Inc.

Lo mas Importante. (Spanish Early Intervention Levels Ser.). (SPA.). 31.14 (978-0-7362-0340-1(0)) Hampton-Brown Bks.

Lo Mas Importante (J), Vol. 24. (Spanish Early Intervention Levels Ser.). (SPA.). 5.19 (978-0-7362-0315-9(X)) Hampton-Brown Bks.

Lo mas quieto que Puedo: 6 Small Books. (Saludos Ser.: Vol. 3). (SPA.). (gr. 2-3). 31.00 (978-0-7635-9549-4(7)) Rigby Education.

Lo Que Sale De Un Huevo: Big Book Packages. 2003. 64.95 (978-0-673-58590-5(5)) Celebration Pr.

Lolita Y Su Familia: Individual 6-packs. 2003. 23.95 (978-0-673-78062-1(7)) Celebration Pr.

Lolita's Family, 6 Packs. 2003. 23.95 (978-0-673-78126-0(7)) Celebration Pr.

Lomba, Ana. Easy Spanish Storybook: Goldilocks & the Three Bears. 2005. (ENG & SPA., Illus.). 41p. 14.95 incl. cd-rom (978-0-07-146170-2(1) , 9780071461702) McGraw-Hill Cos., The.

—Easy Spanish Storybook: Little Red Riding Hood. 2005. (ENG & SPA., Illus.). 41p. 14.95 incl. cd-rom (978-0-07-146164-1(7) , 9780071461641) McGraw-Hill Cos., The.

London, Jonathan. Froggy Apprende a Nadar. 2003. (Froggy Ser.). (SPA., Illus.). (J). (gr. k-2). pap. 3.16 net. (978-0-439-20435-4(6) , SO30917) Scholastic, Inc.

—Froggy Juega al Futbol. 2003. (Froggy Ser.). (SPA., Illus.). (J). (gr. k-2). pap. 3.16 net. (978-0-439-24321-6(1) , SO30406) Scholastic, Inc.

—El Primer Beso de Froggy. 2003. (Froggy Ser.). (SPA., Illus.). (J). (gr. k-2). pap. 3.16 net. (978-0-439-26024-4(8) , SO30356) Scholastic, Inc.

Los animales Astutos: Individual Title Six-Packs. (Literatura 2000 Ser.). (SPA.). (gr. 2-3). 33.00 (978-0-7635-1082-4(3)) Rigby Education.

Los animalitos de Oaxaca: Lap Book. (Pebble Soup Exploraciones Ser.). (SPA.). 16p. (ps up). 21.00 (978-0-7578-1688-8(6)) Rigby Education.

Los animalitos de Oaxaca: Small Book. (Pebble Soup Exploraciones Ser.). (SPA.). 16p. (ps up). 5.00 (978-0-7578-1728-1(9)) Rigby Education.

Los cinco Pollitos: Individual Title Six-Packs. (Literatura 2000 Ser.). (SPA.). (gr. 1-2). 28.00 (978-0-7635-1062-6(9)) Rigby Education.

Los Comilones: Individual Title Six-Packs. (Literatura 2000 Ser.). (SPA.). (gr. k-1). 28.00 (978-0-7635-1012-1(2)) Rigby Education.

Los Disfraces: Individual Title Six-Packs. (Coleccion Pm Ser.: Vol. 1). Tr. of Dressing up. (SPA.). 16p. (gr. k-1). 26.00 (978-0-7578-0664-3(3)) Rigby Education.

A los dos Anos: 6 Small Books. (SPA.). (gr. k-1). 20.00 (978-0-7635-6254-0(8)) Rigby Education.

Los fideos de Papa: Individual Title Six-Packs. (Literatura 2000 Ser.). (SPA.). (gr. 1-2). 28.00 (978-0-7635-1070-1(X)) Rigby Education.

Los Perros. 2004. (Los Mascotas de mi Casa). 24p. (J). 14.95 (978-1-4034-6033-2(7)) Heinemann Library.

Los recuerdos de mi Abuelita: Individual Title Six-Packs. (Literatura 2000 Ser.). (SPA.). (gr. 1-2). 28.00 (978-0-7635-1077-0(7)) Rigby Education.

Los regalos de Abuelita: Individual Title Six-Packs. (Coleccion Pm Ser.). (SPA.). 16p. (gr. 1 up). 26.00 (978-0-7578-3018-1(8)) Rigby Education.

Los regalos de mi Abuelito. (Spanish Early Intervention Levels Ser.). (SPA.). 23.10 (978-1-56334-790-0(3)) Hampton-Brown Bks.

Los Sentidos. (Spanish Early Intervention Levels Ser.). (SPA.). 23.10 (978-1-56334-787-0(3)) Hampton-Brown Bks.

Los tres chivos Vivos: Video Tape. (ENG & SPA.). (gr. k-1). 26.00 (978-0-7635-6280-9(7)) Rigby Education.

Los tres Cochinitos: Video Tape. (ENG & SPA.). (gr. k-1). 26.00 (978-0-7635-6228-1(9)) Rigby Education.

Los trucos de Paco: Individual Title Six-Packs. (Literatura 2000 Ser.). (SPA.). (gr. 1-2). 28.00 (978-0-7635-1056-5(4)) Rigby Education.

Los zapatos de Mari: Individual Title Six-Packs. (Coleccion Pm Ser.: Vol. 2). Tr. of Sally's new shoes. (SPA.). 16p. (gr. k-1). 26.00 (978-0-7578-0682-7(1)) Rigby Education.

Lucia encuentra un Dragon: Individual Title, 6 packs. (Literatura 2000 Ser.). (SPA.). (gr. 2-3). 33.00 (978-0-7635-1095-4(5)) Rigby Education.

Luis y la Mariposa: Individual Title Six-Packs. (Literatura 2000 Ser.). (SPA.). (gr. 2-3). 33.00 (978-0-7635-1263-7(X)) Rigby Education.

Luna Rising Staff, ed. Elmo's Big Word Book. 2006. (Elmo's World Ser.). (SPA & ENG., Illus.). 12p. (J). 6.95 (978-0-87358-906-2(8) , Luna Rising) Northland Publishing.

—Elmo's Guessing Game about Colors. 2006. (SPA & ENG., Illus.). 12p. (J). 5.95 (978-0-87358-905-5(X) , Luna Rising) Northland Publishing.

MacHado, Ana Maria. Eso No Me lo Quita Nadie.Tr. of No One Can Take That Away from Me. (SPA.). (YA). (gr. 7-8). 8.95 (978-958-04-4530-2(3) , NR4358) Norma S.A. COL. *Dist:* Distribuidora Norma, Inc., Lectorum Pubns., Inc.

Mahoney, Judy. Teach Me Even More Spanish Book Box: Twenty-One Songs to Sing & a Story about Pen Pals. (Foreign Language Ser.). (SPA.). (J). incl. audio NewSound, LLC.

Mama y papa Trabajan: Individual Title Six-Packs. (Coleccion Pm Ser.: Vol. 1). Tr. of Mom & Dad work. (SPA.). 16p. (gr. k-1). 26.00 (978-0-7578-0668-1(6)) Rigby Education.

Mami, Mami! (Spanish Early Intervention Levels Ser.). (SPA.). 21.30 (978-0-7362-0801-7(1)) Hampton-Brown Bks.

La Manana: Individual Title Two-Packs. (Chiquilibros Ser.). (SPA.). (ps-1). 12.00 (978-0-7635-8551-8(3)) Rigby Education.

Many Hats: Matching English, 6-packs. 2003. 23.95 (978-0-673-57561-6(6)) Celebration Pr.

La maquina de Imprimir: Individual Title Six-Packs. (Literatura 2000 Ser.). (SPA.). (gr. 1-2). 28.00 (978-0-7635-1046-6(7)) Rigby Education.

El mar de Marta 22: Leveled Books. 2001. (McGraw-Hill. Lectura Ser.). (ENG & SPA.). (gr. 2 up). (978-0-02-188047-8(6)) Macmillan/McGraw-Hill Schl. Div.

Maracana: Individual Title Six-Packs. (On Deck en Espanol Ser.).Tr. of Maracana. (SPA.). 24p. (gr. 4-5). 35.00 (978-0-7578-6446-9(5)) Rigby Education.

La Marca en la Roca. 2000. (SPA., Illus.). 70p. (YA). (gr. 8-10). pap. 11.95 (978-88-8148-466-9(8)) European Language Institute ITA. *Dist:* Distribooks, Inc., Midwest European Pubns.

Margulies, Teddy Slater. El Dia de las Sorpresas. Orlando, Studio, illus. 2002. (Clifford Big Red Readers Ser.). (SPA.). 32p. (J). pap. 3.99 (978-0-439-25038-2(2) , SO30537) Scholastic, Inc.

Mari y la cubeta Roja: Individual Title Six-Packs. (Coleccion Pm Ser.).Tr. of Sally's red bucket. (SPA.). 16p. (gr. 1 up). 26.00 (978-0-7578-3003-7(X)) Rigby Education.

Mari y la Margarita: Individual Title Six-Packs. (Coleccion Pm Ser.).Tr. of Sally & the daisy. (SPA.). 16p. (gr. 1 up). 26.00 (978-0-7578-2966-6(X)) Rigby Education.

Mari y los Gorriones: Individual Title Six-Packs. (Coleccion Pm Ser.).Tr. of Sally & the sparrows. (SPA.). 16p. (gr. 1 up). 26.00 (978-0-7578-3004-4(8)) Rigby Education.

El Mariachi: Big Book Packages. 2003. 64.95 (978-0-673-58585-1(9)) Celebration Pr.

Mariachi 6 Packs: Matching English. 2003. 23.95 (978-0-673-57562-3(4)) Celebration Pr.

Marianela. (Coleccion Centro Literario). (SPA.). (J). pap., stu. ed. 7.95 (978-958-02-0483-1(7) , CAR017) Editorial Voluntad S.A. COL. *Dist:* Continental Bk. Co., Inc.

Marina la Ballena. 2003. 28.95 (978-0-673-78090-4(2)) Celebration Pr.

Marino, Ricardo. Lo Unico del Mundo. (Torre de Papel Ser.). (SPA.). (YA). (gr. 6 up). 8.95 (978-958-04-3812-0(9)) Norma S.A. COL. *Dist:* Distribuidora Norma, Inc.

Martin, Ann M. Claudia y la Nueva Alumna. (SPA.). (J). 11.95 (978-84-272-3662-2(X)) Molino, Editorial ESP. *Dist:* AIMS International Bks., Inc.

—Claudia y la Triste... (SPA.). (J). 11.95 (978-84-272-3676-9(X)) Molino, Editorial ESP. *Dist:* AIMS International Bks., Inc.

—Kristy y el Secreto de Susan. (SPA.). 152p. (J). 11.95 (978-84-272-3682-0(4)) Molino, Editorial ESP. *Dist:* AIMS International Bks., Inc.

—Kristy y los Esnobs. (SPA.). 168p. (J). 11.95 (978-84-272-3661-5(1)) Molino, Editorial ESP. *Dist:* AIMS International Bks., Inc.

—Mala Suerte de Mary Anne. (SPA.). 144p. (J). 11.95 (978-84-272-3667-7(0)) Molino, Editorial ESP. *Dist:* AIMS International Bks., Inc.

Marzollo, Jean. Soy el Fuego. Moffatt, Judith, illus. 2002. (Coleccion "Hola, Lector" Ser.).Tr. of I Am Fire. (SPA.). 32p. (J). (ps-1). pap. 3.99 (978-0-439-17309-4(4) , SO5702, Scholastic en Espanol) Scholastic, Inc.

—Soy el Fuego. 2001. Tr. of I Am Fire. (SPA.). (gr. 3-6). lib. bdg. 11.80 (978-0-613-81409-6(6)) Tandem Library Bks.

—Soy una Oruga. Moffatt, Judith, illus. 2002. (Coleccion "Hola, Lector" Ser.). (SPA.). 32p. (J). (ps-1). pap. 3.99 (978-0-439-08697-4(3) , SO5358, Scholastic en Espanol) Scholastic, Inc.

—Soy una Semilla. Moffatt, Judith, illus. 2002. (Coleccion "Hola, Lector" Ser.). (SPA.). 32p. (J). (ps-1). pap. 3.99 (978-0-439-08698-1(1) , SO0770, Scholastic en Espanol) Scholastic, Inc.

Mas Pizza! 2003. 28.95 (978-0-673-78089-8(9)) Celebration Pr.

Masters, Susan Rowan. La Vida Secreta de Hubie Hatzel. (Torre de Papel Ser.). (SPA.). (J). (gr. 4 up). 7.95 (978-958-04-1900-6(0)) Norma S.A. COL. *Dist:* Distribuidora Norma, Inc.

Mayra y el baile de Disfraces: Individual Title Six-Packs. (Literatura 2000 Ser.). (SPA.). (gr. 2-3). 33.00 (978-0-7635-1096-1(3)) Rigby Education.

McGraw-Hill Staff. !Buen Viaje!, Level 1. 2005. (C). stu. ed. 106.00 incl. cd-rom (978-0-07-868622-1(9) , 9780078686226) Glencoe/McGraw-Hill.

—Buen viaje!, Level 2, StudentWorks Plus CD-ROM. 2005. (C). cd-rom 106.00 (978-0-07-868623-8(7) , 9780078686238) Glencoe/McGraw-Hill.

—Buen Viaje!, Level 3. 2004. stu. ed. 107.32 incl. cd-rom (978-0-07-868624-5(5) , 9780078686245) Glencoe/McGraw-Hill.

—Ibuen Viaje!, Level I. 3rd ed. 2001. (SPA.). stu. ed. 82.64 (978-0-07-825680-6(1) , 9780078256806) Glencoe/McGraw-Hill.

Me Encontre Una Piedra: Big Book Packages. 2003. 64.95 (978-0-673-58591-2(3)) Celebration Pr.

Me gusta Leer. (Spanish Early Intervention Levels Ser.). (SPA.). 21.30 (978-0-7362-0806-2(2)) Hampton-Brown Bks.

Me Gusta Leer, Vol. 3. (Spanish Early Intervention Levels Ser.). (SPA.). 3.55 (978-0-7362-0764-5(3)) Hampton-Brown Bks.

Me gusta Leer: Individual Title Six-Packs. (Coleccion Pm Ser.: Vol. 2). Tr. of I like to read. (SPA.). 16p. (gr. k-1). 26.00 (978-0-7578-0688-9(0)) Rigby Education.

Mejías, Monica. Aprendiendo a Leer con Mili y Molo: Learn How to Read in Spanish. Mejías, Monica, illus. 2004. Tr. of Lernen Sie Spanish Lesen, Impara a leggere in Spagnolo, Aprenda a ler Espanhol, Apprenez a lire L'espagnol. (Illus.). 40p. (J). audio compact disk 12.00 (978-0-9753799-0-5(9)) Ediciones Alas, Inc.

El mejor Pastel, 6 vols., Pack. (Coleccion Pm Ser.).Tr. of Best Cake. (SPA.). 16p. (gr. 1 up). 26.00 (978-0-7578-3014-3(5)) Rigby Education.

El mejor regalo de Cumpleanos: Individual Title Six-Packs. (Literatura 2000 Ser.). (SPA.). (gr. 2-3). 33.00 (978-0-7635-1264-4(8)) Rigby Education.

El mensaje de las Estrellas: Lap Book. (Pebble Soup Exploraciones Ser.). (SPA.). 16p. (ps up). 21.00 (978-0-7578-1677-2(0)) Rigby Education.

El mensaje de las Estrellas: Small Book. (Pebble Soup Exploraciones Ser.). (SPA.). 16p. (ps up). 5.00 (978-0-7578-1717-5(3)) Rigby Education.

Los Meses Del Ano. 2003. 23.95 (978-0-673-77168-1(7)) Celebration Pr.

Mi amiga Laura. (Spanish Early Intervention Levels Ser.). (SPA.). 31.14 (978-0-7362-0329-6(X)) Hampton-Brown Bks.

Mi Amiga Laura (H), Vol. 14. (Spanish Early Intervention Levels Ser.). (SPA.). 5.19 (978-0-7362-0304-3(4)) Hampton-Brown Bks.

Mi Amigo. 2003. 35.50 (978-0-8136-8137-5(5)) Modern Curriculum Pr.

Mi Caballito. (Spanish Early Intervention Levels Ser.). (SPA.). 23.10 (978-1-56334-775-7(X)); Vol. 3. 3.85 (978-1-56334-446-6(7)) Hampton-Brown Bks.

Mi Caja: Individual Title-Six Packs. (Chiquilibros Ser.). (SPA.). (gr. k-1). 23.00 (978-0-7635-8604-1(8)) Rigby Education.

Mi conejito y Yo: Big Book. (Pebble Soup Exploraciones Ser.). (SPA.). 16p. (ps up). 31.00 (978-0-7578-1690-1(8)) Rigby Education.

Mi conejito y Yo: Small Book. (Pebble Soup Exploraciones Ser.). (SPA.). 16p. (ps up). 5.00 (978-0-7578-1730-4(0)) Rigby Education.

Mi Dia. (Spanish Early Intervention Levels Ser.). (SPA.). 23.10 (978-1-56334-771-9(7)); Vol. 3. 3.85 (978-1-56334-442-8(4)) Hampton-Brown Bks.

Mi Escuelita: Individual 6-packs. 2003. 23.95 (978-0-673-77142-1(3)) Celebration Pr.

Mi Familia. (Spanish Early Intervention Levels Ser.). (SPA.). 31.14 (978-0-7362-0327-2(3)) Hampton-Brown Bks.

Mi Familia: Individual 6-packs. 2003. 23.95 (978-0-673-77133-9(4)) Celebration Pr.

Mi Familia (E), Vol. 10. (Spanish Early Intervention Levels Ser.). (SPA.). 5.19 (978-0-7362-0302-9(8)) Hampton-Brown Bks.

Mi Hermanita: Individual Title Six-Packs. (Literatura 2000 Ser.). (SPA.). (ps-1). 28.00 (978-0-7635-1196-8(X)) Rigby Education.

Mi hermanita y Yo, 6 Packs. (Coleccion Pm Ser.).Tr. of My little sister. (SPA.). 16p. (gr. 1 up). 26.00 (978-0-7578-3001-3(3)) Rigby Education.

Mi Hermanito. (Spanish Early Intervention Levels Ser.). (SPA.). 23.10 (978-1-56334-772-6(5)); Vol. 2. 3.85 (978-1-56334-443-5(2)) Hampton-Brown Bks.

Mi Hogar: Individual Title-Six Packs. (Chiquilibros Ser.). (SPA.). (gr. k-1). 23.00 (978-0-7635-8621-8(8)) Rigby Education.

Mi Maestra, 6 Packs. 2003. 23.95 (978-0-673-77148-3(2)) Celebration Pr.

Mi Mami: Individual 6-packs. 2003. 23.95 (978-0-673-77143-8(1)) Celebration Pr.

Mi Mochila, 6 Packs. (Coleccion Pm Ser.: Vol. 2). Tr. of Packing my bag. (SPA.). 16p. (gr. k-1). 26.00 (978-0-7578-0679-7(1)) Rigby Education.

Mi Perrita Chata, 6 Packs. 2003. 23.95 (978-0-673-77149-0(0)) Celebration Pr.

Mi primer Papalote, 6 Packs. (Coleccion Pm Ser.). (SPA.). 16p. (gr. 1 up). 26.00 (978-0-7578-3041-9(2)) Rigby Education.

Mi primera Pinata: Individual Title Six-Packs. (Coleccion Pm Ser.). (SPA.). 16p. (gr. 1 up). 26.00 (978-0-7578-3023-5(4)) Rigby Education.

Mi Taco, 6 Packs. (Coleccion Pm Ser.).Tr. of My taco. (SPA.). 16p. (gr. 1 up). 26.00 (978-0-7578-2985-7(6)) Rigby Education.

Mi Tata Chuy, 6 Packs. 2003. 23.95 (978-0-673-77139-1(3)) Celebration Pr.

Miel para Osito Marcos, 6 vols., Pack. (Coleccion Pm Ser.).Tr. of Honey for baby bear. (SPA.). 16p. (gr. 1 up). 26.00 (978-0-7578-3011-2(0)) Rigby Education.

Miller, Heather. Obrero de Construccion. 2003. (Esto es lo Que Quiero Ser (This Is What I Want to Be) Ser.). (SPA., Illus.). 24p. (J). (ps-1). lib. bdg. 18.50 (978-1-4034-0375-9(9)) Heinemann Library.

Miller, Sara Swan. La Gatita en la Maleta. Mahan, Benton, illus. 2002. (Rookie Reader Espanol Ser.). (J). (gr. k-2). pap. 4.95 (978-0-516-26211-6(4) , Children's Pr.) Scholastic Library Publishing.

Mira el Dinosaurio! (Spanish Early Intervention Levels Ser.). (SPA.). 31.14 (978-0-7362-0334-0(6)) Hampton-Brown Bks.

Mira el Dinosaurio! (K), Vol. 22. (Spanish Early Intervention Levels Ser.). (SPA.). 5.19 (978-0-7362-0309-8(5)) Hampton-Brown Bks.

Mira lo que hizo Tomas, 6 vols., Pack. (Literatura 2000 Ser.). (SPA.). (gr. 1-2). 28.00 (978-0-7635-1072-5(6)) Rigby Education.

Mirame, 6 Packs. (Coleccion Pm Ser.: Vol. 1). (SPA.). 16p. (gr. k-1). 26.00 (978-0-7578-0672-8(4)) Rigby Education.

Miranos, 6 vols., Pack. (Coleccion Pm Ser.: Vol. 2). Tr. of Out in the weather. (SPA.). 16p. (gr. k-1). 26.00 (978-0-7578-0676-6(7)) Rigby Education.

Mis Abuelitos: Individual Title Six-Packs. (Coleccion Pm Ser.).Tr. of My grandma & grandpa. (SPA.). 16p. (gr. 1 up). 26.00 (978-0-7578-2998-7(8)) Rigby Education.

Mis Animalitos: Individual Title Six-Packs. (Literatura 2000 Ser.). (SPA.). (gr. k-1). 28.00 (978-0-7635-1024-4(6)) Rigby Education.

Mis Cinco Perritos: Big Book Packages. 2003. 64.95 (978-0-673-58580-6(8)) Celebration Pr.

Mis Cumpleanos: Individual 6-packs. 2003. 23.95 (978-0-673-77150-6(4)) Celebration Pr.

Mis Juguetes, 6 Packs. 2003. 23.95 (978-0-673-77141-4(5)) Celebration Pr.

Mis Quehaceres, 6 Packs. 2003. 23.95 (978-0-673-77145-2(8)) Celebration Pr.

El misterio del Arroz: Aventuras (Adventure Books) 2000. (Aventuras A Traves Del Tiempo Ser.). (ENG & SPA.). (gr. 6 up). (978-0-02-148747-9(2)) Macmillan/McGraw-Hill Schl. Div.

Mitchell. Escuelas de Todo el Mundo. 1999. pap. 5.18 (978-0-7398-0733-0(1)) Steck-Vaughn.

El Modelo: Individual Title Six-Packs. (Chiquilibros Ser.). (SPA.). (gr. k-1). 23.00 (978-0-7635-8596-9(3)) Rigby Education.

Los Monstruos, 6 packs. 2003. 23.95 (978-0-673-77144-5(X)) Celebration Pr.

La Montana que Llora. (Saludos Ser.: Vol. 1). (SPA.). (gr. 3-5). 31.00 (978-0-7635-3221-5(5)) Rigby Education.

La Montana que Llora: 6 Small Books. (Saludos Ser.: Vol. 1). (SPA.). (gr. 3-5). 31.00 (978-0-7635-1848-6(4)) Rigby Education.

Montoya, Martha, creator. Cenando con el Monstruo: Take-Home. 2005. (Los Kitos Ser.). (SPA.). (YA). (gr. 1-3). 15.00 (978-0-8215-8813-0(3)) Sadlier, William H. Inc.

—Mi heroe Favorito: Take-Home. 2005. (Los Kitos Ser.). (SPA.). (YA). (gr. 1-3). 15.00 (978-0-8215-8811-6(7)) Sadlier, William H. Inc.

—No, no a la Biblioteca! Take-Home. 2005. (Los Kitos Ser.). (SPA.). (YA). (gr. 1-3). 15.00 (978-0-8215-8812-3(5)) Sadlier, William H. Inc.

Mora, Pat. ¡Marimba! Animales from A to Z. Cushman, Doug, illus. 2006. 32p. (J). (gr. k-3). 16.00 (978-0-618-19453-7(3) , Clarion Bks.) Houghton Mifflin Co. Trade & Reference Div.

More Than a Meal. (Early Intervention Levels Ser.). (Illus.). 4.76 (978-0-7362-0956-4(5)) Hampton-Brown Bks.

Morton, Lone & Risk, Mary. Feliz Cumpleanos. 1998. (I Can Read Bks.).Tr. of Happy Birthday. (ENG & SPA., Illus.). 28p. (J). (ps up). audio 9.95 (978-0-7641-7192-5(5)) Barron's Educational Series, Inc.

—I'm Too Big. 1998. (I Can Read Bks.).Tr. of Je Suis Mucho Grande. (ENG & SPA., Illus.). 28p. (J). (ps up). audio 9.95 (978-0-7641-7193-2(3)) Barron's Educational Series, Inc.

La Mosquita Lista. 2003. 23.95 (978-0-673-77122-3(9)) Celebration Pr.

Multicultural Activities Blackline Masters: Fuerzas de la Naturaleza. (Saludos Ser.). (SPA.). (gr. 3-5). 21.00 (978-0-7635-2228-5(7)) Rigby Education.

Multicultural Activities Blackline Masters: Regalos de la Tierra. (Saludos Ser.). (SPA.). (gr. 3-5). 21.00 (978-0-7635-2227-8(9)) Rigby Education.

Multicultural Activities Blackline Masters: Vivan las Tradiciones. (Saludos Ser.). (SPA.). (gr. 3-5). 21.00 (978-0-7635-2226-1(0)) Rigby Education.

El mundo de los Pajaros. (Spanish Early Intervention Levels Ser.). (SPA.). 23.10 (978-0-7362-0325-8(7)) Hampton-Brown Bks.

El Mundo de los Pajaros (I), Vol. 14. (Spanish Early Intervention Levels Ser.). (SPA.). 3.85 (978-0-7362-0300-5(1)) Hampton-Brown Bks.

La Muneca De Galleta: Individual 6-packs. 2003. 23.95 (978-0-673-77152-0(0)) Celebration Pr.

El muneco de Nieve, 6 vols., Pack. (Chiquilibros Ser.).Tr. of Little Snowman. (SPA.). (gr. k-1). 23.00 (978-0-7635-8592-1(0)) Rigby Education.

El muneco de Nieve: Individual Title Six-Packs. (Coleccion Pm Ser.).Tr. of Little Snowman. (SPA.). 16p. (gr. 1 up). 26.00 (978-0-7578-2956-7(2)) Rigby Education.

Munoz, Rosana Acquaroni. Sonar un Crimen. 1998. (SPA.). (gr. 7-12). lib. bdg. 14.10 (978-0-613-80804-0(5)) Tandem Library Bks.

El mural de Maya 9: Leveled Books. 2001. (McGraw-Hill. Lectura Ser.). (ENG & SPA.). (gr. 5 up). (978-0-02-188233-5(9)) Macmillan/McGraw-Hill Schl. Div.

Murphy. Betcha! Estimating. 1999. (Illus.). pap. 5.20 (978-0-7398-2563-1(1)) Steck-Vaughn.

Muy bien, Mayra! (Spanish Early Intervention Levels Ser.). (SPA.). 28.38 (978-0-7362-0836-9(4)) Hampton-Brown Bks.

Muy Bien, Mayra? (I), Vol. 16. (Spanish Early Intervention Levels Ser.). (SPA.). 4.73 (978-0-7362-0812-3(7)) Hampton-Brown Bks.

My Cook Book. 2003. 28.95 (978-0-673-78108-6(9)) Celebration Pr.

My Family Set - Spanish 800799, 6. 2005. (J). bds. (978-1-59794-043-6(7)) Environments, Inc.

My Read, Write, & Listen Practice Book. 2000. (My Read, Write, & Listen Practice Book Ser.). (SPA.). (gr. k up). 11.05 (978-0-673-60576-4(0)); (gr. 4 up). stu. ed. 45.15 (978-0-673-60610-5(4)); (gr. 5 up). stu. ed. 45.15 (978-0-673-60611-2(2)) Addison-Wesley Educational Pubs., Inc.

My Read, Write, & Listen Practice Book 1.1. 2000. (My Read, Write, & Listen Practice Book Ser.). (SPA.). (gr. 1 up). stu. ed. 7.35 (978-0-673-64016-1(7)) Addison-Wesley Educational Pubs., Inc.

My Read, Write, & Listen Practice Book 1.2. 2000. (SPA.). (gr. 1 up). 24.70 (978-0-673-59652-9(4)); wbk. ed. 5.80 (978-0-673-60578-8(7)) Addison-Wesley Educational Pubs., Inc.

My Read, Write, & Listen Practice Book 1.3. 2000. (SPA.). (gr. 1 up). 24.70 (978-0-673-60548-1(5)); wbk. ed. 5.80 (978-0-673-60579-5(5)) Addison-Wesley Educational Pubs., Inc.

My Read, Write, & Listen Practice Book 1.4. 2000. (SPA.). (gr. 1 up). 24.70 (978-0-673-60549-8(3)); wbk. ed. 5.80 (978-0-673-60580-1(9)) Addison-Wesley Educational Pubs., Inc.

My Read, Write, & Listen Practice Book 1.5. 2000. (SPA.). (gr. 1 up). 24.70 (978-0-673-60550-4(7)); wbk. ed. 5.80 (978-0-673-60581-8(7)) Addison-Wesley Educational Pubs., Inc.

My Read, Write, & Listen Practice Book 1.6. 2000. (SPA.). (gr. 1 up). 24.70 (978-0-673-60551-1(5)); wbk. ed. 5.80 (978-0-673-60582-5(5)) Addison-Wesley Educational Pubs., Inc.

My Read, Write, & Listen Practice Book 2.1. 2000. (SPA.). (gr. 2 up). stu. ed., wbk. ed. 5.80 (978-0-673-60583-2(3)); 2nd ed. stu. ed. 31.75 (978-0-673-59653-6(2)) Addison-Wesley Educational Pubs., Inc.

My Read, Write, & Listen Practice Book 2.2. 2000. (SPA.). (gr. 2 up). stu. ed., wbk. ed. 5.80 (978-0-673-60584-9(1)); 2nd ed. stu. ed. 31.75 (978-0-673-60552-8(3)) Addison-Wesley Educational Pubs., Inc.

My Read, Write, & Listen Practice Book 3.1. 2000. (SPA.). (gr. 3 up). wbk. ed. 5.80 (978-0-673-60585-6(X)); 3rd ed. stu. ed. 35.20 (978-0-673-59654-3(0)) Addison-Wesley Educational Pubs., Inc.

My Read, Write, & Listen Practice Book 3.2. 2000. (SPA.). (gr. 3 up). wbk. ed. 5.80 (978-0-673-60586-3(8)); 3rd ed. stu. ed. 35.20 (978-0-673-60553-5(1)) Addison-Wesley Educational Pubs., Inc.

My Snowman: Matching English 6-packs. 2003. 23.95 (978-0-673-57563-0(2)) Celebration Pr.

Nada Extra: Individual Title Six-Packs. (Literatura 2000 Ser.). (SPA.). (gr. 1-2). 28.00 (978-0-7635-1048-0(3)) Rigby Education.

Nassi, Robert J. & Bernstein, Bernard. Workbook in Spanish Two Years. 2001. (SPA & ENG., Illus.). (YA). (gr. 8-10). pap., wbk. ed. (978-0-87720-506-7(X) , R707W) AMSCO Schl. Pubns., Inc.

Niebisch, Jackie. La Escuela de los Vampiritos. (SPA.). (J). (gr. 4 up). 8.95 (978-958-04-5042-9(0)) Norma S.A. COL. *Dist:* Distribuidora Norma, Inc.

—La Escuela de los Vampiritos - Examen. (SPA.). (J). 8.95 (978-958-04-5641-4(0)) Norma S.A. COL. *Dist:* Distribuidora Norma, Inc.

La Nina Del Poncho. 2003. (J). (ps-2). 28.95 (978-0-673-77378-4(7)) Celebration Pr.

El Nino que fue al Viento Norte: Individual Title, 6 packs. (Literatura 2000 Ser.). (SPA.). (gr. 2-3). 33.00 (978-0-7635-1266-8(4)) Rigby Education.

El nino y el Carabao 7: Leveled Books. 2001. (McGraw-Hill. Lectura Ser.). (ENG & SPA.). (gr. 3 up). (978-0-02-188128-4(6)) Macmillan/McGraw-Hill Schl. Div.

S

Niven, David. Los 100 Secretos de la Gente Feliz: Lo que los Cientificos han Descubierto y como Puede Aplicarlo a su Vida. (SPA.). (J). 12.00 (978-958-04-7180-6(0)) Norma S.A. COL. *Dist:* Distribuidora Norma, Inc.

No, Chayito, No: Individual 6-packs. 2003. 23.95 (978-0-673-78074-4(0)) Celebration Pr.

No Les Tengo Miedo: Big Book Packages. 2003. 64.95 (978-0-673-58581-3(6)) Celebration Pr.

No podemos Entrar: Individual Title Six-Packs. (Coleccion Pm Ser.).Tr. of Locked out!. (SPA.). 16p. (gr. 1 up). 26.00 (978-0-7578-3025-9(0)) Rigby Education.

No te dejes de Laura Sue: Social/Emotional Lap Book. (Pebble Soup Exploraciones Ser.). (SPA.). (ps up). 16.00 (978-0-7578-1793-9(9)) Rigby Education.

No te Preocupes: Individual Title, 6 packs. (Literatura 2000 Ser.). (SPA.). (gr. 2-3). 33.00 (978-0-7635-1098-5(X)) Rigby Education.

Nonfiction Packs. (SPA.). 288.75 (978-0-7362-2578-6(1)) Hampton-Brown Bks.

Nonfiction Packs: Spanish Nonfiction Pack, 33 vols. 117.53 (978-0-7362-1511-4(5)) Hampton-Brown Bks.

Nos traen Agua. (Saludos Ser.: Vol. 3). (SPA.). (gr. 3-5). 31.00 (978-0-7635-3268-0(1)) Rigby Education.

Nos traen Agua: 6 Small Books. (Saludos Ser.: Vol. 3). (SPA.). (gr. 3-5). 31.00 (978-0-7635-1827-1(1)) Rigby Education.

Nosotros Interactive Packages: Aqui me Tienen. (Pebble Soup Exploraciones Ser.). (ps up). 52.00 (978-0-7578-5251-0(3)) Rigby Education.

Nostlinger, Christine. Las Enfermedades de Franz. (Torre de Papel Ser.). (SPA.). (J). 7.95 (978-958-04-1930-3(2)) Norma S.A. COL. *Dist:* Distribuidora Norma, Inc.

—Franz Se Mete en Problemas de Amor. (Torre de Papel Ser.). (SPA.). (J). 7.95 (978-958-04-2697-4(X)) Norma S.A. COL. *Dist:* Distribuidora Norma, Inc.

—El Lobo y los Siete Cabritos. (Torre de Papel Ser.). (SPA., Illus.). (J). (gr. 2). 7.95 (978-958-04-4532-6(X)) Norma S.A. COL. *Dist:* Distribuidora Norma, Inc.

—Un Marido para Mama. (Torre de Papel Ser.). (SPA.). (YA). (gr. 6 up). 8.95 (978-958-04-2382-9(2)) Norma S.A. COL. *Dist:* Distribuidora Norma, Inc.

—Las Vacaciones de Franz. (Torre de Papel Ser.). (SPA.). (J). (gr. 2). 7.95 (978-958-04-1931-0(0)) Norma S.A. COL. *Dist:* Distribuidora Norma, Inc.

Nuestra casa de Adobe. (Saludos Ser.: Vol. 2). (SPA.). (gr. 2-3). 31.00 (978-0-7635-5862-8(1)) Rigby Education.

Nuestra casa de Adobe: 6 Small Books. (Saludos Ser.: Vol. 2). (SPA.). (gr. 2-3). 31.00 (978-0-7635-9543-2(8)) Rigby Education.

Nuestras geniales Orejas. (Spanish Early Intervention Levels Ser.). (SPA.). 28.38 (978-0-7362-0841-3(0)) Hampton-Brown Bks.

Nuestras Geniales Orejas (M(, Vol. 26. (Spanish Early Intervention Levels Ser.). (SPA.). 4.73 (978-0-7362-0817-8(8)) Hampton-Brown Bks.

Nuestro Mundo. (Nuevos Horizontes Ser.). (SPA.). (J). (gr. 1). No. 1. wbk. ed. 7.95 (978-1-56014-504-2(8)); No. 2. wbk. ed. 7.95 (978-1-56014-505-9(6)) Santillana USA Publishing Co., Inc.

Nuestro Mundo: Evaluations, Grade 1. (Nuevos Horizontes Ser.). (SPA.). (J). 22.50 (978-1-56014-506-6(4)) Santillana USA Publishing Co., Inc.

Nuestro Mundo No. 1: Student Anthology. (Nuevos Horizontes Ser.). (SPA.). (J). (gr. 1). 14.95 (978-1-56014-502-8(1)) Santillana USA Publishing Co., Inc.

Nuestro Mundo No. 2: Student Anthology. (Nuevos Horizontes Ser.). (SPA.). (J). (gr. 1). 14.95 (978-1-56014-503-5(X)) Santillana USA Publishing Co., Inc.

Nuestro perro Sam 6 Packs. Individual Title. (Literatura 2000 Ser.). (SPA.). (gr. k-1). 28.00 (978-0-7635-1025-1(4)) Rigby Education.

Nuestro viaje hacia la Libertad: 6 Small Books. (Saludos Ser.: Vol. 3). (SPA.). (gr. 3-5). 31.00 (978-0-7635-1782-3(8)) Rigby Education.

Nuevas Aventuras. (Nuevos Horizontes Ser.). (SPA.). (J). (gr. 3). wbk. ed. 8.95 (978-1-56014-515-8(3)) Santillana USA Publishing Co., Inc.

Nuevas Aventuras: Evaluations, Grade 3. (Nuevos Horizontes Ser.). (SPA.). (J). 22.50 (978-1-56014-516-5(1)) Santillana USA Publishing Co., Inc.

Nuevas Aventuras: Student Anthology. (Nuevos Horizontes Ser.). (SPA.). (J). (gr. 3). 18.95 (978-1-56014-514-1(5)) Santillana USA Publishing Co., Inc.

Nuevas Fronteras. (Nuevos Horizontes Ser.). (SPA.). (J). (gr. 4). wbk. ed. 8.95 (978-1-56014-519-6(6)) Santillana USA Publishing Co., Inc.

Nuevas Fronteras: Evaluations, Grade 4. (Nuevos Horizontes Ser.). (SPA.). (J). 22.50 (978-1-56014-520-2(X)) Santillana USA Publishing Co., Inc.

Nuevas Fronteras: Student Anthology. (Nuevos Horizontes Ser.). (SPA.). (J). (gr. 4). 18.95 (978-1-56014-518-9(8)) Santillana USA Publishing Co., Inc.

El Nuevo 2: Leveled Books. 2001. (McGraw-Hill. Lectura Ser.). (ENG & SPA.). (gr. 3 up). (978-0-02-188075-1(1)) Macmillan/McGraw-Hill Schl. Div.

Ohara, Maricarmen. Amiguitos. (SPA., Illus.). 144p. (J). (gr. k-3). 23.00 (978-0-944356-22-7(2)) Alegria Hispana Pubns.

—Capullitos. (SPA., Illus.). 70p. (J). (gr. k-3). 15.00 (978-0-944356-03-6(6)) Alegria Hispana Pubns.

—Tesoro de Poesia Juvenil. (SPA.). 144p. 20.00 (978-0-944356-09-8(5)) Alegria Hispana Pubns.

Ojos, Orejas y Pecas. (SPA.). (J). 12.00 (978-958-02-1236-2(8)) Editorial Voluntad S.A. COL. *Dist:* Distribuidora Norma, Inc.

Olivieri, Cindy, illus. Viento Del Sur. 2000. (SPA.). 426p. (YA). (gr. 12 up). 22.00 (978-0-9707974-0-7(0)) Leon, Ines Publishing Network.

Omar batea un Johron: Individual Title Six-Packs. (Coleccion Pm Ser.). (SPA.). 16p. (gr. 1 up). 26.00 (978-0-7578-3008-2(0)) Rigby Education.

Omar va al Desfile: Individual Title Six-Packs. (Coleccion Pm Ser.). (SPA.). 16p. (gr. 1 up). 26.00 (978-0-7578-3012-9(9)) Rigby Education.

On Safari: Individual Title-Six Packs. (Chiquilibros Ser.). (gr. k-1). 23.00 (978-0-7635-0434-2(3)) Rigby Education.

Once upon a Time Spanish Version-Little Red Riding Hood. 2005. (J). (978-1-57022-562-8(1)) ECS Learning Systems, Inc.

Once upon a Time Spanish Version-the Boy Who Cried Wolf. 2005. (J). (978-1-57022-557-4(5)) ECS Learning Systems, Inc.

Once upon a Time Spanish Version-the Elves & the Shoemaker. 2005. (J). (978-1-57022-559-8(1)) ECS Learning Systems, Inc.

Once upon a Time Spanish Version-the Gingerbread Man. 2005. (J). (978-1-57022-556-7(7)) ECS Learning Systems, Inc.

Once upon a Time Spanish Version-the Little Red Hen. 2005. (J). (978-1-57022-561-1(3)) ECS Learning Systems, Inc.

Once upon a Time Spanish Version-the Three Bears. 2005. (J). (978-1-57022-563-5(X)) ECS Learning Systems, Inc.

Once upon a Time Spanish Version-the Three Billy Goats Gruff. 2005. (J). (978-1-57022-564-2(8)) ECS Learning Systems, Inc.

Once upon a Time Spanish Version-the Three Little Pigs. 2005. (J). (978-1-57022-565-9(6)) ECS Learning Systems, Inc.

Onetti, Juan Carlos. Los Adioses. (SPA.). (J). 9.00 (978-958-04-7258-2(0)) Norma S.A. COL. *Dist:* Distribuidora Norma, Inc.

Onieva Morales, Juan Luis. Como Dominar la Ortografia: Ortografia Moderna. (SPA.). 176p. 18.95 (978-84-359-0467-4(9) , ARG502) Playor, Editorial, S.A. ESP. *Dist:* Continental Bk. Co., Inc.

La Optometrista: Individual Title Six-Packs. (Coleccion Pm Ser.).Tr. of Optometrist. (SPA.). 16p. (gr. 1 up). 26.00 (978-0-7578-3030-3(7)) Rigby Education.

Orange Collection. (Elefonetica Ser.). (SPA.). (gr. 1-2). 296.76 (978-0-7362-0790-4(2)) Hampton-Brown Bks.

Orejas. (Spanish Early Intervention Levels Ser.). (SPA.). 23.10 (978-1-56334-783-2(0)); Vol. 3. 3.85 (978-1-56334-456-5(4)) Hampton-Brown Bks.

Orlev, Uri. La Pequena Nina Grande. Gleich, Jacky, illus. (Buenas Noches Coleccion). (SPA.). (J). 8.95 (978-958-04-4902-7(3)) Norma S.A. COL. *Dist:* Distribuidora Norma, Inc., Lectorum Pubns., Inc.

Osito Marcos quiere Pescar: Individual Title Six-Packs. (Coleccion Pm Ser.).Tr. of Baby Bear goes fishing. (SPA.). 16p. (gr. 1 up). 26.00 (978-0-7578-2988-8(0)) Rigby Education.

El Oso Meno, 6 Packs. 2003. 23.95 (978-0-673-78067-6(8)) Celebration Pr.

Los Osos. 2003. (J). (ps-2). 28.95 (978-0-673-77404-0(X)) Celebration Pr.

Las Ovejitas, Vol. 8. (Spanish Early Intervention Levels Ser.). (SPA.). 3.55 (978-0-7362-0771-3(6)) Hampton-Brown Bks.

Pacheco, Sindo. Maria Virginia, Mi Amor. (Torre de Papel Ser.). (SPA.). (YA). (gr. 6). 8.95 (978-958-04-4523-4(0)) Norma S.A. COL. *Dist:* Distribuidora Norma, Inc.

Pacho, el Oso. (Coleccion Leo Con Figuras). (SPA., Illus.). 14p. (J). pap. 5.50 (978-950-11-0838-5(4) , SGM384) Sigmar ARG. *Dist:* Continental Bk. Co., Inc.

El pajarito Tito 23: Leveled Books. 2001. (McGraw-Hill. Lectura Ser.). (ENG & SPA.). (gr. 1 up). (978-0-02-188000-3(X)) Macmillan/McGraw-Hill Schl. Div.

Palabras. (Coleccion Libritos Acordeon). (SPA., Illus.). 10p. (J). pap. 5.50 (978-950-11-0824-8(4) , SGM244) Sigmar ARG. *Dist:* Continental Bk. Co., Inc.

Palermo, Miguel Angel. Lo Que Cuentan los Tehuelches. (Cuentamerica Ser.). (SPA.). (YA). (gr. 4 up). pap. (978-950-07-1405-1(1) , SA30067) Editorial Sudamericana S.A. ARG. *Dist:* Lectorum Pubns., Inc.

—Lo Que Cuentan los Wichis. (Cuentamerica Ser.). (SPA.). (YA). (gr. 4 up). (978-950-07-1616-1(X) , SA30068) Editorial Sudamericana S.A. ARG. *Dist:* Lectorum Pubns., Inc.

Pan y Canela: Collection C. (SPA.). (gr. k-2). 522.85 (978-0-7362-0342-5(7)); 615.30 (978-0-7362-0343-2(5)) Hampton-Brown Bks.

Papa: Individual Title Six-Packs. (Coleccion Pm Ser.: Vol. 1). Tr. of Dad. (SPA.). 16p. (gr. k-1). 26.00 (978-0-7578-0660-5(0)) Rigby Education.

El papa de Julio: Individual Title Six-Packs. (Coleccion Pm Ser.).Tr. of Ben's dad. (SPA.). 16p. (gr. 1 up). 26.00 (978-0-7578-2992-5(9)) Rigby Education.

A Papa no le Molesto: Individual Title Six-Packs. (Literatura 2000 Ser.). (SPA.). (gr. 1-2). 28.00 (978-0-7635-1057-2(2)) Rigby Education.

Papa Oso y los Peces: Individual Title Six-Packs. (Coleccion Pm Ser.).Tr. of Father Bear goes fishing. (SPA.). 16p. (gr. 1 up). 26.00 (978-0-7578-2973-4(2)) Rigby Education.

Papa salvo la Fiesta: Six-Pack. (Saludos Ser.: Vol. 3). (SPA.). (gr. 2-3). 31.00 (978-0-7635-9528-9(4)) Rigby Education.

Papas. (Spanish Early Intervention Levels Ser.). (SPA.). 21.30 (978-0-7362-0802-4(X)); Vol. 2. 3.55 (978-0-7362-0760-7(0)) Hampton-Brown Bks.

Papi y Yo. (Spanish Early Intervention Levels Ser.). (SPA.). 23.10 (978-1-56334-786-3(5)); Vol. 4. 3.85 (978-1-56334-459-6(9)) Hampton-Brown Bks.

Paquito y los frijoles Magicos: Video Tape. (ENG & SPA.). (gr. k-1). 26.00 (978-0-7635-6278-6(5)) Rigby Education.

Parramon, José María. Mi Calle. Borday, Irene, illus. (Coleccion Estoy En...).Tr. of My Street. (SPA.). 32p. (J). (gr. k-3). 6.36 (978-84-342-1003-5(7)) Parramon Ediciones S.A. ESP. *Dist:* Lectorum Pubns., Inc.

—Mi Casa. Borday, Irene, illus. (Coleccion Estoy En...).Tr. of My House. (SPA.). 32p. (J). (gr. k-3). 6.36 (978-84-342-1002-8(9)) Parramon Ediciones S.A. ESP. *Dist:* Lectorum Pubns., Inc.

—Mi Jardin. Borday, Irene, illus. (Coleccion Estoy En...).Tr. of My Garden. (SPA.). 32p. (J). (gr. k-3). 6.36 (978-84-342-1005-9(3)) Parramon Ediciones S.A. ESP. *Dist:* Lectorum Pubns., Inc.

Parramon, José María & Bordoy, Irene. Mi Calle.Tr. of My Street. (SPA., Illus.). (J). (ps-1). 6.95 (978-958-04-1277-9(4)) Norma S.A. COL. *Dist:* Distribuidora Norma, Inc.

Pastel de Lodo: Individual Title Six-Packs. (Literatura 2000 Ser.). (SPA.). (ps-1). 28.00 (978-0-7635-1000-8(9)) Rigby Education.

Patas, 6 Packs. (Literatura 2000 Ser.). (SPA.). (gr. 1-2). 28.00 (978-0-7635-1049-7(1)) Rigby Education.

El patito y los Gusanos. (Spanish Early Intervention Levels Ser.). (SPA.). 21.30 (978-0-7362-0811-6(9)) Hampton-Brown Bks.

El Patito y los Gusanos, Vol. 8. (Spanish Early Intervention Levels Ser.). (SPA.). 3.55 (978-0-7362-0769-0(4)) Hampton-Brown Bks.

Paty la Pequenita, 6 Packs. (Literatura 2000 Ser.). (SPA.). (gr. 1-2). 28.00 (978-0-7635-1050-3(5)) Rigby Education.

Pebble Soup Exploraciones: Complete Pebble Soup Exploraciones Package. 1650.00 (978-0-7578-3315-1(2)) Rigby Education.

El Pececito Andres: Individual 6-packs. 2003. 23.95 (978-0-673-78065-2(1)) Celebration Pr.

La Pelota: Individual Title Six-Packs. (Coleccion Pm Ser.).Tr. of Big Kick. (SPA.). 16p. (gr. 1 up). 26.00 (978-0-7578-2965-9(1)) Rigby Education.

Pennac, Daniel. La Mirada del Lobo. (Torre de Papel Ser.). (SPA.). (J). (gr. 4 up). 8.95 (978-958-04-4145-8(6)) Norma S.A. COL. *Dist:* Distribuidora Norma, Inc.

Penner, Lucille Recht. Donde Esta ese Hueso? Math Matters en Espanol. Adams, Lynne, illus. 2005. 32p. pap. 4.95 (978-1-57565-156-9(4)) Kane Pr., The.

Pensando. (Coleccion Mil Preguntas). (SPA., Illus.). 24p. (J). pap. 5.50 (978-950-11-0661-9(6) , SGM629) Sigmar ARG. *Dist:* Continental Bk. Co., Inc.

Pepe El Panadero, 6 Packs. 2003. 23.95 (978-0-673-78061-4(9)) Celebration Pr.

Perdido en el parque de Diversiones: Individual Title, 6 packs. (Coleccion Pm Ser.).Tr. of Lost at the Fun Park. (SPA.). 16p. (gr. 1 up). 26.00 (978-0-7578-3022-8(6)) Rigby Education.

Perrin. (Spanish Early Intervention Levels Ser.). (SPA.). 21.30 (978-0-7362-0834-5(8)) Hampton-Brown Bks.

Perrin (E), Vol. 4. (Spanish Early Intervention Levels Ser.). (SPA.). 3.55 (978-0-7362-0780-5(5)) Hampton-Brown Bks.

Perritos, 6 Packs. 2003. 23.95 (978-0-673-78063-8(5)) Celebration Pr.

Pesce, Elena. La Cola de los Ingleses. (SPA.). (J). (gr. 4 up). 7.95 (978-958-04-5033-7(1)) Norma S.A. COL. *Dist:* Distribuidora Norma, Inc.

Pez, Alberto. El Microscopio de Nicolas. (Torre de Papel Ser.). (SPA., Illus.). (J). 7.95 (978-958-04-5644-5(5)) Norma S.A. COL. *Dist:* Distribuidora Norma, Inc.

Phonemic Awareness & Phonics Manipulatives Kit. 2000. (SPA.). (gr. k up). suppl. ed. 370.45 (978-0-673-64907-2(5)); (gr. 1 up). suppl. ed. 370.45 (978-0-673-64908-9(3)); (gr. 2 up). 370.45 (978-0-673-64909-6(1)); (gr. 3 up). 370.45 (978-0-673-64910-2(5)) Addison-Wesley Educational Pubs., Inc.

Phonics Skills of the Week Flip Chart. 2000. (SPA.). (gr. 1 up). suppl. ed. 116.50 (978-0-673-64115-1(5)); (gr. 2 up). 116.50 (978-0-673-64116-8(3)) Addison-Wesley Educational Pubs., Inc.

Phonics Songs & Rhymes. 2000. (SPA.). (gr. k up). suppl. ed. 116.50 (978-0-673-60597-9(3)) Addison-Wesley Educational Pubs., Inc.

Phonics Songs & Rhymes Flip Chart. 2004. (gr. k up). suppl. ed. 109.15 (978-0-328-02213-7(6)); 2004. (gr. 2 up). suppl. ed. 109.15 (978-0-673-59717-5(2)); 2004. (gr. 3 up). suppl. ed. 109.50 (978-0-673-59718-2(0)); 2000. (SPA.). (gr. 2 up). 116.50 (978-0-673-60599-3(X)); 2000. (SPA.). (gr. 3 up). suppl. ed. 19.49 (978-0-673-60600-6(7)) Addison-Wesley Educational Pubs., Inc.

Pin uno, pin dos, pin Tres: Individual Title Six-Packs. (Literatura 2000 Ser.). (SPA.). (gr. 2-3). 33.00 (978-0-7635-1269-9(9)) Rigby Education.

La Pinata, 6 Packs. 2003. 23.95 (978-0-673-77134-6(2)) Celebration Pr.

Pinata: Mas Pinata Package. 2003. 1744.95 (978-0-673-58718-3(5)) Celebration Pr.

La pinata de Omar: Individual Title Six-Packs. (Coleccion Pm Ser.).Tr. of Omar's Pinata. (SPA.). 16p. (gr. 1 up). 26.00 (978-0-7578-2989-5(9)) Rigby Education.

Las Pinatas, Vol. 4. (Spanish Early Intervention Levels Ser.). (SPA.). 3.55 (978-0-7362-0766-9(X)) Hampton-Brown Bks.

Pinguete y Miguela. (Spanish Early Intervention Levels Ser.). (SPA.). 28.38 (978-0-7362-0842-0(9)) Hampton-Brown Bks.

Pinguete y Miguela (M), Vol. 28. (Spanish Early Intervention Levels Ser.). (SPA.). 4.73 (978-0-7362-0818-5(6)) Hampton-Brown Bks.

Los pinguinos Listos: Individual Title Six-Packs. (Coleccion Pm Ser.).Tr. of Clever Penguin. (SPA.). 16p. (gr. 1 up). 26.00 (978-0-7578-3044-0(7)) Rigby Education.

Pinto, Pinto. (Spanish Early Intervention Levels Ser.). (SPA.). 23.10 (978-1-56334-769-6(5)); Vol. 2. 3.85 (978-1-56334-440-4(8)) Hampton-Brown Bks.

Pinto va a la Escuela: Individual Title Six-Packs. (Coleccion Pm Ser.).Tr. of Lucky goes to dog school. (SPA.). 16p. (gr. 1 up). 26.00 (978-0-7578-2991-8(0)) Rigby Education.

Pisa Y Ve! Little Books, Level 6, Vol. 10. 2003. (Fonolibros Ser.). 25.50 (978-0-7652-0087-7(2)) Modern Curriculum Pr.

La Playa: Individual Title Six-Packs. (Literatura 2000 Ser.). (SPA.). (ps-1). 28.00 (978-0-7635-1001-5(7)) Rigby Education.

Polacco, Patricia. Pink y Say. 2003. (SPA.). (gr. k-3). lib. bdg. 16.40 (978-0-613-83096-6(2)) Tandem Library Bks.

Polette, Keith. Isabel & the Hungry Coyote/Isabel y el Coyote Hambriento. de la Vega, Eida, tr. Szegedy, Esther, illus. 2006. Tr. of Isabel y el coyote Hambriento. (SPA.). (J). 4.99 (978-0-9770906-4-8(7)) Raven Tree Pr.

La pollita Vivita: Video Tape. (ENG & SPA.). (gr. k-1). 26.00 (978-0-7635-6279-3(3)) Rigby Education.

El Pollito Huerfanito: Individual 6-packs. 2003. 23.95 (978-0-673-77153-7(9)) Celebration Pr.

Los Pollitos. 2003. (J). (ps-2). 28.95 (978-0-673-77405-7(8)) Celebration Pr.

Por amor a las Tortugas: Six-Pack. (Saludos Ser.: Vol. 1). (SPA.). (gr. 2-3). 31.00 (978-0-7635-9537-1(3)) Rigby Education.

Por Que? (Coleccion Mil Preguntas). (SPA., Illus.). 24p. (J). pap. 5.50 (978-950-11-0611-4(X) , SGM11X) Sigmar ARG. *Dist:* Continental Bk. Co., Inc.

Por que el conejo tiene las orejas tan Largas? Lap Book. (Pebble Soup Exploraciones Ser.). (SPA.). 16p. (ps up). 21.00 (978-0-7578-1691-8(6)) Rigby Education.

Por que el conejo tiene las orejas tan Largas? Small Book. (Pebble Soup Exploraciones Ser.). (SPA.). 16p. (ps up). 5.00 (978-0-7578-1731-1(9)) Rigby Education.

Por que el mar es Salado: Individual Title Six-Packs. (Literatura 2000 Ser.). (SPA.). (gr. 2-3). 33.00 (978-0-7635-1270-5(2)) Rigby Education.

Por que los conejos tienen las orejas Largas: Individual Title Six-Packs. (Literatura 2000 Ser.). (SPA.). (gr. 2-3). 33.00 (978-0-7635-1271-2(0)) Rigby Education.

Por que soplan los vientos Salvajes: 6 Softcover Books. (Saludos Ser.: Vol. 1). (SPA.). (gr. 3-5). 31.00 (978-0-7635-1845-5(X)) Rigby Education.

Porque los elefantes tienen narices Largas: Individual Title Six-Packs. (Literatura 2000 Ser.). (SPA.). (gr. 1-2). 28.00 (978-0-7635-1073-2(4)) Rigby Education.

Porristas: Individual Title Six-Packs. (On Deck en Espanol Ser.).Tr. of Cheerleading. (SPA.). 24p. (gr. 4-5). 35.00 (978-0-7578-6400-1(7)) Rigby Education.

Power Out. (Early Intervention Levels Ser.). (Illus.). 3.57 (978-0-7362-0963-2(8)) Hampton-Brown Bks.

Preparandose para la Fiesta, 6 Packs. (Literatura 2000 Ser.). (SPA.). (ps-1). 28.00 (978-0-7635-1002-2(5)) Rigby Education.

Price. Las Estaciones de Esteban. 1999. (SPA.). pap. 5.18 (978-0-7398-0720-0(X)) Steck-Vaughn.

—Las Estaciones del Ano. 1999. (SPA.). pap. 5.18 (978-0-7398-0721-7(8)) Steck-Vaughn.

—Los Grandes Tiburones Blancos. 1999. (SPA.). pap. 5.18 (978-0-7398-0719-4(6)) Steck-Vaughn.

Price, Mathew. Vueltas y Vueltas en Patin. (SPA.). pap. 3.95 (978-950-07-2062-5(0)) Editorial Sudamericana S.A. ARG. *Dist:* Distribooks, Inc.

Prieto, Iliana. La Princesa del Retrato y el Dragon Rey. (Torre de Papel Ser.). (SPA.). (J). (gr. 4 up). 8.95 (978-958-04-4219-6(3)) Norma S.A. COL. *Dist:* Distribuidora Norma, Inc.

El primer libro de Rob sobre el cuidado de Mascotas 2: Leveled Books. 2001. (McGraw-Hill. Lectura Ser.). (ENG & SPA.). (gr. 2 up). (978-0-02-188051-5(4)) Macmillan/McGraw-Hill Schl. Div.

La Princesa De Verdad. 2003. 28.95 (978-0-673-78087-4(2)) Celebration Pr.

Problem of the Day Flip Chart. 1999. (SPA.). (gr. 2 up). suppl. ed. 86.00 (978-0-201-36532-0(4)); (gr. 3 up). suppl. ed. 86.00 (978-0-201-36540-5(5)); (gr. 4 up). suppl. ed. 86.00 (978-0-201-36548-1(0)); (gr. 5 up). suppl. ed. 86.00 (978-0-201-36556-6(1)) Addison-Wesley Educational Pubs., Inc.

Problem of the Day Flip Chart & Blackline Masters. 1999. (SPA.). (gr. k up). suppl. ed. 78.75 (978-0-201-36517-7(0)) Addison-Wesley Educational Pubs., Inc.

El problema de Ema, 6 Packs. (Literatura 2000 Ser.). (SPA.). (gr. 1-2). 28.00 (978-0-7635-1074-9(2)) Rigby Education.

Puedo Salir? Big Book. 2003. 35.50 (978-0-8136-8101-6(4)) Modern Curriculum Pr.

El puente Akashi Kaikyo: Individual Title Six-Packs. (On Deck en Espanol Ser.).Tr. of Akashi Kaikyo Bridge. (SPA.). 24p. (gr. 4-5). 35.00 (978-0-7578-6442-1(2)) Rigby Education.

Puertas al sol / Gold Set. (SPA.). (J). (gr. 3-5). 65.00 (978-1-59437-849-2(5)) Santillana USA Publishing Co., Inc.

Puertas al sol / Silver Set. (SPA.). (J). (gr. k-2). 65.00 (978-1-59437-848-5(7)) Santillana USA Publishing Co., Inc.

Pullman, Philip. Luces del Norte. Berdage, Roser, tr. 8th ed. 2005. (Escritura desatada Ser.). (SPA., Illus.). 384p. (YA). (gr. 7-11). 13.95 (978-84-406-3296-8(7)) Ediciones B ESP. *Dist:* Independent Pubs. Group.

—Luces del Norte. (SPA.). 672p. 18.95 (978-84-663-0673-7(0)) Suma de Letras, S.L. ESP. *Dist:* Distribooks, Inc.

Puppies. 2003. 23.95 (978-0-673-78127-7(5)) Celebration Pr.

Puppies. 10.95 (978-3-8238-4703-8(1)) teNeues Publishing Co.

Puzo, Mario. Las Extranas Vacaciones de Davie Shaw. (SPA.). 124p. (YA). (gr. 5 up). (978-84-279-3318-7(5) , NG2827) Noguer y Caralt Editores, S. A. ESP. *Dist:* Lectorum Pubns., Inc.

Que agarro Rigo? Individual Title Six-Packs. (Literatura 2000 Ser.). (SPA.). (gr. k-1). 28.00 (978-0-7635-1027-5(0)) Rigby Education.

Que debes decir? Que debes Hacer? Social/Emotional Lap Book. (Pebble Soup Exploraciones Ser.). (SPA.). (ps up). 16.00 (978-0-7578-1791-5(2)) Rigby Education.

Que es Chiquito? (Spanish Early Intervention Levels Ser.). (SPA.). 3.85 (978-1-56334-431-2(9)); 23.10 (978-1-56334-760-3(1)) Hampton-Brown Bks.

Que es Rojo? (Spanish Early Intervention Levels Ser.). (SPA.). 31.14 (978-0-7362-0339-5(7)); Vol. 20. 5.19 (978-0-7362-0314-2(1)) Hampton-Brown Bks.

Que Es un Murcielago? Individual Title Six-Packs. (Literatura 2000 Ser.). (SPA.). (gr. 1-2). 28.00 (978-0-7635-1051-0(3)) Rigby Education.

Que hay a la vuelta de la Esquina? Individual Title Six-Packs. (Literatura 2000 Ser.). (SPA.). (gr. 1-2). 28.00 (978-0-7635-1075-6(0)) Rigby Education.

Que hizo Zoe Zapata? (Spanish Early Intervention Levels Ser.). (SPA.). 21.30 (978-0-7362-0828-4(3)) Hampton-Brown Bks.

Que Hizo Zoe Zapataz?, Vol. 4. (Spanish Early Intervention Levels Ser.). (SPA.). 3.55 (978-0-7362-0774-4(0)) Hampton-Brown Bks.

Que Patatus! Big Books. 1999. (Cuentamundos Ser.). (ENG & SPA.). (gr. 1 up). (978-0-02-181968-3(8)) Macmillan/McGraw-Hill Schl. Div.

Que puede Volar? Individual Title Six-Packs. (Literatura 2000 Ser.). (SPA.). (gr. k-1). 28.00 (978-0-7635-1028-2(9)) Rigby Education.

Que puedo yo Hacer? 6 Small Books. (Saludos Ser.: Vol. 1). (SPA.). (gr. 2-3). 31.00 (978-0-7635-9539-5(X)) Rigby Education.

Que quiere Beto? Individual Title-Six Packs. (Chiquilibros Ser.). (SPA.). (gr. k-1). 23.00 (978-0-7635-8610-2(2)) Rigby Education.

Que quieren Ellos? Individual Title-Six Packs. (Chiquilibros Ser.). (SPA.). (gr. k-1). 23.00 (978-0-7635-8611-9(0)) Rigby Education.

Que Revoltijo! Individual Title Six-Packs. (Chiquilibros Ser.). (SPA.). (gr. k-1). 23.00 (978-0-7635-8593-8(9)) Rigby Education.

Que sale de las Semillas? (Spanish Early Intervention Levels Ser.). (SPA.). 23.10 (978-1-56334-768-9(7)) Hampton-Brown Bks.

Que Sale de las Semillas?, Vol. 2. (Spanish Early Intervention Levels Ser.). (SPA.). 3.85 (978-1-56334-439-8(4)) Hampton-Brown Bks.

Que Sera? 2003. 28.95 (978-0-673-78093-5(7)) Celebration Pr.

Que Sera? Big Book. (Pebble Soup Exploraciones Ser.). (SPA.). 16p. (ps up). 31.00 (978-0-7578-1689-5(4)) Rigby Education.

Que Sera? Small Book. (Pebble Soup Exploraciones Ser.). (SPA.). 16p. (ps up). 5.00 (978-0-7578-1729-8(7)) Rigby Education.

Que Sigue? Big Book Packages. 2003. 64.95 (978-0-673-58584-4(0)) Celebration Pr.

Que suerte Tengo! Individual Title Six-Packs. (Literatura 2000 Ser.). (SPA.). (gr. 1-2). 28.00 (978-0-7635-1076-3(9)) Rigby Education.

Que va en la Tina? Individual Title Six-Packs. (Literatura 2000 Ser.). (SPA.). (gr. k-1). 28.00 (978-0-7635-1029-9(7)) Rigby Education.

Querida Abuelita: 6 Small Books. (Saludos Ser.: Vol. 2). (SPA.). (gr. 3-5). 31.00 (978-0-7635-1770-0(4)) Rigby Education.

Querida Gilda. (Spanish Early Intervention Levels Ser.). (SPA.). 23.10 (978-0-7362-0322-7(2)) Hampton-Brown Bks.

Querida Gilda (E), Vol. 6. (Spanish Early Intervention Levels Ser.). (SPA.). 3.85 (978-0-7362-0297-8(8)) Hampton-Brown Bks.

Querido Santa, 6 Packs. (Literatura 2000 Ser.). (SPA.). (gr. k-1). 28.00 (978-0-7635-1030-5(0)) Rigby Education.

Quien? (Coleccion Mil Preguntas) (SPA., Illus.). 24p. (J). pap. 5.50 (978-950-11-0607-7(1) , SGM110) Sigmar ARG. *Dist:* Continental Bk. Co., Inc.

Quien es Michael Ramirez? 2003. 28.95 (978-0-673-78084-3(8)) Celebration Pr.

A quien le gusta la Noche? (Spanish Early Intervention Levels Ser.). (SPA.). 31.14 (978-0-7362-0330-2(3)) Hampton-Brown Bks.

A Quien le Gusta la Noche? (I), Vol. 12. (Spanish Early Intervention Levels Ser.). (SPA.). 5.19 (978-0-7362-0305-0(2)) Hampton-Brown Bks.

Quien lee con Omar? Individual Title Six-Packs. (Coleccion Pm Ser.).Tr. of Who Reads with Omar?. (SPA.). 16p. (gr. 1 up). 26.00 (978-0-7578-2961-1(9)) Rigby Education.

Quien paso por Aqui? (Spanish Early Intervention Levels Ser.). (SPA.). 23.10 (978-1-56334-788-7(1)) Hampton-Brown Bks.

Quien Paso Por Aqui?, Vol. 2. (Spanish Early Intervention Levels Ser.). (SPA.). 3.85 (978-1-56334-461-9(0)) Hampton-Brown Bks.

Quien soy Yo? (Spanish Early Intervention Levels Ser.). (SPA.). 23.10 (978-1-56334-793-1(8)) Hampton-Brown Bks.

Quien Soy Yo?, Vol. 4. (Spanish Early Intervention Levels Ser.). (SPA.). 3.85 (978-1-56334-466-4(1)) Hampton-Brown Bks.

Quienes Son Tus Amigos? 2003. 35.50 (978-0-8136-8047-7(6)) Modern Curriculum Pr.

Quieres Jugar? Big Book. (Pebble Soup Exploraciones Ser.). 16p. (ps up). 31.00 (978-0-7578-1672-7(X)) Rigby Education.

Quieres Jugar? Small Book. (Pebble Soup Exploraciones Ser.). 16p. (ps up). 5.00 (978-0-7578-1712-0(2)) Rigby Education.

Rabbits: Individual Title Six-Packs. (Literatura 2000 Ser.). (gr. 2-3). 33.00 (978-0-7635-0235-5(9)) Rigby Education.

Raintree Steck-Vaughn Staff. A Dar Palmadas! 1999. (Coleccion en Parejas). (SPA.). (J). pap., stu. ed. 21.50 (978-0-7398-0843-6(5)) Steck-Vaughn.

—El Concurso de Castillos de Arena. 2000. (SPA.). (J). pap. 29.12 (978-0-7398-0738-5(2)) Steck-Vaughn.

—¡Despegue! 1999. (SPA.). (J). pap., stu. ed. 31.05 (978-0-7398-0772-9(2)) Steck-Vaughn.

—Escuelas de Todo el Mundo. 1999. (SPA.). (J). pap., stu. ed. 31.05 (978-0-7398-0768-2(4)) Steck-Vaughn.

—Las Estaciones de Esteban. 1999. (SPA.). (J). pap., stu. ed. 31.05 (978-0-7398-0755-2(2)) Steck-Vaughn.

—Los Lobos. 2000. (SPA.). (J). pap. 29.12 (978-0-7398-0741-5(2)) Steck-Vaughn.

—The Pioneer Way. 1999. (Illus.). (J). pap. 35.60 (978-0-7398-0914-3(8)) Steck-Vaughn.

—¡Por Todas Partes! 1999. (Coleccion en Parejas). (SPA.). (J). pap., stu. ed. 21.50 (978-0-7398-0842-9(7)) Steck-Vaughn.

—El Regreso de Ricitos de Oro. 1999. (SPA.). (J). pap., stu. ed. 31.05 (978-0-7398-0757-6(9)) Steck-Vaughn.

—The Secret of the Silver Shoes. 1999. (Illus.). (J). pap. 35.60 (978-0-7398-0911-2(3)) Steck-Vaughn.

—Somos un Par. 1999. (Coleccion en Parejas). (SPA.). (J). pap., stu. ed. 21.50 (978-0-7398-0838-2(9)) Steck-Vaughn.

Ramos & Tobella. La Nueva Casa. (SPA.). 32p. (J). 10.00 (978-84-342-2517-6(4)) Parramon Ediciones S.A. ESP. *Dist:* Distribuidora Norma, Inc.

Ramos, Maria Cristina. De Barrio Somos. (Torre de Papel Ser.). (SPA.). (J). (gr. 4). 7.95 (978-958-04-4221-9(5)) Norma S.A. COL. *Dist:* Distribuidora Norma, Inc.

La rana que se creia Caballo: Individual Title Six-Packs. (Literatura 2000 Ser.). (SPA.). (gr. 2-3). 33.00 (978-0-7635-1272-9(9)) Rigby Education.

El Ranchito. (Spanish Early Intervention Levels Ser.). (SPA.). 3.85 (978-1-56334-433-6(5)); 23.10 (978-1-56334-764-1(4)) Hampton-Brown Bks.

El Rancho: Individual Title Six-Packs. (Literatura 2000 Ser.). (SPA.). (ps-1). 28.00 (978-0-7635-1006-0(8)) Rigby Education.

Randell, Beverley & Bruere, Julian, contrib. by. Mimosa y el Arbol, 6 vols., Pack. (Coleccion Pm Ser.).Tr. of Tabby in the tree. (SPA.). 16p. (gr. 1 up). 26.00 (978-0-7578-3015-0(3)) Rigby Education.

Randell, Beverley & Hill, Trish, contrib. by. El cochinito Dormilon: Individual Title Six-Packs. (Coleccion Pm Ser.).Tr. of Lazy Pig. (SPA.). 16p. (gr. 1 up). 26.00 (978-0-7578-2968-0(6)) Rigby Education.

Randell, Beverley & Lacey, Elspeth, contrib. by. Donde Estan los Sombreros? Individual Title Six-Packs. (Coleccion Pm Ser.).Tr. of Where Are the Sunhats?. (SPA.). 16p. (gr. 1 up). 26.00 (978-0-7578-2987-1(2)) Rigby Education.

Randell, Beverley & Ruth, Trevor, contrib. by. El carro de Luisa: Individual Title Six-Packs. (Coleccion Pm Ser.).Tr. of Jane's car. (SPA.). 16p. (gr. 1 up). 26.00 (978-0-7578-3016-7(1)) Rigby Education.

Randell, Beverley & Stewart, Chantal, contrib. by. Una Casa para Osito: Individual Title Six-Packs. (Coleccion Pm Ser.).Tr. of Home for Little Teddy. (SPA.). 16p. (gr. 1 up). 26.00 (978-0-7578-2976-5(7)) Rigby Education.

Los Raspados. 2003. 23.95 (978-0-673-77786-7(3)) Celebration Pr.

Ratita y Raton. (Spanish Early Intervention Levels Ser.). (SPA.). 21.30 (978-0-7362-0810-9(0)); Vol. 4. 3.55 (978-0-7362-0768-3(6)) Hampton-Brown Bks.

El raton Audaz. (Spanish Early Intervention Levels Ser.). (SPA.). 28.38 (978-0-7362-0839-0(9)) Hampton-Brown Bks.

El Raton Audaz (L), Vol. 20. (Spanish Early Intervention Levels Ser.). (SPA.). 4.73 (978-0-7362-0815-4(1)) Hampton-Brown Bks.

Rau, Dana Meachen. Cansada de Esperar. Fitzpatrick, Brad, illus. 2006. (Read-It! Readers en Espanol Ser.).Tr. of Tired of Waiting. (SPA.). 32p. (J). (ps-3). 19.95 (978-1-4048-1695-4(X)) Picture Window Bks.

—Vamos a Compartir. Favereau, Beatrice, illus. 2006. (Read-It! Readers en Espanol Ser.).Tr. of Let's Share. (SPA.). 32p. (J). (ps-3). 19.95 (978-1-4048-1693-0(3)) Picture Window Bks.

Ray, Blaine. Pobre Ana: Level 1. 1999. (TPRS First-Year Spanish Novels Ser.). (SPA.). ii, 39p. (YA). (gr. 7-12). pap. 5.95 (978-0-929724-47-8(X) ; BR001) Command Performance Language Institute.

Reach for Reading: Reaching up en espanol Self-Training Package. (SPA.). (gr. 1-3). 675.00 (978-0-7578-5933-5(X)) Rigby Education.

Reaching up en espanol Additional Resources: Additional Tutor's Manual. (Reach for Reading Ser.). (SPA.). (gr. 1-3). 31.00 (978-0-7635-7622-6(0)) Rigby Education.

Reaching up en espanol Additional Resources: Spanish Books (75 Titles) (Reach for Reading Ser.). (SPA.). (gr. 1-3). 205.00 (978-0-7578-4878-0(8)) Rigby Education.

Reaching up en espanol Additional Workstations: With Books. (Reach for Reading Ser.). (SPA.). (gr. 1-3). 390.00 (978-0-7635-3711-1(X)) Rigby Education.

Reaching up en espanol Additional Workstations: Without Books. (Reach for Reading Ser.). (SPA.). (gr. 1-3). 285.00 (978-0-7578-3544-5(9)) Rigby Education.

Read Aloud Package, 18 bks., Set. 2000. (SPA.). (gr. k up). 105.85 (978-0-673-64933-1(4)) Addison-Wesley Educational Pubs., Inc.

Read & Understand Spanish / English, Fiction. 2005. (J). 29.99 (978-1-59673-075-5(7) , EMC 5310) Evan-Moor Educational Pubs.

Read & Understand Spanish / English, Nonfiction. 2005. (J). 29.99 (978-1-59673-076-2(5) , EMC 5311) Evan-Moor Educational Pubs.

Read & Understand Spanish / English, Science. 2005. (J). 29.99 (978-1-59673-077-9(3) , EMC 5312) Evan-Moor Educational Pubs.

Reading Strategies for Problem Solving. 1999. (SPA.). (gr. k up). 115.90 (978-0-201-36975-5(3)); (gr. 1 up). 115.90 (978-0-201-36976-2(1)); (gr. 2 up). 115.90 (978-0-201-36977-9(X)); (gr. 3 up). 115.90 (978-0-201-36978-6(8)); (gr. 4 up). 115.90 (978-0-201-36979-3(6)); (gr. 5 up). 115.90 (978-0-201-36980-9(X)); (gr. 6 up). 115.90 (978-0-201-36981-6(8)) Addison-Wesley Educational Pubs., Inc.

Ready, Dee. Autobuses Escolares. Schon, Isabel, ed. Ferrer, Martín Luis Guzman, tr. from ENG. 1998. (Coleccion Primeros Lectores). (SPA., Illus.). 24p. (J). (gr. k-3). lib. bdg. 18.60 (978-1-56065-792-7(8) , CAP1073, Bridgestone Bks.) Capstone Pr., Inc.

—Enfermeras y Enfermeros. Schon, Isabel, ed. Ferrer, Martín Luis Guzman, tr. from ENG. 1998. (Servidores Comunitarios Ser.). (SPA., Illus.). 24p. (J). (gr. 1-2). lib. bdg. 18.60 (978-1-56065-801-6(0) , Bridgestone Bks.) Capstone Pr., Inc.

—Policias. Schon, Isabel, ed. Ferrer, Martín Luis Guzman, tr. from ENG. 1998. (Servidores Comunitarios Ser.). (SPA., Illus.). 24p. (J). (gr. 1-2). lib. bdg. 18.60 (978-1-56065-802-3(9) , Bridgestone Bks.) Capstone Pr., Inc.

—Veterinarios y Veterinarias. Schon, Isabel, ed. Ferrer, Martín Luis Guzman, tr. from ENG. 1998. (Servidores Comunitarios Ser.). (SPA., Illus.). 24p. (J). (gr. 1-2). lib. bdg. 18.60 (978-1-56065-804-7(5) , Bridgestone Bks.) Capstone Pr., Inc.

El Rebozo De Elsa, 6 packs. 2003. 23.95 (978-0-673-78068-3(6)) Celebration Pr.

Recoge tus Juguetes: Individual Title, 6 packs. (Coleccion Pm Ser.: Vol. 2). Tr. of Pick up your toys. (SPA.). 16p. (gr. k-1). 26.00 (978-0-7578-0691-9(0)) Rigby Education.

Recortes. (Spanish Early Intervention Levels Ser.). (SPA.). 23.10 (978-1-56334-779-5(2)); Vol. 2. 3.85 (978-1-56334-452-7(1)) Hampton-Brown Bks.

Recuerdos: Individual Title Six-Packs. (Literatura 2000 Ser.). (SPA.). (gr. 2-3). 33.00 (978-0-7635-1099-2(8)) Rigby Education.

El regalo de Osito Marcos: Individual Title Six-Packs. (Coleccion Pm Ser.).Tr. of Baby Bear's present. (SPA.). 16p. (gr. 1 up). 26.00 (978-0-7578-3013-6(7)) Rigby Education.

Un Regalo del Mar, 6 Packs. (Literatura 2000 Ser.). (SPA.). (gr. 2-3). 33.00 (978-0-7635-1273-6(7)) Rigby Education.

Los Regalos de Mi Abuelito, Vol. 3. (Spanish Early Intervention Levels Ser.). (SPA.). 3.85 (978-1-56334-464-0(5)) Hampton-Brown Bks.

Regalos de Navidad, 6 Packs. (Literatura 2000 Ser.). (SPA.). (gr. 1-2). 28.00 (978-0-7635-1052-7(1)) Rigby Education.

El Regreso de Maggie 16: Leveled Books. 2001. (McGraw-Hill. Lectura Ser.). (ENG & SPA.). (gr. 5 up). (978-0-02-188288-5(6)) Macmillan/McGraw-Hill Schl. Div.

Reiche, Dietlof. Fredy, el Hamster. (SPA.). (J). 8.95 (978-958-04-6027-5(2)) Norma S.A. COL. *Dist:* Distribuidora Norma, Inc.

Reiser, Lynn. My Way/Mi Manera: A Margaret & Margarita Story/Un Cuento de Margarita y Margaret. Reiser, Lynn, illus. 2007. Tr. of A mi Manera: Un cuento de Margarita y Margaret. (ENG & SPA., Illus.). 32p. (J). (ps-1). 15.99 (978-0-06-084101-0(X)) HarperCollins Pubs.

El Renacuajo: Big Book Packages. 2003. 64.95 (978-0-673-58587-5(5)) Celebration Pr.

Reno ensucia/Messy Moose. 2005. (Libros en Espanol Para Ninos Ser.). (SPA.). (YA). (ps-1). 11.97 (978-0-8215-0991-3(8)); 15.75 (978-0-8215-1201-2(3)) Sadlier, William H. Inc.

El rey de la Laguna. (Spanish Early Intervention Levels Ser.). (SPA.). 31.14 (978-0-7362-0328-9(1)) Hampton-Brown Bks.

El Rey de la Laguna (G), Vol. 12. (Spanish Early Intervention Levels Ser.). (SPA.). 5.19 (978-0-7362-0303-6(6)) Hampton-Brown Bks.

Rico, Lolo. Si Tu Hijo Te Pide un Libro. 2000. (SPA., Illus.). 304p. (J). pap. (978-84-239-7996-3(X)) Espasa Calpe, S.A.

El Rio: Big Book. (Pebble Soup Exploraciones Ser.). (SPA.). 16p. (ps up). 31.00 (978-0-7578-1683-3(5)) Rigby Education.

El Rio: Small Book. (Pebble Soup Exploraciones Ser.). (SPA.). 16p. (ps up). 5.00 (978-0-7578-1723-6(8)) Rigby Education.

El rio es mi Vida: 6 Small Books. (Saludos Ser.: Vol. 3). (SPA.). (gr. 3-5). 31.00 (978-0-7635-1829-5(8)) Rigby Education.

Riqui y el Carnaval. (Spanish Early Intervention Levels Ser.). (SPA.). 21.30 (978-0-7362-0832-1(1)) Hampton-Brown Bks.

Riqui y el Carnaval (F), Vol. 10. (Spanish Early Intervention Levels Ser.). (SPA.). 3.55 (978-0-7362-0778-2(3)) Hampton-Brown Bks.

Rivera, Jose E. La Voragine (The Vortex) (Coleccion Centro Literario). (SPA.). (J). pap., stu. ed. 7.95 (978-958-02-0502-9(7) , CAR027) Editorial Voluntad S.A. COL. *Dist:* Continental Bk. Co., Inc.

Robinson, Bryan, ed. Bilingual Baby Vol. 2: Introduce Your Child to Spanish. 2000. (SPA.). (J). pap., stu. ed. 16.95 incl. VHS (978-1-892703-10-1(6)) Small Fry Productions.

El Robot, 6, Pack. (Chiquilibros Ser.). (SPA.). (gr. k-1). 23.00 (978-0-7635-8612-6(9)) Rigby Education.

Roca, Nuria. Como nos Movemos? How We Move Around (Spanish Edition) Curto, Rosa M., illus. 2007. (What Do You Know about? Bks.). 36p. (J). (gr. k-1). pap. 6.99 (978-0-7641-3654-2(2)) Barron's Educational Series, Inc.

—De que estan hechas las Cosas: What Are Things Made of? (Spanish Edition) Curto, Rosa M., illus. 2007. (What Do You Know about? Bks.). 36p. (J). (gr. k-1). pap. 6.99 (978-0-7641-3652-8(6)) Barron's Educational Series, Inc.

Rojas, Emilio. Ortografía Real de la Lengua Española: Libro con Ejercicios. 2003. 328p. (YA). (gr. 5 up). 17.95 (978-968-6966-15-2(3)) EDITER'S Publishing Hse. MEX. *Dist:* EDITER'S Publishing Hse.

El Rompecabezas: Individual Title-Six Packs. (Chiquilibros Ser.). (SPA.). (gr. k-1). 23.00 (978-0-7635-8614-0(5)) Rigby Education.

Ronron, el Gato. (Coleccion Leo Con Figuras). (SPA., Illus.). 14p. (J). pap. 5.50 (978-950-11-0839-2(2) , SGM392) Sigmar ARG. *Dist:* Continental Bk. Co., Inc.

Roop, Connie & Roop, Peter. Un Pulpo en el Mar. Schwartz, Carol, illus. 2002. (Coleccion "Hola, Lector" Ser.).Tr. of Octopus under the Sea. (SPA.). 32p. (J). pap. 3.99 (978-0-439-25041-2(2) , SO30880, Scholastic en Espanol) Scholastic, Inc.

Rosa-Mendoza, Gladys, creator. I Can! 2004. (English-Spanish Foundations Ser.: Vol. 11). Tr. of ¡Yo Puedo!. (SPA & ENG., Illus.). 20p. (J). bds. 6.95 (978-1-931398-11-4(9)) Me+Mi Publishing.

Ruedas. (Spanish Early Intervention Levels Ser.). (SPA.). 23.10 (978-1-56334-789-4(X)); Vol. 2. 3.85 (978-1-56334-462-6(9)) Hampton-Brown Bks.

Ruedas, 6 Packs. (Literatura 2000 Ser.). (SPA.). (gr. k-1). 28.00 (978-0-7635-1031-2(9)) Rigby Education.

Ruiz, Olivia, et al. La Amiga Nueva De Roberto: Guias De Observacion, Level 12. 2003. 3.95 (978-0-673-61538-1(3)) Celebration Pr.

—Las Cajas De Zapatos: Guias De Observacion, Level 10. 2003. 3.95 (978-0-673-61537-4(5)) Celebration Pr.

—Debes Ser Atento Con Jesefina: Resumen Del Cuento, Level 34. 2003. 3.95 (978-0-673-61562-6(6)) Celebration Pr.

—Debes Ser Atento Con Josefina: Guias De Observacion, Level 34. 2003. (SPA.). 3.95 (978-0-673-61546-6(4)) Celebration Pr.

—El Dia Mas Maravilloso: Guias De Observacion, Level 24. 2003. 3.95 (978-0-673-61543-5(X)) Celebration Pr.

—Donde Esta Mi Gorra? Guias De Observacion, Level 4. 2003. 3.95 (978-0-673-61534-3(0)) Celebration Pr.

—Duque: Guias De Observacion, Level 8. 2003. 3.95 (978-0-673-61536-7(7)) Celebration Pr.

—Evaluacion Del Desarrollo De la Lectura Package. 2003. 123.50 (978-0-673-61724-8(6)) Celebration Pr.

—Un Gigante En El Bosque: Guias De Observacion, Level 18. 2003. 3.95 (978-0-673-61541-1(3)) Celebration Pr.

—Mas Astuto Que El Viejo Camilo Canoso: Guias De Observacion, Level 40. 2003. 3.95 (978-0-673-61548-0(0)) Celebration Pr.

—La Olla De Oro: Guias De Observacion, Level 16. 2003. 3.95 (978-0-673-61540-4(5)) Celebration Pr.

—Peligro En las Profundidades: Guias De Observacion, Level 44. 2003. 3.95 (978-0-673-61549-7(9)) Celebration Pr.

—Por Que Paramos? Guias De Observacion, Level 6. 2003. 3.95 (978-0-673-61535-0(9)) Celebration Pr.

—Que Te Gusta? Guias De Observacion, Level 3. 2003. 3.95 (978-0-673-61533-6(2)) Celebration Pr.

—Reni la Rana: Guias De Observacion, Level 20. 2003. 3.95 (978-0-673-61542-8(1)) Celebration Pr.

—Sabes Cantar? Mira Lo Que Se Va: Registro De la Lectura Oral. 2003. (SPA.). 3.95 (978-0-673-61566-4(9)) Celebration Pr.

—Sabes Cantar? Mira Lo Que Se Va Yo Veo: Guias De Observacion, Level 2. 2003. (SPA.). 3.95 (978-0-673-61532-9(4)) Celebration Pr.

—El Vagon: Guias De Observacion, Level 14. 2003. (SPA.). 3.95 (978-0-673-61539-8(1)) Celebration Pr.

—Yo No Te Veo Hermosa: Guias De Observacion, Level 28. 2003. (SPA.). 3.95 (978-0-673-61544-2(8)) Celebration Pr.

—Yo Veo Que Te Gusta? Registro De la Lectura Oral, Level 3. 2003. (SPA.). 3.95 (978-0-673-61567-1(7)) Celebration Pr.

Rusty the Rooster. 2003. 23.95 (978-0-673-78134-5(8)) Celebration Pr.

Rylant, Cynthia. El Caso de la Perezosa Dormilona. (SPA.). (J). 7.95 (978-958-04-7539-2(3)) Norma S.A. COL. *Dist:* Distribuidora Norma, Inc.

El sacudon de San Francisco: 6 Small Books. (Saludos Ser.: Vol. 3). (SPA.). (gr. 3-5). 31.00 (978-0-7635-2081-6(0)) Rigby Education.

Sad Ladybug: Matching English 6-packs. 2003. 23.95 (978-0-673-57564-7(0)) Celebration Pr.

Sal, Solecito. (Spanish Early Intervention Levels Ser.). (SPA.). 23.10 (978-0-7362-0321-0(4)); Vol. 8. 3.85 (978-0-7362-0296-1(X)) Hampton-Brown Bks.

Salas, Macarena, ed. Baby Donald Makes A Snowfriend/beb Donald Hace un Amigo de Nieve: A Book about Shapes/Un Libro Sobre Las Formas. 2005. (SPA.). 10p. (J). bds. 3.99 (978-0-439-66362-5(8) , Scholastic en Espanol) Scholastic, Inc.

—Disney Bil: Follow Your Nose, Baby Pluto/sigue Tu Nariz, Beb Pluto. 2005. (SPA & ENG.). 10p. (J). bds. 3.99 (978-0-439-66365-6(2) , Scholastic en Espanol) Scholastic, Inc.

—Disney Bil: What Will You Do Today/ qu Vas a Hacer Hoy? 2005. (SPA.). 10p. (J). bds. 3.99 (978-0-439-66368-7(7) , Scholastic en Espanol) Scholastic, Inc.

—Dopey's Bedtime/Tontin Se Va la Cama: A Book about Routines/Un Libro Sobre Rutinas. 2005. (SPA.). 6p. (J). bds. 3.99 (978-0-439-66360-1(1) , Scholastic en Espanol) Scholastic, Inc.

—A New Doll for Baby Daisy/Un Mueco para Beb Daisy: A Book about Classifying/Un Libro Sobre Clasificaciones. 2005. (SPA.). 10p. (J). bds. 3.99 (978-0-439-66361-8(X) , Scholastic en Espanol) Scholastic, Inc.

—Promesa de Lealtad/The Pledge of Allegiance. 2002. (SPA & ENG., Illus.). 24p. (J). pap. 4.95 (978-0-439-31738-2(X) , Scholastic en Espanol) Scholastic, Inc.

Sale un Patito. (Spanish Early Intervention Levels Ser.). (SPA.). 21.30 (978-0-7362-0804-8(6)); Vol. 3. 3.55 (978-0-7362-0762-1(7)) Hampton-Brown Bks.

Saltzberg, Barney. Besos Cucu. Campoy, F. Isabel, tr. 2005. (SPA., Illus.). 14p. (J). bds. 8.95 (978-0-15-205579-0(7) , Red Wagon Bks.) Harcourt Children's Bks.

Saludos! Add-to Pack. (SPA.). 47.00 (978-0-7635-9515-9(2)) Rigby Education.

Saludos! Complete Blue Level Packages. (SPA.). 697.00 (978-0-7635-9509-8(8)); (ENG & SPA.). 1279.00 (978-0-7635-9511-1(X)) Rigby Education.

Saludos! Complete Pasado valioso, futuro Brillante. (SPA.). 385.00 (978-0-7635-9512-8(8)) Rigby Education.

Saludos! Complete Pasado valioso, futuro brillante Rich Past, Bright Future Theme Packages. (ENG & SPA.). 693.00 (978-0-7635-9514-2(4)) Rigby Education.

Saludos! Rich Past, Bright Future Theme Packages. 385.00 (978-0-7635-9513-5(6)) Rigby Education.

Samaniego. mundo 21: Used With ... Samaniego-Mundo 21. 3rd ed. 2004. (YA). cd-rom 3.96 (978-0-618-27582-3(7) , 351022) Houghton Mifflin College Div.

Sanchez, Isidro. Mi Gato. Ruis, Maria, illus. (Coleccion Mis Animales Preferidos).Tr. of My Cat. (SPA.). 32p. (J). (gr. k-3). 6.36 (978-84-342-1127-8(0) , PR0482) Parramon Ediciones S.A. ESP. *Dist:* Lectorum Pubns., Inc.

—Mi Hamster. Ruis, Maria, illus. (Coleccion Mis Animales Preferidos).Tr. of My Hamster. (SPA.). 32p. (J). (gr. k-3). 6.36 (978-84-342-1129-2(7) , PR0485) Parramon Ediciones S.A. ESP. *Dist:* Lectorum Pubns., Inc.

—Mi Pajaro. Ruis, Maria, illus. (Coleccion Mis Animales Preferidos).Tr. of My Bird. (SPA.). 32p. (J). (gr. k-3). 6.36 (978-84-342-1128-5(9) , PR0483) Parramon Ediciones S.A. ESP. *Dist:* Lectorum Pubns., Inc.

—Mi Perro. Ruis, Maria, illus. (Coleccion Mis Animales Preferidos).Tr. of My Dog. (SPA.). 32p. (J). (gr. k-3). (978-84-342-1126-1(2) , PR0481) Parramon Ediciones S.A. ESP. *Dist:* Lectorum Pubns., Inc.

Sanchez Lobato, J., et al. Espanol Sin Fronteras: Level 2. 2001. (SPA, ENG & JPN., Illus.). 1p. 26.95 (978-84-7143-710-5(4) , SGS7104); wbk. ed. 26.95 (978-84-7143-711-2(2) , SGS7112) Sociedad General Espanola de Libreria ESP. *Dist:* Continental Bk. Co., Inc.

La Sandia. (Spanish Early Intervention Levels Ser.). (SPA.). 23.10 (978-1-56334-795-5(4)); Vol. 6. 3.85 (978-1-56334-468-8(8)) Hampton-Brown Bks.

Sastrias, Martha. Como Motivar a los Ninos a Leer: Lecto-Juegos y Algo Mas. 2005. (SPA., Illus.). 180p. (gr. 2-4). pap. 11.95 (978-968-860-449-6(6)) Editorial Pax MEX. *Dist:* Independent Pubs. Group.

Schaefer, Lola M. Animales Resbalosos, 8 bks., Set. Cano, Patricia, tr. 2002. Tr. of Ooey-Gooey Animals. (SPA.). (J). (ps-1). lib. bdg. 90.65 (978-1-58810-770-1(1)) Heinemann Library.

School Specialty Publishing. Artes de Idioma. 2006. (Aprendamos Ser.). 64p. (J). pap. 3.99 (978-0-7696-4325-0(6) , Brighter Child) School Specialty Publishing.

Schreiber-Wicke, Edith. Cuando Decir No. (SPA.). (J). 8.95 (978-958-04-6534-8(7)) Norma S.A. COL. *Dist:* Distribuidora Norma, Inc.

Schwartz, David M. Cuanto Es un Millon? Kellogg, Steven, illus. 2003. (SPA.). (J). (gr. k-3). pap. 3.96 net. (978-0-590-47393-4(X) , SO30942) Scholastic, Inc.

Scott, Ann Herbert. En Las Piernas de Mama: On Mother's Lap. Coalson, Glo, illus. 2007. 14p. (J). (gr. k-ps). bds. 5.95 (978-0-618-75247-8(1) , Clarion Bks.) Houghton Mifflin Co. Trade & Reference Div.

Scott Foresman Family Reading Guide. 2004. (gr. k up). 13.25 (978-0-673-63394-1(2)); 2004. (gr. 1 up). 13.25 (978-0-673-63395-8(0)); 2004. (gr. 2 up). 13.25 (978-0-673-63396-5(9)); 2004. (gr. 3 up). 13.50 (978-0-673-63397-2(7)); 2004. (gr. 4 up). 13.50 (978-0-673-63398-9(5)); 2004. (gr. 5 up). 13.50 (978-0-673-63399-6(3)); 2000. (SPA.). (gr. k up). 12.75 (978-0-673-65048-1(0)); 2000. (SPA.). (gr. 1 up). 12.75 (978-0-673-65049-8(9)); 2000. (SPA.). (gr. 2 up). 12.75 (978-0-673-65050-4(2)); 2000. (SPA.). (gr. 3 up). 12.75 (978-0-673-65051-1(0)); 2000. (SPA.). (gr. 4 up). 19.49 (978-0-673-65052-8(9)); 2000. (SPA.). (gr. 5 up). 12.75 (978-0-673-65053-5(7)) Addison-Wesley Educational Pubs., Inc.

Se venden Pasteles. (Spanish Early Intervention Levels Ser.). (SPA.). 31.14 (978-0-7362-0333-3(8)) Hampton-Brown Bks.

Se Venden Pasteles (G), Vol. 16. (Spanish Early Intervention Levels Ser.). (SPA.). 5.19 (978-0-7362-0308-1(7)) Hampton-Brown Bks.

Un Segundo Cumpleanos. (Saludos Ser.: Vol. 2). (SPA.). 24p. (gr. 2-3). 31.00 (978-0-7635-5723-2(4)) Rigby Education.

Un Segundo Cumpleanos: 6 Small Books. (Saludos Ser.: Vol. 2). (SPA.). 24p. (gr. 2-3). 31.00 (978-0-7635-9524-1(1)) Rigby Education.

Senor Cascaron: Big Book Packages. 2003. (SPA.). 64.95 (978-0-673-58592-9(1)) Celebration Pr.

El senor que domesticaba Espejos 2: Leveled Books. 2001. (McGraw-Hill. Lectura Ser.). (ENG & SPA.). (gr. 4 up). (978-0-02-188147-5(2)) Macmillan/McGraw-Hill Schl. Div.

La Senora Audaz, 6 Pack. (Literatura 2000 Ser.). (SPA.). (gr. 1-2). 28.00 (978-0-7635-1053-4(X)) Rigby Education.

Los Sentidos, Vol. 4. (Spanish Early Intervention Levels Ser.). (SPA.). 3.85 (978-1-56334-460-2(2)) Hampton-Brown Bks.

Set of 10 Titles, Vol. 4. (Spanish Early Intervention Levels Ser.). (SPA.). 37.00 (978-0-7362-1180-2(2)) Hampton-Brown Bks.

Set of 10 Titles: Levels 14-18. (Spanish Early Intervention Levels Ser.). (SPA.). 51.44 (978-0-7362-1184-0(5)) Hampton-Brown Bks.

Set of 11 Titles, Vol. 3. (Spanish Early Intervention Levels Ser.). (SPA.). 41.15 (978-0-7362-1179-6(9)) Hampton-Brown Bks.

Set of 11 Titles: Levels 19-20. (Spanish Early Intervention Levels Ser.). (SPA.). 52.03 (978-0-7362-1185-7(3)) Hampton-Brown Bks.

Set of 14 Titles: Levels 5-7. (Spanish Early Intervention Levels Ser.). (SPA.). 52.10 (978-0-7362-1181-9(0)) Hampton-Brown Bks.

Set of 20 Titles: Level B. (Spanish Guided Reading Levels Ser.). (SPA.). 75.80 (978-0-7362-1195-6(0)) Hampton-Brown Bks.

Set of 8 Titles. (Spanish Early Intervention Levels Ser.). (SPA.). 30.80 (978-0-7362-1010-2(5)) Hampton-Brown Bks.

Set of 9 Titles: Levels 10-13. (Spanish Early Intervention Levels Ser.). (SPA.). 42.09 (978-0-7362-1183-3(7)) Hampton-Brown Bks.

Set of 9 Titles: Levels 8-9. (Spanish Early Intervention Levels Ser.). (SPA.). 33.75 (978-0-7362-1182-6(9)) Hampton-Brown Bks.

Sh! Sh! 2003. 23.95 (978-0-673-78060-7(0)) Celebration Pr.

Shake It, Morena! And Other Folklore from Puerto Rico. 2007. (J). pap. 6.95 (***978-0-8225-7026-4(2)*** , First Avenue Editions) Lerner Publishing Group.

Shaw, Diana. Dias de Terror. (Torre de Papel Ser.). (SPA.). (YA). (gr. 6 up). 8.95 (978-958-04-1504-6(8)) Norma S.A. COL. *Dist:* Distribuidora Norma, Inc.

Si Camino Por Laz Ciudad... 2003. (SPA.). 35.50 (978-0-8136-8089-7(1)) Modern Curriculum Pr.

Silver Dolphin en Español Editors. Baby Senses: el Gusto? Baby Senses: Taste, Spanish-Language Edition. 2007. (Illus.). 8p. (J). bds. 5.95 (***978-970-718-473-2(6)*** , Silver Dolphin en Español) Advanced Marketing, S. de R. L. de C. V. MEX. *Dist:* Perseus Distribution.

—Baby Senses: el Olfato: Baby Senses: Smell, Spanish-Language Edition. 2007. (Illus.). 8p. (J). bds. 5.95 (***978-970-718-471-8(X)*** , Silver Dolphin en Español) Advanced Marketing, S. de R. L. de C. V. MEX. *Dist:* Perseus Distribution.

—Baby Senses: la Vista: Baby Senses: Sight, Spanish-Langage Edition. 2007. (Illus.). 8p. (J). bds. 5.95 (***978-970-718-472-5(8)*** , Silver Dolphin en Español) Advanced Marketing, S. de R. L. de C. V. MEX. *Dist:* Perseus Distribution.

—Caritas felices: Ariel: Happy Faces: Ariel, Spanish-Language Edition. 2007. (Illus.). 8p. (J). bds. 7.95 (***978-970-718-389-6(6)*** , Silver Dolphin en Español) Advanced Marketing, S. de R. L. de C. V. MEX. *Dist:* Perseus Distribution.

—Caritas felices: Cenicienta: Happy faces: Cinderella, Spanish-Language Edition. 2007. (Illus.). 8p. (J). bds. 7.95 (***978-970-718-390-2(X)*** , Silver Dolphin en Español) Advanced Marketing, S. de R. L. de C. V. MEX. *Dist:* Perseus Distribution.

—Caritas felices: Dumbo: Happy Faces: Dumbo, Spanish-Language Edition. 2007. (Illus.). 8p. (J). bds. 7.95 (***978-970-718-394-0(2)*** , Silver Dolphin en Español) Advanced Marketing, S. de R. L. de C. V. MEX. *Dist:* Perseus Distribution.

—Caritas felices: Simba: Happy Faces: Simba, Spanish-Language Edition. 2007. (Illus.). 8p. (J). bds. 7.95 (***978-970-718-392-6(6)*** , Silver Dolphin en Español) Advanced Marketing, S. de R. L. de C. V. MEX. *Dist:* Perseus Distribution.

—Caritas felices: Tigger: Happy Faces: Tigger, Spanish-Language Edition. 2007. (Illus.). 8p. (J). bds. 7.95 (***978-970-718-391-9(8)*** , Silver Dolphin en Español) Advanced Marketing, S. de R. L. de C. V. MEX. *Dist:* Perseus Distribution.

—Caritas felices: Winnie the Pooh: Happy Faces: Winnie the Pooh, Spanish-Language Edition. 2007. (Illus.). 8p. (J). bds. 7.95 (***978-970-718-393-3(4)*** , Silver Dolphin en Español) Advanced Marketing, S. de R. L. de C. V. MEX. *Dist:* Perseus Distribution.

—Disney Learning: Animales: Disney Learning: Animals, Spanish-Language Edition. 2006. (Illus.). 20p. (J). 3.99 (***978-970-718-431-2(0)*** , Silver Dolphin en Español) Advanced Marketing, S. de R. L. de C. V. MEX. *Dist:* Perseus Distribution.

—Disney Learning: Colores: Disney Learning: Colors, Spanish-Language Edition. 2006. (Illus.). 20p. (J). 3.99 (***978-970-718-430-5(2)*** , Silver Dolphin en Español) Advanced Marketing, S. de R. L. de C. V. MEX. *Dist:* Perseus Distribution.

—Disney Learning: Contrarios: Disney Learning: Opposites, Spanish-Language Edition. 2006. (Illus.). 20p. (J). 3.99 (***978-970-718-428-2(0)*** , Silver Dolphin en Español) Advanced Marketing, S. de R. L. de C. V. MEX. *Dist:* Perseus Distribution.

—Disney Learning: Formas: Disney Learning: Shapes, Spanish-Language Edition. 2006. (Illus.). 12p. (J). 3.99 (***978-970-718-429-9(9)*** , Silver Dolphin en Español) Advanced Marketing, S. de R. L. de C. V. MEX. *Dist:* Perseus Distribution.

—Disney princesas: Felices para Siempre: Disney Princesses: Happily Ever after, Spanish-Language Editon. 2007. (Illus.). 5p. (J). 14.99 (***978-970-718-448-0(5)*** , Silver Dolphin en Español) Advanced Marketing, S. de R. L. de C. V. MEX. *Dist:* Perseus Distribution.

—Disney Tesoro de libros de Calcomanias: Disney Sticker Book Treasury, Spanish-Language Edition. 2007. (Illus.). 48p. (J). 14.95 (***978-970-718-447-3(7)*** , Silver Dolphin en Español) Advanced Marketing, S. de R. L. de C. V. MEX. *Dist:* Perseus Distribution.

Sinon Sinonimo y Horacio Contrario. (SPA.). (J). 12.00 (978-958-02-1238-6(4)) Editorial Voluntad S.A. COL. *Dist:* Distribuidora Norma, Inc.

La Sirenita: Family, the Weather, Gardens, Underwater Life. 2000. (SPA & ENG., Illus.). (J). (ps-5). pap. 7.95 (978-88-8148-363-1(7)) European Language Institute ITA. *Dist:* Distribooks, Inc., Midwest European Pubns.

Skinner, Daphne. Tod el Apretado: Math Matters en Espanol. Nez, John, illus. 2005. 32p. pap. 4.95 (978-1-57565-155-2(6)) Kane Pr., The.

Small Book Classroom Set: Green Series. (Rimas y Risas Ser.). (SPA.). (ps-2). 337.22 (978-1-56334-129-8(8)) Hampton-Brown Bks.

Small Book Classroom Set: Green Series with addition of Manipulatives. (Rimas Y Risas Ser.). (SPA.). (ps-2). 461.82 (978-0-7362-0882-6(8)) Hampton-Brown Bks.

Smith. Los Lobos. 1999. pap. 5.18 (978-0-7398-0735-4(8)) Steck-Vaughn.

—Manzanas y Mas Manzanas. 1999. pap. 5.18 (978-0-7398-0725-5(0)) Steck-Vaughn.

El Soldadito de Plomo: Toys, in Town, at the Market, Prepositions of Place. 2000. (SPA & ENG., Illus.). (J). (ps-5). pap. 7.95 (978-88-8148-293-1(2)) European Language Institute ITA. *Dist:* Distribooks, Inc., Midwest European Pubns.

El Sombrero de Juan/Harry's Hat. 2005. (Libros en Espanol Para Ninos Ser.). (SPA.). (YA). (ps-1). 11.97 (978-0-8215-0993-7(4)); 15.75 (978-0-8215-1203-6(X)) Sadlier, William H. Inc.

Somos Amigos. (Spanish Early Intervention Levels Ser.). (SPA.). 23.10 (978-1-56334-763-4(6)); Vol. 2. 3.85 (978-1-56334-434-3(3)) Hampton-Brown Bks.

La sopa Especial: Individual Title, 6 packs. (Literatura 2000 Ser.). (SPA.). (gr. 1-2). 28.00 (978-0-7635-1054-1(8)) Rigby Education.

La sorpresa de Papa Oso: Individual Title Six-Packs. (Coleccion Pm Ser.).Tr. of Father Bear's surprise. (SPA.). 16p. (gr. 1 up). 26.00 (978-0-7578-3046-4(3)) Rigby Education.

Una sorpresa para Monica: 6 Small Books. (Saludos Ser.: Vol. 2). (SPA.). (gr. 3-5). 31.00 (978-0-7635-1816-5(6)) Rigby Education.

Spanish, Set. 2004. 13.99 incl. audio compact disk (978-1-57583-299-9(2)) Twin Sisters Productions, LLC.

Spanish Board Book Set 800782, 7. 2005. (J). bds. (978-1-59794-017-7(8)) Environments, Inc.

Spanish Book Set #2 800875, 8 vols. 2005. (J). pap. (978-1-59794-053-5(4)) Environments, Inc.

Spanish DRA Levels, 7 bks., Set. (Spanish Dra Levels Ser.). (SPA.). Level 1. 26.65 (978-0-7362-1213-7(2)); Level 10-14. 49.19 (978-0-7362-1219-9(1)); Level 16-18. 35.41 (978-0-7362-1220-5(5)); Level 20-28. 68.06 (978-0-7362-1221-2(3)); Level A. 18.65 (978-0-7362-1212-0(4)); Vol. 2. 61.00 (978-0-7362-1214-4(0)); Vol. 3. 49.15 (978-0-7362-1215-1(9)); Vol. 4. 33.15 (978-0-7362-1216-8(7)); Vol. 6. 22.20 (978-0-7362-1217-5(5)); Vol. 8. 29.60 (978-0-7362-1218-2(3)) Hampton-Brown Bks.

Spanish Emergent Reader 1, 2003. Tr. of Libritos Mios. (SPA., Illus.). 8p. (J). 100.00 net. (978-1-893986-24-4(1)) Keep Bks.

Spanish-English Books 800878, 4 vols. 2005. (J). bds. (978-1-59794-056-6(9)) Environments, Inc.

Spanish Guided Reading Levels, 28 bks., Set. (Spanish Guided Reading Levels Ser.). (SPA.). Level C. 105.10 (978-0-7362-1196-3(9)); Level D. 14.80 (978-0-7362-1197-0(7)); Level A. 15.40 (978-0-7362-1194-9(2)); Levels E-F. 46.78 (978-0-7362-1198-7(5)); Levels G-J. 77.96 (978-0-7362-1199-4(3)); Levels K-M. 57.22 (978-0-7362-1200-7(0)); Vol. 2. 52.70 (978-0-7362-1178-9(0)) Hampton-Brown Bks.

Spanish Guided Reading Levels Series, 96 vols. (Spanish Early Intervention Levels Ser.). (SPA.). 393.06 (978-0-7362-1177-2(2)) Hampton-Brown Bks.

Spanish Paperbacks 800718, 10. 2005. (J). (978-1-59794-016-0(X)) Environments, Inc.

Spanish School-to-Home Book, Early Level. (SPA.). (gr. k-2). 29.99 (978-0-7368-2983-0(0) , Yellow Umbrella Bks.) Capstone Pr., Inc.

Spanish School-to-Home Book, Emergent Level. (SPA.). (gr. k-2). 29.95 (978-0-7368-3112-3(6) , Yellow Umbrella Bks.) Capstone Pr., Inc.

Spanish TAKS MASTER Reading Grade 3. 2004. (978-1-57022-464-5(1)) ECS Learning Systems, Inc.

Spanish TAKS MASTER Reading Grade 4. 2004. (978-1-57022-465-2(X)) ECS Learning Systems, Inc.

Spanish/English Reproducible Emergent Readers. 2005. 128p. (J). per. 12.99 (978-1-59441-150-2(6) , CD-104046) Carson-Dellosa Publishing Co., Inc.

Stanley, Diane. El Caballero y la Doncella.Tr. of Gentleman & the Kitchen Maid. (SPA.). 30p. (J). (gr. 3-5). 11.96 (978-84-261-2876-8(9)) Juventud, Editorial ESP. *Dist:* Lectorum Pubns., Inc.

Steck-Vaughn Staff. Despegue. 1999. pap. 5.18 (978-0-7398-0737-8(4)) Steck-Vaughn.

—Raintree New Product Package: Summer 1999. 1999. (Illus.). pap. 175.80 (978-0-7398-1362-1(5)) Steck-Vaughn.

—Skimper Skamper. 1999. (SPA., Illus.). (J). pap. (978-0-8172-8706-1(X)) Steck-Vaughn.

Student Pack. (Cuentacuentos Ser.). (SPA.). (gr. k up). 83.31 (978-1-56334-798-6(9)) Hampton-Brown Bks.

Suenos y Fantasias. (Nuevos Horizontes Ser.). (SPA.). (J). (gr. 2). No. 1. wbk. ed. 8.95 (978-1-56014-510-3(2)); No. 2. wbk. ed. 8.95 (978-1-56014-511-0(0)) Santillana USA Publishing Co., Inc.

Suenos y Fantasias: Evaluations, Grade 2. (Nuevos Horizontes Ser.). (SPA.). (J). 22.50 (978-1-56014-512-7(9)) Santillana USA Publishing Co., Inc.

Suenos y Fantasias No. 1: Student Anthology. (Nuevos Horizontes Ser.). (SPA.). (J). (gr. 2). 14.95 (978-1-56014-508-0(0)) Santillana USA Publishing Co., Inc.

Suenos y Fantasias No. 2: Student Anthology. (Nuevos Horizontes Ser.). (SPA.). (J). (gr. 2). 16.95 (978-1-56014-509-7(9)) Santillana USA Publishing Co., Inc.

Super Classroom Set. (Elefonetica Ser.). (SPA.). (gr. 1-2). 939.56 (978-0-7362-0782-9(1)) Hampton-Brown Bks.

Superflaco! (Spanish Early Intervention Levels Ser.). (SPA.). 28.38 (978-0-7362-0843-7(7)) Hampton-Brown Bks.

Superflaco! (L), Vol. 22. (Spanish Early Intervention Levels Ser.). (SPA.). 4.73 (978-0-7362-0819-2(4)) Hampton-Brown Bks.

TAKS Reading Preparation Grade 3 - Spanish. 2004. (SPA.). per., wbk. ed. (978-1-932524-91-8(6)) Region IV Education Service Ctr.

TAKS Reading Preparation Grade 4 - Spanish. 2004. (SPA.). stu. ed., per., wbk. ed. (978-1-932524-92-5(4)) Region IV Education Service Ctr.

TAKS Reading Preparation Grade 5 - Spanish. 2004. (SPA.). stu. ed., per., wbk. ed. (978-1-932524-93-2(2)) Region IV Education Service Ctr.

El Taller de Pinatas. 2003. (SPA.). 23.95 (978-0-673-78082-9(1)) Celebration Pr.

Los Tamales. 2003. 23.95 (978-0-673-77132-2(6)) Celebration Pr.

Taylor, Mildred D. Lloro por la Tierra. (SPA.). (YA). 10.95 (978-958-04-1838-2(1)) Norma S.A. COL. *Dist:* AIMS International Bks., Inc., Distribuidora Norma, Inc.

El te de Chacota Milenio 10: Leveled Books. 2001. (McGraw-Hill. Lectura Ser.). (ENG & SPA.). (gr. 5 up). (978-0-02-188234-2(7)) Macmillan/McGraw-Hill Schl. Div.

Teague, Mark. El Chiquero. 2002. (SPA., Illus.). 32p. (J). (gr. k-2). pap. 5.99 (978-0-439-27000-7(6) , SO30911, Scholastic en Espanol) Scholastic, Inc.

Un techo y una Puerta: Individual Title Six-Packs. (Coleccion Pm Ser.).Tr. of Roof & a Door. (SPA.). 16p. (gr. 1 up). 26.00 (978-0-7578-2977-2(5)) Rigby Education.

El tesoro de Tono: Individual Title Six-Packs. (Literatura 2000 Ser.). (SPA.). (gr. 2-3). 33.00 (978-0-7635-1252-1(4)) Rigby Education.

Tesoro Escondido, 6, Pack. (Chiquilibros Ser.). (SPA.). (gr. k-1). 23.00 (978-0-7635-8589-1(0)) Rigby Education.

El tesoro Escondido 11: Leveled Books. 2001. (McGraw-Hill. Lectura Ser.). (ENG & SPA.). (gr. 3 up). (978-0-02-188132-1(4)) Macmillan/McGraw-Hill Schl. Div.

Theme Library, 10 vols. (High Point Ser.). (gr. 6-12). Level C. 74.53 (978-0-7362-0983-0(2)); Level A. 2000. (Illus.). 116.69 (978-0-7362-0919-9(0)); Level B. (Illus.). 91.19 (978-0-7362-0951-9(4)) Hampton-Brown Bks.

Thompson. Caperucita Roja Y Lobo Feroz. 1999. pap. 5.18 (978-0-7398-0734-7(X)) Steck-Vaughn.

—Pasteles de Manzana en Familia. 1999. (SPA.). pap. 5.18 (978-0-7398-0724-8(2)) Steck-Vaughn.

La tia Rosalia: Individual Title Six-Packs. (Literatura 2000 Ser.). (SPA.). (gr. 1-2). 28.00 (978-0-7635-1079-4(3)) Rigby Education.

Tiburones. 2003. Tr. of Sharks. (SPA.). 23.95 (978-0-673-78080-5(5)) Celebration Pr.

Tiburones. 2000. (McGraw-Hill Ciencias Ser.).Tr. of Sharks. (ENG & SPA.). (gr. 3 up). (978-0-02-279634-1(7)) Macmillan/McGraw-Hill Schl. Div.

Tich, Jan. Pope & Ba. 2006. (Adventures in Unusual Places Ser.). (Illus.). 28p. (J). 12.95 (978-9974-7925-8-6(4)) Hardenville SA URY. *Dist:* Independent Pubs. Group.

El Tiempo: Individual Title Six-Packs. (Chiquilibros Ser.). (SPA.). (gr. k-1). 23.00 (978-0-7635-8588-4(2)) Rigby Education.

El tigre Comilon, 6, Pack. (Literatura 2000 Ser.). (SPA.). (ps-1). 28.00 (978-0-7635-1007-7(6)) Rigby Education.

El tigre que volo en un Globo 23: Leveled Books. 2001. (McGraw-Hill. Lectura Ser.). (ENG & SPA.). (gr. 1 up). (978-0-02-187952-6(4)) Macmillan/McGraw-Hill Schl. Div.

Time for Bed: Individual Title Six-Packs. (Chiquilibros Ser.). (gr. k-1). 23.00 (978-0-7635-0425-0(4)) Rigby Education.

A Tina le gustan las Herramientas: Lap Book. (Pebble Soup Exploraciones Ser.). (SPA.). 16p. (ps up). 21.00 (978-0-7578-1686-4(X)) Rigby Education.

A Tina le gustan las Herramientas: Small Book. (Pebble Soup Exploraciones Ser.). (SPA.). 16p. (ps up). 5.00 (978-0-7578-1726-7(2)) Rigby Education.

Titanes de la Literatura Infantil.Tr. of Infant Literature. (SPA.). (J). (978-968-15-0412-0(7)) Editores Mexicanos Unidos.

A Tocar! Individual 6-packs. 2003. 23.95 (978-0-673-78075-1(9)) Celebration Pr.

Toconayo. 2003. 28.95 (978-0-673-78101-7(1)) Celebration Pr.

Todas las Mananas: Lap Book. (Pebble Soup Exploraciones Ser.). 16p. (ps up). 21.00 (978-0-7578-1673-4(8)) Rigby Education.

Todas las Mananas: Small Book. (Pebble Soup Exploraciones Ser.). 16p. (ps up). 5.00 (978-0-7578-1713-7(0)) Rigby Education.

Todo cambia Interactive Packages: El agua Cambia. (Pebble Soup Exploraciones Ser.). (SPA.). (ps up). 52.00 (978-0-7578-5263-3(7)) Rigby Education.

Todo cambia Interactive Packages: Los Sentimientos. (Pebble Soup Exploraciones Ser.). (SPA.). (ps up). 52.00 (978-0-7578-5266-4(1)) Rigby Education.

Todo Rojo. (Spanish Early Intervention Levels Ser.). (SPA.). 21.30 (978-0-7362-0803-1(8)); Vol. 2. 3.55 (978-0-7362-0761-4(9)) Hampton-Brown Bks.

Todos Enojados: Social/Emotional Lap Book. (Pebble Soup Exploraciones Ser.). (SPA.). (ps up). 16.00 (978-0-7578-1788-5(2)) Rigby Education.

Todos Somos Amigos: Big Book Packages. 2003. 64.95 (978-0-673-58593-6(X)) Celebration Pr.

Tolstoy, Leo. La Muerte de Ivan Ilich. (SPA.). 6.25 (978-958-04-2126-9(9)) Norma S.A. COL. *Dist:* Distribuidora Norma, Inc.

Tomas: Individual Title Six-Packs. (Literatura 2000 Ser.). (SPA.). (gr. 1-2). 28.00 (978-0-7635-1055-8(6)) Rigby Education.

Tomas es Valiente: Individual Title Six-Packs. (Coleccion Pm Ser.).Tr. of Tom is Brave. (SPA.). 16p. (gr. 1 up). 26.00 (978-0-7578-2964-2(3)) Rigby Education.

Tomas's Tops. 2003. 23.95 (978-0-673-78131-4(3)) Celebration Pr.

Tosal, Oscar. Asesinato en el Barrio Gotico Level 2. 1998. (SPA.). (gr. 7-12). lib. bdg. 14.10 (978-0-613-80706-7(5)) Tandem Library Bks.

Tostada: Matching English 6-packs. 2003. 23.95 (978-0-673-57565-4(9)) Celebration Pr.

Trade Book Library, 12 bks., Set. 2000. (Trade Book Library). (SPA.). (gr. 1 up). 112.90 (978-0-673-65087-0(1)); (gr. 2 up). 112.90 (978-0-673-65088-7(X)); (gr. 3 up). 112.90 (978-0-673-65089-4(8)); (gr. 4 up). 112.90 (978-0-673-65090-0(1)); (gr. 5 up). 112.90 (978-0-673-65091-7(X)) Addison-Wesley Educational Pubs., Inc.

El Traje Perdido. (Spanish Early Intervention Levels Ser.). (SPA.). 31.14 (978-0-7362-0335-7(4)) Hampton-Brown Bks.

El Traje Perdido (G), Vol. 18. (Spanish Early Intervention Levels Ser.). (SPA.). 5.19 (978-0-7362-0310-4(9)) Hampton-Brown Bks.

Trapp, Kyrima. Que? Como? Por que?: Los Colores: What? How? Why?: the Colors, Spanish-Language Edition. 2007. (Illus.). 16p. (J). 9.95 (***978-970-718-491-6(4)*** , Silver Dolphin en Español) Advanced Marketing, S. de R. L. de C. V. MEX. *Dist:* Perseus Distribution.

Los tres Bobos: Individual Title, 6 Packs. (Literatura 2000 Ser.). (SPA.). (gr. 2-3). 33.00 (978-0-7635-1274-3(5)) Rigby Education.

Los tres Cerditos: Lap Book. (Pebble Soup Exploraciones Ser.). (SPA.). 16p. (ps up). 21.00 (978-0-7578-1674-1(6)) Rigby Education.

Los tres Cerditos: Small Book. (Pebble Soup Exploraciones Ser.). (SPA.). 16p. (ps up). 5.00 (978-0-7578-1714-4(9)) Rigby Education.

Los Tres Cerditos Desobedientes: Individual 6-packs. 2003. 23.95 (978-0-673-77155-1(5)) Celebration Pr.

Los tres Magos: Individual Title, 6 Packs. (Literatura 2000 Ser.). (SPA.). (gr. 2-3). 33.00 (978-0-7635-1275-0(3)) Rigby Education.

Triceratops es Valiente: Individual Title Six-Packs. (Coleccion Pm Ser.).Tr. of Brave Triceratops. (SPA.). 16p. (gr. 1 up). 26.00 (978-0-7578-3033-4(1)) Rigby Education.

Los Trillizos: Individual Title, 6 Packs. (Literatura 2000 Ser.). (SPA.). (gr. 2-3). 33.00 (978-0-7635-1253-8(2)) Rigby Education.

Los Trompos De Tomas, 6 packs. 2003. 23.95 (978-0-673-78069-0(4)) Celebration Pr.

Los trucos de Chico: Individual Title, 6 Packs. (Coleccion Pm Ser.). (SPA.). 16p. (gr. 1 up). 26.00 (978-0-7578-2996-3(1)) Rigby Education.

El tunel ferroviario Sei: Individual Title Six-Packs. (On Deck en Espanol Ser.).Tr. of Seikan Railroad Tunnel. (SPA.). 24p. (gr. 4-5). 35.00 (978-0-7578-6443-8(0)) Rigby Education.

Two Volcanoes. 2003. 28.95 (978-0-673-78117-8(8)) Celebration Pr.

Los uniformes Amarillos: Individual Title, 6 Packs. (Literatura 2000 Ser.). (SPA.). (gr. 2-3). 33.00 (978-0-7635-1276-7(1)) Rigby Education.

Uno, dos, tres y Cuatro. (Spanish Early Intervention Levels Ser.). (SPA.). 23.10 (978-1-56334-792-4(X)) Hampton-Brown Bks.

Uno, Dos, Tres y Cuatro, Vol. 8. (Spanish Early Intervention Levels Ser.). (SPA.). 3.85 (978-1-56334-465-7(3)) Hampton-Brown Bks.

Uria, Fernando. Una Mano en la Arena. 1998. (SPA.). (gr. 7-12). lib. bdg. 14.10 (978-0-613-80711-1(1)) Tandem Library Bks.

Urraca, Maraca, Urraca: Little Books, Level 1, Vol. 13. 2003. (Fonolibros Ser.). 25.50 (978-0-7652-0090-7(2)) Modern Curriculum Pr.

Usen la Cabeza: Social/Emotional Lap Book. (Pebble Soup Exploraciones Ser.). (SPA.). (ps up). 16.00 (978-0-7578-1784-7(X)) Rigby Education.

Vacas en el Jardin: Individual Title Six-Packs. (Coleccion Pm Ser.).Tr. of Cows in the garden. (SPA.). 16p. (gr. 1 up). 26.00 (978-0-7578-3027-3(7)) Rigby Education.

El valiente Papa Raton, 6 Packs. (Coleccion Pm Ser.).Tr. of Brave Father mouse. (SPA.). 16p. (gr. 1 up). 26.00 (978-0-7578-2984-0(8)) Rigby Education.

Vamos! (Spanish Early Intervention Levels Ser.). (SPA.). 21.30 (978-0-7362-0809-3(7)) ; Vol. 6. 3.55 (978-0-7362-0767-6(8)) Hampton-Brown Bks.

Vamos a la Escuela: Individual Title Six-Packs. (Coleccion Pm Ser.: Vol. 1). Tr. of Way I Go to School. (SPA.). 16p. (gr. k-1). 26.00 (978-0-7578-0673-5(2)) Rigby Education.

Vamos a Pasear, 6 Packs. (Coleccion Pm Ser.: Vol. 1). Tr. of We go out. (SPA.). 16p. (gr. k-1). 26.00 (978-0-7578-0667-4(8)) Rigby Education.

Vamos De Viaje. 2003. (SPA.). 23.95 (978-0-673-77179-7(2)) Celebration Pr.

Vaughan, Richard. Levantemos el Cielo, Level 3. 2003. (Dejame Leer Ser.). (SPA., Illus.). (J). (ps-3). 4.50 (978-0-673-36332-9(5) , Good Year Bks.) Celebration Pr.

—El Universo, Level 2. 2003. (Dejame Leer Ser.). (SPA., Illus.). (J). (ps-3). 6.50 (978-0-673-36329-9(5) , Good Year Bks.) Celebration Pr.

Vazquez-Figueroa, Alberto. Anaconda. 2001. (SPA.). 400p. 9.95 (978-84-01-49901-2(1)) Astran, Inc.

—Anaconda. (SPA.). 400p. 12.95 (978-84-01-46951-0(1)) Plaza & Janes Editories, S.A. ESP. *Dist:* Distribooks, Inc.

El Veliz De los Recuerdos. 2003. 28.95 (978-0-673-78088-1(0)) Celebration Pr.

El venado de Mario. (Spanish Early Intervention Levels Ser.). (SPA.). 28.38 (978-0-7362-0837-6(2)) Hampton-Brown Bks.

El Venado de Mario (M), Vol. 24. (Spanish Early Intervention Levels Ser.). (SPA.). 4.73 (978-0-7362-0813-0(5)) Hampton-Brown Bks.

El venado y el Cocodrilo: Individual Title Six-Packs. (Literatura 2000 Ser.). (SPA.). (gr. 1-2). 28.00 (978-0-7635-1080-0(7)) Rigby Education.

Veo, veo Colas. (Spanish Early Intervention Levels Ser.). (SPA.). 23.10 (978-1-56334-766-5(0)) Hampton-Brown Bks.

Veo, Veo Colas, Vol. 2. (Spanish Early Intervention Levels Ser.). (SPA.). 3.85 (978-1-56334-436-7(X)) Hampton-Brown Bks.

Vestimos con Orgullo: 6 Small Books. (Saludos Ser.: Vol. 2). (SPA.). (gr. 3-5). 31.00 (978-0-7635-1769-4(0)) Rigby Education.

El viaje de la abuelita Jenny: 6 Small Books. (Saludos Ser.: Vol. 3). (SPA.). (gr. 3-5). 31.00 (978-0-7635-1783-0(6)) Rigby Education.

El viaje de Martin 1: Leveled Books. 2001. (McGraw-Hill. Lectura Ser.). (ENG & SPA.). (gr. 4 up). (978-0-02-188177-2(4)) Macmillan/McGraw-Hill Schl. Div.

El viento Bravo. (Spanish Early Intervention Levels Ser.). (SPA.). 28.38 (978-0-7362-0845-1(3)) Hampton-Brown Bks.

El Viento Bravo (M), Vol. 20. (Spanish Early Intervention Levels Ser.). (SPA.). 4.73 (978-0-7362-0821-5(6)) Hampton-Brown Bks.

Vingan A Ver Mi Rancho! Individual 6-packs. 2003. 23.95 (978-0-673-78066-9(X)) Celebration Pr.

Viva la Musica! (Spanish Early Intervention Levels Ser.). (SPA.). 31.14 (978-0-7362-0331-9(1)) Hampton-Brown Bks.

Viva la Musica! (I), Vol. 14. (Spanish Early Intervention Levels Ser.). (SPA.). 5.19 (978-0-7362-0306-7(0)) Hampton-Brown Bks.

Vjva el Midsommar! (Saludos Ser.: Vol. 1). (SPA.). 24p. (gr. 2-3). 31.00 (978-0-7635-5719-5(6)) Rigby Education.

Vjva el Midsommar! 6 Small Books. (Saludos Ser.: Vol. 1). (SPA.). 24p. (gr. 2-3). 31.00 (978-0-7635-9519-7(5)) Rigby Education.

Las Vocales: Big Book Packages. 2003. 64.95 (978-0-673-58588-2(3)) Celebration Pr.

Volver a Empezar: 6 Softcover Books. (Saludos Ser.: Vol. 3). (SPA.). (gr. 3-5). 31.00 (978-0-7635-2079-3(9)) Rigby Education.

Wall Chart. 2003. (gr. k up). suppl. ed. 81.90 (978-0-673-59354-2(1)); 2003. (gr. 1 up). suppl. ed. 81.90 (978-0-673-59355-9(X)); 2000. (SPA.). (gr. k up). suppl. ed. 85.95 (978-0-673-59490-7(4)); 2000. (SPA.). (gr. 1 up). suppl. ed. 85.95 (978-0-673-59491-4(2)); 2000. (SPA.). (gr. 2 up). suppl. ed. 85.95 (978-0-673-59492-1(0)); 2000. (SPA.). (gr. 3 up). suppl. ed. 85.95 (978-0-673-65119-8(3)) Addison-Wesley Educational Pubs., Inc.

Walqui-Van Lier, Aída, et al. Sendas Literarias, Level 1. 2001. (SPA.). (J). stu. ed. 44.97 (978-0-8384-0301-3(8)) Thomson Heinle.

Wasserman, Marvin & Wasserman, Carol. Susana y Javier en Espana. 2nd ed. 2000. (SPA & ENG.). 214p. (YA). (gr. 7-12). pap. (978-0-87720-502-9(7) , R686P) AMSCO Schl. Pubns., Inc.

The Wedding: Individual Title Six-Packs. (Literatura 2000 Ser.). (gr. k-1). 28.00 (978-0-7635-0071-9(2)) Rigby Education.

Weinhold, Angela. Que? Como? Por que?: el Bosque: What? How? Why?: the Forest, Spanish-Language Edition. 2007. 16p. (J). 9.95 (***978-970-718-493-0(0)*** , Silver Dolphin en Español) Advanced Marketing, S. de R. L. de C. V. MEX. *Dist:* Perseus Distribution.

Werther, Scott P. Autos low Rider: Individual Title Six-Packs. (On Deck en Espanol Ser.).Tr. of Low Riders. (SPA.). 24p. (gr. 4-5). 35.00 (978-0-7578-6421-6(X)) Rigby Education.

—Dragsters: Individual Title Six-Packs. (On Deck en Espanol Ser.). (SPA.). 24p. (gr. 4-5). 35.00 (978-0-7578-6420-9(1)) Rigby Education.

What's in the Box? 2003. 28.95 (978-0-673-78114-7(3)) Celebration Pr.

The White Horse: Individual Title Six-Packs. (Literatura 2000 Ser.). (gr. 2-3). 33.00 (978-0-7635-0244-7(8)) Rigby Education.

White, Mark. El Leon y el Raton: Version de la Fabula de Esopo. Rojo, Sara, illus. 2006. (Read-It! Readers en Espanol Ser.).Tr. of Lion & the Mouse: A Retelling of Aesop's Fable. (SPA.). 32p. (J). (ps-3). 19.95 (978-1-4048-1623-7(2)) Picture Window Bks.

—El Lobo con Piel de Oveja: Version de la Fabula de Esopo. Rojo, Sara, illus. 2006. (Read-It! Readers en Espanol Ser.).Tr. of Wolf in Sheep's Clothing: A Retelling of Aesop's Fable. (SPA.). 32p. (J). (ps-3). 19.95 (978-1-4048-1625-1(9)) Picture Window Bks.

Whitehouse, Patricia. Alimantos Blancos. 2002. (Colores Para Comer (The Colors We Eat) Ser.). (SPA.). 24p. (J). (ps-1). lib. bdg. 18.50 (978-1-58810-792-3(2)) Heinemann Library.

—Alimentos Amarillos. 2002. (SPA.). 24p. (J). (ps-1). pap. 5.25 (978-1-58810-838-8(4) , 91573); lib. bdg. 18.50 (978-1-58810-791-6(4)) Heinemann Library.

—Alimentos Verdes. 2002. (Colores Para Comer (The Colors We Eat) Ser.). (SPA.). 24p. (J). (ps-1). pap. 5.25 (978-1-58810-836-4(8) , 91576); lib. bdg. 18.50 (978-1-58810-789-3(2)) Heinemann Library.

—La Hora en el Zoologico. 2002. (Matematicas del Zoologico (Zoo Math) Ser.). 24p. (J). (ps-1). pap. 5.25 (978-1-58810-865-4(1) , 91626); (SPA.). lib. bdg. 18.50 (978-1-58810-806-7(6)) Heinemann Library.

—Que Esta Despierto?, 8 vols., Set. Cano, Patricia, tr. 2003. (SPA., Illus.). (J). (ps-1). lib. bdg. 148.00 (978-1-4034-0401-5(1)) Heinemann Library.

—Que Puede Construir? Abello, Patricia, tr. 2004. 24p. (J). 12.95 (978-1-4034-4390-8(4)) Heinemann Library.

—Que Puede Correr? Abello, Patricia, tr. 2004. (SPA.). 24p. (J). 12.95 (978-1-4034-4387-8(4)) Heinemann Library.

—Que Puede Excavar? Abello, Patricia, tr. 2004. (SPA.). 24p. (J). 12.95 (978-1-4034-4389-2(0)) Heinemann Library.

—Que Puede Nadar? Abello, Patricia, tr. 2004. (SPA.). 24p. (J). 12.95 (978-1-4034-4388-5(2)) Heinemann Library.

—La Rata. 2003. (Que Esta Despierto? (What's Awake?) Ser.).Tr. of Rats. (ENG & SPA.). 24p. (J). (ps-1). lib. bdg. 17.08 (978-1-4034-0397-1(X)) Heinemann.

—La Rata. 2003. (¿Qué esta despierto? Ser.).Tr. of Rats. (SPA., Illus.). 24p. pap. 5.25 (978-1-4034-0638-5(3)) Heinemann Library.

—Tamanos en el Zoologico. 2002. (Matematicas del Zoologico (Zoo Math) Ser.). (SPA.). 24p. (J). (ps-1). pap. 5.25 (978-1-58810-864-7(3) , 91630); lib. bdg. 18.50 (978-1-58810-805-0(8)) Heinemann Library.

—El Zoologico Matematico. 2002. (Matematicas del Zoologico (Zoo Math) Ser.). 24p. (J). (ps-1). (SPA.). 18.50 (978-1-58810-802-9(3)); pap. 5.25 (978-1-58810-861-6(9) , 91625) Heinemann Library.

Wilde, Oscar. El Fantasma de Canterville: Y otros Cuentos. (SPA.). (YA). 8.75 (978-958-04-6746-5(3)) Norma S.A. COL. *Dist:* Distribuidora Norma, Inc.

Wilhelm, Hans. No Me Gusta Mi Mono. Wilhelm, Hans, illus. 2002. (Coleccion "Hola, Lector" Ser.). (SPA., Illus.). 32p. (J). (ps-1). pap. 3.99 (978-0-439-22645-5(7) , SO5389, Scholastic en Espanol) Scholastic, Inc.

—Se Me Cayo un Diente! Wilhelm, Hans, illus. 2002. (Coleccion "Hola, Lector" Ser.).Tr. of I Lost My Tooth. (SPA., Illus.). 32p. (J). (ps-1). pap. 3.99 (978-0-439-22646-2(5) , SO0823, Scholastic en Espanol) Scholastic, Inc.

Williams, Vera B. More More More, Said the Baby. Williams, Vera B., illus. 2007. (SPA.). 40p. (J). 16.99 (***978-0-06-122876-6(1)*** , Rayo) HarperCollins Pubs.

Willis, Shirley. Dime Cuanto Pesa. 2000. (gr. k-3). (SPA.). lib. bdg. 14.10 (978-0-613-72666-5(9)); (J). 12.75 (978-0-606-20148-3(3)) Tandem Library Bks.

—Dime por Que Es Mojada la Lluvia. 1999. (Coleccion los Estupendos). (SPA., Illus.). 32p. (J). (gr. 2-4). 20.00 (978-0-531-11849-8(5) , OD30029, Watts, Franklin) Scholastic Library Publishing.

—Dime por Que Es Mojada la Lluvia. 2000. (Estupendos Ser.). (J). 12.75 (978-0-606-20150-6(5)) Tandem Library Bks.

—Dime Que Tan Lejos Esta de Aqui. 2000. (gr. k-3). (SPA.). lib. bdg. 14.10 (978-0-613-72672-6(3)); (J). 12.75 (978-0-606-20153-7(X)) Tandem Library Bks.

—Dime Que Tan Rapidamente Va. 2000. (Los Estupendos Whiz Kids, Spanish Edition Ser.). (SPA., Illus.). 32p. (J). (gr. 1-3). pap. 5.95 (978-0-531-15993-4(0) , OD30044, Watts, Franklin) Scholastic Library Publishing.

—Dime Que Tan Rapidamente Va. 2000. (gr. k-3). (SPA.). lib. bdg. 14.10 (978-0-613-72673-3(1)); (J). 12.75 (978-0-606-20154-4(8)) Tandem Library Bks.

Winitz, Harris & Sagarna, Blanca. Basic Structures, Spanish Bk. 2: A Textbook for the Learnables. Trimino, Andres M., ed. Baker, Sydney M. & Nixon, Gloria, illus. 2nd ed. 1998. 362p. (YA). (gr. 7 up). pap. 59.00 (978-1-887371-19-3(2) , 372) International Linguistics Corp.

With addition of Elefonetica & Pan y Canela. (De Canciones A Cuentos Ser.). (SPA.). (gr. 1 up). 1413.46 (978-0-7362-0704-1(X)); (gr. 2 up). 1261.41 (978-0-7362-0706-5(6)) Hampton-Brown Bks.

A With Addition of Pan y Canela Collection. (Cuentacuentos Ser.). (SPA.). (gr. k up). 1238.34 (978-1-56334-801-3(2)) Hampton-Brown Bks.

A With Addition of Pan y Canela Little Reader Collection. (De Canciones A Cuentos Ser.). (SPA.). (gr. k up). 870.44 (978-1-56334-571-5(4)) Hampton-Brown Bks.

With Addition of Pan y Canela Little Reader Collection B. (De Canciones A Cuentos Ser.). (SPA.). (gr. 1 up). 860.93 (978-1-56334-993-5(0)) Hampton-Brown Bks.

With addition of Pan y Canela Little Reader Collection C. (De Canciones A Cuentos Ser.) (SPA.). (gr. 2 up). 929.66 (978-0-7362-0442-2(3)) Hampton-Brown Bks.

Word Pocket with Letras Moviles. (SPA.). (gr. 2 up). 7.40 (978-0-7362-0853-6(4)) Hampton-Brown Bks.

Y Ahora, Que Leo? 2003. (J). 28.95 (978-0-673-78098-0(8)) Celebration Pr.

Yellow Umbrella Spanish & English Add-on Set. (ENG & SPA.). (gr. k-2). 693.95 (978-0-7368-3179-6(7) , Yellow Umbrella Bks.) Capstone Pr., Inc.

Yellow Umbrella Spanish, Early Level. (SPA.). (gr. k-2). 999.95 (978-0-7368-3058-4(8) , Yellow Umbrella Bks.) Capstone Pr., Inc.

Yellow Umbrella Spanish, Early Level Add-on Set. (SPA.). (gr. k-2). 172.95 (978-0-7368-3059-1(6) , Yellow Umbrella Bks.) Capstone Pr., Inc.

Yellow Umbrella Spanish, Emergent Level. (SPA.). (gr. k-2). 999.95 (978-0-7368-3149-9(5) , Yellow Umbrella Bks.) Capstone Pr., Inc.

Yellow Umbrella Spanish, Emergent Level Add-on Set. (SPA.). (gr. k-2). 172.95 (978-0-7368-3150-5(9) , Yellow Umbrella Bks.) Capstone Pr., Inc.

Yo: Individual Title Six-Packs. (Coleccion Pm Ser.: Vol. 1). Tr. of Me. (SPA.). 16p. (gr. k-1). 26.00 (978-0-7578-0658-2(9)) Rigby Education.

Yo ayudo en mi Casa: Individual Title Six-Packs. (Coleccion Pm Ser.).Tr. of I help at home. (SPA.). 16p. (gr. 1 up). 26.00 (978-0-7578-2958-1(9)) Rigby Education.

Yo Juego: Individual Title Six-Packs. (Coleccion Pm Ser.: Vol. 1). Tr. of Playing. (SPA.). 16p. (gr. k-1). 26.00 (978-0-7578-0665-0(1)) Rigby Education.

Yo Me Visto Solo, 6-packs. 2003. (J). 23.95 (978-0-673-77140-7(7)) Celebration Pr.

Yo puedo Ver, 6 Packs. (Coleccion Pm Ser.: Vol. 2). Tr. of I can see. (SPA.). 16p. (gr. k-1). 26.00 (978-0-7578-0687-2(2)) Rigby Education.

Yo quiero Ser. (Spanish Early Intervention Levels Ser.). (SPA.). 23.10 (978-1-56334-782-5(2)) Hampton-Brown Bks.

Yo Quiero Ser, Vol. 2. (Spanish Early Intervention Levels Ser.). (SPA.). 3.85 (978-1-56334-455-8(6)) Hampton-Brown Bks.

Yo Vivo Aqui: Big Book Packages. 2003. (J). 64.95 (978-0-673-58586-8(7)) Celebration Pr.

Young, Caroline. Mi Primer Libro de Palabras. Litchfield, Jo, illus. 2004. (Titles in Spanish Ser.). (SPA.). 16p. (J). 11.99 (978-0-7945-0951-4(7) , Usborne) EDC Publishing.

Your Friend, Jorge. 2003. 28.95 (978-0-673-78118-5(6)) Celebration Pr.

El yoyo de Mayito. (Spanish Early Intervention Levels Ser.). (SPA.). 21.30 (978-0-7362-0829-1(1)) Hampton-Brown Bks.

El Yoyo de Mayito (F), Vol. 10. (Spanish Early Intervention Levels Ser.). (SPA.). 3.55 (978-0-7362-0775-1(9)) Hampton-Brown Bks.

Zapatos, Vol. 3. (Spanish Early Intervention Levels Ser.). (SPA.). 3.85 (978-1-56334-435-0(1)) Hampton-Brown Bks.

Zimmermann, Natalie. Un Principe para Lila. (Torre de Papel Ser.). (SPA., Illus.). (J). 7.95 (978-958-04-5051-1(X)) Norma S.A. COL. *Dist:* Distribuidora Norma, Inc.

Un Zoologico, 6 Packs. (Literatura 2000 Ser.). (SPA.). (ps-1). 28.00 (978-0-7635-1008-4(4)) Rigby Education.

6-Pack Collection: Includes 180 books (30 6-Packs) 2003. (J). 769.95 (978-0-7652-0558-2(0)) Modern Curriculum Pr.

S

SPANISH LITERATURE

Harcourt School Publishers Staff. Student Journal. 93rd ed. 1998. (Estrellas de Literatura Ser.). (gr. 1). 20.30 (978-0-15-304452-6(7)); (gr. 2). 20.30 (978-0-15-304453-3(5)) Harcourt Schl. Pubs.

Pascal, Francine. Rebelde con Causa. Orig. Title: Taking Charge. (SPA.). 136p. (J). 6.95 (978-84-272-3796-4(0)) Molino, Editorial ESP. *Dist:* AIMS International Bks., Inc.

SPANISH MAIN

Malam, John. You Wouldn't Want to Be a Pirate's Prisoner! Antram, David, illus. 2002. (You Wouldn't Want to Ser.). 32p. (J). (gr. 2-5). 28.50 (978-0-531-14607-1(3)); pap. 9.95 (978-0-531-16368-9(7)) Scholastic Library Publishing. (Watts, Franklin).

—You Wouldn't Want to Be a Pirate's Prisoner! 2002. (gr. 3-6). lib. bdg. 18.75 (978-0-613-53885-5(4)) Tandem Library Bks.

Patent, Dorothy Hinshaw. Treasures of the Spanish Main. 2000. (Frozen in Time Ser.). (Illus.). (J). (gr. 5-9). lib. bdg. 28.50 (978-0-7614-0786-7(3) , Benchmark Bks.) Cavendish, Marshall Corp.

SPANISH MAIN—FICTION

Batson, Wayne Thomas. Isle of Swords. 2007. 352p. (J). 16.99 (***978-1-4003-1018-0(0)***) Nelson, Thomas Inc.

Henty, A. G. Under Drakes Flag A Tale of the Spanish. 2007. 97.99 (***978-1-4280-5259-8(3)***); pap. 91.99 (***978-1-4280-5245-1(3)***) IndyPublish.com.

Lewis, C. S. El Caballo y Su Nino. 2000. (978-0-606-22687-5(7)) Tandem Library Bks.

SPANISH POETRY—COLLECTIONS

Del Rosario Marquez, Nieves. Raices y Alas (Poesias para Ninos y Jovenes) Montes, Jesus, illus. 2001. (Coleccion Espejo de Paciencia). (SPA.). 64p. (Orig.). (gr. 6). 9.00 (978-0-89729-289-4(8)) Ediciones Universal.

Lujan, Jorge Elias. Alba y Ocaso. Monroy, Manuel, illus. 2003. (SPA.). 32p. (J). 15.95 (978-0-88899-535-3(0)) Groundwood Bks. CAN. *Dist:* Perseus Distribution.

Medina, Jane. The Dream on Blanca's Wall: Poems in English & Spanish. Casilla, Robert, illus. 2004. (SPA & ENG.). 48p. (YA). (gr. 2-4). pap. 9.95 (978-1-59078-264-4(X)) Boyds Mills Pr.

Polo, Eduardo. Chamario. Ballester, Arnal, illus. 2005. (SPA.). 48p. (J). 8.99 (978-980-257-278-6(0)) Ekare, Ediciones VEN. *Dist:* Iaconi, Mariuccia Bk. Imports.

SPARRING

see Boxing

SPARROWS

Webster, Christine. Sparrows. 2007. (J). (***978-1-59036-681-3(6)***); (***978-1-59036-682-0(4)***) Weigl Pubs., Inc.

SPARROWS—FICTION

Adams, Michelle Medlock. The Sparrow's Easter Song. Eldridge, Marion, illus. 2003. 32p. (J). 14.95 (978-0-8249-5470-3(X)) Ideals Pubns.

Albright, Ann. Samuel Sparrow & the Tree of Light. Albright, Ann, illus. 2003. (J). (978-0-9715472-5-4(4)) Ascension Lutheran Church.

Bentley, Susan E. The Adventures of Twitcher & Solomon. 2005. 96p. (J). pap. 10.99 (978-1-4141-0467-6(7)) Pleasant Word.

Cowley, Joy. The Video Shop Sparrow. Bishop, Gavin, illus. 2003. 32p. (YA). (gr. k-2). 15.95 (978-1-56397-826-5(1)) Boyds Mills Pr.

Doney, Meryl. The Very Worried Sparrow. Hansen, Gaby, illus. 2008. (J). 12.95 (***978-0-8198-8038-3(8)***) Pauline Bks. & Media.

DuFalla, Anita, illus. Sumac & the Magic Lake: Levels F-M (9-28) ed. 2004. (Reader's Theater Ser.). 16p. (J). pap. 22.00 (978-1-4108-2291-8(5) , A22915) Benchmark Education Co.

Ebers, Georg. A Question. 2005. 96p. pap. 10.95 (978-1-4218-0443-9(3) , 1st World Library - Literary Society) 1st World Publishing, Inc.

Gerstein, Mordicai. Sparrow Jack. Gerstein, Mordicai, illus. 2003. (Illus.). 32p. (J). 16.00 (978-0-374-37139-5(3) , Farrar, Straus & Giroux (BYR)) Farrar, Straus & Giroux.

Glass, Stephen. Sara Sparrow. 2006. (J). per. 16.95 (978-1-59858-065-5(5)) Dog Ear Publishing, LLC.

Grandmother Sparrow: Copyright TXu1-280-697. 2007. (J). (***978-0-9792641-0-8(3)***) Shelle, Carole Creative Arts.

Hansen, Brooks. Caesar's Antlers. 2001. (978-0-606-22624-0(9)) Tandem Library Bks.

Kerven, Rosalind. Sparrow, the Crow & the Pearl. Williamson, Melanie, illus. 2005. 24p. (J). lib. bdg. 22.65 (***978-1-59646-754-5(1)***) Dingles & Co.

Kidd, Rob. The Age of Bronze. 5th rev. ed. 2006. (Pirates of the Caribbean Ser.: Bk. 5). 144p. (gr. 3-7). pap. 4.99 (978-1-4231-0168-0(5)) Disney Pr.

—The Coming Storm. 2006. (Pirates of the Caribbean Ser.: Bk. 1). (Illus.). 144p. (gr. 3-7). pap. 4.99 (978-1-4231-0018-8(2)) Disney Pr.

—The Pirate Chase. 3rd rev. ed. 2006. (Pirates of the Caribbean Ser.: Bk. 3). (Illus.). 128p. (gr. 3-7). pap. 4.99 (978-1-4231-0020-1(4)) Disney Pr.

—The Siren Song. 2nd rev. ed. 2006. (Pirates of the Caribbean Ser.: Vol. 2). (Illus.). 128p. (gr. 3-7). pap. 4.99 (978-1-4231-0019-5(0)) Disney Pr.

—The Sword of Cortes. 4th rev. ed. 2006. (Pirates of the Caribbean Ser.: Bk. 4). (Illus.). 128p. (gr. 3-7). pap. 4.99 (978-1-4231-0061-4(1)) Disney Pr.

Lodi, Mario. Cipi. 2000. (SPA., Illus.). 116p. (J). pap. (978-84-204-4779-7(X)) Aguilar, S. A. de Ediciones-Grupo Santillana.

Maddox, Tony. Spike's Best Nest. 1998. (Illus.). 32p. (J). pap. 5.95 (978-0-7641-0548-7(5)) Barron's Educational Series, Inc.

Maguire, Thomas Aquinas. A Growling Place. 2007. (Illus.). 32p. (J). (gr. k up). 16.95 (***978-1-894965-74-3(4)***) Simply Read Bks. CAN. *Dist:* Perseus Distribution.

Mari y los Gorriones: Individual Title Six-Packs. (Coleccion Pm Ser.).Tr. of Sally & the sparrows. (SPA.). 16p. (gr. 1 up). 26.00 (978-0-7578-3004-4(8)) Rigby Education.

Moore, Sherry. The Crab Is Back in Town. 2007. (J). per. (***978-1-894936-78-1(7)***) Saga Bks.

Myers, Christopher A. Fly! Myers, Christopher A., illus. 2001. (Illus.). 32p. (ps-17). 16.49 (978-0-7868-2373-4(9) , Jump at the Sun) Hyperion Bks. for Children.

Narvaez, Concha Lopez. El Cernicalo Porque. Salmeron, Rafael, illus. (Pajaros de Cuento Coleccion). (SPA.). 84p. (YA). (gr. 5-8). (978-84-241-7927-4(7)) Everest de Ediciones y Distribucion, S.L. ESP. *Dist:* Lectorum Pubns., Inc.

Pugliano-Martin, Carol. The el rey malo & Very Mean King. 2005. spiral bd. 66.00 (***978-1-4108-5648-7(8)***) Benchmark Education Co.

Sargent, Dave. Cindy Sparrow. Lenoir, Jane, illus. 2000. (Feather Tale Ser.). ix, 36p. (J). pap. 6.95 (978-1-56763-472-3(9)); lib. bdg. 19.95 (978-1-56763-471-6(0)) Ozark Publishing.

Sargent, Dave & Sargent, David M. Cindy Sparrow: Respect the Property of Others, 19, 6. Lenoir, Jane, illus. 2003. (Feather Tales Ser.: 6). 42p. (J). pap. 6.95 (978-1-56763-730-4(2)); 2nd ed. lib. bdg. 19.95 (978-1-56763-729-8(9)) Ozark Publishing.

The Sparrow's Gift: Second Grade Guided Reading Level L. (On Our Way to English Ser.). (gr. 2 up). 34.50 (978-0-7578-7100-9(3)) Rigby Education.

Watson, Kit. The Day the Birds Sang. 2007. (J). per. 13.99 (***978-1-59886-875-3(6)***) Tate Publishing & Enterprises, L.L.C.

SPARTA (EXTINCT CITY)—HISTORY—FICTION

Harcourt School Publishers Staff. Greetings from Ancient Greece On Level. 3rd ed. 2002. (Trophies Reading Program Ser.). (Illus.). pap. 5.10 (978-0-15-323445-3(8)) Harcourt Schl. Pubs.

SPASTIC PARALYSIS

see Cerebral Palsy

SPEAKING

see Debates and Debating; Public Speaking; Rhetoric; Voice

SPECIE

see Money

SPECIES DIVERSITY

Kelsey, Elin. Strange New Species: Astonishing Discoveries of Life on Earth. 2005. (Illus.). 96p. (J). (gr. 4-7). 24.95 (978-1-897066-31-7(7)); pap. 16.95 (978-1-897066-32-4(5)) Maple Tree Pr. CAN. *Dist:* Perseus Distribution.

SPECTACLES

see Eyeglasses

SPECTERS

see Apparitions; Ghosts

SPEECH

see also Language and Languages; Phonetics; Voice

Apel, Melanie Ann. Coping with Stuttering. 2005. (Coping Ser.). (Illus.). 192p. (YA). (gr. 7-12). lib. bdg. 26.50 (978-0-8239-2970-2(1) , COSTUT) Rosen Publishing Group, Inc., The.

Beaumont, Susanna. Baby Senses Speech: Look! I'm Talking! 2005. (Baby Senses Ser.). (Illus.). 16p. (ps-k). bds. 14.95 (978-1-905051-52-6(2)) Make Believe Ideas GBR. *Dist:* Ingram Pub. Services.

Dorling Kindersley Publishing Staff, ed. Learning to Talk. 2004. (Johnson's Everyday Babycare Ser.). (Illus.). 64p. pap. 8.00 (978-0-7566-0569-8(5)) Dorling Kindersley Publishing, Inc.

First Experiences - Going to the Doctor. 2005. (J). per. 8.95 (978-1-59566-130-2(1)) QEB Publishing Inc.

Glencoe McGraw-Hill Staff. The Basics of Speech: Learning to Be a Competent Communicator. 4th ed. 2004. (C). stu. ed. 76.00 (978-0-07-861620-4(4) , 9780078616204) Glencoe/McGraw-Hill.

Kent, Susan. Let's Talk about Stuttering. 2000. (Let's Talk Library). (Illus.). 24p. (J). (gr. 3). lib. bdg. 18.75 (978-0-8239-5423-0(4) , PowerKids Pr.) Rosen Publishing Group, Inc., The.

Lenny's Lost Spots. 2005. (J). per. 8.95 (978-1-59566-131-9(X)) QEB Publishing Inc.

Life Cycles - from Seed to Sunflower. 2005. (J). per. 8.95 (978-1-59566-145-6(X)) QEB Publishing Inc.

Life Cycles: From Caterpillar to Butterfly. 2005. (J). per. 8.95 (978-1-59566-129-6(8)) QEB Publishing Inc.

LoGiudice, Carolyn & McConnell, Nancy. Room 28 a Social Language Program. 2004. (YA). per. 25.95 (978-0-7606-0530-1(0)) LinguiSystems, Inc.

MagneTalk' Match-up Adventure Kit (without Barrier) 2006. (J). 34.95 (***978-1-58650-616-2(1)***); 34.95 (***978-1-58650-653-7(6)***) Super Duper Pubns.

MagneTalk' Match-up Around the World. 2006. (J). 34.95 (***978-1-58650-644-5(7)***) Super Duper Pubns.

MagneTalk' Match-up Around the World (with Barrier) 2006. (J). 44.95 (***978-1-58650-610-0(2)***) Super Duper Pubns.

McGraw-Hill Staff, et al. Glencoe Speech. 3rd ed. 2004. stu. ed. 80.00 (978-0-07-861618-1(2) , 9780078616181) Glencoe/McGraw-Hill.

O'Connor, Frances. Frequently Asked Questions about Stuttering. 2007. (J). (***978-1-4042-1931-1(5)***) Rosen Publishing Group, Inc., The.

Rouse, Toni. How to Use Parts of Speech. Arquilevich, Gabriel, ed. Chaney, Howard, illus. 1999. (How to Ser.). 48p. (J). (gr. 5-8). pap., act. bk. ed. 7.99 (978-1-57690-500-5(4) , TCA2500) Teacher Created Materials, Inc.

School Specialty Publishing. Making Speeches. 2003. 48p. (J). (gr. 3 up). pap. 6.99 (978-0-7424-1843-1(X) , FS99154); (gr. 4 up). pap. 6.99 (978-0-7424-1844-8(8) , FS99155); (gr. 5 up). pap. 6.99 (978-0-7424-1845-5(6) , FS99156) School Specialty Publishing.

Sleeper, Amanda A. Speech & Language. 2007. (Gray Matter Ser.). (Illus.). 128p. (J). (gr. 9). 32.95 (978-0-7910-8952-1(5) , Chelsea Hse.) Facts On File, Inc.

Smith, J. L. How to Use Parts of Speech. Arquilevich, Gabriel, ed. Chaney, Howard, illus. 1999. (How to Ser.). 48p. (gr. k-3). pap., tchr. ed. 7.99 (978-1-57690-355-1(9) , TCA2355) Teacher Created Materials, Inc.

Snodgrass, Catherine S. Super Silly Sayings That Are over Your Head: A Children's Illustrated Book of Idioms. 2004. (Illus.). 29p. (J). (gr. 1-4). bds. 16.95 (978-0-9666529-4-9(0)) Starfish Specialty Pr., LLC.

Speech Improvement Reproducible Masters. 2000. 56p. spiral bd. 24.00 (978-1-886143-51-7(X)) Great Ideas for Teaching, Inc.

Stanley, Mandy. Mis Primeras Palabras. 2003. Tr. of Very First Words. (SPA.). 12p. (J). (ps-k). 4.95 (978-0-7534-5692-7(3)) Houghton Mifflin Co. Trade & Reference Div.

Talking to Our Friends: Individual Title Six-Packs. (Rigby Focus Ser.). 16p. (gr. 1 up). 28.00 (978-0-7578-5311-1(0)); 30.00 (978-0-7578-5543-6(1)) Rigby Education.

SPEECH, LIBERTY OF

see Freedom of Speech

SPEECH THERAPY

Gustafson, Monica. Quick Make Artic Activities. 2006. (J). per. 27.95 (978-0-7606-0656-8(0)) LinguiSystems, Inc.

kaufman, Nancy. Kaufman Speech Praxis Workout Book. 2005. (Illus.). 127p. (J). pap. (978-0-9765497-1-0(9)) Northern Speech Services.

Libal, Joyce. Finding My Voice: Youth with Speech Impairment. 2004. (Youth with Special Needs Ser.). (Illus.). 128p. (J). (978-1-59084-738-1(5)) Mason Crest Pubs.

Sargisson, Lisa. Quick Connect Articulation 1. 2006. (J). 15.95 (978-0-7606-0661-2(7)) LinguiSystems, Inc.

Sarrgisson, Lisa. Quick Connect Articulaton 2. 2006. (J). 15.95 (978-0-7606-0662-9(5)) LinguiSystems, Inc.

Wojcicki, Ronda. Speech Class Rules: An Introduction to Speech Therapy for Children. 2007. (J). 19.95 (***978-0-9794102-0-8(7)***) Speech Place Publishing, The.

SPEECH THERAPY—FICTION

Feiffer, Jules. Bark, George. 2004. 24.95 incl. audio (978-1-55592-690-8(8)); 29.95 incl. cd-rom (978-1-55592-700-4(9)); pap. 14.95 incl. audio (978-1-55592-696-0(7)); pap. 18.95 incl. audio compact disk (978-1-55592-706-6(8)) Weston Woods Studios, Inc.

Hulme, Joy N. Through the Open Door. 2000. 176p. (J). (gr. 4-6). 14.95 (978-0-380-97870-0(9)) HarperCollins Pubs.

SPEED

Barkan, Joanne. What Is Velocity? 2005. (Rookie Read-About Science Ser.). (Illus.). 32p. (J). (gr. 1-2). pap. 4.95 (978-0-516-24664-2(X) , Children's Pr.) Scholastic Library Publishing.

Barraclough, Sue. Fast & Slow. 2006. (Illus.). 24p. (J). (978-1-4109-2266-3(9)); (978-1-4109-2261-8(8)) Steck-Vaughn.

Butterfield, Moira, et al. Record Breakers & Other Speed Machines. (Illus.). 32p. (J). mass mkt. 8.99 (978-0-590-24653-8(4)) Scholastic, Inc.

Dintiman, George Blough. Speed Improvement for Young Athletes: How to Sprint Faster in Your Sport in 30 Workouts. rev. ed. 2006. Vol. 2. (Illus.). 153p. pap. 17.95 (978-0-938074-26-7(1)) National Assn. of Speed & Explosion.

Discovery Channel & Staff. Speed. 2004. (Planet's Most Extreme Ser.). (Illus.). 48p. (J). (gr. 4-7). 24.95 (978-1-4103-0379-0(9) , Blackbirch Pr., Inc.) Thomson Gale.

Gardner, Robert. Bicycle Science Projects: Physics on Wheels. 2004. (Science Fair Success Ser.). (Illus.). 112p. (J). lib. bdg. 26.60 (978-0-7660-1630-9(7)) Enslow Pubs., Inc.

—Split-Second Science Projects with Speed: How Fast Does It Go? 2003. (Sensational Science Experiments Ser.). (Illus.). 48p. (J). (gr. 1-4). lib. bdg. 23.93 (978-0-7660-2017-7(7)) Enslow Pubs., Inc.

Gordon, Sharon. Fast Slow (Rapido Lento) 2006. (Bookworms Ser.). (ENG & SPA., Illus.). 24p. (J). lib. bdg. 22.79 (978-0-7614-2447-5(4)) Cavendish, Marshall Corp.

—Rapido Lento. 2006. (Bookworms Ser.). (SPA & ENG., Illus.). 24p. (J). lib. bdg. 22.79 (978-0-7614-2367-6(2)) Cavendish, Marshall Corp.

Graham, Ian. The Best Book of Speed Machines. (Best Book of... Ser.). (Illus.). 32p. (J). 2008. pap. 6.95 (***978-0-7534-6168-6(4)***); 2002. tchr. ed. 12.95 (978-0-7534-5436-7(X)) Houghton Mifflin Co. Trade & Reference Div. (Kingfisher).

Group/McGraw-Hill, Wright. Speed: Magazine Anthology: Level 6, 6 vols. (Comprehension Strand Ser.). (gr. 4-8). 54.00 (978-0-322-06040-1(0)) Wright Group, The.

Harris, Nicholas. How Fast? 2003. (How? Ser.). (Illus.). 30p. (J). 23.70 (978-1-4103-0067-6(6)); 11.20 (978-1-4103-0196-3(6)) Thomson Gale. (Blackbirch Pr., Inc.).

Hibbert, Clare & Dorling Kindersley Publishing Staff. The Flash's Book of Speed. 2005. (Dk Readers Ser.). (Illus.). 48p. (J). 12.99 (978-0-7566-1014-2(1)); pap. 3.99 (978-0-7566-1015-9(X)) Dorling Kindersley Publishing, Inc.

O'Neil, Sarah. Going Fast. 2001. (gr. k-3). lib. bdg. 11.65 (978-0-613-33370-2(5)) Tandem Library Bks.

Orme, David. Speed. 2008. (Trailblazers Ser.). (Illus.). 36p. pap. 7.95 (***978-1-84167-647-0(0)***) Ransom Publishing Ltd. GBR. *Dist:* International Publishers Marketing.

Parham, Jerrill. Thrills & Spills: Fast Sports. 2007. (Shockwave: the Human Experience Ser.). 36p. (J). pap. 6.95 (***978-0-531-18796-8(9)***); (Illus.). (gr. 4-6). lib. bdg. 25.00 (***978-0-531-17762-4(9)***) Scholastic Library Publishing. (Children's Pr.).

Roza, Greg. Severe Storms: Measuring Velocity. 2006. (Math for the Real World Ser.). (Illus.). 32p. pap. (978-1-4042-6085-6(4)); lib. bdg. (978-1-4042-3366-9(0)) Rosen Publishing Group, Inc., The.

Rubin, Alan. Fast & Faster. 2003. (Yellow Umbrella Books). (Illus.). 16p. (J). (gr. 1). lib. bdg. 14.60 (978-0-7368-2018-9(3) , Pebble Bks.) Capstone Pr., Inc.

—Fast & Faster! 2003. (J). (978-0-7368-1710-3(7)) Yellow Umbrella Pr.

Schuh, Mari C. Full Speed Ahead: The Science of Going Fast. (Shockwave: Earth & Physical Science Ser.). (J). 2008. 32p. pap. 6.95 (***978-0-531-18835-4(3)***); 2007. (Illus.). 36p. (gr. 4-6). lib. bdg. 25.00 (***978-0-531-17792-1(0)***) Scholastic Library Publishing. (Children's Pr.).

Spilsbury, Richard. Speed & Acceleration. 2006. (Fantastic Forces Ser.). (Illus.). 32p. (J). pap. (978-1-4034-8178-8(4)); lib. bdg. (978-1-4034-8173-3(3)) Heinemann Library.

Starke, John. Speed Machines: Mission Xtreme 3D. 2004. (Mission Xtreme 3D Ser.). (Illus.). 18p. (J). pap. 5.95 (978-1-902626-50-5(8)) Red Bird Publishing GBR. *Dist:* Weatherhill, Inc.

Sullivan, Navin. Speed. 2006. (Measure Up! Ser.). (Illus.). 48p. (J). (gr. 4-7). lib. bdg. 29.93 (978-0-7614-2325-6(7) , Benchmark Bks.) Cavendish, Marshall Corp.

VanVoorst, Jennifer. Rapido y mas Rapido. 2005. Tr. of Fast & Faster!. (SPA., Illus.). 16p. (J). (gr. 1 up). lib. bdg. 15.93 (978-0-7368-4135-1(0)) Capstone Pr., Inc.

Villard, Raymond. Trenes de Alta Velocidad: Por Dentro y por Fuera. 2002. (Tecnología Ser.). (SPA.). 48p. (YA). lib. bdg. 26.50 (978-0-8239-6155-9(9) , Buenas Letras) Rosen Publishing Group, Inc., The.

What Is Fast?, 6 Packs. (gr. 1-2). 22.00 (978-0-7635-9104-5(1)) Rigby Education.

Willis, Shirley. Dime Que Tan Rapidamente Va. 2000. (Los Estupendos Whiz Kids, Spanish Edition Ser.). (SPA., Illus.). 32p. (J). (gr. 1-3). pap. 5.95 (978-0-531-15993-4(0) , OD30044, Watts, Franklin) Scholastic Library Publishing.

—Dime Que Tan Rapidamente Va. 2000. (gr. k-3). (SPA.). lib. bdg. 14.10 (978-0-613-72673-3(1)); (J). 12.75 (978-0-606-20154-4(8)) Tandem Library Bks.

—Tell Me How Fast It Goes. 2000. (Whiz Kids Ser.). (Illus.). 32p. (J). (gr. 1-3). pap. 5.95 (978-0-531-15976-7(0) , Watts, Franklin) Scholastic Library Publishing.

Woodford, Chris. Speed. 2005. (J). 11.20 (978-1-4103-0526-8(0)); 32p. (gr. 2-5). 23.70 (978-1-4103-0370-7(5)) Thomson Gale. (Blackbirch Pr., Inc.).

SPEED, SUPERSONIC

see Aerodynamics, Supersonic

SPELEOLOGY

see Caves

SPELLERS

Campbell, Rod. I Can Spell! With Consonants B C D F G H. 2000. (Illus.). 24p. (J). (ps-k). pap. (978-1-85292-172-9(2) , Campbell Bks.) Pan Macmillan.

—I Can Spell! With Consonants R S T V W Z. 2000. (Illus.). 24p. (J). (ps-k). pap. (978-1-85292-174-3(9) , Campbell Bks.) Pan Macmillan.

—I Can Spell! With Vowels A E I O U. 2000. (Illus.). 24p. (J). (ps-k). pap. (978-1-85292-171-2(4) , Campbell Bks.) Pan Macmillan.

Siede Preis Photography (Firm) Staff & Brian Warling Photography (Firm) Staff, contrib. by. First Words. 2003. (Lift-A-Flap Ser.). (Illus.). 12p. (J). bds. 12.98 (978-0-7853-8624-7(6) , 7188400) Publications International, Ltd.

—I Can Spell. 2003. (Lift-A-Flap Ser.). (Illus.). 12p. (J). bds. (978-0-7853-8238-6(0) , 7190100) Publications International, Ltd.

—Phonics for Fun. 2003. (Lift-A-Flap Ser.). (Illus.). 12p. (J). bds. (978-0-7853-8623-0(8) , 7188300) Publications International, Ltd.

SPELLING

see names of languages with the subdivision Spelling, e.g. English Language—Spelling

American Education Publishing, Inc. Staff & Barr, Linda. Spelling & Writing: Grade 6. 2003. (Brighter Child Workbooks Ser.). (Illus.). 24p. (J). (gr. 6). pap. 2.25 (978-1-56189-136-8(3) , American Education Publishing) School Specialty Publishing.

Barbaresi, Nina. Spelling Fun. 1998. (Illus.). 32p. (J). pap. 1.00 (978-0-486-40044-0(1)) Dover Pubns., Inc.

The Battle of Bowling Street: Level 4, 6 vols. (Fluency Strand Ser.). (gr. 4-8). 45.00 (978-1-4045-1224-5(1)) Wright Group, The.

Blanton, Lynne & Foss, Flora. Spelling Made Easy. 2005. (Learning Made Easy Ser.). (Illus.). 128p. (J). per. (978-0-7853-8845-6(1) , 7192200) Publications International, Ltd.

Buckton, Chris & Corbett, Pie. Searchlights for Spelling Year 3. 2002. (Searchlights for Spelling Ser.). (Illus.). 48p. (J). pap., stu. ed. 9.00 (978-0-521-89169-1(8)) Cambridge Univ. Pr.

—Searchlights for Spelling Year 6. 2002. (Searchlights for Spelling Ser.). (Illus.). 48p. pap., stu. ed. 9.00 (978-0-521-89172-1(8)) Cambridge Univ. Pr.

Carter, Cathy. My Junior Spelling Journal. 2000. 72p. pap. 7.95 (978-1-58324-069-4(1) , World Teachers Pr.) Didax Educational Resources, Inc.

Cunningham, Patricia M. Making More Words: Multilevel, Hands-on Phonics & Spelling Activities. 2001. (Illus.). 208p. (J). (gr. 1-3). pap. 18.99 (978-1-56417-900-5(1) , GA1588) Schaffer, Frank Pubns.

Dalmatian Press Staff. Spelling 2. 2003. (Tools Ser.). 32p. (J). (gr. 2 up). pap. 2.29 (978-1-4037-0213-5(6)) Dalmatian Pr.

—Spelling 3. 2003. (Tools Ser.). 32p. (J). (gr. 2-3). pap. 2.29 (978-1-4037-0214-2(4)) Dalmatian Pr.

Diaz-Cubero, Jose H. Practicas de Ortografia: 6 Grado. (SPA & ENG.). (J). (gr. 6). 9.95 (978-84-357-0124-2(7) , CPR94) Ediciones y Distribuciones Codice, S.A. ESP. *Dist:* Continental Bk. Co., Inc.

Douglas, Vincent & School Specialty Publishing Staff. Spectrum Spelling, Grade 1. 2002. (Starburst Spectrum Workbook Ser.). (Illus.). 150p. (J). (gr. 1-1). pap. 8.95 (978-1-56189-921-0(6) , American Education Publishing) School Specialty Publishing.

—Spectrum Spelling, Grade 2. 2002. (Starburst Spectrum Ser.). (Illus.). 150p. (J). (gr. 2-2). pap. 8.95 (978-1-56189-922-7(4) , American Education Publishing) School Specialty Publishing.

—Spectrum Spelling, Grade 4. 2002. (Starburst Spectrum Ser.). (Illus.). 150p. (J). (gr. 4-4). pap. 8.95 (978-1-56189-924-1(0) , American Education Publishing) School Specialty Publishing.

—Spectrum Spelling, Grade 5. 2002. (Starburst Spectrum Workbook Ser.). (Illus.). 150p. (J). (gr. 5-5). pap. 8.95 (978-1-56189-925-8(9) , American Education Publishing) School Specialty Publishing.

—Spectrum Spelling, Grade 6. 2002. (Starburst Spectrum Workbook Ser.). (Illus.). 150p. (J). (gr. 6-6). pap. 8.95 (978-1-56189-926-5(7) , American Education Publishing) School Specialty Publishing.

—Theme-Based Phonics, Grade 1. 2003. (100+ Ser.). (Illus.). 128p. (J). (gr. 1-1). pap. 14.99 (978-0-7424-1911-7(8) , IFG99104, Instructional Fair) Schaffer, Frank Pubns.

—Theme-Based Phonics, Grade 2. 2003. (100+ Ser.). (Illus.). 128p. (J). (gr. 2-2). pap. 14.99 (978-0-7424-1912-4(6) , IFG99105, Instructional Fair) Schaffer, Frank Pubns.

Dr Awkward: Level 6, 6 vols. (Fluency Strand Ser.). (gr. 4-8). 45.00 (978-1-4045-1239-9(X)) Wright Group, The.

Fry. Spelling Book. 2004. (Spelling Ser.). (Illus.). 48p. (J). (gr. 1-2). 7.99 (978-1-57690-751-1(1)); (gr. 2-3). 7.99 (978-1-57690-752-8(X)); (gr. 3-4). 7.99 (978-1-57690-753-5(8)); (gr. 4-5). 7.99 (978-1-57690-754-2(6)); (gr. 5-6). 7.99 (978-1-57690-755-9(4)) Teacher Created Materials, Inc.

Gidgup, Sue. My Spelling Journal. 2000. 80p. pap. 8.95 (978-1-58324-068-7(3) , World Teachers Pr.) Didax Educational Resources, Inc.

Glassman, Jackie. Play with Your Words: A Spelling Adventure. 2001. (Boggle Jr. Ser.). 32p. (J). pap. 3.99 (978-0-439-31793-1(2)) Scholastic, Inc.

Greenberg, Dan. More Proofreading Practice, Please! Grade 4. 2003. (Funnybone Bks.). 48p. (ps-1). pap. 10.95 (978-0-439-18840-1(7) , Teaching Resources) Scholastic, Inc.

—More Proofreading Practice, Please! Grade 5. 2003. (Funnybone Bks.). 48p. (ps-1). pap. 10.95 (978-0-439-18841-8(5) , Teaching Resources) Scholastic, Inc.

Harcourt School Publishers Staff. Harcourt Brace Spelling. 1998. (Harcourt Brace Spelling Ser.). (Illus.). (gr. 2). pupil's gde. ed. 36.70 (978-0-15-313644-3(8)); (gr. 3). pupil's gde. ed. 36.70 (978-0-15-313645-0(6)); (gr. 4). pupil's gde. ed. 36.70 (978-0-15-313646-7(4)); (gr. 6). pupil's gde. ed. 36.70 (978-0-15-313649-8(9)) Harcourt Schl. Pubs.

—Harcourt Brace Spelling: Consumable Edition. (Harcourt Brace Spelling Ser.). (Illus.). 1999. (gr. 3). pap., pupil's gde. ed. 18.70 (978-0-15-313652-8(9)); 1998. (gr. 1). pap., pupil's gde. ed. 17.40 (978-0-15-313650-4(2)); 1998. (gr. 2). pap., pupil's gde. ed. 18.70 (978-0-15-313651-1(0)); 1998. (gr. 4). pap., pupil's gde. ed. 18.70 (978-0-15-313653-5(7)); 1998. (gr. 5). pap., pupil's gde. ed. 18.70 (978-0-15-313654-2(5)); 1998. (gr. 6). pap., pupil's gde. ed. 18.70 (978-0-15-313656-6(1)) Harcourt Schl. Pubs.

—Vamos de Fiesta, Grade 2: Spelling Practice. 1999. (SPA.). pap., tchr. ed. 18.80 (978-0-15-316140-7(X)) Harcourt Schl. Pubs.

—Vamos de Fiesta, Grade 3: Spelling Practice. 1999. (SPA.). pap., tchr. ed. 18.80 (978-0-15-316147-6(7)) Harcourt Schl. Pubs.

Heinrichs, Ann. Spelling Rules. 2005. (Magic of Language Ser.). (Illus.). 32p. (J). (gr. 1-5). 27.07 (978-1-59296-435-2(4)) Child's World, Inc.

Heley, John. Spelling Practice. 1999. (Illus.). 30p. (J). (gr. 2-6). Bk. 1. pap. 22.00 (978-0-7217-0379-4(8)); Bk. 2. pap. 22.00 (978-0-7217-0380-0(1)); Bk. 4. pap. 22.00 (978-0-7217-0382-4(8)) Schofield & Sims Ltd. GBR. *Dist:* State Mutual Bk. & Periodical Service, Ltd.

Herbold, Marvin. Marvin Teaches Fingerspelling. 2003. (YA). cd-rom 19.95 (978-0-9752933-3-1(8)) Institute for Disabilities Research & Training, Inc.

Hoffman, Joan. Spelling Puzzles 3-4. 2001. (Teacher Edition Wkbks.). (Illus.). 32p. (J). (gr. 3-4). pap., tchr. ed. 3.99 (978-0-88743-481-5(9) , 02869) School Zone Publishing Co.

Holt, Rinehart and Winston Staff. Elements of Language: Spelling - Grade 6. 2003. (Elements of Language Ser.). 13.86 (978-0-03-056326-3(7)) Holt, Rinehart & Winston.

—Elements of Language: Spelling - Grade 7. 2000. pap., tchr. ed. 13.86 (978-0-03-063998-2(0)); pap. 13.86 (978-0-03-056327-0(5)) Holt, Rinehart & Winston.

—Elements of Language: Spelling - Grade 8. 2000. pap. 13.86 (978-0-03-056328-7(3)) Holt, Rinehart & Winston.

—Elements of Language: Spelling & Decoding Worksheets. 1999. pap. 13.86 (978-0-03-052463-9(6)); pap. 13.86 (978-0-03-052464-6(4)) Holt, Rinehart & Winston.

Hop, L. L. C. Hooked on First-Grade Super Workbook. 2006. 320p. 12.99 (978-1-931020-74-9(4)) HOP, LLC.

HOP, LLC. Hooked on Spelling. 2006. 99.99 (978-1-933863-98-6(6)); 64.99 (978-1-60143-000-7(0)); 24.99 (978-1-60143-001-4(9)) HOP, LLC.

Housel, Debra J. Spelling Grade 2. 2003. (Practice Makes Perfect Ser.). (Illus.). 48p. (gr. 2). pap. 4.99 (978-0-7439-3772-6(4)) Teacher Created Materials, Inc.

Josephina, M., et al. Word Power Through Spelling, 7 vols., Set. 1999. (Illus.). (J). (gr. 3-9). 75.00 (978-0-911845-89-1(5)) Neumann Pr., The.

The Language of Literature: Vocabulary & Spelling Book. 2001. (gr. 7 up). (978-0-618-13668-1(1) , 2-04032) McDougal Littell Inc.

The Language of Literature: Vocabulary & Spelling Book Answer Key. 2001. (gr. 7 up). (978-0-618-15371-8(3) , 2-04128) McDougal Littell Inc.

Learning Company Books Staff, ed. Reader Rabbit Spelling Challenge. 2004. (Illus.). 64p. (J). (gr. 1 up). pap. 6.99 (978-0-7630-7740-2(2)); (gr. 2 up). pap. 6.99 (978-0-7630-7741-9(0)) Learning Co. Bks.

Lessie, Par. How to Spell Homophones. Kelly, Walter, ed. Bauer, Larry, illus. 1999. (How to Ser.). 48p. (J). (gr. 3-5). pap., act. bk. ed. 7.99 (978-1-57690-499-2(7) , TCA2499) Teacher Created Materials, Inc.

Maher, Kristina Arcuri. Weekly Word Sorts That Build Spelling Skills: Easy Week-by-Week Reproducibles & Activities That Teach Kids the Key Spelling Rules & Patterns They Need to Become Effective Spellers. 2003. (Illus.). 64p. pap. 11.99 (978-0-439-21615-9(X) , Teaching Resources) Scholastic, Inc.

Marcel Meringue: Level 2, 6 vols. (Fluency Strand Ser.). (gr. 4-8). 45.00 (978-1-4045-1212-2(8)) Wright Group, The.

Mayer, Mercer, illus. Spelling: Grade 1. 2001. (Spectrum Spelling Ser.). 160p. (J). (gr. 1-1). pap., wbk. ed. 8.95 (978-1-57768-831-0(7) , Spectrum) School Specialty Publishing.

—Spelling: Grade K. 2001. (Spectrum Spelling Ser.). 144p. (J). (gr. k-k). pap., wbk. ed. 8.95 (978-1-57768-830-3(9) , Spectrum) School Specialty Publishing.

—Spelling & Writing: Grade 2. 2001. (Spectrum Spelling Ser.). 160p. (J). (gr. 2-2). pap., wbk. ed. 8.95 (978-1-57768-832-7(5) , Spectrum) School Specialty Publishing.

McGraw-Hill Staff. Spelling: Grades 1-3. 1999. (J). pap. 19.95 (978-1-57768-300-1(5)) School Specialty Publishing.

McGraw-Hill Staff, et al. Spectrum Spelling, Grade 3. 2002. (Starburst Spectrum Workbook Ser.). (Illus.). 150p. (J). (gr. 3-3). pap., wbk. ed. 8.95 (978-1-56189-923-4(2) , American Education Publishing) School Specialty Publishing.

Moats, Louisa & Rosow, Bruce. Spellography: A Student Road Map to Better Spelling: Student Lesson Book A. 2002. (Illus.). 128p. (J). per. (978-1-57035-604-9(1) , 166STUDA) Sopris West Educational Services.

—Spellography: A Student Road Map to Better Spelling: Student Lesson Book B. 2002. (Illus.). 152p. (J). per. (978-1-57035-605-6(X) , 166STUDB) Sopris West Educational Services.

—Spellography: A Student Road Map to Better Spelling: Student Lesson Book C. 2002. (Illus.). 136p. (J). per. (978-1-57035-606-3(8) , 166STUDC) Sopris West Educational Services.

More Spelling. 2004. (Help with Homework Ser.). 32p. (J). (gr. 1-4). wbk. ed. 3.99 (978-1-904586-27-2(9)) Byeway Bks.

Night Mare Trip: Level 5, 6 vols. (Fluency Strand Ser.). (gr. 4-8). 45.00 (978-1-4045-1230-6(6)) Wright Group, The.

Olo: Level 6, 6 vols. (Fluency Strand Ser.). (gr. 4-8). 45.00 (978-1-4045-1237-5(3)) Wright Group, The.

Once, Twice, Boom: Level 7, 6 vols. (Fluency Strand Ser.). (gr. 4-8). 45.00 (978-1-4045-1240-5(3)) Wright Group, The.

Parker, Victoria. Improve Your Spelling. 2001. (Better English Ser.). 32p. (YA). (gr. 5 up). lib. bdg. 14.95 (978-1-58086-327-8(2)); (Illus.). pap. 6.95 (978-0-7460-4239-7(6)) EDC Publishing.

—Improve Your Spelling - Internet Linked. 2004. (Better English Ser.). 32p. (J). pap. 6.95 (978-0-7945-0878-4(2) , Usborne) EDC Publishing.

Pennington, Mark. Better Spelling in 5 Minutes a Day: Fun Spelling Activities for Kids & Parents on the Go. 4th ed. 2001: (Five Minutes a Day Ser.). (Illus.). 144p. (J). pap. 10.99 (978-0-7615-2430-4(4) , Three Rivers Pr.) Crown Publishing Group.

Pulse- Fun with Vocabulary & Spelling. 2006. cd-rom 4.99 (***978-1-60245-041-7(2)***) GDL Multimedia, LLC.

Rainbow Bridge Publishing Staff. Spelling Practice Second Grade: Skill Builders. 2002. (Skill Builders Ser.). (Illus.). 64p. (gr. 2 up). 2.49 (978-1-887923-44-6(6)) Rainbow Bridge Publishing.

Rechtschreibung und Wortkunde. (Duden-Schuelerduden Ser.). (GER.). 384p. (YA). (gr. 4 up). pap. (978-3-411-05175-5(2)) Bibliographisches Institut & F. A. Brockhaus AG DEU. *Dist:* International Bk. Import Service, Inc.

Rieder, E. & Toth, M. Das ABC-Haus: Arbeitsheft 1. (Illus.). 64p. pap. (978-3-12-675645-7(X)) Klett, Ernst, Verlag GmbH DEU. *Dist:* International Bk. Import Service, Inc.

—Das ABC-Haus: Arbeitsheft 2. (Illus.). 64p. pap. (978-3-12-675648-8(4)) Klett, Ernst, Verlag GmbH DEU. *Dist:* International Bk. Import Service, Inc.

—Das ABC-Haus: Schuelerbuch. (Illus.). 96p. (J). pap. (978-3-12-675644-0(1)) Klett, Ernst, Verlag GmbH DEU. *Dist:* International Bk. Import Service, Inc.

Rigby. Spelling Puzzlers. (Illus.). (J). 2002. (gr. 3). pap. (978-0-7578-2419-7(6)); 2001. (gr. 1). pap. (978-0-7635-7343-0(4)); 2001. (gr. 2). pap. (978-0-7635-7753-7(7)) Steck-Vaughn.

—Successful Spelling Strategies. 2001. pap. (978-0-7635-7923-4(8)) Steck-Vaughn.

Sanseri, Wanda. Spelling Rule Cards: Large. 2002. (J). pap. 12.95 (978-1-880045-29-9(X)) Back Home Industries.

—Spelling Rule Cards: Small. 2002. (J). pap. 7.95 (978-1-880045-23-7(0)) Back Home Industries.

School Zone Publishing. Spelling Puzzles. 2003. (Language Arts Ser.). cd-rom 19.99 (978-1-58947-914-2(9)) School Zone Publishing Co.

Schwartz, Linda. Conquer Spelling: Word Lists, Roles, & Activities to Help Kids Become Spelling Heros. Scott, Kelly, ed. Armstrong, Beverly & Grayson, Rick, illus. 2003. 112p. (J). pap. 13.99 (978-0-88160-362-0(7) , LW-420, Learning Works, The) Creative Teaching Pr., Inc.

Slater, Teddy. N-O Es No! Johnson, Meredith, illus. 2003. (Coleccion "Hola, Lector" Ser.). (SPA.). 32p. (J). (gr. k-2). pap. 3.99 (978-0-439-05402-7(8) , SO6009) Scholastic, Inc.

Spelling & Vocabulary, Set. 2004. (gr. 2). 38.95 (978-0-7403-0219-0(1) , Horizons) Alpha Omega Pubns., Inc.

Spelling Grade 1. 2003. (Practice Makes Perfect Ser.). 48p. (J). (gr. 1). pap. 4.99 (978-0-7439-3771-9(6)) Teacher Created Materials, Inc.

Spelling Grade 3. 2003. (Practice Makes Perfect Ser.). 48p. (J). (gr. 3). pap. 4.99 (978-0-7439-3773-3(2)) Teacher Created Materials, Inc.

Spelling Workout. (J). Bk. A. 3rd ed. (gr. 1). 11.95 net. (978-0-8136-2815-8(6)); Bk. F. 3rd ed. (gr. 6). 11.95 net. (978-0-8136-2820-2(2)); Bk. G. 3rd ed. (gr. 7). 11.95 net. (978-0-8136-2821-9(0)); Bk. H. 3rd ed. (gr. 8). 11.95 net. (978-0-8136-2822-6(9)); Bk. H. 3rd ed. (gr. 8). 12.50 net. (978-0-8136-2847-9(4)); Rev. B. (gr. 2). (978-0-8136-2808-0(3)) Modern Curriculum Pr.

Steck-Vaughn Staff. Steck-Vaughn Spelling Book: Level 3. 2001. (J). pap., stu. ed. 19.90 (978-0-7398-5055-8(5)) Steck-Vaughn.

—Steck-Vaughn Spelling Book: Level 4. 2001. (J). pap., stu. ed. 19.90 (978-0-7398-5056-5(3)) Steck-Vaughn.

—Steck-Vaughn Spelling Book: Level 5. 2001. (J). pap., stu. ed. 19.90 (978-0-7398-5057-2(1)) Steck-Vaughn.

—Steck-Vaughn Spelling Book: Level 6. 2001. (J). pap., stu. ed. 19.90 (978-0-7398-5058-9(X)) Steck-Vaughn.

—Vocabulary Usage & Spelling Core Skills. 2001. pap. (978-0-7398-4902-6(6)) Steck-Vaughn.

Terror Bear Canyon: Level 5, 6 vols. (Fluency Strand Ser.). (gr. 4-8). 45.00 (978-1-4045-1225-2(X)) Wright Group, The.

Timeless Voices, Timeless Themes: The American Experience, Vocabulary & Spelling Practice Book. 2000. (YA). (gr. 11). pap. 6.97 (978-0-13-437579-3(3)) Prentice Hall PTR.

Timeless Voices, Timeless Themes: The British Tradition, Vocabulary & Spelling Practice Book. 2000. (YA). (gr. 12). pap. 6.97 (978-0-13-437582-3(3)) Prentice Hall PTR.

To Catch a Thief: Level 3, 6 vols. (Fluency Strand Ser.). (gr. 4-8). 45.00 (978-1-4045-1219-1(5)) Wright Group, The.

Trocki, Phillip. Spelling Workout. rev. ed. 2003. (Illus.). Level C. (J). (gr. 3). tchr. ed. 10.50 (978-0-7652-2490-3(9)); Level C. (J). (gr. 3). stu. ed. 9.95 (978-0-7652-2482-8(8)); Level D. (J). (gr. 4). stu. ed. 9.95 (978-0-7652-2483-5(6)); Level A. (J). (gr. 1). tchr. ed. 10.50 (978-0-7652-2488-0(7)); Level B. (J). (gr. 2). tchr. ed. 10.50 (978-0-7652-2489-7(5)); Level B. (J). (gr. 2). stu. ed. 9.95 (978-0-7652-2481-1(X)); Level E. (J). (gr. 5). stu. ed. 9.95 (978-0-7652-2484-2(4)); Level F. (J). (gr. 6). stu. ed. 9.95 (978-0-7652-2485-9(2)); Level G. (YA). (gr. 7). stu. ed. 9.95 (978-0-7652-2486-6(0)); Level H. (YA). (gr. 8). stu. ed. 9.95 (978-0-7652-2487-3(9)) Modern Curriculum Pr.

Turrell, Linda. Mastering Spelling Skills Student Activities Book: Mastering Language Arts Series. Matthews, Douglas L., ed. 2003. (Illus.). stu. ed., wbk. ed. (978-1-931680-69-1(8) , Expert Systems for Teachers) Teaching Point, Inc.

Unccor: Level 5, 6 vols. (Fluency Strand Ser.). (gr. 4-8). 45.00 (978-1-4045-1231-3(4)) Wright Group, The.

Vinopol, Corinne. Spell Well: CD-ROM American Sign Language Spelling Game. 2003. (YA). cd-rom 19.95 (978-0-9752933-0-0(3)) Institute for Disabilities Research & Training, Inc.

Zone Zoomers: Level 2, 6 vols. (Fluency Strand Ser.). (gr. 4-8). 45.00 (978-1-4045-1213-9(6)) Wright Group, The.

SPELLS

see Charms

SPHERICAL TRIGONOMETRY

see Trigonometry

SPICES

Lilly, Melinda. Spices. 2001. (Around the World with Food & Spices Ser.). (Illus.). 32p. (J). (gr. 3-5). lib. bdg. 26.60 (978-1-58952-049-3(1)) Rourke Publishing, LLC.

Raab, Brigitte. And Where Does Pepper Come From? 2006. (Illus.). 32p. (J). 15.95 (978-0-7358-2070-8(8)) North-South Bks., Inc.

Rodger, Ellen. The Biography of Spices. 2005. (How Did That Get Here? Ser.). (Illus.). 32p. (J). (gr. 3-9). (978-0-7787-2484-1(0)); pap. (978-0-7787-2520-6(0)) Crabtree Publishing Co.

Wells, Donald. The Spice Trade. 2004. (Great Journeys Ser.). (Illus.). 32p. (J). lib. bdg. 26.00 (978-1-59036-208-2(X)) Weigl Pubs., Inc.

SPIDER-MAN (FICTITIOUS CHARACTER)—FICTION

Andrews, Kaare. Spider-Man Legend of the Spider-Clan, 3 vols. Young, Skott, illus. 2003. (Mangaverse Ser.: Vol. 3). 128p. (YA). pap. 11.99 (978-0-7851-1114-6(X)) Marvel Enterprises, Inc.

Aptekar, Devan. Webslinger! Mada Design Staff, illus. 2004. (Spider Man Ser.). 32p. (J). 4.99 (978-0-439-35452-3(8) , Scholastic Paperbacks) Scholastic, Inc.

Avery, Fiona & Brooks, Mark. Arana: The Heart of the Spider. 2005. (Spider-Man Ser.). (Illus.). 144p. pap. 7.99 (978-0-7851-1506-9(4)) Marvel Enterprises, Inc.

Bagley, Mark, illus. Ultimate Spider-Man: Double Trouble. 2002. (Ultimate Spider-Man Ser.). 27.19 (978-1-4046-2382-8(5)) Book Wholesalers, Inc.

—Ultimate Spider-Man: Learning Curve. 2002. 21.09 (978-1-4046-2220-3(9)) Book Wholesalers, Inc.

—Ultimate Spider-Man: Legacy. 2002. (Ultimate Spider-Man Ser.). 20.83 (978-1-4046-2353-8(1)) Book Wholesalers, Inc.

—Ultimate Spider-Man: Power & Responsibility. 2002. (YA). 23.04 (978-1-4046-0900-6(8)) Book Wholesalers, Inc.

Bendis, Brian Michael. Carnage. Bagley, Mark, illus. 2004. 100p. lib. bdg. 24.35 (978-1-4176-6038-4(4)) Tandem Library Bks.

—Cats & Kings. Bagley, Mark, illus. 2004. 184p. lib. bdg. 30.15 (978-1-4176-6035-3(X)) Tandem Library Bks.

—Irresponsible, 8 vols., Vol. 7. Bagley, Mark, illus. 2003. (Ultimate Spider-man Ser.). 144p. (J). pap. 12.99 (978-0-7851-1092-7(5)) Marvel Enterprises, Inc.

—Public Scrutiny, 5, Vol. 5. Bagley, Mark, illus. 2003. (Ultimate Spider-man Ser.). 128p. (J). pap. 11.99 (978-0-7851-1087-3(9)) Marvel Enterprises, Inc.

—Ultimate Spider-Man, 2 vols., Vol. 2. Bagley, Mark, illus. 2003. (Ultimate Spider-man Ser.). 336p. 29.99 (978-0-7851-1061-3(5)) Marvel Enterprises, Inc.

Bendis, Brian Michael & Bagley, Mark. Ultimate Spider-Man Vol. 11: Carnage. 2004. (Spider-Man Ser.). (Illus.). 144p. pap. 12.99 (978-0-7851-1403-1(3)) Marvel Enterprises, Inc.

Buckley, James, Jr. Los Asombrosos Poderes de Spider-Man. O'Neill, Cynthia, ed. 2005. (Dk Readers Ser.). (Illus.). 48p. (J). (ps-7). 14.99 (978-0-7566-1500-0(3)) Dorling Kindersley Publishing, Inc.

Buckley, James. Los Asombrosos Poderes de Spider-Man. O'Neill, Cynthia, ed. 2005. (Dk Readers Ser.). (Illus.). 48p. (J). (ps-7). pap. 3.99 (978-0-7566-1499-7(6)) Dorling Kindersley Publishing, Inc.

Castro, Adam Troy. Spider-Man: The Secret of the Sinister Six. 2002. (Illus.). 448p. (978-0-7434-4464-4(7)) ibooks, Inc.

Cooke, Darwyn, et al. Spider-Man's Tangled Web, 4 vols., Vol. 4. Cooke, Darwyn et al, illus. 2003. (Spider-Man's Tangled Web Ser.). 176p. (YA). 15.99 (978-0-7851-1064-4(X)) Marvel Enterprises, Inc.

Curry, Don, ed. Spider-Man 3: Deluxe Sound Storybook. 2007. 22p. (J). 15.95 (978-0-696-23409-5(2)) Meredith Bks.

Curry, Don, ed. Spider-Man 3 Board Game Book. 2007. 10p. (J). bds. 12.99 (***978-0-696-23411-8(4)***) Meredith Bks.

David, Erica. Prison Break. 2007. 21.35 (978-1-59961-214-0(3)) Spotlight.

—Sinister Six. 2007. 21.35 (978-1-59961-216-4(X)) Spotlight.

David, Peter. Spider-Man. 2002. 311p. (gr. 3-6). per. 15.30 (978-0-613-51042-4(9)) Tandem Library Bks.

Davis, Alan. Killraven. Davis, Alan, illus. 2003. (Spider-Man Ser.). (Illus.). 144p. (YA). pap. 16.99 (978-0-7851-1083-5(6)) Marvel Enterprises, Inc.

DeFalco, Tom. Bedeviled. 2006. (Illus.). (J). (gr. 2-6). 21.35 (978-1-59961-027-6(2)) Spotlight.

DeFalco, Tom & Reader's Digest Staff. Marvel Heroes the Battle Unfolds Fold-Out Flap Book. 2007. 10p. (J). 12.99 (***978-0-7944-1306-4(4)***) Reader's Digest Assn., Inc., The.

DeMatteis, J. M., et al. Son of the Goblin. 2004. (Spider-Man Ser.). (Illus.). 144p. (YA). 15.99 (978-0-7851-1563-2(3)) Marvel Enterprises, Inc.

Dezago, Todd. Captain America: Stars, Stripes, & Spiders! 2006. (Spider-Man Team up Ser.). (Illus.). (J). (gr. 2-6). 21.35 (978-1-59961-001-6(9)) Spotlight.

—Duel with Daredevil! 2006. (Illus.). (J). (gr. 2-6). 21.35 (978-1-59961-013-9(2)) Spotlight.

—Enforcers! 2006. (Illus.). (J). (gr. 2-6). 21.35 (978-1-59961-019-1(1)) Spotlight.

—Fantastic Four: The Chameleon Strikes! 2006. (Spider-Man Team up Ser.). (Illus.). (J). (gr. 2-6). 21.35 (978-1-59961-005-4(1)) Spotlight.

—Fantastic Four: The Menace of Monster Isle! 2006. (Spider-Man Team up Ser.). (Illus.). (J). (gr. 2-6). 21.35 (978-1-59961-006-1(X)) Spotlight.

—Man Called Electro! 2006. (Illus.). (J). (gr. 2-6). 21.35 (978-1-59961-021-4(3)) Spotlight.

—Spider-Man & the Terrible Threat of the Living Brain! 2006. (Illus.). (J). (gr. 2-6). 21.35 (978-1-59961-008-5(6)) Spotlight.

—Spidey Strikes Back! 2006. (Illus.). (J). (gr. 2-6). 21.35 (978-1-59961-017-7(5)) Spotlight.

—Storm: Change the Weather. 2006. (Spider-Man Team up Ser.). (Illus.). (J). (gr. 2-6). 21.35 (978-1-59961-003-0(5)) Spotlight.

—Thor: Out of Time! 2006. (Spider-Man Team up Ser.). (Illus.). (J). (gr. 2-6). 21.35 (978-1-59961-004-7(3)) Spotlight.

Dezago, Todd & Raicht, Mike. The Goblin Strikes Digest, Vol. 4. 2004. (Spider-Man Ser.: Vol. 4). (Illus.). 96p. 5.99 (978-0-7851-1549-6(8)) Marvel Enterprises, Inc.

—Spidey Strikes Back!, Vol. 5. 2005. (Spider-Man Ser.). (Illus.). 96p. pap. 5.99 (978-0-7851-1632-5(X)) Marvel Enterprises, Inc.

—Swingtime. 2004. (Spider-Man Ser.: Vol. 3). (Illus.). 96p. (YA). pap. 5.99 (978-0-7851-1548-9(X)) Marvel Enterprises, Inc.

DK Publishing Staff. Spider-Man: The Visual Guide to the Complete Movie Trilogy. 2007. 128p. (J). 19.99 (978-0-7566-2705-8(2)) Dorling Kindersley Publishing, Inc.

Dorling Kindersley Publishing Staff. Glow-in-the-Dark Spider-Man. 2006. (Ultimate Sticker Bks.). 16p. (J). pap. 6.99 (978-0-7566-1999-2(8)) Dorling Kindersley Publishing, Inc.

Egan, Kate. Spider-Man 2: Hands off, Doc Ock! Mones, Isidre et al, illus. 2004. (Spider-Man Ser.). 24p. (J). (ps-2). pap. 3.99 (978-0-06-057138-2(1) , Harper Festival) HarperCollins Pubs.

—Spider-Man 3: The Movie Storybook. 2007. (Spider-Man Ser.). 48p. (J). pap. 8.99 (978-0-06-083723-5(3) , Harper Entertainment) HarperCollins Pubs.

Figueroa, Acton. I Am Spider-Man. 2002. (Festival Reader Ser.). (Illus.). 32p. (J). (ps-2). pap. 3.99 (978-0-694-01644-0(6) , Harper Festival) HarperCollins Pubs.

—Spider-Man 2: Everyday Hero. Vasquez, Ivan & Redondo, Jesus, illus. movie tie-in ed. 2004. (Festival Reader Ser.). 32p. (J). (ps-2). pap. 3.99 (978-0-06-057363-8(5) , Harper Festival) HarperCollins Pubs.

—Spider-Man 2: Spider-Man Versus Doc Ock. Redondo, Jesus, illus. 2004. (Festival Reader Ser.). 32p. (J). (ps-2). pap. 3.99 (978-0-06-057364-5(3) , Harper Festival) HarperCollins Pubs.

—Spider-Man Saves the Day. Lim, Ron, illus. 2002. (Festival Reader Ser.). 32p. (J). (ps-2). pap. 3.99 (978-0-694-01645-7(4) , Harper Festival) HarperCollins Pubs.

—Spider-Man Saves the Day. 2002. (ps-2). lib. bdg. 11.80 (978-0-613-50503-1(4)) Tandem Library Bks.

Fingeroth, Danny. The New Goblin. 2007. (Spider-Man Ser.: No. 3). 64p. (J). pap. 4.99 (978-0-06-083724-2(1) , Harper Entertainment) HarperCollins Pubs.

Fross, Kitty. Here Comes Spider-Man. 2007. 21.35 (978-1-59961-210-2(0)) Spotlight.

Goldman, Leslie. Spider-Man: Spider Bite. 2002. (gr. 3-6). lib. bdg. 13.00 (978-0-613-50747-9(9)) Tandem Library Bks.

Hamilton, Tisha. Ahead by Thread. Mada Design Staff, illus. 2004. (Spider Man Ser.). 32p. (J). 4.99 (978-0-439-35676-3(8) , Scholastic Paperbacks) Scholastic, Inc.

Harper, Benjamin. Marvel Swinging into Action. 2007. 10p. (J). bds. 14.99 (978-0-7944-1228-9(9)) Reader's Digest Assn., Inc., The.

Jenkins, Paul. Here There Be the Monsters, Vol. 3. Scott, Damion, illus. 2004. (Spider-Man Ser.). 144p. (YA). 9.99 (978-0-7851-1333-1(9)) Marvel Enterprises, Inc.

—Trials & Tribulations, 4 vols., Vol. 4. Buckingham, Mark, illus. 2003. (Peter Parker, Spider-Man Ser.: Vol. 4). 128p. (YA). 11.99 (978-0-7851-1150-4(6)) Marvel Enterprises, Inc.

Kiefer, Kit. Spider-Man, 4 vols., Vol. 4. Youngquist, Jeff, ed. 2003. (Marvel Encyclopedia Ser.: Vol. 4). (Illus.). 240p. (YA). (gr. 7 up). 24.99 (978-0-7851-1304-1(5)) Marvel Enterprises, Inc.

Lime, Harry. Spider-Man 3: Meet the Heroes & Villains. Gordon, Steven E., illus. 2007. (I Can Read Bks.). 32p. (J). pap. 3.99 (978-0-06-083721-1(7) , Harper Trophy) HarperCollins Pubs.

—Spider-Man 3: Spider-Man Versus Sandman. Gordon, Steven, illus. 2007. (I Can Read Bks.). 32p. (J). pap. 3.99 (978-0-06-083722-8(5) , Harper Trophy) HarperCollins Pubs.

Loeb, Jeph. Blue. Sale, Tim, illus. 2003. (Spider-Man Ser.). 160p. (YA). 21.99 (978-0-7851-1062-0(3)) Marvel Enterprises, Inc.

McDonnell, David, ed. Spiderman & Other Amazing Heroes. 2004. (Starlog Movie Magic Ser.). (YA). pap. (978-0-88013-065-3(2)) Profile Entertainment, Inc.

McKeever, Sean. Doom with a View. 2007. 21.35 (978-1-59961-208-9(9)) Spotlight.

—Make Mine Mysterio. 2007. 21.35 (978-1-59961-211-9(9)) Spotlight.

—Picture-Perfect Peril. 2007. 21.35 (978-1-59961-212-6(7)) Spotlight.

—Power Struggle. 2007. 21.35 (978-1-59961-213-3(5)) Spotlight.

—Rush Hour. 2007. 21.35 (978-1-59961-215-7(1)) Spotlight.

—Vulture Hunt. 2007. 21.35 (978-1-59961-217-1(8)) Spotlight.

Meredith Books Staff & Marvel Comics Staff. Spider-Man Party Book. Dahlstrom, Carol, ed. 2004. (Illus.). 96p. (J). pap. 9.95 (978-0-696-21996-2(4)) Meredith Bks.

—Spider-Man Poster Book. Holcomb, Carrie, ed. 2004. (Illus.). 48p. (J). pap. 9.95 (978-0-696-21997-9(2)) Meredith Bks.

Ostrom, Bob, illus. Spider-Man 2: Hurry up, Spider-Man! 2004. (Spider-Man Ser.). 24p. (J). (ps-2). pap. 3.99 (978-0-06-057137-5(3) , Harper Festival) HarperCollins Pubs.

Papademetriou, Lisa & Jones, Jasmine. Spider-Man 3: The Junior Novel. 2007. (Spider-Man Ser.: Vol. 3). 144p. (J). pap. 4.99 (978-0-06-083725-9(X) , Harper Entertainment) HarperCollins Pubs.

Parker, Jeff. Goom Got Game. 2007. 21.35 (978-1-59961-209-6(7)) Spotlight.

Quantz, Daniel. Face-to-Face with the Lizard! 2006. (Illus.). (J). (gr. 2-6). 21.35 (978-1-59961-014-6(0)) Spotlight.

—Marked for Destruction by Dr. Doom! 2006. (Illus.). (J). (gr. 2-6). 21.35 (978-1-59961-015-3(9)) Spotlight.

—Nothing Can Stop the Sandman! 2006. (Illus.). (J). (gr. 2-6). 21.35 (978-1-59961-016-0(7)) Spotlight.

—Spider-Man versus Doctor Octopus. 2006. (Illus.). (J). (gr. 2-6). 21.35 (978-1-59961-011-5(6)) Spotlight.

—Unmasked by Doctor Octopus! 2006. (Illus.). (J). (gr. 2-6). 21.35 (978-1-59961-010-8(8)) Spotlight.

Raicht, Mike. Grotesque Adventure of the Green Goblin! 2006. (Illus.). (J). (gr. 2-6). 21.35 (978-1-59961-020-7(5)) Spotlight.

—Kraven the Hunter. 2006. (Illus.). (J). (gr. 2-6). 21.35 (978-1-59961-009-2(4)) Spotlight.

—Menace of Mysterio. 2006. (Illus.). (J). (gr. 2-6). 21.35 (978-1-59961-022-1(1)) Spotlight.

—Where Flies the Beetle... ! 2006. (Illus.). (J). (gr. 2-6). 21.35 (978-1-59961-023-8(X)) Spotlight.

Raymond, N. T. Spider-Man's New Suit. 2007. (Spider-Man Ser.: No. 3). 24p. (J). pap. 3.99 (978-0-06-083718-1(7) , Harper Entertainment) HarperCollins Pubs.

Raymond, N. T., et al, illus. I Am Venom. 2007. (Spider-Man Ser.: No. 3). 24p. (J). pap. 3.99 (978-0-06-083719-8(5) , Harper Entertainment) HarperCollins Pubs.

Redman, Rich. Spider-Man: Mysterio's Ways. rev. ed. 2000. (Marvel Super Heroes Adventures Ser.). (Illus.). 32p. pap. 4.95 (978-0-7869-1669-6(9)) Wizards of the Coast.

Repchuk, Caroline, ed. The Amazing Spiderman Pop-up. Marvel Comics Staff, illus. 2007. 16p. (J). (gr. k-12). 300.00 (978-0-7636-3267-0(8)) Candlewick Pr.

Richards, Kitty. Spider-Man: Your Friendly Neighborhood Spider-Man. 2002. (gr. 3-6). lib. bdg. 13.00 (978-0-613-50750-9(9)) Tandem Library Bks.

Saunders, Catherine. Spider-Man: The Amazing Story. 2006. (Dk Readers Ser.). (Illus.). (J). 1p. pap. 3.99 (978-0-7566-2025-7(2)); 32p. pap. 14.99 (978-0-7566-2026-4(0)) Dorling Kindersley Publishing, Inc.

—Spider-Man's Worst Enemies. 2006. (Dk Readers Ser.). (Illus.). 32p. (J). 14.99 (978-0-7566-2024-0(4)); pap. 3.99 (978-0-7566-2023-3(6)) Dorling Kindersley Publishing, Inc.

Seidman, David & Marvel Comics Staff. A Great Day. Curry, Don & Meredith Books Staff, eds. Stewart, Scott, illus. 2005. (Spider-Man Ser.). 24p. (J). pap. 3.99 (978-0-696-22515-4(8)) Meredith Bks.

—The Super Spider. Curry, Don & Meredith Books Staff, eds. De Martinis, Louie, illus. 2005. (Spider-Man Ser.). 24p. (J). pap. 3.99 (978-0-696-22516-1(6)) Meredith Bks.

Simone, Gail. Gus Beezer with Spider-Man. 2006. (Marvelous Adventures of Gus Beezer Ser.). (Illus.). (J). (gr. 2-6). 21.35 (978-1-59961-047-4(7)) Spotlight.

—Gus Beezer with Spider-Man: Along Came a Spidey! 2006. (Marvelous Adventures of Gus Beezer Ser.). (Illus.). (J). (gr. 2-6). 21.35 (978-1-59961-048-1(5)) Spotlight.

Spider-Man & Friends. 2003. (J). per. (978-1-57657-858-2(5)) Paradise Pr., Inc.

Stern. Spiderman. (Illus.). (J). mass mkt. (978-0-671-00093-6(4)); Vol. 2. mass mkt. (978-0-671-00087-5(X)) Simon & Schuster. (Pocket).

Stern, Roger. Spider-Man: Hobgoblin Lives. Frenz, Ron et al, illus. 1998. 112p. (YA). (gr. 5-12). pap. 14.95 (978-0-7851-0585-5(9)) Marvel Enterprises, Inc.

The Story of Spider-Man. 2003. (Dk Readers Ser.). (J). pap. 3.99 (978-0-7894-4703-6(7)) Dorling Kindersley Publishing, Inc.

Straczynski, J. Amazing Spiderman: Coming Home. 2001. (gr. 5-8). lib. bdg. 25.70 (978-0-613-60526-7(8)) Tandem Library Bks.

Straczynski, J. Michael. Amazing Spider-Man: The Life & Death of Spiders, 4 vols., Vol. 4. Romita, John, Jr., illus. 2003. (Amazing Spider-man Ser.). 120p. (YA). 11.99 (978-0-7851-1097-2(6)) Marvel Enterprises, Inc.

—Best of Spider-Man, Vol. 3. Youngquist, Jeff, ed. 2004. (Spider-Man Ser.). (Illus.). 368p. (YA). 29.99 (978-0-7851-1339-3(8)) Marvel Enterprises, Inc.

—Best of Spider-Man HC, Vol. 5. 2006. (Illus.). 240p. 29.99 (978-0-7851-2128-2(5)) Marvel Enterprises, Inc.

—The Book of Ezekiel, Vol. 7. Romita, John, Jr., illus. 2004. (Spider-Man Ser.). 144p. (YA). 12.99 (978-0-7851-1525-0(0)) Marvel Enterprises, Inc.

—Sins Past. Deodato, Mike, Jr., illus. 2005. (Spider-Man Ser.: Vol. 8). 144p. (YA). pap. 12.99 (978-0-7851-1509-0(9)) Marvel Enterprises, Inc.

—Until the Stars Turn Cold, Vol. 3. Romita, John, Jr., illus. 2002. 144p. (YA). (gr. 7). 12.99 (978-0-7851-1075-0(5)) Marvel Enterprises, Inc.

Straczynski, J. Michael & Jenkins, Paul. Best of Spider-Man, 2 vols., Vol. 2. annual Romita, John, Jr. & Ramos, Humberto, illus. 2003. (Spider-Man Ser.: Vol. 2). 368p. (YA). 29.99 (978-0-7851-1100-9(X)) Marvel Enterprises, Inc.

Teitelbaum, Michael. La Historia de Spider-Man. 2005. (Dk Readers Ser.). (Illus.). 48p. (J). (ps-7). pap. 3.99 (978-0-7566-1506-2(2)) Dorling Kindersley Publishing, Inc.

—Spider-Man. Mada Design Staff, illus. 2004. (Spider Man Ser.). 32p. (J). 3.99 (978-0-439-32953-8(1) , Scholastic Paperbacks) Scholastic, Inc.

—Spider-Man: Amazing Powers. 2001. lib. bdg. 11.80 (978-0-613-43958-9(9)) Tandem Library Bks.

Teitelbaum, Michael & O'Neill, Cynthia. La Historia de Spider-Man. 2005. (Dk Readers Ser.). (Illus.). 48p. (J). (ps-7). 14.99 (978-0-7566-1502-4(X)) Dorling Kindersley Publishing, Inc.

Van Lente, Fred. Breaking up Is Venomous to Do! 2007. (Spider-Man Set III Ser.). 24p. (J). (gr. 2-6). 21.35 ***978-1-59961-393-2(X))** Spotlight.

—Dust-up in Aisle Seven! 2007. (Spider-Man Set III Ser.). 24p. (J). (gr. 2-6). 21.35 ***978-1-59961-394-9(8))** Spotlight.

—Fasion Victims. 2007. (Spider-Man Set III Ser.). 24p. (J). (gr. 2-6). 21.35 ***978-1-59961-395-6(6))** Spotlight.

—World War G. 2007. (Spider-Man Set III Ser.). 24p. (J). (gr. 2-6). 21.35 ***978-1-59961-396-3(4))** Spotlight.

Wells, Zeb. Spider-Man/Doctor Octopus: Year One. Andrews, Kaare, illus. 2005. (Spider-Man Ser.). 120p. pap. 13.99 (978-0-7851-1532-8(3)) Marvel Enterprises, Inc.

Wizard Spiderman Masterpiece Edition, Vol. 11. 2004. 254p. 79.99 (978-0-9743253-6-1(8)) Wizard Entertainment.

SPIDERS

Abejas: Por Dentro y Por Fuera. 2004. (SPA., Illus.). 32p. lib. bdg. 21.25 (978-1-4042-2862-7(4)) Rosen Publishing Group, Inc., The.

Allen, Judy. Are You a Spider? 2003. (ps-2). lib. bdg. 12.95 (978-0-613-90776-7(0)) Tandem Library Bks.

—Are You a Spider? Humphries, Tudor, illus. 2003. (Backyard Bks.). 32p. (J). (ps up). pap. 5.95 (978-0-7534-5609-5(5) , Kingfisher) Houghton Mifflin Co. Trade & Reference Div.

Allman, Toney. From Spider Webs to Man-Made Silk. 2005. (Imitating Nature Ser.). (Illus.). 32p. (J). (ps-8). lib. bdg. 24.95 (978-0-7377-3124-8(9) , Greenhaven Pr., Inc.) Thomson Gale.

—Spiders. 2004. (Illus.). 48p. (J). (gr. 4-7). 26.20 (978-0-7377-2601-5(6) , Greenhaven Pr., Inc.) Thomson Gale.

Anastasio, Dina. Spiders. 2002. (Illus.). 16p. (J). pap. (978-0-439-35100-3(6)) Scholastic, Inc.

Anderson, Catherine. Daddylonglegs. 2003. (Bug Books). (Illus.). 32p. (J). lib. bdg. 22.79 (978-1-4034-0763-4(0)); pap. 6.50 (978-1-4034-0994-2(3)) Heinemann Library.

Animal Lives: Spiders. 2006. pap. 4.99 (978-1-4206-8162-8(1)) Teacher Created Materials, Inc.

Aranas: Por Dentro y Por Fuera. 2004. (SPA., Illus.). 32p. lib. bdg. 21.25 (978-1-4042-2867-2(5)) Rosen Publishing Group, Inc., The.

Las Aranas Tejen Telas. (SPA.). 32p. (J). (gr. 3-5). (978-84-241-1966-9(5)) Everest de Ediciones y Distribucion, S.L. ESP. *Dist:* Lectorum Pubns., Inc.

Bailey, Jill. Bug Dictionary: An A to Z of Insects & Creepy Crawlies. 2002. (Illus.). 64p. (J). 26.20 (978-1-56711-547-5(0) , Blackbirch Pr., Inc.) Thomson Gale.

Berger, Melvin. Do All Spiders Spin Webs? 2000. (gr. 3-6). lib. bdg. 14.10 (978-0-613-24865-5(1)) Tandem Library Bks.

—Do Spiders Spin Webs? 2000. (Question & Answer Ser.). (J). 12.75 (978-0-606-19553-9(X)) Tandem Library Bks.

—Do Tarantulas Have Teeth? 2000. (Question & Answer Ser.). (J). 12.75 (978-0-606-19554-6(8)) Tandem Library Bks.

—Spinning Spiders. Schindler, S. D., illus. 2003. (Let's-Read-&-Find-Out Science Bks.: Vol. 2). 40p. (J). (gr. k-4). lib. bdg. 16.89 (978-0-06-028697-2(0)) HarperCollins Pubs.

—Spinning Spiders. 2003. (gr. k-3). lib. bdg. 13.00 (978-0-613-66670-1(4)) Tandem Library Bks.

Berger, Melvin & Berger, Gilda. Do All Spiders Spin Webs? Questions & Answers about Spiders. Osti, Roberto, illus. 2000. (Question & Answer Ser.). 48p. (J). (gr. 2-7). pap. 14.95 (978-0-439-09586-0(7)) Scholastic, Inc.

—Do Tarantulas Have Teeth? Questions & Answers about Poisonous Creatures. Effler, Jim, illus. 2000. 48p. (J). (ps-7). lib. bdg. 14.10 (978-0-613-24866-2(X)) Tandem Library Bks.

—Spiders. 2002. (Scholastic Readers Ser.). (Illus.). 14p. (J). pap. (978-0-439-44542-9(6)) Scholastic, Inc.

Berger, Melvin, et al. Do All Spiders Spin Webs? Questions & Answers about Spiders. 2000. (Question & Answer Ser.). (Illus.). 48p. (J). pap. (978-0-439-09587-7(5)) Scholastic, Inc.

Berkowitz, Henry. Insects & Spiders: An Educational Coloring Book. Berkowitz, Henry, illus. 2001. (Illus.). 32p. (J). (ps-3). pap. 4.95 (978-0-932855-67-1(9)) Winner Enterprises.

Berman, Ruth. Spinning Spiders. Roberts, David T. & Schleser, David M., photos by. 1998. (Pull Ahead Bks.). (Illus.). 32p. (J). (gr. k-2). pap. 5.95 (978-0-8225-3610-9(2)); lib. bdg. 22.60 (978-0-8225-3604-8(8) , Lerner Pubns.) Lerner Publishing Group.

Biel, Timothy Levi. Aranas. Rountree, Monica, tr. 2003. (Zoobooks). Orig. Title: Spiders. (SPA., Illus.). 24p. (J). (gr. 1-7). lib. bdg. 15.95 (978-1-888153-82-8(2)) Wildlife Education, Ltd.

A Big Spider: Individual Title Six-Packs. (Sails Literacy Ser.). (gr. 1-2). 36.00 (978-0-7578-6726-2(X)) Rigby Education.

Birch. Spiders up Close, 6 Packs. 2004. pap. 40.50 (978-1-4109-1156-8(X)) Harcourt Schl. Pubs.

Birch, Robin. Spiders Up Close. 2004. (Raintree Perspectives Ser.). (Illus.). 32p. (J). pap. 7.50 (978-1-4109-1149-0(7)); (gr. 3-5). 26.36 (978-1-4109-1142-1(X)) Harcourt Schl. Pubs.

Bishop, Nic. Nic Bishop Spiders. 2007. 48p. (J). (ps-3). 16.99 ***978-0-439-87756-5(3)** , Scholastic Nonfiction) Scholastic, Inc.

Books Are Fun 8 Title Animal Lives Set: Spiders. 2006. (J). (978-1-59566-313-9(4)) QEB Publishing Inc.

Boutilier, Joanna. Pigs Aren't Dirty, Bears Aren't Slow: And Other Truths about Misunderstood Animals. Hodson, Ben, illus. 2005. 40p. (J). (gr. 2-4). pap. 7.95 (978-1-55037-848-1(1)); lib. bdg. 19.95 (978-1-55037-849-8(X)) Annick Pr., Ltd. CAN. *Dist:* Firefly Bks., Ltd.

Bradley, Richard A. Spiders. 2000. (In Ohio's Backyard Ser.: Vol. 4). (Illus.). 150p. (YA). (gr. 6 up). 15.00 (978-0-86727-140-9(X)) Ohio Biological Survey.

Bredeson, Carmen. Tarantulas up Close. 2008. (Zoom in on Animals! Ser.). (Illus.). 24p. (J). (gr. 1-3). lib. bdg. 21.26 ***978-0-7660-3076-3(8))** Enslow Pubs., Inc.

Breene, Robert G., III. A Widow Spider in Its Web. 2003. (Where Do Animals Live? Ser.). (J). (978-1-58417-186-7(3)); pap. (978-1-58417-187-4(1)) Lake Street Pubs.

Carle, Eric. My Own Very Busy Spider Coloring Book. Carle, Eric, illus. 2004. (Illus.). 32p. (J). (ps-1). pap. 5.99 (978-0-399-24309-7(7) , Philomel) Penguin Group (USA) Inc.

Chardiet, Bernice & Brenner, Barbara. Where's That Spider? Schwartz, Carol, illus. 1999. (Hide & Seek Science Ser.). (J). 20.01 (978-0-590-12818-6(3)) Scholastic, Inc.

Childrens Press Staff, ed. Insects, Spiders & Worms. 1998. (Rookie Read-About Science Ser.). pap. 19.90 (978-0-516-29985-3(9) , Children's Pr.) Scholastic Library Publishing.

Clarke, Penny. Spiders, Insects, & Minibeasts. 2003. (gr. 3-6). lib. bdg. 15.25 (978-0-613-54362-0(9)) Tandem Library Bks.

Claybourne, Anna. Spiders & Scorpions. 2004. (Awesome Bugs Ser.). (J). lib. bdg. 27.10 (978-1-932799-53-8(2)) Stargazer Bks.

Cooper, Jason. Black Widow Spiders. 2006. (Rourke Discovery Library). (Illus.). 24p. (J). (gr. 2-5). 14.95 (978-1-59515-445-3(0)) Rourke Publishing, LLC.

—Fishing Spiders. 2006. (Rourke Discovery Library). (Illus.). 24p. (J). (gr. 2-5). 14.95 (978-1-59515-446-0(9)) Rourke Publishing, LLC.

—Garden Spiders. 2006. (Rourke Discovery Library). (Illus.). 24p. (J). (gr. 2-5). 14.95 (978-1-59515-447-7(7)) Rourke Publishing, LLC.

—Jumping Spiders. 2006. (Rourke Discovery Library). (Illus.). 24p. (J). (gr. 2-5). 14.95 (978-1-59515-448-4(5)) Rourke Publishing, LLC.

—Spider. 2003. (Life Cycles II Ser.). (Illus.). 24p. (J). 25.64 (978-1-58952-707-2(0)) Rourke Publishing, LLC.

—Tarantulas. 2006. (Spiders Discovery Ser.). (Illus.). 24p. (gr. 2-5). 14.95 (978-1-59515-449-1(3)) Rourke Publishing, LLC.

—Wolf Spiders. 2006. (Rourke Discovery Library). (Illus.). 24p. (gr. 2-5). 14.95 (978-1-59515-450-7(7)) Rourke Publishing, LLC.

Davies, Valerie. The Spectacular Spider Book. Mendez, Simon, illus. 2006. (Beautiful Bug Ser.). 24p. (J). (gr. k-2). spiral bd. 17.95 (978-0-7696-4429-5(5)) School Specialty Publishing.

Dinaberg, Leslie. Spider Life. 2006. (Boys Rock! Ser.). (Illus.). 32p. (J). (gr. 1-5). 24.21 (978-1-59296-737-7(X)) Child's World, Inc.

Eckart, Edana. Tarantula. 2005. (Welcome Bks.). (Illus.). 24p. (ps-2). (J). pap. 4.95 (978-0-516-25167-7(8)); 18.00 (978-0-516-25051-9(5)) Scholastic Library Publishing. (Children's Pr.).

Einhorn, Kama. Word Family Tales -Ap: A Nap for Zap. Jabar, Cynthia, illus. 2002. (Word Family Tales Ser.). 16p. (ps-2). pap. 2.95 (978-0-439-26269-9(0)) Scholastic, Inc.

Ethan, Eric. Aranas Amarillas de Bolsa. Acosta, Tatiana & Gutiérrez, Guillermo, trs. 2003. (Arañas Peligrosas Ser.). (Illus.). 24p. (J). (gr. 2 up). lib. bdg. 22.00 (978-0-8368-3772-8(X)) Stevens, Gareth Inc.

—Aranas Cafe. Acosta, Tatiana & Gutiérrez, Guillermo, trs. 2003. (Arañas Peligrosas Ser.). (SPA., Illus.). 24p. (J). (gr. 2 up). lib. bdg. 22.00 (978-0-8368-3773-5(8)) Stevens, Gareth Inc.

—Aranas de Tela en Embudo. Acosta, Tatiana & Gutiérrez, Guillermo, trs. 2003. (Arañas Peligrosas Ser.). (SPA., Illus.). 24p. (J). (gr. 2 up). lib. bdg. 22.00 (978-0-8368-3774-2(6)) Stevens, Gareth Inc.

—Aranas Hobo. Acosta, Tatiana & Gutiérrez, Guillermo, trs. 2003. (Arañas Peligrosas Ser.). (SPA., Illus.). 24p. (J). (gr. 2 up). lib. bdg. 22.00 (978-0-8368-3775-9(4)) Stevens, Gareth Inc.

—Aranas Peligrosas, 6 bks. Acosta, Tatiana & Gutiérrez, Guillermo, trs. Incl. Aranas Amarillas de Bolsa. lib. bdg. 22.00 (978-0-8368-3772-8(X)); Aranas Cafe. lib. bdg. 22.00 (978-0-8368-3773-5(8)); Aranas de Tela en Embudo. lib. bdg. 22.00 (978-0-8368-3774-2(6)); Aranas Hobo. lib. bdg. 22.00 (978-0-8368-3775-9(4)); Aranas Viudas Negras. lib. bdg. 22.00 (978-0-8368-3776-6(2)); Tarantulas. lib. bdg. 22.00 (978-0-8368-3777-3(0)); 24p. (J). (gr. 2 up). (SPA., Illus.). 2003. Set lib. bdg. 132.00 (978-0-8368-3771-1(1)) Stevens, Gareth Inc.

—Aranas Viudas Negras. Acosta, Tatiana & Gutiérrez, Guillermo, trs. 2003. (Arañas Peligrosas Ser.). (SPA., Illus.). 24p. (J). (gr. 2 up). lib. bdg. 22.00 (978-0-8368-3776-6(2)) Stevens, Gareth Inc.

—Black Widow Spiders. 2003. (Dangerous Spiders Ser.). (Illus.). 24p. (J). (gr. 2 up). lib. bdg. 22.00 (978-0-8368-3765-0(7)) Stevens, Gareth Inc.

—Brown Recluse Spiders. 2003. (Dangerous Spiders Ser.). (Illus.). 24p. (J). (gr. 2 up). lib. bdg. 22.00 (978-0-8368-3766-7(5)) Stevens, Gareth Inc.

—Dangerous Spiders, 6 bks. Incl. Black Widow Spiders. lib. bdg. 22.00 (978-0-8368-3765-0(7)); Brown Recluse Spiders. lib. bdg. 22.00 (978-0-8368-3766-7(5)); Funnel Web Spiders. lib. bdg. 22.00 (978-0-8368-3767-4(3)); Hobo Spiders. lib. bdg. 22.00 (978-0-8368-3768-1(1)); Tarantulas. lib. bdg. 22.00 (978-0-8368-3769-8(X)); Yellow Sac Spiders. lib. bdg. 22.00 (978-0-8368-3770-4(3)); 24p. (J). (gr. 2 up). (Illus.). 2003. Set lib. bdg. 132.00 (978-0-8368-3764-3(9)) Stevens, Gareth Inc.

—Funnel Web Spiders. 2003. (Dangerous Spiders Ser.). (Illus.). 24p. (J). (gr. 2 up). lib. bdg. 22.00 (978-0-8368-3767-4(3)) Stevens, Gareth Inc.

—Hobo Spiders. 2003. (Dangerous Spiders Ser.). (Illus.). 24p. (J). (gr. 2 up). lib. bdg. 22.00 (978-0-8368-3768-1(1)) Stevens, Gareth Inc.

—Tarantulas. 2003. (Dangerous Spiders Ser.). (Illus.). 24p. (J). (gr. 2 up). lib. bdg. 22.00 (978-0-8368-3769-8(X)) Stevens, Gareth Inc.

—Tarantulas. Acosta, Tatiana & Gutiérrez, Guillermo, trs. 2003. (Arañas Peligrosas Ser.). (SPA & ENG., Illus.). 24p. (J). (gr. 2 up). lib. bdg. 22.00 (978-0-8368-3777-3(0)) Stevens, Gareth Inc.

—Yellow Sac Spiders. 2003. (Dangerous Spiders Ser.). (Illus.). 24p. (J). (gr. 2 up). lib. bdg. 22.00 (978-0-8368-3770-4(3)) Stevens, Gareth Inc.

Evans, Arthur V., et al. Grzimek's Student Animal Life Resource, 2 vols. 2005. (Illus.). l, 442p. (J). (978-0-7876-9244-5(1)); (978-0-7876-9245-2(X)) Thomson Gale. (UXL).

Facklam, Margery. Spiders & Their Web Sites. Male, Alan, illus. 2004. 32p. (J). (gr. 4-8). reprint ed. 16.00 (978-0-7567-7321-2(0)) DIANE Publishing Co.

Franks, Katie. Spiders up Close. 2008. (J). lib. bdg. ***978-1-4042-4138-1(8)** , PowerKids Pr.) Rosen Publishing Group, Inc., The.

Fridell, Ron & Walsh, Patricia. Life Cycle of a Spider. 2001. (Heinemann First Library). (Illus.). 32p. (J). (gr. k-2). lib. bdg. 21.36 (978-1-58810-095-5(2)) Heinemann Library.

Frost, Helen. Tarantulas. Saunders-Smith, Gail, ed. 2002. (Rain Forest Animals Ser.). (Illus.). 24p. (J). (gr. k-1). lib. bdg. 15.93 (978-0-7368-1195-8(8) , Pebble Bks.) Capstone Pr., Inc.

Ganeri, Anita. From Egg to Spider. 2006. (Illus.). 32p. (J). 25.36 (978-1-4034-7860-3(0)); pap. (978-1-4034-7869-6(4)) Heinemann Library.

Gareth Stevens Publishing Staff, contrib. by. Spiders. 2004. (All about Wild Animals Ser.). (Illus.). 32p. (J). (gr. 2 up). lib. bdg. 23.33 (978-0-8368-4172-5(7)) Stevens, Gareth Inc.

Gibbons, Gail. Spiders. Gibbons, Gail, illus. unabr. ed. 1999. (Gail Gibbons' Creatures Great & Small Ser.). (Illus.). (J). (gr. 1-6). pap. 16.95 incl. audio (978-0-87499-587-9(6)) BBC Audiobooks America.

—Spiders. Gibbons, Gail, illus. 2002. (Illus.). (J). 15.49 (978-0-7587-3675-8(4)) Book Wholesalers, Inc.

—Spiders. Gibbons, Gail, illus. 1999. (Illus.). 28.95 incl. audio compact disk (978-1-59519-086-4(4)); pap. 39.95 incl. audio compact disk (978-1-59519-085-7(6)); (J). pap. 18.95 incl. audio compact disk (978-1-59519-084-0(8)) Live Oak Media.

—Spiders. unabr. ed. 1999. (Gail Gibbons' Creatures Great & Small Ser.). (Illus.). (J). 25.95 incl. audio (978-0-87499-588-6(4)) Live Oak Media.

Gilpin, Rebecca. Spiders (Level 1) - Internet Referenced. 2006. 32p. (J). 4.99 (978-0-7945-1398-6(0) , Usborne) EDC Publishing.

Glaser, Linda. Spectacular Spiders. Holland, Gary, illus. 1999. 32p. (J). (gr. k-3). pap. 8.95 (978-0-7613-0386-2(3) , Millbrook Pr.) Lerner Publishing Group.

—Spectacular Spiders. Holland, Gay W., illus. 1998. (Linda Glaser's Classic Creatures Ser.). 32p. (ps-3). lib. bdg. 22.90 (978-0-7613-0353-4(7) , Millbrook Pr.) Lerner Publishing Group.

Goldish, Meish. Goliath Bird-Eating Tarantula: The World's Biggest Spider. 2007. (SuperSized! Ser.). (Illus.). 24p. (J). lib. bdg. 21.28 (978-1-59716-389-7(9) , 1265934) Bearport Publishing Co., Inc.

Gordon, David George. Uncover a Tarantula: Take a Three-Dimensional Look Inside a Tarantula! 2004. (Uncover Bks.). (Illus.). 16p. 18.95 (978-1-59223-237-6(X)) Advantage Pubs. Group.

Gordon, Sharon. Guess Who Spins. 2004. (SPA & ENG., Illus.). 31p. (J). 21.36 (978-0-7614-1768-2(0) , Benchmark Bks.) Cavendish, Marshall Corp.

Gordon, Sharon. Guess Who Spins: Adivina Quién Teje. 2007. (SPA & ENG.). (J). ***978-0-7614-2887-9(9)); (*978-0-7614-2871-8(2))** Cavendish, Marshall Bks., Ltd.

Greenaway, Theresa. Spiders. 2001. (Secret World Of... Ser.). (Illus.). 48p. (J). (gr. 4-7). lib. bdg. 27.12 (978-0-7398-3509-8(2)) Raintree.

—Spiders. 1999. (Minipets Ser.). (Illus.). 32p. (gr. 1-5). pap. 7.95 (978-0-8172-4206-0(6)) Steck-Vaughn.

Greenberg, Daniel A. Spiders. 2001. (Animals Animals Ser.). (Illus.). 48p. (J). (gr. 3-5). lib. bdg. 25.64 (978-0-7614-1263-2(8) , Benchmark Bks.) Cavendish, Marshall Corp.

Grosset and Dunlap Staff & Heller, Ruth. Insects & Spiders. 2000. (Designs for Coloring Ser.). (Illus.). 64p. (J). (ps-3). pap. 5.99 (978-0-448-42250-3(6) , Grosset & Dunlap) Penguin Group (USA) Inc.

Group/McGraw-Hill, Wright. Spider & Buffalo: Level N, 6 vols. 128p. (gr. 3-6). 36.95 (978-0-322-05887-3(2)) Wright Group, The.

Halfmann, Janet. Spiders. 2001. (Let's Investigate Ser.). (Illus.). 32p. (J). 18.95 (978-1-58341-195-7(X) , Creative Education) Creative Co., The.

Hall, Margaret. Spiders. 2004. (Pebble Plus: Bugs, Bugs, Bugs! Ser.). (Illus.). 24p. (J). lib. bdg. 19.93 (978-0-7368-2591-7(6) , Pebble Bks.) Capstone Pr., Inc.

Harcourt School Publishers Staff. Amazing Spiders: Take-Home Book. 2001. (Collections Ser.). (Illus.). (J). (gr. 4). pap. 1.90 (978-0-15-319491-7(X)) Harcourt Schl. Pubs.

—Insects & Spiders: Independent Reader. 3rd ed. 2002. (Trophies Reading Program Ser.). (Illus.). (J). pap. 2.90 (978-0-15-325486-4(6)) Harcourt Schl. Pubs.

Harris, Monica. Black Widow Spider. 2003. (Bug Books). (Illus.). 32p. (J). lib. bdg. 22.79 (978-1-4034-0762-7(2)); pap. 6.95 (978-1-4034-0992-8(7)) Heinemann Library.

—Tarantula. 2003. (Bug Books). (Illus.). 32p. (J). lib. bdg. 22.79 (978-1-4034-0764-1(9)); pap. (978-1-4034-0993-5(5)) Heinemann Library.

Hayward, Tim & Greenaway, Theresa. Spiders. 1999. (Minipets Ser.). (Illus.). 32p. (J). (gr. 1-5). lib. bdg. 25.69 (978-0-8172-5589-3(3)) Raintree.

Heinrichs, Ann. Spiders. 2004. (Illus.). 32p. (J). (gr. 2 up). lib. bdg. 15.95 (978-0-7565-0590-5(9)) Compass Point Bks.

Himmelman, John. A House Spider's Life. 2000. (Nature Upclose Ser.). (Illus.). 32p. (J). (gr. k-2). pap. 6.95 (978-0-516-26536-0(9) , Children's Pr.) Scholastic Library Publishing.

—A House Spider's Life. Himmelman, John, illus. 1999. (Nature Upclose Ser.). (Illus.). 32p. (J). (gr. k-2). 25.00 (978-0-516-21185-5(4) , Children's Pr.) Scholastic Library Publishing.

—A House Spider's Life. 1999. (gr. k-3). lib. bdg. 15.25 (978-0-613-37387-6(1)) Tandem Library Bks.

Houghton, Gillian. Spider. 2004. (Getting into Nature Ser.). (Illus.). 32p. (J). lib. bdg. 21.25 (978-0-8239-4209-1(0)) Rosen Publishing Group, Inc., The.

Hovanec, Erin M. I Wonder What It's Like to Be a Spider. 2000. (Life Science Wonder Bks.). (Illus.). 24p. (J). (gr. k-4). lib. bdg. 18.75 (978-0-8239-5453-7(6) , PowerKids Pr.) Rosen Publishing Group, Inc., The.

How Spiders Live, 6 vols. (Sunshinetm Science Ser.). 24p. (gr. 1-2). 31.50 (978-0-7802-0283-2(X)); 36.95 (978-0-7802-0534-5(0)) Wright Group, The.

Huggins-Cooper, Lynn. Minibeasts. McNicholas, Shelagh & Burroughs, Dave, trs. McNicholas, Shelagh & Burroughs, Dave, illus. 2004. 30p. (J). lib. bdg. (978-1-58340-444-7(9)) Smart Apple Media.

—Minibeasts. 2003. (Starters Ser.). 24p. (J). lib. bdg. 21.35 (978-1-58340-263-4(2)) Smart Apple Media.

Huggins-Cooper, Lynn. Scary Spiders. 2007. (Killer Nature! Ser.). (Illus.). 32p. (J). (gr. 3-5). lib. bdg. 28.50 (***978-1-58340-935-0(1)***) Smart Apple Media.

Hughes, Monica. Spiders. 2003. (Raintree Sprouts Ser.). (Illus.). 24p. (J). pap. 5.50 (978-1-4109-0648-9(5)); lib. bdg. 18.56 (978-1-4109-0622-9(1)) Raintree.

—Spiders. 2003. (ps-2). lib. bdg. 13.55 (978-0-613-78257-9(7)) Tandem Library Bks.

Insects & Spiders. (Action Bks.). 64p. (J). (gr. 3-7). pap. (978-1-882210-67-1(0)) Action Publishing, Inc.

Iorio, Nicole. Spiders! 2005. 48p. (J). lib. bdg. 13.85 (***978-1-4242-0862-3(9)***) Fitzgerald Bks.

Iorio, Nicole & Time for Kids Editors. Spiders! 2005. (Time for Kids Science Scoops Ser.). (Illus.). 48p. (J). 14.99 (978-0-06-057635-6(9)); pap. 3.99 (978-0-06-057634-9(0)) HarperCollins Pubs.

Jacobs, Liza. Spiders. 2003. (Wild Wild World Ser.). (Illus.). 24p. (J). 22.45 (978-1-4103-0044-7(7) , Blackbirch Pr., Inc.) Thomson Gale.

Jumping Spiders: Individual Title Six-Packs. (Sails Literacy Ser.). (gr. 1-2). 36.00 (978-0-7578-6736-1(7)) Rigby Education.

Kallen, Stuart A. Spiders. 2001. (Nature's Predators Ser.). (Illus.). 48p. (J). (gr. 3-5). 23.70 (978-0-7377-0630-7(9) , LML00902-178554, Kidhaven) Thomson Gale.

Kalman, Bobbie. The Life Cycle of a Spider. 2002. (Life Cycle Ser.). (Illus.). 32p. (J). (gr. 2-3). (978-0-7787-0658-8(3)); pap. (978-0-7787-0688-5(5)) Crabtree Publishing Co.

—Life Cycle of a Spider. 2002. (gr. 3-6). lib. bdg. 14.10 (978-0-613-52975-4(8)) Tandem Library Bks.

Kalman, Bobbie & Smithyman, Kathryn. Les Araignees. 2005. (FRE., Illus.). 32p. (J). pap. (978-2-89579-023-5(X)) Crabtree Publishing Co.

—El Ciclo de vida de la Arana. 2006. (SPA., Illus.). 32p. (gr. 2-3). pap. (978-0-7787-8714-3(1)) Crabtree Publishing Co.

Kaplan, Leslie C. Daddy Longlegs Spiders. 2004. (Library of Spiders). (Illus.). 24p. (J). lib. bdg. 18.75 (978-0-8239-6706-3(9) , PowerKids Pr.) Rosen Publishing Group, Inc., The.

Kubler, Annie, illus. Incey Wincey Spider. 2005. 12p. (J). bds. 4.99 (978-1-904550-03-7(7)) Child's Play-International.

Landau, Elaine. Creepy Spiders. 2003. (Fearsome, Scary, & Creepy Animals Ser.). (Illus.). 48p. (J). (gr. 1-4). lib. bdg. 23.93 (978-0-7660-2059-7(2)) Enslow Pubs., Inc.

Leavitt, Amie. Care for a Pet Tarantula. 2007. (How to Convince Your Parents You Can ... Ser.). (Illus.). 32p. (J). (gr. 1-4). lib. bdg. 25.70 (***978-1-58415-603-1(1)***) Mitchell Lane Pubs., Inc.

Llewellyn, Claire. Spiders. 2002. (gr. k-3). lib. bdg. 12.95 (978-0-613-54361-3(0)) Tandem Library Bks.

Llewellyn, Claire & Watts, Barrie. Spiders. 2002. (Minibeasts Ser.). (Illus.). 32p. (J). (gr. k-3). pap. 4.95 (978-0-531-14827-3(0) , Watts, Franklin) Scholastic Library Publishing.

Loewen, Nancy. Weaving Wonders: Spiders in Your Backyard. Peterson, Rick, illus. 2005. 24p. (J). (ps-ps). lib. bdg. 22.60 (978-1-4048-1145-4(1)) Picture Window Bks.

Lomberg, Michelle. Caring for Your Spider. 2004. (Caring for Your Pet Ser.). (J). pap. 7.95 (978-1-59036-155-9(5)); (Illus.). 32p. lib. bdg. 16.95 (978-1-59036-120-7(2)) Weigl Pubs., Inc.

Macro, Chris. Spider. 2002. (Bug Bks.). (Illus.). 32p. (J). (ps-2). pap. 6.95 (978-1-58810-322-2(6) , 91030) Heinemann Library.

Markle, Sandra. Outside & Inside Spiders. 1999. (978-0-606-17318-6(8)) Tandem Library Bks.

—Spiders Biggest! Littlest! Pollard, Simon, photos by. 2004. (Illus.). 32p. (J). (ps-17). 15.95 (978-1-59078-190-6(2)) Boyds Mills Pr.

Marshall Cavendish Corporation Staff, contrib. by. Insects & Spiders of the World, 11 vols., Set. 2003. (Illus.). 704p. lib. bdg. 471.36 (978-0-7614-7334-3(3) , Cavendish, Marshall Reference Bks.) Cavendish, Marshall Corp.

Matuszak, Pat. Spiders! Sheldon, David, illus. 2004. (Bible Critters Ser.). 36p. (J). pap. 4.99 (978-0-310-70812-4(5)) Zonderkidz.

McEvey, Shane F. Insects & Spiders Series, 6 bks. Incl. Beetles. 32p. 28.00 (978-0-7910-6600-3(2) , 010551); Bugs. 32p. 28.00 (978-0-7910-6595-2(2) , 010552); Dragonflies. 32p. 28.00 (978-0-7910-6597-6(9) , 010553); Flies. 32p. 28.00 (978-0-7910-6596-9(0) , 010554); Moths & Butterflies. 16.95 (978-0-7910-6598-3(7) , 010555); Spiders. 32p. 28.00 (978-0-7910-6599-0(5) , 010556); (J). (gr. 4 up). 2001. (Illus.). 101.70 (978-0-7910-6594-5(4) , 010550S, Chelsea Hse.) Facts On File, Inc.

—Spiders. 2001. (Insects & Spiders Ser.). (Illus.). 32p. (J). (gr. 4 up). 28.00 (978-0-7910-6599-0(5) , 010556, Chelsea Hse.) Facts On File, Inc.

McGinty, Alice B. The Black Widow Spider. 2002. (Library of Spiders). (Illus.). 24p. (J). (gr. 3-6). lib. bdg. 18.75 (978-0-8239-5565-7(6) , PowerKids Pr.) Rosen Publishing Group, Inc., The.

—The Crab Spider. 2002. (Library of Spiders). (Illus.). 24p. (J). (gr. 3-5). lib. bdg. 18.75 (978-0-8239-5570-1(2) , PowerKids Pr.) Rosen Publishing Group, Inc., The.

—The Jumping Spider. 2002. (Library of Spiders). (Illus.). 24p. (J). (gr. 3-6). lib. bdg. 18.75 (978-0-8239-5568-8(0) , PowerKids Pr.) Rosen Publishing Group, Inc., The.

—The Orb Weaver. 2002. (Library of Spiders). (Illus.). 24p. (J). (gr. 3-5). lib. bdg. 18.75 (978-0-8239-5569-5(9) , PowerKids Pr.) Rosen Publishing Group, Inc., The.

—Tarantula. 2002. (Library of Spiders). (Illus.). 24p. (J). (gr. 3-6). lib. bdg. 18.75 (978-0-8239-5566-4(4) , PowerKids Pr.) Rosen Publishing Group, Inc., The.

—The Wolf Spider. 2002. (Library of Spiders). (Illus.). 24p. (J). (gr. 3-5). lib. bdg. 18.75 (978-0-8239-5567-1(2) , PowerKids Pr.) Rosen Publishing Group, Inc., The.

McGrath, Patrick. Spider. 2000. (Observing Nature Ser.). (J). lib. bdg. 21.40 (978-0-8172-4952-6(4)) Raintree.

McNab, Chris. Dangerous Insects & Spiders. 2006. (Nature's Monsters Ser.). (Illus.). 32p. (J). lib. bdg. (978-0-8368-6848-7(X)) Stevens, Gareth Inc.

—Giant Spiders & Insects. 2006. (Nature's Monsters Ser.). (Illus.). 32p. (J). lib. bdg. (978-0-8368-6850-0(1)) Stevens, Gareth Inc.

Merlino, Kim. Insects & Spiders: Grades 2 & 3. (Illus.). (J). pap., wbk. ed. 4.99 (978-0-88743-960-5(8)) School Zone Publishing Co.

Miller, Heather. Black Widow. 2004. (Bugs Ser.). (Illus.). 32p. (J). (gr. 4-7). 24.95 (978-0-7377-1765-5(3) , Greenhaven Pr., Inc.) Thomson Gale.

—Tarantula. 2004. (Bugs Ser.). (J). 24.95 (978-0-7377-1775-4(0) , Greenhaven Pr., Inc.) Thomson Gale.

Miller, Jake. Brown Recluse Spiders. 2004. (Library of Spiders). (Illus.). 24p. (J). lib. bdg. 18.75 (978-0-8239-6707-0(7) , PowerKids Pr.) Rosen Publishing Group, Inc., The.

—Cobweb Weavers. 2004. (Library of Spiders). (Illus.). 24p. (J). lib. bdg. 18.75 (978-0-8239-6708-7(5) , PowerKids Pr.) Rosen Publishing Group, Inc., The.

—Fishing Spiders. 2004. (Library of Spiders). (Illus.). 24p. (J). lib. bdg. 18.75 (978-0-8239-6711-7(5) , PowerKids Pr.) Rosen Publishing Group, Inc., The.

—Funnel Weavers. 2004. (Library of Spiders). (Illus.). 24p. (J). lib. bdg. 18.75 (978-0-8239-6709-4(3) , PowerKids Pr.) Rosen Publishing Group, Inc., The.

—Trap Door Spiders. 2004. (Library of Spiders). (Illus.). 24p. (J). lib. bdg. 18.75 (978-0-8239-6710-0(7) , PowerKids Pr.) Rosen Publishing Group, Inc., The.

Montgomery, Sy. The Tarantula Scientist. Bishop, Nic, photos by. 2004. (Scientists in the Field Ser.). (Illus.). 80p. (J). (gr. 3-5). tchr. ed. 18.00 (978-0-618-14799-1(3)) Houghton Mifflin Co. Trade & Reference Div.

Montgomery, Sy. Tarantula Scientist. Bishop, Nic, photos by. 2007. (Illus.). 80p. (J). (gr. 4-7). pap. 7.95 (***978-0-618-91577-4(X)***) Houghton Mifflin Co. Trade & Reference Div.

Morgan, Sally. Spiders. 2004. (QEB Animal Lives Ser.). (Illus.). 32p. (J). lib. bdg. 18.95 (978-1-59566-036-7(4)) QEB Publishing Inc.

—Spiders, Centipedes, & Millipedes. 2000. (Looking at Minibeasts Ser.). (Illus.). 32p. (J). (gr. 1-4). lib. bdg. 16.95 (978-1-929298-82-2(X)) Chrysalis Education.

Morley, Christine & Morrison, Phillip. Freaky Facts about Spiders. Morrison, Phillip, illus. 2007. (Freaky Facts Ser.). 32p. (gr. 3-6). 13.95 (978-1-58728-596-7(7)); (J). pap. 8.95 (978-1-58728-597-4(5)) T&N Children's Publishing. (Two Can Publishing).

Morris, Neil & Morris, Ting. Spider. 2003. (Illus.). 32p. (J). lib. bdg. (978-1-58340-377-8(9)) Smart Apple Media.

Murawski, Darlyne. Spiders & Their Webs. 2004. (Illus.). 32p. (J). (gr. 1-4). 16.95 (978-0-7922-6979-3(9)); 25.90 (978-0-7922-6994-6(2)) National Geographic Society. (National Geographic Children's Bks.).

Murawski, Darlyne A. Spiders & Their Webs. Murawski, Darlyne A., photos by. 2007. (Illus.). 31p. (J). reprint ed. 17.00 (***978-1-4223-6813-8(0)***) DIANE Publishing Co.

Murray, Julie. Black Widow Spiders. 2002. (Buddy Book Ser.). (Illus.). 24p. (J). (gr. k-4). lib. bdg. 21.35 (978-1-57765-728-6(4)) ABDO Publishing Co.

—Jumping Spiders. 2005. (Animal Kingdom Set Ii Ser.). (Illus.). 24p. (J). (gr. k-4). lib. bdg. 21.35 (978-1-59197-323-2(6)) ABDO Publishing Co.

—Tarantula Spiders. 2002. (Buddy Book Ser.). (Illus.). 24p. (J). (gr. k-4). lib. bdg. 21.35 (978-1-57765-729-3(2)) ABDO Publishing Co.

—Wolf Spiders. 2005. (Animal Kingdom Set Ii Ser.). (Illus.). 24p. (J). (gr. k-4). lib. bdg. 21.35 (978-1-59197-339-3(2)) ABDO Publishing Co.

Murray, Peter. Black Widows. 2003. (Naturebooks: Creepy Crawlers Ser.). (Illus.). 32p. (J). (gr. 1-5). 25.64 (978-1-56766-977-0(8)) Child's World, Inc.

—Spiders & Scorpions. 2004. (Science Around Us Ser.). 32p. (J). (gr. 2-6). 27.07 (978-1-59296-273-0(4)) Child's World, Inc.

—Tarantulas. 2003. (Naturebooks: Creepy Crawlers Ser.). (Illus.). 32p. (J). (gr. 1-5). 25.64 (978-1-56766-980-0(8)) Child's World, Inc.

O'Neill, Amanda. I Wonder Why Spiders Spin Webs: And Other Questions about Creepy Crawlies. 2003. (I Wonder Why Ser.). 32p. (J). (gr. k-3). pap. 6.95 (978-0-7534-5613-2(3) , Kingfisher) Houghton Mifflin Co. Trade & Reference Div.

—I Wonder Why Spiders Spin Webs: And Other Questions about Creepy Crawlies. 2003. (gr. k-3). lib. bdg. 14.10 (978-0-613-63162-4(5)) Tandem Library Bks.

Otfinoski, Steven. Spiders & Other Arachnids, Vol. 9. World Book, Inc. Staff, ed. 2001. (World Book's Animals of the World Ser.: Set 2). (Illus.). 64p. (J). (978-0-7166-1220-9(8)) World Bk., Inc.

Otto, Carolyn B. Spiders. (Science Readers Ser.). (Illus.). 32p. (J). (gr. k-1). 2002. pap. 3.99 (978-0-439-38245-8(9) , Scholastic Reference); 2001. (978-0-439-26989-6(X)) Scholastic, Inc.

—Spiders. 2002. (gr. k-3). lib. bdg. 11.80 (978-0-613-57138-8(X)) Tandem Library Bks.

Parker, Edward, photos by. Insects & Spiders. 2002. (Rain Forest Pilot Ser.). (Illus.). 48p. (J). lib. bdg. 27.12 (978-0-7398-5240-8(X)) Raintree.

Parker, Steve. 10 Things You Should Know about Spiders. Gallagher, Belinda & Borton, Paula, eds. Draper, Richard, illus. 2004. (10 Things You Should Know Ser.). 24p. (J). 6.99 (978-1-84236-122-1(8)) Miles Kelly Publishing, Ltd. GBR. *Dist:* Independent Pubs. Group.

Pascoe, Elaine. How & Why Spiders Spin Silk. Kupperstein, Joel, ed. Kuhn, Dwight, photos by. 2000. (How & Why Ser.). (Illus.). 16p. (J). (gr. 1-3). pap. 2.99 (978-1-57471-661-0(1) , 2968) Creative Teaching Pr., Inc.

—Spiders Spin Silk. Kuhn, Dwight, photos by. 2002. (Springboards into Science Ser.). (Illus.). 24p. (J). (gr. 1 up). lib. bdg. 20.67 (978-0-8368-3013-2(X)) Stevens, Gareth Inc.

Phillips, Dee. Bugs & Spiders (Blue Zoo Guides) 2006. (Blue Zoo Guides Ser.). (Illus.). 96p. 18.95 (978-1-58728-520-2(7) , Two Can Publishing) T&N Children's Publishing.

Platt, Richard. Spiders' Secrets. 2002. (Readers Ser.). (Illus.). 48p. (J). (gr. 2-3). pap. 3.99 (978-0-7894-8373-7(4)) Dorling Kindersley Publishing, Inc.

—Spiders' Secrets. 2002. (gr. k-3). lib. bdg. 11.80 (978-0-613-45623-4(8)) Tandem Library Bks.

Platt, Richard & Dorling Kindersley Publishing Staff. Spiders' Secrets. 2002. (Readers Ser.). (Illus.). 48p. (J). (gr. 2-3). 14.99 (978-0-7894-8372-0(6)) Dorling Kindersley Publishing, Inc.

Powell, Patricia Hruby. Zinnia: How the Corn Was Saved. Ruffenach, Jessie, ed. Thomas, Peter, tr. Benally, Kendrick, illus. 2004. (ENG & NAV.). 32p. 17.95 (978-1-893354-38-8(5)) Salina Bookshelf.

Prims, Marta & Roca, Nuria. I Am a Little Spider. 2001. (Barron's Little Animal Ser.). (Illus.). 24p. (J). (ps-k). 9.95 (978-0-7641-5345-7(5)) Barron's Educational Series, Inc.

Randolph, Joanne. Tarantulas. 2007. (Classroom Pets Ser.). (Illus.). 24p. (J). (gr. k-5). lib. bdg. 21.25 (***978-1-4042-3678-3(3)*** , PowerKids Pr.) Rosen Publishing Group, Inc., The.

Rankin, Wayne & Walls, Jerry G. Tarantulas & Scorpions. 1999. (Basic Domestic Reptile & Amphibian Library). (Illus.). 64p. (YA). (gr. 4-7). lib. bdg. 19.75 (978-0-7910-5081-1(5) , Chelsea Hse.) Facts On File, Inc.

Rau, Dana Meachen. Spin, Spider, Spin! 2007. (Go, Critter, Go! Ser.). (Illus.). 23p. (J). (ps-3). lib. bdg. 22.79 (***978-0-7614-2653-0(1)*** , Benchmark Bks.) Cavendish, Marshall Corp.

—Spin, Spider, Spin!/¡Teje Araña, Teje! 2007. (Go, Critter, Go!/¡Vamos Criaturita, Vamos! Ser.). (SPA & ENG.). 24p. (J). lib. bdg. 22.79 (***978-0-7614-2818-3(6)*** , Benchmark Bks.) Cavendish, Marshall Corp.

—¡Teje, Araña, Teje! 2007. (¡Vamos Criaturita, Vamos! Ser.). (SPA.). 24p. (J). lib. bdg. 22.79 (***978-0-7614-2794-0(5)*** , Benchmark Bks.) Cavendish, Marshall Corp.

Resnick, Jane Parker. Spiders. 2001. (Nature's Wild Ser.). (J). lib. bdg. (978-1-58952-205-3(2)) Rourke Publishing, LLC.

Richardson, Adele D. Spiders: Spinners & Trappers. 2001. (Wild World of Animals Ser.). (Illus.). 24p. (J). (gr. 1-2). lib. bdg. 18.60 (978-0-7368-0829-3(9) , Bridgestone Bks.) Capstone Pr., Inc.

Rigby Education Staff. Spiders Web. (Sails Literacy Ser.). (Illus.). 16p. (gr. k-1). 27.00 (978-0-7635-9859-4(3)) Rigby Education.

Riley, Joelle. Hairy Tarantulas. 2007. (Pull Ahead Books-Animals Ser.). (J). 22.60 (***978-0-8225-6702-8(4)*** , Lerner Pubns.) Lerner Publishing Group.

Riley Joelle. Hairy Tarantulas. 2007. (Pull Ahead Books-Animals Ser.). (J). pap. 6.95 (***978-0-8225-6705-9(9)*** , First Avenue Editions) Lerner Publishing Group.

Robb, Jackie & Stringle, Berny. The Story of Spider. Duncan, Karen & Stringle, Sam, illus. 2004. (Bang on the Door Ser.). 32p. (YA). pap. (978-1-85602-318-4(4)) Chrysalis Children's Bks.

Robinson, W. Wright. How Spiders & Other Silkmakers Build Their Amazing Homes. Calvert, Trudy L., illus. 1999. (Animal Architects Ser.). 64p. (J). (gr. 5-9). 24.95 (978-1-56711-378-5(8) , Blackbirch Pr., Inc.) Thomson Gale.

Ross, Michael. Millipedeology. 2000. (gr. 3-6). lib. bdg. 15.25 (978-0-613-44312-8(8)) Tandem Library Bks.

—Spiderology. 2000. (gr. 3-6). lib. bdg. 15.25 (978-0-613-36685-4(9)) Tandem Library Bks.

Ross, Michael Elsohn. Spiderology. Erickson, Darren, illus. Grogan, Brian, photos by. (Backyard Buddies Ser.). 48p. (gr. 3-6). 2005. lib. bdg. 19.93 (978-1-57505-387-5(X)); 2003. (YA). 6.95 (978-1-57505-438-4(8) , Carolrhoda Bks.) Lerner Publishing Group.

Ruttle, Kate & Brown, Richard. Itsy Bitsy Spider American English Edtion. 2000. (Cambridge Reading Ser.). 8p. pap. 5.00 (978-0-521-79516-6(8)) Cambridge Univ. Pr.

School Zone Publishing Company Staff. Insects & Spiders. (Illus.). (J). 19.99 incl. audio compact disk (978-0-88743-944-5(6)); 19.99 incl. audio compact disk (978-0-88743-977-3(2)) School Zone Publishing Co.

Schwartz, David M. La Arana Saltadora. Kuhn, Dwight, photos by. 2001. (Springboards into Science Ser.). (SPA., Illus.). 24p. (J). (gr. 1 up). lib. bdg. 20.67 (978-0-8368-2989-1(1) , GHS31408) Stevens, Gareth Inc.

—Jumping Spider. Kuhn, Dwight, photos by. 2001. (Springboards into Science Ser.). (Illus.). 24p. (J). (gr. 1 up). lib. bdg. 20.67 (978-0-8368-2976-1(X)) Stevens, Gareth Inc.

S

Shea, Therese. Spider Biters. 2006. (Illus.). 24p. (J). lib. bdg. 24.77 (978-1-4042-3521-2(3) , PowerKids Pr.) Rosen Publishing Group, Inc., The.

Sill, Cathryn P. & Sill, John. About Arachnids: A Guide for Children. Sill, Cathryn P. & Sill, John, illus. 2003. (About...Ser.). (Illus.). 40p. (J). 15.95 (978-1-56145-038-1(3)) Peachtree Pubs., Ltd.

Simon, Seymour. Spiders. 32p. (J). (gr. k-4). 2007. 16.99 (***978-0-06-089104-6(1)***); 2007. (Illus.). pap. 6.99 (***978-0-06-089103-9(3)***); 2003. (Illus.). 16.99 (978-0-06-028391-9(2)); 2003. (Illus.). lib. bdg. 17.89 (978-0-06-028392-6(0)) HarperCollins Pubs.

Simons, Lisa M. B. From Egg to Spider. 2003. (Grow up! Ser.). (J). pap. (978-1-58417-178-2(2)); lib. bdg. (978-1-58417-172-0(3)) Lake Street Pubs.

Smith. Insects & Spiders: Sticker Book. 1998. (J). pap. 2.99 (978-0-87628-444-5(6)) Ctr. for Applied Research in Education, The.

Solway, Andrew. Deadly Spiders & Scorpions. 2004. (J). 29.93 (978-1-4034-5767-7(0)); pap. 8.50 (978-1-4034-5773-8(5)) Heinemann Library.

—Spiders & Other Invertebrates. 2006. (Illus.). 48p. (J). (978-1-4034-8223-5(3)); pap. (978-1-4034-8230-3(6)) Heinemann Library.

Sovak, Jan. Learning about Spiders. 2001. (Learning about Ser.). (Illus.). 16p. (J). (gr. 3-5). pap. 1.50 (978-0-486-41852-0(9)) Dover Pubns., Inc.

The Spider: First Wave Satellite Individual Title Six-Packs. (Sails Literacy Ser.). 16p. (gr. k up). 27.00 (978-0-7578-6856-6(8)) Rigby Education.

The Spider Bank: Individual Title Six-Packs. (Story Steps Ser.). (gr. k-2). 32.00 (978-0-7635-9845-7(3)) Rigby Education.

Spiders. (Eyes on Nature Ser.). 32p. (J). (gr. 1). pap. (978-1-882210-59-6(X)) Action Publishing, Inc.

Spiders. 2000. (Illus.). 12p. (J). (ps up). pap. 7.99 (978-0-85953-004-0(3)) Child's Play-International.

Spiders. (Eyes on Nature Ser.). (Illus.). 32p. (J). (gr. 1 up). 7.95 (978-1-56156-462-0(1)) Kidsbooks, Inc.

Spiders: Level I, 6 vols. (Wonder Worldtm Ser.). 16p. 29.95 (978-0-7802-1237-4(1)) Wright Group, The.

The Spiders: MainSails Individual Title, 6 Packs. (Sails Literacy Ser.). (gr. 5 up). 37.00 (978-0-7578-8059-9(2)) Rigby Education.

Spiders & Other Creepy-Crawlies. 2002. (Wild, Wild World Ser.). 32p. (J). 9.95 (978-0-7525-4680-3(5)) Parragon, Inc.

Spiders & Their Webs. (Animal Homes Ser.). 24p. (J). 6.95 (978-0-7368-5125-1(9)) Capstone Pr., Inc.

Spiders & their Webs, 6 vols. (Sunshinetm Science Ser.). 24p. (gr. 1-2). 31.50 (978-0-7802-0284-9(8)); 36.95 (978-0-7802-0535-2(9)) Wright Group, The.

Spiders are Special Animals, 6 vols. (Sunshinetm Science Ser.). 24p. (gr. 1-2). 31.50 (978-0-7802-0285-6(6)); 36.95 (978-0-7802-0536-9(7)) Wright Group, The.

Spiders Kid Kit. 2003. 64p. 10.95 (978-1-58086-528-9(3)) EDC Publishing.

Spiders Set II. 2006. (J). (gr. k-6). 128.10 (978-1-59679-291-3(4) , Checkerboard Library) ABDO Publishing Co.

Squire, Ann O. Spiders. (True Bks.). (J). 2004. 47p. (gr. 3-5). pap. 6.95 (978-0-516-29361-5(3)); 2003. (Illus.). 48p. 25.00 (978-0-516-22661-3(4)) Scholastic Library Publishing. (Children's Pr.).

—Spiders of North America. 2000. (Animals in Order Ser.). (Illus.). 48p. (J). (gr. 4-6). 26.50 (978-0-531-11516-9(X) , Watts, Franklin) Scholastic Library Publishing.

—Spiders of North America. 2000. (gr. 3-6). lib. bdg. 15.25 (978-0-613-34969-7(5)) Tandem Library Bks.

Steele, Christy. Tarantulas. Sloan, Frank, ed. 2001. (Animals of the Rain Forest Ser.). (Illus.). 32p. (J). (gr. 4-7). lib. bdg. 22.83 (978-0-7398-3556-2(4)) Raintree.

Stefoff, Rebecca. Spider. 1999. (Living Things Ser.). (Illus.). 32p. (J). (gr. 1-12). lib. bdg. 22.79 (978-0-7614-0442-2(2) , Benchmark Bks.) Cavendish, Marshall Corp.

Stewart, Jennifer, ed. Backyard Bugs. Birmingham, Lloyd, illus. 1999. 28p. (J). (ps-2). 3.29 (978-0-7847-1093-7(7) , 22077, Bean Sprouts) Standard Publishing.

Stewart, Melissa. How Do Spiders Make Webs? 2008. (J). (***978-0-7614-2920-3(4)***) Cavendish, Marshall Bks., Ltd.

Stone, Lynn M. Tarantulas. 2001. (Weird Pets Ser.). (Illus.). 24p. (J). (gr. 1-4). lib. bdg. 20.64 (978-1-58952-041-7(6)) Rourke Publishing, LLC.

Stradling, Jan. Spy on Spiders: Level K, 6 vols., Vol. 2. (First Explorers Ser.). 24p. (gr. 1-2). 34.95 (978-0-7699-1465-7(9)) Shortland Pubns. (U. S. A.) Inc.

Sund, Mike, intro. Creepy Crawly Creatures. 2007. 7p. 16.95 (***978-1-58117-623-0(6)***, Intervisual/Piggy Toes) Dalmatian Pr.

Tagliaferro, Linda. Spiders & Their Webs. 2004. (Pebble Plus Ser.). (Illus.). 24p. (J). 13.95 (978-0-7368-2385-2(9), Pebble Bks.) Capstone Pr., Inc.

Taylor, Barbara. Bugs & Spiders. Eye View Staff, ed. 2003. (Eye View Ser.). (Illus.). 32p. (J). 14.95 (978-1-57768-564-7(4), Waterbird Bks.) School Specialty Publishing.

—Nature Factfile: Spiders. 2000. (Nature Fact Files Ser.). (Illus.). 64p. (gr. 3-7). pap. 7.95 (978-1-84215-016-0(2), Southwater) Anness Publishing GBR. *Dist:* National Bk. Network.

Townsend. Incredible Arachnids, 6 Packs. 2004. (Illus.). (J). pap. 51.30 (978-1-4109-0859-9(3)) Harcourt Schl. Pubs.

Townsend, John. Incredible Arachnids. 2004. (J). pap. 9.50 (978-1-4109-0850-6(X)); (Illus.). 56p. lib. bdg. 31.36 (978-1-4109-0526-0(8)) Harcourt Schl. Pubs.

Twist, Clint. Tarantulas. 2006. (Illus.). 32p. (J). lib. bdg. 23.33 (978-0-8368-6377-2(1)) Stevens, Gareth Inc.

Underwater Spiders: Early Level Satellite Individual Title Six-Packs. (Sails Literacy Ser.). 16p. (gr. 1-2). 27.00 (978-0-7578-3162-1(1)) Rigby Education.

VanCleave, Janice Pratt. Janice VanCleave's Play & Find Out about Bugs: Easy Experiments for Young Children. 1999. (Play & Find Out Ser.: Vol. 9). (Illus.). 122p. (ps-2). pap. 12.95 (978-0-471-17663-3(X), Wiley) Wiley, John & Sons, Inc.

Ward, Allison, ed. Investigating Science - Insects & Spiders. 2003. 48p. 9.95 (978-1-56234-571-6(0), Mailbox Bks., The) Education Ctr., Inc.

Ward, Beck. A Bug's World. 2005. (Illus.). 10p. (J). pap. 7.95 (978-0-7624-1985-2(7), Running Pr. Kids) Running Pr. Bk. Pubs.

Wawrychuk, Carol & McSweeney, Cherie. Insects & Spiders: Active Learning about Nature. Chalk, Philip, illus. 1999. 48p. (J). (ps-1). pap. 7.95 (978-1-57612-074-3(0), MM2088) Monday Morning Bks., Inc.

Weaving Wonders. 2006. (Backyard Bugs Ser.). 24p. (J). 7.95 (978-1-4048-1758-6(1)) Picture Window Bks.

Wells, Rosemary. The Itsy-Bitsy Spider. Wells, Rosemary, illus. 1998. (Bruno & Boots Book Ser.). (Illus.). 18p. (J). (ps). bds. 5.99 (978-0-590-02911-7(8)) Scholastic, Inc.

What's This Spider Doing? Individual Title Six-Packs. (Story Steps Ser.). (gr. k-2). 32.00 (978-0-7635-9617-0(5)) Rigby Education.

Wheeler, Jill C. Crab Spiders. 2006. (Illus.). 24p. (J). (gr. k-6). 21.35 (978-1-59679-292-0(2), Checkerboard Library) ABDO Publishing Co.

—Daddy Longlegs Spiders. 2006. (Checkerboard Animal Library). (Illus.). 24p. (J). (gr. k-6). 21.35 (978-1-59679-293-7(0), Checkerboard Library) ABDO Publishing Co.

—Funnel-Web Spiders. 2006. (Illus.). 24p. (J). (gr. k-6). 21.35 (978-1-59679-294-4(9), Checkerboard Library) ABDO Publishing Co.

—Hobo Spiders. 2006. (J). (gr. k-6). 21.35 (978-1-59679-295-1(7), Checkerboard Library) ABDO Publishing Co.

—Recluse Spiders. 2006. (Illus.). 24p. (J). (gr. k-6). 21.35 (978-1-59679-296-8(5), Checkerboard Library) ABDO Publishing Co.

—White-Tailed Spiders. 2006. (Checkerboard Animal Library). (Illus.). 24p. (J). (gr. k-6). 21.35 (978-1-59679-297-5(3), Checkerboard Library) ABDO Publishing Co.

Whitecap Books Staff. Spiders. 2000. (Investigate Ser.). (Illus.). 64p. (J). (gr. 1-7). pap. 3.95 (978-1-55285-127-2(3)) Whitecap Bks., Ltd. CAN. *Dist:* Firefly Bks., Ltd.

Whitehouse, Patricia. Trap-Door Spiders. 2003. (Heinemann Read & Learn Ser.). (Illus.). 24p. (J). pap. 5.75 (978-1-4034-4327-4(0)); lib. bdg. 18.50 (978-1-4034-4318-2(1)) Heinemann Library.

Wildlife Education, Ltd. Staff & Levibiel, Timothy. Spiders. Stuart, Walter, illus. 2001. (Zoobooks Ser.). 24p. (J). 15.95 (978-0-937934-88-3(7)) Wildlife Education, Ltd.

Wimmer, Teresa. Spiders. 2006. (My First Look at Insects Ser.). 24p. (gr. k-2). 15.95 (978-1-58341-456-9(8), Creative Education) Creative Co., The.

Winer, Yvonne. Spiders Spin Webs. Lloyd-Jones, Karen, illus. 1998. 32p. (J). (ps-3). 15.95 (978-0-88106-983-9(3)); pap. 6.95 (978-0-88106-984-6(1)) Charlesbridge Publishing, Inc.

Winner, Cherie. Everything Bug. 2004. (Kids' FAQs Ser.). (Illus.). 64p. (YA). (gr. 2-6). ring bd. 10.95 (978-1-55971-890-5(0), NorthWord Bks. for Young Readers) T&N Children's Publishing.

Woelflein, Luise. The Spider. Narashima, Tomo, illus. 2000. (Giant Look at Little Bugs Ser.). 14p. (J). (ps-k). 12.95 (978-1-58117-097-9(1), Intervisual/Piggy Toes) Dalmatian Pr.

World Book, Inc Staff, contrib. by. Insects, Spiders, & Creepy Crawlers: A Supplement to Childcraft, the How & Why Library. 2007. (J). (***978-0-7166-0618-5(6)***) World Bk., Inc.

World Book, Inc Staff, contrib. by. Pinktoes & Other Tarantulas. 2007. (World Book's Animals of the World Ser.). (Illus.). 64p. (J). (978-0-7166-1332-9(8)) World Bk., Inc.

Zabludoff, Marc. Spiders. 2005. (Animalways Ser.). (Illus.). 112p. (J). (gr. 3-7). lib. bdg. (978-0-7614-1747-7(8), Benchmark Bks.) Cavendish, Marshall Corp.

Zollman, Pam. A Spiderling Grows Up. 2005. (Scholastic News Nonfiction Readers Ser.). (Illus.). 24p. (J). (gr. 1-2). 19.00 (978-0-516-24946-9(0), Children's Pr.) Scholastic Library Publishing.

SPIDERS—FICTION

Ada, Alma Flor. Turkey for Thanksgiving Dinner? No Thanks! 2000. (gr. k-3). lib. bdg. 17.60 (978-0-613-79397-1(8)) Tandem Library Bks.

Aggs, Patrice, illus. Itsy Bitsy Spider: Level One, Red. 1999. (Reading Together Ser.). 32p. (J). pap. (978-0-7636-0872-9(6)) Candlewick Pr.

Anansi the Spider. 2000. (J). 9.95 (978-1-56137-278-2(1)) Novel Units, Inc.

Anansi the Spider. 2004. (J). 24.95 incl. audio (978-0-89719-858-5(1)); pap. 32.75 incl. audio (978-1-55592-185-9(X)); pap. 32.75 incl. audio (978-1-55592-186-6(8)) Weston Woods Studios, Inc.

Anasti, Tedd, et al. Reign of the Soul Eater. 2006. (Spider Riders Ser.). (Illus.). 224p. (YA). pap. 5.99 (978-1-55704-728-1(6)) Newmarket Pr.

Anderson, Jane. Anansi the Spider & the Sky King: A Tale from Africa. 2006. 23.00 (***978-1-4108-6175-7(9)***) Benchmark Education Co.

Azordegan, Kambiz. Dukunoo Island: Anancy the Spider. Sajem, Johnny, illus. abr. l.t. ed. 1998. (Tootee's Magical Stories Ser.: Vol. 3). 34p. (J). 9.95 (978-1-890571-27-6(X)) Positive Children's Programming Corp.

Beetle Dan & the Big Purple Slide. 2006. 32p. pap. 14.99 (978-1-59185-921-5(2), Creation Hse.) Strang Communications Co.

Bentley, Dawn. The Not-So Itsy Bitsy Spider: A Pop-Up Book. Heo, Yumi, illus. 1999. 12p. (J). (ps up). 12.95 (978-1-58117-051-1(3), Intervisual/Piggy Toes) Dalmatian Pr.

Berger, Melvin. Spinning Spiders. Schindler, S. D., illus. 2003. (Let's-Read-and-Find-Out Science Ser.). 40p. (J). (gr. k-4). 15.99 (978-0-06-028696-5(2)); pap. 5.99 (978-0-06-445207-6(7), Harper Trophy) HarperCollins Pubs.

Brightwood, Laura, illus. Anansi & the Turtle. Brightwood, Laura, . 2006. (J). (978-0-9779290-0-9(0)) 3-C Institute for Social Development.

Cameron-Anasti, Patsy, et al, contrib. by. Spider Riders Bk. 1: Shards of the Oracle. movie tie-in ed. 2005. (Illus.). 224p. (J). 15.00 (978-1-55704-653-6(0)); pap. 5.99 (978-1-55704-652-9(2)) Newmarket Pr.

Carle, Eric. La Arana Muy Ocupada. Carle, Eric, illus. 2004. (SPA., Illus.). 32p. (J). (ps-1). 19.99 (978-0-399-24241-0(4), Philomel) Penguin Group (USA) Inc.

—Tell Time with the Very Busy Spider. 2006. (World of Eric Carle Ser.). 18p. (J). (ps-1). bds. 8.99 (978-0-448-44419-2(4), Grosset & Dunlap) Penguin Group (USA) Inc.

—The Very Busy Spider. 2006. (World of Eric Carle Ser.). (Illus.). 24p. (J). (ps-1). pap. 5.99 (978-0-448-44421-5(6), Grosset & Dunlap) Penguin Group (USA) Inc.

—The Very Busy Spider. Carle, Eric, illus. ed. 2000. (Illus.). 32p. (J). 63.96 (978-0-399-23566-5(3), Philomel) Penguin Group (USA) Inc.

Carlson, Melody. Bitsy's Harvest Party. Reagan, Susan Joy, illus. 2005. 32p. (J). (ps-4). 12.99 (978-0-8054-2684-7(1)) B&H Publishing Grp.

Chapman, Keith. Itsy Bitsy Spider. Tickle, Jack, illus. 2006. 32p. (J). 15.95 (978-1-58925-055-0(9), tiger tales) ME Media LLC.

Charlotte's Web. 1998. 40p. (J). 11.95 (978-1-56137-630-8(2), NU6302SP) Novel Units, Inc.

Contijoch, Josefa. Mariquilla va de Fiesta. Filella, Lluis, illus. 2003. (Caballo Alado Ser.). (SPA & ENG.). 24p. 6.95 (978-84-7864-648-7(5)) Combel Editorial, S.A. ESP. *Dist:* Independent Pubs. Group.

Cook, Sherry & Johnson, Terri. Susie Sound, 26. Kuhn, Jesse, illus. l.t. ed. 2006. 32p. (J). 7.99 (978-1-933815-18-3(3), Quirkles, The) Creative 3, LLC.

Cronin, Doreen. Diary of a Spider. Bliss, Harry, illus. 2005. 40p. (J). (ps-3). 15.99 (978-0-06-000153-7(4)); lib. bdg. 16.89 (978-0-06-000154-4(2)) HarperCollins Pubs. (Cotler, Joanna Books).

—Diary of a Spider. Bliss, Harry, illus. unabr. ed. 2006. (Picture Book Readalong Ser.). (J). (ps-3). 25.95 incl. audio (978-1-59519-482-4(7)); 28.95 incl. audio compact disk (978-1-59519-486-2(X)) Live Oak Media.

—Diary of a Spider. Bliss, Harry, illus. unabr. ed. 2006. (J). (ps-3). 24.95 incl. audio (***978-0-439-90573-2(7)***); 29.95 incl. audio compact disk (***978-0-439-90579-4(6)***) Weston Woods Studios, Inc.

Dahl, Roald. James & the Giant Peach. Blake, Quentin, illus. 2002. (J). 13.19 (978-0-7587-6619-9(X)) Book Wholesalers, Inc.

—James & the Giant Peach. 2001. (gr. 3-6). lib. bdg. 14.15 (978-0-613-35965-8(8)); (Illus.). (J). 12.64 (978-0-606-20734-8(1)) Tandem Library Bks.

Dewey, Jennifer Owings. Once I Knew a Spider. Cassels, Jean, illus. 2002. 32p. (J). (ps-3). 16.95 (978-0-8027-8700-2(2)) Walker & Co.

Donaldson, Julia. Spinderella. Pichon, Liz, illus. 2005. (Blue Go Bananas Ser.). 48p. (J). (978-0-7787-2628-9(2)) Crabtree Publishing Co.

—Spinderella. Pochon, Liz, illus. 2005. (Blue Go Bananas Ser.). 48p. (J). pap. (978-0-7787-2650-0(9)) Crabtree Publishing Co.

Dubarle-Bossy, Philippe & Shulman, Mark. Spooky Spider. Jennings, Patti, illus. 2004. 8p. (J). bds. 7.95 (978-1-4027-1590-7(0), Sterling/Pinwheel) Sterling Publishing Co., Inc.

Evenson, Inge, text. Serafina's Silver Web: A Project to Benefit Noah's Children. 1999. (Illus.). 40p. (J). (978-0-9674273-0-0(4)) Noah's Children, Inc.

Ewers, Hans Heinz. The Spider. 2004. reprint ed. pap. 15.95 (978-1-4191-8326-3(5)); pap. 1.99 (978-1-4192-8326-0(X)) Kessinger Publishing, LLC.

Finn, Isobel. La Mariquita Perezosa. 2003. (SPA., Illus.). 26p. (J). (978-84-8418-029-6(8), ZZ4475) Zendrera Zariquiey, Editorial ESP. *Dist:* Lectorum Pubns., Inc.

Fletcher, Ralph. Spider Boy. 1998. 183p. (J). (ps-7). per. 13.00 (978-0-613-08798-8(4)) Tandem Library Bks.

Fogelin, Adrian. Sister Spider Knows All. 2003. 224p. (J). (gr. 3-6). 14.95 (978-1-56145-290-3(4), Q35925) Peachtree Pubs., Ltd.

Foglio, Phil & Foglio, Kaja. Agatha Heterodyne & the Circus of Dreams. 2006. (Girl Genius Ser.: Bk. 4). (Illus.). 128p. pap. 20.95 (978-1-890856-36-6(3)) Studio Foglio, LLC.

Foote, Norman. Spider Dan. Mitchell, Charlie, illus. 2001. 32p. (J). (ps). pap. 4.95 (978-1-55285-276-7(8)) Whitecap Bks., Ltd. CAN. *Dist:* Firefly Bks., Ltd.

Freeman, Don. Manuelo, the Playing Mantis. McCue, Lisa, illus. 2004. 32p. (J). (ps-8). 15.99 (978-0-670-03684-4(6), Viking Juvenile) Penguin Group (USA) Inc.

—Manuelo, the Playing Mantis. 2006. (Illus.). 32p. (J). reprint ed. pap. 5.99 (978-0-14-240560-4(4), Puffin) Penguin Group (USA) Inc.

Frontiera, Deborah. Eric & the Enchanted Leaf. 2002. (Illus.). 20p. 4.99 (978-1-58608-653-4(7)) New Concepts Publishing.

Galajda, Kathleen L. The Spiders Meet the Children. 2004. 163p. pap. 19.95 (978-1-4137-4923-6(2)) PublishAmerica, Inc.

Gilson, Jamie. Gotcha! Wummer, Amy, illus. 2006. 80p. (J). (gr. k-3). 15.00 (978-0-618-54356-4(2), Clarion Bks.) Houghton Mifflin Co. Trade & Reference Div.

The Granpa Spider Stories. 2002. (J). pap., tchr.'s training gde. ed. 12.95 (978-0-9676256-5-2(3)) Golden Quill Pr.

Graves, Sue. Miss Muffet & the Spider. Warburton, Sarah, illus. 2005. (Reading Corner Ser.). 24p. (J). (gr. k-3). lib. bdg. 22.80 (978-1-932889-99-4(X)) Sea-To-Sea Pubns.

Harper, Charise Mericle. Itsy Bitsy, the Smart Spider. Harper, Charise Mericle, illus. 2004. (Illus.). 32p. (J). (ps). 9.99 (978-0-8037-2901-8(4), Dial) Penguin Group (USA) Inc.

Heiner, Garth Farr. Unwanted Muddy. Melander, Eric, illus. l.t. unabr. ed. 2001. (Fun-with-the-Law Ser.: No. 5). 32p. (J). (gr. k-7). pap. 5.95 (978-1-929905-05-8(X)) Fun With the Law, Inc.

Herman, Gail. Spiders Everywhere. Zimmerman, Jerry, illus. 2000. (Hello Reader! Ser.). (J). pap. (978-0-439-20540-5(9)) Scholastic, Inc.

Hilton, Nette. Web. 1998. (Illus.). 88p. (ps-3). 5.95 (978-0-207-17245-8(5)) HarperCollins Pubs.

Holub, Joan. More Snacks! A Thanksgiving Play. Terry, Will, illus. 2006. (Ant Hill Ser.). 24p. (J). pap. 3.99 (978-1-4169-0954-5(0), Aladdin); lib. bdg. 11.89 (978-1-4169-2559-0(7), Aladdin Library) Simon & Schuster Children's Publishing.

ImageBooks. Little Spider: Finger Puppet Book. 2007. (Illus.). 12p. (J). (ps). 6.95 (***978-0-8118-6104-5(X)***) Chronicle Bks. LLC.

The Itsy Bitsy Spider. 2001. (Take-Home Bks.). (YA). (ps-k). 15.00 (978-0-8215-6986-3(4)) Sadlier, William H. Inc.

Johnson, Kimberly P. The Adventures of the Itty Bitty Spider & the Itty Bitty Mouse. 2004. (Illus.). 31p. (gr. k-2). 14.95 (978-1-57197-236-1(6)) Pentland Pr., Inc.

Kahn, Katherine Janus & Rouss, Sylvia A. Sammy Spider's First Sukkot. 2004. (Illus.). 32p. (J). (ps-3). (978-1-58013-142-1(5)); pap. (978-1-58013-083-7(6)) Kar-Ben Publishing.

Kain, Kathleen E. Acid Attack: The Science Spiders(TM) Demonstrate Acids & Bases. 1999. (Illus.). 32p. (J). (gr. k-3). pap. 5.95 (978-1-892221-07-0(1), RW0567) Ranch Works.

—Broken Bones: The Science Spiders(TM) Investigate Forces. 1999. (Illus.). 32p. (J). (gr. k-3). pap. 5.95 (978-1-892221-06-3(3), RW0566) Ranch Works.

—The Experience: The Science Spiders Learn Colors. 1999. (Illus.). 32p. (J). (gr. k-3). pap. 5.95 (978-1-892221-01-8(2), RW0561) Ranch Works.

—Secret Tricks: The Science Spiders(TM) Investigate Air Pressure. 1999. (Illus.). 32p. (J). (gr. k-3). pap. 5.95 (978-1-892221-05-6(5), RW0565) Ranch Works.

Kean, Lorraine. Spiders in the Woods. 2002. 113p. pap. 16.95 (978-1-59129-580-8(7)) PublishAmerica, Inc.

Keens-Douglas, Richardo. Anancy & the Haunted House. Jorisch, Stephane, illus. 2002. 32p. (J). (ps-2). pap. 7.95 (978-1-55037-736-1(1)); lib. bdg. 19.95 (978-1-55037-737-8(X)) Annick Pr., Ltd. CAN. *Dist:* Firefly Bks., Ltd.

—Anancy & the Haunted House. 2002. (ps-2). lib. bdg. 16.40 (978-0-613-51104-9(2)) Tandem Library Bks.

Kelly, Martin & Legris, Phil. Itsy Bitsy Spider. (Illus.). 6p. (J). 4.95 (978-1-929766-25-3(4)) Handprint Bks.

Kimmel, Eric A. Anansi Series. Stevens, Janet, illus. 2003. pap. 68.95 incl. audio compact disk (978-1-59112-840-3(4)); Set. (J). pap. 61.95 incl. audio (978-0-87499-469-8(1)) Live Oak Media.

King-Smith, David. Emily's Legs. 2002. (Illus.). 64p. (J). pap. 7.99 (978-0-340-85408-2(1), Hodder & Stoughton) Hodder General Publishing Division GBR. *Dist:* Trafalgar Square Publishing.

Kirk, David. Basketberry Blues. 2006. (Miss Spider Ser.). (Illus.). 32p. (J). 6.99 (978-0-448-44118-4(7), Grosset & Dunlap) Penguin Group (USA) Inc.

—Bedtime Story. 2006. (Miss Spider Ser.). (Illus.). 32p. (J). 6.99 (978-0-448-44367-6(8)) Penguin Group (USA) Inc.

—Bedtime Story/David Kirk. 2006. (Illus.). 32p. (J). (***978-1-4156-8869-4(9)***); (***978-0-448-44514-4(X)***) Penguin Group (USA) Inc.

—A Bug-a-Boo Day Play. 2005. (Miss Spider's Sunny Patch Friends Ser.). (Illus.). 24p. (J). (ps-2). pap. 3.99 (978-0-448-43803-0(8), Grosset & Dunlap) Penguin Group (USA) Inc.

—The Bug Flu. 2007. 32p. (J). (ps-2). 6.99 (***978-0-448-44691-2(X)***) Callaway Editions, Inc.

—Bug Your Mom Day. 2006. (Miss Spider Ser.). 24p. (J). (ps-2). pap. 5.99 (978-0-448-44269-3(8), Grosset & Dunlap) Penguin Group (USA) Inc.

—Bug's Away. 2005. (Miss Spider's Sunny Patch Friends Ser.). 24p. (J). (ps-1). pap. 4.99 (978-0-448-43990-7(5), Grosset & Dunlap) Penguin Group (USA) Inc.

—Busy, Buggy Day. 2005. (Miss Spider Ser.). (Illus.). 8p. (J). (ps-1). bds. 7.99 (978-0-448-43989-1(1), Grosset & Dunlap) Penguin Group (USA) Inc.

—Captain Sunny Patch. 2006. (Illus.). 32p. (J). (***978-1-4156-8868-7(0)***); (***978-0-448-44515-1(8)***) Callaway Editions, Inc.

—A Cloudy Day in Sunny Patch. 2005. (Miss Spider Ser.). (Illus.). 32p. (J). (gr. k-1). 6.99 (978-0-448-43897-9(6)) Callaway Editions, Inc.

—Fun with Bounce. 2005. (Miss Spider's Sunny Patch Friends Ser.). 32p. (J). (ps-1). pap. 4.99 (978-0-448-43804-7(6), Grosset & Dunlap) Penguin Group (USA) Inc.

—Little Miss Spider. (Miss Spider Ser.). (J). 2003. (Illus.). 32p. pap. 5.99 (978-0-439-54315-6(0)); 1999. 155.40 (978-0-439-11737-1(2)) Scholastic, Inc.

—Little Miss Spider. Kirk, David, illus. 1999. (Miss Spider Ser.). (Illus.). 32p. (J). (ps-2). pap. 12.95 (978-0-439-08389-8(3)) Scholastic, Inc.

—Little Miss Spider at Sunny Patch School. Kirk, David, illus. (Miss Spider Ser.). (Illus.). 32p. (J). 2003. pap. 5.99 (978-0-439-54316-3(9)); 2000. pap. 12.95 (978-0-439-08727-8(9)) Scholastic, Inc.

—Little Miss Spider at Sunnypatch School. Kirk, David, illus. 2002. (Little Miss Spider Ser.). (Illus.). (J). 21.85 (978-0-7587-3008-4(X)) Book Wholesalers, Inc.

—Little Miss Spider's Christmas Wish: A Christmas Wish. Kirk, David, illus. 2001. (Miss Spider Ser.). (Illus.). 32p. (J). (ps-2). pap. 12.95 (978-0-439-31463-3(1), Levine, Arthur A. Bks.) Scholastic, Inc.

—Miss Spider: All Pupa'ed Out. 2005. (Miss Spider Ser.). 32p. (J). (ps-2). pap. 3.99 (978-0-448-43802-3(X), Grosset & Dunlap) Penguin Group (USA) Inc.

—Miss Spider Boxset: The Counting Book; New Car; ABC. 2003. (Illus.). (J). 12.95 (978-0-439-54317-0(7)) Scholastic, Inc.

—Miss Spider's ABC. Kirk, David, illus. 1998. (Miss Spider Ser.). (Illus.). 32p. (J). (ps-2). pap. 16.95 (978-0-590-28279-6(4)) Scholastic, Inc.

—Miss Spider's ABC: New Board Book Edition. Kirk, David, illus. 2000. (Miss Spider Ser.). (Illus.). 32p. (J). (ps-2). bds. 8.95 (978-0-439-13747-8(0), Scholastic Reference) Scholastic, Inc.

—Miss Spider's Family Album. 2005. (Miss Spider's Sunny Patch Friends Ser.). (Illus.). 16p. (J). (ps-1). bds. 7.99 (978-0-448-43829-0(1), Grosset & Dunlap) Penguin Group (USA) Inc.

—Miss Spider's New Car. Kirk, David, illus. 1999. (Miss Spider Ser.). (Illus.). 32p. (J). (ps-2). bds. 8.95 (978-0-439-04675-6(0)) Scholastic, Inc.

—Miss Spider's Sunny Patch Surprise. 2005. (Play-a-Sound Ser.). (Illus.). 24p. (J). 15.98 (978-1-4127-3558-2(0), 7262900) Publications International, Ltd.

—The Most Perfect Parent: Miss Spiders Sunny Patch Friends. 2007. 32p. (J). (ps-2). 6.99 (***978-0-448-44692-9(8)***) Callaway Editions, Inc.

—Sing It, Sister! 2005. (Miss Spider's Sunny Patch Friends Ser.). (Illus.). 32p. (J). (ps-1). pap. 3.99 (978-0-448-43974-7(3), Grosset & Dunlap) Penguin Group (USA) Inc.

—Spotlight on Shimmer! 2005. (Miss Spider Ser.). 10p. (J). bds. 7.99 (978-0-448-44252-5(3), Grosset & Dunlap) Penguin Group (USA) Inc.

—Top O' Big Tree. 2006. (Miss Spider Ser.). (Illus.). 32p. (J). 6.99 (978-0-448-44120-7(9), Grosset & Dunlap) Penguin Group (USA) Inc.

Kirk, David & Scholastic, Inc. Staff. Miss Spider's Sunny Patch Kids. Rees, Jenifer, ed. 2004. (Illus.). 40p. (J). pap. 14.95 (978-0-439-40870-7(9), Scholastic Pr.) Scholastic, Inc.

Kompelien, Tracy. Spider Web. Haberstroh, Anne, illus. 2007. (Fact & Fiction Ser.). 24p. (J). pap. (978-1-59928-475-0(8)); 21.35 (978-1-59928-474-3(X)) ABDO Publishing Co.

Krenina, Katya, illus. The Spider's Gift: A Ukrainian Christmas Story. 2005. (J). (978-0-8234-1743-8(3)) Holiday Hse., Inc.

Lasky, Kathryn. Show & Tell Bunnies. Hafner, Marylin, illus. 2001. 32p. (J). (ps-3). pap. 5.99 (978-0-7636-1050-0(X)) Candlewick Pr.

—Show & Tell Bunnies. 2001. (ps-2). lib. bdg. 14.15 (978-0-613-44257-2(1)) Tandem Library Bks.

Law, Felicia. Rumble Meets Chester the Chef. Pak, Yoon Mi, illus. 2006. (Read-It! Readers Ser.). 32p. (J). (gr. 2-4). 18.60 (978-1-4048-1335-9(7)) Picture Window Bks.

—Rumble Meets Lucas Lizard. Pak, Yoon Mi, illus. 2006. (Read-It! Readers Ser.). 32p. (J). (gr. 2-4). 18.60 (978-1-4048-1334-2(9)) Picture Window Bks.

—Rumble Meets Randy Rabbit. Pak, Yoon Mi, illus. 2006. (Read-It! Readers Ser.). 32p. (J). (gr. 2-4). 18.60 (978-1-4048-1337-3(3)) Picture Window Bks.

—Rumble Meets Shelby Spider. 2005. (Read-It! Readers Ser.). (Illus.). 32p. (J). (ps-k). lib. bdg. 18.60 (978-1-4048-1286-4(5)) Picture Window Bks.

—Rumble Meets Wally Warthog. 2005. (Read-It! Readers Ser.). (Illus.). 32p. (J). (ps-k). lib. bdg. 18.60 (978-1-4048-1289-5(X)) Picture Window Bks.

Leaney, Cindy. Super Sale. Whitehouse, Patty, ed. King, Sue & Wilks, Peter, illus. 2004. (Friendly Phonics Ser.). 24p. (J). lib. bdg. 14.95 (978-1-59054-231-6(2)) Fitzgerald Bks.

Lombardi, Kristine. Little Spider's First Web. Williamson, James, illus. 2006. 10p. (J). bds. 14.99 (978-0-7944-1008-7(1)) Reader's Digest Assn., Inc., The.

London, Jonathan. Dream Weaver. Baviera, Rocco, illus. 1998. 32p. (YA). (ps-4). 17.00 (978-0-15-200944-1(2) , Silver Whistle) Harcourt Trade Pubs.

Lucado, Max. Hermie y Wormie en un Diluvio de Mentiras. 2004. (SPA.). 24p. (J). bds. 10.99 (978-0-88113-775-0(8)) Grupo Nelson.

Lucado, Max, creator. Webster, the Scaredy Spider. 2004. (Max Lucado's Hermie & Friends Ser.). 16p. (J). bds. 6.99 (978-1-4003-0508-7(X)) Nelson, Thomas Inc.

Lucado, Max & Schmidt, Troy. Webster, the Scaredy Spider. 2005. 32p. (J). pap. 3.99 (978-1-4003-0665-7(5)) Nelson, Thomas Inc.

Lyssenko, Taras. Wendy's Fear of Heights. 2003. 14p. (J). (978-0-9740542-0-9(8)) Prairie Shore Creative, Inc.

Mabee, Kerri. If Spiders Were Purple & Sparkly. Wise, Noreen, ed. Wethington, Liz, illus. 2000. (Book-a-Day Collection). 32p. (YA). pap. 5.95 (978-1-58584-401-2(2)) Huckleberry Pr.

Maguire, Gregory. Seven Spiders Spinning: Y Gregory Maguire. l.t. ed. 2002. (J). 21.95 (978-0-7862-4419-5(4)) Thorndike Pr.

Martin, Patricia. Lulu Atlantis & the Quest for True Blue Love. 2008. (J). (***978-0-375-84016-6(8));** 240p. (gr. 2-6). lib. bdg. 17.99 (***978-0-375-94016-3(2))*** Random Hse. Children's Bks. (Schwartz & Wade Bks.).

Max, Jill, compiled by. Spider Spins a Story: Fourteen Legends from Native America. 2007. (J). pap. 7.95 (***978-0-87358-936-9(X)*** , Rising Moon Bks. for Young Readers) Northland Publishing.

McDermott, Gerald. Anansi the Spider: A Tale from the Ashanti. McDermott, Gerald, illus. 2002. (Illus.). (J). 15.49 (978-0-7587-0090-2(3)) Book Wholesalers, Inc.

Miller, Alan. The Litluns & the Golden Spider Web. 2005. 61p. pap. 12.95 (978-1-4137-6444-4(4)) PublishAmerica, Inc.

Miss Spider & Kirk, David. Oh Boy, It's Bounce! Miss Spider's Sunny Patch Friends. 2005. (Miss Spider Ser.). (Illus.). 8p. (J). (ps-2). bds. 7.99 (978-0-448-44010-1(5) , Grosset & Dunlap) Penguin Group (USA) Inc.

Miss Spider Activity Kit. 2005. (Illus.). (J). (978-0-448-44063-7(6) , Grosset & Dunlap) Penguin Group (USA) Inc.

Miss Spider's Tea Party. 2003. (J). pap. 19.95 (978-0-439-54314-9(2)) Scholastic, Inc.

Monks, Lydia. Aaaarrgghh, Spider! 2004. (Illus.). 32p. (J). (***978-1-4052-0688-4(8));*** pap. (***978-1-4052-1044-7(3))*** Egmont Bks., Ltd.

—Aaaarrgghh, Spider! (Illus.). 32p. (J). (gr. k-3). 2007. pap. 7.95 (***978-0-618-73751-2(0));*** 2004. 16.00 (978-0-618-43250-9(7)) Houghton Mifflin Co. Trade & Reference Div.

Moore. Dark at the Foot of the Stairs. (Illus.). 92p. (J). pap. (978-0-340-64873-5(2) , Hodder & Stoughton) Hodder General Publishing Division.

Morgan, C. M. Silver Doorway #2: Dwarves in the Dark. 2003. 104p. (J). pap. (978-0-9702189-3-3(1)) Sabledrake Enterprises.

Moulton, Mark Kimball. One Enchanted Evening. Crouch, Karen Hillard, illus. 2003. 32p. (J). 14.95 (978-0-8249-5480-2(7)) Ideals Pubns.

—One Enchanted Evening. Crouch, Karen Hillard, illus. 2000. 32p. (J). (gr. k-3). 18.00 (978-0-7412-0439-4(8)) Lang Graphics, Ltd.

Moulton, Mark Kimball. A Royal Wedding. Good, Karen Hillard, illus. 2007. 32p. (J). (gr. k-3). 14.99 (***978-0-8249-8677-3(6))*** Ideals Pubns.

Nagda, Ann Whitehead. Tarantula Power! Roth, Stéphanie, illus. 2007. 96p. (J). (gr. 2-5). 15.95 (978-0-8234-1991-3(6)) Holiday Hse., Inc.

Norfolk, Bobby. Anansi & the Pot of Beans. 2006. (Illus.). 32p. (J). pap. 3.95 (978-0-87483-811-4(8)) August Hse. Pubs., Inc.

Olson, Kevin Noel. Eerey Tocsin in the Cryptoid Zoo. Hammack, Debi, illus. 2006. (YA). per. 15.95 (***978-1-887560-17-7(3)*** , Cornerstone Bk. Publishers) Poll, Michael Publishing.

Osborne, Mary Pope. The Mysteries of Spider Kane. 2006. 240p. (J). (gr. 4-7). 5.99 (978-0-440-42097-2(0) , Yearling) Random Hse. Children's Bks.

Pantelides, Sherry. Make A Choice to Rejoice! A Story about Being Cheerful. Perez, Debi, illus. 2007. 32p. (J). 12.99 (***978-0-9771076-2-9(0))*** Lacey Productions.

Petty, Kate. Nightspinners. Smith, Mary Claire, illus. 2005. 32p. (J). 14.99 (978-1-85881-836-8(2)) Orion Children's Bks. GBR. *Dist:* Trafalgar Square Publishing.

Phillips, Gina & Martin, Stuart. Ants & Caterpillars. 2003. (Busy Bugs Ser.). 12p. (J). bds. 14.95 (978-1-74047-240-1(3)) Book Co. Publishing Pty, Ltd., The AUS. *Dist:* Penton Overseas, Inc.

Posner, Fran. Halloween Makes Me Batty! 2007. (Illus.). 12p. (J). (gr. k-k). bds. 3.99 (***978-0-7364-2458-5(X)*** , Golden Bks.) Random Hse. Children's Bks.

Powell, Richard. Tiny Spider. Martín Larrañaga, Ana, illus. 2001. 10p. bds. 5.95 (978-1-58925-663-7(8) , tiger tales) ME Media LLC.

Rand, Jonathan. Sinister Spiders or Saginaw. 2001. (Michigan Chillers: Vol. 9). 265p. (YA). pap. 5.99 (978-1-893699-15-1(3)) AudioCraft Publishing, Inc.

Randall, Rod. Along Came a Spider. 2000. (Heebie Jeebies Ser.: Vol. 7). 138p. (J). (gr. 3-7). pap. 5.99 (978-0-8054-1981-8(0)) B&H Publishing Grp.

Rigby Education Staff. Baby Kangaroo. (Sails Literacy Ser.). (Illus.). 16p. (gr. k-1). 27.00 (978-0-7635-9879-2(8) , 698798C99) Rigby Education.

Rouss, Sylvia A. Lots of Latkes. Kahn, Katherine Janus, illus. 2003. 32p. (J). (ps-3). pap. 6.95 (978-1-58013-061-5(5)) Kar-Ben Publishing.

—Sammy Spider Series, 11 vols., Set. Kahn, Katherine Janus, illus. 2003. (J). (ps-3). 70.61 (978-1-58013-046-2(1)) Kar-Ben Publishing.

—Sammy Spider's First Haggadah. Kahn, Katherine Janus, illus. 2007. 32p. (J). pap. 5.95 (***978-1-58013-230-5(8))*** Kar-Ben Publishing.

—Sammy Spider's First Israel: A Book about the Five Senses. Kahn, Katherine Janus, illus. 2002. 32p. (J). (ps-3). pap. 7.95 (978-1-58013-035-6(6)) Kar-Ben Publishing.

—Sammy Spider's First Israel: A Book about the Five Senses. 2002. lib. bdg. 16.40 (978-0-613-81763-9(X)) Tandem Library Bks.

—Sammy Spider's First Purim. Kahn, Katherine Janus, illus. 2000. 32p. (J). (ps-3). pap. 7.95 (978-1-58013-062-2(3)) Kar-Ben Publishing.

—Sammy Spider's First Shavuot. Kahn, Katherine, illus. 2008. (J). lib. bdg. (***978-0-8225-7224-4(9))*** Kar-Ben Publishing.

—Sammy Spider's First Tu B'Shevat. Kahn, Katherine Janus, illus. 2000. 32p. (J). (ps-3). pap. 7.95 (978-1-58013-065-3(8)) Kar-Ben Publishing.

—Sammy Spider's Hanukkah Fun Book. Kahn, Katherine Janus, illus. 2003. 24p. (J). (ps-3). pap. 4.95 (978-1-58013-032-5(1)) Kar-Ben Publishing.

—Sammy Spider's Israel Fun Book. (Illus.). 24p. (J). (ps-3). pap. (978-1-58013-119-3(0)) Kar-Ben Publishing.

Sanders, Terri L. Rainbow Spider. 2003. E-Book 4.95 incl. cd-rom (978-1-59201-011-0(3)) Bks. Unbound E-Publishing Co.

Schandle, Julie. Little Wishes Big Dreams: Around the World. 2005. (Illus.). 22p. (J). 11.95 (978-0-9771868-0-8(6) , 303-503-3289) Big Dreams Publishing.

Scholastic, Inc. Staff. Taggies Libros con Lacitos: La Arana Chiquitita. 2007. (My First Taggies Book Ser.). 10p. (J). bds. 6.99 (***978-0-439-92737-6(4)*** , Scholastic en Espanol) Scholastic, Inc.

Schuyer, Silvia. Arana Madrina. Bernalene, Poly, illus. 2001. Tr. of Godmother Spider. (SPA.). 24p. (J). 12.50 (978-950-08-2572-6(4)) Atlantida ARG. *Dist:* AIMS International Bks., Inc.

Scorpions. 1999. (YA). 9.95 (978-1-56137-293-5(5)) Novel Units, Inc.

Scorpions. 2003. 50p. (YA). tchr. ed., ring bd. (978-1-58049-470-0(6) , TU226) Prestwick Hse., Inc.

Seuling, Barbara. Robert & the Attack of the Giant Tarantula. Brewer, Paul, illus. 2003. (Oh No, It's Robert Ser.). 64p. (J). pap. 3.99 (978-0-439-23545-7(6) , Scholastic Paperbacks) Scholastic, Inc.

Shan, Darren, pseud. A Living Nightmare. 2001. (Cirque du Freak: Bk. 1). (J). 272p. (gr. k-3). 15.95 (978-0-316-60340-9(6)); (Illus.). viii, 279p. (gr. 3-6). pap. (978-0-316-64852-3(3)) Little, Brown Bks. for Young Readers.

Shen, Michele. The Spider & the Bee. Shen, Michele, illus. 2002. (Illus.). 32p. (J). 4.95 (978-1-929132-25-6(5)) Kane/Miller Bk. Pubs., Inc.

Shields, Carol Diggory. The Bugliest Bug. Nash, Scott, illus. 2002. 32p. (J). (ps-3). 16.99 (978-0-7636-0784-5(3)) Candlewick Pr.

Smith, Pamela Colman. Annancy Stories. 2006. (YA). reprint ed. pap. 19.99 (978-0-9769612-2-2(9) , Pixiefire) Darker Intentiona Pr.

Smith, Todd Aaron. The Scarecrow & the Spider. 2005. (Illus.). 32p. (J). 9.99 (978-1-4003-0550-6(0)) Nelson, Thomas Inc.

Soundprints. Itsy Bitsy Spider: And Other Favorites. (Meet Mother Goose Ser.). (Illus.). 36p. (J). 2005. bds. 10.95 incl. audio compact disk (978-1-931465-31-2(1) , MD1100); 2005. bds. 14.95 incl. audio compact disk (978-1-931465-51-9(7) , MPD1100); 2002. bds. 8.95 (978-1-931465-25-0(8) , Little Soundprints) Soundprints.

Spider Night! (Early Intervention Levels Ser.). 28.38 (978-0-7362-0411-8(3)) Hampton-Brown Bks.

The Spider Who Never Gave Up. 2004. (J). (978-0-9759077-0-2(0)) Flores, Travis.

Spinelli, Eileen & Dyer, Jane. Sophie's Masterpiece: A Spider's Tale. (Illus.). 32p. (J). (ps). 2001. 16.99 (978-0-689-80112-9(2)); 2004. reprint ed. pap. 6.99 (978-0-689-86680-7(1) , Aladdin) Simon & Schuster Children's Publishing.

Stanley, George Edward. Cobweb Confession. 2001. (gr. 3-6). lib. bdg. 11.80 (978-0-613-35666-4(7)) Tandem Library Bks.

—The Cobweb Confession, No. 4. 2001. (Third Grade Detectives Ser.). (Illus.). (J). 10.79 (978-0-606-20942-7(5)) Tandem Library Bks.

Strockyj, Sonia. The Spider & the Christmas Tree. 2004. 12p. per. 7.95 (978-1-59453-537-6(X) , 2727) Airleaf Publishing & Bookselling.

Sydor, Colleen. Raising a Little Stink. Constantin, Pascale, illus. 2006. 32p. 16.95 (978-1-55337-896-9(2)) Kids Can Pr., Ltd. CAN. *Dist:* Wybel Marketing Group.

Taylor, Sean. Purple Class & the Flying Spider. Bate, Helen, illus. 2006. 96p. (J). pap. 7.95 (978-1-84507-627-6(3)) Lincoln, Frances Ltd. GBR. *Dist:* Perseus Distribution.

Trapani, Iza. The Itsy Bitsy Spider. Trapani, Iza, illus. 1998. (Illus.). 26p. (J). (ps-1). bds. 6.95 (978-1-58089-014-4(8)) Charlesbridge Publishing, Inc.

—Sing along with Iza & Friends: The Itsy Bitsy Spider. Trapani, Iza, illus. 2004. (Illus.). 32p. (J). pap. 9.95 incl. audio compact disk (978-1-58089-100-4(4)) Charlesbridge Publishing, Inc.

Wang, Margaret. Eency Weency Spider. Rueda, Claudia, illus. 2005. 22p. (J). (ps-ps). 10.95 (978-1-58117-418-2(7) , Intervisual/Piggy Toes) Dalmatian Pr.

—Mini Eency Weency Spider. 2006. 12p. (J). 5.95 (978-1-58117-505-9(1) , Intervisual/Piggy Toes) Dalmatian Pr.

Ward, Nick. Squash the Spider! 2004. (Illus.). 40p. (J). (gr. k-3). 9.95 (978-0-385-75017-2(X) , Fickling, David Bks.) Random Hse. Children's Bks.

Weber, Lou, ed. Miss Spider Musical Treasury. 2005. 38p. 12.98 (978-1-4127-3488-2(6)) Publications International, Ltd.

Wenzel, Karen M. The Fan Tom Spider: A Flower Forest Wedding. Stadlberger, Kristy G., illus. 1999. 39p. (J). (gr. 6-12). pap. (978-0-9656714-7-7(X)) WNZ Pubns.

White. Tela di Carlotta. pap. 13.95 (978-88-04-46241-5(8)) Mondadori ITA. *Dist:* Distribooks, Inc.

White, E. B. Charlotte's Web. Williams, Garth, illus. 2002. (J). 34.64 (978-0-7587-0178-7(0)) Book Wholesalers, Inc.

—Charlotte's Web. Williams, Garth & Wells, Rosemary, illus. 2001. 192p. (J). (gr. 5 up). pap. 8.99 (978-0-06-441093-9(5) , Harper Trophy) HarperCollins Pubs.

—Charlotte's Web. Williams, Garth, illus. collector's ed. 192p. (J). 1999. (gr. 4-7). 24.99 (978-0-06-028298-1(3)); 2006. mass mkt. 7.99 (978-0-06-122874-2(5) , Harper Trophy) HarperCollins Pubs.

—Charlotte's Web. Williams, Garth & Wells, Rosemary, illus. 50th anniv. ed. 2002. (J). 29.95 (978-0-06-000698-3(6)) HarperCollins Pubs.

—Charlotte's Web. Williams, Garth, illus. l.t. ed. 1999. (LRS Large Print Cornerstone Ser.). 310p. (J). (gr. 2-8). lib. bdg. 29.95 (978-1-58118-050-3(0) , 22772) LRS.

—Charlotte's Web. Williams, Garth, illus. 184p. (J). pap. 5.95 (978-0-8072-8305-9(3) , Listening Library) Random Hse. Audio Publishing Group.

—Charlotte's Web. unabr. ed. 2004. 184p. (J). (gr. 3-7). pap. 36.00 incl. audio (978-0-8072-8304-2(5) , YYA156SP, Listening Library) Random Hse. Audio Publishing Group.

—Charlotte's Web. 2001. (gr. 3-6). lib. bdg. 17.60 (978-0-613-81689-2(7)) Tandem Library Bks.

—Charlotte's Web/Stuart Little Slipcase, Set. Williams, Garth, illus. collector's gif. ed. 2004. (J). 49.99 (978-0-06-073940-9(1)) HarperCollins Pubs.

—Wilbur's Adventure. Kneen, Maggie, illus. 2008. (Charlotte's Web Ser.). 32p. (J). (gr. k-2). 16.99 (***978-0-06-078164-4(5))*** HarperCollins Pubs.

—Wilbur's Adventure: A Charlotte's Web Picture Book. Kneen, Maggie, illus. 2008. (Charlotte's Web Ser.). 32p. (J). 17.89 (***978-0-06-078165-1(3))*** HarperCollins Pubs.

Willner-Pardo, Gina. Spider Storch's Desperate Deal. Sharratt, Nick, illus. 1999. 69p. (J). (gr. 2-5). pap. 3.95 (978-0-8075-7589-5(5)) Whitman, Albert & Co.

Wilson, David Henry. Can a Spider Learn to Fly? Scheffler, Axel, illus. l.t. ed. 2000. 143p. (J). pap. 16.95 (978-0-7540-6112-0(4) , Galaxy Children's Large Print) BBC Audiobooks America.

Wilson, George H. The Message of the Writing Spider. 2008. (Illus.). 50p. (J). 14.99 (***978-0-9778477-1-6(3))*** Storyplus, Inc., A.

Winter, Barbara. Spider Saga. 2004. (Amazing Dictionary Ser.). (Illus.). 64p. pap. 4.95 (978-0-921156-96-3(0)) Rubicon Publishing, Inc. CAN. *Dist:* International Publishers Marketing.

SPIES

see also Secret Service; World War, 1939-1945—Underground Movements

see also subdivisions Secret Service and Underground Movements under individual wars, e.g. World War, 1939-1945—Secret Service; World War, 1939-1945—Underground Movements.

Abraham, Philip. The CIA. 2003. (High-Top Secret Ser.). (Illus.). 48p. (J). 23.00 (978-0-516-24316-0(0) , Children's Pr.) Scholastic Library Publishing.

Allen, Thomas B. George Washington, Spymaster: How the Americans Outspied the British & Won the Revolutionary War. 2007. (Illus.). 192p. (J). (gr. 5). pap. 5.95 (978-1-4263-0041-7(7) , National Geographic Children's Bks.) National Geographic Society.

Baker, David. Infiltration & Spying. 2006. (Fighting Terrorism Ser.). (Illus.). 48p. (gr. 4-8). 20.95 (978-1-59515-486-6(8)) Rourke Publishing, LLC.

Beck, Esther. Cool Spy Supplies: Fun Top Secret Science Projects. 2007. (Cool Science Ser.). (Illus.). 32p. (J). (gr. k-6). lib. bdg. 24.21 (***978-1-59928 911-3(3)*** , Checkerboard Library) ABDO Publishing Co.

Becker, Helaine. Secret Agent Y. O. U. The Official Guide to Secret Codes, Disguises, Surveillance, & More. Perez, Ramon & Whamond, Dave, illus. 2006. 64p. 21.95 (978-1-897066-68-3(6)); pap. 9.95 (978-1-897066-69-0(4)) Maple Tree Pr. CAN. *Dist:* Perseus Distribution.

Bodie, Idella. Spunky Revolutionary War Heroine. 2000. (Heroes & Heroines of the American Revolution Ser.). (Illus.). 38p. (J). 5.95 (978-0-87844-154-9(9)) Sandlapper Publishing Co., Inc.

Botones para el General Washington (Buttons for General Washington) 2006. (J). pap. 5.95 (978-0-8225-6617-5(6) , Ediciones Lerner) Lerner Publishing Group.

Brian, Sarah Jane. Brainiac's Secret Agent: Fun Activities for Spies of All Ages. 2005. (Activity Journal Ser.). 128p. act. bk. ed. 12.99 (978-0-88088-446-4(0)) Peter Pauper Pr. Inc.

Buranelli, Vincent. American Spies & Traitors. 2004. (Collective Biographies Ser.). (Illus.). 112p. (J). lib. bdg. 26.60 (978-0-7660-2006-1(1)) Enslow Pubs., Inc.

Burgan, Michael. Spying & the Cold War. 2006. (On the Front Line Ser.). (Illus.). 48p. (J). (978-1-4109-2195-6(6)); pap. (978-1-4109-2202-1(2)) Steck-Vaughn.

—Spying in the Cold War. 2004. (On the Front Line Ser.). (Illus.). 48p. (J). (gr. 4-6). 29.93 (978-1-4109-1465-1(8)) Raintree.

Bursztynski, Sue. It's True! This Book Is Bugged. Vane, Mitch, illus. 2007. (It's True! Ser.). 88p. (J). (gr. 5-8). 19.95 (***978-1-55451-080-1(5));*** pap. 5.95 (***978-1-55451-079-5(1))*** Annick Pr., Ltd. CAN. *Dist:* Firefly Bks., Ltd.

Canizares, Susan. Spider Names. 1998. (Science Emergent Readers Ser.). (Illus.). (J). pap. 2.50 (978-0-590-39795-7(8)) Scholastic, Inc.

Caravantes, Peggy. Petticoat Spies: Six Women Spies of the US Civil War. 2004. (Notable Americans Ser.). (Illus.). 112p. (YA). (gr. 6-12). 23.95 (978-1-883846-88-6(9) , First Biographies) Reynolds, Morgan Inc.

Deary, Terry. The Nuclear Winter Man. 2004. (Classified Ser.). 96p. (J). (gr. 5-8). pap. 4.95 (978-0-7534-5827-3(6) , Kingfisher) Houghton Mifflin Co. Trade & Reference Div.

Denega, Danielle. The Cold War Pigeon Patrols: And Other Animal Spies. 2007. (24/7: Science Behind the Scenes: Spy Files Ser.). 64p. (YA). (gr. 5 up). pap. 7.95 (***978-0-531-17534-7(0));*** (gr. 8-12). 26.00 (978-0-531-12081-1(3)) Scholastic Library Publishing. (Watts, Franklin).

Dowswell, Paul & Fleming, Fergus. True Spy Stories. 2004. (True Adventure Stories Ser.). 144p. (J). pap. 4.95 (978-0-7945-0088-7(9) , Usborne) EDC Publishing.

Eye Spy: 6 Each of 1 Anthology, 6 vols. (Wildcats Ser.). 32p. (gr. 2-8). (978-0-322-00592-1(2)) Wright Group, The.

Farman, John. The Short & Bloody History of Spies. 2005. (Short & Bloody Histories Ser.). (Illus.). 96p. (gr. 6-12). lib. bdg. 19.93 (978-0-8225-0845-8(1)) Lerner Publishing Group.

—The Short & Bloody History of Spies. 2002. (Illus.). 96p. (YA). (gr. 8-12). per. 14.10 (978-0-613-52499-5(3)) Tandem Library Bks.

Fleming, Fergus. Tales of Real Spies. 1998. (Usborne Reader's Library). (Illus.). 64p. (YA). (gr. 7 up). pap. 8.95 (978-0-7460-2709-7(5)); lib. bdg. 16.95 (978-1-58086-015-4(X)) EDC Publishing.

Fridell, Ron. Spy Technology. 2007. (Cool Science Ser.). (Illus.). 48p. (J). (gr. 4-8). lib. bdg. 26.60 (978-0-8225-5934-4(X) , Lerner Pubns.) Lerner Publishing Group.

—Spying, Modern World of Espionage. 2002. (Single Titles Ser.). (Illus.). 144p. (gr. 7 up). lib. bdg. 24.90 (978-0-7613-1662-6(0) , Millbrook Pr.) Lerner Publishing Group.

Gifford, Clive. Spies. 2004. (Kingfisher Knowledge Ser.). (Illus.). 64p. (J). (gr. 5-9). 12.95 (978-0-7534-5777-1(6) , Kingfisher) Houghton Mifflin Co. Trade & Reference Div.

Harvey, Gill. True Stories of Crime & Detection. Chisholm, Jane, ed. 2004. (True Adventure Stories Ser.). 144p. (J). pap. 4.95 (978-0-7945-0613-1(5) , Usborne) EDC Publishing.

Hunter, Ryan Ann. In Disguise: Stories of Real Women Spies. 2004. (Illus.). 133p. (YA). (gr. 4-12). pap. (978-1-58270-095-3(8)) Beyond Words Publishing, Inc.

Im, Angela, ed. Spy Surveillance. 2005. (Fun Pack Ser.). (J). lthr. 7.99 (978-0-439-67614-4(2) , Tangerine Pr.) Scholastic, Inc.

International Spy Museum Staff, et al. Secrets, Lies, Gizmos & Spies: A History of Spies & Espionage. 2006. (Illus.). 128p. (gr. 8-17). 24.95 (978-0-8109-5756-5(6)) Abrams, Harry N. , Inc.

Kallen, Stuart A. Primary Sources. 2003. (Illus.). 112p. (J). 29.95 (978-1-59018-243-7(X) , Lucent Bks.) Thomson Gale.

Keeley, Jennifer. Espionage. 2002. (American War Library). (Illus.). 112p. (J). 29.95 (978-1-59018-210-9(3) , Lucent Bks.) Thomson Gale.

Khan, Hena & Melton, H. Keith. The Spy's Guide to Escape & Evasion. 2003. (Illus.). 48p. (J). (978-0-439-33648-2(1)) Scholastic, Inc.

King, C. Spy's Guidebook. Sims, Lesley, ed. 2000. (Spy's Guidebooks Ser.). (Illus.). 48p. (J). (gr. 3-7). pap. 9.95 (978-0-7460-3680-8(9)) EDC Publishing.

Koestler-Grack, Rachel A. Nathan Hale: Courageous Spy. 2005. (Leaders of the American Revolution Ser.). (Illus.). 124p. (J). (gr. 4-8). lib. bdg. 30.00 (978-0-7910-8623-0(2) , Chelsea Hse.) Facts On File, Inc.

Locke, Ian. Super Spies. Rowe, Alan, illus. 2003. 61p. (J). pap. 3.99 (978-0-330-37499-6(0) , Pan) Pan Macmillan GBR. *Dist:* Trafalgar Square Publishing.

Lough, Loree. Nathan Hale. 1999. (Revolutionary War Leaders Ser.). (Illus.). 80p. (gr. 3 up). (J). 31.00 (978-0-7910-5361-4(X)); (YA). pap. 27.50 (978-0-7910-5704-9(6)) Facts On File, Inc. (Chelsea Hse.).

—Nathan Hale: Revolutionary Hero. 2000. (Illus.). 80p. (J). (gr. 3-17). lib. bdg. 17.60 (978-0-613-43357-0(2)) Tandem Library Bks.

Manley, Claudia B. Secret Agents: Life as a Professional Spy. 2005. (Extreme Careers Ser.). (Illus.). 64p. (YA). (gr. 5-8). 26.50 (978-0-8239-3369-3(5)) Rosen Publishing Group, Inc., The.

Mendez, Antonio J. & Mendez, Jonna. Gathering Info: Getting the Scoop by Using Your Wits. 2007. (Illus.). 32p. (J). (***978-0-439-90849-8(3))*** Scholastic, Inc.

Monroe, Judy. The Rosenberg Cold War Spy Trial: A Headline Court Case. 2001. (Headline Court Cases Ser.). (Illus.). 128p. (J). (gr. 6-12). lib. bdg. 20.95 (978-0-7660-1479-4(7)) Enslow Pubs., Inc.

Narayan, Natasha. Spies, Secret Agents & Spooks of London. 2004. (Illus.). 96p. 8.99 (978-1-904153-14-6(3)) Watling St., Ltd. GBR. *Dist:* Trafalgar Square Publishing.

Newcomb, Rain. The Master Spy Handbook: Help Our Intrepid Hero Use Gadgets, Codes & Top-Secret Tactics to Save the World from Evildoers. Chin, Jason, illus. 2005. 96p. (gr. 3-7). 17.95 (978-1-57990-626-9(5) , 1249637) Lark Bks.

Nofi, Albert A. Spies in the Civil War. 1999. (Untold History of the Civil War Ser.). (Illus.). 64p. (YA). (gr. 3-7). 25.00 (978-0-7910-5427-7(6) , Chelsea Hse.) Facts On File, Inc.

Olson, Nathan. Nathan Hale: Revolutionary Spy. Martin, Cynthia & Schoonover, Brent, illus. 2005. 25.26 (Graphic Library). 32p. (J). (gr. 3-7). lib. bdg. 25.26 (978-0-7368-4968-5(8)) Capstone Pr., Inc.

Owen, David. Hidden Secrets: A Complete History of Espionage & the Technology Used to Support It. 2002. (Illus.). 224p. (gr. 7-12). per. 36.15 (978-0-613-51111-7(5)) Tandem Library Bks.

—Spies: The Undercover World of Secrets, Gadgets & Lies. 2004. (Illus.). 128p. (J). (gr. 5-9). 19.95 (978-1-55297-795-8(1)); pap. 9.95 (978-1-55297-794-1(3)) Firefly Bks., Ltd.

Patton, Geoff. The Spying Game. 2005. (X-Zone Ser.). (Illus.), 30p. (gr. 4-8). 23.00 (978-0-7910-8972-9(X)) Facts On File, Inc.

Perrin, Pat & Coleman, Wim. The Mystery of the Murdered Playwright. 2004. (Cover-To-Cover Books). (Illus.). 56p. pap. (*978-0-7891-6001-0(3)); (gr. 4-7). lib. bdg. 17.95 (*978-0-7569-1353-3(5)) Perfection Learning Corp.

Platt, Richard. Spies. 2000. (gr. k-3). lib. bdg. 11.80 (978-0-613-33081-7(1)) Tandem Library Bks.

—Spies!, Vol. 3. 2000. (Readers Ser.). (Illus.). 48p. (J). (gr. 5-3). pap. 3.99 (978-0-7894-5713-4(X)) Dorling Kindersley Publishing, Inc.

Platt, Richard & Dorling Kindersley Publishing Staff. Spies! 2000. (Readers Ser.). (Illus.). 48p. (J). (ps-3). 12.99 (978-0-7894-5712-7(1)) Dorling Kindersley Publishing, Inc.

Portalupi, Laura. Spies! Real People, Real Stories. 2003. (High Five Reading Ser.). (Illus.). (J). 64p. lib. bdg. 22.60 (978-0-7368-2788-1(9)); 48p. pap. 23.93 (978-0-7368-2830-7(3)) Capstone Pr., Inc.

Price, Sean. Top Secret: Spy Equipment & the Cold War. 2006. (American History Through Primary Sources Ser.). (Illus.). 32p. (J). (978-1-4109-2417-9(3)); pap. (978-1-4109-2428-5(9)) Steck-Vaughn.

Rauf, Don. Killer Lipstick: And Other Spy Gadgets. 2007. (24/7: Science Behind the Scenes: Spy Files Ser.). 64p. (J). pap. 7.95 (*978-0-531-17536-1(7)); (YA). (gr. 8-12). 26.00 (978-0-531-12084-2(8)) Scholastic Library Publishing. (Watts, Franklin).

Reit, Seymour V. Behind Rebel Lines: The Incredible Story of Emma Edmonds, Civil War Spy. 2001. (gr. 5-8). lib. bdg. 14.15 (978-0-613-37187-2(9)) Tandem Library Bks.

Rigby Education Staff. Spy Manual. (Sails Literacy Ser.). (Illus.). 16p. (gr. 2-3). 27.00 (978-0-7635-9938-6(7) , 699387C99) Rigby Education.

Ritchie, Scot. Everything Kids' Spies Puzzle & Activity Book: Discover the secrets, tricks, & tools of Spies. 2008. 184p. pap. 7.95 (*978-1-59869-409-3(X)) Adams Media Corp.

Rooney, Anne. Spies. 2003. (Wicked Wallets Ser.). (Illus.). 96p. (YA). pap. (978-1-84347-036-6(5)) Chrysalis Children's Bks.

Roop, Peter & Roop, Connie. Botones para el General Washington (Buttons for General Washington) Hanson, Peter E., illus. 2006. (Yo Solo - Historia (on My Own - History) Ser.). (SPA.). 48p. (J). (gr. 2-4). lib. bdg. 25.26 (978-0-8225-6261-0(8) , Ediciones Lerner) Lerner Publishing Group.

Schoof, Heidi. Elizabeth Van Lew: Civil War Spy. 2005. (Signature Lives Ser.). (Illus.). 112p. (J). (gr. 5-7). (978-0-7565-0985-9(8)) Compass Point Bks.

Shea, Pegi Deitz. Patience Wright: America's First Sculptor, & Revolutionary Spy. Andersen, Bethanne, illus. 2007. (J). (*978-1-4287-3694-8(8)) Holt, Henry & Co.

The Spies: First Wave Satellite Individual Title Six-Packs. (Sails Literacy Ser.). 16p. (gr. k up). 27.00 (978-0-7578-6873-3(8)) Rigby Education.

The Spy, 6 vols., Pack. (Sails Literacy Ser.). 16p. (gr. k up). 27.00 (978-0-7635-4437-9(X)) Rigby Education.

Spy Files, 6 vols., Set. Incl. Bioterror : Deadly Invisible Weapons. Rudy, Lisa Jo. (Illus.). (J). 26.00 (*978-0-531-12080-4(5)); Cold War Pigeon Patrols : And Other Animal Spies. Denega, Danielle. (YA). 26.00 (978-0-531-12081-1(3)); Eyes in the Sky : Satellite Spies Are Watching You! Rudy, Lisa Jo. (YA). 26.00 (978-0-531-12082-8(1)); Killer Lipstick : And Other Spy Gadgets. Rauf, Don. (YA). 26.00 (978-0-531-12084-2(8)); Micro Spies : Spy Planes the Size of a Bird! Rudy, Lisa Jo. (YA). 26.00 (978-0-531-12083-5(X)); 64p. (gr. 8-12). , Watts, Franklin (24/7 Ser.). (Illus.). 2007. 150.00 (*978-0-531-12477-2(0)) Scholastic Library Publishing.

Spy Surveillance. 2004. (Illus.). 48p. (J). (978-0-439-69067-6(6)) Scholastic, Inc.

Stemple, Heidi E. Y. Ready for Anything! Training Your Brain for Expert Espionage. 2006. (Illus.). 32p. (J). (*978-0-439-90504-6(4)) Scholastic, Inc.

Stewart, James. Spies & Traitors. 2007. (*978-1-59920-109-2(7)) Smart Apple Media.

Thomas, Paul. Secret Agents. 2002. (History Makers Ser.). (Illus.). 48p. (J). lib. bdg. 28.50 (978-1-931983-42-6(9)) Chrysalis Education.

Townsend, John. Spies. 48p. (J). 2006. pap. 8.90 (978-1-4109-1431-6(3)); 2005. lib. bdg. 31.43 (978-1-4109-1425-5(9)) Raintree.

Walker, Kate & Argaet, Elaine. Famous Spy Cases. 2003. (Spies & Spying Ser.). 32p. (J). lib. bdg. 24.25 (978-1-58340-342-6(6)) Smart Apple Media.

—So You Want to Be a Spy? 2003. (Spies & Spying Ser.). 32p. (J). lib. bdg. 24.25 (978-1-58340-343-3(4)) Smart Apple Media.

—Spies & Their Gadgets. 2003. (Spies & Spying Ser.). 32p. (J). lib. bdg. 24.25 (978-1-58340-341-9(8)) Smart Apple Media.

—Spies in History. 2003. (Spies & Spying Ser.). 32p. (J). lib. bdg. 24.25 (978-1-58340-338-9(8)) Smart Apple Media.

—Super Spies of World War I. 2003. (Spies & Spying Ser.). 32p. (J). lib. bdg. 24.25 (978-1-58340-339-6(6)) Smart Apple Media.

—Super Spies of World War II. 2003. (Spies & Spying Ser.). 32p. (J). lib. bdg. 24.25 (978-1-58340-340-2(X)) Smart Apple Media.

Wiese, Jim & Melton, H. Keith. The Spy's Guide to Counterintelligence. 2003. (Illus.). 48p. (J). (978-0-439-33646-8(5)) Scholastic, Inc.

Zemlicka, Shannon. Nathan Hale: Patriot Spy. 2002. (On My Own Biographies Ser.). (Illus.). 48p. (J). lib. bdg. 23.93 (978-0-87614-597-5(7) , Carolrhoda Bks.) Lerner Publishing Group.

Ziff, John. Espionage & Treason. 1999. (Crime, Justice & Punishment Ser.). (Illus.). 80p. (J). (gr. 7-12). 30.00 (978-0-7910-4263-2(4) , Chelsea Hse.) Facts On File, Inc.

SPIES—FICTION

A&J Studios. Super Spies. 2007. (Backyardigans Ser.). 24p. (J). pap. 3.99 (*978-1-4169-3825-5(7) , Simon Spotlight/Nickelodeon) Simon & Schuster Children's Publishing.

Abela, Deborah. In Search of the Time & Space Machine. Murphy, Jobi, illus. 2005. (Spy Force Ser.). vi, 248p. (Orig.). (J). 14.95 (978-1-74051-765-2(2) , Simon & Schuster Children's Publishing) Simon & Schuster Children's Publishing.

—Mission: Hollywood. O'Connor, George, illus. 2006. (Spy Force Ser.). 240p. (J). 9.95 (978-0-689-87360-7(3)) Simon & Schuster Children's Publishing.

—Mission: In Search of the Time & Space Machine. O'Connor, George, illus. (Spy Force Ser.). (J). (gr. 4-7). 2006. 240p. pap. 2.99 (978-1-4169-2501-9(5) , Aladdin); 2005. 224p. 9.95 (978-0-689-87357-7(3) , Simon & Schuster Children's Publishing) Simon & Schuster Children's Publishing.

—Mission: Spy Force Revealed. O'Connor, George, illus. (Spy Force Ser.). 288p. (J). 2006. pap. 5.99 (978-1-4169-4024-1(3) , Aladdin); 2005. (gr. 4-7). 9.95 (978-0-689-87358-4(1) , Simon & Schuster Children's Publishing) Simon & Schuster Children's Publishing.

—Mission: The Amazon Experiment. O'Connor, George, illus. 2007. (Spy Force Ser.). 288p. (J). pap. 5.99 (978-0-689-87361-4(1) , Simon & Schuster/Paula Wiseman Bks.) Simon & Schuster Children's Publishing.

—Mission: Hollywood. O'Connor, George, illus. 2007. (Spy Force Ser.). 240p. (J). pap. 5.99 (*978-1-4169-3969-6(5) , Aladdin) Simon & Schuster Children's Publishing.

—Mission: in Search of the Time & Space Machine. O'Connor, George, illus. 2006. (Spy Force Ser.). 240p. (J). pap. 5.99 (978-1-4169-2752-5(2) , Aladdin) Simon & Schuster Children's Publishing.

—Mission: the Nightmare Vortex. O'Connor, George, illus. 2007. (Spy Force Ser.). 256p. (J). pap. 5.99 (978-1-4169-3484-4(7) , Aladdin) Simon & Schuster Children's Publishing.

—The Nightmare Vortex. O'Connor, George, illus. 2005. (Spy Force Ser.). 256p. (J). (gr. 3-7). 9.95 (978-0-689-87359-1(X) , Simon & Schuster/Paula Wiseman Bks.) Simon & Schuster Children's Publishing.

Arena, Felice & Kettle, Phil. Secret Agent Heroes. Vane, Mitch, illus. 2004. (J). pap. (978-1-59336-355-0(9)) Mondo Publishing.

Avi. The Traitors' Gate. Raude, Karina, illus. 2007. 368p. (J). (gr. 6-9). 17.99 (978-0-689-85335-7(1) , Atheneum/Richard Jackson Bks.) Simon & Schuster Children's Publishing.

The Balloon Ride, 6, Pack. (Sails Literacy Ser.). 16p. (gr. k up). 27.00 (978-0-7635-4427-0(2)) Rigby Education.

The Balloon Ride: KinderConcepts Individual Title Six-Packs. (Kinderstarters Ser.). 8p. (ps-1). 21.00 (978-0-7635-8736-9(2)) Rigby Education.

Balocco, Patrizia & Francia, Giada, eds. Alex & Penny Ballooning over Italy. 2007. (Illus.). 80p. (J). (gr. 2-5). 14.95 (978-88-544-0160-0(9) , White Star) Rizzoli International Pubns., Inc.

Barba, Rick. The Massively Multiplayer Mystery. Steccati, Eve, illus. 2006. (Spy Gear Adventures Ser.). 240p. (J). pap. 4.99 (978-1-4169-0888-3(9) , Aladdin) Simon & Schuster Children's Publishing.

—The Secret of Stoneship Woods. Steccati, Eve, illus. 2006. (Spy Gear Adventures Ser.). 160p. (J). pap. 4.99 (978-1-4169-0887-6(0) , Aladdin) Simon & Schuster Children's Publishing.

Barnes, Jennifer. Perfect Cover. 2008. (The Squad). 288p. (YA). (gr. 7). mass mkt. 6.99 (*978-0-385-73454-7(9) , Delacorte Pr.) Dell Publishing.

—Skin Deep. 2008. (J). (*978-0-385-90477-3(0) , Delacorte Pr.) Dell Publishing.

Bell, Mary Reeves. Secret of Mezuzah. 1999. (J). (978-0-606-18974-3(2)) Tandem Library Bks.

Bell, Michele Ashman. Dragon's Jaw: A Heart-Pounding Adventure. 2005. 241p. (J). (978-1-59156-880-3(3)) Covenant Communications.

—Spyhunt: A Heart-Pounding Adventure: A Novel. 2004. 187p. (J). (978-1-59156-457-7(3)) Covenant Communications.

Blair, Margaret Whitman. House of Spies: Danger in the Civil War. 1999. (White Mane Kids Ser.: Vol. 7). (Illus.). 169p. (YA). (ps up). pap. 8.95 (978-1-57249-161-8(2) , White Mane Kids) White Mane Publishing Co., Inc.

Boyd, David. Hidden Message. Alward, Jeff, illus. 2007. 48p. (J). lib. bdg. 23.08 (*978-1-4242-1637-6(0)) Fitzgerald Bks.

Bradley, Kimberly Brubaker. For Freedom: The Story of a French Spy. 2005. 192p. (J). (gr. 5-9). pap. 5.50 (978-0-440-41831-3(3) , Laurel Leaf) Random Hse. Children's Bks.

Bruchac, Joseph. Code Talker: A Novel about the Navajo Marines of World War Two. 2005. 240p. (YA). (gr. 5). 16.99 (978-0-8037-2921-6(9) , Dial) Penguin Group (USA) Inc.

Bryant-Mole, Karen. Mortimer Plays I-Spy. Mukhida, Zul, illus. 2000. (Mortimer's Fun with Words Ser.). 24p. (J). (ps up). lib. bdg. 22.00 (978-0-8368-2749-1(X)) Stevens, Gareth Inc.

Burrows, Geraldine. Miss Sedgewick & the Spy. 2000. (Five Star First Edition Romance Ser.). 263p. (J). 26.95 (978-0-7862-2215-5(8) , Five Star) Thomson Gale.

Butcher, A. J. Chaos Rising. 2004. (Spy High Ser.: Vol. 2). (Illus.). 240p. (J). (gr. 5-8). pap. 6.99 (978-0-316-73765-4(8)) Little, Brown Bks. for Young Readers.

—The Serpent Scenario. 2004. (Spy High Ser.: Vol. 3). 224p. (J). (gr. 5-8). pap. 6.99 (978-0-316-73766-1(6)) Little, Brown Bks. for Young Readers.

—Spy High Mission One. 2004. 224p. (J). (gr. 5-8). pap. 6.99 (978-0-316-73760-9(7)) Little, Brown Bks. for Young Readers.

Butcher, A.J. Agent Orange. 2005. 256p. (YA). pap. 9.95 (*978-1-904233-39-8(2)) Little, Brown Bk. Group Ltd. GBR. *Dist:* Independent Pubs. Group.

Cage, Elizabeth. Spy Girls. Date not set. (Spy Girls Ser.: No. 7). (YA). (gr. 7 up). mass mkt. (978-0-671-03637-9(8)); mass mkt. (978-0-671-03638-6(6)) Simon & Schuster Children's Publishing. (Simon Pulse).

Carey, John. Cook Spies. 2005. 34p. (J). per. (978-0-9773723-2-4(4)) Trent's Prints.

Carter, Ally. Cross My Heart & Hope to Spy. rev. ed. 2007. (Gallagher Girls Ser.). 240p. (J). (gr. 6 up). 16.99 (*978-1-4231-0005-8(0)) Hyperion Pr.

Carter, Ally. I'd Tell You I Love You, but Then I'd Have to Kill You. (Gallagher Girls Ser.). 288p. (gr. 7 up). 2007. pap. 8.99 (*978-1-4231-0004-1(2)); 2006. (978-1-4231-0003-4(4)) Hyperion Pr.

Clancy, Tom. Hidden Agendas. 1999. (gr. 7-12). lib. bdg. 16.45 (978-0-613-33473-0(6)) Tandem Library Bks.

Clancy, Tom, et al. Safe House. 2000. (Tom Clancy's Net Force Ser.: V). 1p. (gr. 7-12). mass mkt. 4.99 (978-0-425-17431-9(X) , Berkley) Penguin Group (USA) Inc.

Clifford, Mary Louise. The Shalamar Code. 2006. 192p. (J). (gr. 7 up). pap. 8.95 (978-0-7387-0934-5(4) , Flux) Llewellyn Pubns.

Coburn, Jake. LoveSick. 2005. 240p. (YA). (gr. 8-12). 16.99 (978-0-525-47383-1(1) , Dutton Juvenile) Penguin Group (USA) Inc.

Cook, Lyn. Flight from the Fortress. 2004. 200p. (J). (gr. 4 up). (978-1-55041-790-6(8)) Fitzhenry & Whiteside, Ltd.

Costain, Meredith, ed. My Brother, the Spy. Tulloch, Coral, illus. 1999. (Supa Doopers Ser.). 64p. (J). (978-0-7608-1930-2(0)) Sundance/Newbridge Educational Publishing.

Crane, Laura Dent. The Automobile Girls at Washington. rev. ed. 2006. (ENG.). 196p. 26.95 (978-1-4218-2096-5(X) , 1st World Library - Literary Society) 1st World Publishing, Inc.

Dale, Anna. Dawn Undercover. 2006. 368p. (J). pap. 7.95 (978-1-59990-002-5(5) , Bloomsbury Children) Bloomsbury Publishing.

David, Peter, et al. Spy-School Confidential, Vol. 5. 2002. (SpyBoy Ser.). (Illus.). 96p. (YA). pap. 12.95 (978-1-56971-834-6(2)) Dark Horse Comics.

Deary, Terry. Breakout! 2004. (Classified Ser.). 96p. (J). (gr. 5-8). pap. 4.95 (978-0-7534-5826-6(8) , Kingfisher) Houghton Mifflin Co. Trade & Reference Div.

Dell, Pamela. Freedom's Light: A Story about Paul Revere's Midnight Ride. 2002. (Scrapbooks of America Ser.). (Illus.). 48p. (J). (gr. 2-6). 28.50 (978-1-59187-016-6(X)) Child's World, Inc.

Denenberg, Barry. Atticus of Rome, 30 B. C. 2004. (Life & Times Ser.). 176p. (J). (gr. 4-7). pap. 10.95 (978-0-439-52453-7(9)) Scholastic, Inc.

Dennis, Jeanne Gowen & Seifert, Sheila. Trapped! Hohn, David, tr. Hohn, David, illus. 2003. (Survivor Ser.). 96p. (J). pap., pap. 5.99 (978-0-7814-3898-8(5) , 0781438985) Cook, David C. Publishing Co.

Duble, Kathleen Benner. Quest. 2008. 256p. (J). 15.99 (*978-1-4169-3386-1(7) , McElderry, Margaret K.) Simon & Schuster Children's Publishing.

Dubosarsky, Ursula. The Red Shoe. 2007. 192p. (J). (gr. 7 up). 16.95 (978-1-59643-265-9(9)) Roaring Brook Pr.

Eggleton, Jill. Spy Maps, 6 vols., Pack. Pye, Trevor, illus. (Sails Literacy Ser.). 16p. (gr. 2-3). 27.00 (978-0-7578-0702-2(X)) Rigby Education.

Ericson, Helen. Harriet Spies Again. 2004. 240p. (J). (gr. 3-7). pap. 36.00 incl. audio (978-0-8072-2091-7(4) , Listening Library) Random Hse. Audio Publishing Group.

—Harriet Spies Again. 2003. 256p. (J). (gr. 5). mass mkt. 6.50 (978-0-440-41688-3(4) , Yearling) Random Hse. Children's Bks.

Ericson, Helen & Fitzhugh, Louise. Harriet Spies Again. 2002. 240p. (gr. 5 up). 15.95 (978-0-385-32786-2(2)); lib. bdg. 17.99 (978-0-385-90022-5(8)) Random Hse. Children's Bks. (Delacorte Bks. for Young Readers).

Fisher, Linda C. A Will of Her Own. 2006. (YA). pap. (978-0-88092-641-6(4)); lib. bdg. (978-0-88092-640-9(6)) Royal Fireworks Publishing Co.

Fitzhugh, Louise. Harriet l Espionne. (FRE.). pap. 19.95 (978-2-07-058141-2(1)) Gallimard, Editions FRA. *Dist:* Distribooks, Inc.

—Harriet the Spy. 298p. (J). (gr. 3-5). pap. 5.95 (978-0-8072-1535-7(X)); 1999. pap. 38.00 incl. audio (978-0-8072-8069-0(0) , YA993SP) Random Hse. Audio Publishing Group. (Listening Library).

—Harriet the Spy. (Illus.). (gr. 5-7). 2001. 320p. pap. 6.50 (978-0-440-41679-1(5) , Yearling); 2000. 304p. (J). 15.95 (978-0-385-32783-1(8) , Delacorte Bks. for Young Readers) Random Hse. Children's Bks.

Fitzhugh, Louise & Gold, Maya. Harriet the Spy, Double Agent. 2007. 160p. (J). (gr. 4-7). 6.50 (978-0-440-41691-3(4) , Yearling) Random Hse. Children's Bks.

Frederick, Heather Vogel. The Black Paw. Comport, Sally Wern, illus. (Spy Mice Ser.). (J). 2006. 256p. pap. 5.99 (978-1-4169-2770-9(0) , Aladdin); 2006. 256p. pap. 2.99 (978-1-4169-2502-6(3) , Aladdin); 2005. 240p. 9.95 (978-0-689-87753-7(6) , Simon & Schuster Children's Publishing) Simon & Schuster Children's Publishing.

—For Your Paws Only. Comport, Sally Wern, illus. 2006. (Spy Mice Ser.). 272p. (J). pap. 5.99 (978-1-4169-4025-8(1) , Aladdin) Simon & Schuster Children's Publishing.

—Goldwhiskers. Comport, Sally Wern, illus. 2007. (Spy Mice Ser.). 256p. (J). pap. 5.99 (978-1-4169-1442-6(0) , Simon & Schuster Children's Publishing) Simon & Schuster Children's Publishing.

Gershon, Dann. Goldstinger. Robinson, David, illus. 1999. (Hangin' with the Hombeez Ser.: Vol. 4). 40p. (J). (gr. k-6). 9.95 (978-0-9656985-6-6(4)) Noware Bks.

Gifford, Griselda. House of Spies. 2006. 160p. (J). pap. 8.99 (*978-1-84270-459-2(1)) Andersen GBR. *Dist:* Independent Pubs. Group.

Gold, Maya & Fitzhugh, Louise. Harriet the Spy, Double Agent. 2005. 160p. (J). (gr. 5 up). 15.95 (978-0-385-32787-9(0) , Delacorte Bks. for Young Readers) Random Hse. Children's Bks.

Golden Books Staff. Spy Race! 2008. (Color Plus Chunky Crayons Ser.). (Illus.). 48p. (J). (ps-2). pap. 3.99 (*978-0-375-84008-1(7) , Golden Bks.) Random Hse., Inc.

Gray, Kes. 006 & a Half: A Daisy Book. Sharratt, Nick, illus. 2007. 32p. (J). (ps-1). 10.95 (*978-0-8109-1719-4(X) , Abrams Bks. for Young Readers) Abrams, Harry N. , Inc.

Greene, Stephanie. Owen Foote, Super Spy. Weston, Martha, illus. 2005. 96p. (J). (gr. k-3). pap. 5.95 (978-0-618-55159-0(X) , Clarion Bks.) Houghton Mifflin Co. Trade & Reference Div.

Greenland, Shannon. Down to the Wire. 2007. (Specialists Ser.). 224p. (J). (gr. 5). 6.99 (*978-0-14-240917-6(0) , Puffin) Penguin Group (USA) Inc.

—Model Spy. 2007. (Specialists Ser.). 224p. (YA). pap. 6.99 (978-0-14-240849-0(2) , Puffin) Penguin Group (USA) Inc.

Greenland, Shannon. The Winning Element. 2008. (Specialists Ser.). 224p. (J). (gr. 5). 6.99 (*978-0-14-241052-3(7) , Puffin) Penguin Group (USA) Inc.

Griffin, Judith Berry. Phoebe the Spy. 1998. (J). (gr. 4). pap. 3.95 (978-0-439-04466-0(9)) Scholastic, Inc.

—Phoebe, the Spy. Tomes, Margot, illus. 2002. 48p. (J). pap. 6.99 (978-0-698-11956-7(8) , Putnam Juvenile) Penguin Group (USA) Inc.

Griffis, Molly Levite. The Feester Filibuster. 2002. (gr. 3-6). lib. bdg. 17.60 (978-0-613-79188-5(6)) Tandem Library Bks.

—The Rachel Resistance. 224p. 8.95 (978-1-57168-553-7(7)) Eakin Pr.

Gutman, Dan. Mrs. Cooney Is Loony! Paillot, Jim, illus. 2005. (My Weird School Ser.). 112p. (J). pap. 3.99 (978-0-06-074522-6(3)); lib. bdg. 15.89 (978-0-06-074523-3(1)) HarperCollins Pubs. (Harper Trophy).

Guzman, Lila. Lorenzo's Revolutionary Quest. 2003. (gr. 7-12). lib. bdg. 18.75 (978-0-613-84279-2(0)) Tandem Library Bks.

Guzman, Lila & Guzman, Rick. Lorenzo's Revolutionary Quest. 176p. (YA). pap. 9.95 (978-1-55885-392-8(8) , Piñata Books) Arte Publico Pr.

Haddon, Mark. Agent Z Goes Wild. 1999. (Illus.). 170p. (J). pap. (978-0-09-940073-8(1) , Red Fox) Random Hse. Children's Bks.

Hale, Shannon. River Secrets. 2006. (Illus.). 304p. (J). 17.95 (978-1-58234-901-5(0)) Bloomsbury Publishing.

Harcourt School Publishers Staff. The Root Cellar Below Level. 3rd ed. 2002. (Trophies Reading Program Ser.). (Illus.). pap. 5.10 (978-0-15-323406-4(7)) Harcourt Schl. Pubs.

Harlow, Joan Hiatt. Midnight Rider. 2006. 384p. (J). pap. 5.99 (978-0-689-87010-1(8) , Aladdin) Simon & Schuster Children's Publishing.

Harlow, Joan Hiatt & Minor, Wendell. Midnight Rider. 2005. (Illus.). 416p. (J). 15.95 (978-0-689-87009-5(4) , McElderry, Margaret K.) Simon & Schuster Children's Publishing.

Harris, Christine. Nightmare. 2006. (Undercover Girl Ser.). 176p. (Orig.). (J). pap. 4.99 (978-0-439-76127-7(1) , Scholastic Paperbacks) Scholastic, Inc.

—Secrets. 2005. (Undercover Girl Ser.: No. 1). 128p. (Orig.). (J). (ps-7). pap. 4.99 (978-0-439-76125-3(5) , Scholastic Paperbacks) Scholastic, Inc.

Hart, Alison. A Spy on the Homefront: A Molly Mystery. 2005. (Illus.). 165p. (J). (gr. 4-7). per. 14.90 (978-0-606-33680-2(X)) Tandem Library Bks.

Haynes, Betsy. Spies on the Devils Belt. 2000. (J). pap. 1.75 (978-0-590-04006-8(5)) Scholastic, Inc.

Herman, Gail & Hughes, Francine. Cats & Dogs. 2001. (Illus.). 32p. (J). (gr. k-3). pap. 3.50 (978-0-439-22573-1(6)) Scholastic, Inc.

Higson, Charlie. Blood Fever. 2nd rev. ed. 2007. (Young Bond Ser.). 368p. (gr. 7 up). pap. 7.99 (*978-1-4231-0029-4(8)) Miramax Bks.

Hill, Laban. The Spy's Survival Handbook. Rath, Robert, illus. 2004. 96p. (J). pap. 9.99 (978-0-439-56125-9(6) , Tangerine Pr.) Scholastic, Inc.

Holm, Jennifer & Hamel. To Scratch a Thief. Weinman, Brad, illus. 2005. (Stink Files Ser.: Bk.2). 144p. pap. 4.99 (978-0-06-052984-0(9) , Harper Trophy) HarperCollins Pubs.

Holm, Jennifer L. & Hamel. To Scratch a Thief. Weinman, Brad, illus. 2004. (Stink Files, Dossier Ser.: No. 2). 144p. (J). 14.99 (978-0-06-052982-6(2)) HarperCollins Pubs.

Holm, Jennifer L. & Hamel, Jonathan. The Postman Always Brings Mice. Weinman, Brad, illus. 2004. (Stink Files, Dossier Ser.). 144p. (J). 14.99 (978-0-06-052979-6(2)); lib. bdg. 15.89 (978-0-06-052980-2(6)) HarperCollins Pubs.

—You Only Have Nine Lives. Weinman, Brad, illus. 2007. (Stink Files, Dossier Ser.: No. 3). 144p. (J). pap. 4.99 (978-0-06-052987-1(3)) HarperCollins Pubs.

Hopkins, Cathy. Midsummer Meltdown. 2006. (Truth or Dare Ser.: No. 6). (Illus.). 224p. (YA). (gr. 7 up). mass mkt. 5.99 (978-1-4169-0654-4(1) , Simon Pulse) Simon & Schuster Children's Publishing.

Horowitz, Anthony. Ark Angel. (Alex Rider Ser.: Bk. 6). 2007. 336p. (J). 7.99 (978-0-14-240738-7(0) , Puffin); 2006. 326p. (YA). (gr. 5). 17.99 (978-0-399-24152-9(3) , Philomel) Penguin Group (USA) Inc.

—Eagle Strike. (Alex Rider Ser.: Bk. 4). 2006. 352p. (J). (gr. 7). pap. 7.99 (978-0-14-240613-7(9) , Puffin); 2004. (Illus.). 272p. (YA). (gr. 4). 17.99 (978-0-399-23979-3(0) , Philomel) Penguin Group (USA) Inc.

—Eagle Strike. 2003. 352p. (YA). pap. (978-0-7445-9057-9(4)) Walker & Co.

—The Falcon's Malteser. 2004. (Diamond Brothers Ser.: No. 1). 208p. (J). (gr. 3-6). pap. 6.99 (978-0-14-240219-1(2) , Puffin) Penguin Group (USA) Inc.

—Gadgets. 2006. (Alex Rider Ser.). (Illus.). 56p. (J). (gr. 5). 15.99 (978-0-399-24486-5(7) , Philomel) Penguin Group (USA) Inc.

—Point Blank. (Alex Rider Ser.: Bk. 2). 2006. 304p. (J). (gr. 7). pap. 7.99 (978-0-14-240612-0(0) , Puffin); 2002. 208p. (YA). (gr. 5 up). 17.99 (978-0-399-23621-1(X) , Philomel) Penguin Group (USA) Inc.

—Scorpia. (Alex Rider Ser.: Bk. 5). (YA). (gr. 5). 2006. 400p. pap. 7.99 (978-0-14-240578-9(7) , Puffin); 2005. 320p. 17.99 (978-0-399-24151-2(5) , Philomel) Penguin Group (USA) Inc.

—Skeleton Key. (Alex Rider Ser.: Bk. 3). 2006. 352p. (J). (gr. 7). pap. 7.99 (978-0-14-240614-4(7) , Puffin); 2003. 240p. (YA). (gr. 5). 17.99 (978-0-399-23777-5(1) , Philomel) Penguin Group (USA) Inc.

—Snakehead. 2007. 400p. (J). (gr. 5). 17.99 (***978-0-399-24161-1(2)*** , Philomel) Penguin Group (USA) Inc.

—South by Southeast. 2005. (Diamond Brothers Ser.). 160p. (YA). (gr. 5-9). 16.99 (978-0-399-24155-0(8) , Philomel) Penguin Group (USA) Inc.

—Stormbreaker. (Alex Rider Ser.: Bk. 1). 2006. 256p. (J). (gr. 7). pap. 7.99 (978-0-14-240611-3(2) , Puffin); 2002. (Illus.). (J). (gr. 4-7). 5.99 (978-0-698-11932-1(0) , Puffin); 2001. (Illus.). 1p. (YA). (gr. 5 up). 17.99 (978-0-399-23620-4(1) , Philomel); 2006. 264p. (J). (gr. 5). 7.99 (978-0-14-240656-4(2) , Puffin) Penguin Group (USA) Inc.

—Stormbreaker. 2004. (Alex Rider Ser.: Bk. 1). 208p. (J). (gr. 4-7). pap. 38.00 incl. audio (978-0-8072-2277-5(1) , Listening Library) Random Hse. Audio Publishing Group.

—Stormbreaker: The Graphic Novel. Kanako & Yuzuru, illus. 2006. (Alex Rider Ser.). 144p. (J). (gr. 4). pap. 14.99 (978-0-399-24633-3(9) , Philomel) Penguin Group (USA) Inc.

Hunter, John P. Red Thunder: Secrets, Spies, & Scoundrels at Yorktown. 2006. (J). (***978-0-87935-231-8(0)***) Colonial Williamsburg Foundation.

I Spy: Individual Title Six-Pack Pouch - Level B. (Lighthouse Ser.). 12p. (gr. k-1). 24.00 (978-0-7578-0818-0(2)) Rigby Education.

I Spy: Individual Title Six-Packs. (Story Steps Ser.). (gr. k-2). 29.00 (978-0-7635-9571-5(3)) Rigby Education.

International Spy Museum Staff & Shugaar, Antony. I Lie for a Living: Greatest Spies of All Time. Guarnaccia, Steven, illus. 2006. 192p. (J). 14.95 (978-0-7922-5316-7(7) , National Geographic) National Geographic Society.

Isabella, Tony, et al. Champions Classic, Vol. 1. 2006. (Illus.). 208p. pap. 19.99 (978-0-7851-2097-1(1)) Marvel Enterprises, Inc.

Jacobs, Edgar P. Blake & Mortimer the Yellow M. 2007. (Illus.). 48p. pap. 14.45 (***978-1-905460-21-2(X)***) Cinebook GBR. *Dist:* Biblio Distribution.

Jacobson, Ryan. Santa Claus: Super Spy: The Case of the Florida Freeze. Belkholm, Erica, illus. l.t. ed. 2005. 80p. (J). per. 4.99 (978-0-9774122-0-4(2)) Lake 7 Creative.

James, Brian. Port of Spies. Zivoin, Jennifer, illus. 2007. (Pirate School Ser.: No. 4). 64p. (J). (gr. 1-3). pap. 3.99 (***978-0-448-44646-2(4)*** , Grosset & Dunlap) Penguin Group (USA) Inc.

Jolley, Dan. Alex Unlimited: The Vosarak Code. 2007. (Illus.). 224p. (YA). (gr. 8 up). pap. 7.99 (***978-1-4278-0122-7(3)*** , Tokyopop Kids) TOKYOPOP, Inc.

Jones, Elizabeth McDavid. The Night Flyers. 1999. (978-0-606-17518-0(0)) Tandem Library Bks.

Kacer, Kathy. Night Spies. 2003. (gr. 3-6). lib. bdg. 14.10 (978-0-613-85822-9(0)) Tandem Library Bks.

Kehret, Peg. Spy Cat. 2004. 192p. (J). (gr. 3 up). pap. 5.99 (978-0-14-240151-4(X) , Puffin) Penguin Group (USA) Inc.

Kelly, John & Simkins, Kate. The Spy-Catcher Gang. Inklink, illus. 2008. 48p. (J). (gr. 3-4). 14.99 (***978-0-7566-3850-4(X)***); pap. 3.99 (***978-0-7566-3849-8(6)***) Dorling Kindersley Publishing, Inc.

Kelly, John & Tincknell, Cathy. Scoop! An Exclusive by Monty Molenski. Kelly, John & Tincknell, Cathy, illus. 2007. (Illus.). 32p. (J). (gr. k-3). 15.99 (978-0-7636-3059-1(4)) Candlewick Pr.

Kidd, Ronald. Undercover Kid: Comic Book King. Sklar, Andy, illus. 2007. (All Aboard Mystery Reader Ser.). 48p. (J). pap. 3.99 (***978-0-448-44438-3(0)*** , Grosset & Dunlap) Penguin Group (USA) Inc.

Kindt, Matt. Super Spy. 2007. 304p. (YA). pap. 19.95 (***978-1-891830-96-9(1)***) Top Shelf Productions.

Kirkpatrick, Katherine. Redcoats & Petticoats. Himler, Ronald, illus. 1999. 32p. (J). (gr. 4-6). tchr. ed. 16.95 (978-0-8234-1416-1(7)) Holiday Hse., Inc.

Kowitt, Holly. Cold Hard Cash. 2003. (gr. k-3). lib. bdg. 11.80 (978-0-613-72169-1(1)) Tandem Library Bks.

Larry, H. I. Zac Power #1: Poison Island. Oswald, Ash, illus. 2008. (Zac Power Ser.). 96p. (J). pap. 3.99 (***978-0-312-34659-1(X)***) Feiwel & Friends.

—Zac Power #2: Deep Waters. Oswald, Ash, illus. 2008. (Zac Power Ser.). 96p. (J). pap. 3.99 (***978-0-312-34655-3(7)***) Feiwel & Friends.

Lasky, Kathryn. The Shattering. 2004. (Guardians of Ga'Hoole Ser.: Bk. 5). (Illus.). 192p. (J). (gr. 3-7). pap. 4.99 (978-0-439-40561-4(0) , Scholastic Paperbacks) Scholastic, Inc.

Lenhard, Elizabeth. Game Over: The Official Movie Scrapboook. 2003. (Spy Kids 3-D Ser.). (Illus.). 32p. pap. 5.99 (978-0-7868-1763-4(1) , Volo) Hyperion Bks. for Children.

—Off Sides. 10th rev. ed. 2004. (Spykids Adventures Ser.: Bk. 10). (Illus.). 128p. (gr. 3-7). pap. 4.99 (978-0-7868-0990-5(6)) Hyperion Bks. for Children.

—OSS Wilderness. 2003. (Spykids Adventures Ser.: Vol. 4). 160p. (Orig.). (J). (gr. 3-7). pap. 4.99 (978-0-7868-1718-4(6) , Volo) Hyperion Bks. for Children.

Lerangis, Peter. Spy X: The Code. 2004. (Spy X Ser.). 144p. (Orig.). (J). 4.99 (978-0-439-50725-7(1) , Scholastic Paperbacks) Scholastic, Inc.

LeSourd, Nancy. Liberty Letters: The Personal Correspondence of Emma Edmonds & Mollie Turner, Civil War Spies, 1862. 2004. (Liberty Letters Ser.). 224p. (J). 9.99 (978-0-310-70352-5(2)) Zonderkidz.

Lisle, Janet Taylor. Sirens & Spies. l.t. ed. 2003. 22.95 (978-0-7862-5378-4(9)) Thorndike Pr.

Lorimer, Janet. Tuesday Raven. 2001. (PageTurner Spy Ser.). 80p. (YA). per. 3.95 (978-1-56254-140-8(4) , SP 1404) Saddleback Educational Publishing.

—Tuesday Raven. 2001. (gr. 7-12). lib. bdg. 11.80 (978-0-613-34513-2(4)) Tandem Library Bks.

MacLean, Alistair. Circus. (J). 24.95 (978-0-89190-672-8(X)) Amereon LTD.

Mah, Adeline Yen. Chinese Cinderella & the Secret Dragon Society. (Illus.). 256p. (J). 2006. pap. 5.99 (978-0-06-056736-1(8) , Harper Trophy); 2005. (gr. 5 up). 15.99 (978-0-06-056734-7(1)) HarperCollins Pubs.

Martin, Ann M. Karen's Spy Mystery. 1999. (Babysitters Little Sister Ser.: No. 111). (Illus.). 109p. (J). (gr. 3-7). pap. 3.99 (978-0-590-52356-1(2)) Scholastic, Inc.

Marzollo, Jean. I Spy Lightning in the Sky. Wick, Walter, illus. 2005. (Scholastic Reader Ser.). 32p. (J). 3.99 (978-0-439-68052-3(2) , Cartwheel Bks.) Scholastic, Inc.

Mason, Lynn. Disappeared. 2003. (gr. 7-12). lib. bdg. 14.15 (978-0-613-72717-4(7)) Tandem Library Bks.

—Recruited. 2002. (Alias Ser.). 224p. (YA). (gr. 7). mass mkt. 5.99 (978-0-553-49398-6(1) , Bantam Bks. for Young Readers) Random Hse. Children's Bks.

—Recruited. 2002. (gr. 7-12). lib. bdg. 14.15 (978-0-613-72715-0(0)) Tandem Library Bks.

McCarthy, Meghan. Steal Back the Mona Lisa! 2006. (Illus.). 40p. (J). 16.00 (978-0-15-205368-0(9)) Harcourt Trade Pubs.

McDivitt, Barry. The Youngest Spy. 2007. 176p. (J). (gr. 3-9). pap. 10.95 (***978-1-897235-17-1(8)***) Thistledown Pr., Ltd. CAN. *Dist:* Fitzhenry & Whiteside, Ltd.

McGraw, Eloise Jarvis. Mara, Daughter of the Nile. 1999. (J). (gr. 5-8). lib. bdg. 14.15 (978-0-613-03326-8(4)) Tandem Library Bks.

McNab, Andy & Rigby, Robert. Meltdown. 2008. 276p. (YA). (gr. 7). 16.99 (***978-0-399-24686-9(X)*** , Putnam Juvenile) Penguin Group (USA) Inc.

—Payback. 2006. 272p. (YA). (ps-k). 16.99 (978-0-399-24465-0(4) , Putnam Juvenile) Penguin Group (USA) Inc.

—Traitor. 2006. 288p. (YA). (gr. 7). pap. 6.99 (978-0-14-240727-1(5) , Puffin) Penguin Group (USA) Inc.

Montgomery, R. A. Evasion. 2002. Tr. of Escape. (SPA.). (J). 6.50 (978-84-7176-650-2(7)) Timun Mas, Editorial S.A. ESP. *Dist:* AIMS International Bks., Inc.

Morgan, Richard K. Black Widow: the Things They Say about Her TPB: The Things They Say about Her TPB. 2006. (Illus.). 144p. (YA). pap. 15.99 (978-0-7851-1768-1(7)) Marvel Enterprises, Inc.

Moss, Marissa. Emma's Journal: The Story of a Colonial Girl. Moss, Marissa, illus. 2001. (Young American Voices Ser.: Bk. 2). (Illus.). 56p. (YA). (gr. 3-7). pap. 7.00 (978-0-15-216325-9(5) , Silver Whistle) Harcourt Trade Pubs.

Muchamore, Robert. The Killing. 2006. (Cherub Ser.). 336p. (YA). mass mkt. 5.99 (978-1-4169-2459-3(0) , Simon Pulse) Simon & Schuster Children's Publishing.

—Man vs. Beast. 2007. (Cherub Ser.). 336p. (YA). mass mkt. 5.99 (978-1-4169-2725-9(5) , Simon Pulse) Simon & Schuster Children's Publishing.

Myers, Bill. My Life as a Screaming Skydiver, Vol. 14. 1998. (Incredible Worlds of Wally McDoogle Ser.: No. 14). (Illus.). 128p. (J). (gr. 3-7). pap. 6.99 (978-0-8499-4023-1(0)) Nelson, Thomas Inc.

Myers, Bill & Wimbish, David. Room with a Boo. 2002. (Bloodhounds Inc Ser.). 128p. (J). pap. 5.99 (978-0-7642-2624-3(X)) Bethany Hse. Pubs.

Noble, Trinka Hakes. The Scarlet Stockings Spy. Papp, Robert, illus. 2004. 48p. (J). (gr. 1-7). 16.95 (978-1-58536-230-1(1)) Sleeping Bear Pr.

Nolan, Peggy. The Spy Who Came in from the Sea. 144p. (J). 2001. pap. 8.95 (978-1-56164-245-8(2)); 2000. (gr. 5-9). 14.95 (978-1-56164-186-4(3)) Pineapple Pr., Inc.

O'Malley, Kevin. Herbert Fieldmouse, Secret Agent. 2003. (Illus.). 32p. (J). pap. (978-1-59336-043-6(6)); (gr. 1-6). 15.95 (978-1-59336-042-9(8)) Mondo Publishing.

Ostrow, Kim. Makeup Mayhem. Durk, Jim, illus. 2006. (Ready-To-Read Ser.: Vol. 2). 32p. (J). pap. 3.99 (978-0-689-87724-7(2) , Simon Spotlight) Simon & Schuster Children's Publishing.

Perlman, Rhea. The Brink of Ex-stink-tion. Santat, Dan, illus. 2007. (Otto Undercover Ser.: No. 5). 128p. (J). pap. 3.99 (978-0-06-075503-4(2) , Harper Trophy) HarperCollins Pubs.

—Canyon Catastrophe. Santat, Dan, illus. 2006. (Otto Undercover Ser.). 128p. (J). 14.99 (978-0-06-075498-3(2)); pap. 3.99 (978-0-06-075497-6(4)) HarperCollins Pubs.

Platt, Richard & Dorling Kindersley Publishing Staff. Spy. 2000. (Eyewitness Bks.). (Illus.). 64p. (J). (gr. 4-7). lib. bdg. 19.99 (978-0-7894-6616-7(3)) Dorling Kindersley Publishing, Inc.

Prins, Piet. The Grim Reaper. 2006. (Illus.). 130p. (J). pap. (978-1-894666-74-9(7)) Inheritance Pubns.

Ransom, Candice. Bones in the Badlands. Call, Greg, illus. 2006. 128p. (J). (gr. 2-4). pap. 4.99 (978-0-7869-4028-8(X) , Mirrorstone) Wizards of the Coast.

—Signals in the Sky. 2007. 128p. (J). 4.99 (978-0-7869-4353-1(X) , Mirrorstone) Wizards of the Coast.

Rash, Andy. Agent A to Agent Z. 2004. (Illus.). (J). (978-0-439-36883-4(9) , Levine, Arthur A. Bks.) Scholastic, Inc.

—Agent A to Agent Z. Rash, Andy, illus. 2004. (Illus.). 40p. (J). (gr. 1-3). pap. 16.95 (978-0-439-36882-7(0) , Levine, Arthur A. Bks.) Scholastic, Inc.

Readler, Blaine C. Under the Radar: The Spy Drone Adventure. 2006. 248p. (J). pap. 14.95 (978-1-933255-18-7(8)) DNA Pr.

Reeve, Philip. Starcross: An Intergalactic Adventure of Spies & Time Travel. Wyatt, David, illus. 2007. 320p. (J). (gr. 5 up). 16.95 (***978-1-59990-121-3(8)*** , Bloomsbury Children) Bloomsbury Publishing.

Richards, Kitty. Game Over: The Official Movie Scrapbook - Junior Novel. 2003. (Spy Kids 3-D Ser.). (Illus.). 128p. (gr. 3-7). pap. 4.99 (978-0-7868-1762-7(3) , Volo) Hyperion Bks. for Children.

Richardson, Bill. Sally Dog Little Undercover Agent. Malépart, Céline, illus. 2003. 24p. (J). (ps-2). pap. 6.95 (978-1-55037-824-5(4)) Annick Pr., Ltd. CAN. *Dist:* Firefly Bks., Ltd.

—Sally Dog Little Undercover Agent. Malepart, Celine, illus. 2003. 24p. (J). (ps-2). lib. bdg. 18.95 (978-1-55037-825-2(2)) Annick Pr., Ltd. CAN. *Dist:* Firefly Bks., Ltd.

Richler, Mordecai. Jacob Two-Two's First Spy Case. Eyolfson, Norman, illus. 2003. 144p. (J). (gr. 3-7). pap. 6.95 (978-0-88776-694-7(3)) Tundra Bks., Inc./Livres Toundra, Inc. CAN. *Dist:* Random Hse., Inc.

Rinaldi, Ann. Finishing Becca: A Story about Peggy Shippen & Benedict Arnold. 2004. (Great Episodes Ser.). 384p. (YA). pap. 6.95 (978-0-15-205079-5(5) , Gulliver Bks.) Harcourt Children's Bks.

—Girl in Blue. 2005. 320p. (J). pap. 5.99 (978-0-439-67646-5(0) , Scholastic Paperbacks) Scholastic, Inc.

—The Secret of Sarah Revere. 2003. (Great Episodes Ser.). 336p. (YA). pap. 6.95 (978-0-15-204684-2(4) , Gulliver Bks.) Harcourt Children's Bks.

Rodriguez, Robert. New Kind of Super Spy. 2003. (gr. 3-6). lib. bdg. 13.00 (978-0-613-68269-5(6)) Tandem Library Bks.

Rogers, Kirby. Operation Dewey. 2002. (Illus.). ix, 100p. (J). pap. (978-1-877633-65-2(8)) Luthers.

Roper, Robert, illus. Dolls of Danger. 2005. (Ready-To-Read Ser.). 32p. (J). pap. 3.99 (978-0-689-87722-3(6) , Simon Spotlight) Simon & Schuster Children's Publishing.

—Space Case. 2006. (Totally Spies! Ser.). 32p. (J). pap. 3.99 (978-1-4169-1571-3(0) , Simon Spotlight) Simon & Schuster Children's Publishing.

Roy, Ron. A Spy in the White House. Bush, Timothy, tr. Bush, Timothy, illus. 2004. (Capital Mysteries Ser.: Vol. 4). 96p. (J). (gr. 1-4). pap. 3.99 (978-0-375-82557-6(6)); lib. bdg. 11.99 (978-0-375-92557-3(0)) Random Hse. Children's Bks. (Random Hse. Bks. for Young Readers).

Rucka, Greg. Operation Vol. 4: Blackwall, 4 vols. 2003. (Queen & Country Ser.: Vol. 4). (Illus.). 88p. pap. 8.95 (978-1-929998-68-5(6)) Oni Pr., Inc.

Rylant, Cynthia. Henry & Mudge & the Sneaky Crackers. Stevenson, Sucie, illus. 2002. (Henry & Mudge Ser.). (J). 11.91 (978-0-7587-1271-4(5)) Book Wholesalers, Inc.

—Henry & Mudge & the Sneaky Crackers. Stevenson, Sucie, illus. 2002. (Henry & Mudge Ser.). 28.95 incl. audio compact disk (978-1-59112-639-3(8)); pap. 31.95 incl. audio compact disk (978-1-59112-640-9(1)) Live Oak Media.

—Henry & Mudge & the Sneaky Crackers. Stevenson, Sucie, illus. 1999. (Henry & Mudge Ser.). 48p. (J). (gr. k-3). pap. 3.99 (978-0-689-82525-5(0) , Aladdin) Simon & Schuster Children's Publishing.

Saito, Takao. Golgo 13. 2006. (Golgo 13 Ser.). 208p. (YA). Vol. 3. pap. 9.99 (978-1-4215-0462-9(6)); Vol. 4. pap. 9.99 (978-1-4215-0463-6(4)) Viz Media.

Schmidt, Suzy. Spy Master. Pinkney, Myles C., illus. 2002. 32p. (J). (gr. 3-7). 12.95 (978-0-439-32540-0(4)) Scholastic, Inc.

Sharmat, Marjorie Weinman, et al. The Sly Spy. Brunkus, Denise, illus. 2005. (Oliver Sharp Ser.: Vol. 2). 80p. (J). (gr. 1-4). pap. 4.50 (978-0-440-42062-0(8) , Yearling) Random Hse. Children's Bks.

Skillchecks for Spy. 2005. (Double Fastback Ser.). (J). (gr. 6-12). 64p. pap. 5.95 (978-0-13-024475-8(9)); 32p. pap. 5.95 (978-0-13-024458-1(9)) Globe Fearon Educational Publishing.

Smith, Annie Laura. The Legacy of Bletchley Park. 2004. (YA). mass mkt. 6.99 (***978-0-9753367-1-7(1)***) Onstage Publishing, LLC.

Smith, Justine. How to Be a Spy in 7 Days or Less. Lewis, Jan, illus. 2007. (How to Be a... Ser.). 32p. (J). (gr. 1-5). 12.95 (***978-0-7534-6135-8(8)*** , Kingfisher) Houghton Mifflin Co. Trade & Reference Div.

Snell, J. Roy. Triple Spies. 2006. 32.99 (***978-1-4280-1776-4(3)***) IndyPublish.com.

Sobol, Donald J. Secret Agents Four. 2003. (Adventure Library). (Illus.). 140p. (J). pap. 10.95 (978-1-883937-65-2(5)) Bethlehem Bks.

Spies Go Shopping: Individual Title Six-Packs. (Sails Literacy Ser.). (gr. 1-2). 36.00 (978-0-7578-6707-1(3)) Rigby Education.

Spradlin, Michael P. Live & Let Shop. 2006. (Spy Goddess Ser.). (Illus.). 288p. (J). pap. 5.99 (978-0-06-059409-1(8)) HarperCollins Pubs.

—Spy Goddess, Book Two: to Hawaii, with Love. 2008. (Spy Goddess Ser.). 288p. (J). pap. 6.99 (***978-0-06-059412-1(8)*** , HarperTeen) HarperCollins Pubs.

Spradlin, Michael P. To Hawaii, with Love. 2006. (Spy Goddess Ser.). (Illus.). 208p. (J). lib. bdg. 16.89 (978-0-06-059411-4(X)); (YA). 15.99 (978-0-06-059410-7(1)) HarperCollins Pubs.

Spradlin, Michael P., illus. & reader. Live & Let Shop. Spradlin, Michael P., reader. 2005. (Spy Goddess Ser.: Bk. 1). 224p. (gr. 7 up). 15.99 (978-0-06-059407-7(1)) HarperCollins Pubs.

Spy, 10 vols. 2005. (Double Fastback Ser.). (J). (gr. 6-12). 64p. pap. 54.95 (978-0-13-024468-0(6)); 32p. pap. 44.95 (978-0-13-024440-6(6)) Globe Fearon Educational Publishing.

The Spy down the Street, 6 vols., Vol. 2. (Woodland Mysteriestm Ser.). 133p. (gr. 3-7). 42.50 (978-0-7802-7938-4(7)) Wright Group, The.

Spy School: Individual Title, 6 packs. (Sails Literacy Ser.). (gr. 1-2). 36.00 (978-0-7578-4000-5(0)) Rigby Education.

Spyboy. 2002. (Spyboy Ser.). (Illus.). 18.66 (978-1-4046-2811-3(8)) Book Wholesalers, Inc.

Spyboy: The Deadly Gourmet Affair. 2002. (Spyboy Ser.). (Illus.). 17.62 (978-1-4046-2267-8(5)) Book Wholesalers, Inc.

Spyboy: Trial & Terror. 2002. (Spyboy Ser.). (Illus.). 17.60 (978-1-4046-2810-6(X)) Book Wholesalers, Inc.

Spyboy: Undercover, Underwear! 2002. (Spyboy Ser.). (Illus.). 18.66 (978-1-4046-2812-0(6)) Book Wholesalers, Inc.

Stanley, George Edward. Adam Sharp No. 5: Moose Master. 2004. (gr. k-3). lib. bdg. 11.80 (978-0-613-86694-1(0)) Tandem Library Bks.

—Adam Sharp, the Spy Who Barked. 2002. (gr. 3-6). lib. bdg. 11.80 (978-0-613-50173-6(X)) Tandem Library Bks.

—Operation Spy School. Francis, Guy, illus. 2003. (Stepping Stone Bks.: Bk. 4). 48p. (J). (gr. 1-4). pap. 3.99 (978-0-375-82404-3(9) , Random Hse. Bks. for Young Readers) Random Hse. Children's Bks.

—The Spy Who Barked. Francis, Guy, illus. 2002. (Adam Sharp Ser.: No. 1). 48p. (J). (gr. 2-4). pap. 3.99 (978-0-307-26412-1(2) , Random Hse. Bks. for Young Readers) Random Hse. Children's Bks.

—Swimming with Sharks. Francis, Guy, illus. 2003. (Adam Sharp Ser.: No. 3). 48p. (J). (gr. 2-4). pap. 3.99 (978-0-307-26418-3(1) , Random Hse. Bks. for Young Readers) Random Hse. Children's Bks.

Strange, Spencer. Operation Billion Gazillion. 2005. (Spy Five Ser.). 93p. (***978-0-439-70352-9(2)***) Scholastic, Inc.

Taylor, Mary Ann. Spies: A Gander's Cove Mystery. Casteel, Kay, illus. 2006. (J). mass mkt. 5.99 (***978-0-9753367-7-9(0)***) Onstage Publishing, LLC.

—Traitors: A Gander's Cove Mystery. Casteel, Kay, illus. 2006. (J). mass mkt. 5.99 (***978-0-9753367-9-3(7)***) Onstage Publishing, LLC.

Teitelbaum, Michael. The Spy Who Was Me. Goldberg, Barry, illus. 2004. (Jimmy Neutron Boy Genius Ser.). 24p. (J). pap. 3.50 (978-0-689-86318-9(7) , Simon Spotlight/Nickelodeon) Simon & Schuster Children's Publishing.

Thomas, Jane Resh. The Counterfeit Princess. 2005. (J). 208p. (gr. 5-9). 15.00 (978-0-395-93870-6(8)); 197p. (978-0-618-93780-6(3)) Houghton Mifflin Co. Trade & Reference Div. (Clarion Bks.).

Van Draanen, Wendelin. Enemy Spy. 2006. (Shredderman Ser.: Bk. 4). 192p. (J). (gr. 2-5). 5.50 (978-0-440-41915-0(8) , Yearling) Random Hse. Children's Bks.

Wax, Wendy. Secret Agents. 2007. 24p. (J). 21.35 (***978-1-59961-161-7(9)***) Spotlight.

Wax, Wendy. Sticky Situations: A Totally Spies! Guide to Getting Out in a Clutch! Style Guide Staff, illus. 2006. (Totally Spies! Ser.). 64p. (J). pap. 6.99 (978-1-4169-0840-1(4) , Simon Spotlight) Simon & Schuster Children's Publishing.

West, Tracey. Scrambled Brains! Roper, Robert, illus. 2006. (Totally Spies! Ser.). 64p. (J). pap. 4.99 (978-1-4169-1313-9(0) , Simon Spotlight) Simon & Schuster Children's Publishing.

Weston, Martha & Greene, Stephanie. Owen Foote, Super Spy. Weston, Martha, illus. 2001. (Illus.). 96p. (J). (gr. 4-6). tchr. ed. 15.00 (978-0-618-11752-9(0) , Clarion Bks.) Houghton Mifflin Co. Trade & Reference Div.

Whelan, Gerard. A Winter of Spies. 2003. 191p. (YA). (gr. 5 up). pap. 6.95 (978-0-86278-566-6(9)) O'Brien Pr., Ltd., The IRL. *Dist:* Independent Pubs. Group.

Whelan, Gloria. Parade of Shadows. 2007. 304p. (J). (gr. 5 up). 15.99 (***978-0-06-089028-5(2)***); lib. bdg. 16.89 (***978-0-06-089029-2(0)***) HarperCollins Pubs.

Where Is the Spy? Early Level Satellite Individual Title Six-Packs. (Sails Literacy Ser.). 16p. (gr. 1-2). 27.00 (978-0-7578-2924-6(4)) Rigby Education.

S

Wickstrom, Lois June & Darling, Lucrecia. The Orange Forest Rabbit Mysteries: Book One. 2003. (J). per. 13.95 (978-0-916176-23-5(1)) Gripper Products.

Wild, Kate. Fight Game. 2007. 288p. (J). (gr. 4-7). 16.99 (***978-0-439-87175-4(1)***) Scholastic, Inc.

Willson, Sarah & Artful Doodlers Limited Staff. Mystery Messages. 2006. (Totally Spies! Ser.). (Illus.). 48p. (J). pap. 3.99 (978-1-4169-1188-3(X) , Simon Spotlight) Simon & Schuster Children's Publishing.

—Valentine Villains. 2005. (Totally Spies! Ser.). (Illus.). 64p. (J). pap. 4.99 (978-1-4169-0283-6(X) , Simon Spotlight) Simon & Schuster Children's Publishing.

Young, Emma. STORM: the Infinity Code: The Infinity Code. 2008. (J). (gr. 5). 16.99 (***978-0-8037-3265-0(1)*** , Dial) Penguin Group (USA) Inc.

Zindel, Paul. The Gadget. 2003. (Illus.). 192p. (YA). (gr. 7). pap. 6.50 (978-0-440-22951-3(0) , Laurel Leaf) Random Hse. Children's Bks.

—The Gadget. 2003. (gr. 5-8). lib. bdg. 13.55 (978-0-613-62203-5(0)) Tandem Library Bks.

SPINAL PARALYSIS, ANTERIOR

see Poliomyelitis

SPIRIT OF ST. LOUIS (AIRPLANE)

Kent, Zachary. Charles Lindbergh & the Spirit of St. Louis in American History. 2001. (In American History Ser.). (Illus.). 128p. (YA). (gr. 5-12). lib. bdg. 26.60 (978-0-7660-1683-5(8)) Enslow Pubs., Inc.

Koestler-Grack, Rachel A. Spirit of St. Louis. 2005. (American Moments Ser.). (Illus.). 48p. (J). (gr. 4-8). lib. bdg. 25.65 (978-1-59197-940-1(4)) ABDO Publishing Co.

Kramer, Sydelle A. Night Flight: Charles Lindbergh's Incredible Adventure. 2002. (gr. k-3). lib. bdg. 11.80 (978-0-613-43635-9(0)) Tandem Library Bks.

SPIRITS

see also Angels; Apparitions; Ghosts; Witchcraft

Krensky, Stephen. Zombies. 2007. (Monster Chronicles Ser.). 48p. (J). (gr. 4-8). lib. bdg. 26.60 (***978-0-8225-6759-2(8)*** , Lerner Pubns.) Lerner Publishing Group.

SPIRITUAL HEALING

Amos, Terri. Message Sent: Retrieving the Gift of Love. 2002. pap. 14.95 (978-0-9719694-0-7(X) , 01) Worldof-Lite Publishing.

Interlude with Sally Hemings: Diary of a Spiritual Healing. 2000. 124p. (J). per. 11.95 (978-0-9700001-0-1(3)) Free To Soar Enterprises.

Penn, John I., Sr. About Caring & Healing: A Coloring & Activities Book about a Loving & Healing God. Rains, Wanda, illus. rev. l.t. ed. 2002. 36p. (J). 5.95 (978-0-9720785-0-4(9) , 821448) Penn, John.

Penn, John I. Getting Well: A Study for Children on Spiritual & Physical Healing. 2005. 32p. pap. 10.00 (978-0-687-00720-2(8)) Abingdon Pr.

Perez, Jaime O. Traditional Ceremonial Pathways: A Pilgrim's Journey. l.t. ed. 2003. (Illus.). 170p. per. 9.99 net. (978-0-9729612-0-2(8) , 44444) Sun Circle Pr.

Raintree Steck-Vaughn Staff. Mysterious Healing. 1999. (Unsolved Mysteries Ser.). (Illus.). (J). pap. 8.05 (978-0-8172-5851-1(5)) Steck-Vaughn.

Taylor, Mary J. God's Miracle Process: Trauma Transformed into Treasures. 2005. (Illus.). 144p. per. 12.95 (978-0-9768530-0-8(0)) Choices International.

SPIRITUAL HEALING—FICTION

Campbell, Tara. The Boy Who Called Heaven. 2006. pap. 32.49 (***978-1-4208-5456-5(9)***) AuthorHouse.

Clinton, Cathryn. The Calling. 2007. (Illus.). 176p. (YA). (gr. 5 up). pap. 5.99 (***978-0-7636-3373-8(9)***) Candlewick Pr.

Conley, Autumn. Colby's Peace. 2005. 197p. pap. 19.95 (978-1-4137-8937-9(4)) PublishAmerica, Inc.

Corley, Theresa. The Journey Home: The Story of Michael Thomas & the Seven Angels. ed. 2003. ix, 226p. pap. 13.95 (978-1-56170-987-8(5)) Hay Hse., Inc.

Hart, Chrissi. Under the Grapevine: A Miracle by St. Kendeas of Cyprus. 2006. 32p. 15.95 (***978-1-888212-84-6(5)***) Conciliar Pr.

Harwell, Wiley D. Knowing Truth by Name: The Stories of White Bear. 2006. 144p. per. (978-1-59298-130-4(5)) Beaver's Pond Pr., Inc.

An Inner Child Speaks. 2006. (J). 17.99 (978-0-9779130-0-8(7)) Zy Iman Pubng.

Kolb, Joseph J. Reservation Dreams. 2004. 185p. pap. 19.95 (978-1-4137-3054-8(X)) PublishAmerica, Inc.

Pitcher. Pitcher - Cloud Cat Quartet Bind-up. 2008. 320p. (YA). pap. 9.95 (***978-1-4052-0851-2(1)***) Egmont Bks., Ltd. GBR. *Dist:* Independent Pubs. Group.

Richardson, Faith. Tree Root & River Rat. 2003. (Illus.). 248p. (J). pap. 12.95 (978-0-9744989-5-9(5)) Fox Song Bks.

SPIRITUAL LIFE

see also Christian Life; Faith

Adams, Patricia E. Help My Shadow Is Chasing Me: Traumas Aftershock. 2006. pap. 10.95 (978-0-9700976-8-2(9) , Shekinah Publishing Hse.) Shekinah Publishing Hse.

Adi Da Samra, Ruchira Avatar. What, Where, When, How, Why & Who to Remember to Be Happy. Van der Veer, Maja, illus. 2nd exp. ed. 2000. 44p. (J). 14.95 (978-1-57097-074-0(2)) Dawn Horse Pr.

Albright, Jim & Albright, Kim Y. Fight Right! A Christian Approach to Conflict. 1998. (Generation Why Ser.: Vol. 3:7). 36p. (J). (gr. 9-12). pap. 12.95 (978-0-87303-279-7(9)) Faith & Life Pr.

Allah in Person, Royall. The Center Page, Volume 1. 2003. (Illus.). 241p. 51.00 (978-0-9768502-0-5(6)) United Nation of Islam, The.

AMC World, ed. He Shall Live & Not Die. 2002. 128p. (YA). E-Book 15.99 incl. cd-rom (978-0-9720750-0-8(3)) AMC World, LLC.

Anderson, Carolyn B. Exchanging God's Glory for the Pleasures of the Flesh. 2004. 120p. (YA). per. 8.95 (978-0-9718249-8-0(3)) Anderson Publishing.

Armbrecht, Doug, compiled by. Quiet Time Prepack for Families (Quiet Time Devotionals). 21. 2006. (Illus.). (YA). per. 347.79 (978-1-931235-53-2(8) , gbookpack) Word of Life Fellowship, Inc.

Arons, Marsha. Teen Miracles: Extraordinary Life-Changing Stories by America's Teenagers. 2004. (Illus.), 256p. pap. 9.95 (978-1-58062-758-0(7)) Adams Media Corp.

Artworks. Faith, Hope & Love. 2004. (YA). 16.95 (978-1-57938-856-0(6)) Artworks International.

Berkley, Deborah Hall. They All Come. 2001. (Illus.). 32p. 19.95 (978-1-890306-33-5(9)) Warwick Hse. Publishing.

Bowman, Crystal & Kucharik, Elena. Is God Always with Me? 2005. (Little Blessings Ser.). (Illus.). 64p. (J). 9.99 (978-1-4143-0287-4(8)) Tyndale Hse. Pubs.

Box, Su. You Are Very Special. Poole, Susie, illus. 2003. 32p. (J). pap. 6.95 (978-0-8198-8807-5(9) , 332-417) Pauline Bks. & Media.

Bussard, Paula. Bug Beepers for Promise Keepers: Critter County Activity Book. 1998. (Nineteen Ninety-Nine 50-Day Spiritual Adventure Ser.). (Illus.). 64p. (J). pap. 7.00 (978-1-57849-109-4(6)) Mainstay Church Resources.

Canfield, Jack L. Chicken Soup for the Kid's Soul: 101 Stories of Courage, Hope & Laughter. 2000. (Illus.). (J). 19.60 (978-0-606-18203-4(9)) Tandem Library Bks.

Cardero, Patrick & JFA Productions Staff. Hello It's Me: An Ineterview with God. 2003. 225p. pap. 19.95 (978-0-9723024-0-1(9)) JFA Productions.

Carlson, Dale. Stop the Pain: Teen Meditations. Nicklaus, Carol, illus. 2000. (Psychology for Teenagers Ser.: No. 3). 189p. (gr. 5-9). pap. 14.95 (978-1-884158-23-0(4)) Bick Publishing Hse.

Carr, Dan. God, I Need to Talk to You about Lying. Clark, Bartholomew & Clark, Bill, illus. 16p. (J). (978-0-7586-0512-2(9)) Concordia Publishing Hse.

—God, I Need to Talk to You about Sharing. Clark, Bartholomew & Clark, Bill, illus. 16p. (J). (978-0-7586-0511-5(0)) Concordia Publishing Hse.

—God, I Need to Talk to You about Stealing. Clark, Bartholomew & Clark, Bill, illus. 16p. (J). (978-0-7586-0509-2(9)) Concordia Publishing Hse.

—God, I Need to Talk to You about Vandalism. Clark, Bartholomew & Clark, Bill, illus. 16p. (J). (978-0-7586-0510-8(2)) Concordia Publishing Hse.

Cavallaro, Gloria. My Beloved's Israel. Wootten, Batya R. et al, eds. Lenhart, Crystal & Yisrael, Miriam, illus. 2001. 384p. (YA). pap. 16.95 (978-1-886987-05-0(X)) House of David.

Chopra, Deepak. Fire in the Heart: A Spiritual Guide for Teens. 208p. (YA). 2006. pap. 9.95 (978-0-689-86217-5(2) , Simon Pulse); 2004. (Illus.). 14.95 (978-0-689-86216-8(4)) Simon & Schuster Children's Publishing.

—Teens Ask Deepak: All the Right Questions. Barchowsky, Damien, illus. 2005. 208p. (YA). pap. 12.95 (978-0-689-86218-2(0) , Simon Pulse) Simon & Schuster Children's Publishing.

Crook, Carol. Spiritual Warfare Manual. 2000. 252p. (YA). (gr. 10 up). stu. ed., spiral bd. 36.75 (978-0-939399-55-0(5)) Books of Truth.

Cummings Moore, Thelma Wyatt. Living with a Passion. 2003. 103p. (YA). (gr. 8 up). pap. 5.95 (978-0-942683-40-0(4)) Publishing Assocs., Inc.

Dent, Jenny. The Giant Jigsaw Puzzle: Democratic Committee Assignments in the Modern House. (Spiritual Teachings for Children Ser.). (Illus.). 32p. (J). (gr. k-9). 17.95 (978-0-85487-053-0(9)) White Eagle Publishing Trust GBR. *Dist:* DeVorss & Co.

Dobson, Shirley. God Helps Me Share: Coloring Book about Abigail & David. 2004. (Illus.). 12p. pap. 1.49 (978-0-8307-2894-7(5) , Gospel Light) Gospel Light Pubns.

—God Made the World Coloring Book. 2004. (Illus.). 16p. 1.49 (978-0-8307-2487-1(7) , Gospel Light) Gospel Light Pubns.

—God Made the World Coloring Book: 100-Unit Counter Merchandiser. 2004. 16p. 99.00 (978-0-8307-2488-8(5) , Gospel Light) Gospel Light Pubns.

—God's Little Helper Coloring Book. 2004. (Illus.). 16p. pap. 1.49 (978-0-8307-2188-7(6) , Gospel Light) Gospel Light Pubns.

—Growing as God's Child Coloring Book. 2004. (Illus.). 16p. pap. 1.49 (978-0-8307-2622-6(5) , Gospel Light) Gospel Light Pubns.

Dobson, Shirley, contrib. by. God Gives Me Joy Coloring Book. 2004. 16p. 1.49 (978-0-8307-3054-4(0) , Gospel Light) Gospel Light Pubns.

Dunagan, Cindy. Journaling Toward Moral Excellence Volume Four for Young Adults: A Character Building Workbook of 100 Thought-Provoking Questions to Help the Young Discover the Value of Moral Strength. 2004. (Journaling Toward Moral Excellence Ser.: Vol. 4). 107p. (YA). (gr. 11 up). 11.95 (978-0-9759871-3-1(5)) Straight Paths Pr.

—Journaling Toward Moral Excellence Volume Three for Teenagers: A Character Building Workbook of 100 Thought-Provoking Questions to Help the Young Discover the Value of Moral Strength. 2004. (Journaling Toward Moral Excellence Ser.: Vol. 3). 107p. (YA). (gr. 8-10). 11.95 (978-0-9759871-2-4(7)) Straight Paths Pr.

—Journaling Toward Moral Excellence Volume Two for Pre-Teens Vol. 2: A Character Building Workbook of 100 Thought-Provoking Questions to Help the Young Discover the Value of Moral Strength. 2004. (Journaling Toward Moral Excellence Ser.: Vol. 2). 107p. (J). (gr. 5-7). 11.95 (978-0-9759871-1-7(9)) Straight Paths Pr.

Eagle, Golden. It's Good to Laugh at Yourself (Coyote Medicine. l.t. ed. 2004. (Illus.). 22p. (J). per. 9.95 (978-1-932338-36-2(5)) Lifevest Publishing, Inc.

Enloe, Rochelle & Enloe, Tim. Kid-Power! How Kids Can Get the Holy Spirit's Power! 2007. (J). per. 5.99 (***978-0-9794331-0-8(X)***) E M Pubns.

Fear Not My Child, I Am Here: Emerging from the Spiral of Fear the Practical Mystic's Guide for Embracing Your Heart's Desire. 2003rd ed. 2003. 240p. per. 15.95 (978-0-9742213-0-4(9)) Community Works!.

Feinberg, Margaret & Gillespie, Natalie. Text Messages from God for Kids. 2005. (Instant Messages Ser.). 160p. mass mkt. 9.99 (978-1-59379-040-0(6)) White Stone Bks.

Fitzhugh, Steve. Who Will Survive: The Teenager's Ultimate Struggle for Survival. 2003. (YA). per. 10.00 (978-0-9748298-0-7(3)) PowerMoves.

Flynn, Leslie B. 19 Gifts of the Spirit. rev. ed. 2003. 240p. reprint ed. pap., pap. 12.99 (978-1-56476-337-2(4) , 1564763374) Cook, David C. Publishing Co.

Forgiveness & Healing. 1999. (Conversations with Teens Ser.). 16p. (YA). pap. 7.95 (978-0-937997-68-0(4) , 3825) Pflaum Publishing Group.

Foster, Kathryn Joy. Always Room for One More. l.t. ed. 2004. (Illus.). 12p. (J). spiral bd. 13.00 (978-0-9728779-6-1(7) , TBK-21007) Read All Over Publishing.

—Pathway to Prosperity. l.t. ed. 2000. 59p. (YA). 15.00 (978-0-9728779-3-0(2) , TBK-21004) Read All Over Publishing.

—Press Toward the Mark: Mountain Moving Faith, 1. l.t. ed. 2000. 54p. (YA). 15.00 (978-0-9728779-2-3(4) , TBK-21003) Read All Over Publishing.

—Royal Seed. l.t. ed. 2000. 30p. (YA). spiral bd. 20.00 (978-0-9728779-4-7(0) , TBK-21005) Read All Over Publishing.

—What if Noah Rocked the Boat? l.t. ed. 2002. 32p. (J). spiral bd. 20.00 (978-0-9728779-5-4(9) , TBK-21006) Read All Over Publishing.

Freed, Shirley & Moon, Louise. Put God First. Morelan, Bill, ed. Harrell, Rob, illus. 2003. 8p. (J). (gr. 1 up). pap. 3.99 (978-1-58938-106-3(8)) Concerned Communications.

Fuller, Robert C. Stairways to Heaven: Drugs in American Religious History. 2000. 237p. (YA). reprint ed. 27.00 (978-0-7567-6120-2(4)) DIANE Publishing Co.

Gilven, Edwin. Blubaugh, Spiritually Speaking. 2005. 27p. spiral bd. 13.58 (978-1-4116-4623-0(1)) Lulu.com.

God Created Animals. 2004. (In Celebration Coloring & Activity Book Ser.). 32p. (J). (gr. k-2). pap. 1.99 (978-0-7647-1014-8(1) , In Celebration) Schaffer, Frank Pubns.

Hamilton, Dennis Stephen. We Shall Come Rejoicing: Improving Your Service. 2001. 120p. (YA). per. 8.95 (978-0-9653904-3-9(8)) DCTS Publishing.

Hanh, Thich Nhat. Under the Rose-Apple Tree. 2002. 64p. (J). pap. 8.00 (978-1-888375-04-6(3)) Parallax Pr.

Haskins, Jim. African American Religious Leaders. 2008. (Black Stars Ser.). 168p. 24.95 (978-0-471-73632-5(5) , Wiley) Wiley, John & Sons, Inc.

Havergal, Frances Ridley. Little Pillows & Morning Bells: Good-Night Thoughts & Waking Thoughts for the Little Ones. 2004. 200p. (J). per. 14.95 (978-1-932474-25-1(0)) Solid Ground Christian Bks.

Hershberger, Tessa Sean. Confessions of a Girl: Truth to Be Told. 2005. (Fresh Voices Ser.). 226p. (J). (gr. 8-17). pap. 7.95 (978-1-932802-97-9(5) , Holy Macro! Bks.) MrExcel.com Publishing.

Hodgson, Joan. Hullo Sun. Ripper, Peter, illus. 2003. 32p. (ps-3). 8.95 (978-0-85487-072-1(5)) White Eagle Publishing Trust GBR. *Dist:* DeVorss & Co.

How to Hear the Voice of God Today! 2003. 52p. per. (978-1-932833-09-6(9)) Dickow, Gregory Ministries.

Hughes-Calero, Heather & Winged Wolf. Life Around Us. l.t. ed. 1999. (Illus.). 34p. (J). (ps-3). spiral bd. (978-0-932927-15-6(7)) Higher Consciousness Bks.

Johnson, Julie T. Teen Psychic: Exploring Your Intuitive Spiritual Powers. 2003. (gr. 7-12). lib. bdg. 24.55 (978-0-613-90834-4(1)) Tandem Library Bks.

Jones, Nona C. When the Soul Won't Let Go: No-Nonsense Answers to a Broken Woman's Questions. 2004. 90p. (YA). pap. 10.00 (978-0-9762770-0-2(X)) TNJ Ministries.

Klemp, Harold. Le Maitre des Reves. 2002. (Mahanta Transcripts Ser.: 8). (FRE.). (YA). pap. 14.00 (978-1-57043-166-1(3) , 021273) Eckankar.

Krishnamurti, Jiddu. What Are You Doing with Your Life? Carlson, Dale, ed. Nicklaus, Carol, illus. 2002. (Books on Living for Teens Ser.: Vol. 1). 272p. (gr. 8-12). pap. 14.95 (978-1-888004-24-3(X)) Krishnamurti Pubns. of America.

Lingo, Susan L. Discover-N-Do Object Talks That Teach about the Holy Spirit: 23 Messages That Teach Kids Ways to Explore God's Spirit. Becker, Paula, illus. 2006. 48p. (J). pap. 6.99 (978-0-7847-1373-0(1) , 02903) Standard Publishing.

The Man of Destiny. 2005. (YA). per. 8.95 (978-1-59872-161-4(5)) Instantpublisher.com.

McCarroll, Tolbert. A Winter Walk: Glimpses of the Sacred in Ordinary Life. 2006. (Illus.). 160p. 14.95 (978-0-8245-2416-6(0)) Crossroad Publishing Co.

McIntosh, Kenneth & McIntosh, Marsha. The Popularity of Meditation & Spiritual Practices: Seeking Inner Peace. 2005. (Religion & Modern Culture Ser.). (Illus.). 112p. (YA). (gr. 7 up). (978-1-59084-980-4(9)) Mason Crest Pubs.

Meyer, Richard. This Faith Is Mine. 2005. 176p. 8.99 (978-0-7586-0727-0(X)) Concordia Publishing Hse.

Morrow, Louis L. My Catholic Faith: A Manual of Religion. 2000. (Illus.). 415p. (YA). (gr. 6 up). 39.95 (978-0-9639032-6-6(8)) Sarto Hse.

Moving in the Spirit Confirmation Student Sessions. 2002. (J). pap. 4.00 (978-1-885996-19-0(5)) Good Ground Pr.

Murphy, Lynda. Total Image: Personal Development Inside & Out. 2003. 172p. (J). pap. 13.99 (978-1-57921-601-6(3)) Pleasant Word.

Noel, N. A. & Sisson, John W. On Earth As It Is in Heaven. Noel, N. A., illus. 1999. (Illus.). 32p. (J). (gr. k-8). 19.95 (978-0-9652531-3-0(9)) Noel Studio, Inc.

Osborne, Rick. God Quest: Dare to Live the Adventure. Close, Alan, illus. 2005. (2:52 Soul Gear Ser.). (J). pap. 7.99 (978-0-310-70868-1(0)) Zonderkidz.

Overstreet, Betty. The Lord Still Speaks - Are You Listening?. 1 book. 2004. 113p. (YA). per. 14.95 (978-0-9746253-0-0(2)) Overstreet Pub. & Mktg.

Parr, Susan Sherwood. 30 Days Out of Depression. 2003. (Illus.). 58p. pap. 4.95 (978-0-9728590-5-9(5)) Word Prodns.

Power Twins Handbook Volume One. 2006. (J). spiral bd. (***978-0-9742355-1-6(2)***) Brda, Tracy.

Ries, Julien. Man & the Divine in Hinduism. 2002. (Religions of Mankind Ser.). (Illus.). 32p. (YA). (gr. 5 up). 21.95 (978-0-7910-6625-6(8) , Chelsea Hse.) Facts On File, Inc.

Selby, John. Meditation the Cool Way to Calm: Solve Your Problems, Find Peace of Mind, & Discover the Real You. 2004. 224p. pap. 10.95 (978-0-8048-3486-5(5)) Tuttle Publishing.

Spiritual Leaders & Thinkers. 2005. 120p. pap. 390.00 (978-0-7910-8734-3(4) , Chelsea Hse.) Facts On File, Inc.

Spiritual Warfare. ldr.'s ed. 1998. (Cross Training Ser.: Vol. 3). 64p. (YA). (gr. 10-12). pap. 15.00 incl. VHS (978-1-57405-025-7(7)) CharismaLife Pubs.

Stevens, Joyce Ann. From the Heart. 2001. (Illus.). 284p. per. 20.00 (978-0-9708645-1-2(5)) Divine Power Publishing.

Stillman, Sarah. Soul Searching Journal: A Guide to Self Discovery for Girls. Gross, Susan, illus. 2001. 88p. (YA). (gr. 7-12). 11.95 (978-1-58270-056-4(7)) Beyond Words Publishing, Inc.

Urne, Anne. A Spiritual Trilogy. Hudson, David W., photos by. 2003. (Illus.). 352p. (YA). pap. 21.00 (978-0-9727967-0-5(3) , 77707) Bois Pubns.

VonSeggen, Liz. Join the Hall of Faith. 2004. 20p. (J). 18.00 (978-1-58302-256-6(2)) One Way St., Inc.

Walker, Peggy, illus. My First Book of Buddhist Treasures. 2003. 38p. (J). 8.95 (978-0-915678-81-5(0)) World Tribune Pr.

Walsch, Neale Donald. The Little Soul & the Earth: A Children's Parable Adapted from Conversations with God. Riccio, Frank, illus. 2005. (Young Spirit Books). 32p. (J). 17.95 (978-1-57174-451-7(7)) Hampton Roads Publishing Co., Inc.

Walter, Pamela. Gramela Pamela Explains What's a YEBEN! ??? unabr. ed. 1999. (J). (gr. k-3). 7.95 incl. audio (978-1-929110-27-8(8) , 0-92791-1) Colter Enterprises, Inc.

Watson, W. Hamp, Jr. Frederick Wilson Still Speaks - Big Words for Our Time. Watson, W. Hamp, Jr., ed. l.t. ed. 2004. (J). per. 12.95 (978-0-9746976-0-4(5)) Cambridge Way Publishing.

Willow Creek Association. 5-G Challenge Winter Quarter Kit: Doing Life with God in the Picture. 2003. (Promiseland Ser.). (J). 299.00 (978-0-7441-2369-2(0)) Zonderkidz.

—5-G Impact Winter Quarter Kit: Doing Life with God in the Picture. 2003. (Promiseland Ser.). (J). 299.00 (978-0-7441-2370-8(4)) Zonderkidz.

SPIRITUALS (SONGS)

Bryan, Ashley. Let It Shine: Three Favorite Spirituals. Bryan, Ashley, illus. 2007. (Illus.). 48p. (J). (ps-3). 16.99 (978-0-689-84732-5(7) , Atheneum) Simon & Schuster Children's Publishing.

Corr, Christopher. Whole World. 2007. (Illus.). 32p. (J). (ps-4). 16.99 incl. audio compact disk (***978-1-84686-043-0(1)***) Barefoot Bks., Inc.

Giovanni, Nikki. On My Journey Now: Looking at African-American History Through the Spirituals. 2007. (Illus.). 128p. (J). (gr. 6-9). 18.99 (978-0-7636-2885-7(9)) Candlewick Pr.

Holiday, Billie. God Bless the Child. Pinkney, Jerry, illus. (J). 2008. 40p. 7.99 (978-0-06-443646-5(2)); 2004. 32p. lib. bdg. 17.89 (978-0-06-029487-8(6) , Amistad) HarperCollins Pubs.

Holiday, Billie & Herzog, Arthur. God Bless the Child. Pinkney, Jerry, illus. 2004. 32p. (J). 16.99 incl. audio compact disk (978-0-06-028797-9(7)) HarperCollins Pubs.

Pinkney, Gloria Jean. Music from Our Lord's Holy Heaven. Pinkney, Jerry et al, illus. 2005. 48p. (J). (ps up). lib. bdg. 18.89 incl. audio compact disk (978-0-06-000769-0(9)) HarperCollins Pubs.

SPLICING

see Knots and Splices

SPONGEBOB SQUAREPANTS (FICTITIOUS CHARACTER)—FICTION

Artifact Group. Atlantis SquarePantis. 2007. (SpongeBob SquarePants Ser.). 24p. (J). pap. 3.99 (***978-1-4169-3799-9(4)*** , Simon Spotlight/Nickelodeon) Simon & Schuster Children's Publishing.

—My Trip to Atlantis: By SpongeBob SquarePants. 2007. (SpongeBob SquarePants Ser.). 32p. (J). pap. 3.99 (***978-1-4169-3794-4(3)*** , Simon Spotlight/Nickelodeon) Simon & Schuster Children's Publishing.

Auerbach, Annie. SpongeBob Superstar. 2001. (gr. 3-6). lib. bdg. 11.80 (978-0-613-43974-9(0)) Tandem Library Bks.

Banks, Steven. Amazing SpongeBobini. 2007. 24p. (J). 21.35 (***978-1-59961-362-8(X)***) Spotlight.

—The Amazing Spongebobini. Martinez, Heather, illus. ed. 2005. (SpongeBob Squarepants Ser.: Garden & No. 1). 22p. (J). lib. bdg. 15.00 (978-1-59054-829-5(9)) Fitzgerald Bks.

—The Art Contest: No Cheating Allowed. Dress, Robert, illus. 2006. (SpongeBob Squarepants Ser.). 24p. (J). pap. 3.99 (978-1-4169-0667-4(3) , Simon Spotlight/Nickelodeon) Simon & Schuster Children's Publishing.

—Dear SpongeBob . . . A Funny Fill-Ins Book. Style Guide Staff, illus. 2003. (SpongeBob SquarePants Ser.). 48p. (J). pap. 2.99 (978-0-689-85997-7(X) , Simon Spotlight) Simon & Schuster Children's Publishing.

—Dear Spongebob: A Funny Fill-Ins Book. 2003. (gr. 3-6). lib. bdg. 10.65 (978-0-613-86194-6(9)) Tandem Library Bks.

—Lost in Time. The Artifact Group, illus. 2006. 22p. (J). lib. bdg. 15.00 (***978-1-4242-0977-4(3)***) Fitzgerald Bks.

—Lost in Time. 2007. 24p. (J). 21.35 (***978-1-59961-367-3(0)***) Spotlight.

—Sandy's Rocket. 2001. (gr. 3-6). lib. bdg. 11.80 (978-0-613-43971-8(6)) Tandem Library Bks.

—Show Me the Bunny! Greenblatt, C. H. & Reiss, William, illus. ed. 2005. 32p. (J). lib. bdg. 15.00 (978-1-59054-985-8(6)) Fitzgerald Bks.

—The Song That Never Ends. DePorter, Vince, illus. ed. 2005. 32p. (J). lib. bdg. 15.00 (978-1-59054-984-1(8)) Fitzgerald Bks.

—The Song That Never Ends. DePorter, Vince, illus. 2004. (Ready-to-Read Ser.: Vol. 4). 32p. (J). pap. 3.99 (978-0-689-86528-2(7) , Simon Spotlight/Nickelodeon) Simon & Schuster Children's Publishing.

—SpongeBob Exposed! The Insider's Guide to SpongeBob SquarePants. Schigiel, Gregg & Bond, Clint, illus. 2004. (Spongebob Squarepants Ser.). 96p. (J). 8.99 (978-0-689-86870-2(7) , Simon Spotlight/Nickelodeon) Simon & Schuster Children's Publishing.

—SpongeBob Goes to the Doctor. Saunders, Zina, illus. 2005. (Spongebob Squarepants Ser.). 24p. (J). pap. 3.99 (978-1-4169-0359-8(3) , Simon Spotlight/Nickelodeon) Simon & Schuster Children's Publishing.

—Spongebob Goes to the Doctor. Saunders, Zina, illus. 2005. 22p. (J). lib. bdg. 15.00 (***978-1-4242-0976-7(5)***) Fitzgerald Bks.

—SpongeBob Pops Up! Martinez, Heather, illus. 2004. (SpongeBob SquarePants Ser.). 16p. (J). 8.99 (978-0-689-86328-8(4) , Simon Spotlight/Nickelodeon) Simon & Schuster Children's Publishing.

—SpongeBob's Easter Parade. Goldberg, Barry, illus. 2005. (Spongebob Squarepants Ser.). 24p. (J). pap. 3.99 (978-0-689-87314-0(X) , Simon Spotlight/Nickelodeon) Simon & Schuster Children's Publishing.

—Spongebob's Easter Parade. Goldberg, Barry, illus. ed. 2005. (SpongeBob Squarepants Ser.: No. 7). 22p. (J). lib. bdg. 15.00 (978-1-59054-827-1(2)) Fitzgerald Bks.

Banks, Steven. Stop the Presses! DePorter, Vince, illus. 2005. 22p. (J). lib. bdg. 15.00 (***978-1-4242-0973-6(0)***) Fitzgerald Bks.

—Stop the Presses! DePorter, Vince, illus. 2005. (Spongebob Squarepants Ser.). 24p. (J). pap. 3.99 (978-0-689-87726-1(9) , Simon Spotlight/Nickelodeon) Simon & Schuster Children's Publishing.

Banks, Steven & Artifact Group. Lost in Time: A Medieval Adventure. 2006. (SpongeBob SquarePants Ser.). (Illus.). 24p. (J). pap. 3.99 (978-1-4169-1464-8(1) , Simon Spotlight/Nickelodeon) Simon & Schuster Children's Publishing.

Banks, Steven & Hillenburg, Stephen. SpongeBob Goes to the Doctor. Saunders, Zina, illus. 2005. (J). (***978-1-4156-3131-7(X)*** , Simon Spotlight/Nickelodeon) Simon & Schuster Children's Publishing.

Boczkowski, Tricia. Meet Patrick. Style Guide Staff, illus. 2003. (SpongeBob SquarePants Ser.). 12p. (J). bds. 7.99 (978-0-689-85904-5(X) , Simon Spotlight/Nickelodeon) Simon & Schuster Children's Publishing.

Bond, Clint & Clark, Andy, illus. The Great Snail Race. 2005. (Spongebob Squarepants Ser.). 24p. (J). pap. 3.99 (978-0-689-87313-3(1) , Simon Spotlight/Nickelodeon) Simon & Schuster Children's Publishing.

Bubble Trouble. 2001. (SpongeBob SquarePants Ser.). (Illus.). (J). pap. 3.99 (978-0-307-10981-1(X) , 10981, Golden Bks.) Random Hse. Children's Bks.

Cerasini, Marc. The SpongeBob Squarepants Movie: A Novelization of the Hit Movie! novel ed. 2004. (Spongebob Squarepants Ser.). (Illus.). 144p. (J). pap. 4.99 (978-0-689-86840-5(5) , Simon Spotlight) Simon & Schuster Children's Publishing.

Chanda, J-P. Happy Birthday Spongebob! Martinez, Heather, illus. ed. 2005. 22p. (J). lib. bdg. 15.00 (978-1-59054-965-0(1)) Fitzgerald Bks.

Chipponeri, Kelli. Hoedown Showdown. DePorter, Vince & Goldberg, Barry, illus. 2006. (Ready-To-Read Ser.). 32p. (J). pap. 3.99 (978-1-4169-0689-6(4) , Simon Spotlight) Simon & Schuster Children's Publishing.

Chipponeri, Kelli. Hoedown Showdown: SpongeBob Squarepants. DePorter, Vince & Goldberg, Barry, illus. 2006. 32p. (J). lib. bdg. 15.00 (***978-1-4242-0960-6(9)***) Fitzgerald Bks.

Collins, Terry. Deep-Sea Tales: 6 Salty Sea Stories. 2005. (Spongebob Squarepants Ser.). (Illus.). 336p. (J). pap. 7.99 (978-0-689-87704-9(8) , Simon Spotlight/Nickelodeon) Simon & Schuster Children's Publishing.

—SpongeBob Naturepants. 2001. (gr. 3-6). lib. bdg. 11.80 (978-0-613-43972-5(4)) Tandem Library Bks.

—SpongeBob Squarepants the World's Greatest Valentine. 2001. (gr. 3-6). lib. bdg. 11.80 (978-0-613-43973-2(2)) Tandem Library Bks.

Dart, Allan, ed. SpongeBob SquarePants & Other TV Tunes, No. 2. 2003. (Illus.). 16p. (J). pap. 3.99 (978-0-88013-060-8(1)) Profile Entertainment, Inc.

Dorling Kindersley Publishing Staff. SpongeBob SquarePants. 2005. (Ultimate sticker Bks.). 16p. (J). (ps-12). pap. 6.99 (978-0-7566-1559-8(3)) Dorling Kindersley Publishing, Inc.

Fry, Sonali. Beyond Bikini Bottom! DePorter, Vince, illus. 2005. (Spongebob Squarepants Ser.). 16p. (J). (ps-ps). 7.99 (978-0-689-87738-4(2) , Simon Spotlight/Nickelodeon) Simon & Schuster Children's Publishing.

—Wheel of Wishes. Saunders, Zina, illus. 2005. (Spongebob Squarepants Ser.). 14p. (J). 5.99 (978-0-689-87420-8(0) , Simon Spotlight/Nickelodeon) Simon & Schuster Children's Publishing.

Giddy Up Staff. SpongeBob Abraca Dazzle. 2006. 24p. 4.99 (978-1-59524-079-8(9)) Giddy Up, LLC.

Goldberg, Barry, illus. Bubble Blowers, Beware! 2004. (Spongebob Squarepants Ser.). 24p. (J). pap. 3.99 (978-0-689-86862-7(6) , Simon Spotlight/Nickelodeon) Simon & Schuster Children's Publishing.

Golden Books Staff. Bring on the Rock! Schigiel, Gregg, illus. 2004. 32p. (J). (ps). pap. 4.99 (978-0-375-82989-5(X) , Golden Bks.) Random Hse. Children's Bks.

—Brush with Greatness. 2002. (SpongeBob SquarePants Ser.). (Illus.). 32p. (J). (ps-2). pap. 4.99 (978-0-307-29958-1(9) , Golden Bks.) Random Hse. Children's Bks.

—Full Speed Ahead! 2005. (Illus.). 32p. (J). (ps-3). 4.99 (978-0-375-83103-4(7) , Golden Bks.) Random Hse. Children's Bks.

—I'm Ready! Schigiel, Gregg, illus. 2004. (Color Plus Growing Characters Ser.). 32p. (J). (ps). pap. 4.99 (978-0-375-82988-8(1) , Golden Bks.) Random Hse. Children's Bks.

—Shell City, Here We Come! 2004. (Illus.). 32p. (J). (ps). pap. 3.99 (978-0-375-82947-5(4) , Golden Bks.) Random Hse. Children's Bks.

—Sponge on the Run. Meurer, Caleb, illus. 2002. 56p. (J). (ps-2). pap. 4.99 (978-0-307-12562-0(9) , Golden Bks.) Random Hse. Children's Bks.

—Stick Together! 2007. (Illus.). 32p. (J). (ps-3). 2.99 (978-0-375-83485-1(0) , Golden Bks.) Random Hse. Children's Bks.

The Greetings from Bikini Bottom. 2003. 32p. mass mkt. 2.64 (978-0-689-85651-8(2) , Simon Spotlight/Nickelodeon) Simon & Schuster Children's Publishing.

Hillenburg, Steven. Gone Jellyfishin', Vol. 7. 2005. (Spongebob Squarepants Ser.). (Illus.). pap. 7.99 (978-1-59532-678-2(2) , Tokyopop Kids) TOKYOPOP, Inc.

—SpongeBob SquarePants: Another Day Another Dollar, Vol. 5. 2004. (Nickelodeon Ser.). (Illus.). 96p. pap. 7.99 (978-1-59532-209-8(4) , Tokyopop Kids) TOKYOPOP, Inc.

Hillenburg, Steven, creator. SpongeBob SquarePants: Tales from Bikini Bottom, 7 vols., Vol. 3. 2004. (Illus.). 96p. pap. 7.99 (978-1-59182-575-3(X) , Tokyopop Kids) TOKYOPOP, Inc.

—SpongeBob SquarePants Vol. 1: Krusty Krab Adventures, 2 vols. 2003. (Illus.). 96p. pap. 7.99 (978-1-59182-398-8(6) , Tokyopop Kids) TOKYOPOP, Inc.

—SpongeBob SquarePants Crime & Funishment Vol. 4, 7 vols. 2004. (Illus.). 96p. (gr. 2-5). pap. 7.99 (978-1-59182-576-0(8) , Tokyopop Kids) TOKYOPOP, Inc.

—SpongeBob SquarePantsTM: Friends Forever. 2003. (Illus.). 96p. pap. 7.99 (978-1-59182-399-5(4) , Tokyopop Kids) TOKYOPOP, Inc.

Koeppel, Ruth. SpongeBob's Day Off. DePorter, Vince, illus. 2004. (Spongebob Squarepants Ser.). 12p. (J). bds. 7.99 (978-0-689-87652-3(1) , Simon Spotlight/Nickelodeon) Simon & Schuster Children's Publishing.

Kowitt, Holly. Belly Laughs from Bikini Bottom. 2003. (SpongeBob SquarePants Ser.). (Illus.). 48p. (J). pap. 3.99 (978-0-689-86165-9(6) , Simon Spotlight) Simon & Schuster Children's Publishing.

—Belly Laughs from Bikini Bottom. 2003. (gr. k-3). lib. bdg. 10.65 (978-0-613-85671-3(6)) Tandem Library Bks.

—SpongeBob's Book of Excuses. Style Guide Staff, illus. 2005. (Spongebob Squarepants Ser.). 48p. (J). pap. 3.99 (978-0-689-87211-2(9) , Simon Spotlight) Simon & Schuster Children's Publishing.

Krulik, Nancy E. Ice-Cream Dreams. Martinez, Heather, illus. 2004. 22p. (J). lib. bdg. 15.00 (***978-1-4242-0975-0(7)***) Fitzgerald Bks.

—Ice-Cream Dreams. 2007. 24p. (J). 21.35 (***978-1-59961-366-6(2)***) Spotlight.

Lewman, David. Bikini Bottom Riddles. Style Guide Staff, illus. 2005. (Spongebob Squarepants Ser.). 48p. (J). pap. 3.99 (978-0-689-87875-6(3) , Simon Spotlight) Simon & Schuster Children's Publishing.

—Blizzard Bluster! SpongeBob's Book of Frosty Funnies. 2008. (SpongeBob SquarePants Ser.). 48p. (J). pap. 3.99 (***978-1-4169-4747-9(7)*** , Simon Spotlight) Simon & Schuster Children's Publishing.

—Go, Graduate! All the Best from Bikini Bottom. 2005. (Spongebob Squarepants Ser.). (Illus.). 32p. (J). 6.99 (978-1-4169-0291-1(0) , Simon Spotlight/Nickelodeon) Simon & Schuster Children's Publishing.

—Hands Off! 2003. (gr. k-3). lib. bdg. 11.25 (978-0-613-66358-8(6)) Tandem Library Bks.

—Hands Off. 2007. 24p. (J). 21.35 (***978-1-59961-365-9(4)***) Spotlight.

—Hands Off! Greenblatt, C. H. & Reiss, William, illus. ed. 2005. (SpongeBob Squarepants Ser.: 2). 22p. (J). lib. bdg. 15.00 (978-1-59054-825-7(6)) Fitzgerald Bks.

—Oh, Barnacles! SpongeBob's Handbook for Bad Days. Style Guide Staff, illus. 2005. (Spongebob Squarepants Ser.). 48p. (J). pap. 3.99 (978-1-4169-0641-4(X) , Simon Spotlight/Nickelodeon) Simon & Schuster Children's Publishing.

—Pirates of Bikini Bottom. Moore, Harry, illus. 2007. (SpongeBob SquarePants Ser.). 64p. (J). pap. 4.99 (***978-1-4169-3560-5(6)*** , Simon Spotlight/Nickelodeon) Simon & Schuster Children's Publishing.

—SpongeBob: Scavenger Hunt. Wang, Teale & Clark, Andy, illus. 2004. (Interactive Play-A-Sound Ser.). 24p. (J). (978-0-7853-9960-5(7) , 7209700) Publications International, Ltd.

—SpongeBob & the Princess. Bond, Clint, illus. 2004. (SpongeBob SquarePants 8 X 8 Paperback ; #5 Ser.). 24p. (J). pap. 3.99 (978-0-689-86581-7(3) , Simon Spotlight/Nickelodeon) Simon & Schuster Children's Publishing.

—Spongebob & the Princess. Bond, Clint, illus. ed. 2005. (SpongeBob Squarepants Ser.: 5). 22p. (J). lib. bdg. 15.00 (978-1-59054-826-4(4)) Fitzgerald Bks.

—SpongeBob DetectivePants: The Case of the Missing Spatula. Moore, Harry, illus. 2006. (SpongeBob SquarePants Ser.). 16p. (J). pap. 5.99 (978-1-4169-1319-1(X) , Simon Spotlight/Nickelodeon) Simon & Schuster Children's Publishing.

—Spongebob Jokepants. 2002. (ps-2). lib. bdg. 10.65 (978-0-613-58155-4(5)) Tandem Library Bks.

—SpongeBob JokePants. Style Guide Staff, illus. 2003. (SpongeBob SquarePants Ser.). 48p. (J). pap. 3.99 (978-0-689-85568-9(0) , Simon Spotlight) Simon & Schuster Children's Publishing.

—The SpongeBob SquarePants Oracle: The Oracle. 2003. (Illus.). 288p. pap. 10.00 (978-0-7434-8316-2(2) , Pocket) Simon & Schuster.

—SpongeBob SquarePants Survival Guide. 2002. (Illus.). 144p. pap. 10.95 (978-0-7434-6987-6(9) , Pocket) Simon & Schuster.

—Spongebob's Secret Valentine. Martinez, Heather, illus. ed. 2005. (SpongeBob Squarepants Ser.: No. 3). 22p. (J). lib. bdg. 15.00 (978-1-59054-828-8(0)) Fitzgerald Bks.

—The Three Little Neighbors. DePorter, Vince, illus. 2006. (SpongeBob SquarePants Ser.). 20p. (J). 8.99 (978-1-4169-0688-9(6) , Simon Spotlight/Nickelodeon) Simon & Schuster Children's Publishing.

Lewman, David & Dorling Kindersley Publishing Staff. The Essential Guide. 2005. (Illus.). 48p. (J). (ps-7). 12.99 (978-0-7566-1640-3(9)) Dorling Kindersley Publishing, Inc.

Lewman, David, et al. Zoo Day Disaster. Dress, Robert, illus. 2005. (SpongeBob SquarePants Chapter Book Ser.: Vol. 10). 60p. (J). (***978-1-4156-0765-7(6)*** , Simon Spotlight/Nickelodeon) Simon & Schuster Children's Publishing.

Lou Weber Staff, ed. Bubbly Beats. 2005. 14p. (J). (ps-ps). 15.98 (978-1-4127-3164-5(X) , 7232500) Publications International, Ltd.

—Spongebob Clock It's Time Sound Book. 2004. 10p. (J). bds. 16.98 (978-1-4127-3030-3(9) , 7226500) Publications International, Ltd.

Meurer, Caleb & Schigiel, Gregg, illus. Bikini Bottom Confidential. 2003. 32p. (J). (ps-3). pap. 3.99 (978-0-307-10455-7(9) , Golden Bks.) Random Hse. Children's Bks.

Miglis, Jenny. And the Winner Is... Meurer, Caleb, illus. ed. 2005. (SpongeBob Squarepants Ser.: 4). 22p. (J). lib. bdg. 15.00 (978-1-59054-824-0(8)) Fitzgerald Bks.

—New Student Starfish. Martinez, Heather, illus. 2003. (SpongeBob SquarePants Ser.). 64p. (J). pap. 3.99 (978-0-689-86164-2(8) , Simon Spotlight) Simon & Schuster Children's Publishing.

—New Student Starfish. 2003. (gr. 3-6). lib. bdg. 11.80 (978-0-613-86195-3(7)) Tandem Library Bks.

Nick Ready-to-Read Boxed Set: Learn to Read with SpongeBob & Friends! 2004. (Ready-to-Reads Ser.). (Illus.). 32p. (J). pap. 9.99 (978-0-689-87053-8(1) , Simon Spotlight/Nickelodeon) Simon & Schuster Children's Publishing.

Ostrow, Kim. Great Snail Race. 2007. 24p. (J). 21.35 (***978-1-59961-364-2(6)***) Spotlight.

Ostrow, Kim. The Great Snail Race. Bond, Clint & Clark, Andy, illus. ed. 2005. (SpongeBob Squarepants Ser.: No. 6). 22p. (J). lib. bdg. 15.00 (978-1-59054-830-1(2)) Fitzgerald Bks.

Pass, Erica. SpongeBob LovePants. Schigiel, Gregg, illus. 2006. (Ready-To-Read Ser.). 32p. (J). pap. 3.99 (978-1-4169-1758-8(6) , Simon Spotlight/Nickelodeon) Simon & Schuster Children's Publishing.

—SpongeBob SantaPants. Martinez, Heather, illus. 2005. (Spongebob Squarepants Ser.). 14p. (J). bds. 6.99 (978-1-4169-0575-2(8) , Simon Spotlight/Nickelodeon) Simon & Schuster Children's Publishing.

Pass, Erica. Vote for SpongeBob! Moore, Harry, illus. 2008. (SpongeBob SquarePants Ser.). 24p. (J). pap. 3.99 (***978-1-4169-4986-2(0)*** , Simon Spotlight/Nickelodeon) Simon & Schuster Children's Publishing.

Reisner, Molly & Ostrow, Kim. Camp SpongeBob. Martinez, Heather, illus. 2004. (SpongeBob SquarePants Ready-To-Read Ser.: Vol. 5). 32p. (J). pap. 3.99 (978-0-689-86593-0(7) , Simon Spotlight/Nickelodeon) Simon & Schuster Children's Publishing.

—Camp Spongebob. Martinez, Heather, illus. ed. 2005. 32p. (J). lib. bdg. 15.00 (978-1-59054-983-4(X)) Fitzgerald Bks.

Reiss, William & Greenblatt, C. H., illus. SpongeBob's Christmas Wish. 2003. (SpongeBob SquarePants Ser.). 32p. (J). 5.99 (978-0-689-85878-9(7) , Simon Spotlight/Nickelodeon) Simon & Schuster Children's Publishing.

Richards, Kitty. SpongeBob Airpants: The Lost Episode. Martinez, Heather, illus. 2003. (SpongeBob SquarePants Ser.). 64p. (J). pap. 3.99 (978-0-689-86163-5(X) , Simon Spotlight) Simon & Schuster Children's Publishing.

Schigiel, Gregg & Meurer, Caleb, illus. Star Power! 2005. 64p. (J). (ps-3). pap. 3.99 (978-0-375-83090-7(1) , Golden Bks.) Random Hse. Children's Bks.

Silverhardt, Lauryn. SpongeBob SpookyPants. Style Guide Staff, illus. 2004. (Spongebob Squarepants Ser.). 16p. (J). bds. 5.99 (978-0-689-87320-1(4) , Simon Spotlight/Nickelodeon) Simon & Schuster Children's Publishing.

Simon and Schuster Children's Staff, ed. Adventures in Bikini Bottom. 2006. (SpongeBob SquarePants Ser.). 144p. (J). pap. 7.99 (978-1-4169-1562-1(1) , Simon Spotlight/Nickelodeon) Simon & Schuster Children's Publishing.

Sollinger, Emily. SpongeBob's Valentine's Surprise. Martinez, Heather, illus. 2005. (Spongebob Squarepants Ser.). 14p. (J). bds. 6.99 (978-1-4169-0574-5(X) , Simon Spotlight/Nickelodeon) Simon & Schuster Children's Publishing.

Spongebob. 2002. mass mkt. 111.76 (978-0-689-02679-9(X) , Simon Spotlight/Nickelodeon) Simon & Schuster Children's Publishing.

SpongeBob SquarePants. 2007. (J). 128.10 (***978-1-59961-361-1(1)***) Spotlight.

SpongeBob Squarepants WOW! Scratchers. 2005. 4p. (J). 6.99 (978-1-59524-031-6(4)) Giddy Up, LLC.

SpongeBob WOW Paper Scribble & Giggle Pad. 2004. 36p. (J). 7.99 (978-1-59524-006-4(3)) Giddy Up, LLC.

SpongeBob WOW! Surprise & Shine. 2005. 4p. (J). 6.99 (978-1-59524-049-1(7)) Giddy Up, LLC.

Spongebob's Backpack Book Proprietary. 2003. (Illus.). 16p. (J). bds. 6.99 (978-0-689-86392-9(6) , Simon Spotlight/Nickelodeon) Simon & Schuster Children's Publishing.

SpongeBob's Box of Books. 2005. (Spongebob Squarepants Ser.). 144p. (J). pap. 9.99 (978-1-4169-1186-9(3) , Simon Spotlight/Nickelodeon) Simon & Schuster Children's Publishing.

Style Guide Staff, illus. Patricks Backpack Book. 2003. (SpongeBob SquarePants Ser.). 16p. (J). bds. 6.99 (978-0-689-85649-5(0) , Simon Spotlight/Nickelodeon) Simon & Schuster Children's Publishing.

—Spongebob Squarepants: Backpack Book. 2003. (SpongeBob SquarePants Ser.). 16p. (J). bds. 6.99 (978-0-689-85648-8(2) , Simon Spotlight/Nickelodeon) Simon & Schuster Children's Publishing.

Wax, Wendy. Nautical Nonsense: A SpongeBob Joke Book. Style Guide Staff, illus. 2006. (SpongeBob SquarePants Ser.). 48p. (J). pap. 3.99 (978-1-4169-1316-0(5) , Simon Spotlight) Simon & Schuster Children's Publishing.

Weber, Lou, ed. Spongebob Color Me Sound. 2004. 32p. (J). 7.98 (978-1-4127-3053-2(8) , 7226100) Publications International, Ltd.

—Spongebob Wipe off Sound Book. 2005. 16p. (J). spiral bd., bds. 12.98 (978-1-4127-3540-7(8) , 7264700) Publications International, Ltd.

Willson, Sarah. Behold, No Cavities! A Visit to the Dentist. Moore, Harry, illus. 2007. (SpongeBob SquarePants Ser.). 24p. (J). pap. 3.99 (***978-1-4169-3566-7(5)*** , Simon Spotlight/Nickelodeon) Simon & Schuster Children's Publishing.

—Just Say Please! Moore, Harry, illus. 2007. (SpongeBob SquarePants Ser.). 32p. (J). pap. 3.99 (978-1-4169-4129-3(0) , Simon Spotlight/Nickelodeon) Simon & Schuster Children's Publishing.

—Mother Knows Best. Dress, Robert, illus. 2006. (SpongeBob SquarePants Chapter Book Ser.: Vol. 11). 64p. (J). pap. 4.99 (978-1-4169-0793-0(9) , Simon Spotlight/Nickelodeon) Simon & Schuster Children's Publishing.

Willson, Sarah. SpongeBob RippedPants. Martinez, Heather, illus. 2007. (SpongeBob SquarePants Ser.). 16p. (J). pap. 5.99 (***978-1-4169-4750-9(7)*** , Simon Spotlight/Nickelodeon) Simon & Schuster Children's Publishing.

Zuravicky, Orli. SpongeBob PartyPants. Goldberg, Barry, illus. 2007. (SpongeBob SquarePants Ser.). 12p. (J). bds. 6.99 (978-1-4169-2776-1(X) , Simon Spotlight/Nickelodeon) Simon & Schuster Children's Publishing.

SPORTS

see also Aeronautical Sports; Amusements; Aquatic Sports; Athletics; Coaching (Athletics); Games; Gymnastics; Olympics; Outdoor Life; Physical Education and Training; Rodeos; School Sports; Winter Sports

also names of sports, e.g. baseball; etc.

Action Sports. 2003. (Illus.). (J). 107.70 (978-0-7910-7062-8(X) , Chelsea Hse.) Facts On File, Inc.

Action Sports, 24 bks. Incl. Bicycling. Gutman, Bill. 1995. lib. bdg. 21.26 (978-1-56065-264-9(0)); BMX Racing. Gutman, Bill. 1995. lib. bdg. 21.26 (978-1-56065-262-5(4)); Hang Gliding & Parasailing. Will-Harris, Toni. 1994. lib. bdg. 21.26 (978-1-56065-058-4(3)); Horseback Riding. Stewart, Gail B. 1995. lib. bdg. 21.26 (978-1-56065-263-2(2)); Hot Air Ballooning. Constanzo, Christie. 1994. lib. bdg. 21.26 (978-1-56065-049-2(4)); Hot Dogging & Snowboarding. Guthrie, Robert. 1994. lib. bdg. 21.26 (978-1-56065-052-2(4)); In-Line Skating. Martin, John. 1994. lib. bdg. 21.26 (978-1-56065-202-1(0)); Judo. Gutman, Bill. 1995. lib. bdg. 21.26 (978-1-56065-265-6(9)); Karate. Gutman, Bill. 1995. lib. bdg. 21.26 (978-1-56065-233-5(0)); Kickboxing : The Modern Martial Art. Sipe, Daniel. 1994. lib. bdg. 21.26 (978-1-56065-203-8(9)); Kung Fu. Gutman, Bill. 1995. lib. bdg. 21.26 (978-1-56065-267-0(5)); Landsailing. Hays, Scott. 1994. lib. bdg. 21.26 (978-1-56065-057-7(5)); Mountain Biking. Gutman, Bill. 1995. lib. bdg. 21.26 (978-1-56065-234-2(9)); Roller Hockey. Gutman, Bill. 1995. lib. bdg. 21.26 (978-1-56065-250-2(0)); Roller Skating. Kulper, Eileen. 1994. lib. bdg. 21.26 (978-1-56065-050-8(8)); Skateboarding. Gould, Marilyn. 1994. lib. bdg. 21.26 (978-1-56065-048-5(6)); Skateboarding Streetstyle. Schoemaker, Joel. 1995. lib. bdg. 21.26 (978-1-56065-261-8(6)); Skydiving. Meeks, Christopher. 1994. lib. bdg. 21.26 (978-1-56065-051-5(6)); Sumo Wrestling. Gutman, Bill. 1995. lib. bdg. 21.26 (978-1-56065-273-1(X)); Surfing. Gutman, Bill. 1995. lib. bdg. 21.26 (978-1-56065-235-9(7)); Tae Kwon Do. Gutman, Bill. 1995. lib. bdg. 21.26 (978-1-56065-266-3(7)); Waterskiing & Kneeboarding. Walker, Cheryl. 1994. lib. bdg. 21.26 (978-1-56065-056-0(7)); White Water Rafting. Nabhan, Marty. 1994. lib. bdg. 21.26 (978-1-56065-053-9(2)); Wind Surfing. Wray, Amanda. 1994. lib. bdg. 21.26 (978-1-56065-055-3(9)); 48p. (J). (gr. 3-4). (Illus.). Set lib. bdg. 510.24 (978-1-56065-625-8(5) , Capstone High-Interest Bks.) Capstone Pr., Inc.

Ajmera, Maya. Let the Games Begin! 2000. (gr. k-3). lib. bdg. 15.25 (978-0-613-28299-4(X)); (Illus.). (J). (978-0-606-18804-3(5)) Tandem Library Bks.

S

Ajmera, Maya & Regan, Michael J. Let the Games Begin! 2004. (Illus.). 32p. (J). 16.95 (978-0-88106-067-6(4)) Charlesbridge Publishing, Inc.

Ajmera, Maya, et al. Let the Games Begin! 2004. (Illus.). 32p. (J). pap. 6.95 (978-0-88106-068-3(2)) Charlesbridge Publishing, Inc.

All-Star Sports Stars, 6 bks. Incl. Baseball All-Stars : Today's Greatest Players. Schwarz, Alan. lib. bdg. 27.95 (978-0-8239-3688-5(0)); Basketball All-Stars : The NBA's Best. Paul, Alan & Kramer, Jon. lib. bdg. 25.25 (978-0-8239-3689-2(9)); Football All-Stars : The NFL's Best. Bradley, Michael. lib. bdg. 27.95 (978-0-8239-3690-8(2)); Gridiron Greats : 8 of Today's Hottest NFL Stars. Collie, Ashley Jude. lib. bdg. 25.25 (978-0-8239-3691-5(0)); Ken Griffey, Jr : Superstar Centerfielder. Rolfe, John. lib. bdg. 30.50 (978-0-8239-3687-8(2)); Sports Superstars : 8 of Today's Hottest Athletes. Knotts, Bob. lib. bdg. 27.95 (978-0-8239-3692-2(9)); (YA). (gr. 7-12). (Illus.). 176p. 2005. Set lib. bdg. 164.85 (978-0-8239-9732-9(4)) Rosen Publishing Group, Inc., The.

American Heritage Dictionary Editors, ed. What Am I Playing? Zagarenski, Pamela, illus. 2004. (Good Beginnings Ser.). 4p. (J). (ps-k). bds. 3.95 (978-0-618-43169-4(1)) Houghton Mifflin Co. Trade & Reference Div.

Anderson, Lars. NASCAR Stars & Cars. Holder, Sherie, ed. 1999. (Illus.). 32p. (J). (gr. 2-8). pap. 3.99 (978-1-886749-78-8(7)) Sports Illustrated For Kids.

Barcelo, Josefina. Vamos a Jugar. Alvarez, Mrinalí, illus. 2006. (SPA.). (J). 8.95 (978-0-8477-1560-2(4)) Univ. of Puerto Rico Pr.

Barrett, John E., photos by. Balls! 2000. (Elmo's World Ser.). (Illus.). 12p. (J). (gr. k-ps). bds. 4.99 (978-0-375-80574-5(5) , Random Hse. Bks. for Young Readers) Random Hse. Children's Bks.

Bates, Cynthia. Courage on the Line. 1999. (Sports Stories Ser.). 117p. (J). (gr. 3-8). 7.95 (978-1-55028-648-9(X)) Lorimer, James & Co., Ltd., Pubs. CAN. *Dist:* Casemate Pubs. & Bk. Distributors, LLC.

Be a Plant Scientist: Level L, 6 vols. (Take-Twostm Ser.). 16p. 36.95 (978-0-322-03403-7(5)) Wright Group, The.

Behr, Steve. Mountain Biking. 1998. (Extreme Sports Ser.). (Illus.). 32p. (J). (gr. 5-9). pap. 6.95 (978-0-7641-0796-2(8)) Barron's Educational Series, Inc.

Berendes, Mary. Sports & Games/Los Deportes y Los Juegos. 2007. (WordBooks/Libros de Palabras Ser.). (SPA & ENG.). 24p. (J). 19.93 (***978-1-59296-802-2(3)***) Child's World, Inc.

Berman, Len. And Nobody Got Hurt! The World's Weirdest, Wackiest True Sports Stories. Gamble, Kent, illus. 2005. 128p. (J). (gr. 3-7). pap. 6.99 (978-0-316-01029-0(4)) Little Brown & Co.

Berman, Len. And Nobody Got Hurt 2! The World's Weirdest, Wackiest Most Amazing True Sports Stories. Gamble, Kent, illus. rev. ed. 2007. 133p. (J). (gr. 3-7). 16.99 (***978-0-316-06706-5(7)***); (gr. 4-7). per. 6.99 (***978-0-316-06705-8(9)***) Little, Brown Bks. for Young Readers.

Best Young Players in Sports, 6 bks. Incl. Grant Hill : Superstar Forward. Rolfe, John & Ross, Dalton. lib. bdg. 30.50 (978-0-8239-3578-9(7)); Rising Stars : The 10 Best Young Players in Baseball. Schwarz, Alan. lib. bdg. 32.00 (978-0-8239-3576-5(0)); Rising Stars : The 10 Best Young Players in the NFL. Dietsch, Richard & Schwarz, Alan. lib. bdg. 32.00 (978-0-8239-3573-4(6)); Rising Stars : The 10 Best Young Players in the NHL. Brehm, Mike & Russo, Michael. lib. bdg. 32.00 (978-0-8239-3575-8(2)); Rising Stars : The Ten Best Young Players in the NBA. Nelson, Glenn. lib. bdg. 32.00 (978-0-8239-3574-1(4)); Shaquille O'Neal : Superhero at Center. Smith, Pohla & Wilson, Steve. lib. bdg. 25.25 (978-0-8239-3577-2(9)); (YA). (gr. 7-12). (Illus.). 176p. 2005. Set lib. bdg. 183.75 (978-0-8239-9731-2(6)) Rosen Publishing Group, Inc., The.

Big Time. 64p. (YA). (gr. 6-12). pap. (978-0-8224-2390-4(1)) Globe Fearon Educational Publishing.

Billings. Extreme Sports. 1998. (Wild Side Ser.). (Illus.). (YA). (gr. 6-12). 13.00 (978-0-89061-800-4(3) , R0800-3E) Jamestown.

Bledsoe, Drew & Brown, Greg. Make the Right Call. 1998. (Illus.). 40p. (gr. 2-7). 14.95 (978-0-87833-215-1(4)) Taylor Trade Publishing.

Blomquist, Christopher. Motocross in the X Games. 2003. (Kids Guide to the X Games Ser.). (Illus.). 24p. (J). lib. bdg. 19.95 (978-0-8239-6303-4(9) , PowerKids Pr.) Rosen Publishing Group, Inc., The.

—Wakeboarding in the X Games. 2003. (Kids Guide to the X Games Ser.). (Illus.). 24p. (J). lib. bdg. 19.95 (978-0-8239-6301-0(2) , PowerKids Pr.) Rosen Publishing Group, Inc., The.

Bloomquist, Christopher. Skateboarding in the X Games. 2003. (Kids Guide to the X Games Ser.). (Illus.). 24p. (J). lib. bdg. 19.95 (978-0-8239-6300-3(4) , PowerKids Pr.) Rosen Publishing Group, Inc., The.

—Street Luge in the X Games. 2003. (Kids Guide to the X Games Ser.). (Illus.). 24p. (J). lib. bdg. 19.95 (978-0-8239-6299-0(7) , PowerKids Pr.) Rosen Publishing Group, Inc., The.

Bourassa, Barbara. Bat & Ball Sports. 2007. (J). lib. bdg. 18.95 (***978-1-59566-350-4(9)***) QEB Publishing Inc.

Bowman, Amy. Sports. 2001. (It's All about! Ser.). (Illus.). 32p. (J). (gr. 2-5). lib. bdg. 25.27 (978-1-58952-161-2(7)) Rourke Publishing, LLC.

Branon, Dave. Undefeated: Catching Inspiration & Hope Thrown by Athletes of Integrity. 2006. 176p. (J). pap. 10.99 (978-0-7642-0293-3(6)) Bethany Hse. Pubs.

Brocker, Susan. Sports Legends. 2004. (Navigators Ser.). (J). pap. 38.00 (978-1-4108-0406-8(2)) Benchmark Education Co.

Brown, Jonatha A. My Favorite Sport. 24p. (YA). 115.98 (978-0-8368-4336-1(3)) Stevens, Gareth Inc.

Bruce, Linda, et al. Sports Technology. 2006. (How Does It Work? Ser.). (Illus.). 32p. (J). (978-1-58340-794-3(4)) Smart Apple Media.

Bryan, Gayle. Professional Athlete. 2008. (Virtual Apprentice Ser.). 64p. (J). (gr. 6-12). 29.95 (***978-0-8160-6759-6(7)*** , Ferguson Publishing Co.) Facts On File, Inc.

Bundey, Nikki. On the Field. Gray, Virginia, illus. 1999. (First Sports Science Ser.). 32p. (J). (gr. 2-4). lib. bdg. 21.27 (978-1-57505-357-8(8) , Carolrhoda Bks.) Lerner Publishing Group.

Burke, Rick & Sherman, Josepha. Sports Files, 6 bks., Set. 2003. (J). (gr. 1-3). lib. bdg. 136.74 (978-1-58810-023-8(5)) Heinemann Library.

Buxton, Paul K., et al. Keeping Score. Adams, Alison, ed. 1999. (Early Connections Ser.). 16p. (J). (gr. k-2). pap. 4.50 (978-1-58344-068-1(2)) Benchmark Education Co.

Canizares, Susan & Chanko, Pamela. Ready, Set, Go! 1999. (J). 2.50 (978-0-439-04565-0(7)) Scholastic, Inc.

—Ready, Set, Go. 1999. (ps-2). lib. bdg. 10.10 (978-0-613-22246-4(6)) Tandem Library Bks.

Carey, Craig Robert. Below Zero. 2000. (Extreme Sports Ser.). (Illus.). (J). 10.79 (978-0-606-21687-6(1)) Tandem Library Bks.

—Hit the Dirt. 2000. (Extreme Sports Ser.). (Illus.). (J). (978-0-606-21689-0(8)) Tandem Library Bks.

Carter, André & Nicholls, Shawn. You Call That a Sport? Strange Sports from Around the Globe. 2003. (J). 3.99 (978-1-930623-32-3(1)) Sports Illustrated For Kids.

Carty, Michelle. Racing to the Finish Vol. 4557: The Olympic Sport of Triathlon, Samoiloff, Sheri, ed. Allsport Staff, photos by. 2002. (Illus.). 16p. (J). (gr. 3-6). pap. 3.49 (978-1-57471-928-4(9)) Creative Teaching Pr., Inc.

—Reach for Your Goal! Vol. 4558: The Olympic Sport of Soccer, Samoiloff, Sheri, ed. Allsport Staff, photos by. 2002. (Illus.). 16p. (J). (gr. 3-6). pap. 3.49 (978-1-57471-929-1(7)) Creative Teaching Pr., Inc.

—Teamwork Counts! Vol. 4551: The Olympic Sport of Bobsledding, Samoiloff, Sheri, ed. Allsport Staff, photos by. 2002. (Illus.). 16p. (J). (gr. 3-6). pap. 3.49 (978-1-57471-922-2(X)) Creative Teaching Pr., Inc.

Chapman, Garry. Extreme Sports, 6 bks. Incl. Air. 28.00 (978-0-7910-6609-6(6) , 010951); Mountains. 28.00 (978-0-7910-6610-2(X) , 010952); Rivers. 28.00 (978-0-7910-6608-9(8) , 010953); Snow. 28.00 (978-0-7910-6607-2(X) , 010954); Streets. 28.00 (978-0-7910-6612-6(6) , 010955); Surf. 28.00 (978-0-7910-6611-9(8) , 010956); (YA). (gr. 5 up). 2001. (Illus.). 32p. 2005. Set pap. 168.00 (978-0-7910-6606-5(1) , 010950S, Chelsea Hse.) Facts On File, Inc.

Cherry Lake Publishing, compiled by. Heathly for Life. 2008. lib. bdg. (***978-1-60279-105-3(8)***) Cherry Lake Publishing.

Cipriano, Jeri S. It's a Rule. 2003. (Yellow Umbrella Books). (Illus.). 16p. (J). (gr. 1). lib. bdg. 14.60 (978-0-7368-2027-1(2) , Pebble Bks.) Capstone Pr., Inc.

—It's a Rule. 2003. (J). (978-0-7368-1724-0(7)) Yellow Umbrella Pr.

Clayton, Lawrence. Everything You Need to Know about Sports Injuries. rev. ed. 1999. (Need to Know Library). (Illus.). 64p. (YA). (gr. 7-12). lib. bdg. 25.25 (978-0-8239-2875-0(6) , NTSPIN) Rosen Publishing Group, Inc., The.

Cohen, Joel H. Odd Moments in Sports, Vol. 2. 2000. (Odd Sports Stories Ser.: Vol. 2). (Illus.). 96p. (YA). (gr. 4-7). pap. 4.50 (978-0-590-37067-7(7)) Scholastic, Inc.

The Complete Book of Learning with Sports. 1999. (Complete Book Ser.). (Illus.). 352p. (J). (gr. 1-2). pap. 14.95 (978-1-56189-506-9(7) , 31150 , American Education Publishing) School Specialty Publishing.

Complete Set. (For Fun Ser.). (gr. 3-5). 293.80 (978-0-7565-0703-9(0)) Compass Point Bks.

Coupe, Robert. Sports for All. 2002. (Junior Adventure Ser.). (Illus.). 32p. (J). (gr. 3 up). lib. bdg. (978-1-59084-180-8(8)) Mason Crest Pubs.

Creighton, Jayne, contrib. by. Boomerangs, Blades & Basketballs: The Science of Sports. 1999. (Science @ Work Ser.). (Illus.). 48p. (J). (gr. 4-6). lib. bdg. 27.12 (978-0-7398-0132-1(5)) Raintree.

Crossingham, John. Lacrosse in Action. (Sports in Action Ser.). (Illus.). 32p. (J). (gr. 4). 2003. pap. (978-0-7787-0349-5(5)); 2002. (978-0-7787-0329-7(0)) Crabtree Publishing Co.

—Lacrosse in Action. 2003. (gr. 3-6). lib. bdg. 15.25 (978-0-613-52865-8(4)) Tandem Library Bks.

Currie, Stephen. Cheating. 2007. (J). (***978-1-60217-011-7(8)***) Erickson Pr.

Dalmatian Press Staff. Spiral Girls: Spiral. 2003. (Illus.). 96p. (J). spiral bd., act. bk. ed. 8.99 (978-1-4037-0437-5(6)) Dalmatian Pr.

David C. Cook. Families, the Environment, Sports & Competition. 2003. (Domain 456 Ser.). 128p. (J). (gr. 4-6). pap., pap. 15.99 (978-0-7814-5514-5(6) , 0781455146) Cook, David C. Publishing Co.

Deportes Atleticos, 6 vols., Vol. 2. (Explorers. Exploradores Nonfiction Sets Ser.). (SPA.). 32p. (gr. 3-6). 44.95 (978-0-7699-0648-5(6)) Shortland Pubns. (U. S. A.) Inc.

Deportes Con Pelota, 6 vols., Vol. 3. (Explorers. Exploradores Nonfiction Sets Ser.). (SPA.). (gr. 3-6). (978-0-7699-0660-7(5)) Shortland Pubns. (U. S. A.) Inc.

DeVito, Carlo. The Ultimate Dictionary of Sports Quotations: From Hank Aaron to the Zone. 2001. (Illus.). 352p. (YA). (gr. 9 up). 45.00 (978-0-8160-3980-7(1)) Facts On File, Inc.

Diehl, David. Sports A to Z. 2007. (Illus.). 28p. (J). (gr. 1). bds. 5.95 (***978-1-60059-113-6(2)***) Lark Bks.

Dillon, Christine J. Sports. rev. ed. 1999. (My First Report Ser.). (Illus.). 56p. (J). ring bd. 5.95 (978-1-57896-051-4(7) , 2572, Hewitt Homeschooling Resources) Hewitt Research Foundation, Inc.

Domnauer, Teresa. Ultimate Sports: Level 3. 2006. (Extreme Readers Ser.). (Illus.). 32p. (J). (gr. 1-2). pap. 3.95 (978-0-7696-4338-0(8)) School Specialty Publishing.

Dorling Kindersley Publishing Staff. Barbie Sports Doll. 2000. (Ultimate Sticker Bks.). (Illus.). 16p. (J). pap. 6.99 (978-0-7894-5451-5(3)) Dorling Kindersley Publishing, Inc.

Doudna, Kelly. Play Fair! 2007. (Illus.). 24p. (J). 19.93 (***978-1-59928-739-3(0)***) ABDO Publishing Co.

Dover Staff. Crazy Lunch: Silly Sticker Story. 2004. 4p. (J). pap. 1.50 (978-0-486-43768-2(X)) Dover Pubns., Inc.

Driscoll, Anne M. Girl to Girl - Sports & You! The Real Deal on Being Fit & Having Fun. 2000. (Illus.). 160p. (YA). (gr. 3 up). pap. 4.95 (978-1-902618-92-0(0)) Element Children's Bks.

Dubois, Muriel L. I Like Sports: What Can I Be? 2000. (What Can I Be? Ser.). (Illus.). 24p. (J). (gr. 1-2). lib. bdg. 18.60 (978-0-7368-0633-6(4) , Bridgestone Bks.) Capstone Pr., Inc.

Eck, Kristin. Extreme Sports, 6 bks. Incl. Bicycle Stunt Riding : Check It Out. (gr. 1). lib. bdg. 17.25 (978-0-8239-5697-5(0) , PowerKids Pr.); In-Line Skating : Check It Out. (gr. 1). lib. bdg. 17.25 (978-0-8239-5699-9(7) , PKINSK, Rosen Central); Mountain Biking : Check It Out. (gr. 2-4). lib. bdg. 17.25 (978-0-8239-5698-2(9) , PKMOBI, PowerKids Pr.); Skateboarding : Check It Out. (gr. 1). lib. bdg. 17.25 (978-0-8239-5695-1(4) , PKSKBO, PowerKids Pr.); Snowboarding : Check It Out. (gr. 1). lib. bdg. 17.25 (978-0-8239-5694-4(6) , PKSNBO, PowerKids Pr.); Wakeboarding : Check It Out. (gr. 1). lib. bdg. 17.25 (978-0-8239-5696-8(2) , PKWABO, Rosen Central); 24p. (J). (Illus.). 2001. Set lib. bdg. 96.00 (978-0-8239-7076-6(0) , PKSPOR, PowerKids Pr.) Rosen Publishing Group, Inc., The.

—Wakeboarding: Check It Out. 2001. (Reading Power Ser.). (Illus.). 24p. (J). (gr. 1). lib. bdg. 17.25 (978-0-8239-5696-8(2) , PKWABO, Rosen Central) Rosen Publishing Group, Inc., The.

Eckart, Edana. Sports, 6 vols, Set. 2004. (Illus.). 24p. (J). (ps-2). 174.00 (978-0-516-29312-7(5)) Scholastic Library Publishing.

Egan, Lorraine Hopping & Egan, Christopher. Sports Math Mania! Cool Stats & Number Facts. McGinty, Mick, illus. 2000. 48p. (J). (gr. 2-8). 2.99 (978-1-886749-96-2(5)) Sports Illustrated For Kids.

Egendorf, Laura K. Performance Enhancing Drugs. 2007. (Compact Research Ser.). 112p. (YA). (gr. 7-10). lib. bdg. (***978-1-60152-003-6(4)***) ReferencePoint Pr., Inc.

El-Hewie, Mohamed F. Essentials of Weightlifting & Strength Training. 2nd rev. exp. ed. 2005. (Illus.). 700p. lib. bdg. 85.00 (978-0-9719581-9-7(X)) Shaymaa Publishing Corp.

Ellenport, Craig. Playoff Sensations. Simpson, Fiona, ed. 2004. (NFL Reader Ser.). 32p. (J). pap. 3.99 (978-0-439-69180-2(X)) Scholastic, Inc.

Emra, Bruce & McGraw-Hill Staff. Sports in Literature. 2nd ed. 1999. (Illus.). 368p. (C). pap., stu. ed. 39.96 (978-0-8442-8096-7(8) , 9780844280967) Glencoe/McGraw-Hill.

Encarnacion, Elizabeth. Sports Stadiums. 2007. (J). lib. bdg. 19.95 (***978-1-59566-372-6(X)***) QEB Publishing Inc.

Endres, Hollie J. Es una Regla. 2005. Tr. of It's a Rule. (SPA., Illus.). 16p. (J). (gr. 1 up). lib. bdg. 15.93 (978-0-7368-4143-6(1)) Capstone Pr., Inc.

Entrenamiento Deportivo Series, 6 bks., Set. 2003. (Entrenamiento Deportivo Ser.). (SPA & ENG., Illus.). (J). 103.50 (978-0-8239-6913-5(4) , Buenas Letra) Rosen Publishing Group, Inc., The.

Epstein, Brad M. University of Iowa Hawkeyes 123: My first counting Book. l.t. ed. 2006. (Illus.). 22p. (J), bds. 14.95 (***978-1-932530-48-3(7)*** , 123 Bk.) Michaelson Entertainment.

—University of South Carolina 101: My First Text-Board-Book. l.t. ed. 2007. (101—My First Text-Board Books). (Illus.). 20p. (J). bds. 10.95 (***978-1-932530-41-4(X)*** , 101 Bk.) Michaelson Entertainment.

—University of Texas Longhorns 123: My first counting Book. l.t. ed. 2006. (Illus.). 22p. (J). bds. 14.95 (***978-1-932530-54-4(1)*** , 123 Bk.) Michaelson Entertainment.

ESPN Staff. The ESPN Book, No. 9. 2005. 96p. (J). pap. 3.99 (978-0-7868-1261-5(3)) Hyperion Pr.

Evans, Gwydion, et al. Ar Dîm Duw: Cyfres o Sesiynau Sydd Yn Defnyddio Byd Chwaraeon I Son Am y Ffydd Gristnogol. 2005. (WEL., Illus.). 24p. (978-1-85994-036-5(6)) Cyhoeddiadau'r Gair.

Extreme Sports, 20 bks. Incl. Aggressive In-Line Skating. McKenna, Anne T. 1999. lib. bdg. 21.26 (978-0-7368-0164-5(2)); Barefoot Waterskiing. Oleksy, Walter. 2000. lib. bdg. 21.26 (978-0-7368-0480-6(3)); Bicycle Stunt Riding. Glaser, Jason. 1999. lib. bdg. 21.26 (978-0-7368-0167-6(7)); Big-Air Snowboarding. McKenna, Anne T. 1999. lib. bdg. 21.26 (978-0-7368-0166-9(9)); Boardsailing. Perry, Phyllis Jean. 2000. lib. bdg. 21.26 (978-0-7368-0481-3(1)); Bungee Jumping. Glaser, Jason. 1999. lib. bdg. 21.26 (978-0-7368-0168-3(5)); Downhill In-Line Skating. Cook, Nick. 2000. lib. bdg. 21.26 (978-0-7368-0482-0(X)); Extreme Mountain Biking. Molzahn, Arlene Bourgeois. 2000. lib. bdg. 21.26 (978-0-7368-0483-7(8)); Extreme Skateboarding. Ryan, Pat. 1997. lib. bdg. 21.26 (978-1-56065-535-0(6)); Extreme Snowboarding. Ryan, Pat. 1997. lib. bdg. 21.26 (978-1-56065-536-7(4)); Extreme Surfing. Voeller, Edward A. 2000. lib. bdg. 21.26 (978-0-7368-0485-1(4)); Extreme Wakeboarding. McKenna, Anne T. 1999. lib. bdg. 21.26 (978-0-7368-0165-2(0)); Kayaking. Lund, Bill. 1996. lib. bdg. 21.26 (978-1-56065-428-5(7)); Rock Climbing. Lund, Bill. 1996. lib. bdg. 21.26 (978-1-56065-429-2(5)); Sky Surfing. Ryan, Pat. 1997. lib. bdg. 21.26 (978-1-56065-537-4(2)); Snow Mountain Biking. Glaser, Jason. 1999. lib. bdg. 21.26 (978-0-7368-0169-0(3)); Sport Climbing. Voeller, Edward A. 2000. lib. bdg. 21.26 (978-0-7368-0484-4(6)); Street Luge Racing. Ryan, Pat. 1997. lib. bdg. 21.26 (978-1-56065-538-1(0)); Triathlon. Lund, Bill. 1996. lib. bdg. 21.26 (978-1-56065-430-8(9)); Weight Lifting. Lund, Bill. 1996. lib. bdg. 21.26 (978-1-56065-431-5(7)); 48p. (J). (gr. 3-4). (Illus.). Set lib. bdg. 425.20 (978-0-7368-0552-0(4) , Capstone High-Interest Bks.) Capstone Pr., Inc.

Extreme Sports, 6 bks. Incl. In-Line Skating. Woods, Bob. (gr. 2 up). lib. bdg. 22.00 (978-0-8368-3722-3(3)); Mountain Biking. Kelley, K. C. (gr. 2 up). lib. bdg. 22.00 (978-0-8368-3723-0(1)); Skateboarding. Kelley, K. C. lib. bdg. 22.00 (978-0-8368-3724-7(X)); Snowboarding. Woods, Bob. (gr. 2 up). lib. bdg. 22.00 (978-0-8368-3725-4(8)); Stunt Bicycle Riding. Kelley, K. C. (gr. 2 up). lib. bdg. 22.00 (978-0-8368-3726-1(6)); Water Sports. Woods, Bob. (gr. 2 up). lib. bdg. 22.00 (978-0-8368-3727-8(4)); 24p. (J). (Illus.). 2003. Set lib. bdg. 127.60 (978-0-8368-3721-6(5)) Stevens, Gareth Inc.

Extreme Sports: High-Low Reading, 6 bks., Set. 2001. (Illus.). (YA). 145.56 (978-0-7398-4693-3(0)) Raintree.

Extreme Sports: Individual Title, 6 pack. (Bookweb Ser.). 32p. (gr. 4 up). 34.00 (978-0-7635-3740-1(3)) Rigby Education.

Extreme Sports: Individual Title Six-Packs. 32p. (gr. 4 up). 44.00 (978-0-7578-0609-4(0)) Rigby Education.

The Extreme Sports Collection, 8 bks. Incl. Bicycle Stunt Riding! Catch Air. Hayhurst, Chris. (YA). 2000. lib. bdg. 26.50 (978-0-8239-3011-1(4) , EXBIST); In-Line Skating! Get Aggressive. Kaminker, Laura. (YA). 1999. lib. bdg. 26.50 (978-0-8239-3012-8(2) , EXSKAT); Mountain Biking! Get on the Trail. Hayhurst, Chris. (YA). 2000. lib. bdg. 26.50 (978-0-8239-3013-5(0) , EXMOBI); Rock & Ice Climbing! Top the Tower. Roberts, Jeremy. (YA). 2000. lib. bdg. 26.50 (978-0-8239-3009-8(2) , EXROIC); Skateboarding! Surf the Pavement. Burke, L. M. (J). 2000. lib. bdg. 26.50 (978-0-8239-3014-2(9) , EXSKBO); Skydiving! Take the Leap. Roberts, Jeremy. (YA). 1999. lib. bdg. 26.50 (978-0-8239-3015-9(7) , EXSKDI); Snowboarding! Shred the Powder. Hayhurst, Chris. (YA). 1999. lib. bdg. 26.50 (978-0-8239-3010-4(6) , EXSNBO); Wakeboarding! Throw a Tantrum. Hayhurst, Chris. (YA). 2000. lib. bdg. 26.50 (978-0-8239-3008-1(4) , EXWABO); 64p. (gr. 5-8). (Illus.). Set lib. bdg. 212.00 o.p. (978-0-8239-9038-2(9) , EXSPCO, Rosen Central) Rosen Publishing Group, Inc., The.

Facts on File, Inc. Staff, contrib. by. Careers in Focus. 2004. (Careers in Focus Ser.). (Illus.). 192p. (J). (gr. 6-12). 22.95 (978-0-8160-5548-7(3) , Ferguson Publishing Co.) Facts On File, Inc.

Fast/Sports Staff, Markers. 2002. 32p. (YA). (gr. 6-12). pap. (978-0-8224-6493-8(4)) Globe Fearon Educational Publishing.

Fauchald, Nick. Game Day, 4 bks. Dickson, Bill, illus. Incl. Jump Ball! You Can Play Basketball. 22.60 (978-1-4048-0261-2(4) , 1229515); Nice Hit! You Can Play Baseball. 22.60 (978-1-4048-0259-9(2) , 1229516); Score! You Can Play Soccer. 22.60 (978-1-4048-0262-9(2) , 1229517); Touchdown! You Can Play Football. 22.60 (978-1-4048-0260-5(6) , 1229518); 24p. (J). (gr. k-3). 2004. (Illus.). 2004. 85.04 (978-1-4048-0258-2(4)) Picture Window Bks.

Feldman, Heather. Superstars of Sports, 6 bks. Incl. Derek Jeter : Baseball's Best. lib. bdg. 17.25 (978-0-8239-5719-4(5) , PKDEJE); Hulk Hogan : Wrestling Pro. lib. bdg. 17.25 (978-0-8239-5720-0(9) , PKHUHO); Marion Jones : World-Class Runner. lib. bdg. 17.25 (978-0-8239-5718-7(7) , PKMAJO); Mia Hamm : Soccer Superstar. lib. bdg. 17.25 (978-0-8239-5716-3(0) , PKHAMM); Venus Williams : Tennis Champion. lib. bdg. 17.25 (978-0-8239-5717-0(9) , PKSUST); Wayne Gretzky : Hockey Star. lib. bdg. 17.25 (978-0-8239-5715-6(2) , PKGRET); 24p. (J). (gr. 1). (Illus.). 2001. Set lib. bdg. 96.00 (978-0-8239-7075-9(2) , PKSUST, PowerKids Pr.) Rosen Publishing Group, Inc., The.

Ferguson. What Can I Do Now: Sports. 2nd rev. ed. 2007. (What Can I Do Now Ser.). 184p. (J). (gr. 6-12). 29.95 (***978-0-8160-6034-4(7)*** , Ferguson Publishing Co.) Facts On File, Inc.

Fetty, Maurice A. High Interest Sports. 1999. (J). (gr. 3). pap. (978-0-8172-3822-3(0)); (gr. 4). pap. (978-0-8172-3823-0(9)); (gr. 5). pap. (978-0-8172-3824-7(7)) Steck-Vaughn.

Fieffe, Kathleen, ed. Laugh Out Loud: Funny Photos, Comic Cards & Other Sports Funnies. rev. ed. 2000. (J). (gr. 3-9). pap. (978-1-930623-14-9(3)) Sports Illustrated For Kids.

For Fun!, 21 vols. 2006. 48p. (YA). (gr. 3-5). 474.60 (978-0-7565-1867-7(9)); 90.40 (978-0-7565-1868-4(7)) Compass Point Bks.

Fried, Mark. Great Teams in Classic College Sports. 2005. pap. 51.00 (978-1-4109-1503-0(4)) Raintree.

Frost, Shelley. Throw Like a Girl: Discovering the Body, Mind, & Spirit of the Athlete in You! 2000. (gr. 3-6). lib. bdg. 19.90 (978-0-613-33445-7(0)) Tandem Library Bks.

Frost, Shelley & Troussieux, Ann. Throw Like a Girl: Discovering the Body, Mind & Spirit of the Athlete in You! l.t. ed. 2000. (Girls Know Best Ser.). (Illus.). 128p. (J). (gr. 3 up). lib. bdg. 23.33 (978-0-8368-2674-6(4)) Stevens, Gareth Inc.

Gaines, Ann Graham. Extreme Sports. 2000. (Composite Guides Ser.). (Illus.). (YA). (gr. 8-12). 12.95 (978-0-7910-5862-6(X) , Chelsea Hse.) Facts On File, Inc.

Gardner, Robert & Conklin, Barbara Gardner. Health Science Projects about Sports Performance. 2002. (Science Projects Ser.). (Illus.). 112p. (YA). (gr. 6-12). lib. bdg. 26.60 (978-0-7660-1441-1(X)) Enslow Pubs., Inc.

George, Charles & George, Linda. Sports Alive!, 4 bks. Incl. Ice Climbing. 1998. lib. bdg. 21.26 (978-0-7368-0052-5(2)); Roller Hockey. 1998. lib. bdg. 21.26 (978-0-7368-0053-2(0)); Team Skydiving. 1998. lib. bdg.

21.26 (978-0-7368-0054-9(9)); White-Water Rafting. 1999. lib. bdg. 21.26 (978-0-7368-0055-6(7)); (J). (gr. 3-4). (Illus.). 48p. Set lib. bdg. 63.80 (978-0-7368-0463-9(3) , Capstone High-Interest Bks.) Capstone Pr., Inc.

—White-Water Rafting. 1999. (Sports Alive! Ser.). (Illus.). 48p. (J). (gr. 3-4). lib. bdg. 21.26 (978-0-7368-0055-6(7) , Capstone High-Interest Bks.) Capstone Pr., Inc.

Getting into Sports. 2005. (Illus.). 32p. (gr. 4-8). pap. 168.00 (978-0-7910-9067-1(1) , Chelsea Clubhouse) Facts On File, Inc.

Ginsburg, Richard D., et al. Whose Game Is It Anyway? A Guide to Helping Your Child Get the Most from Sports, Organized by Age & Stage. 2006. 320p. pap. 15.00 (978-0-618-47460-8(9)) Houghton Mifflin Co. Trade & Reference Div.

Gonzalez, Tony & Brown, Greg. Tony Gonzalez: Catch & Connect. 2004. (Football Ser.). (Illus.). 48p. (J). 15.95 (978-0-9634650-8-5(2)) Positively for Kids, Inc.

Good Sports: Individual Title, 6 packs. (Rigby Infoquest Ser.). (gr. 5 up). 37.00 (978-0-7578-6496-4(1)) Rigby Education.

Goranson, Christopher D. Danny Harf: Wakeboarding Superstar. 2005. (Illus.). 64p. (J). (gr. 5-8). lib. bdg. 26.50 (978-1-4042-0066-1(5)) Rosen Publishing Group, Inc., The.

Gordeeva, Ekaterina. Letter for Daria. 1998. 96p. (J). (ps-4). 12.95 (978-0-316-32994-1(0)) Little Brown & Co.

Gordon, Sharon. Somos un Equipo. 2006. (Bookworms Ser.). (SPA & ENG., Illus.). 24p. (J). lib. bdg. 22.79 (978-0-7614-2357-7(5) , Benchmark Bks.) Cavendish, Marshall Corp.

—We Are a Team. 2005. (Bookworms Ser.). (ENG & SPA., Illus.). 24p. (J). (gr. 3-7). lib. bdg. (978-0-7614-1994-5(2) , Benchmark Bks.) Cavendish, Marshall Corp.

—We Are a Team (Somos un Equipo) 2006. (Bookworms Ser.). (ENG & SPA., Illus.). 24p. (J). lib. bdg. 22.79 (978-0-7614-2436-9(9)) Cavendish, Marshall Corp.

Gorman, Jacqueline Laks. The Playground: El Parque. 2005. (Illus.). 24p. (J). (ENG & SPA.). pap. (978-0-8368-4605-8(2)); (SPA & ENG., lib. bdg. 19.33 (978-0-8368-4598-3(6)) Stevens, Gareth Inc.

Gould, Marilyn. Playground Sports: A Book of Ball Games. rev. ed. 1999. (Illus.). 64p. (J). (gr. 2 up). pap. 10.95 (978-0-9632305-2-2(2)) Allied Crafts Pr.

Gramling, Scott, ed. Totally Michael. 1998. (YA). (gr. 3-6). pap. 4.95 (978-1-886749-32-0(9)) Sports Illustrated For Kids.

Greatest Sports Heroes, 6 vols. 2006. (Illus.). (YA). (gr. 7-12). 144.00 (***978-0-531-12471-0(1)***) Scholastic Library Publishing.

Gregg, Lauren. The Champion Within: Training for Excellence. Nash, Tim, ed. 1999. (Illus.). (YA). (gr. 9 up). pap. 24.95 (978-1-887791-07-6(8)) JTC Sports, Inc.

Group/McGraw-Hill, Wright. Take-Twos Sports Vol. 2: Early Fluency - Complete Kit. (gr. 2 up). 420.50 (978-0-322-09173-3(X)) Wright Group, The.

—Take-Twos Sports Vol. 2: Early Fluency - Student Book Set - 1 Each of 12 Titles. (gr. 2 up). 69.95 (978-0-322-09301-0(5)) Wright Group, The.

Hall, Margaret C. Sports. 2002. (Around the World Ser.). (Illus.). 32p. (J). (gr. k-2). lib. bdg. 22.79 (978-1-58810-478-6(8)) Heinemann Library.

Hammond, Tim & Buller, Laura. Sports. 2005. (Dk eyewitness Bks.). (Illus.). 72p. (J). lib. bdg. 19.99 (978-0-7566-1399-0(X)); (gr. 4-7). 15.99 (978-0-7566-1390-7(6)) Dorling Kindersley Publishing, Inc.

Harcourt School Publishers Staff. All Sorts of Sports Advanced Level. 3rd ed. 2002. (Trophies Reading Program Ser.). (Illus.). (J). pap. 3.70 (978-0-15-323017-2(7)) Harcourt Schl. Pubs.

—All Sorts of Sports 5-Pack, Advanced Level. 3rd ed. 2002. (Trophies Reading Program Ser.). (Illus.). (gr. 1). pap. 20.10 (978-0-15-326867-0(0)) Harcourt Schl. Pubs.

—Let's Talk about Games. 3rd ed. 2002. (Trophies English Language Learners Ser.). pap. 5.10 (978-0-15-327693-4(2)) Harcourt Schl. Pubs.

—Make the Right Moves: Take-Home Book. 1999. (Collections Ser.). (Illus.). (J). pap. 1.90 (978-0-15-317302-8(5)) Harcourt Schl. Pubs.

—The Race Across Alaska Below Level. 3rd ed. 2002. (Trophies Reading Program Ser.). (Illus.). pap. 5.10 (978-0-15-323137-7(8)) Harcourt Schl. Pubs.

—Race the Wind. 3rd ed. 2002. (Trophies English Language Learners Ser.). (Illus.). pap. 5.10 (978-0-15-327817-4(X)) Harcourt Schl. Pubs.

—Team, Yes! 3rd ed. 2002. (Trophies English Language Learners Ser.). (Illus.). pap. 5.10 (978-0-15-327891-4(9)) Harcourt Schl. Pubs.

—Trofeos Advanced Level: Los Deportes. 3rd ed. 2002. (SPA., Illus.). pap. 5.50 (978-0-15-323928-1(X)) Harcourt Schl. Pubs.

—What Sport Will I Try? Below Level. 3rd ed. 2002. (Trophies Reading Program Ser.). (Illus.). (J). pap. 3.20 (978-0-15-322949-7(7)) Harcourt Schl. Pubs.

Harpster, Steven. Be a Good Sport. 1999. (Illus.). 48p. (J). (ps-2). 2.99 (978-0-7847-0983-2(1) , 22053, Bean Sprouts) Standard Publishing.

Hauserman, Angie. I Love Sports!, 8 vols., Vol. 5. 2002. (Illus.). (J). per. (978-1-932062-31-1(9)) Hability Solution Services, Inc.

Hawes, Alison. You Can't Catch Me: Individual Title Six-Pack Pouch - Level D. Roberts, David, illus. (Lighthouse Ser.). 12p. (gr. k-1). 24.00 (978-0-7578-0830-2(1)) Rigby Education.

Hay DeSimone, Corkey. Future Sports Legend Board Book: An Early Introduction to Sports in Maryland. Hay DeSimone, Corkey, illus. 2006. (J). bds. 4.99 (978-0-9747921-5-6(2)) Gentle Giraffe Pr.

Hayhurst, Chris. Snowboarding! Shred the Powder. 1999. (Extreme Sports Collection). (Illus.). 64p. (YA). (gr. 5-8). lib. bdg. 26.50 (978-0-8239-3010-4(6) , EXSNBO, Rosen Central) Rosen Publishing Group, Inc., The.

—Wakeboarding! Throw a Tantrum. 2000. (Extreme Sports Collection). (Illus.). 64p. (YA). (gr. 5-8). lib. bdg. 26.50 (978-0-8239-3008-1(4) , EXWABO, Rosen Central) Rosen Publishing Group, Inc., The.

Herzog, Brad. Heads Up! Puzzles for Sports Brains. 1999. (Sports Illustrated for Kids Bks.). 64p. (J). (gr. 4-6). pap. 3.99 (978-1-886749-62-7(0)) Sports Illustrated For Kids.

—Tons of Top 10 Sports Lists. 2001. 48p. (J). (gr. 3-9). pap. 2.99 (978-1-930623-17-0(8)) Sports Illustrated For Kids.

Herzog, Brad & Labrecque, Jeff. Sports Illustrated for Kids Millenium 2000: A Celebration of Sports. Gramling, Scott, ed. 1999. (Illus.). 48p. (J). (gr. 2-8). pap. 4.99 (978-1-886749-74-0(4)) Sports Illustrated For Kids.

Herzog, Brad & Lerner, Andy. All-Star Sports Puzzle Book. Goehner, Amy Lennard, ed. Staake, Bob, illus. 2000. 48p. (J). (gr. 2-8). pap. 2.99 (978-1-886749-93-1(0)) Sports Illustrated For Kids.

Herzog, Brad & Sports Illustrated for Kids Editors. MVP Sports Puzzles. Gramling, Scott, ed. Gustafson, Glenn & Staake, Bob, illus. rev. ed. 1999. (Sports Illustrated for Kids Bks.). 48p. (J). (gr. 4-6). pap. (978-1-886749-70-2(1)) Sports Illustrated For Kids.

—MVP Sports Puzzles. Gramling, Scott, ed. rev. ed. 1999. (Sports Illustrated for Kids Bks.). (Illus.). 64p. (J). (gr. 4-6). pap. 3.99 (978-1-886749-60-3(4)) Sports Illustrated For Kids.

Hofstetter, Adam B. People Who Love Sports. 2006. (Cool Careers Without College Ser.). (Illus.). 144p. (J). (gr. 5-8). lib. bdg. 33.25 (978-1-4042-0749-3(X)) Rosen Publishing Group, Inc., The.

Hogenkamp, Susan. All Sorts of Sports: Learning the OR Sound. (PowerPhonics Ser.). (Illus.). (J). 2002. 24p. (gr. 1). lib. bdg. 18.50 (978-0-8239-5949-5(X)); 2001. 23p. pap. (978-0-8239-8294-3(7)) Rosen Publishing Group, Inc., The. (PowerKids Pr.).

Holder, Sherie. More Amazing Sports Photos: More Funny, Famous, & Fantastic Photographs from the World of Sports. rev. ed. Date not set. 32p. (J). pap. 3.95 (978-1-886749-13-9(2)) Sports Illustrated For Kids.

Holder, Sherie, ed. Amazing Sports Photos: Funny, Famous, & Fantastic Photographs from the World of Sports. rev. ed. 1998. 32p. (J). (gr. 3-6). pap. 3.95 (978-1-886749-48-1(5)) Sports Illustrated For Kids.

—Strange but True Facts & Fun. 1998. (Illus.). 16p. (J). (gr. 3-6). pap. 2.95 (978-1-886749-43-6(4)) Sports Illustrated For Kids.

Hollow, Michele C. Nifty Thrifty Sports Crafts. 2007. (Nifty Thrifty Crafts for Kids Ser.). (Illus.). 32p. (J). (gr. 3-4). lib. bdg. 22.60 (978-0-7660-2782-4(1) , Enslow Elementary) Enslow Pubs., Inc.

Hopkins, Lee Bennett. Sports! Sports! Sports! A Poetry Collection. 2000. (I Can Read Bks.). (Illus.). 48p. (J). (ps-3). pap. 3.99 (978-0-06-443713-4(2) , Harper Trophy) HarperCollins Pubs.

Hughes, Morgan. Cheerleading. 2005. (Junior Sports Ser.). (Illus.). 32p. (J). (gr. 2-4). 19.95 (978-1-59515-194-0(X)) Rourke Publishing, LLC.

—Scooters. 2003. (Wheels in Motion Ser.). (Illus.). 24p. (J). 20.64 (978-1-58952-667-9(8)) Rourke Publishing, LLC.

—Sports Hall of Fame. 2000. (Halls of Fame Ser.). (Illus.). 24p. (J). (gr. 2-6). lib. bdg. 23.93 (978-1-55916-271-5(6)) Rourke Publishing, LLC.

Hughes, Sarah. Play Time, 6 bks., Set. 2004. (Welcome Books Ser.). (Illus.). 24p. (J). (ps-2). 87.00 (978-0-516-23231-7(2) , Children's Pr.) Scholastic Library Publishing.

J. G. Ferguson Publishing Company Staff, contrib. by. Careers in Focus. 2003. (Careers in Focus Ser.). (Illus.). (J). (gr. 6-12). 176p. 22.95 (978-0-8160-5484-8(3)); 3rd ed. 208p. 22.95 (978-0-8160-5486-2(X)) Facts On File, Inc. (Ferguson Publishing Co.).

Jefferis, David. Water Sports. 2001. (Young Library - Super Sports). (Illus.). 32p. (J). lib. bdg. 25.69 (978-0-7398-4344-4(3)) Raintree.

Kalman, Bobbie. Sports from a to Z. 2000. (gr. 3-6). lib. bdg. 16.40 (978-0-613-22426-0(4)) Tandem Library Bks.

Kalman, Bobbie & Calder, Kate. Sports from A to Z. 1999. (AlphaBasiCs Ser.). (Illus.). 32p. (J). (gr. 2-3). pap. (978-0-86505-416-5(9)); lib. bdg. (978-0-86505-386-1(3)) Crabtree Publishing Co.

Kalman, Bobbie & Crossingham, John. Extreme Sports. 2004. (Extreme Sports - No Limits Ser.). (Illus.). 32p. (J). (978-0-7787-1673-0(2)); pap. (978-0-7787-1719-5(4)) Crabtree Publishing Co.

Kaplan, Ben. Sports Illustrated for Kids Super Sports Stars: The Coolest Athletes in the World. Seik, Margaret, ed. 1999. 48p. (J). (gr. 2-8). pap. 4.99 (978-1-886749-72-6(8)) Sports Illustrated For Kids.

Kaufman, Gabriel. Sporting Events: From Baseball to Skateboarding. 2006. (Which Came First? Ser.). (Illus.). 32p. (J). lib. bdg. 25.27 (978-1-59716-132-9(2)) Bearport Publishing Co., Inc.

Kemper, Bitsy. Out & about at the Stadium. Trover, Zachary, illus. 2006. (Field Trips Ser.). 24p. (J). (gr. 2-4). lib. bdg. 25.26 (978-1-4048-2280-1(1)) Picture Window Bks.

Kennedy, Mike. Roller Hockey. 2001. (Sports Library). (Illus.). 64p. (J). (gr. 5-7). 25.50 (978-0-531-13953-0(0) , Watts, Franklin) Scholastic Library Publishing.

Koeppel, Dan. Extreme Sports Almanac. rev. ed. 2000. (Illus.). 135p. (J). pap. 7.95 (978-0-7373-0435-0(9) , Roxbury Park) Lowell Hse.

—Extreme Sports Almanac. 1998. (Illus.). 128p. (J). (gr. 4-7). pap. 7.95 (978-0-7373-0032-1(9) , 00329W) McGraw-Hill/Contemporary.

Lancaster, Scott B. Fair Play: Making Organized Sports a Great Experience for Your Kids. 2004. 194p. reprint ed. pap. 15.00 (978-0-7567-8419-5(0)) DIANE Publishing Co.

Larsen, Kathy. Celebrate the Fire Within. Decker, Cynthia, illus. 2001. 23p. (J). 15.95 (978-1-930458-01-7(0)) North Star Pubns.

Layden, Joe. Behind the Scenes. 2003. (gr. 3-6). lib. bdg. 14.15 (978-0-613-82747-8(3)) Tandem Library Bks.

Lee, Veronica. Field Hockey. 2003. (Sports Injuries Ser.). (Illus.). 64p. (J). lib. bdg. (978-1-59084-631-5(1)) Mason Crest Pubs.

Leeper, Angela. I Can Play Fairly. 2004. (You & Me Ser.). (Illus.). 24p. (J). (978-1-4034-6083-7(3)); pap. (978-1-4034-6091-2(4)) Heinemann Library.

Lennard-Brown, Sarah. Sports Injuries. 2004. (Health Issues Ser.). (Illus.). 64p. (J). 28.56 (978-0-7398-6892-8(6)) Harcourt Schl. Pubs.

Levine, Shar & Johnstone, Leslie. Sports Science. 2006. (Illus.). 80p. (gr. 2-5). 19.95 (978-1-4027-1520-4(X) , 1252963) Sterling Publishing Co., Inc.

Lobosco, Teresa. Galloping to the Gold Vol. 4562: The Olympic Sport of Equestrian. Samoiloff, Sheri, ed. Allsport Staff, photos by. 2002. (Inspiring Athletes Ser.: Vol. 4562). (Illus.). 16p. (J). (gr. 3-6). pap. 3.49 (978-1-57471-933-8(5)) Creative Teaching Pr., Inc.

—Practice Makes Perfect Vol. 4556: The Olympic Sport of Snowboarding. Samoiloff, Sheri, ed. Allsport Staff, photos by. 2002. (Illus.). 16p. (J). (gr. 3-6). pap. 3.49 (978-1-57471-927-7(0)) Creative Teaching Pr., Inc.

—Soaring to the Top Vol. 4555: The Olympic Sport of Skiing. Samoiloff, Sheri, ed. Allsport Staff, photos by. 2002. (Illus.). 16p. (J). (gr. 3-6). pap. 3.49 (978-1-57471-926-0(2)) Creative Teaching Pr., Inc.

—Take the Plunge! Vol. 4552: The Olympic Sport of Diving. Samoiloff, Sheri, ed. Allsport Staff, photos by. 2002. (Illus.). 16p. (J). (gr. 3-6). pap. 3.49 (978-1-57471-923-9(8)) Creative Teaching Pr., Inc.

Louck, Cheryl. The ABC's of Motocross. Zielinski, Dave, photos by. 2003. (Illus.). 24p. (J). per. 14.95 (978-0-9744230-0-5(9)) Louck, Cheryl.

Lowriders, 6 vols. (gr. 4 up). 39.95 (978-0-7368-9291-9(5)) Red Brick Learning.

Macht, Norman L. Track & Field. 1999. (Composite Guide Ser.). (Illus.). 64p. (J). (gr. 4-7). 28.00 (978-0-7910-4720-0(2) , Chelsea Hse.) Facts On File, Inc.

MacNab, Chris. Weight Training. 2003. (Sports Injuries Ser.). (Illus.). 64p. (J). lib. bdg. (978-1-59084-641-4(9)) Mason Crest Pubs.

Mann, Bob. The Sports Fan's Ultimate Trivia Book. 2001. (Illus.). 104p. (YA). (gr. 5 up). pap. 5.95 (978-1-896184-98-2(7)) Roussan Pubs., Inc./Roussan Editeur, Inc. CAN. *Dist:* Orca Bk. Pubs. USA.

Map of Your Future: For the Student Athlete. 2001. 18p. pap. 7.95 (978-0-9670275-6-2(X)) McCloud Publishing.

Margolis, Jeffrey A. Violence in Sports: Victory at What Price? 1999. (Issues in Focus Ser.). (Illus.). 128p. (YA). (gr. 6-12). lib. bdg. 26.60 (978-0-89490-961-0(4)) Enslow Pubs., Inc.

Martin, Oscar, Jr., creator. Sports Legends, l.t. ed. 2003. (Illus.). 25p. (J). E-Book 19.95 incl. cd-rom (978-0-9748416-6-3(8)) Build Your Story.

Marzilli, Alan. Amateur Athletics. 2004. (Point/Counterpoint Ser.). (Illus.). 112p. (gr. 9-13). 32.95 (978-0-7910-7921-8(X) , Chelsea Hse.) Facts On File, Inc.

Mason, Paul. Kayaking & Rafting. 2007. (J). (***978-1-59920-133-7(X)***) Smart Apple Media.

Mattern, Joanne. Famous Mystics & Psychics. 2004. (gr. 7-10). 27.45 (978-1-59018-558-2(7)) Thomson Gale.

—LeBron James. 2004. (Robbie Reader Ser.). (Illus.). 32p. (J). (gr. 1-4). lib. bdg. 25.70 (978-1-58415-293-4(1)) Mitchell Lane Pubs., Inc.

Maurer, Tracy. Radsports Guides II. 2002. 179.57 (978-1-58952-275-6(3)) Rourke Publishing, LLC.

—Skateboarding. 2001. (Radsports Guides). (Illus.). 48p. (J). (gr. 4-8). lib. bdg. 29.93 (978-1-58952-104-9(8)) Rourke Publishing, LLC.

Maxwell, John C. Leading Your Sports Team. 2001. (PowerPak Collection Ser.). 88p. (J). (gr. 5-9). pap. 3.99 (978-0-8499-7725-1(8)) Nelson, Thomas Inc.

McCoy, Lisa. Lacrosse. 2003. (Sports Injuries Ser.). (Illus.). 64p. (J). lib. bdg. (978-1-59084-636-0(2)) Mason Crest Pubs.

McDaniel, Melissa. Pushing the Limits: A Chapter Book. (True Tales Ser.). (Illus.). 48p. (J). 2005. (gr. 2-4). pap. 4.95 (978-0-516-24688-8(7)); 2004. 22.50 (978-0-516-23734-3(9)) Scholastic Library Publishing. (Children's Pr.).

McKay, Lucia & Guscott, Maggie. Sports & Hobbies. 2004. 104p. (YA). per. 9.95 (978-1-56254-766-0(6) , SP7666) Saddleback Educational Publishing.

McLeese, Tex. Carrera de Barril. Palacios, Argentina, tr. 2002. (Rodeo Ser.).Tr. of Rodeo Barrel Racing. (SPA., Illus.). 24p. mass mkt. 5.95 (978-1-58952-253-4(2) , RK31468) Rourke Publishing, LLC.

—Lucha con Novillos. Palacios, Argentina, tr. 2002. (Rodeo Ser.).Tr. of Steer Wrestling. (SPA., Illus.). 24p. mass mkt. 5.95 (978-1-58952-256-5(7) , RK31471) Rourke Publishing, LLC.

—Monta de Toro y Toreo. Palacios, Argentina, tr. 2002. (Rodeo Ser.).Tr. of Bull Riding & Bullfighting. (SPA., Illus.). 24p. mass mkt. 5.95 (978-1-58952-257-2(5) , RK31472) Rourke Publishing, LLC.

—Monta en Silla y a Pelo. Palacios, Argentina, tr. 2002. (Rodeo Ser.).Tr. of Bronc & Bareback Riding. (SPA., Illus.). 24p. mass mkt. 5.95 (978-1-58952-258-9(3) , RK31473) Rourke Publishing, LLC.

McNeil, Niki, et al. HOCPP 1128 the History of Sports. 2006. spiral bd. 12.50 (***978-1-60308-128-3(3)***) In the Hands of a Child.

Menard, Valerie. Careers in Sports. 2001. (Latinos at Work Ser.). (Illus.). 96p. (gr. 5-12). lib. bdg. 32.75 (978-1-58415-086-2(6)) Mitchell Lane Pubs., Inc.

Mental X, 2003. (Illus.). 32p. (YA). pap. 5.50 (978-0-9745066-8-5(0)) Sports In Mind.

Mia Hamm, 6 vols. (gr. 4 up). 39.95 (978-0-7368-9275-9(3)) Red Brick Learning.

Michelle Kwan, 6 vols. (gr. 4 up). 39.95 (978-0-7368-9276-6(1)) Red Brick Learning.

Miller, Ray. Beat the Clock Sports. Crabtree, Andrew, illus. 1999. 24p. (J). pap. 6.95 (978-1-58295-014-3(8) , Beehive Bk.) Pace Products, Inc.

Molzahn, Arlene Bourgeois. Extreme Mountain Biking. 2000. (Extreme Sports Ser.). (Illus.). 48p. (J). (gr. 3-4). lib. bdg. 21.26 (978-0-7368-0483-7(8) , Capstone High-Interest Bks.) Capstone Pr., Inc.

Morina, Barbara. Sports: An Athlete's Journal. 2000. (Write It down Ser.: Vol. 23). 202p. (YA). (gr. 2 up). 19.95 (978-1-892033-21-5(6)) Journals Unlimited, Inc.

Morris, Neil. Food for Sports. 2006. (Making Healthy Food Choices Ser.). (Illus.). 56p. (J). pap. (978-1-4034-8579-3(8)); (YA). (gr. 6-10). lib. bdg. 32.86 (978-1-4034-8573-1(9)) Heinemann Library.

Mullins, Patty Rutland. All about Sports. Ebert, Len, illus. 2004. (Treasure Tree Ser.). 32p. (J). (978-0-7166-1645-0(9)) World Bk., Inc.

Murphy, Bernadette & Surridge, Gerry. Sport Readiness. 2004. (Illus.). 160p. pap. (978-0-673-58914-9(5)) Good Year Bks.

Nardo, Don. Arts. Leisure & Sport in Ancient Egypt. 2005. (Lucent Library of Historical Eras Ser.). (Illus.). 112p. (YA). (gr. 7-10). lib. bdg. 32.45 (978-1-59018-706-7(7) , Lucent Bks.) Thomson Gale.

—A Roman Gladiator. 2004. (Working Life Ser.). (Illus.). 112p. (J). 29.95 (978-1-59018-480-6(7) , Lucent Bks.) Thomson Gale.

Nathan, Emma. Deportes. 2002. (Abre los Ojos y Aprende Serie).Tr. of Eyeopeners: Sports. (SPA.). 24p. (J). (-3). 24.94 (978-1-4103-0024-9(2) , Blackbirch Pr., Inc.) Thomson Gale.

—Sports. 2002. (Eyeopeners Ser.). (Illus.). 24p. (J). 22.45 (978-1-56711-653-3(1) , Blackbirch Pr., Inc.) Thomson Gale.

Nelson, Cordner. Careers in Pro Sports. rev. ed. 1999. (Careers). (Illus.). 192p. (YA). (gr. 7-12). lib. bdg. 26.50 (978-0-8239-2896-5(9) , CAPRSP) Rosen Publishing Group, Inc., The.

Nelson, Elizabeth Ann. Coping with Drugs & Sports. rev. ed. 1999. (Coping Ser.). (Illus.). 118p. (YA). (gr. 7-12). lib. bdg. 26.50 (978-0-8239-2864-4(0) , CODRSP) Rosen Publishing Group, Inc., The.

Newton, Nick & Minutaglio, Bill. Locker Room Mojo: True Tales of Superstitions in Sports. 1999. 114p. (YA). 32.95 (978-0-9670466-4-8(5)) Middlefork Pr.

Nicholson, Lois. Lacrosse. 1999. (Composite Guide Ser.). (Illus.). 64p. (YA). (gr. 4-7). lib. bdg. 18.65 (978-0-7910-4719-4(9) , Chelsea Hse.) Facts On File, Inc.

Nitz, Kristin Wolden. Track. 2003. (Play-By-Play Ser.). (Illus.). 80p. (J). (gr. 5 up). pap. 7.95 (978-0-8225-9873-2(6)) Lerner Publishing Group.

Otten, Jack. Sports Training, 6 bks. Incl. Baseball. lib. bdg. 17.25 (978-0-8239-5971-6(6)); Basketball. (gr. 1). lib. bdg. 17.25 (978-0-8239-5974-7(0)); Ice Hockey. (gr. 1). lib. bdg. 17.25 (978-0-8239-5976-1(7)); Soccer. (gr. 1). lib. bdg. 17.25 (978-0-8239-5972-3(4)); Tennis. (gr. 1). lib. bdg. 17.25 (978-0-8239-5975-4(9)); Track. (gr. 1). lib. bdg. 17.25 (978-0-8239-5973-0(2)); 24p. (J). 2002. (Illus.). 2001. Set lib. bdg. 96.00 (978-0-8239-7120-6(1) , PowerKids Pr.) Rosen Publishing Group, Inc., The.

Paintball Player's Safety Guide. 2001. 74p. (J). spiral bd. 14.95 (978-0-9708678-2-7(4)) Pro Star Sports, Inc.

Palmer, Edward. Getting Started Sports Books: Soccer Instructional Coloring Book. Howard, Robert & Flynn Sabatino and Day Staff, photos by. rev. ed. 1998. (Illus.). 24p. (J). (ps-4). pap. 4.95 (978-1-890527-02-0(5)) Nuway Youth Sports.

—Getting Started Sports Books: T-Ball Instructional Coloring Book. Howard, Robert & Flynn Sabatino and Day Staff, photos by. 2nd rev. ed. 1998. (Illus.). 24p. (J). (ps-4). pap. 3.95 (978-1-890527-03-7(3)) Nuway Youth Sports.

Pasternak, Ceel. Cool Careers for Girls in Sports. (Cool Careers for Girls Ser.). 1999. 135p. pap. 12.95 (978-1-57023-104-9(4)); 1998. (J). 19.95 (978-1-57023-107-0(9)) Impact Pubns.

Petelinsek, Kathleen & Primm, E. Russell. At Play/En el Juego. 2006. (Talking Hands Ser.). (ENG & SPA., Illus.). 24p. (J). 21.36 (978-1-59296-683-7(7)) Child's World, Inc.

Petruccio, Steven James. I Love Sports. 2006. 32p. (J). (ps-3). pap. 3.95 (978-0-486-44477-2(5)) Dover Pubns., Inc.

—Invisible Sports Magic Picture Book. 2000. (Illus.). 16p. (J). (ps-2). pap. 1.50 (978-0-486-41288-7(1)) Dover Pubns., Inc.

Phelan, Glen. Forces & Motion in Sports. 2005. (Navigators Ser.). (J). pap. 44.00 (***978-1-4108-5088-1(9)***) Benchmark Education Co.

Platt, Richard. Extreme Sports. 2001. (Dk Readers Ser.). (Illus.). 48p. (J). (gr. 5-5). pap. 3.99 (978-0-7894-7884-9(6)) Dorling Kindersley Publishing, Inc.

—Extreme Sports. 2001. (gr. k-3). lib. bdg. 11.80 (978-0-613-43930-5(9)) Tandem Library Bks.

Platt, Richard & Dorling Kindersley Publishing Staff. Extreme Sports. 2001. (Dk Readers Ser.). (Illus.). 48p. (J). (gr. 3-5). 12.95 (978-0-7894-7883-2(8)) Dorling Kindersley Publishing, Inc.

Pollack, Pamela. Ski! Your Guide to Jumping, Racing, Skiboarding, Nordic, Backcountry, Aerobatic. 2002. (gr. 5-8). lib. bdg. 17.60 (978-0-613-60609-7(4)) Tandem Library Bks.

S

Primm III, E. Russell. Questions & Answers/Preguntas y Respuestas. 2006. (Talking Hands Ser.). (ENG & SPA., Illus.). 24p. (J). (ps). 21.36 (978-1-59296-455-0(9)) Child's World, Inc.

Publ, Griffin. Easy Olympic Sports Reader, 6 Bks, Set. 2004. (U. S. Olympic Committee Easy Olympic Sports Readers Ser.). (Illus.). 16p. (J). pap. 17.95 (978-1-58000-116-8(5)) Griffin Publishing Group.

Raatma, Lucia. Sportsmanship. 2002. (Character Education Ser.). (Illus.). 24p. (J). (gr. 1-2). lib. bdg. 18.60 (978-0-7368-1135-4(4) , Bridgestone Bks.) Capstone Pr., Inc.

Rad Sports. 2005. (Illus.). 48p. (gr. 5-8). lib. bdg. 212.00 (978-0-8239-4056-1(X)) Rosen Publishing Group, Inc., The.

Radical Sports, 6 bks., Set 2. 2002. (J). (gr. 5-7). lib. bdg. 153.84 (978-1-58810-629-2(2)) Heinemann Library.

Radtke, Becky. Sports. 1998. (Illus.). 64p. (J). (ps-3). pap., act. bk. ed. 1.50 (978-0-486-40303-8(3)) Dover Pubns., Inc.

Rau, Dana Meachen. Jump Rope. 2004. (Games Around the World Ser.). 32p. (J). (gr. 3 up). lib. bdg. 22.60 (978-0-7565-0677-3(8)) Compass Point Bks.

Reader's Clubhouse Staff. Coach Bo Will Show You. 2007. (Reader's Clubhouse Ser.). 24p. (J). (gr. k-2). pap. 3.99 (978-0-7641-3723-5(9)) Barron's Educational Series, Inc.

Reeves, Diane Lindsey. Career Ideas for Kids Who Like Sports. 2nd rev. ed. (Career Ideas for Kids Ser.). (J). (gr. 4-9). 2008. 48p. pap. 18.95 ***(978-0-8160-6552-3(7))***; 2007. 208p. 32.95 ***(978-0-8160-6551-6(9))*** Facts On File, Inc. (Checkmark Bks.).

Reeves, Diane Lindsey & Kent, Peter. Career Ideas for Kids Who Like Sports. 1998. (Career Ideas for Kids Ser.). (Illus.). 176p. (J). (gr. 4-8). pap. 12.95 (978-0-8160-3690-5(X)) Facts On File, Inc.

Riddle, John. Professional Athlete & Sports Official. 2003. (Careers with Character Ser.). (Illus.). 96p. (J). (gr. 7 up). lib. bdg. 22.95 (978-1-59084-321-5(5)) Mason Crest Pubs.

Roberts, Robin. Careers for Women Who Love Sports. 2000. (Illus.). (J). (978-0-606-18281-2(0)) Tandem Library Bks.

—Sports for Life: How Athletes Have More Fun. 2000. (Get in the Game! with Robin Roberts Ser.). (Illus.). 48p. (gr. 4-8). lib. bdg. (978-0-7613-1407-3(5) , Millbrook Pr.) Lerner Publishing Group.

—Which Sport is Right for You? 2001. (978-0-606-22374-4(6)) Tandem Library Bks.

—Which Sport Is Right for You? 2001. (Illus.). 48p. (gr. 4-8). lib. bdg. 23.90 (978-0-7613-2117-0(9) , Millbrook Pr.) Lerner Publishing Group.

Robinson, Garrick & Kjeldsen, Neil. Having A Ball: Youth Sports Done Right, 1 book. 2006. (ENG & SPA., Illus.). 44p. (J). per. 14.95 (978-0-9777437-0-4(5)) Zeus Sports Florida LLC.

Rolfe, John & Ross, Dalton. Grant Hill. 2001. 112p. (J). (gr. 3-9). pap. 3.99 (978-1-930623-21-7(6)) Sports Illustrated For Kids.

Rosen, Michael J. Balls! Margeson, John, illus. 2006. 72p. (J). (gr. 5 up). 18.95 (978-1-58196-030-3(1)) Darby Creek Publishing.

Rosenberg, Aaron. A Beginner's Guide to Very Cool Skateboarding Tricks. 2005. (World of Skateboarding Ser.). (Illus.). 48p. (YA). (gr. 5-8). lib. bdg. 26.50 (978-0-8239-3646-5(5)) Rosen Publishing Group, Inc., The.

Ross, Dalton. Top Teams Ever. Sieck, Margaret, ed. 1999. 96p. (J). (gr. 1-9). pap. 3.99 (978-1-886749-63-4(9)) Sports Illustrated For Kids.

Salzmann, Mary Elizabeth. Angling to Zorbing: Sports from A to Z. 2007. (Let's See A to Z Ser.). (Illus.). 32p. (J). (ps-3). lib. bdg. 25.65 ***(978-1-59928-881-9(8)*** , Super SandCastle) ABDO Publishing Co.

Savage, Jeff. Top 10 Sports Bloopers & Who Made Them. 2000. (Sports Top 10 Ser.). (Illus.). 48p. (YA). (gr. 4-10). lib. bdg. 23.93 (978-0-7660-1271-4(9)) Enslow Pubs., Inc.

Schaefer, A. R. Extreme Wakeboarding Moves. 2003. (Behind the Moves Ser.). (Illus.). 32p. (J). (gr. 3-4). lib. bdg. 21.26 (978-0-7368-1515-4(5) , Capstone High-Interest Bks.) Capstone Pr., Inc.

Scholastic, Inc. Staff. Sports Illustrated Kids Year in Sports 2008. 2007. 320p. (J). (gr. 4-7). pap. 9.99 ***(978-0-439-91659-2(3)*** , Scholastic Reference) Scholastic, Inc.

Schwarz, Alan. Baseball Big Shots. Holder, Sherie, ed. 1998. (Big Shots Ser.). 32p. (YA). (gr. 3-6). pap. 3.95 (978-1-886749-42-9(6)) Sports Illustrated For Kids.

—Sports Illustrated for Kids Baseball All-Stars. Gramling, Scott, ed. 1999. (Illus.). 96p. (J). (gr. 2-8). pap. 3.99 (978-1-886749-73-3(6)) Sports Illustrated For Kids.

—Sports Illustrated for Kids Baseball's Best. Northrop, Michael & Gramling, Scott, eds. 1999. 32p. (J). (gr. 2-8). pap. 3.99 (978-1-886749-71-9(X)) Sports Illustrated For Kids.

Scott, John, text. Athletic Quest Total Sports System. 2004. (YA). 30.00 (978-1-879498-82-2(0)) SportAmerica.

—Seniors: How to Get Recruited. 2004. (YA). 30.00 (978-1-879498-77-8(4)) SportAmerica.

—Sophomore: How to Make the Team. 2004. (YA). 30.00 (978-1-879498-79-2(0)) SportAmerica.

SI For Kids. Sports illustrated for kids yr in Sports 2007. 2006. 336p. (J). pap. 9.99 (978-0-439-82767-6(1) , Scholastic Reference) Scholastic, Inc.

SI for Kids Staff, ed. What's the Call? 2000. Orig. Title: Trumpet Club. 48p. (J). (gr. 2-8). reprint ed. pap. 2.99 (978-1-886749-84-9(1)) Sports Illustrated For Kids.

Smith, Roger. Teens & Rural Sports: Rodeos, Horses, Hunting, & Fishing. 2008. (J). ***(978-1-4222-0022-3(1))*** Mason Crest Pubs.

So Many Sports! (Girls' World Ser.). 16p. (J). (978-2-7643-0143-2(X)) Phidal Publishing, Inc./Editions Phidal, Inc.

Sosieski, Shanti. Who's Next: The Hottest Young Stars in Action Sports. 2004. (J). 3.99 (978-1-930623-34-7(8)) Sports Illustrated For Kids.

Sports, 10 vols. 2005. (Double Fastback Ser.). (J). (gr. 6-12). 64p. pap. 54.95 (978-0-13-024465-9(1)); 32p. pap. 44.95 (978-0-13-024446-8(5)) Globe Fearon Educational Publishing.

Sports. 1999. (Start Me Up Ser.). (J). pap. 3.95 (978-1-58185-104-5(9)) Quadrillion Media LLC.

Sports & Fitness (Gr. PreK-5) 2003. (J). (978-1-58232-026-7(8)) Bryan Hse. Pubs., Inc.

Sports Around the World, 6 vols. (Book2WebTM Ser.). (gr. 4-8). 36.50 (978-0-322-02989-7(9)) Wright Group, The.

Sports for All: Level P, 6 vols., Vol. 2. (Explorers Ser.). 32p. (gr. 3-6). 44.95 (978-0-7699-0612-6(5)) Shortland Pubns. (U. S. A.) Inc.

Sports from Coast to Coast. 2005. (Illus.). 48p. (gr. 5-8). lib. bdg. 159.00 (978-1-4042-0347-1(8)) Rosen Publishing Group, Inc., The.

Sports from Coast to Coast, 6 bks., Set 2. Incl. Baseball : Rules, Tips, Strategy, & Safety. Porterfield, Jason. (J). lib. bdg. 26.50 (978-1-4042-0991-6(3)); Basketball : Rules, Tips, Strategy, & Safety. Ramen, Fred. (YA). lib. bdg. 26.50 (978-1-4042-0992-3(1)); Football : Rules, Tips, Strategy, & Safety. Wingate, Brian. (YA). lib. bdg. 26.50 (978-1-4042-0993-0(X)); Paintball : Rules, Tips, Strategy, & Safety. Roza, Greg. (YA). lib. bdg. 26.50 (978-1-4042-0994-7(8)); Soccer : Rules, Tips, Strategy, & Safety. Wingate, Brian. (J). lib. bdg. 26.50 (978-1-4042-0995-4(6)); Softball : Rules, Tips, Strategy, & Safety. Hofstetter, Adam B. (J). lib. bdg. 26.50 (978-1-4042-0996-1(4)); (Illus.). 48p. (gr. 5-8). 2006. 2007. Set lib. bdg. 159.00 ***(978-1-4042-1044-8(X))*** Rosen Publishing Group, Inc., The.

Sports Great Books. (Illus.). (YA). (gr. 4-10). lib. bdg. (978-0-89490-342-7(X)) Enslow Pubs., Inc.

Sports Heroes, 6 vols., Pack. 32p. (gr. 4 up). 44.00 (978-0-7578-0611-7(2)) Rigby Education.

Sports Illustrated 2004 Almanac. 2003. (gr. 7-12). lib. bdg. 22.25 (978-0-613-68936-6(4)) Tandem Library Bks.

Sports Illustrated for Kids: Year in Sports 2006. 2005. (J). 99.90 (978-0-439-82763-8(9)) Scholastic, Inc.

Sports Illustrated for Kids Books. 2005. (Illus.). 176p. (gr. 7-12). lib. bdg. 388.65 (978-0-8239-3925-1(1)) Rosen Publishing Group, Inc., The.

Sports Illustrated for Kids Editors. What's the Call? You Are the Referee. 2000. (Illus.). 48p. (J). (gr. 2-8). pap. 2.99 (978-1-930623-12-5(7)) Sports Illustrated For Kids.

Sports on Wheels: Individual Title, 6 packs. 32p. (gr. 4 up). 44.00 (978-0-7578-0606-3(6)) Rigby Education.

Sports Reports, 50 bks., Set. (Illus.). (YA). (gr. 4-10). lib. bdg. 1047.50 (978-0-89490-568-1(6)) Enslow Pubs., Inc.

Sports Technology: Individual Title, 6 packs. 32p. (gr. 4 up). 44.00 (978-0-7578-0607-0(4)) Rigby Education.

Sports Top 10, 48 bks. , Set. 2001. (Illus.). (YA). (gr. 4-10). lib. bdg. 909.60 (978-0-89490-582-7(1)) Enslow Pubs., Inc.

SportsGirl, 8 bks. Incl. Competitive Basketball for Girls. Gettelman, Elizabeth. lib. bdg. 26.50 (978-0-8239-3402-7(0)); Competitive Fastpitch Softball for Girls. Wesley, Ann. lib. bdg. 26.50 (978-0-8239-3409-6(8)); Competitive Figure Skating for Girls. Moncrief, Kathryn. lib. bdg. 26.50 (978-0-8239-3403-4(9)); Competitive Gymnastics for Girls. Wesley, Ann. lib. bdg. 26.50 (978-0-8239-3406-5(3)); Competitive Soccer for Girls. Sherman, Josepha. lib. bdg. 26.50 (978-0-8239-3405-8(5)); Competitive Tennis for Girls. Guillermo-Newton, Judith. lib. bdg. 26.50 (978-0-8239-3407-2(1)); Competitive Track & Field for Girls. Manley, Claudia B. lib. bdg. 26.50 (978-0-8239-3408-9(X)); Competitive Volleyball for Girls. Manley, Claudia B. lib. bdg. 26.50 (978-0-8239-3404-1(7)); (YA). (gr. 5-8). (Illus.). 64p. 2005. Set lib. bdg. 212.00 (978-0-8239-9426-7(0)) Rosen Publishing Group, Inc., The.

Spring, Albert. Steroids & Your Muscles: The Incredibly Disgusting Story. 2005. (Incredibly Disgusting Drugs Ser.). (Illus.). 48p. (YA). (gr. 5-8). lib. bdg. 25.25 (978-0-8239-3393-8(8)) Rosen Publishing Group, Inc., The.

Steck-Vaughn Staff. Sports Around the World. 2002. (Illus.). (J). pap. (978-0-7398-5978-0(1)) Steck-Vaughn.

—Sports/Exercise: Rabbit Turtle. 1998. (Illus.). (J). pap. (978-0-8172-8647-7(0)) Steck-Vaughn.

Stewart, Mark. Vince Carter: The Fire Burns Bright. 2001. (New Wave Ser.). 48p. (J). (gr. 4-8). pap. 7.95 (978-0-7613-1499-8(7) , Millbrook Pr.) Lerner Publishing Group.

Stock Car Racers. (Cool Cars Ser.). 16p. (J). (978-2-7643-0131-9(6)) Phidal Publishing, Inc./Editions Phidal, Inc.

Strange but True: Weird Stories from the Wacky World of Sports. 2002. (J). 3.99 (978-1-930623-25-5(9)) Sports Illustrated For Kids.

Sullivan, Erin. Sports Math/Matematicas en los Deportes: English/Spanish Pair, 12 tests, 2 titles, Vol. 2. ed. 2004. (Navigators Ser.). (J). pap., instr.'s gde. ed. 84.00 (978-1-4108-1774-7(1) , 17741) Benchmark Education Co.

Sullivan, George. Any Number Can Play: The Numbers Athletes Wear. Green, Anne Canevari, illus. 2000. (Sports Trivia from George Sullivan Ser.). 64p. (J). (gr. 5-8). lib. bdg. 23.90 (978-0-7613-1557-5(8) , Millbrook Pr.) Lerner Publishing Group.

—Don't Step on the Foul Line: Sports Superstitions. Green, Anne Canevari, illus. 2000. (Sports Trivia from George Sullivan Ser.). 64p. (gr. 5-8). lib. bdg. 23.90 (978-0-7613-1558-2(6) , Millbrook Pr.) Lerner Publishing Group.

—Don't Step on the Foul Line: Sports Superstitions. 2001. (J). 15.75 (978-0-606-21158-1(6)) Tandem Library Bks.

Super Racing. (Cool Cars Ser.). 16p. (J). (978-2-7643-0002-2(6)) Phidal Publishing, Inc./Editions Phidal, Inc.

Super Speeders. (Cool Cars Ser.). 16p. (J). (978-2-7643-0004-6(2)) Phidal Publishing, Inc./Editions Phidal, Inc.

Super Sports Star, 17 bks. , Set. Incl. Super Sports Star Gary Payton. Mandell, Judith J. lib. bdg. 23.93 (978-0-7660-1519-7(X)); Super Sports Star Grant Hill. Lowenstein, Felicia. lib. bdg. 23.93 (978-0-7660-1517-3(3)); Super Sports Star Kevin Garnett. Thornley, Stew. lib. bdg. 23.93 (978-0-7660-1515-9(7)); Super Sports Star Kobe Bryant. Thornley, Stew. lib. bdg. 23.93 (978-0-7660-1514-2(9)); Super Sports Star Penny Hardaway. Rappoport, Ken. lib. bdg. 23.93 (978-0-7660-1516-6(5)); Super Sports Star Tim Duncan. Thornley, Stew. lib. bdg. 23.93 (978-0-7660-1513-5(0)); 48p. (J). (gr. 1-4). 2001. (Illus.). Set lib. bdg. 322.15 (978-0-7660-1802-0(4)) Enslow Pubs., Inc.

Sylvester, Kevin. Sports Hall of Weird. 2005. (Illus.). 96p. (YA). (gr. 2 up). (978-1-55337-635-4(8)) Kids Can Pr., Ltd.

Tallarico, Tony. I Can Draw Sports. 2000. (J). 4.99 (978-0-689-81451-8(8) , Simon & Schuster Children's Publishing) Simon & Schuster Children's Publishing.

Technosports: Individual Title, 6 packs. (Bookweb Ser.). 32p. (gr. 4 up). 34.00 (978-0-7635-3746-3(2)) Rigby Education.

Teitelbaum, Michael. Sportsmanship. 2003. (Illus.). 32p. (J). pap. 7.50 (978-1-4109-0327-3(3)); lib. bdg. 24.28 (978-0-7398-7008-2(4)) Raintree.

—Sportsmanship. 2003. (gr. 3-6). lib. bdg. 15.90 (978-0-613-78296-8(8)) Tandem Library Bks.

Tejada, Justin & Higgins, Matt. Bails, Biffs, & Wipeouts: The Wildest Slams in Action Sports. 2002. (J). (gr. 3-9). 3.99 (978-1-930623-27-9(5)) Sports Illustrated For Kids.

—Extreme: Inside Info & Big Tricks from Top Action Sports Stars. 2001. (J). (gr. 3-9). pap. 3.99 (978-1-930623-23-1(2)) Sports Illustrated For Kids.

Time Out: Star Athletes Who Shine off the Field. (Illus.). 32p. (J). (gr. 3-9). pap. 3.99 (978-1-930623-19-4(4)) Sports Illustrated For Kids.

To the Extreme. 2005. (Blazers Ser.). (Illus.). (J). (gr. 1-2). lib. bdg. 239.16 (978-0-7368-4628-8(X)) Capstone Pr., Inc.

To the Limit, 6 bks., Set. Incl. In-Line Skating. Smith, Martin. lib. bdg. 25.69 (978-0-7398-3166-3(6)); Motocross. Freeman, Gary. lib. bdg. 25.69 (978-0-7398-3275-2(1)); Mountain Biking. Mason, Paul. lib. bdg. 25.69 (978-0-7398-3274-5(3)); Skateboarding. Horsley, Andy. lib. bdg. 25.69 (978-0-7398-3163-2(1)); Snowboarding. Mason, Paul. lib. bdg. 25.69 (978-0-7398-3164-9(X)); Surfing. Mason, Paul. lib. bdg. 25.69 (978-0-7398-3165-6(8)); 32p. (J). (gr. 4-7). (Illus.). 2001. Set lib. bdg. 154.14 (978-0-7398-3167-0(4)) Raintree.

Tocci, Salvatore. Experiments with Sports. 2004. (True Bks.). (J). (gr. 3-5). pap. 6.95 (978-0-516-27807-0(X) , Children's Pr.) Scholastic Library Publishing.

U. S. Olympic Committee. A Basic Guide to Bobsledding. 2002. (Olympic Guides). (Illus.). 160p. (J). (gr. 6 up). lib. bdg. 23.33 (978-0-8368-3101-6(2)) Stevens, Gareth Inc.

Ultimate Sports Force Staff. Super Squad: Basketball's Superstars. 2003. (Illus.). 56p. (J). pap. 7.95 (978-1-57243-601-5(8)) Triumph Bks.

Ultra Sports, 6 bks. Incl. Adventure Racing. Ching, Jacqueline. lib. bdg. 26.50 (978-0-8239-3555-0(8)); Ironman Triathlon. Scheppler, Bill. lib. bdg. 26.50 (978-0-8239-3556-7(6)); Marathon Cycling. Turner, Cherie. lib. bdg. 26.50 (978-0-8239-3553-6(1)); Marathon Skiing. Stiefer, Sandy. lib. bdg. 26.50 (978-0-8239-3554-3(X)); Ultra Marathon Running. Hayhurst, Chris. lib. bdg. 26.50 (978-0-8239-3557-4(4)); Ultra Swimming. Manley, Claudia B. lib. bdg. 26.50 (978-0-8239-3558-1(2)); 64p. (YA). (gr. 5-8). 2002. (Illus.). 2001. Set lib. bdg. 159.00 (978-0-8239-9697-1(2) , Rosen Central) Rosen Publishing Group, Inc., The.

Valat, Pierre-Marie & Gallimard Jeunesse Publishing Staff. Sports. 1998. (First Discovery Book Ser.). (Illus.). 24p. (J). (ps-2). 12.95 (978-0-590-11617-6(7) , Scholastic Reference) Scholastic, Inc.

Vv. El Deporte. (Coleccion Mundo Maravilloso). (SPA., Illus.). 168p. (J). (gr. 2-4). 13.56 (978-84-348-4486-5(9) , SM1438) SM Ediciones ESP. *Dist:* Lectorum Pubns., Inc.

Wale, Michael & Locke, Ian. No Sweat! A Guide to 50 TV Sports. Parkin, Geo, illus. 2003. 160p. (J). pap. 6.99 (978-0-330-34281-0(9) , Pan) Pan Macmillan GBR. *Dist:* Trafalgar Square Publishing.

Wallace, Paula S. The World of Sports. 2003. (Life Around the World Ser.). (Illus.). 48p. (J). (gr. 2 up). lib. bdg. 24.67 (978-0-8368-3662-2(6)) Stevens, Gareth Inc.

Walsh, Kieran. Sports Math. 2005. (Math & My World Ser.). (Illus.). 48p. (gr. 4-6). 20.95 (978-1-59515-495-8(7)) Rourke Publishing, LLC.

Watkins, Michele. Good Sports. 1999. (J). (978-0-606-19869-1(5)) Tandem Library Bks.

Weber, Jason. Wakeboarding on the Edge: Instruction & Advice for Beginner Through Expert Riders. 2000. (Illus.). 80p. spiral bd. 39.95 incl. cd-rom (978-0-9676408-0-8(6)) Sports On The Edge, LLC.

Wells, Don. Lacrosse. 2005. (For the Love of Sports Ser.). (Illus.). 24p. (J). (ps-6). lib. bdg. 24.45 (978-1-59036-297-6(7)); pap. 6.95 (978-1-59036-301-0(9)) Weigl Pubs., Inc.

Wheelchair Sports, 4 bks. Incl. Wheelchair Basketball. Labanowich, Stan. lib. bdg. 21.26 (978-1-56065-614-2(X)); Wheelchair Field Events. Little, Jim. lib. bdg. 21.26 (978-1-56065-617-3(4)); Wheelchair Road Racing. Little, Jim. lib. bdg. 21.26 (978-1-56065-615-9(8)); Wheelchair Track Events. Labanowich, Stan. lib. bdg. 21.26 (978-1-56065-616-6(6)); (J). (gr. 3-4). 1998. (Illus.). 48p. Set lib. bdg. 85.04 (978-0-7368-0460-8(9) , Capstone High-Interest Bks.) Capstone Pr., Inc.

Who Rules? The Best in Almost Everything in Sports. 2002. (J). (gr. 3-9). 3.99 (978-1-930623-26-2(7)) Sports Illustrated For Kids.

Will, Sandra. Lacrosse for Fun! 2006. (Sports for Fun! Ser.). (Illus.). 48p. (J). (gr. 3-5). 22.60 (978-0-7565-1685-7(4)) Compass Point Bks.

Williams, Brian. Sport & Entertainment: Biggest & Best. 2003. (Biggest & Best Ser.). (Illus.). 40p. (J). pap. 7.95 (978-1-84236-063-7(9)) Miles Kelly Publishing, Ltd. GBR. *Dist:* Independent Pubs. Group.

Windsor, Jo. Kitesurfing: Individual Title Six-Packs. (Sails Literacy Ser.). 20p. (gr. 2-3). 27.00 (978-0-7578-0716-9(X)) Rigby Education.

Wolf, Catherine, ed. Sports Break Two. rev. ed. 2000. (J). (gr. 3-9). reprint ed. pap. (978-1-930623-15-6(1)) Sports Illustrated For Kids.

Wolff, Virginia Euwer & Woodson, Jacqueline. Girls Got Game: Sports Stories & Poems. Macy, Sue, ed. rev. ed. 2001. (Illus.). 160p. (YA). (gr. 6-9). 17.95 (978-0-8050-6568-8(7) , Holt, Henry & Co. Bks. For Young Readers) Holt, Henry & Co.

Wood, Tracey & Maring, Therese, eds. Sports Secrets & Spirit Stuff. 2006. (J). 17.95 (978-1-59369-107-3(6) , American Girl) American Girl Publishing, Inc.

World of Sport. 1998. (Eyewitness Fun Fax Inserts Ser.). (Illus.). (J). (gr. 4-8). pap. 2.95 (978-0-7894-3014-4(2)) Dorling Kindersley Publishing, Inc.

You Can Canoe! Individual Title Six-Packs. (Action Packs Ser.). 120p. (gr. 3-5). 44.00 (978-0-7635-8393-4(6)) Rigby Education.

Young, Ian & Rasinski, Timothy V. X Games: Action Sports Grab in Spotlight. 2002. (High Five Reading Ser.). (J). (Illus.). 48p. (gr. 2-3). lib. bdg. 22.60 (978-0-7368-9546-0(9) , Capstone High-Interest Bks.); pap. (978-0-7368-9524-8(8)) Capstone Pr., Inc.

Zeigler, Heidi. Hang Gliding. 2003. (gr. 7-12). lib. bdg. 15.25 (978-0-613-59628-2(5)) Tandem Library Bks.

Ziegler, Mark. Goofballs! A Book of Sport Jokes. Haberstroh, Anne, illus. 2005. (Read-It! Readers Ser.). 24p. (C). (gr. 1-3). 18.60 (978-1-4048-0965-9(1)) Picture Window Bks.

SPORTS—BIOGRAPHY

Abbey, Cherie D., ed. Biography Today Sports: Profiles of People of Interest to Young Readers. 2006. (Sports Ser.: Vol. 14). 202p. (YA). (gr. 4 up). lib. bdg. 44.00 (978-0-7808-0941-3(6)) Omnigraphics, Inc.

Adams, Sean. Tim Duncan. 2004. (Sports Heroes & Legends Ser.). (Illus.). 112p. (J). (gr. 6-12). lib. bdg. 27.93 (978-0-8225-1793-1(0)) Lerner Publishing Group.

Alexander, Kyle. Wrestling's Most Punishing Finishing Moves. 2000. (Pro Wrestling Legends Ser.). (Illus.). 64p. (J). (gr. 8-12). pap. 25.00 (978-0-7910-5834-3(4)); (gr. 4-7). 25.00 (978-0-7910-5833-6(6)) Facts On File, Inc. (Chelsea Hse.).

Allyson, Jackie. Chris "Jesus" Ferguson. 2008. (J). ***(978-1-4222-0218-0(6))*** Mason Crest Pubs.

—Doyle "Texas Dolly" Brunson. 2008. (J). ***(978-1-4222-0216-6(X))*** Mason Crest Pubs.

—Gus "The Great Dane" Hansen. 2008. (J). ***(978-1-4222-0219-7(4))*** Mason Crest Pubs.

Anthony, Carmelo & Brown, Greg. Carmelo Anthony: It's Just the Beginning. 2004. (Basketball Ser.). (Illus.). 48p. (J). 15.95 (978-0-9634650-7-8(4)) Positively for Kids, Inc.

Armentrout, David & Armentrout, Patricia. Tony Hawk. 2005. (Discover the Life of a Sports Star Ser.). (Illus.). 24p. (gr. 1-4). 14.95 (978-1-59515-129-2(X)) Rourke Publishing, LLC.

Benchmark All-Stars: Group 2, 6 Bks, Set. 2004. (J). 162.43 (978-0-7614-1755-2(9)) Cavendish, Marshall Corp.

Braun, Eric. Wilma Rudolph. 2005. (Pebble Books). (Illus.). 24p. (J). 15.93 (978-0-7368-4234-1(9) , Pebble Bks.) Capstone Pr., Inc.

Brennan, Kristine. Scott Hamilton. 1999. (Overcoming Adversity Ser.). (J). (978-0-606-19354-2(5)) Tandem Library Bks.

Buckley, James. Landon Donovan. 2006. (World's Greatest Athletes Ser.). (Illus.). 32p. (J). (gr. 1-5). 27.07 (978-1-59296-754-4(X)) Child's World, Inc.

—Soccer Superstars. 2006. (Boys Rock! Ser.). (Illus.). 32p. (J). (gr. 1-5). 24.21 (978-1-59296-736-0(1)) Child's World, Inc.

—Soccer Superwomen. 2006. (Girls Rock! Ser.). 32p. (J). (gr. 1-5). 24.21 (978-1-59296-750-6(7)) Child's World, Inc.

Buckley, Steve. Sports Buddies: Superstar Athletes & Their Best Friends. Sieck, Margaret, ed. 1999. 32p. (J). (gr. 1-9). pap. 3.99 (978-1-886749-56-6(6)) Sports Illustrated For Kids.

Carter, Vince & Brown, Greg. Vince Carter: Choose Your Course. 2004. (Basketball Ser.). (Illus.). 48p. (J). 15.95 (978-0-9634650-2-3(3)) Positively for Kids, Inc.

Christopher, Matt. On the Court with... Yao Ming. 2004. (Matt Christopher Sports Biographies Ser.). (Illus.). 112p. (J). (gr. 5-8). pap. 4.99 (978-0-316-73574-2(4) , Tingley, Megan Bks.) Little, Brown Bks. for Young Readers.

—On the Halfpipe with... Tony Hawk. 2001. (gr. 3-6). lib. bdg. 13.00 (978-0-613-44173-5(7)) Tandem Library Bks.

—On the Ice with... Tara Lipinski. 1999. (978-0-606-16725-3(0)) Tandem Library Bks.

Cohen, Daniel. Wrestling Renegades: An in Depth Look at Today's Superstars of Pro Wrestling. 1999. (J). (978-0-606-18955-2(6)) Tandem Library Bks.

Cohen, Sasha & Maciel, Amanda. Sasha Cohen: Fire on Ice: Autobiography of a Champion Figure Skater. Goedeken, Kathy, illus. rev. ed. 2006. 224p. (J). pap. 9.99 (978-0-06-115385-3(0)) HarperCollins Pubs.

Cole, Andy & Fitton, Peter. Andy Cole: Autobiography. 1999. (Illus.). 256p. (J). 35.00 (978-0-233-99737-7(7)) Andre Deutsch GBR. *Dist:* Independent Pubs. Group.

Debon, Nicolas. The Strongest Man in the World: Louis Cyr. Debon, Nicolas, illus. 2007. (Illus.). 36p. (J). (gr. 2 up). 17.95 (978-0-88899-731-9(0)) Groundwood Bks. CAN. *Dist:* Perseus Distribution.

Dieterich, Alice & Chipponeri, Kelli. Tony Hawk & Andy MacDonald: Ride to the Top. 2003. (All Aboard Reading Ser.: Vol. 3). (Illus.). 48p. (J). (gr. 2-4). pap. 3.99 (978-0-448-43160-4(2) , Grosset & Dunlap) Penguin Group (USA) Inc.

Engfer, Lee. Wilma Rudolph: Olympic Track Star. Martin, Cynthia, illus. 2006. (Graphic Library). 32p. (J). (978-0-7368-5489-4(4)) Capstone Pr., Inc.

Extreme Sports Biographies. (Illus.). (J). (gr. k-5). 119.70 (978-1-4042-2954-9(X)); 2005. 64p. (gr. 5-8). lib. bdg. 159.00 (978-1-4042-0344-0(3)) Rosen Publishing Group, Inc., The.

Fitzpatrick, Jim. Tony Hawk. 2006. (World's Greatest Athletes Ser.). (Illus.). 32p. (J). (gr. 1-5). 27.07 (978-1-59296-760-5(4)) Child's World, Inc.

Foley, Mick. Have a Nice Day! A Tale of Blood & Sweatsocks. 2000. (gr. 7-12). lib. bdg. 16.45 (978-0-613-33590-4(2)) Tandem Library Bks.

Fuller, Barbara. Great Britain. 2004. (Illus.). 48p. (J). 27.07 (978-0-7614-1760-6(5) , Benchmark Bks.) Cavendish, Marshall Corp.

Galan, Johnn. Luis Tejada -Vida Breve, Crítica Cronica. 2006. 192p. pap. (978-958-30-1692-9(6)) Panamericana Editorial.

Gigliotti, Jim & Dorling Kindersley Publishing Staff. Record Breakers. 2003. (Major League Baseball Readers Ser.). (Illus.). 48p. (J). 12.99 (978-0-7894-9843-4(X)) Dorling Kindersley Publishing, Inc.

Gikow, Louise A. Extreme Sports: A Chapter Book. 2005. (True Tales Ser.). (Illus.). 48p. (J). (gr. 2-4). pap. 4.95 (978-0-516-24683-3(6) , Children's Pr.) Scholastic Library Publishing.

Golus, Carrie. Muhammad Ali. 2006. (Sports Heroes & Legends Ser.). (Illus.). 110p. (J). 27.93 (978-0-8225-5960-3(9) , Lerner Pubns.) Lerner Publishing Group.

Goodman, Michael E. Monica Seles. 1998. (Ovations Ser.). (Illus.). 32p. (YA). (gr. 4-7). lib. bdg. 21.30 (978-0-88682-699-4(3) , Creative Education) Creative Co., The.

—Shaquille O'Neal. 1998. (Ovations Ser.). (Illus.). 32p. (YA). (gr. 4-7). lib. bdg. (978-0-88682-633-8(0) , Creative Education) Creative Co., The.

Goranson, Christopher D. Danny Harf: Wakeboarding Superstar. 2005. (Illus.). 64p. (J). (gr. 5-8). lib. bdg. 26.50 (978-1-4042-0066-1(5)) Rosen Publishing Group, Inc., The.

Hall, Kirsten. Kids in Sports: A Chapter Book. (True Tales Ser.). (J). 2005. (Illus.). 48p. (gr. 2-4). pap. 4.95 (978-0-516-24685-7(2)); 2004. 22.50 (978-0-516-23733-6(0)) Scholastic Library Publishing. (Children's Pr.).

Hawk, Tony. Tony Hawk: Professional Skateboarder. 2002. (gr. 7-12). lib. bdg. 15.30 (978-0-613-70951-4(9)) Tandem Library Bks.

Hocking, Justin. Famous Skateboarders. 2006. (Illus.). 24p. (J). (978-1-4042-3050-7(5) , PowerKids Pr.) Rosen Publishing Group, Inc., The.

Horn, Geoffrey M. Today's Superstars: Sports, 6 bks., Set. Incl. Albert Pujols. lib. bdg. 23.93 (978-0-8368-6185-3(X)); Dale Earnhardt, Jr. lib. bdg. 23.93 (978-0-8368-6182-2(5)); Laila Ali. lib. bdg. 23.93 (978-0-8368-6181-5(7)); Michelle Wie. lib. bdg. 23.33 (978-0-8368-6186-0(8)); Peyton Manning. lib. bdg. 23.93 (978-0-8368-6183-9(3)); Rafael Nadal. lib. bdg. 23.93 (978-0-8368-6184-6(1)); (Illus.). (YA). (gr. 5 up). 2006. 32p. 2007. Set lib. bdg. 143.58 (978-0-8368-6180-8(9)) Stevens, Gareth Inc.

Hunter, Matt. Ric Flair: The Story of the Wrestler They Call "The Nature Boy" 2000. (Pro Wrestling Legends Ser.). (Illus.). 64p. (J). (gr. 8-12). pap. 25.00 (978-0-7910-5826-8(3) , Chelsea Hse.) Facts On File, Inc.

Johnson, Brad & Brown, Greg. Brad Johnson: Play with Passion. 2004. (Football Ser.). (Illus.). 48p. (J). 15.95 (978-0-9634650-1-7(X)) Positively for Kids, Inc.

Kaelberer, Angie Peterson. Hulk Hogan: Pro Wrestler Terry Bollea. 2003. (Pro Wrestlers Ser.). (Illus.). 48p. (J). lib. bdg. 22.60 (978-0-7368-2140-7(6) , Capstone High/Low Bks.) Capstone Pr., Inc.

Kirkpatrick, Rob. Hot Shots, 6 bks. Incl. Alexia Lalas : Soccer Sensation. lib. bdg. 17.25 (978-0-8239-5541-1(9)); Cobi Jones : Soccer Star. lib. bdg. 17.25 (978-0-8239-5540-4(0)); Dale Earnhardt, Jr. NASCAR Road Racer. lib. bdg. 17.25 (978-0-8239-5545-9(1) , PKDAEA); Evander Holyfield : Heavyweight Champion. lib. bdg. 17.25 (978-0-8239-5542-8(7)); Jeff Gordon : NASCAR Champion. lib. bdg. 17.25 (978-0-8239-5544-2(3) , PKJEGO); Oscar de la Hoya : Gold-Medal Boxer. lib. bdg. 17.25 (978-0-8239-5543-5(5)); 24p. (J). (gr. 1). 2000. (Illus.). Set lib. bdg. 96.00 (978-0-8239-7001-8(9) , PKPOHS, PowerKids Pr.) Rosen Publishing Group, Inc., The.

—Power Players, 6 bks. Incl. Doug Flutie : International Football Star. 2003. lib. bdg. 17.25 (978-0-8239-5537-4(0)); Grant Hill : Basketball All-Star. 2003. lib. bdg. 17.25 (978-0-8239-5538-1(9)); Kobe Bryant : "Slam Dunk" Champion. 2000. lib. bdg. 17.25 (978-0-8239-5539-8(7)); Mark McGwire : Record Breaker. 2000. lib. bdg. 17.25 (978-0-8239-5535-0(4)); Sammy Sosa : Home Run Hitter. 2002. lib. bdg. 17.25 (978-0-8239-5534-3(6)); Terrell Davis : Super Bowl Running Back. 2000. lib. bdg. 17.25 (978-0-8239-5536-7(2)); 24p. (J). (gr. 1). (Illus.). Set lib. bdg. 96.00 (978-0-8239-7000-1(0) , PowerKids Pr.) Rosen Publishing Group, Inc., The.

Kule, Elaine A. Kristi Yamaguchi. 2005. (Asian-American Biographies Ser.). (Illus.). 64p. (J). (gr. 6-9). pap. 9.50 (978-1-4109-1130-8(6)) Raintree.

Lewis, Wendy A. Fire on the Water: The Red-hot Career of Superstar Rower Ned Hanlan. 2007. (Recordbooks Ser.). (Illus.). 112p. (J). (gr. 7-12). 8.95 (***978-1-55028-972-5(1)***); (***978-1-55028-973-2(X)***) Lorimer, James & Co., Ltd., Pubs. CAN. *Dist:* Casemate Pubs. & Bk. Distributors, LLC.

Lincoln Library of Sports Champions, 14 volumes, 14 volume set. 7th ed. 2004. (Illus.). 1800p. (J). lib. bdg. 498.00 (978-0-912168-19-7(6) , 800-516-2656, Lincoln Library) Lincoln Library Press, The.

Macnow, Glen. Sports Great Kevin Garnett. 2000. (Sports Great Bks.). (Illus.). 64p. (YA). (gr. 4-10). lib. bdg. 17.95 (978-0-7660-1263-9(8)) Enslow Pubs., Inc.

Mahaney, Ian. Tony Hawk: Skateboarding Champ. 2005. (Extreme Sports Biographies Ser.). (Illus.). 24p. (J). 19.95 (978-1-4042-2747-7(4) , PowerKids Pr.) Rosen Publishing Group, Inc., The.

Mahaney, Ian F. Kevin Jones: Snowboarding Champion. 2005. (Extreme Sports Biographies Ser.). (Illus.). 24p. (J). 19.95 (978-1-4042-2745-3(8) , PowerKids Pr.) Rosen Publishing Group, Inc., The.

—Taig Khris: In-Line Skate Champion. 2005. (Extreme Sports Biographies Ser.). (Illus.). 24p. (J). 19.95 (978-1-4042-2746-0(6) , PowerKids Pr.) Rosen Publishing Group, Inc., The.

Maxwell, E. J. Xtreme Sports: Cutting Edge. 2003. (Xtreme Sports Ser.). (Illus.). 96p. (J). (gr. 3-6). pap. 4.99 (978-0-439-46854-1(X) , Scholastic Paperbacks) Scholastic, Inc.

—Xtreme Sports: Cutting Edge. 2003. (gr. 3-6). lib. bdg. 13.00 (978-0-613-71994-0(8)) Tandem Library Bks.

McCarthy, Meghan. Strong Man: The Story of Charles Atlas. McCarthy, Meghan, illus. 2007. (Illus.). 40p. (J). (gr. k-3). 15.99 (978-0-375-82940-6(7)); lib. bdg. 18.99 (978-0-375-92940-3(1)) Random Hse. Children's Bks. (Knopf Bks. for Young Readers).

Miller, Raymond H. Tony Hawk. 2004. (Stars of Sport Ser.). (Illus.). 48p. (J). 26.20 (978-0-7377-1568-2(5) , Greenhaven Pr., Inc.) Thomson Gale.

Moore, Bob. Drivers Series: Dale Earnhardt Sr. 2002. (NASCAR Wonder Boy Collector's Ser.). (Illus.). 48p. (J). pap. 7.99 (978-1-57243-526-1(7)) Triumph Bks.

Morelli, Jack. Heroes of the Negro Leagues. 2007. 128p. 19.95 (***978-0-8109-9434-8(8)***) Abrams, Harry N. , Inc.

Mudge, Jacqueline. Diamond Dallas Page: The Story of the Wrestler They Call "Diamond Dallas Page" 2000. (Pro Wrestling Legends Ser.). (Illus.). 64p. (J). (gr. 8-12). pap. 25.00 (978-0-7910-5830-5(1) , Chelsea Hse.) Facts On File, Inc.

—Kevin Nash. 2000. (Pro Wrestling Legends Ser.). (Illus.). 64p. (J). (gr. 8-12). pap. 25.00 (978-0-7910-5828-2(X)); (gr. 4-7). 25.00 (978-0-7910-5827-5(1)) Facts On File, Inc. (Chelsea Hse.).

—Kevin Nash. 2001. (gr. 5-8). lib. bdg. 17.60 (978-0-613-32741-1(1)) Tandem Library Bks.

Myler, Patrick. A Century of Boxing Greats: Inside the Ring with the Hundred Best Boxers. 1998. (Illus.). 394p. (YA). pap. (978-1-86105-258-2(8) , Robson Bks. Ltd.) Anova Bks.

O'Brien, Jim. Hometown Heroes: Profiles in Sports & Spirit. Zirwas, Sarah O'Brien, ed. 1999. (Pittsburgh Proud Sports Book Ser.). (Illus.). 432p. (YA). (gr. 4 up). 29.95 (978-1-886348-04-2(9)) O'Brien, James P. Publishing.

Parham, Jerrill. Thrills & Spills: Fast Sports. 2007. (Shockwave: the Human Experience Ser.). (Illus.). 36p. (J). (gr. 4-6). lib. bdg. 25.00 (***978-0-531-17762-4(9)*** , Children's Pr.) Scholastic Library Publishing.

Raintree Steck-Vaughn Staff. Overcoming the Odds 1b Reading Group. 2002. pap. 399.00 (978-1-58702-852-6(2)) Johnston, Don Inc.

Rapoport, Ron. See How She Runs: Marion Jones & the Making of a Champion. 2001. (J). (978-0-606-21706-4(1)) Tandem Library Bks.

Rappoport, Ken. Profiles in Sports Courage. 2006. (Illus.). 160p. (J). 15.95 (978-1-56145-368-9(4) , Peachtree Junior) Peachtree Pubs., Ltd.

Roberts, Jeremy. Tiger Woods. 2007. (J). pap. 8.95 (***978-0-8225-8563-3(4)*** , First Avenue Editions) Lerner Publishing Group.

Rosenberg, Aaron. Dave Mirra. 2005. (Illus.). 64p. (J). (gr. 5-8). lib. bdg. 26.50 (978-1-4042-0067-8(3)) Rosen Publishing Group, Inc., The.

Ross, Dan. The Rock: The Story of the Wrestler They Call "The Rock" 2000. (Pro Wrestling Legends Ser.). (Illus.). 64p. (J). (gr. 8-12). pap. 25.00 (978-0-7910-5832-9(8) , Chelsea Hse.) Facts On File, Inc.

Savage, Jeff. James Stewart. 2007. (Amazing Athletes Ser.). (J). 23.93 (***978-0-8225-7663-1(5)*** , Lerner Pubns.) Lerner Publishing Group.

Savage, Jeff. Marion Jones. 2005. (J). pap. 5.95 (978-0-8225-2040-5(0) , First Avenue Editions); (Illus.). (gr. 3-4). lib. bdg. 22.60 (978-0-8225-3657-4(9)) Lerner Publishing Group.

Schraff, Anne. Wilma Rudolph: The Greatest Woman Sprinter in History. 2004. (African-American Biographies Ser.). (Illus.). 112p. (J). lib. bdg. 26.60 (978-0-7660-2291-1(9)) Enslow Pubs., Inc.

Sherrow, Victoria. Wilma Rudolph. Johnson, Larry, illus. 2006. (Yo Solo Biografías Ser.). (ENG & SPA.). (J). 23.93 (978-0-8225-6260-3(X) , Ediciones Lerner) Lerner Publishing Group.

Smithwicks, John. All-Star Players, 6 bks., Set. Incl. Meet Alex Rodriguez : Baseball's Lightning Rod. lib. bdg. 23.95 (978-1-4042-3636-3(8)); Meet David Ortiz : Baseball's Top Slugger. lib. bdg. 23.95 (978-1-4042-3637-0(6)); Meet Dwyane Wade : Basketball's Rising Star. lib. bdg. 23.95 (978-1-4042-3639-4(2)); Meet LeBron James : Basketball's King James. lib. bdg. 23.95 (978-1-4042-3638-7(4)); Meet Peyton Manning : Football's Top Quarterback. lib. bdg. 23.95 (978-1-4042-3634-9(1)); Meet Shaun Alexander : Football's Top Running Back. lib. bdg. 23.95 (978-1-4042-3635-6(X)); (Illus.). 32p. (J). (gr. 4-6). 2007. , PowerKids Pr. 2007. Set lib. bdg. 143.70 (***978-1-4042-3601-1(5)***) Rosen Publishing Group, Inc., The.

Sorensen, Lita. Tony Hawk & His Team: Skateboarding Superstars. 2005. (Illus.). 64p. (J). (gr. 5-8). lib. bdg. 26.50 (978-1-4042-0070-8(3)) Rosen Publishing Group, Inc., The.

Sporting Heroes. Date not set. 32p. (J). 3.98 (978-0-7525-9875-8(9)) Parragon, Inc.

Steck-Vaughn Staff. Overcoming the Odds. 2002. pap. 99.00 incl. cd-rom (978-1-58702-940-0(5)); 2002. pap. 99.00 (978-1-58702-941-7(3)); Set. 2001. pap., tchr. ed. 8.00 (978-1-58702-576-1(0)) Johnston, Don Inc.

—Overcoming the Odds: Book Pack. 2002. pap. 30.00 (978-1-58702-346-0(6)); pap. 30.00 (978-1-58702-418-4(7)) Johnston, Don Inc.

—Overcoming the Odds: New York City Edition. 2002. pap. 150.00 (978-1-58702-064-3(5)); pap. 150.00 (978-1-58702-065-0(3)) Johnston, Don Inc.

—Overcoming the Odds: Reading Group Pack. 2001. pap. 399.00 (978-1-58702-414-6(4)); 2000. pap. 399.00 (978-1-893376-89-2(3)) Johnston, Don Inc.

—Overcoming the Odds: Single User Packs. 2001. pap. 174.00 (978-1-58702-410-8(1)); 2000. pap. 174.00 (978-1-893376-85-4(0)) Johnston, Don Inc.

—Overcoming the Odds 1 Single User Packs. 2002. pap. 174.00 (978-1-58702-850-2(6)) Johnston, Don Inc.

Stewart, Mark. New Wave, 27 vols. Incl. Alex Rodriguez : Gunning for Greatness. 1999. lib. bdg. 22.90 (978-0-7613-1515-5(2)); Allen Iverson : Motion & Emotion. 2001. lib. bdg. 22.90 (978-0-7613-1958-0(1)); Andruw Jones : Love That Glove. 2001. lib. bdg. 22.90 (978-0-7613-1967-2(0)); Chamique Holdsclaw : Driving Force. 2000. lib. bdg. 22.90 (978-0-7613-1801-9(1)); Daunte Culpepper : Command & Control. 2002. lib. bdg. 22.90 (978-0-7613-2613-7(8)); Derek Jeter : Substance & Style. 1999. lib. bdg. 22.90 (978-0-7613-1516-2(0)); Ichiro Suzuki : The Best in the West. 2002. lib. bdg. 22.90 (978-0-7613-2616-8(2)); Jackie Stiles : Gym Dandy. 2002. lib. bdg. 22.90 (978-0-7613-2614-4(6)); Jeff Gordon : Rainbow Warrior. 2000. lib. bdg. 22.90 (978-0-7613-1871-2(2)); Jevon Kearse : Force of One. 2001. lib. bdg. 22.90 (978-0-7613-2269-6(8)); Kevin Garnett/Shake up the Game. 2002. lib. bdg. 22.90 (978-0-7613-2615-1(4)); Kobe Bryant : Hard to the Hoop. 2000. lib. bdg. 22.90 (978-0-7613-1800-2(3)); Kurt Warner : Can't Keep Him Down. 2001. lib. bdg. 22.90 (978-0-7613-1953-5(0)); Marion Jones : Fast & Fearless. 2000. lib. bdg. 22.90 (978-0-7613-1870-5(4)); Mia Hamm : Striking Superstar. 2000. lib. bdg. 22.90 (978-0-7613-1802-6(X)); Nomar Garciaparra : Non-Stop Shortstop. 2000. lib. bdg. 22.90 (978-0-7613-1520-9(9)); Peyton Manning : Rising Son. 2000. lib. bdg. 22.90 (978-0-7613-1517-9(9)); Randy Moss : First in Flight. 2000. lib. bdg. 22.90 (978-0-7613-1518-6(7)); Scott Gomez : Open up the Ice. 2001. lib. bdg. 22.90 (978-0-7613-2268-9(X)); Se Ri Pak : The Drive to Win. 2000. lib. bdg. 22.90 (978-0-7613-1519-3(5)); Terrell Davis : Toughing It Out. 1999. lib. bdg. 22.90 (978-0-7613-1514-8(4)); Tim Duncan : Tower of Power. 1999. lib. bdg. 22.90 (978-0-7613-1513-1(6)); Todd Helton : The Hits Keep Coming. 2001. lib. bdg. 22.90 (978-0-7613-2271-9(X)); Venus & Serena Williams : Sisters in Arms. 2000. lib. bdg. 22.90 (978-0-7613-1803-3(8)); Vince Carter : The Fire Burns Bright. 2001. lib. bdg. 22.90 (978-0-7613-2270-2(1)); 48p. (gr. 4 up). , Millbrook Pr. (Illus.). 2004. 595.40 (978-0-7613-3080-6(1) , Twenty-First Century Bks.) Lerner Publishing Group.

—Vince Carter: The Fire Burns Bright. 2001. (New Wave Ser.). 48p. (J). (gr. 4-8). pap. 7.95 (978-0-7613-1499-8(7) , Millbrook Pr.) Lerner Publishing Group.

Stewart, Mark Alan. Brett Favre: Leader of the Pack. 1999. (Sports Stars Ser.). (Illus.). 48p. (J). (gr. 3-4). pap. 5.95 (978-0-516-26422-6(2) , Children's Pr.) Scholastic Library Publishing.

Sword of a Champion: The Sharon Monplaisir Story. 2003. (Anything You Can Do. . .Ser.: Vol. 2). (Illus.). 96p. (J). (gr. 2-5). pap. 9.95 (978-1-930546-39-4(4)) Wish Publishing.

Taylor, Gail. Livewire Real Lives David Campese. 1998. (Livewire Real Lives Ser.). (Illus.). 32p. (J). pap. 5.50 (978-0-7336-0709-7(8)) Cambridge Univ. Pr.

—Livewire Real Lives Laurie Daley. 1998. (Livewires Ser.). (Illus.). 32p. (J). pap. 5.50 (978-0-7336-0708-0(X)) Cambridge Univ. Pr.

Who's Who in Sports 2003-2004: High School Edition. 26th ed. 2004. (YA). 39.95 (978-0-9724667-2-1(X) , Who's Who In Sports) Guidry Assocs., Inc.

Wood, Ted. Iditarod Dream: Dusty & His Sled Dogs Compete in Alaska's Jr. Iditarod. 2002. (gr. 3-6). lib. bdg. 17.60 (978-0-613-57306-1(4)) Tandem Library Bks.

—Iditarod Dream: Dusty & His Sled Dogs Compete in Alaska's Jr. Iditarod. 2002. (Illus.). 48p. (J). (gr. 3-6). pap. 8.95 (978-0-8027-7535-1(7)) Walker & Co.

Woods, Bob. Mat Hoffman. 2006. (World's Greatest Athletes Ser.). (Illus.). 32p. (J). (gr. 1-5). 27.07 (978-1-59296-755-1(8)) Child's World, Inc.

Wrestling Greats. 2005. (Illus.). 112p. (gr. 7-12). lib. bdg. 265.30 (978-0-8239-3911-4(1)) Rosen Publishing Group, Inc., The.

Wrestling Greats Set 2. 2005. (Illus.). (gr. 7-12). lib. bdg. 151.50 (978-0-8239-9717-6(0)) Rosen Publishing Group, Inc., The.

Zuehlke, Jeffrey. Ben Roethlisberger. 2007. (Amazing Athletes Ser.). (J). 23.93 (***978-0-8225-7660-0(0)*** , Lerner Pubns.) Lerner Publishing Group.

—Dirk Nowitzki. 2007. (Amazing Athletes Ser.). (J). 23.93 (***978-0-8225-7661-7(9)*** , Lerner Pubns.) Lerner Publishing Group.

SPORTS—DICTIONARIES

Owens, Jesse, intro. The Lincoln Library of Sports Champions, 14 vols., Set. 8th ed. 2006. (Illus.). (J). (gr. 4 up). lib. bdg. 523.00 (978-0-912168-25-8(0) , 800-516-2656, Lincoln Library) Lincoln Library Press, The.

Wukovits, John F. The Encyclopedia of World Sports. 2000. (Watts Reference Ser.). (Illus.). 192p. (J). (gr. 5). 41.00 (978-0-531-11777-4(4) , Watts, Franklin) Scholastic Library Publishing.

—Encyclopedia of World Sports. 2000. (gr. 5-8). lib. bdg. 36.15 (978-0-613-51640-2(0)) Tandem Library Bks.

SPORTS—FICTION

Alexander, Samantha. Team Spirit, Bk. 2. 117p. (J). mass mkt. 6.99 (978-0-330-34534-7(6) , Pan) Pan Macmillan GBR. *Dist:* Trafalgar Square Publishing.

Anderson, Joseph P. The Kickball Game. 2007. (Illus.). 24p. (J). (***978-1-4048-2443-0(X)***) Picture Window Bks.

—The Kickball Game. Greathouse, Justin, illus. 2006. 24p. (J). (***978-1-4048-2413-3(8)***) Picture Window Bks.

Armstrong, Robb. Got Game? Smith, Bruce, illus. 1998. (Patrick's Pals Ser.: No. 3). 96p. (J). (gr. 2-7). mass mkt. 3.99 (978-0-06-107069-3(6) , Harper Entertainment) HarperCollins Pubs.

Artifact Group. The Crystal Caper: A Lift-the-Flap Story. 2006. (LazyTown Ser.). 16p. (J). pap. 6.99 (978-1-4169-2464-7(7) , Simon Spotlight/Nickelodeon) Simon & Schuster Children's Publishing.

Aryal, Aimee. Hello, Brutus! 2006. (J). 14.95 (***978-1-932888-51-5(9)***) Mascot Bks., Inc.

—Hello, Paws! 2007. (YA). 14.95 (***978-1-932888-74-4(8)***) Mascot Bks., Inc.

—Let's Go, Giants! de Angel, Miguel, illus. 2007. (J). 14.95 (***978-1-932888-92-8(6)***) Mascot Bks., Inc.

Aryal, Aimee & Halligan, Chris. Meet Cort the Sport. 2006. (J). pap. 5.95 (978-1-932888-61-4(6) , 91-100-01) Mascot Bks., Inc.

Ashworth, Sherry. Paralysed. 2007. 304p. (J). pap. 12.00 (***978-1-4169-0094-8(2)***) Simon & Schuster, Ltd. GBR. *Dist:* Independent Pubs. Group.

The Autumn Marathon. 2005. (J). 16.95 (978-0-9771495-0-6(1)) Artistic Ventures LLC.

Averett, Edward. The Rhyming Season. 2005. 224p. (YA). (gr. 7-7). 16.00 (978-0-618-46948-2(6) , Clarion Bks.) Houghton Mifflin Co. Trade & Reference Div.

Axelrod, Amy. Pigs on the Ball: Fun with Math & Sports. McGinley-Nally, Sharon, illus. 1998. (Pigs Will Be Pigs Ser.). 40p. (J). (ps-3). 15.95 (978-0-689-81565-2(4)) Simon & Schuster Children's Publishing.

—Pigs on the Ball: Fun with Math & Sports. 2000. (gr. k-3). lib. bdg. 14.10 (978-0-613-26595-9(5)) Tandem Library Bks.

Axelrod, Amy & McGinley-Nally, Sharon. Pigs on the Ball. 2000. (Illus.). 40p. (J). (ps-4). pap. 6.99 (978-0-689-83537-7(X) , Aladdin) Simon & Schuster Children's Publishing.

Axelrod, Mitchell. Little Billy & Baseball Bob. Campbell, Ron, illus. Lt. ed. 2002. 32p. (J). per. 5.95 (978-0-9710591-2-2(8)) Wynn Publishing, Inc.

Bates, Cynthia. Courage on the Line. 1999. (Sports Stories Ser.). 117p. (J). (gr. 3-8). 7.95 (978-1-55028-649-6(X)); (***978-1-55028-649-6(8)***) Lorimer, James & Co., Ltd., Pubs. CAN. *Dist:* Casemate Pubs. & Bk. Distributors, LLC.

—Courage on the Line. 1999. (gr. 3-6). lib. bdg. 13.55 (978-0-613-29585-7(4)) Tandem Library Bks.

Bee, Clair. Backboard Fever, Vol. 10. 1999. (Chip Hilton Sports Ser.: No. 10). (Illus.). viii, 224p. (J). reprint ed. pap. 5.99 (978-0-8054-1992-4(6)) B&H Publishing Grp.

—Backboard Fever. 1999. (gr. 7-12). lib. bdg. 14.15 (978-0-613-90140-6(1)) Tandem Library Bks.

—Championship Ball, Vol. 2. Farley, Cynthia B. & Farley, Randall, eds. rev. ed. 1998. (Chip Hilton Ser.: Vol. 2). (Illus.). 194p. (J). pap. 5.99 (978-0-8054-1815-6(6)) B&H Publishing Grp.

—Championship Ball. 1998. (gr. 5-8). lib. bdg. 14.15 (978-0-613-90137-6(1)) Tandem Library Bks.

—Fourth down Shutdown, Vol. 13. rev. ed. 2000. (Chip Hilton Sports Ser.: No. 13). (Illus.). x, 221p. (J). pap. 5.99 (978-0-8054-2092-0(4)) B&H Publishing Grp.

—Strike Three, Vol. 3. Farley, Cynthia B. & Farley, Randall K., eds. rev. ed. 1998. (Chip Hilton Ser.: Vol. 3). 211p. (J). pap. 5.99 (978-0-8054-1816-3(4)) B&H Publishing Grp.

—Touchdown Pass. Farley, Cynthia B. & Farley, Randall, eds. rev. ed. 1998. (Chip Hilton Ser.: Vol. 1). 198p. (J). 5.99 (978-0-8054-1686-2(2)) B&H Publishing Grp.

—Tournament Crises, Vol. 14. Farley, Cynthia Bee & Farley, Randall, eds. 2000. (Chip Hilton Sports Ser.: Vol. 14). (Illus.). viii, 223p. (J). reprint ed. pap. 5.99 (978-0-8054-2093-7(2)) B&H Publishing Grp.

—Triple-Threat Trouble, Vol. 18. 2001. (Chip Hilton Sports Ser.: No. 18). (Illus.). viii, 183p. (J). (gr. 3-8). pap. 5.99 (978-0-8054-2097-5(5)) B&H Publishing Grp.

Berenstain, Stan & Berenstain, Jan. The Berenstain Bears' Report Card Trouble. ed. 2004. (Berenstain Bears First Time Bks.). (J). (gr. k-3). spiral bd. (978-0-616-11095-9(2)); spiral bd. (978-0-616-11096-6(0)) Canadian National Institute for the Blind/Institut National Canadien pour les Aveugles.

—The Berenstain Bears' Report Card Trouble. 2002. (Berenstain Bears First Time Bks.). (Illus.). 32p. (J). (gr. k-3). pap. 3.99 (978-0-375-81127-2(3) , Random Hse. Bks. for Young Readers) Random Hse. Children's Bks.

—The Berenstain Bears' Report Card Trouble. 2002. (Berenstain Bears First Time Bks.). (J). (gr. k-3). lib. bdg. 3.80 (978-0-613-70585-1(8)) Tandem Library Bks.

Betancourt, Jeanne. Fight, Bulldogs, Fight! 1999. (Cheer USA Ser.: Vol. 2). 128p. (J). (gr. 3-7). pap. 4.50 (978-0-590-97808-8(X)) Scholastic, Inc.

S

—Go, Girl, Go! 1999. (Cheer USA Ser.: Vol. 1). 128p. (J). (gr. 3-7). pap. 4.50 (978-0-590-97806-4(3)) Scholastic, Inc.

—Ready, Shoot, Score, 1 vol., Vol. 4. 1999. (Cheer USA Ser.: Vol. 3). 128p. (J). (gr. 3-7). pap. 4.50 (978-0-590-97809-5(8)) Scholastic, Inc.

—We've Got Spirit! 1999. (Cheer USA Ser.). (J). pap. 36.00 (978-0-439-11748-7(8)); Vol. 4. 128p. (gr. 3-7). pap. 4.50 (978-0-590-97876-7(4)) Scholastic, Inc.

Bildner, Phil. The Greatest Game Ever Played. Pullen, Zachary, illus. 2006. 40p. (J). (ps-3). 16.99 (978-0-399-24171-0(X) , Putnam Juvenile) Penguin Group (USA) Inc.

Bloor, Edward. Tangerine. 2001. (J). (978-0-606-21480-3(1)) Tandem Library Bks.

Bonehill, Ralph. Guns & Snowshoes or the Winter Outing of the Young Hunters. 2004. reprint ed. pap. 19.95 (978-1-4191-2252-1(5)); pap. 1.99 (978-1-4192-2252-8(X)) Kessinger Publishing, LLC.

Bossley, Michele Martin. Breathing Not Required. 1999. (gr. 7-12). lib. bdg. 13.55 (978-0-613-18215-7(4)) Tandem Library Bks.

—Goon Squad. 2003. (Sports Stories Ser.). 104p. (J). (gr. 4-8). 7.95 (978-1-55028-808-7(3)); (*978-1-55028-809-4(1)) Lorimer, James & Co., Ltd., Pubs. CAN. *Dist:* Casemate Pubs. & Bk. Distributors, LLC.

—Leap of Faith. 1999. (Sports Stories Ser.). 96p. (gr. 3-8). (J). (978-1-55028-685-4(4)); 7.95 (978-1-55028-686-1(2)) Lorimer, James & Co., Ltd., Pubs. CAN. *Dist:* Casemate Pubs. & Bk. Distributors, LLC.

Bossley, Michele Martin. Trapped! 2002. (Sports Stories Ser.). 128p. (gr. 3-8). (J). (*978-1-55028-759-2(1)); 7.95 (978-1-55028-758-5(3)) Lorimer, James & Co., Ltd., Pubs. CAN. *Dist:* Casemate Pubs. & Bk. Distributors, LLC.

—Trapped! 2002. (gr. 3-6). lib. bdg. 13.55 (978-0-613-78321-7(2)) Tandem Library Bks.

Bosworth, Richard. The Box Seat Dream. Cioffi, Joseph, illus. 2000. 126p. (YA). (gr. 3-10). pap. 6.95 (978-0-9679395-0-6(X) , 33) Boz Imagineering.

Boushell, Mike. Freshman Flash. Dodge, Chris, illus. 2002. 120p. (YA). (gr. 5-8). 9.99 (978-0-88092-600-3(7) , 600-7) Royal Fireworks Publishing Co.

Bowen, Fred. Winners Take All. Casale, Paul, illus. 2000. (All-Star Sport Story Ser.). 104p. (J). (gr. 3-7). pap. 4.95 (978-1-56145-229-3(7) , Q26776) Peachtree Pubs., Ltd.

—Winners Take All. 2000. (J). (978-0-606-19863-9(6)); (gr. 3-6). lib. bdg. 12.95 (978-0-613-36750-9(2)) Tandem Library Bks.

Bradman, Tony. Good Sports: Bag of Sports Stories. 2000. (Illus.). 224p. (J). pap. 8.99 (978-0-552-54296-8(2)) Transworld Publishers Ltd. GBR. *Dist:* Trafalgar Square Publishing.

Brewster, Jim. Wild League on Ice. 1998. (J). pap. 5.95 (978-0-9683303-4-0(7)) Tumbleweed Pr.

Bridwell, Norman. Clifford's Sports Day. Bridwell, Norman, illus. 2002. (Clifford, the Big Red Dog Ser.). (Illus.). (J). 11.45 (978-0-7587-6710-3(2)) Book Wholesalers, Inc.

—Clifford's Sports Day. (Clifford, the Big Red Dog Ser.). (Illus.). 32p. (J). (gr. k-2). pap. 5.99 (978-0-590-16002-5(8)) Scholastic, Inc.

Briggs-Pattison, Sue & Harvey, Bev. Home Team. Jones, Helen, illus. 2006. 64p. (J). (gr. 2-4). 19.95 (978-1-4048-1667-1(4)) Picture Window Bks.

Brimner, Larry Dane. The Big Tee Ball Game. Tripp, Christine, illus. 2001. (Rookie Choices Ser.). 32p. (J). (gr. 1-2). 20.50 (978-0-516-22158-8(2) , Children's Pr.) Scholastic Library Publishing.

Brooks, Bruce. All That Remains. 2002. 176p. (YA). (gr. 7 up). pap. 6.99 (978-0-689-83442-4(X) , Simon Pulse) Simon & Schuster Children's Publishing.

—All That Remains: 3 Stories. 2001. (Illus.). 176p. (J). (gr. 7 up). 16.00 (978-0-689-83351-9(2) , Atheneum) Simon & Schuster Children's Publishing.

—All That Remains: 3 Stories. 2002. (gr. 7-12). lib. bdg. 15.30 (978-0-613-62371-1(1)) Tandem Library Bks.

—Reed. 1998. (Wolfbay Wings Ser.: No. 9). (Illus.). 96p. (J). (gr. 5 up). 14.89 (978-0-06-028055-0(7)) HarperCollins Pubs.

Brooks, Jillian. Team Player. 2002. (Wondergirls Ser.: No. 2). 142p. (J). (gr. 3-7). pap. 4.99 (978-0-439-35490-5(0) , Scholastic Paperbacks) Scholastic, Inc.

Brown, Marc. Arthur & the Best Coach Ever. 2001. (Arthur Good Sports Ser.: Bk. 4). (J). 4.25 (978-0-316-12216-0(5)) Little, Brown Bks. for Young Readers.

—Arthur & the Recess Rookie. 2001. (Arthur Good Sports Ser.: Bk. 3). (Illus.). 64p. (J). (gr. 2-4). 13.95 (978-0-316-11916-0(4)); 3rd ed. pap. 4.25 (978-0-316-12105-7(3)) Little, Brown Bks. for Young Readers.

—Arthur & the Recess Rookie. 2001. (Arthur Good Sports Ser.: Bk. 3). (gr. 3-6). lib. bdg. 11.80 (978-0-613-35629-9(2)); (Illus.). (J). 10.75 (978-0-606-21909-9(9)) Tandem Library Bks.

—Arthur & the Seventh-Inning Stretcher. 2001. (Arthur Good Sports Ser.: Bk. 2). (Illus.). (J). 11.05 (978-0-606-21042-3(3)) Tandem Library Bks.

—The Good Sport, 18 vols., Vol. 16. 2001. (Illus.). 28p. (J). (ps-3). 3.79 (978-1-57973-122-9(8)) Advance Pubs. LLC.

Brownridge, William Roy. Victory at Paradise Hill. Brownridge, William Roy, illus. 2002. (Illus.). 32p. (J). (ps-2). 16.95 (978-1-55143-219-9(6)) Orca Bk. Pubs. USA.

Bruchac, Joseph, et al. Sports Shorts: An Anthology of Short Stories. 2005. (Illus.). 127p. (J). (gr. 4-7). per. 15.99 (978-1-58196-040-2(9)) Darby Creek Publishing.

Bruchac, Joseph, et al. Sports Shorts: Eight Short Stories. 2007. (J). pap. 4.99 (*978-1-58196-058-7(1)) Darby Creek Publishing.

Bump, Set, SERVE (2000-2001 Children's Reading Book) 2000. 80p. (J). pap. 6.90 (978-0-8341-1857-7(2)) Beacon Hill Pr. of Kansas City.

Bunting, Eve. Trouble on the T-Ball Team. Trivas, Irene, illus. 2002. 32p. (J). (gr. k-3). pap. 5.95 (978-0-618-24617-5(7) , Clarion Bks.) Houghton Mifflin Co. Trade & Reference Div.

—Trouble on the T-Ball Team. 2002. (gr. k-3). lib. bdg. 14.10 (978-0-613-70964-4(0)) Tandem Library Bks.

Burkett, Kathy & Korman, Gordon. Foul Play! Ethan Flask & Professor Von Offel's Sports Science Match. 2001. (Mad Science Ser.). (Illus.). 67p. (J). (978-0-439-23579-2(0)) Scholastic, Inc.

Burron, Arnold. One Man to Beat. 2002. 156p. (YA). (gr. 6-12). pap. 6.99 (978-0-9673697-2-3(X)) Diamond Peak Pr.

Burton, Jennifer. Christopher's Dilemma. 2003. (Topeka Heights Ser.). (YA). (gr. 9-12). pap. 10.99 (978-0-9724733-1-6(9)) Allen Publishing, USA.

Campbell, Tonie. The Highest Stand. 2003. (Dream Series Ser.). 160p. 9.95 (978-0-9708992-5-5(4)) Scobre Pr. Corp.

Carter, Anne Laurel. In the Clear. 2001. 176p. (J). (gr. 3-7). pap. 6.95 (978-1-55143-192-5(0)) Orca Bk. Pubs. USA.

Chardiet, Jon. Parker Penguin & the Winter Games. Micucci, Charles, illus. 1999. (Read with Me Ser.). 32p. (J). (gr. k-2). pap. 3.25 (978-0-590-14925-9(3)) Scholastic, Inc.

Childs, Rob. Big Day. 2000. (Young Corgi Ser.). (Illus.). 89p. (J). pap. 7.99 (978-0-552-52581-7(2)) Transworld Publishers Ltd. GBR. *Dist:* Independent Pubs. Group.

—Strike! Chatterton, Martin, illus. 2004. (Corgi Pups Ser.). 64p. (J). (gr. k-2). pap. 7.50 (978-0-552-55031-4(0) , Corgi) Transworld Publishers Ltd. GBR. *Dist:* Independent Pubs. Group.

—Wicked Catch! 2003. (Corgi Pups Ser.). (Illus.). 64p. pap. 7.99 (978-0-552-54792-5(1) , Corgi) Transworld Publishers Ltd. GBR. *Dist:* Independent Pubs. Group.

Choyce, Lesley. Roid Rage. unabr. ed. 1999. 112p. (978-1-55017-206-5(9)) Harbour Publishing Co., Ltd.

—Roid Rage. 1999. (gr. 7-12). lib. bdg. 15.25 (978-0-613-83360-8(0)) Tandem Library Bks.

Christopher, Matt. Comeback of the Home Run Kid. 2006. 128p. (J). (gr. 2-5). pap. 4.99 (978-0-316-05987-9(0)) Little Brown & Co.

—Lacrosse Face-Off. 2006. 128p. (J). (gr. 3-7). pap. 4.99 (978-0-316-79641-5(7)) Little Brown & Co.

—Snowboard Showdown. 1999. (978-0-606-17506-7(7)); (gr. 3-6). lib. bdg. 12.40 (978-0-613-22399-7(3)) Tandem Library Bks.

—Snowboard Showdown: Out-of Control Competition Leads to Disaster. 1999. (Matt Christopher Sports Classics Ser.). 144p. (J). (gr. 3-7). pap. 4.99 (978-0-316-13512-2(7)) Little, Brown Bks. for Young Readers.

—Spike It! 1999. 147p. (J). (gr. 3-7). pap. 4.50 (978-0-316-13401-9(5)) Little Brown & Co.

Chronicle Books. Sport Stories You'll Have a Ball With. 2001. (Illus.). 64p. (J). (ps-3). pap. 3.99 (978-1-58717-086-7(8) , SeaStar Bks.) Chronicle Bks. LLC.

Clancy, Tom, et al. Death Match. 2003. (Tom Clancy's Net Force Ser.: No. 18). 192p. (Orig.). (gr. 12). mass mkt. 4.99 (978-0-425-18448-6(X) , Berkley) Penguin Group (USA) Inc.

Collins, Terry. High-Flying Sam. Date not set. (Rocket Power Ready-to-Read Ser.: Vol. 5). (J). pap. 3.50 (978-0-689-86582-4(1) , Simon Spotlight/Nickelodeon) Simon & Schuster Children's Publishing.

Cook, Julia. My Mom Thinks She's My Volleyball Coach... but She's Not! 2007. (J). pap. 9.95 (*978-1-934073-09-4(1)); (YA). 15.95 (*978-1-934073-10-0(5)) CTC Publishing.

Cowell, Cressida. Claydon Was a Clingy Child. 2002. (Illus.). 32p. (J). mass mkt. 9.99 (978-0-340-75724-6(8) , Hodder & Stoughton) Hodder General Publishing Division GBR. *Dist:* Trafalgar Square Publishing.

Cowley, Joy. Agapanthus Hum & the Eyeglasses Hour. 2001. (Easy-to-Read Ser.). (C). (978-0-606-20535-1(7)) Tandem Library Bks.

Crutcher, Chris. Whale Talk. 2001. 224p. (J). (gr. 7 up). 16.99 (978-0-688-18019-5(1)) HarperCollins Pubs.

—Whale Talk. 2004. 224p. (J). (gr. 7 up). pap. 38.00 incl. audio (978-0-8072-2289-8(5) , Listening Library) Random Hse. Audio Publishing Group.

—Whale Talk. 2002. 224p. (YA). (gr. 7). pap. 6.99 (978-0-440-22938-4(3) , Laurel Leaf) Random Hse. Children's Bks.

—Whale Talk. 2002. (gr. 5-8). lib. bdg. 13.55 (978-0-613-61739-0(8)) Tandem Library Bks.

—Whale Talk. l.t. ed. 2005. 323p. 21.95 (978-0-7862-7787-2(4) , Large Print Pr.) Thorndike Pr.

Curtis, Gavin. The Bat Boy & His Violin. Lewis, Earl, illus. 2002. (J). 26.13 (978-0-7587-0338-5(4)) Book Wholesalers, Inc.

—The Bat Boy & His Violin. 2001. (Illus.). (J). 13.79 (978-0-606-20563-4(2)) Tandem Library Bks.

Daniels, Teri. The Feet in the Gym. Foster, Travis, illus. 1999. 40p. (J). (ps-3). 15.95 (978-1-890817-12-1(0)) Winslow Pr.

Deans, Sis Boulos. Racing the Past. 2005. 160p. (J). (gr. 3-9). reprint ed. pap. 5.99 (978-0-14-240308-2(3) , Puffin) Penguin Group (USA) Inc.

Diersch, Sandra. Alecia's Challenge. 1999. (Sports Stories Ser.: Vol. 32). 101p. (J). (gr. 3-8). 7.95 (978-1-55028-650-2(1)) Lorimer, James & Co., Ltd., Pubs. CAN. *Dist:* Casemate Pubs. & Bk. Distributors, LLC.

—Alecia's Challenge. 1999. (gr. 3-6). lib. bdg. 13.55 (978-0-613-29543-7(9)) Tandem Library Bks.

—Ceiling Stars. 2004. (SideStreets Ser.). 144p. (gr. 7-12). 7.95 (978-1-55028-834-6(2)); (*978-1-55028-835-3(0)) Lorimer, James & Co., Ltd., Pubs. CAN. *Dist:* Casemate Pubs. & Bk. Distributors, LLC.

—Home Court Advantage. 2002. (gr. 5-8). lib. bdg. 13.55 (978-0-613-78318-7(2)) Tandem Library Bks.

Diersch, Sandra. Offside! 2000. (Sports Stories Ser.). 94p. (J). (*978-1-55028-723-3(0)); (gr. 3-8). 7.95 (978-1-55028-722-6(2)) Lorimer, James & Co., Ltd., Pubs. CAN. *Dist:* Casemate Pubs. & Bk. Distributors, LLC.

Disney Staff. Need for Speed. 2001. (Jersey Ser.). (Illus.). (J). (978-0-606-21266-3(3)) Tandem Library Bks.

Dubowski, Cathy East. Field Day Foul Up. 2000. (gr. 3-6). lib. bdg. 11.80 (978-0-613-27824-9(0)) Tandem Library Bks.

Durant, Alan. Sports Stories. 2000. (Story Library). (Illus.). 221p. (J). pap. (978-0-7534-5192-2(1) , Kingfisher) Houghton Mifflin Co. Trade & Reference Div.

—Sports Stories. Kearney, David, illus. 2000. (Story Library). 224p. (J). (gr. 4-9). tchr. ed. 14.95 (978-0-7534-5322-3(3) , Kingfisher) Houghton Mifflin Co. Trade & Reference Div.

—Sports Stories. 2001. (978-0-606-21450-6(X)); 2000. (gr. 5-8). lib. bdg. 15.25 (978-0-613-67435-5(9)) Tandem Library Bks.

Dygard, Thomas J. Second Stringer. 1998. 192p. (J). (gr. 7-12). 15.99 (978-0-688-15981-8(8)) HarperCollins Pubs.

Escaich, Bertrand & Roque, Caroline. The Rugger Boys: Why Are We Here Again? Spear, Luke, tr. from FRE. 2007. (Illus.). 52p. pap. 9.99 (*978-1-905460-33-5(3)) CineBook GBR. *Dist:* Biblio Distribution.

Fast/Sports Staff. Redmond's Shot. 2001. 32p. (YA). (gr. 6-12). pap. (978-0-8224-6498-3(5)) Globe Fearon Educational Publishing.

Feinstein, John. Cover-up: Mystery at the Super Bowl. 2007. 304p. (J). (gr. 5). lib. bdg. 19.99 (*978-0-375-94247-1(5) , Knopf Bks. for Young Readers) Random Hse. Children's Bks.

—Cover-Up: Mystery at the Super Bowl. 2007. 304p. (J). (gr. 5 up). 16.99 (*978-0-375-84247-4(0) , Knopf Bks. for Young Readers) Random Hse. Children's Bks.

Forsyth, C. A. Hockey Heat Wave. 1999. (gr. 7-12). lib. bdg. 13.55 (978-0-613-18219-5(7)) Tandem Library Bks.

Friesen, Gayle. Men of stone. unabr. ed. 2002. (Gayle Friesen Ser.). (Illus.). 216p. (YA). (gr. 13 up). (978-1-55074-782-9(7)) Kids Can Pr., Ltd.

Galloway, Priscilla. Atalante: La Coureuse la Plus Rapide au Monde. Cousineau, Normand, illus. 2006. (FRE.). 75p. (J). (gr. k-4). reprint ed. pap. 15.00 (978-1-4223-5394-3(X)) DIANE Publishing Co.

Garant, Andre J. I'm Gonna Win. Aguiar, David, illus. 1999. 154p. (J). (gr. 5-8). pap. 4.75 (978-0-7392-0210-4(3) , PO3228) Morris Publishing.

Gibbons, Alan. Ganging Up. 2nd ed. 2006. (Illus.). 96p. (J). pap. 11.99 (*978-1-85881-194-9(5)) Orion Publishing Group, Ltd. GBR. *Dist:* Independent Pubs. Group.

Golden Books Staff. Fly Like a Fish/Short-Order Showdown. Meurer, Caleb, illus. 2003. 64p. (J). (ps-2). pap. 2.99 (978-0-307-10124-2(X) , Golden Bks.) Random Hse. Children's Bks.

—Team Players. Hall, Susan, illus. 2002. (Dora the Explorer Ser.). 16p. (J). (ps-3). pap. 4.99 (978-0-307-10289-8(0) , Golden Bks.) Random Hse. Children's Bks.

Graham, Georgia. A Team Like No Other. Graham, Georgia, illus. 2004. (Illus.). 32p. (J). (gr. 1-3). 17.95 (978-0-88995-290-4(6)) Red Deer Pr. CAN. *Dist:* Fitzhenry & Whiteside, Ltd.

Greene, Stephanie. Owen Foote, Soccer Star. Weston, Martha, illus. 1998. 96p. (J). (gr. k-3). tchr. ed. 14.00 (978-0-395-86143-1(8) , Clarion Bks.) Houghton Mifflin Co. Trade & Reference Div.

Griffeth, Rodger W. The Reluctant Star. 2000. 108p. (YA). (gr. 4-7). pap. 9.95 (978-0-595-13025-2(9)) iUniverse, Inc.

Guest, Jacqueline. Free Throw. 1999. (Sports Stories Ser.). 128p. (J). (gr. 3-8). (*978-1-55028-665-6(X)) Lorimer, James & Co., Ltd., Pubs. CAN. *Dist:* Casemate Pubs. & Bk. Distributors, LLC.

—Rink Rivals. 2001. (Sports Stories Ser.). 104p. (gr. 3-8). (J). (*978-1-55028-745-5(1)); 7.95 (978-1-55028-744-8(3)) Lorimer, James & Co., Ltd., Pubs. CAN. *Dist:* Casemate Pubs. & Bk. Distributors, LLC.

—Rink Rivals. 2002. (gr. 5-8). lib. bdg. 13.55 (978-0-613-78413-9(8)) Tandem Library Bks.

—Rookie Season. 2000. (Sports Stories Ser.). 115p. (gr. 3-8). (J). (*978-1-55028-725-7(7)); 7.95 (978-1-55028-724-0(9)) Lorimer, James & Co., Ltd., Pubs. CAN. *Dist:* Casemate Pubs. & Bk. Distributors, LLC.

Guest, Jacqueline. Triple Threat. 1999. (Sports Stories Ser.). 123p. (gr. 3-8). (J). (*978-1-55028-681-6(1)); 7.95 (978-1-55028-682-3(X)) Lorimer, James & Co., Ltd., Pubs. CAN. *Dist:* Casemate Pubs. & Bk. Distributors, LLC.

Gutman, Dan. The Million Dollar Strike. 2004. 192p. (gr. 3-7). 15.99 (978-0-7868-1880-8(8)) Hyperion Bks. for Children.

H. Irving Hancock. The High School Captain of the Team: Dick & Co. Leading the Athletic Vanguard. 2007. 156p. pap. 11.99 (*978-1-4264-6386-0(3)) BiblioBazaar.

Hall, Donald. When Willard Met Babe Ruth. 2001. (J). (978-0-606-21521-3(2)) Tandem Library Bks.

Hallinan, P. K. Let's Play As a Team. 2003. (Illus.). 28p. (J). 7.95 (978-0-8249-5452-9(1)) Ideals Pubns.

Hancock, H. Irving. The High School Captain of the Team: Dick & Co. Leading the Athletic Vanguard. l.t. ed. 2007. 172p. pap. 14.99 (*978-1-4264-6460-7(6)) BiblioBazaar.

—The High School Freshmen. rev. ed. 2006. 212p. 27.95 (978-1-4218-1741-5(1)); pap. 12.95 (978-1-4218-1841-2(8)) 1st World Publishing, Inc. (1st World Library - Literary Society).

—The High School Pitcher. rev. ed. 2006. 212p. 27.95 (978-1-4218-1743-9(8)); pap. 12.95 (978-1-4218-1843-6(4)) 1st World Publishing, Inc. (1st World Library - Literary Society).

Hancock, Irving H. The High School Freshmen or Dick & Co. 's. 2006. 78.99 (*978-1-4219-9898-5(X)); pap. 72.99 (*978-1-4219-9901-2(3)) IndyPublish.com.

Harcourt School Publishers Staff. The Derby On Level. 3rd ed. 2002. (Trophies Reading Program Ser.). (Illus.). pap. 5.10 (978-0-15-323165-0(3)) Harcourt Schl. Pubs.

—A Good Sport: On Level. 3rd ed. 2002. (Trophies Reading Program Ser.). (Illus.). (J). (gr. 1). pap. 4.10 (978-0-15-322983-1(7)) Harcourt Schl. Pubs.

—A Good Sport Advanced Level. 3rd ed. 2002. (Trophies Reading Program Ser.). (Illus.). pap. 5.10 (978-0-15-323203-9(X)) Harcourt Schl. Pubs.

—A Good Sport 5-Pack, On Level. 3rd ed. 2002. (Trophies Reading Program Ser.). (Illus.). (gr. 1). pap. 20.10 (978-0-15-326833-5(6)) Harcourt Schl. Pubs.

—I Can't Play Baseball: Take-Home Book. 2001. (Collections Ser.). (Illus.). (J). pap. 1.90 (978-0-15-319546-4(0)) Harcourt Schl. Pubs.

—Sports Day. 3rd ed. 2002. (Trophies English Language Learners Ser.). (Illus.). (J). pap. 3.20 (978-0-15-327572-2(3)) Harcourt Schl. Pubs.

Harris, Devon D. Yes I Can. 2006. (Illus.). 48p. (J). (978-0-9764082-4-6(4)) Waterhouse Publishing.

Hartman, Mike. Take Your Dreams to the ICE. 2003. (Illus.). 60p. (YA). per. 9.99 (978-0-9760419-1-7(X)) ThatsMyLife Co.

Hello, Cy! 2007. (J). 14.95 (*978-1-932888-53-9(5)) Mascot Bks., Inc.

Higgins, Kitty. Mushing in Alaska. 2005. 40.00 (*978-1-4108-4228-2(2)) Benchmark Education Co.

Hill, David. Time Out. 2001. 128p. (YA). (gr. 6-9). 15.95 (978-0-8126-2899-9(3)) Cricket Bks.

Hird, Nancy E. & Mishica, Clare. Sports Stories: 3 Fun-to-Read-Aloud Stories with a Message. Estes, Kathleen et al, illus. 1999. (Read-Aloud Stories Ser.). 24p. (J). (ps-3). 5.99 (978-0-7847-0819-4(3) , 03729, Bean Sprouts) Standard Publishing.

Hitchhiking Flat Kid. 2004. (J). ring bd. 4.50 (978-0-9763328-0-0(9) , Flat Kids) Smart Smiles Co., The.

Hoban, Russell. How Tom Beat Captain Najork. Blake, Quentin, illus. 2006. 32p. (J). pap. 7.95 (*978-1-56792-322-3(4)) Godine, David R. Pub.

Hobbs, Will. River Thunder. 1999. (gr. 7-12). lib. bdg. 13.55 (978-0-613-12037-1(X)) Tandem Library Bks.

Hoese, Ray. My Dad Is an Ironman. Steinbach, Coreen, illus. 2004. 32p. 15.00 (978-1-891369-51-3(2)) Breakaway Bks.

Horton, Randy. The Big Sundae. Taylor, Marjorie, illus. 1999. (Take Ten Ser.). 49p. (YA). (gr. 4-12). pap. 3.95 (978-1-58659-034-5(0)) Artesian Pr.

Hughes, Dean. Grand Slam. 1999. (Scrappers Ser.: No. 9). (J). (gr. 3-7). 10.64 (978-0-606-17514-2(8)) Tandem Library Bks.

—Team Picture. 1998. (J). (978-0-606-13840-6(4)) Tandem Library Bks.

Hunter, Dawn. Hit & Run. 1999. (gr. 3-6). lib. bdg. 13.55 (978-0-613-29639-7(7)) Tandem Library Bks.

Hunter, Dawn & Hunter, Karen. Hit & Run. 1999. (Sports Stories Ser.). 92p. (gr. 3-8). (J). (*978-1-55028-673-1(0)); 7.95 (978-1-55028-672-4(2)) Lorimer, James & Co., Ltd., Pubs. CAN. *Dist:* Casemate Pubs. & Bk. Distributors, LLC.

Hutchins, H. J. TJ & the Sports Fanatic. 2006. (Illus.). 144p. (gr. 3-6). pap. 5.95 (978-1-55143-461-2(X)) Orca Bk. Pubs. USA.

I Play for Notre Dame. 2004. (J). bds. (978-0-9749156-0-9(2)) Mandell, Ted.

Impact Books, 10 bks., Set. 2007. (J). (gr. 4-8). 226.00 (*978-1-59889-462-2(5)) Stone Arch Bks.

Jackson, Joan. Elim, the Determined Athlete: A Pups Journey to Be Part of the Team. l.t. ed. 1998. (Illus.). 32p. (gr. 3-6). 9.95 (978-1-888125-32-0(2)) Publication Consultants.

James, Timothy. Coming from Nowhere. 2002. (ENG.). 164p. 22.95 (*978-0-595-74291-2(2)); 162p. (YA). pap. 12.95 (978-0-595-26000-3(4)) iUniverse, Inc. (Writers Club Pr.).

John Brown Publishing Ltd. Diego in Action! Follow the Reader Level II. 2007. (Go, Diego, Go! Ser.). 24p. (J). 24.99 (*978-1-4169-4993-0(3) , Simon Scribbles) Simon & Schuster Children's Publishing.

Johns, Linda. I Can Bowl! 2002. (Rookie Readers Ser.). (J). lib. bdg. 19.00 (978-0-516-22565-4(0) , Children's Pr.) Scholastic Library Publishing.

—I Can Bowl! Caputo, Jim, illus. 2002. (Rookie Readers Ser.). 32p. (J). (gr. 1-2). 19.50 (978-0-516-22374-2(7) , Children's Pr.) Scholastic Library Publishing.

Johnson, Scott. Safe at Second. 2001. 256p. (YA). pap. 6.99 (978-0-698-11877-5(4) , Putnam Juvenile) Penguin Group (USA) Inc.

—Safe at Second. 2001. (J). (978-0-606-21407-0(0)); (gr. 5-8). lib. bdg. 14.15 (978-0-613-36009-8(5)) Tandem Library Bks.

Jones, Jasmine. Coach Carter. 2004. (Amistad Ser.). 144p. (J). (gr. 7 up). pap. 6.99 (978-0-06-077252-9(2)) HarperCollins Pubs.

Jones, Melanie Davis. Balls. Bronson, Linda, illus. 2003. (Rookie Reader Skill Set Ser.). 24p. (J). (gr. k-2). pap. 4.95 (978-0-516-26967-2(4) , Children's Pr.) Scholastic Library Publishing.

—Balls. 2002. (Rookie Readers Ser.). (J). lib. bdg. 16.00 (978-0-516-22532-6(4) , Children's Pr.) Scholastic Library Publishing.

—Balls. Bronson, Linda, illus. 2002. (Rookie Readers Ser.). 23p. (J). (gr. k-2). 19.50 (978-0-516-22596-8(0) , Children's Pr.) Scholastic Library Publishing.

—Balls. 2002. (gr. k-3). lib. bdg. 12.95 (978-0-613-59448-6(7)) Tandem Library Bks.

Kearney, David, illus. Sports Stories. 2003. (Red Hot Reads Ser.). 224p. (YA). (gr. 4-8). pap. 6.95 (978-0-7534-5641-5(9) , Kingfisher) Houghton Mifflin Co. Trade & Reference Div.

Keene, Carolyn. Strike-Out Scare. Jones, Jan Naimo, illus. 2005. 70p. (J). (978-1-4155-7741-7(2) , Aladdin) Simon & Schuster Children's Publishing.

Kehl, Mark. Tournament of Fear: And Other Martial Arts Stories. Artenstein, Michael, ed. 1999. (Sports Shorts Ser.). (Illus.). (J). (gr. 3-7). 96p. 12.95 (978-1-56565-889-9(2) , 08892W); 95p. pap. 5.95 (978-1-56565-949-0(X) , 09499W) Lowell Hse. (Roxbury Park).

Kessler, Leonard. Sport Stories You'll Have a Ball With. 2001. (gr. 3-6). lib. bdg. 11.80 (978-0-613-56618-6(1)) Tandem Library Bks.

Kim, Kenneth H. Half & Half. Taylor, Marjorie, illus. rev. ed. 1999. (Take Ten Ser.). 51p. (YA). (gr. 4-12). pap. 3.95 (978-1-58659-032-1(4)) Artesian Pr.

Kindig, Tess Eileen. Sixth Man Switch. 2000. (Slam Dunk Ser.: Vol. 1). 96p. (J). (gr. 1-4). 4.99 (978-0-570-07016-0(3)) Concordia Publishing Hse.

—Sixth Man Switch. 2000. (gr. k-3). lib. bdg. 13.00 (978-0-613-72839-3(4)) Tandem Library Bks.

Kline, Suzy. Molly Gets Mad. Bluthenthal, Diana Cain, illus. 2001. 1p. (J). (gr. 1-4). 14.99 (978-0-399-23408-8(X) , Putnam Juvenile) Penguin Group (USA) Inc.

Koch, Edward T. & Koch Thaler, Pat. Eddie: Harold's Little Brother. Warhola, James, illus. 2004. 32p. (J). (ps). 16.99 (978-0-399-24210-6(4) , Putnam Juvenile) Penguin Group (USA) Inc.

Krakow, Amy. The Matt & the Morster 60 Sking & Snowboarding. Williams, Steve, illus. 2005. 32p. (J). (gr. k-6). 15.00 (978-0-9715224-2-8(1)) Wagging Tales Publishing.

Krulik, Nancy E. Doug Makes the Team. 1999. (Doug Ser.). (Illus.). 32p. (J). (gr. k-4). 8.99 (978-0-7868-3193-7(6)) Disney Pr.

Lakin, Patricia. Snow Day! Nash, Scott, illus. 2002. 32p. (J). (ps-2). 15.99 (978-0-8037-2642-0(2) , Dial) Penguin Group (USA) Inc.

Lasky, Kathryn. Tumble Bunnies. Hafner, Marylin, illus. 2005. 32p. (J). (gr. k-3). 15.99 (978-0-7636-2265-7(6)) Candlewick Pr.

Layden, Joe. Against the Odds. 1998. (Fast Breaks Ser.: Vol. 4). (Illus.). (J). (gr. 2-5). pap. 3.99 (978-0-590-12082-1(4)) Scholastic, Inc.

—Against the Odds. 1998. (Fast Breaks Ser.). (978-0-606-13377-7(1)) Tandem Library Bks.

Lefevre, Arthur. What Price Life? 2005. reprint ed. pap. 15.95 (978-1-4191-6801-7(0)) Kessinger Publishing, LLC.

Levine, Anna. Running on Eggs. 1999. 128p. (J). (gr. 5-9). 15.95 (978-0-8126-2875-3(6)) Cricket Bks.

Lewman, David. Bottoms Up! Jokes from Bikini Bottom. Meurer, Caleb, illus. 2002. (SpongeBob SquarePants Ser.). 16p. (J). pap. 5.99 (978-0-689-85181-0(2) , Simon Spotlight/Nickelodeon) Simon & Schuster Children's Publishing.

Ley, Mary. Tri-Son: The Little Triathlete. Ley, Mary, illus. 2003. per. (978-0-9707547-1-4(X)) Woodburn Graphics, Inc.

Lionni, Leo. Swimmy. Lionni, Leo, illus. 2002. (Illus.). (J). 13.83 (978-1-4046-6222-3(7)) Book Wholesalers, Inc.

Little, Kimberley Griffiths. Enchanted Runner. 1999. (Avon Camelot Bks.). 149p. (J). (gr. 5-7). 15.00 (978-0-380-97623-2(4)) HarperCollins Pubs.

Lohans, Alison. Skateboard Kids. 1999. (Early Chapters Bks.). 78p. (J). (gr. 1-4). pap. 4.95 (978-1-896184-64-7(2)) Roussan Pubs., Inc./Roussan Editeur, Inc. CAN. *Dist:* Orca Bk. Pubs. USA.

London, Jonathan. Froggy Plays Soccer. Remkiewicz, Frank, illus. 2001. 32p. (J). (ps-3). pap. 5.99 (978-0-14-056809-7(3) , Puffin) Penguin Group (USA) Inc.

Lowell House Juvenile Staff. Million Dollar Bucket: And Other Stories about Your Favorite Sports. 2000. (Sports Shorts Ser.). (Illus.). 160p. (J). (gr. 3-7). pap. 5.95 (978-0-7373-0433-6(2) , 04332W, Roxbury Park) Lowell Hse.

Lynch, Chris. Slot Machine. 2003. 21.75 (978-0-8446-7249-6(1)) Smith, Peter Pub., Inc.

MacDonald, Kelly. They Shoot! They Score! Life's Lessons on Ice. Luca, Bogdan, illus. 2005. 32p. 9.99 (978-0-9736893-0-3(7)) MacDonald, Kelly CAN. *Dist:* Hushion Hse. Publishing, Ltd.

Maddox, Jake. On the Line. Tiffany, Sean, illus. 2007. (Jake Maddox Sports Story Ser.). 65p. (J). (gr. 4-8). lib. bdg. 21.26 (978-1-59889-062-4(X)) Stone Arch Bks.

Maddox, Jake. Soccer Shootout. Tiffany, Sean, illus. 2008. (J). lib. bdg. ***(978-1-59889-844-6(2))*** Stone Arch Bks.

Maiocco, Chris & Maiocco, Kimberly. Things My Father Taught Me Through Sports. . . Playing the Game of Baseball: Playing the Game of Baseball. Cox, Tom, illus. 2003. 20p. (J). 12.99 (978-0-9720417-0-6(2) , 0-9720417-0-2) His Kids Publishing, Inc.

Marsh, Carole. The Castaway Cheerleaders. 2006. 64p. (gr. 2-4). 14.95 ***(978-0-635-06224-6(0));*** pap. 3.99 ***(978-0-635-06218-5(6))*** Gallopade International.

Martin, Ann M. Karen's Field Day. 1999. (Baby-Sitters Little Sister Ser.: No. 108). 112p. (J). (gr. 3-7). pap. 3.99 (978-0-590-50060-9(0)) Scholastic, Inc.

Mayer, Mercer. Play Ball. 2002. (Little Critter Ser.). (Illus.). 24p. (J). (ps-k). pap. 3.95 (978-1-57768-803-7(1)) School Specialty Publishing.

—Play Ball. 2001. (gr. k-3). lib. bdg. 11.80 (978-0-613-86831-0(5)) Tandem Library Bks.

McBride, Earvin, Jr. The Mice. McBride, Earvin, Jr., illus. unabr. ed. 2002. (Earvin MacBride's Fun Fun Lovable Cartoons Ser.). (Illus.). 123p. (J). (gr. 7-12). pap. 3.95 (978-1-892511-04-1(5)) MacBride, E. J. Pubn., Inc.

McDonnell, Vincent. Race Against Time. 2005. (SPA.). 96p. pap. 10.95 (978-1-903464-62-5(5)) Collins Pr., The IRL. *Dist:* Dufour Editions, Inc.

McEwan, Jamie. Willy the Scrub. Kennedy, Victor, illus. 2004. (Junior Library Guild Selection Ser.). 64p. (J). (gr. 2-5). 14.95 (978-1-58196-010-5(7)) Darby Creek Publishing.

McKay, Sharon E. Rodney's Race. 2001. (Welcome to Truck Town Ser.). (Illus.). 40p. (J). pap. 6.95 (978-1-894454-03-2(0)) Balmur Entertainment, Ltd. CAN. *Dist:* General Distribution Services, Inc.

McKissack, Robert L. Try Your Best. Cepeda, Joe, illus. 2004. (Green Light Readers Level 2 Ser.). 24p. (J). 11.95 (978-0-15-205089-4(2)); pap. 3.95 (978-0-15-205090-0(6)) Harcourt Children's Bks. (Green Light Readers).

—Try Your Best. 2004. (gr. k-3). lib. bdg. 11.80 (978-0-613-81420-1(7)) Tandem Library Bks.

McMullan, Kate. Go for the Gold, Atlanta! 2003. (Myth-o-Mania Ser.: No. 8). (Illus.). 160p. (J). 9.99 (978-0-7868-0864-9(0)) Hyperion Bks. for Children.

McOmber, Rachel B., ed. McOmber Phonics Storybooks: A Game for Champions. rev. ed. (Illus.). (J). (978-0-944991-68-8(8)) Swift Learning Resources.

Morningstar, Jeremy. My Own Special Angel. 2005. 24p. 7.00 (978-1-4116-6574-3(0)) Lulu.com.

Myers, Walter Dean. Game. 2008. 240p. (J). 16.99 ***(978-0-06-058294-4(4));*** lib. bdg. 17.89 ***(978-0-06-058295-1(2))*** HarperCollins Pubs. (HarperTeen).

Napoli, Donna Jo & Furrow, Robert. Sly the Sleuth & the Sports Mysteries. Maione, Heather Harms, illus. 2006. 128p. (J). 15.99 (978-0-8037-2994-0(4) , Dial) Penguin Group (USA) Inc.

Neuhaus, David. His Finest Hour. 2004. (Illus.). 32p. 14.95 (978-1-931382-49-6(2)) VeloPress.

New Coach Blues. 2003. (Illus.). pap. 5.60 (978-0-7398-7509-4(4)) Steck-Vaughn.

Nishiyama, Yuriko. Rebound, 11 vols. 2003. (Illus.). 192p. Vol. 1. (gr. 2 up). pap. 9.99 (978-1-931514-02-6(X)); Vol. 2. rev. ed. (gr. 8 up). pap. 9.99 (978-1-59182-074-1(X)); Vol. 3. 3rd rev. ed. (gr. 2 up). pap. 9.99 (978-1-59182-221-9(1)); Vol. 4. 4th rev. ed. pap. 9.99 (978-1-59182-222-6(X)); Vol. 5. 5th rev. ed. pap. 9.99 (978-1-59182-223-3(8)) TOKYOPOP, Inc. (Tokyopop Adult).

—Rebound, 11 vols., Vol. 6. Nishiyama, Yuriko, illus. 6th rev. ed. 2004. (Illus.). 192p. pap. 9.99 (978-1-59182-530-2(X) , Tokyopop Adult) TOKYOPOP, Inc.

—Rebound, 11 vols. 2004. (Illus.). 192p. Vol. 7. 7th rev. ed. pap. 9.99 (978-1-59182-531-9(8)); Vol. 8. 8th rev. ed. pap. 9.99 (978-1-59182-532-6(6)); Vol. 9. 9th rev. ed. pap. 9.99 (978-1-59182-533-3(4)) TOKYOPOP, Inc. (Tokyopop Adult).

Nishiyama, Yuriko, creator. Rebound, 11 vols. 2004. (Teen Ser.). (Illus.). 192p. Vol. 10. 10th rev. ed. pap. 9.99 (978-1-59182-534-0(2)); Vol. 11. rev. ed. (gr. 7 up). pap. 9.99 (978-1-59182-535-7(0)) TOKYOPOP, Inc. (Tokyopop Adult).

Offit, Sidney. Soupbone. 2002. (J). per. 12.95 (978-0-931761-76-8(X)) Beckham Pubns. Group, Inc.

Olivas, Daniel. Benjamin & Word Benjamin Y la Palabra. (SPA & ENG., Illus.). 32p. 15.95 (978-1-55885-413-0(4) , Piñata Books) Arte Publico Pr.

Olsen, Mary-Kate. Switching Goals. 2000. (gr. 3-6). lib. bdg. 13.00 (978-0-613-27146-2(7)) Tandem Library Bks.

Olsen, Mary-Kate & Olsen, Ashley. Mary-Kate & Ashley Switching Goals. 2000. (Mary-Kate & Ashley Ser.). 128p. (gr. 2-4). mass mkt. 4.99 (978-0-06-107603-9(1) , Harper Entertainment) HarperCollins Pubs.

Paratore, Coleen. Mack McGinn's Big Win. 2007. 192p. (J). (gr. 4-7). 15.99 ***(978-1-4169-1613-0(X)*** , Simon & Schuster Children's Publishing) Simon & Schuster Children's Publishing.

Pasnak, William. Sink or Swim. 1999. (gr. 7-12). lib. bdg. 13.55 (978-0-613-18221-8(9)) Tandem Library Bks.

Pee-Wee T-Ball. 2003. (J). per. (978-1-57657-942-8(5)) Paradise Pr., Inc.

Peers, Judi. Sayonara Sharks. 2001. (Sports Stories Ser.). (Illus.). 84p. (gr. 3-8). (J). ***(978-1-55028-731-8(1));*** 7.95 (978-1-55028-730-1(3)) Lorimer, James & Co., Ltd., Pubs. CAN. *Dist:* Casemate Pubs. & Bk. Distributors, LLC.

Penner, Lucille Recht. Slowpoke. Fiammenghi, Gioia, illus. 2001. (Math Matters Ser.). 32p. (J). (gr. 1-3). pap. 4.95 (978-1-57565-108-8(4)) Kane Pr., The.

—Slowpoke. 2001. (gr. k-3). lib. bdg. 12.95 (978-0-613-39363-8(5)) Tandem Library Bks.

Petersen, P. J. White Water. 1999. (978-0-606-16710-9(2)) Tandem Library Bks.

Powell, Randy. The Whistling Toilets. 2001. (Illus.). (J). (978-0-606-21523-7(9)) Tandem Library Bks.

Preller, James. The Case of the Great Sled Race. 1999. (Jigsaw Jones Mystery Ser.: No. 8). (Illus.). (J). (gr. 1-4). 10.79 (978-0-606-18527-1(5)) Tandem Library Bks.

Preller, James & Preller, Jimmy. The Great Sled Race. Alley, R. W., illus. 2001. (Jigsaw Jones Mystery Ser.: No. 8). 80p. (J). (gr. 1-4). pap. 3.99 (978-0-439-11427-1(6) , Scholastic Paperbacks) Scholastic, Inc.

Press, Skip. Knucklehead. Taylor, Marjorie, illus. rev. ed. 1999. (Take Ten Ser.). 50p. (YA). (gr. 4-12). pap. 3.95 (978-1-58659-033-8(2)) Artesian Pr.

—Knucklehead. 2000. (gr. 7-12). lib. bdg. 11.80 (978-0-613-51052-3(6)) Tandem Library Bks.

Pruett, Scott & Pruett, Judy. Twelve Little Race Cars. Eytchison, Glen, ed. Dietz, Mike & Toft, Kevin, illus. 1999. 32p. (J). (ps-3). 12.95 (978-0-9670600-0-2(1)) Word Weaver Bks., Inc.

Rayner, Robert. Just for Kicks. 2004. (Sports Stories Ser.). 120p. (J). (gr. 3-8). 7.95 (978-1-55028-824-7(5)); ***(978-1-55028-825-4(3))*** Lorimer, James & Co., Ltd., Pubs. CAN. *Dist:* Casemate Pubs. & Bk. Distributors, LLC.

Rayner, Robert J. Walker's Runners. 2002. (gr. 3-6). lib. bdg. 13.55 (978-0-613-78323-1(9)) Tandem Library Bks.

Redmond, Diane. Penalty. 2000. (Illus.). 62p. (J). pap. 6.95 (978-0-552-54559-4(7)) Transworld Publishers Ltd. GBR. *Dist:* Trafalgar Square Publishing.

Regan, Peter. Riverside vs. City Slickers. 1998. (Illus.). 128p. pap. 8.95 (978-1-901737-07-3(1)) Anvil Bks., Ltd. IRL. *Dist:* Dufour Editions, Inc.

Reilly, Matthew. Crash Course. Raimondi, Pablo, illus. 2006. (Hover Car Racer Ser.). 240p. (J). pap. 2.99 (978-1-4169-2503-3(1) , Aladdin) Simon & Schuster Children's Publishing.

Reiser, Lynn W. The Lost Ball/La Pelota Perdida. Infante, M. J., tr. Reiser, Lynn W., illus. 2002. (ENG & SPA., Illus.). 32p. (J). 15.99 (978-0-06-029763-3(8)) HarperCollins Pubs.

Rex, Michael. Dunk Skunk. Rex, Michael, illus. 2005. (Illus.). 32p. (J). 10.99 (978-0-399-24281-6(3) , Putnam Juvenile) Penguin Group (USA) Inc.

Richardson, Charisse K. The Real Slam Dunk. Richardson, Charisse K. & Palmer, Charly, illus. 2002. 52p. (J). (gr. 3-6). pap. 7.99 (978-0-615-11989-2(1)); lib. bdg. 15.95 (978-0-9720689-0-1(2)) EnRich Communications.

—The Real Slam Dunk. Richardson, Charisse K. & Nelson, Kadir, illus. 2005. 64p. (J). (gr. 2-5). 15.99 (978-0-8037-3050-2(0) , Dial) Penguin Group (USA) Inc.

—The Real Slam Dunk. Nelson, Kadir, illus. 2005. 80p. (J). (gr. 2-5). pap. 4.99 (978-0-14-240212-2(5) , Puffin) Penguin Group (USA) Inc.

Rivers, Camilla Reghelini. Shut-Out! 2000. (Sports Stories Ser.). 108p. (gr. 3-8). ***(978-1-55028-669-4(2));*** (Illus.). 7.95 (978-1-55028-667-0(6)) Lorimer, James & Co., Ltd., Pubs. CAN. *Dist:* Casemate Pubs. & Bk. Distributors, LLC.

Roberts, Kristi. My Thirteenth Season. rev. ed. 2005. (Illus.). 160p. (J). 15.95 (978-0-8050-7495-6(3) , Holt, Henry & Co. Bks. For Young Readers) Holt, Henry & Co.

Rocking & Rolling Along, 6 vols., Set B. 32p. (gr. 1-3). 26.50 (978-0-7802-8053-3(9)) Wright Group, The.

Rosseau, Paul. Docteur Soccer. Mongeau, Marc, illus. 2002. (Roman Jeunesse Ser.). (FRE.). 96p. (J). (gr. 4-7). pap. (978-2-89021-582-5(2)) Diffusion du livre Mirabel.

Rosselson, Leon. Gordon & the Giant Killers. (Illus.). 127p. (J). pap. 7.99 (978-0-340-64072-2(3) , Hodder & Stoughton) Hodder General Publishing Division GBR. *Dist:* Trafalgar Square Publishing.

Rud, Jeff. High & Inside. 2006. 176p. (gr. 3-7). pap. 7.95 (978-1-55143-532-9(2)) Orca Bk. Pubs. USA.

Russo, David Anson. Go for It! Sports Treasure Hunt. 1998. (J). pap. 7.95 (978-0-671-86804-8(7) , Simon & Schuster Children's Publishing) Simon & Schuster Children's Publishing.

Sanchez, Juanvi. Ocho. Sanchez, Juanvi, illus. 2001. (SPA., Illus.). 12p. (J). (ps). (978-84-348-7851-8(8)) SM Ediciones ESP. *Dist:* Lectorum Pubns., Inc.

Scheving, Magnus & Artful Doodlers Limited Staff. It's Sports Day! 2006. (LazyTown Ser.). (Illus.). 16p. (J). pap. 4.99 (978-1-4169-0721-3(1) , Simon Spotlight/Nickelodeon) Simon & Schuster Children's Publishing.

Scholastic, Inc. Staff. Duel Masters Bk. 3: Winning Streak. 2005. (Duel Masters Ser.). (Illus.). 64p. (J). 3.99 (978-0-439-69111-6(7) , Scholastic Paperbacks) Scholastic, Inc.

Schraff, Anne. The Phantom Falcon. Taylor, Marjorie, illus. rev. ed. 1999. (Take Ten Ser.). 51p. (YA). (gr. 4-12). pap. 3.95 (978-1-58659-031-4(6)) Artesian Pr.

Schubert, Leda. Winnie Plays Ball. Benedict, William, illus. 2000. (Brand New Readers Ser.). 1p. (J). (ps-2). pap. 4.99 (978-0-7636-0673-2(1)) Candlewick Pr.

Scott, Kieran. Brunettes Strike Back. 2006. 256p. (YA). (gr. 5). 16.99 (978-0-399-24493-3(X) , Putnam Juvenile) Penguin Group (USA) Inc.

Seastar Books, creator. Sports Stories You'll Have a Ball With. 2001. (Reading Rainbow Readers Ser.). (Illus.). 64p. (J). (ps-ps). lib. bdg. 10.79 (978-0-606-21451-3(8)) Tandem Library Bks.

Shaw, Mary. Brady Brady & the Big Mistake, 11vols. Temple, Chuck, illus. l.t. ed. 2004. 32p. (J). per. (978-0-9735557-4-5(2)) Brady Brady, Inc.

—Brady Brady & the Big Mistake. Temple, Chuck, illus. 2002. 32p. (ps-3). 4.95 (978-0-7737-6304-3(X)) Stoddart Kids CAN. *Dist:* Fitzhenry & Whiteside, Ltd.

—Brady Brady & the Great Exchange, 11 vols. Temple, Chuck, illus. l.t. ed. 2003. 32p. (J). per. (978-0-9735557-5-2(0)) Brady Brady, Inc.

—Brady Brady & the Great Exchange. Temple, Chuck, illus. 2002. 32p. (gr. k-3). 4.95 (978-0-7737-6303-6(1)) Stoddart Kids CAN. *Dist:* Fitzhenry & Whiteside, Ltd.

—Brady Brady & the Great Exchange. 2003. (gr. k-3). lib. bdg. 12.95 (978-0-613-81881-0(4)) Tandem Library Bks.

Shaw, Michael. Slider: The Leo Butterburger Story. 2004. per. 14.95 (978-0-9747666-4-5(X)) American Retrospects, LLC.

Shields, Carol Diggory. Sports. Junakovic, Svjetlan, illus. 2001. (Animagicals Ser.). 32p. (J). 9.95 (978-1-929766-28-4(9)) Handprint Bks.

Shulman, Mark. Super Sports. Harris, Jenny B., illus. 2003. (Funny Fingers Ser.). 14p. (J). bds. 3.95 (978-1-4027-0706-3(1)) Sterling Publishing Co., Inc.

Siebold, Jan. Rope Burn. 2000. (978-0-606-18775-6(8)) Tandem Library Bks.

Sis, Peter. Madlenka's Soccer Ball. 2005. (J). (978-0-375-82852-2(4)); lib. bdg. (978-0-375-92852-9(9)) Random Hse., Inc.

Skateboard City. 2002. (J). pap. (978-0-7398-5069-5(5)) Steck-Vaughn.

Skillchecks for Sports. 2005. (Double Fastback Ser.). (J). (gr. 6-12). 64p. pap. 5.95 (978-0-13-024471-0(6)); 32p. pap. 5.95 (978-0-13-024454-3(6)) Globe Fearon Educational Publishing.

Slam Dunk. Date not set. 9.95 (978-0-89868-289-2(4)); pap. 3.95 (978-0-89868-288-5(6)) ARO Publishing Co.

Smith, Stephen & Caldwell, Lise. Downhill Challenge. 2006. (Game on for Girls Ser.). 128p. (J). pap. 5.99 (978-0-7847-1735-6(4) , 42145) Standard Publishing.

Sporteller Staff. Race to Win (Auto Racing) 64p. (YA). (gr. 6-12). pap. 10.95 (978-0-8224-6479-2(9)) Globe Fearon Educational Publishing.

Sports Day: Individual Title Six-Packs. (ps-2). 23.00 (978-0-7635-8804-5(0)) Rigby Education.

Sports Double Fastbacks, 10 bks. (YA). (gr. 6-12). pap. 59.95 (978-0-8224-2389-8(8)) Globe Fearon Educational Publishing.

Sports Stories Theme Pack, 3 vols. 2001. (Illus.). (J). (gr. 3-5). 11.95 (978-1-56762-145-7(7)) Modern Learning Pr.

Standish, Burt L. Dick Merriwell at Fardale. Rudman, Jack, ed. 2003. (Frank Merriwell Ser.). 29.95 (978-0-8373-9376-6(0)) Merriwell, Frank Inc.

—Dick Merriwell, Freshman. Rudman, Jack, ed. 2003. (Frank Merriwell Ser.). pap. 9.95 (978-0-8373-9142-7(3)) Merriwell, Frank Inc.

—Dick Merriwell in the Wilds. Rudman, Jack, ed. 2003. (Frank Merriwell Ser.). pap. 9.95 (978-0-8373-9167-0(9)) Merriwell, Frank Inc.

—Dick Merriwell on the Gridiron. Rudman, Jack, ed. 2003. (Frank Merriwell Ser.). pap. 9.95 (978-0-8373-9102-1(4)) Merriwell, Frank Inc.

—Dick Merriwell, the Wizard. Rudman, Jack, ed. 2003. (Frank Merriwell Ser.). pap. 9.95 (978-0-8373-9126-7(1)) Merriwell, Frank Inc.

—Dick Merriwell's Ability. Rudman, Jack, ed. 2003. (Frank Merriwell Ser.). 29.95 (978-0-8373-9390-2(6)); pap. 9.95 (978-0-8373-9090-1(7)) Merriwell, Frank Inc.

—Dick Merriwell's Assurance. Rudman, Jack, ed. 2003. (Frank Merriwell Ser.). pap. 9.95 (978-0-8373-9109-0(1)) Merriwell, Frank Inc.

—Dick Merriwell's Backers. Rudman, Jack, ed. 2003. (Frank Merriwell Ser.). pap. 9.95 (978-0-8373-9149-6(0)) Merriwell, Frank Inc.

—Dick Merriwell's Backstop. Rudman, Jack, ed. 2003. (Frank Merriwell Ser.). 29.95 (978-0-8373-9396-4(5)); pap. 9.95 (978-0-8373-9096-3(6)) Merriwell, Frank Inc.

—Dick Merriwell's Best Work. Rudman, Jack, ed. 2003. (Frank Merriwell Ser.). pap. 9.95 (978-0-8373-9150-2(4)) Merriwell, Frank Inc.

—Dick Merriwell's Black Star. Rudman, Jack, ed. 2003. (Frank Merriwell Ser.). pap. 9.95 (978-0-8373-9158-8(X)) Merriwell, Frank Inc.

—Dick Merriwell's Cleverness. Rudman, Jack, ed. 2003. (Frank Merriwell Ser.). pap. 9.95 (978-0-8373-9124-3(5)) Merriwell, Frank Inc.

—Dick Merriwell's Close Call. Rudman, Jack, ed. 2003. (Frank Merriwell Ser.). pap. 9.95 (978-0-8373-9156-4(3)) Merriwell, Frank Inc.

—Dick Merriwell's Dare. Rudman, Jack, ed. 2003. (Frank Merriwell Ser.). pap. 9.95 (978-0-8373-9136-6(9)) Merriwell, Frank Inc.

—Dick Merriwell's Dash. Rudman, Jack, ed. 2003. (Frank Merriwell Ser.). 29.95 (978-0-8373-9389-6(2)); pap. 9.95 (978-0-8373-9089-5(3)) Merriwell, Frank Inc.

—Dick Merriwell's Day. Rudman, Jack, ed. 2003. (Frank Merriwell Ser.). pap. 9.95 (978-0-8373-9114-4(8)) Merriwell, Frank Inc.

—Dick Merriwell's Debt. Rudman, Jack, ed. 2003. (Frank Merriwell Ser.). pap. 9.95 (978-0-8373-9152-6(0)) Merriwell, Frank Inc.

—Dick Merriwell's Defense. Rudman, Jack, ed. 2003. (Frank Merriwell Ser.). 29.95 (978-0-8373-9392-6(2)); pap. 9.95 (978-0-8373-9092-5(3)) Merriwell, Frank Inc.

—Dick Merriwell's Delivery. Rudman, Jack, ed. 2003. (Frank Merriwell Ser.). 29.95 (978-0-8373-9384-1(1)); pap. 9.95 (978-0-8373-9084-0(2)) Merriwell, Frank Inc.

—Dick Merriwell's Diamond. Rudman, Jack, ed. 2003. (Frank Merriwell Ser.). 29.95 (978-0-8373-9387-2(6)); pap. 9.95 (978-0-8373-9087-1(7)) Merriwell, Frank Inc.

—Dick Merriwell's Disguise. Rudman, Jack, ed. 2003. (Frank Merriwell Ser.). pap. 9.95 (978-0-8373-9103-8(2)) Merriwell, Frank Inc.

—Dick Merriwell's Distrust. Rudman, Jack, ed. 2003. (Frank Merriwell Ser.). pap. 9.95 (978-0-8373-9151-9(2)) Merriwell, Frank Inc.

—Dick Merriwell's Downfall. Rudman, Jack, ed. 2003. (Frank Merriwell Ser.). pap. 9.95 (978-0-8373-9116-8(4)) Merriwell, Frank Inc.

—Dick Merriwell's Example. Rudman, Jack, ed. 2003. (Frank Merriwell Ser.). pap. 9.95 (978-0-8373-9166-3(0)) Merriwell, Frank Inc.

—Dick Merriwell's Five. Rudman, Jack, ed. 2003. (Frank Merriwell Ser.). pap. 9.95 (978-0-8373-9130-4(X)) Merriwell, Frank Inc.

—Dick Merriwell's Glory. Rudman, Jack, ed. 2003. (Frank Merriwell Ser.). 29.95 (978-0-8373-9377-3(9)); pap. 9.95 (978-0-8373-9077-2(X)) Merriwell, Frank Inc.

—Dick Merriwell's Grit. Rudman, Jack, ed. 2003. (Frank Merriwell Ser.). pap. 9.95 (978-0-8373-9108-3(3)) Merriwell, Frank Inc.

—Dick Merriwell's Home Run. Rudman, Jack, ed. 2003. (Frank Merriwell Ser.). pap. 9.95 (978-0-8373-9135-9(0)) Merriwell, Frank Inc.

—Dick Merriwell's Honors. Rudman, Jack, ed. 2003. (Frank Merriwell Ser.). pap. 9.95 (978-0-8373-9173-1(3)) Merriwell, Frank Inc.

—Dick Merriwell's Influence. Rudman, Jack, ed. 2003. (Frank Merriwell Ser.). pap. 9.95 (978-0-8373-9141-0(5)) Merriwell, Frank Inc.

—Dick Merriwell's Joke. Rudman, Jack, ed. 2003. (Frank Merriwell Ser.). pap. 9.95 (978-0-8373-9144-1(X)) Merriwell, Frank Inc.

—Dick Merriwell's Long Slide. Rudman, Jack, ed. 2003. (Frank Merriwell Ser.). pap. 9.95 (978-0-8373-9110-6(5)) Merriwell, Frank Inc.

—Dick Merriwell's Magnetism. Rudman, Jack, ed. 2003. (Frank Merriwell Ser.). pap. 9.95 (978-0-8373-9148-9(2)) Merriwell, Frank Inc.

—Dick Merriwell's Marked Money. Rudman, Jack, ed. 2003. (Frank Merriwell Ser.). pap. 9.95 (978-0-8373-9100-7(8)) Merriwell, Frank Inc.

—Dick Merriwell's Mastery. Rudman, Jack, ed. 2003. (Frank Merriwell Ser.). pap. 9.95 (978-0-8373-9153-3(9)) Merriwell, Frank Inc.

—Dick Merriwell's Model. Rudman, Jack, ed. 2003. (Frank Merriwell Ser.). 29.95 (978-0-8373-9393-3(0)); pap. 9.95 (978-0-8373-9093-2(1)) Merriwell, Frank Inc.

—Dick Merriwell's Mystery. Rudman, Jack, ed. 2003. (Frank Merriwell Ser.). 29.95 (978-0-8373-9394-0(9)); pap. 9.95 (978-0-8373-9094-9(X)) Merriwell, Frank Inc.

—Dick Merriwell's Narrow Escape. Rudman, Jack, ed. 2003. (Frank Merriwell Ser.). 29.95 (978-0-8373-9380-3(9)); pap. 9.95 (978-0-8373-9080-2(X)) Merriwell, Frank Inc.

—Dick Merriwell's Persistence. Rudman, Jack, ed. 2003. (Frank Merriwell Ser.). pap. 9.95 (978-0-8373-9113-7(X)) Merriwell, Frank Inc.

—Dick Merriwell's Polo Team. Rudman, Jack, ed. 2003. (Frank Merriwell Ser.). pap. 9.95 (978-0-8373-9132-8(6)) Merriwell, Frank Inc.

—Dick Merriwell's Pranks. Rudman, Jack, ed. 2003. (Frank Merriwell Ser.). pap. 9.95 (978-0-8373-9120-5(2)) Merriwell, Frank Inc.

—Dick Merriwell's Promise. Rudman, Jack, ed. 2003. (Frank Merriwell Ser.). 29.95 (978-0-8373-9378-0(7)); pap. 9.95 (978-0-8373-9078-9(8)) Merriwell, Frank Inc.

—Dick Merriwell's Racket. Rudman, Jack, ed. 2003. (Frank Merriwell Ser.). 29.95 (978-0-8373-9381-0(7)); pap. 9.95 (978-0-8373-9081-9(8)) Merriwell, Frank Inc.

—Dick Merriwell's Regret. Rudman, Jack, ed. 2003. (Frank Merriwell Ser.). pap. 9.95 (978-0-8373-9147-2(4)) Merriwell, Frank Inc.

—Dick Merriwell's Reputation. Rudman, Jack, ed. 2003. (Frank Merriwell Ser.). pap. 9.95 (978-0-8373-9171-7(7)) Merriwell, Frank Inc.

—Dick Merriwell's Rescue. Rudman, Jack, ed. 2003. (Frank Merriwell Ser.). 29.95 (978-0-8373-9379-7(5)); pap. 9.95 (978-0-8373-9079-6(6)) Merriwell, Frank Inc.

—Dick Merriwell's Resource. Rudman, Jack, ed. 2003. (Frank Merriwell Ser.). pap. 9.95 (978-0-8373-9129-8(6)) Merriwell, Frank Inc.

—Dick Merriwell's Return. Rudman, Jack, ed. 2003. (Frank Merriwell Ser.). pap. 9.95 (978-0-8373-9128-1(8)) Merriwell, Frank Inc.

—Dick Merriwell's Revenge. Rudman, Jack, ed. 2003. (Frank Merriwell Ser.). 29.95 (978-0-8373-9382-7(5)); pap. 9.95 (978-0-8373-9082-6(6)) Merriwell, Frank Inc.

—Dick Merriwell's Ruse. Rudman, Jack, ed. 2003. (Frank Merriwell Ser.). 29.95 (978-0-8373-9383-4(3)); pap. 9.95 (978-0-8373-9083-3(4)) Merriwell, Frank Inc.

—Dick Merriwell's Stanchness. Rudman, Jack, ed. 2003. (Frank Merriwell Ser.). pap. 9.95 (978-0-8373-9161-8(X)) Merriwell, Frank Inc.

—Dick Merriwell's Stand. Rudman, Jack, ed. 2003. (Frank Merriwell Ser.). pap. 9.95 (978-0-8373-9163-2(6)) Merriwell, Frank Inc.

—Dick Merriwell's Staying Power. Rudman, Jack, ed. 2003. (Frank Merriwell Ser.). pap. 9.95 (978-0-8373-9143-4(1)) Merriwell, Frank Inc.

—Dick Merriwell's Stroke. Rudman, Jack, ed. 2003. (Frank Merriwell Ser.). pap. 9.95 (978-0-8373-9127-4(X)) Merriwell, Frank Inc.

—Dick Merriwell's Team Mate. Rudman, Jack, ed. 2003. (Frank Merriwell Ser.). pap. 9.95 (978-0-8373-9138-0(5)) Merriwell, Frank Inc.

—Dick Merriwell's Test. Rudman, Jack, ed. 2003. (Frank Merriwell Ser.). pap. 9.95 (978-0-8373-9104-5(0)) Merriwell, Frank Inc.

—Frank Merriwell as Coach. Rudman, Jack, ed. 2003. (Frank Merriwell Ser.). 29.95 (978-0-8373-9372-8(8)); pap. 9.95 (978-0-8373-9072-7(9)) Merriwell, Frank Inc.

—Frank Merriwell Facing His Foes. Rudman, Jack, ed. 2003. (Frank Merriwell Ser.). pap. 9.95 (978-0-8373-9160-1(1)) Merriwell, Frank Inc.

—Frank Merriwell in Camp. Rudman, Jack, ed. 2003. (Frank Merriwell Ser.). (YA). (gr. 9 up). 29.95 (978-0-8373-9324-7(8)); pap. 9.95 (978-0-8373-9024-6(9) , FM-024) Merriwell, Frank Inc.

—Frank Merriwell in Maine. Rudman, Jack, ed. 2003. (Frank Merriwell Ser.). (YA). (gr. 9 up). 29.95 (978-0-8373-9328-5(0)); pap. 9.95 (978-0-8373-9028-4(1) , FM-028) Merriwell, Frank Inc.

—Frank Merriwell's Alarm. Rudman, Jack, ed. 2003. (Frank Merriwell Ser.). (YA). (gr. 9 up). 29.95 (978-0-8373-9316-2(7)); pap. 9.95 (978-0-8373-9016-1(8) , FM-016) Merriwell, Frank Inc.

—Frank Merriwell's Athletes. Rudman, Jack, ed. 2003. (Frank Merriwell Ser.). (YA). (gr. 9 up). 29.95 (978-0-8373-9317-9(5)); pap. 9.95 (978-0-8373-9017-8(6) , FM-017) Merriwell, Frank Inc.

—Frank Merriwell's Champions. Rudman, Jack, ed. 2003. (Frank Merriwell Ser.). (YA). (gr. 9 up). 29.95 (978-0-8373-9319-3(1)); pap. 9.95 (978-0-8373-9019-2(2) , FM-019) Merriwell, Frank Inc.

—Frank Merriwell's Chase. Rudman, Jack, ed. 2003. (Frank Merriwell Ser.). (YA). (gr. 9 up). 29.95 (978-0-8373-9327-8(2)); pap. 9.95 (978-0-8373-9027-7(3) , FM-027) Merriwell, Frank Inc.

—Frank Merriwell's Courage. Rudman, Jack, ed. 2003. (Frank Merriwell Ser.). (YA). (gr. 9 up). 29.95 (978-0-8373-9314-8(0)); pap. 9.95 (978-0-8373-9014-7(1) , FM-014) Merriwell, Frank Inc.

—Frank Merriwell's Double Shot. Rudman, Jack, ed. 2003. (Frank Merriwell Ser.). 29.95 (978-0-8373-9347-6(7)); pap. 9.95 (978-0-8373-9047-5(8)) Merriwell, Frank Inc.

—Frank Merriwell's Hard Luck. Rudman, Jack, ed. 2003. (Frank Merriwell Ser.). 29.95 (978-0-8373-9332-2(9)); pap. 9.95 (978-0-8373-9032-1(X)) Merriwell, Frank Inc.

—Frank Merriwell's Honor. Rudman, Jack, ed. 2003. (Frank Merriwell Ser.). 29.95 (978-0-8373-9386-5(8)); pap. 9.95 (978-0-8373-9086-4(9)) Merriwell, Frank Inc.

—Frank Merriwell's Leaguers. Rudman, Jack, ed. 2003. (Frank Merriwell Ser.). pap. 9.95 (978-0-8373-9139-7(3)) Merriwell, Frank Inc.

—Frank Merriwell's Lesson. Rudman, Jack, ed. 2003. (Frank Merriwell Ser.). pap. 9.95 (978-0-8373-9170-0(9)) Merriwell, Frank Inc.

—Frank Merriwell's Luck. Rudman, Jack, ed. 2003. (Frank Merriwell Ser.). 29.95 (978-0-8373-9356-8(6)); pap. 9.95 (978-0-8373-9056-7(7)) Merriwell, Frank Inc.

—Frank Merriwell's Marvel. Rudman, Jack, ed. 2003. (Frank Merriwell Ser.). 29.95 (978-0-8373-9374-2(4)); pap. 9.95 (978-0-8373-9074-1(5)) Merriwell, Frank Inc.

—Frank Merriwell's Mascot. Rudman, Jack, ed. 2003. (Frank Merriwell Ser.). 29.95 (978-0-8373-9357-5(4)); pap. 9.95 (978-0-8373-9057-4(5)) Merriwell, Frank Inc.

—Frank Merriwell's New Comedian. Rudman, Jack, ed. 2003. (Frank Merriwell Ser.). 29.95 (978-0-8373-9340-7(X)); pap. 29.95 (978-0-8373-9040-6(0)) Merriwell, Frank Inc.

—Frank Merriwell's Nomads. Rudman, Jack, ed. 2003. (Frank Merriwell Ser.). pap. 9.95 (978-0-8373-9101-4(6)) Merriwell, Frank Inc.

—Frank Merriwell's Opportunity. Rudman, Jack, ed. 2003. (Frank Merriwell Ser.). 29.95 (978-0-8373-9331-5(0)); pap. 9.95 (978-0-8373-9031-4(1)) Merriwell, Frank Inc.

—Frank Merriwell's Own Company. Rudman, Jack, ed. 2003. (Frank Merriwell Ser.). 29.95 (978-0-8373-9335-3(3)); pap. 9.95 (978-0-8373-9035-2(4)) Merriwell, Frank Inc.

—Frank Merriwell's Peril. Rudman, Jack, ed. 2003. (Frank Merriwell Ser.). pap. 9.95 (978-0-8373-9115-1(6)) Merriwell, Frank Inc.

—Frank Merriwell's Phantom. Rudman, Jack, ed. 2003. (Frank Merriwell Ser.). 29.95 (978-0-8373-9359-9(0)); pap. 9.95 (978-0-8373-9059-8(1)) Merriwell, Frank Inc.

—Frank Merriwell's Power. Rudman, Jack, ed. 2003. (Frank Merriwell Ser.). 29.95 (978-0-8373-9364-3(7)); pap. 9.95 (978-0-8373-9064-2(8)) Merriwell, Frank Inc.

—Frank Merriwell's Pride. Rudman, Jack, ed. 2003. (Frank Merriwell Ser.). pap. 9.95 (978-0-8373-9121-2(0)) Merriwell, Frank Inc.

—Frank Merriwell's Problem. Rudman, Jack, ed. 2003. (Frank Merriwell Ser.). 29.95 (978-0-8373-9338-4(8)); pap. 9.95 (978-0-8373-9038-3(9)) Merriwell, Frank Inc.

—Frank Merriwell's Prosperity. Rudman, Jack, ed. 2003. (Frank Merriwell Ser.). 29.95 (978-0-8373-9341-4(8)); pap. 9.95 (978-0-8373-9041-3(9)) Merriwell, Frank Inc.

—Frank Merriwell's Protege. Rudman, Jack, ed. 2003. (Frank Merriwell Ser.). 29.95 (978-0-8373-9333-9(7)); pap. 9.95 (978-0-8373-9033-8(8)) Merriwell, Frank Inc.

—Frank Merriwell's Pursuit. Rudman, Jack, ed. 2003. (Frank Merriwell Ser.). pap. 9.95 (978-0-8373-9117-5(2)) Merriwell, Frank Inc.

—Frank Merriwell's Rescue. Rudman, Jack, ed. 2003. (Frank Merriwell Ser.). 29.95 (978-0-8373-9398-8(1)); pap. 9.95 (978-0-8373-9098-7(2)) Merriwell, Frank Inc.

—Frank Merriwell's Reward. Rudman, Jack, ed. 2003. (Frank Merriwell Ser.). 29.95 (978-0-8373-9358-2(2)); pap. 9.95 (978-0-8373-9058-1(3)) Merriwell, Frank Inc.

—Frank Merriwell's Rough Deal. Rudman, Jack, ed. 2003. (Frank Merriwell Ser.). pap. 9.95 (978-0-8373-9111-3(3)) Merriwell, Frank Inc.

—Frank Merriwell's Search. Rudman, Jack, ed. 2003. (Frank Merriwell Ser.). 29.95 (978-0-8373-9367-4(1)); pap. 9.95 (978-0-8373-9067-3(2)) Merriwell, Frank Inc.

—Frank Merriwell's Setback. Rudman, Jack, ed. 2003. (Frank Merriwell Ser.). 29.95 (978-0-8373-9366-7(3)); pap. 9.95 (978-0-8373-9066-6(4)) Merriwell, Frank Inc.

—Frank Merriwell's Shrewdness. Rudman, Jack, ed. 2003. (Frank Merriwell Ser.). 29.95 (978-0-8373-9365-0(5)); pap. 9.95 (978-0-8373-9065-9(6)) Merriwell, Frank Inc.

—Frank Merriwell's Sports Afield. Rudman, Jack, ed. (Frank Merriwell Ser.). (YA). (gr. 9 up). 29.95 (978-0-8373-9310-0(8)); pap. 9.95 (978-0-8373-9010-9(9) , FM-010) Merriwell, Frank Inc.

—Frank Merriwell's Stage Hit. Rudman, Jack, ed. 2003. (Frank Merriwell Ser.). 29.95 (978-0-8373-9342-1(6)); pap. 9.95 (978-0-8373-9042-0(7)) Merriwell, Frank Inc.

—Frank Merriwell's Steadying Hand. Rudman, Jack, ed. 2003. (Frank Merriwell Ser.). pap. 9.95 (978-0-8373-9165-6(2)) Merriwell, Frank Inc.

—Frank Merriwell's Strategy. Rudman, Jack, ed. 2003. (Frank Merriwell Ser.). pap. 9.95 (978-0-8373-9106-9(7)) Merriwell, Frank Inc.

—Frank Merriwell's Strong Arm. Rudman, Jack, ed. 2003. (Frank Merriwell Ser.). 29.95 (978-0-8373-9371-1(X)); pap. 9.95 (978-0-8373-9071-0(0)) Merriwell, Frank Inc.

—Frank Merriwell's Support. Rudman, Jack, ed. 2003. (Frank Merriwell Ser.). 29.95 (978-0-8373-9375-9(2)); pap. 9.95 (978-0-8373-9075-8(3)) Merriwell, Frank Inc.

—Frank Merriwell's Talisman. Rudman, Jack, ed. 2003. (Frank Merriwell Ser.). pap. 9.95 (978-0-8373-9145-8(8)) Merriwell, Frank Inc.

—Frank Merriwell's Temptation. Rudman, Jack, ed. 2003. (Frank Merriwell Ser.). 29.95 (978-0-8373-9354-4(X)); pap. 9.95 (978-0-8373-9054-3(0)) Merriwell, Frank Inc.

—Frank Merriwell's Tigers. Rudman, Jack, ed. 2003. (Frank Merriwell Ser.). pap. 9.95 (978-0-8373-9131-1(8)) Merriwell, Frank Inc.

—Frank Merriwell's Tricks. Rudman, Jack, ed. 2003. (Frank Merriwell Ser.). 29.95 (978-0-8373-9353-7(1)); pap. 9.95 (978-0-8373-9053-6(2)) Merriwell, Frank Inc.

—Frank Merriwell's Triumph. Rudman, Jack, ed. 2003. (Frank Merriwell Ser.). pap. 9.95 (978-0-8373-9107-6(5)) Merriwell, Frank Inc.

—Frank Merriwell's Trump Card. Rudman, Jack, ed. 2003. (Frank Merriwell Ser.). pap. 9.95 (978-0-8373-9105-2(9)) Merriwell, Frank Inc.

—Frank Merriwell's Trust. Rudman, Jack, ed. 2003. (Frank Merriwell Ser.). 29.95 (978-0-8373-9369-8(8)); pap. 9.95 (978-0-8373-9069-7(9)) Merriwell, Frank Inc.

—Frank Merriwell's Victories. Rudman, Jack, ed. 2003. (Frank Merriwell Ser.). 29.95 (978-0-8373-9361-2(2)); pap. 9.95 (978-0-8373-9061-1(3)) Merriwell, Frank Inc.

—Frank Merriwell's Winners. Rudman, Jack, ed. 2003. (Frank Merriwell Ser.). 29.95 (978-0-8373-9388-9(4)); pap. 9.95 (978-0-8373-9088-8(5)) Merriwell, Frank Inc.

—Frank Merriwell's Wizard. Rudman, Jack, ed. 2003. (Frank Merriwell Ser.). pap. 9.95 (978-0-8373-9174-8(1)) Merriwell, Frank Inc.

—Frank Merriwell's Worst Boy. Rudman, Jack, ed. 2003. (Frank Merriwell Ser.). pap. 9.95 (978-0-8373-9155-7(5)) Merriwell, Frank Inc.

Stanwood Pier, Arthu. The Jester of St. Timothy's. 2006. pap. 14.95 (****978-1-55742-546-1(9)***) Wildside Pr.

Stewart, Melanie. Pushing the Limits. 1999. (gr. 3-6). lib. bdg. 11.80 (978-0-613-28030-3(X)) Tandem Library Bks.

Stickers N Shapes, Cherrington, et al. The Ojo Lympics. 2000. (Bear in the Big Blue House Ser.). (Illus.). 32p. (J). per. (978-0-7434-0839-4(X) , Simon & Schuster Children's Publishing) Simon & Schuster Children's Publishing.

Still, James. Sporty Creek. Johnson, Paul Brett, illus. 1999. 119p. (YA). (gr. 8-12). pap. 14.00 (978-0-8131-0965-7(5)) Univ. Pr. of Kentucky.

Strasser, Todd. Close Out. 2004. 304p. (YA). pap. 5.99 (978-0-689-87031-6(0) , Simon Pulse) Simon & Schuster Children's Publishing.

Stroke of Luck (Swimming) 64p. (YA). (gr. 6-12). pap. 10.95 (978-0-8224-6482-2(9)) Globe Fearon Educational Publishing.

Swan, Bill. Corner Kick. 2004. (Sports Stories Ser.). 120p. (J). (gr. 3-8). 7.95 (978-1-55028-816-2(4)); (****978-1-55028-817-9(2)***) Lorimer, James & Co., Ltd., Pubs. CAN. *Dist:* Casemate Pubs. & Bk. Distributors, LLC.

—Mud Happens. 2005. (Sports Stories Ser.). 112p. (J). (gr. 3-8). (****978-1-55028-899-5(7));*** 7.95 (978-1-55028-898-8(9)) Lorimer, James & Co., Ltd., Pubs. CAN. *Dist:* Casemate Pubs. & Bk. Distributors, LLC.

Swan, Bill. Road Rage. 2006. (Sports Stories Ser.). 120p. (J). (gr. 3-8). 7.95 (978-1-55028-916-9(0)) Lorimer, James & Co., Ltd., Pubs. CAN. *Dist:* Casemate Pubs. & Bk. Distributors, LLC.

Takanashi, Mitsuba. Crimson Hero, Vol. 3. 2006. (Crimson Hero Ser.). 208p. (YA). pap. 8.99 (978-1-4215-0577-0(0)) Viz Media.

Teitelbaum, Michael. Red Flag. 2001. (NASCAR Racers Ser.: Vol. 7). (Illus.). 128p. (J). (gr. 2-6). pap. 4.50 (978-0-06-107201-7(X) , Harper Entertainment) HarperCollins Pubs.

Thaler, Mike. The Field Day from the Black Lagoon. Lee, Jared D., illus. 2008. (Little Apple Ser.). 64p. (J). 3.99 (****978-0-439-68076-9(X)***) Scholastic, Inc.

—Field Day from the Black Lagoon. Lee, Jared D., illus. 2005. 64p. (J). lib. bdg. 15.00 (****978-1-4242-2261-2(3)***) Fitzgerald Bks.

Thornton-Jones, Marcia. Champ. 2007. 192p. (J). (gr. 4-7). pap. 4.99 (****978-0-439-79399-5(8)***) Scholastic, Inc.

Tocher, Timothy. Close Call. 2002. mass mkt. 3.95 (978-0-689-02121-3(6)) Meadowbrook Pr.

Tomlinson, Everett T. Winning His W. 2006. pap. (****978-1-4068-1194-0(7)***) Echo Library.

Truckey, Don. The Adventures of Caraway Kim— Southpaw. 2005. 192p. pap. 8.95 (978-1-894345-90-3(8)) Thistledown Pr., Ltd. CAN. *Dist:* Literary Pr. Group of Canada.

Twelve More Little Race Cars. 2001. (Illus.). (J). lib. bdg. 12.95 (978-0-9670600-1-9(X)) Word Weaver Bks., Inc.

Twigg, Aeres. The Green Hawk. 2003. (Illus.). 87p. (J). pap. 12.95 (978-1-85902-787-5(3)) Beekman Bks., Inc.

Urandangi State School Staff. Goanna Jumps High. 2000. (Illus.). 24p. pap. 4.95 (978-1-875641-45-1(9)) Magabala Bks. AUS. *Dist:* International Specialized Bk. Services.

Van Steenwyk, Elizabeth. Three Dog Winter. 1999. (978-0-606-16440-5(5)) Tandem Library Bks.

Voigt, Cynthia. Bad Girls, Bad Girls, Whatcha Gonna Do? 2006. (Bad Girls Ser.). 448p. (YA). (gr. 7 up). 17.95 (978-0-689-82474-6(2)) Simon & Schuster Children's Publishing.

Waldron, Kathleen Cook. Rough Day at Loon Lake. Griffiths, Dean, illus. 2002. 32p. (J). (ps-2). 7.95 (978-1-55143-195-6(5)) Orca Bk. Pubs. USA.

Wallace, Rich. Fast Company. 2005. (Winning Season Ser.: Vol. 3). 128p. (J). (gr. 3-6). pap. 4.99 (978-0-14-240468-3(3) , Puffin) Penguin Group (USA) Inc.

—Fast Company No. 3. 2005. 128p. (J). (gr. 3-7). 14.99 (978-0-670-05942-3(0) , Viking Juvenile) Penguin Group (USA) Inc.

—Losing Is Not an Option. 144p. (YA). 2005. (gr. 7 up). pap. 5.99 (978-0-440-23844-7(7) , Laurel Leaf); 2003. (gr. 5-9). 15.95 (978-0-375-81351-1(9) , Knopf Bks. for Young Readers) Random Hse. Children's Bks.

—The Roar of the Crowd. 2004. (Winning Season Ser.: Bk. 1). 112p. (J). (gr. 4). 14.99 (978-0-670-05940-9(4) , Viking Juvenile) Penguin Group (USA) Inc.

—Takedown: Winning Season 8. 2006. (Winning Season Ser.). 128p. (J). (gr. 3). 14.99 (978-0-670-06096-2(8) , Viking Juvenile) Penguin Group (USA) Inc.

—Technical Foul. 2004. (Winning Season Ser.: Bk. 2). 112p. (J). (gr. 3-7). 15.99 (978-0-670-05941-6(2) , Viking Juvenile) Penguin Group (USA) Inc.

—Winning Season 4 Double Fake Pt. 4. 2006. 128p. (J). (gr. 3). pap. 4.99 (978-0-14-240588-8(4) , Puffin) Penguin Group (USA) Inc.

Walters, Eric. Grind. 2004. (Orca Soundings Ser.). 112p. (J). (gr. 7-12). pap. 7.95 (978-1-55143-317-2(6)) Orca Bk. Pubs. USA.

—Hoop Crazy! 2001. (Young Reader Ser.). (Illus.). 144p. (J). (gr. 3-6). pap. 5.95 (978-1-55143-184-0(X)) Orca Bk. Pubs. USA.

—Hoop Crazy! 2001. (gr. 3-6). lib. bdg. 13.00 (978-0-613-50205-4(1)) Tandem Library Bks.

—Rebound. 2001. 262p. (gr. 5-9). mass mkt. 6.95 (978-0-7736-7485-1(3)); (YA). 15.95 (978-0-7737-3303-9(5)) Stoddart Kids CAN. *Dist:* Fitzhenry & Whiteside, Ltd.

—Rebound. 2000. (gr. 3-6). lib. bdg. 15.25 (978-0-613-50233-7(7)) Tandem Library Bks.

—Three on Three. 1999. (Young Reader Ser.). (Illus.). 144p. (J). (gr. 3-6). pap. 4.99 (978-1-55143-170-3(X)) Orca Bk. Pubs. USA.

—Three on Three. 2000. (Illus.). 122p. (J). (gr. 2-6). lib. bdg. 13.00 (978-0-613-36704-2(9)) Tandem Library Bks.

—Underdog. 2004. (Orca Young Readers Ser.). (Illus.). 144p. (J). (gr. 3-6). pap., tchr. ed. 4.99 (978-1-55143-302-8(8) , 1234544) Orca Bk. Pubs. USA.

Warner, Gertrude Chandler. The Hockey Mystery. 2001. (Boxcar Children Ser.: Vol. 80). (J). (978-0-606-20300-5(1)) Tandem Library Bks.

Weaver, Will. Farm Team. 1999. 288p. (J). (gr. 6 up). pap. 7.99 (978-0-06-447118-3(7) , Harper Trophy) HarperCollins Pubs.

Wells, Rosemary. Bubble Gum Radar. 2002. (gr. k-3). lib. bdg. 11.80 (978-0-613-74978-7(2)) Tandem Library Bks.

Wheeler, Lee Alden. Bucking the Odds, 2004. (YA). pap. 13.00 (978-0-9760824-0-8(3)) United Writers Pr., Inc.

Whitney, Kim Ablon. The Perfect Distance: A Novel. 2005. 256p. (YA). (gr. 7 up). 15.95 (978-0-375-83243-7(2) , Knopf Bks. for Young Readers) Random Hse. Children's Bks.

Williams, Tamara L. Shadow Ride. 1999. (Sports Stories Ser.). 96p. (gr. 3-8). (J). (978-1-55028-683-0(8)); 7.95 (978-1-55028-684-7(6)) Lorimer, James & Co., Ltd., Pubs. CAN. *Dist:* Casemate Pubs. & Bk. Distributors, LLC.

—Shadow Ride. 2000. (gr. 5-8). lib. bdg. 13.55 (978-0-613-86086-4(1)) Tandem Library Bks.

Willner-Pardo, Gina. Spider Storch, Rotten Runner. Sharratt, Nick, illus. 2001. 88p. (J). (gr. 2-5). lib. bdg. 11.95 (978-0-8075-7594-9(1)) Whitman, Albert & Co.

Wilson, George. Arron the Royal Archer. 2008. (Illus.). 50p. (J). 14.99 (****978-0-9778477-3-0(X)***) Storyplus, Inc., A.

Wilson, J. M. & Zolkowski, Cathy A. Breathless: The Adventures of a Gymnast. 1999. 150p. (gr. 6-12). (J). pap. 5.95 (978-0-9667037-0-2(7) , 035); (YA). lib. bdg. 7.95 (978-0-9667037-1-9(5) , 035) Verona (Bk.) Publishing, Inc.

Winfield, Arthur M. Putnam Hall Champions or Bound to Win Ou. 2006. pap. 28.95 (****978-1-4286-2346-0(9)***) Kessinger Publishing, LLC.

Winkler, Henry & Oliver, Lin. My Secret Life as a Ping-Pong Wizard. 2006. (Hank Zipzer Ser.: No. 9). (J). (gr. 3-8). 24.21 (978-1-59961-110-5(4)) Spotlight.

SPORTS—HISTORY

Beginnings of Sports: Individual Title Six-Packs. 32p. (gr. 4 up). 44.00 (978-0-7578-0608-7(2)) Rigby Education.

Brignall, Richard. Forever Champions: The Enduring Legacy of the Edmonton Grads Women's Basketball Team. 2007. (Recordbooks Ser.). (Illus.). 112p. (gr. 7-12). (J). 8.95 (****978-1-55028-976-3(4)); *978-1-55028-977-0(2))*** Lorimer, James & Co., Ltd., Pubs. CAN. *Dist:* Casemate Pubs. & Bk. Distributors, LLC.

Cannarella, Deborah & Fournier, Jane. Sports. 1999. (Into the Next Millennium Ser.). (Illus.). 32p. (J). (gr. 4-8). lib. bdg. 27.93 (978-1-57103-275-1(4)) Rourke Publishing, LLC.

Deitsch, Richard. (Quarter)Backs-to-(Running)Backs: The NFL's Finest Passers & Rushers. Wolf, Cathrine, ed. 1998. 32p. (J). (gr. 4-6). pap. 3.95 (978-1-886749-45-0(0)) Sports Illustrated For Kids.

—Super Bowl Heroes: Read about the Super Bowl's Biggest Stars. Sieck, Margaret, ed. 1999. 32p. (J). (gr. 2-7). pap. 3.99 (978-1-886749-53-5(1)) Sports Illustrated For Kids.

Gatto, Steve. Da Curse of the Billy Goat: The Chicago Cubs, Pennant Races, & Curses. 2004. 144p. per. 19.95 (978-0-9720910-4-6(1)) Protar Hse., LLC.

Herzog, Brad. The 20 Greatest Athletes of the 20th Century. 2005. (Sports Illustrated for Kids Bks.). (Illus.). 176p. (YA). (gr. 7-12). lib. bdg. 27.95 (978-0-8239-3694-6(5)) Rosen Publishing Group, Inc., The.

Historia de los Deportes Series, 6 bks., Set. 2003. (Historia de los Deportes Ser.). (SPA & ENG., Illus.). (J). 103.50 (978-0-8239-6917-3(7) , Buenas Letra) Rosen Publishing Group, Inc., The.

Mandell, Richard D. Sport: A Cultural History. 1999. (Illus.). 388p. reprint ed. pap. 18.95 (978-1-58348-282-7(2)) iUniverse, Inc.

Mattern, Joanne & Mattern, James. Teamwork: Working Together to Win. 2002. (Cover-To-Cover Books). (Illus.). 60p. (J). pap. (978-0-7891-5514-6(1)) Perfection Learning Corp.

Morgan, Brendan. Sports Illustrated for Kids Game Time! An Inside Look at Football. Holder, Sherie, ed. 1999. 32p. (J). (gr. 2-8). pap. 3.99 (978-1-886749-65-8(5)) Sports Illustrated For Kids.

Platt, Richard. They Played What?! The Weird History of Sports & Recreation. 2007. 48p. (****978-1-58728-585-1(1));*** (J). pap. (****978-1-58728-586-8(X)***) T&N Children's Publishing. (Two Can Publishing).

Ross, Dalton. Top Teams Ever. Sieck, Margaret, ed. 1999. 96p. (J). (gr. 1-9). pap. 3.99 (978-1-886749-63-4(9)) Sports Illustrated For Kids.

Rutledge, Rachel. The Best of the Best in Soccer. (Women of Sports Ser.: up). (Illus.). 64p. (gr. 5 up). 1998. lib. bdg. 24.90 (978-0-7613-1315-1(X)); 2000. pap. (978-0-7613-1392-2(3)) Lerner Publishing Group. (Twenty-First Century Bks.).

Samuel, Charlie. Entertainment in Colonial America. 2003. (Primary Sources of Everyday Life in Colonial America Ser.). (Illus.). 24p. (J). lib. bdg. 21.25 (978-0-8239-6600-4(3) , PowerKids Pr.) Rosen Publishing Group, Inc., The.

Sports Illustrated Editors. The Amazing World of Sports. 2006. (Sports Illustrated for Kids Ser.). 176p. (J). 18.95 (978-1-933821-00-9(0)) Time, Inc. Home Entertainment.

Stokes, Erica M. Sports of Mexico. 2002. (Encyclopedia of Mexico Ser.). (Illus.). 64,80p. (YA). (gr. 5 up). lib. bdg. (978-1-59084-082-5(8)) Mason Crest Pubs.

Suen, Anastasia. Sports History, 6 bks. Incl. Story of Baseball. lib. bdg. 17.25 (978-0-8239-6000-2(5)); Story of Basketball. lib. bdg. 17.25 (978-0-8239-5995-2(3)); Story of Figure Skating. lib. bdg. 17.25 (978-0-8239-5999-0(6)); Story of Football. lib. bdg. 17.25 (978-0-8239-5996-9(1)); Story of Hockey. lib. bdg. 17.25 (978-0-8239-5997-6(X)); Story of Soccer. lib. bdg. 17.25 (978-0-8239-5998-3(8)); 24p. (J). (gr. 2). 2002. (Illus.). 2001. Set lib. bdg. 96.00 (978-0-8239-7174-9(0) , PowerKids Pr.) Rosen Publishing Group, Inc., The.

Sullivan, George. Any Number Can Play: The Numbers Athletes Wear. Green, Anne Canevari, illus. 2000. (Sports Trivia from George Sullivan Ser.). 64p. (J). (gr. 5-8). lib. bdg. 23.90 (978-0-7613-1557-5(8) , Millbrook Pr.) Lerner Publishing Group.

Wulffson, Don L. Pro Sports: How Did They Begin? 2000. (gr. 3-6). lib. bdg. 14.10 (978-0-613-28028-0(8)) Tandem Library Bks.

SPORTS—POETRY

Burleigh, Robert. Hoops. Johnson, Stephen T., illus. 2001. 32p. (J). (gr. k-3). pap. 6.00 (978-0-15-216380-8(8) , Voyager Bks./Libros Viajeros) Harcourt Children's Bks.

—Hoops. 2001. (gr. k-3). lib. bdg. 14.15 (978-0-613-83779-8(7)) Tandem Library Bks.

Fehler, Gene. The Silly (And Sometimes Serious) Side of Sports: Sports Poems. 1999. 72p. (J). (gr. 3-12). pap. 7.95 (978-0-9650793-1-0(7)) Mailbox Pr.

Greenfield, Eloise. For the Love of the Game: Michael Jordan & Me. Gilchrist, Jan Spivey, illus. 1999. (Trophy Picture Bk.). 32p. (J). (ps-3). pap. 6.99 (978-0-06-443555-0(5) , Harper Trophy) HarperCollins Pubs.

—For the Love of the Game: Michael Jordan & Me. 1999. (gr. k-3). lib. bdg. 15.30 (978-0-613-17800-6(9)) Tandem Library Bks.

Hopkins, Lee Bennett. Sports! Sports! Sports! A Poetry Collection. Floca, Brian, illus. 1999. (I Can Read Bks.: Vol. 2). 48p. (J). (gr. k-3). 15.89 (978-0-06-027801-4(3)) HarperCollins Pubs.

Lansky, Bruce. I Hope I Don't Strike Out! & Other Funny Sports Poems. Carpenter, Stephen, illus. 2008. ***978-0-88166-535-2(5))** Meadowbrook Pr.

Low, Alice. A Pie Plate in the Sky & Other Poems about How Sports Began. O'Brien, John, illus. 2008. (J). ***978-0-8234-1905-0(3))** Holiday Hse., Inc.

Morrison, Lillia. Way to Go. Spellman, Susan, illus. 2007. 40p. pap. 9.95 ***978-1-59078-481-5(2))** Boyds Mills Pr.

Prelutsky, Jack. Good Sports: Rhymes about Running, Jumping, Throwing, & More. Raschka, Christopher, illus. 2007. 40p. (J). (gr. 3). 16.99 (978-0-375-83700-5(0)); lib. bdg. 19.99 (978-0-375-93700-2(5)) Random Hse. Children's Bks. (Knopf Bks. for Young Readers).

Smith, Charles R., Jr. Hoop Kings. 2004. (Illus.). 42p. (J). (gr. 3-8). 14.99 (978-0-7636-1423-2(8)) Candlewick Pr.

Smith, Charles R. Hoop Kings. 2007. (Illus.). 40p. (J). (gr. 3). 5.99 ***978-0-7636-3560-2(X))** Candlewick Pr.

—Hoop Queens. 2007. (Illus.). 40p. (J). (gr. 3). 5.99 ***978-0-7636-3561-9(8))** Candlewick Pr.

Wesley, Sonya L. Life Is a Game of Sports: Sport Poetry. 2000. (Illus.). 2000p. spiral bd. 10.00 (978-0-9706421-1-0(3)) Game Plan Pubns.

Wolff, Virginia Euwer & Woodson, Jacqueline. Girls Got Game: Sports Stories & Poems. Macy, Sue, ed. rev. ed. 2001. (Illus.). 160p. (YA). (gr. 6-9). 17.95 (978-0-8050-6568-8(7) , Holt, Henry & Co. Bks. For Young Readers) Holt, Henry & Co.

SPORTS—YEARBOOKS

Brown, Garry. ESPN Almanac, 2001. 2000. (Illus.). (YA). pap. (978-0-7868-8665-4(X)) Hyperion Pr.

Brown, Gerry & Morrison, Michael. 2000 ESPN Sports Almanac. 1999. (978-0-606-18249-2(7)) Tandem Library Bks.

Martin, Clare. An Insider's Guide to the WNBA. 2002. (Wnba Sticker Book Ser.). 24p. (J). pap. 7.99 (978-0-439-38013-3(8)) Scholastic, Inc.

Morgan, Brendan. Sports Illustrated for Kids Game Time! An Inside Look at Football. Holder, Sherie, ed. 1999. 32p. (J). (gr. 2-8). pap. 3.99 (978-1-886749-65-8(5)) Sports Illustrated For Kids.

Scholastic, Inc. Staff. Sports Illustrated for Kids Year in Sports. 2003. 336p. (J). pap. 9.95 (978-0-439-52027-0(4)) Scholastic, Inc.

SI for Kids Staff. Sports Illustrated for Kids Year in Sports 2004. 2004. (Illus.). 320p. (J). (gr. 3 up). 9.95 (978-0-439-65082-3(8) , Scholastic Reference) Scholastic, Inc.

1966 Season Replay Yearbook. 2nd rev. ed. 2002. 65p. (J). per. 29.95 (978-0-9700351-8-9(7)) Replay Publishing.

SPORTS IN ART

Court, Rob. How to Draw Sports Things. 2008. (Doodle Bks.). 32p. (J). 21.36 ***978-1-59296-956-2(9))** Child's World, Inc.

Lacey, Sue. Sports & Leisure. 2000. (gr. 3-6). lib. bdg. 15.25 (978-0-613-27041-0(X)) Tandem Library Bks.

Peterson, Tiffany. Sports Stars. Westerfield, David, illus. 2003. (Draw It! Ser.). 32p. (J). (gr. 3-5). lib. bdg. 24.22 (978-1-4034-0213-4(2)); pap. 7.50 (978-1-4034-4032-7(8)) Heinemann Library.

—Sports Stars. 2003. (gr. 3-6). lib. bdg. 15.25 (978-0-613-60988-3(3)) Tandem Library Bks.

SPORTS JOURNALISM

Thomas, Stephen, ed. Hot Summer Fun, Cool Summer Stars. Staake, Bob et al, illus. Date not set. 28p. (Orig.). (J). (gr. 3-7). pap. (978-1-886749-26-9(4)) Sports Illustrated For Kids.

Tracy, Kathleen. Matt Christopher. 2007. (Classic Storytellers Ser.). (J). lib. bdg. ***978-1-58415-535-5(3))** Mitchell Lane Pubs., Inc.

SPRING

Anderson, Maxine. Explore Spring! 25 Great Ways to Learn about Spring. 2007. (Explore the Seasons Ser.). 96p. (J). (gr. 1-4). pap. 12.95 ***978-0-9785037-4-1(0))** Nomad Pr.

Bryant, Margaret A., et al. Learning about Spring with Children's Literature. 2006. 160p. (J). pap. 14.95 (978-1-56976-206-6(6) , Zephyr Pr.) Chicago Review Pr., Inc.

Burke, Betty & Finer, Susie. Activites de Printemps. (FRE.). pap. (978-0-439-98520-8(X)) Scholastic Canada, Ltd.

Burton, Jane & Taylor, Kim. The Nature & Science of Spring. Burton, Jane & Taylor, Kim, photos by. 1999. (Exploring the Science of Nature Ser.). (Illus.). 32p. (J). (gr. 3 up). lib. bdg. 24.67 (978-0-8368-2188-8(2)) Stevens, Gareth Inc.

Butterfield, Moira. Spring. James, Helen, illus. 2005. 32p. (J). (gr. 2-5). lib. bdg. 27.10 (978-1-58340-614-4(X)) Smart Apple Media.

Casado, Dami & Casado, Alicia. La Primavera. 2005. (Brujita Mo). (SPA & ESP., Illus.). 14p. (J). (ps-ps). per. 7.99 (978-84-272-6238-6(8)) Molino, Editorial ESP. *Dist:* Santillana USA Publishing Co., Inc.

Claybourne, Anna. Spring. 2001. (Seasons Ser.). (Illus.). 32p. (J). lib. bdg. 24.25 (978-1-930643-06-2(3)) Chrysalis Education.

Davis, Rebecca Fjelland. Flowers & Showers: A Spring Counting Book. 2006. (J). (978-0-7368-6890-7(9)); (Illus.). 32p. (978-0-7368-5377-4(4)) Capstone Pr., Inc.

Declus, Jennifer. What Might I Find in a Geyser. Kalasea, illus. 2004. (J). (978-0-9743690-0-6(4)) Britt Allcroft Productions.

DeGezelle, Terri. Spring. 2002. (Bridgestone Science Library). (Illus.). 24p. (J). (gr. 1-2). lib. bdg. 18.60 (978-0-7368-1410-2(8) , Bridgestone Bks.) Capstone Pr., Inc.

Fisher, Ann Richmond. Spring. Mitchell, Judy, ed. Bradshaw, Cara H., illus. 2001. (Bulletin Board-in-a-Book Ser.). 16p. pap. 7.95 (978-1-57310-287-2(3)) Teaching & Learning Co.

Gerard, Valerie J. Spring: Signs of the Season Around North America. Thomas, Eric, illus. 2004. (Through the Seasons Ser.). 24p. (C). (gr. k-1). 22.60 (978-1-4048-0002-1(6)) Picture Window Bks.

Golden Books Staff. Springtime Joys. Butcher, Samuel J., illus. 2000. (Precious Moments Ser.). 64p. (ps-2). pap. 2.99 (978-0-307-03423-6(2) , 03423, Golden Bks.) Random Hse. Children's Bks.

Hamaguchi, Carla, ed. Spring Stickety-Splits, 12 vols., 0647. Schamber, Kimberly, illus. 2001. 10p. (Orig.). (J). pap. 6.99 (978-1-57471-895-9(9)) Creative Teaching Pr., Inc.

Hensley, Sarah M. One Spring Day. Middleton, Mikell, illus. 2003. 10p. (J). (ps-1). bds. 10.95 (978-1-57332-227-0(X)) HighReach Learning, Inc.

Here Comes Spring! 2003. (J). per. (978-1-57657-968-8(9)) Paradise Pr., Inc.

Herriges, Ann. Spring. 2006. (Blastoff! Readers Ser.). (Illus.). 24p. (J). lib. bdg. 16.95 (978-1-60014-031-0(9)) Bellwether Media.

Is It Spring? 2003. (YA). (978-0-8374-0009-9(0)); lib. bdg. (978-0-8374-0008-2(2)) Weekly Reader Corp.

Kalz, Jill. Spring. 2005. (Illus.). 24p. (gr. k-3). 15.95 (978-1-58341-363-0(4) , Creative Education) Creative Co., The.

Latta, Sara L. What Happens in Spring? 2006. (I Like the Seasons! Ser.). (Illus.). 24p. (J). lib. bdg. 21.26 (978-0-7660-2419-9(9) , Enslow Elementary) Enslow Pubs., Inc.

The Letter Ss: Spring & Summer, 6 vols. (gr. k-2). 17.50 (978-0-7368-4118-4(0)) Red Brick Learning.

Macken, JoAnn Early. Spring. 2006. (Illus.). 16p. (J). pap. (978-0-8368-6359-8(3)); lib. bdg. 16.67 (978-0-8368-6354-3(2)) Stevens, Gareth Inc.

—Spring: Primavera. 2006. (ENG & SPA., Illus.). 16p. (J). pap. (978-0-8368-6538-7(3)); lib. bdg. 16.67 (978-0-8368-6533-2(2)) Stevens, Gareth Inc.

Maurer, Tracy. Spring. 2006. (to Z Ser.). (Illus.). 32p. (gr. k-2). 20.95 (978-1-58952-197-1(8)) Rourke Publishing, LLC.

Meyer, Mary L. Spring. 2002. (J). 21.35 (978-1-58340-143-9(1)) Smart Apple Media.

Parker, Victoria. Days In... Spring. 2004. (Raintree Sprouts Ser.). (Illus.). 24p. (J). pap. 5.50 (978-1-4109-0741-7(4)) Raintree.

—Spring. 2004. (Raintree Sprouts Ser.). (Illus.). 24p. (J). lib. bdg. 18.56 (978-1-4109-0736-3(8)) Raintree.

Roca, Nuria. La Primavera. 2004. (Cuatro Estaciones Ser.).Tr. of Spring. (SPA., Illus.). 36p. (J). pap. 7.99 (978-0-7641-2734-2(9)) Barron's Educational Series, Inc.

—Spring. 2004. (Four Seasons Ser.). (Illus.). 36p. (J). pap. 6.95 (978-0-7641-2733-5(0)) Barron's Educational Series, Inc.

Saunders-Smith, Gail. Spring. 1998. (Seasons Ser.). (Illus.). 24p. (J). (ps-2). pap. 13.25 (978-0-516-21327-9(X) , Children's Pr.) Scholastic Library Publishing.

—Spring, Vol. 4. 2005. (Our Seasons & Weather Ser.). 24p. (YA). (gr. k-3). pap. 3.99 (978-1-56065-844-3(4) , Pebble Bks.) Capstone Pr., Inc.

Schnur, Steven. Spring: An Alphabet Acrostic. Evans, Leslie, illus. 1999. 32p. (J). (gr. k-3). tchr. ed. 15.00 (978-0-395-82269-2(6) , Clarion Bks.) Houghton Mifflin Co. Trade & Reference Div.

Schuette, Sarah L. Let's Look at Spring. 2007. (Pebble Plus Ser.). (Illus.). 24p. (J). (978-0-7368-6707-8(4) , 1264872) Capstone Pr., Inc.

Spring Seasons. 2006. (Illus.). 24p. (J). (gr. k-2). 18.50 ***978-0-531-17883-6(8))** Scholastic Library Publishing.

Stille, Darlene R. Spring. 2001. (Simply Science Ser.). (Illus.). 32p. (J). (gr. 3 up). lib. bdg. 19.93 (978-0-7565-0094-8(X)) Compass Point Bks.

Thayer, Tanya. Spring. 2005. (First Step Nonfiction Ser.). (Illus.). 24p. (gr. k-2). lib. bdg. 17.27 (978-0-8225-1986-7(0)) Lerner Publishing Group.

—Spring. 2001. (gr. k-3). lib. bdg. 11.80 (978-0-613-76623-4(7)) Tandem Library Bks.

Waters, Jennifer. Spring Has Sprung. 2002. (Spyglass Books). (Illus.). 24p. (J). (gr. 1 up). lib. bdg. 18.60 (978-0-7565-0243-0(8)) Compass Point Bks.

Whitehouse, Patricia. Spring. (Seasons Ser.). (Illus.). 24p. (J). (ps-1). 2003. lib. bdg. 17.08 (978-1-58810-894-4(5)); 2002. pap. 5.25 (978-1-4034-0540-1(9)) Heinemann Library.

—Spring. 2003. (ps-2). lib. bdg. 13.30 (978-0-613-86435-0(2)) Tandem Library Bks.

SPRING—FICTION

Barham, Olivia. Springtime in Chubbytown. 2002. (Chubby Puppies Ser.: Vol. 1). (Illus.). 32p. (J). (ps-3). pap. 3.50 (978-0-439-35566-7(4)) Scholastic, Inc.

Barker, Cicely Mary. Flower Fairy Springtime Dance. 2006. (Flower Fairies Ser.). (Illus.). 24p. (J). 4.99 (978-0-7232-5726-4(4) , Warne) Penguin Group (USA) Inc.

Barklem, Jill. Cuento de Primavera.Tr. of Spring Story. (SPA.). (J). pap. 8.95 (978-84-233-2618-1(7)) Ediciones Destino ESP. *Dist:* Planeta Publishing Corp.

Bergen, Lara. Diego's Springtime Fiesta. Oesch, Brian, illus. 2008. (Go, Diego, Go! Ser.). 24p. (J). pap. 3.99 ***978-1-4169-4800-1(7)** , Simon Spotlight/Nickelodeon) Simon & Schuster Children's Publishing.

Bonnell, Kris. Spring Is Coming! 2007. (J). 3.95 ***978-1-933727-64-6(0))** Reading Reading Bks., LLC.

Brown. Little Bear Friendship Box: Love Song of Spring. 2002. (J). bds. (978-0-7868-0896-0(9)) Hyperion Bks. for Children.

Brown, Craig. In the Spring. Brown, Craig, illus. 2004. (Illus.). 21p. (J). reprint ed. 14.00 (978-0-7567-8298-6(8)) DIANE Publishing Co.

Bryant, Megan E. Welcome Spring! Nunn, Paul E., illus. 2008. 32p. (J). (gr. 1-4). 6.99 ***978-0-448-44778-0(9)** , Grosset & Dunlap) Penguin Group (USA) Inc.

Clark, Brenda, illus. Franklin's Baby Sister. 2002. (Franklin Ser.). (J). 14.40 (978-0-7587-6436-2(7)) Book Wholesalers, Inc.

Crane Johnson, Amy. Cinnamon & the April Shower/Canela y el aquacero de Abril: A Solomon Raven Story/un cuento del cuervo Salomon, 4 vols. de la Vega, Eida, tr. Mommaerts, Robb, illus. 2003. (Solomon Raven Ser. : 3). Tr. of Canela y el aguacero de abril:un cuento del cuervo Salomon. (SPA & ENG.). 32p. (J). (gr. k-3). 16.95 (978-0-9720192-2-4(7) , 626999) Raven Tree Pr.

Curry, Don L. In My Backyard. Brown, Erin O'Leary, illus. 2004. 24p. (J). (gr. k-1). lib. bdg. 12.15 (978-0-606-30812-0(1)) Tandem Library Bks.

de Brunhoff, Laurent & Weiss, Ellen. Babar & the Runaway Egg. Gibert, Jean Claude & Gray, Judith, illus. 2004. 24p. (J). (ps-1). 9.95 (978-0-8109-4838-9(9)) Abrams, Harry N. , Inc.

de Paola, Tomie. Four Friends in Summer. de Paola, Tomie, illus. 2003. (Illus.). 32p. (J). reprint ed. 14.95 (978-0-689-85693-8(8)) Simon & Schuster Children's Publishing.

DeKok, Joy. It Is Good. 2005. (ENG.). 28p. (J). per. 15.99 (978-1-4141-0390-7(5)) Pleasant Word.

Ernst, Lisa Campbell. Wake up, It's Spring! Ernst, Lisa Campbell, illus. 2004. (Illus.). 40p. (J). (ps-3). 16.99 (978-0-06-008985-6(7)) HarperCollins Pubs.

—Wake Up, It's Spring! Ernst, Lisa Campbell, illus. 2004. (Illus.). 40p. (J). (ps-3). lib. bdg. 17.89 (978-0-06-008986-3(5)) HarperCollins Pubs.

Fakkema, Julie Ann. Water Is A Wonderful Thing. 2007. (J). per. 10.99 ***978-1-59886-927-9(2))** Tate Publishing & Enterprises, L.L.C.

Fontes, Justine. The Easter Cub. McQueen, Lucinda, illus. 2003. (Hello Reader! Ser.). 32p. (J). (gr. k-2). pap. 3.99 (978-0-439-44340-1(7) , Cartwheel Bks.) Scholastic, Inc.

—Signs of Spring. Hefferan, Rob, illus. 2002. 24p. (J). pap. (978-1-59034-180-3(5)); 14.95 (978-1-59034-189-6(9)) Mondo Publishing.

Francis-Harris, Annabel. The Other Side of the Forest. 2006. pap. 19.95 ***978-1-59526-458-9(2))** Media Creations, Inc.

Glaser, Linda. It's Spring! Swan, Susan, illus. 2002. (Celebrate the Seasons! Ser.). 32p. (J). (gr. 1-3). pap. 7.95 (978-0-7613-1345-8(1) , First Avenue Editions) Lerner Publishing Group.

—It's Spring. 2002. (gr. k-3). lib. bdg. 16.40 (978-0-613-50625-0(1)) Tandem Library Bks.

Gomi, Taro. Spring Is Here/Llego la Primavera. 2006. (ENG & SPA., Illus.). 40p. (J). 14.50 (978-0-8118-4759-9(4)) Chronicle Bks. LLC.

Hanson, Bonnie Compton. A Stormy Spring. 2004. (Ponytail Girls Ser.). (Illus.). 192p. (J). pap. 7.99 (978-1-58411-032-3(5) , Legacy Pr.) Rainbow Pubs. & Legacy Pr.

Harcourt School Publishers Staff. Just Around the Corner Advanced Level. 3rd ed. 2002. (Trophies Reading Program Ser.). (Illus.). pap. 5.10 (978-0-15-323034-9(7)) Harcourt Schl. Pubs.

Hercules's Spring Adventure Pack. 2001. (978-1-883772-01-7(X)) Flying Rhinoceros, Inc.

Hubbell, Patricia. Hurray for Spring. Morley, Taia, illus. 2005. (Picture Book Ser.). 32p. 15.95 (978-1-55971-913-1(3) , Two Can Publishing) T&N Children's Publishing.

Inches, Alison. Hello, Spring! Chernichaw, Ian, illus. 2004. (Blue's Clues Ser.: Vol. 8). 24p. (J). pap. 3.99 (978-0-689-86316-5(0) , Simon Spotlight/Nickelodeon) Simon & Schuster Children's Publishing.

—Hello, Spring! 2004. (ps-2). lib. bdg. 11.80 (978-0-613-73462-2(9)) Tandem Library Bks.

—Spring Is Here! Chernichaw, Ian, illus. 2006. (Blue's Clues Ser.). 16p. (J). pap. 5.99 (978-1-4169-0920-0(6) , Simon Spotlight/Nickelodeon) Simon & Schuster Children's Publishing.

Jordan, Apple. The Sweetest Spring. Matta, Gabriella & Legramandi, Francesco, illus. 2008. (Step into Reading Ser.). 32p. (J). (ps-1). lib. bdg. 11.99 ***978-0-375-94810-7(4)** , RH/Disney) Random Hse. Children's Bks.

—The Sweetest Spring. Matta, Gabriella & Legramandi, Francesco, illus. 2008. 32p. (J). pap. ***978-0-375-84810-0(X))** Random Hse., Inc.

Krensky, Stephen. Lionel in the Spring. 2000. (J). (gr. 2 up). pap., stu. ed. 21.75 incl. audio (978-0-7887-4177-7(2) , 41105) Recorded Bks., LLC.

Lindbergh, Reeve. North Country Spring. Sivertson, Liz, illus. 2007. 32p. (J). (gr. k-3). 6.95 ***978-0-618-80906-6(6))** Houghton Mifflin Co. Trade & Reference Div.

Mack, Lizzie. Hello, Spring! G Studios, illus. 2008. (Land of Milk & Honey Ser.). 12p. (J). bds. 7.99 ***978-1-4169-4933-6(X)** , Little Simon Inspirations) Simon & Schuster Children's Publishing.

Maguire, Gregory. Three Rotten Eggs. Clayton, Elaine, illus. 2002. 192p. (J). (gr. 4-6). 16.00 (978-0-618-09655-8(8) , Clarion Bks.) Houghton Mifflin Co. Trade & Reference Div.

Marzollo, Jean. Once upon a Springtime. 1998. (978-0-606-13680-8(0)) Tandem Library Bks.

Mazur, Kathy. It's Springtime in My Backyard. 2005. (J). bds. 16.95 (978-0-9761076-0-6(0)) Spring Ducks Bks., LLC.

Melancon, Gail. Good Morning Sunshine. 2006. pap. 13.99 (978-1-4196-2105-5(X)) BookSurge, LLC.

Nelson, Ray, et al. Hercules' Spring Book. Siegel, Joseph & Habecker, Mary Beth, eds. Peeples, Aaron et al, illus. 2000. 32p. (J). (gr. 1-3). pap. 12.00 (978-1-883772-23-9(0)) Flying Rhinoceros, Inc.

Neusner, Dena Wallenstein & McKee, Darren. Barney's Colors of Spring: Paint with Water Color Activity Book. 2003. (Barney Ser.). (Illus.). 32p. (J). act. bk. ed. 3.99 (978-1-58668-305-4(5)) Scholastic, Inc.

Oppenheim, Joanne. Could It Be? Schindler, S. D., illus. 1998. (Bank Street Reader Collection). 48p. (J). (gr. 1-3). lib. bdg. 22.60 (978-0-8368-1770-6(2)) Stevens, Gareth Inc.

Page, Nick & Claire. The King of Spring. 2006. (Read with Me (Make Believe Ideas) Ser.). (Illus.). 31p. (J). (gr. k-2). 3.95 (978-1-84610-169-4(7)) Make Believe Ideas GBR. *Dist:* Ingram Pub. Services.

Pearson, Tracey Campbell. Where Does Joe Go? Pearson, Tracey Campbell, illus. 2002. (Illus.). 32p. (J). pap. 5.95 (978-0-374-48366-1(3) , Sunburst) Farrar, Straus & Giroux.

Pelletier, Andrew. Sixteen Miles to Spring. Krenina, Katya, illus. 2002. 32p. (J). (gr. 1-4). 16.95 (978-0-8075-7388-4(4)) Whitman, Albert & Co.

Peters, Lisa. Cold Little Duck, Duck, Duck. Williams, Sam, illus. 2005. 32p. (J). (ps up). 6.99 (978-0-06-072223-4(1) , Harper Festival) HarperCollins Pubs.

Pickering, Jimmy. It's Spring. 2003. (Illus.). 32p. (J). 16.95 (978-1-931290-22-7(9)) Tallfellow Pr

Pitcher, Caroline. Are You Spring? 2000. (J). (978-0-606-20115-5(7)) Tandem Library Bks.

Plourde, Lynn & Couch, Greg. Spring's Sprung. 2002. (Illus.). 32p. (J). (ps-3). 16.00 (978-0-689-84229-0(5)) Simon & Schuster Children's Publishing.

Preller, James. Wake Me in Spring. Scherer, Jeffrey, illus. 2004. 32p. (J). lib. bdg. 15.00 (978-1-59054-397-9(1)) Fitzgerald Bks.

Pugliano-Martin, Carol. See You in Spring! 2006. (Early Explorers Ser.). (J). 34.00 ***978-1-4108-6105-4(8))** Benchmark Education Co.

Raczka, Bob. Spring Things. Stead, Judy, illus. 2007. 32p. (J). 16.95 (978-0-8075-7596-3(8)) Whitman, Albert & Co.

Ratoff, Michael. Silent Noisy Spring, 3 vols. Painter, Laurie, illus. l.t. ed. 2001. (Every Thing in an Empty Box Ser.). 56p. (J). (ps-3). lib. bdg. 9.95 (978-0-9627986-4-1(9)) Rebel Butterfly Pr.

Ray, Mary. Mud. 2001. (ps-2). lib. bdg. 14.15 (978-0-613-35541-4(5)) Tandem Library Bks.

Ray, Mary Lyn. Mud. 2001. (J). (978-0-606-21339-4(2)) Tandem Library Bks.

Reber, Deborah. Blue's Egg Hunt. Norden, Carolyn, illus. 2001. (Blue's Clues Ser.). 24p. (J). (ps-k). pap. 3.50 (978-0-689-83873-6(5) , Simon Spotlight/Nickelodeon) Simon & Schuster Children's Publishing.

—Blue's Egg Hunt. 2001. (gr. k-3). lib. bdg. 11.25 (978-0-613-31009-3(8)) Tandem Library Bks.

Rylant, Cynthia. Henry & Mudge in Puddle Trouble. Stevenson, Sucie, illus. 2002. (Henry & Mudge Ser.). (J). 11.91 (978-0-7587-1261-5(8)) Book Wholesalers, Inc.

—Henry & Mudge in Puddle Trouble. 2006. (Henry & Mudge Ser.). (J). (gr. 1-6). 24.21 (978-1-59961-085-6(X)) Spotlight.

S

Saltzman, Ruth E. Poppy Bear: The Garden That Overslept. Deeter, Catherine, illus. 2001. 32p. (J). (gr. k-2). 16.95 (978-1-58270-042-7(7)) Beyond Words Publishing, Inc.

Schnur, Steven. Spring Thaw. Schuett, Stacey, illus. 2000. 32p. (J). (ps-3). 15.99 (978-0-670-87961-8(4) , Viking Juvenile) Penguin Group (USA) Inc.

Singer, Marilyn. On the Same Day in March: A Tour of the World's Weather. Lessac, Frane, illus. 2002. 40p. (J). (ps-3). pap. 6.99 (978-0-06-443528-4(8) , Harper Trophy) HarperCollins Pubs.

Stephens, Monique Z. Spring for Strawberry Shortcake. Yee, Josie, tr. Yee, Josie, illus. 2004. (Strawberry Shortcake Ser.). 32p. (J). (ps-2). mass mkt. 3.99 (978-0-448-43373-8(7) , Grosset & Dunlap) Penguin Group (USA) Inc.

—Spring for Strawberry Shortcake. 2004. (gr. k-3). lib. bdg. 11.25 (978-0-613-72570-5(0)) Tandem Library Bks.

Stevenson, James. Mud Flat Spring. 1999. (Illus.). 40p. (J). (gr. k-3). 14.89 (978-0-688-15773-9(4)) HarperCollins Pubs.

Stone, Tanya Lee. B Is for Bunny: A Springtime Alphabet Book. Rama, Sue, illus. 2006. 24p. (J). (ps-1). pap. 4.99 (978-0-8431-1826-1(1) , Price Stern Sloan) Penguin Group (USA) Inc.

Thompson, Lauren. Mouse's First Spring. Erdogan, Buket, illus. 2005. 32p. (J). 12.95 (978-0-689-85838-3(8) , Simon & Schuster Children's Publishing) Simon & Schuster Children's Publishing.

Thorpe, Kiki. Spring Has Sprung! 2000. (gr. k-3). lib. bdg. 11.25 (978-0-613-22429-1(9)) Tandem Library Bks.

Trisler, Alana & Cardiel, Patrice Howe. My Spring Journal. 1999. 72p. (J). (gr. 2-3). pap., wbk. ed. 2.10 (978-1-56762-106-8(6)) Modern Learning Pr.

Voorheis, Tracy. Nibbles... a strawberry Tale. Voorheis, Tracy, illus. 2007. (Illus.). 60p. (J). per. 19.00 (***978-0-9787113-0-6(0)*** , Ithaca Pr.) Authors & Artists Publishers of New York, Inc.

Weinberger, Kimberly. Spring Is Here, Hello, Kitty! 2003. (Illus.). 32p. (J). (978-0-439-45079-9(9)) Scholastic, Inc.

Wilder, Laura Ingalls. Santa Comes to Little House. Graef, Renee, illus. 2004. (Little House Ser.). 32p. (J). (ps-3). pap. 5.99 (978-0-06-058694-2(X) , Harper Trophy) HarperCollins Pubs.

Zoehfeld, Kathleen Weidner. Pooh's Favorite Things about Spring. 2000. (My Very First Winnie the Pooh Ser.). (Illus.). 32p. (J). (ps-k). 12.99 (978-0-7868-3251-4(7)) Disney Pr.

Zoehfeld, Kathleen Weidner & Random House Disney Staff. Hello, Spring! Cuddy, Robbin & Marrucchi, Elisa, illus. 2001. (Disney's Winnie the Pooh Ser.). 24p. (J). (gr. k-k). pap. 3.99 (978-0-7364-1109-7(7) , RH/Disney) Random Hse. Children's Bks.

Zolotow, Charlotte. One Step, Two ... 2001. (J). 16.95 (978-0-8050-6307-3(2) , Holt, Henry & Co. Bks. For Young Readers) Holt, Henry & Co.

SPRING—POETRY

Carr, Jan. Splish, Splash, Spring. Donohue, Dorothy, illus. 2005. 32p. (J). (gr. k-3). 6.95 (978-0-8234-1754-4(9)) Holiday Hse., Inc.

Florian, Douglas. Handsprings: Poems & Paintings. Florian, Douglas, illus. 2006. (Illus.). 48p. (J). 15.99 (978-0-06-009280-1(7)) HarperCollins Pubs.

Lenski, Lois. Spring Is Here. 2005. 56p. (J). (ps-1). 9.95 (978-0-375-82729-7(3) , Random Hse. Bks. for Young Readers) Random Hse. Children's Bks.

Mass, Wendy, compiled by. Spring: Poems, Songs, Prayers. 2001. (Illus.). 10p. (J). (ps-2). 6.99 (978-0-570-07164-8(X)) Concordia Publishing Hse.

Rogasky, Barbara, compiled by. Spring Poems. 2007. (978-0-8234-1744-5(1)) Holiday Hse., Inc.

SQUANTO, WAMPANOAG INDIAN, D. 1622

Ghiglieri, Carol. Easy Reader Biographies: Squanto: A Friend to the Pilgrims. 2007. 16p. pap. 2.99 (***978-0-439-77422-2(5)*** , Teaching Resources) Scholastic, Inc.

Hirschfelder, Arlene B. Squanto1585-1622. 2004. (American Indian Biographies Ser.). (Illus.). 32p. (J). (gr. 3-4). lib. bdg. 23.93 (978-0-7368-2446-0(4) , Blue Earth Bks.) Capstone Pr., Inc.

Kessel, Joyce K. Squanto & the First Thanksgiving. Donze, Lisa, illus. rev. ed. 2004. (On My Own Holidays Ser.). 48p. (J). (gr. 2-4). lib. bdg. 25.26 (978-0-87614-941-6(7)) Lerner Publishing Group.

—Squanto & the First Thanksgiving. 2004. (gr. k-3). lib. bdg. 14.10 (978-0-613-63654-4(6)) Tandem Library Bks.

Kessel Joyce K. Squanto y el primer Día de Accion de Gracias (Squanto & the First Thanksgiving) Donze, Lisa, illus. 2007. (Yo solo Festividades (on My Own Holidays) Ser.). (J). pap. 6.95 (***978-0-8225-7795-9(X)*** , Ediciones Lerner) Lerner Publishing Group.

Kessel, Joyce K. Squanto y el Primer Día de Accion de Gracias (Squanto & the First Thanksgiving) Donze, Lisa, illus. 2007. (Yo Solo Festividades (On My Own Holidays) Ser.). (SPA.). 48p. (J). (gr. 2-4). lib. bdg. 25.26 (***978-0-8225-7792-8(5)*** , Ediciones Lerner) Lerner Publishing Group.

Metaxas, Eric. Squanto & the First Thanksgiving: The Legendary American Tale. Donato, Michael A., illus. 2004. 36p. (J). (gr. 3-8). reprint ed. 19.00 (978-0-7567-7123-2(4)) DIANE Publishing Co.

—Squanto & the Miracle of Thanksgiving. Stirnweis, Shannon, illus. 1999. 32p. (J). (gr. k-5). 9.99 (978-0-8499-5864-9(4)) Nelson, Thomas Inc.

SQUARE DANCING

Thomas, Mark. Square Dancing. 2001. (Welcome Bks.). (Illus.). 24p. (J). (ps-2). pap. 4.95 (978-0-516-23070-2(0) , Children's Pr.) Scholastic Library Publishing.

SQUIDS

Coldiron, Deborah. Squid. 2007. (Underwater World Ser.). (ENG., Illus.). 32p. (J). (gr. k-4). lib. bdg. 24.21 (***978-1-59928-816-1(8)*** , Buddy Bks.) ABDO Publishing Co.

Dussling, Jennifer. Giant Squid: Mystery of the Deep. Johnson, Pamela, illus. 1999. (All Aboard Reading Ser.). 48p. (J). (gr. 1-3). pap. 3.99 (978-0-448-41995-4(5) , Grosset & Dunlap) Penguin Group (USA) Inc.

—Giant Squid: Mystery of the Deep. 1999. (J). 10.79 (978-0-606-18938-5(6)); lib. bdg. 11.80 (978-0-613-21593-0(1)) Tandem Library Bks.

Ellis, Richard. Search for the Giant Squid. 1999. (gr. 7-12). lib. bdg. 24.55 (978-0-613-26874-5(1)) Tandem Library Bks.

Legg, Gerald. Octopuses & Squid. Francis, John, illus. 2004. (Scary Creatures Ser.). (J). 22.50 (978-0-531-12377-5(4)); 32p. (gr. 2-4). pap. 6.95 (978-0-531-16748-9(8)) Scholastic Library Publishing. (Watts, Franklin).

Iunis, Natalie. Startling Squids. 2008. (J). lib. bdg. 21.28 (***978-1-59716-513-6(1)***) Bearport Publishing Co., Inc.

Markle, Sandra. Outside & Inside Giant Squid. (Illus.). 40p. (J). 2005. (gr. 1-5). pap. 8.95 (978-0-8027-7724-9(4)); 2003. 17.85 (978-0-8027-8873-3(4)); 2003. 16.95 (978-0-8027-8872-6(6)) Walker & Co.

Matsen, Bradford. The Incredible Hunt for the Giant Squid. 2003. (Incredible Deep-Sea Adventures Ser.). (Illus.). 48p. (J). lib. bdg. 23.93 (978-0-7660-2192-1(0)) Enslow Pubs., Inc.

Nyikos, Stacy Ann. Squirt. Sisneros, Shawn, illus. l.t. ed. 2005. 32p. (J). lib. bdg. 15.95 (978-0-9764199-0-7(4)) Stonehorse Publishing, LLC.

Rake, Jody Sullivan. Squids. 2006. (Illus.). 24p. (J). (978-0-7368-6367-4(2) , Pebble Bks.) Capstone Pr., Inc.

Rhodes, Mary Jo & Hall, David. Octopuses & Squids. Hall, David, photos by. 2005. (Undersea Encounters Ser.). (Illus.). 48p. (J). (ps-7). 27.00 (978-0-516-24394-8(2) , Children's Pr.) Scholastic Library Publishing.

Sharth, Sharon. Squid. 2003. (Spirit of America: Our Colonies Ser.). (Illus.). 40p. (J). (gr. 2-6). 28.50 (978-1-56766-615-1(9)) Child's World, Inc.

Souza, Dorothy M. Sea Creatures with Many Arms. 1998. (Creatures All Around Us Ser.). (Illus.). 40p. (J). (gr. 2-4). lib. bdg. (978-1-57505-262-5(8) , Carolrhoda Bks.) Lerner Publishing Group.

Weber, Valerie. Squids. 2005. (Weird Wonders of the Deep Ser.). (Illus.). 24p. (J). lib. bdg. 22.00 (978-0-8368-4564-8(1)) Stevens, Gareth Inc.

Yin, Robert, illus. & photos by. Octopuses, Squid & Cuttlefish. Yin, Robert, photos by. 1999. 24p. (J). 6.50 (978-0-7685-0351-7(5)) Dominie Pr., Inc.

SQUIRRELS

Berger, Melvin & Berger, Gilda. Squirrels. 2002. (Scholastic Readers Ser.). (Illus.). (J). (978-0-439-44531-3(0)) Scholastic, Inc.

Bieri, Arthur Peter Martin. A Squirrel's Dilemma. 2007. pap. 9.00 (***978-0-8059-8718-8(5)***) Dorrance Publishing Co., Inc.

Booth, Anita K., illus. & photos by. Squirrels!!! An Informative & Entertaining Book about Our Favorite Mountain Mammal. Booth, Anita K., photos by. 2nd ed. 2004. 68p. 9.95 (978-0-9748702-1-2(8)) AKB Design.

Boring, Mel. Rabbits, Squirrels & Chipmunks. Garrow, Linda, illus. 1999. (Young Naturalist Field Guides Ser.). 40p. (J). (gr. 3 up). lib. bdg. 24.67 (978-0-8368-2146-8(7)) Stevens, Gareth Inc.

Bradley, James V. The Squirrel. 2006. (Nature Walk Ser.). (Illus.). 64p. (J). 28.00 (978-0-7910-9116-6(3) , Chelsea Hse.) Facts On File, Inc.

Capstone Press, contrib. by. Animals in the Fall, Vol. 3. 2005. (Our Seasons & Weather Ser.). 24p. (YA). (gr. k-3). pap. (978-1-56065-961-7(0) , Pebble Bks.) Capstone Pr., Inc.

Ciovacco, Justine. Squirrels. 2007. (J). (***978-1-59939-133-5(3)*** , Reader's Digest Young Families, Inc.) Reader's Digest Children's Publishing, Inc.

Diemer, Lauren. Squirrels. 2007. (J). (***978-1-59036-671-4(9)***); (***978-1-59036-672-1(7)***) Weigl Pubs., Inc.

Do Squirrels Swarm? (Animals All Around Ser.). 24p. (J). 7.95 (978-1-4048-0376-3(9)) Picture Window Bks.

Gilkerson, Patricia. My Adventure with Squirrels. 2007. 44p. (J). 8.99 (978-1-59092-470-9(3) , Orchard Academy Pr.) Windstorm Creative.

Glaser, Linda. Hello, Squirrels! Scampering through the Seasons. Holland, Gay W., illus. 2006. (Linda Glaser's Classic Creatures Ser.). 32p. (J). 22.60 (978-0-7613-2887-2(4) , Millbrook Pr.) Lerner Publishing Group.

Jacobs, Lee. Squirrel. 2002. (Illus.). 24p. (J). 24.94 (978-1-56711-642-7(6) , Blackbirch Pr., Inc.) Thomson Gale.

Jango-Cohen, Judith. Flying Squirrels. 2004. (Pull Ahead Bks.). (Illus.). 32p. (J). 22.60 (978-0-8225-3772-4(9) , Lerner Pubns.) Lerner Publishing Group.

Johannes, Avril & Branham, Jan. Squeak an Alaskan Squirrel. Tessama, C., illus. 2001. 32p. (J). 6.95 (978-1-57833-172-7(2)) Todd Communications.

Morris, Ting. Squirrel. Rosewarne, Graham, illus. 2005. 32p. (J). (gr. 3-7). lib. bdg. 27.10 (978-1-58340-520-8(8)) Smart Apple Media.

Murray, Peter. Squirrels. 2005. (World of Mammals Ser.). 40p. (J). (gr. 2-6). 29.93 (978-1-59296-503-8(2)) Child's World, Inc.

Olien, Becky. Squirrels: Furry Scurriers. 2002. (Wild World of Animals Ser.). (Illus.). 24p. (J). (gr. 1-2). lib. bdg. 18.60 (978-0-7368-1139-2(7) , Bridgestone Bks.) Capstone Pr., Inc.

Rustad, Martha E. H. Squirrels & Their Nests. 2004. (Animal Homes Ser.). (Illus.). 24p. (J). lib. bdg. 19.93 (978-0-7368-2585-6(1) , Pebble Bks.) Capstone Pr., Inc.

Schaefer, Lola M. Squirrels. 2004. (J). pap. 5.75 (978-1-4034-5737-0(9)); lib. bdg. (978-1-4034-5049-4(8)) Heinemann Library.

Somervill, Barbara. Gray Squirrel. 2008. (J). lib. bdg. 25.26 (***978-1-60279-116-9(3)***) Cherry Lake Publishing.

Squirrel Monkeys, 6 vols., Pack. (Sails Literacy Ser.). (gr. 1-2). 36.00 (978-0-7578-6768-2(5)) Rigby Education.

Squirrels & Their Nests. (Animal Homes Ser.). 24p. (J). 6.95 (978-0-7368-5129-9(1)) Capstone Pr., Inc.

Swanson, Diane. Squirrels. 2003. (Welcome to the World of Animals Ser.). (Illus.). 32p. (J). (gr. 3 up). lib. bdg. 23.33 (978-0-8368-3564-9(6)) Stevens, Gareth Inc.

—Welcome to the World of Squirrels. 2001. (Welcome to the World Ser.). (Illus.). 32p. (J). (ps-2). 9.95 (978-1-55285-309-2(8)); pap. 5.95 (978-1-55285-259-0(8)) Whitecap Bks., Ltd. CAN. *Dist:* Firefly Bks., Ltd.

Townsend, Emily Rose. Squirrels. Saunders-Smith, Gail, ed. 2004. (Woodland Animals Ser.). (Illus.). 24p. (J). (gr. k-1). lib. bdg. 15.93 (978-0-7368-2069-1(8) , Pebble Bks.) Capstone Pr., Inc.

Winkelman, Barbara Gaines. Flying Squirrel at Acorn Place. Kest, Kristin, illus. 1998. (Smithsonian's Backyard Ser.: Vol. 16). 32p. (J). (ps-2). 15.95 (978-1-56899-669-1(1)); Incl. toy. 32.95 (978-1-56899-673-8(X)) Soundprints.

—Flying Squirrel at Acorn Place: Micro Book. Kest, Kristin, illus. 1998. (Smithsonian's Backyard Ser.: Vol. 16). 32p. (J). (ps-2). 4.95 (978-1-56899-670-7(5)); Incl. micro toy. incl. audio (978-1-56899-676-9(4)) Soundprints.

SQUIRRELS—FICTION

Addis, Sandra. Flashlight One, Night Fright Off. 2005. 18.00 (978-0-8059-9782-8(2)) Dorrance Publishing Co., Inc.

Alexander, Jessica & Shore, Diane Z. Look Both Ways: A Cautionary Tale. Weidner, Teri, illus. 2005. 32p. (J). (ps-ps). 15.95 (978-1-58234-968-8(1)) Bloomsbury Publishing.

Allred, Sylvester. Rascal, the Tassel-Eared Squirrel. Iverson, Diane, illus. 2007. (J). (***978-0-938216-88-9(0)***) Grand Canyon Assn.

Aryal, Aimee. Hello Bucky! Reynolds, Rose, illus. 2004. (J). 19.95 (978-1-932888-11-9(X)) Mascot Bks., Inc.

—Hello Buzz! Moore, Danny, illus. 2004. (J). 19.95 (978-1-932888-27-0(6)) Mascot Bks., Inc.

Avi. The Mayor of Central Park. Floca, Brian, illus. 208p. (J). 2003. (gr. 3-6). 15.99 (978-0-06-000682-2(X)); 2003. (gr. 3-6). lib. bdg. 16.89 (978-0-06-051556-0(2)); 2005. reprint ed. pap. 5.99 (978-0-06-051557-7(0) , Harper Trophy) HarperCollins Pubs.

Baglio, Ben M. Squirrels in the School. 2000. (gr. 3-6). lib. bdg. 11.80 (978-0-613-27050-2(9)) Tandem Library Bks.

Bailey, Scott Arthur. The Tale of Frisky Squirrel. 2006. pap. 33.99 (***978-1-4280-4058-8(7)***) IndyPublish.com.

Bauman, Jill, illus. The Tale of Squirrel Nutkin. 2006. (J). 6.99 (978-1-59939-017-8(5) , Reader's Digest Young Families, Inc.) Reader's Digest Children's Publishing, Inc.

Biederman, Judy. Bushy Tail Squirrel's First Day Out. 2004. (J). lib. bdg. (978-0-9725485-2-6(1)) Waterfall Ridge.

Bonnell, Kris. A House for Squirrel. 2007. (J). 3.95 (***978-1-933727-46-2(2)***) Reading Reading Bks., LLC.

Bowers, Tim. A New Home. 2003. (Green Light Readers Level 1 Ser.). (Illus.). 24p. (J). 11.95 (978-0-15-204808-2(1)); pap. 3.95 (978-0-15-204848-8(0)) Harcourt Children's Bks. (Green Light Readers).

—New Home. 2002. (gr. k-3). lib. bdg. 11.80 (978-0-613-63169-3(2)) Tandem Library Bks.

Bradman, Tony. Elvis the Squirrel. Finlay, Lizzie, illus. 2006. (Read-It! Chapter Books). 48p. (J). (***978-1-4048-3119-3(3)*** , 1265806) Picture Window Bks.

Bruhac, Joseph. How Chipmunk Got His Stripes. 2001. (gr. k-3). lib. bdg. 15.30 (978-0-613-61631-7(6)) Tandem Library Bks.

Burgess, Thornton. The Adventures of Chatterer the Red Squirrel. 2006. pap. 10.95 (***978-1-59605-783-8(1)*** , Cosimo Classics) Cosimo, Inc.

Burgess, Thornton W. The Adventures of Chatterer the Red Squirrel. (J). 18.95 (978-0-8488-0376-6(0)) Amereon LTD.

—The Adventures of Happy Jack. 2004. (Dover Children's Thrift Classics Ser.). (Illus.). 128p. (J). (gr. 3-6). pap. 2.00 (978-0-486-43321-9(8)) Dover Pubns., Inc.

Bynum, Janie. Nutmeg & Barley: A Budding Friendship. Bynum, Janie, illus. 2006. (Illus.). 32p. (J). (ps-2). 15.99 (978-0-7636-2382-1(2)) Candlewick Pr.

Cardano, Sheila. Tail of A Squirrel & Other Tales Stor. 2006. pap. 28.99 (***978-1-4259-4760-6(3)***) AuthorHouse.

Carman, Patrick. Saving Mister Nibbles. 2008. (Elliot's Park Ser.). 80p. (J). 8.99 (***978-0-545-01930-9(3)*** , Orchard Bks.) Scholastic, Inc.

Chamberlain, Lyn. Quonby & the Tree Den. Weltner, Dave, illus. l.t. ed. 2004. 12p. (J). 7.95 (978-0-9706654-8-5(2)) Sprite Pr.

Cherry, Lynne. How Groundhog's Garden Grew. Cherry, Lynne, illus. 2003. (Illus.). 40p. (J). (ps up). pap. 15.95 (978-0-439-32371-0(1) , Blue Sky Pr., The) Scholastic, Inc.

Chinnery, Karen. Secret Agent Squirrel. 2006. (ENG.). 48p. per. 12.95 (***978-1-4241-5459-3(6)***) PublishAmerica, Inc.

Chips, Nathan. Winston's First Day of School. 2006. 24p. pap. 9.95 (978-1-929661-23-7(1) , 379-007) Transpersonal Publishing.

Clark, Emma Chicester. Will & Squill. 2006. (Illus.). 32p. (J). 15.95 (978-1-57505-936-5(3) , Carolrhoda Bks.) Lerner Publishing Group.

Cook, Sherry & Johnson, Terri. Vinnie Volcano, 26. Kuhn, Jesse, illus. l.t. ed. 2006. (Quirkles—Exploring Phonics through Science Ser.: 22). 32p. (J). 7.99 (978-1-933815-21-3(3) , Quirkles, The) Creative 3, LLC.

Cooper, Helen. Delicious! A Pumpkin Soup Story. 2007. (Illus.). 32p. (J). (ps-3). 16.00 (***978-0-374-31756-0(9)*** , Farrar, Straus & Giroux (BYR)) Farrar, Straus & Giroux.

Cooper, Helen. Pumpkin Soup. Cooper, Helen, illus. 1999. (Illus.). 32p. (J). (ps-3). 16.00 (978-0-374-36164-8(9) , Farrar, Straus & Giroux (BYR)) Farrar, Straus & Giroux.

Crane Johnson, Amy. A Home for Pearl Squirrel/una casa para la ardilla Perla: A Solomon Raven Story/ un cuento del cuervo Salomon, 4 vols. de la Vega, Eida, tr. Mommaerts, Robb, illus. rev. ed. 2004. (Solomon Raven Ser. : 1). Tr. of casa para la ardilla Perla. (SPA & ENG.). 32p. (J). 16.95 (978-0-9724973-4-3(X) , 626999) Raven Tree Pr.

Cullen, Lynn. Stink Bomb. 128p. (J). (gr. 3-7). 1999. pap. 3.99 (978-0-380-78507-0(2) , Harper Trophy); 1998. 14.00 (978-0-380-97647-8(1)) HarperCollins Pubs.

Cummins, Judi, creator. It's Raining Acorns & Ladybugs. 2005. (Illus.). 28p. (J). per. (978-0-9760377-4-3(2)) Cummins, Judi.

Davies, Caroline & Martin, Sharon. Chwarae Cuddio. 2005. (WEL., Illus.). 12p. (978-1-86101-080-3(X)) Acen Limited.

—Cotiau Newydd. 2005. (WEL., Illus.). 12p. (978-1-86101-081-0(8)) Acen Limited.

—Y Frech Goch. 2005. (WEL., Illus.). 12p. (978-1-86101-079-7(6)) Acen Limited.

Davis, Holly. Thankful Together. Sokolova, Valerie, illus. 2006. 36p. (J). 5.99 (978-0-7847-1436-2(3) , 04077) Standard Publishing.

Delittle, Cathy. The Squirrel Who Loved Picnics. Delittle, Cathy, illus. 1998. (Illus.). 9p. (J). (ps-1). spiral bd. 7.95 (978-1-892633-05-7(1) , OOCD209) Delittle Storyteller Co.

D'Lacey, Chris. The Fire Within. 2007. 352p. (J). pap. 7.99 (978-0-439-67244-3(9) , Orchard Bks.) Scholastic, Inc.

Dong, Seung. Where Is My Black Belt? 2005. 151p. pap. 19.95 (978-1-4137-8132-8(2)) PublishAmerica, Inc.

Doodle, Nanny. Divorced at Six. 2006. 158p. pap. 19.95 (978-1-4241-3963-7(5)) PublishAmerica, Inc.

Doudna, Kelly. Squirrel Hollow. Chawla, Neena, illus. 2006. (Fact & Fiction Ser.). (J). 21.35 (978-1-59679-967-7(6) , SandCastle); pap. (978-1-59679-968-4(4)) ABDO Publishing Co.

Dower, Laura. Let the Fur Fly. 2002. (gr. k-3). lib. bdg. 11.25 (978-0-613-64743-4(2)) Tandem Library Bks.

Dubowski, Cathy East. Adventures of Rocky & Bullwinkle. 2000. (gr. 3-6). lib. bdg. 11.80 (978-0-613-24090-1(1)) Tandem Library Bks.

Duracell and the National Center for Missing & Exploited Children (NCMEC), creator. The Great Tomato Adventure: A Story about Smart Safety Choices. 2007. 0.00 (***978-0-9795307-0-8(9)***) Duracell & the National Ctr. for Missing & Exploited Children (NCMEC).

Earl the Squirrel & the Great Acorn Caper. None. 2003. (J). pap. 24.95 incl. cd-rom (978-0-9749041-0-8(4)) Big Lil' Bks.

Ehlert, Lois. Nuts to You! 1998. pap. 6.00 (978-0-15-201600-5(7)) Harcourt Trade Pubs.

Elschner, G. & Devos, X. Friends for All Seasons. 2006. (Illus.). 32p. (J). 15.95 (978-0-7358-2003-6(1)) North-South Bks., Inc.

Evenson, Carol. Chatture's Rainbow. 2005. 47p. spiral bd. 7.93 (978-1-4116-4106-8(X)) Lulu.com.

Fiol, Doreen. Pookha Moon. 2006. pap. 11.99 (***978-1-4259-6686-7(1)***) AuthorHouse.

Forbing, Shirley E. Sylvester: A Squirrel for Suzie. Zapp, Marilyn, illus. 2001. (YA). pap. 21.95 incl. audio compact disk Wild Animal XPress.

Freeman, Don. Earl the Squirrel. 2005. (Illus.). 48p. (J). (ps-2). 15.99 (978-0-670-06019-1(4) , Viking Juvenile) Penguin Group (USA) Inc.

Freeman, Don. Earl the Squirrel. 2007. 48p. (J). (gr. k up). pap. 6.99 (***978-0-14-240893-3(X)*** , Puffin) Penguin Group (USA) Inc.

Galjanic, Lisa. When Series 6 Volume Set, 6, 6. 2007. (Illus.). 100p. (J). 34.95 (***978-1-933532-06-6(8)***) LSG Pubns.

Galjanic, Lisa. When Squirrels Try. Hope, Michelle, illus. 2007. (J). 9.95 (978-1-933532-02-8(5)) LSG Pubns.

Giddens, Martha Anne. The Unluckiest Kid in the Universe. 2006. 56p. pap. (***978-1-4120-7935-8(7)***) Trafford Publishing.

Grambling, Lois G. Shoo! Scat! Newman, Barbara Johansen, illus. 2004. 32p. (J). 16.95 (978-0-7614-5167-9(6)) Cavendish, Marshall Corp.

Gray Squirrel's Daring Day. 2002. (Backyard Mini Bks.). (Illus.). 32p. (J). (978-1-59069-018-5(4) , H2007) Studio Mouse LLC.

Harcourt School Publishers Staff. The Giant's Sock Advanced Level. 3rd ed. 2002. (Trophies Reading Program Ser.). (Illus.). pap. 5.10 (978-0-15-323113-1(0)) Harcourt Schl. Pubs.

—Talent Night: On Level. 3rd ed. 2002. (Trophies Reading Program Ser.). (Illus.). (J). pap. 4.10 (978-0-15-322988-6(8)) Harcourt Schl. Pubs.

—Trofeos On Level: El Concurso. 3rd ed. 2002. (SPA., Illus.). pap. 5.50 (978-0-15-323899-4(2)) Harcourt Schl. Pubs.

Harper, Charise Mericle. The Trouble with Normal. 2003. (Illus.). 32p. (J). (gr. k-3). tchr. ed. 15.00 (978-0-618-15626-9(7)) Houghton Mifflin Co. Trade & Reference Div.

Heigh, Stephen. Mr. George & the Red Hat. Burton, Kevin, ed. Heigh, Stephen, illus. 2004. (Illus.). 32p. (J). 18.95 (978-0-9745715-2-2(0)) KRBY Creations, LLC.

Hein, Connie L. Toliver in Time; for a Journey West: History in a Nutshell. Theobald, Denise, illus. l.t. ed. 2005. 28p. (J). lib. bdg. 17.95 (978-0-9740855-6-2(1)); per. 9.95 (978-0-9740855-7-9(X)) Still Water Publishing.

Hiebert, Elfrieda H. & Juel, Connie. Squirrels. (Little Book Practice Reader Ser.). (J). (978-0-8136-0823-5(6)) Modern Curriculum Pr.

Hixson, Jon, et al. Caterpillar Jones & the Adventures of Nut E. Squirrel. 2002. (Mulberry Meadow Ser.: Vol. 2). iv, 184p. (J). (gr. 2-6). pap. 8.95 (978-0-9718774-0-5(8)) Foundation Publishing.

Houser, Marlin L. The Adventures of Little Fox, Book Two, the Secret of Squirrel Meadow. 2006. (Illus.). 194p. 16.95 (978-0-9752703-4-9(6)); pap. 7.95 (978-0-9752703-5-6(4)) Marhouse, Inc.

Hughes, Diane Marie. Meet Wilbur the Squirrel. 2004. 21p. pap. 14.95 (978-1-4137-2758-6(1)) PublishAmerica, Inc.

Humphreys, Dolores, illus. The Adventures of J. G. & Echo: The Land of All Creatures & the Swamp Creature, 1. 2003. 81p. (J). per. 16.00 (978-0-9727415-2-1(6)) Cuccia, Louis.

Hunter, Alixander. The Handicapped Squirrel. l.t. ed. 1998. (Illus.). 32p. 19.95 (978-0-9665582-0-3(0)) Alixander Group.

Hurwitz, Johanna. Lexi's Tale. Brewster, Patience, illus. 2002. (Park Pals Adventure Ser.). 112p. (J). (gr. 2-5). pap. 4.95 (978-1-58717-160-4(0) , SeaStar Bks.) Chronicle Bks. LLC.

—Lexi's Tale. 2002. (gr. 3-6). lib. bdg. 11.80 (978-0-613-54420-7(X)) Tandem Library Bks.

—Pee-Wee's Tale. Brewster, Patience, illus. 2000. (J). 104p. pap. 14.95 (978-1-58717-028-7(0)); 96p. (gr. 2-5). 14.95 (978-1-58717-027-0(2)) Chronicle Bks. LLC. (SeaStar Bks.).

—Pee-Wee's Tale. Brewster, Patience, illus. 2001. 104p. (J). (ps-3). per. 11.80 (978-0-613-54426-9(9)) Tandem Library Bks.

Hurwitz, Johanna & Brewster, Patience. Pee-Wee's Tale. 2001. (Park Pals Adventure Ser.). (Illus.). 112p. (J). (gr. 2-5). pap. 4.95 (978-1-58717-111-6(2) , SeaStar Bks.) Chronicle Bks. LLC.

Hurwitz, Johanna & Chronicle Books LLC Staff. Squirrel World. Garry-McCord, Kathleen & McCord, Kathi, illus. 2007. (Park Pals Adventure Ser.). 128p. (J). (gr. 1-5). 14.95 (978-0-8118-5660-7(7)) Chronicle Bks. LLC.

Jacques, Brian. Rakkety Tam. David, Elliot, illus. 2006. (Redwall Ser.). 384p. (J). (gr. 5). pap. 8.99 (978-0-14-240683-0(X) , Puffin) Penguin Group (USA) Inc.

—Rakkety Tam. 2005. (Redwall Ser.). 384p. (gr. 12). mass mkt. 7.99 (978-0-441-01318-0(X) , Ace Bks.) Penguin Group (USA) Inc.

—Rakkety Tam. Elliot, David, illus. 2004. (Redwall Ser.). 432p. (YA). (gr. 4-6). 23.99 (978-0-399-23725-6(9) , Philomel) Penguin Group (USA) Inc.

Jarvis, Robin. Oaken Throne. 2005. (Illus.). 384p. (J). 17.95 (978-1-58717-277-9(1) , SeaStar Bks.) Chronicle Bks. LLC.

Jennings, Sharon. Priscilla's Paw de Deux. Hendry, Linda, illus. 2002. 36p. (J). (ps-2). (978-1-55041-718-0(5)) Fitzhenry & Whiteside, Ltd.

Johnson, Donna. The Story of the Little Red Leaf. Johnson, Emily, illus. l.t. ed. 2006. 22p. (J). 25.00 ***(978-0-9778774-0-9(X))*** Choicepoint Editions.

Johnson, William Crow. The Adventures of Sara Springborn & Mr. Wollo Bushtail. 2001. 208p. (gr. 7). pap. 14.95 (978-0-595-17616-8(X)) iUniverse, Inc.

Jones, Dorothy Ann. Learn to Recycle with Mary & Goofy Gopher. 2006. 26p. pap. 7.95 (978-0-533-15131-8(7)) Vantage Pr., Inc.

Keller, George. Squirrelly Whirrly & the Haunted House. 2005. 21p. 7.45 (978-1-4116-4425-0(5)) Lulu.com.

Kindley, Jeff. Scamper's Year. Rader, Laura, illus. 1999. (Bank Street Reader Collection). 48p. (J). (ps-2). lib. bdg. 22.60 (978-0-8368-1777-5(X)) Stevens, Gareth Inc.

Kitamura, Satoshi. Ardilla Tiene Hambre. 1998. (SPA., Illus.). 16p. (J). (ps). per. (978-968-16-5539-6(7)) Fondo de Cultura Economica MEX. *Dist:* Lectorum Pubns., Inc.

Kochalka, James. Squirrelly Gray. 2007. (Picture Book Ser.). (Illus.). 40p. (J). (gr. k-2). 12.99 ***(978-0-375-83975-7(5));*** lib. bdg. 15.99 ***(978-0-375-93975-4(X))*** Random Hse. Children's Bks. (Random Hse. Bks. for Young Readers).

LaReau, Kara. Rabbit & Squirrel. Magoon, Scott, illus. 2008. (J). ***(978-0-15-206307-8(2))*** Harcourt Trade Pubs.

Levy, Elizabeth. The Mixed-Up Mask Mystery: A Fletcher Mystery. Gorstein, Mordicai, illus. unabr. ed. 2006. (First Chapter Bks.). (J). (gr. 2-4). pap. 20.95 incl. audio compact disk ***(978-1-59519-711-5(7));*** pap. 17.95 incl. audio ***(978-1-59519-710-8(9))*** Live Oak Media.

Lipe, Riki. Hanging with Yum-Yum & Yuck. 2007. (J). 10.00 ***(978-0-9659381-6-7(6))*** Hoot N' Cackle Pr.

Lithgow, John. Micawber. Payne, C. F., illus. 2002. 44p. (J). (gr. k-3). 17.95 incl. audio compact disk (978-0-689-83341-0(5)) Simon & Schuster Children's Publishing.

—Micawber. Payne, C. F., illus. 2005. 40p. (J). reprint ed. pap. 6.99 (978-0-689-83542-1(6) , Aladdin) Simon & Schuster Children's Publishing.

Loughead, Deb. A Pocketful of Fur. Birke, Lisa, tr. 2005. (Illus.). 60p. (J). (gr. 2-4). 6.95 (978-0-9730831-6-3(6)) Hodgepog Bks. CAN. *Dist:* Coteau Bks., Fitzhenry & Whiteside, Ltd.

Luberto, Bradley. Clide & Druce: A Repulsive Tale of Trolls & Tax Money. 2006. (ENG.). 48p. per. 12.95 ***(978-1-4241-5012-0(4))*** PublishAmerica, Inc.

The Magical Adventures of Samuel the Squirrel & Oscar the Owl Journey to Mars. 2005. (J). per. 12.95 (978-0-9762929-0-6(4)) Morning Glory Pubns.

Marciano, John Bemelmans. Harold's Tail. 2003. (Illus.). 144p. (J). (gr. 3-7). 15.99 (978-0-670-03660-8(9) , Viking Juvenile) Penguin Group (USA) Inc.

McAllister, M. I. Mistmantle Chronicles, the: Urchin & the Heartstone - Book #2. Rayyan, Omar, illus. 2nd rev. ed. 2007. 304p. (gr. 3-7). pap. 7.99 ***(978-0-7868-5489-9(8))*** Miramax Bks.

—The Urchin & the Heartstone. Rayyan, Omar, illus. 2nd rev. ed. 2006. (Mistmantle Chronicles Ser.: Bk. 2). 304p. (gr. 3-7). 17.95 (978-0-7868-5488-2(X)) Hyperion Bks. for Children.

—Urchin of the Riding Stars. Rayyan, Omar, illus. 2006. (Mistmantle Chronicles Ser.: Bk. 1). 288p. (gr. 3-7). pap. 7.99 (978-0-7868-5487-5(0)) Hyperion Bks. for Children.

McCartney, Paul & Ardagh, Philip. High in the Clouds. Dunbar, Geoff, illus. 2007. 93p. (J). 20.00 ***(978-1-4223-6720-9(7))*** DIANE Publishing Co.

McCartney, Paul, et al. High in the Clouds. 2005. (Illus.). 96p. (J). (gr. 1-5). 19.99 (978-0-525-47733-4(0) , Dutton Juvenile) Penguin Group (USA) Inc.

McCorkle, Barbara. Bandit Raccoon. Taylor, David, illus. l.t. ed. 2006. 39p. (J). 19.95 ***(978-1-59879-170-9(2));*** per. 13.99 ***(978-1-59879-123-5(0))*** Lifevest Publishing, Inc.

McCorkle, Barbara. Brutis' New Friend. 2005. (Illus.). 23p. (J). per. 8.99 (978-1-932338-60-7(8)) Lifevest Publishing, Inc.

McKelvey, Lonnie. Ralph & His New Friends. 2007. (J). ***(978-0-9796519-1-5(3))*** Mirror Publishing.

McNease, Mitzy. Chester's Presents. Cox, Kim, illus. ed. 2006. 28p. (J). 10.96 (978-0-9779488-0-2(3)) Blancmange Publishing.

Miller, Donna C. Me & Mister Squirrel. 2005. (J). pap. 8.00 (978-0-8059-6523-0(8)) Dorrance Publishing Co., Inc.

Morgan, Allen. Matthew & the Midnight Hospital. ed. 2004. (Illus.). (J). (gr. k-3). spiral bd. (978-0-616-01529-2(1)) Canadian National Institute for the Blind/Institut National Canadien pour les Aveugles.

Morgan, Allen & Martchenko, Michael. Matthew & the Midnight Hospital. 1999. (Matthew's Midnight Adventures Ser.). (Illus.). 32p. (J). (ps-3). 6.99 (978-0-7737-6014-1(8)) Stoddart Kids CAN. *Dist:* Fitzhenry & Whiteside, Ltd.

Moser, Lisa. Squirrel's World. Gorbachev, Valeri, illus. 2007. 48p. (J). (gr. k-2). 14.99 ***(978-0-7636-2929-8(4))*** Candlewick Pr.

—Sticky Burr: Adventures in Burrwood Forest. Gorbachev, Valeri, illus. 2007. (J). ***(978-0-7636-3567-1(7))*** Candlewick Pr.

Nair, Anita. Adventures of Nonu, the Skating Squirrel. 2006. (Illus.). 44p. (J). ***(978-81-291-0892-0(5))*** Rupa & Co.

Nakagawa, Rieko. Guri & Gura Cd Edition. 2006. (Illus.). 32p. (J). 12.95 (978-0-8048-3782-8(1)) Tuttle Publishing.

Osuna, Rosa, illus. No es Facil, Pequena Ardilla. 2004. Tr. of It's Not Easy, Little Squirrel. (SPA.). (J). 15.99 (978-84-8464-202-2(X)) Kalandraka Editora, S.L. ESP. *Dist:* Lectorum Pubns., Inc.

Page, Frank. Sometimes a Squirrel Is Just a Squirrel. 2005. 106p. pap. 9.99 (978-1-4116-6062-5(5)) Lulu.com.

Parry, Alan. Never Mind Squirrel. Parry, Linda, illus. 2004. (Oaktree Wood Ser.). (ps-3). 5.00 (978-0-687-09710-4(X)) Abingdon Pr.

Patch. Squirrel World. 2005. 81p. pap. 14.95 (978-1-4137-4408-8(7)) PublishAmerica, Inc.

Pearce, Philippa. The Squirrel Wife. Anderson, Wayne, illus. 2007. 32p. (J). (gr. k-3). 16.99 ***(978-0-7636-3551-0(0))*** Candlewick Pr.

Pearson, Iris & Merrill, Mike. The Adventures of Lady: The Big Storm. Pearson, Iris, ed. Project Firefly Animation Studios, illus. rev. ed. 2007. 34p. (J). 15.99 ***(978-0-9789984-2-4(1))*** Adventures of Lady LLC, The.

—The Adventures of Lady: The Big Storm Coloring Book. Pearson, Iris, ed. Project Firefly Animation Studios, illus. 2007. 34p. (J). pap. 6.99 ***(978-0-9789984-3-1(X))*** Adventures of Lady LLC, The.

Pellant, Terry. The Real Valentine's Story. 2004. 27p. (J). pap. 14.95 (978-1-4137-2146-1(X)) PublishAmerica, Inc.

Potter, Beatrix. The Tale of Squirrel Nutkin. Potter, Beatrix, illus. 2002. (Illus.). (J). 15.23 (978-0-7587-3753-3(X)) Book Wholesalers, Inc.

—The Tale of Squirrel Nutkin. 2002. (Illus.). 64p. (J). 6.99 (978-0-7232-4771-5(4) , Warne) Penguin Group (USA) Inc.

—The Tale of Squirrel Nutkin. (Beatrix Potter Bookmark Board Book Ser.). (Illus.). 6p. (J). bds. 3.95 (978-1-58989-203-3(8)) Thurman Hse., LLC.

Powers, Paul. Tales of the Swamp Creatures. 2003. 71p. pap. 11.95 (978-1-4137-0160-9(4)) PublishAmerica, Inc.

Priscella the Monarch Butterfly. l.t. ed. 2000. 10p. (J). 5.95 (978-0-9716507-1-8(3)) Foglestories.

Pyle, Hugh F. Scamper Squirrel Goes to Camp. 2000. (Illus.). 72p. (J). (gr. 4-7). pap. 7.95 (978-0-87398-774-5(8)) Sword of the Lord Pubs.

Quinn, Daniel. Work, Work, Work. Quinn, Daniel, illus. 2006. (Illus.). 32p. (J). 14.95 (978-1-58642-114-4(X)) Knopf Canada CAN. *Dist:* Random Hse., Inc.

Raye, Rebekah. The Very Best Bed. Raye, Rebekah, illus. 2006. (Illus.). 32p. (J). (ps-3). 16.95 (978-0-88448-284-0(7)) Tilbury Hse. Pubs.

Reitz, Ric. The Journey of Sir Douglas Fir: A Reader's Musical. Bell, Suzanne, ed. Brewer, David, illus. 1999. 48p. (J). (gr. 2-6). per. 19.95 (978-0-9670160-0-9(2) , Sir Fir Bks. & Music) Sir Fir Enterprises, LLC.

Rey, H. A. & Rey, Margret. CG TV Curious George Plants a Seed Spanish Bilingual Edition. 2007. 24p. (J). (gr. k-3). mass mkt. 3.99 ***(978-0-618-89688-2(0))*** Houghton Mifflin Co. Trade & Reference Div.

Rivett, Rachel. Little Grey & the Great Mystery. 2007. (Illus.). 32p. (J). pap. 10.95 ***(978-0-7459-4909-3(6))*** Lion Hudson plc GBR. *Dist:* Independent Pubs. Group.

Rock, John P. Earl & Pearl, the Christmas Squirrels. Cohen, Stephen Z., illus. 1998. 24p. (J). (gr. 1-6). pap. 4.95 (978-0-9665625-3-8(4) , 0024) Habitat Pubns.

Rockas, Leo. Mice Make War. 2007. 53p. 12.95 ***(978-1-4241-5708-2(0))*** PublishAmerica, Inc.

Rylant, Cynthia. Gooseberry Park. 2007. (Illus.). 144p. (J). pap. 5.95 ***(978-0-15-206159-3(2)*** , Harcourt Paperbacks) Harcourt Children's Bks.

Sargent, Dave. Cindy Sparrow. Lenoir, Jane, illus. 2000. (Feather Tale Ser.). ix, 36p. (J). pap. 6.95 (978-1-56763-472-3(9)); lib. bdg. 19.95 (978-1-56763-471-6(0)) Ozark Publishing.

Sargent, Dave & Sargent, David M. Cindy Sparrow: Respect the Property of Others, 19, 6. Lenoir, Jane, illus. 2003. (Feather Tales Ser.: 6). 42p. (J). pap. 6.95 (978-1-56763-730-4(2)); 2nd ed. lib. bdg. 19.95 (978-1-56763-729-8(9)) Ozark Publishing.

Scheber, George. Earl Joins the Circus. Spicer, Bridgett, illus. l.t. ed. 2005. (Adventures of Earl the Squirrel Ser.). 32p. (J). (ps-3). 12.95 (978-1-878847-01-0(5)) Make Me A Story Pr.

—Earl the Squirrel. Spicer, Bridgett, illus. l.t. ed. 2005. (Adventures of Earl the Squirrel Ser.). 32p. (J). (ps-2). 12.95 (978-1-878847-00-3(7)) Make Me A Story Pr.

Sculthorp, Jeffrey A. Squirrels Don't Read, Shakespeare. Wingate, Lynae & Kober, John R., eds. Walter, Lorin, illus. 2000. (Wickleville Woods Ser.). 28p. (J). (ps-2). pap. 4.99 (978-1-889319-73-5(2) , Wickleville Woods) Trend Enterprises, Inc.

Shavatt, Donna & Shavatt, Eve. Sammy Squirrel & Friends' Medical Adventures. Mays, Luke, illus. 2000. 40p. (J). pap. 11.95 (978-0-9678630-1-6(5)) Shavatt Enterprises.

Shelton, Ricky V. Quacker Meets His Dad the Squirrel: Tales from a Duck Named Quacker. Williams, Shan, illus. Date not set. (J). (ps-1). pap. 7.00 (978-0-9634257-3-7(0)) RVS Bks., Inc.

Simon and Schuster Children's Staff, ed. Rocky & Bullwinkle & the Jet Fuel Formula. 2000. pap. 3.99 (978-0-689-82478-4(5) , Simon Spotlight) Simon & Schuster Children's Publishing.

—Rocky & Bullwinkle & the Rue Brittania. 1999. pap. 3.99 (978-0-689-82479-1(3) , Simon Spotlight) Simon & Schuster Children's Publishing.

Simon, Mary Manz. Squirrel Says Thank You. Couri, Kathy & Clearwater, Linda, illus. 2006. (First Virtues for Toddlers Ser.). 20p. (J). 5.99 (978-0-7847-1415-7(0) , 04067) Standard Publishing.

Simpson, Richard. The Squirrel Who Was Afraid to Climb Trees. Hoch, Kevin, illus. 2003. 55p. (J). pap. 9.95 (978-0-7414-1825-8(8)) Infinity Publishing.

The Snowman, 6 vols., Pack. (Chiquilibros Ser.). (gr. k-1). 23.00 (978-0-7635-0417-5(3)) Rigby Education.

The Snowman: Individual Title Six-Pack. (Story Steps Ser.). (gr. k-2). 20.00 (978-0-7635-9578-4(0)) Rigby Education.

Sommer, Carl. No One Will Ever Know. 2003. (Another Sommer-Time Story Ser.). (Illus.). 48p. (J). (gr. 1-4). 16.95 incl. audio compact disk (978-1-57537-506-9(0)); 16.95 incl. audio (978-1-57537-555-7(9)) Advance Publishing, Inc.

Spellman, Frankie. Pinky & Bubs' Stinky Night Out: Adventures on Martha's Vineyard. Spellman, Susan, illus. 2005. (J). per. 12.95 (978-1-933002-16-3(6)) PublishingWorks.

Stone, Chuck. Squizzy the Black Squirrel: A Fabulous Fable of Friendship. Jackson, Jeannie, tr. Jackson, Jeannie, illus. 2003. 30p. (J). 16.95 (978-0-940880-71-9(7)) Open Hand Publishing, LLC.

Swallow, Pamela C. Groundhog Gets a Say. Bunkus, Denise, illus. 2007. 40p. (J). (ps). pap. 6.99 ***(978-0-14-240896-4(4)*** , Puffin) Penguin Group (USA) Inc.

—Groundhog Gets a Say. Brunkus, Denise, illus. 2005. 40p. (J). (ps). 15.99 (978-0-399-23876-5(X) , Putnam Juvenile) Penguin Group (USA) Inc.

Tafuri, Nancy. The Busy Little Squirrel. Tafuri, Nancy, illus. 2007. 32p. (J). (ps-k). 15.99 (978-0-689-87341-6(7) , Simon & Schuster Children's Publishing) Simon & Schuster Children's Publishing.

Utsler, Elaine. The Black Cherry Forest: Storybook 1. Wendle, Stan, ed. Jeannotte, Lawrence, illus. 2nd ed. 2003. 48p. (J). per. 6.95 (978-0-9727787-1-8(3) , BCF1B) EV Publishing Corp.

Watt, Melanie. Scaredy Squirrel. 2006. (Illus.). 40p. (J). 14.95 (978-1-55337-959-1(4)) Kids Can Pr., Ltd. CAN. *Dist:* Wybel Marketing Group.

Watt, Mélanie. Scaredy Squirrel Makes a Friend. Watt, Mélanie, illus. 2007. (Illus.). 32p. (J). (ps-3). ***(978-1-55453-181-3(0))*** Kids Can Pr., Ltd.

Weidner Zoehfeld, Kathleen & Harrington, Geri. Smithsonian Backyard Fawn & Gray Squirrel Box. Snyder, Joel & Chopin Roosevelt, Michele, illus. 2002. (Smithsonian Soundprints Ser.). 64p. (J). 19.95 (978-1-931465-55-7(X) , Silver Dolphin Bks.) Advantage Pubs. Group.

Wheeler, Kathryn. The Suspicious Stranger: A Tale in Which Kindness Is Repaid. Anderson, Julie, illus. 1999. (Stories to Grow By Ser.). 20p. (C). 3.99 (978-1-56822-592-0(X) , Instructional Fair) Schaffer, Frank Pubns.

White, Frances. Beaufort Squirrel of Rainbow Springs. Smith, Marve, illus. 2002. 24p. (J). (ps-1). lib. bdg. 14.95 (978-0-9712158-0-1(4)) Randolph Publishing.

Wiles, Deborah. One Wide Sky: A Bedtime Lullaby. Bowers, Tim, illus. 2003. 32p. (J). 16.00 (978-0-15-202334-8(8)) Harcourt Children's Bks.

Williamgoldenpen. Quacker's Bedtime Stories. 2006. 49p. pap. 12.95 (978-1-4241-2236-3(8)) PublishAmerica, Inc.

Williams, Levester. The Adventures od Crunchy & Munchy Squirrel: Field Nuts. 2005. pap. ***(978-0-9774418-0-8(6))*** L.Patrick Publishing.

Winkelman, Barbara Gaines. Flying Squirrel at Acorn Place. Kest, Kristin, illus. 1998. (Smithsonian's Backyard Ser.: Vol. 16). 32p. (J). (ps-2). 15.95 (978-1-56899-669-1(1)) Soundprints.

Yang, Stella, illus. The Snowman, 6 vols., Pack. (Sails Literacy Ser.). 16p. (gr. k up). lib. bdg. 27.00 (978-0-7635-4439-3(6)) Rigby Education.

Young, Miriam. Miss Suzy. Lobel, Arnold, illus. 40th anniv. ed. 2004. 44p. (J). 17.95 (978-1-930900-28-8(7)) Purple Hse. Pr.

SRI LANKA

Grolier Educational Staff, contrib. by. Sri Lanka. 2003. (Illus.). 32p. (J). (978-0-7172-5801-7(7) , Grolier) Scholastic Library Publishing.

Guruswamy, Krishnan. Sri Lanka. 2002. (Countries of the World Ser.). (Illus.). 96p. (J). (gr. 6 up). lib. bdg. 30.00 (978-0-8368-2354-7(0)) Stevens, Gareth Inc.

Hoffmann, Sara. Sri Lanka in Pictures. 2006. (Visual Geography Series, Second Ser.). (Illus.). 80p. (J). 27.93 (978-0-8225-3481-5(9) , Twenty-First Century Bks.) Lerner Publishing Group.

Lee, Vanessa & Guruswamy, Krishnan. Welcome to Sri Lanka. 2003. (Welcome to My Country Ser.). (Illus.). 48p. (J). (gr. 2 up). lib. bdg. 26.00 (978-0-8368-2554-1(3)) Stevens, Gareth Inc.

Miller, Debra A. Sri Lanka. 2005. (Modern Nations Ser.). (Illus.). 96-144p. (J). (gr. 7-10). 29.95 (978-1-59018-626-8(5) , Lucent Bks.) Thomson Gale.

Wanasundera, Nanda P. Sri Lanka. 2002. (Cultures of the World Ser.). (Illus.). 144p. (gr. 5 up). lib. bdg. 37.07 (978-0-7614-1477-3(0) , Cavendish, Marshall Reference Bks.) Cavendish, Marshall Corp.

SRI LANKA—FICTION

Lipp, Frederick J. Tea Leaves. Coloma, Lester, tr. Coloma, Lester, illus. 2003. (J). 32p. (gr. 1-6). 15.95 (978-1-59034-998-4(9)); 33p. pap. (978-1-59034-999-1(7)) Mondo Publishing.

Selvadurai, Shyam. Swimming in the Monsoon Sea. 2007. 280p. (J). (gr. 8). pap. 9.95 ***(978-0-88776-834-7(2))*** Tundra Bks., Inc./Livres Toundra, Inc. CAN. *Dist:* Random Hse., Inc.

S

STABILIZATION IN INDUSTRY

see Economic History

STAGE

see Acting; Actors and Actresses; Theater

STAGE SCENERY

see Theaters—Stage Setting and Scenery

STAGE SETTING

see Theaters—Stage Setting and Scenery

STAINED GLASS

see Glass Painting and Staining

STAIRCASES

Freeman, Marcia S. Going Up? 2006. (City Science Ser.). (Illus.). 24p. (J). (gr. k-3). 14.95 (978-1-59515-409-5(4)) Rourke Publishing, LLC.

STALIN, JOSEPH, 1879-1953

Barter, James. Joseph Stalin. 2005. (Heroes & Villans Ser.). (Illus.). 96-112p. (J). (gr. 7-10). 29.95 (978-1-59018-557-5(9) , Lucent Bks.) Thomson Gale.

Downing, David. Joseph Stalin. 2001. (Leading Lives Ser.). (Illus.). 64p. (J). (gr. 5-7). lib. bdg. 27.86 (978-1-58810-165-5(7)) Heinemann Library.

—Leading Lives, 4 bks., Set 2. 2002. (J). (gr. 5-7). lib. bdg. 114.00 (978-1-58810-576-9(8)) Heinemann Library.

Downing, David, et al. Leading Lives, 17 bks. 2003. (Illus.). (J). Set 1-3. lib. bdg. 484.50 (978-1-4034-0838-9(6)); Set 3. (gr. 5-7). lib. bdg. 199.50 (978-1-4034-0837-2(8)) Heinemann Library.

Gottfried, Ted. The Stalinist Empire. Reim, Melanie K., illus. 2002. (Rise & Fall of the Soviet Union Ser.). 128p. (gr. 7 up). lib. bdg. 28.90 (978-0-7613-2558-1(1) , Twenty-First Century Bks.) Lerner Publishing Group.

Haugen, Brenda. Joseph Stalin: Dictator of the Soviet Union. 2006. (Signature Lives Ser.). (Illus.). 112p. (J). (gr. 5-7). 30.60 (978-0-7565-1597-3(1)) Compass Point Bks.

Joihnson, Robert, compiled by. Lenin, Stalin & Communist Russia: The Myth & Reality of Communism. 2003. (Studymates Ser.). (Illus.). 132p. (C). pap. 27.50 (978-1-84285-039-8(3)) Studymates Ltd. GBR. *Dist:* Trans-Atlantic Pubns., Inc.

Kenworthy, Joyce. Joseph Stalin. 2002. (History's Villains Ser.). (Illus.). 112p. (J). 29.94 (978-1-56711-626-7(4) , Blackbirch Pr., Inc.) Thomson Gale.

Marrin, Albert. Stalin. 2002. 244p. (J). 13.95 (978-1-893103-09-2(9)) Beautiful Feet Bks.

Zuehlke, Jeffrey. Joseph Stalin. 2006. (Illus.). 112p. (J). 27.93 (978-0-8225-3421-1(5) , Twenty-First Century Bks.) Lerner Publishing Group.

STALINGRAD, BATTLE OF, VOLGOGRAD, RUSSIA, 1942-1943

Wilson, John. Four Steps to Death. 2005. 208p. (YA). (gr. 7-9). (978-1-55337-705-4(2)); (978-1-55337-704-7(4)) Kids Can Pr., Ltd.

STAMINA, PHYSICAL

see Physical Fitness

STAMPS, POSTAGE

see Postage Stamps

STANDARD OF VALUE

see Money

STANDARD TIME

see Time

STANDISH, MYLES, 1584?-1656

Harness, Cheryl. The Adventurous Life of Myles Standish & the Amazing-But-True Survival Story of the Plymouth Colony. Harness, Cheryl, illus. 2006. (Illus.). 144p. (J). (gr. 5-9). lib. bdg. 25.90 (978-0-7922-5919-0(X) , National Geographic Children's Bks.) National Geographic Society.

—The Adventurous Life of Myles Standish & the Amazing-but-True Survival Story of the Plymouth Colony. Harness, Cheryl, illus. 2006. (Illus.). 144p. (J). (gr. 5-9). 16.95 (978-0-7922-5918-3(1) , National Geographic Children's Bks.) National Geographic Society.

Miles Standish. (Colonial America Biographies Ser.). 48p. (YA). 7.95 (978-0-7368-4485-7(6)) Capstone Pr., Inc.

Miller, Susan Martins. Miles Standish. (Colonial Leaders Ser.). (Illus.). 80p. (gr. 3 up). 2000. (YA). 27.50 (978-0-7910-5350-8(4)); 1999. (J). pap. 27.50 (978-0-7910-5693-6(7)) Facts On File, Inc. (Chelsea Hse.).

Witteman, Barbara. Miles Standish: Colonial Leader. 2004. (Let Freedom Ring Ser.). (Illus.). 48p. (J). 17.95 (978-0-7368-2457-6(X) , Bridgestone Bks.) Capstone Pr., Inc.

STANLEY, HENRY M. (HENRY MORTON), SIR, 1841-1904

Fish, Bruce & Fish, Becky Durost. The Congo. 2001. (Exploration of Africa Ser.). (Illus.). 112p. (J). 35.00 (978-0-7910-6198-5(1) , Chelsea Hse.) Facts On File, Inc.

Worth, Richard. Stanley & Livingstone & the Exploration of Africa in World History. 2000. (In World History Ser.). (Illus.). 128p. (YA). (gr. 5-12). lib. bdg. 26.60 (978-0-7660-1400-8(2)) Enslow Pubs., Inc.

STANTON, ELIZABETH CADY, 1815-1902

Bohannon, Lisa Frederiksen. Women's Rights & Nothing Less: The Story of Elizabeth Cady Stanton. 2004. (Feminist Voices Ser.). (Illus.). 112p. (YA). (gr. 6-12). 23.95 (978-1-883846-66-4(8) , First Biographies) Reynolds, Morgan Inc.

Davis, Lucile. Elizabeth Cady Stanton. 1998. (Read-and-Discover Biographies Ser.). (J). pap. 14.00 (978-0-516-21271-5(0) , Children's Pr.) Scholastic Library Publishing.

Elizabeth Cady Stanton. (Photo Illustrated Biographies Ser.). 24p. (J). 6.95 (978-0-7368-8428-0(9)) Capstone Pr., Inc.

Elizabeth Cady Stanton, 6 vols. (gr. 2-5). 36.95 (978-0-7368-8439-6(4)) Red Brick Learning.

Fritz, Jean. You Want Women to Vote, Lizzie Stanton? DiSalvo-Ryan, DyAnne, illus. 1999. 96p. (J). (gr. 3-7). pap. 6.99 (978-0-698-11764-8(6) , Putnam Juvenile) Penguin Group (USA) Inc.

—You Want Women to Vote, Lizzie Stanton? 1999. (978-0-606-16848-9(6)); (gr. 3-6). lib. bdg. 15.30 (978-0-613-17893-8(9)) Tandem Library Bks.

Fry, Erin. The Power of Friendship. 2005. (Illus.). 16p. (J). pap. (978-0-7367-2920-8(8)) Zaner-Bloser, Inc.

Hilgartner, Carol. Elizabeth Cady Stanton. 2004. (Illus.). 32p. (ps-3). pap. 6.95 (978-0-87659-151-2(9) , 10018) Gryphon Hse., Inc.

Loos, Pamela. Elizabeth Cady Stanton: Woman Suffragist. 2000. (Women of Achievement Ser.). (Illus.). 112p. (J). (gr. 4-7). 30.00 (978-0-7910-5293-8(1) , Chelsea Hse.) Facts On File, Inc.

Mattern, Joanne. Elizabeth Cady Stanton & Susan B. Anthony: Fighting Together for Women's Rights. 2003. (Reading Power Ser.). (Illus.). 24p. (J). lib. bdg. 17.25 (978-0-8239-6503-8(1) , PowerKids Pr.) Rosen Publishing Group, Inc., The.

McCully, Emily Arnold. The Ballot Box Battle. 1998. (Dragonfly Books Ser.). (Illus.). 32p. (J). (gr. k-3). pap. 6.99 (978-0-679-89312-7(1) , Dragonfly Bks.) Random Hse. Children's Bks.

Miller, Connie Colwell. Elizabeth Cady Stanton: Women's Rights Pioneer. Webb, James, illus. 2006. (Graphic Library). 32p. (J). 25.26 (978-0-7368-4971-5(8)) Capstone Pr., Inc.

Moore, Heidi. Elizabeth Cady Stanton. 2004. (American Lives (Heinemann Library (Firm))). (Illus.). 32p. (J). pap. 6.95 (978-1-4034-5705-9(0)); lib. bdg. (978-1-4034-4994-8(5)) Heinemann Library.

Salisbury, Cynthia. Elizabeth Cady Stanton: Leader of the Fight for Women's Rights. 2002. (Historical American Biographies Ser.). (Illus.). 128p. (YA). (gr. 6-9). lib. bdg. 26.60 (978-0-7660-1616-3(1)) Enslow Pubs., Inc.

Sigerman, Harriet. Elizabeth Cady Stanton: The Right Is Ours. 2001. (Oxford Portraits Ser.). (Illus.). 144p. (YA). (gr. 8 up). suppl. ed. 28.00 (978-0-19-511969-5(X)) Oxford Univ. Pr., Inc.

Stone, Tanya Lee. Elizabeth Leads the Way. 2008. (Illus.). 32p. (J). 16.95 (***978-0-8050-7903-6(3)***) Holt, Henry & Co.

STANTON, WILL (FICTITIOUS CHARACTER)—FICTION

Cooper, Susan. The Dark Is Rising. (Dark Is Rising Sequence Ser.). 244p. (YA). (gr. 5 up). pap. 4.99 (978-0-8072-1533-3(3) , Listening Library) Random Hse. Audio Publishing Group.

—The Dark Is Rising. (Dark Is Rising Sequence Ser.). 2007. 272p. (YA). pap. 8.99 (***978-1-4169-4965-7(8)*** , Simon Pulse); 2005. 232p. pap. 2.99 (978-1-4169-0528-8(6) , Aladdin); 1999. 232p. (J). (gr. 7 up). pap. 5.99 (978-0-689-82983-3(3) , Aladdin); 2007. 256p. (J). (gr. 4-8). pap. 6.99 (***978-1-4169-4995-4(X)*** , Aladdin); 2007. 272p. (YA). (gr. 7). pap. 8.99 (***978-1-4169-4969-5(0)*** , Simon Pulse) Simon & Schuster Children's Publishing.

—The Dark Is Rising. 1999. (Dark Is Rising Sequence Ser.). (gr. 5-8). lib. bdg. 13.00 (978-0-613-90606-7(3)) Tandem Library Bks.

—The Dark Is Rising. l.t. ed. 2001. (Dark Is Rising Sequence Ser.). 395p. (J). (gr. 4-7). 21.95 (978-0-7862-2920-8(9)) Thorndike Pr.

—The Dark Is Rising Boxed Set: The Dark Is Rising, Greenwitch, over Sea, under Stone, Silver on the Tree, the Grey King. 2007. (Dark Is Rising Sequence Ser.). 1088p. (J). pap., pap. 29.99 (***978-1-4169-4996-1(8)*** , Aladdin) Simon & Schuster Children's Publishing.

—Greenwitch. (Dark Is Rising Sequence Ser.). 2007. 176p. (YA). pap. 8.99 (***978-1-4169-4966-4(6)*** , Simon Pulse); 2000. 144p. (J). (gr. 4-7). pap. 5.99 (978-0-689-84034-0(9) , Aladdin) Simon & Schuster Children's Publishing.

—Greenwitch. 2000. (Dark Is Rising Sequence Ser.). (J). 11.64 (978-0-606-19710-6(9)); (gr. 3-6). lib. bdg. 13.00 (978-0-613-29971-8(X)) Tandem Library Bks.

—Greenwitch. l.t. ed. 2001. (Dark Is Rising Sequence Ser.). 131p. (J). 21.95 (978-0-7862-2923-9(3)) Thorndike Pr.

—The Grey King. 2002. (Dark Is Rising Sequence Ser.). (Illus.). (J). 13.40 (978-0-7587-0188-6(8)) Book Wholesalers, Inc.

—The Grey King. (Dark Is Rising Sequence Ser.). 2007. 192p. (YA). pap. 8.99 (***978-1-4169-4967-1(4)*** , Simon Pulse); 1999. 176p. (J). (gr. 4-7). pap. 5.99 (978-0-689-82984-0(1) , Aladdin) Simon & Schuster Children's Publishing.

—The Grey King. 1999. (Dark Is Rising Sequence Ser.). (gr. 5-8). lib. bdg. 13.00 (978-0-613-73286-4(3)) Tandem Library Bks.

—The Grey King. l.t. ed. 2002. (Dark Is Rising Sequence Ser.). 262p. (J). 21.95 (978-0-7862-2919-2(5)) Thomson Gale.

—Over Sea, under Stone. 2002. (Dark Is Rising Sequence Ser.). (Illus.). (J). 13.40 (978-0-7587-5635-0(6)) Book Wholesalers, Inc.

—Over Sea, under Stone. 2007. (Dark Is Rising Sequence Ser.). 224p. (YA). pap. 8.99 (***978-1-4169-4964-0(X)*** , Simon Pulse) Simon & Schuster Children's Publishing.

—Over Sea, under Stone. Wiesner, David, illus. 2000. (Dark Is Rising Sequence Ser.). 208p. (J). (gr. 4-7). pap. 5.99 (978-0-689-84035-7(7) , Aladdin) Simon & Schuster Children's Publishing.

—Over Sea, under Stone. 2000. (Dark Is Rising Sequence Ser.). (gr. 7-12). lib. bdg. 13.00 (978-0-613-30082-7(3)) Tandem Library Bks.

—Over Sea, under Stone. l.t. ed. 2000. (Dark Is Rising Sequence Ser.). 332p. (J). (gr. 4-7). 22.95 (978-0-7862-2918-5(7)) Thorndike Pr.

Cooper, Susan. Silver on the Tree. 2002. (Dark Is Rising Sequence Ser.). (Illus.). (J). 13.40 (978-0-7587-5639-8(9)) Book Wholesalers, Inc.

—Silver on the Tree. (Dark Is Rising Sequence Ser.). 288p. 2007. (YA). pap. 8.99 (***978-1-4169-4968-8(2)*** , Simon Pulse); 2000. (J). (gr. 4-7). pap. 5.99 (978-0-689-84033-3(0) , Aladdin) Simon & Schuster Children's Publishing.

—Silver on the Tree. 2000. (Dark Is Rising Sequence Ser.). (gr. 5-8). lib. bdg. 13.00 (978-0-613-30127-5(7)) Tandem Library Bks.

—Silver on the Tree. l.t. ed. 2002. (Dark Is Rising Sequence Ser.). (Illus.). 430p. (J). 23.95 (978-0-7862-2921-5(7)) Thomson Gale.

STAR TREK TELEVISION PROGRAMS

Last Unicorn Games Staff & Hite, Kenneth. Star Trek: Core Game Book. 1999. (Star Trek Ser.). (Illus.). 288p. (J). 35.00 (978-0-671-04014-7(6)) Wizards of the Coast.

STARFISHES

Andersen, Honey. Starfish. 2000. (gr. k-3). lib. bdg. 11.80 (978-0-613-33441-9(8)) Tandem Library Bks.

Coldiron, Deborah. Starfish. 2007. (Underwater World Ser.). (Illus.). 32p. (J). (gr. k-4). lib. bdg. 24.21 (***978-1-59928-813-0(3)*** , Buddy Bks.) ABDO Publishing Co.

Dahl, Michael. Starry Arms: Counting by 5s. Ouren, Todd, illus. 2004. (Know Your Numbers Ser.). 24p. (C). (gr. k-3). 22.60 (978-1-4048-0947-5(3)) Picture Window Bks.

Douglas, Lloyd G. Starfish. 2005. (Ocean Life Ser.). (Illus.). 24p. (J). (ps-2). pap. 4.95 (978-0-516-23743-5(8)); 18.00 (978-0-516-25030-4(2)) Scholastic Library Publishing. (Children's Pr.).

Fowler, Allan. Stars of the Sea. 2000. (gr. k-3). lib. bdg. 12.95 (978-0-613-54859-5(0)) Tandem Library Bks.

Gay, Marie-Louise. Stella, Etoile de la Mer. braille ed. 2004. (FRE.). (J). (ps-3). spiral bd. (978-0-616-03072-1(X)) Canadian National Institute for the Blind/Institut National Canadien pour les Aveugles.

Gilpin, Daniel. Starfish, Urchins & Other Echinoderms. 2006. (Animal Kingdom Classification Ser.). (Illus.). 48p. (J). (gr. 4-6). 26.60 (978-0-7565-1611-6(0)) Compass Point Bks.

Herriges, Ann. Sea Stars. 2006. (Blastoff! Readers Ser.). (Illus.). 24p. (J). (gr. k-3). lib. bdg. 16.95 (978-1-60014-021-1(1)) Bellwether Media.

Hurd, Edith Thacher. Starfish. 2000. (gr. k-3). lib. bdg. 13.00 (978-0-613-27058-8(4)) Tandem Library Bks.

Logue, Mary. Sea Stars. 2004. (Science Around Us Ser.). 32p. (J). (gr. 2-6). 27.07 (978-1-59296-275-4(0)) Child's World, Inc.

Lunis, Natalie. Prickly Sea Stars. 2008. (No Backbone Ser.). (J). lib. bdg. 21.28 (***978-1-59716-508-2(5)***) Bearport Publishing Co., Inc.

Roop, Connie. Starfish: The Stars of the Sea. Schwartz, Carol, illus. 2002. (J). pap. 1.95 (978-0-439-33209-5(5)) Scholastic, Inc.

Sea Stars. 2006. (Under the Sea Ser.). 24p. (J). 6.95 (978-0-7368-6135-9(1)) Capstone Pr., Inc.

Sea Stars Oceans Alive. 2006. (Illus.). 24p. (J). (gr. k-2). 18.50 (***978-0-531-17873-7(0)***) Scholastic Library Publishing.

Starfish: Individual Title Six-Packs. (Sails Literacy Ser.). (gr. 1-2). 36.00 (978-0-7578-6740-8(5)) Rigby Education.

Stone, Lynn M. Sea Stars. 2005. (Rourke Discovery Library). (Illus.). 24p. (J). (ps-ps). lib. bdg. 21.36 (978-1-59515-442-2(6)) Rourke Publishing, LLC.

Sullivan, Jody. Sea Stars. 2006. (Illus.). 24p. (J). (978-0-7368-4272-3(1)) Capstone Pr., Inc.

Svancara, Theresa. Sea Stars & Other Echinoderms, Vol. 7. World Book, Inc. Staff, ed. 2002. (World Book's Animals of the World Ser.: Set 3). (Illus.). 64p. (J). (978-0-7166-1230-8(5)) World Bk., Inc.

Zuchora-Walske, Christine. Spiny Sea Stars. (Pull Ahead Bks.). (Illus.). 32p. (J). (gr. k-2). 2003. pap. 5.95 (978-0-8225-3770-0(2)); 2001. lib. bdg. 22.60 (978-0-8225-3765-6(6) , Lerner Pubns.) Lerner Publishing Group.

—Spiny Sea Stars. 2001. (gr. k-3). lib. bdg. 14.10 (978-0-613-58877-5(0)) Tandem Library Bks.

STARR, BELLE, 1848-1899

Rau, Margaret. Belle of the West: The True Story of Belle Starr. 2004. (Women of the Frontier Ser.). (Illus.). 160p. (YA). (gr. 6-12). 23.95 (978-1-883846-68-8(4) , First Biographies) Reynolds, Morgan Inc.

Sargent, Dave & Sargent, Pat. Lily: (Lilac Dun) A Second Chance, 30, 38. Lenoir, Jane, illus. 2003. (Saddle Up Ser.: Vol. 38). 42p. (J). pap. 6.95 (978-1-56763-698-7(5)); lib. bdg. 22.60 (978-1-56763-697-0(7)) Ozark Publishing.

STARR, EMILY (FICTITIOUS CHARACTER)—FICTION

see Emily (Fictitious Character)—Fiction

STARS

see also Astrology; Astronomy; Astrophysics; Meteors; Planets; Solar System

Adamson, Thomas K. Stars. 2007. 24p. (J). (978-0-7368-6746-7(5)) Capstone Pr., Inc.

Asimov, Isaac & Hantula, Richard. The Life & Death of Stars. 2005. (Isaac Asimov's 21st Century Library of the Universe). (Illus.). 32p. (J). lib. bdg. 24.67 (978-0-8368-3967-8(6)) Stevens, Gareth Inc.

—A Stargazer's Guide. 2004. (Isaac Asimov's 21st Century Library of the Universe). (Illus.). 32p. (J). lib. bdg. 24.67 (978-0-8368-3953-1(6)) Stevens, Gareth Inc.

Barner, Bob. Stars! Stars! Stars! 2002. (Illus.). 32p. (J). (ps-3). 14.95 (978-0-8118-3159-8(0)) Chronicle Bks. LLC.

Berger, Melvin. Do Stars Have Points? 1999. (Question & Answer Ser.). (J). 12.75 (978-0-606-20054-7(1)) Tandem Library Bks.

Berger, Melvin & Berger, Gilda. Do Stars Have Points? Questions & Answers about Stars & Planets. Di Fate, Vincent, illus. 1999. (Scholastic Question & Answer Ser.). 48p. (J). (gr. 2-4). pap. 6.99 (978-0-439-08570-0(5) , Scholastic Reference) Scholastic, Inc.

—Where Are the Stars During the Day? A Book about Stars. 1999. (Discovery Readers Ser.). (Illus.). 48p. (J). (ps-3). lib. bdg. 15.95 (978-0-7910-5071-2(8) , Chelsea Hse.) Facts On File, Inc.

Birch, Robin. Stars. (Solar System Ser.). (Illus.). 32p. 2004. (gr. 3-5). 23.00 (978-0-7910-7933-1(3)); 2002. (gr. k-2). 23.00 (978-0-7910-6971-4(0)) Facts On File, Inc. (Chelsea Hse.).

Bocknek, Jonathan. Stars. 2002. (Science Matters Ser.). (Illus.). 24p. (J). lib. bdg. 15.95 (978-1-59036-087-3(7)) Weigl Pubs., Inc.

Borg, Janet. My Favorite Nature Book: Stars & Planets: Includes an Activity Kit with Posters, Stickers & Glow-in-the-Dark Stars. Weiss, Anne & Estellon, Pascale, illus. 2006. 24p. 9.95 (978-1-57990-923-9(X)) Lark Bks.

Bown, Deni & Becklake, Sue. Space, Stars, Planets, & Spacecraft: See & Explore Library. 1998. (See & Explore Library Ser.). (Illus.). 64p. (J). (gr. 4-7). pap. 7.99 (978-0-7894-2966-7(7)) Dorling Kindersley Publishing, Inc.

Bredeson, Carmen. What Are Stars? 2008. (I Like Space! Ser.). (Illus.). 32p. (J). (gr. 1-3). lib. bdg. 22.60 (***978-0-7660-2943-9(3)*** , Enslow Elementary) Enslow Pubs., Inc.

Carroll, Michael W., et al. Space & Time. 2005. (God's Creation Ser.). (Illus.). 40p. (J). 7.99 (978-0-310-70578-9(9)) Zonderkidz.

Childrens Press Staff. The Galaxy, 4 vols., Set. 1998. (J). pap. 56.00 (978-0-516-29712-5(0) , Children's Pr.) Scholastic Library Publishing.

Cobb, Allan B. How Do We Know How Stars Shine? 2001. (Great Scientific Questions & the Scientists Who Answered Them Ser.). (Illus.). 112p. (YA). (gr. 4-6). lib. bdg. 26.50 (978-0-8239-3380-8(6)) Rosen Publishing Group, Inc., The.

Cole, Joanna. El Autobus Magico Viaja al Espacio. Schick, Joel, illus. 1999. (Coleccion El Autobus Magico). (SPA.). 32p. (J). (gr. k-4). pap. 3.50 (978-0-439-05613-7(6) , SO4180) Scholastic, Inc.

—Sees Stars: A Book about Stars. 1999. (Magic School Bus Ser.). (Illus.). 32p. (J). (gr. k-2). pap. 3.50 (978-0-590-52102-4(0)) Scholastic, Inc.

—Sees Stars: A Book about Stars. 1999. (Magic School Bus Ser.). (J). (gr. 1-4). (978-0-606-15833-6(2)) Tandem Library Bks.

Curry, Don L. Stars. 2000. (Yellow Umbrella Books). (Illus.). 16p. (J). (gr. 1). lib. bdg. 14.60 (978-0-7368-0726-5(8) , Pebble Bks.) Capstone Pr., Inc.

Deutsch, Stacia & Cohon, Rhody. Life of a Star. 2006. (Navigators Ser.). (J). pap. 44.00 (***978-1-4108-6241-9(0)***) Benchmark Education Co.

DK Publishing Staff. Stars & Planets. 2007. (Eyewitness Workbks.). 48p. (J). pap., wbk. ed. 9.99 (978-0-7566-3034-8(7)) Dorling Kindersley Publishing, Inc.

Driscoll, Michael & Hamilton, Meredith. Child's Introduction to the Night Sky: The Story of the Stars, Planets & Constellations—And How You Can Find Them in the Sky. 2004. (Illus.). 96p. tchr. ed. 19.95 (978-1-57912-366-6(X) , 81366) Black Dog & Leventhal Pubs., Inc.

Dyson, Marianne J. The Space Explorer's Guide to Stars & Galaxies. 2004. (Space University Ser.). (Illus.). 48p. (J). (978-0-439-55746-7(1)) Scholastic, Inc.

Eckart, Edana. Watching the Stars. 2004. (Welcome Bks.). (Illus.). 24p. (J). (ps-2). pap. 4.95 (978-0-516-25938-3(5) , Children's Pr.) Scholastic Library Publishing.

Las Estrellas. (SPA.). (J). 10.00 (978-84-342-1469-9(5)) Parramon Ediciones S.A. ESP. *Dist:* Distribuidora Norma, Inc.

Evert, Laura. Planets, Moons & Stars. Garrow, Linda, illus. (Take-Along Guide Ser.). 48p. (gr. 2-5). 2004. (J). pap. 7.95 (978-1-55971-842-4(0)); 2003. 11.95 (978-1-55971-877-6(3)) T&N Children's Publishing. (North-Word Bks. for Young Readers).

Fried, Ellen. Stars & Galaxies. 2004. (National Geographic Reading Expeditions Ser.). (Illus.). 32p. (J). pap. (978-0-7922-4574-2(1)) National Geographic Society.

Gallant, Roy A. Stars. 2000. (Kaleidoscope Ser.). (Illus.). 48p. (J). (gr. 3 up). lib. bdg. 25.64 (978-0-7614-1036-2(8) , Benchmark Bks.) Cavendish, Marshall Corp.

—When the Sun Dies. 1998. (Accelerated Reader Bks.). (Illus.). 128p. (J). (gr. 5-9). 14.95 (978-0-7614-5036-8(X) , Cavendish Children's Bks.) Cavendish, Marshall Corp.

George, Michael. Stars: Beacons in the Sky. 2003. (Life-Views Ser.). (Illus.). 32p. (J). lib. bdg. (978-1-58341-250-3(6) , Creative Education) Creative Co., The.

Goldstein, Margaret J. Stars. 2005. (Pull Ahead Bks.). (Illus.). 32p. (gr. 2-4). lib. bdg. 22.60 (978-0-8225-4646-7(9)) Lerner Publishing Group.

Grady, Monica, et al. Stardust from Space. 2007. (Illus.). 32p. (J). (gr. 2 up). 16.95 (***978-1-84507-570-5(6)***) Lincoln, Frances Ltd. GBR. *Dist:* Perseus Distribution.

Graham, Ian. Stars & Galaxies. 2007. (J). (***978-1-59920-073-6(2)***) Smart Apple Media.

Graun, Ken. Our Constellations & Their Stars. 2004. (Twenty-First Century Astronomy Ser.: 3). (Illus.). 36p. (J). 15.95 (978-1-928771-09-8(2)) Ken Pr.

Hamaguchi, Carla, ed. Stars Stickety-Splits, 12 vols., 0648. Schamber, Kimberly, illus. 2001. 10p. (J). pap. 6.99 (978-1-57471-896-6(7)) Creative Teaching Pr., Inc.

Harcourt School Publishers Staff. How the Sky Got Its Starr. 3rd ed. 2004. (Trophies Reading Program Ser.). (Illus.). (gr. k). pap. 11.50 (978-0-15-340895-3(2)) Harcourt Schl. Pubs.

Harris, Nicholas. Stars & Planets. 2006. (First Library of Knowledge). 32p. (J). (gr. 2-4). 23.70 (978-1-4103-0343-1(8) , Blackbirch Pr., Inc.) Thomson Gale.

Hobson, Charles. Seeing Stars: An Introduction to the Night Sky. 2001. (Illus.). 48p. (J). 14.95 (978-0-8118-3205-2(8)) Chronicle Bks. LLC.

Jayawardhana, Ray. Star Factories: The Birth of Stars & Planets. 1999. (Space Explorer Ser.). (Illus.). 64p. (J). (gr. 6-8). lib. bdg. 28.54 (978-0-7398-2212-8(8)) Raintree.

Jefferis, David. Black Holes. 2006. (Science Frontiers Ser.). (Illus.). 32p. (J). (gr. 3-9). pap. (978-0-7787-2870-2(6) , 1253434); lib. bdg. (978-0-7787-2856-6(0) , 1253434) Crabtree Publishing Co.

Kerrod, Robin. The Stars & Galaxies. 2001. (Exploring the Universe Ser.). (Illus.). 48p. (J). lib. bdg. 27.12 (978-0-7398-2816-8(9)) Raintree.

—Stars & Galaxies. 2001. (Illus.). 32p. (J). lib. bdg. 24.25 (978-1-930643-28-4(4)) Chrysalis Education.

Klutz Press Staff. Backyard Stars. 1998. (Klutz Guides). (Illus.). (YA). (gr. 4-7). 4.95 (978-1-57054-172-8(8)) Klutz.

Lee, Fran. Wishing on a Star: Constellation Stories & Stargazing Activities for Kids. Lee, Fran, illus. 2001. (Illus.). 64p. (YA). (gr. 2 up). pap. 9.95 (978-1-58685-029-6(6)) Gibbs Smith, Publisher.

—Wishing on a Star: Constellation Stories & Stargazing Activities for Kids. 2001. (gr. 3-6). lib. bdg. 18.75 (978-0-613-52644-9(9)) Tandem Library Bks.

Look at the Stars: Individual Title Six-Packs. (Rigby Focus Ser.). 16p. (gr. 1 up). 28.00 (978-0-7578-5313-5(7)); 30.00 (978-0-7578-5545-0(8)) Rigby Education.

Lowry, Lois. Number the Stars. 2004. 144p. (J). (gr. 5-9). pap. 29.00 incl. audio (978-1-4000-8637-5(X) , Listening Library) Random Hse. Audio Publishing Group.

—Number the Stars. 1998. 144p. (YA). (gr. 5-7). reprint ed. mass mkt. 6.50 (978-0-440-22753-3(4) , Laurel Leaf) Random Hse. Children's Bks.

—Number the Stars. 1998. (J). (978-0-606-13670-9(3)); (gr. 5-8). lib. bdg. 14.15 (978-0-613-72319-0(8)) Tandem Library Bks.

—Number the Stars - Musical. 1998. 33p. (J). pap. 6.95 (978-0-87129-834-8(1) , N03) Dramatic Publishing Co.

Mackall, Dandi Daley. Seeing Stars. Gévry, Claudine, illus. 2006. 16p. (J). 9.99 (978-1-4169-0361-1(5) , Little Simon) Simon & Schuster Children's Publishing.

Marzollo, Jean. I Am a Star. Moffatt, Judith, illus. 2001. (Hello Reader! Science Ser.). 32p. (J). (gr. k-2). pap. 3.99 (978-0-439-11320-5(2)) Scholastic, Inc.

—I Am a Star. 2001. (Hello Reader! Ser.). (Illus.). (J). 10.79 (978-0-606-21024-9(5)) Tandem Library Bks.

Mechler, Gary. Night Sky. 1999. (National Audubon Society First Field Guides). (Illus.). 160p. (gr. 3-7). (J). pap. 8.95 (978-0-590-64086-2(0)); (YA). pap. 17.95 (978-0-590-64085-5(2)) Scholastic, Inc. (Scholastic Reference).

Miller, Ron. Stars & Galaxies. 2006. (Worlds Beyond Ser.). (Illus.). 96p. (J). (gr. 5-9). 27.93 (978-0-7613-3466-8(1) , Twenty-First Century Bks.) Lerner Publishing Group.

Mistral, Gabriela. Ronda de Astros. 3rd ed. (SPA., Illus.). 128p. (YA). (gr. 5). 9.95 (978-84-239-9019-1(2) , EC5264) Espasa Calpe, S.A. ESP. *Dist:* Lectorum Pubns., Inc., Libros Sin Fronteras.

Mitchell, Melanie S. Stars. 2004. (First Step Nonfiction Ser.). (Illus.). 24p. (J). (gr. k-2). lib. bdg. 18.60 (978-0-8225-5138-6(1)) Lerner Publishing Group.

—The Stars. 2003. (First Step Nonfiction Ser.). (Illus.). 22p. (J). pap. 3.95 (978-0-8225-3592-8(0) , Lerner Pubns.) Lerner Publishing Group.

Mitton, Jacqueline. Zoo in the Sky: A Book of Animal Constellations. Balit, Christina, illus. 2006. 32p. (J). (gr. 1-4). pap. 7.95 (978-0-7922-5935-0(1) , National Geographic Children's Bks.) National Geographic Society.

Mitton, Jacqueline & Balit, Christina. Once upon a Starry Night: A Book of Constellations. 2004. (Illus.). 32p. (J). (gr. 1-4). 16.95 (978-0-7922-6332-6(4) , National Geographic Children's Bks.) National Geographic Society.

Mitton, Jacqueline & Milton. Zoo in the Sky: A Book of Animal Constellations. Ballit, Christina, illus. 1998. 32p. (J). (gr. 5-3). 16.95 (978-0-7922-7069-0(X) , National Geographic Children's Bks.) National Geographic Society.

Morris, Rick. Stars & Planets. 2005. (Time for Learning Ser.). (Illus.). 96p. (J). (978-1-4127-1135-7(5) , 7255300) Publications International, Ltd.

Nadeau, Isaac. Learning about the Movement of the Sun & Other Stars with Graphic Organizers. 2005. (Graphic Organizers in Science Ser.). (Illus.). 24p. (J). 19.95 (978-1-4042-2805-4(5)); pap. (978-1-4042-5040-6(9)) Rosen Publishing Group, Inc., The. (PowerKids Pr.).

National Geographic Society Staff. Stars & Planets. 2002. (My First Pocket Guides Ser.). (Illus.). 80p. (J). (gr. 1-5). pap. 5.95 (978-0-7922-6580-1(7) , National Geographic Children's Bks.) National Geographic Society.

Nickel, James. Lift up Your Eyes on High: Understanding the Stars. 1999. (Illus.). 132p. (YA). (gr. 7-12). spiral bd. 9.95 (978-1-930367-37-1(6) , CLP 9595) Christian Liberty Pr.

Nicolson, Cynthia. Discover the Stars. Slavin, Bill, illus. 2006. 32p. (J). lib. bdg. 15.38 (***978-1-4242-1196-8(4)***) Fitzgerald Bks.

Nicolson, Cynthia Pratt. Discover the Stars. Slavin, Bill, illus. 2006. (Kids Can Read Ser.). 32p. (J). (gr. 2-4). (978-1-55337-898-3(9)) Kids Can Pr., Ltd.

—Discover the Stars. Slavin, Bill, illus. 2006. 32p. 3.95 (978-1-55337-899-0(7)) Kids Can Pr., Ltd. CAN. *Dist:* Wybel Marketing Group.

—The Stars. Slavin, Bill, illus. (Starting with Space Ser.). 40p. (J). (gr. 4-6). 1999. (978-1-55074-659-4(6)); 1998. (978-1-55074-524-5(7)) Kids Can Pr., Ltd.

—Starting with Space: The Stars. 1999. (J). (978-0-606-19024-4(4)) Tandem Library Bks.

Olson, Nathan. Stars Around Town. 2007. (Illus.). 32p. (J). (978-0-7368-6372-8(9)) Capstone Pr., Inc.

Parker, Steve. Beyond the Solar System. 2007. (J). lib. bdg. (***978-1-4042-3739-1(9)*** , Rosen Central) Rosen Publishing Group, Inc., The.

Peddicord, Jane Ann. Night Wonders. Peddicord, Jane Ann, illus. 2005. (Illus.). 32p. (J). 16.95 (978-1-57091-877-3(5)) Charlesbridge Publishing, Inc.

—Night Wonders. 2005. (Illus.). 32p. (J). pap. 6.95 (978-1-57091-878-0(3)) Charlesbridge Publishing, Inc.

Perez, Miguel. Stars & Galaxies. Rius, María, illus. 1998. (Universe Ser.). 36p. (J). (ps-1). pap. 6.95 (978-0-7641-0686-6(4)) Barron's Educational Series, Inc.

Peters, Stephanie True. Andromeda. 2003. (Library of Constellations Ser.). (Illus.). 24p. (J). lib. bdg. 21.25 (978-0-8239-6165-8(6) , PowerKids Pr.) Rosen Publishing Group, Inc., The.

—The Big Dipper. 2003. (Library of Constellations Ser.). (Illus.). 24p. (J). lib. bdg. 21.25 (978-0-8239-6162-7(1) , PowerKids Pr.) Rosen Publishing Group, Inc., The.

—Gemini. 2003. (Library of Constellations Ser.). (Illus.). 24p. (J). lib. bdg. 21.25 (978-0-8239-6167-2(2) , PowerKids Pr.) Rosen Publishing Group, Inc., The.

—The Little Dipper. 2003. (Library of Constellations Ser.). (Illus.). 24p. (J). lib. bdg. 21.25 (978-0-8239-6163-4(X) , PowerKids Pr.) Rosen Publishing Group, Inc., The.

—Orion. 2003. (Library of Constellations Ser.). (Illus.). 24p. (J). lib. bdg. 21.25 (978-0-8239-6164-1(8) , PowerKids Pr.) Rosen Publishing Group, Inc., The.

—Pisces. 2003. (Library of Constellations Ser.). (Illus.). 24p. (J). lib. bdg. 21.25 (978-0-8239-6166-5(4) , PowerKids Pr.) Rosen Publishing Group, Inc., The.

Prinja, Raman. Stars & Constellations. (Universe Ser.). (J). 2003. (Illus.). 32p. (gr. 3-5). lib. bdg. 22.79 (978-1-58810-916-3(X)); 2002. pap. (978-1-4034-0617-0(0)) Heinemann Library.

Rau, Dana Meachen. Constellations. 2004. (Our Solar System Ser.). (Illus.). 32p. (J). 22.60 (978-0-7565-0850-0(9)) Compass Point Bks.

—Spots of Light: A Book about Stars. Shea, Denise, illus. 2005. (Amazing Science Ser.). 24p. (J). (ps-k). lib. bdg. 22.60 (978-1-4048-1139-3(7)) Picture Window Bks.

Rau, Dana Meachen & Shea, Denise. Puntos de Luz: Un Libro Sobre Las Estrellas. Shea, Denise, illus. 2006. (SPA.). (J). lib. bdg. (***978-1-4048-3233-6(5)***) Picture Window Bks.

Ridpath, Ian. Facts on File Stars & Planets Atlas: New Edition. 3rd ed. (Facts on File Atlas Ser.). 80p. (gr. 4-9). 18.95 (978-0-8160-6294-2(3) , Checkmark Bks.) Facts On File, Inc.

Rockwell, Anne F. Our Stars. 2002. (gr. k-3). lib. bdg. 14.15 (978-0-613-53848-0(X)) Tandem Library Bks.

Romero, Libby. Discover Stars. 2006. pap. 39.00 (***978-1-4108-6509-0(6)***) Benchmark Education Co.

—Stars. 2006. pap. 42.00 (***978-1-4108-6506-9(1)***) Benchmark Education Co.

Rustad, Martha E. H. The Stars. Saunders-Smith, Gail, ed. 2002. (Out in Space Ser.). (Illus.). 24p. (J). (gr. k-1). lib. bdg. 15.93 (978-0-7368-1179-8(6) , Pebble Bks.) Capstone Pr., Inc.

Ryback, Carol. The Stars. 2006. (Illus.). 24p. (J). pap. (978-0-8368-6350-5(X)); lib. bdg. 19.33 (978-0-8368-6345-1(3)) Stevens, Gareth Inc.

—The Sun. 2006. (Illus.). 24p. (J). pap. (978-0-8368-6351-2(8)); lib. bdg. 19.33 (978-0-8368-6346-8(1)) Stevens, Gareth Inc.

Salzmann, Mary Elizabeth. Stars. l.t. ed. 1999. (What Shape Is It? Ser.). (Illus.). 24p. (J). (ps-3). lib. bdg. 19.93 (978-1-57765-166-6(9) , SandCastle) ABDO Publishing Co.

Sasaki, Chris. The Constellations: Stars & Stories. 2003. (Illus.). 128p. (J). pap. 12.95 (978-1-4027-0800-8(9)) Sterling Publishing Co., Inc.

—Constellations: Stars & Stories. 2003. (gr. 3-6). lib. bdg. 22.20 (978-0-613-78016-2(7)) Tandem Library Bks.

Scholastic, Inc. Staff. Night Sky: Teaching Kit. Cooper, Terry, ed. 2000. (Super Science Readers Ser.). (Illus.). 16p. pap. 10.95 (978-0-439-18618-6(8)) Scholastic, Inc.

Sian revision Planets&stars. 2004. (J). (978-1-59242-057-5(5)) Delta Education, LLC.

Simon, Seymour. Stars. 2006. 32p. (J). 16.99 (978-0-06-089000-1(2)); (Illus.). pap. 6.99 (978-0-06-089001-8(0)) HarperCollins Pubs.

Sneider, Cary I. Earth, Moon & Stars. Bergman, Lincoln & Fairwell, Kay, eds. Baker, Lisa H. et al, illus. Sneider, Cary I., photos by. rev. ed. 1998. (Great Explorations in Math & Science Ser.). 100p. (YA). (gr. 5-8). pap. 13.50 (978-0-924886-05-8(6) , GEMS) Univ. of California, Berkeley, Lawrence Hall of Science.

Solway, Andrew. What's Inside a Black Hole? Deep Space Objects & Mysteries. 2006. (Stargazers Guides Ser.). (Illus.). 48p. (J). (978-1-4034-7710-1(8)); pap. (978-1-4034-7717-0(5)) Heinemann Library.

Sparrow, Giles. Stars & Galaxies. 2006. (Illus.). 48p. (J). pap. (978-0-8368-7247-3(8)); lib. bdg. (978-0-8368-7280-4(0)) Stevens, Gareth Inc. (World Almanac Library).

The Stars, 6 vols. 2005. (Earth & Outer Space Ser.). (gr. k-2). 28.95 (978-0-7368-3261-8(0)) Red Brick Learning.

Stars & Planets. 2001. 63p. (YA). 8.65 (978-0-7525-4879-1(4)) Parragon, Inc.

Stars & Planets. 2002. (Super Science Activities Ser.). 48p. (J). (gr. 2-5). 7.99 (978-0-7439-3663-7(9) , 3663) Teacher Created Materials, Inc.

Stars! Stars! Stars! 2005. (J). 24.95 incl. audio (978-0-439-80462-2(0)); 29.95 incl. audio compact disk (978-0-439-80468-4(X)) Weston Woods Studios, Inc.

Stott, Carole. I Wonder Why Stars Twinkle: And Other Questions about Space. 2003. (I Wonder Why Ser.). 32p. (J). (gr. k-3). pap. 6.95 (978-0-7534-5614-9(1) , Kingfisher) Houghton Mifflin Co. Trade & Reference Div.

Thomson, Sarah L. Extreme Stars! Q&A. 2006. (Illus.). 48p. (J). 16.99 (978-0-06-089934-9(4)); pap. 6.99 (978-0-06-089933-2(6)) HarperCollins Pubs.

Tomecek, Steve. Stars. Guida, Liisa C., illus. 2003. (Jump into Science Ser.). (J). 16.95 (978-0-7922-8203-7(5)) National Geographic Society.

—Stars. Yoshikawa, Sachiko, illus. 2003. (Jump into Science Ser.). 32p. (J). (ps-3). 16.95 (978-0-7922-6955-7(1) , National Geographic Children's Bks.) National Geographic Society.

Tomecek, Steve & Yoshikawa, Sachiko. Jump into Science: Stars. 2006. 32p. (J). (ps-3). 6.95 (978-0-7922-5581-9(X) , National Geographic Children's Bks.) National Geographic Society.

Tompkins, Pat. Stars. Barr, Marilynn G., illus. 1999. 48p. (J). (gr. 3-6). pap. 7.95 (978-1-57612-078-1(3) , MM2092) Monday Morning Bks., Inc.

Turnbull, Stephanie. Sun, Moon & Stars (Level 2) - Internet Referenced. 2006. 32p. (J). 4.99 (978-0-7945-1399-3(9) , Usborne) EDC Publishing.

Twist, Clint. The Stars. 2006. (Stories of the Sun). 28p. (J). (gr. 3-8). 14.95 (978-0-7696-4492-9(9)) School Specialty Publishing.

Vogt, Gregory L. Constellations. 2002. (Galaxy Ser.). (Illus.). 24p. (J). (gr. 2-3). lib. bdg. 18.60 (978-0-7368-1382-2(9) , Bridgestone Bks.) Capstone Pr., Inc.

—Constellations. (Galaxy Ser.). 24p. (J). pap. 6.95 (978-0-7368-3460-5(5)) Capstone Pr., Inc.

—Nebulas. 2000. (Our Universe Ser.). (Illus.). 48p. (YA). (gr. 5-12). lib. bdg. 22.83 (978-0-7398-3108-3(9)) Raintree.

—Nebulas. 2000. (Our Universe Ser.). (Illus.). (J). pap. (978-0-7398-3347-6(2)) Steck-Vaughn.

—Stars. 2002. (Galaxy Ser.). (Illus.). 24p. (J). (gr. 2-3). lib. bdg. 18.60 (978-0-7368-1121-7(4) , Bridgestone Bks.) Capstone Pr., Inc.

White, Nancy. The Magic School Bus Sees Stars: A Book About Stars. 1999. (gr. k-3). lib. bdg. 11.25 (978-0-613-70765-7(6)) Tandem Library Bks.

—Sees Stars: A Book about Stars. Ruiz, Art, illus. 1999. (Magic School Bus Ser.). 32p. (J). (ps-3). pap. 3.50 (978-0-590-18732-9(5)) Scholastic, Inc.

Whitehouse, Patricia. Stars. 2004. (J). lib. bdg. 24.21 (978-1-4034-5156-9(7)) Heinemann Library.

—The Stars. 2004. (Illus.). 32p. (J). (ps). pap. 7.25 (978-1-4034-5660-1(7)) Heinemann Library.

World Book, contrib. by. The Sun & Other Stars. 2nd ed. 2006. (Illus.). 64p. (J). (***978-0-7166-9521-9(9)***) World Bk., Inc.

World Book, Inc Staff, contrib. by. The Sun & Other Stars. 2006. (World Book's Solar System & Space Exploration Library). 63p. (J). (978-0-7166-9501-1(4)) World Bk., Inc.

Wright, Holly. Star. 2004. (J). (978-0-9743690-6-8(3)) Britt Allcroft Productions.

STARS, FALLING

see Meteors

STARS—FICTION

Akers Johnson, Anne. Wishing Stars. 2007. 30p. (J). pap. 5.95 (***978-1-59174-485-6(7)***) Klutz.

Allen, Marky. There Are 508 Stars in the Sky. Fulton, Karen, illus. 2001. 24 pagesp. (J). pap. 6.99 (978-1-929974-00-9(0)) Penniman Publishing Co.

Awdry, Wilbert V. & Random House Staff. Thomas & the Shooting Star. Stubbs, Tommy, illus. 2002. (Thomas & Friends Ser.). 32p. (J). (ps-2). 8.99 (978-0-375-81523-2(6) , Random Hse. Bks. for Young Readers) Random Hse. Children's Bks.

Ayasta, Ayasta. Star. 2007. 117p. 34.95 (***978-1-4303-1520-9(2)***) Lulu.com.

Babcock, Bruce. I Wished upon a Falling Star. Babcock, Bruce, illus. unabr. ed. 1998. (Illus.). 54p. (J). (ps-6). pap. 7.95 (978-1-892161-03-1(6)) Babcock Publishing Co.

Barker, Cicely Mary. Jasmine's Starry Night. 2008. (Flower Fairies Ser.). 168p. (gr. 2). 3.99 (***978-0-7232-5922-0(4)*** , Warne) Penguin Group (USA) Inc.

Barlow, Steve & Skidmore, Steve. Star Bores: May the Farce Be with You. 2004. 416p. 9.95 (978-0-00-719208-3(8)) HarperCollins Pubs. Ltd. GBR. *Dist:* Independent Pubs. Group.

Barracca, Debra. Maxi, the Star. Buehner, Mark, illus. 2002. 13.19 (978-1-4046-0284-7(4)) Book Wholesalers, Inc.

Barwin, Gary. Seeing Stars. 2002. 181p. (J). (gr. 5-7). pap. 7.95 (978-0-7737-6227-5(2)) Stoddart Kids CAN. *Dist:* Fitzhenry & Whiteside, Ltd.

Baumgart, Klaus. Laura's Secret. Waite, Judy, tr. from GER. 2003. Orig. Title: German. (Illus.). 32p. (J). (ps-2). tchr. ed. 16.95 (978-1-58925-031-4(1) , tiger tales) ME Media LLC.

—Laura's Star. 2002. (Illus.). 32p. (J). pap. 7.95 (978-1-58925-374-2(4) , tiger tales) ME Media LLC.

—Laura's Star. 2002. (gr. k-3). lib. bdg. 16.40 (978-0-613-62788-7(1)) Tandem Library Bks.

Beinstein, Phoebe. Dora's Bedtime Wishes. Roper, Robert, illus. 2003. (Dora the Explorer Ser.). 14p. (J). bds. 11.95 (978-0-689-85499-6(4) , Simon Spotlight/ Nickelodeon) Simon & Schuster Children's Publishing.

Book Company Staff. Stella Stars: Charm Treasury Adventure Book with Bracelet. 2002. (Novelty Bks.). 20p. (J). 12.95 (978-1-74047-177-0(6)) Book Co. Publishing Pty, Ltd., The AUS. *Dist:* Penton Overseas, Inc.

Bowman, Alice W. Twinkle Dust - His Awesome Adventure. Pelella, Holly L., illus. 1998. (Twinkle Dust Ser.: No. 2). 24p. (Orig.). (J). (ps-6). pap. 6.95 (978-0-9645870-2-1(5)) Big Foot Publishing.

Bowman, Crystal. A Star for Jesus. Gèvry, Claudine, illus. 2006. 14p. (J). 6.99 (978-0-310-71216-9(5)) Zonderkidz.

Boyd, Dee. Only the Stars. Rich, Anna, illus. 2004. 32p. (J). lib. bdg. 15.00 (***978-1-4242-0230-0(2)***) Fitzgerald Bks.

Boyle, Alison. Twinkle, Twinkle, Little Star. Pichon, Liz, illus. 2000. (Finger Puppet Bks.). 16p. (J). (ps-k). 10.95 (978-1-86233-111-2(1)) Sterling Publishing Co., Inc.

Brady, Kymberli W. The Sleepy Little Star. 2002. (Illus.). 32p. (J). 14.99 (978-0-9711758-0-8(2)) Get Graphic Publishing.

Bridges, Mitzi Pool. The Magic Star Book III: The Delaney Family Mysteries. 2001. 112p. pap. 9.95 (978-0-595-19145-1(2) , Writers Club Pr.) iUniverse, Inc.

Brown, Carl & Brown, Kay. The Little Star. 2006. 123p. pap. (***978-1-4120-9079-7(2)***) Trafford Publishing.

Burge, Kenneth Dean. Lena's Star. Burge, Deborah Lynn, illus. l.t. ed. 2001. 36p. (J). per. 10.00 (978-0-9715953-0-9(5) , Verner Publishing) Verner Advertising, LLC.

Butler, M. Christina. A Star So Bright: A Christmas Tale. Pedler, Caroline, illus. 2006. 21p. (J). (ps-2). 14.95 (978-1-56148-536-9(5)) Good Bks.

Cara al Cielo Vol.3: Six-Pack. (Saludos Ser.: Vol. 3). (SPA.). (gr. 2-3). 31.00 (978-0-7635-9547-0(0)) Rigby Education.

Chapin Carpenter, Mary. Halley Came to Jackson. Andreasen, Dan, illus. 1998. 40p. (J). (ps up). 15.95 incl. audio (978-0-06-025400-1(9)) HarperCollins Pubs.

Clontz, Jay F. The Tiny Star. 2004. 39p. pap. 17.95 (978-1-4137-2339-7(X)) PublishAmerica, Inc.

Cole, Joanna. Sees Stars: A Book about Stars. 2002. (Magic School Bus Ser.). (Illus.). (J). 11.45 (978-0-7587-6704-2(8)) Book Wholesalers, Inc.

Cordes, Jayne A. The Hope Star. 1999. (Illus.). 24p. (J). 16.95 (978-0-9662670-6-0(1)) J. Kid Productions, Ltd.

Crelin, Bob. There Once Was Sky Full of Stars. 2006. 232p. pap. 17.95 (978-1-931559-37-9(6)) Sky Publishing.

Dale, Jenny. Little Star. Reid, Mick, illus. 2003. 109p. (J). (978-0-439-54363-7(0)) Scholastic, Inc.

Das, Christina. Swinging under the Stars. l.t. ed. 2005. (Illus.). 32p. (J). 15.95 (978-0-9763082-1-8(5) , A JuneOne Production) JuneOne Publishing Hub.

De Montano, Marty K. Coyote in Love with a Star. Coffin, Tom, illus. 1998. (Tales of the People Ser.). 30p. (ps up). 14.95 (978-0-7892-0162-1(3)) Abbeville Pr., Inc.

Dent, Jenny. Peter Parrot & His Magic Star. 2001. (Peter Parrot Ser.). (Illus.). 32p. (gr. k-3). 12.95 (978-0-85487-119-3(5)) White Eagle Publishing Trust GBR. *Dist:* De-Vorss & Co.

Dukovich, Amanda J. A Star Named Little One: (Female Version) Pride, Mathew, illus. l.t. ed. 2006. 22p. (J). 15.99 (978-1-59879-190-0(0)) Lifevest Publishing, Inc.

—A Star Named Little One: (Male Version) Pride, Mathew, illus. l.t. ed. 2006. 22p. (J). 15.99 (978-1-59879-189-1(2)) Lifevest Publishing, Inc.

Ellis, Kiersten. Do Planets Hang on Strings? 2006. 24p. (J). per. 11.99 (***978-1-59886-688-9(5)***); 14.99 (***978-1-59886-992-7(2)***) Tate Publishing & Enterprises, L.L.C.

Fabra, Jordi Sierra. El Nino Que Vivia en las Estrellas. (SPA.). 120p. (YA). (gr. 5-8). 8.95 (978-84-204-4429-1(4)) Alfaguara, Ediciones, S.A.- Grupo Santillana ESP. *Dist:* Santillana USA Publishing Co., Inc.

Face to the Sky, 6 pack. (Greetings Ser.: Vol. 3). 24p. (gr. 2-3). 31.00 (978-0-7635-9431-2(8)) Rigby Education.

Facklam, Margery. Only a Star. Carpenter, Nancy, illus. 2004. 32p. (J). (ps-3). pap. 8.00 (978-0-8028-5174-1(6)) Eerdmans, William B. Publishing Co.

Fancher, Lou. Star Climbing. Johnson, Steve, illus. 2006. 32p. (J). 15.99 (978-0-06-073901-0(0)); lib. bdg. 16.89 (978-0-06-073902-7(9)) HarperCollins Pubs. (Geringer, Laura Book).

Fernandez, Roberto Peredo. Acoyani: El Nino y el Poeta. Arte y Diseno, Tane, illus. 2nd rev. ed. 2006. (Castillo de la Lectura Naranja Ser.). (SPA.). 166p. (J). pap. 7.95 (978-970-20-0146-1(3)) Castillo, Ediciones, S. A. de C. V. MEX. *Dist:* Macmillan.

Filigenzi, Tracy. The special little Star. 2007. (***978-0-533-15012-0(4)***) Vantage Pr., Inc.

Fischer, Scott M. Twinkle. 2007. 40p. (J). (ps-1). 15.99 (***978-1-4169-3980-1(6)***) Simon & Schuster Children's Publishing.

Fleming, Sarah. Pictures in the Stars. 2000. (Cambridge Reading Ser.). (Illus.). 10p. pap. 5.00 (978-0-521-77461-1(6)) Cambridge Univ. Pr.

Fry, Sonali. Let's Catch Stars! Aikins, Dave, illus. 2004. (Dora the Explorer Ser.). 14p. (J). bds. 6.99 (978-0-689-86454-4(X) , Simon Spotlight/Nickelodeon) Simon & Schuster Children's Publishing.

Ginolfi, Art. The Tiny Star. 2005. 32p. (J). pap. 3.99 (978-1-4003-0683-1(3)) Nelson, Thomas Inc.

Gooch, T. It Was My Star. 2003. (Illus.). 32p. 19.97 (978-0-9726119-0-9(8)) Dancing Force, The.

Grizzell, Larry. The Star: A Christmas Song. 2006. (Illus.). 25p. (J). 19.95 (978-0-9759542-2-5(9)) Adventures Galore.

Guillet, Jean-Pierre. La Puce Cosmique et le Rayon Bleuge. Guillet, Francois, illus. 2004. (Des 9 Ans. Ser.). (FRE.). 120p. (J). (978-2-922565-98-0(X)) Editions de la Paix CAN. *Dist:* World of Reading, Ltd.

S

Harcourt School Publishers Staff. Friends Forever On Level. 3rd ed. 2002. (Trophies Reading Program Ser.). (Illus.). pap. 5.10 (978-0-15-323177-3(7)) Harcourt Schl. Pubs.

—From Here to There Below Level. 3rd ed. 2002. (Trophies Reading Program Ser.). (Illus.). pap. 5.10 (978-0-15-323159-9(9)) Harcourt Schl. Pubs.

—Harry el Miedoso Advanced Level. 3rd ed. 2002. (Trofeos Ser.).Tr. of Harry Is Scared. (SPA., Illus.). pap. 6.80 (978-0-15-324112-3(8)) Harcourt Schl. Pubs.

—Jordi's Star: Library Edition. 1999. (Collections Ser.). (Illus.). (J). 5.30 (978-0-15-314328-1(2)) Harcourt Schl. Pubs.

—Little Star: Take-Home Book. 1999. (Collections Ser.). (Illus.). (J). pap. 1.90 (978-0-15-317217-5(7)) Harcourt Schl. Pubs.

—Maria's Comet: Reader's Choice Book. 2001. (Collections Ser.). (Illus.). (J). 4.70 (978-0-15-314399-1(1)) Harcourt Schl. Pubs.

—Sky Tales Advanced Level. 3rd ed. 2002. (Trophies Reading Program Ser.). (Illus.). pap. 5.10 (978-0-15-323220-6(X)) Harcourt Schl. Pubs.

Harper, Charise Mericle. There Was a Bold Lady Who Wanted a Star. Harper, Charise Mericle, illus. 2002. (Illus.). 32p. (J). (ps-3). 15.95 (978-0-316-14673-9(0) , Tingley, Megan Bks.) Little, Brown Bks. for Young Readers.

Hartinger, Brent. Dreamquest: Tales of Slumberia. 2007. 160p. (J). (gr. 8 up). 16.95 (***978-0-7653-1397-3(9)*** , Starscape) Doherty, Tom Assocs., LLC.

He Who Listens: Individual Title Six-Packs. (Literatura 2000 Ser.). (gr. 2-3). 33.00 (978-0-7635-0171-6(9)) Rigby Education.

Heine, Theresa. Star Seeker: A Journey to Outer Space. Tavares, Victor, illus. 2006. 32p. (J). 16.99 (978-1-905236-36-7(0)) Barefoot Bks., Inc.

Henkes, Kevin. Wemberly's Ice-Cream Star. Henkes, Kevin, illus. 2003. (Illus.). 24p. (J). 6.99 (978-0-06-050405-2(6)) HarperCollins Pubs.

Hoffman, Mary. Cuentos del Sol, la Luna y las Estrellas: Mitos, Leyendas y Tradiciones de Todas las Culturas. Ray, Jane, illus. 2002. (SPA & ENG.). 80p. (gr. 1-7). 19.95 (978-84-89396-52-4(3)) Blume ESP. *Dist:* Independent Pubs. Group.

Holston-Holloway, Angela M. The Apple Pie Kids. 2006. (J). pap. 8.00 (***978-0-8059-6899-6(7)***) Dorrance Publishing Co., Inc.

Huizenga, Pam. Twinkle. V'in, Anica, illus. 2000. 10p. (J). (ps-k). 7.95 (978-1-929774-01-2(X)) Greenleaf Book Group Pr.

Jeffers, Oliver. How to Catch a Star. Jeffers, Oliver, illus. 2004. (Illus.). 32p. (J). (ps-1). 14.99 (978-0-399-24286-1(4) , Philomel) Penguin Group (USA) Inc.

Jones, Diana Wynne. Dogsbody. 2001. (gr. 7-12). lib. bdg. 15.25 (978-0-613-57404-4(4)) Tandem Library Bks.

Kubler, Annie. Twinkle,Twinkle Little Star. 2002. (Illus.). 16p. (J). 19.99 (978-0-85953-125-2(2)) Child's Play-International.

Kubler, Annie, illus. Twinkle, Twinkle. 2002. 16p. (J). 6.99 (978-0-85953-941-8(5)) Child's Play-International.

The Land Beyond Forever. 2006. 25.00 (***978-0-9785570-0-3(X)***) Three Sisters Publishing Hse., Ltd.

Langley, Karen. Shine! Langley, Jonathan, illus. 2002. 32p. (J). (gr. k-3). 15.95 (978-0-7614-5127-3(7)) Cavendish, Marshall Corp.

Lemieux, Jean. Toby Shoots for Infinity. Cummins, Sarah, tr. from FRE. Casson, Sophie, illus. 2005. (First Novel Ser.). 64p. (J). (gr. 2-5). (***978-0-88780-685-8(6)***); 4.95 (978-0-88780-684-1(8)) Formac Publishing Co., Ltd. CAN. *Dist:* Casemate Pubs. & Bk. Distributors, LLC.

L'Engle, Madeleine. Troubling a Star. 2002. (Austin Family Ser.: No. 7). (YA). 14.47 (978-0-7587-9606-6(4)) Book Wholesalers, Inc.

L'Homme, Erik. Book of Stars 1: Quadehar the Sorcerer. 2006. 288p. (J). pap. 5.99 (978-0-439-53648-6(0) , Scholastic Paperbacks) Scholastic, Inc.

Lobel, Gillian. Little Bear's Special Wish. Hansen, Gaby, illus. 2004. 32p. (J). tchr. ed. 16.95 (978-1-58925-034-5(6) , tiger tales) ME Media LLC.

Lowry, Lois. Number the Stars. 2004. 144p. (J). (gr. 5-9). pap. 29.00 incl. audio (978-1-4000-8637-5(X) , Listening Library) Random Hse. Audio Publishing Group.

—Number the Stars. 1998. 144p. (YA). (gr. 5-7). reprint ed. mass mkt. 6.50 (978-0-440-22753-3(4) , Laurel Leaf) Random Hse. Children's Bks.

—Number the Stars. 1998. (J). (978-0-606-13670-9(3)); (gr. 5-8). lib. bdg. 14.15 (978-0-613-72319-0(8)) Tandem Library Bks.

—Number the Stars - Musical. 1998. 33p. (J). pap. 6.95 (978-0-87129-834-8(1) , N03) Dramatic Publishing Co.

—Quien Cuenta las Estrellas. 2003. (Espasa Juvenil Ser.: Vol. 20). (SPA., Illus.). 152p. (J). (gr. 7 up). 14.95 (978-84-239-8887-7(2) , EC3743) Espasa Calpe, S.A. ESP. *Dist:* Distribooks, Inc., Lectorum Pubns., Inc.

Lyon, George Ella. My Friend, the Starfinder. Gammell, Stephen, illus. 2008. 40p. (J). 16.99 (***978-1-4169-2738-9(7)***) Simon & Schuster Children's Publishing.

March-Settle, Michelle. A Shining Star: A Journey for All Ages. 2004. (J). pap. 8.00 (978-0-8059-6368-7(5)) Dorrance Publishing Co., Inc.

McCarthy, Tara. Number the Stars: Everything You Need for Successful Literature Circles That Get Kids Thinking, Talking, Writing-and Loving Literature. 2002. (Literature Circle Guides Ser.). (Illus.). 32p. (gr. 4-8). pap. 5.95 (978-0-439-27170-7(3)) Scholastic, Inc.

McDonald, Megan. My House Has Stars. 2001. (Illus.). (J). (978-0-606-21563-3(8)) Tandem Library Bks.

The Message in the Stars: Lap Book. (Pebble Soup Explorations Ser.). 16p. (ps up). 21.00 (978-0-7578-2113-4(8)) Rigby Education.

The Message in the Stars: Small Book. (Pebble Soup Explorations Ser.). 16p. (ps up). 5.00 (978-0-7578-2114-1(6)) Rigby Education.

Milliman, Linda & Soles, Gail. Briny the Starfish. 2002. (Illus.). 26p. (J). (ps-4). pap. 15.00 (978-0-9717603-0-1(6)) Isaiah's Promise Publishing Co.

Mills, Nancy Libbey. The Knight the Moon & the Stars Got Stuck. Thieves, Sam, illus. 2000. 32p. (J). (ps-4). 15.95 (978-1-893815-01-8(3)) Pie in the Sky Publishing, LLC.

Morgan, Beverly. Gregory & the Stars: A Little Story about Independence. Joyful Noise, ed. 2005. (Illus.). 26p. (J). 4.95 (978-0-9772109-0-9(1)) Joyful Noise.

Moroney, Tracey, illus. Follow the Star. 1999. (Christmas Bible Play Bks.). 18p. (ps-k). 5.99 (978-0-7847-1050-0(3) , 03998, Bean Sprouts) Standard Publishing.

Murphy, Mary. Little Owl & the Star: A Christmas Story. Murphy, Mary, illus. 2003. (Illus.). 32p. (J). (gr. k-k). 12.99 (978-0-7636-2268-8(0)) Candlewick Pr.

Nash, Deborah. The Little Star. Morgan, Richard, illus. 2004. (Read-It! Readers Ser.). 32p. (C). (gr. k-3). 18.60 (978-1-4048-0065-6(4)) Picture Window Bks.

Nelson, S. D. The Star People: A Lakota Story. 2003. (Illus.). 36p. (J). (ps-3). 14.95 (978-0-8109-4584-5(3)) Abrams, Harry N. , Inc.

Orion the Skateboard Kid. 2001. 63p. (YA). per. 9.95 (978-0-9672585-0-8(2)) CyPress Pubns.

Owner, Victor James. Why Am I?! Grimes, H. J., illus. 2006. 40p. 14.95 (978-0-9764981-8-6(9)) Synergy Bks.

Peirce-Bale, Mary. Twinkle, Twinkle Little Girl. 2005. (J). 6.95 (978-0-9743869-9-7(5)) Mother's Hse. Publishing.

—Wilma Wombat's Trek to Back of Beyond. 2006. (J). 9.90 (978-0-9773990-4-8(4)) Mother's Hse. Publishing.

Perry, Tina. Where Do Stars Come from, Nana? 2007. pap. 10.99 (***978-1-60247-070-5(7)***) Tate Publishing & Enterprises, L.L.C.

Puttock, Simon. A Ladder to the Stars. Jay, Alison, illus. 2006. 32p. (J). pap. 7.95 (978-1-84507-512-5(9)) Lincoln, Frances Ltd. GBR. *Dist:* Perseus Distribution.

Rabley, Stephen. Marcel & the White Star. 2002. (Illus.). 16p. pap. (978-0-582-40290-4(5) , Putnam Juvenile) Penguin Group (USA) Inc.

Ridinger, Gayle. A Star at the Bottom of the Sea. Parpajola, Andreina, illus. 2002. 32p. (J). (ps up). lib. bdg. 24.67 (978-0-8368-3175-7(6)) Stevens, Gareth Inc.

Riordan, James. The Storytelling Star: Tales of the Sun, Moon & Stars. Hill, Amanda, illus. 1999. 60p. (J). (gr. 2-7). 19.99 (978-1-86205-202-4(6) , Pavilion Bks., Ltd.) Anova Bks. GBR. *Dist:* Independent Pubs. Group.

Roberg, Robert & Whiting, Chuck. The Littlest Star: A Musical Story. 2003rd gif. l.t. ed. 2003. (Illus.). 40p. 10.95 incl. audio compact disk (978-0-9712398-0-7(0)) Shine Time Records & Bks.

Roberts, Phyllis. Teeny Tiny Star. 2007. (Illus.). 30p. (J). lib. bdg. 19.95 (***978-1-933732-40-4(7)*** , Bear Hug Bks.) MidAmerica Publishing Co.

Runnells, Treesha. Five Wishing Stars: Disappearing Die Cut. Dillard, Sarah, illus. 2005. 12p. (J). 14.95 (978-1-58117-265-2(6) , Intervisual/Piggy Toes) Dalmatian Pr.

Rylant, Cynthia. Poppleton Everyday. Teague, Mark, illus. 2002. (Poppleton Ser.). (J). 11.91 (978-0-7587-1586-9(2)) Book Wholesalers, Inc.

—Poppleton Everyday. Teague, Mark, illus. 1998. (Poppleton Ser.). (J). (gr. k-3). 48p. pap. 15.95 (978-0-590-84845-9(3) , Blue Sky Pr., The); 56p. pap. 3.99 (978-0-590-84853-4(4)) Scholastic, Inc.

—Poppleton Everyday. 1998. (Poppleton Ser.). (J). (gr. k-3). (978-0-606-13717-1(3)) Tandem Library Bks.

Santillo, LuAnn. The Wish. Santillo, LuAnn, ed. 2003. (Half-Pint Kids Readers Ser.). (Illus.). 7p. (J). (ps-1). pap. (978-1-59256-048-6(2)) Half-Pint Kids, Inc.

Scholastic, Inc. Staff & Boyd, Dee. Only the Stars. Rich, Anna, illus. 2004. (Just for You! Ser.). 32p. pap. 3.99 (978-0-439-56862-3(5) , Teaching Resources) Scholastic, Inc.

Serna, Ana. Una Estrella Muy Especial. 4th ed. 2000. (Cuentos de Ahora Ser.).Tr. of Very Special Star. (SPA., Illus.). 32p. (J). 12.95 (978-84-348-5159-7(8)) SM Ediciones ESP. *Dist:* Distribooks, Inc.

The Shooting Star, 6 vols., Pack. 16p. (gr. 2 up). 35.00 (978-0-7635-9386-5(9)) Rigby Education.

Sills, Elizabeth & Patrice, Elena. Nana Star Book. Saker, Linda, illus. 2004. 15p. (J). 17.99 (978-0-9753843-0-5(9)) ee publishing & productions, inc.

Silver Dolphin en Español Editors, creator. Mis Figuras Geometricas, Srita Estrella. 2005. (Mis figuras Geometricas Ser.). (SPA., Illus.). 6p. (J). (ps-k). 9.95 (978-970-718-295-0(4) , Silver Dolphin en Español) Advanced Marketing, S. de R. L. de C. V. MEX. *Dist:* Perseus Distribution.

Slate, Joseph. The Secret Stars. Davalos, Felipe, illus. 32p. (J). 2005. pap. 5.95 (978-0-7614-5152-5(8)); 1998. 15.95 (978-0-7614-5027-6(0) , Cavendish Children's Bks.) Cavendish, Marshall Corp.

Smith, Debbie Powell. Seymour's Wish. 2000. 21p. (J). pap. 8.99 (978-1-930673-03-8(5)) Childhood Friends, Inc.

Star Gazer. 1998. (Eyewitness Fun Fax Inserts Ser.). (Illus.). (J). (gr. 4-8). pap. 2.95 (978-0-7894-3015-1(0)) Dorling Kindersley Publishing, Inc.

Stars of the Sky. 2004. (Illus.). 32p. (J). 12.95 (978-0-9759468-0-0(3)) Balanced Families.

Steck-Vaughn Staff. How the Sky Got Its Stars. 1999. (Illus.). pap. (978-0-8172-8717-7(5)) Steck-Vaughn.

Steven, Kenneth. The Sea Mice & the Stars. Ho, Louise, illus. 2005. 28p. (J). 16.00 (978-1-56148-490-4(3)) Good Bks.

Stutson, Caroline. Star Comes Home. 1998. (J). (gr. 2-5). pap. 5.95 (978-1-58021-046-1(5)) Benefactory, Inc., The.

Supernova! Individual Chapter Book Title Six-Packs. Vol. 28. 32p. (gr. 4 up). 44.00 (978-0-7635-4498-0(1)) Rigby Education.

Thomas Nelson Publishing Staff. My Christmas Collection: Three Favorite Stories. 2006. 80p. (J). 14.99 (978-1-4003-0843-9(7)) Nelson, Thomas Inc.

Toms, Kate. Twinkle, Twinkle, Little Star. 2007. (Illus.). 26p. (ps). bds. 7.99 (***978-1-84610-485-5(8)***) Make Believe Ideas GBR. *Dist:* Ingram Pub. Services.

Towell, Katy. The Little Girl Who Was Forgotten by Absolutely Everyone (Even the Postman) 2005. 56p. (YA). pap. 16.99 (978-1-4116-5919-3(8)) Lulu.com.

Trapani, Iza. Sing along with Iza & Friends: Twinkle, Twinkle Little Star. Trapani, Iza, illus. 2004. (Illus.). 32p. (J). pap. 9.95 incl. audio compact disk (978-1-58089-101-1(2)) Charlesbridge Publishing, Inc.

—Twinkle, Twinkle, Little Star. Trapani, Iza, illus. 1998. (Illus.). 26p. (J). (ps-k). bds. 6.95 (978-1-58089-015-1(6)) Charlesbridge Publishing, Inc.

True, Preston John. Iron Star & What It Saw on Its Journey. 2006. 62.99 (***978-1-4280-2316-1(X)***) IndyPublish.com.

Twinkle Twinkle Little Star. 2005. (J). bds. 6.99 (978-0-9753127-3-5(1)) Family Bks. at Home.

Walsh, T. B. R. Merlin & the Black Star. 2002. (Illus.). 56p. (J). per. 7.00 (978-0-9720307-0-0(0)) TMC Bks. L.L.C.

Walters, Eric. Stars. unabr. ed. 1998. 315p. (YA). (gr. 7-9). mass mkt. 6.95 (978-0-7736-7447-9(0)) Stoddart Kids CAN. *Dist:* Fitzhenry & Whiteside, Ltd.

Watkins, Dawn L. Very Like a Star/The Cranky Blue Crab, 2 vols. 2000. (Illus.). (J). (ps-3). pap. 14.98 incl. audio (978-0-89084-902-6(1) , 100073) Jones, Bob Univ. Pr.

Wax, Wendy & A&J Studios Staff. Five Stars for Abuela! 2006. (Dora the Explorer Ser.). 14p. (J). 6.99 (978-1-4169-1301-6(7) , Simon Spotlight/Nickelodeon) Simon & Schuster Children's Publishing.

Weiner, Eric, contrib. by. Little Star. 2002. (Illus.). 22p. (J). (ps-1). lib. bdg. 11.25 (978-0-613-83494-0(1)) Tandem Library Bks.

Where Do the Stars Go? ed. 2007. (J). 19.95 (***978-0-9795877-1-9(9)***) Pitcher, Jan.

Williamson, Ray A. & Monroe, Jean Guard. They Dance in the Sky: Native American Star Myths. Stewart, Edgar, illus. 2007. 144p. (J). (gr. 4-6). pap. 8.95 (***978-0-618-80912-7(0)***) Houghton Mifflin Co. Trade & Reference Div.

Willson, Sarah. Estrellita. Thompson Brothers Studio Staff, illus. 2003. (Dora the Explorer Ser.).Tr. of Little Star. (SPA.). 24p. (J). pap. 3.99 (978-0-689-86307-3(1) , Libros Para Ninos) Simon & Schuster Children's Publishing.

—Little Star. Thompson Brothers Staff, illus. 2002. (Dora the Explorer Ser.). 24p. (J). pap. 3.50 (978-0-689-84721-9(1) , Simon Spotlight/Nickelodeon) Simon & Schuster Children's Publishing.

Witschen, Kay. Clinker's Christmas Star. Witschen, Kay, illus. 2004. (Illus.). 24p. (J). 6.95 (978-0-9741352-1-2(6)) Dwitt Publishing.

Wohlford, Martha Crikelair. Little Star's Big Day: A Children's Christmas Story. Schaefer, Heather Leigh, illus. l.t. ed. 2003. 36p. (J). (ps-7). per. 14.95 (978-1-59453-033-3(5) , 1) Airleaf Publishing & Bookselling.

Wolfel, Ursula. Fliegender Stern. pap. 14.95 (978-3-570-26064-7(X)) Bertelsman, Verlagsgruppe C. GmbH DEU. *Dist:* Distribooks, Inc.

Wordshop Editorial Staff. Twink 'n' Twinkle: The Beginning. 1999. (Illus.). 28p. (J). (ps-4). 19.95 (978-0-9668469-0-4(7)) WordSHOP, Inc.

STARS—POETRY

Brown, Margaret Wise. I Like Stars. 2002. (Illus.). (J). 11.91 (978-0-7587-1324-7(X)) Book Wholesalers, Inc.

—I Like Stars. Paley, Joan, illus. (Step into Reading Ser.). 32p. (J). (ps-k). 2004. lib. bdg. 11.99 (978-0-375-99994-9(9)); 1998. pap. 3.99 (978-0-307-26105-2(0) , 26105) Random Hse. Children's Bks. (Random Hse. Bks. for Young Readers).

—I Like Stars. 1998. (gr. k-3). lib. bdg. 11.80 (978-0-613-81156-9(9)) Tandem Library Bks.

Davis, Phyllis Rowe. On a Clear Night: Poetic Description of Constellations. Wolff, Glenn, illus. 2001. 60p. (Orig.). (YA). (gr. 10 up). pap. 11.95 (978-0-9714964-0-8(4)) Fidjus.

Tagel, Peggy, illus. Twinkle Twinkle Little Star: I Squeak! 2005. (***978-1-4127-3573-5(4)***) Publications International, Ltd.

Trapani, Iza. Twinkle, Twinkle, Little Star. Trapani, Iza, illus. 1998. (Illus.). 26p. (J). (ps-k). bds. 6.95 (978-1-58089-015-1(6)) Charlesbridge Publishing, Inc.

Wallace, Nancy Elizabeth. The Sun, the Moon, & the Stars. Wallace, Nancy Elizabeth, illus. 2003. (Illus.). 40p. (J). (gr. k-3). tchr. ed. 12.00 (978-0-618-26353-0(5)) Houghton Mifflin Co. Trade & Reference Div.

STATE AND CHURCH

see Church and State

STATE AND EDUCATION

see Education and State

STATE BIRDS

Cooper, Jason. Aves/Birds. 2003. (La Guia De Rourke Para Los Simbolos De Los Estados). (ENG & SPA., Illus.). 63p. (gr. 3-8). 20.95 (978-1-58952-396-8(2)) Rourke Publishing, LLC.

Talbott, Hudson. United Tweets of America. 2008. 64p. (J). (gr. 1-3). 17.99 (***978-0-399-24520-6(0)*** , Putnam Juvenile) Penguin Group (USA) Inc.

STATE CHURCH

see Church and State

STATE FLOWERS

Cooper, Jason. Flores/Flowers. 2003. (La Guia De Rourke Para Los Simbolos De Los Estados). (ENG & SPA., Illus.). 64p. (gr. 3-8). 20.95 (978-1-58952-398-2(9)) Rourke Publishing, LLC.

STATE GOVERNMENTS

see also Governors

also names of states with the subdivision Politics and Government, e.g. New York (State)—Politics and government; etc.

Benchmark Education Staff. Local & State GOVT. 2005. 2.00 (***978-1-4108-4639-6(3)***) Benchmark Education Co.

Benchmark Education Staff, compiled by. Social Studies Theme: GOVT & Citizenship. 2005. spiral bd. 115.00 (***978-1-4108-5331-8(4)***) Benchmark Education Co.

Brannon, Barbara. Discover Local & State GOVT. 2005. 39.00 (***978-1-4108-5145-1(1)***) Benchmark Education Co.

Cefrey, Holly. Your Governor: State Government in Action. 2003. (Primary Source Library of American Citizenship). (Illus.). 32p. (J). pap. (978-1-4042-5094-9(8)) Rosen Publishing Group, Inc., The.

Firestone, Mary. The State Governor. 2004. (First Facts Ser.). (Illus.). 24p. (J). 15.95 (978-0-7368-2500-9(2)) Capstone Pr., Inc.

—The State Legislative Branch. 2004. (First Facts Ser.). (Illus.). 24p. (J). 15.95 (978-0-7368-2501-6(0)) Capstone Pr., Inc.

Harris, Nancy. What's a Governor? 2007. (J). (***978-1-4034-9508-2(4)***); pap. (***978-1-4034-9514-3(9)***) Heinemann Library.

Johnson, Etta. Local & State GOVT. 2005. 39.00 (***978-1-4108-4591-7(5)***) Benchmark Education Co.

Marsh, Carole. Alabama Government Projects: 30 Cool, Activities, Crafts, Experiments & More for Kids to Do to Learn about Your State! 2003. (Alabama Experience Ser.). 32p. (gr. k-5). pap. 5.95 (978-0-635-01920-2(5) , Marsh, Carole Bks.) Gallopade International.

—Alaska Government Projects: 30 Cool, Activities, Crafts, Experiments & More for Kids to Do to Learn about Your State! 2003. (Alaska Experience Ser.). 32p. (gr. k-5). pap. 5.95 (978-0-635-01921-9(3) , Marsh, Carole Bks.) Gallopade International.

—Arizona Government Projects: 30 Cool, Activities, Crafts, Experiments & More for Kids to Do to Learn about Your State! 2003. (Arizona Experience Ser.). 32p. (gr. k-5). pap. 5.95 (978-0-635-01922-6(1) , Marsh, Carole Bks.) Gallopade International.

—Arkansas Government Projects: 30 Cool, Activities, Crafts, Experiments & More for Kids to Do to Learn about Your State! 2003. (Arkansas Experience Ser.). 32p. (gr. k-5). pap. 5.95 (978-0-635-01923-3(X) , Marsh, Carole Bks.) Gallopade International.

—California Government Projects: 30 Cool, Activities, Crafts, Experiments & More for Kids to Do to Learn about Your State! 2003. (California Experience Ser.). 32p. (gr. k-5). pap. 5.95 (978-0-635-01924-0(8) , Marsh, Carole Bks.) Gallopade International.

—Colorado Government Projects: 30 Cool, Activities, Crafts, Experiments & More for Kids to Do to Learn about Your State! 2003. (Colorado Experience Ser.). 32p. (gr. k-5). pap. 5.95 (978-0-635-01925-7(6) , Marsh, Carole Bks.) Gallopade International.

—Connecticut Government Projects: 30 Cool, Activities, Crafts, Experiments & More for Kids to Do to Learn about Your State! 2003. (Connecticut Experience Ser.). 32p. (gr. k-5). pap. 5.95 (978-0-635-01926-4(4) , Marsh, Carole Bks.) Gallopade International.

—Delaware Government Projects: 30 Cool, Activities, Crafts, Experiments & More for Kids to Do to Learn about Your State! 2003. (Delaware Experience Ser.). 32p. (gr. k-5). pap. 5.95 (978-0-635-01927-1(2) , Marsh, Carole Bks.) Gallopade International.

—Florida Government Projects: 30 Cool, Activities, Crafts, Experiments & More for Kids to Do to Learn about Your State! 2003. (Florida Experience Ser.). 32p. (gr. k-5). pap. 5.95 (978-0-635-01928-8(0) , Marsh, Carole Bks.) Gallopade International.

—Georgia Government Projects: 30 Cool, Activities, Crafts, Experiments & More for Kids to Do to Learn about Your State! 2003. (Georgia Experience Ser.). 32p. (gr. k-5). pap. 5.95 (978-0-635-01929-5(9) , Marsh, Carole Bks.) Gallopade International.

—Hawaii Government Projects: 30 Cool, Activities, Crafts, Experiments & More for Kids to Do to Learn about Your State! 2003. (Hawaii Experience Ser.). 32p. (gr. k-5). pap. 5.95 (978-0-635-01930-1(2) , Marsh, Carole Bks.) Gallopade International.

—Idaho Government Projects: 30 Cool, Activities, Crafts, Experiments & More for Kids to Do to Learn about Your State! 2003. (Idaho Experience Ser.). 32p. (gr. k-5). pap. 5.95 (978-0-635-01931-8(0) , Marsh, Carole Bks.) Gallopade International.

—Illinois Government Projects: 30 Cool, Activities, Crafts, Experiments & More for Kids to Do to Learn about Your State! 2003. (Illinois Experience Ser.). 32p. (gr. k-5). pap. 5.95 (978-0-635-01932-5(9) , Marsh, Carole Bks.) Gallopade International.

—Indiana Government Projects: 30 Cool, Activities, Crafts, Experiments & More for Kids to Do to Learn about Your State! 2003. (Indiana Experience Ser.). 32p. (gr. k-5). pap. 5.95 (978-0-635-01933-2(7) , Marsh, Carole Bks.) Gallopade International.

—Iowa Government Projects: 30 Cool, Activities, Crafts, Experiments & More for Kids to Do to Learn about Your State! 2003. (Iowa Experience Ser.). 32p. (gr. k-5). pap. 5.95 (978-0-635-01934-9(5) , Marsh, Carole Bks.) Gallopade International.

—Kansas Government Projects: 30 Cool, Activities, Crafts, Experiments & More for Kids to Do to Learn about Your State! 2003. (Kansas Experience Ser.). 32p. (gr. k-5). pap. 5.95 (978-0-635-01935-6(3) , Marsh, Carole Bks.) Gallopade International.

—Kentucky Government Projects: 30 Cool, Activities, Crafts, Experiments & More for Kids to Do to Learn about Your State! 2003. (Kentucky Experience Ser.). 32p. (gr. k-5). pap. 5.95 (978-0-635-01936-3(1) , Marsh, Carole Bks.) Gallopade International.

—Louisiana Government Projects: 30 Cool, Activities, Crafts, Experiments & More for Kids to Do to Learn about Your State! 2003. (Louisiana Experience Ser.). 32p. (gr. k-5). pap. 5.95 (978-0-635-01937-0(X) , Marsh, Carole Bks.) Gallopade International.

—Maine Government Projects: 30 Cool, Activities, Crafts, Experiments & More for Kids to Do to Learn about Your State! 2003. (Maine Experience Ser.). 32p. (gr. k-5). pap. 5.95 (978-0-635-01938-7(8) , Marsh, Carole Bks.) Gallopade International.

—Maryland Government Projects: 30 Cool, Activities, Crafts, Experiments & More for Kids to Do to Learn about Your State! 2003. (Maryland Experience Ser.). 32p. (gr. k-5). pap. 5.95 (978-0-635-01939-4(6) , Marsh, Carole Bks.) Gallopade International.

—Massachusetts Government Projects: 30 Cool, Activities, Crafts, Experiments & More for Kids to Do to Learn about Your State! 2003. (Massachusetts Experience Ser.). 32p. (gr. k-5). pap. 5.95 (978-0-635-01940-0(X) , Marsh, Carole Bks.) Gallopade International.

—Michigan Government Projects: 30 Cool, Activities, Crafts, Experiments & More for Kids to Do to Learn about Your State! 2003. (Michigan Experience Ser.). 32p. (gr. k-5). pap. 5.95 (978-0-635-01941-7(8) , Marsh, Carole Bks.) Gallopade International.

—Minnesota Government Projects: 30 Cool, Activities, Crafts, Experiments & More for Kids to Do to Learn about Your State! 2003. (Minnesota Experience Ser.). 32p. (gr. k-5). pap. 5.95 (978-0-635-01942-4(6) , Marsh, Carole Bks.) Gallopade International.

—Mississippi Government Projects: 30 Cool, Activities, Crafts, Experiments & More for Kids to Do to Learn about Your State! 2003. (Mississippi Experience Ser.). 32p. (gr. k-5). pap. 5.95 (978-0-635-01943-1(4) , Marsh, Carole Bks.) Gallopade International.

—Missouri Government Projects: 30 Cool, Activities, Crafts, Experiments & More for Kids to Do to Learn about Your State! 2003. (Missouri Experience Ser.). 32p. (gr. k-5). pap. 5.95 (978-0-635-01944-8(2) , Marsh, Carole Bks.) Gallopade International.

—Montana Government Projects: 30 Cool, Activities, Crafts, Experiments & More for Kids to Do to Learn about Your State! 2003. (Montana Experience Ser.). 32p. (gr. k-5). pap. 5.95 (978-0-635-01945-5(0) , Marsh, Carole Bks.) Gallopade International.

—Nebraska Government Projects: 30 Cool, Activities, Crafts, Experiments & More for Kids to Do to Learn about Your State! 2003. (Nebraska Experience Ser.). 32p. (gr. k-5). pap. 5.95 (978-0-635-01946-2(9) , Marsh, Carole Bks.) Gallopade International.

—Nevada Government Projects: 30 Cool, Activities, Crafts, Experiments & More for Kids to Do to Learn about Your State! 2003. (Nevada Experience Ser.). 32p. (gr. k-5). pap. 5.95 (978-0-635-01947-9(7) , Marsh, Carole Bks.) Gallopade International.

—New Hampshire Government Projects: 30 Cool, Activities, Crafts, Experiments & More for Kids to Do to Learn about Your State! 2003. (New Hampshire Experience Ser.). 32p. (gr. k-5). pap. 5.95 (978-0-635-01948-6(5) , Marsh, Carole Bks.) Gallopade International.

—New Jersey Government Projects: 30 Cool, Activities, Crafts, Experiments & More for Kids to Do to Learn about Your State! 2003. (New Jersey Experience Ser.). 32p. (gr. k-5). pap. 5.95 (978-0-635-01949-3(3) , Marsh, Carole Bks.) Gallopade International.

—New Mexico Government Projects: 30 Cool, Activities, Crafts, Experiments & More for Kids to Do to Learn about Your State! 2003. (New Mexico Experience Ser.). 32p. (gr. k-5). pap. 5.95 (978-0-635-01950-9(7) , Marsh, Carole Bks.) Gallopade International.

—North Carolina Government Projects: 30 Cool, Activities, Crafts, Experiments & More for Kids to Do to Learn about Your State! 2003. (North Carolina Experience Ser.). 32p. (gr. k-5). pap. 5.95 (978-0-635-01952-3(3) , Marsh, Carole Bks.) Gallopade International.

—North Dakota Government Projects: 30 Cool, Activities, Crafts, Experiments & More for Kids to Do to Learn about Your State! 2003. (North Dakota Experience Ser.). 32p. (gr. k-5). pap. 5.95 (978-0-635-01953-0(1) , Marsh, Carole Bks.) Gallopade International.

—Ohio Government Projects: 30 Cool, Activities, Crafts, Experiments & More for Kids to Do to Learn about Your State! 2003. (Ohio Experience Ser.). 32p. (gr. k-5). pap. 5.95 (978-0-635-01954-7(X) , Marsh, Carole Bks.) Gallopade International.

—Oklahoma Government Projects: 30 Cool, Activities, Crafts, Experiments & More for Kids to Do to Learn about Your State! 2003. (Oklahoma Experience Ser.). 32p. (gr. k-5). pap. 5.95 (978-0-635-01955-4(8) , Marsh, Carole Bks.) Gallopade International.

—Oregon Government Projects: 30 Cool, Activities, Crafts, Experiments & More for Kids to Do to Learn about Your State! 2003. (Oregon Experience Ser.). 32p. (gr. k-5). pap. 5.95 (978-0-635-01956-1(6) , Marsh, Carole Bks.) Gallopade International.

—Pennsylvania Government Projects: 30 Cool, Activities, Crafts, Experiments & More for Kids to Do to Learn about Your State! 2003. (Pennsylvania Experience Ser.). 32p. (gr. k-5). pap. 5.95 (978-0-635-01957-8(4) , Marsh, Carole Bks.) Gallopade International.

—Rhode Island Government Projects: 30 Cool, Activities, Crafts, Experiments & More for Kids to Do to Learn about Your State! 2003. (Rhode Island Experience Ser.). 32p. (gr. k-5). pap. 5.95 (978-0-635-01958-5(2) , Marsh, Carole Bks.) Gallopade International.

—South Carolina Government Projects: 30 Cool, Activities, Crafts, Experiments & More for Kids to Do to Learn about Your State! 2003. (South Carolina Experience Ser.). 32p. (gr. k-5). pap. 5.95 (978-0-635-01959-2(0) , Marsh, Carole Bks.) Gallopade International.

—South Dakota Government Projects: 30 Cool, Activities, Crafts, Experiments & More for Kids to Do to Learn about Your State! 2003. (South Dakota Experience Ser.). 32p. (gr. k-5). pap. 5.95 (978-0-635-01960-8(4) , Marsh, Carole Bks.) Gallopade International.

—Tennessee Government Projects: 30 Cool, Activities, Crafts, Experiments & More for Kids to Do to Learn about Your State! 2003. (Tennessee Experience Ser.). 32p. (gr. k-5). pap. 5.95 (978-0-635-01961-5(2) , Marsh, Carole Bks.) Gallopade International.

—Texas Government Projects: 30 Cool, Activities, Crafts, Experiments & More for Kids to Do to Learn about Your State! 2003. (Texas Experience Ser.). 32p. (gr. k-5). pap. 5.95 (978-0-635-01962-2(0) , Marsh, Carole Bks.) Gallopade International.

—Utah Government Projects: 30 Cool, Activities, Crafts, Experiments & More for Kids to Do to Learn about Your State! 2003. (Utah Experience Ser.). 32p. (gr. k-5). pap. 5.95 (978-0-635-01963-9(9) , Marsh, Carole Bks.) Gallopade International.

—Vermont Government Projects: 30 Cool, Activities, Crafts, Experiments & More for Kids to Do to Learn about Your State! 2003. (Vermont Experience Ser.). 32p. (gr. k-5). pap. 5.95 (978-0-635-01964-6(7) , Marsh, Carole Bks.) Gallopade International.

—Virginia Government Projects: 30 Cool, Activities, Crafts, Experiments & More for Kids to Do to Learn about Your State! 2003. (Virginia Experience Ser.). 32p. (gr. k-5). pap. 5.95 (978-0-635-01965-3(5) , Marsh, Carole Bks.) Gallopade International.

Maurer, Tracy. State Capitals. 1999. (Guide to State Symbols Ser.). (Illus.). 48p. (J). (gr. 3-8). lib. bdg. 29.93 (978-1-57103-296-6(7)) Rourke Publishing, LLC.

Othello: Activity Pack. 2003. 156p. (YA). pap. (978-1-58049-631-5(8) , PA6318) Prestwick Hse., Inc.

Remy, Richard C., ed. American Government at Work, 9 vols. 2000. (Illus.). 864p. (J). (gr. 7 up). lib. bdg. 319.00 (978-0-7172-9557-9(5) , Grolier) Scholastic Library Publishing.

STATE PLANNING

see Regional Planning; Social Policy

STATE TREES

Cooper, Jason. Trees. 1998. (Guide to State Symbols Ser.). (Illus.). 48p. (J). (gr. 3-8). lib. bdg. 29.93 (978-1-57103-195-2(2)) Rourke Publishing, LLC.

STATESMEN

see also Diplomats

Adler, David A. & Adler, Michael S. A Picture Book of John Hancock. Himler, Ronald, illus. 2007. 32p. (J). (ps-3). 16.95 (***978-0-8234-2005-6(1)***) Holiday Hse., Inc.

Adler, David A. & Adler, Peter S. Heroes of the Revolution. 2003. (Illus.). 32p. (J). (gr. 1-5). tchr. ed. 16.95 (978-0-8234-1471-0(X)) Holiday Hse., Inc.

African-American Politicians. 2000. (My Ancestors—My Heroes Ser.: Vol. 20). (J). (gr. 3-4). (978-1-893091-19-1(8)) Parker Publishing Co.

Anderson, Dale. Leaders of the American Revolution. 2005. (World Almanac Library of the American Revolution). (J). pap. (978-0-8368-5940-9(5)); lib. bdg. 30.00 (978-0-8368-5931-7(6)) Stevens, Gareth Inc. (World Almanac Library).

Baldwin, James. Four Great Americans. 2006. pap. (***978-1-4065-0509-2(9)***) Dodo Pr.

Baldwin, James. Four Great Americans: Washington, Franklin, Webster, Lincoln: A Book for Young Americans. 2000. (Illus.). (J). (978-0-89526-203-5(7)) Regnery Publishing, Inc., An Eagle Publishing Co.

Beardsley, Laura E. Benjamin Franklin. 2007. (Essential Lives Ser.). (ENG., Illus.). 112p. (YA). (gr. 8-12). lib. bdg. 32.79 (***978-1-59928-840-6(0)*** , Essential Library) ABDO Publishing Co.

Benge, Janet & Benge, Geoff. Benjamin Franklin: A Useful Life. 2005. (Illus.). 197p. (J). (978-1-932096-14-9(0)) Emerald Bks.

Bennett, William. Our Country's Founders: Words of Advice from the Founders in Stories, Lteers, Po. 2001. (gr. 7-12). lib. bdg. 18.80 (978-0-613-37163-6(1)) Tandem Library Bks.

Boekhoff, P. M. & Kallen, Stuart A. Benjamin Franklin. 2006. (Illus.). 48p. (J). (gr. 4-8). 17.00 (978-1-4223-5322-6(2)) DIANE Publishing Co.

Burton, Alma Holman. Four American Patriots: Patrick Henry, Alexander Hamilton, Andrew Jackson, Ulysses S. Grant: A Book for Young Americans. 2000. (Illus.). (J). (978-0-89526-204-2(5)) Regnery Publishing, Inc., An Eagle Publishing Co.

Chelsea House Publishing Staff. Colonial Leaders. 1999. (Illus.). (J). 169.50 (978-0-7910-5340-9(7)); pap. 89.50 (978-0-7910-5694-3(5)) Facts On File, Inc. (Chelsea Hse.).

Collard, Sneed B., III. Benjamin Franklin: The Man Who Could Do Just about Anything. 2006. (American Heroes Ser.). (Illus.). 48p. (J). (gr. 3-5). lib. bdg. 28.50 (***978-0-7614-2161-0(0)*** , Benchmark Bks.) Cavendish, Marshall Corp.

Collier, James Lincoln. The Benjamin Franklin You Never Knew. 2004. (You Never Knew Ser.). (Illus.). 80p. (J). 25.50 (978-0-516-24427-3(2) , Children's Pr.) Scholastic Library Publishing.

Conway, John Richard. A Look at the Constitution: Creating a More Perfect Union. 2008. (J). (***978-1-59845-072-9(7)*** , MyReportLinks.com Bks.) Enslow Pubs., Inc.

Cox, Vicki. Fidel Castro. 2003. (Major World Leaders Ser.). (Illus.). 112p. (gr. 6-12). 30.00 (978-0-7910-7651-4(2) , Chelsea Hse.) Facts On File, Inc.

Crompton, Samuel Willard. Thomas More: And His Struggles of Conscience. 2005. (Makers of the Middle Ages & Renaissance Ser.). (Illus.). 140p. (J). (gr. 4-8). lib. bdg. 30.00 (978-0-7910-8636-0(4) , Chelsea Hse.) Facts On File, Inc.

Daugherty, James. Poor Richard. 2001. (Illus.). (J). pap. 16.95 (978-1-893103-03-0(X)) Beautiful Feet Bks.

DeCarolis, Lisa. Alexander Hamilton: Federalist & Founding Father. 2005. (Library of American Lives & Times). (Illus.). 112p. (J). (gr. 4-8). lib. bdg. 31.95 (978-0-8239-5735-4(7)) Rosen Publishing Group, Inc., The.

Demi. Gandhi. Demi, illus. 2001. (Illus.). 40p. (J). (gr. 2-5). 21.99 (978-0-689-84149-1(3) , McElderry, Margaret K.) Simon & Schuster Children's Publishing.

Donlan, Leni. A Life Well Lived: Ben Franklin. 2007. (J). (***978-1-4109-2698-2(2));*** pap. (***978-1-4109-2709-5(1))*** Steck-Vaughn.

Espinosa, Rod. Benjamin Franklin. 2007. (Bio-Graphics Ser.). (Illus.). 32p. (J). (gr. 3-6). lib. bdg. 27.07 (***978-1-60270-066-6(4)*** , Graphic Planet) Magic Wagon.

Feinstein, Stephen. Colin Powell. 2007. (African-American Heroes Ser.). (Illus.). 24p. (J). (gr. 1-3). lib. bdg. 21.26 (978-0-7660-2761-9(9) , Enslow Elementary) Enslow Pubs., Inc.

—Read about Benjamin Franklin. 2006. (I Like Biographies! Ser.). (Illus.). 24p. (J). lib. bdg. 21.26 (978-0-7660-2596-7(9) ; Enslow Elementary) Enslow Pubs., Inc.

Finlayson, Reggie. Colin Powell. 2005. (Biography Ser.). (Illus.). 112p. (gr. 6-12). lib. bdg. 27.93 (978-0-8225-4966-6(2)) Lerner Publishing Group.

—Colin Powell. 2004. (gr. 7-12). lib. bdg. 16.40 (978-0-613-76660-9(1)) Tandem Library Bks.

Fish, Bruce. Benjamin Franklin: American Statesman, Scientist & Writer. 1999. (Colonial Leaders Ser.). (Illus.). 80p. (J). (gr. 3 up). pap. 8.95 (978-0-7910-5690-5(2) , Chelsea Hse.) Facts On File, Inc.

Flanagan, Alice K. Colin Powell: U. S. Army General & Secretary of State. 2001. (Career Biographies Ser.). (Illus.). 128p. (J). (gr. 6-12). 25.00 (978-0-89434-372-8(6) , F415, Ferguson Publishing Co.) Facts On File, Inc.

Fleming, Candace. Ben Franklin's Almanac. 2003. (Illus.). 128p. (J). (gr. 5-9). 19.95 (978-0-689-83549-0(3) , Atheneum/Anne Schwartz Bks.) Simon & Schuster Children's Publishing.

Fleming, Thomas. Sterling Point Books: Ben Franklin: Inventing America. 2007. (Sterling Point Bks.). (Illus.). 192p. (J). 12.95 (978-1-4027-4523-2(0)); pap. 6.95 (978-1-4027-4143-2(X)) Sterling Publishing Co., Inc.

Fleming, Thomas J. Benjamin Franklin: Inventing America. 2007. (Sterling Point Bks.). (Illus.). viii, 177p. (J). (***978-1-4287-2411-2(7))*** Sterling Publishing Co., Inc.

Ford, Nick. Niccolo Machiavelli: Florentine Statesman, Playwright, & Poet. 2004. (Rulers, Scholars, & Artists of Renaissance Europe Ser.). (J). lib. bdg. 31.95 (978-1-4042-0316-7(8)) Rosen Publishing Group, Inc., The.

Fradin, Dennis Brindell. The Founders: The 39 Stories Behind the U. S. Constitution. McCurdy, Michael, illus. 2005. 144p. (J). (gr. 5-9). 23.85 (978-0-8027-8973-0(0)); 22.95 (978-0-8027-8972-3(2)) Walker & Co.

—The Signers: The 56 Stories Behind the Declaration of Independence. McCurdy, Michael, illus. 2003. (J). (gr. 5 up). 144p. 23.85 (978-0-8027-8850-4(5)); 160p. 22.95 (978-0-8027-8849-8(1)) Walker & Co.

Fredriksen, John C. Biographical Dictionary of Modern World Leaders Set, 2 vols. 2005. (Illus.). 1120p. (gr. 6-12). 125.00 (978-0-8160-6036-8(3)) Facts On File, Inc.

Fritz, Jean. Why Not, Lafayette? Himler, Ronald, illus. 1999. 1p. (J). (gr. 5-9). 17.99 (978-0-399-23411-8(X) , Putnam Juvenile) Penguin Group (USA) Inc.

Gaustad, Edwin S. Benjamin Franklin: Inventing America. 2006. 143p. (J). (gr. 4-8). reprint ed. 22.00 (978-1-4223-5227-4(7)) DIANE Publishing Co.

Giblin, James. The Many Rides of Paul Revere. 2007. 96p. (J). pap. 17.99 (***978-0-439-57290-3(8)*** , Scholastic Pr.) Scholastic, Inc.

Gillis, Jennifer Blizin. Benjamin Franklin. 2004. (Illus.). 32p. (J). pap. 6.50 (978-1-4034-5332-7(2)); lib. bdg. 22.79 (978-1-4034-5324-2(1)) Heinemann Library.

Gimpel, Lee. Fighting Wars, Planning for Peace: The Story of George C. Marshall. 2005. (World Leaders Ser.). (Illus.). 176p. (J). (gr. 8 up). lib. bdg. 26.95 (978-1-931798-66-2(4)) Reynolds, Morgan Inc.

Glass, Maya. Benjamin Franklin: Early American Genius. 2003. (Primary Sources of Famous People in American History Ser.). (Illus.). 32p. (YA). pap. (978-0-8239-4175-9(2)) Rosen Publishing Group, Inc., The.

Great Life Stories: Social Leaders, 3 bks. 2004. 88.50 (978-0-531-12396-6(0) , Children's Pr.) Scholastic Library Publishing.

Gregson, Susan R. Benjamin Franklin. 2000. (Let Freedom Ring Ser.). (Illus.). 48p. (J). (gr. 3-4). lib. bdg. 22.60 (978-0-7368-1031-9(5) , Bridgestone Bks.) Capstone Pr., Inc.

Hale, Sarah Elder, ed. Jefferson Davis & the Confederacy. 2005. (Cobblestone the Civil War Ser.). (Illus.). 48p. (J). 17.95 (978-0-8126-7908-3(3)) Cobblestone Publishing Co.

Hancock, Lee. Lorenzo de' Medici: Florence's Great Leader & Patron of the Arts. 2004. (Rulers, Scholars, & Artists of Renaissance Europe Ser.). (Illus.). 112p. (J). lib. bdg. 31.95 (978-1-4042-0315-0(X)) Rosen Publishing Group, Inc., The.

Harcourt School Publishers Staff. Almqu/Ben Franklin On Level. 3rd ed. 2002. (Trofeos Ser.). (SPA., Illus.). pap. 6.80 (978-0-15-324086-7(5)) Harcourt Schl. Pubs.

Harness, Cheryl. The Remarkable Benjamin Franklin. 2005. (Illus.). 48p. (J). (gr. 2 up). 17.95 (978-0-7922-7882-5(8)); 27.90 (978-0-7922-7884-9(4)) National Geographic Society. (National Geographic Children's Bks.).

Harris, Nancy. What's a Governor? 2007. (J). (***978-1-4034-9508-2(4));*** pap. (***978-1-4034-9514-3(9))*** Heinemann Library.

Haugen, Brenda & Santella, Andrew. Alexander Hamilton: Founding Father & Statesman. 2004. (Signature Lives Ser.). (Illus.). 112p. (J). 30.60 (978-0-7565-0827-2(4) , 1240126) Compass Point Bks.

Higgins, Maria Mihalik. Sterling Biographies: Benjamin Franklin: Revolutionary Inventor. 2007. (Sterling Biographies Ser.). (Illus.). 128p. (J). 12.95 (***978-1-4027-4952-0(X))*** Sterling Publishing Co., Inc.

Horn, Geoffrey M. Colin Powell. 2004. (Trailblazers of the Modern World Ser.). (Illus.). 48p. (J). pap. 11.95 (978-0-8368-5267-7(2)); (YA). lib. bdg. 30.00 (978-0-8368-5498-5(5)) Stevens, Gareth Inc. (World Almanac Library).

Hughes, Chris. The Constitutional Convention. 2005. (People at the Center of Ser.). (Illus.). 48p. (J). (ps-7). lib. bdg. 24.95 (978-1-56711-918-3(2) , Blackbirch Pr., Inc.) Thomson Gale.

Jefferson Davis. (Civil War Biographies Ser.). 48p. (YA). 7.95 (978-0-7368-4524-3(0)) Capstone Pr., Inc.

Kallen, Stuart A. Alexander Hamilton. 2001. (Founding Fathers Ser.). (Illus.). 64p. (J). (gr. 3-8). lib. bdg. 25.65 (978-1-57765-006-5(9) , ABDO & Daughters) ABDO Publishing Co.

—Benjamin Franklin. 2001. (Founding Fathers Ser.). (Illus.). 64p. (J). (gr. 3-8). lib. bdg. 25.65 (978-1-57765-009-6(3) , ABDO & Daughters) ABDO Publishing Co.

Kelly, Jack. Benjamin Franklin. Tafalla, Ortiz, illus. 2005. (Heroes of America Ser.). 240p. (J). (gr. 3-8). lib. bdg. 21.35 (978-1-59679-257-9(4)) ABDO Publishing Co.

Kent, Zachary. Alexander Hamilton: Creating a Nation. 2004. (America's Founding Fathers Ser.). (Illus.). 128p. (J). lib. bdg. 26.60 (978-0-7660-2181-5(5)) Enslow Pubs., Inc.

—William Seward: The Mastermind of the Alaska Purchase. 2001. (Historical American Biographies Ser.). (Illus.). 128p. (J). (gr. 6-12). lib. bdg. 26.60 (978-0-7660-1391-9(X)) Enslow Pubs., Inc.

Koestler-Grack, Rachel. Kofi Annan: Guiding the United Nations. 2007. (Modern Peacemakers Ser.). (Illus.). 128p. (YA). (gr. 9 up). 30.00 (978-0-7910-8996-5(7) , Chelsea Hse.) Facts On File, Inc.

Landau, Elaine. Meet Ben Franklin with Elaine Landau. 2006. (Explore Colonial America with Elaine Landau Ser.). (Illus.). 48p. (J). lib. bdg. 23.93 (978-0-7660-2555-4(1) , Enslow Elementary) Enslow Pubs., Inc.

Leaders of the American Revolution Set, 11-Volumes. 2006. (Leaders of the American Revolution Ser.). 100p. (gr. 5-8). 330.00 (978-0-7910-9320-7(4) , Chelsea Hse.) Facts On File, Inc.

Major World Leaders. 2005. 112-144p. pap. 720.00 (978-0-7910-8410-6(8) , Chelsea Hse.) Facts On File, Inc.

Makers of the Middle Ages & Renaissance. 2005. (Illus.). 100p. (gr. 4-8). pap. 300.00 (978-0-7910-9064-0(7) , Chelsea Hse.) Facts On File, Inc.

Malaspina, Ann. Mahatma Gandhi & India's Independence in World History. 2000. (In World History Ser.). (Illus.). 128p. (YA). (gr. 5-12). lib. bdg. 26.60 (978-0-7660-1398-8(7)) Enslow Pubs., Inc.

Mara, Wil. Benjamin Franklin. rev. ed. 2006. (Rookie Biography Ser.). (Illus.). 31p. (J). (978-0-531-12450-5(9)) Children's Pr., Ltd.

—Paul Revere. (Rookie Biographies Ser.). (J). 2005. (Illus.). 32p. (gr. 1-2). pap. 4.95 (978-0-516-25820-1(6)); 2004. 20.50 (978-0-516-21841-0(7)) Scholastic Library Publishing. (Children's Pr.).

Marcovitz, Hal. Benjamin Franklin: Scientist, Inventor, Printer, & Statesman. 2006. (Leaders of the American Revolution Ser.). (Illus.). 176p. (J). (gr. 5-8). 30.00 (978-0-7910-9219-4(4) , Chelsea Hse.) Facts On File, Inc.

Marsh, Carole. George Mason. 2002. (One Thousand Readers Ser.). (Illus.). 12p. (J). (gr. k-4). 2.95 (978-0-635-01548-8(X) , 1548X) Gallopade International.

Marti, Jose. Jose Marti: Cuatro cuentos Infantiles. Martinez, Enrique & Graullera, Fabiola, illus. (SPA.). 28p. (J). (gr. 3-5). 9.95 (978-970-29-0522-6(2)) Santillana, S.A. de C.V., Editorial MEX. *Dist:* Santillana USA Publishing Co., Inc.

Mayer, Cassie. Benjamin Franklin. 2007. (J). (***978-1-4034-9970-7(5));*** pap. (***978-1-4034-9979-0(9))*** Heinemann Library.

McCurdy, Michael. So Said Ben. 2007. (Illus.). 32p. (YA). (gr. 4 up). 17.95 (***978-1-56846-147-2(X)*** , Creative Editions) Creative Co., The.

McDonough, Yona Zeldis. The Life of Benjamin Franklin: An American Original. Zeldis, Malcah, illus. 2006. 48p. (J). 17.95 (978-0-8050-7856-5(8)) Holt, Henry & Co.

McLeese, Don. Alexander Hamilton. 2005. (Heroes of the American Revolution Ser.). (Illus.). 32p. (gr. 2-5). 19.95 (978-1-59515-219-0(9)) Rourke Publishing, LLC.

—Benjamin Franklin. 2005. (Heroes of the American Revolution Ser.). (Illus.). 32p. (gr. 2-5). 19.95 (978-1-59515-216-9(4)) Rourke Publishing, LLC.

McNeese, Tim. Alexander Hamilton: Framer of the Constitution. 2005. (Leaders of the American Revolution Ser.). (Illus.). 152p. (J). (gr. 4-8). lib. bdg. 30.00 (978-0-7910-8616-2(X) , Chelsea Hse.) Facts On File, Inc.

Meisner, James, Jr. & Ruth, Amy. American Revolutionaries & Founders of the Nation. 1999. (Collective Biographies Ser.). (Illus.). 112p. (YA). (gr. 6-12). lib. bdg. 26.60 (978-0-7660-1115-1(1)) Enslow Pubs., Inc.

Melchiore, Susan McCarthy. Caesar Rodney. 2001. (gr. 3-6). lib. bdg. 17.60 (978-0-613-32357-4(2)) Tandem Library Bks.

Mills, Clifford W. Angela Merkel. 2007. (Modern World Leaders Ser.). 120p. (J). (gr. 6-12). 30.00 (***978-0-7910-9496-9(0)*** , Chelsea Hse.) Facts On File, Inc.

Murphy, John. Ali Khamenei. 2007. (Modern World Leaders Ser.). 144p. (gr. 6-12). 30.00 (***978-0-7910-9517-1(7)*** , Chelsea Hse.) Facts On File, Inc.

Nardo, Don. Pericles: Great Leader of Ancient Athens. 2006. (Rulers of the Ancient World Ser.). (Illus.). 160p. (J). lib. bdg. 27.93 (978-0-7660-2561-5(6)) Enslow Pubs., Inc.

Nava, Julian. Julian Nava: My Mexican-American Journey. 2002. (Hispanic Civil Rights Ser.). 248p. (YA). 16.95 (978-1-55885-364-5(2) , Piñata Books) Arte Publico Pr.

—Julian Nava: My Mexican-American Journey. 2002. (gr. 7-12). lib. bdg. 18.75 (978-0-613-82668-6(X)) Tandem Library Bks.

Nicholson, Michael. Mahatma Gandhi. (Pacificadores Mundiales Ser.). 64p. (gr. 5-8). 28.70 (978-1-4103-0541-1(4) , Blackbirch Pr., Inc.) Thomson Gale.

Niz, Xavier. Paul Revere's Ride. Bascle, Brian, illus. 2005. (Graphic Library). 32p. (J). (gr. 3-7). lib. bdg. 25.26 (978-0-7368-4965-4(3)) Capstone Pr., Inc.

Olson, Kay Melchisedech. Benjamin Franklin: An American Genius. Purcell, Gordon & Schulz, Barbara, illus. 2005. (Graphic Library). 32p. (J). (gr. 3-7). lib. bdg. 25.26 (978-0-7368-4629-5(8)) Capstone Pr., Inc.

Parks, Peggy J. Benjamin Franklin: Genius Inventor & Electricity Pioneer. 2002. (Giants of Science Ser.). (Illus.). 64p. (J). 26.20 (978-1-56711-658-8(2) , Blackbirch Pr., Inc.) Thomson Gale.

Powell, Phelan. John Jay: First Chief Justice of the Supreme Court. 2001. (gr. 5-8). lib. bdg. 17.60 (978-0-613-32726-8(8)) Tandem Library Bks.

Randolph, Ryan P. Benjamin Franklin: Inventor, Writer & Patriot. 2005. (Library of American Lives & Times). (Illus.). 112p. (YA). (gr. 4-8). lib. bdg. 31.95 (978-0-8239-5751-4(9)) Rosen Publishing Group, Inc., The.

Ransom, Candice F. John Hancock. 2005. (History Maker Bios Ser.). (Illus.). 48p. (J). (gr. 3-4). 26.60 (978-0-8225-1547-0(4) , Lerner Pubns.) Lerner Publishing Group.

Raum, Elizabeth. Leaders. 2007. (***978-1-4109-2978-5(7));*** pap. (***978-1-4109-2999-0(X))*** Steck-Vaughn.

Rausch, Monica. Benjamin Franklin. 2006. (J). (ENG & SPA.). pap. (***978-0-8368-7988-9(0));*** (ENG & SPA.). lib. bdg. (***978-0-8368-7981-0(3));*** (Illus.). 24p. pap. (***978-0-8368-7689-5(X));*** (Illus.). 24p. lib. bdg. (***978-0-8368-7682-6(2))*** Stevens, Gareth Inc. (Weekly Reader Early Learning Library).

Riley, Gail Blasser. Benjamin Franklin & Electricity. 2004. (Cornerstones of Freedom Ser.). (Illus.). 48p. (J). 26.00 (978-0-516-24240-8(7) , Children's Pr.) Scholastic Library Publishing.

Riley, John B. Benjamin Franklin: A Photo Biography. l.t. ed. 2004. (First Biographies Ser.). (Illus.). 24p. (YA). (gr. 5 up). 16.95 (978-1-883846-64-0(1) , First Biographies) Reynolds, Morgan Inc.

Rivera, Sheila. Mohandas Gandhi: A Life of Integrity. 2007. (Pull Ahead Books). (Illus.). 32p. (J). 22.60 (978-0-8225-6383-9(5) , Lerner Pubns.) Lerner Publishing Group.

Rosenburg, John M. Alexander Hamilton: America's Bold Lion. 2000. (Single Titles Ser.: up). (Illus.). 192p. (gr. 7-12). lib. bdg. (978-0-7613-1617-6(5) , Millbrook Pr.) Lerner Publishing Group.

Ross, Stewart. Big J. Shields, Sue, illus. 32p. pap. 9.99 (978-0-7502-2852-7(0) , Hodder & Stoughton) Hodder General Publishing Division GBR. *Dist:* Trafalgar Square Publishing.

Satterfield, Kathryn Hoffman. Benjamin Franklin A Man of Many Talents. 2005. 44p. (J). lib. bdg. 15.00 (***978-1-4242-0846-3(7))*** Fitzgerald Bks.

Shaw, Maura D. Gandhi: India's Great Soul. Marchesi, Stephen, illus. 2003. (Spiritual Biographies for Young Readers Ser.). 32p. (J). (gr. 1-3). 12.95 (978-1-893361-91-1(8)) SkyLight Paths Publishing.

Sherrow, Victoria. Benjamin Franklin. 2002. (History Maker Bios Ser.). (Illus.). (J). 47p. pap. 6.95 (978-0-8225-0383-5(2) , Lerner Pubns.); 48p. (gr. 3-5). lib. bdg. 26.60 (978-0-8225-0198-5(8)) Lerner Publishing Group.

Somervill, Barbara A. John Hancock: Signer for Independence. 2004. (Signature Lives Ser.). (Illus.). 112p. (J). 30.60 (978-0-7565-0828-9(2) , 1240133) Compass Point Bks.

The Story of Benjamin Franklin. 2002. (Illus.). 24p. (J). (ps-k). 6.95 (978-0-8249-4227-4(2)) Ideals Pubns.

S

Streissguth, Tom. Benjamin Franklin. 2005. (Bios for Challenged Readers Ser.). (Illus.). 112p. (J). (gr. 6-12). lib. bdg. 27.93 (978-0-8225-2210-2(1)) Lerner Publishing Group.

Strong, Mike. Colin Powell: It Can Be Done! 2002. (High Five Reading Ser.). (Illus.). 48p. (J). (gr. 3-4). lib. bdg. 22.60 (978-0-7368-9551-4(5) , Capstone High-Interest Bks.); pap. (978-0-7368-9529-3(9)) Capstone Pr., Inc.

Sullivan, George. Paul Revere. 1999. (gr. 3-6). lib. bdg. 12.40 (978-0-613-26542-3(4)) Tandem Library Bks.

Sullivan, George E. Paul Revere. 2000. (J). 11.15 (978-0-606-19925-4(X)) Tandem Library Bks.

Tessitore, John. Kofi Annan: The Peacekeeper. 2000. (Book Report Biographies Ser.). (Illus.). 112p. (YA). (gr. 6-8). pap. 6.95 (978-0-531-16458-7(6) , Watts, Franklin) Scholastic Library Publishing.

Thayer, William M. From Boyhood to Manhood - the Life of Be. 2006. pap. (***978-1-4068-0906-0(3)***) Echo Library.

Tieck, Sarah. Paul Revere. 2007. (First Biographies Ser.). (Illus.). 32p. (J). (gr. k-3). lib. bdg. 22.78 (978-1-59679-787-1(8)) ABDO Publishing Co.

Time for Kids Editors. Benjamin Franklin: A Man of Many Talents. 2005. (Time for Kids Ser.). (Illus.). 48p. (J). 14.99 (978-0-06-057610-3(3)); pap. 3.99 (978-0-06-057609-7(X)) HarperCollins Pubs.

Todd, Anne M. Mohandas Gandhi. 2004. (Spiritual Leaders & Thinkers Ser.). (Illus.). 120p. (gr. 9-13). (J). 30.00 (978-0-7910-7864-8(7)); 30.00 (978-0-7910-7865-5(5)) Facts On File, Inc. (Chelsea Hse.).

Tracy, Kathleen. Cicero. 2006. (Biography from Ancient Civilizations Ser.). (Illus.). 48p. (J). lib. bdg. 20.95 (978-1-58415-510-2(8)) Mitchell Lane Pubs., Inc.

—Lorenzo de Zavala. 2002. (Latinos in American History). (Illus.). 56p. (gr. 4-8). lib. bdg. 29.95 (978-1-58415-154-8(4)) Mitchell Lane Pubs., Inc.

Wade, Linda R. Leaders of the American Revolution. 2001. (American Revolution Ser.). (Illus.). 32p. (J). (gr. 3-8). lib. bdg. 24.21 (978-1-57765-156-7(1) , ABDO & Daughters) ABDO Publishing Co.

Wagner, Heather Lehr. Machiavelli: Renaissance Political Analyst & Author. 2005. (Makers of the Middle Ages & Renaissance Ser.). (Illus.). 138p. (J). (gr. 4-8). lib. bdg. 30.00 (978-0-7910-8629-2(1) , Chelsea Hse.) Facts On File, Inc.

—Paul Revere: Messenger for Freedom. 2005. (Leaders of the American Revolution Ser.). (Illus.). 116p. (J). (ps-8). lib. bdg. 30.00 (978-0-7910-8624-7(0) , Chelsea Hse.) Facts On File, Inc.

Waxman, Laura Hamilton. Colin Powell. 2005. (History Maker Bios Ser.). 48p. (J). pap. 6.95 (978-0-8225-5463-9(1)); (Illus.). 26.60 (978-0-8225-2433-5(3) , Lerner Pubns.) Lerner Publishing Group.

Where Was Patrick Henry on the 29th of May? 2004. 29.95 incl. cd-rom (978-1-55592-484-3(0)); pap. 14.95 incl. audio (978-1-56008-222-4(4)); pap. 18.95 incl. audio compact disk (978-1-55592-483-6(2)); pap. 18.95 incl. audio compact disk (978-1-55592-486-7(7)); pap. 32.75 incl. audio (978-1-55592-356-3(9)); pap. 32.75 incl. audio (978-1-55592-348-8(8)); pap. 32.75 incl. audio (978-1-55592-487-4(5)) Weston Woods Studios, Inc.

White, Casey. John Jay. 2005. (Library of American Thinkers). (Illus.). 112p. (J). (978-1-4042-0507-9(1)) Rosen Publishing Group, Inc., The.

Whiting, Jim. Benjamin Franklin. 2006. (Profiles in American History Ser.). (Illus.). 48p. (J). (gr. 4-8). lib. bdg. 20.95 (978-1-58415-435-8(7)) Mitchell Lane Pubs., Inc.

—The Life & Times of Pericles. 2005. (Biography from Ancient Civilizations Ser.). (Illus.). 48p. (J). (ps-7). lib. bdg. 29.95 (978-1-58415-339-9(3)) Mitchell Lane Pubs., Inc.

Williams, Jean Kinney. Jefferson Davis: President of the Confederate States. 2004. (Signature Lives Ser.). (Illus.). 112p. (J). 30.60 (978-0-7565-0817-3(7) , 1240142) Compass Point Bks.

Wilson, Richard L. American Political Leaders. 2002. (American Biographies Ser.). (Illus.). 464p. (gr. 9). 65.00 (978-0-8160-4536-5(4)) Facts On File, Inc.

Winter, Jonah. Paul Revere & the Bell Ringers. Dodson, Bert, illus. 2003. (Ready-to-Read Ser.). 32p. (J). pap. 3.99 (978-0-689-85635-8(0) , Aladdin) Simon & Schuster Children's Publishing.

—Paul Revere & the Bell Ringers. 2003. (gr. k-3). lib. bdg. 11.80 (978-0-613-89003-8(5)) Tandem Library Bks.

Wise, William. Aaron Burr. 2001. 196p. (gr. 7-12). pap. 13.95 (978-0-595-19630-2(6)) iUniverse, Inc.

Yero, Judith Lloyd. The Declaration of Independence. 2004. (National Geographic Reading Expeditions Ser.). (Illus.). 32p. (J). pap. (978-0-7922-4554-4(7)) National Geographic Society.

STATISTICS

see also Probabilities

also general subjects and names of countries, cities, etc. with the subdivision Statistics, e.g. U. S.—Statistics; etc.

Accelerated Math West Virginia State Tagged Probablilty & Statistics Library. 2004. cd-rom 1199.00 (978-1-59455-117-8(0)) Renaissance Learning, Inc.

Adams, Colleen. The Everglades: Analyzing Graphs, Tables, & Charts. 2005. (PowerMath Ser.). (J). 22.50 (978-1-4042-2933-4(7)); pap. (978-1-4042-5127-4(8)) Rosen Publishing Group, Inc., The. (PowerKids Pr.).

American Statistical Association Staff. Exploring Statistics in the Elementary Grades, Bk. 1. 1998. (Illus.). 152p. (J). 18.95 (978-1-57232-344-5(2)) Seymour, Dale Pubns.

Brase. Brase, Understandable Statistics, 8th Edition Plus Eduspace 1. 8th ed. 2005. (YA). pap. 133.56 (978-0-618-64444-5(X) , 396104) Houghton Mifflin College Div.

—Student Solutions Manual: Used with ... Brase-Understandable Statistics: Concepts & Methods. 7th ed. 2002. (YA). (gr. 11-12). stu. ed. 41.96 (978-0-618-20558-5(6) , 307004) Houghton Mifflin College Div.

—Student Solutions Manual: Used with ... Brase-Understanding Basic Statistics. 3rd ed. 2003. (YA). (gr. 6-12). stu. ed. 35.56 (978-0-618-33362-2(2) , 306134) Houghton Mifflin College Div.

—Understandable Statistics, Concepts & Methods. 7th ed. 2002. (YA). (gr. 11-12). stu. ed. 3.96 incl. cd-rom (978-0-618-20562-2(4) , 307009) Houghton Mifflin College Div.

—Understanding Basic Statistics: Highschool Version. 3rd ed. 2003. (YA). (gr. 6-12). 101.16 (978-0-618-33359-2(2) , 306131) Houghton Mifflin College Div.

—Understanding Basic Statistics AP: Concepts & Methods. 7th ed. 2002. (YA). (gr. 11-12). stu. ed. 133.56 incl. cd-rom (978-0-618-26674-6(7) , 307023) Houghton Mifflin College Div.

—Understanding Basic Statistics Brief Highschool with Statpass Cd 3rd Edition. 3rd ed. 2003. (YA). (gr. 6-12). 101.16 incl. cd-rom (978-0-618-39358-9(7) , 384996) Houghton Mifflin College Div.

—Understanding Basic Statistics Brief with Cd Plus Excel Guide Plus Technology Guide 3rd Edition Plus Smarthinking. 3rd ed. 2004. (YA). pap., pap., pap. 115.56 (978-0-618-48897-1(9) , 389043) Houghton Mifflin College Div.

Brase, Charles & Brase, Corinne Pellillo. Understandable Statistics: Concepts & Methods. 6th ed. 1999. 1008p. (gr. 11-12). 107.16 (978-0-395-90768-9(3) , 3-06036) McDougal Littell Inc.

Brase, Charles Henry & Brase, Corinne Pellillo. Understandable Statistics: Advanced Placement Edition. 7th ed. 2002. (Illus.). xxiv, 750p. (YA). (gr. 11-12). stu. ed. 133.56 (978-0-618-26509-1(0) , 307018) Houghton Mifflin College Div.

—Understandable Statistics: Used with ... Brase-Understandable Statistics: Concepts & Methods. 7th ed. 2002. (YA). (gr. 11-12). 41.96 (978-0-618-20557-8(8) , 307003) Houghton Mifflin College Div.

—Understanding Basic Statistics. 3rd ed. 2003. 569p. (YA). 105.96 (978-0-618-31553-6(5) , 306130) Houghton Mifflin College Div.

Brase, Henry Charles & Brase, Corinne Pellillo. Understandble Statistics: Concepts & Methods: Study & Solution Guide. 6th ed. 1999. (gr. 11-12). stu. ed. (978-0-395-90774-0(8) , 3-06040) McDougal Littell Inc.

Burrill, Gail F., et al. Exploring Regression. (Data-Driven Mathematics Ser.). 96p. (YA). (gr. 7-12). pap., stu. ed. 18.95 (978-1-57232-245-5(4)) Seymour, Dale Pubns.

Drawing Conclusions & Inferences (Gr. 4-5) 2004. (J). (978-1-58232-134-9(5)) Bryan Hse. Pubs., Inc.

Freudenthal. Insights into Data. 3rd ed. 2003. (Math in Context Ser.). (Illus.). 7.86 (978-0-03-071699-7(3)) Holt, Rinehart & Winston.

—Math in Context: Statistics & Environment. 3rd ed. 2002. 8.33 (978-0-85229-890-9(0)) Encyclopaedia Britannica, Inc.

—Statistics & Environment. 3rd ed. 2003. (Math in Context Ser.). (Illus.). 8.33 (978-0-03-071549-5(0)) Holt, Rinehart & Winston.

Gnanadesikan, Mrudulla. Art & Technique of Simulation. (YA). (gr. 7-12). pap., stu. ed. 12.95 (978-0-86651-336-4(1) , DSO1704) Globe Fearon Educational Publishing.

Heiman. Basic Statistics Brief Plus Study Guide Brief. 2003. (YA). pap. 101.16 (978-0-618-45486-0(1) , 387298) Houghton Mifflin College Div.

Holt, Rinehart and Winston Staff. Math in Context: Statistics. 3rd ed. 2002. tchr. ed. 33.53 (978-0-85229-900-5(1)) Encyclopaedia Britannica, Inc.

Jacobs Krieger, Melanie. Using Statistics in Science Projects, Internet Enhanced. 2002. (Science Fair Success Ser.). (Illus.). 144p. (YA). (gr. 6-12). lib. bdg. 26.60 (978-0-7660-1629-3(3)) Enslow Pubs., Inc.

Job, Barbara & Morley, Diane. Key Maths. 2nd rev. ed. 2001. (Illus.). 424p. pap. 37.50 (978-0-7487-6549-2(2)) Nelson Thornes Ltd. GBR. *Dist:* Trans-Atlantic Pubns., Inc.

Kompelien, Tracy. You can Estimate, That's Really Great! 2007. (Math Made Fun Ser.). (Illus.). 24p. (J). 19.93 (978-1-59928-551-1(7) , SandCastle) ABDO Publishing Co.

Locke, Ian. Magnificent Monarchs. Rowe, Alan, illus. 2003. 63p. (J). pap. 3.99 (978-0-330-37496-5(6) , Pan) Pan Macmillan GBR. *Dist:* Trafalgar Square Publishing.

McGill, Fiona, et al. Statistics: Complete Advanced Level Mathematics. 1999. (Illus.). 552p. (YA). (gr. 11 up). pap. 59.50 (978-0-7487-3560-0(7)) Nelson Thornes Ltd. GBR. *Dist:* Trans-Atlantic Pubns., Inc.

Moore, David S., et al. Study Guide for Moore's the Basic Practice of Statistics. 3rd ed. 2003. 205p. (C). pap., stu. ed. 28.95 (978-0-7167-5886-0(5)) Freeman, W. H. & Co.

Probability & Statistics. 2003. (Mathematical Mind Ser.). 48p. (gr. 6-8). 5.99 (978-0-7424-0084-9(0) , IF2904) School Specialty Publishing.

Raintree Steck-Vaughn Staff. Statistics & Probability. 1999. pap. (978-0-8172-7478-8(2)); pap. (978-0-8172-7479-5(0)) Steck-Vaughn.

Robinson, C. L. MATH1on1 Statistics Foundation. 2006. (YA). per. 9.99 (978-0-9786767-9-7(3)) Robinson, Consuelo.

Understandable Statistics, Concepts & Methods. 7th ed. 2003. (gr. 11-12). instr.'s gde. ed. (978-0-618-20560-8(8) , 3-07006); cd-rom (978-0-618-20563-9(2) , 3-07010); cd-rom (978-0-618-20564-6(0) , 3-07011) McDougal Littell Inc.

Understanding Basic Statistics: Test Bank. 2nd ed. 2001. (gr. 6-12). (978-0-618-06092-4(8) , 3-06106) McDougal Littell Inc.

Using Cuisenaire Rods: Probability & Statistics. 2002. (J). pap. (978-1-56911-743-9(8)) Learning Resources, Inc.

Velleman, Paul F., et al. STATS: Data & Models. 2004. (DeVeaux/Velleman/Bock Ser.). (Illus.). 840p. (C). 124.67 (978-0-321-20054-9(3)) Addison-Wesley Longman, Inc.

Wingard-Nelson, Rebecca. Data, Graphing, & Statistics. 2004. (Math Success Ser.). (Illus.). 64p. (J). lib. bdg. 22.60 (978-0-7660-2567-7(5)) Enslow Pubs., Inc.

Work with Probability & Statistics. 2004. (Math "How To" Ser.). (Illus.). 48p. (J). (gr. 4-6). 7.99 (978-1-57690-960-7(3)); (YA). (gr. 6-8). 7.99 (978-1-57690-968-3(9)) Teacher Created Materials, Inc.

STATISTICS—GRAPHIC METHODS

Burstein, John. Collecting Data: Pick a Pancake. Destiny Images Staff, illus. 2003. (Math Monsters Ser.). 24p. (YA). (gr. 1 up). lib. bdg. 19.33 (978-0-8368-3805-3(X) , Weekly Reader Early Learning Library) Stevens, Gareth Inc.

—Collecting Data: Pick a Pancake. 2003. (Weekly Reader Early Learning Library). (Illus.). 24p. (J). (gr. 1 up). pap. 7.93 (978-0-8368-3820-6(3) , Weekly Reader Early Learning Library) Stevens, Gareth Inc.

Harris, Nancy. Mashed Potatoes: Collecting & Reporting Data. 2008. (J). (***978-1-60044-640-5(X)***) Rourke Publishing, LLC.

Wilson, Natashya. The Census & America's People: Analyzing Data Using Line Graphs & Tables. 2004. (PowerMath Ser.). (Illus.). 32p. (J). lib. bdg. (978-0-8239-8903-4(8)); lib. bdg. 22.50 (978-0-8239-8990-4(9)) Rosen Publishing Group, Inc., The. (PowerKids Pr.).

STATUE OF LIBERTY (NEW YORK, N.Y.)

Ashley, Susan. The Statue of Liberty. 2004. (Weekly Reader Early Learning Library). (Illus.). 24p. (J). (gr. 2 up). pap. 5.95 (978-0-8368-4150-3(6)); lib. bdg. 19.33 (978-0-8368-4143-5(3)) Stevens, Gareth Inc. (Weekly Reader Early Learning Library).

Bauer, Marion Dane. The Statue of Liberty. Wallace, John, illus. 2007. (Wonders of America Ser.). 32p. (J). (ps-1). lib. bdg. 13.89 (***978-1-4169-3480-6(4)*** , Aladdin Library); per. 3.99 (***978-1-4169-3479-0(0)*** , Aladdin) Simon & Schuster Children's Publishing.

Binns, Tristan Boyer. La Estatua de Libertad. 2003. (Simbolos de Libertad Ser.). (SPA & ENG., 32p. (J). Illus.). lib. bdg. 22.79 (978-1-4034-2999-5(5)); pap. 6.95 (978-1-4034-3022-9(5)) Heinemann Library.

—Simbolos de Libertad, 5 bks., Set. 2003. Tr. of Symbols of Freedom. (SPA & ENG., Illus.). (J). (gr. k-2). lib. bdg. 113.95 (978-1-4034-2996-4(0)) Heinemann Library.

—The Statue of Liberty. (Symbols of Freedom Ser.). (Illus.). 32p. (J). (gr. k-2). 2002. pap. 6.95 (978-1-58810-405-2(2) , 91147); 2001. lib. bdg. 21.36 (978-1-58810-121-1(5)) Heinemann Library.

—Statue of Liberty. 2001. (978-0-606-22575-5(7)) Tandem Library Bks.

Braithwaite, Jill. La Estatua de la Libertad. 2005. (Libros para Avanzar (Pull Ahead Bks.)). (SPA., Illus.). 32p. (J). (gr. k-3). pap. 5.95 (978-0-8225-3137-1(2) , Ediciones Lerner) Lerner Publishing Group.

—The Statue of Liberty. (Pull Ahead Bks.). 32p. (J). (gr. k-3). 2004. (Illus.). lib. bdg. 22.60 (978-0-8225-3802-8(4)); 2003. pap. 5.95 (978-0-8225-3756-4(7)) Lerner Publishing Group.

—Statue of Liberty. 2004. (ps-2). lib. bdg. 14.10 (978-0-613-81322-8(7)) Tandem Library Bks.

Curlee, Lynn. Liberty. Curlee, Lynn, illus. 2003. (Illus.). 48p. (J). (gr. 2-7). pap. 6.99 (978-0-689-85683-9(0) , Aladdin) Simon & Schuster Children's Publishing.

—Liberty. 2000. (Illus.). 48p. (J). (gr. 2-7). 18.95 (978-0-689-82823-2(3) , Atheneum) Simon & Schuster Children's Publishing.

—Liberty. 2003. (gr. 3-6). lib. bdg. 15.30 (978-0-613-61638-6(3)) Tandem Library Bks.

Deady, Kathleen W. The Statue of Liberty. 2002. (National Landmarks Ser.). (Illus.). 24p. (J). (gr. 2-3). lib. bdg. 18.60 (978-0-7368-1115-6(X) , Bridgestone Bks.) Capstone Pr., Inc.

Douglas, Lloyd G. The Statue of Liberty. 2003. (Welcome Bks.). (Illus.). 24p. (J). (ps-2). pap. 4.95 (978-0-516-27877-3(0) , Children's Pr.); 18.00 (978-0-516-25854-6(0)) Scholastic Library Publishing.

—Statue of Liberty. 2003. (gr. k-3). lib. bdg. 12.95 (978-0-613-67770-7(6)) Tandem Library Bks.

Fandel, Jennifer. The Statue of Liberty. 2005. (What in the World? Ser.). (Illus.). 48p. (gr. 5-9). 21.95 (978-1-58341-377-7(4) , Creative Education) Creative Co., The.

Faria, Joseph D. The Statue of Liberty & Ellis Island: A MyReportLinks.com Book. 2005. (Virtual Field Trips Ser.). (Illus.). 48p. (J). (gr. 4-10). lib. bdg. 25.26 (978-0-7660-5226-0(5) , MyReportLinks.com Bks.) Enslow Pubs., Inc.

Firestone, Mary. The Statue of Liberty. Skeens, Matthew, illus. 2006. 24p. (J). (ps-2). lib. bdg. 23.93 (978-1-4048-2216-0(X)) Picture Window Bks.

Hancock, Maryann. The Statue of Liberty. 2006. (Illus.). 32p. (J). pap. (978-1-4034-7011-9(1)) Heinemann Library.

—The Staute of Liberty. 2006. (Land of the Free Ser.). (Illus.). 32p. (J). lib. bdg. 28.21 (978-1-4034-7004-1(9)) Heinemann Library.

Harcourt School Publishers Staff. Liberty Advanced Level. 3rd ed. 2002. (Trophies Reading Program Ser.). (Illus.). pap. 5.10 (978-0-15-323217-6(X)) Harcourt Schl. Pubs.

—The Statue of Liberty. 3rd ed. 2002. (Horizons Ser.). (Illus.). (J). pap. 3.70 (978-0-15-333131-2(3)) Harcourt Schl. Pubs.

Harris, Nancy. The Statue of Liberty. 2007. (J). (***978-1-4034-9382-8(0)***); pap. (***978-1-4034-9389-7(8)***) Heinemann Library.

Healy, Nick. The Statue of Liberty. 2003. (J). pap. (978-1-58417-117-1(0)); lib. bdg. (978-1-58417-054-9(9)) Lake Street Pubs.

Heinrichs, Ann. The Statue of Liberty. 2001. (We the People Ser.). (Illus.). 48p. (J). (gr. 4 up). lib. bdg. 22.60 (978-0-7565-0100-6(8)) Compass Point Bks.

Hicks, Terry Allan. Symbols of America Group 2, 6 bks., Set. Incl. Bald Eagle. lib. bdg. 28.50 (978-0-7614-2133-7(5)); Capitol. lib. bdg. 28.50 (978-0-7614-2132-0(7)); Declaration of Independence. lib. bdg. 28.50 (978-0-7614-2135-1(1)); Ellis Island. lib. bdg. 28.50 (978-0-7614-2134-4(3)); Pledge of Allegiance. lib. bdg. 28.50 (978-0-7614-2136-8(X)); Uncle Sam. lib. bdg. 28.50 (978-0-7614-2137-5(8)); (Illus.). 40p. (J). 2006. 2007. Set lib. bdg. 171.00 (***978-0-7614-2130-6(0)*** , Benchmark Bks.) Cavendish, Marshall Corp.

Hochain, Serge. Building Liberty: A Statue Is Born. Hochain, Serge, illus. 2006. (Illus.). 46p. (J). (gr. 4-8). reprint ed. 25.00 (978-1-4223-5181-9(5)) DIANE Publishing Co.

—Building Liberty: A Statue Is Born. 2004. (Illus.). 48p. (J). (gr. 3-7). 25.90 (978-0-7922-6969-4(1)); 16.95 (978-0-7922-6765-2(6)) National Geographic Society. (National Geographic Children's Bks.).

Landau, Elaine. The Statue of Liberty. (True Booktrade;: American History Ser.). 48p. (J). 2008. pap. 6.95 (***978-0-531-14785-6(1)***); 2007. (Illus.). (gr. 3-5). lib. bdg. 26.00 (***978-0-531-12635-6(8)***); 2004. (Illus.). 26.00 (978-0-516-24233-0(4)) Scholastic Library Publishing. (Children's Pr.).

Lewison, Wendy Cheyette. L Is for Liberty. Hines, Laura Freeman, illus. 2003. (Reading Railroad Bks.). 32p. (J). (ps-4). pap. 3.49 (978-0-448-43228-1(5) , Grosset & Dunlap) Penguin Group (USA) Inc.

—L Is for Liberty. 2003. (gr. k-3). lib. bdg. 11.25 (978-0-613-70592-9(0)) Tandem Library Bks.

Marcovitz, Hal. The Statue of Liberty. 2002. (American Symbols & Their Meanings Ser.). (Illus.). 48p. (YA). (gr. 4 up). lib. bdg. (978-1-59084-022-1(4)) Mason Crest Pubs.

Niz, Xavier. The Story of the Statue of Liberty. Martin, Cynthia & Schoonover, Brent, illus. 2006. (Graphic Library). 32p. (J). (978-0-7368-5494-8(0)) Capstone Pr., Inc.

Nobleman, Marc Tyler. The Statue of Liberty. 2003. (American Symbols Ser.). (Illus.). 24p. (J). (gr. 1-2). lib. bdg. 18.60 (978-0-7368-1632-8(1) , Bridgestone Bks.) Capstone Pr., Inc.

Rau, Dana Meachen. The Statue of Liberty. 2001. (Let's See Library). (Illus.). 24p. (J). (gr. 1 up). lib. bdg. 19.93 (978-0-7565-0143-3(1)) Compass Point Bks.

Shea, Pegi Deitz. Liberty Rising: The Story of the Statue of Liberty. Zahares, Wade, illus. rev. ed. 2005. 44p. (J). (gr. 1-4). 17.95 (978-0-8050-7220-4(9) , Holt, Henry & Co. Bks. For Young Readers) Holt, Henry & Co.

Silate, Jennifer. The Statue of Liberty. 2005. (Illus.). 24p. (J). lib. bdg. (978-1-4042-2696-8(6)) Rosen Publishing Group, Inc., The.

Sorensen, Lynda. La Estatua de la Libertad. Palacios, Argentina, tr. 2002. (Simbolos Americanos Ser.). (SPA., Illus.). 24p. mass mkt. 5.95 (978-1-58952-271-8(0) , RK31484) Rourke Publishing, LLC.

The Statue of Liberty: Third Grade Guided Reading Level L. (On Our Way to English Ser.). (gr. 3 up). 34.50 (978-0-7578-7129-0(1)) Rigby Education.

Stevenson, Harvey. Looking at Liberty. Stevenson, Harvey, illus. 2003. (Illus.). 40p. (J). (ps-2). 17.89 (978-0-06-000101-8(1)) HarperCollins Pubs.

STEALING

see Theft

STEAM-ENGINES

Barron's Educational Editorial Staff. Railways. 1998. (History Ser.). (Illus.). 32p. (J). (gr. 5). pap. 5.95 (978-0-7641-0538-8(8)) Barron's Educational Series, Inc.

Collier, James Lincoln. The Steam Engine. 2005. (Great Inventions Ser.). (Illus.). 112p. (J). (gr. 8-12). lib. bdg. (978-0-7614-1880-1(6) , Benchmark Bks.) Cavendish, Marshall Corp.

Kras, Sara Louise. Steam Engine. 2003. (Transforming Power of Technology Ser.). (Illus.). 112p. (J). (gr. 9-13). 30.00 (978-0-7910-7453-4(6) , Chelsea Hse.) Facts On File, Inc.

Mattern, Joanne. The Steam Engine: Fueling the Industrial Revolution. 2003. (Reading Power Ser.). (Illus.). 24p. (J). lib. bdg. 17.25 (978-0-8239-6490-1(6) , PowerKids Pr.) Rosen Publishing Group, Inc., The.

Orr, Tamra. The Steam Engine. 2005. (Inventions That Shaped the World Ser.). (Illus.). 80p. (J). 30.50 (978-0-531-12400-0(2) , Watts, Franklin) Scholastic Library Publishing.

—Steam Engine. 2006. 80p. (YA). (gr. 5-8). pap. 9.95 (978-0-531-16724-3(0) , Watts, Franklin) Scholastic Library Publishing.

The Steam Engine: Fueling the Industrial Revolution: Individual Title Six-Packs. (On Deck Ser.: Vol. 2). 24p. (gr. 4-5). 35.00 (978-0-7578-5862-8(7)) Rigby Education.

Steam Power: Individual Title Six-Packs. (Rigby Focus Ser.). 24p. (gr. 2 up). 28.00 (978-0-7578-5352-4(8)); 30.00 (978-0-7578-5582-5(2)) Rigby Education.

STEAM-SHOVELS—FICTION

Burton, Virginia Lee. Mike Mulligan & His Steam Shovel. Burton, Virginia Lee, illus. 2002. (Illus.). (J). 14.66 (978-0-7587-3132-6(9)) Book Wholesalers, Inc.

—Mike Mulligan & His Steam Shovel. 2007. (Illus.). 40p. (J). (ps-k). bds. 7.99 (***978-0-618-84019-9(2)***) Houghton Mifflin Co. Trade & Reference Div.

Burton, Virginia Lee. Mike Mulligan y Su Maquina Maravillosa. 1999. (SPA., Illus.). 56p. (J). (gr. k-3). pap. 9.95 incl. audio (978-0-618-01136-0(6) , HM5003) Houghton Mifflin Co. Trade & Reference Div.

Zimmerman, Andrea. Digger Man. Clemesha, David, illus. 2007. 32p. (J). (ps-k). pap. 6.95 (***978-0-8050-8203-6(4)***, Holt, Henry & Co. Bks. For Young Readers) Holt, Henry & Co.

STEAMBOATS

Bednarz, Robert, et al. TIME for Kids Readers: The Last Voyage of the Lusitania. 3rd ed. 2002. (Harcourt Horizons Ser.). (gr. k-7). pap. 38.10 (978-0-15-335288-1(4)) Harcourt Schl. Pubs.

Boothroyd, Jennifer. Robert Fulton: A Life of Innovation. 2007. (Pull Ahead Books-Biographies Ser.). (J). 22.60 (978-0-8225-6458-4(0), Lerner Pubns.) Lerner Publishing Group.

Flammang, James M. Robert Fulton: Inventor & Steamboat Builder. 1999. (Historical American Biographies Ser.). (Illus.). 128p. (YA). (gr. 6-12). lib. bdg. 26.60 (978-0-7660-1141-0(0)) Enslow Pubs., Inc.

Ford, Carin T. Robert Fulton: The Steamboat Man. 2004. (Famous Inventors Ser.). (Illus.). 32p. (J). lib. bdg. 22.60 (978-0-7660-2248-5(X)) Enslow Pubs., Inc.

Gillis, Jennifer Blizin. Robert Fulton. 2004. (Illus.). 32p. (J). pap. 6.50 (978-1-4034-5336-5(5)); lib. bdg. 22.79 (978-1-4034-5328-0(4)) Heinemann Library.

Kroll, Steven. Robert Fulton: From Submarine to Steamboat. Farnsworth, Bill, illus. 1999. 32p. (J). (gr. 4-6). tchr. ed. 16.95 (978-0-8234-1433-8(7)) Holiday Hse., Inc.

McLeese, Don. Robert Fulton. 2006. (Rourke Discovery Library). (Illus.). 24p. (gr. 2-5). 14.95 (978-1-59515-434-7(5), 1244323) Rourke Publishing, LLC.

Murdico, Suzanne J. Railroads & Steamships: Important Developments in American Transportation. 2003. (America's Industrial Society in the Nineteenth Century Ser.). (Illus.). 32p. (J). (978-0-8239-4278-7(3)) Rosen Publishing Group, Inc., The.

Parks, Peggy J. Robert Fulton: Innovator with Steam Power. 2003. (Giants of Science Ser.). (Illus.). 64p. (J). 26.20 (978-1-56711-492-8(X), Blackbirch Pr., Inc.) Thomson Gale.

Pierce, Morris A. Robert Fulton & the Development of the Steamboat. 2005. (Library of American Lives & Times). (Illus.). 112p. (YA). (gr. 4-8). lib. bdg. 31.95 (978-0-8239-5737-8(3)) Rosen Publishing Group, Inc., The.

Rosenberg, Pam. Robert Fulton: Engineer & Inventor. 2003. (Spirit of America: Our People Ser.). (Illus.). 32p. (J). (gr. 2-6). 27.07 (978-1-56766-448-5(2)) Child's World, Inc.

Schaefer, Lola M. Robert Fulton. 2000. (Famous People in Transportation Ser.). (Illus.). 24p. (J). (gr. k-1). lib. bdg. 15.93 (978-0-7368-0547-6(8), Pebble Bks.) Capstone Pr., Inc.

Youngblood, Wayne. Mark Twain along the Mississippi. 2006. (In the Footsteps of American Heroes Ser.). (Illus.). 64p. (J). pap. (978-0-8368-6435-9(2)); lib. bdg. 32.67 (978-0-8368-6430-4(1)) Stevens, Gareth Inc. (World Almanac Library).

STEAMSHIPS

see Steamboats

STEEL

see also Iron

also headings beginning with the word Steel

Kassinger, Ruth. Iron & Steel: From Thor's Hammer to the Space Shuttle. 2003. (Material World Ser.). (Illus.). 80p. (gr. 6-8). lib. bdg. 25.90 (978-0-7613-2111-8(X), Twenty-First Century Bks.) Lerner Publishing Group.

Walker, Kate. Steel. 2004. (Recycle, Reduce, Reuse, Rethink Ser.). lib. bdg. 27.10 (978-1-58340-560-4(7)) Smart Apple Media.

STEEL INDUSTRY AND TRADE

Jarnow, Jesse. Oil, Steel, & Railroads: America's Big Businesses in the Late 1800s. 2003. (America's Industrial Society in the Nineteenth Century Ser.). (Illus.). 32p. (J). pap. (978-0-8239-4276-3(7)) Rosen Publishing Group, Inc., The.

Parker, Lewis K. Andrew Carnegie & the Steel Industry. 6 vols. Pack. (On Deck Ser.: Vol. 2). 24p. (gr. 4-5). 35.00 (978-0-7578-5847-5(3)) Rigby Education.

—Andrew Carnegie & the Steel Industry. 2003. (Reading Power Ser.). (Illus.). 24p. (J). lib. bdg. 17.25 (978-0-8239-6448-2(5), PowerKids Pr.) Rosen Publishing Group, Inc., The.

STEFANSSON, VILHJALMUR, 1879-1962

Montgomery, Richard. Pechuck. 2005. reprint ed. pap. 31.95 (978-1-4179-9755-8(9)) Kessinger Publishing, LLC.

STEINBECK, JOHN, 1902-1968

Florence, Donne. John Steinbeck: America's Author. 2000. (People to Know Ser.). (Illus.). 128p. (YA). (gr. 6-12). lib. bdg. 26.60 (978-0-7660-1150-2(X)) Enslow Pubs., Inc.

Kordich, Catherine J. Bloom's How to Write about John Steinbeck. 2007. (Bloom's How to Write about Literature Ser.). 256p. (YA). (gr. 9 up). 45.00 (***978-0-7910-9486-0(3)***, Chelsea Hse.) Facts On File, Inc.

Newman, Gerald. A Student's Guide to John Steinbeck. 2004. (Understanding Literature Ser.). (Illus.). 176p. (YA). lib. bdg. 27.93 (978-0-7660-2259-1(5)) Enslow Pubs., Inc.

Rice, Kathleen Shores. Of Mice & Men. 2002. (Understanding Great Literature Ser.). 104p. (YA). (gr. 8-11). lib. bdg. 29.95 (978-1-56006-644-6(X), Lucent Bks.) Thomson Gale.

Sanna, Ellyn. John Steinbeck. 2003. (gr. 7-12). lib. bdg. 21.05 (978-0-613-57179-1(7)) Tandem Library Bks.

Tracy, Kathleen. John Steinbeck. 2004. (Classic Storytellers Ser.). (Illus.). 48p. (J). (gr. 4-8). lib. bdg. 20.95 (978-1-58415-271-2(0)) Mitchell Lane Pubs., Inc.

Welsch, Gabriel. Of Mice & Men. 2006. (Bloom's Guides Ser.). 136p. 30.00 (978-0-7910-8581-3(3), Chelsea Hse.) Facts On File, Inc.

Williams, Brian. The Story Behind John Steinbeck's of Mice & Men. 2006. (History in Literature Ser.). (Illus.). 56p. (YA). (gr. 6-9). lib. bdg. 32.86 (978-1-4034-8207-5(1)) Heinemann Library.

STENCIL WORK

Bater, Lucy. Small Dinosaur Stenciling Book. Robbins, Jim, illus. 2006. 24p. (J). (gr. 3-9). bds. 10.95 (978-1-59125-638-0(0), Penton Kids) Penton Overseas, Inc.

—Small Shark Stenciling Book: Learn How to Draw Sharks & Discover Shark Facts at Your Fingertips. Penton Overseas, Inc. Staff, ed. Robbins, Jim, illus. 2006. 24p. (J). (gr. 3-9). bds. 10.95 (978-1-59125-639-7(9), Penton Kids) Penton Overseas, Inc.

Brocklehurst, Ruth. Animal Stencil Bk. Cleyet-Merle, Laurence, illus. 2006. 14p. (J). bds. 12.99 (978-0-7945-1140-1(6), Usborne) EDC Publishing.

Brooks, Sue. Fun with African Animal Stencils. 1999. (Illus.). 6p. (J). pap. 1.50 (978-0-486-40758-6(6)) Dover Pubns., Inc.

Cartwright, Stephen, illus. Christmas Stencil Book. 2005. 10p. (J). (ps-3). bds. 9.95 (978-0-7945-1142-5(2), Usborne) EDC Publishing.

Caterpillar Inc. Staff, contrib. by. Drawing Trucks & Diggers: A Book of 10 Stencils. 2001. (Illus.). 30p. (J). (gr. k up). 9.95 (978-0-8118-3174-1(4)) Chronicle Bks. LLC.

Davis, Billy. Design My Ride. 2006. (J). 9.99 (978-0-439-77764-3(X), Tangerine Pr.) Scholastic, Inc.

Doherty, Gillian. Stencil Book. 2005. (Stencil Book Ser.). 14p. (J). 9.95 (978-0-7945-0866-1(9), Usborne) EDC Publishing.

Flanagan, Jennifer. Spectacular Stencil Art. 2002. (I Am an Artist Club Ser.). (Illus.). 32p. (J). (978-0-439-33626-0(0)) Scholastic, Inc.

Gottesman, Eric. Fun with Wizards Stencils. 2003. (Dover Little Activity Bks.). (Illus.). 6p. (J). pap. 1.50 (978-0-486-42633-4(5)) Dover Pubns., Inc.

Green, John. Fun with Horseback Riding Stencils. 2004. (Stencils Ser.). (Illus.). 6p. (J). pap. 1.50 (978-0-486-43419-3(2)) Dover Pubns., Inc.

—Fun with Ponies Stencils. 2006. (Illus.). 6p. (J). (gr. k). pap. 1.50 (978-0-486-44438-3(4)) Dover Pubns., Inc.

Harper, Ellen. Fun with Chinese Animals Stencils. 2003. (Dover Little Activity Bks.). (Illus.). 6p. (J). pap. 1.50 (978-0-486-43108-6(8)) Dover Pubns., Inc.

—Fun with Egyptian Symbols Stencils. 2003. (Dover Little Activity Bks.). (Illus.). 6p. (J). (gr. k-5). pap. 1.50 (978-0-486-43109-3(6)) Dover Pubns., Inc.

—Fun with Japanese Animals Stencils. 2001. 6p. (J). pap. 1.50 (978-0-486-41635-9(6)) Dover Pubns., Inc.

—Fun with Old MacDonald's Farm Stencils. 2004. (Stencils Ser.). 6p. (J). pap. 1.50 (978-0-486-43420-9(6)) Dover Pubns., Inc.

Kennedy, Paul E. Fun with Swampland Animals Stencils. 1998. 6p. (J). pap. 1.00 (978-0-486-40328-1(9)) Dover Pubns., Inc.

Leonard, Barry, ed. Drawing Trucks & Diggers: A Book of 10 Stencils. 2004. (Illus.). 34p. (J). (gr. k-4). reprint ed. ring bd. 10.00 (978-0-7567-8505-5(7)) DIANE Publishing Co.

Meredith Books Staff & Marshall, Paula, eds. Over the Hedge Stencil Activity Book: With Stickers. 2006. 22p. (J). 9.95 (978-0-696-23067-7(4)) Meredith Bks.

Noble, Marty. Fun with African Design Stencils. 2000. (Illus.). 6p. (J). (gr. k-5). pap. 1.50 (978-0-486-41001-2(3)) Dover Pubns., Inc.

—Fun with Bugs Stencils. 1999. (Illus.). 6p. (J). pap. 1.50 (978-0-486-40759-3(4)) Dover Pubns., Inc.

—Fun with Chinese Symbols Stencils. 2001. 6p. (J). (gr. k-5). pap. 1.50 (978-0-486-41638-0(0)) Dover Pubns., Inc.

—Fun with Christmas Ornaments Stencils. 2006. (Dover Little Activity Bks.). 6p. (J). pap. 1.50 (978-0-486-44893-0(2)) Dover Pubns., Inc.

—Fun with Cretaceous Dinosaurs Stencils. 2002. 6p. (J). pap. 1.50 (978-0-486-42094-3(9)) Dover Pubns., Inc.

—Fun with Emergency Vehicles Stencils. 2003. (Dover Little Activity Bks.). (Illus.). 6p. (J). pap. 1.50 (978-0-486-42634-1(3)) Dover Pubns., Inc.

—Fun with Good Luck Symbols Stencils. 2004. 6p. (J). pap. 1.50 (978-0-486-43692-0(6)) Dover Pubns., Inc.

—Fun with Knights Stencils. 2000. (Illus.). 6p. (J). pap. 1.50 (978-0-486-41004-3(8)) Dover Pubns., Inc.

—Fun with Mother Goose Stencils. 2003. 6p. (J). pap. 1.50 (978-0-486-42351-7(4)) Dover Pubns., Inc.

—Fun with Native American Design Stencils. 2002. (Illus.). 6p. (J). pap. 1.50 (978-0-486-42093-6(0)) Dover Pubns., Inc.

—Fun with Native American Masks Stencils. 2003. (Illus.). 6p. (J). pap. 1.50 (978-0-486-42352-4(2)) Dover Pubns., Inc.

—Fun with Noah's Ark Stencils. 2006. (Dover Little Activity Bks.). 6p. (J). pap. 1.50 (978-0-486-44881-7(9)) Dover Pubns., Inc.

—Fun with Soldiers Stencils. 2001. (Illus.). 6p. (J). pap. 1.00 (978-0-486-41283-2(0)) Dover Pubns., Inc.

—Fun with Tropical Flowers Stencils. 2001. (Illus.). 6p. (J). pap. 1.00 (978-0-486-41284-9(9)) Dover Pubns., Inc.

—Fun with Unicorns Stencils. 2001. (Glitter Stickers Ser.). (Illus.). 6p. (J). pap. 1.50 (978-0-486-41637-3(2)) Dover Pubns., Inc.

—Fun with Wedding Stencils. 2004. 6p. (J). pap. 1.50 (978-0-486-43683-8(7)) Dover Pubns., Inc.

Princess Stencil Book. 2007. (Illus.). 22p. (J). (gr. 3-7). bds. 12.95 (***978-1-59125-793-6(X)***, Penton Kids) Penton Overseas, Inc.

QEB Learn Art National Book Stores Edition: Stencils & Prints. 2006. (J). per. (978-1-59566-283-5(9)) QEB Publishing Inc.

Robins, Deri. Stencils & Prints. 2006. (Illus.). 32p. (J). 9.95 (978-1-58728-544-8(4), Two Can Publishing) T&N Children's Publishing.

School Zone Staff. Fun & Festive. 2004. (J). 12.99 (978-1-58947-471-0(6), 03602) School Zone Publishing Co.

—On the Farm. 2004. (J). 12.99 (978-1-58947-470-3(8), 03601) School Zone Publishing Co.

—Things That Go. 2004. (J). 12.99 (978-1-58947-472-7(4), 03603) School Zone Publishing Co.

Shark Stencilling Book: Learn How to Draw Sharks & Discover Shark Facts at Your Fingertips! 2007. (Illus.). 24p. (J). (gr. 3-7). bds. 12.95 (978-1-59125-553-6(8), Penton Kids) Penton Overseas, Inc.

Silver Dolphin en Español Editors. Libro de actividades con plantillas: Disney Animales: Animals Stencil. 2007. (Illus.). 10p. (J). bds. 12.95 (***978-970-718-435-0(3)***, Silver Dolphin en Español) Advanced Marketing, S. de R. L. de C. V. MEX. *Dist:* Perseus Distribution.

Silver Dolphin en Español Staff, ed. Libro de actividades con plantillas: Disney Pixar: Disney Pixar Stencil. 2007. (Illus.). 20p. (J). bds. 12.95 (***978-970-718-433-6(7)***, Silver Dolphin en Español) Advanced Marketing, S. de R. L. de C. V. MEX. *Dist:* Perseus Distribution.

—Libro de actividades con plantillas: Disney Princesa: Disney Princess Stencil. 2007. (Illus.). 20p. (J). bds. 12.95 (***978-970-718-434-3(5)***, Silver Dolphin en Español) Advanced Marketing, S. de R. L. de C. V. MEX. *Dist:* Perseus Distribution.

Smith, A. G. Fun with Backyard Animals Stencils. 2006. 6p. (J). (gr. k). pap. 1.50 (978-0-486-44490-1(2)) Dover Pubns., Inc.

—Fun with Construction Trucks Stencils. 2000. (Illus.). 6p. (J). pap. 1.50 (978-0-486-40999-3(6)) Dover Pubns., Inc.

—Fun with Favorite Pets Stencils. 1998. (Illus.). 6p. (J). pap. 1.50 (978-0-486-25451-7(8)) Dover Pubns., Inc.

—Fun with Vikings Stencils. 2001. (Illus.). 6p. (J). pap. 1.50 (978-0-486-41285-6(7)) Dover Pubns., Inc.

Stencils & Prints, 6 bks. 2005. (QEB Learn Art Ser.). (Illus.). 32p. (J). per. 8.95 (978-1-59566-127-2(1)) QEB Publishing Inc.

Stowell, Louie. Diggers Stencil Bk. 2007. 14p. (J). bds. 12.99 (978-0-7945-1576-8(2), Usborne) EDC Publishing.

Watt, Fiona. Christmas Stencil Cards. 2007. (Christmas Stencil Cards Ser.). 16p. (J). 9.99 (***978-0-7945-1896-7(6)***, Usborne) EDC Publishing.

Wilson, Phil, illus. Stencil Fun: Dinosaurs. 2003. (Active Minds Ser.). 22p. (J). spiral bd., bds. (978-0-7853-8613-1(0), 7187900) Publications International, Ltd.

STEPFAMILIES

Bernstein, Robin. Terrible, Terrible! A Folktale Retold. Kawasaki, Shauna Mooney, illus. 1998. 32p. (J). (ps-5). 15.95 (978-1-58013-016-5(X)); pap. 6.95 (978-1-58013-017-2(8)) Kar-Ben Publishing.

Beyl, Charles, illus. My Parents Are Divorced Too: A Book for Kids by Kids. 2nd ed. 2006. 71p. (J). 14.95 (978-1-59147-241-4(5)); pap. 9.95 (978-1-59147-242-1(3)) American Psychological Assn. (Magination Pr.).

Block, Joel D. Stepliving for Teens: Getting along with Step-Parents & Siblings. 2001. (gr. 7-12). lib. bdg. 13.00 (978-0-613-89162-2(7)) Tandem Library Bks.

Block, Joel D. & Bartell, Susan S. Stepliving for Teens: Getting along with Stepparents & Siblings. 2001. (Plugged in Ser.). (Illus.). 96p. (J). (gr. 4-12). pap. 4.99 (978-0-8431-7568-4(0), Price Stern Sloan) Penguin Group (USA) Inc.

Clark, Jan. Family Survival. 2004. (Illus.). 32p. (J). lib. bdg. 25.64 (978-1-4109-0569-7(1)) Raintree.

Johnson, Julie. Our Stepfamily. 2007. (J). (***978-1-59604-154-7(4)***) Stargazer Bks.

Lavete, Sarah. Step Families. 2005. (Illus.). 32p. (J). (gr. 3-7). lib. bdg. 27.10 (978-1-59604-048-9(3)) Stargazer Bks.

Leibowitz, Julie. Finding Your Place. A Teen Guide to Life in a Blended Family. 2005. (Divorce Resource Ser.). (Illus.). 64p. (YA). (gr. 7-12). lib. bdg. 26.50 (978-0-8239-3114-9(5), DIFIPL) Rosen Publishing Group, Inc., The.

MacGregor, Cynthia. Jigsaw Puzzle Family: The Stepkids' Guide to Fitting It Together. 2005. 106p. (J). (ps-7). pap. 12.95 (978-1-886230-63-7(3), Rebuilding Bks.) Impact Pubs., Inc.

Pleasant Company Staff. Help! A Girl's Guide to Divorce & Stepfamilies. 1999. (J). (978-0-606-19870-7(9)) Tandem Library Bks.

Price, Elizabeth. Divorce & Teens: When a Family Splits Apart. 2004. (Teen Issues Ser.). (Illus.). 64p. (J). lib. bdg. 22.60 (978-0-7660-1670-5(6)) Enslow Pubs., Inc.

Rogers, Fred. Let's Talk about It: Stepfamilies. 2001. (ps-2). lib. bdg. 15.30 (978-0-613-44223-7(7)) Tandem Library Bks.

—Stepfamilies. 2001. (Illus.). 32p. (J). pap. 6.99 (978-0-698-11665-8(8), Putnam Juvenile) Penguin Group (USA) Inc.

Ruth, Angie. My Step-Dad: Early My Adventure. 2007. 44p. (J). 8.99 (978-1-59092-485-3(1), Orchard Academy Pr.) Windstorm Creative.

—My Step-Mom: Early My Adventure. 2007. 44p. (J). 8.99 (978-1-59092-486-0(X), Orchard Academy Pr.) Windstorm Creative.

Smook, Rachel Gaillard. Stepfamilies: How a New Family Works. 2001. (Teen Issues Ser.). (Illus.). 64p. (J). (gr. 6-12). lib. bdg. 22.60 (978-0-7660-1666-8(8)) Enslow Pubs., Inc.

Stern, Ellen S., et al. Divorce Is Not the End of the World: Zoe's & Evan's Coping Guide for Kids. 2004. (Illus.). 96p. (YA). (gr. 4-8). pap. 8.95 (978-1-883672-44-7(9), Tricycle Pr.) Ten Speed Pr.

Wagner, Heather Lehr. The Blending of Foster & Adopted Children into the Family. 2002. (Focus on Family Matters Ser.). (Illus.). 64p. (J). 25.00 (978-0-7910-6694-2(0), Chelsea Hse.) Facts On File, Inc.

STEPFAMILIES—FICTION

Abel, Heather & McKnight, Gillian. To Catch a Prince. 2005. 192p. (YA). 14.95 (978-0-689-87733-9(1)) Simon & Schuster Children's Publishing.

Adler, C. S. The No Place Cat. 2002. 160p. (YA). (gr. 5-9). 15.00 (978-0-618-09644-2(2), Clarion Bks.) Houghton Mifflin Co. Trade & Reference Div.

Altman, Adam. Liliana's Fan. 2001. 116p. (gr. 4-7). pap. 9.95 (978-0-595-15873-7(0)) iUniverse, Inc.

Amery, Heather & Howell, Laura. Cinderella Sticker Bk. 2006. 16p. (J). pap. 6.99 (978-0-7945-1311-5(5), Usborne) EDC Publishing.

Ballard, Robin. When I Am a Sister. 1998. (Illus.). 24p. (J). (ps-3). 15.00 (978-0-688-15397-7(6)) HarperCollins Pubs.

Barwin, Steven. Icebreaker. 2006. (Sports Stories Ser.). 128p. (J). (gr. 3-8). (***978-1-55028-951-0(9)***); 7.95 (***978-1-55028-950-3(0)***) Lorimer, James & Co., Ltd., Pubs. CAN. *Dist:* Casemate Pubs. & Bk. Distributors, LLC.

Bender, Esther. Search for a Fawn. Bender, Edna, illus. 1998. 32p. (J). (gr. k-5). pap. 8.99 (978-0-8361-9099-1(8)) Herald Pr.

Bennerson, Denise. Daniel Gets a New Daddy. Vega, Edwin, illus. 2001. 12p. (J). 4.00 (978-0-9646279-4-9(9)) Bennerson, Denise.

Boada, Francesc. Cinderella. Surges, James, tr. Fransoy, Monse, illus. 2001. (SPA & ENG.). 32p. (J). (ps-3). pap. 6.95 (978-0-8118-3090-4(X)) Chronicle Bks. LLC.

Bowdish, Lynea. How to Be Nice— & Other Lessons I Didn't Learn. Gray, Leslie, illus. 2006. 47p. (J). pap. (978-1-59336-726-8(0)) Mondo Publishing.

BOWVAYNE. Spell Behind Bars. Snow, Alan, illus. 2006. 208p. (J). pap. 4.99 (978-0-7945-1293-4(3), Usborne) EDC Publishing.

Bowvayne, A. E. Turn in the Grave. Snow, Alan, illus. 2006. 144p. (J). pap. 4.99 (978-0-7945-1292-7(5), Usborne) EDC Publishing.

Bryant, Ann. Billie & the Parent Plan. 2007. (Billie & the Parent Plan Ser.). 192p. (J). pap. 4.99 (***978-0-7945-1721-2(8)***, Usborne) EDC Publishing.

Bryant, Ann. You Can't Fall for Your Step-Sister. 2004. (Step-Chain Ser.). 190p. (J). (gr. 3-8). pap. 4.95 (978-1-894222-77-8(6)) Lobster Pr. CAN. *Dist:* Univ. of Toronto Pr.

Bullard, Lisa. Trick-or-Treat on Milton Street. Oeltjenbruns, Joni, illus. 2003. (Picture Bks.). 32p. (J). (ps-3). 15.95 (978-1-57505-158-1(3), Carolrhoda Bks.) Lerner Publishing Group.

Burke, David. Cinderella (English to German - Level 1) Learn GERMAN Through Fairy Tales. 2007. (Learn German Through Fairy Tales Ser.). (ENG & GER., Illus.). (J). per. 14.95 incl. audio compact disk (***978-1-891888-76-2(5)***) Slangman Publishing.

Burke, David, adapted by. Cinderella (English to Chinese - Level 1) Learn MANDARIN CHINESE Through Fairy Tales. 2007. (Learn Chinese Through Fairy Tales Ser.). (ENG & CHI., Illus.). (J). per. 14.95 incl. cd-rom (***978-1-891888-79-3(X)***) Slangman Publishing.

—Cinderella (English to French - Level 1) Learn FRENCH Through Fairy Tales. 2007. (Learn French Through Fairy Tales Ser.). (ENG & FRE., Illus.). (J). per. 14.95 incl. audio compact disk (***978-1-891888-75-5(7)***) Slangman Publishing.

Butler, Charles. Timon's Tide. Smith, George, illus. 2000. 192p. (YA). (gr. 7-12). 16.00 (978-0-689-82593-4(5), McElderry, Margaret K.) Simon & Schuster Children's Publishing.

Butler, Dori Hillestad. Tank Talbott's Guide to Girls. 2006. (Illus.). 135p. (J). 15.95 (978-0-8075-7761-5(8)) Whitman, Albert & Co.

Carlson, Melody. Moon White. 2007. 224p. (YA). pap. 12.99 (978-1-57683-951-5(6), Th1nk Bks.) NavPress Publishing Group.

Cassidy, Cathy. Scarlett. 2006. 272p. (YA). 16.99 (978-0-670-06068-9(2), Viking Juvenile) Penguin Group (USA) Inc.

Charles, Norma M. All the Way to Mexico. 2003. (Illus.). 168p. (J). pap. 6.95 (978-1-55192-598-1(2)) Raincoast Bk. Distribution CAN. *Dist:* Perseus Distribution.

Christopher, Matt. Spike It! 1999. 147p. (J). (gr. 3-7). pap. 4.50 (978-0-316-13401-9(5)) Little Brown & Co.

Cinderella. 1999. (Little Golden Bks.). (J). pap. 4.99 (978-0-307-98064-9(2), 98064, Golden Bks.) Random Hse. Children's Bks.

Cinderella. 2002. (Classic Tales Ser.). (Illus.). 32p. (J). incl. audio compact disk (978-1-59069-101-4(6), T1103); (978-1-59069-034-5(6), T1003) Studio Mouse LLC.

Cinderella. unabr. ed. (Read-Along Ser.). (J). 7.99 incl. audio (978-1-55723-007-2(2)) Walt Disney Records.

Climo, Shirley. Persian Cinderella. 2001. (gr. k-3). lib. bdg. 14.10 (978-0-613-44245-9(8)) Tandem Library Bks.

Cohn, Rachel. Cupcake. 2007. 256p. (YA). 15.99 (978-1-4169-1217-0(7), Simon & Schuster Children's Publishing) Simon & Schuster Children's Publishing.

—Gingerbread. 2002. (Illus.). 176p. (J). (gr. 9 up). 15.95 (978-0-689-84337-2(2)) Simon & Schuster Children's Publishing.

—Gingerbread. 2003. (gr. 7-12). lib. bdg. 15.30 (978-0-613-60473-4(3)) Tandem Library Bks.

—Shrimp. 288p. (YA). (gr. 7 up). 2005. 15.95 (978-0-689-86612-8(7), Simon & Schuster Children's Publishing); 2006. reprint ed. pap. 6.99 (978-0-689-86613-5(5), Simon Pulse) Simon & Schuster Children's Publishing.

—The Steps. 144p. (J). 2003. (Illus.). (gr. 3-7). 15.95 (978-0-689-84549-9(9)); 2004. reprint ed. pap. 4.99 (978-0-689-87414-7(6), Aladdin) Simon & Schuster Children's Publishing.

Cohn, Rachel. Two Steps Forward. 2007. 240p. (J). (gr. 4-8). pap. 8.99 (*978-0-689-86615-9(1)) Kaplan Bks.

—Two Steps Forward. 2006. (Illus.). 240p. (J). 15.95 (978-0-689-86614-2(3)) Simon & Schuster Children's Publishing.

Cohn, Rachel & Wattenberg, Jane. Gingerbread. 2003. 176p. (YA). pap. 6.99 (978-0-689-86020-1(X) , Simon Pulse) Simon & Schuster Children's Publishing.

Cooper, Ilene. The Worst Noel: A Novel. 2006. 143p. (J). (gr. 4-8). reprint ed. pap. 4.00 (978-1-4223-5411-7(3)) DIANE Publishing Co.

Culver, Carol. Manderley Prep: A BFF Novel. 2007. 224p. (gr. 12 up). 9.99 (*978-0-425-21747-4(7) , Berkley Trade) Penguin Group (USA) Inc.

Cumbie, Patricia. Where People Like Us Live. 2008. 224p. (J). 16.99 (*978-0-06-137597-2(7)); lib. bdg. 17.89 (*978-0-06-137598-9(5)) HarperCollins Pubs. (Geringer, Laura Book).

Daniels, Sara. Pieces of the Sky. 2005. 135p. pap. 15.99 (978-1-4116-4291-1(0)) Lulu.com.

Danziger, Paula. It's an Aardvark-Eat-Turtle World. 2000. (Illus.). (J). 11.64 (978-0-606-18469-4(4)) Tandem Library Bks.

Deem, James M. 3 NBs of Julian Drew. 2004. 208p. (YA). (gr. 7 up). pap. 6.99 (978-0-618-43907-2(2) , Graphia) Houghton Mifflin Co. Trade & Reference Div.

Delton, Judy. Angel Spreads Her Wings. Weber, Jill, illus. 2002. 160p. (J). (gr. 2-5). pap. 4.95 (978-0-618-21617-8(0)) Houghton Mifflin Co. Trade & Reference Div.

—Angel Spreads Her Wings. 2002. (gr. 3-6). lib. bdg. 12.95 (978-0-613-90475-9(3)) Tandem Library Bks.

Deriso, Christine Hurley. The Right-Under Club. 2007. 208p. (J). (gr. 4-7). lib. bdg. 18.99 (*978-0-385-90351-6(0) , Delacorte Bks. for Young Readers) Random Hse. Children's Bks.

Dessen, Sarah. This Lullaby. 2004. 352p. (J). reprint ed. pap. 7.99 (978-0-14-250155-9(7) , Puffin) Penguin Group (USA) Inc.

Dokey, Cameron & McClatchy, Lisa. Before Midnight: A Retelling of Cinderella. Lyon, Tammie, illus. 2007. (Once upon a Time Ser.). 208p. (YA). (gr. 6-10). pap. 5.99 (978-1-4169-3471-4(5) , Simon Pulse) Simon & Schuster Children's Publishing.

Draper, Sharon M. Forged by Fire. 2002. (Illus.). (J). 13.40 (978-0-7587-0354-5(6)) Book Wholesalers, Inc.

—Forged by Fire. l.t. ed. 2006. 199p. pap. 10.95 (978-0-7862-8358-3(0)) Thorndike Pr.

—Forged by Fire No. 2: Hazelwood High Trilogy. l.t. ed. 2005. 199p. 21.95 (978-0-7862-7417-8(4)) Thorndike Pr.

Ehrenhaft, Daniel. The After Life. 2006. 272p. (YA). (gr. 9-12). pap. 8.99 (978-1-59514-080-7(8) , Razorbill) Penguin Group (USA) Inc.

Ehrlich, Amy. Cinderella. Battcock, Gregory, ed. Jeffers, Susan, illus. 2004. 32p. (J). (ps). 16.99 (978-0-525-47345-9(9) , Dutton Juvenile) Penguin Group (USA) Inc.

Elkeles, Simone. How to Ruin a Summer Vacation. 2006. 240p. (J). pap. 9.95 (978-0-7387-0961-1(1) , Flux) Llewellyn Pubns.

Evans, Clay Bonnyman. The Winter Witch. Bender, Robert, illus. 2005. 32p. (J). (ps-ps). 16.95 (978-0-8234-1615-8(1)) Holiday Hse., Inc.

Fowles, Shelley. Climbing Rosa. 2006. (Illus.). 32p. (J). 15.95 (978-1-84507-079-3(8)) Lincoln, Frances Ltd. GBR. *Dist:* Perseus Distribution.

Frances, Ellen. Looking for Dad. White, Annie, illus. 1999. (Supa Doopers Ser.). 64p. (J). (978-0-7608-3292-9(7)) Sundance/Newbridge Educational Publishing.

—Looking for Dad. 1999. (gr. 3-6). lib. bdg. 12.60 (978-0-613-30565-5(5)) Tandem Library Bks.

Fransoy, Monse, illus. Cinderella. 2001. (SPA & ENG.). 32p. (J). (ps-3). 12.95 (978-0-8118-3084-3(5)) Chronicle Bks. LLC.

Friend, Natasha. Bounce. 2007. 192p. (YA). (gr. 6-8). pap. 16.99 (*978-0-439-85350-7(8) , Scholastic Pr.) Scholastic, Inc.

Friesen, Gayle. Losing Forever. (Gayle Friessen Ser.). (Illus.). 248p. (YA). (gr. 13 up). 2003. (978-1-55337-032-1(5)); 2002. (978-1-55337-031-4(7)) Kids Can Pr., Ltd.

—Losing Forever. 2003. (gr. 5-8). lib. bdg. 15.25 (978-0-613-84418-5(1)) Tandem Library Bks.

Greene, Stephanie. Falling into Place. 128p. (J). (gr. 4-6). 2006. pap. 5.95 (978-0-618-68928-6(1)); 2002. (Illus.). tchr. ed. 15.00 (978-0-618-17744-8(2)) Houghton Mifflin Co. Trade & Reference Div. (Clarion Bks.).

Griffin, Adele. Dive. 2001. (J). 12.64 (978-0-606-21151-2(9)); (gr. 5-8). lib. bdg. 14.15 (978-0-613-46066-8(9)) Tandem Library Bks.

Grimes, Nikki. Oh, Brother! Benny, Mike, illus. 2008. 32p. (J). 17.89 (978-0-688-17295-4(4)); 16.99 (978-0-688-17294-7(6)) HarperCollins Pubs.

Grimm. 630 - Cenicienta. 2001. Tr. of Cinderella. (SPA.). (978-968-6347-30-2(5)) Larousse, Ediciones, S. A. de C. V.

Hayes, Joe. Little Gold Star: A Cinderella Cuento. 2002. (gr. k-3). lib. bdg. 16.40 (978-0-613-77773-5(5)) Tandem Library Bks.

Hicks, Betty. Out of Order. 2005. 176p. (J). (ps-7). 16.95 (978-1-59643-061-7(3)) Roaring Brook Pr.

—Out of Order. 2007. 176p. (J). pap. 6.99 (*978-0-312-37355-9(4)) Square Fish.

Hinton, S. E. Esto Ya Es Otra Historia. (SPA.). (J). 6.95 (978-84-204-4121-4(X)) Santillana USA Publishing Co., Inc.

—That Was Then, This Is Now. 1998. 160p. (YA). (gr. 7-12). pap. 7.99 (978-0-14-038966-1(0) , Puffin) Penguin Group (USA) Inc.

—That Was Then, This Is Now. 1998. (Puffin Book Ser.). (YA). (978-0-606-12861-2(1)) Tandem Library Bks.

Hoffman, Mary. Boundless Grace. Binch, Caroline, illus. 2002. (J). 25.45 (978-0-7587-2139-6(0)) Book Wholesalers, Inc.

—Boundless Grace. Binch, Caroline, illus. 2000. 32p. (J). (ps-3). pap. 6.99 (978-0-14-055667-4(2) , Puffin) Penguin Group (USA) Inc.

—Boundless Grace. Binch, Caroline, illus. 2000. (J). (ps-ps). 26p. 12.79 (978-0-606-20350-0(8)); lib. bdg. 14.15 (978-0-613-33678-9(X)) Tandem Library Bks.

—Boundless Grace. 2000. (J). (978-0-606-20224-4(2)) Tandem Library Bks.

—City of Stars. 2003. (Stravaganza Ser.: Vol. 2). (Illus.). 300p. (J). 17.95 (978-1-58234-839-1(1) , Bloomsbury Children) Bloomsbury Publishing.

Hughes, Shirley. Ella's Big Chance. Hughes, Shirley, illus. 2004. (Illus.). 48p. (J). 16.95 (978-0-689-87399-7(9) , Simon & Schuster Children's Publishing) Simon & Schuster Children's Publishing.

Hutchins, Elizabeth. Personal Best: Snowbored, All That Jazz, Thief! 2005. (Triple Play Ser.). (Illus.). 48p. (gr. 4-8). 41.85 (978-0-7910-9075-6(2)) Facts On File, Inc.

Johnson, Angela. Bird. 2004. 144p. (J). (gr. 4). 16.99 (978-0-8037-2847-9(6) , Dial) Penguin Group (USA) Inc.

Johnson, Tim. Never So Green. 2002. 240p. (YA). 18.00 (978-0-374-35509-8(6) , Farrar, Straus & Giroux (BYR)) Farrar, Straus & Giroux.

Jones, Diana Wynne. Ogre Downstairs. 2002. (gr. 3-6). lib. bdg. 14.10 (978-0-613-68455-2(9)) Tandem Library Bks.

Jukes, Mavis. Cinderella 2000. 2001. (Illus.). (J). (978-0-606-20605-1(1)) Tandem Library Bks.

Kantor, Melissa. If I Have a Wicked Stepmother, Where's My Prince? 2007. 320p. (gr. 7 up). pap. 8.99 (*978-0-7868-0961-5(2)); 2005. 288p. (J). (gr. 7-17). 15.99 (978-0-7868-0960-8(4)); 2005. 283p. (YA). (*978-1-4156-2763-1(0)) Hyperion Pr.

Kelly, Theresa. Living on Nothing Atoll. 1999. (Aloha Cove Ser.: Vol. 1). (Illus.). 272p. (YA). (gr. 8-12). 5.99 (978-0-570-05483-2(4)) Concordia Publishing Hse.

—Living on Nothing Atoll. 1999. (gr. 7-12). lib. bdg. 14.15 (978-0-613-72659-7(6)) Tandem Library Bks.

—Place in the Heart. 1999. (gr. 7-12). lib. bdg. 14.15 (978-0-613-72783-9(5)) Tandem Library Bks.

—Seaside High, Vol. 2. 1999. (Aloha Cove Ser.: Vol. 2). (Illus.). 272p. (YA). (gr. 8-12). 5.99 (978-0-570-05484-9(2)) Concordia Publishing Hse.

—Seaside High. 1999. (gr. 7-12). lib. bdg. 14.15 (978-0-613-72660-3(X)) Tandem Library Bks.

—Tomorrow I'll Miss You, Vol. 3. 1999. (Aloha Cove Ser.: Vol. 3). (Illus.). 272p. (YA). (gr. 8-12). 5.99 (978-0-570-05485-6(0)) Concordia Publishing Hse.

—Tomorrow I'll Miss You. 1999. (gr. 7-12). lib. bdg. 14.15 (978-0-613-72575-0(1)) Tandem Library Bks.

Kirby, Susan E. Ellen's Story. 2000. (gr. 3-6). lib. bdg. 13.00 (978-0-613-31156-4(6)) Tandem Library Bks.

Klise, Kate. Deliver Us from Normal. 2006. 256p. (YA). (gr. 5-9). pap. 5.99 (978-0-439-52323-3(0) , Scholastic Paperbacks) Scholastic, Inc.

Korba, Joanna. Yeh-shen: A Cinderella Tale from China. 2006. 42.00 (*978-1-4108-6162-7(7)) Benchmark Education Co.

Korman, Gordon. Maxx Comedy: The Funniest Kid in America. 2006. 160p. (gr. 3-7). pap. 5.99 (978-0-7868-3895-0(7)) Hyperion Pr.

Lantz, Francess L. Stepbaby from Planet Weird. 2001. (Illus.). (J). 3.99 (978-0-375-81259-0(8) , Random Hse. Bks. for Young Readers) Random Hse. Children's Bks.

Lewis, Beverly. California Crazy. 2002. (Holly's Heart Ser.: Bk. 5). 160p. (YA). pap. 6.99 (978-0-7642-2504-8(9)) Bethany Hse. Pubs.

—Eight Is Enough. 2003. (Holly's Heart Ser.: Bk. 13). 160p. (Orig.). (YA). pap. 6.99 (978-0-7642-2620-5(7)) Bethany Hse. Pubs.

—It's a Girl Thing. 2003. (Holly's Heart Ser.: Bk. 14). 160p. (Orig.). (YA). pap. 6.99 (978-0-7642-2621-2(5)) Bethany Hse. Pubs.

—Little White Lies. 2003. (Holly's Heart Ser.: Bk. 10). 160p. (YA). (gr. 5-9). reprint ed. pap. 6.99 (978-0-7642-2617-5(7)) Bethany Hse. Pubs.

—Second-Best Friend. 2002. (Holly's Heart Ser.: Bk. 6). 160p. (YA). pap. 6.99 (978-0-7642-2505-5(7)) Bethany Hse. Pubs.

Lockwood, Cara. Wuthering High. 2006. (Bard Academy Ser.: No. 1). 272p. pap. 9.95 (978-1-4165-2475-5(4) , MTV) Simon & Schuster.

Love, D. Anne. A Year Without Rain. 2000. (Illus.). 128p. (J). (gr. 4-6). tchr. ed. 15.95 (978-0-8234-1488-8(4)) Holiday Hse., Inc.

Lynn, Tracy. Snow: A Retelling of Snow White & the Seven Dwarfs. 2006. (Once upon a Time Ser.). 272p. (YA). pap. 5.99 (978-1-4169-4015-9(4) , Simon Pulse) Simon & Schuster Children's Publishing.

MacCullough, Carolyn. Stealing Henry. rev. ed. 2005. 208p. (YA). 16.95 (978-1-59643-045-7(1)) Roaring Brook Pr.

Mackall, Dandi Daley. Grace Notes. 2006. (Faithgirlz Ser.). (Illus.). 128p. (J). pap. 6.99 (978-0-310-71093-6(6)) Zonderkidz.

Mangum, Kay Lynn. When the Bough Breaks. 2007. 352p. (YA). pap. 15.95 (*978-1-59038-748-1(1)) Deseret Bk. Co.

McCombie, Karen. Being Grown-up Is Cool (Not!) Monks, Lydia, illus. 2007. (Indie Kidd Ser.). 160p. (J). (gr. 2-5). lib. bdg. 9.99 (*978-0-440-42200-6(0)); per. 5.99 (*978-0-440-42199-3(3)) Random Hse. Children's Bks. (Yearling).

McKnight, Gillian. The Frog Prince. 2006. 240p. (J). mass mkt. 5.99 (978-0-689-87735-3(8) , Simon Pulse) Simon & Schuster Children's Publishing.

McNeal, Laura & McNeal, Tom. Zipped. 2003. 288p. (J). (gr. 7). 15.95 (978-0-375-81491-4(4)); lib. bdg. 17.99 (978-0-375-91491-1(9)) Random Hse. Children's Bks. (Knopf Bks. for Young Readers).

McVeity, Jen. On Different Shores. 1998. (Illus.). 167p. (YA). (gr. 5-9). 17.99 (978-0-531-33115-6(6)); pap. 16.95 (978-0-531-30115-9(X)) Scholastic, Inc. (Orchard Bks.).

Miller, Mary Jane. Upside Down. 2000. 160p. (YA). (gr. 4-7). pap. 11.95 (978-0-595-00332-7(X)) iUniverse, Inc.

Minh Quoc. Tam & Cam/Tam Cam: The Ancient Vietnamese Cinderella Story. Smith, William, tr. from VIE. Mai Long, illus. 2006. (ENG & VIE.). 32p. (J). (gr. 1-4). 16.95 (978-0-9701654-4-2(7)) East West Discovery Pr.

Mulford, Philippa Greene. The Holly Sisters on Their Own. 1998. (Accelerated Reader Bks.). 160p. (J). (gr. 5-9). lib. bdg. 14.95 (978-0-7614-5022-1(X) , Cavendish Children's Bks.) Cavendish, Marshall Corp.

Oldham, Mary. No Fire, No Candle. 2001. 217p. (YA). pap. 12.95 (978-1-85902-945-9(0)) Beekman Bks., Inc.

Olsen, Sylvia. White Girl. 2005. (Illus.). 200p. (J). pap. 8.95 (978-1-55039-147-3(X)) Sono Nis Pr. CAN. *Dist:* Orca Bk. Pubs. USA.

Peck, Dale. Drift House: The First Voyage. (J). 2006. 448p. pap. 7.95 (978-1-59990-005-6(X)); 2005. 420p. 16.95 (978-1-58234-969-5(X)) Bloomsbury Publishing. (Bloomsbury Children).

Perrault, Charles. Cinderella. 2002. (gr. k-3). lib. bdg. 15.25 (978-0-613-73574-2(9)) Tandem Library Bks.

Peters, Julie Anne. Keeping You a Secret. 2005. 272p. (YA). (gr. 9-17). pap. 7.99 (978-0-316-00985-0(7) , Tingley, Megan Bks.) Little, Brown Bks. for Young Readers.

Pielichaty, Helena. Starring Brody ... 2006. (Girls of Avenue Z Ser.). 144p. (J). pap. 4.99 (978-1-4169-0062-7(4) , Aladdin) Simon & Schuster Children's Publishing.

Pryor, Bonnie. Joseph: 1861 - A Rumble of War. Dodson, Bert, illus. 1999. (American Adventures Ser.). 176p. (J). (gr. 3-7). 14.95 (978-0-688-15671-8(1)) HarperCollins Pubs.

—Joseph: 1861 - A Rumble of War. 2000. (Illus.). (J). (978-0-606-17975-1(5)) Tandem Library Bks.

—Joseph: 1861—A Rumble of War. 2000. (American Adventures Ser.). (Illus.). 176p. (J). (gr. 3-7). pap. 4.50 (978-0-380-73103-9(7) , Harper Trophy) HarperCollins Pubs.

Rallison, Janette. How to Take the Ex Out of Ex-Boyfriend. 2007. 272p. (YA). (gr. 7 up). 15.99 (978-0-399-24617-3(7) , Putnam Juvenile) Penguin Group (USA) Inc.

Random House Disney Staff. Cinderella. 2002. (Illus.). (J). 2.99 (978-0-7364-2076-1(2) , RH/Disney) Random Hse. Children's Bks.

Random House Disney Staff & Posner-Sanchez, Andrea. Lovely Cinderella. 2004. (Illus.). 16p. (J). (gr. k-ps). bds. 3.99 (978-0-7364-2212-3(9) , RH/Disney) Random Hse. Children's Bks.

Ransom, Candice F. More Than a Name. 1999. 115p. (J). (gr. 2-5). reprint ed. 14.00 (978-0-7881-6609-9(3)) DIANE Publishing Co.

Readler, Blaine C. Under the Radar: The Spy Drone Adventure. 2006. 248p. (J). pap. 14.95 (978-1-933255-18-7(8)) DNA Pr.

Reinhardt, Dana. How to Build a House. 2008. 240p. (YA). (gr. 7). lib. bdg. 18.99 (*978-0-375-94454-3(0) , Lamb, Wendy) Random Hse. Children's Bks.

Reinhart, Matthew. Cinderella: A Pop-up Fairy Tale. Reinhart, Matthew, illus. 2005. (Illus.). 12p. (J). 25.99 (978-1-4169-0501-1(4) , Little Simon) Simon & Schuster Children's Publishing.

Reiss, Kathryn. Sweet Miss Honeywell's Revenge: A Ghost Story. 2005. 444p. (J). (gr. 7-17). pap. 6.95 (978-0-15-205471-7(5) , Harcourt Paperbacks) Harcourt Children's Bks.

Richardson, E. E. The Intruders. 2006. 208p. (J). (gr. 7). 15.95 (978-0-385-73264-2(3) , Delacorte Bks. for Young Readers) Random Hse. Children's Bks.

Rinn, Miriam. The Saturday Secret. 1999. (Illus.). 144p. (J). (gr. 4-7). pap. 7.95 (978-1-881283-26-3(7)) Alef Design Group.

Salenas, Bobbi. Cinderella Latina - Cinicienta Latina. La Madrid, Enriquee, tr. Salenas, Bobbi, illus. 2003. (SPA.). (YA). (gr. 3-12). 19.95 (978-0-934925-06-8(2)) Pinata Pubns.

Salisbury, Graham. Lord of the Deep. braille ed. 2003. (J). (gr. 2). spiral bd. (978-0-616-15872-2(6)) Canadian National Institute for the Blind/Institut National Canadien pour les Aveugles.

—Lord of the Deep. 2003. 192p. (J). (gr. 5). pap. 5.99 (978-0-440-22911-7(1) , Laurel Leaf) Random Hse. Children's Bks.

—Lord of the Deep. 2003. (gr. 5-8). lib. bdg. 13.55 (978-0-613-61296-8(5)) Tandem Library Bks.

Salisbury, Graham. Lord of the Deep: A Novel. 2006. 182p. (J). (gr. 6-10). reprint ed. 16.00 (*978-1-4223-5841-2(0)) DIANE Publishing Co.

San Souci, Robert D. Cendrillon: A Caribbean Cinderella. Pinkney, Brian, illus. 2002. 40p. (J). (gr. k-5). 7.99 (978-0-689-84888-9(9) , Aladdin) Simon & Schuster Children's Publishing.

—Cendrillon: A Caribbean Cinderella. 2002. (gr. 3-6). lib. bdg. 15.30 (978-0-613-45021-8(3)) Tandem Library Bks.

Sasman, Irene D. H. Cinderella Around the World Children's Library, Set. 1998. (Illus.). (J). (ps-4). pap. 89.95 (978-1-56831-380-1(2)) Learning Connection, The.

Stacy, Lori. Island Girl. 2001. (Seasons: Vol. 2). 124p. pap. 4.95 (978-0-9678285-2-7(X)) Lunchbox Pr.

Stengel, Joyce A. Mystery of the Island Jewels. 2002. 208p. (J). (gr. 3-7). pap. 4.99 (978-0-689-85049-3(2) , Aladdin) Simon & Schuster Children's Publishing.

—Mystery of the Island Jewels. 2002. (gr. 3-6). lib. bdg. 13.00 (978-0-613-70940-8(3)) Tandem Library Bks.

Stewart, Sharon. Spider's Web. 1998. 160p. (J). (gr. 4-9). pap. 7.95 (978-0-88995-177-8(2)) Red Deer Pr. CAN. *Dist:* Fitzhenry & Whiteside, Ltd.

Stine, R.L. Stepsister. 2005. 165p. (J). lib. bdg. 13.00 (*978-1-4242-0998-9(6)) Fitzgerald Bks.

Strong, Jeremy. Stuff: The Life of a Cool Demented Dude. Armstrong, Matthew S., illus. 2007. 240p. (J). (gr. 7 up). 15.99 (978-0-06-084105-8(2) , HarperTeen) HarperCollins Pubs.

—Stuff: The Life of a Cool Demented Dude. Armstrong, Matthew, illus. 2007. 240p. (J). (gr. 7 up). lib. bdg. 16.89 (978-0-06-084106-5(0) , HarperTeen) HarperCollins Pubs.

Thomas, Joyce Carol. The Gospel Cinderella. Diaz, David, illus. 2004. 40p. (J). (gr. k-5). 15.99 (978-0-06-025387-5(8) , Amistad) HarperCollins Pubs.

Thompson, Kate. Only Human. 2006. (Missing Link Trilogy Ser.: Bk. 2). 320p. (YA). 16.95 (978-1-58234-651-9(8) , Bloomsbury Children) Bloomsbury Publishing.

Tucker, Charlotte Maria. Driven into Exile: A Story of the Huguenots. 2003. (Huguenot Inheritance Ser.: Vol. 5). (Illus.). 141p. (J). (978-0-921100-66-9(3)) Inheritance Pubns.

Voigt, Cynthia. When She Hollers. 2003. 192p. (J). (gr. 7 up). pap. 5.99 (978-0-590-46715-5(8) , Scholastic Paperbacks) Scholastic, Inc.

Werner, Jane. Cinderella. Worcester, Retta Scott, illus. 2002. (Little Golden Book Ser.). 24p. (J). (gr. k-k). 2.99 (978-0-7364-2151-5(3) , Golden/Disney) Random Hse. Children's Bks.

Wilkins, Rose. So Super Stylish. 2006. 288p. (J). (gr. 6). 16.99 (978-0-8037-3064-9(0) , Dial) Penguin Group (USA) Inc.

Wilson, Jacqueline. Girls Out Late. 2003. 224p. (YA). (gr. 7). mass mkt. 5.50 (978-0-440-22959-9(6) , Laurel Leaf) Random Hse. Children's Bks.

—Girls Out Late. Sharratt, Nick, illus. 2003. 192p. (YA). mass mkt. (978-0-552-54523-5(6) , Corgi) Transworld Publishers Ltd. GBR. *Dist:* Random Hse. of Canada, Ltd.

—The Suitcase Kid. Hu, Ying-Hwa, illus. 1998. 144p. (gr. 3-7). 5.50 (978-0-440-41371-4(0) , Yearling) Random Hse. Children's Bks.

Wyss, Thelma Hatch. Ten Miles from Winnemucca. 2002. 144p. (J). (gr. 7 up). 15.95 (978-0-06-029783-1(2)) HarperCollins Pubs.

Zeises, Lara M. Anyone but You. 256p. (YA). (gr. 9). 2007. mass mkt. 6.50 (*978-0-440-23858-4(7) , Laurel Leaf); 2005. 15.95 (978-0-385-73145-4(0) , Delacorte Bks. for Young Readers) Random Hse. Children's Bks.

STEPHENSON, GEORGE, 1781-1848

Wooten, Sara McIntosh. The Industrial Revolution. 2003. (People at the Center of Ser.). (Illus.). 48p. (J). 24.95 (978-1-56711-766-0(X) , Blackbirch Pr., Inc.) Thomson Gale.

STEPPARENTS

Block, Joel D. Stepliving for Teens: Getting along with Step-Parents & Siblings. 2001. (gr. 7-12). lib. bdg. 13.00 (978-0-613-89162-2(7)) Tandem Library Bks.

Hancock, Rusty. Dedicated Dads: Stepfathers of Famous People. Van Kampen, Megan, illus. 2004. 138p. (978-0-934981-12-5(4)) Lawells Publishing.

Hunter, Rebecca. My New Dad. 2007. (First Times Ser.). (Illus.). 24p. (J). pap. 10.95 (*978-0-237-53180-5(1) , Evans Brothers, Limited) Evans Publishing Group GBR. *Dist:* Independent Pubs. Group.

MacGregor, Cynthia. Jigsaw Puzzle Family: The Stepkids' Guide to Fitting It Together. 2005. 106p. (J). (ps-7). pap. 12.95 (978-1-886230-63-7(3) , Rebuilding Bks.) Impact Pubs., Inc.

Wells, Sherry A. Warm & Wonderful Stepmothers of Famous People. Van Kampen, Megan, illus. 2004. 131p. 20.00 (978-0-934981-10-1(8)) Lawells Publishing.

STEPPARENTS—FICTION

Alger, Horatio. Luck & Pluck: Or, John Oakley's Inheritance. unabr. ed. 2002. (Polyglot Press Alger Ser.). (Illus.). (J). pap. 17.95 (978-1-4115-0019-8(9)) Polyglot Pr., Inc.

Archer, Lily. The Poison Apples. 2007. 288p. (YA). (gr. 6 up). 16.95 (*978-0-312-36762-6(7)) Feiwel & Friends.

Boyd, David. Bottom Drawer. 2002. 126p. pap. 4.95 (978-0-921156-58-1(8)) Rubicon Publishing, Inc. CAN. *Dist:* International Publishers Marketing.

—Bottom Drawer. 2002. (gr. 7-12). lib. bdg. 12.95 (978-0-613-77607-3(0)) Tandem Library Bks.

Brooks, Martha. Being with Henry. 1999. (J). (978-0-88899-377-9(3)) Douglas & McIntyre, Ltd.

—Being with Henry. pap. 8.95 (978-0-88899-502-5(4)) Groundwood Bks. CAN. *Dist:* Transition Vendor.

Bryant, Ann. One Mom Too Many! 2004. (Step-Chain Ser.: Vol. 1). 190p. (J). (gr. 3-8). pap. 4.95 (978-1-894222-78-5(4)) Lobster Pr. CAN. *Dist:* Univ. of Toronto Pr.

—One Mom Too Many! 2003. (gr. 5-8). lib. bdg. 11.80 (978-0-613-82599-3(3)) Tandem Library Bks.

Bunting, Eve. The Memory String. Rand, Ted, illus. 2000. 40p. (J). (gr. k-3). tchr. ed. 16.00 (978-0-395-86146-2(2) , Clarion Bks.) Houghton Mifflin Co. Trade & Reference Div.

Caletti, Deb. Wild Roses. (YA). (gr. 7 up). 2006. 320p. pap. 6.99 (978-0-689-86475-9(2) , Simon Pulse); 2005. 304p. 15.95 (978-0-689-86766-8(2)) Simon & Schuster Children's Publishing.

Candido, Jeane H. Levi: The Smartest Boy in the World. Lester, Susie, illus. 2nd rev. ed. 2001. 42p. (J). pap. 9.99 (978-1-883573-87-4(4) , Little Blue Works) Windstorm Creative.

Connor, Leslie. Waiting for Normal. 2008. 304p. (J). 16.99 (*978-0-06-089088-9(6)); lib. bdg. 17.89 (*978-0-06-089089-6(4)) HarperCollins Pubs.

Couloumbis, Audrey. Say Yes. 2003. 208p. (J). pap. 6.99 (978-0-14-250186-3(7) , Puffin) Penguin Group (USA) Inc.

Cullen, Lynn. Diary of Nelly Vandorn. (gr. 3 up). Date not set. 128p. mass mkt. 4.99 (978-0-06-440926-1(0)); 2002. 192p. (J). 15.95 (978-0-06-029133-4(8)) HarperCollins Pubs.

Dunbar, Fiona. The Truth Cookie. 2005. 224p. (J). (gr. 4-7). pap. 15.99 (978-0-439-74022-7(3) , Orchard Bks.) Scholastic, Inc.

Ensor, Barbara. Cinderella (As If You Didn't Already Know the Story) Ensor, Barbara, illus. 2006. (Illus.). 128p. (J). (gr. 2-7). 12.95 (978-0-375-83620-6(9) , Schwartz & Wade Bks.) Random Hse. Children's Bks.

Fairy Tale- Cinderella. 2005. (J). bds. (978-1-4194-0039-1(8)) Paradise Pr., Inc.

Fairy tales - Cinderella. 2005. (J). bds. (978-1-4194-0100-8(9)) Paradise Pr., Inc.

Fairy talse s/s - CInderella. 2005. (J). bds. (978-1-4194-0066-7(5)) Paradise Pr., Inc.

Ferguson, Tina. The Day i Disappeared. 2005. 83p. pap. 14.95 (978-1-4137-9243-0(X)) PublishAmerica, Inc.

Fietzek, Petra. Trommeln, Trommeln. 2002. (GER.). 128p. pap. 15.00 (978-1-4000-3958-6(4) , New Media German Language) Random House Foreign Language Publishing.

Freeman, Martha. The Trouble with Cats. Smith, Cat Bowman, illus. 2000. 80p. (J). (gr. 4-6). tchr. ed. 15.95 (978-0-8234-1479-6(5)) Holiday Hse., Inc.

French, Simon. Where in the World. 2003. 208p. (J). (gr. 3-6). 14.95 (978-1-56145-292-7(0) , Q34443) Peachtree Pubs., Ltd.

Geras, Adele. Pictures of the Night. 2005. (Egerton Hall Novels: Vol. 3). 192p. (YA). (gr. 7-17). pap. 6.95 (978-0-15-205543-1(6) , Harcourt Paperbacks) Harcourt Children's Bks.

Gleitzman, Morris. Sticky Beak. l.t. ed. 2005. 200p. (J). pap. (978-0-7540-6180-9(9) , CLP 374) BBC Audio.

Hamilton, Morse. The Garden of Eden Motel. 1999. (Illus.). 160p. (J). (gr. 5 up). 16.00 (978-0-688-16814-8(0)) HarperCollins Pubs.

Hanson-Roberts, Mary, illus. Cinderella: A Tale of Kindness. 2006. (J). 6.99 (978-1-59939-001-7(9) , Reader's Digest Young Families, Inc.) Reader's Digest Children's Publishing, Inc.

Hendry, Frances. Quest for a Queen: The Falcon. 2006. pap. ***978-1-905665-06-8(7))** Pollinger In Print.

Henry, April. Shock Point. 2006. 192p. (YA). (gr. 6). 16.99 (978-0-399-24385-1(2) , Putnam Juvenile) Penguin Group (USA) Inc.

Hinman, Bonnie. San Francisco Earthquake. 32nd ed. 1998. (American Adventure Ser.: No. 32). (Illus.). (J). (gr. 3-7). pap. 3.97 (978-1-57748-393-9(6)) Barbour Publishing, Inc.

James, Brian. Dirty Liar. 2006. 304p. (J). (gr. 10 up). pap. 16.99 (978-0-439-79623-1(7) , PUSH) Scholastic, Inc.

Johnson, Kathleen Jeffrie. The Parallel Universe of Liars. 2004. 240p. (YA). (gr. 9). reprint ed. pap. 5.99 (978-0-440-23852-2(8) , Laurel Leaf) Random Hse. Children's Bks.

Jukes, Mavis. Like Jake & Me. 2005. (Illus.). 64p. (J). (gr. 5). 6.50 (978-0-440-42122-1(5) , Yearling) Random Hse. Children's Bks.

Little Reader Digital Storybook: Cinderella. 2005. (J). cd-rom 8.99 (978-0-9767657-7-6(2)) Mullings Media.

Lopez, Lorraine. Call Me Henri. 2006. 242p. 17.95 (978-1-931896-27-6(5)) Curbstone Pr.

Lurie, April. Dancing in the Streets of Brooklyn. 208p. (gr. 3-7). 2004. pap. 5.99 (978-0-440-41825-2(9) , Yearling); 2002. lib. bdg. 17.99 (978-0-385-90066-9(X) , Delacorte Bks. for Young Readers) Random Hse. Children's Bks.

Lutz, Norma Jean. Smallpox Strikes! Cotton Mather's Bold Experiment. 1999. (American Adventure Ser.: No. 7). (Illus.). 144p. (J). (gr. 3-7). lib. bdg. 15.95 (978-0-7910-5047-7(5) , Chelsea Hse.) Facts On File, Inc.

MacLachlan, Patricia. Sarah, Plain & Tall. l.t. ed. 2005. 82p. (YA). pap. 10.95 (978-0-7862-8064-3(6)) Thorndike Pr.

Mason, Jane B. & Stephens, Sarah Hines. Appley Ever After. 2005. (Princess School Ser.: No. 6). (Illus.). 128p. (J). (ps-7). pap. 4.99 (978-0-439-69814-6(6) , Scholastic Paperbacks) Scholastic, Inc.

Matheson, Shirlee Smith. Gambler's Daughter. 2008. 144p. (YA). pap. 11.99 ***978-1-55002-718-1(2)** , Sandcastle Bks.) Dundurn Group, The CAN. *Dist:* Univ. of Toronto Pr.

McClintock, Norah. Tell. 2006. 112p. (YA). (gr. 7 up). pap. 8.95 (978-1-55143-511-4(X)); lib. bdg. 14.95 (978-1-55143-672-2(8)) Orca Bk. Pubs. USA.

Meade, L. T. The Children's Pilgrimage. 2004. reprint ed. pap. 24.95 (978-1-4191-5659-5(4)); pap. 1.99 (978-1-4192-5659-2(9)) Kessinger Publishing, LLC.

Meyers, Susan A. Callie & the Stepmother. Gauss, Rose, illus. l.t. ed. 2005. 64p. (J). pap. 6.95 (978-0-9718348-0-4(6)) Blooming Tree Pr.

Miller, Lisa K. The Range of Light. 2005. (Illus.). 112p. (YA). pap. 11.95 (978-1-58736-538-6(3)) Wheatmark.

Napoli, Donna Jo. Bound. 2004. (Illus.). 192p. (YA). (gr. 6 up). 16.95 (978-0-689-86175-8(3) , Atheneum) Simon & Schuster Children's Publishing.

Narsimhan, Mahtab. The Third Eye. 2007. 240p. (YA). pap. 11.99 ***978-1-55002-750-1(6)** , Boardwalk Bks.) Dundurn Group, The CAN. *Dist:* Univ. of Toronto Pr.

Naylor, Phyllis Reynolds. Alice on Her Way. 2006. (Alice Ser.). 352p. (YA). mass mkt. 5.99 (978-0-689-87091-0(4) , Simon Pulse) Simon & Schuster Children's Publishing.

Naylor, Phyllis Reynolds & Vaccaro, Nick. Alice on Her Way. 2005. (Alice Ser.). 336p. (YA). 16.99 (978-0-689-87090-3(6) , Atheneum) Simon & Schuster Children's Publishing.

Nixon, Joan Lowery. Nancy's Story, 1765. 2004. (J). (978-0-87935-225-7(6)) Colonial Williamsburg Foundation.

Ostrow, Kim. Chuckie's New Mommy. 2007. 24p. (J). 21.35 ***978-1-59961-356-7(5))** Spotlight.

Paterson, Katherine. The Field of the Dogs. McCully, Emily Arnold, illus. (J). 2002. 112p. pap. 5.99 (978-0-06-442147-8(3)); 2001. 96p. (gr. 4-7). 14.89 (978-0-06-029475-5(2)) HarperCollins Pubs.

—The Field of the Dogs. 2002. (gr. 3-6). lib. bdg. 13.00 (978-0-613-62947-8(7)) Tandem Library Bks.

Patneaude, David. Framed in Fire. 2001. (gr. 5-8). lib. bdg. 14.10 (978-0-613-35946-7(1)) Tandem Library Bks.

—Framed in Fire. 224p. (J). (gr. 6-9). 2004. pap. 5.95 (978-0-8075-9096-6(7)); 1999. (Illus.). 15.95 (978-0-8075-9098-0(3)) Whitman, Albert & Co.

Peters, Julie Anne. Keeping You a Secret. 2005. 250p. (YA). (gr. 8-12). per. 14.64 (978-0-606-33459-4(9)) Tandem Library Bks.

Pfeffer, Susan Beth. Devil's Den. 1998. 115p. (J). (gr. 3-7). 15.95 (978-0-8027-8650-0(2)) Walker & Co.

Platt, Randall Beth. Honor Bright. 1998. (978-0-606-13486-6(7)) Tandem Library Bks.

Polak, Monique. Home Invasion. 2005. (Orca Soundings Ser.). 112p. (J). (gr. 7-12). pap. 7.95 (978-1-55143-482-7(2)) Orca Bk. Pubs. USA.

Rallison, Janette. How to Take the Ex Out of Ex-Boyfriend. 2007. 272p. (YA). (gr. 7 up). 15.99 (978-0-399-24617-3(7) , Putnam Juvenile) Penguin Group (USA) Inc.

Random House Disney Staff. Cinderella. 2002. (gr. k-3). lib. bdg. 10.95 (978-0-613-73670-1(2)) Tandem Library Bks.

—Cinderella III: A Twist in Time. 2006. (Pictureback(R) Ser.). (Illus.). 24p. (J). (gr. k-3). pap. 3.99 (978-0-7364-2429-5(6) , RH/Disney) Random Hse. Children's Bks.

Rinaldi, Ann. Keep Smiling Through. 2005. 208p. (J). pap. 6.95 (978-0-15-205399-4(9) , Gulliver Bks.) Harcourt Children's Bks.

Rinn, Miriam. The Saturday Secret. 1999. (Illus.). 144p. (J). (gr. 4-7). pap. 7.95 (978-1-881283-26-3(7)) Alef Design Group.

Roberts, Rachel. Song of the Unicorns. 2003. (Avalon Ser.). 175p. (J). (gr. 3-7). pap. 4.99 (978-1-59315-002-0(4)) Perseus Bks. Group.

Schraff, Anne. When Sleeping Dogs Awaken. 2001. (PageTurner Mystery Ser.). 80p. (YA). per. 3.95 (978-1-56254-180-4(3) , SP 1803) Saddleback Educational Publishing.

—When Sleeping Dogs Awaken. 2001. (gr. 7-12). lib. bdg. 11.80 (978-0-613-33238-5(5)) Tandem Library Bks.

Sherrard, Valerie. Three Million Acres of Flame. 2007. 180p. (YA). pap. 10.99 ***978-1-55002-727-3(1)** , Boardwalk Bks.) Dundurn Group, The CAN. *Dist:* Univ. of Toronto Pr.

Sorrells, Walter. Silent Room. 2006. 240p. (YA). (gr. 7). 16.99 (978-0-525-47697-9(0) , Dutton Juvenile) Penguin Group (USA) Inc.

Souci, Robert D. San. Well at the End of the World. Walsh, Rebecca, illus. 2004. 48p. (J). 16.95 (978-1-58717-212-0(7) , SeaStar Bks.) Chronicle Bks. LLC.

Spinelli, Eileen. Lizzie Logan, Second Banana. 2000. (978-0-606-17827-3(9)) Tandem Library Bks.

Stewart, Jennifer J. The Bean King's Daughter. 2002. 144p. (J). (gr. 4-6). tchr. ed. 15.95 (978-0-8234-1644-8(5)) Holiday Hse., Inc.

Sturtevant, Katherine. At the Sign of the Star. 2000. 144p. (YA). (gr. 5 up). 16.00 (978-0-374-30449-2(1) , Farrar, Straus & Giroux (BYR)) Farrar, Straus & Giroux.

Tullson, Diane. Red Sea. 2005. 176p. (J). (gr. 7-12). pap. 7.95 (978-1-55143-331-8(1)) Orca Bk. Pubs. USA.

Venable, Leslie Allgood. The Not So Wicked Stepmother. Harrison, Julie M., illus. 1999. 24p. (J). (gr. 1-7). per. 9.95 (978-0-9666817-0-3(3)) Venable, L.A. Publishing Co.

Voigt, Cynthia. When She Hollers. 2003. 192p. (J). (gr. 7 up). pap. 5.99 (978-0-590-46715-5(8) , Scholastic Paperbacks) Scholastic, Inc.

Weber, Lenora Mattingly. Beany Has a Secret Life. 1999. (Beany Malone Ser.). 296p. (J). pap. 12.95 (978-0-9639607-7-1(6)) Image Cascade Publishing.

Wilkes, Maria D. On Top of Concord Hill. Andreasen, Dan, illus. 2000. (Little House Ser.). 288p. (J). (gr. 3-7). 15.89 (978-0-06-027003-2(9)) HarperCollins Pubs.

Wilson, Jacqueline. Double Act. 1999. (J). (978-0-606-16442-9(1)); (gr. 3-6). lib. bdg. 12.40 (978-0-613-16097-1(5)) Tandem Library Bks.

—Double Act. 2001. (Corgi Yearling Ser.). (Illus.). 32p. 9.99 (978-0-440-86334-2(1) , Corgi) Transworld Publishers Ltd. GBR. *Dist:* Trafalgar Square Publishing.

—Secrets. l.t. ed. 2003. (Illus.). 208p. (J). 16.95 (978-0-7540-7854-8(X) , Galaxy Children's Large Print) BBC Audiobooks America.

Zimmer, Tracie Vaughn. Sketches from a Spy Tree. Glass, Andrew, illus. 2005. 64p. (J). (gr. 4-6). 16.00 (978-0-618-23479-0(9) , Clarion Bks.) Houghton Mifflin Co. Trade & Reference Div.

STEROIDS

Aretha, David. Steroids & Other Performance-Enhancing Drugs: A MyReportLinks. com Book. 2005. (Drugs Ser.). (Illus.). 48p. (J). lib. bdg. 25.26 (978-0-7660-5277-2(X) , MyReportLinks.com Bks.) Enslow Pubs., Inc.

Connolly, Sean. Steroids. 2000. (Just the Facts Ser.). (Illus.). 56p. (YA). (gr. 6-8). lib. bdg. 24.22 (978-1-57572-259-7(3)) Heinemann Library.

Fitzhugh, Karla. Steroids. 2005. (What's the Deal? Ser.). (Illus.). 54p. (J). (978-1-4034-7025-6(1)) Heinemann Library.

—Steroids. 2003. (Health Issues Ser.). (Illus.). 64p. (J). lib. bdg. 28.56 (978-0-7398-6426-5(2)) Raintree.

Jaffe, Steven L., ed. Steroids. 1999. (Junior Drug Awareness Ser.). (Illus.). 80p. (J). (gr. 4-8). 27.50 (978-0-7910-5179-5(X) , Chelsea Hse.) Facts On File, Inc.

Kutz-Mellem, Sharon. Honest Talk about Eating Disorders. 2000. 28p. (YA). (978-1-57895-096-6(1)) Bridge Resources.

Lukas, Scott E. Steroids. 2001. (Drug Library). (Illus.). 128p. (YA). (gr. 6-12). pap. 13.26 (978-0-7660-1930-0(6)) Enslow Pubs., Inc.

Mintzer, Richard. Steroids=Busted! 2006. (Busted! Ser.). (Illus.). 112p. (J). lib. bdg. 31.93 (978-0-7660-2471-7(7)) Enslow Pubs., Inc.

Monroe, Judy. Steroid Drug Dangers. (Drug Dangers Ser.). (Illus.). 64p. (YA). (gr. 4-10). 2000. pap. 13.26 (978-0-7660-1742-9(7)); 1999. lib. bdg. 27.93 (978-0-7660-1154-0(2)) Enslow Pubs., Inc.

—Steroids, Sports, & Body Image: The Risks of Performance-Enhancing Drugs. 2004. (Issues in Focus Ser.). (Illus.). 128p. (J). lib. bdg. 26.60 (978-0-7660-2160-0(2)) Enslow Pubs., Inc.

Walker, Ida. Steroids: Pumped up & Dangerous. 2008. (J). ***978-1-4222-0164-0(3))** Mason Crest Pubs.

STEUBEN, FRIEDRICH WILHELM LUDOLF GERHARD, BARON VON, 1730-1794

Adelson, Bruce. Baron Von Steuben. 2001. (Revolutionary War Leaders Ser.). (Illus.). 80p. (J). pap. 27.50 (978-0-7910-6393-4(3)); 27.50 (978-0-7910-6392-7(5)) Facts On File, Inc. (Chelsea Hse.).

STEVENSON, ROBERT LOUIS, 1850-1894

Hamilton, John. Man-Made Horrors. 2007. (ENG., Illus.). 32p. (YA). lib. bdg. 24.21 ***978-1-59928-769-0(2)** , ABDO & Daughters) ABDO Publishing Co.

Murphy, Jim. Across America on an Emigrant Train. 2003. (Illus.). 168p. (J). (gr. 4-6). pap. 10.95 (978-0-395-76483-1(1) , Clarion Bks.) Houghton Mifflin Co. Trade & Reference Div.

—Across America on an Emigrant Train. unabr. ed. 1998. (YA). (gr. 7 up). Class Set. 198.80 incl. audio (978-0-7887-2559-3(9) , 46729); Homework Set. 44.95 incl. audio (978-0-7887-2272-1(7) , 40739) Recorded Bks., LLC.

STILTON, GERONIMO (FICTITIOUS CHARACTER)—FICTION

Geronimo Stilton 12: 12-Copy Solid Prepack. 2004. (J). (978-0-439-64102-9(0) , Scholastic Paperbacks) Scholastic, Inc.

Geronimo Stilton 12: 12-copy Solid Self Shipper. 2004. (J). (978-0-439-64101-2(2) , Scholastic Paperbacks) Scholastic, Inc.

Stilton, Geronimo. All Because of a Cup of Coffee. 2004. (Geronimo Stilton Ser.: No. 10). (Illus.). 128p. (J). mass mkt. 6.99 (978-0-439-55972-0(3) , Scholastic Paperbacks) Scholastic, Inc.

—Attack of the Bandit Cats. 2004. (Geronimo Stilton Ser.: No. 8). (Illus.). 128p. (J). pap. 5.99 (978-0-439-55970-6(7) , Scholastic Paperbacks) Scholastic, Inc.

—Cat & Mouse in a Haunted House. Wolf, Matt & Keys, Larry, illus. 2004. (Geronimo Stilton Ser.: No. 3). 128p. (J). pap. 6.99 (978-0-439-55965-2(0) , Scholastic Paperbacks) Scholastic, Inc.

—Cat & Mouse in a Haunted House. 2004. (Geronimo Stilton Ser.: No. 3). (gr. 3-6). lib. bdg. 14.15 (978-0-613-72224-7(8)) Tandem Library Bks.

—A Christmas Tale. ed. 2005. (Geronimo Stilton Ser.). (Illus.). 64p. (J). (gr. 2-5). pap. 6.99 (978-0-439-79131-1(6) , Scholastic Paperbacks) Scholastic, Inc.

—The Curse of the Cheese Pyramid. Wolf, Matt, illus. 2004. (Geronimo Stilton Ser.: No. 2). 113p. (J). lib. bdg. 10.00 ***978-1-4242-0696-4(0))** Fitzgerald Bks.

—The Curse of the Cheese Pyramid. Wolf, Matt & Keys, Larry, illus. 2004. (Geronimo Stilton Ser.: No. 2). 128p. (J). pap. 5.99 (978-0-439-55964-5(2)) Scholastic, Inc.

—The Curse of the Cheese Pyramid. 2004. (Geronimo Stilton Ser.: No. 2). (gr. 3-6). lib. bdg. 14.15 (978-0-613-72223-0(X)) Tandem Library Bks.

—A Fabumouse Vacation for Geronimo. Keys, Larry, illus. 2004. (Geronimo Stilton Ser.: No. 9). 128p. (J). pap. 6.99 (978-0-439-55971-3(5) , Scholastic Paperbacks) Scholastic, Inc.

—A Fabumouse Vacation for Geronimo. 2004. (Geronimo Stilton Ser.: No. 9). (Illus.). 113p. (J). (gr. 2-5). lib. bdg. 13.94 (978-0-606-33272-9(3)) Tandem Library Bks.

—Field Trip to Niagara Falls. Keys, Larry et al, illus. 2005. (Geronimo Stilton Ser.: No. 24). 121p. (J). lib. bdg. 18.46 ***978-1-4242-0293-5(0))** Fitzgerald Bks.

—Field Trip to Niagara Falls. 2006. (Geronimo Stilton Ser.: No. 24). 128p. (J). pap. 6.99 (978-0-439-69146-8(X) , Scholastic Paperbacks) Scholastic, Inc.

—Four Mice Deep in the Jungle. Wolf, Matt & Keys, Larry, illus. 2004. (Geronimo Stilton Ser.: No. 5). 128p. (J). pap. 6.99 (978-0-439-55967-6(7) , Scholastic Paperbacks) Scholastic, Inc.

—Geronimo Stilton 12-Copy Prepack. 2004. (J). 71.88 (978-0-439-70121-1(X) , Scholastic Paperbacks) Scholastic, Inc.

—I'm Too Fond of My Fur! Wolf, Matt & Keys, Larry, illus. 2004. (Geronimo Stilton Ser.: No. 4). 128p. (J). pap. 6.99 (978-0-439-55966-9(9) , Scholastic Paperbacks) Scholastic, Inc.

—I'm Too Fond of My Fur! 2004. (Geronimo Stilton Ser.: No. 4). (gr. 3-6). lib. bdg. 14.15 (978-0-613-72225-4(6)) Tandem Library Bks.

—It's Halloween, You 'Fraidy Mouse! 2004. (Geronimo Stilton Ser.: No. 11). (Illus.). 128p. (J). (gr. 2-3). pap. 5.99 (978-0-439-55973-7(1) , Scholastic Paperbacks) Scholastic, Inc.

—Lost Treasure of the Emerald Eye. 2007. (Geronimo Stilton Ser.: No. 1). 128p. (J). pap. 2.99 ***978-0-545-01032-0(2)** , Scholastic Paperbacks) Scholastic, Inc.

—Lost Treasure of the Emerald Eye. Wolf, Matt & Keys, Larry, illus. 2004. (Geronimo Stilton Ser.: No. 1). 128p. (J). (gr. 2-5). pap. 6.99 (978-0-439-55963-8(4) , Scholastic Paperbacks) Scholastic, Inc.

—Merry Christmas, Geronimo! 2004. (Geronimo Stilton Ser.: No. 12). (Illus.). 128p. (J). (gr. 2-5). pap. 6.99 (978-0-439-55974-4(X) , Scholastic Paperbacks) Scholastic, Inc.

—The Mona Mousa Code. Wolf, Matt, illus. 2005. (Geronimo Stilton Ser.: No. 15). 113p. (J). lib. bdg. 10.00 ***978-1-4242-0284-3(1))** Fitzgerald Bks.

—The Mona Mousa Code. Wolf, Matt, illus. 2005. (Geronimo Stilton Ser.: No. 15). 113p. (J). (ps-k). lib. bdg. 13.54 (978-0-606-33278-1(2)) Tandem Library Bks.

—The Mummy with No Name. 2006. (Geronimo Stilton Ser.: No. 26). 128p. (J). pap. 6.99 (978-0-439-84117-7(8) , Scholastic Paperbacks) Scholastic, Inc.

—My Name Is Stilton, Geronimo Stilton. 2005. (Geronimo Stilton Ser.: No. 19). (Illus.). 128p. (J). pap. 5.99 (978-0-439-69142-0(7) , Scholastic Paperbacks) Scholastic, Inc.

—Paws off, Cheddarface! Wolf, Matt & Keys, Larry, illus. 2004. (Geronimo Stilton Ser.: No. 6). 128p. (J). mass mkt. 6.99 (978-0-439-55968-3(5)) Scholastic, Inc.

—The Phantom of the Subway. 2004. (Geronimo Stilton Ser.: No. 13). (Illus.). 128p. (J). (gr. 2-5). pap. 5.99 (978-0-439-66162-1(5) , Scholastic Paperbacks) Scholastic, Inc.

—Red Pizzas for a Blue Count. Wolf, Matt & Keys, Larry, illus. 2004. (Geronimo Stilton Ser.: No. 7). 128p. (J). pap. 6.99 (978-0-439-55969-0(3)) Scholastic, Inc.

—The Search for Sunken Treasure. Wolf, Matt, illus. 2006. (Geronimo Stilton Ser.: No. 25). 111p. (J). lib. bdg. 10.00 ***978-1-4242-1519-5(6))** Fitzgerald Bks.

—The Temple of the Ruby of Fire. 2004. (Geronimo Stilton Ser.: No. 14). (Illus.). 128p. (J). (gr. 2-5). pap. 6.99 (978-0-439-66163-8(3) , Scholastic Paperbacks) Scholastic, Inc.

—Valentine's Day Disaster. 2006. (Geronimo Stilton Ser.: No. 23). (Illus.). 91p. (J). (978-1-4156-4780-6(1)) Scholastic, Inc.

Stilton, Geronimo, text. A Cheese-Colored Camper. 2005. (Geronimo Stilton Ser.: No. 16). (Illus.). 111p. (J). (ps-k). lib. bdg. 12.64 (978-0-606-33281-1(2)) Tandem Library Bks.

The Wild, Wild West. 2005. (Illus.). 106p. (J). (978-1-4156-0684-1(6)) Scholastic, Inc.

STOCK EXCHANGES

see also Bonds; Investments; Securities; Stocks; Wall Street (New York, N.Y.)

Caes, Charles J. The Young Zillionaire's Guide to the Stock Market. 2000. (Be a Zillionaire Ser.). (Illus.). 48p. (YA). (gr. 5-8). lib. bdg. 23.95 (978-0-8239-3265-8(6) , ZISTMA, Rosen Central) Rosen Publishing Group, Inc., The.

Crewe, Sabrina & Ingram, Scott. The Stock Market Crash of 1929. 2005. (Events That Shaped America Ser.). (Illus.). 32p. (J). lib. bdg. 24.67 (978-0-8368-3416-1(X)) Stevens, Gareth Inc.

Doak, Robin S. Black Tuesday: Prelude to the Great Depression. 2007. (J). lib. bdg. ***978-0-7565-3327-4(9))** Compass Point Bks.

Fuller, Donna Jo. The Stock Market. 2006. (How Economics Works). (Illus.). 48p. (J). (ps-7). 25.26 (978-0-8225-2635-3(2) , Lerner Pubns.) Lerner Publishing Group.

Garman. Goventure Stock Market Simulation. 7th ed. 2002. (YA). cd-rom 39.16 (978-0-618-34517-5(5) , 317431) Houghton Mifflin College Div.

Kohut, Kathy. Stock Market Simulations. 2000. (Illus.). 48p. (YA). pap., tchr. ed. 7.99 (978-1-57690-589-0(6) , TCA2589) Teacher Created Materials, Inc.

Loewen, Nancy. Ups & Downs: A Book about the Stock Market. Fitzpatrick, Brad, illus. 2004. (Money Matters Ser.). 24p. (J). 22.60 (978-1-4048-0954-3(6)) Picture Window Bks.

Zuravicky, Orli. The Stock Market: Understanding & Applying Ratios, Decimals, Fractions, & Percentages. 2005. (PowerMath Ser.). (Illus.). 32p. (J). 22.50 (978-1-4042-2929-7(9) , PowerKids Pr.); (978-1-4042-5122-9(7) , PowerKids Pr.); pap. (978-1-4042-5121-2(9)) Rosen Publishing Group, Inc., The.

STOCK MARKET

see Stock Exchanges

STOCK RAISING

see Livestock

STOCKS

see also Bonds; Investments; Securities; Stock Exchanges

Beach, Byron & Keck, Gayle. Stock Matters: An Introduction to Stock & Ownership for Kids. 2006. (Illus.). 72p. (J). pap. 6.99 (978-0-9788438-0-9(0)) OneShare Educational Pr.

Condon, Daniel. Playing the Market: Stocks & Bonds. (Everyday Economics Ser.). (Illus.). 48p. (J). 2003. (gr. 3-5). lib. bdg. (978-1-58810-495-3(8)); 2002. pap. 8.50 (978-1-58810-958-3(5)) Heinemann Library.

Cooper, Terry, ed. Stock Market: Scholastic Technology Activity Folder. 2001. (Instant Internet Activities Folder Ser.). 6p. 3.95 (978-0-439-30952-3(2)) Scholastic, Inc.

Davidson, Avelyn. The Bull & the Bear. 2007. (Shockwave: Economics & Geography Ser.). (Illus.). 36p. (J). (gr. 4-6). lib. bdg. 25.00 ***978-0-531-17797-6(1)** , Children's Pr.) Scholastic Library Publishing.

Fuller, Donna Jo. The Stock Market. 2006. (How Economics Works). (Illus.). 48p. (J). (ps-7). 25.26 (978-0-8225-2635-3(2) , Lerner Pubns.) Lerner Publishing Group.

Giesecke, Ernestine. Playing the Market: Stocks & Bonds. 2003. (gr. 3-6). lib. bdg. 16.40 (978-0-613-45812-2(5)) Tandem Library Bks.

S

Loewen, Nancy. Ups & Downs: A Book about the Stock Market. Fitzpatrick, Brad, illus. 2004. (Money Matters Ser.). 24p. (J). 22.60 (978-1-4048-0954-3(6)) Picture Window Bks.

McGowan, Eileen Nixon & Dumas, Nancy Lagow. Stock Market Smart. 2002. (Sports Palaces Ser.). (Illus.). 64p. (gr. 5-8). lib. bdg. 23.90 (978-0-7613-2113-2(6), Millbrook Pr.) Lerner Publishing Group.

Minden, Cecilia. Investing: Making Your Money Work for You. 2008. (J). lib. bdg. 25.26 ***(978-1-60279-003-2(5))*** Cherry Lake Publishing.

Stock Market Crash. 2002. (History in the Headlines Ser.). 32p. (gr. 6-8). 6.99 (978-0-7682-0471-1(2), GA131696) School Specialty Publishing.

STOCKYARDS

see Meat Industry and Trade

STONE

see also Rocks

Auster, Michael A. Stone Is Strong. 2005. (Illus.). 16p. (978-0-7368-5264-7(6)); (978-0-7368-5300-2(6)) Capstone Pr., Inc.

Oxlade, Chris. Rock. 2002. (Materials, Materials, Materials Ser.). (Illus.). 32p. (J). (gr. k-2). lib. bdg. 22.79 (978-1-58810-585-1(7)); pap. 6.95 (978-1-4034-0086-4(5), 91527) Heinemann Library.

—Rock. 2002. (gr. k-3). lib. bdg. 14.75 (978-0-613-45820-7(6)) Tandem Library Bks.

Royston, Angela. Rock: Let's Look at a Pebble. 2005. (J). (978-1-4109-1826-0(2)); pap. (978-1-4109-1833-8(5)) Steck-Vaughn.

—Vidrio: Miremos unas Canicas. 2005. (Heinemann Lee y Aprende Ser.). (ENG & SPA., Illus.). 24p. (978-1-4034-7542-8(3)) Heinemann Library.

Storey, Rita. Rocks & Stones. 2007. (J). ***(978-1-59920-006-4(6))*** Smart Apple Media.

STONE AGE

see also Prehistoric Peoples

Harcourt School Publishers Staff. Stone Age Farmers Level D: Library Edition. 2001. (Collections Ser.). (Illus.). (J). 5.90 (978-0-15-314442-4(4)) Harcourt Schl. Pubs.

Haslam, Andrew. Stone Age People. 2004. (Make It Work! History Ser.). (Illus.). 64p. (gr. 3-6). (J). pap. 7.95 (978-1-58728-302-4(6)); 14.95 (978-1-58728-306-2(9)) T&N Children's Publishing. (Two Can Publishing).

Hurdman, Charlotte. Step into: The Stone Age. 2007. (Illus.). 64p. pap. 10.99 ***(978-1-84476-421-1(4)***, Southwater) Anness Publishing GBR. *Dist:* National Bk. Network.

MacDonald, Fiona. The Stone Age News. 2001. (History News Ser.). (Illus.). 32p. (J). (gr. 3 up). lib. bdg. 24.67 (978-0-8368-2778-1(3)) Stevens, Gareth Inc.

Spizzirri, Linda, ed. Prehistoric Birds. Spizzirri, Peter M., illus. 32p. (J). (gr. 1-8). pap. 4.98 incl. audio (978-0-86545-023-3(4)) Spizzirri Pr., Inc.

—Prehistoric Sea Life. Kohn, Arnie, illus. 32p. (J). (gr. 1-8). pap. 4.98 incl. audio (978-0-86545-020-2(X)) Spizzirri Pr., Inc.

Steele, Philip. The Stone Age. 1998. (Step into Ser.). (Illus.). 64p. (gr. 4-7). 12.95 (978-1-85967-684-4(7)) Anness Publishing GBR. *Dist:* National Bk. Network.

STONE AGE—FICTION

Dagg, Stephanie. Flint Dog. 1999. (Illus.). 96p. (J). (gr. 4-8). per. (978-1-902586-51-9(4)) Mentor Bks.

Harcourt School Publishers Staff. An Interview with Otzi Advanced Level. 3rd ed. 2002. (Trophies Reading Program Ser.). (Illus.). pap. 5.10 (978-0-15-323471-2(7)) Harcourt Schl. Pubs.

Hardy, Linda. Come into My Cave: A Prehistoric Novel. 1998. 104p. (J). (gr. 4-9). pap. 12.95 (978-0-9656945-2-0(6)) LHA Bks.

McDonnell, Vincent. Children of Stone. 2006. 206p. (J). pap. 9.95 (978-1-903464-88-5(9)) Collins Pr., The IRL. *Dist:* Dufour Editions, Inc.

Scieszka, Jon. Your Mother Was a Neanderthal, Vol. 4. Smith, Lane, illus. 2004. (Time Warp Trio Ser.: No. 4). 80p. (J). (gr. 2-6). pap. 4.99 (978-0-14-240048-7(3), Puffin) Penguin Group (USA) Inc.

STONEHENGE (ENGLAND)

Dunn, Mary. My Adventure at Stonehenge. 2006. 44p. (J). 8.99 (978-1-59092-412-9(6), Orchard Academy Pr.) Windstorm Creative.

Lace, William W. Stonehenge. 2003. (Mystery Library). (Illus.). 104p. (J). 29.95 (978-1-59018-131-7(X), Lucent Bks.) Thomson Gale.

Mass, Wendy. Stonehenge. 1998. (Building History Ser.). (Illus.). 96p. (YA). (gr. 6-9). 27.45 (978-1-56006-432-9(3), Lucent Bks.) Thomson Gale.

McMorrow, Catherine. Stonehenge. 1999. (J). (978-0-679-87499-7(2), Random Hse. Bks. for Young Readers) Random Hse. Children's Bks.

Petrini, Catherine M. Stonehenge. 2005. (Wonders of the World Ser.). (Illus.). 48p. (J). (gr. 4-8). lib. bdg. 26.20 (978-0-7377-3073-9(0), Greenhaven Pr., Inc.) Thomson Gale.

Richards, Julian. Amazing Pop-Up Stonehenge. 2005. (Illus.). 16p. (J). ***(978-1-85074-926-4(4))*** English Heritage.

Shofner, Shawndra. Stonehenge. 2005. (Ancient Wonders of the World Ser.). (Illus.). 32p. (gr. 4-7). 18.95 (978-1-58341-360-9(X), Creative Education) Creative Co., The.

STONES, PRECIOUS

see Precious Stones

STONEWARE

see Pottery

STORIES

see also Anecdotes; Animals—Fiction; Ballet—Fiction; Bible Stories; Birds—Fiction; Christmas—Fiction; Fairy Tales; Horror Stories; Legends; Mystery and Detective Stories; Operas—Stories, Plots, Etc.; Sea Stories; Short Stories; Storytelling; Trees—Fiction

Alexander, Ian. Big Book: Do You See a Dozen?, Vol. 2. l.t. ed. 2005. (Sadlier Phonics Reading Program). (Illus.). 8p. (YA). (ps-1). 22.50 (978-0-8215-7347-1(0)) Sadlier, William H. Inc.

Amery, H. Cuentos Populares del Mundo. 2004. (Titles in Spanish Ser.). (SPA.). (J). 16.95 (978-0-7460-5084-2(4)) EDC Publishing.

Anderson, Jon. Bad Guys Beware! Steck, Jim, illus. 2004. (Story Cards Ser.). 6p. (J). (gr. 1-17). bds. 9.99 (978-1-58476-271-3(3)) Innovative Kids.

Angela's Bookshelf Publishing Staff. Choice Stories for Children. Date not set. (Illus.). 144p. (J). pap. 6.95 (978-1-878726-08-7(0)) A B Publishing.

Antologia Staff. Cuentos Picarescos para Ninos de America Latina. 2002. Tr. of Picaresque Tales for Latin American Children. (SPA.). 78p. (YA). pap. (978-980-257-137-6(7), Ek8604) Ekare, Ediciones.

Arnott, Kathleen. Tales from Africa. 2000. (Oxford Myths & Legends Ser.). (Illus.). 224p. (YA). 11.95 (978-0-19-275079-2(8)) Oxford Univ. Pr., Inc.

Asher, Sandy. But That's Another Story: Favorite Authors Introduce Popular Genres. 1999. (J). (978-0-606-16876-2(1)) Tandem Library Bks.

Bailey, Etta Lorene. Etta's Collection of Children's Stories. 2000. 48p. (J). (gr. k-6). pap. 8.00 (978-0-8059-4677-2(2)) Dorrance Publishing Co., Inc.

Bair, Linda & Andrews, Jill. Fiddle-Dee-Dee: Songs, Stories & Activities. 2000. (Illus.). 120p. (J). (ps-2). pap. 16.95 (978-1-57950-037-5(4), Upstart Bks.) Highsmith Inc.

Baldner, Jean V. Pebbles in the Wind. Webster, Carroll, illus. 52p. (Orig.). (YA). (gr. 7 up). pap. 5.95 (978-0-9615317-0-6(3)) Baldner, Jean V.

Barber, Antonia. Hidden Tales from Eastern Europe. Guild, Shena, ed. Hess, Paul, illus. 2004. 48p. (J). pap. 9.95 (978-1-84507-147-9(6)) Lincoln, Frances Ltd. GBR. *Dist:* Perseus Distribution.

Barber, Tony. Tony Barber's Book of Stories. 2002. (Illus.). (J). (ps-6). (978-1-876973-04-9(8)) Wizard Bks.

Baum, L. Frank. Adventures of the Magical Monarch of Mo & His People. Date not set. (J). (gr. 5-6). lib. bdg. 20.95 (978-0-88411-771-1(5)) Amereon LTD.

Baxter, Nicole. 5 Minute Bedtime Stories. Press, Jenny, illus. 1999. 80p. (J). pap. 12.98 (978-1-58048-062-8(4)) Sandvik Publishing.

Beck, Jerry. Looney Tunes: The Ultimate Visual Guide. 2003. (Illus.). 143p. (J). 24.99 (978-0-7894-9758-1(1)) Dorling Kindersley Publishing, Inc.

Benchabbat, Edie C., et al. My Little Guardian Storybook. Date not set. (Illus.). 28p. (J). (ps-5). pap. 5.99 (978-0-9660879-0-1(9)) Little Guardians, Inc.

Berger, Melvin & Peck, Marshall H., III. A Whale Is Not a Fish & Other Animal Mix-Ups. (FRE., Illus.). 64p. (J). pap. 6.99 (978-0-590-16026-1(5)) Scholastic, Inc.

Big Box of Board Books: A Hedgehog; a Mallard Duckling; a Ladybug & a Chipmunk, 4 bks., Set. 2002. (Backyard Mini Bks.). (Illus.). (J). bds. (978-1-59069-070-3(2), KS2001) Studio Mouse LLC.

Big Box of Board Books: A Sea Turtle; an Orca Whale; a Dolphin & a Walrus, 4 bks., Set. 2002. (Oceanic Mini Bks.). (Illus.). (J). bds. (978-1-59069-075-8(3), KS1001) Studio Mouse LLC.

Big Box of Board Books: Early Learning. 2002. (Illus.). (J). bds. (978-1-59069-090-1(7), 14-2001) Studio Mouse LLC.

Big Box of Board Books: Grey Wolf; Snowshoe Hare; Prairie Dog & Polar Bear, 4 bks., Set. 2002. (Wild Heritage Collection Mini Bks.). (Illus.). (J). bds. (978-1-59069-254-7(3), KS3001) Studio Mouse LLC.

Birmingham, Christian, illus. Dick King-Smith's Countryside Treasury. 2001. 144p. (J). (gr. 2 up). 27.50 (978-0-00-198161-4(7)) Zondervan.

Bloom, Harold. Stories & Poems for Extremely Intelligent Children of All Ages. 2001. (Illus.). 576p. (gr. 3-8). 30.00 (978-0-684-86873-8(3), Scribner) Simon & Schuster.

—Stories & Poems for Extremely Intelligent Children of All Ages. Bloom, Harold, ed. 2002. (Illus.). 576p. reprint ed. pap. 16.00 (978-0-684-86874-5(1), Scribner) Simon & Schuster.

—Stories & Poems for Extremely Intelligent Children of All Ages. 2002. (gr. 3-6). lib. bdg. 25.75 (978-0-613-90932-7(1)) Tandem Library Bks.

Blume, Judy, ed. Places I Never Meant to Be: Original Stories by Censored Writers. 2001. 208p. (YA). (gr. 7 up). pap. 10.00 (978-0-689-84258-0(9), Simon Pulse) Simon & Schuster Children's Publishing.

Blyton, Enid. Mr Twiddle Stories. (Illus.). 224p. (J). pap. 5.95 (978-0-09-965560-2(8)) Random Hse. GBR. *Dist:* Trafalgar Square Publishing.

—Well, Really, Mr Twiddle! 2nd ed. (Illus.). 111p. (J). pap. 6.95 (978-0-7475-3852-3(2)) Bloomsbury Publishing Plc GBR. *Dist:* Trafalgar Square Publishing.

Bourgeois, Paulette. Franklin's Holiday Treasury. Clark, Brenda, illus. 2002. (Franklin Treasuries Ser.). 128p. (J). (gr. k-3). (978-1-55337-045-1(7)) Kids Can Pr., Ltd.

Brahe, Carl. PNI Healing Stories for Children, Vol. I. Hall, Victoria, ed. 1999. 84p. (J). (ps-6). pap. 11.95 (978-1-893351-05-9(X)) Asclepian Pr.

Brewster, Betty. Stories That Rhyme: Reading Fun Time. Tolan, R., illus. 1998. 20p. (J). (ps-2). pap. (978-1-57579-120-3(X)) Pine Hill Pr., Inc.

Brock, Melea J. Right-Side-Up Stories for Upside-Down-People Vols. 3-4: Listen with Your Heart. 2001. (YA). (gr. 2 up). 10.98 incl. audio (978-0-9667455-9-7(0)) Right-Side-Up Stories.

Brooks, Martha. Traveling on into the Light: And Other Stories. (J). 16.95 (978-0-88899-220-8(3)) Groundwood Bks. CAN. *Dist:* Transition Vendor.

Brovelli, Tito Alberto. La Nubecita Panza de Agua: Cuentos Bilingues. Anderson, Kirk, tr. Munoz, Rafael Sanchez, illus. 2000. Tr. of Water Belly, the Little Cloud: Bilingual Stories. (ENG & SPA.). 24p. (J). (gr. k up). 14.00 (978-0-9673032-0-8(6)) Sweet Dreams Bilingual Pubs.

Brown, Irene Bennett. Answer Me, Answer Me. 2000. 208p. (YA). (gr. 7-12). pap. 13.95 (978-0-595-14505-8(1), Backinprint.com) iUniverse, Inc.

Brown, Richard & Ruttle, Kate. Looking for Dragons ELT Edition. Lewis, Jan, illus. 2001. (Cambridge Storybooks Ser.). 8p. pap. 3.00 (978-0-521-00705-4(4)) Cambridge Univ. Pr.

Burton, Virginia Lee. Mike Mulligan & More: A Virginia Lee Burton Treasury. 2002. (Illus.). 208p. (J). (gr. k-3). tchr. ed. 20.00 (978-0-618-25627-3(X)) Houghton Mifflin Co. Trade & Reference Div.

Bybee, Faith. Stories for Brittany. 2001. (Illus.). (J). (gr. 3-7). pap. 7.95 (978-1-56167-700-9(0)) American Literary Pr.

Calderone-Stewart, Lisa-Marie & Kunzman, Ed. Better Than Natural & Other Stories. 2003. (Stories for Teens Ser.: Vol. 3). 72p. (YA). (gr. 7-12). pap. 4.95 (978-0-88489-591-6(2)) St. Mary's Pr.

—Meeting Frankenstein & Other Stories. 2003. (Stories for Teens Ser.: Vol. 5). 72p. (YA). (gr. 7-12). pap. 4.95 (978-0-88489-593-0(9)) St. Mary's Pr.

—My Wish List & Other Stories. 2003. (Stories for Teens Ser.: Vol. 2). 72p. (YA). (gr. 7-12). pap. 4.95 (978-0-88489-590-9(4)) St. Mary's Pr.

Capucilli, Alyssa Satin. Biscuit Storybook Collection. Schories, Pat, illus. 2005. (Biscuit Ser.). 192p. (J). (ps-1). 10.99 (978-0-06-075904-9(6), Harper Festival) HarperCollins Pubs.

Castroviejo, Concha & Fedorchek, Robert M., trs. from SPA. The Garden with Seven Gates. 2003. (Illus.). 112p. (J). 32.50 (978-0-8387-5559-4(3)) Bucknell Univ. Pr.

Charming Classics: Charming Favorites Library. 2001. (Charming Classics: Vol. 1). 32p. (J). (ps-2). pap., pap. 20.97 (978-0-694-01647-1(0), Harper Festival) HarperCollins Pubs.

Children's Bedtime Treasury. 2002. 384p. (J). 14.98 (978-0-7525-4516-5(7)) Parragon, Inc.

Classic Tales Carrying Case, 8 bks., Set. 2002. (Classic Tales Ser.). (Illus.). (J). incl. audio compact disk (978-1-59069-110-6(5), TD1102) Studio Mouse LLC.

Clevenger, Roy L. Limericks & 8 Childrens Stories: Lee Tales. deluxe ed. 2002. (Illus.). 21p. (J). (gr. 1-4). 10.00 (978-0-9720089-2-1(6), 3) Clevenger, Roy L.

Coleman, Catherine. The Cape Cod Collection: Stories & Poems for Children. Nowell, Justin A. & Nowell, Thomas H., illus. 1998. 55p. (J). (gr. k-8). pap. 15.00 (978-1-891331-10-7(8)) Nebbadoon Pr.

Cooling, Wendy. Puffin Book of Stories for Eight-Year-Olds. (Illus.). 160p. (J). (gr. 3). pap. 8.95 (978-0-14-038052-1(3)) Penguin Bks., Ltd. GBR. *Dist:* Trafalgar Square Publishing.

Cooper, Terry, ed. Historical Fiction: A Complete Unit That Helps Students Explore This Exciting Genre & Become Better Readers & Writers. 2001. (Illus.). 48p. (ps-3). pap. 12.95 (978-0-439-23797-0(1)) Scholastic, Inc.

Corbett, Pie. Fiction. 2006. (I-read Ser.). (Illus.). 56p. pap. 10.00 (978-0-521-61889-2(4)) Cambridge Univ. Pr.

Craats, Rennay. E. B. White. 2002. (My Favorite Writer Ser.). (Illus.). 32p. (J). lib. bdg. 16.95 (978-1-59036-026-2(5)) Weigl Pubs., Inc.

Cross, Gillian. Rent a Genius. (Illus.). 96p. (J). 13.95 (978-0-241-13061-2(1), Hamilton, Hamish) Penguin Bks., Ltd. GBR. *Dist:* Trafalgar Square Publishing.

Cutler, Jane. Rats! Pearson, Tracey Campbell, illus. 1998. 128p. (J). (ps-k). pap. 5.95 (978-0-374-46203-1(8), Sunburst) Farrar, Straus & Giroux.

Dale, Jenny. Boomerang Bob. Reid, Mick, illus. 2003. 105p. (J). (978-0-439-45348-6(8)) Scholastic, Inc.

—Dognapped! Reid, Mick, illus. 2003. 102p. (J). (978-0-439-45350-9(X)) Scholastic, Inc.

—Homeward Bound. Reid, Mick, illus. 2003. 110p. (J). (978-0-439-45354-7(2)) Scholastic, Inc.

Dalmatian Press Staff. Sesame Street's Carry along Stories. rev. ed. 144p. pap. 9.99 (978-1-4037-2066-5(5)) Dalmatian Pr.

Davis, Julia A. Classic Stories for Today's Students. 2002. (Illus.). 183p. (gr. 4-12). 9.95 (978-0-9631110-0-5(0)) Epps-Alford Publishing.

Deary, Terry. True Detective Stories. l.t. ed. 2005. (Illus.). 192p. (J). pap. (978-0-7540-6126-7(4), CLP 320) BBC Audio.

—True Detective Stories. unabr. l.t. ed. 2003. (Read-Along Ser.). 176p. (J). 29.95 incl. audio (978-0-7540-6240-0(6), RAO41, Galaxy Children's Large Print) BBC Audiobooks America.

—True Mystery Stories. l.t. ed. 2005. (Illus.). 240p. (J). pap. (978-0-7540-7810-4(8), CLP 420) BBC Audio.

DiGiacomo, Anthony W. Rachel's Stories for Tough Kids. DiGiacomo, Anthony W., illus. 1998. (Illus.). 30p. (J). (gr. 1-4). pap. 7.95 (978-1-58265-001-2(2)) Orphan Pr.

Disney Staff. La Belle et la Bete.Tr. of Beauty & the Beast. (FRE., Illus.). 96p. (J). (ps-4). 11.95 (978-2-89393-145-6(6)) Phidal Publishing, Inc./Editions Phidal, Inc. CAN. *Dist:* AIMS International Bks., Inc.

Dover Staff. Favorite Children's Stories, 5 vols., Set. 1998. (Dover Children's Thrift Classics Ser.). 480p. (J). pap. 5.00 (978-0-486-28182-7(5)) Dover Pubns., Inc.

—7 Childrens' Sticker Storybooks. 1998. (Illus.). 112p. (J). 7.00 (978-0-486-29983-9(X)) Dover Pubns., Inc.

Doyle, Alfreda C. Story Course - Mask: Stories, Poetry & Color Therapy. 1998. (Illus.). 40p. (J). pap., wbk. ed. 29.95 (978-1-56820-377-5(2)) Story Time Stories That Rhyme.

Doyon, Mark W. Bonneville Stories. Hetrick, J. Thomas, ed. Doyon, Robin, illus. 2001. 144p. (C). pap. 12.95 (978-1-929763-09-2(3), 7) Pocol Pr.

Dragon Tales Music Maker. 2002. (Illus.). (J). 15.98 (978-0-7853-6404-7(8)) Publications International, Ltd.

Duffey, William, Jr. Riddles & Short Stories & Mini Plays. 2002. 32p. pap. 8.00 (978-0-8059-5927-7(0)) Dorrance Publishing Co., Inc.

Edwards, Dorothy. More Naughty Little Sister Stories. Hughes, Shirley, illus. 2002. (My Naughty Little Sister Ser.). 128p. (J). pap. 7.50 (978-1-4052-0290-9(4)) Egmont Bks., Ltd. GBR. *Dist:* Independent Pubs. Group.

Elkins, Stephen. Special Times Bible Rhymes for Toddlers. 2005. (Special Times Ser.). (Illus.). 32p. (J). (ps up). 9.97 (978-0-8054-2659-5(0)) B&H Publishing Grp.

—Special Times Bible Stories for Toddlers. 2005. (Special Times Ser.). (Illus.). 32p. (J). (ps up). 9.97 (978-0-8054-2681-6(7)) B&H Publishing Grp.

—Stories That End with a Prayer. Menck, Kevin, illus. 32p. (J). (gr. k-8). 12.98 (978-1-56919-003-6(8)) Wonder Workshop.

Fajardo, Renee & Ruby, Carl. Pinch a Lotta Enchiladas & Other Tummy Tales. Fajardo, Renee & Ruby, Carl, eds. 2002. (Illus.). 104p. (YA). (gr. 4-8). pap. 14.00 (978-0-9724472-0-1(2)) Just Enjoyable Memorable Story Bks.

Family Storytime Collection, 5 vols., Vol. 1. 2000. (Family Storytime Ser.: Bk. 1). (Illus.). (J). (ps-3). 49.99 (978-0-307-19558-6(9), Golden Bks.) Random Hse. Children's Bks.

Federici, Elaine. The Rose Tales for Children: Inspirational Collection of Stories for Childen. 2000. (J). pap. 10.95 (978-1-930574-03-8(7)) Rose International Publishing Hse., Inc.

Ferber, Jeannie, et al, compiled by. Six Inches to England: An Anthology of International Children's Stories. 2001. (Illus.). 192p. (J). (gr. 3-7). pap. 21.00 (978-1-885934-07-9(6)) Andover Green Bk. Pubs.

First Animal Stories. 2000. (J). bds. 19.95 (978-0-7525-6555-2(9)) Parragon, Inc.

First Teddy Bear Stories. 2001. (J). bds. 19.95 (978-0-7525-6556-9(7)) Parragon, Inc.

Fitzgerald, F. Scott. Bernice Bobs Her Hair & Other Stories. Date not set. (Nelson Readers Ser.). (Illus.). 86p. (J). pap. (978-0-17-557051-5(5)) Addison-Wesley Longman, Inc.

Foster, Elizabeth Vincent. Lyrico: The Only Horse of His Kind. Buba, Joy, illus. 2nd ed. 2004. 230p. (gr. 6-8). reprint ed. 8.95 (978-0-930407-21-6(0)) Parabola Bks.

Franco, Eloise. Little Stories. Bredius, Rein, illus. 2003. 66p. (gr. k-5). 5.95 (978-0-87516-384-0(X), Devorss Pubns.) DeVorss & Co.

French, Vivian. The Kingfisher Book of Nursery Tales. Lambert, Stephen, illus. 2003. (Kingfisher Book of Ser.). 96p. (J). (ps-k). tchr. ed. 15.00 (978-0-7534-5482-4(3), Kingfisher) Houghton Mifflin Co. Trade & Reference Div.

Gaines, Ann Graham. Christopher Paul Curtis. 2001. (Real-Life Reader Biography Ser.). (Illus.). 32p. (J). (gr. 3-8). lib. bdg. 15.95 (978-1-58415-076-3(9)) Mitchell Lane Pubs., Inc.

Garay, Luis, illus. La Piedra y el Metal: Cuentos, Mitos y Leyendas de America Latina. 2000. (SPA.). 64p. (YA). (gr. 3-5). pap. 14.95 (978-980-257-228-1(4), EK3109) Ekare, Ediciones VEN. *Dist:* Lectorum Pubns., Inc.

Gavin, Fred. Bedtime Stories. Klemek, Ryan, illus. Date not set. 64p. (J). (gr. k-3). pap. (978-0-935668-00-1(4)) Gavin, Fred Enterprises.

Gliori, Debi. Bedtime Stories. 2005. (Illus.). 80p. (J). 19.99 (978-0-7566-1466-9(X)) Dorling Kindersley Publishing, Inc.

Glyman, Caroline A. Forest House Firsts: Supplemental Selected Early Childhood Stories, 2 bks. Biser, Dee, illus. (J). (gr. k-3). lib. bdg. 29.90 (978-1-56674-910-7(7)) Forest Hse. Publishing Co., Inc.

Golden Books Staff. Farm Tales. 2005. (Little Golden Book Ser.). (Illus.). 320p. (J). 14.95 (978-0-375-83190-4(8), Golden Bks.) Random Hse. Children's Bks.

—Little Golden Book Boxed Set Classic Collection, Set. 2002. (Illus.). 24p. (J). (ps-3). 17.94 (978-0-307-34080-1(5), Golden Bks.) Random Hse. Children's Bks.

—Little Golden Book Collection: Animal Tales. 2004. (Illus.). 320p. (J). (gr. k-k). 14.95 (978-0-375-83128-7(2), Golden Bks.) Random Hse. Children's Bks.

Gonzales Bertrand, Diane. Upside down & Backwards. Hernandez, Karina, tr. Tr. of De Cabeza y al Revés. (ENG & SPA., Illus.). 64p. (gr. 2-5). pap. 9.95 (978-1-55885-408-6(8), Piñata Books) Arte Publico Pr.

Grandma's Magical Storybook. 2003. (Illus.). 256p. (J). 12.98 (978-1-4054-0968-1(1)) Parragon, Inc.

Griffin, Leon. A Beautiful Day, Vol. 8. 1999. (Illus.). 50p. (J). (978-1-884083-40-2(4)) Maval Publishing, Inc.

Grimm, Jacob W. Treasury of Classic Children's Stories. 2002. 29.95 (978-0-7407-2572-2(6)) Andrews McMeel Publishing.

Grosset and Dunlap Staff, ed. Storybook Treasury of Dick & Jane & Friends. 2003. (Dick & Jane Ser.). (Illus.). 200p. (J). (ps-3). 10.99 (978-0-448-43340-0(0), Grosset & Dunlap) Penguin Group (USA) Inc.

Guild, Shena. Hidden Tales from Eastern Europe. Hess, Paul, illus. 2004. 48p. (J). (978-0-7112-1949-6(4)) Lincoln, Frances Ltd. GBR. *Dist:* Transition Vendor.

Hamilton, Martha & Weiss, Mitch. How & Why Stories: World Tales Kids Can Read & Tell. Lyon, Carol, illus. 1999. (World Storytelling from August House Ser.). 96p. (gr. 1-7). 24.95 (978-0-87483-562-5(3)); pap. 14.95 (978-0-87483-561-8(5)) August Hse. Pubs., Inc.

HarperCollins Staff. Charming Classics Box Set No. 3: Charming Horse Library. 2003. (Charming Classics). (J). (gr. 3-7). pap. 19.99 (978-0-06-056141-3(6)) HarperCollins Pubs.

Hayes, Joe. Here Comes the Storyteller. Barron, Richard, photos by. 2004. (Illus.). 80p. (gr. 4-7). pap. 12.95 (978-0-938317-25-8(3)) Cinco Puntos Pr.

Henderson, Kathy, ed. The Bedtime Book. Ives, Penny, illus. 2004. 72p. (J). pap. 10.95 (978-1-84507-139-4(5)) Lincoln, Frances Ltd. GBR. *Dist:* Perseus Distribution.

Hernandez, Mary L. Everything Is All Right Now. 1999. (Daddy's Collection: Bk. 5). (Illus.). 50p. (J). 7.50 (978-1-884083-43-3(9)) Maval Publishing, Inc.

—Sarah's Oak Tree Swing. 1999. (Daddy's Collection: Bk. 7). (Illus.). 50p. (J). per. 7.50 (978-1-884083-41-9(2)) Maval Publishing, Inc.

Hernandez, Mary L., ed. El Columpio de Sara, Vol. 6. 1999. (SPA., Illus.). 50p. (J). (978-1-884083-42-6(0)) Maval Publishing, Inc.

—Todo Esta Bien Ahora, Vol. 4. 1999. (Illus.). 50p. (J). (978-1-884083-44-0(7)) Maval Publishing, Inc.

Herrera, Mario, et al. English for Me. 1999. Vol. 1. (Illus.). 16p. (C). pap. 8.00 (978-0-201-35143-9(9)) Longman Publishing Group.

—English for Me Storybook 5: Mixed up Monday. 1999. Vol. 5. (Illus.). 16p. (C). pap. 7.66 (978-0-201-35147-7(1)) Longman Publishing Group.

Hetzer, Michael. Footprints on the Ceiling: Your Child's Footprint Completes the Story. Clayton, Kim, illus. 2nd ed. 2005. 32p. (J). 18.95 (978-0-9728222-2-0(4)) Webster Henrietta Publishing.

—Footprints on the Ceiling (Collector's Edition) Your Child's Footprint Completes the Story. Clayton, Kim, illus. 2004. 32p. (J). 18.95 (978-0-9728222-1-3(6)) Webster Henrietta Publishing.

Hillman, Manny. A Nest of Birdlets, Vol. 3. 1999. (Illus.). 50p. (J). 7.50 (978-1-884083-45-7(5)) Maval Publishing, Inc.

Homer, Larona. The Shore Ghosts & Other Stories of New Jersey. Bock, William Sauts, illus. 2005. 154p. (J). (gr. 4-8). pap. (978-0-912608-82-2(X)) Middle Atlantic Pr.

Hughes, Shirley. The Big Alfie Out of Doors Storybook. 2007. (Illus.). 64p. (J). pap. 12.95 (***978-0-09-925891-9(9)***, Red Fox) Random Hse. Children's Bks. GBR. *Dist:* Independent Pubs. Group.

Idaho Writers League Coeur d'Alene Chapter. Kaleidoscope: A Collection of Tantalizing Tales. 2003. (Illus.). (YA). (gr. 6 up). pap. 15.00 (978-0-9740481-0-9(0)) Children's Village Foundation, Inc.

The Illustrated Treasury. 2003. (Illus.). lib. bdg. 42.80 (978-1-56846-179-3(8)) Creative Co., The.

Iparraguirre, Sylvia, et al. Terminemos el Cuento. 2003. (SPA., Illus.). 128p. (YA). (gr. 9-12). 9.95 (978-84-204-4965-4(2)) Alfaguara, Ediciones, S.A.- Grupo Santillana ESP. *Dist:* Santillana USA Publishing Co., Inc.

Jarman, Julia. The Jessame Stories. 2006. (Illus.). 162p. (J). pap. 8.99 (***978-1-84270-454-7(0)***) Andersen GBR. *Dist:* Independent Pubs. Group.

Jarvis, Martin & Crompton, Richmal. William's Haunted House & Other Stories, Vol. 5. Ross, Tony, illus. 2003. (Meet Just William Ser.). 76p. (J). pap. 8.99 (978-0-330-39101-6(1), Pan) Pan Macmillan GBR. *Dist:* Trafalgar Square Publishing.

—William's Wonderful Plan & Other Stories, No. 3. Ross, Tony, illus. 2003. 78p. (J). pap. 8.99 (978-0-330-39102-3(X), Pan) Pan Macmillan GBR. *Dist:* Trafalgar Square Publishing.

Joyce, William. Rolie Polie Olie. 2003. 32p. (J). pap. 3.50 (978-0-7868-4536-1(8)) Disney Pr.

Jungle Book. 2003. (Illus.). (J). 12.99 (978-0-7868-3477-8(3)) Disney Pr.

Jungle Book. 2000. (Illus.). 80p. (YA). per. 6.95 (978-1-56254-291-7(5), SP2915) Saddleback Educational Publishing.

Kinney, Robert & Kinney, Donald. Stories for Young Readers. 2000. (Illus.). 100p. (YA). Vol. 1. (gr. 3-10). per. (978-0-9702889-0-5(5)); Vol. 2. (gr. 9 up). per. (978-0-9702889-1-2(3)) Kinney Brothers Publishing.

Lanners, Karen & Schwartzenberger, Ken. Therapeutic Stories for Children in Foster Care. Lanners, Karen, illus. 2nd rev. ed. 1998. (Illus.). x, 60p. (Orig.). (J). (ps-6). pap. 15.95 (978-0-9652163-1-9(4)) Therapeutic Stories.

Lansky, Bruce. Girls to the Rescue: Folk Tales from Around the World. 1999. (Illus.). (J). 78.00 (978-0-684-81211-3(8)) Meadowbrook Pr.

Lansky, Bruce, ed. Girls to the Rescue, Bk. 1. 1998. (J). 3.95 (978-0-88166-314-3(X)) Meadowbrook Pr.

Lansky, Bruce & Johnson, Martha. Girls to the Rescue, Bk. 5. 108p. (J). pap. (978-0-88166-315-0(8)) Meadowbrook Pr.

Larsen, Carolyn. Little Girl's Bible Storybook for Fathers & Daughters. Turk, Caron, illus. 2000. 360p. (J). (gr. 1-4). 16.99 (978-0-8010-4469-4(3), New Kids Media) Baker Bks.

Las Moras: Individual Title Six-Packs. (Coleccion Pm Ser.).Tr. of Blackberries. (SPA.). 16p. (gr. 1 up). 26.00 (978-0-7578-2983-3(X)) Rigby Education.

Laybourn, Emma. Megamouse. 2001. 92p. (J). pap. 8.99 (978-1-84270-013-6(8)) Andersen GBR. *Dist:* Independent Pubs. Group.

LeapFrog Schoolhouse Staff. Read-It-All Books: 2nd Grade & Up. 2003. tchr. ed. 19.95 (978-1-59319-016-3(6), LeapFrog Schl. Hse.) LeapFrog Enterprises, Inc.

Leeson, Robert. All the Gold in the World. Leplar, Anna, illus. 2004. 96p. 8.95 (978-0-7136-4059-5(6)) A & C Black GBR. *Dist:* Consortium Bk. Sales & Distribution.

Legends, Myths, & Folktales. (Britannica Learning Library). (J). (gr. 2-5). 14.95 (978-1-59339-006-8(8), 049907-EN-REF) Encyclopaedia Britannica, Inc.

Lilly, Melinda & Reasoner, Charles. Aletin & the Falling Sky: A Mocovi Myth. 1999. (Latin American Tales & Myths Ser.). (Illus.). 32p. (J). (gr. 2-5). lib. bdg. 26.60 (978-1-57103-262-1(2)) Rourke Publishing, LLC.

—Mira & the Stone Tortoise: A Kulina Tale. 1999. (Illus.). 32p. (J). (gr. 2-5). lib. bdg. 26.60 (978-1-57103-264-5(9)) Rourke Publishing, LLC.

—The Moon People. 1999. (Illus.). 31p. (J). (gr. 2-5). lib. bdg. 26.60 (978-1-57103-265-2(7)) Rourke Publishing, LLC.

—Song of the Sun: An Aztec Myth. 1999. (Illus.). 32p. (J). (gr. 2-5). lib. bdg. 26.60 (978-1-57103-267-6(3)) Rourke Publishing, LLC.

Lopdrop, Kjeld. The Grandparents Story Book. 2001. pap. 8.95 (978-0-533-13962-0(7)) Vantage Pr., Inc.

Luder, George, ed. Daddy's Collection. 1999. (Illus.). 50p. (J). Bk. 2. (978-1-884083-46-4(3)); Bk. 9. (978-1-884083-39-6(0)) Maval Publishing, Inc.

MacDonald, George. At the Back of the North Wind. 1998. (Twelve-Point Ser.). 280p. reprint ed. lib. bdg. 25.00 (978-1-58287-015-1(2)) North Bks.

MacIntyre, R. P. The Blue Camaro. 2004. 160p. pap. (978-1-895449-23-5(5)) Thistledown Pr., Ltd.

March, Julia. Looney TunesTM: The Ultimate Sticker Book. 2003. (Ultimate Sticker Bks.). (Illus.). 12p. (J). pap. 6.99 (978-0-7894-9757-4(3)) Dorling Kindersley Publishing, Inc.

Marcovitz, Hal. Will Hobbs. 2005. (Who Wrote That? Ser.). (Illus.). 124p. (J). (gr. 6-12). lib. bdg. 30.00 (978-0-7910-8657-5(7), Chelsea Hse.) Facts On File, Inc.

Marshall, Hallie. Winnie the Pooh's Many Adventures, Set. Kurtz, John, illus. 2003. 176p. (J). 15.99 (978-0-7868-3440-2(4)) Disney Pr.

Mason, Victor & Beal, Gillian. Balinese Children's Favorite Stories. Bohan-Tyrie, Trina, illus. 2001. 96p. (gr. 1-5). 16.95 (978-962-593-440-2(5)) Periplus Editions (HK), Ltd. HKG. *Dist:* Tuttle Publishing.

Mayer, Mercer. Little Critter First Readers Assortment. Mayer, Mercer, illus. 2003. (Illus.). 189.60 (978-1-57768-847-1(3)) School Specialty Publishing.

—Mercer Mayer Storybook Set. 2000. (Little Critter Ser.). (J). (ps-3). 23.99 (978-0-307-19565-4(1), Golden Bks.) Random Hse. Children's Bks.

McCaughrean, Geraldine. My First Oxford Book of Stories. Green, Ruby, illus. 2001. 96p. (YA). 13.95 (978-0-19-278187-1(1)) Oxford Univ. Pr., Inc.

McKinley, Robin & Dickinson, Peter. Water: Tales of Elemental Spirits. 2002. (Illus.). 272p. (YA). (gr. 4 up). 18.99 (978-0-399-23796-6(8), Putnam Juvenile) Penguin Group (USA) Inc.

McOmber, Rachel B., ed. McOmber Phonics Storybooks: A Trip to China. rev. ed. (Illus.). (J). (978-0-944991-70-1(X)) Swift Learning Resources.

—McOmber Phonics Storybooks: Choose Which One - 1. rev. ed. (Illus.). (J). (978-0-944991-67-1(X)) Swift Learning Resources.

—McOmber Phonics Storybooks: Humps & Lumps. rev. ed. (Illus.). (J). (978-0-944991-62-6(9)) Swift Learning Resources.

—McOmber Phonics Storybooks: Kim. rev. ed. (Illus.). (J). (978-0-944991-07-7(6)) Swift Learning Resources.

—McOmber Phonics Storybooks: Razz. rev. ed. (Illus.). (J). (978-0-944991-06-0(8)) Swift Learning Resources.

—McOmber Phonics Storybooks: Ten in the Hut. rev. ed. (Illus.). (J). (978-0-944991-27-5(0)) Swift Learning Resources.

—McOmber Phonics Storybooks: The Bag. rev. ed. (Illus.). (J). (978-0-944991-03-9(3)) Swift Learning Resources.

—McOmber Phonics Storybooks: The Big Deal. rev. ed. (Illus.). (J). (978-0-944991-47-3(5)) Swift Learning Resources.

—McOmber Phonics Storybooks: The Big Hole. rev. ed. (Illus.). (J). (978-0-944991-38-1(6)) Swift Learning Resources.

—McOmber Phonics Storybooks: The Bon-Bon Box. rev. ed. (Illus.). (J). (978-0-944991-14-5(9)) Swift Learning Resources.

—McOmber Phonics Storybooks: The Box Mix. rev. ed. (Illus.). (J). (978-0-944991-15-2(7)) Swift Learning Resources.

—McOmber Phonics Storybooks: The Fumes. rev. ed. (Illus.). (J). (978-0-944991-39-8(4)) Swift Learning Resources.

—McOmber Phonics Storybooks: The Kit. rev. ed. (Illus.). (J). (978-0-944991-08-4(4)) Swift Learning Resources.

—McOmber Phonics Storybooks: The Land of Morning. rev. ed. (Illus.). (J). (978-0-944991-82-4(3)) Swift Learning Resources.

—McOmber Phonics Storybooks: The Map. rev. ed. (Illus.). (J). (978-0-944991-05-3(X)) Swift Learning Resources.

—McOmber Phonics Storybooks: The Pit Kit. rev. ed. (Illus.). (J). (978-0-944991-09-1(2)) Swift Learning Resources.

—McOmber Phonics Storybooks: The Prize. rev. ed. (Illus.). (J). (978-0-944991-49-7(1)) Swift Learning Resources.

—McOmber Phonics Storybooks: The Quiz Is (1) rev. ed. (Illus.). (J). (978-0-944991-34-3(3)) Swift Learning Resources.

—McOmber Phonics Storybooks: The Quiz Is (2) rev. ed. (Illus.). (J). (978-0-944991-35-0(1)) Swift Learning Resources.

—McOmber Phonics Storybooks: The Rope. rev. ed. (Illus.). (J). (978-0-944991-45-9(9)) Swift Learning Resources.

—McOmber Phonics Storybooks: The Tin Lid. rev. ed. (Illus.). (J). (978-0-944991-10-7(6)) Swift Learning Resources.

—McOmber Phonics Storybooks: Tid Bits. rev. ed. (Illus.). (J). (978-0-944991-36-7(X)) Swift Learning Resources.

Mindel, Nissan. Dertzeil Mir a Maaseh, Vol. 3. Kleinman, Zalman & Dershowitz, Yosef, illus. 1999. Tr. of Storyteller. (YID.). 316p. (J). (gr. 4-8). 13.95 (978-0-8266-0388-3(2)) Kehot Pubn. Society.

Modern Staff. Kites in Flight & Mosquito Bites. (J). 7.95 (978-0-8136-4839-2(4)) Modern Curriculum Pr.

Monster Stories. 256p. (J). 2003. 5.98 (978-1-4054-1008-3(6)); 2002. 25.95 (978-0-7525-5673-4(8)) Parragon, Inc.

Morpurgo, Michael. The Kingfisher Book of Great Boy Stories: A Treasury of Classics from Children's Literature. 2000. (Kingfisher Treasury of Stories Ser.). (Illus.). 160p. (J). (gr. k-3). tchr. ed. 19.95 (978-0-7534-5320-9(7), Kingfisher) Houghton Mifflin Co. Trade & Reference Div.

Mouse Works Staff. Minnie Mouse. 1998. (Friendly Tales Ser.). (Illus.). 10p. (J). (ps). 6.99 (978-1-57082-930-7(6)) Mouse Works.

Munsch, Robert, et al. Mini-Book Fun Pack: The Annick ABC, the Boy in the Drawer, a Friend Like You, The Dark, Henry & the Cow Problem, Red Is Best, Norman's Snowball, & You Can Be the Cat, the Too Big Bear. 2004. (Annikins Ser.). (Illus.). 24p. (J). (ps-k). pap. 4.99 (978-1-55037-552-7(0)) Annick Pr., Ltd. CAN. *Dist:* Firefly Bks., Ltd.

My Big Book of Bedtime Tales. 2001. 284p. (J). 29.95 (978-0-7525-4082-5(3)) Parragon, Inc.

Nault, Jennifer. Judy Blume. 2002. (My Favorite Writer Ser.). (Illus.). 32p. (J). lib. bdg. 18.20 (978-1-59036-025-5(7)) Weigl Pubs., Inc.

No te dejes de Laura Sue: Social/Emotional Lap Book. (Pebble Soup Exploraciones Ser.). (SPA.). (ps up). 16.00 (978-0-7578-1793-9(9)) Rigby Education.

Nye, Naomi Shihab. The Tree Is Older Than You Are: A Bilingual Gathering of Poems & Stories from Mexico with Paintings by Mexican Artists. 1998. (ENG & SPA.). (J). (978-0-606-13867-3(6)) Tandem Library Bks.

Obiols, Anna. Dali & the Path of Dreams. Subirana, Joan, illus. 2004. 32p. (J). 15.95 (978-1-84507-282-7(0)) Lincoln, Frances Ltd. GBR. *Dist:* Perseus Distribution.

Old MacDonald's Farmyard Tales. (Little Treasuries Ser.). 256p. (J). 2002. 5.98 (978-0-7525-7689-3(5)); 2000. 25.95 (978-0-7525-3758-0(X)) Parragon, Inc.

Oravecz, Kathy Sabbath. The Frog & the Footbridge, Vol. 10. 2001. (Illus.). 50p. (J). per. 7.50 (978-1-884083-05-1(6)) Maval Publishing, Inc.

Parent, Nancy, ed. Coleccion de Cuentos. 2002. (Tesoros de Disney Ser.). (SPA., Illus.). 320p. (J). 15.95 (978-968-5308-74-8(8), Silver Dolphin en Español) Advanced Marketing, S. de R. L. de C. V. MEX. *Dist:* Bilingual Pubns. Co., The, Perseus Distribution, Transition Vendor.

Paterson, Katherine. Angels & Other Strangers: Family Christmas Stories. 2006. 192p. (J). 9.99 (978-0-06-078376-1(1)) HarperCollins Pubs.

Potter, Beatrix. The Complete Tales of Beatrix Potter: The 23 Original Peter Rabbit Bookss & 4 Unpublished Works. 2002. (Illus.). 400p. (J). 35.00 (978-0-7232-4760-9(9), Warne) Penguin Group (USA) Inc.

Prap, Lila. 1001 Stories. Prap, Lila, illus. 2006. (Illus.). 32p. (J). 15.95 (978-1-929132-92-8(1)) Kane/Miller Bk. Pubs., Inc.

Quiroga, Horacio. Cuentos de la Selva. 2nd ed. 2002. (Clover Ser.). (SPA., Illus.). 156p. (YA). 13.95 (978-84-392-8050-7(5), EV4408) Lectorum Pubns., Inc.

Ratoff, Michael. Every Thing in an Empty Box, Vol. 3. Painter, Laurie, illus. l.t. ed. 2001. 168p. (J). (ps-3). lib. bdg. 24.00 (978-0-9627986-5-8(7)) Rebel Butterfly Pr.

Read Magazine Editorial Staff. Read in A Different Light: Stories of Loners, Outcasts & Rebels. 2000. (Best of READ Ser.). 160p. (gr. 5 up). lib. bdg. 24.90 (978-0-7613-1615-2(9), Millbrook Pr.) Lerner Publishing Group.

Read to Me Grandma. 2002. (Read to Me Ser.). 192p. (J). 14.98 (978-0-7525-4075-7(0)) Parragon, Inc.

Read to Me Grandpa. 2002. (Read to Me Ser.). 192p. (J). 14.98 (978-0-7525-4076-4(9)) Parragon, Inc.

Reading Friends Staff. Benjamin. (J). pap. (978-0-8136-3840-9(2)) Modern Curriculum Pr.

Ready Reader Staff. Stan Packs, 6 bks., set, Level 8, Bk. 41. 2003. (J). (ps-3). pap. 33.50 (978-0-8136-2077-0(5)) Modern Curriculum Pr.

Richardson, Arleta. Stories from the Growing Years. 2003. (Grandma's Attic Ser.). 144p. (J). pap., pap. 6.99 (978-0-7814-3905-3(1), 0781439051) Cook, David C. Publishing Co.

Rock, Lois. My Very First Bedtime Storybook. Ayliffe, Alex, illus. 2004. 128p. (J). (ps). 14.99 (978-1-56148-448-5(2)) Good Bks.

Rockwell, Anne F. Long Ago Yesterday. Rockwell, Anne F., illus. 1999. (Illus.). 24p. (J). (ps up). 16.00 (978-0-688-14411-1(X)) HarperCollins Pubs.

Romulo, Liana & De Leon, Joanne. Filipino Children's Favorite Stories. 2000. (Illus.). 96p. (ps-3). 16.95 (978-962-593-765-6(X)) Periplus Editions (HK), Ltd. HKG. *Dist:* Tuttle Publishing.

Rosenberg, Teya. Diana Wynne Jones: An Exciting & Exacting Wisdom. 2002. (Studies in Children's Literature Ser.: Vol. 1). 187p. pap. 29.95 (978-0-8204-5687-4(X)) Lang, Peter Publishing, Inc.

Rosenstein, Richard. One, Two... Where's the Shoe? Ambrus, Victor G., illus. 1998. 24p. (J). (ps-3). 16.95 (978-0-86315-261-0(9)) Floris Bks. GBR. *Dist:* Gryphon Hse., Inc., SteinerBooks, Inc.

Rothman, Cynthia Anne. Big Book: A Party for Nine. l.t. ed. 2005. (Sadlier Phonics Reading Program). (Illus.). 8p. (YA). (gr. k-2). 22.50 (978-0-8215-7349-5(7)) Sadlier, William H. Inc.

Rubel, William & Mandel, Gerry, eds. Animal Stories by Young Writers. 2004. 96p. (YA). (gr. 3-8). pap., tchr. ed. 9.95 (978-1-58246-017-8(5), Tricycle Pr.) Ten Speed Pr.

Sandberg, Rosemary, ed. The Kingfisher Book of Great Girl Stories: A Treasury of Classics from Children's Literature. Blake, Quentin, illus. 2006. (Story Collections). 160p. (J). (gr. k-3). tchr. ed. 19.95 (978-0-7534-5207-3(3), Kingfisher) Houghton Mifflin Co. Trade & Reference Div.

Sandberg, Rosemary & Morpurgo, Michael, compiled by. The Kingfisher Treasury of Classic Stories. 2002. (Story Collections). (Illus.). 320p. (J). (gr. 3-5). tchr. ed. 24.95 (978-0-7534-5483-1(1), Kingfisher) Houghton Mifflin Co. Trade & Reference Div.

Schram, Peninnah. Ten Classic Jewish Children's Stories. Allon, Jeffrey, illus. 48p. (J). 2000. (ps-3). pap. 9.95 (978-0-943706-88-7(2)); 1998. (Jewish Storyteller Ser.: Vol. 3). (gr. 1-4). 16.95 (978-0-943706-96-2(3)) Pitspopany Pr.

Selected Children's Stories Published in Other Lands, 7 bks. (Illus.). (J). (gr. k-3). lib. bdg. 101.65 (978-1-56674-905-3(0)) Forest Hse. Publishing Co., Inc.

Singer, Marilyn. Stay True: Short Stories for Strong Girls. 1999. 208p. (J). (gr. 6-9). pap. 4.99 (978-0-590-36033-3(7)) Scholastic, Inc.

—Stay True: Short Stories for Strong Girls. 1999. (978-0-606-16590-7(8)) Tandem Library Bks.

Singh, Rina. Moon Tales. Lush, Debbie, illus. 2001. 80p. (J). pap. 16.99 (978-0-7475-4795-2(5)) Bloomsbury Publishing Plc GBR. *Dist:* Trafalgar Square Publishing.

Speirs, Roger. Pearls: Bedtime Stories. Speirs, Megan, illus. 1998. (Orig.). (J). (ps-5). pap. 5.95 (978-0-9667544-0-7(9)) UCanDo Bks.

Sprick, Marilyn, et al. Read Well Student Storybooks, 16 vols., Set. 1998. (Read Well Ser.). (Illus.). 72p. (J). (gr. 1-3). pap. 35.00 (978-1-57035-158-7(9), 93SET) Sopris West Educational Services.

Stalcup, Ann & Politi, Leo. Leo Politi: Artist of the Angels. 2004. (J). 24.95 (978-1-893110-38-0(9)) Silver Moon Pr.

Stories for 6 Year Olds. 2002. 80p. (J). 7.98 (978-0-7525-4071-9(8)) Parragon, Inc.

Story Rhyme Staff. Self-Esteem: Stories, Poetry & Activity Pages. Story Rhyme Staff, illus. Date not set. (Illus.). 28p. (YA). (gr. 4-9). ring bd. 19.95 (978-1-56820-107-8(9)) Story Time Stories That Rhyme.

Story Time Staff. Story Time Kit: Story Rhymes, Art Activities, Assessments & More. 2001. (Illus.). (J). (gr. 3-8). wbk. ed. 59.95 (978-1-56820-346-1(2)) Story Time Stories That Rhyme.

Strelchun, Rory T. Writings & Stories by RTS: A Collection of Writings & Stories. l.t. ed. 2002. (YA). (gr. 6-8). mass mkt. 11.88 (978-0-9671942-3-3(7)) Top Tek Corp.

Sweet Dreams Stories: A Collection of Bedtime Tales. 2002. 232p. (J). 5.98 (978-0-7525-8911-4(3)) Parragon, Inc.

Taylor. Seven Silly Stories. Date not set. (Illus.). pap. 129.15 (978-0-582-18518-0(1)) Addison-Wesley Longman, Ltd. GBR. *Dist:* Trans-Atlantic Pubns., Inc.

Traditional Tales of Long, Long Ago. 2001. (Little Treasuries Ser.). 256p. (J). 11.95 (978-0-7525-4514-1(0)) Parragon, Inc.

Treasured Tales. 2002. 224p. (J). 5.98 (978-0-7525-8912-1(1)) Parragon, Inc.

Troughton, Joanna, et al. A Friend for the King & Other Stories. 2002. (Illus.). 48p. pap. 0.40 (978-0-521-89006-9(3)) Cambridge Univ. Pr.

Tunnell, Michael O. The Prydain Companion: A Reference Guide to Lloyd Alexander's Prydain Chronicles. rev. ed. 2003. (Illus.). 304p. (YA). (gr. 7 up). pap. 19.95 (978-0-8050-7271-6(3), Holt, Henry & Co. Bks. For Young Readers) Holt, Henry & Co.

Turner, Megan Whalen. Instead of Three Wishes: Magical Short Stories. 1998. (978-0-606-13521-4(9)) Tandem Library Bks.

Urmston, Kathleen & Evans, Karen. Sammy Collection: Includes Dressed up Sammy, Sammy at the Farm, Sammy Gets a Ride, Sammy's Moving, A Rainy Day for Sammy, Sammy's Hamburger Caper, Sammy & Sammy's Slippery Day, 8 books. Gedeon, Gloria, illus. 2006. (J). pap. 37.95 (978-1-57874-068-0(1)) Kaeden Corp.

Vyner, Sue. If Only: One Day He'd Find His Dad, He Just Knew It... Lawrie, Robin, illus. 2001. (Go for It! Ser.). 127p. pap. 12.00 (978-0-237-52331-2(0), Evans Brothers, Limited) Evans Publishing Group GBR. *Dist:* Independent Pubs. Group.

—Kids' Stuff: No One Understood, No One.. Lawrie, Robin, illus. 2001. (Go for It! Ser.). 127p. pap. 12.00 (978-0-237-52330-5(2), Evans Brothers, Limited) Evans Publishing Group GBR. *Dist:* Independent Pubs. Group.

We Read More Stories. (J). tchr. ed. 4.72 (978-0-917186-12-7(5)); Set. pap. 10.62 (978-0-917186-11-0(7)) McQueen Publishing Co.

Webb, Kaye, ed. Let the Sun Shine: Stories & Poems for Reading Aloud. 1998. (Illus.). 72p. (J). (ps-3). pap. 9.99 (978-0-7112-1247-3(3)) Lincoln, Frances Ltd. GBR. *Dist:* Transition Vendor.

Weinbach, Shaindel. Cartons in the Air & Other Stories. Dershowitz, Yosef, illus. (J). 14.99 (978-0-89906-992-0(4), CARH) Mesorah Pubns., Ltd.

—The Friendly Persuader & Other Stories. Dershowitz, Yosef, illus. (J). 14.99 (978-0-89906-970-8(3), FRIH) Mesorah Pubns., Ltd.

Wells, Rosemary. Yoko's World of Kindness: Golden Rules for a Happy Classroom. Nez, John & Wheeler, Jody, illus. 2005. 160p. (J). (gr. k-2). 19.99 (978-0-7868-5109-6(0)) Hyperion Bks. for Children.

Wethington, Liz. Pansy Ann & Eva Stories. Wise, Noreen, ed. 2001. (Gold Mixed Collection). (Illus.). 54p. (J). (ps up). pap. 7.50 (978-1-58584-419-7(5)) Huckleberry Pr.

Whelan, Gerard. Out of Nowhere. 2003. 240p. (YA). (gr. 5 up). pap. 7.95 (978-0-86278-637-3(1)) O'Brien Pr., Ltd., The IRL. *Dist:* Independent Pubs. Group.

White, E. B. E. B. White: Charlotte's Web, Stuart Little, & the Trumpet of the Swan, 3 bks., Set. 2003. (Illus.). (J). pap. 14.99 (978-0-06-055416-3(9)) HarperCollins Pubs.

White, Stephen. Barney's Storybook Treasury. Sharp, Chris & McGlothin, David, illus. 1999. (Barney Ser.). 176p. (J). (ps-k). pap. 10.95 (978-1-57064-579-2(5)) Scholastic, Inc.

Wick, Walter. Seymour Makes New Friends. Wick, Walter, illus. 2006. (Can You See What I See Ser.). (Illus.). 32p. (J). (ps-k). pap. 8.99 (978-0-439-61780-2(4)) Scholastic, Inc.

Wiggin, Eric. The Texas Rodeo Showdown. 1998. (Hannah's Island Ser.: Bk. 6). 192p. (Orig.). (gr. 3-7). pap. 5.99 (978-1-883002-29-9(X)) Emerald Bks.

Willard, Nancy. The Tale I Told Sasha. Christiana, David, illus. 1999. 32p. (J). (ps-3). 15.95 (978-0-316-94115-0(8)) Little Brown & Co.

Winter, Jeanette. Beatrix: Various Episodes from the Life of Beatrix Potter. Winter, Jeanette, illus. 2003. (Illus.). 64p. (J). (gr. k-3). 15.00 (978-0-374-30655-7(9) , Farrar, Straus & Giroux (BYR)) Farrar, Straus & Giroux.

STORIES IN RHYME

Abolade, Caroline, told to. I'm Going to Be a Big Brother. 2003. 14p. 9.44 (978-1-4116-0123-9(8)) Lulu.com.

Abrams, Harry N. Campbell Kids Alphabet Soup: An ABC Book. 2004. (Illus.). 40p. (J). (ps-1). 10.95 (978-0-8109-5041-2(3)) Abrams, Harry N. , Inc.

Ada, Alma Flor. The Golden Cage. 2000. (gr. k-3). lib. bdg. 17.60 (978-0-613-79387-2(0)) Tandem Library Bks.

—Kite. 2000. (gr. k-3). lib. bdg. 17.60 (978-0-613-79386-5(2)) Tandem Library Bks.

—Quien Nacera Aqui? (Libros para Contar Ser.).Tr. of Who's Hatching Here?. (SPA., Illus.). 24p. (J). (gr. k-3). pap. 6.95 (978-1-58105-198-8(0)) Santillana USA Publishing Co., Inc.

—Quien Nacera Aqui? 2000. Tr. of Who's Hatching Here?. (SPA.). (gr. k-3). lib. bdg. 15.25 (978-0-613-79382-7(X)) Tandem Library Bks.

Adams, Diane. Zoom! Luthardt, Kevin, illus. 2005. 32p. (J). 15.95 (978-1-56145-332-0(3)) Peachtree Pubs., Ltd.

Adams, Michelle Medlock. Little Colt's Palm Sunday. Parmenter, Wayne, illus. 2005. 28p. (J). 14.95 (978-0-8249-5503-8(X)) Ideals Pubns.

—The Sparrow's Easter Song. Eldridge, Marion, illus. 2003. 32p. (J). 14.95 (978-0-8249-5470-3(X)) Ideals Pubns.

Adams, Michelle Medlock. What Is Halloween? Wummer, Amy, illus. 2007. 26p. (J). (ps-k). bds. 6.99 (****978-0-8249-6712-3(7)*** , Candy Cane Pr.) Ideals Pubns.

Adams, Pam. This Is the House That Jack Built. 2001. (Illus.). 16p. (J). (ps-1). bds. 5.99 (978-0-85953-468-0(5)) Child's Play-International.

Adlerman, Daniel. Rock-a-Bye Baby. Adlerman, Kimberly M., illus. 2004. 32p. (J). 15.95 (978-1-58089-082-3(2)) Charlesbridge Publishing, Inc.

Adoff, Arnold. Black Is Brown Is Tan. McCully, Emily Arnold, illus. 40p. (J). (ps-3). 2004. reprint ed. pap. 6.99 (978-0-06-443644-1(6)); 2002. 16.99 (978-0-06-028776-4(4)) HarperCollins Pubs.

Ahlberg, Allan. The Jolly Postman: Or, Other People's Letters. Ahlberg, Janet, illus. 2006. 28p. (J). (gr. k-3). 19.99 (978-0-316-01776-3(0)) Little Brown & Co.

—One, Two, Flea! McNaughton, Colin, illus. 1999. (Read & Share Ser.). 32p. (J). (gr. k). pap. 3.99 (978-0-7636-0859-0(9)) Candlewick Pr.

Ahlberg, Janet. Each Peach Pear Plum. 2004. pap. 14.95 incl. audio (978-1-56008-194-4(5)); (J). 24.95 incl. audio (978-1-56008-193-7(7)) Weston Woods Studios, Inc.

Ahlberg, Janet & Ahlberg, Allan. Each Peach Pear Plum. Ahlberg, Janet, illus. 2002. (Illus.). (J). 12.34 (978-0-7587-2427-4(6)) Book Wholesalers, Inc.

—Each Peach Pear Plum. (Illus.). 32p. (J). pap. 9.95 (978-0-14-050919-9(4)) Penguin Bks., Ltd. GBR. *Dist:* Trafalgar Square Publishing.

—Each Peach Pear Plum. Ahlberg, Janet & Ahlberg, Allan, illus. 1999. (Illus.). 34p. (J). (ps up). 6.99 (978-0-670-88278-6(X) , Viking Juvenile) Penguin Group (USA) Inc.

Ahrens, Robin Isabel. Dee & Bee. Haley, Amanda, illus. 2000. 40p. (J). (ps-1). 14.95 (978-1-890817-26-8(0)) Winslow Pr.

Aigner-Clark, Julie. Baby Einstein: Las rimas de Bard : Bard4s Rhyme Time, Spanish-Language Edition. Zaidi, Nadeem, illus. 2005. (Baby Einstein: Libros de Carton Ser.). (SPA.). 16p. (J). 6.95 (978-970-718-304-9(7) , Silver Dolphin en Español) Advanced Marketing, S. de R. L. de C. V. MEX. *Dist:* Perseus Distribution.

—Baby MacDonald Magnetic Puzzle Book. 2008. 8p. (ps-17). 12.99 (****978-1-4231-0205-2(3)***) Hyperion Bks. for Children.

—Bard's Rhyme Time. Zaidi, Nadeem, illus. 2002. (Baby Einstein Ser.). 16p. (J). (ps). bds. 6.99 (978-0-7868-0842-7(X)) Hyperion Bks. for Children.

—What's Bigger Than Me? Zaidi, Nadeem, illus. 2006. 16p. (ps-17). 5.99 (978-0-7868-4974-1(6)) Hyperion Bks. for Children.

—World Around Me: Oceans. 2003. (Baby Einstein Ser.). 12p. (ps-17). 15.99 (978-0-7868-1913-3(8)) Disney Pr.

Aignier-Clark, Julie. Peek-a-Boo Bard. 2008. 10p. 9.99 (****978-1-4231-0860-3(4)***) Hyperion Bks. for Children.

Akley, Jason. Sweet Pea & the Bumblebee. 2007. (ENG.). 36p. (J). per. 16.95 (****978-1-4327-0341-7(2)***) Outskirts Press, Inc.

Alarcon, Karen Beaumont. Louella Mae, She's Run Away! Litzinger, Rosanne, illus. rev. ed. 2002. 32p. (J). (ps-1). pap. 7.95 (978-0-8050-6830-6(9) , Holt, Henry & Co. Bks. For Young Readers) Holt, Henry & Co.

—Louella Mae, She's Run Away! 2002. (ps-2). lib. bdg. 15.25 (978-0-613-75399-9(2)) Tandem Library Bks.

Albee, Sarah. Hello, Cat, Hello, Dog. Leigh, Tom, illus. 2006. (Step-By-Step Readers Ser.). (J). pap. (978-1-59939-054-3(X) , Reader's Digest Young Families, Inc.) Reader's Digest Children's Publishing, Inc.

—Hic! Brannon, Tom, illus. 2006. (Step-By-Step Readers Ser.). (J). pap. (978-1-59939-061-1(2) , Reader's Digest Young Families, Inc.) Reader's Digest Children's Publishing, Inc.

Alborough, Jez. Duck in the Truck. Alborough, Jez, illus. 2008. (Illus.). 32p. (J). pap. 7.95 (****978-1-933605-76-0(6)***) Kane/Miller Bk. Pubs., Inc.

—Fix-It Duck. Alborough, Jez, illus. 2002. (Illus.). 40p. (J). (ps-1). 16.99 (978-0-06-000699-0(4)) HarperCollins Pubs.

—Some Dogs Do. Alborough, Jez, illus. 2003. (Illus.). 40p. (J). (ps-2). 15.99 (978-0-7636-2201-5(X)) Candlewick Pr.

—Tall. Alborough, Jez, illus. 2005. (Illus.). 40p. (J). (ps up). 15.99 (978-0-7636-2784-3(4)) Candlewick Pr.

—Tall. Alborough, Jez, illus. 2007. (Illus.). 34p. (J). (gr. k-ps). bds. 6.99 (978-0-7636-3328-8(3)) Candlewick Pr.

Aldis, Dorothy & Collins, Heather. Hiding. (FRE.). (J). pap. 7.99 (978-0-590-24195-3(8)) Scholastic, Inc.

Alekos. Aroma de Nispero y Otros Versos de Papel. (SPA.). 48p. (J). (gr. k-2). (978-958-30-0567-1(3)) Panamericana Editorial COL. *Dist:* Lectorum Pubns., Inc.

Alexander, Jessica & Shore, Diane Z. Look Both Ways: A Cautionary Tale. Weidner, Teri, illus. 2005. 32p. (J). (ps-ps). 15.95 (978-1-58234-968-8(1)) Bloomsbury Publishing.

Allen, Kathryn Madeline. This Little Piggy's Book of Manners. Wolff, Nancy, illus. rev. ed. 2003. 32p. (J). 15.95 (978-0-8050-6769-9(8) , Holt, Henry & Co. Bks. For Young Readers) Holt, Henry & Co.

Allen, Lisa & Sharp, Julis. Time for Bed - The Secret of Shadows: Shadow Theater Inside. Johnson, Vickie, illus. 26p. (J). (ps-2). pap. (978-1-56021-355-0(8) , 206) W.J. Fantasy, Inc.

Almy, Judy. My Name Is Ick: A Rhyming Story of an Alaska Caribou. 2005. 9.95 (978-1-59433-009-4(3)) Publication Consultants.

Alyson Publications Staff & Valentine, Johnny. The Daddy Machine. 2nd ed. 2004. (Illus.). 16.95 (978-1-55583-887-4(1)) Alyson Pubns.

Anastas, Margaret. A Hug for You. Winter, Susan, photos by. 2005. (Illus.). 32p. (J). (ps-1). 15.99 (978-0-06-623613-1(4)) HarperCollins Pubs.

—Mommy's Best Kisses. Winter, Susan, illus. 32p. (J). (ps-1). 2003. 15.99 (978-0-06-623601-8(0)); 2000. reprint ed. pap. 6.99 (978-0-06-443839-1(2)) HarperCollins Pubs.

Anderson, Derek & Child, Lydia Maria. Over the River: A Turkey's Tale. 2005. (Illus.). 40p. (J). 14.95 (978-0-689-87635-6(1)) Simon & Schuster Children's Publishing.

Anderson, Doug. Too Big to Dance. Anderson, Sara, illus. 2004. 32p. (J). 15.95 (978-1-59354-046-3(9)) Handprint Bks.

Anderson, Lena. Hedgehog, Pig, & the Sweet Little Friend. Sandin, Joan, tr. from SWE. 2007. (Illus.). 32p. (J). (ps-1). 16.00 (****978-91-29-66742-4(9)***) R & S Bks. SWE. *Dist:* Macmillan.

Anderson, M. T. The Serpent Came to Gloucester. Ibatoulline, Bagram, illus. 2005. 40p. (J). (gr. 1-5). 16.99 (978-0-7636-2038-7(6)) Candlewick Pr.

Anderson, Peggy Perry. Chuck's Band. 2008. 32p. (J). 16.00 (****978-0-618-96506-9(8)***) Houghton Mifflin Co.

—Chuck's Truck. 2006. (Illus.). 32p. (J). (gr. k-3). 16.00 (978-0-618-66836-6(5)) Houghton Mifflin Co.

—Joe on the Go. 2007. (Illus.). 32p. (J). (gr. 3-5). 16.00 (978-0-618-77331-2(2)) Houghton Mifflin Co.

—Let's Clean Up! (Illus.). 32p. (J). (gr. k-3). 2005. 5.95 (978-0-618-55523-9(4)); 2002. 15.00 (978-0-618-19602-9(1)) Houghton Mifflin Co. Trade & Reference Div. (Walter Lorraine).

Anderson, Sara. Noisy City Day. 2005. (Illus.). 6p. (J). bds. 7.95 (978-1-59354-054-8(X)) Handprint Bks.

—Noisy City Night. 2005. (Illus.). 6p. (J). bds. 7.95 (978-1-59354-055-5(8)) Handprint Bks.

—Octopus Oyster Hermit Crab Snail: A Poem of the Sea. 2005. (Illus.). 32p. (J). (gr. 1-3). 16.95 (978-1-59354-079-1(5)) Handprint Bks.

Andreae, Giles. Giraffes Can't Dance. Parker-Rees, Guy, illus. (J). (ps-1). 2001. 32p. pap. 16.95 (978-0-439-28719-7(7) , Orchard Bks.); 2007. 29.95 incl. audio compact disk (****978-0-439-02734-2(9)***); 2007. 24.95 incl. audio (****978-0-439-02733-5(0)***) Scholastic, Inc.

—Heaven Is Having You. Cabban, Vanessa, illus. (J). (ps-k). 2007. 24p. bds. 7.95 (****978-1-58925-820-4(7)***); 2002. 32p. tchr. ed. 15.95 (978-1-58925-016-1(8)) ME Media LLC. (tiger tales).

—Keep Love in Your Heart, Little One. Vulliamy, Clara, illus. 2007. 32p. (J). (ps-2). 15.95 (****978-1-58925-066-6(4)*** , tiger tales) ME Media LLC.

—The Lion Who Wanted to Love. Wojtowycz, David, illus. 1998. 32p. (J). (ps-2). 14.95 (978-1-888444-25-4(8) , 21023) Little Tiger Pr.

—Love Is a Handful of Honey. Cabban, Vanessa, illus. 1999. 32p. (J). (ps-2). 14.95 (978-1-888444-58-2(4)) Little Tiger Pr.

—Love Is a Handful of Honey. Cabban, Vanessa, illus. 2004. 32p. (J). (ps-k). 5.95 (978-1-58925-353-7(1)); tchr. ed. 15.95 (978-1-58925-003-1(6)) ME Media LLC. (tiger tales).

—Love Is a Handful of Honey. 2001. (ps-2). lib. bdg. 14.10 (978-0-613-57645-1(4)) Tandem Library Bks.

—There's a House Inside My Mommy. Cabban, Vanessa, illus. 2002. (Concept Book Ser.). 32p. (J). (ps-3). 15.95 (978-0-8075-7853-7(3)) Whitman, Albert & Co.

Andreasen, Dan. The Baker's Dozen: A Counting Book. 2007. (Illus.). 32p. (J). (ps-1). 16.95 (****978-0-8050-7809-1(6)***) Holt, Henry & Co.

Anglemyer, Jordan, illus. Grandpa's Favorites: A collection of quotes, things to ponder, stories, bits of verse, & Humor. 2007. 77p. (YA). per. 10.95 (****978-0-9796251-2-1(2)***) Robertson Publishing.

Anonymous. Story Time Book: Rhyme Time & Story Time. 2004. reprint ed. pap. 15.95 (978-1-4191-1380-2(1)) Kessinger Publishing, LLC.

Anson-Weber, Joan. Snuffles Goes to Scotland Yard. Russell, Judith, illus. 2001. (J). 16.95 (978-0-87797-293-8(1)) Cherokee Publishing Co.

Appelt, Kathi. The Alley Cat's Meow. Goodell, Jon, illus. 2002. 32p. (J). (gr. k-2). 16.00 (978-0-15-201980-8(4)) Harcourt Children's Bks.

—Incredible Me! Karas, G. Brian, illus. 2003. 32p. (J). (ps-1). 15.99 (978-0-06-028622-4(9)) HarperCollins Pubs.

—Merry Christmas, Merry Crow. Goodell, Jon, illus. 2005. 32p. (J). (ps-ps). 16.00 (978-0-15-202651-6(7) , Harcourt Children's Bks) Harcourt Children's Bks.

—Oh My Baby, Little One. Dyer, Jane, illus. 2006. 32p. (J). pap. 3.99 (978-0-15-206031-2(6) , Voyager Bks./Libros Viajeros) Harcourt Children's Bks.

—Piggies in a Polka. Pham, LeUyen, illus. 2003. 40p. (J). 16.00 (978-0-15-216483-6(9)) Harcourt Children's Bks.

—Someone's Come to Our House. Carpenter, Nancy, illus. 1999. 24p. (J). (ps-3). 16.00 (978-0-8028-5144-4(4) , Eerdmans Bks For Young Readers) Eerdmans, William B. Publishing Co.

Apperley, Dawn. Good Night, Sleep Tight, Little Bunnies. Apperley, Dawn, illus. 2002. (Illus.). 32p. (J). (ps-k). pap. 9.95 (978-0-439-22525-0(6) , Cartwheel Bks.) Scholastic, Inc.

—Hello Little Chicks. Apperley, Dawn, illus. 2000. (Hello Bks.). (Illus.). 12p. (J). bds. 3.95 (978-1-86233-181-5(2)) David & Charles Children's Bks. GBR. *Dist:* Sterling Publishing Co., Inc.

—Hello Little Ducklings. Apperley, Dawn, illus. 2000. (Hello Bks.). (Illus.). 12p. (J). bds. 3.95 (978-1-86233-176-1(6)) David & Charles Children's Bks. GBR. *Dist:* Sterling Publishing Co., Inc.

Apperley, Dawn, illus. Santa Claus Will Come Tonight. 2002. 24p. (J). (ps-1). pap. 6.95 (978-0-439-40449-5(5) , Cartwheel Bks.) Scholastic, Inc.

April, Elyse. We Like to Move: Exercise Is Fun. Iverson, Diane, illus. 2006. 32p. (J). pap. 9.95 (978-1-890772-60-4(7)) Hohm Pr.

Archambault, John. Boom Chicka Rock. Chitwood, Suzanne Tanner, illus. 2004. 36p. (J). (ps-2). 15.99 (978-0-399-23587-0(6) , Philomel) Penguin Group (USA) Inc.

Arciero, Susan. Nantucket 1, 2, 3. Arciero, Susan, illus. l.t. ed. 2000. (Illus.). (J). (ps). 7.95 (978-0-9677548-2-6(8)) Pigtail Publishing.

Arcure, Suzanne. Little Angels. 2002. 36p. pap. 9.95 (978-0-7414-0791-7(4)) Infinity Publishing.

Argueta, Jorge. Talking with Mother Earth/Hablando con Madre Tierra: Poems/Poemas. Perez, Lucia Angela, illus. 2006. (ENG & SPA.). 32p. (J). 15.95 (978-0-88899-626-8(8)) Groundwood Bks. CAN. *Dist:* Perseus Distribution.

Armstrong, Jennifer. Sunshine, Moonshine. 2003. (Early Step into Reading Ser.). (Illus.). 32p. (J). (ps-1). 11.99 (978-0-679-96442-1(8) , Random Hse. Bks. for Young Readers) Random Hse. Children's Bks.

Arnold, Marsha Diane. Roar of a Snore. Pratt, Pierre, illus. 2006. (J). (****978-1-4156-8271-5(2)*** , Dial) Penguin Group (USA) Inc.

Arnold, Tedd. Even More Parts. Arnold, Tedd, illus. 2007. 40p. (J). pap. 6.99 (978-0-14-240714-1(3) , Puffin) Penguin Group (USA) Inc.

—Even More Parts: Idioms from Head to Toe. Arnold, Tedd, illus. 2004. (Illus.). 40p. (J). (ps-3). 16.99 (978-0-8037-2938-4(3) , Dial) Penguin Group (USA) Inc.

—Parts. 2000. (Illus.). 32p. (J). (ps-3). pap. 5.99 (978-0-14-056533-1(7) , Puffin) Penguin Group (USA) Inc.

—Parts. 2000. (978-0-606-20368-5(0)); (J). (978-0-606-20249-7(8)); lib. bdg. 14.15 (978-0-613-30085-8(8)) Tandem Library Bks.

Arnold, Tedd, et al. Five Ugly Monsters. Arnold, Tedd, illus. 2003. 28p. (J). bds. 6.99 (978-0-439-52465-0(2) , Cartwheel Bks.) Scholastic, Inc.

Artell, Mike. Petite Rouge: A Cajun Red Riding Hood. Harris, Jim, illus. 2003. 32p. (J). pap. 6.99 (978-0-14-250070-5(4) , Puffin) Penguin Group (USA) Inc.

—Petite Rouge: A Cajun Red Riding Hood. 2001. (Illus.). 32p. (J). (gr. k up). 16.99 (978-0-8037-2514-0(0) , Dial) Penguin Group (USA) Inc.

—Petite Rouge: A Cajun Red Riding Hood. 2001. lib. bdg. 15.30 (978-0-613-67470-6(7)) Tandem Library Bks.

Ashburn, Boni. Hush, Little Dragon. Murphy, Kelly, illus. 2008. 32p. (J). 15.95 (****978-0-8109-9491-1(7)*** , Abrams Bks. for Young Readers) Abrams, Harry N. , Inc.

Ashman, Linda. Can You Make a Piggy Giggle? Cole, Henry, illus. 2002. 32p. (J). 12.99 (978-0-525-46881-3(1) , Dutton Juvenile) Penguin Group (USA) Inc.

—Castles, Caves, & Honeycombs. Stringer, Lauren, illus. 2001. 32p. (J). (ps-k). 17.00 (978-0-15-202211-2(2)) Harcourt Children's Bks.

—How to Make a Night. Tusa, Tricia, illus. (J). (ps-3). Date not set. 32p. pap. 5.99 (978-0-06-443699-1(3)); 2004. 40p. 15.99 (978-0-06-029032-0(3)) HarperCollins Pubs.

—Just Another Morning. Munoz, Claudio, illus. 2004. 32p. (J). (ps-3). 15.99 (978-0-06-029053-5(6)) HarperCollins Pubs.

—Mama's Day. Ormerod, Jan, illus. 2006. 32p. (J). (ps-1). 15.95 (978-0-689-83475-2(6)) Simon & Schuster Children's Publishing.

—Maxwell's Magic Mix-up. Dunnick, Regan, illus. 2004. 30p. (J). (gr. k-3). reprint ed. 16.00 (978-0-7567-7156-0(0)) DIANE Publishing Co.

—Starry Safari. Mack, Jeff, illus. 2005. 40p. (J). 16.00 (978-0-15-204766-5(2)) Harcourt Children's Bks.

—To the Beach! Westcott, Nadine Bernard, illus. 2005. 32p. (J). 16.00 (978-0-15-216490-4(1)) Harcourt Children's Bks.

Asim, Jabari. Daddy Goes to Work. Boyd, Aaron, illus. 2006. 32p. (J). (ps-3). 15.99 (978-0-316-73575-9(2)) Little Brown & Co.

—Whose Knees Are These? Pham, LeUyen, illus. 2006. 20p. (J). (ps-ps). bds. 6.99 (978-0-316-73576-6(0)) Little Brown & Co.

—Whose Toes Are Those? Pham, LeUyen, illus. 2006. 11p. (J). (ps-3). bds. 6.99 (978-0-316-73609-1(0)) Little Brown & Co.

Asquith, Ros & Childs, Sam. Baby's Shoe. 2005. (Illus.). 32p. (J). (ps-7). pap., pap. 9.99 (978-0-09-945107-5(7) , Red Fox) Random Hse. Children's Bks. GBR. *Dist:* Trafalgar Square Publishing.

Aston, Dianna Hutts. Bless This Mouse: A Soft-to-Touch Book. 2004. (Illus.). 24p. (J). 14.95 (978-1-59354-050-0(7)) Handprint Bks.

Atkinson, Greg. Skuborm & His Super Hat. Ford Wilson, Melanie, illus. l.t. ed. 2002. 32p. per. (978-0-9730527-0-1(8)) Red Hare Pr.

Atlas, Ron. Ten Pigs Fiddling. Flint, Stacie, illus. 2nd rev. ed. 2006. 32p. (J). 17.95 (978-0-9630243-3-6(7)) Amberwood Pr.

Augustine, Kristen. Can I Tell You? 2005. 9.00 (978-0-8059-8071-4(7)) Dorrance Publishing Co., Inc.

Awdry, Wilbert V. Blue Train, Green Train. Stubbs, Tommy, illus. 2006. 36p. (J). (gr. k-1). 8.99 (978-0-375-83463-9(X) , Random Hse. Bks. for Young Readers) Random Hse. Children's Bks.

—Blue Train, Green Train. Stubbs, Tommy, illus. (J). (gr. k-ps). 2007. 24p. bds. 4.99 (****978-0-375-83984-9(4)***); 2006. 36p. lib. bdg. 12.99 (978-0-375-93463-6(4)) Random Hse. Children's Bks. (Random Hse. Bks. for Young Readers).

Awdry, Wilbert V. & Gerver, Jane E. A Crack in the Track: A Thomas the Tank Engine Story. Stubbs, Tommy & Nelson, Mary Beth, illus. 2001. (Beginner Bks.). 48p. (J). (gr. k-3). 8.99 (978-0-375-81246-0(6) , Random Hse. Bks. for Young Readers) Random Hse. Children's Bks.

Awdry, Wilbert V. & Hooke, R. Schuyler. Railway Rhymes. Courtney, Richard, illus. 2005. (Thomas & Friends Ser.). 36p. (J). (gr. k-2). bds. 11.99 (978-0-375-83175-1(4) , Random Hse. Bks. for Young Readers) Random Hse. Children's Bks.

Aylesworth, Jim. Little Bitty Mousie. Hague, Michael, illus. 2007. 32p. (J). 17.85 (****978-0-8027-9638-7(9)***); 16.95 (****978-0-8027-9637-0(0)***) Walker & Co.

—Naughty Little Monkeys. Cole, Henry, illus. 2006. 32p. (J). reprint ed. pap. 6.99 (978-0-14-240562-8(0) , Puffin) Penguin Group (USA) Inc.

—Old Black Fly. 2002. (Illus.). (J). 15.49 (978-0-7587-3302-3(X)) Book Wholesalers, Inc.

Ayres, Katherine. Up, Down, & Around. Westcott, Nadine Bernard, illus. 2007. 32p. (J). (gr. k). 16.99 (978-0-7636-2378-4(4)) Candlewick Pr.

Azr, Teferu. The Ronin Poetz: Hip-Hop's First Novel in Rhyme. 2002. (Illus.). 184p. (YA). per. 15.95 (978-0-9762627-1-8(1)) DaChosen Publishing.

Baa, Baa Black Sheep. 2003. (J). per. (978-1-57657-799-8(6)) Paradise Pr., Inc.

Baby Looney Tunes Visit a Haunted House. 2005. (Baby Looney Tunes Ser.). (Illus.). 14p. (J). (ps-3). bds. 9.95 (978-0-8249-6609-6(0)) Ideals Pubns.

Backx, Patsy. Skippy & Jack. Backx, Patsy, illus. 2002. (Illus.). 32p. (J). (ps up). lib. bdg. 24.67 (978-0-8368-3080-4(6)) Stevens, Gareth Inc.

Baer, Edith. Words are like Faces. Teis, Kyra, illus. 2007. 32p. (J). 15.95 (****978-1-59572-108-2(8)***) Star Bright Bks., Inc.

Baicker, Karen. I Can Do It Too! Wilson-Max, Ken, illus. 2003. 24p. (J). 13.95 (978-1-929766-83-3(1)) Handprint Bks.

—Tumble Me Tumbly. Williams, Sam, illus. 2002. 40p. (J). 15.95 (978-1-929766-61-1(0)) Handprint Bks.

Bailey, Beth. Raining Fish. 2006. (Illus.). 32p. (J). per. 14.95 (978-1-933148-34-2(9)) Tate Publishing & Enterprises, L.L.C.

Bair, Sheila. Rock, Brock, & the Savings Shock. Gott, Barry, illus. 2006. (Way I ACT Ser.). 32p. (J). 15.95 (978-0-8075-7094-4(X)) Whitman, Albert & Co.

Bajaj, Varsha. How Many Kisses Do You Want Tonight? Bates, Ivan, illus. 2004. 28p. (J). (ps-3). 15.99 (978-0-316-82381-4(3)) Little, Brown Bks. for Young Readers.

Baker, Keith. Little Green. (Illus.). (J). (ps-k). 2001. 32p. 16.00 (978-0-15-292859-9(6)); 2005. 30p. bds. 6.95 (978-0-15-205308-6(5) , Red Wagon Bks.) Harcourt Children's Bks.

—Quien es la Bestia? Ada, Alma Flor, tr. 2005. (SPA., Illus.). 28p. (J). bds. 6.95 (978-0-15-205596-7(7) , Red Wagon Bks.) Harcourt Children's Bks.

—Who Is the Beast? 2003. (Illus.). 28p. (J). bds. 6.95 (978-0-15-204752-8(2) , Red Wagon Bks.) Harcourt Children's Bks.

Baker, Liza. I Love You Because You're You. 2008. (Scooby-Doo Ser.). 24p. (J). bds. 8.99 (****978-0-545-02931-5(7)*** , Cartwheel Bks.) Scholastic, Inc.

—I Love You Because You're You. McPhail, David M., illus. 2001. 32p. (J). (ps-k). pap. 9.95 (978-0-439-20638-9(3) , Cartwheel Bks.) Scholastic, Inc.

Baker, Ryan. How I Would Paint the World? 2006. (ENG.). 48p. per. 15.95 (****978-1-59800-969-9(9)***) Outskirts Press, Inc.

Balaam, Lisa & Balaam, Steven. Abbey the Cavi in Miami Beach. 2006. 52p. (J). 19.95 (978-1-4196-1004-2(X)) BookSurge, LLC.

Balan, Bruce. Cows Going Past. Nash, Scott, illus. 2005. 32p. (J). (ps-ps). 9.99 (978-0-8037-2902-5(2)) Penguin Group (USA) Inc.

Ballentine, Joyce. Nana's Nursery Rhymes 2. 2003. (J). pap. 12.00 (978-0-8059-9211-3(1) , RoseDog Bks.) Dorrance Publishing Co., Inc.

Banana-Tail. 2003. lib. bdg. 13.95 (978-0-9727681-0-8(6)) Active Media Publishing, LLC.

Bandsuh, Jim. Helmet Hank. 2007. (J). per. 15.99 (*978-1-933156-19-4(8)*, Visikid Bks.) GSVQ Publishing.
Barkan, Joanne. There's A Mouse in My House! 2006. (Illus.). 10p. (J). bds. 14.99 (978-0-7944-1138-1(X)) Reader's Digest Assn., Inc., The.
Barkly, Bob. A Puppy to Love. Kurtz, John, illus. 2001. (Clifford, the Big Red Dog Ser.). (J). (gr. k-2). pap. (978-0-439-22004-0(1)) Scholastic, Inc.
Barner, Bob. Parade Day: Marching Through the Calendar Year. 2003. (Illus.). 32p. (J). (gr. k-3). tchr. ed. 16.95 (978-0-8234-1690-5(9)) Holiday Hse., Inc.
Barnes, Derrick. The Low-down, Bad-Day Blues. Boyd, Aaron, illus. 2004. 32p. (J). (gr. k-1). lib. bdg. 11.19 (978-0-606-33352-8(5)) Tandem Library Bks.
Barnes, Derrick D. The Low-down, Bad-Day Blues. Boyd, Aaron, illus. 2004. 32p. (J). lib. bdg. 15.00 (*978-1-4242-0222-5(1)*) Fitzgerald Bks.
—Stop, Drop, & Chill. Phillips-Duke, Barbara Jean, illus. 2004. 32p. (J). lib. bdg. 15.00 (*978-1-4242-0231-7(0)*) Fitzgerald Bks.
Barnes, Peter W. Woodrow, the White House Mouse. Barnes, Cheryl Shaw, illus. 2nd rev. ed. 1998. 32p. (J). (gr. 1-3). (978-0-9637688-9-6(1)) Vacation Spot Publishing.
Barnes, Peter W. & Barnes, Cheryl Shaw. Woodrow, the White House Mouse. 2000. 32p. (J). (gr. k-3). pap. 5.99 (978-0-439-12952-7(4)) Scholastic, Inc.
Barns, Peter & Barns, Cheryl. Woodrow, the White House Mouse. 2000. (978-0-606-18617-9(4)) Tandem Library Bks.
Barracca, Debra. Adventures of Taxi Dog. 2000. (ps-2). lib. bdg. 14.15 (978-0-613-28397-7(X)) Tandem Library Bks.
Barry, Robert. Mr. Willowby's Christmas Tree. Date not set. 32p. (J). 16.95 (978-0-8488-2206-4(4)) Amereon LTD.
—Mr. Willowby's Christmas Tree. Barry, Robert, illus. 2000. (Illus.). 32p. (J). (gr. k-3). 15.95 (978-0-385-32721-3(8), Doubleday Bks. for Young Readers) Random Hse. Children's Bks.
Barton, Byron. The Three Bears. 1999. 32p. (J). (ps-1). pap. 4.95 (978-0-06-443365-5(X)) HarperCollins Pubs.
Base, Graeme. The Sign of the Seahorse: A Tale of Greed & High Adventure in Two Acts. 1998. (Picture Puffin Ser.). (Illus.). 48p. (J). (gr. 1-4). pap. 8.99 (978-0-14-056387-0(3), Puffin) Penguin Group (USA) Inc.
Baskwill, Jane. If Peace Is... Carter, Stephanie, illus. 2003. (J). 23p. pap. 7.95 (978-1-59034-449-1(9)); 24p. (gr. 11 up). 15.95 (978-1-59034-448-4(0)) Mondo Publishing.
Bateman, Teresa. April Foolishness. Westcott, Nadine Bernard, illus. 32p. (J). 2007. pap. 6.95 (*978-0-8075-0405-5(X)*); 2004. 16.95 (978-0-8075-0404-8(1)) Whitman, Albert & Co.
—Farm Flu. Westcott, Nadine Bernard, illus. 2001. 32p. (J). (ps-2). pap. 7.95 (978-0-8075-2275-2(9)) Whitman, Albert & Co.
—Fluffy, Scourge of the Sea. Chesworth, Michael, illus. 32p. (J). 2006. pap. 6.95 (978-1-58089-152-3(7)); 2005. 14.95 (978-1-58089-099-1(7)) Charlesbridge Publishing, Inc.
—Hamster Camp: How Harry Got Fit. Cote, Nancy, illus. 2005. 32p. (J). (gr. k-4). 15.95 (978-0-8075-3139-6(1)) Whitman, Albert & Co.
—Hunting the Daddyosaurus. Huang, Benrei, illus. 2004. 29p. (J). (gr. k-4). reprint ed. 16.00 (978-0-7567-7796-8(8)) DIANE Publishing Co.
—Hunting the Daddyosaurus. Huang, Benrei, illus. 2002. 32p. (J). (ps-1). 15.95 (978-0-8075-1433-7(0)) Whitman, Albert & Co.
—A Plump & Perky Turkey. Shelly, Jeff, illus. 2005. 32p. (J). pap. 5.95 (978-0-7614-5188-4(9)) Cavendish, Marshall Corp.
—A Plump & Perky Turkey. Shelly, Jeff, illus. 2001. 40p. (J). (ps-3). 15.95 (978-1-890817-91-6(0)) Winslow Pr.
—Will You Be My Valenswine? Stephenson, Kristina, illus. 2005. 24p. (J). (ps-2). lib. bdg. 15.95 (978-0-8075-9195-6(5)) Whitman, Albert & Co.
Bauer, Marion Dane. My Mother Is Mine. Elwell, Peter, illus. 40p. (J). (ps-k). 2001. 13.00 (978-0-689-82267-4(7)); 2004. reprint ed. pap. 6.99 (978-0-689-86695-1(X), Aladdin) Simon & Schuster Children's Publishing.
—My Mother Is Mine. 2004. (ps-2). lib. bdg. 14.15 (978-0-613-88067-1(6)) Tandem Library Bks.
Bauer, Marion Dane. One Brown Bunny. Bates, Ivan, illus. 2008. (J). (*978-0-439-68010-3(7)*, Orchard Bks.) Scholastic, Inc.
Bauer, Marion Dane & Wu, Leslie. The Very Best Daddy of All. 2007. 40p. (J). pap. 6.99 (978-1-4169-2736-5(0), Aladdin) Simon & Schuster Children's Publishing.
Baum, L. Frank. Mother Goose in Prose. l.t. ed. 2005. 268p. pap. (978-1-84637-097-7(3)) Echo Library.
Baynes, Pauline, illus. The Elephant's Ball. 2007. 32p. (J). 17.00 (978-0-8028-5316-5(1), Eerdmans Bks For Young Readers) Eerdmans, William B. Publishing Co.
Bea, Holly. Bless Your Heart. Howard, Kim, illus. 2001. 32p. (J). (ps-1). 16.00 (978-0-915811-94-6(4)) Kramer, H.J. Inc.
—Lucy Goose Goes to Texas. Boddy, Joe, illus. 2005. 32p. (J). 15.95 (978-1-932073-15-7(9)) New World Library.
Bea, Holly & Howard, Kim. God Believes in You. 2004. (Illus.). 32p. (J). 15.00 (978-1-932073-08-9(6)) Kramer, H.J. Inc.
Beardsley, Martyn. Five Naughty Kittens. East, Jacqueline, illus. 2005. (Reading Corner Ser.). 24p. (J). (gr. k-3). lib. bdg. 22.80 (978-1-59771-006-0(7)) Sea-To-Sea Pubns.
Beaton, Clare, illus. Daisy Gets Dressed. 2005. 24p. (J). 15.99 (978-1-84148-794-6(5)) Barefoot Bks., Inc.
Beaty, Andrea. Iggy Peck, Architect. Roberts, David, illus. 2007. 32p. (J). (ps-3). 15.95 (978-0-8109-1106-2(X), Abrams Bks. for Young Readers) Abrams, Harry N., Inc.
Beaumont, Karen. Baby Danced the Polka. Plecas, Jennifer, illus. 2004. 32p. (J). (ps). 12.99 (978-0-8037-2587-4(6), Dial) Penguin Group (USA) Inc.
—Doggone Dogs! Catrow, David, illus. 2008. (J). (*978-0-8037-3157-8(4)*, Dial) Penguin Group (USA) Inc.
—Duck, Duck, Goose! (A Coyote's on the Loose!) Aruego, Jose, illus. 2004. 32p. (J). (ps-2). 16.99 (978-0-06-050802-9(7)); lib. bdg. 17.89 (978-0-06-050804-3(3)) HarperCollins Pubs.
—I Ain't Gonna Paint No More! Catrow, David, illus. 2005. 32p. (J). 16.00 (978-0-15-202488-8(3)) Harcourt Trade Pubs.
—I Like Myself! Catrow, David, illus. 2004. 32p. (J). 16.00 (978-0-15-202013-2(6)) Harcourt Children's Bks.
—Move Over, Rover! Dyer, Jane, illus. 2006. (J). (*978-1-4287-0246-2(6)*) Harcourt Trade Pubs.
—Who Ate All the Cookie Dough? Yelchin, Eugene, illus. 2008. 32p. (J). 16.95 (*978-0-8050-8267-8(0)*) Holt, Henry & Co.
Beccia, Carlyn. Who Put the "B" in Ballyhoo? The Most Amazing, Bizarre, & Celebrated Circus Performers. 2007. (Illus.). 32p. (J). (ps-k). 16.00 (978-0-618-71718-7(8)) Houghton Mifflin Co. Trade & Reference Div.
Beccia, Carlyn. Who Put the B in the Ballyhoo? 2007. (Illus.). (J). (*978-1-4287-3570-5(4)*) Houghton Mifflin Co.
Beck, Scott. Little House, Little Town. 2004. (Illus.). 32p. (J). (ps-1). 14.95 (978-0-8109-4930-0(X)) Abrams, Harry N., Inc.
Becker, Helaine. Mother Goose Unplucked: Crazy Comics, Zany Activities, Nutty Facts, & Other Twisted Takes on Childhood Favorites. Davila, Claudia, illus. 2007. 160p. (J). (gr. 3-7). 22.95 (978-1-897066-83-6(X)); pap. 10.95 (978-1-897066-84-3(8)) Maple Tree Pr. CAN. *Dist:* Perseus Distribution.
Becker, John E. Seven Little Rabbits. Cooney, Barbara, illus. 2007. 32p. (J). 8.85 (978-0-8027-9635-6(4)); 7.95 (978-0-8027-9634-9(6)) Walker & Co.
Becker, Shelly. Mine! Mine! Mine! Takahashi, Hideko, illus. 2006. 32p. (J). 14.95 (978-1-4027-2538-8(8)) Sterling Publishing Co., Inc.
Beckerman, Menucha. The Candy Kids. 2004. (My Smiling World Ser.: No. 3). (Illus.). 32p. (J). 11.95 (978-1-931681-54-4(6)) Israel Bk. Shop.
Bedtime Stories & Rhymes. 2002. 224p. (J). 5.98 (978-0-7525-8909-1(1)) Parragon, Inc.
Been, Sherry. If I Were a Frog. 2001. (Illus.). 42p. (J). (gr. k-3). 14.95 (978-0-9705693-0-1(0)) SherMar Pubns.
Bell, Russell, illus. Herbert Hilligan's Tropical Adventure, Vol. 3. rev. ed. 1999. (Herbert Hilligan Ser.). 15.95 (978-1-57168-314-4(3)) Eakin Pr.
Bellido, Mary Ellen, illus. A Princess Smiled: A Story Book Rhyme Collection. 2001. 24p. (J). 13.95 (978-1-886185-22-7(0)) Mosley Publishing Group.
Bemelmans, Ludwig. Madeline: Edicion en Espanol. Anasal, Arshes, ed. 2005. (SPA., Illus.). 44p. (J). (gr. k-4). reprint ed. 16.00 (978-0-7567-8842-1(0)) DIANE Publishing Co.
—Madeline's Christmas. Bemelmans, Ludwig, illus. 2007. (Puffin Storytime Ser.). 32p. (J). (ps). 9.99 (*978-0-14-240897-1(2)*, Puffin) Penguin Group (USA) Inc.
Bemelmans, Ludwig. Madeline's Rescue. ed. 2004. (J). (ps-2). spiral bd. (978-0-616-11864-1(3)) Canadian National Institute for the Blind/Institut National Canadien pour les Aveugles.
Bemelsman, Ludwig. Madeleine. 2000. (Adventures of Madeleine Ser.). (FRE.). (J). pap. 14.95 (978-2-211-02156-2(5)) Archimede Editions FRA. *Dist:* Distribooks, Inc.
Benenfeld, Rikki. I Go Visiting. 2007. (Illus.). 32p. (J). 10.95 (978-1-929628-33-9(1)) Hachai Publishing.
Bennett, Caroline Coleman. Charley's Columbia Backyard. Bowers, Paula Hayne, illus. 2006. 49p. (J). (978-0-9745284-5-8(5)) Palmetto Conservation Foundation.
Bentley, Dawn. I'm a Pink Piggy. Tom-Nellis, Susan, illus. 1998. (Baby Buddy Bks.: No. 4). 12p. (YA). (ps up). bds. 4.95 (978-1-888443-70-7(7), Intervisual/Piggy Toes) Dalmatian Pr.
—Little Lost Duck. Tom-Nellis, Susan, illus. 1998. (Baby Buddy Bks.). 12p. (YA). (ps up). bds. 4.95 (978-1-888443-72-1(3), Intervisual/Piggy Toes) Dalmatian Pr.
—Who's in the Jungle. Valderrama, Rosario, illus. 2001. (Sneak-A-Peek Board Book Ser.: Vol. 1). 10p. (ps-k). bds. 6.95 (978-1-58117-141-9(2), Intervisual/Piggy Toes) Dalmatian Pr.
Berenstain, Jan, et al. The Berenstain Bears Save Christmas. Berenstain, Michael, illus. 2003. (Berenstain Bears Ser.). 48p. (J). (ps-3). 12.99 (978-0-06-052670-2(X)) HarperCollins Pubs.
Berenstain, Stan & Berenstain, Jan. The Berenstain Bears down on the Farm. Berenstain, Stan & Berenstain, Jan, illus. 2006. (Berenstain Bears Ser.). (Illus.). 32p. (J). 15.99 (978-0-06-058350-7(9)) HarperCollins Pubs.
—The Berenstain Bears down on the Farm. 2006. (Berenstain Bears Ser.). (Illus.). 32p. (J). pap. 3.99 (978-0-06-058351-4(7), Harper Trophy); (*978-1-4156-8342-2(5)*) HarperCollins Pubs.
—Berenstain Bears down on the Farm. 2006. (Illus.). 32p. (J). lib. bdg. 15.00 (*978-1-4242-1537-9(4)*) Fitzgerald Bks.
—The Berenstain Bears Go on Vacation. 2006. (Berenstain Bears Ser.: No. 1). (Illus.). 32p. (J). 9.99 (978-0-06-057431-4(3)); Bk. 1. lib. bdg. 15.89 (978-0-06-057432-1(1)) HarperCollins Pubs.
—The Berenstain Bears Out West. Berenstain, Stan & Berenstain, Jan, illus. 2006. (Berenstain Bears Ser.). (Illus.). 32p. (J). 15.99 (978-0-06-058353-8(3)); pap. 3.99 (978-0-06-058354-5(1), Harper Trophy) HarperCollins Pubs.
—The Berenstain Bears We Like Kites. 2004. (Berenstain Bears Ser.). (J). (ps-2). lib. bdg. 11.80 (978-0-613-87779-4(9)) Tandem Library Bks.
Berger, Samantha. Honk! Toot! Beep! Elliott, Gloria, illus. 2001. (My First Hello Reader! Ser.). 32p. (J). (gr. k-2). pap. 3.99 (978-0-439-21037-9(2)) Scholastic, Inc.
—It's Spring! 2001. (Hello Reader! Ser.). (Illus.). (J). (978-0-606-21257-1(4)) Tandem Library Bks.
Berger, Samantha & Chanko, Pamela. It's Spring. Sweet, Melissa, illus. 2003. 30p. (J). bds. 5.99 (978-0-439-44238-1(9), Cartwheel Bks.) Scholastic, Inc.
Berger, Samantha, et al. It's Spring! 2001. (Hello Reader! Ser.). (Illus.). 32p. (J). (gr. k-2). pap. 3.99 (978-0-439-08754-4(6)) Scholastic, Inc.
Bergman, Mara. Oliver Who Would Not Sleep! Maland, Nick, illus. 2007. (J). (*978-0-439-92827-4(3)*); 40p. pap. 16.99 (*978-0-439-92826-7(5)*) Scholastic, Inc. (Levine, Arthur A. Bks.).
Berkes, Marianne Collins. Marsh Music. Noreika, Robert, illus. 2000. 3. 32p. (J). (gr. k-3). 14.95 (978-0-7613-1850-7(X), Millbrook Pr.) Lerner Publishing Group.
Berman, Ron. Old MacDonald Had a Wedding. Gerrity, Brian, illus. 2007. 24p. (J). pap. 5.99 (978-0-8431-2189-6(0), Price Stern Sloan) Penguin Group (USA) Inc.
Bermiss, Aamir. I Hate to Be Sick! Wilson-Max, Ken, illus. 2004. 32p. (J). (gr. k-1). lib. bdg. 11.19 (978-0-606-33350-4(9)) Tandem Library Bks.
Bermiss, Aamir Lee. I Hate to Be Sick! Wilson-Max, Ken, illus. 2004. 32p. (J). lib. bdg. 15.00 (*978-1-4242-0220-1(5)*) Fitzgerald Bks.
Bernal, Mitchell. Skelanimals: Dead Animals Need Love Too, Bernal, Mitchell, illus. l.t. ed. 2005. (Illus.). 22p. (J). per. 12.95 (978-0-9766621-0-5(8), 818 554-8965) Kreations.
Bernstein, Lee. Barney's Sing-Along Stories: I Love You. Valentine-Ruppe, June, illus. 2003. (Barney Ser.). 24p. (J). (ps-1). pap. 3.50 (978-1-58668-299-6(7)) Scholastic, Inc.
Bernstein, Margery. My Brother, the Pest. Handelman, Dorothy, photos by. 1999. (Real Kids Readers Ser.). (Illus.). 32p. (gr. k-2). (J). pap. 4.99 (978-0-7613-2080-7(6)); lib. bdg. 18.90 (978-0-7613-2055-5(5)) Lerner Publishing Group. (Millbrook Pr.).
—My Brother, the Pest. 1999. (J). (978-0-606-19164-7(X)); lib. bdg. 11.80 (978-0-613-16773-4(2)) Tandem Library Bks.
Bernthal, Mark & Exclaim Entertainment Staff. Boz/Good Morning Boz. Jeffords, Brandon, illus. 2006. (BOZ#8482; Ser.). 14p. (J). 4.99 (978-0-310-71207-7(6)) Zondervan.
—Boz/Good Night Boz. Jeffords, Brandon, illus. 2006. (BOZ#8482; Ser.). 14p. (J). 4.99 (978-0-310-71206-0(8)) Zondervan.
Bernthal, Mark S. & Scholastic, Inc. Staff. Barney's ABC Animals! Baker, Darrell, illus. 1999. (Barney Ser.). 32p. (J). (ps-k). pap. 3.50 (978-1-57064-453-5(5)) Scholastic, Inc.
Berry, Lynne. Duck Dunks. Nakata, Hiroe, illus. 2008. 32p. (J). 16.95 (*978-0-8050-8128-2(3)*) Holt, Henry & Co.
Bertram, Debbie & Bloom, Susan. The Best Place to Read. Garland, Michael, illus. 2003. 32p. (J). (ps-1). 14.95 (978-0-375-82293-3(3), Random Hse. Bks. for Young Readers) Random Hse. Children's Bks.
—The Best Time to Read. Garland, Michael, illus. 2005. 32p. (J). (ps-2). 14.95 (978-0-375-83025-9(1)); lib. bdg. 16.99 (978-0-375-93025-6(6)) Random Hse. Children's Bks. (Random Hse. Bks. for Young Readers).
Bicknell, Joanna. Tickle Monsters. 2007. (Finger Puppet Books Ser.). (Illus.). 12p. (ps). bds. 12.99 (*978-1-84610-427-5(0)*) Make Believe Ideas GBR. *Dist:* Ingram Pub. Services.
Billstrom, Diane. You Can't Go to School Naked! Kilpatrick III, Don, illus. 2008. 32p. (J). (ps-k). 16.99 (*978-0-399-24738-5(6)*, Putnam Juvenile) Penguin Group (USA) Inc.
Bingham, Kelly L. Shark Girl. 2007. 276p. (YA). (*978-1-4287-4705-0(2)*) Candlewick Pr.
Birrer, Cynthia & Birrer, Bill, illus. The Confused Zebra. 1999. (J). 16.95 (978-0-86543-795-1(5)) Africa World Pr.
Bjorkman, Steve. Good Night, Little One. Bjorkman, Steve, illus. 1999. (Illus.). 40p. (J). (ps-3). 9.99 (978-1-57856-275-6(9), WaterBrook Pr.) WaterBrook Pr.
Black, Michael Ian. Chicken Cheeks. Hawkes, Kevin, illus. 2008. (J). (*978-1-4169-4864-3(3)*, Simon & Schuster Children's Publishing) Simon & Schuster Children's Publishing.
Black, Robyn Hood. Sir Mike. Murphy, David, illus. (J). (gr. k-2). 2006. 32p. pap. 4.95 (978-0-516-25020-5(5)); 2005. 31p. 19.50 (978-0-516-24862-2(6)) Scholastic Library Publishing. (Children's Pr.).
Black, Sonia W. Hanging Out with Mom. 2000. (Hello Reader! Ser.). (Illus.). (J). 10.79 (978-0-606-18554-7(2)) Tandem Library Bks.
—Hanging Out with Mom: Level. 1. Ford, George C., illus. 2000. (Hello Reader! Ser.). 32p. (J). (ps-3). pap. 3.99 (978-0-590-86636-1(2)) Scholastic, Inc.
Black, Sonia W. & MacCombie, Turi. Follow the Polar Bears. 2000. (Hello Reader! Science Ser.). (Illus.). (J). (ps-3). pap. 3.99 (978-0-439-20641-9(3)) Scholastic, Inc.
Blackaby, Susan. Ann Plants a Garden. Collier-Morales, Roberta, illus. 2005. (Read-It! Readers Ser.). 32p. (J). (gr. k-3). 18.60 (978-1-4048-1010-5(2)) Picture Window Bks.
—Wes Gets a Pet. Gallagher-Cole, Mernie, illus. 2005. (Read-It! Readers Ser.). 32p. (J). (gr. k-3). 18.60 (978-1-4048-1060-0(9)) Picture Window Bks.
Blackstone, Stella. Alligator Alphabet. Bauer, Stephanie, illus. 2005. 48p. (J). (ps-k). 16.99 (978-1-84148-494-5(6)) Barefoot Bks., Inc.
—Cleo's Color Book. Mockford, Caroline, illus. 2006. 0032p. (J). 15.99 (978-1-905236-30-5(1)) Barefoot Bks., Inc.
—A Dragon on the Doorstep. Harter, Debbie, illus. 2005. 32p. (J). (ps-1). 15.99 (978-1-84148-227-9(7)) Barefoot Bks., Inc.
—La Familia activa de Oso (Bear's Busy Family) Sarfatti, Esther, tr. Harter, Debbie, illus. 2003. (Bear Ser.). (SPA.). 24p. (J). 5.99 (978-1-84148-777-9(5)) Barefoot Bks., Inc.
—Hay una Vaca Entre las Coles. Beaton, Clare, illus. 2003. (SPA.). 32p. (J). (gr. k-2). 6.99 (978-1-84148-965-0(4)) Barefoot Bks., Inc.
—I Dreamt I Was a Dinosaur. Beaton, Clare, illus. 2005. 32p. (J). (ps-3). 15.99 (978-1-84148-238-5(2)) Barefoot Bks., Inc.
—I Wish I Were a Pilot. Grover, Max, illus. 2005. 32p. (J). (ps-ps). pap. 15.99 (978-1-84148-341-2(9)) Barefoot Bks., Inc.
—An Island in the Sun. Ceccoli, Nicoletta, illus. 2005. 24p. (J). pap. 6.99 (978-1-84148-079-4(7)); 15.99 (978-1-84148-193-7(9)) Barefoot Bks., Inc.
—Jump into January. Carluccio, Maria, illus. 2004. 32p. (J). 15.99 (978-1-84148-629-1(9)) Barefoot Bks., Inc.
—My Granny Went to Market: A Round-the-World Counting Rhyme. Corr, Christopher, illus. 2005. 24p. (J). 16.99 (978-1-84148-792-2(9)) Barefoot Bks., Inc.
—Oso bajo el sol (Bear in Sunshine) Sarfatti, Esther, tr. Harter, Debbie, illus. 2003. (Bear Ser.). (SPA.). 24p. (J). 5.99 (978-1-84148-778-6(3)) Barefoot Bks., Inc.
—Oso en bicicleta (Bear on a Bike) Sarfatti, Esther, tr. Harter, Debbie, illus. 2003. (Bear Ser.). (SPA.). 32p. (J). 5.99 (978-1-84148-775-5(9)) Barefoot Bks., Inc.
—Oso en casa (Bear at Home) Sarfatti, Esther, tr. Harter, Debbie, illus. 2003. (Bear Ser.). (SPA.). 24p. (J). 5.99 (978-1-84148-779-3(1)) Barefoot Bks., Inc.
—Oso en la ciudad (Bear About Town) Sarfatti, Esther, tr. Harter, Debbie, illus. 2003. (Bear Ser.). (SPA.). 24p. (J). 5.99 (978-1-84148-776-2(7)) Barefoot Bks., Inc.
—Oso en un cuadrado (Bear in a Square) Sarfatti, Esther, tr. Harter, Debbie, illus. 2003. (Bear Ser.). (SPA.). 24p. (J). 5.99 (978-1-84148-774-8(0)) Barefoot Bks., Inc.
—Secret Seahorse. Beaton, Clare, illus. 24p. (J). 2005. pap. 6.99 (978-1-84148-937-7(9)); 2005. 15.99 (978-1-84148-704-5(X)); 2004. per. 6.99 (978-1-905236-15-2(8)) Barefoot Bks., Inc.
—Secret Seahorse. Beaton, Clare, illus. 2005. (ps-ps). lib. bdg. 14.19 (978-0-606-33158-6(1)) Tandem Library Bks.
—Ship Shapes. Bell, Siobhan, illus. 2006. (J). 0024p. 15.99 (978-1-905236-34-3(4)); (*978-1-4156-6474-2(9)*) Barefoot Bks., Inc.
—Skip through the Seasons. Carluccio, Maria, illus. 2006. 32p. (J). (ps-2). pap. 6.99 (978-1-905236-71-8(9)) Barefoot Bks., Inc.
—Walking Through the Jungle. Harter, Debbie, illus. 2004. 32p. (J). 9.99 (978-1-84148-182-1(3)) Barefoot Bks., Inc.
—Who Are You? Harter, Debbie, illus. 2003. 24p. (J). (gr. k-2). bds. 6.99 (978-1-84148-609-3(4)) Barefoot Bks., Inc.
—Who Are You, Baby Kangaroo? Beaton, Clare, illus. 2004. 32p. (J). 14.99 (978-1-84148-217-0(X)) Barefoot Bks., Inc.
Blake, Anne Catharine. Sheep Lost. 1998. (ENG., Illus.). 20p. (J). (ps). bds. 4.99 (978-0-570-05091-9(X)) Concordia Publishing Hse.
Blake, Quentin. Fantastic Daisy Artichoke. 2001. (Illus.). 32p. (J). (ps-1). pap. 11.99 (978-0-09-940006-6(5)) Random Hse. GBR. *Dist:* Trafalgar Square Publishing.
Blomgren, Jennifer. Where Do I Sleep? A Pacific Northwest Lullaby. Gabriel, Andrea, illus. 2002. 32p. (J). (ps-1). 16.95 (978-1-57061-258-9(7)) Sasquatch Bks.
Bloom, Susan & Bertram, Debbie. The Best Place to Read. Garland, Michael, illus. 2007. 32p. (J). (ps-3). pap. 6.99 (978-0-375-83757-9(4), Dragonfly Bks.) Random Hse. Children's Bks.
Bloom, Suzanne. We Keep a Pig in the Parlor. 2004. (Illus.). 24p. (J). (gr. k-2). reprint ed. pap. 7.95 (978-1-59078-084-8(1)) Boyds Mills Pr.
Bock, Suzanne, illus. Meet the Angels, l.t. ed. 2004. 10p. (J). bds. 12.99 (978-0-9758709-4-5(7), 13401) Journey Stone Creations, LLC.
Boedoe, Geefwee. Arrowville. Boedoe, Geefwee, illus. 2004. (Illus.). 40p. (J). (ps-2). 16.89 (978-0-06-055599-3(8), Geringer, Laura Book) HarperCollins Pubs.
Boelts, Maribeth. The Firefighters' Thanksgiving. Widener, Terry, illus. 32p. (J). (ps). 2006. pap. 6.99 (978-0-14-240631-1(7), Puffin); 2004. 15.99 (978-0-399-23600-6(7), Putnam Juvenile) Penguin Group (USA) Inc.
Boey, Stephanie. Undersea Treasure Hunt: Find the Treasure with Little Fish & Friends. Boey, Stephanie, illus. 2005. (Illus.). 20p. (J). 15.95 (978-0-8118-4622-6(9)) Chronicle Bks. LLC.
Bolam, Emily, illus. I'm Going to Read (Level 2): Fooba Wooba John. 2006. (I'm Going to Read Ser.). 32p. (J). pap. 3.95 (978-1-4027-3420-5(4)) Sterling Publishing Co., Inc.
Bond, Juliana. Pixie Tales the Wobbly Tooth. 2005. 30p. spiral bd. 12.08 (978-1-4116-6046-5(3)) Lulu.com.
—Salad Cream. 2005. 31p. spiral bd. 12.28 (978-1-4116-6047-2(1)) Lulu.com.
Bond, Rebecca. The Great Doughnut Parade. 2007. (Illus.). 40p. (J). (ps-k). 17.00 (*978-0-618-77705-1(9)*) Houghton Mifflin Co.
Boniface, William. The Treasure Hunter. Harris, Jim, illus. 1998. 32p. (J). 15.99 (978-0-939251-97-1(3)) Accord Publishing, Ltd.
—The Treasure Hunter. Harris, Jim, illus. 2007. 28p. bds. 9.99 (*978-1-57939-354-0(3)*) Andrews McMeel Publishing.

S

Boniface, William. Trim the Tree for Christmas! Palen, Debbie, illus. 2000. 12p. (J). (ps-2). bds. 9.99 (978-0-8431-7558-5(3) , Price Stern Sloan) Penguin Group (USA) Inc.

Bonnet-Rampersaud, Louise. My Nose Is Running. 1999. (Illus.). 24p. (J). (ps-k). 12.95 (978-1-886388-14-7(8)) Flower Valley Pr., Inc.

Bono, Mary. Ugh! a Bug. 2001. (Illus.). (J). 16.85 (978-0-8027-8800-9(9)) Walker & Co.

Bott, Elizabeth. Vinnie in Egypt. Frosini, Guido & Cecchetti, Alessandra, illus. l.t. ed. 2000. (Laugh & Learn Travel Ser.: No. 1). 54p. (J). (gr. k-8). 15.95 (978-0-9704678-0-5(X)) Pageturner Bks.

Bowdish, Lynea. A Dog for Each Day. Brooks, Karen Stormer, illus. 2003. (Rookie Reader Ser.). 32p. (J). 19.50 (978-0-516-22849-5(8) , Children's Pr.) Scholastic Library Publishing.

—One Glad Man. Sorra, Kristin, illus. 1999. (Rookie Readers Ser.). 32p. (J). (gr. 1-2). 19.50 (978-0-516-21595-2(7) , Children's Pr.) Scholastic Library Publishing.

—One Glad Man. Sorra, Kristin, illus. 2000. 31p. (J). (ps-3). lib. bdg. 12.95 (978-0-613-54628-7(8)) Tandem Library Bks.

—Preguntas Tontitas. Doty, Eldon C., illus. 2002. (Rookie Reader Espanol Ser.). (SPA.). (J). (gr. k-2). pap. 4.95 (978-0-516-26319-9(6) , Children's Pr.) Scholastic Library Publishing.

—Silly Questions Level C. Doty, Eldon C., illus. 2001. (Rookie Readers Ser.). 32p. (J). (gr. 1-2). 19.50 (978-0-516-22230-1(9) , Children's Pr.) Scholastic Library Publishing.

Bowen, Anne. What Do Teachers Do? After YOU Leave School. Gott, Barry, illus. 2006. 32p. (J). 15.95 (978-1-57505-922-8(3) , Carolrhoda Bks.) Lerner Publishing Group.

Bowie, C. W. Busy Fingers. Willingham, Fred, illus. 2004. (J). 28p. bds. 6.95 (978-1-58089-048-9(2)); 32p. 16.95 (978-1-58089-036-6(9)); 32p. pap. 6.95 (978-1-58089-037-3(7)) Charlesbridge Publishing, Inc.

—Busy Fingers. 2003. (ps-2). lib. bdg. 15.25 (978-0-613-87431-1(5)) Tandem Library Bks.

—Busy Toes. Willingham, Fred, illus. (J). (ps-1). 2004. 28p. bds. 6.95 (978-1-58089-056-4(3)); 2002. 32p. pap. 6.95 (978-1-58089-081-6(4)) Charlesbridge Publishing, Inc.

—Busy Toes. 1999. (Metro Reading Program Ser.). (J). (gr. k). 29.95 (978-1-58120-107-9(9)) Metropolitan Teaching & Learning Co.

Bowman, Crystal. J Is for Jesus: The Sweetest Story Ever Told. Gèvry, Claudine, illus. 2005. 20p. (J). (ps). 6.99 (978-0-310-70891-9(5)) Zonderkidz.

—Jesus, Me, & My Christmas Tree. Gèvry, Claudine, illus. 2005. 20p. (J). (ps). 6.99 (978-0-310-70874-2(5)) Zonderkidz.

—A Star for Jesus. Gèvry, Claudine, illus. 2006. 14p. (J). 6.99 (978-0-310-71216-9(5)) Zonderkidz.

Boynton, Sandra. But Not the Hippopotamus. 2001. (Illus.). (J). bds. 4.99 (978-0-689-83626-8(0) , Simon & Schuster Children's Publishing) Simon & Schuster Children's Publishing.

—Dinos to Go. Boynton, Sandra, illus. 2000. (Illus.). 18p. (J). (ps-k). 7.99 (978-0-689-84007-4(1)) Simon & Schuster Children's Publishing.

—Dinosaur's Binkit. 1998. (Illus.). 14p. (J). (ps-k). bds. 10.95 (978-0-689-82203-2(0) , Little Simon) Simon & Schuster Children's Publishing.

—The Going to Bed Book. Boynton, Sandra, illus. 2006. 14p. (J). 12.95 (978-1-4169-2794-5(8) , Little Simon) Simon & Schuster Children's Publishing.

—Hey! Wake Up! ed. 2004. (Illus.). (J). (ps up). spiral bd., bds. (978-0-616-14611-8(6)) Canadian National Institute for the Blind/Institut National Canadien pour les Aveugles.

—Hey! Wake Up! 2000. (Illus.). 24p. (J). (ps). bds. 6.95 (978-0-7611-1976-0(0) , 11976) Workman Publishing Co., Inc.

—Moo, Baa, La La La! braille ed. 2004. (J). (gr. 1). spiral bd., bds. (978-0-616-03082-0(7)) Canadian National Institute for the Blind/Institut National Canadien pour les Aveugles.

—Muu. Beee. ¡Asi Fue! Boynton, Sandra, illus. 2003. (SPA., Illus.). 14p. (J). bds. 5.99 (978-0-689-86302-8(0) , Libros Para Ninos) Simon & Schuster Children's Publishing.

—Sandra Boynton's Moo, Baa, la la La! Book & Rattle. Boynton, Sandra, illus. 2009. 16p. (J). bds. 16.99 (***978-1-4169-5035-6(4)** , Little Simon) Simon & Schuster Children's Publishing.

—Snuggle Puppy! A Love Song. 2003. (Illus.). 24p. (J). bds. 6.95 (978-0-7611-3067-3(5) , 13067) Workman Publishing Co., Inc.

—What's Wrong, Little Pookie? 2007. (Illus.). 18p. (J). (ps). bds. 5.99 (***978-0-375-84552-9(6)** , Robin Corey Bks.) Random Hse. Children's Bks.

Boynton, Sandra. Yay, You! Moving Out, Moving up, Moving On. Boynton, Sandra, illus. 2001. (Illus.). 32p. (J). (ps-3). 14.95 (978-0-689-84283-2(X) , Little Simon) Simon & Schuster Children's Publishing.

Bradby, Marie. Once upon a Farm. Rand, Ted, illus. 2002. 32p. (J). (ps-2). pap. 16.95 (978-0-439-31766-5(5) , Orchard Bks.) Scholastic, Inc.

Bradford, William. Jeremy Mcbright Was Afraid of the Night. 2006. (Illus.). 36p. (J). lib. bdg. 13.95 (978-0-9672585-2-2(9)) CyPress Pubns.

Bradman, Tony. Stack of Story Poems. 2000. (Illus.). 176p. (J). pap. 6.95 (978-0-552-52709-5(2)) Transworld Publishers Ltd. GBR. *Dist:* Trafalgar Square Publishing.

Brady, Karen. God Is Great: A Collection of 13 Story Book Poems. 1. l.t. ed. 2004. (Illus.). 20p. (J). 12.50 (978-0-9754169-0-7(1)) Bradybooks.biz.

Bramwell, Wendie, et al. The Friendship Alphabet. Ziegler, Michael, illus. Ziegler, Michael, photos by. 2003. 32p. (J). pap. (978-0-9741388-3-1(5)) Committee for Children.

Breathed, Berkeley. Edwurd Fudwupper Fibbed Big. 2000. (Illus.). 48p. (J). (ps-17). 15.99 (978-0-316-10675-7(5)) Little Brown & Co.

—Edwurd Fudwupper Fibbed Big. Breathed, Berkeley, illus. 2003. (Illus.). 40p. (J). (gr. 1-4). pap. 6.99 (978-0-316-14425-4(8)) Little, Brown Bks. for Young Readers.

—Edwurd Fudwupper Fibbed Big. 2003. (gr. k-3). lib. bdg. 15.30 (978-0-613-71786-1(4)) Tandem Library Bks.

Bremmer, Patricia A. The Christmas Westie. 2007. 48p. (J). kivar 17.99 (***978-0-9745884-5-2(8))** Windcall Publishing.

Brennan, Linda Crotta. Flannel Kisses. Takabayashi, Mari, illus. 2006. 32p. (J). (gr. k-3). 6.95 (978-0-618-73752-9(9)) Houghton Mifflin Co. Trade & Reference Div.

Brennan, Linda Crotta. Marshmallow Kisses. Takabayashi, Mari, illus. 2007. 32p. (J). (gr. k-3). 6.95 (***978-0-618-80903-5(1))** Houghton Mifflin Co. Trade & Reference Div.

Brennan, Martin. I Saw It in the Garden. Monroe, Michael Glenn, illus. 2006. 32p. (J). 17.95 (978-1-58726-296-8(7) , Mitten Pr.) Ann Arbor Media Group, LLC.

Brennan, Martin. Three Lessons for Astair the Bear. Huntington, Amy, illus. 2007. 40p. (J). 18.95 (***978-1-58726-435-1(8)** , Mitten Pr.) Ann Arbor Media Group, LLC.

Brennan-Nelson, Denise. Buzzy the Bumblebee. Monroe, Michael Glenn, illus. 32p. (J). (gr. k-3). 2003. pap. 6.95 (978-1-58536-166-3(6)); 1999. 15.00 (978-1-886947-82-5(1)) Sleeping Bear Pr.

—Buzzy the Bumblebee. 2003. (gr. k-3). lib. bdg. 15.25 (978-0-613-79710-8(8)) Tandem Library Bks.

Brenner, Barbara. Good Morning, Garden. Ortakales, Denise, illus. 2004. 32p. (ps up). 15.95 (978-1-55971-888-2(9) , NorthWord Bks. for Young Readers) T&N Children's Publishing.

Brenner, Emily. On the First Day of Grade School. Whatley, Bruce, illus. 2004. 32p. (J). (ps-1). 15.99 (978-0-06-028013-0(1)); lib. bdg. 16.89 (978-0-06-051041-1(2)) HarperCollins Pubs.

Brett, Jan. The Twelve Days of Christmas. Brett, Jan, illus. 2004. (Illus.). 32p. (J). (ps-1). bds. 6.99 (978-0-399-24329-5(1) , Putnam Juvenile) Penguin Group (USA) Inc.

Brian Cleary Staff. Eight Wild Nights. 2006. (J). pap. 7.95 (978-1-58013-229-9(4)) Kar-Ben Publishing.

Briggs-Ward, Barbara. Snarly Sally's Garden of ABC. (Illus.). 32p. 14.95 (978-1-890621-30-8(7)) Landauer Corp.

Bright, Paul. I'm Not Going Out There! Cort, Ben, illus. 2006. 28p. (J). (ps-2). 16.00 (978-1-56148-535-2(7)) Good Bks.

—Under the Bed. Cort, Ben, illus. 2004. 32p. (J). 16.00 (978-1-56148-434-8(2)) Good Bks.

Brimner, Larry Dane. Here Comes Trouble. Torrecilla, Pablo, illus. 2002. (Rookie Reader Skill Set Ser.). 32p. (J). (gr. k-2). pap. 4.95 (978-0-516-25968-0(7) , Children's Pr.) Scholastic Library Publishing.

—Here Comes Trouble. 2001. (gr. k-3). lib. bdg. 12.95 (978-0-613-54535-8(4)) Tandem Library Bks.

—Here Comes Trouble Level B. Torrecilla, Pablo, illus. 2001. (Rookie Readers Ser.). 32p. (J). (gr. 1-2). 19.50 (978-0-516-22220-2(1) , Children's Pr.) Scholastic Library Publishing.

—Monkey Math. Kulka, Joe, illus. 2006. (Rookie Reader Skill Set Ser.). 32p. (J). (gr. k-2). 19.50 (978-0-531-12463-5(0) , Children's Pr.) Scholastic Library Publishing.

—Nana's Fiddle. Miller, Susan, illus. 2002. (Rookie Reader Ser.). 32p. (J). (gr. 1-2). 19.50 (978-0-516-22373-5(9) , Children's Pr.) Scholastic Library Publishing.

—Nana's Fiddle. 2002. (gr. k-3). lib. bdg. 12.95 (978-0-613-59521-6(1)) Tandem Library Bks.

—Nana's Hog. Miller, Susan, illus. (Rookie Reader Skill Set Ser.). 32p. (J). 1999. (gr. k-2). pap. 4.95 (978-0-516-26412-7(5)); 1998. (gr. 1-2). 19.50 (978-0-516-20755-1(5)) Scholastic Library Publishing. (Children's Pr.).

Brisson, Pat. Beach Is to Fun: A Book of Relationships. Yoshikawa, Sachiko, illus. rev. ed. 2004. 80p. (J). 16.95 (978-0-8050-7315-7(9) , Holt, Henry & Co. Bks. For Young Readers) Holt, Henry & Co.

Broadley, Leo. Pedro the Brave. Swain, Holly, illus. 2002. (J). 5.95 (978-1-58925-375-9(2)); 32p. tchr. ed. 14.95 (978-1-58925-024-6(9)) ME Media LLC. (tiger tales).

—Pedro the Brave. 2002. (gr. k-3). lib. bdg. 14.10 (978-0-613-56567-7(3)) Tandem Library Bks.

Brody, Lazer. The Worry Worm. Shapiro, Rebecca, illus. 2007. 26p. (J). 26.95 (***978-0-9797530-1-5(5))** Kalcom Publishing.

Brooks, David. You Can Count at the Ocean. 2005. (Illus.). 24p. (J). bds. (978-1-55971-930-8(3) , NorthWord Bks. for Young Readers) T&N Children's Publishing.

—You Can Count in the Jungle. 2005. (Illus.). 24p. (J). bds. (978-1-55971-931-5(1) , NorthWord Bks. for Young Readers) T&N Children's Publishing.

Brooks, Erik, illus. Octavius Bloom & the House of Doom. 2003. 32p. (J). (gr. 1-3). 15.95 (978-0-8075-5820-1(6)) Whitman, Albert & Co.

Brooks, Regina. Never Finished, Never Done! Borgella, Marjorie, illus. 2004. 32p. (J). lib. bdg. 15.00 (***978-1-4242-0229-4(9))** Fitzgerald Bks.

Brooks, Stephen. Creatures of the Night. Wilson, Rodger, illus. 2005. 32p. (J). 19.95 (978-0-9769017-1-6(4)) Purple Sky Publishing.

Brooks, Stephen J. Alexander Asenby's Great Adventure. Rajesh, illus. 2006. 32p. (J). 16.96 (978-0-9769017-2-3(2)) Purple Sky Publishing.

Brouillard, Anne. The Bathtub Prima Donna. Brouillard, Anne, illus. 2004. (Illus.). 24p. (J). (gr. k-4). reprint ed. 13.00 (978-0-7567-7755-5(0)) DIANE Publishing Co.

Brown, Calef. Tippintown: A Guided Tour. 2003. (Illus.). 32p. (J). (gr. k-3). tchr. ed. 16.00 (978-0-618-14972-8(4)) Houghton Mifflin Co. Trade & Reference Div.

Brown, Margaret Wise. A Child Is Born: Picture Book. Cooper, Floyd, illus. 2000. 32p. (ps-ps). 16.99 (978-0-7868-0673-7(7)) Hyperion Bks. for Children.

—Christmas in the Barn. Goode, Diane, illus. 32p. (J). 2007. pap. 6.99 (***978-0-06-052636-8(X)** , Harper Trophy); 2004. 16.99 (978-0-06-052634-4(3)) HarperCollins Pubs.

—Goodnight Moon. Hurd, Clement, illus. 2005. 32p. (J). lib. bdg. 17.89 (978-0-06-077586-5(6)); 60th anniv. ed. 16.99 (978-0-06-077585-8(8)) HarperCollins Pubs.

—Goodnight Moon 123: A Counting Book. Hurd, Clement, illus. 2007. 32p. (J). lib. bdg. 17.89 (978-0-06-112594-2(6)); 16.99 (978-0-06-112593-5(8)) HarperCollins Pubs.

—Goodnight Moon 123/Buenas Noches, Luna 123: A Counting Book/Un Libro para Contar. Hurd, Clement, illus. 2007. (ENG & SPA.). 32p. (J). (ps-k). 16.99 (***978-0-06-117325-7(8)** , Rayo) HarperCollins Pubs.

—Goodnight Moon Big Book. Hurd, Clement, illus. 2007. 32p. (J). pap. 24.99 (***978-0-06-111977-4(6)** , Harper Festival) HarperCollins Pubs.

—My World of Color. Krupinski, Loretta, illus. 2002. 32p. (ps-k). 15.99 (978-0-7868-0605-8(2)); 16.49 (978-0-7868-2519-6(7)) Hyperion Bks. for Children.

—A Pussycat's Christmas. 1998. (ps-2). lib. bdg. 14.10 (978-0-613-81428-7(2)) Tandem Library Bks.

—Two Little Trains. Dillon, Leo & Dillon, Diane, illus. 32p. (J). (ps-1). 2003. pap. 6.99 (978-0-06-443568-0(7)); 2001. 16.99 (978-0-06-028376-6(9)) HarperCollins Pubs.

—Two Little Trains. 2001. (gr. 3-6). lib. bdg. 15.25 (978-0-613-49533-2(0)) Tandem Library Bks.

—Where Have You Been? Dillon, Leo & Dillon, Diane, illus. 2004. 32p. (J). (ps-1). 16.99 (978-0-06-028378-0(5)) HarperCollins Pubs.

Brown, Margaret Wise & Andreasen, Dan. Sailor Boy Jig. 2002. (Illus.). 32p. (J). (ps-k). 16.00 (978-0-689-83348-9(2) , McElderry, Margaret K.) Simon & Schuster Children's Publishing.

Brown, Richard, illus. Street Music. 2006. (I'm Going to Read Ser.). 24p. (J). pap. 3.95 (978-1-4027-3073-3(X)) Sterling Publishing Co., Inc.

Brown, Rick, illus. I'm Going to Read (Level 2): Hooray for the 4th of July. 2007. (I'm Going to Read Ser.). 28p. (J). pap. 3.95 (978-1-4027-4241-5(X)) Sterling Publishing Co., Inc.

Broyles, Beverly Ashley, illus. Grandmother's Alligator/Burukenge Wa Nyanya Activity Guide. 2005. (ENG & SWA.). (J). 12.95 (978-0-9703632-7-5(3)) Wakefield Connection, The.

Bruel, Nick. Little Red Bird. 2008. 32p. (J). 16.95 (***978-1-59643-339-7(6))** Roaring Brook Pr.

Bruna, Dick. Miffy Goes Flying. 1998. (Miffy Ser.). (Illus.). 28p. (J). (ps-k). pap. 4.95 (978-1-56836-221-2(8)) Kodansha America, Inc.

Bryan, Sean. A Bear & His Boy. Murphy, Tom, illus. rev. ed. 2007. 32p. (J). (ps-1). 14.99 (***978-1-55970-838-8(7))** Arcade Publishing, Inc.

—A Boy & His Bunny. Murphy, Tom, illus. rev. ed. 2005. 32p. (J). (ps-1). pap. 14.99 (978-1-55970-725-1(9)) Arcade Publishing, Inc.

—A Girl & Her Gator. Murphy, Tom, illus. rev. ed. 2006. 36p. (J). (ps-1). 14.99 (978-1-55970-798-5(4)) Arcade Publishing, Inc.

Bryant, Janine. Yucky Green Beans. l.t. ed. 2005. 12p. (J). per. 5.00 (978-0-9703474-8-0(0)) Pinninti Pubs.

Bryant, Jennifer. Ringside, 1925: Views from the Scopes Trial. 2008. (J). (***978-0-375-84047-0(8));** lib. bdg. (***978-0-375-94047-7(2))** Knopf, Alfred A. Inc.

Bryant, Raymond. On the Tracks. 2004. (Funtime Rhymes Ser.). 10p. (J). bds. 4.95 (978-0-7641-5718-9(3)) Barron's Educational Series, Inc.

Buck, Nola. Oh, Cats! 1998. (My First I Can Read Bks.). (J). (ps-k). (978-0-606-13005-9(5)) Tandem Library Bks.

Buck, Nola & Godwin, Laura. Central Park Serenade. Root, Barry, illus. 2002. 32p. (J). (ps-k). 16.99 (978-0-06-025891-7(8) , Cotler, Joanna Books) HarperCollins Pubs.

Buckner, Arlene. Elphina. Klementz-Harte, Lauren, illus. 1998. 32p. (J). (gr. k-2). 17.95 (978-1-890309-56-5(7)) Tern Bk. Co., Inc., The.

Budgell, Gill & Ruttle, Kate. One, Two, Buckle My Shoe. 2001. (Cambridge Reading Ser.). (Illus.). 8p. pap. 5.00 (978-0-521-00201-1(X)) Cambridge Univ. Pr.

Buehner, Caralyn. Snowmen at Christmas. Buehner, Mark, illus. 2005. 32p. (J). (ps). 16.99 (978-0-8037-2995-7(2) , Dial) Penguin Group (USA) Inc.

—Snowmen at Night. Buehner, Mark, illus. (J). (ps). 2004. 26p. bds. 6.99 (978-0-8037-3041-0(1)); 2002. 32p. 15.99 (978-0-8037-2550-8(7)); Set. 2003. 26p. 16.99 (978-0-8037-2975-9(8)) Penguin Group (USA) Inc. (Dial).

—Snowmen at Night Jigsaw Puzzle Book. Buehner, Mark, illus. 2007. 12p. (J). (ps). 10.99 (***978-0-8037-3254-4(6)** , Dial) Penguin Group (USA) Inc.

Buehner, Caralyn. Would I Ever Lie to You? Davis, Jack E., illus. 2007. 32p. (J). (ps up). 16.99 (978-0-8037-2793-9(3) , Dial) Penguin Group (USA) Inc.

Buell, Janet. Sail Away, Little Boat. Ishida, Jui, illus. 2006. 32p. (J). 15.95 (978-1-57505-821-4(9) , Carolrhoda Bks.) Lerner Publishing Group.

Bullard, Lisa. Not Enough Beds! A Christmas Alphabet Book. Oeltjenbruns, Joni, illus. 2004. (Picture Bks.). 32p. (J). (ps-3). 15.95 (978-1-57505-356-1(X) , Carolrhoda Bks.) Lerner Publishing Group.

—Not Enough Beds: A Christmas Alphabet Book. Oeltjenbruns, Joni, illus. 2004. 26p. (J). (ps-ps). lib. bdg. 13.75 (978-0-606-30541-9(6)) Tandem Library Bks.

Bunting, Eve. The Baby Shower. Love, Judy, illus. 2007. 28p. (J). (ps-1). 15.95 (978-1-58089-139-4(X)) Charlesbridge Publishing, Inc.

—The Bones of Fred McFee. Cyrus, Kurt, illus. 32p. (J). (ps-ps). 2005. pap. 6.00 (978-0-15-205423-6(5) , Voyager Bks./Libros Viajeros); 2002. 16.00 (978-0-15-202004-0(7)) Harcourt Children's Bks.

—Dear Wish Fairy. Bjhorkman, Steve, illus. 2000. (Hello Reader! Ser.). (J). (978-0-439-20634-1(0)) Scholastic, Inc.

—Flower Garden. 2002. (Illus.). (J). 13.19 (978-0-7587-2519-6(1)) Book Wholesalers, Inc.

—Flower Garden. Hewitt, Kathryn, illus. 2000. 32p. (J). (ps-3). pap. 7.00 (978-0-15-202372-0(0)) Harcourt Children's Bks.

—Flower Garden. Hewitt, Kathryn, illus. 1999. 32p. (J). (ps-3). 25.95 (978-0-15-201968-6(5)) Harcourt Trade Pubs.

—Flower Garden. Hewitt, Kathryn, illus. 2000. (J). (ps-ps). lib. bdg. 14.15 (978-0-613-28490-5(9)) Tandem Library Bks.

—Flower Garden. 2000. 12.80 (978-0-606-17842-6(2)) Tandem Library Bks.

—Flower Garden: Lap-Sized Board Book. Hewitt, Kathryn, illus. 2008. 30p. (J). bds. 10.95 (***978-0-15-206516-4(4)** , Red Wagon Bks.) Harcourt Children's Bks.

Bunting, Eve. The Wedding. Trapani, Iza, illus. 32p. (J). (ps). 2005. pap. 6.95 (978-1-58089-118-9(7)); 2004. 15.95 (978-1-58089-040-3(7)) Charlesbridge Publishing, Inc.

Burgess, Karin Whiting. It's Always a Good Day for Crabbing. 2005. (J). 16.95 (978-0-9718303-4-9(7)) Flat Hammock Pr.

Burleigh, Robert. I Love Going Through This Book. Yaccarino, Dan, illus. 40p. (J). (ps-3). Date not set. pap. 5.99 (978-0-06-443647-2(0)); 2001. 15.99 (978-0-06-028805-1(1) , Cotler, Joanna Books); 2001. 15.89 (978-0-06-028806-8(X) , Cotler, Joanna Books) HarperCollins Pubs.

Burnham, Janet Hayward. The Dragoness Mess. 2003. (Illus.). 32p. (J). (gr. k-1). pap. 12.95 (978-0-9740743-1-3(4)) My Little Jessie Pr.

Burns, Joanne. Abigail Is a Big Girl Now. 2005. 20p. (J). 8.99 (978-1-4116-2042-1(9)) Lulu.com.

—Annibelle Is a Big Girl Now Weaning Two Year-Olds. 2005. 20p. 8.99 (978-1-4116-2044-5(5)) Lulu.com.

—No Says the Baby When You Say Yes, a book about the terrible Twos. 2005. 1p. 5.68 (978-1-4116-3386-5(5)) Lulu.com.

—What Is Heaven Like? 2005. 35p. (J). 10.99 (978-1-4116-3360-5(1)) Lulu.com.

Burton, Katherine. One Gray Mouse. Fernandes, Kim, illus. 2006. 24p. 6.95 (978-1-55453-026-7(1)) Kids Can Pr., Ltd. CAN. *Dist:* Wybel Marketing Group.

Bushar, Carol. Robby the Lion Doesn't Eat Meat. 2006. 30p. 12.96 (978-1-4116-9113-1(X)) Lulu.com.

Butler, John. Can You Cuddle Like a Koala? Butler, John, illus. (Illus.). (J). 2005. 20p. bds. 6.95 (978-1-56145-347-4(1)); 2003. 32p. 15.95 (978-1-56145-298-9(X)) Peachtree Pubs., Ltd.

—Can You Growl Like a Bear? Butler, John, illus. 2007. (Illus.). 40p. (J). (ps-1). pap. 15.95 (***978-1-56145-396-2(X)** , Peachtree Junior) Peachtree Pubs., Ltd.

Butler, John. Hush, Little Ones. Butler, John, illus. 2002. (Illus.). 32p. (J). (ps-k). 15.95 (978-1-56145-269-9(6)) Peachtree Pubs., Ltd.

Butler, Kristi T. A Big Surprise. Paparone, Pamela, illus. 2005. (Green Light Readers Level 1 Ser.). 24p. (J). (ps-ps). 12.95 (978-0-15-205142-6(2)); pap. 3.95 (978-0-15-205141-9(4)) Harcourt Trade Pubs.

Butler, Kristi T. Big Surprise. Paparone, Pamela, illus. 2005. 24p. (J). lib. bdg. 10.00 (***978-1-4242-0175-4(6))** Fitzgerald Bks.

Butler, M. Christina. A Star So Bright: A Christmas Tale. Pedler, Caroline, illus. 2006. 21p. (J). (ps-2). 14.95 (978-1-56148-536-9(5)) Good Bks.

By the Light of the Halloween Moon. 2004. pap. 18.95 incl. audio compact disk (978-1-55592-800-1(5)); (J). pap. 38.75 incl. audio compact disk (978-1-55592-817-9(X)); (J). pap. 32.75 incl. audio (978-1-55592-198-9(1)) Weston Woods Studios, Inc.

Bynum, Janie. Altoona Baboona. 2002. (Illus.). 36p. (J). (ps-2). pap. 7.00 (978-0-15-216404-1(9) , Voyager Bks./Libros Viajeros) Harcourt Children's Bks.

Cabrera, Jane. Over in the Meadow. Cabrera, Jane, illus. 2000. (Illus.). 32p. (J). (ps-1). 16.95 (978-0-8234-1490-1(6)) Holiday Hse., Inc.

Caffey, Donna. Tengo Piojos! Girouard, Patrick, illus. (SPA.). 28p. (J). (gr. k-3). 15.50 (978-84-261-3098-3(4) , JV7082) Juventud, Editorial ESP. *Dist:* Lectorum Pubns., Inc.

Calitri, Susan Chapma. The Ants Go Marching. Gruetzke, Mary, ed. Scherer, Jeffrey, illus. 2005. (Sing & Read Ser.). 32p. (J). (ps-ps). pap. 4.99 incl. audio compact disk (978-0-439-75560-3(3) , Cartwheel Bks.) Scholastic, Inc.

—There Were Ten in the Bed. Gruetzke, Mary, ed. 2005. (Sing & Read Ser.). (Illus.). 24p. (J). (ps-ps). pap. 4.99 (978-0-439-75559-7(X) , Cartwheel Bks.) Scholastic, Inc.

Calmenson, Stephanie. Birthday at the Panda Palace. Cushman, Doug, illus. 2007. 32p. (J). (ps-1). 15.99 (978-0-06-052663-4(7)); lib. bdg. 16.89 (978-0-06-052664-1(5)) HarperCollins Pubs.

Calmenson, Stephanie. Jazzmatazz! Degen, Bruce, illus. 2008. 32p. (J). 16.99 (***978-0-06-077289-5(1)***); lib. bdg. 17.89 (***978-0-06-077290-1(5))*** HarperCollins Pubs.

Calmenson, Stephanie, et al, illus. What's My Job? 2000. (Hello Reader! Ser.). (J). pap. (978-0-439-20473-6(9)) Scholastic, Inc.

Caloggero, Lynne. New Home, New School. Higgins, Don, illus. 2000. 40p. (J). (ps-3). 6.50 (978-0-9700250-0-5(9)) L. Lemon O'Pea Productions.

Calvert, Deanna. Feeding the Gulls. Ulrich, George, illus. 2004. (Rookie Reader Skill Set Ser.). 32p. (J). (gr. k-2). pap. 4.95 (978-0-516-24622-2(4) , Children's Pr.) Scholastic Library Publishing.

—Shadows. Lester, Mike, illus. 2004. (Rookie Reader Espanol Ser.). 24p. (J). (gr. k-2). pap. 4.95 (978-0-516-25840-9(0) , Children's Pr.) Scholastic Library Publishing.

—Las Sombras. Lester, Mike, illus. 2005. (Rookie Reader Espanol Ser.). (SPA & ESP.). 23p. (J). (gr. k-2). pap. 4.95 (978-0-516-24697-0(6) , Children's Pr.) Scholastic Library Publishing.

Candlewick Press Staff. Love & Kisses Ams Ed. 2002. (J). bds. 12.99 (978-0-7636-1823-0(3)) Candlewick Pr.

Capucilli, Alyssa Satin. Inside a Zoo in the City: A Rebus Read along Story. Arnold, Tedd, illus. 2000. (J). (ps-2). pap. 11.95 (978-0-590-99715-7(7)) Scholastic, Inc.

Carlson, Melody. Farmer Brown's Field Trip. Bjorkman, Steve, illus. 2004. 40p. (ps-3). 9.99 (978-1-58134-142-3(3)) Crossway Bks.

—Forgive Others. Reagan, Susan Joy, illus. 2004. (Just Like Jesus Said Ser.). 32p. (J). (ps-5). 12.99 (978-0-8054-2385-3(0)) B&H Publishing Grp.

—Love Your Neighbor. Reagan, Susan Joy, illus. 2004. (Just Like Jesus Said Ser.). 32p. (J). (ps-5). 12.99 (978-0-8054-2383-9(4)) B&H Publishing Grp.

—My Happy Heart. Osborn, Jim, illus. 2001. 32p. (J). (ps-5). 12.99 (978-0-8054-2382-2(6)) B&H Publishing Grp.

—Secretly Do Good Deeds. Reagan, Susan Joy, illus. 2004. (Just Like Jesus Said Ser.). 32p. (J). (ps-5). 12.99 (978-0-8054-2384-6(2)) B&H Publishing Grp.

Carlstrom, Nancy White. Happy Birthday, Jesse Bear! 2000. (Illus.). (J). 13.79 (978-0-606-17922-5(4)) Tandem Library Bks.

—Jesse Bear, What Will You Wear? Degen, Bruce, illus. 2nd ed. 2005. (Stories to Go! Ser.). (J). (***978-1-4156-3022-8(4)*** , Aladdin) Simon & Schuster Children's Publishing.

—Let's Count It Out Jesse Bear. 2001. (Illus.). (J). (978-0-606-20763-8(5)) Tandem Library Bks.

—Where Is Christmas, Jesse Bear? 2003. (ps-2). lib. bdg. 15.30 (978-0-613-88993-3(2)) Tandem Library Bks.

Carpenter, Dimitrea. Together. 2006. 24p. (J). pap. 8.99 (978-0-439-80323-6(3) , Orchard Bks.) Scholastic, Inc.

Carr, Jan. Dappled Apples. Donohue, Dorothy, illus. 2001. 32p. (J). (gr. k-3). tchr. ed. 15.95 (978-0-8234-1583-0(X)) Holiday Hse., Inc.

Carrier, Lark. Five Little Goblins. 2001. (Illus.). 18p. (J). (ps-1). 6.95 (978-0-694-01576-4(8) , Harper Festival) HarperCollins Pubs.

Carta, Karla K. Chocolate in My Pocket. 2006. 21p. (J). 10.68 (978-1-4116-9312-8(4)) Lulu.com.

Carter, David A. Feely Bugs: To Touch & Feel. Carter, David A., illus. ed. 2005. (Illus.). 14p. (J). (ps-ps). pap. 9.99 (978-1-4169-0326-0(7) , Little Simon) Simon & Schuster Children's Publishing.

Carter, Don. Old MacDonald Drives a Tractor. 2007. (Illus.). 24p. (J). (ps-2). 14.95 (978-1-59643-023-5(0)) Roaring Brook Pr.

Cartwright, Reg. What We Do. 2005. (Illus.). 32p. (J). (ps). 7.95 (978-0-8050-7671-4(9) , Holt, Henry & Co. Bks. For Young Readers) Holt, Henry & Co.

Casanova, Mary. One Dog Canoe. Goodrich, Carter, illus. 1999. (978-0-7894-2582-9(3)) Dorling Kindersley Publishing, Inc.

—One-Dog Canoe. Hoyt, Ard, illus. 2003. 32p. (J). (ps-1). 16.50 (978-0-374-35638-5(6) , Farrar, Straus & Giroux (BYR)) Farrar, Straus & Giroux.

Catchpool, Michael. Where There's a Bear, There's Trouble! Cabban, Vanessa, illus. 2002. 28p. (J). (ps-k). tchr. ed. 14.95 (978-1-58925-022-2(2) , tiger tales) ME Media LLC.

Celia, Shannon Casey. Nature's Music, 2003. (Illus.). 12p. (J). spiral bd. 10.95 (978-1-931844-07-9(0) , PP1019) Piano Pr.

Celsi, Teresa. The Fourth Little Pig. (Metro Reading Program Ser.). (J). (gr. k). 2000. 45.95 (978-1-58830-030-0(7)); 1999. 29.95 (978-1-58120-118-5(4)) Metropolitan Teaching & Learning Co.

Centeio, Tara Jaye. Mommy Loves Her Baby. Date not set. 32p. (J). (ps-1). pap. 5.99 (978-0-06-443715-8(9)) HarperCollins Pubs.

Chaconas, Dori. When Cows Come Home for Christmas. Chapman, Lynne, illus. 2005. 32p. (J). (gr. k-3). 15.95 (978-0-8075-8877-2(6)) Whitman, Albert & Co.

Chaconas, Doris J. One Little Mouse. Pham, Le Uyen, illus. 2002. 32p. (J). 15.99 (978-0-670-88947-1(4) , Viking Juvenile) Penguin Group (USA) Inc.

Changizi, Mandana S. The Plain Blue Caterpillar. 2000. (Illus.). 16p. (J). (ps-5). pap. 9.95 (978-0-9637240-9-0(6)) Biographical Publishing Co.

Chapman, Jane, illus. Bear Wants More. unabr. ed. 2006. (J). (ps-2). 24.95 incl. audio (***978-0-439-90572-5(9)***); 29.95 incl. audio compact disk (***978-0-439-90578-7(8))*** Weston Woods Studios, Inc.

Chapman, Keith. Itsy Bitsy Spider. Tickle, Jack, illus. 2006. 32p. (J). 15.95 (978-1-58925-055-0(9) , tiger tales) ME Media LLC.

Chapman, Lynn. When You're Not Looking. 2006. (Illus.). 10p. (J). bds. 12.95 (978-0-7696-4638-1(7) , Gingham Dog Pr.) School Specialty Publishing.

Chapman, Mary Beth & Chapman, Steven Curtis. Shaoey & Dot: A Trip to Dr. Betterbee. 2005. 20p. (J). 6.99 (978-1-4003-0568-1(3)) Nelson, Thomas Inc.

—Shaoey & Dot: Back in A Bug's Blink. 2005. 20p. (J). 6.99 (978-1-4003-0569-8(1)) Nelson, Thomas Inc.

—Shaoey & Dot: Thunder & Lightning Bugs. 2005. 20p. (J). 6.99 (978-1-4003-0570-4(5)) Nelson, Thomas Inc.

—Shoey & Dot: A Thunder & Lightning Bug Story. Chapman, Jim, illus. 2006. 32p. (J). 10.99 (978-1-4003-0743-2(0)) Nelson, Thomas Inc.

Chapman, Steven Curtis & Chapman, Mary Beth. Shaoey & Dot: Bug Meets Bundle. 2004. (Illus.). 32p. (J). 16.99 (978-1-4003-0482-0(2)) Nelson, Thomas Inc.

Charley's Columbia Backyard. 2006. (J). 14.95 (***978-0-9793808-0-8(4))*** Backyard Ambassador Reader Publishing Co.

Charlie Canoe & Other Boats, Too. 2006. (J). (978-0-9755348-2-3(3)) Kids Life Pr.

Charlip, Remy. Baby Hearts & Baby Flowers. 2001. (Illus.). 24p. (J). (ps-3). 15.89 (978-0-06-029592-9(9)) HarperCollins Pubs.

—A Perfect Day. Charlip, Remy, illus. 2007. 40p. (J). lib. bdg. 17.89 (978-0-06-051973-5(8)); 16.99 (978-0-06-051972-8(X)) HarperCollins Pubs.

Charlip, Remy & Supree, Burton. Mother Mother I Feel Sick Send for the Doctor Quick Quick Quick. 2004. (Illus.). 46p. (J). (ps-2). 16.95 (978-1-58246-043-7(4) , Tricycle Pr.) Ten Speed Pr.

Charnan, Simon. I've Lost My Hat. 2006. (Rookie Reader Skill Set Ser.). (Illus.). 32p. (J). (gr. k-2). 19.50 (978-0-531-12088-0(0) , Children's Pr.) Scholastic Library Publishing.

Cheng, Andrea. Where the Steps Were. 2008. (J). (***978-1-932425-88-8(8)*** , Front Street) Boyds Mills Pr.

Cherry, Lynne. Armadillo from Amarillo. 1999. (gr. k-3). lib. bdg. 14.15 (978-0-613-18298-0(7)) Tandem Library Bks.

Chess, Sharon. Grandma's Ready. 2007. 30p. pap. (***978-1-933916-04-0(4))*** Nelson Publishing & Marketing.

Chesworth, Michael. Alphaboat. Chesworth, Michael D., illus. 2002. 32p. (J). 16.00 (978-0-374-30244-3(8) , Farrar, Straus & Giroux (BYR)) Farrar, Straus & Giroux.

—Colors. Holmes, Stephen, illus. 1999. (Touch & Feel Surprises Ser.: 5). 12p. (ps-k). pap. 6.95 (978-0-7613-0979-6(9) , Millbrook Pr.) Lerner Publishing Group.

Chetkowski, Emily. Pumpkin Smile. Peterson, Dawn, illus. 2001. 32p. (J). (gr. k-3). 16.95 (978-0-9700974-2-2(5)); (gr. 1-3). pap. 11.95 (978-0-9700974-3-9(3)) Seven Coin Pr.

Chin, Oliver Clyde. Harriet's Hairballs. Crawford, Gregory, tr. Crawford, Gregory, illus. 2003. 32p. (J). 15.95 (978-1-58394-078-5(2) , Frog Ltd.) North Atlantic Bks.

Chitwood, Suzanne. Wake Up, Big Barn. Chitwood, Suzanne, illus. 2002. (Illus.). 40p. (J). (ps-2). pap. 15.95 (978-0-439-26627-7(0) , Cartwheel Bks.) Scholastic, Inc.

Chivus, Mitch. Fartsy Claus. Reed, Mike, illus. 2007. 32p. (J). lib. bdg. 17.89 (***978-0-06-089467-2(9)***); 16.99 (***978-0-06-089466-5(0))*** HarperCollins Pubs.

Christelow, Eileen. En un Arbol Estan los Cinco Monitos / Five Little Monkeys Sitting in a Tree. 2007. Tr. of Five Little Monkeys Sitting in a Tree. (ENG & SPA., Illus.). 28p. (J). (gr. k-ps). bds. 5.95 (978-0-618-75248-5(X) , Clarion Bks.) Houghton Mifflin Co. Trade & Reference Div.

—Five Little Monkeys Jumping on the Bed Big Book. 2006. 32p. (J). (ps-k). 25.00 (978-0-618-83682-6(9)) Houghton Mifflin Co. Trade & Reference Div.

—Five Little Monkeys Wash the Car. (Illus.). 40p. (J). (ps-1). 2004. 5.95 (978-0-618-48602-1(X)); 2000. tchr. ed. 15.00 (978-0-395-92566-9(5)) Houghton Mifflin Co. Trade & Reference Div. (Clarion Bks.).

Chronicle Books LLC Staff. Castaway Pirates. 2008. (J). 19.99 (978-0-8118-5923-3(1)) Chronicle Bks. LLC.

Chukovskii, Kornei. Doctor Ouch. Seabaugh, Jan, tr. from RUS. Seabaugh, Jan, illus. 2004. (Children's International Ser.: 1). Orig. Title: Aibolit. 50p. (J). pap. 6.99 (978-0-9740551-0-7(7)) Smith, Viveca Publishing.

Chung, Jenny. A Subtler Shade: Poems in Prose. 2007. 60p. per. 8.95 (***978-0-595-45997-1(8))*** iUniverse, Inc.

Cipolletti, George. Once upon an Elephant. Cipolletti, Suzanne, illus. 2006. (ENG.). 40p. (J). per. 16.99 (***978-1-4259-6441-2(9))*** AuthorHouse.

Cirici, David. Libro de Voliches, Laguidamios y Otras Especies. Balaguer, Marta, illus. 2000. Tr. of Book of Voliches, Laguidamios & Other Species. (SPA.). 56p. (J). (gr. 2-4). 13.95 (978-84-233-3217-5(9)) Ediciones Destino ESP. *Dist:* Baker & Taylor Bks.

Ciundziewicki, Lech. Glupcio Zeglarz: Zbior Bajek I Wierszy. 2004. 114p. (J). per. (978-1-59196-597-8(7)) Instantpublisher.com.

Clammer, Virginia Grant. The Big Box. Handelman, Dorothy, photos by. 1999. (Real Kids Readers Ser.). (Illus.). 32p. (gr. k-1). (J). pap. 4.99 (978-0-7613-2049-4(0)); lib. bdg. 18.90 (978-0-7613-2024-1(5)) Lerner Publishing Group. (Millbrook Pr.).

—The Big Box. 1999. (J). 11.79 (978-0-606-19146-3(1)) Tandem Library Bks.

—Big Box. 1999. (ps-2). lib. bdg. 13.00 (978-0-613-16606-5(X)) Tandem Library Bks.

Clare, James. The Zoo Rap. Vagnozzi, Barbara, illus. 2005. (Reading Corner Ser.). 24p. (J). (gr. k-3). lib. bdg. 22.80 (978-1-59771-003-9(2)) Sea-To-Sea Pubns.

Clark, Emma Chicester. Will & Squill. 2006. (Illus.). 32p. (J). 15.95 (978-1-57505-936-5(3) , Carolrhoda Bks.) Lerner Publishing Group.

Clark, Emma Chichester. Mimi's Book of Opposites. Clark, Emma Chichester, illus. 2004. (Illus.). 24p. (J). 9.95 (978-1-57091-574-1(1)) Charlesbridge Publishing, Inc.

Clark, Seneca & Giardi, Sandy. The Yellowest Yellow Lab. Decedue, Julie, illus. 2005. 32p. (J). 10.95 (978-0-9767276-2-0(5)) Three Bean Pr.

Clawson, Kimberly. Fun O' Licious. Bellomy, Gail, illus. 2007. (ENG.). 56p. per. 12.95 (***978-1-4241-5556-9(8))*** PublishAmerica, Inc.

Cleary, Beverly. The Hullabaloo ABC. 2000. pap. (978-0-688-17715-7(8)) HarperCollins Pubs.

Cleary, Brian P. Eight Wild Nights: A Family Hanukkah Tale. Udovic, David, illus. 2006. 24p. (J). 16.95 (978-1-58013-152-0(2)) Kar-Ben Publishing.

Clerk, Jessica. The Wriggly, Wriggly Baby. Rankin, Laura, illus. 2002. 32p. (J). pap. 16.95 (978-0-590-96067-0(9) , Levine, Arthur A. Bks.) Scholastic, Inc.

Clifton, Lucille. Everett Anderson's 1-2-3. Grifalconi, Ann, illus. rev. ed. 2002. 32p. (J). (ps-3). pap. 6.95 (978-0-8050-7048-4(6) , Holt, Henry & Co. Bks. For Young Readers) Holt, Henry & Co.

—One of the Problems of Everett Anderson. Grifalconi, Ann, illus. rev. ed. 2001. 32p. (J). (gr. k-3). 16.95 (978-0-8050-5201-5(1) , Holt, Henry & Co. Bks. For Young Readers) Holt, Henry & Co.

Cocca-Leffler, Maryann. Jungle Halloween. Cocca-Leffler, Maryann, illus. 2000. (Illus.). 32p. (J). (ps-1). pap. 6.95 (978-0-8075-4057-2(9)) Whitman, Albert & Co.

Cochran, Jean M. Off I Go. Gullens, Lee, illus. 2007. 32p. (J). 16.95 (***978-0-9792035-1-0(1))*** Pleasant St. Pr.

Cohen, Caron Lee. How Many Fish? Schindler, S. D., illus. 2000. (My First I Can Read Bks.). 32p. (J). (ps up). pap. 3.99 (978-0-06-444273-2(X)) HarperCollins Pubs.

—How Many Fish? 2000. (gr. k-3). lib. bdg. 11.80 (978-0-613-22995-1(9)) Tandem Library Bks.

Cohen, Shari. Alfie's Bark Mitzvah. 2006. (Illus.). (J). per. 18.00 net. (978-1-58985-055-2(6)) Five Star Pubns., Inc.

Cohn, Arlen. Firsts: Reflections of a 7-Year Old. Vasconsellos, Daniel, tr. Vasconsellos, Daniel, illus. gif. ed. 2004. 28p. bds. 9.99 (978-1-57939-168-3(0)) Accord Publishing, Ltd.

Colandro, Lucille. There Was a Cold Lady Who Swallowed Some Snow. unabr. ed. 2006. (J). (gr. k-2). pap. 9.95 incl. audio compact disk (978-0-439-89556-9(1)) Scholastic, Inc.

—There Was a Cold Lady Who Swallowed Some Snow. 2003. (gr. k-3). lib. bdg. 14.10 (978-0-613-72229-2(9)) Tandem Library Bks.

—There Was A Cold Lady Who Swallowed Some Snow -library. 2006. (J). 18.95 (978-0-439-89841-6(2)) Scholastic, Inc.

Colburn, Mary Palenick. Rainy Day Slug. Grover, Lorie A., illus. 2002. 32p. (J). (ps-1). 15.95 (978-1-57061-238-1(2)) Sasquatch Bks.

Cole, Gina, illus. Adapt. 2005. 40p. (J). 17.00 (978-0-9659538-3-2(1)) Soul Vision Works Publishing.

Cole, Stephen & Gardner, Lousie. Alien Olympics. 1998. (Alien Pop-Ups Ser.). (Illus.). 10p. (J). 4.95 (978-1-899607-65-5(X)) Sterling Publishing Co., Inc.

Coll, Ivar Da. Cinco Amigos. (SPA.). (J). bds. (978-958-04-4909-6(0)) Norma S.A. COL. *Dist:* Lectorum Pubns., Inc.

Collins, Suzanne. When Charlie McButton Lost Power. Lester, Mike, illus. 2005. 32p. (J). (ps-3). 15.99 (978-0-399-24000-3(4) , Putnam Juvenile) Penguin Group (USA) Inc.

Collins, Suzanne. When Charlie Mcbutton Lost Power. Lester, Mike, illus. 2007. 32p. (J). (ps). pap. 5.99 (***978-0-14-240857-5(3)*** , Puffin) Penguin Group (USA) Inc.

Colors All Day. (J). 26.20 (978-0-8136-8399-7(8)); 59.50 (978-0-8136-7918-1(4)); 1998. pap. (978-0-8136-8292-1(4)) Modern Curriculum Pr.

Coniglio, John. The Cat Who Slept All Day: What Happens While the Cat Sleeps. Key, Pamela, illus. 2006. 24p. (J). per. 2.99 (978-1-59958-004-3(7)) Journey Stone Creations, LLC.

Connelly, Wendy. Fiona the Firefly! 2003. (Illus.). (J). 12.95 (978-1-929039-16-6(6)) Ambassador Bks., Inc.

Connor, Leslie. Dead on Town Line. Triplett, Gina, illus. 2006. 144p. (YA). (gr. 6). pap. 6.99 (978-0-14-240697-7(X) , Puffin) Penguin Group (USA) Inc.

Conover, Chris. Over the Hills & Far Away. 2004. (Illus.). 40p. (J). 16.00 (978-0-374-38043-4(0) , Farrar, Straus & Giroux (BYR)) Farrar, Straus & Giroux.

Conversations on the Ark. 2003. (Illus.). 28p. (J). 14.95 (978-0-8249-5440-6(8)) Ideals Pubns.

Cook, Julie Kidd. One Is Enough. Iwai, Melissa, illus. 2005. (Rookie Reader Skill Set Ser.). 32p. (J). (gr. k-2). pap. 4.95 (978-0-516-25283-4(6)); (gr. 1-2). 19.50 (978-0-516-25152-3(X)) Scholastic Library Publishing. (Children's Pr.).

Cook, Sally. Good Night Pillow Fight. Cornell, Laura, illus. 2004. 32p. (J). lib. bdg. 16.89 (978-0-06-205190-5(3) , Cotler, Joanna Books) HarperCollins Pubs.

Copeland, Cynthia L. & Lewis, Alexandra P. Splashy Fins, Flashy Skins: Deep-Sea Rhymes to Make You Grin. 2003. (Silly Millies Ser.: 4). (Illus.). 32p. lib. bdg. 17.90 (978-0-7613-2906-0(4) , Millbrook Pr.) Lerner Publishing Group.

Cordsen, Carol Foskett. The Milkman. Jones, Douglas B., illus. 2007. 32p. (J). (ps). pap. 6.99 (978-0-14-240804-9(2) , Puffin) Penguin Group (USA) Inc.

Corey, Shana. Boats. Reed, Mike, illus. 2001. (Early Step into Reading Ser.). 32p. (J). (ps-1). pap. 3.99 (978-0-375-80221-8(5) , Random Hse. Bks. for Young Readers) Random Hse. Children's Bks.

—Boats. 2001. (ps-2). lib. bdg. 11.80 (978-0-613-33792-2(1)); (Illus.). (J). 10.79 (978-0-606-21076-8(8)) Tandem Library Bks.

Corke, Estelle. Cheetah Tale. 2001. (Bendy Tales Ser.). 8p. (J). (ps). 4.95 (978-0-7641-5368-6(4)) Barron's Educational Series, Inc.

—Little Elephant Tale. 2001. (Bendy Tales Ser.). (Illus.). 8p. (J). (ps). bds. 4.95 (978-0-7641-5369-3(2)) Barron's Educational Series, Inc.

—Monkey Tale. 2001. (Bendy Tales Ser.). 8p. (J). (ps). bds. 4.95 (978-0-7641-5371-6(4)) Barron's Educational Series, Inc.

Corkran, Alice. Bairn's Annual of Old Fashioned Fairy Tales. 2003. (gr. k-3). lib. bdg. 26.90 (978-0-613-74872-8(7)) Tandem Library Bks.

Cortes, Mary. Where on Earth Did My Sock Go? 2006. (J). per. 15.95 (***978-0-9787788-3-5(9))*** LUMEN-US Pubns.

Costales, Amy. Hello Night: Hola Noche. McDonald, Mercedes, illus. 2007. (ENG & SPA.). 24p. 12.95 (***978-0-87358-927-7(0)*** , Luna Rising) Northland Publishing.

Costello, David. Here They Come! 2004. (Illus.). 32p. (J). 15.00 (978-0-374-33051-4(4) , Farrar, Straus & Giroux (BYR)) Farrar, Straus & Giroux.

Cotten, Cynthia. Some Babies Sleep. Tong, Paul, illus. 2007. 32p. (J). 12.99 (978-0-399-24030-0(6) , Philomel) Penguin Group (USA) Inc.

Cotten, Cynthia S. At the Edge of the Woods: A Counting Book. Cartwright, Reg, illus. rev. ed. 2002. 32p. (J). (ps-1). 16.95 (978-0-8050-6354-7(4) , Holt, Henry & Co. Bks. For Young Readers) Holt, Henry & Co.

—This Is the Stable. Bettoli, Delana, illus. rev. ed. 2006. 32p. (J). (ps-3). 16.95 (978-0-8050-7556-4(9) , Holt, Henry & Co. Bks. For Young Readers) Holt, Henry & Co.

S

Couric, Katie. The Blue Ribbon Day. Priceman, Marjorie, illus. 2004. 32p. (gr. k-2). 15.95 (978-0-385-50142-2(0) , Doubleday) Doubleday Publishing.

—The Brand New Kid. Priceman, Marjorie, illus. 2000. 32p. (J). (gr. 2-3). 15.95 (978-0-385-50030-2(0) , Doubleday) Doubleday Publishing.

Cousins, Lucy. Hooray for Fish! Cousins, Lucy, illus. 2005. (Illus.). 40p. (J). (gr. k-k). 14.99 (978-0-7636-2741-6(0)) Candlewick Pr.

Cowley, Joy. The Bedtime Train. Odone, Jamison, illus. 2008. (J). (***978-1-59078-493-8(6)*** , Front Street) Boyds Mills Pr.

Cowley, Joy. Mrs. Wishy-Washy's Farm. Fuller, Elizabeth, illus. 32p. (J). (ps). 2006. pap. 5.99 (978-0-14-240299-3(0) , Puffin); 2003. 15.99 (978-0-399-23872-7(7) , Philomel) Penguin Group (USA) Inc.

Cox, Phil Roxbee. Fat Cat on A Mat. Cartwright, Stephen, illus. rev. ed. 2006. 16p. (J). pap. 6.99 (978-0-7945-1502-7(9) , Usborne) EDC Publishing.

—Ted's Shed. Cartwright, Stephen, illus. rev. ed. 2006. 16p. (J). pap. 6.99 (978-0-7945-1511-9(8) , Usborne) EDC Publishing.

Cox, Phil Roxbee & Cartwright, S. Goose on the Loose. 2004. (Easy Words to Read Ser.). 16p. (J). (gr. 1 up). pap. 6.95 (978-0-7945-0036-8(6) , Usborne) EDC Publishing.

Cox, Phil Roxbee & Cartwright, Stephen. Goose on the Loose. 2004. (Phonics Board Bks.). (Illus.). 10p. (J). 4.99 (978-0-7945-0305-5(5) , Usborne) EDC Publishing.

Coxe, Molly. Bookworm. 2000. (J). (978-0-606-18920-0(3)) Tandem Library Bks.

—Fox Trot. 1999. (Road to Reading Ser.). (J). lib. bdg. (978-0-03-074629-1(9) , Saunders) Elsevier - Health Sciences Division.

Coyle, Carmela LaVigna. Do Princesses Really Kiss Frogs? Gordon, Mike & Gordon, Carl, illus. 2005. 32p. (gr. 1-4). 15.95 (978-0-87358-880-5(0) , Rising Moon Bks. for Young Readers) Northland Publishing.

—Do Princesses Scrape Their Knees? 2006. (Illus.). 32p. (J). 15.95 (978-0-87358-909-3(2)) Northland Publishing.

—Do Princesses Wear Hiking Boots? Gordon, Mike & Gordon, Carl, illus. 2003. 32p. (J). 15.95 (978-0-87358-828-7(2) , Rising Moon Bks. for Young Readers) Northland Publishing.

Crabtree, Sally. Magic Train Ride. Esplugas, Sonia, illus. 2006. 0032p. (J). 16.99 (978-1-905236-52-7(2)) Barefoot Bks., Inc.

Crabtree, Sally & Mathieson, Roberta. Jungle Boogie. Jennings, Patti, illus. 2004. 12p. (J). bds. 7.99 (978-0-689-86184-0(2) , Little Simon) Simon & Schuster Children's Publishing.

Crabtree, Sally & Wallace, John. Ten Buzzy Bees. 2000. (Finger Puppet Bks.). (Illus.). 24p. (J). (ps-k). 10.95 (978-1-86233-162-4(6)) Sterling Publishing Co., Inc.

Craig, Gary. Where Does the Sun Go? Craig, Gary, illus. 2006. 40p. (J). 14.95 (978-0-9786813-0-2(4)) Elora Pr.

—You Can Be Anything. Craig, Gary, illus. 2006. 32p. (J). 14.95 (978-0-9786813-1-9(2)) Elora Pr.

Craig, Helen. This Is the Bear. 2003. (ps-2). lib. bdg. 11.80 (978-0-613-74748-6(8)) Tandem Library Bks.

Craig, Paula M. Mr. Wiggle's Book. Sharp, Dan, illus. 2000. 20p. (J). 3.99 (978-1-56822-975-1(5) , IF22085) School Specialty Publishing.

Crawford, Laura. In Arctic Waters. Hodson, Ben, illus. 2007. 32p. (J). pap. 8.95 (***978-1-934359-34-1(3))*** Sylvan Dell Pubng.

Crazy Animals. 2002. (Tap My Nose Ser.). (J). (ps-k). 4.98 (978-0-7525-8726-4(9)) Parragon, Inc.

Crites, Susan E. I Love You More Than Rainbows. Jarman, Rosemary & Jarman, Mark, illus. 2008. 32p. (J). 14.99 (***978-1-4003-1089-0(X))*** Nelson, Thomas Inc.

Crocker, Nancy. Betty Lou Blue. Kulikov, Boris, illus. 2006. 32p. (J). (ps). 16.99 (978-0-8037-2937-7(5) , Dial) Penguin Group (USA) Inc.

Cronin, Doreen. Bounce. Menchin, Scott, illus. 2007. 40p. (J). (ps). 14.00 (978-1-4169-1627-7(X) , Atheneum) Simon & Schuster Children's Publishing.

—Click, Clack, Splish, Splash. 2006. (J). (ps-3). 22.78 (978-1-59961-090-0(6)) Spotlight.

—Click, Clack, Splish, Splash: A Counting Adventure. Lewin, Betsy, illus. 2006. 24p. (J). (ps-k). 12.95 (978-0-689-87716-2(1) , Atheneum) Simon & Schuster Children's Publishing.

—Wiggle. Menchin, Scott, illus. 2005. 40p. (J). 12.95 (978-0-689-86375-2(6) , Atheneum) Simon & Schuster Children's Publishing.

Crow, Kristyn. Cool Daddy Rat. Lester, Mike, illus. 2008. 32p. (J). (ps). 16.99 (***978-0-399-24375-2(5)*** , Putnam Juvenile) Penguin Group (USA) Inc.

Crozon, Alain & Lanchais, Aurelie. Wild Animals Who Am I? 2002. (Illus.). 14p. (J). 7.95 (978-0-8118-3321-9(6)) Chronicle Bks. LLC.

Cruickshank, Margrit. Down by the Pond: A Surprise Farmyard Book. Saunders, Dave, illus. 1999. 32p. (J). (ps-k). pap. 7.99 (978-0-7112-0978-7(2)) Lincoln, Frances Ltd. GBR. *Dist:* Transition Vendor.

Crum, Shutta. The House in the Meadow. Billin-Frye, Paige, illus. 2003. 32p. (J). (ps-2). 16.95 (978-0-8075-3393-2(9)) Whitman, Albert & Co.

Crummel, Susan Stevens. All in One Hour. Donohue, Dorothy, illus. 2003. 32p. (J). 16.95 (978-0-7614-5129-7(3)) Cavendish, Marshall Corp.

Crystal, Billy. Grandpa's Little One. 2008. 40p. (J). (ps-k). pap. 6.99 (978-0-06-078175-0(0) , Harper Trophy) HarperCollins Pubs.

—Grandpa's Little One. Porfirio, Guy, illus. 2006. 40p. (J). (ps-k). lib. bdg. 17.89 (978-0-06-078174-3(2)) HarperCollins Pubs.

—I Already Know I Love You. Sayles, Elizabeth, illus. 40p. (J). (ps-3). 2007. pap. 6.99 (978-0-06-059393-8(8) , Harper Trophy); 2004. 16.99 (978-0-06-059391-9(1)) HarperCollins Pubs.

Cummings, Pat. Clean Your Room, Harvey Moon! Cummings, Pat, illus. 2002. (Illus.). (J). 14.47 (978-0-7587-2248-5(6)) Book Wholesalers, Inc.

—Clean Your Room, Harvey Moon! 1998. (J). pap. 4.95 (978-0-87628-335-6(0)) Ctr. for Applied Research in Education, The.

—Harvey Moon Museum Boy. Cummings, Pat, illus. 2008. (Illus.). 32p. (J). 16.99 (978-0-688-17889-5(8)) HarperCollins Pubs.

—Harvey Moon Museum Boy. 2008. (Illus.). 32p. (J). lib. bdg. 17.89 (978-0-06-057861-9(0)) HarperCollins Pubs.

Curry, Don L. Willie's Word World. Stromoski, Rick, illus. 2005. (Rookie Reader Skill Set Ser.). 31p. (J). (gr. k-2). pap. 4.95 (978-0-516-25288-9(7) , Children's Pr.) Scholastic Library Publishing.

Curtis, Carolyn. I Took the Moon for a Walk. Jay, Alison, illus. 2004. 32p. (J). 16.99 (978-1-84148-611-6(6)) Barefoot Bks., Inc.

Curtis, Jamie Lee. I'm Gonna Like Me: Letting off a Little Self-Esteem. Cornell, Laura, illus. 2002. (J). (ps-3). 32p. 16.99 (978-0-06-028761-0(6)); 40p. lib. bdg. 17.89 (978-0-06-028762-7(4)) HarperCollins Pubs. (Cotler, Joanna Books).

—Is There Really a Human Race? Cornell, Laura, illus. 2006. 40p. 16.99 (978-0-06-075346-7(3)); lib. bdg. 17.89 (978-0-06-075348-1(X)) HarperCollins Pubs. (Cotler, Joanna Books).

—It's Hard to Be Five: Learning How to Work My Control Panel. Cornell, Laura, illus. 2004. 40p. (J). (ps-3). 16.99 (978-0-06-008095-2(7)); lib. bdg. 17.89 (978-0-06-008096-9(5)) HarperCollins Pubs. (Cotler, Joanna Books).

—Today I Feel Silly Activity Book. 1998. (Illus.). (J). pap. (978-0-06-028099-4(9)) HarperCollins Pubs.

—Today I Feel Silly & Other Moods That Make My Day. (J). (ps). 2001. 32p. 6.95 (978-0-694-01343-2(9)); 2000. (Illus.). 32p. 15.95 incl. audio (978-0-06-028257-8(6)); 2000. 19.95 (978-0-00-225528-8(6)) HarperCollins Pubs.

—Today I Feel Silly & Other Moods That Make My Day. Cornell, Laura, illus. 1999. 40p. (J). (ps-3). 16.99 (978-0-06-024560-3(3) , Cotler, Joanna Books) HarperCollins Pubs.

—Today I Feely Silly / Canadian Edition. Cornell, Laura, illus. 1999. (J). (ps-3). (978-0-06-028842-6(6)) HarperCollins Pubs.

—Where Do Balloons Go? An Uplifting Mystery. 2001. (J). 135.60 (978-0-06-623707-7(6)) HarperCollins Pubs.

—Where Do Balloons Go? An Uplifting Mystery. Cornell, Laura, illus. 2000. 36p. (J). (ps-3). 16.89 (978-0-06-027981-3(8)); 16.99 (978-0-06-027980-6(X) , Cotler, Joanna Books) HarperCollins Pubs.

Curtis, Marci. Big Brother, Little Brother. 2004. (Illus.). 40p. (J). (gr. k). 12.99 (978-0-8037-2870-7(0) , Dial) Penguin Group (USA) Inc.

Cuscuna, Susan. Molly & Me & Manny Magee. 2007. (J). (***978-0-7666-2839-7(6)***) Modern Publishing.

Cusimano, Maryann K. You Are My I Love You. Ichikawa, Satomi, illus. 2001. 32p. (J). (ps-1). 16.99 (978-0-399-23392-0(X) , Philomel) Penguin Group (USA) Inc.

Cuyler, Margery. Monster Mess! Schindler, S. D., illus. 2008. (J). (978-0-689-86405-6(1) , McElderry, Margaret K.) Simon & Schuster Children's Publishing.

Cyrus, Kurt. Tadpole Rex. 2008. (J). (***978-0-15-205990-3(3)***) Harcourt Trade Pubs.

Dacey, Richard. Spinner McClock & the Christmas Visit. Gillett, Hallie, illus. 2004. 32p. (J). 13.95 (978-1-929039-24-1(7)) Ambassador Bks., Inc.

Daddy Is a Doodlebug Doodle Pad. 2000. (J). (978-0-06-029068-9(4)) HarperCollins Pubs.

Dahl, Michael. Dust Bunnies. Yi, Hye Won, illus. 2005. (Read-It! Readers Ser.). 32p. (J). (ps). lib. bdg. 18.60 (978-1-4048-1168-3(0)) Picture Window Bks.

Daley Mackall, Dandi. I Love You Daddy. Lee Schmidt, Karen, illus. 2006. (I Love You Ser.). 20p. (J). bds. 7.99 (978-0-7847-1816-2(4) , 04138) Standard Publishing.

—I Love You Mommy. Lee Schmidt, Karen, illus. 2005. (I Love You Ser.). 20p. (J). bds. 7.99 (978-0-7847-1815-5(6) , 04137) Standard Publishing.

Dalmatian Press Staff. Abby Cadabby's Rhyme BK. 2007. 24p. pap. 3.50 (***978-1-4037-3609-3(X)***) Dalmatian Pr.

—Bunny Tale: Soft Spot Board Book. 2002. (Soft Spot Bks.). (Illus.). 10p. (J). bds. 3.99 (978-1-57759-626-4(9)) Dalmatian Pr.

—Little Chick: Soft Spot Board Book. 2002. (Soft Spot Bks.). (Illus.). 10p. (J). bds. 3.99 (978-1-57759-652-3(8)) Dalmatian Pr.

Dalmatian Press Staff, ed. A Perfect Picnic. rev. ed. 2005. 24p. (J). pap. 3.50 (978-1-4037-1695-8(1)) Dalmatian Pr.

Dalmation Press. Storytime & Favorite Rhymes: A Storybook Collection. (Keepsake Quality Ser.). (Illus.). 224p. (J). 10.99 (978-1-4037-0527-3(5)) Dalmatian Pr.

Daly, Niki, illus. A Family for Old Mill Farm. 2007. 32p. (J). (gr. k-3). 16.00 (978-0-618-42846-5(1) , Clarion Bks.) Houghton Mifflin Co. Trade & Reference Div.

Danis, Naomi. Splish-Splash, into the Bath! Kreloff, Elliot, illus. 2007. 16p. (J). (***978-1-59354-609-0(2)***) Handprint Bks.

Darling, Helen. Hide-n-seek Monday. Glickstein, Jennifer, ed. Sona and Jacob, illus. 2007. (J). 10.00 (***978-0-9797674-0-1(7)***) My Darling-Tots Pubns.

Darrow, Sharon. Trash. 2006. 160p. (J). (gr. 7). 16.99 (978-0-7636-2624-2(4)) Candlewick Pr.

Davidson, Alice Joyce. A Christmas Candy Cane. 2006. (Christmas Minis Ser.). 14p. (J). 3.99 (978-0-310-70848-3(6)) Zonderkidz.

Davies, Jacqueline. The Night Is Singing Lullabies. Brooker, Kyrsten, illus. 2006. 40p. (J). (ps). 16.99 (978-0-8037-3004-5(7) , Dial) Penguin Group (USA) Inc.

Davies, Timothy, Sr. The Polka-Dotted Elephant. 2007. (J). per. 12.00 (***978-0-9793207-0-5(4)***) Wildlife Tales Publishing.

Davis, David. Jazz Cats. Galey, Chuck, illus. 2001. 32p. (J). (gr. 2-4). pap. 15.95 (978-1-56554-859-6(0)) Pelican Publishing Co., Inc.

Davis, Jennifer. Before You Were Big. Cornell, Laura, illus. 2003. 36p. (J). 11.95 (978-0-7611-2732-1(1) , 12732) Workman Publishing Co., Inc.

Davis, Lee. Where Is P. B. Bear? 2001. (P. B. Bear Ser.). (Illus.). 24p. (J). (ps). pap. 4.95 (978-0-7894-2222-4(0) , D K Ink) Dorling Kindersley Publishing, Inc.

Day, Robert O. & Day, Linda S. There's a Frog on a Log in the Bog. Day, Linda S., illus. 2002. (Florida Tales Ser.: Vol. 1). (Illus.). 112p. (J). (gr. 4-6). pap. 8.95 (978-1-890905-20-0(8)) Day to Day Enterprises.

de Alba, Arlette, tr. Musica en Casa: Libro de Cuentos. 2005. (SPA., Illus.). 40p. (J). (ps-7). 24.95 (978-970-718-290-5(3) , Silver Dolphin en Español) Advanced Marketing, S. de R. L. de C. V. MEX. *Dist:* Perseus Distribution.

De Regniers, Beatrice Schenk. May I Bring A Friend? Montresor, Beni, illus. 2002. (J). 14.47 (978-0-7587-0057-5(1)) Book Wholesalers, Inc.

—Was It a Good Trade? Haas, Irene, illus. rev. ed. 2002. 32p. (J). (ps-1). 15.95 (978-0-06-029359-8(4)) HarperCollins Pubs.

Dealey, Erin. Goldie Locks Has Chicken Pox. ed. 2004. (Illus.). (J). (gr. k-3). spiral bd. (978-0-616-14572-2(1)); spiral bd. (978-0-616-14573-9(X)) Canadian National Institute for the Blind/Institut National Canadien pour les Aveugles.

—Goldie Locks Has Chicken Pox. Wakiyama, Hanako, illus. 40p. (J). 2002. 17.99 (978-0-689-82981-9(7) , Atheneum); 2005. reprint ed. 6.99 (978-0-689-87610-3(6) , Aladdin) Simon & Schuster Children's Publishing.

DeBoer, Jesslyn. Countdown to Christmas. 2006. 14p. (J). 3.99 (978-0-310-70845-2(1)) Zondervan.

Debowski, Sharon. The Snowman, the Owl, & the Groundhog. 2007. (J). lib. bdg. 15.95 (***978-1-60227-468-6(1)***); (Illus.). 32p. 14.95 (***978-1-60227-470-9(3)***) Above the Clouds Publishing.

Degen, Bruce, illus. Happy Birthday, Jesse Bear! 2002. (J). 14.47 (978-0-7587-2685-8(6)) Book Wholesalers, Inc.

—How Do You Say It Today, Jesse Bear? 2002. (Jesse Bear Ser.). (J). 14.47 (978-0-7587-2760-2(7)) Book Wholesalers, Inc.

—It's about Time, Jesse Bear: And Other Rhymes. 2002. (Jesse Bear Ser.). (J). 14.47 (978-0-7587-2875-3(1)) Book Wholesalers, Inc.

—Jesse Bear, What Will You Wear? 2002. (Jesse Bear Ser.). (J). 15.53 (978-0-7587-2900-2(6)) Book Wholesalers, Inc.

Deich, Cheri Bivin. The Messy Monkey Tea Party. Genth, Christina, illus. 2007. 32p. (J). 15.95 (978-1-60108-006-6(9)) Red Cygnet Pr.

Delessert, Etienne. Humpty Dumpty. 2006. (Illus.). 32p. (J). (gr. k-3). 17.00 (978-0-618-56987-8(1)) Houghton Mifflin Co.

Denise, Anika. Pigs Love Potatoes. Denise, Christopher, illus. 2007. 40p. (J). (ps-1). 15.99 (978-0-399-24036-2(5) , Philomel) Penguin Group (USA) Inc.

DePalma, Johnny. The Raindrop Keeper: (Limited Edition Hardcover) Crabapple, Molly, illus. 2006. 50p. (J). 16.50 (***978-0-9791127-8-2(8)***) Umbrelly Bks.

DePaola, Tomie. Get Dressed, Santa! 2006. (Illus.). 12p. (J). (ps-1). bds. 6.99 (978-0-448-44446-8(1) , Grosset & Dunlap) Penguin Group (USA) Inc.

DePrisco, Dorothea & Barnard, Lucy. Lullaby & Good Night. 2006. 12.95 (978-1-58117-450-2(0) , Intervisual/Piggy Toes) Dalmatian Pr.

deRubertis, Barbara. Marty Aardvark. Cockrille, Eva V., illus. 1998. (Let's Read Together Ser.). 32p. (J). (ps-3). pap. 8.95 (978-1-57565-047-0(9)) Kane Pr., The.

—Rooney 'Roo. Cockrille, Eva V., illus. 1998. (Let's Read Together Ser.). 32p. (J). (ps-3). pap. 4.95 (978-1-57565-044-9(4)); pap. 8.95 incl. audio (978-1-57565-049-4(5)) Kane Pr., The.

Dewdney, Anna. Grumpy Gloria. Dewdney, Anna, illus. 2006. (Illus.). 28p. (J). (ps). 15.99 (978-0-670-06123-5(9) , Viking Juvenile) Penguin Group (USA) Inc.

Dewdney, Anna. Llama Llama Mad at Mama. Dewdney, Anna, illus. 2007. (Illus.). 40p. (J). (ps-k). 15.99 (***978-0-670-06240-9(5)*** , Viking Juvenile) Penguin Group (USA) Inc.

Diaz-Pimienta, Alexis. Cuentos Clasicos en Verso.Tr. of Classic Stories in Verse. (SPA.). (J). (gr. 2-4). pap. 7.98 (978-970-643-142-4(X)) Selector, S.A. de C.V. MEX. *Dist:* Lectorum Pubns., Inc.

Dickinson, Rebecca. Monster Cake. Dickinson, Rebecca, illus. 2000. (Illus.). 32p. (J). (ps-2). pap. 4.99 (978-0-439-06752-2(9)) Scholastic, Inc.

—Monster Cake. 2000. (J). (978-0-606-19579-9(3)) Tandem Library Bks.

Dickinson, Rebecca, tr. & illus. Over in the Hollow. Dickinson, Rebecca, illus. 2002. (J). (978-0-385-74620-5(2) , Doubleday Bks. for Young Readers) Random Hse. Children's Bks.

Diesen, Deborah. The Pout-Pout Fish. Hanna, Dan, illus. 2008. 32p. (J). 16.00 (***978-0-374-36096-2(0)***) Farrar, Straus & Giroux.

Dillon-Butler, Marybeth. Myrtle the Hurdler & Her Pink & Purple, Polka-Dotted Girdle. Messing, David, illus. 2005. 32p. (J). pap. 11.95 (978-0-9785075-9-6(2) , Ferne Pr.) Nelson Publishing & Marketing.

Dillon, Leo & Dillon, Diane. Rap a Tap Tap: Here's Bojangles - Think of That! 2005. (J). 25.95 incl. audio (978-1-59519-365-0(0)); 28.95 incl. audio compact disk (978-1-59519-369-8(3)) Live Oak Media.

—Rap a Tap Tap: Here's Bojangles - Think of That! Dillon, Leo & Dillon, Diane, illus. 2002. (Illus.). 32p. (J). pap. 15.95 (978-0-590-47883-0(4) , Blue Sky Pr., The) Scholastic, Inc.

Dining with Prunella. 1998. (Books to Go). (J). pap. (978-0-8136-7877-1(3)) Modern Curriculum Pr.

Dionne, Wanda. Little Thumb. Dillon, Jana, illus. 2001. 32p. (J). (gr. k-3). pap. 7.95 (978-1-56554-754-4(3)) Pelican Publishing Co., Inc.

Dippold, Jane, illus. I Love My Baby. 1999. (Leap Frog Lift-a-Flap Ser.). (J). (978-0-7853-3367-8(3)) Publications International, Ltd.

DiPucchio, Kelly. Dinosnores. Goembel, Ponder, illus. 2005. 32p. (J). (ps-1). lib. bdg. 16.89 (978-0-06-051578-2(3)); 15.99 (978-0-06-051577-5(5)) HarperCollins Pubs.

Dipucchio, Kelly. What's the Magic Word? Winborn, Marsha, illus. 2005. 32p. (J). (ps-1). 15.99 (978-0-06-000578-8(5)) HarperCollins Pubs.

DiPucchio, Kelly S. Bed Hogs. Fine, Howard, illus. 2004. 32p. (ps-k). 15.99 (978-0-7868-1884-6(0)) Hyperion Bks. for Children.

—Monster Makeovers. Pham, LeUyen, illus. 2006. (J). (978-0-7868-5181-2(3)) Hyperion Bks. for Children.

Disney Staff. Winnie the Pooh CD Storybook: Winnie the Pooh & the Blustery Day, Winnie the Pooh & the Honey Tree, Winnie the Pooh & a Day for Eeyore, Winnie the Pooh & Tigger Too. Milne, A. A. & Shepard, Ernest H., eds. rev. ed. 2004. (Disney CD Storybooks Ser.). (Illus.). 128p. (J). (gr. 4-12). 14.95 incl. cd-rom (978-1-86515-303-2(6)) Hinkler Bks. Pty, Ltd. AUS. *Dist:* Penton Overseas, Inc.

Dixon, Ann. Winter Is. Dwyer, Mindy, illus. 2005. 32p. (ps-1). 15.95 (978-0-88240-543-8(8)); pap. 8.95 (978-0-88240-544-5(6)) Graphic Arts Ctr. Publishing Co.

—Winter Is. 2002. (ps-2). lib. bdg. 17.60 (978-0-613-61929-5(3)) Tandem Library Bks.

Dockweiler, Sharon. No Buttons for Suzy Cow. Silbert, Barbara Briggs, illus. 1999. (J). (978-1-929453-00-9(0)) Sharon's Small Pr.

Dodd, Emma. Amazing Baby: on the Move! Jolley, Mike, illus. 2007. (Amazing Baby Ser.). 10p. (J). bds. 6.95 (***978-1-59223-800-2(9)*** , Silver Dolphin Bks.) Advantage Pubs. Group.

—Amazing Baby: Rain or Shine! Jolley, Mike, illus. 2007. (Amazing Baby Ser.). 10p. (J). bds. 6.95 (***978-1-59223-801-9(7)*** , Silver Dolphin Bks.) Advantage Pubs. Group.

—Just Like You. 2008. 24p. (J). (ps). 10.99 (***978-0-525-47933-8(3)*** , Dutton Juvenile) Penguin Group (USA) Inc.

Dodd, Lynley. A Dragon in a Wagon. Dodd, Lynley, illus. 2000. (Gold Star First Readers Ser.). (Illus.). 32p. (J). (gr. 1 up). lib. bdg. 22.00 (978-0-8368-2687-6(6)) Stevens, Gareth Inc.

—Find Me a Tiger. Dodd, Lynley, illus. 2001. (Gold Star First Readers Ser.). (Illus.). 32p. (J). (gr. 1 up). lib. bdg. 22.00 (978-0-8368-2781-1(3)) Stevens, Gareth Inc.

—Hairy Maclary & Zachary Quack. Dodd, Lynley, illus. 2000. (Gold Star First Readers Ser.). (Illus.). 32p. (J). (gr. 1 up). lib. bdg. 22.00 (978-0-8368-2676-0(0)) Stevens, Gareth Inc.

—Hairy Maclary & Zachary Quack. 2005. (Illus.). 32p. (J). reprint ed. 5.95 (978-1-58246-147-2(3) , Tricycle Pr.) Ten Speed Pr.

—Hairy Maclary from Donaldson's Dairy. Dodd, Lynley, illus. 2000. (Gold Star First Readers Ser.). (Illus.). 32p. (J). (gr. 1 up). lib. bdg. 21.26 (978-0-8368-2688-3(4)) Stevens, Gareth Inc.

—Hairy Maclary from Donaldson's Dairy. 2005. (Illus.). 36p. (J). 5.95 (978-1-58246-059-8(0) , Tricycle Pr.) Ten Speed Pr.

—Hairy Maclary Scattercat. Dodd, Lynley, illus. 2000. (Gold Star First Readers Ser.). (Illus.). 32p. (J). (gr. 1 up). lib. bdg. 22.00 (978-0-8368-2689-0(2)) Stevens, Gareth Inc.

—Hairy Maclary Scattercat. 2005. (Illus.). 32p. (J). 5.95 (978-1-58246-095-6(7) , Tricycle Pr.) Ten Speed Pr.

—Hairy Maclary, Sit. Dodd, Lynley, illus. 2001. (Gold Star First Readers Ser.). (Illus.). 32p. (J). (gr. 1 up). lib. bdg. 22.00 (978-0-8368-2808-5(9)) Stevens, Gareth Inc.

—Hairy Maclary's Bone. Dodd, Lynley, illus. 2001. (Gold Star First Readers Ser.). (Illus.). 32p. (J). (gr. 1 up). lib. bdg. 22.00 (978-0-8368-2782-8(1)) Stevens, Gareth Inc.

—Hairy Maclary's Bone. 2005. (Illus.). 36p. (J). 5.95 (978-1-58246-060-4(4) , Tricycle Pr.) Ten Speed Pr.

—Hairy Maclary's Caterwaul Caper. Dodd, Lynley, illus. 2000. (Gold Star First Readers Ser.). (Illus.). 32p. (J). (gr. 1 up). lib. bdg. 22.00 (978-0-8368-2690-6(6)) Stevens, Gareth Inc.

—Hairy Maclary's Rumpus at the Vet. Dodd, Lynley, illus. 2000. (Gold Star First Readers Ser.). (Illus.). 32p. (J). (gr. 1 up). lib. bdg. 21.26 (978-0-8368-2691-3(4)) Stevens, Gareth Inc.

—Hairy Maclary's Rumpus at the Vet. 2005. (Illus.). 32p. (J). 5.95 (978-1-58246-094-9(9) , Tricycle Pr.) Ten Speed Pr.

—Hairy Maclary's Showbusiness. 2006. (Illus.). 32p. (J). 5.95 (***978-1-58246-208-0(9)*** , Tricycle Pr.) Ten Speed Pr.

—Scarface Claw. Dodd, Lynley, illus. 2002. (Gold Star First Readers Ser.). (Illus.). 32p. (J). (gr. 1 up). lib. bdg. 22.00 (978-0-8368-3161-0(6)) Stevens, Gareth Inc.

—Schnitzel Von Krumm, Dogs Never Climb Trees. 2004. (Gold Star First Readers Ser.). (Illus.). 32p. (J). (gr. 1 up). lib. bdg. 22.00 (978-0-8368-4092-6(5)) Stevens, Gareth Inc.

—Schnitzel Von Krumm's Basketwork. Dodd, Lynley, illus. 2001. (Gold Star First Readers Ser.). (Illus.). 32p. (J). (gr. 1 up). lib. bdg. 22.00 (978-0-8368-2783-5(X)) Stevens, Gareth Inc.

—Slinky Malinki. Dodd, Lynley, illus. 2001. (Gold Star First Readers Ser.). (Illus.). 32p. (J). (gr. 1 up). lib. bdg. 22.00 (978-0-8368-2784-2(8)) Stevens, Gareth Inc.

—Slinky Malinki. 2005. (Illus.). 32p. (J). reprint ed. 5.95 (978-1-58246-148-9(1) , Tricycle Pr.) Ten Speed Pr.

—Slinky Malinki Catflaps. Dodd, Lynley, illus. 1999. (Gold Star First Readers Ser.). (Illus.). 32p. (J). (gr. 1 up). lib. bdg. 22.00 (978-0-8368-2249-6(8)) Stevens, Gareth Inc.

—Slinky Malinki Catflaps. 2006. (Illus.). 0032p. (J). pap. 5.95 (978-1-58246-175-5(9) , Tricycle Pr.) Ten Speed Pr.

—Slinky Malinki, Open the Door. Dodd, Lynley, illus. 2001. (Gold Star First Readers Ser.). (Illus.). 32p. (J). (gr. 1 up). lib. bdg. 22.00 (978-0-8368-2785-9(6)) Stevens, Gareth Inc.

—Slinky Malinki, Open the Door. 2006. (Illus.). 0032p. (J). pap. 5.95 (978-1-58246-176-2(7) , Tricycle Pr.) Ten Speed Pr.

—Sniff-Snuff-Snap! Dodd, Lynley, illus. 2000. (Gold Star First Readers Ser.). (Illus.). 32p. (J). (gr. 1 up). lib. bdg. 22.00 (978-0-8368-2677-7(9)) Stevens, Gareth Inc.

—Zachary Quack Minimonster. 2006. (Gold Star First Readers Ser.). (Illus.). 31p. (J). 22.00 (978-0-8368-6187-7(6)) Stevens, Gareth Inc.

Dodds, Dayle Ann. Minnie's Diner: A Multiplying Menu. Manders, John, illus. 2004. 40p. (J). (gr. k-3). 16.99 (978-0-7636-1736-3(9)) Candlewick Pr.

—Minnie's Diner: A Multiplying Menu. Manders, John, illus. 2007. 40p. (J). (gr. k-3). pap. 6.99 (978-0-7636-3313-4(5)) Candlewick Pr.

—The Prince Won't Go to Bed. Brooker, Kyrsten, illus. 2007. 32p. (J). (ps-1). 16.00 (978-0-374-36108-2(8)) Farrar, Straus & Giroux.

Dolan, Penny. Eight Enormous Elephants. Bradley, Leo, illus. 2004. (Read-It! Readers Ser.). 32p. (C). (gr. k-3). 18.60 (978-1-4048-0054-0(9)) Picture Window Bks.

Donahue, Jill L. Rudy Helps Out. Previn, Stacey, illus. 2006. (Read-It! Readers Ser.). (J). 19.93 (978-1-4048-2420-1(0)) Picture Window Bks.

Donahue, Jill L. The Zoo Band. 2007. (Illus.). 24p. (J). (***978-1-4048-2381-5(6)***) Picture Window Bks.

—The Zoo Band. Eroglu, Aysin D., illus. 2006. 24p. (J). (***978-1-4048-3165-0(7)***) Picture Window Bks.

Donahue, Jill L. Urban. Wendell the Worrier. Spence, Tom, illus. 2006. (Read-It! Readers Ser.). (J). 19.93 (978-1-4048-2425-6(1)) Picture Window Bks.

Donaldson, Julia. Charlie Cook's Favourite Book. Scheffler, Axel, illus. 2006. 32p. (J). (ps). 16.99 (978-0-8037-3142-4(6) , Dial) Penguin Group (USA) Inc.

—The Fish Who Cried Wolf. Scheffler, Axel, illus. 2008. (J). pap. (***978-0-545-03454-8(X)***); 40p. 15.99 (***978-0-439-92825-0(7)***) Scholastic, Inc. (Levine, Arthur A. Bks.).

—The Gruffalo. 2006. 32p. (J). pap. 5.99 (978-0-14-240387-7(3) , Puffin) Penguin Group (USA) Inc.

—The Gruffalo's Child. Scheffler, Axel, illus. 2005. 32p. (J). (ps). 16.99 (978-0-8037-3009-0(8) , Dial) Penguin Group (USA) Inc.

—One Ted Falls Out of Bed. Currey, Anna, illus. 2006. 32p. (J). 15.95 (978-0-8050-7787-2(1)) Holt, Henry & Co.

—Room on the Broom. Scheffler, Axel, illus. (J). (gr. k-3). 2003. pap. 6.99 (978-0-14-250112-2(3) , Puffin); 2001. 16.99 (978-0-8037-2657-4(0) , Dial) Penguin Group (USA) Inc.

—Room on the Broom. 2003. (gr. k-3). lib. bdg. 15.30 (978-0-613-83001-0(6)) Tandem Library Bks.

—The Snail & the Whale. Scheffler, Axel, tr. Scheffler, Axel, illus. 2004. 32p. (J). (gr. k-3). 16.99 (978-0-8037-2922-3(7) , Dial) Penguin Group (USA) Inc.

—The Snail & the Whale. Scheffler, Axel, illus. 2006. 32p. (J). reprint ed. pap. 6.99 (978-0-14-240580-2(9) , Puffin) Penguin Group (USA) Inc.

Donaldson, Julia. Where's My Mom? Scheffler, Axel, illus. 2008. 32p. (J). (ps). 16.99 (***978-0-8037-3228-5(7)*** , Dial) Penguin Group (USA) Inc.

Doran, Margie. Sunflower Serenade. 2001. (Illus.). 14p. (J). (ps-3). 10.00 (978-0-9629270-7-2(4)) C&D Productions JimMar, Inc.

Dorfman, Craig. I Knew You Could! A Book for All the Stops in Your Life. Ong, Cristina, illus. 2003. (Little Engine That Could Ser.). 32p. (J). (gr. 1-2). 11.99 (978-0-448-43148-2(3) , Grosset & Dunlap) Penguin Group (USA) Inc.

Dorfman, Craig. I Knew You Could! Celebrate All the Stops in Your Life. Ong, Cristina, illus. 2008. (Little Engine That Could Ser.). 32p. (J). (ps). 12.99 (***978-0-448-44813-8(0)*** , Grosset & Dunlap) Penguin Group (USA) Inc.

Dorfman, Gladys E. Locked in the Zoo, What Will They Do? 2000. (Illus.). 28p. (J). (gr. k-4). 12.95 (978-0-9671111-2-4(9)) Hannah Mae Enterprises, Inc.

Dorling Kindersley Publishing Staff. Babies Love. 2003. (Baby's World Ser.). (Illus.). 12p. (J). bds. 6.99 (978-0-7894-9212-8(1)) Dorling Kindersley Publishing, Inc.

—Look at Me: I Can Clap. 2002. (Baby's World Board Books Ser.). (Illus.). 12p. (J). bds. 6.99 (978-0-7894-8827-5(2)) Dorling Kindersley Publishing, Inc.

Dorling Kindersley Publishing Staff, contrib. by. Love & Kisses. 2005. (Glitter Stickers Ser.). (Illus.). 16p. (J). (ps-3). pap. 6.99 (978-0-7566-1413-3(9)) Dorling Kindersley Publishing, Inc.

Dorling Kindersley Publishing Staff & Millard, Anne. Good Morning. 2002. (Baby's World Shaped Board Bks.). (Illus.). 12p. (J). bds. 4.99 (978-0-7894-8563-2(X)) Dorling Kindersley Publishing, Inc.

—Halloween. 2002. (Jumbo Shaped Board Bks.). (Illus.). 12p. (J). bds. 6.99 (978-0-7894-8589-2(3)) Dorling Kindersley Publishing, Inc.

Las Dos Iguanas.Tr. of Two Iguanas. (SPA.). (J). 9.95 (978-968-6044-78-2(7)) Corunda, Ediciones, S.A. de C.V. MEX. *Dist:* AIMS International Bks., Inc.

Dotlich, Rebecca Kai & Boyds Mills Press Staff. In the Spin of Things: Poetry of Motion. Dugan, Karen M., illus. 2003. 32p. (J). (gr. k-2). 16.95 (978-1-56397-145-7(3)) Boyds Mills Pr.

Dougherty, Terri. Days of the Week. Greathouse, Justin, illus. 2006. (Read-It! Readers Ser.). 32p. (J). (ps-3). 18.60 (978-1-4048-1581-0(3)) Picture Window Bks.

Douglis, Carole. Tessa & the Fishy Mystery. Kennaway, Adrienne, tr. 2005. (Tunza Environmental Series for Children). (Illus.). 30p. (J). pap. 8.00 (978-92-807-2462-2(2) , E.04.III.D.29) United Nations Environment Programme KEN. *Dist:* United Nations Pubns.

Downey, Lynn. The Flea's Sneeze. Firehammer, Karla, illus. rev. ed. 2000. 32p. (J). (ps-1). 17.95 (978-0-8050-6103-1(7) , Holt, Henry & Co. Bks. For Young Readers) Holt, Henry & Co.

Downs, Mike. You See a Circus, I See... McGrory, Anik, illus. (J). 2006. pap. 6.95 (978-1-58089-155-4(1)); 2005. 32p. 14.95 (978-1-58089-097-7(0)) Charlesbridge Publishing, Inc.

Downs Webb, Michelle. What Color Is Love? 2005. 24p. 10.95 (978-1-4116-2783-3(0)) Lulu.com.

Doyle, Alfreda C. Easter Story Rhymes. unabr. ed. 1998. (Alfreda's Radio Ser.: Vol. 8). (J). (gr. 5-9). 16.95 incl. audio (978-1-56820-312-6(8)) Story Time Stories That Rhyme.

Doyle, Charlotte. The Bouncing, Dancing, Galloping ABC. Gorton, Julia, illus. 2006. 32p. (J). (ps-1). 10.99 (978-0-399-23778-2(X) , Putnam Juvenile) Penguin Group (USA) Inc.

—It's Twins! Gorton, Julia, illus. 2003. 32p. (J). (ps-1). 10.99 (978-0-399-23718-8(6) , Putnam Juvenile) Penguin Group (USA) Inc.

—Supermarket! Westcott, Nadine Bernard, tr. Westcott, Nadine Bernard, illus. 2004. (Super Study Picture Book Ser.). 24p. (J). (gr. k-ps). 8.99 (978-0-7636-2218-3(4)) Candlewick Pr.

Doyle, Malachy. One, Two, Three O'Leary. Hillenbrand, Will, tr. Hillenbrand, Will, illus. 2004. 32p. (J). 15.95 (978-0-689-85513-9(3) , McElderry, Margaret K.) Simon & Schuster Children's Publishing.

Dr. Seuss Enterprises Staff. Hop on Pop. 2004. (Illus.). 24p. (J). (gr. k-ps). bds. 4.99 (978-0-375-82837-9(0) , Random Hse. Bks. for Young Readers) Random Hse. Children's Bks.

Dragonwagon, Crescent. The Sun Begun. Shaffer, Terea, illus. 1999. (J). 16.00 (978-0-689-81159-3(4) , Atheneum) Simon & Schuster Children's Publishing.

Dreyer, Nicole E. The Parable of the Talents. Morris, Susan, illus. 2007. 16p. (J). (gr. k-4). 1.99 (***978-0-7586-1282-3(6)***) Concordia Publishing Hse.

Dudley, Linda. Aunt Linda's Mommy & Me Book. 2003. (J). pap. 15.99 (978-1-4134-3830-7(X)) Borders Personal Publishing.

Duksta, Laura. I Love You More. Keesler, Karen, illus. 2007. 34p. (J). (gr. 4-7). 16.99 (***978-1-4022-1126-3(0)*** , Sourcebooks Jabberwocky) Sourcebooks, Inc.

Dulaney, Kim. I Love Me! 1998. 9.95 (978-1-891636-02-8(2)) Unique Expression.

Dunbar, Joyce. Shoe Baby. Dunbar, Polly, illus. 2005. 40p. (J). (gr. k-k). 15.99 (978-0-7636-2779-9(8)) Candlewick Pr.

Dunn, Opal. Number Rhymes to Say & Play! Gon, Adriano, illus. 2005. 32p. (J). (ps). pap. 7.95 (978-1-84507-441-8(6)) Lincoln, Frances Ltd. GBR. *Dist:* Perseus Distribution.

Dunn, Todd. We Go Together! Sakamoto, Miki, illus. 2007. 24p. (J). (ps). 12.95 (978-1-4027-3260-7(0)) Sterling Publishing Co., Inc.

Dunphy, Madeleine. Here Is the Arctic Winter. Robinson, Alan James, illus. 2007. (Web of Life Ser.). 32p. (J). 16.95 (978-0-9777539-1-8(3)); pap. 9.95 (978-0-9777539-0-1(5)) Web of Life Children's Bks.

Dunrea, Olivier, illus. Goslings on the Prowl! 2005. (J). (978-0-618-53241-4(2)) Houghton Mifflin Co.

DuQuette, Keith. Cock-a-Doodle Moooo! A Mixed-Up Menagerie. DuQuette, Keith, illus. 2004. (Illus.). 32p. (J). (ps-3). 15.99 (978-0-399-23889-5(1) , Putnam Juvenile) Penguin Group (USA) Inc.

Durango, Julia. Dream Hop. Lee, Jared D., illus. 2005. 32p. (J). (gr. k-2). 15.95 (978-0-689-87163-4(5)) Simon & Schuster Children's Publishing.

DuTemple, Lesley A. One Little Balsam Fir: A Northwoods Counting Book. Robinson, Susan, illus. 2006. (J). (***978-1-892384-37-9(X)***) Avery Color Studios, Inc.

Dver, Alyssa. When Whizzly Wanders. 2005. 15p. 6.78 (978-1-4116-4667-4(3)) Lulu.com.

Dwyer, Mindy. Sweet Dreams, Polar Bear. 2005. (Illus.). 32p. (J). 15.95 (978-0-88240-554-4(3)); pap. 8.95 (978-0-88240-555-1(1)) Graphic Arts Ctr. Publishing Co.

Eastwood, J. G. Dragon: Enter the Realm. 2007. (YA). per. (***978-0-9792030-7-7(4)***) Light Sword Publishing LLC.

Eaton, Seymour. Teddy Bears Traveling Adventures. Akmon, Nancy, ed. Akmon, Roni, illus. 2004. 46p. (J). (gr. k-4). reprint ed. 15.00 (978-0-7567-8171-2(X)) DIANE Publishing Co.

Eberhard, Phyllis Lunde Brees. Little Miss Neat-A-Pin. Jacoby, Nickolina Dye, illus. 2007. (J). (***978-0-9722741-7-3(0)***) Publishing Factory, The.

Edens, Cooper. Santa Cow Island. 1999. (J). (978-0-606-18952-1(1)) Tandem Library Bks.

Edwards, David. The Pen That Pa Built. Wolff, Ashley, illus. 2007. 32p. (J). (ps-1). 14.95 (***978-1-58246-153-3(8)*** , Tricycle Pr.) Ten Speed Pr.

Edwards, Julie Andrews & Hamilton, Emma Walton. Thanks to You: Wisdom from Mother & Child. 2007. (Illus.). 40p. 14.99 (978-0-06-124002-7(8)) HarperCollins Pubs.

Edwards, Pamela Duncan. Miss Polly Has a Dolly. Castaldi, Elicia, illus. 2003. 32p. (J). (ps-2). 15.99 (978-0-399-23857-4(3) , Putnam Juvenile) Penguin Group (USA) Inc.

—Roar! Cole, Henry, illus. Date not set. 32p. (J). (ps-2). pap. 5.99 (978-0-06-443572-7(5)) HarperCollins Pubs.

—Roar! A Noisy Counting Book. Cole, Henry, illus. 2000. 32p. (J). (ps-2). 16.99 (978-0-06-028384-1(X)); 15.89 (978-0-06-028385-8(8)) HarperCollins Pubs.

—Warthogs Paint: A Messy Color Book. Cole, Henry, illus. 2001. 32p. (ps-4). 15.49 (978-0-7868-2412-0(3)) Hyperion Bks. for Children.

Egan, Kate. The Movie Storybook. 2006. (Open Season Ser.). 48p. (J). 8.99 (978-0-06-084609-1(7)) HarperCollins Pubs.

Ehlert, Lois. Fish Eyes: A Book You Can Count On. Ehlert, Lois, illus. 2001. (Illus.). 40p. (J). bds. 6.95 (978-0-15-216281-8(X) , Red Wagon Bks.) Harcourt Children's Bks.

—Market Day: A Story Told with Folk Art. Ehlert, Lois, illus. 2002. (Illus.). (J). 23.40 (978-0-7587-4281-0(9)) Book Wholesalers, Inc.

—Market Day: A Story Told with Folk Art. (Illus.). 36p. (J). (gr. k-2). 2002. pap. 7.00 (978-0-15-216820-9(6) , Voyager Bks./Libros Viajeros); 2000. 16.00 (978-0-15-202158-0(2)) Harcourt Children's Bks.

—Market Day: A Story Told with Folk Art. 2002. (gr. k-3). lib. bdg. 14.15 (978-0-613-53833-6(1)) Tandem Library Bks.

—Oodles of Animals. 2008. (J). (***978-0-15-206274-3(2)***) Harcourt Trade Pubs.

—Top Cat. Ehlert, Lois, illus. 2002. (Illus.). (J). 21.70 (978-0-7587-3843-1(9)) Book Wholesalers, Inc.

—Top Cat. 2001. (J). (978-0-606-21492-6(5)); lib. bdg. 14.15 (978-0-613-35585-8(7)) Tandem Library Bks.

—Wag a Tail. 2007. (Illus.). 40p. (J). (ps-2). 16.00 (978-0-15-205843-2(5)) Harcourt Trade Pubs.

Ehrhardt, Karen. This Jazz Man. Roth, Robert, illus. 2006. 32p. (J). (ps-2). 16.00 (978-0-15-205307-9(7)) Harcourt Trade Pubs.

Ehrlich, H. M. Dr. Duck & the New Babies. Rader, Laura, illus. 2005. 36p. (J). 15.95 (978-1-59354-073-9(6)) Blue Apple Bks.

Ehrlich, H. M., et al. Dr. Duck. Rader, Laura, illus. 2000. 36p. (J). (ps-1). pap. 14.95 (978-0-531-30254-5(7) , Orchard Bks.) Scholastic, Inc.

Elin Hirschman, Jessica & Bright, Bonnie. The Tangle Tower. 2006. (Illus.). 32p. (J). 14.95 (978-0-9701155-6-0(3)) Cookie Bear Pr., Inc.

Elliott, David. And Here's to You! Cecil, Randy, illus. 2004. 32p. (J). (ps-2). 15.99 (978-0-7636-1427-0(0)) Candlewick Pr.

Elliott, David. One Little Chicken: A Counting Book. Long, Ethan, illus. 2007. 24p. (J). (ps-k). 16.95 (***978-0-8234-1983-8(5)***) Holiday Hse., Inc.

Ellis, Kiersten. Do Planets Hang on Strings? 2006. 24p. (J). per. 11.99 (***978-1-59886-688-9(5)***); 14.99 (***978-1-59886-992-7(2)***) Tate Publishing & Enterprises, L.L.C.

Ellis, Libby. Midge & Max's Scavenger Hunt. Jonason, Dave, illus. 2005. 12p. (J). (ps-3). act. bk. ed. 14.95 (978-1-58117-109-9(9) , Intervisual/Piggy Toes) Dalmatian Pr.

Elmo's Christmas. 2000. (J). 9.99 (978-1-931312-29-5(X)) SoftPlay, Inc.

Elya, Susan Middleton. Bebé Goes Shopping. Salerno, Steven, illus. 2006. (ENG & SPA.). 40p. (J). 16.00 (978-0-15-205426-7(X)) Harcourt Trade Pubs.

—Bebe Goes Shopping. Salerno, Steven, illus. 2008. 36p. (J). pap. 6.00 (***978-0-15-206142-5(8)*** , Voyager Bks./Libros Viajeros) Harcourt Children's Bks.

—Bebé Goes to the Beach. Salerno, Steven, illus. 2008. (ENG & SPA.). (J). (***978-0-15-206000-8(6)***) Harcourt Trade Pubs.

—Cowboy Jose. Raglin, Tim, illus. 2005. 32p. (J). 15.99 (978-0-399-23570-2(1) , Putnam Juvenile) Penguin Group (USA) Inc.

—Eight Animals Bake a Cake. Chapman, Lee, illus. 2002. (ENG & SPA.). 32p. (J). (ps-3). 15.99 (978-0-399-23468-2(3) , Putnam Juvenile) Penguin Group (USA) Inc.

—Eight Animals on the Town. Chapman, Lee, illus. (SPA.). (J). 2002. 32p. pap. 6.99 (978-0-698-11961-1(4)); 2000. 1p. 15.99 (978-0-399-23437-8(3)) Penguin Group (USA) Inc. (Putnam Juvenile).

—Eight Animals on the Town. 2002. (gr. k-3). lib. bdg. 15.30 (978-0-613-73480-6(7)) Tandem Library Bks.

—F Is for Fiesta. Karas, G. Brian, illus. 2006. 32p. (J). (ps-2). 12.99 (978-0-399-24225-0(2) , Putnam Juvenile) Penguin Group (USA) Inc.

—Fairy Trails: A Story Told in English & Spanish. McDonald, Mercedes, illus. 2005. 32p. (J). (ps-ps). 16.95 (978-1-58234-927-5(4)) Bloomsbury Publishing.

—Oh No, Gotta Go! Karas, G. Brian, illus. 2005. 29p. (J). (gr. k-4). reprint ed. 15.00 (978-0-7567-8946-6(X)) DIANE Publishing Co.

—Oh No, Gotta Go! Karas, G. Brian, illus. 32p. (J). 2006. pap. 5.99 (978-0-14-240334-1(2) , Puffin); 2003. (SPA.). 15.99 (978-0-399-23493-4(4) , Putnam Juvenile) Penguin Group (USA) Inc.

—Oh No, Gotta Go, No. 2. Cravath, Lynne Woodcock & Avril, Lynne, illus. 2007. 32p. (J). (ps-k). 15.99 (978-0-399-24308-0(9) , Putnam Juvenile) Penguin Group (USA) Inc.

Elya, Susan Middleton. Tooth on the Loose. Mattheson, Jenny, illus. 2008. (SPA & ENG.). 32p. (J). (ps-k). 16.99 (***978-0-399-24459-9(X)*** , Putnam Juvenile) Penguin Group (USA) Inc.

Elya, Susan Middleton & Banks, Merry. N Is for Navidad. Cepeda, Joe, illus. 2007. 40p. (J). (ps-3). 14.95 (978-0-8118-5205-0(9)) Chronicle Bks. LLC.

Emery, Joanna. Stinky Clothes. Rossi, Richard, illus. 2005. (Rookie Reader Skill Set Ser.). (J). 31p. (gr. k-2). pap. 4.95 (978-0-516-25284-1(4)); 32p. (gr. 1-2). 19.50 (978-0-516-25151-6(1)) Scholastic Library Publishing. (Children's Pr.).

Emmett, Jonathan. A Mouse in the Marmalade. Church, Caroline, illus. 2002. (J). tchr. ed. 14.95 (978-1-58925-687-3(5) , tiger tales) ME Media LLC.

—Someone Bigger. Reynolds, Adrian, illus. 2004. 32p. (J). (gr. k-3). 16.00 (978-0-618-44397-0(5) , Clarion Bks.) Houghton Mifflin Co. Trade & Reference Div.

—Through the Heart of the Jungle. Gomez, Elena, illus. 2003. 32p. (J). tchr. ed. 15.95 (978-1-58925-029-1(X)); pap. 5.95 (978-1-58925-380-3(9)) ME Media LLC. (tiger tales).

—Through the Heart of the Jungle. 2003. (gr. k-3). lib. bdg. 14.10 (978-0-613-85249-4(4)) Tandem Library Bks.

—A Turtle in the Toilet. Jayne Church, Caroline, illus. 2002. 16p. (J). tchr. ed. 14.95 (978-1-58925-688-0(3) , tiger tales) ME Media LLC.

Emzer, Counselor. Duane, You Must be Insane. 2005. 20p. 7.97 (978-1-4116-3091-8(2)) Lulu.com.

Enderle, Judith Ross. Six Creepy Sheep. 2001. (ps-2). lib. bdg. 17.60 (978-0-613-78778-9(1)); (Illus.). (J). (978-0-606-20918-2(2)) Tandem Library Bks.

Engelbreit, Mary. Mary Engelbreit's A Merry Little Christmas: Celebrate from A to Z. Engelbreit, Mary, illus. 2006. (Illus.). 40p. (J). lib. bdg. 17.89 (978-0-06-074159-4(7)) HarperCollins Pubs.

—Mary Engelbreit's a Merry Little Christmas: Celebrate from A to Z. Engelbreit, Mary, illus. 2006. (Illus.). 40p. (J). 16.99 (978-0-06-074158-7(9)) HarperCollins Pubs.

England, Brooke. Guardian Fairies. 2006. 17p. 12.00 (978-1-4116-7923-8(7)) Lulu.com.

Epner, Paul. Herbert Hilligan & His Magical Adventure. Kuon, Vuthy & Nguyen, Duke, illus. 2003. 32p. (J). 15.95 (978-0-9743335-0-2(6)) Imaginative Publishing, Ltd.

—Herbert Hilligan & His Magical Lunchbox. Kuon, Vuthy & Nguyen, Duke, illus. rev. ed. (Herbert Hilligan Ser.). 15.95 (978-1-57168-549-0(9)) Eakin Pr.

—Herbert Hilligan's Lone Star Adventure, Vol. 4. Kuon, Vuthy & Nguyen, Duke, illus. 2002. (Herbert Hilligan Ser.). 15.95 (978-1-57168-678-7(9)) Eakin Pr.

—Herbert Hilligan's Lone Star Adventure. Kuon, Vuthy & Nguyen, Duke, illus. 2003. 32p. (J). 15.95 (978-0-9743335-3-3(0)) Imaginative Publishing, Ltd.

—Herbert Hilligan's Tropical Adventure. Kuon, Vuthy & Nguyen, Duke, illus. 2003. 32p. (J). 15.95 (978-0-9743335-2-6(2)) Imaginative Publishing, Ltd.

Erickson, Gina Clegg & Foster, Kelli C. The Pancake Day. Gifford, Kerri, illus. 2004. 30p. (J). (ps-ps). lib. bdg. 11.30 (978-0-606-30082-7(1)) Tandem Library Bks.

Erlich, Bev. Pink Roses Everywhere. gif. ed. 2004. (Illus.). 64p. (J). 14.95 (978-0-9743913-0-4(1)) Snojoy Publishing.

Ernst, Lisa Campbell, illus. This Is the Van That Dad Cleaned. 2005. 40p. (J). 15.95 (978-0-689-86190-1(7) , Simon & Schuster Children's Publishing) Simon & Schuster Children's Publishing.

Esbaum, Jill. Estelle Takes a Bath. DePalma, Mary Newell, illus. rev. ed. 2006. 32p. (J). 16.95 (978-0-8050-7741-4(3)) Holt, Henry & Co.

Eschbacher, Roger. Road Trip! Wickstrom, Thor, illus. 2006. 32p. (J). (ps). 16.99 (978-0-8037-2927-8(8) , Dial) Penguin Group (USA) Inc.

Estefan, Gloria & Garland, Michael. The Magically Mysterious Adventures of Noelle the Bulldog. 32p. 2006. pap. 6.99 (978-0-06-082625-3(8)); 2005. (Illus.). 17.99 (978-0-06-082623-9(1)) HarperCollins Pubs. (Rayo).

—Las Magicas y Misteriosas Aventuras de una Bulldog Llamada Noelle. 2005. (Illus.). 32p. (ps). 17.99 (978-0-06-082626-0(6) , Rayo) HarperCollins Pubs.

Eubank, Patti Reeder, tr. ABCs of Halloween. 2003. (Illus.). 40p. (J). (ps-k). 8.95 (978-0-8249-5467-3(X)) Ideals Pubns.

Evans, Lezlie. The Bunnies' Trip. Chorao, Kay, illus. 2008. 32p. 16.99 (***978-0-7868-1898-3(0)***) Hyperion Bks. for Children.

Everson, Chance. Beginnings Vol. 2: Tales of the Mandrasaurs, Volume the Second. Geary, Steve, illus. 2004. cd-rom 9.95 (978-0-9760303-1-7(4)) R.A.R.E. TALES.

—Discoveries: Tales of the Mandrasaurs, Volume the Third. Geary, Steve, illus. 2004. cd-rom 9.95 (978-0-9760303-2-4(2)) R.A.R.E. TALES.

—Forever & a Day Vol. 1: Tales of the Mandrasaurs, Volume the First. Geary, Steve, illus. 2004. cd-rom 9.95 (978-0-9760303-0-0(6)) R.A.R.E. TALES.

—Verlin's Magical Blunder: Tales of the Mandrasaurs, Volume the Seventh. Geary, Steve, illus. 2004. cd-rom 9.95 (978-0-9760303-6-2(5)) R.A.R.E. TALES.

Ewart, Claire. Fossil. Ewart, Claire, illus. 2004. (Illus.). 32p. (J). 16.95 (978-0-8027-8890-0(4)) Walker & Co.

Fagan, Cary. Directed by Kaspar Snit. 2007. 160p. (J). (gr. 3-7). pap. 9.95 (978-0-88776-753-1(2) , Delacorte Bks. for Young Readers) Random Hse. Children's Bks.

Fallon, Jimmy. Snowball Fight! Stower, Adam, illus. 2005. 32p. (J). (ps). 15.99 (978-0-525-47456-2(0) , Dutton Juvenile) Penguin Group (USA) Inc.

Fallon, Joe & Scarborough, Ken. Halfway Hank. Davis, Jack E., illus. 2005. 40p. (J). 15.99 (978-0-06-623636-0(3)) HarperCollins Pubs.

Falwell, Cathryn. Scoot! 2008. 32p. (J). 16.99 (***978-0-06-128882-1(9)***); lib. bdg. 17.89 (***978-0-06-128883-8(7)***) HarperCollins Pubs. (Greenwillow Bks.).

—Shape Capers. Falwell, Cathryn, illus. 2007. 32p. (J). (ps-k). 16.99 (***978-0-06-123699-0(3)*** , Greenwillow Bks.) HarperCollins Pubs.

—Shape Capers. 2007. 32p. (J). (ps-k). lib. bdg. 17.89 (***978-0-06-123700-3(0)*** , Greenwillow Bks.) HarperCollins Pubs.

—Turtle Splash! Countdown at the Pond. Falwell, Cathryn, illus. 2002. (Illus.). (J). 25.04 (978-0-7587-8827-6(4)) Book Wholesalers, Inc.

—Turtle Splash! Countdown at the Pond. Falwell, Cathryn, illus. 32p. (J). 2008. pap. 6.99 (***978-0-06-142927-9(9)*** , Harper Trophy); 2001. (Illus.). (gr. 7 up). 16.99 (978-0-06-029462-5(0)); 2001. (Illus.). (gr. 7 up). lib. bdg. 17.89 (978-0-06-029463-2(9)) HarperCollins Pubs.

Famoriyo, Olusegun. The Handkerchief. 2005. 111p. pap. 16.95 (978-1-4137-2162-1(1)) PublishAmerica, Inc.

Farrell, John. Dear Child. Manning, Maurie, illus. 2008. (J). (***978-1-59078-495-2(2)***) Boyds Mills Pr.

Fatus, Sophie, illus. A Hen, a Chick & a String Guitar. 2005. 32p. (J). 17.99 incl. audio compact disk (978-1-84148-796-0(1)) Barefoot Bks., Inc.

Faulkner, Keith. The Five Senses. Lambert, Jonathan, illus. 2002. 14p. (J). pap. 9.95 (978-0-439-38882-5(1) , Scholastic Pr.) Scholastic, Inc.

—Ten Little Monkeys: A Counting Story Book. Lambert, Jonathan, illus. 2004. 12p. (J). reprint ed. 20.00 (978-0-7567-8203-0(1)) DIANE Publishing Co.

Feely, Jenny. Pig's Skin. 2001. (gr. k-3). lib. bdg. 11.80 (978-0-613-33412-9(4)) Tandem Library Bks.

Fehlner, Paul. Dog & Cat. Chambliss, Maxie, illus. 2003. (My First Reader Ser.). 32p. (J). 18.50 (978-0-516-22924-9(9) , Children's Pr.) Scholastic Library Publishing.

Feldman, Estelle. Snowy Winter Day. Demarest, Chris L., illus. 2002. (Rhyme Time Readers Ser.). 32p. (J). 3.99 (978-0-439-33401-3(2)) Scholastic, Inc.

Fennell, Kristen & Petruccelli, Jessica, illus. A World of Hope: Written by Hope's Parents Laurie & Mike. l.t. ed. 2005. 18p. (J). per. 9.99 (978-1-59879-069-6(2)) Lifevest Publishing, Inc.

Fernandes, Eugenie. Busy Little Mouse. Fernandes, Kim, illus. 2006. 24p. 6.95 (978-1-55453-027-4(X)) Kids Can Pr., Ltd. CAN. *Dist:* Wybel Marketing Group.

—Busy Little Mouse. Fernandes, Kim, illus. 2004. 20p. (ps-ps). lib. bdg. 12.75 (978-0-606-31383-4(4)) Tandem Library Bks.

Ferreri, Della Ross. How Will I Ever Sleep in This Bed? Mazille, Capucine, illus. 2007. 24p. (J). bds. 5.95 (978-1-4027-4324-5(6)); 2005. 32p. 12.95 (978-1-4027-1492-4(0)) Sterling Publishing Co., Inc.

Ficocelli, Elizabeth. Kid Tea. Dibley, Glin, illus. 2007. 40p. (J). (ps-2). 14.99 (978-0-7614-5333-8(4)) Cavendish, Marshall Corp.

Fireman Bear: New Heroes Backpack Story. 2002. (J). (978-1-931312-58-5(3)) SoftPlay, Inc.

Fisher, Aileen. Know What I Saw. DeSaix, Deborah Durland, illus. 2005. 32p. (J). 16.95 (978-1-59643-055-6(9)) Roaring Brook Pr.

—You Don't Look Like Your Mother. Jones, Lilith, illus. 2001. 31p. (J). pap. 6.00 (978-1-59034-061-5(2)); 15.95 (978-1-58653-856-9(X)) Mondo Publishing.

Fisher, Doris & Sneed, Dani. My Even Day. Lee, Karen, illus. 2007. 32p. (J). (ps-3). 8.95 (***978-1-934359-22-8(X)***) Sylvan Dell Pubng.

—One Odd Day, 2 Books, Book 1. Lee, Karen, illus. 2007. 32p. (J). pap. 8.95 (***978-1-934359-33-4(5)***) Sylvan Dell Pubng.

Fitzkee, Jeremy. One, Two, Three, Me. Budde, Nadia, illus. 2006. 24p. (J). (ps). 8.99 (978-0-670-06124-2(7) , Viking Adult) Penguin Group (USA) Inc.

Fitzpatrick, Marie-Louise. I'm a Tiger, Too! Fitzpatrick, Marie-Louise, illus. 2002. (Illus.). 6.95 (978-0-86327-871-6(X)) Interlink Publishing Group, Inc.

Flanagan, Alice K. Cats: The Sound of Short A. 1999. (Wonder Books Phonics: Vowels Ser.). (Illus.). 24p. (J). (ps-3). 21.36 (978-1-56766-691-5(4)) Child's World, Inc.

Flaxman, Jessica & Hall, Kirsten. Who Says? Becker, Wayne, illus. 2003. (My First Reader Ser.). 32p. (J). 18.50 (978-0-516-22958-4(3) , Children's Pr.) Scholastic Library Publishing.

Fleming, Candace & Smith, Maggie. This Is the Baby. 2004. (Illus.). 40p. (J). 16.50 (978-0-374-37486-0(4) , Farrar, Straus & Giroux (BYR)) Farrar, Straus & Giroux.

Fleming, Denise. Beetle Bop. 2007. (Illus.). 32p. (J). (ps-2). 16.00 (978-0-15-205936-1(9)) Harcourt Trade Pubs.

S

—In the Small, Small Pond. Fleming, Denise, illus. 2002. (Illus.). (J). 15.49 (978-0-7587-0119-0(5)) Book Wholesalers, Inc.

—In the Small, Small Pond. 2007. (Illus.). 32p. (J). pap. 22.95 (*978-0-8050-8117-6(8)* , Holt, Henry & Co. Bks. For Young Readers) Holt, Henry & Co.

—In the Small, Small Pond. Fleming, Denise, illus. rev. ed. 1998. (Illus.). 32p. (J). (ps-1). pap. 7.95 (978-0-8050-5983-0(0) , Holt, Henry & Co. Bks. For Young Readers) Holt, Henry & Co.

—In the Tall, Tall Grass. Fleming, Denise, illus. 2002. (Illus.). (J). 15.49 (978-0-7587-2843-2(3)) Book Wholesalers, Inc.

—Pumpkin Eye. rev. ed. (Illus.). 32p. (J). 2005. reprint ed. pap. 6.95 (978-0-8050-7635-6(2) , Owlet Paperbacks for Young Readers); 2001. 16.95 (978-0-8050-6681-4(0) , Holt, Henry & Co. Bks. For Young Readers) Holt, Henry & Co.

Fleming, Maria. Jumping Jill Went down the Hill. Weissman, Bart, illus. 2002. (Word Family Tales Ser.). 16p. (ps-2). pap. 2.95 (978-0-439-26267-5(4)) Scholastic, Inc.

Florian, Douglas. Vegetable Garden. Florian, Douglas, illus. 2002. (Illus.). (J). 13.19 (978-0-7587-3896-7(X)) Book Wholesalers, Inc.

—Vegetable Garden. 2000. (Illus.). 31p. (J). (gr. 2-3). reprint ed. pap. 20.00 (978-0-7881-9459-7(3)) DIANE Publishing Co.

Follow the Fish: A Touch & Say ABC Book. 2002. (DK Ladybird Ser.). 12p. (J). bds. 6.95 (978-0-7894-8470-3(6)) Dorling Kindersley Publishing, Inc.

Fontanez, Edwin. En esta hermosa Isla. Fontanez, Edwin, illus. 2005. (SPA., Illus.). 32p. (J). 16.95 (978-0-9640868-7-6(5)) Exit Studio.

Ford, Bernette. Don't Hit Me! Grier, Gary, illus. 2004. 32p. (J). lib. bdg. 15.00 (*978-1-4242-0218-8(3)*) Fitzgerald Bks.

Forever Friends! 2003. (Illus.). 28p. (J). (ps-k). bds. 7.95 (978-0-8249-5454-3(8)) Ideals Pubns.

Foster, Chad. Dear God: Thank-You Notes to God from Baby Boys & Girls. 2004. (J). bds. 8.99 (978-0-9644456-1-1(1)) Rising Bks.

Fox, Mem. Boo to a Goose. 2001. (gr. k-3). lib. bdg. 14.15 (978-0-613-35910-8(0)); (Illus.). (J). 13.79 (978-0-606-20576-4(4)) Tandem Library Bks.

—A Cat Called Kite. Slack, Michael H., illus. 2008. (J). (*978-0-15-204909-6(6)*) Harcourt Trade Pubs.

—The Magic Hat. Tusa, Tricia, illus. 2002. 32p. (J). (ps-3). 16.00 (978-0-15-201025-6(4)) Harcourt Children's Bks.

—Ten Little Fingers & Ten Little Toes. Oxenbury, Helen, illus. 2008. (J). (*978-0-15-206057-2(X)*) Harcourt Trade Pubs.

—Time for Bed. Dyer, Jane, illus. 2005. 28p. (J). bds. 10.95 (978-0-15-205349-9(2) , Red Wagon Bks.) Harcourt Children's Bks.

—Where the Giant Sleeps. Radunsky, Vladimir, illus. 2007. 32p. (J). (ps-2). 16.00 (978-0-15-205785-5(4)) Harcourt Trade Pubs.

—Zoo-Looking. Love, Judith DuFour & Whitman, Candace, illus. 2001. (J). (ps-2). pap. 6.00 (978-1-57255-011-7(2)) Mondo Publishing.

—Zoo-Looking. 2001. (ps-2). lib. bdg. 14.15 (978-0-613-86395-7(X)) Tandem Library Bks.

Fox, Mem & Horacek, Judy. Where Is the Green Sheep? 2004. (Illus.). 32p. (J). (ps-k). 16.00 (978-0-15-204907-2(X)) Harcourt Children's Bks.

Fox, Mem & Rodunsky, Vladimir. Where the Giant Sleeps. 2007. (Illus.). 32p. (J). (gr. k-2). 16.00 (978-0-15-206092-3(8)) Harcourt Trade Pubs.

Frampton, David. The Whole Night Through. Frampton, David, illus. Date not set. (Illus.). 32p. (J). (ps-1). pap. 5.99 (978-0-06-443652-6(7)) HarperCollins Pubs.

—The Whole Night Through: A Lullaby. Frampton, David, illus. 2004. (Illus.). 30p. (J). (gr. k-4). reprint ed. (978-0-7567-7723-4(2)) DIANE Publishing Co.

—The Whole Night Through: A Lullaby. Frampton, David, illus. 2001. (Illus.). 32p. (J). (ps-1). 15.89 (978-0-06-028826-6(4)); 15.95 (978-0-06-028825-9(6)) HarperCollins Pubs.

Francis, Snip & Gilbert, Melanie. Hey Look! the Happy Book. 1998. (Hey Look! Ser.: Vol. 1). (Illus.). 32p. (J). (ps-3). 15.95 (978-1-890616-22-9(2)) Salamander Group, Inc., The.

Franco, Betsy. Mi Dedo Menique. Lucas, Margeaux, illus. (Rookie Reader Espanol Ser.). (SPA.). (J). (gr. k-2). 2002. 24p. pap. 4.95 (978-0-516-26318-2(8)); 2001. 32p. 19.50 (978-0-516-22359-9(3)) Scholastic Library Publishing. (Children's Pr.).

—My Pinkie Finger. Lucas, Margeaux, illus. 2001. (Rookie Reader Espanol Ser.). 32p. (J). (gr. k-2). pap. 4.95 (978-0-516-27295-5(0)); (gr. 1-2). 19.50 (978-0-516-22221-9(X)) Scholastic Library Publishing. (Children's Pr.).

—My Pinkie Finger. 2001. (gr. k-3). lib. bdg. 12.95 (978-0-613-54620-1(2)) Tandem Library Bks.

—Shells. Sorra, Kristin, illus. 2000. (Rookie Readers Ser.). 32p. (J). (gr. 1-2). 19.50 (978-0-516-22012-3(8) , Children's Pr.) Scholastic Library Publishing.

—Summer's Beat. Middleton, Charlotte, illus. 2007. 40p. (J). 15.99 (978-1-4169-1237-8(1) , McElderry, Margaret K.) Simon & Schuster Children's Publishing.

—Vamos a la Granja de la Abuela. 2004. (Rookie Reader Espanol Ser.). (J). (gr. k-2). pap. 4.95 (978-0-516-24616-1(X) , Children's Pr.) Scholastic Library Publishing.

Frank, John. How to Catch a Fish. Sylvada, Peter, illus. 2007. (Neal Porter Bks.). 32p. (J). (ps-3). 17.95 (*978-1-59643-163-8(6)*) Roaring Brook Pr.

Frankau, Gilbert. One of Us: A Novel in Verse. 2005. pap. 22.95 (978-1-4179-6045-3(0)) Kessinger Publishing, LLC.

Freedman, Claire. One Magical Day. Macnaughton, Tina, illus. 2007. 28p. (J). (ps-1). 16.95 (*978-1-56148-567-3(5)*) Good Bks.

—Snuggle up, Sleepy Ones. Macnaughton, Tina, illus. 28p. (J). (ps). 2007. bds. 8.95 (*978-1-56148-562-8(4)*); 2005. 16.00 (978-1-56148-475-1(X)) Good Bks.

Freeman, Claire. One Magical Morning. Ho, Louise, illus. 2005. 28p. (J). 16.00 (978-1-56148-472-0(5)) Good Bks.

Freeman, Don. Rhymes & Riddles with Corduroy. 2002. (gr. k-3). lib. bdg. 11.25 (978-0-613-51510-8(2)) Tandem Library Bks.

Freeman, Tammy A. The Earthworm Jamboree. Zangrillo, Robert P., illus. 1999. (J). (978-0-9670675-1-3(0)) Largesse Publishing, Inc.

Freeman, Tina. Ten Little Monkeys: Jumping on the Bed. 2001. (gr. k-3). lib. bdg. 15.30 (978-0-613-77001-9(3)) Tandem Library Bks.

French, Vivian. Cat in a Coat. Bartlett, Alison, illus. 2005. 32p. (J). (ps-k). lib. bdg. 11.15 (978-0-606-33583-6(8)) Tandem Library Bks.

—The Daddy Goose Treasury. Collins, Ross, illus. 2006. 96p. (J). pap. 18.99 (978-0-439-79608-8(3) , Chicken Hse., The) Scholastic, Inc.

—Pig in Love, Level 3. Archbold, Tim, illus. 2005. (Lightning Readers Ser.). 32p. (J). (gr. 1-2). pap., pap. 3.95 (978-0-7696-4221-5(7) , Gingham Dog Pr.) School Specialty Publishing.

French/Archbold, Vivian/Tim. Pig in Love. 2005. (Illus.). 32p. (J). lib. bdg. 9.00 (*978-1-4242-0889-0(0)*) Fitzgerald Bks.

Freymann, Saxton & Elffers, Joost. Gus & Button. Freymann, Saxton & Elffers, Joost, illus. 2001. (Illus.). 40p. (J). pap. 15.95 (978-0-439-11015-0(7) , Levine, Arthur A. Bks.) Scholastic, Inc.

Freysinger, Karen. Adventures of Countess Pigula Her Royal Imagination. Freysinger, Karen, illus. 2006. (J). 15.95 (978-0-9786729-0-4(9)) Aha! Elora Danan Productions.

Friedlander, Eleanor. Mrs. Digger's Roots. Traverso, Laura, illus. 1999. 44p. (J). (ps-3). 17.95 (978-0-9672124-0-1(5)) Jadeda Pr.

Friedlander, Tim. The I Like Me Dance. 2007. 32p. (J). (ps-3). 14.95 (*978-1-933721-07-1(3)*) Playdate Kids Publishing.

Friedman, Carol. Nicky's Jazz Christmas. 2006. (Illus.). 32p. (J). 16.95 (978-1-57687-341-0(2)) powerHouse Cultural Entertainment, Inc.

Friedman, Dawn. Dance, Annie. Bosch, Nicole in den, illus. 2001. (Rookie Reader Skill Set Ser.). 24p. (J). (gr. k-2). pap. 4.95 (978-0-516-27289-4(6) , Children's Pr.) Scholastic Library Publishing.

—Dance, Annie. 2001. (gr. k-3). lib. bdg. 12.95 (978-0-613-54158-9(8)) Tandem Library Bks.

Friedman, Laurie. Love, Ruby Valentine. Cravath, Lynne Avril, illus. 2006. 32p. (J). 15.95 (978-1-57505-899-3(5) , Carolrhoda Bks.) Lerner Publishing Group.

Friedman, Laurie B. I'm Not Afraid of This Haunted House. Murfin, Teresa, illus. 2005. 32p. (J). (ps-ps). 15.95 (978-1-57505-751-4(4) , Carolrhoda Bks.) Lerner Publishing Group.

Friedman, Rainey L. Monsters in Your Bed... Monsters in Your Head. Dill, Betsy, illus. 1999. 32p. (J). 15.95 (978-0-9666199-1-1(9)) DreamDog Pr.

Frost, Helen. Spinning Through the Universe. 2004. (Illus.). 112p. (J). 16.00 (978-0-374-37159-3(8) , Farrar, Straus & Giroux (BYR)) Farrar, Straus & Giroux.

Frosty the Snowman. 2003. (Illus.). 24p. (J). bds. 6.95 (978-0-8249-6500-6(0)) Ideals Pubns.

Fullerton, Alma. Walking on Glass. 2007. 144p. (J). (gr. 9 up). 15.99 (978-0-06-077851-4(2)); lib. bdg. 16.89 (978-0-06-077852-1(0)) HarperCollins Pubs. (HarperTeen).

Fulmer, Jeffrey. My Imagination Kit. Pickering, Jimmy, tr. Pickering, Jimmy, illus. 2003. (J). 24p. 15.95 (978-1-59336-008-5(8)); 23p. pap. (978-1-59336-009-2(6)) Mondo Publishing.

Gabriel, Andrea. My Favorite Bear. Gabriel, Andrea, illus. 2004. (Illus.). 32p. (J). pap. 6.95 (978-1-58089-039-7(3)) Charlesbridge Publishing, Inc.

—My Favorite Bear. 2003. (Illus.). 32p. (J). 15.95 (978-1-58089-038-0(5)) Charlesbridge Publishing, Inc.

Gabriel, Nat. Day with May. 2000. (ps-2). lib. bdg. 11.80 (978-0-613-24786-3(8)) Tandem Library Bks.

Gaiman, Neil. Blueberry Girl. Vess, Charles, illus. 2008. (J). (*978-0-06-083808-9(6)*) HarperCollins Pubs.

—Dangerous Alphabet. Grimly, Gris, illus. 2008. 32p. (J). 17.99 (*978-0-06-078333-4(8)*); lib. bdg. 18.89 (*978-0-06-078334-1(6)*) HarperCollins Pubs.

Galbraith, Kathryn Osebold. One Shy Bunny, One Dark Night. Mack, Jeff, illus. 2008. (J). (*978-0-15-216246-7(1)*) Harcourt Trade Pubs.

Gallyp, Tracy. King Cat. Gallyp, Tracy, illus. 2006. (Illus.). 32p. (J). (978-0-9749145-8-9(4)) Mackinac Island Pr., Inc.

Gamble, Adam. Good Night Arizona. Hansen, Red, illus. 2008. (Good Night Our World Ser.). 20p. (J). bds. 9.95 (*978-1-60219-000-9(3)*) Our World of Books.

—Good Night California. Kelly, Cooper, illus. 2008. (Good Night Our World Ser.). 24p. (J). bds. 9.95 (*978-1-60219-021-4(6)*) Our World of Books.

—Good Night Tennessee. Veno, Joe, illus. 2007. (Good Night Our World Ser.). 20p. (J). bds. 9.95 (*978-1-60219-019-1(4)*) Our World of Books.

—Good Night Texas. Hansen, Red, illus. 2007. (Good Night Our World Ser.). 20p. (J). bds. 9.95 (*978-1-60219-015-3(1)*) Our World of Books.

Gamble, Jeremiah. Hold the Boat! Allen, Joy, illus. 1999. 32p. (J). (ps-3). 14.99 (978-0-7642-2199-6(X)) Bethany Hse. Pubs.

Garcia, Joan. Footsteps of Angels. 2003. 52p. (J). pap. 11.95 (978-0-7414-1602-5(6)) Infinity Publishing.

A Garden Circus. 2003. (J). 9.99 (978-0-9740847-5-6(1)) GiGi Bks.

Garden, Randa Sue. Penny the Penguin. 2003. 48p. per. 7.95 (978-0-615-12322-6(8)) Garden, Randa.

Gardeski, Christina Mia. All Kinds of Kids. McMahon, Bob, illus. 2002. 19.95 (978-1-932715-38-5(X)) UMI (Urban Ministries, Inc.).

—All Kinds of Kids Level A. McMahon, Bob, illus. 2002. (Rookie Readers Ser.). 24p. (J). (gr. k-1). 19.50 (978-0-516-22370-4(4) , Children's Pr.) Scholastic Library Publishing.

—Toda Clase de Ninos. 2002. Tr. of All Kinds of Kids. (gr. k-3). lib. bdg. 12.95 (978-0-613-59552-0(1)) Tandem Library Bks.

Garland, Michael. Hooray Jose! 2007. (Illus.). 32p. (J). 14.99 (*978-0-7614-5345-1(8)*) Cavendish, Marshall Corp.

Garland, Michael, illus. Hooray José! 2007. (J). (*978-1-4287-3591-0(7)* , Cavendish Children's Bks.) Cavendish, Marshall Corp.

Garofoli, Viviana. Princess! 2008. (J). (*978-0-7614-5450-2(0)*) Cavendish, Marshall Corp.

Garren, Devorah-Leah. Shabbos Is Coming! We're Lost in the Zoo! Katz, Maya S., illus. 1999. 32p. (J). (ps-3). 12.95 (978-1-880582-32-9(5)) Judaica Pr., Inc., The.

Garriel, Barbara S. I Know a Shy Fellow Who Swallowed a Cello. O'Brian, John, illus. 2004. 32p. (J). (gr. k-2). 15.95 (978-1-59078-043-5(4)) Boyds Mills Pr.

Gates, Larry Kenneth. The Sad, Glad Story of Johnny B. Gull. Rubinstein, Abby, illus. 2000. Tr. of Las Tristezas y Alegrias de Juancho C. Gaviota. (ENG & SPA.). 44p. (J). 9.00 (978-0-9705154-0-7(5)) Wildfire Starts.

Gauthier, Lance C., text. The One-Eared Mouse of Pasture Hill. 2003. 55p. (J). per. 6.95 (978-1-884540-70-7(8)) Haley's.

Gautier, Gary. Spaghetti & Peas. Bailey, Sheila, illus. 2007. (ENG.). 40p. (J). pap. 15.95 (978-0-9744446-1-1(8)) All About Kids Publishing.

Gayzagian, Doris. One White Wishing Stone: A Beach Day Counting Book. 2006. (Illus.). 32p. (J). (ps-1). 16.95 (978-0-7922-5110-1(5)); 25.90 (978-0-7922-5573-4(9)) National Geographic Society. (National Geographic Children's Bks.).

Geiger, Lorraine Lynch. A Wild & Woolly Night. Vargo, Sharon, illus. 2007. (J). (*978-1-891795-25-1(2)*) RGU Group, The.

Gelman, Rita Goldman. More Spaghetti, I Say: Quiero Mas Fideos! 2003. (SPA.). 32p. (J). pap. 3.99 (978-0-590-29377-8(X)) Scholastic, Inc.

Gelman, Rita Golden. Hello, Cat, You Need a Hat. 1999. (Hello Reader! Ser.). (Illus.). (J). (978-0-606-18557-8(7)) Tandem Library Bks.

—Pizza Pat. 1999. (Step into Reading Ser.). (978-0-606-16891-5(5)) Tandem Library Bks.

Gemmen, Heather. But It's True. Lagares, Luciano, illus. 2004. (Tough Stuff for Kids Ser.). 36p. (J). (gr. 4-7). pap., pap. 5.99 (978-0-7814-4033-2(5) , 0781440335) Cook, David C. Publishing Co.

—I Don't Like It. Lagares, Luciano, illus. 2004. (Tough Stuff for Kids Ser.). 36p. (J). (gr. 4-7). pap., pap. 5.99 (978-0-7814-4036-3(X) , 078144036X) Cook, David C. Publishing Co.

—Quit Looking at Me! Lagares, Luciano, illus. 2003. (Tough Stuff for Kids Ser.). 32p. (J). pap., pap. 5.99 (978-0-7814-3852-0(7) , 0781438527) Cook, David C. Publishing Co.

George, Audra. Vagabonding. George, Audra, illus. 2006. (Illus.). 32p. (J). 17.95 (978-1-60108-010-3(7)) Red Cygnet Pr.

George, Kristine O'Connell. Hummingbird Nest: A Journal of Poems. Moser, Barry, illus. 2004. 48p. (J). 16.00 (978-0-15-202325-6(9)) Harcourt Children's Bks.

—One Mitten. Smith, Maggie, illus. 2004. 32p. (J). (gr. k-3). tchr. ed. 15.00 (978-0-618-11756-7(3) , Clarion Bks.) Houghton Mifflin Co. Trade & Reference Div.

—Up! Nakata, Hiroe, illus. 2005. 32p. (J). (gr. k-ps). 15.00 (978-0-618-06489-2(3) , Clarion Bks.) Houghton Mifflin Co. Trade & Reference Div.

George, Olivia. Copy Cat. Hudson, Brett, illus. (My First Reader Ser.). (J). (gr. k-1). 2005. 32p. pap. 3.95 (978-0-516-25113-4(9)); 2004. 18.50 (978-0-516-24679-6(8)) Scholastic Library Publishing. (Children's Pr.).

—My Birthday Cake. Aviles, Martha, illus. 2005. (My First Reader Ser.). 31p. (J). (gr. k-1). pap. 3.95 (978-0-516-25276-6(3) , Children's Pr.) Scholastic Library Publishing.

—My Birthday Cake. Aviles Junco, Martha, illus. 2005. (My First Reader Ser.). 32p. (J). (gr. k-1). 18.50 (978-0-516-25178-3(3) , Children's Pr.) Scholastic Library Publishing.

Gerber, Carole. Baa Baa Black Sheep. Husted, Marty, illus. 2004. 26p. (J). bds. 6.95 (978-1-58089-089-2(X)) Charlesbridge Publishing, Inc.

—Blizzard. Husted, Marty, illus. 2001. (J). pap. (978-1-58089-065-6(2)); 15.95 (978-1-58089-064-9(4)) Charlesbridge Publishing, Inc.

—Firefly Night. Husted, Marty, illus. 2000. 32p. (J). (ps-1). 16.95 (978-1-58089-051-9(2)); pap. 6.95 (978-1-58089-066-3(0)) Charlesbridge Publishing, Inc.

—Firefly Night. Husted, Marty, illus. 2000. (J). (ps-3). lib. bdg. 15.25 (978-0-613-35117-1(7)) Tandem Library Bks.

—Firefly Night. 2000. (J). (978-0-606-19687-1(0)) Tandem Library Bks.

Geringer, Lucy T. Rhymes & Times of Cleo-cat-tra. Kollock, Bernardita Cox, illus. 2002. 34p. (J). (ps-1). pap. 8.95 (978-0-9719483-0-3(5)) Cleo Cat Bks.

—Rhymes & Times of Cleo-cat-tra. Kollock, Bernardita Cox, illus. l.t. ed. 2000. (Cleo-Cat-Tra Easy-to-Read Book Ser.). 28p. (J). (ps-2). pap. 7.95 (978-0-9600962-7-5(2)) Displays for Schls., Inc.

Gerrard, Roy. Croco'nile. 2001. (Illus.). (J). 13.75 (978-0-606-21130-7(6)) Tandem Library Bks.

—Wagons West! Gerrard, Roy, illus. 2000. (Illus.). 32p. (J). (ps-3). pap. 5.95 (978-0-374-48210-7(1) , Sunburst) Farrar, Straus & Giroux.

—Wagons West! 2000. (J). (ps-ps). (Illus.). lib. bdg. 14.10 (978-0-613-30179-4(X)); (978-0-606-20138-4(6)); (Illus.). (978-0-606-20401-9(6)) Tandem Library Bks.

Gershator, Phillis. Listen, Listen. Jay, Alison, illus. 2008. 32p. (J). (ps-4). 16.99 (*978-1-84686-084-3(9)*) Barefoot Bks., Inc.

—Old House, New House. Potter, Katherine, illus. 2008. (J). (*978-0-7614-5386-4(5)*) Cavendish, Marshall Corp.

Gershator, Phillis. When It Starts to Snow. Matje, Martin, illus. rev. ed. 2001. 32p. (J). (ps-2). pap. 7.95 (978-0-8050-6765-1(5) , Holt, Henry & Co. Bks. For Young Readers) Holt, Henry & Co.

—When It Starts to Snow. 2001. (ps-2). lib. bdg. 15.25 (978-0-613-51425-5(4)) Tandem Library Bks.

Gershator, Phillis & Gershator, David. Greetings, Sun. 2000. (978-0-606-17809-9(0)) Tandem Library Bks.

Gershenson, Harold P. Freddy Flamingo & the Kindertown Five. Mills, Christopher, illus. 2005. 27p. (J). (978-1-58987-070-3(0)) Kindermusik International.

—The Kindertown Fire Brigade. Mills, Christopher, illus. 2006. (J). (978-1-58987-019-2(0)) Kindermusik International.

—Noodles from Scratch. Mills, Christopher, illus. 2006. (J). (978-1-58987-007-9(7)) Kindermusik International.

Gershon, Dann. Extra Large. Robinson, David, illus. 1999. (Hangin' with the Hombeez Ser.: Vol. 3). 40p. (J). (gr. k-6). 14.95 (978-0-9656985-5-9(6)) Noware Bks.

Gerver, Jane E. Bath Time. Ovresat, Laura, illus. (My First Reader Ser.). (J). (gr. k-1). 2005. 32p. pap. 3.95 (978-0-516-25111-0(2)); 2004. 31p. 18.50 (978-0-516-24677-2(1)) Scholastic Library Publishing. (Children's Pr.).

—The Big Red Sled. Burris, Priscilla, illus. 2001. (Hello Reader! Ser.). 32p. (J). (ps-1). 3.99 (978-0-439-20434-7(8) , Cartwheel Bks.) Scholastic, Inc.

—The Big Red Sled. Burris, Priscilla, illus. 2001. (J). (ps-3). lib. bdg. 11.80 (978-0-613-43797-4(7)) Tandem Library Bks.

—The Big Red Sled. 2001. 10.79 (978-0-606-22227-3(8)) Tandem Library Bks.

—A Crack in the Track: A Thomas the Tank Engine Story. Stubbs, Tommy, illus. 2001. (Beginner Bks. Ser.). 48p. (J). (ps-3). lib. bdg. 11.99 (978-0-375-91246-7(0) , Random Hse. Bks. for Young Readers) Random Hse. Children's Bks.

—Sweetest Valentines. 2003. (gr. k-3). lib. bdg. 11.80 (978-0-613-63569-1(8)) Tandem Library Bks.

—Wait for Me! Reid, Mick, illus. (My First Reader Ser.). (J). (gr. k-1). 2005. 32p. pap. 3.95 (978-0-516-25116-5(3)); 2004. 31p. 18.50 (978-0-516-24676-5(3)) Scholastic Library Publishing. (Children's Pr.).

Ghigna, Charles. The Alphabet Parade. Woods, Patti, illus. 2002. 32p. (J). 17.95 (978-1-880216-74-3(4)) River City Publishing.

—Oh My, Pumpkin Pie! Spengler, Kenneth, illus. 2005. (Step into Reading Ser.). 32p. (J). (ps-2). pap. 3.99 (978-0-375-82945-1(8)); lib. bdg. 11.99 (978-0-375-92945-8(2)) Random Hse. Children's Bks. (Random Hse. Bks. for Young Readers).

—Oh My, Pumpkin Pie! Spengler, Ken, illus. 2005. (J). (ps-2). lib. bdg. 11.19 (978-0-606-33714-4(8)) Tandem Library Bks.

Gibbons, Joyce. The Little Brown Owl & Me. Lenoir, Jane, illus. 2001. (J). (gr. k-5). lib. bdg. 14.95 (978-0-9705727-6-9(X)) Coastal Publishing Carolina, Inc.

Gikow, Louise. The Big Game. Garner, Phil, illus. 2004. (My First Reader Pb Ser.). 32p. (J). (gr. k-1). pap. 3.95 (978-0-516-25500-2(2) , Children's Pr.) Scholastic Library Publishing.

—The Big Game. Garner, Phil, tr. Garner, Phil, illus. 2004. (My First Reader Ser.). 31p. (J). 18.50 (978-0-516-24408-2(6) , Children's Pr.) Scholastic Library Publishing.

—A Day with Daddy. Mazali, Gustavo, tr. Mazali, Gustavo, illus. 2004. (My First Reader Ser.). 31p. (J). 18.50 (978-0-516-24410-5(8) , Children's Pr.) Scholastic Library Publishing.

—I Can Read. Patience, John, illus. 2004. (My First Reader Ser.). 31p. (J). 18.50 (978-0-516-24678-9(X) , Children's Pr.) Scholastic Library Publishing.

Gill, Shelley. Sitka Rose. Cartwright, Shannon, illus. 2005. (J). 16.95 (978-1-57091-353-2(6)); 32p. pap. 7.95 (978-1-57091-364-8(1)) Charlesbridge Publishing, Inc.

Ginkel, Anne. I've Got an Elephant. Bynum, Janie, illus. 2006. 32p. (J). 16.95 (978-1-56145-373-3(0) , Peachtree Junior) Peachtree Pubs., Ltd.

Ginsburg, Mirra. The Sun's Asleep Behind the Hill. 2002. (Illus.). (J). 15.49 (978-0-7587-9822-0(9)) Book Wholesalers, Inc.

—The Sun's Asleep Behind the Hill. 2000. (J). (978-0-606-20412-5(1)); (978-0-606-20297-8(8)) Tandem Library Bks.

Giogas, Valerie. In My Backyard. Zecca, Katherine, illus. 2007. 32p. (J). (ps-3). 15.95 (*978-0-9777423-1-8(8)*) Sylvan Dell Pubng.

Gisler, David. Addition Annie. Beise, Sarah A., illus. rev. ed. 2002. (Rookie Reader Skill Set Ser.). 32p. (J). (gr. k-2). pap. 4.95 (978-0-516-27378-5(7) , Children's Pr.) Scholastic Library Publishing.

—Addition Annie. 2002. (gr. k-3). lib. bdg. 12.95 (978-0-613-53789-6(0)) Tandem Library Bks.

—Addition Annie Level C. Beise, Sarah A., illus. rev. ed. 2002. (Rookie Readers Ser.). 32p. (J). (gr. 1-2). 19.50 (978-0-516-22560-9(X) , Children's Pr.) Scholastic Library Publishing.

Glass, Beth Raisner & Lubner, Susan. Noises at Night. Whatley, Bruce, illus. 2005. 32p. (J). (ps-3). 15.95 (978-0-8109-5750-3(7) , Abrams Bks. for Young Readers) Abrams, Harry N. , Inc.

Glass, Julie. A Dollar for Penny. Allen, Joy, illus. 2000. (Step into Reading Ser.: No. 3). 32p. (J). (gr. k-3). pap. 3.99 (978-0-679-88973-1(6) , Random Hse. Bks. for Young Readers) Random Hse. Children's Bks.

—A Dollar for Penny. Allen, Joy, illus. 2000. 32p. (J). (ps-ps). lib. bdg. 11.80 (978-0-613-07631-9(1)) Tandem Library Bks.

—A Dollar for Penny. 2000. (Illus.). (J). 10.79 (978-0-606-18492-2(9)) Tandem Library Bks.

Glassman, Bruce. Zoolidays. Kiaulevicius, Rolandas, illus. 2006. 32p. (J). 15.95 (978-1-60108-011-0(5)) Red Cygnet Pr.

Glinski, Donita. A Smile in My Pocket. Simpson-Baucom, Charlotte Q., illus. 2006. 32p. 14.95 (978-1-57197-465-5(2) , Ivy House Publishing Group) Pentland Pr., Inc.

Gliori, Debi. No Matter What. (Illus.). (J). 2008. 24p. bds. 6.95 (***978-0-15-206343-6(9)*** , Red Wagon Bks.); 1999. 32p. 16.00 (978-0-15-202061-3(6)) Harcourt Children's Bks.

—Polar Bolero: A Bedtime Dance. 2001. (Illus.). 40p. (J). (ps-2). 16.00 (978-0-15-202436-9(0)) Harcourt Children's Bks.

—Where Did That Baby Come From? 2005. (Illus.). 32p. (J). 16.00 (978-0-15-205373-4(5)) Harcourt Children's Bks.

Gmeyner, Elizabeth. The Key of the Kingdom: A Book of Stories & Poems for Children. Russell, Joyce, illus. 2004. 100p. (J). pap. 15.00 (978-0-88010-549-1(6) , Bell Pond Bks.) SteinerBooks, Inc.

Gobo Books Staff. Santa Baby. 2006. 8p. 9.95 (978-1-932915-30-3(3)) Sandvik Innovations, LLC.

Goddard, Mary Beth. How Would It Feel? Mycek-Wodecki, Anna, illus. 2005. 32p. (J). 15.95 (978-1-59143-050-6(2) , Bear Cub Bks.) Bear & Co.

Godwin, Laura. Flower Girl. Wallace, John, illus. 2000. 24p. (ps-k). 12.99 (978-0-7868-0408-5(4)) Hyperion Bks. for Children.

—Little White Dog. 2000. (ps-2). lib. bdg. 14.15 (978-0-613-31428-2(X)) Tandem Library Bks.

—The Little White Dog. Yaccarino, Dan, illus. 2000. 32p. (ps-k). pap. 5.99 (978-0-7868-1515-9(9)) Disney Pr.

—What the Baby Hears. 2002. (Illus.). 32p. (ps-k). 16.49 (978-0-7868-2484-7(0)) Hyperion Bks. for Children.

Gold-Vukson, Marji & Evans, Leslie. Grandpa & Me on Tu B'Shevat. 2004. (Illus.). 32p. (J). (ps-3). pap. (978-1-58013-122-3(0)) Kar-Ben Publishing.

Goldberg, Malky. What Else Do I Say? A Lift the Flap Book. Argoff, Patti, illus. 2007. (J). (ps-k). bds. 9.95 (***978-1-929628-34-6(X)***) Hachai Publishing.

Golden Books Staff. Blue's Dress-up Day. Miller, Victoria, illus. 2005. 48p. (J). (ps-2). pap. 2.99 (978-0-375-83172-0(X) , Golden Bks.) Random Hse. Children's Bks.

—It's Snow Place Like Home. 2001. 32p. (J). (ps-3). pap. 4.99 (978-0-307-27621-6(X) , Golden Bks.) Random Hse. Children's Bks.

—Trick or Treat. Borlasca, Hector, illus. 2006. 12p. (J). (gr. k-1). bds. 3.99 (978-0-375-87490-1(9) , Golden Bks.) Random Hse. Children's Bks.

Golden Books Staff & Hill, Stuart. Wreck the Halls. 2001. 8p. (J). (ps-3). pap. 3.99 (978-0-307-25300-2(7) , Golden Bks.) Random Hse. Children's Bks.

Goldman, Todd Harris. The Zoo I Drew. 2008. (J). (***978-0-375-85201-5(8)); (*978-0-375-95201-2(2)***) Random Hse., Inc.

Goldstone, Bruce. The Beastly Feast. Lent, Blair, illus. 2001. 32p. (J). (ps-1). pap. 7.95 (978-0-8050-6709-5(4) , Holt, Henry & Co. Bks. For Young Readers) Holt, Henry & Co.

—The Beastly Feast. 2001. 13.75 (978-0-606-22584-7(6)) Tandem Library Bks.

—Beastly Feast. 2001. (ps-2). lib. bdg. 15.25 (978-0-613-75496-5(4)) Tandem Library Bks.

Gollub, Matthew. Ten Oni Drummers. Stone, Kazuko G., illus. 2000. (JPN & ENG.). 32p. (J). (ps-3). 15.95 (978-1-58430-011-3(6)) Lee & Low Bks., Inc.

Gomez, Rebecca. Scholastic Reader Level 1: It's St. Patrick's Day! 2004. (gr. k-3). lib. bdg. 11.80 (978-0-613-72120-2(9)) Tandem Library Bks.

Gonzales, Alysia. Mikey & Monster Vacuum. Cook, Joel, illus. 2004. 28p. 15.95 (978-0-9707906-0-6(0)) Providence Publishing.

Good, Merle, et al. Dan's Pants: The Adventures of Dan, the Fabric Man. Benner, Cheryl A., illus. 2000. 32p. (J). (ps-3). 16.00 (978-1-56148-307-5(9)) Good Bks.

Goodhart, Pippa. Three Little Ghosties. Cantone, Anna-Laura, illus. 2007. 32p. (J). (ps-1). 16.95 (***978-1-58234-711-0(5)***) Bloomsbury Publishing.

Goodings, Christina. Around the Year: A Calendar & Counting Rhyme. Lewis, Jan, illus. 2001. 32p. (J). pap. 13.99 (978-0-7459-4451-7(5) , Lion) Lion Hudson plc GBR. *Dist:* Independent Pubs. Group.

Goodman, Larry. The Cowboy. unabr. ed. 2000. (Illus.). (J). pap. 18.00 incl. audio (978-1-58807-038-8(7)) Americana Publishing, Inc.

Goodnight Moon. 2004. (J). 24.95 incl. audio (978-0-89719-774-8(7)); pap. 32.75 incl. audio (978-1-55592-233-7(3)); pap. 32.75 incl. audio (978-1-55592-234-4(1)) Weston Woods Studios, Inc.

Goodrich, Carter & Moore, Clement Clarke. A Creature Was Stirring. Goodrich, Carter, illus. 2006. (Illus.). 40p. (J). 16.95 (978-0-689-86399-8(3) , Simon & Schuster Children's Publishing) Simon & Schuster Children's Publishing.

Gordon, Benjamin. Sea Monkeys & Other Disappointments. 2002. (Illus.). 68p. per. 10.00 net. (978-0-9722885-0-7(3)) Raise Giant Frogs Publishing.

Gordon, Beth. Wish upon a Star: Whimsical Rhymes to Read & Sing. G Studios, illus. 2007. (Land of Milk & Honey Ser.). 30p. (J). bds. 10.99 (978-1-4169-3654-1(8) , Little Simon Inspirations) Simon & Schuster Children's Publishing.

Gorey, Edward. The Wuggly Ump. Gorey, Edward, illus. 2007. 32p. 12.95 (***978-0-7649-4192-4(5)*** , A142) Pomegranate Communications, Inc.

Gosline, Andrea Alban. January's Child: The Birthday Month Book. Bossi, Lisa Burnett, illus. 2007. 32p. (J). (ps-3). pap. 12.99 (978-0-439-67268-9(6) , Scholastic Pr.) Scholastic, Inc.

—Ten Little Wishes: A Baby Animal Counting Book. Bossi, Lisa Burnett, illus. 2007. 40p. (J). (ps-k). 15.99 (978-0-06-053410-3(9)); lib. bdg. 16.89 (978-0-06-053411-0(7)) HarperCollins Pubs.

Goss, Leon. By the Light of the Moon. Luo, Shiyin Sean, illus. 2005. (J). pap. (978-1-933156-12-5(0)); per. (978-1-933156-05-7(8)) GSVQ Publishing. (VisionQuest Kids).

—I'm Good, I'm Beautiful, I'm Smart. Mailey, Maria C. & Neuburger, Jenny, illus. 2005. (J). per. (978-1-933156-02-6(3) , VisionQuest Kids) GSVQ Publishing.

—King for a Day. Nichols, Chris, illus. 2005. (J). pap. (978-1-933156-09-5(0)); per. (978-1-933156-01-9(5)) GSVQ Publishing. (VisionQuest Kids).

—Selfus Esteemus Personalitus Low. Tunell, Ken, illus. 2005. (J). pap. (978-1-933156-08-8(2) , VisionQuest Kids) GSVQ Publishing.

Goss, Leon, 3rd. Selfus Esteemus Personalitus Low. Tunell, Ken, illus. ed. 2005. 32p. (J). per. 17.95 (978-1-933156-00-2(7) , VisionQuest Kids) GSVQ Publishing.

The Gracious Mother Goose. 2004. 64p. (J). pap. 9.99 (978-0-88724-217-5(0) , CD-2038) Carson-Dellosa Publishing Co., Inc.

Gralley, Jean. The Moon Came down on Milk Street. rev. ed. 2004. (Illus.). 32p. (J). 16.95 (978-0-8050-7266-2(7) , Holt, Henry & Co. Bks. For Young Readers) Holt, Henry & Co.

—Very Boring Alligator. rev. ed. 2001. (Illus.). 32p. (J). (ps-3). 15.95 (978-0-8050-6328-8(5) , Holt, Henry & Co. Bks. For Young Readers) Holt, Henry & Co.

Graves, Keith. Three Nasty Gnarlies. Graves, Keith, illus. 2003. (Illus.). 40p. (J). pap. 16.95 (978-0-439-24090-1(5)) Scholastic, Inc.

Graves, Sue. Bug in a Rug. 2007. (Fun with Phonics Ser.). 20p. (J). pap. 4.99 (***978-0-439-02550-8(8)***) Scholastic, Inc.

—A Busy Week. Sharp, Melanie, illus. 2005. (Reading Corner Ser.). 24p. (J). (gr. k-3). lib. bdg. 22.80 (978-1-59771-005-3(9)) Sea-To-Sea Pubns.

—Dog in the Fog. 2007. (Fun with Phonics Ser.). 20p. (J). pap. 4.99 (***978-0-439-02551-5(6)***) Scholastic, Inc.

—Fat Cat. 2007. (Fun with Phonics Ser.). 20p. (J). pap. 4.99 (***978-0-439-02552-2(4)***) Scholastic, Inc.

Gray, Kes. Cluck O'Clock. McQuillan, Mary, tr. McQuillan, Mary, illus. 2004. 32p. (J). (gr. k-3). tchr. ed. 16.95 (978-0-8234-1809-1(X)) Holiday Hse., Inc.

Gray, Rita. Easy Street. Bono, Mary, illus. 2006. 32p. (J). (ps-ps). 15.99 (978-0-525-47657-3(1) , Dutton Juvenile) Penguin Group (USA) Inc.

—Mama Mine, Mama Mine. Goembel, Ponder, illus. 2008. 32p. (J). (ps). 15.99 (***978-0-525-47206-3(1)*** , Dutton Juvenile) Penguin Group (USA) Inc.

Gray, Rita. The Wild Little Horse. Wolff, Ashley, illus. 2005. 32p. (J). (ps-ps). 15.99 (978-0-525-47455-5(2) , Dutton Juvenile) Penguin Group (USA) Inc.

The Great Redwall Feast. 2002. (Redwall Ser.). (Illus.). (J). 25.47 (978-0-7587-2657-5(0)) Book Wholesalers, Inc.

Green, George & Brooke, Amy/ J. George Green's, the Lion Who Couldn't Roar. 2007. (J). per. 17.99 (***978-1-933156-14-9(7)*** , Visikid Bks.) GSVQ Publishing.

Green, Lucyna A. M., illus. Love You Little Brother. 2006. (J). (***978-1-58669-186-8(4)); (*978-1-58669-185-1(6)***) Childcraft Education Corp.

Greenberg, David T. Crocs! 2008. 32p. (J). (978-0-316-07306-6(7)) Little Brown & Co.

Greenburg, Dan. The Day That Went from Bad to Verse. Davis, Jack E., illus. 2000. (Zack Files Ser.: No. 20). 64p. (J). (gr. 2-5). pap. 4.99 (978-0-448-42042-4(2) , Grosset & Dunlap) Penguin Group (USA) Inc.

—The Day That Went from Bad to Verse. 2000. (gr. 3-6). lib. bdg. 13.00 (978-0-613-24777-1(9)) Tandem Library Bks.

Greene, Rhonda. Santa's Stuck. Cole, Henry, illus. 2006. 32p. (J). (ps). pap. 5.99 (978-0-14-240686-1(4) , Puffin) Penguin Group (USA) Inc.

Greene, Rhonda Gowler. At Grandma's. Firehammer, Karla, illus. rev. ed. 2003. 32p. (J). (ps-k). 15.95 (978-0-8050-6336-3(6) , Holt, Henry & Co. Bks. For Young Readers) Holt, Henry & Co.

—Barnyard Song. 2001. (ps-2). lib. bdg. 14.15 (978-0-613-34598-9(3)) Tandem Library Bks.

—Firebears, the Rescue Team. Andreasen, Dan, illus. rev. ed. 2005. 32p. (J). 15.95 (978-0-8050-7010-1(9) , Holt, Henry & Co. Bks. For Young Readers) Holt, Henry & Co.

—Santa's Stuck. Cole, Henry, illus. 2004. 32p. (J). (ps). 16.99 (978-0-525-47292-6(4) , Dutton Juvenile) Penguin Group (USA) Inc.

—Sing Praise. Broxon, Janet, illus. 2005. 32p. (J). (ps-3). pap. 16.99 (978-0-8066-5120-0(2) , Augsburg Bks.) Augsburg Fortress, Pubs.

—This Is the Teacher. Lester, Mike, illus. 32p. (J). (gr. k). 2004. 15.99 (978-0-525-47125-7(1) , Dutton Juvenile); 2006. reprint ed. pap. 5.99 (978-0-14-240653-3(8) , Puffin) Penguin Group (USA) Inc.

—The Very First Thanksgiving Day. Gaber, Susan, illus. 32p. (J). 2006. 6.99 (978-1-4169-1916-2(3) , Aladdin); 2002. 15.95 (978-0-689-83301-4(6) , Atheneum) Simon & Schuster Children's Publishing.

—When a Line Bends... A Shape Begins. 2001. (978-0-606-22586-1(2)); lib. bdg. 14.10 (978-0-613-35592-6(X)) Tandem Library Bks.

Greenfield Educational Center Staff. I Can Read Series: Level 1, 12 bks., Set. 2000. (Illus.). (J). pap. 35.00 incl. audio (978-962-563-140-0(2)) Greenfield Enterprises, Ltd. HKG. *Dist:* Cheng & Tsui Co.

—I Can Read Series: Level 2, 12 bks., Set. 2000. (Illus.). (J). pap. 35.00 incl. audio (978-962-563-141-7(0)) Greenfield Enterprises, Ltd. HKG. *Dist:* Cheng & Tsui Co.

—I Can Read Series: Level 3, 12 bks., Set. 2000. (Illus.). (J). pap. 35.00 incl. audio (978-962-563-142-4(9)) Greenfield Enterprises, Ltd. HKG. *Dist:* Cheng & Tsui Co.

Greenhut, Elyse. The Littlest Kitten. 2003. 33p. pap. 14.95 (978-1-59286-986-2(6)) PublishAmerica, Inc.

Griffin, Claire Janosik. Imagine That! Foley, Timothy, illus. 2000. (Rollicking Rhymes Ser.). 20p. (J). (gr. k-1). 3.99 (978-1-56822-977-5(1) , IF40211-E4, Instructional Fair) Schaffer, Frank Pubns.

—Kidding Around. Wright, Jane Chambless, illus. 2000. (Rollicking Rhymes Ser.). 20p. (J). (gr. k-1). 3.99 (978-1-56822-978-2(X) , IF40212-E4, Instructional Fair) Schaffer, Frank Pubns.

—The Mother Goose News. Foley, Timothy, illus. 2000. (Rollicking Rhymes Ser.). 20p. (J). (gr. k-1). 3.99 (978-1-56822-976-8(3) , IF40210-E4, Instructional Fair) Schaffer, Frank Pubns.

Griffis, Molly. The Buffalo in the Mall. Doner, Kim, illus. 32p. 8.95 (978-1-57168-635-0(5)) Eakin Pr.

Griffiths, Andy. The Cat on the Mat Is Flat. Denton, Terry, illus. 2007. 176p. (J). (ps-3). 9.95 (***978-0-312-36787-9(2)***) Feiwel & Friends.

Grimes, Nikki. Danitra Brown, Class Clown. Lewis, Earl, illus. 2005. 32p. (J). 16.99 (978-0-688-17290-9(3)); lib. bdg. 16.89 (978-0-688-17291-6(1)) HarperCollins Pubs.

—A Day with Daddy. Tadgell, Nicole, illus. 2004. 32p. (J). lib. bdg. 15.00 (***978-1-4242-0226-3(4)***) Fitzgerald Bks.

—Talkin' about Bessie: The Story of Aviator Elizabeth Coleman. Lewis, Earl B & Moser, B., illus. 2002. 48p. (J). pap. 16.95 (978-0-439-35243-7(6) , Orchard Bks.) Scholastic, Inc.

—When Gorilla Goes Walking. Evans, Shane, illus. 2007. 32p. (J). (ps-3). pap. 16.99 (978-0-439-31770-2(3) , Orchard Bks.) Scholastic, Inc.

—Wild, Wild Hair. Ford, George, illus. 2002. (J). 11.91 (978-0-7587-1855-6(1)) Book Wholesalers, Inc.

Grimm, Lana & Bloch, Tania. How Butterbees Came to Bee! 2001. (Illus.). (J). (978-0-9662048-2-7(4)) Bee Unlimited, Inc.

—How Butterbees Came to Bee! Michener, David, illus. 2nd ed. 2001. 48p. 19.95 (978-0-9662048-3-4(2)) Bee Unlimited, Inc.

Gritz, Ona, et al. Rolling Stone 1,000 Covers: A History of the Most Influential Magazine in Pop Culture. Heo, Yumi, illus. 2006. 568p. 35.00 (978-0-8109-5865-4(1)) Abrams, Harry N. , Inc.

Grossman, Bill. My Little Sister Hugged an Ape. Hawkes, Kevin, illus. 2004. 40p. (J). (gr. k-3). 16.95 (978-0-517-80017-1(9)); lib. bdg. 18.99 (978-0-517-80018-8(7)) Random Hse. Children's Bks. (Knopf Bks. for Young Readers).

Grove, Ella. A Surprise for Tommy. 2005. (Illus.). 24p. (ps-5). 2.70 (978-0-7399-2341-2(2) , 2780) Rod & Staff Pubs., Inc.

Guarino, Deborah. Is Your Mama a Llama? Kellogg, Steven, illus. (Scholastic Bookshelf Ser.). (J). 2004. 32p. 6.99 (978-0-439-59842-2(7) , Scholastic Paperbacks); 2006. 9.95 (978-0-439-87588-2(9)) Scholastic, Inc.

Guenther, James. Turnagain, Ptarmigan, Where Did You Go? Cartwright, Shannon, illus. 2002. 32p. (J). (ps-2). pap. 8.95 (978-1-57061-237-4(4)) Sasquatch Bks.

Gugler, Laurel Dee. Facing the Day. Betteridge, Deirdre, illus. 1999. 24p. (J). (gr. k-ps). pap. 5.95 (978-1-55037-576-3(8)) Annick Pr., Ltd. CAN. *Dist:* Firefly Bks., Ltd.

Gulbis, Stephen, illus. Old MacDonald Had a Barn. 2003. 22p. (YA). (978-1-85602-453-2(9)) Chrysalis Children's Bks.

—The Wheels on the Bus. 2003. 22p. (YA). (978-1-85602-454-9(7)) Chrysalis Children's Bks.

Guthrie, Woody. New Baby Train. Frazee, Marla, illus. 2004. 32p. (J). 15.99 (978-0-316-07020-1(3) , Tingley, Megan Bks.) Little, Brown Bks. for Young Readers.

Gutman, Dan. Casey Back at the Bat. Johnson, Steve & Fancher, Lou, illus. 2007. 32p. (J). (gr. k-4). 16.99 (978-0-06-056025-6(8) , HarperCollins) HarperCollins Pubs.

Guy, Ginger Foglesong. Go Back to Bed! Bernardin, James, illus. 2006. (J). 15.95 (978-1-57505-750-7(6) , Carolrhoda Bks.) Lerner Publishing Group.

Hacking, Norm. When Cats Go Wrong. Nugent, Cynthia, illus. 2006. 32p. (J). pap. 9.95 (978-1-55192-917-0(1)) Raincoast Bk. Distribution CAN. *Dist:* Perseus Distribution.

Hager, Sarah. Dancing Matilda. Murphy, Kelly, illus. 2005. 40p. (J). (ps-2). 15.99 (978-0-06-051452-5(3)); lib. bdg. 16.89 (978-0-06-051453-2(1)) HarperCollins Pubs.

Hague, Kathleen. Alphabears: An ABC Book. Hague, Michael, illus. rev. ed. 1999. 28p. (J). (ps-k). bds. 6.95 (978-0-8050-6208-3(4) , Holt, Henry & Co. Bks. For Young Readers) Holt, Henry & Co.

—Numbears: A Counting Book. Hague, Michael, illus. rev. ed. 1999. 28p. (J). (ps-k). bds. 6.95 (978-0-8050-6207-6(6) , Holt, Henry & Co. Bks. For Young Readers) Holt, Henry & Co.

Hague, Michael. Mama Gansa. 2000. (SPA., Illus.). 72p. (J). 14.50 (978-84-241-3347-4(1) , EV1153) Everest de Ediciones y Distribucion, S.L. ESP. *Dist:* Lectorum Pubns., Inc.

Haley, Amanda, illus. Music Class. 2006. (I'm Going to Read Ser.). 32p. (J). pap. 3.95 (978-1-4027-3081-8(0)) Sterling Publishing Co., Inc.

Hall, Kirsten. A Bear for You. Rosa, Iole, illus. (My First Reader Ser.). (J). (gr. k-1). 2005. 32p. pap. 3.95 (978-0-516-25112-7(0)); 2004. 31p. 18.50 (978-0-516-24675-8(5)) Scholastic Library Publishing. (Children's Pr.).

—The Big Race: All about Safety. Luedecke, Bev, illus. (Beastieville Ser.). (J). (gr. k-1). 2005. 32p. pap. 3.95 (978-0-516-25517-0(7)); 2004. 19.50 (978-0-516-23671-1(7)) Scholastic Library Publishing. (Children's Pr.).

—Birthday Beastie: All about Counting. Luedecke, Bev, illus. 2003. (Beastieville Ser.). 32p. (J). 19.50 (978-0-516-22891-4(9) , Children's Pr.) Scholastic Library Publishing.

—Buried Treasure: All about Using a Map. Luedecke, Bev, illus. 2003. (Beastieville Ser.). 32p. (J). 19.50 (978-0-516-22894-5(3) , Children's Pr.) Scholastic Library Publishing.

—Busy Chipmunk. Phillips, Cary, illus. 2001. (My First Hello Reader! Ser.). (J). pap. (978-0-439-31703-0(7) , Cartwheel Bks.) Scholastic, Inc.

—First Day of School: All about Shapes & Sizes. Luedecke, Bev, illus. 2003. (Beastieville Ser.). 32p. (J). (ps-1). 19.50 (978-0-516-22893-8(5) , Children's Pr.) Scholastic Library Publishing.

—Good Times: All about the Seasons. Luedecke, Bev, illus. (Beastieville Ser.). (J). (gr. k-1). 2005. 32p. pap. 3.95 (978-0-516-25518-7(5)); 2004. 19.50 (978-0-516-23648-3(2)) Scholastic Library Publishing. (Children's Pr.).

—Grandma's House. Calderas, Gloria, illus. 2004. (My First Reader Ser.). 32p. (J). (gr. k-1). pap. 3.95 (978-0-516-25502-6(9) , Children's Pr.) Scholastic Library Publishing.

—Grandma's House. Calderas Lim, Gloria, illus. 2004. (My First Reader Ser.). 31p. (J). 18.50 (978-0-516-24411-2(6) , Children's Pr.) Scholastic Library Publishing.

—Help! All about Telling Time. Luedecke, Bev, illus. 2003. (Concept Bks.). 32p. (J). 19.50 (978-0-516-22890-7(0) , Children's Pr.) Scholastic Library Publishing.

—Hide-And-Seek: All about Location. Luedecke, Bev, illus. 2004. (Beastieville Ser.). (J). 19.50 (978-0-516-23649-0(0) , Children's Pr.) Scholastic Library Publishing.

—I'm a Princess. DeRosa, Dee, illus. 2003. (My First Reader Ser.). 32p. (J). 18.50 (978-0-516-22928-7(1) , Children's Pr.) Scholastic Library Publishing.

—I'm Not Scared. Holub, Joan, illus. 2003. (My First Reader Ser.). 32p. (J). 18.50 (978-0-516-22929-4(X) , Children's Pr.) Scholastic Library Publishing.

—I'm So Scared! Eugenie, illus. 2002. (My First Hello Reader! Ser.). (J). 2.95 (978-0-439-32098-6(4)) Scholastic, Inc.

—Let's Trade: All about Trading. Luedecke, Bev, illus. (Beastieville Ser.). (J). (gr. k-1). 2005. 32p. pap. 3.95 (978-0-516-25520-0(7)); 2004. 19.50 (978-0-516-22999-7(0)) Scholastic Library Publishing. (Children's Pr.).

—Little Lies: All about Math. Luedecke, Bev, illus. 2003. (Beastieville Ser.). 32p. (J). 19.50 (978-0-516-22896-9(X) , Children's Pr.) Scholastic Library Publishing.

—My New School. Gott, Barry, illus. 2004. (My First Reader Ser.). 32p. (J). (gr. k-1). pap. 3.95 (978-0-516-25505-7(3) , Children's Pr.) Scholastic Library Publishing.

—My New School. Gott, Barry, tr. Gott, Barry, illus. 2004. (My First Reader Ser.). 31p. (J). 18.50 (978-0-516-24413-6(2) , Children's Pr.) Scholastic Library Publishing.

—On the Farm. Gurney, John Steven, illus. 2005. (My First Reader Ser.). 32p. (J). (gr. k-1). pap. 3.95 (978-0-516-25115-8(5) , Children's Pr.) Scholastic Library Publishing.

—On the Farm. Gurney, John. illus. 2004. (My First Reader Ser.). 31p. (J). 18.50 (978-0-516-24680-2(1) , Children's Pr.) Scholastic Library Publishing.

—A Perfect Day: All about the Five Senses. Luedecke, Bev, illus. (Beastieville Ser.). (J). (gr. k-1). 2005. 32p. pap. 3.95 (978-0-516-25521-7(5)); 2004. 19.50 (978-0-516-24437-2(X)) Scholastic Library Publishing. (Children's Pr.).

—Slider's Pet: All about Nature. Luedecke, Bev, illus. (Beastieville Ser.). (J). (gr. k-1). 2005. 32p. pap. 3.95 (978-0-516-25522-4(3)); 2004. 19.50 (978-0-516-22898-3(6)) Scholastic Library Publishing. (Children's Pr.).

—Tug-of-War: All about Balance. Luedecke, Bev, illus. (Beastieville Ser.). (J). (gr. k-1). 2005. 32p. pap. 3.95 (978-0-516-25523-1(1)); 2004. 31p. 19.50 (978-0-516-22899-0(4)) Scholastic Library Publishing. (Children's Pr.).

—What a Mess! All about Numbers. Luedecke, Bev, illus. (Beastieville Ser.). (J). (gr. k-1). 2005. 32p. pap. 3.95 (978-0-516-25524-8(X)); 2004. 19.50 (978-0-516-23670-4(9)) Scholastic Library Publishing. (Children's Pr.).

Hallinan, P. K. ABC I Love You. 2003. (Illus.). 26p. (J). bds. 7.95 (978-0-8249-5458-1(0)) Ideals Pubns.

—Happy Birthday! 2003. (J). (Illus.). 26p. bds. 7.95 (978-0-8249-5453-6(X)); (978-0-8249-6507-5(8) , Candy Cane Pr.) Ideals Pubns.

—Heartprints. 2004. (Illus.). 26p. (J). bds. 6.95 (978-0-8249-6564-8(7)) Ideals Pubns.

—How Do I Love You? 2006. (Illus.). 32p. (J). pap. 3.95 (978-0-8249-5518-2(8) , Ideals Children's Bks.) Ideals Pubns.

—How Do I Love You/Como Te Amo. 2003. (SPA & ENG., Illus.). 32p. (J). 3.95 (978-0-8249-5471-0(8)) Ideals Pubns.

—I Know Jesus Loves Me. Hallinan, P. K., illus. 2007. (Illus.). 28p. (J). (ps-3). 8.99 (***978-0-8249-5553-3(6)*** , Ideals Children's Bks.) Ideals Pubns.

—Just Open a Book. (J). 24p. 7.95 (978-0-8249-5353-9(3) , Ideals); 22p. pap. 5.95 (978-0-8249-5354-6(1)); 24p. lib. bdg. 11.00 (978-0-8249-5355-3(X) , Ideals); 2004. (Illus.). 48p. pap. 9.95 (978-0-8249-5490-1(4)) Ideals Pubns.

—Let's Be Happy. 2005. (Illus.). 26p. (J). (ps-k). bds. 7.95 (978-0-8249-6588-4(4)) Ideals Pubns.

—Let's Be Helpful. 2004. (Illus.). 26p. (J). bds. 7.95 (978-0-8249-6563-1(9)) Ideals Pubns.

—Let's Be Honest. 2003. (Illus.). 24p. (J). bds. 7.95 (978-0-8249-5478-9(5)) Ideals Pubns.

—Let's Be Kind. 2003. (Illus.). 24p. (J). bds. 7.95 (978-0-8249-5477-2(7)) Ideals Pubns.

—Let's Be Polite. 2004. (Illus.). 26p. (J). bds. 7.95 (978-0-8249-6562-4(0)) Ideals Pubns.

—Let's Be Safe. 2007. 32p. (J). 8.99 (*978-0-8249-5529-8(3) , Candy Cane Pr.) Ideals Pubns.

—Let's Learn All We Can! (J). 2004. (Illus.). 48p. pap. 9.95 (978-0-8249-5491-8(2)); 2002. 24p. 7.95 (978-0-8249-5307-2(X) , Ideals) Ideals Pubns.

—Let's Play As a Team. 2003. (Illus.). 28p. (J). 7.95 (978-0-8249-5452-9(1)) Ideals Pubns.

—My Daddy & I. (Illus.). (J). 2006. 32p. pap. 3.95 (978-0-8249-5521-2(8) , Ideals Children's Bks.); 2002. 26p. bds. 7.95 (978-0-8249-4217-5(5)) Ideals Pubns.

—My Mommy & I. 2006. (Illus.). 32p. (J). pap. 3.95 (978-0-8249-5520-5(X) , Ideals Children's Bks.) Ideals Pubns.

—That's What a Friend Is. 2001. (Illus.). 24p. (J). 7.95 (978-0-8249-5390-4(8)) Ideals Pubns.

Hallwood, Cheri L. Winter's First Snowflake. Rose, Patricia M., illus. l.t. ed. 2006. 32p. (J). per. 15.99 (978-0-9774422-0-1(9)) Forever Young Pubs.

Ham, David A. & Sibley, Janice B. Magic Baseball Cap. Bostick, Blair, illus. 2006. 48p. (J). 16.95 (978-0-9746920-2-9(6)) CRM Pubs., LLC.

Hamanaka, Sheila. All the Colors of the Earth. Hamanaka, Sheila, illus. 1999. (Illus.). 32p. (J). (ps-3). pap. 6.99 (978-0-688-17062-2(5) , Harper Trophy) HarperCollins Pubs.

—All the Colors of the Earth. 1999. (J). 12.79 (978-0-606-17242-4(4)); (gr. 3-6). lib. bdg. 14.15 (978-0-613-22808-4(1)) Tandem Library Bks.

—Grandparents Song. Hamanaka, Sheila, illus. 2003. (Illus.). 32p. (J). 15.99 (978-0-688-17852-9(9)) HarperCollins Pubs.

Hamburger, Carole. The Zippity-Do-Dot: The Dot Who Dared to Pick Her Knows. Hamburger, Carole, illus. 2008. (Illus.). 40p. (J). 16.95 (*978-0-9764921-1-5(3)) Cherry Street Pr.

Hamilton, Richard. Let's Take over the Kindergarten. Heap, Sue, illus. 2007. 32p. (J). (ps-1). 15.95 (978-1-58234-707-3(7)) Bloomsbury Publishing.

Hamilton, Richard & Williams, Sophy. Polly's Picnic. 2003. (Illus.). 32p. (J). (ps-2). 16.95 (978-1-58234-819-3(7) , Bloomsbury Children) Bloomsbury Publishing.

Hample, Stoo. I Will Kiss You (Lots & Lots & Lots!) 2006. (Illus.). 32p. (J). (ps up). 15.99 (978-0-7636-2787-4(9)) Candlewick Pr.

Hamsa, Bobbie. Dirty Larry. Catanese, Donna, illus. rev. ed. 2003. (Rookie Reader Espanol Ser.). 24p. (J). (gr. k-2). pap. 4.95 (978-0-516-27493-5(7) , Children's Pr.) Scholastic Library Publishing.

—Dirty Larry. rev. ed. 2002. (Rookie Readers Ser.). (J). lib. bdg. 16.00 (978-0-516-22561-6(8) , Children's Pr.) Scholastic Library Publishing.

—Dirty Larry. Catanese, Donna, illus. rev. ed. 2002. (Rookie Readers Ser.). 23p. (J). (gr. k-1). 19.50 (978-0-516-22668-2(1) , Children's Pr.) Scholastic Library Publishing.

—Dirty Larry. 2002. (ps-2). lib. bdg. 12.95 (978-0-613-59125-6(9)) Tandem Library Bks.

—Fast-Draw Freddie. Miller, Susan, illus. rev. ed. 2001. (Rookie Reader Skill Set Ser.). 32p. (J). (gr. k-2). pap. 4.95 (978-0-516-27150-7(4) , Children's Pr.) Scholastic Library Publishing.

—Fast-Draw Freddie. rev. ed. 2000. (gr. k-3). lib. bdg. 12.95 (978-0-613-54482-5(X)) Tandem Library Bks.

Hanken, Sandra. Sky Castle. Bergsma, Jody Lynn, illus. 1998. 32p. (ps-3). 15.95 (978-0-935699-14-2(7)) Illumination Arts Publishing Co., Inc.

Hankey, Sandy. Sweet Little Girl. Gay, Maria T., illus. 2004. 20p. pap. 14.95 (978-1-4137-3329-7(8)) PublishAmerica, Inc.

Hanson, Warren. Bugtown Boogie. 2008. 32p. (J). 16.99 (*978-0-06-059937-9(5)); lib. bdg. 17.89 (*978-0-06-059938-6(3)) HarperCollins Pubs. (Geringer, Laura Book).

Hanson, Warren, illus. Kiki's Hats. 2007. (J). (*978-0-931674-94-5(8)) Waldman Hse. Pr., Inc.

Hapka, Cathy. Pretend & Play Kitty: With Real Crown You Can Wear! Borlasca, Hector, illus. 2004. (Role Play Ser.). 10p. (J). (ps up). bds. 6.99 (978-1-57151-742-5(1)) Playhouse Publishing.

Harcourt School Publishers Staff. Coyote: Library Edition. 1999. (Collections Ser.). (Illus.). (J). 4.70 (978-0-15-314331-1(2)) Harcourt Schl. Pubs.

—Go out in the Rain: Take-Home Book. 1999. (Collections Ser.). (Illus.). (J). pap. 1.90 (978-0-15-317212-0(6)) Harcourt Schl. Pubs.

—Monkey Fun: Take-Home Book. 1999. (Collections Ser.). (Illus.). (J). pap. 1.90 (978-0-15-317216-8(9)) Harcourt Schl. Pubs.

—Off We Go! 3rd ed. 2002. (Illus.). pap. 55.10 (978-0-15-325444-4(0)) Harcourt Schl. Pubs.

—Off We Go! Little Book. 3rd ed. 2002. (Trophies Reading Program Ser.). (Illus.). (J). pap. 10.20 (978-0-15-325449-9(1)) Harcourt Schl. Pubs.

—PB & Jelly: Little Book. 2000. (Collections Ser.). (Illus.). (J). pap. 10.20 (978-0-15-314497-4(1)) Harcourt Schl. Pubs.

Harder Tangvald, Christine. Whoo! Moo! Cock-a-Doodle-Doo! Conteh-Morgan, Jane, illus. 2000. 24p. (J). (ps-k). bds. 7.99 (978-0-570-07096-2(1)) Concordia Publishing Hse.

Harley, Bill. Dirty Joe, the Pirate: A True Story. Davis, Jack E., illus. 2008. 32p. (J). 16.99 (*978-0-06-623780-0(7)); lib. bdg. 17.89 (*978-0-06-623781-7(5)) HarperCollins Pubs.

Harper, Charise Mericle. Itsy Bitsy, the Smart Spider. Harper, Charise Mericle, illus. 2004. (Illus.). 32p. (J). (ps). 9.99 (978-0-8037-2901-8(4) , Dial) Penguin Group (USA) Inc.

Harper, Jessica. I Like Where I Am. Osborn, Kathy & Karas, G. Brian, illus. 2004. 32p. (J). (ps-3). 15.99 (978-0-399-23479-8(9) , Putnam Juvenile) Penguin Group (USA) Inc.

—I'm Not Going to Chase the Cat Today! 2000. (Illus.). 32p. (J). (ps-3). 15.89 (978-0-688-17637-2(2)) HarperCollins Pubs.

—I'm Not Going to Chase the Cat Today! Dupont, Lindsay Harper, illus. 2000. 32p. (J). (ps-3). 15.95 (978-0-688-17636-5(4)) HarperCollins Pubs.

—Lizzy's Do's & Don'ts. Dupont, Lindsay Harper, illus. 2002. 32p. (J). (ps-3). 15.95 (978-0-06-623860-9(9)); lib. bdg. 15.89 (978-0-06-623861-6(7)) HarperCollins Pubs.

—Nora's Room. Dupont, Lindsay Harper, illus. 2001. 32p. (J). (ps-3). 15.95 (978-0-06-029136-5(2)); 15.89 (978-0-06-029137-2(0)) HarperCollins Pubs.

Harper, Jo. I Could Eat You Up! Chorao, Kay, illus. 2007. 32p. (J). (ps-k). 16.95 (978-0-8234-1733-9(6)) Holiday Hse., Inc.

Harris, Annmarie. The Countdown to Halloween. Lucas, Margeaux, illus. 2003. 24p. (J). (ps-4). pap. 3.99 (978-0-8431-0462-2(7) , Price Stern Sloan) Penguin Group (USA) Inc.

—The Countdown to the First Day of School. Motoyama, Keiko, illus. 2003. 24p. (J). (ps-4). pap. 3.99 (978-0-8431-0463-9(5) , Price Stern Sloan) Penguin Group (USA) Inc.

Harris, Emma. Bedtime, Little Monsters! Cherrill, Paul, illus. 2002. 20p. (J). tchr. ed. 14.95 (978-1-58925-689-7(1) , tiger tales) ME Media LLC.

Harris, Jay M. The Moon Is la Luna: A Fun & Easy Way to Learn 55 Spanish Words. Cordell, Matthew, illus. 2007. 32p. (J). (gr. 3-5). 15.00 (*978-0-618-64645-6(0)) Houghton Mifflin Co.

Harris, Joe. The Belly Book. 2008. (J). (978-0-375-84340-2(X)); lib. bdg. (978-0-375-94340-9(4)) Random Hse. Children's Bks.

Harris, Joe. Halloween Ball. 2008. (J). (*978-0-375-84975-6(0)); (*978-0-375-84373-0(6)); lib. bdg. (*978-0-375-94975-3(5)) Random Hse., Inc.

Harris, Sue. Butterfly Garden. Boey, Stephanie, illus. 2006. 20p. (J). 15.95 (978-0-8118-5247-0(4)) Chronicle Bks. LLC.

Harris, Trudy. Jenny Found a Penny. Hovell, John, illus. 2008. (J). lib. bdg. (*978-0-8225-6725-7(3) , Millbrook Pr.) Lerner Publishing Group.

Harris, Trudy. Over, under, in, & Ouch! 2003. (Silly Millies Ser.). 32p. lib. bdg. 17.90 (978-0-7613-2912-1(9)); (Illus.). (J). (gr. 1-3). pap. 4.99 (978-0-7613-1946-7(8)) Lerner Publishing Group. (Millbrook Pr.).

Harrison, David L. The Alligator in the Closet: And Other Poems Around the House. Kendall, Jane, illus. 2003. 48p. (J). (gr. 2-4). 16.95 (978-1-56397-994-1(2)) Boyds Mills Pr.

—Animals' Song. 2003. (ps-2). lib. bdg. 17.60 (978-0-613-59274-1(3)) Tandem Library Bks.

Harrison, David Lee. The Big Sleepover. Edwards, Ken, illus. 2001. (Clifford, the Big Red Dog Ser.). (J). pap. (978-0-439-22364-5(4)) Scholastic, Inc.

Harshman, Cheryl Ryan. Christmas Morning. Mattheson, Jenny, illus. 2004. 40p. (J). pap. 6.99 (978-0-439-41425-8(3) , Cartwheel Bks.) Scholastic, Inc.

Harshman, Marc & Ryan, Cheryl. Red Are the Apples. Zahares, Wade, illus. 32p. (J). 2007. pap. 6.00 (*978-0-15-206065-7(0) , Voyager Bks./Libros Viajeros); 2001. 17.00 (978-0-15-201917-4(0)) Harcourt Children's Bks.

Harshman, Terry Webb. Bessie's Bed. Vargo, Sharon Hawkins, illus. 2003. (Silly Millies Ser.). 32p. lib. bdg. 17.90 (978-0-7613-2742-4(8) , Millbrook Pr.) Lerner Publishing Group.

Harter, Debbie. The Animal Boogie. 2005. (Illus.). (J). pap. (*978-1-905236-49-7(2)) Barefoot Bks., Inc.

Harter, Debbie. Walking Through the Jungle. 2001. (Illus.). 32p. (J). (ps-k). pap. 5.95 (978-0-531-07185-4(5) , Orchard Bks.) Scholastic, Inc.

Harter, Debbie, illus. Walking Through the Jungle. 2004. 30p. (J). (ps). pap. 6.99 (978-1-84148-548-5(9)) Barefoot Bks., Inc.

—Walking Through the Jungle. 2004. 30p. (J). (TAM, CZE, VIE, SPA & GUJ.). (978-1-85269-811-9(X)); (TAM, CZE, VIE, SPA & GUJ.). (978-1-85269-816-4(0)); (TAM, CZE, VIE, SPA & GUJ.). (978-1-85269-821-8(7)); (TAM, CZE, VIE, SPA & GUJ.). (978-1-85269-826-3(8)); (TAM, CZE, VIE, SPA & GUJ.). (978-1-85269-831-7(4)); (TAM, CZE, VIE, SPA & GUJ.). (978-1-85269-841-6(1)); (TAM, CZE, VIE, SPA & GUJ.). (978-1-85269-846-1(2)); (TAM, CZE, VIE, SPA & GUJ.). (978-1-85269-807-2(1)); (TAM, CZE, VIE, SPA & GUJ.). (978-1-85269-851-5(9)); (TAM, CZE, VIE, SPA & GUJ.). (978-1-85269-861-4(6)); (TAM, CZE, VIE, SPA & GUJ.). (978-1-85269-866-9(7)); (TAM, CZE, VIE, SPA & GUJ.). (978-1-85269-871-3(3)); (CZE, TAM, VIE, SPA & GUJ.). (978-1-85269-876-8(4)); (TAM, CZE, VIE, SPA & GUJ.). (978-1-85269-881-2(0)); (TAM, CZE, VIE, SPA & GUJ.). (978-1-85269-886-7(1)); (TAM, CZE, SPA, VIE & GUJ.). (978-1-85269-891-1(8)); (TAM, CZE, VIE, SPA & GUJ.). (978-1-85269-856-0(X)) Mantra Publishing, Ltd.

Hartman, Sara. When Jesus Was Born. Mitter, Kathy, illus. 2007. 16p. (J). (gr. k-4). 1.99 (*978-0-7586-1281-6(8)) Concordia Publishing Hse.

Harvey, Damian. Oggy & the Dinosaur. Hall, Francois, illus. 2005. (Reading Corner Ser.). 24p. (J). (gr. k-3). lib. bdg. 22.80 (978-1-59771-008-4(3)) Sea-To-Sea Pubns.

Haskins, Lori. Ducks in Muck. Petrone, Valeria, illus. 2007. (For Baby Board Bks.). 24p. (J). (gr. k-ps). bds. 4.99 (978-0-375-84028-9(1) , Random Hse. Bks. for Young Readers) Random Hse. Children's Bks.

—Ducks in Muck. Petrone, Valeria, illus. 2000. 32p. (J). (ps-ps). lib. bdg. 11.80 (978-0-613-21470-4(6)) Tandem Library Bks.

Hasling, Jack. Salamander the Great! 2006. (J). per. 10.00 (*978-0-9786988-1-2(9)) Hazel Street Productions.

Hasse, John Edward. I Love You When... Obligado, Lilian, illus. 2001. (Pictureback Shape Ser.). 24p. (J). (gr. k-3). pap. 3.25 (978-0-375-81063-3(3) , Random Hse. Bks. for Young Readers) Random Hse. Children's Bks.

Hatch, Elizabeth. Halloween Night. Pickering, Jimmy, illus. 2005. 32p. (J). (ps-1). 15.95 (978-0-385-74622-9(9)); lib. bdg. 17.99 (978-0-385-90887-0(3)) Random Hse. Children's Bks. (Doubleday Bks. for Young Readers).

Hay DeSimone, Corkey. Dinosaur Explore Activity & Coloring Book: Dinosaurs designed for their littlest Fans. Hay DeSimone, Corkey, illus. 2006. (J). 4.95 (978-0-9777394-0-0(6)) Gentle Giraffe Pr.

—Dinosaur Explore Board Book: Dinosaurs Designed for Their Littlest Fans. Hay DeSimone, Corkey, illus. 2006. (J). bds. 7.95 (978-0-9777394-1-7(4)) Gentle Giraffe Pr.

—Panda Promise Activity & Coloring Book. Hay DeSimone, Corkey, illus. 2006. (J). 4.95 (978-0-9747921-9-4(5)) Gentle Giraffe Pr.

—Panda Promise Hard Bound: Hard Bound Book. Hay DeSimone, Corkey, illus. 2006. (J). 9.95 (978-0-9747921-7-0(9)) Gentle Giraffe Pr.

Hays, Anna Jane. Here Comes Silent E! Adinolfi, JoAnn, illus. 2004. 32p. (J). (ps-2). pap. 3.99 (978-0-375-81233-0(4) , Random Hse. Bks. for Young Readers) Random Hse. Children's Bks.

—Here Comes Silent E! A Phonics Reader. Adinolfi, JoAnn, illus. 2004. 32p. (J). (ps-2). lib. bdg. 11.99 (978-0-375-91233-7(9) , Random Hse. Bks. for Young Readers) Random Hse. Children's Bks.

—Kindergarten Countdown. Davick, Linda, illus. 2007. 24p. (J). (ps-1). lib. bdg. 11.99 (978-0-375-94252-5(1)); 8.99 (978-0-375-84252-8(7)) Random Hse. Children's Bks. (Knopf Bks. for Young Readers).

—Silly Sara: A Phonics Reader. Wickstrom, Sylvie K., illus. 2002. (Step into Reading Early Bks.). 32p. (J). (gr. k-3). pap. 3.99 (978-0-375-81231-6(8) , Random Hse. Bks. for Young Readers) Random Hse. Children's Bks.

Hayward, Linda. It Takes Three. Koontz, Robin Michal, illus. 2003. (Silly Millies Ser.: 3). 32p. lib. bdg. 17.90 (978-0-7613-2902-2(1) , Millbrook Pr.) Lerner Publishing Group.

Hebson, Dennis. Robots Everywhere. Hoffman, Todd, tr. Hoffman, Todd, illus. 2004. 32p. (J). 16.85 (978-0-8027-8893-1(9)) Walker & Co.

Hegg, Tom. A Silent Night for Peef. Hanson, Warren, illus. 1998. 48p. (J). (ps-3). 15.95 (978-0-931674-35-8(2)) Waldman Hse. Pr., Inc.

Hegg, Tom & Hanson, Warren. Peef & the Baby Sister. Hegg, Tom & Hanson, Warren, illus. 2006. (J). (978-0-931674-67-9(0)) Waldman Hse. Pr., Inc.

Heidenreich, Elke & Buchholz, Quint. Some Folk Say the South Pole's Hot: The Three Tenors Play the Antarctic. 2001. (Illus.). 64p. (J). 17.95 (978-1-56792-170-0(1)) Godine, David R. Pub.

Heiligman, Deborah. Fun Dog, Sun Dog/Deborah Heiligman ; Illustrated by Tim Bowers. Bowers, Tim, illus. 2005. 32p. (J). 14.95 (978-0-7614-5162-4(5)) Cavendish, Marshall Corp.

Heine, Theresa. Star Seeker: A Journey to Outer Space. Tavares, Victor, illus. 2006. 32p. (J). 16.99 (978-1-905236-36-7(0)) Barefoot Bks., Inc.

Heinz, Brian J. The Alley Cat. Blair, June H., illus. l.t. ed. 2002. 32p. (J). 14.95 (978-0-936335-05-6(X)); pap. 6.95 (978-0-936335-06-3(8)) Ballyhoo BookWorks, Inc.

—The Barnyard Cat. Blair, June H., illus. 2000. 32p. (J). (gr. k-4). 14.95 (978-0-936335-04-9(1)) Ballyhoo BookWorks, Inc.

—The Barnyard Cat. l.t. ed. 2003. (Illus.). 32p. (J). pap. 6.96 (978-0-936335-07-0(6)) Ballyhoo BookWorks, Inc.

—Red Fox at McCloskey's Farm. Sheban, Chris, illus. 2006. 32p. (J). 17.95 (978-1-56846-195-3(X) , Creative Editions) Creative Co., The.

Heling, Kathryn. Mouse Makes Words: A Phonics Reader. 2002. (ps-2). lib. bdg. 11.80 (978-0-613-83542-8(5)) Tandem Library Bks.

—Mouse's Hide-and-Seek Words: A Phonics Reader. 2003. (ps-2). lib. bdg. 11.80 (978-0-613-89790-7(0)) Tandem Library Bks.

Heling, Kathryn & Hembrook, Deborah. Mouse Makes Words: A Phonics Reader. Joseph, Patrick, illus. 2002. (Early Step into Reading Ser.). 32p. (J). (ps-1). pap. 3.99 (978-0-375-81399-3(3) , Random Hse. Bks. for Young Readers) Random Hse. Children's Bks.

—Mouse's Hide-and-Seek Words. Joseph, Patrick, illus. 2003. (Early Step into Reading Ser.: Vol. 1). 32p. (J). (ps-1). pap. 3.99 (978-0-375-82185-1(6) , Random Hse. Bks. for Young Readers) Random Hse. Children's Bks.

—Mouse's Hide-and-Seek Words: A Phonics Reader. Joseph, Patrick, illus. 2003. (Early Step into Reading Ser.). 32p. (J). (ps-1). lib. bdg. 11.99 (978-0-375-92185-8(0) , Random Hse. Bks. for Young Readers) Random Hse. Children's Bks.

Helmore, Jim. Letterbox Lil: A Cautionary Tale. 2006. (Illus.). (J). (*978-1-4156-4110-1(2)) Barron's Educational Series, Inc.

Helton, Dianne. I Like Pumpkins! Me Gustan Las Calabazas! 2006. 32p. per. 13.99 (*978-1-59886-670-4(2)) Tate Publishing & Enterprises, L.L.C.

Hemphill, Stephanie. Things Left Unsaid: A Novel in Poems. 2007. 272p. (gr. 7-17). pap. 7.99 (*978-0-7868-3745-8(4)) Hyperion Pr.

Henderson, Kathy. 15 Ways to Go to Bed. 1999. (Illus.). 32p. (J). (ps-3). pap. (978-0-7112-0589-5(2)) Lincoln, Frances Ltd. GBR. *Dist:* Transition Vendor.

Henkel, Donald G. A Legend of Santa & His Brother Fred. Henkel, Donald B., illus. 2000. 46p. (J). 20.50 (978-0-9673504-0-0(9)) Quillpen.

—Painted Treasures or the Original 288 Tree Gnomes. Henkel, D. B., VIII, illus. 2006. (J). mass mkt. 20.50 (978-0-9673504-1-7(7)) Quillpen.

Henning, Heather. Christmas. Chapman, Gillian, illus. 2007. (ENG.). 16p. (J). pap. 9.99 (*978-0-7586-1383-7(0)) Concordia Publishing Hse.

—Creation. Chapman, Gillian, illus. 2007. (ENG.). 16p. (J). pap. 9.99 (*978-0-7586-1384-4(9)) Concordia Publishing Hse.

Henry, Sandy. A Child's Bedtime Companion. Pavlova, Vera, illus. 2005. 26p. (J). (ps-2). per. 12.95 (978-1-929039-31-9(X)) Ambassador Bks., Inc.

Henson, John, illus. Sarah Lynn's Christmas Present. 2002. (J). 24.95 (978-0-9711706-8-1(1)) Waiver Publishing.

Henson, Laura J. & Grooms, Duffy. Ten Little Elvi. Gorissen, Dean, illus. 2004. 30p. (J). 12.95 (978-1-58246-124-3(4) , Tricycle Pr.) Ten Speed Pr.

Herman Horatio Hornblower III. 2005. (YA). per. 5.00 (978-1-59872-239-0(5)) Instantpublisher.com.

Herrera, Juan Felipe. Crashboomlove: A Novel in Verse. 2000. (J). 20.60 (978-0-606-19432-7(0)); 1999. (gr. 7-12). lib. bdg. 22.20 (978-0-613-33880-6(4)) Tandem Library Bks.

—CrashBoomLove: A Novel in Verse. 2004. 165p. (gr. 8-12). pap. 14.95 (978-0-8263-2114-5(3)); 1999. 176p. 18.95 (978-0-8263-2113-8(5)) Univ. of New Mexico Pr.

Herrick, Steven. Naked Bunyip Dancing. Norling, Beth, illus. 2008. (J). (*978-1-59078-499-0(5) , Front Street) Boyds Mills Pr.

Herrick, Steven. The Simple Gift. 2004. 192p. (YA). pap. 6.99 (978-0-689-86867-2(7) , Simon Pulse) Simon & Schuster Children's Publishing.

Hesse, Karen. Lejos del Polvo. 1999. (SPA.). (gr. 5-8). lib. bdg. 18.75 (978-0-613-18124-2(7)) Tandem Library Bks.

Hicks, Barbara Jean. I Like Black & White. Prap, Lila, illus. 2006. 32p. (J). 9.95 (978-1-58925-056-7(7) , tiger tales) ME Media LLC.

Hicks, Linda & Ashman, Linda. What Could Be Better Than This? Wingerter, Linda S., illus. 2006. 32p. (J). (ps-2). 16.99 (978-0-525-46954-4(0) , Dutton Juvenile) Penguin Group (USA) Inc.

Hicks, Robert Z. Tommie Turtle's Secret. Rolseth, Ruthie, illus. 2007. 40p. (J). 16.95 (*978-0-9792031-0-7(4)) R.Z. Enterprises of Florida.

Hill, Karen. Grandmother's Book of Promises. Clar, David Austin, illus. 2000. 48p. (J). (ps-2). 9.99 (978-1-57856-221-3(X) , WaterBrook Pr.) WaterBrook Pr.

Hillert, Margaret. The Cow That Got Her Wish. (J). 4.95 (978-0-87895-694-4(8)) Modern Curriculum Pr.

—Fun Days. (J). 4.95 (978-0-87895-678-4(6)) Modern Curriculum Pr.

Hills, Jodi. Hope-So. Bjornson, Barbara, illus. 2004. 36p. (J). 16.95 (978-0-9726504-2-7(3)) Tristan Publishing, Inc.

Hindley, Judy. Baby Talk: A Book of First Words & Phrases. Granstrom, Brita, illus. 2006. 32p. (J). (gr. k-k). 15.99 (978-0-7636-2971-7(5)) Candlewick Pr.

—Do Like a Duck Does! Bates, Ivan, illus. 40p. (J). (ps-k). 2007. pap. 4.99 (978-0-7636-3284-7(8)); 2002. 14.99 (978-0-7636-1668-7(0)) Candlewick Pr.

—Sleepy Places. Freeman, Tor, illus. 2006. 32p. (J). (ps-1). 15.99 (978-0-7636-2983-0(9)) Candlewick Pr.

Hinker Books. Disney Pixar Storybook: Finding Nemo: Monsters, Inc.: A Bug's Life: Toy Story. rev. ed. 2004. (Disney CD Storybooks Ser.). (Illus.). 128p. (J). (gr. 4-12). 14.95 incl. cd-rom (978-1-86515-517-3(9)) Hinkler Bks. Pty, Ltd. AUS. *Dist:* Penton Overseas, Inc.

Hinman, Bobbie. The Knot Fairy. 2007. 32p. 15.95 (*978-0-9786791-0-1(5)) Hinman, Bobbie E. Inc.

Hippely, Hilary Horder. Adventure on Klickitat Island. Upton, Barbara, illus. 2000. (J). (ps-ps). lib. bdg. 15.30 (978-0-613-24092-5(8)) Tandem Library Bks.

Ho, Minfong. Peek! A Thai Hide-and-Seek. Ho, Minfong & Meade, Holly, illus. 2004. 40p. (J). (ps-1). 16.99 (978-0-7636-2041-7(6)) Candlewick Pr.

Hobbie, Nathaniel. Priscilla & the Pink Planet. Hobbie, Jocelyn, illus. 2008. 32p. (J). (ps-1). pap. 6.99 (978-0-316-11349-6(2)) Little Brown & Co.

—Priscilla & the Pink Planet. Hobbie, Jocelyn, illus. 2004. 32p. (J). (ps-1). 15.99 (978-0-316-73579-7(5)) Little, Brown Bks. for Young Readers.

—Priscilla & the Splish-Splash Surprise. Hobbie, Jocelyn, illus. 2006. 32p. (J). (ps-1). 15.99 (978-0-316-01046-7(4)) Little Brown & Co.

—Priscilla, Superstar. Hobbie, Jocelyn, illus. 2007. 36p. (J). (ps-1). 16.99 (978-0-316-01386-4(2)) Little Brown & Co.

Hoberman, Mary Ann. A House Is a House for Me. Fraser, Betty, illus. 2000. (J). pap. 19.97 incl. audio (978-0-7366-9199-4(5)) Books on Tape, Inc.

—A House Is a House for Me. Betty, Fraser, illus. 2007. 48p. (J). (ps). 7.99 (*978-0-14-240773-8(9) , Puffin) Penguin Group (USA) Inc.

—I'm Going to Grandma's. Beeke, Tiphanie, illus. 2007. 32p. (J). (ps-2). 16.00 (978-0-15-216592-5(4)) Harcourt Trade Pubs.

—One of Each. Priceman, Marjorie, illus. 2000. 32p. (J). (ps-3). pap. 7.99 (978-0-316-36644-1(7)) Little, Brown Bks. for Young Readers.

—One of Each. Priceman, Marjorie, illus. 2000. (J). (ps-ps). lib. bdg. 14.10 (978-0-613-30077-3(7)) Tandem Library Bks.

—One of Each. 2000. (978-0-606-22189-4(1)) Tandem Library Bks.

—Right Outside My Window. Wilton, Nicholas, illus. 2002. 24p. (J). pap. (978-1-59034-181-0(3)); 15.95 (978-1-59034-194-0(5)) Mondo Publishing.

—The Seven Silly Eaters. Frazee, Marla, illus. 2000. 40p. (J). (ps-3). pap. 7.00 (978-0-15-202440-6(9) , Voyager Bks./Libros Viajeros) Harcourt Children's Bks.

—Seven Silly Eaters. 2000. (ps-2). lib. bdg. 14.15 (978-0-613-30122-0(6)) Tandem Library Bks.

—The Seven Silly Eaters. Frazee, Marla, illus. ed. 2004. (J). (gr. k-3). spiral bd. (978-0-616-14576-0(4)) Canadian National Institute for the Blind/Institut National Canadien pour les Aveugles.

—Sing-along Stories 3: Mary Had a Little Lamb, Yankee Doodle, Bill Grogan's Goat, 3 vols. Westcott, Nadine Bernard, illus. 3rd ed. 2005. (Sing-Along Stories Ser.). 33p. (J). (ps-k). 14.99 (978-0-316-01139-6(8) , Tingley, Megan Bks.) Little, Brown Bks. for Young Readers.

—Skip to My Lou. Westcott, Nadine Bernard, illus. 2006. 32p. (J). (ps-1). pap. 6.99 (978-0-316-73405-9(5)) Little Brown & Co.

—Whose Garden Is It? Dyer, Jane, illus. 2004. 40p. (J). 16.00 (978-0-15-202631-8(2) , Gulliver Bks.) Harcourt Children's Bks.

—You Read to Me, I'll Read to You. 2005. (J). (ps-7). 13.58 (978-0-316-16223-4(X) , Tingley, Megan Bks.) Little, Brown Bks. for Young Readers.

—You Read to Me, I'll Read to You: Very Short Stories to Read Together. Emberley, Michael, illus. 2001. (J). (ps-2). 15.95 (978-0-316-14672-2(2)) Little Brown & Co.

Hodges, James. The Trail of Truth. 2004. 36p. (J). pap. 18.99 (978-1-4141-0284-9(4)) Pleasant Word.

Hodges, Lynn, et al. Count Yourself to Sleep. 2005. (Song of God's Love Ser.). (Illus.). 32p. (J). 14.99 (978-0-310-70717-2(X)) Zonderkidz.

Hodges, Susan. Up in Space. Barr, Marilynn G., illus. 1999. (Rhyme & Reason Workbook Ser.). 32p. (J). (ps-k). pap. 3.95 (978-1-57029-254-5(X) , WPH 01106, Totline Pubns.) Schaffer, Frank Pubns.

Hodgson, Mona Gansberg. Bedtime in the Southwest. Graef, Renee, illus. 2004. 32p. 14.95 (978-0-87358-871-3(1) , Rising Moon Bks. for Young Readers) Northland Publishing.

Hogan, Robb Dragon Taz. Moonlight's Spell: Rhymes for Younger Readers by TAZ. 2003. (Illus.). 61p. (J). spiral bd. 9.95 (978-0-9742178-1-9(6)) TazTales.

Hollon, Frank. Glitter Girl & the Crazy Cheese. Dulemba, Elizabeth O., illus. 2006. 32p. (J). 14.95 (978-1-59692-137-5(4)) MacAdam/Cage Publishing, Inc.

Holub, Joan. Big Heart! A Valentine's Day Tale. Terry, Will, illus. 2007. (Ant Hill Ser.). 24p. (J). lib. bdg. 13.89 (*978-1-4169-2562-0(7)); pap. 3.99 (*978-1-4169-0957-6(5)) Simon & Schuster Children's Publishing. (Aladdin).

—The Garden That We Grew. Nakata, Hiroe, illus. 2001. (J). (ps-3). lib. bdg. 11.80 (978-0-613-35612-1(8)) Tandem Library Bks.

—Good Luck! A St. Patrick's Day Story. Terry, Will, illus. 2007. (Ant Hill Ser.). 24p. (J). pap. 3.99 (978-1-4169-0955-2(9) , Aladdin) ; lib. bdg. 11.89 (978-1-4169-2560-6(0) , Aladdin Library) Simon & Schuster Children's Publishing.

—The Halloween Queen. Smythe, Theresa, illus. 2004. 32p. (J). (gr. k-3). 15.95 (978-0-8075-3138-9(3)) Whitman, Albert & Co.

—Pajama Party. Durrell, Julie, illus. 1998. (All Aboard Reading Ser.). 32p. (J). (gr. k-2). pap. 3.99 (978-0-448-41739-4(1) , Grosset & Dunlap) Penguin Group (USA) Inc.

—The Pizza That We Made. Cravath, Lynne W., illus. 2001. (Puffin-Easy-to-Read Ser.). 32p. (J). pap. 3.99 (978-0-14-230019-0(5) , Puffin) Penguin Group (USA) Inc.

—Pizza That We Made. 2001. (gr. k-3). lib. bdg. 11.80 (978-0-613-64422-8(0)) Tandem Library Bks.

—Scaredy-Pants: A Halloween Story. Terry, Will, illus. 2007. (Ant Hill Ser.). 24p. (J). lib. bdg. 13.89 (*978-1-4169-2561-3(9) , Aladdin) Simon & Schuster Children's Publishing.

—Scaredy-Pants! A Halloween Story. Terry, Will, illus. 2007. (Ant Hill Ser.). 24p. (J). pap. 3.99 (*978-1-4169-0956-9(7) , Aladdin) Simon & Schuster Children's Publishing.

—Scat Cats! Davis, Rich, illus. 2001. (Viking Easy-to-Read Ser.). 32p. (J). (gr. k-2). pap. 3.99 (978-0-14-130905-7(9) , Puffin) Penguin Group (USA) Inc.

—Scat Cats! 2001. (Puffin Easy-to-Read Ser.). (Illus.). (J). (978-0-606-21412-4(7)) Tandem Library Bks.

—Scat, Cats! 2001. (ps-2). lib. bdg. 11.80 (978-0-613-35620-6(9)) Tandem Library Bks.

—Silly Bears. Burris, Priscilla, illus. 2001. (My First Hello Reader! Ser.). (J). pap. (978-0-439-32473-1(4)) Scholastic, Inc.

Holub, Joan. Spring Time! A Story about Seeds. Terry, Will, illus. 2008. (Ant Hill Ser.). 24p. (J). 13.89 (*978-1-4169-5132-2(6)); pap. 3.99 (*978-1-4169-5131-5(8)) Simon & Schuster Children's Publishing. (Aladdin).

Holub, Joan & Kurisu, Jane. Backwards Day. 2000. (Hello Reader! Ser.). (J). pap. (978-0-439-12964-0(8)) Scholastic, Inc.

Holwitz, Peter. Scribbleville. Holwitz, Peter, illus. 2005. (Illus.). 40p. (J). (ps-3). 15.99 (978-0-399-24303-5(8) , Philomel) Penguin Group (USA) Inc.

Honeycutt, Scarlet. Quit Waking Us Up. We're Trying to Sleep! Aarvig, Cindy, illus. 2001. 28p. (J). 16.85 (978-1-55618-194-8(9)) Brunswick Publishing Corp.

Hood, Susan. Bad Hair Day. 1999. (gr. k-3). lib. bdg. 11.80 (978-0-613-21160-4(X)) Tandem Library Bks.

—I Am Mad! Handelman, Dorothy, photos by. 1999. (Real Kids Readers Ser.). (Illus.). 32p. (gr. k-1). (J). pap. 4.99 (978-0-7613-2086-9(5)); lib. bdg. 18.90 (978-0-7613-2061-6(X)) Lerner Publishing Group. (Millbrook Pr.).

—I Am Mad! 1999. (J). 11.79 (978-0-606-19155-5(0)); lib. bdg. 13.00 (978-0-613-18156-3(5)) Tandem Library Bks.

—Look! I Can Read! Wummer, Amy, illus. 2000. (All Aboard Reading Ser.). 32p. (J). (ps-3). mass mkt. 3.99 (978-0-448-41967-1(X) , Grosset & Dunlap) Penguin Group (USA) Inc.

—Look! I Can Read! 2000. (gr. k-3). lib. bdg. 11.80 (978-0-613-26053-4(8)); field. (Illus.). (J). (978-0-606-18470-0(8)) Tandem Library Bks.

—Look! I Can Tie My Shoes! Wummer, Amy, illus. 2002. (All Aboard Reading Ser.). 32p. (J). pap. 3.99 (978-0-448-42676-1(5) , Grosset & Dunlap) Penguin Group (USA) Inc.

—Look! I Can Tie My Shoes! 2002. (gr. k-3). lib. bdg. 11.80 (978-0-613-45289-2(5)) Tandem Library Bks.

—Show & Tell. Handelman, Dorothy, photos by. 1999. (Real Kids Readers Ser.). (Illus.). 32p. (gr. k-2). (J). pap. 4.99 (978-0-7613-2081-4(4)); lib. bdg. 18.90 (978-0-7613-2056-2(3)) Lerner Publishing Group. (Millbrook Pr.).

—Show & Tell. 1999. (J). (978-0-606-19173-9(9)); lib. bdg. 11.80 (978-0-613-16835-9(6)) Tandem Library Bks.

—Time for Bed? 1999. (Real Kids Readers Ser.: 2). (Illus.). 32p. (J). (gr. k-2). pap. 4.99 (978-0-7613-2094-4(6) , Millbrook Pr.) Lerner Publishing Group.

—Time for Bed? Handelman, Dorothy, photos by. 1999. (Real Kids Readers Ser.). (Illus.). 32p. (gr. k-2). lib. bdg. 18.90 (978-0-7613-2069-2(5) , Millbrook Pr.) Lerner Publishing Group.

—Time for Bed? 1999. (J). (978-0-606-19178-4(X)); lib. bdg. 11.80 (978-0-613-18165-5(4)) Tandem Library Bks.

Hood, Susan & Gevry, Claudine. Caterpillar Spring, Butterfly Summer. 2006. 10p. (J). bds. 6.99 (978-0-7944-1217-3(3)) Reader's Digest Assn., Inc., The.

hooks, bell. Skin Again. Raschka, Chris, illus. 2004. 32p. (ps-3). 16.99 (978-0-7868-0825-0(X)) Hyperion Bks. for Children.

Hope Music. 2006. (J). per. 12.00 (*978-0-9773608-4-0(9)) Shiny Red Ball Publishing.

Hopkinson, Deborah. Maria's Comet. Lanino, Deborah, illus. 2003. 32p. (J). (ps-3). pap. 6.99 (978-0-689-85678-5(4) , Aladdin) Simon & Schuster Children's Publishing.

Hopper, Karyn. There's a Monster in My Opu. 2006. (Illus.). 24p. (J). mass mkt. 11.95 (978-1-57306-244-2(8)) Bess Pr., Inc.

Hoppes, Lyn L. Freefall. 1998. (J). 12.95 (978-1-58021-044-7(9)); pap. 5.95 (978-1-58021-039-3(2)) Benefactory, Inc., The.

Horowitz, Dave. Beware of Tigers. Horowitz, Dave, illus. 2006. (Illus.). 40p. (J). (ps-3). 12.99 (978-0-399-24508-4(1)) Penguin Group (USA) Inc.

—Five Little Gefiltes. Horowitz, Dave, illus. 2007. (Illus.). 32p. (J). (ps-2). 12.99 (978-0-399-24608-1(8) , Putnam Juvenile) Penguin Group (USA) Inc.

—Twenty-Six Princesses. Horowitz, Dave, illus. 2008. 32p. (J). (ps). 15.99 (*978-0-399-24607-4(X) , Putnam Juvenile) Penguin Group (USA) Inc.

Horowitz, Dave. The Ugly Pumpkin: A Thanksgiving Story. Horowitz, Dave, illus. 2005. (Illus.). 40p. (J). (ps-2). 16.99 (978-0-399-24267-0(8) , Putnam Juvenile) Penguin Group (USA) Inc.

Horsbrugh, Wilma. The Train to Glasgow. Cox, Paul, illus. 2004. 32p. (J). (gr. k-3). 16.00 (978-0-618-38143-2(0) , Clarion Bks.) Houghton Mifflin Co. Trade & Reference Div.

Horton, Joan. Hippopotamus Stew & Other Silly Animal Poems. Adinolfi, JoAnn, illus. rev. ed. 2006. 32p. (J). 16.95 (978-0-8050-7350-8(7) , Holt, Henry & Co. Bks. For Young Readers) Holt, Henry & Co.

Houk, Randy. Rico's Hawk. Lane, Nancy, illus. 1998. 32p. (J). 12.95 (978-1-58021-029-4(5)); pap. 5.95 (978-1-58021-030-0(9)); (gr. 1-4). pap. 9.95 incl. audio (978-1-58021-033-1(3)); (gr. 1-4). pap. 19.95 incl. audio (978-1-58021-031-7(7)) Benefactory, Inc., The.

—Rico's Hawk: Includes Plush Toy Animal. Lane, Nancy, illus. 1998. 32p. (J). 29.95 (978-1-58021-038-6(4)); pap. 14.95 (978-1-58021-032-4(5)) Benefactory, Inc., The.

—Rico's Hawk: Includes Tape & Plush Toy Animal. Lane, Nancy, illus. 1998. 32p. (J). 34.95 incl. audio (978-1-58021-037-9(6)) Benefactory, Inc., The.

Howard, Reginald. Big, Big Wall. 2001. (gr. k-3). lib. bdg. 11.80 (978-0-613-66350-2(0)) Tandem Library Bks.

Howe, Tina Field. Snailsworth, a Slow Little Story. Howe, Tina Field, illus. l.t. ed. 2005. (Illus.). 24p. (J). 12.95 (978-0-9768585-0-8(9) , 001) Howe, Tina Field.

Hsu, Stacey W. Old Mo. Ritter, Adam, illus. 2006. (Rookie Reader Skill Set Ser.). 32p. (J). (gr. k-2). 19.50 (978-0-516-24981-0(9) , Children's Pr.) Scholastic Library Publishing.

Hsu, Stacey W. & Ritter, Adam. Old Mo. 2006. (Rookie Reader Ser.). (Illus.). 32p. (J). pap. 4.95 (978-0-516-24762-5(X) , Children's Pr.) Scholastic Library Publishing.

Hubbell, Patricia. Airplanes: Soaring! Diving! Turning! Halsey, Megan & Addy, Sean, illus. 2008. (J). (*978-0-7614-5388-8(1)) Cavendish, Marshall Corp.

—Black All Around! Tate, Don, illus. 2003. 32p. (J). 16.95 (978-1-58430-048-9(5)) Lee & Low Bks., Inc.

—Bouncing Time. Sweet, Melissa, illus. 2000. 32p. (YA). (ps up). 15.95 (978-0-688-17376-0(4)) HarperCollins Pubs.

—Cars: Rushing! Honking! Zooming! Halsey, Megan & Addy, Sean, illus. 2006. 32p. (J). 14.99 (978-0-7614-5296-6(6)) Cavendish, Marshall Corp.

—Firefighters! Speeding! Spraying! Saving! Garofoli, Viviana, illus. (J). 2007. (*978-1-4287-3584-2(4) , Cavendish Children's Bks.); 2006. 14.99 (978-0-7614-5337-6(7)) Cavendish, Marshall Corp.

—Hurray for Spring. Morley, Taia, illus. 2005. (Picture Book Ser.). 32p. 15.95 (978-1-55971-913-1(3) , Two Can Publishing) T&N Children's Publishing.

—Rabbit Moon: A Book of Holidays & Celebrations. Watson, Wendy, illus. 2002. 32p. (J). (ps-3). 15.95 (978-0-7614-5103-7(X) , Cavendish Children's Bks.) Cavendish, Marshall Corp.

—Sea, Sand, Me! Ernst, Lisa Campbell, illus. 2001. 32p. (J). (ps-3). 16.99 (978-0-688-17378-4(0)) HarperCollins Pubs.

—Trains: Steaming! Pulling! Huffing! Halsey, Megan & Addy, Sean, illus. 2005. 32p. (J). (ps-3). per. 14.95 (978-0-7614-5194-5(3)) Cavendish, Marshall Corp.

—Trucks. Halsey, Megan, illus. 2006. 32p. 5.99 (978-0-7614-5328-4(8)) Cavendish, Marshall Corp.

—Trucks: Whizz! Zoom! Rumble! Halsey, Megan, illus. 2003. 32p. (J). 14.95 (978-0-7614-5124-2(2)) Cavendish, Marshall Corp.

Hubbell, Patricia & Westcott, Nadine Bernard. Pig Picnic. 1999. (Road to Reading Ser.). (Illus.). 32p. (J). (ps-1). 11.99 (978-0-307-46108-7(4) , Random Hse. Bks. for Young Readers) Random Hse. Children's Bks.

Hudson, Cheryl Willis. Hands Can. Bourke, John-Francis, photos by. 2007. (Illus.). 24p. (J). (gr. k-ps). bds. 7.99 (978-0-7636-3292-2(9)) Candlewick Pr.

—Hands Can. Bourke, John-Francis, illus. Bourke, John-Francis, photos by. 2003. 32p. (J). (gr. k-ps). 15.99 (978-0-7636-1667-0(2)) Candlewick Pr.

Hudson, Eleanor. The Best Thing about Valentines. Melcher, Mary, tr. Melcher, Mary, illus. 2004. 32p. (J). pap. 3.50 (978-0-439-52119-3(2) , Cartwheel Bks.) Scholastic, Inc.

Huelin, Jodi. Countdown to Thanksgiving. Motoyama, Keiko, illus. 2002. 24p. (J). pap. 3.99 (978-0-8431-4880-0(2) , Price Stern Sloan) Penguin Group (USA) Inc.

—Countdown to Valentine's Day. Haskamp, Steve, illus. 2002. 24p. (J). pap. 3.99 (978-0-8431-4882-4(9) , Price Stern Sloan) Penguin Group (USA) Inc.

Hughes, Shirley. Alfie's Weather. 2007. (Illus.). 48p. (J). pap. 8.95 (*978-0-09-940425-5(7) , Red Fox) Random Hse. Children's Bks. GBR. *Dist:* Independent Pubs. Group.

—Alfie's Weather. 2007. (Illus.). 48p. (J). 18.95 (*978-0-370-32561-3(3)) Transworld Publishers Ltd. GBR. *Dist:* Independent Pubs. Group.

Hughes, Shirley. Olly & Me. Hughes, Shirley, illus. 2004. (Illus.). 32p. (J). (ps-2). 15.99 (978-0-7636-2374-6(1)) Candlewick Pr.

Huizenga, Pam. My Best Friend. V'in, Anica, illus. 2000. 12p. (J). (ps-k). 7.95 (978-1-929774-00-5(1)) Greenleaf Book Group Pr.

—Twinkle. V'in, Anica, illus. 2000. 10p. (J). (ps-k). 7.95 (978-1-929774-01-2(X)) Greenleaf Book Group Pr.

Hulme, Joy N. Bubble Trouble. 1999. (gr. k-3). lib. bdg. 12.95 (978-0-613-37298-5(0)) Tandem Library Bks.

—Eerie Feary Feeling: A Hairy Scary Pop-up Book. Ely, Paul & Dudley, Dick, illus. 2006. 12p. (J). (gr. k-4). reprint ed. 14.00 (978-1-4223-5171-0(8)) DIANE Publishing Co.

Hulme, Joy N. Stable in Bethlehem: A Christmas Counting Book. Andreasen, Dan, illus. 2007. 24p. (J). (ps-k). 9.95 (*978-1-4027-4121-0(9)) Sterling Publishing Co., Inc.

Hundal, Nancy. Camping. Deines, Brian, illus. 2002. 32p. (ps-3). (978-1-55041-668-8(5)) Fitzhenry & Whiteside, Ltd.

—Camping. Deines, Brian, illus. 2006. 32p. pap. 7.95 (978-1-55041-686-2(3)) Fitzhenry & Whiteside, Ltd. CAN. *Dist:* F & W Pubns., Inc.

Hunter, Jana Novotny. When Daddy Picks Me Up. Miller, Thomas O., illus. 2004. (J). (gr. k-3). 12.95 (978-0-7696-3169-1(X) , Gingham Dog Pr.) School Specialty Publishing.

—When Daddy's Truck Picks Me Up. Thompson, Carol, illus. 2006. 32p. (J). 15.95 (978-0-8075-8914-4(4)) Whitman, Albert & Co.

Hutchins, Hazel J. I'd Know You Anywhere. Ohi, Ruth, illus. 2002. 24p. (J). (ps-k). pap. 7.95 (978-1-55037-746-0(9)); lib. bdg. 19.95 (978-1-55037-747-7(7)) Annick Pr., Ltd. CAN. *Dist:* Firefly Bks., Ltd.

—I'd Know You Anywhere. ed. 2004. (Illus.). (J). (ps up). spiral bd. (978-0-616-14577-7(2)); spiral bd. (978-0-616-14578-4(0)) Canadian National Institute for the Blind/Institut National Canadien pour les Aveugles.

Hutchins, Pat. Barn Dance! Hutchins, Pat, illus. 2007. (Illus.). 32p. (J). (ps-k). 16.99 (*978-0-06-089120-6(3)); lib. bdg. 17.89 (*978-0-06-089122-0(X)) HarperCollins Pubs. (Greenwillow Bks.).

Hutchins, Pat. The Wind Blew. Hutchins, Pat, illus. 2002. (Illus.). 14.47 (978-0-7587-4036-6(0)) Book Wholesalers, Inc.

Hyde, Judith Jensen. Rainy-Day Music. Abbott, Jason, illus. 2006. (Rookie Reader Skill Set Ser.). 32p. (J). (gr. k-2). 19.50 (978-0-516-24983-4(5) , Children's Pr.) Scholastic Library Publishing.

Hyde, Judith Jensen & Abbott, Jason. Rainy-day Music. 2006. (Illus.). 32p. (YA). pap. 4.95 (978-0-516-24998-8(3) , Children's Pr.) Scholastic Library Publishing.

Ide, Laurie Shimizu. Okazu at the Zoo. Kanekuni, Daniel, illus. 2006. (J). (978-1-56647-776-5(X)) Mutual Publishing LLC.

I'm Glad I'm Your Grandma. 2006. 16p. (J). pap. 1.99 (978-0-7847-1686-1(2) , 02988) Standard Publishing.

The Imaginary Zoo. 2007. (J). 16.95 (978-0-9789880-0-5(0)) Wild About Learning, Inc.

Inches, Alison. The Stuffed Animals Get Ready for Bed. Langdo, Bryan, illus. 2006. 32p. (J). 16.00 (978-0-15-216466-9(9)) Harcourt Children's Bks.

The Internal Adventures of Marcus Snarkis Adventure Pack. 2001. (978-1-883772-32-1(X)) Flying Rhinoceros, Inc.

Intrater, Roberta Grobel. Baby Faces. 2002. (Baby Faces Ser.). 10p. (J). bds. 4.95 (978-0-439-42005-1(9) , Cartwheel Bks.) Scholastic, Inc.

—Eat! 2002. (Baby Faces Ser.). 10p. (J). bds. 4.95 (978-0-439-42006-8(7) , Cartwheel Bks.) Scholastic, Inc.

—Hugs & Kisses. 2002. (Baby Faces Ser.). 10p. (J). bds. 4.95 (978-0-439-42003-7(2) , Cartwheel Bks.) Scholastic, Inc.

—Peek-a-Boo, You! Intrater, Roberta Grobel, photos by. 2nd rev. l.t. ed. 2005. (Illus.). 14p. (J). 14.99 (978-0-9764985-0-6(2)) 1212 Pr.

—Peek-a-Boo, You! Intrater, Roberta Grobel, photos by. 2002. (Illus.). 7p. (J). pap. 9.95 (978-0-439-33961-2(8) , Cartwheel Bks.) Scholastic, Inc.

—Sleep. 2002. (Baby Faces Ser.). (Illus.). 10p. (J). bds. 4.95 (978-0-439-42004-4(0) , Cartwheel Bks.) Scholastic, Inc.

Ipcar, Dahlov. My Wonderful Christmas Tree. 1999. 28p. (J). (ps-3). 9.95 (978-0-89272-475-8(7)) Down East Bks.

Ireland, Karin. Don't Take Your Snake for a Stroll. Catrow, David, illus. 2003. 32p. (J). 16.00 (978-0-15-202361-4(5)) Harcourt Children's Bks.

Irly, I. R. Why Crocodile Does Not Smile. 2004. (Illus.). (J). bds. (978-0-9753075-4-0(1)) M-Graphics Publishing.

Isadora, Rachel. Bring on That Beat. 2002. (Illus.). 32p. (J). (ps-3). 15.99 (978-0-399-23232-9(X) , Putnam Juvenile) Penguin Group (USA) Inc.

Isom, Lori Boyd. Swoosh! Wise, Noreen, ed. 2004. (Illus.). 64p. (J). per. 6.95 (978-1-58584-560-6(4)) Huckleberry Pr.

Ives, Penny. Five Little Ducks. 2002. (Illus.). 16p. (J). 19.99 (978-0-85953-124-5(4)) Child's Play-International.

Ives, Penny, illus. Five Little Ducks. 2002. 16p. (J). 6.99 (978-0-85953-935-7(0)); bds. 5.99 (978-0-85953-141-2(4)) Child's Play-International.

Jabar, Cynthia. Wow! It Sure Is Good to Be You! Jabar, Cynthia, illus. 2006. (Illus.). 32p. (J). (gr. k-3). 9.95 (978-0-618-58132-0(4)) Houghton Mifflin Co.

Jackson, Alison. Ballad of Valentine. Tusa, Tricia, illus. 2002. 32p. (J). (gr. k-3). 16.99 (978-0-525-46720-5(3) , Dutton Juvenile) Penguin Group (USA) Inc.

—The Ballad of Valentine. Tusa, Tricia, illus. 2006. 32p. (J). (gr. 3). reprint ed. pap. 6.99 (978-0-14-240400-3(4) , Puffin) Penguin Group (USA) Inc.

—I Know an Old Lady Who Swallowed a Pie. Schachner, Judith B., illus. 2002. 32p. (J). (ps-3). pap. 6.99 (978-0-14-056595-9(7) , Puffin) Penguin Group (USA) Inc.

—I Know an Old Lady Who Swallowed a Pie. Schachner, Judith Byron, illus. 2002. (J). (ps-k). lib. bdg. 15.30 (978-0-613-55215-8(6)) Tandem Library Bks.

Jackson, Ann. Rags the Recycled Doll. O'Connor, Shannon, illus. 2004. 49p. 12.95 (978-1-57197-405-1(9)) Pentland Pr., Inc.

Jackson, Ellen B. Jean Henry. 1999. (J). 15.00 (978-0-15-202225-9(2)) Assessment Systems, Inc.

Jacobs, Paul DuBois & Swender, Jennifer. My Taxi Ride. Alko, Selina, illus. 2006. 32p. (J). 15.95 (978-1-4236-0073-2(8)) Gibbs Smith, Publisher.

Jacobson, David, illus. Three Wishes. 2006. (I'm Going to Read Ser.). 32p. (J). pap. 3.95 (978-1-4027-3130-3(2)) Sterling Publishing Co., Inc.

Jacobson, John. A Tree in Tappen Wood: A Musical Tale of Growing & Gratitude, Adventure & Peace. 2006. 48p. 19.95 incl. audio compact disk (978-1-4234-1263-2(X) , 142341263X) Leonard, Hal Corp.

Jacques, Brian. The Great Redwall Feast. Denise, Christopher, illus. 2000. 64p. (J). (ps-ps). lib. bdg. 15.30 (978-0-613-29968-8(X)) Tandem Library Bks.

Jam, Teddy. Night Cars. Beddows, Eric, illus. 2006. 32p. 9.95 (978-0-88899-748-7(5)) Groundwood Bks. CAN. *Dist:* Perseus Distribution.

James, Brian. The Shark Who Was Afraid of Everything. 2006. (Illus.). 32p. (J). pap. 5.99 (978-0-439-78672-0(X) , Cartwheel Bks.) Scholastic, Inc.

—The Shark Who Was Afraid of Everything. McNally, Bruce J., illus. 2002. (J). (978-0-439-36865-0(0)) Scholastic, Inc.

Jane, Pamela. Monster Countdown: A Spooky Counting Book. Zarin-Ackerman, Nick, illus. 2001. (J). (ps-2). 14.95 (978-1-58653-857-6(8)) Mondo Publishing.

Janovitz, Marilyn. Can I Help? 1998. (Illus.). 32p. (J). (ps-3). pap. 5.95 (978-1-55858-904-9(X)) North-South Bks., Inc.

—We Love Christmas! 32p. (J). 9.95 (978-1-59014-126-7(1)); (Illus.). pap. 3.50 (978-1-59014-125-0(3)) Night Sky Bks.

Jantti, Mariana. Cuanta gente! Quienes Son? Amelio-Ortiz, Osvaldo P. & Rodriguez Vidal, Andrea, illus. 2005. (SPA.). 28p. (J). 14.95 (978-9974-7799-2-1(8) , nicanitas) Hardenville SA URY. *Dist:* Independent Pubs. Group.

Jareckie, Ellen. A House-Mouse Christmas: House-Mouse Tales. 4th ed. 2004. (Illus.). 22p. (J). (ps-k). bds. 6.99 (978-0-316-73806-4(9)) Little, Brown Bks. for Young Readers.

Jarman, Julia. Big Red Tub. Reynolds, Adrian, illus. 2004. (Clifford Big Red Reader Ser.). 32p. (J). pap. 14.95 (978-0-439-67232-0(5) , Orchard Bks.) Scholastic, Inc.

Jarman, Julia. Class Two at the Zoo. Chapman, Lynne, illus. 2007. (Carolrhoda Picture Bks.). 32p. (J). (gr. k-3). 16.95 (*978-0-8225-7132-2(3) , Carolrhoda Bks.) Lerner Publishing Group.

Jasper, Mark. Good Night Charleston. Kelly, Cooper, illus. 2007. (Good Night Our World Ser.). 20p. (J). bds. 9.95 (*978-1-60219-022-1(4)) Our World of Books.

—Good Night Florida Keys. Rosen, Anne, illus. 2008. (Good Night Our World Ser.). 20p. (J). bds. 9.95 (*978-1-60219-020-7(8)) Our World of Books.

Jenkins, Barbie. The Legend of Christmas Kiss. 2005. 32p. 13.99 (978-1-4165-3382-5(6) , Howard Bks.) Simon & Schuster.

Jenkins, Jane John. The Adventures of Harry the Hamster. Grenda, Janet W., illus. 2001. (J). (978-0-9674867-2-7(6)) Campbell Hse. Museum.

Jerome, Kate Boehm. Maggie's Rocky Shore Adventure. Garry-McCord, Kathleen, illus. 2002. (J). (978-1-878244-41-3(8)) Monterey Bay Aquarium.

Jill & the Beanstalk. 2004. (J). (ENG & ITA.). (978-1-84444-480-9(5)); (ALB & ENG.). (978-1-84444-492-2(9)); (ARA & ENG.). (978-1-84444-486-1(4)); (BEN & ENG.). (978-1-84444-478-6(3)); (CHI & ENG.). (978-1-84444-488-5(0)); (SBC & ENG.). (978-1-84444-483-0(X)); (ENG & PER.). (978-1-84444-491-5(0)); (ENG & FRE.). (978-1-84444-489-2(9)); (ENG & GUJ.). (978-1-84444-479-3(1)); (ENG & PAN.). (978-1-84444-494-6(5)); (ENG & POR.). (978-1-84444-481-6(3)); (ENG & RUS.). (978-1-84444-482-3(1)); (ENG & SOM.). (978-1-84444-487-8(2)); (ENG & SPA.). (978-1-84444-490-8(2)); (ENG & TAM.). (978-1-84444-484-7(8)); (ENG & TUR.). (978-1-84444-495-3(3)); (ENG & URD.). (978-1-84444-485-4(6)); (ENG & VIE.). (978-1-84444-496-0(1)); E-Book incl. cd-rom (978-1-84444-463-2(5)) Mantra Publishing, Ltd.

Joel, Billy. Goodnight, My Angel: A Lullabye. Gilbert, Yvonne, illus. 2004. (Goodnight, My Angel Ser.). (J). 32p. pap. 16.95 (978-0-439-55376-6(8) , Scholastic Pr.); pap. (978-0-439-55378-0(4)) Scholastic, Inc.

Johns, Linda. I Can Bowl! 2002. (Rookie Readers Ser.). (J). lib. bdg. 19.00 (978-0-516-22565-4(0) , Children's Pr.) Scholastic Library Publishing.

—I Can Bowl! Caputo, Jim, illus. 2002. (Rookie Readers Ser.). 32p. (J). (gr. 1-2). 19.50 (978-0-516-22374-2(7) , Children's Pr.) Scholastic Library Publishing.

Johnson, Gillian. My Sister Gracie. Johnson, Gillian, illus. 2000. (Illus.). 32p. (J). (ps-k). 16.95 (978-0-88776-514-8(9)) Tundra Bks., Inc./Livres Toundra, Inc. CAN. *Dist:* Random Hse., Inc.

Johnson, Julia. One Humpy Grumpy Camel. Styles, Emily, illus. 2003. 32p. (J). (gr. 3-6). 15.95 (978-1-900988-75-9(5)) Stacey International Pubs. GBR. *Dist:* Interlink Publishing Group, Inc.

Johnson, Kathleen A. A Voice Came to Me. 2006. lib. bdg. 17.95 (978-0-9785623-0-4(5)) Voice of Light Pubns.

Johnson, Kimberly P. The Adventures of the Itty Bitty Spider & the Itty Bitty Mouse. 2004. (Illus.). 31p. (gr. k-2). 14.95 (978-1-57197-236-1(6)) Pentland Pr., Inc.

Johnston-Brown, A. M. The Chronicles of Pleasant Grove. 2006. (J). pap. 12.95 (978-0-9760718-5-3(1)) Retriever Pr.

Johnston, Tony. Cat, What Is That? Minor, Wendell, illus. 2001. 32p. (J). 15.95 (978-0-06-027742-0(4)); lib. bdg. 16.89 (978-0-06-027743-7(2)) HarperCollins Pubs.

—Chicken in the Kitchen. Taylor, Eleanor, illus. 2005. 32p. (J). 15.95 (978-0-689-85641-9(5) , Simon & Schuster Children's Publishing) Simon & Schuster Children's Publishing.

—Desert Dog. Weatherford, Robert, illus. 2001. 32p. (J). (gr. 1-5). 15.95 (978-0-87156-979-0(5)) Gibbs Smith, Publisher.

—Gopher up Your Sleeve. Park, Trip, illus. 2001. 32p. (J). (ps-3). 15.95 (978-0-87358-794-5(4) , Rising Moon Bks. for Young Readers) Northland Publishing.

—Off to Kindergarten. Sweet, Melissa, illus. 2007. 32p. (J). (ps-3). 7.99 (***978-0-439-73090-7(2)*** , Cartwheel Bks.) Scholastic, Inc.

—Ten Fat Turkeys. Deas, Richard F., illus. 2004. 32p. (J). (gr. k-ps). pap. 3.99 (978-0-439-45948-8(6) , Cartwheel Bks.) Scholastic, Inc.

—The Whole Green World. Kleven, Elisa, illus. 2005. 32p. (J). 15.00 (978-0-374-38400-5(2) , Farrar, Straus & Giroux (BYR)) Farrar, Straus & Giroux.

Jones, Christianne C. Eric No Juega. Demski, James, Jr., illus. 2006. (Read-It! Readers en Espanol Ser.).Tr. of Eric Won't Do It. (SPA.). 32p. (J). (ps-3). 19.95 (978-1-4048-1683-1(6)) Picture Window Bks.

—Eric Won't Do It. Demski, James, illus. 2005. (Read It! Readers Ser.). 24p. (J). (ps). lib. bdg. 18.60 (978-1-4048-1188-1(5)) Picture Window Bks.

Jones, Kelly. Mama. Kewley, Ken, illus. 2004. 32p. (J). (978-0-9745930-0-5(1)) Stunt Publishing.

Jones, Melanie Davis. Balls. Bronson, Linda, illus. 2003. (Rookie Reader Skill Set Ser.). 24p. (J). (gr. k-2). pap. 4.95 (978-0-516-26967-2(4) , Children's Pr.) Scholastic Library Publishing.

—Balls. 2002. (Rookie Readers Ser.). (J). lib. bdg. 16.00 (978-0-516-22532-6(4) , Children's Pr.) Scholastic Library Publishing.

—Balls. Bronson, Linda, illus. 2002. (Rookie Readers Ser.). 23p. (J). (gr. k-2). 19.50 (978-0-516-22596-8(0) , Children's Pr.) Scholastic Library Publishing.

—Balls. 2002. (gr. k-3). lib. bdg. 12.95 (978-0-613-59448-6(7)) Tandem Library Bks.

—I Can Ski! 2004. (Rookie Reader Skill Set Ser.). (Illus.). 31p. (J). (gr. k-2). pap. 4.95 (978-0-516-27901-5(7) , Children's Pr.) Scholastic Library Publishing.

—I Can Ski! Boles, Terry, illus. 2003. (Rookie Reader - Level B Ser.). 32p. (J). 19.50 (978-0-516-22878-5(1) , Children's Pr.) Scholastic Library Publishing.

—Pigs Rock! 2003. (Illus.). 32p. (J). (ps-1). 15.99 (978-0-670-03581-6(5) , Viking Juvenile) Penguin Group (USA) Inc.

Jones, Nathan Smith. The Boy Who Ate America. Nelson, Carey, illus. 2007. 32p. (J). (ps-3). 16.95 (***978-1-59038-814-3(3)*** , Shadow Mountain) Deseret Bk. Co.

Jones, Sylvie. Who's in the Tub? Constantin, Pascale, illus. 2007. 38p. (ps-3). 15.95 (***978-1-59354-612-0(2))*** Handprint Bks.

Jones, T. L. Santa Takes a Holiday! 2005. (Santa Chronicles Ser.: Bk. 1). (Illus.). 100p. (J). per. 12.00 (978-0-9707594-4-3(4) , 00001) Mercury/Hula Babe Productions.

Jordan, Apple. Bug Stew! 2003. (gr. k-3). lib. bdg. 11.80 (978-0-613-73701-2(6)) Tandem Library Bks.

—The Sweetest Spring. Matta, Gabriella & Legramandi, Francesco, illus. 2008. (Step into Reading Ser.). 32p. (J). (ps-1). lib. bdg. 11.99 (***978-0-375-94810-7(4)*** , RH/Disney) Random Hse. Children's Bks.

—The Sweetest Spring. Matta, Gabriella & Legramandi, Francesco, illus. 2008. 32p. (J). pap. (***978-0-375-84810-0(X))*** Random Hse., Inc.

Jordan, Apple. Winter Wishes. Marrucchi, Elisa, illus. 2006. (Step into Reading Ser.). 32p. (J). (ps-2). pap. 3.99 (978-0-7364-2409-7(1)); lib. bdg. 11.99 (978-0-7364-8049-9(8)) Random Hse. Children's Bks. (RH/Disney).

Jordan, Deloris & Jordan, Roslyn. Did I Tell You I Love You Today? Evans, Shane, tr. Evans, Shane, illus. 2004. 32p. (J). 16.95 (978-0-689-85271-8(1)) Simon & Schuster Children's Publishing.

Jorgensen, Richard. Reading with Dad. Hanson, Warren, illus. 2000. 40p. (J). (ps-k). 15.95 (978-0-931674-41-9(7)) Waldman Hse. Pr., Inc.

Joyce, William. Rolie Polie Olie. 2003. 32p. (J). pap. 3.50 (978-0-7868-4533-0(3)); pap. 3.50 (978-0-7868-4534-7(1)); pap. 3.50 (978-0-7868-4535-4(X)) Disney Pr.

—Rolie Polie Olie. Joyce, William, illus. 1999. (Laura Geringer Bks.). (Illus.). 48p. (J). (ps-k). 16.99 (978-0-06-027163-3(9) , Geringer, Laura Book) HarperCollins Pubs.

—Rolie Polie Olie. 1999. (Laura Geringer Bks.). (Illus.). 48p. (J). (ps-3). 15.89 (978-0-06-027164-0(7)) HarperCollins Pubs.

—Rolie Polie Olie. Joyce, William, illus. 2003. (Rolie Polie Olie Ser.). (Illus.). 32p. (J). (ps-k). 6.99 (978-0-06-055716-4(8) , Harper Festival) HarperCollins Pubs.

—Rolie Polie Olie. Joyce, William, illus. 2006. (Rolie Polie Olie Ser.). (Illus.). 48p. (J). reprint ed. pap. 6.99 (978-0-06-053484-4(2) , Harper Trophy) HarperCollins Pubs.

—Sleepy Time Olie. Joyce, William, illus. 2001. (Rolie Polie Olie Ser.). (Illus.). 40p. (J). (ps-3). 15.95 (978-0-06-029613-1(5) , Geringer, Laura Book) HarperCollins Pubs.

—Sleepy Time Olie. 2001. (Rolie Polie Olie Ser.). (Illus.). 40p. (J). (ps-3). 15.89 (978-0-06-029614-8(3) , Geringer, Laura Book) HarperCollins Pubs.

—Sleepy Time Olie. Joyce, William, illus. 2006. (Rolie Polie Olie Ser.). 40p. (J). pap. 6.99 (978-0-06-084222-2(9) , Harper Trophy) HarperCollins Pubs.

Jungle Limbo. l.t. ed. 2003. (Illus.). 31p. (J). spiral bd. 7.95 (978-0-9741074-0-0(9)) Catterfly Pr.

Kadair, Deborah Ousley. There Was an Ol' Cajun. Kadair, Deborah Ousley, illus. 2002. (Illus.). 32p. (J). (gr. k-3). 15.95 (978-1-56554-917-3(1)) Pelican Publishing Co., Inc.

Kahn, Peggy, et al. Welcome to Birdwell Island. 2001. (Clifford, the Big Red Dog Ser.). (Illus.). (J). pap. (978-0-439-22005-7(X)) Scholastic, Inc.

Kaldor, Connie & Campagne, Carmen. Lullaby Berceuse: A Warm Prairie Night. Deines, Brian, illus. 2006. 40p. (J). 16.95 incl. audio compact disk (978-2-923163-22-2(2)) La Montagne Secrete CAN. *Dist:* National Bk. Network.

Kalin, Julia. Peek-a-Boo Moon: A Reader Illustrated Storybook. unabr. ed. 1999. (Picture-It Storybook Ser.). 8p. (J). (ps-3). pap. 10.95 (978-0-9672430-3-0(3) , 9904) Stay, Play & Learn.

—Runaway Balloon: A Picture-It Storybook; A Reader Illustrated Storybook. unabr. ed. 1999. 12p. (J). (ps-3). pap. 12.95 (978-0-9672430-4-7(1) , 9905) Stay, Play & Learn.

Katz, Alan. Don't Say That Word! Catrow, David, illus. 2007. 40p. (J). (ps-3). 16.99 (978-0-689-86971-6(1) , McElderry, Margaret K.) Simon & Schuster Children's Publishing.

Katz, Bobbi. Lots of Lice. Bjorkman, Steve, illus. 1998. (Hello Reader! Science Ser.). 40p. (J). (gr. 1-3). pap. 3.99 (978-0-590-10834-8(4)) Scholastic, Inc.

—Lots of Lice. 1998. (Hello Reader! Science Ser.). (J). (gr. 1-3). (978-0-606-13583-2(9)) Tandem Library Bks.

Kavanagh, Peter. I Love My Mama. Chapman, Jane, illus. 2003. 32p. (J). (ps-1). 14.99 (978-0-689-85691-4(1)) Simon & Schuster Children's Publishing.

—I Love My Mama. Chapman, Jane, tr. Chapman, Jane, illus. 2003. 32p. (J). 12.95 (978-1-85430-806-1(8) , Simon & Schuster Children's Publishing) Simon & Schuster Children's Publishing.

Kay, Julia. Gulliver Snip & the Clipper Ship. 2008. 32p. (J). 16.95 (***978-0-8050-7992-0(0))*** Holt, Henry & Co.

Kay, Verla. Gold Fever. Schindler, S. D., illus. (Picture Puffin Ser.). (J). (gr. k-3). 2003. 32p. pap. 6.99 (978-0-14-250183-2(2) , Puffin); 1999. 1p. 15.99 (978-0-399-23027-1(0) , Putnam Juvenile) Penguin Group (USA) Inc.

—Gold Fever. 2003. (gr. k-3). lib. bdg. 15.30 (978-0-613-89796-9(X)) Tandem Library Bks.

—Homespun Sarah. Rand, Ted, illus. 2003. 32p. (J). (ps-3). 16.99 (978-0-399-23417-0(9) , Putnam Juvenile) Penguin Group (USA) Inc.

—Iron Horses. McCurdy, Michael, illus. 1999. 32p. (J). (ps-3). 16.99 (978-0-399-23119-3(6) , Putnam Juvenile) Penguin Group (USA) Inc.

—Tattered Sails. Andreasen, Dan, illus. 2001. 32p. (J). 15.99 (978-0-399-23345-6(8) , Putnam Juvenile) Penguin Group (USA) Inc.

Keckler, Ben. From Here to There. 2005. (Express Yourself Ser.). (Illus.). 48p. (J). lib. bdg. 16.95 (978-0-9769093-0-9(8)) Eagle Creek Pubns., LLC.

Keckler, Ben. Incredibly Lonely, That's Me. Davis, Dick, illus. 2007. (J). (gr. 2-7). lib. bdg. 17.95 (***978-0-9769093-2-3(4))*** Eagle Creek Pubns., LLC.

Keenan, Sheila. What Time Is It? a Book of Math Riddles. 1999. (gr. k-3). lib. bdg. 11.80 (978-0-613-22609-7(7)) Tandem Library Bks.

Keenan, Sheila & Burns, Marilyn. Lizzy's Dizzy Day. Snider, Jackie, illus. 2001. (Hello Reader! Math Ser.). (J). (gr. k-2). pap. 3.99 (978-0-439-05963-5(1) , Cartwheel Bks.) Scholastic, Inc.

—What's up with That Cup? Snider, Jackie, illus. 2001. (Hello Reader! Math Ser.). 32p. (J). (gr. k-2). pap. 3.99 (978-0-439-09954-7(4)) Scholastic, Inc.

Keep, Richard Cleminson, illus. Clatter Bash! A Day of the Dead Celebration. 2004. 32p. (J). (ps-3). 15.95 (978-1-56145-322-1(6)) Peachtree Pubs., Ltd.

Keffer, Lois. Fancy the Filly's Not Selfish or Silly. 1999. (J). 9.99 (978-1-57673-442-1(0)) Zondervan.

—Mercury Mouse Slows down in the House. 1999. (J). 9.99 (978-1-57673-437-7(4)) Zondervan.

—Wiggledy Worm Learns Not to Squirm. 1999. (J). 9.99 (978-1-57673-439-1(0)) Zondervan.

Keffer, Lois & Haidle, Helen. Ripples Raccoon Shares His Balloon. Spengler, Ken, illus. 1999. (Read-To-Me Puppet Buddies Ser.: Vol. 9). 24p. (J). (ps-1). 9.99 (978-1-57673-438-4(2) , Multnomah) WaterBrook Pr.

Keillor, Garrison. The Old Man Who Loved Cheese. braille ed. 2004. (Illus.). (J). (gr. k-3). spiral bd. (978-0-616-01687-9(5)) Canadian National Institute for the Blind/Institut National Canadien pour les Aveugles.

—The Old Man Who Loved Cheese. Wilsdorf, Anne, illus. 1998. (978-0-606-13674-7(6)) Tandem Library Bks.

Keiser, Frances. The Adventures of Pelican Pete: A Bird Is Born. Keiser, Hugh, illus. 1999. 32p. (J). (ps-3). 15.00 (978-0-9668845-0-0(7)) Sagaponack Bks.

—Preening for Flight: The Adventures of Pelican Pete. Keiser, Hugh, illus. 2001. Orig. Title: The Adventures of Pelican Pete: Preening for Flight. 32p. (J). 17.00 (978-0-9668845-1-7(5)) Sagaponack Bks.

Keiser, Frances R. Annie the River Otter: The Adventures of Pelican Pete. Keiser, Hugh M., illus. l.t. ed. 2006. 32p. (J). 17.00 (978-0-9668845-4-8(X)) Sagaponack Bks.

Keller, Holly. What I See. 2003. (Green Light Readers Level 1 Ser.). (Illus.). 24p. (J). 11.95 (978-0-15-204814-3(6)); pap. 3.95 (978-0-15-204854-9(5)) Harcourt Children's Bks. (Green Light Readers).

—What I See. 2000. (gr. k-3). lib. bdg. 11.80 (978-0-613-66389-2(6)) Tandem Library Bks.

Keller, Laurie S. Grandpa Gazillion's Number Yard. 2005. (Illus.). 32p. (J). (ps-ps). 16.95 (978-0-8050-6282-3(3) , Holt, Henry & Co. Bks. For Young Readers) Holt, Henry & Co.

Kelley, Ellen A. My Life As a Chicken. Slack, Michael H., illus. 2007. 40p. (J). (ps-2). 16.00 (978-0-15-205306-2(9)) Harcourt Trade Pubs.

Kelley, Maria Felicia. Buz Words: Discovering Words in Pairs. Kelley, Maria Felicia, illus. 2006. (Illus.). 32p. (J). 14.95 (978-0-9650918-1-7(3)) April Arts Press & Productions.

Kelley, Marty. The Rules. Kelley, Marty, illus. 2000. (Illus.). 32p. (J). (ps-4). 12.95 (978-1-55933-284-2(0)) Zino Pr. Children's Bks.

—Summer Stinks. 2001. (Illus.). 32p. (J). (ps-1). 12.95 (978-1-55933-291-0(3)) Zino Pr. Children's Bks.

Kelley, Marty, illus. Winter Woes. 2003. 32p. (J). 12.95 (978-1-55933-306-1(5)) Zino Pr. Children's Bks.

Kellogg, Steven. I Was Born about 10,000 Years Ago: A Tall Tale. 1998. (Illus.). 48p. (J). (ps-3). pap. 5.95 (978-0-688-16156-9(1) , Harper Trophy) HarperCollins Pubs.

—There Was an Old Woman Who Swallowed a Fly. 2003. (Illus.). (J). 16.00 (978-0-689-81703-8(7) , Simon & Schuster Children's Publishing) Simon & Schuster Children's Publishing.

Kelly, Ellen A. Buckamoo Girls. Curry, Tom, illus. 2006. 32p. (J). (ps-3). 15.95 (978-0-8109-5471-7(0) , Abrams Bks. for Young Readers) Abrams, Harry N. , Inc.

Kelly, Mij. One More Sheep. Ayto, Russell, illus. 2006. 30p. (J). 16.95 (978-1-56145-378-8(1) , Peachtree Junior) Peachtree Pubs., Ltd.

—Where's My Darling Daughter? McEwen, Katharine, illus. 2006. 28p. (J). 16.00 (978-1-56148-537-6(3)) Good Bks.

Kelly, Sharon L. C. M. Coco's Vineyard Vacation: Double Fun on Martha's Vineyard. Galbraith, Alison L., illus. 2005. 40p. (J). 16.95 (978-0-9766283-0-9(9)) Secret Garden Bookworks.

Kemble, Mai. The Moon & the Night Sweeper. Kemble, Mai, illus. 2007. 32p. (J). (ps-2). 15.95 (***978-1-60108-013-4(1))*** Red Cygnet Pr.

Kemp, Jane & Walters, Clare. My Favorite Toys! Williams, Sam, illus. 2006. 24p. (J). 9.95 (978-1-58925-793-1(6) , tiger tales) ME Media LLC.

Kenah, Katharine & Lithgow, John. A Den, a Tree, a Nest Is Best, Level 3: An Animal Adventure. 2005. (Lithgow Palooza Readers Ser.). (Illus.). 32p. (J). (gr. 1-2). pap. 3.95 (978-0-7696-4263-5(2)) School Specialty Publishing.

Kenney, Cindy. Love Your Neighbor. 2004. (Illus.). 22p. bds. 4.99 (978-0-310-70783-7(8)) Zonderkidz.

—The Stable That Bob Built. 2004. (Big Idea Books). (Illus.). 32p. 9.99 (978-0-310-70472-0(3)) Zonderkidz.

Kenrick, Angela. The Quilt That Wouldn't Be Built. Hunt, Devin, illus. 2001. (J). (978-1-57102-177-9(9) , Ideals Children's Bks.) Ideals Pubns.

Kido, Yukiko. Flip-a-Word. 2006. 32p. pap. 5.95 (978-1-59354-179-8(1)) Blue Apple Bks.

—Snake Cake. 2006. 32p. 12.95 (978-1-59354-176-7(7)) Blue Apple Bks.

Kido, Yukiko, illus. I'm Going to Read (Level 3): A Dozen Dozens. 2007. (I'm Going to Read Ser.). 32p. (J). pap. 3.95 (978-1-4027-4246-0(0)) Sterling Publishing Co., Inc.

Killion, Bette. Just Think. 2001. (Growing Tree Ser.). (Illus.). 24p. (J). (ps). 9.95 (978-0-694-01315-9(3) , Harper Festival) HarperCollins Pubs.

Kimmel, Eric A. The Erie Canal Pirates. Glass, Andrew, illus. 2002. 32p. (J). (gr. k-3). tchr. ed. 16.95 (978-0-8234-1657-8(7)) Holiday Hse., Inc.

Kimmelman, Leslie. Everybody Bonjours! McMenemy, Sarah, illus. 2008. (J). 16.99 (***978-0-375-84443-0(0));*** lib. bdg. 19.99 (***978-0-375-94443-7(5))*** Knopf, Alfred A. Inc.

—Happy 4th of July, Jenny Sweeney! Cote, Nancy, illus. 2003. 32p. (J). (ps-1). 16.95 (978-0-8075-3152-5(9)) Whitman, Albert & Co.

—How Do I Love You? McCue, Lisa, illus. 2005. 32p. (J). 14.99 (978-0-06-001200-7(5)); lib. bdg. 16.89 (978-0-06-001201-4(3)) HarperCollins Pubs.

Kindermans, Martine. You & Me. Quinton, Sasha, tr. from GER. Kindermans, Martine, illus. 2006. (Illus.). 32p. (J). (ps-3). 15.99 (978-0-399-24471-1(9) , Philomel) Penguin Group (USA) Inc.

Kinerk, Robert. Clorinda. Kellogg, Steven, illus. 2007. 40p. (J). (ps-3). pap. 6.99 (***978-1-4169-3964-1(4)*** , Aladdin) Simon & Schuster Children's Publishing.

—Clorinda Takes Flight. Kellogg, Steven, illus. 2007. 40p. (J). (ps-3). 16.99 (978-0-689-86864-1(2) , Simon & Schuster/Paula Wiseman Bks.) Simon & Schuster Children's Publishing.

—Slim & Miss Prim. Harris, Jim, illus. (J). pap. 7.95 (978-0-87358-819-5(3) , Rising Moon Bks. for Young Readers) Northland Publishing.

—Timothy Cox Will Not Change His Socks. Gammell, Stephen, illus. 2005. 32p. (J). 16.95 (978-0-689-87181-8(3) , Simon & Schuster Children's Publishing) Simon & Schuster Children's Publishing.

Kinerk, Robert & Kellogg, Steven. Clorinda. 2003. (Illus.). 40p. (J). (gr. k-3). 15.95 (978-0-689-86449-0(3) , Simon & Schuster/Paula Wiseman Bks.) Simon & Schuster Children's Publishing.

King, Dave, photos by. My Christmas Scratch & Sniff Book. 2004. (First Holiday Bks.). (Illus.). 12p. (J). (gr. k-3). bds. 7.95 (978-0-7534-5731-3(8) , Kingfisher) Houghton Mifflin Co. Trade & Reference Div.

Kingfisher Editors, creator. My Halloween Sound Book. 2004. (First Holiday Bks.). (Illus.). 12p. (J). (gr. k-3). bds. 7.95 (978-0-7534-5730-6(X) , Kingfisher) Houghton Mifflin Co. Trade & Reference Div.

Kingsbury, Karen. Let's Go on a Mommy Date. Andreasen, Dan, illus. 2008. 32p. (J). 15.99 (978-0-310-71214-5(9)) Zonderkidz.

—We Believe in Christmas. 2008. (J). (978-0-310-71212-1(2)) Zonderkidz.

Kirk, Daniel. Keisha Ann Can! Kirk, Daniel, illus. 2008. 32p. (J). (ps-k). 16.99 (***978-0-399-24179-6(5)*** , Putnam Juvenile) Penguin Group (USA) Inc.

Kirk, David, illus. Little Mouse, Biddle Mouse. 2002. (Biddle Bks.). 32p. (J). pap. 9.95 (978-0-439-28051-8(6) , Scholastic Pr.) Scholastic, Inc.

Kirk, David & Scholastic, Inc. Staff. Miss Spider's Sunny Patch Kids. Rees, Jenifer, ed. 2004. (Illus.). 40p. (J). pap. 14.95 (978-0-439-40870-7(9) , Scholastic Pr.) Scholastic, Inc.

Kirkham, Teresa. Tattle Tom. 2003. 27p. pap. 9.95 (978-1-4137-0141-8(8)) PublishAmerica, Inc.

Kittinger, Jo S. Feeding the Gulls. Lucas, Margeaux, tr. Lucas, Margeaux, illus. 2004. (Rookie Reader Ser.). 31p. (J). 19.50 (978-0-516-24407-5(8) , Children's Pr.) Scholastic Library Publishing.

—A Lunch with Punch. 2004. (Rookie Reader Espanol Ser.). (Illus.). 31p. (J). (gr. k-2). pap. 4.95 (978-0-516-27785-1(5) , Children's Pr.) Scholastic Library Publishing.

—A Lunch with Punch. Medoff, Jack, illus. 2003. (Rookie Reader - Level B Ser.). 32p. (J). 19.50 (978-0-516-22879-2(X) , Children's Pr.) Scholastic Library Publishing.

—Moving Day. Richard, Ilene, illus. 2003. (Rookie Reader Ser.). 24p. (J). 19.50 (978-0-516-22846-4(3) , Children's Pr.) Scholastic Library Publishing.

Kitzmiller, Brenda. Muddy Mud — an Easy to Read Beginning Reader Book. 2005. 24p. 7.85 (978-1-4116-2937-0(X)) Lulu.com.

Klein-Higger, Joni. Ten Tzedakah Pennies. Leff, Tova, illus. 2005. 30p. (J). 10.95 (978-1-929628-19-3(6)) Hachai Publishing.

Kleinhenz, Sydnie Meltzer. Pleased to Eat You. 2003. (Silly Millies Ser.: 3). (Illus.). 32p. lib. bdg. 17.90 (978-0-7613-2909-1(9) , Millbrook Pr.) Lerner Publishing Group.

—Work & Play. Reasor, Mick, illus. 2005. (Rookie Reader Skill Set Ser.). 23p. (J). (gr. k-2). pap. 4.95 (978-0-516-25282-7(8) , Children's Pr.) Scholastic Library Publishing.

Kleven, Elisa. Sun Bread. 2004. (gr. k-3). lib. bdg. 15.30 (978-0-613-83005-8(9)) Tandem Library Bks.

Klier, Kimberly. Firefly Friend. Garland, Michael, illus. 2004. (Rookie Reader Ser.). 32p. (J). 19.50 (978-0-516-25895-9(8) , Children's Pr.) Scholastic Library Publishing.

Klier, Kimberly Wagner. Firefly Friend. Garland, Michael, illus. 2005. (Rookie Reader Skill Set Ser.). 32p. (J). (gr. k-2). pap. 4.95 (978-0-516-26817-0(1) , Children's Pr.) Scholastic Library Publishing.

—Firefly Friend. Garland, Michael, illus. 2005. 32p. (J). (gr. 1-2). lib. bdg. 12.15 (978-0-606-33169-2(7)) Tandem Library Bks.

Klingel, Cynthia Fitterer & Ballard, Peg. Fun! The Sound of Short U. 1999. (Wonder Books Phonics: Vowels Ser.). (Illus.). 24p. (J). (ps-3). 21.36 (978-1-56766-725-7(2)) Child's World, Inc.

Klug, Eric. The Monster in My Closet. Klug, Eric, illus. 2007. (Illus.). 32p. (J). 15.95 (978-1-60108-007-3(7)) Red Cygnet Pr.

Kneen, Maggie. The Christmas Surprise. Kneen, Maggie, illus. 2006. (Illus.). 18p. (J). (gr. k-4). reprint ed. 16.00 (978-0-7567-9837-6(X)) DIANE Publishing Co.

—Halloween Kittens. Kneen, Maggie, illus. 2004. (Illus.). 20p. (J). 15.95 (978-0-8118-4228-0(2)) Chronicle Bks. LLC.

Knott, Anthony & Kneen, Maggie. An Angel Came to Nazareth. Kneen, Maggie, illus. 2005. (Illus.). 24p. (J). (ps-3). 15.95 (978-0-8118-4798-8(5)) Chronicle Bks. LLC.

Knowles, Kent. Lucius & the Storm. Knowles, Kent, illus. 2007. (Illus.). 32p. (J). 15.95 (978-1-60108-005-9(0)) Red Cygnet Pr.

Knudsen, Michelle. Autumn Is for Apples. Denise, Fernando, illus. 2001. 24p. (J). (ps-1). pap. 3.25 (978-0-375-81090-9(0) , Random Hse. Bks. for Young Readers) Random Hse. Children's Bks.

Knutson, Kimberley. Jungle Jamboree. 1998. (Accelerated Reader Bks.). (Illus.). 32p. (J). (ps-3). 15.95 (978-0-7614-5032-0(7) , Cavendish Children's Bks.) Cavendish, Marshall Corp.

Kochalka, James. Squirrelly Gray. 2007. (Picture Book Ser.). (Illus.). 40p. (J). (gr. k-2). 12.99 ***(978-0-375-83975-7(5));*** lib. bdg. 15.99 ***(978-0-375-93975-4(X))*** Random Hse. Children's Bks. (Random Hse. Bks. for Young Readers).

Koda-Callan, Elizabeth, illus. The Squiggly Wigglys. 2003. 24p. (J). (gr. k-3). 14.95 (978-0-7611-2821-2(2) , 12821) Workman Publishing Co., Inc.

Koller, Jackie French. One Monkey Too Many. Munsinger, Lynn, illus. 2003. 32p. (J). (ps-2). pap. 7.00 (978-0-15-204764-1(6) , Voyager Bks./Libros Viajeros) Harcourt Children's Bks.

—One Monkey Too Many. Munsinger, Lynn, illus. 1999. 28p. (J). (ps-2). lib. bdg. 14.15 (978-0-613-70500-4(9)) Tandem Library Bks.

—Seven Spunky Monkeys. Munsinger, Lynn M., illus. 2005. 32p. (J). (ps-ps). 16.00 (978-0-15-202519-9(7)) Harcourt Trade Pubs.

Komaiko, Leah. Earl's Too Cool for Me. Cornell, Laura, illus. 2004. 48p. (J). (ps-3). lib. bdg. 13.19 (978-0-606-30512-9(2)) Tandem Library Bks.

—Earl's Too Cool for Me. 2003. (gr. k-3). lib. bdg. 14.15 (978-0-613-65690-0(3)) Tandem Library Bks.

—Just My Dad & Me. Greene, Jeffrey, illus. 1999. (Trophy Picture Bk.). 32p. (J). (ps-2). pap. 5.95 (978-0-06-443562-8(8) , Harper Trophy) HarperCollins Pubs.

—Just My Dad & Me. 1999. (J). (978-0-606-16691-1(2)); lib. bdg. 14.10 (978-0-613-18259-1(6)) Tandem Library Bks.

Kono, Erin Eitter. Hula Lullaby. 2005. (Illus.). 32p. (J). (ps-1). 15.99 (978-0-316-73591-9(4)) Little Brown & Co.

Koontz, Dean. Robot Santa: The Further Adventures of Santa's Twin. Parks, Phil, illus. 2004. 72p. (J). 20.89 (978-0-06-050944-6(9)) HarperCollins Pubs.

—Santa's Twin. Parks, Phil, illus. 2004. 64p. pap. 12.95 (978-0-06-057223-5(X)) HarperCollins Pubs.

Koontz, Robin Michal. Why a Dog? By A. Cat. 2000. (Hello Reader! Ser.). (978-0-606-18892-0(4)) Tandem Library Bks.

Kramer, Jennifer E. Good Luck, Charlie. Moores, Jeff, illus. 2004. (Rookie Reader Ser.). 31p. (J). 19.50 (978-0-516-21722-2(4) , Children's Pr.) Scholastic Library Publishing.

—Good Luck Charlie. Moores, Jeff, illus. 2005. (Rookie Reader Skill Set Ser.). 32p. (J). (gr. k-2). pap. 4.95 (978-0-516-25826-3(5) , Children's Pr.) Scholastic Library Publishing.

Kranking, Kathy & Kranking, Kathleen W. The Ocean Is. . . Wu, Norbert, photos by. 2003. (Illus.). 32p. (J). (ps-2). 17.95 (978-0-8050-7097-2(4) , Holt, Henry & Co. Bks. For Young Readers) Holt, Henry & Co.

Kraus, Robert. Mouse in Love. Aruego, Jose & Dewey, Ariane, illus. 2000. 32p. (J). (ps 2). 16.99 (978 0 531 33297-9(7) , Orchard Bks.) Scholastic, Inc.

Krauss, Ruth. I Can Fly. Blair, Mary, illus. 2003. (Little Golden Bks.). (J). (gr. k-k). 24p. 2.99 (978-0-307-00146-7(6) , 312-12); 48p. 12.95 (978-0-307-10548-6(2)) Random Hse. Children's Bks. (Golden Bks.).

Krebs, Laurie. We're Sailing down the Nile: A Journey Through Egypt. Wilson, Anne, illus. 2007. 32p. (J). (ps-3). 16.99 ***(978-1-84686-040-9(7))*** Barefoot Bks., Inc.

Kreib. We're off to Find the Witch's House. Alley, R. W., illus. 2007. 32p. (J). (gr. k). pap. 5.99 (978-0-14-240854-4(9) , Puffin) Penguin Group (USA) Inc.

—We're off to Find the Witch's House. Alley, Robert W., illus. 2005. 32p. (J). (ps-ps). 14.99 (978-0-525-47003-8(4) , Dutton Juvenile) Penguin Group (USA) Inc.

Kreloff, Elliot. Harry Bear & Friends Count Fish. 2007. (Illus.). 16p. (ps-k). bds. 7.95 ***(978-1-59354-619-9(X))*** Handprint Bks.

Krensky, Stephen. Fraidy Cats. Lewin, Betsy, illus. 2004. 32p. (J). lib. bdg. 15.00 (978-1-59054-383-2(1)) Fitzgerald Bks.

—My Loose Tooth. Takahashi, Hideko, illus. 1999. (Step into Reading Ser.: Vol. 1). 32p. (J). (gr. k-3). pap. 3.99 (978-0-679-88847-5(0) , Random Hse. Bks. for Young Readers) Random Hse. Children's Bks.

—My Loose Tooth. 1999. (Step into Reading Ser.). (J). (978-0-606-16758-1(7)); lib. bdg. 11.80 (978-0-613-11897-2(9)) Tandem Library Bks.

Krensky, Stephen. Snack Attack. Curtis, Stacy, illus. 2008. (Ready-to-Reads Ser.). 32p. (J). pap. 3.99 ***(978-1-4169-0238-6(4));*** lib. bdg. 13.89 ***(978-1-4169-0239-3(2))*** Simon & Schuster Children's Publishing. (Aladdin).

Kret, Itzah C. The Man with the Sneezes. 2003. per. 16.99 (978-1-4134-2895-7(9)) Xlibris Corp.

Kristina Learns about Fishing. 2007. (J). ***(978-0-9792728-0-6(7))*** Tracepaper Bks. Inc.

Kroll, Virginia L. Boy, You're Amazing! Yoshikawa, Sachiko, illus. 2004. 32p. (J). (ps-2). 15.95 (978-0-8075-0868-8(3)) Whitman, Albert & Co.

—Everybody Has a Teddy. Allsopp, Sophie, illus. 2007. 24p. (J). 12.95 (978-1-4027-3580-6(4)) Sterling Publishing Co., Inc.

—Girl, You're Amazing! Potter, Melisande, illus. 2001. 32p. (J). (gr. k-4). 15.95 (978-0-8075-2930-0(3)) Whitman, Albert & Co.

—Motherlove. Washburn, Lucia, illus. 1998. 32p. (J). (ps-3). 16.95 (978-1-883220-81-5(5)) Dawn Pubns.

—On the Way to Kindergarten. Schlossberg, Elisabeth, illus. 2006. 32p. (J). (ps). 15.99 (978-0-399-24168-0(X) , Putnam Juvenile) Penguin Group (USA) Inc.

Kruckvich, Francis. The Blue Chequered Harlequin. 2004. (Illus.). (YA). pap. (978-0-9746226-2-0(1)) Scribolin.

Kruckvich, Francis, text. A Hero & a Great Man. 2003. (Illus.). 33p. (YA). pap. 4.95 (978-0-9746226-0-6(5)) Scribolin.

Krushner, Tony. Brundibar. 2002. 64p. (J). (978-0-7868-0905-9(1) , Di Capua, Michael) Scholastic, Inc.

Kubler, Annie. Dingle Dangle Scarecrow. 2003. (Illus.). 12p. (J). (ps). bds. 4.99 (978-0-85953-626-4(2)) Child's Play-International.

—Man's Work. 2000. (All in a Day Boardbooks Ser.). (Illus.). 14p. (J). (ps-k). bds. 3.99 (978-0-85953-587-8(8)) Child's Play-International.

—Ring Around the Rosie. 2000. (Illus.). 12p. (J). bds. 4.99 (978-0-85953-628-8(9)) Child's Play-International.

—Twinkle,Twinkle Little Star. 2002. (Illus.). 16p. (J). 19.99 (978-0-85953-125-2(2)) Child's Play-International.

Kubler, Annie, illus. Head, Shoulders, Knees & Toes ... 2003. 12p. (J). (ps). bds. 4.99 (978-0-85953-728-5(5)) Child's Play-International.

—Twinkle, Twinkle. 2002. 16p. (J). 6.99 (978-0-85953-941-8(5)) Child's Play-International.

Kupchella, Rick. Girls Can! Make it Happen. Brown, Marilyn, illus. 2004. 40p. (J). 16.95 (978-0-9726504-3-4(1)) Tristan Publishing, Inc.

—Tell Me What We Did Today. Hanson, Warren, illus. 32p. (J). 15.95 (978-0-9726504-0-3(7)) Tristan Publishing, Inc.

Kurtz, Jane. Rain Romp: Stomping Away a Grouchy Day. Wolcott, Dyanna, illus. 2002. 32p. (J). (ps up). 16.99 (978-0-06-029805-0(7)) HarperCollins Pubs.

Kurtz, Kevin. A Day in the Salt Marsh. 2007. (Illus.). 32p. (J). (ps-3). 15.95 (978-0-9768823-5-0(3)) Sylvan Dell Pubng.

Kuskin, Karla. A Boy Had a Mother Who Bought Him Hat. 2008. (J). ***(978-0-06-075330-6(7)); (978-0-06-075331-3(5))*** HarperCollins Pubs. (Geringer, Laura Book).

—City Dog. Kuskin, Karla, illus. 1998. (Illus.). 32p. (J). (gr. k-3). 6.95 (978-0-395-90016-1(6) , Clarion Bks.) Houghton Mifflin Co. Trade & Reference Div.

—Green as a Bean. Iwai, Melissa, illus. 2007. 32p. (J). lib. bdg. 17.89 (978-0-06-075334-4(X)); 16.99 (978-0-06-075332-0(3)) HarperCollins Pubs. (Geringer, Laura Book).

—So, What's It Like to Be a Cat? Lewin, Betsy, illus. (J). 2008. 40p. 6.99 ***(978-0-689-85930-4(9) ,*** Aladdin); 2005. 32p. 15.95 (978-0-689-84733-2(5) , Atheneum) Simon & Schuster Children's Publishing.

Kuskin, Karla. The Upstairs Cat. Fine, Howard, illus. 2003. 32p. (J). (gr. k-3). 5.95 (978-0-618-31676-2(0) , Clarion Bks.) Houghton Mifflin Co. Trade & Reference Div.

Kutner, Merrily. The Zombie Nite Cafe. Long, Ethan, illus. 2007. 32p. (J). (ps-3). 16.95 (978-0-8234-1963-0(0)) Holiday Hse., Inc.

Lach, William. Baby Loves. Cassatt, Mary, illus. 2002. (J). (978-1-58839-052-3(7)) Metropolitan Museum of Art, The.

Laden, Nina. Grow Up. 2003. (Illus.). 26p. (J). bds. 6.95 (978-0-8118-3761-3(0)) Chronicle Bks. LLC.

Ladybird Books Staff. Downy Duckling. (Rhyming Stories Ser.: No. 401-5). (Illus.). 52p. (J). (ps). 3.50 (978-0-7214-0210-9(0) , Dutton Juvenile) Penguin Group (USA) Inc.

Lagonegro, Melissa. Friends for a Princess. Harchy, Atelier Philippe, illus. 2004. (Disney Princess Ser.). 32p. (J). (ps-1). pap. 3.99 (978-0-7364-2208-6(0) , RH/Disney) Random Hse. Children's Bks.

—Friends for a Princess. 2004. (Disney Princess Ser.). (ps-2). lib. bdg. 11.80 (978-0-613-73713-5(X)) Tandem Library Bks.

—Happy Halloween! 2003. (Teenie Halloweenies Ser.). (Illus.). 24p. (J). (gr. k-3). 3.25 (978-0-375-82532-3(0) , Golden Bks.) Random Hse. Children's Bks.

—Happy Halloween! 2003. (gr. k-3). lib. bdg. 10.95 (978-0-613-71930-8(1)) Tandem Library Bks.

—Just Keep Swimming. Harchy, Atelier Philippe, illus. 2005. (Step into Reading Ser.). 32p. (ps-2). pap. 3.99 (978-0-7364-2319-9(2) , RH/Disney) Random Hse. Children's Bks.

Lakeshore Learning Materials Staff, contrib. by. The Gingerbread Boy Packet. 2000. (J). pap. 19.95 (978-1-929255-32-0(2)) Lakeshore Learning Materials.

Lakin, Patricia. Rainy Day! Nash, Scott, illus. 2007. 40p. (J). (ps-1). 16.99 (978-0-8037-3092-2(6) , Dial) Penguin Group (USA) Inc.

Lamar, Gail Renfroe. Moon of the Wishing Night. Mask, Cynthia, illus. 2004. 32p. (J). 17.95 (978-1-57966-047-5(9) , River City Kids) River City Publishing.

Lambert, Patricia. The Blue Ribbon Chicken. 2005. 36p. (J). pap. 14.93 (978-1-4116-6163-9(X)) Lulu.com.

LaMear, Arline. Lewis & Clark, the Astoria Cats. Goza, Benjamin, illus. 2002. 32p. (J). (gr. 3-7). pap. 9.95 (978-0-9720394-0-6(6)) Lucky Cat Publishing.

Lang, Aubrey. Baby Sea Turtle. Lynch, Wayne, photos by. 2007. (Nature Babies Ser.). (Illus.). 32p. (J). (gr. k-3). ***(978-1-55041-728-9(2))*** Fitzhenry & Whiteside, Ltd.

Langcaon, Jeff, illus. My Grandpa's Battleship Missouri Tour. 2007. (J). 14.95 ***(978-1-56647-831-1(6))*** Mutual Publishing LLC.

Langham, Tony. Creepy Crawly Calypso. Harter, Debbie, illus. 2004. 32p. (J). 16.99 incl. audio compact disk (978-1-84148-699-4(X)) Barefoot Bks., Inc.

Langham, Tony & Harter, Debbie. Creepy Crawly Calypso. 2006. 32p. pap. 9.99 incl. cd-rom (978-1-902283-46-3(5)) Barefoot Bks., Inc.

Lappin, Amber. My, You Have Your Hands Full! Galey, Chuck, illus. 2000. 16p. (J). pap. 5.95 (978-1-891846-21-2(3)) Business Word, The.

Lawler, Janet. A Father's Song. Corvino, Lucy, illus. 2006. 24p. (J). 12.95 (978-1-4027-2501-2(9)) Sterling Publishing Co., Inc.

—If Kisses Were Colors. Jay, Alison, illus. 2003. 32p. (J). (ps). 15.99 (978-0-8037-2617-8(1) , Dial) Penguin Group (USA) Inc.

Lawless, Mary Ann. The Proud Christmas Tree. McCool, Arlene, illus. 2006. (J). 12.95 ***(978-0-9772795-0-0(2))*** Tuesday's Child.

Lawrence, John. This Little Chick. Lawrence, John, illus. (Illus.). (gr. k-ps). 2006. 24p. (YA). bds. 6.99 (978-0-7636-2882-6(4)); 2002. 32p. (J). 15.99 (978-0-7636-1716-5(4)) Candlewick Pr.

Lawson, Carol, et al, illus. Once upon a Poem: Favorite Poems That Tell Stories. 2004. 128p. (J). (gr. 3 up). pap. 18.95 (978-0-439-65108-0(5) , Chicken Hse., The) Scholastic, Inc.

Lazo, Caroline. Someday When My Cat Can Talk. Brooker, Kyrsten, illus. 2008. 32p. (J). (ps-3). lib. bdg. 19.99 ***(978-0-375-93754-5(4) ,*** Schwartz & Wade Bks.) Random Hse. Children's Bks.

Lazo, Caroline Evensen. Someday When My Cat Can Talk. Brooker, Kyrsten, illus. 2008. 32p. (J). ***(978-0-375-83754-8(X) ,*** Schwartz & Wade Bks.) Random Hse. Children's Bks.

LeapFrog Staff, compiled by. Once upon a Time. 2001. (J). (ps-1). spiral bd. 14.99 (978-1-58605-081-8(8)) LeapFrog Enterprises, Inc.

Lee, Betsy B. 10,000 White Horses 10,000 Caballos Blancos. Cruz-Torres, Natty, tr. Varnedoe, Catharine E., illus. l.t. ed. 2002. (SPA & ENG.). 24p. (J). pap. 5.95 (978-0-9720267-2-7(X)) Learning Abilities Bks.

Leedy, Loreen, illus. Missing Math. 2008. (J). ***(978-0-7614-5385-7(7))*** Cavendish, Marshall Corp.

Leman, Nora. The Alpha Building Crew. Hartmann, April, illus. 2005. (J). (978-1-58987-110-6(3)) Kindermusik International.

Lendroth, Susan. Ocean Wide, Ocean Deep. Allen, Raul, illus. 2007. (J). ***(978-1-58246-232-5(1) ,*** Tricycle Pr.) Ten Speed Pr.

Lendroth, Susan. Why Explore? Moreiro, Enrique S., illus. 2005. 32p. (J). (ps-ps). 15.95 (978-1-58246-150-2(3) , Tricycle Pr.) Ten Speed Pr.

Lennard, Kate & Flynn, Dermot. Smile! 2007. (Illus.). 16p. (J). (ps-2). 11.95 ***(978-0-8027-9709-4(1))*** Walker & Co.

Leon, Loni. Can you Imagine...., 1. Leon, Loni & Huston, Kyle, illus. 2006. 49p. (J). 21.95 (978-0-9728556-0-0(2)) Sullivan, Kelley Enterprises.

Leonard, Marcia. Best Friends. Handelman, Dorothy, photos by. 1999. (Real Kids Readers Ser.). (Illus.). 32p. (ps-1). lib. bdg. 18.90 (978-0-7613-2064-7(4) , Millbrook Pr.) Lerner Publishing Group.

—Best Friends. (J). (978-0-606-19144-9(5)); 1999. lib. bdg. 13.00 (978-0-613-18155-6(7)) Tandem Library Bks.

—Dress-Up. Handelman, Dorothy, photos by. 1999. (Real Kids Readers Ser.). (Illus.). 32p. (J). (ps-1). lib. bdg. 18.90 (978-0-7613-2053-1(9)); pap. 4.99 (978-0-7613-2078-4(4)) Lerner Publishing Group. (Millbrook Pr.).

—Dress-Up. 1999. (J). 11.79 (978-0-606-19154-8(2)) Tandem Library Bks.

—Let's Go Baby-O! 2000. (Hanna Bks.). (Illus.). 24p. (J). (ps-k). 7.95 (978-0-694-01367-8(6) , Harper Festival) HarperCollins Pubs.

Leonard Marcia. Me gusta el desorden (I Like Mess) 2007. (Lecturas para niños de verdad - Nivel 1 (Real Kids Readers - Level 1) Ser.). (J). pap. 5.95 ***(978-0-8225-7800-0(X) ,*** Ediciones Lerner) Lerner Publishing Group.

—Mi día de campamento (My Camp-Out) 2007. (Lecturas para niños de verdad - Nivel 1 (Real Kids Readers - Level 1) Ser.). (J). pap. 5.95 ***(978-0-8225-7798-0(4) ,*** Ediciones Lerner) Lerner Publishing Group.

Leonard, Marcia. My Camp-Out. Handelman, Dorothy, photos by. 1999. (Real Kids Readers Ser.). (Illus.). 32p. (ps-1). lib. bdg. 18.90 (978-0-7613-2052-4(0)); (J). pap. 4.99 (978-0-7613-2077-7(6)) Lerner Publishing Group. (Millbrook Pr.).

—My Camp-Out. 1999. (J). (978-0-606-19165-4(8)); lib. bdg. 13.00 (978-0-613-16774-1(0)) Tandem Library Bks.

—No New Pants! Handelman, Dorothy, photos by. 1999. (Real Kids Readers Ser.). (Illus.). 32p. (ps-1). lib. bdg. 18.90 (978-0-7613-2063-0(6)); (J). pap. 4.99 (978-0-7613-2088-3(1)) Lerner Publishing Group. (Millbrook Pr.).

—No New Pants! 1999. (J). (978-0-606-19166-1(6)); lib. bdg. 11.80 (978-0-613-18161-7(1)) Tandem Library Bks.

—The Pet Vet. Handelman, Dorothy, photos by. 1999. (Real Kids Readers Ser.). (Illus.). 32p. (gr. k-1). (J). pap. 4.99 (978-0-7613-2075-3(X)); lib. bdg. 18.90 (978-0-7613-2050-0(4)) Lerner Publishing Group. (Millbrook Pr.).

—The Pet Vet. 1999. (J). (978-0-606-19168-5(2)) Tandem Library Bks.

—Pet Vet. 1999. (ps-2). lib. bdg. 13.00 (978-0-613-16795-6(3)) Tandem Library Bks.

Leonard Marcia. Saltar, brincar, correr (Hop, Skip, Run) 2007. (Lecturas para niños de verdad - Nivel 1 (Real Kids Readers - Level 1) Ser.). (J). pap. 5.95 ***(978-0-8225-7799-7(2) ,*** Ediciones Lerner) Lerner Publishing Group.

Leonard, Marcia. Splish, Splash! Handelman, Dorothy, photos by. 2000. (Hanna Bks.). (Illus.). 24p. (J). (ps up). 7.95 (978-0-694-01365-4(X)) HarperCollins Pubs.

—The Tin Can Man. Handelman, Dorothy, photos by. 1998. (Real Kids Readers Ser.: 1). (Illus.). 32p. (J). (gr. k-1). pap. 4.99 (978-0-7613-2037-1(7) , Millbrook Pr.) Lerner Publishing Group.

—Trae la Pelota, Tito. Handelman, Dorothy, photos by. 2005. (Lecturas para Niños de Verdad (Real Kids Readers) Ser.). (Illus.). 32p. (J). (ps-1). (SPA.). pap. 4.99 (978-0-8225-3292-7(1) , Ediciones Lerner); (ENG & SPA., pap. 4.99 (978-0-8225-3293-4(X)) Lerner Publishing Group.

Leonard, Marcia & Handelman, Dorothy. The Pet Vet. Handelman, Dorothy, illus. Leonard, Marcia, photos by. 2005. (ENG & SPA., Illus.). 32p. (J). (ps-1). pap. 4.99 (978-0-8225-3299-6(9)) Lerner Publishing Group.

LeSieg, Theo. The Eye Book. Mathieu, Joe, illus. 1999. (Bright & Early Bks.). 36p. (J). (gr. k-1). lib. bdg. 11.99 (978-0-375-90033-4(0) , Random Hse. Bks. for Young Readers) Random Hse. Children's Bks.

LeSieg, Theo., ed. & illus. The Eye Book. LeSieg, Theo., illus. Mathieu, Joe, illus. (J). (gr. k-ps). 2001. 24p. bds. 4.99 (978-0-375-81240-8(7)); 1999. 36p. 8.99 (978-0-375-80033-7(6)) Random Hse. Children's Bks. (Random Hse. Bks. for Young Readers).

S

Less, Emma. Snail's Journey Through the Jungle. Moon, Jo, illus. 2006. (Snail#39;s Adventures Ser.). 10p. (J). bds. 15.95 (978-0-7696-4608-4(5) , Brighter Child) School Specialty Publishing.

—Snail's Race Around the World. Moon, Jo, illus. 2006. (Snail#39;s Adventures Ser.). 10p. (J). bds. 15.95 (978-0-7696-4607-7(7) , Brighter Child) School Specialty Publishing.

Lessac, Frane. Island Counting 1 2 3. Lessac, Frane, illus. 2007. (Illus.). 24p. (J). (gr. k-ps). bds. 6.99 ***(978-0-7636-3518-3(9))*** Candlewick Pr.

Lessac, Frané. Island Counting 123. 2005. (Illus.). 24p. (J). (gr. k-ps). 12.99 (978-0-7636-1960-2(4)) Candlewick Pr.

Lester, Alison. Magic Beach. 2006. (Illus.). 32p. (J). (ps-k). pap. 7.95 (978-1-74114-488-8(4)) Allen & Unwin AUS. *Dist:* Independent Pubs. Group.

Lesynski, Loris. Rocksy. Lesynski, Loris, illus. 2002. (Illus.). 32p. (J). (ps-3). pap. 5.95 (978-1-55037-750-7(7)); lib. bdg. 19.95 (978-1-55037-751-4(5)) Annick Pr., Ltd. CAN. *Dist:* Firefly Bks., Ltd.

Let's Be Friends. 2005. (Illus.). 26p. (J). (ps-k). bds. 7.95 (978-0-8249-6587-7(6)) Ideals Pubns.

Let's Learn All We Can! (Illus.). 24p. (J). 5.95 (978-0-8249-5449-9(1)) Ideals Pubns.

Let's Share. 2003. (Illus.). 24p. (J). bds. 7.95 (978-0-8249-5451-2(3)) Ideals Pubns.

Leuck, Laura. Goodnight Baby Monster. Date not set. 32p. (J). (ps-1). pap. 4.99 (978-0-06-443723-3(X)) HarperCollins Pubs.

—Goodnight, Baby Monster. 2002. (Illus.). 32p. (J). (ps-1). 14.99 (978-0-06-029151-8(6)); 16.89 (978-0-06-029152-5(4)) HarperCollins Pubs.

—I Love My Pirate Papa. Stone, Kyle M., illus. 2007. 32p. (J). (ps-2). 16.00 (978-0-15-205664-3(5)) Harcourt Trade Pubs.

—Jeepers Creepers: A Monstrous ABC. Parkins, David, illus. 2003. 32p. (J). 15.95 (978-0-8118-3509-1(X) , 53408263) Chronicle Bks. LLC.

—My Creature Teacher. Nash, Scott, illus. 2004. 32p. (J). (ps-1). 15.99 (978-0-06-029694-0(1)) HarperCollins Pubs.

—My Monster Mama Loves Me So. Buehner, Mark, illus. 24p. (J). (ps-3). 2002. pap. 6.99 (978-0-06-008860-6(5) , Harper Trophy); 1999. 15.89 (978-0-688-16867-4(1)); 1999. 15.99 (978 0 688 16866 7(3)) HarperCollins Pubs.

—My Monster Mama Loves Me So. 2002. (gr. k-3). lib. bdg. 14.15 (978-0-613-53844-2(7)) Tandem Library Bks.

—One Witch. Schindler, S. D., illus. 32p. (J). 2005. pap. 6.95 (978-0-8027-7729-4(5)); 2004. 15.95 (978-0-8027-8860-3(2)) Walker & Co.

—Santa Claws: A Scary Christmas to All. Grimly, Gris, illus. 2006. 32p. (J). 16.95 (978-0-8118-4992-0(9)) Chronicle Bks. LLC.

Levin, Bridget. Rules of the Wild: An Unruly Book of Manners. Shepherd, Amanda, illus. 2004. 36p. (J). 14.95 (978-0-8118-4226-6(6)) Chronicle Bks. LLC.

Levine, Abby. Daddies Give You Horsey Rides. Bendall-Brunello, John, illus. 2004. 32p. (J). (ps-k). 16.95 (978-0-8075-1429-0(2)) Whitman, Albert & Co.

—This Is the Dreidel. Billin-Frye, Paige, tr. Billin-Frye, Paige, illus. 2003. 24p. (J). (ps-1). 15.95 (978-0-8075-7884-1(3)) Whitman, Albert & Co.

—This Is the Matzah. Billin-Frye, Paige, illus. 2005. 32p. (J). (ps-2). 15.95 (978-0-8075-7885-8(1)) Whitman, Albert & Co.

—This Is the Turkey. Billin-Frye, Paige, illus. 2000. 32p. (J). (ps-1). pap. 6.95 (978-0-8075-7889-6(4)) Whitman, Albert & Co.

Levine, Martha Peaslee. Stop That Nose! White, Lee, illus. 2006. (J). (978-0-7614-5222-5(2)); 32p. 14.95 (978-0-7614-5280-5(X)) Cavendish, Marshall Corp.

Lewis, Anne Margaret. Gitchi Gumee. Chaney Fritz, Kathleen, illus. 2006. (J). 18.95 (978-0-9749145-9-6(2)) Mackinac Island Pr., Inc.

Lewis, Anthony, illus. So Much to Love. 1999. (Leap Frog Lift-a-Flap Ser.). (J). (978-0-7853-3368-5(1)) Publications International, Ltd.

Lewis, J. Patrick. The Snowflake Sisters. Desimini, Lisa, illus. 2003. 32p. (J). 16.95 (978-0-689-85029-5(8) , Atheneum/Anne Schwartz Bks.) Simon & Schuster Children's Publishing.

Lewis, Kevin. Chugga Chugga Choo Choo. Kirk, Daniel, illus. 1999. 32p. (ps-k). 12.99 (978-0-7868-0429-0(7)) Disney Pr.

—Chugga Chugga Choo-Choo Big Book. Kirk, Daniel, illus. 2001. 32p. (ps-k). 6.99 (978-0-7868-0760-4(1)) Hyperion Bks. for Children.

—Dinosaur, Dinosaur. Kirk, Daniel, illus. 2006. (J). (978-0-439-78228-9(7)); 32p. pap. 15.99 (978-0-439-60371-3(4)) Scholastic, Inc. (Orchard Bks.).

—Lot at the End of My Block. Cartwright, Reg, illus. 2001. 32p. (ps-1). 15.49 (978-0-7868-2512-7(X)) Hyperion Bks. for Children.

—My Truck Is Stuck! Kirk, Daniel, illus. (ps-ps). 2006. 30p. 6.99 (978-0-7868-3739-7(X)); 2002. 40p. 14.99 (978-0-7868-0534-1(X)) Hyperion Bks. for Children.

—The Runaway Pumpkin. Schindler, S. D., illus. 2003. 32p. (J). (gr. k-2). pap. 15.95 (978-0-439-43974-9(4) , Orchard Bks.) Scholastic, Inc.

—Tugga Tugga Tug Boat. Kirk, Daniel, illus. 2006. 32p. (ps-k). 15.99 (978-0-7868-5615-2(7)) Hyperion Pr.

Lewis, Kevin & Reeves, Howard. There Was an Old Witch Paperback. Catrow, David, illus. abr. ed. 2000. 32p. (ps-3). pap. 5.99 (978-0-7868-1492-3(6)) Disney Pr.

Lewison, Wendy Cheyette. Baby Faces. Moroney, Christopher, illus. 2002. 14p. (J). (gr. k). bds. 6.99 (978-0-375-81538-6(4) , Random Hse. Bks. for Young Readers) Random Hse. Children's Bks.

—Big Snowball. 2000. (All Aboard Reading Ser.). 10.79 (978-0-606-20402-6(4)); (J). (978-0-606-20266-4(8)); lib. bdg. 11.80 (978-0-613-30995-0(2)) Tandem Library Bks.

—Raindrop, Plop! Paparone, Pamela, tr. Paparone, Pamela, illus. 2004. 32p. (J). (ps-3). 15.99 (978-0-670-03620-2(X) , Viking Juvenile) Penguin Group (USA) Inc.

—Two Is for Twins. Nakata, Hiroe, illus. 2006. 40p. (J). (ps). 16.99 (978-0-670-06128-0(X) , Viking Juvenile) Penguin Group (USA) Inc.

Lewison, Wendy Cheyette & Basso, Bill. Mud. 2001. (Hello Reader! Ser.). (Illus.). (J). (978-0-439-17932-4(7)) Scholastic, Inc.

Lewison, Wendy Cheyette & Greigo, Tony. So Many Boots. 2000. (My First Hello Reader! Ser.). (J). 3.99 (978-0-439-09865-6(3)) Scholastic, Inc.

Liberto, Lorenzo. Matt the Rat & His Magic Cloud / Raton Mateo y Su Nube Magica: A Day at School / un Dia de Escuela. Gomez, Rocio, ed. Torres, Irving, illus. 2003. (Matt the Rat Ser. / La Serie de Raton Mateo). (ENG & SPA.). 32p. (J). lib. bdg. 20.00 (978-0-9743668-0-7(3)) Harvest Sun Pr., LLC.

Liberts, Jennifer. Piglet Feels Small. Yee, Josie, illus. 2002. (Early Step into Reading Ser.). 32p. (J). (ps-1). pap. 3.99 (978-0-7364-1226-1(3) , RH/Disney) Random Hse. Children's Bks.

Lies, Brian. Bats at the Beach. 2006. (Illus.). 32p. (J). (gr. k-3). 16.00 (978-0-618-55744-8(X)) Houghton Mifflin Co.

Lieurance, Suzanne. Pennies. Payne, Tom, illus. (Rookie Reader Skill Set Ser.). (J). 2003. 32p. (gr. k-2). pap. 4.95 (978-0-516-27818-6(5)); 2002. 31p. (gr. 1-2). 19.50 (978-0-516-22286-8(4)) Scholastic Library Publishing. (Children's Pr.).

—Shoelaces. Girouard, Patrick, illus. 2000. (Rookie Reader Skill Set Ser.). 32p. (J). (gr. k-2). pap. 4.95 (978-0-516-26546-9(6)); (gr. 1-2). 19.50 (978-0-516-21613-3(9)) Scholastic Library Publishing. (Children's Pr.).

Lillegard, Dee. Balloons, Balloons, Balloons. Pons, Bernadette, illus. 2007. 32p. (J). (ps-1). 16.99 (978-0-525-45940-8(5) , Dutton Juvenile) Penguin Group (USA) Inc.

Lillegard, Dee. Who Will Sing a Lullaby? Yaccarino, Dan, illus. 2007. 32p. (J). (ps-1). 15.99 ***(978-0-375-81573-7(2));*** lib. bdg. 18.99 ***(978-0-375-91573-4(7))*** Random Hse. Children's Bks. (Knopf Bks. for Young Readers).

Lindbergh, Reeve. My Hippie Grandmother. Carter, Abby, illus. 2003. 24p. (J). (ps). 15.99 (978-0-7636-0671-8(5)) Candlewick Pr.

—My Little Grandmother Often Forgets. Brown, Kathryn, illus. 2007. (J). (ps-1). 32p. 16.99 (978-0-7636-1989-3(2)); ***(978-1-4287-3962-8(9))*** Candlewick Pr.

—Nobody Owns the Sky. Paparone, Pamela, illus. 2004. 32p. (J). (VIE, CHI, BEN, GUJ & ENG.). (978-1-85269-342-8(8)); (VIE, CHI, BEN, GUJ & ENG.). (978-1-85269-343-5(6)); (VIE, CHI, BEN, GUJ & ENG.). (978-1-85269-344-2(4)); (CHI, VIE, BEN, GUJ & ENG.). (978-1-85269-345-9(2)); (VIE, CHI, BEN, GUJ & ENG.). (978-1-85269-347-3(9)) Mantra Publishing, Ltd.

—North Country Spring. Sivertson, Liz, illus. 2007. 32p. (J). (gr. k-3). 6.95 ***(978-0-618-80906-6(6))*** Houghton Mifflin Co. Trade & Reference Div.

Lindbergh, Reeve. Our Nest. McElmurry, Jill, illus. 2004. 32p. (J). (ps-1). 15.99 (978-0-7636-1286-3(3)) Candlewick Pr.

Lingard, Joan. The Same Only Different. Whelan, Olwyn, illus. 2001. 32p. (J). (ps-1). pap. (978-1-871512-64-9(6)) Glowworm Bks., Ltd.

Lionni, Leo. A Color of His Own. Lionni, Leo, illus. 2002. (Illus.). (J). 14.79 (978-0-7587-5604-6(6)) Book Wholesalers, Inc.

—A Color of His Own. Boughton, Simon, ed. Lionni, Leo, illus. 2000. (Illus.). 30p. (J). (gr. k-ps). bds. 6.99 (978-0-375-81091-6(9) , Knopf Bks. for Young Readers) Random Hse. Children's Bks.

Listening with Zachary. (J). pap. 13.75 (978-0-8136-4655-8(3)) Modern Curriculum Pr.

Lithgow, John. The Carnival of the Animals. Kulikov, Boris, illus. 2004. 40p. (J). (ps-3). 17.95 (978-0-689-86721-7(2)) Simon & Schuster Children's Publishing.

—Carnival of the Animals. Kulikov, Boris, illus. 2007. 40p. (J). (gr. k-5). pap. 7.99 ***(978-0-689-87343-0(3)*** , Aladdin) Simon & Schuster Children's Publishing.

—I'm a Manatee. Hoyt, Ard, illus. 2003. 32p. (J). 17.95 incl. audio compact disk (978-0-689-85427-9(7)) Simon & Schuster Children's Publishing.

—I'm a Manatee. Hoyt, Ard, illus. 2007. 32p. (J). 9.99 (978-0-689-85452-1(8) , Aladdin) Simon & Schuster Children's Publishing.

—Mahalia Mouse Goes to College. Oleynikov, Igor, illus. 2007. 40p. (J). 17.99 (978-1-4169-2715-0(8) , Simon & Schuster Children's Publishing) Simon & Schuster Children's Publishing.

—Marsupial Sue. Davis, Jack E., illus. 2001. 40p. (J). (ps-3). 17.95 incl. audio compact disk (978-0-689-84394-5(1)) Simon & Schuster Children's Publishing.

—Micawber. Payne, C. F., illus. 2002. 44p. (J). (gr. k-3). 17.95 incl. audio compact disk (978-0-689-83341-0(5)) Simon & Schuster Children's Publishing.

—The Remarkable Farkle McBride: 52 Unexpected Ways to Make a Birthday, Holiday, or Any Day a Celebration. Payne, C. F., illus. 2000. 40p. (J). (ps-3). 16.00 (978-0-689-83340-3(7)) Simon & Schuster Children's Publishing.

Lithgow, John & Davis, Jack E. Marsupial Sue. 2004. (Illus.). 40p. (J). reprint ed. pap. 6.99 (978-0-689-87410-9(3) , Aladdin) Simon & Schuster Children's Publishing.

Little, Jean. I Know an Old Laddie. ed. 2004. (Illus.). (J). (gr. k-3). spiral bd. (978-0-616-01703-6(0)) Canadian National Institute for the Blind/Institut National Canadien pour les Aveugles.

Little Softy, 4 bks., Set. alt. ed. 2002. (J). (978-1-931312-86-8(9)) SoftPlay, Inc.

Little Softy Cow. 2002. (J). (978-1-931312-90-5(7)) SoftPlay, Inc.

Little Softy Pig. 2002. (J). (978-1-931312-91-2(5)) SoftPlay, Inc.

Little Softy Pony. 2002. (J). (978-1-931312-92-9(3)) SoftPlay, Inc.

Little Softy Sheep. 2002. (J). (978-1-931312-93-6(1)) SoftPlay, Inc.

Livermore, Edward. Phebe the Blackberry Girl. 2004. reprint ed. pap. 15.95 (978-1-4191-4126-3(0)); pap. 1.99 (978-1-4192-4126-0(5)) Kessinger Publishing, LLC.

Livingston, Irene. Finklehopper Frog. Lies, Brian, illus. 2004. 30p. (J). (ps-2). 14.95 (978-1-58246-075-8(2) , Tricycle Pr.) Ten Speed Pr.

—Finklehopper Frog Cheers. Lies, Brian, illus. 2005. 32p. (J). 14.95 (978-1-58246-138-0(4) , Tricycle Pr.) Ten Speed Pr.

Ljungkvist, Laura. Follow the Line Through the House. 2007. (Illus.). 32p. (J). (gr. k-3). 16.99 (978-0-670-06225-6(1) , Viking Juvenile) Penguin Group (USA) Inc.

Lloyd-Jones, Sally. Old MacNoah Had an Ark. 2008. (HarperBlessings Ser.). (Illus.). 32p. (J). 17.89 (978-0-06-055718-8(4)) HarperCollins Pubs.

—Old MacNoah Had an Ark. Newton, Jill, illus. 2008. (HarperBlessings Ser.). 32p. (J). 16.99 (978-0-06-055717-1(6)) HarperCollins Pubs.

—Time to Say Goodnight. Chapman, Jane, illus. 2006. 32p. (J). 15.99 (978-0-06-054328-0(0)); lib. bdg. 16.89 (978-0-06-054329-7(9)) HarperCollins Pubs.

Lodge, Alison. Clever Chameleon. Lodge, Alison, illus. 2005. (Illus.). 24p. (J). 15.99 (978-1-84148-347-4(8)) Barefoot Bks., Inc.

Loehr, Patrick, illus. Mucumber McGee & the Lunch Lady's Liver. 2008. (J). ***(978-0-06-082330-6(5));*** lib. bdg. ***(978-0-06-082331-3(3))*** HarperCollins Pubs.

London, Jonathan. The Gruffalo's Child. Moore, Margie, illus. 2007. 32p. (J). pap. 5.99 (978-0-14-240754-7(2) , Puffin) Penguin Group (USA) Inc.

—Park Beat: Rhymin' Through the Seasons. Hubbard, Woodleigh Marx, illus. 2001. 32p. (J). (ps-3). 15.95 (978-0-688-13994-0(9)) HarperCollins Pubs.

—What Do You Love? Schmidt, Karen Lee, illus. 2004. 30p. (J). bds. 6.95 (978-0-15-205054-2(X) , Red Wagon Bks.) Harcourt Children's Bks.

Long, D. J. I Wish I Was the Baby. Johnson, Gary, illus. 2002. 32p. (J). 5.95 (978-0-8249-5441-3(6)) Ideals Pubns.

Looking for Lewis. 1999. (Books to Go Ser.). (J). pap. (978-0-8136-7879-5(X)) Modern Curriculum Pr.

Loomis, Christine. Astro Bunnies. Loomis, Christine & Eitan, Ora, illus. 2001. 1p. (J). (ps-3). 15.99 (978-0-399-23175-9(7) , Putnam Juvenile) Penguin Group (USA) Inc.

—Cowboy Bunnies. Eitan, Ora, illus. 2000. (J). (978-0-606-18397-0(3)) Tandem Library Bks.

—The Ten Best Things about My Dad. Urbanovic, Jackie, tr. Urbanovic, Jackie, illus. 2004. 32p. (J). (ps-3). pap. 3.99 (978-0-439-57769-4(1) , Cartwheel Bks.) Scholastic, Inc.

Lopshire, Robert. Put Me in the Zoo. 2001. (Bright & Early Board Bks.). (Illus.). 24p. (J). (gr. k-ps). bds. 4.99 (978-0-375-81215-6(6) , Random Hse. Bks. for Young Readers) Random Hse. Children's Bks.

Lorbiecki, Marybeth. Sister Anne's Hands. Popp, Wendy, illus. 2000. 32p. (J). (ps-3). pap. 6.99 (978-0-14-056534-8(5) , Puffin) Penguin Group (USA) Inc.

—Sister Anne's Hands. 2000. (J). (978-0-606-20253-4(6)); lib. bdg. 15.30 (978-0-613-33728-1(X)) Tandem Library Bks.

Lord, John Vernon & Burroway, Janet. The Giant Jam Sandwich. 2007. (Illus.). 32p. (J). (ps-k). pap. 9.95 incl. audio compact disk ***(978-0-618-83952-0(6))*** Houghton Mifflin Co. Trade & Reference Div.

Lorenz Editors. My Day, 4 vols. 2002. Tr. of Mi dia. (Illus.). 48p. pap. 12.95 (978-0-7548-0876-3(9) , Lorenz Bks.) Anness Publishing, Inc.

Lost & Found in JumpStart Town. 2000. (ps-2). lib. bdg. 11.80 (978-0-613-26061-9(9)) Tandem Library Bks.

Love, Maryann Cusimano. You Are My Miracle. Ichikawa, Satomi, illus. 2005. 32p. (J). (ps-1). 15.99 (978-0-399-24037-9(3) , Philomel) Penguin Group (USA) Inc.

Love, Pamela. Two Feet up, Two Feet Down. Chapman, Lynne, illus. (Rookie Reader Espanol Ser.). 32p. (J). (gr. k-2). 2005. pap. 4.95 (978-0-516-24646-8(1)); 2004. 19.50 (978-0-516-23612-4(1)) Scholastic Library Publishing. (Children's Pr.).

Lovejoy, Sharon. The Little Green Island with a Little Red House: A Book of Colors & Critters. 2005. (Illus.). 32p. 9.95 (978-0-89272-673-8(3)) Down East Bks.

Low, Alice. Aunt Lucy Went to Buy a Hat. Huliska-Beith, Laura, illus. 2004. 32p. (J). (ps-3). lib. bdg. 16.89 (978-0-06-008972-6(5)) HarperCollins Pubs.

—Aunt Lucy Went to Buy a Hat. Huliska-Beith, Laura, tr. Huliska-Beith, Laura, illus. 2004. 32p. (J). (ps-3). 15.99 (978-0-06-008971-9(7)) HarperCollins Pubs.

—Blueberry Mouse. Friend, David Michael, tr. Friend, David Michael, illus. 2004. (J). 15.95 (978-1-59336-111-2(4)); pap. (978-1-59336-112-9(2)) Mondo Publishing.

Lowery, Paul. Do You Know Where Sea Turtles Go? 2007. (J). 15.99 ***(978-0-9792379-0-4(4))*** PBL Stories LLC.

Lubner, Susan. A Horse's Tale. Moore, Margie, illus. 2008. 32p. (J). 16.95 ***(978-0-8109-9490-4(9)*** , Abrams Bks. for Young Readers) Abrams, Harry N. , Inc.

Lubner, Susan Emple. Ruthie Bon Bair: Do Not Go to Bed with Wringing Wet Hair! Whatley, Bruce, illus. 2006. 32p. (J). (ps-3). 15.95 (978-0-8109-5470-0(2)) Abrams, Harry N. , Inc.

Lucas, Sally & Lucas, Margeaux. Dancing Dinos Go to School. 2006. (Step into Reading Ser.). (Illus.). 32p. (J). (ps-1). lib. bdg. 11.99 (978-0-375-93241-0(0)); pap. 3.99 (978-0-375-83241-3(6)) Random Hse. Children's Bks. (Random Hse. Bks. for Young Readers).

Lue, Grammy. Tuffy Turtle. 2007. pap. 11.99 ***(978-1-4259-4872-6(3))*** AuthorHouse.

Luke, Deanna. Chris Mouse & the Christmas House Audio Story Book. 2001. (J). cd-rom 5.95 (978-1-928777-35-9(X) , BOW Bks.) Blessing Our World, Inc.

Lumley, Jemima. The Journey Home from Grandpa's. Fatus, Sophie, illus. 2006. 24p. (J). (978-1-905236-37-4(9)) Barefoot Bks., Inc.

Lund, Deb. Dinosailors. Fine, Howard, illus. 2003. 40p. (J). (ps-2). 16.00 (978-0-15-204609-5(7)) Harcourt Children's Bks.

Lund, Deb. Monsters on Machines. Neubecker, Robert, illus. 2008. (J). ***(978-0-15-205365-9(4))*** Harcourt Trade Pubs.

Lund, Deborah. All Aboard the Dinotrain. Fine, Howard, illus. 2006. 40p. (J). 16.00 (978-0-15-205237-9(2)) Harcourt Trade Pubs.

Lundgren, Mary Beth. Seven Scary Monsters. Fine, Howard, illus. 2003. 32p. (J). (gr. k-3). tchr. ed. 15.00 (978-0-395-88913-8(8) , Clarion Bks.) Houghton Mifflin Co. Trade & Reference Div.

Luneau, Terri Roberts. Big Woods Bird: An Ivory-bill Story. Trevor, Bennett, illus. 2005. 36p. (J). per. 8.95 (978-0-9768839-0-6(2)) Kury Lane Inc.

Lyon, George Ella. Trucks Roll! Frazier, Craig, illus. 2007. 40p. (J). (ps-2). 14.99 (978-1-4169-2435-7(3)) Simon & Schuster Children's Publishing.

Lyon, Justice. The King of Meat-Yuk-Land. 2002. 20p. (J). 4.95 (978-0-9716596-0-5(5)) 7 Heads Publishing.

Lyons, Dana. The Tree. Danioth, David, illus. l.t. ed. 2002. 32p. 16.95 (978-0-9701907-1-0(9)) Illumination Arts Publishing Co., Inc.

Maccabe, Catherine. Teddy Bear, Piglet, Kitten & Me. Scruton, Clive, illus. 2004. 28p. 11.99 (978-0-8066-4148-5(7) , Augsburg Bks.) Augsburg Fortress, Pubs.

Maccarone, Grace. The Class Trip. Lewin, Betsy, illus. 2004. 32p. (J). lib. bdg. 15.00 (978-1-59054-663-5(6)) Fitzgerald Bks.

—The Class Trip. Lewin, Betsy, illus. 1999. (Hello Reader! Science Ser.: Level 1). 32p. (J). (ps-3). pap. 3.99 (978-0-439-06755-3(3) , Cartwheel Bks.) Scholastic, Inc.

—Class Trip. 1999. (gr. k-3). lib. bdg. 11.80 (978-0-613-21357-8(2)) Tandem Library Bks.

—Fun with First-grade Friends. 2007. (Scholastic Reader Level 1 Ser.). 64p. (J). pap. 4.99 ***(978-0-439-93444-2(3)*** , Cartwheel Bks.) Scholastic, Inc.

—Graduation Day Is Here! Brown, Rick, illus. 2006. (Scholastic Reader Ser.). 32p. (J). pap. 3.99 (978-0-439-83298-4(5) , Cartwheel Bks.) Scholastic, Inc.

—I Have a Cold. Lewin, Betsy, illus. 1999. (Hello Reader! Ser.: Level 1). 32p. (J). (ps-3). pap. 3.99 (978-0-590-39638-7(2) , Cartwheel Bks.) Scholastic, Inc.

—I Shop with My Daddy. Brunkus, Denise, illus. 2004. 32p. (J). lib. bdg. 15.00 (978-1-59054-659-8(8)) Fitzgerald Bks.

—I Shop with My Daddy. Brunkus, Denise, illus. 1998. (Hello Reader! Ser.). 32p. (J). (ps-1). pap. 3.99 (978-0-590-50196-5(8)) Scholastic, Inc.

—Sleepover. Lewin, Betsy, illus. 2005. (Hello Reader! Ser.). 32p. (J). pap. 3.99 (978-0-439-38575-6(X) , Cartwheel Bks.) Scholastic, Inc.

—"What Is That?" Said the Cat, Level 1. Scherer, Jeffrey, illus. 1998. (Hello Reader! Ser.). 32p. (J). (ps-1). pap. 3.99 (978-0-590-25945-3(8) , Cartwheel Bks.) Scholastic, Inc.

Mack, Lizzie. Catch a Ride to the Moon: Whimsical Rhymes to Read & Sing. G Studios, illus. 2007. (Land of Milk & Honey Ser.). 30p. (J). (ps). 10.99 ***(978-1-4169-2764-8(6)*** , Little Simon Inspirations) Simon & Schuster Children's Publishing.

Mackall, Dandi Daley. Don't Cry, Lion! 2007. 26p. (J). bds. 6.99 ***(978-1-4003-1008-1(3))*** Nelson, Thomas Inc.

MacKall, Dandi Daley. First Day. Beeke, Tiphanie, illus. 2003. 32p. (J). 16.00 (978-0-15-216577-2(0) , Silver Whistle) Harcourt Trade Pubs.

Mackall, Dandi Daley. A Gaggle of Geese & a Clutter of Cats. Hohn, David, illus. 2007. (Dandilion Rhymes Ser.). 32p. (J). (ps-3). 9.99 ***(978-1-4000-7204-0(2)*** , WaterBrook Pr.) WaterBrook Pr.

—The Light of Christmas. Walker, John, illus. 2007. 32p. (J). (ps-3). 14.99 ***(978-0-7586-1270-0(2))*** Concordia Publishing Hse.

—Little Lost Donkey. 2007. 26p. (J). bds. 6.99 ***(978-1-4003-1009-8(1))*** Nelson, Thomas Inc.

—Merry Creature Christmas. 2006. 24p. (J). bds. 9.99 (978-1-4003-0823-1(2)) Nelson, Thomas Inc.

—My Big Birthday. O'Neill, Rachael, illus. 2005. (Carry Me Along Ser.). 24p. (J). (ps). 6.99 (978-0-310-70939-8(3)) Zonderkidz.

—No, No, Noah! Kucharik, Elena, illus. 2002. (I'm Not Afraid Ser.). 24p. (J). (ps-2). 6.99 (978-0-8499-7750-3(9)) Nelson, Thomas Inc.

Mackall, Dandi Daley. No, No Noah! 2007. 26p. (J). bds. 6.99 ***(978-1-4003-1007-4(5))*** Nelson, Thomas Inc.

Macveety, Sue Maney. Singing Sea/el Mar Que Canta. Zantay, Valerie, tr. 2005. (SPA., Illus.). 36p. per. 15.99 (978-1-4134-7275-2(3)) Xlibris Corp.

Magnus, Kellie. Little Lion Goes to School. Robinson, Michael, illus. l.t. ed. 2003. 16p. (J). 9.99 (978-0-9744211-0-0(3)) Media Magic New York.

Magsamen, Sandra. Butterfly Kisses. rev. ed. 2007. (Snuggle-Me Stories Ser.). 20p. (J). (ps). 7.99 ***(978-0-316-06595-5(1))*** Little, Brown Bks. for Young Readers.

—Love Bug. rev. ed. 2007. (Snuggle-Me Stories Ser.). 20p. (J). (ps-ps). 7.99 ***(978-0-316-06596-2(X))*** Little, Brown Bks. for Young Readers.

Maguire, Gregory. Crabby Cratchitt. Glass, Andrew, illus. 2000. 32p. (J). (gr. k-3). tchr. ed. 15.00 (978-0-395-60485-4(0) , Clarion Bks.) Houghton Mifflin Co. Trade & Reference Div.

Mahy, Margaret. Down the Back of the Chair. Dunbar, Polly, illus. 2006. 32p. (J). (gr. k-3). 16.00 (978-0-618-69395-5(5) , Clarion Bks.) Houghton Mifflin Co. Trade & Reference Div.

—Summery Saturday Morning. 2000. (J). (978-0-606-19071-8(6)) Tandem Library Bks.

Majors, Ursula. The Bear. Spengler, Kenneth J., illus. 2002. 32p. (J). pap. 15.95 (978-1-59034-182-7(1)) Mondo Publishing.

Maloney, Peter. Belly Button Boy. 2003. (gr. k-3). lib. bdg. 15.30 (978-0-613-61603-4(0)) Tandem Library Bks.

Maloney, Peter & Zekauskas, Felicia. Belly Button Boy. Maloney, Peter & Zekauskas, Felicia, illus. (Illus.). 40p. (J). (ps-2). 2003. pap. 6.99 (978-0-14-250017-0(8) , Puffin); 2000. 16.99 (978-0-8037-2542-3(6) , Dial) Penguin Group (USA) Inc.

Manalang, Dan. Ambrosia. Wong, Nichole, illus. 2006. 32p. (J). 14.99 (978-0-9769342-0-2(5)) Flip Publishing.

Manivong, Laura. One Smart Fish. Beaky, Suzanne, illus. 2006. (Rookie Reader Skill Set Ser.). 32p. (J). (gr. k-2). 19.50 (978-0-516-24982-7(7) , Children's Pr.) Scholastic Library Publishing.

Manivong, Laura & Beaky, Suzanne. One Smart Fish. 2006. (Rookie Reader Ser.). (Illus.). 32p. (J). pap. 4.95 (978-0-516-24996-4(7) , Children's Pr.) Scholastic Library Publishing.

Mann, Paul. Meet My Monster. 1999. (gr. k-3). lib. bdg. 11.80 (978-0-613-26180-7(1)) Tandem Library Bks.

Mann, Paul Z. I Can Jump Higher! 2000. (gr. k-3). lib. bdg. 11.80 (978-0-613-71007-7(X)) Tandem Library Bks.

Manushkin, Fran. The Tushy Book. Lemaître, Pascal, illus. 2007. (J). (978-0-15-205335-2(2)) Harcourt Trade Pubs.

Marchus, Linda. The Gorilla Who Wanted to Dance. Marchus, Linda, illus. 2003. (Illus.). 32p. (J). lib. bdg. 15.95 (978-0-9723122-1-9(8)) Wee Read Publishing.

Markell, Denis. The Great Stroller Adventure. Iwai, Melissa, illus. 2004. 16p. (J). pap. 9.95 (978-0-439-54651-5(6) , Cartwheel Bks.) Scholastic, Inc.

Markes, Julie. Shhhhh! Everybody's Sleeping. Parkins, David, illus. 2005. 32p. (J). (ps-1). 14.99 (978-0-06-053790-6(6)); lib. bdg. 16.89 (978-0-06-053791-3(4)) HarperCollins Pubs.

—Thanks for Thanksgiving. Barrette, Doris, illus. 2004. 32p. (J). (ps-2). 12.99 (978-0-06-051096-1(X)) HarperCollins Pubs.

Marks, Lisa Rey. Joy Is the Greatest Gift. 2007. (Illus.). 32p. (J). 16.99 ***(978-0-9786028-0-2(3))*** Focus Friends, LLC.

Marks, Nancy Freeman. Just As You Are: The Story of Leon & Sam. Buchheim, Su Jen, illus. 2003. 32p. (J). 15.00 (978-0-9722430-1-8(1)) Wave Publishing.

Markun, Alan F. New Revolution. (J). 8.95 (978-0-8022-1062-3(7)) Philosophical Library, Inc.

Marsh, T. J. & Ward, Jennifer. Way Out in the Desert. Spengler, Kenneth J., illus. 2002. 20p. (J). bds. 6.95 (978-0-87358-802-7(9)); 1999. 32p. 15.95 (978-0-87358-687-0(5)) Northland Publishing. (Rising Moon Bks. for Young Readers).

Marshall, Judy. Morning. Annelli, Nikki, illus. l.t. ed. 2005. 21p. (J). per. 9.99 (978-1-59879-050-4(1)) Lifevest Publishing, Inc.

Marshall, Mark. Imagine! 2006. (Illus.). 10p. (J). (gr. k-k). bds. 12.95 (978-0-7696-4647-3(6) , Gingham Dog Pr.) School Specialty Publishing.

Martin. The Maestro Plays. 2001. 13.95 (978-0-15-200259-6(6)) Harcourt Trade Pubs.

—The Turning of the Year. Shed, Greg, illus. 2007. 28p. (J). pap. 6.00 (978-0-15-204555-5(4) , Voyager Bks./Libros Viajeros) Harcourt Children's Bks.

Martin, Bill, Jr. Baby Bear, Baby Bear, What Do You See? Carle, Eric, illus. 2007. 32p. (J). (ps-3). 16.95 ***(978-0-8050-8336-1(7)*** , Holt, Henry & Co. Bks. For Young Readers) Holt, Henry & Co.

Martin, Bill. Beasty Story. 2002. (gr. k-3). lib. bdg. 15.30 (978-0-613-53796-4(3)) Tandem Library Bks.

Martin, Bill, Jr. Brown Bear, Brown Bear, What Do You See? 2002. (Illus.). (J). 26.49 (978-0-7587-2157-0(9)) Book Wholesalers, Inc.

—Chicka Chicka Boom Boom. 2002. (Illus.). (J). 15.53 (978-0-7587-2222-5(2)) Book Wholesalers, Inc.

—Chicka Chicka Boom Boom. 2000. (gr. 3-6). lib. bdg. 15.30 (978-0-613-28443-1(7)); (Illus.). (J). 13.79 (978-0-606-18798-5(7)) Tandem Library Bks.

—Fire! Fire! Said Mrs. Mcguire. Radunsky, Vladimir, illus. 2006. 32p. (J). 16.00 (978-0-15-205725-1(0) , Gulliver Bks.) Harcourt Children's Bks.

Martin, Bill. The Maestro Plays. 2002. (Illus.). (J). 26.47 (978-0-7587-6796-7(X)) Book Wholesalers, Inc.

Martin, Bill, Jr. Oso Polar, Oso Polar, Que Es Ese Ruido? Carle, Eric, illus. rev. ed. 2000. (SPA.). 32p. (J). (ps-k). 15.95 (978-0-8050-6427-8(3) , Holt, Henry & Co. Bks. For Young Readers) Holt, Henry & Co.

Martin, Bill. Oso Polar, Oso Polar, Que es Ese Ruido? Mlawer, Teresa, tr. Carle, Eric, illus. rev. ed. 2002. (SPA.). 28p. (J). (ps-k). bds. 7.95 (978-0-8050-6902-0(X) , Holt, Henry & Co. Bks. For Young Readers) Holt, Henry & Co.

—Panda Bear, Panda Bear, What Do You See? Carle, Eric, illus. 2007. 32p. (J). 22.95 (***978-0-8050-8102-2(X)*** , Holt, Henry & Co. Bks. For Young Readers) Holt, Henry & Co.

—Panda Bear, Panda Bear, What Do You See? Carlen, Eric, illus. 2006. 28p. (J). bds. 7.95 (978-0-8050-8078-0(3) , Holt, Henry & Co. Bks. For Young Readers) Holt, Henry & Co.

Martin, Bill, Jr. Polar Bear, Polar Bear, What Do You Hear? 2002. (Illus.). (J). 26.47 (978-0-7587-3432-7(8)) Book Wholesalers, Inc.

—The Turning of the Year. Shed, Greg, illus. 1998. 28p. (J). (ps-3). 15.00 (978-0-15-201085-0(8)) Harcourt Children's Bks.

Martin, Bill, Jr. & Archambault, John. Chicka Chicka Boom Boom. Ehlert, Lois, illus. 40p. (J). 2006. pap. 9.99 incl. audio compact disk (978-1-4169-2718-1(2) , Little Simon); 2000. pap. 7.99 (978-0-689-83568-1(X) , Aladdin) Simon & Schuster Children's Publishing.

Martin, Bill & Archambault, John. Here Are My Hands. Rand, Ted, illus. 2007. 32p. (J). 22.95 (***978-0-8050-8119-0(4)*** , Holt, Henry & Co. Bks. For Young Readers) Holt, Henry & Co.

Martin, Bill, Jr. & Sampson, Michael. Chicka Chicka 1, 2, 3. Ehlert, Lois, illus. 2005. (J). (ps-3). 24.95 incl. audio (978-0-439-76675-3(3) , WHRA669); 29.95 incl. audio compact disk (978-0-439-76677-7(X) , WHCD669) Weston Woods Studios, Inc.

Martin, Bill, Jr. & Sampson, Michael R. Chicka Chicka 1, 2, 3. Ehlert, Lois, illus. 2004. 40p. (J). 16.99 (978-0-689-85881-9(7)) Simon & Schuster Children's Publishing.

Martin, David. We've All Got Bellybuttons! Cecil, Randy, illus. 2005. 32p. (J). (ps-1). 15.99 (978-0-7636-1775-2(X)) Candlewick Pr.

Martin, Joy. Bear Story: A Rhyme from A to Zzzz's. Cartwright, Shannon, illus. 2001. 32p. 15.95 (978-0-936425-69-6(5)); 9.95 (978-0-936425-70-2(9)) Greatland Graphics.

Martin, Linda. When Dinosaurs Go to School. 2002. (Illus.). 32p. (J). (gr. k-1). pap. 6.95 (978-0-8118-3514-5(6)) Chronicle Bks. LLC.

—When Dinosaurs Go to School. 2002. (ps-2). lib. bdg. 15.25 (978-0-613-51424-8(6)) Tandem Library Bks.

Martin, Mike. 365 Stories & Rhymes for Girls. Date not set. 384p. (J). 9.98 (978-1-4054-1959-8(8)) Parragon, Inc.

Martin, Steve & Chast, Roz. The Alphabet from A to Y, with Bonus Letter Z! 2007. (Illus.). 64p. (J). 17.95 (***978-0-385-51662-4(2)***); lib. bdg. 17.95 (***978-0-385-52377-6(7)***) Doubleday Publishing. (Flying Dolphin Pr.).

Marzollo, Jean. Doctor Show, No. 2. Evans, Shane W., illus. 2001. 24p. (J). lib. bdg. 13.49 (978-0-7868-2548-6(0) , Jump at the Sun) Hyperion Bks. for Children.

—Mama Mama. Regan, Laura, illus. 1999. (Growing Tree Ser.). 16p. (J). (ps up). 5.99 (978-0-694-01245-9(9) , Harper Festival) HarperCollins Pubs.

—Papa Papa. Regan, Laura, illus. 2000. (Growing Tree Ser.). 14p. (J). (ps up). 5.99 (978-0-694-01246-6(7) , Harper Festival) HarperCollins Pubs.

—Shanna's Pizza Parlor. 2004. (Shanna Show! Ser.). 32p. (ps-1). pap. 3.99 (978-0-7868-1831-0(X) , Jump at the Sun) Hyperion Bks. for Children.

—Shanna's Princess Show, No. 1. Evans, Shane W., illus. 2001. 24p. (J). 13.49 (978-0-7868-2549-3(9) , Jump at the Sun) Hyperion Bks. for Children.

—Shanna's Princess Show. 2003. (ps-2). lib. bdg. 11.25 (978-0-613-91009-5(5)) Tandem Library Bks.

—Ten Little Christmas Presents. 2008. (J). (***978-0-545-02791-5(8)***) Scholastic, Inc.

—Thanksgiving Cats. 1999. (978-0-606-17282-0(3)) Tandem Library Bks.

—What's the Matter with Mother Goose? Trivas, Irene, illus. 2000. 32p. (J). pap. 14.95 (978-0-06-027276-0(7)) HarperCollins Pubs.

Marzollo, Jean, et al. What's the Matter with Mother Goose? Trivas, Irene, illus. 2000. 32p. (J). (ps-k). lib. bdg. 14.89 (978-0-06-027277-7(5)) HarperCollins Pubs.

Masaurel, Claire. Ten Dogs in the Window. 2000. (978-0-606-18323-9(X)) Tandem Library Bks.

Maslyn, Stacie K. B. Mad Maddie Maxwell. 2004. (ps-2). lib. bdg. 13.00 (978-0-613-71695-6(7)) Tandem Library Bks.

—Mad Maddie Maxwell. Schettle, Jane, illus. 2004. 24p. (J). pap. 4.99 (978-0-310-70817-9(6)) Zonderkidz.

—Mad Maddie Maxwell. 2000. (Illus.). 24p. (J). 7.99 (978-0-310-23207-0(4)) Zondervan.

Masurel, Claire. Diez Perros en la Tienda: Un Libro Para Contar. 2000. (SPA., Illus.). (J). 13.75 (978-0-606-18318-5(3)) Tandem Library Bks.

—Diez Perros en la Tienda: Un Libro para Contar. Moro, Elena, tr. from ENG. Paparone, Pamela, illus. 2000. (SPA.). 32p. (J). (ps-1). pap. 6.95 (978-0-7358-1303-8(5) , NS3643) North-South Bks., Inc.

—Ten Dogs in the Window: A Countdown Book. Paparone, Pamela, illus. 2000. 32p. (J). (ps-1). pap. 6.95 (978-0-7358-1301-4(9)) North-South Bks., Inc.

Mathes, Charles. In Every Moon There Is a Face. Graston, Arlene, illus. 2003. 32p. 15.95 (978-0-9701907-4-1(3)) Illumination Arts Publishing Co., Inc.

Mathews, Judith. Nathaniel Willy, Scared Silly. 1999. (J). (978-0-606-18951-4(3)) Tandem Library Bks.

Mau, Connie. Catch me if you Can. Lemus, Kristina, illus. l.t. ed. 2006. 28p. (J). 14.95 (978-0-9778843-0-8(9)) Mau, C. Publishing Co.

Maurer, Amy J. A Purple Hippopotamus Pillow & Pink Penguin Sheets. Smith, Rachael, illus. 2006. 56p. (J). per. 19.99 (***978-1-59879-239-3(3)***); per. 15.99 (***978-1-59879-167-9(2)***) Lifevest Publishing, Inc.

May, Robert L. Rudolph the Red-Nosed Reindeer. Wenzel, David, illus. 2001. 40p. (J). (gr. k-3). 9.99 (978-0-448-42534-4(3) , Grosset & Dunlap) Penguin Group (USA) Inc.

Mayhew, James. Who Wants a Dragon? Gardiner, Lindsey, illus. 2004. 32p. (J). (gr. k-ps). pap. 15.95 (978-0-439-67237-5(6) , Orchard Bks.) Scholastic, Inc.

Maynard, Bill. Incredible Ned: If You Could See What He Said. 1999. (J). (978-0-606-17417-6(6)) Tandem Library Bks.

Mayo, Margaret. Emergency! Ayliffe, Alex, illus. 2003. 32p. (J). (ps-1). 14.95 (978-0-87614-922-5(0) , Carolrhoda Bks.) Lerner Publishing Group.

Mazer, Norma Fox. Has Anyone Seen My Emily Greene? Davenier, Christine, illus. 2007. (J). (ps-2). 32p. 15.99 (***978-0-7636-1384-6(3)***); (***978-1-4287-4761-6(3)***) Candlewick Pr.

McBratney, Sam. The Caterpillow Fight. 2002. (Illus.). (J). 11.23 (978-0-7587-2207-2(9)) Book Wholesalers, Inc.

McBride, Martha J. Avery Finds Five Dollars. l.t. ed. 2004. 36p. (J). per. 19.99 (978-1-59196-434-6(2)) Instantpublisher.com.

McCabe, Lauren A. How Many Spots Have I Got? Foulke, Nancy, illus. 2005. (J). 16.00 (978-1-893516-02-1(4)) Our Child Pr.

McCafferty, Catherine. Picture Me as Dad's Little Helper. Rasmussen, Wendy, illus. 2001. (Picture Me Ser.). 10p. (J). (ps up). bds. 4.99 (978-1-57151-588-9(7)) Playhouse Publishing.

—Picture Me as Mom's Little Helper. Rasmussen, Wendy, illus. 2001. (Picture Me Ser.). 10p. (J). (ps up). bds. 4.99 (978-1-57151-587-2(9)) Playhouse Publishing.

—Picture Me with My Grandpa. Rasmussen, Wendy, illus. 2000. (Picture Me Ser.). 10p. (J). (ps up). bds. 4.99 (978-1-57151-579-7(8)) Playhouse Publishing.

McCardell, Kenneth/W. Bible Rhymes' Christmas Story. Chirco, Antonella, illus. 2007. 32p. (J). 17.95 (***978-0-9790605-2-6(4)*** , BibleRhymes) BibleRhymes Publishing, L.L.C.

—Bible Rhymes' Creation. Chirco, Antonella, illus. 2007. 32p. (J). 17.95 (***978-0-9790605-0-2(8)*** , BibleRhymes) BibleRhymes Publishing, L.L.C.

—Bible Rhymes' Noah & the Ark. Chirco, Antonella, illus. 2007. 32p. (J). 17.95 (***978-0-9790605-1-9(6)*** , BibleRhymes) BibleRhymes Publishing, L.L.C.

McCarthy, Michael. The Story of Daniel in the Lions' Den. Ferri, Giuliano, illus. 2003. 32p. (J). (gr. 1-3). 16.99 (978-1-84148-209-5(9)) Barefoot Bks., Inc.

McClure, Brian D. Who Am I? 2006. (Illus.). 52p. (J). 12.95 (978-1-933426-03-7(9)) Universal Flag Publishing.

McCormick, Patricia. Sold. 2006. 272p. (gr. 7 up). 15.99 (978-0-7868-5171-3(6)) Hyperion Pr.

McCully, Emily Arnold & Schertle, Alice. 1, 2, I Love You. 2004. (Illus.). 32p. (J). (ps-k). 16.95 (978-0-8118-3518-3(9)) Chronicle Bks. LLC.

McDonald, Rae. A Fishing Surprise. Kemly, Kathleen Hadam, illus. 2007. 32p. (J). (***978-1-55971-977-3(X)*** , NorthWord Bks. for Young Readers) T&N Children's Publishing.

McDonnell, Patrick. Art. 2006. (Illus.). 44p. (J). (ps-1). 14.99 (978-0-316-11491-2(X)) Little Brown & Co.

McDonnell, Patrick. Hug Time. 2007. (Illus.). 48p. (J). (ps-1). 14.99 (***978-0-316-11494-3(4)***) Little Brown & Co.

—Hug Time. 2007. 14.99 (***978-0-316-02373-3(6)***) Little, Brown Bks. for Young Readers.

McGee, Marni. While Angels Watch. Macnaughton, Tina, illus. 2006. 26p. (J). (ps-2). 16.00 (978-1-56148-513-0(6)) Good Bks.

McGinty, Alice B. Thank You, World. Halperin, Wendy Anderson, illus. 2007. 32p. (J). (ps-k). 16.99 (978-0-8037-2705-2(4) , Dial) Penguin Group (USA) Inc.

McGrath, Barbara Barbieri. The Pepperidge Farm Goldfish Fun Book. Bolster, Rob & Mazzola, Frank, Jr., illus. 1999. 16p. (J). (ps up). 5.99 (978-0-694-01450-7(8) , Harper Festival) HarperCollins Pubs.

McGraw, Jason. Beating the Odds. 2007. 30p. 47.88 (***978-0-615-13681-3(8)***) McGraw, Jason A.

McGuire, Leslie & Brunelle, Lynn. Animal Singalong. Voo, Rhonda, illus. 1999. 12p. (J). 5.95 (978-1-892374-16-5(1)) Weldon Owen, Inc.

McHenry, E. B. Has Anyone Seen Winnie & Jean? McHenry, E. B., illus. 2007. (Illus.). 32p. (J). (gr. k-2). 16.95 (978-1-58234-999-2(1)) Bloomsbury Publishing.

—Poodlena. McHenry, E. B., illus. 2005. (Illus.). 32p. (J). (ps-3). pap. 6.95 (978-1-58234-698-4(4) , Bloomsbury Children) Bloomsbury Publishing.

—Poodlena. 2004. (Illus.). (J). (978-1-58234-962-6(2)); 32p. (gr. 1 up). 16.95 (978-1-58234-824-7(3) , Bloomsbury Children) Bloomsbury Publishing.

McKay, Sindy. New Red Bed. 1999. (gr. k-3). lib. bdg. 11.80 (978-0-613-82080-6(0)) Tandem Library Bks.

—We Both Read-My Car Trip. Johnson, Meredith, illus. 2005. (J). (***978-1-4156-3785-2(7)***) Book Wholesalers, Inc.

—We Both Read-My Day (Picture Book Edition) Johnson, Meredith, illus. 2007. (We Both Read Ser.). 44p. (J). 14.95 (***978-1-60115-005-9(9)***) Treasure Bay, Inc.

McKenna, Mark, et al, illus. Banana Tail. 2003. 32p. (J). 12.95 (978-0-9727681-3-9(0)) Active Media Publishing, LLC.

McKissack, Pat. Stitchin' & Pullin' A Gee's Bend Quilt. Cabrera, Cozbi S., illus. 2007. (J). (***978-0-375-83163-8(0)***); lib. bdg. (***978-0-375-93163-5(5)***) Random Hse., Inc.

McKissack, Patricia C. Messy Bessey's Closet. 2001. (gr. k-3). lib. bdg. 12.95 (978-0-613-54440-5(4)) Tandem Library Bks.

—Messy Bessey's Garden. 2002. (gr. k-3). lib. bdg. 12.95 (978-0-613-53836-7(6)) Tandem Library Bks.

—Messy Bessey's Holidays. 1999. (gr. k-3). lib. bdg. 12.95 (978-0-613-37457-6(6)) Tandem Library Bks.

McKissack, Patricia C. & McKissack, Fredrick L. Messy Bessey & the Birthday Overnight. Regan, Dana, illus. 1998. (Rookie Readers Ser.). 32p. (J). (gr. 1-2). 19.50 (978-0-516-20828-2(4) , Children's Pr.) Scholastic Library Publishing.

—Messy Bessey's Family Reunion. Regan, Dana, illus. 2000. (Rookie Reader Skill Set Ser.). 32p. (J). (gr. k-2). pap. 4.95 (978-0-516-26552-0(0) , Children's Pr.) Scholastic Library Publishing.

—Messy Bessey's Garden. Regan, Dana, illus. rev. ed. 2002. (Rookie Reader Espanol Ser.). 32p. (J). (gr. k-2). pap. 4.95 (978-0-516-27386-0(8) , Children's Pr.) Scholastic Library Publishing.

—Messy Bessey's Garden Level C. Regan, Dana, illus. rev. ed. 2002. (Rookie Readers Ser.). 32p. (J). (gr. 1-2). 19.50 (978-0-516-22491-6(3) , Children's Pr.) Scholastic Library Publishing.

—Messy Bessey's Holidays. Regan, Dana, illus. 1999. (Rookie Readers Ser.). 32p. (J). (gr. 1-2). 19.50 (978-0-516-20829-9(2) , Children's Pr.) Scholastic Library Publishing.

McKissack, Patricia C. & McKissack, Pat. Where Crocodiles Have Wings. Barner, Bob, illus. 2005. 32p. (J). (ps-ps). 16.95 (978-0-8234-1748-3(4)) Holiday Hse., Inc.

McKissack, Patricia C., et al. Messy Bessey's Closet, Level C. rev. ed. 2001. (Rookie Readers Ser.). (Illus.). 32p. (J). (gr. 1-2). 19.50 (978-0-516-21659-1(7) , Children's Pr.) Scholastic Library Publishing.

—Messy Bessey's Family Reunion. 2000. (Rookie Readers Ser.). (Illus.). 32p. (J). (gr. 1-2). 19.50 (978-0-516-20830-5(6) , Children's Pr.) Scholastic Library Publishing.

McLaren, Chesley. Zat Cat! A Haute Couture Tail. McLaren, Chesley, illus. 2002. (Illus.). 40p. (J). (ps-3). pap. 16.95 (978-0-439-27316-9(1) , Scholastic Pr.) Scholastic, Inc.

McLaughlin, Julie. Hungry Mr. Gator. McKay, Ann Marie, illus. 2002. 32p. (J). (gr. k-2). pap. (978-0-615-12335-6(X)) JAM Publishers.

—Hungry Mr. Gator. McKay, Ann Marie, illus. 2005. (J). 15.99 (978-0-933101-24-1(4)) Legacy Pubns.

McLaughlin, Marie. Those Toes. Rohr, Roni, illus. l.t. ed. 2000. 32p. (J). (ps-3). 15.95 (978-1-929115-01-3(6)) Azro Pr., Inc.

McLelland, Michael J. Beating the Bully. Kirk, Andrea Cope, illus. 2007. 16p. (J). 15.99 (***978-1-59955-006-0(7)***) Cedar Fort, Inc./CFI Distribution.

McMillan, Bruce. Puffins Climb, Penguins Rhyme. 2001. (gr. k-3). lib. bdg. 14.15 (978-0-613-35557-5(1)); (Illus.). (J). (978-0-606-21388-2(0)) Tandem Library Bks.

McMillan, Ernest. Psalms of Passion. 2006. 48p. pap. 8.95 (978-1-59800-224-9(4)) Outskirts Press, Inc.

McNaughton, Colin. When I Grow Up. McNaughton, Colin, illus. 2005. (Illus.). 40p. (J). (ps-1). 12.99 (978-0-7636-2675-4(9)) Candlewick Pr.

McNease, Mitzy. Chester's Presents. Cox, Kim, illus. ed. 2006. 28p. (J). 10.96 (978-0-9779488-0-2(3)) Blancmange Publishing.

McNeil, Florence. Sail Away. 2001. (gr. k-3). lib. bdg 16.40 (978-0-613-88506-5(6)); (Illus.). (J). (978-0-606-21408-7(9)) Tandem Library Bks.

McPhail, David. Big Brown Bear/El gran oso Pardo. Campoy, F. Isabel & Ada, Alma Flor, trs. from ENG. 2007. (Green Light Readers Level 1 Ser.). (ENG & SPA., Illus.). 28p. (J). 12.95 (978-0-15-205965-1(2)); pap. 3.95 (978-0-15-205970-5(9)) Harcourt Trade Pubs.

McWilliams, Amanda & Moore, Clement C. Ozark Night Before Christmas. Rice, James, illus. 2004. 32p. pap. 15.95 (978-1-58980-056-4(7)) Pelican Publishing Co., Inc.

Meade, Holly. A Place to Sleep. 2001. (Illus.). 32p. (J). (ps-1). 15.95 (978-0-7614-5096-2(3) , Cavendish Children's Bks.) Cavendish, Marshall Corp.

Medearis, Angela Shelf. Best Friends in the Snow. Wilson-Max, Ken, illus. 2002. (My First Hello Reader! Ser.). 32p. (J). (ps-k). pap. 3.99 (978-0-590-52284-7(1) , Cartwheel Bks.); pap. 3.99 (978-0-439-61912-7(2) , Scholastic, Inc.) Scholastic, Inc.

—Dancing with the Indians. Byrd, Samuel, illus. 2000. pap. 18.95 incl. audio compact disk (978-1-59519-248-6(4)); pap. 39.95 incl. audio compact disk (978-1-59519-249-3(2)); (J). (gr. 1-6). 24.95 incl. audio (978-0-87499-333-2(4)); (J). (gr. 1-6). pap. 16.95 incl. audio (978-0-87499-332-5(6)) Live Oak Media.

—Dancing with the Indians, Grades 1-6. Byrd, Samuel, illus. unabr. ed. 2000. (J). pap., tchr. ed. 37.95 incl. audio (978-0-87499-334-9(2)) Live Oak Media.

—Lights Out! Tadgell, Nicole, illus. 2004. 32p. (J). lib. bdg. 15.00 (***978-1-4242-0221-8(3)***) Fitzgerald Bks.

Medearis, Angela Shelf. Snug in Mama's Arms. Sandford, John, illus. 2004. 32p. (J). 14.95 (978-1-57768-430-5(3) , Gingham Dog Pr.) School Specialty Publishing.

Meister, Cari. I Love Rocks. Sirrell, Terry, illus. 2001. (Rookie Readers Ser.). 32p. (J). (gr. 1-2). 19.50 (978-0-516-22152-6(3) , Children's Pr.) Scholastic Library Publishing.

—I Love Trees. Sirrell, Terry, illus. (Rookie Reader Espanol Ser.). (J). (gr. k-2). 2005. 32p. pap. 4.95 (978-0-516-26827-9(9)); 2004. 31p. 19.50 (978-0-516-25900-0(8)) Scholastic Library Publishing. (Children's Pr.).

—I Love Trees. Sirrell, Terry, illus. 2005. 32p. (J). (gr. 1-2). lib. bdg. 12.15 (978-0-606-33170-8(0)) Tandem Library Bks.

—My Pony Jack. Young, Amy, illus. 2005. (Viking Easy-To-Read Ser.). 32p. (J). (ps-3). 13.99 (978-0-670-05917-1(X) , Viking Adult) Penguin Group (USA) Inc.

—My Pony Jack at Riding Lessons. Young, Amy, illus. 2005. (Viking Easy-To-Read Ser.). 32p. (J). (ps-ps). 13.99 (978-0-670-05918-8(8) , Viking Juvenile) Penguin Group (USA) Inc.

—My Pony Jack at the Horse Show: Viking Easy to Read Level 1. Young, Amy, illus. 2006. (Easy-to-Read,Viking Children's Ser.). 32p. (J). (ps). 13.99 (978-0-670-05919-5(6) , Viking Adult) Penguin Group (USA) Inc.

—What Can I Be? Phillips, Matt, illus. 2003. (Rookie Reader Ser.). 24p. (J). 19.50 (978-0-516-22876-1(5) , Children's Pr.) Scholastic Library Publishing.

Melmed, Laura Krauss. Fright Night Flight. Cole, Henry, illus. 2002. 32p. (J). (ps-3). 15.99 (978-0-06-029701-5(8)) HarperCollins Pubs.

—I Love You as Much... Sorensen, Henri, illus. 1998. 11p. (J). (ps-2). bds. 7.99 (978-0-688-15978-8(8)) HarperCollins Pubs.

—I Love You As Much... Sorensen, Henri, illus. (J). (ps-2). 2005. 24p. pap. 5.99 (978-0-06-000202-2(6)); 2001. 22p. 12.99 (978-0-06-001011-9(8)) HarperCollins Pubs. (Harper Festival).

—I Love You As Much... 2001. (Illus.). 32p. (J). (ps up). pap. 6.95 (978-0-688-16806-3(X)) HarperCollins Pubs.

—I Love You As Much... Board Book & Picture Frame. 2003. (Illus.). 22p. (J). (ps-2). 12.99 (978-0-06-008659-6(9) , Harper Festival) HarperCollins Pubs.

—Jumbo's Lullaby. Sorensen, Henri, illus. 1999. 24p. (J). (ps-k). lib. bdg. 15.89 (978-0-688-16996-1(1)) HarperCollins Pubs.

Meltzer Kleinhenz, Sydnie. Work & Play. Reasor, Mick, illus. 2005. (Rookie Reader Ser.). 24p. (J). (gr. k-1). 17.00 (978-0-516-24433-4(7) , Children's Pr.) Scholastic Library Publishing.

Merberg, Julie & Bober, Suzanne. Dreaming with Rousseau. 2007. (Illus.). 22p. (J). (ps). bds. 6.95 (978-0-8118-5712-3(3)) Chronicle Bks. LLC.

—In the Garden with Van Gogh. 2002. (Illus.). 22p. (J). (ps). bds. 6.95 (978-0-8118-3415-5(8)) Chronicle Bks. LLC.

—A Magical Day with Matisse. 2002. (Illus.). 22p. (J). (ps). bds. 6.95 (978-0-8118-3414-8(X)) Chronicle Bks. LLC.

—Sharing with Renoir. 2005. (Illus.). 22p. (J). (ps-ps). bds. 6.95 (978-0-8118-4757-5(8)) Chronicle Bks. LLC.

—Sunday with Seurat. 2005. (Illus.). 16p. (J). (ps-ps). bds. 6.95 (978-0-8118-4758-2(6)) Chronicle Bks. LLC.

Merberg, Julie, et al. Painting with Picasso. 2006. (Illus.). 22p. (J). bds. 6.95 (978-0-8118-5505-1(8)) Chronicle Bks. LLC.

Merritt, Kate, illus. Peekaboo, Baby! A Rhyming Flap Book. 2002. (DK Ladybird Ser.). 12p. (J). bds. 6.95 (978-0-7894-8467-3(6)) Dorling Kindersley Publishing, Inc.

Merz, Jennifer. Playground Day. 2007. 32p. 16.00 (***978-978-061-896-4(1)*** , Clarion Bks.) Houghton Mifflin Co. Trade & Reference Div.

Merz, Jennifer J. Playground Day! Merz, Jennifer J., illus. 2007. (Illus.). 32p. (J). (ps-1). 16.00 (***978-0-618-81696-5(8)*** , Clarion Bks.) Houghton Mifflin Co. Trade & Reference Div.

Messinger, Midge. Freddie Q. Freckle. Messinger, Robert, ed. Ferraro-Oster, Margaret, illus. unabr. ed. 2003. 40p. (ps-2). 12.95 (978-1-893237-00-1(1)) Little Mai Pr.

Messinger, Robert. I've Got Mail! Salerno, John, illus. 2003. 40p. 12.95 (978-1-893237-01-8(X)) Little Mai Pr.

Metzger, Steve. Five Spooky Ghosts Playing Tricks at School. Harrald-Pilz, Marilee, illus. 2005. (J). (***978-0-439-80381-6(0)***) Scholastic, Inc.

Metzger, Steve. My Bossy Dolly. Demarest, Chris L., illus. 2006. 24p. (J). pap. 3.50 (978-0-439-74055-5(X) , Cartwheel Bks.) Scholastic, Inc.

Meyers, Susan. Everywhere Babies. Frazee, Marla, illus. 2001. 32p. (J). (ps-k). 16.00 (978-0-15-202226-6(0)) Harcourt Children's Bks.

—Kittens! Kittens! Kittens! Walker, David, illus. 2007. (J). (ps-1). 32p. 15.95 (978-0-8109-1218-2(X)); (***978-1-4287-3986-4(6)***) Abrams, Harry N. , Inc. (Abrams Bks. for Young Readers).

—Puppies! Puppies! Puppies! Walker, David, illus. 2005. 32p. (J). (ps-1). 15.95 (978-0-8109-5856-2(2)) Abrams, Harry N. , Inc.

—This Is the Way a Baby Rides. Nakata, Hiroe, illus. 2005. 32p. (J). (ps-1). 15.95 (978-0-8109-5763-3(9) , Abrams Bks. for Young Readers) Abrams, Harry N. , Inc.

Michelson, Richard. Oh No, Not Ghosts! McCauley, Adam, illus. 2006. 44p. (J). 16.00 (978-0-15-205186-0(4)) Harcourt Trade Pubs.

Mighty Fine, Inc. Staff. French Kitty in Las Vegas Pair-a-Dice. 2005. (Illus.). 56p. 12.95 (978-0-8109-5861-6(9)) Abrams, Harry N. , Inc.

Milam, Mary Kay. The Zooming Star Babies. Date not set. (J). pap. (978-1-890622-65-7(6)) Leathers Publishing.

Mileto, Richard. Superbird. 2005. per. 15.50 (978-0-8059-9658-6(3)) Dorrance Publishing Co., Inc.

Milgrim, David. Amelia Makes a Movie. Milgrim, David, illus. 2008. 32p. (J). (ps). 16.99 (***978-0-399-24670-8(3)*** , Putnam Juvenile) Penguin Group (USA) Inc.

S

Milgrim, David. Time to Get up, Time to Go. 2006. (Illus.). 32p. (J). (ps-k). 15.00 (978-0-618-51998-9(X) , Clarion Bks.) Houghton Mifflin Co. Trade & Reference Div.

Milios, Rita. Bears Bears Everywhere. 2003. (gr. k-3). lib. bdg. 12.95 (978-0-613-66348-9(9)) Tandem Library Bks.

—Bears, Bears, Everywhere. Motoyama, Keiko, illus. rev. ed. 2003. (Rookie Reader Ser.). 32p. (J). 19.50 (978-0-516-22847-1(1) , Children's Pr.) Scholastic Library Publishing.

Millen, C. M. Blue Bowl Down: An Appalachian Rhyme. Meade, Holly, illus. 2004. 32p. (J). (gr. k-k). 16.99 (978-0-7636-1817-9(9)) Candlewick Pr.

Miller, Deborah U. & Ostrove, Karen. Fins & Scales: A Kosher Tale. Ostrove, Karen, illus. 2004. (Israel Ser.). (Illus.). 32p. (J). (gr. 1-3). pap. 4.95 (978-0-929371-25-2(9)) Kar-Ben Publishing.

Miller, Jessel. Calico Cat. Miller, Jessel, illus. 1999. (Illus.). 24p. (J). (ps-3). 20.00 (978-0-9660381-8-7(5)) Jessel Gallery.

Miller, Pam. Wrinkles. Ostrom, Bob, illus. 32p. (J). (gr. k-2). 2006. pap. 4.95 (978-0-516-25021-2(3)); 2005. 19.50 (978-0-516-24860-8(X)) Scholastic Library Publishing. (Children's Pr.).

Miller, Shannon Terry & Warner, Timothy. Tub Toys. Calderon, Lee, illus. 2007. 32p. (J). pap. 6.95 (***978-1-58246-235-6(6)*** , Tricycle Pr.) Ten Speed Pr.

Mills, Elizabeth. Tick-Tock Sharks. Bettoli, Delana, illus. 2005. 40p. (J). (ps-ps). 9.99 (978-0-439-72308-4(6) , Cartwheel Bks.) Scholastic, Inc.

Mills, Nancy Libbey. Hug a Bug. Wells, Shan, illus. 2001. 32p. (J). pap. 7.95 (978-1-893815-05-6(6)) Pie in the Sky Publishing, LLC.

Mimi. Jake Is Up! Dubin, Jill, illus. 1999. (Jake's World Ser.: Vol. 2). 26p. (J). (ps-k). bds. 6.95 (978-1-892780-01-0(1)) Giggles Group, Inc., The.

Minor, Florence. Christmas Tree! Minor, Wendell & Minor, Florence, illus. 2005. 40p. (J). lib. bdg. 16.89 (978-0-06-056035-5(5) , Tegen, Katherine Bks) HarperCollins Pubs.

Miranda, Anne. Beep! Beep! 2000. (ps-2). lib. bdg. 16.40 (978-0-613-27731-0(7)) Tandem Library Bks.

—Beep! Beep! A Vehicle Imagination Book. Murphy, David, illus. 2000. 32p. (J). (ps up). pap. 7.95 (978-1-890515-20-1(5)) Turtle Bks.

—Pignic. Hoffman, Rosekrans, illus. 2004. 32p. (J). pap. 7.95 (978-1-59078-328-3(X)) Boyds Mills Pr.

—Vroom, Chugga, Vroom-Vroom. 2000. (ps-2). lib. bdg. 16.40 (978-0-613-28127-0(6)) Tandem Library Bks.

Mitchard, Jacquelyn. Baby Bat's Lullaby. Noonan, Julia, illus. 2004. 32p. (J). (ps-1). 15.99 (978-0-06-050760-2(8)) HarperCollins Pubs.

Mitchell, Dawn. Always Zany Abcs. Molnar, Albert, illus. 2001. 16p. (J). pap. 5.95 (978-1-891846-25-0(6)) Business Word, The.

Mitton, Tony. All Afloat on Noah's Boat! Parker-Rees, Guy, illus. 2007. 32p. (J). (ps-3). pap. 16.99 (978-0-439-87397-0(5) , Orchard Bks.) Scholastic, Inc.

—Dazzling Diggers. Parker, Ant, illus. 2000. (Amazing Machines Ser.). 24p. (J). (ps-k). pap. 3.95 (978-0-7534-5304-9(5) , Kingfisher) Houghton Mifflin Co. Trade & Reference Div.

—Dazzling Diggers. 2000. (ps-2). lib. bdg. 11.80 (978-0-613-51344-9(4)) Tandem Library Bks.

—Dinosaurumpus! Parker-Rees, Guy, illus. 2003. 32p. (J). (ps-1). pap. 15.95 (978-0-439-39514-4(3) , Orchard Bks.) Scholastic, Inc.

—Down by the Cool of the Pool. Parker-Rees, Guy, illus. 2002. 32p. (J). (ps-k). pap. 15.95 (978-0-439-30915-8(8) , Orchard Bks.) Scholastic, Inc.

—Once upon a Tide. Young, Selina, illus. 2006. 40p. (J). (gr. k-1). 16.95 (978-0-385-75100-1(1)); lib. bdg. 18.99 (978-0-385-75101-8(X)) Random Hse. Children's Bks. (Fickling, David Bks.).

—Playful Little Penguins. Parker-Rees, Guy, illus. 2007. 32p. (J). (ps-1). 15.95 (***978-0-8027-9710-0(5)***) Walker & Co.

—Spooky Hour. Parker-Rees, Guy, illus. 2004. 32p. (J). pap. 16.95 (978-0-439-60373-7(0) , Orchard Bks.) Scholastic, Inc.

Mitton, Tony. Truckload of Fun. Parker, Ant, illus. 2007. (Amazing Machines Ser.). 24p. (J). (ps-1). 19.95 (***978-0-7534-6154-9(4)*** , Kingfisher) Houghton Mifflin Co. Trade & Reference Div.

Modesitt, Jeanne. Oh, What a Beautiful Day! Spowart, Robin, illus. 2008. (J). (***978-1-56397-409-0(6)***) Boyds Mills Pr.

Moffatt, Judith. Pumpkin Man. 2000. (Hello Reader! Ser.). (978-0-606-18885-2(1)) Tandem Library Bks.

Moncure, Jane Belk. My Sound Parade. King, Colin, illus. 2000. (New Sound Box Library). 32p. (J). (ps-3). 22.79 (978-1-56766-766-0(X)) Child's World, Inc.

Monks, Lydia. The Cat Barked? 2001. (J). 12.79 (978-0-606-21102-4(0)) Tandem Library Bks.

Monroe, Colleen. A Is for Ark: Noah's Journey. Monroe, Michael Glenn, illus. 2004. 38p. (ps-1). pap. 17.95 (978-0-9754942-0-2(1)) Storytime Pr., Inc.

—A Wish to Be a Christmas Tree. Monroe, Michael Glenn, illus. 2005. 32p. (J). (ps-3). bds. 6.99 (978-1-58536-269-1(7)) Sleeping Bear Pr.

Montenegro, Laura Nyman. A Poet's Bird Garden. 2007. (Illus.). 32p. (J). (ps-3). 16.00 (978-0-374-36038-2(3)) Farrar, Straus & Giroux.

Montes, Marisa. Los Gatos Black on Halloween. Morales, Yuyi, illus. rev. ed. 2006. 32p. (J). 16.95 (978-0-8050-7429-1(5) , Holt, Henry & Co. Bks. For Young Readers) Holt, Henry & Co.

Moore, Clement C. Grumpy Santa. Spiridellis, Gregg & Spiridellis, Evan, illus. 2003. (J). pap. (978-0-439-53039-2(3) , Orchard Bks.) Scholastic, Inc.

—The Night Before Christmas. 2004. (Illus.). 20p. (J). bds. 6.95 (978-0-8118-3933-4(8)) Chronicle Bks. LLC.

Moore, Clement C., ed. & illus. The Night Before Christmas. Moore, Clement C., illus. Price, Margaret Evans, illus. 2004. 16p. (J). (ps-3). pap. 9.95 (978-1-59583-009-8(X) , Green Tiger Pr.) Laughing Elephant.

Mora, Pat. ¡Marimba! Animales from A to Z. Cushman, Doug, illus. 2006. 32p. (J). (gr. k-3). 16.00 (978-0-618-19453-7(3) , Clarion Bks.) Houghton Mifflin Co. Trade & Reference Div.

— Uno, Dos, Tres. Lavallee, Barbara, illus. 2002. Tr. of One, Two, Three. (SPA.). (J). 14.74 (978-0-7587-3892-9(7)) Book Wholesalers, Inc.

—Uno, Dos, Tres. Lavallee, Barbara, illus. 2000. Tr. of One, Two, Three. (SPA & ENG.). 48p. (J). (gr. k-3). pap. 6.95 (978-0-618-05468-8(5) , Clarion Bks.) Houghton Mifflin Co. Trade & Reference Div.

—Uno, Dos, Tres: One, Two, Three. Lavallee, Barbara, illus. 2000. (SPA.). 43p. (ps-ps). lib. bdg. 15.25 (978-0-613-28687-9(1)) Tandem Library Bks.

Moreillon, Judi. Read to Me. Teis, Kyra, illus. 24p. (J). (ps-ps). 2004. per. 6.95 (978-1-59572-014-6(6)); 2003. 6.95 (978-1-932065-49-7(0) , 1-718-784-9112) Star Bright Bks., Inc.

Morris, Jackie. The Snow Leopard. 2007. (Illus.). 32p. (J). (ps-3). 16.95 (***978-1-84507-600-9(1)***) Lincoln, Frances Ltd. GBR. *Dist:* Perseus Distribution.

Morrow, Tara Jaye. Just Mommy & Me. Bratun, Katy, illus. 2004. 32p. (J). 13.89 (978-0-06-000725-6(7)) HarperCollins Pubs.

—Mommy Loves Her Baby/Daddy Loves His Baby. Beeke, Tiphanie, illus. 2003. 32p. (J). (ps-1). 15.99 (978-0-06-029077-1(3)); lib. bdg. 16.89 (978-0-06-029078-8(1)) HarperCollins Pubs.

Mortensen, Denise Dowling. Good Night Engines. Iwai, Melissa, illus. 2003. 32p. (J). (gr. k-3). 15.00 (978-0-618-13537-0(5) , Clarion Bks.) Houghton Mifflin Co. Trade & Reference Div.

—Ohio Thunder. Kiesler, Kate, illus. 2006. 32p. (J). (gr. k-3). 16.00 (978-0-618-59542-6(2) , Clarion Bks.) Houghton Mifflin Co. Trade & Reference Div.

—Wake up Engines. Iwai, Melissa, illus. 2007. 32p. (J). (ps-k). 16.00 (978-0-618-51736-7(7) , Clarion Bks.) Houghton Mifflin Co. Trade & Reference Div.

Morton, Jane & Dreier, Ted. Moozie's Cow Wisdom for Loving to the "Uddermost" Royse, Jane, illus. 2003. (J). pap. 4.95 (978-0-9662268-3-6(6)) Best Friends Bks.

Moses, Brian. Trouble at the Dinosaur Cafe. Parsons, Garry, illus. 2006. 32p. (J). 16.95 (978-0-8027-9599-1(4)) Walker & Co.

Moss, Lloyd. Music Is. Petit-Roulet, Philippe, illus. 2003. 32p. (J). (ps-2). 14.99 (978-0-399-23336-4(9) , Putnam Juvenile) Penguin Group (USA) Inc.

—Our Marching Band. Bluthenthal, Diana Cain, illus. 2001. 1p. (J). (ps-3). 15.99 (978-0-399-23335-7(0) , Putnam Juvenile) Penguin Group (USA) Inc.

—Zin! Zin! Zin! A Violin. Priceman, Marjorie, illus. 2002. (J). 15.53 (978-0-7587-0170-1(5)) Book Wholesalers, Inc.

—Zin! Zin! Zin! A Violin. Priceman, Marjorie, illus. (Stories to Go! Ser.). 32p. (J). 2005. 4.99 (978-1-4169-0838-8(2)); 2000. pap. 6.99 (978-0-689-83524-7(8)) Simon & Schuster Children's Publishing. (Aladdin).

Moss, Miriam. Bare Bear. McQuillan, Mary, illus. 2005. 32p. (J). 16.95 (978-0-8234-1934-0(7)) Holiday Hse., Inc.

Moulton, Mark K. The Visit. Winget, Susan, illus. 2003. 56p. (J). 14.95 (978-0-8249-5475-8(0)) Ideals Pubns.

Moulton, Mark Kimball. A Cricket's Carol. Blowers, Lisa, illus. 2004. 32p. (J). 14.95 (978-0-8249-5488-8(2)) Ideals Pubns.

—A Cricket's Carol. Blowers, Lisa, illus. 2000. 32p. (J). (gr. k-3). 18.00 (978-0-7412-0735-7(4)) Lang Graphics, Ltd.

—Everyday Angels. Winget, Susan, illus. 2003. 32p. (J). 14.95 (978-0-8249-5479-6(3)) Ideals Pubns.

—Everyday Angels. Winget, Susan, illus. 3rd ed. 2000. 32p. (J). (gr. k-3). 18.00 (978-0-7412-0737-1(0)) Lang Graphics, Ltd.

—Miss Fiona's Stupendous Pumpkin Pies. Crouch, Karen Hillard, illus. 2004. 28p. (J). 14.95 (978-0-8249-5489-5(0)) Ideals Pubns.

—Miss Fiona's Stupendous Pumpkin Pies. Crouch, Karen Hillard, illus. 2001. 21p. (J). (gr. k-3). 18.00 (978-0-7412-0865-1(2)) Lang Graphics, Ltd.

—One Enchanted Evening. Crouch, Karen Hillard, illus. 2003. 32p. (J). 14.95 (978-0-8249-5480-2(7)) Ideals Pubns.

—One Enchanted Evening. Crouch, Karen Hillard, illus. 2000. 32p. (J). (gr. k-3). 18.00 (978-0-7412-0439-4(8)) Lang Graphics, Ltd.

—A Royal Wedding. Good, Karen Hillard, illus. 2007. 32p. (J). (gr. k-3). 14.99 (***978-0-8249-8677-3(6)***) Ideals Pubns.

—Sadie McGee Who Lived in a Tree. Good, Karen Hillard, illus. 2006. 32p. (J). (ps). 16.95 (978-0-8249-5152-8(2) , Ideals Children's Bks.) Ideals Pubns.

—Scarecrow Pete & His Suitcase of Dreams. Crouch, Karen Hillard, illus. 2005. 36p. (J). (ps-3). 14.95 (978-0-8249-5151-1(4)) Ideals Pubns.

—A Snowgirl Named Just Sue. Good, Karen Hillard, illus. 2005. 36p. (J). (ps-3). 14.95 (978-0-8249-5150-4(6)) Ideals Pubns.

—A Snowman Named Just Bob. Crouch, Karen Hillard, illus. 2003. 36p. (J). 14.95 (978-0-8249-5860-2(8) , 53876801) Ideals Pubns.

—A Snowman Named Just Bob. Crouch, Karen Hillard, illus. 1999. 32p. (J). pap. 18.00 (978-0-7412-0283-3(2)) Lang Graphics, Ltd.

—A Snowman Named Just Bob: Boxed Notecards. Good, Karen Hillard, illus. 2006. 16p. (J). 14.95 (978-0-8249-1707-4(3)) Ideals Pubns.

—The Visit. Winget, Susan, tr. Winget, Susan, illus. 2003. 56p. (J). 14.95 (978-0-8249-5859-6(4)) Ideals Pubns.

—The Visit. Winget, Susan, illus. 2001. 48p. (J). (gr. 3-6). 22.00 (978-0-7412-0866-8(0)) Lang Graphics, Ltd.

Moulton, Mark Kimballl. The Annual Snowman's Ball. Hillaard, Karen, illus. 2007. 32p. (J). (ps-3). 14.99 (***978-0-8249-5564-9(1)*** , Ideals Children's Bks.) Ideals Pubns.

Mouse Works Staff. Dumbo. 2000. (Read-Aloud Storybook Ser.). 64p. (J). 6.99 (978-0-7364-1052-6(X)) Hyperion Bks. for Children.

—Dumbo. 1999. (Disney's Friendly Tales Ser.). (Illus.). 10p. (J). (ps-k). 6.99 (978-0-7364-1012-0(0)) Mouse Works.

—Simba. 1999. (Disney's Friendly Tales Ser.). (Illus.). 10p. (J). (ps-k). 6.99 (978-0-7364-1011-3(2)) Mouse Works.

Murphy. Best Bug Parade: Comparing Sizes Big Book. 2002. (Illus.), (J). pap. (978-0-7398-6775-4(X)) Steck-Vaughn.

—Circus Shapes: Recognizing Shapes Big Book. 2002. (Illus.). (J). pap. (978-0-7398-6779-2(2)) Steck-Vaughn.

—Every Buddy Counts: Counting Big Book. 2002. (Illus.). pap. (978-0-7398-6777-8(6)) Steck-Vaughn.

Murphy, Bonnie. Can A Rooster Drive A Tractor? Richardson, Shelley, illus. 2001. 32p. (J). 14.95 (978-0-9714419-0-3(1)) Alabama Farmers Federation.

Murphy, Patricia J. I Need You. Bryant, Laura J., illus. 2003. (Rookie Reader Ser.). 32p. (J). 19.50 (978-0-516-22595-1(2) , Children's Pr.) Scholastic Library Publishing.

Murphy, Stuart J. Spunky Monkeys on Parade. 1999. (MathStart Ser.). (Illus.). 40p. (YA). (gr. 1 up). 15.95 (978-0-06-028014-7(X)) HarperCollins Pubs.

—Spunky Monkeys on Parade. 1999. (Math Start Ser.). (978-0-606-17496-1(6)); lib. bdg. 13.00 (978-0-613-22430-7(2)) Tandem Library Bks.

Murray, Carol. Hurry Up! Garbot, Dave, illus. 2003. (Rookie Reader Ser.). 32p. (J). 19.50 (978-0-516-22585-2(5) , Children's Pr.) Scholastic Library Publishing.

—Jenny's Socks. Burris, Priscilla, tr. Burris, Priscilla, illus. 2004. (Rookie Reader Ser.). 31p. (J). 19.50 (978-0-516-25899-7(0) , Children's Pr.) Scholastic Library Publishing.

—Jennys Socks. Burris, Priscilla, illus. 2004. (Rookie Reader Skill Set Ser.). 32p. (J). (gr. k-2). pap. 4.95 (978-0-516-26826-2(0) , Children's Pr.) Scholastic Library Publishing.

My Brother & I. 2003. (Illus.). 24p. (J). (ps-k). bds. 7.95 (978-0-8249-5455-0(6)) Ideals Pubns.

My Crazy Christmas Catastrophe Cat. 2003. (Illus.). 22p. (J). 9.95 (978-0-9744751-1-0(4)) Timothy Lane Pr.

My Doctor, My Friend. 2002. (Illus.). 24p. (J). (ps-3). 5.95 (978-0-8249-5389-8(4)) Ideals Pubns.

My First Book of Bedtime Stories. 2003. (J). 8.99 (978-1-59384-013-6(6)) Parklane Publishing.

My First Reader, 10 Bks., Set. 2004. 175.00 (978-0-516-23716-9(0) , Children's Pr.) Scholastic Library Publishing.

My Grandma & I! 2002. (Illus.). 24p. (J). (ps-k). bds. 7.95 (978-0-8249-4220-5(5)) Ideals Pubns.

My Grandpa & I! 2002. (Illus.). 24p. (J). (ps-k). bds. 7.95 (978-0-8249-4219-9(1)) Ideals Pubns.

My Little Softplay Cube Books. 2002. (J). (978-1-931312-69-1(9)) SoftPlay, Inc.

My Mommy & I! 2002. (Illus.). 24p. (J). (ps-k). bds. 7.95 (978-0-8249-4218-2(3)) Ideals Pubns.

My Sister & I. 2003. (Illus.). 24p. (J). (ps-k). bds. 7.95 (978-0-8249-5456-7(4)) Ideals Pubns.

Myers, Bill. The House That Went Ker-Splat! The Parable of the Wise & Foolish Builder. Smith, Andy J., illus. 2008. (J). (***978-0-310-71220-6(3)***) Zonderkidz.

—Stink Bug Saves the Day! The Parable of the Good Samaritan. Smith, Andy J., illus. 2008. (J). (***978-0-310-71219-0(X)***) Zonderkidz.

Myers, Walter Dean. Jazz. Myers, Christopher, illus. 2006. 48p. (J). (gr. 4-8). 18.95 (978-0-8234-1545-8(7)) Holiday Hse., Inc.

—Street Love. (J). 2007. 160p. pap. 7.99 (***978-0-06-440732-8(2)***); 2006. 144p. 15.99 (978-0-06-028079-6(4)) HarperCollins Pubs. (Amistad).

Mykowski, Michelle. Explore God's Forest. Ring, Laura, ed. Mykowski, Michelle, illus. 1999. (Shaped Paperback Bks.). (Illus.). 24p. (J). (ps-1). pap. 3.99 (978-0-7847-0900-9(9) , 03790, Bean Sprouts) Standard Publishing.

Myra, Harold. Santa, Are You for Real? Kurisu, Jane, illus. 2005. 18p. (J). (ps-3). bds. 6.99 (978-1-4003-0629-9(9)) Nelson, Thomas Inc.

Nagel, Karen B. Snow? Let's Go! Croll, Carolyn, illus. 2000. (My First Hello Reader! Ser.). 32p. (J). (ps-1). pap. 3.99 (978-0-439-09906-6(4)) Scholastic, Inc.

—Snow? Let's Go! 2000. (Hello Reader! Ser.). (J). (978-0-606-19613-0(7)) Tandem Library Bks.

Nagy, Gloria & Chwast, Seymour. The Wizard Who Wanted to Be Santa. 2000. (Illus.). (J). (ps-3). 16.95 (978-0-9679436-0-2(4)) Sheer Bliss Communications, LLC.

Namm, Diane. Guess Who? Sheldon, David, illus. 2004. (My First Reader Ser.). 32p. (J). (gr. k-1). pap. 3.95 (978-0-516-25503-3(7) , Children's Pr.) Scholastic Library Publishing.

—Guess Who? Sheldon, David, tr. Sheldon, David, illus. 2004. (My First Reader Ser.). 31p. (J). 18.50 (978-0-516-24412-9(4) , Children's Pr.) Scholastic Library Publishing.

—Little Bear. McCue, Lisa, illus. 2003. (My First Reader Ser.). 32p. (J). 18.50 (978-0-516-22931-7(1) , Children's Pr.) Scholastic Library Publishing.

—My Best Friend. Gordon, Mike, illus. 2004. (My First Reader Ser.). 32p. (J). (gr. k-1). pap. 3.95 (978-0-516-25504-0(5) , Children's Pr.) Scholastic Library Publishing.

—My Best Friend. Gordon, Mike, tr. Gordon, Mike, illus. 2004. (My First Reader Ser.). 31p. (J). 18.50 (978-0-516-24416-7(7) , Children's Pr.) Scholastic Library Publishing.

—Pick a Pet. Suarez, Maribel, tr. Suarez, Maribel, illus. 2004. (My First Reader Ser.). 31p. (J). 18.50 (978-0-516-24417-4(5) , Children's Pr.) Scholastic Library Publishing.

Nash, Ogden. Custard the Dragon & the Wicked Knight. Munsinger, Lynn, illus. 1999. 32p. (J). (ps-3). pap. 6.99 (978-0-316-59905-4(0)) Little Brown & Co.

—Custard the Dragon & the Wicked Knight. 1999. (J). (gr. k up). pap., stu. ed. 25.20 incl. audio (978-0-7887-2986-7(1) , 40868); Class set. pap. 91.30 incl. audio (978-0-7887-3016-0(9) , 46833) Recorded Bks., LLC.

—The Tale of Custard the Dragon. Munsinger, Lynn, illus. 1998. 32p. (J). (ps-3). pap. 6.99 (978-0-316-59031-0(2)) Little Brown & Co.

—The Tale of Custard the Dragon. 1998. (J). (978-0-606-13833-8(1)) Tandem Library Bks.

Neitzel, Shirley. I'm Not Feeling Well Today. Parker, Nancy Winslow, illus. 2001. 32p. (J). (gr. k-2). 15.95 (978-0-688-17380-7(2)) HarperCollins Pubs.

—Who Will I Be? A Halloween Rebus Story. Parker, Nancy Winslow, illus. 2005. 32p. (J). 12.99 (978-0-06-056067-6(3)); lib. bdg. 13.89 (978-0-06-056068-3(1)) HarperCollins Pubs.

Nelsen, Michael & Nelsen, Wendy. My CTR Ring. Jensen, Jodi, illus. 2000. 32p. (J). (978-1-57345-467-4(2)) Scribbulations LLC.

Nelson, Esther. Blocks Are to Build. Hirsch, Davida, ed. Behr, Joyce, illus. l.t. ed. 1999. 28p. (Orig.). (J). (gr. k-1). pap. 7.95 (978-0-945110-15-6(4)) Granny Pr.

—Chairs Are to Sit. Hirsch, Davida, ed. Behr, Joyce, illus. l.t. ed. 1999. 28p. (Orig.). (J). (gr. k-1). pap. 7.95 (978-0-945110-14-9(6)) Granny Pr.

Nelson, Kadir A. He's Got the Whole World in His Hands. Nelson, Kadir A., illus. 2005. (Illus.). 32p. (J). (ps). 16.99 (978-0-8037-2850-9(6) , Dial) Penguin Group (USA) Inc.

Neubecker, Robert. Beasty Bath. 2005. (Illus.). 32p. (J). (ps-1). pap. 14.99 (978-0-439-64000-8(8) , Orchard Bks.) Scholastic, Inc.

Nevius, Carol. Building with Dad. Thomson, Bill, illus. 2006. 32p. (J). (ps-3). 16.99 (978-0-7614-5312-3(1)) Cavendish, Marshall Corp.

—Karate Hour. Thomson, Bill, illus. 2004. 32p. (J). 14.95 (978-0-7614-5169-3(2)) Cavendish, Marshall Corp.

New Pet. l.t. ed. 2005. (Illus.). 32p. (J). lib. bdg. 14.95 (978-0-9658365-8-6(4)) Beetle Bug Bks.

, New Players Club LLC, New Players Club L. L. C. Coco Boom Boom. 2006. 32p. 12.99 (978-1-4116-8191-0(6)) Lulu.com.

Newman, Barbara Johansen. Tex & Sugar: A Big City Kitty Ditty. Newman, Barbara Johansen, illus. 2007. (Illus.). 32p. (J). (gr. k-2). 14.95 (978-1-4027-3887-6(0)) Sterling Publishing Co., Inc.

Newman, Leslea. The Boy Who Cried Fabulous. Ferguson, Peter, illus. 32p. (J). (ps-2). 2007. pap. 7.95 (***978-1-58246-224-0(0)***); 2004. 15.95 (978-1-58246-101-4(5)) Ten Speed Pr. (Tricycle Pr.).

Newman, Leslea. Cats, Cats, Cats! Oller, Erika, illus. 2001. 32p. (J). (ps-1). 16.00 (978-0-689-83077-8(7)) Simon & Schuster Children's Publishing.

—Cats, Cats, Cats! 2001. (978-0-606-22791-9(1)) Tandem Library Bks.

Newman, Lesléa. Cats, Cats, Cats! Oller, Erika, illus. 2004. 32p. (J). reprint ed. pap. 6.99 (978-0-689-86697-5(6) , Aladdin) Simon & Schuster Children's Publishing.

Newman, Leslea. Runaway Dreidel! Brooker, Kyrsten, illus. 2007. 32p. (J). pap. 6.99 (***978-0-312-37142-5(X)***) Square Fish.

Newman, Lesléa. Skunk's Spring Surprise. Gorbachev, Valeri, illus. 2007. 44p. (J). 16.00 (978-0-15-205683-4(1)) Harcourt Trade Pubs.

Newman, Leslea. Where Is Bear? Gorbachev, Valeri, illus. 2004. 44p. (J). 16.00 (978-0-15-204936-2(3) , Gulliver Bks.) Harcourt Children's Bks.

Newman, Leslea & Gorbachev, Valeri. Where Is Bear? 2006. (Illus.). 44p. (J). pap. 6.00 (978-0-15-205918-7(0) , Voyager Bks./Libros Viajeros) Harcourt Children's Bks.

Newman, Leslea & Oller, Erika. Dogs, Dogs, Dogs! 2002. (Illus.). 32p. (J). (ps-3). 16.00 (978-0-689-84492-8(1)) Simon & Schuster Children's Publishing.

Nicola, Robbin. Fighter Joe: The Fish of Which Dreams Are Made. Wolf, Claudia, illus. 2006. 24p. (J). per. 2.99 (978-1-59958-001-2(2)) Journey Stone Creations, LLC.

Nikola-Lisa, W. My Teacher Can Teach—Anyone! Galindo, Felipe, illus. 2004. 32p. (J). (ps-2). 16.95 (978-1-58430-163-9(5)) Lee & Low Bks., Inc.

—Shake D'em Halloween Bones. 2000. (978-0-606-22080-4(1)) Tandem Library Bks.

—Shake Dem Halloween Bones. Reed, Mike, illus. 2000. 32p. (J). (gr. k-3). 6.95 (978-0-618-07034-3(6)) Houghton Mifflin Co. Trade & Reference Div.

—Summer Sun Risin' Tate, Don, illus. 32p. (J). (ps-ps). 2005. pap. 7.95 (978-1-58430-252-0(6)); 2002. 16.95 (978-1-58430-034-2(5)) Lee & Low Bks., Inc.

Nister, Ernest, illus. Merry Magic-Go-Round: An Antique Book of Changing Pictures. 2005. 14p. (J). (gr. k-4). reprint ed. 19.00 (978-0-7567-9156-8(1)) DIANE Publishing Co.

Nobisso, Josephine. Hot Cha Cha!, Holub, Joan, illus. 2004. 32p. (J). 16.95 (978-0-940112-18-6(3)) Gingerbread Hse.

—The Numbers Dance: A Counting Comedy. Ziborova, Dasha, illus. 2005. 32p. (J). (ps-4). 16.95 (978-0-940112-11-7(6)); pap. 8.95 (978-0-940112-12-4(4)) Gingerbread Hse.

Noonan, Julia. My Pumpkin. Lawson, Peter, illus. (J). (gr. k-1). 2006. 32p. pap. 3.95 (978-0-516-24973-5(8)); 2005. 31p. 18.50 (978-0-516-24876-9(6)) Scholastic Library Publishing. (Children's Pr.).

Noonen, Tom. Pelicans Belly Can. Fredericksen, Alison, illus. 1999. 38p. (J). (ps-3). 14.95 (978-1-893385-04-7(3)) Little Leaf Pr., Inc.

Novak, Matt. Flip Flop Bop. Novak, Matt, illus. rev. ed. 2005. (Illus.). 32p. (J). 15.95 (978-1-59643-049-5(4)) Roaring Brook Pr.

Noyes, Diana. The Tickle Bug. Noyes, Diana, illus. l.t. ed. 2005. (Illus.). 20p. (J). per. 9.99 (978-1-59879-080-1(3)) Lifevest Publishing, Inc.

Nozick, Betsy. Grandma & Me & Her Secret Recipe. Morgan, Polsky, illus. 2000. 32p. (J). 16.95 (978-1-57168-473-8(5)) Eakin Pr.

Numeroff, Laura Joffe. Chimps Don't Wear Glasses. Mathieu, Joe, illus. 2006. (Stories to Go! Ser.). 32p. (J). pap. 4.99 (978-1-4169-1859-2(0) , Aladdin) Simon & Schuster Children's Publishing.

—Chimps Don't Wear Glasses. 1998. (J). (ps-2). pap. 14.00 (978-0-671-87007-2(6) , Simon & Schuster Children's Publishing) Simon & Schuster Children's Publishing.

—Dogs Don't Wear Sneakers. Mathieu, Joe, illus. 2005. (Stories to Go! Ser.). 40p. (J). pap. 4.99 (978-0-689-87828-2(1) , Aladdin) Simon & Schuster Children's Publishing.

—Two for Stew. 1999. (978-0-606-17515-9(6)) Tandem Library Bks.

—When Sheep Sleep. McPhail, David, illus. 2006. 24p. (J). (ps-3). 15.95 (978-0-8109-5469-4(9)) Abrams, Harry N. , Inc.

Nyquist, Kate. Maggie's Coral Reef Adventure. McCord, Kathleen, illus. 2001. 32p. (J). (ps-2). 12.95 (978-1-878244-34-5(5)) Monterey Bay Aquarium.

Oades, Joy. Willie the Whale. Vagnozzi, Barbara, illus. 2004. (Read-It! Readers Ser.). 32p. (C). (gr. k-3). 18.60 (978-1-4048-0557-6(5)) Picture Window Bks.

Ochiltree, Dianne. It's a Firefly Night. Snyder, Betsy, illus. 2008. (J). (*978-1-55971-991-9(5) , NorthWord Bks. for Young Readers) T&N Children's Publishing.

Ochiltree, Dianne. Lull-a-Bye, Little One. Takahashi, Hideko, illus. 2006. 32p. (J). (gr. 1-ps). 16.99 (978-0-399-24305-9(4)) Penguin Group (USA) Inc.

Ochiltree, Dianne & D'Allance, Mireille. Pillow Pup. 2002. (Illus.). 32p. (J). (gr. k-3). 14.95 (978-0-689-83408-0(X) , McElderry, Margaret K.) Simon & Schuster Children's Publishing.

Ochiltree, Dianne & Lanquetin, Anne-Sophie. Sixteen Runaway Pumpkins. 2004. (Illus.). 24p. (J). 16.95 (978-0-689-85090-5(5) , McElderry, Margaret K.) Simon & Schuster Children's Publishing.

Ocker, Christ Holder. A Mouse Without a House. 2006. (J). per. (*978-1-59872-711-1(7)) Instantpublisher.com.

O'Clair, Rita M. & Hocker, Katherine M. Where Is Dinah Diatom? 2000. (Illus.). 16p. (J). (ps-4). pap. (978-0-9664245-2-2(2)) Plant Pr.

O'Connor, Jane. Ready, Set, Skip! James, Ann, illus. 2007. 32p. (J). (ps-k). 15.99 (978-0-670-06216-4(2) , Viking Adult) Penguin Group (USA) Inc.

Odanaka, Barbara. Skateboard Mom. Adinolfi, JoAnn, illus. 2004. 32p. (J). (ps-3). 15.99 (978-0-399-23867-3(0) , Putnam Juvenile) Penguin Group (USA) Inc.

—Smash! Mash! Crash! There Goes the Trash! Hillenbrand, Will, illus. 2006. 32p. (J). (ps-3). 15.95 (978-0-689-85160-5(X) , McElderry, Margaret K.) Simon & Schuster Children's Publishing.

Odziemek, John. Catching Wayward Sheep. 2006. 128p. 21.99 (978-1-4141-0563-5(0)) Pleasant Word.

O'Garden, Irene. The Scrubbly-Bubbly Car Wash. Jabar, Cynthia, illus. 2003. 32p. (J). (ps-1). 15.99 (978-0-694-00871-1(0)) HarperCollins Pubs.

O'Hair, Margaret. My Pup. Lyon, Tammie, illus. 2008. (J). (*978-0-7614-5389-5(X)) Cavendish, Marshall Corp.

—Star Baby. Kono, Erin Eitter, illus. 2005. 32p. (J). (gr. k-ps). 16.00 (978-0-618-30668-8(4) , Clarion Bks.) Houghton Mifflin Co. Trade & Reference Div.

—Twin to Twin. Courtin, Thierry, illus. 2003. 32p. (J). 16.99 (978-0-689-84494-2(8) , McElderry, Margaret K.) Simon & Schuster Children's Publishing.

Ohi, Ruth. Me & My Sister. Ohi, Ruth, illus. 2005. (Illus.). 24p. (J). (gr. k-ps). pap. 5.95 (978-1-55037-892-4(9)); lib. bdg. 19.95 (978-1-55037-893-1(7)) Annick Pr., Ltd. CAN. *Dist:* Firefly Bks., Ltd.

O'Keefe, Susan Heyboer. Baby Day. Spowart, Robin, illus. 2006. 32p. (J). 15.95 (978-1-56397-981-1(0)) Boyds Mills Pr.

—Christmas Gifts. Emery, Jennifer, illus. 2004. 32p. (J). (ps up). 15.95 (978-1-59078-083-1(3)) Boyds Mills Pr.

—Hungry Monster ABC: An Alphabet Book. Munsinger, Lynn, illus. 2007. 32p. (J). (ps-1). 12.99 (978-0-316-15574-8(8)) Little Brown & Co.

—Love Me, Love You. Spowart, Robin, illus. 2003. 32p. (J). (ps up). 15.95 (978-1-56397-837-1(7)) Boyds Mills Pr.

—One Hungry Monster: A Counting Book in Rhyme. Munsinger, Lynn, illus. 2001. 10p. (J). (ps-k). bds. 6.99 (978-0-316-60804-6(1)) Little Brown & Co.

Old MacDonald's Pigs. 2002. 16p. (J). pap. 2.98 (978-0-7525-7062-4(5)) Parragon, Inc.

Old MacDonald's Sheep. 2002. 16p. (J). pap. 2.98 (978-0-7525-7058-7(7)) Parragon, Inc.

Olson-Brown, Ellen. Ten Stinky Babies. 2005. (Illus.). 28p. (J). (ps-ps). 12.95 (978-1-58246-137-3(6) , Tricycle Pr.) Ten Speed Pr.

Olson, David. The Thunderstruck Stork. Munsinger, Lynn, illus. 2007. (J). (ps-2). 15.95 (*978-0-8075-7910-7(6)) Whitman, Albert & Co.

One Baby Jesus. 2005. (Ideals Christmas Classic Ser.). (Illus.). 30p. (J). 3.95 (978-0-8249-5511-3(0)) Ideals Pubns.

Ong, Christina. Little Engine That Could ABC Time. 2000. (ps-2). lib. bdg. 11.25 (978-0-613-26024-4(4)) Tandem Library Bks.

Oppenheim, Joanne. The Prince's Bedtime. Latimer, Miriam, illus. 2005. 32p. (J). 16.99 (978-1-84148-597-3(7)) Barefoot Bks., Inc.

Orgel, Doris. Sarah's Room. Sendak, Maurice, illus. 2005. 47p. (J). (gr. k-4). reprint ed. 15.00 (978-0-7567-9683-9(0)) DIANE Publishing Co.

Orleans, Daniel Elliot. Snow Buddies. 2007. (Illus.). 14p. (ps). bds. 9.95 (*978-1-59354-605-2(X)) Blue Apple Bks.

Orloff, Karen Kaufman. If Mom Had Three Arms. Whitehead, Pete, illus. 2006. 32p. 14.95 (978-1-4027-2356-8(3)) Sterling Publishing Co., Inc.

Ormerod, Jan. If You're Happy & You Know It! Gardiner, Lindsey, illus. 2003. 32p. (J). (ps-3). pap. 5.95 (978-1-932065-10-7(5)); 15.95 (978-1-932065-07-7(5)) Star Bright Bks., Inc.

—If You're Happy & You Know It! 2003. (gr. k-3). lib. bdg. 14.10 (978-0-613-80469-1(4)) Tandem Library Bks.

Ornstein, Mike. The Daddy Longlegs Blues. Kopelke, Lisa, illus. 2008. (J). (*978-1-4027-4359-7(9)) Sterling Publishing Co., Inc.

Otto, Gina. Cassandra's Angel. Joost, Trudy, illus. 2001. 32p. (ps-3). 15.95 (978-0-935699-20-3(1)) Illumination Arts Publishing Co., Inc.

Out on the Tundra. 2005. 14.95 (978-1-888125-96-2(9)) Publication Consultants.

Owens, Mary Beth. Panda Whispers. 2007. (Illus.). 32p. (J). (ps-2). 16.99 (978-0-525-47171-4(5) , Dutton Juvenile) Penguin Group (USA) Inc.

Oxenbury, Helen. Pig Tale. Oxenbury, Helen, illus. 2005. (Illus.). 32p. (J). 16.95 (978-1-4169-0277-5(5) , McElderry, Margaret K.) Simon & Schuster Children's Publishing.

Pace, Dianne. Odel's Diner. 2007. (J). per. 12.95 (*978-0-89315-419-6(9)) Lambert Bk. Hse., Inc.

Packard, Mary. It's Thanksgiving Day! Ewing, C. S., illus. 2001. (Hello Reader! Ser.). (J). pap. (978-0-439-32101-3(8)) Scholastic, Inc.

—The Missing Tooth. Ulrich, George, illus. 2002. (Hello Reader! Ser.). (J). 3.99 (978-0-439-32094-8(1)) Scholastic, Inc.

—The New Baby. Haley, Amanda, illus. 2004. (My First Reader Ser.). 32p. (J). (gr. k-1). pap. 3.95 (978-0-516-25506-4(1) , Children's Pr.) Scholastic Library Publishing.

—The New Baby. Haley, Amanda, tr. Haley, Amanda, illus. 2004. (My First Reader Ser.). 31p. (J). 18.50 (978-0-516-24409-9(4) , Children's Pr.) Scholastic Library Publishing.

—The Shy Scarecrow. Huang, Benrei, illus. 2001. (Hello Reader! Ser.). (J). (978-0-439-31704-7(5)) Scholastic, Inc.

—The Very Bad Day. Allen, Joy, tr. Allen, Joy, illus. 2004. (My First Reader Ser.). 31p. (J). 18.50 (978-0-516-24415-0(9) , Children's Pr.) Scholastic Library Publishing.

Packard, Mary & Mitier, Matt. Same & Different: Comparison Rhymes. Banta, Susan & Cushman, Doug, illus. 2004. (Rhyme Time Learning Ser.). 16p. (J). (gr. 1 up). lib. bdg. 20.67 (978-0-8368-4097-1(6)) Stevens, Gareth Inc.

Packard, Mary & Mitier, Matt. Once upon a Rhyme: Story Rhymes. Banta, Susan & Cushman, Doug, illus. 2004. (Rhyme Time Learning Ser.). 16p. (J). (gr. 1 up). lib. bdg. 20.67 (978-0-8368-4096-4(8)) Stevens, Gareth Inc.

—1, 2, 3: Counting Rymes. Cushman, Doug & Banta, Susan, illus. 2004. (Rhyme Time Learning Ser.). 16p. (J). (gr. 1 up). lib. bdg. 20.67 (978-0-8368-4094-0(1)) Stevens, Gareth Inc.

Page, Nick & Claire. Elves & the Shoemaker. 2006. (Read with Me (Make Believe Ideas) Ser.). (Illus.). 32p. (J). (gr. k-2). 3.95 (978-1-84610-161-8(1)) Make Believe Ideas GBR. *Dist:* Ingram Pub. Services.

—Jack & the Beanstalk. 2006. (Read with Me (Make Believe Ideas) Ser.). (Illus.). 32p. (J). (gr. k-2). 3.95 (978-1-84610-164-9(6)) Make Believe Ideas GBR. *Dist:* Ingram Pub. Services.

Paluch, Beily. Braid the Challah: A Playful Action Rhyme. Argoff, Beily, illus. 2004. 10p. (J). bds. 5.95 (978-1-929628-17-9(X)) Hachai Publishing.

Panahi, H. L. The Bebop Express. Johnson, Steve & Fancher, Lou, illus. 2005. 32p. (J). (ps-3). 15.99 (978-0-06-057190-0(X)); lib. bdg. 16.89 (978-0-06-057191-7(8)) HarperCollins Pubs. (Geringer, Laura Book).

Paraskevas, Betty. Peter Pepper's Pet Spectacular. Paraskevas, Michael, illus. 2007. 32p. (J). (gr. 2-6). pap. 14.95 (*978-1-60095-257-9(7)) Carson-Dellosa Publishing Co., Inc.

Park, Barbara. Ma! There's Nothing to Do Here! A Word from Your Baby-In-Waiting. Garofoli, Viviana, illus. 2008. 40p. (J). (*978-0-375-83852-1(X)); lib. bdg. (*978-0-375-93852-8(4)) Random Hse., Inc.

Park, Linda Sue. Bee-Bim Bop! Lee, Ho Baek, illus. 2005. 32p. (J). (gr. k-3). 15.00 (978-0-618-26511-4(2) , Clarion Bks.) Houghton Mifflin Co. Trade & Reference Div.

—What Does Bunny See? A Book of Colors & Flowers. Smith, Maggie, illus. 2005. 32p. (J). (ps-k). 15.00 (978-0-618-23485-1(3) , Clarion Bks.) Houghton Mifflin Co. Trade & Reference Div.

Parker, Jessie, et al. Barbie: A Dress-up Day. S. I. International Staff, illus. 2003. (Step into Reading Ser.). 32p. (J). (ps-1). pap. 3.99 (978-0-375-82501-9(0) , Random Hse. Bks. for Young Readers) Random Hse. Children's Bks.

Parker, Marjorie. Hello, Fire Truck! Kolar, Bob, illus. 2004. (Scholastic Reader Ser.). 32p. (J). (ps-3). pap. 3.99 (978-0-439-59890-3(7) , Cartwheel Bks.) Scholastic, Inc.

—Hello, Freight Train Level 1. Kolar, Bob, illus. 2005. (Scholastic Reader Ser.). 32p. (J). pap. 3.99 (978-0-439-59891-0(5)) Scholastic, Inc.

Parker, Marjorie Blain. Hello, Freight Train! Kolar, Bob, illus. 2005. (Scholastic Reader Ser.). (J). (*978-1-4155-7966-4(0)) Scholastic, Inc.

—Hello, Freight Train! Kolar, Bob, illus. 2005. 28p. (J). (ps-ps). lib. bdg. 10.79 (978-0-606-33279-8(0)) Tandem Library Bks.

—Hello, School Bus! Kolar, Bob, tr. Kolar, Bob, illus. 2004. (Scholastic Reader Ser.). 32p. (J). pap. 3.99 (978-0-439-59889-7(3) , Cartwheel Bks.) Scholastic, Inc.

—Hello, School Bus! Kolar, Bob, illus. 2004. 28p. (ps-ps). lib. bdg. 11.19 (978-0-606-30604-1(8)) Tandem Library Bks.

—Ice Cream Everywhere! Roth, Stephanie, illus. 2002. (Rhyme Time Readers Ser.). (J). 1.95 (978-0-439-33397-9(0)) Scholastic, Inc.

Parker, Toni Trent. Snowflake Kisses & Gingerbread Smiles. Anderson, Earl, illus. 2002. 16p. (J). pap. 6.95 (978-0-439-33872-1(7) , Cartwheel Bks.) Scholastic, Inc.

—Sweets & Treats. Anderson, Earl, illus. 2002. 16p. (J). pap. 6.95 (978-0-439-33871-4(9) , Cartwheel Bks.) Scholastic, Inc.

Paul, Alison. The Crow (A Not So Scary Story) 2007. (Illus.). 40p. (J). (gr. 3-5). 16.00 (*978-0-618-66380-4(0)) Houghton Mifflin Co.

Paul, Ann W. Hello Toes! Hello Feet! Wescott, Nadine Bernard, illus. 2000. (J). (978-0-606-19770-0(2)) Tandem Library Bks.

Paul, Ann Whitford. Everything to Spend the Night: From A to Z. 2001. (978-0-606-22366-9(5)) Tandem Library Bks.

Paulsen, Gary. Worksong. Paulsen, Ruth Wright, illus. 2000. 32p. (J). (ps-3). pap. 7.00 (978-0-15-202371-3(2) , Harcourt Paperbacks) Harcourt Children's Bks.

—Worksong. 2000. (978-0-606-18199-0(7)); lib. bdg. 15.30 (978-0-613-28707-4(X)) Tandem Library Bks.

Pawlitz, Gail. Sing Glory Glory! Jesus Is Born! Jung, Sehee, illus. 2007. 10p. (J). (ps). bds. 6.99 (*978-0-7586-1310-3(5)) Concordia Publishing Hse.

Paxton, Tom. Jennifer's Rabbit. Miles, Elizabeth, illus. 2001. 32p. (J). (ps-3). 15.89 (978-0-06-029216-4(4)); 15.95 (978-0-688-15262-8(7)) HarperCollins Pubs.

—The Marvelous Toy. 2000. (Metro Reading Program Ser.). (J). (gr. k). 7.98 (978-1-58120-970-9(3)); 45.95 (978-1-58830-028-7(5)) Metropolitan Teaching & Learning Co.

Payne, Nina. Summertime Waltz. Swiatkowska, Gabi, illus. 2005. 32p. (J). 16.00 (978-0-374-37291-0(8) , Farrar, Straus & Giroux (BYR)) Farrar, Straus & Giroux.

Pearson, Debora. Big City Song! Reed, Lynn Rowe, illus. 2006. 32p. (J). 16.95 (978-0-8234-1988-3(6)) Holiday Hse., Inc.

Pearson, Mary. Pickles in My Soup. Payne, Tom, illus. 2000. 31p. (J). (ps-3). lib. bdg. 12.95 (978-0-613-54634-8(2)) Tandem Library Bks.

Pearson, Mary E. Fast Dan. Doty, Eldon C., illus. 2003. (Rookie Reader Skill Set Ser.). 32p. (J). (gr. k-2). pap. 4.95 (978-0-516-27494-2(5) , Children's Pr.) Scholastic Library Publishing.

—Fast Dan. 2002. (Rookie Readers Ser.). (J). lib. bdg. 19.00 (978-0-516-22563-0(4) , Children's Pr.) Scholastic Library Publishing.

—Fast Dan. Doty, Eldon C., illus. 2002. (Rookie Readers Ser.). 31p. (J). (gr. 1-2). 19.50 (978-0-516-22239-4(2) , Children's Pr.) Scholastic Library Publishing.

—Fast Dan. 2002. (gr. k-3). lib. bdg. 12.95 (978-0-613-59476-9(2)) Tandem Library Bks.

—Generous Me. Krejca, Gary, illus. (Rookie Reader Espanol Ser.). (J). 2003. 32p. (gr. k-2). pap. 4.95 (978-0-516-27819-3(3)); 2002. 31p. (gr. 1-2). 19.50 (978-0-516-22253-0(8)) Scholastic Library Publishing. (Children's Pr.).

—Generous Me. 2002. (gr. k-3). lib. bdg. 12.95 (978-0-613-59484-4(3)) Tandem Library Bks.

—I Can Do It All: Level B. Shelly, Jeff, illus. 2002. (Rookie Readers Ser.). 32p. (J). (gr. 1-2). 19.50 (978-0-516-22240-0(6) , Children's Pr.) Scholastic Library Publishing.

—Pickles in My Soup. Payne, Tom, illus. 2000. (Rookie Reader Skill Set Ser.). 32p. (J). (gr. k-2). pap. 4.95 (978-0-516-26550-6(4) , Children's Pr.) Scholastic Library Publishing.

Pearson, Tracey Campbell. Little Bo-Peep. 2004. (Mother Goose Board Bks.). (Illus.). 14p. (J). bds. 5.95 (978-0-374-30859-9(4) , Farrar, Straus & Giroux (BYR)) Farrar, Straus & Giroux.

Peck, Jan. Way down Deep in the Deep Blue Sea. Petrone, Valeria, illus. 2004. 32p. (J). 16.99 (978-0-689-85110-0(3)) Simon & Schuster Children's Publishing.

—Way up High in a Tall Green Tree. Petrone, Valeria, illus. 2005. 32p. (J). (ps-ps). 15.95 (978-1-4169-0071-9(3)) Simon & Schuster Children's Publishing.

Peck, Judith. The Bright Blue Button & the Button-Hole. Stasolla, Mario, illus. 2004. 28p. (J). 18.95 (978-0-9746119-5-2(6)) Imagination Arts Pubns.

Peddicord, Jane Ann & So, Meilo. That Special Little Baby. 2007. (Illus.). 40p. (J). (ps-2). 16.00 (978-0-15-205430-4(8)) Harcourt Trade Pubs.

Pepin, Rebecca. Bobby Dog & the Flying Frog. Fuller, Cari, illus. 2004. (J). 16.99 (978-0-9760684-0-2(0)); pap. 11.99 (978-0-9760684-1-9(9)) FullofPep Pubns.

Perez-Mercado, Mary Margaret. Splat! 2000. (Rookie Reader Espanol Ser.). (Illus.). 24p. (J). (gr. k-2). pap. 4.95 (978-0-516-26543-8(1) , Children's Pr.) Scholastic Library Publishing.

—Splat! Torrey, Richard L., illus. 1999. (Rookie Readers Ser.). 24p. (J). (gr. k-1). 19.50 (978-0-516-21615-7(5) , Children's Pr.) Scholastic Library Publishing.

—Splat! 1999. (gr. k-3). lib. bdg. 12.95 (978-0-613-54858-8(2)) Tandem Library Bks.

Perkins, Al. The Ear Book. Payne, Henry, illus. 2007. 36p. (J). (gr. k-1). 8.99 (978-0-375-84251-1(9)); lib. bdg. 12.99 (978-0-375-94251-8(3)) Random Hse. Children's Bks. (Random Hse. Bks. for Young Readers).

—The Nose Book. Perkins, Al, illus. 2002. (Illus.). (J). 15.74 (978-0-7587-1509-8(9)) Book Wholesalers, Inc.

—The Nose Book. Mathieu, Joe, illus. 2002. 36p. (J). (gr. k-3). 8.99 (978-0-375-81212-5(1) , Random Hse. Bks. for Young Readers) Random Hse. Children's Bks.

Perl, Erica S. Chicken Bedtime Is Really Early. Bates, George, illus. 2005. 32p. (J). (ps-1). 14.95 (978-0-8109-4926-3(1)) Abrams, Harry N. , Inc.

—Ninety-Three in My Family. Lester, Mike, illus. 2006. 32p. (J). (ps-3). 15.95 (978-0-8109-5760-2(4)) Abrams, Harry N. , Inc.

Perry, Michael. Turntable Timmy. Cunningham, Douglas, illus. 2002. 32p. (J). (gr. 2-5). 18.95 incl. audio compact disk (978-0-9701771-7-9(8)) Free Will Pr.

Perry, Rex, illus. All Things Bright & Beautiful. 2004. 24p. (J). lib. bdg. 8.00 (*978-1-4242-0638-4(3)) Fitzgerald Bks.

Persun, Morgan R. No Pets Allowed. Banks, Timothy, illus. 1998. 32p. (J). (ps-1). pap. 5.49 (978-1-57924-077-6(1)) Jones, Bob Univ. Pr.

—No Pets Allowed. 1998. (gr. k-3). lib. bdg. 13.55 (978-0-613-81217-7(4)) Tandem Library Bks.

Peters, Lisa. Cold Little Duck, Duck, Duck. Williams, Sam, illus. 2005. 32p. (J). (ps up). 6.99 (978-0-06-072223-4(1) , Harper Festival) HarperCollins Pubs.

Peters, Lisa Westberg. Sleepyhead Bear. Schoenherr, Ian, illus. 2006. (J). 32p. 16.99 (978-0-06-059675-0(9)); 40p. lib. bdg. 17.89 (978-0-06-059676-7(7)) HarperCollins Pubs.

—We're Rabbits! Mack, Jeff, illus. 2004. 32p. (J). 16.00 (978-0-15-204671-2(2)) Harcourt Children's Bks.

Petrosino, Tamara, illus. No Plain Hair. 2006. (I'm Going to Read Ser.). 32p. (J). pap. 3.95 (978-1-4027-3083-2(7)) Sterling Publishing Co., Inc.

Petty, Dini. The Queen, the Bear & the Bumblebee. Cowles, Rose, illus. 32p. (J). 19.95 (978-1-55285-151-7(6)) Whitecap Bks., Ltd. CAN. *Dist:* Graphic Arts Ctr. Publishing Co.

Pham, LeUyen. Big Sister, Little Sister. 2005. (Illus.). 40p. (ps-3). 15.99 (978-0-7868-5182-9(1)) Hyperion Bks. for Children.

Philip, Neil. The Fish Is Me! Bathtime Rhymes. Henley, Claire, illus. 2002. 32p. (J). (gr. k-3). tchr. ed. 16.00 (978-0-618-15939-0(8) , Clarion Bks.) Houghton Mifflin Co. Trade & Reference Div.

Phillips, Jan. Just for Today. Shapiro, Alison Bonds, illus. 2005. 32p. (J). (ps-5). 15.95 (978-1-932073-07-2(8)) Kramer, H.J. Inc.

Phillips, Jean. The Meaning of Christmas: A Children's Story in Picture & Verse. 2005. (ENG., Illus.). 24p. pap. 7.95 (978-0-929292-67-0(7) , 800-747-0738) Hannibal Bks.

Phillips, Leigh Hope. Birthday Wishes. Fountain, John, illus. 2005. (J). pap. (978-1-933156-10-1(4)); per. (978-1-933156-03-3(1)) GSVQ Publishing. (VisionQuest Kids).

Phillips, Sally Kahler. Nonsense! 2006. (Illus.). 32p. (J). (ps-2). 14.95 (978-0-375-83306-9(4) , Random Hse. Bks. for Young Readers) Random Hse. Children's Bks.

Phillips, Terrie. The Ski Trip. 2006. (Illus.). 38p. (J). lib. bdg. 12.95 (*978-0-9789449-0-2(9)) Tbooks Publishing Co.

Pierce, Craig. A Greyhound's Tale: Running for Glory, Walking for Home. Santiago, Tony, illus. 2004. (J). per. 15.00 (978-0-9762564-0-3(1) , American Dog) Ideate Prairie.

Pierce, Terry. Tae Kwon Do! Bonita, Todd, illus. 2006. (Step into Reading Ser.). 32p. (J). (ps-1). pap. 3.99 (978-0-375-83448-6(6)); lib. bdg. 11.99 (978-0-375-93448-3(0)) Random Hse. Children's Bks. (Random Hse. Bks. for Young Readers).

Piernas-Davenport, Gail. Shanté Keys & the New Year's Peas. Eldridge, Marion, illus. 2007. 32p. (J). (gr. k-4). 16.95 (*978-0-8075-7330-3(2)) Whitman, Albert & Co.

Pinczes, Elinor J. Inchworm & a Half. Enos, Randall, illus. 2003. 32p. (J). pap. 5.95 (978-0-618-31101-9(7)) Houghton Mifflin Co. Trade & Reference Div.

—Inchworm & a Half. Mackain, Bonnie & Enos, Randall, illus. 2001. 32p. (J). (gr. k-3). tchr. ed. 15.00 (978-0-395-82849-6(X)) Houghton Mifflin Co. Trade & Reference Div.

—Inchworm & a Half. 2001. (gr. k-3). lib. bdg. 14.10 (978-0-613-60769-8(4)) Tandem Library Bks.

—My Full Moon Is Square. Enos, Randall, illus. 2002. 32p. (J). (gr. k-3). tchr. ed. 15.00 (978-0-618-15489-0(2)) Houghton Mifflin Co. Trade & Reference Div.

—A Remainder of One. MacKain, Bonnie, illus. 2002. 32p. (J). (gr. k-3). pap. 5.95 (978-0-618-25077-6(8)) Houghton Mifflin Co. Trade & Reference Div.

Pingry, Patricia A. Noses & Toes. Rose, Drew, illus. 2005. (J). (978-0-8249-6594-5(9) , Candy Cane Pr.) Ideals Pubns.

—On Christmas Morning. Barretta, Gene, illus. 2007. 26p. (J). (ps-k). bds. 6.99 (*978-0-8249-6713-0(5) , Candy Cane Pr.) Ideals Pubns.

Pingry, Patricia A. Sounds. Rose, Drew, illus. 2005. (J). (978-0-8249-6596-9(5) , Candy Cane Pr.) Ideals Pubns.

Plourde, Lynn. Dino Pets. Kendall, Gideon, illus. 2007. 32p. (J). (ps-1). 15.99 (978-0-525-47778-5(0) , Dutton Juvenile) Penguin Group (USA) Inc.

—Grandpappy Snippy Snappies. Santoro, Christopher, illus. (J). Date not set. 16.89 (978-0-06-029528-8(7)); 2002. 15.99 (978-0-06-028050-5(6)) HarperCollins Pubs.

Plourde, Lynn & Couch, Greg. Spring's Sprung. 2002. (Illus.). 32p. (J). (ps-3). 16.00 (978-0-689-84229-0(5)) Simon & Schuster Children's Publishing.

Plourde, Paulette. My Magic Pillow. 2005. (Illus.). 40p. (J). per. 8.99 (978-1-932338-76-8(4)) Lifevest Publishing, Inc.

S

Plume, Ilse, illus. The Twelve Days of Christmas. 2005. 32p. (J). 17.95 (978-1-56792-300-1(3)) Godine, David R. Pub.

Polacco, Patricia. G Is for Goat. Gauch, Patricia Lee, ed. Polacco, Patricia, illus. 2003. (Illus.). 32p. (J). (ps-1). 16.99 (978-0-399-24018-8(7) , Philomel) Penguin Group (USA) Inc.

—G Is for Goat. Polacco, Patricia, illus. 32p. (J). 2007. 6.99 (978-0-399-24530-5(8) , Philomel); 2006. (Illus.). reprint ed. pap. 6.99 (978-0-14-240550-5(7) , Puffin) Penguin Group (USA) Inc.

Polette, Nancy. Flying with Mother Goose. 2003. pap. 7.95 (978-1-931334-19-8(6) , CLC0285) Pieces of Learning.

Polette, Nancy & Shaw, Charles. Grandma's Patchy Pocket. 2004. (Illus.). 16p. (J). (gr. k-3). pap. 4.95 (978-1-57874-075-8(4)) Kaeden Corp.

Pollack, Pam & Belviso, Meg. Halloween Night on Shivermore Street. DuBurke, Randy, illus. 2004. 32p. (J). 15.95 (978-0-8118-3946-4(X)) Chronicle Bks. LLC.

Porter, Annaliese & Bancroft, Bronwyn. The Outback. 2005. (Illus.). 28p. (J). 20.95 (978-1-875641-86-4(6)) Magabala Bks. AUS. *Dist:* International Specialized Bk. Services.

Porter, Pamela. The Crazy Man. 2005. 176p. (J). (gr. 4-7). 15.95 (978-0-88899-694-7(2)) Groundwood Bks. CAN. *Dist:* Perseus Distribution.

Post, Jim. Frog in the Kitchen Sink. Vasconsellos, Daniel, illus. 2001. 28p. bds. 9.99 (978-1-57939-098-3(6)) Accord Publishing, Ltd.

Post, Jim & Post, Janet. Barnyard Boogie. Vasconsellos, Daniel, illus. gif. ed. 2003. 32p. (J). 15.99 (978-1-57939-130-0(3)) Accord Publishing, Ltd.

Powers, Christine. Love Is a Rainbow. 1999. (Leap Frog Lift-A-Flap Ser.). (Illus.). (J). (978-0-7853-3370-8(3)) Publications International, Ltd.

Price, Hope Lynne. These Hands. Collier, Bryan, illus. rev. ed. 2007. 24p. (ps-1). pap. 6.99 (***978-1-4231-0633-3(4)*** , Jump at the Sun) Hyperion Bks. for Children.

Price, Mary Ellizabeth. Wallbaby Bumblebees. 2004. (Illus.). 40p. (J). per. 15.75 (978-0-9715402-2-4(5) , 410-707-6686) Barnhardt & Ashe Publishing, Inc.

Prince, April Jones. Valentine Friends. Schlossberg, Elisabeth, illus. 2007. 24p. (J). pap. 3.99 (978-0-439-79999-7(6)) Scholastic, Inc.

Prince, Joshua. I Saw an Ant in a Parking Lot. Pamintuan, Macky, illus. 2007. 24p. (J). (ps-k). 14.95 (978-1-4027-3823-4(4)) Sterling Publishing Co., Inc.

—I Saw an Ant on the Railroad Track. Pamintuan, Macky, illus. 2006. 24p. (J). 14.95 (978-1-4027-2183-0(8) , 1252268) Sterling Publishing Co., Inc.

Protopopescu, Orel Odinov. Two Sticks. Wilsdorf, Anne, illus. 2007. 32p. (J). (ps-1). 16.00 (978-0-374-38022-9(8)) Farrar, Straus & Giroux.

Provencher, Rose-Marie. Slithery Jake. Carter, Abby, illus. 2004. 32p. (J). 15.99 (978-0-06-623820-3(X)) HarperCollins Pubs.

—Slithery Jake. Provencher, Rose-Marie & Carter, Abby, illus. 2004. 32p. (J). lib. bdg. 17.89 (978-0-06-623821-0(8)) HarperCollins Pubs.

Provost, Elizabeth. Ten Little Sleepyheads. Saaf, Donald, illus. 2005. 32p. (J). 16.95 (978-1-58234-838-4(3)) Bloomsbury Publishing.

Pumphrey, Jerome & Pumphrey, Jarrett. Creepy Things Are Scaring Me! Litzinger, Rosanne, illus. 2003. 32p. (J). (ps-3). lib. bdg. 15.89 (978-0-06-028963-8(5)) HarperCollins Pubs.

Pumphrey, W. Jerome. Creepy Things Are Scaring Me! (Illus.). 32p. (J). (ps-3). 5.99 (978-0-06-443680-9(2)) HarperCollins Pubs.

Purdy, Betty Jane. Aunt Hattie, Aunt Mattie, & Aunt Pattie. 2005. (ENG., Illus.). 32p. (J). per. (978-1-4141-0365-5(4)) Pleasant Word.

Rabe, Tish. Pigs of a Feather. 1998. (J). 7.99 (978-0-679-89089-8(0) , Random Hse. Bks. for Young Readers) Random Hse. Children's Bks.

Raczka, Bob. Spring Things. Stead, Judy, illus. 2007. 32p. (J). 16.95 (978-0-8075-7596-3(8)) Whitman, Albert & Co.

Raczka, Bob. Who Loves the Fall? Stead, Judy, illus. 2007. 29p. (J). (ps-1). 16.95 (***978-0-8075-9037-9(1)***) Whitman, Albert & Co.

Radzinski, Kandy. What Cats Want for Christmas. rev. ed. 2007. (Holiday Ser.). 32p. (J). 16.95 (***978-1-58536-340-7(5)***) Sleeping Bear Pr.

Rae, Jennifer. Gilbert de la Frogponde: A Swamp Story. braille ed. 2004. (Illus.). (J). (gr. k-3). spiral bd. (978-0-616-03054-7(1)); spiral bd. (978-0-616-04561-9(1)) Canadian National Institute for the Blind/Institut National Canadien pour les Aveugles.

—Gilbert de la Frogponde: A Swamp Story. Cowles, Rose, illus. 2000. 32p. (J). (ps-12). pap. 9.95 (978-1-55285-087-9(0)) Whitecap Bks., Ltd. CAN. *Dist:* Firefly Bks., Ltd.

Raintree Steck-Vaughn Staff, contrib. by. I Went Walking. 1999. (J). (ps-3). pap. 23.95 (978-0-8172-9788-6(X)) Steck-Vaughn.

Ralph, Brian. Crum Bums. 2007. (Illus.). 208p. (YA). pap. 15.00 (***978-1-60309-002-5(9)***) Top Shelf Productions.

Rand, Ann & Rand, Paul. Little 1. 2006. (Illus.). 40p. (J). 15.95 (978-0-8118-5004-9(8)) Chronicle Bks. LLC.

Random House Disney Staff. Run, Remy, Run! 2007. (Step into Reading Ser.). (Illus.). 32p. (J). (ps-1). pap. 3.99 (978-0-7364-2476-9(8)); lib. bdg. 11.99 (978-0-7364-8054-3(4)) Random Hse. Children's Bks. (RH/Disney).

Ransom, Candice. I Like Shoes. LaFleur, David, illus. 2006. 24p. (J). (gr. k-2). pap. 4.95 (978-0-516-25017-5(5) , Children's Pr.) Scholastic Library Publishing.

Ransom, Candice F. I Like Shoes. LaFleur, David, illus. 2005. (Rookie Reader Ser.). 23p. (J). (ps-ps). 19.50 (978-0-516-24858-5(8) , Children's Pr.) Scholastic Library Publishing.

—Tractor Day. Bryant, Laura J., illus. 2007. 32p. (J). (ps). 17.85 (978-0-8027-8091-1(1)) Walker & Co.

Ransom, Candice F. & Bryant, Laura. Tractor Day. Bryant, Laura, illus. 2007. (Illus.). 32p. (J). (ps). 16.95 (978-0-8027-8090-4(3)) Walker & Co.

Rao, Rama Pemmaraju. Nine Tales from the Heart: Stories with Unique, Inspiring Messages for School-Ag. 2001. (gr. 3-6). lib. bdg. 28.00 (978-0-613-74700-4(3)) Tandem Library Bks.

Raschka, Chris. Can't Sleep. Raschka, Chris, illus. 1999. (Illus.). (J). (ps-1). 32p. 15.99 (978-0-531-08779-4(4)); 16p. bds. 6.95 (978-0-531-30201-9(6)); 32p. pap. 14.95 (978-0-531-09479-2(0)) Scholastic, Inc. (Orchard Bks.).

—Five for a Little One. Raschka, Chris, illus. 2006. (Illus.). 48p. (J). (ps-k). 16.95 (978-0-689-84599-4(5) , Atheneum/Richard Jackson Bks.) Simon & Schuster Children's Publishing.

Rash, Andy. Agent A to Agent Z. 2004. (Illus.). (J). (978-0-439-36883-4(9) , Levine, Arthur A. Bks.) Scholastic, Inc.

—Agent A to Agent Z. Rash, Andy, illus. 2004. (Illus.). 40p. (J). (gr. 1-3). pap. 16.95 (978-0-439-36882-7(0) , Levine, Arthur A. Bks.) Scholastic, Inc.

Rasmussen, Halfdan Wedel. The Ladder. Nelson, Marilyn, tr. from DAN. Pratt, Pierre, illus. 2006. 62p. (J). (ps-2). 17.99 (978-0-7636-2282-4(6)) Candlewick Pr.

Rathmann, Peggy. The Day the Babies Crawled Away. Rathmann, Peggy, illus. 2003. (Illus.). 40p. (J). (ps-2). 16.99 (978-0-399-23196-4(X) , Putnam Juvenile) Penguin Group (USA) Inc.

Ratnett, Michael. Dracula Steps Out. Goulding, June & Smyth, Iain, illus. 2005. 12p. (J). (gr. k-4). reprint ed. 16.00 (978-0-7567-8585-7(5)) DIANE Publishing Co.

Rau, Dana Meachen. Carlitos Friolento. Lemelman, Martin, illus. (Rookie Reader Espanol Ser.). (SPA.). 24p. (J). (gr. k-2). 2002. pap. 4.95 (978-0-516-26208-6(4)); 2001. 19.50 (978-0-516-22352-0(6) , CP1128) Scholastic Library Publishing. (Children's Pr.).

—Chilly Charlie. Lemelman, Martin, illus. 2001. (Rookie Reader Espanol Ser.). 24p. (J). (gr. k-2). pap. 4.95 (978-0-516-27288-7(8) , Children's Pr.) Scholastic Library Publishing.

—Chilly Charlie. 2001. (gr. k-3). lib. bdg. 12.95 (978-0-613-54123-7(5)) Tandem Library Bks.

—Clown Around, Level B. Evans, Nate, illus. 2001. (Early Reader Ser.). 32p. (J). (gr. k up). lib. bdg. 18.60 (978-0-7565-0074-0(5)) Compass Point Bks.

—Feet. Stromoski, Rick, illus. 2000. (Rookie Reader Espanol Ser.). 24p. (J). (gr. k-2). pap. 4.95 (978-0-516-27042-5(7)); 19.50 (978-0-516-22008-6(X)) Scholastic Library Publishing. (Children's Pr.).

—Feet. 2000. (gr. k-3). lib. bdg. 12.95 (978-0-613-54486-3(2)) Tandem Library Bks.

—Hands. Stromoski, Rick, illus. 2000. (Rookie Reader Espanol Ser.). 24p. (J). (gr. k-2). pap. 4.95 (978-0-516-27043-2(5)); 19.50 (978-0-516-22009-3(8)) Scholastic Library Publishing. (Children's Pr.).

—Hands. 2000. (gr. k-3). lib. bdg. 12.95 (978-0-613-54531-0(1)) Tandem Library Bks.

—Hats!, Level B. Harvey, Paul, illus. 2001. (Early Reader Ser.). 32p. (J). (gr. k up). lib. bdg. 18.60 (978-0-7565-0073-3(7)) Compass Point Bks.

—I'll Make You a Card, Level C. Bryan-Hunt, Jan, illus. 2002. (Compass Point Early Reader Ser.). 32p. (J). (gr. k up). lib. bdg. 18.60 (978-0-7565-0172-3(5)) Compass Point Bks.

—Look down Low, Level A. Adnet, Bernard, illus. 2002. (Compass Point Early Reader Ser.). 24p. (J). (gr. k up). lib. bdg. 18.60 (978-0-7565-0173-0(3)) Compass Point Bks.

—Look for Ladybugs. Schneider, Christine, illus. 2007. (Rookie Reader Ser.). 30p. (J). pap. (***978-0-531-12493-2(2)***) Children's Pr., Ltd.

—Look for Ladybugs. 2006. (Rookie Reader Skill Set Ser.). (Illus.). 32p. (J). (gr. k-2). 19.50 (978-0-531-12470-3(3) , Children's Pr.) Scholastic Library Publishing.

—Mi Lugar Preferido. Kim, Julie J., illus. 2005. (Rookie Reader Espanol Ser.). (SPA & ESP.). 31p. (J). (gr. k-2). pap. 4.95 (978-0-516-25534-7(7) , Children's Pr.) Scholastic Library Publishing.

—My Special Space. 2004. (Rookie Reader Espanol Ser.). (Illus.). 31p. (J). (gr. k-2). pap. 4.95 (978-0-516-27788-2(X) , Children's Pr.) Scholastic Library Publishing.

—My Special Space. Kim, Julie J., illus. 2003. (Rookie Reader - Level C Ser.). 32p. (J). 19.50 (978-0-516-22881-5(1) , Children's Pr.) Scholastic Library Publishing.

—Pet Your Pet, Level B. Scherer, Jeffrey, illus. 2002. (Compass Point Early Reader Ser.). 32p. (J). (gr. k up). lib. bdg. 18.60 (978-0-7565-0175-4(X)) Compass Point Bks.

—Rubber Duck, Level C. Girouard, Patrick, illus. 2001. (Early Reader Ser.). 32p. (J). (gr. k up). lib. bdg. 18.60 (978-0-7565-0121-1(0)) Compass Point Bks.

—Say "Hi" up High, Level A. Dammer, Mike, illus. 2002. (Compass Point Early Reader Ser.). 24p. (J). (gr. k up). lib. bdg. 18.60 (978-0-7565-0176-1(8)) Compass Point Bks.

—Stickers, Shells, & Snow Globes. Thivierge, Claude, illus. 2004. (Read-It! Readers Ser.). 32p. (C). (gr. k-3). 18.60 (978-1-4048-0648-1(2)) Picture Window Bks.

—Stickers, Shells, & Snowglobes. 2004. (Compass Point Early Reader Ser.). (J). 18.60 (978-0-7565-0574-5(7)) Compass Point Bks.

Rau, Dana Meachen & Rojas, Mary G. Shoo Crow, Shoo!, Level A. 2001. (Early Reader Ser.). (Illus.). 24p. (J). (gr. k up). lib. bdg. 18.60 (978-0-7565-0072-6(9)) Compass Point Bks.

Rauchwerger, Diane Levin. Dinosaur on Hanukkah. Wolff, Jason, illus. 2005. 24p. (J). (ps-6). pap. 6.95 (978-1-58013-143-8(3)); 15.95 (978-1-58013-145-2(X)) Kar-Ben Publishing.

—Dinosaur on Shabbat. Wolff, Jason, illus. 2006. (J). 15.95 (978-1-58013-159-9(X)) Kar-Ben Publishing.

Ravishankar, Anushka. Excuse Me, Is This India? Leutwiler, Anita, illus. 2003. 28p. (J). 7.99 (978-81-86211-56-4(X)) Penguin Group (USA) Inc.

—Tiger on a Tree. Biswas, Pulak, illus. 2004. 48p. (J). 15.00 (978-0-374-37555-3(0) , Farrar, Straus & Giroux (BYR)) Farrar, Straus & Giroux.

Reber, Deborah. Magenta & Me. Bishop, Don, illus. 2000. (Blues Clue's Ready to Read Ser.: No. 2). 24p. (J). (ps-1). pap. 3.99 (978-0-689-83123-2(4) , Simon Spotlight/Nickelodeon) Simon & Schuster Children's Publishing.

—Magenta & Me. 2000. (gr. k-3). lib. bdg. 11.80 (978-0-613-26094-7(5)) Tandem Library Bks.

Redding, Sue. Up above & down Below. 2006. (Illus.). 32p. (J). 14.95 (978-0-8118-4876-3(0)) Chronicle Bks. LLC.

Redfield, James & Lillegard, Dee. The Song of Celestine. Morrissey, Dean, illus. 2004. 46p. (J). (gr. 4-8). reprint ed. 15.00 (978-0-7567-8115-6(9)) DIANE Publishing Co.

Redmond, Shirley-Raye. The Princesses' Lucky Day. 2007. (Illus.). 24p. (J). (***978-1-4048-1242-0(3)***) Picture Window Bks.

—The Princesses' Lucky Day. Rooney, Ronnie, illus. 2006. 24p. (J). (***978-1-4048-3143-8(6)***) Picture Window Bks.

Reece, Robert. Freeman A. Freelander. Gallina, Todd, illus. 2002. 40p. (J). 11.95 (978-0-9702308-1-2(8)) Dark Horse Pr.

Reed, Lynn R. Julius Anteater, Misunderstood. rev. ed. 2005. (Illus.). 32p. (J). 15.95 (978-1-59643-042-6(7)) Roaring Brook Pr.

Reeves, Howard. There Was an Old Witch. 2000. (gr. k-3). lib. bdg. 14.15 (978-0-613-31797-9(1)) Tandem Library Bks.

Refrrolo, C. T. Grandchild of Mine: You & I. 2006. (J). 12.00 (978-0-8059-6845-3(8)) Dorrance Publishing Co., Inc.

Regan, Dana. Monkey See, Monkey Do. Regan, Dana, illus. 2000. (All Aboard Reading Ser.). (Illus.). 32p. (J). (ps-3). pap. 3.99 (978-0-448-42299-2(9) , Grosset & Dunlap) Penguin Group (USA) Inc.

Regan, Dana, illus. Messy Bessey's School Desk. 2002. (Messy Bessey Ser.). (J). 12.83 (978-0-7587-7189-6(4)) Book Wholesalers, Inc.

Reich, Ashley. Izzy Lizzy. Reich, Ashley, illus. 2005. (Illus.). 32p. (J). per. 16.00 (978-0-9754298-3-9(3) , Ithaca Pr.) Authors & Artists Publishers of New York, Inc.

Reichert, Amy. While Mama Had a Quick Little Chat. Boiger, Alexandra, illus. 2005. 40p. (J). 15.95 (978-0-689-85170-4(7) , Atheneum) Simon & Schuster Children's Publishing.

Reiser, Lynn. My Baby & Me. Gentieu, Penny, illus. 2008. 32p. (J). (ps-1). 16.99 (***978-0-375-85205-3(0)*** , Knopf Bks. for Young Readers) Random Hse. Children's Bks.

Reiser, Lynn. You & Me, Baby. Gentieu, Penny, illus. 2006. 40p. (J). (gr. k-ps). lib. bdg. 17.99 (978-0-375-93401-8(4) , Knopf Bks. for Young Readers) Random Hse. Children's Bks.

—You & Me, Baby. Gentieu, Penny, photos by. 2006. (Illus.). 40p. (J). (gr. k-ps). 15.95 (978-0-375-83401-1(X) , Knopf Bks. for Young Readers) Random Hse. Children's Bks.

Reiss, Mike. The Great Show & Tell Disaster! Cressy, Mike, illus. 2001. 32p. (J). 13.99 (978-0-8431-7680-3(6) , Price Stern Sloan) Penguin Group (USA) Inc.

—How Murray Saved Christmas. Catrow, David, illus. 2000. 32p. (J). (ps-3). 10.99 (978-0-8431-7610-0(5) , Price Stern Sloan) Penguin Group (USA) Inc.

—Late for School. Austin, Michael, illus. 2003. 32p. (J). (gr. 1-5). 16.95 (978-1-56145-286-6(6) , Q35957) Peachtree Pubs., Ltd.

—Santa Claustrophobia. Catrow, David, illus. 2002. 32p. (J). (gr. 2-5). 10.99 (978-0-8431-7756-5(X) , Price Stern Sloan) Penguin Group (USA) Inc.

—Santa Claustrophobia. Catrow, David, illus. 2006. 32p. (J). (ps). pap. 5.99 (978-0-14-240376-1(8) , Puffin) Penguin Group (USA) Inc.

Reiss, Mike. Santa's Eleven Months Off. Montgomery, Michael, illus. 2007. 32p. (J). (ps-3). 16.95 (***978-1-56145-421-1(4)*** , Peachtree Junior) Peachtree Pubs., Ltd.

Reiss-Weimann, Elayne. Who's New at the Zoo? Wetzel, Rick, illus. 2002. (Read-To-Me Ser.). 25p. (J). (978-0-7665-1226-9(6)) Abrams, Harry N., Inc.

Reitman, Andrea. Mouse in the House: Pop-Up Playset. Bell, Karen, illus. 2001. 3p. (J). (ps-k). 16.95 (978-1-58117-156-3(0) , Intervisual/Piggy Toes) Dalmatian Pr.

Rex, Adam. Tree-Ring Circus. 2006. (Illus.). 32p. (J). 16.00 (978-0-15-205363-5(8)) Harcourt Trade Pubs.

Rex, Michael. Dunk Skunk. Rex, Michael, illus. 2005. (Illus.). 32p. (J). 10.99 (978-0-399-24281-6(3) , Putnam Juvenile) Penguin Group (USA) Inc.

—Goodnight Goon. 2008. 32p. (J). (ps-k). 14.99 (***978-0-399-24534-3(0)*** , Putnam Juvenile) Penguin Group (USA) Inc.

Rex, Michael. Truck Duck. Rex, Michael, illus. (J). (ps-ps). 2008. 28p. bds. 6.99 (***978-0-399-25092-7(1)***); 2004. (Illus.). 34p. 9.99 (978-0-399-24009-6(8)) Penguin Group (USA) Inc. (Putnam Juvenile).

Rexroth, Sharon. America from the Sky. 2006. (J). 9.95 (***978-1-57166-429-7(7)***); per. 22.95 (***978-1-57166-430-3(0)***) Quixote Pr.

—Ohio. 2006. (J). per. 19.95 (***978-1-57166-421-1(1)***) Quixote Pr.

Rey, H. A. Elizabite: Adventures of A Carnivorous Plant. 1999. (gr. k-3). lib. bdg. 14.10 (978-0-613-21489-6(7)) Tandem Library Bks.

Reynolds, Aaron. Breaking Out of the Bungle Bird: Based on Proverbs 13:10. Whitehead, Peter, illus. 2005. (Insect-Inside Ser.). 40p. (J). 9.99 (978-0-310-70956-5(3)) Zonderkidz.

Rhoades, Heather. Picture Me in the Circus. 2000. (Picture Me Ser.). (Illus.). 10p. (J). (ps up). bds. 4.99 (978-1-57151-586-5(0)) Playhouse Publishing.

Rich, Francine Poppo. Small, Not Tall. Difilippi, Thomas, illus. 2001. 32p. (J). (ps-3). 16.00 (978-0-9674602-2-2(0)) Blue Marlin Pubns.

Richards, Arlene. That's Bingzy! Busy Building Self-Esteem. 2007. (J). per. 15.95 (***978-0-9794323-2-3(4)***) Bing Note, Inc.

Richards, Chuck. Jungle Gym Jitters. Richards, Chuck, illus. 2004. (Illus.). 32p. (J). 17.85 (978-0-8027-8932-7(3)); 16.95 (978-0-8027-8931-0(5)) Walker & Co.

Richards, Helene. Disney Winnie the Pooh Music Play Storybook. 2005. (RD Innovative Book & Player Format Ser.). (Illus.). 40p. (J). 24.99 (978-0-7944-0768-1(4)) Reader's Digest Assn., Inc., The.

Richards, Jean, reader. Madeline & the Gypsies. 2004. (Illus.). (J). pap. 18.95 incl. audio compact disk (978-1-59112-821-2(8)) Live Oak Media.

—Madeline in London. 2004. (Illus.). (J). pap. 18.95 incl. audio compact disk (978-1-59112-817-5(X)) Live Oak Media.

—Madeline's Rescue. 2004. (Illus.). (J). pap. 18.95 incl. audio compact disk (978-1-59112-809-0(9)) Live Oak Media.

Ridley, Sharon, illus. My Wildflower Friends. Phillips, Marilyn, photos by. 2006. (J). (978-0-9786168-0-9(4)) Rio Wildflower Pubns.

Ries, Lori Anne. Mrs. Fickle's Pickles. Cote, Nancy, illus. 2006. (J). 15.95 (978-1-59078-195-1(3)) Boyds Mills Pr.

Ringler, Matt. One Little, Two Little, Three Little Apples. Kennedy, Anne, illus. 2005. (J). pap. (***978-0-439-77500-7(0)***) Scholastic, Inc.

Rink, Cindy. Where Does the Wind Blow? 2002. (gr. k-3). lib. bdg. 16.40 (978-0-613-52797-2(6)) Tandem Library Bks.

Rink, Cynthia A. Where Does the Wind Blow? Rink, Cynthia A., illus. 2004. (Sharing Nature with Children Book Ser.). (Illus.). 32p. (J). (gr. k-5). 16.95 (978-1-58469-041-2(0)) Dawn Pubns.

Rink, Cynthia A., illus. Where Does the Wind Blow? 2004. (Sharing Nature with Children Book Ser.). 32p. (J). pap. 7.95 (978-1-58469-040-5(2)) Dawn Pubns.

Ritchie, Alison. Me & My Dad! Edgson, Alison, illus. 2007. 28p. (J). (ps-2). 16.95 (***978-1-56148-565-9(9)***) Good Bks.

Ritchie, Joseph R. Frosty the Snowman Returns. Rose, Drew, illus. 2006. 14p. (J). (ps). bds. 9.95 (978-0-8249-6670-6(8) , Candy Cane Pr.) Ideals Pubns.

—Peek-a-Boo! Halverson, Lydia, illus. 2004. 14p. (J). bds. 7.95 (978-0-8249-6550-1(7)) Ideals Pubns.

—Peter Cottontail's Busy Day. Halverson, Lydia, illus. 2005. 16p. (J). bds. 9.95 (978-0-8249-6571-6(X)) Ideals Pubns.

—Peter Cottontail's Easter Egg Hunt. Thornburgh, Rebecca McKillip, illus. 2004. 12p. (J). (ps-k). bds. 9.95 (978-0-8249-6522-8(1)) Ideals Pubns.

—Where's Santa? Halverson, Lydia, illus. 2006. 14p. (J). (ps). bds. 7.95 (978-0-8249-6673-7(2) , Candy Cane Pr.) Ideals Pubns.

Ritter, Philip. Tales in Rhyme from Three Little Mischief Maker's Country Time: The Escapades of Three Little Mischief Makers. 2005. (J). pap. 10.00 (978-0-8059-6928-3(4)) Dorrance Publishing Co., Inc.

Roberson, Karla. My Shoelaces Are Hard to Tie! Holley, Vanessa D., illus. 2004. 32p. (J). lib. bdg. 15.00 (***978-1-4242-0224-9(8)***) Fitzgerald Bks.

Roberts, Bethany. Cat Skidoo. Alley, R. W., tr. Alley, R. W., illus. rev. ed. 2004. 32p. (J). 16.95 (978-0-8050-6710-1(8) , Holt, Henry & Co. Bks. For Young Readers) Holt, Henry & Co.

—Christmas Mice. Cushman, Doug, illus. 2004. 32p. (J). (gr. k-ps). 5.95 (978-0-618-48601-4(1) , Clarion Bks.) Houghton Mifflin Co. Trade & Reference Div.

—Easter Mice! Cushman, Doug, illus. 2003. 32p. (J). (gr. k-ps). tchr. ed. 13.00 (978-0-618-16455-4(3) , Clarion Bks.) Houghton Mifflin Co. Trade & Reference Div.

—Fourth of July Mice! Cushman, Doug, illus. 2004. (Holiday Mice Ser.). 32p. (J). (gr. k-ps). 13.00 (978-0-618-31366-2(4) , Clarion Bks.) Houghton Mifflin Co. Trade & Reference Div.

—Thanksgiving Mice! Cushman, Doug, illus. 32p. (J). (ps-k). 2005. 5.95 (978-0-618-60486-9(3)); 2001. tchr. ed. 13.00 (978-0-618-12040-6(8)) Houghton Mifflin Co. Trade & Reference Div. (Clarion Bks.).

Robertson, Patrisha. Cirque du Soleil: Parade of Colors. Robertson, Patrisha, tr. Cirque du Soleil Group, illus. Seib, Al, photos by. 2003. 40p. (J). (ps-3). 15.95 (978-0-8109-4515-9(0)) Abrams, Harry N., Inc.

Robinson, Don Leonard, illus. G Is for Gecko: An Alphabet Adventure in Hawaii. 2006. (J). (***978-1-933067-18-6(7)***) Beachhouse Publishing, LLC.

Robinson, Hilary. Croc by the Rock. Gordon, Mike, illus. 2005. 32p. (J). lib. bdg. 9.00 (***978-1-4242-0885-2(8)***) Fitzgerald Bks.

—The Croc by the Rock, Level 1. Gordon, Mike, illus. 2005. (Lightning Readers Ser.). 32p. (J). (ps-k). pap., pap. 3.95 (978-0-7696-4219-2(5) , Gingham Dog Pr.) School Specialty Publishing.

—Freddie's Fears. Collins, Ross, illus. 2004. (Read-It! Readers Ser.). 32p. (C). (gr. k-3). 18.60 (978-1-4048-0056-4(5)) Picture Window Bks.

Robinson, Tim. Tobias, the Quig & the Rumplenut Tree. Robinson, Tim, illus. 2000. (Illus.). 40p. (J). (ps-3). 16.95 (978-1-890817-20-6(1)) Winslow Pr.

Robleda, Margarita. Ramon y Su Raton. Suarez, Maribel, illus. (Rana, Rema, Rimas Ser.). (SPA.). 16p. (J). (gr. k-3). 7.95 (978-1-59437-818-8(5)) Santillana USA Publishing Co., Inc.

Roche, Denis & London, Jonathan. Train Goes Clickety-clack. 2007. (Illus.). 32p. (J). (ps-k). 15.95 (***978-0-8050-7972-2(6)***) Holt, Henry & Co.

Rock, Lois. I Wish Tonight. Wilson, Anne, illus. 2001. 28p. (J). (ps-3). 16.00 (978-1-56148-315-0(X)) Good Bks.

—I Wonder Why? Corr, Christopher, illus. 2000. 32p. (J). pap. 9.99 (978-0-7459-4461-6(2) , Lion) Lion Hudson plc GBR. *Dist:* Independent Pubs. Group.

Rock, Lois & Buckingham, Gabriella. Now You Are. 2002. (Illus.). 28p. 4.99 (978-1-56148-394-5(X)); 2nd ed. 4.99 (978-1-56148-395-2(8)); 3rd ed. 4.99 (978-1-56148-396-9(6)) Good Bks.

—Now You Are 4. 2002. (Illus.). 28p. 4.99 (978-1-56148-397-6(4)) Good Bks.

Rock Steady. 2001. (J). 101.70 incl. cd-rom (978-0-06-623706-0(8)) HarperCollins Pubs.

Rodriguez, Antonio Orlando. Mi Bicicleta es un Hada y Otros Secretos Por el Estilo. (SPA.). 68p. (J). (gr. k-2). (978-958-30-0797-2(8)) Panamericana Editorial COL. *Dist:* Lectorum Pubns., Inc.

Rohmann, Eric. Cinder-Eyed Cat. 2001. (gr. k-3). lib. bdg. 15.30 (978-0-613-36797-4(9)) Tandem Library Bks.

—The Cinder-Eyed Cats. 2001. 40p. (J). (gr. k-3). pap. 6.99 (978-0-440-41743-9(0) , Dragonfly Bks.) Random Hse. Children's Bks.

—The Cinder-Eyed Cats. 2001. 13.79 (978-0-606-22187-0(5)) Tandem Library Bks.

Rondon, Javier. The Absent-Minded Toad. Cabrera, Marcela, illus. 2002. 28p. (J). pap. 6.95 (978-1-929132-39-3(5)) Kane/Miller Bk. Pubs., Inc.

Roop, Connie. Octopus under the Sea. 2001. (gr. k-3). lib. bdg. 11.80 (978-0-613-35544-5(X)); (Illus.). (J). (978-0-606-21363-9(5)) Tandem Library Bks.

Roosa, Karen. Beach Day. Smith, Maggie, illus. 2001. 40p. (J). (gr. k-3). tchr. ed. 16.00 (978-0-618-02923-5(0) , Clarion Bks.) Houghton Mifflin Co. Trade & Reference Div.

Root, Phyllis. Looking for a Moose. Cecil, Randy, illus. 2006. 40p. (J). (ps-k). 15.99 (978-0-7636-2005-9(X)) Candlewick Pr.

—One Duck Stuck. Chapman, Jane, illus. 2001. 32p. (J). (gr. k-ps). bds. 6.99 (978-0-7636-1104-0(2)) Candlewick Pr.

—One Duck Stuck. 2003. (gr. k-3). lib. bdg. 14.15 (978-0-613-60361-4(3)) Tandem Library Bks.

—One Duck Stuck: A Mucky Ducky Counting Book. Chapman, Jane, illus. 2003. 40p. (J). (gr. k-k). pap. 5.99 (978-0-7636-1566-6(8)) Candlewick Pr.

—Ten Sleepy Sheep. Gaber, Susan, illus. 2004. 32p. (J). (gr. k-k). 15.99 (978-0-7636-1545-1(5)) Candlewick Pr.

Rosario, Joann. Swiggly Swiggly Do! Rosario, Joann, illus. 2004. (Illus.). 5p. (J). (ps-5). pap. 10.00 (978-0-9758746-6-0(7) , 1246169) J.G.R. Enterprises.

Rose, Deborah Lee. Birthday Zoo. Munsinger, Lynn, illus. 2002. 24p. (J). (ps-1). 15.95 (978-0-8075-0776-6(8)) Whitman, Albert & Co.

Rosebush, Beatrice. What Would I Do if I Met a Moose? Cooke, Sean, illus. 1999. 24p. (J). pap. 8.00 (978-0-9678193-0-3(X)) Ebeemee Pubs.

Rosen, Wendy & End, Jackie. Chicken Fingers, Mac & Cheese... Why Do You Always Have to Say Please? Tuck-Bernstein, Cheryl, illus. 2005. 32p. (J). 14.99 (978-0-7666-1986-9(9)) Modern Publishing.

Rosenbaum, Andria Warmflash. A Grandma Like Yours: A Grandpa Like Yours. Bjornson, Barbara, illus. 2006. (J). 16.95 (978-1-58013-167-4(0)) Kar-Ben Publishing.

Rosenthal, Amy Krouse. It's Not Fair. Lichtenheld, Tom, illus. 2008. 40p. (J). 16.99 (***978-0-06-115257-3(9)***); lib. bdg. 17.89 (***978-0-06-115258-0(7)***) HarperCollins Pubs.

Rosenwald, Laurie. And to Name but Just a Few: Red, Yellow, Green, Blue. 2007. (Illus.). 40p. (ps-3). 16.95 (978-1-59354-596-3(7)) Blue Apple Bks.

Ross, Michael Elsohn. Mama's Milk. Wolff, Ashley, illus. 2007. 32p. (J). 12.95 (***978-1-58246-181-6(3)*** , Tricycle Pr.) Ten Speed Pr.

Ross, Tim. Brewster the Rain Makin' Rooster. Ross, Scott, illus. 1999. (Professor Wigglestix & the Weather Ser.). 32p. (ps-3). 14.95 (978-1-57168-332-8(1)) Eakin Pr.

—Brewster, the Rain-Makin' Rooster. 1999. (Professor Wigglestix & the Weather Ser.). (Illus.). 32p. (ps-3). 7.95 (978-1-57168-357-1(7)) Eakin Pr.

Ross, Tim & Ross, Scott, illus. Twinkle Twinkle Little Twister, Vol. 2. 2001. (Professor Wigglestix & the Weather Ser.). 32p. 14.95 (978-1-57168-447-9(6)); 7.95 (978-1-57168-619-0(3)) Eakin Pr.

Ross, Tony. Is it Because? 2005. (Illus.). 32p. (J). 9.95 (978-0-7641-5830-8(9)) Barron's Educational Series, Inc.

Roth, Carol. Here Comes the Choo Choo! Cushman, Doug, illus. 2007. (J). (***978-0-15-205582-0(7)***) Harcourt Trade Pubs.

—The Little School Bus. 2004. (Illus.). 32p. (J). (gr. k-1). pap. 6.95 (978-0-7358-1905-4(X)) North-South Bks., Inc.

—The Little School Bus. Paparone, Pamela, illus. 2002. 32p. (J). (ps-1). 14.95 (978-0-7358-1646-6(8)) North-South Bks., Inc.

—Who Will Tuck Me in Tonight? Gorbachev, Valeri, illus. 2003. 32p. (J). 15.95 (978-0-7358-1772-2(3)); 16.50 (978-0-7358-1773-9(1)) North-South Bks., Inc.

—Who Will Tuck Me in Tonight Sp. 2007. (J). 16.50 (978-0-7358-2108-8(9)); (Illus.). pap. 6.95 (978-0-7358-2107-1(0)) North-South Bks., Inc.

Rothstein, Gloria L. Sheep Asleep. Date not set. 224p. (J). (ps-1). pap. 4.99 (978-0-06-443717-2(5)) HarperCollins Pubs.

Rotner, Shelley. Parts. 2001. (Illus.). 32p. (J). (ps-1). 17.85 (978-0-8027-8754-5(1)) Walker & Co.

Rouss, Sylvia A. The Littlest Pair. Hannon, Holly, illus. 2005. 32p. (J). (ps-1). 14.95 (978-1-930143-17-3(6) , Devora Publishing) Pitspopany Pr.

Rovetch, Lissa. I Need a Kazoot! Castillon, Carly, illus. 2006. (J). (978-1-58987-055-0(7)) Kindermusik International.

—1,2,3 Octopus & Me. Gévry, Claudine, illus. 2006. (J). (978-1-58987-011-6(5)) Kindermusik International.

Roxbee-Cox, Phil. Find the Teddy. 2007. (Find-its Board Bks). 12p. (J). bds. 6.99 (***978-0-7945-1805-9(2)*** , Usborne) EDC Publishing.

Ruble, Kam. Princess Annado Tandy's Versery-Rhymes. McMullen, T. C., illus. 2007. (J). per. (***978-0-9779680-4-6(9)***) Global Authors Pubns.

Ruckman, Kathleen, told to. The Big Book: God Made Giant Things, Too! 2002. (Illus.). 24p. (J). pap. 5.99 (978-0-89051-358-3(9)) Master Bks.

Rueda, Claudia, illus. I Know an Old Lady Who Swallowed a Fly. 2005. 14p. (J). 12.95 (978-1-58117-267-6(2) , Intervisual/Piggy Toes) Dalmatian Pr.

Rundstrom, T. S. The Adventures of Tommy Toad. Marshall, Setsu, illus. 2002. 34p. (J). per. 16.00 (978-1-932062-03-8(3)) Hability Solution Services, Inc.

Rundstrom, Teressa. The Adventures of Tommy Toad. Marshall, Setsu, illus. 2004. 40p. (J). per. (978-1-932062-41-0(6)) Hability Solution Services, Inc.

Ruurs, Margriet. A Pacific Alphabet. Bonder, Dianna, illus. 2004. 32p. (J). (ps-2). 16.95 (978-1-55285-264-4(4)); pap. 8.95 (978-1-55285-521-8(X)) Whitecap Bks., Ltd. CAN. *Dist:* Firefly Bks., Ltd.

Ryan, Pam Muñoz. Hello, Ocean. Astrella, Mark, illus. 2001. Tr. of Hola Mar. 32p. (J). (ps-3). 16.95 (978-0-88106-987-7(6)); pap. 6.95 (978-0-88106-988-4(4)) Charlesbridge Publishing, Inc.

—Hello, Ocean. 2001. Tr. of Hola Mar. (Illus.). (J). 13.75 (978-0-606-20698-3(1)) Tandem Library Bks.

—Hello, Ocean: Hola Mar. Canetti, Yanitzia, tr. Astrella, Mark, illus. 2004. (ENG & SPA.). 32p. (J). (gr. k-3). pap. 7.95 (978-1-57091-372-3(2)) Charlesbridge Publishing, Inc.

Ryder, Joanne. Bear of My Heart. Moore, Margie, illus. 32p. (J). 2010. bds. 8.99 (***978-1-4169-5472-9(4)*** , Little Simon Inspirations); 2006. 12.95 (978-0-689-85947-2(3) , Simon & Schuster Children's Publishing) Simon & Schuster Children's Publishing.

—Big Bear Ball. Kellogg, Steven, illus. 2002. 32p. (J). (ps-1). 15.95 (978-0-06-027955-4(9)) HarperCollins Pubs.

—Won't You Be My Hugaroo? Sweet, Melissa, illus. 2006. 40p. (J). 16.00 (978-0-15-205778-7(1)) Harcourt Trade Pubs.

Ryder, Joanne & Sweet, Melissa. Won't You Be My Hugaroo? 2008. (Illus.). 30p. (J). (ps). bds. 6.95 (***978-0-15-206298-9(X)*** , Red Wagon Bks.) Harcourt Children's Bks.

—Won't You Be My Kissaroo? 2008. (Illus.). 30p. (J). (ps). bds. 6.95 (***978-0-15-206060-2(X)*** , Red Wagon Bks.) Harcourt Children's Bks.

Rylant, Cynthia. If You'll Be My Valentine. Kosaka, Fumi, illus. 32p. (J). 2005. pap. 6.99 (978-0-06-009271-9(8)); 2004. 14.99 (978-0-06-009270-2(X)) HarperCollins Pubs.

—Puppies & Piggies. Bates, Ivan, illus. 2008. 32p. (J). 16.00 (978-0-15-202321-8(6)) Harcourt Trade Pubs.

—The Stars Will Still Shine. Beeke, Tiphanie, illus. 2005. 40p. (J). lib. bdg. 16.89 (978-0-06-054640-3(9)); 15.99 (978-0-06-054639-7(5)) HarperCollins Pubs.

Rynders, Dawn & Wallingford, Stephanie. A Day at the Lake. Villnave, Erica Pelton, illus. 2008. (J). (***978-1-55971-990-2(7)*** , NorthWord Bks. for Young Readers) T&N Children's Publishing.

Sadler, Marilyn & Bollen, Roger. Money, Money, Honey Bunny! 2006. (Bright & Early Bks.). (Illus.). 36p. (J). 8.99 (978-0-375-83370-0(6)); lib. bdg. 12.99 (978-0-375-93370-7(0)) Random Hse. Children's Bks. (Random Hse. Bks. for Young Readers).

Saltzberg, Barney. I Love Cats. Saltzberg, Barney, illus. 2005. (Super Sturdy Picture Book Ser.). (Illus.). 24p. (J). (ps-17). 8.99 (978-0-7636-2588-7(4)) Candlewick Pr.

—I Love Dogs. Saltzberg, Barney, illus. 2005. (Super Sturdy Picture Book Ser.). (Illus.). 24p. (J). (ps up). 8.99 (978-0-7636-2587-0(6)) Candlewick Pr.

Saltzman, Ruth E. Poppy Bear: The Garden That Overslept. Deeter, Catherine, illus. 2001. 32p. (J). (gr. k-2). 16.95 (978-1-58270-042-7(7)) Beyond Words Publishing, Inc.

San Souci, Robert D. Cinderella Skeleton. Catrow, David, illus. 2004. 32p. (J). reprint ed. pap. 6.00 (978-0-15-205069-6(8) , Voyager Bks./Libros Viajeros) Harcourt Children's Bks.

Sandage, Charley. ALL AROUND ARKANSAS student Edition. 2005. (J). pap. (***978-0-9638956-5-3(6)***) Archeological Assessments, Inc.

Sanders, Karen Nordberg. Ruth & Naomi. Rooney, Ronnie, illus. 2007. 16p. (J). (gr. k-4). 1.99 (***978-0-7586-1283-0(4)***) Concordia Publishing Hse.

Sandhaus, Ellen. The Runaway Balloon (El Globo Que Se Escapo) Blanco, Osvaldo J., tr. unabr. ed. 1999. (SPA & ENG., Illus.). 24p. (J). (gr. k-4). pap. 4.95 (978-1-893266-01-8(X)) Sandhaus, Paul Assocs., Inc.

—Santa's Scavenger Hunt (Santa Claus en Busca de Regalos Raros) Blanco, Osvaldo J., tr. unabr. ed. 1999. (SPA & ENG., Illus.). 16p. (J). (gr. k-4). pap. 4.95 (978-1-893266-04-9(4)) Sandhaus, Paul Assocs., Inc.

—Stop Rhyming! (Deja de Hablar en Rima!) Blanco, Osvaldo J., tr. unabr. ed. 1999. (SPA & ENG., Illus.). 15p. (J). (ps-3). pap. 4.95 (978-1-893266-03-2(6)) Sandhaus, Paul Assocs., Inc.

—Where Do Lost Balloons Go? (Adonde Van los Globos Perdidos?) Blanco, Osvaldo J., tr. unabr. ed. 1999. (ENG & SPA., Illus.). 24p. (J). (gr. k-4). pap. 4.95 (978-1-893266-00-1(1)) Sandhaus, Paul Assocs., Inc.

Sanger, Amy Wilson. Hola! Jalapeno. 2004. (Illus.). 20p. (J). bds. 6.95 (978-1-58246-072-7(8) , Tricycle Pr.) Ten Speed Pr.

—A Little Bit of Soul Food. 2004. (World Snacks Ser.). (Illus.). 20p. (J). bds. 6.95 (978-1-58246-109-0(0) , Tricycle Pr.) Ten Speed Pr.

—Yum Yum Dim Sum. 2004. (Illus.). 20p. (J). bds. 6.95 (978-1-58246-108-3(2) , Tricycle Pr.) Ten Speed Pr.

Santa's Busy Christmas Eve. 2003. (J). 4.99 (978-1-59384-011-2(X)) Parklane Publishing.

Sargent, Dave. Autumn's Emergency. Huff, Jean Lirley, illus. 2000. (J). pap. (978-1-56763-566-9(0)) Ozark Publishing.

Sargent, Dave M., Jr. Buffy's Haircut, 9. Huff, Jeane Lirley, illus. 2004. (Doggie Tails Ser.: 9). (J). pap. 9.95 (978-1-56763-860-8(0)) Ozark Publishing.

—Vicious Vera, 9. Huff, Jeane Lirley, illus. 2004. (Doggie Tails Ser.: 9). (J). pap. 9.95 (978-1-56763-854-7(6)); lib. bdg. 19.95 (978-1-56763-853-0(8)) Ozark Publishing.

Sargent, David M., Jr. Buffy's Haircut, 9. Huff, Jeane Lirley, illus. 2004. (Doggie Tails Ser.: 9). (J). lib. bdg. 19.95 (978-1-56763-859-2(7)) Ozark Publishing.

Sarrazin, Marisol. Peppy, Patch, & the Postman. 2005. (Read-It! Readers Ser.). (Illus.). 32p. (C). (gr. k-3). 18.60 (978-1-4048-1034-1(X)) Picture Window Bks.

—Peppy, Patch, & the Socks. 2005. (Read-It! Readers Ser.). (Illus.). 32p. (C). (gr. k-3). 18.60 (978-1-4048-1023-5(4)) Picture Window Bks.

Sarrazin, Marisol, illus. Peppy, Patch, & the Bath. 2005. (Read-It! Readers Ser.). 32p. (C). (gr. k-3). 18.60 (978-1-4048-1032-7(3)) Picture Window Bks.

Sarta, Jon. Your Adoption Story. 2005. 20p. 9.99 (978-1-4116-6439-5(6)) Lulu.com.

Saul, Carol P. Barn Cat. Azarian, Mary, illus. 2002. (J). 21.66 (978-0-7587-2036-8(X)) Book Wholesalers, Inc.

—Barn Cat: A Counting Book. Azarian, Mary, illus. 2000. (J). 12.75 (978-0-606-19836-3(9)) Tandem Library Bks.

Sauro, Joan. Does God Ever Sleep? Sauro, Joan, photos by. 2005. (Illus.). 32p. (J). (ps-3). 8.99 (978-1-59473-110-5(1)) SkyLight Paths Publishing.

Sayles, Elizabeth. The Goldfish Yawned. Sayles, Elizabeth, illus. rev. ed. 2005. (Illus.). 40p. (J). (ps-1). 16.95 (978-0-8050-7624-0(7)) Holt, Henry & Co.

Scaglione, Joanne & Small, Gail. The Big Squeal: A Wild, True, & Twisted Tail. Endelman, David, illus. 2005. 56p. pap. 19.95 (978-1-57886-256-6(6)) Rowman & Littlefield Education.

Scagliotti, Loti. Silly Number Nonsense. 2006. (Silly Word & Number Stories Ser.). (Illus.). 28p. (J). 12.95 (978-9974-7960-1-0(6)) Hardenville SA URY. *Dist:* Independent Pubs. Group.

Scelsa, Greg & Debney, John. Friends Forever. Faulkner, Stacey, ed. Mahan, Benton, illus. 2006. (J). pap. 2.99 (***978-1-59198-322-4(3)***) Creative Teaching Pr., Inc.

Schade, Susan. Cat at Bat. 2000. (gr. k-3). lib. bdg. 11.80 (978-0-613-27765-5(1)) Tandem Library Bks.

—Cat on Ice. 2001. (Road to Reading Ser.). (Illus.). (J). 10.79 (978-0-606-20596-2(9)) Tandem Library Bks.

Schade, Susan & Buller, Jon. Cat at Bat. 2000. (Road to Reading Ser.). (Illus.). 32p. (J). (ps-1). pap. 3.99 (978-0-307-26211-0(1) , Random Hse. Bks. for Young Readers) Random Hse. Children's Bks.

—Cat on the Mat. 1998. (Step into Reading Ser.: Vol. 2). (Illus.). 32p. (J). (ps-1). pap. 3.99 (978-0-307-26207-3(3) , Random Hse. Bks. for Young Readers) Random Hse. Children's Bks.

—Cat on the Mat. 1998. (Illus.). 32p. (J). (ps-ps). lib. bdg. 11.80 (978-0-613-16623-2(X)) Tandem Library Bks.

—Space Dog Jack. 2001. (Hello Reader! Ser.). (Illus.). 32p. (J). (ps-1). pap. (978-0-439-20541-2(7)) Scholastic, Inc.

—Space Dog Jack & the Haunted Spaceship. 2002. (Hello Reader! Ser.). (Illus.). 32p. (J). pap. 3.99 (978-0-439-32315-4(0) , Cartwheel Bks.) Scholastic, Inc.

Schaefer, Lola. Toolbox Twins. Iwai, Melissa, illus. rev. ed. 2006. 32p. (J). 16.95 (978-0-8050-7733-9(2)) Holt, Henry & Co.

Schaefer, Lola M. An Island Grows. Felstead, Cathie, illus. 2006. 40p. (J). (gr. k-2). 16.99 (978-0-06-623930-9(3)); lib. bdg. 17.89 (978-0-06-623931-6(1)) HarperCollins Pubs.

—Loose Tooth. Wickstrom, Sylvie K., tr. Wickstrom, Sylvie K., illus. 2004. (My First I Can Read Bks.). 32p. (J). (ps up). 14.99 (978-0-06-052776-1(5)) HarperCollins Pubs.

—Loose Tooth. Wickstrom, Sylvie Kantorovitz, illus. 2005. 32p. (J). (ps-ps). lib. bdg. 11.19 (978-0-606-33932-2(9)) Tandem Library Bks.

—This Is the Rain. Wattenberg, Jane, illus. 2001. 40p. (J). 16.99 (978-0-688-17039-4(0)); 16.89 (978-0-688-17040-0(4)) HarperCollins Pubs.

Schafer, Milton. I'm Big! Lew-Vriethoff, Joanne, illus. 2006. (J). (***978-1-4156-8150-3(3)*** , Dial) Penguin Group (USA) Inc.

Schatzer, Jeffery. The Runaway Garden. Ebbeler, Jeffrey, illus. 2007. 32p. (J). 17.95 (***978-1-58726-436-8(6)*** , Mitten Pr.) Ann Arbor Media Group, LLC.

Schertle, Alice. The Adventures of Old Bo Bear. Parkins, David, illus. 2005. (J). 16.95 (978-978-081-183-9(4)) Chronicle Bks. LLC.

—All You Need for a Beach. Lavallee, Barbara, illus. 2004. 32p. (J). 16.00 (978-0-15-216755-4(2) , Silver Whistle) Harcourt Trade Pubs.

—The Skeleton in the Closet. Jobling, Curtis, illus. 2003. 32p. (J). (gr. 1 up). 15.99 (978-0-688-17738-6(7)) HarperCollins Pubs.

Schertle, Alice & Parkins, Schertle. The Adventures of Old Bo Bear. 2006. (Illus.). 32p. (J). 16.95 (978-0-8118-3476-6(X)) Chronicle Bks. LLC.

Schindel, John. Busy Kitties. Franzen, Sean, photos by. 2004. (Illus.). 20p. (J). bds. 6.95 (978-1-58246-130-4(9) , Tricycle Pr.) Ten Speed Pr.

—Busy Piggies. Holt, Steven, illus. Holt, Steven, photos by. 2006. 20p. (J). bds. 6.95 (978-1-58246-169-4(4) , Tricycle Pr.) Ten Speed Pr.

Schindel, John & Marigo, Luiz Claudio. Busy Monkeys. 2004. (Illus.). 20p. (J). bds. 6.95 (978-1-58246-082-6(5) , Tricycle Pr.) Ten Speed Pr.

Schneider, Christine. Picky Mrs. Pickle. 2001. (978-0-606-22744-5(X)) Tandem Library Bks.

Schnitzlein, Danny. The Monster Who Ate My Peas. Faulkner, Matt, illus. 2001. 32p. (J). (gr. k-3). 15.95 (978-1-56145-216-3(5) , Q32689) Peachtree Pubs., Ltd.

Schnitzlein, Danny. The Monster Who Did My Math. Mayer, Bill, illus. 2007. 32p. (J). (gr. 1-5). 16.95 (***978-1-56145-420-4(6)*** , Peachtree Junior) Peachtree Pubs., Ltd.

Schoberle, Cecile. Everyday Heroes. Lopez, Paul, illus. 2005. (Ready-to-Read Ser. Level 1). 32p. (J). lib. bdg. 15.00 (978-1-59054-925-4(2)) Fitzgerald Bks.

—Everyday Heroes. Ewers, Joe & Lopez, Paul, illus. 2003. (Matchbox Ser.). 32p. (J). pap. 3.99 (978-0-689-85899-4(X) , Little Simon) Simon & Schuster Children's Publishing.

—Everyday Heroes. 2003. (gr. k-3). lib. bdg. 11.80 (978-0-613-66498-1(1)) Tandem Library Bks.

—To the Rescue! Mones, Isidre et al, illus. 2003. (Matchbox Ser.: Vol. 1). 32p. (J). 3.99 (978-0-689-85898-7(1) , Little Simon) Simon & Schuster Children's Publishing.

—To the Rescue! 2003. (gr. k-3). lib. bdg. 11.80 (978-0-613-66550-6(3)) Tandem Library Bks.

Scholastic, Inc. Staff. Cars & Trucks. 2008. (Littlest Pet Shop Ser.). (SPA.). 24p. (J). pap. 3.99 (***978-0-545-02728-1(4)*** , Scholastic en Espanol) Scholastic, Inc.

—The Real Mother Goose. 2005. (Humpty Dumpty Musical Toy Ser.). (J). pap. 24.99 (978-0-439-72694-8(8) , Side-Kicks TM Baby) Scholastic, Inc.

Scholastic, Inc. Staff. Taggies Libros con Lacitos: La Arana Chiquitita. 2007. (My First Taggies Book Ser.). 10p. (J). bds. 6.99 (***978-0-439-92737-6(4)*** , Scholastic en Espanol) Scholastic, Inc.

Scholastic, Inc. Staff & Barnes, Derrick D. Low-Down Bad-Day Blues. Boyd, Aaron, illus. 2004. (Just for You! Ser.). 32p. (J). (gr. k-1). pap. 3.99 (978-0-439-56867-8(6) , Teaching Resources) Scholastic, Inc.

Scholastic, Inc. Staff & Bermiss, Aamir Lee. Just for You: I Hate to Be Sick. Wilson-Max, Ken, illus. 2004. (Just for You! Ser.). 32p. (gr. k-3). pap. 3.99 (978-0-439-56877-7(3) , Teaching Resources) Scholastic, Inc.

Scholastic, Inc. Staff & Ford, Bernette G. Don't Hit Me! Grier, Gary, illus. 2004. (Just for You! Ser.). 32p. (gr. k-1). pap. 3.99 (978-0-439-56860-9(9) , Teaching Resources) Scholastic, Inc.

Scholastic, Inc. Staff & Roberson, Karla. My Shoelaces Are Hard to Tie. Holley, Vanessa, illus. 2004. (Just for You! Ser.). 32p. pap. 3.99 (978-0-439-56869-2(2) , Teaching Resources) Scholastic, Inc.

Scholastic, Inc. Staff, et al. Lights Out! Tadgell, Nicole, illus. 2004. (Just for You! Ser.). 32p. (J). (gr. k-1). pap. 3.99 (978-0-439-56868-5(4) , Teaching Resources) Scholastic, Inc.

Schomer Wendel, Gretchen & Schomer, Adam Anthony. Becka & the Big Bubble: All Around Town. 2007. (Illus.). 32p. (J). 11.99 (***978-1-933754-10-9(9)***) Waterside Publishing.

—Becka & the Big Bubble: Becka Goes to India. 2007. (Illus.). 32p. (J). 11.99 (***978-1-933754-13-0(3)***) Waterside Publishing.

—Becka & the Big Bubble: Becka Goes to San Francisco. 2007. (Illus.). 32p. (J). 11.99 (***978-1-933754-12-3(5)***) Waterside Publishing.

—Becka & the Big Bubble: Becka Goes to the North Pole. 2007. (Illus.). 28p. (J). 11.99 (***978-1-933754-11-6(7)***) Waterside Publishing.

School Specialty Publishing. Learning Letters. 2004. (Kindergarten Standards Ser.). 144p. (C). pap. 16.99 (978-0-7682-2820-5(4) , FS99276) Schaffer, Frank Pubns.

School Specialty Publishing, et al. Christmas Stories, 2 Pack. Gabriel, Andrea & Riley, R. W., illus. 2006. 36p. (J). bds. 14.98 (978-0-7696-4966-5(1)) School Specialty Publishing.

Schotter, Roni. Passover! Kono, Erin Eitter, illus. 2006. 28p. (J). (ps-1). 12.99 (978-0-316-93991-1(9)) Little Brown & Co.

Schroeder, Lisa. Baby Can't Sleep. Garofoli, Viviana, illus. 2005. 32p. (J). (ps). 12.95 (978-1-4027-2171-7(4)) Sterling Publishing Co., Inc.

Schuepbach, Lynnette. Cat Time. 2006. 28p. pap. 12.95 (978-0-9759613-2-2(2)) Creative Sources.

Schulman, Elayne. This Year We Took a Special Trip. Bowser, Ken, illus. 2000. (This Year We... Ser.: Vol. 2). 32p. (J). (ps up). 14.95 (978-1-892780-04-1(6)) Giggles Group, Inc., The.

Schulman, Janet. 10 Trick-Or-Treaters: A Halloween Counting Book. Davick, Linda, illus. 2005. 32p. (J). (ps-3). 8.95 (978-0-375-83225-3(4)); lib. bdg. 10.99 (978-0-375-93225-0(9)) Random Hse. Children's Bks. (Knopf Bks. for Young Readers).

Schultz, Kathy. Get Out of My Chair. Payne, Tom, illus. 2002. (Rookie Reader Skill Set Ser.). 24p. (J). (gr. k-2). pap. 4.95 (978-0-516-25965-9(2) , Children's Pr.) Scholastic Library Publishing.

—Get Out of My Chair. 2001. (gr. k-3). lib. bdg. 12.95 (978-0-613-54233-3(9)) Tandem Library Bks.

Schulz, Kathy. I Do Not Want To. Rescek, Sanja, illus. 2004. (Rookie Reader Skill Set Ser.). 32p. (J). (gr. k-2). pap. 4.95 (978-0-516-27845-2(2) , Children's Pr.) Scholastic Library Publishing.

—I Do Not Want To. Rescek, Sanja, tr. Rescek, Sanja, illus. 2004. (Rookie Reader Ser.). 31p. (J). 19.50 (978-0-516-24403-7(5) , Children's Pr.) Scholastic Library Publishing.

S

—I Need a Little Help. 2004. (Rookie Reader Skill Set Ser.). (Illus.). 23p. (J). (gr. k-2). pap. 4.95 (978-0-516-27833-9(9) , Children's Pr.) Scholastic Library Publishing.

—I Need a Little Help. Losa, Ann, illus. 2003. (Rookie Reader - Level a Ser.). 24p. (J). 19.50 (978-0-516-22877-8(3) , Children's Pr.) Scholastic Library Publishing.

—I Need a Little Help. Iosa, Ann, illus. 2004. 24p. lib. bdg. 12.15 (978-0-606-30160-2(7)) Tandem Library Bks.

Schwartz, Noa. Old Timers: The One That Got Away. Vipond, Erica, illus. 1998. (J). pap. 5.95 (978-0-9683303-1-9(2)) Tumbleweed Pr.

Scillian, Devin. Brewster the Rooster. White, Lee, illus. rev. ed. 2007. 32p. (J). (gr. k-2). 16.95 (***978-1-58536-311-7(1)***) Sleeping Bear Pr.

Scillian, Devin. Fibblestax. K.L., Darnell, illus. 2003. 32p. (J). pap. 7.95 (978-1-58536-165-6(8)) Sleeping Bear Pr.

—Fibblestax. 2003. (gr. k-3). lib. bdg. 16.40 (978-0-613-79709-2(4)) Tandem Library Bks.

Scott, Janine. Fun in the Sun. Forss, Ian, illus. 2006. (Farmer Claude & Farmer Maude Ser.). 32p. (J). (gr. k-2). 22.60 (978-1-4048-1697-8(6) , 1253180) Picture Window Bks.

—Rain on the Roof. Forss, Ian, illus. 2006. 32p. (J). (gr. k-2). 22.60 (978-1-4048-1698-5(4)) Picture Window Bks.

—The Rowdy Rooster. Forss, Ian, illus. 2006. 32p. (J). (gr. k-2). 22.60 (978-1-4048-1699-2(2)) Picture Window Bks.

—Sunny Sunday Drive. Forss, Ian, illus. 2006. 32p. (J). (gr. k-2). 22.60 (978-1-4048-1696-1(8)) Picture Window Bks.

Scruton, Clive, illus. I Love You! 1999. (Leap Frog Lift-A-Flap Ser.). (J). (978-0-7853-3369-2(X)) Publications International, Ltd.

Sedgwick, Marcus & Andersen, Hans Christian. Emperor's New Clothes. Jay, Alison, illus. 2004. 32p. (J). 16.95 (978-0-8118-4569-4(9)) Chronicle Bks. LLC.

Seeley, Laura L. The Magical Moonballs. Seeley, Laura L., illus. 1998. (Illus.). 48p. (J). (ps-3). reprint ed. pap. 7.95 (978-1-56145-189-0(4)) Peachtree Pubs., Ltd.

Seigerman, Michelle. A Christmastime Book of Rhymes. 2005. 35p. pap. 13.08 (978-1-4116-4960-6(5)) Lulu-.com.

Self, Timothy. Davy the Dolphin. l.t. ed. 2003. (Illus.). 22p. (J). per. 8.99 (978-1-932338-30-0(6)) Lifevest Publishing, Inc.

Seltzer, Eric. Doodle Dog. Seltzer, Eric, illus. 2005. (Ready-to-Reads Ser.). (Illus.). 32p. (J). pap. 3.99 (978-0-689-85910-6(4) , Aladdin) Simon & Schuster Children's Publishing.

—Doodle Dog. 2005. (Ready-to-Reads Ser.). (Illus.). 32p. (J). lib. bdg. 11.89 (978-0-689-85913-7(9) , Aladdin Library) Simon & Schuster Children's Publishing.

—Doodle Dog in Space. Seltzer, Eric, illus. 2005. (Ready-to-Reads Ser.). (Illus.). 32p. (J). (ps-3). pap. 3.99 (978-0-689-85912-0(0) , Aladdin) Simon & Schuster Children's Publishing.

—Granny Doodle Day. Seltzer, Eric, illus. 2006. (Ready-to-Reads Ser.). (Illus.). 32p. (J). pap. 3.99 (978-0-689-85911-3(2) , Aladdin) Simon & Schuster Children's Publishing.

Sensel, Joni. Bears Barge In. Bivins, Christopher, illus. 2003. 32p. (J). (ps up). 14.95 (978-0-9701195-0-6(X)) Dream Factory Bks.

Serfozo, Mary. Big Bug Dug. Maccarone, Grace, ed. Scherer, Jeffrey, illus. 2003. 32p. (J). pap. 3.99 (978-0-439-59426-4(X)) Scholastic, Inc.

—A Head Is for Hats. Bratun, Katy, illus. 2000. (Hello Reader! Ser.). 32p. (J). (gr. k-2). pap. 3.99 (978-0-439-09909-7(9)) Scholastic, Inc.

—A Head Is for Hats. 2000. (Hello Reader! Ser.). (Illus.). (J). (978-0-606-18876-0(2)) Tandem Library Bks.

—Plumply, Dumply Pumpkin. Petrone, Valeria, illus. (Classic Board Bks.). (J). 2006. 28p. 6.99 (978-0-689-86277-9(6) , Little Simon); 2001. 32p. 12.95 (978-0-689-83834-7(4) , McElderry, Margaret K.) Simon & Schuster Children's Publishing.

—Whooo's There? Scherer, Jeffrey, illus. 2007. 40p. (J). (gr. k-1). 9.99 (978-0-375-84050-0(8)); lib. bdg. 12.99 (978-0-375-94050-7(2)) Random Hse. Children's Bks. (Random Hse. Bks. for Young Readers).

Serfozo, Mary & Petrone, Valeria. Plumply, Dumply Pumpkin. 2004. 32p. (J). pap. 6.99 (978-0-689-87135-1(X) , Aladdin) Simon & Schuster Children's Publishing.

Sesame Street Storybook COLL 2. 2007. 10.99 (***978-1-4037-3614-7(6)***) Dalmatian Pr.

Seskin Steve & Shamblin Allen. Chance to Shine. 2006. (Illus.). 32p. 16.95 incl. audio compact disk (978-1-58246-167-0(8) , Tricycle Pr.) Ten Speed Pr.

Seuling, Barbara & Altshuler, Miriam. Whose House? Chorao, Kay, tr. Chorao, Kay, illus. 2004. 32p. (J). 16.00 (978-0-15-216347-1(6) , Gulliver Bks.) Harcourt Children's Bks.

Seuss, Dr. The Cat in the Hat. 1999. (Illus.). (J). 12.99 (978-0-679-89267-0(2) , Random Hse. Bks. for Young Readers) Random Hse. Children's Bks.

—The Cat in the Hat. Seuss, Dr., illus. l.t. ed. 2007. (I Can Read It All by Myself). (Illus.). 72p. (J). (gr. k-3). 8.99 (978-0-394-80001-1(X) , Random Hse. Bks. for Young Readers) Random Hse. Children's Bks.

—The Cat in the Hat's Great Big Flap Book. Ruiz, Aristides, illus. 1999. 12p. (J). (gr. k-ps). bds. 11.99 (978-0-679-89360-8(1) , Random Hse. Bks. for Young Readers) Random Hse. Children's Bks.

—Cattus Petasatus. Tunberg, Jennifer Morrish & Tunberg, Terence O., trs. from ENG. 2000. Tr. of Cat in the Hat. (LAT., Illus.). 80p. (YA). (ps-3). 20.00 (978-0-86516-472-7(X)); 26.00 (978-0-86516-471-0(1)) Bolchazy-Carducci Pubs.

—Green Eggs & Ham. 2001. (Nifty Lift-and-Look Bks.). (Illus.). 12p. (J). (gr. k-ps). bds. 7.99 (978-0-375-81088-6(9) , Random Hse. Bks. for Young Readers) Random Hse. Children's Bks.

—The Grinch Meets His Max. 1998. (J). (ps-3). lib. bdg. 11.99 (978-0-679-98836-6(X) , Random Hse. Bks. for Young Readers) Random Hse. Children's Bks.

—How the Grinch Stole Christmas! 1999. (J). 12.99 (978-0-679-89270-0(2) , Random Hse. Bks. for Young Readers) Random Hse. Children's Bks.

—How the Grinch Stole Christmas! A 50th Anniversary Retrospective. 50th anniv. ed. 2007. (Illus.). 85p. (J). (gr. 1-4). lib. bdg. 32.99 (***978-0-375-93847-4(8)***); 24.99 (***978-0-375-83847-7(3)***) Random Hse. Children's Bks. (Random Hse. Bks. for Young Readers).

—My Many Colored Days. Johnson, Stephen T. & Fancher, Lou, illus. 1998. 16p. (J). (gr. k-ps). bds. 6.99 (978-0-679-89344-8(X) , Knopf Bks. for Young Readers) Random Hse. Children's Bks.

—Oh, the Places You'll Go! 2003. 7.95 (978-1-56890-373-6(1)) Peaceable Kingdom Pr.

—Ten Apples up on Top! 1998. (Bright & Early Bks.). (Illus.). (J). bds. 4.99 (978-0-679-89343-1(1) , Random Hse. Bks. for Young Readers) Random Hse. Children's Bks.

—The Tooth Book. Jonaitis, Alice, ed. Mathieu, Joe, illus. 2000. (Bright & Early Bks.). 48p. (J). (gr. k-1). lib. bdg. 11.99 (978-0-375-91039-5(5) , Random Hse. Bks. for Young Readers) Random Hse. Children's Bks.

—The Tooth Book. Mathieu, Joe, illus. 2000. (Bright & Early Bks.: Vol. 25). 48p. (J). (gr. k-1). 8.99 (978-0-375-81039-8(0) , Random Hse. Bks. for Young Readers) Random Hse. Children's Bks.

—Virent Ova! Viret Perna! Tunberg, Jennifer Morrish & Tunberg, Terence O., trs. 2003. Tr. of Green Eggs & Ham. (LAT., Illus.). 72p. (J). 26.00 (978-0-86516-555-7(6)) Bolchazy-Carducci Pubs.

—Y Pensar Que lo Vi por la Calle Porvenir. Canetti, Yanitzia, tr. Seuss, Dr., illus. 2006. (SPA., Illus.). (J). 14.99 (***978-1-933032-07-8(3)***) Lectorum Pubns., Inc.

Seuss, Dr. Your Favorite Seuss: A Baker's Dozen by the One & Only Dr. Seuss. 2004. (Illus.). 368p. (J). (gr. k-3). 34.95 (978-0-375-81061-9(7) , Random Hse. Bks. for Young Readers) Random Hse. Children's Bks.

Seuss, Dr. & Prelutsky, Jack. Hooray for Diffendoofer Day! Smith, Lane, illus. 1998. 56p. (J). (gr. k-3). 17.00 (978-0-679-89008-9(4)); lib. bdg. 18.99 (978-0-679-99008-6(9)) Random Hse. Children's Bks. (Knopf Bks. for Young Readers).

Shackman, Julie. Olivia's Orchestra. 2000. (Illus.). 24p. (J). (ps-1). pap. (978-1-84210-008-0(4)) Mentor Bks.

Shannon, Joe. Tennis Shoe Love. Huskins, Suzie, illus. 2006. (J). (978-1-933251-40-0(9)) Parkway Pubs., Inc.

Shannon, Terry Miller & Warner, Tim. Tub Toys. Calderon, Lee, illus. 2004. 30p. (J). (gr. k-2). 14.95 (978-1-58246-066-6(3) , Tricycle Pr.) Ten Speed Pr.

Shaw, Nancy. Raccoon Tune. Fine, Howard, illus. rev. ed. 2003. 32p. (J). (ps-2). 16.95 (978-0-8050-6544-2(X) , Holt, Henry & Co. Bks. For Young Readers) Holt, Henry & Co.

—Sheep in a Jeep. Apple, Margot, illus. 2002. (J). 12.83 (978-0-7587-3608-6(8)) Book Wholesalers, Inc.

—Sheep in a Shop. Apple, Margot, illus. 2002. (J). 12.81 (978-0-7587-3609-3(6)) Book Wholesalers, Inc.

—Sheep on a Ship. Apple, Margot, illus. 2002. (J). 12.81 (978-0-7587-3611-6(8)) Book Wholesalers, Inc.

—Sheep Out to Eat. Apple, Margot, illus. 2002. (J). 12.81 (978-0-7587-3612-3(6)) Book Wholesalers, Inc.

—Sheep Take a Hike. Apple, Margot, illus. 2002. (J). 12.81 (978-0-7587-3613-0(4)) Book Wholesalers, Inc.

Shaw, Nancy E. Sheep Out to Eat. Apple, Margot, illus. 2005. 13p. (J). (gr. k-ps). bds. 5.95 (978-0-618-58339-3(4)) Houghton Mifflin Co. Trade & Reference Div.

Shelton, Jayne C. In Grandmother's Arms. Katz, Karen, illus. 2001. 32p. (J). pap. 3.25 (978-0-439-21314-1(2)) Scholastic, Inc.

Shields, Carol Diggory. The Bugliest Bug. Nash, Scott, illus. 2002. 32p. (J). (ps-3). 16.99 (978-0-7636-0784-5(3)) Candlewick Pr.

—Homes. Junakovic, Svjetlan, illus. 2001. (Animagicals Ser.). 32p. (J). (ps-2). 9.95 (978-1-929766-27-7(0)) Handprint Bks.

—Patterns. Junakovic, Svjetlan, illus. 2001. (Animagicals Ser.). 32p. (J). (ps-1). bds. 9.95 (978-1-929766-15-4(7)) Handprint Bks.

—Sports. Junakovic, Svjetlan, illus. 2001. (Animagicals Ser.). 32p. (J). 9.95 (978-1-929766-28-4(9)) Handprint Bks.

Shields, Carol Diggory & Junakovic, Svjetlan. On the Go. 2001. (Animagicals Ser.). (Illus.). 32p. (J). (ps-1). bds. 9.95 (978-1-929766-14-7(9)) Handprint Bks.

Shields, Carol Diggory, et al. Music. 2000. (Animagicals Ser.). (Illus.). 12p. (J). (ps-1). 9.95 (978-1-929766-05-5(X)) Handprint Bks.

Shindler, Ramon & Graniczewski, Wojciech. Found Alphabet. Andrzejewska, Anita & Pilichowski-Ragno, Andrzej, illus. 2005. 32p. (J). (gr. k-3). 16.00 (978-0-618-44232-4(4)) Houghton Mifflin Co. Trade & Reference Div.

Shively, Julie. What Belongs? Kurtz, John, illus. 2004. (Baby Looney Toons Ser.). 16p. (J). 6.95 (978-0-8249-6561-7(2)) Ideals Pubns.

Shook, Babs. A House for Mouse, Level 1. Couri, Kathy, illus. 2000. (All-Star Readers Ser.). 32p. (J). (ps-1). pap. 3.99 (978-1-57584-383-4(8) , Reader's Digest Children's Bks.) Reader's Digest Children's Publishing, Inc.

Shook-Hazen, Barbara. House for Mouse. 2000. (ps-2). lib. bdg. 11.80 (978-0-613-25577-6(1)) Tandem Library Bks.

Shore, Diane Z. Bus-a-Saurus Bop. Clark, David, illus. 2003. 32p. (J). (gr. k-3). 16.95 (978-1-58234-850-6(2) , Bloomsbury Children) Bloomsbury Publishing.

Shulman, Lisa. Old MacDonald Had a Woodshop. Wolff, Ashley, illus. 2002. 32p. (J). 16.99 (978-0-399-23596-2(5) , Putnam Juvenile) Penguin Group (USA) Inc.

—Over in the Meadow at the Big Ballet. Massini, Sarah, illus. 2007. 32p. (J). (gr. k). 16.99 (978-0-399-24289-2(9)) Penguin Group (USA) Inc.

Shulman, Lisa & Wolff, Ashley. Old MacDonald Had a Woodshop. 2004. (Illus.). 32p. (J). reprint ed. pap. 6.99 (978-0-14-240186-6(2) , Puffin) Penguin Group (USA) Inc.

Sidle, Christian. Murphy Dog at the Circus. Lynn, Dianne, illus. l.t. ed. 2001. 80p. (J). (ps-3). per. 12.50 (978-0-9708053-6-2(5)) Authors & Artists Publishers of New York, Inc.

Siegel, Phil. Simon the Daredevil Centipede: He Learned to Skate - & Much, Much More. Caiarelli, Alisa, illus. 1998. 28p. (J). pap. 8.95 (978-0-932991-58-4(0) , Different Bks.) Place In The Woods, The.

Sierra, Judy. Born to Read. Brown, Marc, illus. 2008. (J). (***978-0-375-84687-8(5)***); lib. bdg. (***978-0-375-94687-5(X)***) Knopf, Alfred A. Inc.

—Counting Crocodiles. Hillenbrand, Will, illus. 2001. 40p. (J). (gr. k-2). pap. 7.00 (978-0-15-216356-3(5) , Voyager Bks./Libros Viajeros) Harcourt Children's Bks.

—Counting Crocodiles. 2001. (ps-2). lib. bdg. 15.30 (978-0-613-82223-7(4)); 13.80 (978-0-606-22596-0(X)) Tandem Library Bks.

—The House That Drac Built. Hillenbrand, Will, illus. 1998. (J). (ps-ps). lib. bdg. 14.15 (978-0-613-09949-3(4)) Tandem Library Bks.

—Preschool to the Rescue. Hillenbrand, Will, illus. 2001. 32p. (J). (ps-2). 16.00 (978-0-15-202035-4(7) , Gulliver Bks.) Harcourt Children's Bks.

—The Secret Science Project That Almost Ate the School. Gammell, Stephen, illus. 2006. 32p. (J). (gr. 1-4). 16.95 (978-1-4169-1175-3(8) , Simon & Schuster Children's Publishing) Simon & Schuster Children's Publishing.

—Thelonius Monster's Sky-High Fly-Pie. Koren, Edward, illus. 2006. 40p. (J). (ps-3). 16.95 (978-0-375-83218-5(1)); lib. bdg. 18.99 (978-0-375-93218-2(6)) Random Hse. Children's Bks. (Knopf Bks. for Young Readers).

—Twas the Fright Before Christmas. Hillenbrand, Will, illus. 2005. 32p. (J). (ps-ps). reprint ed. pap., pap. 7.00 (978-0-15-205640-7(8) , Voyager Bks./Libros Viajeros) Harcourt Children's Bks.

—What Time Is It, Mr. Crocodile? Cushman, Doug, illus. 2007. 32p. (J). pap. 7.00 (978-0-15-205850-0(8) , Voyager Bks./Libros Viajeros) Harcourt Children's Bks.

—What Time Is It, Mr. Crocodile? Cushman, Doug, tr. Cushman, Doug, illus. 2004. 32p. (J). 16.00 (978-0-15-216445-4(6) , Gulliver Bks.) Harcourt Children's Bks.

—Wild about Books. Brown, Marc, tr. Brown, Marc, illus. 2004. 40p. (J). (ps-3). 16.95 (978-0-375-82538-5(X)); lib. bdg. 18.99 (978-0-375-92538-2(4)) Random Hse. Children's Bks. (Knopf Bks. for Young Readers).

Signorino, Slug, illus. I Know an Old Lady Who Swallowed a Fly: A Traditional Rhyme. 2004. 16p. (J). (gr. k-4). reprint ed. pap. 10.00 (978-0-7567-9066-0(2)) DIANE Publishing Co.

Silverman, Erica. The Halloween House. Agee, Jon, illus. 2008. 32p. (J). pap. 6.99 (***978-0-312-38013-7(5)***) Square Fish.

Silverman, Erica. Halloween House. 1999. (J). (978-0-606-17220-2(3)) Tandem Library Bks.

Silverman, Erika. Wee Woman Who Lived in a Shoe. Date not set. (J). (978-0-374-38253-7(0) , Farrar, Straus & Giroux (BYR)) Farrar, Straus & Giroux.

Simmons, Andrea. What Anna Loves. Capaldi, Gina, illus. 2006. 32p. (J). 15.95 (978-1-59714-044-7(9)) Heyday Bks.

Simms Taback Staff, illus. There Was an Old Lady Who Swallowed a Fly. 2004. (J). pap. 18.95 incl. audio compact disk (978-1-55592-145-3(0)); pap. 18.95 incl. audio compact disk (978-1-55592-146-0(9)) Weston Woods Studios, Inc.

Simon, Charnan. I Like to Win! Handelman, Dorothy, photos by. 1999. (Real Kids Readers Ser.). (Illus.). 32p. (J). (gr. k-1). pap. 4.99 (978-0-7613-2087-6(3) , Millbrook Pr.) Lerner Publishing Group.

—I Like to Win! 1999. (ps-2). lib. bdg. 13.00 (978-0-613-18157-0(3)) Tandem Library Bks.

—I've Lost My Hat. 2007. (Rookie Reader Ser.). (Illus.). 31p. (J). pap. (***978-0-531-12490-1(8)***) Children's Pr., Ltd.

—Lodo! Handelman, Dorothy, photos by. 2005. Tr. of Mud!. (ENG & SPA., Illus.). 32p. (J). (ps-1). pap. 4.99 (978-0-8225-3295-8(6)) Lerner Publishing Group.

—Lodo! Nivel 1. Handelman, Dorothy, photos by. 2005. (Lecturas para Niños de Verdad (Real Kids Readers) Ser.). (SPA., Illus.). 32p. (J). (gr. 1-1). pap. 4.99 (978-0-8225-3294-1(8) , Ediciones Lerner) Lerner Publishing Group.

—Mud! Handelman, Dorothy, photos by. 1999. (Real Kids Readers Ser.). (Illus.). 32p. (ps-1). lib. bdg. 18.90 (978-0-7613-2051-7(2)); (J). pap. 4.99 (978-0-7613-2076-0(8)) Lerner Publishing Group. (Millbrook Pr.).

—Mud! 1999. (J). (978-0-606-19163-0(1)) Tandem Library Bks.

—The Sillies. Petelinsek, Kathleen, illus. 2006. (Magic Door to Learning Ser.). 24p. (J). 21.36 (978-1-59296-627-1(6)) Child's World, Inc.

—Wash Day. Handelman, Dorothy, photos by. 1999. (Real Kids Readers Ser.). (Illus.). 32p. (ps-1). lib. bdg. 18.90 (978-0-7613-2065-4(2) , Millbrook Pr.) Lerner Publishing Group.

—Wash Day. Handelman, Dorothy, illus. 1999. (Real Kids Readers Ser.). 32p. (J). (gr. k-1). pap. 4.99 (978-0-7613-2090-6(3) , Millbrook Pr.) Lerner Publishing Group.

—Wash Day. 1999. (J). (978-0-606-19179-1(8)); lib. bdg. 11.80 (978-0-613-45236-6(4)) Tandem Library Bks.

—What Makes You Happy? Bryan-Hunt, Jan, illus. 2006. (Magic Door to Learning Ser.). 24p. (J). 21.36 (978-1-59296-623-3(3)) Child's World, Inc.

Singer, Marilyn. City Lullaby. Cneut, Carll, illus. 2007. 32p. (J). (ps-3). 16.00 (***978-0-618-60703-7(X)*** , Clarion Bks.) Houghton Mifflin Co. Trade & Reference Div.

—Let's Build a Clubhouse. Bush, Timothy, illus. 2006. 32p. (J). (gr. k-3). 16.00 (978-0-618-30670-1(6) , Clarion Bks.) Houghton Mifflin Co. Trade & Reference Div.

—The One & Only Me. Rubel, Nicole, illus. 2000. (Growing Tree Ser.). 24p. (J). (ps-k). 9.95 (978-0-694-01279-4(3) , Harper Festival) HarperCollins Pubs.

Sinke, Janet. Grandma's Christmas Tree. l.t. ed. 2004. (Illus.). 48p. (J). (978-0-9742732-1-1(X)) My Grandma & Me Pubs.

Siomades, Lorianne. Cuckoo Can't Find You. Siomades, Lorianne, illus. 2003. (Illus.). 32p. (J). (ps up). 12.95 (978-1-56397-778-7(8)) Boyds Mills Pr.

Sion Charnan. ¡Me gusta ganar! (I Like to Win!) 2007. (Lecturas para niños de verdad - Nivel 1 (Real Kids Readers - Level 1) Ser.). (J). pap. 5.95 (***978-0-8225-7801-7(8)*** , Ediciones Lerner) Lerner Publishing Group.

Siwak, Brenda S. Counting on the Bay. Dodge, Barbara A., illus. 2006. (J). per. 14.95 (***978-0-9790906-0-8(1)***) Pleasant Plains Pr.

Siy, Alexandra. Old Macdonald had a Farm. Rogers, Jacqueline, illus. 2008. (J). (***978-0-8234-1923-4(1)***) Holiday Hse., Inc.

Skalak, Barbara Anne. Waddle, Waddle, Quack, Quack, Quack. Long, Sylvia, illus. 2005. 36p. (J). 14.95 (978-0-8118-4342-3(4)) Chronicle Bks. LLC.

Skalak, Daniel. All Summer's Fun. Skalak, Daniel, illus. 2006. (Illus.). 32p. (J). 15.95 (978-1-60108-000-4(X)) Red Cygnet Pr.

Skene, Pat. The Whoosh of Gadoosh. Keith, Doug, illus. 2002. 32p. 15.95 (978-0-9701907-0-3(0)) Illumination Arts Publishing Co., Inc.

Sklansky, Amy E. The Duck Who Played the Kazoo. Beeke, Tiphanie, illus. 2008. 32p. (J). (ps-1). 16.00 (***978-0-618-42854-0(2)*** , Clarion Bks.) Houghton Mifflin Co. Trade & Reference Div.

Sklansky, Amy E. My Daddy & Me. Hoyt, Ard, illus. 2005. 24p. (J). 3.50 (978-0-439-74046-3(0) , Cartwheel Bks.) Scholastic, Inc.

Slate, Joseph. Miss Bindergarten Celebrates the 100th Day of Kindergarten. 2002. (Miss Bindergarten Ser.). (Illus.). (YA). 15.53 (978-1-4046-2578-5(X)) Book Wholesalers, Inc.

—Miss Bindergarten Has a Wild Day in Kindergarten. Wolff, Ashley, illus. 2006. 40p. (J). (ps). reprint ed. pap. 6.99 (978-0-14-240709-7(7) , Puffin) Penguin Group (USA) Inc.

—Miss Bindergarten Takes a Field Trip with Kindergarten. Wolff, Ashley, illus. 2001. 32p. (J). (ps-1). 16.99 (978-0-525-46710-6(6) , Dutton Juvenile) Penguin Group (USA) Inc.

—Miss Bindergarten's Wild Day. Wolff, Ashley, illus. 2005. 40p. (J). (ps). 16.99 (978-0-525-47084-7(0) , Dutton Juvenile) Penguin Group (USA) Inc.

—What Star Is This? Jay, Alison, illus. 2005. 32p. (J). (ps-3). 15.99 (978-0-399-24014-0(4) , Putnam Juvenile) Penguin Group (USA) Inc.

Slater, Dashka. Baby Shoes. Nakata, Hiroe, illus. 2006. 32p. (J). 15.95 (978-1-58234-684-7(4) , Bloomsbury Children) Bloomsbury Publishing.

Sloat, Teri. Farmer Brown Goes Round & Round. 2001. (978-0-606-22359-1(2)) Tandem Library Bks.

—I'm a Duck! 2008. 32p. (J). (ps). pap. 6.99 (***978-0-14-241062-2(4)*** , Puffin) Penguin Group (USA) Inc.

—I'm a Duck! Sloat, Teri, illus. 2006. (Illus.). 32p. (J). (ps-2). 15.99 (978-0-399-24274-8(0) , Putnam Juvenile) Penguin Group (USA) Inc.

—Patty's Pumpkin Patch. 1999. (Illus.). 32p. (J). (ps-3). 15.99 (978-0-399-23010-3(6) , Putnam Juvenile) Penguin Group (USA) Inc.

—There Was an Old Man Who Painted the Sky. Date not set. (J). 17.00 (978-0-8050-6751-4(5) , Holt, Henry & Co. Bks. For Young Readers) Holt, Henry & Co.

—This Is the House That Was Tidy & Neat. Alley, R. W., illus. rev. ed. 2005. 32p. (J). 16.95 (978-0-8050-6921-1(6) , Holt, Henry & Co. Bks. For Young Readers) Holt, Henry & Co.

Small, David. Hoover's Bride. 2006. (Illus.). 40p. (J). pap. 5.99 (978-0-439-81218-4(6) , Scholastic Paperbacks) Scholastic, Inc.

Smalls-Hector, Irene. I Can't Take a Bath. Boyd, Aaron, illus. 2004. (Just for You! Ser.). 32p. (J). pap. 3.99 (978-0-439-56852-4(8)) Scholastic, Inc.

Smalls, Irene. My Pop Pop & Me. Johnson, Cathy Ann, illus. 2006. 24p. (J). (ps-3). 15.99 (978-0-316-73422-6(5)) Little Brown & Co.

Smaridge, Norah. The Big Tidy-Up. 2008. (Golden Classic Ser.). (Illus.). 32p. (J). (gr. k-k). lib. bdg. 11.99 (***978-0-375-95821-2(5)*** , Golden Bks.) Random Hse. Children's Bks.

Smath, Jerry. I Like Pumpkins. Smath, Jerry, illus. 2003. (Illus.). 32p. (J). (gr. k-3). pap. 3.50 (978-0-439-52110-9(6) , Cartwheel Bks.) Scholastic, Inc.

—I Like Pumpkins. 2003. (gr. k-3). lib. bdg. 11.25 (978-0-613-72237-7(X)) Tandem Library Bks.

Smee, Nicola. No Bed Without Ted. 2005. (Illus.). 24p. (J). (ps-ps). 14.95 (978-1-58234-963-3(0)) Bloomsbury Publishing.

Smeltzer, Jennifer. Scrolls & Coals. 2004. (J). 14.95 (978-0-9754804-3-4(X) , Rockhill Bks.) Kansas City Star Bks.

Smerek, Kim. What Is Zazu?, 1 bk. Smerek, Kim, illus. 2003. (Illus.). 24p. (J). bds. 7.95 (978-0-9745116-0-3(9)) Sunshine Bks. for Children.

Smith. When the Moon Fell Down. Date not set. 32p. (J). (ps up). pap. 4.99 (978-0-06-443550-5(4)) HarperCollins Pubs.

Smith, Jennifer Lynne. Things I Wonder. Perez, Angela J., ed. Gray, Angela M., illus. 2007. 36p. (J). 17.95 (***978-0-9778328-5-9(6)***) His Work Christian Publishing.

Smith, Linda. Mrs. Biddlebox: Her Bad Day... And What She Did about It! Frazee, Marla, illus. 2007. 32p. (J). (ps-2). 15.00 (***978-0-15-206349-8(8)***) Harcourt Trade Pubs.

Smith, Maggie. One Naked Baby. 2007. (Illus.). 40p. (J). (ps-k). 15.99 (978-0-375-83329-8(3)); lib. bdg. 17.99 (978-0-375-93329-5(8)) Random Hse. Children's Bks. (Knopf Bks. for Young Readers).

Smith, Stu. Goldilocks & the Three Martians. Garland, Michael, tr. Garland, Michael, illus. 2004. 32p. (J). (ps). 15.99 (978-0-525-46972-8(9) , Dutton Juvenile) Penguin Group (USA) Inc.

Snyder, Susan. There's a Frog Trapped in the Bathroom. McCabe, Susan, ed. Johanson, Anna, illus. 2005. 24p. (J). (ps-ps). 9.95 (978-0-9715411-0-8(8)) Kotzig Publishing, Inc.

—The Very Stubborn Centipede. McCabe, Susan, ed. Johanson, Anna, illus. 2005. 24p. (J). (ps-ps). 9.95 (978-0-9767163-0-3(5)) Kotzig Publishing, Inc.

Snyder, Susan E. Shivers & Shakes. 2007. (Illus.). 24p. (J). 9.95 (978-0-9767163-5-8(6)) Kotzig Publishing, Inc.

Sobel, June. B Is for Bulldozer: A Construction ABC. Iwai, Melissa, illus. 2003. 32p. (J). 16.00 (978-0-15-202250-1(3)) Harcourt Children's Bks.

—B Is for Bulldozer: A Construction ABC. Iwai, Melissa, illus. 2006. 32p. (J). pap. 6.00 (978-0-15-205774-9(9) , Voyager Bks./Libros Viajeros) Harcourt Children's Bks.

—The Goodnight Train. Huliska-Beith, Laura, illus. 2006. 32p. (J). 16.00 (978-0-15-205436-6(7)) Harcourt Trade Pubs.

—Shiver Me Letters: A Pirate ABC. Cole, Henry, illus. 2006. 32p. (J). 16.00 (978-0-15-216732-5(3)) Harcourt Trade Pubs.

Souhami, Jessica. The Famous Adventure of a Bird-Brained Hen. (Illus.). 36p. (978-0-7112-2025-6(5)); 2004. (J). 15.95 (978-1-84507-263-6(4)); 2004. (J). reprint ed. pap. 6.95 (978-1-84507-310-7(X)) Lincoln, Frances Ltd. GBR. *Dist:* Transition Vendor, Perseus Distribution.

Souhami, Jessica. In the Dark, Dark Wood. 2007. (Illus.). 24p. (J). 7.95 (***978-1-84507-755-6(5)***) Lincoln, Frances Ltd. GBR. *Dist:* Perseus Distribution.

Soule, Jean Conder. Never Tease a Weasel. Booth, George, illus. 2007. (Picture Book Ser.). 40p. (J). (ps-2). 15.99 (978-0-375-83420-2(6)); lib. bdg. 18.99 (978-0-375-93420-9(0)) Random Hse. Children's Bks. (Random Hse. Bks. for Young Readers).

Soundprints. Here We Go Round the Mulberry Bush: And Other Favorites. 2002. (Illus.). 36p. (J). bds. 8.95 (978-1-931465-26-7(6)); bds. 10.95 incl. audio compact disk (978-1-931465-32-8(0)) Soundprints. (Little Soundprints).

Sparks, Evan. Freddy's Tale. 2006. 44p. pap. 14.88 (978-1-4116-7427-1(8)) Lulu.com.

Sparks, Michal. My Very First Tea Party. 2000. (Illus.). 10p. (ps). 5.99 (978-0-7369-0243-4(0)) Harvest Hse. Pubs.

Spence, Rob & Spence, Amy. Clickety Clack. Spengler, Margaret, illus. 1999. 32p. (J). (ps-3). 15.99 (978-0-670-87946-5(0) , Viking Juvenile) Penguin Group (USA) Inc.

Spengler, Kenneth J. The Bear: An American Folk Song. Spengler, Kenneth J., illus. 2002. (Illus.). 32p. (J). (ps-3). 15.95 (978-1-59034-190-2(2)) Mondo Publishing.

Spinelli, Eileen. Bath Time. Pedersen, Janet, illus. 2003. 32p. (J). 14.95 (978-0-7614-5117-4(X)) Cavendish, Marshall Corp.

—The Best Time of Day. Langdo, Bryan, illus. 2007. 32p. (J). pap. 6.00 (978-0-15-205862-3(1) , Voyager Bks./Libros Viajeros) Harcourt Children's Bks.

—The Best Time of Day. Langdo, Bryan, illus. 2005. 32p. (J). (ps-ps). 16.00 (978-0-15-205051-1(5)) Harcourt Trade Pubs.

—Here Comes the Year. Narahashi, Keiko, illus. rev. ed. 2002. 32p. (J). (ps-3). 16.95 (978-0-8050-6685-2(3) , Holt, Henry & Co. Bks. For Young Readers) Holt, Henry & Co.

—Hug a Bug. Andreasen, Dan, illus. 2008. (J). (***978-0-06-051832-5(4)); lib. bdg. (978-0-06-051833-2(2))*** HarperCollins Pubs.

—I Know It's Autumn. Hayashi, Nancy, tr. Hayashi, Nancy, illus. 2004. 32p. (J). (ps-2). 16.99 (978-0-06-029422-9(1)); lib. bdg. 17.89 (978-0-06-029423-6(X)) HarperCollins Pubs.

—Kittycat Lullaby. Mortimer, Anne, illus. 2001. 32p. (J). 13.49 (978-0-7868-2400-7(X)) Disney Pr.

—Kittycat Lullaby. Mortimer, Anne, illus. 2001. 32p. (ps-1). 14.99 (978-0-7868-0458-0(0)) Hyperion Bks. for Children.

—Night Shift Daddy. Iwai, Melissa, illus. 2000. 32p. (ps-2). 14.99 (978-0-7868-0495-5(5)) Hyperion Pr.

—The Perfect Thanksgiving. Adinolfi, JoAnn, illus. 2007. 32p. (J). pap. 6.99 (***978-0-312-37505-8(0)***) Square Fish.

—A Safe Place Called Home. Hale, Christy, illus. 2001. 32p. (J). (gr. k-3). 15.95 (978-0-7614-5085-6(8) , Cavendish Children's Bks.) Cavendish, Marshall Corp.

—When Mama Comes Home Tonight. Dyer, Jane, illus. (Classic Board Bks.). (J). (ps-k). 2001. 30p. bds. 7.99 (978-0-689-84220-7(1) , Little Simon); 1998. 32p. 14.00 (978-0-689-81065-7(2)) Simon & Schuster Children's Publishing.

Spires, Elizabeth. The Mouse of Amherst: A Tale of Young Readers. Nivola, Claire A., illus. 2001. (Sunburst Bks.). 64p. (J). (gr. 3-7). pap. 5.95 (978-0-374-45411-1(6) , Sunburst) Farrar, Straus & Giroux.

Spiridellis, Gregg & Spiridellis, Evan. Are You Grumpy, Santa? 2006. 32p. (ps-3). pap. 6.99 (978-0-7868-0997-4(3)) Hyperion Pr.

Splash! 2001. (SPA.). 24p. (J). 15.95 (978-980-6437-19-7(5)) Playco Editores, C.A.

Spowart, Robin. Ten Little Bunnies. Spowart, Robin, illus. 2001. (Illus.). 24p. (J). (ps). pap. 7.95 (978-0-439-20863-5(7)) Scholastic, Inc.

Spruill, Ed & Spruill, Sonya. Jordan's Hair. Peringer, Stephen Mercer, illus. 2005. 16p. (J). 8.00 (978-0-8170-1484-1(5)) Judson Pr.

Spurr, Elizabeth. Halloween Sky Ride. Long, Ethan, illus. 32p. (J). (ps). 16.95 (978-0-8234-1870-1(7)) Holiday Hse., Inc.

Squillace, Elisa, illus. Down in the Jungle. 2005. (Classic Books with Holes). 16p. (J). bds. 5.99 (978-1-904550-61-7(4)) Child's Play-International.

Staake, Bob. The Red Lemon. 2006. (Deluxe Golden Book Ser.). (Illus.). 40p. (J). (ps-3). 14.95 (978-0-375-83593-3(8)); lib. bdg. 16.99 (978-0-375-93593-0(2)) Random Hse. Children's Bks. (Golden Bks.).

Staffier, Jane Sarah. Casey's History of the World: Or "Roots" Casey. l.t. ed. 1999. (Casey the Beacon Hill Cat Ser.: Vol. 4). 32p. (J). (gr. k-5). spiral bd. 9.95 (978-1-928895-03-9(4)) B.A.B., Ltd.

Stair, Karen Smith. Glasses, Glasses Oh What Do I See. 2004. (Illus.). 32p. 14.95 (978-0-9755407-1-8(8)) Bk. Pubs. Network.

Stead, Judy, illus. Mister Sun. 2006. (J). (978-1-58987-097-0(2)) Kindermusik International.

Steed, Alice. I Am Three - I Am Four. Trapani, Iza, illus. 2000. 16p. (J). (ps-k). bds. 5.95 (978-1-58089-068-7(7)) Charlesbridge Publishing, Inc.

Steer, Dugald. Snappy Little Halloween. Matthews, Derek, illus. 2004. 20p. (J). (gr. k-4). reprint ed. 13.00 (978-0-7567-7403-5(9)) DIANE Publishing Co.

Steig, Jeanne. Tales from Gizzard's Grill. Turner, Sandy, illus. 2004. 80p. (J). 17.89 (978-0-06-000960-1(8)); 16.99 (978-0-06-000959-5(4)) HarperCollins Pubs. (Cotler, Joanna Books).

Stein, Kristen. The Vegetarian Lion. 2006. 36p. (J). pap. 13.28 (978-1-4116-6459-3(0)) Lulu.com.

Stein, Mathilde. Monstersong. Linden, Gerdien van der, illus. 2007. 32p. (J). 15.95 (978-1-932425-90-1(X) , Lemniscaat) Boyds Mills Pr.

Steinberg, Laya. All Around Me, I See. Arbo, Cris, illus. 2005. (Sharing Nature with Children Book Ser.). 32p. (J). 16.95 (978-1-58469-068-9(2)); pap. 8.95 (978-1-58469-069-6(0)) Dawn Pubns.

—Thesaurus Rex Finds a Friend. Harter, Debbie, illus. 2006. (J). (978-1-905236-48-0(4)) Barefoot Bks., Inc.

Stewart, Maddie. Peg. Willey, Bee, illus. 2001. (Blue Bananas Ser.). 48p. (J). (gr. 1-2). (978-0-7787-0841-4(1)); pap. (978-0-7787-0887-2(X)) Crabtree Publishing Co.

—Peg. 2002. (gr. k-3). lib. bdg. 12.95 (978-0-613-52895-5(6)) Tandem Library Bks.

Stewart, Madeleine. Clever Daddy. Granstrom, Brita, illus. 2001. (J). pap. (978-0-7636-1376-1(2)) Candlewick Pr.

Stewart, Sarah. The Friend. Small, David, illus. 2004. 48p. (J). 16.00 (978-0-374-32463-6(8) , Farrar, Straus & Giroux (BYR)) Farrar, Straus & Giroux.

—The Friend. Small, David, illus. unabr. ed. 2007. (Picture Book Readalong Ser.). (J). (ps-3). 28.95 incl. audio compact disk (***978-1-59519-918-8(7)***); 25.95 incl. audio (***978-1-59519-914-0(4)***) Live Oak Media.

Stewart, Sarah. The Library. Small, David, illus. 2002. (J). 14.43 (978-0-7587-2983-5(9)) Book Wholesalers, Inc.

—The Library. Small, David, illus. 2000. (J). pap. 19.97 incl. audio (978-0-7366-9189-5(8)) Books on Tape, Inc.

—The Library. Small, David, illus. 1999. (Sunburst Bks.). 40p. (J). (ps-3). pap. 6.95 (978-0-374-44394-8(7) , Sunburst) Farrar, Straus & Giroux.

—The Library. Small, David, illus. 28.95 incl. audio compact disk (978-1-59519-011-6(2)); pap. 35.95 incl. audio compact disk (978-1-59519-010-9(4)); 2004. (J). 18.95 (978-1-59519-009-3(0)) Live Oak Media.

—The Library. Small, David, illus. 1999. (J). (ps-ps). lib. bdg. 14.10 (978-0-613-22882-4(0)) Tandem Library Bks.

Stewart, Wilson N. Cock-a-Doodle-Who? 2007. (Illus.). 6p. (J). 15.99 (978-0-7868-0826-7(8)) Hyperion Bks. for Children.

Stickland, Paul. Dinosaur Roar. 2001. (ps-2). lib. bdg. 14.15 (978-0-613-35933-7(X)) Tandem Library Bks.

Stiegemeyer, Julie. Bethlehem Night. Capaldi, Gina, illus. 2005. 32p. (J). (ps-ps). 12.99 (978-0-7586-0907-6(8)) Concordia Publishing Hse.

—Cheep! Cheep! Baicker-McKee, Carol, illus. 2006. 24p. (J). 9.95 (978-1-58234-682-3(8)) Bloomsbury Publishing.

—Merry Christmas, Cheeps! Baicker-McKee, Carol, illus. 2007. 24p. (J). (ps). 9.95 (978-1-59990-064-3(5)) Bloomsbury Publishing.

Sting. Rock Steady: A Story of Noah's Ark. Whyte, Hugh, illus. 2006. 28p. (J). (gr. k-4). reprint ed. 17.00 (978-1-4223-5556-5(X)) DIANE Publishing Co.

Stockham, Jessica. Runaway Train. 2004. (Illus.). 24p. (J). 9.99 (978-0-85953-144-3(9)) Child's Play-International.

Stodghill, Pat & Briley, Rita, illus. Jake's Snapping Catastrophe. 2000. 15.95 (978-1-57168-379-3(8)) Eakin Pr.

Stoeke, Janet Morgan. The Bus Stop. Stoeke, Janet Morgan, illus. 2007. (Illus.). 24p. (J). (ps-k). 12.99 (978-0-525-47805-8(1) , Dutton Juvenile) Penguin Group (USA) Inc.

Stohs, Reith Anita. Oh Come, Little Children. Huang, Benrei, illus. 2006. 32p. (J). 14.99 (978-0-7586-1215-1(X)) Concordia Publishing Hse.

Stone, Tanya Lee. B Is for Bunny: A Springtime Alphabet Book. Rama, Sue, illus. 2006. 24p. (J). (ps-1). pap. 4.99 (978-0-8431-1826-1(1) , Price Stern Sloan) Penguin Group (USA) Inc.

Stonecipher, Philiip. Boudreau of de Bayou. Perez Sanchez, Delia, tr. from ENG. 1999. (SPA & ENG., Illus.). ii, 22p. (J). (gr. 2-3). 6.95 (978-0-943864-92-1(5)) Davenport, May Pubs.

Stories & Rhymes for Every Bedtime. 2001. 384p. (J). 29.95 (978-0-7525-6432-6(3)) Parragon, Inc.

Stowe, Dorothy Bye. Bearly "Sew" Big. Stowe, Dorothy Bye, illus. 2000. (Illus.). 2p. (J). (ps-1). pap. 9.95 (978-0-9704586-0-5(6)) Verse-a-Tale Pr.

Strickland, Paul. Ten Terrible Dinosaurs. 2000. (J). (978-0-606-20260-2(9)) Tandem Library Bks.

Strong, Cynda. Where Do Angels Sleep? Denos, Julia, illus. 2007. 32p. (J). (ps-3). 14.99 (***978-0-7586-1298-4(2)***) Concordia Publishing Hse.

Stubbs, Tommy, illus. A Crack in the Track: A Thomas the Tank Engine Story. 2004. (Bright & Early Board Bks.). 24p. (J). (gr. k-ps). bds. 4.99 (978-0-375-82755-6(2) , Random Hse. Bks. for Young Readers) Random Hse. Children's Bks.

Sturges, Philemon. I Love Bugs! Halpern, Shari, illus. 2005. 32p. (J). (ps-1). 14.99 (978-0-06-056168-0(8)); lib. bdg. 14.89 (978-0-06-056169-7(6)) HarperCollins Pubs.

—I Love School! Halpern, Shari, illus. 32p. (J). (ps-1). 2004. 12.99 (978-0-06-009284-9(X)); 2004. lib. bdg. 14.89 (978-0-06-009285-6(8)); 2006. reprint ed. pap. 5.99 (978-0-06-009286-3(6) , Harper Trophy) HarperCollins Pubs.

—I Love Tools! Halpern, Shari, illus. 2006. 32p. (J). 12.99 (978-0-06-009287-0(4)); lib. bdg. 14.89 (978-0-06-009288-7(2)) HarperCollins Pubs.

—I Love Trains! Halpern, Shari, illus. (J). 2006. 28p. 6.99 (978-0-06-083774-7(8) , Harper Festival); 2003. 32p. pap. 6.99 (978-0-06-443667-0(5)) HarperCollins Pubs.

—I Love Trains! Halpern, Shari, illus. 2003. (ps-ps). lib. bdg. 14.15 (978-0-613-65696-2(2)) Tandem Library Bks.

—This Little Pirate. Walrod, Amy, illus. 2005. 40p. (J). (ps). 16.99 (978-0-525-46440-2(9) , Dutton Juvenile) Penguin Group (USA) Inc.

Stutson, Caroline. Mama Loves You. Segal, John, illus. 2005. 32p. (J). pap. 6.99 (978-0-439-57842-4(6)) Scholastic, Inc.

—Pirate Pup. Rayevsky, Robert, illus. 2005. 32p. (J). 15.95 (978-0-8118-4239-6(8)) Chronicle Bks. LLC.

—Prairie Primer: A to Z. Lamb, Susan Condie, illus. 2006. 29p. (J). (ps-2). reprint ed. 16.00 (978-1-4223-5585-5(3)) DIANE Publishing Co.

—Prairie Primer A to Z. 1999. (978-0-606-16783-3(8)) Tandem Library Bks.

Suarez, Maribel, illus. Rebecca. (Rowing Frog's Rhymes Ser.). 16p. (J). (gr. k-3). 7.95 (978-1-59437-840-9(1)) Santillana USA Publishing Co., Inc.

Suen, Anastasia. Delivery. 2001. (978-0-606-22519-9(6)) Tandem Library Bks.

—Raise the Roof! Smith, Elwood H., illus. 2003. 32p. (J). (ps-1). 15.99 (978-0-670-89282-2(3) , Viking Juvenile) Penguin Group (USA) Inc.

—Red Light, Green Light. Wilson-Max, Ken, illus. 2005. 40p. (J). (ps-k). 16.00 (978-0-15-202582-3(0) , Gulliver Bks.) Harcourt Children's Bks.

—Window Music. 2000. (978-0-606-20382-1(6)); (J). (978-0-606-20305-0(2)) Tandem Library Bks.

Suen, Anastasia & Katz, Karen. Subway. 2004. (Illus.). 40p. (J). (gr. k-1). 15.99 (978-0-670-03622-6(6) , Viking Juvenile) Penguin Group (USA) Inc.

Sullivan, Kevin. Best Hawaiian Style Mother Goose Ever. Aoki, Deb, illus. 2006. 40p. 16.95 incl. cd-rom (***978-0-9644149-6-9(1)***) Hawaya, Inc.

Sutherland, Marc. The Waiting Place. Sutherland, Marc, illus. 2004. (Illus.). 24p. (J). (gr. k-4). reprint ed. 15.00 (978-0-7567-8382-2(8)) DIANE Publishing Co.

Svendsen, Mark. Circus Carnivore. Redlich, Ben, illus. 2006. 40p. (J). (gr. 3-5). 16.00 (978-0-618-56328-9(8)) Houghton Mifflin Co. Trade & Reference Div.

Swaim, Jessica. The Hound from the Pound. McElmurry, Jill, illus. 2007. 32p. (J). (ps-3). 15.99 (***978-0-7636-2330-2(X)***) Candlewick Pr.

Swope, Sam. Krazees. 2003. lib. bdg. 15.25 (978-0-613-59656-5(0)) Tandem Library Bks.

t, Randolph (Il. Frog He Would AWooing Go Illustrated Edi. 2006. pap. (***978-1-4065-1224-3(9)***) Dodo Pr.

Taback, Simms. I Miss You Everyday. Taback, Simms, illus. 2007. (Illus.). 40p. (YA). (gr. 12-2). 16.99 (***978-0-670-06192-1(1)*** , Viking Juvenile) Penguin Group (USA) Inc.

Tabby, Abigail. Snap! Button! Zip! Moroney, Christopher, illus. 2003. (Sesame Beginnings Ser.). 14p. (J). (gr. k). bds. 7.99 (978-0-375-82369-5(7) , Random Hse. Bks. for Young Readers) Random Hse. Children's Bks.

Tafolla, Carmen. What Can You Do with a Rebozo? 2007. (J). (***978-1-58246-220-2(8)*** , Tricycle Pr.) Ten Speed Pr.

Tafuri, Nancy. Snowy Flowy Blowy: A Twelve Months Rhyme. 1999. (Illus.). (J). pap. (978-0-590-18974-3(3)) Scholastic Reading Counts.

Tagg, Christine. A Very Special Valentine. Kneen, Maggie, illus. 2003. (J). 15.95 (978-0-8118-4073-6(5)) Chronicle Bks. LLC.

Tanen, Sloane. C Is for Coco: A Little Chick's First Book of Letters. Hagen, Stefan, illus. Hagen, Stefan, photos by. 2007. 24p. (J). (ps). 6.95 (978-1-59990-071-1(8)) Bloomsbury Publishing.

—Coco All Year Round. Hagen, Stefan, photos by. 2006. (Illus.). 32p. (J). 15.95 (978-1-58234-709-7(3) , Bloomsbury Children) Bloomsbury Publishing.

Tanen, Sloane. Coco Counts: A Little Chick's First Book of Numbers. Hagen, Stefan, illus. Hagen, Stefan, photos by. 2007. 24p. (J). (ps). 6.95 (***978-1-59990-072-8(6)***) Bloomsbury Publishing.

Tango Hampton, Doreen. I Like Gum. 2007. 32p. (J). 15.95 (***978-0-9726614-2-3(5)***) Shenanigan Bks.

Tara, Stephanie Lisa. Gwynne, Fair & Shining. Fodi, Lee Edward, illus. 2006. (J). lib. bdg. 16.95 (***978-1-933285-62-7(1)***) Brown Bks. Publishing Group.

Tarbox, A. D. Already Asleep. Olson, Julie, illus. 2006. 32p. 12.95 (978-0-9766805-6-7(4) , Moo Pr.) Keene Publishing.

Taylor, Bonnie Highsmith. Simon Can't Say Hippopotamus. Hornung, Phyllis, tr. Hornung, Phyllis, illus. 2003. 24p. (J). 14.95 (978-1-59336-017-7(7)); pap. (978-1-59336-018-4(5)) Mondo Publishing.

Taylor-Butler, Christine. Ah-Choo. Koeller, Carol, illus. 2005. (My First Reader Ser.). (J). (gr. k-1). 31p. pap. 3.95 (978-0-516-25275-9(5)); 32p. 18.50 (978-0-516-25175-2(9)) Scholastic Library Publishing. (Children's Pr.).

Taylor-Butler, Christine. A Mom Like No Other. Devard, Nancy, illus. 2004. 32p. (J). lib. bdg. 15.00 (***978-1-4242-0227-0(2)***) Fitzgerald Bks.

Taylor, Yvonne. Hartlie: The Streak. Taylor, Yvonne, ed. (Hartlie: Vol. 1). (Illus.). 32p. (J). 10.99 (978-0-9709187-0-3(4)) Peaceable Productions.

Terheyden, Linda, reader. Madeline & the Bad Hat. 2004. (Illus.). (J). pap. 18.95 incl. audio compact disk (978-1-59112-813-7(7)) Live Oak Media.

Testa, Maria. Becoming Joe Dimaggio. Hunt, Scott, illus. 2002. 64p. (J). (gr. 5-9). 14.99 (978-0-7636-1537-6(4)) Candlewick Pr.

—Becoming Joe DiMaggio. Hunt, Scott, illus. 2005. 64p. (J). (gr. 5-9). reprint ed. pap. 5.99 (978-0-7636-2444-6(6)) Candlewick Pr.

S

Thach, James Otis. A Child's Guide to Common Household Monsters. Udovic, David, illus. 2007. 32p. (J). (ps-1). 16.95 (***978-1-932425-58-1(6)*** , Front Street) Boyds Mills Pr.

Thank You, God. 2003. (Illus.). 28p. (J). (ps-k). bds. 7.95 (978-0-8249-5457-4(2)) Ideals Pubns.

That's What a Friend Is. 2001. (Illus.). 24p. (J). pap. 5.95 (978-0-8249-5391-1(6)) Ideals Pubns.

Thomas, Frances. Little Monster's Book of Numbers. Collins, Ross, illus. 2005. 10p. (J). (ps-k). bds. 5.95 (978-1-58234-979-4(7)) Bloomsbury Publishing.

—Little Monster's Book of Opposites. Collins, Ross, illus. 2005. 10p. (J). (ps-k). bds. 5.95 (978-1-58234-980-0(0)) Bloomsbury Publishing.

Thomas Nelson Publishing Staff. My Christmas Collection: Three Favorite Stories. 2006. 80p. (J). 14.99 (978-1-4003-0843-9(7)) Nelson, Thomas Inc.

Thomas, Rosie. Cowgirl Rosie & Her Five Baby Bison. 2001. (Illus.). 24p. (J). (ps-3). 12.95 (978-0-316-64712-0(8)) Little Brown & Co.

Thomas, Scott. The Yawn Heard 'Round the World. Mai-Wyss, Tatjana, illus. 2004. 30p. (J). 14.95 (978-1-58246-051-2(5) , Tricycle Pr.) Ten Speed Pr.

Thompson. The Follower. 2003. 32p. (J). pap. (978-1-55041-880-4(7)) Fitzhenry & Whiteside, Ltd.

Thompson, Kay. Eloise's Christmas Trinkles. Knight, Hilary, illus. 2007. (Eloise Ser.). 48p. (J). (ps-3). 9.99 (***978-0-689-87425-3(1)***) Simon & Schuster Children's Publishing.

Thompson, Shannon Raines. Mad about Miller. Stone, Kathrine Thompson, ed. Shehan, Terece, illus. 2006. 24p. (YA). 12.95 (978-1-59971-853-8(7)) Aardvark Global Publishing.

—Nuts about Neal. Stone, Kathrine Thompson, ed. Shehan, Terece, illus. 2006. 24p. (YA). 12.95 (978-1-59971-852-1(9)) Aardvark Global Publishing.

Thong, Roseanne. Gai See: What You Can See in Chinatown. Choi, Yangsook, illus. 2007. 40p. (J). (ps-3). 16.95 (***978-0-8109-9337-2(6)*** , Abrams Bks. for Young Readers) Abrams, Harry N. , Inc.

—Red Is a Dragon. Lin, Grace, illus. 2001. 40p. (J). 15.95 (978-0-8118-3177-2(9)) Chronicle Bks. LLC.

—Round Is a Mooncake: A Book of Shapes. Lin, Grace, illus. 2000. 40p. (J). (ps-k). 14.95 (978-0-8118-2676-1(7)) Chronicle Bks. LLC.

Thornhill, Jan. A Tree in the Forest. 1999. 40p. (Orig.). (J). (gr. 3). pap. 10.11 (978-0-382-24374-5(9)) Silver, Burdett & Ginn, Inc.

Thornton, E. J. I Have a Secret: Do I Keep It? 2004. (Illus.). 24p. per. 8.95 (978-1-932344-66-0(7)) Thornton Publishing.

Tillman, Nancy. On the Night You Were Born. 2006. (Illus.). 32p. (J). (gr. k-2). 16.95 (978-0-312-34606-5(9) , Feiwel & Friends) Feiwel & Friends.

Tini Sisters Staff. Finny Finds Friends in the Forest: A Letter-Sound * Listen & Retell Adventure. Mauterer, Erin Marie, illus. 2002. (Letter-Sound Listen & Retell Adventure Ser.). (J). 18.95 incl. audio compact disk (978-0-9678459-3-7(9)) Atori Publishing, Inc.

Tobiassen, Virginia Hege. The Gift of the Magi Retold in Rhyme. 2002. viii, 40p. pap. 12.95 (978-0-9723095-0-9(0)) Ashe Street Hse., The.

Tocco, Nicole. Toothbrush, Jammies, Man in the Moon—Why Is It Bedtime So Soon? 2006. (J). (978-0-7666-2463-4(3)) Modern Publishing.

Todd, Mark. Monster Trucks! Todd, Mark, illus. 2003. (Illus.). 32p. (J). (gr. k-ps). tchr. ed. 15.00 (978-0-618-18208-4(X)) Houghton Mifflin Co. Trade & Reference Div.

—Monster Trucks. 2005. 13p. (J). (gr. k-ps). bds. 8.95 (978-0-618-58119-1(7)) Houghton Mifflin Co. Trade & Reference Div.

Todd, Traci N. Wiggle, Waggle, Loop-De-Loo! Barner, Bob, illus. 2006. (J). (978-1-58987-009-3(3)) Kindermusik International.

Tokunbo, Dimitrea. Together. Oliver, Jennifer, illus. 2005. (J). pap. (978-0-439-79654-5(7)) Scholastic, Inc.

Toms, Kate. I Udderly Love You. 2007. (Illus.). 25p. (ps). per., bds. 7.95 (978-1-84610-460-2(2)) Make Believe Ideas GBR. *Dist:* Ingram Pub. Services.

Toms, Kate. Twinkle, Twinkle, Little Star. 2007. (Illus.). 26p. (ps). bds. 7.99 (*978-1-84610-485-5(8)) Make Believe Ideas GBR. *Dist:* Ingram Pub. Services.

Triti. Changes: A True Story about Oscar Turtle & Amazon Red. 2000. (Illus.). (J). (978-0-915180-36-3(7)) Harrowood Bks.

Trumbauer, Lisa. A Tooth Is Loose. Gray, Steve, illus. (Rookie Reader Espanol Ser.). (J). (gr. k-2). 2005. 24p. pap. 4.95 (978-0-516-25841-6(9)); 2004. 23p. 19.50 (978-0-516-23445-8(5)) Scholastic Library Publishing. (Children's Pr.).

—A Tooth Is Loose. Gray, Steve, illus. 2005. 24p. (J). (gr. k-1). lib. bdg. 12.15 (978-0-606-33168-5(9)) Tandem Library Bks.

Tucker Slingsby Ltd., Staff. My Big Book of Fairy Tales in Rhyme! Lewis, Jan, illus. 2004. 224p. (J). (978-1-902272-31-3(5)) Tucker Slingsby, Ltd.

Tudor, Tasha. Around the Year. Tudor, Tasha, illus. 64p. (J). 2004. pap. 6.99 (978-0-689-87350-8(6) , Aladdin); 2001. (Illus.). 17.99 (978-0-689-82847-8(0)) Simon & Schuster Children's Publishing.

—1 Is One. Tudor, Tasha, illus. (Classic Board Bks.). (Illus.). (J). 2002. 24p. 6.99 (978-0-689-85142-1(1) , Little Simon); 2000. 48p. 16.00 (978-0-689-82843-0(8)) Simon & Schuster Children's Publishing.

Tunley, Annabel & Tellis, Annabel. If My Dad Were A Dog. 2007. 32p. (J). pap. 16.99 (*978-0-439-91387-4(X) , Chicken Hse., The) Scholastic, Inc.

Tutu Nene - Hawaiian Mother Goose Rhymes. 2004. (J). audio compact disk 14.99 (978-0-931548-60-4(8)) Island Heritage Publishing.

Tyler, Jenny & Hawthorn, Phillip. Who's Making that Smell? 2007. (Luxury Flap Bks). 16p. (J). 9.99 (*978-0-7945-1696-3(3) , Usborne) EDC Publishing.

Tym, Kate. We Love the Seaside. 2007. (J). lib. bdg. 16.95 (*978-1-59566-369-6(X)) QEB Publishing Inc.

Tyrrell, Melissa. Here Comes Santa! A Little Foil Book. 1998. (Merry Little Foil Bks.). (Illus.). 10p. (YA). (ps up). 2.95 (978-1-58117-007-8(6) , Intervisual/Piggy Toes) Dalmatian Pr.

Urbigkit, Cat. Puppies, Puppies Everywhere! Urbigkit, Cat, photos by. (Illus.). 24p. (J). (ps-1). 12.95 (978-1-59078-363-4(8)) Boyds Mills Pr.

Uslander, Arlene. That's What Grandparents Are For. Levin, Freddie, illus. 2001. 32p. (J). (ps-3). (978-0-939217-60-1(0)) Peel Productions, Inc.

Valentine, Johnny. The Daddy Machine. Schmidt, Lynette, illus. 2nd ed. 2004. 32p. (Orig.). pap. 10.95 (978-1-55583-846-1(4)) Alyson Pubns.

—One Dad, Two Dads, Brown Dad, Blue Dads. Sarecky, Melody, illus. 2004. 32p. (J). pap. 10.95 (978-1-55583-848-5(0)) Alyson Pubns.

Van Dusen, Chris. A Camping Spree with Mr. Magee. 2003. (Illus.). 36p. (J). 14.95 (978-0-8118-3603-6(7)) Chronicle Bks. LLC.

—Down to the Sea with Mr. Magee. (Illus.). 36p. (J). 2006. pap. 6.95 (978-0-8118-5225-8(3)); 2000. 14.95 (978-0-8118-2499-6(3)) Chronicle Bks. LLC.

—If I Built a Car. Van Dusen, Chris, illus. (J). (gr. k). 2007. 40p. pap. 6.99 (978-0-14-240825-4(5) , Puffin); 2005. (Illus.). 32p. 15.99 (978-0-525-47400-5(5) , Dutton Juvenile) Penguin Group (USA) Inc.

Van Fleet, Mara. Up the Water Spout & Other Nursery Rhymes. 2005. (Illus.). 10p. (J). (ps-k). bds. 12.99 (978-0-7944-0766-7(8)) Reader's Digest Assn., Inc., The.

Van Fleet, Matthew. Tails. 2003. (Illus.). 20p. (J). 13.95 (978-0-15-216773-8(0) , Red Wagon Bks.) Harcourt Children's Bks.

Vantrease, Norma. Ants in My Pants. Vantrease, Norma & Cox, Steve, trs. Cox, Steve, illus. 2004. (Rookie Reader Ser.). 31p. (J). 19.50 (978-0-516-23443-4(9) , Children's Pr.) Scholastic Library Publishing.

Varela, Barry. Gizmo. Briant, Ed, illus. 2007. 32p. (J). (ps-3). 16.95 (978-1-59643-115-7(6)) Roaring Brook Pr.

Vasconsellos, Daniel. Frog in the Kitchen Sink: And Hand Puppet. gif. ed. 2004. (Illus.). (J). bds. 16.99 (978-1-57939-169-0(9)) Accord Publishing, Ltd.

—Max Makes Millions: The Adventures of Max Continued... 2005. (Illus.). 32p. (J). 15.99 (978-1-57939-198-0(2)) Accord Publishing, Ltd.

Vassallo, Rebecca. Listen to Luther. 2006. 24p. (J). 10.87 (978-1-4116-8169-9(X)) Lulu.com.

Vaughan, Marcia. We're Going on a Ghost Hunt. Schweninger, Ann, illus. 2001. 32p. (J). (gr. k-2). 15.00 (978-0-15-202353-9(4)) Harcourt Children's Bks.

Vaughn Zimmer, Tracie. Reaching for Sun. 2007. 144p. (J). (gr. 7 up). 14.95 (978-1-59990-037-7(8) , Bloomsbury Children) Bloomsbury Publishing.

Vazov, George D. The Other Side of the Mushroom. 2006. 12.00 (978-0-8059-9018-8(6)) Dorrance Publishing Co., Inc.

Veggietales. Thankfulness Song. 2007. (Veggie Tales Gift Book Ser.). 32p. (J). 7.99 (978-1-4165-3393-1(1) , Howard Bks.) Simon & Schuster.

Velde, Marie. Laundry Day. 2007. (J). bds. 22.95 (*978-1-933156-17-0(1) , Visikid Bks.) GSVQ Publishing.

Venn, Cecilia. Puppy Parade, Level 2. 1998. (Disney's First Readers Ser.). (Illus.). 32p. (J). (gr. 1-3). pap. 2.95 (978-0-7868-4170-7(2)) Disney Pr.

Verlander, Susan. Goodnight Country. 2004. (Illus.). 28p. (J). 13.95 (978-0-8118-4172-6(3)) Chronicle Bks. LLC.

Vestergaard, Hope. Hello, Snow! Westcott, Nadine Bernard, illus. 2004. 32p. (J). 16.00 (978-0-374-32949-5(4) , Farrar, Straus & Giroux (BYR)) Farrar, Straus & Giroux.

—Hillside Lullaby. Moore, Margie, tr. Moore, Margie, illus. 2006. 32p. (J). (ps). 15.99 (978-0-525-47215-5(0) , Dutton Juvenile) Penguin Group (USA) Inc.

—What Do You Do— When a Monster Says Boo? Smith, Maggie, illus. 2006. 32p. (J). (ps-1). 15.99 (978-0-525-47737-2(3) , Dutton Juvenile) Penguin Group (USA) Inc.

Viorst, Judith. Nobody Here but Me. Davenier, Christine, illus. 2008. (J). (*978-0-374-35540-1(1)) Farrar, Straus & Giroux.

Viscardi, Dolly. All Around Cats, , Brooks, David, illus. 2004. 32p. (gr. k-3). 15.95 (978-1-55971-072-5(1) , NorthWord Bks. for Young Readers) T&N Children's Publishing.

Vischer, Phil. How Many Veggies? A Veggiecational Book about Numbers! 1999. (Veggiecational Ser.: Vol. 1). (Illus.). 12p. (J). (ps). 8.99 (978-0-8499-5985-1(3)) Nelson, Thomas Inc.

—More Veggiecational Fun: A Book about Time & Opposites! 1999. (Veggiecational Ser.). (Illus.). 64p. (J). (ps-2). 10.99 (978-0-8499-7531-8(X)) Nelson, Thomas Inc.

—The Veggiecational Book: A Book about Numbers, Colors, Shapes & Letters! 1998. (Veggiecational Ser.: Vol. 7). (Illus.). 128p. (J). (ps-2). 19.99 (978-0-8499-5865-6(2)) Nelson, Thomas Inc.

—47 Beavers in the Big Blue Sea. 2007. (Illus.). 48p. (J). 15.99 (978-1-4003-0836-1(4)) Nelson, Thomas Inc.

Vision, Mutiya Sahar. Disabilities?! Alcantara, Ignacio, illus. 2005. 40p. (J). mass mkt. 17.00 (978-0-9659538-9-4(0)) Soul Vision Works Publishing.

Voce, Louise, ed. & illus. Over in the Meadow: A Counting Rhyme. Voce, Louise, illus. 2000. (Big Books! Ser.). 32p. (J). (gr. k-2). pap. 19.99 (978-0-7636-1285-6(5)) Candlewick Pr.

Waber, Bernard. Fast Food! Gulp! Gulp! 2001. (Illus.). 32p. (J). (gr. k-3). tchr. ed. 16.00 (978-0-618-14189-0(8) , Walter Lorraine) Houghton Mifflin Co. Trade & Reference Div.

—Fast Food! Gulp! Gulp! 2005. (Illus.). 32p. (J). (gr. k-3). reprint ed. 5.95 (978-0-618-55561-1(7) , Walter Lorraine) Houghton Mifflin Co. Trade & Reference Div.

—The Mouse That Snored. 2004. (Illus.). 32p. (J). (gr. k-3). 5.95 (978-0-618-43954-6(4) , Walter Lorraine) Houghton Mifflin Co. Trade & Reference Div.

Wade, Connie. Noah's Ark. Overstreet, Laura, illus. 2006. (Sing A Story Ser.). 20p. (J). bds. 4.99 (978-0-7847-1812-4(1) , 04134) Standard Publishing.

Wahl, Jan. Elf Night. Weevers, Peter, illus. 2005. (Picture Bks.). 32p. (gr. k-2). 15.25 (978-1-57505-512-1(0)) Lerner Publishing Group.

—The Enchanted Sled. Felix, Monique, illus. 2005. (Creative Editions Ser.). 32p. (J). 16.95 (978-1-56846-187-8(9)) Creative Co., The.

—I Met a Dinosaur. 2002. (gr. k-3). lib. bdg. 16.40 (978-0-613-77489-5(2)) Tandem Library Bks.

Wahl, Jan & Sheban, Chris. I Met a Dinosaur. 2002. (Illus.). 32p. (J). (gr. 1-5). pap. 7.95 (978-0-89812-331-9(3) , Creative Paperbacks) Creative Co., The.

Waldron, Jan L. John Pig's Halloween. 2001. (gr. 3-6). lib. bdg. 15.30 (978-0-613-58416-6(3)) Tandem Library Bks.

Walker, Isenberg. Blankie Book. (J). 12.95 (978-0-8118-4137-5(5)) Chronicle Bks. LLC.

Walker, Rob D. Once upon a Cloud. Mahurin, Matt, illus. 2005. 40p. (J). pap. 16.95 (978-0-439-68879-6(5) , Blue Sky Pr., The) Scholastic, Inc.

Walker, Sylvia L. & Lisberg, Rachel. Little Light of Mine. Gruetzke, Mary, ed. 2005. (Sing & Read Ser.). (Illus.). 24p. (J). (ps). pap. 4.99 incl. audio compact disk (978-0-439-75558-0(1) , Cartwheel Bks.) Scholastic, Inc.

Wallace, Nancy Elizabeth. Baby Day! 2003. (Illus.). 32p. (J). (gr. k-ps). 9.95 (978-0-618-27576-2(2)) Houghton Mifflin Co. Trade & Reference Div.

Walsh, Sheila. Hello, Stars! A Sleepytime Tale of God's Loving Presence. Maze, Deborah, illus. 2001. 40p. (J). 9.95 (978-1-57856-336-4(4) , WaterBrook Pr.) WaterBrook Pr.

Walters, Virginia. Are We There Yet, Daddy? Schindler, S. D., illus. 2002. 32p. (J). pap. 6.99 (978-0-14-230013-8(6) , Puffin) Penguin Group (USA) Inc.

—Are We There Yet, Daddy? 2002. (gr. k-3). lib. bdg. 15.30 (978-0-613-83552-7(2)) Tandem Library Bks.

—Are We There yet, Daddy? Schindler, S. D., illus. 2005. 27p. (J). (gr. k-4). reprint ed. 16.00 (978-0-7567-9708-9(X)) DIANE Publishing Co.

Walton, Rick. Bunnies on the Go: Getting from Place to Place. Miglio, Paige, illus. 2003. 32p. (J). 16.99 (978-0-06-029185-3(0)) HarperCollins Pubs.

—Bunny Christmas: A Family Celebration. Miglio, Paige, illus. 2004. 32p. (J). 15.99 (978-0-06-008415-8(4)); lib. bdg. 16.89 (978-0-06-008416-5(2)) HarperCollins Pubs.

—Bunny Day: Telling Time from Breakfast to Bedtime. Miglio, Paige, illus. 2002. 32p. (J). (gr. 2 up). 16.99 (978-0-06-029183-9(4)) HarperCollins Pubs.

—Bunny School: A Learning Fun-for-All. Miglio, Paige, illus. 2005. 32p. (J). 15.99 (978-0-06-057508-3(5)); lib. bdg. 16.89 (978-0-06-057509-0(3)) HarperCollins Pubs.

—How Can You Dance? Lopez-Escriva, Ana, illus. 2001. 1p. (J). (ps-3). 13.99 (978-0-399-23229-9(X) , Putnam Juvenile) Penguin Group (USA) Inc.

—The Remarkable Friendship of Mr. Cat & Mr. Rat. McCue, Lisa, illus. 2006. 32p. (J). (ps-3). 14.99 (978-0-399-23899-4(9) , Putnam Juvenile) Penguin Group (USA) Inc.

—So Many Bunnies: A Bedtime ABC & Counting Book. Miglio, Paige, illus. 32p. (J). (ps-3). 2002. pap. 5.95 (978-0-06-443751-6(5) , Harper Trophy); 2000. 6.99 (978-0-688-17364-7(0) , Harper Festival) HarperCollins Pubs.

—So Many Bunnies: A Bedtime ABC & Counting Book. 1998. (Illus.). 32p. (J). (ps-1). 15.89 (978-0-688-13657-4(5)) HarperCollins Pubs.

—So Many Bunnies: A Bedtime ABC & Counting Book. Miglio, Paige, illus. 1998. 32p. (J). (ps-3). 17.99 (978-0-688-13656-7(7)) HarperCollins Pubs.

Walton, Rick & Bardhan-Quallen, Sudipta. A Very Hairy Scary Story. Clark, David, illus. 2004. 32p. (J). (ps-3). 15.99 (978-0-399-23858-1(1) , Putnam Juvenile) Penguin Group (USA) Inc.

Walvoord, Linda. Razzamadaddy. Yoshikawa, Sachiko, tr. Yoshikawa, Sachiko, illus. 2004. 32p. (J). 14.95 (978-0-7614-5158-7(7)) Cavendish, Marshall Corp.

Wang, Margaret. Eency Weency Spider. Rueda, Claudia, illus. 2005. 22p. (J). (ps-ps). 10.95 (978-1-58117-418-2(7) , Intervisual/Piggy Toes) Dalmatian Pr.

—Who Stole the Cookie Form the Cookie Jar? Schneider, Christine, illus. 2005. 12p. (J). (ps-ps). 4.95 (978-1-58117-429-8(2) , Intervisual/Piggy Toes) Dalmatian Pr.

Ward, Helen. The Animals' Christmas Carol. 2001. (Picture Books for Holidays). (Illus.). 40p. lib. bdg. 24.90 (978-0-7613-2408-9(9) , Millbrook Pr.) Lerner Publishing Group.

—The Animals Christmas Carol. 2001. (Illus.). 40p. (J). 16.95 (978-0-7613-1496-7(2) , Millbrook Pr.) Lerner Publishing Group.

Ward, Jennifer. Because You Are My Baby. Long, Sylvia, illus. 2007. 32p. 15.95 (*978-0-87358-911-6(4) , Rising Moon Bks. for Young Readers) Northland Publishing.

—Over in the Garden. Spengler, Kenneth J., illus. 2002. 32p. (ps-2). 15.95 (978-0-87358-793-8(6) , Rising Moon Bks. for Young Readers) Northland Publishing.

—The Seed & the Giant Saguaro. Rangner, Mike, illus. 2003. 32p. (gr. 4-8). 15.95 (978-0-87358-845-4(2) , Rising Moon Bks. for Young Readers) Northland Publishing.

—Somewhere in the Ocean. 2000. (J). (978-0-606-19468-6(1)) Tandem Library Bks.

Ward, Jennifer. Way up in the Arctic. Spengler, Kenneth J., illus. 2007. (SPA & ENG.). 32p. 15.95 (*978-0-87358-928-4(9) , Rising Moon Bks. for Young Readers) Northland Publishing.

Ward, Jennifer, et al. Somewhere in the Ocean. Spengler, Kenneth J., illus. 2000. 32p. (ps-2). 15.95 (978-0-87358-748-8(0) , Rising Moon Bks. for Young Readers) Northland Publishing.

Wardlaw, Lee. The Chair Where Bear Sits. Benfanti, Russell, illus. 2001. 56p. (J). (ps-2). 23.00 (978-1-890817-85-5(6)) Winslow Pr.

Wargin, Kathy-Jo. P Is for Pumpkin. Pang, Ariel Ya-Wen, illus. 2008. (J). (978-0-310-71180-3(0)) Zonderkidz.

Warnes, Tim. Daddy Hug. Chapman, Jane, illus. 2008. 32p. (J). 16.99 (978-0-06-058950-9(7)); lib. bdg. 17.89 (978-0-06-058951-6(5)) HarperCollins Pubs.

—Mommy Mine. Chapman, Jane, illus. 2005. 32p. (J). (ps-k). 15.99 (978-0-06-058947-9(7)); lib. bdg. 16.89 (978-0-06-058948-6(5)) HarperCollins Pubs.

Watson, Clyde. Midnight Moon. Natti, Susanna, illus. 2006. 24p. (J). 12.95 (978-1-59692-162-7(5)) MacAdam/Cage Publishing, Inc.

Watson, Richard A. In the Dark Cave. Norman, Dean, illus. 2005. 40p. (J). (ps-ps). pap. 5.95 (978-1-59572-038-2(3)) Star Bright Bks., Inc.

Wax, Wendy. What Do You Say? Please & Thank You. Dillard, Sarah, illus. 2005. (J). (978-1-58987-108-3(1)) Kindermusik International.

Wax, Wendy & Kwiat, Ernie. Sesame Street Guess Who? Elmo. 2007. 10p. (J). bds. 10.99 (978-0-7944-1211-1(4)) Reader's Digest Assn., Inc., The.

Waysman, Dvora. My Jewish Days of the Week. Rosenfeld, D. L., ed. Schmidt, Melanie, illus. 2001. 32p. (J). (ps-k). 9.95 (978-1-929628-03-2(X)) Hachai Publishing.

Weare, Tim. I'm A Little Puppy: A Finger-Puppet Pal. 2002. (I'm A Little Ser.). (Illus.). 12p. (J). (ps-k). bds. 6.95 (978-0-439-40642-0(0) , Cartwheel Bks.) Scholastic, Inc.

Weare, Tim, illus. I'm a Little Giraffe: A Finger-Puppet Pal. 2002. (I'm A Little Ser.). 12p. (J). (ps-k). bds. 6.95 (978-0-439-40641-3(2) , Cartwheel Bks.) Scholastic, Inc.

Weatherford, Carole Boston. Jazz Baby. Freeman, Laura, illus. 2002. 24p. (J). (ps). 11.95 (978-1-58430-039-7(6)) Lee & Low Bks., Inc.

Weaver, Katie McAllaster. Bill in a China Shop. Raglin, Tim, illus. 2003. 32p. (J). 16.95 (978-1-58234-832-2(4) , Bloomsbury Children) Bloomsbury Publishing.

Weeks, Sarah. Baa-Choo! Manning, Jane, illus. (I Can Read Bks.). 32p. (J). (ps-3). 2006. pap. 3.99 (978-0-06-443740-0(X)); 2004. 15.99 (978-0-06-029236-2(9)); 2004. lib. bdg. 16.89 (978-0-06-029237-9(7)) HarperCollins Pubs.

—Bunny Fun. Williams, Sam, illus. 2008. 40p. (J). (ps-k). 14.00 (978-0-15-205838-8(9)) Harcourt Trade Pubs.

—Drip Drop. 2002. (gr. k-3). lib. bdg. 11.80 (978-0-613-44518-4(X)) Tandem Library Bks.

—Drip, Drop. Manning, Jane, illus. rev. ed. 2000. (I Can Read Bks.). 32p. (J). (gr. k-3). 14.95 (978-0-06-028523-4(0)) HarperCollins Pubs.

—If I Were a Lion. Solomon, Heather M., illus. 2004. 40p. (J). 16.99 (978-0-689-84836-0(6) , Atheneum) Simon & Schuster Children's Publishing.

—Mrs. McNosh Hangs up Her Wash. Westcott, Nadine Bernard, illus. 2002. 24p. (J). pap. 6.99 (978-0-06-000479-8(7) , Harper Trophy) HarperCollins Pubs.

—Mrs. McNosh Hangs up Her Wash. 2002. (ps-2). lib. bdg. 18.75 (978-0-613-57646-8(2)) Tandem Library Bks.

—Oh My Gosh, Mrs. McNosh. Westcott, Nadine Bernard, illus. 2002. 32p. (J). (ps up). 15.99 (978-0-694-01204-6(1)); lib. bdg. 15.89 (978-0-06-008858-3(3)) HarperCollins Pubs. (Geringer, Laura Book).

—Overboard! Williams, Sam, illus. 2006. 40p. (J). 14.00 (978-0-15-205046-7(9)) Harcourt Trade Pubs.

—Piece of Jungle. Duranceau, Suzanne, illus. 1999. 32p. (J). (ps-3). 15.95 incl. audio (978-0-06-028409-1(9) , Geringer, Laura Book) HarperCollins Pubs.

—Pip Squeak. Manning, Jane, illus. 2007. (I Can Read Bks.). 32p. (J). lib. bdg. 16.89 (978-0-06-075637-6(3)); 15.99 (978-0-06-075635-2(7)) HarperCollins Pubs. (Geringer, Laura Book).

Weeks, Sarah & Carter, David A. Peek in My Pocket. 2007. (Illus.). 16p. (J). (ps). 10.95 (*978-0-15-205807-4(9)) Harcourt Trade Pubs.

Weigel, Jeff. Atomic Ace: (He's Just My Dad) Weigel, Jeff, illus. 2004. (Illus.). 32p. (J). (gr. 1-4). pap. 6.95 (978-0-8075-3217-1(7)) Whitman, Albert & Co.

Weigel, Jeff, illus. Atomic Ace & the Robot Rampage. 2006. 32p. (J). 15.95 (978-0-8075-0484-0(X)); pap. 6.95 (978-0-8075-0485-7(8)) Whitman, Albert & Co.

Weimer, Heidi R. Love from My Heart: To a Snuggly Cuddly Little Boy (Parent Love Letters) Sharp, Chris, illus. 2005. 14p. (J). bds. 12.99 (978-0-8249-6654-6(6)) Ideals Pubns.

—Love from My Heart: To a Precious Sweet Little Girl (Parent Love Letters) Sharp, Chris, illus. 2005. 14p. (J). bds. 12.99 (978-0-8249-6655-3(4)) Ideals Pubns.

Weinberger, Kimberly. Our Thanksgiving. deGroat, Diane, illus. 2000. (My First Hello Reader! Ser.). 32p. (J). (ps-3). pap. 3.99 (978-0-439-09908-0(0)) Scholastic, Inc.

—Our Thanksgiving. 2000. (Hello Reader! Ser.). (J). (978-0-606-19586-7(6)) Tandem Library Bks.

Weiss, Ellen. Twins Have a Fight. Williams, Sam, tr. Williams, Sam, illus. 2004. (Ready-to-Read Ser.). 24p. (J). pap. 3.99 (978-0-689-86515-2(5) , Aladdin) Simon & Schuster Children's Publishing.

—Twins in the Park. Williams, Sam, illus. 2003. (Ready-to-Read Ser.). 24p. (J). pap. 3.99 (978-0-689-85742-3(X) , Aladdin) Simon & Schuster Children's Publishing.

—Twins Take a Bath. Williams, Sam, illus. 2003. (Ready-to-Read Ser.). 24p. (J). pap. 3.99 (978-0-689-85740-9(3) , Aladdin) Simon & Schuster Children's Publishing.

Weiss, Ellen & Weiss, Ellen. Twins Go to Bed. 2004. (Ready-to-Read Ser.). (Illus.). 24p. (J). pap. 3.99 (978-0-689-86517-6(1) , Aladdin) Simon & Schuster Children's Publishing.

Welch, Willy. Grumbly Bunnies. Lyon, Tammie, illus. 2004. 28p. (J). bds. 6.95 (978-1-58089-088-5(1)) Charlesbridge Publishing, Inc.

—Grumbly Bunnies. Lyon, Tammie Speer, illus. 2004. 32p. (J). 15.95 (978-1-58089-086-1(5)); pap. 6.95 (978-1-58089-087-8(3)) Charlesbridge Publishing, Inc.

—Grumpy Bunnies. Lyon, Tammie Speer, illus. 2000. 32p. (J). (ps-2). 16.95 (978-1-58089-053-3(9)); pap. 6.95 (978-1-58089-060-1(1)) Charlesbridge Publishing, Inc.

—Grumpy Bunnies. 2000. (Illus.). (J). 13.75 (978-0-606-18749-7(9)) Tandem Library Bks.

Wells, Philip. Daddy Island. Daly, Niki, illus. 2001. 24p. (J). (ps-2). 15.99 (978-1-84148-197-5(1)) Barefoot Bks., Inc.

Wells, Rosemary. Noisy Nora. 2000. (gr. k-3). lib. bdg. 15.30 (978-0-8085-3632-1(X)) Tandem Library Bks.

—Read to Your Bunny. Wells, Rosemary, illus. (Illus.). (J). 2003. 12p. bds. 7.99 (978-0-439-54337-8(1) , Cartwheel Bks.); 1999. 32p. pap. 3.99 (978-0-439-08717-9(1)) Scholastic, Inc.

—Read to Your Bunny. 1998. (Bruno & Boots Book Ser.). (Illus.). 32p. (J). (ps). bds. 7.95 (978-0-590-30284-5(1)) Scholastic, Inc.

—Read to Your Bunny. 1999. (978-0-606-17056-7(1)); lib. bdg. 10.65 (978-0-613-16996-7(4)) Tandem Library Bks.

—Read to Your Bunny Very First Library Gift Set. 2006. 64p. (J). pap. 19.99 (978-0-439-87190-7(5) , Scholastic Pr.) Scholastic, Inc.

—Shy Charles. 2001. (ps-2). lib. bdg. 14.15 (978-0-613-36076-0(1)) Tandem Library Bks.

Weston, Martha. Space Guys: A Holiday House Reader. Weston, Martha, illus. 2000. (Holiday House Reader Ser.). (Illus.). 32p. (J). (gr. k-3). tchr. ed. 14.95 (978-0-8234-1487-1(6)) Holiday Hse., Inc.

Weston, Tamson. Hey, Pancakes! Gammell, Stephen, illus. 2003. 32p. (J). 17.00 (978-0-15-216502-4(9)) Harcourt Trade Pubs.

Whatley, Bruce. That Magnetic Dog. 2001. (Illus.). 81p. (J). (ps-3). pap. 6.95 (978-0-207-18420-8(8)) HarperCollins Pubs.

Whayne, Susanne Santoro. Petropolis. Santoro, Christopher, illus. 2004. 40p. (J). 16.95 (978-1-59354-001-2(9)) Handprint Bks.

Wheeler, Lisa. Bubble Gum, Bubble Gum. Huliska-Beith, Laura & Harriet Kasak Portfolio Staff, illus. 2004. 32p. (J). (ps-3). 15.99 (978-0-316-98894-0(4)) Little Brown & Co.

—Castaway Cats. Goembel, Ponder, illus. 2006. 32p. (J). (ps-2). 16.95 (978-0-689-86232-8(6) , Atheneum) Simon & Schuster Children's Publishing.

—Dino-Hockey. Gott, Barry, illus. 2007. (Carolrhoda Picture Bks.). 32p. (J). (gr. k-4). 16.95 (*978-0-8225-6191-0(3) , Carolrhoda Bks.) Lerner Publishing Group.

—Farmer Dale's Red Pickup Truck. Bates, Ivan, illus. 2006. 40p. (J). pap. 6.00 (978-0-15-205912-5(1) , Voyager Bks./Libros Viajeros) Harcourt Children's Bks.

—Farmer Dale's Red Pickup Truck. Bates, Ivan, tr. Bates, Ivan, illus. 2004. 40p. (J). 16.00 (978-0-15-202319-5(4)) Harcourt Children's Bks.

—Jazz Baby. Christie, Gregory R., illus. 2007. 40p. (J). (ps-2). 16.00 (978-0-15-202522-9(7)) Harcourt Trade Pubs.

—One Dark Night. Bates, Ivan, illus. 2006. 32p. (J). reprint ed. pap. 6.00 (978-0-15-205888-3(5) , Voyager Bks./Libros Viajeros) Harcourt Children's Bks.

—Seadogs: An Epic Ocean Operetta. Siegel, Mark, illus. 2006. 40p. (J). reprint ed. 7.99 (978-1-4169-4103-3(7) , Aladdin) Simon & Schuster Children's Publishing.

—Sixteen Cows. Cyrus, Kurt, illus. 2002. 32p. (J). (ps-2). 16.00 (978-0-15-202676-9(2)) Harcourt Children's Bks.

—Where, Oh Where, Is Santa Claus? Bates, Ivan, illus. 2007. 32p. (J). (ps-2). 16.00 (978-0-15-216408-9(1)) Harcourt Trade Pubs.

Whitaker, Kent. Big Mo's Tennis Ball Hunt. 2007. (J). ***(978-0-9779053-8-6(1))*** Great American Pubs.

White-Carlstrom, Nancy. How Do You Say it Today, Jesse Bear? 1999. (J). (978-0-606-16941-7(5)) Tandem Library Bks.

White, Kimberly. Mood Music, 2003. (Musical Colors Rhyming Story Coloring Book Ser.). (Illus.). 16p. (J). spiral bd. 10.95 (978-1-931844-06-2(2) , PP1018) Piano Pr.

Whose Mouse Are You? 2004. (J). 24.95 incl. audio (978-0-7882-0560-6(9)) ; pap. 14.95 incl. audio (978-0-7882-0627-6(3)) Weston Woods Studios, Inc.

Whybrow, Ian & Ayliffe, Alex. Faraway Farm. 2006. (Illus.). 32p. (J). 14.95 (978-1-57505-938-9(X) , Carolrhoda Bks.) Lerner Publishing Group.

Wickberg, Susan. Hey Mr. Choo-Choo, Where Are You Going? Heo, Yumi, illus. 2008. 32p. (J). (ps). 16.99 ***(978-0-399-23993-9(6)*** , Putnam Juvenile) Penguin Group (USA) Inc.

Wiersum, Gale. The Animals' Christmas Eve. 2007. (Illus.). 24p. (J). (gr. k-k). 2.99 ***(978-0-375-83923-8(2)*** , Golden Inspirational) Random Hse. Children's Bks.

Wiggins, Leah Holder. My Neighbor Is Gone. Wiggins, Margaret W., illus. 2006. 28p. (J). per. 17.99 ***(978-0-9768579-5-2(2))*** eVision, LLC.

Wilcox, Leah. Falling for Rapunzel. Monks, Lydia, illus. 2003. 32p. (J). (ps-3). 14.99 (978-0-399-23794-2(1) , Putnam Juvenile) Penguin Group (USA) Inc.

Wilcox, Leah. Waking Beauty. Monks, Lydia, illus. 2008. 32p. (J). (ps). 16.99 ***(978-0-399-24615-9(0)*** , Putnam Juvenile) Penguin Group (USA) Inc.

Wild Imagination Series. 2000. (978-1-883772-36-9(2)) Flying Rhinoceros, Inc.

Wilde, Gloria. Lucifer, Good Angel Gone Bad. Bauer, John, illus. 2007. 36p. (J). 14.95 ***(978-1-57258-462-4(9)*** , 945-6323) TEACH Services, Inc.

Wildman, Dale. Do You Know the Way to Find an A? A Rhyming ABC Book. Sisung, Peter, illus. 2006. 24p. (J). per. 2.99 (978-1-59958-002-9(0)) Journey Stone Creations, LLC.

Williams, David. The Picnic. Ovresat, Laura, illus. 2006. (Green Light Readers Level 1 Ser.). 24p. (J). 12.95 (978-0-15-205776-3(5)); pap. 3.95 (978-0-15-205782-4(X)) Harcourt Trade Pubs.

—Tick Tock. Ovresat, Laura, illus. 2006. (Green Light Reader Ser.). 24p. (J). 12.95 (978-0-15-205581-3(9)); pap. 3.95 (978-0-15-205605-6(X)) Harcourt Trade Pubs.

Williams, Harland. The Kid with Too Many Nightmares. 2006. (Illus.). 32p. (J). (ps-2). pap. 3.99 (978-0-448-44365-2(1) , Grosset & Dunlap) Penguin Group (USA) Inc.

Williams, Harland, illus. The Kid with Too Many Nightmares. 2004. (J). (978-0-8431-1582-6(3) , Price Stern Sloan) Penguin Group (USA) Inc.

Williams, Rozanne Lanczak. Purple Snerd. 2000. (Green Light Readers Ser.). (978-0-606-20333-3(8)); lib. bdg. 11.80 (978-0-613-66373-1(X)) Tandem Library Bks.

Williams, Sam. That's Love. Moriuchi, Mique, illus. 2007. 32p. (J). 16.95 (978-0-8234-2028-5(0)) Holiday Hse., Inc.

Williams, Sue. I Went Walking. Vivas, Julie, illus. 2005. 30p. (ps-ps). bds. 10.95 (978-0-15-205626-1(2) , Red Wagon Bks.) Harcourt Children's Bks.

—I Went Walking. 2003. (Illus.). (J). pap. 18.95 incl. audio compact disk (978-1-59112-719-2(X)) Live Oak Media.

—I Went Walking. Vivas, Julie, illus. 2003. 28.95 incl. audio compact disk (978-1-59112-720-8(3)); 2003. pap. 39.95 incl. audio compact disk (978-1-59112-721-5(1)); 2000. (J). 25.95 incl. audio (978-0-87499-664-7(3)) Live Oak Media.

—I Went Walking/Sali de Paseo: Lap-Sized Board Book. Ada, Alma Flor, tr. from ENG. Vivas, Julie, illus. 2006 (ENG & SPA.). 30p. (J). bds. 10.95 (978-0-15-205895-1(8) , Voyager Bks./Libros Viajeros) Harcourt Children's Bks.

—Let's Go Visiting. Vivas, Julie, illus. 32p. (J). 2006. bds. 10.95 (978-0-15-205539-4(8) , Red Wagon Bks.); 2003. bds. 6.95 (978-0-15-204638-5(0) , Red Wagon Bks.); 2000. pap. 7.00 (978-0-15-202410-9(7) , Voyager Bks./Libros Viajeros) Harcourt Children's Bks.

—Let's Go Visiting. 1998. 90.00 (978-0-15-202036-1(5) , Gulliver Bks.) Harcourt Children's Bks.

—Let's Go Visiting. Vivas, Julie, illus. 1998. 32p. (J). (ps). 16.00 (978-0-15-201823-8(9) , Gulliver Bks.) Harcourt Children's Bks.

—Let's Go Visiting. 2000. (978-0-606-20330-2(3)); (J). (978-0-606-20167-4(X)) Tandem Library Bks.

—Sali de Paseo. Ada, Alma Flor, tr. Vivas, Julie, illus. 2005. (SPA.). 30p. (J). (ps-ps). bds. 6.95 (978-0-15-205614-8(9) , Red Wagon Bks.) Harcourt Children's Bks.

Williams, Ted. Curly Hare Gets It Straight. 2001. (Kiss a Me Teacher Creature Stories Ser.). (Illus.). (J). (978-1-890343-35-4(8)) Kiss A Me Productions, Inc.

Williams, Vera B. Amber Was Brave, Essie Was Smart. Williams, Vera B., illus. 2004. (Illus.). 72p. (J). (gr. 2 up). reprint ed. pap. 7.99 (978-0-06-057182-5(9) , Harper Trophy) HarperCollins Pubs.

Willis, J. Tale of Fearsome Fritz. 1999. (Illus.). 24p. (J). pap. 11.99 (978-0-86264-887-9(4)) Andersen GBR. *Dist:* Independent Pubs. Group.

Willis, Jeanne. Do Little Mermaids Wet Their Beds? Jossen, Penelope, illus. 2001. (Concept Book Ser.). 32p. (J). (ps-1). 15.95 (978-0-8075-1668-3(6)) Whitman, Albert & Co.

—I Want to Be a Cowgirl. Ross, Tony, illus. rev. ed. 2002. 32p. (J). 15.95 (978-0-8050-6997-6(6) , Holt, Henry & Co. Bks. For Young Readers) Holt, Henry & Co.

—Monster Bed. 1999. (J). (978-0-606-17392-6(7)) Tandem Library Bks.

Willson, Sarah. Do Not Wake Jake. Johnson, Meredith, illus. 2006. (Step-By-Step Readers Ser.). (J). (978-1-59939-059-8(0) , Reader's Digest Young Families, Inc.) Reader's Digest Children's Publishing, Inc.

Wilson, Bob. Stanley Bagshaw & Twenty Two Foot Whale. 2006. (Stanley Bagshaw Ser.). (Illus.). 32p. (J). pap. 6.95 (978-1-903015-50-6(2)) Barn Owl Bks, London GBR. *Dist:* Independent Pubs. Group.

Wilson, Karma. Animal Strike at the Zoo: It's True! Spengler, Margaret, illus. 2006. 32p. (J). 15.99 (978-0-06-057502-1(6)); lib. bdg. 17.89 (978-0-06-057503-8(4)) HarperCollins Pubs.

—Bear Feels Sick. Chapman, Jane, illus. 2007. 40p. (J). (ps-2). 16.99 (978-0-689-85985-4(6) , McElderry, Margaret K.) Simon & Schuster Children's Publishing.

—Bear Snores On. Chapman, Jane, illus. 2002. (J). 25.11 (978-0-7587-9751-3(6)) Book Wholesalers, Inc.

—Bear Snores On. Chapman, Jane, illus. (Classic Board Bks.). (J). 2005. 34p. bds. 7.99 (978-1-4169-0272-0(4) , Little Simon); 2002. 40p. 16.95 (978-0-689-83187-4(0) , McElderry, Margaret K.) Simon & Schuster Children's Publishing.

—Bear Snores On. 2005. (J). (ps-2). 29.95 incl. audio compact disk (978-0-439-76664-7(8) , WHCD666); 24.95 incl. audio (978-0-439-76660-9(5) , WHRA666) Weston Woods Studios, Inc.

—Bear Stays up for Christmas. Chapman, Jane, illus. 2004. 40p. (J). (ps-2). 16.95 (978-0-689-85278-7(9) , McElderry, Margaret K.) Simon & Schuster Children's Publishing.

—Bear Wants More. Chapman, Jane, illus. (Classic Board Bks.). (J). 2008. 34p. 7.99 ***(978-1-4169-4922-0(4)*** , Little Simon); 2003. 40p. 16.95 (978-0-689-84509-3(X) , McElderry, Margaret K.) Simon & Schuster Children's Publishing.

—Bear's New Friend. Chapman, Jane, illus. 2006. 40p. (J). (ps-2). 16.95 (978-0-689-85984-7(8) , McElderry, Margaret K.) Simon & Schuster Children's Publishing.

—A Frog in the Bog. Rankin, Joan, illus. 2003. 32p. (J). 16.95 (978-0-689-84081-4(0) , McElderry, Margaret K.) Simon & Schuster Children's Publishing.

—How to Bake an American Pie. Colon, Raul, illus. 2007. 40p. (J). (ps-3). 16.99 (978-0-689-86506-0(6) , McElderry, Margaret K.) Simon & Schuster Children's Publishing.

—Mama Always Comes Home. Dyer, Brooke, illus. 32p. (J). 2007. pap. 6.99 (978-0-06-057507-6(7) , Harper Trophy); 2005. 15.99 (978-0-06-057505-2(0)); 2005. lib. bdg. 16.89 (978-0-06-057506-9(9)) HarperCollins Pubs.

—Moose Tracks! Davis, Jack E., illus. 2006. 32p. (J). (ps-2). 16.95 (978-0-689-83437-0(3) , McElderry, Margaret K.) Simon & Schuster Children's Publishing.

—Never, Ever Shout in a Zoo. Cushman, Douglas, illus. 2004. 32p. (J). (ps-3). 16.99 (978-0-316-98564-2(3)) Little Brown & Co.

—Princess Me. Unzner-Fischer, Christa, illus. 2007. 32p. (J). (ps-2). 16.99 (978-1-4169-4098-2(7) , McElderry, Margaret K.) Simon & Schuster Children's Publishing.

—Sakes Alive! A Cattle Drive. Firehammer, Karla, illus. 2005. (J). (ps-3). 32p. 15.99 (978-0-316-98841-4(3)); ***(978-1-4156-0890-6(3))*** Little Brown & Co.

—Sleepyhead. Segal, John, illus. 2006. 32p. (J). (ps-2). 15.95 (978-1-4169-1241-5(X) , McElderry, Margaret K.) Simon & Schuster Children's Publishing.

—Whopper Cake. Hillenbrand, Will, illus. 2007. 40p. (J). (ps-3). 16.99 (978-0-689-83844-6(1) , McElderry, Margaret K.) Simon & Schuster Children's Publishing.

Wilson, Karma & Rankin, Joan. A Frog in the Bog. 2007. 32p. (J). pap. 6.99 (978-1-4169-2727-3(1) , Aladdin) Simon & Schuster Children's Publishing.

Wilson, Karma & Watts, Suzanne. Hilda Must Be Dancing. 2004. (Illus.). 32p. (J). 16.99 (978-0-689-84788-2(2) , McElderry, Margaret K.) Simon & Schuster Children's Publishing.

Wilson, Sarah. Friends & Pals & Brothers, Too. Landry, Leo, illus. 2008. 32p. (J). 16.95 ***(978-0-8050-7643-1(3))*** Holt, Henry & Co.

Wilson, Zachary. A Circle in the Sky. Adinolfi, JoAnn, illus. 2007. (Rookie Reader Ser.). 31p. (J). pap. ***(978-0-531-12589-2(0))*** Children's Pr., Ltd.

—A Circle in the Sky. 2006. (Rookie Reader Skill Set Ser.). (Illus.). 32p. (J). (gr. k-2). 19.50 (978-0-531-12570-0(X) , Children's Pr.) Scholastic Library Publishing.

Wing, Natasha. The Night Before First Grade. Zemke, Deborah, illus. 2005. 32p. (J). (ps-4). 3.99 (978-0-448-43747-7(3) , Grosset & Dunlap) Penguin Group (USA) Inc.

—The Night Before the Night Before Christmas. Lester, Mike, illus. 2002. (Reading Railroad Bks.). 32p. (J). (gr. k-3). pap. 3.99 (978-0-448-42872-7(5) , Grosset & Dunlap) Penguin Group (USA) Inc.

—The Night Before the Night Before Christmas. 2002. (gr. k-3). lib. bdg. 11.25 (978-0-613-72485-2(2)) Tandem Library Bks.

—The Night Before the Tooth Fairy. Newman, Barbara Johansen, illus. 2003. (Reading Railroad Bks.). 32p. (J). (ps-4). pap. 3.99 (978-0-448-43252-6(8) , Grosset & Dunlap) Penguin Group (USA) Inc.

—The Night Before Valentine's Day. Petach, Heidi, illus. 2001. (Reading Rainbow Bks.). 32p. (J). (ps-3). mass mkt. 3.99 (978-0-448-42188-9(7) , Grosset & Dunlap) Penguin Group (USA) Inc.

—The Night Before Valentine's Day. 2000. (gr. k-3). lib. bdg. 11.25 (978-0-613-31527-2(8)) Tandem Library Bks.

Winn, L. B. Butterpod Jerome & the Planet of Gabool. Winn, L. B., illus. 2007. (J). pap. 18.95 ***(978-0-9791884-0-4(7))*** Winn, Lynnette.

Winthrop, Elizabeth. Dancing Granny. Murdocca, Sal, illus. 2003. 32p. (J). 16.95 (978-0-7614-5141-9(2)) Cavendish, Marshall Corp.

—Dumpy la Rue. Lewin, Betsy, illus. rev. ed. 40p. (J). 2004. reprint ed. pap. 7.95 (978-0-8050-7535-9(6)); 2001. 16.95 (978-0-8050-6385-1(4)) Holt, Henry & Co. (Holt, Henry & Co. Bks. For Young Readers).

—Dumpy la Rue. Lewin, Betsy, illus. 2004. 48p. (J). (ps-4). lib. bdg. 14.15 (978-0-606-30292-0(1)) Tandem Library Bks.

Wise, William. Ten Sly Piranhas: A Counting Story in Reverse (A Tale of Wickedness - And Worse!) 2004. (Illus.). 32p. (J). pap. 5.99 (978-0-14-240074-6(2) , Puffin) Penguin Group (USA) Inc.

—Zany Zoo. Munsinger, Lynn, illus. 32p. (J). (gr. k-3). 2006. 16.00 (978-0-618-18891-8(6) , Walter Lorraine); 11th ed. 2007. 6.95 ***(978-0-618-95686-9(7))*** Houghton Mifflin Co. Trade & Reference Div.

Wiseman, Lisa, ed. Disney's Nursery Rhymes & Fairy Tales. 2005. (Illus.). 320p. (J). (ps-3). 15.99 (978-0-7868-3463-1(3)) Disney Pr.

Wishinsky, Frieda. Jennifer Jones Won't Leave Me Alone. Layton, Neal, illus. 2005. 32p. (gr. k-2). 15.95 (978-0-87614-921-8(2)) Lerner Publishing Group.

Wishinsky, Frieda. Jennifer Jones Won't Leave Me Alone. Layton, Neal, illus. 2005. 32p. (J). (gr. k-2). pap. 6.95 (978-1-57505-921-1(5)) Lerner Publishing Group.

Wiskur, Darrell. Dinky Dinosaur: Creation Days. 2002. (Illus.). 16p. (J). (ps-1). 6.99 (978-0-89051-361-3(9) , 303-075) Master Bks.

—Really Big Barn on Noah's Farm. 2001. (Illus.). 40p. (J). 11.99 (978-0-89051-353-8(8)) Master Bks.

Wiskur, Darrell, told to. Dinky Dinosaur - Who's My Friend? 2001. (Illus.). 16p. (J). 6.99 (978-0-89051-362-0(7)) Master Bks.

Witte, Anna. The Parrot Tico Tango. Witte, Anna, illus. (Illus.). 24p. (J). (gr. k-3). 2005. 15.99 (978-1-84148-243-9(9)); 2004. pap. 6.99 (978-1-905236-11-4(5)) Barefoot Bks., Inc.

Wojtusik, Elizabeth. Kitty Up! Yoshikawa, Sachiko, illus. 2008. (J). (978-0-8037-3045-8(4) , Dial) Penguin Group (USA) Inc.

Wolf, Allan. New Found Land: Lewis & Clark's Voyage of Discovery. 2007. (Illus.). 512p. (YA). (gr. 7). pap. 8.99 ***(978-0-7636-3288-5(0))*** Candlewick Pr.

Wolf, Joan. How the Selves Became Elves. Squassoni, Christine, illus. 2001. (J). (ps-2). 19.95 (978-0-9711445-1-4(6)) Cruzane Mountain Publishing.

Wolf, Sallie. Truck Stuck. Davies, Andrew Robert, illus. 2008. (J). ***(978-1-58089-119-6(5))*** Charlesbridge Publishing, Inc.

Wolff, Ashley. Me Baby, You Baby. Wolff, Ashley, illus. 2004. (Illus.). 32p. (J). (ps). 14.99 (978-0-525-46952-0(4) , Dutton Juvenile) Penguin Group (USA) Inc.

Wolff, Virginia Euwer. True Believer. 2004. (Make Lemonade Trilogy Ser.). 272p. (J). (gr. 7 up). pap. 38.00 incl. audio (978-0-8072-2283-6(6) , Listening Library) Random Hse. Audio Publishing Group.

—True Believer. Gordon, Russell, illus. 2002. 272p. (YA). pap. 8.99 (978-0-689-85288-6(6) , Simon Pulse) Simon & Schuster Children's Publishing.

—True Believer. 2002. (gr. 7-12). lib. bdg. 16.45 (978-0-613-60942-5(5)) Tandem Library Bks.

Wong, Janet S. Hide & Seek. Chodos-Irvine, Margaret, illus. 2005. 40p. (J). 16.00 (978-0-15-204934-8(7)) Harcourt Trade Pubs.

Wood, A. & Hawkins, Emily A. Amazing Baby Night-Night, Baby! Jolley, Mike, illus. 2007. (Amazing Baby Ser.). 16p. (J). bds. 5.95 ***(978-1-59223-802-6(5)*** , Silver Dolphin Bks.) Advantage Pubs. Group.

—Amazing Baby Yum-Yum, Baby! Jolley, Mike, illus. 2007. (Amazing Baby Ser.). 16p. (J). bds. 5.95 ***(978-1-59223-803-3(3)*** , Silver Dolphin Bks.) Advantage Pubs. Group.

Wood, Audrey. A Dog Needs a Bone. 2007. (J). pap. ***(978-0-545-00006-2(8))*** Blue Sky Pr.

—A Dog Needs a Bone. 2007. (Illus.). 40p. (J). (ps-k). pap. 16.99 ***(978-0-545-00005-5(X)*** , Blue Sky Pr., The) Scholastic, Inc.

—Piggy Pie Po. 2001. (J). 16.00 (978-0-15-202494-9(8)) Harcourt Children's Bks.

—Quick As a Cricket: Nrawm Npaum Le Ih Tug Kaab Roj/ Nrawm Npaum Li Ib Tug Kab Npis. Vang, Mao J., tr. Wood, Don, illus. 2000. 32p. (J). (ps-3). pap. 6.95 (978-0-9629298-3-0(2) , MHC-3-2) Minnesota Humanities Commission.

—Silly Sally. Wood, Audrey, illus. 2002. (Illus.). (J). 23.40 (978-0-7587-3621-5(5)) Book Wholesalers, Inc.

—Silly Sally. braille ed. 2004. (J). (gr. 1). spiral bd., bds. (978-0-616-01864-4(9)) Canadian National Institute for the Blind/Institut National Canadien pour les Aveugles.

—Silly Sally. 1999. (Illus.). 30p. (J). (ps). bds. 6.95 (978-0-15-201990-7(1) , Red Wagon Bks.) Harcourt Children's Bks.

—Silly Sally: Lap-Sized Board Book. 2007. (Illus.). 30p. (J). bds. 10.95 (978-0-15-205902-6(4) , Red Wagon Bks.) Harcourt Children's Bks.

—Ten Little Fish. Wood, Bruce, illus. 2004. 40p. (J). (ps up). pap. 15.95 (978-0-439-63569-1(0) , Blue Sky Pr., The) Scholastic, Inc.

Wood, Jakki. Baby Parade. 2004. (Illus.). 32p. (J). reprint ed. pap. 7.95 (978-1-84507-042-7(9)) Lincoln, Frances Ltd. GBR. *Dist:* Perseus Distribution.

Woodend, Rosetta. Sammy Salmon's Big Adventure: The lifecycle of a Salmon, 1. ed. 2005. (Illus.). 12p. (J). per. 9.95 (978-0-9760342-0-9(4)) Animal Tracks Pr.

Woodruff, Liza. What Time Is It? Woodruff, Liza, illus. 2005. (My First Reader Ser.). (Illus.). 32p. (J). (gr. k-1). 18.50 (978-0-516-25180-6(5) , Children's Pr.) Scholastic Library Publishing.

Woodruff, Liza, illus. What Time Is It? 2005. (My First Reader Ser.). 31p. (J). (gr. k-1). pap. 3.95 (978-0-516-25279-7(8) , Children's Pr.) Scholastic Library Publishing.

Worth, Bonnie. The Cat in the Hat: Cooking with the Cat. Moroney, Christopher, illus. 2003. (Step into Reading Ser.). 32p. (J). (ps-1). lib. bdg. 11.99 (978-0-375-92494-1(9) , Random Hse. Bks. for Young Readers) Random Hse. Children's Bks.

—Cooking with the Cat. Moroney, Christopher, illus. 2003. (Step into Reading Ser.). 32p. (J). (ps-1). pap. 3.99 (978-0-375-82494-4(4) , 53560581, Random Hse. Bks. for Young Readers) Random Hse. Children's Bks.

—A Great Day for Pup. Ruiz, Aristides, illus. 2002. (Cat in the Hat's Learning Library). 48p. (J). (gr. k-3). 8.99 (978-0-375-81096-1(X) , Random Hse. Bks. for Young Readers) Random Hse. Children's Bks.

Wright, Cliff. Bear & Ball. 2005. (Illus.). 16p. (J). bds. 5.95 (978-0-8118-4819-0(1)) Chronicle Bks. LLC.

—Bear & Kite. 2005. (Illus.). 16p. (J). bds. 5.95 (978-0-8118-4820-6(5)) Chronicle Bks. LLC.

Yackle, Deanne. Jenny & Me. 2005. (J). lib. bdg. 15.95 (978-0-9725485-4-0(8)) Waterfall Ridge.

Yates, Gene, illus. The Chameleon Colors Book. 2006. (J). ***(978-1-58865-361-1(7))*** Kidsbooks, Inc.

—The Giraffe Numbers Book. 2006. (J). ***(978-1-58865-364-2(1))*** Kidsbooks, Inc.

S

Yates, Philip. Ten Little Mummies: An Egyptian Counting Book. Karas, G. Brian, illus. 2005. 40p. (J). pap. 6.99 (978-0-14-240367-9(9) , Puffin) Penguin Group (USA) Inc.

Yee, Brenda Shannon. Hide & Seek. Tilley, Debbie, illus. 2001. 32p. (J). (ps). pap. 15.95 (978-0-531-30302-3(0) , Orchard Bks.) Scholastic, Inc.

Yee, Brenda Shannon & Tilley, Debbie, illus. Hide & Seek. 2000. (J). lib. bdg. (978-0-531-33302-0(7) , Orchard Bks.) Scholastic, Inc.

Yee, Wong Herbert. Detective Small in the Amazing Banana Caper. 2007. (Illus.). 32p. (J). (gr. k-3). 15.00 (978-0-618-47285-7(1)) Houghton Mifflin Co.

—Fireman Small - Fire down Below! 32p. (J). (gr. k-3). 2004. pap. 5.95 (978-0-618-49492-7(8)); 2001. (Illus.). tchr. ed. 15.00 (978-0-618-00707-3(5)) Houghton Mifflin Co. Trade & Reference Div.

—Hamburger Heaven. Yee, Wong Herbert, illus. 1999. (Illus.). 32p. (J). (gr. k-3). tchr. ed. 16.00 (978-0-395-87548-3(X)) Houghton Mifflin Co. Trade & Reference Div.

—Hamburger Heaven. 2005. (Illus.). 32p. (J). (gr. k-3). reprint ed. 5.95 (978-0-618-54885-9(8)) Houghton Mifflin Co. Trade & Reference Div.

—Here Come Train Mice! 2000. (Illus.). 9p. (J). (gr. k-ps). bds. 4.95 (978-0-395-98401-7(7)) Houghton Mifflin Co. Trade & Reference Div.

—Mrs Brown Went to Town. 2003. (gr. k-3). lib. bdg. 14.10 (978-0-613-91047-7(8)) Tandem Library Bks.

—A Small Christmas. 2004. (Illus.). 32p. (J). (gr. k-3). tchr. ed. 12.95 (978-0-618-32612-9(X)) Houghton Mifflin Co. Trade & Reference Div.

—Small Christmas. 2007. (Illus.). 32p. (J). (ps-3). 6.95 ***(978-0-618-91534-7(6))*** Houghton Mifflin Co. Trade & Reference Div.

—Tracks in the Snow. Yee, Wong Herbert, illus. rev. ed. 2003. (Illus.). 32p. (J). 15.95 (978-0-8050-6771-2(X) , Holt, Henry & Co. Bks. For Young Readers) Holt, Henry & Co.

—Tracks in the Snow. 2007. (Illus.). 32p. (J). pap. 6.99 ***(978-0-312-37134-0(9))*** Square Fish.

—Who Likes Rain? 2007. (Illus.). (J). ***(978-1-4287-3979-6(3));*** 32p. 14.95 (978-0-8050-7734-6(0)) Holt, Henry & Co.

Yolen, Jane. Baby Bear's Big Dreams. Sweet, Melissa, illus. 2007. 40p. (J). (ps-k). 16.00 (978-0-15-205291-1(7)) Harcourt Trade Pubs.

—Baby Bear's Books. Sweet, Melissa, illus. 2006. 40p. (J). 16.00 (978-0-15-205290-4(9)) Harcourt Trade Pubs.

—Baby Bear's Chairs. Sweet, Melissa, illus. 2005. 40p. (J). (ps). 16.00 (978-0-15-205114-3(7)) Harcourt Children's Bks.

—The Ballad of the Pirate Queens. Shannon, David, illus. 1998. (J). (ps-7). lib. bdg. 15.30 (978-0-613-09936-3(2)) Tandem Library Bks.

—Dimity Duck. Braun, Sebastien, illus. 2008. 30p. (J). (ps). bds. 6.99 ***(978-0-399-25060-6(3)*** , Philomel) Penguin Group (USA) Inc.

—Dimity Duck. Braun, Sebastien, illus. 2006. 32p. (J). (ps). 15.99 (978-0-399-24632-6(0) , Philomel) Penguin Group (USA) Inc.

—Hoptoad. Schmidt, Karen Lee, illus. 2003. 32p. (J). 16.00 (978-0-15-216352-5(2) , Silver Whistle) Harcourt Trade Pubs.

—How Do Dinosaurs Clean Their Rooms? Teague, Mark, illus. 2004. 12p. (J). (ps up). bds. 6.99 (978-0-439-64950-6(1) , Blue Sky Pr., The) Scholastic, Inc.

—How Do Dinosaurs Count to Ten? Teague, Mark, illus. 2004. 12p. (J). (ps up). bds. 6.99 (978-0-439-64949-0(8) , Blue Sky Pr., The) Scholastic, Inc.

—How Do Dinosaurs Eat Their Food? Teague, Mark, illus. 2005. 40p. (J). (ps-k). pap. 15.99 (978-0-439-24102-1(2) , Blue Sky Pr., The) Scholastic, Inc.

—How Do Dinosaurs Get Well Soon? Teague, Mark, illus. 2003. 40p. (J). (ps-1). pap. 15.95 (978-0-439-24100-7(6) , Blue Sky Pr., The) Scholastic, Inc.

—How Do Dinosaurs Go to School? Teague, Mark, illus. 2007. 40p. (J). (ps-2). 16.99 ***(978-0-439-02081-7(6))*** Scholastic, Inc.

—How Do Dinosaurs Learn Their Colors? Teague, Mark, illus. 2006. 12p. (J). bds. 6.99 (978-0-439-85653-9(1) , Blue Sky Pr., The) Scholastic, Inc.

—How Do Dinosaurs Learn Their Colors (Como Aprenden los Dinosaurios los Colores) 2006. 12p. (J). bds. 6.99 (978-0-439-87192-1(1) , Scholastic en Espanol) Scholastic, Inc.

—How Do Dinosaurs Play with Their Friends? Teague, Mark, illus. 2006. 12p. (J). bds. 6.99 (978-0-439-85654-6(X) , Blue Sky Pr., The) Scholastic, Inc.

—How Do Dinosaurs Play with Their Friends (Como Juegan los Dinosaurios con Sus Amigos) 2006. 12p. (J). bds. 6.99 (978-0-439-87193-8(X) , Scholastic en Espanol) Scholastic, Inc.

—How Do Dinosaurs Say Good Night? Teague, Mark, illus. 2000. 40p. (J). (ps up). pap. 15.95 (978-0-590-31681-1(8) , Blue Sky Pr., The) Scholastic, Inc.

—How Do Dinosaurs Say Good Night? Book & Plush Set. 2002. (Illus.). (J). 25.04 (978-0-7587-2759-6(3)) Book Wholesalers, Inc.

—How Do Dinosaurs Say Good Night? Book & Plush Set. 2004. (J). (ps-1). 24.95 incl. audio (978-1-55592-099-9(3)) Weston Woods Studios, Inc.

—Off We Go! 2002. (Illus.). (J). 18.89 (978-0-7587-3295-8(3)) Book Wholesalers, Inc.

—Off We Go! Molk, Laurel, illus. 2000. 32p. (J). (ps-1). 14.99 (978-0-316-90228-1(4)) Little Brown & Co.

—Off We Go! Molk, Laurel, illus. 2002. 8p. (J). (ps-k). bds. 5.95 (978-0-316-90972-3(6)) Little, Brown Bks. for Young Readers.

—Where Have the Unicorns Gone. Sanderson, Ruth, illus. 2003. 32p. (J). 6.99 (978-0-689-86359-2(4) , Aladdin) Simon & Schuster Children's Publishing.

—Where Have the Unicorns Gone. 2003. (gr. k-3). lib. bdg. 15.30 (978-0-613-90038-6(3)) Tandem Library Bks.

Yolen, Jane & Stemple, Heidi E. Y. Sleep, Black Bear, Sleep. Dyer, Brooke, illus. 2007. 32p. (J). (ps-1). 15.99 (978-0-06-081560-8(4) , HarperCollins); lib. bdg. 16.89 (978-0-06-081561-5(2)) HarperCollins Pubs.

Yoon, Salina. Count My Blessings, One Through Ten. Yoon, Salina, illus. 2006. (Illus.). 32p. (J). (ps-k). 9.99 (978-0-399-24660-9(6) , Putnam Juvenile) Penguin Group (USA) Inc.

—Good Night, Little One. 2005. (Illus.). 16p. (J). pap. 6.99 (978-0-439-66373-1(3) , Cartwheel Bks.) Scholastic, Inc.

—Halloween Party. 2007. (Salina Yoon Bks.). 10p. (J). (ps-k). bds. 5.99 (978-0-8431-2485-9(7) , Price Stern Sloan) Penguin Group (USA) Inc.

Yorinks, Arthur. Happy Bees! Armstrong-Ellis, Carey, illus. 2005. 24p. (J). (ps-1). 15.95 (978-0-8109-5866-1(X)) Abrams, Harry N. , Inc.

Young, Diane B. Wee Willy Weasel. Bienvenu, Lisa, illus. 2001. 23p. (Orig.). (J). (ps-k). pap. (978-0-9706269-0-5(8)) Young, Diane B.

Young, Shelley. Doc Broc's Cave Adventure. Young, Shelley, illus. 2005. (Illus.). 44p. 19.95 (978-1-58054-406-1(1)) Woodland Publishing, Inc.

Yuko, G. The Castle That Kai Built. 2001. (J). 8.99 (978-0-89610-360-3(9)) Island Heritage Publishing.

Yurcheshen, Richard P. My Gum Is Gone. Flanagan, Kate, illus. 2000. 32p. (J). (ps-3). pap. (978-1-55798-662-7(2) , 441-6622, Magination Pr.) American Psychological Assn.

Zabel, Alanna. A Chair in the Air. 2006. 35p. pap. 16.00 (978-1-4116-7436-3(7)) Lulu.com.

Zalben, Jane Breskin. Hey, Mama Goose. Chollat, Emilie, illus. 2005. 32p. (J). (ps). 15.99 (978-0-525-47097-7(2) , Dutton Juvenile) Penguin Group (USA) Inc.

The Zany Zanimal Zoo. 2005. (Illus.). 40p. (J). 14.95 (978-0-9769738-0-5(4)) Redel, Nicole.

Ziefert, Harriet. April Fool! Demarest, Chris L., illus. 2000. (Viking Easy-to-Read Ser.). 32p. (J). (ps-2). pap. 3.99 (978-0-14-130582-0(7) , Puffin) Penguin Group (USA) Inc.

—April Fool! 2000. (ps-2). lib. bdg. 11.80 (978-0-613-24229-5(7)); (Illus.). (J). 10.79 (978-0-606-18387-1(6)) Tandem Library Bks.

—Buzzy's Big Bedtime Book. Bolam, Emily, illus. 2004. 40p. 9.95 (978-1-59354-059-3(0)) Blue Apple Bks.

—Buzzy's Birthday. Bolam, Emily, illus. 2004. 24p. 9.95 (978-1-59354-062-3(0)) Blue Apple Bks.

—Clara Ann Cookie, Go to Bed! Bolam, Emily, illus. 2000. 32p. (J). (gr. k-3). tchr. ed. 15.00 (978-0-395-97381-3(3) , Walter Lorraine) Houghton Mifflin Co. Trade & Reference Div.

—Dancing Class. Haley, Amanda, illus. 2006. (I'm Going to Read Ser.). 32p. (J). pap. 3.95 (978-1-4027-3427-4(1)) Sterling Publishing Co., Inc.

—From Kalamazoo to Timbuktu. Miller, Gustaf, illus. 2002. (J). (978-0-399-23730-0(5)) Penguin Group (USA) Inc.

—From Kalamazoo to Timbuktu! Roitman, Tanya, illus. 2005. 40p. (ps-ps). 15.95 (978-1-59354-091-3(4)) Blue Apple Bks.

—Hats off for the Fourth of July! Miller, Gustaf, illus. 2002. 32p. (J). (ps-ps). pap. 6.99 (978-0-14-056709-0(7) , Puffin) Penguin Group (USA) Inc.

—Messy Bessie: Where's My Homework. De Muth, Roger, illus. 2007. 36p. 12.95 (978-1-59354-181-1(3)) Handprint Bks.

—Ode to Humpty Dumpty. Chwast, Seymour, illus. 2001. 32p. (J). (gr. k-3). tchr. ed. 15.00 (978-0-618-05047-5(7) , Walter Lorraine) Houghton Mifflin Co. Trade & Reference Div.

—Presents for Santa. Rader, Laura, illus. 2000. (Easy-to-Read Ser.). 32p. (J). (gr. k-3). 13.89 (978-0-670-88390-5(5) , Viking Juvenile) Penguin Group (USA) Inc.

—Schools Have Learn. 2004. (Illus.). 36p. 15.95 (978-1-59354-056-2(6)) Blue Apple Bks.

—Swapped My Dog. 2000. (J). 12.75 (978-0-606-19429-7(0)) Tandem Library Bks.

Ziefert, Harriet, text. A Dozen Dozens. 2007. (I'm Going to Read Ser.). (Illus.). (J). (*978-1-4287-2803-5(1)*) Sterling Publishing Co., Inc.

Ziefert, Harriet & Ehrlich, H. M. Dancing Class. Rader, Laura, illus. 2001. 32p. (J). (ps-1). pap. 12.95 (978-0-531-30300-9(4) , Orchard Bks.) Scholastic, Inc.

Ziefert, Harriet & Saaf, Donald. Train Song. 2000. (Illus.). 32p. (J). pap. 14.95 (978-0-531-30204-0(0) , Orchard Bks.) Scholastic, Inc.

Zinsmeister, Elke, illus. Ten Fat Sausages. 2005. (Classic Books with Holes). 16p. (J). bds. 5.99 (978-1-904550-59-4(2)) Child's Play-International.

Zobel-Nolan, Allia. The Secret Fairy Garden. Ember, Kathi, illus. 2005. 12p. (J). bds. 12.99 (978-0-7944-0513-7(4)) Reader's Digest Assn., Inc., The.

365 Stories & Rhymes for Boys. Date not set. 384p. (J). 9.98 (978-1-4054-1958-1(X)) Parragon, Inc.

1000 Stories & Rhymes. 2002. 1024p. (J). 24.98 (978-0-7525-9096-7(0)) Parragon, Inc.

STORIES WITHOUT WORDS

Arnosky, Jim. Mouse Colors: A Very First Book. Arnosky, Jim, illus. 2001. (Illus.). 48p. (J). (gr. k-ps). tchr. ed. 5.95 (978-0-618-01521-4(3) , Clarion Bks.) Houghton Mifflin Co. Trade & Reference Div.

Baker, Liza. Under the Sea. 2003. (Festival Reader Ser.). (Illus.). 32p. (J). (ps-2). pap. 3.99 (978-0-06-000178-0(X)) HarperCollins Pubs.

Bang, Molly Garrett. The Grey Lady & the Strawberry Snatcher. Bang, Molly Garrett, illus. 2002. (Illus.). (J). 15.53 (978-0-7587-0113-8(6)) Book Wholesalers, Inc.

Banyai, Istvan. The Other Side. Banyai, Istvan, illus. 2005. (Illus.). 48p. (J). (ps). 15.95 (978-0-8118-4608-0(3)) Chronicle Bks. LLC.

Bartlett, T. C. Tuba Lessons. Felix, Monique, illus. 2004. 32p. pap. 9.95 (978-0-89812-522-1(7) , Creative Paperbacks) Creative Co., The.

Briggs, Raymond. The Snowman. Briggs, Raymond, illus. 2002. (Illus.). (J). 16.60 (978-0-7587-3649-9(5)) Book Wholesalers, Inc.

—The Snowman. Labrack, Joy, ed. 2000. (Bright & Early Board Bks.). (Illus.). 24p. (J). (gr. k-ps). bds. 4.99 (978-0-375-81067-1(6) , Random Hse. Bks. for Young Readers) Random Hse. Children's Bks.

—The Snowman, 1 vol. Downer, Maggie, illus. 1999. (Early Step into Reading Ser.). 32p. (J). (gr. k-ps). pap. 3.99 (978-0-679-89443-8(8) , Random Hse. Bks. for Young Readers) Random Hse. Children's Bks.

—The Snowman. Briggs, Raymond, illus. 1998. (Nifty Lift-and-Look Bks.). (Illus.). 12p. (J). (gr. k-1). bds. 5.99 (978-0-679-88896-3(9) , Random Hse. Bks. for Young Readers) Random Hse. Children's Bks.

Briggs, Raymond & Knudsen, Michelle. The Snowman. Downer, Maggie, illus. 1999. (Step into Reading Ser.). 32p. (J). (ps-2). lib. bdg. 11.99 (978-0-679-99443-5(2) , Random Hse. Bks. for Young Readers) Random Hse. Children's Bks.

Burg, Sarah, illus. The Secret of Love. 2006. 56p. (J). (ps). 11.00 (978-0-698-40050-4(X) , Minedition) Penguin Group (USA) Inc.

Carle, Eric. Do You Want to Be My Friend? Carle, Eric, illus. 2002. (Illus.). (J). 15.49 (978-0-7587-8917-4(3)) Book Wholesalers, Inc.

Carmi, Giora. A Circle of Friends. Carmi, Giora, illus. 2003. (Illus.). 40p. (J). 15.95 (978-1-932065-00-8(8)) Star Bright Bks., Inc.

Carmi, Giora, illus. A Circle of Friends. 2006. 40p. pap. 5.95 (978-1-59572-060-3(X)) Star Bright Bks., Inc.

Collington, Peter. A Small Miracle. Collington, Peter, illus. 2002. (Illus.). 32p. (J). (ps-3). reprint ed. 15.95 (978-0-679-88725-6(3) , Knopf Bks. for Young Readers) Random Hse. Children's Bks.

Cosentino, Ralph. The Marvelous Misadventures of Fun Boy. 2006. (Illus.). 32p. (J). (ps-1). 15.99 (978-0-670-05961-4(7) , Viking Juvenile) Penguin Group (USA) Inc.

Day, Alexandra. Follow Carl! Day, Alexandra, illus. 1998. (Carl Ser.). (Illus.). 32p. (J). (ps-1). 12.95 (978-0-374-34380-4(2) , Farrar, Straus & Giroux (BYR)) Farrar, Straus & Giroux.

Dematons, Charlotte. Yellow Balloon. 2004. (Illus.). 32p. (J). 15.95 (978-1-932425-01-7(2) , Lemniscaat) Boyds Mills Pr.

Dewey, Ariane & Aruego, Jose. The Last Laugh. 2006. (Illus.). 32p. (J). (ps). 12.99 (978-0-8037-3093-9(4) , Dial) Penguin Group (USA) Inc.

Dornbusch, Erica. Finding Kate's Shoes. 2001. (Illus.). 32p. (J). (gr. k-ps). pap. 6.95 (978-1-55037-670-8(5)); lib. bdg. 17.95 (978-1-55037-671-5(3)) Annick Pr.; Ltd. CAN. *Dist:* Firefly Bks., Ltd.

Drooker, Eric. Blood Song: A Silent Ballad. 2002. (gr. 7-12). lib. bdg. 30.40 (978-0-613-54897-7(3)) Tandem Library Bks.

Enderle, Judith Ross & Tessler, Stephanie Gordon. Six Creepy Sheep. O'Brien, John, illus. 2003. 24p. (J). (ps up). pap. 8.95 (978-1-56397-242-3(5)) Boyds Mills Pr.

Fleischman, Paul. Sidewalk Circus. Hawkes, Kevin, illus. 2004. 32p. (J). (gr. k-4). 15.99 (978-0-7636-1107-1(7)) Candlewick Pr.

Geisert, Arthur. Hogwash. 2008. (J). (*978-0-618-77332-9(0)*) Houghton Mifflin Co.

Geisert, Arthur. Oops! 2006. (Illus.). 32p. (J). (gr. k-3). 16.00 (978-0-618-60904-8(0)) Houghton Mifflin Co.

Goodale, Rebecca, illus. Island Dog. 1999. 38p. (J). (ps up). 17.95 (978-1-891090-03-5(8)) Two Dog Pr.

Gutierrez, Elisa. Picturescape. 2005. (Illus.). 32p. (J). (gr. k). 16.95 (978-1-894965-24-8(8)) Simply Read Bks. CAN. *Dist:* Perseus Distribution.

Harcourt School Publishers Staff. Dear Juno: Library Book. 3rd ed. 2002. (Trophies Reading Program Ser.). (Illus.). pap. 13.50 (978-0-15-326528-0(0)) Harcourt Schl. Pubs.

Himler, Ronald. Dancing Boy. Himler, Ronald, illus. 2005. (Illus.). 40p. (J). (ps-ps). 15.95 (978-1-59572-020-7(0)) Star Bright Bks., Inc.

Hutchins, Pat. Changes, Changes. Hutchins, Pat, illus. 2002. (Illus.). (J). 14.47 (978-0-7587-2213-3(3)) Book Wholesalers, Inc.

Johnson, Crockett. Harold & the Purple Crayon: Under the Sea. 2003. (gr. k-3). lib. bdg. 11.80 (978-0-613-69129-1(6)) Tandem Library Bks.

Keats, Ezra Jack. Clementina's Cactus. Keats, Ezra Jack, illus. 2002. (Illus.). (J). 21.81 (978-0-7587-2249-2(4)) Book Wholesalers, Inc.

—Clementina's Cactus. Keats, Ezra Jack, illus. 1999. (Illus.). 40p. (J). (ps-3). 16.99 (978-0-670-88545-9(2) , Viking Juvenile) Penguin Group (USA) Inc.

Kubler, Annie. Baby-Sitter. 2000. (All in a Day Boardbooks Ser.). (Illus.). 14p. (J). (ps-k). bds. 3.99 (978-0-85953-588-5(6)) Child's Play-International.

—Bedtime. 2000. (All in a Day Boardbooks Ser.). (Illus.). 14p. (J). (ps-k). bds. 3.99 (978-0-85953-589-2(4)) Child's Play-International.

Kubler, Annie, illus. Waiting for Baby. 2nd ed. 2000. 14p. (J). (ps-k). bds. 3.99 (978-0-85953-973-9(3)) Child's Play-International.

Lehman, Barbara. Museum Trip. 2006. (Illus.). 32p. (J). (gr. k-3). 15.00 (978-0-618-58125-2(1)) Houghton Mifflin Co.

—Rainstorm. 2007. (Illus.). (J). (ps-k). 32p. 16.00 (978-0-618-75639-1(6)); 30p. (*978-1-4287-3564-4(X)*) Houghton Mifflin Co.

Lehman, Barbara. Train Stop. 2008. 32p. (J). (ps-k). 16.00 (*978-0-618-75640-7(X)*) Houghton Mifflin Co.

Liu, Jae Soo. Yellow Umbrella. Liu, Jae Soo, illus. 2002. (Illus.). 32p. (J). (gr. k-3). 19.95 incl. audio compact disk (978-1-929132-36-2(0)) Kane/Miller Bk. Pubs., Inc.

Luthardt, Kevin. Peep! Luthardt, Kevin, illus. 2003. (Illus.). 36p. (J). 15.95 (978-1-56145-046-6(4)) Peachtree Pubs., Ltd.

Macaroni & Baloney: Wordless Edition. 2001. 22p. (J). spiral bd. 14.95 (978-0-9702698-2-9(X)) Special Reads for Special Needs.

Mayer, Mercer. Frog Goes to Dinner. Mayer, Mercer, illus. 2003. (Illus.). 32p. (J). (gr. k-1). 6.99 (978-0-8037-2884-4(0) , Dial) Penguin Group (USA) Inc.

McCully, Emily Arnold. Picnic. McCully, Emily Arnold, illus. 2003. (Illus.). 32p. (J). (ps-k). 16.89 (978-0-06-623855-5(2)); 16.99 (978-0-06-623854-8(4)) HarperCollins Pubs.

—School. McCully, Emily Arnold, illus. 2005. (Illus.). 32p. (J). 15.99 (978-0-06-623856-2(0)); lib. bdg. 16.89 (978-0-06-623857-9(9)) HarperCollins Pubs.

McGrath, Meggan. My Grapes. McGrath, Meggan, illus. 2001. (Illus.). 48p. (J). (ps-1). pap. 16.95 (978-0-439-09259-3(0)) Scholastic, Inc.

Muller, Jorg. The Changing Countryside. 2006. (Illus.). 7p. (J). 17.95 (978-0-9762056-4-7(5)) Heryin Publishing Corp.

Ommen, Sylvia Van. The Surprise. 2007. 24p. (J). (ps). 15.95 (978-1-932425-85-7(3) , Front Street) Boyds Mills Pr.

Ormerod, Jan. Moonlight. 2005. (Illus.). 32p. pap. 14.95 (978-1-84507-391-6(6)) Lincoln, Frances Ltd. GBR. *Dist:* Transition Vendor.

—Sunshine. 2005. (Illus.). 32p. pap. 14.95 (978-1-84507-390-9(8)) Lincoln, Frances Ltd. GBR. *Dist:* Transition Vendor.

Polhemus, Coleman. The Crocodile Blues. Polhemus, Coleman, illus. 2007. (Illus.). 48p. (J). (ps-1). 16.99 (*978-0-7636-3543-5(X)*) Candlewick Pr.

Schories, Pat. Breakfast for Jack. 2004. (Illus.). 32p. (J). 13.95 (978-1-932425-16-1(0) , Lemniscaat) Boyds Mills Pr.

—Jack & the Night Visitors. 2006. (Illus.). 32p. (J). 13.95 (978-1-932425-33-8(0) , Lemniscaat) Boyds Mills Pr.

Sis, Peter. Dinosaur! Sis, Peter, illus. (J). (ps-1). 2005. 28p. bds. 6.99 (978-0-06-075967-4(4) , Harper Festival); 2000. (Illus.). 24p. 16.99 (978-0-688-17049-3(8)) HarperCollins Pubs.

—An Ocean World. Sis, Peter, illus. 2002. (Illus.). (YA). 14.43 (978-1-4046-0278-6(X)) Book Wholesalers, Inc.

Strang Communications Company Staff, ed. Ages 1-2 Teaching Pictures. 2001. (J). pap., tchr.'s training gde. ed. 10.99 (978-1-57405-770-6(7) , TOTP) CharismaLife Pubs.

Suen, Anastasia. Dos Anos. Cheon, Winnie, illus. 2002. (SPA.). 20p. (J). (ps). bds. 6.95 (978-1-58430-053-3(1)) Lee & Low Bks., Inc.

Tan, Shaun. The Arrival. 2007. (J). 128p. (gr. 7 up). pap. 19.99 (978-0-439-89529-3(4)); (978-0-439-89530-9(8)) Scholastic, Inc. (Levine, Arthur A. Bks.).

Tanaka, Shinsuke, illus. Wings. 2006. 80p. (J). 14.95 (978-1-933327-19-8(7)) Purple Bear Bks., Inc.

Tildes, Phyllis L. Baby Animals Black & White. Tildes, Phyllis L., illus. 1998. (Illus.). 10p. (J). (ps). bds. 5.95 (978-0-88106-313-4(4)) Charlesbridge Publishing, Inc.

Toy Box Innovations Staff, creator. Disney Pixar: Finding Nemo/A Bug's Life/Monsters, Inc. unabr. abr. ed. 2005. (Disney's Read along Collection). (J). audio compact disk 14.99 (978-0-7634-1151-0(5)) Walt Disney Records.

Trondheim, Lewis. Li'l Santa. Robin, Thierry, illus. 2003. 48p. 14.95 (978-1-56163-335-7(6)) NBM Publishing Co.

Weitzman, Jacqueline Preiss. You Can't Take a Balloon into the Metropolitan Museum. Bonnell, J., ed. Glasser, Robin Preiss, illus. 2001. 40p. (J). (ps-3). pap. 6.99 (978-0-14-056816-5(6) , Puffin) Penguin Group (USA) Inc.

—You Can't Take a Balloon into the Metropolitan Museum. Glasser, Robin, illus. 1998. 40p. (J). (gr. k-3). 18.99 (978-0-8037-2301-6(6) , Dial) Penguin Group (USA) Inc.

—You Can't Take a Balloon into the Metropolitan Museum. 2000. (gr. k-3). lib. bdg. 15.30 (978-0-613-33742-7(5)) Tandem Library Bks.

—You Can't Take a Balloon into the Museum of Fine Arts. Glasser, Robin Preiss, illus. 2002. 40p. (J). (gr. k-4). 18.99 (978-0-8037-2570-6(1) , Dial) Penguin Group (USA) Inc.

—You Can't Take a Balloon into the National Gallery. Glasser, Robin Preiss, illus. 2002. 40p. (J). pap. 7.99 (978-0-14-230131-9(0) , Puffin) Penguin Group (USA) Inc.

—You Can't Take a Balloon into the National Gallery. 2002. (ps-2). lib. bdg. 16.45 (978-0-613-83550-3(6)) Tandem Library Bks.

Wiesner, David. Free Fall. Wiesner, David, illus. 2008. 32p. (J). 17.99 (*978-0-06-156741-4(8)*) HarperCollins Pubs.

Wiesner, David. Sector 7. Wiesner, David, illus. 2002. (Illus.). (J). 23.40 (978-0-7587-0142-8(X)) Book Wholesalers, Inc.

—Sector 7. Wiesner, David, illus. 1999. (Illus.). 48p. (J). (gr. k-3). tchr. ed. 16.00 (978-0-395-74656-1(6) , Clarion Bks.) Houghton Mifflin Co. Trade & Reference Div.

STORKS

World Book, Inc. Staff, contrib. by. Storks & Other Large Wading Birds. 2005. (World Book's Animals of the World Ser.). (Illus.). 64p. (J). (978-0-7166-1267-4(4)) World Bk., Inc.

—World Book's Animals of the World Set 4. 2005. (World Book's Animals of the World Ser.). (Illus.). 64p. (gr. 2-8). 189.00 (978-0-7166-1261-2(5)) World Bk., Inc.

STORKS—FICTION

Alonso, Fernando. Feral y las Ciguenas. (SPA.). 96p. (J). (gr. 3-5). (978-84-279-3332-3(0) , NG2826) Noguer y Caralt Editores, S. A. ESP. *Dist:* Lectorum Pubns., Inc.

Clarke, Jane. The Best of Both Nests. Kennedy, Anne, illus. 2007. 32p. (J). 15.95 (*978-0-8075-0668-4(0)*) Whitman, Albert & Co.

Drescher, Henrik. The Strange Appearance of Howard Cranebill. Drescher, Henrik, illus. 2006. (Illus.). 32p. (J). 14.95 (978-1-59692-134-4(X)) MacAdam/Cage Publishing, Inc.

The Fox & the Stork, Vol. 2. l.t. ed. 1999. (Illus.). 43p. (J). (gr. k-6). reprint ed. pap. 2.50 (978-1-893688-06-3(2)) Carroll Schl., The.

Mackinnon, Mairi. Fox & the Stork. 2007. (First Reading Level 1 Ser.). 32p. (J). 8.99 (*978-0-7945-1812-7(5)* , Usborne) EDC Publishing.

McDermott, Gerald. The Fox & the Stork. 2003. (Green Light Readers Level 2 Ser.). (Illus.). 24p. (J). 11.95 (978-0-15-204877-8(4)); pap. 3.95 (978-0-15-204837-2(5)) Harcourt Children's Bks. (Green Light Readers).

—The Fox & the Stork. 1999. (Illus.). (J). (978-0-606-18173-0(3)) Tandem Library Bks.

—Fox & the Stork. 1999. (gr. k-3). lib. bdg. 11.80 (978-0-613-63154-9(4)) Tandem Library Bks.

Olson, David. The Thunderstruck Stork. Munsinger, Lynn, illus. 2007. (J). (ps-2). 15.95 (*978-0-8075-7910-7(6)*) Whitman, Albert & Co.

STORMALONG, ALFRED BULLTOP

Metaxas, Eric. Stormalong. Vanderbeek, Don, illus. 2005. (Rabbit Ears-A Classic Tale Ser.). 40p. (J). (gr. k-5). 25.65 (978-1-59197-772-8(X)) Spotlight.

STORMS

see also Hurricanes; Meteorology; Rain and Rainfall; Snow; Thunderstorms; Tornadoes; Winds

also other kinds of storms

Aarons, Jacob. Stormy Weather. 2005. (Illus.). 20p. (J). (*978-0-328-13452-6(X)* , Scott Foresman) Addison-Wesley Educational Pubs., Inc.

Baird, Audrey B. Storm Coming! O'Brien, Patrick, illus. 2003. 32p. (J). (gr. 2-4). 15.95 (978-1-56397-887-6(3)) Boyds Mills Pr.

Benchmark Education Staff. The Power of Storms. 2005. 2.00 (*978-1-4108-4636-5(9)*) Benchmark Education Co.

Benchmark Education Staff, compiled by. Storms. 2006. spiral bd. 99.00 (*978-1-4108-7080-3(4)*) Benchmark Education Co.

Berger, Melvin & Berger, Gilda. Hurricanes Have Eyes but Can't See: And Other Amazing Facts about Wild Weather. 2003. (Illus.). 48p. (J). (978-0-439-54980-6(9)) Scholastic, Inc.

Bonar, Samantha. Tsunamis. 2001. (Natural Disasters Ser.). (Illus.). 48p. (J). (gr. 3-4). lib. bdg. 21.26 (978-0-7368-0902-3(3) , Capstone High-Interest Bks.) Capstone Pr., Inc.

Brannon, Barbara. Discover Storms. 2005. 39.00 (*978-1-4108-5124-6(9)*) Benchmark Education Co.

Bundey, Nikki. Storms & People. 2005. (Science of Weather Ser.). (Illus.). 32p. (J). (gr. 4-6). lib. bdg. 21.27 (978-1-57505-499-5(X)) Lerner Publishing Group.

—Storms & the Earth. 2005. (Science of Weather Ser.). (Illus.). 32p. (J). (gr. 4-6). lib. bdg. 21.27 (978-1-57505-474-2(4)) Lerner Publishing Group.

Burby, Liza N. Blizzards. 1999. (Extreme Weather Ser.). 24p. (J). (gr. k-4). lib. bdg. 18.75 (978-0-8239-5291-5(6) , PowerKids Pr.) Rosen Publishing Group, Inc., The.

—Tropical Storms & Hurricanes. 1999. (Extreme Weather Ser.). 24p. (J). (gr. k-4). lib. bdg. 18.75 (978-0-8239-5290-8(8) , PowerKids Pr.) Rosen Publishing Group, Inc., The.

Canizares, Susan & Chessen, Betsey. Storms: Tormentas. 2004. (Science Emergent Readers Ser.). (ENG & SPA., Illus.). (J). (978-0-439-66392-2(X)) Scholastic, Inc.

Challoner, Jack & Dorling Kindersley Publishing Staff. Hurricane & Tornado. 2004. (Eyewitness Books). (Illus.). 72p. (J). lib. bdg. 19.99 (978-0-7566-0689-3(6)) Dorling Kindersley Publishing, Inc.

Chambers, Catherine. Blizzard. 2002. (Wild Weather Ser.). 32p. (J). (gr. k-2). (Illus.). lib. bdg. 21.36 (978-1-58810-654-4(3)); pap. (978-1-4034-0110-6(1) , 91677) Heinemann Library.

Connell, Kate. Hoping for Rain: The Dust Bowl Adventures of Patty & Earl Buckler. 2004. (I Am American Ser.). (Illus.). 40p. (J). (gr. 3-7). pap. 6.99 (978-0-7922-6903-8(9) , National Geographic Children's Bks.) National Geographic Society.

Connolly, Sean. Storms. 2004. (Illus.). 31p. (J). lib. bdg. (978-1-58340-393-8(0)) Smart Apple Media.

Curry, Don, ed. Super Storms That Rocked the World. 2008. 40p. (J). pap. 6.99 (***978-0-696-23978-6(7)***) Meredith Bks.

Davies, Jon. Project Storm Chaser: A Kids' Guide to Safe Storm Chasing. 2007. (J). (***978-1-56037-407-7(1)***) Farcountry Pr.

De Hahn, Tracee. The Blizzard of 1888. 2000. (Great Disasters Ser.). (Illus.). 104p. (J). (gr. 5-9). 21.95 (978-0-7910-5787-2(9) , Chelsea Hse.) Facts On File, Inc.

DeAngelis, Therese & DeAngelis, Gina. The Dust Bowl. 2001. (Great Disasters, Reforms & Ramifications Ser.). (Illus.). 112p. (J). 30.00 (978-0-7910-6323-1(2) , Chelsea Hse.) Facts On File, Inc.

Desmond, Jones. Eye of the Storm Vol. 2: Storm, E Weather, Set. abr. ed. 1999. (YA). (gr. 7-12). pap. 30.00 incl. audio (978-0-9669585-3-9(5)) Eye of the Storm.

—Eye of the Storm Vol. 2: Storm, E Weather, Set. Golden Arts Photos and Graphics Staff, tr. 2nd abr. rev. ed. 1999. 72p. (YA). (gr. 7-12). 22.00 incl. audio (978-0-9669585-4-6(3)) Eye of the Storm.

Dickstein, Leslie. Storms! 2006. 32p. (J). lib. bdg. 13.85 (***978-1-4242-1009-1(7)***) Fitzgerald Bks.

Dineen, Jacqueline. Hurricanes & Typhoons. 2004. (Natural Disasters Ser.). (J). lib. bdg. 27.10 (978-1-932799-06-4(0)) Stargazer Bks.

Donnelly, Karen J. Storms of the Past & the Future. 2003. (Earths Changing Weather & Climate Ser.). (Illus.). 24p. (J). lib. bdg. 18.75 (978-0-8239-6216-7(4) , PowerKids Pr.) Rosen Publishing Group, Inc., The.

Doudna, Kelly. It Is Stormy. 2003. (Weather Ser.). (Illus.). 23p. (J). (ps-3). lib. bdg. 19.93 (978-1-57765-776-7(4)) ABDO Publishing Co.

Egan, Lorraine Hopping. Wild Weather No. 3: Blizzards. Wheeler, Jody, illus. 1999. (Hello Reader! Ser.). 48p. (J). (gr. 2-4). pap. 3.99 (978-0-590-39730-8(3)) Scholastic, Inc.

Eye of the Storm. 2006. (Amazing Science Ser.). 24p. (J). 7.95 (978-1-4048-1845-3(6)) Picture Window Bks.

Faidley, Warren, Jr. How to Survive Any Storm: Severe Weather Handbook. 2003. (Illus.). 213p. spiral bd. 17.95 (978-0-9728107-0-8(6)) Weatherstock, Inc.

Gleason, Carrie. Ocean Storm Alert! 2004. (Disaster Alert! Ser.). (Illus.). 32p. (J). (978-0-7787-1579-5(5)); pap. (978-0-7787-1611-2(2)) Crabtree Publishing Co.

Group/McGraw-Hill, Wright. Savage Storms: Tornadoes & Hurricanes, 6 vols. (Book2WebTM Ser.). (gr. 4-8). 36.50 (978-0-322-04424-1(3)) Wright Group, The.

Harcourt School Publishers Staff. Storm Watch: Below Level. 3rd ed. 2002. (Trophies Reading Program Ser.). (Illus.). (J). pap. 4.10 (978-0-15-322969-5(1)) Harcourt Schl. Pubs.

—Storm Watch 5-Pack, Below Level. 3rd ed. 2002. (Trophies Reading Program Ser.). (Illus.). (gr. 1). pap. 20.10 (978-0-15-326819-9(0)) Harcourt Schl. Pubs.

Harris, Caroline & Faidley, Warren. Wild Weather. 2005. (Kingfisher Voyages Ser.). (Illus.). 60p. (J). (gr. 4-6). 14.95 (978-0-7534-5911-9(6) , Kingfisher) Houghton Mifflin Co. Trade & Reference Div.

Hiscock, Bruce. The Big Storm. 2000. (Illus.). (J). (978-0-606-17912-6(7)) Tandem Library Bks.

Isaacs, Sally Senzell. Life in the Dust Bowl. (Picture the Past Ser.). (Illus.). 32p. (J). 2002. (gr. k-3). 7.50 (978-1-58810-413-7(3) , 91186); 2001. (gr. 2-4). lib. bdg. (978-1-58810-248-5(3)) Heinemann Library.

—Life in the Dust Bowl. 2002. (gr. k-3). lib. bdg. 15.90 (978-0-613-84255-6(3)) Tandem Library Bks.

Jeffrey, Gary. Tornadoes & Superstorms. Riley, Terry, illus. 2007. 48p. (J). (***978-1-4042-1986-1(2)***); pap. (***978-1-4042-1985-4(4)***); (gr. 5-8). lib. bdg. 29.25 (978-1-4042-1993-9(5)) Rosen Publishing Group, Inc., The.

Jennings, Terry. Extreme Weather. 2005. (Illus.). 48p. (J). (gr. 6-9). lib. bdg. 29.95 (978-1-58340-727-1(8)) Smart Apple Media.

Kalz, Jill. Snow. 2002. (Illus.). 23p. (J). 21.35 (978-1-58340-155-2(5)) Smart Apple Media.

Kliman, Gilbert, et al. My Personal Story about Tropical Storm Stan: A Guided Activity Workbook for Children, Adolescents & Families. 2006. spiral bd. 19.00 (***978-0-9790846-8-3(7)***) Children's Psychological Health Ctr., Inc., The.

Kramer, Stephen P. Eye of the Storm: Chasing Storms with Warren Faidley. 1999. (J). (978-0-606-16125-1(2)) Tandem Library Bks.

Lassieur, Allison. Storm Tracker. 2006. (Illus.). 32p. (J). (978-1-4109-2576-3(5)); pap. (978-1-4109-2605-0(2)) Steck-Vaughn.

Levey, Richard H. Dust Bowl! The 1930s Black Blizzard. 2005. (X-Treme Disasters That Changed America Ser.). (J). lib. bdg. 25.27 (978-1-59716-007-0(5)) Bearport Publishing Co., Inc.

Linde, Barbara M. The Power of Storms. 2005. 39.00 (***978-1-4108-4588-7(5)***) Benchmark Education Co.

Mac Aulay, Kelly. Cambios del Estado del Tiempo: Las Tormentas. 2006. (SPA., Illus.). 32p. (J). pap. (978-0-7787-8390-9(1)) Crabtree Publishing Co.

MacAulay, Kelley & Kalman, Bobbie. Cambios Del Estado Del Tiempo: Las Tormentas. 2006. (SPA., Illus.). 32p. (J). (978-0-7787-8376-3(6)) Crabtree Publishing Co.

—Changing Weather: Storms. 2006. (Nature's Changes Ser.). (Illus.). 32p. (J). (gr. k-6). pap. (978-0-7787-2314-1(3)); (978-0-7787-2280-9(5)) Crabtree Publishing Co.

MacAulay, Kelley & Kalman, Bobbie. Les Tempêtes. 2007. (FRE.). 32p. pap. 8.95 (***978-2-89579-166-9(X)***) Editions Banjo CAN. *Dist:* Crabtree Publishing Co.

Maslin, Mark. Storms. 1999. (Restless Planet Ser.). (Illus.). 48p. (J). (gr. 4-6). lib. bdg. 27.12 (978-0-7398-1330-0(7)) Raintree.

McMorrow, Annalisa. Storms. Chalk, Philip, illus. 1998. 48p. (J). (gr. 1-3). pap. 7.95 (978-1-57612-057-6(0) , MM2071) Monday Morning Bks., Inc.

Meister, Cari. Blizzards. 1999. (Nature's Fury Ser.). (Illus.). 32p. (J). (gr. 3-8). lib. bdg. 24.21 (978-1-57765-085-0(9) , ABDO & Daughters) ABDO Publishing Co.

Merk, A. Storms. 2003. (Weather Report Discovery Library). (Illus.). 24p. (gr. 1-4). 14.95 (978-1-58952-572-6(8)) Rourke Publishing, LLC.

Mezzanotte, Jim. Dust Storms. 2006. (J). pap. (***978-0-8368-7918-6(X)***); lib. bdg. (***978-0-8368-7911-7(2)***) Stevens, Gareth Inc. (Weekly Reader Early Learning Library).

—Hail Storms. 2006. (J). pap. (***978-0-8368-7919-3(8)***); lib. bdg. (***978-0-8368-7912-4(0)***) Stevens, Gareth Inc. (Weekly Reader Early Learning Library).

—Snow Storms. 2006. (J). pap. (***978-0-8368-7921-6(X)***); lib. bdg. (***978-0-8368-7914-8(7)***) Stevens, Gareth Inc. (Weekly Reader Early Learning Library).

—Tormentas de Polvo. 2006. (ENG & SPA.). (J). lib. bdg. (***978-0-8368-8073-1(0)***); (Illus.). 24p. (gr. 2). pap. (***978-0-8368-8080-9(3)***) Stevens, Gareth Inc. (Weekly Reader Early Learning Library).

Morris, Neil. Inside Hurricanes & Tornadoes. 2006. (Inside Nature's Disasters Ser.). (Illus.). 36p. (J). lib. bdg. (978-0-8368-7249-1(5)) Stevens, Gareth Inc.

Murphy, Jim. Blizzard. 2006. (Illus.). 144p. (J). pap. 8.99 (978-0-590-67310-5(6) , Scholastic Paperbacks) Scholastic, Inc.

—Blizzard! The Storm That Changed America. Murphy, Jim, illus. 2000. (Illus.). 136p. (J). (gr. 5 up). pap. 18.95 (978-0-590-67309-9(2)) Scholastic, Inc.

Olson, Nathan. Blizzards. 2005. (Bridgestone Books. Weather Update). (Illus.). 24p. (J). (ps-7). lib. bdg. 21.26 (978-0-7368-4330-0(2) , 1243957, Bridgestone Bks.) Capstone Pr., Inc.

Osborne, Will & Osborne, Mary Pope. Twisters & Other Terrible Storms. Murdocca, Sal, illus. 2003. (Magic Tree House Research Guide Ser.: No. 8). 128p. (J). (gr. k-3). 4.99 (978-0-375-81358-0(6) , Random Hse. Bks. for Young Readers) Random Hse. Children's Bks.

—Twisters & Other Terrible Storms: A Nonfiction Companion to Twister on Tuesday. Murdocca, Sal, illus. 2003. (Magic Tree House Research Guide Ser.: No. 8). 128p. (J). (gr. k-3). lib. bdg. 11.99 (978-0-375-91358-7(0) , Random Hse. Bks. for Young Readers) Random Hse. Children's Bks.

—Twisters & Other Terrible Storms: A Nonfiction Companion to Twister on Tuesday. Murdocca, Sal, illus. 2003. (Magic Tree House Research Guide Ser.: No. 8). 119p. (J). (gr. k-3). per. 13.00 (978-0-613-62411-4(4)) Tandem Library Bks.

Oxlade, Chris. Storm Warning: Tornadoes. 2004. (Turbulent Planet Ser.). (Illus.). 48p. (J). 28.56 (978-1-4109-1099-8(7)); pap. 8.50 (978-1-4109-1206-0(X)) Harcourt Schl. Pubs.

—Storm Warning: Tornadoes. 2005. (Turbulent Planet Ser.). (Illus.). 48p. (J). (gr. 4-7). pap. 9.35 (978-1-4109-1750-8(9)); (978-1-4109-1740-9(1)) Steck-Vaughn.

Paul, Gil. See-Through Storms. Baker, Julian & Baker, Janet, illus. 2006. 32p. (J). (gr. 5-7). 15.95 (978-0-7624-2662-1(4)) Running Pr. Bk. Pubs.

Peppas, Lynn. Severe Storm & Blizzard Alert! 2004. (Disaster Alert! Ser.). (Illus.). 32p. (J). pap. (978-0-7787-1605-1(8)); (978-0-7787-1573-3(6)) Crabtree Publishing Co.

Phelan, Glen. Extreme Weather. 2004. (National Geographic Reading Expeditions Ser.). (Illus.). 32p. (J). pap. (978-0-7922-4575-9(X)) National Geographic Society.

Preszler, June. Where Does Lightning Come From? A Book about Weather. 2007. 24p. (J). (978-0-7368-6754-2(6)) Capstone Pr., Inc.

Richards, Julie. It's Stormy! 2004. (J). lib. bdg. 27.10 (978-1-58340-534-5(8)) Smart Apple Media.

Rosado, Maria. Blizzards & Ice Storms. 1999. (978-0-606-17527-2(X)) Tandem Library Bks.

Roza, Greg. Severe Storms: Measuring Velocity. 2006. (Math for the Real World Ser.). (Illus.). 32p. pap. (978-1-4042-6085-6(4)); lib. bdg. (978-1-4042-3366-9(0)) Rosen Publishing Group, Inc., The.

Sandler, Michael. Catastrophic Storms. 2005. (Navigators Ser.). (J). pap. 42.00 (***978-1-4108-5082-9(X)***) Benchmark Education Co.

Scheff, Duncan. Ice & Hailstorms. 2001. (Nature on the Rampage Ser.). (Illus.). 32p. (J). lib. bdg. 22.83 (978-0-7398-4703-9(1)) Raintree.

Sievert, Terri. Storms. 2005. (Weather Update Ser.). (Illus.). 24p. (J). 21.26 (978-0-7368-3738-5(8)) Capstone Pr., Inc.

Simon, Seymour. Seemore Super Tormentas. 2007. (ENG & SPA.). 32p. (J). 15.50 (978-0-8118-5767-3(0)); (Illus.). pap. 3.95 (978-0-8118-5808-3(1)) Chronicle Bks. LLC.

—Super Storms. 2002. (See More Readers Ser.). (Illus.). 32p. (J). 13.95 (978-1-58717-137-6(6)); Vol. 2. pap. 3.95 (978-1-58717-138-3(4)) Chronicle Bks. LLC. (SeaStar Bks.).

—Super Storms. 2002. (gr. 3-6). lib. bdg. 11.80 (978-0-613-58440-1(6)) Tandem Library Bks.

Steele, Christy. Tsunamis. 2001. (Nature on the Rampage Ser.). (Illus.). 32p. (J). (ps-3). lib. bdg. 22.83 (978-0-7398-4706-0(6)) Raintree.

Stein, Paul. Storms of the Future. 2001. (Library of Future Weather & Climate). (Illus.). 64p. (YA). (gr. 4-6). lib. bdg. 26.50 (978-0-8239-3417-1(9)) Rosen Publishing Group, Inc., The.

Storm: Level Q, 6 vols. (Wonder Worldtm Ser.). 48p. 39.95 (978-0-7802-2953-2(3)) Wright Group, The.

Storm Trackers: Six-Pack. (Greetings Ser.: Vol. 3). (gr. 3-5). 31.00 (978-0-7635-2076-2(4)) Rigby Education.

Storms, 6 vols., Pack. (Sails Literacy Ser.). (gr. 1-2). 36.00 (978-0-7578-6741-5(3)) Rigby Education.

Temple, Bob. Ice Storm! The 1998 Freeze. 2007. (X-Treme Disasters That Changed America Ser.). (Illus.). 32p. (J). lib. bdg. 25.27 (978-1-59716-275-3(2)) Bearport Publishing Co., Inc.

Thomas, Rick. Whiteout! A Book about Blizzards. Shea, Denise, illus. 2005. (Amazing Science Ser.). 24p. (C). (gr. k-3). 22.60 (978-1-4048-0925-3(2)) Picture Window Bks.

Time for Kids Editors. Storms! 2006. (Time for Kids Science Scoops Ser.). (Illus.). 32p. (J). 14.99 (978-0-06-078205-4(6)) HarperCollins Pubs.

Time for Kids Editors & Dickstein, Leslie. Storms! 2006. (Time for Kids Science Scoops Ser.). (Illus.). 32p. (J). pap. 3.99 (978-0-06-078204-7(8)) HarperCollins Pubs.

Tras las Tormentas: 6 Small Books. (Saludos Ser.: Vol. 3). (SPA.). (gr. 3-5). 31.00 (978-0-7635-2082-3(9)) Rigby Education.

Trueit, Trudi Strain. Storm Chasers. 2002. (Watts Library). (Illus.). 64p. (J). (gr. 5-7). 25.50 (978-0-531-11971-6(8) , Watts, Franklin) Scholastic Library Publishing.

Turck, Mary. Blizzard! Snowstorm Fury. 2000. (Cover-to-Cover Bks.). (Illus.). 56p. (J). pap. 8.95 (978-0-7891-5056-1(5)); (gr. 4-7). lib. bdg. 17.95 (978-0-7807-9020-9(0)) Perfection Learning Corp.

Watts, Claire. White-Out: Blizzards. 2004. (Turbulent Planet Ser.). (Illus.). 48p. (J). 28.56 (978-1-4109-1101-8(2)); pap. 8.50 (978-1-4109-1208-4(6)) Harcourt Schl. Pubs.

—Whiteout Blizzards. 2005. (Turbulent Planet Ser.). (Illus.). 48p. (J). (978-1-4109-1739-3(8)); pap. (978-1-4109-1749-2(5)) Steck-Vaughn.

Webster, Christine. Storms. 2006. (Science Matters Ser.). (J). (978-1-59036-412-3(0)); pap. (978-1-59036-418-5(X)) Weigl Pubs., Inc.

Weil, Ann. Deadly Storms. 2003. (Illus.). 64p. (YA). per. 3.95 (978-1-56254-664-9(3) , SP6643) Saddleback Educational Publishing.

Wetterer, Charles M. & Wetterer, Margaret K. The Snow Walker. Young, Mary O'Keefe, illus. 1998. (On My Own History Ser.). 48p. (J). (gr. 1-3). pap. 5.95 (978-0-87614-959-1(X) , Carolrhoda Bks.) Lerner Publishing Group.

White, Matt. Storm Chasers: On the Trail of Deadly Tornadoes, 6 vols. (gr. 4 up). 49.95 (978-0-7368-9541-5(8) , High Five) Red Brick Learning.

Wind & Storms: 6 Each of 1 Student Book, 6 vols. (Sunshinetm Science Ser.). 24p. (gr. 1-2). 41.95 (978-0-7802-1376-0(9)) Wright Group, The.

Wind & Storms: Big Book. (Sunshinetm Science Ser.). 24p. (gr. 1-2). 37.50 (978-0-7802-1377-7(7)) Wright Group, The.

Winner, Cherie. Clouds, Storms, & Rainbows. Recher, Andrew & Rogge, Rachel, illus. 2008. (J). (***978-1-55971-992-6(3)***); pap. (***978-1-55971-993-3(1)***) T&N Children's Publishing. (NorthWord Bks. for Young Readers).

Wood, Jennifer. Storms. 2004. (Interfact Ser.). (SPA., Illus.). 48p. (J). (gr. 3-6). 14.95 incl. cd-rom (978-1-58728-466-3(9) , Two Can Publishing) T&N Children's Publishing.

Woods, Michael & Woods, Mary B. Blizzards. 2008. (Disasters up Close Ser.). (J). lib. bdg. 27.93 (***978-0-8225-6575-8(7)*** , Lerner Pubns.) Lerner Publishing Group.

Woods, Michael & Woods, Mary B. Hurricanes. 2007. (Disasters up Close Ser.). (Illus.). 64p. (J). (gr. 4-6). 27.93 (978-0-8225-4710-5(4) , Lerner Pubns.) Lerner Publishing Group.

World Book, Inc Staff, contrib. by. Blizzards. 2007. (J). (***978-0-7166-9802-9(1)***) World Bk., Inc.

Ylvisaker, Anne. Ice Storms. 2003. (Natural Disasters Ser.). (Illus.). 48p. (J). (gr. 3-4). lib. bdg. 21.26 (978-0-7368-1506-2(6) , Capstone High-Interest Bks.) Capstone Pr., Inc.

STORMS—FICTION

Ada, Alma Flor. After the Storm. 1998. (Stories the Year 'Round Ser.). (J). (gr. k-12). pap. 7.95 (978-1-56014-337-6(1)) Santillana USA Publishing Co., Inc.

Anholt, Laurence & Anholt, Catherine. Chimp & Zee: Words & Pictures. 2006. (Chimp & Zee Ser.). (Illus.). 32p. (J). (ps). 15.95 (978-1-84507-375-6(4)) Lincoln, Frances Ltd. GBR. *Dist:* Perseus Distribution.

Asare, Meshack. Sosu's Call. Asare, Meshack, illus. 2002. (Illus.). 40p. (J). (gr. k-4). 15.95 (978-1-929132-21-8(2)) Kane/Miller Bk. Pubs., Inc.

Baglio, Ben M. Into the Blue. 2002. (gr. 3-6). lib. bdg. 12.40 (978-0-613-70893-7(8)) Tandem Library Bks.

Baguley, Elizabeth. The Little Lost Robin. Macnaughton, Tina, illus. 2007. 28p. (J). (ps-2). 16.95 (***978-1-56148-590-1(X)***) Good Bks.

Banks, Kate. El Pajaro, el Mono y la Serpiente en la Selva. Bogacki, Tomek, illus. (SPA.). 24p. (J). (gr. k-2). (978-84-261-3129-4(8) , JV2823) Juventud, Editorial ESP. *Dist:* Lectorum Pubns., Inc.

Beech, Linda. Alive! Hollander, Wendy Born, illus. 2002. 16p. (J). (978-0-439-35177-5(4)) Scholastic, Inc.

Bodett, Tom. Williwaw! unabr. ed. 2004. 208p. (J). (gr. 5-9). pap. 38.00 incl. audio (978-0-8072-8226-7(X) , LL0169, Listening Library) Random Hse. Audio Publishing Group.

—Williwaw! 2000. 208p. (YA). (gr. 5-8). pap. 5.99 (978-0-375-80687-2(3) , Yearling) Random Hse. Children's Bks.

—Williwaw! 2000. (J). (978-0-606-19440-2(1)); (gr. 5-8). lib. bdg. 13.55 (978-0-613-28363-2(5)) Tandem Library Bks.

Bolme, Edward Sarah. Jesus Stops a Storm. Gillette, Tim, illus. l.t. ed. 2003. 20p. (J). bds. 6.99 (978-0-9725546-3-3(7)) CREST Pubns.

Brave Irene. 2004. pap. 32.75 incl. audio (978-1-55592-195-8(7)); (J). 24.95 incl. audio (978-1-56008-006-0(X)) Weston Woods Studios, Inc.

Bridwell, Norman. The Stormy Day Rescue. Bridwell, Norman, illus. 2002. (Big Red Readers Ser.). (Illus.). (J). 11.91 (978-0-7587-5220-8(2)) Book Wholesalers, Inc.

Brin, Susannah. Under the Waterfall. 2001. (gr. 5-8). lib. bdg. 11.80 (978-0-613-63136-5(6)) Tandem Library Bks.

Bryant, Megan E. The Berry Big Storm. S. I. Artists Staff & Querol, Marga, illus. 2003. (All Aboard Reading Station Stop Ser.). 32p. (J). (ps-2). pap. 3.99 (978-0-448-43135-2(1) , Grosset & Dunlap) Penguin Group (USA) Inc.

Butterworth, Nick. Despues de la Tormenta. 2001. Tr. of After the Storm. (SPA.). (J). 12.76 (978-84-233-2284-8(X)) Ediciones Destino ESP. *Dist:* Lectorum Pubns., Inc.

Carinos, Lydie: Libros Aventuras (Adventure Books) 2000. (MacMillan/McGraw-Hill. Estudios Sociales Ser.). (ENG & SPA.). (gr. 5 up). (978-0-02-148732-5(4)) Macmillan/McGraw-Hill Schl. Div.

Carrasco, Ledo & Munoz, Norma. Los Cuentos de la Casa del Arbol. Olson, Johan, illus. rev. ed. 2004. (Castillo de la Lectura Blanca Ser.). (SPA.). 72p. (J). pap. 6.95 (978-970-20-0124-9(2)) Castillo, Ediciones, S. A. de C. V. MEX. *Dist:* Macmillan.

S

Caught in the Storm: Individual Title Six-Packs. (gr. k-1). 23.00 (978-0-7635-9046-8(0)) Rigby Education.

Cole, Joanna & White, Nancy. The Magic School Bus Kicks up a Storm: A Book about Weather. 2000. (Magic School Bus Ser.). (J). (gr. 1-4). (978-0-606-18577-6(1)) Tandem Library Bks.

Courtin, Thierry. T'choupi a Peur de l'Orage. 2000. (FRE.). (J). 13.95 (978-2-09-202033-3(1)) Nathan, Fernand FRA. *Dist:* Distribooks, Inc.

Crossley-Holland, Kevin. Storm. Marks, Alan, illus. 2002. (Yellow Bananas Ser.). 48p. (J). (gr. 3-4). (978-0-7787-0934-3(5)); pap. (978-0-7787-0980-0(9)) Crabtree Publishing Co.

D'Amico, Carmela & D'Amico, Steven. Ella Sets Sail. 2008. (J). (***978-0-439-83156-7(3)***); pap. (***978-0-439-83155-0(5)***) Scholastic, Inc. (Levine, Arthur A. Bks.).

Dearen, Patrick. When the Sky Rained Dust. 2004. 132p. (J). pap. 12.95 (978-1-57168-830-9(7) , Eakin Pr.) Eakin Pr.

Dodds, Dayle Ann. Sing, Sophie! 1999. (J). (978-0-606-19321-4(9)) Tandem Library Bks.

Doyle, Malachy. Storm Cats. Trotter, Stuart, illus. 2002. 32p. (J). (ps-1). 15.95 (978-0-689-84464-5(6) , McElderry, Margaret K.) Simon & Schuster Children's Publishing.

Duey, Kathleen & Bale, Karen A. Blizzard: Colorado, 1886. 1998. (Survival! Ser.: No. 3). (J). (gr. 4-7). (978-0-606-13827-7(7)) Tandem Library Bks.

Edwards, Carol. Jacy Meets Betsy: Jacy's Search for Jesus Book II. Frey, Daniel, illus. 2006. 32p. (J). 15.95 (978-0-9755314-1-9(7)) Majestic Publishing, LLC.

Edwards, Julie Andrews. Dumpy & the Big Storm. Walton, Tony, illus. 2002. (Dumpy Ser.: Vol. 4). 32p. (ps-2). 15.99 (978-0-7868-0742-0(3)) Hyperion Bks. for Children.

Erickson, John R. The Case of the Swirling Killer Tornado. Holmes, Gerald L., illus. 1998. (Hank the Cowdog Ser.: No. 25). 144p. (J). (gr. 2-5). 14.99 (978-0-670-88432-2(4) , Viking Juvenile); Vol. 25. pap. 4.99 (978-0-14-130401-4(4) , Puffin) Penguin Group (USA) Inc.

—Lost in the Blinded Blizzard. Holmes, Gerald L., illus. 1998. (Hank the Cowdog Ser.: No. 16). 144p. (J). (gr. 2-5). 14.99 (978-0-670-88423-0(5) , Viking Juvenile); pap. 4.99 (978-0-14-130392-5(1) , Puffin) Penguin Group (USA) Inc.

Erickson, Mary Ellen. Snowstorm. 2005. (J). (978-0-9765453-3-0(0)) Dr. Mary's Bks.

Frenette, Liza. Soft Shoulders: An Adirondack Story. 1998. (J). 9.95 (978-0-925168-70-2(X)) North Country Bks., Inc.

Fudge, Keith. The Rainy Day Discovery. 2006. (J). per. 11.95 (978-1-889743-37-0(2)) Robbie Dean Pr.

Fulcher, Dean. The Grand Island Adventure. 2006. 238p. (J). per. 18.95 (978-1-59886-074-0(7)) Tate Publishing & Enterprises, L.L.C.

Gerritsen, Paula. Nuts. 2006. 32p. (J). 15.95 (978-1-932425-66-6(7) , Lemniscaat) Boyds Mills Pr.

Giff, Patricia Reilly. Tempestalenos Retumbatruenos. 2000. (Kids of Polk Street School Ser.).Tr. of Snaggle Doodles. (SPA.). (YA). (gr. 1 up). 4.50 (978-0-922852-49-9(9)) AIMS International Bks., Inc.

Graham, Georgia. The Strongest Man This Side of Cremona. Graham, Georgia, illus. 1998. (Illus.). 32p. (J). (ps-3). pap. 15.95 (978-0-88995-182-2(9)) Red Deer Pr. CAN. *Dist:* Fitzhenry & Whiteside, Ltd.

Gramatky, Hardie. Little Toot. Gramatky, Hardie, illus. 2007. 104p. (J). (ps). 17.99 (978-0-399-24713-2(0) , Putnam Juvenile) Penguin Group (USA) Inc.

Hall, Rose. After the Storm. jazvic, Beryl, illus. 2005. (J). bds. 19.95 (978-0-9770503-0-7(0)) Institute For Behavior Change Incorporated The.

Hamilton, Tisha. Oops! I Polluted Again. Noel, Aragon & Hwan, Choi Sung, illus. 2006. (Trollz Ser.). 80p. (J). pap. 3.99 (978-0-439-70003-0(5)) Scholastic, Inc.

Harcourt School Publishers Staff. Rescue at Fox Creek On Level. 3rd ed. 2002. (Trophies Reading Program Ser.). (Illus.). pap. 5.10 (978-0-15-323350-0(8)) Harcourt Schl. Pubs.

—The Tree House: Take-Home Book. 1999. (Collections Ser.). (Illus.). (J). pap. 1.90 (978-0-15-317227-4(4)) Harcourt Schl. Pubs.

Haughton, Emma. Rainy Day. Rinaldi, Angelo, illus. (Carolrhoda Picture Books Ser.). 32p. (J). 2004. pap. 6.95 (978-1-57505-668-5(2)); 2003. 6.95 (978-1-57505-452-0(3) , Carolrhoda Bks.) Lerner Publishing Group.

High, Linda Oatman. City of Snow: The Great Blizzard Of 1888. Filippucci, Laura Francesca, illus. 2004. 32p. (J). 17.85 (978-0-8027-8911-2(0)); 16.95 (978-0-8027-8910-5(2)) Walker & Co.

Hippely, Hilary Horder. Adventure on Klickitat Island. Upton, Barbara, illus. 2000. (J). (ps-ps). lib. bdg. 15.30 (978-0-613-24092-5(8)) Tandem Library Bks.

Hobbie, Holly. You Are My Sunshine. Hobbie, Holly, illus. 3rd ed. 1999. (Toot & Puddle Ser.). (Illus.). 32p. (J). (ps-3). 16.99 (978-0-316-36562-8(9)) Little Brown & Co.

Jax, T. L. Fraidy-Frieda's Light Show. Jax, T. L., illus. l.t. ed. 2004. (Illus.). 30p. (J). 9.95 (978-0-9743890-2-8(1)) Flaxenfluff Pr., LLC.

Johnson, D. B. Henry Works. 2004. 32p. (J). (gr. k-3). 15.00 (978-0-618-55204-7(9)) Houghton Mifflin Co. Trade & Reference Div.

Ketteman, Helen. The Christmas Blizzard. 1999. (J). (978-0-606-17293-6(9)) Tandem Library Bks.

Ketteman, Helen & Warhola, James. Christmas Blizzard. 1999. (Illus.). 32p. (ps-3). pap. 5.99 (978-0-590-13609-9(7)) Scholastic, Inc.

Lake, Julie. Galveston's Summer of the Storm. 2003. (Chaparral Book for Young Readers Ser.). 210p. 16.95 (978-0-87565-272-6(7)) Texas Christian Univ. Pr.

Lance, Scott. Pourman's Library. 2003. 108p. (YA). pap. 10.95 (978-0-595-30148-5(7)) iUniverse, Inc.

Landstrom, Olof. Boo & Baa Get Wet. 2000. (978-0-606-22355-3(X)) Tandem Library Bks.

Leeson, Christine. Molly & the Storm. Hansen, Gaby, illus. 2003. 32p. (J). (gr. k-2). tchr. ed. 15.95 (978-1-58925-027-7(3) , tiger tales) ME Media LLC.

Lepp, Royden. Barnabas Helps a Friend. 2008. 32p. (J). pap. 3.99 (***978-0-310-71585-6(7)***) Zondervan.

Levithan, David. In the Eye of the Tornado. 1998. (Disaster Zone Ser.: Vol. 1). (J). pap. 3.99 (978-0-590-12915-2(5)) Scholastic, Inc.

—In the Eye of the Tornado. 1998. (Disaster Zone Ser.). (978-0-606-13334-0(8)) Tandem Library Bks.

Maguire, Gregory. What-the-Dickens: The Story of a Rogue Tooth Fairy. 2007. (Illus.). 304p. (J). (gr. 5-8). 15.99 (***978-0-7636-2961-8(8)***) Candlewick Pr.

Maurer, Tracy. Storm Codes. Rodriguez, Christina, illus. 2007. 40p. (J). pap. 8.95 (***978-0-89317-064-6(X)*** , WW-064X); (gr. 1-7). lib. bdg. 17.95 (***978-0-89317-063-9(1)*** , WW-0631) Finney Co., Inc. (Windward Publishing).

McBratney, Sam. Just You & Me. Bates, Ivan, illus. 2000. 32p. (J). (gr. k-1). pap. 5.99 (978-0-7636-1078-4(X)) Candlewick Pr.

—Just You & Me. 2000. (gr. k-3). lib. bdg. 14.15 (978-0-613-28545-2(X)) Tandem Library Bks.

McPhail, David. The Searcher & Old Tree. 2008. (J). (***978-1-58089-223-0(X)***) Charlesbridge Publishing, Inc.

Meyer, Marianne. Snow Problem: The Case of the Mushing Madness. 1998. (Kinetic City Super Crew: No. 9). (Illus.). 160p. (gr. 4-7). pap. 4.25 (978-0-07-006693-9(0) , 9780070066939) McGraw-Hill Cos., The.

Miller, S. K., illus. & creator. Jesse's Color Field. Miller, S. K., creator. l.t. ed. 2002. 68p. (J). (gr. k-5). pap. 16.95 (978-0-9714636-0-8(3)) Treehouse Treasures Corp.

Naylor, Phyllis Reynolds. Blizzard's Wake. (YA). 2004. (Illus.). 240p. pap. 5.99 (978-0-689-85221-3(5) , Simon Pulse); 2002. 224p. 16.95 (978-0-689-85220-6(7) , Atheneum) Simon & Schuster Children's Publishing.

—Blizzard's Wake. 2004. (gr. 7-12). lib. bdg. 14.15 (978-0-613-73409-7(2)) Tandem Library Bks.

—Blizzard's Wake. l.t. ed. 2003. 260p. (J). 22.95 (978-0-7862-5815-4(2)) Thorndike Pr.

Oldfield, Jenny. Midnight Snow 4. 2007. (Illus.). 128p. pap. 6.95 (***978-0-340-91076-4(3)***) Hodder Children's Division GBR. *Dist:* Independent Pubs. Group.

Pearson, Iris & Merrill, Mike. The Adventures of Lady: The Big Storm. Pearson, Iris, ed. Project Firefly Animation Studios, illus. rev. ed. 2007. 34p. (J). 15.99 (***978-0-9789984-2-4(1)***) Adventures of Lady LLC, The.

—The Adventures of Lady: The Big Storm Coloring Book. Pearson, Iris, ed. Project Firefly Animation Studios, illus. 2007. 34p. (J). pap. 6.99 (***978-0-9789984-3-1(X)***) Adventures of Lady LLC, The.

Peterson, John. The Littles & the Summer Storm. Rogers, Jacqueline, illus. 2002. (Littles First Readers Ser.: No. 10). 32p. (J). pap. 3.99 (978-0-439-31719-1(3) , Scholastic Paperbacks) Scholastic, Inc.

Pfister, Marcus. Rainbow Fish Finds His Way. James, J. Alison, tr. from GER. 2006. (Illus.). 32p. (J). 18.95 (978-0-7358-2084-5(8)) North-South Bks., Inc.

—Rainbow Fish Finds His Way. 2006. (Illus.). 32p. (J). 18.88 (978-0-7358-2085-2(6)) North-South Bks., Inc.

Preller, James. Case of the Great Sled Race. 2000. (gr. 3-6). lib. bdg. 11.80 (978-0-613-21298-4(3)) Tandem Library Bks.

Reinoso, Carlos. Little Ducky Jr. & the Whirlwind Storm: A Tale of Loss, Hope,and Renewal. Reinoso, Carlos, illus. l.t. ed. 2005. (Illus.). 50p. (J). 8.99 (978-0-9777672-0-5(5)) Behavioral Health & Human Development Ctr.

Rossi. El Chaparron Torrencial. 2000. Tr. of Gullywasher. (SPA.). (J). 14.75 (978-0-606-19852-3(0)) Tandem Library Bks.

Rossi, Joyce. The Gullywasher (El Chaparron Torrencial) 1998. (ENG & SPA., Illus.). 32p. (J). (gr. k-3). 7.95 (978-0-87358-728-0(6) , Rising Moon Bks. for Young Readers) Northland Publishing.

Runyon, Anne Marshall. The Sheltering Cedar. Runyon, Anne Marshall, illus. 2007. (Illus.). 32p. (J). (***978-1-933454-02-3(4)***) Portal Pr.

Rylant, Cynthia. The Storm. 2003. (Lighthouse Family Ser.). (gr. 3-6). lib. bdg. 11.80 (978-0-613-87052-8(2)) Tandem Library Bks.

Rylant, Cynthia & McDaniels, Preston. The Storm. 2003. (Lighthouse Family Ser.). (Illus.). 80p. (J). pap. 3.99 (978-0-689-84882-7(X) , Aladdin) Simon & Schuster Children's Publishing.

Sargent, Dave & Sargent, Pat. The Chuck Wagon: Don't Be Stubborn, 10. Lenoir, Jane, illus. 2005. (Colorado Cowboys Ser.: 7). 32p. (J). 7. lib. bdg. 22.60 (978-1-59381-098-6(9)); Vol. 7. pap. 9.95 (978-1-59381-099-3(7)) Ozark Publishing.

—The Colorado Blizzard: Be Determined, 10 vols., Vol. 8. Lenoir, Jane, illus. 2005. (Colorado Cowboys Ser.: 10). 32p. (J). pap. 9.95 (978-1-59381-027-6(X)) Ozark Publishing.

—The Drought: Have Faith, 10. Lenoir, Jane, illus. 2005. (Colorado Cowboys Ser.: 9). 32p. (J). 9. lib. bdg. 22.60 (978-1-59381-102-0(0)); Vol. 9. pap. 9.95 (978-1-59381-103-7(9)) Ozark Publishing.

Sawyer, Walter. The Storm. O'Malley, Kathleen, illus. 1999. (Books for Young Learners). 8p. (J). (gr. k-2). pap. 5.00 (978-1-57274-149-2(X)) Owen, Richard C. Pubs., Inc.

Seeger, Laura Vaccaro. Walter Was Worried. 2005. (Illus.). 40p. (J). 15.95 (978-1-59643-068-6(0)) Roaring Brook Pr.

Shearer, Alex. Professor Sniff & the Lost Spring Breezes. Kenyon, Tony, illus. 1998. 102p. (J). (gr. 3-7). pap. 14.95 (978-0-531-30079-4(X) , Orchard Bks.) Scholastic, Inc.

Simmons, Derek. Flash of Life. 2006. 85p. pap. 14.95 (***978-1-4241-3890-6(6)***) PublishAmerica, Inc.

Skevington, Andrea. The Little Christmas Tree. Hussey, Lorna, illus. 2002. 32p. (J). (gr. k-2). pap. 8.99 (978-0-7459-4588-0(0) , Lion) Lion Hudson plc GBR. *Dist:* Independent Pubs. Group.

Spafford, Suzy. Tales from Duckport: Stick Together! 2003. (Suzy's Zoo Ser.). (Illus.). 40p. (J). (gr. k-3). pap. 3.99 (978-0-439-38357-8(9)) Scholastic, Inc.

—Tales from Duckport: Stick Together! 2003. (gr. k-3). lib. bdg. 11.80 (978-0-613-63568-4(X)) Tandem Library Bks.

Stevens, Carla. Anna, Grandpa, & the Big Storm. Tomes, Margot, illus. 1998. (Puffin Chapters for Readers on the Move Ser.). 64p. (J). (gr. 2-5). pap. 5.99 (978-0-14-130083-2(3) , Puffin) Penguin Group (USA) Inc.

A Stormy Adventure: Facing the Fear of Storms. 2004. (J). 6.99 (978-0-9753870-3-0(0)) Write On!.

A Sudden Storm. 2002. (Illus.). (J). pap. (978-0-7398-5102-9(0)) Steck-Vaughn.

Tekavec, Heather. Storm Is Coming! Spengler, Margaret, illus. 32p. (J). (ps). 2002. 15.99 (978-0-8037-2626-0(0) , Dial); 2004. reprint ed. pap. 6.99 (978-0-14-240070-8(X) , Puffin) Penguin Group (USA) Inc.

Trimble, Marcia. Witchy's Turned-Around House. Cameron, Chad, illus. 1998. 32p. (J). (ps-5). 15.95 (978-1-891577-27-7(1)) Images Pr.

Urale, Makerita. The Magic Seashell. Sakaria, Samuel, illus. 1999. 24p. (J). pap. (978-1-877228-06-3(0)) Steele Roberts Publishing Ltd.

Vaughan, Marcia. Abbie Against the Storm: The True Story of a Young Heroine & a Lighthouse. Farnsworth, Bill, illus. 1999. 30p. (J). (gr. 1-3). 15.95 (978-1-58270-007-6(9)) Beyond Words Publishing, Inc.

Wasserman, Robin. The Stormy Night. del Sur, Duendes, illus. 2003. (Scooby-Doo! Picture Clue Book Ser.: Vol. 16). 32p. (J). pap. 3.99 (978-0-439-44418-7(7)) Scholastic, Inc.

Weinberger, Kimberly. The Stormy Day Rescue. Thompson, Del, illus. 2001. (J). 10.79 (978-0-606-19914-8(4)) Tandem Library Bks.

—Stormy Day Rescue. 2001. (ps-2). lib. bdg. 11.80 (978-0-613-33106-7(0)) Tandem Library Bks.

Weinberger, Kimberly & Bridwell, Norman. The Stormy Day Rescue. 2001. (Clifford, the Big Red Dog Ser.). (Illus.). 32p. (J). (gr. k-2). pap. 3.99 (978-0-439-21360-8(6)) Scholastic, Inc.

White, Nancy. The Magic School Bus Kicks up a Storm: A Book about Weather. Ruiz, Art, illus. 2000. (Magic School Bus Ser.). 32p. (J). (gr. 1-4). pap. 3.50 (978-0-439-10275-9(8)) Scholastic, Inc.

—The Magic School Bus Kicks up a Storm: A Book about Weather. 2000. (gr. k-3). lib. bdg. 11.25 (978-0-613-21949-5(X)) Tandem Library Bks.

Willis, Jeanne. La Tormenta Monstruosa. (Cotton Cloud Ser.). (SPA.). (J). (gr. 1-3). pap. (978-84-480-0180-3(X)) Timun Mas, Editorial S.A. ESP. *Dist:* Lectorum Pubns., Inc.

STORYTELLING

Bicknell, Joanna. Build a Story Book. 2007. (Illus.). 20p. (J). (gr. k-5). pap. (***978-1-84610-426-8(2)***) Make Believe Ideas.

Cranium. Cranium Silly Stories. 2007. (Play It Again Book Ser.). (Illus.). 52p. (J). (gr. 1). 9.99 (***978-0-316-01206-5(8)***) Little, Brown Bks. for Young Readers.

Doyle, Alfreda C. Story Time Literacy Coach: Literacy, Storytelling & Rhyme. unabr. ed. 2005. (Alfreda's Radio Ser.: Vol. 1). (gr. 5-9). spiral bd. 39.95 (978-1-56820-305-8(5)) Story Time Stories That Rhyme.

Dubrovin, Vivian. Storytelling for the Fun of It: A Handbook for Children. Shupe, Bobbie, illus. 2nd rev. ed. 1999. 204p. (J). (gr. 4-6). pap. 19.90 (978-0-9638339-3-8(6)) Storycraft Publishing.

Dubrovin, Vivian & Dubrovin, Barbara. Storytelling Discoveries: Favorite Activities for Young Tellers. Dubrovin, Barbara, illus. 2002. (Illus.). 72p. (J). pap. 17.50 (978-0-9638339-5-2(2)) Storycraft Publishing.

Heurtelou, Maude. Dekouvet. Louissaint, Louis, illus. 1999. Tr. of Discovery. (CRP.). 20p. (J). (gr. k-2). pap. 8.50 (978-1-58432-017-3(6)) Educa Vision.

—Dekouvet: Discovery. 1999. (Big Book Ser.). (CRP & ENG., Illus.). 20p. (J). (gr. k-2). 19.50 (978-1-58432-050-0(8)) Educa Vision.

How Rabbit Caught the Sun: Individual Title Six-Packs. (Story Steps Ser.). (gr. k-2). 32.00 (978-0-7635-9811-2(9)) Rigby Education.

How the Geese Saved Rome: Individual Title Six-Packs. (Story Steps Ser.). (gr. k-2). 32.00 (978-0-7635-9801-3(1)) Rigby Education.

Lingo, Susan L. Collect-n-Tell Bible Stories for Kids: 34 Awesome Bible Stories with Powerful Points from a Few Simple Supplies! Barr, Marilynn G., illus. 2006. 112p. (YA). 15.99 (978-0-7847-1418-8(5) , 02456) Standard Publishing.

Lyon, Carol, illus. Through the Grapevine: World Tales Kids Can Read & Tell. 2001. 128p. (gr. 2-7). 24.95 (978-0-87483-625-7(5)); pap. 14.95 (978-0-87483-624-0(7)) August Hse. Pubs., Inc.

Marsh, Valerie. Storytelling with Shapes & Numbers. 1999. (Illus.). 86p. (J). (ps-1). pap. 15.95 (978-1-57950-024-5(2) , Upstart Bks.) Highsmith Inc.

McKay, Todd. TPR Storytelling Especially for Elementary & Middle School: Student Book for Year 1 English, Vol. 1. Asher, James T. & Porrata, Samuel, eds. Arantowicz, Gerard, illus. 2000. 38p. (J). (gr. 1-9). pap., stu. ed. 12.00 (978-1-56018-017-3(X) , 400) Sky Oaks Productions, Inc.

—TPR Storytelling Especially for Elementary & Middle School Vol. 1: Student Book for Year 1 French. Asher, James T. & Porrata, Samuel, eds. Arantowicz, Gerard, illus. 2000. (FRE & ENG.). 38p. (J). (gr. 1-9). pap., stu. ed. 12.00 (978-1-56018-014-2(5) , 420) Sky Oaks Productions, Inc.

—TPR Storytelling Especially for Elementary & Middle School Vol. 1: Student Book for Year 1 Spanish. Porrata, Samuel & Asher, James T., eds. Arantowicz, Gerard, illus. 2000. (SPA.). 38p. (J). (gr. 1-9). pap., stu. ed. 12.00 (978-1-56018-023-4(4) , 410) Sky Oaks Productions, Inc.

—TPR Storytelling Especially for Elementary & Middle School Vol. 2: Student Book for Year 2 English. Asher, James T. & Porrata, Samuel, eds. Arantowicz, Gerard, illus. 2000. 38p. (J). (gr. 1-9). pap., stu. ed. 12.00 (978-1-56018-018-0(8) , 401) Sky Oaks Productions, Inc.

—TPR Storytelling Especially for Elementary & Middle School Vol. 2: Student Book for Year 2 French. Asher, James T. & Porrata, Samuel, eds. Arantowicz, Gerard, illus. 2000. (FRE & ENG.). 38p. (J). (gr. 1-9). pap., stu. ed. 12.00 (978-1-56018-015-9(3) , 421) Sky Oaks Productions, Inc.

—TPR Storytelling Especially for Elementary & Middle School Vol. 2: Student Book for Year 2 Spanish. Porrata, Samuel & Asher, James T., eds. Arantowicz, Gerard, illus. 2000. (SPA.). 38p. (J). (gr. 1-9). pap., stu. ed. 12.00 (978-1-56018-024-1(2) , 411) Sky Oaks Productions, Inc.

—TPR Storytelling Especially for Elementary & Middle School Vol. 3: Student Book for Year 3 English. Asher, James T. & Porrata, Samuel, eds. Arantowicz, Gerard, illus. 2000. 38p. (J). (gr. 1-9). pap., stu. ed. 12.00 (978-1-56018-019-7(6) , 402) Sky Oaks Productions, Inc.

—TPR Storytelling Especially for Elementary & Middle School Vol. 3: Student Book for Year 3 French. Asher, James T. & Porrata, Samuel, eds. Arantowicz, Gerard, illus. 2000. (FRE & ENG.). 38p. (J). (gr. 1-9). pap., stu. ed. 12.00 (978-1-56018-016-6(1) , 422) Sky Oaks Productions, Inc.

—TPR Storytelling Especially for Elementary & Middle School Vol. 3: Student Book for Year 3 Spanish. Porrata, Samuel & Asher, James T., eds. Arantowicz, Gerard, illus. 2000. (SPA.). 38p. (J). (gr. 1-9). pap., stu. ed. 12.00 (978-1-56018-025-8(0) , 412) Sky Oaks Productions, Inc.

Reid, Rob. Storytime Slam! 15 Lesson Plans for Preschool & Primary Story Programs. 2006. (Illus.). 85p. (J). pap. 16.95 (***978-1-932146-52-3(0)*** , Upstart Bks.) Highsmith Inc.

Roper, Ingrid. Storyteller Journal. Gordon-Lucas, Bonnie, illus. 2002. 128p. (J). (gr. 3 up). pap. 9.99 (978-0-439-39996-8(3) , Tangerine Pr.) Scholastic, Inc.

Set of 7 StoryTellers. (Classic Storytellers Ser.). (Illus.). (gr. 4-8). lib. bdg. (978-1-58415-321-4(0)) Mitchell Lane Pubs., Inc.

Story Elements: Middle School. 2004. 48p. (YA). (gr. 7-8). pap. 6.99 (978-0-7696-3400-5(1) , MH1033) School Specialty Publishing.

A Storyteller's Journey, 6 Pack. (Bookweb Ser.). 32p. (gr. 4 up). 34.00 (978-0-7635-3738-8(1)) Rigby Education.

Storytelling Guide with Cassette. 2000. (Illus.). incl. audio (978-0-525-46549-2(9) , Dutton Juvenile) Penguin Group (USA) Inc.

Tell Me a Story, 6 Packs. (Rigby Infoquest Ser.). 32p. (gr. 4 up). 37.00 (978-0-7578-5740-9(X)) Rigby Education.

The Tug of War: Individual Title Six-Pack. (Story Steps Ser.). (gr. k-2). 23.00 (978-0-7635-9620-0(5)) Rigby Education.

STORYTELLING—COLLECTIONS

DeSpain, Pleasant. Sweet Land of Story: Thirty-Six American Tales to Tell. 2001. (Illus.). 176p. (J). (gr. 3-7). 19.95 (978-0-87483-569-4(0)); pap. 12.95 (978-0-87483-600-4(X)) August Hse. Pubs., Inc.

—Sweet Land of Story: Thirty-Six American Tales to Tell. Bell, Donald-, illus. 2000. 176p. (J). (gr. 3-7). lib. bdg. 22.20 (978-0-613-35886-6(4)) Tandem Library Bks.

Hamilton, Martha, et al. Noodlehead Stories: World Tales Kids Can Read & Tell. 2000. (Illus.). 96p. (J). (gr. 3-7). pap. 14.95 (978-0-87483-585-4(2)) August Hse. Pubs., Inc.

Raines, Shirley C. Easy to Tell Stories with Activities for Young Children. (Tell It Again Ser.). (Illus.). (J). 1999. (978-0-606-21572-5(7)); No. 2. 2000. (978-0-606-21571-8(9)) Tandem Library Bks.

Sierra, Judy. Silly & Sillier: Read Aloud Tales from Around the World. Gorbachev, Valeri, illus. 2002. 96p. (J). (gr. k-3). lib. bdg. 21.99 (978-0-375-90609-1(6) , Knopf Bks. for Young Readers) Random Hse. Children's Bks.

—Silly & Sillier: Read-Aloud Tales from Around the World. Gorbachev, Valeri, illus. 2002. 96p. (J). (gr. k-3). 19.95 (978-0-375-80609-4(1) , Knopf Bks. for Young Readers) Random Hse. Children's Bks.

STORYTELLING—FICTION

Abbott, Jacob. Stories Told to Rollo's Cousin Lucy. 2005. pap. 22.95 (978-1-4179-5651-7(8)) Kessinger Publishing, LLC.

Adams, H. J. The Song of the Blackbirds in the Reeds: In Which Great-Grandpa Nicholas Winslow Applewood Entertains Young Folk with Stories & Fables & Has Some Remarkable Betimes. Adams, Denise, illus. 1998. 168p. (J). lib. bdg. 20.00 (978-0-923687-48-9(3)) Celo Valley Bks.

Adams, W. Royce. Raid on Rairarubia. 2000. (Rairarubia Tales Ser.: Bk. 3). 144p. (J). (gr. 4-7). pap. 10.95 (978-1-882897-56-8(0)) Lost Coast Pr.

—Raid on Rairarubia. 2000. (gr. 3-6). lib. bdg. 19.90 (978-0-613-85833-5(6)) Tandem Library Bks.

—Rairarubia. 1999. (Rairarubia Tales Ser.: Bk. 1). (Illus.). 138p. (J). (gr. 3-7). pap. 10.95 (978-1-882897-36-0(6)) Lost Coast Pr.

—Return to Rairarubia. 2000. (Rairarubia Tales Ser.: Bk. 2). 138p. (J). (gr. 3-7). pap. 10.95 (978-1-882897-44-5(7)) Lost Coast Pr.

—Return to Rairarubia. 2000. (gr. 3-6). lib. bdg. 19.90 (978-0-613-86348-3(8)) Tandem Library Bks.

—Revenge on Rairarubia. 2001. (Rairarubia Tales Ser.: Vol. 4). (Illus.). 134p. (J). (gr. 4-6). pap. 10.95 (978-0-9712206-0-7(3)) Rairarubia Bks.

BAtey, Kathey. Exaggeration Aggravation. 2006. (J). per. 15.00 (978-0-9790017-1-0(4)) Spirited Presentations.

—Exaggeration Aggravation. GEbhard, Andy, illus. 2006. (J). 8.00 (978-0-9790017-0-3(6)) Spirited Presentations.

Beck, Ian. The Secret History of Tom Trueheart. 2007. (Illus.). 352p. (J). (gr. 4-7). 16.99 (978-0-06-115210-8(2)); lib. bdg. 17.89 (978-0-06-115211-5(0)) HarperCollins Pubs.

Blume, Lesley. Cornelia & the Audacious Escapades of the Somerset Sisters. 2006. 272p. (J). (gr. 3-7). 15.95 (978-0-375-83523-0(7) , Knopf Bks. for Young Readers) Random Hse. Children's Bks.

Blume, Lesley M. M. Cornelia & the Audacious Escapades of the Somerset Sisters. 2006. 272p. (J). (gr. 3-7). lib. bdg. 17.99 (978-0-375-93523-7(1) , Knopf Bks. for Young Readers) Random Hse. Children's Bks.

Broyles, Beverly Ashley, illus. Grandmother's Alligator/ Burukenge Wa Nyanya Activity Guide. 2005. (ENG & SWA.). (J). 12.95 (978-0-9703632-7-5(3)) Wakefield Connection, The.

Brutschy, Jennifer. Just One More Story. Smith, Cat Bowman, illus. 2000. (J). (978-0-531-33296-2(9)); lib. bdg. (978-0-531-30296-5(2)) Scholastic, Inc. (Orchard Bks.).

Burford, Lorrimer. A Jamaican Storyteller's Tale. 2005. 197p. 7.99 (978-976-8184-84-9(1)) Penguin Group (USA) Inc.

Byars, Betsy, et al. The SOS File. Howard, Arthur, illus. rev. ed. 2004. 80p. (J). 16.95 (978-0-8050-6888-7(0) , Holt, Henry & Co. Bks. For Young Readers) Holt, Henry & Co.

Byars, Betsy Cromer, et al. The Dog Diaries: Secret Writings of the WOOF Society. Brooks, Erik, illus. 2007. 80p. (J). 15.95 (978-0-8050-7957-9(2)) Holt, Henry & Co.

Byars, Betsy Cromer, et al. Dog Diaries: Secret Writings of the WOOF Society. Brooks, Erik, illus. 2007. 72p. (J). (***978-1-4287-4611-4(0)***) Holt, Henry & Co.

Cahill, Byron. The Legend of Skywoman. 2005. 40.00 (***978-1-4108-4232-9(0)***) Benchmark Education Co.

Catalanotto, Peter. Ivan the Terrier. Catalanotto, Peter, illus. 2007. 32p. (J). (ps-k). 16.99 (978-1-4169-1247-7(9)) Simon & Schuster Children's Publishing.

Cazet, Denys. Grandpa Spanielson's Chicken Pox Stories No. 1: The Octopus. Cazet, Denys, illus. 2005. (I Can Read Bks.). (Illus.). 48p. (J). (ps-3). lib. bdg. 16.89 (978-0-06-051089-3(7)) HarperCollins Pubs.

—Octopus. Cazet, Denys, illus. 2005. (I Can Read Bks.). (Illus.). 48p. (J). (ps-3). 15.99 (978-0-06-051088-6(9)) HarperCollins Pubs.

—Octopus No. 1: Grandpa Spanielson's Chicken Pox Stories. Cazet, Denys, illus. 2006. (I Can Read Bks.). 48p. (J). pap. 3.99 (978-0-06-051092-3(7) , Harper Trophy) HarperCollins Pubs.

—Shrunken Head. Cazet, Denys, illus. 2008. (I Can Read Bks.: No. 3). 48p. (J). pap. 3.99 (***978-0-06-073015-4(3)*** , Harper Trophy) HarperCollins Pubs.

—Shrunken Head No. 3: Grandpa Spanielson's Chicken Pox Stories. Cazet, Denys, illus. 2007. (I Can Read Bks.). (Illus.). 48p. (J). (gr. k-2). 15.99 (978-0-06-073013-0(7)); lib. bdg. 16.89 (978-0-06-073014-7(5)) HarperCollins Pubs.

—Snout for Chocolate: Grandpa Spanielson's Chicken Pox Stories. Cazet, Denys, illus. 2007. (I Can Read Bks.). 48p. (J). pap. 3.99 (978-0-06-051095-4(1) , Harper Trophy) HarperCollins Pubs.

—Snout for Chocolate No. 2: Grandpa Spanielson's Chicken Pox Stories. Cazet, Denys, illus. 2006. (I Can Read Bks.). (Illus.). 48p. (J). 15.99 (978-0-06-051093-0(5)); lib. bdg. 16.89 (978-0-06-051094-7(3)) HarperCollins Pubs.

Connolly, Brian A. Hawk. 2007. 156p. 20.95 (***978-1-60264-030-6(0)***); 160p. per. 13.95 (***978-1-60264-029-0(7)***) Virtualbookworm.com Publishing, Inc.

Cornwell, Nikki. Christophe's Story. Littlewood, Karin, illus. 2007. 96p. (J). (gr. 3 up). 14.95 (***978-1-84507-765-5(2)***) Lincoln, Frances Ltd. GBR. *Dist:* Perseus Distribution.

Dann, Penny, illus. Read Me a Story, Please. 1998. 256p. (J). (978-1-85881-548-0(7)) Orion Children's Bks.

DiSalvo-Ryan, DyAnne. The Sloppy Copy Slipup. 2005. (Illus.). 128p. (J). 16.95 (978-0-8234-1947-0(9)) Holiday Hse., Inc.

Dokey, Cameron. The Storyteller's Daughter: A Retelling of the Arabian Nights. 2007. (Once upon a Time Ser.). 240p. (YA). pap. 5.99 (978-1-4169-3776-0(5) , Simon Pulse) Simon & Schuster Children's Publishing.

Donaldson, Julia. The Fish Who Cried Wolf. Scheffler, Axel, illus. 2008. (J). pap. ***978-0-545-03454-8(X));*** 40p. 15.99 ***(978-0-439-92825-0(7))*** Scholastic, Inc. (Levine, Arthur A. Bks.).

Downey, Lynn. Matilda's Humdinger. Bowers, Tim, illus. 2006. 40p. (J). (gr. k-4). 15.95 (978-0-375-82403-6(0)); lib. bdg. 17.99 (978-0-375-92403-3(5)) Random Hse. Children's Bks. (Knopf Bks. for Young Readers).

Foreman, Mark. Grandpa Jack's Tattoo Tales. 2007. (Illus.). 40p. (J). (ps-3). 16.00 (978-0-374-32768-2(8)) Farrar, Straus & Giroux.

Gavrilovskiy, Olga, illus. Elf Night: A Christmas Story. 2006. 52p. (J). 16.95 ***(*978-0-9788085-0-1(9))*** Tetoca Pr.

Gilmore, Rachna. The Sower of Tales. 348p. 2007. (YA). (gr. 6-8). pap. ***(*978-1-55041-590-2(5));*** 2005. (J). (978-1-55041-945-0(5)) Fitzhenry & Whiteside, Ltd.

Gutsche, Brigitte. The Intruder. 2006. (J). pap. ***(*978-0-88092-743-7(7))*** Royal Fireworks Publishing Co.

Hadley, Caroline. Woodside or Look Listen & Learn. 2007. pap. 87.99 ***(*978-1-4280-5242-0(9))*** IndyPublish.com.

—Woodside; or, Look, Listen & Learn. 2007. (ENG., Illus.). 80p. per. ***(*978-1-4065-1557-2(4))*** Dodo Pr.

Hanson, Mary Elizabeth. How to Save Your Tail: If You Are a Rat Nabbed by Cats Who Really Like Stories about Magic Spoons, Wolves with Snout-Warts, Big Hairy Chimney Trolls—And Cookies Too. Hendrix, John, illus. 2007. 112p. (J). (gr. 1-5). 15.99 (978-0-375-83755-5(8) , Schwartz & Wade Bks.) Random Hse. Children's Bks.

—How to Save Your Tail: If You Are a Rat Nabbed by Cats Who Really Like Stories about Magic Spoons, Wolves with Snout-Warts, Big Hairy Chimney Trolls—and Cookies Too. 2007. (Illus.). 112p. (J). (gr. 1-5). lib. bdg. 18.99 (978-0-375-93755-2(2) , Schwartz & Wade Bks.) Random Hse. Children's Bks.

Hanson, Regina. A Season for Mangoes. Velasquez, Eric, illus. 2005. 40p. (J). (gr. k-3). 15.00 (978-0-618-15972-7(X) , Clarion Bks.) Houghton Mifflin Co. Trade & Reference Div.

Harley Bill. Sarahs Story. Aldridge Eve, illus. 2006. 32p. (J). 6.95 (978-1-58246-178-6(3) , Tricycle Pr.) Ten Speed Pr.

Hartnett, Sonya. The Silver Donkey. Powers, Don, illus. 272p. (J). (gr. 5). 2007. pap. 7.99 ***(*978-0-7636-3681-4(9));*** 2006. 15.99 (978-0-7636-2937-3(5)) Candlewick Pr.

—The Silver Donkey. Spudvilas, Anne, illus. 2004. viii, 193p. (J). (978-0-670-04240-1(4) , Viking Adult) Penguin Group (USA) Inc.

Haselhurst, Maureen. The Tickety Tale Teller. 2007. (J). lib. bdg. 16.95 ***(*978-1-59566-335-1(5))*** QEB Publishing Inc.

Hughes, V. I. Aziz the Story Teller. Czernecki, Stefan, illus. 2006. 29p. (J). (gr. k-4). reprint ed. 17.00 (978-1-4223-5298-4(6)) DIANE Publishing Co.

Hughes, Vi. Aziz the Story Teller. Czernecki, Stefan, illus. 2002. 32p. (J). (ps-3). 15.95 (978-1-56656-456-4(5) , Crocodile Bks.) Interlink Publishing Group, Inc.

Jinkins, Jim. Pinky Dinky Doo: Pinky Stinky Doo. 2006. (Illus.). 48p. (J). (gr. 1-3). pap. 3.99 (978-0-375-83511-7(3)); lib. bdg. 11.99 (978-0-375-93511-4(8)) Random Hse. Children's Bks. (Random Hse. Bks. for Young Readers).

—Pinky Dinky Doo: Polka Dot Pox. 2004. (Illus.). 48p. (J). (gr. 1-3). pap. 3.99 (978-0-375-82713-6(7) , Random Hse. Bks. for Young Readers) Random Hse. Children's Bks.

—Pinky Dinky Doo: Think Pink! 2006. (Step into Reading Ser.). (Illus.). 48p. (J). (gr. 1-3). pap. 3.99 (978-0-375-83573-5(3)); lib. bdg. 11.99 (978-0-375-93573-2(8)) Random Hse. Children's Bks. (Random Hse. Bks. for Young Readers).

—Pinky Dinky Doo: Where Are My Shoes? 2004. (Illus.). 48p. (J). (gr. 1-3). pap. 3.99 (978-0-375-82712-9(9) , Random Hse. Bks. for Young Readers) Random Hse. Children's Bks.

—Pinky Dinky Doo: Shrinky Pinky! 2005. (Step into Reading Ser.). (Illus.). 48p. (J). (gr. 1-3). pap. 3.99 (978-0-375-83235-2(1) , Random Hse. Bks. for Young Readers) Random Hse. Children's Bks.

Jones, Katina. Cool School Story: Little Lucy & Friends. Ottinger, Jon, illus. Zaidan, Rick, photos by. 2001. (Little Lucy & Friends Ser.). 24p. (J). (ps-3). 9.99 (978-1-57151-700-5(6)) Playhouse Publishing.

Kemp, Moira. Tell Me a Story, Daddy. 2006. (Illus.). 32p. (J). pap. (978-0-340-87560-5(7) , Hodder Children's Books) Hodder Children's Division.

Kurtz, Jane. In the Small, Small Night. Isadora, Rachel, illus. 2005. (Amistad Ser.). 32p. (J). 16.99 (978-0-06-623814-2(5)); lib. bdg. 17.89 (978-0-06-623813-5(7)) HarperCollins Pubs.

Lobel, Arnold. Historias de Ratones. 2003. (SPA.). 64p. (978-84-95123-95-4(9) , KA7695) Kalandraka Editora, S.L. ESP. *Dist:* Lectorum Pubns., Inc.

Lowry, Lois. Gooney Bird Greene. Thomas, Middy Chilman, illus. 2002. 96p. (J). (gr. 3-5). tchr. ed. 15.00 (978-0-618-23848-4(4) , Walter Lorraine) Houghton Mifflin Co. Trade & Reference Div.

—Gooney Bird Greene. 2004. (Illus.). 96p. (J). (gr. 2-5). reprint ed. pap. 5.50 (978-0-440-41960-0(3) , Yearling) Random Hse. Children's Bks.

—Gooney Bird Greene. 2004. (gr. 3-6). lib. bdg. 13.55 (978-0-613-82980-9(8)) Tandem Library Bks.

Lyon, George Ella. My Friend, the Starfinder. Gammell, Stephen, illus. 2008. 40p. (J). 16.99 ***(*978-1-4169-2738-9(7))*** Simon & Schuster Children's Publishing.

Maguire, Gregory. What-the-Dickens: The Story of a Rogue Tooth Fairy. 2007. (Illus.). 304p. (J). (gr. 5-8). 15.99 ***(*978-0-7636-2961-8(8))*** Candlewick Pr.

Manley, Craig. The Rammarg Files. 2006. (J). lib. bdg. ***(*978-0-88092-742-0(9))*** Royal Fireworks Publishing Co.

Martel, Yann. Life of Pi: A Novel. 2003. (gr. 7-12). lib. bdg. 23.45 (978-0-613-59907-8(1)) Tandem Library Bks.

Martin, Rafe. Storytelling Princess. 2003. (gr. 3-6). lib. bdg. 15.30 (978-0-613-67306-8(9)) Tandem Library Bks.

McCaffrey, Laura Williams. Water Shaper. 2006. 224p. (J). (gr. 5-9). 16.00 (978-0-618-61489-9(3) , Clarion Bks.) Houghton Mifflin Co. Trade & Reference Div.

Mitton, Tony. Tale of Tales. Bailey, Peter, illus. 2004. 112p. (J). (gr. k-7). 15.95 (978-0-385-75016-5(1) , Fickling, David Bks.) Random Hse. Children's Bks.

Montgomery, L. M. Midnight Madness & Mayhem. Griffin, Jim, illus. 2005. (Story Girl Ser.). 112p. (J). (gr. 3-7). pap. 4.99 (978-0-310-70861-2(3)) Zonderkidz.

—Summer Shenanigans, Bk. 3. 2004. (Story Girl Ser.: Bk. 3). (Illus.). 112p. (J). pap. 4.99 (978-0-310-70600-7(9)) Zonderkidz.

—The Winds of Change. 2005. (Story Girl#8482; Ser.). (Illus.). 112p. (J). (gr. 3-7). pap. 4.99 (978-0-310-70862-9(1)) Zonderkidz.

Morpurgo, Michael. I Believe in Unicorns. Blythe, Gary, illus. 2006. 80p. (J). (gr. 1-4). 12.99 (978-0-7636-3050-8(0)) Candlewick Pr.

Muth, Jon J. Zen Shorts. Muth, Jon J., illus. 2005. (Illus.). 40p. (J). pap. 16.95 (978-0-439-33911-7(1)) Scholastic, Inc.

Muth, Jon J. Zen Shorts (Collector's Edition) 2008. 40p. (J). 25.00 ***(*978-0-545-04087-7(6)*** , Scholastic) Scholastic, Inc.

Nash, Scott. Tuff Fluff: The Case of Duckie's Missing Brain. Nash, Scott, illus. 2004. (Illus.). (J). 101.94 (978-0-7636-2503-0(5)) Candlewick Pr.

—Tuff Fluff: The Case of Duckie's Missing Brain. 2004. (Illus.). 40p. (J). (gr. 1-4). 16.99 (978-0-7636-1882-7(9)) Candlewick Pr.

Nolan, Janet. The St. Patrick's Day Shillelagh. Stahl, Ben, illus. 2002. 32p. (J). (gr. 2-5). 16.95 (978-0-8075-7344-0(2)) Whitman, Albert & Co.

—The St. Patrick's Day Shillelagh. Stahl, Ben F., illus. 2002. 32p. (J). (gr. 2-5). pap. 6.95 (978-0-8075-7345-7(0)) Whitman, Albert & Co.

Priestley, Chris. Uncle Montague's Tales of Terror. Roberts, David, illus. 2007. 192p. (J). (gr. 3-7). 12.95 ***(*978-1-59990-118-3(8)*** , Bloomsbury Children) Bloomsbury Publishing.

Prose, Francine. Leopold: The Liar of Leipzig. Aviram, Einav, illus. 2005. 32p. (J). 15.99 (978-0-06-008075-4(2) , Cotler, Joanna Books) HarperCollins Pubs.

Robberecht, Thierry. Sam Tells Stories. Goossens, Philippe, illus. 2007. 32p. (J). (gr. k-3). 12.00 (978-0-618-73280-7(2) , Clarion Bks.) Houghton Mifflin Co. Trade & Reference Div.

Rushdie, Salman. Haroun & the Sea of Stories. 1999. 96p. 13.00 (978-0-571-19693-7(4)) Faber & Faber, Inc.

Say, Allen. Kamishibai Man. 2005. (Illus.). 32p. (J). (gr. k-3). 17.00 (978-0-618-47954-2(6) , Walter Lorraine) Houghton Mifflin Co. Trade & Reference Div.

Schaefer, Carole Lexa. The Biggest Soap. Dressen-McQueen, Stacey, illus. 2004. 32p. (J). 16.00 (978-0-374-30690-8(7) , Farrar, Straus & Giroux (BYR)) Farrar, Straus & Giroux.

Schmidt, Gary. Mara's Stories: Glimmers in the Darkness. 2008. 128p. (J). pap. 6.99 ***(*978-0-312-37388-7(0))*** Square Fish.

Slate, Joseph. Story Time for Little Porcupine. Rogers, Jacqueline, illus. 2000. 32p. (J). (gr. k-3). 15.95 (978-0-7614-5073-3(4) , Cavendish Children's Bks.) Cavendish, Marshall Corp.

Spinner, Stephanie. It's a Miracle! A Hanukkah Storybook. 2007. (Illus.). 40p. (J). (ps-3). 6.99 ***(*978-1-4169-5001-1(X)*** , Aladdin) Simon & Schuster Children's Publishing.

Stewart, Paul & Riddell, Chris. Hugo Pepper. 2007. (Far-Flung Adventures Ser.). (Illus.). 272p. (J). (gr. 3-7). 14.99 (978-0-385-75092-9(7)); lib. bdg. 16.99 (978-0-385-75093-6(5)) Random Hse. Children's Bks. (Fickling, David Bks.).

Strong, Jeremy. Don't Go in the Cellar. Anderson, Scoular, illus. 2006. 72;88p. (J). (gr. 2-3). lib. bdg. 21.26 (978-1-59889-002-0(6)) Stone Arch Bks.

Tate, Nikki. Cave of Departure. 2002. (Illus.). 239p. (J). (gr. 5-9). pap. 6.95 (978-1-55039-119-0(4)) Sono Nis Pr. CAN. *Dist:* Orca Bk. Pubs. USA.

—Cave of Departure. 2002. (gr. 5-8). lib. bdg. 15.25 (978-0-613-78607-2(6)) Tandem Library Bks.

Theroux, Phyllis. Serefina under the Circumstances. Priceman, Marjorie, illus. 2004. 30p. (J). (gr. k-4). reprint ed. (978-0-7567-7756-2(9)) DIANE Publishing Co.

—Serefina under the Circumstances. 2000. (J). 16.00 (978-0-689-80450-2(4) , Simon & Schuster Children's Publishing) Simon & Schuster Children's Publishing.

Trimble, Marcia. Jonah's Riddle. Ulrich, George, illus. 2000. 32p. (J). (ps-3). 15.95 (978-1-891577-32-1(8)) Images Pr.

Walde, Christine. The Candy Darlings. 2006. 320p. (YA). (gr. 10). pap. 8.99 (978-0-618-58969-2(4) , Graphia) Houghton Mifflin Co. Trade & Reference Div.

Watts, Jeri Hanel. Keepers. 2000. (J). (978-0-606-19832-5(6)) Tandem Library Bks.

Whitethorne, Baje, Sr. Father's Boots: Azhe'e bikenidoots'osii. Marvin, Yellowhair & Jerrold, Johnson, eds. Darlene, Redhair, tr. Whitethorne, Baje, Sr., illus. 2001. (ENG & NAV., Illus.). 32p. (gr. 1-6). 17.95 (978-1-893354-29-6(6)) Salina Bookshelf.

Wolfson, Jill. What I Call Life. rev. ed. 2005. (Illus.). 272p. (J). (ps-7). 16.95 (978-0-8050-7669-1(7)) Holt, Henry & Co.

—What I Call Life. 2008. 288p. (J). pap. 6.99 ***(*978-0-312-37752-6(5))*** Square Fish.

Wooding, Chris. Poison. 288p. (J). 2006. pap. 7.99 (978-0-439-75571-9(9) , Scholastic Paperbacks); 2005. (gr. 7 up). pap. 16.99 (978-0-439-75570-2(0) , Orchard Bks.) Scholastic, Inc.

Zusak, Markus. The Book Thief. (YA). (gr. 7 up). 2007. 576p. pap. 11.99 ***(*978-0-375-84220-7(9));*** 2006. 560p. 16.95 (978-0-375-83100-3(2)); 2006. 560p. lib. bdg. 18.99 (978-0-375-93100-0(7)) Random Hse. Children's Bks. (Knopf Bks. for Young Readers).

STOVES—FICTION

Fussell, Bonnie. More Than a Stove. Sadler, Dale, illus. l.t. ed. 2004. 32p. (J). pap. 7.99 (978-0-615-12702-6(9)) Blackberry Pubs.

STOWE, HARRIET BEECHER, 1811-1896

Adler, David A. A Picture Book of Harriet Beecher Stowe. Bootman, Colin, illus. 2003. 32p. (J). (gr. k-3). 6.95 (978-0-8234-1878-7(2)); tchr. ed. 16.95 (978-0-8234-1646-2(1)) Holiday Hse., Inc.

Fritz, Jean. Harriet Beecher Stowe & the Beecher Preachers. 1998. (Unforgettable Americans Ser.). 144p. (J). (gr. 3-7). pap. 5.99 (978-0-698-11660-3(7) , Putnam Juvenile) Penguin Group (USA) Inc.

Gelletly, LeeAnne. Harriet Beecher Stowe. 2001. (gr. 5-8). lib. bdg. 17.60 (978-0-613-32632-2(6)) Tandem Library Bks.

—Harriet Beecher Stowe: Author of Uncle Tom's Cabin. (Famous Figures of the Civil War Era Ser.). (Illus.). 80p. (J). (gr. 4-7). 2001. 25.00 (978-0-7910-6009-4(8)); 2000. pap. 25.00 (978-0-7910-6147-3(7)) Facts On File, Inc. (Chelsea Hse.).

Griskey, Michele. Harriet Beecher Stowe. 2005. (Classic Storytellers Ser.). (Illus.). 48p. (J). lib. bdg. 29.95 (978-1-58415-375-7(X)) Mitchell Lane Pubs., Inc.

Haugen, Brenda. Harriet Beecher Stowe: Author & Advocate. 2004. (Signature Lives Ser.). (Illus.). 112p. (J). 30.60 (978-0-7565-0822-7(3) , 1240140) Compass Point Bks.

Hill, Mary. Harriet Beecher Stowe. 2003. (Welcome Book Ser.). (Illus.). 24p. (J). 18.00 (978-0-516-25865-2(6) , Children's Pr.) Scholastic Library Publishing.

Hougen, Brenda. Harriet Beecher Stowe: Author & Advocate. 2005. (Signature Lives Ser.). (YA). (978-0-7565-0872-2(X)) Compass Point Bks.

Randolph, Ryan P. Harriet Beecher Stowe: Author & Abolitionist. 2005. (Library of American Lives & Times). (Illus.). 112p. (J). (gr. 4-8). lib. bdg. 31.95 (978-0-8239-6623-3(2)) Rosen Publishing Group, Inc., The.

Tackach, James. Uncle Tom's Cabin: Indictment of Slavery. 2000. (Words That Changed History Ser.). (Illus.). 128p. (YA). (gr. 4-12). lib. bdg. 27.45 (978-1-56006-591-3(5) , LML00902-177946, Lucent Bks.) Thomson Gale.

STRATEGIC MATERIALS

see Materials

STRATIGRAPHIC GEOLOGY

see Geology, Stratigraphic

STRATOSPHERE

Burning up: Losing Our Ozone Layer: Individual Title Six-Packs. (On Deck Ser.: Vol. 2). 24p. (gr. 4-5). 35.00 (978-0-7578-5829-1(5)) Rigby Education.

Morgan, Sally. Ozone Hole. 2007. (Illus.). 32p. (J). ***(*978-1-59771-068-8(7))*** Sea-To-Sea Pubns.

STRAVINSKY, IGOR, 1882-1971

Schubert, Leda. Ballet of the Elephants. Parker, Robert Andrew, illus. 2006. 34p. (J). 17.95 (978-1-59643-075-4(3)) Roaring Brook Pr.

Vernon, Roland. Stravinsky: Introducing. 2000. (Introducing Composers Ser.). (Illus.). 32p. (J). (gr. 4-7). 21.95 (978-0-7910-6042-1(X) , Chelsea Hse.) Facts On File, Inc.

Whiting, Jim. The Life & Times of Igor Stravinsky. 2004. (Masters of Music Ser.). (Illus.). 48p. (gr. 4-8). lib. bdg. 20.95 (978-1-58415-277-4(X)) Mitchell Lane Pubs., Inc.

STRAWBERRY SHORTCAKE (FICTITIOUS CHARACTER)—FICTION

Bryant, Megan E. The Berry Big Storm. S. I. Artists Staff & Querol, Marga, illus. 2003. (All Aboard Reading Station Stop Ser.). 32p. (J). (ps-2). pap. 3.99 (978-0-448-43135-2(1) , Grosset & Dunlap) Penguin Group (USA) Inc.

—Strawberry Shortcake at the Beach. 2003. (Strawberry Shortcake Ser.). (Illus.). 32p. (J). (ps-2). mass mkt. 3.99 (978-0-448-43187-1(4) , Grosset & Dunlap) Penguin Group (USA) Inc.

—Strawberry Shortcake's Filly Friends: All Aboard Reading Station Stop 1. 2004. (Strawberry Shortcake Ser.: 1). (Illus.). 32p. (J). (ps-2). mass mkt. 3.99 (978-0-448-43574-9(8) , Grosset & Dunlap) Penguin Group (USA) Inc.

—Strawberry Shortcake's Show-and-Tell Surprise: All Aboard Reading Station Stop 1. Neely, Scott, illus. 2005. (All Aboard Reading Ser.). 32p. (J). (ps-2). pap. 3.99 (978-0-448-43848-1(8) , Grosset & Dunlap) Penguin Group (USA) Inc.

—Strawberry Shortcake's World of Friends: 4 Scratch & Sniff Postcards & over 25 Stickers! Workman, Lisa, illus. 2006. (Strawberry Shortcake Ser.). 32p. (J). (ps-2). pap. 4.99 (978-0-448-44101-6(2) , Grosset & Dunlap) Penguin Group (USA) Inc.

Bryant, Megan E., et al. Strawberry Shortcake Storybook Treasury. Durk, Jim et al, illus. 2005. (Strawberry Shortcake Ser.). 192p. (J). (ps-2). 10.99 (978-0-448-44303-4(1) , Grosset & Dunlap) Penguin Group (USA) Inc.

Ciminera, Siobhan. Strawberry Shortcake Sleeps Over. 2004. (Strawberry Shortcake Ser.). (Illus.). 24p. (J). (ps-2). pap. 4.99 (978-0-448-43516-9(0) , Grosset & Dunlap) Penguin Group (USA) Inc.

Curry, Kelli. Strawberry Shortcake & the Butterfly Garden. 2005. (All Aboard Reading Ser.). (Illus.). 32p. (J). (ps-2). mass mkt. 3.99 (978-0-448-43643-2(4) , Grosset & Dunlap) Penguin Group (USA) Inc.

—Strawberry Shortcake & the Butterfly Garden. Artful Doodlers Limited Staff, illus. 2005. 31p. (J). (ps-ps). lib. bdg. 10.79 (978-0-606-33096-1(8)) Tandem Library Bks.

Dalmatian Press Staff. Strawberry Shortcake: Halloween Dress Up. 2005. (Illus.). 48p. (J). pap. 2.99 (978-1-4037-1489-3(4)) Dalmatian Pr.

Dalmatian Press Staff, ed. Strawberry Shortcake: Dream & Believe (movie tie In) 48p. 2.99 (978-1-4037-2397-0(4)) Dalmatian Pr.

—Strawberry Shortcake: Life's Berry Hoppin' (movie tie In) 48p. 2.99 (978-1-4037-2396-3(6)) Dalmatian Pr.

Glassman, Jackie. The Berry Best Friends' Picnic: Strawberry Shortcake. S. I. Artists Staff et al, illus. 2003. (All Aboard Reading Station Stop Ser.). 32p. (J). (ps-2). pap. 3.99 (978-0-448-43134-5(3) , Grosset & Dunlap) Penguin Group (USA) Inc.

Mason, Eva. Halloween Play. Huxtable, John, illus. 2005. (Strawberry Shortcake Ser.). 32p. (J). (ps-2). pap. 3.99 (978-0-448-43910-5(7) , Grosset & Dunlap) Penguin Group (USA) Inc.

S. I. Artists Staff, illus. Strawberry Shortcake's Ballet Recital: Sticker Stories. 2005. (Strawberry Shortcake Ser.). 16p. (J). (ps-1). pap. 4.99 (978-0-448-43573-2(X) , Grosset & Dunlap) Penguin Group (USA) Inc.

Sander, Sonia. Strawberry Shortcake's Seaberry Mystery. Yee, Josie & Durk, Jim, illus. 2005. (Strawberry Shortcake Ser.). 32p. (J). (ps-2). mass mkt. 3.99 (978-0-448-43639-5(6) , Grosset & Dunlap) Penguin Group (USA) Inc.

Sollinger, Emily. Strawberry Shortcake Goes to School. S. I. Artists Staff, illus. 2003. (Strawberry Shortcake Ser.). 24p. (J). (ps-2). mass mkt. 4.99 (978-0-448-43188-8(2) , Grosset & Dunlap) Penguin Group (USA) Inc.

Stephens, Monique. Berry Merry Christmas. Thomas, Laura & Ungrey, Tom, illus. 2003. (Strawberry Shortcake Ser.). 32p. (J). (gr. k-1). 9.99 (978-0-448-43200-7(5) , Grosset & Dunlap) Penguin Group (USA) Inc.

Stephens, Monique Z. The Berrylicious Bake-off: A Scratch-and-Sniff Story. S. I. Artists Staff, illus. 2003. (Strawberry Shortcake Ser.). 16p. (J). (ps-2). mass mkt. 4.99 (978-0-448-43186-4(6) , Grosset & Dunlap) Penguin Group (USA) Inc.

—Spring for Strawberry Shortcake. Yee, Josie, tr. Yee, Josie, illus. 2004. (Strawberry Shortcake Ser.). 32p. (J). (ps-2). mass mkt. 3.99 (978-0-448-43373-8(7) , Grosset & Dunlap) Penguin Group (USA) Inc.

—Spring for Strawberry Shortcake. 2004. (gr. k-3). lib. bdg. 11.25 (978-0-613-72570-5(0)) Tandem Library Bks.

—Strawberry Shortcake & the Friendship Party. Bracken, Carolyn, illus. 2003. (Strawberry Shortcake Ser.). 24p. (J). (ps-3). mass mkt. 4.99 (978-0-448-43222-9(6) , Grosset & Dunlap) Penguin Group (USA) Inc.

Strawberry Shortcake Activity Book Collection. 2005. (J). (978-1-59487-137-5(X)) Artist Studios, Ltd.

Strawberry Shortcake Berry Loveable Diary. 2005. 7.95 (978-1-59487-083-5(7)) Artist Studios, Ltd.

Unknown. Strawberry Shortcake's Country Fair Fun. 2008. (Strawberry Shortcake Ser.). 32p. (J). (ps-1). pap. 5.99 ***(*978-0-448-44861-9(0)*** , Grosset & Dunlap) Penguin Group (USA) Inc.

Weber, Lou. Strawberry Shortcake Little Music Note. 12p. 9.98 (978-1-4127-6209-0(X) , PIL Kids) Publications International, Ltd.

Workman, Lisa, illus. Meet Strawberry Shortcake. 2003. (Strawberry Shortcake Ser.). 32p. (J). (ps-2). mass mkt. 3.99 (978-0-448-43132-1(7) , Grosset & Dunlap) Penguin Group (USA) Inc.

STREAMLINING

see Aerodynamics

STREET TRAFFIC

see Traffic Regulations

STREETS

see also Roads

Our Street: Big Book: Level D. Group 1. (Sunshinetm Ser.). 8p. 20.95 (978-0-7802-5732-0(4)) Wright Group, The.

Riggs, Sandy. Safe Streets. 2006. (Reader's Clubhouse Set B Ser.). (Illus.). 24p. (J). pap. 3.99 (978-0-7641-3300-8(4)) Barron's Educational Series, Inc.

STRINGED INSTRUMENTS

see also names of stringed instruments, e.g. Guitar; etc.

Dearling, Robert. String Instruments. 2000. (Encyclopedia of Musical Instruments Ser.). (Illus.). 48p. (J). (gr. 4-7). 22.95 (978-0-7910-6092-6(6) , Chelsea Hse.) Facts On File, Inc.

Dick, William & Scott, Laurie. Mastery for Strings, 3 vols. 2004. 109p. spiral bd. 15.95 (978-0-9753919-0-7(9)) Mastery For Strings Pubns.

Harcourt School Publishers Staff. Ancient Stringed Instruments Advanced Level. 3rd ed. 2002. (Trophies Reading Program Ser.). (Illus.). pap. 5.10 (978-0-15-323462-0(8)) Harcourt Schl. Pubs.

—Strings Around the World On Level. 3rd ed. 2002. (Trophies Reading Program Ser.). (Illus.). pap. 5.10 (978-0-15-323343-2(5)) Harcourt Schl. Pubs.

S

Hunka, Alison & Bunting, Philippa. Playing the Violin & Stringed Instruments. 2004. (Young Musician Ser.). (J). lib. bdg. (978-1-932799-61-3(3)) Stargazer Bks.

Knight, M. J. Stringed Instruments. 2005. (Musical Instruments of the World Ser.). (Illus.). 32p. (J). (gr. 3-7). lib. bdg. 27.10 (978-1-58340-414-0(7)) Smart Apple Media.

Kreutzer, Rudolph. Forty-Two Studies for Violin. Singer, Edmund, ed. (Carl Fischer Music Library: No. 120). 73p. (J). pap. 10.95 (978-0-8258-0025-2(0)) Fischer, Carl LLC.

Lynch, Wendy. Strings. 2001. (Musical Instruments Ser.). (Illus.). 32p. (J). (gr. k-2). lib. bdg. 21.36 (978-1-58810-236-2(X)) Heinemann Library.

Smith, Erica. Making Music with Stringed Instruments. 2002. (Reading Room Collection). (Illus.). 24p. (J). lib. bdg. 18.75 (978-0-8239-3740-0(2)) Rosen Publishing Group, Inc., The.

Stevens, Kathryn. Cellos. 2002. (Music Makers Ser.). (Illus.). 24p. (J). (gr. 1-5). 22.79 (978-1-56766-043-2(6)) Child's World, Inc.

Taylor, Michael. Pull the Other One Bk. 1: String Games & Stories. 2000. (Illus.). 128p. (gr. k-4). pap. 16.95 (978-1-869890-49-0(3)) Hawthorn Pr. GBR. *Dist:* Steiner-Books, Inc.

Thomas, Roger. Strings. 2001. (Soundbites Ser.). (Illus.). 32p. (YA). (gr. 6-8). lib. bdg. 22.79 (978-1-58810-266-9(1)) Heinemann Library.

Thomson, Ryan J. Banjo Tab Book: 19 Clawhammer Tabs from the Great Bay Stomp CD. 1999. (Illus.). 52p. (YA). spiral bd. 12.95 (978-0-931877-29-2(6)) Captain Fiddle Pubns.

Turner, Barrie Carson. Strings. 1998. (Musical Instruments of the World Ser.). (Illus.). 32p. (J). (gr. 1-5). lib. bdg. 16.95 (978-1-887068-47-5(3)) Smart Apple Media.

Von Wasielewski, Wilhelm J. The Violoncello & Its History. 2001. 225p. (YA). reprint ed. 98.00 (978-0-7222-6026-5(1)) Library Reprints, Inc.

STRINGED INSTRUMENTS—FICTION

Brimner, Larry Dane. Nana's Fiddle. Miller, Susan, illus. 2002. (Rookie Reader Ser.). 32p. (J). (gr. 1-2). 19.50 (978-0-516-22373-5(9), Children's Pr.) Scholastic Library Publishing.

—Nana's Fiddle. 2002. (gr. k-3). lib. bdg. 12.95 (978-0-613-59521-6(1)) Tandem Library Bks.

STRUCTURAL BOTANY

see Plant Anatomy

STRUCTURAL DRAFTING

see Mechanical Drawing

STUART, JEB, 1833-1864

Greene, Meg. Jeb Stuart: Confederate General. 2001. (Famous Figures of the Civil War Era Ser.). (Illus.). 80p. (J). (gr. 5 up). pap. 25.00 (978-0-7910-6415-3(8)); 25.00 (978-0-7910-6414-6(X)) Facts On File, Inc. (Chelsea Hse.).

Marsh, Carole. J. E. B. Stuart. 2002. (One Thousand Readers Ser.). (Illus.). 12p. (J). (gr. k-4). 2.95 (978-0-635-01502-0(1), 15021) Gallopade International.

—The Virginia Reader: J. E. B. Stuart. 2001. (Virginia Experience! Ser.). (Illus.). 12p. (J). (gr. k-5). pap. 2.95 (978-0-635-00371-3(6)) Gallopade International.

McLeese, Don. Jeb Stuart. 2006. (Civil War Military Leaders Ser.). (Illus.). 32p. (gr. 3-6). 19.95 (978-1-59515-479-8(5)) Rourke Publishing, LLC.

Mcleese, Don. Jeb Stuart. 2005. 32p. pap. 6.45 (978-1-59515-793-5(X)) Rourke Publishing, LLC.

Pflueger, Lynda. Jeb Stuart: Confederate Cavalry General. 1998. (Historical American Biographies Ser.). (Illus.). 128p. (YA). (gr. 6-12). lib. bdg. 20.95 (978-0-7660-1013-0(9)) Enslow Pubs., Inc.

STUDENT ACTIVITIES

see also College and School Journalism; School Sports

Aboff, Marcie. The Northern Lights Carry-along Coloring Kit. 2007. (Frosty the Snowman Ser.). (Illus.). 80p. (J). (ps-3). pap. 5.99 (*978-1-4169-3548-3(7)*, Simon Scribbles) Simon & Schuster Children's Publishing.

Actividades Escolares Series, 6 bks, Set. 2003. (Actividades Escolares Ser.). (Illus.). (J). lib. bdg. 103.50 (978-0-8239-6910-4(X), Buenas Letra) Rosen Publishing Group, Inc., The.

Activities & Events. 48p. (978-0-86388-508-2(X), 001-1541) Speechmark Publishing Ltd.

Adams, Lynn. Irish. 1998. (Dover Little Activity Bks.). (Illus.). (J). pap., act. bk. ed. 1.00 (978-0-486-40000-6(X)) Dover Pubns., Inc.

Adventures in Suburbia-Boston. 2nd ed. 2003. (J). per. 19.95 (978-0-9743319-1-0(0)) Kiwi Media Group, Inc.

Amer Ed Pub, ed. More SkillBuilding Act Gr1. 2007. (Skill Building Learning Activities Ser.). 416p. (J). pap. 15.95 (*978-0-7696-8441-3(6)*, American Education Publishing) School Specialty Publishing.

—More SkillBuilding Act GrK. 2007. (Skill Building Learning Activities Ser.). 416p. (J). pap. 15.95 (*978-0-7696-8440-6(8)*, American Education Publishing) School Specialty Publishing.

—More SkillBuilding Act PreK. 2007. (Skill Building Learning Activities Ser.). 416p. (J). pap. 15.95 (*978-0-7696-8439-0(4)*, American Education Publishing) School Specialty Publishing.

—SkillBuilding Activities Gr1. 2007. (Skill Building Learning Activities Ser.). 416p. (J). pap. 15.95 (*978-0-7696-8431-4(9)*, American Education Publishing) School Specialty Publishing.

—SkillBuilding Activities GrK. 2007. (Skill Building Learning Activities Ser.). 416p. (J). pap. 15.95 (*978-0-7696-8430-7(0)*, American Education Publishing) School Specialty Publishing.

—SkillBuilding Activities PreK. 2007. (Skill Building Learning Activities Ser.). 416p. (J). pap. 15.95 (*978-0-7696-8429-1(7)*, American Education Publishing) School Specialty Publishing.

Baker, Yaba. Princess Briana. 2004. (Illus.). 72p. (J). 17.99 (978-1-928889-05-2(0), 262-002) Just Like Me, Inc.

Balaban, Mariah, ed. Mystery Machine. 2006. (Scooby-Doo Ser.). 8p. (J). pap. 5.99 (978-0-439-87443-4(2)) Scholastic, Inc.

Ball, Liz, illus. A Standardbred Star: Learn about Harness Racing with Star & Friends. 2007. (YA). 3.95 (*978-0-9793891-0-8(0)*) United States Trotting Association.

Balloon Books. Make a Garage. 2001. (Press Out & Play Bks.). (Illus.). 16p. (J). (gr. k-3). pap. 5.95 (978-0-8069-2278-2(8), Balloon Bks.) Sterling Publishing Co., Inc.

Balloon Books Staff, ed. Sticker Fun: Stick & Learn 2 Years. 2003. (Stick & Learn Bks.). (Illus.). 20p. (J). pap. 3.95 (978-0-8069-8061-4(3)) Sterling Publishing Co., Inc.

—Sticker Play: Stick & Learn 3 Years. 2001. (Stick & Learn Bks.). (Illus.). 20p. (J). pap. 3.95 (978-0-8069-8062-1(1)) Sterling Publishing Co., Inc.

Batty Bears: Make Hundreds of Funny Faces with Re-Usable Stickers! 1999. (Funny Faces Ser.: Vol. 12). (Illus.). 10p. (J). (ps-7). 1.99 (978-1-86091-115-6(3), 80) Trident Pr. International.

Bauer, Susan Wise. Activity Book: Ancient Times. 2002. (Story of the World: Vol. 1). (Illus.). 275p. (J). pap., act. bk. ed. 34.50 (978-0-9714129-1-0(X)) Peace Hill Pr.

Bear, Magdalen. Walking Automata: A Collection of Self-Moving Models to Cut Out & Make. 2004. (Illus.). 32p. 10.00 (978-1-899618-50-7(3)) Tarquin Pubns. GBR. *Dist:* Parkwest Pubns., Inc.

Bee Smarter Starter Kit Grade 3. l.t. ed. 2002. (Illus.). 72p. (J). per. 14.99 (978-0-9717643-9-2(5), Bee Smarter Study Kits) Verde Publishing, Inc.

Bell, Robin. My Adventure with Pirates. 2007. 44p. (J). 8.99 (978-1-59092-462-4(2), Orchard Academy Pr.) Windstorm Creative.

Benchmark Education Staff, compiled by. Sort & Classify. 2006. spiral bd. 205.00 (*978-1-4108-7051-3(0)*) Benchmark Education Co.

Bentley, Linda. Big Book of Quick & Easy Art Activities: More Than 75 Creative Activities with Curriculum Connections That Keep Kids Creating & Learning All Year Long! 2007. 208p. pap. 26.99 (*978-0-439-58060-1(9)*, Teaching Resources) Scholastic, Inc.

Benton, Jim. Monster Maker. Benton, Jim, illus. 2007. (Franny K. Stein, Mad Scientist Ser.). 64p. (J). pap. 3.99 (*978-1-4169-3657-2(2)*, Simon Scribbles) Simon & Schuster Children's Publishing.

—Spooky Science. Benton, Jim, illus. 2007. (Franny K. Stein, Mad Scientist Ser.). 64p. (J). pap. 3.99 (*978-1-4169-3553-7(3)*, Simon Scribbles) Simon & Schuster Children's Publishing.

Beylon, Cathy. Fairy Tale Princesses. 1999. (Sticker Styles Ser.). (Illus.). 16p. (J). (ps-1). pap. 4.99 (978-0-448-42078-3(3), Grosset & Dunlap) Penguin Group (USA) Inc.

—Shiny Dinosaurs. 2004. (Shiny Stickers Ser.). (Illus.). 2p. (J). (ps-5). 1.50 (978-0-486-43536-7(9)) Dover Pubns., Inc.

Bicknell, Joanna & Horne, Jane. My Scrapbook about Me. 2007. (Illus.). 20p. (J). (gr. k-2). 12.99 (*978-1-84610-424-4(6)*) Make Believe Ideas GBR. *Dist:* Ingram Pub. Services.

Biggs, Kathy. Dragonflies of North America: A Color & learn Book for All Ages, with Activities. MAnolis, Tim, illus. l.t. ed. 2007. 48p. (J). (*978-0-9677934-4-3(0)*) Azalea Creek Publishing.

—Dragonflies of North America: A Color & Learn Book for All Ages, with Activities. Manolis, Tim, illus. l.t. ed. 2007. 48p. (J). cd-rom (*978-0-9677934-5-0(9)*) Azalea Creek Publishing.

Black, Jessica L. What Do the Animals Say? Board Book & Felt Puppet Set. Coates, Jennifer, illus. 2005. (J). bds. (978-1-57332-360-4(8)) HighReach Learning, Inc.

blackbird. Mr. HookWorm Coloring Book. 2007. 32p. (J). per. 1.50 (*978-0-9789798-7-4(7)*) Blackbird's World Publishing Co.

Blakey, Nancy. The Mudpies Book of Boredom Busters. 2004. (Illus.). 120p. (J). (ps-7). 8.95 (978-1-883672-86-7(4), Tricycle Pr.) Ten Speed Pr.

Bork, Rhoda. Pioneering: Activities to Live History. 2007. (J). (*978-0-9786018-6-7(6)*) Sparrow Media Group, Inc.

Boutan, Mila. Rousseau: Art Activity Pack. 2005. (Illus.). 22p. (J). (gr. 4-8). pap. 10.00 (978-0-7567-9413-2(7)) DIANE Publishing Co.

Boy Scouts of America Staff. Bear Cub Scout Book. rev. ed. 1998. 264p. (J). (gr. 3). 4.95 (978-0-8395-3107-4(9)) Boy Scouts of America.

—Wolf Cub Scout Book. rev. ed. 1998. (Illus.). 232p. (J). (gr. 2). pap. 4.95 (978-0-8395-3106-7(0)) Boy Scouts of America.

Boyle, Helen. Battle of Britain. 2008. 30p. (J). pap. 8.95 (*978-1-84425-464-4(X)*) Haynes Publishing PLC GBR. *Dist:* MBI Distribution Services.

—Planes of the Raf. 2008. 30p. pap. 8.95 (*978-1-84425-465-1(8)*) Haynes Publishing PLC GBR. *Dist:* MBI Distribution Services.

Bree, Loris & Bree, Marlin. Kid's Travel Fun Book: Draw, Make Stuff, Play Games, Have Fun for Hours! 2nd ed. 2007. (Kid's Travel Ser.). 96p. (J). pap. 6.95 (*978-1-892147-13-4(0)*) Marlor Pr., Inc.

Briant, Monta Z. & Z, Susan. Songs for Little Hands Activity Guide & CD. 2008. pap. 12.95 (*978-1-4019-1797-5(6)*, Hay Hse. Lifestyles) Hay Hse., Inc.

Bright & Beyond - 1 Ano. 2007. (J). 9.95 (*978-0-9763648-3-2(2)*) Pal Toys, LLC.

Bright & Beyond - 2 Anos. 2007. (SPA.). (J). 9.95 (*978-0-9763648-4-9(0)*) Pal Toys, LLC.

Bright & Beyond - Preescolar: Anos 3 To 5. 2007. Orig. Title: Bright & Beyond - Preschool. (SPA.). (J). 9.95 (*978-0-9763648-5-6(9)*) Pal Toys, LLC.

Bright Ideas - Age 0. 2002. (J). (978-0-9726170-0-0(0)) Pal Toys, LLC.

Bright Ideas - Age 1. 2002. (J). (978-0-9726170-1-7(9)) Pal Toys, LLC.

Bright Ideas - Age 2. 2002. (J). (978-0-9726170-2-4(7)) Pal Toys, LLC.

Bright Ideas - Preschool. 2002. (J). (978-0-9726170-3-1(5)) Pal Toys, LLC.

Brighter Vision Publishing Staff. Five's. 1998. (Year of Fun Ser.). 32p. (ps-k). pap. 3.99 (978-1-55254-018-3(9)) Brighter Vision Pubns.

—Four's. 1998. (Year of Fun Ser.). 32p. (ps-k). pap. 3.99 (978-1-55254-017-6(0)) Brighter Vision Pubns.

—One's. 1998. (Year of Fun Ser.). 32p. (ps-k). pap. 3.99 (978-1-55254-014-5(6)) Brighter Vision Pubns.

—Three's. 1998. (Year of Fun Ser.). 32p. (ps-k). pap. 3.99 (978-1-55254-016-9(2)) Brighter Vision Pubns.

—Two's. 1998. (Year of Fun Ser.). 32p. (ps-k). pap. 3.99 (978-1-55254-015-2(4)) Brighter Vision Pubns.

Bunny Days. (Happy Days Ser.). 48p. 5.99 (978-1-57029-271-2(X), WPH28007, Totline Pubns.) Schaffer, Frank Pubns.

Callella, Trisha. I Have, Who Has?, Language Arts — Grades 5-6: 38 Interactive Card Games. Hamaguchi, Carla, ed. 2006. (I Have, Who Has? Ser.). 208p. pap. 19.99 (978-1-59198-229-6(4)) Creative Teaching Pr., Inc.

—I Have, Who Has, Language Arts — Grades 3-4: 38 Interactive Card Games, Vol. 2206. Hamaguchi, Carla, ed. 2006. (Illus.). 208p. (gr. 3-4). pap. 19.99 (978-1-59198-228-9(6), 2206) Creative Teaching Pr., Inc.

Candle Books, creator. More 365 Activities for Kids. 2005. (Illus.). 366p. (J). (ps-3). spiral bd. 7.99 (978-0-8254-7292-3(X)) Kregel Pubns.

Carle, Eric. Eric Carle Activity Kit. 2000. (J). (978-0-06-028837-2(X)) HarperCollins Pubs.

Carlton Books Staff, creator. The Mr. Bean. 2002. (Illus.). 24p. (J). (ps-3). pap., act. bk. ed. 6.99 (978-1-84222-679-7(7)) Carlton Bks., Ltd. GBR. *Dist:* Independent Pubs. Group.

Carole, Jane. Get Ready for Kindergarten! 1,107 Interactive & Educational Exercises for Curriculum-Based Learning That's Fun! 2005. (Illus.). 320p. spiral bd., spiral bd. 17.95 (978-1-57912-450-2(X), 81450) Black Dog & Leventhal Pubs., Inc.

—Get Ready for Pre-K. 2006. (Illus.). 320p. (J). spiral bd. 17.95 (978-1-57912-549-3(2)) Black Dog & Leventhal Pubs., Inc.

Carole Marsh. Los Angeles Coloring & Activity Book. 2004. (City Bks.). 24p. (J). (gr. k-5). pap. 3.95 (978-0-635-02229-5(X)) Gallopade International.

—San Francisco Coloring & Activity Book. 2004. (City Bks.). 24p. (J). (gr. k-5). pap., act. bk. ed. 3.95 (978-0-635-02228-8(1)) Gallopade International.

Carter, David A. 600 Black Spots: A Pop-up Book for Children of All Ages. 2007. (Classic Collectible Pop-up Ser.). (Illus.). 20p. (J). (ps-3). 19.99 (*978-1-4169-4092-0(8)*, Little Simon) Simon & Schuster Children's Publishing.

Cartoon Network Staff, contrib. by. Hyper Activities. 2000. (Illus.). 24p. (J). (ps-3). pap. 3.99 (978-0-307-10774-9(4), Golden Bks.) Random Hse. Children's Bks.

Castafero, Jeanne Crane & Van Roden, Janet. Summer Smarts. 2007. (Summer Smarts Ser.). 92p. (J). (gr. 5). Vol. 4. pap. 8.95 (978-0-7534-6114-3(5)); Vol. 5. pap. 8.95 (978-0-7534-6115-0(3)) Houghton Mifflin Co. Trade & Reference Div. (Kingfisher).

—Summer Smarts 1. 2007. (Summer Smarts Ser.). 92p. (J). (gr. k-3). pap. 8.95 (978-0-7534-6111-2(0), Kingfisher) Houghton Mifflin Co. Trade & Reference Div.

—Summer Smarts 2. 2007. (Summer Smarts Ser.). 92p. (J). (gr. k-3). pap. 8.95 (978-0-7534-6112-9(9), Kingfisher) Houghton Mifflin Co. Trade & Reference Div.

—Summer Smarts 3. 2007. (Summer Smarts Ser.). 92p. (J). (gr. k-3). pap. 8.95 (978-0-7534-6113-6(7), Kingfisher) Houghton Mifflin Co. Trade & Reference Div.

Castaldo, Nancy F. Sunny Days & Starry Nights: Nature Activities for Ages 2-6. 2005. (Illus.). 144p. (J). pap. 12.95 (978-1-55652-556-8(7)) Chicago Review Pr., Inc.

Charlesworth, Liza, ed. Sight Word Tales. 2008. pap. 77.99 (*978-0-545-01642-1(8)*, Teaching Resources) Scholastic, Inc.

Cheney, Martha C. Things That Go Workbook: For Preschoolers. Kaminski, Karol, illus. 2000. (Gifted & Talented Ser.). 48p. (J). (ps-k). pap., wbk. ed. 5.95 (978-0-7373-0340-7(9), 03409W, Roxbury Park Juvenile) Lowell Hse. Juvenile.

Chihak, Sheena, ed. It's a Big Big World Jumbo Color & Activity Book. 2007. 400p. (J). pap. 5.99 (*978-0-696-23549-8(8)*) Meredith Bks.

Chihuly, Dale. Chihuly Art Kit. 2006. (J). 28.00 (978-1-57684-157-0(X)) Portland Pr., Inc.

Church, Ellen Booth. Best-Ever Circle Time Activities: Back to School. 2003. (Best-ever Circle Time Activities Ser.). 64p. 11.95 (978-0-439-43114-9(X)) Scholastic, Inc.

Clarke, Catriona. 50 Things to Do on Vacation. 2007. (Activity Cards Ser.). 50p. (J). 9.99 (*978-0-7945-1704-5(8)*, Usborne) EDC Publishing.

Clibbon, Meg. Imagine You're a Knight! Lady Megavere, Lucy D'Ancealot. Clibbon, Lucy, illus. 2005. (Imagine This! Ser.). 32p. (J). (ps-4). 19.95 (978-1-55037-919-8(4)); pap. 7.95 (978-1-55037-918-1(6)) Annick Pr., Ltd. CAN. *Dist:* Firefly Bks., Ltd.

—Imagine You're a Princess! Princess Megerella & Princess Lulubelle. Clibbon, Lucy, illus. 2005. (Imagine This! Ser.). 32p. (J). (ps-4). 19.95 (978-1-55037-921-1(6)); pap. 7.95 (978-1-55037-920-4(8)) Annick Pr., Ltd. CAN. *Dist:* Firefly Bks., Ltd.

Cline, Mike & Yi-Cline, Nancy. Franky Fox's Fun with English Activity Book, Level A1. Yi-Cline, Nancy, ed. Cline, Mike, illus. 2007. 62p. pap. 7.99 (*978-0-9777419-1-5(5)*, SIAB) Lingo Pr. LLC.

—Franky Fox's Fun with English Level A1. Yi-Cline, Nancy, ed. Cline, Mike, illus. 2007. 65p. 14.99 (*978-0-9777419-0-8(7)*, SITB) Lingo Pr. LLC.

Clineff, Jeff. Too Many Kitties. Movshina, Marina, illus. 2007. (ESK.). 24p. (J). 9.95 (978-1-933090-10-8(3)) Guardian Angel Publishing, Inc.

Code Busters. 2002. 96p. (J). pap. 2.98 (978-0-7525-7518-6(X)) Parragon, Inc.

Collins, Elaine Banks. See What I Can Do. Floyd, John, Jr., illus. 2005. (J). bds. 5.95 (*978-0-9752860-4-3(8)*) Our-Rainbow Pr., LLC.

Color Mouse Puppet Set. 2006. (J). per. (978-1-57332-431-1(0)) HighReach Learning, Inc.

Coloring Fun: Coloring/Activity Book (English/Spanish) Low Price Point. 2006. (Illus.). (J). (*978-0-9770455-9-4(5)*) Educational Adventures.

Community Helpers Puppet Set, Series 2. 2006. (J). per. (978-1-57332-430-4(2)) HighReach Learning, Inc.

Coon, Cyndi, illus. Art That Pops! How to Make Wacky 3-D Creations That Jump, Spin, & Spring! 2006. 48p. (J). pap. (*978-0-439-81337-2(9)*) Scholastic, Inc.

Cranium. Cranium Silly Stories. 2007. (Play It Again Book Ser.). (Illus.). 52p. (J). (gr. 1). 9.99 (*978-0-316-01206-5(8)*) Little, Brown Bks. for Young Readers.

—Super Sculpting. 2007. (Play It Again Book Ser.). (Illus.). 44p. (J). (gr. 1). 9.99 (*978-0-316-01205-8(X)*) Little, Brown Bks. for Young Readers.

Cranium Inc. Staff. Cranium - Funfolio Family Edition Level 2, Vol. 1. 2006. (Illus.). 40p. (J). (gr. k-17). 14.99 (978-0-316-01202-7(5)) Little Brown & Co.

—Cranium FunFolio, Vol. 1. 2006. (Illus.). 40p. (J). (gr. 2-17). 14.99 (978-0-316-01204-1(1)) Little Brown & Co.

Cranium Inc. Staff. The Cranium Ultimate Book of Fantastic Fun & Games. 2007. 54p. (J). (ps-3). 19.99 (*978-0-316-01208-9(4)*) Little, Brown Bks. for Young Readers.

Crazy Cats: Make Hundreds of Funny Faces with Re-Usable Stickers! 1999. (Funny Faces Ser.). (Illus.). 10p. (J). (ps-5). 1.99 (978-1-86091-019-7(X), 81) Trident Pr. International.

Crazy Pop Stars: Make Hundreds of Funny Faces with Re-Usable Stickers! 1999. (Funny Faces Ser.). (Illus.). 10p. (J). (ps-7). 1.99 (978-1-86091-017-3(3), 82) Trident Pr. International.

Creepy Crawlies Discover & Do. 2006. (J). pap. (*978-1-57332-391-8(8)*) HighReach Learning, Inc.

Curry, Don, ed. Kong Stencil Book with Stickers. 2005. (Illus.). 22p. (J). (ps-3). bds., act. bk. ed. 9.95 (978-0-696-22815-5(7)) Meredith Bks.

Cyber Creeps: Make Hundreds of Funny Faces with Re-Usable Stickers! 1999. (Funny Faces Ser.). (Illus.). 10p. (J). (ps-7). 1.99 (978-1-86091-122-4(6), 83) Trident Pr. International.

Dalmatian Press, ed. Dinosaur Discovery. rev. ed. 2007. 48p. pap. 3.99 (*978-1-4037-3383-2(X)*) Dalmatian Pr.

Dalmatian Press Staff. Disney's Mickey Mouse Clubhouse Wipe-off Activity Book. 2007. 24p. pap. 3.99 (*978-1-4037-3209-5(4)*) Dalmatian Pr.

—Mega Fun. 2004. (Illus.). 304p. (J). pap., act. bk. ed. 3.99 (978-1-4037-0115-2(6)) Dalmatian Pr.

—Same or Different. rev. ed. 2002. (Tools Ser.). (Illus.). 32p. (J). (ps up). pap. 2.29 (978-1-57759-145-0(3)) Dalmatian Pr.

—Strawberry Shortcake Growing Sweet Surprises Spiral. 2004. (Strawberry Shortcake Ser.). (Illus.). 64p. (J). act. bk. ed. 8.99 (978-1-4037-0722-2(7)) Dalmatian Pr.

Danks, Fiona & Schofield, Jo. Nature's Playground: Activities, Crafts, & Games to Encourage Children to Get Outdoors. 2007. 192p. (J). (gr. 2-4). pap. 16.95 (*978-1-55652-723-4(3)*) Chicago Review Pr., Inc.

Danziger, Paula. Amber Brown Scrap Book. Ross, Tony, illus. 2006. 24p. (J). (gr. 2). pap. 7.99 (978-0-14-240620-5(1), Puffin) Penguin Group (USA) Inc.

Davis, Guy, et al. Barney's Search & Spot Book Set. 2001. (Barney Ser.). 9p. (J). pap. 10.99 (978-1-58668-127-2(3)) Scholastic, Inc.

Desso, Karen. Early Learning Reading Games A to D. 2007. (J). spiral bd. 15.99 (*978-0-9793576-8-8(3)*) New Learning Publishing.

Dickinson, Gill. Crafts for Kids: Birthdays*Easter*Halloween*Christmas*Mother's Day*Thanksgiving*and More. 2006. (Illus.). 144p. (J). pap. 12.95 (978-0-600-61506-4(5), Hamlyn) Octopus Publishing Group GBR. *Dist:* Sterling Publishing Co., Inc.

DK Publishing. Cirque du Soleil. 2008. (Ultimate Sticker Bks.). 1p. (J). (gr. 5-12). pap. 6.99 (*978-0-7566-3806-1(2)*) Dorling Kindersley Publishing, Inc.

—Go for the Gold. 2008. 16p. (J). pap. 2.49 (*978-0-7566-3321-9(4)*) Dorling Kindersley Publishing, Inc.

—Rockets Galore: Cub Scout Activity Series. 2007. (J). (gr. 12). pap. 2.49 (*978-0-7566-3300-4(1)*) Dorling Kindersley Publishing, Inc.

—Toddler on the Move: Busy Day: Activity Pack. 2008. 75p. (J). (ps-k). 9.99 (*978-0-7566-3807-8(0)*) Dorling Kindersley Publishing, Inc.

DK Publishing Staff. Ballerina. 2007. 12p. (J). bds. 6.99 (*978-0-7566-3106-2(8)*) Dorling Kindersley Publishing, Inc.

—The Nativity. 2007. 12p. (J). (ps-2). bds. 12.99 (*978-0-7566-3094-2(0)*) Dorling Kindersley Publishing, Inc.

—Poles Apart: North & South Poles: Cub Scout Activity Series. 2006. 24p. (J). pap. 2.49 (978-0-7566-2966-3(7)) Dorling Kindersley Publishing, Inc.

—Weather Watch: Cub Scout Activity Series. 2006. 16p. (J). pap. 2.49 (*978-0-7566-3108-6(4)*) Dorling Kindersley Publishing, Inc.

—Wheel Adventures: Cub Scout Activity Series. 2007. 16p. (J). pap. 2.49 (***978-0-7566-3220-5(X)***) Dorling Kindersley Publishing, Inc.

DK Publishing Staff & Smith, Justine. The First Christmas. 2007. 16p. (J). (gr. k-1). 19.99 (***978-0-7566-3147-5(5)***) Dorling Kindersley Publishing, Inc.

Doherty, Gillian. 1001 Things to Spot Long Ago. rev. ed. 2006. (Illus.). 32p. (J). pap. 6.99 (978-0-7945-0716-9(6) , Usborne) EDC Publishing.

Dora the Explorer Preschool Adventure. 2006. (J). pap. 5.95 (***978-1-58610-992-9(8)***) Learning Horizons, Inc.

Dora the Explorer We Go Together. 2007. (J). pap. 4.99 (***978-1-59545-121-7(8)***) Learning Horizons, Inc.

Dorling Kindersley Publishing Staff. Barbie My Big Book of Activity Fun. 2006. (Illus.). 128p. (J). pap. 9.99 (978-0-7566-1838-4(X)) Dorling Kindersley Publishing, Inc.

Dot-to-Dot 1-100+ Spanish Version. 2007. (J). per. (***978-1-58232-163-9(9)***) Bryan Hse. Pubs., Inc.

Douglas, Kathy M. Center Activities for Early Childhood. 1999. 160p. (J). (ps-1). pap. 15.99 (978-0-513-02363-5(1) , TSD23631, Instructional Fair) Schaffer, Frank Pubns.

Duncan, Dennis. Strategies & Games for Improving Critical-Thinking & Questioning Skills. 2007. 80p. pap. 11.99 (***978-1-4206-8599-2(6)***) Teacher Created Resources, Inc.

Dunn, Mary. My Adventure in the Southeast: Advanced My Adventure. 2007. 44p. (J). pap. 8.99 (978-1-59092-436-5(3) , Orchard Academy Pr.) Windstorm Creative.

—My Adventure on a Dinosaur Dig. 2006. 44p. (J). 8.99 (978-1-59092-281-1(6) , Orchard Academy Pr.) Windstorm Creative.

—My Adventure with Mozart. 2006. 44p. (J). 8.99 (978-1-59092-459-4(2) , Orchard Academy Pr.) Windstorm Creative.

—My Adventure with Rembrandt. 2006. 44p. (J). 8.99 (978-1-59092-463-1(0) , Orchard Academy Pr.) Windstorm Creative.

e-Educators. Full-Color Standards-Based Language Arts: Activities & Games. 2007. 176p. pap. 21.99 (***978-1-4206-8717-0(4)***) Teacher Created Resources, Inc.

—Full-Color Standards-Based Math: Activities & Games. 2007. 176p. pap. 21.99 (***978-1-4206-8719-4(0)***) Teacher Created Resources, Inc.

The Education of Little Tree: Activity Pack. 2003. 118p. (YA). pap. (978-1-58049-627-8(X) , PA0127) Prestwick Hse., Inc.

Educational Adventures, creator. Blazin' Hot: Coloring/Activity Book (Spanish) w/ Snipe. 2006. (SPA., Illus.). (J). (***978-0-9770455-5-6(2)***) Educational Adventures.

Etringer, Kathy. Mrs. EOs Extraordinary Number Activities. Mitchell, Judy & Sussman, Ellen, eds. Rojas, Mary Galan, illus. 2006. 128p. (J). pap. 13.95 (***978-1-57310-506-4(6)***) Teaching & Learning Co.

Falligant, Erin, ed. Doll Scrapbook. 2007. 32p. (J). 17.95 (***978-1-59369-173-8(4)*** , Pleasant Co.) American Girl Publishing, Inc.

Fearnley, Jan. Mr Wolf's Activity Book. 2006. (Illus.). 32p. (J). (ps). pap. 7.99 (978-1-4052-2425-3(8)) Egmont Bks., Ltd. GBR. *Dist:* Independent Pubs. Group.

Feelings Garden Coloring & Activity Book. 2005. (J). (978-0-9768827-2-5(8)) Prevention Through Puppetry, Inc.

Fifty-Five Fun Book Projects. 1999. 64p. (J). pap., stu. ed. 24.95 (978-1-58303-080-6(8)) Pathways Publishing.

Fitchett, Jilda, 4th. Aunt Molly's Transition—Seeing Death in A New Light. 2006. (Illus.). 91p. (J). per. 15.95 (***978-0-9773244-0-8(0)***) Light Line.

Floss, Laura. Doin' My Thing Carry-Along Coloring Kit. Riley, Kellee, illus. 2008. (Holly Hobbie & Friends Ser.). 80p. (J). (ps-3). 5.99 (***978-1-4169-4786-8(8)*** , Simon Scribbles) Simon & Schuster Children's Publishing.

Fogle, Robin. A Christmas Story. 2006. (J). pap. 1.79 (***978-1-59317-159-9(5)***) Warner Pr. Pubs.

Forthun, Angela. Joozu! Activities for Beginners. 2004. (JPN.). 80p. (J). 49.95 (978-1-86366-717-3(2)) Curriculum Corporation AUS. *Dist:* Cheng & Tsui Co.

Friedman, Pamela & Bauer, Larry. Activites de Fin d'Annee Scolaire. (FRE.). pap. (978-0-439-98519-2(6)) Scholastic Canada, Ltd.

Fritz, Pat, ed. The PowerGuide Logbook. 2000. 96p. (J). pap. 3.99 (978-0-8280-1504-2(X) , 164-290) Review & Herald Publishing Assn.

Fun to Learn Activity Book - Blue. 2005. (J). per. (978-1-933581-50-7(6)) Byeway Bks.

Fun to Learn Activity Book - Red. 2005. (J). per. (978-1-933581-49-1(2)) Byeway Bks.

Fun with Food Discover & Do. 2006. (J). pap. (***978-1-57332-394-9(2)***) HighReach Learning, Inc.

Funny Friends: Make Hundreds of Funny Faces with Re-Usable Stickers! 1999. (Funny Faces Ser.). (Illus.). 10p. (J). 1.99 (978-1-86091-016-6(5) , 85) Trident Pr. International.

Funny Monsters: Make Hundreds of Funny Faces with Re-Usable Stickers! 1999. (Funny Faces Ser.). (Illus.). 10p. (J). (ps-5). 1.99 (978-1-86091-018-0(1) , 86) Trident Pr. International.

Geiser, Traci Ferguson. Standards-Based Class Books Grades PreK-K: 30 Seasonal Activities for Emergent Writers. Butler, Heather, ed. 2006. (J). pap. (***978-1-59198-325-5(8)***) Creative Teaching Pr., Inc.

Giglio, Judy. Third Grade Scholar. Boyer, Robin, illus. 2004. 32p. (J). pap. 2.49 (978-1-58947-458-1(9)) School Zone Publishing Co.

Gilkerson, Patricia. My Adventure in the Desert. 2006. 44p. (J). 8.99 (978-1-59092-278-1(6) , Orchard Academy Pr.) Windstorm Creative.

—My Adventure on a Ranch. 2006. 44p. (J). 8.99 (978-1-59092-282-8(4) , Orchard Academy Pr.) Windstorm Creative.

—My Adventure Scuba Diving. 2006. 44p. (J). 8.99 (978-1-59092-286-6(7) , Orchard Academy Pr.) Windstorm Creative.

—My Adventure with Dogs. 2007. 44p. (J). 8.99 (978-1-59092-451-8(7) , Orchard Academy Pr.) Windstorm Creative.

—My Adventure with Eagles. 2006. 44p. (J). 8.99 (978-1-59092-453-2(3) , Orchard Academy Pr.) Windstorm Creative.

—My Adventure with Owls. 2007. 44p. (J). 8.99 (978-1-59092-460-0(6) , Orchard Academy Pr.) Windstorm Creative.

—My Adventure with Sea Horses. 2007. 44p. (J). 8.99 (978-1-59092-465-5(7) , Orchard Academy Pr.) Windstorm Creative.

—My Adventure with Sea Turtles. 2007. 44p. (J). 8.99 (978-1-59092-466-2(5) , Orchard Academy Pr.) Windstorm Creative.

—My Adventure with Sharks. 2006. 44p. (J). 8.99 (978-1-59092-468-6(1) , Orchard Academy Pr.) Windstorm Creative.

—My Adventure with Squirrels. 2007. 44p. (J). 8.99 (978-1-59092-470-9(3) , Orchard Academy Pr.) Windstorm Creative.

—My Adventure with Whales. 2007. 44p. (J). 8.99 (978-1-59092-475-4(4) , Orchard Academy Pr.) Windstorm Creative.

—My Adventure with Wild Horses. 2006. 44p. (J). 8.99 (978-1-59092-312-2(X) , Orchard Academy Pr.) Windstorm Creative.

—My Adventure with Wolves. 2006. 44p. (J). 8.99 (978-1-59092-476-1(2) , Orchard Academy Pr.) Windstorm Creative.

Gilpin, Rebecca. Cosas de Hadas. 2005. (Titles in Spanish Ser.). (SPA.). 32p. (J). pap. 8.95 (978-0-7460-6393-4(8) , Usborne) EDC Publishing.

—50 Travel Games & Activities. 2006. 50p. (J). 9.99 (978-0-7945-1319-1(0) , Usborne) EDC Publishing.

Gingold, Janet. My Adventure on a Lake: Advanced My Adventure. 2007. 44p. (J). pap. 8.99 (978-1-59092-442-6(8) , Orchard Academy Pr.) Windstorm Creative.

—My Adventure with Arthropods: Advanced My Adventure. 2007. 44p. (J). pap. 8.99 (978-1-59092-447-1(9) , Orchard Academy Pr.) Windstorm Creative.

—My Adventure with Reptiles: Advanced My Adventure. 2007. 44p. (J). pap. 8.99 (978-1-59092-464-8(9) , Orchard Academy Pr.) Windstorm Creative.

Golden Books Staff. Backyardigans Make Your Own Little Golden Book. 2006. (Illus.). 16p. (J). (ps-k). 5.99 (978-0-375-83845-3(7) , Golden Bks.) Random Hse. Children's Bks.

—Forever Fairytopia. 2007. (Super Stickerific Ser.). (Illus.). 64p. (J). (ps-2). 12.99 (***978-0-375-84717-2(0)*** , Golden Bks.) Random Hse. Children's Bks.

—Friends Around the World. 2006. (Illus.). 32p. (J). (ps-2). pap. 3.99 (978-0-375-83714-2(0) , Golden Bks.) Random Hse. Children's Bks.

—Go Diego Go Fun Kit. 2007. (Fun Kit Ser.). (Illus.). 48p. (J). (ps-2). pap. 9.99 (***978-0-375-84692-2(1)*** , Golden Bks.) Random Hse. Children's Bks.

—Halloween Book Bag. 2007. (Bookbag Ser.). (Illus.). 32p. (J). (ps-2). 4.99 (***978-0-375-84179-8(2)*** , Golden Bks.) Random Hse. Children's Bks.

—Ho-Ho-Ho-Oh, No! Zalme, Ron, illus. 2005. 32p. (J). (ps-3). pap. 3.99 (978-0-375-83091-4(X) , Golden Bks.) Random Hse. Children's Bks.

—Make Your Own Little Golden Book. 2006. (Illus.). 16p. (J). (ps-k). 5.99 (978-0-375-83844-6(9) , Golden Bks.) Random Hse. Children's Bks.

—Meet the Lazytown Gang! Saunders, Zina, illus. 2005. 32p. (J). (ps-2). pap. 3.99 (978-0-375-83139-3(8) , Golden Bks.) Random Hse. Children's Bks.

—Nick Book & CD Gift Set. 2007. (Book & CD Ser.). (Illus.). 32p. (J). (ps-2). 10.99 (***978-0-375-84221-4(7)*** , Golden Bks.) Random Hse. Children's Bks.

—No Matter How Small. 2008. (Deluxe Coloring Book Ser.). (Illus.). 96p. (J). (ps-2). pap. 3.99 (***978-0-375-83821-7(X)*** , Golden Bks.) Random Hse. Children's Bks.

—Princess Party. 2007. (Color Plus Gatefold Sticker Ser.). (Illus.). 16p. (J). (ps-2). pap. 3.99 (978-0-375-84149-1(0) , Golden Bks.) Random Hse. Children's Bks.

—Race Team! Simpson, Howard, illus. 2005. 32p. (J). (ps-2). pap. 3.99 (978-0-375-83138-6(X) , Golden Bks.) Random Hse. Children's Bks.

—Sleeping Beauty. 2006. (Illus.). 48p. (J). (ps-2). pap. 2.99 (978-0-375-83476-9(1) , Golden Bks.) Random Hse. Children's Bks.

Golden Books Staff & Artful Doodlers Limited Staff. Blue's Quilt. 2005. (Illus.). 32p. (J). (ps-2). pap. 0.48 (978-0-375-87512-0(3) , Golden Bks.) Random Hse. Children's Bks.

Goldstein, Alrica, ed. Polly Pocket Groovy Getaway Activity Kit. 2007. 32p. (J). 14.99 (***978-0-696-23200-8(6)***) Meredith Bks.

Golliher, Bill & Vaughan, Jack, illus. Webber' Interactive WH Questions Level 2. 2006. (J). cd-rom 39.99 (***978-1-58650-647-6(1)***) Super Duper Pubns.

Goodwin, Brenda L., concept. The Mangoes & the Kids: Teach A Child, Change the World. 2007. (Illus.). 37p. 10.00 (***978-0-9745861-2-0(9)***) Science & God, Inc.

Gordon, Lynn. 52 Activities to Share with Your Grandchildren. Johnson, Karen, illus. 2004. 6.95 (978-0-8118-4125-2(1)) Chronicle Bks. LLC.

Gospel Light Staff. Adventures with God's Family: Student Activity Pages. 2001. (Kids on the Rock Ser.). (J). (gr. 1-3). pap. 3.00 (978-0-8307-2295-2(5)) Gospel Light Pubns.

—I Learn about God's Plans: Student Activity Pages. 2001. (Movers & Shakers Ser.). (J). (ps). pap. 3.00 (978-0-8307-2289-1(0)) Gospel Light Pubns.

—My Bible Tells about God's Plan: Student Activity Pages. 2001. (Movers & Shakers Ser.). (J). (ps-k). pap. 3.00 (978-0-8307-2293-8(9)) Gospel Light Pubns.

Graham, Ian. Build Your Own Cool Cars. 2004. (Illus.). 48p. (***978-0-439-67662-5(2)***) Scholastic, Inc.

Gravois, Michael. Reading Response Scrapbooking Activities: Reproducible Fonts, Clip Art, & Templates with Easy Step-by-Step Directions & Presentation Tips to Help All Students Showcase Their Learning. 2007. 80p. pap. 12.99 (978-0-439-54893-9(4) , Teaching Resources) Scholastic, Inc.

Green, John. Beowulf. 2007. 32p. pap. 3.95 (***978-0-486-45655-3(2)***) Dover Pubns., Inc.

Green, John & Blaisdell, Bob. Great Scenes from Dickens' Novels. 2005. (Illus.). 32p. (J). pap. 3.95 (978-0-486-43985-3(2)) Dover Pubns., Inc.

Gresham, Starla T. Creative Problem Solving: Using Only Supplies from Your Classroom Closet. 2000. 40p. (J). pap. 15.95 (978-0-945984-94-8(4) , Zephyr Pr.) Chicago Review Pr., Inc.

Groeneweg, Nicole. Interactive Projects & Displays: Ideas for a Student-Created Learning Environment. F, Stacey, ed. Yamada, Jane, illus. 2006. (J). pap. 13.99 (***978-1-59198-315-6(0)***) Creative Teaching Pr., Inc.

Hamaguchi, Carla. Letters, Numbers, Colors & Shapes — Activity Pages. Dobelmann, Collene, ed. Yamada, Jane & Grayson, Rick, illus. 2006. 144p. pap. 15.99 (978-1-59198-225-8(1) , 2227) Creative Teaching Pr., Inc.

—Letters, Numbers, Colors & Shapes — Learning Centers. Dobelmann, Collene, ed. Yamada, Jane, illus. 2006. 96p. pap. 20.99 (978-1-59198-214-2(6) , 2228) Creative Teaching Pr., Inc.

Hamlet: Activity Pack. 2003. 133p. (YA). pap. (978-1-58049-622-3(9) , PA0121) Prestwick Hse., Inc.

Harcourt School Publishers Staff. Activity Book 2005. 3rd ed. 2003. (Horizons Ser.). (gr. 3). pap., tchr. ed. 20.90 (978-0-15-340299-9(7)) Harcourt Schl. Pubs.

—Alone Time, Together Time: Take-Home Book. 1999. (Illus.). (J). pap. 1.90 (978-0-15-317220-5(7)) Harcourt Schl. Pubs.

—Harcourt: Challenge Workbook. 2nd ed. 2002. (gr. 2). pap., wbk. ed. 23.10 (978-0-15-336516-4(1)) Harcourt Schl. Pubs.

—Instant Intervention Kit Grade 1. 99th ed. 1999. (Harcourt Title I Reading Programs Ser.). (gr. 1 up). pap. 1092.80 (978-0-15-315188-0(9)) Harcourt Schl. Pubs.

—Instant Intervention Kit Grade 2. 99th ed. 1999. (Harcourt Title I Reading Programs Ser.). (gr. 2 up). pap. 461.80 (978-0-15-315189-7(7)) Harcourt Schl. Pubs.

Hargrove, Julia. Tomb of the Unknowns. 2003. (Illus.). 48p. (J). pap. 6.95 (978-1-57310-405-0(1)) Teaching & Learning Co.

Harpster, Steve. Travelin' Harpster, Steve, illus. 2006. (Scribble & Sing Ser.). (Illus.). 80p. (J). 4.99 (978-1-4169-2691-7(7) , Simon Scribbles) Simon & Schuster Children's Publishing.

Haugen-McLane, Janie. Real-World Picture Words Software - Household Words. 2004. (J). cd-rom 69.95 (978-1-58804-374-0(6)) PCI Educational Publishing.

—Real-World Picture Words Software - Kitchen/Bathroom Words. 2004. (J). cd-rom 69.95 (978-1-58804-375-7(4)) PCI Educational Publishing.

Haunted House: Make Hundreds of Funny Faces with Re-Usable Stickers! 1999. (Funny Faces Ser.). (Illus.). 10p. (J). (ps-5). 1.99 (978-1-86091-123-1(4) , 87) Trident Pr. International.

Hauser, Savlan, illus. Kindergarten Success: Helping Children Excel Right from the Start. 2005. (Williamson Little Hands Book Ser.). 128p. (J). (gr. 3-7). 14.95 (978-0-8249-6777-2(1) , Williamson Bks.) Ideals Pubns.

—Kindergarten Success: Helping Children Excel Right from the Start. 2005. (Williamson Little Hands Book Ser.). 128p. (J). (gr. 3-7). pap. 12.95 (978-0-8249-6758-1(5) , Williamson Bks.) Ideals Pubns.

Haynes, Betsy. My Adventure Panning for Gold. 2007. 44p. (J). 8.99 (978-1-59092-444-0(4) , Orchard Academy Pr.) Windstorm Creative.

Haynes-Mayes, Ingrid. A Recipe of Ideas for Phonemic Awareness & Phonics: Hands-on Activities for Primary Grades. 2006. (J). per. (978-1-59872-635-0(8)) Instant-publisher.com.

Headway Level A Thinking Book. (J). (978-0-89688-280-5(2) , 88-280) Open Court Publishing Co.

Herbert, Janis. Abraham Lincoln for Kids: His Life & Times with 21 Activities. 2007. (For Kids Ser.). 160p. (J). pap. 14.95 (***978-1-55652-656-5(3)***) Chicago Review Pr., Inc.

Herrick, Mark J., illus. Core Democratic Values CONNECT-IT. 2003. (J). per. 24.95 (978-0-9749412-0-2(4)) EDCO Publishing, Inc.

Hollenbeck, Kathleen M. 20 Manipulative Mini-Books: Neighborhood & Community:Easy-to-Make, Interactive Mini-Books That Engage Kids in Reading & Writing-and Teach Key Social Studies Concepts & Vocabulary. 2004. 64p. pap. 11.99 (978-0-439-33167-8(6) , Teaching Resources) Scholastic, Inc.

Hood, Karen Jean Matsko. Fun with Foster Kids Activity & Coloring Book. 2008. (Illus.). 128p. (J). 22.95 (***978-1-59808-542-6(5)***); cd-rom 13.95 (***978-1-59808-541-9(7)***) Whispering Pine Pr., Inc.

—Oregon State Activity & Coloring Book. 2007. (Educational Activity & Coloring Book Ser.). (J). 22.95 (***978-1-59210-015-6(5)***); ring bd. 24.95 (***978-1-59210-014-9(7)***) Whispering Pine Pr., Inc.

House, Katherine L. Lighthouses for Kids: History, Science, & Lore with 21 Activities. 2008. (For Kids Ser.). 144p. (J). (gr. 4-7). pap. 14.95 (***978-1-55652-720-3(9)***) Chicago Review Pr., Inc.

Houts, Amy. Traza y Dibuja. 2006. (Dora The Explorer Ser.). (SPA & ENG., Illus.). 24p. (J). wbk. ed. 4.99 (***978-1-59545-064-7(5)***) Learning Horizons, Inc.

Huggins-Cooper, Lynn. Play, Laugh & Learn Celebrate the Seasons. 2003. (Illus.). 96p. pap. 20.00 (978-1-903258-68-2(5)) Carroll & Brown Pubs., Ltd. GBR. *Dist:* Independent Pubs. Group.

It's Circle Time: Themes to Enrich Shared Learning. 2003. 80p. (J). per. 9.99 (978-0-88724-915-0(9)) Carson-Dellosa Publishing Co., Inc.

Jackson, Bridgette. SAround the World. 2006. pap. 9.95 (***978-1-84728-101-2(X)***) Lulu.com.

Joel's Library Jam, 1 VHS cassette. 2005. (J). VHS, cd-rom (978-0-9744419-1-7(0) , CET) Greater Cincinnati TV Educational Foundation.

Johnson, Dirk, illus. Purdue University Coloring & Activity Adventure Book. 2007. 52p. (J). pap. (***978-0-9790923-0-5(2)***) DirkDesigns, LLC.

Johnson, Erik O. Limerick Stickies: 100 Rhymes to Write & Leave Behind. 2007. (Illus.). 208p. (J). pap. 4.95 (***978-1-60059-175-4(2)***) Lark Bks.

Kagan, Miguel. Match Mine: Language Builder. 2008. per. 19.00 (***978-1-879097-21-6(4)***) Kagan Publishing.

Kawasaki, Shauna Mooney. 2006 Primary Theme Resource. 2005. 64p. pap. 12.95 incl. cd-rom (978-1-59038-492-3(X)) Deseret Bk. Co.

Kessler, Colleen. Hands-on Ecology. 2006. 200p. pap. 19.95 (978-1-59363-201-4(0)) Prufrock Pr.

Key Porter Books Staff. Gymboree in a Princess Castle. rev. ed. 2007. (Illus.). 1p. (J). 16.95 (***978-1-55263-923-8(1)***) Key Porter Bks. CAN. *Dist:* Perseus Distribution.

—Gymboree on a Pirate Ship. rev. ed. 2007. (Illus.). 1p. (J). 16.95 (***978-1-55263-921-4(5)***) Key Porter Bks. CAN. *Dist:* Perseus Distribution.

Kids: Watershed Protection. 2003. (J). (978-1-888631-29-6(5)) Watercourse, The.

Kindergarten Coloring & Activity. 2006. (J). per. 4.99 (***978-1-59545-032-6(7)***) Learning Horizons, Inc.

Kindersley, Dorling. 1St Cooking Act Bk. 2008. 48p. (J). (gr. 3). ring bd. 9.99 (***978-0-7566-3503-9(9)***) Dorling Kindersley Publishing, Inc.

Kinney, Mary Lou & Witt Ahrens, Patricia. Tangling with Toddlers. 1999. 48p. (J). pap. 6.99 (978-0-513-02376-5(3) , TSD23763, Instructional Fair) Schaffer, Frank Pubns.

Kitch, Anne E. What We Do in Lent: A Child's Activity Book. Perez, Dorothy Thompson, illus. 2007. 48p. 8.00 (***978-0-8192-2278-7(X)***) Morehouse Publishing.

Klawitter, Pamela Amick. Centers on the Go: Fun, Creative Activity Folders to Take to Your Seat. VanBlaricum, Pam, ed. Armstrong, Bev & Baker, Don, illus. 2005. 192p. pap. 19.99 (978-0-88160-378-1(3) , LW435, Learning Works, The) Creative Teaching Pr., Inc.

Kliman, Gilbert. My Personal Story about Hurricanes Katrina & Rita: A Guided Activity Workbook for Middle & High School Students. 2005. (YA). spiral bd. 19.00 (***978-0-9790846-9-0(5)***) Children's Psychological Health Ctr., Inc., The.

Kliman, Gilbert, et al. My Personal Story about Tropical Storm Stan: A Guided Activity Workbook for Children, Adolescents & Families. 2006. spiral bd. 19.00 (***978-0-9790846-8-3(7)***) Children's Psychological Health Ctr., Inc., The.

Kline, Trish & Donev, Mary. The Busy Preschooler's Guide to Learning. 2007. (Illus.). 128p. (J). per. 60.00 (***978-1-934307-17-5(3)***) Ghost Hunter Productions.

—Celebration of Letters A & B: Busy Preschoolers. 2007. (Illus.). 16p. (J). per. 20.00 (***978-1-934307-04-5(1)***) Ghost Hunter Productions.

—Celebration of Letters C & D: Busy Preschoolers. 2007. (Illus.). 16p. (J). per. 20.00 (***978-1-934307-05-2(X)***) Ghost Hunter Productions.

—Celebration of Letters E & F: Busy Preschoolers. 2007. (Illus.). 16p. (J). per. 20.00 (***978-1-934307-06-9(8)***) Ghost Hunter Productions.

—Celebration of Letters G & H: Busy Preschoolers. 2007. (Illus.). 16p. (J). per. 20.00 (***978-1-934307-07-6(6)***) Ghost Hunter Productions.

—Celebration of Letters I & J: Busy Preschoolers. 2007. (Illus.). 16p. (J). per. 20.00 (***978-1-934307-08-3(4)***) Ghost Hunter Productions.

—Celebration of Letters K & L: Busy Preschoolers. 2007. (Illus.). 16p. (J). per. 20.00 (***978-1-934307-09-0(2)***) Ghost Hunter Productions.

—Celebration of Letters M & N: Busy Preschoolers. 2007. (Illus.). 16p. (J). per. 20.00 (***978-1-934307-10-6(6)***) Ghost Hunter Productions.

—Celebration of Letters O & Q: Busy Preschoolers. 2007. (Illus.). 16p. (J). per. 20.00 (***978-1-934307-11-3(4)***) Ghost Hunter Productions.

—Celebration of Letters P & R: Busy Preschoolers. 2007. (Illus.). 16p. (J). per. 20.00 (***978-1-934307-12-0(2)***) Ghost Hunter Productions.

—Celebration of Letters S & T: Busy Preschoolers. 2007. (Illus.). 16p. (J). per. 20.00 (***978-1-934307-13-7(0)***) Ghost Hunter Productions.

—Celebration of Letters U & V: Busy Preschoolers. 2007. (Illus.). 16p. (J). per. 20.00 (***978-1-934307-14-4(9)***) Ghost Hunter Productions.

—Celebration of Letters W & X: Busy Preschoolers. 2007. (Illus.). 16p. (J). per. 20.00 (***978-1-934307-15-1(7)***) Ghost Hunter Productions.

—Celebration of Letters Y & Z: Busy Preschoolers. 2007. (Illus.). 16p. (J). per. 20.00 (***978-1-934307-16-8(5)***) Ghost Hunter Productions.

Klutz Editors & Dzwonik, Cristian. De las 1000 y una Actividades. 2005. (SPA., Illus.). 120p. (J). spiral bd. 15.95 (978-968-5528-17-7(9)) Klutz Latino MEX. *Dist:* Independent Pubs. Group.

Klutz Press Staff. El libro del body Crayon. 2004. (SPA., Illus.). 42p. (J). spiral bd. 17.95 (978-968-5528-02-3(0)) Klutz Latino MEX. *Dist:* Independent Pubs. Group.

S

Koh, Susan G. & Green, Helen. Get Ready for Kindergarten Book & Activity Kit: 201 Interactive Lessons & 370 Illustrations that Make Learning Fun. 2007. (Illus.). 208p. pap. 15.95 (*978-1-57912-725-1(8)) Black Dog & Leventhal Pubs., Inc.

Kuligowski, Step. Get up Get Noisy Get Writing. 2007. 80p. pap. 11.99 (*978-1-4206-3709-0(6)) Teacher Created Resources, Inc.

Larson, Jennifer. Category Cut-ups, Workbook with CD-ROM. Prince, Audrey & Webber, Thomas, eds. 2006. (J). 12.95 (*978-1-58650-635-3(8)) Super Duper Pubns.

Leap Frog Kindergarten Basic Skills. 2006. (J). spiral bd. 3.95 (*978-1-59545-087-6(4)) Learning Horizons, Inc.

Leap Frog Pre-K Basic Skills. 2006. (J). spiral bd. 3.95 (*978-1-59545-086-9(6)) Learning Horizons, Inc.

LeapFrog Get Started Bindup. 2007. (J). spiral bd. 8.95 (*978-1-59545-163-7(3)) Learning Horizons, Inc.

Learning Activities. 2003. 80p. (J). (ps-5). pap. 9.99 (978-0-7647-0977-7(1)) School Specialty Publishing.

Learning by Coloring: Mini-Book Set Linking Beginning Skill with Self-Esteem. (J). (ps-2). 5.98 (978-0-89544-315-1(5) , 315) Silbert & Bress Pubns.

Lee, Martin & Miller, Marcia. 40 Elaboration Activities That Take Writing from Bland to Brilliant! Grades 2-4. 2007. 80p. pap. 12.99 (*978-0-439-55433-6(0) , Teaching Resources) Scholastic, Inc.

—40 Elaboration Activities That Take Writing from Bland to Brilliant! Grades 5-8. 2007. 80p. pap. 12.99 (*978-0-439-55434-3(9) , Teaching Resources) Scholastic, Inc.

Legrand, Njeri, ed. Games Galore Language Arts. 2002. 96p. (gr. 1-3). 14.95 (978-1-56234-494-8(3) , Mailbox Bks., The) Education Ctr., Inc.

Levin, Michael. Start to Finish: Word Searches. 2006. 64p. pap. 5.99 (978-1-4206-5994-8(4)); pap. 5.99 (978-1-4206-5995-5(2)) Austin & Company, Inc.

Lil' Bratz 5 in 1 Superly Duperly. 2005. 52p. pap. 3.99 (978-0-7666-2251-7(7)) Modern Publishing.

Lil' Bratz Activity Box Set. 2006. N/Ap. pap. 9.99 (978-0-7666-1466-6(2)) Modern Publishing.

Linaker, Kathryn. Nursery. 1999. (Illus.). 23p. (J). (ps). Bk. 1. pap., wbk. ed., act. bk. ed. 15.00 (978-0-7217-6500-6(9)); Bk. 2. pap., wbk. ed. 15.00 (978-0-7217-6501-3(7)); Bk. 3. pap., wbk. ed. 15.00 (978-0-7217-6502-0(5)); Bk. 4. pap., wbk. ed. 15.00 (978-0-7217-6503-7(3)); Bk. 5. pap., wbk. ed. 15.00 (978-0-7217-6504-4(1)); Bk. 6. pap., wbk. ed. 15.00 (978-0-7217-6505-1(X)) Schofield & Sims Ltd. GBR. Dist: State Mutual Bk. & Periodical Service, Ltd.

Lithgow, John. Boredom Blasters: Home Sick Edition. 2005. (Illus.). 64p. (J). pap. 14.95 (978-0-7624-2233-3(5) , Running Pr. Kids) Running Pr. Bk. Pubs.

Littler, Keith. Merlin, the Magical Puppy Activity Book. 2002. (Illus.). 24p. pap. 6.99 (978-1-84222-651-3(7)) Carlton Bks., Ltd. GBR. Dist: Independent Pubs. Group.

Lock, Deborah & Dorling Kindersley Publishing Staff. Knights in Shining Armor: Cub Scout Activity Series. 2006. 16p. (J). pap. 2.49 (978-0-7566-2726-3(5)) Dorling Kindersley Publishing, Inc.

Lombardo, Michelle. Pepto's Place. Herron, Mark, illus. 2003. (J). pap., act. bk. ed. 4.95 (978-1-931212-52-6(X)) Wellness, Inc.

Lorenz Books Staff. Mix & Match with Stickers. 1999. (Sticker Fun Ser.). (Illus.). 16p. (ps-k). pap. 4.95 (978-0-7548-0279-2(5)) Anness Publishing GBR. Dist: National Bk. Network.

Mack, Julia. God's Very Special People: An Activity Book for Children Who Grieve. 2007. 32p. (J). per. 13.99 (*978-1-59886-585-1(4)) Tate Publishing & Enterprises, L.L.C.

Manualidades y Otro Actividades. 2006. 32p. (J). pap. 8.99 (978-0-7460-6647-8(3) , Usborne) EDC Publishing.

Marshall, Paula, ed. Shrek the Third Book with Activity Kit. 2007. 32p. (J). 14.99 (*978-0-696-23383-8(5)) Meredith Bks.

Martinez, Kathleen & Edwards, Sue. Colossal Clubs: Activities-Based Curriculum for School-Age Programs. Edwards, Mark, illus. 2006. per. 29.95 (978-0-917505-39-3(5)) School Age Notes.

Mason, Jane B. & Hines Stephens, Sarah. Gymboree Face Painting: Imaginative Designs Plus Fun-Filled Activities! rev. ed. 2007. (Illus.). 36p. (J). (ps-2). bds. 16.95 (*978-1-55263-962-7(2)) Key Porter Bks. CAN. Dist: Perseus Distribution.

—Gymboree Music Play. rev. ed. 2007. (Illus.). 36p. (J). bds. 16.95 (*978-1-55263-964-1(9)) Key Porter Bks. CAN. Dist: Perseus Distribution.

McBride, Susan. The I'm-So-Bored Doodle Notebook. 2006. (Illus.). 128p. (J). 7.95 (978-1-57990-767-9(9)) Lark Bks.

McLaughlin, Kari Massie. My Adventure with Dragonflies. 2007. 44p. (J). 8.99 (978-1-59092-452-5(5) , Orchard Academy Pr.) Windstorm Creative.

—My Adventure with Flamingos. 2007. 44p. (J). 8.99 (978-1-59092-454-9(1) , Orchard Academy Pr.) Windstorm Creative.

—My Adventure with Ladybugs. 2007. 44p. (J). 8.99 (978-1-59092-457-0(6) , Orchard Academy Pr.) Windstorm Creative.

—My Adventure with Penguins. 2007. 44p. (J). 8.99 (978-1-59092-461-7(4) , Orchard Academy Pr.) Windstorm Creative.

—My Adventure with the Cherokee. 2007. 44p. (J). 8.99 (978-1-59092-446-4(0) , Orchard Academy Pr.) Windstorm Creative.

—My Adventure with the Wright Brothers. 2007. 44p. (J). 8.99 (978-1-59092-471-6(1) , Orchard Academy Pr.) Windstorm Creative.

—My Adventure with Thomas Edison. 2007. 44p. (J). 8.99 (978-1-59092-472-3(X) , Orchard Academy Pr.) Windstorm Creative.

McNeil, Niki, et al. HOCPP 1053 Narnia. 2005. spiral bd. 15.50 (*978-1-60308-053-8(8)) In the Hands of a Child.

—HOCPP 1072 Katy's Big Snow Day. 2006. spiral bd. 15.50 (*978-1-60308-072-9(4)) In the Hands of a Child.

—HOCPP 1073 Charlotte & Wilbur. 2006. spiral bd. 24.50 (*978-1-60308-073-6(2)) In the Hands of a Child.

Meloche, R. T. Heroes for Young Readers Activity Guide for Books 13-16. 2006. (ENG.). pap. 12.99 (*978-1-57658-370-8(8)) YWAM Publishing.

Merrell, Patrick. Everything Kids' Racecars Puzzle & Activity Book: Put the pedal to the metal for laps & laps of Fun! 2008. 144p. pap. 7.95 (*978-1-59869-243-3(7)) Adams Media Corp.

Micheletti, Judy. Snibbles: Really Creative Problem Solving Lessons & Mind-Stimulating Exercises for Gifted Students & Their Teachers, Ages 5 through Really Old! 2005. (Illus.). 70p. (978-0-910609-50-0(0)) Gifted Education Pr.

Midgley, Elizabeth Cole. Daily Discoveries for August. Mitchell, Judith, ed. Guymon, Jennette King, illus. 2005. 192p. (J). pap. 12.95 (978-1-57310-452-4(3)) Teaching & Learning Co.

—Daily Discoveries for October. Mitchell, Judith, ed. Guymon, Jennette King, illus. 2005. 192p. (J). pap. 12.95 (978-1-57310-454-8(X)) Teaching & Learning Co.

—Daily Discoveries for September. Mitchess, Judith, ed. Guymon, Jennette King, illus. 2005. 192p. (J). pap. 12.95 (978-1-57310-453-1(1)) Teaching & Learning Co.

Modern Publishing Staff, ed. Lots of Fun in Care a Lot. 2005. 12p. pap. 3.99 (978-0-7666-1868-8(4)) Modern Publishing.

—Record Breaking Racers. 2005. 32p. pap. 2.99 (978-0-7666-1909-8(5)) Modern Publishing.

—Sun & Fun in Care a Lot. 2005. 12p. pap. 3.99 (978-0-7666-1869-5(2)) Modern Publishing.

—Tuned up Challengers. 2005. 12p. pap. 2.99 (978-0-7666-1908-1(7)) Modern Publishing.

Moon, Jo, illus. How to Build a Snowman. 2007. (Little Scholastic Ser.). 10p. (J). (ps). 9.99 (*978-0-545-00066-6(1) , Cartwheel Bks.) Scholastic, Inc.

Moon, Rising. The Great Colorado Activity Book. 2007. (J). pap. 7.95 (*978-0-87358-921-5(1) , Rising Moon Bks. for Young Readers) Northland Publishing.

Multicultural Activities Blackline Masters. (Greetings Ser.). (gr. 3-5). 21.00 (978-0-7635-2230-8(9)); 21.00 (978-0-7635-2231-5(7)) Rigby Education.

Mussler-Wright, Richard & Baran, Laura. PCS Edventures! Bricklab Grade 3. 2007. (Illus.). spiral bd. (*978-0-9753193-5-2(3)) PCS Edventures, Inc.

—PCS Edventures! Bricklab Grade 4. 2006. spiral bd. (*978-0-9753193-6-9(1)) PCS Edventures, Inc.

Mutant Monsters: Make Hundreds of Funny Faces with Re-Usable Stickers! 1999. (Funny Faces Ser.). (Illus.). 10p. (J). (ps-7). 1.99 (978-1-86091-125-5(0) , 88) Trident Pr. International.

My Puptatl Book. 2006. (J). spiral bd. 8.00 (*978-0-9786947-0-8(8)) Puptattle Pr., Inc.

My Puptatl Youth Book. 2006. (J). spiral bd. 8.00 (*978-0-9786947-1-5(6)) Puptattle Pr., Inc.

My Very Own Activity Pages: Summer 2004. 2004. (J). pap. 1.79 (*978-1-59317-067-7(X)) Warner Pr. Pubs.

Never-Bored Kid, Ages 6-7, Bk. 2. 2006. (J). 14.99 (978-1-59673-158-5(3) , EMC 6309) Evan-Moor Educational Pubs.

Never-Bored Kid, Ages 7-8, Bk. 2. 2006. (J). 14.99 (978-1-59673-159-2(1) , EMC6310) Evan-Moor Educational Pubs.

Never-Bored Kid, Ages 8-9, Bk. 2. 2006. (J). 14.99 (978-1-59673-160-8(5) , EMC 6311) Evan-Moor Educational Pubs.

The Never-Bored Kid Book, Ages 5-6. 2006. (J). 14.99 (978-1-59673-154-7(0) , EMC 6303) Evan-Moor Educational Pubs.

The Never-Bored Kid Book, Ages 7-8. 2006. (J). 14.99 (978-1-59673-155-4(9) , EMC 6304) Evan-Moor Educational Pubs.

Newman-D'Amico, Fran. Birthday. 2006. 64p. (J). (ps-2). pap., act. bk. ed. 1.50 (978-0-486-44441-3(4)) Dover Pubns., Inc.

—Fun on the Go Travel Activity Book. 2005. 64p. (J). (ps-2). pap. 1.50 (978-0-486-44456-7(2)) Dover Pubns., Inc.

—Make Your Own Pizza. 2006. 4p. (J). pap. 1.50 (978-0-486-45224-1(7)) Dover Pubns., Inc.

—Vacation Fun Activity Book. 2007. 64p. (J). pap. 4.95 (*978-0-486-45896-0(2)) Dover Pubns., Inc.

Newman-D'Amico, Fran. What's Different. 2002. (Dover Little Activity Bks.). 64p. (J). (ps-3). pap. 1.50 (978-0-486-42334-0(4)) Dover Pubns., Inc.

Nickelodeon Staff. Nick Jr All about Me. 2004. (Illus.). 32p. (J). 12.95 (978-0-8118-4193-1(6)) Chronicle Bks. LLC.

O'Brien, Joan. Christmas Village Sticker Activity Book. 2002. (Illus.). 4p. (J). pap. 1.50 (978-0-486-42074-5(4)) Dover Pubns., Inc.

Oppenheimer, C. Pirkei Avos Activity Book: For Teachers & Students. Fruchter, Rabbi Y., ed. 1999. (HEB., Illus.). 75p. 13.00 (978-1-878895-26-4(5)) Torah Umesorah Pubns.

O'Reilly, Wenda. Art Ditto. 2007. 24.95 (978-1-889613-56-7(8)) Birdcage Pr.

Osborne, Nancy. Rhyming Words: Cut & Paste. l.t. ed. 2007. (Illus.). 52p. ring bd. 9.95 (*978-1-928856-07-8(1)) Osborne Pr.

O'Sullivan, Joanne. 101 Things You Gotta Do Before You're 12! 2007. (Illus.). 144p. (J). (gr. 1 up). pap. 9.95 (978-1-57990-859-1(4)) Lark Bks.

Pacheco, Luis Gabriel & Pacheco, Alma Rosa, illus. Juegos Recreativos para Ninos. 2003. (SPA.). 182p. (J). pap. (978-970-651-625-1(5)) Editorial Oceano De Mexico, S.A. DE C.V.

Pal Toys, creator. Bright & Beyond - Bebes. 2007. (J). 9.95 (*978-0-9763648-2-5(4)) Pal Toys, LLC.

Panchyk, Richard. Franklin Delano Roosevelt for Kids: His Life & Times with 21 Activities. 2007. (For Kids Ser.). 160p. (J). pap. 14.95 (*978-1-55652-657-2(1)) Chicago Review Pr., Inc.

Patterning & Sequencing. 2003. pap. 7.99 (978-0-7439-3231-8(5)) Teacher Created Materials, Inc.

Perry, Phyllis J. Colorado Fun: Activities for on the Road & at Home. Tarr, Lisa M., illus. 2007. 80p. (J). pap. 12.95 (*978-1-55566-402-2(4)) Johnson Bks.

Petruccio, Steven James. Create Your Own Dream Car Sticker Activity Book. 2006. 4p. (J). pap. 1.50 (978-0-486-44737-7(5)) Dover Pubns., Inc.

—Create Your Own Robot: Sticker Activity Book. 2006. 4p. (J). pap. 1.50 (978-0-486-44878-7(9)) Dover Pubns., Inc.

Petty Power. 1998. (Hot Wheels Ser.). (Illus.). (J). (ps-1). pap. (978-0-7666-0098-0(X) , Honey Bear Bks.) Modern Publishing.

Piano, Maureen. My Adventure to the Wonders of the World. 2006. 44p. (J). 8.99 (978-1-59092-445-7(2) , Orchard Academy Pr.) Windstorm Creative.

—My Adventure with Tidepools. 2007. 44p. (J). 8.99 (978-1-59092-473-0(8) , Orchard Academy Pr.) Windstorm Creative.

Pirate's Cove Bonus Eye Patch. 2006. 48p. pap. 3.99 (978-0-7666-2303-3(3)) Modern Publishing.

Playdays Staff. All Around Me. Date not set. (Illus.). 32p. (J). pap. (978-0-563-36704-8(0)) BBC Worldwide.

Polette, Nancy. A-Z Activities for the K-2 Student. 2005. (J). pap. 19.95 (978-1-931334-71-6(4)) Pieces of Learning.

Power & Light for Kids: Kidsbook. 2005. (J). pap., stu. ed. 5.95 (978-0-8309-1135-6(9)) Herald Publishing Hse.

Pratt, Leonie. Mermaid Things to Make & Do Kid Kit. 2005. 32p. (J). 15.99 (978-1-58086-842-6(8) , Usborne) EDC Publishing.

Preschool Coloring & Activity. 2006. (J). per. 4.99 (*978-1-59545-031-9(9)) Learning Horizons, Inc.

Price, Roger & Stern, Leonard. The Backyardigans My First Mad Libs. 2007. 16p. (J). (ps). pap. 4.99 (*978-0-8431-2673-0(6) , Price Stern Sloan) Penguin Group (USA) Inc.

Price, Roger & Stern, Leonard. Napoleon Dynamite Mad Libs. 2005. (Mad Libs Ser.). (Illus.). 48p. (J). (gr. 3). 3.99 (978-0-8431-2011-0(8) , Price Stern Sloan) Penguin Group (USA) Inc.

Priddy, ed. Wipe Clean Early Learning Activity Book Time. rev. ed. 2007. 12p. (J). bds. 4.75 (*978-0-312-49988-4(4) , Priddy Bks.) St. Martin's Pr.

Priddy, Roger. Baby Shaker Teethers Farm. 2005. (Bright Baby Ser.). (Illus.). 24p. (J). bds. 5.95 (978-0-312-49439-1(4) , Priddy Bks.) St. Martin's Pr.

—Baby Shaker Teethers Girl. 2005. (Illus.). 24p. (J). bds. 5.95 (978-0-312-49442-1(4) , Priddy Bks.) St. Martin's Pr.

—Baby Teethers: Boy. 2005. (Illus.). 24p. (J). bds. 5.95 (978-0-312-49441-4(6) , Priddy Bks.) St. Martin's Pr.

—Baby Teethers: Zoo. 2005. (Priddy Books Big Ideas for Little People). (Illus.). 24p. (J). bds. 5.95 (978-0-312-49440-7(8) , Priddy Bks.) St. Martin's Pr.

—Baby Touch & Feel: Puppy Love. rev. ed. 2005. 14p. (J). bds. 8.95 (978-0-312-49536-7(6) , Priddy Bks.) St. Martin's Pr.

—Bath Book: Rubber Duck & Friends. 2005. (Illus.). 10p. (J). 8.95 (978-0-312-49443-8(2) , Priddy Bks.) St. Martin's Pr.

—Fluffy Chick & Friends. 2005. (Illus.). 10p. (J). 8.95 (978-0-312-49430-8(0) , Priddy Bks.) St. Martin's Pr.

—Giant Sticker Activity Fun Book: Teddy Bears, Animals, Farm. 2006. 132p. (J). 12.95 (978-0-312-49740-8(7) , Priddy Bks.) St. Martin's Pr.

—Let's Pretend Al's Auto Workshop. 2007. 24p. (J). bds. 14.95 (*978-0-312-50018-4(1) , Priddy Bks.) St. Martin's Pr.

—My Big Book of Stickers. 2005. (Illus.). 120p. (J). pap. 12.95 (978-0-312-49432-2(7) , Priddy Bks.) St. Martin's Pr.

—My Day. 2005. (Illus.). 10p. (J). (ps-ps). bds. 4.95 (978-0-312-49514-5(5) , Priddy Bks.) St. Martin's Pr.

—My Giant Sticker Puzzle Book 2 (with CD) 2nd ed. 2007. (J). pap. 12.95 (*978-0-312-50094-8(7) , Priddy Bks.) St. Martin's Pr.

—My Giant Sticker Work Book (with CD) 2007. (J). pap. 12.95 (*978-0-312-50089-4(0) , Priddy Bks.) St. Martin's Pr.

—Touch & Feel: Baby Hugs. rev. ed. 2005. 10p. (J). 9.95 (978-0-312-49542-8(0) , Priddy Bks.) St. Martin's Pr.

—Wipe Clean: 40 Wipe-Clean Pages of Early Learning. 2006. (Wipe Clean Ser.). (Illus.). 40p. (J). bds., bds. 14.95 (978-0-312-49710-1(5) , Priddy Bks.) St. Martin's Pr.

—Wipe Clean Early Learning Activity Book. 2007. 56p. (J). spiral bd. 12.95 (978-0-312-49922-8(1) , Priddy Bks.) St. Martin's Pr.

—Wipe Clean Early Learning Activity Book Pirate. 2007. 12p. (J). bds. 3.47 (978-0-312-49928-0(0) , Priddy Bks.) St. Martin's Pr.

—Wipe Clean Early Learning Activity Book Princess. rev. ed. 2007. 12p. (J). bds. 3.47 (978-0-312-49927-3(2) , Priddy Bks.) St. Martin's Pr.

Radtke, Becky. Fairy Tales. 2004. (Illus.). 64p. (J). pap., act. bk. ed. 1.50 (978-0-486-43854-2(6)) Dover Pubns., Inc.

—Little Cars & Trucks Activity Book. 2007. 64p. (J). pap. 1.50 (*978-0-486-45685-0(4)) Dover Pubns., Inc.

—Pets Activity Book. 2005. 64p. (J). (ps-3). pap. 1.50 (978-0-486-44491-8(0)) Dover Pubns., Inc.

Radtke, Becky. Trains Activity Book. 2007. 64p. (J). pap. 1.50 (*978-0-486-45683-6(8)) Dover Pubns., Inc.

Random House Disney Staff. Crown Jewels. 2008. (Super Stickerific Ser.). (Illus.). 64p. (J). (ps-2). pap. 12.99 (*978-0-7364-2498-1(9) , Golden/Disney) Random Hse. Children's Bks.

—Little Red Riding Pooh's Adventure. Emslie, Peter, illus. 2005. 32p. (J). (ps-2). pap. 4.99 (978-0-7364-2320-5(6) , Golden/Disney) Random Hse. Children's Bks.

—Love at First Sight. 2003. (Disney Princess Ser.). (gr. k-3). lib. bdg. 11.80 (978-0-613-73762-3(8)) Tandem Library Bks.

Random House Disney Staff. Nuts & Bolts. 2008. (Paint Box Book Ser.). 48p. (J). (ps-2). pap. 3.99 (*978-0-7364-2521-6(7) , Golden/Disney) Random Hse. Children's Bks.

Ransom, Sharon L., ed. Cocurricular Activities: Their Values & Benefits, 11 vols. 2005. (Illus.). 64p. (YA). lib. bdg. 219.45 (978-1-59084-888-3(8)) Mason Crest Pubs.

Reader, Jenny. Girl 2 Girl: The Swap Book You Share with Your Friends. Martin, Caroline & Davies, Nic, illus. 2003. 96p. (J). pap. (978-0-439-56743-5(2)) Scholastic, Inc.

Redmond, Lindy. Choosing & Charting: Helping Students Select, Map Out, & Embark on Independent Projects. 2002. 94p. spiral bd. 19.95 (978-0-936386-91-1(6) , 154) Creative Learning Pr., Inc.

Rentschler, Nancy, illus. Hand Puppet & Board Book Jumbo Set. 2006. (J). per. (978-1-57332-398-7(5)) HighReach Learning, Inc.

Rhodes, Karen. Do You Know Jesus? 2005. (J). pap. 1.79 (*978-1-59317-111-7(0)) Warner Pr. Pubs.

Ritchie, Scot. Everything Kids' Spies Puzzle & Activity Book: Discover the secrets, tricks, & tools of Spies. 2008. 184p. pap. 7.95 (*978-1-59869-409-3(X)) Adams Media Corp.

Roche, Denis. Oodles to Do with Loo-Loo & Boo: The Collected Art Adventures. Roche, Denis, illus. 2001. (Illus.). 64p. (J). (gr. k-3). pap. 9.95 (978-0-618-15423-4(X)) Houghton Mifflin Co. Trade & Reference Div.

Romeo & Juliet: Activity Pack. 2003. 130p. (YA). pap. (978-1-58049-621-6(0) , PA0126) Prestwick Hse., Inc.

Ronkko, Kevin. My Adventure with Smooth Jazz: Advanced My Adventure. 2007. 44p. (J). pap. 8.99 (978-1-59092-469-3(X) , Orchard Academy Pr.) Windstorm Creative.

Ross, Kathy. Step-by-Step Crafts for Gifts. Emery, Jennifer, illus. 2007. 48p. (J). (gr. k up). pap. 6.95 (*978-1-59078-478-5(2)) Boyds Mills Pr.

Ross, Suzanne. Halloween Mazes. 1998. (Illus.). 64p. (J). (ps-3). pap. 1.50 (978-0-486-40208-6(8)) Dover Pubns., Inc.

Rouss, Slyvia. Sammy Spider's Shabbat Fun Book. 2006. (J). pap. 5.95 (978-1-58013-147-6(6)) Kar-Ben Publishing.

Rouss, Sylvia A. Sammy Spider's Passover Fun Book. Kahn, Katherine Janus, illus. 2003. 32p. (J). (ps-3). pap. 4.95 (978-1-58013-033-2(X)) Kar-Ben Publishing.

Ruth, Angie. My Adventure in Italy. 2007. 44p. (J). 8.99 (978-1-59092-430-3(4) , Orchard Academy Pr.) Windstorm Creative.

—My Adventure in Japan. 2007. 44p. (J). 8.99 (978-1-59092-431-0(2) , Orchard Academy Pr.) Windstorm Creative.

—My Adventure in Mexico. 2007. 44p. (J). 8.99 (978-1-59092-432-7(0) , Orchard Academy Pr.) Windstorm Creative.

—My Adventure in Scotland. 2007. 44p. (J). 8.99 (978-1-59092-433-4(9) , Orchard Academy Pr.) Windstorm Creative.

—My Adventure in the Snow. 2006. 44p. (J). 8.99 (978-1-59092-435-8(5) , Orchard Academy Pr.) Windstorm Creative.

—My Adventure in the United States of America. 2007. 44p. (J). 8.99 (978-1-59092-438-9(X) , Orchard Academy Pr.) Windstorm Creative.

—My Adventure on a Volcano. 2006. 44p. (J). 8.99 (978-1-59092-443-3(6) , Orchard Academy Pr.) Windstorm Creative.

—My Adventure with Bugs. 2006. 44p. (J). 8.99 (978-1-59092-448-8(7) , Orchard Academy Pr.) Windstorm Creative.

—My Aunt: Early My Adventure. 2007. 44p. (J). 8.99 (978-1-59092-477-8(0) , Orchard Academy Pr.) Windstorm Creative.

—My Cousin: Early My Adventure. 2007. 44p. (J). 8.99 (978-1-59092-479-2(7) , Orchard Academy Pr.) Windstorm Creative.

—My Daddy: Early My Adventure. 2007. 44p. (J). 8.99 (978-1-59092-480-8(0) , Orchard Academy Pr.) Windstorm Creative.

—My Grandma: Early My Adventure. 2007. 44p. (J). 8.99 (978-1-59092-481-5(9) , Orchard Academy Pr.) Windstorm Creative.

—My Grandpa: Early My Adventure. 2007. 44p. (J). 8.99 (978-1-59092-482-2(7) , Orchard Academy Pr.) Windstorm Creative.

—My Mommy: Early My Adventure. 2007. 44p. (J). 8.99 (978-1-59092-483-9(5) , Orchard Academy Pr.) Windstorm Creative.

—My Sister: Early My Adventure. 2007. 44p. (J). 8.99 (978-1-59092-484-6(3) , Orchard Academy Pr.) Windstorm Creative.

Salch, Megan. 100+ Activities for Houston Kids 2006. 2005. (Illus.). 40p. pap. 19.95 (978-0-9776154-0-7(5)) Salch, Megan F.

Sanders, Lori & Kimble, Linda. Book Projects to Send Home, Grade 3. rev. ed. 2004. (Basic Skills Ser.). (Illus.). 48p. (J). (gr. 3-3). pap. 6.99 (978-0-7424-2733-4(1) , IFG99161, Instructional Fair) Schaffer, Frank Pubns.

Schmidt, Carol. Butterfly Alphabet Coloring Book. 2007. (Illus.). 32p. (J). pap. 3.95 (*978-0-486-45843-4(1)) Dover Pubns., Inc.

Scholastic, Inc. Staff. Baby Days: A Collection of 9 Board Books, 9 vols. 2007. (Little Scholastic Ser.). (Illus.). (J). bds. 9.99 (*978-0-545-00070-3(X) , Cartwheel Bks.) Scholastic, Inc.

—Star. 2007. (Little Scholastic Ser.). 10p. (J). bds. 4.99 (*978-0-545-02070-1(0) , Cartwheel Bks.) Scholastic, Inc.

School Specialty Publishing. Best Buy Bargain Plus, Fifth Grade Skills & Practice. 2007. (Best Buy Bargain Bks.). 320p. (J). (gr. 5-6). pap. 16.99 (*978-0-7682-3795-5(5) , Schaffer, Frank) Schaffer, Frank Pubns.

—Best Buy Bargain Plus, First Grade Skills & Practice. 2007. (Best Buy Bargain Bks.). 320p. (J). (gr. 1-2). pap. 16.99 (*978-0-7682-3791-7(2) , Schaffer, Frank) Schaffer, Frank Pubns.

—Best Buy Bargain Plus, Fourth Grade Skills & Practice. 2007. (Best Buy Bargain Bks.). 320p. (C). pap. 16.99 (*978-0-7682-3794-8(7) , Schaffer, Frank) Schaffer, Frank Pubns.

—Best Buy Bargain Plus, Second Grade Skills & Practice. 2007. (Best Buy Bargain Bks.). 320p. (J). (gr. 2-3). pap. 16.99 (*978-0-7682-3792-4(0) , Schaffer, Frank) Schaffer, Frank Pubns.

—Best Buy Bargain Plus, Sixth Grade Skills & Practice. 2007. (Best Buy Bargain Bks.). 320p. (J). (gr. 6-6). pap. 16.99 (*978-0-7682-3796-2(3) , Schaffer, Frank) Schaffer, Frank Pubns.

—Best Buy Bargain Plus, Third Grade Skills & Practice. 2007. (Best Buy Bargain Bks.). 320p. (J). (gr. 3-4). pap. 16.99 (*978-0-7682-3793-1(9) , Schaffer, Frank) Schaffer, Frank Pubns.

—Best Buy Bargian Plus, Kindergarten Skills & Practice. 2007. (Best Buy Bargain Bks.). 320p. (J). (gr. 1). pap. 16.99 (*978-0-7682-3790-0(4) , Schaffer, Frank) Schaffer, Frank Pubns.

—The Construction Site. 2003. (Brighter Child Activity Bks.). 32p. (J). (ps-1). pap. 2.99 (978-0-7696-3227-8(0) , Brighter Child) School Specialty Publishing.

—The Fire Station. 2003. (Brighter Child Activity Bks.). 32p. (J). (ps-1). pap. 2.99 (978-0-7696-3213-1(0) , Brighter Child) School Specialty Publishing.

—Learning Activities, Grade 2. 2006. (Skills for Scholars Ser.). 80p. (C). pap. 4.99 (*978-0-7696-7992-1(7) , Schaffer, Frank) Schaffer, Frank Pubns.

—Learning Activities, Kindergarten. 2006. (Skills for Scholars Ser.). 80p. (C). pap. 4.99 (*978-0-7696-7990-7(0) , Schaffer, Frank) Schaffer, Frank Pubns.

—Learning Activities, Preschool. 2006. (Skills for Scholars Ser.). 80p. (C). pap. 4.99 (*978-0-7696-7989-1(7) , Schaffer, Frank) Schaffer, Frank Pubns.

—Space Travel. 2004. (Brighter Child Activity Bks.). 32p. (J). (gr. 1-3). pap. 2.99 (978-0-7696-3580-4(6) , Brighter Child) School Specialty Publishing.

—Total English Spanish Learning Kit. 2007. (Total Learning Kits Ser.). 563p. (J). pap. 49.95 (*978-0-7696-5489-8(4)) School Specialty Publishing.

—Total Numbers & Counting Learn. 2007. (Total Learning Kits Ser.). 1028p. (J). pap. 49.95 (*978-0-7696-5499-7(1)) School Specialty Publishing.

—Total Reading Learning Kit. 2007. (Total Learning Kits Ser.). 868p. (J). pap. 49.95 (*978-0-7696-5509-3(2)) School Specialty Publishing.

School Specialty Publishing. The Zoo. 2003. (Brighter Child Activity Bks.). 32p. (J). (ps-1). pap. 2.99 (978-0-7696-3215-5(7) , Brighter Child) School Specialty Publishing.

School Zone Interactive Staff. Dot-to-Dots. 2006. 64p. (J). (gr. 1-2). pap. 7.99 (*978-1-58947-302-7(7)) School Zone Publishing Co.

—Hidden Pictures. rev. ed. 2006. 64p. (J). (gr. 1-2). pap. 7.99 (*978-1-58947-301-0(9)) School Zone Publishing Co.

Schwartz, Linda. Creepy Crawly Readiness Activities. Clark, Kim, ed. Armstrong, Beverly, illus. 2001. 80p. (J). pap. 10.99 (978-1-57471-796-9(0) , 2354) Creative Teaching Pr., Inc.

Scott, James. Holes: Activity Pack. 2002. (Illus.). 143p. (YA). pap. (978-1-58049-617-9(2) , PA0120) Prestwick Hse., Inc.

—The Indian in the Cupboard: Activity Pack. 2003. 138p. (YA). pap. (978-1-58049-625-4(3) , PA0124) Prestwick Hse., Inc.

Sesame Street Ready, Set, Preschool. 2006. (J). pap. 5.95 (*978-1-59545-008-1(4)) Learning Horizons, Inc.

Sevaly, Karen. Matching Animals & Babies Lace Up Cards. Chang, Maria, ed. 2007. (It's Happy Bunny Ser.). 16p. 9.99 (*978-0-439-91219-8(9) , Teaching Resources) Scholastic, Inc.

—Matching Animals & Habitats Lace up Cards. 2007. 48p. 9.99 (*978-0-439-91221-1(0) , Teaching Resources) Scholastic, Inc.

Shaffer, Christy. Learning about Mythical Creatures. 2005. (Illus.). 16p. (J). (ps-ps). pap. 1.50 (978-0-486-44047-7(8)) Dover Pubns., Inc.

Share Time with Me. 2004. (J). per. 5.95 (978-0-9760282-0-8(4)) RAPC - Sparkle & Shine Project.

Silly Spooks: Make Hundreds of Funny Faces with Re-Usable Stickers! 1999. (Funny Faces Ser.). (Illus.). 10p. (J). (ps-5). 1.99 (978-1-86091-114-9(5) , 90) Trident Pr. International.

Slade, Suzanne. My Adventure Inventing the Radio. 2007. 44p. (J). 8.99 (978-1-59092-440-2(1) , Orchard Academy Pr.) Windstorm Creative.

—My Adventure Inventing the Television. 2007. 44p. (J). 8.99 (978-1-59092-441-9(X) , Orchard Academy Pr.) Windstorm Creative.

—My Adventure with Henry Ford. 2007. 44p. (J). 8.99 (978-1-59092-455-6(X) , Orchard Academy Pr.) Windstorm Creative.

Slam! Activity Pack. 2003. 172p. (YA). pap. (978-1-58049-624-7(5) , PA0123) Prestwick Hse., Inc.

Smart Kids Publishing Staff. My Snuggle up Bedtime Book. Smart Kids Publishing Staff, illus. 2007. 16p. 14.99 (*978-0-8249-6695-9(3)) Ideals Pubns.

Smith, Naniloa. The Children Are Happy Activity Book with Animals from the Southwest. 2003. (J). 11.00 (978-0-9744005-0-1(5)) In the Desert.

Soffer, Ruth. Animal Illustrations to Paint or Color. 2007. 48p. (J). pap. 4.95 (*978-0-486-45696-6(X)) Dover Pubns., Inc.

Sosa, Carlos. Celebrations. 2007. (Familia Banderas Ser.). (Illus.). 48p. (J). (gr. 3-7). per. 9.95 (*978-1-933669-11-3(X)) Literary Architects, LLC.

—Cultures. 2007. (Familia Banderas Ser.). (Illus.). 48p. (J). (gr. 3-7). per. 9.95 (*978-1-933669-12-0(8)) Literary Architects, LLC.

Spear, Kevin. My Very Own Activity Pages: Spring 2004. 2004. (J). pap. 1.79 (*978-1-59317-077-6(7)) Warner Pr. Pubs.

Stafford, Lonnie. I'm a Child of God: Songs & Activities for Preschool Choirs & School Programs. Tyree, Debra, ed. 2004. 96p. 20.00 (978-0-687-09762-3(2)) Abingdon Pr.

Stangl, Jean. Toddler Time Creative Experiences for Toddlers. 1999. 96p. (J). pap. 10.99 (978-0-513-02257-7(0) , TSD22570, Instructional Fair) Schaffer, Frank Pubns.

Start to Finish: More Pictures to Finish. 2006. 64p. pap. 5.99 (978-1-4206-5993-1(6)) Austin & Company, Inc.

Staying Focused. 2007. (J). per. 10.00 (*978-0-9788937-2-9(7)) Amani Publishing.

Steck-Vaughn Staff. Monthly Activity Books: November. 2004. (Illus.). (ps-k). pap. 12.99 (978-0-7398-9310-4(6)) Steck-Vaughn.

Stephens, Monique Z. Sweetest Easter Ever! 2008. (Littlest Pet Shop Ser.). 32p. (J). pap. 5.99 (*978-0-545-03940-6(1) , Scholastic) Scholastic, Inc.

Stern, Leonard & Price, Roger. Letters to Mom & Dad Mad Libs. 2007. (Mad Libs Ser.). 48p. (J). pap. 4.99 (978-0-8431-2135-3(1) , Price Stern Sloan) Penguin Group (USA) Inc.

Stern, Leonard & Price, Roger. Merry Christmas! My First Mad Libs. Daugherty, Heather, illus. 2007. 16p. (J). (ps). pap. 4.99 (*978-0-8431-2674-7(4)) Penguin Group (USA) Inc.

Stevens, Eric. Exo-Force. 2007. (Lego Ser.). 32p. (J). pap., act. bk. ed. 4.99 (*978-0-439-92327-9(1)) Scholastic, Inc.

Stillerman, Robbie. Mix & Match Jewelry Sticker Activity Book. 2006. (Dover Little Activity Bks.). 4p. (J). pap. 1.50 (978-0-486-44880-0(0)) Dover Pubns., Inc.

Stilson, Linda J. Sew Easy Felt Puppets. 2005. (Illus.). 118p. 23.25 (978-0-9770043-8-6(4)) New Global Publishing.

Stohs, Anita Reith. Praise God with Paper Cups: 45 Easy Bible Crafts. 2005. (ENG., Illus.). 64p. (J). 9.99 (978-0-7586-0842-0(X)) Concordia Publishing Hse.

Stone, Sandra. Playing: A Kid's Curriculum. 2nd ed. 2005. 240p. pap. (978-1-59647-003-3(8)) Good Year Bks.

Strait, Mark, et al, creators. Webber' Interactive WH Questions Level 1: Sentence-Based Activities. 2006. (J). cd-rom 39.95 (*978-1-58650-642-1(0)) Super Duper Pubns.

Strang Communications Company Staff, ed. Kidz Chat: Spring 2002. 2002. (J). pap. 14.99 (978-1-57405-941-0(6)) CharismaLife Pubs.

Summer Activites K-1. 2005. 128p. (J). per. 4.99 (978-1-59441-322-3(3) , C04002) Carson-Dellosa Publishing Co., Inc.

Summer Activites P-K. 2005. 128p. (J). per. 4.99 (978-1-59441-321-6(5) , C04001) Carson-Dellosa Publishing Co., Inc.

Summer Activities 1-2. 2005. 128p. (J). per. 4.99 (978-1-59441-323-0(1) , C04003) Carson-Dellosa Publishing Co., Inc.

Summer Activities 2-3. 2005. 128p. (J). per. 4.99 (978-1-59441-324-7(X) , C04004) Carson-Dellosa Publishing Co., Inc.

Summer Activities 3-4. 2005. 128p. (J). per. 4.99 (978-1-59441-325-4(8) , C04005) Carson-Dellosa Publishing Co., Inc.

Summer Activities 4-5. 2005. 128p. (J). per. 4.99 (978-1-59441-326-1(6) , C04006) Carson-Dellosa Publishing Co., Inc.

Summer Activities 4 Set. 2005. (J). per. 51.80 (978-1-59441-387-2(8) , C48106) Carson-Dellosa Publishing Co., Inc.

Super Duper Publications Staff. Spinner 1-6. 2007. (J). 8.95 (*978-1-58650-744-2(3)) Super Duper Pubns.

Suzuki, Genevieve A. & Murakami, Jon J. The Original Poi Cats on Oahu. 2005. 24p. (J). pap. 5.95 (978-1-56647-731-4(X)) Mutual Publishing LLC.

Tainsh, Robert. Zoo's Who. 2005. (Baby Touch & Feel Ser.). (Illus.). 14p. (J). bds. 8.95 (978-0-312-49431-5(9) , Priddy Bks.) St. Martin's Pr.

Talhamy, Sarah. Children's Workbook. 2005. (J). ring bd. (978-0-615-12907-5(2)) SLG.

Terrific Themes for Year-Round Fun. 2004. 352p. (J). per. 22.99 (978-0-88724-913-6(2) , CD-0817) Carson-Dellosa Publishing Co., Inc.

Theodore, Elizabeth. Lily's Lollipop Moments. 2006. (Illus.). 60p. (J). ring bd. 22.50 (*978-0-9792472-2-4(5)) Lily Wish Factory.

Thomas, John & Thomas, Danita. Ingeniosos inventos y recetas para Niños. 2007. (Illus.). 80p. (J). pap. 14.99 (*978-0-8054-4498-8(X) , B&H Bks.) B&H Publishing Grp.

Thompson, Karen & Mitzo Thompson, Kim. Preschool: Songs That Teach Preschool. 2006. (Sing along Activity Books with CDs Ser.). (Illus.). 32p. (J). pap. 4.99 (978-0-7696-4574-2(7)) School Specialty Publishing.

Timmerman, Charles & Timmerman, Calla. Everything Kids' Fairies Puzzle & Activity Book: Enter the make-believe world of these magical creatures. 2007. 144p. pap. 7.95 (*978-1-59869-394-2(8)) Adams Media Corp.

Toms, Kate. Sticky Little Fingers Rainy Day Activity Book. 2007. (Illus.). 48p. (J). (ps-3). 6.95 (*978-1-84610-483-1(1)) Make Believe Ideas GBR. *Dist:* Ingram Pub. Services.

Tonka 5 in 1 Superly Duperly. 2005. 52p. pap. 3.99 (978-0-7666-2249-4(5)) Modern Publishing.

Top That Publishing Staff, ed. Build Your Own Willy Wonkas Chocolate Factory. Dahl, Ronald, illus. 2005. 24p. pap. (978-1-905359-58-5(6)) Top That! Publishing PLC.

—Funny Monsters. 2005. 12p. (978-1-84510-734-5(9)) Top That! Publishing PLC.

Torres, Laura & Sherman, Michael. Limpiapipas de Locura. 2004. (SPA., Illus.). 46p. (J). spiral bd. 15.95 (978-968-5528-09-2(8)) Klutz Latino MEX. *Dist:* Independent Pubs. Group.

Tsukamoto, Allen. Somethin Fishy for the Small Fry. 2006. 28p. (J). pap. 5.95 (978-0-944462-50-8(2)) Hawaii Fishing News.

Tucker, Mary. Stories & Activities David. 2007. 48p. pap. 7.99 (*978-1-4206-7067-7(0)) Teacher Created Resources, Inc.

—Stories & Activities Paul. 2007. 48p. pap. 7.99 (*978-1-4206-7069-1(7)) Teacher Created Resources, Inc.

—Stories & Activities Ruth. 2007. 48p. pap. 7.99 (*978-1-4206-7068-4(9)) Teacher Created Resources, Inc.

Turrell, Linda. Complete Library Skills, Grade 5. rev. ed. 2004. (Illus.). 128p. (J). (gr. 5-5). pap. 13.99 (978-0-7424-1955-1(X) , IFG99136, Instructional Fair) Schaffer, Frank Pubns.

—Mastering Spelling Skills Student Activities Book: Mastering Language Arts Series. Matthews, Douglas L., ed. 2003. (Illus.). stu. ed., wbk. ed. (978-1-931680-69-1(8) , Expert Systems for Teachers) Teaching Point, Inc.

Twin Sisters Productions Staff, prod. Gross & Annoying Songs: Songs That Teach. 2005. (J). per. 12.99 (978-1-57583-821-2(4)) Twin Sisters Productions, LLC.

Van Leeuwen, Wendy. The Ten Commandments Activity Book. 2007. (Illus.). 16p. (J). pap. 1.89 (*978-1-59317-210-7(9)) Warner Pr. Pubs.

Van Vleet, Carmella. Explore Ancient Egypt! 25 Great Projects, Activities, & Experiments. 2008. (Explore Your World Ser.). 96p. (J). (gr. 1-4). pap. 12.95 (*978-0-9792268-3-0(X)) Nomad Pr.

—Explore Ancient Rome! 25 Great Projects, Activities, & Experiments. 2008. (Explore Your World Ser.). 96p. (J). (gr. 1-4). pap. 12.95 (*978-0-9792268-4-7(8)) Nomad Pr.

Volke, Gordon. Big World Activity Sticker Book, Vol. 2. 2004. (Illus.). 16p. 7.25 (978-1-84161-130-3(1)) Ravette Publishing, Ltd. GBR. *Dist:* Parkwest Pubns., Inc.

Ward, Kathi. More Primary Quarterly Activities. 2003. (J). pap. 6.95 (978-1-57665-095-0(2)) Muggli Graphics.

—Primary Quarterly Activities. 2003. (J). pap. 6.95 (978-1-57665-094-3(4)) Muggli Graphics.

Wesleyan Publishing House Staff. Knowing God's Truth: Student Activity Book, Middle School. 2006. pap. 15.99 (978-0-89827-342-7(0)) Wesleyan Publishing Hse.

White, Mia. CAREFUL, YOU Could HURT the DOLPHINS. White, Mia, illus. 2007. per. 24.00 (*978-1-60361-710-9(8)) MW International, Belle Lumiere.

Wick, Walter. Once upon a Time. 2006. (Can You See What I See Ser.). (Illus.). 40p. (J). (gr. k-4). pap. 13.99 (978-0-439-61777-2(4) , Cartwheel Bks.) Scholastic, Inc.

Wiggles 5 in 1 Superly Duperly. 2005. 52p. pap. 3.99 (978-0-7666-2252-4(5)) Modern Publishing.

Williams, Colleen Madonna Flood. My Adventure in the Midwest: Advanced My Adventure. 2007. 44p. (J). pap. 8.99 (978-1-59092-564-5(5) , Orchard Academy Pr.) Windstorm Creative.

—My Adventure in the Northeast: Advanced My Adventure. 2007. 44p. (J). pap. 8.99 (978-1-59092-565-2(3) , Orchard Academy Pr.) Windstorm Creative.

—My Adventure in the Pacific Northwest: Advanced My Adventure. 2007. 44p. (J). pap. 8.99 (978-1-59092-566-9(1) , Orchard Academy Pr.) Windstorm Creative.

—My Adventure in the Triassic Period: Advanced My Adventure. 2007. 44p. (J). pap. 8.99 (978-1-59092-437-2(1) , Orchard Academy Pr.) Windstorm Creative.

—My Adventure in the Wild West. 2007. 44p. (J). 8.99 (978-1-59092-439-6(8) , Orchard Academy Pr.) Windstorm Creative.

—My Adventure on April Fool's Day. 2007. 44p. (J). 8.99 (978-1-59092-544-7(0) , Orchard Academy Pr.) Windstorm Creative.

—My Adventure on Christmas. 2006. 44p. (J). 8.99 (978-1-59092-545-4(9) , Orchard Academy Pr.) Windstorm Creative.

—My Adventure on Easter. 2007. 44p. (J). 8.99 (978-1-59092-546-1(7) , Orchard Academy Pr.) Windstorm Creative.

—My Adventure on Father's Day. 2007. 44p. (J). 8.99 (978-1-59092-547-8(5) , Orchard Academy Pr.) Windstorm Creative.

—My Adventure on Groundhog Day. 2007. 44p. (J). 8.99 (978-1-59092-548-5(3) , Orchard Academy Pr.) Windstorm Creative.

—My Adventure on Halloween. 2006. 44p. (J). 8.99 (978-1-59092-549-2(1) , Orchard Academy Pr.) Windstorm Creative.

—My Adventure on Martin Luther King Jr. Day. 2007. 44p. (J). 8.99 (978-1-59092-551-5(3) , Orchard Academy Pr.) Windstorm Creative.

—My Adventure on Mother's Day. 2007. 44p. (J). 8.99 (978-1-59092-552-2(1) , Orchard Academy Pr.) Windstorm Creative.

—My Adventure on My Birthday. 2007. 44p. (J). 8.99 (978-1-59092-553-9(X) , Orchard Academy Pr.) Windstorm Creative.

—My Adventure on New Year's Day. 2006. 44p. (J). 8.99 (978-1-59092-554-6(8) , Orchard Academy Pr.) Windstorm Creative.

—My Adventure on President's Day. 2007. 44p. (J). 8.99 (978-1-59092-555-3(6) , Orchard Academy Pr.) Windstorm Creative.

—My Adventure on St. Patrick's Day. 2007. 44p. (J). 8.99 (978-1-59092-556-0(4) , Orchard Academy Pr.) Windstorm Creative.

—My Adventure on Thanksgiving Day. 2006. 44p. (J). 8.99 (978-1-59092-557-7(2) , Orchard Academy Pr.) Windstorm Creative.

—My Adventure on the Fourth of July. 2007. 44p. (J). 8.99 (978-1-59092-560-7(2) , Orchard Academy Pr.) Windstorm Creative.

—My Adventure on Valentine's Day. 2007. 44p. (J). 8.99 (978-1-59092-558-4(0) , Orchard Academy Pr.) Windstorm Creative.

—My Adventure on Veteran's Day. 2006. 44p. (J). 8.99 (978-1-59092-559-1(9) , Orchard Academy Pr.) Windstorm Creative.

—My Adventure with Knights. 2007. 44p. (J). 8.99 (978-1-59092-456-3(8) , Orchard Academy Pr.) Windstorm Creative.

—My Adventure with Leonardo da Vinci. 2007. 44p. (J). 8.99 (978-1-59092-458-7(4) , Orchard Academy Pr.) Windstorm Creative.

—My Adventure with Shakespeare. 2007. 44p. (J). 8.99 (978-1-59092-467-9(3) , Orchard Academy Pr.) Windstorm Creative.

—My Adventure with Vikings. 2007. 44p. (J). 8.99 (978-1-59092-474-7(6) , Orchard Academy Pr.) Windstorm Creative.

—Schooling Day-by-day in May. 2007. 44p. (J). 8.99 (978-1-59092-521-8(1) , Orchard Academy Pr.) Windstorm Creative.

Willis, Tammy A., ed. Community Helpers Puppet Set, Series 1. 2006. (J). per. (978-1-57332-400-7(0)) High-Reach Learning, Inc.

Wolf, Jackie. Little Tikes(r) Building: Pretend Play Book. 2001. (Picture Me Ser.). 10p. (J). (ps up). bds. 4.99 (978-1-57151-590-2(9)) Playhouse Publishing.

Wonderful Winter. 2000. (Learning Fun for Little Ones Ser.). (Illus.). 64p. (J). pap. 8.99 (978-0-88724-577-0(3) , CD-6409) Carson-Dellosa Publishing Co., Inc.

Wood, Mark. Beyond Classroom Enrichment: Creative Units for Gifted Students. 2004. (Illus.). 80p. (978-0-910609-48-7(9)) Gifted Education Pr.

Wootton, Kathy. Making Memories Month-by-Month: Poems, Art Projects, & Activity Ideas for Creating Student Scrapbooks. Hamaguchi, Carla, ed. Tom, Darcy, illus. 2001. 144p. (J). pap. 15.99 (978-1-57471-783-9(9) , 2399) Creative Teaching Pr., Inc.

Working Together: Individual Title Six-Packs. (Rigby Focus Ser.). 24p. (gr. 2 up). 28.00 (978-0-7578-5339-5(0)); 30.00 (978-0-7578-5569-6(5)) Rigby Education.

The World of Eric Carle My Alphabet Activity Kit. 2007. (J). 16.99 (*978-0-9794445-0-0(0)) Loew-Cornell, Inc.

The World of Eric Carle My Animals Activity Kit. 2007. (J). 16.99 (*978-0-9794445-4-8(3)) Loew-Cornell, Inc.

The World of Eric Carle My Numbers Activity Kit. 2007. (J). 16.99 (*978-0-9794445-1-7(9)) Loew-Cornell, Inc.

The World of Eric Carle My Shapes Activity Kit. 2007. (J). 16.99 (*978-0-9794445-3-1(5)) Loew-Cornell, Inc.

Wynne, Patricia J. Butterfly Activity Book. 2007. (Illus.). 46p. per. 4.95 (*978-0-486-45692-8(7)) Dover Pubns., Inc.

Zelinski, E. J. Pensar a lo Grande: Ejercicios Simples y Divertidos para Potenciar la Creatividad. (SPA.). 212p. 16.00 (978-84-95456-79-3(6) , 87420) Ediciones Oniro S.A. ESP. *Dist:* Bilingual Pubns. Co., The, Lectorum Pubns., Inc., Libros Sin Fronteras.

Zschock, Martha. Flower Fairies Scratch & Sketch: An Art Activity Book for Magical Artists & Believers of All Ages. Zschock, Martha, illus. 2007. (Activity Book Ser.). (Illus.). 64p. (J). 12.99 (*978-1-59359-870-9(X)) Peter Pauper Pr. Inc.

Zucker, Zoey. Can I Trust You with My Secret? Yee, Josie, illus. 2006. (Groovy Girls Ser.). 32p. (J). act. bk. ed. 4.99 (978-1-4169-2832-4(4) , Simon Scribbles) Simon & Schuster Children's Publishing.

50 Learning Center Activities. 2005. 84p. (J). spiral bd. 14.99 (978-1-59441-471-8(8) , K04022) Carson-Dellosa Publishing Co., Inc.

2004 Summer Vacation First Grade Workbook. 2005. (J). spiral bd. 12.99 (978-1-58553-775-4(6)) Entertainment Publications, Inc.

2005 Summer Vacation Fifth Grade. 2005. (J). spiral bd., wbk. ed. 12.99 (978-1-58553-973-4(2)) Entertainment Publications, Inc.

2005 Summer Vacation First Grade. 2005. (J). ring bd., wbk. ed. 12.99 (978-1-58553-969-7(4)) Entertainment Publications, Inc.

2005 Summer Vacation Fourth Grade. 2005. (J). spiral bd., wbk. ed. 12.99 (978-1-58553-972-7(4)) Entertainment Publications, Inc.

2005 Summer Vacation Second Grade Workbook. 2005. (J). spiral bd. 12.99 (978-1-58553-970-3(8)) Entertainment Publications, Inc.

2005 Summer Vacation Sixth Grade. 2005. (J). spiral bd., wbk. ed. 12.99 (978-1-58553-974-1(0)) Entertainment Publications, Inc.

2005 Summer Vacation Third Grade. 2005. (J). spiral bd., wbk. ed. 12.99 (978-1-58553-971-0(6)) Entertainment Publications, Inc.

STUDENT AID

see Scholarships; Student Loan Funds

STUDENT GUIDANCE

see Educational Counseling; Vocational Guidance

STUDENT LIFE AND CUSTOMS

see Students

STUDENT LOAN FUNDS

see also Scholarships

S

Aresty, Reecy. Getting into College & Paying for It: Solutions for High School & College Families Guaranteed to Cut the Cost! l.t. ed. 2003. Tr. of Sueno Americano: Como Ingresar a la Universidad Y Pagar Los Mas Bajos Costos!. (SPA., Illus.). 258p. (YA). per. 27.95 (978-0-9760251-1-5(6)) College Assistance, Inc.

Edwards, Christina. Gardner's Guide to Finding Money for School Online. 2004. (Gardner's Guide Ser.). 208p. pap. 19.95 (978-1-58965-012-1(3) , 703 793 8604) Gardner, Garth Co., Inc. (GGC).

Rugg, Frederick E. Financial Aid in Less Than 3000 Words. 7th rev. ed. 2001. 5p. (J). (gr. 11-12). pap. 6.95 (978-1-883062-42-2(X)); 8th rev. ed. 2002. 5p. (YA). (gr. 11-12). pap. 6.95 (978-1-883062-47-7(0)); 9th rev. ed. 2003. 6p. (YA). pap. 6.95 (978-1-883062-51-4(9)); 10th rev. ed. 2004. 6p. (YA). pap. 6.95 (978-1-883062-57-6(8)) Rugg's Recommendations.

—Thirty Questions & Answers on the Colleges. (YA). 7th ed. 2001. 20p. (gr. 11-12). pap. 9.95 (978-1-883062-31-6(4)); 9th rev. ed. 2003. 20p. pap. 9.95 (978-1-883062-52-1(7)); 10th rev. ed. 2004. 20p. pap. 9.95 (978-1-883062-56-9(X)); 11th rev. ed. 2005. 21p. pap. 9.95 (978-1-883062-61-3(6)) Rugg's Recommendations.

STUDENT MOVEMENTS

see Youth Movement

STUDENT PROTESTS

see Youth Movement

STUDENT REVOLT

see Youth Movement

STUDENT STRIKES

McGregor, Tony L., illus. Victory Week. 1998. 40p. (J). lib. bdg. 22.95 (978-0-9634016-9-4(6) , Deaf Life Pr.) MSM Productions, Ltd.

STUDENTS

Ahlberg, Janet & Ahlberg, Allan. Starting School. ed. 2004. (J). (gr. k-3). spiral bd. (978-0-616-11861-0(9)) Canadian National Institute for the Blind/Institut National Canadien pour les Aveugles.

Anonymous. Diary of a Junior Year. (Real Teens Ser.: Vol. 4). (YA). (gr. 7 up). 2000. 196p. pap. 4.99 (978-0-439-08411-6(3) , Scholastic Paperbacks); 1999. pap. 59.88 (978-0-439-13483-5(8)); 1999. mass mkt. 59.88 (978-0-439-11746-3(1)); 1999. mass mkt. 59.88 (978-0-439-09275-3(2)) Scholastic, Inc.

—Diary of a Junior Year. 1999. (Real Teens Ser.: Vol. 1). (YA). (gr. 7 up). 11.64 (978-0-606-17278-3(5)); (978-0-606-17547-0(4)) Tandem Library Bks.

Buchanan, Jonathan J. Inside the Torii Gate: The Journal of an Exchange Student in Japan. 1999. 275p. (J). pap. (978-0-9683945-0-2(7)) The Beresford Pr.

Carriero, John P. Staying on Top of Things Before It's Too Late, Vol. 1. 2nd unabr. rev. ed. 2000. (Illus.). 54p. (YA). (gr. 8-10). 15.00 (978-0-9703109-0-3(0)) McQuaid Jesuit High Schl.

Davidson, Tish. School Conflict. 2003. (Life Balance Ser.). (Illus.). 80p. (J). 20.50 (978-0-531-12251-8(4) , Watts, Franklin) Scholastic Library Publishing.

Dewin, Howie. Scooby Doo's Guide to School. 2003. (ps-2). lib. bdg. 11.80 (978-0-613-72117-2(9)) Tandem Library Bks.

The Diaries. 2001. (True Stories from Senior Tear Ser.: No. 3). 160p. pap. 5.99 (978-1-931497-33-6(8)); pap. 5.99 (978-1-931497-32-9(X)) 17th Street Productions, An Alloy Online Inc. Co.

The Diaries No. 1: True Stories from Senior Year. 2001. 224p. (J). (gr. 4-7). pap. 5.99 (978-1-931497-30-5(3)) 17th Street Productions, An Alloy Online Inc. Co.

The Diaries No. 2: True Stories from Senior Year. 2001. 224p. (J). (gr. 4-7). pap. 5.99 (978-1-931497-31-2(1)) 17th Street Productions, An Alloy Online Inc. Co.

Diary of a Junior Year. 2000. (Real Teens Ser.: Vol. 6). 160p. (YA). (gr. 7 up). pap. 4.99 (978-0-439-08413-0(X)) Scholastic, Inc.

Doudna, Kelly. School Around the World. 2004. (Around the World Ser.). (Illus.). 23p. (J). (ps-3). lib. bdg. 19.93 (978-1-59197-569-4(7)) ABDO Publishing Co.

Dream Soup: Stories from San Francisco Youth, 2 vols. 1999. (J). (Illus.). 176p. spiral bd. (978-0-9646977-5-1(0)); Vol. 2. 196p. spiral bd. 15.00 (978-0-9646977-6-8(9)) Streetside Stories, Inc.

Everything's Different Now: Stories of Change by San Francisco Youth, 2002. (Illus.). 278p. (J). per. 15.00 (978-0-9710606-1-6(4)) Streetside Stories, Inc.

Farrell, Juliana & Mayall, Beth. Middle School: The Real Deal: From Cafeteria Food to Combination Locks. 2007. 176p. (J). (gr. 4-7). pap. 7.99 (*978-0-06-122742-4(0)) HarperCollins Pubs.

Gold, Susan Dudley. Tinker v. Des Moines: Free Speech for Students. 2006. (Supreme Court Milestones Ser.). (Illus.). 143p. (J). lib. bdg. 39.93 (978-0-7614-2142-9(4) , Benchmark Bks.) Cavendish, Marshall Corp.

Hall, Margaret. Schools. (Around the World Ser.). 32p. pap. 6.95 (978-1-4034-4006-8(9)) Heinemann Library.

Hall, Margaret C. Schools. 2002. (Around the World Ser.). (Illus.). 32p. (J). (gr. k-2). lib. bdg. 22.79 (978-1-58810-477-9(X)) Heinemann Library.

Harcourt School Publishers Staff. Social Science: Oklahoma State. 2000. (Illus.). pap., act. bk. ed. 11.50 (978-0-15-319764-2(1)) Harcourt Schl. Pubs.

—Social Studies: Mississippi State Activity Book Answer Key. 1999. (Illus.). (gr. 4). pap. 10.40 (978-0-15-317757-6(8)) Harcourt Schl. Pubs.

Hooray! Stories of Celebrations by San Francisco Youth, 2 vols. 2001. (Illus.). (J). 226p. spiral bd. 15.00 (978-0-9646977-9-9(3)); Vol. 2. 238p. spiral bd. 15.00 (978-0-9710606-0-9(6)) Streetside Stories, Inc.

Howe, Randy. 101 Ways to Adjust to High School: Randy Howe. 2007. (G - Reference,Information & Interdisciplinary Subjects Ser.). 224p. pap. 9.95 (978-1-4195-4177-3(3)) Kaplan Publishing.

Hudson, David. Rights of Students. 2004. (Point/Counterpoint Ser.). (Illus.). 120p. (J). (gr. 9-13). 32.95 (978-0-7910-7920-1(1) , Chelsea Hse.) Facts On File, Inc.

Johnston, Kurt & Oestreicher, Mark. My School. 2007. 144p. (J). pap. 9.99 (*978-0-310-27882-5(1)) Zondervan.

Mattern, Joanne. After School: Después de la Escuela. 2006. (ENG & SPA., Illus.). 24p. (J). pap. (978-0-8368-7364-1(5)); lib. bdg. (978-0-8368-7357-3(2)) Stevens, Gareth Inc. (Weekly Reader Early Learning Library).

Maxwell, John C. Leading at School. 2001. (PowerPak Collection Ser.). 88p. (J). (gr. 5-9). pap. 3.99 (978-0-8499-7724-4(X)) Nelson, Thomas Inc.

Messina, Noreen E. TeenWork: Four Teens Tell All: A Guide for Finding Jobs. 2006. (Illus.). 126p. (gr. 6-12). pap. 12.75 (978-1-59070-598-8(X)) Goodheart-Willcox Pub.

Miller, Jake. Who's Who in a School Community. 2005. (Communities at Work Ser.). (Illus.). 24p. (J). 19.95 (978-1-4042-2788-0(1)); pap. (978-1-4042-5030-7(1)) Rosen Publishing Group, Inc., The. (PowerKids Pr.).

Mosatche, Harriet S. Too Old for This, Too Young for That: Your Survival Guide for the Middle-School. 2000. (gr. 5-8). lib. bdg. 24.55 (978-0-613-89619-1(X)) Tandem Library Bks.

My School Memories: Scrapbook. 1999. (gr. 3-7). 12.95 (978-0-439-09253-1(1)) Scholastic, Inc.

National Honor Roll Staff. National Honor Roll 2001-2002: CT, DE, DC, ME, MD, MA, ,NH, NJ, NY, PA, RI, VT, WV, Foreign. 2001. (Illus.). 435p. (YA). 46.95 (978-0-9714201-0-6(6)) River City Pr.

National Honor Roll Staff & Photo Disc, Inc., Staff. National Honor Roll 2001-2002: AL, FL, GA, SC, Vol. 5. 2001. (Illus.). 471p. (YA). 46.95 (978-0-9714201-4-4(9)) River City Pr.

—National Honor Roll 2001-2002: AR, LA, MS, OK, TX, Vol. 4. 2001. (Illus.). 519p. (YA). 46.95 (978-0-9714201-3-7(0)) River City Pr.

—National Honor Roll 2001-2002: IL, IN, IA, KA, MN, MO, NE, ND, SD, WI, Vol. 2. 2001. (Illus.). 494p. (YA). 46.95 (978-0-9714201-1-3(4)) River City Pr.

—National Honor Roll 2001-2002: KY, MI, NC, OH, IN, VA, Vol. 3. 2001. (Illus.). 541p. (YA). 46.95 (978-0-9714201-2-0(2)) River City Pr.

National Honor Roll Staff & Photo Disc, Inc., Staff, eds. National Honor Roll 2001-2002: AK, AZ, CA, CO, HI, ID, MT, NV, NM, OR, UT, WA, WY, Vol. 6. 2001. (Illus.). 513p. (YA). 46.95 (978-0-9714201-5-1(7)) River City Pr.

Newsom, Tony. Student Safety Tips: 40 that Every 1st - 2nd Grader Must Know! 2007. pap. 6.99 (*978-0-9787143-4-5(2)) Carrington Bks.

Newsom, Tony. Student Safety Tips: 45 that Every 3rd - 5th Grader Must Know! 2007. pap. 6.99 (978-0-9787143-2-1(6)); pap. 6.99 (*978-0-9787143-5-2(0)) Carrington Bks.

Nuwer, Hank. High School Hazing: When Rites Become Wrongs. 2000. (Single Titles Ser.). (Illus.). 144p. (YA). (gr. 8-12). 24.00 (978-0-531-11682-1(4) , Watts, Franklin) Scholastic Library Publishing.

Persico, Deborah A. Vernonia School District vs. Acton: Drug Testing in Schools. 1999. (Landmark Supreme Court Cases Ser.). (Illus.). 128p. (YA). (gr. 6-12). lib. bdg. 26.60 (978-0-7660-1087-1(2)) Enslow Pubs., Inc.

Robert Seaman School Students Staff. Reflections Journal 2001. 2001. 180p. pap. (978-0-940429-26-0(8)) Glass, Michael B. & Assocs., Inc.

Trespacz, Karen L. Ferrell vs. Dallas I. S. D. Hairstyles in Schools. 1998. (Landmark Supreme Court Cases Ser.). (Illus.). 128p. (YA). (gr. 6-12). lib. bdg. 26.60 (978-0-7660-1054-3(6)) Enslow Pubs., Inc.

Trumbauer, Lisa. At School. 2000. (Yellow Umbrella Books). (Illus.). 16p. (J). (gr. 1). lib. bdg. 14.60 (978-0-7368-0741-8(1) , Pebble Bks.) Capstone Pr., Inc.

Vizzini, Ned. Teen Angst? Naaah. 2000. (gr. 7-12). lib. bdg. 22.20 (978-0-613-35333-5(1)) Tandem Library Bks.

—Teen Angst? Naaah: A Quasi-Autobiography. 2002. (gr. 7-12). lib. bdg. 13.55 (978-0-613-72265-0(5)) Tandem Library Bks.

Woloschak, Gayle E. & Paunesku, Tatjana Jovanovic. More Challenge Questions on Orthodoxy for Students, 2 vols., Vol. 2. 2002. 104p. (J). pap. (978-1-880971-72-7(0)) Light & Life Publishing Co.

Yates, Vicki. Life at School. 2007. (J). (*978-1-4034-9835-9(0)); pap. (*978-1-4034-9843-4(1)) Heinemann Library.

STUDENTS—EMPLOYMENT

Messina, Noreen E. TeenWork: Four Teens Tell All: A Guide for Finding Jobs. 2006. (Illus.). 126p. (gr. 6-12). pap. 12.75 (978-1-59070-598-8(X)) Goodheart-Willcox Pub.

Troutman, Kathryn K. Creating Your High School Resume: A Step-by-Step Guide to Preparing an Effective Resume for Jobs, College & Training Programs. 2nd ed. 2003. (Illus.). 160p. pap. 8.95 (978-1-56370-902-9(3) , JIST Works) JIST Publishing.

STUDENTS—FICTION

Advantage Publishers Group. Clara Goes to School. 2000. (Let's Start! Teacher's Pets Ser.). (Illus.). 32p. (J). (ps-1). 6.95 (978-1-57145-437-9(3) , Silver Dolphin Bks.) Advantage Pubs. Group.

Alfonsi, Alice. Freaked Out. 2004. 148p. (J). lib. bdg. 16.92 (*978-1-4242-0687-2(1)) Fitzgerald Bks.

Anna, Jennifer. Yen Shei & the American Bonsai. 2007. (Illus.). 88p. (YA). pap. 14.99 (*978-1-59092-153-1(4) , Blue Works) Windstorm Creative.

Banim, Lisa. Hands off My Crush-Boy! 2004. 125p. (J). lib. bdg. 16.92 (*978-1-4242-0684-1(7)) Fitzgerald Bks.

Bennett, W. J., Jr. Sydney & Garrett's Great Arkansas Adventury. 2005. (J). pap. (*978-0-9794044-6-7(0)) Archeological Assessments, Inc.

Brent-Dyer, Elinor M. The Chalet School at War. 2001. (Chalet School Ser.). (Illus.). 300p. mass mkt. 5.99 (978-0-00-692944-4(3)) Zondervan.

Burleigh, Cyril. Hilltop Boys on Lost Island. 2006. 77.99 (*978-1-4280-3214-9(2)) IndyPublish.com.

Burleigh, Cyril. The Hilltop Boys on the River. 2005. 26.95 (978-1-4218-0327-2(5) , 1st World Library - Literary Society) 1st World Publishing, Inc.

—The Hilltop Boys on the River. 2006. 77.99 (*978-1-4280-0122-0(0)); pap. 71.99 (*978-1-4280-0141-1(7)) IndyPublish.com.

Cabot, Meg. Party Princess. l.t. rev. ed. 2007. (Princess Diaries: Vol. 7). 335p. (YA). 23.95 (*978-0-7862-9273-8(3)) Thorndike Pr.

Caseley, Judith. Field Day Friday. 2000. (Illus.). 32p. (J). (ps up). 16.89 (978-0-688-16762-2(4)) HarperCollins Pubs.

Chapman, Allen. Frank Roscoes Secret or the Darewell Chu. 2007. pap. (*978-1-4065-1431-5(4)) Dodo Pr.

Cheat, Sheet & Krulik, Nancy E. Cheat Sheet. 2008. (How I Survived Middle School Ser.). 112p. (J). 4.99 (*978-0-545-01304-8(6) , Scholastic Paperbacks) Scholastic, Inc.

Cheng, Haw. Sixth Grade Was a Nightmare, & Seventh Is Worse: A 12-Year Old Speaks Out. Thurman, Joann M., ed. Costner, Howard, illus. Date not set. 128p. (J). (gr. 3-9). 11.95 (978-0-89896-335-9(4)) Larksdale.

Cho, Jerry, et al. Stray Little Devil. 2006. (Illus.). 200p. (YA). pap. 9.95 (978-1-59796-043-4(8)) DrMaster Pubns. Inc.

Cipriano, A. G. Bertie. 1999. 294p. (YA). (gr. 6-12). pap. 5.99 (978-0-9672074-0-7(1)) Gold Lace Publishing, LLC.

Clements, Andrew. Frindle. Selznick, Brian, illus. l.t. ed. 2000. (LRS Large Print Cornerstone Ser.). 116p. (YA). (gr. 4-10). lib. bdg. 24.95 (978-1-58118-062-6(4) , 23476) LRS.

—Frindle. Selznick, Brian, illus. 105p. (J). (gr. 3-5). pap. 4.50 (978-0-8072-1522-7(8) , Listening Library) Random Hse. Audio Publishing Group.

—Frindle, unabr. ed. 2004. (Middle Grade Cassette Librariestm Ser.). 105p. (J). (gr. 3-7). pap. 29.00 incl. audio (978-0-8072-7994-6(3) , S YA 961 SP, Listening Library) Random Hse. Audio Publishing Group.

—Frindle. Selznick, Brian, illus. 1998. 112p. (J). (gr. 3-7). pap. 5.99 (978-0-689-81876-9(9) , Aladdin) Simon & Schuster Children's Publishing.

—Frindle. Selznick, Brian, illus. 1998. (J). 11.64 (978-0-606-12939-8(1)) Tandem Library Bks.

—Jake Drake, Class Clown. Frazee, Marla & Pedersen, Janet, illus. 2007. (Jake Drake Ser.). 96p. (J). pap. 4.99 (*978-1-4169-4912-1(7) , Aladdin) Simon & Schuster Children's Publishing.

—Teacher's Pet. Pedersen, Janet, illus. 2007. (Jake Drake Ser.). 96p. (J). pap. 4.99 (*978-1-4169-3932-0(6) , Aladdin) Simon & Schuster Children's Publishing.

Cohen, Miriam. It's George! 1998. (978-0-606-13530-6(8)) Tandem Library Bks.

—So What? 1998. (Welcome to First Grade! Ser.). (978-0-606-13783-6(1)) Tandem Library Bks.

Cormier, Robert. The Chocolate War. 2003. 253p. reprint ed. 25.00 (978-0-7567-6585-9(4)) DIANE Publishing Co.

Crilley, Mark. Autumn. Crilley, Mark, illus. 2007. (Miki Falls Ser.). 176p. (J). (gr. 7 up). pap. 7.99 (*978-0-06-084618-3(6) , HarperTeen) HarperCollins Pubs.

Dadey, Debbie & Jones, Marcia Thornton. Hercules Doesn't Pull Teeth. 1998. (Adventures of the Bailey School Kids Ser.: No. 30). (J). (gr. 2-4). 10.79 (978-0-606-13475-0(1)) Tandem Library Bks.

—Trolls Don't Ride Roller Coasters. Gurney, John Steven, illus. 1999. (Adventures of the Bailey School Kids Ser.: No. 35). 80p. (J). (gr. 2-4). 3.99 (978-0-590-18985-9(9) , Scholastic Paperbacks) Scholastic, Inc.

—Trolls Don't Ride Roller Coasters. 1999. (Adventures of the Bailey School Kids Ser.: No. 35). (J). (gr. 2-4). (978-0-606-16587-7(8)); (gr. 3-6). lib. bdg. 11.80 (978-0-613-17030-7(X)) Tandem Library Bks.

Danziger, Paula. It's a Fair Day, Amber Brown. Ross, Tony, illus. 2003. (Readalongs for Beginning Readers Ser.). (J). 25.95 incl. audio (978-1-59112-246-3(5)); pap. 16.95 incl. audio (978-1-59112-245-6(7)); pap. 29.95 incl. audio (978-1-59112-247-0(3)); pap. 18.95 incl. audio compact disk (978-1-59112-362-0(3)) Live Oak Media.

Danzinger, Paula. Get Ready for Second Grade, Amber Brown. Ross, Tony, illus. 2003. (Readalongs for Beginning Readers Ser.). (J). 25.95 incl. audio (978-1-59112-234-0(1)); pap. 16.95 incl. audio (978-1-59112-233-3(3)); pap. 29.95 incl. audio (978-1-59112-235-7(X)) Live Oak Media.

David, Christopher. Denholme & the Skeleton Mystery. 2006. 274p. pap. (*978-1-4120-8014-9(2)) Trafford Publishing.

Decampi, Alex & Federica Manfredi. Kat & Mouse, Vol. 2. 2007. (Illus.). pap. 5.99 (978-1-59816-549-4(6) , Tokyopop Kids) TOKYOPOP, Inc.

Duffield, W. J. The Radio Boys in the Thousand Islands. 2007. 150p. pap. 11.99 (*978-1-4264-6513-0(0)); 166p. pap. 14.99 (*978-1-4264-6572-7(6)) BiblioBazaar.

Duncan, Lois. Killing Mr. Griffin. 223p. (YA). (gr. 7 up). pap. 4.50 (978-0-8072-1373-5(X) , Listening Library) Random Hse. Audio Publishing Group.

Ellis, Deborah & Walters, Eric. Bifocal. 2007. 240p. (YA). (gr. 7 up). (*978-1-55455-036-4(X)) Fitzhenry & Whiteside, Ltd.

Esham, Barbara. Last to Finish A Story about the Smartest Boy in Math Class. Gordon, Mike, illus. 2007. 32p. (J). 16.99 (*978-1-60336-456-0(0)) Mainstream Connections, Inc.

Ferguson, Donald. The Chums of Scranton High at Ice Hockey. 2006. 77.99 (*978-1-4142-5876-8(3)); pap. 70.99 (*978-1-4142-5881-2(X)) IndyPublish.com.

Ferguson, John B. Cindy Before. 2003. (YA). per. 10.95 (978-0-9728144-7-7(2)) Caslon Pr.

Fietzek, Petra. Trommeln, Trommeln. 2002. (GER.). 128p. pap. 15.00 (978-1-4000-3958-6(4) , New Media German Language) Random House Foreign Language Publishing.

Flower, Graham Jessie. Grace Harlowes Return to Overton Campus. 2006. 63.99 (*978-1-4280-2335-2(6)) IndyPublish.com.

Flower, Jessie Graham. Grace Harlowe's Return to Overton Campus. l.t. ed. 2006. 154p. pap. 11.99 (*978-1-4264-3783-0(8)); 174p. pap. 14.99 (*978-1-4264-3853-0(2)) BiblioBazaar.

—Grace Harlowe's Return to Overton Campus. 2004. reprint ed. pap. 20.95 (978-1-4191-2222-4(3)); pap. 1.99 (978-1-4192-2222-1(8)) Kessinger Publishing, LLC.

—Grace Harlowe's Second Year at Overton College. 2004. reprint ed. pap. 20.95 (978-1-4191-2223-1(1)); pap. 1.99 (978-1-4192-2223-8(6)) Kessinger Publishing, LLC.

Foglio, Phil & Foglio, Kaja. Agatha Heterodyne & the Clockwork Princess. 2006. (Girl Genius Ser.: Vol. 5). (Illus.). 112p. (YA). pap. 19.95 (978-1-890856-39-7(8)) Studio Foglio, LLC.

Frank, E. R. Friction. 208p. (YA). 2003. (Illus.). 16.95 (978-0-689-85384-5(X) , Atheneum/Richard Jackson Bks.); 2004. reprint ed. pap. 6.99 (978-0-689-85385-2(8) , Simon Pulse) Simon & Schuster Children's Publishing.

Frankel, Valerie. American Fringe. 2008. 272p. (gr. 12 up). 9.99 (*978-0-451-22292-3(X) , N A L Trade) Penguin Group (USA) Inc.

Fujishima, Kosuke. Oh My Goddess!, Vol. 25. 2007. 176p. (J). pap. 10.95 (978-1-59307-644-3(4)) Dark Horse Comics.

Fuller, Mary. Tattletale, Tattletail. 2007. 32p. (J). per. 10.99 (*978-1-60247-303-4(X)) Tate Publishing & Enterprises, L.L.C.

Gallegos, Manuel. El Cisne y la Luna. 2001. (YA). (978-956-240-301-6(7)) Arrayan Editores S.A.

Gephart, Donna. As If Being 12 3/4 Isn't Bad Enough, My Mother Is Running for President! 2008. (J). (gr. 3-7). 240p. 15.99 (*978-0-385-73481-3(6)); 192p. lib. bdg. 18.99 (*978-0-385-90479-7(7)) Random Hse. Children's Bks. (Delacorte Bks. for Young Readers).

Goodman, Susan E. Adventures in the Amazon Rain Forest. 1999. (978-0-606-16324-8(7)) Tandem Library Bks.

Grace, N. B. Broadway Dreams. rev. ed. 2007. (High School Musical Ser.: No. 5). 128p. (gr. 3-7). pap. 4.99 (*978-1-4231-0623-4(7)) Disney Pr.

Grant, Robert. Jack in the Bush or A Summer on a Salmon River. 2005. pap. 33.95 (978-1-4179-5573-2(2)) Kessinger Publishing, LLC.

Greene, Janice. The Plot: Set 3. 2002. 32p. (YA). 2.95 (978-1-56254-431-7(4) , SP 4314) Saddleback Educational Publishing.

Hagen, Michael. The African Term. Kemnitz, Myrna, ed. 1998. 81p. (YA). (gr. 8 up). 9.99 (978-0-88092-368-2(7)) Royal Fireworks Publishing Co.

Haigh, Liz. The Dragon's Ring. 2002. (Illus.). 80p. pap. 11.95 (978-1-85902-724-0(5)) Beekman Bks., Inc.

Hancock, H. Irving. The High School Captain of the Team. rev. ed. 2006. 212p. 27.95 (978-1-4218-1740-8(3)); pap. 12.95 (978-1-4218-1840-5(X)) 1st World Publishing, Inc. (1st World Library - Literary Society).

—The High School Freshmen. rev. ed. 2006. 212p. 27.95 (978-1-4218-1741-5(1)); pap. 12.95 (978-1-4218-1841-2(8)) 1st World Publishing, Inc. (1st World Library - Literary Society).

—The High School Left End. rev. ed. 2006. 212p. 27.95 (978-1-4218-1742-2(X)); pap. 12.95 (978-1-4218-1842-9(6)) 1st World Publishing, Inc. (1st World Library - Literary Society).

Hancock, Irving H. The High School Captain of the Team or D. 2006. 78.99 (*978-1-4219-9894-7(7)); pap. 71.99 (*978-1-4219-9905-0(6)) IndyPublish.com.

—The High School Freshmen or Dick & Co. 's. 2006. 78.99 (*978-1-4219-9898-5(X)); pap. 72.99 (*978-1-4219-9901-2(3)) IndyPublish.com.

—The High School Left End or Dick & Co. G. 2006. 78.99 (*978-1-4219-9906-7(4)); pap. 72.99 (*978-1-4219-9911-1(0)) IndyPublish.com.

—The High School Pitcher or Dick & Co. on. 2006. 78.99 (*978-1-4219-9918-0(8)); pap. 72.99 (*978-1-4219-9929-6(3)) IndyPublish.com.

Harcourt School Publishers Staff. Two Fridas. 3rd ed. 2002. (Trophies English Language Learners Ser.). (Illus.). pap. 5.10 (978-0-15-327770-2(X)) Harcourt Schl. Pubs.

Harrison, Emma & SparkNotes Staff. Busted. 2004. (SAT Vocabulary Novels Ser.). (Illus.). 192p. pap. 7.95 (978-1-4114-0081-8(X)) Spark Publishing Group.

Herman, Gail. Everybody Hates Romeo & Juliet. 2007. (Everybody Hates Chris Ser.). 96p. (J). pap. 5.99 (*978-1-4169-3570-4(3) , Simon Spotlight) Simon & Schuster Children's Publishing.

Herman, Gail. Lucky Goes to School. Gorbaty, Norman, illus. 2001. (All Aboard Reading Ser.). 1p. (J). (ps-1). pap. 3.99 (978-0-448-42498-9(3) , Grosset & Dunlap) Penguin Group (USA) Inc.

High School Musical: All-Access. rev. ed. 2007. 32p. (J). (gr. 2-7). 19.99 (*978-1-4231-1066-8(8)) Disney Pr.

Hoffman, Alice. The River King. 2001. (gr. 7-12). lib. bdg. 23.45 (978-0-613-35818-7(X)) Tandem Library Bks.

Howe, James. Pinky & Rex & the School Play. 1999. (Pinky & Rex Ser.). (J). (gr. 1-4). pap., stu. ed. 22.24 incl. audio (978-0-7887-2984-3(5) , 40866) Recorded Bks., LLC.

—Pinky & Rex & the School Play. Sweet, Melissa, illus. 1998. (Pinky & Rex Ser.). (J). (gr. 1-4). (978-0-606-13707-2(6)) Tandem Library Bks.

James, Brian. Everybody Hates School Dances. 2007. (Everybody Hates Chris Ser.). 96p. (J). pap. 5.99 (*978-1-4169-3562-9(2) , Simon Spotlight) Simon & Schuster Children's Publishing.

Jones, Carrie. Tips on Having a Gay (ex) Boyfriend. 2007. (Illus.). 288p. (J). (gr. 7 up). 16.95 (978-0-7387-1050-1(4)) Llewellyn Pubns.

Jones, Jasmine. Best Dressed. 2004. 138p. (J). lib. bdg. 16.92 (*978-1-4242-0678-0(2)) Fitzgerald Bks.

—Mirror,Mirror. 2004. 151p. (J). lib. bdg. 16.92 (*978-1-4242-0675-9(8)) Fitzgerald Bks.

Jones, Jasmine. Picture This! 2003. (gr. 3-6). lib. bdg. 13.00 (978-0-613-68277-0(7)) Tandem Library Bks.

Jones, Jasmine, adapted by. Oh, Brother! 2005. 146p. (J). lib. bdg. 16.92 (*978-1-4242-0682-7(0)) Fitzgerald Bks.

Krulik, Nancy E. I Heard a Rumor. 2007. (How I Survived Middle School Ser.: No. 3). 112p. (J). pap. 4.99 (*978-0-439-02557-7(5)) Scholastic, Inc.

Langan, Paul. The Gun. Langan, Paul, ed. 2002. (Bluford Ser.: 6). 123p. (YA). mass mkt. 4.95 (978-0-944210-04-8(X)) Townsend Pr.

Langan, Paul. Payback. 2007. (Bluford Ser.: No. 6). 144p. (J). pap. 3.99 (*978-0-439-90487-2(0) , Scholastic Paperbacks) Scholastic, Inc.

Langan, Paul & Alirez, Ben. Brothers in Arms. 2008. (Bluford Ser.: No. 9). 160p. (J). pap. 3.99 (*978-0-439-90490-2(0) , Scholastic Paperbacks) Scholastic, Inc.

Langan, Paul & Blackwell, D. M. Blood Is Thicker. 2007. (Bluford Ser.: No. 8). (Illus.). 176p. (J). pap. 3.99 (*978-0-439-90489-6(7) , Scholastic Paperbacks) Scholastic, Inc.

Lasky, Kathryn. Show & Tell Bunnies. Hafner, Marylin, illus. 2001. 32p. (J). (ps-3). pap. 5.99 (978-0-7636-1050-0(X)) Candlewick Pr.

—Show & Tell Bunnies. 2001. (ps-2). lib. bdg. 14.15 (978-0-613-44257-2(1)) Tandem Library Bks.

Lee, YoungHee. You're So Cool Volume 2. 2007. (Illus.). 200p. (YA). pap. 10.95 (*978-89-527-4718-1(6)) ICE Kunion KOR. Dist: Diamond Bk. Distributors.

Lee, Younghee. You're So Cool Volume 3. 2007. 200p. (YA). pap. 10.95 (*978-89-527-4874-4(3)) ICE Kunion KOR. Dist: Diamond Bk. Distributors.

Lefevre, Arthur. What Price Life? 2005. reprint ed. pap. 15.95 (978-1-4191-6801-7(0)) Kessinger Publishing, LLC.

Lekich, John. King of the Lost & Found. 2007. 304p. (J). (gr. 7 up). pap. 9.95 (*978-1-55192-802-9(7)) Raincoast Bk. Distribution CAN. Dist: Perseus Distribution.

Lerangis, Peter. The Big Production, No. 2. 2007. (Drama Club Ser.). 240p. (YA). (gr. 7). 7.99 (*978-0-14-240887-2(5) , Puffin) Penguin Group (USA) Inc.

—The Fall Musical, No. 1. 2007. (Drama Club Ser.). 224p. (YA). (gr. 7). 7.99 (*978-0-14-240886-5(7) , Puffin) Penguin Group (USA) Inc.

Levy, Elizabeth. Parents' Night Fright, 6. 1998. (Invisible Ink Ser.). (978-0-606-13526-9(X)) Tandem Library Bks.

—Third Grade Bullies. 1998. (Hyperion Chapters Ser.). (978-0-606-13844-4(7)) Tandem Library Bks.

Lewis, Corey & Ko, Erik. Rival Schools. 2007. (Illus.). 200p. (YA). pap. 12.95 (*978-0-9738652-2-6(9)) URON Entertainment Corp. CAN. Dist: Diamond Bk. Distributors.

Lockwood, Cara. The Scarlet Letterman. 2007. (Bard Academy Ser.). 320p. pap. 9.95 (978-1-4165-2490-8(8) , MTV) Simon & Schuster.

Lutzen, Hanna. Vlad the Undead. 2001. (gr. 7-12). lib. bdg. 14.10 (978-0-613-88930-8(4)) Tandem Library Bks.

Madonna. A Rose by Any Other Name. Fulvimari, Jeffrey, illus. 2007. (English Roses Ser.). 125p. (J). (gr. 2). 9.99 (*978-0-14-240885-8(9) , Puffin) Penguin Group (USA) Inc.

Marrs, Christie, creator. The Perfect Gift. l.t. ed. 2004. (Illus.). 57p. (J). mass mkt. 5.99 (978-1-928890-19-5(9)) I.B. Hoofinit Co.

Mazer, Anne. Declaration of Independence. 2000. (Amazing Days of Abby Hayes Ser.: No. 2). (J). 11.64 (978-0-606-19552-2(1)) Tandem Library Bks.

McEwan, Jamie. Rufus the Scrub Does Not Wear a Tutu! Margeson, John, illus. 2007. 64p. (J). (gr. 2-3). 14.95 (*978-1-58196-060-0(3)) Darby Creek Publishing.

Miglis, Jenny. New Student Starfish. Martinez, Heather, illus. 2003. (SpongeBob SquarePants Ser.). 64p. (J). pap. 3.99 (978-0-689-86164-2(8) , Simon Spotlight) Simon & Schuster Children's Publishing.

—New Student Starfish. 2003. (gr. 3-6). lib. bdg. 11.80 (978-0-613-86195-3(7)) Tandem Library Bks.

Millman, Selena. Anyone Can Make A Difference. 2006. 109p. (YA). per. (*978-0-9793058-6-3(1)) Millman, Selena.

Mori, Kotaro. Stray Little Devil. 2006. (Illus.). 200p. (YA). Vol. 2. pap. 9.95 (*978-1-59796-044-1(6)); Vol. 3. pap. 9.95 (*978-1-59796-045-8(4)) DrMaster Pubns. Inc.

—Stray Little Devil Volume 4. 2007. (Illus.). 200p. (YA). pap. 9.95 (*978-1-59796-046-5(2)) DrMaster Pubns. Inc.

Napoli, Donna Jo. Running Away. 2000. (Angelwings Ser.: No. 10). 96p. (J). (gr. 2-6). pap. 7.95 (978-0-689-83210-9(9) , Aladdin) Simon & Schuster Children's Publishing.

—Running Away. 2000. (Angelwings Ser.: No. 10). (Illus.). (J). (978-0-606-20384-5(2)) Tandem Library Bks.

Oboh, Rolic. Treasure Hunt. 2006. pap. (*978-1-84426-318-9(5)) Upfront Publishing Ltd.

Ostow, Micol. Westminster Abby. 2005. (S. A. S. S. (Students Across the Seven Seas) Ser.). (Illus.). 192p. (YA). (gr. 6). pap. 6.99 (978-0-14-240413-3(6) , Puffin) Penguin Group (USA) Inc.

Pahls, E. S. It's My Heaven. 2002. (gr. 7-12). lib. bdg. 30.35 (978-0-613-78040-7(X)) Tandem Library Bks.

Park, Barbara. Junie B., First Grader: Cheater Pants. 2004. (Junie B. Jones Ser.: No. 21). (J). (gr. k-3). lib. bdg. 11.80 (978-0-613-85713-0(5)) Tandem Library Bks.

Pascal, Francine. Elizabeth. 2000. (Secret Love Diaries). (gr. 7-12). lib. bdg. 12.40 (978-0-613-33043-5(9)) Tandem Library Bks.

—Una Larga Noche.Tr. of All Night Long. (SPA.). 128p. (J). 7.95 (978-84-272-3875-6(4)) Molino, Editorial ESP. Dist: AIMS International Bks., Inc.

—Peligrosa Tentacion.Tr. of Dangerous Love. (SPA., Illus.). 136p. (J). 7.95 (978-84-272-3876-3(2)) Molino, Editorial ESP. Dist: AIMS International Bks., Inc.

—Querida Hermana.Tr. of Dear Sister. (SPA., Illus.). 168p. (J). 7.95 (978-84-272-3877-0(0)) Molino, Editorial ESP. Dist: AIMS International Bks., Inc.

Paterson, Katherine. Marvin One Too Many. Clark Brown, Jane, illus. 2003. (Readalongs for Beginning Readers Ser.). (J). pap. 29.95 incl. audio (978-1-59112-255-5(4)); pap. 16.95 incl. audio (978-1-59112-253-1(8)) Live Oak Media.

Perelman-Bernstein, Helen. Heart to Heart. 6th rev. ed. 2007. (High School Musical Ser.: No. 6). 128p. (gr. 3-7). pap. 4.99 (*978-1-4231-0624-1(5)) Disney Pr.

Peretti, Frank E. Hangman's Curse. movie tie-in ed. 2003. (Veritas Project Ser.). 312p. (YA). pap. 9.99 (978-1-4003-0371-7(0)) Nelson, Thomas Inc.

—Hangman's Curse. 2003. (gr. 3-6). lib. bdg. 18.80 (978-0-613-77934-0(7)) Tandem Library Bks.

Pike, Christopher, pseud. The Graduation. 1998. (Final Friends Ser.: Vol. 3). (978-0-606-13883-8(6)) Tandem Library Bks.

Pinkwater, Daniel M. Second-Grade Ape. 1998. (978-0-606-13768-3(8)) Tandem Library Bks.

Pollack, Pam. The Exchange Student. 2001. (Malcolm in the Middle Ser.: Vol. 4). (Illus.). 112p. (J). (gr. 8). pap. 4.99 (978-0-439-22850-3(6)) Scholastic, Inc.

Pugin-Rodas, M. C. The Eight Ball Club: Ocean of Fire. 2007. (Illus.). 144p. pap. 15.95 (*978-0-9793761-2-2(2)) ESOL Publishing.

r, Edward (Winf. Rover Boys at College. 2006. pap. (*978-1-4068-3128-3(X)) Echo Library.

—Rover Boys at School. 2006. pap. (*978-1-4068-3129-0(8)) Echo Library.

Ramsey, R. M. The Browser Bunch: The Browser Files Presents... the Big Lie. 2006. (J). pap. 8.00 (*978-0-8059-7172-9(6)) Dorrance Publishing Co., Inc.

Regan, Dian Curtis. Cyberpals According to Kaley. 2006. 128p. (J). (gr. 3-5). 15.95 (978-1-58196-051-8(4)) Darby Creek Publishing.

Roach, Hesta. First Grade Again. 1998. (Illus.). 22p. (J). pap. 7.95 (978-0-9660583-1-4(3)) Sakura Pr.

Rogers, Karen M. Good Thinking! Ahers-Johnson, Patrizia, illus. 1998. (Think-Kids Book Collection). 16p. (J). (gr. 1-4). pap. 2.95 (978-1-58237-015-6(X)) Creative Thinkers, Inc.

Sachar, Louis. Sideways Stories from Wayside School. McCauley, Adam, illus. rev. ed. 1998. (Wayside School Ser.). 128p. (J). (gr. 5 up). pap. 5.99 (978-0-380-73148-0(7) , Harper Trophy) HarperCollins Pubs.

Saenz, Benjamin Alire. Sammy & Juliana in Hollywood. 2004. 240p. (YA). 19.95 (978-0-938317-81-4(4)) Cinco Puntos Pr.

Scholastic, Inc. Staff. Have a Great Summer, 30 vols. 1999. (J). pap. 3.95 (978-0-439-07235-9(2)) Scholastic, Inc.

Schraff, Anne. Twin. 2000. (gr. 7-12). lib. bdg. 12.95 (978-0-613-51059-2(3)) Tandem Library Bks.

Schuck, Philip. A Ricochet from Circumstance. 2005. (YA). 19.95 (978-0-9764670-0-7(3)) Smithfield Capital Corp.

Seymour, Tres. The Revelation of Saint Bruce. 1998. (Illus.). 128p. (YA). (gr. 7-12). pap. 16.95 (978-0-531-30109-8(5) , Orchard Bks.) Scholastic, Inc.

Sherman, Deborah. Triple Chocolate Brownie Genius. 2007. 120p. (J). (gr. 4-6). pap. (*978-1-55455-035-7(1)) Fitzhenry & Whiteside, Ltd.

Sherrill, Ronda Scott. Going to Long Valley. 2004. 199p. pap. 19.95 (978-1-4137-3160-6(0)) PublishAmerica, Inc.

The Shoe Grabber: Individual Title Six-Pack. (Story Steps Ser.). (gr. k-2). 23.00 (978-0-7635-9832-7(1)) Rigby Education.

Smith, Betty. Joy in the Morning. 2000. (gr. 7-12). lib. bdg. 22.25 (978-0-8085-1474-9(1)) Tandem Library Bks.

Standish, Burt L. Frank Merriwell's Pupils. Rudman, Jack, ed. 2003. (Frank Merriwell Ser.). pap. 9.95 (978-0-8373-9133-5(4)) Merriwell, Frank Inc.

Strasser, Todd. Help! I'm Trapped in My Lunch Lady's Body. 1999. (Help! I'm Trapped Ser.). 144p. (gr. 4-7). pap. 4.50 (978-0-590-97805-7(5)) Scholastic, Inc.

—Help! I'm Trapped in My Lunch Lady's Body. 1999. (Help! I'm Trapped Ser.). (J). (gr. 4-7). (978-0-606-17543-2(1)) Tandem Library Bks.

Stratemeyer, Edward. The Rover Boys at College or the Right R. 2004. reprint ed. pap. 22.95 (978-1-4191-8114-6(9)) Kessinger Publishing, LLC.

—The Rover Boys at College or the Right Road & the Wrong. 2004. reprint ed. pap. 1.99 (978-1-4192-8114-3(3)) Kessinger Publishing, LLC.

Tchudi, Steven. The Valedictorian. 2001. 217p. (YA). (gr. 9-17). pap. 9.99 (978-0-88092-448-1(9)) Royal Fireworks Publishing Co.

There's No Room for You, Maddie Morrison. 2006. (J). per. 6.99 (978-0-9786117-0-5(5)) Neal Morgan Publishing.

Thomas, Paul R., reader. The Reeve's Tale. 2006. pap. 10.00 (*978-0-8425-2667-8(6)) Brigham Young Univ.

Thompson, Michelle. Annie's Secret. 2004. 83p. pap. 14.95 (978-1-4137-3362-4(X)) PublishAmerica, Inc.

Thouin, Juanita. Eight O'Clock Classes: And Other Life-Threatening Situations. 1998. (Illus.). 144p. (YA). pap. 9.99 (978-1-57921-104-2(6)) WinePress Publishing.

Tierno, Susan F. Have You Done Your Homework? Ramirez, Michael, illus. 1998. (Think-Kids Book Collection). 16p. (J). (gr. 1-4). pap. 2.95 (978-1-58237-012-5(5)) Creative Thinkers, Inc.

—I Hate Projects. Schiffman, Jessica, illus. 1998. (Think-Kids Book Collection). 16p. (J). (gr. 1-4). pap. 2.95 (978-1-58237-017-0(6)) Creative Thinkers, Inc.

Tomlinson, Everett T. Winning His W. 2006. pap. (*978-1-4068-1194-0(7)) Echo Library.

Tripathi, Namrata. Happy Graduation. Couri, Kathy, illus. 2003. (Sing-Along Storybks.). 12p. (J). (ps-1). bds. 6.99 (978-0-06-001009-6(6) , Harper Entertainment) HarperCollins Pubs.

Umezu, Kazuo. The Drifting Classroom, Vol. 8. Roman, Annette, ed. Umezu, Kazuo, illus. 2007. (Drifting Classroom Ser.). 192p. (YA). pap. 9.99 (*978-1-4215-0960-0(1)) Viz Media.

Uncle Tom's Cabin: Response Journal. 2003. 48p. (YA). (978-1-58049-983-5(X) , RJ83) Prestwick Hse., Inc.

Wallace, Karen. Climbing a Monkey Puzzle Tree. 2004. 208p. (YA). (gr. 7-9). pap. 9.99 (978-0-689-83763-0(1)) Simon & Schuster, Ltd. GBR. Dist: Independent Pubs. Group.

Walters, Eric. Stuffed. 2006. 112p. (gr. 3-6). lib. bdg. 14.95 (978-1-55143-519-0(5)); (gr. 7-12). pap. 7.95 (978-1-55143-500-8(4)) Orca Bk. Pubs. USA.

Warde, Margaret. Betty Wales, Sophomore. 2006. 63.99 (*978-1-4219-9626-4(X)); pap. 57.99 (*978-1-4219-9627-1(8)) IndyPublish.com.

Webster, Jean. Daddy Long Legs. 2004. reprint ed. pap. 19.95 (978-1-4191-1490-8(5)); pap. 1.99 (978-1-4192-1490-5(X)) Kessinger Publishing, LLC.

Weinberger, Kimberly. Wizz. 2000. (Teacher's Pet Ser.: Vol. 4). (J). pap. 4.95 (978-0-439-13247-3(9)) Scholastic, Inc.

Weisberg, Joseph. 10th Grade: A Novel. 2003. (gr. 7-12). lib. bdg. 21.05 (978-0-613-62920-1(5)) Tandem Library Bks.

West, Tracey. Game On! 2007. (Yu-gi-oh Ser.: No. 1). (Illus.). 96p. (J). pap. 4.99 (*978-0-439-87394-9(0)) Scholastic, Inc.

Weston, Alan & Gempko, Gloria. The Girl from Keelonia. 2003. (J). pap. 7.95 (978-0-9742808-0-6(1)) Lill-Till Pr.

White, Ellen Emerson. Long May She Reign. 2007. 720p. (YA). (gr. 7 up). pap. 15.95 (*978-0-312-36767-1(8)) Feiwel & Friends.

Winfield, Arthur M. Rover Boys at College or the Right Road. 2006. pap. 30.95 (*978-1-4286-4106-8(8)) Kessinger Publishing, LLC.

—The Rover Boys down East or the Struggle for the Stanhope Fortune. 2006. (ENG.). 316p. per. 30.95 (*978-1-4286-4113-6(0)) Kessinger Publishing, LLC.

—Rover Boys in Alaska or Lost in the Fiel. 2006. pap. 30.95 (*978-1-4286-4107-5(6)) Kessinger Publishing, LLC.

—The Rover Boys in Business or the Search for the Missing Bonds. 2006. (ENG.). 316p. per. 30.95 (*978-1-4286-4098-6(3)) Kessinger Publishing, LLC.

—The Rover Boys in the Air or from College Campus to the Clouds. 2006. (ENG.). 316p. per. 30.95 (*978-1-4286-4103-7(3)) Kessinger Publishing, LLC.

—Rover Boys on A Tour or Last Days at Bri. 2006. pap. 31.95 (*978-1-4286-4389-5(3)) Kessinger Publishing, LLC.

Winfield, M. Arthur. The Rover Boys at College or the Right R. 2006. 96.99 (*978-1-4219-7415-6(0)); pap. 90.99 (*978-1-4219-7402-6(9)) IndyPublish.com.

Wing, Natasha. The Night Before Kindergarten. Durrell, Julie, illus. 2001. (Reading Railroad Bks.). 32p. (J). (ps-1). mass mkt. 3.99 (978-0-448-42500-9(9) , Grosset & Dunlap) Penguin Group (USA) Inc.

Woo, Soo Jung. Legend Volume 3. 2007. (Illus.). 200p. (YA). pap. 10.95 (*978-89-527-4712-9(7)) ICE Kunion KOR. Dist: Diamond Bk. Distributors.

—Legend Volume 4. 2007. 200p. (YA). pap. 10.95 (*978-89-527-4871-3(9)) ICE Kunion KOR. Dist: Diamond Bk. Distributors.

—Legend Volume 5. 2007. 200p. (YA). pap. 10.95 (*978-89-527-4883-6(2)) ICE Kunion KOR. Dist: Diamond Bk. Distributors.

Zoehfeld, Kathleen Weidner & Random House Disney Staff. Time for School, Pooh. Cuddy, Robbin, illus. 2001. 24p. (J). (gr. k-3). pap. 3.25 (978-0-7364-1179-0(8) , RH/Disney) Random Hse. Children's Bks.

STUDENTS—PERSONNEL WORK

see Educational Counseling

STUDY, METHOD OF

see Study Skills

STUDY SKILLS

see also Self-Culture

also subjects with the subdivision Study and Teaching, e.g. Art—Study and Teaching, etc.

Albrecht, Jeff. Watch Me Grow. 2001. (gr. k-3). lib. bdg. 10.65 (978-0-613-86249-3(X)) Tandem Library Bks.

Alphabet, Colors, & Numbers. . . 2000. (Kelley Wingate Ser.). 80p. (J). (ps-k). pap. 9.99 (978-0-88724-591-6(9)) Carson-Dellosa Publishing Co., Inc.

American Girl Editors, ed. School Smarts Planner. 2007. 112p. (J). pap. 9.95 (*978-1-59369-168-4(8) , Pleasant Co.) American Girl Publishing, Inc.

Anhalt, Edward. Raise Your GPA 1 Full Grade. 2003. 265p. (YA). pap. 19.95 (978-0-595-24645-8(1) , Writers Club Pr.) iUniverse, Inc.

Ashley, Susan A. I Can Do It! 24p. 115.98 (978-0-8368-4322-4(3)) Stevens, Gareth Inc.

Bautista, Veltisezar B. Improve Your Grades: How to Become an Honor Student. 3rd ed. 2000. (Illus.). 256p. pap. 16.95 (978-0-931613-16-6(7)) Bookhaus Pubs.

Beck, Isabel. Questioning the Author: An Approach for Enhancing Student Engagement with Text. 122p. 84.95 incl. DVD (978-0-322-04355-8(7)) Wright Group, The.

Bergstrom, Joan M. Cuaderno Ayuda Tareas. 1999. Tr. of Homework Helper. (SPA., Illus.). 27p. (J). (gr. k-6). 20.00 (978-1-931042-25-3(X)) Activities Club, Inc., The.

Berry, Ron. What Nerds Don't Want You to Know! Sharp, Chris, illus. 2000. (Nerds' Secrets Ser.). 40p. (YA). 12.99 (978-1-891100-72-7(6)) Smart Kids Publishing.

Bidaisee, Sharlini. Toddler's Basic Knowledge. 2006. 13p. (J). 10.30 (978-1-4116-6849-2(9)) Lulu.com.

Black, Howard, et al. Learning on Purpose: A Self-Management Approach to Study Skills. 2003. (YA). pap. 34.99 (978-0-89455-753-8(X)) Critical Thinking Bks. & Software.

Caillou: Thinking Skills. 2003. 32p. pap., wbk. ed. 14.95 incl. cd-rom (978-1-57791-030-5(3)) Brighter Minds Children's Publishing.

Cali, Charlene C. The Nature of Study Skills: Hardworking Helen K Honeybee Study Skills 3. Norcross, Harry, illus. 56p. (J). (gr. 8-9). 14.95 (978-1-57543-101-7(7)) MAR*CO Products, Inc.

Carriero, John Peter. Staying on Top of Things Before It's Too Late: High School Handbook - 1st Year Academic Excellence & More, 1 cass. Carriero, John Peter, ed. 2001st rev. ed. 2001. (Illus.). 54p. (YA). per. 9.00 (978-0-9703109-1-0(9)) McQuaid Jesuit High Schl.

Cassel, Katrina L. The Junior High Survival Manual. 1998. 128p. (YA). (gr. 8-12). 7.99 (978-0-570-05062-9(6)) Concordia Publishing Hse.

—Junior High Survival Manual. 1998. (gr. 7-12). lib. bdg. 16.45 (978-0-613-72804-1(1)) Tandem Library Bks.

Childs, Mattie S. Lesson Helpers. 2004. 74p. (YA). per. 19.99 (978-1-4116-0948-8(4)) Lulu.com.

Creative Imaging. 2nd ed. 2004. 116p. (YA). pap. (978-0-938465-01-0(5)) Zo Publishing.

Dalmatian Press Staff. Kindergarten Workbook: Complete Curriculum of Basic Skills. 2002. (Home Learning Tools Ser.). (Illus.). 384p. (J). (gr. k-1). pap., wbk. ed. 12.99 (978-1-57759-622-6(6)) Dalmatian Pr.

—Preschool Workbook: Complete Curriculum of Basic Skills. 2002. (Home Learning Tools Ser.). (Illus.). 384p. (J). (ps up). pap., wbk. ed. 12.99 (978-1-57759-621-9(8)) Dalmatian Pr.

—Second Grade Workbook: Complete Curriculum of Basic Skills. 2002. (Home Learning Tools Ser.). (Illus.). 384p. (J). (gr. 2-3). pap., wbk. ed. 12.99 (978-1-57759-624-0(2)) Dalmatian Pr.

Daly, Gayle H. Scissors, Glue & Phonological Processes, Too! 1999. (Scissors, Glue Ser.). (Illus.). 174p. (J). (ps-4). stu. ed., spiral bd. 37.95 (978-0-7606-0303-1(0) , 6-0303-0A1) LinguiSystems, Inc.

Davis. Test Practice. 1999. (Illus.). (J). (gr. 2). pap. (978-0-8172-3786-8(0)); (gr. 3). pap. (978-0-8172-3787-5(9)); (gr. 4). pap. (978-0-8172-3788-2(7)); (gr. 5). pap. (978-0-8172-3789-9(5)); (gr. 6). pap. (978-0-8172-3790-5(9)) Steck-Vaughn.

Dimitrova, Evelina & Galaczi, Arpad. Scott Foresman Proulex, in Charge, Vol. 1. 2nd ed. 2002. (Illus.). 128p. (C). pap. 18.66 (978-0-13-098693-1(3)) Longman Publishing Group.

Doherty, Edith J. S. Primary Independent. 60p. (J). pap., stu. ed. 14.95 (978-0-945984-06-1(5) , Zephyr Pr.) Chicago Review Pr., Inc.

Doherty, Edith J. S. & Evans, Louise C. Primary Independent Study. 2003. 60p. (J). pap. 14.95 (978-0-945984-05-4(7) , Zephyr Pr.) Chicago Review Pr., Inc.

—Self-Starter Kit for Independent Study. 2000. 166p. (J). spiral bd. 27.95 (978-0-945984-95-5(2) , Zephyr Pr.) Chicago Review Pr., Inc.

Dot-to-Dot Stories. 2004. (Kids Can Learn with Franklin Ser.). (Illus.). 32p. (J). (gr. k-3). (978-1-55337-600-2(5)) Kids Can Pr., Ltd.

Douglas, Vincent. Comprehensive Curriculum Plus Test Practice. Grade 2. 2003. (Comprehensive Curriculum Plus Test Practice Ser.). (Illus.). 616p. (J). (ps-6). pap. 24.95 (978-0-7696-2902-5(4) , American Education Publishing) School Specialty Publishing.

—Comprehensive Curriculum Plus Test Practice: Grade K. 2003. (Comprehensive Curriculum Plus Test Practice Ser.). (Illus.). 616p. (J). (ps-6). pap. 24.95 (978-0-7696-2900-1(8) , American Education Publishing) School Specialty Publishing.

—Early School Skills. 2004. (C). 16.95 (978-1-58845-661-8(7)) School Specialty Publishing.

Douglas, Vincent & School Specialty Publishing Staff. Comprehensive Curriculum of Basic Skills, Grade 1. 2001. (Comprehensive Curriculum of Basic Skills Ser.). (Illus.). 544p. (J). (ps-6). pap., wbk. ed. 19.95 (978-1-56189-368-3(4) , 60011, American Education Publishing) School Specialty Publishing.

—Comprehensive Curriculum Plus Test Practice, Grade 1. 2003. (Comprehensive Curriculum Plus Test Practice Ser.). (Illus.). 616p. (J). (ps-6). pap. 24.95 (978-0-7696-2901-8(6) , American Education Publishing) School Specialty Publishing.

—Comprehensive Curriculum Plus Test Practice, Grade 3. 2003. (Comprehensive Curriculum Plus Test Practice Ser.). (Illus.). 616p. (J). (ps-6). pap. 24.95 (978-0-7696-2903-2(2) , American Education Publishing) School Specialty Publishing.

—Comprehensive Curriculum Plus Test Practice, Grade 4. 2003. (Comprehensive Curriculum Plus Test Practice Ser.). (Illus.). 616p. (J). (ps-6). pap. 24.95 (978-0-7696-2904-9(0) , American Education Publishing) School Specialty Publishing.

—Kindergarten. 2001. (Comprehensive Curriculum of Basic Skills Ser.). (Illus.). 544p. (J). (ps-6). pap., wbk. ed. 19.95 (978-1-56189-367-6(6) , 60010, American Education Publishing) School Specialty Publishing.

S

—Smart 2 the Max Basic Skills, Grade 1. 2004. (Smart 2 the Max Ser.). (Illus.). 416p. (J). (ps-1). pap. 12.99 (978-0-7696-3361-9(7) , American Education Publishing) School Specialty Publishing.

—Smart 2 the Max Basic Skills, Kindergarten. 2004. (Smart 2 the Max Ser.). (Illus.). 416p. (J). (ps-1). pap. 12.99 (978-0-7696-3360-2(9) , American Education Publishing) School Specialty Publishing.

—Smart 2 the Max Learning Activities, Grade 1. 2004. (Smart 2 the Max Ser.). (Illus.). 416p. (J). (ps-1). pap. 12.99 (978-0-7696-3371-8(4) , American Education Publishing) School Specialty Publishing.

—Using the Standards in Grade Five. 2003. (Illus.). 128p. (J). (gr. 5-5). pap. 13.99 (978-0-7424-1945-2(2) , IFG99114, Instructional Fair) Schaffer, Frank Pubns.

—Using the Standards in Grade Four. 2003. (Illus.). 128p. (J). (gr. 4-4). pap. 13.99 (978-0-7424-1944-5(4) , IFG99115, Instructional Fair) Schaffer, Frank Pubns.

—Using the Standards in Grade One. 2003. (Illus.). 128p. (J). (gr. 1-1). pap. 13.99 (978-0-7424-1941-4(X) , IFG99116, Instructional Fair) Schaffer, Frank Pubns.

—Using the Standards in Grade Six. 2003. (Illus.). 128p. (J). (gr. 6-6). pap. 13.99 (978-0-7424-1946-9(0) , IFG99117, Instructional Fair) Schaffer, Frank Pubns.

—Using the Standards in Grade Three. 2003. (Illus.). 128p. (J). (gr. 3-3). pap. 13.99 (978-0-7424-1943-8(6) , IFG99118, Instructional Fair) Schaffer, Frank Pubns.

—Using the Standards in Grade Two. 2003. (Illus.). 128p. (J). (gr. 2-2). pap. 13.99 (978-0-7424-1942-1(8) , IFG99119, Instructional Fair) Schaffer, Frank Pubns.

DynaNotes Test Taking Tips. 2006. (J). pap. (978-1-933854-37-3(5)) DynaStudy, Inc.

DynaNotes Test Taking Tips Transparency Set. 2006. (J). trans. (978-1-933854-38-0(3)) DynaStudy, Inc.

Elms, Mae D. My A B C's to Learning. l.t. ed. 2000. 28p. (J). (gr. 1-6). pap. 12.95 (978-1-930002-25-8(4)) I & L Publishing.

Falligant, Erin, ed. School Smarts Homework Survival Guide. 2007. 84p. (J). pap. 8.95 (***978-1-59369-174-5(2)** , Pleasant Co.) American Girl Publishing, Inc.

Farrell, Juliana. High School: The Real Deal. 2001. (gr. 7-12). lib. bdg. 16.40 (978-0-613-81954-1(3)) Tandem Library Bks.

Fisher, Ann. Quick Thinkers: 365 Challenges to Fill Those Idle Moments. 1999. 96p. (J). (gr. 5-8). pap. 10.99 (978-1-56822-623-1(3) , IF2524) School Specialty Publishing.

For the 1st Grade Graduate. (Summer Skills Ser.). 104p. (ps-4). 12.99 (978-0-7682-0039-3(3) , FS23403) Schaffer, Frank Pubns.

For the 2nd Grade Graduate. (Summer Skills Ser.). 104p. (ps-4). 12.99 (978-0-7682-0040-9(7) , FS23404) Schaffer, Frank Pubns.

For the 3rd Grade Graduate. (Summer Skills Ser.). 104p. (ps-4). 12.99 (978-0-7682-0041-6(5) , FS23405) Schaffer, Frank Pubns.

For the 4th Grade Graduate. (Summer Skills Ser.). 104p. (ps-4). 12.99 (978-0-7682-0042-3(3) , FS23406) Schaffer, Frank Pubns.

For the Kindergarten Graduate. (Summer Skills Ser.). 104p. (ps-4). 12.99 (978-0-7682-0038-6(5) , FS23402) Schaffer, Frank Pubns.

For the Preschool Graduate. (Summer Skills Ser.). 104p. (ps-4). 12.99 (978-0-7682-0037-9(7) , FS23401) Schaffer, Frank Pubns.

Fox, Janet S. Get Organized Without Losing It. 2005. (Laugh & Learn Ser.). (Illus.). 112p. (J). (gr. 3-8). pap. 8.95 (978-1-57542-193-3(3)) Free Spirit Publishing, Inc.

Freitag, Jan Armstrong. Fresh & Fun Calendar Activities. 2000. (Fresh & Fun Ser.). (Illus.). 32p. (J). 8.95 (978-0-439-10613-9(3)) Scholastic, Inc.

Fry, Ron. Como Planificar Tus Actividades Diarias. 2000. Tr. of Manage Your Time. (SPA.). 156p. (YA). 10.95 (978-84-241-2585-1(1) , EV11877) Everest de Ediciones y Distribucion, S.L. ESP. *Dist:* Lectorum Pubns., Inc.

Fulfilling the Dream: Going to College: Curriculum for College Transitions. 2001. (YA). 279p. pap., stu. ed. 30.00 (978-0-9710666-0-1(4)); 171p. spiral bd., wbk. ed. 30.00 (978-0-9710666-1-8(2)) Helping Teens Succeed, Inc.

Gabe, Janice E. Making the Grade: The Teen's Guide to Homework Success. Word Works Staff, illus. 2000. 72p. (YA). pap. 7.95 (978-0-9639023-1-3(8)) Professional Resource Pubns.

Gehret, Jeanne. The Don't-Give-Up Kid: And Learning Differences. DePauw, Sandra A., illus. 2nd rev. ed. 2003. 40p. (J). (gr. 1-5). 13.95 (978-0-9625136-3-3(6)) Verbal Images Pr.

Geiser, Traci Ferguson. Celebrate Reading: Teaching Reading Skills Using Multicultural Celebrations. Dobelmann, Collene, ed. 2005. (Celebrate the Months Ser.). (Illus.). 112p. (J). pap. (978-1-59198-179-4(4) , 4548) Creative Teaching Pr., Inc.

Golden, Nancy. School Smarts. 2002. (Smarts Ser.). (Illus.). (YA). (gr. 7-12). 44p. pap. 23.00 (978-0-516-23930-9(9)); 48p. pap. 6.95 (978-0-516-24015-2(3)) Scholastic Library Publishing. (Children's Pr.).

Goldhammer, Richard. Gotta Do Homework! Elephant Notes - Study Tips You'll Never Forget. 2003. (Elephant Notes Ser.). (YA). (gr. 6-8). spiral bd. (978-0-9716873-0-1(7)) ElephantSide Pr.

Green, Bea, et al. Five-Minute Warm-Ups for Elementary Grades. rev. ed. 2004. 96p. (J). per. 11.95 (978-0-86530-625-7(7)) Incentive Pubns., Inc.

—Five-Minute Warm-Ups for Middle Grades. rev. ed. 2004. 96p. (YA). per. 11.95 (978-0-86530-626-4(5)) Incentive Pubns., Inc.

Green, Gordon W. How to Get Straight A's In School & Have Fun at the Same Time. 1999. (Illus.). (YA). 17.60 (978-0-606-18630-8(1)) Tandem Library Bks.

Green, Gordon W., Jr. How to Get Straight A's in School & Have Fun at the Same Time. rev. ed. 1999. 192p. pap. 10.95 (978-0-312-86659-4(3) , Forge Bks.) Doherty, Tom Assocs., LLC.

Greene, Lawrence J. Winning the Study Game (Consumable Edition) Learning How to Succeed in School. 2002. 250p. (gr. 6-11). lib. bdg., stu. ed. 14.95 (978-1-890455-47-7(4) , P801) Peytral Pubns., Inc.

—Winning the Study Game (Reproducible Edition) Learning How to Succeed in School. 2002. 240p. (gr. 6-11). pap., stu. ed. 34.95 (978-1-890455-48-4(2) , P802) Peytral Pubns., Inc.

Grundon, Holly & Novelli, Joan. Smart Pads! Following Directions: 40 Fun Games to Help Kids Master Following Directions. 2005. 48p. pap. 7.99 (978-0-439-72077-9(X) , Teaching Resources) Scholastic, Inc.

Hagerty, Carol, ed. Dracula Study Guide. 1998. (Classics Ser.: Set II). 48p. (YA). (gr. 5-12). pap., stu. ed. 17.95 (978-1-56254-263-4(X) , SP263X) Saddleback Educational Publishing.

Hands-On Literacy Center - Farm Set. (J). (ps-1). pap. 149.00 (978-0-9673268-9-4(3)) Learning Fasten-Ations, Inc.

Harcourt School Publishers Staff. Horizon: Test Prep Answer Key: Indiana Edition. 2nd ed. 2002. (Illus.). (gr. 4). pap. 14.90 (978-0-15-335693-3(6)) Harcourt Schl. Pubs.

—Horizon: Test Prep Answer Key: North Carolina. 2nd ed. 2002. (gr. 4). pap. 14.40 (978-0-15-335722-0(3)) Harcourt Schl. Pubs.

—Horizon: Test Prep Answer Key: Virginia Edition. 2nd ed. 2002. (gr. 3). pap. 14.00 (978-0-15-335707-7(X)); (gr. 4). pap. 14.90 (978-0-15-335708-4(8)) Harcourt Schl. Pubs.

—Horizons: Test Prep Answer Key: Indiana Edition. 2nd ed. 2002. (Illus.). (gr. 3). pap. 14.00 (978-0-15-335692-6(8)) Harcourt Schl. Pubs.

—Horizons: Test Prep Answer Key: North Carolina Edition. 2nd ed. 2002. (gr. 3). pap. 14.40 (978-0-15-335721-3(5)) Harcourt Schl. Pubs.

—Horizons: Test Prep: Indiana Edition. 2nd ed. 2002. (Illus.). (J). (gr. 3). pap. 7.40 (978-0-15-335688-9(X)) Harcourt Health Sciences Group.

—Horizons: Test Prep: Indiana Edition. 2nd ed. 2002. (Illus.). (gr. 4). pap. 10.80 (978-0-15-335689-6(8)) Harcourt Schl. Pubs.

—Horizons: Test Prep: Virginia Edition. 2nd ed. 2002. (Illus.). (J). (gr. 3). pap. 7.40 (978-0-15-335702-2(9)) Harcourt Health Sciences Group.

—Horizons: Test Prep: Virginia Edition. 2nd ed. 2002. (gr. 4). pap. 9.80 (978-0-15-335703-9(7)) Harcourt Schl. Pubs.

Harter, Faybeth, et al. Grade Boosters Second Grade. 1999. (Grade Boosters Ser.). (Illus.). 320p. (J). (gr. 1-3). pap. 18.95 (978-0-7373-0151-9(1) , 01511W) McGraw-Hill/Contemporary.

Hegarty, Carol, ed. The Adventures of Huckleberry Finn. 1998. (Classics Ser.: Set I). 48p. (YA). (gr. 5-12). pap., stu. ed. 17.95 (978-1-56254-251-1(6) , SP2516) Saddleback Educational Publishing.

—The Adventures of Tom Sawyer Study Guide. 1998. (Classics Ser.: Set II). 48p. (YA). (gr. 5-12). pap., stu. ed. 17.95 (978-1-56254-253-5(2) , SP2532) Saddleback Educational Publishing.

—The Call of the Wild. 1998. (Classics Ser.: Set I). 48p. (YA). (gr. 5-12). pap., stu. ed. 17.95 (978-1-56254-255-9(9) , SP2559) Saddleback Educational Publishing.

—A Christmas Carol Study Guide. 1998. (Classics Ser.: Set I). 48p. (YA). (gr. 5-12). pap., stu. ed. 17.95 (978-1-56254-257-3(5) , SP2575) Saddleback Educational Publishing.

—Dr. Jekyll & Mr. Hyde. 1998. (Classics Ser.: Set II). 48p. (YA). (gr. 5-12). stu. ed., per. 17.95 (978-1-56254-261-0(3) , SP2613) Saddleback Educational Publishing.

—Frankenstein. 1998. (Classics Ser.: Set I). 48p. (YA). (gr. 5-12). pap., stu. ed. 17.95 (978-1-56254-265-8(6) , SP2656) Saddleback Educational Publishing.

—Great Expectation. 1998. (Classics Ser.: Set II). 48p. (YA). (gr. 5-12). pap., stu. ed. 17.95 (978-1-56254-267-2(2) , SP2672) Saddleback Educational Publishing.

—Jayne Eyre Study Guide. 1998. (Classics Ser.: Set II). 48p. (YA). (gr. 5-12). pap., stu. ed. 17.95 (978-1-56254-269-6(9) , SP2699) Saddleback Educational Publishing.

—The Red Badge of Courage Study Guide. 1998. (Classics Ser.: Set I). 48p. (YA). (gr. 5-12). pap., stu. ed. 17.95 (978-1-56254-271-9(0) , SP2710) Saddleback Educational Publishing.

—Robinson Crusoe Study Guide. 1998. (Classics Ser.: Set II). 48p. (YA). (gr. 5-12). pap., stu. ed. 17.95 (978-1-56254-273-3(7) , SP2737) Saddleback Educational Publishing.

—A Tale of Two Cities. 1998. (Classics Ser.: Set I). 48p. (YA). (gr. 5-12). pap., stu. ed. 17.95 (978-1-56254-278-8(8) , SP2788) Saddleback Educational Publishing.

—The Time Machine. 1998. (Classics Ser.: Set II). 48p. (YA). (gr. 5-12). pap., stu. ed. 17.95 (978-1-56254-280-1(X) , SP280X) Saddleback Educational Publishing.

—Treasure Island. 1998. (Classics Ser.: Set I). 48p. (YA). (gr. 5-12). pap., stu. ed. 17.95 (978-1-56254-282-5(6) , SP2826) Saddleback Educational Publishing.

Heiderer, Conrad. Alpha-Blocke: Alpha-Blocke.com Learning Forum Animals, Art & the Alphabet Series with Case & Talking CD. 2004. (Illus.). 32p. spiral bd. 39.95 incl. audio compact disk (978-0-9746699-0-8(3)) Heiderer, Conrad.

HM Group Staff. HM Learning & Study Skills, Level I. 3rd ed. 2002. (HM Study Skills Group Ser.). (Illus.). 288p. pap., stu. ed. 12.95 (978-0-8108-4640-1(3)) Scarecrow Pr., Inc.

—HM Learning & Study Skills Program. 2000. pap., ldr.'s hndbk. ed. 9.95 (978-0-8108-3826-0(5)); Level I. ring bd., ldr.'s hndbk. ed. 9.95 (978-0-8108-3830-7(3)); Level II. pap., ldr.'s hndbk. ed. 9.95 (978-0-8108-3832-1(X)); Level A. 64p. pap., stu. ed. 9.95 (978-0-8108-3810-9(9)); Level B. 96p. pap., stu. ed. 12.95 (978-0-8108-3812-3(5)) Scarecrow Pr., Inc.

—HMS Level 2. 3rd ed. 2000. 112p. pap. 12.95 (978-0-8108-3802-4(8)) Scarecrow Pr., Inc.

—HMS Level 3. 2000. 64p. pap. 9.95 (978-0-8108-3804-8(4)) Scarecrow Pr., Inc.

Hollingsworth, Patricia L. Student's Overview Book. 2000. (Students' Active Interdisciplinary Learning Ser.). (Illus.). 72p. (YA). (gr. 1-13). pap. 20.00 (978-1-893413-08-5(X)) Univ. Schl. at the Univ. of Tulsa.

Holt, Rinehart and Winston Staff. Holt Science & Technology: Directed Reading Answer Key. 4th ed. 2004. (Illus.). pap. 11.20 (978-0-03-037018-2(3)); pap. 11.20 (978-0-03-037019-9(1)); pap. 11.20 (978-0-03-037021-2(3)) Holt, Rinehart & Winston.

—Holt Science & Technology: Directed Reading Worksheets. 4th ed. 2004. pap. 15.00 (978-0-03-036992-6(4)); pap. 15.00 (978-0-03-036993-3(2)); pap. 15.00 (978-0-03-036994-0(0)) Holt, Rinehart & Winston.

HOP, LLC. Hooked on Kindergarten. 2006. 99.99 (978-1-933863-88-7(9)) HOP, LLC.

—Hooked on Pre-K. 2006. 99.99 (978-1-933863-89-4(7)) HOP, LLC.

—Sylvan School Success. 2006. 199.99 (978-1-931020-76-3(0)) HOP, LLC.

Howe, Wally. Life's Little Study Tips. 99p. (YA). pap. 6.00 (978-0-86806-534-2(X)) Hale & Iremonger Pty., Ltd. AUS. *Dist:* Empire Publishing Service.

Howes, Jacqueline Johnson. Instant & Interactive Math Picturepages with Activities. 2000. (J). 12.95 (978-0-439-07748-4(6)) Scholastic, Inc.

Hubbard, L. Ron. Learning How to Learn. (Illus.). 208p. (J). (gr. 3-7). 43.75 (978-0-88404-771-1(7)) Bridge Pubns., Inc.

Hubbard, L.Ron. Learning How to Learn. 2000. (CHI, CZE, DAN, FRE & GER., Illus.). 208p. (J). (gr. 3-7). per. 14.95 (978-1-58460-005-3(5)) Effective Education Publishing.

—Study Skills for Life. 2000. (CHI., Illus.). 142p. (YA). (gr. 7-10). per. 14.95 (978-1-58460-003-9(9)) Effective Education Publishing.

Jeffrey, Stephen A. How to Fail at College. 2003. (ENG.). 116p. 19.95 (***978-0-595-65581-6(5)***); 114p. (YA). pap. 9.95 (978-0-595-26338-7(0)) iUniverse, Inc. (Writers Club Pr.).

Jensen, Eric. Student Success Secrets. 5th ed. 2003. (Illus.). 256p. pap. 8.99 (978-0-7641-2007-7(7)) Barron's Educational Series, Inc.

Kaplan Staff. SCORE! Mountain Challenge Language Arts Workbook: Grade 2 (Ages 7-8) 2007. (Score Mountain Challenge Ser.). 160p. pap. 10.95 (978-1-4195-9460-1(5)) Kaplan Publishing.

—Score! Mountian Challenge Language Arts Workbook, Grade 3 (Ages 8-9) 2007. (Score Mountain Challenge Ser.). 192p. pap. 10.95 (978-1-4195-9461-8(3)) Kaplan Publishing.

—Score! Mountian Challenge Language Arts Workbook, Grade 4 (Ages 9-10) 2007. (Score Mountain Challenge Ser.). 192p. pap. 10.95 (978-1-4195-9462-5(1)) Kaplan Publishing.

—Score Mountain Challenge Language Arts Workbook, Grade 5 (Ages 10-11) 2007. (Score Mountain Challenge Ser.). 192p. pap. 10.95 (978-1-4195-9463-2(X)) Kaplan Publishing.

—SCORE! Mountain Challenge Language Arts Workbook, Grade 6 (Ages 11-12) 2007. (Score Mountain Challenge Ser.). 192p. 10.95 (978-1-4195-9464-9(8)) Kaplan Publishing.

Kids Can Press Staff, Press Can. Measurement. 2004. (Kids Can Learn with Franklin Ser.). (Illus.). 32p. (J). (gr. k-3). (978-1-55337-595-1(5)) Kids Can Pr., Ltd.

Kindergarten Skills Booster. 2005. (J). per. 0.00 (978-1-59441-501-2(3) , C04033) Carson-Dellosa Publishing Co., Inc.

Lakeshore Learning Materials Staff, contrib. by. Big Book Theme Packets - Complete Set. 2000. (J). pap. 279.00 (978-1-929255-99-3(3)) Lakeshore Learning Materials.

—Classic Literature Theme Packets - Complete Set, 8 vols., Set. 2000. (J). 149.00 (978-1-929255-37-5(3)) Lakeshore Learning Materials.

Lambert, Monica & Algozzine, Bob. Strategies That Make Learning Fun. 2003. (Illus.). 184p. spiral bd. (978-1-57035-915-6(6) , 211LEARN) Sopris West Educational Services.

LeapFrog Staff & Disney Staff, compiled by. Monsters, Inc. 2002. (J). (gr. k-2). spiral bd. 14.99 (978-1-58605-187-7(3)) LeapFrog Enterprises, Inc.

Learning Company Books Staff, ed. Reader Rabbit 1st Grade Workbook. 2003. (Illus.). 320p. (J). (gr. 1 up). pap., wbk. ed. 14.99 (978-0-7630-7543-9(4)) Learning Co. Bks.

—Reader Rabbit Kindergarten Workbook. 2003. (Illus.). 320p. (J). (gr. k up). pap., wbk. ed. 14.99 (978-0-7630-7542-2(6)) Learning Co. Bks.

—Reader Rabbit Preschool Workbook. 2003. (Illus.). 320p. (J). (ps up). pap., wbk. ed. 14.99 (978-0-7630-7541-5(8)) Learning Co. Bks.

Learning Launchers Staff, et al. Curriculum Yellow Pages: 501 Web Sites Featuring Free Worksheets, Unit Studies, Lesson Plans, Tools & Resources for Grades K-12. 2002. 120p. (gr. k-12). per. 19.95 (978-1-891400-04-9(5)) Champion Pr., Ltd.

Learning-to-Go. (Illus.). (J). pap. 8.95 (978-1-55254-122-7(3) , BV24008) Brighter Vision Pubns.

Lowe, Dave C. & Guianan, Eve, illus. Grade Boosters First Grade Language. 1999. (Grade Boosters Ser.). 320p. (J). (ps-3). pap. 18.95 (978-0-7373-0149-6(X) , 0149XW) McGraw-Hill/Contemporary.

Mastering Fifth Grade Skills. 2006. 240p. (J). (gr. 5). 18.99 (978-1-4206-3941-4(2)) Teacher Created Resources, Inc.

McCutcheon, Randall. Get off My Brain: A Survival Guide for Lazy Students. 1998. (gr. 7-12). lib. bdg. 22.20 (978-0-613-82294-7(3)) Tandem Library Bks.

—Get off My Brain: A Survival Guide for Lazy* Students (*Bored, Frustrated, & Otherwise Sick of School) Wagner, Pete, illus. rev. ed. 1998. 112p. (YA). (gr. 10 up). pap. 12.95 (978-1-57542-037-0(6) , FS03) Free Spirit Publishing, Inc.

McGraw-Hill Staff. Magic Apple House: Basic Skills Builder. 1999. (J). (gr. k-2). pap. 19.95 (978-1-57768-302-5(1)) School Specialty Publishing.

—Scoring High. 1999. (J). (gr. 6-8). pap. 19.95 (978-1-57768-307-0(2)) School Specialty Publishing.

Moore, Gary W. Becoming a Master Student: Keys to Student Success. 2004. 305p. 38.00 (978-0-9760939-0-9(1) , 0-9760939-0-1) Tudor Assocs. Pr.

Morris, Daphne. Trevor Romain's How to Do Homework Without Throwing up DVD Educator Kit. 2007. (J). 69.99 (***978-1-934365-00-7(9)***) Trevor Romain Co., The.

—Trevor Romain's How to Do Homework Without Throwing up VHS Educator Kit. 2007. (J). 69.99 (***978-1-934365-01-4(7)***) Trevor Romain Co., The.

Moss, Marissa. Amelia's Book of Notes & Note Passing. Moss, Marissa, illus. 2006. (Amelia's Notebooks). (Illus.). 80p. (J). 9.95 (978-0-689-87446-8(4)) Simon & Schuster Children's Publishing.

Musso, Lori Licciardo. Teaching with Favorite Newbery Books. 1999. (978-0-606-17041-3(3)) Tandem Library Bks.

Nathan, Amy. Surviving Homework: Tips That Really Work! Green, Anne Canevari, illus. 1998. (Single Titles Ser.: 8). 80p. (gr. 4-8). pap. 8.95 (978-0-7613-0137-0(2) , Millbrook Pr.) Lerner Publishing Group.

The Need to Know Library: For Empowering Students with Knowledge, 8 bks. Incl. Everything You Need to Know about ADD/ADHD (Attention Deficit Disorder/Attention Deficit Hyperactivity Disorder) Beal, Eileen J. 1998. lib. bdg. 25.25 (978-0-8239-2748-7(2) , NTADDA); Everything You Need to Know about Anger. Licata, Renora. 1999. lib. bdg. 25.25 (978-0-8239-2953-5(1) , NTANGE); Everything You Need to Know about Being a Vegetarian. Serafin, Kim. 1999. lib. bdg. 25.25 (978-0-8239-2951-1(5) , NTVEGE); Everything You Need to Know about Drug Addiction. Nagle, Jeanne M. 1999. lib. bdg. 25.25 (978-0-8239-2772-2(5) , NTDRAD); Everything You Need to Know about Going to the Gynecologist. Diamond, Shifra N. 1999. lib. bdg. 25.25 (978-0-8239-2839-2(X) , NTGOGY); Everything You Need to Know about Sports Injuries. Clayton, Lawrence. 1999. lib. bdg. 25.25 (978-0-8239-2875-0(6) , NTSPIN); Everything You Need to Know about Staying Safe in Cyberspace. Croft, Jennifer. 1999. lib. bdg. 25.25 (978-0-8239-2957-3(4) , NTCYBE); Everything You Need to Know about Teen Suicide. Schleifer, Jay. 1999. lib. bdg. 25.25 (978-0-8239-3038-8(6) , NT-TESU); 64p. (YA). (gr. 7-12). (Illus.). 2005. Set lib. bdg. 202.00 (978-0-8239-9286-7(1)) Rosen Publishing Group, Inc., The.

Nessel, Denise & Graham, Joyce Marie. Follow the Directions: 180 Quick Daily Exercises That Help Kids Learn to Read & Follow Written & Oral Directions ... All by Themselves! 2001. (Joyful Learning Ser.). 80p. pap. 11.95 (978-0-439-40812-7(1) , Teaching Resources) Scholastic, Inc.

Nessel, Denise D. Follow the Directions. 2001. 80p. pap. 11.95 (978-0-439-21861-0(6)) Scholastic, Inc.

Newsom, Mary T. & Jones, Joy. The Homework Survival Kit. (J). (978-0-9637644-2-3(X)) Spoken Word, The.

Novelli, Joan. Hands-On Homework Pages: 50 Fun-Filled, Reproducible Activities, Games, & Manipulatives That Help Stregthen Skills in Reading, Writing, Math, & More. 2000. (Illus.). 80p. pap. 11.95 (978-0-439-04385-4(9)) Scholastic, Inc.

Nuzum, Margaret. Study Skills That Stick: Surefire Strategies, Reproducible Checklists, & Planning Sheets That Help Every Student Get Organized, Stay Focused, & Become More Effective Learners & Test-Takers. 2001. 80p. (gr. 4). pap. 10.95 (978-0-439-06070-7(2)) Scholastic, Inc.

O'Brien, Jonathan. Longman Brain Trainer. 1998. (Illus.). 64p. (J). pap. 17.50 (978-0-582-36875-0(8)) Pearson Education.

On the Road Through 2nd Grade. 2002. (On the Road Ser.). 160p. per. 14.99 (978-0-88724-751-4(2) , CD-0318) Carson-Dellosa Publishing Co., Inc.

On the Road Through 3rd Grade. 2002. (On the Road Ser.). 160p. per. 14.99 (978-0-88724-752-1(0) , CD-0319) Carson-Dellosa Publishing Co., Inc.

On the Road Through 4th Grade. 2002. (On the Road Ser.). 160p. per. 14.99 (978-0-88724-753-8(9) , CD-0320) Carson-Dellosa Publishing Co., Inc.

On the Road Through Kindergarten. 2002. 160p. per. 14.99 (978-0-88724-749-1(0) , CD-0316) Carson-Dellosa Publishing Co., Inc.

On the Road Through Preschool. 2002. 160p. per. 14.99 (978-0-88724-748-4(2) , CD-0315) Carson-Dellosa Publishing Co., Inc.

Osborne, Corinne. Picture Book Learning, Vol. 1. 2004. Tr. of Picture Book Learning. (ENG & AFA.). 60p. per. 11.99 (978-0-9760725-0-8(5) , PBLSSV1P) Picture Bk Learning, Inc.

Petersen, Evelyn. 1-2-3 Blocks. Bittinger, Gayle, ed. Ekberg, Marion H., illus. 1998. (1-2-3 Ser.). 80p. (J). (ps). pap. 8.95 (978-1-57029-185-2(3) , WPH0412, Totline Pubns.) Schaffer, Frank Pubns.

Play Bac Publishing Staff, ed. Homework Helpsters Grade 3. 2007. 248p. (J). spiral bd. 12.95 (***978-1-60214-000-4(6)***) Play Bac Publishing, USA.

—Homework Helpsters Grade 4. 2007. 248p. (J). spiral bd. 12.95 (***978-1-60214-001-1(4)***) Play Bac Publishing, USA.

—Homework Helpsters Grade 5. 2007. 248p. (J). spiral bd. 12.95 (***978-1-60214-002-8(2)***) Play Bac Publishing, USA.

Power Ranger Skill Builder Workbooks: Blue Cover. 1999. (Illus.). 32p. (J). (gr. 1-2). pap., wbk. ed. (978-0-7666-0565-7(5)) Modern Publishing.

Power Ranger Skill Builder Workbooks: Green Cover. 1999. (Illus.). 32p. (J). (gr. 1-2). pap., wbk. ed. (978-0-7666-0564-0(7)) Modern Publishing.

Power Ranger Skill Builder Workbooks: Red Cover. 1999. (Illus.). 32p. (J). (gr. 1-2). pap., wbk. ed. (978-0-7666-0563-3(9)) Modern Publishing.

Power Ranger Skill Builder Workbooks: Yellow Cover. 1999. (Illus.). 32p. (J). (gr. 1-2). pap., wbk. ed. (978-0-7666-0566-4(3)) Modern Publishing.

Power Rangers Learning Pad: Blue Cover. 1999. (Illus.). 48p. (J). (gr. 1-2). pap. (978-0-7666-0512-1(4)) Modern Publishing.

Power Rangers Learning Pad: Green Cover. 1999. (Illus.). 48p. (J). (gr. 1-2). pap. (978-0-7666-0513-8(2)) Modern Publishing.

Power Rangers Learning Pad: Red Cover. 1999. (Illus.). 48p. (J). (gr. 1-2). pap. (978-0-7666-0510-7(8)) Modern Publishing.

Power Rangers Learning Pad: Yellow Cover. 1999. (Illus.). 48p. (J). (gr. 1-2). pap. (978-0-7666-0511-4(6)) Modern Publishing.

Practice Book. 2000. (SPA.). (gr. 4 up). 5.80 (978-0-673-60587-0(6)); (gr. 5 up). 5.80 (978-0-673-60588-7(4)) Addison-Wesley Educational Pubs., Inc.

Preschool & Kindergarten Skills. 2002. (Home Workbooks Ser.). 64p. pap. 2.49 (978-0-88724-708-8(3) , CD-4510) Carson-Dellosa Publishing Co., Inc.

Preschool Daily Planbook: CD-8201. 2002. 64p. pap. 4.99 (978-0-88724-754-5(7)) Carson-Dellosa Publishing Co., Inc.

Preschool Skills Booster. 2005. (J). per. 0.00 (978-1-59441-500-5(5) , C04032) Carson-Dellosa Publishing Co., Inc.

Priddy Books Staff & Priddy, Roger. My Big Creative. 2004. (Smart Kids Ser.). (Illus.). 70p. (J). act. bk. ed. 14.95 (978-0-312-49330-1(4) , Priddy Bks.) St. Martin's Pr.

Rainbow Bridge Publishing Staff. Listening Skills Third Grade: Mastering Basic Skills. 2002. (Mastering Basic Skills Ser.). 32p. (gr. 3 up). 4.95 (978-1-887923-71-2(3)) Rainbow Bridge Publishing.

Realtime Associates and Mazer Corporation Staff, et al, compiled by. Understand Figurative Language. 2002. (J). (978-1-58605-420-5(1)) LeapFrog Enterprises, Inc.

Realtime Associates and Mazer Corporation Staff & Leap-Frog Staff, compiled by. Differentiate Fact from Opinion. 2002. (J). (gr. 3). 66.75 (978-1-58605-374-1(4)); (gr. 4). 66.75 (978-1-58605-432-8(5)); (gr. 5). 66.75 (978-1-58605-494-6(5)) LeapFrog Enterprises, Inc. (LeapFrog Schl. Hse.).

—Differentiate Fiction from Nonfiction. 2002. (J). (gr. 3). 66.75 (978-1-58605-373-4(6)); (gr. 4). 66.75 (978-1-58605-431-1(7)); (gr. 5). 66.75 (978-1-58605-493-9(7)) LeapFrog Enterprises, Inc. (LeapFrog Schl. Hse.).

—Differentiate Reality from Fantasy. 2002. (J). (gr. 2). 66.75 (978-1-58605-306-2(X)); (gr. 3). 66.75 (978-1-58605-372-7(8)); (gr. 4). 66.75 (978-1-58605-430-4(9)) LeapFrog Enterprises, Inc. (LeapFrog Schl. Hse.).

—Make Inferences. 2002. (J). (gr. 2). 66.75 (978-1-58605-300-0(0)); (gr. 3). 66.75 (978-1-58605-362-8(0)); (gr. 4). 66.75 (978-1-58605-418-2(X)); (gr. 5). 66.75 (978-1-58605-477-9(5)) LeapFrog Enterprises, Inc. (LeapFrog Schl. Hse.).

—Understand Figurative Language. 2002. (J). (gr. 3). 66.75 (978-1-58605-364-2(7)); (gr. 5). 66.75 (978-1-58605-478-6(3)) LeapFrog Enterprises, Inc. (LeapFrog Schl. Hse.).

Rigby. Let's Get Ready for Kindergarten. 2002. (J). pap. 16.99 (978-0-7578-2420-3(X)) Rigby Education.

Roberts, James. How to Take Great Notes in Class & from Textbooks. 2nd rev. ed. 1999. 50p. (gr. 7 up). pap. 7.00 (978-1-891707-03-2(5)) Lawrence Hsc. Pubs.

Romain, Trevor. True or False: Tests Stink! 1999. (gr. 5-8). lib. bdg. 18.75 (978-0-613-86530-2(8)) Tandem Library Bks.

Rozakis, Laurie. Get Test Smart! 2007. 128p. (J). pap. 6.99 (978-0-439-87880-7(2) , Scholastic Reference) Scholastic, Inc.

—Super Study Skills: The Ultimate Guide to Tests & Studying. Cain, David, illus. 2002. 128p. (J). pap. 7.95 (978-0-439-21607-4(9)); pap. 12.95 (978-0-439-21601-2(X)) Scholastic, Inc. (Scholastic Reference).

—Super Study Skills: The Ultimate Guide to Tests & Studying. 2002. (gr. 3-6). lib. bdg. 15.25 (978-0-613-53110-8(8)) Tandem Library Bks.

School Skills. (My First Homework Booklets Ser.). 80p. 2.99 (978-1-56822-764-1(7) , IF0314) School Specialty Publishing.

School Specialty Publishing. Basic Skills Helpers, Grade 1. 2006. (Skills for Scholars Ser.). 80p. (C). pap. 4.99 (***978-0-7696-7951-8(X)*** , Schaffer, Frank) Schaffer, Frank Pubns.

—Basic Skills Helpers, Grade 2. 2006. (Skills for Scholars Ser.). 80p. (C). pap. 4.99 (***978-0-7696-7952-5(8)*** , Schaffer, Frank) Schaffer, Frank Pubns.

—Basic Skills Helpers, Kindergarten. 2006. (Skills for Scholars Ser.). 80p. (C). pap. 4.99 (***978-0-7696-7950-1(1)*** , Schaffer, Frank) Schaffer, Frank Pubns.

—Basic Skills Helpers, Preschool. 2006. (Skills for Scholars Ser.). 80p. (C). pap. 4.99 (***978-0-7696-7949-5(8)*** , Schaffer, Frank) Schaffer, Frank Pubns.

—Following Directions, Grades 1-2. 2006. (Frank Schaffer Classic Reproducibles Ser.). 48p. (J). (gr. 1-2). pap. 6.99 (978-0-7682-3531-9(6) , Schaffer, Frank) Schaffer, Frank Pubns.

—Learning Activities, Grade 1. 2006. (Skills for Scholars Ser.). 80p. (C). pap. 4.99 (***978-0-7696-7991-4(9)*** , Schaffer, Frank) Schaffer, Frank Pubns.

—Sequencing & Memory, Preschool. 2006. (Skills for Scholars Ser.). 80p. (C). pap. 4.99 (***978-0-7696-5029-6(5)*** , Schaffer, Frank) Schaffer, Frank Pubns.

School Zone Publishing Company Staff. Following Directions. (Illus.). (J). 19.99 incl. audio compact disk (978-0-88743-930-8(6)) School Zone Publishing Co.

Schroeder, Linda M. Becoming Excellent Students Today: Academic Organizer. 102p. (YA). (gr. 9-12). pap. 6.95 (978-1-883583-01-9(2)) Gratitude Publishing & Printing.

Schumm, Jeanne Shay. School Power: Study Skill Strategies for Succeeding in School. rev. ed. 2004. (Illus.). 144p. (J). (gr. 6 up). pap. 16.95 (978-1-57542-096-7(1)) Free Spirit Publishing, Inc.

Scott, John, suppl. How to Study. 2004. (YA). 30.00 (978-1-879498-80-8(4)) SportAmerica.

Shields, Charles J. Standardized Test Practice for 6th Grade. 1999. 96p. (J). (gr. 6). pap., tchr. ed. 11.99 (978-1-57690-681-1(7) , TCA2681) Teacher Created Materials, Inc.

Silver, Harvey F., et al. The Multiple Intelligences Indicator Grade 6 - Adult. 2001. 11p. 5.00 (978-1-58284-100-7(4) , Thoughtful Education Pr., The) Silver Strong & Associates.

Silverman, Sharon Hernes. 13 Steps to Better Grades. 1998. (Illus.). 144p. (YA). (gr. 4-9). pap. 15.95 (978-1-882732-71-5(5) , 63590) Childswork/Childsplay.

Sims, C. A. Guide Lines. 1999. (J). (gr. 1-3). Bk. 1. pap., wbk. ed. 20.00 (978-0-7217-0275-9(9)); Bk. 2. (Illus.). 32p. pap., wbk. ed. 20.00 (978-0-7217-0276-6(7)); Bk. 3. (Illus.). 32p. pap., wbk. ed. 20.00 (978-0-7217-0277-3(5)); Bk. 4. pap., wbk. ed. 20.00 (978-0-7217-0278-0(3)); Bk. 5. (Illus.). 32p. pap., wbk. ed. 20.00 (978-0-7217-0279-7(1)) Schofield & Sims Ltd. GBR. *Dist:* State Mutual Bk. & Periodical Service, Ltd.

Sirotowitz, Sandi, et al. Study Strategies for Early School Success: Seven Steps to Improve Your Learning. Dimatteo, Richard, illus. 2003. (Seven Steps Family Guides Ser.). 146p. (J). pap. 18.00 (978-1-886941-55-7(6)) Specialty Pr., Inc.

—Study Strategies Made Easy: A Practical Plan for School Success. DiMatteo, Richard A., illus. 2003. (School Success Ser.). 160p. (J). (gr. 6-12). pap. 18.95 (978-1-886941-03-8(3) , 0931) Specialty Pr., Inc.

Southwater Staff. It's Really Fun to Learn. 2002. (Illus.). 256p. pap. 19.95 (978-1-84215-462-5(1) , Southwater) Anness Publishing GBR. *Dist:* National Bk. Network.

Steck-Vaughn Staff. At-Home Workbooks: Math. 2004. (Illus.). (gr. 1). pap., wbk. ed. (978-0-7398-8519-2(7)) Steck-Vaughn.

—Core Skills Test Preparation. 2002. (Illus.). (J). (gr. 1). pap. (978-0-7398-6496-8(3)); (J). (gr. 2). pap. (978-0-7398-5735-9(5)); (J). (gr. 3). pap. (978-0-7398-5736-6(3)); (J). (gr. 4). pap. (978-0-7398-5737-3(1)); (J). (gr. 5). pap. (978-0-7398-5738-0(X)); (J). (gr. 6). pap. (978-0-7398-5739-7(8)); (YA). (gr. 7). pap. (978-0-7398-5740-3(1)); (YA). (gr. 8). pap. 9.99 (978-0-7398-5741-0(X)) Steck-Vaughn.

—English ASAP: Level 1. 2000. (J). pap., tchr. ed. (978-0-7398-2965-3(3)) Steck-Vaughn.

—Estimation. 1999. (Illus.). (J). (gr. 1). pap. (978-0-7398-2921-9(1)); (gr. 2). pap. (978-0-7398-2922-6(X)); (gr. 3). pap. (978-0-7398-2923-3(8)); (gr. 4). pap. 7.99 (978-0-7398-2924-0(6)); (gr. 5). pap. (978-0-7398-2925-7(4)) Steck-Vaughn.

—Expository Writing. 1999. pap. (978-0-7398-2928-8(9)) Steck-Vaughn.

—Goal Setting Strategies-Start Smart. 2002. (J). pap. (978-0-7398-6011-3(9)) Steck-Vaughn.

—Learning Skills-Start Smart. 2002. (J). pap. (978-0-7398-6009-0(7)) Steck-Vaughn.

—Study Skills-Start Smart. 2002. (J). pap. (978-0-7398-6020 5(8)) Steck-Vaughn.

—Test Best Success Pack: High School, 10. rev. ed. 2002. (YA). (gr. 9-12). pap. (978-0-7398-6716-7(4)) Steck-Vaughn.

—Test Preparation Strategies-Start Smart. 2002. (J). pap. (978-0-7398-6010-6(0)) Steck-Vaughn.

—We Are Friends. 2000. pap. (978-0-7398-4482-3(2)) Steck-Vaughn.

Step up to Grade 3. 2000. (Smart Summer Ser.). (Illus.). 112p. (J). (gr. 3-4). pap. (978-1-58273-520-7(4)) Sundance/Newbridge Educational Publishing.

Step up to Grade 4. 2000. (Smart Summer Ser.). (Illus.). 112p. (J). (gr. 4-5). pap. (978-1-58273-521-4(2)) Sundance/Newbridge Educational Publishing.

Step up to Grade 5. 2000. (Smart Summer Ser.). (Illus.). 112p. (J). (gr. 5-6). pap. (978-1-58273-522-1(0)) Sundance/Newbridge Educational Publishing.

Step up to Grade 6. 2000. (Smart Summer Ser.). (Illus.). 112p. (YA). (gr. 6-7). pap. (978-1-58273-523-8(9)) Sundance/Newbridge Educational Publishing.

Student Resource Advantage 2001: Lab Pack (15) 2000. (Advantage 2001). (YA). cd-rom 399.99 (978-1-58263-150-9(6)) Encore Software, Inc.

Student Resource Advantage 2001: Lab Pack (30) 2000. (Advantage 2001). (YA). cd-rom 699.99 (978-1-58263-151-6(4)) Encore Software, Inc.

Student Resource Advantage 2001: Lab Pack (5) 2000. (Advantage 2001). (YA). cd-rom 139.99 (978-1-58263-149-3(2)) Encore Software, Inc.

Study Skills & Strategies for Students in High School. 2005. spiral bd. 40.00 (978-0-9745999-4-6(8)) Mangrum-Strichart Learning Resources.

Study Skills Fun. 2003. 34.95 (978-1-57543-115-4(7)) MAR*CO Products, Inc.

Study Skills Wheel. 2004. (Region IV ESC Resources for Diverse Learners Ser.). pap. (978-1-932797-11-4(4)) Region IV Education Service Ctr.

Summer School Program: Grade 1 Complete Package. (gr. 1 up). 650.00 (978-0-7578-3236-9(9)) Rigby Education.

Summer School Program: Grade 2 Complete Package. (gr. 2 up). 750.00 (978-0-7578-3237-6(7)) Rigby Education.

Summer School Program: Grade 3 Complete Package. (gr. 3 up). 750.00 (978-0-7578-3238-3(5)) Rigby Education.

Summer School Program: Grade 4 Complete Package. (gr. 4 up). 750.00 (978-0-7578-3239-0(3)) Rigby Education.

Summer School Program: Grade 5 Complete Package. (gr. 5 up). 650.00 (978-0-7578-3240-6(7)) Rigby Education.

Summer School Program: Grade 6 Complete Package. (gr. 6 up). 725.00 (978-0-7578-3241-3(5)) Rigby Education.

Summer School Program: Grade 7 Complete Package. (gr. 7 up). 725.00 (978-0-7578-3242-0(3)) Rigby Education.

Summer School Program: Grade 8 Complete Package. (gr. 8 up). 725.00 (978-0-7578-3243-7(1)) Rigby Education.

Summer School Program: Grade K Complete Package. (gr. k up). 650.00 (978-0-7578-3235-2(0)) Rigby Education.

ThemeMaker Student Tool. 2005. 3.95 (***978-0-9769527-9-4(3)***) Mindwing Concepts, Inc.

Toft, Doug & Master Students Staff. Master Student Guide to Academic Success. 2004. 341p. (YA). stu. ed. 38.76 (978-0-618-38256-9(9) , 308180) Houghton Mifflin College Div.

Vener, Diane. Study Skills: A Landmark School Student Guide. 2002. 125p. (YA). (gr. 9 up). stu. ed., spiral bd. 30.00 (978-0-9624119-7-7(3)) Landmark Schl., Inc.

Venit, Corinne. Study Skills. 1998. 140p. (YA). (gr. 2-12). (978-1-930288-05-8(0)) Carney Educational Services.

Verbansky, Peter. The Secrets of Academic Excellence: How to Get the Grades You Want & Deserve. Verbansky, Pal, illus. Verbansky, Pal, photos by. 1998. xiv, 306p. (YA). (gr. 7-12). pap. 16.95 (978-0-9663965-0-8(2)) Palson Publishing.

Verde, B. Bee Smarter Study Kit Grade 1. 2002. 208p. (J). per. 39.99 (978-0-9717643-1-6(X) , Bee Smarter Study Kits) Verde Publishing, Inc.

Verdick, Elizabeth & Romain, Trevor. True or False? Tests Stink! 2004. (Laugh & Learn Ser.). (Illus.). 88p. (YA). (gr. 3-8). pap. 8.95 (978-1-57542-073-8(2)) Free Spirit Publishing, Inc.

Viviers, Susan. Survive Your Studies: Tips for Teens. 2000. 244p. pap. (978-0-947465-70-4(7)) Cambridge Univ. Pr.

Watkins, Dewhite. Quick & Dirty Secrets of College Success: A Professor Tells It All. 2004. 128p. (YA). per. 14.95 (978-0-9742632-1-2(4)) Blue Boy Publishing Co.

The Weaver Curriculum. 2004. (gr. k-12). Vol. 1. 145.00 (978-1-58095-842-4(7) , WV001, Weaver); Vol. 2. 145.00 (978-1-58095-843-1(5) , WV002, Weaver); Vol. 3. 145.00 (978-1-58095-844-8(3) , WV003, Lifepac); Vol. 4. 145.00 (978-1-58095-845-5(1) , WV004, Lifepac); Vol. 5. 145.00 (978-1-58095-846-2(X) , WV005, Weaver) Alpha Omega Pubns., Inc.

Wenz-Gross, Melodie. Moving on to Middle School: Life Skills & Coping Skills for Successful Student Transition. 2002. 150p. pap. 19.95 (978-1-931061-34-6(3)) Jalmar Pr.

Whale, Janeen. Object Mysteries: Using Critical Questioning to Identify Thingamajigs, Doohickeys, & Gadgets. 2001. (J). pap. 21.99 (978-0-89455-795-8(5)); pap. 11.99 (978-0-89455-796-5(3)) Critical Thinking Bks. & Software.

What Nerds Don't Want You to Know! 2000. (Nerds' Secrets Ser.). 80p. (J). 9.99 (978-1-891100-69-7(6)) Smart Kids Publishing.

Whitney, Brooks. School Smarts: All the Right Answers to Homework, Teachers, Popularity, & More! McGuinness, Tracy, illus. 2000. (American Girl Library). 96p. (J). (gr. 3 up). pap. 8.95 (978-1-58485-165-3(1)) American Girl Publishing, Inc.

Willis, Mariaemma & Kindle Hodson, Victoria. Mid-life Crisis Begins in Kindergarten: How we learn the habit of settling for Less. 2004. spiral bd. 10.00 (***978-0-9772350-0-1(9)***) LearningSuccess Pr.

Wirasinha, Anushka. Study Buddy. 2000. (Study Buddy). 55p. (J). per. (978-955-97038-0-8(3)) Computer Literate Generation (Private), Ltd.

World Book, Inc. Staff. How to Study. 2001. (YA). (gr. 5 up). cd-rom 25.00 (978-0-7166-3313-6(2)) World Bk., Inc.

Young Minds at Play. 240p. 16.99 (978-1-56822-528-9(8) , IF24131) School Specialty Publishing.

50 Student Books. 2005. 95p. (J). spiral bd. 14.99 (978-1-59441-466-4(1) , K04017) Carson-Dellosa Publishing Co., Inc.

50 Student Mobiles. 2005. 83p. (J). spiral bd. 14.99 (978-1-59441-467-1(X) , K04018) Carson-Dellosa Publishing Co., Inc.

101Things First Graders Should Know. 2005. 128p. (J). (978-1-4127-1065-7(0) , 5519500) Publications International, Ltd.

3118902. HMS Level 1. 2000. pap., stu. ed. 10.95 (978-0-8108-3800-0(1)) Rowman & Littlefield Education.

STUNT PERFORMERS

Bledsoe, Karen & Bledsoe, Glen. The Blue Angels: The U. S. Navy Flight Demonstration Squadron. 2001. (Serving Your Country Ser.). (Illus.). 48p. (J). (gr. 3-4). lib. bdg. 21.26 (978-0-7368-0773-9(X) , Capstone High-Interest Bks.) Capstone Pr., Inc.

Clemson, Wendy, et al. Using Math to Create a Movie Stunt. 2004. (Mathworks!). (Illus.). 31p. (J). lib. bdg. 24.67 (978-0-8368-4211-1(1)) Stevens, Gareth Inc.

Gonzalez, Lissette. Stunt Performers & Stunt Doubles. 2008. (J). lib. bdg. (***978-1-4042-3780-3(1)*** , PowerKids Pr.) Rosen Publishing Group, Inc., The.

Horn, Geoffrey M. Movie Stunts & Special Effects. 2006. (Making Movies Ser.). (Illus.). 32p. (J). (gr. 4-6). lib. bdg. 23.93 (978-0-8368-6840-1(4)) Stevens, Gareth Inc.

Mello, Tara Baukus. Stunt Driving. 1999. (Race Car Legends Ser.). (Illus.). 64p. (YA). (gr. 4-7). pap. 25.00 (978-0-7910-5681-3(3)); 25.00 (978-0-7910-5415-4(2)) Facts On File, Inc. (Chelsea Hse.).

—Stunt Driving. rev. ed. 2007. (Race Car Legends: Ser.). 72p. (J). (gr. 5-8). 25.00 (978-0-7910-8666-7(6) , Chelsea Hse.) Facts On File, Inc.

Oberle, Lora Polack. The Canadian Forces Snowbirds: 431 Air Demonstration Squadron. 2001. (Serving Your Country Ser.). (Illus.). 48p. (J). (gr. 3-4). lib. bdg. 21.26 (978-0-7368-0774-6(8) , Capstone High-Interest Bks.) Capstone Pr., Inc.

Turner, Cherie. Stunt Performers: Life Before the Camera. 2005. (Extreme Careers Ser.). (Illus.). 64p. (YA). (gr. 5-8). 26.50 (978-0-8239-3371-6(7)) Rosen Publishing Group, Inc., The.

Watts, Claire & Nicholson, Robert. Daredevils. 2000. (Info Adventure Ser.). (Illus.). 32p. (J). (gr. 3-6). pap. 3.95 (978-1-58728-104-4(X) , Two Can Publishing) T&N Children's Publishing.

Weintraub, Aileen. Stunt Double. 2003. (High Interest Bks.). (Illus.). 48p. (J). 24.00 (978-0-516-24338-2(1)); (YA). (gr. 7-12). pap. 6.95 (978-0-516-27867-4(3)) Scholastic Library Publishing. (Children's Pr.).

—Stunt Double. 2003. (gr. 7-12). lib. bdg. 15.25 (978-0-613-67936-7(9)) Tandem Library Bks.

STUYVESANT, PETER, 1592-1672

Banks, Joan. Peter Stuyvesant. (Colonial Leaders Ser.). (Illus.). 80p. (gr. 3 up). 2000. (YA). 27.50 (978-0-7910-5346-1(6)); 1999. (J). pap. (978-0-7910-5689-9(9)) Facts On File, Inc. (Chelsea Hse.).

—Peter Stuyvesant: Dutch Military Leader. 2000. (gr. 5-8). lib. bdg. 17.60 (978-0-613-43365-5(3)) Tandem Library Bks.

Krizner, L. J. & Sita, Lisa. Peter Stuyvesant: New Amsterdam & the Origins of New York. 2005. (Library of American Lives & Times). (Illus.). 112p. (J). (gr. 4-8). lib. bdg. 31.95 (978-0-8239-5732-3(2)) Rosen Publishing Group, Inc., The.

Lilly, Melinda. The Dutch in New Amsterdam. 2003. (Rourke Discovery Library). (Illus.). 24p. (gr. 1-4). 14.95 (978-1-58952-367-8(9)) Rourke Publishing, LLC.

Whiting, Jim. The Life & Times of Peter Stuyvesant. 2007. (Profiles in American History Ser.). (Illus.). 48p. (J). lib. bdg. 29.95 (***978-1-58415-526-3(4)***) Mitchell Lane Pubs., Inc.

STYLE IN DRESS

see Costume; Fashion

SU DOKU

see Sudoku

SUBMARINE DIVING

see Deep Diving

SUBMARINE EXPLORATION

see Underwater Exploration

SUBMARINE GEOLOGY

Davis, Wendy & Knight, Bertram T. Working at a Marine Institute. 1998. (Working Here Ser.). (Illus.). 32p. (J). (gr. 2-4). 23.50 (978-0-516-21223-4(0) , Children's Pr.) Scholastic Library Publishing.

SUBMARINE WARFARE

see also Submarines (Ships)

Brooks, Victor D. Secret Weapons in the Civil War. 1999. (Untold History of the Civil War Ser.). (Illus.). 64p. (YA). (gr. 3 up). 29.50 (978-0-7910-5433-8(0) , Chelsea Hse.) Facts On File, Inc.

Payan, Gregory. Fast Attack Submarine: The SSN Seawolf. 2000. (High Interest Bks.). (Illus.). 48p. (YA). (gr. 7-12). pap. 6.95 (978-0-516-23538-7(9) , Children's Pr.) Scholastic Library Publishing.

West, Krista. Underwater Warfare of the Future. 2005. (Library of Future Weaponry). (Illus.). 64p. (J). (978-1-4042-0522-2(5)) Rosen Publishing Group, Inc., The.

SUBMARINE WARFARE—FICTION

Driscoll, R. James. The Brighton Boys with the Submarine Fle. 2006. 32.99 (***978-1-4219-7846-8(6)***); pap. 26.99 (***978-1-4219-7867-3(9)***) IndyPublish.com.

Nolan, Peggy. Spy Who Came in from the Sea. 1999. (gr. 5-8). lib. bdg. 17.60 (978-0-613-37048-6(1)) Tandem Library Bks.

SUBMARINES (SHIPS)

Abramson, Andra Serlin. Submarines: Up Close. 2008. 28p. (J). 9.95 (***978-1-4027-4797-7(7)*** , Sterling Innovation) Sterling Publishing Co., Inc.

Barron's Educational Editorial Staff. Submarines. 1998. (History Ser.). (Illus.). 32p. (J). (gr. 5). pap. 5.95 (978-0-7641-0536-4(1)) Barron's Educational Series, Inc.

Doeden, Matt. Submarines. 2006. (Pull Ahead Books). (Illus.). 32p. (J). (ps-ps). 22.60 (978-0-8225-2669-8(7) , Lerner Pubns.) Lerner Publishing Group.

Doyle, Kevin. Submarines. 2004. (Military Hardware in Action Ser.). (Illus.). 48p. (J). (gr. 4-9). lib. bdg. 25.26 (978-0-8225-4704-4(X)) Lerner Publishing Group.

Ellis, Catherine. Submarines. 2007. (Mega Military Machines Ser.). (Illus.). 24p. (J). (gr. k-5). lib. bdg. 21.25 (978-1-4042-3665-3(1)) Rosen Publishing Group, Inc., The.

Fein, Eric. The USS Greeneville Submarine Disaster: When Disaster Strikes! 2005. (When Disaster Strikes! Ser.). (Illus.). 48p. (YA). (gr. 5-8). lib. bdg. 23.95 (978-0-8239-3676-2(7)) Rosen Publishing Group, Inc., The.

Graham, Ian. Ships & Submarines. 2000. (Fast Forward Ser.). (Illus.). 32p. (J). (gr. 4-8). pap. 9.95 (978-0-531-16446-4(2) , Watts, Franklin) Scholastic Library Publishing.

—Ships & Submarines. Antram, David, illus. 2000. (Fast Forward Ser.). 32p. (J). (gr. 4-8). 29.00 (978-0-531-11880-1(0) , Watts, Franklin) Scholastic Library Publishing.

—Ships & Submarines. 2000. (J). (978-0-606-19793-9(1)); (gr. 3-6). lib. bdg. 18.75 (978-0-613-34945-1(8)) Tandem Library Bks.

Green, Michael & Green, Gladys. Attack Submarines: The Seawolf Class. 2004. (Edge Books, War Machines). (Illus.). 32p. (J). lib. bdg. 22.60 (978-0-7368-2721-8(8)) Capstone Pr., Inc.

Harcourt School Publishers Staff. The Secrets of the Hunley. 3rd ed. 2002. (Horizons Ser.). (Illus.). (J). pap. 7.30 (978-0-15-333583-9(1)) Harcourt Schl. Pubs.

Jefferis, David. Super Subs: Opening up Undersea Frontiers. 2002. (Megatech Ser.). (Illus.). 32p. (J). (gr. 4-5). pap. (978-0-7787-0063-0(1)); lib. bdg. (978-0-7787-0053-1(4)) Crabtree Publishing Co.

—Super Subs: Opening up Undersea Frontiers. 2002. (gr. 3-6). lib. bdg. 17.60 (978-0-613-52999-0(5)) Tandem Library Bks.

Jerome, Kate Boehm. Civil War Sub Vol. 3: The Mystery of the Hunley. Sofo, Frank & Farnsworth, Bill, illus. 2002. (All Aboard Reading Ser.). 48p. (J). pap. 3.99 (978-0-448-42597-9(1) , Grosset & Dunlap) Penguin Group (USA) Inc.

—Civil War Sub Vol. 3: The Mystery of the Hunley. 2002. (gr. k-3). lib. bdg. 11.80 (978-0-613-64032-9(2)) Tandem Library Bks.

Lock, Deborah. Submarines & Submersibles. 2007. (Dk Readers Ser.). (Illus.). 32p. (J). pap. 14.99 (978-0-7566-2551-1(3)); pap. 3.99 (978-0-7566-2550-4(5)) Dorling Kindersley Publishing, Inc.

Mallard, Neil. Submarine. 2003. (Eyewitness Bks.). (Illus.). 64p. (J). lib. bdg. 19.99 (978-0-7894-9503-7(1)); 15.99 (978-0-7894-9501-3(5)) Dorling Kindersley Publishing, Inc.

Matsen, Bradford. The Incredible Submersible Alvin Discovers a Strange Deep-Sea World. 2003. (Incredible Deep-Sea Adventures Ser.). (Illus.). 48p. (J). (gr. 4-10). lib. bdg. 23.93 (978-0-7660-2189-1(0)) Enslow Pubs., Inc.

Milton, Keith. Subs Against the Rising Sun: U. S. Submarines in the Pacific. 2000. (Illus.). 403p. (J). 30.00 (978-1-881325-45-1(8)) Barbed Wire Publishing.

Pascoe, Elaine, ed. Seawolf Submarine. 2003. (Super Structures of the World Ser.). (J). 24.95 (978-1-56711-868-1(2)); 11.20 (978-1-4103-0188-8(5)) Thomson Gale. (Blackbirch Pr., Inc.).

Patton, Geoff. Giants of the Sea. 2005. (X-Zone Ser.). (Illus.). 30p. (gr. 4-8). 23.00 (978-0-7910-8978-1(9)) Facts On File, Inc.

Reed, Jennifer. Submarines. 2008. (J). (*978-1-4296-0031-6(4) , Pebble Bks.) Capstone Pr., Inc.

Shipwreck Search: Discovery of the H. L. Hunley. 2007. (J). pap. 5.95 (*978-0-8225-6449-2(1) , First Avenue Editions) Lerner Publishing Group.

Stefoff, Rebecca. Submarines. 2006. (Great Inventions Ser.). (Illus.). 127p. (J). lib. bdg. 39.93 (978-0-7614-2229-7(3) , Benchmark Bks.) Cavendish, Marshall Corp.

Stille, Darlene R. Submarines. 2004. (Illus.). 32p. (J). (gr. 1 up). lib. bdg. 21.26 (978-0-7565-0610-0(7)) Compass Point Bks.

Stone, Lynn M. Submarines. 2006. (Fighting Forces Ser.). (Illus.). 32p. (gr. 4-8). 19.95 (978-1-59515-466-8(3) , 1244408) Rourke Publishing, LLC.

Submarinos Nucleares, 6 vols., Pack. (On Deck en Espanol Ser.). (SPA.). 24p. (gr. 4-5). 35.00 (978-0-7578-6432-2(5)) Rigby Education.

Teitelbaum, Michael. Submarines: Underwater Stealth. 2006. (Mighty Military Machines Ser.). (Illus.). 48p. (J). (gr. 4-10). lib. bdg. 23.93 (978-0-7660-2659-9(0)) Enslow Pubs., Inc.

Thomas, Isabel. Dive! Dive! 2006. (Illus.). 32p. (J). (978-1-4109-2588-6(9)); pap. (978-1-4109-2617-3(6)) Steck-Vaughn.

Walker, Sally M. Secrets of a Civil War Submarine: Solving the Mysteries of the H.L. Hunley. 2005. (Illus.). 112p. (J). (gr. 6-8). 18.95 (978-1-57505-830-6(8) , Carolrhoda Bks.) Lerner Publishing Group.

—Shipwreck Search: Discovery of the H. L. Hunley. Verstraete, Elaine, illus. 2006. (On My Own Science Ser.). 48p. (J). (gr. 2-4). lib. bdg. 25.26 (978-1-57505-878-8(2) , Millbrook Pr.) Lerner Publishing Group.

Weller, George. The Story of Submarines. 2003. 210p. pap. 29.00 (978-0-7581-4985-5(9)) Textbook Pubs.

West, Krista. Underwater Warfare of the Future. 2005. (Library of Future Weaponry). (Illus.). 64p. (J). (978-1-4042-0522-2(5)) Rosen Publishing Group, Inc., The.

Zuehlke, Jeffrey. Indonesia in Pictures. 2nd ed. 2006. (Visual Geography Series, Second Ser.). (Illus.). 80p. (J). (gr. 3-7). 27.93 (978-0-8225-2074-0(5) , Lerner Pubns.) Lerner Publishing Group.

SUBMARINES (SHIPS)—FICTION

Appleton, Victor. Into the Abyss. 2007. (Tom Swift, Young Inventor Ser.). 160p. (J). (gr. 4-7). 27.07 (*978-1-59961-350-5(6)) Spotlight.

—Tom Swift & His Submarine Boat. 2000. (Tom Swift Original Ser.: Vol. No. 4). 114p. (gr. 3-7). pap. 7.95 (978-1-57646-204-1(8)) Quiet Vision Publishing.

Appleton, Victor. Tom Swift & His Submarine Boat or Unde. 2006. pap. (*978-1-4065-0908-3(6)) Dodo Pr.

Blaine, John. The Boy Scouts on a Submarine. 2006. 62.99 (*978-1-4280-0926-4(4)); pap. 55.99 (*978-1-4280-0929-5(9)) IndyPublish.com.

Carlson, Drew. Attack of the Turtle. Johnson, David A., illus. 2007. 160p. (J). (gr. 3-7). 16.00 (978-0-8028-5308-0(0) , Eerdmans Bks For Young Readers) Eerdmans, William B. Publishing Co.

Carter, Joey. Lost in a Submarine! A Cantor Kids! Book. 2006. 56p. pap. 9.95 (978-1-59800-312-3(7)) Outskirts Press, Inc.

Clary, Margie Willis. Make It Three: The Story of the CSS H. L. Hunley, Civil War Submarine. Rickenbaker, Becky, illus. 2001. 110p. (J). 9.95 (978-0-87844-158-7(1)) Sandlapper Publishing Co., Inc.

Cummings, Mary. And the Baker's Boy Went to Sea. 2006. (Illus.). 195p. (YA). 16.95 (978-0-9774855-0-5(1)) Sparkling Pr.

Foster, Teresa. Big Green Submarine. 1999. (Window Board Bks.). (Illus.). 14p. (J). (ps-k). bds. 4.99 (978-0-7847-0988-7(2) , 03785, Bean Sprouts) Standard Publishing.

Gardner, Charlie. The Beatles Yellow Submarine. Edelmann, Heinz, illus. 2006. 37p. (J). (gr. 4-8). reprint ed. 18.00 (978-1-4223-5184-0(X)) DIANE Publishing Co.

Gilson, Jamie. Thirteen Ways to Sink a Sub. Edwards, Linda S., illus. 1999. (Avon Camelot Bks.). 128p. (J). (gr. 3-7). pap. 5.99 (978-0-380-73251-7(3)) HarperCollins Pubs.

—Thirteen Ways to Sink a Sub. (J). 4.50 (978-0-8072-1387-2(X) , Listening Library) Random Hse. Audio Publishing Group.

—Thirteen Ways to Sink a Sub. 1999. (978-0-606-17980-5(1)) Tandem Library Bks.

Larry, H. I. Zac Power #2: Deep Waters. Oswald, Ash, illus. 2008. (Zac Power Ser.). 96p. (J). pap. 3.99 (*978-0-312-34655-3(7)) Feiwel & Friends.

McOmber, Rachel B., ed. McOmber Phonics Storybooks: The Sub. rev. ed. (Illus.). (J). (978-0-944991-22-0(X)) Swift Learning Resources.

Miller, Ron & Verne, Jules. 20,000 Leagues under the Sea. Wright, Paul, illus. 1998. (Eyewitness Classics Ser.). 64p. (J). (gr. 3-6). 14.99 (978-0-7894-3428-9(8)) Dorling Kindersley Publishing, Inc.

Mitton, Tony. Super Submarines. Parker, Ant, illus. 2006. (Amazing Machines Ser.). 24p. (J). (ps-k). 9.95 (978-0-7534-5940-9(X) , Kingfisher) Houghton Mifflin Co. Trade & Reference Div.

My Day in a Submarine. 2004. (J). ring bd. 3.25 (978-0-9762740-3-2(5) , Flat Kids) Smart Smiles Co., The.

Orme, David. Something Evil. Savage, Paul, illus. 2006. 40p. (J). (gr. 2-3). lib. bdg. (978-1-59889-017-4(4)) Stone Arch Bks.

Osborne, Mary Pope. Magische Baumhaus der Ruf. 18.95 (978-3-7855-4185-2(6)) Loewe Verlag GmbH DEU. *Dist:* Distribooks, Inc.

Verne, Jules. Twenty Thousand Leagues under the Sea. l.t. ed. 2006. 592p. pap. (978-1-84702-222-6(7)) Echo Library.

—Veinte Mil Leguas de Viaje Submarino.Tr. of Twenty Thousand Leagues under the Sea. (SPA., Illus.). 160p. (YA). 11.95 (978-84-7281-075-4(5) , AF1075) Auriga, Ediciones S.A. ESP. *Dist:* Continental Bk. Co., Inc.

—20,000 Leagues under the Sea. Dillon, Leo & Dillon, Diane, illus. 2000. (Books of Wonder). 384p. (gr. 4-7). 24.99 (978-0-688-10535-8(1)) HarperCollins Pubs.

—20,000 Leagues under the Sea. 2003. (gr. 5-8). lib. bdg. 13.00 (978-0-613-66744-9(1)) Tandem Library Bks.

—20,000 Leagues under the Sea: Level 4. Solimene, Laura, ed. 2005. (Illus.). 72p. (YA). (gr. 4 up). act. bk. ed. 9.95 (978-1-55576-091-5(0) , EDCTR405B) AV Concepts Corp.

—20,000 Leagues under the Sea: Retold from the Jules Verne Original. Andreasen, Dan, illus. 2006. (Classic Starts Ser.). 160p. 4.95 (978-1-4027-2533-3(7)) Sterling Publishing Co., Inc.

Ward, Beck. Submarine Sam. Crowson, Andrew, illus. 2005. 8p. (J). (ps-k). 12.95 (978-0-7624-2418-4(4) , Running Pr. Kids) Running Pr. Bk. Pubs.

Wilson-Max, Ken. The Little Orange Submarine. Wilson-Max, Ken, illus. 2001. (Illus.). 14p. (J). (ps-1). bds. 7.95 (978-0-439-24025-3(5)) Scholastic, Inc.

SUBSTANCE ABUSE

see also Alcoholism; Drug Abuse; Tobacco Habit

Aretha, David. Inhalants: A MyReportLinks. com Book. 2005. (Drugs Ser.). (Illus.). 48p. (J). lib. bdg. 25.26 (978-0-7660-5280-2(X) , MyReportLinks.com Bks.) Enslow Pubs., Inc.

Austin, James. Underage Drinking. 2007. (Issues that Concern You Ser.). 144p. (gr. 7-10). 32.45 (978-0-7377-3091-3(9) , Greenhaven Pr., Inc.) Thomson Gale.

Bankston, John. Inhalants = Busted! 2006. (Busted! Ser.). (Illus.). 104p. (J). lib. bdg. 31.93 (978-0-7660-2472-4(5) , 1250497) Enslow Pubs., Inc.

Berry, Joy Wilt. Substance Abuse: Good Answers to Tough Questions. Bartholomew, illus. rev. ed. 2000. (Good Answers to Tough Questions Ser.: Vol. 8). 48p. (J). (gr. 4-7). pap. 4.95 (978-1-58634-218-0(5) , 01-0901-08) Goldstar Publishing, Inc.

Bigelow, Barbara C. & Edgar, Kathleen J. The UXL Encyclopedia of Drugs & Addictive Substances, 5 vols. 2005. (Illus.). (J). (978-1-4144-0445-5(X)); (978-1-4144-0446-2(8)); (978-1-4144-0447-9(6)); (978-1-4144-0448-6(4)); (978-1-4144-0449-3(2)) Thomson Gale.

Brinkerhoff, Shirley. Drug Therapy & Substance-Related Disorders. 2003. (Encyclopedia of Psychiatric Drugs & Their Disorders Ser.). (Illus.). 128p. (J). lib. bdg. (978-1-59084-577-6(3)) Mason Crest Pubs.

Carson-DeWitt, Rosalyn, ed. Drugs, Alcohol, & Tobacco: Learning about Addictive Behavior, 3 vols., Vol. 3. 2002. (Illus.). (J). (978-0-02-865759-2(4) , Macmillan Reference USA) Thomson Gale.

Clued in! on Addiction & Your Brain. 2005. (J). 4.95 (978-1-55548-050-9(0) , 674) Human Relations Media.

Connolly, Sean. Inhalants. 2006. (J). (978-1-58340-648-9(4)) Smart Apple Media.

Crist, James J. When Someone You Love Abuses Alcohol or Drugs - A Guide for Kids. 2003. (gr. 3-6). lib. bdg. 22.20 (978-0-613-79732-0(9)) Tandem Library Bks.

Curriculum in a Box: Substance Abuse. 2005. (YA). 924.95 incl. DVD (978-1-55548-256-5(2) , 377dv) Human Relations Media.

Flynn, Noa. Inhalants & Solvents: Sniffing Disaster. 2008. (J). (*978-1-4222-0157-2(0)) Mason Crest Pubs.

Gottfried, Ted. The Facts about Marijuana. 2004. (J). 37.07 (978-0-7614-1806-1(7) , Benchmark Bks.) Cavendish, Marshall Corp.

Harrow, Jeremy. Crystal Meth. 2007. (J). lib. bdg. (*978-1-4042-1953-3(6)) Rosen Publishing Group, Inc., The.

Hiber, Amanda. Are Americans Overmedicated? 2006. (Illus.). 128p. (J). (gr. 10-12). 21.20 (978-0-7377-3402-7(7)); pap. 29.95 (978-0-7377-3401-0(9)) Thomson Gale. (Greenhaven Pr., Inc.).

Incredibly Disgusting Drugs: Set 1, 6 bks. Incl. Alcohol & Your Liver : The Incredibly Disgusting Story. Miller, Andrew. 2005. lib. bdg. 25.25 (978-0-8239-3254-2(0) , DDALLI); Cocaine & Your Nose : The Incredibly Disgusting Story. Apel, Melanie Ann. 2005. lib. bdg. 25.25 (978-0-8239-3251-1(6) , DDCONO); Heroin & Your Veins : The Incredibly Disgusting Story. Cobb, Allan B. 2005. lib. bdg. 25.25 (978-0-8239-3249-8(4) , DDHEVE); Marijuana & Your Lungs : The Incredibly Disgusting Story. Stanley, Debbie. 2005. lib. bdg. 25.25 (978-0-8239-3252-8(4) , DDMALU); Speed & Your Brain : The Incredibly Disgusting Story. Cobb, Allan B. 2000. lib. bdg. 25.25 (978-0-8239-3253-5(2) , DDSPBR, Rosen Central); Tobacco & Your Mouth : The Incredibly Disgusting Story. Winters, Adam & Sommers, Michael A. 2005. lib. bdg. 25.25 (978-0-8239-3250-4(8) , DDTOMO); 48p. (YA). (gr. 5-8). (Illus.). 2000. Set lib. bdg. 151.50 (978-0-8239-9168-6(7) , DDDIDR, Rosen Central) Rosen Publishing Group, Inc., The.

Information Plus Alcohol & Tobacco November 2005, Vol. 2005. 2005. 45.00 (978-1-4144-0405-9(0)) Thomson Gale.

Information Plus Illegal Drugs November 2005. 2005. 45.00 (978-1-4144-0419-6(0)) Thomson Gale.

Ingram, Scott & Brogan, Ronald J. Marijuana. 2008. (Junior Drug Awareness Ser.). 112p. (J). (gr. 5-8). 30.00 (*978-0-7910-9695-6(5) , Chelsea Hse.) Facts On File, Inc.

Karson, Jill. Teen Addiction. 2006. (Contemporary Issues Companion Ser.). (Illus.). 244p. (gr. 10-12). 24.95 (978-0-7377-3266-5(0)); pap. 36.20 (978-0-7377-3265-8(2)) Thomson Gale. (Greenhaven Pr., Inc.).

Keegan, Kyle, et al. Chasing the High: A Firsthand Account of One Young Person's Experience with Substance Abuse. 2008. (Illus.). 192p. 30.00 (*978-0-19-531471-7(9)); pap. 9.95 (*978-0-19-531472-4(7)) Oxford Univ. Pr., Inc.

Koellhoffer, Tara. Inhalants & Solvents. 2008. (Junior Drug Awareness Ser.). 112p. (J). (gr. 5-8). 30.00 (*978-0-7910-9698-7(X) , Chelsea Hse.) Facts On File, Inc.

Libal, Autumn. The FDA & Psychiatric Drugs: Drugs & Psychology for the Mind & Body, 19 vols., Set. 2004. (Psychiatric Disorders Ser.). (Illus.). 128p. (J). lib. bdg. (978-1-59084-559-2(5)) Mason Crest Pubs.

Lobo, Ingrid A. Inhalants. 2004. (Drugs, the Straight Facts Ser.). (Illus.). 112p. (gr. 9-13). 30.00 (978-0-7910-7636-1(9) , Chelsea Hse.) Facts On File, Inc.

Marcovitz, Hal. Inhalants. 2005. (Drug Education Library). (Illus.). 112p. (J). (gr. 5-8). lib. bdg. 32.45 (978-1-59018-416-5(5) , Lucent Bks.) Thomson Gale.

Rebman, Renee C. Addictions & Risky Behaviors: Cutting, Bingeing, Snorting, & Other Dangers. 2006. (Issues in Focus Today). (Illus.). 104p. (J). (gr. 6-12). lib. bdg. 31.93 (978-0-7660-2165-5(3)) Enslow Pubs., Inc.

Schaefer, Wyatt. Addiction. 2007. (Social Issues Firsthand Ser.). 192p. (gr. 10-12). 29.95 (*978-0-7377-2494-3(3) , Greenhaven Pr., Inc.) Thomson Gale.

Schwartzenberger, Tina. Substance Use & Abuse. 2004. (Understanding Global Issues Ser.). (J). lib. bdg. (978-1-59036-232-7(2)) Weigl Pubs., Inc.

Sheen, Barbara. Chemical Dependency. 2003. (Lucent Overview Ser.). (Illus.). 112p. (J). 29.95 (978-1-56006-657-6(1) , Lucent Bks.) Thomson Gale.

Substance Abuse A2Z Transparencies. 2006. (J). 74.95 (978-1-55548-072-1(1) , 711) Human Relations Media.

SUBSTANCE ABUSE—FICTION

Adams, M.F.T., C.A.C. III, Juanita Beasley, MA. Clancy & the Bear Dance: One Ute Mountain Boy's Journey from Alcoholism & Abuse to Wholeness! 2007. 104p. pap. 11.95 (*978-0-615-14729-1(1)) Out-of-Body Travel Foundation, The.

Atkinson, I. J. I Might be Just a Freshman, But... 2002. 130p. pap. 19.95 (978-1-59129-640-9(4)) PublishAmerica, Inc.

Cohn, Rachel. You Know Where to Find Me. 2008. 208p. (YA). 15.99 (*978-0-689-87859-6(1) , Simon & Schuster Children's Publishing) Simon & Schuster Children's Publishing.

Dean, Zoey. Girls on Film. 2004. 250p. (YA). (gr. 8-12). per. 16.64 (978-0-606-33460-0(2)) Tandem Library Bks.

—Tall Cool One. 2005. (A-List Ser.: No. 4). 295p. (YA). (gr. 7-17). per. 16.64 (978-0-606-33462-4(9)) Tandem Library Bks.

Hopkins, Ellen. Crank. 2004. 544p. (YA). (gr. 9 up). pap. 8.99 (978-0-689-86519-0(8) , Simon Pulse) Simon & Schuster Children's Publishing.

Hyde, Catherine Ryan. The Year of My Miraculous Reappearance. 2007. 240p. (gr. 7). (J). lib. bdg. 18.99 (978-0-375-93257-1(7)); (YA). 15.99 (978-0-375-83257-4(2)) Random Hse. Children's Bks. (Knopf Bks. for Young Readers).

Iversen, Jeremy. 21. 2005. 272p. (YA). pap. 6.99 (978-0-689-87623-3(8) , Simon Pulse) Simon & Schuster Children's Publishing.

Koertge, Ronald. Stoner & Spaz. 2004. (gr. 7-12). lib. bdg. 15.30 (978-0-613-74820-9(4)) Tandem Library Bks.

Page, Katherine Hall. Club Meds. 2006. 176p. (YA). pap. 6.99 (978-1-4169-0903-3(6) , Simon Pulse) Simon & Schuster Children's Publishing.

Smith-Leckie, Nina. The Fall & Rise of Abuse-a-Saurus Rex. Gordon, Danny, illus. 2003. 28p. (YA). (gr. 5 up). pap. 6.95 (978-0-9725382-0-6(8)) Prairie Arts, Inc.

SUBURBAN AREAS

see Metropolitan Areas

SUBURBAN HOMES

see Architecture, Domestic

SUBURBAN LIFE

Bodden, Valerie. A Suburb. 2007. (J). (978-1-58341-514-6(9) , Creative Education) Creative Co., The.

Miller, Jake. Who's Who in a Suburban Community. 2005. (Communities at Work Ser.). (Illus.). 24p. (J). (gr. 2-4). lib. bdg. 19.95 (978-1-4042-2789-7(X) , PowerKids Pr.) Rosen Publishing Group, Inc., The.

Pancella, Peggy. Suburb. 2005. (Illus.). 32p. (J). pap. (978-1-4034-6225-1(9)); lib. bdg. 25.36 (978-1-4034-6219-0(4)) Heinemann Library.

Sterling, Kristin. Suburban Communities. 2008. (First Step Nonfiction - Communities Ser.). (J). lib. bdg. 18.60 (*978-0-8225-8598-5(7) , Lerner Pubns.) Lerner Publishing Group.

Thompson, Gare. A Suburban Community of the 1950s. 2002. (Reading Expeditions Ser.). (Illus.). 24p. (J). pap. (978-0-7922-8691-2(X)) National Geographic Society.

Trumbauer, Lisa. Living in a Suburb. 2005. (Communities Ser.). (Illus.). 24p. (J). 15.93 (978-0-7368-3632-6(2) , Pebble Bks.) Capstone Pr., Inc.

SUBVERSIVE ACTIVITIES

see also Political Crimes and Offenses; Spies; Terrorism

Owen, David. Hidden Secrets: A Complete History of Espionage & the Technology Used to Support It. 2002. (Illus.). 224p. (gr. 7-12). per. 36.15 (978-0-613-51111-7(5)) Tandem Library Bks.

SUBWAYS

Blevins, Wiley. Found Underground: Art, Music, & Poetry of the New York City Subways. 2002. (Illus.). 16p. (J). pap. (978-0-439-35143-0(X)) Scholastic, Inc.

Brimner, Larry Dane. Subway: A Brief History of Underground Mass Transit. Waldman, Neil, illus. 2004. 32p. (YA). (gr. 2-4). 15.95 (978-1-59078-176-0(7)) Boyds Mills Pr.

New York Transit Museum Staff, creator. New York City Subway Trains: 12 Classic Punch-and-Build Trains. 2003. (Illus.). 48p. (J). (gr. 1-7). pap. 16.95 (978-1-58685-324-2(4)) Gibbs Smith, Publisher.

Pascoe, Elaine, ed. London Underground. 2003. (Super Structures of the World Ser.). (Illus.). 48p. (J). 24.95 (978-1-56711-866-7(6)); 11.20 (978-1-4103-0190-1(7)) Thomson Gale. (Blackbirch Pr., Inc.).

Santella, Andrew. Building the New York City Subway. 2007. (Cornerstones of Freedom). (Illus.). 48p. (J). (gr. 4-6). 26.00 (978-0-516-23638-4(5) , Children's Pr.) Scholastic Library Publishing.

Subways. 2007. (J). pap. 5.95 (*978-0-8225-6424-9(6) , First Avenue Editions) Lerner Publishing Group.

Walker, Pam. Subway Rides. 2000. (Let's Go Ser.). (Illus.). 24p. (J). (ps-2). 18.00 (978-0-516-23103-7(0) , Children's Pr.) Scholastic Library Publishing.

—Subway Rides. 2000. (gr. k-3). lib. bdg. 12.95 (978-0-613-52192-5(7)) Tandem Library Bks.

Weitzman, David L. A Subway for New York. 2005. (Illus.). 40p. (J). (gr. 4-7). 17.00 (978-0-374-37284-2(5)) Farrar, Straus & Giroux.

Winget, Mary. Subways. 2007. (Pull Ahead Books). (J). 22.60 (978-0-8225-6418-8(1) , Lerner Pubns.) Lerner Publishing Group.

SUBWAYS—FICTION

Cohen, Miriam. Down in the Subway. Greenberg, Melanie Hope, illus. 2003. 40p. (J). (gr. k-3). pap. 5.95 (978-1-932065-24-4(5)); 15.95 (978-1-932065-08-4(3)) Star Bright Bks., Inc.

Derrick, Patricia. Rathbone the Rat. 2007. 32p. 18.95 (978-1-933818-17-7(4)) Animalations.

Holman, Felice. Slake's Limbo. unabr. ed. 2004. 117p. (J). (gr. 7 up). pap. 29.00 incl. audio (978-0-8072-8744-6(X) , YA254SP, Listening Library) Random Hse. Audio Publishing Group.

Jacobs, Paul DuBois & Swender, Jennifer. My Subway Ride. Alko, Selina, illus. 2004. 32p. (J). 15.95 (978-1-58685-357-0(0)) Gibbs Smith, Publisher.

Lakin, Patricia. Subway Sonata. Maione, Heather Harms, illus. 2001. 32p. (J). (gr. k-4). lib. bdg. (978-0-7613-1464-6(4) , Millbrook Pr.) Lerner Publishing Group.

Mercier, Johanne & Brignaud, Pierre. Caillou on the Subway. rev. ed. 2006. (Out & about Ser.). (Illus.). 24p. (J). pap. 3.95 (*978-2-89450-584-7(1)) Chouette Publishing CAN. *Dist:* Independent Pubs. Group.

Potter, Ellen. Olivia Kidney & the Secret Beneath the City. 2007. 336p. (YA). (gr. 4 up). 16.99 (978-0-399-24701-9(7) , Philomel) Penguin Group (USA) Inc.

Quattlebaum, Mary. Underground Train. Smith, Cat Bowman, illus. 1999. (J). (ps-ps). lib. bdg. 12.54 (978-0-606-20025-7(8)) Tandem Library Bks.

Reid, Barbara. The Subway Mouse. Reid, Barbara, illus. 2005. (Illus.). 40p. (J). 15.95 (978-0-439-72827-0(4)) Scholastic, Inc.

—The Subway Mouse. 2005. (Illus.). (J). (978-0-439-77430-7(6)) Scholastic, Inc.

Shusterman, Neal. Downsiders. l.t. ed. 2000. 336p. (YA). (gr. 6-12). lib. bdg. 29.95 (978-1-58118-071-8(3)) LRS.

—Downsiders. 2001. 256p. (YA). (gr. 8-12). mass mkt. 5.99 (978-0-689-83969-6(3) , Simon Pulse) Simon & Schuster Children's Publishing.

Slake's Limbo. 2001. stu. ed., wbk. ed. (978-1-58130-749-8(7)) Novel Units, Inc.

Stilton, Geronimo. The Phantom of the Subway. Wolf, Matt, illus. 2004. (Geronimo Stilton Ser.: No. 13). 112p. (J). lib. bdg. 10.00 (*978-1-4242-0282-9(5)) Fitzgerald Bks.

—The Phantom of the Subway. 2004. (Geronimo Stilton Ser.: No. 13). (Illus.). 112p. (J). (gr. 2-5). lib. bdg. 13.94 (978-0-606-33276-7(6)) Tandem Library Bks.

Suen, Anastasia & Katz, Karen. Subway. 2004. (Illus.). 40p. (J). (gr. k-1). 15.99 (978-0-670-03622-6(6) , Viking Juvenile) Penguin Group (USA) Inc.

SUCCESS

see also Business; Leadership; Life Skills

The Action Principles: Armed Service Tribute Edition. 2nd ed. 2003. mass mkt. 20.00 (978-1-884864-19-3(8)) American Success Institute, Inc.

Adler, Mia Sharon. Essential Proteen: A Life Skills Program for Helping Teens Succeed: Student Journal. 2006. viii, 39p. (YA). pap. 14.95 (978-0-87822-582-8(X) , 5284) Research Pr.

Afflick, Lloyd E. Teenager's Guide to Success. 2002. (gr. 7-12). lib. bdg. 20.50 (978-0-613-74662-5(7)) Tandem Library Bks.

Asgedom, Mawi. Code: The 5 Secrets of Teen Success. 2003. (gr. 7-12). lib. bdg. 18.80 (978-0-613-70576-9(9)) Tandem Library Bks.

Bachel, Beverly K. What Do You Really Want? How to Set a Goal & Go for It! A Guide for Teens. 2004. (Illus.). 144p. (YA). (gr. 6 up). pap. 12.95 (978-1-57542-085-1(6)) Free Spirit Publishing, Inc.

Benson, Peter L. What Teens Need to Succeed: Proven, Practical Ways to Shape Your Own Future. 1998. (gr. 7-12). lib. bdg. 25.70 (978-0-613-84383-6(5)) Tandem Library Bks.

Benson, Peter L., et al. What Teens Need to Succeed: Proven, Practical Ways to Shape Your Own Future. 1998. (Illus.). 368p. (YA). (gr. 6 up). pap. 15.95 (978-1-57542-027-1(9)) Free Spirit Publishing, Inc.

Bishop, John. Goal Setting for Students: Winner of three national parenting book Awards. 2003. (Illus.). (YA). pap. 11.95 (978-0-9743700-0-2(2)) Accent On Success.

Blair, Gary R. The Kid's Guide to Goal-Setting. 1998. 48p. (J). (gr. 2 up). pap. 6.95 (978-1-889770-15-4(9) , GSK) GoalsGuy Learning Systems, Inc.

—The Teenager's Guide to Goal-Setting. 1998. 48p. (YA). pap. 6.95 (978-1-889770-16-1(7) , GST) GoalsGuy Learning Systems, Inc.

Clark, Sondra. Snap 2 It! A Real Girl's Guide to Keeping a Positive Outlook (even when you're having a bad hair day, just got a pimple on your nose & you & your best friend are fighting) 2007. 128p. pap. 7.95 (***978-1-4022-0954-3(1)***) Sourcebooks, Inc.

Conway, Hollis. Grasshopper: The Hollis Conway Story. 2004. 30p. (J). per. (978-1-59196-584-8(5)) Instantpublisher.com.

Crow, Gary & Crow, Marissa. The Success Train. 2003. (Illus.). 73p. (J). pap. 9.95 (978-0-9741685-5-6(6)) Koenisha Pubns.

Dyer, Wayne W. & Dyer, Summer. 10 Secrets for Success & Inner Peace for Teens. 2004. 12.95 (978-1-4019-0270-4(7) , 2707, Hay Hse. Lifestyles) Hay Hse., Inc.

Dyer, Wayne W. & Tracy, Kristina. Incredible You! (Spanish) 10 Ways to Let Your Greatness Shine Through. Siegel, Melanie, illus. 2007. Tr. of ¡Eres increíble!:10 formas de permitir que tu GRANDEZA brille a través de Ti. (SPA.). 32p. 14.95 (978-1-4019-1700-5(3)) Hay Hse., Inc.

Espeland, Pamela. Succeed Every Day: Daily Readings for Teens. 2004. (Illus.). 408p. (YA). (gr. 6 up). pap. 10.95 (978-1-57542-083-7(X)) Free Spirit Publishing, Inc.

Evans, Kristina. Cherish Today: A Celebration of Life's Moments. Collier, Bryan, illus. 2007. (J). (***978-1-4287-3968-0(8)*** , Jump at the Sun) Hyperion Bks. for Children.

Fiszer, Edward P. Thoughts to Inspire: Daily Messages for Young People. 2004. 176p. pap. 29.95 (978-1-57886-124-8(1)) Scarecrow Pr., Inc.

Frankel Hauser, Jill. The Kids Guide to Becoming the Best You Can Be! Developing 5 Traits You Need to Achieve Your Personal Best. 2006. (Illus.). 128p. (J). pap. 12.95 (978-0-8249-6788-8(7) , Williamson Bks.) Ideals Pubns.

Friel, John C. Seven Best Things Smart Teens Do. 2000. (gr. 7-12). lib. bdg. 22.20 (978-0-613-30721-5(6)) Tandem Library Bks.

Goldish, Meish. Kids & Co. Pellaton, Karen E., illus. 2002. 16p. (J). (978-0-439-35179-9(0)) Scholastic, Inc.

Graham, Stedman. Move Without the Ball: Put Your Skills & Your Magic to Work for You. 2004. (Illus.). 208p. pap. 14.00 (978-0-7432-3440-5(5) , Fireside) Simon & Schuster.

—Teens Can Make It Happen. 2001. (Illus.). 176p. pap., wbk. ed. 12.00 (978-0-7432-2558-8(9) , Fireside) Simon & Schuster.

—Teens Can Make It Happen: Nine Steps to Success. 2000. (gr. 7-12). lib. bdg. 23.45 (978-0-613-87778-7(0)) Tandem Library Bks.

Gratzon, Fred. The Lazy Way to Success: How to Do Nothing & Accomplish Everything. Sheaff, Lawrence, illus. 2002. 216p. (YA). 27.95 (978-0-9720464-0-4(2)) Soma Pr.

Hauser, Jill Frankel. The Kids Guide to Becoming the Best You Can Be. 2006. 128p. (J). 16.95 (978-0-8249-6789-5(5) , Williamson Bks.) Ideals Pubns.

Hearst Books (Firm) Staff. CosmoGirl! Secrets of Success. 2007. (Illus.). 176p. (J). (gr. 7 up). pap. 7.95 (***978-1-58816-666-1(X)***) Hearst Bks.

Hunt, Christopher. Victory after High School: Survive or Thrive—You Choose! 2005. 144p. (YA). per. 16.95 (978-0-9765973-4-6(9)) Adjust Communications.

Hunt, Rameck, et al. We Beat the Street: How a Friendship Pact Led to Success. 2006. (Illus.). 208p. (J). (gr. 5). pap. 6.99 (978-0-14-240627-4(9) , Puffin) Penguin Group (USA) Inc.

Imai, Carol. True Success: An Interactive Guide for Achieving Career, Academic & Personal Goals: Instructor's Guide. Berry, Mike, ed. 2002. (True Success Book). 212p. (J). per. 55.00 (978-1-893320-29-1(4)) True Colors, Inc. Publishing.

Kiefer, Jeanne. Jobs for Kids: A Smart Kid's Q & A Guide. Green, Anne Canevari, illus. 2003. (Single Titles Ser.). 112p. (gr. 5-8). lib. bdg. 25.90 (978-0-7613-2611-3(1) , Millbrook Pr.) Lerner Publishing Group.

Kuitenbrouwer, Peter. 7 Secrets of Highly Successful Kids. Flook, Helen, illus. 2001. (Millennium Generation Ser.). 80p. (J). (gr. 4-7). pap. 9.95 (978-1-894222-39-6(3)) Lobster Pr. CAN. *Dist:* Univ. of Toronto Pr.

Leslie, Roger. Success Express for Teens: 50 Life-Changing Activities. 2004. (Illus.). 224p. pap. 14.95 (978-1-886298-09-5(2)) Bayou Publishing.

Lewis, Carole. Pathway to Success. 2004. (First Place Bible Studies). 240p. pap. 19.99 (978-0-8307-2927-2(5) , Gospel Light) Gospel Light Pubns.

Mandino, Og. Og Mandino's Great Trilogy: The Greatest Salesman in the World, the Greatest Secret in the World & the Greatest Miracle in the World. 2008. 420p. (J). (978-0-8119-0428-5(8)) Lifetime Bks.

McDuffie, Daryl L. ABC's to Unlimited Success: How to Turn All Your Dreams into Reality. 2003. (YA). per. 9.97 (978-0-9727582-0-8(8)) G Publishing LLC.

McGraw, Jay. Life Strategies for Teens. 2000. (Illus.). 240p. (YA). (gr. 8-12). pap. 14.95 (978-0-7432-1546-6(X) , Fireside) Simon & Schuster.

Miller, Brandy & Wittmaier, Jeffrey B., eds. Success: In Your Career & Personal Life, a How-to Guide. Leonard, David, illus. l.t. ed. 2002. 160p. (YA). per. 16.95 (978-0-9720961-0-2(8)) Miller, Larry.

Norris, David A. Lasting Success: Quality Decisions, Relationships & Untamed Emotions. 2003. (Illus.). 256p. per. (978-0-943177-12-0(X) , 0-943177-12-x) Heartland Foundation, Inc.

Ogg, Jim, et al, eds. The Achiever, Elementary. 1999. (Illus.). (J). (gr. 3-6). pap. (978-0-9678649-0-7(9)) Coole Schl.

—The Achiever, Elementary. Tate, Lori, illus. 2nd ed. 2000. (J). (gr. 3-6). pap. (978-0-9678649-4-5(1)) Coole Schl.

Ogg, Jim & Koslow, Paula. The Achiever, Middle. Hassenmiller, Steve, ed. 1999. (Illus.). (YA). (gr. 6-9). pap. (978-0-9678649-1-4(7)) Coole Schl.

Overcoming Obstacles: A Program for Success: High School Level, 16 vols. 1999. (YA). (gr. 9-12). pap. (978-1-929393-13-8(X)) Community for Education Foundation.

Paxson, Jillip Naysinthe, told to. The First Thirty. 2005. 96p. (YA). 15.00 (978-0-9758794-1-2(3)) IdeaList Enterprises, Inc.

Paxson, Jillip Naysinthe & Siegman, Greg Forbes. The First Thirty. 2005. 96p. (YA). per. 10.00 (978-0-9758794-0-5(5)) IdeaList Enterprises, Inc.

Rayel, Michael G. A 31-Day Success Principles for Kids & Teens. 2006. 64p. (J). pap. (***978-0-9737070-3-8(8)***) Soar Dime, Limited/Oikos Global.

Richardson, Dot. Go for It: Conversations on Being You. 2004. (Girls Explore, Reach for the Stars Ser.). (Illus.). 140p. (J). 20.00 (978-0-9749456-0-6(9) , Girls Explore) Girls Explore LLC.

Rimm, Sylvia. See Jane Win for Girls: A Smart Girl's Guide to Success. 2004. (Illus.). 144p. (YA). (gr. 4-8). pap. 13.95 (978-1-57542-122-3(4)) Free Spirit Publishing, Inc.

—See Jane Win for Girls: A Smart Girl's Guide to Success. 2003. (gr. 7-12). lib. bdg. 23.40 (978-0-613-67161-3(9)) Tandem Library Bks.

Roets, Lois F. Understanding Success & Failure: Life's Two Biggest Challenges. 3rd rev. ed. 2001. 36p. (J). (gr. k-12). pap. 10.00 (978-0-911943-81-8(1)) Leadership Pub., Inc.

Ross, Margaret. Casey & the Amazing Good Finder: Teaching Adults & Children How to Succeed in School, Work, Life & Relationships. l.t. ed. 2005. (Illus.). 32p. (J). 9.99 (978-0-9715713-5-8(X)) Kamaron Institute Pr.

Rossi, Debra M. No Horsing Around: Kick off to Success in School. 2004. (Illus.). 32p. (J). 5.95 (978-0-9758982-0-8(5)) Rossi, Debra.

Scott, John, text. Juniors: How to Make the Team. 2004. (YA). 30.00 (978-1-879498-78-5(2)) SportAmerica.

Silverman, Robin Landew. Reaching Your Goals. 2004. (Life Balance Ser.). 80p. (J). 20.50 (978-0-531-12342-3(1) , Watts, Franklin) Scholastic Library Publishing.

Stacy, Lori Moore. Discover Yourself! 2000. (All about You Ser.). 112p. (J). (gr. 4-7). pap. 4.50 (978-0-439-15529-8(0)) Scholastic, Inc.

Success in the World of Work: Getting a Job. (Success in the World of Work Ser.). (YA). cd-rom 159.95 (978-1-56191-659-7(5)) Films Media Group.

Tate, Lori. The Achiever, K-2. Ogg, Jim et al, eds. Tate, Lori, illus. 2000. (Illus.). (J). (gr. k-2). pap. (978-0-9678649-3-8(3)) Coole Schl.

—The Achiever, Middle. Ogg, Jim et al, eds. Tate, Lori, illus. 2nd ed. 2000. (Illus.). (YA). (gr. 6-9). pap. (978-0-9678649-5-2(X)) Coole Schl.

Upsets & Comebacks. 2006. (Upsets & Comebacks Ser.). (J). lib. bdg. 143.76 (978-1-59716-201-2(9)) Bearport Publishing Co., Inc.

SUDOKU

Balaban, Mariah, ed. Scooby Doo Sudoku. 2006. 24p. (J). pap. 4.99 (978-0-439-87921-7(3)) Scholastic, Inc.

Benton, Jim & Sirkis, Rafael. Sudoku. Glazer, Joshua, ed. 2006. (It's Happy Bunny Ser.). 144p. (J). pap. 4.99 (978-0-439-87320-8(7) , Scholastic) Scholastic, Inc.

Carey, Craig Robert. Sudoku Puzzles. 2006. (SpongeBob SquarePants Ser.: No. 3). 32p. (J). pap. 5.99 (978-1-4169-2428-9(0) , Simon Spotlight/Nickelodeon) Simon & Schuster Children's Publishing.

—Sudoku Puzzles #1. 2006. (SpongeBob SquarePants Ser.). 32p. (J). pap. 5.99 (978-1-4169-2426-5(4) , Simon Spotlight/Nickelodeon) Simon & Schuster Children's Publishing.

—Sudoku Puzzles #2. 2006. (SpongeBob SquarePants Ser.). 32p. (J). pap. 5.99 (978-1-4169-2427-2(2) , Simon Spotlight/Nickelodeon) Simon & Schuster Children's Publishing.

Chisholm, Alastair. The Kids' Book of Sudoku 1!, Bk. 1. Catlow, Nikalas, illus. 2005. 224p. (J). mass mkt. 5.99 (978-1-4169-1761-8(6)) Simon & Schuster Children's Publishing.

—The Kids' Book of Sudoku 2!, Bk. 2. Catlow, Nikalas, illus. 2005. 224p. (J). mass mkt. 5.99 (978-1-4169-1789-2(6)) Simon & Schuster Children's Publishing.

Conceptis Puzzles. The 21-Foot-Long Sudoku Puzzle Book: Fold-Out Fun for More Than One. 2007. 64p. (J). 9.95 (978-1-4027-4551-5(6) , Sterling Innovation) Sterling Publishing Co., Inc.

Coussement, Frank & De Schepper, Peter. Farm Animal Sudoku. 2007. (Illus.). 96p. (J). pap. 5.95 (978-1-4027-4365-8(3)) Sterling Publishing Co., Inc.

—Spaceship Sudoku. 2007. (Illus.). 96p. (J). pap. 5.95 (978-1-4027-4367-2(X)) Sterling Publishing Co., Inc.

—Wild Animal Sudoku. 2007. (Illus.). 96p. (J). pap. 5.95 (978-1-4027-4366-5(1)) Sterling Publishing Co., Inc.

Eddy, Ron & Stelluto, Jim. Sudoku Puzzles, No. 1. Style Guide Staff, illus. 2006. (VeggieTales Ser.). 32p. (J). pap. 5.99 (978-1-4169-4117-0(7) , Simon Scribbles) Simon & Schuster Children's Publishing.

Gould, Wayne. Grand Master Junior Su Doku. 2005. (Illus.). 240p. (J). (gr. 3-7). pap. 4.99 (978-0-06-112412-9(5)) HarperCollins Pubs.

Griffiths-Jones, Sam & Moog, Bob. Sudoku for Kids. 2005. 160p. (J). pap. (978-1-57528-963-2(6)) University Games.

Heron, Andrew. Kids' Sudoku for Dummies. 2006. 278p. pap. 7.99 (978-0-470-12447-5(4) , For Dummies) Wiley, John & Sons, Inc.

Higginson, Sheila. Scary Sudoku & Spooky Puzzles. Disney Storybook Artists Staff, illus. 2007. 32p. (ps-k). pap., act. bk. ed. 5.99 (***978-1-4231-0650-0(4)***) Disney Pr.

Hodder and Stoughton Staff, ed. Sudoku for Beginners 1. 2006. (Illus.). (J). mass mkt. 4.99 (978-0-340-91721-3(0) , Hodder & Stoughton) Hodder General Publishing Division GBR. *Dist:* Trafalgar Square Publishing.

—Sudoku for Beginners 2. 2006. (Illus.). (J). mass mkt. 4.99 (978-0-340-91722-0(9) , Hodder & Stoughton) Hodder General Publishing Division GBR. *Dist:* Trafalgar Square Publishing.

—Sudoku for Beginners 3. 2006. (Illus.). (J). mass mkt. 4.99 (978-0-340-91828-9(4) , Hodder & Stoughton) Hodder General Publishing Division GBR. *Dist:* Trafalgar Square Publishing.

—Sudoku for Beginners 4. 2006. (Illus.). (J). mass mkt. 4.99 (978-0-340-91829-6(2) , Hodder & Stoughton) Hodder General Publishing Division GBR. *Dist:* Trafalgar Square Publishing.

Kattan, Peter & Kattan, Nicola. Kindergarten Sudoku: 4x4 Sudoku Puzzles for Kids. 2007. 48p. pap. 7.50 (***978-0-615-15334-6(8)***) Kattan, Peter I.

Kingfisher Editors, ed. More Sudoku for Kids. 2006. 64p. (J). (gr. 3-5). pap. 3.95 (978-0-7534-6109-9(9) , Kingfisher) Houghton Mifflin Co. Trade & Reference Div.

—Sudoku. 2005. 64p. (J). (gr. 3-5). pap. 3.95 (978-0-7534-6029-0(7) , Kingfisher) Houghton Mifflin Co. Trade & Reference Div.

Longo, Frank. The Big Book of Sudoku Puzzles for Kids: 818 Super Puzzles! 2006. 320p. pap. 14.95 (978-1-4027-4272-9(X)) Sterling Publishing Co., Inc.

Molski, Carol. Bible Word Suduko. 2007. (ENG.). 64p. (J). 10.99 (***978-0-7586-1344-8(X)***) Concordia Publishing Hse.

Moog, Bob. Do You Sudoku Spicy. Over 200 Puzzles for Experienced Sudoku Solvers. 2006. 160p. pap. (978-1-57528-899-4(0)) University Games.

Moore, Gareth. Sudoku Makes You Smarter! Catlow, Nikalas, illus. 2007. 192p. (J). pap. 5.99 (***978-1-4169-3663-3(7)*** , Simon Scribbles) Simon & Schuster Children's Publishing.

Moore, Gareth & Moore, Gustav. The Kids' Book of Sudoku! Challenge Edition! Catlow, Nikalas, illus. 2006. 224p. (J). mass mkt. 5.99 (978-1-4169-4116-3(9) , Simon Scribbles) Simon & Schuster Children's Publishing.

Newmarket Press. Junior Su Doku. 2005. (Illus.). 112p. (gr. 3-7). pap. 4.95 (978-1-55704-706-9(5)) Newmarket Pr.

—Junior Su Doku: Easter. 2006. (Illus.). 128p. (YA). pap. 4.95 (978-1-55704-715-1(4)) Newmarket Pr.

—Junior Su Doku Christmas. 2005. (Illus.). 128p. (YA). pap. 4.95 (978-1-55704-707-6(3)) Newmarket Pr.

—Junior Su Doku Halloween. 2006. (Sudoku Ser.). (Illus.). 128p. (YA). pap. 4.95 (978-1-55704-730-4(8)) Newmarket Pr.

—Junior Su Doku Valentine's Day: Newmarket Press Puzzle Book. 2006. (Illus.). 128p. (YA). pap. 4.95 (978-1-55704-713-7(8)) Newmarket Pr.

Pazzelli, John. A First Sudoku Book. Zourelias, Diana, illus. 2006. 64p. (J). pap. 3.95 (978-0-486-45074-2(0)) Dover Pubns., Inc.

Puzzler Media Staff. More Original Sudoku for Kids: 100 More of the World's Most Popular Puzzle! 2005. (Illus.). 144p. (gr. 4-7). pap. 5.95 (978-1-56025-877-3(2)) Running Pr. Bk. Pubs.

—Original Sudoku for Kids: With Complete Instructions, Hints, 10 Puzzles & Solutions for the World's Most Popular Puzzle! 2005. (Illus.). 144p. (gr. 4-7). pap. 5.95 (978-1-56025-876-6(4)) Running Pr. Bk. Pubs.

Puzzler Media Staff & Hamlyn. Sudoku for Smart Kids: 200 Puzzles for Brainy Children. 2006. (Illus.). 288p. (J). pap. 7.95 (978-0-600-61533-0(2) , Hamlyn) Octopus Publishing Group GBR. *Dist:* Sterling Publishing Co., Inc.

Rios, Michael. Sudoku Puzzles for Kids. 2005. 96p. (J). pap. 4.95 (978-1-4027-3602-5(9)) Sterling Publishing Co., Inc.

—Super Sudoku Puzzles for Kids. 2006. 96p. (J). pap. 4.95 (978-1-4027-3765-7(3)) Sterling Publishing Co., Inc.

Sander, Sonia. Easy Sudoku Puzzles, No. 3. 2006. (Dora the Explorer Ser.). 32p. (J). pap. 5.99 (978-1-4169-2431-9(0) , Simon Spotlight/Nickelodeon) Simon & Schuster Children's Publishing.

—Easy Sudoku Puzzles #1. 2006. (Dora the Explorer Ser.). 32p. (J). pap. 5.99 (978-1-4169-2429-6(9) , Simon Spotlight/Nickelodeon) Simon & Schuster Children's Publishing.

—Easy Sudoku Puzzles #2. 2006. (Dora the Explorer Ser.). 32p. (J). pap. 5.99 (978-1-4169-2430-2(2) , Simon Spotlight/Nickelodeon) Simon & Schuster Children's Publishing.

Scholastic, Inc. Staff. Su Doku: Jokes! Jokes! Jokes! 2007. (Su Doku Ser.). 144p. (J). pap. 4.99 (***978-0-439-02279-8(7)***) Scholastic, Inc.

Shortz, Will. Will Shortz Presents the Monster Book of Sudoku for Kids. 2006. 176p. pap. 5.95 (978-0-312-36842-5(9) , St. Martin's Griffin) St. Martin's Pr.

Sirkis, Rafael. My First Book of Su Doku. Ackerman, Daria, illus. 2007. 24p. (J). pap. 4.99 (***978-0-545-00016-1(5)***) Scholastic, Inc.

Small, Lindsay. Superstar Sudoku for Kids. 2005. (Illus.). 288p. (J). (gr. 3-7). mass mkt. 4.99 (978-0-8431-2029-5(0) , Price Stern Sloan) Penguin Group (USA) Inc.

—Superstar Sudoku for Kids on the Go. 2006. 288p. (J). (gr. 3). pap. 4.99 (978-0-8431-2095-0(9) , Price Stern Sloan) Penguin Group (USA) Inc.

Su Doku: Wacky Facts. 2007. 144p. (J). pap. 4.99 (***978-0-439-02280-4(0)***) Scholastic, Inc.

Suzuki, Yukio. Wizard Su Doku for Kids. 2006. 125p. (J). pap. 4.99 (978-0-7858-2102-1(3) , Chartwell) Book Sales, Inc.

Teora, ed. Sudoku 42 Puzzles for Kids. 2005. 24p. pap. 3.95 (978-1-59496-126-7(3)); pap. 3.95 (978-1-59496-127-4(1)) Teora USA LLC.

YOE! Studio Staff. Easy Puzzles. Style Guide Staff, illus. 2007. (Care Bears Ser.). 32p. (J). pap. 5.99 (978-1-4169-3411-0(1)); pap. 5.99 (978-1-4169-3410-3(3)) Simon & Schuster Children's Publishing. (Simon Scribbles).

YOE! Studio Staff, des. The Backyardigans Easy Sudoku Puzzles, No. 1. 2007. (Backyardigans Ser.). 32p. (J). pap. 5.99 (978-1-4169-3556-8(8) , Simon Spotlight) Simon & Schuster Children's Publishing.

—Go, Diego, Go! Sudoku Puzzles. 2007. (Go, Diego, Go! Ser.: No. 1). 32p. (J). pap. 5.99 (978-1-4169-3554-4(1) , Simon Spotlight) Simon & Schuster Children's Publishing.

SUEZ CANAL (EGYPT)

Bodden, Valerie. Suez Canal. 2006. (Modern Wonders of the World Ser.). (Illus.). 32p. 18.95 (***978-1-58341-441-5(X)*** , Creative Education) Creative Co., The.

Stewart, Gail B. The Suez Canal. 2001. (Building History Ser.). (Illus.). 112p. (YA). (gr. 6-9). 32.45 (978-1-56006-842-6(6) , Lucent Bks.) Thomson Gale.

SUFFRAGE

see also classes of people with the subdivision Suffrage, e.g. Women—Suffrage; etc.

Connolly, Sean. The Right to Vote. 2005. (Campaigns for Change Ser.). (Illus.). 48p. (J). (gr. 6-9). lib. bdg. 29.95 (978-1-58340-517-8(8)) Smart Apple Media.

Cunningham, Kevin. U. S. Congress: Who Represents You. 2004. (Our Government & Citizenship Ser.). (Illus.). 32p. (J). (gr. 2-6). 27.07 (978-1-59296-327-0(7)) Child's World, Inc.

Decapua, Sarah. Voting. 2002. (gr. 3-6). lib. bdg. 15.25 (978-0-613-54380-4(7)) Tandem Library Bks.

Durrett, Deanne. Right to Vote. 2005. (American Rights Ser.). (Illus.). 148p. (J). (gr. 4-9). per. 35.00 (978-0-8160-5661-3(7)) Facts On File, Inc.

Egan, Tracie. Voting. 2004. (Primary Source Library of American Citizenship). (Illus.). 32p. (YA). lib. bdg. (978-1-4042-5093-2(X)) Rosen Publishing Group, Inc., The.

Hamilton, John. Voting in an Election. 2005. (Government in Action! Ser.). (J). (gr. k-6). lib. bdg. 22.78 (978-1-59197-647-9(2)) ABDO Publishing Co.

Kamma, Anne. If You Lived When Women Won Their Rights. 2008. 64p. pap. 5.99 (***978-0-439-74869-8(0)*** , Scholastic Reference) Scholastic, Inc.

Price Hossell, Karen. The Nineteenth Amendment: Women Get the Vote. 2003. (Point of Impact Ser.). (Illus.). 32p. (J). (gr. 5-7). lib. bdg. 25.64 (978-1-58810-908-8(9)) Heinemann Library.

Richardson, Jane & Dawson, Ian. Dying for the Vote: Britain 1750-1900: a Key Stage 3 Depth Study on the Chartists & the Suffragettes. 2002. (Illus.). 72p. pap., stu. ed. 26.00 (***978-0-7195-8563-0(5)*** , Hodder Murray) Hodder Education GBR. *Dist:* Trans-Atlantic Pubns., Inc.

SUFFRAGETTES

see Suffragists

SUFFRAGISTS

Bjornlund, Lydia D. Women of the Suffrage Movement. 2003. (Women in History Ser.). (Illus.). 112p. (J). 32.45 (978-1-59018-173-7(5) , Lucent Bks.) Thomson Gale.

Bohannon, Lisa Frederiksen. Failure Is Impossible: The Story of Susan B. Anthony. 2004. (Feminist Voices Ser.). (Illus.). 112p. (YA). (gr. 6-12). 23.95 (978-1-883846-77-0(3) , First Biographies) Reynolds, Morgan Inc.

Boothroyd, Jennifer. Susan B. Anthony: A Life of Fairness. 2006. (Pull Ahead Books). (J). lib. bdg. (978-978-082-253-8(4)); (Illus.). 32p. 22.60 (978-0-8225-3479-2(7)) Lerner Publishing Group. (Lerner Pubns.).

—Susan B. Anthony: Una Vida de Igualdad. 2006. (Libros para Avanzar Ser.). (ENG & SPA., Illus.). 32p. (J). lib. bdg. 22.60 (978-0-8225-6234-4(0)) Lerner Publishing Group.

Brown, Don. A Voice from the Wilderness: The Story of Anna Howard Shaw. 32p. (J). (gr. k-3). 2010. pap. 5.95 (978-0-618-58544-1(3)); 2001. (Illus.). tchr. ed. 16.00 (978-0-618-08362-6(6)) Houghton Mifflin Co. Trade & Reference Div.

Collier, James Lincoln. The Susan B. Anthony You Never Knew. 2004. (You Never Knew Ser.). (J). 25.50 (978-0-516-24428-0(0) , Children's Pr.) Scholastic Library Publishing.

Elizabeth Cady Stanton. (Photo Illustrated Biographies Ser.). 24p. (J). 6.95 (978-0-7368-8428-0(9)) Capstone Pr., Inc.

Fritz, Jean. You Want Women to Vote, Lizzie Stanton? DiSalvo-Ryan, DyAnne, illus. 1999. 96p. (J). (gr. 3-7). pap. 6.99 (978-0-698-11764-8(6) , Putnam Juvenile) Penguin Group (USA) Inc.

—You Want Women to Vote, Lizzie Stanton? 1999. (978-0-606-16848-9(6)); (gr. 3-6). lib. bdg. 15.30 (978-0-613-17893-8(9)) Tandem Library Bks.

Havelin, Kate. Victoria Woodhull: Fearless Feminist. 2007. (Trailblazer Biographies Ser.). (Illus.). 112p. (J). 30.60 (978-0-8225-5986-3(2) , Lerner Pubns.) Lerner Publishing Group.

Hopkinson, Deborah. Susan B. Anthony: Fighter for Women's Rights. Bates, Amy, illus. 2005. 32p. (J). lib. bdg. 15.00 (*978-1-4242-1563-8(3))* Fitzgerald Bks.

—Susan B. Anthony: Fighter for Women's Rights. Bates, Amy June, illus. 2005. (Ready-To-Read Stories of Famous Americans Ser.). 32p. (J). (gr. 1-3). pap. 3.99 (978-0-689-86909-9(6)); lib. bdg. 11.89 (978-0-689-86910-5(X)) Simon & Schuster Children's Publishing. (Aladdin).

Kops, Deborah. The Women Suffrage Movement. 2003. (People at the Center of Ser.). (Illus.). 48p. (J). 24.95 (978-1-56711-772-1(4) , Blackbirch Pr., Inc.) Thomson Gale.

Krull, Kathleen. A Woman for President: The Story of Victoria Woodhull. Dyer, Jane, illus. 32p. (J). 2004. 16.95 (978-0-8027-8908-2(0)); 2006. reprint ed. pap. 6.95 (978-0-8027-9615-8(X)) Walker & Co.

Landau, Elaine. Women's Right to Vote. (Cornerstones of Freedomtrade;, Second Ser.). 48p. (J). 2007. (gr. 4-6). pap. 5.95 (*978-0-531-18833-0(7));* 2005. (Illus.). 26.00 (978-0-516-23639-1(3)) Scholastic Library Publishing. (Children's Pr.).

Loos, Pamela. Elizabeth Cady Stanton: Woman Suffragist. 2000. (Women of Achievement Ser.). (Illus.). 112p. (J). (gr. 4-7). 30.00 (978-0-7910-5293-8(1) , Chelsea Hse.) Facts On File, Inc.

Mattern, Joanne. Elizabeth Cady Stanton & Susan B. Anthony: Fighting Together for Women's Rights. 2003. (Reading Power Ser.). (Illus.). 24p. (J). lib. bdg. 17.25 (978-0-8239-6503-8(1) , PowerKids Pr.) Rosen Publishing Group, Inc., The.

McCully, Emily Arnold. The Ballot Box Battle. 1998. (Dragonfly Books Ser.). (Illus.). 32p. (J). (gr. k-3). pap. 6.99 (978-0-679-89312-7(1) , Dragonfly Bks.) Random Hse. Children's Bks.

McPherson, Stephanie Sammartino. Susan B. Anthony. 2006. (History Maker Bios Ser.). (Illus.). 48p. (J). 26.60 (978-0-8225-5938-2(2) , Lerner Pubns.) Lerner Publishing Group.

Miller, Connie Colwell. Elizabeth Cady Stanton: Women's Rights Pioneer. Webb, James, illus. 2006. (Graphic Library). 32p. (J). 25.26 (978-0-7368-4971-5(8)) Capstone Pr., Inc.

Moore, Heidi. Elizabeth Cady Stanton. 2004. (American Lives (Heinemann Library (Firm))). (Illus.). 32p. (J). pap. 6.95 (978-1-4034-5705-9(0)); lib. bdg. (978-1-4034-4994-8(5)) Heinemann Library.

Mosley, Shelley & Charles, John. The Suffragists in Literature for Youth: The Fight for the Vote. 2006. (Literature for Youth Ser.: Vol. 10). 336p. (J). pap. 45.00 (978-0-8108-5372-0(8)) Scarecrow Pr., Inc.

Noyed, Robert B. Susan B. Anthony: Reformer. 2002. (Spirit of America: Our People Ser.). (Illus.). 32p. (J). (gr. 2-6). 27.07 (978-1-56766-171-2(8)) Child's World, Inc.

Orr, Tamra B. Susan B. Anthony. 2006. (Profiles in American History Ser.). (Illus.). 48p. (J). (gr. 4-8). lib. bdg. 29.95 (*978-1-58415-445-7(4))* Mitchell Lane Pubs., Inc.

Raatma, Lucia. Susan B. Anthony. 2001. (Compass Point Early Biographies Ser.). (Illus.). 32p. (J). (gr. 2 up). lib. bdg. 21.26 (978-0-7565-0069-6(9)) Compass Point Bks.

Randolph, Ryan P. Harriet Beecher Stowe: Author & Abolitionist. 2005. (Library of American Lives & Times). (Illus.). 112p. (J). (gr. 4-8). lib. bdg. 31.95 (978-0-8239-6623-3(2)) Rosen Publishing Group, Inc., The.

Rau, Dana Meachen. Great Women of the Suffrage Movement. 2005. (We the People Ser.). (Illus.). 48p. (J). (gr. 4-6). (978-0-7565-1270-5(0)) Compass Point Bks.

Raum, Elizabeth. Alice Paul. 2004. (American Lives (Heinemann Library (Firm))). (Illus.). 32p. (J). pap. 7.50 (978-1-4034-5703-5(4)); lib. bdg. (978-1-4034-4996-2(1)) Heinemann Library.

Rossi, Ann. Created Equal: Women Campaign for the Right to Vote, 1840-1920. 2005. (Crossroads America Ser.). (Illus.). 40p. (J). (978-0-7922-8626-4(X)) National Geographic Society.

Salisbury, Cynthia. Elizabeth Cady Stanton: Leader of the Fight for Women's Rights. 2002. (Historical American Biographies Ser.). (Illus.). 128p. (YA). (gr. 6-9). lib. bdg. 26.60 (978-0-7660-1616-3(1)) Enslow Pubs., Inc.

Sigerman, Harriet. Elizabeth Cady Stanton: The Right Is Ours. 2001. (Oxford Portraits Ser.). (Illus.). 144p. (YA). (gr. 8 up). suppl. ed. 28.00 (978-0-19-511969-5(X)) Oxford Univ. Pr., Inc.

Slade, Suzanne. Susan B. Anthony: Fighter for Freedom & Equality. Orback, Craig, illus. 2006. (Biographies Ser.). 24p. (J). (gr. k-3). lib. bdg. 23.93 (*978-1-4048-3104-9(5))* Picture Window Bks.

Somervill, Barbara A. Votes for Women! The Story of Carrie Chapman Catt. 2004. (Feminist Voices Ser.). (Illus.). 128p. (YA). (gr. 6-12). 23.95 (978-1-883846-96-1(X) , First Biographies) Reynolds, Morgan Inc.

Stone, Tanya Lee. Elizabeth Leads the Way. 2008. (Illus.). 32p. (J). 16.95 (*978-0-8050-7903-6(3))* Holt, Henry & Co.

Wheeler, Jill C. Susan B. Anthony. 2003. (Breaking Barriers Ser.). (Illus.). 64p. (J). (gr. 3-8). lib. bdg. 25.65 (978-1-57765-903-7(1)) ABDO Publishing Co.

White, Linda Arms. I Could Do That! Esther Morris Gets Women the Vote. Carpenter, Nancy, illus. 2005. 40p. (J). (ps-7). 16.00 (978-0-374-33527-4(3) , Farrar, Straus & Giroux (BYR)) Farrar, Straus & Giroux.

—I Could Do That! Esther Morris Gets Women the Vote. unabr. ed. 2006. (J). (gr. 2-4). 24.95 incl. audio (*978-0-439-90576-3(1)* , WHRA692); 29.95 incl. audio compact disk (*978-0-439-90582-4(6)* , WHCD692) Weston Woods Studios, Inc.

Wooldridge, Connie N. When Esther Morris Headed West: Women, Wyoming, & the Right to Vote. Rogers, Jacqueline, illus. 2001. 32p. (J). (gr. k-3). tchr. ed. 16.95 (978-0-8234-1597-7(X)) Holiday Hse., Inc.

SUGAR

Basel, Roberta. From Cane to Sugar. 2005. (First Facts Ser.). (Illus.). 24p. (J). (ps-7). lib. bdg. 21.26 (978-0-7368-4283-9(7)) Capstone Pr., Inc.

Braithwaite, Jill. From Cane to Sugar. 2004. (Start to Finish Ser.). (Illus.). 24p. (J). (gr. k-2). lib. bdg. 18.60 (978-0-8225-0940-0(7)) Lerner Publishing Group.

Dalton, Cindy Devine. Eat Carbohydrates That Grow. 2000. (Why Should I... Ser.). (Illus.). 24p. (J). (gr. 1-4). lib. bdg. 19.27 (978-1-55916-303-3(8)) Rourke Publishing, LLC.

Eagen, Rachel. The Biography of Sugar. 2005. (How Did That Get Here? Ser.). (Illus.). 32p. (J). (gr. 3-9). (978-0-7787-2485-8(9)); pap. (978-0-7787-2521-3(9)) Crabtree Publishing Co.

Franck, Irene M. & Brownstone, David M. Sugar. 2003. (Illus.). 32p. (J). (978-0-7172-5725-6(8) , Grolier) Scholastic Library Publishing.

Frost, Helen. Fats, Oils & Sweets. Saunders-Smith, Gail, ed. 2000. (Food Guide Pyramid Ser.). (Illus.). 24p. (J). (gr. k-1). lib. bdg. 15.93 (978-0-7368-0536-0(2) , Pebble Bks.) Capstone Pr., Inc.

Landau, Elaine. Sugar. 1999. (True Bks.). (Illus.). 48p. (J). (gr. 3-5). 25.00 (978-0-516-21027-8(0) , Children's Pr.) Scholastic Library Publishing.

—Sugar. 1999. (gr. 3-6). lib. bdg. 15.25 (978-0-613-37553-5(X)) Tandem Library Bks.

Murray, Julie. Cane to Sugar. 2007. (Illus.). 24p. (J). 21.35 (978-1-59679-834-2(3) , Buddy Bks.) ABDO Publishing Co.

Peterson, Sheryl. Sugar. 2001. (Let's Investigate Ser.). (Illus.). 32p. (J). (978-1-58341-190-2(9) , Creative Education) Creative Co., The.

SUGAR-CANE

Eagen, Rachel. The Biography of Sugar. 2005. (How Did That Get Here? Ser.). (Illus.). 32p. (J). (gr. 3-9). (978-0-7787-2485-8(9)) Crabtree Publishing Co.

SUICIDE

see also Assisted Suicide

Carlson-Berne, Emma. Suicide. 2006. (History of Issues Ser.). (Illus.). 240p. (gr. 10-12). 36.20 (978-0-7377-2873-6(6) , Greenhaven Pr., Inc.) Thomson Gale.

Esherick, Joan. The Silent Cry: Teen Suicide & Self-Destructive Behaviors. 2005. (Science of Health Ser.). (Illus.). 128p. (J). lib. bdg. 24.95 (978-1-59084-851-7(9)) Mason Crest Pubs.

Espejo, Roman. Suicide. 2003. (Opposing Viewpoints Ser.). (Illus.). 207p. (J). lib. bdg. 36.20 (978-0-7377-1242-1(2) , Greenhaven Pr., Inc.) Thomson Gale.

Goldman, Linda. Bart Speaks Out! Breaking the Silence on Suicide. 1998. (Illus.). 42p. (J). (ps-7). pap., wbk. ed. 15.95 (978-0-87424-352-9(1) , W-352) Manson Western Corp.

Kuehn, Eileen. After Suicide: Living with the Questions. 2000. (Grief & Loss Ser.). (Illus.). 64p. (J). (gr. 4-6). lib. bdg. 23.93 (978-0-7368-0748-7(9) , LifeMatters Bks.) Capstone Pr., Inc.

Libal, Joyce. Antidepressants & Suicide: When Treatment Kills. 2006. (Antidepressants Ser.). (Illus.). 120p. (J). (gr. 7 up). (978-1-4222-0099-5(X)) Mason Crest Pubs.

Marcovitz, Hal. Teens & Suicide. 2004. (Gallup Youth Survey, Major Issues & Trends Ser.). (Illus.). 112,128p. (YA). (gr. 7-9). lib. bdg. 22.95 (978-1-59084-724-4(5)) Mason Crest Pubs.

McDowell, Josh & Stewart, Ed. Friendship 911 Collection: My Friend Is Struggling With... Thoughts of Suicide. 2000. (Friendship 911 Ser.). (Illus.). 64p. (gr. 8-12). pap. 7.98 (978-0-8499-3792-7(2)) Nelson, Thomas Inc.

Miller, Leslie A. & Rose, Paul A. Suicide. 2000. (Current Controversies Ser.). (Illus.). 160p. (YA). (gr. 7-12). pap. 24.95 (978-0-7377-0317-7(2) , Greenhaven Pr., Inc.) Thomson Gale.

Murphy, James M. Coping with Teen Suicide. 1999. (Coping Ser.). (Illus.). 128-192p. (YA). (gr. 7-12). lib. bdg. 26.50 (978-0-8239-2824-8(1) , COTESU) Rosen Publishing Group, Inc., The.

Nelson, Richard E. & Galas, Judith C. The Power to Prevent Suicide: A Guide for Teens Helping Teens. 2006. 128p. pap. 13.95 (978-1-57542-206-0(9)) Free Spirit Publishing, Inc.

Peacock, Judith. Teen Suicide. 2000. (Perspectives on Mental Health Ser.). (Illus.). 64p. (J). (gr. 4-6). lib. bdg. 23.93 (978-0-7368-0436-3(6) , LifeMatters Bks.) Capstone Pr., Inc.

Salomon, Ron, et al. Suicide. 2007. (Psychological Disorders Ser.). 120p. (gr. 9). 37.50 (*978-0-7910-9007-7(8)* , Chelsea Hse.) Facts On File, Inc.

Schleifer, Jay. Everything You Need to Know about Teen Suicide. rev. ed. 1999. (Need to Know Library). (Illus.). 64p. (YA). (gr. 7-12). lib. bdg. 25.25 (978-0-8239-3038-8(6) , NTTESU) Rosen Publishing Group, Inc., The.

Shannon, Joyce Brennfleck, ed. Suicide Information for Teens: Health Tips about Suicide Causes & Prevention, Including Facts about Depression, Hopelessness, Risk Factors, Getting Help, Survivor Support, & More. 2004. (Teen Health Ser.). 368p. (J). 65.00 (978-0-7808-0737-2(5)) Omnigraphics, Inc.

Slomski, Genevieve. Suicide. 2007. (Current Controversies Ser.). (Illus.). 240p. (J). (gr. 10-12). pap. 24.95 (978-0-7377-2489-9(7) , Greenhaven Pr., Inc.) Thomson Gale.

Slomski, Genevieve & Connors, Paul. Suicide. 2007. (Current Controversies Ser.). (Illus.). 240p. (J). (gr. 10-12). 36.20 (978-0-7377-2488-2(9) , Greenhaven Pr., Inc.) Thomson Gale.

Sperekas, Nicole B. SuicideWise: Taking Steps Against Teen Suicide. 2000. (Teen Issues Ser.). (Illus.). 64p. (YA). (gr. 6-12). lib. bdg. 22.60 (978-0-7660-1360-5(X)) Enslow Pubs., Inc.

Thiele, Christine. What Catholic Teens Should Know about Suicide. Larkin, Jean K., ed. 2004. (What Catholic Teens Should Know Ser.). (Illus.). 8p. (YA). 7.95 (978-0-89837-240-3(2) , 441110) Pflaum Publishing Group.

Torr, James D. Problems of Death. 2000. (Opposing Viewpoints Ser.). (Illus.). 189p. (YA). (gr. 10-12). pap. 24.95 (978-0-7377-0349-8(0) , Greenhaven Pr., Inc.) Thomson Gale.

Wallerstein, Claire. Teen Suicide. 2003. (Just the Facts Ser.). (Illus.). 56p. (J). lib. bdg. 25.64 (978-1-4034-0820-4(3)) Heinemann Library.

SUICIDE—FICTION

Air Conditioning and Refrigeration Institute Staff, . Suicidal Destiny. 2005. 91p. pap. 14.95 (978-1-4137-4018-9(9)) PublishAmerica, Inc.

Allison, Jennifer. Gilda Joyce: Psychic Investigator. 2005. 208p. (YA). 12.99 (978-0-525-47375-6(0) , Dutton Juvenile); 2006. 336p. (J). (gr. 5). reprint ed. pap. 6.99 (978-0-14-240698-4(8) , Puffin) Penguin Group (USA) Inc.

Asher, Jay. Thirteen Reasons Why. 2007. 256p. (YA). (gr. 7). 16.99 (*978-1-59514-171-2(5)* , Razorbill) Penguin Group (USA) Inc.

Banting, Celia. I only said I Couldn't Cope. 2006. 240p. (YA). per. 14.99 (*978-0-9786648-2-4(5))* Wighita Pr.

—I Only Said Yes So That They'd Like Me. 2006. 224p. (YA). per. 14.99 (*978-0-9786648-1-7(7))* Wighita Pr.

Boyd, David. Bottom Drawer. 2002. 126p. pap. 4.95 (978-0-921156-58-1(8)) Rubicon Publishing, Inc. CAN. *Dist:* International Publishers Marketing.

—Bottom Drawer. 2002. (gr. 7-12). lib. bdg. 12.95 (978-0-613-77607-3(0)) Tandem Library Bks.

Brill, Sarah. Glory. 2002. 140p. pap. 10.95 (978-1-876756-25-3(X)) Spinifex Pr. AUS. *Dist:* Independent Pubs. Group.

—Glory. 2002. (gr. 7-12). lib. bdg. 19.90 (978-0-613-85840-3(9)) Tandem Library Bks.

Brugman, Alyssa. Walking Naked. 2004. 192p. (YA). (gr. 7). 15.95 (978-0-385-73115-7(9) , Delacorte Bks. for Young Readers) Random Hse. Children's Bks.

Carlson, Melody. Beyond Reach. 2007. (Secret Life Samantha Mcgregor Ser.). 258p. (YA). pap. 11.99 (978-1-59052-693-4(7) , Multnomah Fiction) WaterBrook Pr.

Carlson, Melody. Beyond Reach: A Novel. 2007. 250p. (YA). (*978-1-4287-2412-9(5)* , Multnomah) WaterBrook Pr.

Chalifour, Francis. After. 2005. 144p. (J). (gr. 7). pap. 7.95 (978-0-88776-705-0(2)) Tundra Bks., Inc./Livres Toundra, Inc. CAN. *Dist:* Random Hse., Inc.

—Le Fils du Pendu. 2006. (FRE.). 168p. (J). (gr. 7). pap. 7.95 (978-0-88776-795-1(8) , Livres Toundra) Tundra Bks., Inc./Livres Toundra, Inc. CAN. *Dist:* Random Hse., Inc.

Cohn, Rachel. You Know Where to Find Me. 2008. 208p. (YA). 15.99 (*978-0-689-87859-6(1)* , Simon & Schuster Children's Publishing) Simon & Schuster Children's Publishing.

Crutcher, Chris. Chinese Handcuffs. 2004. 304p. (J). pap. 7.99 (978-0-06-059839-6(5) , HarperTeen) HarperCollins Pubs.

Davis, Terry. Mysterious Ways. 2002. 284p. (YA). pap. 15.95 (978-0-910055-81-9(5)) Eastern Washington Univ. Pr.

Deal, Paul. Lighting Candles. 2003. 122p. (YA). 20.95 (978-0-595-65804-6(0)); pap. 10.95 (978-0-595-28457-3(4)) iUniverse, Inc.

Deuker, Carl. High Heat. 2005. 352p. (J). (gr. 7 up). pap. 6.99 (978-0-06-057248-8(5) , Harper Trophy) HarperCollins Pubs.

—High Heat. 2003. 288p. (J). (gr. 7-9). tchr. ed. 16.00 (978-0-618-31117-0(3)) Houghton Mifflin Co. Trade & Reference Div.

Dewey, Jennifer Owings. Borderlands. 2002. 192p. (YA). 14.95 (978-0-7614-5114-3(5) , Cavendish Children's Bks.) Cavendish, Marshall Corp.

Fine, Anne. Up on Cloud Nine. l.t. ed. 2005. (Illus.). 232p. (J). pap. incl. audio (978-0-7540-7878-4(7) , CLP 455) BBC Audio.

—Up on Cloud Nine. 2003. 160p. (J). (gr. 5-17). 4.99 (978-0-440-41916-7(6) , Yearling) Random Hse. Children's Bks.

Fine, Anne & Glover, Jamie. Up on Cloud Nine. 2004. (J). pap. 29.95 incl. audio (978-0-7540-6276-9(7) , Chivers Children's Audio Bks.) BBC Audiobooks America.

Freymann-Weyr, Garret. Stay with Me. 2006. 320p. (YA). (gr. 8). 16.00 (978-0-618-60571-2(1)) Houghton Mifflin Co.

—Stay with Me. 2007. 320p. (YA). (gr. 9 up). pap. 8.99 (*978-0-618-88404-9(1))* Houghton Mifflin Co. Trade & Reference Div.

Fullerton, Alma. Walking on Glass. 2007. 144p. (J). (gr. 9 up). 15.99 (978-0-06-077851-4(2)); lib. bdg. 16.89 (978-0-06-077852-1(0)) HarperCollins Pubs. (HarperTeen).

Gibbons, Alan. Hold On, Bk. 1. 2006. 176p. (J). pap. 11.99 (*978-1-84255-176-9(0))* Orion Publishing Group, Ltd. GBR. *Dist:* Independent Pubs. Group.

Giles, Gail. What Happened to Cass Mcbride. 2007. 240p. (J). (gr. 7-17). pap. 7.99 (*978-0-316-16639-3(1))* Little, Brown Bks. for Young Readers.

Giles, Gail. What Happened to Cass McBride? 2006. 212p. (YA). pap. 16.99 (*978-0-316-01703-9(5));* 224p. (J). (gr. 7-17). 16.99 (978-0-316-16638-6(3)) Little Brown & Co.

Going, K. L. Fat Kid Rules the World. (YA). 2004. (gr. 8-12). 17.99 (978-0-8037-2948-3(0) , Dial); 2003. 224p. (gr. 4 up). 17.99 (978-0-399-23990-8(1) , Putnam Juvenile); 2004. 192p. (gr. 6). reprint ed. pap. 6.99 (978-0-14-240208-5(7) , Puffin) Penguin Group (USA) Inc.

Goobie, Beth. Who Owns Kelly Paddik? 2003. (Orca Soundings Ser.). 96p. (J). (gr. 7-12). pap. 7.95 (978-1-55143-239-7(0)) Orca Bk. Pubs. USA.

—Who Owns Kelly Paddik? 2003. (gr. 7-12). lib. bdg. 16.40 (978-0-613-63005-4(X)) Tandem Library Bks.

Holt, Kimberly Willis. Keeper of the Night. 2005. 336p. (YA). (gr. 7). reprint ed. mass mkt. 6.50 (978-0-553-49441-9(4) , Laurel Leaf) Random Hse. Children's Bks.

—Keeper of the Night. l.t. ed. 2004. 336p. (J). 23.95 (978-0-7862-6431-5(4)) Thorndike Pr.

Honeycutt, Natalie. Twilight in Grace Falls. 1999. 192p. (J). (gr. 3-7). pap. 4.50 (978-0-380-73128-2(2)) HarperCollins Pubs.

—Twilight in Grace Falls. 1999. (978-0-606-15928-9(2)) Tandem Library Bks.

Hopkins, Ellen. Impulse. 2007. 672p. (YA). (gr. 9 up). 16.99 (978-1-4169-0356-7(9) , McElderry, Margaret K.) Simon & Schuster Children's Publishing.

Johnston, Jeffry. Fragments. 2007. 208p. (YA). pap. 6.99 (978-1-4169-2486-9(8) , Simon Pulse) Simon & Schuster Children's Publishing.

Levy, Robert Joseph & Matsuda, Jeff. The Suicide King. 2005. (Buffy the Vampire Slayer Ser.). 160p. (YA). pap. 6.99 (978-0-689-86957-0(6) , Simon Spotlight Entertainment) Simon & Schuster.

Lynch, Chris. Freewill. 2006. 148p. (YA). (gr. 7-10). reprint ed. 16.00 (978-0-7567-9869-7(8)) DIANE Publishing Co.

Maynard, Joyce. The Cloud Chamber. 288p. (YA). 2006. (gr. 9). pap. 7.99 (978-1-4169-2699-3(2) , Simon Pulse); 2005. (gr. 6-9). 16.95 (978-0-689-87152-8(X) , Atheneum) Simon & Schuster Children's Publishing.

Mazetti, Katerina. God & I Broke Up. Lundin, Maria, tr. from SWE. 2004. 160p. (J). 15.95 (978-0-88899-584-1(9)) Groundwood Bks. CAN. *Dist:* Perseus Distribution.

McDaniel, Lurlene. So Much to Live For. 2005. (Dawn Rochelle Ser.: No. 3). (Illus.). 160p. (gr. 6-12). reprint ed. pap. 4.99 (978-1-58196-005-1(0)) Lerner Publishing Group.

—So Much to Live For. 2003. (Dawn Rochelle Ser.: No. 3). (gr. 7-12). lib. bdg. 13.00 (978-0-613-84379-9(7)) Tandem Library Bks.

Messer, Celeste M. A Message from Teddy. Hoeffner, Deb, illus. 2004. 82-92p. 4.95 (978-0-9702171-5-8(3)) AshleyAlan Enterprises.

Mickle, Shelley Fraser. The Turning Hour. 2004. 264p. (YA). pap. 16.95 (978-1-57966-008-6(8)) River City Publishing.

O'Hara, John. Appointment in Samarra. 2003. (gr. 7-12). lib. bdg. 22.25 (978-0-613-68488-0(5)) Tandem Library Bks.

Rapp, Adam. Under the Wolf, under the Dog. 320p. (YA). (gr. 9). 2007. pap. 8.99 (978-0-7636-3365-3(8)); 2004. 16.99 (978-0-7636-1818-6(7)) Candlewick Pr.

Seidler, Tor. Terpin. 2002. (Illus.). 112p. (J). 14.89 (978-0-06-623608-7(8) , Geringer, Laura Book) HarperCollins Pubs.

—Terpin. 2004. (gr. 3-6). lib. bdg. 14.15 (978-0-613-81688-5(9)) Tandem Library Bks.

Stein, Tammar. Light Years. 2005. 272p. (YA). (gr. 9). 15.95 (978-0-375-83023-5(5) , Knopf Bks. for Young Readers) Random Hse. Children's Bks.

—Light Years: A Novel. 2005. 272p. (J). (gr. 9). lib. bdg. 17.99 (978-0-375-93023-2(X) , Knopf Bks. for Young Readers) Random Hse. Children's Bks.

Taylor, William. Jerome: A Novel. 1999. 96p. (gr. 9 up). pap. 9.95 (978-1-55583-512-5(0)) Alyson Pubns.

Trueman, Terry. Inside Out. 128p. (J). 2003. 15.99 (978-0-06-623962-0(1)); 2003. lib. bdg. 16.89 (978-0-06-623963-7(X)); 2004. reprint ed. pap. 6.99 (978-0-06-447376-7(7) , HarperTeen) HarperCollins Pubs.

—No Right Turn. 2006. 176p. (J). 16.99 (978-0-06-057491-8(7)); lib. bdg. 16.89 (978-0-06-057492-5(5)) HarperCollins Pubs. (HarperTeen).

Vaught, Susan. Trigger. 2006. 304p. (YA). 16.95 (978-1-58234-920-6(7) , Bloomsbury Children) Bloomsbury Publishing.

Youmans, Marly. Little Jordan. 1999. 112p. (YA). (gr. 7-12). pap. 6.99 (978-0-380-73136-7(3)) HarperCollins Pubs.

SUKKOT

Fishman, Cathy Goldberg. On Sukkot & Simchat Torah. Hall, Melanie W., illus. (J). (ps-4). 2006. 32p. lib. bdg. 17.95 (978-1-58013-165-0(4)); 2005. pap. (978-1-58013-166-7(2)) Kar-Ben Publishing.

Groner, Judyth Saypol & Wikler, Madeline. All about Sukkot. Kreiswirth, Kinny, illus. 1998. Orig. Title: My Very Own Sukkot. 32p. (J). (gr. k-5). pap. 5.95 (978-1-58013-018-9(6)) Kar-Ben Publishing.

Kropf, Latifa Berry. It's Sukkah Time. Cohen, Tod, illus. Cohen, Tod, photos by. 2003. (Sukkot & Simchat Torah Ser.). 24p. (J). (ps-1). (978-1-58013-084-4(4)) Kar-Ben Publishing.

Nason, Ruth. Celebrating Harvest. 2005. (Start up Religion Ser.). (Illus.). 24p. (J). (gr. 1-4). lib. bdg. (978-1-84234-338-8(6) , Cherrytree Books) Evans Publishing Group.

SUKKOT—FICTION

Kahn, Katherine Janus & Rouss, Sylvia A. Sammy Spider's First Sukkot. 2004. (Illus.). 32p. (J). (ps-3). (978-1-58013-142-1(5)); pap. (978-1-58013-083-7(6)) Kar-Ben Publishing.

Terwilliger, Kelly. Bubbe Isabella & the Sukkot Cake. Hornung, Phyllis, illus. 2005. 24p. (J). (ps-2). pap. 6.95 (978-1-58013-128-5(X)) Kar-Ben Publishing.

SULLIVAN, ANNIE, 1866-1936

Adams, Colleen. The Courage of Helen Keller. 2003. (Reading Room Collection). (Illus.). 24p. (J). lib. bdg. 18.75 (978-0-8239-3710-3(0)) Rosen Publishing Group, Inc., The.

Adler, David A. Helen Keller. Wallner, John, illus. 32p. (J). 4.95 (978-0-8234-2042-1(6)) Holiday Hse., Inc.

—Helen Keller. Wallner, John C., illus. 32p. (J). (gr. k-3). tchr. ed. 14.95 (978-0-8234-1606-6(2)) Holiday Hse., Inc.

Devillier, Christy. Helen Keller. 2004. (First Biographies Set Iv Ser.). (Illus.). 32p. (J). (gr. k-4). lib. bdg. 22.78 (978-1-59197-514-4(X)) ABDO Publishing Co.

Koestler-Grack, Rachel A. The Story of Helen Keller. 2003. (Breakthrough Biographies Ser.). (Illus.). 32p. (J). (gr. 3-5). 23.00 (978-0-7910-7315-5(7) , Chelsea Hse.) Facts On File, Inc.

Lakin, Patricia. Helen Keller & the Big Storm. Magnuson, Diana, illus. 2002. (Ready-to-Read Ser.: Level 2). 32p. (J). pap. 3.99 (978-0-689-84104-0(3) , Aladdin) Simon & Schuster Children's Publishing.

Lynch, Emma. Helen Keller. 2005. (Lives & Times Ser.). 32p. (J). (Illus.). (gr. 2-4). lib. bdg. 24.21 (978-1-4034-6350-0(6)); pap. (978-1-4034-6364-7(6)) Heinemann Library.

MacLeod, Elizabeth. Helen Keller: A Determined Life. Krystoforski, Andrej, illus. 2007. 32p. pap. (***978-1-55453-000-7(8)***) Kids Can Pr., Ltd.

—Helen Keller: A Determined Life. 2004. (Snapshots Ser.). (Illus.). 32p. (J). (gr. 4-6). (978-1-55337-509-8(2)); (978-1-55337-508-1(4)) Kids Can Pr., Ltd.

Roop, Peter & Roop, Connie. Give Me a Sign, Helen Keller! 2004. (Scholastic Chapter Book Biography Ser.). (Illus.). 55p. (J). (978-0-439-55444-2(6)) Scholastic, Inc.

SULLIVAN, ARTHUR, SIR, 1842-1900

Findon, Benjamin W. Sir Arthur Sullivan, His Life & Music. 2001. 214p. (YA). reprint ed. 98.00 (978-0-7222-5538-4(1)) Library Reprints, Inc.

Wyndham, Henry S. Arthur Seymour Sullivan, 1842-1900. 2001. 276p. (YA). reprint ed. 98.00 (978-0-7222-5546-9(2)) Library Reprints, Inc.

SUMERIANS

Fine, Jil. Writing in Ancient Mesopotamia. 2003. (Writing in the Ancient World Ser.). (Illus.). 24p. (J). lib. bdg. 17.25 (978-0-8239-6509-0(0) , PowerKids Pr.) Rosen Publishing Group, Inc., The.

Kirkpatrick, Naida. The Sumerians. 2003. (Understanding People in the Past Ser.: Set 3). (J). pap. 8.95 (978-1-4034-0609-5(X)); (Illus.). 64p. (gr. 4-6). pap. 28.50 (978-1-4034-0389-6(9)) Heinemann Library.

—Sumerians. 2003. (gr. 3-6). lib. bdg. 17.60 (978-0-613-60933-3(6)) Tandem Library Bks.

Moss, Carol. Science in Mesopotamia. rev. ed. 1999. (Science of the Past Ser.). (Illus.). 64p. (J). (gr. 5-7). pap. 8.95 (978-0-531-15930-9(2) , Watts, Franklin) Scholastic Library Publishing.

Shuter, Jane. Mesopotamia. 2005. (Excavating the Past Ser.). (Illus.). 48p. (J). lib. bdg. (978-1-4034-5998-5(3)) Heinemann Library.

—The Sumerians. 2002. (History Opens Windows Ser.). (Illus.). 32p. (J). (gr. 2-4). lib. bdg. 22.79 (978-1-58810-592-9(X)) Heinemann Library.

SUMMER

Albert, Toni. A Kid's Summer EcoJournal: With Nature Activities for Exploring the Season. Brandt, Margaret, illus. 1998. 56p. (J). (gr. 3 up). pap. 9.95 (978-0-9640742-4-8(9)) Trickle Creek Bks.

Barklem, Jill. Cuento de Verano.Tr. of Summer Story. (J). pap. 8.95 (978-84-233-2619-8(5)) Ediciones Destino ESP. *Dist:* Planeta Publishing Corp.

Bull, Jane. The Vacation Activity Book. 2007. 48p. (J). (gr. 1-3). 12.99 (978-0-7566-2942-7(X)) Dorling Kindersley Publishing, Inc.

Burton, Jane & Taylor, Kim. The Nature & Science of Summer. Burton, Jane & Taylor, Kim, photos by. 1999. (Exploring the Science of Nature Ser.). (Illus.). 32p. (J). (gr. 3 up). lib. bdg. 24.67 (978-0-8368-2189-5(0)) Stevens, Gareth Inc.

Butterworth Moira. Summer. James, Helen, illus. 2005. 32p. (J). (gr. 2-5). lib. bdg. 27.10 (978-1-58340-615-1(8)) Smart Apple Media.

Casado, Dami & Casado, Alicia. El Verano. 2005. (Brujita Mo). (SPA & ESP., Illus.). 14p. (J). (ps-ps). per. 7.99 (978-84-272-6235-5(3)) Molino, Editorial ESP. *Dist:* Santillana USA Publishing Co., Inc.

Claybourne, Anna. Summer. 2001. (J). 24.25 (978-1-930643-07-9(1)) Chrysalis Education.

Davis, Rebecca Fjelland. Beaches & Bicycles: A Summer Counting Book. 2006. (J). (978-0-7368-6891-4(7)); (Illus.). 32p. (978-0-7368-5378-1(2)) Capstone Pr., Inc.

DeGezelle, Terri. Summer. 2002. (Bridgestone Science Library). (Illus.). 24p. (J). (gr. 1-2). lib. bdg. 18.60 (978-0-7368-1411-9(6) , Bridgestone Bks.) Capstone Pr., Inc.

George, Jean Craighead. Summer Moon. 2002. (Seasons of the Moon Ser.). (Illus.). 112p. (J). pap. 5.95 (978-0-06-440995-7(3) , Harper Trophy) HarperCollins Pubs.

—Summer Moon. 2003. (J). (gr. 3-7). 20.75 (978-0-8446-7243-4(2)) Smith, Peter Pub., Inc.

Gerard, Valerie J. Summer: Signs of the Season Around North America. Thomas, Eric, illus. 2004. (Through the Seasons Ser.). 24p. (C). (gr. k-1). 22.60 (978-1-4048-0003-8(4)) Picture Window Bks.

Here Comes Summer! 2003. (J). per. (978-1-57657-969-5(7)) Paradise Pr., Inc.

Herriges, Ann. Summer. 2006. (Blastoff! Readers Ser.). (Illus.). 24p. (J). lib. bdg. 16.95 (978-1-60014-032-7(7)) Bellwether Media.

Hiebert, Elfrieda H. & Juel, Connie. Summer at Cove Lake. 1998. (Little Book Practice Reader Ser.). (J). (978-0-8136-0955-3(0)) Modern Curriculum Pr.

A Hot Day, Vol. 2. 2005. (Our Seasons & Weather Ser.). (YA). (gr. k-3). (978-0-7368-8621-5(4) , Pebble Bks.) Capstone Pr., Inc.

Jackson, Ellen B. The Summer Solstice. 2003. (Illus.). 32p. (J). (gr. 3-6). pap. 7.95 (978-0-7613-1985-6(9) , Millbrook Pr.) Lerner Publishing Group.

—The Summer Solstice. Ellis, Jan Davey, illus. 2001. 4. 32p. (J). (gr. 4-7). 14.95 (978-0-7613-1283-3(8) , Millbrook Pr.) Lerner Publishing Group.

Kalz, Jill. Summer. 2005. (Illus.). 24p. (J). (gr. k-3). 15.95 (978-1-58341-364-7(2) , Creative Education) Creative Co., The.

Latta, Sara L. What Happens in Summer? 2006. (I Like the Seasons! Ser.). (Illus.). 24p. (J). lib. bdg. 21.26 (978-0-7660-2416-8(4) , Enslow Elementary) Enslow Pubs., Inc.

The Letter Ss: Spring & Summer, 6 vols. (gr. k-2). 17.50 (978-0-7368-4118-4(0)) Red Brick Learning.

Low, Alice. Summer. McKie, Roy, illus. 2007. 24p. (J). (gr. k-ps). bds. 4.99 (978-0-375-83870-5(8) , Random Hse. Bks. for Young Readers) Random Hse. Children's Bks.

Macken, JoAnn Early. Summer. 2006. (Illus.). 16p. (J). pap. 4.50 (978-0-8368-6360-4(7)); lib. bdg. 16.67 (978-0-8368-6355-0(0)) Stevens, Gareth Inc.

—Summer: Verano. 2006. (ENG & SPA., Illus.). 16p. (J). pap. (978-0-8368-6539-4(1)); lib. bdg. 16.67 (978-0-8368-6534-9(0)) Stevens, Gareth Inc.

Maurer, Tracy. Summer. 2006. (to Z Ser.). (Illus.). 32p. (gr. k-2). 20.95 (978-1-58952-198-8(6)) Rourke Publishing, LLC.

—Summer. 2003. (gr. k-3). lib. bdg. 14.10 (978-0-613-81751-6(6)) Tandem Library Bks.

McMahon, Patricia. Summer Tunes: A Martha's Vineyard Vacation. Simon, Peter, illus. 2003. 48p. (J). (gr. 4-6). 16.95 (978-1-56397-572-1(6)) Boyds Mills Pr.

Meyer, Mary L. Summer. 2002. (Illus.). 24p. (J). lib. bdg. 21.35 (978-1-58340-140-8(7)) Smart Apple Media.

Parker, Victoria. Days In... Summer. 2004. (Raintree Sprouts Ser.). (Illus.). 24p. (J). pap. 5.50 (978-1-4109-0742-4(2)) Raintree.

—Summer. 2004. (Raintree Sprouts Ser.). (Illus.). 24p. (J). lib. bdg. 18.56 (978-1-4109-0737-0(6)) Raintree.

Rius, Maria. Summer. 1998. (Four Seasons Ser.). (Illus.). 32p. (J). (ps-k). pap. 6.95 (978-0-7641-0556-2(6)) Barron's Educational Series, Inc.

Roca, Nuria. Summer. 2004. (Four Seasons Ser.). (Illus.). 36p. (J). pap. 6.99 (978-0-7641-2735-9(7)) Barron's Educational Series, Inc.

—El Verano. 2004. (Cuatro Estaciones Ser.).Tr. of Summer. (SPA., Illus.). 36p. (J). pap. 6.95 (978-0-7641-2736-6(5)) Barron's Educational Series, Inc.

Saunders, Gail. Summer. 1998. (Seasons Ser.). 24p. (J). (ps-2). pap. 13.25 (978-0-516-21328-6(8) , Children's Pr.) Scholastic Library Publishing.

Saunders-Smith, Gail. Summer, Vol. 4. 2005. (Our Seasons & Weather Ser.). 24p. (YA). (gr. k-3). pap. (978-1-56065-845-0(2) , Pebble Bks.) Capstone Pr., Inc.

Schuette, Sarah L. Let's Look at Summer. 2007. (Pebble Plus Ser.). (Illus.). 24p. (J). (978-0-7368-6708-5(2) , 1264873) Capstone Pr., Inc.

Simon, Seymour. Summer Across America. 1999. (J). (978-0-7868-0181-7(6)) Hyperion Pr.

Stille, Darlene R. Summer. 2001. (Simply Science Ser.). (Illus.). 32p. (J). (gr. 3 up). lib. bdg. 19.93 (978-0-7565-0095-5(8)) Compass Point Bks.

Summer Seasons. 2006. (Illus.). 24p. (J). (gr. k-2). 18.50 (***978-0-531-17884-3(6)***) Scholastic Library Publishing.

Thayer, Tanya. Summer. 2005. (First Step Nonfiction Ser.). (Illus.). 24p. (gr. k-2). lib. bdg. 17.27 (978-0-8225-1984-3(4)) Lerner Publishing Group.

Waters, Jennifer. Summer Fun. 2002. (Spyglass Books). (Illus.). 24p. (J). (gr. 1 up). lib. bdg. 18.60 (978-0-7565-0244-7(6)) Compass Point Bks.

Whitehouse, Patricia. Summer. (Seasons Ser.). (Illus.). 24p. (J). (ps-1). 2003. lib. bdg. 17.08 (978-1-58810-891-3(0)); 2002. pap. 5.25 (978-1-4034-0542-5(5)) Heinemann Library.

Willson, Sarah. The Summer Camp Survival Guide. 1999. (Nick Reference Ser.). (Illus.). (J). mass mkt. 5.99 (978-0-689-84557-4(X) , Simon Spotlight/Nickelodeon) Simon & Schuster Children's Publishing.

SUMMER—FICTION

Abbott, Hailey. Next Summer: A Summer Boys Novel. 2005. (Summer Boys Ser.). 224p. (YA). (gr. 10 up). 8.99 (978-0-439-75540-5(9)) Scholastic, Inc.

—Summer Boys. 2004. 224p. (J). 8.99 (978-0-439-54020-9(8)) Scholastic, Inc.

Aldridge, James. The Girl from the Sea. 2004. 216p. pap. 9.99 (978-0-14-300112-6(4) , Penguin Global) Penguin Group (USA) Inc.

Andrews, Jan. The Twelve Days of Summer. Jolliffe, Susan Rennick, illus. 2007. 32p. (J). (ps-3). (***978-1-55143-735-4(X)***) Orca Bk. Pubs.

—The Twelve Days of Summer. Jolliffe, Susan Rennick, illus. 2005. 112p. (J). (gr. 4-10). 16.95 (978-1-55143-365-3(6)) Orca Bk. Pubs. USA.

Angstrom, Gwen. Ruthie's Extraordinarily Ordinary Summer: A Tale of Happy Valley. 2005. 59p. pap. 12.95 (978-1-4137-6323-2(5)) PublishAmerica, Inc.

Barbour, Ralph Henry. The Lilac Girl. 2006. (Illus.). pap. (***978-1-4065-0778-2(4)***) Dodo Pr.

Barclay, Jane. How Hot Was It? Cole, Kathryn, ed. Donato, Janice, illus. 24p. (J). 14.95 (978-1-894222-70-9(9)) Lobster Pr. CAN. *Dist:* Univ. of Toronto Pr.

Barkan, Joanne. Good Night, Summer Lights. Bryant, Laura, illus. 2005. (Fiber Optic Book Ser.). 10p. (J). bds. 12.99 (978-0-7944-0671-4(8)) Reader's Digest Assn., Inc., The.

Barra, Nancy. Monica y la Fiesta de Verano. Zuman, John, ed. Deming, Linda, illus. 2002. (Sunflower/Girasol Ser.). (SPA.). 20p. tchr. ed., spiral bd. 5.95 (978-1-58332-055-6(5)) Intercultural Center for Research in Education (I N C R E).

—Monica y la Fiesta de Verano. Deming, Linda, illus. 2002. (Sunflower/Girasol Ser.). (SPA.). 38p. (J). 5.95 (978-1-58332-054-9(7)) Intercultural Center for Research in Education (I N C R E).

Behrens, Andy. All the Way (Splashproof Edition) 2007. 224p. (YA). (gr. 9). pap. 7.99 (978-0-14-240833-9(6) , Puffin) Penguin Group (USA) Inc.

Blackwell-Burke, Melissa & Kunkel, Kristen. Summertime Surprise. 2003. (J). spiral bd. 14.95 (978-1-58605-956-9(4) , LeapFrog Schl. Hse.) LeapFrog Enterprises, Inc.

Blume, Judy. Otherwise Known As Sheila the Great. 2004. (Fudge Ser.). 160p. (gr. 12). mass mkt. 5.99 (978-0-425-19380-8(2) , Berkley) Penguin Group (USA) Inc.

Blumenthal, Deborah. The Pink House at the Seashore. Chayka, Doug, illus. 2005. 32p. (J). (gr. 3-5). 16.00 (978-0-618-37886-9(3) , Clarion Bks.) Houghton Mifflin Co. Trade & Reference Div.

Boeve, Eunice. The Summer of the Crow. 2000. 224p. (J). pap. 12.95 (978-1-58597-059-9(X)) Leathers Publishing.

Boyd, David. Champlain Summer. 2002. 202p. pap. 4.95 (978-0-921156-40-6(5)) Rubicon Publishing, Inc. CAN. *Dist:* International Publishers Marketing.

Brennan, Linda Crotta. Marshmallow Kisses. Takabayashi, Mari, illus. 2007. 32p. (J). (gr. k-3). 6.95 (***978-0-618-80903-5(1)***) Houghton Mifflin Co. Trade & Reference Div.

Brigitte, Luciani. How Will We Get to the Beach? Tharlet, Eve, illus. 2003. 36p. (J). (ps). pap. 6.95 (978-0-7358-1783-8(9)) North-South Bks., Inc.

Brimner, Larry Dane. Summer Fun. Tripp, Christine, illus. 2003. (Rookie Choices Ser.). (gr. 1-2). pap. 5.95 (978-0-516-27836-0(3) , Children's Pr.) Scholastic Library Publishing.

—Summer Fun. 2003. (gr. k-3). lib. bdg. 14.10 (978-0-613-67672-4(6)) Tandem Library Bks.

Brown. Little Bear Friendship Box: Love Song of Summer. 2002. (J). bds. (978-0-7868-0897-7(7)) Hyperion Bks. for Children.

Buffie, Margaret. Who Is Frances Rain? 20th ed. 2007. 184p. pap. (***978-1-55453-209-4(4)***) Kids Can Pr., Ltd.

Bunting, Eve. The Summer of Riley. 176p. (J). 2002. (gr. 3-7). pap. 5.99 (978-0-06-440927-8(9)); 2001. (gr. 4-6). lib. bdg. 16.89 (978-0-06-029142-6(7) , Cotler, Joanna Books) HarperCollins Pubs.

Cernyar, Anne Clay. Summer at Steller's Creek. Clay, Joan, illus. 2000. 188p. (gr. 4-7). pap. 11.95 (978-0-595-13729-9(6)) iUniverse, Inc.

Chapman, Brenda. Where Trouble Leads. 2007. (Illus.). 136p. (YA). (gr. 5 up). pap. 8.95 (***978-1-894917-44-5(8)***) Napoleon Publishing/Rendezvous Pr. CAN. *Dist:* AtlasBooks Distribution.

Cheney, Cora. The Doll of Lilac Valley. Cassidy, Nancy White, illus. 2003. 128p. 11.95 (978-0-9714612-5-3(2)) Green Mansion Pr. LLC.

Colebank, Susan. Black Tuesday. 2007. 208p. (YA). 16.99 (978-0-525-47766-2(7) , Dutton Juvenile) Penguin Group (USA) Inc.

Come on Rain. 2004. (J). pap. 14.95 incl. audio (978-0-7882-0513-2(7)) Weston Woods Studios, Inc.

Conly, Jane Leslie. Trout Summer. 1998. (J). (978-0-606-13872-7(2)) Tandem Library Bks.

Couloumbis, Audrey. Summer's End. 2005. 192p. (YA). (gr. 4). 16.99 (978-0-399-23555-9(8) , Putnam Juvenile) Penguin Group (USA) Inc.

Coxe, Molly. Hot Dog. Coxe, Molly, illus. 1998. (Road to Reading Ser.). (Illus.). 32p. (J). (ps-1). pap. 3.99 (978-0-307-26101-4(8) , 26101, Random Hse. Bks. for Young Readers) Random Hse. Children's Bks.

—Hot Dog. (Road to Reading Ser.). 1999. (Illus.). (J). 10.79 (978-0-606-16255-5(0)); 1998. lib. bdg. 11.80 (978-0-613-71623-9(X)) Tandem Library Bks.

Creech, Sharon. Absolutely Normal Chaos. 1999. (J). pap. 50.20 incl. audio (978-0-7887-2994-2(2) , 40876); Class Set. pap., wbk. ed. 107.30 incl. audio (978-0-7887-3024-5(X) , 46841) Recorded Bks., LLC.

Daly, Maureen. Seventeenth Summer. 2002. 320p. (YA). 17.95 (978-0-689-85383-8(1)) Simon & Schuster Children's Publishing.

Dangerous Summer 2. 2006. (J). (978-1-933343-19-8(2)) Stabenfeldt Inc.

Daringer, Helen Fern. Adopted Jane. Seredy, Kate, illus. 2002. 224p. (gr. 3-6). reprint ed. 12.95 (978-0-9714612-4-6(4)) Green Mansion Pr. LLC.

de Paola, Tomie. Four Friends in Summer. de Paola, Tomie, illus. 2003. (Illus.). 32p. (J). reprint ed. 14.95 (978-0-689-85693-8(8)) Simon & Schuster Children's Publishing.

Dessen, Sarah. That Summer. 208p. (YA). (gr. 7). 2006. 16.99 (978-0-670-06110-5(7) , Viking Juvenile); 2004. pap. 7.99 (978-0-14-240172-9(2) , Puffin) Penguin Group (USA) Inc.

Dewey, Jennifer Owings. Navajo Summer. 2003. (Illus.). 136p. (YA). (gr. 6-9). 10.95 (978-1-56397-855-5(5)) Boyds Mills Pr.

—Navajo Summer. 2000. (J). (978-0-606-19306-1(5)) Tandem Library Bks.

Dobson, Rosemary. Summer Press. 132p. pap. 11.95 (978-0-7022-2083-8(3)) Univ. of Queensland Pr. AUS. *Dist:* International Specialized Bk. Services.

Dower, Laura. From the Files of Madison Finn: Only the Lonely. 2001. (gr. 3-6). lib. bdg. 13.00 (978-0-613-44497-2(3)) Tandem Library Bks.

Doyle, Patrick H. T. Edgar Font's Hunt for a House to Haunt: Adventure One: the Castle Tower Lighthouse. 2006. (Illus.). 232p. (J). per. 6.99 (978-0-9786132-0-4(1)) Armadillo Bks.

Doyle, Patrick H. T. Edgar Font's Hunt for a House to Haunt: Adventure Two: the Fakersville Power Station. 2007. (J). per. 7.99 (***978-0-9786132-1-1(X)***) Armadillo Bks.

Duncan, Lois. I Know What You Did Last Summer. 1999. 208p. (YA). (gr. 7-12). mass mkt. 5.99 (978-0-440-22844-8(1) , Laurel Leaf) Random Hse. Children's Bks.

Dunevant, Darlene J. An A+ Alaskan Adventure. 2002. 110p. pap. 9.95 (978-0-595-22991-8(3) , Writers Club Pr.) iUniverse, Inc.

DuVall, Nell. Summer Day. Weltner, Dave, illus. l.t. ed. 2003. 13p. 7.95 (978-0-9706654-6-1(6)) Sprite Pr.

Emerson, Carl. Old Oak & the Summer Playground. Doerrfeld, Cori, illus. 2007. (J). (978-1-4048-2626-7(2)) Picture Window Bks.

Emzer, Counselor. The Day Before Summer Vacation. 2004. 31p. pap. 17.95 (978-1-4137-2680-0(1)) PublishAmerica, Inc.

English, Karen. Hot Day on Abbott Avenue. Steptoe, Javaka, illus. 2004. 32p. (J). (gr. k-3). 16.00 (978-0-395-98527-4(7) , Clarion Bks.) Houghton Mifflin Co. Trade & Reference Div.

Enright, Elizabeth. Thimble Summer. unabr. ed. 2004. 136p. (J). (gr. 3-7). pap. 36.00 incl. audio (978-0-8072-0671-3(7) , Listening Library) Random Hse. Audio Publishing Group.

—Thimble Summer. 2008. (Illus.). 124p. (J). pap. 6.99 (***978-0-312-38002-1(X)***) Square Fish.

Fakkema, Julie Ann. Water Is A Wonderful Thing. 2007. (J). per. 10.99 (***978-1-59886-927-9(2)***) Tate Publishing & Enterprises, L.L.C.

Finley, Martha & Mission City Press Staff. Violet's Amazing Summer, Bk. 2. 2004. (Life of Faith Ser.). 224p. (YA). 12.99 (978-1-928749-18-9(6)) Zonderkidz.

Fisher, Rick. Unknown Heroes. 2007. (ENG., Illus.). 32p. (J). per. 14.95 (***978-1-59800-899-9(4)***) Outskirts Press, Inc.

Fitzhugh, Louise. The Long Secret. 2001. (Illus.). 288p. (J). (gr. 5 up). 15.95 (978-0-385-32784-8(6) , Delacorte Bks. for Young Readers) Random Hse. Children's Bks.

Fitzhugh, Percy K. Pee-Wee Harris. 2004. reprint ed. pap. 1.99 (978-1-4192-4057-7(9)); pap. 15.95 (978-1-4191-4057-0(4)) Kessinger Publishing, LLC.

Fox, Red. The Big Book of Summer Love. 2001. 480p. (J). pap. 11.99 (978-0-09-941758-3(8)) Random Hse. GBR. *Dist:* Independent Pubs. Group.

—The Big Book of Summer Snogs. 2001. 480p. (J). pap. 11.99 (978-0-09-940967-0(4)) Random Hse. GBR. *Dist:* Independent Pubs. Group.

Franco, Betsy. Summer's Beat. Middleton, Charlotte, illus. 2007. 40p. (J). 15.99 (978-1-4169-1237-8(1) , McElderry, Margaret K.) Simon & Schuster Children's Publishing.

Franklin, Emily. Labor of Love: The Principles of Love. 2007. 256p. (gr. 12 up). pap. 9.99 (***978-0-451-22211-4(3)*** , N A L Trade) Penguin Group (USA) Inc.

Franklin, Rosalind. Bodrick & the Magic Petals. 2006. (Illus.). (J). lib. bdg. (978-1-84685-020-2(7) , Exposure Publishing) Meadow Bks.

Freedman, Claire. One Magical Day. Macnaughton, Tina, illus. 2007. 28p. (J). (ps-1). 16.95 (***978-1-56148-567-3(5)***) Good Bks.

Fuchs, Menucha. The Yellow Ball & Other Summer Adventures. Shlomo, Bat, illus. 2000. (Children's Learning Ser.: Vol. 11). 48p. (J). (gr. k-5). pap. 4.95 (978-1-880582-53-4(8)) Judaica Pr., Inc., The.

Furgang, Kathy. A Happy Summer Day. ed. 2003. (Early Connections Ser.). (J). pap. 33.00 (978-1-4108-1371-8(1)) Benchmark Education Co.

Furgang, Kathy. A un día feliz de verano & Happy Summer Day. 2005. spiral bd. 66.00 (***978-1-4108-5656-2(9)***) Benchmark Education Co.

Gagliano, Eugene M. Falling Stars. 2004. 68p. pap. 14.95 (978-1-58851-419-6(6)) PublishAmerica, Inc.

Garcia-Huidobro, Beatriz. Misterio en Los Pinones. 2001. (J). (978-956-240-300-9(9)) Arrayan Editores S.A.

Garelick, May & Whitman, Candace. Sounds of a Summer Night. 2000. (Illus.). 32p. (J). (ps-3). 15.95 (978-1-57255-745-1(1)) Mondo Publishing.

The Gauntlet. (J). 14.00 (978-1-931555-16-6(8)) Our Lady of Victory Schl.

Gehrman, Jody. Confessions of a Triple Shot Betty. 2008. 256p. (J). (gr. 9). 16.99 (***978-0-8037-3247-6(3)*** , Dial) Penguin Group (USA) Inc.

Gershator, Phillis. Old House, New House. Potter, Katherine, illus. 2008. (J). (***978-0-7614-5386-4(5)***) Cavendish, Marshall Corp.

S

Giff, Patricia Reilly. Horas de Sol. 2000. Tr. of Sunny Side Up. (SPA.). (YA). (gr. 1 up). 3.95 (978-0-922852-48-2(0)) AIMS International Bks., Inc.

Gifford, Peggy. Moxy Maxwell Does Not Love Stuart Little. Fisher, Valorie, photos by. 2007. (Illus.). 104p. (J). (gr. 2-6). 12.99 (978-0-375-83915-3(1)); lib. bdg. 15.99 (978-0-375-93915-0(6)) Random Hse. Children's Bks. (Schwartz & Wade Bks.).

Gifford, Peggy. Moxy Maxwell Does Not Love Stuart Little. Fisher, Valorie, photos by. 2008. (Illus.). 112p. (J). (gr. 2-6). 5.50 (*978-0-440-42230-3(2) , Yearling) Random Hse. Children's Bks.

Gill, Amber. Joseph's Summer. 2006. 71p. pap. 14.95 (978-1-4241-0122-1(0)) PublishAmerica, Inc.

Glaser, Linda. It's Summer! 2003. (gr. k-3). lib. bdg. 16.40 (978-0-613-58978-9(5)) Tandem Library Bks.

Glasscock, Sarah. My Prairie Summer. 2001. lib. bdg. 13.00 (978-0-613-76467-4(6)) Tandem Library Bks.

Golden Books Staff & Scott, Evelyn. The Fourteen Bears in Summer & Winter. 2005. (Illus.). 64p. (J). (gr. k-k). lib. bdg. 16.99 (978-0-375-93279-3(8) , Golden Bks.) Random Hse. Children's Bks.

Goode, Suzi. The Lost Wizard Series Bk 1. 2007. pap. 11.95 (*978-1-59374-817-3(5)) Whiskey Creek Pr., LLC.

Green, Holly. Don't Slam the Door! Scott, Sarah Chamberlin, illus. 2005. (J). 19.95 (978-0-9744803-7-4(1)) PublishingWorks.

Greenberg, Melanie Hope. The Mermaid Parade. Greenberg, Melanie Hope, illus. 2008. 32p. (J). (ps-k). 16.99 (*978-0-399-24708-8(4) , Putnam Juvenile) Penguin Group (USA) Inc.

Griese, Arnold A. Anna's Athabaskan Summer. Ragins, Charles, illus. 2003. 32p. (J). (gr. k-2). pap. 9.95 (978-1-56397-650-6(1)) Boyds Mills Pr.

Grosch, Greta & Grosch, Heidi. What We Did Last Summer Bk. 1: Some Silly Sisters' Summer Stories. Grosch, Heidi, illus. 1998. (Illus.). 70p. (J). (ps-6). pap. 8.95 (978-0-9668728-0-4(0)) Oh, You Girls!.

Hall, Donald. Lucy's Summer. 1998. (978-0-606-13585-6(5)) Tandem Library Bks.

Hall, Katy, pseud. Summer Camp Crack-Ups: And Lots S'more Knock-Knock Jokes to Write Home About. 2001. (Lift-the-Flap Knock-Knock Bk.). (Illus.). 16p. (J). (gr. k-3). 6.95 (978-0-694-01357-9(9) , Harper Festival) HarperCollins Pubs.

Hall, Zoe. It's Pumpkin Time! Halpern, Sheri, illus. 2002. (SPA.). 40p. (J). (gr. k-1). pap. 5.99 (978-0-439-18731-2(1) , SO30069, Scholastic en Espanol) Scholastic, Inc.

Harcourt School Publishers Staff. G. Hopper's Summer Fun Advanced Level. 3rd ed. 2002. (Trophies Reading Program Ser.). (Illus.). pap. 5.10 (978-0-15-323109-4(2)) Harcourt Schl. Pubs.

—A Record-Breakng Summer: Take-Home Book. 2001. (Collections Ser.). (Illus.). (J). pap. 1.90 (978-0-15-319519-8(3)) Harcourt Schl. Pubs.

—Summer/Maizon Level D: Library Edition. 2001. (Collections Ser.). (Illus.). pap. 12.10 (978-0-15-314435-6(1)) Harcourt Schl. Pubs.

Harrington, Jane. Lucy's E-Journal. 2002. 176p. (J). pap. 4.50 (978-0-439-32373-4(8)) Scholastic, Inc.

Hartgraves, Richard. Little Cedar. 2006. 130p. pap. 19.95 (*978-1-4241-4603-1(8)) PublishAmerica, Inc.

Hawthorne, Rachel. Island Girls & Boys. 2005. 336p. pap. 5.99 (978-0-06-075546-1(6)) HarperCollins Pubs.

Hecker, Robert. The Greatest Summer Job in the Whole Wide World. 2001. 253p. pap. 14.99 (978-1-928767-11-4(7)) Royal Fireworks Publishing Co.

Heidtke, John. A Summer's Passage on Sutter's Bay. 2005. (J). per. (978-0-9748426-6-0(4)) Accent Pubns.

Hesse, Karen. Come on, Rain! 1999. (J). (ps up). (978-0-439-06015-8(X)) Scholastic, Inc.

—Come on, Rain! 2004. (J). 24.95 incl. audio (978-1-55592-177-4(9)); 29.95 incl. cd-rom (978-1-55592-500-0(6)) Weston Woods Studios, Inc.

—Come on, Rain. Muth, Jon J., illus. 1999. 32p. (J). (ps-2). pap. 16.95 (978-0-590-33125-8(6)) Scholastic, Inc.

Hoffman, Mary. Starring Grace. Binch, Caroline, illus. (Chapters Ser.). 96p. (J). 2001. (gr. 2-6). pap. 4.99 (978-0-14-230022-0(5) , Puffin); 2000. (gr. k-4). 14.99 (978-0-8037-2559-1(0) , Dial) Penguin Group (USA) Inc.

—Starring Grace. 2001. (gr. 3-6). lib. bdg. 13.00 (978-0-613-44418-7(3)) Tandem Library Bks.

Hopkinson, Deborah. Pioneer Summer. Faricy, Patrick, illus. ed. 2005. 74p. (J). lib. bdg. 15.00 (978-1-59054-911-7(2)) Fitzgerald Bks.

Howe, James. The Watcher. 2001. 192p. (YA). (gr. 8-12). pap. 5.99 (978-0-689-83533-9(7) , Simon Pulse) Simon & Schuster Children's Publishing.

Hundal, Nancy. Prairie Summer. Deines, Brian, illus. 1999. 34p. (J). (gr. k-3). (978-1-55041-403-5(8)) Fitzhenry & Whiteside, Ltd.

Hurwitz, Johanna. Faraway Summer. Azarian, Mary, illus. 2000. 160p. (J). (gr. 3-7). pap. 5.99 (978-0-380-73256-2(4) , Harper Trophy) HarperCollins Pubs.

—Faraway Summer. 2000. 11.60 (978-0-606-17880-8(5)); (gr. 3-6). lib. bdg. 12.95 (978-0-613-28480-6(1)) Tandem Library Bks.

—Summer with Elisa. Maione, Heather Harms & Tilley, Debbie, illus. 2000. 96p. (J). (ps-2). 16.99 (978-0-688-17095-0(1)) HarperCollins Pubs.

I Love Summer the Best... 2000. 22p. (J). pap. 6.95 (978-0-9704420-0-0(9)) Dancing Crows Unlimited.

Irwin, Inez Haynes. Maida's Little House. 2004. reprint ed. pap. 27.95 (978-1-4179-4236-7(3)) Kessinger Publishing, LLC.

Jacobs, E. Caroline. The S. W. F. Club. 2006. 77.99 (*978-1-4280-4783-9(2)); pap. 71.99 (*978-1-4280-4779-2(4)) IndyPublish.com.

Jocelyn, Marthe. Mayfly. 2004. (Illus.). 32p. (J). (ps-k). 14.95 (978-0-88776-676-3(5)) Tundra Bks., Inc./Livres Toundra, Inc. CAN. *Dist:* Random Hse., Inc.

Johnson, Amy Crane. Mason Moves Away/Mason se Muda: A Solomon Raven Story: un cuento del cuervo Salomon, 4 vols. de la Vega, Eida, tr. Mommaerts, Robb, illus. 2004. (Solomon Raven Ser. : 4). Tr. of Mason se Muda. (SPA & ENG.). 32p. (J). (gr. k-3). 16.95 (978-0-9720192-3-5(1) , 626999) Raven Tree Pr.

Joosse, Barbara M. Hot City. Gauch, Patricia Lee, ed. Christie, Gregory R., illus. 2004. 32p. (J). (ps-3). 16.99 (978-0-399-23640-2(6) , Philomel) Penguin Group (USA) Inc.

Kelley, Marty. Summer Stinks. 2001. (Illus.). 32p. (J). (ps-1). 12.95 (978-1-55933-291-0(3)) Zino Pr. Children's Bks.

Kelly, Katy. Lucy Rose: Big on Plans. Rex, Adam, illus. 2005. 176p. (gr. 3-7). (J). 12.95 (978-0-385-73204-8(X)); lib. bdg. 14.99 (978-0-385-90235-9(2)) Random Hse. Children's Bks. (Delacorte Bks. for Young Readers).

—Lucy Rose: Big on Plans. Rex, Adam, illus. 2007. 192p. (gr. 3-5). 5.50 (978-0-440-42027-9(X) , Yearling) Random Hse. Children's Bks.

Kraft, Erik P. Lenny & Mel's Summer Vacation. Kraft, Erik P., illus. 2004. (Ready-for-Chapters Ser.). (Illus.). 64p. (J). pap. 3.99 (978-0-689-86874-0(X) , Aladdin) Simon & Schuster Children's Publishing.

Krensky, Stephen. Lionel in the Summer. Natti, Susanna, illus. 2000. (Easy-to-Read Ser.). 48p. (J). (gr. 1-4). pap. 3.99 (978-0-14-130824-1(9) , Puffin) Penguin Group (USA) Inc.

—Lionel in the Summer. 1999. (J). (gr. 1 up). pap., stu. ed. 30.99 incl. audio (978-0-7887-2987-4(X) , 40869) Recorded Bks., LLC.

—Lionel in the Summer. 2000. (gr. k-3). lib. bdg. 11.80 (978-0-613-28555-1(7)); (Illus.). (J). (978-0-606-18419-9(8)) Tandem Library Bks.

Lembcke, Marjaleena & Santos, Nuria G. El Verano en el Que Todos Estabamos Enamorados. Santos, Nuria G., tr. 2002. (Joven Coleccion Ser.). (SPA., Illus.). 128p. (978-84-89804-34-0(6)) Loguez Ediciones ESP. *Dist:* Lectorum Pubns., Inc.

Lenhard, Elizabeth. OSS Wilderness. 2003. (gr. 3-6). lib. bdg. 13.00 (978-0-613-68274-9(2)) Tandem Library Bks.

—OSS Wilderness. 2003. (Spykids Adventures Ser.: Vol. 4). 160p. (Orig.). (J). (gr. 3-7). pap. 4.99 (978-0-7868-1718-4(6) , Volo) Hyperion Bks. for Children.

Limb, Sue. Girl, (Nearly) 16: Absolute Torture. (Girl, 15 Ser.). 224p. (YA). (gr. 5-11). 2008. mass mkt. 6.50 (*978-0-440-23897-3(8) , Laurel Leaf); 2006. pap. 8.95 (978-0-385-73217-8(1) , Delacorte Bks. for Young Readers) Random Hse. Children's Bks.

Little, Jean. Somebody Else's Summer. 2007. 192p. (J). 16.00 (978-0-670-04466-5(0) , Penguin Global) Penguin Group (USA) Inc.

London, Jonathan. When the Fireflies Come. Widener, Terry, illus. 2003. 32p. (J). (ps). 15.99 (978-0-525-45404-5(7) , Dutton Juvenile) Penguin Group (USA) Inc.

Love, D. Anne. My Lone Star Summer. 1998. (978-0-606-13636-5(3)) Tandem Library Bks.

Lowry, Lois. Un Verano para Morir. 1998. (SPA., Illus.). 124p. (YA). (gr. 5-8). pap. 10.99 (978-84-241-3267-5(X) , EV7788) Everest Publishing.

Lubar, David. Dog Days. 80p. (J). (gr. 4-8). 2005. pap. 4.99 (978-1-58196-025-9(5)); 2004. 15.95 (978-1-58196-013-6(1)) Darby Creek Publishing.

Lubbert, Constance. Killdeer. 2004. 81p. pap. 14.95 (978-1-4137-1138-7(3)) PublishAmerica, Inc.

Luxa, Sue. One Golden Summer. 2004. (Illus.). 80p. (J). pap. 8.95 (978-1-890437-99-2(9) , 1234248) Western Reflections Publishing Co.

Mahy, Margaret. Summery Saturday Morning. 2000. (J). (978-0-606-19071-8(6)) Tandem Library Bks.

Malkin, Nina. Orange Is the New Pink. 2007. 272p. (YA). (gr. 7 up). 8.99 (*978-0-439-89965-9(6)) Scholastic, Inc.

Manutoli, Sophie. Uksuq Wallu-qaa Kiak? Andrew, John et al, illus. 1998. Tr. of Winter or Summer?. (ESK.). 20p. (J). (gr. k-3). pap. 8.00 (978-1-58084-042-2(6)) Lower Kuskokwim Schl. District.

Maridan, Samantha. A Totally Hottie Summer: Junior Novel. 2nd rev. ed. 2006. (Lizzie McGuire Super Special Ser.). (Illus.). 272p. (gr. 3-7). pap. 6.99 (978-0-7868-3842-4(6)) Disney Pr.

Marks, Cindy. Another Summer: If Only There Was. Pickar, Steve, illus. l.t. ed. 1999. 56p. (J). (gr. 1-4). pap. 3.95 (978-0-9655425-0-0(5)) TiaraMoon Publishing.

The Marsh Runners. 2004. (J). per. 14.95 (978-0-9761178-0-3(0)) Maritime Kids Quest Pr.

Mazer, Anne. The Best Is Yet to Come. 2004. (Amazing Days of Abby Hayes Ser.: No. 1). 109p. (J). lib. bdg. 16.92 (*978-1-4242-1197-5(2)) Fitzgerald Bks.

McLain, Tanya. A Different Kind of Summer. 2007. (ENG.). 72p. (J). per. 10.99 (*978-1-4141-0848-3(6)) Pleasant Word.

McMullan, Kate. Fluffy's Silly Summer. 2000. (Hello Reader! Ser.). (Illus.). (J). 10.79 (978-0-606-18873-9(8)) Tandem Library Bks.

Meadows, Daisy. Joy the Summer Vacation Fairy. 2007. (Rainbow Magic Ser.). 192p. (J). pap. 6.99 (*978-0-439-93442-8(7) , Scholastic Paperbacks) Scholastic, Inc.

Menefee, Angelo K. Billy's First Summer Vacation. 2007. (J). per. 16.95 (*978-1-60002-249-4(9) , Airleaf Publishing) Airleaf Publishing & Bookselling.

Miller, J. P. Over the River & Through the Woods: A Journey with Harriet Tubman. 2004. 74p. pap. 14.95 (978-1-4137-1604-7(0)) PublishAmerica, Inc.

Moore, Ishbel. Dolina's Decision. 2001. 132p. (YA). (gr. 9 up). pap. (978-1-896184-74-6(X)) Roussan Pubs., Inc./ Roussan Editeur, Inc.

Muldrow, Diane. Sweet-and-Sour Summer, No. 9. Pollack, Barbara, illus. 2007. (Dish Ser.). 160p. (J). (gr. 4-7). pap. 4.99 (*978-0-448-44661-5(8) , Grosset & Dunlap) Penguin Group (USA) Inc.

—Sweet-and-Sour Summer. 2003. (gr. 3-6). lib. bdg. 13.00 (978-0-613-72478-4(X)) Tandem Library Bks.

Nabb, Magdalen. Josie Smith in Summer. l.t. ed. 2005. (Illus.). 112p. (J). pap. (978-0-7540-6164-9(7) , CLP 356) BBC Audio.

Natti, Susanna, illus. Lionel in the Summer. 2002. (Lionel Ser.). (J). 11.49 (978-0-7587-4120-2(0)) Book Wholesalers, Inc.

Naylor, Phyllis Reynolds. Boys Rock! 144p. (gr. 4-7). 2007. 5.50 (*978-0-440-41990-7(5) , Yearling); 2005. (J). 15.95 (978-0-385-73140-9(X) , Delacorte Bks. for Young Readers); 2005. (J). lib. bdg. 17.99 (978-0-385-90171-0(2) , Delacorte Bks. for Young Readers) Random Hse. Children's Bks.

Naylor, Phyllis Reynolds. The Grooming of Alice. Elliott, Mark, illus. (Alice Ser.). 224p. (J). (gr. 5-9). 2001. pap. 4.99 (978-0-689-84618-2(5) , Aladdin); 2000. 16.99 (978-0-689-82633-7(8) , Atheneum) Simon & Schuster Children's Publishing.

—The Grooming of Alice. 2001. (Alice Ser.). 11.64 (978-0-606-22125-2(5)) Tandem Library Bks.

Nelson, Ray, et al. Porkchop's Summer Book. Siegel, Joseph & Habecker, Mary Beth, eds. Peeples, Aaron, illus. 1999. 32p. (J). (gr. k-3). pap. 9.95 (978-1-883772-24-6(9)) Flying Rhinoceros, Inc.

A New & Different Summer. 2000. (Katie Rose/Stacy Belford Ser.). (YA). (gr. 5-9). per. 12.95 (978-1-930009-12-7(7)) Image Cascade Publishing.

Nicholson, John & Nicholson, Ed. Shall We Gather. 2002. (Illus.). 123p. reprint ed. pap. (978-0-9720828-0-8(8)) Nicholson, Ed.

Ormondroyd, Edward. Castaways on Long Ago. 2003. (Illus.). 188p. (gr. 5 up). 12.95 (978-0-9714612-8-4(7)) Green Mansion Pr. LLC.

Pantelo, Amber. The Totally Meaningless Summer. 2004. 75p. (YA). pap. 12.95 (978-0-7414-1914-9(9)) Infinity Publishing.

Parr, Letitia. When Sea & Sky Are Blue. Watts, John, illus. 32p. (J). (ps-3). 13.95 (978-0-87592-059-7(4)) Scroll Pr., Inc.

Paulsen, Gary. Canoe Days. Paulsen, Ruth Wright, illus. 2001. 32p. (J). (ps-3). reprint ed. pap. 6.99 (978-0-440-41441-4(5) , Dragonfly Bks.) Random Hse. Children's Bks.

—Canoe Days. Paulsen, Ruth Wright, illus. 2001. (J). (ps-ps). lib. bdg. 15.30 (978-0-613-33747-2(6)) Tandem Library Bks.

—Canoe Days. 2001. (J). 13.79 (978-0-606-21100-0(4)) Tandem Library Bks.

Payne, Nina. Summertime Waltz. Swiatkowska, Gabi, illus. 2005. 32p. (J). 16.00 (978-0-374-37291-0(8) , Farrar, Straus & Giroux (BYR)) Farrar, Straus & Giroux.

Perez, Angela J. Zack Attack! Hazard, Andrea, illus. 2007. 36p. (J). 17.95 (*978-0-9778328-9-7(9)) His Work Christian Publishing.

Pickering, Jimmy. It's Summer. 2003. (Illus.). 32p. (J). 16.95 (978-1-931290-23-4(7)) Tallfellow Pr.

Pittar, Gill. Milly, Molly & Special Friends (book W/dolls) 2006. 28p. pap. (978-1-86972-104-6(7)) Milly Molly Bks.

Posner, Renee & Quinton, Sasha. Suzy Season Loves Summer. D'Argo, Laura, illus. (Be Mine Bears Ser.). (J). bds. 4.99 (978-1-58209-351-2(2)) Books Are Fun, Ltd.

Rawls, Wilson. Summer of the Monkeys. 1998. 288p. (J). (gr. 5-9). pap. 5.99 (978-0-440-41580-0(2) , Yearling) Random Hse. Children's Bks.

—Summer of the Monkeys. 1998. (gr. 5-8). lib. bdg. 14.15 (978-0-613-83533-6(6)) Tandem Library Bks.

Recorvits, Helen. Where Heroes Hide. 2002. (Illus.). 144p. (J). (gr. 4-6). 16.00 (978-0-374-33057-6(3) , Farrar, Straus & Giroux (BYR)) Farrar, Straus & Giroux.

Reynolds, Bill. Willy Woodchuck. 2002. 52p. pap. 9.95 (978-0-7414-1012-2(5)) Infinity Publishing.

Richards, Martha. Dizzy Days: My Amazing 13th Summer. Wise, Noreen, ed. 2002. (Lemonade Collection). 256p. (YA). (gr. 5 up). pap. 13.95 (978-1-58584-285-8(0)) Huckleberry Pr.

Rodgers, Mary. Summer Switch. 224p. (J). (gr. 4-6). pap. 4.95 (978-0-8072-1550-0(3) , Listening Library) Random Hse. Audio Publishing Group.

—Summer Switch. 2003. (gr. 3-6). lib. bdg. 14.15 (978-0-613-58737-2(5)) Tandem Library Bks.

Romer, Ruth. The Great Lemonade Stand-off. 2005. 22.00 (*978-1-4108-4200-8(2)) Benchmark Education Co.

Roop, Meg. Summer Mystery, 2002. (Illus.). 172p. (YA). pap. 13.95 (978-1-58736-072-5(1) , Starbound Bks.) Wheatmark.

Rue, Nancy N. Sophie's Stormy Summer, Vol. 6. Chen, Grace, illus. 2005. (Faithgirlz Ser.). 128p. (J). pap. 6.99 (978-0-310-70761-5(7)) Zonderkidz.

Rylant, Cynthia. Henry & Mudge in the Green Time. Stevenson, Sucie, illus. 2002. (Henry & Mudge Ser.). (J). 11.91 (978-0-7587-1264-6(2)) Book Wholesalers, Inc.

—Henry & Mudge in the Green Time. Stevenson, Sucie, illus. 1999. (Henry & Mudge Ser.). 28.95 incl. audio compact disk (978-1-59112-579-2(0)); pap. 31.95 incl. audio compact disk (978-1-59112-578-5(2)) Live Oak Media.

Sam's Last Summer. 2006. (J). per. 5.95 (*978-0-9790796-3-4(2)) PJR Assocs., Ltd.

Scholastic, Inc. Staff. Have a Great Summer, 30 vols. 1999. (J). pap. 3.95 (978-0-439-07235-9(2)) Scholastic, Inc.

Schraff, Anne. Horse Called Courage. 2001. (gr. 7-12). lib. bdg. 11.80 (978-0-613-32650-6(4)) Tandem Library Bks.

Schumacher, Julie. Grass Angel. 2005. 196p. (J). (gr. k-9). per. 12.55 (978-0-606-33725-0(3)) Tandem Library Bks.

Scott, Evelyn & Golden Books Staff. The Fourteen Bears in Summer & Winter. Parsons, Virginia, illus. 2005. 64p. (J). (gr. k-k). reprint ed. 14.95 (978-0-375-83279-6(3) , Golden Bks.) Random Hse. Children's Bks.

Shreve, Susan. Under the Watsons' Porch. 2006. 208p. (J). (gr. 5-8). reprint ed. pap. 4.99 (978-0-440-41969-3(7) , Yearling) Random Hse. Children's Bks.

Shreve, Susan Richards. Under the Watsons' Porch. (J). 2006. 199p. (*978-1-4156-7020-0(X) , Yearling); 2004. 208p. (gr. 5-8). 15.95 (978-0-375-82630-6(0) , Knopf Bks. for Young Readers) Random Hse. Children's Bks.

Siburt, Ruth. The Trouble with Alex. 1998. 93p. (J). (gr. k-9). pap. 9.99 (978-0-88092-366-8(0) , 3660) Royal Fireworks Publishing Co.

Sierra Summer. 2003. (Illus.). pap. 15.99 (978-0-7868-4561-3(9)) Disney Pr.

Skalak, Daniel. All Summer's Fun. Skalak, Daniel, illus. 2006. (Illus.). 32p. (J). 15.95 (978-1-60108-000-4(X)) Red Cygnet Pr.

Smith, Montez Roller. A Summer to Grow On: House upon a Hill Series - Book 1. 2005. 220p. per. 14.95 (978-1-933148-95-3(0)) Tate Publishing & Enterprises, L.L.C.

Smoot, Madeline, compiled by. Summer Shorts: A Short Story Collection. 2006. (Illus.). 428p. (J). pap. 8.95 (978-0-9769417-5-0(9)) Blooming Tree Pr.

Spinelli, Eileen. Summerhouse Time. Lew-Vriethoff, Joanne, illus. 2007. 224p. (J). (gr. 3-7). 12.99 (978-0-375-84061-6(3)); lib. bdg. 15.99 (978-0-375-94061-3(8)) Random Hse. Children's Bks. (Knopf Bks. for Young Readers).

Spinelli, Eileen & Lisker, Emily, illus. Summerhouse Time. 2001. (J). 16.00 (978-0-689-82418-0(1) , Simon & Schuster Children's Publishing) Simon & Schuster Children's Publishing.

Staples, Suzanne Fisher. The Green Dog: A Mostly True Story. 2003. (Illus.). 128p. (J). 16.00 (978-0-374-32779-8(3) , Farrar, Straus & Giroux (BYR)) Farrar, Straus & Giroux.

—The Green Dog: A Mostly True Story. 2005. 144p. (J). (ps-7). reprint ed. pap. 5.99 (978-0-06-076045-8(1) , Harper Trophy) HarperCollins Pubs.

—The Green Dog: A Mostly True Story. l.t. ed. 2004. 140p. (J). 21.95 (978-0-7862-6577-0(9)) Thorndike Pr.

Star Spangled Summer. 2001. (Penny Parrish Story Ser.). 281p. (YA). (gr. 5 up). pap. 12.95 (978-1-930009-26-4(7)) Image Cascade Publishing.

Stock, Catherine. Island Summer. 1999. (Illus.). 192p. (J). (gr. k-3). 16.00 (978-0-688-12780-0(0)) HarperCollins Pubs.

Sumerak, Mark. I Know What We Did That Summer. 2006. (Illus.). (J). (gr. 2-6). 21.35 (978-1-59961-033-7(7)) Spotlight.

Summer Fun: Individual Title Six-Packs. (Literatura 2000 Ser.). (ps-1). 28.00 (978-0-7635-0064-1(X)) Rigby Education.

Summer Is a Special Season. 2004. (YA). (978-0-8374-0013-6(9)); lib. bdg. (978-0-8374-0012-9(0)) Weekly Reader Corp.

Summer of the Monkeys. 1999. (J). 9.95 (978-1-56137-065-8(7)) Novel Units, Inc.

Summer Success. 2002. 96p. (J). (ps-3). pap. 166.80 (978-1-57768-352-0(8)) School Specialty Publishing.

Ten Book Summer. 2002. (Illus.). (J). pap. (978-0-7398-5106-7(3)) Steck-Vaughn.

Thomas, Patricia. Firefly Mountain. Sylvada, Peter, illus. 2007. 32p. (J). (gr. k-2). 16.95 (*978-1-56145-360-3(9) , Peachtree Junior) Peachtree Pubs., Ltd.

Thomson, Sarah L. Feel the Summer. Yamada, Kana, illus. 2006. 32p. 14.95 (978-1-59687-174-8(1)) ibooks, Inc.

Tich, Jan & Jantti, Mariana. Te dare un pedacito de Sol. 2006. (Pequenos cuentos para grandes lectores Ser.). (SPA., Illus.). 32p. (J). 9.95 (978-84-96448-02-5(9)) Hardenville SA URY. *Dist:* Independent Pubs. Group.

Trisler, Alana & Cardiel, Patrice Howe. My Summer Journal. 1999. 72p. (J). (gr. 2-3). pap., wbk. ed. 2.10 (978-1-56762-107-5(4)) Modern Learning Pr.

Turner, Julie Anne. A Tale of Summerland. 2007. (Illus.). 72p. pap. (*978-1-84401-902-1(0)) Athena Pr.

Wallington, Aury. Bait & Switch. novel ed. 2005. (O. C. Ser.: No. 6). 264p. (J). pap. 6.99 (978-0-439-74570-3(5)) Scholastic, Inc.

Ware, Cheryl. Flea Circus Summer. 1998. (Illus.). 144p. (J). (gr. 3-7). pap. 3.99 (978-0-380-72939-5(3) , Harper Trophy) HarperCollins Pubs.

—Flea Circus Summer. 1998. (J). (978-0-606-13391-3(7)); (gr. 3-6). lib. bdg. 11.80 (978-0-613-89786-0(2)) Tandem Library Bks.

Warner, Gertrude Chandler, creator. The Boxcar Children Summer Special. 2007. (Boxcar Children Mysteries Ser.). 376p. (J). pap. 7.95 (*978-0-8075-0885-5(3)) Whitman, Albert & Co.

Waucaush, Clair. Pokey's World. 2004. 72p. pap. 14.95 (978-1-4137-3923-7(7)) PublishAmerica, Inc.

Weihrich, Carroll. On Jim Street. 2003. 144p. 24.50 (978-1-932621-19-8(9)); per. 15.00 (978-1-932621-18-1(0)) Open Bk. Publishing.

Welles, Lee. Gaia Girls Enter the Earth. 2006. (Gaia Girls Ser.). (Illus.). 336p. (YA). 18.95 (978-1-933609-00-3(1)) Daisyworld Pr.

Weyn, Suzanne. Sleepover. novel ed. 2004. (Illus.). 104p. (J). pap. 4.99 (978-0-439-65787-7(3) , Scholastic Paperbacks) Scholastic, Inc.

Whelan, Gloria. That Wild Berries Should Grow. 2003. (gr. 3-6). lib. bdg. 16.45 (978-0-613-75569-6(3)) Tandem Library Bks.

Wiebe, Kathleen. Willow Creek Summer. 2005. 217p. (J). (gr. 7-12). 7.95 (978-1-55050-169-8(0)) Coteau Bks. CAN. *Dist:* Fitzhenry & Whiteside, Ltd.

—Willow Creek Summer. 2001. (gr. 7-12). lib. bdg. 16.40 (978-0-613-78445-0(6)) Tandem Library Bks.

Williams, Dell. If I Forget, You Remember. 1999. (J). 11.64 (978-0-606-16171-8(6)) Tandem Library Bks.
Winkler, Henry & Oliver, Lin. Summer School! What Genius Thought That Up? 2006. (Hank Zipzer Ser.: No. 8). (J). (gr. 3-8). 24.21 (978-1-59961-107-5(4)) Spotlight.
—Summer School! What Genius Thought That Up? 2005. (Hank Zipzer Ser.: No. 8). (Illus.). 157p. (J). (ps-7). per. 11.64 (978-0-606-33097-8(6)) Tandem Library Bks.
Woodbury, Mary. The Ghost in the Machine. 2005. 222p. (J). (gr. 6-9). pap. 7.95 (978-1-55050-227-5(1)) Coteau Bks. CAN. *Dist:* Fitzhenry & Whiteside, Ltd.
Woodson, Jacqueline. The Other Side. Lewis, Earl, illus. 2001. 1p. (J). (gr. k up). 16.99 (978-0-399-23116-2(1), Putnam Juvenile) Penguin Group (USA) Inc.
Wright, Betty Ren. Haunted Summer. 2001. 112p. (gr. 4-7). pap. 3.99 (978-0-439-24402-2(1)) Scholastic, Inc.
Yeomans, Ellen. Jubilee. Ladwig, Tim, illus. 2004. 32p. (J). 16.00 (978-0-8028-5230-4(0)) Eerdmans, William B. Publishing Co.
Ylitalo, Gail. Blackberry Summer. 2003. 153p. pap. 16.95 (978-1-59286-784-4(7)) PublishAmerica, Inc.
Young, D. Jean. Quicksilver Summer. 1998. 162p. (YA). (gr. 7-12). pap. 9.95 (978-1-896184-36-4(7)) Roussan Pubs., Inc./Roussan Editeur, Inc. CAN. *Dist:* Orca Bk. Pubs. USA.

SUMMER—POETRY

Forman, Ruth. Young Cornrows Callin Out the Moon: Poem. Bayoc, Cbabi, illus. 2007. 24p. (J). (gr. 1-3). 16.95 (978-0-89239-218-6(5)) Children's Bk. Pr.
London, Jonathan. Sun Dance, Water Dance. Couch, Greg, illus. 2001. 40p. (J). (ps-3). 15.99 (978-0-525-46682-6(7), Dutton Juvenile) Penguin Group (USA) Inc.
Mass, Wendy, compiled by. Summer: Poems, Songs, Prayers. 2001. (Illus.). 10p. (J). (ps-2). 6.99 (978-0-570-07165-5(8)) Concordia Publishing Hse.

SUMMER HOMES

see Architecture, Domestic; Houses

SUMMER RESORTS—FICTION

Harcourt School Publishers Staff. Thunder Lake Advanced Level. 3rd ed. 2002. (Trophies Reading Program Ser.). (Illus.). pap. 5.10 (978-0-15-323469-9(5)) Harcourt Schl. Pubs.
Jewett, Sarah Orne. The Country of the Pointed Firs & Other Stories. 2000. (gr. 7-12). lib. bdg. 11.80 (978-0-613-27778-5(3)) Tandem Library Bks.

SUMMER THEATER—FICTION

Lambert, Janet. Stagestruck Parri. 2001. (Parri MacDonald Series by Janet Lambert: Vol. 3). (YA). pap. 12.95 (978-1-930009-43-1(7)) Image Cascade Publishing.
Ryan, Sarah. The Rules for Hearts: A Family Drama. 2007. 224p. (YA). (gr. 9 up). 16.99 (978-0-670-05906-5(4), Viking Juvenile) Penguin Group (USA) Inc.

SUN

see also Solar Energy; Solar System

Adamson, Thomas K. The Sun. 2007. (Illus.). 24p. (J). (978-0-7368-6757-3(0)) Capstone Pr., Inc.
Asch, Frank. The Sun Is My Favorite Star. 2000. (Illus.). 32p. (J). 16.00 (978-0-15-202127-6(2), Gulliver Bks.) Harcourt Children's Bks.
Asch, Frank. The Sun Is My Favorite Star. 2008. (Illus.). 32p. (J). pap. 7.00 (*978-0-15-206397-9(8), Voyager Bks./Libros Viajeros) Harcourt Children's Bks.
Asimov, Isaac. The Solar System: The Sun. 2004. (Isaac Asimov's 21st Century Library of the Universe). (Illus.). 32p. 14.00 (978-1-59102-122-3(7)) Prometheus Bks., Pubs.
Asimov, Isaac & Hantula, Richard. El Sol. Porras, Carlos & D'Andrea, Patricia, trs. 2003. (Isaac Asimov's Biblioteca del Universo del Siglo XXI). (SPA., Illus.). 32p. (J). (gr. 3 up). lib. bdg. 24.67 (978-0-8368-3861-9(0)); pap. 8.95 (978-0-8368-3874-9(2), Weekly Reader Early Learning Library) Stevens, Gareth Inc.
—The Sun. 2003. (Isaac Asimov's 21st Century Library of the Universe). (Illus.). 32p. (gr. 3 up). (J). pap. 0.00 (978-0-8368-3946-3(3), Weekly Reader Early Learning Library); (YA). lib. bdg. 24.67 (978-0-8368-3242-6(6)) Stevens, Gareth Inc.
Bailey, Jacqui. Sun Up, Sun Down: The Story of Day & Night. Lilly, Matthew, illus. 2004. (Science Works Ser.). 32p. (J). (gr. 3-6). 23.93 (978-1-4048-0567-5(2)) Picture Window Bks.
Barnes-Svarney, Patricia L. Secrets of the Sun: A Closer Look at Our Star. 2000. (Space Explorer Ser.). (Illus.). 64p. (J). (gr. 6-8). lib. bdg. 28.54 (978-0-7398-2214-2(4)) Raintree.
—Secrets of the Sun: Closer Look. 1999. (Illus.). (J). pap. (978-0-7398-2502-0(X)) Steck-Vaughn.
Barry, Frances. Duckie's Rainbow. Barry, Frances, illus. 2004. (Illus.). 14p. (J). (gr. k-ps). 7.99 (978-0-7636-2066-0(1)) Candlewick Pr.
Bell, Trudy E. The Sun: Our Nearest Star. 2003. (New Solar System Ser.). (J). lib. bdg. 28.50 (978-1-58340-286-3(1)) Smart Apple Media.
Birch, Robin. Earth, Sun, & Moon. 2002. (Space Ser.). (Illus.). 32p. (gr. k-2). 23.00 (978-0-7910-6970-7(2), Chelsea Hse.) Facts On File, Inc.
—The Sun. 2004. (Solar System Ser.). (Illus.). 32p. (gr. 3-5). 23.00 (978-0-7910-7934-8(1), Chelsea Hse.) Facts On File, Inc.
Bourgeois, Paulette. The Sun. Slavin, Bill, illus. unabr. ed. 1999. (Starting with Space Ser.). 40p. (J). (gr. 4-6). (978-1-55074-330-2(9)) Kids Can Pr., Ltd.
Branley, Franklyn M. The Sun: Our Nearest Star. Miller, Edward, illus. 2002. (Let's-Read-and-Find-Out Science Ser.). 32p. (J). (gr. k-4). pap. 5.99 (978-0-06-445202-1(6)) HarperCollins Pubs.
—Sun: Our Nearest Star. 2002. (gr. k-3). lib. bdg. 12.95 (978-0-613-59381-6(2)) Tandem Library Bks.
—Sunshine Makes the Seasons. Rex, Michael, illus. 2005. (Let's-Read-and-Find-Out Science Ser.). 40p. (J). (gr. k-4). pap. 5.99 (978-0-06-059205-9(2)) HarperCollins Pubs.
Branley, Franklyn Mansfield. Sunshine Makes the Seasons. Rex, Michael, illus. 2005. (Let's-Read-and-Find-Out Science Ser.). (J). (ps-ps). 31p. 15.99 (978-0-06-059203-5(6)); 40p. lib. bdg. 16.89 (978-0-06-059204-2(4)) HarperCollins Pubs.
Bredeson, Carmen. What Do You Know about the Sun? 2008. (I Like Space! Ser.). (Illus.). 32p. (J). (gr. 1-3). lib. bdg. 22.60 (*978-0-7660-2941-5(7), Enslow Elementary) Enslow Pubs., Inc.
Brinkman, Patricia. Discover the Sun. 2006. pap. 39.00 (*978-1-4108-6477-2(4)) Benchmark Education Co.
—The Sun. 2006. pap. 39.00 (*978-1-4108-6474-1(X)) Benchmark Education Co.
Canizares, Susan & Moreton, D. Sun. 1998. (Science Emergent Readers Ser.). (Illus.). 16p. (J). pap. 3.25 (978-0-590-10731-0(3)) Scholastic, Inc.
Capstone Press, contrib. by. Sunshine. 2005. (Our Seasons & Weather Ser.). 24p. (YA). (gr. k-3). pap. (978-1-56065-843-6(6), Pebble Bks.) Capstone Pr., Inc.
Chrismer, Melanie. The Sun. (Scholastic News Nonfiction Readers: Space Science Ser.). 24p. (J). 2008. pap. 6.95 (*978-0-531-14768-9(1)); 2007. (Illus.). (gr. 1-2). lib. bdg. 20.00 (*978-0-531-14753-5(3)) Scholastic Library Publishing. (Children's Pr.).
Cole, Michael D. The Sun: The Center of the Solar System. 2001. (Countdown to Space Ser.). (Illus.). 48p. (J). (gr. 4-10). lib. bdg. 23.93 (978-0-7660-1508-1(4)) Enslow Pubs., Inc.
Daronco, Mickey & Ohanesian, Diane. Fun in the Sun. 2nd rev. ed. 2003. (BuildUp Ser.). (J). pap. 22.00 (978-1-4108-0741-0(X)) Benchmark Education Co.
Un día soleado (A Sunny Day) 2006. (J). 18.60 (978-0-8225-6213-9(8), Ediciones Lerner) Lerner Publishing Group.
Un Día Soleado (A Sunny Day) 2007. (J). pap. 4.25 (978-0-8225-6552-9(8), Ediciones Lerner) Lerner Publishing Group.
Dobeck, Maryann. Circling the Sun. 2004. (Illus.). 16p. (J). (978-0-7608-8917-6(1)) Sundance/Newbridge Educational Publishing.
Doudna, Kelly. It Is Sunny. 2003. (Weather Ser.). (Illus.). 23p. (J). (ps-3). lib. bdg. 19.93 (978-1-57765-777-4(2)) ABDO Publishing Co.
Dubarle-Bossy, Philippe. Hello, Sun! Moon, Jo, illus. 2005. 8p. (J). 9.95 (978-1-4027-2623-1(6), Sterling/Pinwheel) Sterling Publishing Co., Inc.
Eckart, Edana. Watching the Sun. 2004. (Wel-Watching Nature Ser.). (Illus.). 24p. (J). 18.00 (978-0-516-27597-0(6)); pap. 4.95 (978-0-516-25939-0(3)) Scholastic Library Publishing. (Children's Pr.).
Elish, Dan. The Sun. 2006. (Kaleidoscope Space Ser.). (Illus.). 48p. (J). lib. bdg. 28.50 (978-0-7614-2048-4(7), Benchmark Bks.) Cavendish, Marshall Corp.
Excavaciones a pleno Sol: Aventuras (Adventure Books) 2000. (Aventuras A Traves Del Tiempo Ser.). (ENG & SPA.). (gr. 6 up). (978-0-02-148740-0(5)) Macmillan/McGraw-Hill Schl. Div.
Feinstein, Stephen. The Sun: A Myreportlinks. com Book. 2005. (Solar System Ser.). (Illus.). 48p. (J). (ps-10). lib. bdg. 25.26 (978-0-7660-5305-2(9), MyReportLinks.com Bks.) Enslow Pubs., Inc.
Flanagan, Alice K. Sunshine. 2003. (Wonder Books Level 1: Weather Ser.). (Illus.). 24p. (J). (ps-2). 22.79 (978-1-56766-454-6(7)) Child's World, Inc.
Fowler, Allan. Energy from the Sun. 1998. (Rookie Read-About Science Ser.). (Illus.). 32p. (J). (gr. 1-2). pap. 4.95 (978-0-516-26255-0(6), Children's Pr.) Scholastic Library Publishing.
Furniss, Tim. The Sun. 2000. (Spinning Through Space Ser.). (Illus.). 32p. (J). (gr. 2-4). lib. bdg. 25.69 (978-0-7398-2739-0(1)) Raintree.
—The Sun. 2000. (Spinning Through Space Ser.). (Illus.). 32p. (J). (gr. 2-4). pap. 10.34 (978-0-7398-3091-8(0)) Steck-Vaughn.
Gallant, Roy A. When the Sun Dies. 1998. (Accelerated Reader Bks.). (Illus.). 128p. (J). (gr. 5-9). 14.95 (978-0-7614-5036-8(X), Cavendish Children's Bks.) Cavendish, Marshall Corp.
Ganeri, Anita. Sunshine. 2004. (Illus.). 24p. (J). pap. (978-0-8368-4306-4(1)); lib. bdg. 19.33 (978-0-8368-4301-9(0)) Stevens, Gareth Inc.
Gardner, Robert. Far-Out Science Projects about Earth's Sun & Moon. LaBaff, Tom, illus. 2007. (Rockin' Earth Science Experiments Ser.). 48p. (J). (gr. 3-6). lib. bdg. 23.93 (978-0-7660-2736-7(8), Enslow Elementary) Enslow Pubs., Inc.
Goldstein, Margaret J. The Sun. 2005. (Pull Ahead Bks.). (Illus.). 32p. (gr. 2-4). lib. bdg. 22.60 (978-0-8225-4647-4(7)) Lerner Publishing Group.
Graham, Ian. The Sun. 2007. (J). (*978-1-59920-069-9(4)) Smart Apple Media.
Grimshaw, Caroline. Sun: Follow the Journey of a Sunbeam. 2000. (Invisible Journeys Ser.). (Illus.). 32p. (J). (gr. 3-6). 10.95 (978-1-58728-332-1(8)); pap. 5.95 (978-1-58728-329-1(8)) T&N Children's Publishing. (Two Can Publishing).
Hartley, Susan. The Hot Sun! 2nd rev. ed. 2003. (StartUp Ser.). (J). pap. 22.00 (978-1-4108-0722-9(3)) Benchmark Education Co.
Haydon, Julie. The Sun: Individual Title Six-Packs. (Rigby Focus Ser.). 16p. (gr. k up). 26.00 (978-0-7578-5280-0(7)); 28.00 (978-0-7578-5514-6(8)) Rigby Education.
Head, Honor. Sun. 2006. (QEB Weather Watch Ser.). (Illus.). 24p. (J). lib. bdg. 16.95 (978-1-59566-186-9(7)) QEB Publishing Inc.
Hil, Mcgraw. Sciasmtbk the Sun & Its F. 2000. (McGraw-Hill Science Ser.). (gr. 3 up). (978-0-02-277751-7(2)) Macmillan/McGraw-Hill Schl. Div.
—Trfpaswak the Sun & Its F. 2000. (McGraw-Hill Science Ser.). (gr. 3 up). (978-0-02-277632-9(X)) Macmillan/McGraw-Hill Schl. Div.
Hines, Anna Grossnickle. What Can You Do in the Sun? Kliros, Thea, illus. 1999. 10p. (J). (ps-k). pap. 6.95 (978-0-688-16080-7(8)) HarperCollins Pubs.
Howerton, Roger. What's So Hot about the Sun? And Other Questions about Outer Space. 2002. (Illus.). 24p. (J). pap. 5.99 (978-0-89051-364-4(3)) Master Bks.
Hutson, Matt. The Inside Story of the Sun. 2006. (J). 7.80 (978-1-933798-06-6(8)) Sally Ride Science.
Kelly, Harold. El Sol por Dentro. 2002. (Buenas Letras Reading Room Ser.). (SPA.). 24p. (J). lib. bdg. 18.75 (978-0-8239-6514-4(7), Buenas Letra) Rosen Publishing Group, Inc., The.
Kelly, Harold G. Inside the Sun. 2002. (Reading Room Collection). (Illus.). 24p. (J). pap. 4.40 (978-0-8239-8167-0(3)); lib. bdg. 18.75 (978-0-8239-3730-1(5)) Rosen Publishing Group, Inc., The.
Kerrod, Robin. The Sun. 1999. (Planet Library). (Illus.). 32p. (gr. 3-8). lib. bdg. 21.27 (978-0-8225-3901-8(2)) Lerner Publishing Group.
—Sun. 2001. (Illus.). 32p. (J). lib. bdg. 24.25 (978-1-930643-26-0(8)) Chrysalis Education.
—The Sun & the Moon. 2001. (Exploring the Universe Ser.). (Illus.). 48p. (J). lib. bdg. 27.12 (978-0-7398-2818-2(5)) Raintree.
Kerrod, Robin & Posada, Mia. Dandelions: Stars in the Grass. 2003. (Illus.). 32p. (J). pap. 6.95 (978-1-57505-399-8(3)) Lerner Publishing Group.
Kosek, Jane Kelly. What's Inside the Sun? 1999. (What's Inside Library). 24p. (J). (gr. k-4). lib. bdg. 18.75 (978-0-8239-5279-3(7), PowerKids Pr.) Rosen Publishing Group, Inc., The.
Landau, Elaine. The Sun. (True Booktrade;: Space Ser.). 48p. (J). 2008. pap. 6.95 (*978-0-531-14796-2(7)); 2007. (Illus.). (gr. 3-5). lib. bdg. 26.00 (*978-0-531-12568-7(8)) Scholastic Library Publishing. (Children's Pr.).
Lassieur, Allison. The Sun. 2001. (True Bks.). (Illus.). 48p. (J). (gr. 3-5). pap. 6.95 (978-0-516-27188-0(1), Children's Pr.) Scholastic Library Publishing.
Lilly, Melinda. Sun & Moon. 2006. (Rourke Discovery Library). (Illus.). 24p. (gr. 1-4). 14.95 (978-1-59515-405-7(1), 1244276) Rourke Publishing, LLC.
Mayer, Cassie. Sol. 2006. (ENG & SPA., Illus.). 24p. (J). (*978-1-4034-8651-6(4)) Heinemann Library.
—Sol (Sunshine) 2006. (ENG & SPA., Illus.). 24p. (J). pap. (*978-1-4034-8659-2(X)) Heinemann Library.
Mayer, Cassie. Sunshine. 2006. (Illus.). 24p. (J). (978-1-4034-8410-9(4)); pap. 5.99 (978-1-4034-8418-5(X)) Heinemann Library.
McNeil, Niki, et al. HOCPP 1124 the Sun. 2006. spiral bd. 16.00 (*978-1-60308-124-5(0)) In the Hands of a Child.
Miles, Elizabeth. Sunshine. 2004. (J). pap. 7.25 (978-1-4034-5676-2(3)); lib. bdg. 24.21 (978-1-4034-5578-9(3)) Heinemann Library.
Miller, Ron, illus. The Sun. 2002. (Worlds Beyond Ser.). 64p. (gr. 7 up). lib. bdg. 25.90 (978-0-7613-2355-6(4), Twenty-First Century Bks.) Lerner Publishing Group.
Mist, Rosalind. Will the Sun Ever Burn Out? Earth, Sun, & Moon. 2006. (Stargazers Guides Ser.). (Illus.). 48p. (J). (978-1-4034-7707-1(8)); pap. (978-1-4034-7714-9(0)) Heinemann Library.
Mitchell, Melanie. Sun. 2004. (First Step Nonfiction). (J). lib. bdg. 17.76 (978-0-8225-0187-9(2), Lerner Pubns.) Lerner Publishing Group.
Mitchell, Melanie S. Sun. 2004. (First Step Nonfiction Ser.). (Illus.). 24p. (J). (gr. k-2). lib. bdg. 18.60 (978-0-8225-5139-3(X)) Lerner Publishing Group.
—The Sun. 2003. (First Step Nonfiction Ser.). (Illus.). 22p. (J). pap. 3.95 (978-0-8225-3593-5(9), Lerner Pubns.) Lerner Publishing Group.
Morris, Neil. Amazing Sun. 2006. (Amazing World). 28p. (J). (gr. 3-8). 17.95 (978-0-7696-4834-7(7)) School Specialty Publishing.
Murphy, Patricia J. Why Is the Sun So Hot? 2004. (Library of Why?). (Illus.). 24p. (J). lib. bdg. 18.75 (978-0-8239-6235-8(0)) Rosen Publishing Group, Inc., The.
Nadeau, Isaac. Learning about the Movement of the Sun & Other Stars with Graphic Organizers. 2005. (Graphic Organizers in Science Ser.). (Illus.). 24p. (J). 19.95 (978-1-4042-2805-4(5)); pap. (978-1-4042-5040-6(9)) Rosen Publishing Group, Inc., The. (PowerKids Pr.).
Nations, Susan. Hace Sol. 2006. (ENG & SPA.). (J). pap. (*978-0-8368-8116-5(8)); lib. bdg. (*978-0-8368-8111-0(7)) Stevens, Gareth Inc. (Weekly Reader Early Learning Library).
—Let's Read about Sun. 2006. (J). lib. bdg. (*978-0-8368-7807-3(8)); (Illus.). 12p. pap. (*978-0-8368-7812-7(4)) Stevens, Gareth Inc. (Weekly Reader Early Learning Library).
Nelson, Robin. Sunny. 2004. (First Step Nonfiction Ser.). (J). pap. (978-0-8225-5367-0(8), Lerner Pubns.) Lerner Publishing Group.
—A Sunny Day. (First Step Nonfiction Ser.). (Illus.). 24p. (gr. k-2). 2005. lib. bdg. 17.27 (978-0-8225-0176-3(7)); 2003. (J). pap. 4.25 (978-0-8225-1965-2(8)) Lerner Publishing Group.
—Sunny Day. 2001. (gr. k-3). lib. bdg. 11.80 (978-0-613-76620-3(2)) Tandem Library Bks.
Nuestra Estrella: El Sol. (SPA.). (J). 10.00 (978-84-342-1470-5(9)) Parramon Ediciones S.A. ESP. *Dist:* Distribuidora Norma, Inc.
Olien, Rebecca. Exploring the Sun. 2007. (Objects in the Sky Ser.). (Illus.). 24p. (J). (gr. 4-6). lib. bdg. 21.25 (978-1-4042-3464-2(0)); pap. (*978-1-4042-2173-4(5)) Rosen Publishing Group, Inc., The. (PowerKids Pr.).
Orme, Helen & Orme, David. Let's Explore the Sun. 2006. (J). pap. (*978-0-8368-8133-2(8)); lib. bdg. (*978-0-8368-7948-3(1)) Stevens, Gareth Inc.
Our Friend the Sun. 2004. (J). pap. 14.95 (978-1-932762-07-5(8)) Elderberry Press, Inc.
Parker, Steve. The Sun. 2007. (J). lib. bdg. (*978-1-4042-3737-7(2), Rosen Central) Rosen Publishing Group, Inc., The.
Parks, Peggy. The Sun. 2007. (KidHaven Science Library Ser.). (Illus.). 48p. (J). (gr. 4-8). 23.70 (*978-0-7377-3778-3(6), Kidhaven) Thomson Gale.
Phelan, Glen. Earth, Sun, Moon. 2004. (National Geographic Reading Expeditions Ser.). (Illus.). 32p. (J). pap. (978-0-7922-4573-5(3)) National Geographic Society.
Picray, Michael. The Sun. 2002. (Science Matters Ser.). (Illus.). 24p. (J). lib. bdg. 15.95 (978-1-59036-089-7(3)) Weigl Pubs., Inc.
Pipe, Jim. Light: What Is a Shadow? 2005. (Science Starters Ser.). (Illus.). 32p. (J). (gr. 3-7). lib. bdg. 27.10 (978-1-59604-017-5(3)) Stargazer Bks.
—The Sun. 2004. (Earthwise Ser.). (J). lib. bdg. 27.10 (978-1-932799-46-0(X)) Stargazer Bks.
Potts, Steve. The Sun. 2001. (Illus.). 24p. (J). 21.35 (978-1-58340-092-0(3)) Smart Apple Media.
Prinja, Raman. The Sun. 2003. (Universe Ser.). (Illus.). 32p. (J). (gr. 3-5). lib. bdg. 22.79 (978-1-58810-917-0(8)) Heinemann Library.
Rau, Dana Meachen. Hot & Bright: A Book about the Sun. Shea, Denise, illus. 2005. (Amazing Science Ser.). 24p. (J). (ps-k). lib. bdg. 22.60 (978-1-4048-1135-5(4)) Picture Window Bks.
—Sun. 2003. (Our Solar System Ser.). (Illus.). 32p. (J). (gr. 3 up). lib. bdg. 21.26 (978-0-7565-0440-3(6)) Compass Point Bks.
Rhythms of the Sun. 2004. lib. bdg. 30.00 net. (978-0-9749364-0-6(5)) Chuttani, Kabir.
Richards, Julie. It's Sunny! 2004. (J). lib. bdg. 27.10 (978-1-58340-535-2(6)) Smart Apple Media.
Ring, Susan. The Sun. 2003. (Yellow Umbrella Books). (Illus.). 16p. (J). (gr. 1). lib. bdg. 14.60 (978-0-7368-2022-6(1), Pebble Bks.) Capstone Pr., Inc.
—The Sun. 2003. (J). (978-0-7368-1714-1(X)) Yellow Umbrella Pr.
Roberts, Jeremy. Benito Mussolini. 2006. (First Step Nonfiction Ser.). (Illus.). 112p. (J). (gr. 3-7). 29.27 (978-0-8225-2648-3(4), Lerner Pubns.) Lerner Publishing Group.
Rogers, Alan. Sol y Lluvia. 2004. (Pequenos Gigantes Ser.).Tr. of Bright & Breezy. (SPA., Illus.). 16p. (ps-k). 5.95 (978-1-58728-298-0(4), Two Can Publishing) T&N Children's Publishing.
Rosenberg, Pam. Sunny Weather Days. 2006. (Scholastic News Nonfiction Readers Ser.). 24p. (J). (gr. k-2). 19.00 (978-0-531-16770-0(4), Children's Pr.) Scholastic Library Publishing.
Royston, Angela. The Day the Sun Went Out. 2005. (Illus.). 32p. (J). lib. bdg. (978-1-4109-1929-8(3)) Steck-Vaughn.
—The Day the Sun Went Out: The Sun's Energy. 2005. (Illus.). 32p. (J). (gr. 3-5). 7.85 (978-1-4109-1960-1(9)) Steck-Vaughn.
Rushworth, Gary. Our Solar System: The Sun. 2006. (Navigators Ser.). (J). pap. 38.00 (*978-1-4108-6220-4(8)) Benchmark Education Co.
Rustad, Martha E. H. The Sun. Saunders-Smith, Gail, ed. 2002. (Out in Space Ser.). (Illus.). 24p. (J). (gr. k-1). lib. bdg. 15.93 (978-0-7368-1180-4(X), Pebble Bks.) Capstone Pr., Inc.
Ryback, Carol. The Sun. 2006. (Illus.). 24p. (J). pap. (978-0-8368-6351-2(8)); lib. bdg. 19.33 (978-0-8368-6346-8(1)) Stevens, Gareth Inc.
Sasso, Sandy Eisenberg. Adam & Eve's New Day. Rothenberg, Joani Keller, illus. 2006. 24p. (J). bds. 7.99 (978-1-59473-205-8(1)) SkyLight Paths Publishing.
Saunders-Smith, Gail & Guzman Ferrer, Martin Luis. La Luz Del Sol. 2004. (Pebble Bilingual Books). (ENG & SPA., Illus.). 24p. (J). 15.93 (978-0-7368-2310-4(7)) Capstone Pr., Inc.
Schwabacher, Martin. The Sun. 2002. (Blastoff! Ser.). (Illus.). 64p. (J). 28.50 (978-0-7614-1402-5(9), Benchmark Bks.) Cavendish, Marshall Corp.
Sherman, Joseph. Sunshine: A Book about Sunlight. Wesley, Omarr, illus. 2004. (Amazing Science Ser.). 24p. (C). (gr. k-3). 22.60 (978-1-4048-0096-0(4)) Picture Window Bks.
Spangenburg, Ray. Look at the Sun. 2001. (gr. 5-8). lib. bdg. 24.55 (978-0-613-54276-0(2)) Tandem Library Bks.
Spangenburg, Ray & Moser, Kit. The Sun. 2001. (Watts Library). (Illus.). 64p. (J). (gr. 5-7). pap. 8.95 (978-0-531-13991-2(3), Watts, Franklin) Scholastic Library Publishing.
—The Sun. 2001. (Illus.). 63p. (J). (gr. 4-7). lib. bdg. 17.60 (978-0-613-37554-2(8)) Tandem Library Bks.
Spangenburg, Ray, et al. The Sun. 2001. (Space Ser.). (Illus.). 64p. (J). (gr. 5-7). 25.50 (978-0-531-11767-5(7), Watts, Franklin) Scholastic Library Publishing.
Sparrow, Giles. Sun. (Illus.). (J). (gr. 4-6). 2002. 40p. pap. 7.95 (978-1-58810-965-1(8), 91448); 2001. 39p. lib. bdg. 24.22 (978-1-57572-391-4(3)) Heinemann Library.
Steck-Vaughn Staff. Secrets of the Sun: Closer Look. 1999. (J). pap., tchr. ed. (978-0-7398-2505-1(4)) Steck-Vaughn.
Stewart, Melissa. Fun with the Sun. 2004. (Investigate Science Ser.). (Illus.). 32p. (J). (gr. 1 up). lib. bdg. 21.26 (978-0-7565-0593-6(3)) Compass Point Bks.
Stewart, Tobi Stanton. Solar Storms. 2003. (Reading Room Collection). (Illus.). 24p. (J). lib. bdg. 18.75 (978-0-8239-3709-7(7)) Rosen Publishing Group, Inc., The.
Stille, Darlene R. The Sun. 2003. (Planets Ser.). (Illus.). 32p. (J). (gr. 2-6). 27.07 (978-1-59296-055-2(3)) Child's World, Inc.
Sun, 6 vols. (gr. 2-5). 36.95 (978-0-7368-8974-2(4)) Red Brick Learning.

S

The Sun: Level L, 6 vols. (Wonder Worldtm Ser.). 16p. 34.95 (978-0-7802-4607-2(1)) Wright Group, The.

Sun & Its Family. 2000. (McGraw-Hill Science Ser.). (gr. 3 up). (978-0-02-278211-5(7)) Macmillan/McGraw-Hill Schl. Div.

The Sun Science, 6 vols. (gr. k-2). 28.95 (978-0-7368-1750-9(6), Yellow Umbrella Bks.) Capstone Pr., Inc.

A Sunny Day, Vol. 2. 2005. (Our Seasons & Weather Ser.). (YA). (gr. k-3). (978-0-7368-8624-6(9), Pebble Bks.) Capstone Pr., Inc.

A Sunny Day, 6 vols. (gr. k-2). 28.95 (978-0-7368-8630-7(3)) Red Brick Learning.

Tesar, Jenny. The Sun. 1998. (Space Observer Ser.). (Illus.). 24p. (ps-3). lib. bdg. 21.36 (978-1-57572-582-6(7)) Heinemann Library.

Thompson, C. E. Where Does the Sun Go at Night? 1998. (Junior Scientist Ser.). (J). pap. 9.95 (978-0-8362-5329-0(9)) Andrews McMeel Publishing.

Tocci, Salvatore. Experiments with the Sun & the Moon. 2003. (True Bks.). (gr. 3-5). pap. 6.95 (978-0-516-27469-0(4), Children's Pr.) Scholastic Library Publishing.

—Experiments with the Sun & the Moon. 2003. (gr. 3-6). lib. bdg. 15.25 (978-0-613-67892-6(3)) Tandem Library Bks.

Tomecek, Steve. Jump into Science: Sun. 2006. 32p. (J). (ps-3). 6.95 (978-0-7922-5582-6(8), National Geographic Children's Bks.) National Geographic Society.

—Sun. Golembe, Carla, illus. 2001. (Jump into Science Ser.). 32p. (J). (gr. 3-7). 16.95 (978-0-7922-8200-6(0), National Geographic Children's Bks.) National Geographic Society.

Turnbull, Stephanie. Sun, Moon & Stars (Level 2) - Internet Referenced. 2006. 32p. (J). 4.99 (978-0-7945-1399-3(9), Usborne) EDC Publishing.

Vogt. The Sun. 2000. (Our Universe Ser.). (Illus.). (J). pap. (978-0-7398-3344-5(8)) Steck-Vaughn.

Vogt, Gregory L. The Sun. 2000. (Our Universe Ser.). (Illus.). 48p. (YA). (gr. 5-12). lib. bdg. 22.83 (978-0-7398-3105-2(4)) Raintree.

—Sun. (Galaxy Ser.). 24p. (J). pap. 6.95 (978-0-7368-8892-9(6)) Capstone Pr., Inc.

—Sun. 2000. (Galaxy Ser.). (Illus.). 24p. (J). (gr. 2-3). lib. bdg. 18.60 (978-0-7368-0516-2(8), Bridgestone Bks.) Capstone Pr., Inc.

Walker, Niki. The Sun. 2000. (Eye on the Universe Ser.). (Illus.). 32p. (J). (gr. 3-4). pap. (978-0-86505-692-3(7)); lib. bdg. (978-0-86505-682-4(X)) Crabtree Publishing Co.

—Sun. 2001. (gr. 3-6). lib. bdg. 14.10 (978-0-613-33113-5(3)) Tandem Library Bks.

Whitehouse, Patricia. Sun. 2004. (Illus.). 32p. (J). lib. bdg. 24.21 (978-1-4034-5157-6(5)) Heinemann Library.

—The Sun. 2004. (Illus.). 32p. (J). pap. 7.25 (978-1-4034-5661-8(5)) Heinemann Library.

Winrich, Ralph. The Sun. (J). 2008. (***978-1-4296-0721-6(1));*** 2005. (Illus.). 24p. lib. bdg. 21.26 (978-0-7368-3696-8(9)) Capstone Pr., Inc.

World Book, contrib. by. The Sun & Other Stars. 2nd ed. 2006. (Illus.). 64p. (J). (***978-0-7166-9521-9(9)***) World Bk., Inc.

World Book, Inc Staff, contrib. by. The Sun & Other Stars. 2006. (World Book's Solar System & Space Exploration Library). 63p. (J). (978-0-7166-9501-1(4)) World Bk., Inc.

SUN—FICTION

Armstrong, Jennifer. Sunshine, Moonshine. 2003. (Early Step into Reading Ser.). (Illus.). 32p. (J). (ps-1). 11.99 (978-0-679-96442-1(8), Random Hse. Bks. for Young Readers) Random Hse. Children's Bks.

Bailey, Jacqui. Sun up, Sun Down. Lilly, Matthew, illus. (Science Works). 32p. (YA). 8.95 (978-1-4048-1128-7(1)) Picture Window Bks.

Brinkley, Inez. Rainbows & Promises. 2006. 43p. (J). 15.98 (978-1-4116-9579-5(8)) Lulu.com.

Bronn, Charles Heil. The Sun, the Moon, & the Gardener's Son. Kami, Y. Z., illus. 2006. 30p. (J). (gr. 4-12). reprint ed. 16.00 (978-1-4223-5222-9(6)) DIANE Publishing Co.

Bruhac, Joseph. How Chipmunk Got His Stripes. 2001. (gr. k-3). lib. bdg. 15.30 (978-0-613-61631-7(6)) Tandem Library Bks.

Butler, Andrea. El Senor Sol y el Senor Mar, Level 3. Ada, Alma Flor, tr. Hong, Lily T., illus. 2003. (Dejame Leer Ser.). (SPA.). 16p. (J). (ps-3). 6.50 (978-0-673-36302-2(3), Good Year Bks.) Celebration Pr.

Butler, Mary Nyegard. Fantasy Marsh. Butler, Mary Nyegard, illus. 2000. (Illus.). 27p. (J). (ps-2). per. 6.95 (978-0-9701497-0-1(0)) Bay Tree Enterprises.

Byers, Carla Rae. Why Am I Here? Sunshines Story. Kepler, Kit, ed. 2001. Vol. 7. (Illus.). 20p. (gr. 4 up). 7.95 (978-1-930910-02-7(9)) Heyokah Publishing Co.

Cadnum, Michael. Phaeton & the Chariot of the Sun. 2004. (Starfall Ser.). 128p. (J). (gr. 4-7). pap. 16.95 (978-0-439-54533-4(1), Orchard Bks.) Scholastic, Inc.

Canyon, Christopher. John Denver's Sunshine on My Shoulders. 2003. (gr. k-3). lib. bdg. 17.60 (978-0-613-68518-4(0)) Tandem Library Bks.

Climent, Elena. Triste Historia del Sol con Final Feliz. (SPA.). (J). (gr. k-3). pap. 4.76 net. (978-0-8136-1521-9(6), TR4081) Modern Curriculum Pr.

Craig, Gary. Where Does the Sun Go? Craig, Gary, illus. 2006. 40p. (J). 14.95 (978-0-9786813-0-2(4)) Elora Pr.

Denver, John. John Denver's Sunshine on My Shoulders. Canyon, Christopher, illus. 2004. 32p. pap. 8.95 incl. audio compact disk (978-1-58469-050-4(X)) Dawn Pubns.

Desimini, Lisa. The Sun & Moon: A Giant Love Story. 1999. (Illus.). 40p. (YA). (ps-3). pap. 16.95 (978-0-590-18720-6(1), Blue Sky Pr., The) Scholastic, Inc.

Eagle, Golden. Father Sun & Luis the Lizard. l.t. ed. 2005. (Illus.). 22p. (J). per. 9.99 (978-1-59879-026-9(9)) Lifevest Publishing, Inc.

Esteban, Angel. Pablo, Pablo en Busca del Sol. 2003. (SPA.). 48p. (978-84-263-1408-6(2), LV1312) Vives, Luis Editorial (Edelvives) ESP. *Dist:* Lectorum Pubns., Inc.

Forest, Heather & Aesop. The Contest Between the Sun & the Wind: An Aesop's Fable. Gaber, Susan, illus. 2008. 32p. (***978-0-87483-832-9(0)***, August Hse. Little Folk) August Hse. Pubs., Inc.

Freeman, Claire. One Magical Morning. Ho, Louise, illus. 2005. 28p. (J). 16.00 (978-1-56148-472-0(5)) Good Bks.

Gay, Marie-Louise. Mademoiselle Moon. Gay, Marie-Louise, illus. 2006. (Illus.). 32p. pap. 7.95 (978-1-55005-134-6(2)) Fitzhenry & Whiteside, Ltd. CAN. *Dist:* F & W Pubns., Inc.

Gill, Jim. May There Always Be Sunshine: A Traditional. Signorino-Richards, Susie, illus. 2001. 32p. (J). (ps-1). 15.00 (978-0-9679038-6-6(6)) Gill, Jim Music.

Gollub, Matthew. Moon Was at a Fiesta. 2002. (gr. k-3). lib. bdg. 15.25 (978-0-613-70980-4(2)) Tandem Library Bks.

Guess What the Sun Saw? Individual Title Six-Packs. (ps-2). 23.00 (978-0-7635-8808-3(3)) Rigby Education.

Hamilton, Harriet E. The Sunbeam & the Wave. Bowen, Connie, illus. 2000. 33p. (J). (gr. 4-7). 17.95 (978-0-87159-250-7(9)) Unity Schl. of Christianity.

Harcourt School Publishers Staff. Sky Tales Advanced Level. 3rd ed. 2002. (Trophies Reading Program Ser.). (Illus.). pap. 5.10 (978-0-15-323220-6(X)) Harcourt Schl. Pubs.

Hija del Sol y de Luna (Daughter of Sun & Moon) (SPA.). 24p. (J). 4.95 (978-84-246-1610-6(3)) La Galera, S.A. Editorial ESP. *Dist:* AIMS International Bks., Inc.

Hines, Anna Grossnickle. What Can You Do in the Sun? Kliros, Thea, illus. 1999. 10p. (J). (ps-k). pap. 6.95 (978-0-688-16080-7(8)) HarperCollins Pubs.

Hoffman, Mary. Cuentos del Sol, la Luna y las Estrellas: Mitos, Leyendas y Tradiciones de Todas las Culturas. Ray, Jane, illus. 2002. (SPA & ENG.). 80p. (gr. 1-7). 19.95 (978-84-89396-52-4(3)) Blume ESP. *Dist:* Independent Pubs. Group.

Hofmeister, Alan, et al. Mat in the Sun. (Reading for All Learners Ser.). (Illus.). (J). pap. (978-1-56861-094-8(7)) Swift Learning Resources.

Inkpen, Mick. Blue Nose Island Ploo & the Terrible Gnobbler. 2006. (Blue Nose Island Ser.: Bk. 1). (Illus.). (J). (ps). pap. 9.99 (978-0-340-87900-9(9), Hodder & Stoughton) Hodder General Publishing Division GBR. *Dist:* Trafalgar Square Publishing.

—Ploo & the Terrible Gnobbler. 2006. (Blue Nose Island Ser.: Bk. 1). (Illus.). (J). (ps). 19.99 (978-0-340-85573-7(8), Hodder & Stoughton) Hodder General Publishing Division GBR. *Dist:* Trafalgar Square Publishing.

Johnson, Angela. A Cool Moonlight. 2005. 144p. (J). (gr. 3-6). reprint ed. pap. 5.99 (978-0-14-240284-9(2), Puffin) Penguin Group (USA) Inc.

—A Cool Moonlight. 2005. 133p. (J). (ps-7). per. 12.64 (978-0-606-33124-1(7)) Tandem Library Bks.

Kalz, Jill. Henry Shortbull Swallows the Sun. Erkocak, Sahin, illus. 2007. (Pfeffernut County Ser.). 32p. (J). (gr. k-2). lib. bdg. 23.93 (***978-1-4048-3695-2(0)***) Picture Window Bks.

Kleven, Elisa. Sun Bread. 2004. (gr. k-3). lib. bdg. 15.30 (978-0-613-83005-8(9)) Tandem Library Bks.

Kline, Robert. First Sun, Last Sun. 2002. 316p. (YA). per. 13.00 (978-0-9652682-4-0(1)) Galaxy Bks., Inc.

Kochersperger, Jenny. Good Morning, Sun. l.t. ed. 2002. (Illus.). 32p. (J). (gr. k-4). 16.95 (978-0-9715884-0-0(6)) Beyond Borders Bks.

Layman, John S. Armageddon & Son. 2005. (Illus.). 96p. (YA). pap. 9.95 (978-1-932664-33-1(5)) Oni Pr., Inc.

MacDiarmid, Jim. Akerta. Manutoli, Sophie, tr. Andrew, John & Horesh, David, illus. 1998. Tr. of Sun. (ESK.). 16p. (J). (gr. k-3). pap. 6.00 (978-1-58084-047-7(7)) Lower Kuskokwim Schl. District.

Mackinnon, Mairi. Sun & the Wind. 2007. (First Reading Level 1 Ser.). 32p. (J). 8.99 (***978-0-7945-1811-0(7)***, Usborne) EDC Publishing.

McClulre, Brian D. The Sun & the Moon. 2006. (Illus.). 36p. (J). 14.95 (978-1-933426-09-9(8)) Universal Flag Publishing.

Melancon, Gail. Good Morning Sunshine. 2006. pap. 13.99 (978-1-4196-2105-5(X)) BookSurge, LLC.

Mollel, Tololwa M. Kitoto the Mighty. Frost, Kristi, illus. 1998. 28p. (J). (gr. k-3). 14.95 (978-0-7737-3019-9(2)) Stoddart Kids CAN. *Dist:* Fitzhenry & Whiteside, Ltd.

O'Day, Joseph E. I Like Sunshine! Foster, Ron, illus. 2007. (J). (***978-1-929039-41-8(7)***) Ambassador Bks., Inc.

Paratore, Coleen. Catching the Sun. Catalanotto, Peter, illus. 2008. (J). (***978-1-57091-720-2(5)***) Charlesbridge Publishing, Inc.

—Catching the Sun. 2010. (J). (978-0-618-45780-9(1)) Houghton Mifflin Co.

Pittis, Arthur M. Sun So Hot I Froze to Death: A Waldorf Reader for Advanced Fourth Grade. Mitchell, David S., ed. Peacock, Ausa M., illus. 2005. (J). bds. 12.00 (978-1-888365-65-8(X)) Assn. of Waldorf Schls. of North America Pubns. (AWSNA).

Pla Valencia, Nancy. Under Bright Rays & Sparkling Stars. Pla Valencia, Nancy, illus. 1999. (J). (978-1-56492-283-0(9)) Laredo Publishing Co., Inc.

Polacco, Patricia. I Can Hear the Sun. Polacco, Patricia, illus. 1999. (Illus.). 40p. (J). (ps-3). pap. 5.99 (978-0-698-11857-7(X), Putnam Juvenile) Penguin Group (USA) Inc.

—I Can Hear the Sun. 1999. (J). (978-0-606-17412-1(5)); lib. bdg. 14.15 (978-0-613-22873-2(1)) Tandem Library Bks.

Pugliano-Martin, Carol. How Davy Crockett Moved the Sun: An AMER Tall Tale. 2006. 42.00 (***978-1-4108-6168-9(6)***) Benchmark Education Co.

Rivais, Yak. Contes du Cimetiere au Soleil Couchant. 2000. Tr. of Tales of the Cemetery at Sunset. (FRE.). (J). pap. 11.95 (978-2-09-282012-4(5)) Nathan, Fernand FRA. *Dist:* Distribooks, Inc.

Rockwood, Joyce. To Spoil the Sun. rev. ed. 2003. 192p. (J). 16.95 (978-0-8050-7372-0(8), Holt, Henry & Co. Bks. For Young Readers) Holt, Henry & Co.

Root, Phyllis. Lucia & the Light. GrandPré, Mary, illus. 2006. 40p. (J). (gr. k-3). 16.99 (978-0-7636-2296-1(6)) Candlewick Pr.

Rosario, Joann. Where Did Sabrina Go? Rosario, Joann, illus. 2004. (Illus.). 13p. (J). (ps-5). pap. 10.00 (978-0-9758746-1-5(6)) J.G.R. Enterprises.

Salem, Lynn & Stewart, Josie. The Sun's Magic. Terry, Christy, illus. 2000. 8p. (J). (gr. k-2). pap. 3.75 (978-1-58323-013-8(0), Seedling Pubns.) Continental Pr., Inc.

Santillo, LuAnn. The Sun. Santillo, LuAnn, ed. 2003. (Half-Pint Kids Readers Ser.). (Illus.). 7p. (J). (ps-1). pap. (978-1-59256-047-9(4)) Half-Pint Kids, Inc.

Stead, Judy, illus. Mister Sun. 2006. (J). (978-1-58987-097-0(2)) Kindermusik International.

Steck-Vaughn Staff. Folktales & Legends: Moon, Sun. 1998. (Illus.). (J). pap. (978-0-8172-8646-0(2)) Steck-Vaughn.

Straight, Susan. Where's Your Sun? 1999. 32p. (J). (978-0-7868-2157-0(4)) Hyperion Bks. for Children.

—Where's Your Sun? 1999. 32p. (J). (978-0-7868-0186-2(7)) Hyperion Pr.

The Sun in the Sky. 2003. lib. bdg. 12.99 (978-0-9740997-0-5(8)) Lisa The Weather Wonder Inc.

Tomos, Angharad. Diffodd Yr Haul. 2005. (WEL., Illus.). 48p. pap. (978-0-86243-080-1(1)) Y Lolfa.

Tracey & the Sun: Individual Title, 6 packs. (Sails Literacy Ser.). 16p. (gr. 2-3). 27.00 (978-0-7578-0710-7(0)) Rigby Education.

Tsinajinnie, Veronica, et al. Johonaa'éí: Bringer of Dawn. Howard, Winston, illus. 2008. (ENG & NAV.). 32p. 17.95 (978-1-893354-54-8(7)) Salina Bookshelf.

Viola, Karen & Reader's Digest Staff. Good Night Sun, Hello Moon. Chung, Chi, illus. 2004. 16p. (J). bds. 12.99 (978-0-7944-0356-0(5), Reader's Digest Children's Bks.) Reader's Digest Children's Publishing, Inc.

West, Linzi, illus. Soft Sand Warm Sun. 2005. 12p. (J). bds. 5.95 (978-1-84507-342-8(8)) Lincoln, Frances Ltd. GBR. *Dist:* Perseus Distribution.

Whitethorne, Baje, Sr., illus. Sunpainters: Eclipse of the Navajo Sun. 2002. 32p. 17.95 (978-1-893354-33-3(4)) Salina Bookshelf.

Wilhelm, Hans. Hello, Sun! Wilhelm, Hans, illus. 2005. (Illus.). 32p. (gr. k-2). 15.25 (978-1-57505-348-6(9)) Lerner Publishing Group.

Williams, Vereca R. Thank God for Sunshine. White, Malynda, ed. 1998. (Illus.). 64p. (J). (gr. 1-4). pap. 12.00 (978-1-892477-00-2(9)) Nottinghill Bks.

Zeder, Suzan. The Taste of Sunrise. 1999. pap. 7.00 (978-0-87602-378-5(2)) Anchorage Pr.

SUN—RADIATION

see Solar Radiation

SUN-DIALS

see Sundials

SUN GLASSES

see Eyeglasses

SUNDAY

see Sabbath

SUNDIALS

Trionfante, Jeffrey V. Sunclocks: Sundials to Make & Use. Trionfante, Jeffrey V., illus. 1999. (Illus.). 56p. (J). (gr. 3-9). pap. 12.95 (978-1-893812-51-2(0)) JVT Pubns. & Creations.

SUNFLOWERS

Bourbon-Ramirez, Melissa. The Flight of the Sunflower. Guevara, Linda L., ed. Takvorian, Nadine, illus. 2002. 32p. (J). (ps-5). 16.95 (978-0-9700863-0-3(X)) All About Kids Publishing.

Cooper, Jason. Sunflower. 2003. (Life Cycles II Ser.). (Illus.). 24p. (J). 25.64 (978-1-58952-708-9(9)) Rourke Publishing, LLC.

Diary of a Sunflower: Individual Title Six-Packs. (Story Steps Ser.). (gr. k-2). 32.00 (978-0-7635-9839-6(9)) Rigby Education.

Franks, Katie. Sunflowers up Close. 2008. (J). lib. bdg. (***978-1-4042-4141-1(8)***, PowerKids Pr.) Rosen Publishing Group, Inc., The.

Ganeri, Anita. From Seed to Sunflower. 2006. (Heinemann First Library). (Illus.). 32p. (J). (978-1-4034-7857-3(0)); pap. (978-1-4034-7866-5(X)) Heinemann Library.

El Girasol: Por Dentro y Por Fuera. 2004. (SPA., Illus.). 32p. lib. bdg. 21.25 (978-1-4042-2868-9(3)) Rosen Publishing Group, Inc., The.

Gunderson, Jessica. The Sunflower Farmer. Haugen, Ryan, illus. 2007. (J). lib. bdg. (***978-1-4048-2293-1(3)***) Picture Window Bks.

Hibbert, Clare. Life of a Sunflower. 2004. (Raintree Perspectives Ser.). (Illus.). 32p. (J). lib. bdg. 25.70 (978-1-4109-0539-0(X)) Raintree.

—The Life of a Sunflower. 2004. (Illus.). pap. 7.50 (978-1-4109-0927-5(1)) Raintree.

—The Life of a Sunflower 6-Pack. 2004. (Illus.). pap. 40.50 (978-1-4109-0934-3(4)) Raintree.

Hipp, Andrew. Sunflower. 2004. (Getting into Nature Ser.). (Illus.). 32p. (J). lib. bdg. 21.25 (978-0-8239-4210-7(4)) Rosen Publishing Group, Inc., The.

Legg, Gerald. From Seed to Sunflower. Scrace, Carolyn, illus. 1998. (Life Cycles Ser.). 32p. (J). (gr. k-2). pap. 6.95 (978-0-531-15334-5(7)); 25.50 (978-0-531-14492-3(5)) Scholastic Library Publishing. (Watts, Franklin).

Life Cycles - from Seed to Sunflower. 2005. (J). per. 8.95 (978-1-59566-145-6(X)) QEB Publishing Inc.

Morgan, Sally. From Seed to Sunflower. 2002. (How Things Grow Ser.). (Illus.). 32p. (J). lib. bdg. (978-1-930643-89-5(6)) Chrysalis Education.

—Sunflowers & Other Plants. 2001. (Illus.). 32p. (J). lib. bdg. 24.25 (978-1-930643-46-8(2)) Chrysalis Education.

Parker, Victoria. Life as a Sunflower. 2003. (Raintree Sprouts Ser.). (Illus.). 24p. (J). pap. 5.50 (978-1-4109-0655-7(8)); lib. bdg. 18.56 (978-1-4109-0629-8(9)) Raintree.

—Life as a Sunflower. 2003. (ps-2). lib. bdg. 13.55 (978-0-613-78264-7(X)) Tandem Library Bks.

Reid, Barbara. Seed to Sunflower: A First Look Board Book. Crysler, Ian, photos by. 2004. (Illus.). 12p. (J). (gr. k-2). reprint ed. 10.00 (978-0-7567-7853-8(0)) DIANE Publishing Co.

Royston, Angela. Sunflower. 2002. (Life Cycle of a... Ser.). (Illus.). 32p. (J). (gr. k-2). pap. 6.95 (978-1-57572-475-1(8), 90464) Heinemann Library.

Scholastic, Inc. Staff. Diary of a Sunflower: Teaching Kit. Cooper, Terry, ed. 2000. (Super Science Readers Ser.). 16p. pap. 10.95 (978-0-439-18606-3(4)) Scholastic, Inc.

Schwartz, David M. Sunflower. Kuhn, Dwight, photos by. 2001. (Springboards into Science Ser.). (Illus.). 24p. (J). (gr. 1 up). lib. bdg. 20.67 (978-0-8368-2980-8(8)) Stevens, Gareth Inc.

Smith, Ian. How Does it Grow? From Seed to Sunflower. 2004. (Illus.). 24p. (J). lib. bdg. 15.95 (978-1-59566-016-9(X)) QEB Publishing Inc.

Stewart, David. How a Seed Grows into a Sunflower. (Amaze Ser.). 32p. (J). 2008. pap. 8.95 (***978-0-531-20453-5(7));*** 2007. spiral bd. 26.00 (***978-0-531-20442-9(1)***) Scholastic Library Publishing. (Children's Pr.).

Tagliaferro, Linda. The Life Cycle of a Sunflower. 2007. (Pebble Plus Ser.). (Illus.). 24p. (J). (978-0-7368-6714-6(7), 1264880) Capstone Pr., Inc.

Watts, Barrie. Sunflower. 2003. 32p. (J). lib. bdg. 24.25 (978-1-58340-232-0(2)) Smart Apple Media.

SUNFLOWERS—FICTION

Boland, Janice. Girasoles. Romo, Alberto, tr. Veno, Joe, illus. 1998. (Books for Young Learners).Tr. of Sunflowers. (SPA.). 8p. (J). (gr. k-2). pap. 5.00 (978-1-57274-203-1(8), A2860) Owen, Richard C. Pubs., Inc.

Doran, Margie. Sunflower Serenade. 2001. (Illus.). 14p. (J). (ps-3). 10.00 (978-0-9629270-7-2(4)) C&D Productions JimMar, Inc.

Higgs, Liz Curtis. The Sunflower Parable. 10th anniv. ed. 2007. 32p. (J). 7.99 (978-1-4003-0845-3(3)) Nelson, Thomas Inc.

Kieffer, Eduardo Gudino. Giraluna. 2001. (SPA.). (gr. k-3). lib. bdg. 15.25 (978-0-613-64512-6(X)) Tandem Library Bks.

Maile's Sunflower. 2nd ed. 2006. (J). (***978-0-9787864-0-3(8)***) Acrobatic Cats Publishing.

My Sunflowers. 2003. (J). per. (978-1-57657-897-1(6)) Paradise Pr., Inc.

Ochiltree, Dianne. Sunflowers Measure Up! 2003. (Hello Math Reader Ser.). (Illus.). (J). (978-0-439-24228-8(2)) Scholastic, Inc.

Preller, James. Cardinal & Sunflower. Lee, Huy Voun, illus. 1998. 32p. (J). (gr. k-3). 14.95 (978-0-06-026222-8(2)) HarperCollins Pubs.

Stewart, Dianne. El Regalo del Sol. Daly, Jude, illus. 2000. (SPA.). 28p. (J). (ps-3). pap. 6.99 (978-980-257-258-8(6), EK(1977)) Ekare, Ediciones VEN. *Dist:* Kane/Miller Bk. Pubs., Inc., Lectorum Pubns., Inc.

Swanson, Susan Marie. To Be Like the Sun. Chodos-Irvine, Margaret, illus. 2008. 40p. (J). 16.00 (***978-0-15-205796-1(X)***) Harcourt Trade Pubs.

Wagner, Larry. The Adventures of Sally Sunflower. 2004. 23p. pap. 14.95 (978-1-4137-4009-7(X)) PublishAmerica, Inc.

SUNKEN CITIES

see Cities and Towns, Ruined, Extinct, Etc.

SUNKEN TREASURE

see Buried Treasure

SUNNYDALE (CALIF. : IMAGINARY PLACE)—FICTION

Navarro, Yvonne. Willow Files. 1999. (gr. 7-12). lib. bdg. 13.00 (978-0-613-22639-4(9)) Tandem Library Bks.

SUPERIOR, LAKE

Fondrk, Benjamin. Lake Superior & the North. 2004. per. 10.00 (978-0-9673483-0-8(7)) Poseidon Publishing Co.

Stewart, Melissa. Life in a Lake: Lake Superior. 2003. (Ecosystems in Action Ser.). (Illus.). 72p. (J). (gr. 6-12). 26.60 (978-0-8225-2138-9(5)) Lerner Publishing Group.

Ylvisaker, Anne. Lake Superior. 2003. (Fact Finders Ser.). (Illus.). 32p. (J). lib. bdg. 22.60 (978-0-7368-2212-1(7), Bridgestone Bks.) Capstone Pr., Inc.

SUPERIOR, LAKE—FICTION

Erdrich, Louise. The Birchbark House. Erdrich, Louise, illus. 2002. (Illus.). 256p. (gr. 4-17). pap. 6.99 (978-0-7868-1454-1(3)) Hyperion Paperbacks for Children.

—The Birchbark House. 2002. (gr. 5-8). lib. bdg. 15.00 (978-0-613-59384-7(7)) Tandem Library Bks.

—The Game of Silence. 2005. (Illus.). 272p. (J). lib. bdg. 16.89 (978-0-06-029790-9(5)); 15.99 (978-0-06-029789-3(1)) HarperCollins Pubs.

—The Game of Silence. l.t. ed. 2005. (Illus.). 319p. (J). (gr. 3-7). per. 22.95 (978-0-7862-7768-1(8), Large Print Pr.); 2000. 272p. (YA). (gr. 7-12). 20.95 (978-0-7862-2178-3(X)) Thorndike Pr.

Ernst, Kathleen. Trouble at Fort la Pointe. 2000. (American Girl Collection). (Illus.). (J). (978-0-606-20956-4(5)) Tandem Library Bks.

Lewis, Anne Margaret. Gitchi Gumee. Chaney Fritz, Kathleen, illus. 2006. (J). 18.95 (978-0-9749145-9-6(2)) Mackinac Island Pr., Inc.

Martin, Jacqueline Briggs. On Sand Island. Johnson, David A., illus. 2003. 32p. (J). (gr. k-3). tchr. ed. 16.00 (978-0-618-23151-5(X)) Houghton Mifflin Co. Trade & Reference Div.

Root, Phyllis. If You Want to See a Caribou. Meyer, Jim, illus. 2004. 32p. (J). (gr. k-3). tchr. ed. 16.00 (978-0-618-39314-5(5)) Houghton Mifflin Co. Trade & Reference Div.

Wargin, Kathy-Jo. The Voyageur's Paddle. Geister, David, illus. rev. ed. 2007. 40p. (J). (ps-5). 17.95 (978-1-58536-007-9(4)) Sleeping Bear Pr.

SUPERMAN (FICTITIOUS CHARACTER)—FICTION

Allred, Laura, illus. The Superman: Madman Hullabaloo! 1998. 96p. (YA). (gr. 7 up). pap. 8.95 (978-1-56971-301-3(4)) Dark Horse Comics.

Animal Rage. 2003. (gr. 7-12). lib. bdg. 14.15 (978-0-613-50635-9(9)) Tandem Library Bks.

Augustyn, Brian. The One-Man Justice League: 8x8 Stiorybook. Rousseau, Craig, illus. 2003. (Justice League Ser.). 24p. (J). per. 2.99 (978-1-4037-0297-5(7)) Dalmatian Pr.

Byrne, John A. Generations: An Imaginary Tale. Crain, Dale, ed. Byrne, John, illus. rev. ed. 2000. (Superman/Batman Ser.). 208p. pap. 17.95 (978-1-56389-605-7(2)) DC Comics.

Chaykin, Howard. Son of Superman. Tischman, David, illus. 1999. 95p. (YA). 24.95 (978-1-56389-595-1(1)) DC Comics.

DC Comics Staff. Superman Morphing Journal. 2004. (Illus.). 128p. 10.95 (978-0-8118-4198-6(7)) Chronicle Bks. LLC.

—They Saved Luthor's Brain. rev. ed. 2000. (Superman Ser.). (Illus.). 160p. pap. 14.95 (978-1-56389-601-9(X)) DC Comics.

DC Comics Staff & Simonson, Louise. Superman Returns: The Junior Novel. novel ed. 2006. (Illus.). 176p. (J). (ps-17). pap. 4.99 (978-0-316-17805-1(5)) Little, Brown Bks. for Young Readers.

Dorling Kindersley Publishing Staff & Wallace, Daniel. Superman Returns Visual Guide. 2006. (Illus.). 64p. (J). 17.99 (978-0-7566-2066-0(X)) Dorling Kindersley Publishing, Inc.

Finger, Bill, et al. Superman. Swan, Curt, illus. rev. ed. 2005. (Showcase Presents Ser.: Vol. 1). 560p. (YA). pap. 9.99 (978-1-4012-0758-8(8)) DC Comics.

LeapFrog Staff, compiled by. Superman/Read All about It. 2001. (J). (ps-2). spiral bd. 14.99 (978-1-58605-112-9(1)) LeapFrog Enterprises, Inc.

Marvel Staff. The Clone Trap. 2007. 24p. (J). pap. 3.99 (978-0-696-23477-4(7)) Meredith Bks.

Meredith Books Staff. Superman Returns. Curry, Don, ed. 2007. (I Can Find It Ser.). 24p. (J). pap. 4.99 ***(*978-0-696-23728-7(8))*** Meredith Bks.

Meredith Books Staff, ed. Doom in A Box. 2008. 24p. pap. 3.99 ***(*978-0-696-23956-4(6))*** Meredith Bks.

—Robo-Monster. 2008. 24p. pap. 3.99 ***(*978-0-696-23957-1(4))*** Meredith Bks.

Meredith Books Staff & Curry, Don, eds. Be a Hero! movie tie-in ed. 2006. (Superman Returns Ser.). (Illus.). 24p. (J). pap. 3.99 (978-0-696-22904-6(8)) Meredith Bks.

—Coming Home. movie tie-in ed. 2006. (Superman Returns Ser.). (Illus.). 32p. (J). pap. 3.99 (978-0-696-22961-9(7)) Meredith Bks.

—I Am Superman! 2006. (Superman Returns Ser.). (Illus.). 24p. (J). pap. 3.99 (978-0-696-22905-3(6)) Meredith Bks.

—Superman Returns. movie tie-in ed. 2006. (I Can Find It Ser.). 22p. (J). 7.99 (978-0-696-22903-9(X)) Meredith Bks.

—Superman Returns: Deluxe Sound Storybook. movie tie-in ed. 2006. 22p. (J). 15.95 (978-0-696-22897-1(1)) Meredith Bks.

—Superman Returns: Earthquake in Metropolis! 2006. (Superman Returns Ser.). (Illus.). 32p. (J). pap. 3.99 (978-0-696-22909-1(9)) Meredith Bks.

—Superman Returns: The Last Son of Krypton. movie tie-in ed. 2006. (Superman Returns Ser.). (Illus.). 88p. (J). pap. 4.99 (978-0-696-22959-6(5)) Meredith Bks.

—Superman Returns Movie Storybook. movie tie-in ed. 2006. (Illus.). 48p. (J). pap. 7.99 (978-0-696-22901-5(3)) Meredith Bks.

—Superman Returns Stencil Activity Book. movie tie-in ed. 2006. 22p. (J). bds. 9.95 (978-0-696-22899-5(8)) Meredith Bks.

—Thank You, Superman! movie tie-in ed. 2006. (Superman Returns Ser.). 14p. (J). bds. 7.99 (978-0-696-22902-2(1)) Meredith Bks.

Raucci, Richard & Wolverton, Mark. The Science of Superman. 2002. (Illus.). 256p. 22.95 (978-0-7434-5273-1(9)) ibooks, Inc.

Siegel, Jerry. Archives. Shuster, Joe, illus. rev. ed. 2000. (Superman Archives Ser.: Vol. 5). 224p. 49.95 (978-1-56389-602-6(8)) DC Comics.

Superman. 2001. (Look & Find Ser.). (Illus.). (J). lib. bdg. 15.95 (978-1-56674-299-3(4)) Forest Hse. Publishing Co., Inc.

Superman: The Visual Dictionary. 1999. 64p. (J). pap. 19.95 (978-0-7894-4702-9(9)) Dorling Kindersley Publishing, Inc.

SUPERMARKETS

Beylon, Cathy. At the Supermarket. 2004. (Dover Coloring Bks.). (Illus.). 32p. (J). pap. 2.95 (978-0-486-43323-3(4)) Dover Pubns., Inc.

Canizares, Susan & Einhorn, Kama. Supermarket. 2000. (Scholastic Placebook Ser.). (Illus.). 16p. (J). pap. (978-0-439-15368-3(9)) Scholastic, Inc.

Firestone, Mary. Supermarket Managers. 2003. (Community Helpers Ser.). (Illus.). 24p. (J). (gr. 1-2). lib. bdg. (978-0-7368-1614-4(3) , Bridgestone Bks.) Capstone Pr., Inc.

Hoena, B. A. A Visit to the Supermarket. 2004. (Pebble Plus, Let's Visit Ser.). (Illus.). 24p. (J). 13.95 (978-0-7368-2393-7(X) , Pebble Bks.) Capstone Pr., Inc.

Johnston, Marianne. Let's Visit the Supermarket. 2000. (Our Community Ser.). (Illus.). 24p. (J). (gr. 3). lib. bdg. 18.75 (978-0-8239-5436-0(6) , PowerKids Pr.) Rosen Publishing Group, Inc., The.

Leeper, Angela. The Grocery Store. 2004. (Field Trip! Ser.). (Illus.). 24p. (J). pap. 5.75 (978-1-4034-5169-9(9)) Heinemann Library.

—To a Grocery Store. 2004. (Field Trip! Ser.). (Illus.). 24p. (J). lib. bdg. (978-1-4034-5163-7(X)) Heinemann Library.

Mattern, Joanne. I Use Math at the Store. 2005. (Illus.). 24p. (J). pap. (978-0-8368-4863-2(2)); lib. bdg. 19.33 (978-0-8368-4856-4(X)) Stevens, Gareth Inc.

—I Use Math at the Store: Uso Las Matematicas en la Tienda. 2005. (Illus.). 24p. (J). (SPA.). pap. (978-0-8368-6008-5(X)); (ENG & SPA., lib. bdg. 19.33 (978-0-8368-6001-6(2)) Stevens, Gareth Inc.

Out & about at the Supermarket. (Field Trips Ser.). 24p. (J). 8.95 (978-1-4048-0200-1(2)) Picture Window Bks.

Saunders, Gail. The Supermarket. 1998. (Growing Flowers Ser.). 24p. (J). (gr. k-2). pap. 13.25 (978-0-516-21321-7(0) , Children's Pr.) Scholastic Library Publishing.

Saunders-Smith, Gail. The Supermarket. 2005. (Transportation Ser.). 24p. (YA). (gr. k-3). pap. (978-1-56065-839-9(8) , Pebble Bks.) Capstone Pr., Inc.

Schaefer, Lola M. Supermarket. 2000. (Who Works Here? Ser.). (Illus.). 32p. (J). (gr. 1-3). lib. bdg. 21.36 (978-1-57572-518-5(5)) Heinemann Library.

Shea, Kitty. Out & About at the Supermarket. Shipe, Becky, illus. 2004. (Field Trips Ser.). 24p. (C). (gr. k-3). 23.93 (978-1-4048-0295-7(9)) Picture Window Bks.

The Super Supermarket Plan: Individual Title Six-Packs. (gr. k-1). 23.00 (978-0-7635-8844-1(X)) Rigby Education.

The Supermarket, 6 vols. (gr. k-2). 28.95 (978-0-7368-8007-7(0)) Red Brick Learning.

SUPERMARKETS—FICTION

CINAR Corporation Staff, illus. Caillou at the Market. 2002. (Caillou Ser.). 26p. (J). pap. (978-2-89450-294-5(X)) Chouette Publishing.

Corbet, Robert. Shelf Life. 2005. 190p. (YA). 16.95 (978-0-8027-8959-4(5)) Walker & Co.

Curry, Don, ed. Foodfight! 2008. (I Can Find It Ser.). 22p. (J). 7.99 (978-0-696-23425-5(4)) Meredith Bks.

—Foodfight! Deluxe Sound Storybook. 2008. 22p. (J). 15.95 (978-0-696-23424-8(6)) Meredith Bks.

Doyle, Charlotte. Supermarket! Westcott, Nadine Bernard, tr. Westcott, Nadine Bernard, illus. 2004. (Super Study Picture Book Ser.). 24p. (J). (gr. k-ps). 8.99 (978-0-7636-2218-3(4)) Candlewick Pr.

Elya, Susan Middleton. Bebé Goes Shopping. Salerno, Steven, illus. 2006. (ENG & SPA.). 40p. (J). 16.00 (978-0-15-205426-7(X)) Harcourt Trade Pubs.

Elya, Susan Middleton. Bebe Goes Shopping. Salerno, Steven, illus. 2008. 36p. (J). pap. 6.00 ***(*978-0-15-206142-5(8)*** , Voyager Bks./Libros Viajeros) Harcourt Children's Bks.

Food from the Farm: Individual Title Six-Packs. (ps-2). 23.00 (978-0-7635-8994-3(2)) Rigby Education.

Golden Books Staff. The Secret's Inside! 2007. (Illus.). 16p. (J). (ps-3). pap. 6.99 (978-0-375-83792-0(2) , Golden Bks.) Random Hse. Children's Bks.

—Top Dog. 2007. (Deluxe Coloring Book Ser.). (Illus.). 64p. (J). (ps-3). pap. 3.99 (978-0-375-83708-1(6) , Golden Bks.) Random Hse. Children's Bks.

In the Supermarket: Individual Title, 6 Packs. (Chiquilibros Ser.). (gr. k-1). 23.00 (978-0-7635-0453-3(X)) Rigby Education.

Krakower, Dora B. The Dudley Doohinkle Grocery Store. 2000. 83p. (J). pap. 10.95 (978-0-9643273-4-4(1)) AZURE/BMI.

McKee, David. Who Is Mrs. Green? 2003. (Illus.). 32p. (J). 19.99 (978-1-84270-092-1(8)) Andersen GBR. *Dist:* Independent Pubs. Group.

—Who Is Mrs Green? 2005. (Illus.). 32p. (J). pap. 9.99 (978-1-84270-429-5(X)) Trafalgar Square Publishing.

Spitzer, Linda & Myers, Sarah. Tales of the Paper Bag Fairies/Color Version. 2005. 54p. (J). pap. 14.95 (978-1-4116-4095-5(0)) Lulu.com.

Trimble, Irene. Foodfight! Jr Novel. 2007. (Junior Novel Ser.). (Illus.). 128p. (J). (gr. 4-7). mass mkt. 4.99 (978-0-375-83794-4(9) , Golden Bks.) Random Hse. Children's Bks.

When Dad Got Lost: Individual Title, 6 packs. (ps-2). 27.00 (978-0-7635-9484-8(9)) Rigby Education.

SUPERNATURAL

see also Spirits

Baddiel, Ivor & Blezard, Tracey. The Supernatural. 1999. (Mysterious World Bks.). (Illus.). 32p. (YA). (gr. 5 up). pap. 6.95 (978-0-7641-0906-5(5)) Barron's Educational Series, Inc.

Blackwood, Gary L. Extraordinary Events & Oddball Occurrences. 1999. (Secrets of the Unexplained Ser.). (Illus.). 80p. (J). (gr. 5-9). lib. bdg. 29.93 (978-0-7614-0748-5(0) , Benchmark Bks.) Cavendish, Marshall Corp.

Day, Jon. Arswyd Mawr! Yr Anhygoel A'r Anesboniadwy. 2005. (WEL., Illus.). 31p. (978-0-86381-415-0(8)) Gwasg Carreg Gwalch.

—Supernatural. 2004. (Illus.). 32p. pap. (978-1-904516-01-9(7)) Chrysalis Children's Bks.

Ford, Arielle. Hot Chocolate for the Mystical Teen: 101 True Stories of Angels, Miracles, & H. 2000. (gr. 7-12). lib. bdg. 22.20 (978-0-613-72567-5(0)) Tandem Library Bks.

Gardner, Robert. What's So Super about the Supernatural? 1998. (Single Titles Ser.). 80p. (YA). (gr. 4-7). lib. bdg. 24.90 (978-0-7613-3228-2(6) , Twenty-First Century Bks.) Lerner Publishing Group.

Hall, Katy, pseud. Creepy Riddles. 2000. (Easy-to-Read Ser.). (J). 10.79 (978-0-606-20230-5(7)) Tandem Library Bks.

Mason, Paul. Investigating the Supernatural. 2004. (Forensic Files Ser.). (Illus.). 48p. (J). pap. 8.50 (978-1-4034-5472-0(8)) Heinemann Library.

—The Supernatural. 2004. (Forensic Files Ser.). (Illus.). 48p. (J). lib. bdg. 27.07 (978-1-4034-4832-3(9)) Heinemann Library.

Netzley, Patricia D. The Curse of King Tut. 2000. (Mystery Library). (Illus.). 96p. (YA). (gr. 4-12). 27.45 (978-1-56006-684-2(9) , Lucent Bks.) Thomson Gale.

Raintree Steck-Vaughn Staff. Mysterious Healing. 1999. (Unsolved Mysteries Ser.). (Illus.). (J). pap. 8.05 (978-0-8172-5851-1(5)) Steck-Vaughn.

Stevens, C. J. The Supernatural Side of Maine. 2003. (YA). 12.00 (978-1-882425-16-7(2)) Wade, John Pub.

World Book, Inc Staff, contrib. by. Tales of Mystery & the Unknown: A Supplement to Childcraft— the How & Why Library. 2006. (Illus.). 208p. (J). (978-0-7166-0616-1(X)) World Bk., Inc.

SUPERNATURAL—FICTION

Adamchuk, Rachelle G. Disappearance: The First Part of Trickery & Honest Deception. 2006. 169p. pap. ***(*978-1-4120-8991-3(3))*** Trafford Publishing.

Alexander, Lloyd. The Rope Trick. 2002. 192p. (J). (gr. 3-6). 16.99 (978-0-525-47020-5(4) , Dutton Juvenile) Penguin Group (USA) Inc.

Alexander, Lloyd, contrib. by. The Rope Trick. 2004. 195p. (J). (gr. 5). lib. bdg. 13.64 (978-0-606-30794-9(X)) Tandem Library Bks.

Allende, Isabel. City of the Beasts. Peden, Margaret Sayers, tr. from SPA. 2002. Tr. of Ciudad de las Bestias. 416p. (J). (gr. 5 up). 19.99 (978-0-06-050918-7(X)) HarperCollins Pubs.

—City of the Beasts. l.t. ed. 2002. Tr. of Ciudad de las Bestias. 400p. (J). (gr. 5). pap. 19.99 (978-0-06-051195-1(8)) HarperCollins Pubs.

—City of the Beasts. Peden, Margaret Sayers, tr. from SPA. 2004. Tr. of Ciudad de las Bestias. 432p. (J). (gr. 5 up). reprint ed. pap. 7.99 (978-0-06-053503-2(2)) HarperCollins Pubs.

—City of the Beasts. 2004. Tr. of Ciudad de las Bestias. (gr. 5-8). lib. bdg. 16.45 (978-0-613-71427-3(X)) Tandem Library Bks.

—La Ciudad de las Bestias. 2002. (SPA., Illus.). 416p. 19.95 (978-0-06-051031-2(5) , Rayo) HarperCollins Pubs.

Almond, David. Clay. 2006. 256p. (J). (gr. 7). 15.95 (978-0-385-73171-3(X)); lib. bdg. 17.99 (978-0-385-90208-3(5)) Random Hse. Children's Bks. (Delacorte Bks. for Young Readers).

Alter, Stephen. The Phantom Isles. 2007. (Illus.). 244p. (J). (gr. 4-6). 16.95 (978-1-58234-738-7(7) , Bloomsbury Children) Bloomsbury Publishing.

Anagram, Nicholas C. The Compass Has Eight Points, Bk. 1. 2002. 286p. (gr. 4-7). pap. 15.95 (978-0-595-21839-4(3) , Writer's Showcase Pr.) iUniverse, Inc.

Anderson, Janet. Going Through the Gate. 2000. (Illus.). (J). (978-0-606-18407-6(4)) Tandem Library Bks.

Arnold, Marliese. Ghost Park Bks. 1 & 2: The Vanishing Gate & The Imposter. Spry, Alexis L., tr. from GER. Scholz, Barbara, illus. 2007. 215p. (J). (gr. 4-6). 12.95 (978-0-7358-2099-9(6)) North-South Bks., Inc.

Atwater-Rhodes, Amelia. Midnight Predator. l.t. ed. 2004. 195p. 20.95 (978-0-7862-6576-3(0)) Thorndike Pr.

Avi. The Book Without Words: A Fable of Medieval Magic. 2006. 224p. (gr. 5-9). reprint ed. pap. 5.99 (978-0-7868-1659-0(7)) Hyperion Pr.

—The Book Without Words: A Fable of Medieval Magic. l.t. ed. 2005. 220p. (YA). 23.95 (978-0-7862-7940-1(0)) Thorndike Pr.

Banks, John. Doorway to Darkness. Liew, Sonny, illus. 2007. (J). 80p. ***(*978-1-59889-351-9(3));*** 75p. pap. ***(*978-1-59889-446-2(3))*** Stone Arch Bks.

Barnes, Dawn. Beware of the Haunted Eye. 2007. (Black Belt Club Ser.: No. 3). 128p. (J). pap. 4.99 (978-0-439-85657-7(4) , Blue Sky Pr., The) Scholastic, Inc.

Barnes, Jennifer Lynn. Tattoo. 2007. 272p. (YA). (gr. 7 up). pap. 7.99 (978-0-385-73347-2(X)); lib. bdg. 12.99 (978-0-385-90363-9(4)) Random Hse. Children's Bks. (Delacorte Bks. for Young Readers).

Bauer, Marion Dane. The Red Ghost. Ferguson, Peter, illus. 2008. (J). ***(*978-0-375-84081-4(8));*** pap. ***(*978-0-375-84082-1(6));*** lib. bdg. ***(*978-0-375-94081-1(2))*** Random Hse., Inc.

Becker, Tom. Darkside Book 1 Don't Turn Out the Light. 2008. 304p. (J). pap. 16.99 ***(*978-0-545-03739-6(5)*** , Orchard Bks.) Scholastic, Inc.

Bellairs, John. The Ghost in the Mirror. 2002. (J). (gr. 3 up). 20.75 (978-0-8446-7205-2(X)) Smith, Peter Pub., Inc.

—The Revenge of the Wizard's Ghost. 1999. (J). (gr. 3 up). 20.25 (978-0-8446-7010-2(3)) Smith, Peter Pub., Inc.

Bildner, Phil & Long, Loren. Game 1. Long, Loren, illus. 2007. (Barnstormers Ser.). (Illus.). 144p. (J). (gr. 2-5). 9.99 (978-1-4169-1863-9(9)) Simon & Schuster Children's Publishing.

Black, Holly. Ironside: A Modern Faery's Tale. 2007. 336p. (YA). (gr. 4-7). 16.99 (978-0-689-86820-7(0) , McElderry, Margaret K.) Simon & Schuster Children's Publishing.

—Tithe: A Modern Faerie Tale. 2004. 331p. (YA). (gr. 7-17). per. 13.64 (978-0-606-30074-2(0)) Tandem Library Bks.

—Valiant: A Modern Tale of Faerie. 2006. 320p. (YA). pap. 7.99 (978-0-689-86823-8(5) , Simon Pulse) Simon & Schuster Children's Publishing.

—Valiant: A Modern Tale of Faerie. rev. l.t. ed. 353p. 21.95 (978-0-7862-8226-5(6)) Thorndike Pr.

Black, Holly & DiTerlizzi, Tony. Spiderwick Chronicles Set: The Field Guide, the Seeing Stone, Lucinda's Secret, the Ironwood Tree, the Wrath of Mulgarath. DiTerlizzi, Tony, illus. movie tie-in ed. 2008. (Spiderwick Chronicles). 672p. (J). 49.99 ***(*978-1-4169-5016-5(8))*** Simon & Schuster Children's Publishing.

Bouton, Warren Hussey. The Captain's Return: A Spooky Tale from Nantucket. Locke, Barbara Kauffmann, illus. 2004. (J). per. 5.95 ***(*978-0-9700555-4-5(4))*** Hither Creek Pr.

Bray, Libba. A Great & Terrible Beauty. (YA). (gr. 7). 2003. 416p. 16.95 (978-0-385-73028-0(4)); 2005. 432p. reprint ed. pap. 8.95 (978-0-385-73231-4(7)) Random Hse. Children's Bks. (Delacorte Bks. for Young Readers).

—A Great & Terrible Beauty. 2005. 403p. (YA). (gr. 8-12). per. 15.60 (978-0-606-33978-0(7)) Tandem Library Bks.

—A Great & Terrible Beauty. l.t. ed. 2005. 512p. (YA). (gr. 8-12). pap. 10.95 (978-0-7862-8082-7(4)); 2004. 507p. 23.95 (978-0-7862-6504-6(3) , Large Print Pr.) Thorndike Pr.

—Rebel Angels. (gr. 7). 2006. 592p. (YA). pap. 9.99 (978-0-385-73341-0(0)); 2005. 560p. (J). lib. bdg. 18.99 (978-0-385-90257-1(3)); 2005. 560p. (YA). 16.95 (978-0-385-73029-7(2)) Random Hse. Children's Bks. (Delacorte Bks. for Young Readers).

—Rebel Angels. l.t. ed. 2006. (Thorndike Press Large Print the Literacy Bridge Ser.). 655p. (J). 23.95 (978-0-7862-8087-2(5)) Thorndike Pr.

S

Brennan, Herbie. Faerie Lord. 2007. (Faerie Wars Chronicles Ser.). 432p. (YA). (gr. 7 up). 18.95 ***(*978-1-59990-120-6(X)*** , Bloomsbury Children) Bloomsbury Publishing.

—Faerie Wars. 2003. (Illus.). 370p. (J). 17.95 (978-1-58234-810-0(3) , Bloomsbury Children) Bloomsbury Publishing.

—Faerie Wars. 2007. 384p. mass mkt. 6.99 (978-0-7653-5674-1(0) , Tor Bks.) Doherty, Tom Assocs., LLC.

—Faerie Wars. l.t. ed. 2004. 448p. 22.95 (978-0-7862-6831-3(X) , Large Print Pr.) Thorndike Pr.

—The Purple Emperor. 2006. (Faerie Wars Chronicles Ser.). 432p. (J). pap. 8.95 (978-1-58234-746-2(8) , Bloomsbury Children) Bloomsbury Publishing.

—Ruler of the Realm. 2006. (Faerie Wars Chronicles Ser.: Bk. 3). (Illus.). 432p. (YA). 18.95 (978-1-58234-881-0(2)) Bloomsbury Publishing.

Brezenoff, Steven. Alley of Shadows. Martin, Cynthia, illus. 2008. (J). pap. ***(*978-1-59889-922-1(8));*** (YA). (gr. 5-9). lib. bdg. 17.95 ***(*978-1-59889-856-9(6))*** Stone Arch Bks.

—Burning Secrets. Vue, Tou, illus. 2008. (J). pap. ***(*978-1-59889-920-7(1));*** (YA). (gr. 5-9). lib. bdg. 17.95 ***(*978-1-59889-854-5(X))*** Stone Arch Bks.

Brooks, Martha. Bone Dance. 2005. 184p. (J). (gr. 7-16). pap. 6.95 (978-0-88899-336-6(6)) Groundwood Bks. CAN. *Dist:* Perseus Distribution.

—The Bone Dance. 1999. (J). (978-0-606-16716-1(1)) Tandem Library Bks.

Buckingham, Royce. Demonkeeper. 2007. 192p. (J). (gr. 4-7). 15.99 (978-0-399-24649-4(5) , Putnam Juvenile) Penguin Group (USA) Inc.

Buffie, Margaret. The Dark Garden. 2001. (Margaret Buffie Ser.). 240p. (YA). (gr. 13 up). (978-1-55337-091-8(0)) Kids Can Pr., Ltd.

—The Finder. 2005. (Watcher's Quest Ser.). (Illus.). (YA). 406p. (gr. 7-12). (978-1-55337-672-9(2)); 416p. (gr. 5-9). (978-1-55337-671-2(4)) Kids Can Pr., Ltd.

Bunting, Eve. The Presence: A Ghost Story. 2003. 208p. (J). (gr. 5-9). tchr. ed. 16.00 (978-0-618-26919-8(3) , Clarion Bks.) Houghton Mifflin Co. Trade & Reference Div.

Burgoyne, Tom. The Adventures of Super Phanatic. Epstein, Len, illus. 2007. 32p. ***(*978-0-9705804-7-4(9))*** Middle Atlantic Pr.

Butler, Charles. Timon's Tide. Smith, George, illus. 2000. 192p. (YA). (gr. 7-12). 16.00 (978-0-689-82593-4(5) , McElderry, Margaret K.) Simon & Schuster Children's Publishing.

Carroll, Jenny, pseud. Shadowland. unabr. ed. 2005. (Mediator Ser.: Bk. 1). (J). (gr. 3-7). 68.99 incl. audio (978-1-4193-4144-1(8) , 42055) Recorded Bks., LLC.

Chase, Mary. The Wicked, Wicked Ladies in the Haunted House. Sis, Peter, illus. 2003. 144p. (J). (gr. 2-5). lib. bdg. 17.99 (978-0-375-92572-6(4) , Knopf Bks. for Young Readers) Random Hse. Children's Bks.

Chris Wooding. The Haunting of Alaizabel Cray. l.t. ed. 2006. 463p. (YA). 22.95 (978-0-7862-8739-0(X)) Thorndike Pr.

Clare, Cassandra. City of Ashes. 2008. (Mortal Instruments Ser.). 480p. (YA). 17.99 ***(*978-1-4169-1429-7(3)*** , McElderry, Margaret K.) Simon & Schuster Children's Publishing.

Clare, Cassandra. City of Bones. 2007. (Mortal Instruments Ser.). (YA). 496p. (gr. 9 up). 17.99 (978-1-4169-1428-0(5)); 485p. ***(*978-1-4287-3999-4(8))*** Simon & Schuster Children's Publishing. (McElderry, Margaret K.).

Clasicos Fantasticos. (Clasicos Juveniles Coleccion). (SPA.). (YA). (gr. 5-8). pap. (978-950-11-1373-0(6) , SG1702) Sigmar ARG. *Dist:* Lectorum Pubns., Inc.

Climer, Steven Lee. Young of Heart. 2006. (YA). pap. ***(*978-0-9790649-5-1(3))*** Mardi Gras Publishing, LLC.

Cormier, Robert. Fade. 2004. 320p. (YA). (gr. 9-17). pap. 7.99 (978-0-385-73134-8(5) , Delacorte Bks. for Young Readers) Random Hse. Children's Bks.

—Fade. 2002. 20.50 (978-0-8446-7216-8(5)) Smith, Peter Pub., Inc.

Creedon, Catherine. Blue Wolf. Bentley, James, illus. 192p. (J). 2005. pap. 5.99 (978-0-06-050870-8(1)); 2003. lib. bdg. 16.89 (978-0-06-050869-2(8)) HarperCollins Pubs. (Julie Andrews Collection).

Croggon, Alison. The Naming. 2006. (Pellinor Ser.: Bk. 1). 528p. (YA). (gr. 7). pap. 8.99 (978-0-7636-3162-8(0)) Candlewick Pr.

—The Riddle. (Pellinor Ser.: Bk. 2). (Illus.). (YA). (gr. 7). 2007. 528p. pap. 8.99 (*978-0-7636-3414-8(X)); 2006. 512p. 17.99 (978-0-7636-3015-7(2)) Candlewick Pr.

Croggon, Allison. Naming: The First Book of Pellinor, No. 1. 2005. 528p. (YA). (gr. 7 up). 17.99 (978-0-7636-2639-6(2)) Candlewick Pr.

Curran, Casner. The Witch Across the Street. 2002. 113p. pap. 9.95 (978-0-595-21593-5(9) , Writers Club Pr.) iUniverse, Inc.

Curry, Jane Louise. The Egyptian Box. 2002. (Illus.). 192p. (J). (gr. 4-7). 16.95 (978-0-689-84273-3(2) , McElderry, Margaret K.) Simon & Schuster Children's Publishing.

—The Egyptian Box. l.t. ed. 2002. 216p. (J). 21.95 (978-0-7862-4896-4(3)) Thorndike Pr.

Cusick, Richie Tankersley. Blood Brothers Pt. 3. 2006. 304p. (J). (gr. 7). pap. 6.99 (978-0-14-240583-3(3) , Puffin) Penguin Group (USA) Inc.

—The Unseen 1 It Begins. 2005. 304p. (YA). (gr. 7). pap. 6.99 (978-0-14-240463-8(2) , Puffin) Penguin Group (USA) Inc.

Daughters Mo13 & Ewing, Lynne. Final Eclipse. 13th rev. ed. 2007. 288p. (YA). (gr. 7 up). 9.99 (*978-1-4231-0843-6(4)) Hyperion Bks. for Children.

De Haven, Tom. The Orphan's Tent. 2005. (Illus.). 192p. mass mkt. 5.99 (978-0-7434-9772-5(4)) ibooks, Inc.

De Lint, Charles. The Blue Girl. 2006. 384p. (YA). (gr. 7). reprint ed. pap. 7.99 (978-0-14-240545-1(0) , Puffin) Penguin Group (USA) Inc.

—The Dreaming Place. 2002. (gr. 7-12). lib. bdg. 14.15 (978-0-613-56338-3(7)) Tandem Library Bks.

—Waifs & Strays. 2004. 416p. (YA). (gr. 7 up). pap. 8.99 (978-0-14-240158-3(7) , Puffin) Penguin Group (USA) Inc.

De Lint, Charles, contrib. by. Waifs & Strays. 2004. 391p. (YA). (gr. 7-17). lib. bdg. 14.64 (978-0-606-30808-3(3)) Tandem Library Bks.

Del Negro, Janice. Passion & Poison: Tales of Shape-Shifters, Ghosts, & Spirited Women. 2007. 64p. (YA). (gr. 6 up). 16.99 (*978-0-7614-5361-1(X)) Cavendish, Marshall Corp.

Delaney, Joseph. Curse of the Bane. Arrasmith, Patrick, illus. 2006. (Last Apprentice Ser.). 480p. (J). 16.99 (978-0-06-076621-4(2) , Greenwillow Bks.); lib. bdg. 17.89 (978-0-06-076622-1(0)) HarperCollins Pubs.

—Last Apprentice Curse of Bane. 2007. (Last Apprentice Ser.). 480p. (J). pap. 7.99 (*978-0-06-076623-8(9) , Harper Trophy) HarperCollins Pubs.

—Night of the Soul Stealer, No. 3. 2007. (Last Apprentice Ser.). 512p. (J). (gr. 5 up). lib. bdg. 17.89 (*978-0-06-076625-2(5) , Greenwillow Bks.) HarperCollins Pubs.

—Night of the Soul Stealer, No. 3. Arrasmith, Patrick, illus. 2007. (Last Apprentice Ser.). 512p. (J). (gr. 5 up). 16.99 (*978-0-06-076624-5(7) , Greenwillow Bks.) HarperCollins Pubs.

Delaney, Joseph. Revenge of the Witch. Arrasmith, Patrick, illus. (Last Apprentice Ser.). (J). 2005. 368p. 16.99 (978-0-06-076618-4(2)); 2005. 368p. lib. bdg. 17.89 (978-0-06-076619-1(0)); 2006. 384p. reprint ed. pap. 7.99 (978-0-06-076620-7(4) , Harper Trophy) HarperCollins Pubs.

Dickinson, Peter. The Lion Tamer's Daughter & Other Stories. 1998. (978-0-606-13572-6(3)) Tandem Library Bks.

Dinnis, Enid M. God's Fairy Tales: Stories of the Supernatural in Everyday Life. 2005. pap. 24.95 (978-1-4179-5385-1(3)) Kessinger Publishing, LLC.

DiTerlizzi, Tony & Black, Holly. Lucinda's Secret. DiTerlizzi, Tony, illus. movie tie-in ed. 2008. (Spiderwick Chronicles: Bk. 3). 128p. (J). 10.99 (*978-1-4169-5019-6(2)) Simon & Schuster Children's Publishing.

—Lucinda's Secret. l.t. ed. 2006. (Spiderwick Chronicles: Bk. 3). 93p. (YA). 23.95 (978-0-7862-8585-3(0)) Thorndike Pr.

DK Publishing. Marvel Heroes Amazing Powers. 2008. (Dk Readers Ser.). 48p. (J). 14.99 (*978-0-7566-3495-7(4)) Dorling Kindersley Publishing, Inc.

—Marvel Heroes Greatest Battles. 2008. (Dk Readers Ser.). 48p. (J). 14.99 (*978-0-7566-3497-1(0)); pap. 3.99 (*978-0-7566-3496-4(2)) Dorling Kindersley Publishing, Inc.

D'Lacey, Chris. Fire Star. 560p. (J). 2008. pap. 7.99 (978-0-439-90185-7(5)); 2007. (gr. 4-7). pap. 15.99 (978-0-439-84582-3(3)) Scholastic, Inc. (Orchard Bks.).

—The Fire Within. 2007. 352p. (J). pap. 7.99 (978-0-439-67244-3(9) , Orchard Bks.) Scholastic, Inc.

—Icefire. 432p. (J). 2007. pap. 7.99 (978-0-439-67246-7(5)); 2006. pap. 14.99 (978-0-439-67245-0(7)) Scholastic, Inc. (Orchard Bks.).

Dorling Kindersley Publishing Staff & Sauders, Catherine. Marvel Heroes Amazing Powers. 2008. (Dk Readers Ser.). 48p. (J). pap. 3.99 (*978-0-7566-3494-0(6)) Dorling Kindersley Publishing, Inc.

Duncan, Lois. Down a Dark Hall. 181p. (YA). (gr. 7 up). pap. 4.99 (978-0-8072-1370-4(5) , Listening Library) Random Hse. Audio Publishing Group.

Dunne, Robin & Kee, James Montgomery. The Secret of the Shaman. 2007. 64p. (J). (gr. 2-5). pap. 5.99 (*978-0-8431-2666-2(3) , Price Stern Sloan) Penguin Group (USA) Inc.

ElvenWolf. Binding Magic. 2006. 75p. pap. 14.95 (978-1-4241-2700-9(9)) PublishAmerica, Inc.

The Emperor's Fruits. 2002. (YA). pap. 14.00 (978-1-59268-004-7(6)) GMA Publishing & Inspiration Pr.

Enderle, Dotti. Hand of Fate, Vol. 4. Nightingale, Kimberly, ed. 2004. (Fortune Tellers Club Ser.). (Illus.). 144p. (gr. 8-12). pap. 4.99 (978-0-7387-0390-9(7)) Llewellyn Pubns.

—The Magic Shades. 2003. (Fortune Tellers Club Ser.: Bk. 3). (Illus.). 144p. pap. 4.99 (978-0-7387-0341-1(9)) Llewellyn Pubns.

—Mirror, Mirror. 2004. (Illus.). 144p. pap. 4.99 (978-0-7387-0436-4(9)) Llewellyn Pubns.

—Playing with Fire. Leuthner, Sandy, ed. 2003. (Fortune Tellers Club Ser.: Bk. 2). (Illus.). 160p. pap. 4.99 (978-0-7387-0340-4(0)) Llewellyn Pubns.

—Playing with Fire: Fortune Tellers Club. 2003. (gr. 3-6). lib. bdg. 13.00 (978-0-613-90789-7(2)) Tandem Library Bks.

Enthoven, Sam. The Black Tattoo. 2006. 512p. (J). (gr. 5-12). 19.99 (978-1-59514-114-9(6) , Razorbill) Penguin Group (USA) Inc.

Ewing, Lynne. Barbarian. 2004. (Sons of the Dark Ser.: Bk. 1). 272p. (gr. 7-17). 9.99 (978-0-7868-1811-2(5) , Volo) Hyperion Bks. for Children.

—The Becoming. rev. ed. 2004. (Daughters of the Moon Ser.: No. 12). 288p. (J). (gr. 7-17). 9.99 (978-0-7868-1892-1(1) , Volo) Hyperion Bks. for Children.

—Choice. 9th rev. ed. 2003. (Daughters of the Moon Ser.: No. 9). 288p. (gr. 7-17). 9.99 (978-0-7868-0851-9(9) , Volo) Hyperion Bks. for Children.

—Daughters of the Moon. 2000. 160p. (YA). pap. 4.99 (978-0-7868-1409-1(8)); Vol. 2. pap. 4.99 (978-0-7868-1410-7(1)) Disney Pr.

—Divine One. 2nd rev. ed. 2007. (Sisters of Isis Ser.: No. 2). 272p. (gr. 7 up). 9.99 (*978-1-4231-0343-1(2)) Hyperion Pr.

—Goddess of the Night. 2000. (Daughters of the Moon Ser.: Vol. 1). 304p. (J). (gr. 7-17). 9.99 (978-0-7868-0653-9(2)) Disney Pr.

—Into the Cold Fire. 2nd rev. ed. 2000. (Daughters of the Moon Ser.: Vol. 2). (Illus.). 272p. (gr. 7-17). 9.99 (978-0-7868-0654-6(0)) Hyperion Bks. for Children.

—The Lost One. 2001. (Daughters of the Moon Ser.: No. 6). 288p. (J). (gr. 7-17). 9.99 (978-0-7868-0707-9(5) , Volo) Hyperion Bks. for Children.

—Moon Demon, Bk. 7. rev. ed. 2002. (Daughters of the Moon Ser.: No. 7). 289p. (J). (gr. 7-17). 9.99 (978-0-7868-0849-6(7) , Volo) Hyperion Bks. for Children.

—Night Shade. 2001. (Daughters of the Moon Ser.: Vol. 3). 288p. (J). (gr. 7-17). 9.99 (978-0-7868-0708-6(3) , Volo) Hyperion Bks. for Children.

—The Sacrifice. Scalora, Suza, illus. 5th rev. ed. 2001. (Daughters of the Moon Ser.: Bk. 5). 288p. (gr. 7-17). 9.99 (978-0-7868-0706-2(7) , Volo) Hyperion Bks. for Children.

—The Secret Scroll. 2001. (Daughters of the Moon Ser.: Vol. 4). 268p. (J). (gr. 7-17). reprint ed. 9.99 (978-0-7868-0709-3(1) , Volo) Hyperion Bks. for Children.

Ewing, Lynne. The Summoning. 2007. (Sisters of Isis Ser.: No. 1). 272p. (gr. 7 up). 9.99 (*978-1-4231-0342-4(4)) Hyperion Pr.

Farmer, Nancy. A Girl Named Disaster. 1998. 320p. (YA). (gr. 5-9). pap. 6.99 (978-0-14-038635-6(1) , Puffin) Penguin Group (USA) Inc.

—A Girl Named Disaster. 1998. (J). 12.64 (978-0-606-13430-9(1)) Tandem Library Bks.

—A Girl Named Disaster. l.t. ed. 2005. 533p. (J). (gr. 5-9). pap. 10.95 (978-0-7862-8037-7(9)) Thorndike Pr.

Feil, Hila. Blue Moon. 2007. (Illus.). 272p. (YA). pap. 6.95 (978-0-15-205933-0(4) , Harcourt Paperbacks) Harcourt Children's Bks.

Fforde, Jasper. The Eyre Affair. 2003. 374p. (gr. 7-12). per. 23.45 (978-0-613-62901-0(9)) Tandem Library Bks.

Gaiman, Neil. Coraline. McKean, Dave, illus. 3rd ed. 2003. (SPA.). 160p. (978-84-7888-579-4(X) , 1952) Emece Editores.

—Coraline. 2006. (P. S. Ser.). 192p. pap. 12.95 (978-0-06-113937-6(8)) HarperCollins Pubs.

—Coraline. McKean, Dave, illus. (J). 2004. 208p. (gr. 7 up). pap. 6.99 (978-0-06-057591-5(3) , Harper Trophy); 2003. 176p. (gr. 3 up). pap. 6.99 (978-0-380-80734-5(3) , Harper Trophy); 2002. 176p. (gr. 3 up). 15.99 (978-0-380-97778-9(8)); 2002. 176p. (gr. 3 up). lib. bdg. 17.89 (978-0-06-623744-2(0)) HarperCollins Pubs.

—Coraline. 2002. (gr. 5-8). lib. bdg. 14.15 (978-0-613-67322-8(0)) Tandem Library Bks.

—Coraline: Reading Group Guide. McKean, Dave, illus. (978-0-06-056878-8(X)) HarperCollins Pubs.

Geras, Adele. Family Files. Ross, Tony, illus. 1998. (Fabulous Fantoras Ser.: Vol. 1). 144p. (J). (gr. 3-7). 14.00 (978-0-380-97547-1(5)) HarperCollins Pubs.

Gershon, Gina & Gershon, Dann. Camp Creepy Time: The Adventures of Einstein P. Fleet. 2007. 224p. (J). (gr. 5 up). 16.99 (978-0-399-24737-8(8) , Putnam Juvenile) Penguin Group (USA) Inc.

Gibson, Glen. Angel & the Misfits. 2006. 175p. (YA). per. 11.95 (*978-1-59594-114-5(2) , Wingspan Pr.) Wing-Span Publishing.

Gilman, Laura Anne. Deep Water. 2000. (Buffy the Vampire Slayer Ser.: No. 14). (Illus.). (YA). (gr. 7 up). (978-0-606-18365-9(5)) Tandem Library Bks.

Golding, Julia. The Gorgon's Gaze. 2007. (Companions Quartet Ser.). 320p. (YA). (gr. 5 up). 16.99 (*978-0-7614-5377-2(6)) Cavendish, Marshall Corp.

—Mines of the Minotaur. Wyatt, David, illus. 2008. (J). (*978-0-7614-5302-4(4)) Cavendish, Marshall Corp.

—Secret of the Sirens. Wyatt, David, illus. 2007. 384p. (YA). (gr. 5 up). 16.99 (*978-0-7614-5371-0(7)) Cavendish, Marshall Corp.

Gopnik, Adam. The King in the Window. 2005. (Illus.). 416p. (gr. 5-17). 19.95 (978-0-7868-1862-4(X)) Hyperion Bks. for Children.

—The King in the Window. Rayyan, Omar, illus. 2006. 416p. (gr. 5-17). reprint ed. pap. 9.99 (978-0-7868-3894-3(9)) Miramax Bks.

Greenburg, Dan. Yikes! Grandma's a Teenager, Vol. 17. Davis, Jack E., illus. 1999. (Zack Files Ser.: No. 17). 64p. (J). (gr. 2-5). pap. 4.99 (978-0-448-41999-2(8) , Grosset & Dunlap) Penguin Group (USA) Inc.

—Yikes! Grandma's a Teenager. Davis, Jack E., illus. 1999. 58p. (J). (ps-k). lib. bdg. 13.00 (978-0-613-22664-6(X)) Tandem Library Bks.

—Yikes! Grandma's a Teenager. 1999. (Zack Files Ser.: No. 17). (J). (gr. 2-5). (978-0-606-17783-2(3)) Tandem Library Bks.

Haarsma, P. J. The Softwire: Virus on Orbis 1. 2008. (Illus.). 288p. (J). (gr. 5). 6.99 (*978-0-7636-3638-8(X)) Candlewick Pr.

Hassinger, Peter W. The Book of Alfar: A Tale of the Hudson Highlands. 2002. (Illus.). 272p. (J). (gr. 4 up). 15.89 (978-0-06-028470-1(6) , Geringer, Laura Book) HarperCollins Pubs.

Hawthorne, Nathaniel. Nathaniel Hawthorne. McConnell, James, illus. 2004. (Great American Short Stories Ser.). 71p. (J). lib. bdg. 23.33 (978-0-8368-4252-4(9)) Stevens, Gareth Inc.

Hearn, Julie. The Minister's Daughter. 2006. 272p. (YA). pap. 7.99 (978-0-689-87691-2(2) , Simon Pulse) Simon & Schuster Children's Publishing.

Hearn, Julie & Frost, Michael. The Minister's Daughter. 2005. 272p. (YA). (gr. 7 up). 17.99 (978-0-689-87690-5(4) , Atheneum) Simon & Schuster Children's Publishing.

Hinchliffe, Polly. Trio Theo in the Grip of Terror. 2003. 150p. pap. 12.95 (978-0-595-28727-7(1)) iUniverse, Inc.

Horowitz, Anthony. Evil Star. 2006. (Power of Five Ser.: Vol. 2). 320p. (J). pap. 17.99 (978-0-439-67996-1(6) , Scholastic Pr.) Scholastic, Inc.

—Nightrise. 2007. (Gatekeepers Ser.: No. 3). 368p. (YA). pap. 17.99 (*978-0-439-68001-1(8)) Scholastic, Inc.

Horowitz, Anthony. Ravens Gate. (Power of Five Ser.: Vol. 1). 2006. 272p. (J). pap. 6.99 (978-0-439-68009-7(3) , Scholastic Paperbacks); 2005. 256p. (YA). pap. 17.95 (978-0-439-67995-4(8)) Scholastic, Inc.

—Ravens Gate. l.t. ed. 2006. (Power of Five Ser.: Vol. 1). (YA). 23.95 (978-0-7862-8584-6(2)) Thorndike Pr.

Howe, James. Howie Monroe & the Doghouse of Doom. Helquist, Brett, illus. 2003. (Tales from the House of Bunnicula Ser.). 112p. (J). pap. 3.99 (978-0-689-83952-8(9) , Aladdin) Simon & Schuster Children's Publishing.

Humphreys, Chris. Vendetta. 2007. (Runestone Saga Ser.: No. 2). 336p. (YA). (gr. 7 up). 15.99 (*978-0-375-83293-2(9)); lib. bdg. 18.99 (*978-0-375-93293-9(3)) Random Hse. Children's Bks. (Knopf Bks. for Young Readers).

Hutchins, Hazel J. TJ & the Haunted House. 2003. (Orca Young Readers Ser.). (Illus.). 144p. (J). (gr. 3-6). pap. 4.99 (978-1-55143-262-5(5)) Orca Bk. Pubs. USA.

Irving, Washington. Washington Irving. Hall, Tracy, illus. 2004. (Great American Short Stories Ser.). 80p. (J). lib. bdg. 23.33 (978-0-8368-4253-1(7)) Stevens, Gareth Inc.

Jarvis, Robin. The Crystal Prison. (Deptford Mice Ser.: Bk. 2). (Illus.). 256p. (YA). 2002. pap. 6.95 (978-1-58717-161-1(9)); 2001. (gr. 5 up). 17.95 (978-1-58717-107-9(4)) Chronicle Bks. LLC. (SeaStar Bks.).

—Crystal Prison. 2002. (gr. 5-8). lib. bdg. 15.25 (978-0-613-56295-9(X)) Tandem Library Bks.

—The Final Reckoning. 2003. (Deptford Mice Ser.). (Illus.). 304p. (YA). pap. 6.95 (978-1-58717-244-1(5) , SeaStar Bks.) Chronicle Bks. LLC.

—Oaken Throne. 2005. (Illus.). 384p. (J). 17.95 (978-1-58717-277-9(1) , SeaStar Bks.) Chronicle Bks. LLC.

—Thomas. 2006. 400p. (J). 17.95 (978-0-8118-5412-2(4)) Chronicle Bks. LLC.

—The Whitby Witches. Petersen, Jeff, illus. 2006. 296p. (J). 17.95 (978-0-8118-5413-9(2)) Chronicle Bks. LLC.

Johnson, Maureen. Devilish. 2007. 272p. (YA). (gr. 7 up). pap. 8.99 (*978-1-59514-132-3(4) , Razorbill) Penguin Group (USA) Inc.

Jones, Allan Frewin. Ghostlight, Vol. 8. 2003. 176p. (J). mass mkt. 6.99 (978-0-330-39239-6(5) , Pan) Pan Macmillan GBR. Dist: Trafalgar Square Publishing.

Jones, Diana Wynne. The Time of the Ghost. 2002. 304p. (J). (gr. 7 up). 16.99 (978-0-06-029887-6(1)) HarperCollins Pubs.

Joseph Delaney. Revenge of the Witch. l.t. ed. 2006. 375p. 21.95 (978-0-7862-8641-6(5)) Thorndike Pr.

Kalkipsakis, Thalia. Sister Spirit. Oswald, Ash, illus. 2007. (Go Girl! Ser.: Bk. 3). 96p. (Orig.). (J). (gr. 2 up). pap. 3.99 (*978-0-312-34643-0(3)) Feiwel & Friends.

Kavanagh, Herminie Templeton. Darby O'Gill & the Crocks of Gold: And Other Irish Tales. Schluenderfritz, Ted, illus. 2003. ix, 155p. (J). pap. 14.95 (978-1-928832-85-0(7)) Sophia Institute Pr.

Kindl, Patrice. Owl in Love. 2004. 224p. (YA). (gr. 7 up). pap. 6.99 (978-0-618-43910-2(2) , Graphia) Houghton Mifflin Co. Trade & Reference Div.

—Owl in Love. unabr. ed. 1998. (J). Class Set. 102.80 incl. audio (978-0-7887-2562-3(9) , 46732); Homework Set. 49.75 incl. audio (978-0-7887-2106-9(2) , 40701) Recorded Bks., LLC.

Klause, Annette Curtis. Freaks: Alive, on the Inside! 336p. (YA). 2007. pap. 6.99 (*978-0-689-87038-5(8) , Simon Pulse); 2006. (gr. 8). 16.95 (978-0-689-87037-8(X) , McElderry, Margaret K.) Simon & Schuster Children's Publishing.

Lambeth, Robert Jay. Justin Crumble & the Journey of the Dead. 2000. 108p. (YA). pap. 9.95 (978-0-595-14488-4(8)) iUniverse, Inc.

Langrish, Katherine. Troll Blood. Stevens, Tim, illus. 2008. 352p. (J). 16.99 (*978-0-06-111674-2(2)); lib. bdg. 17.89 (*978-0-06-111675-9(0)) HarperCollins Pubs. (Eos).

—Troll Mill. 2008. 384p. (J). 7.99 (*978-0-06-058309-5(6) , Eos) HarperCollins Pubs.

Latta, Ruth. The Revenant & Other Stories for Hallowe'en. 2004. 54p. (*978-0-9683382-8-5(3)) Latta, Roger K.

Layefsky, Virginia. Impossible Things. 1998. (Accelerated Reader Bks.). 208p. (J). (gr. 5-9). 14.95 (978-0-7614-5038-2(6) , Cavendish Children's Bks.) Cavendish, Marshall Corp.

Lehr, Norma. Dance of the Crystal Skull. rev. exp. ed. 2003. (Illus.). 238p. (J). (gr. 3-7). lib. bdg. 15.95 (978-0-87358-724-2(3) , Rising Moon Bks. for Young Readers) Northland Publishing.

—Dance of the Crystal Skull. 1999. (Illus.). (J). (978-0-606-18310-9(8)) Tandem Library Bks.

—Haunting at Black Water Cove. 2000. (Illus.). (J). (978-0-606-18311-6(6)) Tandem Library Bks.

Lewis, Richard. The Demon Queen. 2008. 252p. (J). (*978-1-4169-3589-6(4) , Simon & Schuster Children's Publishing) Simon & Schuster Children's Publishing.

Lincoln, Christopher. Billy Bones. 2007. 208p. (J). (978-0-316-01473-1(7)) Little Brown & Co.

Littlefield, William. The Circus in the Woods. 2001. 208p. (J). (gr. 4-6). tchr. ed. 15.00 (978-0-618-06642-1(X)) Houghton Mifflin Co. Trade & Reference Div.

Llewellyn, Claire. Asi Nace un Pato. Mendez, Simon, illus. (Coleccion Asi Nace... Ser.). (SPA.). T/Ap. (J). (gr. 3-5). pap. 7.95 (978-1-59437-837-9(1)) Santillana USA Publishing Co., Inc.

MacDonald, Alan. Cleaner Genie. Remphry, Martin, illus. 2006. 48p. (J). lib. bdg. (*978-1-4048-3114-8(2)) Picture Window Bks.

Marillier, Juliet. Wildwood Dancing. 2008. 416p. (J). (gr. 7). pap. 9.99 (*978-0-375-84474-4(0) , Knopf Bks. for Young Readers) Random Hse. Children's Bks.

Marino, Ricardo. Cuentos Espantosos. 2002. (SPA.). 64p. (J). pap. (978-1-4000-0037-1(8)) Editorial Sudamericana S.A.

Mariotte, Jeff. Stranger to the Sun. 2002. (gr. 7-12). lib. bdg. 14.15 (978-0-613-63236-2(2)) Tandem Library Bks.

Matas, Carol. The Freak. rev. ed. 2008. 128p. pap. 6.95 (*978-1-55263-930-6(4)) Key Porter Bks. CAN. Dist: Perseus Distribution.

Matthews, L. S. The Outcasts. 2007. 272p. (YA). (gr. 7). 15.99 (*978-0-385-73367-0(4)); lib. bdg. 18.99 (*978-0-385-90382-0(0)) Random Hse. Children's Bks. (Delacorte Bks. for Young Readers).

McAuley, Amy. Over & over You. rev. ed. 2005. 192p. (J). 16.95 (978-1-59643-017-4(6)) Roaring Brook Pr.

McNeal, Laura & McNeal, Tom. The Decoding of Lana Morris. 2007. 304p. (J). (gr. 7). lib. bdg. 18.99 (978-0-375-93106-2(6)); 15.99 (978-0-375-83106-5(1)) Random Hse. Children's Bks. (Knopf Bks. for Young Readers).

Messer, Celeste M. Andi's Choice. Hoeffner, Deb, illus. 2004. 82-92p. 4.95 (978-0-9702171-6-5(1)) AshleyAlan Enterprises.

—The Boy Who Cried Wolf. Hoeffner, Deb, illus. 2004. 82-92p. 4.95 (978-0-9702171-9-6(6)) AshleyAlan Enterprises.

Metz, Melinda. Ravens Point. 2005. pap. (978-0-06-052373-2(5)) HarperCollins Canada, Ltd.

Michael, Livi. The Whispering Road. 2006. 336p. (J). (gr. 5). pap. 6.99 (978-0-14-240724-0(0) , Puffin); 2005. 272p. (YA). (gr. 4). 17.99 (978-0-399-24357-8(7) , Putnam Juvenile) Penguin Group (USA) Inc.

Montes, Graciela. Tengo un Monstruo en el Bolsillo. 2002. (SPA.). 88p. (J). pap. 10.95 (978-1-4000-0046-3(7)) Random Hse., Inc.

Moon, Russell. Witch Boy. 2002. (gr. 7-12). lib. bdg. 15.25 (978-0-613-71472-3(5)) Tandem Library Bks.

Morgan, Melissa J. Charmed Forces No. 19: Super Special. 2008. (Camp Confidential Ser.). 256p. (J). (gr. 4-7). 5.99 (*978-0-448-44722-3(3) , Grosset & Dunlap) Penguin Group (USA) Inc.

Morin, James F. Rothshield Chasing Shadows. 2006. pap. 14.95 (*978-1-59330-422-5(6)) Aventine Pr.

Morrison, P. R. Wave Traveller. 2007. 300p. (J). (gr. 3-7). 16.95 (*978-1-59990-123-7(4)) Bloomsbury Publishing.

Murphy, T. M. The Secrets of Cain's Castle. 2001. (Belltown Mystery Ser.). 144p. (J). (978-1-880158-38-8(8)) Townsend, J.N. Publishing.

Myers, Bill. The Curse. 2002. (Forbidden Doors Ser.: Vol. 7). 176p. (J). mass mkt. 4.99 (978-0-8423-5739-5(4)) Tyndale Hse. Pubs.

Newbery, Linda. At the Firefly Gate. 2007. 160p. (J). (gr. 5). 15.99 (978-0-385-75113-1(3)); lib. bdg. 18.99 (978-0-385-75114-8(1)) Random Hse. Children's Bks. (Fickling, David Bks.).

Nimmo, Jenny. Griffin's Castle. 2007. 288p. (J). 16.99 (*978-0-439-02554-6(0) , Orchard Bks.) Scholastic, Inc.

Nolan, Han. Dancing on the Edge. 2007. (Illus.). 264p. (YA). pap. 6.95 (978-0-15-205884-5(2) , Harcourt Paperbacks) Harcourt Children's Bks.

—Dancing on the Edge. 1999. 256p. (gr. 3-6). pap. 6.99 (978-0-14-130203-4(8) , Puffin) Penguin Group (USA) Inc.

—Dancing on the Edge. 1999. (J). 12.64 (978-0-606-16836-6(2)); (gr. 7-12). lib. bdg. 14.15 (978-0-613-15338-6(3)) Tandem Library Bks.

Parker, Daniel. April. 1999. (Count Down Ser.: No. 4). (YA). (gr. 5-8). (978-0-606-16235-7(6)) Tandem Library Bks.

—July. 1999. (Count Down Ser.: No. 7). (YA). (gr. 5-8). (978-0-606-16238-8(0)) Tandem Library Bks.

—June. 1999. (Count Down Ser.: No. 6). (YA). (gr. 5-8). (978-0-606-16239-5(9)) Tandem Library Bks.

—March. 1999. (Count Down Ser.: No. 3). (YA). (gr. 5-8). (978-0-606-16240-1(2)) Tandem Library Bks.

—May. 1999. (Count Down Ser.: No. 5). (YA). (gr. 5-8). (978-0-606-16241-8(0)) Tandem Library Bks.

—November. 1999. (gr. 7-12). lib. bdg. 11.80 (978-0-613-22112-2(5)) Tandem Library Bks.

—October. 1999. (gr. 7-12). lib. bdg. 11.80 (978-0-613-22120-7(6)) Tandem Library Bks.

Parker, Jeff. The Bird, the Beast & the Lizard. 2007. (X-Men: First Class Ser.). 24p. (J). (gr. 2-6). 21.35 (***978-1-59961-398-7(0)***) Spotlight.

Peretti, Frank. Deadly Curse of Toco Rey: Cooper Kids #6. Life Publishers International, tr. from ENG. 2005. (RUS., Illus.). 156p. (J). (978-0-7361-0347-3(3)) Life Pubs. International.

Peretti, Frank E. The Secret of the Desert Stone. 2005. (Cooper Kids Adventure Ser.: Vol. 5). 160p. (J). pap. 6.99 (978-1-4003-0574-2(8)) Nelson, Thomas Inc.

Perez, Marlene. Dead Is the New Black. 2008. (Illus.). 204p. (YA). pap. 7.95 (***978-0-15-206408-2(7)*** , Harcourt Paperbacks) Harcourt Children's Bks.

Petrucha, Stefan. Snared. 2008. (Wicked Dead Ser.: No.3). 224p. (J). pap. 7.99 (***978-0-06-113851-5(7)*** , HarperTeen) HarperCollins Pubs.

Petrucha, Stefan & Pendleton, Thomas. Crush. 2008. (Wicked Dead Ser.). 224p. (J). pap. 7.99 (***978-0-06-113852-2(5)*** , HarperTeen) HarperCollins Pubs.

Pierce, Tamora. Emperor Mage. 2005. (Immortals Ser.: No. 2). 384p. (YA). pap. 6.99 (978-1-4169-0337-6(2) , Simon Pulse) Simon & Schuster Children's Publishing.

Pike, Christopher, pseud. Witch. 2001. (gr. 7-12). lib. bdg. 14.15 (978-0-613-61002-5(4)) Tandem Library Bks.

Poe, Edgar Allan. Edgar Allan Poe. McConnell, James, illus. 2004. (Great American Short Stories Ser.). 73p. (J). lib. bdg. 23.33 (978-0-8368-4254-8(5)) Stevens, Gareth Inc.

Popescu, Petru. Weregirls: Birth of the Pack. rev. ed. 2007. 352p. (YA). (gr. 8 up). pap. 9.95 (***978-0-7653-1641-7(2)*** , Tor Teen) Doherty, Tom Assocs., LLC.

Pullman, Philip. Clockwork or All Wound Up. Gore, Leonid, illus. 128p. (J). (gr. 3-7). 1999. pap. 4.99 (978-0-590-12998-5(8) , Scholastic Paperbacks); 1998. pap. 14.95 (978-0-590-12999-2(6) , Levine, Arthur A. Bks.) Scholastic, Inc.

Reiss, Kathryn. Pale Phoenix. 2004. 326p. (J). (gr. k-17). lib. bdg. 12.60 (978-0-606-30243-2(3)); 2003. (gr. 7-12). lib. bdg. 14.10 (978-0-613-67837-7(0)) Tandem Library Bks.

—Sweet Miss Honeywell's Revenge: A Ghost Story. 2005. 444p. (J). (gr. 7-17). pap. 6.95 (978-0-15-205471-7(5) , Harcourt Paperbacks) Harcourt Children's Bks.

Richards, Justin. The Chaos Code. 2007. 416p. (YA). (gr. 7 up). 17.95 (***978-1-59990-124-4(2)***) Bloomsbury Publishing.

Richardson, E. E. Devil's Footsteps. 192p. 2006. (YA). (gr. 9). mass mkt. 5.99 (978-0-440-23916-1(8) , Laurel Leaf); 2005. (J). (gr. 7 up). lib. bdg. 17.99 (978-0-385-90279-3(4) , Delacorte Bks. for Young Readers); 2005. (YA). (gr. 7 up). 15.95 (978-0-385-73263-5(5) , Delacorte Bks. for Young Readers) Random Hse. Children's Bks.

Rinaldi, Ann. Millicent's Gift. 2002. (Illus.). 224p. (J). (ps-3). 15.95 (978-0-06-029636-0(4)) HarperCollins Pubs.

Robison, Dan. Death Chant: Kimo's Battle with the Shamanic Forces. 2006. 194p. (J). pap. (978-0-922993-52-9(1)) Marquette Bks., LLC.

Rowe, Jamie. Moon Flower. 2002. 38p. pap. 9.95 (978-1-59129-835-9(0)) PublishAmerica, Inc.

Schaenen, Inda. All the Cats of Cairo. 2007. 232p. (J). (gr. 5-10). pap. 8.95 (***978-0-9768126-5-4(7)***) Brown Barn Bks.

Scott, Michael. The Alchemyst. 2007. (Secrets Imrtl Nicholas Flamel Ser.). (Illus.). 400p. (YA). (gr. 7 up). 16.99 (978-0-385-73357-1(7)); lib. bdg. 19.99 (978-0-385-90372-1(3)) Random Hse. Children's Bks. (Delacorte Bks. for Young Readers).

Shua, Ana María. La Fabrica del Terror. 2002. (SPA.). 120p. (J). pap. (978-1-4000-0057-9(2)) Editorial Sudamericana S.A.

—La Fabrica del Terror II. 2002. (SPA.). 128p. (J). pap. 11.95 (978-1-4000-0058-6(0)) Random Hse., Inc.

Shusterman, Neal. Dread Locks, No. 1. 2006. (Dark Fusion Ser.). 176p. (YA). (gr. 7). pap. 6.99 (978-0-14-240599-4(X) , Puffin) Penguin Group (USA) Inc.

—Dread Locks: Dark Fusion # 1. 2005. 176p. (J). (gr. 6-12). 15.99 (978-0-525-47554-5(0) , Dutton Juvenile) Penguin Group (USA) Inc.

—Duckling Ugly. (Dark Fusion Ser.). 224p. (J). 2007. pap. 6.99 (978-0-14-240684-7(8) , Puffin); 2006. (gr. 5). 15.99 (978-0-525-47585-9(0) , Dutton Juvenile) Penguin Group (USA) Inc.

—Red Rider's Hood. 2006. (Dark Fusion Ser.). 192p. (YA). (gr. 7). pap. 6.99 (978-0-14-240678-6(3) , Puffin) Penguin Group (USA) Inc.

Silverman. Mirror Mirror. 2004. 176p. (J). pap. 4.50 (978-0-439-44086-8(6) , Scholastic Paperbacks) Scholastic, Inc.

Silverman, A. O. Mirror, Mirror: Twisted Tales. 2002. (Illus.). 176p. (J). (gr. 5). pap. 15.95 (978-0-439-29593-2(9) , Chicken Hse., The) Scholastic, Inc.

Simmons, Derek. Flash of Life. 2006. 85p. pap. 14.95 (***978-1-4241-3890-6(6)***) PublishAmerica, Inc.

Singleton, Linda Joy. Don't Die, Dragonfly. Karre, Andrew, ed. 2004. 288p. pap. 6.99 (978-0-7387-0526-2(8)) Llewellyn Pubns.

—Last Dance. 2005. (Seer Ser.: Book 2). 264p. pap. 6.99 (978-0-7387-0638-2(8)) Llewellyn Pubns.

Sisters of Isis3 & Ewing, Lynne. Enchantress. 3rd rev. ed. 2007. 256p. (gr. 7 up). 9.99 (***978-1-4231-0684-5(9)***) Hyperion Bks. for Children.

Sleator, William. Hell Phone. 2007. 288p. (J). (gr. 7-17). pap. 6.95 (***978-0-8109-9360-0(0)***); 2006. 252p. (YA). (gr. 8-11). 16.95 (978-0-8109-5479-3(6) , Amulet Bks.) Abrams, Harry N. , Inc.

Smeltzer, Jennifer. Scrolls & Coals. 2004. (J). 14.95 (978-0-9754804-3-4(X) , Rockhill Bks.) Kansas City Star Bks.

Smith, Cynthia Leitich. Tantalize. 2007. (Illus.). 336p. (YA). (gr. 9). 16.99 (978-0-7636-2791-1(7)) Candlewick Pr.

Sniegoski, Thomas E. The Fallen. 2006. (Fallen Ser.). 272p. (YA). pap. 6.99 (978-1-4169-3877-4(X) , Simon Pulse) Simon & Schuster Children's Publishing.

Snyder, Zilpha Keatley. The Unseen. l.t. ed. 2005. 276p. 22.95 (978-0-7862-7265-5(1) , Large Print Pr.) Thorndike Pr.

Solitaire, Jenna. Keeper of the Waters. 3rd rev. ed. 2006. (Guardian of the Boards Ser.). 256p. (YA). 6.99 (978-0-7653-5359-7(8) , Tor Teen) Doherty, Tom Assocs., LLC.

Spradlin, Michael P. Live & Let Shop. 2006. (Spy Goddess Ser.). (Illus.). 288p. (J). pap. 5.99 (978-0-06-059409-1(8)) HarperCollins Pubs.

—Spy Goddess, Book Two: to Hawaii, with Love. 2008. (Spy Goddess Ser.). 288p. (J). pap. 6.99 (***978-0-06-059412-1(8)*** , HarperTeen) HarperCollins Pubs.

Spradlin, Michael P. To Hawaii, with Love. 2006. (Spy Goddess Ser.). (Illus.). 208p. (J). lib. bdg. 16.89 (978-0-06-059411-4(X)); (YA). 15.99 (978-0-06-059410-7(1)) HarperCollins Pubs.

Spradlin, Michael P., illus. & reader. Live & Let Shop. Spradlin, Michael P., reader. 2005. (Spy Goddess Ser.: Bk. 1). 224p. (gr. 7 up). 15.99 (978-0-06-059407-7(1)) HarperCollins Pubs.

Stahler, David, Jr. Doppelganger. 2006. 272p. (J). 16.99 (978-0-06-087232-8(2)); lib. bdg. 17.89 (978-0-06-087233-5(0)) HarperCollins Pubs.

Stevenson, Robert Louis. Dr. Jekyll & Mr. Hyde. (YA). (gr. 5-12). pap. 6.50 (978-0-8224-9255-9(5)) Globe Fearon Educational Publishing.

Stevermer, Caroline & Wrede, Patricia C. The Grand Tour: Being a Revelation of Matters of High Confidentiality & Greatest Importance, Including Extracts from the Intimate Diary of a Noblewoman & the Sworn Testimony of a Lady of Quality. 2006. (Illus.). 480p. (J). pap. 6.95 (978-0-15-205556-1(8) , Magic Carpet Bks.) Harcourt Children's Bks.

Stine, R. L. Have You Met My Ghoulfriend? 2004. (Mostly Ghostly Ser.). 144p. (J). (gr. 2-5). 6.95 (978-0-385-74664-9(4)); lib. bdg. 8.99 (978-0-385-90914-3(4)) Random Hse. Children's Bks. (Delacorte Bks. for Young Readers).

—Night of the Living Dummy 2. 2004. (Goosebumps Ser.). 144p. (J). 4.99 (978-0-439-57374-0(2)) Scholastic, Inc.

—Say Cheese & Die. . Again! 2004. (Goosebumps Ser.). 144p. (J). 4.99 (978-0-439-57361-0(0)) Scholastic, Inc.

—The Taste of Night. (Dangerous Girls Ser.). (gr. 7 up). 2005. 288p. (YA). pap. 6.99 (978-0-06-059618-7(X)); 2004. 240p. (J). 14.99 (978-0-06-059616-3(3)) HarperCollins Pubs.

—Who Let the Ghosts Out? 2004. (Mostly Ghostly Ser.). 144p. (J). (gr. 2-5). 6.95 (978-0-385-74663-2(6)); lib. bdg. 8.99 (978-0-385-90913-6(6)) Random Hse. Children's Bks. (Delacorte Bks. for Young Readers).

Strickland, Brad. The House Where Nobody Lived. 2006. 176p. (J). (gr. 4-7). 16.99 (978-0-8037-3148-6(5) , Dial) Penguin Group (USA) Inc.

—The Tower at the End of the World. Schindler, S. D., illus. 2001. (Lewis Barnavelt Ser.). 160p. (J). 16.99 (978-0-8037-2620-8(1) , Dial) Penguin Group (USA) Inc.

—The Whistle, the Grave & the Ghost. 2003. (Lewis Barnavelt Ser.). 160p. (J). (gr. 4). 16.99 (978-0-8037-2622-2(8) , Dial) Penguin Group (USA) Inc.

—The Wrath of the Grinning Ghost. 2001. (Illus.). (J). (978-0-606-21537-4(9)) Tandem Library Bks.

Stroud, Jonathan. Buried Fire. 2004. 332p. (J). pap. (978-0-7818-5794-9(5)) Hippocrene Bks., Inc.

—Buried Fire. 2004. 336p. (gr. 5-17). pap. 6.95 (978-0-7868-5194-2(5)) Miramax Bks.

—The Golem's Eye. 2nd rev. ed. 2004. (Bartimaeus Trilogy Ser.: Bk. 2). 576p. (gr. 5-17). 17.95 (978-0-7868-1860-0(3)) Miramax Bks.

—The Leap. 2004. 240p. (gr. 5-17). pap. 6.95 (978-0-7868-5195-9(3)) Miramax Bks.

Teitelbaum, Michael. The Scary States of America. 2007. 416p. (J). (gr. 4-7). pap. 7.99 (978-0-385-73331-1(3)); lib. bdg. 12.99 (***978-0-385-90348-6(0)***) Random Hse. Children's Bks. (Delacorte Bks. for Young Readers).

Thompson, Kate. Midnight's Choice. unabr. ed. 2004. (Switchers Ser.: Vol. 2). 240p. (J). (gr. 5-9). pap. 38.00 incl. audio (978-0-8072-8769-9(5) , Listening Library) Random Hse. Audio Publishing Group.

—Midnight's Choice. 2000. (J). (978-0-606-20189-6(0)) Tandem Library Bks.

—Wild Blood. 2002. 272p. (gr. 5-17). pap. 5.99 (978-0-7868-1422-0(5)) Hyperion Paperbacks for Children.

—Wild Blood. 2002. (gr. 3-6). lib. bdg. 14.15 (978-0-613-74970-1(7)) Tandem Library Bks.

Tiernan, Cate. The Shadows. 2001. (Sweep Ser.: Bk. 1). (Illus.). 192p. (YA). (gr. 7 up). pap. 5.99 (978-0-14-131046-6(4) , Puffin) Penguin Group (USA) Inc.

Townsend, John. Hunter's Moon. Dietrich, Sean, illus. 2007. (J). 80p. (***978-1-59889-352-6(1)***); 71p. pap. (***978-1-59889-447-9(1)***) Stone Arch Bks.

—The Omen & the Ghost. Cunningham, Kelley, illus. 2007. (J). 80p. (***978-1-59889-353-3(X)***); 71p. pap. (***978-1-59889-448-6(X)***) Stone Arch Bks.

Van Belkom, Edo. Wolf Pack. 2004. 184p. (J). (gr. 6). pap. 8.95 (978-0-88776-669-5(2)) Tundra Bks., Inc./Livres Toundra, Inc. CAN. *Dist:* Random Hse., Inc.

Vande Velde, Vivian. All Hallow's Eve: 13 Stories. 2006. (Illus.). 240p. (YA). 17.00 (978-0-15-205576-9(2)) Harcourt Children's Bks.

—Being Dead: Stories. 2001. (gr. 7-12). lib. bdg. 15.25 (978-0-613-68194-0(0)) Tandem Library Bks.

Wade, Rebecca. The Theft & the Miracle. 2007. 368p. (J). (gr. 5-9). 16.99 (978-0-06-077493-6(2)); lib. bdg. 17.89 (978-0-06-077495-0(9)) HarperCollins Pubs.

Walker, Pamela. Daughter of Light. 2006. (Kung Fu Princess Ser.: No. 1). (Illus.). 224p. (J). (gr. 7). pap. 6.99 (978-0-448-44139-9(X) , Grosset & Dunlap) Penguin Group (USA) Inc.

—In Gold & Jade, No. 2. 2006. (Kung Fu Princess Ser.). (Illus.). 224p. (J). (gr. 7). pap. 6.99 (978-0-448-44140-5(3) , Grosset & Dunlap) Penguin Group (USA) Inc.

Wallin, Luke. The Slavery Ghosts. 2001. 132p. (YA). pap. 11.95 (978-0-595-19277-9(7)) iUniverse, Inc.

Watts, Leander. Beautiful City of the Dead. 2006. 256p. (YA). (gr. 7). 16.00 (978-0-618-59443-6(4)) Houghton Mifflin Co.

—Beautiful City of the Dead. 2007. 256p. (YA). (gr. 7). pap. 7.99 (***978-0-618-59499-3(X)***) Houghton Mifflin Co. Trade & Reference Div.

Watts, Leander. Ten Thousand Charms. 2005. 240p. (YA). (gr. 5). 16.00 (978-0-618-44897-5(7)) Houghton Mifflin Co. Trade & Reference Div.

Weiss, Bobbi J. G. & Weiss, David Cody. Trouble on Oak Street. Spaziante, Patrick, illus. 2006. (Monster House Ser.). 32p. (J). pap. 3.99 (978-1-4169-1822-6(1) , Simon Spotlight) Simon & Schuster Children's Publishing.

Welvaert, Scott R. The Curse of the Wendigo: An Agate & Buck Adventure. Garvey, Brann, illus. 2007. (Vortex Books). 105p. (J). (gr. 5 up). lib. bdg. 22.60 (978-1-59889-066-2(2)) Stone Arch Bks.

Welvaert, Scott R. The Mosquito King: An Agate & Buck Adventure. Garvey, Brann, illus. 2008. (J). pap. (***978-1-59889-923-8(6)***); lib. bdg. (***978-1-59889-857-6(4)***) Stone Arch Bks.

West, Tracey, et al. Roxy Hunter & the Secret of the Shaman. 2007. 128p. (J). (gr. 2-5). 4.99 (***978-0-8431-2665-5(5)*** , Price Stern Sloan) Penguin Group (USA) Inc.

Wooding, Chris. The Haunting of Alaizabel Cray. 2005. 304p. (YA). (gr. 7-17). reprint ed. pap. 7.99 (978-0-439-59851-4(6)) Scholastic, Inc.

Wrede, Patricia C. & Stevermer, Caroline. The Grand Tour: Being a Revelation of Matters of High Confidentiality & Greatest Importance, Including Extracts from the Intimate Diary of a Noblewoman & the Sworn Testimony of a Lady of Quality. 2004. (Illus.). 480p. (YA). 17.00 (978-0-15-204616-3(X)) Harcourt Children's Bks.

—The Mislaid Magician or Ten Years After: Being the Private Correspondence Between Two Prominent Families Regarding a Scandal Touching the Highest Levels of Government & the Security of the Realm. 2006. (Illus.). 336p. (J). (gr. 8 up). 17.00 (978-0-15-205548-6(7)) Harcourt Trade Pubs.

—Sorcery & Cecelia or the Enchanted Chocolate Pot: Being the Correspondence of Two Young Ladies of Quality Regarding Various Magical Scandals in London & the Country. 2003. (Illus.). 336p. (YA). 17.00 (978-0-15-204615-6(1)) Harcourt Children's Bks.

Wright, Nina. Homefree. 2006. 240p. (J). pap. 8.95 (978-0-7387-0927-7(1) , Flux) Llewellyn Pubns.

Wright, Nina. Sensitive. 2007. 240p. (J). (gr. 4-7). pap. 9.95 (***978-0-7387-1170-6(5)*** , Flux) Llewellyn Pubns.

Wright, Randall. The Silver Penny. rev. ed. 2005. 208p. (J). 16.95 (978-0-8050-7391-1(4) , Holt, Henry & Co. Bks. For Young Readers) Holt, Henry & Co.

Yamada, Shutaro. R. O. D, Vol. 4. 2006. (Read or Die Ser.). 208p. (YA). pap. 9.99 (978-1-4215-0509-1(6)) Viz Media.

Yep, Laurence. The Imp That Ate My Homework. 2000. 11.75 (978-0-606-17671-2(3)) Tandem Library Bks.

Youmans, Marly. The Curse of the Raven Mocker. 2003. 288p. (J). 18.00 (978-0-374-31667-9(8) , Farrar, Straus & Giroux (BYR)) Farrar, Straus & Giroux.

—The Curse of the Raven Mocker. 2006. 288p. (YA). (gr. 7). pap. 7.99 (978-0-14-240696-0(1) , Puffin) Penguin Group (USA) Inc.

—Ingledove. 2005. (Illus.). 208p. (YA). 16.00 (978-0-374-33599-1(0) , Farrar, Straus & Giroux) Farrar, Straus & Giroux.

—Ingledove. 2006. 208p. (YA). (gr. 7). pap. 7.99 (978-0-14-240704-2(6) , Puffin) Penguin Group (USA) Inc.

Zuravicky, Orli. Dear Diary: Monster House. 2006. (Illus.). 32p. (J). lib. bdg. 15.00 (***978-1-4242-1561-4(7)***) Fitzgerald Bks.

Zydek, Heather. Basil's Search for Miracles. 2007. 160p. pap. 13.95 (***978-1-888212-86-0(1)***) Conciliar Pr.

SUPERSONIC AERODYNAMICS

see Aerodynamics, Supersonic

SUPERSTITION

see also Apparitions; Astrology; Charms; Divination; Dreams; Fairies; Folklore; Fortune-Telling; Ghosts; Occultism; Vampires; Witchcraft

Dineen, Jacqueline. Living with the Gods. Wilkinson, Philip, ed. Ingpen, Robert R., illus. 1999. (People & Customs of the World Ser.). 96p. (YA). lib. bdg. 21.95 (978-0-7910-5135-1(8) , Chelsea Hse.) Facts On File, Inc.

Hughes, Mary. Popular Superstitions. 1999. (Costume, Tradition & Culture). (Illus.). 64p. (YA). (gr. 5 up). 28.00 (978-0-7910-5172-6(2) , Chelsea Hse.) Facts On File, Inc.

Newton, Nick & Minutaglio, Bill. Locker Room Mojo: True Tales of Superstitions in Sports. 1999. 114p. (YA). 32.95 (978-0-9670466-4-8(5)) Middlefork Pr.

Rigby Education Staff. Keep Tradition. (Greetings Ser.). (Illus.). (gr. 3-5). 21.00 (978-0-7635-2229-2(5)) Rigby Education.

Sanna, Ellyn. Folk Customs. 2002. (North American Folklore Ser.). (Illus.). 112p. (YA). (gr. 7 up). lib. bdg. (978-1-59084-336-9(3)) Mason Crest Pubs.

Sullivan, George. Don't Step on the Foul Line: Sports Superstitions. 2000. (gr. 3-6). lib. bdg. 17.60 (978-0-613-55824-2(3)) Tandem Library Bks.

SUPERSTITION—FICTION

The Bad Luck of King Fred: Individual Title Six-Packs. (Action Packs Ser.). 104p. (gr. 3-5). 44.00 (978-0-7635-8408-5(8)) Rigby Education.

Brodeur, Tom. Regina Silsby's Secret War. 2004. 248p. (J). 7.49 (978-1-59166-235-8(4)) Jones, Bob Univ. Pr.

Durrant, George D. The Christmas Marble: A Christmas Story. 2004. 70p. (J). 4.95 (978-1-55517-824-6(3) , Bonneville Bks.) Cedar Fort, Inc./CFI Distribution.

Hassett, John & Hassett, Ann. Father Sun, Mother Moon. 2001. (Illus.). 32p. (J). (gr. k-3). tchr. ed. 16.00 (978-0-395-97565-7(4) , Walter Lorraine) Houghton Mifflin Co. Trade & Reference Div.

Haven, Paul. Two Hot Dogs with Everything. Ferguson, Peter, illus. 2007. 320p. (J). (gr. 4-7). 6.50 (978-0-375-83349-6(8) , Yearling) Random Hse. Children's Bks.

—Two Hot Dogs with Everything. 2006. (J). lib. bdg. (978-0-375-93350-9(6)) Random Hse. Children's Bks.

—Two Hot Dogs with Everything. Ferguson, Peter & Jessell, Tim, illus. 2006. 320p. (J). (gr. 3-7). 15.95 (978-0-375-83348-9(X) , Random Hse. Bks. for Young Readers) Random Hse. Children's Bks.

—Two Hot Dogs with Everything. Ferguson, Peter, illus. 2006. 320p. (J). (gr. 3-7). lib. bdg. 17.99 (978-0-375-93348-6(4) , Random Hse. Bks. for Young Readers) Random Hse. Children's Bks.

McMullan, Kate. Beware! It's Friday the 13th. 2006. (Dragon Slayers' Academy Ser.: No. 13). (Illus.). 107p. (J). (gr. 1-6). 24.21 (978-1-59961-122-8(8)) Spotlight.

Nervelle, Rosemarie. The Witch of Beaver Creek Mine. 2007. 160p. (gr. 5-9). 14.95 (***978-0-89272-741-4(1)***) Down East Bks.

Repp, Gloria. Charlie. 2002. (Illus.). 147p. (J). (gr. 4-7). 7.49 (978-1-57924-817-8(9)) Jones, Bob Univ. Pr.

Rumford, James. Don't Touch My Hat. 2007. (Illus.). 40p. (J). (ps-3). lib. bdg. 18.99 (978-0-375-93782-8(X) , Knopf Bks. for Young Readers) Random Hse. Children's Bks.

—Don't Touch My Hat! 2007. (Illus.). 40p. (J). (ps-3). 16.99 (978-0-375-83782-1(5) , Knopf Bks. for Young Readers) Random Hse. Children's Bks.

Schumacher, Julie. The Chain Letter. 2005. 208p. (J). (gr. 5-9). lib. bdg. 17.99 (978-0-385-90205-2(0) , Delacorte Bks. for Young Readers) Random Hse. Children's Bks.

Sutton, Jane. The Trouble with Cauliflower. Harris, Jim, illus. 2006. 32p. (J). (ps). 16.99 (978-0-8037-2707-6(0) , Dial) Penguin Group (USA) Inc.

SURF

see Ocean Waves

SURFING

Arksey, Neil. Surfer's Result. (Illus.). 128p. (J). 7.95 (978-0-14-130206-5(2)) Penguin Bks., Ltd. GBR. *Dist:* Trafalgar Square Publishing.

Barker, Amanda. Wind Surfing. 1999. (Radical Sports Ser.). 32p. (J). (gr. 5-7). lib. bdg. 24.22 (978-1-57572-948-0(2)) Heinemann Library.

Bass, Scott. Extreme Sports: Your Guide to Longboarding, Shortboarding, Tubing, Aerials, Hanging Ten, & More. 2003. (Illus.). 64p. (J). (gr. 4-7). pap. 8.95 (978-0-7922-5108-8(3) , National Geographic Children's Bks.) National Geographic Society.

Bizley, Kirk. Surfing. 1999. (Radical Sports Ser.). 32p. (J). (gr. 5-7). lib. bdg. 24.22 (978-1-57572-947-3(4)) Heinemann Library.

Brimner, Larry Dane. Surfing. 1998. (First Bks.). (Illus.). 64p. (J). (gr. 5-7). pap. 6.95 (978-0-531-15891-3(8) , Watts, Franklin) Scholastic Library Publishing.

Cooperman, Stephanie. Wakeboarding. 2005. (Rad Sports Techniques, Training, & Tricks Ser.). (Illus.). 48p. (YA). (gr. 5-8). lib. bdg. 26.50 (978-0-8239-3850-6(6)) Rosen Publishing Group, Inc., The.

Crossingham, John & Kalman, Bobbie. Extreme Surfing. 2003. (Extreme Sports - No Limits Ser.). (Illus.). 32p. (J). (gr. 3). (978-0-7787-1669-3(4)); pap. (978-0-7787-1715-7(1)) Crabtree Publishing Co.

Crump, A. K., ed. The Dog's Guide to Surfing: Hanging Ten with Man's Best Friend. 2004. (Illus.). 128p. (gr. 5 up). pap. 14.95 (978-0-9674898-7-2(3)) TCB-Cafe Publishing.

De Macedo, Joao. How to Be a Surfer. 2007. (Illus.). 130p. (J). pap. 19.95 (978-1-84126-201-7(3)) Meyer & Meyer Sport, Ltd. GBR. *Dist:* Perseus Distribution.

DeLa Vega, Timothy T., et al. 200 Years of Surfing Literature: An Annotated Bibliography. 2004. (Illus.). 108p. per. 19.95 (978-0-9754328-0-8(X)) DeLaVega, T.

Diaz, Roberto. My Surf Tricks. 2005. (Illus.). 26p. (J). per. 15.95 (978-0-9764788-5-0(4) , 1-866-238-7759) Olas.

Fitzpatrick, Jim. Surfing. 2008. (J). lib. bdg. 25.26 (***978-1-60279-019-3(1)***) Cherry Lake Publishing.

The 'Goods: 2004 Surfing Calendar of C. J. & Damien Hobgood. 2003. (YA). (978-0-9746953-0-3(0)) Board Sports Management.

Green, Naima. Surfing: Rules, Tips, Strategy, & Safety. 2005. (Sports from Coast to Coast Ser.). (Illus.). 48p. (J). (gr. 5-8). lib. bdg. 26.50 (978-1-4042-0184-2(X)) Rosen Publishing Group, Inc., The.

Herran, Joe & Thomas, Ron. Surfing. 2003. (Action Sports Ser.). (Illus.). 32p. (gr. 4-8). 28.00 (978-0-7910-7538-8(9) , Chelsea Hse.) Facts On File, Inc.

Kampion, Drew. Waves: From Surfing to Tsunami. Drew, Jeff & Peterson, Jeff, illus. 2005. 80p. (YA). 19.95 (978-1-58685-212-2(4)) Gibbs Smith, Publisher.

Labrecque, Ellen. Surfing Stars. 2007. (World's Greatest Athletes Ser.). 32p. (J). (gr. 1-5). 27.07 (978-1-59296-793-3(0)) Child's World, Inc.

Mason, Paul. Surfing. 2005. (Adrenalin! Ser.). (Illus.). 32p. (YA). (gr. 4 up). lib. bdg. 27.10 (978-1-59389-234-0(9)) Chrysalis Education.

—Surfing. 2001. (To the Limit Ser.). (Illus.). 32p. (J). (gr. 4-7). lib. bdg. 25.69 (978-0-7398-3165-6(8)) Raintree.

Maurer, Tracy. Surfing. 2003. (Radsports Guides Ser.). (Illus.). 48p. (gr. 4-8). 20.95 (978-1-58952-280-0(X)) Rourke Publishing, LLC.

McClellan, Ray. Surfing. 2008. (Illus.). 24p. (J). lib. bdg. 19.95 (***978-1-60014-145-4(5)***) Bellwether Media.

Miller, Chuck. Surfing. 2001. (Extreme Sports Ser.). (Illus.). 48p. (J). lib. bdg. 24.26 (978-0-7398-4689-6(2)) Raintree.

S

Peterson, Christine. Extreme Surfing. 2005. (Blazers—To the Extreme Ser.). (Illus.). 32p. (J). (ps). lib. bdg. 19.93 (978-0-7368-3786-6(8)) Capstone Pr., Inc.

—Extreme Surfing. (To the Extreme Ser.). 32p. (YA). pap. 7.95 (978-0-7368-5221-0(2)) Capstone Pr., Inc.

Pierce, Terry. Surfing A to Z Coloring Book. Kofsky, Kristen, illus. 2004. 24p. pap. 4.95 (978-1-57306-178-0(6)) Bess Pr., Inc.

Smalley, Carol. Ride the Giant Waves with Garrett Mcnamara. 2006. (Extreme Sports Ser.). (Illus.). 32p. (J). (gr. 1-4). lib. bdg. (978-1-58415-486-0(1)) Mitchell Lane Pubs., Inc.

Smith, Ryan A. Surfboards. 2006. 32p. (gr. 3-5). 22.45 (978-1-4103-0719-4(0) , Blackbirch Pr., Inc.) Thomson Gale.

The Surf Carnival: Individual Title Six-Packs. 16p. (gr. 2 up). 35.00 (978-0-7635-9237-0(4)) Rigby Education.

Surfing. 2004. (I-Quest Ser.). (J). (978-1-84229-743-8(0)) Top That! Publishing PLC.

Voeller, Edward A. Extreme Surfing. 2000. (Extreme Sports Ser.). (Illus.). 48p. (J). (gr. 3-4). lib. bdg. 21.26 (978-0-7368-0485-1(4) , Capstone High-Interest Bks.) Capstone Pr., Inc.

Wakeboarding. (To the Extreme Ser.). 32p. (YA). 7.95 (978-0-7368-5223-4(9)) Capstone Pr., Inc.

SURFING—FICTION

Advantage Publishers Group & Saidens, Amy. Surfer Girl Sticker Book. 2007. (Illus.). 24p. (J). 14.95 (978-1-59223-632-9(4) , Silver Dolphin Bks.) Advantage Pubs. Group.

Allen, J. Kent. Embritt Waters & the Mark of the Rattlesnake. 2006. 229p. (J). pap. 14.95 (978-0-7414-2769-4(9)) Infinity Publishing.

Axelrod, Amy. The News Hounds Catch a Wave: A Geography Adventure. Bowers, Tim, illus. 2001. (J). 13.00 (978-0-689-82410-4(6) , Simon & Schuster Children's Publishing) Simon & Schuster Children's Publishing.

Barlow, Steve L. Surfers' Mad Myths Must Fly. (Illus.). 128p. (J). 7.95 (978-0-14-038347-8(6)) Penguin Bks., Ltd. GBR. *Dist:* Trafalgar Square Publishing.

Big Wave. 2000. (YA). 9.95 (978-1-56137-120-4(3)) Novel Units, Inc.

Bo, Ben. Skullcrack. 2003. 168p. (J). pap. 6.95 (978-0-8225-3311-5(1)); (gr. 9-12). 14.95 (978-0-8225-3308-5(1)) Lerner Publishing Group.

—Skullcrack. 2000. (gr. 5-8). lib. bdg. 15.25 (978-0-613-58938-3(6)) Tandem Library Bks.

—Xtreme: Skullcrack. 208p. (J). pap. (978-0-7475-4220-9(1)) Bloomsbury Publishing Plc GBR. *Dist:* Raincoast Bk. Distribution.

Brown, Marc. Buster Catches a Wave. 2005. (Postcards from Buster Ser.). (Illus.). 32p. (J). (gr. 1-4). pap. 14.99 (978-0-316-15903-6(4)); 7th ed. pap. 3.99 (978-0-316-00122-9(8)) Little Brown & Co.

Chase, Diana. Surf's Up. 1999. 200p. (J). pap. 12.95 (978-1-86368-250-3(3)) Fremantle Pr. AUS. *Dist:* International Specialized Bk. Services.

Choyce, Lesley. Wave Warrior. 2007. (Orca Soundings Ser.). 112p. (YA). (gr. 7 up). pap. (***978-1-55143-647-0(7)**); lib. bdg. (***978-1-55143-649-4(3)***) Orca Bk. Pubs.

Christopher, Matt. Catching Waves. 2006. 128p. (J). (gr. 3-7). pap. 4.99 (978-0-316-05848-3(3)) Little Brown & Co.

Collins, Terry. Surf's Up! 2001. (gr. 3-6). lib. bdg. 11.80 (978-0-613-87766-4(7)) Tandem Library Bks.

Cox, Rhonda. I Ride the Waves. Cox, Rhonda, photos by. 1999. (Books for Young Learners). (Illus.). 8p. (J). (gr. k-2). pap. 5.00 (978-1-57274-335-9(2) , A2464) Owen, Richard C. Pubs., Inc.

Decter, Ed. Expedition to Surf Island. Yuen Jr., Sammy, illus. 2009. (Outriders Ser.). 224p. (J). pap. 4.99 (***978-1-4169-1308-5(4)*** , Aladdin) Simon & Schuster Children's Publishing.

Denton, Terry. The Obelisk of Eeeno. 2004. (Storymaze Ser.). (Illus.). 144p. (J). pap. 6.95 (978-1-74114-089-7(7)) Allen & Unwin AUS. *Dist:* Independent Pubs. Group.

Hall, Susan, illus. Surf That Wave! 2006. (Backyardigans Ser.). 24p. (J). pap. 3.99 (978-1-4169-1482-2(X) , Simon Spotlight/Nickelodeon) Simon & Schuster Children's Publishing.

Hamilton, Bethany & Bundschuh, Rick. Burned. 2007. (Soul Surfer#8482; Ser.). (Illus.). 144p. (J). pap. 6.99 (978-0-310-71223-7(8)) Zonderkidz.

—Clash. 2007. (Soul Surfer#8482; Ser.). (Illus.). 144p. (J). pap. 6.99 (978-0-310-71222-0(X)) Zonderkidz.

Hemphill, Rick, illus. The Adventures of Kirra & Rincon: Li'l Kids, Big Waves. 2005. 32p. (J). 17.99 (978-0-9766408-0-6(5)) Kerr, Justin & Shelley.

Hill, Donna. Shipwreck Season. 1998. 224p. (J). (gr. 4-6). tchr. ed. 16.00 (978-0-395-86614-6(6) , Clarion Bks.) Houghton Mifflin Co. Trade & Reference Div.

Hoeffner, Karol Ann. Surf Ed. 2007. 288p. (YA). mass mkt. 5.99 (***978-1-4169-3970-2(9)*** , Simon Pulse) Simon & Schuster Children's Publishing.

Johnson, Lissa Halls & Wierenga, Kathy. No Lifeguard on Duty, Vol. 8. 2005. (Brio Girls Ser.). 192p. (YA). (gr. 6-11). pap. 7.99 (978-1-58997-081-6(0)) Focus on the Family Publishing.

Johnson, Pete. Surfers' Mind Reader. (Illus.). 128p. (J). 7.95 (978-0-14-038814-5(1)) Penguin Bks., Ltd. GBR. *Dist:* Trafalgar Square Publishing.

Komaiko, Leah. Malibu Carmie. 2007. 256p. (YA). (gr. 7-11). mass mkt. 5.99 (978-0-440-42014-9(8) , Laurel Leaf) Random Hse. Children's Bks.

Lopez, Jack. In the Break. 2006. (Illus.). 208p. (J). (gr. 7-17). 16.99 (978-0-316-00874-7(5)) Little Brown & Co.

—In the Break. 2007. 208p. (J). (gr. 7-17). pap. 7.99 (***978-0-316-06708-9(3)***) Little, Brown Bks. for Young Readers.

Mammano, Julie. Rhinos Who Surf. 2006. (Illus.). 32p. (J). pap. 6.95 (978-0-8118-5229-6(6)) Chronicle Bks. LLC.

Masters, Anthony. The Haunted Surfboard. Dennis, Peter, illus. 2007. (Graphic Quest Ser.). (J). 88p. (***978-1-59889-215-4(0)*** , 1256167); 80p. (gr. 2-8). lib. bdg. 21.26 (978-1-59889-080-8(8) , 1256167) Stone Arch Bks.

Metzenthen, David. Big Wave Day. 2000. (gr. 7-12). lib. bdg. 12.25 (978-0-613-28757-9(6)) Tandem Library Bks.

—Rodney, the Surfing Duck. Axelsen, Stephen, illus. 1999. (Supa Doopers Ser.). 64p. (J). (978-0-7608-1929-6(7)) Sundance/Newbridge Educational Publishing.

Noël, Alyson & Quiksilver Entertainment. Laguna Cove. 2006. 224p. (YA). pap. 8.95 (978-0-312-34869-4(X) , St. Martin's Griffin) St. Martin's Pr.

Perry, Chrissie. Go Girl! #6 - Surf's Up! Oswald, Ash, illus. 2008. (Go Girl! Ser.). 96p. (J). pap. 3.99 (***978-0-312-34647-8(6)***) Feiwel & Friends.

Ray, Belinda & SparkNotes Staff. Sun-Kissed. 2004. (SparkNotes SAT Vocabulary Novels Ser.). (Illus.). 200p. pap. 7.95 (978-1-4114-0080-1(1)) Spark Publishing Group.

Renaud, Andrea. Sammy the Surfing Pelican Meets Steve the Surf Guru. l.t. ed. 2003. (Illus.). 32p. (J). per. (978-0-9717041-3-8(9)) A Happy Friend, Inc.

Rogo, Thomas Paul. The Surfrider: A Midwestern Odyssey. Rogo, Thomas Paul, illus. 1999. (Illus.). 80p. (J). (gr. 3 up). 19.95 (978-1-57306-082-0(8)); 4.95 (978-1-57306-110-0(7)) Bess Pr., Inc.

Smith, Stephen D. & Caldwell, Lise. Rivals on the Waves. 2006. 128p. (J). pap. 5.99 (978-0-7847-1470-6(3) , 42141) Standard Publishing.

Surfer Girl. 2004. (Illus.). (J). (978-1-59577-014-1(3)) Starfall Education.

Wax, Wendy. Practice Makes Perfect. Date not set. (Rocket Power Ready-to-Read Ser.: Vol. 6). (J). 3.99 (978-0-689-86591-6(0) , Simon Spotlight/Nickelodeon) Simon & Schuster Children's Publishing.

West, J. A. C. Wipeout. Lawrie, Robin, illus. 2008. (J). pap. (***978-1-59889-905-4(8)***); 33p. (YA). (gr. 5-9). lib. bdg. 21.26 (***978-1-59889-853-8(1)***) Stone Arch Bks.

Zindel, Paul. The Surfing Corpse. 2001. (P. C. Hawke Mystery Ser.: No. 2). 128p. pap. 4.99 (978-0-7868-1711-5(9)) Hyperion Bks. for Children.

SURGEONS

African-American Surgeons. 2000. (My Ancestors—My Heroes Ser.: Vol. 18). (J). (gr. 3-4). (978-1-893091-17-7(1)) Parker Publishing Co.

Bankston, John. Joseph Lister & the Story of Antiseptics. 2004. (Uncharted, Unexplored, & Unexplained Ser.). (Illus.). 48p. (J). (gr. 4-8). lib. bdg. 29.95 (978-1-58415-262-0(1)) Mitchell Lane Pubs., Inc.

—Robert Jarvik & the First Artificial Heart. l.t. ed. 2002. (Unlocking the Secrets of Science Ser.). (Illus.). 56p. (gr. 4-10). lib. bdg. 25.70 (978-1-58415-116-6(1)) Mitchell Lane Pubs., Inc.

Parks, Peggy J. Joseph Lister: Father of Antiseptics. 2005. (Giants of Science Ser.). 64p. (J). (gr. 5-7). 26.20 (978-1-4103-0322-6(5) , Blackbirch Pr., Inc.) Thomson Gale.

Salas, Laura Purdie. Charles Drew: Pioneer in Medicine. 2006. (Fact Finders Ser.). (Illus.). 32p. (J). (978-0-7368-5433-7(9)) Capstone Pr., Inc.

Schraff, Anne. Charles Drew: Pioneer in Medicine. 2003. (Famous Inventors Ser.). (Illus.). 32p. (J). (gr. 1-4). lib. bdg. 22.60 (978-0-7660-2008-5(8)) Enslow Pubs., Inc.

—Dr. Charles Drew: Blood Bank Innovator. 2003. (African-American Biographies Ser.). (Illus.). 128p. (J). (gr. 6-12). lib. bdg. 26.60 (978-0-7660-2117-4(3)) Enslow Pubs., Inc.

Trice, Linda. Charles Drew. 2000. (Ideas on Trial Ser.). (Illus.). 121p. (C). (gr. 8-12). pap. 8.95 (978-0-07-135317-5(8)) McGraw-Hill Cos., The.

Uschan, Michael V. A Civil War Doctor. 2005. (Working Life Ser.). (Illus.). 112p. (YA). (gr. 7-10). lib. bdg. 29.95 (978-1-59018-578-0(1) , Lucent Bks.) Thomson Gale.

Wilson, John. Righting Wrongs: The Story of Norman Bethune. 2004. (Stories of Canada Ser.). (Illus.). 65p. (J). (gr. 3-7). 14.95 (978-0-929141-71-8(7)) Napoleon Publishing/Rendezvous Pr. CAN. *Dist:* AtlasBooks Distribution.

Wyckoff, Edwin Brit. Heart Man: Vivien Thomas, African-American Heart Surgery Pioneer. 2007. (Genius at Work! Great Inventor Biographies Ser.). (Illus.). 32p. (J). (gr. 3-4). lib. bdg. 22.60 (***978-0-7660-2849-4(6)*** , Enslow Elementary) Enslow Pubs., Inc.

SURGERY

Alagna, Magdalena. Everything You Need to Know about the Dangers of Cosmetic Surgery. 2005. (Need to Know Library). (Illus.). 64p. (YA). (gr. 4-6). lib. bdg. 25.25 (978-0-8239-3552-9(3)) Rosen Publishing Group, Inc., The.

Apel, Melanie Ann. Let's Talk about When You Have Stitches. 2002. (Let's Talk Library). (Illus.). 24p. (J). lib. bdg. 18.75 (978-0-8239-5861-0(2) , PowerKids Pr.) Rosen Publishing Group, Inc., The.

Bankston, John. Joseph Lister & the Story of Antiseptics. 2004. (Uncharted, Unexplored, & Unexplained Ser.). (Illus.). 48p. (J). (gr. 4-8). lib. bdg. 29.95 (978-1-58415-262-0(1)) Mitchell Lane Pubs., Inc.

—Robert Jarvik & the First Artificial Heart. l.t. ed. 2002. (Unlocking the Secrets of Science Ser.). (Illus.). 56p. (gr. 4-10). lib. bdg. 25.70 (978-1-58415-116-6(1)) Mitchell Lane Pubs., Inc.

Carter, Stephanie & Lederman, JoAnn. Meditapes One - For Your Surgery. 1998. (J). pap. 24.95 incl. audio (978-1-893868-00-7(1)) Meditapes.

Gordon, Melanie Apel. Let's Talk about When You Have to Have Your Tonsils Out. 2000. (Let's Talk Library). (Illus.). 24p. (J). (gr. 3). lib. bdg. 18.75 (978-0-8239-5418-6(8) , PowerKids Pr.) Rosen Publishing Group, Inc., The.

Libal, Autumn. Can I Change the Way I Look? A Teen's Guide to the Health Implications of Cosmetic Surgery, Makeovers, & Beyond. 2004. (Science of Health Ser.). (Illus.). 128p. (J). (978-1-59084-843-2(8)) Mason Crest Pubs.

Morgan, Sally. Body Sculpting. 2005. (Science at the Edge Ser.). (Illus.). 64p. (J). (978-1-4034-7762-0(0)) Heinemann Library.

Townsend, John. Surgery: Scalpels, Stitches & Scars. 2005. (Raintree Freestyle Ser.). (Illus.). 56p. (J). (978-1-4109-1332-6(5)); pap. (978-1-4109-1337-1(6)) Steck-Vaughn.

Winkler, Kathleen. Cosmetic Surgery for Teens: Choices & Consequences. 2003. (Teen Issues Ser.). (Illus.). 64p. (J). lib. bdg. 22.60 (978-0-7660-1957-7(8)) Enslow Pubs., Inc.

SURGERY—VOCATIONAL GUIDANCE

Ellis, Catherine. Planes. 2007. (Mega Military Machines Ser.). (Illus.). 24p. (J). (gr. k-5). lib. bdg. 21.25 (978-1-4042-3667-7(8)) Rosen Publishing Group, Inc., The.

Giddens, Sandra & Giddens, Owen. Future Techniques in Surgery. 2005. (Library of Future Medicine). (Illus.). 64p. (YA). (gr. 7-12). lib. bdg. 26.50 (978-0-8239-3667-0(8)) Rosen Publishing Group, Inc., The.

Primm, E. Russell. Surgical Technician. 1998. (Careers Without College Ser.). (Illus.). 48p. (J). (gr. 3-7). pap. 19.00 (978-0-516-21288-3(5) , Children's Pr.) Scholastic Library Publishing.

SURINAME

Beatty, Noelle Blackmer. Suriname. 1999. (Major World Nations Ser.). (Illus.). 144p. (YA). (gr. 4-7). 29.95 (978-0-7910-4748-4(2) , Chelsea Hse.) Facts On File, Inc.

Williams, Colleen Madonna Flood. Suriname. 2003. (Discovering Latin America Ser.). (Illus.). 64p. (J). (gr. 5 up). lib. bdg. (978-1-59084-295-9(2)) Mason Crest Pubs.

SURVEYING

Anderson, Judith. Ways to Do Surveys. 2007. (***978-1-59920-053-8(8)***) Smart Apple Media.

Morrison, Taylor. The Coast Mappers. 2004. (Illus.). 48p. (J). (gr. 3-5). tchr. ed. 16.00 (978-0-618-25408-8(0) , Walter Lorraine) Houghton Mifflin Co. Trade & Reference Div.

SURVIVAL AFTER AIRPLANE ACCIDENTS, SHIPWRECKS, ETC.

see also Wilderness Survival

Ashcraft, Tami Oldham & McGearhart, Susea. Red Sky in Mourning: A True Story of Love, Loss, & Survival at Sea. 2002. (Illus.). 240p. 31.95 (978-0-7868-6791-2(4)) Hyperion Pr.

—Red Sky in Mourning: The True Story of Love, Loss, & Survival at Sea. 2003. 240p. pap. 19.95 (978-0-7868-8676-0(5)) Hyperion Pr.

Calabro, Marian. The Perilous Journey of the Donner Party. 1999. (Illus.). 192p. (J). (gr. 5-9). tchr. ed. 20.00 (978-0-395-86610-8(3) , Clarion Bks.) Houghton Mifflin Co. Trade & Reference Div.

Cefrey, Holly. Steven Callahan: Adrift at Sea. 2003. (Survivor Ser.). (Illus.). 48p. (J). 23.00 (978-0-516-24330-6(6)); (YA). (gr. 7-12). pap. 6.95 (978-0-516-27868-1(1)) Scholastic Library Publishing. (Children's Pr.).

—Steven Callahan: Adrift at Sea. 2003. lib. bdg. 15.25 (978-0-613-67934-3(2)) Tandem Library Bks.

Cook, Peter. You Wouldn't Want to Sail on 19th Century Whaling Ship. Antram, David, illus. 2004. (You Wouldn't Want to Ser.). 32p. (J). (gr. 2-5). pap. 9.95 (978-0-531-16399-3(7) , Watts, Franklin) Scholastic Library Publishing.

Cook, Peter & Salariya, David. You Wouldn't Want to Sail on a 19th-Century Whaling Ship! Grisly Tasks You'd Rather Not Do. Antram, David, illus. 2004. (You Wouldn't Want To Ser.). (J). 28.50 (978-0-531-12356-0(1) , Watts, Franklin) Scholastic Library Publishing.

Currie, Stephen. Escapes from Natural Disasters. 2003. (Great Escapes Ser.). (Illus.). 112p. (J). 29.95 (978-1-59018-278-9(2) , Lucent Bks.) Thomson Gale.

Deaton, Wendy & Johnson, Kendall. GROW I Am a Survivor: A Child's Workbook about Surviving Disasters. 2002. (Grow Ser.). (Illus.). 32p. (J). pap., stu. ed., wbk. ed. 11.95 (978-0-89793-242-4(0)) Hunter Hse., Inc.

Donkin, Andrew. Zeppelin: The Age of the Airship. 2000. (Eyewitness Readers Ser.). (Illus.). (J). (978-0-606-21008-9(3)) Tandem Library Bks.

Dowswell, P. True Survival Stories. 2004. (True Adventure Stories Ser.). 144p. (J). lib. bdg. 12.95 (978-1-58086-457-2(0)) EDC Publishing.

Harris, David. Survival! 2005. (X-Zone Ser.). (Illus.). 30p. (gr. 4-8). 23.00 (978-0-7910-8984-2(3)) Facts On File, Inc.

High-Interest Nonfiction: Survivors 3-5. 2003. 128p. (J). per. 10.99 (978-0-88724-950-1(7) , CD-4320) Carson-Dellosa Publishing Co., Inc.

Kraske, Robert. Marooned: The Strange but True Adventures of Alexander Selkirk, the Real Robinson Crusoe. Parker, Robert Andrew, illus. 2005. 128p. (J). (gr. 5-9). 15.00 (978-0-618-56843-7(3) , Clarion Bks.) Houghton Mifflin Co. Trade & Reference Div.

Leroe, Ellen. Disaster! 2000. 240p. (gr. 3-7). pap. 5.99 (978-0-7868-1403-9(9)) Hyperion Paperbacks for Children.

—Disaster! Three Real-Life Stories of Survival. 2000. 144p. (J). (gr. 5-9). 15.99 (978-0-7868-0544-0(7)) Hyperion Bks. for Children.

—Disaster! Three Real-Life Stories of Survival. 2000. (gr. 5-8). lib. bdg. 14.15 (978-0-613-36304-4(3)) Tandem Library Bks.

Leroe, Ellen W. Disaster! 2000. 240p. (gr. 3-7). 16.49 (978-0-7868-2474-8(3)) Hyperion Pr.

Lewis, Brenda Ralph. Wilderness Rescue with the U. S. Search & Rescue Task Force. 2003. (Rescue & Prevention Ser.). (Illus.). 96p. (J). (gr. 7 up). lib. bdg. (978-1-59084-404-5(1)) Mason Crest Pubs.

Markle, Sandra. Rescues! 2006. (Illus.). 88p. (J). 25.26 (978-0-8225-3413-6(4) , Millbrook Pr.) Lerner Publishing Group.

McNab, Chris. Elite Forces Survival Guides, 20 vols., Set. 2002. (Illus.). 96p. (YA). (gr. 7 up). lib. bdg. (978-1-59084-000-9(3)) Mason Crest Pubs.

Morris, Deborah. Real Kids Real Adventures in Texas: Blanco River Rescue. 2002. (gr. k-3). lib. bdg. 17.60 (978-0-613-87965-1(1)) Tandem Library Bks.

Nickel, Howard J., tr. The Luftwaffe Guide Book to Basic Survival at Sea. 2002. (Illus.). 56p. (gr. 10-13). pap. 12.95 (978-0-7643-1619-7(2)) Schiffer Publishing, Ltd.

O'Shei, Tim. Shipwreck! Debbie Kiley's Story of Survival. 2008. (J). (***978-1-4296-0089-7(6)***) Capstone Pr., Inc.

Penner, Lucille Recht. Ice Wreck. LaFleur, David, illus. 2004. (Stepping Stones Ser.). 48p. (J). (gr. k-3). pap. 3.99 (978-0-307-26408-4(4) , Random Hse. Bks. for Young Readers) Random Hse. Children's Bks.

Philbrick, Nathaniel. Revenge of the Whale: The True Story of the Whaleship Essex. 176p. 2002. (Illus.). (YA). (gr. 4 up). 16.99 (978-0-399-23795-9(X) , Putnam Juvenile); 2004. (J). (gr. 5-9). reprint ed. pap. 7.99 (978-0-14-240068-5(8) , Puffin) Penguin Group (USA) Inc.

—Revenge of the Whale: The True Story of the Whaleship Essex. 2004. (Illus.). 164p. (J). (gr. k-9). per. 16.65 (978-0-613-97779-1(3)) Tandem Library Bks.

Porterfield, Jason. Shipwreck: True Stories of Survival. 2006. (Survivor Stories Ser.). (Illus.). 48p. (J). (gr. 5-8). lib. bdg. 26.50 (978-1-4042-1000-4(8)) Rosen Publishing Group, Inc., The.

Rohr, Ian. Survival Against the Odds. 2005. (Real Deal Ser.). (Illus.). 32p. (J). 18.50 (978-0-7910-8442-7(6) , Chelsea Hse.) Facts On File, Inc.

Searl, Duncan. Trapped! 2005. (Illus.). 48p. (J). (***978-0-669-51413-1(6)***) Great Source Education Group, Inc.

Shakespeare, William. The Tempest. Ermitage, Kathleen, ed. 2002. (Simply Shakespeare Ser.). (Illus.). 288p. pap. 8.99 (978-0-7641-2087-9(5)) Barron's Educational Series, Inc.

Spalding, Frank. Plane Crash: True Stories of Survival. 2006. (Survivor Stories Ser.). (Illus.). 48p. (J). (gr. 5-8). lib. bdg. 26.50 (978-1-4042-0999-2(9) , 1267009) Rosen Publishing Group, Inc., The.

Stephen Currie. Escapes from Man-Made Disasters. 2004. (Great Escapes Ser.). (Illus.). 112p. (J). 29.95 (978-1-59018-277-2(4)) Thomson Gale.

Storm, Rory. Castaway Survivor's Guide. (Survivors Ser.). (Illus.). (J). 2001. 128p. (gr. 3-7). pap. 4.99 (978-0-439-27055-7(3)); 2000. 120p. (978-0-439-27151-6(7)) Scholastic, Inc.

—Mountain Survivor's Guide. 2001. (Survivors Ser.). 128p. pap. 4.99 (978-0-439-32854-8(3)) Scholastic, Inc.

Werther, Scott P. Alive! Airplane Crash in the Andes Mountains. 2003. (Survivor Ser.). (Illus.). 48p. (J). 24.00 (978-0-516-24329-0(2) , Children's Pr.) Scholastic Library Publishing.

—Alive! Airplane Crash in the Andes Mountains. 2003. (gr. 7-12). lib. bdg. 15.25 (978-0-613-67864-3(8)) Tandem Library Bks.

Wulffson, Don L. The Upside-Down Voyage. Lyall, Dennis, illus. 2005. (J). (978-1-59336-334-5(6)); pap. (978-1-59336-335-2(4)) Mondo Publishing.

SURVIVAL AFTER AIRPLANE ACCIDENTS, SHIPWRECKS, ETC.—FICTION

Allison, Samuel B. An American Robinson Crusoe. 2005. 136p. pap. 10.95 (978-1-4218-0186-5(8) , 1st World Library - Literary Society) 1st World Publishing, Inc.

—An American Robinson Crusoe. 2004. reprint ed. pap. 15.95 (978-1-4191-0613-2(9)); pap. 1.99 (978-1-4192-0613-9(3)) Kessinger Publishing, LLC.

Andersen, C. B. The Book of Mormon Sleuths 2: The Lost Tribe. 2002. 261p. (J). pap. 9.95 (978-1-57008-842-1(X)) Scribbulations LLC.

Appleton, Victor. Tom Swift & His Wireless Message or Th. 2006. pap. (***978-1-4065-0911-3(6)***) Dodo Pr.

Asai, Carrie. Book of the Flame. 2004. lib. bdg. 15.30 (978-0-613-73423-3(8)) Tandem Library Bks.

—Book of the Sword. 2003. (gr. 7-12). lib. bdg. 15.30 (978-0-613-63150-1(1)) Tandem Library Bks.

Benjamin, David. Secrets from Beyond. Rawlings, Steve, illus. 2000. (Sixth Sense Ser.: Vol. 1). 160p. (gr. 4-7). pap. 4.99 (978-0-439-20270-1(1)) Scholastic, Inc.

Birch, Beverley. Tempest. 2007. (Illus.). 80p. 13.95 (***978-0-7502-4961-4(7)*** , Hodder Wayland) Hodder Children's Division GBR. *Dist:* Independent Pubs. Group.

Byars, Betsy. Little Horse on His Own. McPhail, David M., tr. McPhail, David M., illus. rev. ed. 2004. 48p. (J). 15.95 (978-0-8050-7352-2(3) , Holt, Henry & Co. Bks. For Young Readers) Holt, Henry & Co.

Carter, Alden R. Between a Rock & a Hard Place. 1999. (J). (978-0-606-15835-0(9)) Tandem Library Bks.

Collison, Linda. Star-Crossed. 2006. (Illus.). 416p. (YA). (gr. 9). 16.95 (978-0-375-83363-2(3)); lib. bdg. 18.99 (978-0-375-93363-9(8)) Random Hse. Children's Bks. (Knopf Bks. for Young Readers).

Cowley, Joy. Hunter. 2004. 176p. (YA). (gr. 5). 17.99 (978-0-399-24227-4(9) , Philomel) Penguin Group (USA) Inc.

Cummings, Priscilla. A Face First. 2003. (gr. 3-6). lib. bdg. 14.15 (978-0-613-61621-8(9)) Tandem Library Bks.

Danger in the Canyon. 1999. (SmartReader Ser.). (J). pap., tchr. ed. 19.95 incl. audio (978-0-7887-0128-3(2) , 79316T3) Recorded Bks., LLC.

Defoe, Daniel. The Adventures of Robinson Crusoe. 2002. (Great Illustrated Classics Ser.).Tr. of Robinson Crusoe. (Illus.). 240p. (J). (gr. 3-8). 21.35 (978-1-57765-677-7(6) , ABDO & Daughters) ABDO Publishing Co.

—Aventuras de Robinson Crusoe. 2003. (Advanced Reading Ser.: Vol. 73). (SPA., Illus.). 118p. (J). (gr. 4-7). (978-84-239-9043-6(5)) Espasa Calpe, S.A.

—The Farther Adventures of Robinson Crusoe. (Illus.). (J). reprint ed. 32.50 (978-0-404-07912-3(1)) AMS Pr., Inc.

—Robinson Crusoe. Heller, Julek, illus. 1998. (Eyewitness Classics Ser.).Tr. of Robinson Crusoe. 64p. (J). (gr. 3-6). 14.95 (978-0-7894-3625-2(6)) Dorling Kindersley Publishing, Inc.

—Robinson Crusoe. 2001. (Fast Track Classics Ser.).Tr. of Robinson Crusoe. (Illus.). 48p. pap. 9.99 (978-0-237-52283-4(7) , Evans Brothers, Limited) Evans Publishing Group GBR. *Dist:* Independent Pubs. Group.

—Robinson Crusoe. Exams Unlimited, Inc. Staff, ed. Paget, William, illus. 2001. Tr. of Robinson Crusoe. 104p. (J). reprint ed. cd-rom 5.20 (978-1-59132-021-0(6)) Exams Unlimited, Inc.

—Robinson Crusoe. Lindskoog, Kathryn, ed. Chitouras, Barbara, illus. 2002. (Classics for Young Readers Ser.).Tr. of Robinson Crusoe. 192p. (J). per. 7.99 (978-0-87552-735-2(3)) P & R Publishing.

—Robinson Crusoe. 2001. (Modern Library Classics Ser.).Tr. of Robinson Crusoe. 320p. pap. 7.95 (978-0-375-75732-7(5) , Modern Library) Random House Publishing Group.

—Robinson Crusoe. 2001. (Classics Ser.).Tr. of Robinson Crusoe. 304p. (YA). (gr. 3-7). pap. 5.99 (978-0-689-84408-9(5) , Aladdin) Simon & Schuster Children's Publishing.

—Robinson Crusoe. Akib, Jamel, illus. 2006. (Classic Starts Ser.).Tr. of Robinson Crusoe. 160p. (J). 4.95 (978-1-4027-2664-4(3)) Sterling Publishing Co., Inc.

—Robinson Crusoe.Tr. of Robinson Crusoe. 2001. (gr. 3-6). lib. bdg. 11.80 (978-0-613-63226-3(5)); 2001. (gr. 7-12). lib. bdg. 16.45 (978-0-613-64320-7(8)); 1999. (Illus.). (J). (978-0-606-21567-1(0)); 1999. (gr. 7-12). lib. bdg. 15.25 (978-0-613-33002-2(1)) Tandem Library Bks.

—Robinson Crusoe. 2000. (Coleccion "Clasicos Juveniles" Ser.).Tr. of Robinson Crusoe. (SPA., Illus.). 288p. (YA). (gr. 4-7). pap. 13.95 (978-1-58348-782-2(4)) iUniverse, Inc.

—Robinson Crusoe: With a Discussion of Resourcefulness. Landgraf, Kenneth, illus. 2003. (Values in Action Illustrated Classics Ser.). 190p. (J). (978-1-59203-035-4(1)) Learning Challenge, Inc.

Defoe, Daniel, et al. Robinson Crusoe. (Classics Illustrated Ser.).Tr. of Robinson Crusoe. (Illus.). 52p. (YA). pap. 4.95 (978-1-57209-021-7(9)) Classics International Entertainment, Inc.

Duey, Kathleen. San Francisco Earthquake, 1906. 1999. (978-0-606-17951-5(8)) Tandem Library Bks.

Duey, Kathleen & Bale, Karen. Trainwreck: Kansas, 1892. 1999. (Survival! Ser.: No. 8). (J). (gr. 4-7). (978-0-606-16279-1(8)) Tandem Library Bks.

Duey, Kathleen & Bale, Karen A. Blizzard: Colorado, 1886. 1998. (Survival! Ser.: No. 3). (J). (gr. 4-7). (978-0-606-13827-7(7)) Tandem Library Bks.

—Cave-In, St. Claire, Pennsylvania, 1859. 1998. (Survival! Ser.: No. 7). 160p. (J). (gr. 4-7). pap. 3.99 (978-0-689-82350-3(9) , Simon Pulse) Simon & Schuster Children's Publishing.

—Fire, Chicago, 1871. 1998. (Survival! Ser.: No. 4). (J). (gr. 4-7). (978-0-606-13828-4(5)) Tandem Library Bks.

—Flood: Mississippi 1927. 1998. (Survival! Ser.: No. 5). 176p. (J). (gr. 4-7). pap. 4.99 (978-0-689-82116-5(6) , Aladdin) Simon & Schuster Children's Publishing.

—Flood, Mississippi, 1927. 1998. (Survival! Ser.: No. 5). (J). (gr. 4-7). 10.64 (978-0-606-13829-1(3)) Tandem Library Bks.

—Forest Fire, Hinckley, Minnesota, 1894. 1999. (Survival! Ser.: No. 10). (J). (gr. 4-7). (978-0-606-16301-9(8)) Tandem Library Bks.

—Hurricane, New Bedford, Massachusetts, 1784. 1999. (Survival! Ser.: No. 9). 160p. (J). (gr. 4-7). per. 4.50 (978-0-689-82544-6(7) , Simon Pulse) Simon & Schuster Children's Publishing.

Easley, Mary Ann. I Am the Ice Worm. 2003. 128p. (J). (gr. 4-7). 16.95 (978-1-56397-412-0(6)) Boyds Mills Pr.

—I Am the Ice Worm. 1998. (978-0-606-13500-9(6)) Tandem Library Bks.

Eckert, Allan W. Return to Hawk's Hill. 1998. (Illus.). 160p. (J). (gr. 7-12). 15.95 (978-0-316-21593-0(7)) Little Brown & Co.

—Return to Hawk's Hill. 2000. (978-0-606-17850-1(3)) Tandem Library Bks.

—Return to Hawk's Hill: Sequel to the Newbery Honor-Winning Incident at Hawk's Hill. 2000. 208p. (J). (gr. 7-17). pap. 15.99 (978-0-316-00689-7(0)) Little Brown & Co.

Flegg, Aubrey. The Cinnamon Tree: A Novel Set in Africa. 2003. 208p. (YA). reprint ed. pap. 7.95 (978-0-86278-657-1(6)) O'Brien Pr., Ltd., The IRL. *Dist:* Independent Pubs. Group.

George, Jean Craighead. Julie of the Wolves. Schoenherr, John, illus. 2003. (Julie of the Wolves Ser.). 208p. (YA). (gr. 7 up). pap. 5.99 (978-0-06-054095-1(8) , Harper Trophy) HarperCollins Pubs.

—Julie of the Wolves. l.t. ed. 2004. (Beeler Mystery Ser.). 32.95 (978-1-58118-121-0(3)) LRS.

—Julie's Wolf Pack. Minor, Wendell, illus. 1999. (Julie of the Wolves Ser.). 208p. (J). (gr. 5 up). pap. 5.99 (978-0-06-440721-2(7) , Harper Trophy) HarperCollins Pubs.

Godolphin, Mary. The Swiss Family Robinson Told in Words. 2006. 24.99 ***(978-1-4280-4168-4(0));*** pap. 18.99 ***(978-1-4280-4195-0(8))*** IndyPublish.com.

Golding, Theresa Martin & Easley, Mary Ann. I Am the Ice Worm. 2004. (Illus.). 128p. (YA). (gr. 4-6). pap. 9.95 (978-1-59078-281-1(5)) Boyds Mills Pr.

Golding, William. Lord of the Flies. 1999. 27p. (J). (gr. 9-12). 9.95 (978-1-56137-383-3(4) , BK8384) Novel Units, Inc.

—Lord of the Flies. 2002. (YA). pap. 9.99 (978-0-399-52901-6(2)) Penguin Group (USA) Inc.

—Lord of the Flies. 208p. (YA). (gr. 7 up). pap. 6.95 (978-0-8072-1364-3(0) , Listening Library) Random Hse. Audio Publishing Group.

Hill, Kirkpatrick. Toughboy & Sister. 2000. 128p. (J). (gr. 3-7). pap. 9.95 (978-0-689-83978-8(2) , Aladdin) Simon & Schuster Children's Publishing.

Hobbs, William. Wild Man Island. 192p. (J). (gr. 5 up). 2003. pap. 5.99 (978-0-380-73310-1(2) , Harper Trophy); 2002. (Illus.). 19.99 (978-0-688-17473-6(6)); 2002. (Illus.). lib. bdg. 16.89 (978-0-06-029810-4(3)) HarperCollins Pubs.

Holcomb, Jerry K. The Chinquapin Tree. 1998. (Accelerated Reader Bks.). 192p. (J). (gr. 3-7). 14.95 (978-0-7614-5028-3(9) , Cavendish Children's Bks.) Cavendish, Marshall Corp.

Hyland, Hilary. The Wreck of the Ethie. 1999. (978-0-606-22861-9(6)) Tandem Library Bks.

—Wreck of the Ethie. 1999. (gr. 3-6). lib. bdg. 16.40 (978-0-613-23823-6(0)) Tandem Library Bks.

Jenkins, Jerry B. Crash at Cannibal Valley. 2006. (AirQuest Adventures Ser.). 160p. (J). pap. 6.99 (978-0-310-71347-0(1)) Zonderkidz.

Jenner, Caryn. Survivors: The Night the Titanic Sank. Martin, Linda, ed. 2001. (Readers Ser.). (Illus.). 32p. (J). (ps-3). pap. 3.99 (978-0-7894-7373-8(9)) Dorling Kindersley Publishing, Inc.

Jenner, Caryn & Dorling Kindersley Publishing Staff. Survivors: The Night the Titanic Sank. 2001. (Readers Ser.). (Illus.). 32p. (J). (ps-3). 14.99 (978-0-7894-7374-5(7)) Dorling Kindersley Publishing, Inc.

Kurtz, Jane. River Friendly, River Wild. Brennan, Neil, illus. 2007. 40p. (J). 7.99 (978-1-4169-3487-5(1) , Aladdin) Simon & Schuster Children's Publishing.

Lamb, Charles & Lamb, Mary. Tales from Shakespeare: "Twelfth Night" Strang, Kay, ed. Andrews, Gary, illus. rev. ed. 2005. 40p. pap. 4.95 (978-0-9542905-7-3(7)) Capercaillie Bks., Ltd GBR. *Dist:* Wilson & Assocs.

Lansing, Richard D., Jr. The Green Curly-Tailed Lizard. Lansing, Randy, illus. 1999. 48p. (J). (ps-4). mass mkt. 6.00 (978-0-9661844-4-0(0)) Purple Gorilla, LLC, The.

Lawrence, Iain. The Wreckers. 1999. (978-0-606-17565-4(2)) Tandem Library Bks.

—Wreckers. 1999. (gr. 5-8). lib. bdg. 13.55 (978-0-613-22807-7(3)) Tandem Library Bks.

—The Wreckers. 1999. (Dell Yearling Book Ser.). 224p. (J). (gr. 5-9). reprint ed. 5.99 (978-0-440-41545-9(4) , Yearling) Random Hse. Children's Bks.

—The Wreckers. unabr. ed. 2000. (YA). (gr. 7). pap., stu. ed. 59.95 incl. audio (978-0-7887-4195-1(0) , 41097) Recorded Bks., LLC.

Leavitt, Caroline. Robinhound Crusoe. l.t. ed. 1999. (Adventures of Wishbone Ser.: No. 4). (Illus.). 144p. (J). (gr. 4 up). lib. bdg. 22.60 (978-0-8368-2300-4(1)) Stevens, Gareth Inc.

Llewellyn, Sam. Bad Bad Darlings. 2005. 240p. (J). ***(978-0-14-131701-4(9)*** , Puffin) Penguin Group (USA) Inc.

Lowden, Stephanie. Time of the Eagle: A Story of an Ojibwe Winter. 2004. 128p. (J). pap. 12.00 (978-1-883953-34-8(0)) Midwest Traditions, Inc.

Marryat, Frederick. Masterman Ready. l.t. ed. 2006. 276p. pap. 16.99 (978-1-4264-0573-0(1)) BiblioBazaar.

Marsden, John. Darkness Be My Friend. 1999. 288p. (YA). (gr. 7-12). 16.00 (978-0-395-92274-3(7)) Houghton Mifflin Co. Trade & Reference Div.

—The Dead of Night. 1999. (J). (978-0-606-16450-4(2)) Tandem Library Bks.

—A Killing Frost. 2006. (Tomorrow Ser.: No. 3). 288p. (J). pap. 8.99 (978-0-439-82912-0(7) , Scholastic Paperbacks) Scholastic, Inc.

—Tomorrow, When the War Began. ed. 2006. (Tomorrow Ser.: No. 1). 304p. (J). pap. 8.99 (978 0 439 82910 6(0) , Scholastic Paperbacks) Scholastic, Inc.

Martel, Yann. Life of Pi: A Novel. 2003. (gr. 7-12). lib. bdg. 23.45 (978-0-613-59907-8(1)) Tandem Library Bks.

McCaughrean, Geraldine. Smile! 2nd rev. ed. 2004. (Illus.). 128p. (J). (978-0-19-271961-4(0)) Oxford Univ. Pr., Inc.

—The White Darkness. 2007. 384p. (J). (gr. 7 up). 16.99 (978-0-06-089035-3(5)); lib. bdg. 17.89 (978-0-06-089036-0(3)) HarperCollins Pubs. (HarperTeen).

McCullagh, Sheila. Shipwrecked. 2007. (Three Pirates Ser.). (Illus.). 48p. 15.95 ***(978-1-84560-043-3(6))*** Mercury Bks. Ltd. GBR. *Dist:* International Publishers Marketing.

Mikaelsen, Ben. Red Midnight. 2003. 224p. (J). (gr. 5 up). pap. 5.99 (978-0-380-80561-7(8)) HarperCollins Pubs.

—Red Midnight. 2003. (gr. 5-8). lib. bdg. 14.15 (978-0-613-57776-2(0)) Tandem Library Bks.

Neale, Jonathan. Himalaya. 2004. 160p. (J). (gr. 5-9). tchr. ed. 16.00 (978-0-618-41200-6(X)) Houghton Mifflin Co. Trade & Reference Div.

O'Donnell, Liam. Wild Ride. Deas, Michael, illus. 2007. 64p. (J). (gr. 3-7). pap. ***(*978-1-55143-756-9(2))*** Orca Bk. Pubs.

Orr, Wendy. Nim's Island. Millard, Kerry, illus. 2002. 128p. (gr. 3-7). 5.50 (978-0-440-41868-9(2) , Yearling) Random Hse. Children's Bks.

Paulsen, Gary. Hatchet. 2002. (Illus.). (J). 14.47 (978-0-7587-0017-9(2)) Book Wholesalers, Inc.

—Hatchet. 1999. 235p. (J). 17.90 (978-0-03-054626-6(5)) Holt, Rinehart & Winston.

—Hatchet. l.t. ed. 2000. (LRS Large Print Cornerstone Ser.). 205p. (YA). (gr. 4-12). lib. bdg. 28.95 (978-1-58118-055-8(1) , 23469) LRS.

—Hatchet. 2003. 151p. (J). 9.99 (978-0-330-31045-1(3) , Pan) Pan Macmillan GBR. *Dist:* Trafalgar Square Publishing.

—Hatchet. 2000. 195p. (J). (gr. 4-6). pap. 4.99 (978-0-8072-8320-2(7) , Listening Library) Random Hse. Audio Publishing Group.

—Hatchet. 2000. (Illus.). 208p. (YA). 17.99 (978-0-689-84092-0(6) , Atheneum/Richard Jackson Bks.) Simon & Schuster Children's Publishing.

—Hatchet. Willis, Drew, illus. 20th ed. 2007. 188p. (J). (gr. 5-9). 19.99 ***(*978-1-4169-2508-8(2))*** Simon & Schuster Children's Publishing.

Paulson, Gary. Hatchet. unabr. ed. 2004. 195p. (J). (gr. 5-9). pap. 36.00 incl. audio (978-0-8072-8319-6(3) , YA161SP, Listening Library) Random Hse. Audio Publishing Group.

Peck, Robert Newton. Extra Innings. 2003. (gr. 5-8). lib. bdg. 14.15 (978-0-613-61762-8(2)) Tandem Library Bks.

Peretti, Frank E. Mayday at Two Thousand Five Hundred. 2005. (Cooper Kids Adventure Ser.: Vol. 8). 144p. (J). pap. 6.99 (978-1-4003-0577-3(2)) Nelson, Thomas Inc.

—Trapped at the Bottom of the Sea. 144p. 2004. (Cooper Kids Adventures Ser.: No. 4). (gr. 4-7). 5.99 (978-0-89107-594-3(1)); Vol. 4. 2005. (Cooper Kids Adventure Ser.: Vol. 4). (gr. 4-6). pap. 5.99 (978-1-58134-621-3(2) , Crossway Bibles) Crossway Bks.

Pressler, Mirjam. Malka. 2005. 288p. (YA). (gr. 6). reprint ed. pap. 5.99 (978-0-14-240269-6(9) , Puffin) Penguin Group (USA) Inc.

Saltzwedel, Hans H. Hans' Journal: A Young German's Memories of His Family's Survival During Germany's Darkest Days. 2003. (Illus.). 234p. per. 19.95 net. (978-1-931934-17-6(7)) Back Yard Pub.

Schaaf, Ron. BearClaw: Finding Courage Within. 2007. (J). ***(*978-0-9787555-1-5(0))*** Hickory Tales Publishing.

Shaw, Janet Beeler. Kaya's Escape! A Survival Story, Bk. 2. Farnsworth, Bill & McAliley, Susan, illus. 2002. (American Girls Collection: Bk. 2). 88p. (gr. 2-7). (J). 12.95 (978-1-58485-426-5(X)); 6.95 (978-1-58485-425-8(1)) American Girl Publishing, Inc.

Sims, Matt. Deep Sea. 1999. (gr. 3-6). lib. bdg. 10.85 (978-0-613-30351-4(2)) Tandem Library Bks.

Smelcer, John. The Trap. 2007. 192p. (YA). pap. 7.99 ***(*978-0-312-37755-7(X))*** Square Fish.

Smith, Duane. Heritage Revealed Series, 3. (J). (gr. 2-9). pap. 13.95 (978-1-886218-00-0(5)) Azimuth Pr.

Smith, Roland. Peak. 2008. (Illus.). 272p. (YA). pap. 6.95 ***(*978-0-15-206268-2(8)*** , Harcourt Paperbacks) Harcourt Children's Bks.

Sorrells/Sorrells. Scratch. 2006. 222p. (J). lib. bdg. 23.08 ***(*978-1-4242-2214-8(1))*** Fitzgerald Bks.

Strickland, Brad, et al. The Storm: A Novelization. 2006. (Flight 29 down Ser.: Vol. 4). 224p. (J). ***(*978-1-4156-8721-5(8)*** , Grosset & Dunlap) Penguin Group (USA) Inc.

Stroud, Bettye & Lucas, Cedric, illus. The Leaving. 2001. 32p. (J). (gr. 1-4). 15.95 (978-0-7614-5067-2(X) , Cavendish Children's Bks.) Cavendish, Marshall Corp.

Swiss Family Robinson Study Guide. 2002. (Illus.). 48p. (YA). per. 17.95 (978-1-56254-532-1(9) , SP5329) Saddleback Educational Publishing.

Tait, Chris & Wyss, Johann David. The Swiss Family Robinson. Akib, Jamel, illus. 2007. 151p. (J). ***(*978-1-4287-4213-0(1))*** Sterling Publishing Co., Inc.

Taylor, Theodore. The Cay. 2000. 171p. (J). 15.60 (978-0-03-054604-4(4)) Holt, Rinehart & Winston.

—The Cay. 144p. 2003. (J). (gr. 5). mass mkt. 5.99 (978-0-440-22912-4(X) , Laurel Leaf); 2002. (gr. 4-7). 5.99 (978-0-440-41663-0(9) , Yearling) Random Hse. Children's Bks.

—Cay. 2003. (gr. 5-8). lib. bdg. 13.55 (978-0-613-72282-7(5)); 2002. (gr. 3-6). lib. bdg. 13.55 (978-0-613-33748-9(4)) Tandem Library Bks.

—Cayo. 2001. (SPA.). (gr. 3-6). lib. bdg. 17.05 (978-0-613-44195-7(8)) Tandem Library Bks.

Tullson, Diane. The Darwin Expedition. 2007. (Orca Sports Ser.). 112p. (YA). (gr. 7 up). pap. ***(*978-1-55143-676-0(0));*** lib. bdg. ***(*978-1-55143-678-4(7))*** Orca Bk. Pubs.

Twelfth Night Paperback Book. 2006. (YA). 7.95 ***(*978-1-56254-858-2(1))*** Saddleback Educational Publishing.

Twelfth Night Study Guide. 2006. (YA). per. 17.95 ***(*978-1-56254-859-9(X))*** Saddleback Educational Publishing.

Umphenour, Terry. Across a Broken Sky. 2001. 176p. (YA). pap. 12.95 (978-0-595-17949-7(5) , Writer's Showcase Pr.) iUniverse, Inc.

Werlin, Nancy. Locked Inside. 2001. 272p. (YA). (gr. 7). mass mkt. 5.99 (978-0-440-22829-5(8) , Laurel Leaf) Random Hse. Children's Bks.

The Will to Survive. 2002. (Illus.). (J). pap. (978-0-7398-5140-1(3)) Steck-Vaughn.

Williams, M. C. No where to be Found: Time Is Short. l.t. ed. 2006. 38p. per. 3.65 (978-1-59879-099-3(4)) Lifevest Publishing, Inc.

Winfield, Arthur M. The Rover Boys on Land & Sea or the Crusoes of Seven Islands. 2006. (ENG.). 284p. per. 28.95 ***(*978-1-4286-4097-9(5))*** Kessinger Publishing, LLC.

Wyss, Johann David. Swiss Family Robinson. 1998. (Children's Classics). (ENG., Illus.). 192p. (J). (gr. 4-7). pap. (978-1-85326-111-4(4) , 1114WW) Wordsworth Editions, Ltd.

—The Swiss Family Robinson: Critical Reading Series. 2002. (Great Illustrated Classics Ser.). (Illus.). 240p. (J). (gr. 3-8). 21.35 (978-1-57765-801-6(9) , ABDO & Daughters) ABDO Publishing Co.

—The Swiss Family Robinson: Critical Reading Series. (Young Collector's Illustrated Classics Ser.). (Illus.). 192p. (J). (gr. 3-7). 9.95 (978-1-56156-459-0(1)) Kidsbooks, Inc.

—The Swiss Family Robinson: Critical Reading Series. 1999. 336p. (J). (gr. 5-7). pap. 6.50 (978-0-440-41594-7(2) , Yearling) Random Hse. Children's Bks.

—Swiss Family Robinson: With a Discussion of Teamwork. Butterfield, Ned, illus. 2003. (Values in Action Illustrated Classics Ser.). 191p. (J). (978-1-59203-036-1(X)) Learning Challenge, Inc.

Wyss, Johann David, illus. The Swiss Family Robinson. 2004. reprint ed. pap. 30.95 (978-1-4191-5012-8(X)); pap. 1.99 (978-1-4192-5012-5(4)) Kessinger Publishing, LLC.

Wyss, Johann David & McGraw-Hill - Jamestown Education Staff. The Swiss Family Robinson: Critical Reading Series. unabr. ed. 1999. (Wordsworth Classics Ser.). (gr. 6-12). pap. 16.64 (978-0-89061-111-1(4) , 9780890611111) Jamestown.

Zorn, Steven & Defoe, Daniel. Robinson Crusoe. Wyeth, N. C., illus. 2002. 48p. (J). 9.98 (978-0-7624-1419-2(7) , Courage Bks.) Running Pr. Bk. Pubs.

SURVIVAL OF THE FITTEST

see Natural Selection

SUSPENSION BRIDGES

see Bridges

SUTTER, JOHN AUGUSTUS, 1803-1880

Cassanos, Lynda Cohen. Sutter's Fort. 2004. (American Forts & Their Strategic Importance Ser.). (J). (978-1-59084-709-1(1)) Mason Crest Pubs.

Doeden, Matt. John Sutter & the California Gold Rush. Barnett, Charles, III & Frenz, Ron, illus. 2005. (Graphic Library). 32p. (J). (gr. 3-7). lib. bdg. 25.26 (978-0-7368-4370-6(1)) Capstone Pr., Inc.

Dunn, Joeming W. California Gold Rush. Dunn, Ben, illus. 2007. (Graphic History Ser.). 32p. (J). (gr. 3-6). lib. bdg. 27.07 ***(*978-1-60270-076-5(1)*** , Graphic Planet) Magic Wagon.

Engstrand, Iris Wilson & Owens, Kenneth N. John Sutter: Sutter's Fort & the California Gold Rush. 2005. (Library of American Lives & Times). (Illus.). 112p. (J). (gr. 4-8). lib. bdg. 31.95 (978-0-8239-6630-1(5)) Rosen Publishing Group, Inc., The.

Hayhurst, Chris. John Sutter: California Pioneer. 2003. (Primary Sources of Famous People in American History Ser.). (Illus.). 32p. (J). pap. (978-0-8239-4186-5(8)) Rosen Publishing Group, Inc., The.

SUTTER'S FORT (SACRAMENTO, CALIF.)

Cassanos, Lynda Cohen. Sutter's Fort. 2004. (American Forts & Their Strategic Importance Ser.). (J). (978-1-59084-709-1(1)) Mason Crest Pubs.

SWALLOWS

French, Vivian. Swallow Journey. Littlewood, Karin, illus. 2001. (Fantastic Journeys Ser.). 32p. (J). 15.95 (978-1-84089-215-4(3) , Zero to Ten, Limited) Evans Publishing Group GBR. *Dist:* Independent Pubs. Group.

Salariya, David. The Journey of a Swallow. Sorace, Carolyn, photos by. 2000. (Lifecycles Ser.). (Illus.). 32p. (J). (gr. k-2). 25.50 (978-0-531-14519-7(0) , Watts, Franklin) Scholastic Library Publishing.

Savage, Stephen. Swallow. 2003. (Animal Neighbours Ser.). (Illus.). 32p. (978-0-7502-4473-2(9) , Hodder Wayland) Hodder Children's Division.

SWALLOWS—FICTION

Donaldson. Donaldson - Follow the Swallow. 2008. (Illus.). 32p. (J). pap. 9.95 ***(*978-1-4052-1788-0(X))*** Egmont Bks., Ltd. GBR. *Dist:* Independent Pubs. Group.

Howie, Vicki. The Easter Swallows. Grudina, Paola Bertolini, illus. 2007. 32p. (J). 10.95 (978-0-8198-2360-1(0)) Pauline Bks. & Media.

Morpurgo, Michael. Dear Olly. Birmingham, Christian, illus. 2001. 128p. (J). mass mkt. 7.99 (978-0-00-675333-9(7)) HarperCollins Pubs. Ltd. GBR. *Dist:* Independent Pubs. Group.

Ryan, Pam Muñoz. Nacho & Lolita. Rueda, Claudia, illus. 2005. 40p. (J). (ps-3). pap. 16.99 (978-0-439-26968-1(7) , Scholastic Pr.) Scholastic, Inc.

Tirabosco, Tom. At the Same Time. Tirabosco, Tom, illus. 2001. (Illus.). 40p. (J). (ps-1). 8.95 (978-1-929132-17-1(4)) Kane/Miller Bk. Pubs., Inc.

Wilde, Oscar. El Principe Feliz. Fischer, Ursel & Pittau, Francesco, trs. Ray, Jane, illus. 2004. (SPA.). 32p. 9.95 (978-84-95939-36-4(3)) Blume ESP. *Dist:* Independent Pubs. Group.

SWAMPS

see Marshes

SWANS

Harris, Tim. Swans. 2004. (Nature's Children Ser.). (Illus.). 48p. (J). (978-0-7172-5974-8(9) , Grolier) Scholastic Library Publishing.

Helget, Nicole Lea. Swans. 2008. (J). ***(*978-1-58341-659-4(5)*** , Creative Education) Creative Co., The.

Hoff, Mary King. Swans. 2005. (Illus.). 32p. (gr. 2-5). 18.95 (978-1-58341-354-8(5) , Creative Education) Creative Co., The.

Horak, Steven A. Swans & Other Swimming Birds, Vol. 10. World Book, Inc. Staff, ed. 2001. (World Book's Animals of the World Ser.: Set 2). (Illus.). 64p. (J). (978-0-7166-1217-9(8)) World Bk., Inc.

Meyer, Therese. The Little Ballerina & Her Friends the Swans. 2004. (Illus.). 52p. 16.95 (978-0-9750325-0-3(X)) Baby Swan AUS. *Dist:* Biblio Distribution.

—La Petite Ballerine et Ses Amis les Cygnes (The Little Ballerina & Her Friends the Swans) Meyer, Therese, illus. 2004. (FRE.). 52p. 16.95 (978-0-9750325-1-0(8)) Baby Swan AUS. *Dist:* Biblio Distribution.

Miller, Sara Swan. Waterfowl: From Swans to Screamers. 1999. (Animals in Order Ser.). (Illus.). 48p. (J). (gr. 4-6). 26.50 (978-0-531-11584-8(4) , Watts, Franklin) Scholastic Library Publishing.

Osborn, Elinor. Project UltraSwan. Osborn, Elinor, photos by. 2002. (Scientists in the Field Ser.: Vol. 6). (Illus.). 64p. (J). (gr. 3-5). tchr. ed. 16.00 (978-0-618-14528-7(1)) Houghton Mifflin Co. Trade & Reference Div.

—Project Ultraswan. 2006. (Scientists in the Field Ser.). (Illus.). 64p. (J). (gr. 4-6). pap. 6.95 (978-0-618-58545-8(1)) Houghton Mifflin Co.

Steck-Vaughn Staff. The Lifecycles of Swans Level B: Early Reader. 2003. (Illus.). pap. (978-0-7398-8219-1(8)) Steck-Vaughn.

Stewart, Melissa. Swans. 2007. (Animals Animals Ser.). (Illus.). 48p. (J). (gr. 4-7). lib. bdg. 28.50 (978-0-7614-2530-4(6)) Cavendish, Marshall Corp.

Swan's Flight. 2002. (Wild Heritage Collection Mini Bks.). (Illus.). 32p. (J). (978-1-59069-160-1(1) , H3004) Studio Mouse LLC.

Taylor, Bonnie Highsmith. Daphne: A Trumpeter Swan. 2001. (Animal Adventures Ser.). (Illus.). (J). 54p. pap. (978-0-7891-5156-8(1)); 56p. (gr. 1-4). lib. bdg. 16.95 (978-0-7807-9312-5(9)) Perfection Learning Corp.

SWANS—FICTION

Adiccabandhu & Padmasri. Siddhartha & the Swan. Adiccabandhu, illus. 2004. (Illus.). 32p. (gr. k-3). pap. 10.95 (978-1-899579-10-5(9)) Windhorse Pubns. GBR. *Dist:* Consortium Bk. Sales & Distribution.

Andersen, Hans Christian. The Wild Swans. Lewis, Naomi, tr. from DAN. Gilbert, Yvonne, illus. 2005. 48p. (J). 17.99 (978-1-84148-164-7(5)) Barefoot Bks., Inc.

Andersen, Hans Christian. The Wild Swans: A Tale of Persistence. Lohmann, Renate, illus. 2006. (J). (***978-1-59939-093-2(0)*** , Reader's Digest Young Families, Inc.) Reader's Digest Children's Publishing, Inc.

Apperley, Dawn. Princess Rosebud: Perfectly Perfect Princess. 2007. 32p. (J). (gr. k-1). 14.99 (978-0-7641-6033-2(8)) Barron's Educational Series, Inc.

Ariyoshi, Kyoko. Swan. Ariyoshi, Kyoko, illus. 2005. (Illus.). (YA). Vol. 4. 200p. pap. 9.99 (978-1-4012-0538-6(0)); Vol. 5. 192p. pap. 9.99 (978-1-4012-0539-3(9)) DC Comics.

Bordoy, Irene, illus. El Patito Feo / the Ugly Duckling. 2006. (Bilingual Tales Ser.). 24p. (J). pap. 3.50 (978-0-439-77376-8(8) , Scholastic en Espanol) Scholastic, Inc.

Daniel, Patricia A. The Purple Swan. 2007. 12.95 (***978-1-59526-676-7(3)***) Media Creations, Inc.

Edwards, Pamela Duncan. Honk! The Story of a Prima Swanerina. Cole, Henry, illus. 2000. 32p. (gr. k-4). pap. 5.99 (978-0-7868-1298-1(2)) Disney Pr.

Entara Ltd., photos by. What's Hatching? 2008. (Jakers! Ser.). 24p. (J). pap. 3.99 (***978-0-689-87861-9(3)*** , Simon Spotlight) Simon & Schuster Children's Publishing.

Foster, F. Gordon. The Seasons of the Swans. 2006. (Illus.). 203p. (978-0-9760563-3-1(X)) Mechling Bookbindery.

Fox, Mem. Feathers & Fools. Wilton, Nicholas, illus. 2000. 36p. (J). (gr. k-3). pap. 7.00 (978-0-15-202365-2(8) , Harcourt Paperbacks) Harcourt Children's Bks.

—Feathers & Fools. 2000. (gr. k-3). lib. bdg. 14.15 (978-0-613-28482-0(8)); (Illus.). (J). (978-0-606-18740-4(5)) Tandem Library Bks.

Hofer, Ernst & Hofer, Nelly, illus. The Wild Swans. 2003. 40p. (J). (gr. 3-5). 17.95 (978-0-88776-615-2(3)) Tundra Bks., Inc./Livres Toundra, Inc. CAN. *Dist:* Random Hse., Inc.

Jackson, Marianne Bell. The Swan Twins, No. 1. 1999. (Illus.). 22p. (YA). (gr. k up). pap. 5.00 (978-0-9669554-0-8(4)) ColorAnDraw.

Law, Felicia. Rumble Meets Sylvia & Sally Swan. 2005. (Read-It! Readers Ser.). (Illus.). 32p. (J). (ps-k). lib. bdg. 18.60 (978-1-4048-1541-4(4)) Picture Window Bks.

Leonard, Barry, ed. The Ugly Duckling. 2003. (Illus.). 12p. (J). (gr. k-4). reprint ed. 17.00 (978-0-7567-6858-4(6)) DIANE Publishing Co.

Lipe, Riki. The Mystery at Ricena's Pond. Spears-Stewart, Reta, ed. Lipe, Riki, illus. Payton, Leland, photos by. 2000. (Illus.). 36p. (J). (ps-6). 10.00 (978-0-9659381-2-9(3)) Hoot N' Cackle Pr.

Martin, Rafe & Bellm, Dan. Birdwing. (J). 2007. 384p. pap. 6.99 (978-0-439-21168-0(9)); 2005. 368p. pap. 16.99 (978-0-439-21167-3(0)) Scholastic, Inc. (Levine, Arthur A. Bks.).

Maxson, H. A. & Young, Claudia H. Zwaanendael: Valley of the Swans. Etherson, Lesley, illus. 2000. 64p. (J). (gr. 3-5). per. 8.95 (978-0-9704692-0-5(9)) Bay Oak Pubs., Ltd.

McNamee, Barbara Oakley. Kelsey & Seattle. 2007. (J). pap. 15.00 (***978-0-8059-7428-7(8)***) Dorrance Publishing Co., Inc.

Mini Cuentos: Atletas se Entrenan, Zorro y la Ciguena.Tr. of Mini Fairy Tales: Fox & the Swan. (SPA.). (J). (gr. k-4). 4.98 (978-970-607-621-2(2)) Larousse, Ediciones, S. A. de C. V. MEX. *Dist:* Continental Bk. Co., Inc.

Phillips, Vivian A. Swan. Date not set. (Illus.). 20p. (Orig.). (J). pap. (978-1-888413-02-1(6)) Seasoning Quilting (Arts & Crafts).

San José, Christine, et al. The Six Swans. Cole, Jes, illus. 2006. (J). 16.95 (978-1-59078-056-5(6)) Boyds Mills Pr.

Shulman, Lisa. Over in the Meadow at the Big Ballet. Massini, Sarah, illus. 2007. 32p. (J). (gr. k). 16.99 (978-0-399-24289-2(9)) Penguin Group (USA) Inc.

Stein, Meg. Ugly Duckling. 2001. (gr. k-3). lib. bdg. 11.65 (978-0-613-33447-1(7)) Tandem Library Bks.

Tafuri, Nancy. Whose Chick Are You? Tafuri, Nancy, illus. 2007. (Illus.). 40p. (J). (ps-k). 16.99 (978-0-06-082514-0(6)); lib. bdg. 17.89 (978-0-06-082515-7(4)) HarperCollins Pubs.

The Trumpet of the Swan. 1999. (J). 9.95 (978-1-56137-067-2(3)) Novel Units, Inc.

Watson Omura Gail. Have You Ever Seen a Swan Smile. Brooks Susan, illus. 2005. 32p. 16.95 (978-0-9723420-4-9(4)) Belknap Publishing & Design.

White, E. B. The Trumpet of the Swan. l.t. ed. 2005. (Illus.). 225p. (J). pap. (978-0-7540-6173-1(6) , CLP 366) BBC Audio.

—The Trumpet of the Swan. Marcellino, Fred, illus. 272p. (J). 2000. (gr. 4 up). pap. 6.50 (978-0-06-440867-7(1)); 2001. (gr. 2-5). pap. 8.99 (978-0-06-441094-6(3)) HarperCollins Pubs. (Harper Trophy).

—The Trumpet of the Swan. collector's ed. 2000. 224p. (J). 24.95 (978-0-06-028410-7(2)) HarperCollins Pubs.

—The Trumpet of the Swan. Marcellino, Fred, illus. collector's rev. ed. 2000. 272p. (J). (ps-1). 16.99 (978-0-06-028935-5(X)); (gr. 4-7). lib. bdg. 17.89 (978-0-06-028936-2(8)) HarperCollins Pubs.

—The Trumpet of the Swan. 1999. (J). 11.95 (978-1-56137-710-7(4)) Novel Units, Inc.

—The Trumpet of the Swan. unabr. ed. 2004. 210p. (J). (gr. 4-7). pap. 38.00 incl. audio (978-0-8072-8710-1(5) , YA243SP, Listening Library) Random Hse. Audio Publishing Group.

—The Trumpet of the Swan. 2001. (gr. 3-6). lib. bdg. 17.60 (978-0-613-81690-8(0)); 2000. (J). (978-0-606-20002-8(9)); 2000. (gr. 3-6). lib. bdg. 14.75 (978-0-613-30167-1(6)) Tandem Library Bks.

SWEDEN

Alexander, Vimala & Wagner, Michele. Welcome to Sweden. 2002. (Welcome to My Country Ser.). (Illus.). 48p. (J). (gr. 2 up). lib. bdg. 26.00 (978-0-8368-2540-4(3)) Stevens, Gareth Inc.

Barber, Nicola. Focus on Sweden. 2006. (J). pap. (***978-0-8368-6746-6(7)***); lib. bdg. (***978-0-8368-6739-8(4)***) Stevens, Gareth Inc. (World Almanac Library).

Blomquist, Christopher. Sweden, a Primary Source Guide. 2005. (Countries of the World, a Primary Source Journey Ser.). (Illus.). 24p. (J). 19.95 (978-1-4042-2758-3(X) , PowerKids Pr.) Rosen Publishing Group, Inc., The.

Boraas, Tracey. Sweden. 2002. (Countries & Cultures Ser.). (Illus.). 64p. (J). (gr. 4). lib. bdg. 23.93 (978-0-7368-0939-9(2) , Bridgestone Bks.) Capstone Pr., Inc.

Butler, Roberta. Sweden. 2000. (Nations of the World Ser.). (Illus.). 128p. (J). (gr. 6-8). lib. bdg. 34.26 (978-0-8172-5784-2(5)) Raintree.

Carlson, Bo Kage. Sweden. 1999. (Country Fact Files Ser.). (Illus.). 48p. (J). (gr. 4-8). lib. bdg. 27.12 (978-0-8172-5407-0(2)) Raintree.

Docalavich, Heather. Sweden. 2006. (European Union Ser.). (Illus.). 88p. (J). (gr. 5 up). lib. bdg. (978-1-4222-0063-6(9)) Mason Crest Pubs.

Furlong, Kate A. Sweden. 2001. (Countries Ser.). (Illus.). 40p. (J). (gr. k-6). lib. bdg. 22.78 (978-1-57765-550-3(8) , Checkerboard Library) ABDO Publishing Co.

Gan, Delice & Jermyn, Leslie. Sweden. 2nd ed. 2003. (Cultures of the World Ser.). (Illus.). 144p. (gr. 5 up). lib. bdg. 37.07 (978-0-7614-1502-2(5) , Cavendish, Marshall Reference Bks.) Cavendish, Marshall Corp.

Goodman, Polly. Sweden. 2007. (J). (***978-1-84234-463-7(3)***) Cherrytree Pubns., Inc.

Grahame, Deborah A. Sweden. 2006. (Discovering Cultures Ser.). (Illus.). 48p. (J). lib. bdg. 28.50 (978-0-7614-1985-3(3) , Benchmark Bks.) Cavendish, Marshall Corp.

Harcourt School Publishers Staff. Social Studies: Sweden. 2000. (Harcourt Brace Social Studies). (Illus.). (gr. k-7). pap. 33.90 (978-0-15-317436-0(6)) Harcourt Schl. Pubs.

Johnson, Allen LeRoy. Sweden through the Eyes of a Six-year-old: Adventures with Grandchildren, 2005. (Illus.). 180p. 15.00 (978-1-880675-06-9(4)) Creative Enterprises.

Keeler, Stephen. Sweden. 2004. (Changing Face Of... Ser.). 28.56 (978-0-7398-6043-4(7)) Harcourt Schl. Pubs.

Marran, James. Sweden. 2006. (Modern World Nations Ser.). (Illus.). 112p. (J). (gr. 6-12). 30.00 (978-0-7910-8799-2(9) , Chelsea Hse.) Facts On File, Inc.

Olmstead, Mary. Sweden. 2003. (World Tour Ser.). (Illus.). 48p. (J). lib. bdg. 25.70 (978-0-7398-6817-1(9)) Raintree.

Raatma, Lucia. Swedish Americans. 2002. (Spirit of America: Our Cultural Heritage Ser.). (Illus.). 32p. (J). (gr. 2-6). 27.07 (978-1-56766-159-0(9)) Child's World, Inc.

Riehecky, Janet. Sweden. 2000. (Countries of the World Ser.). (Illus.). 126p. (J). (gr. 2-3). 18.60 (978-0-7368-0629-9(6) , Bridgestone Bks.) Capstone Pr., Inc.

Schack-Nielsen, Leif. Sweden. 2006. (Countries of the World Ser.). 64p. (J). (gr. 6-12). 30.00 (978-0-8160-6012-2(6)) Facts On File, Inc.

Thomas, Keltie. Sweden — The Culture. 2003. (Lands, Peoples & Cultures Ser.). (Illus.). 32p. (J). (gr. 4-5). (978-0-7787-9329-8(X)) Crabtree Publishing Co.

Wagner, Michele. Sweden. 2001. (Countries of the World Ser.). (Illus.). 96p. (J). (gr. 6 up). lib. bdg. 30.00 (978-0-8368-2340-0(0)) Stevens, Gareth Inc.

Yanuck, Debbie L. Sweden. 2004. (Many Cultures, One World Ser.). (Illus.). 32p. (J). (gr. 2-3). lib. bdg. 23.93 (978-0-7368-2452-1(9) , Bridgestone Bks.) Capstone Pr., Inc.

Zickgraf, Ralph. Sweden. 1999. (Major World Nations Ser.). (Illus.). 144p. (YA). (gr. 4-7). 29.95 (978-0-7910-4749-1(0) , Chelsea Hse.) Facts On File, Inc.

Zocchi, Judy. In Sweden. Brodie, Neale, illus. 2005. (Global Adventures II Ser.). 32p. (J). pap. 9.95 (978-1-59646-176-5(4)); lib. bdg. 20.65 (978-1-59646-087-4(3)); per. 9.95 (978-1-59646-177-2(2)) Dingles & Co.

—In Sweden/en Suecia. Brodie, Neale, illus. 2005. (Global Adventures I Ser.).Tr. of En Japon. (ENG & SPA.). 32p. (J). pap. 9.95 (978-1-59646-178-9(0)); lib. bdg. 20.65 (978-1-59646-088-1(1)); per. 9.95 (978-1-59646-179-6(9)) Dingles & Co.

SWEDEN—FICTION

Andersen, Hans Christian. Pictures of Sweden. 2006. pap. (***978-1-4065-0860-4(8)***) Dodo Pr.

Apelqvist, Eva. Swede Dreams. 2007. (S. A. S. S. (Students Across the Seven Seas) Ser.). (Illus.). (YA). 224p. pap. 6.99 (978-0-14-240746-2(1)); 202p. (***978-1-4287-2702-1(7)***) Penguin Group (USA) Inc. (Puffin).

Dines, Carol. The Queen's Soprano. 2007. (Illus.). 336p. (YA). pap. 6.95 (***978-0-15-206102-9(9)*** , Harcourt Paperbacks) Harcourt Children's Bks.

Lagerlof, Selma. The Further Adventures of Nils. 2005. pap. 31.95 (978-1-4179-9042-9(2)) Kessinger Publishing, LLC.

—The Further Adventures of Nils. 2006. 384p. pap. 25.45 (***978-1-59462-402-5(X)*** , 438, Book Jungle) Standard Pubns., Inc.

Lagerlof, Selma. The Wonderful Adventures of Nils. 2004. reprint ed. pap. 34.95 (978-1-4191-8845-9(3)); pap. 1.99 (978-1-4192-8845-6(8)) Kessinger Publishing, LLC.

Lewis, Beverly. Annika's Secret Wish. Querin, Pamela, illus. 2004. 32p. (J). 16.99 (978-0-7642-2940-4(0)) Bethany Hse. Pubs.

Lewis, Beverly & Querin, Pamela. Annika's Secret Wish. 2006. (Illus.). 32p. (J). (gr. k-4). reprint ed. 15.00 (978-0-7567-9876-5(0)) DIANE Publishing Co.

Lindgren, Astrid. Pippi Goes to School. 1999. (J). (gr. k-3). lib. bdg. 14.15 (978-0-613-22923-4(1)) Tandem Library Bks.

—Pippi Goes to the Circus. 2000. (J). (gr. k-3). lib. bdg. 14.15 (978-0-613-28608-4(1)) Tandem Library Bks.

—Pippi Longstocking. Glanzman, Louis S., illus. 2005. (Puffin Modern Classics Ser.). 160p. (J). (***978-1-4155-8329-6(3)*** , Puffin) Penguin Group (USA) Inc.

—Pippi's Extraordinary Ordinary Day. Chesworth, Michael, illus. 2001. 32p. (J). (ps-3). lib. bdg. 12.79 (978-0-606-21381-3(3)); lib. bdg. 14.15 (978-0-613-36072-2(9)) Tandem Library Bks.

—The Red Bird. Crampton, Patricia, tr. from SWE. Tornqvist, Marit, illus. 2005. 48p. (J). reprint ed. pap. 16.95 (978-0-439-62796-2(6) , Levine, Arthur A. Bks.) Scholastic, Inc.

Lindgren, Astrid & Crampton, Patricia. The Red Bird. Tornqvist, Marit, illus. 2005. (J). 5.99 (978-0-439-62797-9(4) , Levine, Arthur A. Bks.) Scholastic, Inc.

Mankell, Henning. A Bridge to the Stars. 2007. 176p. (YA). (gr. 7). 15.99 (***978-0-385-73495-0(6)***); lib. bdg. 18.99 (***978-0-385-90489-6(4)***) Random Hse. Children's Bks. (Delacorte Bks. for Young Readers).

Mankell, Henning & Thompson, Laurie. Shadows in the Twilight. 2008. 176p. (J). (***978-0-385-73496-7(4)***); (YA). (gr. 7). lib. bdg. 18.99 (***978-0-385-90490-2(8)***) Dell Publishing. (Delacorte Pr.).

Mazetti, Katerina. God & I Broke Up. Lundin, Maria, tr. from SWE. 2004. 160p. (J). 15.95 (978-0-88899-584-1(9)) Groundwood Bks. CAN. *Dist:* Perseus Distribution.

Meyer, Carolyn. Kristina, the Girl King, Sweden 1638. 2003. (Royal Diaries Ser.). 176p. (J). pap. 10.95 (978-0-439-24976-8(7) , Scholastic Pr.) Scholastic, Inc.

Nilsson, Per. Heart's Delight. Chace, Tara, tr. from SWE. 2005. 192p. (YA). reprint ed. pap. 6.99 (978-0-689-87677-6(7) , Simon Pulse) Simon & Schuster Children's Publishing.

—Heart's Desire. Chace, Tara, tr. from SWE. 2004. 160p. (YA). 16.95 (978-1-886910-92-8(8) , Lemniscaat) Boyds Mills Pr.

Number the Stars. 2004. (Literature Connections Ser.). (gr. 6-12). (978-0-395-88457-7(8) , 2-70863) McDougal Littell Inc.

Uncle Markie. Piglette & Bobo Have Visitors. 2003. (YA). ring bd. 9.95 (978-1-933129-12-9(3)) Studio 403.

SWEDES—UNITED STATES

Gunderson, Cory Gideon. Swedish Americans. 2003. (Immigrants in America Ser.). (Illus.). 112p. (gr. 6-12). 30.00 (978-0-7910-7131-1(6)); lib. bdg. 9.95 (978-0-7910-7514-2(1)) Facts On File, Inc. (Chelsea Hse.).

Peterson, Tiffany. Swedish Americans. 2004. (We Are America Ser.). (Illus.). 30p. (J). lib. bdg. 24.22 (978-1-4034-5024-1(2)) Heinemann Library.

SWEDISH LANGUAGE

Dumont, Deborah, intro. Hippocrene Children's Illustrated Swedish Dictionary: English-Swedish/Swedish-English. 2001. (Hippocrene Children's Illustrated Foreign Language Dictionaries Ser.). (SWE & ENG., Illus.). 94p. (gr. k-5). pap. 11.95 (978-0-7818-0850-7(2)) Hippocrene Bks., Inc.

SWIFT, JONATHAN, 1667-1745

Aykroyd, Clarissa. Savage Satire: The Story of Jonathan Swift. 2006. (World Writers Ser.). (Illus.). 160p. (J). (gr. 6-12). lib. bdg. 27.95 (978-1-59935-027-1(0)) Reynolds, Morgan Inc.

SWIFT, TOM (FICTITIOUS CHARACTER)—FICTION

Appleton, Victor. The Alien Probe. (Tom Swift Ser.). (J). (gr. 3-7). 20.95 (978-0-88411-464-2(3)) Amereon LTD.

—The City in the Stars. (Tom Swift Ser.). (J). (gr. 3-7). 20.95 (978-0-88411-463-5(5)) Amereon LTD.

—Into the Abyss. 2007. (Tom Swift, Young Inventor Ser.). 160p. (J). (gr. 4-7). 27.07 (***978-1-59961-350-5(6)***) Spotlight.

—The Rescue Mission. (Tom Swift Ser.). (J). (gr. 3-7). 20.95 (978-0-88411-458-1(9)) Amereon LTD.

—The Robot Olympics. 2006. (Tom Swift, Young Inventor Ser.). 176p. (J). pap. 4.99 (978-1-4169-1361-0(0) , Aladdin) Simon & Schuster Children's Publishing.

—The Robot Olympics. 2007. (Tom Swift, Young Inventor Ser.). 160p. (J). (gr. 4-7). 27.07 (***978-1-59961-351-2(4)***) Spotlight.

—Rocket Racers. 2007. (Tom Swift, Young Inventor Ser.: No. 4). 160p. (J). pap. 4.99 (978-1-4169-3488-2(X) , Aladdin) Simon & Schuster Children's Publishing.

—Rocket Racers. 2007. (Tom Swift, Young Inventor Ser.). 160p. (J). (gr. 4-7). 27.07 (***978-1-59961-352-9(2)***) Spotlight.

—The Space Hotel. 2006. (Tom Swift, Young Inventor Ser.: No. 3). 160p. (J). pap. 4.99 (978-1-4169-1751-9(9) , Aladdin) Simon & Schuster Children's Publishing.

—The Space Hotel. 2007. (Tom Swift, Young Inventor Ser.). 160p. (J). (gr. 4-7). 27.07 (***978-1-59961-353-6(0)***) Spotlight.

—Terror on the Moons of Jupiter. (Tom Swift Ser.). (J). (gr. 3-7). 20.95 (978-0-88411-460-4(0)) Amereon LTD.

—Tom Swift among the Diamond Makers or Th. 2006. pap. (***978-1-4065-0892-5(6)***) Dodo Pr.

—Tom Swift among the Fire Fighters. 2005. 27.95 (978-1-4218-1088-1(3)); 204p. pap. 12.95 (978-1-4218-1188-8(X)) 1st World Publishing, Inc. (1st World Library - Literary Society).

—Tom Swift among the Fire Fighters. 2006. (ENG.). pap. (***978-1-4068-0726-4(5)***) Echo Library.

—Tom Swift among the Fire Fighters. 2004. reprint ed. pap. 20.95 (978-1-4191-9047-6(4)); pap. 1.99 (978-1-4192-9047-3(9)) Kessinger Publishing, LLC.

—Tom Swift among the Fire Fighters or Bat. 2006. pap. (***978-1-4065-0893-2(4)***) Dodo Pr.

—Tom Swift & His Aerial Warship. 2005. 27.95 (978-1-4218-1092-8(1)); 212p. pap. 12.95 (978-1-4218-1192-5(8)) 1st World Publishing, Inc. (1st World Library - Literary Society).

—Tom Swift & His Aerial Warship. 2004. reprint ed. pap. 1.99 (978-1-4192-8451-9(7)) Kessinger Publishing, LLC.

—Tom Swift & His Aerial Warship or the. 2006. pap. (***978-1-4065-0894-9(2)***) Dodo Pr.

—Tom Swift & His Air Glider. 2004. reprint ed. pap. 20.95 (978-1-4191-8452-9(0)); pap. 1.99 (978-1-4192-8452-6(5)) Kessinger Publishing, LLC.

—Tom Swift & His Air Glider or Seeking. 2006. pap. (***978-1-4065-0895-6(0)***) Dodo Pr.

—Tom Swift & His Air Scout. 2005. 27.95 (978-1-4218-1091-1(3)); 208p. pap. 12.95 (978-1-4218-1191-8(X)) 1st World Publishing, Inc. (1st World Library - Literary Society).

—Tom Swift & His Air Scout. 2004. reprint ed. pap. 20.95 (978-1-4191-9048-3(2)); pap. 1.99 (978-1-4192-9048-0(7)) Kessinger Publishing, LLC.

—Tom Swift & His Air Scout or Uncle Sam. 2006. pap. (***978-1-4065-0896-3(9)***) Dodo Pr.

—Tom Swift & His Airship. 2005. 27.95 (978-1-59540-801-3(0) , 1st World Library - Literary Society) 1st World Publishing, Inc.

—Tom Swift & His Airship. 2004. (Tom Swift Original Ser.: No. 3). 216p. (J). (ps-3). 17.95 (978-1-55709-177-2(3)) Applewood Bks.

—Tom Swift & His Airship. 2006. pap. (***978-1-4065-0897-0(7)***) Dodo Pr.

—Tom Swift & His Airship. 2000. (Tom Swift Original Ser.: Vol. No. 3). 118p. (gr. 3-7). 19.95 (978-1-57646-359-8(1)); 118p. (gr. 3-7). pap. 7.95 (978-1-57646-203-4(X)); 186p. pap. 12.99 (978-1-57646-360-4(5)) Quiet Vision Publishing.

—Tom Swift & His Airship. 2006. 224p. pap. 16.95 (978-1-59462-179-6(9) , 208, Book Jungle) Standard Pubns., Inc.

—Tom Swift & His Big Tunnel. 2005. 27.95 (978-1-4218-1093-5(X)); 216p. pap. 12.95 (978-1-4218-1193-2(6)) 1st World Publishing, Inc. (1st World Library - Literary Society).

—Tom Swift & His Big Tunnel. 2004. reprint ed. pap. 20.95 (978-1-4191-8454-3(7)); pap. 1.99 (978-1-4192-8454-0(1)) Kessinger Publishing, LLC.

—Tom Swift & His Big Tunnel or the Hidd. 2006. pap. (***978-1-4065-0898-7(5)***) Dodo Pr.

—Tom Swift & His Electric Locomotive or. 2006. pap. (***978-1-4065-0899-4(3)***) Dodo Pr.

—Tom Swift & His Electric Rifle. 2005. 26.95 (978-1-59540-802-0(9) , 1st World Library - Literary Society) 1st World Publishing, Inc.

—Tom Swift & His Electric Rifle. 2006. pap. (***978-1-4065-0900-7(0)***) Dodo Pr.

—Tom Swift & His Electric Rifle. 2006. 18.99 (***978-1-4280-3261-3(4)***) IndyPublish.com.

—Tom Swift & His Electric Rifle. 1998. (Tom Swift Original Ser.: No. 10). (J). (gr. 3-7). lib. bdg. 18.95 (978-1-56723-020-8(2)) Yestermorrow, Inc.

—Tom Swift & His Electric Runabout. 2004. reprint ed. pap. 20.95 (978-1-4191-8455-0(5)); pap. 1.99 (978-1-4192-8455-7(X)) Kessinger Publishing, LLC.

—Tom Swift & His Electric Runabout or T. 2006. pap. (***978-1-4065-0901-4(9)***) Dodo Pr.

—Tom Swift & His Electronic Electroscope. (J). (gr. 5-6). 20.95 (978-0-88411-462-8(7)) Amereon LTD.

—Tom Swift & His Giant Cannon. 2005. 27.95 (978-1-4218-1089-8(1)); 204p. pap. 12.95 (978-1-4218-1189-5(8)) 1st World Publishing, Inc. (1st World Library - Literary Society).

—Tom Swift & His Giant Cannon. 2004. reprint ed. pap. 20.95 (978-1-4191-8456-7(3)); pap. 1.99 (978-1-4192-8456-4(8)) Kessinger Publishing, LLC.

—Tom Swift & His Giant Cannon or the lo. 2006. pap. (***978-1-4065-0902-1(7)***) Dodo Pr.

—Tom Swift & His Great Searchlight. 2005. 204p. pap. 12.95 (978-1-4218-1190-1(1) , 1st World Library - Literary Society) 1st World Publishing, Inc.

—Tom Swift & His Great Searchlight. 2004. reprint ed. pap. 20.95 (978-1-4191-8457-4(1)); pap. 1.99 (978-1-4192-8457-1(6)) Kessinger Publishing, LLC.

—Tom Swift & His Great Searchlight or O. 2006. pap. (***978-1-4065-0903-8(5)***) Dodo Pr.

—Tom Swift & His Motor Boat. 2004. (Tom Swift Original Ser.: No. 2). 212p. (J). (ps-3). 14.95 (978-1-55709-176-5(5)) Applewood Bks.

—Tom Swift & His Motor Boat. 2000. (Tom Swift Original Ser.: Vol. No. 2). 112p. (gr. 3-7). 19.95 (978-1-57646-356-7(7)); 112p. (gr. 3-7). pap. 7.95 (978-1-57646-202-7(1)); 182p. pap. 12.99 (978-1-57646-357-4(5)) Quiet Vision Publishing.

—Tom Swift & His Motor Cycle. 2004. (Tom Swift Original Ser.: No. 1). 206p. (J). (ps-3). 17.95 (978-1-55709-175-8(7)) Applewood Bks.

—Tom Swift & His Motor Cycle. 2004. reprint ed. pap. 1.99 (978-1-4192-8459-5(2)) Kessinger Publishing, LLC.

—Tom Swift & His Motor Cycle. 2000. (Tom Swift Original Ser.: Vol. No. 1). 114p. (gr. 3-7). 19.95 (978-1-57646-353-6(2)); 114p. (gr. 3-7). pap. 7.95 (978-1-57646-201-0(3)); 180p. pap. 12.99 (978-1-57646-354-3(0)) Quiet Vision Publishing.

—Tom Swift & His MotorBoat or the Rival. 2006. pap. ***978-1-4065-0904-5(3))** Dodo Pr.

—Tom Swift & His MotorCycle. 2006. 18.99 (***978-1-4280-3267-5(3))** IndyPublish.com.

—Tom Swift & His Photo Telephone. 1998. (Tom Swift Original Ser.: No. 17). (J). (gr. 3-7). lib. bdg. 18.95 (978-1-56723-022-2(9)) Yestermorrow, Inc.

—Tom Swift & His Photo Telephone or the. 2006. pap. (***978-1-4065-0906-9(X))** Dodo Pr.

—Tom Swift & His Sky Racer. 2004. reprint ed. pap. 1.99 (978-1-4192-8461-8(4)) Kessinger Publishing, LLC.

—Tom Swift & His Sky Racer or the Quick. 2006. pap. (***978-1-4065-0907-6(8))** Dodo Pr.

—Tom Swift & His Submarine Boat. 2004. reprint ed. pap. 20.95 (978-1-4191-8462-8(8)); pap. 1.99 (978-1-4192-8462-5(2)) Kessinger Publishing, LLC.

—Tom Swift & His Submarine Boat. 2000. (Tom Swift Original Ser.: Vol. No. 4). 114p. (gr. 3-7). pap. 7.95 (978-1-57646-204-1(8)) Quiet Vision Publishing.

—Tom Swift & His Submarine Boat or Unde. 2006. pap. (***978-1-4065-0908-3(6))** Dodo Pr.

—Tom Swift & His Triphibian Atomicar. (Tom Swift Ser.). (J). (gr. 5-6). 20.95 (978-0-88411-459-8(7)) Amereon LTD.

—Tom Swift & His Undersea Search or the. 2006. pap. (***978-1-4065-0909-0(4))** Dodo Pr.

—Tom Swift & His War Tank. 2004. reprint ed. pap. 20.95 (978-1-4191-9054-4(7)); pap. 1.99 (978-1-4192-9054-1(1)) Kessinger Publishing, LLC.

—Tom Swift & His War Tank or Doing His. 2006. pap. (***978-1-4065-0910-6(8))** Dodo Pr.

—Tom Swift & His Wireless Message or Th. 2006. pap. (***978-1-4065-0911-3(6))** Dodo Pr.

—Tom Swift & His Wizard Camera or Thril. 2006. pap. (***978-1-4065-0912-0(4))** Dodo Pr.

—Tom Swift & the Electronic Hydrolung. 2007. 94.99 (***978-1-4280-5319-9(0));** pap. 88.99 (***978-1-4280-5318-2(2))** IndyPublish.com.

—Tom Swift & the Visitor from Planet X. 2006. pap. (***978-1-4065-0913-7(2))** Dodo Pr.

—Tom Swift & the Visitor from Planet X. 2006. 95.99 (***978-1-4280-1626-2(0));** pap. 88.99 (***978-1-4280-1622-4(8))** IndyPublish.com.

—Tom Swift in Captivity. 2005. 27.95 (978-1-4218-1508-4(7)); 200p. pap. 12.95 (978-1-4218-1608-1(3)) 1st World Publishing, Inc. (1st World Library - Literary Society).

—Tom Swift in Captivity. 2004. reprint ed. pap. 20.95 (978-1-4191-9056-8(3)); pap. 1.99 (978-1-4192-9056-5(8)) Kessinger Publishing, LLC.

—Tom Swift in Captivity or A Daring Escap. 2006. pap. (***978-1-4065-0914-4(0))** Dodo Pr.

—Tom Swift in the Caves of Ice. 1998. (Tom Swift Original Ser.: No. 8). (J). (gr. 3-7). lib. bdg. 18.95 (978-1-56723-021-5(0)) Yestermorrow, Inc.

—Tom Swift in the Caves of Ice or the Wre. 2006. pap. (***978-1-4065-0915-1(9))** Dodo Pr.

—Tom Swift in the City of Gold or Marvelo. 2006. pap. (***978-1-4065-0916-8(7))** Dodo Pr.

—Tom Swift in the Land of Wonders. 2005. 27.95 (978-1-4218-1511-4(7)); 204p. pap. 12.95 (978-1-4218-1611-1(3)) 1st World Publishing, Inc. (1st World Library - Literary Society).

—Tom Swift in the Land of Wonders. 2004. reprint ed. pap. 20.95 (978-1-4191-9057-5(1)); pap. 1.99 (978-1-4192-9057-2(6)) Kessinger Publishing, LLC.

Appleton, Victor. Tom Swift in the Land of Wonders or the. 2006. pap. (***978-1-4065-0917-5(5))** Dodo Pr.

Appleton, Victor & Appleton, Victor, II. Under the Radar. 2007. (Tom Swift, Young Inventor Ser.: No. 6). 146p. (J). (gr. 3-7). per. 4.99 (***978-1-4169-3644-2(0)** , Aladdin) Simon & Schuster Children's Publishing.

SWIMMING

see also Diving

Adler, David A. America's Champion Swimmer: Gertrude Ederle. Widener, Terry, illus. 32p. (J). (gr. k-4). 2000. 16.00 (978-0-15-201969-3(3) , Gulliver Bks.); 2005. reprint ed. pap. 6.00 (978-0-15-205251-5(8) , Voyager Bks./Libros Viajeros) Harcourt Children's Bks.

—America's Champion Swimmer: Gertrude Ederle. 2000. (Illus.). 32p. (J). (gr. 1-4). 18.98 (978-0-7398-2197-8(0)) Raintree.

Atkins, Jeannine. Get Set! Swim! Lee, Hector Viveros, illus. 1998. 32p. (J). (ps up). 15.95 (978-1-880000-66-3(0)) Lee & Low Bks., Inc.

Barr, Linda. The Water Patrol: Saving Surfers' Lives in Big Waves. 2005. (High Five Reading Ser.). (Illus.). 64p. (J). (gr. 4-5). lib. bdg. incl. audio (978-0-7368-5759-8(0)) Capstone Pr., Inc.

Barr, Linda & Rasinski, Timothy V. The Water Patrol: Saving Surfers' Lives in Big Waves. 2005. (High Five Reading Ser.). (Illus.). 48p. (J). (978-0-7368-5749-9(4)); (978-0-7368-5739-0(7)) Capstone Pr., Inc.

Barth, Katrin & Dietze, Jurgen. Swimming: Training. 2004. (Illus.). 152p. pap. 14.95 (978-1-84126-145-4(9)) Meyer & Meyer Sport, Ltd. GBR. *Dist:* Lewis International, Inc.

Compass Point Books, contrib. by. Swimming for Fun! (For Fun Ser.). 48p. (YA). pap. 8.95 (978-0-7565-1162-3(3)) Compass Point Bks.

Crossingham, John. Swimming in Action. 2002. (Sports in Action Ser.). (Illus.). 32p. (J). (gr. 4). (978-0-7787-0331-0(2)); pap. (978-0-7787-0351-8(7)) Crabtree Publishing Co.

—Swimming in Action. 2003. (gr. 3-6). lib. bdg. 15.25 (978-0-613-52918-1(9)) Tandem Library Bks.

Ditchfield, Christin. Swimming & Diving. 2000. (True Bks.). (Illus.). 48p. (J). (gr. 3-5). pap. 6.95 (978-0-516-27030-2(3) , Children's Pr.) Scholastic Library Publishing.

Eckart, Edana. I Can Swim. 2002. (Wel-Sports Ser.). (Illus.). 24p. (J). (ps-2). 18.00 (978-0-516-23970-5(8)); pap. 4.95 (978-0-516-24033-6(1)) Scholastic Library Publishing. (Children's Pr.).

Fox, Martha Capwell. Swimming. 2003. (History of Sports Ser.). (Illus.). 104p. (J). 29.95 (978-1-59018-073-0(9) , Lucent Bks.) Thomson Gale.

Giff, Patricia Reilly. Horas de Sol.Tr. of Sunny Side Up. (SPA.). (J). 3.95 (978-0-922852-52-9(9)) AIMS International Bks., Inc.

Gonsalves, Kelly A. & La Mondia, Susan A. First to the Wall: 100 Years of Olympic Swimming. Gonsalves, Kelly A., illus. Morse, Tim, photos by. 1999. (Illus.). 374p. (J). pap. 24.95 (978-0-9674171-0-3(4)) FreeStyle Pubns., Inc.

Greenberg, Doreen L., et al. Fast Lane to Victory: The Story of Jenny Thompson, Vol. 3. Velikan, Phil, illus. 2003. (Anything You Can Do. . .Ser.: 3). 141p. (J). (gr. 4 up). pap. 12.95 (978-1-930546-38-7(6)) Wish Publishing.

Heston, Lauren. Water Baby: A First Fun Book of Water Skills. 1999. (Illus.). 48p. (J). 16.95 (978-1-902618-51-7(3)) Element Children's Bks.

Hill, Mary. Signs at the Pool. 2003. (Welcome Bks.). (Illus.). 24p. (J). (ps-2). pap. 4.95 (978-0-516-24367-2(5) , Children's Pr.) Scholastic Library Publishing.

Kalman, Bobbie. Swimming with Dolphins. 2003. (gr. 3-6). lib. bdg. 15.25 (978-0-613-52919-8(7)) Tandem Library Bks.

Kehm, Greg. Olympic Swimming & Diving. 2007. (Great Moments in Olympic History Ser.). (Illus.). 48p. (J). (gr. 5-8). lib. bdg. 26.50 (978-1-4042-0970-1(0) , Rosen Central) Rosen Publishing Group, Inc., The.

Keiser, Howard. Superstars of Men's Swimming & Diving. 1999. (Male Sports Stars Ser.). (Illus.). 64p. (YA). (gr. 4-7). 18.65 (978-0-7910-4589-3(7) , Chelsea Hse.) Facts On File, Inc.

Leaney, Cindy. Help!.I Can't Swim! Safety in Water. Wilks, Peter, tr. Wilks, Peter, illus. 2003. 32p. (J). 28.50 (978-1-58952-743-0(7)) Rourke Publishing, LLC.

Lindeen, Carol K. Let's Swim. 2006. (Pebble Plus Ser.). (Illus.). 24p. (J). (978-0-7368-5367-5(7)) Capstone Pr., Inc.

MacCallum, Jess. Swimming with the Fishes. 2nd ed. 2004. per. 4.95 (978-0-9749673-0-1(0)) In Ardua Tendit Pr.

Macken, JoAnn Early. Swimming. 2005. (Illus.). 24p. (J). pap. (978-0-8368-4523-5(4)); (YA). lib. bdg. 19.33 (978-0-8368-4516-7(1)) Stevens, Gareth Inc.

Manley, Claudia B. Ultra Swimming. 2002. (Ultra Sports Ser.). (Illus.). 64p. (YA). (gr. 5-8). lib. bdg. 26.50 (978-0-8239-3558-1(2) , Rosen Central) Rosen Publishing Group, Inc., The.

Mason, Paul. How to Improve at Swimming. 2007. 48p. (J). (gr. 3-9). pap. (***978-0-7787-3592-2(3))** Crabtree Publishing Co.

Mason, Paul. A World-Class Swimmer. 2004. (Making of a Champion Ser.). (Illus.). 48p. (J). pap. 8.50 (978-1-4034-5538-3(4)); lib. bdg. 27.07 (978-1-4034-4671-8(7)) Heinemann Library.

McKay, Kathy & McKay, Rob. Learn to Swim: Step-by-Step Water Confidence & Safty Skills for Babies & Young Children. 2005. (Illus.). 128p. pap. 15.00 (978-0-7566-0955-9(0) , 1241340) Dorling Kindersley Publishing, Inc.

Migliaccio, Eric. Swimming: Easy Olympic Sports Reader. 2004. (U. S. Olympic Committee Easy Olympic Sports Readers Ser.). (Illus.). 16p. (J). pap. 2.99 (978-1-58000-114-4(9)) Griffin Publishing Group.

Nessel, Ed. Swim to Win: Train Like a Champion. 2008. (Illus.). 224p. pap. 17.95 (978-1-4027-3256-0(2)) Sterling Publishing Co., Inc.

Page, Jason. Swimming: Sprints, Medleys, Diving, Water-Polo & Lots, Lots More. Alston, John, illus. 2000. (Zeke's Olympic Pocket Guide Ser.). 32p. (J). pap. 3.95 (978-0-8225-5056-3(3) , LernerSports) Lerner Publishing Group.

Pancella, Peggy. Water Safety. 2004. (Heinemann First Library). (Illus.). 32p. (J). 6.95 (978-1-4034-4945-0(7)); lib. bdg. 22.79 (978-1-4034-4936-8(8)) Heinemann Library.

Peterson, Sue H. Swim with Me: A New Fun Approach to Learning to Swim. 2004. (Illus.). 24p. (ps-2). 12.95 (978-1-883672-94-2(5) , Tricycle Pr.) Ten Speed Pr.

Raatma, Lucia. Water Safety. 2003. (Living Well). (Illus.). 32p. (J). (gr. 2-6). 27.07 (978-1-59296-090-3(1)) Child's World, Inc.

Randolph, Joanne. Swimming. 2001. (Sports Clinic Ser.). (Illus.). 48p. (YA). (gr. 7-12). 23.00 (978-0-516-23165-5(0) , Children's Pr.) Scholastic Library Publishing.

Rodomista, Kim. 101 Cool Pool Games for Children: Fun & Fitness for Swimmers of All Levels. Patterson, Robin, illus. 2006. (Hunter House Smartfun Book Ser.). 160p. pap. 14.95 (978-0-89793-483-1(0)) Hunter Hse., Inc.

Rodomista, Kim & Patterson, Robin. 101 Cool Pool Games for Children: Fun & Fitness for Swimmers of All Levels. 2006. (SmartFun Activity Bks.). (Illus.). 160p. spiral bd. 19.95 (978-0-89793-484-8(9)) Hunter Hse., Inc.

Skinner, Tina. Hot Tubs & Spas: An Inspirational Design Guide. 2003. (Schiffer Design Book Ser.). (Illus.). 144p. (gr. 10-13). pap. 24.95 (978-0-7643-1841-2(1)) Schiffer Publishing, Ltd.

Stanley, Mandy. At the Pool. 2004. (All Aboard Ser.). Orig. Title: Vamos a la Piscina. (ENG & SPA., Illus.). 12p. (J). (ps-k). bds. 3.95 (978-0-7534-5747-4(4) , Kingfisher) Houghton Mifflin Co. Trade & Reference Div.

—Vamos a la Piscina: Todos a Bordo. 2004. (ENG & SPA., Illus.). 12p. (J). (ps-k). bds. 3.95 (978-0-7534-5810-5(1) , Kingfisher) Houghton Mifflin Co. Trade & Reference Div.

Verrier, John. Swimming. 1998. (Successful Sports Ser.). 32p. (J). lib. bdg. (978-1-57572-199-6(6)) Heinemann Library.

—Swimming & Diving. 1998. (Olympic Library). (J). pap. (978-1-57572-039-5(6)) Heinemann Library.

Whitehouse, Patricia. Que Puede Nadar? Abello, Patricia, tr. 2004. (SPA.). 24p. (J). 12.95 (978-1-4034-4388-5(2)) Heinemann Library.

—What Can Swim? 2003. (Illus.). 24p. (J). (ps-ps). lib. bdg. 18.50 (978-1-4034-4368-7(8)); pap. 5.25 (978-1-4034-4375-5(0)) Heinemann Library.

—What Can Swim? 2003. (ps-2). lib. bdg. 28.65 (978-0-613-86882-2(X)) Tandem Library Bks.

Willett, Andy. Swimming for Fun. 2003. (Sports for Fun Ser.). (Illus.). 48p. (J). (gr. 3 up). lib. bdg. 21.26 (978-0-7565-0432-8(5)) Compass Point Bks.

SWIMMING—FICTION

Allen, Margaret. Splish, Splash. 1999. (ps-2). lib. bdg. 10.65 (978-0-613-34489-0(8)) Tandem Library Bks.

Amy's Water Wings: Individual Title Six-Pack Pouch - Level K. (Lighthouse Ser.). 16p. (gr. 2 up). 28.00 (978-0-7578-0883-8(2)) Rigby Education.

Ashley, Chris. Wasim One Star. 2007. (Illus.). 80p. (J). pap. 7.95 (***978-1-84507-744-0(X))** Lincoln, Frances Ltd. GBR. *Dist:* Perseus Distribution.

—Wasim One Star. Pankhurst, Kate, illus. 2007. 80p. (J). 15.95 (***978-1-84507-775-4(X))** Lincoln, Frances Ltd. GBR. *Dist:* Perseus Distribution.

Atkins, Jeannine. Get Set! Swim! Lee, Hector Viveros, illus. 1998. 32p. (J). (ps up). pap. 15.95 (978-1-880000-66-3(0)) Lee & Low Bks., Inc.

—Preparadas... Listas... Ya! ed. 2004. (SPA., Illus.). (J). (gr. k-3). spiral bd. (978-0-616-07274-5(0)) Canadian National Institute for the Blind/Institut National Canadien pour les Aveugles.

—Preparadas... Listas... Ya! Sarfatti, Esther, tr. from ENG. Lee, Hector Viveros, illus. 1998. (SPA.). 32p. (J). (gr. 1-3). 15.95 (978-1-880000-77-9(6) , LW(8473)); pap. 6.95 (978-1-880000-78-6(4) , LW(8474)) Lee & Low Bks., Inc.

Atkins, Jill. Toad Swims for his Life! Mostyn, David, illus. 2004. 24p. (J). lib. bdg. 22.65 (***978-1-59646-712-5(6))** Dingles & Co.

Bauer, Marion Dane. Palabra de Honor. 1998. (SPA., Illus.). 88p. (J). (gr. k-2). (978-84-279-3234-0(0) , NG8010) Noguer y Caralt Editores, S. A. ESP. *Dist:* Lectorum Pubns., Inc.

Borden, Louise. Albie the Lifeguard. 1999. (Illus.). 32p. (J). (ps-3). pap. 5.99 (978-0-590-44586-3(3)) Scholastic, Inc.

Bossley, Michele Martin. Pool Princess. 2001. (Sports Stories Ser.). 94p. (gr. 3-8). (***978-1-55028-729-5(X));** (Illus.). 7.95 (978-1-55028-728-8(1)) Lorimer, James & Co., Ltd., Pubs. CAN. *Dist:* Casemate Pubs. & Bk. Distributors, LLC.

Bowler, Tim. River Boy. l.t. ed. 2003. (Read-Along Ser.). (Illus.). (J). pap. 29.95 incl. audio (978-0-7540-6214-1(7) , Galaxy Children's Large Print) BBC Audiobooks America.

—River Boy. 2002. (Illus.). 160p. (YA). mass mkt. 4.99 (978-0-689-84804-9(8) , Simon Pulse) Simon & Schuster Children's Publishing.

—River Boy. 2002. (gr. 5-8). lib. bdg. 13.00 (978-0-613-67116-3(3)) Tandem Library Bks.

—River Boy. l.t. ed. 2001. 190p. (J). 22.95 (978-0-7862-3507-0(1)) Thorndike Pr.

Brimner, Larry Dane. Unsinkable! Tripp, Christine, illus. (Rookie Choices Ser.). 32p. (J). (gr. 1-2). 2003. pap. 5.95 (978-0-516-27790-5(1)); 2002. pap. 20.50 (978-0-516-22543-2(X)) Scholastic Library Publishing. (Children's Pr.).

—Unsinkable! 2002. (gr. k-3). lib. bdg. 14.10 (978-0-613-59753-1(2)) Tandem Library Bks.

Bruna, Dick. Miffy Goes Swimming. 2004. (Illus.). 12p. bds. 5.99 (978-1-59226-204-5(X)) Big Tent Entertainment, Inc.

—Miffy va a Nadar/Miffy Goes Swimming. 2004. (SPA., Illus.). 12p. bds. 5.99 (978-1-59226-209-0(0)) Big Tent Entertainment, Inc.

Bulion, Leslie. Uncharted Waters. 2006. 155p. (J). 14.95 (978-1-56145-365-8(X) , Peachtree Junior) Peachtree Pubs., Ltd.

Butler, Dori Hillestad. Trading Places with Tank Talbott. 2003. 136p. (J). (gr. 3-6). 15.95 (978-0-8075-1708-6(9)); pap. 6.95 (978-0-8075-8060-8(0)) Whitman, Albert & Co.

Buzzeo, Toni. Little Loon & Papa. Spengler, Margaret, tr. Spengler, Margaret, illus. 2004. 32p. (J). (ps). 16.99 (978-0-8037-2958-2(8) , Dial) Penguin Group (USA) Inc.

Cambridge Young Writers Staff. I'm Telling You!, 6 vols., Pack. 2001. (Cambridge Reading Ser.). (Illus.). 80p. pap. 46.00 (978-0-521-01353-6(4)) Cambridge Univ. Pr.

Capdevila, Roser & Vendrell, Maria Martinez. El Agua Inquieta. 2003. Tr. of Rough Water. (SPA.). 24p. (J). 7.95 (978-84-233-1742-4(0)) Ediciones Destino ESP. *Dist:* Planeta Publishing Corp.

Caruso, D. A. Cool by the Pool. 2005. pap. 19.99 (978-0-9765953-0-4(3)) Educational Adventures.

Cisco's Adventure Downunder. 2002. (Illus.). 80p. (J). per. 5.99 (978-0-9707924-2-6(5)) Tail it Like it is, Publishing.

Coleman, Evelyn. Born in Sin. Duffy, Tony, illus. 2001. 240p. (YA). (gr. 7-12). 16.00 (978-0-689-83833-0(6) , Atheneum/Richard Jackson Bks.) Simon & Schuster Children's Publishing.

Coulman, Valerie. Sink or Swim. Roge, tr. Roge & Girard, Roge, illus. 2004. 32p. (J). 15.95 (978-1-894222-54-9(7)) Lobster Pr. CAN. *Dist:* Univ. of Toronto Pr.

—Sink or Swim. 2005. (Illus.). 32p. (J). reprint ed. pap. 6.95 (978-1-894222-96-9(2)) Lobster Pr. CAN. *Dist:* Univ. of Toronto Pr.

Cousins, Lucy. Maisy's Pool. Cousins, Lucy, illus. 1999. (Maisy Bks.). (Illus.). 24p. (J). pap. 3.99 (978-0-7636-0907-8(2)) Candlewick Pr.

Crouse, Donna J. The Ruby Ring: The Whispering Cove Kids Club. 2005. 114p. pap. 12.99 (978-0-9765339-0-0(1)) Crouse, Donna J.

Crutcher, Chris. Whale Talk. 2001. 224p. (J). (gr. 7 up). 16.99 (978-0-688-18019-5(1)) HarperCollins Pubs.

—Whale Talk. 2004. 224p. (J). (gr. 7 up). pap. 38.00 incl. audio (978-0-8072-2289-8(5) , Listening Library) Random Hse. Audio Publishing Group.

—Whale Talk. 2002. 224p. (YA). (gr. 7). pap. 6.99 (978-0-440-22938-4(3) , Laurel Leaf) Random Hse. Children's Bks.

—Whale Talk. 2002. (gr. 5-8). lib. bdg. 13.55 (978-0-613-61739-0(8)) Tandem Library Bks.

—Whale Talk. l.t. ed. 2005. 323p. 21.95 (978-0-7862-7787-2(4) , Large Print Pr.) Thorndike Pr.

Davis, Lambert. Swimming with Dolphins. Davis, Lambert, illus. 2004. (Illus.). 32p. (J). pap. 15.95 (978-0-439-47257-9(1) , Blue Sky Pr., The) Scholastic, Inc.

Diersch, Sandra. False Start. 2005. (Sports Stories Ser.). 104p. (J). (gr. 3-8). (***978-1-55028-873-5(3));** 7.95 (978-1-55028-872-8(5)) Lorimer, James & Co., Ltd., Pubs. CAN. *Dist:* Casemate Pubs. & Bk. Distributors, LLC.

Diersch, Sandra. Great Lengths. 1999. 12.30 (978-0-606-17668-2(3)) Tandem Library Bks.

The Dolphin on the Wall: Individual Title Six-Packs. (gr. 3 up). 35.00 (978-0-7635-9662-0(0)) Rigby Education.

The Dolphins, 6 Packs. 16p. (gr. 2 up). 35.00 (978-0-7635-9384-1(2)) Rigby Education.

Dorling Kindersley Publishing Staff. I Can Swim! 2004. (Dk Readers Ser.). (Illus.). 32p. (J). pap. 3.99 (978-0-7566-0273-4(4)) Dorling Kindersley Publishing, Inc.

Driscoll, Laura. Sink or Swim. Billin-Frye, Paige, tr. Billin-Frye, Paige, illus. 2004. (Science Solves It! Ser.). (J). pap. 4.99 (978-1-57565-137-8(8)) Kane Pr., The.

Dubovoy, Silvia. Turquesita. (SPA.). (J). pap. (978-968-6465-18-1(9)) Casa de Estudios de Literatura y Talleres Artisticos Amaquemecan A.C. MEX. *Dist:* Lectorum Pubns., Inc.

Duck Wants to Swim. 2002. (J). 4.98 (978-0-7525-7218-5(0)) Parragon, Inc.

Eargle, Michelle. Swim Team. Eargle, Michelle, illus. 2001. (Illus.). 15p. (J). (ps-4). pap. 12.00 (978-1-890703-20-2(6) , Bookmates) Penny Laine Papers, Inc.

Farley, Jeanene. I Can Swim. Strasshofer, Craig, ed. Iniquez, Alex & Cortez, Steve, illus. 2000. (Mighty Minnows Adventure Ser.). 16p. (J). (ps-2). pap. 10.99 (978-0-9700101-0-0(9)) LittleJeanie Publishing Co.

Farrell, Sue. To the Pool with Mama. Lewis, Robin Baird, illus. 2000. 24p. (J). (gr. k-ps). pap. 5.95 (978-1-55037-620-3(9)); lib. bdg. 15.95 (978-1-55037-621-0(7)) Annick Pr., Ltd. CAN. *Dist:* Firefly Bks., Ltd.

Forde, Catherine. Fat Boy Swim. 2004. 240p. (J). (gr. 7). lib. bdg. 17.99 (978-0-385-90237-3(9) , Delacorte Bks. for Young Readers) Random Hse. Children's Bks.

Fuge, Charles. Swim, Little Wombat, Swim! (Illus.). (J). 2006. 32p. bds. 5.95 (978-1-4027-3632-2(0)); 2005. 24p. 12.95 (978-1-4027-2375-9(X)) Sterling Publishing Co., Inc.

Furgang, Kathy. Unlucky Stanley. ed. 2003. (Early Connections Ser.). (J). pap. 33.00 (978-1-4108-1357-2(6)) Benchmark Education Co.

Gillen, Lisa P. Louie the Lifeguard. Gillen, Lisa P., illus. l.t. ed. 2000. (LB Ser.). (Illus.). (J). (ps-1). 6p. pap. 10.95 (978-1-57332-176-1(1)); 10p. pap. 10.95 (978-1-57332-175-4(3)) HighReach Learning, Inc.

Going Swimming: KinderConcepts Individual Title Six-Packs. (Kinderstarters Ser.). 8p. (ps-1). 21.00 (978-0-7635-8731-4(1)) Rigby Education.

Gordon, Wendy. I'm Safe! in the Water. 1999. 24p. (J). (ps-3). pap., act. bk. ed. 2.95 (978-1-891596-07-0(1)) Backyard Pub. Co., Inc.

Gutman, Anne & Hallensleben, Georg. Gaspard at the Seashore. 2002. (Illus.). 32p. (J). (gr. k-3). 9.95 (978-0-375-81118-0(4) , Knopf Bks. for Young Readers) Random Hse. Children's Bks.

Hambleton, Laura. Chameleon Swims. 2005. (Chameleon Ser.). (Illus.). 16p. (J). bds. 7.95 (978-1-84059-435-5(7)); (ARA & ENG., bds. 8.95 (978-1-84059-436-2(5)); (BEN & ENG., bds. 8.95 (978-1-84059-437-9(3)); (ENG, PER & FAR., bds. 8.95 (978-1-84059-438-6(1)); (CHI & ENG., bds. 8.95 (978-1-84059-442-3(X)); (ENG & ITA., bds. 8.95 (978-1-84059-440-9(3)); (ENG & SOM., bds. 8.95 (978-1-84059-443-0(8)); (ENG & SPA., bds. 8.95 (978-1-84059-444-7(6)); (ENG & TUR., bds. 8.95 (978-1-84059-445-4(4)); (ENG & URD., bds. 8.95 (978-1-84059-446-1(2)); (ENG & VIE., bds. 8.95 (978-1-84059-447-8(0)) Milet Publishing.

—Chameleon Swims. Santos, Manolo, tr. 2005. (Chameleon Ser.). (ENG & POR., Illus.). 16p. (J). bds. 8.95 (978-1-84059-441-6(1)) Milet Publishing.

—Chameleon Swims. Sommer, Patricia, tr. 2005. (Chameleon Ser.). (ENG & FRE., Illus.). 16p. (J). bds. 8.95 (978-1-84059-439-3(X)) Milet Publishing.

S

—Chameleon Swims. Astridge, Nissho, tr. 2005. (Chameleon Ser.). (ENG & JPN., Illus.). 16p. (J). bds. 8.95 (978-1-84059-454-6(3)) Milet Publishing.

Hancock, H. Irving. The Grammar School Boys in Summer Athlet. rev. ed. 2006. 216p. 27.95 (978-1-4218-1748-4(9)); pap. 12.95 (978-1-4218-1848-1(5)) 1st World Publishing, Inc. (1st World Library - Literary Society).

Hancock, Irving H. The Grammar School Boys in Summer Athlet. 2006. 78.99 (***978-1-4219-9869-5(6)**); pap. 72.99 (***978-1-4219-9873-2(4)**) IndyPublish.com.

Harcourt School Publishers Staff. Breaking Away: Take-Home Book. 1999. (Collections Ser.). (Illus.). (J). pap. 1.90 (978-0-15-317286-1(X)) Harcourt Schl. Pubs.

—Come Swimming: Take-Home Book. 1999. (Signatures Ser.). (Illus.). (J). pap. 1.70 (978-0-15-313828-7(9)) Harcourt Schl. Pubs.

—Wave Rider. 3rd ed. 2002. (Trophies English Language Learners Ser.). (Illus.). (gr. 5). pap. 5.10 (978-0-15-327819-8(6)) Harcourt Schl. Pubs.

Hedges, Jeremy. Sammy's Breakfast Swim. 2000. (Illus.). 48p. (J). 18.95 (978-1-85776-447-5(1)) Book Guild, Ltd. GBR. *Dist:* Trans-Atlantic Pubns., Inc.

Heiligman, Deborah. Mike Swan, Sink or Swim. 1998. (978-0-606-13610-5(X)) Tandem Library Bks.

Herman, Gail. Splish! Splash! Basso, Bill, illus. 2003. (Hello Reader Ser.). (J). (978-0-439-44164-3(1)) Scholastic, Inc.

Hest, Amy. Make the Team, Baby Duck! Barton, Jill, illus. 2002. (Baby Duck Books! Ser.). 32p. (J). (ps-1). 16.99 (978-0-7636-1541-3(2)) Candlewick Pr.

Hofmeister, Alan, et al. Swim with Us. (Reading for All Learners Ser.). (Illus.). (J). pap. (978-1-56861-140-2(4)) Swift Learning Resources.

Hood, Susan. Lets Jump In! 1999. (ps-2). lib. bdg. 11.80 (978-0-613-25948-4(3)) Tandem Library Bks.

I love to Swim. 2004. (J). per. (978-1-57657-473-7(3)) Paradise Pr., Inc.

Inkpen, Mick. Hissss! 2000. 11.75 (978-0-606-22337-9(1)); 1999. lib. bdg. 12.95 (978-0-613-25527-1(5)) Tandem Library Bks.

Innovative Kids Staff. Ducky Swims. Filipowich, Bob, illus. ed. 2000. (Mini Soft Shapes Ser.). 8p. (J). (ps-ps). 6.99 (978-1-58476-038-2(9)) Innovative Kids.

Ironside, Virginia. Hakiba Kabira Min Al Himoom: The Huge Bag of Worries. 2005. 32p. pap. 12.00 (978-977-6171-02-2(8) , 706-002) Al-Balsam Pubng. Hse. EGY. *Dist:* Bookworld Trade, Inc.

James, Simon. Querido Salvatierra. de la Vega, Eida, tr. from ENG. 2003. Tr. of Dear Mr. Blueberry. (SPA.). (J). (gr. k-2). pap. 6.95 (978-1-930332-45-4(9)) Lectorum Pubns., Inc.

—Querido Salvatierra. 2003. Tr. of Dear Mr. Blueberry. (SPA.). (gr. k-3). lib. bdg. 15.25 (978-0-613-64586-7(3)) Tandem Library Bks.

Jones, Christianne C. Finny Learns to Swim. Schultz, Sara, illus. 2006. (Read-It! Readers Ser.). 24p. (J). (ps-3). 18.60 (978-1-4048-1582-7(1)) Picture Window Bks.

—The Lifeguard. Skeens, Matthew, illus. 2006. (Read-It! Readers Ser.). 32p. (J). (ps-3). 18.60 (978-1-4048-1584-1(8)) Picture Window Bks.

Kessler, Leonard. Last One in Is a Rotten Egg. 1999. (I Can Read Bks.). (Illus.). 64p. (J). (gr. k-3). pap. 3.99 (978-0-06-444262-6(4) , Harper Trophy); 14.95 (978-0-06-028484-8(6)) HarperCollins Pubs.

Kessler, Liz. The Tail of Emily Windsnap. Gibb, Sarah, illus. 2006. (Emily Windsnap Ser.). 224p. (J). (gr. 3-7). reprint ed. 5.99 (978-0-7636-2811-6(5)) Candlewick Pr.

Klam, Cheryl. Learning to Swim. 2007. 224p. (YA). (gr. 7). pap. 8.99 (978-0-385-73372-4(0)); lib. bdg. 13.99 (978-0-385-90387-5(1)) Random Hse. Children's Bks. (Delacorte Bks. for Young Readers).

Koch, Edward T. & Thaler, Pat Koch. Eddie's Little Sister Makes a Splash. Warhola, James, illus. 2007. 32p. (J). (gr. k). 16.99 (978-0-399-24310-3(0) , Putnam Juvenile) Penguin Group (USA) Inc.

Kovalski, Maryann. Omar on Board. 32p. 2007. pap. (***978-1-55455-033-3(5)**); 2005. (Illus.). (J). (978-1-55041-918-4(8)) Fitzhenry & Whiteside, Ltd.

Lagonegro, Melissa. Just Keep Swimming. Harchy, Atelier Philippe, illus. 2005. (Step into Reading Ser.). 32p. (J). (ps-2). pap. 3.99 (978-0-7364-2319-9(2) , RH/Disney) Random Hse. Children's Bks.

Landstrom, Olof & Landstrom, Lena. Will Goes to the Beach. Wilberg, Carla, tr. from SWE. Landstrom, Olof & Landstrom, Lena, illus. 2001. (Illus.). 28p. (J). (ps-1). pap. 4.95 (978-91-29-65305-2(3)) R & S Bks. SWE. *Dist:* Macmillan.

Larsen, Alison. Thomas the Turtle. 2006. (Illus.). 21p. (J). per. 14.95 (978-1-60002-097-1(6) , 3961, Airleaf Publishing) Airleaf Publishing & Bookselling.

Lepp, Royden. Barnabas Goes Swimming. 2008. 32p. (J). pap. 3.99 (***978-0-310-71584-9(9)**) Zondervan.

Lewin, Betsy. Chubbo's Pool. 1998. (Illus.). 32p. (J). (gr. k-3). pap. 6.95 (978-0-395-92863-9(X) , Clarion Bks.) Houghton Mifflin Co. Trade & Reference Div.

Lewis, Edwina. Who Swims? Parker, Ant, illus. 2003. (Who. . . Ser.). 16p. (YA). (978-1-85602-448-8(2)) Chrysalis Children's Bks.

Lin, Grace. Olvina Swims. rev. ed. 2007. (Illus.). 32p. (J). (ps-2). 16.95 (978-0-8050-7661-5(1)) Holt, Henry & Co.

London, Jonathan. Froggy Apprende a Nadar. 2003. (Froggy Ser.). (SPA., Illus.). (J). (gr. k-2). pap. 3.16 net. (978-0-439-20435-4(6) , SO30917) Scholastic, Inc.

Long, Tammy J. Like a Fish. 2007. (J). pap. 7.95 (***978-1-932715-81-1(9)**) UMI (Urban Ministries, Inc.).

Lucke, Deb. The Boy Who Wouldn't Swim. 2008. (J). (***978-0-618-91484-5(6)** , Clarion Bks.) Houghton Mifflin Co. Trade & Reference Div.

Lyles, Tanya. The Frog That Needed an Umbrella. 2006. 17.00 (978-0-8059-9906-8(X)) Dorrance Publishing Co., Inc.

MacGregor, Jill. Swim Safe Little Seals. 2006. (Illus.). 31p. (J). 14.95 (978-0-9774062-0-3(2)) Seal Publishing, LLC.

Martin, Ann M. Karen's Swim Meet. 1999. (Baby-Sitters Little Sister Ser.: No. 110). (Illus.). 102p. (J). (gr. 3-7). pap. 3.99 (978-0-590-50062-3(7) , Scholastic Paperbacks) Scholastic, Inc.

Mayall, Beth. Mermaid Park. 2007. 256p. (YA). pap. 8.99 (978-1-59514-137-8(5) , Razorbill) Penguin Group (USA) Inc.

McMullan, Kate. Fluffy Learns to Swim. Smith, Mavis, illus. 2002. (Hello Reader! Ser.). (J). pap. 3.99 (978-0-439-31946-1(3)) Scholastic, Inc.

McVeity, Jen. On Different Shores. 1998. (Illus.). 167p. (YA). (gr. 5-9). 17.99 (978-0-531-33115-6(6)); pap. 16.95 (978-0-531-30115-9(X)) Scholastic, Inc. (Orchard Bks.).

Metzger, Steve. Five Little Sharks Swimming in the Sea. Bryant, Laura, illus. 2005. 32p. (J). pap. 5.99 (978-0-439-73767-8(2)) Scholastic, Inc.

Morpurgo, Michael & Richards, Lucy. Mairi's Mermaid. 2006. (Blue Bananas Ser.). (Illus.). 43p. (J). (978-0-7787-0851-3(9)) Crabtree Publishing Co.

Murphy, Stuart J. Shark Swimathon. 2001. (gr. k-3). lib. bdg. 13.00 (978-0-613-31686-6(X)) Tandem Library Bks.

Nakagawa, Rieko. Guri y Gura Aprenden a Nadar. Yamawaki, Yuriko, illus. 2001. (SPA.). (J). pap. (978-980-257-256-4(X) , EK6378) Ekare, Ediciones.

No Running! Individual Title Six-Pack Pouch - Level H. (Lighthouse Ser.). 16p. (gr. 1 up). 26.00 (978-0-7578-0850-0(6)) Rigby Education.

Pants Makes the Swim Team. 2004. (J). per. 7.99 (978-0-9755959-2-3(X)) Girl Named Pants, Inc., A.

Picked for the Team, 6 Packs. 16p. (gr. 2 up). 35.00 (978-0-7635-9383-4(4)) Rigby Education.

Polak, Monique. Flip Turn. 2004. (Sports Stories Ser.). 104p. (J). (gr. 3-13). (***978-1-55028-819-3(9)**); 7.95 (978-1-55028-818-6(0)) Lorimer, James & Co., Ltd., Pubs. CAN. *Dist:* Casemate Pubs. & Bk. Distributors, LLC.

Proysen, Alf. Mrs. Pepperpot Learns to Swim. 2006. (Illus.). 32p. (J). pap. 8.99 (***978-0-09-945157-0(3)** , Red Fox) Random Hse. Children's Bks. GBR. *Dist:* Independent Pubs. Group.

Ratto, Linda Lee. Perfection. 2004. (YA). per. (978-0-9748508-3-2(7)) Power Pr.

Remkiewicz, Frank, illus. Froggy Learns to Swim. 2002. (Froggy Ser.). (J). 13.19 (978-0-7587-2553-0(1)) Book Wholesalers, Inc.

Rimes, Leann. Jag. Bernal, Richard, illus. 2003. 40p. (J). (gr. k-3). 15.99 (978-0-525-47155-4(3) , Dutton Juvenile) Penguin Group (USA) Inc.

Rockwell, Anne F. Katie Catz Makes a Splash. Meisel, Paul, illus. 2003. (Good Sports Ser.). 40p. (J). (ps-1). 15.99 (978-0-06-028441-1(2)) HarperCollins Pubs.

—Katie Catz Swims at Last. Meisel, Paul, illus. 1999. 32p. (J). (ps-1). pap. 5.95 (978-0-06-446740-7(6)) HarperCollins Pubs.

Rodriguez, Edel. Sergio Makes a Splash. 2008. 40p. 15.99 (***978-0-316-06616-7(8)**) Little Brown & Co.

Rottman, S. L. Head above Water. 192p. (YA). 2003. pap. 6.95 (978-1-56145-238-5(6) , Q21186); 1999. (gr. 7-11). 14.95 (978-1-56145-185-2(1) , Q21186) Peachtree Pubs., Ltd.

—Head above Water. 2003. (gr. 7-12). lib. bdg. 15.25 (978-0-613-60386-7(9)) Tandem Library Bks.

Schecter, Ellen. Swim Like a Fish. Cymerman, John E., illus. 1998. (Bank Street Reader Collection). 48p. (J). (ps-2). lib. bdg. 22.60 (978-0-8368-1767-6(2)) Stevens, Gareth Inc.

Scheunemann, Pam. Crocodile Tears. Chawla, Neena, illus. 2007. (Fact & Fiction Ser.). 24p. (J). (978-1-59928-437-8(5)); 21.35 (978-1-59928-436-1(7)) ABDO Publishing Co.

Schuurmans, Hilde. Sidney Won't Swim. Schuurmans, Hilde, illus. (Illus.). pap. 6.95 (978-1-57091-515-4(6)); 2001. 32p. (J). 15.95 (978-1-57091-476-8(1)) Charlesbridge Publishing, Inc.

—Sidney Won't Swim. 2002. (gr. k-3). lib. bdg. 15.25 (978-0-613-50062-3(8)) Tandem Library Bks.

Seuling, Barbara. Robert Goes to Camp. Brewer, Paul, illus. 2007. (Robert Bks.). 160p. (J). (gr. 2-4). 16.95 (***978-0-8126-2753-4(9)**) Cricket Bks.

Simon, Seymour. Let's Try It Out in the Water. 2003. (gr. k-3). lib. bdg. 15.30 (978-0-613-67151-4(1)) Tandem Library Bks.

Smith Dinbergs, Holly. Pool Pals. Maddock, Monika, illus. 2005. (Girlz Rock! Ser.). (J). pap. (978-1-59336-705-3(8)) Mondo Publishing.

Stroke of Luck (Swimming) 64p. (YA). (gr. 6-12). pap. 10.95 (978-0-8224-6482-2(9)) Globe Fearon Educational Publishing.

Swimming Lessons with Stewie the Duck. 2005. (J). 9.95 (978-0-9668611-3-6(2)) Kimberly Pr., LLC.

Thomas, Cameron. Mystery of the Lake. Krystoforski, Andrej, illus. 2004. (Jungle of Utt Ser.). 40p. (J). 16.95 (978-0-921800-02-6(9)) MGT Developments, Ltd. CAN. *Dist:* Independent Pubs. Group.

Thomas, Jeana. How Louie Became a Safety Swimmer: Water Safety. Triefenbach, Lisa, illus. l.t. ed. 2002. (Camp of Champs Ser.: Vol. 2). 24p. (J). (ps-3). pap. 6.95 (978-0-9701118-4-5(3) , 050-002) Charm Pubns., Inc.

Wallace, Karen & Dorling Kindersley Publishing Staff. I Can Swim! 2004. (Dk Readers Ser.). (Illus.). 32p. (J). 12.99 (978-0-7566-0274-1(2)) Dorling Kindersley Publishing, Inc.

Walters, Celeste. The Last Race. 2000. (UQP Young Adult Fiction Ser.). 224p. (J). pap. 16.95 (978-0-7022-3172-8(X)) Univ. of Queensland Pr. AUS. *Dist:* International Specialized Bk. Services.

Ward, Nick. Come on, Baby Duck! 2004. (Illus.). 30p. (J). (ps up). 16.00 (978-1-56148-447-8(4)) Good Bks.

Wells, Rosemary. Eduardo: Cumpleanos en la Piscina. Wells, Rosemary, illus. Orig. Title: Edward's Big Splash. (SPA.). 26p. (J). (ps). pap. 8.95 (978-1-59437-477-5(7)) Santillana USA Publishing Co., Inc.

—Eduardo: Cumpleanos en la Piscina. 2003. Orig. Title: Edward's Big Splash. (SPA., Illus.). 22p. (J). (ps-k). 12.95 (978-1-56014-664-3(8)) Santillana USA Publishing Co., Inc.

Wildsmith, Brian. The Little Wood Duck. Wildsmith, Brian, illus. 2006. (Illus.). 32p. (J). 16.95 (978-1-59572-042-9(1)); pap. 6.95 (978-1-59572-049-8(9)) Star Bright Bks., Inc.

Willner-Pardo, Gina. Jumping into Nothing. Chang, Heidi, illus. 1999. 64p. (J). (gr. 4-6). tchr. ed. 14.00 (978-0-395-84130-3(5) , Clarion Bks.) Houghton Mifflin Co. Trade & Reference Div.

Winton, Tim. The Deep. Louise, Karen, illus. 1998. 32p. (YA). 21.95 (978-1-86368-242-8(2)) Fremantle Pr. AUS. *Dist:* International Specialized Bk. Services.

—The Deep. Louise, Karen, illus. 2004. 32p. (ps-2). 14.95 (978-1-58246-024-6(8) , Tricycle Pr.) Ten Speed Pr.

Winton, Tim & Louise, Karen. The Deep. (Illus.). 32p. (YA). pap. 13.95 (978-1-86368-210-7(4)) Fremantle Pr. AUS. *Dist:* International Specialized Bk. Services.

Zalben, Jane Breskin. Leap. 2007. 272p. (J). (gr. 5). 15.99 (978-0-375-83871-2(6)); lib. bdg. 18.99 (978-0-375-93871-9(0)) Random Hse. Children's Bks. (Knopf Bks. for Young Readers).

SWINE

see Pigs

SWITZERLAND

Chelsea House Publishing Staff. Switzerland. 1999. (Major World Nations Ser.). (Illus.). 144p. (gr. 4-7). 29.95 (978-0-7910-5399-7(7) , Chelsea Hse.) Facts On File, Inc.

Graf, Mike. Switzerland. 2002. (Countries of the World Ser.). (Illus.). 24p. (J). (gr. 2-3). lib. bdg. 18.60 (978-0-7368-1109-5(5) , Bridgestone Bks.) Capstone Pr., Inc.

Hammond, Paula. Italy & Switzerland. 2002. (Cultures & Costumes Ser.). (Illus.). 64p. (J). (gr. 7 up). lib. bdg. (978-1-59084-438-0(6)) Mason Crest Pubs.

Harris, Pamela K. Welcome to Switzerland. 2008. (Welcome to the World Ser.). 32p. (J). (gr. 1-5). 27.07 (***978-1-59296-980-7(1)**) Child's World, Inc.

Harvey, Miles. Look What Came from Switzerland. 2003. (Look What Came from Ser.). (Illus.). 32p. (J). (gr. 2-4). pap. 6.95 (978-0-531-16630-7(9) , Watts, Franklin) Scholastic Library Publishing.

—Look What Came from Switzerland. 2002. (gr. 3-6). lib. bdg. 15.25 (978-0-613-59510-0(6)) Tandem Library Bks.

Levy, Patricia. Switzerland. 2nd ed. 2005. (Cultures of the World Ser.). (Illus.). 144p. (YA). 37.07 (978-0-7614-1850-4(4) , Benchmark Bks.) Cavendish, Marshall Corp.

McKay, Susan. Switzerland. 1999. (Festivals of the World Ser.). (Illus.). 32p. (J). (gr. 3 up). lib. bdg. 24.67 (978-0-8368-2027-0(4)) Stevens, Gareth Inc.

Netzley, Patricia D. Switzerland. 2000. (Modern Nations of the World Ser.). (Illus.). 96p. (J). (gr. 4-12). 27.45 (978-1-56006-821-1(3) , Lucent Bks.) Thomson Gale.

Rogers, Lura & Hintz, Martin. Switzerland. 2001. (Enchantment of the World, Second Ser.). (Illus.). 144p. (J). (gr. 5-9). 36.00 (978-0-516-21080-3(7) , Children's Pr.) Scholastic Library Publishing.

Van Cleaf, Kristin. Switzerland. 2007. (Countries Set VI Ser.). (Illus.). 40p. (J). (gr. k-6). lib. bdg. 24.21 (***978-1-59928-786-7(2)** , Checkerboard Library) ABDO Publishing Co.

Zocchi, Judy. In Switzerland. Brodie, Neale, illus. 2005. (Global Adventures I Ser.). 32p. (J). pap. 9.95 (978-1-59646-156-7(X)); lib. bdg. 20.65 (978-1-59646-006-5(7)); per. 9.95 (978-1-59646-157-4(8)) Dingles & Co.

—In Switzerland/en Suiza. Brodie, Neale, illus. 2005. (Global Adventures I Ser.).Tr. of En Suiza. (ENG & SPA.). 32p. (J). pap. 9.95 (978-1-59646-158-1(6)); lib. bdg. 20.65 (978-1-59646-007-2(5)); per. 9.95 (978-1-59646-159-8(4)) Dingles & Co.

SWITZERLAND—FICTION

Buff, Conrad. Apple & the Arrow. 2001. (gr. 3-6). lib. bdg. 14.10 (978-0-613-35484-4(2)) Tandem Library Bks.

Buff, Conrad & Buff, Mary. The Apple & the Arrow. Buff, Conrad & Buff, Mary, illus. 2001. (Illus.). 80p. (J). (gr. 4-6). tchr. ed. 16.00 (978-0-618-12807-5(7)); pap. 8.95 (978-0-618-12809-9(3)) Houghton Mifflin Co. Trade & Reference Div.

Church, Lisa R. & Spyri, Johanna. Heidi. Akib, Jamel, illus. 2007. (Classic Starts Ser.). 152p. (J). (***978-1-4287-4211-6(5)**) Sterling Publishing Co., Inc.

Coats, Lucy. Heidi. 2000. (gr. k-3). lib. bdg. 11.80 (978-0-613-25481-6(3)) Tandem Library Bks.

Coats, Lucy, et al. Heidi, Vol. 3. 2000. (Classic Readers Ser.). (Illus.). 48p. (J). (gr. 2-3). pap. 3.99 (978-0-7894-5390-7(8)) Dorling Kindersley Publishing, Inc.

Creech, Sharon. Bloomability. 288p. (J). (gr. 3-7). 1999. (Illus.). pap. 6.99 (978-0-06-440823-3(X) , Harper Trophy); 1998. 17.99 (978-0-06-026993-7(6) , Cotler, Joanna Books) HarperCollins Pubs.

—Bloomability. unabr. ed. 2004. 273p. (J). (gr. 4-7). pap. 38.00 incl. audio (978-0-8072-8754-5(7) , YA257SP, Listening Library) Random Hse. Audio Publishing Group.

—Bloomability. 1999. 12.64 (978-0-606-17460-2(5)); (gr. 3-6). lib. bdg. 14.15 (978-0-613-22826-8(X)) Tandem Library Bks.

Dalmatian Press Staff, adapted by. Heidi. (SPA., Illus.). (YA). 11.95 (978-84-7281-082-2(8) , AF1082) Auriga, Ediciones S.A. ESP. *Dist:* Continental Bk. Co., Inc.

—Heidi. (Young Collector's Illustrated Classics Ser.). (Illus.). 192p. (J). (gr. 3-7). 9.95 (978-1-56156-455-2(9)) Kidsbooks, Inc.

Fisher, Leonard Everett. William Tell. Fisher, Leonard Everett, illus. 2006. (Illus.). 28p. (J). reprint ed. 16.00 (978-0-7567-9880-2(9)) DIANE Publishing Co.

Franklin, Emily. Balancing Acts: Chalet Girls. 2007. 244p. (YA). (gr. 12 up). per. 9.99 (***978-0-451-22219-0(9)** , N A L Trade) Penguin Group (USA) Inc.

Gallaz, Christophe. The Wolf Who Loved Music. Logue, Mary, tr. from FRE. 2003. (Illus.). 32p. 17.95 (978-1-56846-178-6(X) , Creative Editions) Creative Co., The.

A Gift to Share. 2005. (J). 17.00 (978-0-9721457-1-8(0)) Silent Moon Bks.

Goscinny, René & Uderzo, Albert. Asterix in Switzerland. Uderzo, Albert, illus. 2004. (Illus.). 48p. pap. 9.95 (978-0-7528-6635-2(4)) Orion Bks. Ltd. GBR. *Dist:* Sterling Publishing Co., Inc.

Gudel, Helen. Dear Alexandra: A Story of Switzerland. Gudel, Helen, illus. 1999. (Make Friends Around the World Ser.). Orig. Title: Leiber Alex. (Illus.). 32p. (J). (gr. k-3). 15.95 (978-1-56899-739-1(6) , B8002); pap. 5.95 (978-1-56899-740-7(X) , S8002) Soundprints.

Hasler, E. & Bhend, K. Tale of Two Brothers. 2006. (Illus.). 40p. (J). 16.95 (978-0-7358-2102-6(X)) North-South Bks., Inc.

Hedji, Charles. Fields of Discovery. 2006. 220p. pap. 19.95 (978-1-4241-0605-9(2)) PublishAmerica, Inc.

Hergé. L' Affaire Tournesol. 1999. (Tintin Ser.).Tr. of Calculus Affair. (FRE.). (J). (gr. 4-7). 21.95 (978-2-203-00117-6(8)) Casterman, Editions FRA. *Dist:* Distribooks, Inc.

—The Calculus Affair. (Illus.). 62p. (J). 19.95 (978-0-8288-5014-8(3)) French & European Pubns., Inc.

Montgomery, R. A. Behind the Wheel. 2008. (Choose Your Own Adventure Ser.: No. 26). (Illus.). 144p. (J). per. 5.99 (***978-1-933390-26-0(3)**) Chooseco LLC.

Nascimbene, Yan. Ocean Deep. 1999. 40p. 18.00 (978-1-56846-161-8(5) , Creative Editions) Creative Co., The.

Perkins, Lucy Fitch. The Swiss Twins. 2004. reprint ed. pap. 15.95 (978-1-4191-8467-3(9)); pap. 1.99 (978-1-4192-8467-0(3)) Kessinger Publishing, LLC.

Pullman, Philip. Count Karlstein. Bryan, Diana, illus. 2000. 256p. (YA). (gr. 5-8). 5.99 (978-0-375-80348-2(3) , Yearling) Random Hse. Children's Bks.

—Count Karlstein. 1998. 256p. (J). (gr. 5-8). 17.00 (978-0-679-89255-7(9) , Knopf Bks. for Young Readers) Random Hse. Children's Bks.

—Count Karlstein. 2000. 12.64 (978-0-606-17845-7(7)); (gr. 7-12). lib. bdg. 14.15 (978-0-613-28451-6(8)) Tandem Library Bks.

Random House Value Publishing Staff & Spyri, Johanna. Heidi. 1998. (Children's Classics Ser.). (Illus.). 352p. (J). (gr. 5-9). 5.99 (978-0-517-18967-2(4) , Children's Classics) Random Hse. Value Publishing.

Ruiz, Celia & Spyri, Johanna. Heidi. 2001. (SPA., Illus.). 184p. (J). 15.95 (978-84-372-2237-0(0)) Altea, Ediciones, S.A. - Grupo Santillana ESP. *Dist:* Santillana USA Publishing Co., Inc.

Smith, Alexander McCall. Max & Maddy & the Chocolate Money Mystery. Pamintuan, Macky, illus. 2007. 128p. (J). (gr. 2-4). 9.95 (978-1-59990-036-0(X) , Bloomsbury Children) Bloomsbury Publishing.

Spyri, Johanna. Classic Starts: Heidi. Akib, Jamel, illus. 2007. (Classic Starts Ser.). 160p. (J). 4.95 (978-1-4027-3691-9(6)) Sterling Publishing Co., Inc.

—Heidi. 2002. (Great Illustrated Classics Ser.). (Illus.). 240p. (J). (gr. 3-8). 21.35 (978-1-57765-688-3(1) , ABDO & Daughters) ABDO Publishing Co.

—Heidi. (J). 24.95 (978-0-8488-1179-2(8)) Amereon LTD.

—Heidi. 1999. (Andre Deutsch Classics). 316p. (J). 9.95 (978-0-233-99227-3(8)) Andre Deutsch GBR. *Dist:* Trafalgar Square Publishing.

—Heidi. Rinaldi, Angelo, illus. 2002. (Kingfisher Classics Ser.). 352p. (J). (gr. k-3). tchr. ed. 15.95 (978-0-7534-5494-7(7) , Kingfisher) Houghton Mifflin Co. Trade & Reference Div.

—Heidi. 2001. (Young Reader's Classics Ser.). 94p. (J). pap. 9.95 (978-1-55013-971-6(1) , Key Porter kids) Key Porter Bks. CAN. *Dist:* Firefly Bks., Ltd.

—Heidi. 2002. (Twelve-Point Ser.). lib. bdg. 25.00 (978-1-58287-183-7(3)) North Bks.

—Heidi. 2000. (Aladdin Classics Ser.). (Illus.). 304p. (J). (gr. 4-7). pap. 5.99 (978-0-689-83962-7(6) , Aladdin) Simon & Schuster Children's Publishing.

—Heidi. 1998. (Children's Classics). (ENG., Illus.). 240p. (J). pap. (978-1-85326-125-1(4) , 1254WW) Wordsworth Editions, Ltd.

—Heidi. 2002. (Spot the Classics Ser.). (Illus.). 180p. (J). (gr. k-5). 4.99 (978-1-57759-546-5(7)) Dalmatian Pr.

—Heidi. reprint ed. lib. bdg. 48.00 (978-0-7426-1047-7(0)); 2001. (Illus.). pap. 28.00 (978-0-7426-6047-2(8)) Classic Bks.

—Heidi. unabr. ed. 2000. (Dover Juvenile Classics Ser.). (Illus.). 304p. (J). (gr. 4-7). pap. 3.00 (978-0-486-41235-1(0)) Dover Pubns., Inc.

—Heidi. 2nd ed. (Coleccion Clasicos en Accion). (SPA., Illus.). 80p. (YA). (gr. 5-8). 15.95 (978-84-241-5784-5(2) , EV0790) Everest de Ediciones y Distribucion, S.L. ESP. *Dist:* Lectorum Pubns., Inc.

—Heidi. l.t. ed. 2004. (Large Print Ser.). 433p. 26.00 (978-1-58287-666-5(5)) North Bks.

—Heidi. l.t. ed. 2002. (Perennial Bestsellers Ser.). 394p. 29.95 (978-0-7862-4886-5(6)) Thorndike Pr.

—Heidi: With a Discussion of Optimism. Clift, Eva, illus. 2003. (Values in Action Illustrated Classics Ser.). 190p. (J). (978-1-59203-030-9(0)) Learning Challenge, Inc.
—Heidi Book & Charm. (Charming Classics). (J). 2006. 432p. pap. 6.99 (978-0-06-088217-4(4)); 2000. (gr. 3-7). pap. 6.99 (978-0-694-01453-8(2)) HarperCollins Pubs. (Harper Festival).
—Heidi EasyRead Large Edition. 2006. pap. (***978-1-4250-4150-2(7)***) Assistedreadingbooks.com Inc.
—Maezli (a Story of the Swiss Valleys) 2006. 95.99 (***978-1-4219-7379-1(0)***); pap. 89.99 (***978-1-4219-7364-7(2)***) IndyPublish.com.
Spyri, Johanna. Moni, the Goat Boy: And Other Stories. 2000. (Illus.). 219p. (J). reprint ed. pap. 6.95 (978-1-883453-09-1(7)) Deutsche Buchhandlung-James Lowry.
The Story of William Tell: Individual Title Six-Packs. (gr. 3 up). 35.00 (978-0-7635-9673-6(6)) Rigby Education.
Tetzner, Lisa. The Black Brothers. Binder, Hannes, illus. 2004. 146p. (YA). 16.95 (978-1-932425-04-8(7), Lemniscaat) Boyds Mills Pr.
Ward, John. Secret of the Alchemist. 2003. (gr. 3-6). lib. bdg. 17.60 (978-0-613-78582-2(7)) Tandem Library Bks.

SYMBIOSIS

see Plant Ecology

SYMBOLISM

see also Christian Art and Symbolism; Heraldry

Bateman, Teresa. Red, White, Blue & Uncle Who? The Story Behind Some of America's Patriotic Symbols. (Illus.). 64p. (J). (gr. 4-6). 6.95 (978-0-8234-1784-1(0)) Holiday Hse., Inc.
DeGezelle, Terri. The Great Seal of the United States. 2004. (Illus.). 24p. (J). 15.95 (978-0-7368-2528-3(2)) Capstone Pr., Inc.
Douglas, Lloyd G. The Bald Eagle. 2003. (Welcome Book Ser.). (J). 24p. 18.00 (978-0-516-25851-5(6)); pap. 4.95 (978-0-516-27874-2(6)) Scholastic Library Publishing. (Children's Pr.).
—The Bald Eagle. 2003. (gr. k-3). lib. bdg. 12.95 (978-0-613-67690-8(4)) Tandem Library Bks.
Dubois, Muriel L. Alaska Facts & Symbols. (States & Their Symbols Ser.). 24p. (J). 2000. (Illus.). (gr. 2-3). lib. bdg. 13.95 (978-0-7368-0522-3(2), Bridgestone Bks.); 2003. lib. bdg. 19.93 (978-0-7368-2232-9(1)) Capstone Pr., Inc.
—Maryland Facts & Symbols. (States & Their Symbols Ser.). 24p. (J). 2000. (Illus.). (gr. 2-3). lib. bdg. 18.60 (978-0-7368-0523-0(0), Bridgestone Bks.); 2003. lib. bdg. 19.93 (978-0-7368-2250-3(X)) Capstone Pr., Inc.
—New Hampshire Facts & Symbols. (States & Their Symbols Ser.). 24p. (J). 2000. (Illus.). (gr. 2-3). lib. bdg. 13.95 (978-0-7368-0524-7(9), Bridgestone Bks.); 2003. lib. bdg. 19.93 (978-0-7368-2259-6(3)) Capstone Pr., Inc.
—Wyoming Facts & Symbols. (States & Their Symbols Ser.). 24p. (J). 2000. (Illus.). (gr. 2-3). lib. bdg. 18.60 (978-0-7368-0529-2(X), Bridgestone Bks.); 2003. lib. bdg. 19.93 (978-0-7368-2281-7(X)) Capstone Pr., Inc.
Feeney, Kathy. Puerto Rico Facts & Symbols. (States & Their Symbols Ser.). 24p. (J). 2000. (Illus.). (gr. 2-3). lib. bdg. 18.60 (978-0-7368-0644-2(X), Bridgestone Bks.); 2003. lib. bdg. 19.93 (978-0-7368-2269-5(0)) Capstone Pr., Inc.
—Rhode Island Facts & Symbols. (States & Their Symbols Ser.). 24p. (J). 2000. (Illus.). (gr. 2-3). lib. bdg. 18.60 (978-0-7368-0645-9(8), Bridgestone Bks.); 2003. lib. bdg. 19.93 (978-0-7368-2270-1(4)) Capstone Pr., Inc.
—Tennessee Facts & Symbols. (States & Their Symbols Ser.). 24p. (J). 2000. (Illus.). (gr. 2-3). lib. bdg. 13.95 (978-0-7368-0525-4(7), Bridgestone Bks.); 2003. lib. bdg. 19.93 (978-0-7368-2273-2(9)) Capstone Pr., Inc.
—Utah Facts & Symbols. (States & Their Symbols Ser.). 24p. (J). 2000. (Illus.). (gr. 2-3). lib. bdg. 13.95 (978-0-7368-0526-1(5), Bridgestone Bks.); 2003. lib. bdg. 19.93 (978-0-7368-2274-9(7)) Capstone Pr., Inc.
—Vermont Facts & Symbols. (States & Their Symbols Ser.). 24p. (J). 2000. (Illus.). (gr. 2-3). lib. bdg. 18.60 (978-0-7368-0647-3(4), Bridgestone Bks.); 2003. lib. bdg. 19.93 (978-0-7368-2275-6(5)) Capstone Pr., Inc.
—Washington, D. C. Facts & Symbols. (States & Their Symbols Ser.). 24p. (J). 2000. (Illus.). (gr. 2-3). lib. bdg. 18.60 (978-0-7368-0527-8(3), Bridgestone Bks.); 2003. lib. bdg. 19.93 (978-0-7368-2278-7(X)) Capstone Pr., Inc.
—West Virginia Facts & Symbols. (States & Their Symbols Ser.). 24p. (J). 2000. (Illus.). (gr. 2-3). lib. bdg. 18.60 (978-0-7368-0528-5(1), Bridgestone Bks.); 2003. lib. bdg. 19.93 (978-0-7368-2279-4(8)) Capstone Pr., Inc.
Fein, Eric & Muschinske, Emily. How to Draw Puerto Rico's Sights & Symbols. 2002. (Kid's Guide to Drawing America Ser.). (Illus.). 32p. (J). lib. bdg. 25.25 (978-0-8239-6095-8(1), PowerKids Pr.) Rosen Publishing Group, Inc., The.
Gibson, Karen Bush. Nevada Facts & Symbols. (States & Their Symbols Ser.). 24p. (J). 2000. (Illus.). (gr. 2-3). lib. bdg. 18.60 (978-0-7368-0641-1(5), Bridgestone Bks.); 2003. lib. bdg. 19.93 (978-0-7368-2258-9(5)) Capstone Pr., Inc.
—North Dakota Facts & Symbols. (States & Their Symbols Ser.). 24p. (J). 2000. (Illus.). (gr. 2-3). lib. bdg. 18.60 (978-0-7368-0642-8(3), Bridgestone Bks.); 2003. lib. bdg. 19.93 (978-0-7368-2264-0(X)) Capstone Pr., Inc.
—Oklahoma Facts & Symbols. (States & Their Symbols Ser.). 24p. (J). 2000. (Illus.). (gr. 2-3). lib. bdg. 18.60 (978-0-7368-0643-5(1), Bridgestone Bks.); 2003. lib. bdg. 19.93 (978-0-7368-2266-4(6)) Capstone Pr., Inc.
Hancock, Maryann. The Bald Eagle. 2006. (Illus.). 32p. (J). pap. (978-1-4034-7010-2(3)); lib. bdg. (978-1-4034-7003-4(0)) Heinemann Library.
Harris, Nancy. The Bald Eagle. 2007. (J). (***978-1-4034-9380-4(4)***) Heinemann Library.
Kule, Elaine A. Arkansas Facts & Symbols. (States & Their Symbols Ser.). 24p. (J). 2000. (Illus.). (gr. 2-3). lib. bdg. 18.60 (978-0-7368-0634-3(2), Bridgestone Bks.); 2003. lib. bdg. 19.93 (978-0-7368-2234-3(8)) Capstone Pr., Inc.
—Delaware Facts & Symbols. (States & Their Symbols Ser.). 24p. (J). 2000. (Illus.). (gr. 2-3). lib. bdg. 18.60 (978-0-7368-0635-0(0), Bridgestone Bks.); 2003. lib. bdg. 19.93 (978-0-7368-2238-1(0)) Capstone Pr., Inc.
—Idaho Facts & Symbols. (States & Their Symbols Ser.). 24p. (J). 2000. (Illus.). (gr. 2-3). lib. bdg. 18.60 (978-0-7368-0636-7(9), Bridgestone Bks.); 2003. lib. bdg. 19.93 (978-0-7368-2242-8(9)) Capstone Pr., Inc.
—Iowa Facts & Symbols. (States & Their Symbols Ser.). 24p. (J). 2000. (Illus.). (gr. 2-3). lib. bdg. 18.60 (978-0-7368-0637-4(7), Bridgestone Bks.); 2003. lib. bdg. 19.93 (978-0-7368-2245-9(3)) Capstone Pr., Inc.
Love, Mary A. Learning Through Symbolism & Celebrations. Flournoy, L. Diana, illus. 1998. x, 150p. (J). pap. 18.00 (978-1-929548-00-2(1)) Love's Creative Resources.
McAuliffe, Bill. Indiana: Facts & Symbols. 1999. (J). lib. bdg. 14.00 (978-0-531-11802-3(9)) Capstone Pr., Inc.
—Minnesota: Facts & Symbols. 1999. (J). lib. bdg. 14.00 (978-0-531-11803-0(7)) Capstone Pr., Inc.
—South Carolina: Facts & Symbols. 1999. (J). lib. bdg. 14.00 (978-0-531-11805-4(3)) Capstone Pr., Inc.
—Virginia: Facts & Symbols. 1999. (J). lib. bdg. 14.00 (978-0-531-11807-8(X)) Capstone Pr., Inc.
McAuliffe, Emily. Connecticut Facts & Symbols. 1999. lib. bdg. 14.00 (978-0-531-11800-9(2)) Capstone Pr., Inc.
—Georgia: Facts & Symbols. 1999. (J). lib. bdg. 14.00 (978-0-531-11801-6(0)) Capstone Pr., Inc.
—Oregon Facts & Symbols. 1999. (J). lib. bdg. 14.00 (978-0-531-11804-7(5)) Capstone Pr., Inc.
Quasha, Jennifer. The Birth & Growth of a Nation: Hands-On Projects about Symbols of American Liberty. 2001. (Great Social Studies Projects Ser.). (Illus.). 24p. (J). (gr. 3). lib. bdg. 19.95 (978-0-8239-5703-3(9), PowerKids Pr.) Rosen Publishing Group, Inc., The.
Sateren, Shelley Swanson. New Mexico Facts & Symbols. (States & Their Symbols Ser.). 24p. (J). 2000. (Illus.). (gr. 2-3). lib. bdg. 18.60 (978-0-7368-0380-9(7), Bridgestone Bks.); 2003. lib. bdg. 19.93 (978-0-7368-2261-9(5)) Capstone Pr., Inc.
Stone, Lynn M. Bald Eagle. 2003. (Animals in U.S. History Ser.). (Illus.). 24p. (J). 25.64 (978-1-58952-699-0(6)) Rourke Publishing, LLC.
Yanuck, Debbie L. The Bald Eagle. 2003. (American Symbols Ser.). (Illus.). 24p. (J). (gr. 1-2). lib. bdg. 23.93 (978-0-7368-1629-8(1), Bridgestone Bks.) Capstone Pr., Inc.

SYMMETRY

Kirkby, David. Patterns. 1998. (Mini Math Ser.). (Illus.). 24p. (J). (978-1-57572-003-6(5)) Heinemann Library.
Martin, Elena. Look at Both Sides. 2003. (Yellow Umbrella Books for Early Readers). (Illus.). 16p. (J). 15.93 (978-0-7368-2936-6(9)); pap. (978-0-7368-2895-6(8)) Yellow Umbrella Pr.
Murphy, Stuart J. Let's Fly a Kite: Symmetry. Floca, Brian, illus. 2000. (Mathstart Ser.). (J). (978-0-606-19985-8(3)) Tandem Library Bks.
Realtime Associates and Mazer Corporation Staff & LeapFrog Staff, compiled by. Understand Linear or Rotational Symmetry. 2002. (J). (gr. 3). 66.75 (978-1-58605-403-8(1), LeapFrog Schl. Hse.) LeapFrog Enterprises, Inc.
Rubin, Alan. Mira los dos Lados. 2005. Tr. of Look at Both Sides. (SPA., Illus.). 16p. (J). (gr. k-1). lib. bdg. 15.93 (978-0-7368-4154-2(7)) Capstone Pr., Inc.
That Is Symmetry! First Grade Guided Reading Level E. (On Our Way to English Ser.). (gr. 1 up). 27.75 (978-0-7578-7046-0(5)) Rigby Education.

SYNAGOGUES

Berkson, Marc & VanDusen, Susan. The Synagogue: House of the Jewish People. Collins, Matt, illus. 1999. 96p. (J). (gr. 3-5). pap. 5.95 (978-0-87441-664-0(7)) Behrman Hse., Inc.
Charing, Douglas. Visiting a Synagogue. 2000. (gr. 7-12). lib. bdg. 16.45 (978-0-613-89220-9(8)) Tandem Library Bks.
Hoffman, Lawrence & Wolfson, Ron. What You Will See Inside a Synagogue. Aron, Bill, photos by. 2004. (What You Will See Inside- Ser.). (Illus.). 32p. (J). 17.99 (978-1-59473-012-2(1)) SkyLight Paths Publishing.
Nason, Ruth. Visiting a Synagogue. 2005. (Start up Religion Ser.). (Illus.). 24p. (J). (gr. 1-4). lib. bdg. (978-1-84234-343-2(2), Cherrytree Books) Evans Publishing Group.
Person, Hara & z"l, Faye Tillis Lewy. My Synagogue Scrapbook. Schoenberg-Lam, Dahlia, illus. 2006. pap. 11.95 (***978-0-8074-0990-9(1)***, 164065) URJ Pr.
Rosenberg, Larry. Jewish Synagogue. 2000. (gr. 3-6). lib. bdg. 14.10 (978-0-613-88866-0(9)) Tandem Library Bks.
Rosenberg, Laurie. Jewish Synagogue. 1998. (Illus.). 32p. (J). (978-0-7136-4338-1(2), Adlard Coles) A & C Black.
—Jewish Synagogue. 2000. (Keystones Ser.). (Illus.). 32p. (gr. 2-6). reprint ed. pap. 5.95 (978-0-7136-5343-4(4)) A & C Black GBR. *Dist:* Consortium Bk. Sales & Distribution.
Ross, Mandy. Jewish Synagogues. 2005. (Let's Find Out about Ser.). (Illus.). 32p. (J). 25.36 (978-1-4034-7032-4(4)) Steck-Vaughn.
Wood, Angela. Jewish Synagogue. 1999. (Places of Worship Ser.). (Illus.). 32p. (J). (gr. 2 up). lib. bdg. 23.33 (978-0-8368-2608-1(6)) Stevens, Gareth Inc.

SYRIA

Behnke, Alison. Syria in Pictures. 2005. (Visual Geography Ser.). (Illus.). 80p. (J). (gr. 5-12). 27.93 (978-0-8225-2396-3(5)) Lerner Publishing Group.
Dougherty, Terri. Syria. 2004. (Modern Nations of the World Ser.). (Illus.). 112p. (J). (gr. 7-10). 29.95 (978-1-59018-246-8(4), Lucent Bks.) Thomson Gale.
Englar, Mary. Syria: A Question & Answer Book. 2007. (Fact Finders Ser.). (Illus.). 32p. (J). 22.60 (978-0-7368-6412-1(1)) Capstone Pr., Inc.
Grolier Educational Staff, contrib. by. Syria. 2003. (Illus.). 32p. (J). (978-0-7172-5802-4(5), Grolier) Scholastic Library Publishing.
Kummer, Patricia K. Syria. 2005. (Enchantment of the World, Second Ser.). 144p. (YA). (gr. 5-9). 36.00 (978-0-516-23677-3(6), Children's Pr.) Scholastic Library Publishing.
Morrison, John F. Syria. 2002. (Creation of the Modern Middle East Ser.). (Illus.). 125p. (YA). (gr. 6-12). 35.00 (978-0-7910-6509-9(X), Chelsea Hse.) Facts On File, Inc.
Mulloy, Martin. Syria. 1999. (Major World Nations Ser.). (Illus.). 144p. (YA). (gr. 4-7). lib. bdg. 19.95 (978-0-7910-4983-9(3), Chelsea Hse.) Facts On File, Inc.
Skinner, Patricia. Syria. 2004. (J). lib. bdg. 30.00 (978-0-8368-3118-4(7)) Stevens, Gareth Inc.
South, Coleman. Syria. 2nd ed. 2006. (Cultures of the World Ser.). (Illus.). 144p. (J). (978-0-7614-2054-5(1), Benchmark Bks.) Cavendish, Marshall Corp.
Stanley, Diane. Saladin: Noble Prince of Islam. Stanley, Diane, illus. 2002. (Illus.). 48p. (J). (gr. 5-8). 16.99 (978-0-688-17135-3(4)); lib. bdg. 18.89 (978-0-688-17136-0(2)) HarperCollins Pubs.
Sullivan, Anne Marie. Syria. 2003. (Modern Middle East Nations & Their Strategic Place in the World Ser.). (Illus.). 112,128p. (YA). (gr. 7 up). lib. bdg. (978-1-59084-506-6(4)) Mason Crest Pubs.
Tay, Alan. Welcome to Syria. 2005. (Welcome to My Country Ser.). (Illus.). 48p. (J). lib. bdg. 26.00 (978-0-8368-3136-8(5)) Stevens, Gareth Inc.
Zurlo, Tony. Syria in the News: Past, Present, & Future. 2006. (Middle East Nations in the News Ser.). (Illus.). 128p. (J). lib. bdg. 33.27 (978-1-59845-025-5(5), MyReportLinks.com Bks.) Enslow Pubs., Inc.

T

TABLE

Baylor, Byrd. The Table Where Rich People Sit. Parnell, Peter, illus. 1998. 32p. (J). (gr. 1-4). 6.99 (978-0-689-82008-3(9), Aladdin) Simon & Schuster Children's Publishing.
Evans, Lynn. Peas & Honey: A Young Persons Guide to Gracious Dining. 1999. (Illus.). (J). (gr. k-5). 10.00 (978-0-9669658-6-5(8)) Poole & Smith Publishing.

TADPOLES

Ganeri, Anita. Frogs & Tadpoles. 2007. (J). (***978-1-58340-809-4(6)***) Smart Apple Media.
Ganeri, Anita. From Tadpole to Frog. 2006. (Heinemann First Library). (Illus.). 32p. (J). 25.36 (978-1-4034-7859-7(7)); pap. (978-1-4034-7868-9(6)) Heinemann Library.
Godwin, Sam. The Trouble with Tadpoles: A First Look at the Life Cycle of a Frog. Abel, Simone, illus. 2004. (First Look Science Ser.). 32p. (C). (gr. k-3). 22.60 (978-1-4048-0654-2(7)) Picture Window Bks.
Greenaway, Theresa. Tadpoles. Fairclough, Chris, illus. 1999. (Minipets Ser.). 32p. (J). (gr. 1-5). lib. bdg. 25.69 (978-0-7398-1828-2(7)) Raintree.
—Tadpoles. 2000. (Minipets Ser.). (Illus.). 32p. (J). (gr. 1-5). pap. 7.95 (978-0-7398-2195-4(4)) Steck-Vaughn.
Keeping Tadpoles Alive! Individual Title Six-Packs. (Discovery World Ser.). 24p. (gr. 1-2). 33.00 (978-0-7635-8476-4(2)) Rigby Education.
Milbourne, A. Tadpoles & Frogs. 2004. (Beginners Ser.). 32p. (J). (gr. 1 up). lib. bdg. 12.95 (978-1-58086-465-7(1)); (Illus.). pap. 4.95 (978-0-7945-0164-8(8), Usborne) EDC Publishing.
Milbourne, Anna. Tadpoles & Frogs - Internet Referenced (Level 1) 2007. 32p. (J). 4.99 (978-0-7945-1345-0(X), Usborne) EDC Publishing.
Stewart, David. How a Tadpole Grows into a Frog. (Amaze Ser.). 32p. (J). 2008. pap. 8.95 (***978-0-531-20454-2(5)***); 2007. spiral bd. 26.00 (***978-0-531-20443-6(X)***) Scholastic Library Publishing. (Children's Pr.).
Vern, Alex. Where Do Frogs Come From? 2001. (J). (978-0-606-22610-3(9)) Tandem Library Bks.
Zoehfeld, Kathleen Weidner. From Tadpole to Frog. 2001. (Science Readers Ser.). (Illus.). (J). (978-0-439-20549-8(2)) Scholastic, Inc.
Zollman, Pam. A Tadpole Grows Up. 2005. (Scholastic News Nonfiction Readers Ser.). (Illus.). 24p. (J). (gr. 1-2). 19.00 (978-0-516-24947-6(9), Children's Pr.) Scholastic Library Publishing.

TADPOLES—FICTION

Azore, Barbara. Wanda & the Frogs. Graham, Georgia, illus. 2007. 32p. (J). (ps-2). 18.95 (978-0-88776-761-6(3)) Tundra Bks., Inc./Livres Toundra, Inc. CAN. *Dist:* Random Hse., Inc.
Bennett, Kimberly. The Tale of A Tadpole. 2003. 26p. pap. 14.95 (978-1-4137-1458-6(7)) PublishAmerica, Inc.
Bronson, Tammy Carter. Polliwog. Bronson, Tammy Carter, illus. 2006. (ENG & SPA.). (J). 7.99 (***978-0-9678167-5-3(0)***) Bookaroos Publishing, Inc.
—Polliwog. Davi, Annou, tr. Bronson, Tammy Carter, illus. 2004. (SPA., Illus.). 32p. (J). lib. bdg. 17.00 (978-0-9678167-4-6(2)) Bookaroos Publishing, Inc.
Cain, Sheridan. The Teeny Weeny Tadpole. Tickle, Jack, illus. 2005. 32p. (J). 15.95 (978-1-58925-047-5(8), tiger tales) ME Media LLC.
Clarke, Jane. Only Tadpoles Have Tails. Gray, Jane, illus. 2004. (Flying Foxes Ser.). (J). 46p. (978-0-7787-1484-2(5)); 48p. pap. (978-0-7787-1530-6(2)) Crabtree Publishing Co.
Cyrus, Kurt. Tadpole Rex. 2008. (J). (***978-0-15-205990-3(3)***) Harcourt Trade Pubs.
Farfan, Flores & Antonio, Jose. Axolotl: El Ajolote. Celestino, Cleofas Ramirez, illus. 2003. (SPA.). 40p. (J). (978-968-411-569-9(5)) Ediciones Era.
Ferri, Giuliano. Little Tad Grows Up. Ferri, Giuliano, illus. 2007. (Illus.). 32p. (J). (ps-1). 16.99 (***978-0-698-40060-3(7)***, Minedition) Penguin Group (USA) Inc.
Focus On The Family Staff. Hero of Hoppers Landing. 2002. (J). 12.99 incl. VHS (978-0-310-70507-9(X)) Zonderkidz.
Greene, Stephanie. Owen Foote, Mighty Scientist. Smith, Catharine Bowman, illus. 2004. 96p. (J). (gr. k-3). tchr. ed. 15.00 (978-0-618-43016-1(4), Clarion Bks.) Houghton Mifflin Co. Trade & Reference Div.
Harcourt School Publishers Staff. Sing for the King Advanced Level. 3rd ed. 2002. (Trophies Reading Program Ser.). (Illus.). (J). pap. 3.70 (978-0-15-323016-5(9)) Harcourt Schl. Pubs.
—Slim Grows Up: On Level. 3rd ed. 2002. (Trophies Reading Program Ser.). (Illus.). (J). pap. 4.10 (978-0-15-322982-4(9)) Harcourt Schl. Pubs.
—Slim Grows Up 5-Pack, On Level. 3rd ed. 2002. (Trophies Reading Program Ser.). (Illus.). (gr. 1). pap. 20.10 (978-0-15-326832-8(8)) Harcourt Schl. Pubs.
Kimura, Ken. 999 Tadpoles. Murakami, Yasunari, illus. 2006. 40p. (J). 14.95 (978-1-74126-433-3(2)) R.I.C. Pubns. AUS. *Dist:* SCB Distributors.
Milbourne, Anna. In the Pond. 2007. 24p. (J). 9.99 (978-0-7945-1544-7(4), Usborne) EDC Publishing.
Narvaez, Concha Lopez & Salmeron, Carmelo. Tomas Es Distinto a los Demas.Tr. of Tomas Is Different from the Others. (SPA.). 64p. (J). (gr. 2-4). (978-84-216-3432-5(1)) Bruño, Editorial ESP. *Dist:* Lectorum Pubns., Inc.
Nicholls, Judith. Tiny Tadpole. 2007. (Little Scholastic Ser.). (J). (ps). bds. 7.99 (***978-0-439-02152-4(9)***) Scholastic, Inc.
Rey, H. A. & Rey, Margret. Curious George Tadpole Trouble. 2007. (Illus.). 24p. (J). (ps-k). 3.99 (***978-0-618-77712-9(1)***) Houghton Mifflin Co. Trade & Reference Div.
Rice, Cindy & Stolarski, Jerry. Mr. Mahaffy on Wisdom Pond: The Beginning. 2007. (ENG.). 84p. per. 14.95 (***978-1-4241-3097-9(2)***) PublishAmerica, Inc.
Sargent, Dave & Sargent, Pat. Little Tadpole, 10, 20. Robinson, Laura, illus. 2004. (Learn to Read Ser.: 10). 18p. (J). lib. bdg. 19.95 (978-1-56763-835-6(X)); lib. bdg. 9.95 (978-1-56763-836-3(8)) Ozark Publishing.
—Little Tadpole/el Renacuajo Pequeño, 10. Robinson, Laura, illus. 2004. (Learn to Read Ser.: 10). (ENG & SPA.). 18p. (J). pap. 9.95 (978-1-56763-567-6(9)); lib. bdg. 19.95 (978-1-56763-999-5(2)) Ozark Publishing.
Sparks, Evan. Freddy's Tale. 2006. 44p. pap. 14.88 (978-1-4116-7427-1(8)) Lulu.com.
There's a Rainbow in the River: Individual Title Six-Packs. (gr. k-1). 23.00 (978-0-7635-8850-2(4)) Rigby Education.
Tiny Tiny Tadpole. 2005. (J). bds. 7.99 (978-1-933200-17-0(0)) Family Bks. at Home.
Ward, Nick. The Tadpole Prince. 2003. (Illus.). 32p. (YA). (978-1-84365-016-4(9)) Chrysalis Children's Bks.
Westphal, Hugo, illus. Tad Pole & Dr. Frog: A Self Help Book for Little Ones. 2002. 60p. (J). (gr. 1-7). 19.95 (978-1-893672-07-9(7)) Johnson, Michael Presentations.
Willis, Jeanne. Tadpole's Promise. Ross, Tony, illus. 2005. 32p. (J). 16.99 (978-0-689-86524-4(4), Atheneum) Simon & Schuster Children's Publishing.
Wilson, Kevin. Brown Spot. 2006. 60p. (J). pap. 12.00 (978-1-4116-8059-3(6)) Lulu.com.

TAFT, WILLIAM H. (WILLIAM HOWARD), 1857-1930

Benson, Michael. William Howard Taft. 2005. (Presidential Leaders Ser.). (Illus.). 112p. (J). 29.27 (978-0-8225-0849-6(4), Lerner Pubns.) Lerner Publishing Group.
Burgan, Michael. William Howard Taft. 2003. (Profiles of the Presidents Ser.). (Illus.). 64p. (J). (gr. 4 up). lib. bdg. 23.93 (978-0-7565-0273-7(X)) Compass Point Bks.
Doherty, Kieran. William Howard Taft. 2004. (Encyclopedia of Presidents Ser.). (Illus.). 110p. (J). 34.00 (978-0-516-22967-6(2), Children's Pr.) Scholastic Library Publishing.
Joseph, Paul. William Taft. 2001. (United States Presidents Ser.). (Illus.). 32p. (J). (gr. k-6). lib. bdg. 22.78 (978-1-57765-300-4(9), Checkerboard Library) ABDO Publishing Co.
Marsh, Carole. William Howard Taft: An Ohio Experience Reader. 2001. (J). (gr. k-5). pap. 1.95 (978-0-635-00447-5(X)) Gallopade International.
Maupin, Melissa. William Howard Taft: Our Twenty-Seventh President. 2001. (Spirit of America: Our Presidents Ser.). (Illus.). 48p. (J). (gr. 2-6). 28.50 (978-1-56766-835-3(6)) Child's World, Inc.
O'Connell, Kim A. William Howard Taft: A MyReportLinks.com Book. 2003. (Presidents Ser.). (Illus.). 48p. (J). (gr. 4-10). lib. bdg. 25.26 (978-0-7660-5078-5(5), MyReportLinks.com Bks.) Enslow Pubs., Inc.
Randolph, Ryan P. How to Draw the Life & Times of William Howard Taft. 2007. (Kid's Guide to Drawing the Presidents of the United States of America Ser.). (Illus.). 32p. (J). 25.25 (978-1-4042-3003-3(3), PowerKids Pr.) Rosen Publishing Group, Inc., The.

T U V

Venezia, Mike, illus. William Howard Taft. 2006. 32p. (J). (978-0-516-22631-6(2)) Children's Pr., Ltd.

TAHITI

NgCheong-Lum, Roseline. Tahiti. 2nd ed. 2007. (Cultures of the World Ser.). 144p. (J). lib. bdg. 39.93 (***978-0-7614-2089-7(4)***, Benchmark Bks.) Cavendish, Marshall Corp.

TAHITI—FICTION

Lumry, Amanda & Hurwitz, Laura. Adventures of Riley: Dolphins in Danger. McIntyre, Sarah, illus. 2005. 36p. 15.95 (978-0-9748411-1-3(0)) Eaglemont Pr.

Rees, Douglas. Smoking Mirror. 2005. (Art Encounters Ser.). (Illus.). 176p. (YA). 15.95 (978-0-8230-4863-2(2)) Watson-Guptill Pubns., Inc.

Walls, Pamela June. Trouble in Tahiti. 2002. (gr. 3-6). lib. bdg. 14.15 (978-0-613-76806-1(X)) Tandem Library Bks.

—Trouble in Tahiti. 2002. (Abby & the South Seas Adventures Ser.: Vol. 7). 208p. (J). mass mkt. 5.99 (978-0-8423-3632-1(X)) Tyndale Hse. Pubs.

TAILORS—FICTION

Anholt, Laurence. The Emperor's New Underwear. Robins, Arthur, illus. 1999. (J). pap. (978-0-88166-347-1(6)) Meadowbrook Pr.

Benchmark Education Staff, compiled by. Measuring. 2006. spiral bd. 99.00 (***978-1-4108-7090-2(1)***) Benchmark Education Co.

Giff, Patricia Reilly. A House of Tailors. (gr. 4-7). 2006. 160p. (YA). 5.50 (978-0-440-23800-3(5), Yearling); 2004. 176p. (J). 15.95 (978-0-385-73066-2(7), Lamb, Wendy); 2004. 176p. (J). lib. bdg. 17.99 (978-0-385-90879-5(2), Lamb, Wendy) Random Hse. Children's Bks.

—A House of Tailors. l.t. ed. 2005. 218p. 23.95 (978-0-7862-7262-4(7), Large Print Pr.) Thorndike Pr.

Potter, Beatrix. The Tailor of Gloucester, Vol. 3. 2002. (Illus.). 64p. (J). 6.99 (978-0-7232-4772-2(2), Warne) Penguin Group (USA) Inc.

Principals New Cloth. 1998. (J). pap. 3.95 (978-0-439-04435-6(9)) Scholastic, Inc.

Shaw, David, illus. The Brave LittleTailor: A Retelling of the Grimms' Fairy Tale. 2004. (Read-It! Readers Ser.). 32p. (C). (gr. k-3). 18.60 (978-1-4048-0315-2(7)) Picture Window Bks.

TAIWAN

Behnke, Alison. Taiwan in Pictures. 2007. (J). lib. bdg. (***978-0-8225-7148-3(X)***) Twenty First Century Bks.

Green, Robert. Taiwan. 2000. (Modern Nations of the World Ser.). (Illus.). 112p. (YA). (gr. 7-10). 29.95 (978-1-56006-819-8(1), Lucent Bks.) Thomson Gale.

King, David C. Taiwan. 2006. (Enchantment of the World, Second Ser.). (Illus.). 144p. (J). (gr. 5-9). 36.00 (978-0-516-24856-1(1), Children's Pr.) Scholastic Library Publishing.

Moiz, Azra & Wu, Janice. Taiwan. 2nd ed. 2006. (Cultures of the World Ser.). 144p. (J). lib. bdg. 39.93 (978-0-7614-2069-9(X), Benchmark Bks.) Cavendish, Marshall Corp.

Salter, Christopher L. Taiwan. 2004. (Modern World Nations Ser.). (Illus.). 116p. (J). (gr. 6-12). lib. bdg. 30.00 (978-0-7910-7914-0(7), Chelsea Hse.) Facts On File, Inc.

Wan, Vanessa. Welcome to Taiwan. 2004. (Welcome to My Country Ser.). (Illus.). 48p. (J). lib. bdg. 26.00 (978-0-8368-3122-1(5)) Stevens, Gareth Inc.

Wee, Jessie. Taiwan. abr. ed. 1999. (Major World Nations Ser.). (Illus.). 144p. (YA). (gr. 4-7). lib. bdg. 21.95 (978-0-7910-4986-0(8), Chelsea Hse.) Facts On File, Inc.

TAIWAN—FICTION

Itoh, Shimpei. Hyper Dolls, Vol. 5. 2003. (Illus.). 208p. pap. 15.95 (978-1-929090-67-9(6)) International Comics & Entertainment L.L.C.

TALES

see Fables; Fairy Tales; Folklore; Legends

TALISMANS

see Charms

TALKING

see Speech

TALKING PICTURES

see Motion Pictures

TALL TALES

see also American Wit and Humor; Folklore; Legends

Bertrand, Lynne. Granite Baby. Hawkes, Kevin, illus. 2005. 40p. (J). 16.00 (978-0-374-32761-3(0), Farrar, Straus & Giroux (BYR)) Farrar, Straus & Giroux.

Blair, Eric. Pecos Bill Tames the Wild West: A Retelling of the Classic Traditional Tale. Chambers-Goldbert, Micah, illus. 2005. (Read-It! Readers Ser.). 32p. (C). (gr. k-3). 18.60 (978-1-4048-0977-2(5)) Picture Window Bks.

Boniface, William. The Treasure Hunter. Harris, Jim, illus. 1998. 32p. (J). 15.99 (978-0-939251-97-1(3)) Accord Publishing, Ltd.

Chung, Chi, illus. Captain Stormalong. 2004. (Imagination Ser.). 32p. (C). (gr. 3-5). 22.60 (978-0-7565-0601-8(8)) Compass Point Bks.

Crunk, Tony. Railroad John & the Red Rock Run. Austin, Michael, illus. 2006. 32p. (J). 16.95 (978-1-56145-363-4(3)) Peachtree Pubs., Ltd.

Cuyler, Margery. That's Good! That's Bad! In the Grand Canyon. Catrow, David, illus. rev. ed. 2002. 32p. (J). (ps-2). 16.95 (978-0-8050-5975-5(X), Holt, Henry & Co. Bks. For Young Readers) Holt, Henry & Co.

Cuyler, Margery. That's Good! That's Bad! in Washington, D. C. Garland, Michael, illus. rev. ed. 2007. 32p. (J). (ps-2). 16.95 (***978-0-8050-7727-8(8)***) Holt, Henry & Co.

Dadey, Debbie. Will Rogers: Larger Than Life. Goto, Scott, illus. 1999. 32p. (J). (gr. k-3). 15.95 (978-0-8027-8681-4(2)); lib. bdg. 16.85 (978-0-8027-8682-1(0)) Walker & Co.

Dashney, John. The Ballad of Big Ben's Boots & Other Tales for Telling. Somerville, Sheila, illus. 3rd rev. ed. 2001. 184p. (Orig.). (J). (gr. k-10). pap. 9.95 (978-0-9633236-4-4(4), Wicklewood Bks.) Stage Within Your Mind, The.

Davol, Marguerite W. The Loudest, Fastest, Best Drummer in Kansas. Smith, Cat Bowman, illus. 2000. 32p. (J). (gr. k-4). 16.99 (978-0-531-33191-0(1)); pap. 15.95 (978-0-531-30191-3(5)) Scholastic, Inc. (Orchard Bks.).

Day, Karen. Tall Tales. 2007. 240p. (J). (gr. 4-7). 15.99 (978-0-375-83773-9(6)); lib. bdg. 18.99 (978-0-375-93773-6(0)) Random Hse. Children's Bks. (Lamb, Wendy).

Derby, Sally. Whoosh Went the Wind! Nguyen, Vincent, illus. 2006. 32p. (J). 16.99 (978-0-7614-5309-3(1)) Cavendish, Marshall Corp.

Enderle, Dotti. The Cotton Candy Catastrophe at the Texas State Fair. Galey, Chuck, illus. 2004. 32p. (J). pap. 15.95 (978-1-58980-189-9(X)) Pelican Publishing Co., Inc.

Enderle, Dottie. Granny Gert & the Bunion Brothers. Kulka, Joe, illus. 2006. 32p. (J). (gr. k-3). 15.95 (978-1-58980-373-2(6)) Pelican Publishing Co., Inc.

Fienberg, Anna & Fienberg, Barbara. Tashi & the Big Stinker. Gamble, Kim, illus. 2001. (Tashi Ser.). 64p. (Orig.). (J). (gr. 2-4). pap. 5.95 (978-1-86508-350-6(X)) Allen & Unwin AUS. *Dist:* Independent Pubs. Group.

Fleischman, Sid. A Carnival of Animals. Hafner, Marylin, illus. 2000. 48p. (J). (gr. 2 up). 15.89 (978-0-688-16949-7(X)) HarperCollins Pubs.

—Here Comes McBroom! Three More Tall Tales. 1999. (J). (gr. 2-5). 21.75 (978-0-8446-7029-4(4)) Smith, Peter Pub., Inc.

—Here Comes Mcbroom! Three More Tall Tales. 1998. (Illus.). 79p. (J). (ps-k). lib. bdg. 13.00 (978-0-613-11625-1(9)) Tandem Library Bks.

—Here Comes McBroom! Three More Tall Tales. Blake, Quentin, illus. 1998. 80p. (J). (gr. 2-5). reprint ed. pap. 4.99 (978-0-688-16364-8(5)) HarperCollins Pubs.

—McBroom Tells a Lie. Wummer, Amy, illus. 1999. (Adventures of McBroom Ser.). 64p. (J). (gr. 2-6). pap. 4.99 (978-0-8431-7497-7(8), Price Stern Sloan) Penguin Group (USA) Inc.

—McBroom Tells a Lie. 1999. (J). (978-0-606-19073-2(2)); (gr. 3-6). lib. bdg. 13.00 (978-0-613-14983-9(1)) Tandem Library Bks.

—McBroom Tells the Truth. Wummer, Amy, illus. 1998. (Adventures of McBroom Ser.). 62p. (J). (gr. 2-5). pap. 4.99 (978-0-8431-7947-7(3), Price Stern Sloan) Penguin Group (USA) Inc.

—McBroom the Rainmaker. 1999. (J). (978-0-606-19074-9(0)) Tandem Library Bks.

—McBroom's Ghost. Wummer, Amy, illus. 1998. 62p. lib. bdg. 11.79 (978-0-606-15963-0(0)) Tandem Library Bks.

Gershator, Phillis. Tiny & Bigman. Cravath, Lynne W., illus. 1999. (Accelerated Reader Bks.). 32p. (J). (gr. k-3). 15.95 (978-0-7614-5044-3(0), Cavendish Children's Bks.) Cavendish, Marshall Corp.

Gibson, D. W., et al. Fundorado Island. 2006. (Illus.). 224p. (J). (gr. 3). lib. bdg. 16.99 (978-0-385-90284-7(0), Delacorte Bks. for Young Readers) Random Hse. Children's Bks.

Gill, Shelley. Sitka Rose. Cartwright, Shannon, illus. 2005. (J). 16.95 (978-1-57091-353-2(6)); 32p. pap. 7.95 (978-1-57091-364-8(1)) Charlesbridge Publishing, Inc.

Gleeson, Brian. Paul Bunyan. Meyerowitz, Rick, illus. 2005. (Rabbit Ears-A Classic Tale Ser.). 40p. (J). (gr. k-5). 25.65 (978-1-59197-767-4(3)) Spotlight.

Griffin, Kitty & Combs, Kathy. The Foot-Stomping Adventures of Clementine Sweet. Wohnoutka, Mike, tr. Wohnoutka, Mike, illus. 2004. 32p. (J). (gr. k-3). tchr. ed. 15.00 (978-0-618-24746-2(7), Clarion Bks.) Houghton Mifflin Co. Trade & Reference Div.

Harcourt School Publishers Staff. Pecos Bill On Level. 3rd ed. 2002. (Trophies Reading Program Ser.). (Illus.). pap. 5.10 (978-0-15-323182-7(3)) Harcourt Schl. Pubs.

Hayes, Joe. The Gum-Chewing Rattler. 2006. (Illus.). 32p. (J). (gr. k-3). 16.95 (978-0-938317-99-9(7)) Cinco Puntos Pr.

Healy, Nick. Fawn Braun's Big City Blues. Erkocak, Sahin, illus. 2007. (Pfeffernut County Ser.). 32p. (J). (gr. k-2). lib. bdg. 23.93 (***978-1-4048-3696-9(9)***) Picture Window Bks.

—Louie the Layabout. Erkocak, Sahin, illus. 2007. (Pfeffernut County Ser.). 32p. (J). (gr. k-2). lib. bdg. 23.93 (***978-1-4048-3697-6(7)***) Picture Window Bks.

Henry, Tom. Paul Bunyan on the West Coast. LaFave, Kim, illus. unabr. ed. 56p. (Orig.). (J). pap. (978-1-55017-109-9(7)) Harbour Publishing Co., Ltd.

Hopkinson, Deborah & Carpenter, Nancy. Apples to Oregon: Being the (Slightly) True Narrative of How a Brave Pioneer Father Brought Apples, Peaches, Pears, Plums, Grapes, & Cherries (And Children) Across the Plains. 2004. (Illus.). 40p. (J). 16.95 (978-0-689-84769-1(6), Atheneum) Simon & Schuster Children's Publishing.

Hurston, Zora Neale & Thomas, Joyce Carol. Lies & Other Tall Tales. Myers, Christopher, illus. 2005. 40p. (J). 15.99 (978-0-06-000655-6(2)) HarperCollins Pubs.

Isaacs, Anne. Swamp Angel. Zelinsky, Paul O., illus. 2002. (J). 14.04 (978-0-7587-0152-7(7)) Book Wholesalers, Inc.

—Swamp Angel. Zelinsky, Paul O., illus. 2000. 48p. (J). (ps-3). pap. 6.99 (978-0-14-055908-8(6), Puffin) Penguin Group (USA) Inc.

—Swamp Angel. 2000. (978-0-606-18453-3(8)); lib. bdg. 15.30 (978-0-613-23041-4(8)) Tandem Library Bks.

Jackson, Ellen B. Scatterbrain Sam. Faulkner, Matt, illus. 2001. (J). (gr. k-4). 6.95 (978-0-88106-395-0(9)); 32p. (gr. 3-6). 15.95 (978-0-88106-394-3(0)) Charlesbridge Publishing, Inc.

—Scatterbrain Sam. 2001. (gr. k-3). lib. bdg. 15.25 (978-0-613-60439-0(3)) Tandem Library Bks.

Jacques, Brian. The Tale of Urso Brunov: Little Father of All Bears. Natchev, Alexi, illus. 2003. 45p. (J). (ps-3). 16.99 (978-0-399-23762-1(3), Philomel) Penguin Group (USA) Inc.

—The Tale of Urso Brunov: Little Father of All Bears. Natchev, Alexi, illus. 2006. 48p. (J). (gr. k). reprint ed. pap. 6.99 (978-0-14-240723-3(2), Puffin) Penguin Group (USA) Inc.

Jenkins, Amanda. Pecos Bill & Sluefoot Sue: An AMER Tall Tale. 2006. spiral bd. 23.00 (***978-1-4108-7158-9(4)***) Benchmark Education Co.

Jones, Nathan Smith. The Boy Who Ate America. Nelson, Carey, illus. 2007. 32p. (J). (ps-3). 16.95 (***978-1-59038-814-3(3)***, Shadow Mountain) Deseret Bk. Co.

Kalz, Jill. Farmer Cap. Erkocak, Sahin, illus. 2007. (Pfeffernut County Ser.). 26p. (J). (gr. k-2). lib. bdg. 23.93 (***978-1-4048-3139-1(8)***) Picture Window Bks.

Karas, G. Brian, illus. Carlita Ropes the Twister. 1999. (J). 27.84 (978-0-8172-7256-2(9)) Steck-Vaughn.

Keehn, Sally M. Magpie Gabbard & the Quest for the Buried Moon. 2007. 208p. (YA). (gr. 5-8). 16.99 (978-0-399-24340-0(2), Philomel) Penguin Group (USA) Inc.

Kellogg, Steven. I Was Born about 10,000 Years Ago: A Tall Tale. 1998. (Illus.). 48p. (J). (ps-3). pap. 5.95 (978-0-688-16156-9(1), Harper Trophy) HarperCollins Pubs.

—Mike Fink. Kellogg, Steven, illus. 1998. (Illus.). 48p. (J). (ps-ps). pap., pap. 6.99 (978-0-688-13577-5(3), Harper Trophy) HarperCollins Pubs.

—Paul Bunyan. Kellogg, Steven, illus. 2006. (SPA.). 48p. (J). pap. 6.99 (978-0-06-088705-6(2)) HarperCollins Pubs.

Kellogg, Steven, illus. & retold by. Mike Fink. Kellogg, Steven, retold by. 1998. (J). (ps-ps). lib. bdg. 15.30 (978-0-613-08345-4(8)) Tandem Library Bks.

Ketteman, Helen. The Christmas Blizzard. 1999. (J). (978-0-606-17293-6(9)) Tandem Library Bks.

—Heat Wave! 2000. (J). 13.75 (978-0-606-19679-6(X)) Tandem Library Bks.

—Heat Wave! Goto, Scott, illus. 1998. 32p. (J). (gr. k-3). 15.95 (978-0-8027-8644-9(8)); lib. bdg. 16.85 (978-0-8027-8645-6(6)) Walker & Co.

—Shoeshine Whittaker. Goto, Scott, illus. 1999. 32p. (J). (gr. k-3). lib. bdg. 16.85 (978-0-8027-8715-6(0)) Walker & Co.

Ketteman, Helen & Warhola, James. Christmas Blizzard. 1999. (Illus.). 32p. (ps-3). pap. 5.99 (978-0-590-13609-9(7)) Scholastic, Inc.

Kimmel, Eric A. The Great Texas Hamster Drive: An Original Tall Tale. Whatley, Bruce, illus. 2007. 40p. (J). (ps-2). 16.99 (***978-0-7614-5357-4(1)***) Cavendish, Marshall Corp.

Krensky, Stephen. Pecos Bill. Tong, Paul, illus. 2007. (On My Own Folklore Ser.). 48p. (J). (gr. 2-5). lib. bdg. 25.26 (978-1-57505-889-4(8), Millbrook Pr.) Lerner Publishing Group.

Krensky, Stephen, adapted by. John Henry. 2007. (On My Own Folklore Ser.). (Illus.). 48p. (J). (gr. 2-5). lib. bdg. 25.26 (978-1-57505-887-0(1), Millbrook Pr.) Lerner Publishing Group.

—Mike Fink. 2007. (On My Own Folklore Ser.). 48p. (J). (gr. 2-5). lib. bdg. 25.26 (978-1-57505-891-7(X), Millbrook Pr.) Lerner Publishing Group.

Lloyd, Megan, illus. Davy Gets Hitched. 2007. (J). (978-0-8234-1837-4(5)) Holiday Hse., Inc.

Lorbiecki, Marybeth. Paul Bunyan's Sweetheart. Graef, Renee, illus. rev. ed. 2007. 32p. (J). (gr. 1-4). 16.95 (***978-1-58536-289-9(1)***) Sleeping Bear Pr.

Love, Judith DuFour, illus. Calamity Jane. 2004. (Imagination Ser.). 32p. (C). (gr. 3-5). 22.60 (978-0-7565-0600-1(X)) Compass Point Bks.

Madison, Alan. The Littlest Grape Stomper. Potter, Giselle, illus. 2007. 40p. (J). (ps-3). lib. bdg. 18.99 (978-0-375-93675-3(0)); 16.99 (978-0-375-83675-6(6)) Random Hse. Children's Bks. (Schwartz & Wade Bks.).

Manos, John. Big Ben Helps the Town. 2006. (Early Explorers Ser.). (J). 34.00 (***978-1-4108-6119-1(8)***) Benchmark Education Co.

Mason, Jane, adapted by. Paul Bunyan & Other Tall Tales. 2002. (Illus.). 107p. (J). (978-0-439-40324-5(3)) Scholastic, Inc.

McKissack, Patricia C. Porch Lies: Tales of Slicksters, Tricksters, & Other Wily Characters. Carrilho, André, illus. 2006. 160p. (J). (gr. 3-7). 18.95 (978-0-375-83619-0(5), Schwartz & Wade Bks.) Random Hse. Children's Bks.

Metaxas, Eric. Mose the Fireman. Peck, Everett, illus. 2005. (Rabbit Ears-A Classic Tale Ser.). 40p. (J). (gr. k-5). 25.65 (978-1-59197-766-7(5)) Spotlight.

—Stormalong. Vanderbeek, Don, illus. 2005. (Rabbit Ears-A Classic Tale Ser.). 40p. (J). (gr. k-5). 25.65 (978-1-59197-772-8(X)) Spotlight.

Mora, Pat. Dona Flor: Un Cuento de una Mujer Gigante con un Gran Corazon. Mora, Pat & Mlawer, Teresa, trs. Colon, Raul, illus. 2005. 32p. (J). (ps-3). lib. bdg. 15.19 (978-0-606-33665-9(6)) Tandem Library Bks.

Nolen, Jerdine. Big Jabe. Nelson, Kadir A., illus. 32p. (J). (gr. 1 up). 2004. pap. 6.99 (978-0-06-054061-6(3), Amistad); 2000. 16.89 (978-0-688-13663-5(X)) HarperCollins Pubs.

—Big Jabe. 2004. (gr. k-3). lib. bdg. 15.30 (978-0-613-71462-4(8)) Tandem Library Bks.

—Harvey Potter's Balloon Farm. Buehner, Mark, illus. 1998. 32p. (J). (ps-3). pap. 6.99 (978-0-688-15845-3(5), Harper Trophy) HarperCollins Pubs.

—Harvey Potter's Balloon Farm. 1998. (J). 12.75 (978-0-606-13100-1(0)) Tandem Library Bks.

—Thunder Rose. Nelson, Kadir, illus. 2007. 32p. (J). pap. 7.00 (***978-0-15-206006-0(5)***, Voyager Bks./Libros Viajeros) Harcourt Children's Bks.

—Thunder Rose. Nelson, Kadir A., illus. 2003. 32p. (J). (gr. k-3). 16.00 (978-0-15-216472-0(3)) Harcourt Children's Bks.

Oppel, Kenneth. Peg & the Whale. ed. 2004. (Illus.). (J). (gr. k-3). spiral bd. (978-0-616-07245-5(7)) Canadian National Institute for the Blind/Institut National Canadien pour les Aveugles.

Orback, Craig, illus. Paul Bunyan. 2007. (On My Own Folklore Ser.). 48p. (J). (gr. 2-5). lib. bdg. 25.26 (978-1-57505-888-7(X), Millbrook Pr.) Lerner Publishing Group.

Pinkney, Andrea Davis. Peggony-Po: A Whale of a Tale. Pinkney, Brian, illus. 2006. 32p. (ps-2). 16.99 (978-0-7868-1958-4(8), Jump at the Sun) Hyperion Bks. for Children.

Pugliano-Martin, Carol. Read-Aloud Plays: Tall Tales. 2000. 64p. (J). pap. 10.95 (978-0-439-11367-0(9)) Scholastic, Inc.

Raglin, Tim, illus. Pecos Bill. 2005. (Rabbit Ears-A Classic Tale Ser.). 40p. (J). (gr. k-5). 25.65 (978-1-59197-768-1(1)) Spotlight.

Rossi. El Chaparron Torrencial. 2000. Tr. of Gullywasher. (SPA.). (J). 14.75 (978-0-606-19852-3(0)) Tandem Library Bks.

Rossi, Joyce. The Gullywasher (El Chaparron Torrencial) 1998. (ENG & SPA., Illus.). 32p. (J). (gr. k-3). 7.95 (978-0-87358-728-0(6), Rising Moon Bks. for Young Readers) Northland Publishing.

San Souci, Robert D. Cut from the Same Cloth: American Women of Myth, Legend & Tall Tale. 2000. (gr. 3-6). lib. bdg. 15.30 (978-0-613-28458-5(5)) Tandem Library Bks.

—Cut from the Same Cloth: American Women of Myth, Legend & Tall Tales. Pinkney, Brian, illus. 2000. 160p. (J). (gr. 3-7). pap. 6.99 (978-0-698-11811-9(1), Putnam Juvenile) Penguin Group (USA) Inc.

—Cut from the Same Cloth: American Women of Myth, Legend & Tall Tales. 2000. (Illus.). (J). 13.64 (978-0-606-18398-7(1)) Tandem Library Bks.

Schanzer, Rosalyn. Davy Crockett Saves the World. Schanzer, Rosalyn, illus. 2001. (Illus.). 32p. (J). 17.89 (978-0-688-16992-3(9)) HarperCollins Pubs.

Schnetzler, Pattie L. Widdermaker. Sealock, Rick, illus. 2005. 32p. (gr. k-2). 15.95 (978-0-87614-647-7(7)) Lerner Publishing Group.

Shepard, Aaron. Master Man: A Tale of Nigeria. Wisniewski, David, illus. 2001. 32p. (J). (gr. k-3). 15.95 (978-0-688-13783-0(0)) HarperCollins Pubs.

Sowash, Rick. Ripsnorting Whoppers! A Book of Ohio Tall Tales. 2003. (J). 19.95 (978-0-9762412-1-8(8)); pap. 11.95 (978-0-9762412-0-1(X)) Sowash, Rick Publishing Co.

Stanley, Diane. Raising Sweetness. Karas, G. Brian, illus. 2004. (Live Oak Readalong Ser.). (J). (ps-3). audio compact disk 18.95 (978-1-59112-494-8(8)) Live Oak Media.

—Raising Sweetness. 2003. (Live Oak Readalong Ser.). (Illus.). (J). pap. 16.95 incl. audio (978-1-59112-265-4(1)) Live Oak Media.

Tryon, Micro, et al. Fundorado Island. 2006. (Illus.). 224p. (J). (gr. 3). 14.95 (978-0-385-73267-3(8), Delacorte Bks. for Young Readers) Random Hse. Children's Bks.

Walker, Paul R. Big Men, Big Country: A Collection of American Tall Tales. 2000. (Illus.). (J). (978-0-606-18168-6(7)) Tandem Library Bks.

Webb, Lois. Tall Tales. 2007. (J). per. (***978-0-9791550-4-8(5)***) About Time Publishing.

Welling, Peter J. Darlene Halloween & the Great Chicago Fire. Welling, Peter J., illus. 2007. 32p. (J). (gr. k-3). 15.95 (***978-1-58980-479-1(1)***) Pelican Publishing Co., Inc.

Wheeler, Lisa. Avalanche Annie: A Not-So-Tall Tale. Cyrus, Kurt, illus. 2005. 30p. (J). (gr. k-4). reprint ed. 16.00 (978-0-7567-8536-9(7)) DIANE Publishing Co.

—Avalanche Annie: A Not-So-Tall Tale. Cyrus, Kurt, illus. 2003. 32p. (J). 16.00 (978-0-15-216735-6(8)) Harcourt Children's Bks.

Willey, Margaret. Clever Beatrice. Solomon, Heather M., illus. 2001. 40p. (J). (ps-3). 16.99 (978-0-689-83254-3(0), Atheneum) Simon & Schuster Children's Publishing.

—Clever Beatrice & the Best Little Pony. Solomon, Heather M., illus. 2004. 40p. (J). (ps-3). 16.95 (978-0-689-85339-5(4), Atheneum) Simon & Schuster Children's Publishing.

Wood, Audrey. The Bunyans. Wood, Audrey, illus. 2002. (Illus.). (J). 25.06 (978-0-7587-2160-0(9)) Book Wholesalers, Inc.

—The Bunyans. 2006. (Illus.). 32p. (J). pap. 5.99 (978-0-439-81214-6(3), Scholastic Paperbacks) Scholastic, Inc.

Yolen, Jane & Mannheim, Linda, eds. The Liars' Book. Hawkes, Kevin, illus. 1999. (J). 16.95 (978-0-590-48999-7(2), Blue Sky Pr., The) Scholastic, Inc.

TALLCHIEF, MARIA, 1925-

Gourley, Catherine. Who Is Maria Tallchief? Taylor, Val Paul & Harrison, Nancy, illus. 2002. (Who Was...? Ser.). 112p. (J). mass mkt. 4.99 (978-0-448-42675-4(7), Grosset & Dunlap) Penguin Group (USA) Inc.

—Who Is Maria Tallchief? 2002. (gr. 3-6). lib. bdg. 13.00 (978-0-613-45330-1(1)) Tandem Library Bks.

Tallchief, Maria. Tallchief: America's Prima Ballerina. 2001. (J). (978-0-606-22511-3(0)) Tandem Library Bks.

Tallchief, Maria & Well, Rosemary. Tallchief: America's Prima Ballerina. Kelley, Gary, illus. 2001. 28p. (J). (gr. k-4). lib. bdg. 15.30 (978-0-613-44420-0(5)) Tandem Library Bks.

Tallchief, Maria & Wells, Rosemary. Tallchief: America's Prima Ballerina. Kelley, Gary, illus. 1999. 32p. (J). (gr. k-4). 16.99 (978-0-670-88756-9(0) , Viking Juvenile) Penguin Group (USA) Inc.

TANKS (MILITARY SCIENCE)

Baker, David. M1A1 Abrams Tank. 2007. (Fighting Forces on Land Ser.). (Illus.). 32p. (J). (978-1-60044-248-3(X)) Rourke Publishing, LLC.

Black, Michael A. Tank: The M1A1 Abrams. 2000. (High Interest Bks.). (Illus.). 48p. (YA). (gr. 7-12). 24.00 (978-0-516-23342-0(4) , Children's Pr.) Scholastic Library Publishing.

—Tanks: The M1A1 Abrams. 2000. (High Interest Bks.). (Illus.). 48p. (YA). (gr. 7-12). pap. 6.95 (978-0-516-23542-4(7) , Children's Pr.) Scholastic Library Publishing.

Braulick, Carrie A. U.S. Army Tanks. 2006. (Blazers—Military Vehicles Ser.). (Illus.). 32p. (J). (978-0-7368-5469-6(X)) Capstone Pr., Inc.

Budd, E. S. Tanks. 2001. (Machines at Work Ser.). (Illus.). 24p. (J). (ps-3). 21.36 (978-1-56766-984-8(0)) Child's World, Inc.

Cornish, Geoff. Tanks. 2004. (Military Hardware in Action Ser.). (Illus.). 48p. (J). (gr. 4-9). lib. bdg. 25.26 (978-0-8225-4701-3(5)) Lerner Publishing Group.

David, Jack. Abrams Tanks. 2007. (Illus.). 24p. (J). lib. bdg. 19.95 (978-1-60014-101-0(3)) Bellwether Media.

—Abrams Tanks. 2007. (Torque: Military Machines Ser.). (Illus.). 24p. (J). (gr. 3-7). lib. bdg. 20.00 (***978-0-531-18497-4(8)*** , Children's Pr.) Scholastic Library Publishing.

David West. Tank. 2006. (Illus.). 32p. (J). pap. (978-1-4109-2566-4(8)) Steck-Vaughn.

Doeden, Matt. Tanks. 2005. (Pebble Plus: Mighty Machines Ser.). (Illus.). 24p. (J). 19.93 (978-0-7368-3659-3(4)) Capstone Pr., Inc.

—Tanques. 2006. (ENG & SPA.). (J). (978-0-7368-5877-9(6)) Capstone Pr., Inc.

Ellis, Catherine. Tanks. 2007. (Mega Military Machines Ser.). (Illus.). 24p. (J). (gr. k-5). lib. bdg. 21.25 (978-1-4042-3664-6(3)) Rosen Publishing Group, Inc., The.

Graham, Ian. Military Vehicles. 2003. (Designed for Success Ser.). (Illus.). 32p. pap. 7.50 (978-1-4034-3357-2(7)); (J). 24.22 (978-1-4034-2655-0(4)) Heinemann Library.

—Tanks. 2005. (World's Greatest Ser.). (Illus.). 32p. (J). pap. (978-1-4109-2094-2(1)); lib. bdg. (978-1-4109-2087-4(9)) Steck-Vaughn.

Green, Michael. Main Battle Tanks. 2001. (Land & Sea Ser.). (Illus.). 48p. (J). (gr. 3-4). lib. bdg. 21.26 (978-0-7368-0757-9(8) , Capstone High-Interest Bks.) Capstone Pr., Inc.

Green, Michael & Green, Gladys. Main Battle Tanks: The M1A1 Abrams. 2004. (War Machines Ser.). (Illus.). 32p. (J). 16.95 (978-0-7368-2416-3(2)) Capstone Pr., Inc.

Hama, Larry. Tank of Tomorrow. 2006. (High-Tech Military Weapons Ser.). (Illus.). 48p. (J). (978-0-531-12094-1(5) , Children's Pr.) Scholastic Library Publishing.

Harvey, Ian & Chasemore, Richard. Tanks. (Illus.). 32p. (J). mass mkt. 8.99 (978-0-590-24940-9(1)) Scholastic, Inc.

Jentz, Thomas L. Germany's Tiger Tanks Series Tigers at the Front: A Photo Study Compiled by Thomas L. Jentz. 2001. (Germany's Tiger Tanks Ser.). (Illus.). 208p. (gr. 10-13). 29.95 (978-0-7643-1339-4(8)) Schiffer Publishing, Ltd.

McGowen, Tom. Germany's Lightning War: Panzer Divisions of World War II. 1999. (Military Might Ser.: 8). (Illus.). 64p. (gr. 5-8). lib. bdg. 26.90 (978-0-7613-1511-7(X) , Twenty-First Century Bks.) Lerner Publishing Group.

Parker, Steve. The M1A1 Abrams Main Battle Tank. 2008. (J). (***978-1-4296-0091-0(8)***) Capstone Pr., Inc.

Sautter, Aaron. How to Draw Indestructible Tanks. Whigham, Rod, illus. 2008. (J). (***978-1-4296-1301-9(7)***) Capstone Pr., Inc.

Souter, Gerry. Battle Tanks: Power in the Field. 2006. (Mighty Military Machines Ser.). (Illus.). 48p. (J). (gr. 4-10). lib. bdg. 23.93 (978-0-7660-2658-2(2)) Enslow Pubs., Inc.

Tanks. (Mighty MacHines Ser.). 24p. (J). 6.95 (978-0-7368-5143-5(7)) Capstone Pr., Inc.

Tanks. 2003. (Illus.). 32p. (YA). pap. (978-1-904516-34-7(3)) Chrysalis Children's Bks.

West, David. Why Things Don't Work. 2006. (Illus.). 32p. (J). (978-1-4109-2559-6(5)) Steck-Vaughn.

Zuehlke, Jeffrey. Tanks. 2006. (Pull Ahead Books). (Illus.). 32p. (J). (ps-7). 22.60 (978-0-8225-2865-4(7) , Lerner Pubns.) Lerner Publishing Group.

TANNING

Fisher, Leonard Everett. The Tanners. 2000. (Colonial Craftsmen Ser.). (Illus.). 48p. (J). (gr. 4-8). lib. bdg. 24.21 (978-0-7614-1148-2(8) , Benchmark Bks.) Cavendish, Marshall Corp.

TANZANIA

Here are entered works on the jurisdiction of Tanzania formed in 1964 by the merger of Tanganyika and Zanzibar for all periods and subjects. Works on the island of Zanzibar for all periods are entered under Zanzibar. Works limited in subject coverage to the historical, political or cultural aspects of Tanganyika for the period before the merger in 1964 are entered under Tanganyika. Works on other subjects relating to Tanganyika for any pre-merger period are entered under the name of the present jurisdiction, Tanzania.

Barber, Nicola. Living in the African Savannah. 2007. (J). pap. (***978-1-4109-2823-8(3)***); lib. bdg. (***978-1-4109-2814-6(4)***) Steck-Vaughn.

Corwin, Jeff. Into Wild Zanzibar. 2004. (Jeff Corwin Experience Ser.). (Illus.). 48p. (J). 11.20 (978-1-4103-0256-4(3)); (gr. 4-7). 24.95 (978-1-4103-0255-7(5)) Thomson Gale. (Blackbirch Pr., Inc.).

Dentro de Tanzania Salvaje. 2005. (Jeff Corwin Experience Ser.). (ENG & SPA., Illus.). 48p. (J). (ps-7). lib. bdg. 24.95 (978-1-4103-0686-9(0) , Blackbirch Pr., Inc.) Thomson Gale.

DiPiazza, Francesca. Tanzania in Pictures. 2008. (J). lib. bdg. (***978-0-8225-8571-8(5)***) Twenty First Century Bks.

Ferguson, Amanda. The Attack Against the U. S. Embassies in Kenya & Tanzania. 2005. (Terrorist Attacks Ser.). (Illus.). 64p. (J). (gr. 7-12). lib. bdg. 26.50 (978-0-8239-3652-6(X)) Rosen Publishing Group, Inc., The.

Goodall, Jane. With Love: Ten Heartwarming Stories of Chimpanzees in the Wild. Marks, Alan, illus. 1998. 44p. (J). (gr. 1-5). 15.95 (978-1-55858-911-7(2)) North-South Bks., Inc.

Heale, Jay. Tanzania. 1998. (Cultures of the World Ser.). (Illus.). 128p. (gr. 5-12). lib. bdg. 37.07 (978-0-7614-0809-3(6) , Benchmark Bks.) Cavendish, Marshall Corp.

Krebs, Laurie. We All Went on Safari: A Counting Journey Through Tanzania. Cairns, Julia, illus. 2003. (ENG & SWA.). 32p. (J). (gr. k-3). 15.99 (978-1-84148-478-5(4)) Barefoot Bks., Inc.

Leathers, Dan. The Snows of Kilimanjaro. 2007. (On the Verge of Extinction Ser.). (Illus.). 32p. (J). (gr. 1-4). lib. bdg. 25.70 (***978-1-58415-584-3(1)***) Mitchell Lane Pubs., Inc.

Ling, Chin Oi. Welcome to Tanzania. 2005. (Welcome to My Country Ser.). (Illus.). 48p. (J). lib. bdg. 26.00 (978-0-8368-3137-5(3)) Stevens, Gareth Inc.

MacDonald, Joan Vos. Tanzania. 2004. (Africa Ser.). (Illus.). 85p. (J). lib. bdg. (978-1-59084-813-5(6)) Mason Crest Pubs.

Maillu, David G. Julius Nyerere: Father of Ujamaa. 2005. (Lion Book Ser.). (Illus.). ix, 81p. (J). (978-9966-951-32-8(6)) Sasa Sema Publications Ltd.

Murphy, Patricia J. Tanzania. 2002. (Countries of the World Ser.). (Illus.). 126p. (J). (gr. 2-3). 18.60 (978-0-7368-1373-0(X) , Bridgestone Bks.) Capstone Pr., Inc.

Wakabi, Wairagala. Tanzania. 2004. (Illus.). 96p. (J). lib. bdg. 30.00 (978-0-8368-3119-1(5)) Stevens, Gareth Inc.

Woodward, John & Corwin, Jeff. Into Wild Tanzania. 2004. (Jeff Corwin Experience Ser.). (Illus.). 48p. (J). (gr. 4-7). 24.95 (978-1-4103-0249-6(0)); pap. 11.20 (978-1-4103-0250-2(4)) Thomson Gale. (Blackbirch Pr., Inc.).

TANZANIA—FICTION

Becker, John E. Mugambi's Journey. Clapsadle, Mark, illus. 2004. 32p. (J). 14.95 (978-0-7696-3167-7(3) , Gingham Dog Pr.) School Specialty Publishing.

Dubowski, Cathy East. Wild Thornberrys Movie. 2002. (gr. 3-6). lib. bdg. 13.00 (978-0-613-58171-4(7)) Tandem Library Bks.

Elizabeti's Doll. 2004. 24.95 incl. audio (978-1-55592-053-1(5)); (J). pap. 14.95 incl. audio (978-1-55592-716-5(5)) Weston Woods Studios, Inc.

Kilaka, John. Fresh Fish: A Tale from Tanzania. 2005. (Illus.). 32p. (J). 16.95 (978-0-88899-656-5(X)) Groundwood Bks. CAN. *Dist:* Perseus Distribution.

Krebs, Laurie. We All Went on Safari: A Counting Journey Through Tanzania. Cairns, Julia, illus. 2004. 32p. (J). pap. 6.99 (978-1-84148-119-7(X)) Barefoot Bks., Inc.

Matthews, T. J. The Canoeing Safari. Rheburg, Judy, illus. 2004. (J). (978-0-938978-35-0(7)) Wycliffe Bible Translators.

—The Village Safari. Rheburg, Judy, illus. 2005. (J). (978-0-938978-36-7(5)) Wycliffe Bible Translators.

Mollel, Tololwa M. My Rows & Piles of Coins. Lewis, Earl, illus. 2002. (J). 22.45 (978-0-7587-0385-9(6)) Book Wholesalers, Inc.

—My Rows & Piles of Coins. Lewis, E. B., illus. 1999. 32p. (J). (gr. k-3). tchr. ed. 16.00 (978-0-395-75186-2(1) , Clarion Bks.) Houghton Mifflin Co. Trade & Reference Div.

Murray, Marjorie Dennis. Hippo Goes Bananas! O'Malley, Kevin, illus. 2006. 32p. (J). 14.95 (978-0-7614-5224-9(9)) Cavendish, Marshall Corp.

Newman, Gwill York. Bingo Bear Was Here: A Toy Bear's Climb to the Top of Africa's Highest Mountain. Babcock, Jeff, illus. 2003. 48p. (J). pap. 8.95 (978-0-86534-395-5(0)) Sunstone Pr.

Stuve-Bodeen, Stephanie. Babu's Song. Boyd, Aaron, illus. 2003. 32p. (J). 16.95 (978-1-58430-058-8(2)) Lee & Low Bks., Inc.

—Elizabeti's Doll. Hale, Christy, illus. 2002. (J). 23.19 (978-0-7587-2449-6(7)) Book Wholesalers, Inc.

—Elizabeti's Doll. Hale, Christy, illus. 32p. (YA). 2002. (978-1-58430-081-6(7)); 2000. 19.95 (978-1-880000-70-0(9)) Lee & Low Bks., Inc.

—Elizabeti's School. Hale, Christy, illus. 2002. 32p. (J). (gr. k-3). 16.95 (978-1-58430-043-4(4)) Lee & Low Bks., Inc.

—La escuela de Elizabeti. Christy, Hale, illus. 2007. (SPA.). (J). pap. 7.95 (***978-1-60060-235-1(5)***) Lee & Low Bks., Inc.

—Mama Elizabeti. Hale, Christy, illus. 2000. 32p. (J). (ps up). 12.76 (978-1-58430-002-1(7)) Lee & Low Bks., Inc.

—La Muneca de Elizabeti. Sarfatti, Esther, tr. Hale, Christy, illus. braille ed. 2004. (SPA.). (J). (gr. k-3). spiral bd. (978-0-616-08966-8(X)) Canadian National Institute for the Blind/Institut National Canadien pour les Aveugles.

—La Muneca de Elizabeti. Sarfatti, Esther, tr. from ENG. Hale, Christy, illus. 2000. (SPA.). 32p. (J). (gr. k-1). pap. 6.95 (978-1-58430-001-4(9) , LW5012); lib. bdg. 15.95 (978-1-58430-000-7(0) , LW5352) Lee & Low Bks., Inc.

—La Muneca de Elizabeti. 2000. (978-0-606-17847-1(3)) Tandem Library Bks.

Thorpe, Kiki. Trouble with Darwin. 2001. (gr. k-3). lib. bdg. 14.15 (978-0-613-43965-7(1)) Tandem Library Bks.

Trimble, Marcia. Hello Sun: A True African Travel Tale. Arciero, Susan, illus. 2000. 32p. (J). (gr. k-2). 12.95 (978-1-891577-50-5(6)); pap. 6.95 (978-1-891577-51-2(4)) Images Pr.

TAPE RECORDERS

see Magnetic Recorders and Recording

TAPESTRY

Noble, Marty. Medieval Tapestries Coloring Book. 2004. (Illus.). 32p. (J). pap. 3.95 (978-0-486-43686-9(1)) Dover Pubns., Inc.

TAPESTRY—FICTION

Dobkin, Bonnie. Dream Spinner. 2006. 288p. pap. 8.95 (978-0-7387-0919-2(0) , Flux) Llewellyn Pubns.

Lasky, Kathryn. Born to Rule. Walton, Tony, illus. 2006. (Camp Princess Ser.: No. 1). 160p. (J). pap. 4.99 (978-0-06-058763-5(6) , Harper Trophy); 15.99 (978-0-06-058761-1(X)) HarperCollins Pubs.

Perkins, T J. Image in the Tapestry: A Kim & Kelly Mystery. 2005. (Illus.). 155p. (YA). 10.99 (978-0-9777538-3-3(2)) GumShoe Press.

TARBELL, IDA M. (IDA MINERVA), 1857-1944

Somervill, Barbara A. Ida Tarbell: Pioneer Investigative Reporter. 2004. (World Writers Ser.). (Illus.). 112p. (YA). (gr. 6-12). 23.95 (978-1-883846-87-9(0) , First Biographies) Reynolds, Morgan Inc.

TARKENTON, FRAN, 1940-

Hulm, David. Fran Tarkenton. 2003. (Football Hall of Famers Ser.). (Illus.). 112p. (YA). (gr. 5-8). lib. bdg. 29.25 (978-0-8239-3608-3(2) , Rosen Central) Rosen Publishing Group, Inc., The.

TARZAN (FICTITIOUS CHARACTER)—FICTION

Burroughs, Edgar Rice. Tarzan of the Apes. 1999. Tr. of 320. (gr. 7-12). lib. bdg. 13.00 (978-0-613-17651-4(0)) Tandem Library Bks.

Burroughs, Edgar Rice & Macan, Darko. Tarzan: Carson of Venus. 1999. (Illus.). 120p. (YA). (gr. 7 up). pap. 12.95 (978-1-56971-379-2(0)) Dark Horse Comics.

Burroughs, Edgar Rice, et al. Tarzan & the Jewels of Opar. 1999. (Illus.). 80p. (YA). (gr. 7 up). pap. 10.95 (978-1-56971-417-1(7)) Dark Horse Comics.

Byars, Betsy. Me Tarzan. Cigliano, Bill, illus. 2000. 96p. (J). (ps-3). lib. bdg. 15.89 (978-0-06-028707-8(1)) HarperCollins Pubs.

—Me Tarzan. 2002. (gr. 3-6). lib. bdg. 13.00 (978-0-613-61917-2(X)) Tandem Library Bks.

Capdevilla, Rosa. Tarzan. 2002. (SPA.). (gr. k-3). lib. bdg. 14.10 (978-0-613-64602-4(9)) Tandem Library Bks.

Disney Staff. Tarzan, Me & You. 1999. (Illus.). 10p. (J). (ps). 3.99 (978-0-7364-0132-6(6)) Mouse Works.

—Tarzan's Jungle Adventure. 1999. (Giant Lift-the-Flap Ser.). (Illus.). 10p. (J). (ps). bds. 8.99 (978-0-7364-0066-4(4)) Mouse Works.

DPWW. Tarzan. 1999. (Disney Chapters Ser.). (Illus.). 48p. (J). (gr. 2-4). pap. 3.95 (978-0-7868-4289-6(X)) Disney Pr.

Katschke, Judy. Tarzan Goes Bananas: Disney First Reader Ser. 1999. (Disney's Tarzan Ser.). (Illus.). 32p. (J). (gr. k-2). pap. 2.99 (978-0-7868-4281-0(4)) Hyperion Pr.

McPhail, David M. Edward in the Jungle. McPhail, David M., illus. 2004. (Illus.). 28p. (J). (gr. k-4). reprint ed. lib. bdg. 16.00 (978-0-7567-8009-8(8)) DIANE Publishing Co.

Milnes, Ellen. Tarzan Jungle Jam. Emslie, Peter, illus. 1999. (Chunky Roly-Poly Book Ser.). 16p. (J). bds. 3.50 (978-0-7364-0048-0(6)) Mouse Works.

Moore, Robin. Tarzan of the Apes. 1999. (gr. 3-6). lib. bdg. 11.80 (978-0-613-73242-0(1)) Tandem Library Bks.

Mouse Works Staff. Tarzan. 1999. (Spanish Read-Aloud Storybook Classics). (SPA., Illus.). 64p. (J). (ps-2). 6.99 (978-0-7364-0057-2(5)) Mouse Works.

—Tarzan. 1999. (Disney's Read-Aloud Storybooks Ser.). (Illus.). 72p. (J). (ps-2). 8.99 (978-0-7364-0047-3(8) , RH/Disney) Random Hse. Children's Bks.

Petruccio, Steven James. Tarzan Sticker Activity Book. 1999. (Dover Little Activity Bks.). (Illus.). 4p. (J). act. bk. ed. 1.00 (978-0-486-40933-7(3)) Dover Pubns., Inc.

Souci, Robert D. San & Burroughs, Edgar Rice. Tarzan. McCurdy, Michael, illus. 2004. 31p. (J). (gr. k-4). reprint ed. 16.00 (978-0-7567-7576-6(0)) DIANE Publishing Co.

Suben, Eric, et al, illus. Tarzan. 1999. (Disney Ser.). 24p. (J). (ps-3). pap. 3.29 (978-0-307-13194-2(7) , Golden Bks.) Random Hse. Children's Bks.

Tarzan Read Along. 1999. (J). (ps-3). pap. 6.98 incl. audio (978-0-7634-0530-4(2)) Walt Disney Records.

Tarzan Read & Sing Along. 1999. (J). (ps-3). pap. 14.48 incl. audio (978-0-7634-0525-0(6)) Walt Disney Records.

Terk Friendly Tales. 1999. 10p. (J). 6.99 (978-0-7364-0188-3(1)) Mouse Works.

Zoehfeld, Kathleen Weidner, adapted by. Tarzan. 1999. (Illus.). 48p. (J). (ps-3). 10.99 (978-0-7868-3220-0(7)) Disney Pr.

TASMANIA

Markle, Sandra. Tasmanian Devils. 2006. (Illus.). 39p. (J). pap. 7.95 (978-0-8225-3470-9(3) , First Avenue Editions) Lerner Publishing Group.

Ryan, Marla Felkins & Corwin, Jeff. Into Wild Tasmania. 2004. (Jeff Corwin Experience Ser.). (Illus.). 48p. (J). 11.20 (978-1-4103-0248-9(2)); (gr. 4-7). 24.95 (978-1-4103-0247-2(4)) Thomson Gale. (Blackbirch Pr., Inc.).

TASMANIA—FICTION

Baker, Jeannie. The Hidden Forest. 2000. (Illus.). 40p. (J). (gr. k up). 16.89 (978-0-688-15761-6(0)) HarperCollins Pubs.

Bugmann, Marlies. Golden Wings. 2005. (Green Heart Ser.). 216p. (J). pap. 12.99 (978-1-55410-283-9(9) , PO 00132) Zumaya Pubns. LLC.

Roy, James. Billy Mack's War. 2004. 245p. (J). pap. (***978-0-7022-3479-8(6)***) Univ. of Queensland Pr.

Russon, Penni. Breathe. 2007. (Illus.). 368p. (J). (gr. 9 up). 16.99 (978-0-06-079393-7(7)); lib. bdg. 17.89 (978-0-06-079394-4(5)) HarperCollins Pubs.

TASSEL, LINDA (FICTITIOUS CHARACTER)—FICTION

Charbonneau, Eileen. The Connor Emerald. Williams, Lori, ed. 1999. 170p. (YA). pap. 9.99 (978-1-58365-753-9(3) , Timeless Romance) Sierra Raconteur Publishing.

TAXATION

Grote, JoAnn A. The Internal Revenue Service. 2001. (Your Government Ser.). (Illus.). 64p. (J). (gr. 4-7). 25.00 (978-0-7910-5989-0(8) , Chelsea Hse.) Facts On File, Inc.

Macht, Norman L. Taxes. 2001. (Exploring Business & Economics Ser.). (Illus.). 64p. (YA). (gr. 6-9). 25.00 (978-0-7910-6640-9(1) , Chelsea Hse.) Facts On File, Inc.

TAXATION—UNITED STATES

Bussing-Burks, Maire. The Young Zillionaire's Guide to Taxation & Government Spending. 2000. (Be a Zillionaire Ser.). (Illus.). 48p. (YA). (gr. 5-8). lib. bdg. 23.95 (978-0-8239-3258-0(3) , ZITASP, Rosen Central) Rosen Publishing Group, Inc., The.

De Capua, Sarah. Paying Taxes. 2002. (True Bks.). (Illus.). 48p. (J). (gr. 3-5). pap. 6.95 (978-0-516-27367-9(1) , Children's Pr.) Scholastic Library Publishing.

—Paying Taxes. 2002. (gr. 3-6). lib. bdg. 15.25 (978-0-613-54077-3(8)) Tandem Library Bks.

Giesecke, Ernestine. Your Money at Work: Taxes. (Everyday Economics Ser.). (Illus.). 48p. (J). 2003. (gr. 3-5). lib. bdg. 27.07 (978-1-58810-494-6(X)); 2002. pap. 8.50 (978-1-58810-957-6(7)) Heinemann Library.

Hamilton, John. Funding the Nation. 2005. (Government in Action! Ser.). (J). (gr. k-6). lib. bdg. 22.78 (978-1-59197-823-7(8)) ABDO Publishing Co.

Kowalski, Kathiann M. Taxes. 2005. (Open for Debate Ser.). (Illus.). 139p. (J). (978-0-7614-1887-0(3) , Benchmark Bks.) Cavendish, Marshall Corp.

Loewen, Nancy. Taxes, Taxes! Where the Money Goes. Fitzpatrick, Brad, illus. 2005. (Money Matters Ser.). 24p. (J). (ps). lib. bdg. 22.60 (978-1-4048-1158-4(3)) Picture Window Bks.

—Uncle Sam's Allowance: A Book about Taxes. Fitzpatrick, Brad, illus. 2004. (J). (978-1-4048-0955-0(4)) Picture Window Bks.

Rochford, Stephen. Tax for Teens. 2002. 96p. pap. 20.95 (978-0-538-43711-0(1)) Thomson South-Western.

TAYLOR, ZACHARY, 1784-1850

Brunelli, Carol. Zachary Taylor: Our Twelfth President. 2001. (Spirit of America: Our Presidents Ser.). (Illus.). 48p. (J). (gr. 2-6). 28.50 (978-1-56766-836-0(4)) Child's World, Inc.

Deem, James M. Zachary Taylor: A MyReportLinks.com Book. 2002. (Presidents Ser.). (Illus.). 48p. (J). (gr. 4-10). lib. bdg. 25.26 (978-0-7660-5013-6(0) , MyReportLinks.com Bks.) Enslow Pubs., Inc.

Doak, Robin S. Zachary Taylor. 2003. (Profiles of the Presidents Ser.). (Illus.). 64p. (J). (gr. 4 up). lib. bdg. 23.93 (978-0-7565-0260-7(8)) Compass Point Bks.

Joseph, Paul. Zachary Taylor. 1999. (United States Presidents Ser.). (Illus.). 32p. (J). (gr. k-6). lib. bdg. 22.78 (978-1-57765-233-5(9) , Checkerboard Library) ABDO Publishing Co.

Kops, Deborah. Zachary Taylor. 2004. (Encyclopedia of Presidents Ser.). (Illus.). 110p. (J). 34.00 (978-0-516-23442-7(0) , Children's Pr.) Scholastic Library Publishing.

Roberts, Jeremy. Zachary Taylor. 2005. (Presidential Leaders Ser.). (Illus.). 112p. (J). (gr. 6-12). 29.27 (978-0-8225-1397-1(8)) Lerner Publishing Group.

Schmidt, Roderic. How to Draw the Life & Times of Zachary Taylor. 2006. (Kid's Guide to Drawing the Presidents of the United States of America Ser.). (J). 25.25 (978-1-4042-2989-1(2) , PowerKids Pr.) Rosen Publishing Group, Inc., The.

Venezia, Mike. Zachary Taylor: Twelfth President 1849-1850. Venezia, Mike, illus. 2005. (Getting to Know the U. S. Presidents Ser.). (Illus.). 32p. (J). (gr. 3-4). pap. 7.95 (978-0-516-27486-7(4) , Children's Pr.) Scholastic Library Publishing.

Venezia, Mike, illus. Zachary Taylor: Twelfth President, 1849-1850. 2005. (Getting to Know the U. S. Presidents Ser.). 32p. (J). (gr. 3-4). 27.00 (978-0-516-22617-0(7) , Children's Pr.) Scholastic Library Publishing.

TCHAIKOVSKY, PETER ILICH, 1840-1893

Beier, Jean. Pyotr Ilich Tchaikovsky. 2006. (Lives & Times of Famous Composers Ser.). (J). lib. bdg. (978-1-4042-0725-7(2)) Rosen Publishing Group, Inc., The.

Cencetti, Greta. Tchaikovsky. 2002. (Classic Composers Ser.). (Illus.). 40p. (J). incl. audio compact disk (978-1-59069-095-6(8) , T2105) Studio Mouse LLC.

—Tchaikovsky: Getting to Know Your Classical Composers. 2002. (Illus.). 32p. (978-1-59069-028-4(1) , T2005) Studio Mouse LLC.

Chaikovskii. The Life & Letters of Peter Ilich Tchaikovsky. 2001. 782p. (YA). reprint ed. 148.00 (978-0-7222-5550-6(0)) Library Reprints, Inc.

Evans, Edwin. Tchaikovsky. 2001. 207p. (YA). reprint ed. 98.00 (978-0-7222-5547-6(0)) Library Reprints, Inc.

T U V

TEA

Clough. Time for Tea. 1999. pap. 9.99 (978-0-7369-0076-8(4)) Harvest Hse. Pubs.

Gleason, Carrie. The Biography of Tea. 2007. (How Did That Get Here? Ser.). (Illus.). 32p. (J). (gr. 2-9). ***(978-0-7787-2493-3(X))***; pap. ***(*978-0-7787-2529-9(4))*** Crabtree Publishing Co.

Sato, Shozo. Tea Ceremony. 2005. (Asian Arts & Crafts for Creative Kids Ser.). (Illus.). 64p. 12.95 (978-0-8048-3500-8(4)) Tuttle Publishing.

Wheeler, Susan & Kortepeter, Paul. Let's Have Tea Together: Recipes & Celebrations for Every Season. 2nd gif. ed. 2002. Orig. Title: Tea with Victoria Rose. (Illus.). 80p. 15.99 (978-0-7369-1043-9(3)) Harvest Hse. Pubs.

TEA ROOMS

see Restaurants

TEACH, EDWARD, D. 1718

Hamilton, Sue L. Blackbeard. 2007. (Pirates! Ser.). (ENG., Illus.). 32p. (J). (gr. 3-6). 24.21 ***(*978-1-59928-758-4(7)*** , ABDO & Daughters) ABDO Publishing Co.

Weintraub, Aileen. Blackbeard: 18th-Century Pirate of the Spanish Main & the Carolina Coast. 2002. (Library of Pirates). (Illus.). 24p. (J). (gr. 3). lib. bdg. 18.75 (978-0-8239-5794-1(2) , PowerKids Pr.) Rosen Publishing Group, Inc., The.

TEACH, EDWARD, D. 1718—FICTION

Kimmel, Eric A. Blackbeard's Last Fight. Fisher, Leonard Everett, illus. 2006. 32p. (J). 17.00 (978-0-374-30780-6(6) , Farrar, Straus & Giroux (BYR)) Farrar, Straus & Giroux.

O'Donnell, Liam. Blackbeard's Sword: The Pirate King of the Carolinas. Spoor, Mike, illus. 2007. (J). 46p. pap. ***(*978-1-59889-404-2(8))***; 56p. (gr. 3-5). lib. bdg. 23.93 ***(*978-1-59889-309-0(2))*** Stone Arch Bks.

Pyle, Howard. The Story of Jack Ballister's Fortunes. 2007. (YA). ***(*978-0-486-45467-2(3))*** Dover Pubns., Inc.

Wechter, Nell Wise & Tucker, Bruce. Teach's Light. 1999. (Chapel Hill Book Ser.). (Illus.). 160p. (gr. 4-7). pap. 10.95 (978-0-8078-4793-0(3)) Univ. of North Carolina Pr.

TEACHER-STUDENT RELATIONSHIPS—FICTION

Alexander, Lloyd. The Gawgon & the Boy. 2003. (gr. 3-6). lib. bdg. 14.15 (978-0-613-59809-5(1)) Tandem Library Bks.

Anderson, Laurie Halse. Teacher's Pet. 2003. (Wild at Heart Ser.). (Illus.). 132p. (J). (gr. 4 up). lib. bdg. 23.33 (978-0-8368-3261-7(2)) Stevens, Gareth Inc.

Avi. Don't You Know There's a War On? 2003. 200p. (J). (ps-7). lib. bdg. 14.15 (978-0-613-60338-6(9)) Tandem Library Bks.

Clements, Andrew. Head of the Class: Frindle; the Landry News; the Janitor's Boy. Selznick, Brian, illus. 2007. 416p. (J). 17.99 ***(*978-1-4169-4974-9(7)*** , Aladdin) Simon & Schuster Children's Publishing.

Clements, Andrew. Jake Drake, Class Clown. 2002. (gr. 3-6). lib. bdg. 11.80 (978-0-613-45071-3(X)) Tandem Library Bks.

Codell, Esmé Raji. Sahara Special. 2003. (Illus.). 192p. (gr. 3-7). 15.99 (978-0-7868-0793-2(8)) Hyperion Bks. for Children.

Colon, Suzan. Buried Secrets. 2003. (gr. 5-8). lib. bdg. 14.15 (978-0-613-64658-1(4)) Tandem Library Bks.

D'Agata, Tabatha Jean. Marvin Monster's Teacher Jitters. Newmann, Ed, illus. 2006. 48p. pap. 6.95 (978-0-9766805-3-6(X)) Keene Publishing.

deGroat, Diane. No More Pencils, No More Books, No More Teacher's Dirty Looks! deGroat, Diane, illus. 2006. (Illus.). 32p. (J). 15.99 (978-0-06-079114-8(4)); lib. bdg. 16.89 (978-0-06-079115-5(2)) HarperCollins Pubs.

Gauthier, Gail. Hero of Ticonderoga. 2002. lib. bdg. 15.30 (978-0-613-60807-7(0)) Tandem Library Bks.

Grant, Cynthia D. White Horse. 2000. (978-0-606-17945-4(3)) Tandem Library Bks.

Honey, Elizabeth. Don't Pat the Wombat. 2001. (gr. 3-6). lib. bdg. 12.40 (978-0-613-36095-1(8)) Tandem Library Bks.

Hyde, Catherine Ryan. Pay It Forward. 2000. (gr. 7-12). lib. bdg. 16.45 (978-0-613-33844-8(8)) Tandem Library Bks.

Johnson, Kathleen Jeffrie. Gone. 2007. 176p. (YA). (gr. 9 up). 16.95 (978-1-59643-138-6(5)) Roaring Brook Pr.

Johnson, Sandi. My Teacher Is an Alien. Johnson, Britt, ed. Sturgen, Bobbi, illus. 2002. 16p. (J). (gr. k-5). spiral bd. 5.99 (978-1-929063-75-8(X) , 285) Moons & Stars Publishing For Children.

Jonsberg, Barry. The Crimes & Punishments of Miss Payne. 2006. 288p. (YA). (gr. 7). pap. 8.95 (978-0-375-84022-7(2) , Knopf Bks. for Young Readers) Random Hse. Children's Bks.

Layne, Steven L., et al. T Is for Teachers: A School Alphabet. Ettlinger, Doris, illus. 2005. 40p. (J). (ps-ps). per. 16.95 (978-1-58536-159-5(3)) Sleeping Bear Pr.

Lisle, Janet Taylor. Sirens & Spies. 2002. (gr. 3-6). lib. bdg. 13.00 (978-0-613-45104-8(X)) Tandem Library Bks.

Marshall, James, illus. Miss Nelson Is Missing! 2002. (Miss Nelson Ser.). (J). 13.79 (978-0-7587-3147-0(7)) Book Wholesalers, Inc.

Marvin Redpost: Alone in His Teacher's House. 2002. (Marvin Redpost Ser.). (Illus.). (J). 11.91 (978-0-7587-1428-2(9)) Book Wholesalers, Inc.

Muluka, B. Kandu & the Lake. 2004. (Illus.). 40p. 13.95 (978-9966-25-165-7(0)) Heinemann Kenya, Limited (East African Educational Publishers Ltd E.A.E.P.) KEN. *Dist:* Michigan State Univ. Pr.

Nelson, R. A. Teach Me. 2007. 272p. (J). pap. 8.99 (978-1-59514-085-2(9) , Razorbill) Penguin Group (USA) Inc.

Oates, Joyce Carol. Sexy. (J). 2005. 272p. lib. bdg. 17.89 (978-0-06-054150-7(4)); 2005. 272p. (gr. 7 up). 16.99 (978-0-06-054149-1(0)); 2006. 288p. reprint ed. pap. 7.99 (978-0-06-054151-4(2)) HarperCollins Pubs. (HarperTeen).

Patneaude, David. The Last Man's Reward. 1998. 192p. (J). (gr. 4-7). lib. bdg. 12.95 (978-0-613-62498-5(X)) Tandem Library Bks.

Prestine, Joan Singleton. It's Hard to Share My Teacher: Picture Book & Resource Guide, 2 bks., Set. 2001. (Kids Have Feelings, Too Ser.). (J). (ps-3). 14.99 (978-1-56417-773-5(4) , FE0061, Fearon Teacher Aids) Schaffer, Frank Pubns.

Rathmann, Peggy. Ruby the Copycat Library. 2007. (J). 18.95 ***(*978-0-545-00583-8(3))*** Scholastic, Inc.

Regan, Dian Curtis. The World According to Kaley. 2005. (Illus.). 112p. (J). (gr. 4-7). per. 14.99 (978-1-58196-039-6(5)) Darby Creek Publishing.

Rue, Nancy N. Totally Unfair. 2005. (Invert / 'Nama Beach High Ser.). 160p. (YA). pap. 6.99 (978-0-310-25183-5(4)) Zondervan.

Standiford, Natalie. The Dating Game, No. 1. 2005. 224p. (YA). (gr. 8-17). pap. 9.99 (978-0-316-11040-2(X)) Little Brown & Co.

—Dating Game: Breaking Up Is Really, Really Hard to Do, No. 2. 2005. 224p. (YA). (gr. 8-17). pap. 9.99 (978-0-316-11041-9(8)) Little Brown & Co.

TEACHER TRAINING

see Teachers—Training of

TEACHERS

see also Educators; Teaching

Adamson, Heather. A Day in the Life of a Teacher. 2003. (First Facts Ser.). (Illus.). 24p. (J). lib. bdg. 21.26 (978-0-7368-2286-2(0)) Capstone Pr., Inc.

African-American Teachers. 2000. (My Ancestors—My Heroes Ser.: Vol. 36). (J). (gr. 3-4). (978-1-893091-35-1(X)) Parker Publishing Co.

Ayers, Samuel J. Ella Iles: Early Texas Teacher. Ayers, Samuel J., illus. l.t. ed. 1999. (Illus.). 32p. (J). (gr. 2-6). 13.00 (978-0-9667681-0-7(8)) Hermosa Creations.

Bao, Julie. A Loving Teacher Forever: A True Story of Loving Children, Defying Fate & Achieving Teaching Excellence. 2004. (Illus.). 32p. (J). 15.00 (978-0-9748890-0-9(8)) Dings Bks.

Brooks, Felicity. Tessa the Teacher. 2006. 24p. (J). pap. 6.99 (978-0-7945-0937-8(1) , Usborne) EDC Publishing.

Catala, Ellen. Who Keeps Us Safe? 2006. (Illus.). 18p. (J). (978-0-7368-5984-4(5)) Capstone Pr., Inc.

—Who Keeps Us Safe? 2006. (Illus.). 8,16p. (J). 6.50 (978-0-7368-1720-2(4)) Red Brick Learning.

—Who Keeps Us Safe. 2006. (ENG & SPA., Illus.). 18p. (J). (978-0-7368-6020-8(7)) Yellow Umbrella Pr.

Crane, Natalie. I Go to Work as a Teacher. 2003. (I Go to Work As Ser.). (Illus.). (J). (gr. k-3). (978-1-58417-106-5(5)); lib. bdg. (978-1-58417-043-3(3)); lib. bdg. (978-1-58417-044-0(1)) Lake Street Pubs.

Dahl, Michael. Teacher Says: A Book of Teacher Jokes. Haugen, Ryan, illus. 2004. (Read-It! Joke Books). 24p. (C). (gr. k-3). 18.60 (978-1-4048-0301-5(7)) Picture Window Bks.

Dent, Jenny. Great Teachers. 2003. (Spiritual Teachings for Children Ser.). (Illus.). 32p. (gr. k-9). 17.95 (978-0-85487-054-7(7)) White Eagle Publishing Trust GBR. *Dist:* DeVorss & Co.

Evento, Susan. Mary McLeod Bethune. 2004. (Rookie Biographies Ser.). (Illus.). 31p. (J). 20.50 (978-0-516-21720-8(8) , Children's Pr.) Scholastic Library Publishing.

Flanagan, Alice K. Teachers. 2001. (Community Workers Ser.). (Illus.). 32p. (J). (gr. 1 up). lib. bdg. 21.26 (978-0-7565-0066-5(4)) Compass Point Bks.

Flanagan, Alice K. & Cornwell, Linda. Learning Is Fun with Mrs. Perez. Flanagan, Romie, illus. 1998. (Our Neighborhood Ser.). 32p. (J). (gr. 1-2). 20.00 (978-0-516-20774-2(1) , Children's Pr.) Scholastic Library Publishing.

Freeman, Dallas. Mirth & Misery: Memoirs of a Midwestern Maverick. 2003. 267p. per. 14.95 net. (978-1-931934-22-0(3)) Back Yard Pub.

Hayward, Linda. Day in the Life of a Teacher. 2001. (gr. k-3). lib. bdg. 11.80 (978-0-613-35099-0(5)) Tandem Library Bks.

Hayward, Linda & Dorling Kindersley Publishing Staff. Jobs People Do: A Day in the Life of a Teacher. 2001. (Readers Ser.). (Illus.). 32p. (J). (ps-3). pap. 3.99 (978-0-7894-7367-7(4)) Dorling Kindersley Publishing, Inc.

Hunter, Rebecca. Teacher. 2006. (People Who Help Us Ser.). (Illus.). 32p. 22.95 ***(*978-1-84234-300-5(9)*** , Evans Brothers, Limited) Evans Publishing Group GBR. *Dist:* Independent Pubs. Group.

Inseth, Zachary. Teachers. 2003. (Wonder Books Level 3: Careers Ser.). (Illus.). 32p. (J). (ps-2). 22.79 (978-1-56766-488-1(1)) Child's World, Inc.

J. G. Ferguson Publishing Company Staff, contrib. by. Careers in Focus. (Careers in Focus Ser.). (Illus.). 192p. (J). (gr. 6-12). 2nd ed. 2003. 22.95 (978-0-8160-5485-5(1)); 4th ed. 2004. 22.95 (978-0-8160-5553-1(X)) Facts On File, Inc. (Ferguson Publishing Co.).

Johnston, Lissa Jones. Mary McLeod Bethune: Empowering Educator. 2006. (Fact Finders Ser.). (Illus.). 32p. (J). 22.60 (978-0-7368-6421-3(0)) Capstone Pr., Inc.

Lehn, Barbara. What Is a Teacher? Krauss, Carol, photos by. 2000. (What Is...? Ser.). (Illus.). 32p. (gr. k-3). lib. bdg. 21.90 (978-0-7613-1713-5(9) , Millbrook Pr.) Lerner Publishing Group.

Lesinski, Jeanne M. Bill Gates. 2006. (First Step Nonfiction Ser.). (Illus.). 112p. (J). (gr. 3-7). 27.93 (978-0-8225-2642-1(5) , Lerner Pubns.) Lerner Publishing Group.

Liebman, Daniel. Quiero Ser Maestro. 2001. (Coleccion Quierno Ser.). (SPA., Illus.). 24p. (J). (ps-2). pap. 5.99 (978-1-55209-594-2(0) , AP30397) Firefly Bks., Ltd.

Lieurance, Suzanne. The Space Shuttle Challenger Disaster in American History. 2001. (In American History Ser.). (Illus.). 128p. (J). (gr. 5-12). lib. bdg. 26.60 (978-0-7660-1419-0(3)) Enslow Pubs., Inc.

Lohse, Joyce B. Emily Griffith: Opportunity's Teacher. 2005. (Now You Know Bio Ser.). (Illus.). 50p. (J). pap. 8.95 (978-0-86541-077-0(1)) Filter Pr., LLC.

Lowenstein, Felicia. What Does a Teacher Do? 2006. (What Does a Community Helper Do? Ser.). (Illus.). 24p. (J). lib. bdg. 21.26 (978-0-7660-2321-5(4) , Enslow Elementary) Enslow Pubs., Inc.

Lucas, Eileen. Prudence Crandall. Smith, Kimanne, illus. 2001. (On My Own Biographies Ser.). 48p. (J). (gr. 1-3). lib. bdg. (978-1-57505-480-3(9) , Carolrhoda Bks.) Lerner Publishing Group.

Macken, JoAnn Early. People in My Community: Crossing Guard; Mail Carrier; Nurse; Sanitation Worker; Teacher; Veterinarian, 6 bks. (Weekly Reader Early Learning Library). (Illus.). (J). (ps up). lib. bdg. 111.60 (978-0-8368-3588-5(3) , Weekly Reader Early Learning Library) Stevens, Gareth Inc.

—Teacher/El Maestro. Coffey, Colleen & Carrillo, Consuelo, trs. 2003. (Weekly Reader Early Learning Library). (ENG & SPA., Illus.). 24p. (J). (ps up). lib. bdg. 19.33 (978-0-8368-3675-2(8) , Weekly Reader Early Learning Library) Stevens, Gareth Inc.

Macken, JoAnn Early & Gorman, Jacqueline Laks. Teacher/El Maestro. Coffey, Colleen & Carrillo, Consuelo, trs. Andersen, Gregg, photos by. 2003. (Weekly Reader Early Learning Library). (ENG & SPA., Illus.). 24p. (J). (ps up). pap. 5.95 (978-0-8368-3689-9(8) , Weekly Reader Early Learning Library) Stevens, Gareth Inc.

McDonnell, Peter. Helping Others: The Story of Fanny Jackson Coppin. 2005. (Illus.). 16p. (J). (978-0-7367-2901-7(1)) Zaner-Bloser, Inc.

Mellor, C. Michael. Louis Braille: A Touch of Genius. 2006. (Illus.). 144p. (J). 35.00 (978-0-939173-70-9(0)) National Braille Pr.

Miller, Heather. Maestro. 2003. (Esto es lo Que Quiero Ser (This Is What I Want to Be) Ser.). (SPA., Illus.). 24p. (J). (ps-1). lib. bdg. 18.50 (978-1-4034-0382-7(1)) Heinemann Library.

—Teacher. 2003. (This Is What I Want to Be Ser.). (Illus.). 24p. (J). (ps-1). lib. bdg. (978-1-4034-0372-8(4)); pap. 5.25 (978-1-4034-0594-4(8)) Heinemann Library.

Minden, Cecilia. Teachers. 2006. (Neighborhood Helpers Ser.). (Illus.). 32p. (J). (gr. k-4). 22.79 (978-1-59296-569-4(5)) Child's World, Inc.

Mitchell, Melanie. Teachers. (Pull Ahead Bks.). (Illus.). 32p. (J). 2005. lib. bdg. 22.60 (978-0-8225-1696-5(9)); 2004. pap. (978-0-8225-2536-3(4) , Lerner Pubns.) Lerner Publishing Group.

Morris, Ann. That's Our Teacher! 2003. (That's Our School Ser.). 32p. lib. bdg. 22.90 (978-0-7613-2373-0(2) , Millbrook Pr.) Lerner Publishing Group.

Parks, Peggy J. Teacher. 2003. (Exploring Careers Ser.). (Illus.). 48p. (J). (gr. 3-5). 26.20 (978-0-7377-1487-6(5) , Kidhaven) Thomson Gale.

Picture Window Books, contrib. by. Helping You Learn. (Community Workers Ser.). 24p. (J). pap. 7.95 (978-1-4048-0478-4(1)) Picture Window Bks.

Reece, Colleen L. & Donihue, Anita C. A Teacher's Heart: Thank You for Being My Teacher. 1998. 64p. (J). 5.97 (978-1-57748-220-8(4)) Barbour Publishing, Inc.

Richmond, Marianne R. Thank You Teacher. 2005. (Illus.). 40p. (J). 7.95 (978-0-9763101-0-5(4)) Marianne Richmond Studios, Inc.

Rivera, Sheila. Teacher. 2004. (First Step Nonfiction Ser.). (J). pap. (978-0-8225-5361-8(9) , Lerner Pubns.) Lerner Publishing Group.

Russack, Joy C. Those Wonderful Children. 2000. (Illus.). 32p. (J). pap. 8.00 (978-0-8059-4831-8(7)) Dorrance Publishing Co., Inc.

Scholastic, Inc. Staff. Welcome to My Class. 1999. (J). pap. 3.95 (978-0-439-07230-4(1)) Scholastic, Inc.

Schomp, Virginia. If You Were a Teacher. 2000. (If You Were A... Ser.). (Illus.). 32p. (J). (gr. 2-4). lib. bdg. 22.79 (978-0-7614-0916-8(5) , Benchmark Bks.) Cavendish, Marshall Corp.

Stewart, Tobi Stanton. Colonial Teachers. 2006. (J). lib. bdg. (978-1-4042-3351-5(2) , PowerKids Pr.) Rosen Publishing Group, Inc., The.

Streissguth, Thomas. Christa McAuliffe. 2003. (Explore Space! Ser.). (Illus.). 24p. (J). (gr. 1-2). lib. bdg. 18.60 (978-0-7368-1624-3(0) , Bridgestone Bks.) Capstone Pr., Inc.

Strong, Jeremy. Pandemonium at School. 2004. (J). pap. 24.95 incl. audio (978-0-7540-6272-1(4) , Chivers Children's Audio Bks.) BBC Audiobooks America.

Verdick, Elizabeth & Romain, Trevor. True or False? Tests Stink! 2004. (Laugh & Learn Ser.). (Illus.). 88p. (YA). (gr. 3-8). pap. 8.95 (978-1-57542-073-8(2)) Free Spirit Publishing, Inc.

Vogel, Elizabeth. Meet My Teacher. 2002. (PowerKids Readers Ser.). (Illus.). 24p. (J). (gr. 1). lib. bdg. 16.00 (978-0-8239-6032-3(3) , PowerKids Pr.) Rosen Publishing Group, Inc., The.

We Need Teachers, 6 vols. (gr. k-2). 28.95 (978-0-7368-8741-0(5)) Red Brick Learning.

Wilmore, Kathy. A Day in the Life of a Colonial Schoolteacher. 2000. (Library of Living & Working in Colonial Times). (Illus.). 24p. (J). (gr. 3). lib. bdg. 18.75 (978-0-8239-5429-2(3) , PowerKids Pr.) Rosen Publishing Group, Inc., The.

Wohlrabe, Sarah. Helping You Learn: A Book about Teachers. Thomas, Eric, illus. 2004. (Community Workers Ser.). 24p. (C). (gr. k-3). 22.60 (978-1-4048-0084-7(0)) Picture Window Bks.

TEACHERS—ANECDOTES, FACETIAE, SATIRE, ETC.

Draper, Sharon M. Not Quite Burned Out but Crispy Around the Edges: Inspiration, Laughter, & Encouragement for Teachers. 2001. 128p. pap. 13.95 (978-0-325-00365-8(3) , E00365) Heinemann.

TEACHERS—FICTION

Abdo Publishing Staff, contrib. by. Flower Girl Friends. 2000. (Faithful Friends Ser.). (Illus.). 64p. (J). (gr. 4). lib. bdg. 21.35 (978-1-57765-229-8(0) , ABDO & Daughters) ABDO Publishing Co.

Adams, W. Royce. Teacher, Teacher, I Declare! & Other Little Tattle Tales. 2nd ed. 2001. 228p. pap. 14.95 (978-0-9712206-1-4(1)) Rairarubia Bks.

Adler, David A. Cam Jansen & the Tennis Trophy Mystery. Natti, Susanna, tr. Natti, Susanna, illus. 2003. (Cam Jansen Ser.: No. 24). 64p. (J). 13.99 (978-0-670-03643-1(9) , Viking Juvenile) Penguin Group (USA) Inc.

—School Trouble for Andy Russell. Hillenbrand, Will, illus. 2005. (Andy Russell Ser.). 128p. (J). pap. 4.95 (978-0-15-205428-1(6) , Gulliver Bks.) Harcourt Children's Bks.

—School Trouble for Andy Russell. Hillenbrand, Will, illus. 1999. (Andy Russell Ser.). 118p. (J). (gr. 2-5). per. 11.60 (978-0-606-19004-6(X)) Tandem Library Bks.

—Young Cam Jansen & the Substitute Mystery. Natti, Susanna, illus. 32p. (J). (gr. k). 2006. (Young Cam Jansen Ser.: No. 11). pap. 3.99 (978-0-14-240660-1(0) , Puffin); 2005. (Viking Easy-To-Read Ser.). 13.99 (978-0-670-05988-1(9) , Viking Juvenile) Penguin Group (USA) Inc.

Ahlberg, Allan. The Children Who Smelled a Rat. McEwen, Katharine, illus. 2005. 80p. (J). (gr. 2-4). 15.99 (978-0-7636-2870-3(0)) Candlewick Pr.

Aikawa, Yu. Dark Edge, Vol. 4. 2005. (Illus.). 208p. (YA). pap. 9.95 (978-1-59796-024-3(1)) DrMaster Pubns. Inc.

Alfonsi, Alice, adapted by. 'Rents: Lizzie Mcguire. 2005. 134p. (J). lib. bdg. 16.92 ***(*978-1-4242-0689-6(8))*** Fitzgerald Bks.

Alger, Horatio. Fancy of Hers. 2006. pap. ***(*978-1-4250-3505-1(1))***; pap. ***(*978-1-4250-3545-7(0))***; pap. ***(*978-1-4250-3583-9(3))*** Assistedreadingbooks.com Inc.

Allard, Harry G. La Senorita Nelson Ha Desaparecido! Marshall, James, illus. 1998. (Miss Nelson Ser.). (SPA.). 32p. (J). (gr. k-3). 16.00 (978-0-395-90009-3(3)) Houghton Mifflin Co. Trade & Reference Div.

—La Señorita Nelson Ha Desaparecido! Canetti, Yanitzia, tr. Marshall, James, illus. 1998. (SPA.). 32p. (J). (gr. k-3). pap. 5.95 (978-0-395-90008-6(5) , HM8029) Houghton Mifflin Co. Trade & Reference Div.

Anderson, Janet. Going Through the Gate. 2000. (Illus.). (J). (978-0-606-18407-6(4)) Tandem Library Bks.

Anna, Jennifer. Yen Shei & the American Bonsai. 2007. (Illus.). 88p. (YA). pap. 14.99 ***(*978-1-59092-153-1(4)*** , Blue Works) Windstorm Creative.

Arthur's Teacher Moves In. 2001. (Arthur Adventure Ser.). (Illus.). (J). pap. 5.95 (978-0-316-12206-1(8)) Little Brown & Co.

Avi. The Secret School. 2001. 160p. (YA). (gr. 3-7). 16.00 (978-0-15-216375-4(1)) Harcourt Children's Bks.

—The Secret School. 2003. (gr. 3-6). lib. bdg. 14.10 (978-0-613-70523-3(8)) Tandem Library Bks.

Barth-Grozinger, Inge. Something Remains. Bell, Anthea, tr. from GER. 2006. 400p. (gr. 5-9). 16.99 (978-0-7868-3880-6(9)) Hyperion Pr.

Bartlett, Susan. Seal Island School. Bonnell, J., ed. Tusa, Tricia, illus. 2001. (Chapters Ser.). 80p. (J). (gr. 2-5). pap. 4.99 (978-0-14-131104-3(5) , Puffin) Penguin Group (USA) Inc.

—Seal Island School. Tusa, Tricia, illus. 1999. 80p. (J). (gr. 2-5). 15.99 (978-0-670-88349-3(2) , Viking Juvenile) Penguin Group (USA) Inc.

—Seal Island School. 2001. (gr. 3-6). lib. bdg. 13.00 (978-0-613-63991-0(X)) Tandem Library Bks.

Beasley, Cheryl. Piano Paradise: My Piano Has a Big Secret. 2006. (ENG.). 52p. per. 12.95 ***(*978-1-4241-4590-4(2))*** PublishAmerica, Inc.

Bellamy, Diane. But I Will Teach You. 2004. (YA). pap. 15.00 (978-1-56411-297-2(7)) UBUS Communications Systems.

Bellingham, Brenda. Lilly in the Middle. Owen, Elizabeth, illus. 2003. (First Novel Ser.). 64p. (J). (gr. 1-5). 4.95 (978-0-88780-589-9(2)); ***(*978-0-88780-590-5(6))*** Formac Publishing Co., Ltd. CAN. *Dist:* Casemate Pubs. & Bk. Distributors, LLC.

Bickel, Karla. Teacher's Remarkable Secret. Bickel, Karla, illus. l.t. ed. 2004. (Illus.). 16p. (J). (ps-6). pap. 5.00 (978-1-891452-09-3(6) , 2) Heart Arbor Bks.

Blackman, Malorie. The Monster Crisp-Guzzler. Sweeten, Sami, illus. 2002. (Corgi Pups Ser.). 64p. (J). pap. 7.99 (978-0-552-54783-3(2) , Corgi) Transworld Publishers Ltd. GBR. *Dist:* Independent Pubs. Group.

Boonstra, Jean Elizabeth. Miss Button & the Schoolboard: Sarah 1842-1844. 2002. 95p. (J). (978-0-8163-1874-2(3)) Pacific Pr. Publishing Assn.

Borden, Louise. Good Luck, Mrs. K. ! Gustavson, Adam, illus. 2002. 32p. (J). (gr. 1-5). pap. 6.99 (978-0-689-85119-3(7) , Aladdin) Simon & Schuster Children's Publishing.

—The Last Day of School. Gustavson, Adam, illus. 2006. 40p. (J). (gr. 2-5). 15.95 (978-0-689-86869-6(3) , McElderry, Margaret K.) Simon & Schuster Children's Publishing.

Bowen, Anne. What Do Teachers Do? After YOU Leave School. Gott, Barry, illus. 2006. 32p. (J). 15.95 (978-1-57505-922-8(3) , Carolrhoda Bks.) Lerner Publishing Group.

Bradman, Tony. Spooky Teachers, 2 bks. in 1. 2005. (Illus.). 128p. (J). (gr. k-2). pap. (978-0-552-55347-6(6) , Corgi) Transworld Publishers Ltd.

Brandt, Amy. When Katie Was Our Teacher. de la Vega, Eida, tr. Porter, Janice Lee, illus. 2004. (Child Care Bks. for Kids).Tr. of Cuando Katie Era Nuestra Maestra. (ENG & SPA.). 32p. (J). (ps-2). pap. 11.95 (978-1-884834-78-3(7) , 709901) Redleaf Pr.

Brenner, Emily. On the First Day of Grade School. Whatley, Bruce, illus. 2004. 32p. (J). (ps-1). 15.99 (978-0-06-028013-0(1)); lib. bdg. 16.89 (978-0-06-051041-1(2)) HarperCollins Pubs.

Brink, LeeAnn. The Stuff in the Back of the Desk. Cratty, Aaron, illus. 2006. 24p. (J). per. 10.95 ***(978-1-934246-05-4(0))*** Peppertree Pr., The.

Brisson, Pat. I Remember Miss Perry. Jorisch, Stephane, illus. 2006. 32p. (J). (ps). 16.99 (978-0-8037-2981-0(2) , Dial) Penguin Group (USA) Inc.

Brown, Marc. Arthur's Adventures Four Book Set: Arthur's Computer Disaster, Arthur's TV Troubles, Arthur's Teacher Troubles, Arthur's New Puppy. 2002. pap. 23.80 (978-0-316-16961-5(7)) Little Brown & Co.

—Arthur's Teacher Moves In. 2000. (Arthur Adventure Ser.). (Illus.). (J). 15.95 (978-0-316-11809-5(5)) Little Brown & Co.

—Arthur's Teacher Moves In. Brown, Marc, illus. 2000. (Arthur Adventure Ser.). (Illus.). 32p. (J). (ps-3). 15.95 (978-0-316-11979-5(2)) Little, Brown Bks. for Young Readers.

—Arthur's Teacher Moves In. 2000. (Arthur Adventure Ser.). (J). (gr. k-3). 15.95 (978-0-316-11856-9(7)) Little, Brown Bks. for Young Readers.

—Arthur's Teacher Trouble. ed. 2004. (Arthur Adventure Ser.). (J). (gr. k-3). spiral bd. (978-0-616-00406-7(0)); spiral bd. (978-0-616-01603-9(4)) Canadian National Institute for the Blind/Institut National Canadien pour les Aveugles.

—La Visita del Señor Rataquemada. Sarfatti, Esther, tr. from ENG. 2003. (SPA.). (J). (gr. k-2). pap. 6.95 (978-1-930332-41-6(6)) Lectorum Pubns., Inc.

—La Visita del Senor Rataquemada. 2003. (SPA.). (gr. k-3). lib. bdg. 15.25 (978-0-613-64613-0(4)) Tandem Library Bks.

Bunting, Eve. Our Teacher's Having a Baby. deGroat, Diane, illus. 2001. 32p. (J). (gr. k-3). pap. 6.95 (978-0-618-11138-1(7) , Clarion Bks.) Houghton Mifflin Co. Trade & Reference Div.

—Our Teacher's Having a Baby. 2001. (gr. k-3). lib. bdg. 14.10 (978-0-613-35547-6(4)); (Illus.). (J). (978-0-606-21372-1(4)) Tandem Library Bks.

Calamari, Barbara. The Trouble with Teachers. Brandt, Elizabeth, illus. 2001. (Angela Anaconda Ser.: Vol. 1). 64p. (J). (gr. 4-7). pap. 3.99 (978-0-689-83996-2(0) , Simon Spotlight) Simon & Schuster Children's Publishing.

Campbell, Bebe Moore. I Get So Hungry. Bates, Amy, illus. 2008. 32p. (J). (gr. 1-3). 16.99 ***(978-0-399-24311-0(9)*** , Putnam Juvenile) Penguin Group (USA) Inc.

Capeci, Anne. Now You See It. 2000. (gr. 3-6). lib. bdg. 12.40 (978-0-613-54061-2(1)) Tandem Library Bks.

Carabine, Sue. A Teacher's Night Before Christmas. Kawasaki, Shauna Mooney, illus. 2000. 60p. 5.95 (978-0-87905-764-0(5)) Gibbs Smith, Publisher.

Carney, Mary Lou. Tyler Timothy Bradford & the Birthday Surprise. Warren, Shari, illus. 2004. 32p. (J). 14.95 (978-0-7696-3168-4(1)) School Specialty Publishing.

Carson, Jana. We Both Read-Stop Teasing Taylor! Treatner, Meryl, illus. 2005. (J). ***(978-1-4156-3784-5(9))*** Book Wholesalers, Inc.

Caudwell, Sarah. Sibyl in Her Grave. 2001. (gr. 7-12). lib. bdg. 14.15 (978-0-613-36875-9(4)) Tandem Library Bks.

Cheng, Andrea. Where the Steps Were. 2008. (J). ***(978-1-932425-88-8(8)*** , Front Street) Boyds Mills Pr.

Clarke, Gus. What Would We Do Without Missus Mac. 1999. (Illus.). 24p. (J). 19.99 (978-0-86264-884-8(X)) Andersen GBR. *Dist:* Independent Pubs. Group.

Cleary, Beverly. Querido Senor Henshaw. 2003. (Ramona Collection). (SPA.). 136p. (J). 9.95 (978 84 239 9013 9(3)) Espasa Calpe, S.A. ESP. *Dist:* Planeta Publishing Corp.

Clements, Andrew. Frindle. Selznick, Brian, illus. l.t. ed. 2000. (LRS Large Print Cornerstone Ser.). 116p. (YA). (gr. 4-10). lib. bdg. 24.95 (978-1-58118-062-6(4) , 23476) LRS.

—Frindle. Selznick, Brian, illus. 105p. (J). (gr. 3-5). pap. 4.50 (978-0-8072-1522-7(8) , Listening Library) Random Hse. Audio Publishing Group.

—Frindle. unabr. ed. 2004. (Middle Grade Cassette Librariestm Ser.). 105p. (J). (gr. 3-7). pap. 29.00 incl. audio (978-0-8072-7994-6(3) , S YA 961 SP, Listening Library) Random Hse. Audio Publishing Group.

—Frindle. Selznick, Brian, illus. 1998. 112p. (J). (gr. 3-7). pap. 5.99 (978-0-689-81876-9(9) , Aladdin) Simon & Schuster Children's Publishing.

—Frindle. Selznick, Brian, illus. 1998. (J). 11.64 (978-0-606-12939-8(1)) Tandem Library Bks.

—Head of the Class: Frindle; the Landry News; the Janitor's Boy. Selznick, Brian, illus. 2007. 416p. (J). 17.99 ***(978-1-4169-4974-9(7)*** , Aladdin) Simon & Schuster Children's Publishing.

—Jake Drake, Class Clown. Frazee, Marla & Pedersen, Janet, illus. 2007. (Jake Drake Ser.). 96p. (J). pap. 4.99 ***(978-1-4169-4912-1(7)*** , Aladdin) Simon & Schuster Children's Publishing.

—The Landry News. Murdocca, Sal, illus. 2002. (J). 13.40 (978-0-7587-6519-2(3)) Book Wholesalers, Inc.

—The Landry News. Selznick, Brian, illus. 2000. 144p. (J). (gr. 3-7). pap. 5.99 (978-0-689-82868-3(3) , Aladdin) Simon & Schuster Children's Publishing.

—The Landry News. 2000. (gr. 3-6). lib. bdg. 13.00 (978-0-613-30001-8(7)); 1999. (J). (978-0-606-19720-5(6)) Tandem Library Bks.

—The Landry News. l.t. ed. 2000. (Juvenile Ser.). (Illus.). 138p. (J). (gr. 4-7). 21.95 (978-0-7862-2707-5(9)) Thorndike Pr.

—El Periodico Landry. Selznick, Brian, illus. 2004. Tr. of Landry News. (SPA.). (YA). pap. 9.99 (978-84-241-7886-4(6)) Everest de Ediciones y Distribucion, S.L. ESP. *Dist:* Lectorum Pubns., Inc.

Clements, Andrew. Teacher's Pet. Pedersen, Janet, illus. 2007. (Jake Drake Ser.). 96p. (J). pap. 4.99 ***(978-1-4169-3932-0(6)*** , Aladdin) Simon & Schuster Children's Publishing.

Clements, Andrew & Murdocca, Salvatore. The Landry News. 1999. (Illus.). 128p. (J). (gr. 3-7). 15.95 (978-0-689-81817-2(3)) Simon & Schuster Children's Publishing.

Cooper, Barbara. Emma Exclamation Point. Raynor, Maggie, illus. 2004. 32p. (J). lib. bdg. 23.33 (978-0-8368-4225-8(1)) Stevens, Gareth Inc.

Coville, Bruce. The Attack of the Two-Inch Teacher. unabr. ed. 2000. (I Was a Sixth Grade Alien Ser.). 165p. (J). (gr. 3-5). pap. 28.00 incl. audio (978-0-8072-8354-7(1) , YA170SP, Listening Library) Random Hse. Audio Publishing Group.

—The Attack of the Two-Inch Teacher. 1999. (I Was a Sixth Grade Alien Ser.). (Illus.). (J). 10.64 (978-0-606-18374-1(4)) Tandem Library Bks.

—My Teacher Fried My Brains. 2005. (Illus.). 136p. (J). ***(978-1-4156-1080-0(0)*** , Aladdin) Simon & Schuster Children's Publishing.

—My Teacher Glows in the Dark. 2005. (Illus.). 137p. (J). ***(978-1-4156-1081-7(9)*** , Aladdin) Simon & Schuster Children's Publishing.

Coville, Bruce. My Teacher Is an Alien. (My Teacher Is an Alien Ser.). 123p. (J). (Illus.). (J). (gr. 4-7). pap. 4.50 (978-0-8072-1528-9(7)); 2004. (gr. 3-6). pap. 29.00 incl. audio (978-0-8072-8029-4(1) , S YA 971 SP) Random Hse. Audio Publishing Group. (Listening Library).

—My Teacher Is an Alien. 2005. (Illus.). 123p. (J). ***(978-1-4156-1082-4(7)*** , Aladdin) Simon & Schuster Children's Publishing.

—My Teacher Is an Alien. Wimmer, Mike, illus. 2005. 124p. (J). (ps-7). lib. bdg. 12.04 (978-0-606-33889-9(6)) Tandem Library Bks.

Cox, Judy. Don't Be Silly, Mrs. Millie! Mathieu, Joe, illus. 2005. 32p. (J). (ps-2). 14.95 (978-0-7614-5166-2(8)) Cavendish, Marshall Corp.

Cox, Judy. Mrs. Millie Goes to Philly! Mathieu, Joseph, illus. 2008. (J). ***(978-0-7614-5372-7(5))*** Cavendish, Marshall Corp.

Creech, Sharon. A Fine, Fine School. Bliss, Harry, illus. 32p. (J). (ps-3). 2004. pap. 6.99 (978-0-06-000728-7(1) , Harper Trophy); 2001. 16.99 (978-0-06-027736-9(X) , Cotler, Joanna Books) HarperCollins Pubs.

—A Fine, Fine School. 2003. (Live Oak Readalong Ser.). (Illus.). (J). pap. 16.95 incl. audio (978-1-59112-220-3(1)) Live Oak Media.

—Fine Fine School. 2004. (Live Oak Readalong Ser.). (Illus.). (J). (ps-2). audio compact disk 18.95 (978-1-59112-497-9(2)) Live Oak Media.

—A Fine, Fine School. ed. 2004. (Illus.). (J). (gr. k-3). spiral bd. (978-0-616-11107-9(X)) Canadian National Institute for the Blind/Institut National Canadien pour les Aveugles.

—A Fine, Fine School. Bliss, Harry, illus. ed. 2004. (J). (gr. k-3). spiral bd. (978-0-616-11106-2(1)) Canadian National Institute for the Blind/Institut National Canadien pour les Aveugles.

Croft, Louise. What's Inside Miss Molly's Locket? Baldwin, Sherri Buck, illus. 2000. 32p. (J). 16.00 (978-0-7412-0825-5(3)) Lang Graphics, Ltd.

Croteau, Marie-Danielle. Gabby's School by the Sea. Casson, Sophie, illus. 2005. (Read-It! Readers Ser.). 32p. (J). (gr. k-3). 18.60 (978-1-4048-1072-3(2)) Picture Window Bks.

Cummings, Priscilla. What Mr. Mattero Did. 224p. (J). 2007. (gr. 3). pap. 6.99 (978-0-14-240856-8(5) , Puffin); 2005. (gr. 5-9). 16.99 (978-0-525-47621-4(0) , Dutton Juvenile) Penguin Group (USA) Inc.

Cutler, Jane. Spaceman. 1999. (978-0-606-16980-6(6)) Tandem Library Bks.

Dadey, Debbie. The Worst Name in Third Grade. 2007. 80p. (J). pap. 3.99 ***(978-0-439-72000-7(1))*** Scholastic, Inc.

Dadey, Debbie & Jones, Marcia Thornton. Mrs. Jeepers' Scariest Halloween Ever. Gurney, John Steven, illus. 2005. 103p. (J). (978-1-4156-2066-3(0)) Scholastic, Inc.

Dagg, Stephanie. Oh Teacher! 2001. (Illus.). 48p. (J). (gr. 1-4). per. (978-1-84210-130-8(7)) Mentor Bks.

Danneberg, Julie. First Day Jitters. Love, Judith DuFour, illus. 2000. 32p. (J). (gr. k-4). 16.95 (978-1-58089-054-0(7)) Charlesbridge Publishing, Inc.

—First Day Jitters. Love, Judy, illus. 2000. 32p. (J). (gr. k-4). pap. 6.95 (978-1-58089-061-8(X)) Charlesbridge Publishing, Inc.

—First Day Jitters. 2000. (gr. k-3). lib. bdg. 15.25 (978-0-613-34040-3(X)); (Illus.). (J). 13.75 (978-0-606-18748-0(0)) Tandem Library Bks.

—First Year Letters. Love, Judy, illus. 2003. 32p. (J). (gr. k-4). 16.95 (978-1-58089-084-7(9)) Charlesbridge Publishing, Inc.

—First Year Letters. Love, Judith DuFour, illus. 2003. 32p. (J). (gr. k-4). pap. 6.95 (978-1-58089-085-4(7)) Charlesbridge Publishing, Inc.

—First Year Letters. 2003. (gr. k-3). lib. bdg. 15.25 (978-0-613-62443-5(2)) Tandem Library Bks.

—Last Day Blues. Love, Judy, illus. 2006. 32p. (J). pap. 6.95 (978-1-58089-104-2(7)) Charlesbridge Publishing, Inc.

Danziger, Paula. The Cat Ate My Gymsuit. 2006. 160p. (J). (gr. 5). pap. 5.99 (978-0-14-240654-0(6) , Puffin) Penguin Group (USA) Inc.

—The Cat Ate My Gymsuit. 1998. (Illus.). 147p. (J). (ps-7). lib. bdg. 14.30 (978-0-88103-336-6(7)) Tandem Library Bks.

—The Cat Ate My Gymsuit. l.t. ed. 2005. 174p. 22.95 (978-0-7862-7310-2(0)) Thorndike Pr.

Day, Marlis. Curriculum Murders: A Margo Brown Mystery. 2004. 192p. 12.95 (978-1-56315-316-7(5)) Sterling-House Pubs., Inc.

DeBray, Sherry. The Teacher's Gift. Cauthen, Tommy, illus. 2004. 30p. ***(978-1-59421-007-5(1))*** Seacoast Publishing, Inc.

Decker, Wendy. The Bedazzling Bowl. 2006. pap. 13.99 ***(978-1-60034-468-8(2))*** Xulon Pr., Inc.

Derby, Sally. The Wacky Substitute. Herbert, Jennifer, illus. 2005. 32p. (J). (gr. k-3). 14.95 (978-0-7614-5219-5(2)) Cavendish, Marshall Corp.

—Whoosh Went the Wind! Nguyen, Vincent, illus. 2006. 32p. (J). 16.99 (978-0-7614-5309-3(1)) Cavendish, Marshall Corp.

DiPucchio, Kelly. Mrs. Mcbloom, Clean up Your Classroom! Francis, Guy, illus. 2005. 32p. (gr. k-3). 15.99 (978-0-7868-0932-5(9)) Hyperion Bks. for Children.

Du Bois, William Pene. Twenty-One Balloons. Du Bois, William Pene, illus. 2005. (Illus.). 180p. (J). lib. bdg. 15.00 ***(978-1-4242-2270-4(2))*** Fitzgerald Bks.

Durkee, Sarah. The Fruit Bowl Project. 2006. 160p. (J). (gr. 5-8). 14.95 (978-0-385-73289-5(9)); lib. bdg. 16.99 (978-0-385-90310-3(3)) Random Hse. Children's Bks. (Delacorte Bks. for Young Readers).

Durkee, Sarah. The Fruit Bowl Project: Fifty Ways to Tell a Story. 2007. 160p. (J). (gr. 5). 5.99 ***(978-0-385-73385-4(2)*** , Yearling) Random Hse. Children's Bks.

Dyer, K. C. Ms. Zephyr's Notebook. 2007. 206p. (YA). pap. 12.99 ***(978-1-55002-691-7(7)*** , Boardwalk Bks.) Dundurn Group, The CAN. *Dist:* Univ. of Toronto Pr.

Edwards, Pamela Duncan. Ms. Bitsy Bat's Kindergarten. Cole, Henry, illus. 2005. (J). ***(978-1-4156-2782-2(7))*** Hyperion Bks. for Children.

Esham, Barbaraa. Mrs. Gorski, I Think I Have the Wiggle Fidgets. Gordon, Mike, illus. 2007. (ENG, SPA & FRE.). 32p. (J). 16.99 ***(978-1-60336-469-0(2))*** Mainstream Connections, Inc.

Evangelista, Beth. Gifted. 192p. (J). 2007. pap. 6.95 ***(978-0-8027-9644-8(3));*** 2005. (gr. 5-9). 16.95 (978-0-8027-8994-5(3)) Walker & Co.

Figley, Marty Rhodes. The Schoolchildren's Blizzard. Haas, Shelly O., illus. 2004. (On My Own History Ser.). 48p. (J). lib. bdg. 23.93 (978-1-57505-586-2(4) , Carolrhoda Bks.) Lerner Publishing Group.

Finchler, Judy. Miss Malarkey Won't Be in Today. O'Malley, Kevin, illus. 2000. 32p. (J). (gr. k-4). reprint ed. pap. 6.95 (978-0-8027-7591-7(8)) Walker & Co.

Finchler, Judy & O'Malley, Kevin. Miss Malarkey Leaves No Reader Behind. O'Malley, Kevin, illus. 2006. (Illus.). 32p. (J). 16.95 (978-0-8027-8084-3(9)) Walker & Co.

—Miss Malarkey's Field Trip. 2006. (Illus.). 32p. (J). pap. 6.95 (978-0-8027-8917-4(X)) Walker & Co.

—Miss Malarkey's Field Trip. O'Malley, Kevin, illus. 2004. (Illus.). 32p. (J). 16.95 (978-0-8027-8912-9(9)) Walker & Co.

Flake, Sharon G. The Skin I'm In. 1999. 176p. (gr. 5-17). 14.95 (978-0-7868-0444-3(0)) Hyperion Pr.

—The Skin I'm In. 2000. 171p. (J). (gr. 5-9). lib. bdg. 13.94 (978-0-606-17605-7(5)) Tandem Library Bks.

—Skin I'm In. 2000. (gr. 5-8). lib. bdg. 14.15 (978-0-613-28643-5(X)) Tandem Library Bks.

—The Skin I'm In. l.t. ed. 1999. 173p. (J). (gr. 7-12). 20.95 (978-0-7862-2179-0(8)) Thorndike Pr.

Fleming, Candace. The Fabled Fourth Graders of Aesop Elementary School. 2007. 192p. (J). (gr. 2-6). lib. bdg. 18.99 ***(978-0-375-93672-2(6)*** , Schwartz & Wade Bks.) Random Hse. Children's Bks.

Fletcher, Ralph J. Flying Solo. 1998. (Illus.). 144p. (J). (gr. 4-6). tchr. ed. 15.00 (978-0-395-87323-6(1) , Clarion Bks.) Houghton Mifflin Co. Trade & Reference Div.

—Flying Solo. 2000. (gr. 5-8). lib. bdg. 13.00 (978-0-613-28491-2(7)) Tandem Library Bks.

Fox, Mem. Fairy, Fairy Quite Contrary. Swearingen, Greg, illus. 2005. (J). (978-0-15-202260-0(0)) Holt, Rinehart & Winston.

Frank, E. R. Friction. 208p. (YA). 2003. (Illus.). 16.95 (978-0-689-85384-5(X) , Atheneum/Richard Jackson Bks.); 2004. reprint ed. pap. 6.99 (978-0-689-85385-2(8) , Simon Pulse) Simon & Schuster Children's Publishing.

Friedrich, Joachim. The Disappearing Bio Teacher. Bk. 2. 2001. (4 1/2 Friends Mysteries Ser.). (Illus.). 160p. (gr. 3-7). 14.99 (978-0-7868-0698-0(2) , Volo) Hyperion Bks. for Children.

—The Disappearing Bio Teacher. Date not set. (Illus.). 144p. (J). (gr. 3-7). 14.99 (978-0-7868-0700-0(8)) Hyperion Pr.

—4 1/2 Friends: And the Disappearing Bio Teacher. Crawford, Elizabeth D., tr. from GER. 2001. 144p. (J). lib. bdg. 15.49 (978-0-7868-2588-2(X) , Volo) Hyperion Bks. for Children.

Fuller, Mary. Tattletale, Tattletail. 2007. 32p. (J). per. 10.99 ***(978-1-60247-303-4(X))*** Tate Publishing & Enterprises, L.L.C.

Gallegos, Manuel. El Cisne y la Luna. 2001. (YA). (978-956-240-301-6(7)) Arrayan Editores S.A.

Garland, Michael. Miss Smith Reads Again! Garland, Michael, illus. 2006. (Illus.). 32p. (J). (ps). 15.99 (978-0-525-47722-8(5) , Dutton Juvenile) Penguin Group (USA) Inc.

—Miss Smith Reads Again! 2006. (Illus.). (J). ***(978-1-4156-8098-8(1)*** , Dutton Juvenile) Penguin Group (USA) Inc.

Garland, Michael. Miss Smith's Incredible Storybook. Garland, Michael, illus. 32p. (J). 2005. pap. 6.99 (978-0-14-240282-5(6) , Puffin); 2003. (Illus.). 16.99 (978-0-525-47133-2(2) , Dutton Juvenile) Penguin Group (USA) Inc.

—Miss Smith's Incredible Storybook. 2007. 27.95 incl. audio ***(978-0-8045-6945-3(2));*** 29.95 incl. audio compact disk ***(978-0-8045-4159-6(0))*** Spoken Arts, Inc.

Giff, Patricia Reilly. Horas de Sol. 2000. Tr. of Sunny Side Up. (SPA.). (YA). (gr. 1 up). 3.95 (978-0-922852-48-2(0)) AIMS International Bks., Inc.

Grant, Vicki. Pigboy. 2006. 112p. (J). pap. 8.95 (978-1-55143-643-2(4)); lib. bdg. 14.95 (978-1-55143-666-1(3)) Orca Bk. Pubs. USA.

Greenburg, Dan. My Teacher Ate My Homework, Vol. 27. Davis, Jack E., illus. 2002. (Zack Files Ser.: 27). 64p. (J). pap. 4.99 (978-0-448-42683-9(8) , Grosset & Dunlap) Penguin Group (USA) Inc.

—My Teacher Ate My Homework. 2002. (gr. 3-6). lib. bdg. 13.00 (978-0-613-61645-4(6)) Tandem Library Bks.

Greene, Stephanie. Show & Tell. Clayton, Elaine, illus. 2001. 96p. (J). (gr. 7). pap. 3.99 (978-0-439-14553-4(8)) Scholastic, Inc.

Griffith, Amanda. Two Truths & a Lie. 2006. pap. 15.95 ***(978-1-4259-4458-2(2))*** AuthorHouse.

Guest, Elissa Haden. Iris & Walter & the Substitute Teacher. Davenier, Christine, tr. Davenier, Christine, illus. 2004. (Iris & Walter Ser.). 44p. (J). 15.00 (978-0-15-205013-9(2) , Gulliver Bks.) Harcourt Children's Bks.

Gutman, Dan. Miss Daisy Is Crazy! Paillot, Jim, illus. 2004. (My Weird School Ser.: Bk. 1). 96p. (J). pap. 3.99 (978-0-06-050700-8(4)) HarperCollins Pubs.

—Miss Holly Is Too Jolly! Paillot, Jim, illus. 2006. (My Weird School Ser.: No. 14). 112p. (J). pap. 3.99 (978-0-06-085382-4(4) , Harper Trophy) HarperCollins Pubs.

—Miss Suki Is Kooky! Paillot, Jim, illus. 2007. (My Weird School Ser.: No. 17). 112p. (J). pap. 3.99 ***(978-0-06-123473-6(7)*** , Harper Trophy); lib. bdg. 15.89 ***(978-0-06-123474-3(5))*** HarperCollins Pubs.

—Mr. Docker Is off His Rocker! Paillot, Jim, illus. 2006. (My Weird School Ser.). 112p. (J). pap. 3.99 (978-0-06-082227-9(9) , Harper Trophy); lib. bdg. 15.89 (978-0-06-082228-6(7)) HarperCollins Pubs.

—Mr. Hynde Is Out of His Mind! Paillot, Jim, illus. 2005. 97p. (J). (ps-k). lib. bdg. 10.64 (978-0-606-33934-6(5)) Tandem Library Bks.

—Mrs. Roopy Is Loopy! Paillot, Jim, illus. 2004. (My Weird School Ser.: Bk. 3). 96p. (J). lib. bdg. 15.89 (978-0-06-050705-3(5)) HarperCollins Pubs.

—Mrs. Yonkers Is Bonkers! 2007. (My Weird School Ser.: No. 18). 112p. (J). lib. bdg. 15.89 ***(978-0-06-123476-7(1))*** HarperCollins Pubs.

—Mrs. Yonkers Is Bonkers! Paillot, Jim, illus. 2007. (My Weird School Ser.: No. 18). 112p. (J). pap. 3.99 ***(978-0-06-123475-0(3)*** , Harper Trophy) HarperCollins Pubs.

—Ms. Hannah Is Bananas! Paillot, Jim, illus. 2004. (My Weird School Ser.: Bk. 4). 96p. (J). pap. 3.99 (978-0-06-050706-0(3) , Harper Trophy); lib. bdg. 15.89 (978-0-06-050707-7(1)) HarperCollins Pubs.

Gutman, Dan. My Weird School #21: Ms. Krup Cracks Me Up! 2008. (My Weird School Ser.). 112p. (J). pap. 3.99 ***(978-0-06-134605-7(5)*** , Harper Trophy); lib. bdg. 15.89 ***(978-0-06-134606-4(3))*** HarperCollins Pubs.

Hagen, Michael. The African Term. Kemnitz, Myrna, ed. 1998. 81p. (YA). (gr. 8 up). 9.99 (978-0-88092-368-2(7)) Royal Fireworks Publishing Co.

Hall, Kirsten. First Day of School: All about Shapes & Sizes. Luedecke, Bev, illus. 2003. (Beastieville Ser.). 32p. (J). (ps-1). 19.50 (978-0-516-22893-8(5) , Children's Pr.) Scholastic Library Publishing.

Hallinan, P. K. My Teacher's My Friend. Hallinan, P. K., illus. 1999. (Illus.). 24p. (ps-3). 6.95 (978-1-57102-155-7(8)) Warehousing & Fulfillment Specialists, LLC (WFS, LLC).

Hallinan, P. K., illus. My Teacher's My Friend. 2001. 24p. (J). 7.95 (978-0-8249-5309-6(6) , Ideals) Ideals Pubns.

Hamilton, Richard. Let's Take over the Kindergarten. Heap, Sue, illus. 2007. 32p. (J). (ps-1). 15.95 (978-1-58234-707-3(7)) Bloomsbury Publishing.

Harcourt School Publishers Staff. The New Teacher: Take-Home Book. 1999. (Signatures Ser.). (Illus.). (J). pap. 1.90 (978-0-15-313916-1(1)) Harcourt Schl. Pubs.

Harper, Charise Mericle. Still Just Grace. Harper, Charise Mericle, illus. 2007. (Illus.). 152p. (J). (gr. 3-5). 15.00 ***(978-0-618-64643-2(4))*** Houghton Mifflin Co. Trade & Reference Div.

Harper, Jamie. Miss Mingo & the First Day of School. Harper, Jamie, illus. 2006. (Illus.). 32p. (J). (ps-2). 15.99 (978-0-7636-2410-1(1)) Candlewick Pr.

—Miss Mingo & the First Day of School. 2006. (Illus.). 26p. (J). ***(978-1-4156-9174-8(6))*** Candlewick Pr.

Harris, Valerie F. & Jones, Eula V. My Teacher Doesn't Like Me. Date not set. 22p. (J). (gr. k-6). pap. (978-1-889654-00-3(0)) Enricharamics, Inc.

Harriton, Maxine. A School Trip to the Fruit Planet, 1. l.t. ed. 2006. 34p. (J). (ps-1). lib. bdg. 18.95 (978-0-9787248-0-1(1) , 00-01-851-447X) UpTree Publishing.

Havill, Juanita. Jamaica & the Substitute Teacher. O'Brien, Anne Sibley, illus. 2001. 32p. (J). (gr. k-3). 6.95 (978-0-618-15242-1(3)) Houghton Mifflin Co. Trade & Reference Div.

—Jamaica & the Substitute Teacher. 1999. (gr. k-3). lib. bdg. 14.10 (978-0-613-44221-3(0)) Tandem Library Bks.

Hayes, Rosemary. The Amazing Mr Mulch. 2005. (Cambridge Storybooks Ser.). (Illus.). 32p. pap. 7.00 (978-0-521-67479-9(4)) Cambridge Univ. Pr.

—The Magic Sword. 2005. (Cambridge Storybooks Ser.). 32p. pap. 7.00 (978-0-521-67475-1(1)) Cambridge Univ. Pr.

Henderson, Lyndsey. Dino. 2001. (Teacher's Pet Ser.). 48p. (J). 4.95 (978-0-439-17344-5(2)) Scholastic, Inc.

T U V

Henkes, Kevin. Chrysanthemum. unabr. ed. 1998. (J). (ps-2). 24.95 incl. audio (978-0-7882-0672-6(9) , HRA369); pap. 14.95 incl. audio (978-0-7882-0675-7(3) , PRA369) Weston Woods Studios, Inc.

—The Lilly Book & Toy Box. 1998. (Illus.). 160p. (J). 24.95 (978-0-688-16437-9(4) , Harper Festival) HarperCollins Pubs.

—Lilly's Big Day. Henkes, Kevin, illus. 2006. (Illus.). 40p. (J). 16.99 (978-0-06-074236-2(4)); lib. bdg. 17.89 (978-0-06-074237-9(2)) HarperCollins Pubs.

—Lilly's Purple Plastic Purse. Henkes, Kevin, illus. 10th anniv. ed. 2006. (Illus.). 40p. (J). (ps-3). 16.99 (978-0-688-12897-5(1)) HarperCollins Pubs.

—Lilly's Purple Plastic Purse. Henkes, Kevin, illus. (Illus.). pap. incl. audio (978-0-87499-688-3(0)); pap. 18.95 incl. audio compact disk (978-1-59112-347-7(X)); pap. incl. audio compact disk (978-1-59112-557-0(X)); pap. 16.95 incl. audio (978-0-87499-686-9(4)); 2000. (J). pap. 28.95 incl. audio compact disk (978-1-59112-348-4(8)) Live Oak Media.

—Lily y Su Bolso de Plastico Morado. Mlawer, Teresa, tr. 2001. (SPA., Illus.). 32p. (J). (gr. k-2). 8.99 (978-84-241-7984-7(6) , EV3112) Everest de Ediciones y Distribucion, S.L. ESP. *Dist:* Lectorum Pubns., Inc.

—Lily y Su Bolso de Plastico Morado. 2001. (Illus.). (J). (978-0-606-20767-6(8)) Tandem Library Bks.

Henson, Heather & Wilkins, Celia. A Little House of Their Own. Andreasen, Dan, illus. 2005. (Little House Ser.). 320p. (J). 16.99 (978-0-06-027009-4(8)) HarperCollins Pubs.

Herman, Gail. I've Got the Back-to-School Blues. Peterson, Stacy, illus. 2002. (All Aboard Reading Ser.). 48p. (J). pap. 3.99 (978-0-448-42832-1(6) , Grosset & Dunlap) Penguin Group (USA) Inc.

—I've Got the Back-to-School Blues. 2002. (gr. k-3). lib. bdg. 11.80 (978-0-613-45285-4(2)) Tandem Library Bks.

Herrick, Steven. Naked Bunyip Dancing. Norling, Beth, illus. 2008. (J). (*978-1-59078-499-0(5) , Front Street) Boyds Mills Pr.

Hill, Kirkpatrick. The Year of Miss Agnes. 2002. 128p. (J). (ps-7). mass mkt. 4.99 (978-0-689-85124-7(3) , Aladdin) Simon & Schuster Children's Publishing.

—The Year of Miss Agnes. Knorr, Peter, illus. 2000. 128p. (J). (gr. 3-7). 16.00 (978-0-689-82933-8(7) , McElderry, Margaret K.) Simon & Schuster Children's Publishing.

—The Year of Miss Agnes. 2002. (gr. 3-6). lib. bdg. 13.00 (978-0-613-53884-8(6)) Tandem Library Bks.

Hilton, James. Goodbye, Mr. Chips. 2004. 144p. (J). (gr. 7-17). mass mkt. 5.99 (978-0-316-01013-9(8)) Little Brown & Co.

Hortten, Jacqueline Faye. Pu Beach. l.t. ed. 2004. (Illus.). 27p. (J). pap. 14.95 (978-0-9728393-0-3(5)) Children's Bookshoppe Stop, The.

Howe, James. Day the Teacher Went Bananas. 1999. (Illus.). (J). (gr. k-3). lib. bdg. 14.15 (978-0-8335-0697-9(8)) Tandem Library Bks.

Hubbell, Will. Snow Day Dance. Hubbell, Will, illus. 2005. (Illus.). 32p. (J). (gr. 5-8). 16.95 (978-0-8075-7523-9(2)) Whitman, Albert & Co.

Irwin, Jacqueline. Secrets of Seacrest School. 2005. 85p. pap. 14.95 (978-1-4137-6363-8(4)) PublishAmerica, Inc.

James, Brian. The Fishy Field Trip. Woodman, Ned, illus. 2007. (Catkid Ser.: Bk. 2). 96p. (J). pap. 3.99 (*978-0-439-88855-4(7)) Scholastic, Inc.

Jane, Pamela. Milo & the Flapjack Fiasco! Johnson, Meredith, ed. Johnson, Meredith, tr. 2004. (Illus.). 32p. (J). 13.95 (978-1-59336-113-6(0)); pap. (978-1-59336-114-3(9)) Mondo Publishing.

Jeffs, Stephanie. It's Mine, Christopher Bear! Thomas, Jacqui, illus. 2004. (Christopher Bear Ser.). 32p. 5.99 (978-0-8066-4400-4(1) , Augsburg Bks.) Augsburg Fortress, Pubs.

Jocelyn, Marthe. Mable Riley: A Reliable Record of Humdrum, Peril, & Romance. 2007. 288p. (J). (gr. 5). 6.99 (978-0-7636-3287-8(2)) Candlewick Pr.

Johnson, Doug. Substitute Teacher Plans. Smith, Tammy, illus. rev. ed. 2002. 32p. (J). (gr. k-3). 16.95 (978-0-8050-6520-6(2) , Holt, Henry & Co. Bks. For Young Readers) Holt, Henry & Co.

Johnson, Michael. The Most Special Person. Latta, Doug, illus. 1999. 24p. (J). (gr. k-6). 12.95 (978-1-893672-00-0(X)) Johnson, Michael Presentations.

Katar, Al. Captain Scratch: Island of Sirmanj. 2007. (J). (*978-1-934035-31-3(9)) Trent's Prints.

Katz, T. Miss L'eau. 2007. 44p. (YA). pap. 14.99 (978-1-59092-404-4(5) , Blue Works) Windstorm Creative.

Keene, Carolyn. Alien in the Classroom. Acardo, Anthony, illus. 2004. 72p. (J). lib. bdg. 15.00 (*978-1-4242-0369-7(4)) Fitzgerald Bks.

—Alien in the Classroom. 1998. (Nancy Drew Notebooks: No. 23). (Illus.). 80p. (J). (gr. k-3). pap. 3.99 (978-0-671-00818-5(8) , Aladdin) Simon & Schuster Children's Publishing.

—Alien in the Classroom. 1998. (Nancy Drew Notebooks: No. 23). (J). (gr. k-3). 10.79 (978-0-606-13653-2(3)) Tandem Library Bks.

Kenah, Katharine. The Best Teacher in Second Grade. Carter, Abby, illus. 2007. (I Can Read Bks.). 48p. (J). pap. 3.99 (*978-0-06-053566-7(0) , Harper Trophy) HarperCollins Pubs.

Kendall, Sydney. A Turn for de Wurst. 318p. (J). (gr. 3-5). 9.99 (978-0-88092-461-0(6)) Royal Fireworks Publishing Co.

Kindl, Patrice. Owl in Love. 2004. 224p. (YA). (gr. 7 up). pap. 6.99 (978-0-618-43910-2(2) , Graphia) Houghton Mifflin Co. Trade & Reference Div.

—Owl in Love. unabr. ed. 1998. (J). Class Set. 102.80 incl. audio (978-0-7887-2562-3(9) , 46732); Homework Set. 49.75 incl. audio (978-0-7887-2106-9(2) , 40701) Recorded Bks., LLC.

King, Seth David. The Substitute Teacher Named Mr King. Clark, Matthew Levi, illus. 2005. 24p. (gr. 2-6). 12.00 (978-0-9640837-6-9(0)) Ascension Education.

Kleinberg, Naomi. Elmo's World: Teachers! Nelson, Mary Beth, illus. 2007. 12p. (J). (gr. k-ps). bds. 4.99 (*978-0-375-83788-3(4) , Random Hse. Bks. for Young Readers) Random Hse. Children's Bks.

Kline, Suzy. Horrible Harry & the Dungeon. 1998. (Horrible Harry Ser.: No. 7). (Illus.). 64p. (J). (gr. 2-4). pap. 3.99 (978-0-14-038620-2(3) , Puffin) Penguin Group (USA) Inc.

—Horrible Harry Takes the Cake. Remkiewicz, Frank, illus. (Horrible Harry Ser.). 64p. (J). (gr. 2). 2007. 3.99 (*978-0-14-240939-8(1) , Puffin); 2006. 13.99 (978-0-670-06075-7(5) , Viking Juvenile) Penguin Group (USA) Inc.

Kline, Suzy. Marvin & the Mean Words. 1998. (J). (978-0-606-13599-3(5)) Tandem Library Bks.

Konigsburg, E. L. Throwing Shadows. 1998. 160p. (J). (gr. 5-9). pap. 5.99 (978-0-689-82120-2(4) , Aladdin) Simon & Schuster Children's Publishing.

—The View from Saturday. Konigsburg, E. L., illus. 2002. (Illus.). (J). 25.11 (978-0-7587-0221-0(3)) Book Wholesalers, Inc.

—The View from Saturday. 2000. (J). 11.95 (978-1-56137-936-1(0)) Novel Units, Inc.

—The View from Saturday. 280p. (YA). (gr. 5 up). pap. 4.95 (978-0-8072-1511-1(2) , Listening Library) Random Hse. Audio Publishing Group.

—The View from Saturday. 1998. (Jean Karl Bks.). 176p. (J). (gr. 3-7). reprint ed. pap. 5.99 (978-0-689-81721-2(5) , Aladdin) Simon & Schuster Children's Publishing.

—The View from Saturday. 1998. (J). (978-0-606-13063-9(2)) Tandem Library Bks.

Kremer, Kevin. Santa's Our Substitute Teacher. 2006. 150p. pap. 5.99 (978-0-9663335-4-1(3) , 703-001) Snow In Sarasota Publishing.

Krensky, Stephen. My Teacher's Secret Life. Adinolfi, JoAnn, illus. 1999. 32p. (J). (ps-1). pap. 6.99 (978-0-689-82982-6(5) , Aladdin) Simon & Schuster Children's Publishing.

—My Teacher's Secret Life. 1999. (J). (978-0-606-17317-9(X)) Tandem Library Bks.

Kress, Adrienne. Alex & the Ironic Gentleman. 2007. 320p. (YA). (gr. 3-7). 16.95 (*978-1-60286-005-6(X)) Weinstein Bks.

Krulik, Nancy E. Anyone but Me, No. 1. John and Wendy Staff, illus. 2006. (Katie Kazoo, Switcheroo Ser.: No. 1). 80p. (J). 2.99 (978-0-448-44259-4(0) , Grosset & Dunlap) Penguin Group (USA) Inc.

—Doggone It!, No. 8. John and Wendy Staff, illus. 2003. (Katie Kazoo, Switcheroo Ser.: No. 8). 80p. (J). (gr. 2-4). pap. 3.99 (978-0-448-43172-7(6) , Grosset & Dunlap) Penguin Group (USA) Inc.

—Doggone It!, No. 8. 2003. (Katie Kazoo, Switcheroo Ser.: No. 8). (gr. 3-6). lib. bdg. 11.80 (978-0-613-67541-3(X)) Tandem Library Bks.

—Flower Power, No. 27. 2008. (Katie Kazoo, Switcheroo Ser.: No. 27). 80p. (J). (gr. 2-5). 3.99 (*978-0-448-44674-5(X) , Grosset & Dunlap) Penguin Group (USA) Inc.

Krulik, Nancy E. No Messin' with My Lesson, No. 11. John and Wendy Staff, illus. 2004. (Katie Kazoo, Switcheroo Ser.: No.. 11). 80p. (J). (gr. 2-6). pap. 3.99 (978-0-448-43357-8(5) , Grosset & Dunlap) Penguin Group (USA) Inc.

—No Messin' with My Lesson, No. 11. 2004. (Katie Kazoo, Switcheroo Ser.: No. 11). (gr. 3-6). lib. bdg. 11.80 (978-0-613-72569-9(7)) Tandem Library Bks.

Kuroda, Yosuke & Hayashiya, Shizuru. Onegai Teacher, No. 2. 2003. 120p. pap. 9.95 (978-1-58899-179-9(2)) ComicsOne Corp./Dr. Masters.

Kurzweil, Allen. Leon & the Champion Chip. Bertholf, Bret, illus. 2007. 352p. (J). pap. 6.99 (*978-0-06-053935-1(6) , Harper Trophy) HarperCollins Pubs.

Laminack, Lester L. Snow Day! 2007. 32p. (J). (ps-3). 16.95 (*978-1-56145-418-1(4) , Peachtree Junior) Peachtree Pubs., Ltd.

Lawrence, Jan. Revenge of the Substitute Teacher. 1998. (978-0-606-13739-3(4)) Tandem Library Bks.

—The Revenge of the Substitute Teacher. 1998. (J). (gr. 3-7). pap. 4.50 (978-0-590-05902-2(5) , Scholastic Paperbacks) Scholastic, Inc.

Lems, Kristin. Piano Teacher's Daughter. Daoudi, Karima Lems & Daoudi, Kennan Lems, illus. 2002. pap. 18.00 (978-0-9637048-2-5(6)) Lems-Dworkin, Carol Pubs.

Leppard, Lois Gladys. The Mysterious Teacher. 2003. 160p. (J). mass mkt. 4.99 (978-1-889893-98-3(6) , Ambassador-Emerald, International) Emerald Hse. Group, Inc.

Leuck, Laura. My Creature Teacher. Nash, Scott, illus. 2004. 32p. (J). (ps-1). 15.99 (978-0-06-029694-0(1)) HarperCollins Pubs.

Levchuk, Lisa. Everything Beautiful in the World. 2008. (YA). (*978-0-374-32238-0(4)) Farrar, Straus & Giroux.

Lewis, Beverly. Straight-A Teacher. 2002. (Holly's Heart Ser.: Bk. 8). 160p. (YA). pap. 6.99 (978-0-7642-2615-1(0)) Bethany Hse. Pubs.

Lisle, Janet Taylor. Sirens & Spies. O'Rourke, Ericka, illus. 2002. 176p. (J). (gr. 5 up). pap. 4.99 (978-0-689-84457-7(3) , Aladdin) Simon & Schuster Children's Publishing.

Lodi, Mario. Cipi. 2000. (SPA., Illus.). 116p. (J). pap. (978-84-204-4779-7(X)) Aguilar, S. A. de Ediciones-Grupo Santillana.

Luddy, Karon. Spelldown: The Big-Time Dreams of a Small-Town Word Whiz. 2007. 224p. (YA). 15.99 (978-1-4169-1610-9(5)) Simon & Schuster Children's Publishing.

Lynch, Janet Nichols. Peace Is a Four-Letter Word. 2005. 168p. (YA). pap. 9.95 (978-1-59714-014-0(7) , Great Valley Bks.) Heyday Bks.

Maccarone, Grace. Mr. Rover Takes Over. 2000. (gr. k-3). lib. bdg. 11.80 (978-0-613-35537-7(7)) Tandem Library Bks.

MacDonald, Amy. No More Nasty. Smith, Cat Bowman, illus. 2001. 176p. (J). (gr. 3-7). 16.00 (978-0-374-35529-6(0) , Farrar, Straus & Giroux (BYR)) Farrar, Straus & Giroux.

Madonna. Las Manzanas Del Sr. Peabody. Long, Loren, illus. 2003. Tr. of Mr. Peabody's Apples. (SPA.). 32p. (J). 19.95 (978-0-439-62279-0(4) , Scholastic en Espanol) Scholastic, Inc.

Maguire, Gregory. Four Stupid Cupids. Clayton, Elaine, illus. 2001. 192p. (J). (gr. 4-6). tchr. ed. 16.00 (978-0-395-83895-2(9) , Clarion Bks.) Houghton Mifflin Co. Trade & Reference Div.

—Four Stupid Cupids. 2002. (gr. 3-6). lib. bdg. 12.95 (978-0-613-43035-7(2)) Tandem Library Bks.

—Four Stupid Cupids. l.t. ed. 2001. 225p. (J). 21.95 (978-0-7862-3547-6(0)) Thorndike Pr.

Maguire, Gregory. One Final Firecracker. 2007. (Hamlet Chronicles Ser.). 320p. (J). pap. 6.99 (*978-0-06-085284-9(4) , Harper Trophy) HarperCollins Pubs.

—One Final Firecracker. Clayton, Elaine, illus. 2005. 240p. (J). (gr. 4-6). 17.00 (978-0-618-27480-2(4) , Clarion Bks.) Houghton Mifflin Co. Trade & Reference Div.

Mahy, Margaret. Very Wicked Headmistress. Chamberlain, Margaret, illus. 2006. 94p. (J). pap. 6.95 (978-1-903015-46-9(4)) Barn Owl Bks, London GBR. *Dist:* Independent Pubs. Group.

Marshall, Catherine. Midnight Rescue/the Proposal/Christy's Choice. 2005. (Christy Juvenile Ser.). 384p. (J). pap. 9.99 (978-1-4003-0773-9(2)) Nelson, Thomas Inc.

—The Princess Club/Family Secrets/Mountain Madness. 2005. (Christy Juvenile Ser.). 368p. (J). pap. 9.99 (978-1-4003-0774-6(0)) Nelson, Thomas Inc.

—Stage Fright/Goodbye, Sweet Prince/Brotherly Love. 2005. (Christy Juvenile Ser.). 368p. (J). (gr. 4-7). pap. 9.99 (978-1-4003-0775-3(9)) Nelson, Thomas Inc.

Marshall, James, illus. Miss Nelson Has a Field Day. 2002. (Miss Nelson Ser.). (J). 13.79 (978-0-7587-3145-6(0)) Book Wholesalers, Inc.

Matsuura, Richard & Matsuura, Ruth. Angels Masquerading on Earth. Chao, Linus, illus. (J). 7.95 (978-1-887916-07-3(5)) Orchid Isle Publishing Co.

McDaniel, Lurlene. Prey. 2008. 208p. (YA). (*978-0-385-73453-0(0) , Delacorte Pr.) Dell Publishing.

McGhee, Alison. Mrs. Watson Wants Your Teeth. Bliss, Harry, illus. 2007. 32p. (J). reprint ed. 16.00 (*978-1-4223-6777-3(0)) DIANE Publishing Co.

—Mrs. Watson Wants Your Teeth. Bliss, Harry, illus. 2004. 36p. (J). 16.00 (978-0-15-204931-7(2)) Harcourt Children's Bks.

McKenna, Colleen O'Shaughnessy. Third Grade Wedding Bells. Roth, Stéphanie, illus. 2006. 160p. (J). (gr. 2-5). 15.95 (978-0-8234-1943-2(6)) Holiday Hse., Inc.

McKissack, Patricia C. Miami Sees It Through. 2002. (gr. k-3). lib. bdg. 11.80 (978-0-613-82723-2(6)) Tandem Library Bks.

McKissack, Patricia C. & McKissack, Fredrick L. Miami Jackson Sees It Through. Chesworth, Michael, illus. 2004. (Road to Reading Ser.). 96p. (J). (gr. 2-4). pap. 3.99 (978-0-307-26513-5(7) , Random Hse. Bks. for Young Readers) Random Hse. Children's Bks.

McKissack, Robert L. Try Your Best. Cepeda, Joe, illus. 2004. (Green Light Readers Level 2 Ser.). 24p. (J). 11.95 (978-0-15-205089-4(2)); pap. 3.95 (978-0-15-205090-0(6)) Harcourt Children's Bks. (Green Light Readers).

—Try Your Best. 2004. (gr. k-3). lib. bdg. 11.80 (978-0-613-81420-1(7)) Tandem Library Bks.

McNamara, Margaret. Eloise Has a Lesson. Mitter, Kathryn, illus. 2004. (Eloise Ser.). 32p. (J). pap. 3.99 (978-0-689-87367-6(0) , Aladdin) Simon & Schuster Children's Publishing.

—Eloise Has a Lesson. Mitter, Kathryn, illus. 2005. (Eloise Ser.). 32p. (J). (ps-1). lib. bdg. 11.19 (978-0-606-33476-1(9)) Tandem Library Bks.

McNaughton, Colin. Once upon an Ordinary School Day. Kitamura, Satoshi, illus. 2005. 32p. (J). 16.00 (978-0-374-35634-7(3) , Farrar, Straus & Giroux (BYR)) Farrar, Straus & Giroux.

Meganck, Glenn. Big Deal at the Center of the Earth. 1999. (Illus.). 67p. 11.99 (978-1-892339-02-7(1)); (gr. 4-7). pap. 4.99 (978-1-892339-03-4(X)) Beachfront Publishing.

Miles, Ellen. Taylor-Made Tales. 2006. 144p. (J). pap. 4.99 (978-0-439-59710-4(2) , Scholastic Paperbacks) Scholastic, Inc.

Miller, Sarah Elizabeth. Miss Spitfire: Reaching Helen Keller. 2007. 240p. (J). (gr. 5-9). 16.99 (978-1-4169-2542-2(2)) Simon & Schuster Children's Publishing.

Millman, Selena. Anyone Can Make A Difference. 2006. 109p. (YA). per. (*978-0-9793058-6-3(1)) Millman, Selena.

Mills, Claudia. Standing up to Mr. O. 2000. (978-0-606-18215-7(2)) Tandem Library Bks.

Miss Nelson Is Back; Miss Nelson Is Missing. 1999. (Miss Nelson Ser.). (J). (ps-3). 9.95 (978-1-56137-032-0(0)) Novel Units, Inc.

Montgomery, L. M. Anne of Avonlea. 2000. (Anne of Green Gables Ser.: Vol. No. 2). 194p. (gr. 5-8). pap. 12.99 (978-1-57646-304-8(4)); (YA). 24.95 (978-1-57646-305-5(2)) Quiet Vision Publishing.

—Anne of Avonlea. 2006. (Scholastic Classics Ser.). (Illus.). viii, 239p. (J). 25.00 (978-0-531-16979-7(0) , Watts, Franklin) Scholastic Library Publishing.

—Anne of Avonlea. 2004. 336p. (J). pap. 3.99 (978-0-439-43649-6(4) , Scholastic Paperbacks) Scholastic, Inc.

—Anne of Avonlea. 2005. (Aladdin Classics Ser.). (Illus.). 398p. (J). (gr. 4-7). pap. 4.99 (978-1-4169-0328-4(3) , Aladdin) Simon & Schuster Children's Publishing.

—Anne of Avonlea. unabr. ed. 2002. (Dover Juvenile Classics Ser.). 272p. (J). (gr. 4-7). pap. 3.00 (978-0-486-42239-8(9)) Dover Pubns., Inc.

—Anne of Avonlea. l.t. ed. 2006. (ENG.). pap. (*978-1-4068-3173-3(5)) Echo Library.

—Anne of Avonlea. l.t. ed. 1998. (Avonlea Ser.: No. 2). 401p. (YA). (gr. 5-8). lib. bdg. 35.95 (978-1-58118-039-8(X) , 22507) LRS.

—Anne of Avonlea. 1998. 270p. (YA). (gr. 5-8). reprint ed. lib. bdg. 25.00 (978-1-58287-013-7(6)) North Bks.

—Anne of Avonlea. l.t. ed. 2000. (Anne of Green Gables Ser.: Vol. 2). 366p. (gr. 5-8). pap. 21.99 (978-1-57646-306-2(0)) Quiet Vision Publishing.

—Anne of Avonlea Book & Charm. 2002. (Charming Classics). 256p. (ps-1). pap. 6.99 (978-0-694-01584-9(9) , Harper Festival) HarperCollins Pubs.

—Anne of Windy Willows, Vol. 4. 1999. 336p. (J). pap. 3.99 (978-0-14-036800-0(0) , Putnam Juvenile) Penguin Group (USA) Inc.

Morgenstern, Susie. A Book of Coupons. Rosner, Gill, tr. Bloch, Serge, illus. (J). (gr. 3-6). 2003. 80p. pap. 5.99 (978-0-14-250115-3(8) , Puffin); 2001. 64p. 13.99 (978-0-670-89970-8(4) , Viking Juvenile) Penguin Group (USA) Inc.

Moses, B. More Secret Lives of Teachers. 2003. (Illus.). 62p. (J). pap. 7.99 (978-0-330-34994-9(5) , Pan) Pan Macmillan GBR. *Dist:* Trafalgar Square Publishing.

Moss, Marissa. Amelia's 6th Grade Notebook. Moss, Marissa, illus. 2005. (Amelia's Notebooks). (Illus.). 80p. (J). (gr. k-8). 9.95 (978-0-689-87040-8(X) , Simon & Schuster Children's Publishing) Simon & Schuster Children's Publishing.

Mrs Bold, 6 Packs. (Literatura 2000 Ser.). (gr. 1-2). 28.00 (978-0-7635-0101-3(8)) Rigby Education.

Mrs Keen: Individual Title Six-Packs. (ps-2). 27.00 (978-0-7635-9462-6(8)) Rigby Education.

Murphy, Jill. The Worst Witch Saves the Day. Murphy, Jill, illus. 2007. (Worst Witch Ser.). (Illus.). 160p. (J). (gr. 3). 13.99 (*978-0-7636-3319-6(4)) Candlewick Pr.

My Teacher's My Friend. 22p. (J). 5.95 (978-0-8249-5308-9(8)) Ideals Pubns.

Myers, Christopher. Wings. 2001. (YA). (gr. 2-4). 27.90 incl. audio (978-0-8045-6880-7(4) , 6880) Spoken Arts, Inc.

Myers, Laurie. Earthquake in the Third Grade. Ritz, Karen, illus. 1998. 64p. (J). (gr. 4-6). pap. 5.95 (978-0-395-92866-0(4) , Clarion Bks.) Houghton Mifflin Co. Trade & Reference Div.

Needle, Jan. El Buscapleitos (The Bully) Cross, Juan Elias Tovar, tr. Enriquez, Luis Fernando, illus. 2000. (la Orilla Del Viento Ser.). (SPA.). 138p. (J). 7.99 (978-968-16-6069-7(2) , 132) Fondo de Cultura Economica USA.

Nelson, R. A. Teach Me. 2007. 272p. (J). pap. 8.99 (978-1-59514-085-2(9) , Razorbill) Penguin Group (USA) Inc.

Nikola-Lisa, W. My Teacher Can Teach—Anyone! Galindo, Felipe, illus. 2004. 32p. (J). (ps-2). 16.95 (978-1-58430-163-9(5)) Lee & Low Bks., Inc.

O'Brien, Tim. Tomcat in Love. 1999. (gr. 7-12). lib. bdg. 22.25 (978-0-613-62863-1(2)) Tandem Library Bks.

O'Connor, Jane. Fancy Nancy at the Museum. Glasser, Robin Preiss & Enik, Ted, illus. 2008. (I Can Read Bks.). 32p. (J). 16.99 (*978-0-06-123608-2(X)) HarperCollins Pubs.

—Fancy Nancy at the Museum. Glasser, Robin Preiss, illus. 2008. (I Can Read Bks.). 32p. (J). pap. 3.99 (*978-0-06-123607-5(1) , Harper Trophy) HarperCollins Pubs.

Oliver, Lin. The Mighty Mogul. Lindberg, Jeffrey, illus. 1999. (Great Railway Adventures Ser.: Vol. 2;1). 32p. (J). (gr. k-4). 14.95 (978-1-890647-56-8(X)); pap. 14.99 incl. audio (978-1-890647-57-5(8)) RC2 Corp.

Ormerod, Jan. Ms. MacDonald Has a Class. Ormerod, Jan, illus. 2002. (Illus.). (J). 23.36 (978-0-7587-3197-5(3)) Book Wholesalers, Inc.

—Ms. MacDonald Has a Class. Ormerod, Jan, illus. 2001. (Illus.). 32p. (J). (gr. k-3). pap. 6.95 (978-0-618-13056-6(X) , Clarion Bks.) Houghton Mifflin Co. Trade & Reference Div.

Oshima, Towa & Aikawa, Yu. Dark Edge, Vol. 3. 2005. (Illus.). 208p. (YA). pap. 9.95 (978-1-59796-030-4(6)) DrMaster Pubns. Inc.

Parker, Robert Andrew. Edenville Owls. 2008. 208p. (YA). (gr. 4-6). pap. 7.99 (*978-0-14-241161-2(2) , Puffin) Penguin Group (USA) Inc.

Passen, Lisa. The Abominable Snow Teacher. rev. ed. 2004. (Illus.). 32p. (J). 15.95 (978-0-8050-7379-9(5) , Holt, Henry & Co. Bks. For Young Readers) Holt, Henry & Co.

—Attack of the 50-Foot Teacher. 2005. (Illus.). 28p. (J). (gr. k-4). reprint ed. 16.00 (978-0-7567-9665-5(2)) DIANE Publishing Co.

—Attack of the 50-Foot Teacher. 2003. (gr. k-3). lib. bdg. 15.25 (978-0-613-75618-1(5)) Tandem Library Bks.

—The Attack of the 50-Foot Teacher. Passen, Lisa, illus. rev. ed. (Illus.). 32p. (J). 2003. (gr. 1-3). pap. 6.95 (978-0-8050-7260-0(8)); 2000. (gr. k-3). 16.00 (978-0-8050-6100-0(2)) Holt, Henry & Co. (Holt, Henry & Co. Bks. For Young Readers).

Passen, Lisa. The Incredible Shrinking Teacher, Passen, Lisa, illus. rev. ed. 2002. (Illus.). 32p. (J). (gr. k-3). 15.95 (978-0-8050-6452-0(4) , Holt, Henry & Co. Bks. For Young Readers) Holt, Henry & Co.

—The Incredible Shrinking Teacher. 2008. (Illus.). 32p. (J). pap. 6.99 (*978-0-312-38017-5(8)) Square Fish.

Pattou, Edith. Mrs. Spitzer's Garden. Tusa, Tricia, illus. 2007. 32p. (J). 9.95 (978-0-15-205802-9(8)) Harcourt Children's Bks.

Pearson, Mary E. Donde Esta Max? Cordova, Jacqueline, tr. Walker, Samantha L., illus. (Rookie Reader Espanol Ser.). (SPA.). 24p. (J). (gr. k-2). 2001. pap. 4.95 (978-0-516-27011-1(7)); 2000. 19.50 (978-0-516-22023-9(3)) Scholastic Library Publishing. (Children's Pr.).

—Donde Esta Max? 2000. (SPA.). (gr. k-3). lib. bdg. 12.95 (978-0-613-54176-3(6)) Tandem Library Bks.

Peck, Richard. The Teacher's Funeral: A Comedy in Three Parts. 2004. 208p. (J). (gr. 5). 16.99 (978-0-8037-2736-6(4) , Dial); 2006. 224p. (YA). (gr. 3). reprint ed. pap. 6.99 (978-0-14-240507-9(8) , Puffin) Penguin Group (USA) Inc.

—The Teacher's Funeral: A Comedy in Three Parts. l.t. ed. 2005. 226p. 22.95 (978-0-7862-7750-6(5) , Large Print Pr.) Thorndike Pr.

Pilkey, Dav. Captain Underpants & the Attack of the Talking Toilets. (Captain Underpants Ser.: No. 2). (J). 2004. lib. bdg. 19.95 (978-0-439-68436-1(6) , Scholastic, Inc.); 1999. (Illus.). 144p. (gr. 2-5). pap. 16.95 (978-0-590-63136-5(5) , Blue Sky Pr., The) Scholastic, Inc.

—Captain Underpants & the Attack of the Talking Toilets. Pilkey, Dav, illus. 1999. (Captain Underpants Ser.: No. 2). (Illus.). 144p. (J). (gr. 2-5). pap. 4.99 (978-0-590-63427-4(5)) Scholastic, Inc.

—Captain Underpants & the Attack of the Talking Toilets. 1999. (Captain Underpants Ser.: No. 2). (Illus.). (J). (gr. 2-5). 11.64 (978-0-606-15830-5(8)); (gr. 3-6). lib. bdg. 13.00 (978-0-613-11382-3(9)) Tandem Library Bks.

—Captain Underpants & the Invasion of the Incredibly Naughty Cafeteria Ladies from Outer Space: And the Subsequent Assault of the Equally Evil Lunchroom Zombie Nerds. Pilkey, Dav, illus. 1999. (Captain Underpants Ser.: No. 3). (Illus.). 144p. (J). (gr. 2-5). 4.99 (978-0-439-04996-2(2) , Blue Sky Pr., The) Scholastic, Inc.

—Captain Underpants & the Invasion of the Incredibly Naughty Cafeteria Ladies from Outer Space: And the Subsequent Assault of the Equally Evil Lunchroom Zombie Nerds. 1999. (Captain Underpants Ser.: No. 3). (Illus.). 134p. (J). (gr. 2-5). pap. 16.95 (978-0-439-04995-5(4) , Blue Sky Pr., The) Scholastic, Inc.

—Captain Underpants & the Perilous Plot of Professor Poopypants. ed. 2005. (Captain Underpants Ser.: No. 4). (Illus.). 156p. (J). lib. bdg. 15.00 (978-1-59054-678-9(4)) Fitzgerald Bks.

—Captain Underpants & the Perilous Plot of Professor Poopypants. 2004. (Captain Underpants Ser.: No. 4). (J). lib. bdg. 19.95 (978-0-439-68440-8(4) , Scholastic, Inc.) Scholastic, Inc.

—Captain Underpants & the Perilous Plot of Professor Poopypants. Pilkey, Dav, illus. 2000. (Captain Underpants Ser.: No. 4). (Illus.). 160p. (J). (gr. 2-5). pap. 4.99 (978-0-439-04998-6(9)); pap. 16.95 (978-0-439-04997-9(0)) Scholastic, Inc. (Blue Sky Pr., The).

—Captain Underpants & the Perilous Plot of Professor Poopypants. 2000. (Captain Underpants Ser.: No. 4). (gr. 3-6). lib. bdg. 13.00 (978-0-613-21289-2(4)); (Illus.). (J). (gr. 2-5). 11.64 (978-0-606-18526-4(7)) Tandem Library Bks.

—Captain Underpants & the Wrath of the Wicked Wedgie Woman. 2004. (Captain Underpants Ser.: No. 5). (J). lib. bdg. 19.95 (978-0-439-68441-5(2) , Scholastic, Inc.) Scholastic, Inc.

—Captain Underpants & the Wrath of the Wicked Wedgie Woman. 2001. (Captain Underpants Ser.: No. 5). (gr. 3-6). lib. bdg. 13.00 (978-0-613-35767-8(1)); (Illus.). (J). 11.64 (978-0-606-21101-7(2)) Tandem Library Bks.

Plourde, Lynn. Teacher Appreciation Day. Wickstrom, Thor, illus. (J). 2005. 40p. pap. 6.99 (978-0-14-240283-2(4) , Puffin); 2003. 36p. 16.99 (978-0-525-47113-4(8) , Dutton Juvenile) Penguin Group (USA) Inc.

Polacco, Patricia. Gracias, Senor Falker. Mlawer, Teresa, tr. from ENG. 2001. (SPA., Illus.). (J). (gr. 1-3). lib. bdg. 17.00 (978-1-930332-03-4(3) , LC30185) Lectorum Pubns., Inc.

—The Lemonade Club. Polacco, Patricia, illus. 2007. (Illus.). 48p. (J). (gr. 1). 16.99 (***978-0-399-24540-4(5)*** , Philomel) Penguin Group (USA) Inc.

Polacco, Patricia. Thank You, Mr. Falker. Polacco, Patricia, illus. 2002. (Illus.). (J). 23.64 (978-0-7587-3779-3(3)) Book Wholesalers, Inc.

—Thank You, Mr. Falker. 1998. (Illus.). 40p. (J). (gr. k-4). 16.99 (978-0-399-23166-7(8) , Philomel) Penguin Group (USA) Inc.

—Thank You, Mr. Falker. 2001. (J). (gr. k-4). 27.95 incl. audio (978-0-8045-6854-8(5) , 6854) Spoken Arts, Inc.

Priceman, Marjorie. Emeline at the Circus. (J). (gr. k-3). 2000. pap. 6.99 (978-0-375-80351-2(3) , Random Hse. Bks. for Young Readers); 1999. (Illus.). 40p. pap. 15.00 (978-0-679-87685-4(5) , Knopf Bks. for Young Readers) Random Hse. Children's Bks.

Prinz, Yvonne. Still There, Clare Teacher Guide. 2005. 4p. (J). pap. (978-1-55192-821-0(3)) Raincoast Bk. Distribution CAN. *Dist:* Transition Vendor.

Profilet, Cynthia. Maggie's Golden Moment. Barron, Ann, illus. 2005. (J). (***978-0-9637735-1-7(8)***) Sterling Pr., Inc.

Puttock, Simon. Miss Fox. Swain, Holly, illus. 2006. 32p. (J). (gr. k-4). 15.95 (***978-1-84507-475-3(0)***) Lincoln, Frances Ltd. GBR. *Dist:* Perseus Distribution.

Ransom, Jeanie Franz. Don't Squeal Unless It's a Big Deal: A Tale of Tattletales. Urbanovic, Jackie, illus. 2005. 32p. (J). 14.95 (978-1-59147-239-1(3)); pap. 8.95 (978-1-59147-240-7(7)) American Psychological Assn. (Magination Pr.).

Ray, Delia. Ghost Girl: A Blue Ridge Mountain Story. 2003. 224p. (YA). (gr. 5-9). tchr. ed. 15.00 (978-0-618-33377-6(0) , Clarion Bks.) Houghton Mifflin Co. Trade & Reference Div.

—Ghost Girl: A Blue Ridge Mountain Story. 2006. 236p. (YA). 22.95 (978-0-7862-8876-2(0)) Thorndike Pr.

Red & Green Choices by Green Irene: Niki's Next Grade. 2003. (J). per. 14.50 (978-0-9742280-1-3(X)) Green Irene.

Remkiewicz, Frank, illus. Horrible Harry & the Dungeon. 2002. (Horrible Harry Ser.). (J). 11.49 (978-0-7587-0590-7(5)) Book Wholesalers, Inc.

Richardson, Regina. Maggie's Treasured Stone. 2006. (ENG.). 36p. per. 19.99 (***978-1-4259-3095-0(6)***) AuthorHouse.

Ritchie, Madonna. Mr. Peabody's Apples. Ritchie, Madonna & Long, Loren, illus. 2003. 40p. (J). 19.95 (978-0-670-05883-9(1)) Callaway Editions, Inc.

—Mr. Peabody's Apples. Ritchie, Madonna & Long, Loren, illus. 2003. 40p. (J). 19.95 (978-0-670-04492-4(X)) Penguin Group (USA) Inc.

Rizzo, Cynthia Marie. Angela & the Princess. 2006. 89p. pap. 14.95 (978-1-4241-2599-9(5)) PublishAmerica, Inc.

Robles, Tony. Joey Gonzales, Real American. 2007. (J). 12.95 (***978-0-9767269-3-7(9)***) World Ahead Media.

Rosen, Michael. Totally Wonderful Miss Plumberry. Lee, Chinlun, illus. 2006. 40p. (J). (ps-2). 15.99 (978-0-7636-2744-7(5)) Candlewick Pr.

Salant, Sherry Ann. Skipping School. l.t. ed. 2001. 24p. 6.95 (978-0-9712952-0-9(4)) Storywriter Pr.

Sasaki, Mutsumi. Happy Lesson, Vol.1. 2004. 170p. pap. (978-1-4139-0021-7(6)) ADV Manga.

Schraff, Anne. The Boy from Planet Nowhere. 1999. 125p. (J). pap. (978-0-7891-4927-5(3)); (gr. 5-12). lib. bdg. 13.95 (978-0-7807-8004-0(3)) Perfection Learning Corp.

—Where's Dudley? 2001. (PageTurner Mystery Ser.). 80p. (YA). per. 3.95 (978-1-56254-177-4(3) , SP 1773) Saddleback Educational Publishing.

—Where's Dudley? 2001. (gr. 7-12). lib. bdg. 11.80 (978-0-613-33240-8(7)) Tandem Library Bks.

Seuss, Dr. & Prelutsky, Jack. Hooray for Diffendoofer Day! Smith, Lane, illus. 1998. 56p. (J). (gr. k-3). 17.00 (978-0-679-89008-9(4)); lib. bdg. 18.99 (978-0-679-99008-6(9)) Random Hse. Children's Bks. (Knopf Bks. for Young Readers).

Sherrard, Valerie. Speechless. 2007. 176p. (YA). pap. 12.99 (***978-1-55002-701-3(8)*** , Boardwalk Bks.) Dundurn Group, The CAN. *Dist:* Univ. of Toronto Pr.

Shipton, Paul. Clown School. Blake, Beccy, illus. 2005. 24p. (J). lib. bdg. 22.65 (***978-1-59646-752-1(5)***) Dingles & Co.

The Shoe Grabber: Individual Title Six-Pack. (Story Steps Ser.). (gr. k-2). 23.00 (978-0-7635-9832-7(1)) Rigby Education.

Shubert Sees the Best. 2004. (J). 9.00 (978-1-889609-23-2(4)) Loving Guidance, Inc.

Slate, Joseph. Miss Bindergarten Celebrates the Last Day of Kindergarten. Wolff, Ashley, illus. 40p. (J). (ps). 2008. pap. 6.99 (***978-0-14-241060-8(8)*** , Puffin); 2006. 16.99 (978-0-525-47744-0(6) , Dutton Juvenile) Penguin Group (USA) Inc.

Slate, Joseph. Miss Bindergarten Gets Ready for Kindergarten. Wolff, Ashley, illus. 2001. 40p. (J). pap. 6.99 (978-0-14-056273-6(7) , Puffin) Penguin Group (USA) Inc.

Snyder, Susan E. Shivers & Shakes. 2007. (Illus.). 24p. (J). 9.95 (978-0-9767163-5-8(6)) Kotzig Publishing, Inc.

Soda, Masahito. Firefighter, Vol. 16. 2006. (Firefighter Daigo of Fire Company M Ser.). 208p. (YA). pap. 9.95 (978-1-4215-0452-0(9)) Viz Media.

Sommerdorf, Norma. Red River Girl. 2006. (Illus.). 192p. (J). 16.95 (978-0-8234-1903-6(7)) Holiday Hse., Inc.

Southgate, Martha. Fall of Rome. 2003. (gr. 7-12). lib. bdg. 21.10 (978-0-613-62902-7(7)) Tandem Library Bks.

Spelvin, Justin & Artifact Group. Teacher Trouble. 2006. (LazyTown Ser.). 24p. (J). pap. 3.99 (978-1-4169-1212-5(6) , Simon Spotlight/Nickelodeon) Simon & Schuster Children's Publishing.

Spyri, Johanna. Rico & Wiseli, Rico & Stineli, & H. 2006. 63.99 (***978-1-4280-3033-6(6)***) IndyPublish.com.

Stine, R. L. Creature Teacher. 1998. (Goosebumps Series 2000: No. 3). 125p. (J). (gr. 3-7). pap. 3.99 (978-0-590-39989-0(6) , Scholastic Paperbacks) Scholastic, Inc.

—Creature Teacher. 1998. (Goosebumps Series 2000: No. 3). (J). (gr. 3-7). (978-0-606-13440-8(9)) Tandem Library Bks.

Strand, Jeff. Elrod Mcbugle on the Loose. 2006. (ENG.). 136p. (YA). per. 9.25 (***978-0-7599-4325-4(7)***) Hard Shell Word Factory.

Streep, Meryl, narrated by. Chrysanthemum. unabr. ed. 1998. (SPA.). (J). (ps-2). pap. 14.95 incl. audio (978-0-7882-0126-4(3) , PRA369SP) Weston Woods Studios, Inc.

Strong, R. What Difference Does Seven Days Make? 2005. 140p. pap. 19.95 (978-1-4137-7789-5(9)) PublishAmerica, Inc.

Sustrin, Sheila & Sustrin, Letty. The Teacher Who Would Not Retire. Bone, Thomas H., III, illus. unabr. ed. 2002. 32p. (J). (ps-3). 16.00 (978-0-9674602-3-9(9)) Blue Marlin Pubns.

Taylor, Shane. The Magic of Mortals. 2006. (YA). pap. 11.95 (978-1-58736-542-3(1) , Starbound Bks.) Wheatmark.

Teach Us, Amelia Bedelia. 2002. (Amelia Bedelia Ser.). (Illus.). (J). 11.91 (978-0-7587-1726-9(1)) Book Wholesalers, Inc.

TenNapel, Doug & Koelsch, Mike. Fateful Friday. 1998. (Strange Kid Chronicles: No. 5). 80p. (J). (gr. 2-5). pap. 3.99 (978-0-590-05958-9(0)) Scholastic, Inc.

—Just Thursday. 1998. (Strange Kid Chronicles: No. 4). 80p. (J). (gr. 2-5). pap. 3.99 (978-0-590-05957-2(2)) Scholastic, Inc.

—Tuna Fish Tuesday. 1998. (Strange Kid Chronicles: No. 2). 80p. (J). (gr. 2-5). pap. 3.99 (978-0-590-05955-8(6)) Scholastic, Inc.

—Wisenheimer Wednesday. 1998. (Strange Kid Chronicles: No. 3). 80p. (J). (gr. 2-5). pap. 3.99 (978-0-590-05956-5(4)) Scholastic, Inc.

Thaler, Mike. The Music Teacher from the Black Lagoon. Lee, Jared D., illus. 2000. (Black Lagoon Ser.). 32p. (J). (ps-3). pap. 3.99 (978-0-439-18873-9(3)) Scholastic, Inc.

—The Music Teacher from the Black Lagoon. 2000. (Black Lagoon Ser.). (J). (ps-3). (978-0-606-18882-1(7)) Tandem Library Bks.

—Music Teacher from the Black Lagoon. 2000. (gr. 3-6). lib. bdg. 10.95 (978-0-613-24063-5(4)) Tandem Library Bks.

—Teacher from the Black Lagoon. Lee Jared, illus. 2006. (Scholastic Reader Collection Level 3 Ser.). 144p. (J). pap. 6.99 (978-0-439-84803-9(2) , Cartwheel Bks.) Scholastic, Inc.

—The Teacher from the Black Lagoon. Lee, Jared D., illus. 2004. (YA). (gr. k up). pap. 14.95 incl. audio (978-1-55592-172-9(8)) Weston Woods Studios, Inc.

—The Teacher from the Black Lagoon. Lee, Jared D., illus. unabr. ed. 2006. (J). 9.95 (978-0-439-87590-5(0)) Scholastic, Inc.

—The Teacher from the Black Lagoon. Lee, Jared D., illus. 2004. (J). (gr. k-3). pap. 18.95 incl. audio compact disk (978-1-55592-495-9(6)) Weston Woods Studios, Inc.

Thomas, Carroll, creator. Under the Open Sky: A Matty Trescott Novel. 2005. (Illus.). 184p. (J). per. 12.95 (978-0-9762091-2-6(8)) Antrim Hse.

Thompson, Tate. Senioritis. 2nd ed. 2003. (YA). per. 13.50 (978-0-9743864-47-1(X)) Davenport, May Pubs.

Townsend, Lois Ritter. Our Journey Through Breast Cancer: -a story based on a teacher's journey through breast cancer with her kindergarten Class. 2005. (Illus.). 20p. (J). pap. 6.99 (978-1-933570-93-8(8)) Aardvark Global Publishing.

Trapped by a Teacher: Individual Title Six-Packs. (Action Packs Ser.). 128p. (gr. 3-5). 44.00 (978-0-7635-3309-0(2)) Rigby Education.

Vaughan, Marcia. Up the Learning Tree. Blanks, Derek, illus. 2003. 32p. (J). 16.96 (978-1-58430-049-6(3)) Lee & Low Bks., Inc.

Viguie, Debbie. Miss O & Friends: Trouble with a Capital O. Brindak, Hermine, illus. 2006. (Miss O & Friends Ser.). 128p. (J). pap. 5.99 (978-0-8230-2946-4(8)) Watson-Guptill Pubns., Inc.

Volponi, Paul. The Hand You're Dealt. 2008. 256p. (YA). (***978-1-4169-3989-4(X)***) Simon & Schuster Children's Publishing.

Wardlaw, Lee. 101 Ways to Bug Your Teacher. 256p. 2005. (gr. 5-7). pap. 6.99 (978-0-14-240331-0(8) , Puffin); 2004. (Illus.). (J). (gr. 4). 16.99 (978-0-8037-2658-1(9) , Dial) Penguin Group (USA) Inc.

Warner, Gertrude Chandler. Benny's Saturday Surprise, Vol. 8. Life, Kay, illus. 2004. (Adventures of Benny & Watch: Vol. 8). 32p. (J). (ps-2). pap. 3.95 (978-0-8075-0642-4(7)) Whitman, Albert & Co.

Watson, Richard Jesse. The Boy Who Went Ape. Watson, Benjamin James, illus. 2008. (J). pap. (***978-0-590-47966-0(0)***) Blue Sky Pr.

Weber, Susan. Seal Island School. 2001. (Puffin Chapters Ser.). (Illus.). (J). (978-0-606-21423-0(2)) Tandem Library Bks.

Weil, Zoe. Claude & Medea: The Hellburn Dogs. 2007. 112p. (J). (gr. 4-7). pap. 30.00 (***978-1-59056-105-8(8)***) Lantern Bks.

Wesson, André. Mrs. Applebee & the Sunshine Band, Book 1: Meet the Class! 2007. 48p. pap. 18.40 (***978-0-615-14849-6(2)***) Se7enth Swan Publishing Group, LLC.

Wheatley, Nadia & Ottley, Matt. Luke's Way of Looking. 2001. (Illus.). 36p. (J). (gr. k up). 15.95 (978-1-929132-18-8(2)) Kane/Miller Bk. Pubs., Inc.

White, Russ. Cat Got Your Tongue? A Book of Idioms. Cornelison, Reuel, illus. l.t. ed. 2004. 44p. (J). per. (978-0-9742885-0-5(0) , 00) White, Russ.

Wilder, Laura Ingalls. These Happy Golden Years. 2007. (Little House Ser.). 304p. (J). pap. 6.99 (978-0-06-088544-1(0) , Harper Trophy) HarperCollins Pubs.

Wilkins, Celia. A Little House of Their Own. Andreasen, Dan, illus. 2005. (Little House Ser.). 320p. (J). pap. 6.99 (978-0-06-440736-6(5)) HarperCollins Pubs.

Williams, Quan. The Leopard Man. 2005. 183p. pap. 19.95 (978-1-4137-5214-4(4)) PublishAmerica, Inc.

Willner-Pardo, Gina. Spider Storch's Fumbled Field Trip. Sharratt, Nick, illus. 1998. 68p. (J). (gr. 2-5). pap. 3.95 (978-0-8075-7582-6(8)) Whitman, Albert & Co.

—Spider Storch's Music Mess. Sharratt, Nick, illus. 1998. 80p. (J). (gr. 2-5). lib. bdg. 11.95 (978-0-8075-7583-3(6)) Whitman, Albert & Co.

Winfrey, Michelle Whitaker. It's My Birthday. . . Finally! A Leap Year Story. Turley, Joyce M., illus. 2003. 88p. (J). (gr. 3-7). per. 11.95 (978-0-9727179-0-8(0)) Hobby Hse. Publishing Group.

Winters, Kay. My Teacher for President. Brunkus, Denise, illus. 2004. 32p. (J). (gr. k). 14.99 (978-0-525-47186-8(3) , Dutton Juvenile) Penguin Group (USA) Inc.

Wood, Douglas & Cushman, Doug. What Teachers Can't Do. 2002. (Illus.). 32p. (J). (ps-3). 14.95 (978-0-689-84644-1(4)) Simon & Schuster Children's Publishing.

Zemach, Kaethe. Ms. Mccaw Learns To Draw. (J). 2008. 32p. pap. 16.99 (978-0-439-82914-4(3)); 2006. (978-0-439-82915-1(1)) Scholastic, Inc. (Levine, Arthur A. Bks.).

TEACHERS—TRAINING OF

Here are entered works dealing with the history and methods of training teachers, including the educational functions of teachers colleges. Works on the study of education as a science are entered under Education—Study and teaching.

Gaither, Jennifer. 85 Ways for Teachers to Make the Connection with Students. 2002. 122p. spiral bd. 8.90 (978-0-9664154-1-4(8) , 4103583360) Jenrod, Inc.

J. G. Ferguson Publishing Company Staff, contrib. by. Discovering Careers in Your Future/Teaching. 2002. (Discovering Careers for Your Future Ser.). (Illus.). 96p. (J). (gr. 4-9). 21.95 (978-0-89434-398-8(X) , Ferguson Publishing Co.) Facts On File, Inc.

TEACHERS AND PARENTS

see Home and School

TEACHING

see also Education; Educational Psychology; Kindergarten; Project Method in Teaching; Study Skills; Teachers—Training of

also subjects with the subdivision Study and Teaching, e.g. Science—Study and Teaching

Baltas, Joyce Graham, et al. Follow the Directions, Grades 3-6: 180 Daily Exercises That Help Kids Learn to Follow Written Directions - Independently! 2001. (Joyful Learning Ser.). 80p. (gr. 3-6). pap., tchr. ed. 10.95 (978-0-439-40813-4(X) , Teaching Resources) Scholastic, Inc.

Bigelow, Bill, ed. Rethinking Our Classrooms Vol. 2: Teaching for Equity & Justice. 2001. (Illus.). 240p. (YA). pap. 12.95 (978-0-942961-27-0(7)) Rethinking Schls., Ltd.

Crane, Natalie. I Go to Work as a Teacher. 2003. (I Go to Work As Ser.). (Illus.). (J). lib. bdg. (978-1-58417-044-0(1)) Lake Street Pubs.

The Education of Little Tree: Activity Pack. 2003. 118p. (YA). pap. (978-1-58049-627-8(X) , PA0127) Prestwick Hse., Inc.

Gerngross, Gunter & Puchta, Herbert. Playway to English 2 Picture Cards. 1999. (Playway to English Ser.). 2p. 36.00 (978-0-521-65681-8(8)) Cambridge Univ. Pr.

Hurlstone, Jill. Cornerstones for Writing Ages 7-9 Interactive Single User Version. 2001. (Cornerstones Ser.). cd-rom 92.25 (978-0-521-75193-3(4)) Cambridge Univ. Pr.

—Cornerstones for Writing Ages 9-11 Interactive Single User Version. 2001. (Cornerstones Ser.). cd-rom 92.25 (978-0-521-75195-7(0)) Cambridge Univ. Pr.

Liebman, Daniel. I Want to Be a Teacher. 2001. (I Want to Be Ser.). (Illus.). 24p. (J). (ps-2). pap. 3.99 (978-1-55209-570-6(3)); lib. bdg. 14.95 (978-1-55209-572-0(X)) Firefly Bks., Ltd.

—I Want to Be a Teacher. 2001. (I Want to Be Ser.). (Illus.). (J). 10.79 (978-0-606-21508-4(5)) Tandem Library Bks.

Morris, Ann. That's Our Teacher! 2003. (That's Our School Ser.). 32p. lib. bdg. 22.90 (978-0-7613-2373-0(2) , Millbrook Pr.) Lerner Publishing Group.

Murdoch, Bernard Constantine. A Revolutionary View of Education & Teaching for the Third Millenium. 2002. 142p. pap. 20.00 (978-0-9664283-4-6(X) , 145193) Fore(In)Sight Foundation.

Walk Two Moons Literature Unit. 2003. 48p. (YA). (gr. 5-8). 7.99 (978-0-7439-3160-1(2)) Teacher Created Materials, Inc.

TEACHING—VOCATIONAL GUIDANCE

Adamson, Heather. A Day in the Life of a Teacher. 2003. (First Facts Ser.). (Illus.). 24p. (J). lib. bdg. 21.26 (978-0-7368-2286-2(0)) Capstone Pr., Inc.

Calhoun, Florence. Choosing a Career in Teaching. 2005. (World of Work Ser.). (Illus.). 64p. (YA). (gr. 7-12). lib. bdg. 25.25 (978-0-8239-3247-4(8)) Rosen Publishing Group, Inc., The.

Crane, Natalie. I Go to Work as a Teacher. 2003. (I Go to Work As Ser.). (Illus.). (J). pap. (978-1-58417-106-5(5)); lib. bdg. (978-1-58417-043-3(3)) Lake Street Pubs.

Cutlip, Glen W. & Shockley, Robert J. Careers in Teaching. rev. ed. 2000. (Careers Ser.). (Illus.). 128p. (YA). (gr. 7-12). lib. bdg. 26.50 (978-0-8239-3182-8(X) , CATEAC) Rosen Publishing Group, Inc., The.

Flanagan, Alice K. Teachers. 2001. (Community Workers Ser.). (Illus.). 32p. (J). (gr. 1 up). lib. bdg. 21.26 (978-0-7565 0066 5(4)) Compass Point Bks.

Hayward, Linda. Jobs People Do: A Day in the Life of a Teacher. 2001. (Jobs People Do Ser.). (Illus.). (J). 10.79 (978-0-606-21141-3(1)) Tandem Library Bks.

Hesse, Karen. Out of the Dust: Literature Guide. Cooper, Terry, ed. 2000. (Professional Bks.). (Illus.). 16p. (gr. 4-13). pap. 3.95 (978-0-439-13112-4(X)) Scholastic, Inc.

J. G. Ferguson Publishing Company Staff, contrib. by. Discovering Careers in Your Future/Teaching. 2002. (Discovering Careers for Your Future Ser.). (Illus.). 96p. (J). (gr. 4-9). 21.95 (978-0-89434-398-8(X) , Ferguson Publishing Co.) Facts On File, Inc.

Lesinski, Jeanne M. Bill Gates. 2006. (First Step Nonfiction Ser.). (Illus.). 112p. (J). (gr. 3-7). 27.93 (978-0-8225-2642-1(5) , Lerner Pubns.) Lerner Publishing Group.

Lowenstein, Felicia. What Does a Teacher Do? 2006. (What Does a Community Helper Do? Ser.). (Illus.). 24p. (J). lib. bdg. 21.26 (978-0-7660-2321-5(4) , Enslow Elementary) Enslow Pubs., Inc.

Macken, JoAnn Early. Teacher. 2003. (People in My Community Ser.). (Illus.). 24p. (J). (ps up). lib. bdg. 19.33 (978-0-8368-3593-9(X) , Weekly Reader Early Learning Library) Stevens, Gareth Inc.

Macken, JoAnn Early & Gorman, Jacqueline Laks. Teacher. Andersen, Gregg, photos by. 2003. (Weekly Reader Early Learning Library). (Illus.). 24p. (J). (ps up). pap. 7.93 (978-0-8368-3600-4(6) , Weekly Reader Early Learning Library) Stevens, Gareth Inc.

McAlpine, Margaret. Working with Children. 2004. (My Future Career Ser.). (Illus.). 64p. lib. bdg. 26.00 (978-0-8368-4241-8(3)) Stevens, Gareth Inc.

Miller, Heather. Teacher. 2003. (This Is What I Want to Be Ser.). (Illus.). 24p. (J). (ps-1). lib. bdg. (978-1-4034-0372-8(4)); pap. 5.25 (978-1-4034-0594-4(8)) Heinemann Library.

Mitchell, Melanie. Teachers. (Pull Ahead Bks.). (Illus.). 32p. (J). 2005. lib. bdg. 22.60 (978-0-8225-1696-5(9)); 2004. pap. (978-0-8225-2536-3(4) , Lerner Pubns.) Lerner Publishing Group.

Parks, Peggy J. Teacher. 2003. (Exploring Careers Ser.). (Illus.). 48p. (J). (gr. 3-5). 26.20 (978-0-7377-1487-6(5) , Kidhaven) Thomson Gale.

Reeves, Diane Lindsey & Karlitz, Gail. Career Ideas for Teens in Education & Training. (Career Ideas for Teens Ser.). 192p. (gr. 6-12). pap. 16.95 (978-0-8160-6919-4(0) , Checkmark Bks.); 2005. (Illus.). (J). 40.00 (978-0-8160-5295-0(6) , Ferguson Publishing Co.) Facts On File, Inc.

Rivera, Sheila. Teacher. 2004. (First Step Nonfiction Ser.). (J). pap. (978-0-8225-5361-8(9) , Lerner Pubns.) Lerner Publishing Group.

Sanna, Ellyn. Special Education Teacher. 2002. (Careers with Character Ser.). (Illus.). 96p. (YA). (gr. 7 up). (978-1-59084-325-3(8)) Mason Crest Pubs.

Schomp, Virginia. If You Were a Teacher. 2000. (If You Were A... Ser.). (Illus.). 32p. (J). (gr. 2-4). lib. bdg. 22.79 (978-0-7614-0916-8(5) , Benchmark Bks.) Cavendish, Marshall Corp.

TEACHINGS OF JESUS

see Jesus Christ—Teachings

TEAROOMS

see Restaurants

TECHNICAL EDUCATION

Tech3000. 2003. (J). cd-rom 99.00 (978-1-932166-06-4(8)) Achieve3000.

TECHNICAL SCHOOLS

see Technical Education

TECHNICAL TERMS

see Technology—Dictionaries

TECHNOLOGY

see also Building; Engineering; Inventions; Machinery; Manufactures; Technical Education

Anderson, Jenna. How It Happens at the ATV Plant. Wolfe, Bob & Wolfe, Diane, photos by. 2004. (How It Happens Ser.). (Illus.). 32p. (J). (gr. 2-5). lib. bdg. 19.95 (978-1-881508-94-6(3)) Oliver Pr., Inc.

Angliss, Sarah. Science Now. 2001. (Datafiles Ser.). (Illus.). 84p. (J). (gr. 3-7). 15.95 (978-1-57145-481-2(0) , Silver Dolphin Bks.) Advantage Pubs. Group.

Bacchin, Giorgio, illus. Industrial Revolution, 1800-1850: A Social History. 2002. (Road to Globalization Ser.). 32p. (YA). 22.95 (978-0-7910-7092-5(1)) Facts On File, Inc.

Bailey, Gerry. Age of New Ideas. Boulter, Steve et al, illus. 2005. (Crafty Inventions Ser.). 48p. (C). (gr. 4-6). 26.60 (978-1-4048-1037-2(4)) Picture Window Bks.

—Early Civilizations. Boulter, Steve et al, illus. 2005. (Crafty Inventions Ser.). 48p. (C). (gr. 4-6). 26.60 (978-1-4048-1038-9(2)) Picture Window Bks.

—First Thousand Years. Smith, Jan & Keylock, Andrew, illus. 2005. (Crafty Inventions Ser.). 48p. (C). (gr. 4-6). 26.60 (978-1-4048-1039-6(0)) Picture Window Bks.

—Long, Long Ago. Boulter, Steve et al, illus. 2005. (Crafty Inventions Ser.). 48p. (C). (gr. 4-6). 26.60 (978-1-4048-1043-3(9)) Picture Window Bks.

—Modern Times. Boulter, Steve et al, illus. 2005. (Crafty Inventions Ser.). 48p. (C). (gr. 4-6). 26.60 (978-1-4048-1044-0(7)) Picture Window Bks.

—Trade & Industry. Boulter, Steve et al, illus. 2005. (Crafty Inventions Ser.). 48p. (C). (gr. 4-6). 26.60 (978-1-4048-1047-1(1)) Picture Window Bks.

Baker, Christopher W. New Century Technology, 4 vols. 2004. (Science & Technology Ser.). (Illus.). 48p. (YA). (gr. 5-8). (978-0-7613-3173-5(5) , Twenty-First Century Bks.) Lerner Publishing Group.

Barnes, John, et al. Science, Maths & Technology. 2003. (Illus.). 184p. pap. (978-0-7487-7121-9(2)) Nelson Thornes Ltd.

Baxen, Jean & Sinclair, Peta-Jane. Science & Technology Matters Grade 6 Learner's Book. 2002. 112p. (gr. 6). pap. 5.05 (978-0-521-78839-7(0)) Cambridge Univ. Pr.

Benchmark Education Staff, compiled by. Invention & Technology. 2006. spiral bd. 145.00 (***978-1-4108-7100-8(2)**) Benchmark Education Co.

—Science & Technology. 2006. spiral bd. 115.00 (***978-1-4108-6923-4(7)**); 2006. spiral bd. 105.00 (***978-1-4108-6935-7(0)**); 2005. spiral bd. 60.00 (***978-1-4108-3843-8(9)**); 2005. spiral bd. 115.00 (***978-1-4108-3854-4(4)**); 2005. spiral bd. 55.00 (***978-1-4108-3855-1(2)**); 2005. spiral bd. 110.00 (***978-1-4108-3866-7(8)**); 2005. spiral bd. 42.00 (***978-1-4108-3880-3(3)**); 2005. spiral bd. 235.00 (***978-1-4108-4520-7(6)**); 2005. spiral bd. 255.00 (***978-1-4108-5444-5(2)**); 2005. spiral bd. 145.00 (***978-1-4108-5445-2(0)**); 2005. spiral bd. 170.00 (***978-1-4108-5855-9(3)**); 2005. spiral bd. 130.00 (***978-1-4108-5856-6(1)**); 2005. spiral bd. 125.00 (***978-1-4108-3842-1(0)**) Benchmark Education Co.

—Science, Technology & Society. 2005. spiral bd. 185.00 (***978-1-4108-3753-0(X)**) Benchmark Education Co.

—Science, Technology, & Society. 2005. spiral bd. 70.00 (***978-1-4108-3954-1(0)**); spiral bd. 80.00 (***978-1-4108-3961-9(3)**); spiral bd. 80.00 (***978-1-4108-3962-6(1)**); spiral bd. 145.00 (***978-1-4108-4499-6(4)**); spiral bd. 110.00 (***978-1-4108-5425-4(6)**); spiral bd. 115.00 (***978-1-4108-5841-2(3)**); spiral bd. 74.00 (***978-1-4108-5842-9(1)**) Benchmark Education Co.

—Tools & Technology. 2006. spiral bd. 139.00 (***978-1-4108-7034-6(0)**) Benchmark Education Co.

Beshore, George W. Science in Ancient China. 1998. (Science of the Past Ser.). (Illus.). 64p. (J). (gr. 5-7). pap. 8.95 (978-0-531-15914-9(0) , Watts, Franklin) Scholastic Library Publishing.

—Science in Ancient China. 1998. (gr. 3-6). lib. bdg. 17.60 (978-0-613-72684-9(7)) Tandem Library Bks.

Biesty, Stephen & Platt, Richard. The Coolest Cross-Sections Ever. 2001. (Illus.). 128p. (J). 24.99 (978-0-7894-7964-8(8)) Dorling Kindersley Publishing, Inc.

Biggs, Andy, et al. Product Design for Key Stage 3. 2000. (Design & Make It Ser.). (Illus.). 144p. (J). (gr. 6-9). pap. 22.50 (978-0-7487-4429-9(0)) Nelson Thornes Ltd. GBR. *Dist:* Trans-Atlantic Pubns., Inc.

—Product Design for Key Stage 3: Teacher Support Pack. 2000. (Design & Make It Ser.). (Illus.). 244p. (J). (gr. 6-9). 99.50 (978-0-7487-4430-5(4)) Nelson Thornes Ltd. GBR. *Dist:* Trans-Atlantic Pubns., Inc.

Bitetto, Marco A. V. Science Fact of Space Warfare. 2000. 225p. (YA). pap. 49.95 (978-1-58578-351-9(X)) Institute of Cybernetics Research, Inc.

Book Steps, 6 Pack. (Bookweb Ser.). 32p. (gr. 5 up). 34.00 (978-0-7635-3800-2(0)) Rigby Education.

Brezina, Corona. The Industrial Revolution in America. 2005. (Illus.). 64p. (J). (gr. 5-8). lib. bdg. 29.25 (978-1-4042-0179-8(3)) Rosen Publishing Group, Inc., The.

Brooks, Philip. How Things Work. 2002. (Questions & Answers about... Ser.). (Illus.). 40p. (J). (gr. 4-8). pap. 7.95 (978-0-7534-5490-9(4) , Kingfisher) Houghton Mifflin Co. Trade & Reference Div.

Buckley, Susan Washburn. The Industrial Revolution: 1790-1850. 2002. (Reading Expeditions Ser.). (Illus.). 40p. (J). (978-0-7922-8685-1(5)) National Geographic Society.

Casanellas, Antonio. Great Discoveries & Inventions, 5 bks. Garousi, Ali, illus. Incl. Great Discoveries & Inventions That Advanced Industry & Technology. lib. bdg. 24.67 (978-0-8368-2583-1(7)); Great Discoveries & Inventions That Helped Explore Earth & Space. lib. bdg. 24.67 (978-0-8368-2584-8(5)); Great Discoveries & Inventions That Improved Human Health. lib. bdg. 24.67 (978-0-8368-2585-5(3)); Great Discoveries & Inventions That Improved Our Daily Lives. lib. bdg. 24.67 (978-0-8368-2586-2(1)); Great Discoveries & Inventions That Improved Transportation. lib. bdg. 24.67 (978-0-8368-2587-9(X)); 32p. (J). (gr. 4 up). (Illus.). 2000. Set lib. bdg. 123.35 (978-0-8368-2582-4(9)) Stevens, Gareth Inc.

—Great Discoveries & Inventions That Advanced Industry & Technology. Garousi, Ali, illus. 2000. (Great Discoveries & Inventions Ser.). 32p. (J). (gr. 4 up). lib. bdg. 24.67 (978-0-8368-2583-1(7)) Stevens, Gareth Inc.

Chancellor, Deborah & Murrell, Deborah. Everything You Need to Know: An Encyclopedia for Inquiring Young Minds. 2007. (Illus.). 320p. (J). (ps-3). 24.95 (***978-0-7534-6089-4(0)*** , Kingfisher) Houghton Mifflin Co. Trade & Reference Div.

Davidson, Avelyn. Dollars & Sense: Economics & Science. 2008. (Shockwave: Economics & Geography Ser.). 32p. (J). pap. 6.95 (***978-0-531-18836-1(1)*** , Children's Pr.) Scholastic Library Publishing.

Daynes, Katie. Toilets, Telephones & Other Useful Inventions. 2005. (Young Reading Series 1 Ser.). 48p. (J). (gr. 2 up). pap. 5.95 (978-0-7945-0888-3(X) , Usborne) EDC Publishing.

Dorling Kindersley Publishing Staff. Big Book of Knowledge. 2002. (Illus.). 480p. (J). (gr. 4-7). pap. 17.99 (978-0-7894-8501-4(X)) Dorling Kindersley Publishing, Inc.

—Big Book of Knowledge. 2002. (gr. 3-6). lib. bdg. 28.05 (978-0-613-75146-9(9)) Tandem Library Bks.

—Future. 2004. (Eyewitness Books). (Illus.). 72p. (J). lib. bdg. 19.99 (978-0-7566-0683-1(7)) Dorling Kindersley Publishing, Inc.

—Technology. 2000. (Eyewitness Bks.). (Illus.). 64p. (J). (gr. 4-7). lib. bdg. 19.99 (978-0-7894-6723-2(2)) Dorling Kindersley Publishing, Inc.

Dorling Kindersley Publishing Staff & Bridgman, Roger. Technology. 1999. (Eyewitness Bks.). (Illus.). 64p. (J). (gr. 3-7). 15.99 (978-0-7894-4887-3(4)) Dorling Kindersley Publishing, Inc.

Douglas, Vincent & School Specialty Publishing Staff. Tell Me about Science & Technology. 2004. (Tell Me Ser.). (Illus.). 224p. (J). pap. 14.95 (978-0-7696-3382-4(X) , Waterbird Bks.) School Specialty Publishing.

Encyclopedia of Technology & Applied Sciences, 11 vols. 2000. (Illus.). 1,500p. 657.07 (978-0-7614-7116-5(2) , Cavendish, Marshall Reference Bks.) Cavendish, Marshall Corp.

Faiella, Graham. The Technology of Mesopotamia. 2005. (Technology of the Ancient World Ser.). (Illus.). 48p. (J). (978-1-4042-0560-4(8)) Rosen Publishing Group, Inc., The.

Fourth grade Technology: 32 lessons every fourth grader should Know, 6. 2006. (Illus.). 104p. 22.99 net. (978-0-9787800-4-3(3)) Structured Learning.

Frontiers of Technology: Individual Title Six-Packs. (Rigby Infoquest Ser.). (gr. 5 up). 37.00 (978-0-7578-6522-0(4)) Rigby Education.

Futurekids Staff, creator. Mac 2 PC Study Guide: Grages K-12. 2002. tchr. ed., ring bd. (978-1-58739-400-3(6)) Futurekids, Inc.

Gaff, Jackie & Tyrrell, John. 70s & 80s: The High-Tech Age. 2000. (Twentieth Century Design Ser.). (Illus.). 32p. (J). (gr. 5 up). lib. bdg. 26.00 (978-0-8368-2709-5(0)) Stevens, Gareth Inc.

Gail Stewart. Written Communication. 2004. (Yesterday & Today Ser.). (Illus.). 32p. 23.70 (978-1-56711-834-6(8) , Blackbirch Pr., Inc.) Thomson Gale.

Garassino, Alessandro. La Vida. (SPA.). 40p. (YA). (gr. 5-8). (978-84-207-5697-4(0)) Grupo Anaya, S.A. ESP. *Dist:* Lectorum Pubns., Inc.

Gardner, Robert. Yesterday's Science, Today's Technology. (Illus.). 96p. (978-0-7613-3114-8(X) , Twenty-First Century Bks.) Lerner Publishing Group.

Graham, Ian, et al. Tomorrow's Technology, 4 vols. , Set. 1999. 32p. (J). lib. bdg. 67.80 (978-1-929298-43-3(9)) Chrysalis Education.

Grambo, Rebecca L. Technology. 2001. (It's All about! Ser.). (Illus.). 32p. (J). (gr. 2-5). lib. bdg. 25.27 (978-1-58952-162-9(5)) Rourke Publishing, LLC.

Greenberger, Robert. The Technology of Ancient China. 2005. (Technology of the Ancient World Ser.). (Illus.). 48p. (J). (978-1-4042-0558-1(6)) Rosen Publishing Group, Inc., The.

Greene, Meg. The Technology of Ancient Japan. 2005. (Technology of the Ancient World Ser.). (Illus.). 48p. (J). (978-1-4042-0559-8(4)) Rosen Publishing Group, Inc., The.

Grolier Educational Staff, contrib. by. Inside A—, 16 vols. 2000. (Illus.). 512p. (J). (gr. 5-8). 299.00 (978-0-7172-9521-0(4) , Grolier) Scholastic Library Publishing.

—The New Book of Popular Science, 6 vols. (Illus.). (J). 2003. 279.00 (978-0-7172-1224-8(6)); 2002. 3,798p. (978-0-7172-1223-1(8)); Set. 2000. 3100p. (gr. 6-12). lib. bdg. 269.00 (978-0-7172-1222-4(X)) Scholastic Library Publishing. (Grolier).

Group/McGraw-Hill, Wright. On the Move: Level H, 6 vols. (First Explorers Ser.). 24p. (gr. 1-2). 29.95 (978-0-7699-1449-7(7)) Shortland Pubns. (U. S. A.) Inc.

Groves, Marcia & Findon, Joanna. Science & Technology in the Middle Ages. 2004. (Medieval World Ser.). (Illus.). 32p. (J). (978-0-7787-1354-8(7)); pap. (978-0-7787-1386-9(5)) Crabtree Publishing Co.

Halstead, Rachel & Reid, Struan. Technology. 2004. (Hands-On History Ser.). (Illus.). 64p. pap. 10.99 (978-1-84215-858-6(9) , Southwater) Anness Publishing GBR. *Dist:* National Bk. Network.

Hands-On Science, Math, & Technology. 112p. (gr. 5-8). 14.99 (978-0-7682-0218-2(3) , GA13018) School Specialty Publishing.

Harding, Sandra & Figueroa, Robert, eds. Science & Other Cultures: Diversity in the Philosophy of Science & Technology. 2003. 304p. (gr. 13 up). 32.00 (978-0-415-93992-8(5)) Routledge.

Harms, Henry R. & Swernofsky, Neal. Technology Interactions. 1999. (Illus.). (YA). (gr. 6-12). stu. ed. 30.50 (978-0-02-838779-6(1)) Glencoe/McGraw-Hill.

Harms, Henry R., et al. Experience Technology: Manufacturing & Construction, Student Text. 2nd ed. 1999. (Illus.). 144p. (YA). (gr. 6-12). stu. ed. 28.99 (978-0-02-838739-0(2)) Glencoe/McGraw-Hill.

Harris, Nicholas, ed. High-Tech Science. 2002. (Blackbirch Visual Encyclopedia Ser.). (Illus.). 64p. (J). 38.70 (978-1-56711-522-2(5) , Blackbirch Pr., Inc.) Thomson Gale.

Heinz, Brian J. Nathan of Yesteryear & Michael of Today. Friar, Joanne H., illus. 2006. (Exceptional Social Studies Titles for Intermediate Grades). 32p. (J). lib. bdg. 22.60 (978-0-7613-2893-3(9) , Millbrook Pr.) Lerner Publishing Group.

Holt, Rinehart and Winston Staff. Harcourt Science & Technology: Strategies & Practice Answer Key. 4th ed. 2004. (Illus.). pap. 6.00 (978-0-03-019863-2(1)) Holt, Rinehart & Winston.

—Holt Ciencias y Technologia: Directed Reading Worksheets Answer Key: Texas Edition. 2nd ed. 2001. (gr. 6). pap. 12.00 (978-0-03-064627-0(8)) Holt, Rinehart & Winston.

—Holt Ciencias y Technologia: Directed Reading Worksheets: Texas Edition. 2nd ed. 2001. (J). pap. 20.00 (978-0-03-064628-7(6)) Holt, Rinehart & Winston.

—Holt Ciencias y Technologia: Study Guide with Answer Key: Texas Edition. 2nd ed. 2001. (J). (gr. 6). pap., stu. ed. 10.60 (978-0-03-064447-4(X)) Holt, Rinehart & Winston.

—Holt Ciencias y Technologia: Texas Edition. 2nd ed. 2001. (J). pap., stu. ed. 15.60 (978-0-03-064451-1(8)) Holt, Rinehart & Winston.

—Holt Science & Technology. 4th annot. ed. 2004. tchr. ed. 128.80 (978-0-03-073173-0(9)); tchr. ed. 128.80 (978-0-03-073174-7(7)); tchr. ed. 128.80 (978-0-03-073176-1(3)) Holt, Rinehart & Winston.

—Holt Science & Technology: Chapter Resources. 5th ed. 2005. pap. 87.36 (978-0-03-030632-7(9)) Holt, Rinehart & Winston.

—Holt Science & Technology: Custom A, F, K, M. 2nd ed. 2002. 65.60 (978-0-03-070041-5(8)) Holt, Rinehart & Winston.

—Holt Science & Technology: Custom Edition, C-D & K-L. 2nd ed. 2003. (Illus.). (J). 75.40 (978-0-03-036083-1(8)) Holt, Rinehart & Winston.

—Holt Science & Technology: Custom Edition: C, F, G, I, M. 2nd ed. 2002. 88.60 (978-0-03-070991-3(1)) Holt, Rinehart & Winston.

—Holt Science & Technology: Enhanced Online Edition. 2002. 74.53 (978-0-03-072489-3(9)) Holt, Rinehart & Winston.

—Holt Science & Technology: Online Edition Update, Level G. 2nd ed. 2003. 2.60 (978-0-03-037243-8(7)) Holt, Rinehart & Winston.

—Holt Science & Technology: Strategies & Practice Answer Key. 4th ed. 2004. (Illus.). pap. 6.00 (978-0-03-020022-9(9)); pap. 6.00 (978-0-03-019892-2(5)) Holt, Rinehart & Winston.

—Holt Science & Technology: Texas Edition. 2nd ed. 2002. (SPA.). (YA). (gr. 7). pap., stu. ed. 16.00 (978-0-03-069201-7(6)); (gr. 8). pap., stu. ed. 16.00 (978-0-03-069202-4(4)) Holt, Rinehart & Winston.

—Holt Science & Technology, Grade 7: Reinforcement Worksheets: Texas Edition. 2nd ed. 2001. pap. 21.61 (978-0-03-065983-6(3)) Holt, Rinehart & Winston.

—Holt Science & Technology, Grade 8: Reinforcement Worksheets: Texas Edition. 2nd ed. 2001. pap. 21.61 (978-0-03-065986-7(8)) Holt, Rinehart & Winston.

—NJ One-Stope Lesson Planner 2002. 2002. (Holt Science & Technology Ser.). (J). cd-rom 100.00 (978-0-03-072168-7(7)) Holt, Rinehart & Winston.

Jedicke, Peter. Scientific American. 2007. (Scientific American Ser.). 72p. (J). (gr. 5-8). 30.00 (978-0-7910-9048-0(5) , Chelsea Hse.) Facts On File, Inc.

Jefferis, David. Megatech, 8 bks. Incl. Alien Lifesearch : Quest for Extraterrestrial Organisms. 1999. lib. bdg. (978-0-7787-0049-4(6)); Artificial Intelligence : Robotics & Machine Evolution. 1999. lib. bdg. (978-0-7787-0046-3(1)); BioTech : Frontiers of Medicine. 2002. lib. bdg. (978-0-7787-0051-7(8)); Cloning : Frontiers of Genetic Engineering. 1999. lib. bdg. (978-0-7787-0048-7(8)); Cyberspace : Virtual Reality & the World Wide Web. 1999. lib. bdg. (978-0-7787-0047-0(X)); Internet : Electronic Global Village. 2002. lib. bdg. (978-0-7787-0052-4(6)); Into Infinity : From Earth to the Stars. 2001. lib. bdg. (978-0-7787-0050-0(X)); Super Subs : Opening up Undersea Frontiers. 2002. lib. bdg. (978-0-7787-0053-1(4)); 32p. (J). (gr. 4-5). (Illus.). 1998. Set pap. o.p. (978-0-7787-0045-6(3)); Set pap. (978-0-7787-0055-5(0)) Crabtree Publishing Co.

Jennings, Terry. Pushes & Pulls. 1998. (Find Out about Ser.). (Illus.). 24p. (J). (ps-3). (978-0-563-37467-1(5)) BBC Worldwide.

Johnson, Rebecca L. Nanotechnology. 2006. (Cool Science Ser.). (Illus.). 48p. (J). (gr. 4-8). lib. bdg. 26.60 (978-0-8225-2111-2(3) , Lerner Pubns.) Lerner Publishing Group.

Jones, Charlotte Foltz. Accidents May Happen. 1998. (Illus.). 96p. (J). (gr. 3-7). reprint ed. pap. 11.95 (978-0-385-32240-9(2) , Delacorte Bks. for Young Readers) Random Hse. Children's Bks.

—Accidents May Happen: 50 Inventions Discovered by Mistake. 1998. (J). 18.60 (978-0-606-13109-4(4)) Tandem Library Bks.

Jones, Glenda. Science & Technology Matters: Grade 4 Learner's Book. 2000. 96p. (gr. 4). pap., tchr. ed. 7.35 (978-0-521-78837-3(4)) Cambridge Univ. Pr.

Kindergarten Technology: 32 Lessons Every Kindergartner Should Know. 2006. 18.99 net. (978-0-9787800-0-5(0)) Structured Learning.

Lamb, Annette. Building Treehouses for Learning: Technology in Today's Classrooms. 2nd ed. 1999. (Illus.). 615p. (J). (gr. k-12). pap. 34.95 (978-1-891917-00-4(5)) Vision to Action, Inc.

Lockman, Darcy. Technology, 4 bks. Incl. Computer Animation. lib. bdg. 25.64 (978-0-7614-1048-5(1)); Computers. lib. bdg. 25.64 (978-0-7614-1045-4(7)); Internet. lib. bdg. 25.64 (978-0-7614-1046-1(5)); Robots. lib. bdg. 25.64 (978-0-7614-1047-8(3)); 48p. (J). (gr. 3 up). 2000. (Kaleidoscope Ser.). (Illus.). 2001. Set lib. bdg. 102.57 (978-0-7614-1044-7(9) , Benchmark Bks.) Cavendish, Marshall Corp.

MacDonald, Fiona. Science, Crafts & Technology. 2001. (Through the Ages Ser.). (Illus.). 64p. (gr. 3-7). 12.95 (978-0-7548-0850-3(5)) Anness Publishing GBR. *Dist:* National Bk. Network.

Marcovitz, Hal. Technology. 2006. (Gallup Major Trends & Events Ser.). (Illus.). 112p. (J). (gr. 7 up). lib. bdg. (978-1-59084-969-9(8)) Mason Crest Pubs.

Maynard, Charles W. The Technology of Ancient Greece. 2005. (Technology of the Ancient World Ser.). (Illus.). 48p. (J). (978-1-4042-0555-0(1)) Rosen Publishing Group, Inc., The.

—The Technology of Ancient Rome. 2005. (Technology of the Ancient World Ser.). (Illus.). 48p. (J). (978-1-4042-0556-7(X)) Rosen Publishing Group, Inc., The.

McDonagh, Sorcha, et al. Computers & Technology. 2006. (Science News for Kids Ser.). (Illus.). 64p. (J). 30.00 (978-0-7910-9120-3(1) , Chelsea Clubhouse) Facts On File, Inc.

McGraw-Hill Staff. Technology: Today & Tomorrow. 4th ed. 1998. stu. ed. 59.96 (978-0-02-658569-9(3) , 9780026585699); 5th ed. 2003. (C). (gr. 6-12). pap., stu. ed., wbk. ed. 12.64 (978-0-07-830831-4(3) , 9780078308314) Glencoe/McGraw-Hill.

McGraw-Hill Staff, et al. Technology: Today & Tomorrow. 5th ed. 2003. (gr. 6-12). stu. ed. 57.96 (978-0-07-830829-1(1) , 9780078308291) Glencoe/McGraw-Hill.

Metropolitan Toronto School Board Staff. By Design: Technology Exploration & Integration: Activities for Grades 6-9. 1999. (Illus.). 176p. (YA). pap., tchr. ed. 24.95 (978-1-895579-78-9(3)) Trifolium Bks., Inc. CAN. *Dist:* Fitzhenry & Whiteside, Ltd.

Mitchell, Melanie. From Cloth to American Flag. 2004. (Start to Finish Ser.). (J). pap. 4.95 (978-0-8225-2142-6(3)) Lerner Publishing Group.

Murray, Jacqui. Fifth grade Technology: 32 lessons every fifth grader should Know, 6. 2006. (Illus.). 104p. 22.99 net. (978-0-9787800-5-0(1)) Structured Learning.

NETS Project Staff, et al. NETS*S Curriculum Series: Multidisciplinary Units for Prekindergarten Through Grade 2. 2003. (National Educational Technology Standards for Students Curriculum Ser.). 306p. (J). pap. 34.95 (978-1-56484-200-8(2)) International Society for Technology in Education.

Nsrc. Science & Technology for Children Books, the Technology of Paper. 2004. (Illus.). 64p. (J). (978-1-933008-11-0(3)) National Science Resources Ctr.

O'Hara, Susan & McMahon, Maureen. NETS*S Curriculum Series: Multidisciplinary Units for Grades 6-8. 2003. (National Educational Technology Standards for Students Curriculum Ser.). (Illus.). 241p. (J). pap. 34.95 (978-1-56484-206-0(1)) International Society for Technology in Education.

Out & About: Level Q, 6 vols., Vol. 2. (Explorers Ser.). 32p. (gr. 3-6). 44.95 (978-0-7699-0608-9(7)) Shortland Pubns. (U. S. A.) Inc.

Oxlade, Chris. How Things Work. 2004. (Knowledge Masters Plus Ser.). (Illus.). 32p. (YA). pap. incl. cd-rom (978-1-903954-43-0(6)) Chrysalis Children's Bks.

—How Things Work: The Complete Illustrated Guide to the Amazing World of Technology. 2003. (Illus.). 512p. 45.00 (978-0-7548-1087-2(9) , Lorenz Bks.) Anness Publishing GBR. *Dist:* National Bk. Network.

TUV

—The Inside & Out Guide to Inventions. 2006. (Inside & Out Guides Ser.). (Illus.). 32p. (J). pap. (978-1-4034-9092-6(9)); lib. bdg. (978-1-4034-9085-8(6)) Heinemann Library.

—The Way Things Work: The Complete Illustrated Guide to the Amazing World of Technology. 2005. (Illus.). 512p. 24.99 (978-0-7548-1504-4(8) , Lorenz Bks.) Anness Publishing GBR. *Dist:* National Bk. Network.

Parker, Steve. 1900-20: A Shrinking World. 2001. (Twentieth Century Science & Technology Ser.). (Illus.). 32p. (J). (gr. 5 up). lib. bdg. 26.00 (978-0-8368-2942-6(5)) Stevens, Gareth Inc.

—1920-40: Atoms to Automation. 2001. (Twentieth Century Science & Technology Ser.). (Illus.). 32p. (J). (gr. 5 up). lib. bdg. 26.00 (978-0-8368-2943-3(3)) Stevens, Gareth Inc.

—1940-60: The Nuclear Age. 2001. (Twentieth Century Science & Technology Ser.). (Illus.). 32p. (J). (gr. 5 up). lib. bdg. 26.00 (978-0-8368-2944-0(1)) Stevens, Gareth Inc.

—1960s: Space & Time. 2001. (Twentieth Century Science & Technology Ser.). (Illus.). 32p. (J). (gr. 5 up). lib. bdg. 26.00 (978-0-8368-2945-7(X)) Stevens, Gareth Inc.

Pedal Power: Individual Title Six-Packs. (Bookweb Ser.). 32p. (gr. 6 up). 34.00 (978-0-7578-0913-2(8)) Rigby Education.

Pierce, Alan, et al. Introduction to Technology. 2nd ed. 1998. (Illus.). (C). (gr. 6-12). stu. ed. 61.32 (978-0-02-831275-0(9) , 9780028312750) Glencoe/McGraw-Hill.

Pierce, Franklin. Fiberglass Ding Repair: The Art of Polyester Resin/Fiberglas & Polyurathane Foam Surfboard Repairwork. 2004. (Illus.). 64p. (gr. 7 up). per. 19.95 (978-0-9744247-0-5(6)) Impulse Surf.

Platt, Richard. Technology & Communications. 2001. (Datafiles Ser.). (Illus.). 84p. (J). (gr. 3-7). 15.95 (978-1-57145-479-9(9) , Silver Dolphin Bks.) Advantage Pubs. Group.

Platt, Richard & Biesty, Stephen. Stephen Biesty's Incredible Cross-Sections Book. (Illus.). (J). pap. 24.95 (978-0-590-73870-5(4)) Scholastic, Inc.

Poggio, Pier Paolo & Simoni, Carlo. Development & Underdevelopment, 1945-1975. Bacchin, Giorgio, illus. 2002. (Road to Globalization Ser.). 32p. (YA). 22.95 (978-0-7910-7095-6(6)) Facts On File, Inc.

—The Global Community, 1975-2000. Bacchin, Giorgio, illus. 2002. (Road to Globalization Ser.). 32p. (YA). 22.95 (978-0-7910-7096-3(4)) Facts On File, Inc.

—Progress & the Empires, 1850-1900. Bacchin, Giorgio, illus. 2002. (Road to Globalization Ser.). 32p. (YA). 22.95 (978-0-7910-7093-2(X)) Facts On File, Inc.

—States, Wars, & Technologies, 1900-1945. Bacchin, Giorgio, illus. 2002. (Road to Globalization Ser.). 32p. (YA). 22.95 (978-0-7910-7094-9(8)) Facts On File, Inc.

Quadrillion Media Staff. Technology. 1999. (Start Me Up Ser.). (J). pap. 3.95 (978-1-58185-103-8(0)) Quadrillion Media LLC.

Real Journeys in Technology: Grade 2. 2001. (J). stu. ed., spiral bd., wbk. ed. (978-1-58739-222-1(4)) Futurekids, Inc.

Real Journeys in Technology: Kindergarten. 2001. (J). spiral bd., wbk. ed. (978-1-58739-210-8(0)) Futurekids, Inc.

Relf, Patricia. What's Happening? A Book of Explanations. Schwartz, Francis, illus. 2000. 32p. (J). (gr. 3-7). 15.95 (978-1-57255-841-0(5)) Mondo Publishing.

Relf, Patricia & Schwartz, Francis H. What's Happening? A Book of Explanations. 2000. (J). pap. 4.95 (978-1-57255-807-6(5)) Mondo Publishing.

Ring, Susan. What Is Technology? Date not set. (Early Science Big Bks.). (Illus.). 16p. (J). (ps-2). pap. 16.95 (978-1-58273-119-3(5)) Sundance/Newbridge Educational Publishing.

Romanek, Trudee. Technology Book for Girls: And Other Advanced Beings. Cupples, Pat, illus. unabr. ed. 2001. (Books for Girls Ser.). 56p. (J). (gr. 4-6). (978-1-55074-936-6(6)); (978-1-55074-619-8(7)) Kids Can Pr., Ltd.

—Technology Book for Girls: And Other Advanced Beings. 2001. (gr. 3-6). lib. bdg. 17.60 (978-0-613-49374-1(5)); 2000. (Illus.). (J). (978-0-606-21482-7(8)) Tandem Library Bks.

—The Technology Book for Girls & Other Advanced Beings. Cupples, Pat, tr. Cupples, Pat, illus. 2001. 56p. (J). (978-0-439-35872-9(8)) Scholastic, Inc.

Ross, Frank. Oracle Bones, Stars, & Wheelbarrows: Ancient Chinese Science & Technology. (gr. 5-8). lib. bdg. 15.25 (978-0-8335-6082-7(4)) Tandem Library Bks.

Rourke Publishing Staff. Rourke's World of Science Encyclopedia, 10 vols., Set. 2007. (J). (gr. 3-8). 329.95 (***978-1-60044-646-7(9)*** , 1-6467) Rourke Publishing, LLC.

Sarver, Amy. Science at the Mall. 2004. (National Geographic Reading Expeditions Ser.). (Illus.). 24p. (J). pap. (978-0-7922-4569-8(5)) National Geographic Society.

Scholastic, Inc. Staff. Amazing Air Racers. Im, Angela, ed. 2003. 24p. (J). pap. 9.99 (978-0-439-40965-0(9) , Tangerine Pr.) Scholastic, Inc.

Science & Technology. 2000. (Quick Start Masters Technology Ser.). (J). (gr. 1-2). (978-0-7725-2361-7(4)); (gr. 3-5). (978-0-7725-2365-5(7)); (gr. 5-6). (978-0-7725-2369-3(X)) Thomson Nelson.

Science & Technology for Children Books, Physical Sciences & Technology Library, 6 vols. 2004. (Illus.). 64p. (J). (978-1-933008-26-4(1)) National Science Resources Ctr.

Science & Technology for Children Books, Technology of Paper, 8 vols. 2004. (Illus.). 64p. (J). (978-1-933008-23-3(7)) National Science Resources Ctr.

Science & Technology in Focus, 6 Vols., Set. 2006. 192-208p. (gr. 6-12). 210.00 (978-0-8160-6781-7(3)) Facts On File, Inc.

Science & Technology in Focus Set 1. 2004. (Science & Technology in Focus Ser.). 208-240p. (gr. 9-12). 175.00 (978-0-8160-5836-5(9)) Facts On File, Inc.

Scott Foresman Reading: Technology. 2004. (gr. 1 up). cd-rom (978-0-328-04995-0(6)); (gr. 2-6). cd-rom (978-0-328-08680-1(0)); (gr. 2-6). cd-rom (978-0-328-09384-7(X)); (gr. 2 up). cd-rom (978-0-328-09374-8(2)); (gr. 2 up). cd-rom (978-0-328-09379-3(3)); (gr. 2 up). cd-rom (978-0-328-08681-8(9)); (gr. 2 up). cd-rom (978-0-328-08691-7(6)); (gr. 2 up). cd-rom (978-0-328-04996-7(4)); (gr. 3 up). cd-rom (978-0-328-08682-5(7)); (gr. 3 up). cd-rom (978-0-328-04997-4(2)); (gr. 3 up). cd-rom (978-0-328-08692-4(4)); (gr. 3 up). cd-rom (978-0-328-09375-5(0)); (gr. 3 up). cd-rom (978-0-328-09380-9(7)); (gr. 4 up). cd-rom (978-0-328-08683-2(5)); (gr. 4 up). cd-rom (978-0-328-04998-1(0)); (gr. 4 up). cd-rom (978-0-328-09381-6(5)); (gr. 4 up). cd-rom (978-0-328-08693-1(2)); (gr. 5 up). cd-rom (978-0-328-08694-8(0)); (gr. 5 up). cd-rom (978-0-328-08684-9(3)); (gr. 5 up). cd-rom (978-0-328-09382-3(3)); (gr. 5 up). cd-rom (978-0-328-09377-9(7)); (gr. 5 up). cd-rom (978-0-328-04999-8(9)); (gr. 6 up). cd-rom (978-0-328-09383-0(1)); (gr. 6 up). cd-rom (978-0-328-09378-6(5)); (gr. 6 up). cd-rom (978-0-328-08685-6(1)); (gr. 6 up). cd-rom (978-0-328-08695-5(9)); (gr. 6 up). cd-rom (978-0-328-05000-0(8)) Addison-Wesley Educational Pubs., Inc. (Scott Foresman).

Scott Foresman Science: Grade 4. 2001. tchr. ed. 136.95 incl. cd-rom (978-0-673-59314-6(2) , Scott Foresman) Addison Wesley Schl.

Second Grade Technology: 32 Lessons Every Second Grader Should Know, 6 vols. 2006. (Illus.). 56p. 19.99 net. (978-0-9787800-2-9(7)) Structured Learning.

Simon, Seymour. Destination: Jupiter. (Illus.). 32p. (J). 2000. (gr. k up). pap. 6.99 (978-0-06-443759-2(0) , Harper Trophy); 1998. (gr. 5 up). 15.95 (978-0-688-15620-6(7)) HarperCollins Pubs.

—Destination: Jupiter. 2000. (gr. 3-6). lib. bdg. 15.30 (978-0-613-33691-8(7)) Tandem Library Bks.

—Destination: Mars. 2000. (Illus.). 32p. (J). (ps-3). 15.95 (978-0-688-15770-8(X)) HarperCollins Pubs.

Sinclair, Peta-Jane. Science & Technology Matters: Grade 5. 2001. (gr. 5). pap., tchr. ed. 9.20 (978-0-521-78841-0(2)) Cambridge Univ. Pr.

—Science & Technology Matters: Grade 5 Learner's Book. 2001. (gr. 5). pap., tchr. ed. 6.90 (978-0-521-78838-0(2)) Cambridge Univ. Pr.

Sloan, Peter. What If? 1999. (gr. k-3). lib. bdg. 11.55 (978-0-613-30862-5(X)) Tandem Library Bks.

Sobey, Edwin J. C. What's That? A Field Guide to Technology. 2004. (Watts Reference Ser.). (J). lib. bdg. 39.50 (978-0-531-12221-1(2) , Watts, Franklin) Scholastic Library Publishing.

Solodky, M. The Technology of Ancient Egypt. 2005. (Technology of the Ancient World Ser.). (Illus.). 48p. (J). (978-1-4042-0557-4(8)) Rosen Publishing Group, Inc., The.

Soman & Swernofsky, Neal. Experience Technology: Communication, Production, Transportation, Biotechnology, Student Text. 2nd ed. 1999. (Illus.). 256p. (YA). (gr. 6-12). stu. ed. 28.99 (978-0-02-838719-2(8)) Glencoe/McGraw-Hill.

Steart, David. Brain Power-What's the Big Idea? 2005. (Illus.). 64p. (J). 14.99 (978-0-7641-5898-8(8)) Barron's Educational Series, Inc.

Stevens, Ray, et al. Technology 2. 1998. (Australian Technology Studies). (Illus.). 208p. pap. 23.00 (978-0-521-56574-5(X)) Cambridge Univ. Pr.

Tambini, Michael. Future. 2006. (DK Eyewitness Bks.). 72p. (J). 15.99 (978-0-7566-2244-2(1)); lib. bdg. 19.99 (978-0-7566-2245-9(X)) Dorling Kindersley Publishing, Inc.

Technology - Grade 3: Test Generator. 2000. (McGraw-Hill Science Ser.). (gr. 3 up). (978-0-02-280853-2(1)) Macmillan/McGraw-Hill Schl. Div.

Technology - Grade 4: Test Generator. 2000. (McGraw-Hill Science Ser.). (gr. 4 up). (978-0-02-280854-9(X)) Macmillan/McGraw-Hill Schl. Div.

Technology - Grade 6: Test Generator. 2000. (McGraw-Hill Science Ser.). (gr. 6 up). (978-0-02-280856-3(6)) Macmillan/McGraw-Hill Schl. Div.

Technology: Blueprints of the Future. 2005. (Technology Ser.). (Illus.). (gr. 4-8). lib. bdg. 159.00 (978-0-8239-7192-3(9)) Rosen Publishing Group, Inc., The.

Technology Helps Me: Fifth Grade Newcomer Books. (On Our Way to English Ser.). (gr. 5 up). 34.50 (978-0-7578-7278-5(6)) Rigby Education.

Technology in the Time Of, 6 bks., Set. 2000. (Illus.). (J). (978-0-7398-4217-1(X)) Raintree.

Technology Matters! Fifth Grade Class Collection Books. (On Our Way to English Ser.). (gr. 5 up). 29.95 (978-0-7578-4472-0(3)) Rigby Education.

Technology Matters! Small Versions of Class Collection Books. (On Our Way to English Ser.). (gr. 5 up). 34.50 (978-0-7578-7288-4(3)) Rigby Education.

Technology Through Time, 3 bks., Set. Incl. Communication Through Time. Oxlade, Chris. lib. bdg. 18.98 (978-0-8172-4141-4(8)); Ships Through Time. Richards, Roy. lib. bdg. 18.98 (978-0-8172-4138-4(8)); Toys Through Time. Oxlade, Chris. lib. bdg. 18.98 (978-0-8172-4139-1(6)); 48p. (J). (gr. 4-8). 1996. (Illus.). Set lib. bdg. 56.94 (978-0-7398-3299-8(9)) Raintree.

Technosports: Individual Title, 6 packs. (Bookweb Ser.). 32p. (gr. 4 up). 34.00 (978-0-7635-3746-3(2)) Rigby Education.

Tembo, Wilson. Creative & Technology Studies for Zambia Basic Education Grade 2. 2006. pap., stu. ed. 4.00 (978-0-521-69106-2(0)) Cambridge Univ. Pr.

—Creative Technology Studies for Zambia Basic Education Grade 1 Pupil's Book. 2005. 48p. pap. 3.70 (978-0-521-67364-8(X)) Cambridge Univ. Pr.

Third Grade Technology: 32 lessons every third grader should Know, 6. 2006. (Illus.). 85p. 22.99 net. (978-0-9787800-3-6(5)) Structured Learning.

Thomas, Mark. Maracana: El Estadio de Futbol Mas Grande del Mundo. 2004. (Estructuras Extraordinarias Ser.). (SPA & ENG., Illus.). 24p. (J). (gr. 3-6). lib. bdg. 17.25 (978-0-8239-6863-3(4) , Buenas Letra) Rosen Publishing Group, Inc., The.

—La Represa de Itaipu: La Represa Mas Grande Del Mundo. 2004. (Estructuras Extraordinarias Ser.). (SPA & ENG., Illus.). 24p. (J). (gr. 3-6). lib. bdg. 17.25 (978-0-8239-6865-7(0) , Buenas Letra) Rosen Publishing Group, Inc., The.

Top That Publishing Staff. Today's Technology. 2006. (Illus.). 48p. (978-1-84510-013-1(1)) Top That! Publishing PLC.

Transforming Power of Technology, 6 vols. 2005. (Transforming Power of Technology Ser.). (Illus.). 100+p. (gr. 9-13). pap. 180.00 (978-0-7910-7447-3(1) , Chelsea Hse.) Facts On File, Inc.

Turbulence Ahead: Individual Title Six-Packs. (Rigby Infoquest Ser.). 32p. (gr. 4 up). 37.00 (978-0-7578-5742-3(6)) Rigby Education.

Wagner, Douglas, et al. Stepping into Natural Science & Technology Matters Grade 4 Facilitator's Guide. 2nd rev. ed. 2004. 152p. (AFR.). pap. 14.45 (978-0-521-54449-8(1)); pap. 14.45 (978-0-521-54447-4(5)) Cambridge Univ. Pr.

—Stepping into Natural Science & Technology Matters Grade 4 Learner's Book. rev. ed. 2000. 168p. pap. (978-0-947465-87-2(1)); 2nd ed. 2004. 152p. pap., stu. ed. 8.85 (978-0-521-54446-7(7)) Cambridge Univ. Pr.

—Stepping into Natural Science & Technology Matters Grade 4 Learner's Book (Afrikaans Translation) 2nd rev. ed. 2004. (AFR.). 152p. pap. 8.85 (978-0-521-54448-1(3)) Cambridge Univ. Pr.

—Stepping into Natural Science & Technology Matters Grade 5 Facilitators Guide. 2nd rev. ed. 2000. 178p. pap. (978-0-947465-65-0(0)); 3rd rev. ed. 2004. (AFR.). 128p. pap. 14.35 (978-0-521-54641-6(9)) Cambridge Univ. Pr.

—Stepping into Natural Science & Technology Matters Grade 5 Facilitator's Guide Afrikaans Translation. 2nd rev. ed. 2004. (AFR.). 128p. pap. 14.35 (978-0-521-54643-0(5)) Cambridge Univ. Pr.

—Stepping into Natural Science & Technology Matters Grade 5 Learner's Book. 2nd rev. ed. 2004. 176p. pap. 9.25 (978-0-521-54640-9(0)); 2000. pap. (978-0-947465-66-7(9)) Cambridge Univ. Pr.

—Stepping into Natural Science & Technology Matters Grade 5 Learner's Book Afrikaans Translation. 2nd rev. ed. 2004. (AFR.). 176p. pap. 9.25 (978-0-521-54642-3(7)) Cambridge Univ. Pr.

—Stepping into Natural Science & Technology Matters Grade 6 Facilitators Guide. 2000. 158p. pap. (978-0-947465-77-3(4)) Cambridge Univ. Pr.

Wakumelo, Mubiana. Creative & Technology Studies for Zambia Basic Education Grade 6. 2006. pap., stu. ed. 3.99 (***978-0-521-70085-6(X)***) Cambridge Univ. Pr.

Weaver, Janice. The A to Z of Everyday Things. Blake, Francis, illus. 2004. 128p. (J). (gr. 5). pap. 8.95 (978-0-88776-671-8(4)) Tundra Bks., Inc./Livres Toundra, Inc. CAN. *Dist:* Random Hse., Inc.

Woodcock, John & Woodford, Chris. Cool Stuff 2.0: And How It Works. 2007. (Illus.). 256p. (J). (gr. 4-7). 24.99 (***978-0-7566-3207-6(2)***) Dorling Kindersley Publishing, Inc.

TECHNOLOGY—DICTIONARIES

Engelbert, Phillis. Technology in Action: Science Applied to Everyday Life, 3 vols. 1998. (Illus.). 523p. (J). (gr. 4-7). lib. bdg. 85.00 net. (978-0-7876-2809-3(3) , GML00402-112350, UXL) Thomson Gale.

—Technology Present & Future. 1998. (J). 79.95 (978-0-7876-2810-9(7)); 79.95 (978-0-7876-2811-6(5)) Thomson Gale. (UXL).

—Technology Present & Futures. 1999. (J). 79.95 (978-0-7876-2812-3(3) , UXL) Thomson Gale.

Holt, Rinehart and Winston Staff. Holt Science & Technology. 5th ed. 2003. (Illus.). 75.80 (978-0-03-066476-2(4)); 75.80 (978-0-03-066478-6(0)); 75.80 (978-0-03-066481-6(0)) Holt, Rinehart & Winston.

—Holt Science & Technology: Custom Edition - C, F & K. 2nd ed. 2003. (Illus.). 62.66 (978-0-03-036086-2(2)) Holt, Rinehart & Winston.

—Holt Science & Technology: Custom Edition - E, H-I & M. 2nd ed. 2003. (Illus.). 75.40 (978-0-03-036199-9(0)) Holt, Rinehart & Winston.

—Holt Science & Technology: Custom Edition - F, I & K-M. 2nd ed. 2003. (Illus.). (J). 86.00 (978-0-03-036084-8(6)) Holt, Rinehart & Winston.

—Holt Science & Technology: Custom Edition - H-J & O. 2nd ed. 2003. (Illus.). 75.40 (978-0-03-036198-2(2)) Holt, Rinehart & Winston.

—Holt Science & Technology: Online Edition Upgrade. 2nd ed. 2003. Level I. 10.60 (978-0-03-037203-2(8)); Level I. 2.60 (978-0-03-037246-9(1)); Level L. 10.60 (978-0-03-037207-0(0)); Level L. 2.60 (978-0-03-037249-0(6)); Level C. 10.60 (978-0-03-037196-7(1)); Level C. 2.60 (978-0-03-037238-4(0)); Level D. 10.60 (978-0-03-037197-4(X)); Level D. 2.60 (978-0-03-037239-1(9)); Level M. 10.60 (978-0-03-037208-7(9)); Level M. 2.60 (978-0-03-037251-3(8)); Level A. 10.60 (978-0-03-037193-6(7)); Level A. 2.60 (978-0-03-037236-0(4)); Level B. 10.60 (978-0-03-037194-3(5)); Level B. 2.60 (978-0-03-037237-7(2)); Level E. 10.60 (978-0-03-037198-1(8)); Level E. 2.60 (978-0-03-037241-4(0)); Level F. 10.60 (978-0-03-037199-8(6)); Level F. 2.60 (978-0-03-037242-1(9)); Level G. 10.60 (978-0-03-037201-8(1)); Level H. 10.60 (978-0-03-037202-5(X)); Level H. 2.60 (978-0-03-037244-5(5)); Level J. 10.60 (978-0-03-037204-9(6)); Level J. 2.60 (978-0-03-037247-6(X)); Level K. 10.60 (978-0-03-037206-3(2)); Level K. 2.60 (978-0-03-037248-3(8)); Level N. 10.60 (978-0-03-037209-4(7)); Level N. 2.60 (978-0-03-037252-0(6)); Level O. 10.60 (978-0-03-037211-7(9)); Level O. 2.60 (978-0-03-037253-7(4)) Holt, Rinehart & Winston.

How It Works: Science & Technology, 20 vols. 3rd ed. 2003. (J). (978-0-7614-7315-2(7)); (978-0-7614-7316-9(5)); (978-0-7614-7317-6(3)); (978-0-7614-7318-3(1)); (978-0-7614-7319-0(X)); (978-0-7614-7320-6(3)); (978-0-7614-7321-3(1)); (978-0-7614-7322-0(X)); (978-0-7614-7323-7(8)); (978-0-7614-7324-4(6)); (978-0-7614-7325-1(4)); (978-0-7614-7326-8(2)); (978-0-7614-7327-5(0)); (978-0-7614-7328-2(9)); (978-0-7614-7329-9(7)); (978-0-7614-7330-5(0)); (978-0-7614-7331-2(9)); (978-0-7614-7332-9(7)); (978-0-7614-7333-6(5)); (978-0-7614-7346-6(7)) Cavendish, Marshall Corp.

Nagel, Rob. U-X-L Encyclopedia of Science Vol. 1: A - As, 10 vols. 2nd ed. 2001. (Illus.). (J). (978-0-7876-5433-7(7) , UXL) Thomson Gale.

—U-X-L Encyclopedia of Science Vol. 2: At - Car, 10 vols. 2nd ed. 2001. (Illus.). (J). (978-0-7876-5434-4(5) , UXL) Thomson Gale.

—U-X-L Encyclopedia of Science Vol. 3: Cat - Cy, 10 vols. 2nd ed. 2001. (Illus.). (J). (978-0-7876-5435-1(3) , UXL) Thomson Gale.

—U-X-L Encyclopedia of Science Vol. 4: D - Em, 10 vols. 2nd ed. 2001. (Illus.). (J). (978-0-7876-5436-8(1) , UXL) Thomson Gale.

—U-X-L Encyclopedia of Science Vol. 5: En - G, 10 vols. 2nd ed. 2001. (Illus.). (J). (978-0-7876-5437-5(X) , UXL) Thomson Gale.

—U-X-L Encyclopedia of Science Vol. 6: H- Mar, 10 vols. 2nd ed. 2001. (Illus.). (J). (978-0-7876-5438-2(8) , UXL) Thomson Gale.

—U-X-L Encyclopedia of Science Vol. 7: Mas - O, 10 vols. 2nd ed. 2001. (Illus.). (J). (978-0-7876-5439-9(6) , UXL) Thomson Gale.

—U-X-L Encyclopedia of Science Vol. 8: P - Ra, 10 vols. 2nd ed. 2001. (Illus.). (J). (978-0-7876-5440-5(X) , UXL) Thomson Gale.

—U-X-L Encyclopedia of Science Vol. 9: Re - St, 10 vols. 2nd ed. 2001. (Illus.). (J). (978-0-7876-5441-2(8) , UXL) Thomson Gale.

—U-X-L Encyclopedia of Science Vol. 10: Su - Z, 10 vols. 2nd ed. 2001. (Illus.). (J). (978-0-7876-5775-8(1) , UXL) Thomson Gale.

The New Book of Popular Science 2008, 6 vols., Set. 2008. (YA). (gr. 7-12). lib. bdg. 299.00 (***978-0-7172-1226-2(2)***) Scholastic Library Publishing.

Scholastic Library Publishing Staff, contrib. by. The New Book of Popular Science, 6 vols., Set. 2006. (Illus.). (J). (gr. 7-12). 279.00 (978-0-7172-1225-5(4) , Grolier) Scholastic Library Publishing.

Wilsdon, Christina. Everyday Things: An A-Z Guide. 2002. (gr. 3-6). lib. bdg. 30.35 (978-0-613-72688-7(X)) Tandem Library Bks.

TECHNOLOGY—FICTION

Baker, Barrie. The Village of a Hundred Smiles. Jorisch, Stephane, illus. 1998. 48p. (J). (gr. k-3). lib. bdg. 18.95 (978-1-55037-522-0(9)) Firefly Bks., Ltd.

Home Technology: Individual Title Six-Packs. (Bookweb Ser.). 32p. (gr. 3 up). 34.00 (978-0-7635-3950-4(3)) Rigby Education.

Hulme, John, et al. The Seems: The Glitch in Sleep. 2007. (Illus.). 288p. (J). (gr. 5 up). 16.95 (***978-1-59990-129-9(3)*** , Bloomsbury Children) Bloomsbury Publishing.

McGough, Roger. Dotty Inventions: And Some Real Ones Too! Swain, Holly, illus. 2004. 32p. (J). 15.95 (978-1-84507-036-6(4)) Lincoln, Frances Ltd. GBR. *Dist:* Perseus Distribution.

Nanatsuki, Kyoichi. Project Arms, Vol. 13. Nanatsuki, Kyoichi, illus. 2006. (Project Arms Ser.). 208p. (YA). pap. 9.99 (978-1-4215-0502-2(9)) Viz Media.

Sleator, William. Rewind. 2001. 128p. (J). (ps-7). pap. 5.99 (978-0-14-131101-2(0) , Puffin) Penguin Group (USA) Inc.

Suen, Anastasia. Wired. 2001. (J). 15.95 (978-0-8050-6465-0(6) , Holt, Henry & Co. Bks. For Young Readers) Holt, Henry & Co.

TECHNOLOGY—VOCATIONAL GUIDANCE

Ferguson, J. G. Exploring Tech Careers, 2 vols., Set. 1998. 900p. 89.95 (978-0-8239-2289-5(8) , D2289-8) Rosen Publishing Group, Inc., The.

Granados, Christine & Garcia, Kimberly. Careers in Technology. 2001. (Latinos at Work Ser.). (Illus.). 96p. (gr. 5-12). lib. bdg. 32.75 (978-1-58415-087-9(4)) Mitchell Lane Pubs., Inc.

J. G. Ferguson Publishing Company Staff, ed. Exploring Tech Careers, 2 vols., Set. 3rd ed. 2001. (Illus.). 1000p. (YA). (978-0-89434-310-0(6) , Ferguson Publishing Co.) Facts On File, Inc.

TECHNOLOGY AND CIVILIZATION

Apel, Melanie Ann. Technology of Ancient Greece. 2004. (Primary Sources of Ancient Civilizations Ser.). (Illus.). 24p. (J). lib. bdg. (978-0-8239-8941-6(0)); lib. bdg. 19.95 (978-0-8239-6773-5(5)) Rosen Publishing Group, Inc., The. (PowerKids Pr.).

Bacchin, Giorgio, illus. Industrial Revolution, 1800-1850: A Social History. 2002. (Road to Globalization Ser.). 32p. (YA). 22.95 (978-0-7910-7092-5(1)) Facts On File, Inc.

Carlson, W. Bernard. Technology in World History, 7 vols. 2005. (Illus.). (J). (978-0-19-521823-3(3)); (978-0-19-521823-7(X)); (978-0-19-521824-4(8)); (978-0-19-521825-1(6)); (978-0-19-521826-8(4)); (978-0-19-521827-5(2)) Oxford Univ. Pr., Inc.

Carlson, W. Bernard, ed. Technology in World History, 7 vols. (Illus.). 2003. (J). (978-0-19-521822-0(1)); Set. 2005. 640p. 299.00 (978-0-19-521820-6(5)) Oxford Univ. Pr., Inc.

T U V

Gedacht, Daniel C. Technology of Ancient Rome. 2004. (Primary Sources of Ancient Civilizations Ser.). (Illus.). 24p. (J). lib. bdg. (978-0-8239-8947-8(X)); lib. bdg. 19.95 (978-0-8239-6779-7(4)) Rosen Publishing Group, Inc., The. (PowerKids Pr.).

Haywood, John. Science & Technology. 2004. (Illus.). 64p. pap. 8.99 (978-1-84215-956-9(9) , Southwater) Anness Publishing GBR. *Dist:* National Bk. Network.

Lorenz Books Staff, et al. Science & Technology: Humanity's Quest for Knowledge & Explanations, 4 vols. 2000. (Exploring History Ser.). (Illus.). 64p. (gr. 3-7). 12.95 (978-0-7548-0454-3(2) , Lorenz Bks.) Anness Publishing GBR. *Dist:* National Bk. Network.

Poggio, Pier Paolo & Simoni, Carlo. Development & Underdevelopment, 1945-1975. Bacchin, Giorgio, illus. 2002. (Road to Globalization Ser.). 32p. (YA). 22.95 (978-0-7910-7095-6(6)) Facts On File, Inc.

—Into the 21st Century 2000. Bacchin, Giorgio, illus. 2002. (Road to Globalization Ser.). 32p. (YA). 22.95 (978-0-7910-7097-0(2)) Facts On File, Inc.

—Progress & the Empires, 1850-1900. Bacchin, Giorgio, illus. 2002. (Road to Globalization Ser.). 32p. (YA). 22.95 (978-0-7910-7093-2(X)) Facts On File, Inc.

—States, Wars, & Technologies, 1900-1945. Bacchin, Giorgio, illus. 2002. (Road to Globalization Ser.). 32p. (YA). 22.95 (978-0-7910-7094-9(8)) Facts On File, Inc.

TECUMSEH, SHAWNEE CHIEF, 1768-1813

Aller, Susan Bivin. Tecumseh. 2004. (History Maker Bios Ser.). (J). pap. 6.95 (978-0-8225-2073-3(7)); (Illus.). 48p. 26.60 (978-0-8225-0699-7(8) , Carolrhoda Bks.) Lerner Publishing Group.

Collier, James Lincoln. The Tecumseh You Never Knew. Copeland, Greg, illus. 2004. (You Never Knew Ser.). (J). 25.50 (978-0-516-24426-6(4) , Children's Pr.) Scholastic Library Publishing.

Connell, Kate. These Lands Are Ours: Tecumseh's Fight for the Old Northwest. 2001. (Nonfiction Bookbag Ser.). (J). (gr. 5-6). per. 8.45 (978-1-58830-206-9(7)) Metropolitan Teaching & Learning Co.

Fitterer, C. Ann. Tecumseh: Chief of the Shawnee. 2002. (Spirit of America: Our People Ser.). (Illus.). 32p. (J). (gr. 2-6). 27.07 (978-1-56766-168-2(8)) Child's World, Inc.

Gregson, Susan R. Tecumseh: Shawnee Leader. 2003. (Let Freedom Ring Ser.). (Illus.). 48p. (J). (gr. 3-4). lib. bdg. 22.60 (978-0-7368-1556-7(2) , Bridgestone Bks.) Capstone Pr., Inc.

Koestler-Grack, Rachel A. Tecumseh 1768-1813. 2002. (American Indian Biographies Ser.). (Illus.). 32p. (J). (gr. 3-4). lib. bdg. 23.93 (978-0-7368-1212-2(1) , Blue Earth Bks.) Capstone Pr., Inc.

Marsh, Carole. Tecumseh: An Ohio Experience Reader. 2001. (J). (gr. k-5). pap. 1.95 (978-0-635-00431-4(3)) Gallopade International.

Mayer, Cassie. Tecumseh. 2007. (J). ***(978-1-4034-9975-2(6));*** pap. ***(978-1-4034-9984-4(5))*** Heinemann Library.

McLeese, Don. Tecumseh. 2003. (Native American Legends Ser.). (Illus.). 32p. (J). 28.50 (978-1-58952-731-7(3)) Rourke Publishing, LLC.

Todd, Anne M. Chief Tecumseh. 2004. (Illus.). 32p. (J). pap. 7.50 (978-1-4034-5009-8(9)); lib. bdg. 24.22 (978-1-4034-5002-9(1)) Heinemann Library.

TEDDY BEARS

Ada, Alma Flor & Compoy, F. Isabel. Donde Esta Mi Osito? 3rd ed. 2002. (Trofeos Ser.). (SPA.). (gr. k-6). pap. 19.70 (978-0-15-330488-0(X)) Harcourt Schl. Pubs.

Bart, Kathleen. A Tale of Two Teddies. 2005. 32p. (J). (978-1-932485-23-3(6)) Reverie Publishing Co.

—A Tale of Two Teddies: The First Teddy Bears Tell Their True Stories. Bart, Kathleen, illus. 2001. (Illus.). 40p. pap. 16.95 (978-0-942620-51-1(8)) Portfolio Pr. Corp.

Beck, Isabel L., et al. Trophies Kindergarten: Where's My Teddy? 2003. (Trophies Ser.). (gr. k-6). 13.80 (978-0-15-329517-1(1)) Harcourt Schl. Pubs.

Craven, Lon Eric, illus. ABC Coloring Book: March of the Teddy Bears Kansas City 2002. l.t. ed. 2002. 32p. per. 5.95 (978-0-9717080-9-9(6)) Kansas City Star Bks.

Harcourt School Publishers Staff. Teddy Takes a Vacation On Level. 3rd ed. 2002. (Trophies Reading Program Ser.). (Illus.). pap. 5.10 (978-0-15-323087-5(8)) Harcourt Schl. Pubs.

Kennedy, Jimmy. Teddy Bears' Picnic. 2000. (gr. k-3). lib. bdg. 14.15 (978-0-613-88163-0(X)) Tandem Library Bks.

Lorenz Books Staff. Teddy Bears: With over 50 Reusable Stickers. 1999. (Sticker Fun Ser.). (Illus.). 16p. (ps-k). pap. 4.95 (978-0-7548-0049-1(0) , Lorenz Bks.) Anness Publishing GBR. *Dist:* National Bk. Network.

Lorenz Books Staff & Tuxworth, Nicola. Teddy Bears. 2000. (Very First Picture Bks.). (Illus.). 12p. bds. 4.95 (978-0-7548-0065-1(2) , Lorenz Bks.) Anness Publishing GBR. *Dist:* National Bk. Network.

McCafferty, Jim. Holt & the Teddy Bear. Davis, Florence S., illus. 2001. 40p. (J). pap. 9.95 (978-1-56554-580-9(X)) Pelican Publishing Co., Inc.

Priddy, Roger. Teddy Bears. 2005. (Sticker Activity Fun Workbooks). (Illus.). 48p. (J). pap. 3.47 (978-0-312-49664-7(8) , Priddy Bks.) St. Martin's Pr.

Priddy, Roger & Priddy Books Staff. Sticker Activity Fun Teddy Bears: Play & Learn. rev. ed. 2006. 48p. (J). bds. 3.47 (978-0-312-49799-6(7) , Priddy Bks.) St. Martin's Pr.

Southwater Books Staff. Funtime Teddy Bear Stickers. 2000. (Superstickers Ser.). (Illus.). 64p. (ps-2). pap. 7.95 (978-1-84215-059-7(6) , Southwater) Anness Publishing GBR. *Dist:* National Bk. Network.

TEDDY BEARS—FICTION

Akmon, Roni & Akmon, Nancy C. Roosevelt Bears Traveling Adventures. 2000. (Illus.). 28p. (J). (ps-3). 10.95 (978-1-884807-50-3(X) , EC 750) Blushing Rose Publishing.

Alexander, Martha G. I'll Protect You from the Jungle Beasts. Alexander, Martha G., illus. 2006. (Illus.). 32p. (J). 9.95 (978-1-57091-677-9(2)) Charlesbridge Publishing, Inc.

Allison, Catherine & Scholastic, Inc. Staff. Brown Paper Teddy Bear. Reed, Neil & Harper, Piers, illus. 2004. 32p. (J). (ps-3). pap. 16.95 (978-0-439-63900-2(X) , Cartwheel Bks.) Scholastic, Inc.

Ashforth, Camilla. Willow at Christmas. Ashforth, Camilla, illus. 2005. (Illus.). 32p. (J). (ps-1). pap. 3.99 (978-0-7636-2927-4(8)) Candlewick Pr.

Atkinson, Robert. Daddy Monster Tells the Tale of the Teddy Bear. Atkinson, Robert, illus. 2001. (J). spiral bd. 16.95 (978-0-9717868-6-8(0)) WordWright.biz, Inc.

Aylesworth, Jim. Teddy Bear Tears. 2000. (gr. k-3). lib. bdg. 14.15 (978-0-613-28667-1(7)) Tandem Library Bks.

The Bear Who Had No Name. 2006. (J). 10.00 ***(978-0-9760076-1-6(4))*** Juniper Berry Pr.

Beck, Ian. Lost in the Snow. 2000. (Illus.). (J). pap. (978-0-439-17521-0(6)) Scholastic, Inc.

—The Teddy Robber. 2000. (Illus.). 32p. (J). pap. 8.95 (978-0-552-52593-0(6)) Transworld Publishers Ltd. GBR. *Dist:* Trafalgar Square Publishing.

Blackman, Malorie. Sinclair, Wonder Bear. Allwright, Deborah, illus. 2005. (Blue Go Bananas Ser.). 43p. (J). (978-0-7787-2631-9(2)) Crabtree Publishing Co.

Blizzard, Vicki, ed. Teddy Bear Treasures Transfer Book. 2000. (Illus.). 224p. (J). pap. 24.95 (978-1-882138-57-9(0)) House of White Birches, Inc.

Bowman, Crystal. Morning, Mr. Ted. Conrad, Liz, illus. 2001. 12p. (J). pap. 5.99 (978-0-310-70060-9(4)) Zondervan.

Braybrooks, Ann & Milne, A. A. Pooh, the Great Riddle Contest. 2000. (Illus.). pap. (978-0-307-98915-4(1) , Golden Bks.) Random Hse. Children's Bks.

Brown, Gwen. Clifford & His Bear. 2006. (Illus.). 48p. pap. ***(978-1-84401-650-1(1))*** Athena Pr.

Brown, Janet Allison. Teddy Backpack. O'Neill, Rachael, illus. 2007. 10p. (J). bds. 12.95 (978-1-4027-4481-5(1)) Sterling Publishing Co., Inc.

Brown, Margaret Wise & Wiggins, Beth Foster. Buenas noches Oso. 2006. 24p. (J). 12.95 (978-1-882077-61-8(X)) Sweetwater Pr.

Brown, Ruth. Night-Time Tale. 2007. (Illus.). 32p. (J). pap. 9.95 ***(978-1-84270-475-2(3))*** Andersen GBR. *Dist:* Independent Pubs. Group.

Buckley, Charlie. How to Wash Your Hands. 2007. (Show Jo Language Development Ser.). (Illus.). 16p. (J). (ps-1). per., bds. 14.95 ***(978-1-933669-09-0(8))*** Literary Architects, LLC.

—Show Jo How to Make a Sandwich. 2007. (Show Jo Language Development Ser.). (Illus.). 16p. (J). (ps-1). per., bds. 14.95 ***(978-1-933669-08-3(X))*** Literary Architects, LLC.

Burgess, Mark. Teddy Time. 2001. (Illus.). 32p. (J). (ps-k). pap. 9.99 (978-0-00-664691-4(3)) HarperCollins Pubs. Ltd. GBR. *Dist:* Independent Pubs. Group.

Burke, Ellinor Rozecki. Susana Worrywart & the Magical Teddy Bear Balloon: With CD for Relaxation. Perciopelo, illus. 2003. 32p. (J). 27.00 incl. audio compact disk (978-0-9741586-0-0(7)) Comfort Tales, LLC.

Carmichael, Clay. El Osito Usado. 2000. (SPA., Illus.). (J). (978-0-606-18319-2(1)) Tandem Library Bks.

—Used-up Bear. 2000. (Illus.). (978-0-606-18326-0(4)) Tandem Library Bks.

Clarke, Gus. Eddie & Teddy. 2004. (Illus.). 32p. (J). pap. 8.99 (978-1-84270-373-1(0)) Andersen GBR. *Dist:* Independent Pubs. Group.

Cole, Stephen. The Adventures of Mr. Bean. 2002. (Illus.). 64p. (J). pap. 6.99 (978-1-84222-658-2(4)) Carlton Bks., Ltd. GBR. *Dist:* Independent Pubs. Group.

Conrad, Liz, illus. Bedtime Bear. 1999. (J). (978-1-892374-26-4(9)) Weldon Owen, Inc.

Corser-Gay, Joan. Jennifer Jane's Blanky. Corser-Gay, Joan, illus. 1999. 13p. (J). pap. 8.95 (978-0-7414-0233-2(5)) Infinity Publishing.

Cox, Phil Roxbee. Ted in A Red Bed. Cartwright, Stephen, illus. rev. ed. 2006. 16p. (J). pap. 6.99 (978-0-7945-1510-2(X) , Usborne) EDC Publishing.

—Ted's Shed. Cartwright, Stephen, illus. rev. ed. 2006. 16p. (J). pap. 6.99 (978-0-7945-1511-9(8) , Usborne) EDC Publishing.

Cox, Phil Roxbee & Cartwright, S. Ted's Shed, Toad Makes a Road, Fat Cat on a Mat & Sam Sheep Can't Sleep. 2004. (Easy Words to Read Ser.). (Illus.). 16p. (J). (gr. 1 up). pap. 9.95 (978-0-7945-0245-4(8) , Usborne) EDC Publishing.

Cox, Phil Roxbee & Cartwright, Stephen. Ted's Shed. 2004. (Phonics Board Bks.). (Illus.). 10p. (J). 4.95 (978-0-7945-0304-8(7) , Usborne) EDC Publishing.

Curtiss, A. B. & Lucarelli, Sue. T Bear's Tale. 2005. 40p. 18.95 (978-0-932529-80-0(1)) Oldcastle Publishing.

Davis, Lee. Spooky Game: Bear Read Alone. 2001. (Pajama Bedtime Bear Ser.). (Illus.). 24p. (J). (ps-1). pap. 6.95 (978-0-7894-4945-0(5) , D K Ink) Dorling Kindersley Publishing, Inc.

—Where Is P. B. Bear? 2001. (P. B. Bear Ser.). (Illus.). 24p. (J). (ps-1). pap. 4.95 (978-0-7894-2222-4(0) , D K Ink) Dorling Kindersley Publishing, Inc.

De Bear, Tedrick & Rizzi, Trefoni Michael. Teddy's Travels: America's National Parks. 2006. (Illus.). 128p. (J). spiral bd. 19.95 (978-0-9740494-0-3(9)) TdB Pr. LLC.

Dematons, Charlotte. Worry Bear. 1998. (Illus.). 32p. (J). 15.95 (978-1-886910-83-6(9) , Lemniscaat) Boyds Mills Pr.

Dietrich, Sean, creator. Industriacide. 2004. (Illus.). 120p. (YA). per. 11.99 (978-0-9748654-0-9(0)) Rorschach Entertainment.

Disney Staff. Big Things, Little Things. Disney Staff, illus. 1999. (Pooh's Learn & Grow Ser.: Vol. 9). (Illus.). 12p. (J). 3.49 (978-1-57973-043-7(4)) Advance Pubs. LLC.

—Pooh's Noisy Book. 1999. (Learn & Grow Busy Book Ser.). (Illus.). 12p. (J). (ps-3). 6.99 (978-0-7364-0136-4(9)) Mouse Works.

—Winnie the Pooh. (FRE.). 96p. (J). (gr. k-5). pap. 9.95 (978-0-7859-8848-9(3)) French & European Pubns., Inc.

D'Lacey, Chris. Franklin's Bear. Taylor, Thomas, illus. 2005. (Red Go Bananas Ser.). 42p. (J). lib. bdg. (978-0-7787-2674-6(6)) Crabtree Publishing Co.

Douglas, Babette. Larkspur: And His Wooden Nose. 2005. (J). 9.99 (978-1-890343-23-1(4)) Kiss A Me Productions, Inc.

Doyle, Malachy. Teddybear Blue. Bretschneider, Christina, illus. 2004. 32p. (J). 15.95 (978-1-84507-001-4(1)) Lincoln, Frances Ltd. GBR. *Dist:* Perseus Distribution.

Dracker, Pune. Doll & Teddy Bear Activity Book. Bart, Kathleen & Hofmann, Ginnie, illus. 2005. 96p. (J). pap. (978-1-932485-24-0(4)) Reverie Publishing Co.

Dray, Matt. Dougal, the Garbage Dump Bear. 2005. (Illus.). 40p. (J). (ps-ps). 14.95 (978-1-929132-78-2(6)) Kane/Miller Bk. Pubs., Inc.

—Dougal, the Garbage Dump Bear. Dray, Matt, illus. 2005. (Illus.). 32p. (J). pap. (978-0-14-350097-1(X)) Penguin Group (USA) Inc.

Ellwand, David. Tickle Teddy: A Touch & Feel Book. 2002. (Illus.). 10p. (J). 12.95 (978-1-929766-57-4(2)) Handprint Bks.

Faundez, Anne. Teddy's Birthday. 2004. (QEB Start Talking Ser.). (Illus.). 24p. (J). lib. bdg. 15.95 (978-1-59566-004-6(6)) QEB Publishing Inc.

Feinman, Myke. In Search of the First Teddy Bear. Feinman, Anthony, photos by. 2002. (Illus.). 16p. (J). 4.95 (978-0-9664974-4-1(9)) Ink & Feathers Comics.

First Teddy Bear Stories. (J). 2002. bds. 4.98 (978-0-7525-4109-9(9)); 2001. bds. 19.95 (978-0-7525-6556-9(7)) Parragon, Inc.

Fox, Christyan & Fox, Diane. What Shape Is That, Piggywiggy? 2002. (Illus.). 10p. (J). (ps-k). bds. 5.95 (978-1-929766-44-4(0)) Handprint Bks.

—What's the Opposite, Piggywiggy? 2002. (Illus.). 10p. (J). (ps-k). bds. 5.95 (978-1-929766-43-7(2)) Handprint Bks.

Freedman, Claire. Night-Night, Emily! Massey, Jane, illus. 2005. 32p. (J). 6.95 (978-1-58925-390-2(6) , tiger tales) ME Media LLC.

—Night-Night, Emily! Massey, Jane, tr. Massey, Jane, illus. 2003. 32p. (J). (ps-1). tchr. ed. 15.95 (978-1-58925-032-1(X) , tiger tales) ME Media LLC.

Freeman, Don. Christmas Is Here, Corduroy! 2007. 16p. (J). (ps-1). pap. 5.99 ***(978-0-448-44650-9(2)*** , Grosset & Dunlap) Penguin Group (USA) Inc.

—Corduroy. 2007. (Puffin Storytime Ser.). 32p. (J). (ps). pap. 9.99 (978-0-14-240839-1(5) , Puffin) Penguin Group (USA) Inc.

—Corduroy's ABC Felt Read & Play. McCue, Lisa, illus. 2007. 10p. (J). (ps). pap. 16.99 ***(978-0-670-06197-6(2)*** , Viking Juvenile) Penguin Group (USA) Inc.

—Corduroy's Best Halloween Ever. McCue, Lisa, illus. 2001. (Reading Railroad Bks.). 32p. (J). (gr. k-1). 3.99 (978-0-448-42499-6(1) , Grosset & Dunlap) Penguin Group (USA) Inc.

—Corduroy's Best Halloween Ever. 2001. (gr. k-3). lib. bdg. 11.25 (978-0-613-72457-9(7)); (Illus.). (J). 10.29 (978-0-606-21123-9(3)) Tandem Library Bks.

—A Pocket for Corduroy. Freeman, Don, illus. 2004. (Illus.). (J). pap. 18.95 incl. audio compact disk (978-1-59112-793-2(9)) Live Oak Media.

—Rhymes & Riddles with Corduroy. 2002. (gr. k-3). lib. bdg. 11.25 (978-0-613-51510-8(2)) Tandem Library Bks.

Freeman, Don & Hennessy, B. G. Corduroy's Sleepover. 2007. 20p. (J). 11.99 (978-0-670-06185-3(9) , Viking Juvenile) Penguin Group (USA) Inc.

Freeman, Don & Inches, Alison. Corduroy Makes a Cake. Eitzen, Allan, illus. 2003. 32p. (J). (gr. k-3). pap. 3.99 (978-0-14-250163-4(8) , Puffin) Penguin Group (USA) Inc.

—Corduroy Writes a Letter. Eitzen, Allan, illus. 2004. (Easy-to-Read, Puffin Ser.). 32p. (J). (gr. k-3). pap. 3.99 (978-0-14-240130-9(7) , Puffin) Penguin Group (USA) Inc.

Gaines, Isabel. Eeyore Finds Friends. 1999. (Winnie the Pooh First Readers Ser.: No. 11). (Illus.). 37p. (J). (gr. k-3). pap. 3.99 (978-0-7868-4269-8(5)) Disney Pr.

—Pooh's Easter Egg Hunt. 1999. (Winnie the Pooh First Readers Ser.: No. 10). (Illus.). 40p. (J). (gr. k-3). pap. 3.99 (978-0-7868-4268-1(7)) Disney Pr.

—Pooh's Halloween Pumpkin: Disney Winnie the Pooh. 2003. (ps-2). lib. bdg. 11.80 (978-0-613-73693-0(1)) Tandem Library Bks.

—Pooh's Honey Tree. 2002. (gr. k-3). lib. bdg. 11.80 (978-0-613-65133-2(2)) Tandem Library Bks.

—Pooh's Surprise Basket. 1999. (Winnie the Pooh First Readers Ser.: No. 13). (Illus.). 37p. (J). (gr. k-3). pap. 3.99 (978-0-7868-4332-9(2)) Disney Pr.

—Pooh's Valentine. Marderosian, Mark & Lopez, Paul, illus. 2004. (Step into Reading Ser.). 32p. (J). (ps-1). pap. 3.99 (978-0-7364-2264-2(1) , RH/Disney) Random Hse. Children's Bks.

Gaines, Isabel & Random House Disney Staff. Pooh's Halloween Pumpkin. Yee, Josie, illus. 2003. (Disney Winnie the Pooh Ser.). 32p. (J). (ps-1). pap. 3.99 (978-0-7364-2160-7(2) , RH/Disney) Random Hse. Children's Bks.

Gaines, Isabel, et al. Pooh's Easter Egg Hunt. 2002. (Step into Reading Ser.). (Illus.). 32p. (J). (ps-1). pap. 3.99 (978-0-7364-1208-7(5) , RH/Disney) Random Hse. Children's Bks.

Garcia, Jerry. Jerry Bear. 1999. 9.95 (978-0-694-01300-5(5)) HarperCollins Pubs.

Golden Books Staff. Winnie the Pooh. 2000. (J). (ps-3). pap. 2.99 (978-0-307-05545-3(0) , 05545, Golden Bks.) Random Hse. Children's Bks.

Grams, Kimberly. Smedley & the Sprinkle Machine. 2005. 59p. pap. 12.95 (978-1-4241-0184-9(0)) PublishAmerica, Inc.

Group/McGraw-Hill, Wright. The Humpback Tedy: Level E, 6 vols. (Take Twostm Ser.). 16p. 29.95 (978-0-322-08952-5(2)) Wright Group, The.

Guy, Ginger Foglesong. Siesta. Moreno, Rene King, illus. 2005. (ENG & SPA.). 32p. (J). lib. bdg. 16.89 (978-0-06-056063-8(0)); 15.99 (978-0-06-056061-4(4)) HarperCollins Pubs.

Hachler, Bruno. What Does My Teddy Bear Do All Night? Muller, Birte, illus. 2005. 32p. (J). (ps-2). 14.99 (978-0-698-40029-0(1) , Minedition) Penguin Group (USA) Inc.

Hacke, Alex. Bear Called Sunday. 2004. (Illus.). 32p. (J). 14.95 (978-1-58234-929-9(0) , Bloomsbury Children) Bloomsbury Publishing.

Hale, Nathan. Yellowbelly & Plum Go to School. Hale, Nathan, illus. 2007. (Illus.). 32p. (J). (ps-1). 16.99 (978-0-399-24624-1(X) , Putnam Juvenile) Penguin Group (USA) Inc.

Hall, Margaret. Sebastian in Central Park. Wenzel, David, illus. 2001. (Suitcase Bear Adventures Ser.: Vol. 1). (J). (978-0-9713174-0-6(2) , Bear & Co.) Bear & Co.

Hall, Margaret & Jones, Dawn L. Sebastian at the Tower of London. Wenzel, David, illus. 2001. (Suitcase Bear Adventures Ser.). (J). (978-0-9713174-1-3(0) , Bear & Co.) Bear & Co.

—Sebastian in Egypt. Wenzel, David, illus. 2001. (Suitcase Bear Adventures Ser.). (J). (978-0-9713174-2-0(9) , Bear & Co.) Bear & Co.

Harper, Charise Mericle. Good Night, Leo: A Swashbuckling Bedtime Adventure. 2008. (Illus.). 24p. (J). (gr. k-k). bds. 6.99 ***(978-0-375-84234-4(9)*** , Robin Corey Bks.) Random Hse. Children's Bks.

Hegg, Tom. Peef & His Best Friend. Hanson, Warren, illus. 2001. 48p. (J). (ps up). 15.95 (978-0-931674-49-5(2)) Waldman Hse. Pr., Inc.

—A Silent Night for Peef. Hanson, Warren, illus. 1998. 48p. (J). (ps-3). 15.95 (978-0-931674-35-8(2)) Waldman Hse. Pr., Inc.

Hegg, Tom & Hanson, Warren. Peef & the Baby Sister. Hegg, Tom & Hanson, Warren, illus. 2006. (J). (978-0-931674-67-9(0)) Waldman Hse. Pr., Inc.

Heiney, Peggy Price. Lonely Teddy. Wellman, Megan D., illus. 2006. (J). 18.95 ***(978-1-933916-67-5(2)*** , Ferne Pr.) Nelson Publishing & Marketing.

Hennessy, B. G. Corduroy Lost & Found. Wheeler, Jody, illus. 2006. 32p. (J). (ps). 15.99 (978-0-670-06100-6(X) , Viking Juvenile) Penguin Group (USA) Inc.

Hennessy, B. G. & Freeman, Don. Corduroy Goes to the Library. 2005. 20p. (J). (gr. 1). 11.99 (978-0-670-05991-1(9) , Viking Juvenile) Penguin Group (USA) Inc.

Henny, Rose. Teddy Finds His Way: A Teddy Tale. Henny, Rose, illus. l.t. ed. 2005. (Illus.). 22p. (J). per. 12.95 (978-0-9705458-7-9(8)) Royalty Bks. International.

Henson, John, illus. Sarah Lynn's Christmas Present. 2002. (J). 24.95 (978-0-9711706-8-1(1)) Waiver Publishing.

Herman, Gail. Se Vende un Osito. 2000. (Coleccion "Hola, Lector" Ser.). (SPA., Illus.). (J). pap. (978-0-439-08701-8(5)) Scholastic, Inc.

Herrington, Chris. Harry & Hannah: The American Adventure. Pacheco, Jorge M., illus. 2003. (Adventures of Harry & Hannah Ser.). 72p. (gr. 1-5). 15.00 (978-0-9722343-0-6(6)) Herrington Teddy Bears.

Hill, Eric. Spot Sleeps Over. Hill, Eric, illus. 2004. (Spot Ser.). (Illus.). 24p. (J). (ps-1). pap. 6.99 (978-0-14-240168-2(4) , Puffin) Penguin Group (USA) Inc.

—Spot's Easter Surprise. Hill, Eric, illus. 2007. 10p. (J). (ps-k). bds. 5.99 (978-0-399-24743-9(2) , Putnam Juvenile) Penguin Group (USA) Inc.

Hippely, Hilary Horder. Adventure on Klickitat Island. Upton, Barbara, illus. 2000. (J). (ps-ps). lib. bdg. 15.30 (978-0-613-24092-5(8)) Tandem Library Bks.

Holl, Robert. Apurate, Teddy: Fiction-to-Fact Big Book. Forss, Ian, illus. enl. ed. 2004. (SPA.). (J). pap. 26.00 (978-1-4108-2362-5(8) , 23628) Benchmark Education Co.

—Teddy on the Move. ed. 2004. (Shared Connections Ser.). (J). pap. 27.00 (978-1-4108-1629-0(X)) Benchmark Education Co.

—Teddy on the Move (Big Book) ed. 2004. (Shared Connections Ser.). (J). pap., instr.'s gde. ed. 27.00 (978-1-4108-1605-4(2)) Benchmark Education Co.

Howe, Deborah & Howe, James. Teddy Bear's Scrapbook. Bush, Timothy, illus. 2001. (Ready-for-Chapters Ser.). 80p. (J). (gr. 2-5). pap. 3.99 (978-0-689-84483-6(2) , Aladdin) Simon & Schuster Children's Publishing.

Inches, Alison. Corduroy Makes a Cake. Eitzen, Allan, illus. 2004. 32p. lib. bdg. 10.79 (978-0-606-30118-3(6)) Tandem Library Bks.

—Corduroy Makes a Cake. 2003. (gr. k-3). lib. bdg. 11.80 (978-0-613-87824-1(8)) Tandem Library Bks.

—Corduroy Writes a Letter, Level 2. Eitzen, Allan, illus. 2002. (Easy-to-read, Viking Children's Ser.). 32p. (J). (gr. k-3). 13.99 (978-0-670-03548-9(3) , Viking Juvenile) Penguin Group (USA) Inc.

Inches, Alison & Freeman, Don. Corduroy's Garden. Eitzen, Allan, illus. 2002. (Viking Easy-to-Read Ser.). 32p. (J). (gr. k-3). 13.99 (978-0-670-03547-2(5) , Viking Juvenile) Penguin Group (USA) Inc.

Ira Sleeps Over. 2005. (J). (978-1-59564-973-7(5)) Steps To Literacy, LLC.

Jarrell, Pamela R. Where Is the Teddy Bear? Metzger, Jeanne, illus. l.t. ed. 2001. (Board Bk.). 12p. (J). (ps-1). 4.99 (978-1-57332-191-4(5)) HighReach Learning, Inc.

—Where Is the Teddy Bear? Board Book & Felt Puppet Set. Metzger, Jeanne, illus. 2005. (J). bds. (978-1-57332-358-1(6)) HighReach Learning, Inc.

Jeffs, Stephanie. A Bad Day for Christopher Bear. Thomas, Jacqui, illus. 2004. (Christopher Bear Ser.). 30p. 5.99 (978-0-8066-4367-0(6) , Augsburg Bks.) Augsburg Fortress, Pubs.

—Christopher Bear's First Christmas. Thomas, Jacqui, illus. 2004. (Christopher Bear Ser.). 30p. 5.99 (978-0-8066-4349-6(8) , Augsburg Bks.) Augsburg Fortress, Pubs.

—I Love You, Christopher Bear. Thomas, Jacqui, illus. 2004. (Christopher Bear Ser.). 32p. 5.99 (978-0-8066-4366-3(8) , Augsburg Bks.) Augsburg Fortress, Pubs.

Judd, Christopher M. Bearable Moments. 2005. (J). 18.95 (978-0-9766666-1-5(8)) Arcadian Hse.

Karpinski, David. Sarah's Christmas Presence. 2006. 58p. pap. 8.95 (978-0-7414-3411-1(3)) Infinity Publishing.

Kelly, Katherine, text. Albert Bear & the Big Celebration. 2005. (J). 12.95 (978-0-9773481-0-7(5)) Pink Hyacinth Pr.

King, Dorothea. Teddybears' Garden. King, Dorothea, illus. 1999. (Teddybears Ser.). (Illus.). 8p. (J). bds. 3.95 (978-1-57717-105-8(5)) New Line Bks.

—Teddybears' House. King, Dorothea, illus. 1999. (Teddybears Ser.). (Illus.). 8p. (J). bds. 3.95 (978-1-57717-104-1(7)) New Line Bks.

—Teddybears' Party. King, Dorothea, illus. 1999. (Teddybears Ser.). (Illus.). 8p. (J). bds. 3.95 (978-1-57717-107-2(1)) New Line Bks.

—Teddybears' Vacation. King, Dorothea, illus. 1999. (Teddybears Ser.). (Illus.). 8p. (J). bds. 3.95 (978-1-57717-106-5(3)) New Line Bks.

Krensky, Stephen. Eeyore Has a Birthday. 2001. 10.79 (978-0-606-22514-4(5)) Tandem Library Bks.

—Winnie the Pooh & Some Bees. 2001. (978-0-606-22513-7(7)) Tandem Library Bks.

Kroll, Virginia L. Everybody Has a Teddy. Allsopp, Sophie, illus. 2007. 24p. (J). 12.95 (978-1-4027-3580-6(4)) Sterling Publishing Co., Inc.

Lagonegro, Melissa. Lots of Pots. 2005. (Pooh's Readables Ser.). (J). (978-0-7364-8035-2(8)) Random Hse., Inc.

Lagonegro, Melissa & Random House Disney Staff. Lots of Pots. 2005. (Pooh's Readables Ser.). (Illus.). 32p. (J). (ps-1). 4.99 (978-0-7364-2278-9(1) , RH/Disney) Random Hse. Children's Bks.

Legrand, Martine & Delvaux, Nancy. ¡una nalgada por Favor! 2006. 28p. pap. (978-958-30-1886-2(4)) Panamericana Editorial.

Little Teddy. (Bedtime Babies Ser.). (J). 6.99 (978-1-57755-500-1(7)) Allied Publishing.

Ludde & His Naughty Teddy Bear. 2003. Orig. Title: Ludde Och Busiga Nalle. (NOR, FIN, GER, FLE & DAN.). lib. bdg. 7.95 (978-0-9740419-0-2(4)) words4u.

Luke, Judy. Teddy Goes to Monaco. 2006. (Illus.). 116p. (YA). per. 12.95 (978-0-9769645-6-8(2)) Flo's Productions.

Macaluso, Jennifer. Teddy Bear Waltz. 2006. (ENG.). 40p. per. 16.99 (***978-1-4259-6274-6(2)***) AuthorHouse.

Mangan, Anne. Little Teddy Left Behind. Moss, Joanne, illus. 2006. 26p. (J). 16.00 (978-1-56148-508-6(X)) Good Bks.

Matsutani, Miyoko. Peek-a-Boo. Segawa, Yasuo, illus. 2006. 20p. (J). 10.95 (978-1-74126-047-2(7)) R.I.C. Pubns. AUS. *Dist:* SCB Distributors.

McGough, Roger. Moonthief. Dann, Penny, illus. 2003. 32p. (J). (ps-k). tchr. ed. 15.00 (978-0-7534-5481-7(5) , Kingfisher) Houghton Mifflin Co. Trade & Reference Div.

McKee, David. Elmer & the Lost Teddy. McKee, David, illus. 2004. (Elmer Bks.). 32p. (J). 9.99 (978-0-06-075243-9(2)) HarperCollins Pubs.

McPhail, David. The Teddy Bear. 2005. (Illus.). 32p. (J). reprint ed. pap. 6.95 (978-0-8050-7882-4(7) , Holt, Henry & Co. Bks. For Young Readers) Holt, Henry & Co.

Meridith, Shelley, illus. Hide n' Seek at Home with Josh B'Gosh. 1998. 10p. (J). 6.99 (978-1-929174-10-2(1)) Oshkosh B'Gosh, Inc.

Milios, Rita. Bears Bears Everywhere. 2003. (gr. k-3). lib. bdg. 12.95 (978-0-613-66348-9(9)) Tandem Library Bks.

—Bears, Bears, Everywhere. Motoyama, Keiko, illus. rev. ed. 2003. (Rookie Reader Ser.). 32p. (J). 19.50 (978-0-516-22847-1(1) , Children's Pr.) Scholastic Library Publishing.

Miller, Sara Swan. Three Stories You Can Read to Your Teddy Bear. Kelley, True, tr. Kelley, True, illus. 2004. 48p. (J). (gr. k-3). tchr. ed. 15.00 (978-0-618-30397-7(9)) Houghton Mifflin Co. Trade & Reference Div.

Milne, A. A. Slide & Seek Numbers: A Sliding Window Book. 1999. (Illus.). 8p. (J). 10.99 (978-0-7868-3241-5(X)) Disney Pr.

—Tigger Comes to the Forest. 2002. (gr. k-3). lib. bdg. 11.80 (978-0-613-62575-3(7)) Tandem Library Bks.

Mitchell, Anastasia, illus. Josh B'Gosh at School. 1998. 10p. (J). 6.99 (978-1-929174-08-9(X)) Oshkosh B'Gosh, Inc.

Moffat, Judith. Floaties! Teddy Bear, Teddy Bear, Peek-a-boo! Moffatt, Judith, illus. 2004. (Floaties Ser.). 12p. (J). bds. 7.95 (978-1-4027-2151-9(X)) Sterling Publishing Co., Inc.

Mooney, Bel & Chamberlain, Margaret. Mr. Tubs Is Lost. 2006. (Blue Bananas Ser.). (Illus.). 46p. (J). (978-0-7787-0858-2(6)) Crabtree Publishing Co.

Moore, Mel. Mr P's Tale or Two. 2006. (Illus.). 21p. (J). per. (***978-0-9775919-1-6(3)***) Carpe Diem Publishing.

Mulally, Gucki. Gucki-Bear: The Girl Teddy Bear. 2002. pap. 13.00 (978-0-8059-5836-2(3)) Dorrance Publishing Co., Inc.

Murphy, Frank & van Frankenhuyzen, Gijsbert. The Legend of the Teddy Bear. 2000. (Illus.). 48p. (J). (ps up). 16.95 (978-1-58536-013-0(9)) Sleeping Bear Pr.

My Very Own Teddy Bears' Schoolhouse Play Set. 2004. (J). (978-1-59292-008-2(X)) SoftPlay, Inc.

Naylor, Phyllis Reynolds. Please Do Feed the Bears. Escriva, Ana Lopez, illus. 2002. 40p. (J). (ps-2). 16.00 (978-0-689-82561-3(7) , Atheneum) Simon & Schuster Children's Publishing.

Newman, Robert. Lost Treasures Bk. 3: The Teddy Bear Habit. 2001. 184p. (J). 13.49 (978-0-7868-2599-8(5)) Hyperion Pr.

Nightingale, Sandy. Throwaway Bear. 2001. (Illus.). 32p. (J). 16.99 (978-0-86264-899-2(8)) Andersen GBR. *Dist:* Independent Pubs. Group.

Novak, Matt. Jazzbo & Googy. Novak, Matt, illus. 2000. (Jazzbo & Friends Ser.: Vol. 2). (Illus.). 32p. (ps-k). 14.99 (978-0-7868-0388-0(6)) Hyperion Bks. for Children.

Oliva, Nephi. Elder Teddy & His First Companion. Maruyama, Jerrod, illus. 2005. 32p. (J). per. 4.95 (978-1-886249-30-1(X)) WindRiver Publishing.

El osito de Julio: Individual Title Six-Packs. (Coleccion Pm Ser.).Tr. of Ben's teddy bear. (SPA.). 16p. (gr. 1 up). 26.00 (978-0-7578-2970-3(8)) Rigby Education.

The Pajama Party. 1998. (P. B. Bear Ser.). (Illus.). 24p. (J). (ps). 6.95 (978-0-7894-3107-3(6)) Dorling Kindersley Publishing, Inc.

Peter, Rutherford. Ready for Bed. 2006. (Illus.). 32p. (J). (ps). 12.95 (978-1-904613-95-4(0) , Buster Bks.) O'Mara, Michael Bks., Ltd. GBR. *Dist:* Independent Pubs. Group.

Piper, Sophie. Little Teddy's Birthday Book. Massey, Jane, illus. 2002. 64p. (J). 6.99 (978-0-7459-4709-9(3) , Lion) Lion Hudson plc GBR. *Dist:* Independent Pubs. Group.

Random House Disney Staff & Liberts, Jennifer. Pooh: Tricks & Treats. Alvin & Associates, Inc., illus. 2001. 16p. (J). (ps-3). pap. 2.99 (978-0-7364-1191-2(7) , Golden/Disney) Random Hse. Children's Bks.

Ray, Brenda. Where Is Teddy? Laurie, Gloria J., illus. 2000. 26p. (J). (ps-6). pap. 8.00 (978-0-9701089-0-6(7)) Mourning Dove Studio.

Richter, Dana. Pooh's Snapshot Surprise. 2002. (Illus.). 14p. (J). bds. (978-0-7853-8089-4(2) , 7181300) Publications International, Ltd.

Robinson, Joan G. Dear Teddy Robinson. l.t. ed. 1999. 161p. (J). pap. (978-0-7540-6075-8(6) , CLP 280) BBC Audio.

Robinson, Sue. Bear in the Barnyard. Morris, Tony, illus. 2004. 28p. (J). 16.00 (978-1-56148-430-0(X)) Good Bks.

Roman, Javier. Adventures of Tinturu & Kumachan the M. 2007. (Illus.). 48p. pap. 12.95 (***978-1-4241-1626-3(0)***) PublishAmerica, Inc.

Rose, Alea. There's a Bear in my House. 2007. (J). (***978-0-9803367-1-9(6)***) Buttermoth Pr.

Rossiter-McFarland, Lyn. The Pirate's Parrot. McFarland, Jim, illus. 2004. 40p. (J). (gr. k-2). 14.95 (978-1-58246-014-7(0) , Tricycle Pr.) Ten Speed Pr.

Rowe, John Alfred. J. A. Teddy. Rowe, John Alfred, illus. 2006. 32p. (J). (ps-3). 16.99 (978-0-698-40043-6(7) , Minedition) Penguin Group (USA) Inc.

Schertle, Alice. The Adventures of Old Bo Bear. Parkins, David, illus. 2005. (J). 16.95 (978-978-081-183-9(4)) Chronicle Bks. LLC.

—Teddy Bear, Teddy Bear. Griffith, Linda Hill, illus. 2003. 32p. (J). (gr. 5 up). lib. bdg. 16.89 (978-0-688-16871-1(X)); 15.99 (978-0-688-16870-4(1)) HarperCollins Pubs.

Schertle, Alice & Parkins, Schertle. The Adventures of Old Bo Bear. 2006. (Illus.). 32p. (J). 16.95 (978-0-8118-3476-6(X)) Chronicle Bks, LLC.

Seeger, Laura Vaccaro. Dog & Bear, Too! 2008. 32p. (J). 12.95 (***978-1-59643-273-4(X)***) Roaring Brook Pr.

Senderak, Carol Hunt. Mommy in My Pocket. Nakata, Hiroe, illus. 2006. 32p. (ps-1). 12.99 (978-0-7868-5596-4(7)) Hyperion Pr.

Shanks, Ronnie. Oh Where, Oh Where Is My Teddy Bear? 2004. 22p. pap. 14.95 (978-1-4137-2693-0(3)) PublishAmerica, Inc.

Shustak, Bernadette Rossetti. I Love You Through & Through. Church, Caroline Jay, illus. 2005. 24p. (J). bds. 8.95 (978-0-439-67363-1(1) , Cartwheel Bks.) Scholastic, Inc.

Smee, Nicola. No Bed Without Ted. 2005. (Illus.). 24p. (J). (ps-ps). 14.95 (978-1-58234-963-3(0)) Bloomsbury Publishing.

Spedden, Daisy Corning Stone. Polar the Titanic Bear. 2001. (978-0-606-22559-5(5)) Tandem Library Bks.

Stadler, John. Catilda. Stadler, John, illus. 2003. (Illus.), 32p. (J). (ps-k). 16.95 (978-0-689-84728-8(9) , Atheneum/ Richard Jackson Bks.) Simon & Schuster Children's Publishing.

Teddy Bear. 2000. (J). (978-0-8431-4671-4(0) , Putnam Juvenile) Penguin Group (USA) Inc.

Teddy Bear-Duck. 2003. (J). per. (978-1-57657-160-6(2)) Paradise Pr., Inc.

Teddy Bear Frog. 2003. (J). per. (978-1-57657-161-3(0)) Paradise Pr., Inc.

Teddy Bear-House. 2003. (J). per. (978-1-57657-162-0(9)) Paradise Pr., Inc.

Teddy Bear-Sheep. 2003. (J). per. (978-1-57657-163-7(7)) Paradise Pr., Inc.

Teddy Bear Tales: Teddy Bear Stories & Rhymes. 2000. 96p. (J). 7.95 (978-0-7525-4274-4(5)) Parragon, Inc.

Teddy in the Toyshop. Date not set. (Illus.). (J). bds. 1.98 (978-0-7525-9841-3(4)) Parragon, Inc.

Toews, Sheena. Beary Fun! 2004. 48p. pap. 10.95 (978-1-57377-189-4(9) , 0-1988-4-02506-1) Eas'l Pubns.

—Beary Snowy. 2004. 56p. pap. 10.95 (978-1-57377-196-2(1) , 0-1988-4-02512-2) Eas'l Pubns.

Tulip, Jenny. The Teddy Bear Dance. 2001. (Illus.). 16p. (ps-3). pap. 5.00 (978-0-7548-0113-9(6)) Anness Publishing, Inc.

Waber, Bernard. Quique Duerme Fuera de Casa. Mlawer, Teresa, tr. 2003. (SPA., Illus.). (J). (gr. k-2). pap. (978-968-6579-15-4(X) , SI6510) Sistemas Tecnicos de Edicion, S.A. de C.V. MEX. *Dist:* Lectorum Pubns., Inc.

Wach, Martin & Wach, Delia. The Great West Virginia Snow Adventure. Wach, Delia, illus. 2006. (Illus.). 32p. (J). 16.95 (978-0-929915-42-5(9)) Headline Bks., Inc.

Wahl, Jan. Humphrey's Bear. Joyce, William, illus. 2005. 32p. (J). pap. 6.95 (978-0-8050-7887-9(8) , Holt, Henry & Co. Bks. For Young Readers) Holt, Henry & Co.

Walker, Neva M. Grandma's Teddy Bear Tales. Coonce, Phillip, illus. 2002. 144p. (J). (gr. 2-7). pap. (978-0-9721303-0-1(6)) Neva's Arts & Crafts.

Walling, Lani. Clyde-Fred & the Color of Friendship. 2005. 23p. (J). 9.98 (978-1-4116-6091-5(9)) Lulu.com.

Wang, Margaret. Teddy Bear's Picnic. 2008. 12p. (J). (ps-2). 16.99 (***978-0-7641-6069-1(9)***) Barron's Educational Series, Inc.

Ward, Nick. I Wish. 2007. (Illus.). 24p. (J). pap. 8.99 (***978-1-84458-126-9(8)***) Anova Bks. GBR. *Dist:* Independent Pubs. Group.

Warner, Gertrude Chandler. Stuffed Bear Mystery. 2002. (gr. 3-6). lib. bdg. 11.80 (978-0-613-62574-6(9)) Tandem Library Bks.

Watt, Fiona & Wells, Rachel, eds. That's Not My Teddy: Its Paws Are Too Woolly. 2004. (Touchy-Feely Board Bks.). (SPA., Illus.). 10p. (J). (ps up). bds. 7.95 (978-0-7460-3782-9(1)) EDC Publishing.

Wickstrom, Sylvie K. I Love You, Mister Bear. 2004. (Illus.). 40p. (J). (ps-1). pap. 14.99 (978-0-06-029331-4(4)) HarperCollins Pubs.

—I Love You, Mister Bear. Wickstrom, Sylvie K., illus. 2004. (Illus.). 40p. (J). (ps-1). lib. bdg. 15.89 (978-0-06-029332-1(2)) HarperCollins Pubs.

Williams, Sam. Teddy Bears' Trick-or-Treat. McQuade, Jacqueline, illus. 2001. 12p. (J). (ps-1). pap. 14.95 (978-0-439-20403-3(8) , Cartwheel Bks.) Scholastic, Inc.

—Teddy Bears Trim the Tree: A Christmas Pull-the-Tab Book. McQuade, Jacqueline, illus. 2000. 12p. (J). (ps-1). bds. 14.95 (978-0-439-19285-9(4)) Scholastic, Inc.

Willis, Jeanne & Varley, Susan. The Boy Who Thought He Was a Teddy Bear. 2002. (Illus.). 32p. (J). (ps-2). 15.95 (978-1-56145-270-5(X)) Peachtree Pubs., Ltd.

Winburn, William B., photos by. Teddy Bears, Teddy Bears. 2006. (Illus.). 24p. (J). 9.95 (978-1-4027-3639-1(8)) Sterling Publishing Co., Inc.

Winnie the Pooh & the Blustery Day. 1999. (Disney Ser.). (Illus.). 56p. (J). (ps-3). pap. 2.99 (978-0-307-28029-9(2) , Golden Bks.) Random Hse. Children's Bks.

Wright, Dare. Gift from the Lonely Doll. 2001. (gr. k-3). lib. bdg. 15.25 (978-0-613-35517-9(2)) Tandem Library Bks.

Ziefert, Harriet. Clara Ann Cookie, Go to Bed! Bolam, Emily, illus. 2000. 32p. (J). (gr. k-3). tchr. ed. 15.00 (978-0-395-97381-3(3) , Walter Lorraine) Houghton Mifflin Co. Trade & Reference Div.

Zoehfeld, Kathleen Weidner. Happy New Year, Pooh! 2000. (My Very First Winnie the Pooh Ser.). (Illus.). 32p. (J). (ps-k). pap. 4.99 (978-0-7868-4418-0(3)) Disney Pr.

—Pooh's Bad Dream. 2000. (My Very First Winnie the Pooh Ser.). (Illus.). 32p. (J). (ps-k). pap. 4.99 (978-0-7868-4377-0(2)) Disney Pr.

—Pooh's Bad Dream. Cuddy, Robbin, illus. 1998. (My Very First Winnie the Pooh Ser.). 32p. (J). (ps-k). 11.95 (978-0-7868-3137-1(5)) Disney Pr.

—Pooh's Favorite Things about Spring. 2000. (My Very First Winnie the Pooh Ser.). (Illus.). 32p. (J). (ps-k). 12.99 (978-0-7868-3251-4(7)) Disney Pr.

—Winnie the Pooh's Honey Adventures. 1999. 64p. (J). 6.99 (978-0-7364-0139-5(3)) Mouse Works.

Zoehfeld, Kathleen Weidner & Random House Disney Staff. Hello, Spring! Cuddy, Robbin & Marrucchi, Elisa, illus. 2001. (Disney's Winnie the Pooh Ser.). 24p. (J). (gr. k-k). pap. 3.99 (978-0-7364-1109-7(7) , RH/Disney) Random Hse. Children's Bks.

TEENAGE

see Adolescence; Youth

TEENAGE MUTANT NINJA TURTLES (FICTITIOUS CHARACTERS)—FICTION

Black, Jake. Leonardo Returns. Jourdan, Diego, illus. 2007. (Teenage Mutant Ninja Turtles Ser.). 32p. (J). pap. 3.99 (978-1-4169-4056-2(1) , Simon Spotlight) Simon & Schuster Children's Publishing.

Cerasini, Marc. Meet Casey Jones. 2004. (gr. k-3). lib. bdg. 11.80 (978-0-613-83490-2(9)) Tandem Library Bks.

Chanda, J-P. Four's a Crowd. Let's Draw Studio Staff, illus. ed. 2005. (Teenage Mutant Ninja Turtles Ser.: No. 7). 24p. lib. bdg. 15.00 (978-1-59054-832-5(9)) Fitzgerald Bks.

—Four's a Crowd. Let's Draw Studio Staff, illus. 2005. (Teenage Mutant Ninja Turtles Ser.). 24p. (J). pap. 3.99 (978-0-689-87330-0(1) , Simon Spotlight) Simon & Schuster Children's Publishing.

Clarke, Catherine. Teenage Mutant Ninja Turtles: The Next Mutation. 1998. (J). 3.99 (978-0-679-89302-8(4) , Random Hse. Bks. for Young Readers) Random Hse. Children's Bks.

Dalmatian Press Staff. Power Ranger Ninja Storm: Team Power. 2007. 24p. pap. 3.50 (***978-1-4037-3565-2(4)***) Dalmatian Pr.

—Power Ranger Ninja Storm: Thunderstorm Watch. 2007. 24p. pap. 3.50 (***978-1-4037-3566-9(2)***) Dalmatian Pr.

Denega, Danielle & Artful Doodlers Limited Staff. TMNT: Turtle Power! 2007. (Teenage Mutant Ninja Turtles Ser.). 48p. (J). 3.99 (978-1-4169-3413-4(8) , Simon Scribbles) Simon & Schuster Children's Publishing.

Giles, Mike & Ruiz, Aristides, illus. Comic Book Heroes. 2005. (Teenage Mutant Ninja Turtles Ser.). 32p. (J). pap. 3.99 (978-1-4169-0074-0(8) , Simon Spotlight) Simon & Schuster Children's Publishing.

Hamilton, Tisha & Artful Doodlers Limited Staff. TMNT: the Nightwatcher. 2007. (Teenage Mutant Ninja Turtles Ser.). 48p. (J). 3.99 (978-1-4169-3415-8(4) , Simon Scribbles) Simon & Schuster Children's Publishing.

Harper, Benjamin & Artful Doodlers Limited Staff. TMNT: Turtles Together. 2007. (Teenage Mutant Ninja Turtles Ser.). 96p. (J). 2.99 (978-1-4169-3412-7(X) , Simon Scribbles) Simon & Schuster Children's Publishing.

Kilpatrick, Irene. TMNT Movie Sticker Book. Style Guide, illus. 2007. (Teenage Mutant Ninja Turtles Ser.). 8p. (J). 6.99 (978-1-4169-4055-5(3) , Simon Spotlight) Simon & Schuster Children's Publishing.

Lewman, David. Turtle Talk: A Funny Fill-ins Book. Spaziante, Patrick, illus. 2005. (Teenage Mutant Ninja Turtles Ser.). 48p. (J). pap. 3.99 (978-0-689-87727-8(7) , Simon Spotlight) Simon & Schuster Children's Publishing.

Murphy, Stephen & Murphy, Sonia. The Master's Book. Johnson, Shane L., illus. unabr. ed. 2006. (Teenage Mutant Ninja Turtles Ser.: 1). 64p. (J). pap. 4.99 (978-1-4169-0945-3(1) , Simon Spotlight) Simon & Schuster Children's Publishing.

Murphy, Steve. Lean, Green Smackdown Machine! Ruiz, Aristides & Giles, Mike, illus. ed. 2005. (Teenage Mutant Ninja Turtles Ser.: No. 5). 24p. (J). lib. bdg. 15.00 (978-1-59054-834-9(5)) Fitzgerald Bks.

—Look Out! It's Turtle Titan! Spaziante, Patrick, illus. ed. 2005. (Teenage Mutant Ninja Turtles Ser.: No. 2). 24p. (J). lib. bdg. 15.00 (978-1-59054-835-6(3)) Fitzgerald Bks.

—Look Out! It's Turtle Titan! Spaziante, Patrick, illus. 2004. (Teenage Mutant Ninja Turtles Ser.). 24p. (J). pap. 3.99 (978-0-689-86900-6(2) , Simon Spotlight) Simon & Schuster Children's Publishing.

—Look Out! It's Turtle Titan! 2004. (gr. k-3). lib. bdg. 11.80 (978-0-613-83491-9(7)) Tandem Library Bks.

—Shadows over Chinatown. Spaziante, Patrick, illus. 2005. (Teenage Mutant Ninja Turtles Ser.). 128p. (J). pap. 4.99 (978-0-689-87209-9(7) , Simon Spotlight) Simon & Schuster Children's Publishing.

—Tricks & Treats. Spaziante, Patrick, illus. ed. 2005. (Teenage Mutant Ninja Turtles Ser.: No. 4). 24p. (J). lib. bdg. 15.00 (978-1-59054-837-0(X)) Fitzgerald Bks.

Murphy, Steve, adapted by. TMNT Movie Novelization. movie tie-in ed. 2007. (Teenage Mutant Ninja Turtles Ser.). 128p. (J). pap. 5.99 (978-1-4169-4057-9(X) , Simon Spotlight) Simon & Schuster Children's Publishing.

Nickel, Scott & Artful Doodlers Limited Staff. TMNT: Cowabunga! 2007. (Teenage Mutant Ninja Turtles Ser.). 32p. (J). 3.99 (978-1-4169-3414-1(6) , Simon Scribbles) Simon & Schuster Children's Publishing.

Peterson, Scott. Blackout! Spaziante, Patrick, illus. 2005. (Teenage Mutant Ninja Turtles Ser.). 24p. (J). pap. 3.99 (978-0-689-87329-4(8) , Simon Spotlight) Simon & Schuster Children's Publishing.

Redondo, Jesus, illus. Turtle Rescue! 2004. (Ready-to-Read Ser.). 32p. (J). pap. 3.99 (978-0-689-87007-1(8) , Simon Spotlight) Simon & Schuster Children's Publishing.

Simon Spotlight, creator. Turtles in Action! 2005. (Teenage Mutant Ninja Turtles Ser.). (Illus.). 192p. (J). (ps-ps). per. 10.95 (978-1-4169-0256-0(2) , Simon Spotlight) Simon & Schuster Children's Publishing.

Spaziante, Patrick, illus. Meet Casey Jones. ed. 2005. (Teenage Mutant Ninja Turtles Ser.: No. 1). 24p. (J). lib. bdg. 15.00 (978-1-59054-836-3(1)) Fitzgerald Bks.

—Meet Casey Jones. 2004. (Teenage Mutant Ninja Turtles Ser.). 24p. (J). pap. 3.99 (978-0-689-86899-3(5) , Simon Spotlight) Simon & Schuster Children's Publishing.

Teenage Mutant Ninja Turtles Sticker Activity Books. 2004. (J). act. bk. ed. 3.49 (978-0-7666-1299-0(6) , 69645); act. bk. ed. (978-0-7666-1300-3(3) , 69645) Modern Publishing.

Teitelbaum, Michael. The Return of Shredder. Spaziante, Patrick, illus. 2005. (Teenage Mutant Ninja Turtles Ser.: 3). 128p. (J). pap. 4.99 (978-1-4169-0828-9(5) , Simon Spotlight) Simon & Schuster Children's Publishing.

Thomas, Jim. Super Slam Turtles! Spaziante, Patrick, illus. 2005. 22p. (J). lib. bdg. 15.00 (***978-1-4242-0971-2(4)***) Fitzgerald Bks.

—Turtle Tales: An Insider's Guide by Leonardotrade. George, Chris & Giles, Mike, illus. 2007. (Teenage Mutant Ninja Turtles Ser.). 24p. (J). pap. 3.99 (***978-1-4169-4885-8(6)*** , Simon Spotlight) Simon & Schuster Children's Publishing.

Thomas, LeSean & David, Peter. Attack of the Mousers. 2007. (Illus.). 96p. pap. 12.95 (***978-1-84576-092-2(1)***) Titan Bks. Ltd. GBR. *Dist:* Random Hse., Inc.

TEETH

see also Dentistry

Bagley, Katie. Brush Well: A Look at Dental Care. 2001. (Your Health Ser.). (Illus.). 24p. (J). (gr. 1-2). lib. bdg. 18.60 (978-0-7368-0969-6(4) , Bridgestone Bks.) Capstone Pr., Inc.

Beeler, Selby B. Throw Your Tooth on the Roof: Tooth Traditions from Around the World. Karas, G. Brian, illus. 1998. 32p. (J). (gr. k-3). tchr. ed. 16.00 (978-0-395-89108-7(6)) Houghton Mifflin Co. Trade & Reference Div.

Bozzo, Linda. Amazing Animal Teeth. 2008. (J). lib. bdg. (***978-1-4042-4170-1(1)*** , PowerKids Pr.) Rosen Publishing Group, Inc., The.

Brill, Marlene Targ. Tooth Tales from Around the World. 1998. (J). (978-0-606-13856-7(0)) Tandem Library Bks.

Casado, Dami & Casado, Alicia. Los Dientes. 2005. (Sentidos y Algo Mas). (SPA & ESP.). 16p. 8.99 (978-84-272-6418-2(6)) Molino, Editorial ESP. *Dist:* Santillana USA Publishing Co., Inc.

Chandra, Deborah & Comora, Madeleine. George Washington's Teeth. Cole, Brock, illus. 2007. 40p. (J). pap. 6.99 (*978-0-312-37604-8(9)) Square Fish.

Cherrington, Janelle. Who Needs Teeth? 2003. (Compass Point Phonics Readers Ser.). (Illus.). 16p. (J). (gr. 1 up). 13.26 (978-0-7565-0535-6(6)) Compass Point Bks.

Collard, Sneed B. Teeth. Saroff, Phyllis V., illus. 2008. (J). (*978-1-58089-120-2(9)) Charlesbridge Publishing, Inc.

Copeland, Cynthia L. The Tooth Fairy Tells All. 2002. (Silly Millies Ser.). (Illus.). 32p. lib. bdg. 17.90 (978-0-7613-2805-6(X) , Millbrook Pr.) Lerner Publishing Group.

Curry, Don L. Take Care of Your Teeth. 2005. (Rookie Read-about Health Ser.). (Illus.). (J). (gr. k-2). 31p. pap. 5.95 (978-0-516-27915-2(7)); 32p. 20.50 (978-0-516-25875-1(3)) Scholastic Library Publishing. (Children's Pr.).

Degezelle, Terri. Taking Care of My Teeth. 2005. (Keeping Healthy Ser.). (Illus.). 24p. (J). (ps-2). lib. bdg. 19.93 (978-0-7368-4264-8(0)) Capstone Pr., Inc.

Demuth, Patricia B. Look! My Tooth Is Loose! 2002. (gr. k-3). lib. bdg. 15.30 (978-0-613-72490-6(9)) Tandem Library Bks.

DK Publishing Staff. Brushing My Teeth. 2007. 12p. (J). (ps-1). bds. 6.99 (978-0-7566-3021-8(5)) Dorling Kindersley Publishing, Inc.

Dorling Kindersley Publishing Staff. A Trip to the Dentist. 2006. (Dk Readers Ser.). (Illus.). 32p. (J). 14.99 (978-0-7566-1915-2(7)); pap. 3.99 (978-0-7566-1914-5(9)) Dorling Kindersley Publishing, Inc.

Food for Healthy Teeth, 6 vols. (gr. k-2). 28.95 (978-0-7368-8138-8(7)) Red Brick Learning.

Fowler, Allan. A Look at Teeth. (Rookie Read-About Science Ser.). (Illus.). 32p. (J). (gr. 1-2). 2000. pap. 4.95 (978-0-516-26567-4(9)); 1999. 19.50 (978-0-516-21217-3(6)) Scholastic Library Publishing. (Children's Pr.).

—A Look at Teeth. 1999. (gr. k-3). lib. bdg. 12.95 (978-0-613-54741-3(1)) Tandem Library Bks.

Frost, Helen. Brushing Well. Saunders-Smith, Gail, ed. 1998. (Dental Health Ser.). (Illus.). 24p. (J). (gr. k-1). lib. bdg. 15.93 (978-0-7368-0112-6(X) , Pebble Bks.) Capstone Pr., Inc.

—Brushing Well. 1998. (Dental Health Ser.). (J). lib. bdg. 13.25 (978-0-516-21492-4(6) , Children's Pr.) Scholastic Library Publishing.

—Dental Health, 4 bks. Saunders-Smith, Gail, ed. Incl. Brushing Well. lib. bdg. 15.93 (978-0-7368-0112-6(X)); Food for Healthy Teeth. lib. bdg. 15.93 (978-0-7368-0113-3(8)); Going to the Dentist. lib. bdg. 15.93 (978-0-7368-0114-0(6)); Your Teeth. lib. bdg. 15.93 (978-0-7368-0115-7(4)); 24p. (J). (gr. k-1). 1998. (Illus.). 1998. Set lib. bdg. 63.72 (978-0-7368-0142-3(1) , Pebble Bks.) Capstone Pr., Inc.

—Dental Health, 4 bks., Set. Date not set. (J). 53.00 (978-0-516-29821-4(6) , Children's Pr.) Scholastic Library Publishing.

—Food for Healthy Teeth. Saunders-Smith, Gail, ed. 1998. (Dental Health Ser.). (Illus.). 24p. (J). (gr. k-1). lib. bdg. 15.93 (978-0-7368-0113-3(8) , Pebble Bks.) Capstone Pr., Inc.

—Food for Healthy Teeth. 1998. (Dental Health Ser.). (J). lib. bdg. 13.25 (978-0-516-21493-1(4) , Children's Pr.) Scholastic Library Publishing.

—Your Teeth. Saunders-Smith, Gail, ed. 1998. (Dental Health Ser.). (Illus.). 24p. (J). (gr. k-1). lib. bdg. 15.93 (978-0-7368-0115-7(4) , Pebble Bks.) Capstone Pr., Inc.

—Your Teeth. 1998. (Dental Health Ser.). (J). lib. bdg. 13.25 (978-0-516-21495-5(0) , Children's Pr.) Scholastic Library Publishing.

Gaff, Jackie. Why Must I... Brush My Teeth? 2005. (Illus.). 32p. (J). (gr. 2-5). lib. bdg. (978-1-84234-347-0(5) , Cherrytree Books) Evans Publishing Group.

Goulding, Sylvia. Taking Care of Your Teeth. 2005. (Healthy Kids Ser.). (Illus.). 32p. (J). (gr. 3-6). 19.95 (978-1-59515-203-9(2)) Rourke Publishing, LLC.

Gray, Susan H. Dinosaur Teeth. 2007. (Scholastic News Nonfiction Readers: Prehistoric World Ser.). 24p. (J). pap. 6.95 (*978-0-531-18778-4(0) , Children's Pr.) Scholastic Library Publishing.

Gray, Susan Heinrichs. Dinosaur Teeth. 2007. (Scholastic News Nonfiction Readers Ser.). (Illus.). 24p. (J). (gr. 1-2). 19.00 (978-0-531-17484-5(0) , Children's Pr.) Scholastic Library Publishing.

Harrison, Emma. From Head to Toe: The Girls' Life Guide to Taking Care of You. Montagna, Frank, illus. 2004. 124p. (J). (978-0-439-44983-0(9)) Scholastic, Inc.

Hood, Karen Jean Matsko. My Dentist & the Tooth Fairy Activity & Coloring Book. Scripture-Smith, Mary, illus. 2005. (Educational Activity & Coloring Book Ser.). (J). (ps-11). 15.95 (978-0-9679368-1-9(0)) Whispering Pine Pr., Inc.

Kachlany, Scott C. Infectious Diseases of the Mouth. 2007. (Deadly Diseases & Epidemics Ser.). 96p. (J). (gr. 9). 31.95 (978-0-7910-9242-2(9) , Chelsea Hse.) Facts On File, Inc.

Katz, Bobbi. Make Way for Tooth Decay. Bjorkman, Steve, illus. 2002. (Hello Reader! Science Ser.). 32p. (J). (gr. 1-3). pap. 3.99 (978-0-590-52290-8(6) , Cartwheel Bks.) Scholastic, Inc.

Katz, Bobbie. Make Way for Tooth Decay. 1999. (gr. k-3). lib. bdg. 11.25 (978-0-613-43848-3(5)) Tandem Library Bks.

Labella, Susan. Beavers & Other Animals with Amazing Teeth. 2005. (Scholastic News Nonfiction Readers Ser.). (Illus.). 24p. (J). (gr. 1-2). 19.00 (978-0-516-24930-8(4) , Children's Pr.) Scholastic Library Publishing.

Landau, Elaine. Cavities & Toothaches. 2008. (J). (*978-0-7614-2848-0(8)) Cavendish, Marshall Bks., Ltd.

Lennard, Kate & Flynn, Dermot. Smile! 2007. (Illus.). 16p. (J). (ps-2). 11.95 (*978-0-8027-9709-4(1)) Walker & Co.

Libal, Autumn & Hovius, Christopher. Taking Care of Your Smile: A Teen's Guide to Dental Care. 2005. (Science of Health Ser.). (Illus.). 128p. (J). lib. bdg. 24.95 (978-1-59084-846-3(2)) Mason Crest Pubs.

Llewellyn, Claire. Your Teeth. 2007. (J). (*978-1-59771-099-2(7)) Sea-To-Sea Pubns.

Lynch, Wayne. Whose Teeth Are These? Lynch, Wayne, photos by. 2003. (Name That Animal! Ser.). (Illus.). 32p. (J). (gr. 1 up). lib. bdg. 23.33 (978-0-8368-3643-1(X)) Stevens, Gareth Inc.

—Whose Teeth Are These? 2001. (gr. k-3). lib. bdg. 15.25 (978-0-613-87567-7(2)) Tandem Library Bks.

—Whose Teeth Are These? 2001. (Whose? Animal Ser.). (Illus.). 32p. (J). (ps-2). pap. 6.95 (978-1-55285-204-0(0)) Whitecap Bks., Ltd. CAN. *Dist:* Firefly Bks., Ltd.

Magsamen, Susan. Tooth Fairy Time. 2007. 48p. 17.95 (*978-1-4027-4823-3(X)) Sterling Publishing Co., Inc.

Miles, Elizabeth. Mouths & Teeth. 2003. (Animal Parts Ser.). (Illus.). 32p. (J). (gr. k-2). lib. bdg. 21.36 (978-1-4034-0018-5(0)); pap. 6.95 (978-1-4034-0427-5(5)) Heinemann Library.

Miller, Edward. The Tooth Book: A Guide to Healthy Teeth & Gums. 2008. (J). (*978-0-8234-2092-6(2)) Holiday Hse., Inc.

O'hehir, Trisha. The Toothpaste Secret. O'hehir, Trisha, illus. 2003. 56p. (J). (gr. 2-6). 9.95 (978-0-9659236-1-3(4)) Perio Reports.

The Perfect Prescription for Your Teeth. 2003. 29.95 (978-0-9747253-0-7(7)) Health & Beauty Ctr., LLC.

Perkins, Wendy. Animal Teeth. 2007. (Pebble Plus Ser.). (Illus.). 24p. (J). 19.93 (978-0-7368-6353-7(2) , Pebble Bks.) Capstone Pr., Inc.

Pirotta, Saviour. Teeth. 2003. (Starters Ser.). 24p. (J). lib. bdg. 21.35 (978-1-58340-259-7(4)) Smart Apple Media.

Price, Dan. The Braces Journal. 2007. (Illus.). 72p. (J). (gr. 7 up). pap. 9.95 (*978-1-933662-72-5(7)) Cider Mill Pr. Bk. Pubs. LLC.

QEB Start Reading Together National Book Stores Edition: First Experiences: Going to the Dentist. 2006. (J). per. (978-1-59566-260-6(X)) QEB Publishing Inc.

Rice, Judith Anne. Those Icky Sticky Smelly Cavity-Causing but—Invisible Germs/Esos Sucios Pegajosos Olorosos Causantes de Caries Pero... Invisibles Germenes. Stricklin, Julie A., illus. 2004. (SPA & ENG.). 32p. (J). (gr. k-3). pap. 14.95 (978-1-884834-30-1(2)) Redleaf Pr.

Rogers, Josephine. Dental Health, Beautiful Teeth. 2000. (Illus.). 32p. (J). (ps-7). pap., act. bk. ed. 7.00 (978-0-9679975-0-6(X)) Rogers, Josephine H.

Royston, Angela. Healthy Teeth. 2003. (Illus.). 32p. (J). pap. 6.95 (978-1-4034-4452-3(8)); lib. bdg. 22.79 (978-1-4034-4443-1(9)) Heinemann Library.

—Tooth Decay. 2004. (Heinemann First Library). (Illus.). 32p. (J). lib. bdg. (978-1-4034-4827-9(2)) Heinemann Library.

Salzmann, Mary Elizabeth. Taking Care of Your Teeth. 2004. (Healthy Habits Ser.). (Illus.). 23p. (J). (ps-3). lib. bdg. 19.93 (978-1-59197-554-0(9)) ABDO Publishing Co.

Santillo, LuAnn. The Dentist. Santillo, LuAnn, ed. 2003. (Half-Pint Kids Readers Ser.). (Illus.). 7p. (J). (ps-1). pap. (978-1-59256-120-9(9)) Half-Pint Kids, Inc.

Schuh, Mari C. All about Teeth. 2008. (J). (*978-1-4296-1238-8(X) , Pebble Bks.) Capstone Pr., Inc.

Seuss, Dr. The Tooth Book. Jonaitis, Alice, ed. Mathieu, Joe, illus. 2000. (Bright & Early Bks.). 48p. (J). (gr. k-1). lib. bdg. 11.99 (978-0-375-91039-5(5) , Random Hse. Bks. for Young Readers) Random Hse. Children's Bks.

—The Tooth Book. Mathieu, Joe, illus. 2000. (Bright & Early Bks.: Vol. 25). 48p. (J). (gr. k-1). 8.99 (978-0-375-81039-8(0) , Random Hse. Bks. for Young Readers) Random Hse. Children's Bks.

Shaw, Gina. All about Teeth. Neri, Gregory, illus. 2000. (Hello Reader! Ser.). (J). pap. (978-0-439-20642-6(1)) Scholastic, Inc.

Silverstein, Alvin. Tooth Decay & Cavities. 1999. (gr. 3-6). lib. bdg. 15.25 (978-0-613-31827-3(7)) Tandem Library Bks.

Silverstein, Alvin, et al. Tooth Decay & Cavities. (My Health Ser.). (Illus.). 48p. (J). (gr. 3-5). 2000. pap. 6.95 (978-0-531-16412-9(8)); 1999. 25.50 (978-0-531-11580-0(1)) Scholastic Library Publishing. (Watts, Franklin).

Spilsbury, Louise. Why Should I Brush My Teeth? And Other Questions about Healthy Teeth. 2003. (Body Matters Ser.). (Illus.). 32p. (J). lib. bdg. (978-1-4034-4679-4(2)) Heinemann Library.

Stone, Lynn M. Teeth & Fangs. 2007. (Let's Look at Animals Ser.). (Illus.). 24p. (J). (gr. k-2). lib. bdg. 21.35 (978-1-60044-174-5(2)) Rourke Publishing, LLC.

Swanson, Diane. Dentist & You. 2002. (gr. 5-8). lib. bdg. 16.40 (978-0-613-78435-1(9)) Tandem Library Bks.

—Teeth That Stab & Grind. 2003. (Up Close Ser.). (Illus.). 32p. (J). (gr. 2-4). 5.95 (978-1-55054-770-2(4)) Douglas & McIntyre, Ltd. CAN. *Dist:* Transition Vendor.

Teeth Sets: 1 Each of 3 Big Books. (Sunshinetm Science Ser.). (gr. 1-2). 111.50 (978-0-7802-1449-1(8)) Wright Group, The.

Tooth. 2001. (Human Anatomy Ser.). (J). (gr. k-12). vinyl bd. 4.95 (978-1-58845-083-8(X)) School Specialty Publishing.

Tooth Fairy Book. 2008. 9.95 (978-0-7624-1940-1(7)) Running Pr. Bk. Pubs.

Tuggle, Diane. Spencer's Toothbrush Vol. 1: An Adventure in Preventive Dental Health. 1999. (Illus.). 48p. (J). (gr. k-10). pap. 12.99 (978-0-9674450-1-4(9)) Forerunner Pr.

Verdick, Elizabeth. Teeth Are Not for Biting. Heinlen, Marieka, illus. 2003. (Best Behavior Ser.). 24p. (J). 7.95 (978-1-57542-128-5(3)) Free Spirit Publishing, Inc.

Vogel, Elizabeth. Brushing My Teeth. 2001. (PowerKids Readers Ser.). (Illus.). 24p. (J). (gr. 1). lib. bdg. 16.00 (978-0-8239-5683-8(0) , PKBRTE, PowerKids Pr.) Rosen Publishing Group, Inc., The.

—A Lavarse Los Dientes! 2004. (Limpieza y Salud Todo el Dia Ser.). (SPA & ENG., Illus.). 24p. (J). lib. bdg. 16.00 (978-0-8239-6621-9(6) , Buenas Letra) Rosen Publishing Group, Inc., The.

Who Needs Teeth? Set B, 6 vols. (Phonics Readers Ser.). (gr. k-2). 17.50 (978-0-7368-3211-3(4)) Red Brick Learning.

TEETH—FICTION

Adler, David A. Young Cam Jansen & the Lost Tooth. 1999. (Young Cam Jansen Ser.: No. 3). (gr. k-3). lib. bdg. 11.80 (978-0-613-17895-2(5)) Tandem Library Bks.

Adventures of My Dentist & the Tooth Fairy Activity & Coloring Book Second Edition. 2nd ed. 2005. (J). per. 19.95 (978-1-59649-535-7(9)) Whispering Pine Pr., Inc.

Adventures of My Dentist & the Tooth Fairy Story Book. 2005. (J). 9.95 (978-1-59649-412-1(3)); spiral bd. 9.95 (978-1-59649-542-5(1)); per. 9.95 (978-1-59649-541-8(3)); cd-rom 9.95 (978-1-59649-543-2(X)) Whispering Pine Pr., Inc.

Albee, Sarah. A Visit from the Tooth Fairy. Craig, Karen, illus. 2003. (Blue's Clues Ser.). 24p. (J). pap. 3.50 (978-0-689-86271-7(7) , Simon Spotlight/Nickelodeon) Simon & Schuster Children's Publishing.

Alley, R. W., illus. The Prince's Tooth Is Loose. 2005. (I'm Going to Read Ser.). 28p. (J). (ps-ps). 11.95 (978-1-4027-2722-1(4)) Sterling Publishing Co., Inc.

Andersdatter, Karla Margaret. Marissa the Tooth Fairy. Koff, Deborah, illus. 2nd ed. 2005. (J). (978-0-9717611-2-4(4)) Depot Bks.

Azhdam, Ziva. The Night the Tooth Fairy Came. Burrier, Mark, illus. 2002. 32p. (J). (gr. k-3). pap. 6.95 (978-0-9718952-0-1(1)) Avnner Publishing.

Balzola, Asun. Munia y el Cocolilo Naranja. (SPA.). 32p. (J). (978-84-233-1335-8(2)) Ediciones Destino ESP. *Dist:* Lectorum Pubns., Inc.

Beeler, Selby B. Throw Your Tooth on the Roof: Tooth Traditions from Around the World. Karas, G. Brian, illus. 2001. 32p. (J). (gr. k-3). pap. 6.95 (978-0-618-15238-4(5)) Houghton Mifflin Co. Trade & Reference Div.

—Throw Your Tooth on the Roof: Tooth Traditions from Around the World. 2001. (978-0-606-22587-8(0)) Tandem Library Bks.

Bell-Rehwoldt, Sheri. You Think It's Easy Being the Tooth Fairy? Slonim, David, illus. 2007. 32p. (J). (ps-3). 15.95 (978-0-8118-5460-3(4)) Chronicle Bks. LLC.

Bond, Juliana. Pixie Tales the Wobbly Tooth. 2005. 30p. spiral bd. 12.08 (978-1-4116-6046-5(3)) Lulu.com.

Borden, Louise. The Lost-And-Found Tooth. 2008. 40p. (J). 16.99 (*978-1-4169-1814-1(0) , McElderry, Margaret K.) Simon & Schuster Children's Publishing.

Bourgeois, Paulette. El Diente de Franklin. 2001. (Franklin Ser.). (SPA., Illus.). (J). 12.75 (978-0-606-21171-0(3)) Tandem Library Bks.

—Franklin & the Tooth Fairy. Clark, Brenda, illus. 2002. (Franklin Ser.). 12.40 (978-1-4046-0311-0(5)) Book Wholesalers, Inc.

—Franklin & the Tooth Fairy. 1999. (Franklin Ser.). (Illus.). 180p. (J). (ps-3). (978-1-55074-793-5(2)) Kids Can Pr., Ltd.

Bridwell, Norman & Lewison, Wendy Cheyette. Clifford's Loose Tooth. Kurtz, Sandrina & Kurtz, John, illus. 2002. (Clifford Big Red Readers Ser.). 32p. (J). (ps-1). pap. 3.99 (978-0-439-33245-3(1)) Scholastic, Inc.

Brill, Marlene Targ. Tooth Tales from Around the World. 1998. (J). (978-0-606-13856-7(0)) Tandem Library Bks.

Brown, Marc. Arthur Tricks the Tooth Fairy. 1998. (Arthur Ser.). (Illus.). 24p. (J). (gr. k-3). pap. 3.99 (978-0-679-88464-4(5) , Random Hse. Bks. for Young Readers) Random Hse. Children's Bks.

—Arthur's Tooth. Brown, Marc, illus. 2005. (Arthur Adventure Ser.). 32p. (J). (gr. 1-3). pap. 10.99 (978-0-316-05960-2(9)) Little Brown & Co.

Bunting, Eve. Trouble on the T-Ball Team. Trivas, Irene, illus. 2002. 32p. (J). (gr. k-3). pap. 5.95 (978-0-618-24617-5(7) , Clarion Bks.) Houghton Mifflin Co. Trade & Reference Div.

—Trouble on the T-Ball Team. 2002. (gr. k-3). lib. bdg. 14.10 (978-0-613-70964-4(0)) Tandem Library Bks.

Caldwell, J. Lynn. The Tooth Fairy's Guide to Lost Teeth: A Fortune for Every Day a Tooth Is Lost. Jepson, Beth, illus. 2005. (J). per. 11.95 (978-0-9774463-0-8(1)) Caldwell, Judy.

Capone, Deb. Tooth Fairy Tales. 2005. (J). 14.95 (*978-0-9728666-7-5(1)) As Simple As That Publishing.

Chandra, Deborah & Comora, Madeleine. George Washington's Teeth. Cole, Brock, illus. 2003. 40p. (J). (gr. k-3). 16.00 (978-0-374-32534-3(0) , Farrar, Straus & Giroux (BYR)) Farrar, Straus & Giroux.

Chetkowski, Emily. Pumpkin Smile. Peterson, Dawn, illus. 2001. 32p. (J). (gr. k-3). 16.95 (978-0-9700974-2-2(5)); (gr. 1-3). pap. 11.95 (978-0-9700974-3-9(3)) Seven Coin Pr.

Child, Lauren. My Wobbly Tooth Must Not Ever Never Fall Out. Child, Lauren, illus. 2006. (Charlie & Lola Ser.). (Illus.). 32p. (J). (ps-2). pap. 6.99 (978-0-448-44255-6(8) , Grosset & Dunlap) Penguin Group (USA) Inc.

Clark, CoraMarie. Emily's Magical Journey with Toothena the Tooth Fairy. Lawton, Val, illus. 2007. 32p. (J). (*978-0-9783779-0-8(7)) Strategix Ltd.

Clement, Rod. Grandpa's Teeth. Clement, Rod, illus. 1998. (Illus.). 32p. (J). (ps-3). 16.99 (978-0-06-027671-3(1)) HarperCollins Pubs.

Cooper, Mimi. Me Versus the Tooth. 2006. 17p. (J). 9.99 (978-1-4116-6933-8(9)) Lulu.com.

Copeland, Cynthia L. Tooth Fairy Tells All. 2002. 32p. (J). (gr. 1-3). pap. 4.99 (978-0-7613-1785-2(6) , Millbrook Pr.) Lerner Publishing Group.

Cousins, Lucy. Maisy, Charley, & the Wobbly Tooth. Cousins, Lucy, illus. 2006. (Illus.). 32p. (J). (gr. k-k). 12.99 (978-0-7636-2904-5(9)) Candlewick Pr.

Dalmatian Press Staff. Elmo Visits the Dentist. 2007. 24p. pap. 3.50 (*978-1-4037-3430-3(5)) Dalmatian Pr.

Davis, Katie. Mabel the Tooth Fairy & How She Got Her Job. 2003. (Illus.). 40p. (J). (gr. k-3). 16.00 (978-0-15-216307-5(7)) Harcourt Children's Bks.

Diakite, Penda. I Lost My Tooth in Africa. Diakite, Baba Wague, illus. 2006. 32p. (J). (ps-3). pap. 16.99 (978-0-439-66226-0(5) , Scholastic Pr.) Scholastic, Inc.

El diente de Julio: Individual Title Six-Packs. (Coleccion Pm Ser.).Tr. of Ben's tooth. (SPA.). 16p. (gr. 1 up). 26.00 (978-0-7578-3036-5(6)) Rigby Education.

Donahue, Jill L. Benny & the Birthday Gift. 2007. (Illus.). 24p. (J). (*978-1-4048-0590-3(7)) Picture Window Bks.

—Benny & the Birthday Gift. Senturk, Burak, illus. 2006. (Read It! Readers Ser.). 24p. (J). (gr. 1-2). 19.93 (*978-1-4048-3164-3(9)) Picture Window Bks.

Dr. Seuss Enterprises Staff & LeSieg, Theo. The Tooth Book. Mathieu, Joe, illus. 2003. (Bright & Early Board Bks.). 24p. (J). (gr. k-ps). bds. 4.99 (978-0-375-82492-0(8) , Random Hse. Bks. for Young Readers) Random Hse. Children's Bks.

Durant, Alan. Dear Tooth Fairy. Cabban, Vanessa, illus. 2004. 32p. (J). (ps-2). 14.99 (978-0-7636-2175-9(7)) Candlewick Pr.

Edah, Omatseyin Mark. The Mystery Toothpaste. Eda, Martin M., ed. Edoja, Oke-Wiskee, illus. 2000. 32p. (J). (gr. 4 up). pap. (978-1-928903-03-1(7)) Edah Bks.

Edwards. Dear Tooth Fairy. 2000. mass mkt. 5.95 (978-0-06-443877-3(5)) HarperCollins Pubs.

Edwards, Pamela Duncan. Dear Tooth Fairy. Fitzpatrick, Marie-Louise, illus. 2003. 32p. (J). (ps-2). 15.99 (978-0-06-623972-9(9) , Tegen, Katherine Bks) HarperCollins Pubs.

Elya, Susan Middleton. Tooth on the Loose. Mattheson, Jenny, illus. 2008. (SPA & ENG.). 32p. (J). (ps-k). 16.99 (*978-0-399-24459-9(X) , Putnam Juvenile) Penguin Group (USA) Inc.

Faulkner, Keith. The Mixed-Up Tooth Fairy. Lambert, Jonathan, illus. 2002. 8p. (J). (ps-1). pap. 9.95 (978-0-439-35609-1(1) , Cartwheel Bks.) Scholastic, Inc.

Fruisen, Catherine Myler. Alice & Her Fabulous Teeth. 2000. (Illus.). 32p. (J). (ps-3). 12.95 (978-0-7683-2176-0(X)) CEDCO Publishing.

Ginsburg, Herbert P., et al. Two-Two the Tooth Fairy. 2003. (Illus.). 9.95 (978-0-7690-3039-5(4)) Seymour, Dale Pubns.

Gossett, Dean L. The Hair Angel. 2006. (ENG.). 32p. per. 15.99 (*978-1-4259-7677-4(8)) AuthorHouse.

Govoni, Amanda. Aaron the Toothy Critter. 2004. 23p. pap. 14.95 (978-1-4137-1441-8(2)) PublishAmerica, Inc.

Hall, Kirsten. The Tooth Fairy. 2004. (My First Reader Ser.). (Illus.). 31p. (J). (gr. k-1). pap. 3.95 (978-0-516-24640-6(2) , Children's Pr.) Scholastic Library Publishing.

—The Tooth Fairy. Apperley, Dawn, illus. 2003. (My First Reader Ser.). 32p. (J). 18.50 (978-0-516-22938-6(9) , Children's Pr.) Scholastic Library Publishing.

Harrigan, Michael. What Does the Tooth Fairy Do with All Those Teeth? 2004. 20p. pap. 14.95 (978-1-4137-1159-2(6)) PublishAmerica, Inc.

Hawley, Bill. El Diente Suelto de Carlitos, Level 2. 2003. (Dejame Leer Ser.). (SPA., Illus.). (gr. 1-4). 6.50 (978-0-673-36330-5(9) , Good Year Bks.) Celebration Pr.

Heller, Andrew. A Mouthful of Teeth. 2002. (Illus.). 16p. (J). 7.99 (978-0-9722038-4-5(2)) Mr Do It All, Inc.

Hill, Amanda. A Brush with the Super Dentists. 2007. (Illus.). 22p. (J). 14.99 (*978-0-9798506-0-8(6)) Super Dentists, The.

Hoban, Lillian. Arthur's Loose Tooth. Hoban, Lillian, illus. 2002. (Arthur the Chimpanzee Ser.). (Illus.). (J). 11.37 (978-0-7587-5987-0(8)) Book Wholesalers, Inc.

Hood, Karen Jean Matsko. My Denties & the Tooth Fairy Curriculum Teachers' Edition. 2005. spiral bd. 15.95 (978-1-59649-322-3(4)) Whispering Pine Pr., Inc.

—My Dentist & the Tooth Fairy A Daily Journal. 2002. cd-rom 13.95 (978-1-59210-597-7(1)) Whispering Pine Pr., Inc.

—My Dentist & the Tooth Fairy Activity & Coloring Book. 2002. (J). per. 17.95 (978-1-59210-596-0(3)) Whispering Pine Pr., Inc.

—My Dentist & the Tooth Fairy Adventures in Learning Book. 2005. (J). 15.95 (978-1-59210-286-0(7)); spiral bd. 15.95 (978-1-59210-314-0(6)); cd-rom 13.95 (978-1-59649-317-9(8)) Whispering Pine Pr., Inc.

—My Dentist & the Tooth Fairy Christian Adventures in Learning Book. 2005. (J). 15.95 (978-1-59210-368-3(5)); spiral bd. 15.95 (978-1-59210-369-0(3)) Whispering Pine Pr., Inc.

—My Dentist & the Tooth Fairy Curriculum Teachers' Edition. 2005. 15.95 (978-1-59649-321-6(6)); cd-rom 13.95 (978-1-59649-324-7(0)) Whispering Pine Pr., Inc.

—My Dentist & the Tooth Fairy Educational Curriculum Book. 2005. (J). 15.95 (978-1-59210-302-7(2)); spiral bd. 15.95 (978-1-59210-313-3(8)); cd-rom 13.95 (978-1-59649-318-6(6)) Whispering Pine Pr., Inc.

—My Dentist & the Tooth Fairy Hood Christian Educational Curriculum Book. 2005. (J). 15.95 (978-1-59210-404-8(5)); spiral bd. 15.95 (978-1-59210-405-5(3)) Whispering Pine Pr., Inc.

Impey, Rose. Wanda Witch & the Wobbly Fang. Mcewen, Katharine, illus. 2006. (Scholastic Reader Level 3 Ser.). 32p. (J). pap. 3.99 (978-0-439-78450-4(6) , Cartwheel Bks.) Scholastic, Inc.

Jelly's Loose Tooth. 1999. (PB & J Noodle Stories Ser.). 32p. (J). pap. 3.99 (978-0-7868-4328-2(4)) Disney Pr.

Jensen, Patsy. Loose-Tooth Luke. Handelman, Dorothy, photos by. 1998. (Real Kids Readers Ser.). (Illus.). 48p. (gr. 1-3). lib. bdg. 18.90 (978-0-7613-2009-8(1)); 32p. (J). (gr. 2-4). pap. 4.99 (978-0-7613-2034-0(2)) Lerner Publishing Group. (Millbrook Pr.).

Johnson, Arden. The Lost Tooth Club. 2004. (Illus.). 32p. (J). (ps-3). 6.95 (978-1-58246-041-3(8) , Tricycle Pr.) Ten Speed Pr.

—The Lost Tooth Club. Johnson, Arden, illus. 2004. (Illus.). 32p. (J). (ps-3). 13.95 (978-1-883672-55-3(4) , Tricycle Pr.) Ten Speed Pr.

Keen, Donna. Flossy, a Tooth Fairy Tale: Including Red Velvet Bag for Tooth. Keen, Donna, illus. 2nd ed. 1998. (Illus.). 32p. (YA). (ps up). reprint ed. spiral bd. (978-1-56021-273-7(X) , 171) W.J. Fantasy, Inc.

Klein, Abby. Ready, Freddy! 2006. (Illus.). 96p. (J). pap. 3.99 (978-0-439-78458-0(1) , Blue Sky Pr., The) Scholastic, Inc.

—Tooth Trouble. McKinley, John, illus. 2004. (Ready, Freddy! Ser.: No. 1). 96p. (J). pap. 3.99 (978-0-439-55596-8(5) , Blue Sky Pr., The) Scholastic, Inc.

Krensky, Stephen. My Loose Tooth. Takahashi, Hideko, illus. 1999. (Step into Reading Ser.: Vol. 1). 32p. (J). (gr. k-3). pap. 3.99 (978-0-679-88847-5(0) , Random Hse. Bks. for Young Readers) Random Hse. Children's Bks.

—My Loose Tooth. 1999. (Step into Reading Ser.). (J). (978-0-606-16758-1(7)); lib. bdg. 11.80 (978-0-613-11897-2(9)) Tandem Library Bks.

Krulik, Nancy E. Open Wide, No. 23. John and Wendy Staff, illus. 2007. (Katie Kazoo, Switcheroo Ser.: No. 23). 80p. (J). pap. 3.99 (978-0-448-44439-0(9) , Grosset & Dunlap) Penguin Group (USA) Inc.

Laminack, Lester L. Trevor's Wiggly-Wobbly Tooth. McCord, Kathi Garry, illus. 2002. 32p. (J). pap. 7.95 (978-1-56145-279-8(3)) Peachtree Pubs., Ltd.

—Trevor's Wiggly-Wobbly Tooth. McCord, Kathi G., illus. 1998. 32p. (J). (ps-2). 15.95 (978-1-56145-175-3(4)) Peachtree Pubs., Ltd.

Lane, Jeanette. Magic School Bus & the Missing Tooth. 2007. (Magic School Bus Ser.). 32p. (J). pap. 3.99 (978-0-439-80107-2(9) , Cartwheel Bks.) Scholastic, Inc.

Luppens, Michel. What Do the Fairies Do with All Those Teeth. Bêha, Philippe, illus. 2003. 24p. (J). (gr. k-3). pap. 4.95 (978-1-55209-002-2(7)) Firefly Bks., Ltd.

Luppens, Michel & Bêha, Philippe. What Do the Fairies Do with All Those Teeth? (Illus.). (J). pap. 15.95 (978-0-590-74050-0(4)) Scholastic, Inc.

Lynne, Rustyna. Tyler Brushes His Teeth. Lynne, Rustyna, illus. l.t. ed. 2002. (Illus.). 17p. (J). (gr. k-2). spiral bd. 10.95 (978-0-9719657-4-4(9)) Red Carpet Publishing.

—Tyler Brushes His Teeth: Special Needs Version. Lynne, Rustyna, illus. l.t. ed. 2002. 14p. (YA). (gr. 3-8). spiral bd. 10.95 (978-0-9719657-5-1(7)) Red Carpet Publishing.

Maccarone, Grace. My Tooth Is about to Fall Out. Lewin, Betsy, illus. 2004. Tr. of Ma Dent Va Tomber. 32p. (J). lib. bdg. 15.00 (978-1-59054-661-1(X)) Fitzgerald Bks.

MacDonald, Amy. Cousin Ruth's Tooth. Priceman, Marjorie, illus. 2003. 32p. (J). (gr. k-3). pap. 5.95 (978-0-618-31099-9(1)) Houghton Mifflin Co. Trade & Reference Div.

Maconie, Robin. Alice & Her Fabulous Teeth! Fruisen, Catherine Myler, illus. 2004. 32p. (J). per. (978-1-893974-21-0(9) , Design Pr. Bks.) Savannah College of Art & Design.

Maguire, Gregory. What-the-Dickens: The Story of a Rogue Tooth Fairy. 2007. (Illus.). 304p. (J). (gr. 5-8). 15.99 ***(978-0-7636-2961-8(8))*** Candlewick Pr.

Maloney, Peter & Zekauskas, Felicia. Lose That Tooth! 2005. (Illus.). 32p. (J). ***(978-0-439-67639-7(8))*** Scholastic, Inc.

Marks, Melanie. The Tooth Fairy Rules. Kalis, Jennifer, illus. 2006. 14p. (J). (gr. k-17). 12.99 (978-1-58476-488-5(0) , IKIDS) Innovative Kids.

McClaine, Jamie. Have You Ever Seen a Moose Brushing His Teeth? Willy, April, illus. 2003. 30p. (J). 18.95 (978-0-9709533-2-2(1)) JAFS, Inc.

McGhee, Alison. Mrs. Watson Wants Your Teeth. Bliss, Harry, illus. 2007. 32p. (J). reprint ed. 16.00 ***(978-1-4223-6777-3(0))*** DIANE Publishing Co.

—Mrs. Watson Wants Your Teeth. Bliss, Harry, illus. 2004. 36p. (J). 16.00 (978-0-15-204931-7(2)) Harcourt Children's Bks.

McMullan, Kate. Fluffy Meets the Tooth Fairy. Smith, Mavis, illus. 2003. (Fluffy the Classroom Guinea Pig Ser.). 40p. (J). (gr. 1-3). 3.99 (978-0-439-12918-3(4)) Scholastic, Inc.

—Fluffy Meets the Tooth Fairy. 2000. (gr. k-3). lib. bdg. 11.80 (978-0-613-58150-9(4)) Tandem Library Bks.

McNamara, Margaret. Election Day. Gordon, Mike, illus. ed. 2005. 32p. (J). lib. bdg. 15.00 (978-1-59054-924-7(4)) Fitzgerald Bks.

—A Tooth Story. Gordon, Mike, illus. ed. 2005. 32p. (J). lib. bdg. 15.00 (978-1-59054-937-7(6)) Fitzgerald Bks.

—A Tooth Story. Gordon, Mike, illus. 2004. 32p. (J). (ps-ps). lib. bdg. 10.79 (978-0-606-30721-5(4)) Tandem Library Bks.

Mills, David. Wibble Wobble. Crouth, Julia, illus. 2004. 32p. (J). (TAM, CZE, VIE, SPA & GUJ.). (978-1-85269-926-0(4)); (TAM, CZE, VIE, SPA & GUJ.). (978-1-85269-931-4(0)); (TAM, CZE, VIE, SPA & GUJ.). (978-1-85269-936-9(1)); (TAM, CZE, VIE, SPA & GUJ.). (978-1-85269-902-4(7)); (TAM, CZE, VIE, SPA & GUJ.). (978-1-85269-907-9(8)); (TAM, CZE, VIE, SPA & GUJ.). (978-1-85269-912-3(4)); (TAM, CZE, VIE, SPA & GUJ.). (978-1-85269-917-8(5)); (CZE, TAM, VIE, SPA & GUJ.). (978-1-85269-922-2(1)); (TAM, CZE, VIE, SPA & GUJ.). (978-1-85269-927-7(2)); (TAM, CZE, VIE, SPA & GUJ.). (978-1-85269-932-1(9)); (TAM, CZE, SPA, VIE & GUJ.). (978-1-85269-937-6(X)); (TAM, CZE, VIE, SPA & GUJ.). (978-1-85269-941-3(8)); (TAM, CZE, VIE, SPA & GUJ.). (978-1-85269-946-8(9)); (TAM, CZE, VIE, SPA & GUJ.). (978-1-85269-951-2(5)); (TAM, CZE, VIE, SPA & GUJ.). (978-1-85269-956-7(6)); (TAM, CZE, VIE, SPA & GUJ.). (978-1-85269-961-1(2)); (TAM, CZE, VIE, SPA & GUJ.). (978-1-85269-966-6(3)); (TAM, CZE, VIE, SPA & GUJ.). (978-1-85269-971-0(X)); (TAM, CZE, VIE, SPA & GUJ.). (978-1-85269-976-5(0)); (TAM, CZE, SPA, GUJ & PER.). (978-1-85269-981-9(7)); (TAM, CZE, VIE, SPA & GUJ.). (978-1-85269-986-4(8)); (TAM, CZE, VIE, SPA & GUJ.). (978-1-85269-991-8(4)); (TAM, CZE, VIE, SPA & GUJ.). (978-1-85269-996-3(5)) Mantra Publishing, Ltd.

Minarik, Else Holmelund. Little Bear's Loose Tooth. Hahner, Chris, illus. 2002. (Maurice Sendak's Little Bear Ser.). 32p. (J). (ps-2). pap. 3.95 (978-0-694-01713-3(2) , Harper Festival) HarperCollins Pubs.

—Little Bear's Loose Tooth. 2002. (gr. k-3). lib. bdg. 11.80 (978-0-613-62524-1(2)) Tandem Library Bks.

Morris, Clarine. I Have a Toothache. Leavitt, Deborah, illus. 2000. 12p. (J). (ps-7). pap. 3.00 (978-0-9650312-5-7(X)) Cosmo Starr Bks.

Moss, Miriam. Se Me Mueve un Diente. Mockler, Joanna, illus. 2002. (J). (CAT.). 38p. 16.95 (978-84-8488-021-9(4)); (SPA.). 32p. (gr. 1-2). 16.95 (978-84-8488-020-2(6) , RR30960) Serres, Ediciones, S. L. ESP. *Dist:* Lectorum Pubns., Inc.

—Wibble Wobble. Mockler, Joanna, illus. 2001. 32p. (J). (gr. k-2). tchr. ed. 14.95 (978-1-58925-013-0(3) , tiger tales) ME Media LLC.

Munsch, Robert. Andrew's Loose Tooth. ed. 2004. (Illus.). (J). (gr. k-3). spiral bd. (978-0-616-00403-6(6)); spiral bd. (978-0-616-01732-6(4)) Canadian National Institute for the Blind/Institut National Canadien pour les Aveugles.

—Andrew's Loose Tooth. Martchenko, Michael, illus. (J). 2002. 32p. pap. 3.99 (978-0-439-38850-4(3)); 1999. 32p. pap. 4.99 (978-0-590-34197-4(9) , Cartwheel Bks.); 1998. 29p. 1.95 (978-0-590-21102-4(1) , Cartwheel Bks.) Scholastic, Inc.

—Andrew's Loose Tooth. 2002. (ps-2). lib. bdg. 11.80 (978-0-613-72077-9(6)) Tandem Library Bks.

My Dentist & the Tooth Fairy Hood Christian Educational Curriculum. 2005. (J). 34.95 (978-1-59649-452-7(2)) Whispering Pine Pr., Inc.

My Dentist & the Tooth Fairy Hood Christian Educational Curriculum Book. 2005. (J). cd-rom 13.95 (978-1-59649-320-9(8)) Whispering Pine Pr., Inc.

My Dentist & the Tooth Fairy Story Book. 2005. (J). 15.95 (978-1-59649-432-9(8)) Whispering Pine Pr., Inc.

Naughton, Randi & Oelkers, Allex. The Tooth Fairy Palace. Butler, Tracy, illus. 2001. 20p. pap. 9.95 (978-0-9708422-0-6(1)) Stellar Pr.

O'Connor, Jane. Dear Tooth Fairy, Vol. 2. Allen, Joy, illus. 2002. (All Aboard Reading Ser.). 48p. (J). 3.99 (978-0-448-42849-9(0) , Grosset & Dunlap) Penguin Group (USA) Inc.

—Dear Tooth Fairy. 2002. (gr. k-3). lib. bdg. 11.80 (978-0-613-64036-7(5)) Tandem Library Bks.

Olson, Mary W. & Tillotson, Katherine. Nice Try, Tooth Fairy. 2000. Orig. Title: Dear Tooth Fairy. (Illus.). 32p. (J). (ps-3). 15.00 (978-0-689-82422-7(X)) Simon & Schuster Children's Publishing.

Packard, Mary. The Missing Tooth. Ulrich, George, illus. 2002. (Hello Reader! Ser.). (J). 3.99 (978-0-439-32094-8(1)) Scholastic, Inc.

Palatini, Margie. No Biting, Louise. Reinhart, Matthew, illus. 2007. 32p. (J). (ps-2). 16.99 (978-0-06-052627-6(0)); lib. bdg. 17.89 (978-0-06-052628-3(9)) HarperCollins Pubs. (Tegen, Katherine Bks).

Palatini, Margie & Davis, Jack E. Sweet Tooth. 2004. (Illus.). 40p. (J). 16.95 (978-0-689-85159-9(6)) Simon & Schuster Children's Publishing.

Park, Barbara. Junie B., First Grader: Toothless Wonder. Brunkus, Denise, illus. 2003. (Junie B. Jones Ser.: No. 20). 96p. (J). (gr. k-3). pap. 3.99 (978-0-375-82223-0(2) , Random Hse. Bks. for Young Readers) Random Hse. Children's Bks.

—Junie B., First Grader: Toothless Wonder. 2002. (Junie B. Jones Ser.: No. 20). (Illus.). 96p. (J). (gr. k-3). lib. bdg. 13.99 (978-0-375-90295-6(3) , Random Hse. Bks. for Young Readers) Random Hse. Children's Bks.

—Junie B., First Grader: Toothless Wonder. Brunkus, Denise, illus. 2002. (Junie B. Jones Ser.: No. 20). 96p. (J). (gr. 1-4). 11.95 (978-0-375-80295-9(9) , Random Hse. Bks. for Young Readers) Random Hse. Children's Bks.

—Junie B., First Grader: Toothless Wonder. 2003. (Junie B. Jones Ser.: No. 20). (J). (gr. k-3). lib. bdg. 11.80 (978-0-613-71014-5(2)) Tandem Library Bks.

Paxton, Tom. The Story of the Tooth Fairy. Sauber, Robert G., illus. 2000. 32p. (YA). (ps-3). pap. 5.95 (978-0-688-17523-8(6) , Harper Trophy) HarperCollins Pubs.

Pete's Teeth. 1998. (Fisher-Price Phonics Storybooks Ser.: Vol. 1). (Illus.). (J). pap. (978-0-7666-0175-8(7) , Honey Bear Bks.) Modern Publishing.

Ray, Karen. The T. F. Letters. 2000. (978-0-606-22349-2(5)) Tandem Library Bks.

Rigby Education Staff. Clean My Teeth. (Sails Literacy Ser.). (Illus.). 16p. (gr. k-1). 27.00 (978-0-7635-9882-2(8) , 698828C99) Rigby Education.

Robinson, Robert, et al. Danny Goes to the Dentist. Smee, Nicola, illus. 2002. (First Experiences Ser.). 32p. (J). (gr. k-2). 15.00 (978-1-57768-987-4(9) , Waterbird Bks.) School Specialty Publishing.

Ross, Tony. I Want My Tooth. Ross, Tony, illus. 2005. (Illus.). 28p. (J). (gr. k-2). pap. 4.95 (978-1-929132-85-0(9)) Kane/Miller Bk. Pubs., Inc.

Rowe, Melissa J. When the Tooth Fairy Comes... 2007. (J). per. 10.99 ***(978-1-59879-369-7(1))*** Lifevest Publishing, Inc.

Ruelle, Karen Gray. Dear Tooth Fairy. (Illus.). 32p. (J). 14.95 (978-0-8234-1929-6(0)); 4.95 (978-0-8234-1984-5(3)) Holiday Hse., Inc.

Ryan, Margaret. Smiler Gets a Toothache. Melling, David, tr. Melling, David, illus. 2003. 42p. (J). (978-0-439-45586-2(3)) Scholastic, Inc.

Santa Goes to the Dentist. 2005. (J). 5.95 net. (978-0-9769321-5-4(6)) Steingart, Nathan Publishing.

Sarrazin, Marisol. Peppy, Patch, & the Socks. 2005. (Read-It! Readers Ser.). (Illus.). 32p. (C). (gr. k-3). 18.60 (978-1-4048-1023-5(4)) Picture Window Bks.

Saunders, Helen. So, Where do all the teeth Go? Bolick, Brian, illus. 2006. (J). (978-0-9763143-3-2(9)) Happy Heart Kids Publishing.

Schaefer, Lola M. Loose Tooth. Wickstrom, Sylvie K., tr. Wickstrom, Sylvie K., illus. 2004. (My First I Can Read Bks.). 32p. (J). (ps up). 14.99 (978-0-06-052776-1(5)) HarperCollins Pubs.

—Loose Tooth. Wickstrom, Sylvie Kantorovitz, illus. 2005. 32p. (J). (ps-ps). lib. bdg. 11.19 (978-0-606-33932-2(9)) Tandem Library Bks.

Sis, Peter. Madlenka. Sis, Peter, illus. 2000. (Illus.). 48p. (J). (ps-3). 17.00 (978-0-374-39969-6(7) , Farrar, Straus & Giroux (BYR)) Farrar, Straus & Giroux.

—Madlenka. 2000. (Illus.). (J). (gr. k-3). 19.95 (978-0-88899-412-7(5)) Groundwood Bks. CAN. *Dist:* Transition Vendor.

Smileytooth & the Plaque Attack: The Adventures of Smileytooth. 2006. (J). 6.95 (978-0-9778456-0-6(5)) Pontrelli, Jeany.

Smith, Juanda. I'd Rather Lose a Tooth. 2005. pap. 7.95 (978-0-533-14184-5(2)) Vantage Pr., Inc.

Speakes, Leslie. The Hygiene Mystery. 2004. 31p. pap. 17.95 (978-1-4137-1860-7(4)) PublishAmerica, Inc.

Star the Tooth Fairy from Treasure Cloud Shares Secrets with You! 2006. (J). per. 9.99 ***(978-0-9792992-0-9(9))*** Twinkle Bks.

Star the Tooth Fairy Is Checking on You! 2004. (J). per. 9.99 ***(978-0-9792992-2-3(5))*** Twinkle Bks.

Star the Tooth Fairy Wants to Know if You Need Braces? 2006. (J). per. 9.99 ***(978-0-9792992-1-6(7))*** Twinkle Bks.

Suen, Anastasia. Loose Tooth. 2003. (gr. k-3). lib. bdg. 11.80 (978-0-613-67459-1(6)) Tandem Library Bks.

—The Loose Tooth. Eitzen, Allan, illus. 2003. (Easy-to-Read Ser.). 32p. (J). (gr. k-2). pap. 3.99 (978-0-14-250064-4(X) , Puffin) Penguin Group (USA) Inc.

Thompson, Deanna. 100 Years Old with Baby Teeth: Will Caroline Ever Lose Her Tooth? Wolf, Claudia, illus. 2006. 24p. (J). per. 2.99 (978-1-59958-000-5(4)) Journey Stone Creations, LLC.

Tiourina, Svetlana. Oh, Boris! 2000. (Illus.). 28p. (J). 14.50 (978-1-84059-225-2(7)) Milet Publishing.

Trumbauer, Lisa. Un Diente Esta Flojo. Gray, Steve, illus. 2005. (Rookie Reader Espanol Ser.). (SPA & ESP.). 23p. (J). (gr. k-2). pap. 4.95 (978-0-516-24674-1(7) , Children's Pr.) Scholastic Library Publishing.

—Un Diente esta Flojo: A Tooth Is Loose. Gray, Steve, illus. 2005. (Rookie Reader(R) Espanol Ser.). (SPA & ENG.). 24p. (gr. k-2). 19.50 (978-0-516-24449-5(3) , Children's Pr.) Scholastic Library Publishing.

—A Tooth Is Loose. Gray, Steve, illus. (Rookie Reader Espanol Ser.). (J). (gr. k-2). 2005. 24p. pap. 4.95 (978-0-516-25841-6(9)); 2004. 23p. 19.50 (978-0-516-23445-8(5)) Scholastic Library Publishing. (Children's Pr.).

—A Tooth Is Loose. Gray, Steve, illus. 2005. 24p. (J). (gr. k-1). lib. bdg. 12.15 (978-0-606-33168-5(9)) Tandem Library Bks.

Tuggle, Diane. Spencer's Toothbrush Vol. 1: An Adventure in Preventive Dental Health. 1999. (Illus.). 48p. (J). (gr. k-10). pap. 12.99 (978-0-9674450-1-4(9)) Forerunner Pr.

Van Leeuwen, Jean. Amanda Pig & the Wiggly Tooth. Schweninger, Ann, illus. 2008. 40p. (J). (ps). 14.99 (978-0-8037-3104-2(3) , Dial) Penguin Group (USA) Inc.

Vrombaut, An. Clarabella's Teeth. 2003. (Illus.). 32p. (J). (gr. k-3). 15.00 (978-0-618-33379-0(7) , Clarion Bks.) Houghton Mifflin Co. Trade & Reference Div.

Walden, Joseph. Grandpa's Smile. Walden, Joseph, illus. 2000. (Illus.). 32p. (ps-2). 9.95 (978-1-59093-058-8(4)) Warehousing & Fulfillment Specialists, LLC (WFS, LLC).

Walsh, Alice. Les Dents D'Hector. 1999. (FRE., Illus.). 24p. (J). pap. (978-2-89021-351-7(X)) Diffusion du livre Mirabel.

—Uncle Farley's False Teeth. ed. 2004. (Illus.). (J). (gr. k-3). spiral bd. (978-0-616-01807-1(X)) Canadian National Institute for the Blind/Institut National Canadien pour les Aveugles.

—Uncle Farley's False Teeth. Martchenko, Michael, illus. 1998. 32p. (J). (ps-2). lib. bdg. 15.95 (978-1-55037-543-5(1)) Firefly Bks., Ltd.

Webb, Carla. The Magic in Believing: The Tooth Fairies. Lee, Kim, illus. (Magic in Believing Ser.). 36p. (J). (gr. k-5). (978-0-9705726-0-8(3)) Ageless Treasures.

Wells, Rosemary. The School Play. Wheeler, Jody, illus. 2001. (Yoko & Friends School Days Ser.: No. 2). 32p. (gr. k-2). 9.99 (978-0-7868-0721-5(0)); pap. 3.99 (978-0-7868-1527-2(2)) Hyperion Bks. for Children. (Volo).

—The School Play. 2001. (J). (978-0-606-22547-2(1)); lib. bdg. 11.80 (978-0-613-53555-7(3)) Tandem Library Bks.

Wilhelm, Hans. I Lost My Tooth! 2004. 32p. (J). lib. bdg. 15.00 (978-1-59054-366-5(1)) Fitzgerald Bks.

—I Lost My Tooth! Wilhelm, Hans, illus. 1999. (Hello Reader! Ser.). (Illus.). 32p. (J). (ps-1). pap. 3.99 (978-0-590-64230-9(8) , Cartwheel Bks.) Scholastic, Inc.

—I Lost My Tooth! 1999. (Hello Reader! Ser.). (J). 10.79 (978-0-606-16613-3(0)); lib. bdg. 11.80 (978-0-613-11664-0(X)) Tandem Library Bks.

—Se Me Cayo un Diente! Wilhelm, Hans, illus. 2002. (Coleccion "Hola, Lector" Ser.).Tr. of I Lost My Tooth. (SPA., Illus.). 32p. (J). (ps-1). pap. 3.99 (978-0-439-22646-2(5) , SO0823, Scholastic en Espanol) Scholastic, Inc.

—Se Me Cayo un Diente! 2001. Tr. of I Lost My Tooth. (978-0-606-22704-9(0)) Tandem Library Bks.

Williams, Barbara. Albert's Impossible Toothache. Cushman, Doug, illus. 2003. 40p. (J). (ps-1). 15.99 (978-0-7636-1723-3(7)) Candlewick Pr.

Williams, Jamie P. The Story of the Toothfairie. Brockschmidt, Kevin, illus. 1998. 18p. (J). (ps-4). pap. 10.00 (978-0-9664799-0-4(4)) Soft Stuff.

Wing, Natasha. The Night Before the Tooth Fairy. Newman, Barbara Johansen, illus. 2003. (Reading Railroad Bks.). 32p. (J). (ps-4). pap. 3.99 (978-0-448-43252-6(8) , Grosset & Dunlap) Penguin Group (USA) Inc.

The Wobbly Tooth: Individual Title Six-Packs. (Literatura 2000 Ser.). (gr. 1-2). 28.00 (978-0-7635-0158-7(1)) Rigby Education.

Wood, Audrey. Presto Change-O & Tooth Fairy. (J). audio 10.97 (978-0-85953-374-4(3)) Child's Play-International.

—Tooth Fairy. 2002. (Illus.). 32p. (J). 7.99 (978-0-85953-293-8(3)) Child's Play-International.

—Tooth Fairy. 2003. (ps-2). lib. bdg. 16.45 (978-0-613-76960-0(0)) Tandem Library Bks.

Xavier, Imbeus & Sanders, Martin B. Super Dentist Guy: Attack of the Yukkies. Sanders, Martin B., illus. 2003. (Illus.). 64p. lib. bdg. 11.99 (978-0-9708523-2-8(0)) DeMosi Publishing.

—Super Dentist Guy: Attack of the Yukkies. Sanders, Martin B. et al, illus. 2003. 52p. 7.99 (978-0-9708523-0-4(4)) DeMosi Publishing.

TELECOMMUNICATION

see also Artificial Satellites in Telecommunication; Interstellar Communication; Radio; Telegraph; Telephone; Television

Aaseng, Nathan. Business Builders in Broadcasting. 2005. (Business Builders Ser.: Vol. 8). (Illus.). 160p. (J). (gr. 5 up). lib. bdg. 24.95 (978-1-881508-83-0(8)) Oliver Pr., Inc.

Ball, Jacqueline A., et al. Communication Inventions: From Hieroglyphics to DVDs. 2006. (Which Came First? Ser.). (Illus.). 32p. (J). lib. bdg. 25.27 (978-1-59716-129-9(2)) Bearport Publishing Co., Inc.

Currie-Mcghee, Leanne K. Brittany & Robbie Bergquist: Cell Phones for Soldiers. 2007. (Young Heroes Ser.). (Illus.). 64p. (gr. 4-8). 24.95 ***(978-0-7377-3866-7(9)*** , Kidhaven) Thomson Gale.

Equipo Staff. Suena el Telefono. (Enciclopedia Me Pregunto Por Que). (SPA., Illus.). 124p. (J). (gr. 3-5). (978-84-241-1964-5(9) , EV6623) Everest de Ediciones y Distribucion, S.L. ESP. *Dist:* Lectorum Pubns., Inc.

Gaines, Ann Graham. Hedy Lamarr. 2001. (Discover the Life of an Inventor Ser.). (Illus.). 24p. (J). (gr. 1-4). lib. bdg. 20.64 (978-1-58952-119-3(6)) Rourke Publishing, LLC.

—Hedy Lamarr. Sarfatti, Esther & de la Vega, Eida, trs. from ENG. 2001. (Inventores Famosos Ser.). (SPA., Illus.). 24p. (J). lib. bdg. 19.27 (978-1-58952-176-6(5) , RK7040) Rourke Publishing, LLC.

Graham, Ian. Communications. 2001. (Science Fact Files Ser.). (Illus.). 48p. (J). (gr. 4-7). lib. bdg. 27.12 (978-0-7398-1014-6(9)) Raintree.

—Satellites & Communications. 2001. (Technoworld Ser.). (Illus.). 32p. (J). lib. bdg. 25.69 (978-0-7398-3255-4(7)) Raintree.

—The World of Computers & Communication. 2000. (Inside Look Ser.). (Illus.). 48p. (J). (gr. 4 up). lib. bdg. 26.00 (978-0-8368-2727-9(9)) Stevens, Gareth Inc.

Henderson, Harry. Communications & Broadcasting. 2nd rev. ed. 2006. (Milestones in Discovery & Invention Ser.). 224p. (gr. 6-12). 35.00 (978-0-8160-5748-1(6)) Facts On File, Inc.

J. G. Ferguson Publishing Company Staff, ed. Careers in Focus. 3rd ed. 2006. (Careers in Focus Ser.). (Illus.). 192p. (J). (gr. 6-12). 29.95 (978-0-8160-6564-6(0) , Ferguson Publishing Co.) Facts On File, Inc.

Jefferis, David. Internet: Electronic Global Village. 2002. (Megatech Ser.). (Illus.). 32p. (J). (gr. 4-5). pap. (978-0-7787-0062-3(3)); lib. bdg. (978-0-7787-0052-4(6)) Crabtree Publishing Co.

—Internet: Electronic Global Village. 2002. (gr. 3-6). lib. bdg. 17.60 (978-0-613-52962-4(6)) Tandem Library Bks.

Kallen, Stuart A. The Wireless Society. 2006. 128p. (J). 21.20 (978-0-7377-2750-0(0)); pap. 29.95 (978-0-7377-2749-4(7)) Thomson Gale. (Greenhaven Pr., Inc.).

Maddison, Simon. Telecoms. 2003. 48p. (J). lib. bdg. 27.10 (978-1-58340-352-5(3)) Smart Apple Media.

Mattern, Joanne. From Radio to the Wireless Web. 2002. (Transportation & Communication Ser.). (Illus.). 48p. (J). (gr. 1-4). lib. bdg. 23.93 (978-0-7660-1893-8(8)) Enslow Pubs., Inc.

Parker, Janice. Messengers, Morse Code & Modems: The Science of Communication. 2000. (Science @ Work Ser.). (Illus.). 48p. (J). (gr. 4-6). lib. bdg. 27.12 (978-0-7398-0138-3(4)) Raintree.

Parker, Steve. Communications. 2002. (Tomorrow's Technology Ser.). (Illus.). 32p. (J). lib. bdg. 24.25 (978-1-931983-22-8(4)) Chrysalis Education.

Radios, Phones & Telecommunications. 2005. (Inventions Ser.). (Illus.). 30p. (J). pap. 15.95 incl. audio (978-0-9724983-4-0(6)) Jazwares Distribution, Inc.

Rooney, Anne. Telecommunications. 2005. (Technology All Around Us Ser.). (Illus.). 32p. (J). (gr. 4-7). lib. bdg. 27.10 (978-1-58340-754-7(5)) Smart Apple Media.

Sanders. Communication Technology: Today & Tomorrow. 2nd ed. 1999. (Illus.). 190p. (YA). (gr. 6-12). stu. ed., wbk. ed. 7.99 (978-0-02-838760-4(0)) Glencoe/ McGraw-Hill.

Sawyer, Sarah. Career Building Through Podcasting. 2007. (J). lib. bdg. (*978-1-4042-1944-1(7)) Rosen Publishing Group, Inc., The.

Waters, Jennifer. Let's Talk: How We Communicate. 2002. (Spyglass Books). (Illus.). 24p. (J). (gr. 1 up). lib. bdg. 18.60 (978-0-7565-0381-9(7)) Compass Point Bks.

Whitehouse, Patricia. Loud Sounds, Soft Sounds. 2007. (J). (978-1-60044-191-2(2)) Rourke Publishing, LLC.

Whiting, Jim. John R. Pierce: Pioneer in Satellite Communication. 2003. (Unlocking the Secrets of Science Ser.). (Illus.). 56p. (gr. 4-10). lib. bdg. 25.70 (978-1-58415-205-7(2)) Mitchell Lane Pubs., Inc.

Woodford, Chris. Communication & Computers. 2004. (History of Invention Ser.). (Illus.). 96p. (J). (gr. 6-12). 35.00 (978-0-8160-5443-5(6)) Facts On File, Inc.

TELEGRAPH

Hall, Margaret. Samuel Morse. 2004. (J). pap. 6.50 (978-1-4034-5337-2(3)); lib. bdg. 22.79 (978-1-4034-5329-7(2)) Heinemann Library.

Jarnow, Jesse. Telegraph & Telephone Networks: Ground Breaking Developments in American Communications. 2003. (America's Industrial Society in the 19th Century Ser.). (Illus.). 32p. (J). pap. (978-0-8239-4279-4(1)) Rosen Publishing Group, Inc., The.

McCormick, Anita Louise. The Invention of the Telegraph & Telephone in American History. 2004. (In American History Ser.). (Illus.). 128p. (J). lib. bdg. 26.60 (978-0-7660-1841-9(5)) Enslow Pubs., Inc.

Tucker, Mary. History Hands on! Telegraph & Telephone. Mitchell, Judy, ed. Hierstein, Judith, illus. 2004. 32p. (J). pap. 6.95 (978-1-57310-428-9(0)) Teaching & Learning Co.

Worth, Richard. Telegraph & Telephone. 2005. (Great Inventions Ser.). (Illus.). 48p. (J). lib. bdg. 30.00 (978-0-8368-5879-2(4) , World Almanac Library) Stevens, Gareth Inc.

Zannos, Susan. Samuel Morse & the Telegraph. 2004. (Uncharted, Unexplored, & Unexplained Ser.). (Illus.). 48p. (J). (gr. 4-8). lib. bdg. 29.95 (978-1-58415-269-9(9)). Mitchell Lane Pubs., Inc.

TELEPATHY

see Thought Transference

TELEPHONE

Alphin, Elaine Marie. Telephones. 2001. (Household History Ser.). (Illus.). 48p. (J). (gr. 2-5). lib. bdg. (978-1-57505-432-2(9) , Carolrhoda Bks.) Lerner Publishing Group.

Ashley, Susan. I Can Use the Telephone. 2004. (J). pap. (978-0-8368-4334-7(7)); (Illus.). 24p. (YA). lib. bdg. 19.33 (978-0-8368-4327-9(4)) Stevens, Gareth Inc.

Bankston, John. Alexander Graham Bell & the Story of the Telephone. 2004. (Uncharted, Unexplored, & Unexplained Ser.). (Illus.). 48p. (J). (gr. 4-8). lib. bdg. 29.95 (978-1-58415-243-9(5)) Mitchell Lane Pubs., Inc.

Banting, Erinn. Inventing the Telephone. 2006. (Breakthrough Inventions Ser.). (Illus.). 32p. (J). (gr. 3-9). pap. (978-0-7787-2837-5(4)); (978-0-7787-2815-3(3)) Crabtree Publishing Co.

Berger, Melvin & Berger, Gilda. Did You Invent the Phone All Alone, Alexander Graham Bell? 2007. (Scholastic Science Supergiants Ser.). 48p. (J). pap. 4.99 (978-0-439-83381-3(7) , Scholastic Nonfiction) Scholastic, Inc.

—Telephones, Televisions, & Toilets: How They Work & What Can Go Wrong. Madden, Don, illus. 1999. (Discovery Readers Ser.). 48p. (J). (gr. 4-7). 11.95 (978-0-7910-5065-1(3) , Chelsea Hse.) Facts On File, Inc.

Carson, Mary Kay. Sterling Biographies: Alexander Graham Bell: Giving Voice to the World. 2007. (Sterling Biographies Ser.). (Illus.). 128p. (J). 12.95 (*978-1-4027-4951-3(1)); pap. 5.95 (*978-1-4027-3230-0(9)) Sterling Publishing Co., Inc.

Chambers, Catherine. Telephone. 1998. (Look Inside Ser.). (Illus.). 24p. 19.92 (978-1-57572-625-0(4)) Heinemann Library.

Collins, Lori & Koski, Mary B. Impatient Pamela Says: Learn How to Call 9-1-1. Brown, Dan, illus. 2000. (Impatient Pamela Ser.). 16p. (J). (ps-3). pap., wbk. ed. 4.95 (978-0-9663281-1-0(6)) Trellis Publishing, Inc.

Cunningham, Kevin. Cell Phones. 2008. (J). lib. bdg. 25.26 (*978-1-60279-022-3(1)) Cherry Lake Publishing.

DiCicco, Sue, illus. Hello, It's Elmo. 2000. 5p. (J). bds. 12.98 (978-0-7853-4589-3(2)) Publications International, Ltd.

DK Publishing Staff. On the Phone. 2007. (Keep me Busy Ser.). 12p. (J). (ps-1). bds. 12.99 (978-0-7566-2937-3(3)) Dorling Kindersley Publishing, Inc.

Equipo Staff. El Telefono y los Medios de Communicacion. (Coleccion Mundo Maravilloso). (SPA., Illus.). 40p. (J). (gr. 2-4). (978-84-348-5484-0(8) , SM8407) SM Ediciones ESP. *Dist:* Lectorum Pubns., Inc.

Fandel, Jennifer. Alexander Graham Bell & the Telephone. Tucker, Keith & Barnett, Charles, illus. 2007. (Graphic Library). 32p. (J). 25.26 (978-0-7368-6478-7(4)) Capstone Pr., Inc.

Feinstein, Stephen. Alexander Graham Bell: Genius Behind the Bell. 2008. (Inventors Who Changed the World Ser.). 128p. (gr. 6 up). lib. bdg. 33.27 (*978-1-59845-055-2(7) , MyReportLinks.com Bks.) Enslow Pubs., Inc.

Fox, Susan & Phillips, Karen. Dial with Style 6 W/Display: Decorate Your Cell Phone. 2005. 38p. (J). 77.70 (978-1-57054-876-5(5)) Klutz.

Gaines, Ann Graham. Alexander Graham Bell. 2001. (Discover the Life of an Inventor Ser.). (Illus.). 24p. (J). (gr. 1-4). lib. bdg. 20.64 (978-1-58952-117-9(X)) Rourke Publishing, LLC.

—Alexander Graham Bell. Sarfatti, Esther & de la Vega, Eida, trs. 2001. (Inventores Famosos Ser.). (SPA & ENG., Illus.). 24p. (J). (gr. 1-4). lib. bdg. 19.27 (978-1-58952-173-5(0) , RK5266) Rourke Publishing, LLC.

Jarnow, Jesse. Telegraph & Telephone Networks: Ground Breaking Developments in American Communications. 2003. (America's Industrial Society in the 19th Century Ser.). (Illus.). 32p. (J). pap. (978-0-8239-4279-4(1)) Rosen Publishing Group, Inc., The.

Kulling, Monica. Listen Up! Alexander Graham Bell's Talking Machine. Walz, Richard, illus. 2007. (Step into Reading Ser.). 48p. (J). (gr. 1-3). pap. 3.99 (978-0-375-83115-7(0)); lib. bdg. 11.99 (978-0-375-93115-4(5)) Random Hse. Children's Bks. (Random Hse. Bks. for Young Readers).

Kummer, Patricia K. The Telephone. 2006. 80p. (gr. 5-8). pap. 9.95 (978-0-531-13903-5(4)); (Illus.). (J). 30.50 (978-0-531-12407-9(X)) Scholastic Library Publishing. (Watts, Franklin).

Mander, Lelia. Answer the Telephone. 2003. (Step Back Science Ser.). (Illus.). 48p. (J). 24.95 (978-1-56711-682-3(5) , Blackbirch Pr., Inc.) Thomson Gale.

Mara, Wil. Alexander Graham Bell. 2002. (Rookie Biographies Ser.). (Illus.). 32p. (J). (gr. 1-2). 20.50 (978-0-516-22524-1(3) , Children's Pr.) Scholastic Library Publishing.

Mattern, Joanne. Telephones. 2002. (Transportation & Communication Ser.). (Illus.). 48p. (J). (gr. 1-4). lib. bdg. 23.93 (978-0-7660-1888-4(1)) Enslow Pubs., Inc.

Matthews, Tom L. Always Inventing: A Photobiography of Alexander Graham Bell. 1999. (Illus.). 64p. (J). (gr. 3-13). 17.95 (978-0-7922-7391-2(5) , National Geographic Children's Bks.) National Geographic Society.

McCormick, Anita Louise. The Invention of the Telegraph & Telephone in American History. 2004. (In American History Ser.). (Illus.). 128p. (J). lib. bdg. 26.60 (978-0-7660-1841-9(5)) Enslow Pubs., Inc.

Micklos, John. Alexander Graham Bell Inventor of the Telephone. 2006. 44p. (J). lib. bdg. 15.00 (*978-1-4242-0686-5(3)) Fitzgerald Bks.

Nobleman, Marc Tyler. The Telephone. 2003. (Fact Finders Ser.). (Illus.). 32p. (J). lib. bdg. 22.60 (978-0-7368-2218-3(6)) Capstone Pr., Inc.

—The Telephone, 6 vols. (gr. 2-5). 36.95 (978-0-7368-4617-2(4)) Red Brick Learning.

Pleau-Murissi, Marilyn. Caillou: The Phone Call. 2003. (Clubhouse Ser.). (Illus.). 24p. (J). pap. 2.50 (978-2-89450-446-8(2)) Chouette Publishing CAN. *Dist:* Independent Pubs. Group.

Raatma, Lucia. Alexander Graham Bell. 2004. (Compass Point Early Biographies Ser.). (Illus.). 32p. (J). (gr. 2 up). lib. bdg. 21.26 (978-0-7565-0569-1(0)) Compass Point Bks.

Radios, Phones & Telecommunications. 2005. (Inventions Ser.). (Illus.). 30p. (J). pap. 15.95 incl. audio (978-0-9724983-4-0(6)) Jazwares Distribution, Inc.

Raum, Elizabeth. The History of the Telephone. 2007. (J). (*978-1-4034-9650-8(1)); pap. (*978-1-4034-9656-0(0)) Heinemann Library.

Rivera, Sheila. Alexander Graham Bell: A Life of Helpfulness. 2007. (Pull Ahead Books-Biographies Ser.). (J). 22.60 (978-0-8225-6463-8(7) , Lerner Pubns.) Lerner Publishing Group.

Royston, Angela. Telephone & Fax. 2001. (In Touch Ser.). (Illus.). 32p. (J). (gr. 1-3). lib. bdg. 22.79 (978-1-58810-067-2(7)) Heinemann Library.

Savage, Sharon. How to Dial 9-1-1. 2000. (Illus.). 12p. (J). (ps-5). pap. 10.00 incl. cd-rom (978-0-9650312-6-4(8)) Cosmo Starr Bks.

Schaefer, Lola M. I Know My Phone Number. 2007. (J). (978-1-59515-929-8(0)) Rourke Publishing, LLC.

Somervill, Barbara A. The History of the Telephone. 2004. (Timeline Library Ser.). 32p. (J). (gr. 2-6). 27.07 (978-1-59296-346-1(3)) Child's World, Inc.

Stefoff, Rebecca. The Telephone. 2005. (Great Inventions Ser.). (Illus.). 127p. (J). (gr. 8-12). lib. bdg. (978-0-7614-1879-5(2) , Benchmark Bks.) Cavendish, Marshall Corp.

Stile, Darlene. Telephones. 2001. (Communications Ser.). 24p. (J). (gr. 1 up). lib. bdg. 18.60 (978-0-7565-0138-9(5)) Compass Point Bks.

Telephones, Televisions, & Toilets. (Discovery Readers Ser.). 48p. (J). pap. 3.95 (978-0-8249-5311-9(8) , Ideals Children's Bks.) Ideals Pubns.

Tucker, Mary. History Hands on! Telegraph & Telephone. Mitchell, Judy, ed. Hierstein, Judith, illus. 2004. 32p. (J). pap. 6.95 (978-1-57310-428-9(0)) Teaching & Learning Co.

Washington, Kim M. Cell Phone Massacre: They Come Alive, 1. Blackwell, Jennifer M., illus. 2002. 122p. (YA). per. 13.00 (978-0-9679727-2-5(8)) Washington, Kim M.

Williams, Brian. Bell & the Science of the Telephone. Antram, David, illus. 2006. (Explosion Zone Ser.). 32p. (J). 12.99 (978-0-7641-5972-5(0)); pap. 6.99 (978-0-7641-3488-3(4)) Barron's Educational Series, Inc.

Worth, Richard. Telegraph & Telephone. 2005. (Great Inventions Ser.). (Illus.). 48p. (J). lib. bdg. 30.00 (978-0-8368-5879-2(4) , World Almanac Library) Stevens, Gareth Inc.

TELEPHONE—FICTION

Appleton, Victor. Tom Swift & His Photo Telephone or the. 2006. pap. (*978-1-4065-0906-9(X)) Dodo Pr.

Bour, Daniele. Petit ours brun repond au Teleph. pap. 12.95 (978-2-227-74805-7(2)) Bayard Editions FRA. *Dist:* Distribooks, Inc.

Comfort, Louise. Daisy's Necklace. 2003. (Fairy Phones Ser.). (Illus.). 10p. (J). bds. 4.95 (978-0-7641-5691-5(8)) Barron's Educational Series, Inc.

—Lily's Busy Day. 2003. (Fairy Phones Ser.). (Illus.). 10p. (J). bds. 4.95 (978-0-7641-5692-2(6)) Barron's Educational Series, Inc.

—Poppy's Party. 2003. (Fairy Phones Ser.). (Illus.). 10p. (J). bds. 4.95 (978-0-7641-5694-6(2)) Barron's Educational Series, Inc.

—Rosie's Surprise. 2003. (Fairy Phones Ser.). (Illus.). 10p. (J). bds. 4.95 (978-0-7641-5693-9(4)) Barron's Educational Series, Inc.

Cort, Ben, illus. Adam Astronaut. 2005. (Fun Phones Ser.). 10p. (J). bds. 4.95 (978-0-7641-5792-9(2)) Barron's Educational Series, Inc.

—Cody Cowboy. 2005. (Fun Phones Ser.). 10p. (J). bds. 4.95 (978-0-7641-5793-6(0)) Barron's Educational Series, Inc.

—Pip Pirate. 2005. (Fun Phones Ser.). 10p. (J). bds. 4.95 (978-0-7641-5794-3(9)) Barron's Educational Series, Inc.

Deutsch, Stacia & Cohon, Rhody. Bell's Breakthrough. Wenzel, David, illus. 2005. 105p. (J). (*978-1-4156-2913-0(7) , Aladdin) Simon & Schuster Children's Publishing.

Esbensen, Barbara Juster. Who Is Calling? Date not set. 15.95 (978-0-8050-4899-5(5)) Holt, Henry & Co.

Griffis, Molly Levite. Five Two, Five Blue. Hardgrove, M. W., illus. 1999. 32p. (gr. 1-4). 14.95 (978-1-57168-274-1(0)) Eakin Pr.

Hessel, Brooke. Clifford the Big Red Dog Telephone Book. 2002. (Illus.). (J). 16.98 (978-0-7853-6401-6(3)) Publications International, Ltd.

—Telephone Book. 2002. (Illus.). (J). (978-0-7853-7183-0(4)) Publications International, Ltd.

Kliebenstein, Shane & McCracken, Craig. The Powerpuff Girls Telephone Book. 2002. (Illus.). (J). (978-0-7853-6400-9(5)) Publications International, Ltd.

Koski, Mary B. Impatient Pamela Calls 9-1-1. Brown, Dan, illus. 2005. (Impatient Pamela Series Ser.). 32p. 14.95 (978-1-930650-09-1(4)) Trellis Publishing, Inc.

Koski, Mary B. & Collins, Lori. Impatient Pamela Says: Learn to Call 9-1-1: Learn to Call 9-1-1. Brown, Dan S., illus. 2007. 16p. (J). pap. 2.95 (*978-1-930650-05-3(1)) Trellis Publishing, Inc.

Lang, Greg. I'm on the Phone. 2000. (gr. k-3). lib. bdg. 11.80 (978-0-613-29649-6(4)) Tandem Library Bks.

Reynolds, Wendy. Moby for Justice. 2006. 17.00 (*978-0-8059-8861-1(0)) Dorrance Publishing Co., Inc.

Sefton, Catherine. Ghosts of Cobweb & the TV Battle. (Illus.). 48p. (J). 11.95 (978-0-241-00199-8(4) , Hamilton, Hamish) Penguin Bks., Ltd. GBR. *Dist:* Trafalgar Square Publishing.

Sleator, William. Hell Phone. 2007. 288p. (J). (gr. 7-17). pap. 6.95 (*978-0-8109-9360-0(0)); 2006. 252p. (YA). (gr. 8-11). 16.95 (978-0-8109-5479-3(6) , Amulet Bks.) Abrams, Harry N. , Inc.

Takeshita, Fumiko. Hello, Hello. Takabatake, Jun, illus. 2006. 28p. (J). pap. (978-1-933605-11-1(1)) Kane/Miller Bk. Pubs., Inc.

Upton, Deborah. First Telephone Book. Kleven, Dean, illus. 2001. (J). 16.98 (978-0-7853-4794-1(1)) Publications International, Ltd.

Zucker, Jonny. Creature Chase. Troiano, Enzo, illus. 2007. 33p. (J). pap. (*978-1-59889-424-0(2)); 40p. (YA). (gr. 5-9). 21.26 (*978-1-59889-336-6(X)) Stone Arch Bks.

—Cut-Throat Pirates. Smith, Pete, illus. 2007. 33p. (J). pap. (*978-1-59889-428-8(5)); 40p. (YA). (gr. 5-9). lib. bdg. 21.26 (*978-1-59889-332-8(7)) Stone Arch Bks.

—Inside the Game. Smith, Pete, illus. 2007. 33p. (J). pap. (*978-1-59889-426-4(9)); 40p. (YA). (gr. 5-9). lib. bdg. 21.26 (*978-1-59889-330-4(0)) Stone Arch Bks.

—Safecrackers. Troiano, Enzo, illus. 2007. 33p. (J). pap. (*978-1-59889-427-1(7)); 40p. (YA). (gr. 5-9). lib. bdg. 21.26 (*978-1-59889-331-1(9)) Stone Arch Bks.

—Soccer Showdown. Troiano, Enzo, illus. 2007. 33p. (J). pap. (*978-1-59889-430-1(7)); 40p. (YA). (gr. 5-9). lib. bdg. 21.26 (*978-1-59889-334-2(3)) Stone Arch Bks.

—Speed Star. Troiano, Enzo, illus. 2007. 33p. (J). pap. (*978-1-59889-431-8(5) , 1264997); 40p. (YA). (gr. 5-9). lib. bdg. 21.26 (*978-1-59889-335-9(1) , 1264997) Stone Arch Bks.

—Spin Off. Troiano, Enzo, illus. 2007. 33p. (J). pap. (*978-1-59889-429-5(3)); 40p. (YA). (gr. 5-9). lib. bdg. 21.26 (*978-1-59889-333-5(5)) Stone Arch Bks.

TELESCOPES

Barter, James. Telescopes. 2004. (Lucent Library of Science & Technology). 112p. (YA). (gr. 7-10). lib. bdg. 29.95 (978-1-59018-568-1(4) , Lucent Bks.) Thomson Gale.

Bender, Lionel. Magnification: A Closer Look. Davis, Jon, illus. 2007. (Amazing Science Ser.). (J). 23.93 (978-1-4048-2196-5(1)) Picture Window Bks.

Beyer, Mark T. Supertelescopios: Por Dentro y por Fuera. 2002. (Tecnología Ser.). (SPA.). 48p. (YA). lib. bdg. 26.50 (978-0-8239-6152-8(4) , Buenas Letra) Rosen Publishing Group, Inc., The.

Bocknek, Jonathan. Telescopes. 2002. (Science Matters Ser.). (Illus.). 24p. (J). lib. bdg. 15.95 (978-1-59036-084-2(2)) Weigl Pubs., Inc.

Bortz, Fred & Hammel, Heidi. Beyond Jupiter: The Story of Planetary Astronomer Heidi Hammet. 2006. (Women's Adventures in Science Ser.). 128p. pap. 9.95 (978-0-309-09552-5(2) , Joseph Henry Pr.) National Academies Pr.

Building Blocks of Science: Sky Watchers Teacher's Guide. 2007. (Illus.). ring bd. (*978-0-89278-325-0(7)) Carolina Biological Supply Co.

Bullock, Linda. Looking Through a Telescope. (Rookie Read-About Science Ser.). (Illus.). (J). 2004. 31p. (gr. 1-2). pap. 4.95 (978-0-516-27906-0(8)); 2003. 32p. 20.50 (978-0-516-22873-0(0)) Scholastic Library Publishing. (Children's Pr.).

Doak, Robin S. The Telescope & Microscope. 2005. (Great Inventions Ser.). (Illus.). 48p. (J). lib. bdg. 30.00 (978-0-8368-5880-8(8) , World Almanac Library) Stevens, Gareth Inc.

Matloff, Gregory L. More Telescope Power: All New Activities & Projects for Young Astronomers. 2002. (Illus.). 128p. pap. 12.95 (978-0-471-40985-4(5) , Wiley) Wiley, John & Sons, Inc.

Mattern, Joanne. The Telescope: Looking into Space. 2003. (Reading Power Ser.). (Illus.). 24p. (J). lib. bdg. 17.25 (978-0-8239-6489-5(2) , PowerKids Pr.) Rosen Publishing Group, Inc., The.

Moore, Patrick. The Young Astronomer & his Telescope. 2004. (Illus.). 80p. pap. 8.00 (978-0-904094-09-1(X)) Reid, Keith Ltd. GBR. *Dist:* Parkwest Pubns., Inc.

Nardo, Don. Telescopes. 2005. (KidHaven Science Library). (Illus.). 48p. (J). (ps-8). lib. bdg. 26.20 (978-0-7377-3060-9(9) , Greenhaven Pr., Inc.) Thomson Gale.

Orr, Tamra. The Telescope. (Inventions That Shaped the World Ser.). (Illus.). 80p. (J). 2005. (gr. 5-8). pap. 9.95 (978-0-531-16736-6(4)); 2004. 30.50 (978-0-531-12344-7(8)) Scholastic Library Publishing. (Watts, Franklin).

Price, Sean. Eye on the Universe. 2003. (Science Links Ser.). (Illus.). 32p. (J). (gr. 3-5). 23.00 (978-0-7910-7423-7(4) , Chelsea Hse.) Facts On File, Inc.

Richardson, Adele D. Telescopes. 2004. (First Facts Ser.). (Illus.). 24p. (J). 15.95 (978-0-7368-2518-4(5)) Capstone Pr., Inc.

Roza, Greg. The Hubble Space Telescope: Understanding & Representing Numbers in the Billions. 2005. (Illus.). 32p. (J). (978-1-4042-5130-4(8) , PowerKids Pr.) Rosen Publishing Group, Inc., The.

—The Hubble Space Telescope: Understanding & Representing Numbers up to 1 Billion. 2005. (PowerMath Ser.). (Illus.). 32p. (J). 22.50 (978-1-4042-2931-0(0) , PowerKids Pr.); pap. (978-1-4042-5129-8(4)) Rosen Publishing Group, Inc., The.

—The Incredible Story of Telescopes. 2004. (Kid's Guide to Incredible Technology Ser.). (Illus.). 24p. (J). lib. bdg. 19.95 (978-0-8239-6715-5(8)) Rosen Publishing Group, Inc., The.

Simon, Seymour. Destination: Space. 2004. 32p. (J). pap. 6.99 (978-0-06-059681-1(3) , Harper Trophy) HarperCollins Pubs.

—Out of Sight: Pictures of Hidden World. 2000. (gr. 3-6). lib. bdg. 15.25 (978-0-613-44470-5(1)) Tandem Library Bks.

—Out of Sight: Pictures of Hidden Worlds. 2002. (Illus.). 48p. (J). (gr. k up). 6.95 (978-1-58717-149-9(X) , SeaStar Bks.) Chronicle Bks. LLC.

Spangenburg, Ray. Hubble Space Telescope. 2002. (gr. 5-8). lib. bdg. 24.55 (978-0-613-53820-6(X)) Tandem Library Bks.

Sparrow, Giles. Observing the Universe. 2006. (Illus.). 48p. (J). pap. (978-0-8368-7284-2(3)); lib. bdg. (978-0-8368-7277-4(0)) Stevens, Gareth Inc. (World Almanac Library).

Stefoff, Rebecca. Microscopes & Telescopes. 2006. (Great Inventions Ser.). (Illus.). 128p. (J). lib. bdg. 39.93 (978-0-7614-2230-3(7) , Benchmark Bks.) Cavendish, Marshall Corp.

The Telescope: Looking into Space: Individual Title Six-Packs. (On Deck Ser.: Vol. 2). 24p. (gr. 4-5). 35.00 (978-0-7578-5863-5(5)) Rigby Education.

Telescopes & Space Probes. 2006. (World Book's Solar System & Space Exploration Library). (Illus.). (J). 63p. (978-0-7166-9510-3(3)); 2nd ed. 64p. (*978-0-7166-9520-2(0)) World Bk., Inc.

Villard, Raymond. Large Telescopes: Inside & Out. 2002. (Technology Ser.). (Illus.). 48p. (YA). (gr. 4-8). lib. bdg. 26.50 (978-0-8239-6110-8(9) , PowerKids Pr.) Rosen Publishing Group, Inc., The.

TELETUBBIES (FICTITIOUS CHARACTERS)—FICTION

The Butterfly. 1998. (Teletubbies Ser.). (Illus.). 24p. (J). (ps). pap. (978-0-7666-0259-5(1) , Honey Bear Bks.) Modern Publishing.

Come & Play. 1998. (Teletubbies Ser.). (Illus.). 96p. (J). (ps). pap. (978-0-7666-0266-3(4) , Honey Bear Bks.) Modern Publishing.

Davenport, Andrew. Here Come the Teletubbies. ed. 2004. (Illus.). (J). (ps-2). spiral bd. (978-0-616-03029-5(0)); spiral bd. (978-0-616-04551-0(4)) Canadian National Institute for the Blind/Institut National Canadien pour les Aveugles.

—Teletubbies (Ce p'Tit Agneau) ed. 2004. (J). (ps-2). spiral bd. (978-0-616-03071-4(1)) Canadian National Institute for the Blind/Institut National Canadien pour les Aveugles.

Davenport, Andrew & Baines, Chris. Time for Tubbyrobies. abr. ed. 1998. (Teletubbies Ser.). (Illus.). 22p. (J). (ps). mass mkt. (978-0-563-55855-2(5)) BBC Worldwide.

Dipsy's Day to Dance. 1998. (Teletubbies Ser.). (Illus.). 32p. (J). (ps). pap. (978-0-7666-0256-4(7) , Honey Bear Bks.) Modern Publishing.

Follow the Leader. 2003. (J). per. (978-1-57657-861-2(5)) Paradise Pr., Inc.

A Funny Day. 1998. (Teletubbies Ser.). (Illus.). 32p. (J). (ps). pap. (978-0-7666-0264-9(8) , Honey Bear Bks.) Modern Publishing.

Laa Laa Gets a Guitar. 1998. (Teletubbies Ser.). (Illus.). 32p. (J). (ps). pap. (978-0-7666-0257-1(5) , Honey Bear Bks.) Modern Publishing.

The Magic Cloud. 1998. (Teletubbies Ser.). (Illus.). 24p. (J). (ps). pap. (978-0-7666-0260-1(5) , Honey Bear Bks.) Modern Publishing.

Meet the Teletubbies. 1998. (Teletubbies Ser.). (Illus.). 96p. (J). (ps). pap. (978-0-7666-0265-6(6) , Honey Bear Bks.) Modern Publishing.

Playing Inside the Tubbytronic Superdome. 1999. (Teletubbies Ser.). (Illus.). (J). (ps). 19.99 (978-0-439-10603-0(6)) Scholastic, Inc.

Po Follows a Path. 1998. (Teletubbies Ser.). (Illus.). 32p. (J). (ps). pap. (978-0-7666-0258-8(3) , Honey Bear Bks.) Modern Publishing.

Scholastic, Inc. Staff. Teletubbies: 1999 Edition. 1998. (Teletubbies Ser.). (J). (ps). 10.95 (978-0-590-38611-1(5)) Scholastic, Inc.

Teletubbies' Favorite Things. 1998. (Teletubbies Ser.). (Illus.). 24p. (J). (ps). pap. (978-0-7666-0262-5(1) , Honey Bear Bks.) Modern Publishing.

Teletubbies Happy Time. 2001. (Illus.). (J). 7.95 (978-0-7853-4784-2(4)) Publications International, Ltd.

Teletubby Baby Busy Day! 2001. (J). (978-1-931312-41-7(9)) SoftPlay, Inc.

Time for a Walk. 1998. (Teletubbies Ser.). (Illus.). 32p. (J). (ps). pap. (978-0-7666-0263-2(X) , Honey Bear Bks.) Modern Publishing.

Tinky-Winky's Tubby Toast. 1998. (Teletubbies Ser.). (Illus.). 32p. (J). (ps). pap. (978-0-7666-0255-7(9) , Honey Bear Bks.) Modern Publishing.

Tubby Custard Mess. 1998. (Teletubbies Ser.). (Illus.). 24p. (J). (ps). pap. (978-0-7666-0261-8(3) , Honey Bear Bks.) Modern Publishing.

TELEVISION

Abraham, Philip. Television & Movies. 2004. (High-American Pop Culture Ser.). (Illus.). 48p. (J). 24.00 (978-0-516-24074-9(9) , Watts, Franklin) Scholastic Library Publishing.

Berger, Melvin & Berger, Gilda. Telephones, Televisions, & Toilets: How They Work & What Can Go Wrong. Madden, Don, illus. 1999. (Discovery Readers Ser.). 48p. (J). (gr. 4-7). 11.95 (978-0-7910-5065-1(3) , Chelsea Hse.) Facts On File, Inc.

Bodden, Valerie. Television. 2008. (J). ***978-1-58341-559-7(9)*** , Creative Education) Creative Co., The.

Cantor, Joanne. Teddy's TV Troubles. Lowes, Tom, illus. 2004. 36p. (J). mass mkt. 16.95 (978-0-9647663-7-2(X)) Goblin Fern Pr., Inc.

Carlson-Berne, Emma. Television. 2007. (Introducing Issues with Opposing Viewpoints Ser.). (Illus.). 144p. (gr. 7-10). 33.70 ***(978-0-7377-3853-7(7)*** , Greenhaven Pr., Inc.) Thomson Gale.

Ciovacco, Justine. Turn on the TV. 2003. (Step Back Science Ser.). (Illus.). 48p. (J). 24.95 (978-1-56711-680-9(9) , Blackbirch Pr., Inc.) Thomson Gale.

Feeney, Kathy. Television. 2001. (Transportation & Communication Ser.). (Illus.). 48p. (J). (gr. 1-4). lib. bdg. 23.93 (978-0-7660-1644-6(7)) Enslow Pubs., Inc.

Garth Gardner Company Staff, ed. Gardner's Film, Video & TV Dictionary. 2002. (Gardner's Guide Ser.). 448p. pap. 24.95 (978-1-58965-006-0(9) , 703 793 8604) Gardner, Garth Co., Inc. (GGC).

Gibson, Diane. Television. 1999. (Making Contact Ser.). (Illus.). 32p. (YA). (gr. 4 up). lib. bdg. 16.95 (978-1-887068-64-2(3)) Smart Apple Media.

Krementz, Jill. Keshia: A Very Young Television Star. 1999. (J). (978-0-316-50363-1(0)) Little Brown & Co.

Lafferty, Peter. Radio & Television. Antram, David, illus. 1998. (Worldwise Ser.: Vol. 17). 40p. (J). (gr. 4-7). pap. 7.00 (978-0-531-15317-8(7) , Watts, Franklin) Scholastic Library Publishing.

Mattern, Joanne. Television: Window to the World. 2003. (Reading Power Ser.). (Illus.). 24p. (J). lib. bdg. 17.25 (978-0-8239-6493-2(0) , PowerKids Pr.) Rosen Publishing Group, Inc., The.

Netter, Matt. Meet the Stars of 7th Heaven: The Unofficial Scrapbook. 1999. (Illus.). 48p. (J). (gr. 3-10). pap. 5.99 (978-0-439-04299-4(2)) Scholastic, Inc.

Oxlade, Chris. Television. 2001. (In Touch Ser.). (Illus.). 32p. (J). (gr. 1-3). lib. bdg. 22.79 (978-1-58810-068-9(5)) Heinemann Library.

Price, Roger & Stern, Leonard. Prime-Time Mad Libs'. 2002. (Mad Libs Ser.). 48p. (J). mass mkt. 3.99 (978-0-8431-4886-2(1) , Price Stern Sloan) Penguin Group (USA) Inc.

Richter, Joanne. Inventing the Television. 2006. (Breakthrough Inventions Ser.). (Illus.). 32p. (J). (gr. 3-9). pap. (978-0-7787-2835-1(8)); (978-0-7787-2813-9(7)) Crabtree Publishing Co.

Sheindlin, Judy. Win or Lose by How You Choose! 2000. (J). (978-0-06-028860-0(4)) HarperCollins Pubs.

Slade, Suzanne. My Adventure Inventing the Television. 2007. 44p. (J). 8.99 (978-1-59092-441-9(X) , Orchard Academy Pr.) Windstorm Creative.

Stille, Darlene R. Television. 2001. (Communications Ser.). (Illus.). 24p. (J). (gr. 1 up). lib. bdg. 18.60 (978-0-7565-0139-6(3)) Compass Point Bks.

Teitelbaum, Michael. Radio & Television. 2005. (Great Inventions Ser.). (Illus.). 48p. (YA). lib. bdg. 30.00 (978-0-8368-5802-0(6) , World Almanac Library) Stevens, Gareth Inc.

Telephones, Televisions, & Toilets. (Discovery Readers Ser.). 48p. (J). pap. 3.95 (978-0-8249-5311-9(8) , Ideals Children's Bks.) Ideals Pubns.

The Television: Window to the World. 6 Packs. (On Deck Ser.: Vol. 2). 24p. (gr. 4-5). 35.00 (978-0-7578-5864-2(3)) Rigby Education.

Wyckoff, Edwin Brit. The Teen Who Invented Television: Philo T. Farnsworth & His Awesome Invention. 2007. (Genius at Work! Great Inventor Biographies Ser.). (Illus.). 32p. (J). (gr. 3-4). lib. bdg. 22.60 ***(978-0-7660-2845-6(3)*** , Enslow Elementary) Enslow Pubs., Inc.

TELEVISION—BROADCASTING

see Television Broadcasting

TELEVISION—FICTION

Amelio-Ortiz, Osvaldo P. Nicolas, Donde Estas? Rodriguez Vidal, Andrea, illus. 2006. (SPA.). 28p. (J). pap. 14.95 (978-84-933955-1-3(X)) Hardenville SA URY. *Dist:* Independent Pubs. Group.

American Girl Editorial Staff. Making of the Movie. 2004. (Illus.). 32p. (J). pap. 10.00 (978-1-58485-942-0(3) , American Girl) American Girl Publishing, Inc.

Atinsky, Steve. Tyler on Prime Time. 2004. 176p. (J). (gr. 5-9). pap. 29.00 incl. audio (978-0-8072-2279-9(8) , Listening Library) Random Hse. Audio Publishing Group.

—Tyler on Prime Time. 2003. 176p. (J). (gr. 5-9). pap. 5.50 (978-0-440-41803-0(8) , Yearling) Random Hse. Children's Bks.

—Tyler on Prime Time. l.t. ed. 2002. 218p. (J). 23.95 (978-0-7862-4709-7(6)) Thorndike Pr.

Auerbach, Annie. Spongebob Superstar, Vol. 5. 2004. 64p. (J). (gr. 2-5). pap. 17.00 incl. audio (978-1-4000-8628-3(0) , Listening Library) Random Hse. Audio Publishing Group.

Bell, Christine. Oh No! the Television Won't Work! 2005. (Illus.). 52p. pap. ***(978-1-84401-340-1(5))*** Athena Pr.

Blacker, Terence. Parent Swap. 2006. 240p. (J). 16.00 (978-0-374-35752-8(8) , Farrar, Straus & Giroux (BYR)) Farrar, Straus & Giroux.

Bonin, Liane. Pretty on the Outside: Fame Unlimited. 2007. 288p. (YA). pap. 9.99 ***(978-0-451-22122-3(2)*** , N A L Trade) Penguin Group (USA) Inc.

Caulfield, Annie. Katie Milk Solves Reality TV Crimes. 2007. (Illus.). 208p. (J). pap. 9.95 ***(978-0-440-86687-9(1))*** Transworld Publishers Ltd. GBR. *Dist:* Independent Pubs. Group.

Collier, James Lincoln. The Rich & Famous. 2001. (Lost Treasures Ser.: No. 6). (Illus.). 240p. (gr. 3-7). pap. 1.99 (978-0-7868-1519-7(1) , Volo) Hyperion Bks. for Children.

Cooke, Jordan. Loose Lips. 2008. 224p. (J). (gr. 9). pap. 6.99 ***(978-0-448-44687-5(1)*** , Grosset & Dunlap) Penguin Group (USA) Inc.

Dague, Paige A. & Dague, James. ScribbleMonster & the Broken TV. 2001. (Illus.). 32p. (J). (ps). pap. 5.50 (978-0-9706406-1-1(7)) ScribbleBooks Co., The.

Dixon, Franklin W. Trouble in Warp Space. 2002. (gr. 3-6). lib. bdg. 13.00 (978-0-613-45115-4(5)) Tandem Library Bks.

—Trouble in Warp Space. l.t. ed. 2002. 181p. (J). 21.95 (978-0-7862-4658-8(8)) Thorndike Pr.

Donaldson, Julia & Richards, Lucy. The Quick Brown Fox Club. 2006. (Red Bananas Ser.). (Illus.). 48p. (J). (978-0-7787-1080-6(7)) Crabtree Publishing Co.

Dupasquier, Philippe. No More Television. 1999. (Illus.). 30p. (J). pap. 9.99 (978-0-86264-891-6(2)) Andersen GBR. *Dist:* Independent Pubs. Group.

Dussling, Jennifer. Whatcha Got? Wummer, Amy, illus. 2004. (Social Studies Connects). 32p. (J). (gr. 1-3). pap. 4.99 (978-1-57565-143-9(2)) Kane Pr., The.

Gaberman, Judith. First the Good News. 2001. 164p. pap. 11.95 (978-0-595-15835-5(8) , Backinprint.com) iUniverse, Inc.

Gilmore, Rachna. Ellen's Terrible TV Troubles. Mardon, John, illus. 2000. (First Flight Ser.). 38p. (J). (gr. 1-3). (978-1-55041-525-4(5)); pap. (978-1-55041-527-8(1)) Fitzhenry & Whiteside, Ltd.

—Ellen's Terrible TV Troubles. 2000. (gr. k-3). lib. bdg. 11.80 (978-0-613-90273-1(4)) Tandem Library Bks.

Gordon, Cambria. Reggie the Veggie. (J). 1999. pap. 3.99 (978-0-679-88848-2(9)); 1998. lib. bdg. 11.99 (978-0-679-98848-9(3)) Random Hse. Children's Bks. (Random Hse. Bks. for Young Readers).

Greenburg, Dan. Weird Planet: Lights, Camera... Liftoff! Pamintuan, Macky, illus. 2007. (Weird Planet Ser.: No. 5). 96p. (J). (gr. 2-5). pap. 3.99 ***(978-0-375-84336-5(1)*** , Random Hse. Bks. for Young Readers) Random Hse. Children's Bks.

—Weird Planet No. 5: Lights, Camera... Liftoff! Pamintuan, Macky, illus. 2007. (Stepping Stone Bks.). 96p. (J). (gr. 2-5). lib. bdg. 11.99 ***(978-0-375-94336-2(6)*** , Random Hse. Bks. for Young Readers) Random Hse. Children's Bks.

Hapka, Cathy. Star Bright. 2005. 146p. (J). (978-1-4155-7740-0(4) , Aladdin) Simon & Schuster Children's Publishing.

Harrison, John. Fergal Onions. 2005. (Illus.). 32p. pap. 17.95 (978-0-7022-3481-1(8)) Univ. of Queensland Pr. AUS. *Dist:* International Specialized Bk. Services.

Intercambio Cultural. 2001. (la Orilla Del Viento Ser.).Tr. of Cultural Exchange. (SPA., Illus.). 31p. (J). (ps-ps). pap. 6.99 (978-968-16-6261-5(X) , 136) Fondo de Cultura Economica USA.

Ironside, Virginia. Hakiba Kabira Min Al Himoom: The Huge Bag of Worries. 2005. 32p. pap. 12.00 (978-977-6171-02-2(8) , 706-002) Al-Balsam Pubng. Hse. EGY. *Dist:* Bookworld Trade, Inc.

Lawton, Wendy. Flip Flop. 2004. (Real Tv - Real Transformations Series (Take 2) Ser.). 208p. (J). pap. 10.99 (978-0-8024-5414-0(3)) Moody Pubs.

Leblanc, Louise. Maddie on TV. Gay, Marie-Louise & Cummins, Sarah, trs. from FRE. Gay, Marie-Louise, illus. 2003. 64p. (J). (gr. 2-5). (First Novel Ser.). ***(978-0-88780-613-1(9));*** (First Novels Ser.: Vol. 48). 4.95 (978-0-88780-612-4(0)) Formac Publishing Co., Ltd. CAN. *Dist:* Casemate Pubs. & Bk. Distributors, LLC.

Leroe, Ellen. Confessions of a Teenage TV Addict. (Illus.). (J). (978-0-448-47767-1(X) , Grosset & Dunlap) Penguin Group (USA) Inc.

Magoo, Biz. Pajama Sam's Amazing TV Adventure! Wunderlich, Dirk, illus. 2001. (Humongous Ser.). 24p. (J). (ps-3). pap. 3.99 (978-1-58668-062-6(5)) Lyrick Studios.

Marx, David F. Apagala! Shelly, Jeff, illus. 2001. (Rookie Reader Espanol Ser.). (SPA.). 32p. (J). (gr. k-2). 19.50 (978-0-516-22361-2(5) , Children's Pr.) Scholastic Library Publishing.

—Turn It Off! Shelly, Jeff, illus. 2001. (Rookie Readers Ser.). 32p. (J). (gr. 1-2). 19.50 (978-0-516-22229-5(5) , Children's Pr.) Scholastic Library Publishing.

McOmber, Rachel B., ed. McOmber Phonics Storybooks: On TV. rev. ed. (Illus.). (J). (978-0-944991-17-6(3)) Swift Learning Resources.

—McOmber Phonics Storybooks: The TV Box. rev. ed. (Illus.). (J). (978-0-944991-18-3(1)) Swift Learning Resources.

—McOmber Phonics Storybooks: The Video Show. rev. ed. (Illus.). (J). (978-0-944991-63-3(7)) Swift Learning Resources.

McPhail, David M. Fix It. McPhail, David M., illus. 2002. (Illus.). (J). 12.34 (978-0-7587-2515-8(9)) Book Wholesalers, Inc.

Mooney, E. S. Fuzzy Lumpkins Show. 2003. (gr. k-3). lib. bdg. 11.80 (978-0-613-66356-4(X)) Tandem Library Bks.

Mooney, E. S., et al. Fuzzy Lumpkins Show. Thompson Brothers Staff, illus. 2003. (Powerpuff Girls Ser.). 64p. (J). mass mkt. 3.99 (978-0-439-44226-8(5) , Scholastic Paperbacks) Scholastic, Inc.

Muldrow, Diane. Lights! Camera! Cook! Pollak, Barbara, illus. 2007. (Dish Ser.: No. 8). 160p. (J). pap. 4.99 (978-0-448-44533-5(6) , Grosset & Dunlap) Penguin Group (USA) Inc.

Nickle, John. TV Rex. 2001. (Illus.). 32p. (J). (gr. k-2). pap. 15.95 (978-0-439-12043-2(8)) Scholastic, Inc.

Novak, Matt. Mouse TV. 1998. (Illus.). 32p. (J). (ps-1). pap. 6.95 (978-0-531-07099-4(9) , Orchard Bks.) Scholastic, Inc.

Papademetriou, Lisa. A Very Lizzie Summer. 2005. (Illus.). 272p. (J). (gr. 3-7). pap. 6.99 (978-0-7868-4634-4(8)) Disney Pr.

Polacco, Patricia. Aunt Chip & the Great Triple Creek Dam Affair. Polacco, Patricia, illus. 2002. (Illus.). (J). 23.64 (978-0-7587-1998-0(1)) Book Wholesalers, Inc.

Random House Staff. Elmo's Breakfast Bingo. Womble, Louis, illus. 2005. 32p. (J). (ps-k). 6.99 (978-0-375-83045-7(6) , Random Hse. Bks. for Young Readers) Random Hse. Children's Bks.

—Get Moving with Grover. Womble, Louis, illus. 2005. 32p. (J). (ps-k). 6.99 (978-0-375-83046-4(4) , Random Hse. Bks. for Young Readers) Random Hse. Children's Bks.

Rodgers, Mary. ESP TV. 1999. (Freaky Friday Bks.). 224p. (J). (gr. 5 up). pap. 4.95 (978-0-06-440838-7(8) , Harper Trophy) HarperCollins Pubs.

Roth, Matthue. Never Mind the Goldbergs. 368p. (J). 2006. pap. 7.99 (978-0-439-69189-5(3)); 2005. pap. 16.95 (978-0-439-69188-8(5)) Scholastic, Inc. (PUSH).

Scholastic, Inc. Staff. The Springy Zingy Box. 2004. (Boohbah Ser.). (Illus.). 16p. (J). pap. 5.99 (978-0-439-59093-8(0)) Scholastic, Inc.

—Storyworld Stickers. 2004. (Boohbah Ser.). (Illus.). 16p. (J). 5.99 (978-0-439-62515-9(7)) Scholastic, Inc.

Scholastic, Inc. Staff. Zoey 101: Chapter Book. 2007. (Teenick Ser.). 112p. (J). pap. 4.99 ***(978-0-439-91648-6(8))*** Scholastic, Inc.

Shreve, Susan Richards. Jonah, the Whale. 1999. 128p. (J). (gr. 3-7). pap. 4.99 (978-0-590-37134-6(7) , Scholastic Paperbacks) Scholastic, Inc.

Thompson, Lisa. Wonder Worlds. Thompson, Lisa & Stapleton, Matthew, illus. 2005. (Read-It! Chapter Bks.). 48p. (J). (ps-k). lib. bdg. 19.95 (978-1-4048-1347-2(0)) Picture Window Bks.

Tulloch, Richard. Freaky Stuff. Nagle, Shane, illus. 2007. 208p. (J). (gr. 3-7). 16.95 (978-0-8027-9623-3(0)) Walker & Co.

Van Etten, David. Likely Story (Book 1) 2008. (Likely Story Ser.). 208p. (J). (gr. 7). 15.99 ***(978-0-375-84676-2(X));*** lib. bdg. 18.99 ***(978-0-375-94676-9(4))*** Random Hse. Children's Bks. (Knopf Bks. for Young Readers).

White, Andrea. Surviving Antarctica: Reality TV 2083. 2005. 336p. (J). (gr. 7 up). 16.99 (978-0-06-055454-5(1) , HarperCollins); lib. bdg. 16.89 (978-0-06-055455-2(X)) HarperCollins Pubs.

Wilcox, Mary. The Hollywood Sisters: Backstage Pass. 2006. 256p. (J). (gr. 5). 7.95 (978-0-385-73354-0(2) , Delacorte Bks. for Young Readers) Random Hse. Children's Bks.

—On Location. 2007. (Hollywood Sisters Ser.). 240p. (J). (gr. 5). 7.99 (978-0-385-73355-7(0) , Delacorte Bks. for Young Readers) Random Hse. Children's Bks.

Willson, Sarah. The Rugrats & the Zombies. Goldberg, Barry, illus. 1998. (Rugrats Ser.). 24p. (J). (ps-2). pap. 3.50 (978-0-689-82125-7(5) , Simon Spotlight/ Nickelodeon) Simon & Schuster Children's Publishing.

Zink, Rui. The Boy Who Did Not Like Television. Dreher, Patrick, tr. from POR. Ramos, Manuel Joao, illus. 2004. (J). 14.95 (978-1-931561-96-9(6)) MacAdam/Cage Publishing, Inc.

TELEVISION—HISTORY

Borgenicht, David. Sesame Street Unpaved: Scripts, Stories, Secrets & Songs. 1998. (Illus.). 193p. (YA). (gr. 5 up). 24.95 (978-0-7868-6460-7(5)) Hyperion Pr.

Niz, Ellen Sturm. Philo Farnsworth & the Television. Tucker, Keith, illus. 2007. (Graphic Library). 32p. (J). 25.26 (978-0-7368-6487-9(3)) Capstone Pr., Inc.

Nobleman, Marc Tyler. The Television. 2004. (Fact Finders Ser.). (Illus.). 32p. (J). (gr. 3-5). lib. bdg. 22.60 (978-0-7368-2671-6(8) , Fact Finders) Capstone Pr., Inc.

O'Shei, Tim. Philo T. Farnsworth: Visionary Inventor of Television. 2008. (Inventors Who Changed the World Ser.). 128p. (J). (gr. 6 up). lib. bdg. 33.27 ***(*978-1-59845-075-0(1)*** , MyReportLinks.com Bks.) Enslow Pubs., Inc.

Otfinoski, Steven. Television. 2006. (Great Inventions Ser.). (Illus.). 111p. (J). lib. bdg. 39.93 (978-0-7614-2228-0(5) , Benchmark Bks.) Cavendish, Marshall Corp.

Raum, Elizabeth. The History of the Television. 2007. (J). ***(*978-1-4034-9651-5(X));*** pap. ***(*978-1-4034-9657-7(9))*** Heinemann Library.

Reid, Struan. John Logie Baird. 2000. (Groundbreakers Ser.). (Illus.). 48p. (J). (gr. 5-7). lib. bdg. 25.64 (978-1-57572-372-3(7)) Heinemann Library.

TELEVISION—PRODUCTION AND DIRECTION

Blount, Diana. TV Production Student Activities Book. Matthews, Douglas L., ed. 2003. (Illus.). stu. ed., per., wbk. ed. (978-1-931680-51-6(5) , Expert Systems for Teachers) Teaching Point, Inc.

Dunkleberger, Amy. So You Want to Be a Film or TV Director? 2007. (Careers in Film & Television Ser.). (Illus.). 128p. (YA). (gr. 5-10). lib. bdg. 31.93 (978-0-7660-2738-1(4)) Enslow Pubs., Inc.

Shulman, Mark. Attack of the Killer Video Book: Tips & Tricks for Young Directors. 2004. (gr. 5-8). lib. bdg. 18.75 (978-0-613-78549-5(5)) Tandem Library Bks.

Shulman, Mark & Krog, Hazlitt. Attack of the Killer Video Book: Tips & Tricks for Young Directors. Newbigging, Martha, illus. 2004. 64p. (J). (gr. 5). 24.95 (978-1-55037-841-2(4)); pap. 12.95 (978-1-55037-840-5(6)) Annick Pr., Ltd. CAN. *Dist:* Firefly Bks., Ltd.

Thornton, Craig. Career Diary of a TV Production Manager. 2005. (Gardner's Guide Ser.: No. 003). (Illus.). 178p. pap. 14.95 (978-1-58965-015-2(8)) Gardner, Garth Co., Inc. (GGC).

TELEVISION—VOCATIONAL GUIDANCE

Byrum, R. T. Television. 2005. (Careers for the Twenty-First Century Ser.). (Illus.). 112p. (YA). (gr. 7-10). lib. bdg. 29.95 (978-1-59018-400-4(9) , Lucent Bks.) Thomson Gale.

Davis, Gary W. Working at a TV Station. 1998. (Working Here Ser.). (Illus.). 32p. (J). (gr. 2-4). 23.50 (978-0-516-20750-6(4) , Children's Pr.) Scholastic Library Publishing.

Dunkleberger, Amy. So You Want to Be a Film or TV Director? 2007. (Careers in Film & Television Ser.). (Illus.). 128p. (YA). (gr. 5-10). lib. bdg. 31.93 (978-0-7660-2738-1(4)) Enslow Pubs., Inc.

—So You Want to Be a Film or TV Screenwriter? 2007. (Careers in Film & Television Ser.). (Illus.). 128p. (YA). (gr. 5-10). lib. bdg. 31.93 (978-0-7660-2645-2(0)) Enslow Pubs., Inc.

Facts on File, Inc. Staff. Careers in Focus. 2nd ed. 2004. (Careers in Focus Ser.). (Illus.). 192p. (YA). (gr. 6-12). 22.95 (978-0-8160-5551-7(3) , Ferguson Publishing Co.) Facts On File, Inc.

Facts on File, Inc. Staff, ed. Aviation. 4th ed. 2004. (Careers in Focus Ser.). (Illus.). 192p. (J). (gr. 6-12). 22.95 (978-0-8160-5552-4(1) , Ferguson Publishing Co.) Facts On File, Inc.

Ferguson. Careers in Focus. 2nd ed. 2002. (Careers in Focus Ser.). 192p. (YA). (gr. 6-12). 22.95 (978-0-89434-440-4(4) , Ferguson Publishing Co.) Facts On File, Inc.

J. G. Ferguson Publishing Company Staff. Careers in Focus: Broadcasting. 2001. (Careers in Focus Ser.). 188p. (J). (gr. 7 up). (978-0-89434-333-9(5) , F711, Ferguson Publishing Co.) Facts On File, Inc.

J. G. Ferguson Publishing Company Staff, contrib. by. Careers in Focus. 2nd ed. 2004. (Careers in Focus Ser.). (Illus.). 192p. (J). (gr. 6-12). 22.95 (978-0-8160-5549-4(1) , Ferguson Publishing Co.) Facts On File, Inc.

J. G. Ferguson Publishing Company Staff, ed. Careers in Focus, 12 vols., Set 3. 2001. 2304p. (YA). 186.00 (978-0-89434-423-7(4) , Ferguson Publishing Co.) Facts On File, Inc.

McAlpine, Margaret. Working in Film & Television. 2004. (My Future Career Ser.). (Illus.). 64p. (J). lib. bdg. 26.00 (978-0-8368-4237-1(5)) Stevens, Gareth Inc.

TELEVISION BROADCASTING

see also Television in Politics

Boraas, Tracey. TV Reporters. 1999. (Community Helpers Ser.). (Illus.). 92p. (J). (gr. 1-2). 18.60 (978-0-7368-0075-4(1) , Bridgestone Bks.) Capstone Pr., Inc.

Brandon, Karen & Diani, Stephanie. Nurse. 2005. (How Do I Become a... Ser.). (Illus.). 32p. (J). (gr. 4-7). lib. bdg. 23.70 (978-1-56711-744-8(9) , Blackbirch Pr., Inc.) Thomson Gale.

Chambers, Catherine. Television. 2001. (Behind Media Ser.). (Illus.). 48p. (YA). (gr. 6-8). lib. bdg. 24.22 (978-1-58810-035-1(9)) Heinemann Library.

Davis, Gary. Working at a TV Station. 1999. (Working Here Ser.). (Illus.). 32p. (J). (gr. 2-4). pap. 6.95 (978-0-516-20378-2(9) , Children's Pr.) Scholastic Library Publishing.

Davis, Gary W. Working at a TV Station. 1998. (Working Here Ser.). (Illus.). 32p. (J). (gr. 2-4). 23.50 (978-0-516-20750-6(4) , Children's Pr.) Scholastic Library Publishing.

Gellman, Marc. Bad Stuff in the News: A Guide to Handling the Headlines. 2002. (gr. 5-8). lib. bdg. 12.95 (978-0-613-87927-9(9)) Tandem Library Bks.

Gellman, Marc & Hartman, Tom. Bad Stuff in the News: A Guide to Handling the Headlines. 2002. 128p. (J). (gr. 4-9). reprint ed. pap. 4.95 (978-1-58717-232-8(1) , Sea-Star Bks.) Chronicle Bks. LLC.

Harte, Lawrence. Introduction to IP Television: Why & How Companies are Providing Television Through Data Networks. 2005. (Illus.). per. 14.99 (978-1-932813-35-7(7)) Althos.

—IP TV Dictionary: IP Television, Internet Television & IP CATV. 2005. (Illus.). 600p. per. 39.99 (978-1-932813-34-0(9)) Althos.

Hayward, Linda. A Day in the Life of a TV Reporter. 2001. 10.75 (978-0-606-22627-1(3)) Tandem Library Bks.

Hayward, Linda & Dorling Kindersley Publishing Staff. Jobs People Do: A Day in the Life of a Reporter. 2001. (Dk Readers Ser.). (Illus.). 32p. (J). (ps-3). 14.99 (978-0-7894-7956-3(7)); pap. 3.99 (978-0-7894-7957-0(5)) Dorling Kindersley Publishing, Inc.

Heath, David. Television Production Assistant. 1999. (Careers Without College Ser.). (Illus.). 48p. (J). (gr. 3-4). lib. bdg. 21.26 (978-0-7368-0173-7(1) , LifeMatters Bks.) Capstone Pr., Inc.

McAlpine, Margaret. Working in Film & Television. 2004. (My Future Career Ser.). (Illus.). 64p. (J). lib. bdg. 26.00 (978-0-8368-4237-1(5)) Stevens, Gareth Inc.

Minden, Cecilia & Cupp, Dave. Television Reporters. 2006. (Neighborhood Helpers Ser.). (Illus.). 32p. (J). (gr. k-4). 22.79 (978-1-59296-570-0(9)) Child's World, Inc.

Nagle, Jeanne M. Careers in Television. 2005. (Careers Ser.). (Illus.). 192p. (J). (gr. 7-12). lib. bdg. 26.50 (978-0-8239-3187-3(0)) Rosen Publishing Group, Inc., The.

Oxlade, Chris. Television. 2001. (In Touch Ser.). (Illus.). 32p. (J). (gr. 1-3). lib. bdg. 22.79 (978-1-58810-068-9(5)) Heinemann Library.

Paprocki, Sherry Beck. Katie Couric. 2001. (Women of Achievement Ser.). (Illus.). 112p. (J). (gr. 4-7). 30.00 (978-0-7910-5881-7(6) , Chelsea Hse.) Facts On File, Inc.

Pelusey, Michael & Pelusey, Jane. Film & Television (Media) 2005. (Media Ser.). (Illus.). 32p. (J). (ps-8). lib. bdg. 21.95 (978-0-7910-8802-9(2) , Chelsea Hse.) Facts On File, Inc.

Reeves, Diane Lindsey. Virtual Apprentice: TV Journalist. 2007. (Virtual Apprentice Ser.). 72p. (J). (gr. 6-12). 29.95 (***978-0-8160-6753-4(8)** , Ferguson Publishing Co.) Facts On File, Inc.

Shofner, Shawndra. How it Happens: At the T. V. Station. 2008. (J). lib. bdg. 19.95 net. (***978-1-934545-07-2(4)**) Oliver Pr., Inc.

Somervill, Barbara A. Backstage at a Newscast. 2003. (Backstage Pass Ser.). (Illus.). 48p. (J). 24.00 (978-0-516-24326-9(8)); (YA). (gr. 7-12). pap. 6.95 (978-0-516-24388-7(8)) Scholastic Library Publishing. (Children's Pr.).

—Backstage at a Newscast. 2003. (gr. 7-12). lib. bdg. 15.25 (978-0-613-59579-7(3)) Tandem Library Bks.

Spangenburg, Ray & Moser, Kit. TV News: Can It Be Trusted? 2003. (Issues in Focus Ser.). (Illus.). 128p. (J). (gr. 6-12). lib. bdg. 26.60 (978-0-7660-1942-3(X)) Enslow Pubs., Inc.

TV Reporters. (Community Helpers Ser.). 24p. (J). 6.95 (978-0-7368-8463-1(7)) Capstone Pr., Inc.

Wallace, Shelagh, et al. The TV Book: The Kid's Guide to Talking Back. Tuson, Lorraine & Bean, Brian, illus. 2nd rev. ed. 1998. 112p. (J). (gr. 3 up). pap. 12.95 (978-1-55037-534-3(2)) Annick Pr., Ltd. CAN. *Dist:* Firefly Bks., Ltd.

Wan, Guofang. TV Takeover: Questioning Television. 2007. (Fact Finders Ser.). (Illus.). 32p. (J). (gr. 4-7). lib. bdg. 22.60 (978-0-7368-6763-4(5) , 1264913, Fact Finders) Capstone Pr., Inc.

Wan, Guofang. TV Takeover: Questioning Television. 2007. (Fact Finders Ser.). (Illus.). 32p. (J). (***978-0-7368-7859-3(9)** , 1264913) Capstone Pr., Inc.

Woods, Bob. Live from the Racetrack: NASCAR on TV. 2003. (World of NASCAR Ser.). (Illus.). 32p. (J). (gr. 2-6). 25.64 (978-1-59187-035-7(6)) Child's World, Inc.

T U V

TELEVISION BROADCASTING—BIOGRAPHY

Banting, Erinn. Katie Couric. 2007. (J). (***978-1-59036-643-1(3)**); (***978-1-59036-644-8(1)**) Weigl Pubs., Inc.

Blashfield, Jean F. Oprah Winfrey. 2003. (Trailblazers of the Modern World Ser.). (ENG & SPA., Illus.). 48p. (J). (gr. 5 up). pap. 14.95 (978-0-8368-5247-9(8)); lib. bdg. 30.00 (978-0-8368-5087-1(4)) Stevens, Gareth Inc. (World Almanac Library).

Brooks, Philip. Oprah Winfrey: A Voice for the People. 2000. (Book Report Bios Ppbk Ser.). (Illus.). (YA). pap. 6.95 (978-0-531-16406-8(3) , Watts, Franklin) Scholastic Library Publishing.

—Oprah Winfrey: A Voice for the People. 1999. (978-0-606-18159-4(8)) Tandem Library Bks.

Brown, Jonatha A. Oprah Winfrey. 2004. (Gente Que Hay Que Conocer Ser.). (ENG & SPA.). pap. 5.95 (978-0-8368-4361-3(4)) Stevens, Gareth Inc.

—Oprah Winfrey. Acosta, Tatiana & Gutierrez, Guillermo, trs. 2004. (Gente Que Hay Que Conocer Ser.). (ENG & SPA.). 24p. (J). lib. bdg. 19.33 (978-0-8368-4354-5(1)) Stevens, Gareth Inc.

—Oprah Winfrey. 2004. (Illus.). 24p. pap. (978-0-8368-4319-4(3)); (YA). lib. bdg. 19.33 (978-0-8368-4312-5(6)) Stevens, Gareth Inc.

Canizares, Susan & Berger, Samantha. Meet Jim Henson. 1999. (Social Studies Emergent Readers). (J). 2.50 (978-0-439-04575-9(4)) Scholastic, Inc.

—Meet Jim Henson. 1999. (ps-2). lib. bdg. 10.10 (978-0-613-21981-5(3)) Tandem Library Bks.

Durrett, Deanne. Jim Henson. 2002. (Inventors & Creators Ser.). (Illus.). 48p. (J). (gr. 3-5). 23.70 (978-0-7377-0996-4(0) , LML00902-178605, Kidhaven) Thomson Gale.

Friedrich, Belinda. Oprah Winfrey. 2001. (Women of Achievement Ser.). (Illus.). 112p. (J). pap. (978-0-7910-5892-3(1)); (gr. 4-7). 30.00 (978-0-7910-5891-6(3)) Facts On File, Inc. (Chelsea Hse.).

Guilfoyle, Peg. Oprah Winfrey. 1999. (Ovations Ser.). (Illus.). 32p. (YA). (gr. 4-7). pap. (978-0-88682-941-4(0) , Creative Education) Creative Co., The.

Horner, Matina S., intro. Barbara Walters: Journalist. 1999. (Women of Achievement Ser.). (Illus.). 112p. (gr. 4-7). (J). pap. 9.95 (978-0-7910-4717-0(2)); (YA). 21.95 (978-0-7910-4716-3(4)) Facts On File, Inc. (Chelsea Hse.).

Kallen, Stuart A. Rosie O'Donnell. 1999. (People in the News Ser.). (Illus.). 96p. (YA). (gr. 6-9). 27.45 (978-1-56006-546-3(X) , Lucent Bks.) Thomson Gale.

Krohn, Katherine. Oprah Winfrey. 2005. (Lighting Bolt Bios Ser.). (Illus.). 112p. (J). (gr. 6-12). 27.93 (978-0-8225-2472-4(4)) Lerner Publishing Group.

Krohn, Katherine E. Oprah Winfrey. (Biography Ser.). (Illus.). 112p. (J). (gr. 6 up). 2003. pap. 7.95 (978-0-8225-5000-6(8)); 2001. 27.93 (978-0-8225-4999-4(9) , Lerner Pubns.) Lerner Publishing Group.

—Oprah Winfrey. 2002. (gr. 7-12). lib. bdg. 16.40 (978-0-613-84025-5(9)) Tandem Library Bks.

McIntosh-Wooten, Sara. Oprah Winfrey: Talk Show Legend. 1999. (African-American Biographies Ser.). (Illus.). 128p. (YA). (gr. 6-12). lib. bdg. 26.60 (978-0-7660-1207-3(7)) Enslow Pubs., Inc.

McLeese, Don. Oprah Winfrey. 2002. (Discover the Life of an American Legend Ser.). (Illus.). 24p. (J). lib. bdg. 20.64 (978-1-58952-306-7(7)) Rourke Publishing, LLC.

Norwich, Grace. Ashton! With Poster. 2003. (gr. 5-8). lib. bdg. 14.15 (978-0-613-83489-6(5)) Tandem Library Bks.

Paprocki, Sherry Beck. Katie Couric. 2001. (Women of Achievement Ser.). (Illus.). (YA). (gr. 8-12). pap. 30.00 (978-0-7910-5882-4(4) , Chelsea Hse.) Facts On File, Inc.

Presnall, Judith Janda. Oprah Winfrey. 1998. (People in the News Ser.). (Illus.). 112p. (YA). (gr. 6-9). 27.45 (978-1-56006-360-5(2) , Lucent Bks.) Thomson Gale.

Stanley, George Edward. Mr. Rogers: Young Friend & Neighbor. Henderson, Meryl, illus. 2004. 199p. (J). (ps-7). per. 11.64 (978-0-606-32667-4(7)) Tandem Library Bks.

Stone, Tanya Lee. Oprah Winfrey: Success with an Open Heart. 2001. (Gateway Biography Ser.). (Illus.). 48p. (J). (gr. 2-4). lib. bdg. 23.90 (978-0-7613-1814-9(3) , Millbrook Pr.) Lerner Publishing Group.

Wheeler, Jill C. Oprah Winfrey. 2002. (Breaking Barriers Ser.). (Illus.). 64p. (J). (gr. 3-8). lib. bdg. 25.65 (978-1-57765-319-6(X) , ABDO & Daughters) ABDO Publishing Co.

Woronoff, Kristen. Oprah Winfrey: Media Superstar. 2002. (Famous Women Juniors Ser.). (Illus.). 32p. (J). (gr. 3-5). 24.94 (978-1-56711-588-8(8) , Blackbirch Pr., Inc.) Thomson Gale.

TELEVISION IN POLITICS

Ruschmann, Paul. The FCC/Broadcast Regulations. Marzilli, Alan, ed. 2004. (Point/Counterpoint Ser.). (Illus.). 112p. (gr. 9-13). 32.95 (978-0-7910-8363-5(2) , Chelsea Hse.) Facts On File, Inc.

TELEVISION PLAYS

Crompton, Richmal. Just William As Seen on TV. 2003. (Illus.). 176p. (J). pap. 6.95 (978-0-333-62802-7(0)) Macmillan Publishers Ltd. GBR. *Dist:* Trafalgar Square Publishing.

Reisfeld, Randi. Sarah Michelle Gellar: She is the Slayer. 1998. (J). pap. 3.99 (978-0-590-64308-5(8)) Scholastic, Inc.

Stern, Leonard & Gribbin, Lisa. The Mad Libs Worst-Case Scenario Survival Handbook: Holidays. 2004. (Mad Libs Ser.). 48p. (J). pap. 3.99 (978-0-8431-1151-4(8) , Price Stern Sloan) Penguin Group (USA) Inc.

TELEVISION PROGRAMS

Abraham, Philip. Television & Movies. 2004. (High Interest Bks.). (Illus.). 48p. (J). (gr. 7-12). pap. 6.95 (978-0-516-25946-8(6) , Children's Pr.) Scholastic Library Publishing.

Altman, Sheryl. Way Too Much Information: A Fanatic's Guide to Dawson's Creek. 1998. (Illus.). 128p. (YA). (gr. 5 up). pap. 4.50 (978-0-06-107137-9(4)) HarperCollins Pubs.

Andrews, Scott. Troubled Waters: An Unauthorised & Unofficial Guide to Dawson's Creek. 2001. 384p. pap. 9.95 (978-0-7535-0625-7(4)) Macmillan.

Baby Boomers, 5 cass.; set. 2004. (People's Century Ser.). (gr. 7 up). 59.95 incl. VHS (978-1-57807-186-9(0) , WG590) WGBH Boston Video.

Beatty, Scott & Dorling Kindersley Publishing Staff. Batman Beyond. 2004. (Animated Series Guide). (Illus.). 48p. (J). 9.99 (978-0-7566-0586-5(5)) Dorling Kindersley Publishing, Inc.

Calderone, Samantha. Meet the Stars of Popular. 2000. (gr. 3-6). lib. bdg. 13.00 (978-0-613-32825-8(6)) Tandem Library Bks.

—Meet the Stars of Roswell: An Unauthorized Biography. 2000. (gr. 7-12). lib. bdg. 13.00 (978-0-613-89565-1(7)) Tandem Library Bks.

Cartwright, Nancy. My Life As a Ten Year-Old Boy. 2001. 304p. pap. 17.95 (978-0-7868-8600-5(5)) Hyperion Pr.

—My Life as a Ten Year-Old Boy: Bart, the Simpsons & Me. 2000. (Illus.). 288p. 27.95 (978-0-7868-6696-0(9)) Hyperion Pr.

Cocoro Books Staff, compiled by. The Gundam Explorer: G, Wing, Turn A, & Seed! 2004. (Illus.). 192p. pap. 11.95 (978-0-9723124-8-6(X)) DH Publishing, Inc.

Cole, Stephen. Thunderbirds Annual 2003. 2002. (Illus.). 64p. (J). pap. 16.00 (978-1-84222-675-9(4)) Carlton Bks., Ltd. GBR. *Dist:* Independent Pubs. Group.

Danko, Dan & Mason, Tom. The Official Guide to Battlebots. 2002. (Illus.). 64p. (J). (gr. 4-6). pap. 6.99 (978-0-439-39000-2(1)) Scholastic, Inc.

Dorling Kindersley Publishing Staff & Beatty, Scott. Batman. 2003. (DC Animated Series Guides). (Illus.). 48p. (J). 9.99 (978-0-7894-9580-8(5)) Dorling Kindersley Publishing, Inc.

Englart, Mindi. Televison Show. 2003. (Made in the USA Ser.). 32p. (YA). 24.94 (978-1-56711-413-3(X) , Blackbirch Pr., Inc.) Thomson Gale.

ESCAPE! Because Accidents Happen: Abandon Ship. 2004. (NOVA Ser.). (gr. 7 up). 19.95 incl. VHS (978-1-57807-158-6(5) , WG2607) WGBH Boston Video.

Foster, Walter, ed. Spongebob Squarepants. Martinez, Heather, illus. 2002. (Nick How to Draw Ser.). 32p. (J). pap. 5.95 (978-1-56010-662-3(X)) Foster, Walter Publishing, Inc.

Goleszowski, R. Rex the Runt's Rainy Day Companion. 2000. (Illus.). 126p. (J). pap. 16.95 (978-0-340-74862-6(1) , Hodder & Stoughton) Hodder General Publishing Division GBR. *Dist:* Trafalgar Square Publishing.

Graham, Jefferson. Ultimate Rugrats Fan Book. 1998. (gr. 3-6). lib. bdg. 17.60 (978-0-613-73261-1(8)) Tandem Library Bks.

Green, Rod. The Mr. Bean Annual. 2002. (Illus.). 64p. (J). (gr. 4-7). pap. 13.99 (978-1-84222-632-2(0)) Carlton Bks., Ltd. GBR. *Dist:* Independent Pubs. Group.

Hall, Jason & Dorling Kindersley Publishing Staff. Justice League: The Animated Series Guide. 2004. (Animated Series Guide). (Illus.). 48p. (J). 9.99 (978-0-7566-0587-2(3)) Dorling Kindersley Publishing, Inc.

Holder, Nancy. Watcher's Guide 2. 2000. (gr. 7-12). lib. bdg. 28.00 (978-0-613-63366-6(0)) Tandem Library Bks.

Kent, Brittany. O. C. Undercover: An Unofficial Guide to the Stars & Styles of the O. C. rev. ed. 2004. (Illus.). 192p. (YA). pap. 11.95 (978-0-312-33142-9(8) , St. Martin's Griffin) St. Martin's Pr.

Lewman, David. Eat First Ask Questions Later: Trivia & Advice from the Rugrats. 1999. (Illus.). 48p. (gr. k-3). 2.99 (978-0-671-02873-2(1) , Simon & Schuster Children's Publishing) Simon & Schuster Children's Publishing.

Littler, Keith. Merlin the Magical Puppy Annual 2003. 2002. (Illus.). 64p. (J). (ps-3). pap. 13.99 (978-1-84222-629-2(0)) Carlton Bks., Ltd. GBR. *Dist:* Independent Pubs. Group.

Losty, Shelly Weiss. Dark Shadows A View of Collinsport. l.t. ed. 2002. 177p. 19.95 (978-0-9726299-0-4(4)) Bethany Pr., LLC.

Mara, Wil. Oprah Winfrey. 2005. (Rookie Biographies(R) Ser.). (Illus.). (gr. 1-2). 31p. (J). pap. 4.95 (978-0-516-25819-5(2)); 32p. 20.50 (978-0-516-21724-6(0)) Scholastic Library Publishing. (Children's Pr.).

Mariotte, Jeff. Angel Casefiles. 2002. (gr. 7-12). lib. bdg. 26.85 (978-0-613-63174-7(9)) Tandem Library Bks.

Marsh, Carole. Vermont Millionaire. 2001. (GameBook Ser.). 32p. (J). (gr. 3-8). pap., act. bk. ed. 9.95 (978-0-635-00106-1(3)) Gallopade International.

Mystery of the Senses, 5 cass.; set. 2004. (NOVA Ser.). (gr. 7 up). 69.95 incl. VHS (978-1-884738-57-9(5) , WG2214) WGBH Boston Video.

Ninety in The 90's. 2004. (Wgbh Specials Ser.). (gr. 7 up). 19.95 (978-1-57807-458-7(4) , WG080) WGBH Boston Video.

Pollet, Alison. MTV's the Real World: New Orleans. 2000. (gr. 7-12). lib. bdg. 25.75 (978-0-613-33937-7(1)) Tandem Library Bks.

Reisfeld, Randi, ed. Fear Factor: Yuck! Grossest Stunts Ever! Leon McCann, Jesse, illus. 2006. 88p. (J). pap. 4.99 (978-0-439-79050-5(6)) Scholastic, Inc.

Rizzo, Monica. One Tree Hill: Meet the Stars of One Tree Hill. movie tie-in ed. 2005. (One Tree Hill Ser.). (Illus.). 160p. (J). pap. 5.99 (978-0-439-73036-5(8)) Scholastic, Inc.

Rodriquez, K. S. Dawson's Creek: The Official Scrapbook. 1998. (gr. 7-12). lib. bdg. 17.60 (978-0-613-73071-6(2)) Tandem Library Bks.

Ruditis, Paul. Sabrina the Teenage Witch: The Official Episode Guide. 2002. (Illus.). 192p. (J). pap. (978-0-7522-6493-6(1) , Boxtree) Pan Macmillan.

Sarandon, Susan, narrated by. Dying to Be Thin. 2004. (NOVA Ser.). (gr. 4 up). 19.95 (978-1-57807-232-3(8) , WG2707) WGBH Boston Video.

Sublette, Guen. Here's Lookin' at Lizzie. (978-0-312-32669-2(6)) St. Martin's Pr.

Teitelbaum, Michael. Story of the Incredible Hulk. 2003. (gr. k-3). lib. bdg. 11.80 (978-0-613-62436-7(X)) Tandem Library Bks.

—Transformers Armada Official Guidebook. 2003. (gr. 3-6). lib. bdg. 14.15 (978-0-613-75087-5(X)) Tandem Library Bks.

Tibballs, Geoff. 10 Years of Heartbeat. 2002. (Illus.). 128p. pap. 19.95 (978-0-233-05045-4(0)) Andre Deutsch GBR. *Dist:* Trafalgar Square Publishing.

Vaz, Mark. Alias Declassified: The Official Companion. 2002. (gr. 3-6). lib. bdg. 26.85 (978-0-613-56718-3(8)) Tandem Library Bks.

Woog, Adam. Reality TV. 2007. (Ripped from the Headlines Ser.). 64p. (J). (gr. 5). 23.95 (***978-1-60217-005-6(3)**) Erickson Pr.

TEMPERANCE

Berry, Joy Wilt. A Book about Overdoing It. 2005. (Illus.). (J). (978-0-7172-8575-4(8)) Scholastic, Inc.

Beyer, Mark. Temperance & Prohibition: The Movement to Pass Anti-Liquor Laws in America. 2006. (Progressive Movement, 1900-1920—Efforts to Reform America's New Industrial Society Ser.). (Illus.). 32p. (J). (978-1-4042-0861-2(5)); lib. bdg. (978-1-4042-0195-8(5)) Rosen Publishing Group, Inc., The.

Harvey, Bonnie Carman. Carry A. Nation: Saloon Smasher & Prohibitionist. 2002. (Historical American Biographies Ser.). (Illus.). 128p. (YA). (gr. 6-12). lib. bdg. 26.60 (978-0-7660-1907-2(1)) Enslow Pubs., Inc.

TEMPERATURE

see also Heat; Low Temperatures; Thermometers and Thermometry

Ardley, Neil. The Science Book of Hot & Cold. 1998. (Illus.). (978-0-8172-9801-2(0)) Steck-Vaughn.

Auch, Alison. That's Hot! 2002. (Spyglass Books). (Illus.). 24p. (J). (gr. 1 up). lib. bdg. 18.60 (978-0-7565-0245-4(0)) Compass Point Bks.

Ballard, Carol. Heating & Cooling. 2007. (J). (***978-1-4034-9925-7(X)**); pap. (***978-1-4034-9933-2(0)**) Heinemann Library.

Chappell, Jackie. Do You Think It's Funny When- 2007. (J). (978-1-59515-933-5(9)) Rourke Publishing, LLC.

Cole, Joanna. El Autobus Magico en el Artico: Un Libro Sobre el Calor. 1998. (Coleccion El Autobus Magico). (SPA., Illus.). (J). (gr. k-4). pap. 3.50 (978-0-590-38664-7(6) , SO8203, Scholastic en Espanol) Scholastic, Inc.

—El Autobus Magico en el Artico: Un Libro Sobre el Calor. 1999. (Magic School Bus Ser.). (Illus.). (J). (gr. 1-4). (978-0-606-15520-5(1)) Tandem Library Bks.

Cole, Joanna & Schreiber, Anne. The Magic School Bus in the Arctic: A Book about Heat. Degan, Bruce & Ruiz, Art, illus. 1998. (Magic School Bus Ser.). 32p. (J). (gr. 1-4). pap. 3.99 (978-0-590-18724-4(4)) Scholastic, Inc.

Doudna, Kelly. If You Prefer, I'll Use a Thermometer. 2007. (Illus.). 24p. (J). 19.93 (978-1-59928-594-8(0) , Sand-Castle) ABDO Publishing Co.

—If You Prefer, I'll Use a Thermometer! 2006. (Illus.). 24p. (J). pap. (978-1-59928-595-5(9)) ABDO Publishing Co.

Fiedler, Julie. Learning about Heat & Temperature with Graphic Organizers. 2007. (Graphic Organizers in Science Ser.). (Illus.). 24p. (J). lib. bdg. (978-1-4042-3408-6(X) , PowerKids Pr.) Rosen Publishing Group, Inc., The.

Frisch, Joy. Temperature. 2008. (J). (***978-1-58341-579-5(3)** , Creative Education) Creative Co., The.

Gardner, Robert. Melting, Freezing, & Boiling Science Projects with Matter. 2006. (Fantastic Physical Science Experiments Ser.). (Illus.). 48p. (J). lib. bdg. 23.93 (978-0-7660-2589-9(6) , Enslow Elementary) Enslow Pubs., Inc.

—Really Hot Science Projects with Temperature: How Hot Is It? How Cold Is It? 2003. (Sensational Science Experiments Ser.). (Illus.). 48p. (J). lib. bdg. 23.93 (978-0-7660-2015-3(0)) Enslow Pubs., Inc.

Gish, Melissa. Temperature. 2005. (My First Look at Science Ser.). (Illus.). 24p. (gr. k-3). 15.95 (978-1-58341-375-3(8) , Creative Education) Creative Co., The.

Granowsky, Alvin. Hot & Cold. 2001. 11.79 (978-0-606-22435-2(1)) Tandem Library Bks.

Hewitt, Sally. Heat. 2006. (Science Starters Ser.). (Illus.). 32p. (J). (978-1-59604-080-9(7)) Stargazer Bks.

—Hot & Cold. 2000. (It's Science! Ser.). (Illus.). 32p. (J). (gr. k-3). 23.50 (978-0-516-21654-6(6) , Children's Pr.) Scholastic Library Publishing.

Hidalgo, Maria. Heat. 2006. (My First Look at Weather Ser.). (Illus.). 24p. 15.95 (978-1-58341-449-1(5) , Creative Education) Creative Co., The.

Keeping Warm. 2006. (Yellow Umbrella Science Ser.). 8,16p. (J). 6.50 (978-0-7368-1711-0(5)) Red Brick Learning.

Lilly, Melinda. Hot & Cold. 2006. (Rourke Discovery Library). (Illus.). 24p. (gr. 1-4). 14.95 (978-1-59515-402-6(7) , 1244273) Rourke Publishing, LLC.

Manolis, Kay. Temperature. 2007. (Illus.). 24p. (J). lib. bdg. 19.95 (978-1-60014-100-3(5)) Bellwether Media.

Martin, Elena. Hot or Cold? 2003. (Yellow Umbrella Books). (Illus.). 16p. (J). (gr. 1). lib. bdg. 14.60 (978-0-7368-2012-7(4) , Pebble Bks.) Capstone Pr., Inc.

—Hot or Cold? 2003. (Math Ser.). (J). (978-0-7368-1698-4(4)) Yellow Umbrella Pr.

Moran, Jeffrey B. How Do We Know the Laws of Thermodynamics? 2001. (Great Scientific Questions & the Scientists Who Answered Them Ser.). (Illus.). 112p. (YA). (gr. 4-6). lib. bdg. 26.50 (978-0-8239-3384-6(9)) Rosen Publishing Group, Inc., The.

Olien, Rebecca. Temperature. (Our Physical World Ser.). 24p. (J). pap. 6.95 (978-0-7368-5159-6(3)) Capstone Pr., Inc.

—Temperature. 2004. (First Facts Ser.). 24p. (J). lib. bdg. 21.26 (978-0-7368-2619-8(X)) Capstone Pr., Inc.

Riley, Peter D. Keeping Warm. 2007. (J). (***978-1-59920-027-9(9)**) Smart Apple Media.

Ring, Susan. Como se Calientan? 2005. Tr. of Keeping Warm. (SPA., Illus.). 16p. (J). (gr. 2 up). lib. bdg. 15.93 (978-0-7368-4136-8(9)) Capstone Pr., Inc.

Rodgers, Alan & Streluk, Angella. Temperature. 2002. (Measuring the Weather Ser.). (Illus.). 32p. (J). (gr. 3-5). lib. bdg. 22.79 (978-1-58810-689-6(6)) Heinemann Library.

Sadler, Wendy. Hot & Cold: Feel It! 2005. (Raintree Perspectives Ser.). (Illus.). 32p. (J). pap. (978-1-4109-1562-7(X)); lib. bdg. (978-1-4109-1554-2(9)) Steck-Vaughn.

Schmauss, Judy Kentor. Too, Too Hot. 2006. (Reader's Clubhouse Set A Ser.). (Illus.). 24p. (J). pap. 3.99 (978-0-7641-3285-8(7)) Barron's Educational Series, Inc.

Sheehan, Thomas F. Keeping Warm, Keeping Cool. 2006. (City Science Ser.). (Illus.). 24p. (gr. k-3). 14.95 (978-1-59515-413-2(2)) Rourke Publishing, LLC.

—Para Calentarse, para Refrescarse (Keeping Warm, Keeping Cool) Sarfatti, Esther, tr. from ENG. 2005. (Ciencia Citadina Ser.). (ENG & SPA., Illus.). 24p. (J). (gr. 3-7). lib. bdg. 21.36 (978-1-59515-666-2(6)) Rourke Publishing, LLC.

Simon, Seymour & Fauteux, Nicole. Let's Try It Out with Cold Hands & Warm Feet. Cushman, Doug, illus. 2000. (J). (gr. k-3). per. 15.00 (978-0-689-82920-8(5) , Simon & Schuster Children's Publishing) Simon & Schuster Children's Publishing.

Stille, Darlene R. Hot & Cold. 2001. (Simply Science Ser.). (Illus.). 32p. (J). (gr. 3 up). lib. bdg. 19.93 (978-0-7565-0090-0(7)) Compass Point Bks.

—Temperature: Heating Up & Cooling Down. Boyd, Sheree, illus. 2004. (Amazing Science Ser.). 24p. (C). (gr. k-4). 22.60 (978-1-4048-0247-6(9)) Picture Window Bks.

Sullivan, Navin. Temperature. 2006. (Measure Up! Ser.). (Illus.). 48p. (J). (gr. 4-7). lib. bdg. 29.93 (978-0-7614-2322-5(2) , Benchmark Bks.) Cavendish, Marshall Corp.

Temperature. (Amazing Science Ser.). 24p. (J). 7.95 (978-1-4048-0345-9(9)) Picture Window Bks.

Waiakea High Writer's Group. Hot Lava, Cool Rain. 2001. (gr. 7-12). lib. bdg. 25.20 (978-0-613-74532-1(9)) Tandem Library Bks.

What Temperature Is Safe? 2001. (YA). pap. (978-1-57078-006-6(4)) C E V Multimedia, Ltd.

Woodford, Chris. Temperature. 2005. (J). 11.20 (978-1-4103-0525-1(2)); 32p. (gr. 2-5). 23.70 (978-1-4103-0369-1(1)) Thomson Gale. (Blackbirch Pr., Inc.).

TEMPERATURES, LOW

see Low Temperatures

TEMPLES

Bagley, Val. My Little Book about Temples. 2004. (J). bds. 10.95 (978-1-57734-999-0(7)) Covenant Communications, Inc.

Bingham, Jane. Sikh Gurdwaras. 2005. (Let's Find Out about Ser.). (Illus.). 32p. (J). (978-1-4034-7034-8(0)) Steck-Vaughn.

Bodden, Valerie. Greek Temples. 2008. (J). (***978-1-58341-560-3(2)*** , Creative Education) Creative Co., The.

Dargie, Richard. Look Around a Greek Temple. 2007. (J). (***978-1-84193-720-5(7)***) Smart Apple Media.

Ganeri, Anita. Hindu Mandirs. 2005. (Let's Find Out about Ser.). (Illus.). 32p. (J). 25.36 (978-1-4034-7033-1(2)) Steck-Vaughn.

Geldart, Anne. Buddhist Temples. 2005. (Let's Find Out about Ser.). (J). 25.36 (978-1-4034-7035-5(9)) Steck-Vaughn.

Halfmann, Janet. Greek Temples. 1999. (Designing the Future Ser.). (Illus.). 32p. (J). (gr. 4-7). lib. bdg. 21.30 (978-0-88682-654-3(3) , Creative Education) Creative Co., The.

Hawkins, Chad S. Youth & the Temple. 2002. (Illus.). vii, 136p. (J). pap. 12.95 (978-1-57008-846-9(2)) Scribbulations LLC.

Hegedus, Umar. Muslim Mosque. 1998. (Keystones Ser.). (Illus.). 32p. (J). (gr. 2-6). 16.95 (978-0-7136-4335-0(8)) A & C Black GBR. *Dist:* Lubrecht & Cramer, Ltd.

Jani, Mahendra & Jani, Vandana. What You Will See Inside a Hindu Temple. Bhargava, Neirah & Dave, Vijay, photos by. 2005. (What You Will See Inside- Ser.). (Illus.). 32p. (J). pap. 17.99 (978-1-59473-116-7(0)) SkyLight Paths Publishing.

Kaur-Singh, Kanwaljit & Nason, Ruth. Visiting a Gurdwara. 2005. (Start up Religion Ser.). (Illus.). 24p. (J). (gr. 1-4). lib. bdg. (978-1-84234-345-6(9) , Cherrytree Books) Evans Publishing Group.

Malam, John & Bergin, Mark. An Ancient Greek Temple. 2001. (Magnifications Ser.). (Illus.). 48p. (J). (gr. 3-8). 18.95 (978-0-87226-652-0(4) , Bedrick, Peter Bks.) School Specialty Publishing.

Mead, Jean & Nason, Ruth. Visiting a Mandir. 2005. (Start up Religion Ser.). (Illus.). 24p. (J). (gr. 1-4). lib. bdg. (978-1-84234-346-3(7) , Cherrytree Books) Evans Publishing Group.

Nardo, Don. Greek Temples. 2002. (Watts Library). (J). (gr. 5-7). 63p. pap. 8.95 (978-0-531-16225-5(7)); (Illus.). 64p. 25.50 (978-0-531-12035-4(X)) Scholastic Library Publishing. (Watts, Franklin).

Parker. The Golden Temple. 2003. (Holy Places Ser.). (Illus.). 32p. (J). pap. 6.95 (978-1-4109-0052-4(5)) Raintree.

Parker, Victoria. The Golden Temple. 2003. (Holy Places Ser.). (Illus.). 32p. (J). 24.28 (978-0-7398-6079-3(8)) Raintree.

—Golden Temple. 2003. (gr. k-3). lib. bdg. 15.25 (978-0-613-78216-6(X)) Tandem Library Bks.

Ross, Mandy. The Western Wall. 2003. (Holy Places Ser.). (Illus.). 32p. (J). 24.28 (978-0-7398-6082-3(8)) Raintree.

Shuter, Jane. Life in a Greek Temple. 2005. (Picture the Past Ser.). (Illus.). 32p. (J). (ps-ps). lib. bdg. 26.79 (978-1-4034-6442-2(1)); pap. (978-1-4034-6449-1(9)) Heinemann Library.

Wood, Angela. Hindu Mandir. 1999. (Places of Worship Ser.). (Illus.). 32p. (J). (gr. 2 up). lib. bdg. 23.33 (978-0-8368-2607-4(8)) Stevens, Gareth Inc.

TEN COMMANDMENTS

Allen, Jan. Now I Know the 10 Commandments. Allen, Russ, illus. 2005. 32p. (J). (gr. k-5). (978-0-9765514-0-9(3)) Light Bugs Publishing.

Alsbrooks, Stephanie. The Ten Commandments: The Second Commandment. 2004. (J). bds. 9.99 (978-1-4183-0000-5(4)) Christ Inspired, Inc.

Come & See KIDS, Friends of God. 2006. per. 9.95 (***978-1-931018-41-8(3)***) Emmaus Road Publishing.

Curtis, Ken & Tompkins, Steve. Ten Commandments. 2000. (Illus.). 112p. (YA). pap. 19.99 (978-1-56364-395-8(2)) Christian History Institute.

Curtis, Ken & Tompkinson, Stephen. Ten Commandments. 2000. (Illus.). 48p. (YA). pap., stu. ed., wbk. ed. 5.99 (978-1-56364-430-6(4)) Christian History Institute.

David C. Cook. The Ten Commandments. 2003. (My Jesus Pocket Bks.). (Illus.). 32p. (J). (ps-3). pap., pap. 8.90 (978-1-55513-859-2(4) , 1555138594) Cook, David C. Publishing Co.

Dobson, Shirley, contrib. by. God's Ten Best: The Ten Commandments Coloring Book. 2004. 16p. pap. 1.49 (978-0-8307-3061-2(3) , Gospel Light) Gospel Light Pubns.

—God's Ten Best: The Ten Commandments Comic & Activity Book. 2004. 16p. act. bk. ed. 1.49 (978-0-8307-3060-5(5) , Gospel Light) Gospel Light Pubns.

Forster, Pamela R. Honor Your Father & Mother: The Fifth Commandment for Little Ones. 2006. (J). spiral bd. 10.00 (***978-1-891206-23-8(0)***) Doorposts.

Gortier, Rosemarie & Piscitelli, Donna. Living the 10 commandments for Children. 2007. per. 6.95 (***978-1-59276-231-6(X)***) Our Sunday Visitor, Publishing Div.

Gustafson, Janie. The Commandments: Practical Activities. 2001. (Illus.). 32p. (J). (gr. 4-7). 9.95 (978-1-893757-23-3(4)) Needer, E.T. Publishing.

Jenkins, Sharon I. Remember the Ten Commandments with Jam & Jean Jellybean. l.t. ed. 2006. (Illus.). 32p. (J). per. 10.99 (***978-1-59879-240-9(7)***) Lifevest Publishing, Inc.

Livingstone, creator. K10C Family Fun Pack: Exploring the Ten Commandments. 2004. 226p. (J). spiral bd. 19.99 (978-1-4143-0058-0(1)) Tyndale Hse. Pubs.

Lovasik, Lawrence G. Los Diez Mandamientos. (Illus.). (J). 1.50 (978-0-89942-469-9(4)) Catholic Bk. Publishing Corp.

Mackall, Dandi Daley. God Shows the Way. Gévry, Claudine, illus. 2006. 36p. (J). 9.99 (978-0-7847-1821-6(0)) Standard Publishing.

Mackenzie, Carine. God, the Ten Commandments, & Jesus. 2004. 40p. (J). pap. 12.99 (978-1-85792-850-1(4) , Christian Focus) Christian Focus Pubns. GBR. *Dist:* Riverside.

McNeil, Niki, et al. HOCPP 1134 10 Commandments. 2006. spiral bd. 16.00 (***978-1-60308-134-4(8)***) In the Hands of a Child.

Murphy, W. Ten Commandments for Children. Date not set. (J). (ps-3). pap. 1.95 (978-0-88271-159-1(8)) Regina Pr., Malhame & Co.

O'Connor, Francine M. The Commandments: God's Plan for Our Happy Lives. Larkin, Jean, ed. Lynch, Patricia, illus. 1999. (Active Learning for Catholic Kids Ser.). 28p. (J). (gr. 4-6). pap. 7.95 (978-0-937997-56-7(0)) Pflaum Publishing Group.

Parker, Victoria. Moses & the 10 Commandments. 2002. (Illus.). 64p. pap. 7.95 (978-1-84215-631-5(4)) Anness Publishing GBR. *Dist:* National Bk. Network.

Peters, Craig. Carved in Stone: Exploring the Ten Commandments with Your Children. Mazgaj, Sharon, illus. 2001. 120p. (J). (gr. 1-5). pap. 9.95 (978-0-9715840-0-6(1)) Safe Harbor Pr.

Pingry, Patricia A. La Historia de los Diez Mandamientos. Venturi-Pickett, Stacy, illus. 2000. Tr. of Story of the Ten Commandments. (SPA.). 26p. (J). (ps-k). 6.95 (978-0-8249-4191-8(8)) Ideals Pubns.

—The Story of the Ten Commandments. Venturi-Pickett, Stacy, illus. 2007. 32p. pap. 3.99 (***978-0-8249-5554-0(4)*** , Ideals Children's Bks.) Ideals Pubns.

—The Story of the Ten Commandments. 2006. (Illus.). 26p. (J). bds. 10.95 (978-0-8249-6656-0(2) , Candy Cane Pr.) Ideals Pubns.

Richards, Virginia Helen. The Ten Commandments. Richards, Virginia Helen & Halpin, D. Thomas, illus. 2007. (J). 1.95 (***978-0-8198-7420-7(5)***) Pauline Bks. & Media.

Rock, Lois. The Lord's Prayer & Ten Commandments Bible Words to Know & to Treasure. 2008. (Illus.). 64p. (J). 5.95 (***978-0-7459-4941-3(X)***) Lion Hudson plc GBR. *Dist:* Independent Pubs. Group.

The Story of the Ten Commandments/la Historia de Los Diez Mandamientos. 2002. (SPA & ENG., Illus.). 28p. (J). pap. 3.95 (978-0-8249-4205-2(1)) Ideals Pubns.

Swain Trahan, Kendra. Following Jesus: Obeying His Commandments (Children's Version) 2006. (Illus.). 35p. (J). per. 14.99 (***978-1-59879-201-0(6)***) Lifevest Publishing, Inc.

The Ten Commandments. 2004. (Exploring Luther's Small Catechism Ser.). (gr. 5-6). 2.99 (978-0-8066-6788-1(5)) Augsburg Fortress, Pubs.

Ten Commandments Grades 4-6. 2004. pap. 7.99 (978-1-56417-930-2(3)) School Specialty Publishing.

Topek, Susan R. Ten Good Rules. Schanzer, Rosalyn, illus. 2004. (General Jewish Interest Ser.). 24p. (J). (ps-1). pap. 6.95 (978-0-929371-30-6(5)) Kar-Ben Publishing.

Topek, Susan Remick. Ten Good Rules: A Counting Book. Cohen, Tod, illus. 2007. 24p. (J). (ps-1). 15.95 (***978-0-8225-7293-0(1)***) Kar-Ben Publishing.

Topek, Susan Remick & Cohen, Tod. Ten Good Rules: A Counting Book. 2007. 24p. (J). (ps-1). pap. 7.95 (978-1-58013-209-1(X)) Kar-Ben Publishing.

Van Leeuwen, Wendy. The Ten Commandments Activity Book. 2007. (Illus.). 16p. (J). pap. 1.89 (***978-1-59317-210-7(9)***) Warner Pr. Pubs.

VonSeggen, Liz. The King's Commandments: Teaching Unit. rev. ed. 2003. (Illus.). 228p. (J). spiral bd. 45.00 (978-1-58302-247-4(3)) One Way St., Inc.

Walker, Joni. Gods Ten Commandments. 2004. (Follow & Do Ser.). (Illus.). 32p. (J). 6.99 (978-0-7586-0227-5(8)) Concordia Publishing Hse.

The 10 Commandments. (Illus.). 16p. (J). pap. 1.50 (978-0-87162-872-5(4) , E6037) Warner Pr. Pubs.

TENNESSEE

Barrett, Tracy. Tennessee. 2nd ed. 2006. (Celebrate the States Ser.). (J). lib. bdg. 39.93 (978-0-7614-2151-1(3) , Benchmark Bks.) Cavendish, Marshall Corp.

Berger, Donna, illus. Davy Crockett. 2004. (Imagination Ser.). 32p. (J). (gr. 3 up). 22.60 (978-0-7565-0603-2(4)) Compass Point Bks.

Brown, Vanessa. Tennessee. 2006. (Bilingual Library of the United States of America: Set 2). (ENG & SPA., Illus.). 32p. (J). (gr. 3-6). lib. bdg. 22.50 (978-1-4042-3108-5(0) , Buenas Letra) Rosen Publishing Group, Inc., The.

Feeney, Kathy. Tennessee Facts & Symbols. (States & Their Symbols Ser.). 24p. (J). 2000. (Illus.). (gr. 2-3). lib. bdg. 13.95 (978-0-7368-0525-4(7) , Bridgestone Bks.); 2003. lib. bdg. 19.93 (978-0-7368-2273-2(9)) Capstone Pr., Inc.

Harcourt School Publishers Staff. Primary Black Line Master Harcourt Braise Social Studies: Tennessee Edition. 2nd ed. 2002. (gr. 1). pap. 19.40 (978-0-15-335862-3(9)); (gr. 2). pap. 19.40 (978-0-15-335863-0(7)) Harcourt Schl. Pubs.

Heinrichs, Ann. Tennessee. Kania, Matt, illus. 2005. (Welcome to the USA Ser.). 40p. (J). (gr. 1-5). 27.07 (978-1-59296-484-0(2)) Child's World, Inc.

—Tennessee. 2003. (This Land Is Your Land Ser.). (Illus.). 48p. (J). (gr. 3 up). lib. bdg. 22.60 (978-0-7565-0319-2(1)) Compass Point Bks.

Hodgkins, Fran. Tennessee. 2003. (Land of Liberty Ser.). (Illus.). 64p. (J). lib. bdg. 25.26 (978-0-7368-2199-5(6)) Capstone Pr., Inc.

Knapp, Ron. Tennessee: A MyReportLinks. Com Book. 2003. (States Ser.). (Illus.). 48p. (J). lib. bdg. 25.26 (978-0-7660-5120-1(X) , MyReportLinks.com Bks.) Enslow Pubs., Inc.

Kummer, Patricia K. Tennessee. rev. ed. 2002. (One Nation Ser.). (Illus.). 48p. (J). (gr. 3-4). lib. bdg. 22.60 (978-0-7368-1267-2(9) , Bridgestone Bks.) Capstone Pr., Inc.

Kunstler, James Howard. Davy Crockett. Brodner, Steve, illus. 2005. (Rabbit Ears-A Classic Tale Ser.). 40p. (J). (gr. k-5). 25.65 (978-1-59197-762-9(2)) Spotlight.

Marsh, Carole. The Big Tennessee Reproducible Activity Book. 2004. (Carole Marsh Tennessee Bks.). 96p. (J). (gr. 2-6). pap. 9.95 (978-0-7933-9957-4(2)) Gallopade International.

—My First Book about Tennessee. 2004. (Carole Marsh Tennessee Bks.). 32p. (J). (gr. k-4). pap. 7.95 (978-0-7933-9899-7(1)) Gallopade International.

—Tennessee Classic Christmas Trivia. 2002. (Carole Marsh Tennessee Bks.). 32p. pap. 6.95 (978-0-635-01449-8(1) , 14491); lib. bdg. 21.95 (978-0-635-01450-4(5) , 14505) Gallopade International. (Marsh, Carole Bks.).

—Tennessee Current Events Projects: 30 Cool, Activities, Crafts, Experiments & More for Kids to Do to Learn about Your State! 2003. (Tennessee Experience Ser.). 32p. (gr. k-5). pap. 5.95 (978-0-635-02061-1(0) , Marsh, Carole Bks.) Gallopade International.

—The Tennessee Experience Pocket Guide. 2004. (Carole Marsh Tennessee Bks.). (Illus.). 96p. (J). (gr. 3-8). pap. 6.95 (978-0-7933-9928-4(9)) Gallopade International.

—Tennessee Geography Projects: 30 Cool, Activities, Crafts, Experiments & More for Kids to Do to Learn about Your State! 2003. (Tennessee Experience Ser.). 32p. (gr. k-5). pap. 5.95 (978-0-635-01860-1(8) , Marsh, Carole Bks.) Gallopade International.

—Tennessee Government Projects: 30 Cool, Activities, Crafts, Experiments & More for Kids to Do to Learn about Your State! 2003. (Tennessee Experience Ser.). 32p. (gr. k-5). pap. 5.95 (978-0-635-01961-5(2) , Marsh, Carole Bks.) Gallopade International.

—Tennessee Jeopardy! Answers & Questions about Our State! Line Art Staff, illus. 2004. 32p. (J). (gr. 3-8). pap. 7.95 (978-0-7933-9812-6(6)) Gallopade International.

—Tennessee People Projects: 30 Cool, Activities, Crafts, Experiments & More for Kids to Do to Learn about Your State! 2003. (Tennessee Experience Ser.). 32p. (gr. k-5). pap. 5.95 (978-0-635-02011-6(4) , Marsh, Carole Bks.) Gallopade International.

—Tennessee Symbols & Facts Projects: 30 Cool, Activities, Crafts, Experiments & More for Kids to Do to Learn about Your State! 2003. (Tennessee Experience Ser.). 32p. (gr. k-5). pap. 5.95 (978-0-635-01911-0(6) , Marsh, Carole Bks.) Gallopade International.

McClellan, Adam. Uniquely Tennessee. 2003. (State Studies). (Illus.). 48p. (J). pap. 8.50 (978-1-4034-4512-4(5)); lib. bdg. 27.07 (978-1-4034-4497-4(8)) Heinemann Library.

McNamara, Connie. My First University of Tennessee Words. 2004. (J). bds. 11.95 (978-0-9759703-3-1(X)) Shamrock Publishing, Inc.

Murray, Julie. Tennessee. 2006. (Illus.). 32p. (J). (gr. k-4). lib. bdg. 22.78 (978-1-59197-701-8(0) , Buddy Bks.) ABDO Publishing Co.

Owens, Martha Galyon. A Tennessee Journey: An Interactive Student Workbook. 1999. (Illus.). 32p. (J). (gr. k-7). pap., wbk. ed. 9.95 (978-1-57072-142-7(4)) Overmountain Pr.

Peck, Barbara. Tennessee: The Volunteer State. 2002. (World Almanac Library of the States). (Illus.). 48p. (J). (gr. 5 up). lib. bdg. 30.00 (978-0-8368-5145-8(5)); pap. 14.95 (978-0-8368-5315-5(6)) Stevens, Gareth Inc. (World Almanac Library).

Petreycik, Rick. Tennessee. 2005. (It's My State! Ser.). (Illus.). 80p. (J). (978-0-7614-1909-9(8) , Benchmark Bks.) Cavendish, Marshall Corp.

Semchuk, Rosann. A Guide to Tennessee. 2001. (American States Ser.). (Illus.). 32p. (J). lib. bdg. 16.95 (978-1-930954-79-3(4)) Weigl Pubs., Inc.

Shoulders, Michael. Count on Us: A Tennessee Number Book. Langton, Bruce, illus. 2003. 40p. (J). 16.95 (978-1-58536-131-1(3)) Sleeping Bear Pr.

—V Is for Volunteer: A Tennessee Alphabet. Langton, Bruce, illus. 2001. 40p. (J). 17.95 (978-1-58536-033-8(3)) Sleeping Bear Pr.

Sirvaitis, Karen. Tennessee. 2nd exp. rev. ed. 2003. (Hello U. S. A. Ser.). (Illus.). 84p. (J). (gr. 3-6). 25.26 (978-0-8225-4090-8(8) , Lerner Pubns.) Lerner Publishing Group.

—Tennessee. rev. ed. 2003. (gr. 3-6). lib. bdg. 15.25 (978-0-613-52509-1(4)) Tandem Library Bks.

Sparkman, Winette. Tennessee Trailblazers. Laughbaum, Steve & Crutchfield, Jim, illus. 56p. (J). pap., wbk. ed., act. bk. ed. 6.95 (978-0-9634824-1-9(6)) March Media, Inc.

Tennessee. 2000. (Switched on Schoolhouse Ser.). (Illus.). (YA). (gr. 7-12). pap. 24.95 incl. cd-rom (978-0-7403-0294-7(9) , SOSTN) Alpha Omega Pubns., Inc.

Valzania, Kimberly. Tennessee. 2003. (Rookie Read-About Geography Ser.). (Illus.). (J). (gr. 1-2). pap. 5.95 (978-0-516-27843-8(6)); 32p. 20.50 (978-0-516-22699-6(1)) Scholastic Library Publishing. (Children's Pr.).

—Tennessee. 2003. (gr. k-3). lib. bdg. 14.10 (978-0-613-67937-4(7)) Tandem Library Bks.

Wagner, Heather Lehr. Benjamin Hooks. 2003. (African American Leaders Ser.). (Illus.). 112p. (gr. 6-12). 30.00 (978-0-7910-7685-9(7) , Chelsea Hse.) Facts On File, Inc.

Weatherly, Myra. Tennessee. 2001. (From Sea to Shining Sea Ser.: 2). (Illus.). 80p. (J). (gr. 3-5). 30.50 (978-0-516-22312-4(7) , Children's Pr.) Scholastic Library Publishing.

TENNESSEE—FICTION

Altsheler, A. Joseph. Guns of Shiloh A Story of the Great West. 2006. 26.99 (***978-1-4280-2738-1(6)***) IndyPublish.com.

Applegate, Stan. The Devil's Highway. Watling, James, illus. 1998. 224p. (J). (gr. 3-7). pap. 8.95 (978-1-56145-184-5(3) , Q21196) Peachtree Pubs., Ltd.

Barrett, Tracy. Cold in Summer. rev. ed. 2003. (Illus.). 208p. (YA). (gr. 5-9). 16.95 (978-0-8050-7052-1(4) , Holt, Henry & Co. Bks. For Young Readers) Holt, Henry & Co.

Bradley, Kimberly Brubaker. Weaver's Daughter. l.t. ed. 2002. 173p. (J). 21.95 (978-0-7862-3763-0(5)) Thomson Gale.

Bryant, Jennifer. Ringside, 1925: Views from the Scopes Trial. 2008. (J). (***978-0-375-84047-0(8)***); lib. bdg. (***978-0-375-94047-7(2)***) Knopf, Alfred A. Inc.

Coleman, Evelyn. Circle of Fire. 2001. (American Girl Collection). (Illus.). (J). 12.60 (978-0-606-21249-6(3)) Tandem Library Bks.

Crist-Evans, Craig. Moon over Tennessee: A Boy's Civil War Journal. Christensen, Bonnie, illus. 64p. (J). (gr. 4-6). 2003. pap. 6.95 (978-0-618-31107-1(6)); 1999. tchr. ed. 15.00 (978-0-395-91208-9(3)) Houghton Mifflin Co. Trade & Reference Div.

—Moon over Tennessee: A Boy's Civil War Journal. 1999. (gr. 3-6). lib. bdg. 15.25 (978-0-613-60819-0(4)) Tandem Library Bks.

Dabbs, Douglas, illus. The Legend's Granddaughter: Not Quite Super, Book 1. 2007. 281p. (J). pap. (***978-0-9793168-0-7(4)***) NQSBks.

Denham, Larry Allen. Pioneers. 2007. 392p. per. 21.95 (***978-0-595-41965-4(8)***) iUniverse, Inc.

Disney Press Staff & McElroy, Laurie. Super Sneak. 3rd rev. ed. 2006. (Hannah Montana Ser.: No. 3). 128p. (gr. 3-7). pap. 4.99 (978-1-4231-0276-2(2)) Disney Pr.

Dowell, Frances O'Roark. Where I'd Like to Be. 240p. (J). 2003. (Illus.). (gr. 5-9). 15.95 (978-0-689-84420-1(4) , Atheneum); 2004. reprint ed. pap. 5.99 (978-0-689-87067-5(1) , Aladdin) Simon & Schuster Children's Publishing.

—Where I'd Like to Be. 2004. 232p. (J). (gr. k-9). lib. bdg. 11.64 (978-0-606-32673-5(1)) Tandem Library Bks.

—Where I'd Like to Be. l.t. ed. 2003. 162p. (J). 22.95 (978-0-7862-5741-6(5)) Thorndike Pr.

Eady, Ellen. Pardon Me. . . Is That the Grand Ole Opry? Brown, Emily, illus. 2001. 28p. (J). 15.95 (978-0-9679065-2-2(0)) Majestic Publishing.

—Pardon Me, Is That the Chattanooga Choo-Choo? Guhne, Kelly, illus. 2000. (J). pap. 9.95 (978-0-9679065-1-5(2)) Majestic Publishing.

English, D. N. Downtown Wanderings: Stories & Pictures of Downtown Jackson Tennessee. Galloway, Annette, ed. l.t. ed. 2002. (Illus.). 184p. per. 15.95 (978-0-9710470-0-6(6)) Main St Publishing, Inc.

Ernst, Kathleen. Hearts of Stone. 2006. 240p. (J). (gr. 7). 16.99 (978-0-525-47686-3(5) , Dutton Juvenile) Penguin Group (USA) Inc.

Gamble, Adam. Good Night Tennessee. Veno, Joe, illus. 2007. (Good Night Our World Ser.). 20p. (J). bds. 9.95 (***978-1-60219-019-1(4)***) Our World of Books.

Gratz, Alan M. Something Rotten: A Horatio Wilkes Mystery. 2007. 208p. (J). (gr. 6). 16.99 (***978-0-8037-3216-2(3)*** , Dial) Penguin Group (USA) Inc.

Green, Connie Jordan. The War at Home. 2nd ed. 2003. 144p. (J). pap. (978-0-916078-75-1(2)) Iris Publishing Group, Inc., The.

Hermes, Patricia. Sweet by & By. 2002. 208p. (J). (gr. 3-6). 15.99 (978-0-380-97452-8(5)) HarperCollins Pubs.

Holley, Marietta. Samantha at the World's Fair. 2007. 428p. pap. 16.99 (***978-1-4264-5101-0(6)***) BiblioBazaar.

Hopkinson, Deborah. A Band of Angels: A Story Inspired by the Jubilee Singers. Colon, Raul, illus. 1999. (Anne Schwartz Bks.). 40p. (J). (gr. 1-4). 16.95 (978-0-689-81062-6(8) , Atheneum/Anne Schwartz Bks.) Simon & Schuster Children's Publishing.

Isaacs, Anne. Swamp Angel. Zelinsky, Paul O., illus. 2002. (J). 14.04 (978-0-7587-0152-7(7)) Book Wholesalers, Inc.

—Swamp Angel. Zelinsky, Paul O., illus. 2000. 48p. (J). (ps-3). pap. 6.99 (978-0-14-055908-6(6) , Puffin) Penguin Group (USA) Inc.

—Swamp Angel. 2000. (978-0-606-18453-3(8)); lib. bdg. 15.30 (978-0-613-23041-4(8)) Tandem Library Bks.

Isbell, Rebecca & Buchanan, Marilyn. Everyone Has a Story to Tell. Bledsoe, Wiliam B., illus. 2004. (J). 14.95 (978-0-9755906-0-7(X)) Olde Town Publishing.

John Philip Duck. 2004. (J). 27.95 incl. audio (978-0-8045-6932-3(0)); 29.95 incl. audio compact disk (978-0-8045-4127-5(2)) Spoken Arts, Inc.

Johnston, Tony. Bone by Bone by Bone. 2007. 192p. (YA). (gr. 7 up). 17.95 (***978-1-59643-113-3(X)***) Roaring Brook Pr.

Keehn, Sally M. Gnat Stokes & the Foggy Bottom Swamp Queen. 2005. 160p. (YA). (gr. 5-7). 16.99 (978-0-399-24287-8(2) , Philomel) Penguin Group (USA) Inc.

T U V

Kidd, Ronald. Monkey Town: The Summer of the Scopes Trial. 2006. (Illus.). 272p. (YA). 16.99 (978-1-4169-0572-1(3)) Simon & Schuster Children's Publishing.
—Monkey Town, the Summer of the Scopes Trial. l.t. ed. 2006. 320p. (YA). 22.95 (978-0-7862-9080-2(3)) Thorndike Pr.
Madden, Kerry. Jessie's Mountain. 2008. (J). (gr. 3). 16.99 (*978-0-670-06154-9(9)* , Viking Juvenile) Penguin Group (USA) Inc.
McDaniel, Lurlene. The Girl Death Left Behind. 1999. 192p. (YA). (gr. 7-12). pap. 5.50 (978-0-553-57091-5(9) , Laurel Leaf) Random Hse. Children's Bks.
—The Girl Death Left Behind. 1999. (J). 11.64 (978-0-606-16371-2(9)) Tandem Library Bks.
McKissack, Patricia. Abby Takes a Stand. James, Gordon C., illus. 2006. (Scraps of Time Ser.). 112p. (J). (gr. 3). pap. 4.99 (978-0-14-240687-8(2) , Puffin) Penguin Group (USA) Inc.
McKissack, Patricia C. Abby Takes a Stand. James, Gordon C., illus. 2005. (Scraps of Time Ser.). 112p. (J). (gr. 3). 14.99 (978-0-670-06011-5(9) , Viking Juvenile) Penguin Group (USA) Inc.
—Color Me Dark: The Diary of Nellie Lee Love, the Great Migration North, Chicago, Illinois, 1919. 2000. (Dear America Ser.). (J). 9.95 (978-0-439-26653-6(X)) Scholastic, Inc.
—Color Me Dark: The Diary of Nellie Lee Love, the Great Migration North, Chicago, Illinois, 1919. 2000. (Dear America Ser.). (Illus.). 224p. (J). (gr. 4-9). pap. 10.95 (978-0-590-51159-9(9)) Scholastic, Inc.
—Tippy Lemmey. Keeter, Susan, illus. 2003. (Ready-for-Chapters Ser.). 64p. (J). lib. bdg. 11.89 (978-0-689-85594-8(X) , Aladdin Library) Simon & Schuster Children's Publishing.
—Tippy Lemmey. 2003. (gr. 3-6). lib. bdg. 11.80 (978-0-613-61590-7(5)) Tandem Library Bks.
McKissack, Patricia C. & Pinkney, Jerry. Goin' Someplace Special. 2001. (Illus.). 40p. (J). (ps-3). 16.99 (978-0-689-81885-1(8) , Atheneum/Anne Schwartz Bks.) Simon & Schuster Children's Publishing.
Moonshower, Candie. The Legend of Zoey. 2007. 224p. (J). (gr. 4-7). 5.99 (*978-0-440-23924-6(9)* , Yearling) Random Hse. Children's Bks.
Nilsson, Al. The Tennessee Tater. Nilsson, Al, illus. 2003. (YA). per. (978-0-9741294-9-5(6) , MSP) Main St Publishing, Inc.
O Neil, Elizabeth. Alfred Visits Tennessee. 2006. 24p. pap. 12.00 (978-0-9771836-5-4(3)) Funny Bone Bks.
Polacco, Patricia. John Philip Duck. Polacco, Patricia, illus. 2004. (Illus.). 48p. (J). (ps-5). 16.99 (978-0-399-24262-5(7) , Philomel) Penguin Group (USA) Inc.
Reed, Vernon. Children of the Hollow. 2006. (ENG.). 188p. per. 19.95 (*978-1-4241-3668-1(7)*) PublishAmerica, Inc.
Reinhardt, Dana. How to Build a House. 2008. 240p. (YA). (gr. 7). lib. bdg. 18.99 (*978-0-375-94454-3(0)* , Lamb, Wendy) Random Hse. Children's Bks.
Rennison, Louise. Then He Ate My Boy Entrancers: More Mad, Marvy Confessions of Georgia Nicolson. (Confessions of Georgia Nicolson Ser.). 2006. 336p. (J). pap. 7.99 (978-0-06-058939-4(6)); 2005. 320p. (J). lib. bdg. 16.89 (978-0-06-058938-7(8)); No. 6. 2005. 320p. (YA). 15.99 (978-0-06-058937-0(X)) HarperCollins Pubs. (HarperTeen).
Rodriguez, Elisabeth. Jumping Jack. 2006. pap. 14.99 (*978-1-4259-8197-6(6)*) AuthorHouse.
Schwabach, Karen. The Hope Chest. 2008. 288p. (J). (gr. 4-7). 16.99 (*978-0-375-84095-1(8)*); lib. bdg. 19.99 (*978-0-375-94095-8(2)*) Random Hse., Inc.
Singer, Sarah Jane. Two Bullets for Sergeant Franks. 2003. (Illus.). 112p. (YA). pap. 7.99 (978-0-9721216-9-9(2) , 0972121692) Computer Classics (R).
Steele, William O. Flaming Arrows. 2004. (Illus.). 160p. (J). pap. 5.95 (978-0-15-205213-3(5) , Odyssey Classics) Harcourt Children's Bks.
Street, Jane. Snow Baby. Yandell, Charlene, illus. 2002. 30p. (J). 11.95 (978-1-887905-56-5(1)) Parkway Pubs., Inc.
Tugman, Etta. Smokey Mountain Bears. 2006. 9.00 (978-0-8059-8189-6(6)) Dorrance Publishing Co., Inc.
Turner, Thomas N. Country Music Night Before Christmas. Rice, James, illus. 2003. 32p. (J). pap. 14.95 (978-1-58980-148-6(2)) Pelican Publishing Co., Inc.
Tyler-Vaughn, Savanna. Flour Sack Wear. 2006. (ENG.). 48p. per. 12.95 (*978-1-4241-2501-2(4)*) PublishAmerica, Inc.
Weathers, Anah D. Secrets of the Cave. Weathers, Luther, illus. Weathers, Luther, photos by. unabr. ed. 2000. (Treasures from the Past Ser.). x, 104p. (J). (gr. 4-8). pap. 7.98 (978-0-9702584-0-3(2)) Creative Services.
Wells, Rosemary. The Small World of Binky Braverman. Egielski, Richard, illus. 40p. (J). (ps-3). 2003. 15.99 (978-0-670-03636-3(6) , Viking Juvenile); 2006. reprint ed. pap. 6.99 (978-0-14-240380-8(6) , Puffin) Penguin Group (USA) Inc.

TENNESSEE—HISTORY

De Capua, Sarah. The Wilderness Road. 2006. (We the People Ser.). (Illus.). 48p. (J). (gr. 4-6). 23.93 (978-0-7565-1637-6(4)) Compass Point Bks.
English, D. N. Downtown Wanderings & Memories. 2nd ed. 2003. (Illus.). 190p. (YA). pap. (978-0-9741294-8-8(8) , MSP) Main St Publishing, Inc.
Furstinger, Nancy. Davy Crockett. 2003. (Folk Heroes Ser.). (Illus.). 24p. (J). lib. bdg. 15.95 (978-1-59036-073-6(7)) Weigl Pubs., Inc.
George, Bob. Cleveland, Tennessee. 2000. (Images of America Ser.). (Illus.). 128p. (gr. 5 up). pap. 19.99 (978-0-7385-0659-3(1)) Arcadia Publishing.
Hama, Larry. The Battle of Shiloh: Surprise Attack! 2007. (Graphic Battles of the Civil War Ser.). (J). lib. bdg. (978-1-4042-0779-0(1)) Rosen Publishing Group, Inc., The.
Hemphill, Helen D. Hattie's Carnton: Plantation Life in the Generation of the Civil War. Hotchkiss, Ann, illus. 1998. 32p. (J). (gr. 4-5). pap. 4.95 (978-0-9667267-0-1(7)) Historic Carnton Plantation Assn., Inc.
Hoobler, James A. & Hunter Marks, Sarah. Nashville:From the Collection of Carl & Otto Giers, Vol. 2. 2000. (Images of America Ser.). 128p. pap. 19.99 (978-0-7385-0632-6(X)) Arcadia Publishing.
Lantier, Patricia. Tennessee. 2005. (Portraits of the States Ser.). (Illus.). 32p. (J). pap. (978-0-8368-4653-9(2)); lib. bdg. 23.33 (978-0-8368-4634-8(6)) Stevens, Gareth Inc.
Marsh, Carole. My First Pocket Guide Tennessee. 2000. (Tennessee Experience! Ser.). (Illus.). 96p. (J). (gr. 3-8). 12.95 (978-0-635-01332-3(0) , 13320) Gallopade International.
—The Survivor: A Class Challenge. 2001. (Tennessee Experience! Ser.). (J). lib. bdg. 29.95 (978-0-635-00688-2(X)) Gallopade International.
—Tennessee History Projects: 30 Cool, Activities, Crafts, Experiments & More for Kids to Do to Learn about Your State! 2003. (Tennessee Experience Ser.). 32p. (gr. k-5). pap. 5.95 (978-0-635-01811-3(X) , Marsh, Carole Bks.) Gallopade International.
—Tennessee Survivor. 2001. (GameBook Ser.). 32p. (J). (gr. 3-8). pap., act. bk. ed. 9.95 (978-0-635-00563-2(8)) Gallopade International.
—Tennessee Wheel of Fortune. 2001. (GameBook Ser.). 32p. (J). (gr. 3-8). pap., act. bk. ed. 9.95 (978-0-635-00000-2(8)) Gallopade International.
—Wheel of Fortune. 2001. (Carol Marsh Tennessee Bks.). (J). lib. bdg. 29.95 (978-0-635-00001-9(6)) Gallopade International.
—Who Wants to Be a Millionaire? 2001. (Carole Marsh Tennessee Bks.). (J). lib. bdg. 29.95 (978-0-635-00101-6(2)) Gallopade International.
Weeks, Terry & Womack, Bob. Tennessee: The History of an American State. 3rd ed. 2002. (Illus.). ix, 438p. (J). (978-1-56733-068-7(1)) Clairmont Pr., Inc.
Wheeler, Frank. Tusculum College, Tennessee. 2000. (College History Ser.). 128p. pap. 19.99 (978-0-7385-0611-1(7)) Arcadia Publishing.
Winders, Richard Bruce. Davy Crockett: The Legend of the Wild Frontier. 2005. (Library of American Lives & Times). (Illus.). 112p. (YA). (gr. 4-8). lib. bdg. 31.95 (978-0-8239-5747-7(0)) Rosen Publishing Group, Inc., The.

TENNIS

Armentrout, David & Armentrout, Patricia. Andy Roddick. 2005. (Discover the Life of a Sports Star Ser.). (Illus.). 24p. (gr. 1-4). 14.95 (978-1-59515-128-5(1)) Rourke Publishing, LLC.
—Annika Sorenstam. 2005. (Discover the Life of a Sports Star Ser.). (Illus.). 24p. (gr. 1-4). 14.95 (978-1-59515-130-8(3)) Rourke Publishing, LLC.
Benson, Michael. Althea Gibson: Tennis Player. 2005. (Ferguson Career Biographies Ser.). (Illus.). 144p. (J). (gr. 6-12). 25.00 (978-0-8160-5889-1(X) , Ferguson Publishing Co.) Facts On File, Inc.
Bratton, Deboral B. & Bratton, Ashley D. Record-a-Sport Tennis Organizer. Bratton, Deborah B. & Bratton, Ashley D., eds. 2003. (Illus.). (gr. 1 up). 18.95 (978-1-931746-06-9(0)) Sport Your Stuff Corp.
Brown, Jonatha A. Tennis. 2004. (Illus.). 24p. (J). pap. (978-0-8368-4349-1(5)); lib. bdg. 19.33 (978-0-8368-4342-2(8)) Stevens, Gareth Inc.
Consistent Tennis Wins. 2004. per. 14.95 (978-0-9727444-1-6(X)) Avery's, Tom Totally Tennis.
Ditchfield, Christin. Tennis. 2003. (True Book Ser.). (Illus.). 48p. (J). 25.00 (978-0-516-22589-0(8) , Children's Pr.) Scholastic Library Publishing.
—Tennis. 2003. (gr. 3-6). lib. bdg. 15.25 (978-0-613-67988-6(1)) Tandem Library Bks.
Douglas, Paul. Tennis. 2004. (101 Essential Tips Ser.). (Illus.). 72p. pap. 5.00 (978-0-7566-0225-3(4)) Dorling Kindersley Publishing, Inc.
Drewett, Jim. How to Improve at Tennis. 2007. 48p. (J). (gr. 3-9). pap. (*978-0-7787-3593-9(1)*) Crabtree Publishing Co.
Ganeri, Anita. Super Active Tennis. (Illus.). 126p. pap. (978-0-340-76446-6(5) , Hodder & Stoughton) Hodder General Publishing Division.
Guillermo-Newton, Judith. Competitive Tennis for Girls. 2005. (SportsGirl Ser.). (Illus.). 64p. (YA). (gr. 5-8). lib. bdg. 26.50 (978-0-8239-3407-2(1)) Rosen Publishing Group, Inc., The.
Kalman, Bobbie & Crossingham, John. Tennis in Action. Rouse, Bonna, illus. 2002. (Sports in Action Ser.). 32p. (J). (gr. 3-4). pap. (978-0-7787-0122-4(0)); (978-0-7787-0116-3(6)) Crabtree Publishing Co.
Klingel, Cynthia Fitterer & Noyed, Robert B. Tennis. 2003. (Wonder Books Level 2: Sports Ser.). (Illus.). 24p. (J). (ps-2). 22.79 (978-1-56766-462-1(8)) Child's World, Inc.
Kubik, Jeff. Wimbledon. 2007. (J). (*978-1-59036-697-4(2)*); (*978-1-59036-698-1(0)*) Weigl Pubs., Inc.
Lagunilla, Cheryl, told to. The ABC's of Tennis. 2003. (Illus.). (J). lib. bdg. 24.95 (978-0-9726419-0-6(4)) GHL Publishing LLC.
Muskat, Carrie. Tennis. 1999. (Composite Guide Ser.). (Illus.). 64p. (YA). (gr. 4-7). 12.95 (978-0-7910-4728-6(8) , Chelsea Hse.) Facts On File, Inc.
Otten, Jack. Tenis. 2004. (Entrenamiento Deportivo Ser.). (SPA & ENG., Illus.). 24p. (J). lib. bdg. 17.25 (978-0-8239-6840-0(0) , Buenas Letra) Rosen Publishing Group, Inc., The.
—Tennis. 2002. (Reading Power Ser.). (Illus.). 24p. (J). (gr. 1). lib. bdg. 17.25 (978-0-8239-5975-4(9) , PowerKids Pr.) Rosen Publishing Group, Inc., The.
Reynolds, Keith. Tennis. 1998. (Successful Sports Ser.). 32p. (J). lib. bdg. 21.36 (978-1-57572-200-9(3)) Heinemann Library.
Sanchez Vicario, Arantxa. Jovenes Tenistas. (SPA.). 46p. (YA). (gr. 2 up). 16.76 (978-84-272-4967-7(5)) Molino, Editorial ESP. *Dist:* Lectorum Pubns., Inc.
Simkins, Kate. Let's Play Tennis. 2006. (Dk Readers Ser.). (Illus.). 32p. (J). 14.99 (978-0-7566-2010-3(4)); pap. 3.99 (978-0-7566-2009-7(0)) Dorling Kindersley Publishing, Inc.
Tenis, 6, Pack. (On Deck en Espanol Ser.). (SPA.). 24p. (gr. 4-5). 35.00 (978-0-7578-6391-2(4)) Rigby Education.
Tennis, 6 Packs. (On Deck Ser.). 24p. (gr. 4-5). 35.00 (978-0-7578-1008-4(X)) Rigby Education.
Thomas, Ron & Herran, Joe. Getting into Tennis. 2005. (Getting Into Ser.). (Illus.). 32p. (J). (ps-8). lib. bdg. 28.00 (978-0-7910-8807-4(3) , Chelsea Clubhouse) Facts On File, Inc.
Tym, Wanda. The Illustrated Rules of Tennis. Zuehlke, Paul, illus. 2001. 32p. (J). (ps-3). pap. 5.95 (978-0-8249-5424-6(6) , Ideals Children's Bks.) Ideals Pubns.
Wells, Don. For the Love of Tennis. 2005. (For the Love of Sports Ser.). (Illus.). 24p. (J). (ps-6). lib. bdg. 24.45 (978-1-59036-298-3(5)) Weigl Pubs., Inc.
—Tennis. 2005. (For the Love of Sports Ser.). (Illus.). 24p. (J). (ps-7). pap. 6.95 (978-1-59036-302-7(7)) Weigl Pubs., Inc.
Wheeler, Jill C. Andy Roddick. 2007. (Awesome Athletes Ser.). (Illus.). 32p. (J). 22.78 (978-1-59928-307-4(7)) ABDO Publishing Co.
Williams, Venus & Williams, Serena. How to Play Tennis: Learn How to Play the Williams Sisters' Way. 2004. (Animated Series Guide). (Illus.). 96p. (gr. 3 up). 19.99 (978-0-7566-0582-7(2)) Dorling Kindersley Publishing, Inc.

TENNIS—BIOGRAPHY

Armentrout, David & Armentrout, Patricia, trs. Venus & Serena Williams. 2003. (Discover the Life of a Sports Star Ser.). (Illus.). 24p. (J). 20.64 (978-1-58952-655-6(4)) Rourke Publishing, LLC.
Aronson, Virginia. Venus & Serena Williams. 2000. (Women Who Win Ser.). (Illus.). 64p. (J). (gr. 4-7). pap. 25.00 (978-0-7910-6158-9(2)); 25.00 (978-0-7910-5799-5(2)) Facts On File, Inc. (Chelsea Hse.).
—Venus & Serena Williams. 2000. (Illus.). 64p. (J). (gr. 4-7). lib. bdg. 17.60 (978-0-613-33180-7(X)) Tandem Library Bks.
—Venus Williams. 1999. (Galaxy of Superstars Ser.). (Illus.). 64p. (J). pap. 25.00 (978-0-7910-5329-4(6)); (YA). (gr. 4-7). 25.00 (978-0-7910-5153-5(6)) Facts On File, Inc. (Chelsea Hse.).
—Venus Williams. 1999. (Galaxy of Superstars Ser.). (978-0-606-16419-1(7)); (gr. 5-8). lib. bdg. 17.60 (978-0-613-17759-7(2)) Tandem Library Bks.
Asirvatham, Sandy. Venus Williams. 2001. (Black Americans of Achievement Ser.). (Illus.). (J). 104p. pap. 30.00 (978-0-7910-6290-6(2)); 112p. 30.00 (978-0-7910-6289-0(9)) Facts On File, Inc. (Chelsea Hse.).
Bankston, John. Venus Williams. l.t. ed. 2002. (Real Life Reader Biography Ser.). (Illus.). 32p. (gr. 3-8). lib. bdg. 15.95 (978-1-58415-129-6(3)) Mitchell Lane Pubs., Inc.
Berman, Connie. Anna Kournikova. 2001. (Women Who Win Ser.). (Illus.). 64p. (J). pap. (978-0-7910-6530-3(8)); (gr. 3 up). 25.00 (978-0-7910-6529-7(4)) Facts On File, Inc. (Chelsea Hse.).
Boekhoff, P. M. & Kallen, Stuart A. Venus Williams. 2002. (Stars of Sports Ser.). (Illus.). 48p. (J). 26.20 (978-0-7377-1395-4(X) , Greenhaven Pr., Inc.) Thomson Gale.
Bradley, Jeff. David Beckham. 2008. (World's Greatest Athletes Ser.). 32p. (J). (gr. 1-5). 27.07 (*978-1-59296-879-4(1)*) Child's World, Inc.
Brown, Jonatha A. Venus & Serena Williams. 2005. (People to Know Ser.). (Illus.). 24p. (J). pap. (978-0-8368-4477-1(7)); (YA). lib. bdg. 19.33 (978-0-8368-4470-2(X)) Stevens, Gareth Inc.
Buckley, James, Jr. Venus & Serena Williams. 2003. (Trailblazers of the Modern World Ser.). (Illus.). 48p. (J). (gr. 5 up). pap. 14.95 (978-0-8368-5246-2(X)); lib. bdg. 30.00 (978-0-8368-5086-4(6)) Stevens, Gareth Inc. (World Almanac Library).
Christopher, Matt. On the Court with... Jennifer Capriati. 2004. (Illus.). 96p. (J). (gr. 4-6). pap. 4.99 (978-0-316-16474-0(7)) Little Brown & Co.
—On the Court with... Venus & Serena Williams. 2002. (Matt Christopher Sports Biographies Ser.). (Illus.). 112p. (J). (gr. 4-7). pap. 4.99 (978-0-316-13814-7(2)) Little, Brown Bks. for Young Readers.
—On the Court with... Venus & Serena Williams. 2002. (gr. 3-6). lib. bdg. 12.95 (978-0-613-70947-7(0)) Tandem Library Bks.
Cole, Melanie. Mary Joe Fernandez. 1998. (Real-Life Reader Biographies Ser.). (Illus.). 32p. (J). (gr. 3-8). lib. bdg. 15.95 (978-1-883845-63-6(7)) Mitchell Lane Pubs., Inc.
Deans, Karen. Playing to Win: The Story of Althea Gibson. Brown, Elbrite, illus. 2007. 32p. (J). (ps-3). 16.95 (978-0-8234-1926-5(6)) Holiday Hse., Inc.
Ditchfield, Christin. Martina Hingis. 2000. (Women Who Win Ser.). (Illus.). 64p. (J). (gr. 4-7). pap. 25.00 (978-0-7910-6157-2(4)); (YA). (gr. 8 up). 25.00 (978-0-7910-5797-1(6)) Facts On File, Inc. (Chelsea Hse.).
—Martina Hingis. 2001. (gr. 3-6). lib. bdg. 17.60 (978-0-613-32821-0(3)) Tandem Library Bks.
—Sports Great Michael Chang. 1999. (Sports Great Bks.). (Illus.). 64p. (YA). (gr. 4-10). lib. bdg. 22.60 (978-0-7660-1223-3(9)) Enslow Pubs., Inc.
Donaldson, Madeline. Venus & Serena Williams. 2005. (Amazing Athletes Ser.). (Illus.). 32p. (gr. 3-4). lib. bdg. 22.60 (978-0-8225-3316-0(2)) Lerner Publishing Group.
—Venus & Serena Williams. 2004. (Illus.). 32p. (J). (ps-6). lib. bdg. 12.75 (978-0-606-30527-3(0)) Tandem Library Bks.
Donaldson Madeline. Venus & Serena Willliams (Revised Edition) 2007. (Amazing Athletes Ser.). (J). 23.93 (*978-0-8225-7595-5(7)* , Lerner Pubns.) Lerner Publishing Group.
Dorrie, Roxanne. Venus & Serena Williams: The Smashing Sisters. 2003. (High Five Reading (Red Level) Ser.). (Illus.). (J). 64p. lib. bdg. 22.60 (978-0-7368-2784-3(6)); 48p. pap. 23.93 (978-0-7368-2827-7(3)) Capstone Pr., Inc.
Edelson, Paula. Superstars of Men's Tennis. 1999. (Male Sports Stars Ser.). (Illus.). 64p. (YA). (gr. 4-7). 18.65 (978-0-7910-4590-9(0) , Chelsea Hse.) Facts On File, Inc.
Feldman, Heather. Venus Williams: Tennis Champion. 2001. (Reading Power Ser.). (Illus.). 24p. (J). (gr. 1). lib. bdg. 17.25 (978-0-8239-5717-0(9) , PKSUST, PowerKids Pr.) Rosen Publishing Group, Inc., The.
—Venus Williams, Campeona del Tenis. 2002. (Coleccion Power Kids). (SPA & ENG., Illus.). 24p. (J). (gr. k-2). lib. bdg. 17.25 (978-0-8239-6138-2(9) , RN31300, Buenas Letra) Rosen Publishing Group, Inc., The.
Fillon, Mike. Young Superstars of Tennis: The Venus & Serena Williams Story. 1999. (Illus.). 144p. (YA). (gr. 6-12). lib. bdg. 19.95 (978-1-888105-43-8(7)) Avisson Pr., Inc.
Franzen, Lenore. Venus Williams. 2003. (Ovations Ser.). (Illus.). 32p. (J). (978-1-58341-249-7(2) , Creative Education) Creative Co., The.
Glaser, Jason. Maria Sharapova. 2008. (J). lib. bdg. (*978-1-4042-4181-7(7)* , PowerKids Pr.) Rosen Publishing Group, Inc., The.
Gonzales, Doreen. Richard "Pancho" Gonzales: Tennis Champion. 1998. (Hispanic Biographies Ser.). (Illus.). 128p. (YA). (gr. 6-12). lib. bdg. 20.95 (978-0-89490-891-0(X)) Enslow Pubs., Inc.
Goodman, Michael E. Monica Seles. 1998. (Ovations Ser.). (Illus.). 32p. (YA). (gr. 4-7). lib. bdg. 21.30 (978-0-88682-699-4(3) , Creative Education) Creative Co., The.
Gormley, Beatrice. Althea Gibson: Young Tennis Player. Henderson, Meryl, illus. 2005. (Childhood of Famous Americans Ser.). 224p. (J). pap. 4.99 (978-0-689-87187-0(2) , Aladdin) Simon & Schuster Children's Publishing.
—Althea Gibson: Young Tennis Player. Henderson, Meryl, illus. 2005. 214p. (J). (gr. 3-7). lib. bdg. 12.04 (978-0-606-33374-0(6)) Tandem Library Bks.
Gutman, Bill. Venus & Serena: The Grand Slam Williams Sisters. 2001. (Scholastic Biography Ser.). (Illus.). 144p. (J). (gr. 3-7). pap. 4.50 (978-0-439-27152-3(5)) Scholastic, Inc.
—Venus & Serena: The Grand Slam Williams Sisters. 2001. (Illus.). (978-0-606-21502-2(6)) Tandem Library Bks.
Hill, Mary. Serena & Venus Williams. 2003. (Welcome Bks.). (Illus.). 24p. (J). (ps-2). pap. 4.95 (978-0-516-27889-6(4) , Children's Pr.) Scholastic Library Publishing.
—Serena & Venus Williams. 2003. (gr. k-3). lib. bdg. 12.95 (978-0-613-67764-6(1)) Tandem Library Bks.
Lannin, Joanne. Billie Jean King: Tennis Trailblazer. 1999. (Lerner Biographies Ser.). (Illus.). 128p. (gr. 6-12). lib. bdg. 27.93 (978-0-8225-4959-8(X)) Lerner Publishing Group.
Mantell, Paul. Arthur Ashe: Young Tennis Champion. Henderson, Meryl, illus. 2006. 213p. (J). lib. bdg. 18.46 (*978-1-4242-2203-2(6)*) Fitzgerald Bks.
Martin, Marvin. Arthur Ashe: Of Tennis & the Human Spirit. 1999. (Impact Biographies Ser.). (Illus.). 176p. (J). (gr. 8-12). 18.95 (978-0-531-11432-2(5) , Watts, Franklin) Scholastic Library Publishing.
McCann, John T. Lindsay Davenport. 2001. (Women Who Win Ser.). (J). pap. (978-0-7910-6528-0(6)); (Illus.). 64p. 25.00 (978-0-7910-6527-3(8)) Facts On File, Inc. (Chelsea Hse.).
Miles, Ellen. Superstars of Womens Tennis. 2000. (YA). (978-0-606-19251-4(4)) Tandem Library Bks.
Morgan, Terri. Venus & Serena Williams. 2003. (gr. 3-6). lib. bdg. 14.10 (978-0-613-76644-9(X)) Tandem Library Bks.
—Venus & Serena Williams: Grand Slam Sisters. (Sports Achievers Biographies Ser.). (Illus.). 2005. 80p. (gr. 7-12). lib. bdg. 22.60 (978-0-8225-3684-0(6)); 2003. 64p. (J). (gr. 4-9). pap. 5.95 (978-0-8225-9866-4(3) , Carolrhoda Bks.) Lerner Publishing Group.
Murdico, Suzanne J. Monica Seles. 1998. (Overcoming the Odds Ser.). (Illus.). 48p. (J). (gr. 3-8). (978-0-8172-4128-5(0)) Raintree.
—Monica Seles. 1998. (Overcoming the Odds Ser.). (Illus.). 48p. (J). (gr. 4-7). pap. 7.95 (978-0-8172-8001-7(4)) Steck-Vaughn.
Naden, Corinne J. & Blue, Rose. Monica Seles. 2001. (Overcoming Adversity Ser.). (Illus.). 112p. (J). 30.00 (978-0-7910-5899-2(9) , Chelsea Hse.) Facts On File, Inc.
Pyle, Lydia. Venus & Serena Williams. 2004. (Awesome Athletes Ser.). (Illus.). 32p. (J). (gr. k-6). lib. bdg. 22.78 (978-1-59197-486-4(0)) ABDO Publishing Co.
Rutledge, Rachel. The Best of the Best in Tennis. 1998. (Women of Sports Ser.). (Illus.). 64p. (gr. 5 up). lib. bdg. 24.90 (978-0-7613-1303-8(6) , Twenty-First Century Bks.) Lerner Publishing Group.
Savage, Jeff. Annika Sorenstam. 2005. (Amazing Athletes Ser.). (Illus.). 32p. (J). (gr. 2-5). pap. 5.95 (978-0-8225-3107-4(0)); (gr. 3-4). 23.93 (978-0-8225-2428-1(7)) Lerner Publishing Group.
Schaefer, A. R. Serena & Venus Williams. 2002. (Sports Heroes Ser.). (Illus.). 48p. (J). (gr. 3-4). lib. bdg. 21.26 (978-0-7368-1054-8(4) , Capstone High-Interest Bks.) Capstone Pr., Inc.
Sherman, Josepha. Venus Williams. 2001. (Sports Files Ser.). (Illus.). 32p. (J). (gr. 1-3). lib. bdg. (978-1-58810-116-7(9)) Heinemann Library.

Stauffacher, Sue. Nothing but Trouble: The Story of Althea Gibson. Couch, Greg, illus. 2007. 40p. (J). (gr. k-3). lib. bdg. 19.99 (978-0-375-93408-7(1)); 16.99 (978-0-375-83408-0(7)) Random Hse. Children's Bks. (Knopf Bks. for Young Readers).

Stewart, Mark. Pete Sampras: Strokes of Genius. 2000. (gr. 3-6). lib. bdg. 14.10 (978-0-613-62309-4(6)) Tandem Library Bks.

—Venus & Serena Williams: Sisters in Arms. 2000. (New Wave Ser.). (Illus.). 48p. (gr. 4 up). lib. bdg. 22.90 (978-0-7613-1803-3(8) , Millbrook Pr.) Lerner Publishing Group.

Swanson, June. Venus & Serena Williams. Burke, Susan S., illus. 2003. (You Must Be Joking! Riddle Bks.). 32p. (J). (gr. 2-5). pap. 5.95 (978-0-8225-9842-8(6)) Lerner Publishing Group.

Williams, Venus, et al. Venus & Serena: 10 Rules for Living, Loving, & Winning. 2005. (Illus.). 144p. (YA). (gr. 7). pap. 14.00 (978-0-618-57653-1(3)) Houghton Mifflin Co. Trade & Reference Div.

Wilson, Mike. The Williams Sisters: Venus & Serena. 2005. (Illus.). 32p. pap. 8.50 (978-0-340-84876-0(6)) Cambridge Univ. Pr.

TENNIS—FICTION

Adler, C. S. Winning. 1999. (Illus.). 160p. (J). (gr. 5-9). tchr. ed. 15.00 (978-0-395-65017-2(8) , Clarion Bks.) Houghton Mifflin Co. Trade & Reference Div.

Adler, David A. Cam Jansen & the Tennis Trophy Mystery. Natti, Susanna, tr. Natti, Susanna, illus. 2003. (Cam Jansen Ser.: No. 24). 64p. (J). 13.99 (978-0-670-03643-1(9) , Viking Juvenile) Penguin Group (USA) Inc.

—The Tennis Trophy Mystery, Vol. 23. Natti, Susanna, illus. 2005. (Cam Jansen Ser.). 64p. (J). (gr. 2-4). pap. 3.99 (978-0-14-240290-0(7) , Puffin) Penguin Group (USA) Inc.

Arena, Felice & Kettle, Phil. Tennis Ace. Boyer, Susy, illus. 2004. (J). pap. (978-1-59336-360-4(5)) Mondo Publishing.

Bee, Clair. Hardcourt Upset, Vol. 15. rev. ed. 2000. (Chip Hilton Sports Ser.: No. 15). (Illus.). x, 197p. (J). pap. 5.99 (978-0-8054-2094-4(0)) B&H Publishing Grp.

Berman, Ron. The Kid from Courage. 2003. (Illus.). 160p. 9.95 (978-0-9708992-2-4(X)) Scobre Pr. Corp.

Bray-Moffatt, Naia & Dorling Kindersley Publishing Staff. I Love Tennis. 2005. (Illus.). 48p. (J). (ps-ps). 12.99 (978-0-7566-0309-0(9)) Dorling Kindersley Publishing, Inc.

Christopher, Matt. Tennis Ace. ed. 2005. (Sports Classics IV Ser.). 119p. (J). lib. bdg. 15.00 (978-1-59054-773-1(X)) Fitzgerald Bks.

—Tennis Ace. 2000. (Illus.). 128p. (J). (gr. 3-6). 15.95 (978-0-316-13519-1(4)) Little Brown & Co.

—Tennis Ace. 2000. (978-0-606-18267-6(5)) Tandem Library Bks.

Clippinger, Carol. Open Court. 2007. 272p. (YA). (gr. 5-8). 15.99 (978-0-375-84049-4(4)); lib. bdg. 18.99 (978-0-375-94049-1(9)) Random Hse. Children's Bks. (Knopf Bks. for Young Readers).

Corbet, Robert. Fifteen Love. 2005. 192p. (YA). pap. 6.95 (978-0-8027-7714-0(7)) Walker & Co.

Cruise, Robin. Match Point. Taylor, Marjorie, illus. rev. ed. 1999. (Take Ten Ser.). 52p. (YA). (gr. 4-12). pap. 3.95 (978-1-58659-035-2(9)) Artesian Pr.

—Match Point. 2000. (gr. 7-12). lib. bdg. 11.80 (978-0-613-51053-0(4)) Tandem Library Bks.

Feinstein, John. Vanishing Act. 2008. 288p. (J). (gr. 5). 6.50 (***978-0-440-42125-2(X)*** , Yearling) Random Hse. Children's Bks.

—Vanishing Act: Mystery at the U. S. Open. 2006. 288p. (J). (gr. 5). lib. bdg. 18.99 (978-0-375-93592-3(4) , Knopf Bks. for Young Readers) Random Hse. Children's Bks.

—Vanishing Act: Mystery at the U.S. Open. 2006. 288p. (J). (gr. 5). 16.95 (978-0-375-83592-6(X) , Knopf Bks. for Young Readers) Random Hse. Children's Bks.

Horowitz, Anthony. Skeleton Key. (Alex Rider Ser.: Bk. 3). 2006. 352p. (J). (gr. 5). pap. 7.99 (978-0-14-240614-4(7) , Puffin); 2003. 240p. (YA). (gr. 5). 17.99 (978-0-399-23777-5(1) , Philomel) Penguin Group (USA) Inc.

Jenkins, Jerry B. & Fabry, Chris. Double Fault. 2005. (Tyndale Kids Ser.). 272p. (J). pap. 5.99 (978-1-4143-0146-4(4)) Tyndale Hse. Pubs.

King, Donna. Game, Set & Match. 2007. 144p. (J). (gr. 4-6). pap. 5.95 (978-0-7534-6022-1(X) , Kingfisher) Houghton Mifflin Co. Trade & Reference Div.

McG, Shane. Tennis, Anyone? 2007. 40p. (J). (gr. k-4). 15.95 (978-0-8225-6901-5(9) , Carolrhoda Bks.) Lerner Publishing Group.

O'Sullivan, Mark. More Than a Match. 2001. 202p. (J). pap. 6.95 (978-0-86327-496-1(X)) Interlink Publishing Group, Inc.

Powell, Randy. The Whistling Toilets. 2001. (Aerial Fiction Ser.). 256p. (YA). (gr. 7 up). pap. 5.95 (978-0-374-48369-2(8) , Aerial) Farrar, Straus & Giroux.

—The Whistling Toilets. 2001. (Illus.). (J). (978-0-606-21523-7(9)) Tandem Library Bks.

Power, Tim. Tennis Balls & Rotten Shrimp. Bray, Steven, illus. 2006. (Read-It! Chapter Books). 64p. (J). (gr. 2-4). 19.95 (978-1-4048-1664-0(X)) Picture Window Bks.

Shull, Megan. Amazing Grace. 2006. 256p. (gr. 6-9). pap. 6.99 (978-0-7868-5691-6(2)) Hyperion Pr.

Voigt, Cynthia. Bad Girls, Bad Girls, Whatcha Gonna Do? 2006. (Bad Girls Ser.). 448p. (YA). (gr. 7 up). 17.95 (978-0-689-82474-6(2)) Simon & Schuster Children's Publishing.

Wells, Rosemary. When No One Was Looking. 2000. (gr. 7-12). lib. bdg. 14.15 (978-0-613-30190-9(0)) Tandem Library Bks.

TENPINS

see Bowling

TENTS

Gallagher, Debbie. Portable Homes. 2007. (J). (***978-1-59920-150-4(X)***) Smart Apple Media.

Harcourt School Publishers Staff. A House & a Teepee: Below Level. 3rd ed. 2002. (Trophies Reading Program Ser.). (Illus.). (J). pap. 4.10 (978-0-15-322959-6(4)) Harcourt Schl. Pubs.

Tents: Individual Title Six-Packs. (Sails Literacy Ser.). (gr. 1-2). 36.00 (978-0-7578-6742-2(1)) Rigby Education.

TERESA, MOTHER, 1910-1997

Demi. Mother Teresa. 2005. (Illus.). 40p. (J). (gr. 1-4). 19.95 (978-0-689-86407-0(8) , McElderry, Margaret K.) Simon & Schuster Children's Publishing.

Dils, Tracy. Mother Theresa. 2001. (Women of Achievement Ser.). (Illus.). 112p. (J). pap. 9.95 (978-0-7910-5888-6(3)); (gr. 4-7). 30.00 (978-0-7910-5887-9(5)) Facts On File, Inc. (Chelsea Hse.).

Fitzpatrick, Anne. Mother Teresa. 2005. (Genius Ser.). (Illus.). 48p. (J). (gr. 5-9). 21.95 (978-1-58341-330-2(8) , Creative Education) Creative Co., The.

Glavich, Mary Kathleen. Blessed Teresa of Calcutta: Missionary of Charity. Kiwak, Barbara, tr. Kiwak, Barbara, illus. 2003. (Encounter the Saints Ser.: Vol. 17). 136p. (J). pap. 7.95 (978-0-8198-1160-8(2) , 332-024) Pauline Bks. & Media.

Howden, Iris. Mother Teresa. 2nd rev. ed. 2005. 32p. pap. (978-0-340-87626-8(3)) Cambridge Univ. Pr.

Johnson, Emma. Mother Teresa. 2003. (20th Century History Makers Ser.). (Illus.). 112p. (J). lib. bdg. 32.85 (978-0-7398-6143-1(3)) Raintree.

Jones, Brenn. Learning about Love from the Life of Mother Teresa. 2002. (Character Building Book Ser.). (Illus.). 24p. (J). (gr. 3). lib. bdg. 18.75 (978-0-8239-5777-4(2) , PowerKids Pr.) Rosen Publishing Group, Inc., The.

Kudlinski, Kathleen. Mother Teresa: Friend to the Poor. 2006. 171p. (J). lib. bdg. 18.46 (***978-1-4242-1731-1(8)***) Fitzgerald Bks.

—Mother Teresa: Friend to the Poor. 2006. (Childhood of World Figures Ser.). (Illus.). 176p. (J). pap. 5.99 (978-1-4169-1160-9(X) , Aladdin) Simon & Schuster Children's Publishing.

Middleton, Haydn. Mother Teresa. 2000. (Profiles Ser.). (Illus.). 56p. (J). (gr. 4-6). lib. bdg. 24.22 (978-1-57572-227-6(5)) Heinemann Library.

Morgan, Nina. Mother Teresa: Saint of the Poor. 1998. (Illus.). 48p. (gr. 4-7). pap. 7.95 (978-0-8172-7848-9(6)) Steck-Vaughn.

Nelson, Robin. Mother Teresa: A Life of Caring. 2007. (Pull Ahead Books). (Illus.). 32p. (J). 22.60 (978-0-8225-6384-6(3) , Lerner Pubns.) Lerner Publishing Group.

Ransom, Candice F. Mother Teresa. Verstraete, Elaine, illus. 2000. (On My Own Biographies Ser.). 48p. (J). (gr. 1-3). 23.93 (978-1-57505-441-4(8) , Carolrhoda Bks.) Lerner Publishing Group.

Rice, Tanya. Mother Teresa. 1999. (Life & Times of Ser.). (Illus.). 48p. (YA). (gr. 5 up). 12.95 (978-0-7910-4637-1(0) , Chelsea Hse.) Facts On File, Inc.

Ross, Stewart. The Story of Mother Teresa. 2001. (Illus.). 48p. (J). lib. bdg. 24.25 (978-1-930643-21-5(7)) Chrysalis Education.

Rustad, Martha E. H. Mother Teresa: A Life of Kindness. 2007. (Illus.). 24p. (J). lib. bdg. 19.95 (978-1-60014-092-1(0)) Bellwether Media.

Ruth, Amy. Mother Teresa. 1999. (Biography Ser.). (Illus.). 112p. (YA). (gr. 6-12). lib. bdg. 27.93 (978-0-8225-4943-7(3) , Lerner Pubns.) Lerner Publishing Group.

Schaefer, Lola M. Mother Teresa, Vol. 2. 2005. (First Biographies Ser.). 24p. (YA). (gr. k-3). pap. (978-0-7368-3381-3(1) , Pebble Bks.) Capstone Pr., Inc.

Slavicek, Louise Chipley. Mother Teresa: Caring for the World's Poor. 2007. (Modern Peacemakers Ser.). (Illus.). 120p. (YA). (gr. 9 up). 30.00 (***978-0-7910-9433-4(2)*** , Chelsea Hse.) Facts On File, Inc.

Stone, Elaine Murray. Mother Teresa: A Life of Love. 1999. (Illus.). 128p. (gr. 5-9). 7.95 (978-0-8091-6651-0(8) , 6651-8) Paulist Pr.

Sullivan, Anne Marie. Mother Theresa: Religious Humanitarian. 2002. (Great Names Ser.). (Illus.). 32p. (J). (gr. 3 up). lib. bdg. (978-1-59084-142-6(5)) Mason Crest Pubs.

Tilton, Rafael. Mother Teresa. 1999. (Importance of Ser.). (Illus.). 120p. (YA). (gr. 7-10). 27.45 (978-1-56006-565-4(6) , Lucent Bks.) Thomson Gale.

Valentine, Emily. Mother Teresa: With a Discussion of Compassion. 2004. (Values in Action Ser.). (J). (978-1-59203-070-5(X)) Learning Challenge, Inc.

Wellman, Sam. Mother Teresa: Missionary of Charity. 1999. (Heroes of the Faith Ser.). 208p. (YA). (gr. 4-7). 14.95 (978-0-7910-5033-0(5) , Chelsea Hse.) Facts On File, Inc.

—Mother Teresa: Missionary of Charity. l.t. ed. 2001. (Thorndike Christian Fiction Ser.). 274p. (J). 24.95 (978-0-7862-3250-5(1)) Thorndike Pr.

Wheeler, Jill C. Mother Teresa. 2002. (Breaking Barriers Ser.). (Illus.). 64p. (J). (gr. 3-8). lib. bdg. 25.65 (978-1-57765-315-8(7) , ABDO & Daughters) ABDO Publishing Co.

Woronoff, Kristen. Mother Teresa: Helper of the Poor. 2002. (Famous Women Juniors Ser.). (Illus.). 32p. (J). (gr. 3-5). 23.70 (978-1-56711-591-8(8) , Blackbirch Pr., Inc.) Thomson Gale.

TERMITES

Bach, Mary. Termitas. Romo, Alberto, tr. Lyon, Tammie Speer, illus. 1999. (Books for Young Learners).Tr. of Termites. (SPA.). 16p. (J). (gr. k-2). pap. 5.00 (978-1-57274-291-8(7)) Owen, Richard C. Pubs., Inc.

—Termites. Lyon, Tammie Speer, illus. 1998. (Books for Young Learners). 16p. (J). (gr. k-2). pap. 5.00 (978-1-57274-150-8(3) , A2520) Owen, Richard C. Pubs., Inc.

Carole Telford and Rod Theodorou. Through a Termite City. 2nd ed. 2006. (Illus.). 32p. (J). pap. (***978-1-4034-8798-8(7)***) Heinemann Library.

Claybourne, Anna. Ants & Termites. (Illus.). 32p. (YA). (gr. 3 up). lib. bdg. 27.10 (978-1-932799-57-6(5)) Stargazer Bks.

Green, Jen. Ants, Bees, Wasps & Termites. 2004. (Illus.). 64p. pap. 8.99 (978-1-84215-977-4(1) , Southwater) Anness Publishing GBR. *Dist:* National Bk. Network.

—Termites. 2004. (Nature's Children Ser.). (J). (978-0-7172-5960-1(9) , Grolier) Scholastic Library Publishing.

Hartley, Karen, et al. Termite. 2006. (Illus.). 32p. (J). (***978-1-4034-8302-7(7)***); 2nd ed. pap. (***978-1-4034-8315-7(9)***) Heinemann Library.

Hirschmann, Kris. Termites. 2005. (Bugs Ser.). (Illus.). 32p. (J). (ps-8). lib. bdg. 24.95 (978-0-7377-1776-1(9) , Greenhaven Pr., Inc.) Thomson Gale.

Markle, Sandra. Termites: Hard-Working Insect Families. 2008. (Insect World Ser.). (J). lib. bdg. 27.93 (***978-0-8225-7301-2(6)*** , Lerner Pubns.) Lerner Publishing Group.

Rustad, Martha E. H. Termites. 2007. (Illus.). 24p. (J). lib. bdg. 19.95 (978-1-60014-108-9(0)) Bellwether Media.

Schuh, Mari C. Termites. 2003. (Insects Ser.). (Illus.). 24p. (J). (gr. k-1). lib. bdg. 15.93 (978-0-7368-1667-0(4) , Pebble Bks.) Capstone Pr., Inc.

—Termites, Vol. 2. 2005. (Bugs, Bugs, Bugs Ser.). 24p. (YA). (gr. k-3). pap. (978-0-7368-3389-9(7) , Pebble Bks.) Capstone Pr., Inc.

Squire, Ann O. Termites. (True Bks.). (J). 2004. (gr. 3-5). pap. 6.95 (978-0-516-29360-8(5)); 2003. (Illus.). 48p. 25.00 (978-0-516-22660-6(6)) Scholastic Library Publishing. (Children's Pr.).

Telford & Theodorou, Rod. Through a Termite City. 2002. (Amazing Journeys Ser.). (Illus.). 32p. (J). (gr. k-3). pap. 7.50 (978-1-58810-303-1(X) , 91068) Heinemann Library.

Telford, Carole & Theodorou, Rod. Through a Termite City. (Illus.). 32p. (J). 2006. (***978-1-4034-8791-9(X));*** 1998. (gr. 2-4). lib. bdg. 22.79 (978-1-57572-155-2(4)) Heinemann Library.

TERMITES—FICTION

Brennan, Herbie. Nuff Said: Another Tale of Bluebell Wood. Collins, Ross, illus. 2002. 128p. (J). (gr. 2-5). 13.95 (978-1-58234-771-4(9) , Bloomsbury Children) Bloomsbury Publishing.

Caple, Kathy. Termite Trouble. Caple, Kathy, illus. 2005. (Brand New Readers Ser.). (Illus.). 48p. (J). (ps-2). 14.99 (978-0-7636-2572-6(8)) Candlewick Pr.

Laden, Nina. Roberto Insect Architect. 2000. (Illus.). 40p. (J). (ps-1). 16.95 (978-0-8118-2465-1(9)) Chronicle Bks. LLC.

Roberto the Insect Architect. 2005. (J). 24.95 incl. audio (978-0-439-80450-9(7)); 29.95 incl. audio compact disk (978-0-439-80455-4(8)) Weston Woods Studios, Inc.

Rouss, Sylvia. The Littlest Pair. Hannon, Holly, illus. 2005. 32p. (J). pap. 9.95 (978-1-930143-18-0(4) , Devora Publishing) Pitspopany Pr.

Schreiber, Anne. The Bug & the Bird. Thornburgh, Rebecca McKillip, illus. 1999. (Scholastic At-Home Phonics Reading Program Ser.: Vol. 36). 24p. (J). (978-0-590-68791-1(3)) Scholastic, Inc.

TERRARIUMS

Harcourt School Publishers Staff. Vivarium Tips: Take-Home Book. 2001. (Collections Ser.). (Illus.). (J). pap. 1.90 (978-0-15-319529-7(0)) Harcourt Schl. Pubs.

Weingartz, Jill. Terrariums. 2001. (Created Environments Ser.). (Illus.). 24p. (J). 21.35 (978-1-58340-106-4(7)) Smart Apple Media.

TERRESTRIAL PHYSICS

see Geophysics

TERROR, REIGN OF

see France—History—Revolution, 1789-1799

TERRORISM

see also Bombings

Amer, Joseph. The War on Terror. 2005. (Behind the News Ser.). (Illus.). 112p. (J). (gr. 5 up). lib. bdg. 24.95 (978-1-881508-68-7(4)) Oliver Pr., Inc.

America's Battle Against Terrorism. 2005. (Current Controversies Ser.). 208p. (YA). (gr. 10-13). lib. bdg. 36.20 (978-0-7377-2783-8(7) , Greenhaven Pr., Inc.) Thomson Gale.

Anderson, Dale. The Terrorist Attacks of September, 11, 2001. 2003. (Landmark Events in American History Ser.). (Illus.). 48p. (J). (gr. 5 up). lib. bdg. 30.00 (978-0-8368-5380-3(6)); pap. 14.95 (978-0-8368-5408-4(X)) Stevens, Gareth Inc. (World Almanac Library).

Anderson, Wayne. The ETA: Spain's Basque Terrorists. 2005. (Inside the World's Most Infamous Terrorist Organizations Ser.). (Illus.). 64p. (YA). (gr. 7-12). lib. bdg. 26.50 (978-0-8239-3818-6(2)) Rosen Publishing Group, Inc., The.

Andryszewski, Tricia. Terrorism in America. (Headliners Ser.). 2003. (Illus.). 64p. (gr. 5-8). lib. bdg. 25.90 (978-0-7613-2803-2(3) , Millbrook Pr.); 1999. (J). lib. bdg. (978-0-8225-2629-2(8) , Lerner Pubns.) Lerner Publishing Group.

Baer, Suzie. Peru's MRTA: Tupac Amaru Revolutionary Movement. 2005. (Inside the World's Most Infamous Terrorist Organizations Ser.). (Illus.). 64p. (YA). (gr. 7-12). lib. bdg. 26.50 (978-0-8239-3824-7(7)) Rosen Publishing Group, Inc., The.

Baker, David. Biological, Nuclear, & Chemical Weapons. 2006. (Fighting Terrorism Ser.). (Illus.). 48p. (gr. 4-8). 20.95 (978-1-59515-489-7(2)) Rourke Publishing, LLC.

—CIA & FBI. 2006. (Fighting Terrorism Ser.). (Illus.). 48p. (gr. 4-8). 20.95 (978-1-59515-482-8(5)) Rourke Publishing, LLC.

—The Department of Homeland Security. 2006. (Fighting Terrorism Ser.). (Illus.). 48p. (gr. 4-8). 20.95 (978-1-59515-484-2(1)) Rourke Publishing, LLC.

—Hideouts & Training Camps. 2006. (Fighting Terrorism Ser.). (Illus.). 48p. (gr. 4-8). 20.95 (978-1-59515-485-9(X)) Rourke Publishing, LLC.

—Hijacking & Security. 2006. (Fighting Terrorism Ser.). (Illus.). 48p. (gr. 4-8). 20.95 (978-1-59515-488-0(4)) Rourke Publishing, LLC.

—Infiltration & Spying. 2006. (Fighting Terrorism Ser.). (Illus.). 48p. (gr. 4-8). 20.95 (978-1-59515-486-6(8)) Rourke Publishing, LLC.

Beecroft, Simon. The September 11th Terrorist Attacks. 2004. (Days That Changed the World Ser.). (Illus.). 48p. (J). (gr. 5 up). pap. 11.95 (978-0-8368-5579-1(5) , World Almanac Library) Stevens, Gareth Inc.

Beyer, Mark. Homeland Security & Weapons of Mass Destruction: How Prepared Are We? 2004. (Library of Weapons of Mass Destruction). (Illus.). 64p. (J). lib. bdg. 26.50 (978-1-4042-0289-4(7)) Rosen Publishing Group, Inc., The.

—Sky Marshals. 2003. (High Interest Bks.). (Illus.). 48p. (J). 23.00 (978-0-516-24314-6(4)); (YA). (gr. 7-12). pap. 6.95 (978-0-516-24377-1(2)) Scholastic Library Publishing. (Children's Pr.).

Bingley, Richard. Terrorism. 2003. (Face the Facts Ser.). (Illus.). 56p. (J). pap. 8.95 (978-1-4109-0340-2(0)); lib. bdg. 28.56 (978-0-7398-6852-2(7)) Raintree.

—Terrorism. 2003. (gr. 5-8). lib. bdg. 17.60 (978-0-613-78234-0(8)) Tandem Library Bks.

Brownell, Richard. The Oklahoma City Bombing. 2007. (Crime Scene Investigations Ser.). 128p. (J). (gr. 7-10). 32.45 (***978-1-59018-843-9(8)*** , Lucent Bks.) Thomson Gale.

Broyles, Janell. Chemical & Biological Weapons in a Post-9/11 World. 2004. (Library of Weapons of Mass Destruction). (Illus.). 64p. (J). lib. bdg. 26.50 (978-1-4042-0288-7(9)) Rosen Publishing Group, Inc., The.

Buell, Tonya. The Crash of United Flight 93 on September 11, 2001. 2005. (Terrorist Attacks Ser.). (Illus.). 64p. (YA). (gr. 7-12). lib. bdg. 26.50 (978-0-8239-3857-5(3)) Rosen Publishing Group, Inc., The.

Burnett, Betty. The Attack on the U. S. S. Cole in Yemen on October 12, 2000. 2005. (Terrorist Attacks Ser.). (Illus.). 64p. (YA). (gr. 7-12). lib. bdg. 26.50 (978-0-8239-3860-5(3)) Rosen Publishing Group, Inc., The.

Burt, Peg O'Connor. What in the World Is Going On? Am I Safe? (A Letter to American Kids) 2002. 130p. (J). pap. 10.95 (978-0-595-22777-8(5) , Writers Club Pr.) iUniverse, Inc.

Campbell, Geoffrey A. A Vulnerable America: An Overview of National Security. 2003. (Lucent Library of Homeland Security). (Illus.). 112p. (J). 29.95 (978-1-59018-383-0(5) , Lucent Bks.) Thomson Gale.

Charles, Robert B. Narcotics & Terrorism. 2003. (Securing the Nation Ser.). (Illus.). 112p. (J). (gr. 9-13). 30.00 (978-0-7910-7701-6(2) , Chelsea Hse.) Facts On File, Inc.

Corona, Laurel. Hunting down the Terrorists: Declaring War & Policing Global Violations. 2003. (Lucent Terrorism Library). (Illus.). 112p. (J). 29.95 (978-1-59018-382-3(7) , Lucent Bks.) Thomson Gale.

Crewe, Sabrina & Uschan, Michael V. The Terrorist Attacks of September 11, 2001. 2004. (Events That Shaped America Ser.). (Illus.). 32p. (J). (gr. 3 up). lib. bdg. 24.67 (978-0-8368-3399-7(6)) Stevens, Gareth Inc.

Currie, Stephen. Terrorists & Terrorist Groups. 2002. (Terrorism Library). (Illus.). 112p. (YA). 29.95 (978-1-59018-207-9(3) , LML00902-182194, Lucent Bks.) Thomson Gale.

Davenport, John C. Global Extremism & Terrorism. 2007. (World in Focus Ser.). 224p. (gr. 9). 35.00 (***978-0-7910-9279-8(8)*** , Chelsea Hse.) Facts On File, Inc.

Decker, Janet I. Anthrax. 2003. (Deadly Diseases & Epidemics Ser.). (Illus.). 112p. (gr. 9-13). 31.95 (978-0-7910-7302-5(5) , Chelsea Hse.) Facts On File, Inc.

Dorkins, Susie. The Irish Republican Army. 2005. (Inside the World's Most Infamous Terrorist Organizations Ser.). (Illus.). 64p. (YA). (gr. 7-12). lib. bdg. 26.50 (978-0-8239-3822-3(0)) Rosen Publishing Group, Inc., The.

Docalavich, Heather. UN Action Against Terrorism: Fighting Fear. 2007. (United Nations Ser.). (Illus.). 88p. (J). (gr. 5 up). lib. bdg. 21.95 (978-1-4222-0067-4(1)) Mason Crest Pubs.

Donohoe, Helen. Terrorism. 2007. (J). (***978-1-59604-144-8(7)***) Stargazer Bks.

Donohoe, Helen. Terrorism: A Look at the Way the World Is Today. 2005. (Issues of the World Ser.). (Illus.). 48p. (J). (gr. 6-9). lib. bdg. 29.95 (978-1-59604-070-0(X)) Stargazer Bks.

Donovan, Sandy. Protecting America: A Look at the People Who Keep Our Country Safe. 2004. (How Government Works). (Illus.). 56p. (J). (gr. 4-8). lib. bdg. 25.26 (978-0-8225-1345-2(5)) Lerner Publishing Group.

Downing, David. The Debate about Terrorist Tactics. 2007. (J). lib. bdg. (***978-1-4042-3757-5(7)*** , Rosen Central) Rosen Publishing Group, Inc., The.

Emergency Response to Terrorism. 2nd ed. 2003. cd-rom 89.95 (978-0-9746186-0-9(8)) RESPONDER911, Inc.

Englar, Mary. September 11. 2006. (J). (978-0-7565-2029-8(0)) Compass Point Bks.

Eubank, William & Weinberg, Leonard. What Is Terrorism? 2006. (Roots of Terrorism Ser.). (Illus.). 112p. (J). (gr. 6-12). 35.00 (978-0-7910-8305-5(5) , Chelsea Hse.) Facts On File, Inc.

Evans, Fred. Maritime & Port Security. 2003. (Securing the Nation Ser.). (Illus.). 112p. (J). (gr. 9-13). 30.00 (978-0-7910-7614-9(8) , Chelsea Hse.) Facts On File, Inc.

Ferguson, Amanda. The Attack Against the U. S. Embassies in Kenya & Tanzania. 2005. (Terrorist Attacks Ser.). (Illus.). 64p. (J). (gr. 7-12). lib. bdg. 26.50 (978-0-8239-3652-6(X)) Rosen Publishing Group, Inc., The.

Fighting Terrorism DBA. 2001. spiral bd. 16.95 (978-1-56004-123-8(4)) Social Studies Schl. Service.

Frank, Mitch. Understanding September 11th: Answering Questions about the Attacks on America. 2002. (Illus.). 176p. (gr. 6 up). (J). pap. 8.99 (978-0-670-03587-8(4)); (YA). 16.99 (978-0-670-03582-3(3)) Penguin Group (USA) Inc. (Viking Juvenile).

—Understanding September 11th: Answering Questions about the Attacks on America. 2002. (gr. 5-8). lib. bdg. 17.60 (978-0-613-50113-2(6)) Tandem Library Bks.

Fridell, Ron. Terrorism: Political Violence at Home & Abroad. 2001. (Issues in Focus Ser.). (Illus.). 128p. (J). (gr. 6-12). lib. bdg. 26.60 (978-0-7660-1671-2(4)) Enslow Pubs., Inc.

Gaines, Ann Graham. Terrorism. Sarat, Austin, ed. 1999. (Crime, Justice & Punishment Ser.). (Illus.). 80p. (J). (gr. 8). 30.00 (978-0-7910-4596-1(X) , Chelsea Hse.) Facts On File, Inc.

—Terrorism. 2002. (Crime, Justice & Punishment Ser.). (Illus.). 117p. (J). pap. 30.00 (978-0-7910-6924-0(9) , Chelsea Hse.) Facts On File, Inc.

Gard, Carolyn. The Attack on the Pentagon on September 11, 2001. 2005. (Terrorist Attacks Ser.). (Illus.). 64p. (YA). (gr. 7-12). lib. bdg. 26.50 (978-0-8239-3858-2(1)) Rosen Publishing Group, Inc., The.

—The Attacks on the World Trade Center: February 26, 1993, & September 11, 2001. 2005. (Terrorist Attacks Ser.). (Illus.). 64p. (YA). (gr. 7-12). lib. bdg. 26.50 (978-0-8239-3657-1(0)) Rosen Publishing Group, Inc., The.

Gerdes, Louise, ed. Rogue Nations. 2006. (Opposing Viewpoints Ser.). (Illus.). 244p. (YA). (gr. 6 up). pap. 24.95 (978-0-7377-3422-5(1) , Greenhaven Pr., Inc.) Thomson Gale.

Giordano, Geraldine. The Oklahoma City Bombing. 2005. (Terrorist Attacks Ser.). (Illus.). 64p. (YA). (gr. 7-12). lib. bdg. 26.50 (978-0-8239-3655-7(4)) Rosen Publishing Group, Inc., The.

Gottfried, Ted. Homeland Security vs. Constitutional Rights. 2003. (Single Titles Ser.). (Illus.). 128p. (gr. 7 up). lib. bdg. 24.90 (978-0-7613-2862-9(9)) , Twenty-First Century Bks.) Lerner Publishing Group.

Greenberger, Robert. Suicide Bombers. 2006. (In the News Ser.). (Illus.). 64p. (J). (gr. 7-12). lib. bdg. 27.95 (978-1-4042-0977-0(8)) Rosen Publishing Group, Inc., The.

Grow, Mary L. Attack on America: The Day the Twin Towers Collapsed. 2002. (American Disasters Ser.). 64p. (YA). (gr. 4-10). lib. bdg. 23.93 (978-0-7660-2118-1(1)) Enslow Pubs., Inc.

Gunderson, Cory Gideon. Islamic Fundamentalism. 2004. (World in Conflict-the Middle East Ser.). (Illus.). 48p. (J). (gr. 4-8). lib. bdg. 25.65 (978-1-59197-411-6(9)) ABDO Publishing Co.

—Terrorist Groups. 2004. (World in Conflict-the Middle East Ser.). (Illus.). 48p. (J). (gr. 4-8). lib. bdg. 25.65 (978-1-59197-413-0(5)) ABDO Publishing Co.

Halberstam, David. Firehouse. 2003. 208p. 14.00 (978-0-7868-8851-1(2)) Hyperion Pr.

Hamilton, John. Behind the Terror. 2002. (War on Terrorism Ser.). (Illus.). 24p. (J). (gr. 4-8). lib. bdg. 25.65 (978-1-57765-659-3(8) , ABDO & Daughters) ABDO Publishing Co.

—Operation Enduring Freedom. 2002. (War on Terrorism Ser.). (Illus.). 64p. (J). (gr. 4-8). lib. bdg. 25.65 (978-1-57765-665-4(2) , ABDO & Daughters) ABDO Publishing Co.

—Operation Noble Eagle. 2002. (War on Terrorism Ser.). (Illus.). 64p. (J). (gr. 4-8). lib. bdg. 25.65 (978-1-57765-664-7(4) , ABDO & Daughters) ABDO Publishing Co.

Hampton, Wilborn. September 11, 2001: Attack on New York City. (Illus.). (gr. 5 up). 2007. 160p. (YA). pap. 9.99 (***978-0-7636-3635-7(5)***); 2003. 144p. (J). 17.99 (978-0-7636-1949-7(3)) Candlewick Pr.

Haney, Eric L. Inside Delta Force. 2006. (Illus.). 256p. (YA). (gr. 7). 15.95 (978-0-385-73251-2(1) , Delacorte Bks. for Young Readers) Random Hse. Children's Bks.

Haney;, Eric. Inside Delta Force. 2007. 256p. (YA). (gr. 7). pap. 9.99 (978-0-385-73252-9(X) , Delacorte Bks. for Young Readers) Random Hse. Children's Bks.

Harris, Nathaniel. Terrorism. 2004. (21st Century Issues Ser.). (Illus.). 48p. (J). pap. 11.95 (978-0-8368-5662-0(7)); lib. bdg. 30.00 (978-0-8368-5645-3(7)) Stevens, Gareth Inc. (World Almanac Library).

Hasan, Tahara. Anthrax Attacks Around the World. 2005. (Terrorist Attacks Ser.). (Illus.). 64p. (YA). (gr. 7-12). lib. bdg. 26.50 (978-0-8239-3859-9(X)) Rosen Publishing Group, Inc., The.

Haulley, Fletcher. Critical Perspectives on 9/11. 2005. (Critical Anthologies of Nonfiction Writing Ser.). 176p. (J). (gr. 7-12). lib. bdg. 30.60 (978-1-4042-0060-9(6)) Rosen Publishing Group, Inc., The.

—The Department of Homeland Security. 2005. (This Is Your Government Ser.). (Illus.). 64p. (J). (gr. k-3). pap. 13.25 (978-1-4042-0662-5(0)) Rosen Publishing Group, Inc., The.

—The Department of Homeland Security. 2005. (This Is Your Government Ser.). (Illus.). 64p. (J). lib. bdg. (978-1-4042-0209-2(9)) Rosen Publishing Group, Inc., The.

Hibbert, Adam. Terrorism. 2003. (In the News Ser.). (J). lib. bdg. 24.25 (978-1-58340-395-2(7)) Smart Apple Media.

Houle, Michelle. Terrorism. 2004. (History of Issues Ser.). (Illus.). 170p. (gr. 10-12). 24.95 (978-0-7377-1910-9(9) , Greenhaven Pr., Inc.) Thomson Gale.

Howard, Amanda. Terroist Bombing File: The Lockerbie Investigation. 2008. (J). lib. bdg. (***978-1-59716-552-5(2)***) Bearport Publishing Co., Inc.

Hugen, David & Musser, Susan. Can the War on Terrorism Be Won? 2007. (At Issue Ser.). (Illus.). 128p. (J). (gr. 10-12). 29.95 (***978-0-7377-1973-4(7)***); pap. 21.20 (***978-0-7377-1974-1(5)***) Thomson Gale. (Greenhaven Pr., Inc.).

Innes, Brian. International Terrorism. 2002. (Crime & Detection Ser.). (Illus.). 96p. (J). (gr. 7 up). lib. bdg. (978-1-59084-371-0(1)) Mason Crest Pubs.

Inside the World's Most Infamous Terrorist Organizations. 2005. (Illus.). 64p. (gr. 7-12). lib. bdg. 212.00 (978-0-8239-4062-2(4)) Rosen Publishing Group, Inc., The.

Jacobs, Dale W., ed. World Book Focus on Terrorism. 2002. (Illus.). 160p. (J). (978-0-7166-1295-7(X)) World Bk., Inc.

Katz, Samuel M. At Any Cost: National Liberation Terrorism. 2003. (Terrorists Ser.). (Illus.). 72p. (J). (gr. 6-12). 26.60 (978-0-8225-0949-3(0)) Lerner Publishing Group.

—Global Counterstrike: International Counterterrorism. 2005. (Terrorist Dossiers Ser.). (Illus.). 72p. (J). (gr. 6-12). 26.60 (978-0-8225-1566-1(0)) Lerner Publishing Group.

—Jerusalem or Death: Palestinian Terrorism. 72p. (YA). (gr. 9 up). 19.95 (978-1-58013-208-4(1)) Kar-Ben Publishing.

—Jerusalem or Death: Palestinian Terrorism. 2003. (Terrorist Dossiers Ser.). (Illus.). 72p. (J). (gr. 6-12). 26.60 (978-0-8225-4033-5(9)) Lerner Publishing Group.

—Raging Within: Ideological Terrorism. 2003. (Terrorist Dossiers Ser.). (Illus.). 72p. (J). (gr. 6-12). 26.60 (978-0-8225-4032-8(0)) Lerner Publishing Group.

—U. S. Counterstrike: American Counterterrorism. 2005. (Terrorist Dossiers Ser.). (Illus.). 72p. (J). (gr. 6-12). 26.60 (978-0-8225-1569-2(5)) Lerner Publishing Group.

Keeter, Hunter. The US Homeland Security Forces. 2004. (J). pap. 11.95 (978-0-8368-5689-7(9)); lib. bdg. 30.00 (978-0-8368-5682-8(1)) Stevens, Gareth Inc. (World Almanac Library).

Kennet, M. O. & H. Byron Masterson School 1st Graders. September 12th: We Knew We Would Be All Right. Kennet, M. O., illus. 2002. (Kids Are Authors Ser.). (Illus.). 32p. (J). pap. 3.99 (978-0-439-44246-6(X)) Scholastic, Inc.

Kerrigan, Michael. The Department of Homeland Security. 2002. (Rescue & Prevention Ser.). (Illus.). 96p. (J). (gr. 7 up). lib. bdg. (978-1-59084-409-0(2)) Mason Crest Pubs.

Kjelle, Marylou Morano. Helping Hands: A City & a Nation Lend Their Support at Ground Zero. (United We Stand Ser.). (Illus.). 64p. (gr. 6-12). 2003. pap. 11.95 (978-0-7910-7181-6(2)); 2002. 25.00 (978-0-7910-6959-2(1)) Facts On File, Inc. (Chelsea Hse.).

Koestler-Grack, Rachel A. The Department of Homeland Security. 2007. (U. S. Government Ser.). 104p. (YA). (gr. 5-8). 30.00 (***978-0-7910-9286-6(0)*** , Chelsea Hse.) Facts On File, Inc.

Kowalski, Kathiann M. A Pro/con Look at Homeland Security: Safety vs. Liberty After 9/11. 2008. (Issues in Focus Today Ser.). (Illus.). 104p. (J). (gr. 6 up). lib. bdg. 31.93 (***978-0-7660-2914-9(X)***) Enslow Pubs., Inc.

Lalley, Pat. 9.11.01: Terrorists Attack the U. S. 2002. pap. 45.95 (978-0-7398-6357-2(6)); pap. 8.95 (978-0-7398-6356-5(8)); (Illus.). 48p. (gr. 5-8). lib. bdg. 31.40 (978-0-7398-6021-2(6)) Raintree.

Landau, Elaine. Osama Bin Laden: A War Against the West. 2002. (Single Titles Ser.). (Illus.). 144p. (gr. 7 up). lib. bdg. 23.90 (978-0-7613-1709-8(0) , Twenty-First Century Bks.) Lerner Publishing Group.

Levin, John, et al. Domestic Terrorism. 2006. (Roots of Terrorism Ser.). (Illus.). 104p. (gr. 6-12). 35.00 (978-0-7910-8683-4(6) , Chelsea Hse.) Facts On File, Inc.

Loehfelm, Bill. Osama Bin Laden. 2003. (Heroes & Villains Ser.). (Illus.). 104p. (J). 29.95 (978-1-59018-294-9(4) , Lucent Bks.) Thomson Gale.

Louis, Nancy. Ground Zero. 2002. (War on Terrorism Ser.). (Illus.). 64p. (J). (gr. 4-8). lib. bdg. 25.65 (978-1-57765-657-9(1) , ABDO & Daughters) ABDO Publishing Co.

—Heroes of the Day. 2002. (War on Terrorism Ser.). (Illus.). 64p. (J). (gr. 4-8). lib. bdg. 25.65 (978-1-57765-658-6(X) , ABDO & Daughters) ABDO Publishing Co.

—Osama Bin Laden. 2002. (War on Terrorism Ser.). (Illus.). 24p. (J). (gr. 4-8). lib. bdg. 25.65 (978-1-57765-663-0(6) , ABDO & Daughters) ABDO Publishing Co.

MacDonald, Fiona. The September 11th Terrorist Attacks. 2004. (Days That Changed the World Ser.). (Illus.). 48p. (J). (gr. 5 up). lib. bdg. 30.00 (978-0-8368-5572-2(8) , World Almanac Library) Stevens, Gareth Inc.

Marcovitz, Hal. Guardians of Safety: Law Enforcement at Ground Zero. 2002. (United We Stand: America Responds to the Events of September 11, 2001 Ser.). (Illus.). 64p. (gr. 6-12). 25.00 (978-0-7910-6960-8(5) , Chelsea Hse.) Facts On File, Inc.

—The Munich Olympics. 2002. (Great Disasters, Reforms & Ramifications Ser.). (Illus.). 112p. (J). 30.00 (978-0-7910-6737-6(8)); pap. 13.25 (978-0-7910-6911-0(7)) Facts On File, Inc. (Chelsea Hse.).

—The Oklahoma City Bombing. 2002. (Great Disasters, Reforms & Ramifications Ser.). (Illus.). (J). 114p. pap. 13.25 (978-0-7910-6912-7(5)); 112p. 30.00 (978-0-7910-6738-3(6)) Facts On File, Inc. (Chelsea Hse.).

—Terrorism. 2000. (Great Disasters, Reforms & Ramifications Ser.). (Illus.). 112p. (J). (gr. 4-7). 30.00 (978-0-7910-5264-8(8) , Chelsea Hse.) Facts On File, Inc.

Margulies, Phillip. Al-Qaeda: Osama Bin Laden's Army of Terrorists. 2005. (Inside the World's Most Infamous Terrorist Organizations Ser.). (Illus.). 64p. (YA). (gr. 7-12). lib. bdg. 26.50 (978-0-8239-3817-9(4)) Rosen Publishing Group, Inc., The.

Marquette, Scott. America at War. 2003. (America at War Ser.). (gr. 4-8). 167.60 (978-1-58952-385-2(7)) Rourke Publishing, LLC.

—America under Attack. 2003. (America at War Ser.). (Illus.). 48p. (gr. 4-8). 20.95 (978-1-58952-386-9(5)) Rourke Publishing, LLC.

Marsh, Carole. Terrorists & Terrorism: Who, What, Where, When & Why They Exist. 2002. (J). 48p. lib. bdg. 29.95 (978-0-635-01286-9(3)); 32p. (gr. 3-8). pap. 9.95 (978-0-635-01081-0(X)) Gallopade International.

Maybury, Richard J. World War II: The Rest of the Story & How It Affects You Today, 1930 to September 11 2001. Williams, Jane A., ed. rev. ed. 2003. ("Uncle Eric" Bk.). 349p. (YA). pap. 19.95 (978-0-942617-43-6(6)) Bluestocking Pr.

Meeny, John. Should We Ever Negotiate with Terrorists? 2007. (J). (***978-1-4329-0361-9(6)***) Heinemann Library.

Miller, Debra. The Patriot Act. 2007. (Hot Topics Ser.). (Illus.). 128p. (J). (gr. 7-10). 32.45 (***978-1-59018-981-8(7)*** , Lucent Bks.) Thomson Gale.

Miller, Debra A. Middle East. 2007. (Current Controversies Ser.). (Illus.). 240p. (gr. 10-12). 36.20 (***978-0-7377-3960-2(6)***); pap. 24.95 (***978-0-7377-3961-9(4)***) Thomson Gale. (Greenhaven Pr., Inc.).

Miller, Mara. Terrorist Attacks: Disaster & Survival. 2005. (Deadly Disasters Ser.). (Illus.). 48p. (J). (ps-10). lib. bdg. 23.93 (978-0-7660-2385-7(0)) Enslow Pubs., Inc.

Miller, Raymond H. The War in Afghanistan. 2003. (American War Library). (Illus.). 112p. (J). 29.95 (978-1-59018-331-1(2) , Lucent Bks.) Thomson Gale.

Mintzer, Richard. Keeping the Peace: The U. S. Military Responds to Terror. (United We Stand Ser.). (Illus.). 64p. (gr. 6-12). 2003. pap. 11.95 (978-0-7910-7182-3(0)); 2002. 25.00 (978-0-7910-6961-5(3)) Facts On File, Inc. (Chelsea Hse.).

Nakaya, Andrea C. America's Battle Against Terrorism. 2005. (Current Controversies Ser.). 208p. (gr. 10-12). pap. 24.95 (978-0-7377-2784-5(5) , Greenhaven Pr., Inc.) Thomson Gale.

Netzley, Patricia D. The Greenhaven Encyclopedia of Terrorism. 2007. (Greenhaven Encylopedia of Ser.). (Illus.). 352p. 77.45 (978-0-7377-3235-1(0) , Greenhaven Pr., Inc.) Thomson Gale.

O'Connor, Rebecca. Weapons of Mass Destruction. 2007. (Introducing Issues with Opposing Viewpoints Ser.). 144p. (gr. 7-10). 32.45 (***978-0-7377-3617-5(8)*** , Greenhaven Pr., Inc.) Thomson Gale.

Outman, James L. & Outman, Elisabeth M. Terrorism Reference Library: Almanac, Vol. 1. Sawinski, Diane M., ed. 2002. (Illus.). 652p. (J). lib. bdg. 67.00 (978-0-7876-6566-1(5) , UXL) Thomson Gale.

Payan, Gregory. Chemical & Biological Weapons: Anthrax & Sarin. 2000. (gr. 7-12). lib. bdg. 15.25 (978-0-613-58692-4(1)) Tandem Library Bks.

Peppas, Lynn. Terrorism Alert! 2005. (Disaster Alert! Ser.). (Illus.). 32p. (J). (978-0-7787-1585-6(X)); pap. (978-0-7787-1617-4(1)) Crabtree Publishing Co.

Perliger, Arie, et al. Terrorism in the Middle East. 2006. (Roots of Terrorism Ser.). (Illus.). 120p. (J). (gr. 6-12). 35.00 (978-0-7910-8309-3(8) , Chelsea Hse.) Facts On File, Inc.

Pierce, Alan. September 11, 2001. 2005. (American Moments Set Ii Ser.). (J). (gr. 4-8). lib. bdg. 25.65 (978-1-59197-735-3(5) , ABDO & Daughters) ABDO Publishing Co.

Poffenberger, Nancy. Iraq 2003. 2003. (gr. 3-6). lib. bdg. 18.75 (978-0-613-77719-3(0)) Tandem Library Bks.

Porterfield, Jason. Terrorism, Dirty Bombs, & Weapons of Mass Destruction. 2004. (Library of Weapons of Mass Destruction). (Illus.). 64p. (J). lib. bdg. 26.50 (978-1-4042-0291-7(9)) Rosen Publishing Group, Inc., The.

Raintree Steck-Vaughn Staff. Terrorism. 2000. (Global Issues Ser.). (Illus.). 64p. (YA). (gr. 5-10). lib. bdg. 19.98 (978-0-8172-4862-8(5)) Raintree.

Roleff, Tamara L., ed. America under Attack: Primary Sources. 2002. (Terrorism Library). (Illus.). 112p. (YA). 29.95 (978-1-59018-216-1(2) , LML00902-182494, Lucent Bks.) Thomson Gale.

—The World Trade Center Attack. 2003. (History Firsthand Ser.). (Illus.). 202p. (YA). (gr. 7-10). pap. 21.20 (978-0-7377-1469-2(7)); lib. bdg. 36.20 (978-0-7377-1468-5(9)) Thomson Gale. (Greenhaven Pr., Inc.).

The Roots of Terrorism. 2006. (Illus.). (gr. 9-12). 149.70 (978-0-7910-9099-2(X)); Set. (gr. 6-12). 210.00 (978-0-7910-9322-1(0) , Chelsea Hse.) Facts On File, Inc.

Rosaler, Maxine. Hamas: Palestinian Terrorists. 2005. (Inside the World's Most Infamous Terrorist Organizations Ser.). (Illus.). 64p. (YA). (gr. 7-12). lib. bdg. 26.50 (978-0-8239-3820-9(4)) Rosen Publishing Group, Inc., The.

—Hamas: (Rev) Palestinian Terrorists. 2005. (Illus.). 64p. (J). (ps-7). lib. bdg. 26.50 (978-1-4042-0634-2(5)) Rosen Publishing Group, Inc., The.

Rudy, Lisa Jo. Bioterror: Deadly Invisible Weapons. 2007. (24/7: Science Behind the Scenes: Spy Files Ser.). 64p. (J). pap. 7.95 (***978-0-531-18742-5(X)***); (Illus.). (gr. 8-12). 26.00 (***978-0-531-12080-4(5)***) Scholastic Library Publishing. (Watts, Franklin).

Ruffin, David C. The Duties & Responsibilities of the Secretary of Homeland Security. 2005. (Your Government in Action Ser.). (Illus.). 32p. (J). 21.95 (978-1-4042-2693-7(1) , PowerKids Pr.) Rosen Publishing Group, Inc., The.

Ruschmann, Paul. War on Terror. 2004. (Point/Counterpoint Ser.). (Illus.). 112p. (gr. 9-13). 32.95 (978-0-7910-8091-7(9) , Chelsea Hse.) Facts On File, Inc.

Santella, Andrew. September 11, 2001. 2002. (Cornerstones of Freedom Ser.). (Illus.). 48p. (J). (gr. 4-6). 26.00 (978-0-516-22692-7(4) , Children's Pr.) Scholastic Library Publishing.

Santella, Andrew. September 11 2001. 2007. (Cornerstones of Freedomtrade;, Second Ser.). 48p. (J). pap. 5.95 (***978-0-531-18692-3(X)*** , Children's Pr.) Scholastic Library Publishing.

Schaffer, Donna. Director of Homeland Security. 2003. (America's Leaders Ser.). (Illus.). 32p. (J). 23.70 (978-1-56711-960-2(3) , Blackbirch Pr., Inc.) Thomson Gale.

Scheppler, Bill. The USA Patriot ACT: Antiterror Legislation in Response To 9/11. 2005. (Library of American Laws & Legal Principles). (Illus.). 48p. (J). (ps-ps). lib. bdg. 23.95 (978-1-4042-0457-7(1)) Rosen Publishing Group, Inc., The.

September 11, 2001. 2002. (Illus.). 48p. (J). 6.25 (978-0-7398-6006-9(2)) Steck-Vaughn.

Shahak, Bat-Chen. The Bat-Chen Diaries. 2008. (Israel Ser.). (J). lib. bdg. 16.95 (***978-0-8225-8807-8(2)***) Kar-Ben Publishing.

Sheen, Barbara. Nuclear Weapons. 2007. (Ripped from the Headlines Ser.). 64p. (J). (gr. 5). 23.95 (***978-1-60217-004-9(5)***) Erickson Pr.

Sherrow, Victoria. The Oklahoma City Bombing: Terror in the Heartland. 1998. (American Disasters Ser.). (Illus.). 48p. (YA). (gr. 4-10). lib. bdg. 23.93 (978-0-7660-1061-1(9)) Enslow Pubs., Inc.

—The World Trade Center Bombing: Terror in the Towers. 1998. (American Disasters Ser.). (Illus.). 48p. (YA). (gr. 4-10). lib. bdg. 23.93 (978-0-7660-1056-7(2)) Enslow Pubs., Inc.

Shields, Charles J. The World Trade Center Bombing. 2001. (Great Disasters, Reforms & Ramifications Ser.). (J). pap. 13.25 (978-0-7910-6915-8(X) , Chelsea Hse.) Facts On File, Inc.

—The 1993 World Trade Center Bombing. 2001. (Great Disasters, Reforms & Ramifications Ser.). (Illus.). 112p. (YA). (gr. 6-9). 30.00 (978-0-7910-5789-6(5) , Chelsea Hse.) Facts On File, Inc.

Shostak, Arthur B. Defeating Terrorism: Developing Dreams, 4 vols. 2004. (Defeating Terrorism/Developing Dreams Ser.). (Illus.). 120p. (YA). (gr. 9-13). 31.95 (978-0-7910-7955-3(4)); 31.95 (978-0-7910-7956-0(2)); 31.95 (978-0-7910-7957-7(0)) Facts On File, Inc. (Chelsea Hse.).

—Defeating Terrorism/Developing Dreams: Beyond 9/11 & the Iraq War, 4 vols. 2004. (Defeating Terrorism/ Developing Dreams Ser.). (Illus.). 120p. (YA). (gr. 9-13). 31.95 (978-0-7910-7958-4(9) , Chelsea Hse.) Facts On File, Inc.

Shostak, Arthur B., ed. Defeating Terrorism/Developing Dreams: Beyond 9/11 & the Iraq War. 2005. (Illus.). 120 to 185p. (gr. 9-13). pap. 159.75 (978-0-7910-8421-2(3) , Chelsea Hse.) Facts On File, Inc.

Shuchart, John & Searcy, Steve. Kids' Letters to Terrorists. 2003. (Illus.). 148p. (J). pap. 9.95 (978-1-932181-00-5(8) , PP8100) Personhood Pr.

Silate, Jennifer. Terrorist Attack: True Stories of Survival. 2006. (Survivor Stories Ser.). (Illus.). 48p. (YA). (gr. 5-8). lib. bdg. 26.50 (978-1-4042-1001-1(6)) Rosen Publishing Group, Inc., The.

Sonder, Ben. Militia Movement: Fighters of the Far Right. 2000. (Single Titles Social Studies Ser.). (Illus.). 128p. (YA). (gr. 8-12). pap. 8.95 (978-0-531-16466-2(7) , Watts, Franklin) Scholastic Library Publishing.

—Militia Movement: Fighters of the Far Right. 2000. (J). (978-0-606-19786-1(9)) Tandem Library Bks.

—The Militia Movement: Fighters of the Far Right. 2000. (Illus.). 128p. (YA). (gr. 8-13). per. 17.60 (978-0-613-31476-3(X)) Tandem Library Bks.

Spies, Karen Bornemann. Pan Am Flight 103: Terrorism over Lockerbie. 2003. (American Disasters Ser.). (Illus.). 48p. (J). (gr. 4-10). lib. bdg. 23.93 (978-0-7660-1788-7(5)) Enslow Pubs., Inc.

Stefoff, Rebecca. Security vs. Privacy. 2007. (Open for Debate Ser.). (J). lib. bdg. (***978-0-7614-2578-6(0)*** , Benchmark Bks.) Cavendish, Marshall Corp.

Stein, R. Conrad. The Oklahoma City National Memorial. 2003. (Cornerstones of Freedom). (Illus.). 48p. (J). (gr. 4-6). 26.00 (978-0-516-24205-7(9) , Children's Pr.) Scholastic Library Publishing.

Stewart, Gail B. America under Attack: September 11, 2001. 2002. (Terrorism Library). (Illus.). 112p. (J). 29.95 (978-1-59018-208-6(1) , LML00902-182195, Lucent Bks.) Thomson Gale.

—Defending the Borders: The Role of Border & Immigration Control. 2003. (Lucent Library of Homeland Security). (Illus.). 112p. (J). 29.95 (978-1-59018-376-2(2) , Lucent Bks.) Thomson Gale.

—Terrorism. 2002. (Understanding Issues Ser.). (Illus.). 48p. (J). (gr. 3-5). 26.20 (978-0-7377-1287-2(2) , LML00902-181530, Kidhaven) Thomson Gale.

—The War at Home. 2003. (American War Library). (Illus.). 112p. (J). 29.95 (978-1-59018-330-4(4) , Lucent Bks.) Thomson Gale.

Streissguth, Thomas. International Terrorists. rev. ed. 1999. (Profiles Ser.). (Illus.). 160p. (gr. 5 up). lib. bdg. 19.95 (978-1-881508-07-6(2)) Oliver Pr., Inc.

Streissguth, Thomas, tr. Combating the Global Terrorist Threat. 2003. (American War Library). (Illus.). 112p. (J). 29.95 (978-1-59018-327-4(4) , Lucent Bks.) Thomson Gale.

Taylor, Robert. The History of Terrorism. 2002. (Terrorism Library). (Illus.). 112p. (YA). (gr. 8 up). 29.95 (978-1-59018-206-2(5) , LML00902-182193, Lucent Bks.) Thomson Gale.

Terrorist Attacks. 2005. (Illus.). 64p. (gr. 7-12). lib. bdg. 239.40 (978-0-8239-4077-6(2)) Rosen Publishing Group, Inc., The.

Terrorist Attacks Set 1. 2005. (Illus.). (gr. 7-12). lib. bdg. 159.00 (978-0-8239-3900-8(6)) Rosen Publishing Group, Inc., The.

Terrorist Attacks Set 2. 2005. (Illus.). 64p. (gr. 7-12). lib. bdg. 159.00 (978-0-8239-4063-9(2)) Rosen Publishing Group, Inc., The.

Torr, James D. Civil Liberties in the War on Terrorism. 2004. (Lucent Terrorism Library). (Illus.). 96p. (J). 29.95 (978-1-59018-527-8(7) , Lucent Bks.) Thomson Gale.

—Responding to Attack: Firefighters & Police. 2003. (Lucent Library of Homeland Security). (Illus.). 112p. (J). 29.95 (978-1-59018-375-5(4) , Lucent Bks.) Thomson Gale.

Uschan, Michael V. The Beslan School Siege & Separatist Terrorism, 6 Vols. 2006. 180.00 (978-0-8368-6555-4(3)); (Illus.). 48p. (J). pap. 11.95 (978-0-8368-6563-9(4) , World Almanac Library); (Illus.). 48p. (J). lib. bdg. 30.00 (978-0-8368-6556-1(1) , World Almanac Library) Stevens, Gareth Inc.

—Suicide Bombings in Israel & Palestinian Terrorism. 2006. (Terrorism in Today's World Ser.). (Illus.). 48p. (J). pap. 11.95 (978-0-8368-6568-4(5)); lib. bdg. 30.00 (978-0-8368-6561-5(8)) Stevens, Gareth Inc. (World Almanac Library).

Valdez, Angela. We the People: The U. S. Government's United Response Against Terror. (United We Stand Ser.). (Illus.). 64p. (gr. 6-12). 2003. pap. 11.95 (978-0-7910-7183-0(9)); 2002. 25.00 (978-0-7910-6962-2(1)) Facts On File, Inc. (Chelsea Hse.).

War on Terrorism, Set. Incl. America's Leaders. Wheeler, Jill C. 64p. lib. bdg. 25.65 (978-1-57765-661-6(X)); Armed Forces. Hamilton, John. 64p. lib. bdg. 25.65 (978-1-57765-674-6(1)); Behind the Terror. Hamilton, John. 24p. lib. bdg. 25.65 (978-1-57765-659-3(8)); George W. Bush. Wheeler, Jill C. 64p. lib. bdg. 25.65 (978-1-57765-662-3(8)); Ground Zero. Louis, Nancy. 64p. lib. bdg. 25.65 (978-1-57765-657-9(1)); Heroes of the Day. Louis, Nancy. 64p. lib. bdg. 25.65 (978-1-57765-658-6(X)); Operation Enduring Freedom. Hamilton, John. 64p. lib. bdg. 25.65 (978-1-57765-665-4(2)); Operation Noble Eagle. Hamilton, John. 64p. lib. bdg. 25.65 (978-1-57765-664-7(4)); Osama Bin Laden. Louis, Nancy. 24p. lib. bdg. 25.65 (978-1-57765-663-0(6)); September 11, 2001 : The Day That Changed America. Wheeler, Jill C. 64p. lib. bdg. 25.65 (978-1-57765-656-2(3)); United We Stand. Louis, Nancy. 64p. lib. bdg. 25.65 (978-1-57765-660-9(1)); Weapons of War. Hamilton, John. 64p. lib. bdg. 25.65 (978-1-57765-673-9(3)); (J). (gr. 4-8). (Illus.). 2002. Set lib. bdg. 307.80 (978-1-57765-655-5(5) , ABDO & Daughters) ABDO Publishing Co.

The War on Terrorism: The First Year. 2004. 64p. lib. bdg. 28.56 (978-1-4109-0182-8(3)) Raintree.

Weil, Ann. Terrorism. 2003. (Illus.). 64p. (YA). per. 3.95 (978-1-56254-666-3(X) , SP666X) Saddleback Educational Publishing.

Weitzman, Stanley. Terrorism. 2006. (Global Issues Ser.). (Illus.). 64p. (J). (gr. 4-12). pap. 12.95 (978-1-55285-746-5(8) , Walrus Bks.) Whitecap Bks., Ltd. CAN. *Dist:* Firefly Bks., Ltd.

Wells, Donald. Terrorism. 2004. (Understanding Global Issues Ser.). (J). lib. bdg. (978-1-59036-234-1(9)) Weigl Pubs., Inc.

Wells, Donna. Live Aware, Not in Fear: The 411 After 9-11. 2002. (gr. 7-12). lib. bdg. 18.75 (978-0-613-51313-5(4)) Tandem Library Bks.

Wells, Donna K. & Morris, Bruce C. Live Aware, Not in Fear: The 411 after 9-11, A Book for Teens. 2002. (Illus.). 120p. pap. 9.95 (978-0-7573-0013-4(8)) Health Communications, Inc.

WeWrite Kids Staff. War? I'm Scared! Calmese, Norman E., illus. Andrews, Rob, photos by. l.t. ed. 2001. (WeWrite Kids! Ser.: No. 46). 50p. (J). (gr. 1-7). pap. 8.95 (978-1-57635-057-7(6)) WeWrite LLC.

Wheeler, Jill C. America's Leaders. 2002. (War on Terrorism Ser.). (Illus.). 64p. (J). (gr. 4-8). lib. bdg. 25.65 (978-1-57765-661-6(X) ; ABDO & Daughters) ABDO Publishing Co.

—September 11, 2001: The Day That Changed America. 2002. (War on Terrorism Ser.). (Illus.). 64p. (J). (gr. 4-8). lib. bdg. 25.65 (978-1-57765-656-2(3) , ABDO & Daughters) ABDO Publishing Co.

Wicker, R. Doug. The Bombing of Pan Am Flight 103. 2005. (Terrorist Attacks Ser.). (Illus.). 64p. (YA). (gr. 7-12). lib. bdg. 26.50 (978-0-8239-3656-4(2)) Rosen Publishing Group, Inc., The.

Williams, Brian. America under Attack. 2003. (Dates with History Ser.). 45p. (J). lib. bdg. 28.50 (978-1-58340-406-5(6)) Smart Apple Media.

Woolf, Alex. Osama Bin Laden. 2004. (A&E Biography Ser.). (Illus.). 112p. (J). 29.27 (978-0-8225-5003-7(2) , Lerner Pubns.) Lerner Publishing Group.

—Terrorism. 2003. (21st Century Debates Ser.). (Illus.). 64p. (J). lib. bdg. 28.56 (978-0-7398-6034-2(8)) Raintree.

—Why Are People Terrorists? 2004. (Exploring Tough Issues Ser.). (Illus.). 48p. (J). lib. bdg. (978-0-7398-6686-3(9)) Raintree.

Wright, John D. Counterterrorist Forces with the CIA. 2002. (Rescue & Prevention Ser.). (Illus.). 96p. (J). (gr. 7 up). lib. bdg. (978-1-59084-407-6(6)) Mason Crest Pubs.

Wukovits, John F. The War at Home. 2003. (American War Library). (Illus.). 128p. (J). 29.95 (978-1-59018-262-8(6) , Lucent Bks.) Thomson Gale.

Yancey, Diane. Life of an American Soldier in Afghanistan. 2003. (American War Library). (Illus.). 128p. (J). 29.95 (978-1-59018-329-8(0) , Lucent Bks.) Thomson Gale.

—Terrorism. 2005. (Overview Ser.). (Illus.). 112p. (J). (gr. 7-10). lib. bdg. 29.95 (978-1-59018-194-2(8) , Lucent Bks.) Thomson Gale.

Young, Mitch. Turning Points in World History Anthology. 2003. (Turning Points in World History Ser.). (Illus.). 224p. (YA). (gr. 9-12). pap. 24.95 (978-0-7377-1471-5(9) , Greenhaven Pr., Inc.) Thomson Gale.

—War on Terrorism. 2003. (gr. 7-12). lib. bdg. 33.25 (978-0-613-73877-4(2)) Tandem Library Bks.

TERRORISM—FICTION

Alexander, R. W. Charm Hunter. 2004. 208p. (YA). pap. 14.95 (978-0-7414-2105-0(4)) Infinity Publishing.

Anne, Kimberley. Twin Heroes. McCarthy, Michael, illus. 2002. 32p. (J). (gr. k-6). pap. 12.95 (978-0-9717623-0-5(9)) Power Publishing.

Appleton, Victor. The Robot Olympics. 2007. (Tom Swift, Young Inventor Ser.). 160p. (J). (gr. 4-7). 27.07 (***978-1-59961-351-2(4)***) Spotlight.

Blackman, Malorie. Black & White. 2007. 512p. (YA). (gr. 9 up). pap. 7.99 (978-1-4169-0017-7(9) , Simon Pulse) Simon & Schuster Children's Publishing.

Bongiorno, Patti Lynn. Grandma, Does God Make Mistakes? 2nd ed. 2001. (J). spiral bd. 20.00 (978-0-9715819-3-7(2)) Bongiorno Bks.

—My Dad's Footsteps. Bongiorno, Patti Lynn, illus. 2002. (J). spiral bd. 20.00 (978-0-9715819-8-2(3)) Bongiorno Bks.

Buckman, Carole Duncan. Neighbors & Traitors. 2000. (StarMaker Bks.). 81p. (J). (gr. 6-9). pap. 5.50 (978-0-88489-548-0(3)) St. Mary's Pr.

Bunting, Eve. Man with the Red Bag. 2007. 240p. (J). (gr. 5 up). 15.99 (***978-0-06-081828-9(X));*** lib. bdg. 16.89 (***978-0-06-081835-7(2)***) HarperCollins Pubs. (Cotler, Joanna Books).

Burns, Joanne. What Is Heaven Like? 2005. 35p. (J). 10.99 (978-1-4116-3360-5(1)) Lulu.com.

Butcher, Andrew. Factoria Frankestein. Morales, Andrea, tr. 2004. (SPA., Illus.). 240p. (978-84-95618-57-3(5) , Umbriel) Ediciones Urano S. A.

Cambridge Young Writers Staff. I'm Telling You!, 6 vols., Pack. 2001. (Cambridge Reading Ser.). (Illus.). 80p. pap. 46.00 (978-0-521-01353-6(4)) Cambridge Univ. Pr.

Carver, Bill. Lift. 2004. 84p. pap. 14.95 (978-1-4137-5281-6(0)) PublishAmerica, Inc.

Chin, Oliver. 9 of 1: A Window to the World. 2003. (gr. 7-12). lib. bdg. 19.90 (978-0-613-79605-7(5)) Tandem Library Bks.

Cooney, Caroline B. Terrorist. 1999. (978-0-606-17447-3(8)) Tandem Library Bks.

Cormier, Robert. After the First Death. 2002. 21.75 (978-0-8446-7215-1(7)) Smith, Peter Pub., Inc.

David, Christopher. Denholme & the Skeleton Mystery. 2006. 274p. pap. (***978-1-4120-8014-9(2)***) Trafford Publishing.

Deuker, Carl. Runner. 2007. 224p. (YA). (gr. 7). 2007. pap. 7.99 (***978-0-618-73505-1(4)*** , Graphia); 2005. 16.00 (978-0-618-54298-7(1)) Houghton Mifflin Co. Trade & Reference Div.

Dunlop, Ed. Sherlock Jones: The Assassination Plot. 2004. 116p. (J). (978-1-59166-315-7(6)) Jones, Bob Univ. Pr.

Dunphy, Joan S. The Mouse Family's Most Terrible, Terrifying Day: Helping Children Cope with Terrorism Fears. DePrince, Erik & Volinski, Jessica, illus. 2002. (Let's Talk Ser.). 48p. (J). pap. 12.95 (978-0-88282-227-3(6)) New Horizon Pr. Pubs., Inc.

Forde, Catherine. Tug of War: Two Mums, One Girl, One Choice. 2007. 304p. (J). pap. 9.95 (***978-1-4052-2005-7(8)***) Egmont Bks., Ltd. GBR. *Dist:* Independent Pubs. Group.

Hayes, Rosemary. Mixing It. 2007. 192p. (YA). (gr. 5 up). pap. 7.95 (***978-1-84507-495-1(5)***) Lincoln, Frances Ltd. GBR. *Dist:* Perseus Distribution.

Heneghan, James. Torn Away. 2003. 256p. (J). (gr. 4-7). pap. 6.95 (978-1-55143-263-2(3)) Orca Bk. Pubs. USA.

—Torn Away. 2003. (gr. 7-12). lib. bdg. 15.25 (978-0-613-84756-8(3)) Tandem Library Bks.

Horowitz, Anthony. Ark Angel. (Alex Rider Ser.: Bk. 6). 2007. 336p. (J). 7.99 (978-0-14-240738-7(0) , Puffin); 2006. 326p. (YA). (gr. 5). 17.99 (978-0-399-24152-9(3) , Philomel) Penguin Group (USA) Inc.

—Scorpia. (Alex Rider Ser.: Bk. 5). (YA). (gr. 5). 2006. 400p. pap. 7.99 (978-0-14-240578-9(7) , Puffin); 2005. 320p. 17.99 (978-0-399-24151-2(5) , Philomel) Penguin Group (USA) Inc.

—Skeleton Key. (Alex Rider Ser.: Bk. 3). 2006. 352p. (J). (gr. 7). pap. 7.99 (978-0-14-240614-4(7) , Puffin); 2003. 240p. (YA). (gr. 5). 17.99 (978-0-399-23777-5(1) , Philomel) Penguin Group (USA) Inc.

—Stormbreaker. (Alex Rider Ser.: Bk. 1). 2006. 256p. (J). (gr. 7). pap. 7.99 (978-0-14-240611-3(2) , Puffin); 2002. (Illus.). (J). (gr. 4-7). 5.99 (978-0-698-11932-1(0) , Puffin); 2001. (Illus.). 1p. (YA). (gr. 5 up). 17.99 (978-0-399-23620-4(1) , Philomel); 2006. 264p. (J). (gr. 5). 7.99 (978-0-14-240656-4(2) , Puffin) Penguin Group (USA) Inc.

—Stormbreaker. 2004. (Alex Rider Ser.: Bk. 1). 208p. (J). (gr. 4-7). pap. 38.00 incl. audio (978-0-8072-2277-5(1) , Listening Library) Random Hse. Audio Publishing Group.

—Stormbreaker: The Graphic Novel. Kanako & Yuzuru, illus. 2006. (Alex Rider Ser.). 144p. (J). (gr. 4). pap. 14.99 (978-0-399-24633-3(9) , Philomel) Penguin Group (USA) Inc.

Jenkins, Jerry B. & Fabry, Chris. Dead End. 2006. (Red Rock Mysteries Ser.). 256p. (J). pap. 5.99 (978-1-4143-0154-9(5) , Tyndale Kids) Tyndale Hse. Pubs.

Kaplan, Gloria. Pappou, Where Are You? Olavarria, Hector, illus. 2002. 112p. (YA). per. 11.99 (978-1-889732-28-2(1) , Key-A-Teese Production) Word For Word Publishing Co.

Kass, Pnina Moed. Real Time. 2006. 192p. (YA). (gr. 7). reprint ed. pap. 7.99 (978-0-618-69174-6(X)) Houghton Mifflin Co.

Klein. Operation Firestorm. (Bloomfield 3-in-1 Mini Ser.). (J). 17.99 (978-1-56871-309-0(6)) Targum Pr., Inc.

Lopes, Myra A. Around the Kitchen Table. 2nd ed. 2002. (Illus.). (J). per. 15.50 (978-0-9717984-0-3(0)) Harbor View Publishing Co.

Mason, Tom. Take It to the Max. 2001. (gr. 3-6). lib. bdg. 11.80 (978-0-613-87080-1(8)) Tandem Library Bks.

McNab, Andy & Rigby, Robert. Meltdown. 2008. 276p. (YA). (gr. 7). 16.99 (***978-0-399-24686-9(X)*** , Putnam Juvenile) Penguin Group (USA) Inc.

McNab, Andy & Rigby, Robert. Payback. (YA). 2007. 288p. (gr. 7). 7.99 (***978-0-14-240914-5(6)*** , Puffin); 2006. 272p. (ps-k). 16.99 (978-0-399-24465-0(4) , Putnam Juvenile) Penguin Group (USA) Inc.

Mitchell, Nancy. Global Warning. Christensen, Edie et al, illus. 1999. (Changing Earth Trilogy Ser.: Bk. 3). 178p. (Orig.). (J). (ps-12). mass mkt. 5.95 (978-1-892713-02-5(0)) Lightstream Pubns.

Mohsenian, Javad. 9/11 Children. 2006. 113p. pap. 10.95 (978-0-7414-3218-6(8)) Infinity Publishing.

Morris, Robert. Grandma Ursu, Think Blue. 2003. (Illus.). 32p. (J). 15.95 (978-0-9741634-0-6(6)) Ursu Pubns.

Muchamore, Robert. The Recruit. 2005. (Cherub Ser.). 352p. (YA). mass mkt. 6.99 (978-0-689-87779-7(X) , Simon Pulse) Simon & Schuster Children's Publishing.

Peretti, Frank E. Trapped at the Bottom of the Sea. 144p. 2004. (Cooper Kids Adventures Ser.: No. 4). (gr. 4-7). 5.99 (978-0-89107-594-3(1)); Vol. 4. 2005. (Cooper Kids Adventure Ser.: Vol. 4). (gr. 3-6). pap. 5.99 (978-1-58134-621-3(2) , Crossway Bibles) Crossway Bks.

Prose, Francine. Bullyville. 2007. 272p. (J). (gr. 5-8). 16.99 (***978-0-06-057497-0(6));*** lib. bdg. 17.89 (***978-0-06-057498-7(4)***) HarperCollins Pubs. (HarperTeen).

Reece, Colleen L. Saturday Scare. l.t. ed. 2002. (Juli Scott, Super Sleuth Ser.). (Illus.). 211p. (J). 24.95 (978-0-7862-3195-9(5)) Thomson Gale.

Seabrooke, Brenda. Stonewolf. 2004. 240p. (J). (gr. 7 up). tchr. ed. 16.95 (978-0-8234-1848-0(0)) Holiday Hse., Inc.

Trout, Richard E. Czar of Alaska: The Cross of Charlemagne. 2005. 248p. (J). (gr. 5-8). 15.95 (978-1-58980-328-2(0)) Pelican Publishing Co., Inc.

Wakely, Carolrae. The History Nut. 2005. (Illus.). 81p. 17.95 (978-0-533-14985-8(1)) Vantage Pr., Inc.

White, Ellen Emerson. Long Live the Queen. 2008. (YA). pap. 8.99 (***978-0-312-37490-7(9)***) Feiwel & Friends.

Wilson, Eric G. Disneyland Hostage. 2000. (Illus.). 144p. (J). (gr. 6-8). pap. 4.99 (978-1-55143-174-1(2)) Orca Bk. Pubs. USA.

Windle, Jeanette. Race for the Secret Code, Vol. 6. 2002. (Parker Twins Ser.: No. 6). 160p. pap. 5.99 (978-0-8254-4144-8(7)) Kregel Pubns.

TESLA, NIKOLA, 1856-1943

Aldrich, Lisa J. Nikola Tesla & the Taming of Electricity. 2005. (Profiles in Science Ser.). (Illus.). 160p. (J). (ps-7). lib. bdg. 26.95 (978-1-931798-46-4(X)) Reynolds, Morgan Inc.

O'Shei, Tim. Marconi & Tesla: Pioneers of Radio Communication. 2008. (Inventors Who Changed the World Ser.). (Illus.). 128p. (J). (gr. 6 up). lib. bdg. 33.27 (***978-1-59845-076-7(X)*** , MyReportLinks.com Bks.) Enslow Pubs., Inc.

TEST PILOTS

see Air Pilots; Airplanes—Testing

TESTS

see Educational Tests and Measurements

TEXAS

Alter, Judy. Texas: A MyReportLinks.com Book. 2002. (States Ser.). (Illus.). 48p. (J). (gr. 4-10). lib. bdg. 25.26 (978-0-7660-5018-1(1) , MyReportLinks.com Bks.) Enslow Pubs., Inc.

Altman, Linda Jacobs. Texas. 2002. (It's My State! Ser.). (Illus.). 80p. (J). 27.07 (978-0-7614-1423-0(1) , Benchmark Bks.) Cavendish, Marshall Corp.

Barenblat, Rachel. Texas. Porras, Carlos & D'Andrea, Patricia, trs. 2003. (World Almanac Biblioteca de los Estados). (SPA., Illus.). 48p. (J). (gr. 5 up). lib. bdg. 30.00 (978-0-8368-5547-0(7) , World Almanac Library) Stevens, Gareth Inc.

—Texas: The Lone Star State. 2002. (World Almanac Library of the States). (Illus.). 48p. (J). (gr. 5 up). pap. 14.95 (978-0-8368-5292-9(3)); lib. bdg. 30.00 (978-0-8368-5121-2(8)) Stevens, Gareth Inc. (World Almanac Library).

—Texas: The Lone Star State. 2002. (gr. 5-8). lib. bdg. 24.15 (978-0-613-52511-4(6)) Tandem Library Bks.

Bauld, Jane Scoggins. The Story of MotherTree. l.t. ed. 2000. (J). 12.95 (978-1-929701-03-2(9)) Under the Green Umbrella.

Bredeson, Carmen. Texas. (Rookie Espanol: Geografia Ser.). (J). 2005. (SPA., Illus.). 32p. (gr. k-2). pap. 5.95 (978-0-516-25516-3(9) , Children's Pr.); 2004. 19.50 (978-0-516-25110-3(4) , Watts, Franklin); 2002. (Illus.). 32p. (gr. 1-2). pap. 5.95 (978-0-516-27393-8(0) , Children's Pr.); 2002. (Illus.). 32p. (gr. 1-2). 20.50 (978-0-516-22270-7(8) , Children's Pr.) Scholastic Library Publishing.

—Texas. 2002. (Illus.). 31p. (J). (gr. 4-7). lib. bdg. 14.10 (978-0-613-54365-1(3)) Tandem Library Bks.

Capstone Press Staff, contrib. by. Texas. rev. ed. 2002. (One Nation Ser.). (Illus.). 48p. (J). (gr. 3-4). lib. bdg. 22.60 (978-0-7368-1268-9(7) , Bridgestone Bks.) Capstone Pr., Inc.

Caravantes, Peggy. O. Henry: William Sidney Porter: Texas Cowboy Writer. 2003. (J). (978-1-57168-768-5(8) , Eakin Pr.) Eakin Pr.

Carr, Karen. Dinosaur Hunt: Texas - 115 Million Years Ago. Carr, Karen, illus. 2002. (Illus.). 48p. (J). (gr. 1 up). 17.99 (978-0-06-029703-9(4)) HarperCollins Pubs.

Crane, Carol. L Is for Lonestar: A Texas Alphabet. Stacy, Alan, illus. 2001. 40p. (J). 17.95 (978-1-58536-019-2(8)) Sleeping Bear Pr.

Dorling Kindersley Publishing Staff. Texas. 2003. (Eyewitness Bks.). (Illus.). 64p. (J). pap. 15.99 (978-0-7894-9745-1(X)); (SPA., pap. 15.99 (978-0-7894-9744-4(1)) Dorling Kindersley Publishing, Inc.

Flynn, Jean. Texas Women Who Dared to Be First. 2004. (Illus.). 144p. (gr. 4-7). 18.95 (978-1-57168-232-1(5)) Eakin Pr.

Hanson-Harding, Alexandra. Texas. 80p. (J). 2008. (From Sea to Shining Sea, Second Ser.). pap. 7.95 (***978-0-531-18809-5(4));*** 2001. (From Sea to Shining Sea Ser.: 2). (Illus.). (gr. 3-5). 30.50 (978-0-516-22322-3(4)) Scholastic Library Publishing. (Children's Pr.).

Harcourt School Publishers Staff. North of the Rio Grande: Take-Home Book. 2001. (Collections Ser.). (Illus.). (J). pap. 1.90 (978-0-15-319507-5(X)) Harcourt Schl. Pubs.

—TIME for Kids: Texas. 3rd ed. 2002. (Horizontes (Social Studies) Ser.). (SPA., Illus.). Bk. 3. pap. 7.00 (978-0-15-333823-6(7)); Bk. 4. pap. 7.00 (978-0-15-333825-0(3)); Bk. 5. pap. 7.00 (978-0-15-333827-4(X)); Bk. 6. pap. 7.00 (978-0-15-333829-8(6)); Bk. 7. pap. 7.00 (978-0-15-333831-1(8)); Bk. 8. pap. 7.00 (978-0-15-333833-5(4)); Bk. 9. pap. 7.00 (978-0-15-333835-9(0)); Bk. 10. pap. 7.00 (978-0-15-333837-3(7)); Bk. 11. pap. 7.00 (978-0-15-333839-7(3)); Bk. 12. pap. 7.00 (978-0-15-333841-0(5)); Bk. 13. pap. 7.00 (978-0-15-333843-4(1)); Bk. 14. pap. 7.00 (978-0-15-333845-8(8)); Bk. 15. pap. 7.00 (978-0-15-333847-2(4)); Bk. 16. pap. 7.00 (978-0-15-333849-6(0)); Bk. 17. pap. 7.00 (978-0-15-333851-9(2)); Bk. 18. pap. 7.00 (978-0-15-333853-3(9)) Harcourt Schl. Pubs.

—Time/Kids Readers: Texas Edition. 3rd ed. 2002. (Horizontes (Social Studies) Ser.). pap., tchr. ed. 65.80 (978-0-15-334662-0(0)) Harcourt Schl. Pubs.

Harper, Jo. Big Foot Wallace: A Hero of Early Texas. Roeder, Virginia M., illus. 1999. 48p. (gr. 1-3). 14.95 (978-1-57168-223-9(6)) Eakin Pr.

Heinrichs, Ann. Texas. Kania, Matt, illus. 2005. (Welcome to the USA Ser.). 40p. (J). (gr. 1-5). 27.07 (978-1-59296-485-7(0)) Child's World, Inc.

—Texas. 2002. (This Land Is Your Land Ser.). (Illus.). 48p. (J). (gr. 3 up). lib. bdg. 22.60 (978-0-7565-0312-3(4)) Compass Point Bks.

Herold, Vickey. A Cattle Town: Forth Worth. 2006. pap. 39.00 (***978-1-4108-6427-7(8)***) Benchmark Education Co.

Holt, Rinehart and Winston Staff. Holt Texas: Chapter Summary Overhead Transparencies. 3rd ed. 2002. trans. 141.46 (978-0-03-073208-9(5)) Holt, Rinehart & Winston.

—Taks Every Day! Activities for Holt Texas. 3rd ed. 2002. (Illus.). pap. 45.60 (978-0-03-065706-1(7)) Holt, Rinehart & Winston.

Houston Gold C 2005. 2004. 452p. (YA). pap. 15.00 (978-1-58553-954-3(6) , 05GC0008) Entertainment Publications, Inc.

Kent, Deborah. Dallas. 2001. (Cities of the World Ser.). (Illus.). 64p. (YA). (gr. 4-9). pap. 9.95 (978-0-516-27168-2(7) , Children's Pr.) Scholastic Library Publishing.

—Dallas. 2000. (gr. 5-8). lib. bdg. 18.75 (978-0-613-51485-9(8)) Tandem Library Bks.

Levy, Janey. Juneteenth: Celebrating the End of Slavery. 2003. (Reading Room Collection). (Illus.). 24p. (J). lib. bdg. 18.75 (978-0-8239-3711-0(9)) Rosen Publishing Group, Inc., The.

Lomas Garza, Carmen. In My Family. 2000. Tr. of En Mi Familia. (Illus.). (J). 14.75 (978-0-606-18039-9(7)) Tandem Library Bks.

—In My Family (En Mi Familia) Lomas Garza, Carmen, illus. 2000. (ENG & SPA., Illus.). 32p. (J). (gr. 1-4). pap. 7.95 (978-0-89239-163-9(4)) Children's Bk. Pr.

Marsh, Carole. My First Book about Texas. 2000. (Texas Experience! Ser.). (Illus.). 32p. (J). (gr. k-4). pap. 7.95 (978-0-7933-9527-9(5)) Gallopade International.

—Texas Classic Christmas Trivia. 2002. (Carole Marsh Texas Bks.). (Illus.). 32p. pap. 6.95 (978-0-635-01451-1(3) , 14513); lib. bdg. 21.95 (978-0-635-01452-8(1) , 14521) Gallopade International. (Marsh, Carole Bks.).

—Texas Current Events Projects: 30 Cool, Activities, Crafts, Experiments & More for Kids to Do to Learn about Your State! 2003. (Texas Experience Ser.). 32p. (gr. k-5). pap. 5.95 (978-0-635-02062-8(9) , Marsh, Carole Bks.) Gallopade International.

—The Texas Experience Pocket Guide. 2000. (Texas Experience! Ser.). (Illus.). 96p. (J). (gr. 3-8). pap. 6.95 (978-0-7933-9455-5(4)) Gallopade International.

—Texas Geography Projects: 30 Cool, Activities, Crafts, Experiments & More for Kids to Do to Learn about Your State! 2003. (Texas Experience Ser.). 32p. (gr. k-5). pap. 5.95 (978-0-635-01861-8(6) , Marsh, Carole Bks.) Gallopade International.

—Texas Government Projects: 30 Cool, Activities, Crafts, Experiments & More for Kids to Do to Learn about Your State! 2003. (Texas Experience Ser.). 32p. (gr. k-5). pap. 5.95 (978-0-635-01962-2(0) , Marsh, Carole Bks.) Gallopade International.

—Texas Jeopardy! Answers & Questions about Our State! 2000. (Texas Experience! Ser.). (Illus.). 32p. (J). (gr. 3-8). pap. 7.95 (978-0-7933-9528-6(3)); pap. 7.95 (978-0-7933-9529-3(1)) Gallopade International.

—Texas People Projects: 30 Cool, Activities, Crafts, Experiments & More for Kids to Do to Learn about Your State! 2003. (Texas Experience Ser.). 32p. (gr. k-5). pap. 5.95 (978-0-635-02012-3(2) , Marsh, Carole Bks.) Gallopade International.

—Texas Symbols & Facts Projects: 30 Cool, Activities, Crafts, Experiments & More for Kids to Do to Learn about Your State! 2003. (Texas Experience Ser.). 32p. (gr. k-5). pap. 5.95 (978-0-635-01912-7(4) , Marsh, Carole Bks.) Gallopade International.

—The Totally Texas Coloring Book. 2000. (Texas Experience! Ser.). (Illus.). 32p. (J). (gr. k-2). pap. 3.95 (978-0-7933-9475-3(9)) Gallopade International.

McAdam, Claudia Cangilla & Reynolds, Richard. Do You See What I See? 2007. (J). 14.95 (***978-1-56579-589-1(X)***) Westcliffe Pubs.

McAuliffe, Emily. Texas: Facts & Symbols. 1998. (States & Their Symbols Ser.). 24p. (J). lib. bdg. 13.75 (978-0-531-11553-4(4) , Watts, Franklin) Scholastic Library Publishing.

—Texas Facts & Symbols. rev. ed. 2003. (States & Their Symbols Ser.). 24p. (J). lib. bdg. 19.93 (978-0-7368-1764-6(6)) Capstone Pr., Inc.

TUV

McNamara, Connie. My First University of Texas Words. 2004. (J). bds. 11.95 (978-0-9759703-4-8(8)) Shamrock Publishing, Inc.

McNeil, Niki, et al. HOCPP 1120 Texas. 2006. spiral bd. 24.00 (***978-1-60308-120-7(8)***) In the Hands of a Child.

Mitchell-Burnett, Carolyn. The Sites & Sounds of Texas. 2001. (J). 15.95 (978-1-57168-198-0(1)) Eakin Pr.

Morris, Deborah. Real Kids Real Adventures in Texas: Blanco River Rescue. 2002. (gr. k-3). lib. bdg. 17.60 (978-0-613-87965-1(1)) Tandem Library Bks.

Murray, Julie. Texas. 2006. (Illus.). 32p. (J). (gr. k-4). lib. bdg. 22.78 (978-1-59197-702-5(9) , Buddy Bks.) ABDO Publishing Co.

Obregon, Jose Maria. Texas. de Leon, Mauricio Velazquez, tr. 2005. (Bilingual Library of the United States of America: Set 1). (ENG & SPA., Illus.). 32p. (J). (gr. 2-5). lib. bdg. 22.50 (978-1-4042-3109-2(9) , Buenas Letra) Rosen Publishing Group, Inc., The.

Parker, Janice. A Guide to Texas. 2000. (American States Ser.). (Illus.). 32p. (J). (gr. 3-7). lib. bdg. 16.95 (978-1-930954-40-3(9)) Weigl Pubs., Inc.

Parker, Laurie. Texas Alphabet, 3 vols., Vol. 2. 2000. (State Alphabet Ser.: Vol. 2). (Illus.). 32p. (J). (ps-3). 15.95 (978-1-893062-17-7(1)) Quail Ridge Pr., Inc.

Pelta, Kathy. Texas. 2nd rev. exp. ed. (Hello U. S. A. Ser.). (Illus.). 84p. (J). (gr. 3-6). 2003. pap. 6.95 (978-0-8225-4142-4(4)); 2002. 25.26 (978-0-8225-4064-9(9) , Lerner Pubns.) Lerner Publishing Group.

Pierce, Jill. Meet Little Texas. Colina, Charmaine, illus. 2000. 20p. pap. 7.95 (978-0-87719-356-2(8)) National Bk. Network.

Salch, Megan. 100+ Activities for Houston Kids 2006. 2005. (Illus.). 40p. pap. 19.95 (978-0-9776154-0-7(5)) Salch, Megan F.

Sasek, Miroslav. This Is Texas. 2006. (Illus.). 64p. (J). (gr. k). 17.95 (978-0-7893-1389-8(8) , Prima Games) Random Hse. Information Group.

School Atlas of Texas. 2001. 48p. (J). (gr. 1-12). pap. 9.95 (978-0-87443-129-2(8)) Benson, W. S. & Co., Inc.

Schwartz, Linda. Texas Geodoodles. Grades 4-6: Learning about Texas Through Step-by-Step Drawings. Smith, Stephanie W. & Clark, Kim, eds. Armstrong, Beverly, illus. 2000. 64p. pap., tchr. ed. 9.99 (978-0-88160-352-1(X) , LW-391, Learning Works, The) Creative Teaching Pr., Inc.

Scogginsbauld, Jane. Texas in Bloom: A Wildflower Guide for Children. Waldrup, Gayle, photos by. l.t. ed. 1999. (Illus.). 24p. (J). (ps-3). pap. 14.95 (978-1-929701-00-1(4)) Under the Green Umbrella.

Sievert, Terri. Texas. 2003. (Land of Liberty Ser.). (Illus.). 64p. (J). (gr. 3-4). lib. bdg. 23.93 (978-0-7368-1594-9(5) , Bridgestone Bks.) Capstone Pr., Inc.

Smith, Karla. All Around Texas: Regions & Resources. 2003. (Heinemann State Studies). (Illus.). 48p. (J). lib. bdg. 27.07 (978-1-4034-0686-6(3)) Heinemann Library.

Somervill, Barbara A. Texas. 2008. (J). (***978-0-531-18580-3(X)***) Children's Pr., Ltd.

Texas. 2000. (Switched on Schoolhouse Ser.). (Illus.). (YA). (gr. 7-12). pap. 24.95 incl. cd-rom (978-0-7403-0295-4(7) , SOSTX) Alpha Omega Pubns., Inc.

Wade, Mary Dodson. All Around Texas: Regions & Resources. 2003. (Heinemann State Studies). (Illus.). 48p. (J). pap. 8.50 (978-1-4034-2694-9(5)) Heinemann Library.

—All Around Texas: Regions & Resources. 2003. (gr. 3-6). lib. bdg. 17.05 (978-0-613-88566-9(X)) Tandem Library Bks.

—"T" Is for Texas. Roeder, Virginia M., illus. 2000. (Alpha Flight Bks.). 60p. (J). (ps-3). 17.95 (978-1-892920-28-7(X)) GHB Publishers, LLC.

—Uniquely Texas. 2003. (Heinemann State Studies). (Illus.). 48p. (J). pap. 8.50 (978-1-4034-2699-4(6)); lib. bdg. 27.07 (978-1-4034-0691-0(X)) Heinemann Library.

—Uniquely Texas. 2003. (gr. 3-6). lib. bdg. 17.05 (978-0-613-86890-7(0)) Tandem Library Bks.

Walker, Paul Robert. Remember the Alamo: Texians, Tejanos, & Mexicans Tell Their Stories. 2007. (Illus.). 64p. (J). (gr. 4-8). lib. bdg. 27.90 (978-1-4263-0011-0(5) , National Geographic Children's Bks.) National Geographic Society.

Weintraub, A. How to Draw Texass Sights & Symbols. 2002. (Kids Guide to Drawing America Ser.). 32p. (J). lib. bdg. 25.25 (978-0-8239-6100-9(1) , PowerKids Pr.) Rosen Publishing Group, Inc., The.

Weintraub, Aileen. Texas's Sights & Symbols. 2005. 48p. pap. 8.95 (978-1-4042-8503-3(2)) Rosen Publishing Group, Inc., The.

Willoughby. Texas! 2003. 2001. 86.33 (978-0-03-064678-2(2)) Holt, Rinehart & Winston.

Young, Evan A. Lone Star Justice: A Biography of Justice Tom C. Clark. 1998. (Illus.). 160p. (YA). (gr. 7 up). 12.95 (978-1-885777-11-9(6)) Hendrick-Long Publishing Co.

TEXAS—FICTION

Abernathy, Francis E. How the Critters Created Texas. Sargent, Ben, illus. 2nd rev. ed. 1998. 46p. (J). (gr. 1-6). lib. bdg. 14.95 (978-0-936650-14-2(1)) Temple, Ellen C. Publishing, Inc.

Alter, Judy. Sam Houston Is My Hero. 2003. (Chaparral Book for Young Readers Ser.). 140p. (J). pap. 15.95 (978-0-87565-277-1(8)) Texas Christian Univ. Pr.

Ames, Joseph B. Pete Cow Puncher a Story of the Texas Plains. Perard, Victor, illus. 2005. reprint ed. pap. 31.95 (978-0-7661-9421-2(3)) Kessinger Publishing, LLC.

Anzaldua, Gloria. Prietita & the Ghost Woman. 2001. Tr. of Prietita Y La Llorona. (SPA.). (gr. 3-6). lib. bdg. 16.40 (978-0-613-34419-7(7)) Tandem Library Bks.

Aryal, Aimee. How 'Bout Them Cowboys! Coloring Book. 2007. (YA). pap. 4.95 (***978-1-932888-77-5(2)***) Mascot Bks., Inc.

Bauer, Joan. Rules of the Road. 208p. (gr. 7). 2005. (YA). pap. 7.99 (978-0-14-240425-6(X) , Puffin); 1998. (J). 16.99 (978-0-399-23140-7(4) , Putnam Juvenile) Penguin Group (USA) Inc.

—Rules of the Road. 2000. (YA). (978-0-606-20252-7(8)); 201p. (gr. 7-12). lib. bdg. 13.64 (978-0-606-20370-8(2)) Tandem Library Bks.

Bear Paw. 2001. 180p. (J). per. 11.95 (978-1-891929-63-2(1)) Four Seasons Pubs.

Beecher, Jo. Texas Beau. Quinn, Kenneth M., illus. 1999. 32p. (gr. 3-5). 14.95 (978-1-57168-204-8(X)) Eakin Pr.

Bertrand, Diane Gonzales. Trino's Choice. (Illus.). 128p. (YA). (gr. 5-11). pap., stu. ed. 9.95 (978-1-55885-268-6(9)); 1999. 124p. (J). (gr. 4-7). 16.95 (978-1-55885-279-2(4)) Arte Publico Pr. (Piñata Books).

—Trino's Choice. 1999. (978-0-606-17956-0(9)); (gr. 5-8). lib. bdg. 18.75 (978-0-613-33660-4(7)) Tandem Library Bks.

Booth, Martin. Coyote Moon. 2005. 272p. (J). (gr. 4-6). pap. 8.99 (978-0-552-55001-7(9) , Corgi) Transworld Publishers Ltd. GBR. *Dist:* Independent Pubs. Group.

Borgia, Mary. Tales of the Texas Mermaid: The Boot. 2006. (Illus.). 47p. (J). 17.95 (978-0-9778451-0-1(9)) Goretti Publishing.

Borgia, Mary. Tales of the Texas Mermaid: The Charro. 2007. (J). 17.95 (***978-0-9778451-1-8(7)***) Goretti Publishing.

Borntrager, Mary Christner. Polly. l.t. ed. 2002. 165p. (J). 25.95 (978-0-7862-4030-2(X)) Thomson Gale.

Brett, Jan. Armadillo Rodeo. Brett, Jan, illus. 2002. (Illus.). (J). 23.64 (978-0-7587-1968-3(X)) Book Wholesalers, Inc.

—Armadillo Rodeo. Brett, Jan, illus. 2004. (Illus.). 32p. (J). (ps-1). pap. 6.99 (978-0-14-240125-5(0) , Puffin) Penguin Group (USA) Inc.

Byers, Rob. The Adventures of Pork & Bean. 2006. (ENG.). 124p. (J). per. 13.99 (***978-1-4141-0769-1(2)***) Pleasant Word.

Canales, Viola. The Tequila Worm. 208p. (YA). (gr. 7-11). 2007. pap. 7.99 (978-0-375-84089-0(3)); 2005. 15.95 (978-0-385-74674-8(1)); 2005. 17.99 (978-0-385-90905-1(5)) Random Hse. Children's Bks. (Lamb, Wendy).

Carey, Mary. Two for Texas: The Extraordinary Story of Kian & Jane Long. Finney, Pat, illus. 1999. 88p. 14.95 (978-1-57168-292-5(9)) Eakin Pr.

Casad, Mary Brooke. Bluebonnet at Johnson Space Center. Vincent, Benjamin, illus. 2003. 32p. pap. 7.95 (978-1-58980-101-1(6)) Pelican Publishing Co., Inc.

Casad, Mary Brooke & Brooke Casad, Mary. Bluebonnet at the East Texas Oil Museum. Vincent, Benjamin, illus. 2005. 32p. (J). (gr. k-3). per. 15.95 (978-1-58980-358-9(2)) Pelican Publishing Co., Inc.

Cherry, Lynne. Armadillo from Amarillo. 1999. (gr. k-3). lib. bdg. 14.15 (978-0-613-18298-0(7)) Tandem Library Bks.

Chrismer, Melanie. Phoebe Clappsaddle & The Tumbleweed Gang. Roeder, Virginia M., illus. 2002. 32p. (J). 14.95 (978-1-56554-966-1(X)) Pelican Publishing Co., Inc.

—Phoebe Clappsaddle for Sheriff. Roeder, Virginia M., illus. 2003. 32p. (J). pap. 14.95 (978-1-58980-127-1(X)) Pelican Publishing Co., Inc.

—Phoebe Clappsaddle Has a Tumbleweed Christmas. Roeder, Virginia M., illus. 2004. 32p. (J). 15.95 (978-1-58980-241-4(1)) Pelican Publishing Co., Inc.

Christian, Diana. The Lucky Seven. 2005. 71p. pap. 14.95 (978-1-4137-5471-1(6)) PublishAmerica, Inc.

Clifton Wisler, G. All for Texas. 2004. 140p. (J). lib. bdg. 16.92 (***978-1-4242-0767-1(3)***) Fitzgerald Bks.

Crawford, Ann Fears. Keechee: The Witch of the Woods. 2005. (J). (978-1-931823-21-0(9)) Halcyon Pr.

—Vangie: The Ghost of the Pines. 2002. 142p. (J). 17.95 (978-1-57168-710-4(6) , Eakin Pr.) Eakin Pr.

Crowley, Suzanne Carlisle. The Very Ordered Existence of Merilee Marvelous. 2007. (J). (gr. 5 up). 256p. 16.99 (***978-0-06-123197-1(5)***); 384p. lib. bdg. 17.89 (***978-0-06-123198-8(3)***) HarperCollins Pubs. (Greenwillow Bks.).

Cuate, Melodie A. Journey to San Jacinto. 2007. (Illus.). 160p. (J). 17.95 (***978-0-89672-602-4(9)***) Texas Tech Univ. Pr.

Davis, David. Texas Zeke & the Longhorn. Stacey, Alan, illus. 2006. 32p. (J). 15.95 (978-1-58980-348-0(5)) Pelican Publishing Co., Inc.

Dean, Carolee. Comfort. (J). (gr. 7 up). 2004. 256p. pap. 6.99 (978-0-618-43912-6(9) , Graphia); 2002. 240p. 15.00 (978-0-618-13846-3(3)) Houghton Mifflin Co. Trade & Reference Div.

Dearen, Patrick. Comanche Peace Pipe. 2001. (gr. k-3). lib. bdg. 17.60 (978-0-613-86879-2(X)) Tandem Library Bks.

—Comanche Peace Pipe. 2001. (Lone Star Heroes Ser.). 128p. (ps-3). pap. 8.95 (978-1-55622-831-5(7) , Republic of Texas Pr.) Wordware Publishing, Inc.

—Hidden Treasure of the Chisos. 2001. (gr. 3-6). lib. bdg. 17.60 (978-0-613-83165-9(9)) Tandem Library Bks.

—The Hidden Treasure of the Chisos, Bk. 3. 2001. (Lone Star Heroes Ser.). 117p. pap. 8.95 (978-1-55622-829-2(5) , Republic of Texas Pr.) Wordware Publishing, Inc.

—On the Pecos Trail. 2001. (gr. 3-6). lib. bdg. 17.60 (978-0-613-83166-6(7)) Tandem Library Bks.

—On the Pecos Trail. 2001. (Lone Star Heroes Ser.). 128p. (gr. 4-7). pap. 8.95 (978-1-55622-830-8(9) , Republic of Texas Pr.) Wordware Publishing, Inc.

Dell, Pamela. Blood in the Water: A Story of Friendship During the Mexican War. 2003. (Scrapbooks of America Ser.). (Illus.). 48p. (J). (gr. 2-6). 28.50 (978-1-59187-042-5(9)) Child's World, Inc.

DuCharme, Dede Fox. The Treasure in the Tiny Blue Tin. 1998. (Chaparral Books for Young Readers). 144p. (J). (gr. 5-8). pap. 11.95 (978-0-87565-180-4(1)) Texas Christian Univ. Pr.

Edgell, Ernest. The Cowbears of Texas: The Hero. Haycraft, Marilynn J., illus. 2004. 25p. pap. 14.95 (978-1-4137-3507-9(X)) PublishAmerica, Inc.

Ellis, Tacy. Goat Tales: Stories of Izzy & Her Friends. Collins, Don, illus. 2006. 128p. (J). 17.95 (978-1-931721-78-3(5)) Bright Sky Pr.

Ellsberry, Sharon. The Spaniel Family Goes to the State Fair. Espinosa, Chris, illus. 2004. 24p. (J). 9.00 (978-0-9724637-2-0(0)) Sky Rocket Pr.

Enderle, Dotti. The Cotton Candy Catastrophe at the Texas State Fair. Galey, Chuck, illus. 2004. 32p. (J). pap. 15.95 (978-1-58980-189-9(X)) Pelican Publishing Co., Inc.

Enderle, Dottie. Granny Gert & the Bunion Brothers. Kulka, Joe, illus. 2006. 32p. (J). (gr. k-3). 15.95 (978-1-58980-373-2(6)) Pelican Publishing Co., Inc.

Epner, Paul. Herbert Hilligan's Lone Star Adventure, Vol. 4. Kuon, Vuthy & Nguyen, Duke, illus. 2002. (Herbert Hilligan Ser.). 15.95 (978-1-57168-678-7(9)) Eakin Pr.

—Herbert Hilligan's Lone Star Adventure. Kuon, Vuthy & Nguyen, Duke, illus. 2003. 32p. (J). 15.95 (978-0-9743335-3-3(0)) Imaginative Publishing, Ltd.

Erdman, Loula Grace. The Wind Blows Free: A Tale of the Texas Panhandle. 2006. (Living History Library). 288p. (J). pap. 12.95 (***978-1-932350-09-8(8)***) Bethlehem Bks.

Erickson, John R. The Case of the Blazing Sky, No. 51. Holmes, Gerald L., illus. 2008. (Hank the Cowdog Ser.). 144p. (J). (gr. 3). 5.99 (***978-0-14-241015-8(2)***, Puffin) Penguin Group (USA) Inc.

—The Case of the Blazing Sky #51. Holmes, Gerald L., illus. 2008. (Hank the Cowdog Ser.). 144p. (J). (gr. 3). 15.99 (***978-0-670-06260-7(X)***, Viking Juvenile) Penguin Group (USA) Inc.

Erickson, John R. Moonshiner's Gold. (J). (gr. 5). 2003. (Illus.). 208p. 7.99 (978-0-14-250023-1(2) , Puffin); 2001. 176p. 15.99 (978-0-670-03502-1(5) , Viking Juvenile) Penguin Group (USA) Inc.

—Moonshiner's Gold. 2003. 199p. (J). (gr. 5-8). lib. bdg. 15.30 (978-0-613-61644-7(8)) Tandem Library Bks.

Estevis, Anne. Down Garrapata Road. 128p. pap. 12.95 (978-1-55885-397-3(9)) Arte Publico Pr.

Farish, Terry. The Cat Who Liked Potato Soup. Root, Barry, illus. 40p. (J). (gr. 1). 2007. pap. 6.99 (978-0-7636-3297-7(X)); 2003. 16.99 (978-0-7636-0834-7(3)) Candlewick Pr.

Fern, Tracey E. Buffalo Music. Castillo, Lauren, illus. 2008. 32p. (J). 16.00 (***978-0-618-72341-6(2)***, Clarion Bks.) Houghton Mifflin Co. Trade & Reference Div.

Fitzgibbon, Diana. Somewhere in Texas. Gonzales, Diana, ed. Del Toro, Mark, illus. 2004. 32p. (J). (978-0-9747587-0-1(1)) Mike-Auri Bks.

Flores, Carlos Nicolas. Our House on Hueco. 2006. 248p. (YA). pap. 17.95 (978-0-89672-573-7(1)) Texas Tech Univ. Pr.

Ford, Christine. Scout. 2007. 224p. (J). (gr. 4-7). pap. 5.50 (***978-0-440-42041-5(5)***, Yearling) Random Hse. Children's Bks.

Gaard, Betty. Jericho Ride. 2003. (Illus.). 165p. (J). pap. (978-1-57924-968-7(X)) Jones, Bob Univ. Pr.

Gamble, Adam. Good Night Texas. Hansen, Red, illus. 2007. (Good Night Our World Ser.). 20p. (J). bds. 9.95 (***978-1-60219-015-3(1)***) Our World of Books.

Gardiner, Lorisa Garcia. Nacho Muchacho! Boy of the Valley, 2 bks. 2002. 174p. (J). per. (978-0-9724251-9-3(5)) Aenor Trust, The.

Garza, Xavier. Creepy Creatures & Other Cucuys. 2004. (Illus.). 144p. pap. 9.95 (978-1-55885-410-9(X) , Piñata Books) Arte Publico Pr.

Gilstrap, Robert. We're Going to Hollywood! 2005. 111p. pap. 16.95 (978-1-4137-5378-3(7)) PublishAmerica, Inc.

Gipson, Fred. Old Yeller. Date not set. 192p. (J). 20.95 (978-0-8488-2273-6(0)) Amereon LTD.

—Old Yeller. 2001. 132p. (J). (ps-7). lib. bdg. 16.45 (978-0-613-85744-4(5)) Tandem Library Bks.

—Old Yeller. 1999. (J). lib. bdg. 21.95 (978-1-56723-204-2(3)) Yestermorrow, Inc.

Gipson, Fred & Polson, Steven. Old Yeller. 2001. (Perennial Classics Ser.). (Illus.). 144p. (gr. 4-7). pap. 8.00 (978-0-06-093547-4(2)) HarperCollins Pubs.

Gipson, Frederick. Old Yeller. Burger, Carl, illus. 2002. 14.47 (978-0-7587-0299-9(X)) Book Wholesalers, Inc.

Gonzales Bertrand, Diane, et al. Close to the Heart. 2002. (Illus.). 176p. (J). pap. 9.95 (978-1-55885-319-5(7) , Piñata Books) Arte Publico Pr.

Greene, Thomas J. I Want to Be a Texas Aggie. Pankey, Jill, illus. 1999. 28p. (J). (ps-2). 15.95 (978-0-9670607-0-5(2)) Chalk Stream Publishing.

Griffin, Kitty & Combs, Kathy. The Foot-Stomping Adventures of Clementine Sweet. Wohnoutka, Mike, tr. Wohnoutka, Mike, illus. 2004. 32p. (J). (gr. k-3). tchr. ed. 15.00 (978-0-618-24746-2(7) , Clarion Bks.) Houghton Mifflin Co. Trade & Reference Div.

—Stinker & the Onion Princess. Manders, John, illus. 2005. (J). (978-0-8037-2976-6(6) , Dial) Penguin Group (USA) Inc.

Guzman, Lila. Green Slime & Jam. Guzman, Lila, illus. 2001. (Illus.). v, 168p. (J). pap. 11.95 (978-1-57168-555-1(3) , Eakin Pr.) Eakin Pr.

—Green Slime & Jam. Guzman, Jenny, illus. 2001. 174p. 16.95 (978-1-57168-483-7(2)) Eakin Pr.

Hale, Marian. The Truth about Sparrows. rev. ed 2004. (Illus.). 272p. (J). 16.95 (978-0-8050-7584-7(4) , Holt, Henry & Co. Bks. For Young Readers) Holt, Henry & Co.

—The Truth about Sparrows. 2007. 288p. (J). pap. 6.99 (***978-0-312-37133-3(0)***) Square Fish.

Harper, Jo. Como los Perros de la Pradera. 2000. (SPA.). (gr. k-3). lib. bdg. 17.60 (978-0-613-32422-9(6)) Tandem Library Bks.

—Delfino's Journey. 2000. viii, 184p. (J). (gr. 8-12). 15.95 (978-0-89672-437-2(9)) Texas Tech Univ. Pr.

—Delfino's Journey, Grades 8-12. 2000. (Illus.). viii, 184p. (J). tchr. ed. 5.95 (978-0-89672-442-6(5)) Texas Tech Univ. Pr.

—Jalapeno Hal. Harris, Jennifer Beck, illus. Date not set. 40p. (gr. 4). 8.95 (978-1-57168-206-2(6)) Eakin Pr.

—Mayor Jalapeno Hal from Presidio, Texas. 2003. (Illus.). (J). (978-1-57168-767-8(X) , Eakin Pr.) Eakin Pr.

Harper, Jo & Harper, Josephine. Prairie Dog Pioneers. Spearing, Craig, illus. 48p. (J). (ps-3). 2000. pap. 8.95 (978-1-890515-23-2(X)); 1998. (SPA.). 16.95 (978-1-890515-10-2(8)) Turtle Bks.

Harper, Jo & Harper, Josephine L. Prairie Dog Pioneers. Spearing, Craig, illus. 2000. 44p. (J). (ps-3). lib. bdg. 17.60 (978-0-613-32966-8(X)) Tandem Library Bks.

Harper, Josephin & Harper, Jo. Teresa's Journey. 2006. 192p. (YA). pap. 17.95 (978-0-89672-591-1(X)) Texas Tech Univ. Pr.

Hees, Miriam. The Adventures of Jilly & Brad: Noises in the Attic. Kinneman, D. Michael, illus. 2003. 128p. (J). pap. 5.95 (978-0-9718348-4-2(9)) Blooming Tree Pr.

Henderson, Aileen Kilgore. The Treasure of Panther Peak. Coyle, Mark, illus. 1998. 160p. (J). (gr. 3-8). pap. 6.95 (978-1-57131-619-6(1)) Milkweed Editions.

Herbert Hilligan & His Magical Adventure Curriculum Guide. 2004. ring bd. 24.95 (978-0-9743335-4-0(9)) Imaginative Publishing, Ltd.

Herbert Hilligan's Lone Star Adventure Curriculum Guide. 2004. ring bd. 24.95 (978-0-9743335-7-1(3)) Imaginative Publishing, Ltd.

Hergenrader, Christina. Double Shift. 2004. 208p. (J). 6.99 (978-0-7586-0716-4(4)) Concordia Publishing Hse.

Hest, Amy. The Private Notebook of Katie Roberts, Age 11. Lamut, Sonja, illus. ed. 2005. 192p. (J). (gr. 4-7). 10.99 (978-0-7636-2698-3(8)) Candlewick Pr.

Higman, Anita. The Living Darkness: Texas Caves. 2nd ed. 2003. (Illus.). xiii, 93p. (J). (978-1-57168-783-8(1) , Eakin Pr.) Eakin Pr.

—Texas Twisters. 1999. (Illus.). 64p. 13.95 (978-1-57168-316-8(X)) Eakin Pr.

Hill, William. The Vampire Hunters. 286p. (YA). (gr. 7-12). 2004. 19.95 (978-1-890611-05-7(0)); 1999. pap. 12.95 (978-1-890611-02-6(6)) Otter Creek Pr., Inc.

—The Vampire Hunters Stalked. 2006. 350p. (J). 24.95 (***978-1-890611-41-5(7)***) Otter Creek Pr., Inc.

Hill, William. Vampires Stalked. 2006. (Illus.). 331p. (J). pap. 14.95 (978-1-890611-42-2(5)) Otter Creek Pr., Inc.

Holt, Kimberly Willis. Dancing in Cadillac Light. 2002. 176p. (J). (gr. 5 up). pap. 5.99 (978-0-698-11970-3(3) , Putnam Juvenile) Penguin Group (USA) Inc.

—Dancing in Cadillac Light. 2004. 176p. (J). (gr. 4-7). pap. 36.00 incl. audio (978-0-8072-2095-5(7) , Listening Library) Random Hse. Audio Publishing Group.

—Dancing in Cadillac Light. 2002. (gr. 5-8). lib. bdg. 14.15 (978-0-613-66873-6(1)) Tandem Library Bks.

—When Zachary Beaver Came to Town. rev. ed. 1999. 240p. (YA). (gr. 5-9). 17.95 (978-0-8050-6116-1(9) , Holt, Henry & Co. Bks. For Young Readers) Holt, Henry & Co.

—When Zachary Beaver Came to Town. 2000. (J). tchr. ed. 9.95 (978-1-58130-674-3(1)); (YA), stu. ed. 11.95 (978-1-58130-675-0(X)) Novel Units, Inc.

—When Zachary Beaver Came to Town. unabr. ed. 2004. 227p. (J). (gr. 5-9). pap. 36.00 incl. audio (978-0-8072-8394-3(0) , Listening Library) Random Hse. Audio Publishing Group.

—When Zachary Beaver Came to Town. (gr. 5 up). 2003. (Illus.). 256p. (YA). mass mkt. 6.50 (978-0-440-23841-6(2) , Laurel Leaf); 2001. 240p. (J). pap. 6.50 (978-0-440-22904-9(9) , Yearling) Random Hse. Children's Bks.

—When Zachary Beaver Came to Town. 2003. (gr. 5-8). lib. bdg. 14.15 (978-0-613-72251-3(5)); 2000. (J). (978-0-606-20113-1(0)); 2000. (J). (978-0-606-20114-8(9)) Tandem Library Bks.

—When Zachary Beaver Came to Town. l.t. ed. 2000. 224p. (YA). 22.95 (978-0-7862-2515-6(7)) Thorndike Pr.

Holt, Rinehart and Winston Staff. A Paradise Called Texas: With Connections. 2001. 14.64 (978-0-03-064737-6(1)); pap., stu. ed. 13.16 (978-0-03-064736-9(3)) Holt, Rinehart & Winston.

Horan, Evelyn. Jeannie, a Texas Frontier Girl. 2002. 149p. pap. 14.95 (978-1-59129-750-5(8)) PublishAmerica, Inc.

How 'Bout Them Cowboys! 2007. (J). 17.95 (***978-1-932888-90-4(X)***) Mascot Bks., Inc.

Howard, Jo Ann. The Little Boy Who Made a Difference. 2001. 41p. per. 8.95 (978-0-7414-0575-3(X)) Infinity Publishing.

Inagaki, Riichiro. Eyeshield 21, Volume 12. 2007. (Eyeshield 21 Ser.). 208p. (YA). pap. 7.99 (978-1-4215-1061-3(8)) Viz Media.

—Eyeshield 21, Volume 13. 2007. (Eyeshield 21 Ser.). 216p. (YA). pap. 7.99 (978-1-4215-1062-0(6)) Viz Media.

Ingold, Jeanette. Window. 2003. (gr. 7-12). lib. bdg. 8.10 (978-0-613-70529-5(7)) Tandem Library Bks.

Jackson, Sarah. Preep of Old Washington Square: A Collection of East Texas Tales. Jenkins, Delores, illus. l.t. ed. 2005. 48p. (J). 16.95 (978-1-931823-25-8(1)) Halcyon Pr., Ltd.

Janke, Katelan. Survival in the Storm: The Dust Bowl Diary of Grace Edwards. 2002. (Dear America Ser.). (Illus.). 192p. (J). (gr. 4-9). pap. 10.95 (978-0-439-21599-2(4)) Scholastic, Inc.

Jones, Martha Tannery. Terror from the Gulf: A Hurricane in Galveston. 1999. (Illus.). 134p. (YA). (gr. 4-7). 17.95 (978-1-885777-21-8(3)) Hendrick-Long Publishing Co.

Kahn, Lisa. The Calf Who Fell in Love with a Wolf: And Other Calf Stories from Round Top, Texas. von Schweinitz, Helga, tr. from GER. 1999. (J). (978-1-57168-346-5(1) , Eakin Pr.) Eakin Pr.

Karr, Kathleen. Exiled: Memoirs of a Camel. 2006. 240p. (J). pap. 6.95 (978-0-7614-5291-1(5)) Cavendish, Marshall Corp.

Kelton, Elmer. Cloudy in the West. 1999. (gr. 7-12). lib. bdg. 14.15 (978-0-613-28796-8(7)) Tandem Library Bks.

Kerr, Rita. The Good Old Days. 1999. (Illus.). 120p. 13.95 (978-1-57168-362-5(3)) Eakin Pr.

Ketteman, Helen. Shoeshine Whittaker. Goto, Scott, illus. 1999. 32p. (J). (gr. k-3). lib. bdg. 16.85 (978-0-8027-8715-6(0)) Walker & Co.

Kimmel, Eric A. The Lady in the Blue Cloak: Legends from the Texas Missions. Guevera, Susan, illus. 2005. 40p. (J). 16.95 (978-0-8234-1738-4(7)) Holiday Hse., Inc.

Komechak, Marilyn Gilbert. Paisano Pete: Snake-Killer Bird. 2003. (Illus.). 100p. (J). 9.95 (978-1-57168-770-8(X), Eakin Pr.) Eakin Pr.

Krueger, Kathryn L. Road to Grandma's House. 2005. 128p. pap. 13.95 (978-1-59800-366-6(6)) Outskirts Press, Inc.

Kutchinski, Marjorie. Liberty, Justice & F'Rall: The Dog Heroes of the Texas Republic. 1998. 152p. (gr. k-5). 15.95 (978-1-57168-217-8(1)) Eakin Pr.

Lake, Julie. Galveston's Summer of the Storm. 2003. (Chaparral Book for Young Readers Ser.). 210p. 16.95 (978-0-87565-272-6(7)) Texas Christian Univ. Pr.

Landrey, Wanda A. The Ghost of Spindletop Hill. 2000. (Illus.). 144p. (J). 15.95 (978-1-57168-449-3(2)) Eakin Pr.

Laronde, Gary, illus. Hector Visits His Country Cousin, Vol. 3. 2002. 25p. 14.95 (978-1-57168-601-5(0)); 7.95 (978-1-57168-676-3(2)) Eakin Pr.

Lewis, Preston. Blanca Is My Name: Or, How I Saved the Buffalo on the Texas Plains. Eckhardt, Jason C., illus. 2002. (Animal Legends Ser.: Vol. 2). 188p. 15.95 (978-1-57168-699-2(1)); 9.95 (978-1-57168-700-5(9)) Eakin Pr.

—They Called Me Old Blue: Or How I Helped Charles Goodnight Invent the Chuck Wagon. 2001. (Illus.). 188p. 17.95 (978-1-57168-493-6(X)); 12.95 (978-1-57168-636-7(3)) Eakin Pr.

Liles, Maurine W. Dona Maria, la Ranchera. 2000. (Illus.). 144p. 15.95 (978-1-57168-381-6(X)) Eakin Pr.

Literature Connections English: ... & the Earth Did Not Devour Him. 2004. (gr. 6-12). (978-0-395-77139-6(0), 2-70217) McDougal Littell Inc.

Literature Connections Spanish: ... y No se lo Trago la Tierra (... & the Earth Did Not Devour Him) 2004. (gr. 6-12). (978-0-395-84376-5(6), 2-70789) McDougal Littell Inc.

Love, D. Anne. I Remember the Alamo. 1999. 156p. (J). (gr. 3-7). tchr. ed. 15.95 (978-0-8234-1426-0(4)) Holiday Hse., Inc.

—Picture Perfect. 2007. (YA). 304p. (gr. 7 up). 16.99 (978-0-689-87390-4(5)); 291p. (***978-1-4287-3275-9(6)***) Simon & Schuster Children's Publishing. (McElderry, Margaret K.).

Mackey, Weezie Kerr. Throwing a Like Girl. 2007. 272p. (J). (gr. 7 up). 16.99 (***978-0-7614-5342-0(3)***) Cavendish, Marshall Corp.

Martin, LaJoyce. The Silver Ghost. 2004. (Illus.). 161p. (J). pap. 9.99 (978-1-56722-643-0(4)) Word Aflame Pr.

Martínez, Arturo O. Pedrito's World. 2007. (Illus.). 160p. (J). 16.95 (***978-0-89672-600-0(2)***) Texas Tech Univ. Pr.

Marusak, Elaine. Truly Tales & Girl Fish Stories. 2006. 93p. pap. 14.95 (978-1-4241-3244-7(4)) PublishAmerica, Inc.

Marusak, Elaine Truly. Truly Tales: Aunt Gertie & Uncle George's Haunted House. 2007. (ENG.). 84p. per. 14.95 (***978-1-4241-5959-8(8)***) PublishAmerica, Inc.

McAdoo, Grami. Adventures of Sergeant Socks: The Journey Home. 2003. (gr. 5-8). lib. bdg. 18.75 (978-0-613-85568-6(X)) Tandem Library Bks.

McMahon, P. J. The Case of the Psychic Hamster. 2005. (Freaky Joe Club Ser.: No. 4). (Illus.). 153p. (J). (978-1-4155-7725-7(0), Aladdin) Simon & Schuster Children's Publishing.

—Case of the Psychic Hamster. Manders, John, illus. 2005. 153p. (J). lib. bdg. 15.38 (***978-1-4242-0404-5(6)***) Fitzgerald Bks.

—The Case of the Singing Sea Dragons. 2005. (Freaky Joe Club Ser.: No. 6). (Illus.). 153p. (J). (978-1-4156-4221-4(4), Aladdin) Simon & Schuster Children's Publishing.

—Case of the Singing Sea Dragons. Manders, John, illus. 2005. 153p. (J). lib. bdg. 15.38 (***978-1-4242-0406-9(2)***) Fitzgerald Bks.

—The Mystery of the Diappearing Dinosaurs. 2005. (Illus.). 120p. (J). (***978-1-4156-0778-7(8)***, Aladdin) Simon & Schuster Children's Publishing.

McMurtry, Larry. Duane's Depressed: A Novel. 1999. (Last Picture Show Trilogy: No. 3). (gr. 7-12). lib. bdg. 16.45 (978-0-613-24945-4(3)) Tandem Library Bks.

Mercer, Peggy. Ten Cows to Texas. 2005. (Illus.). 40p. (J). 17.50 (978-1-59354-129-3(5)) Handprint Bks.

—Ten Cows to Texas. Crews, Bill, illus. 2005. 40p. (J). 16.95 (978-1-59354-116-3(3)) Handprint Bks.

Meyer, Carolyn. Jubilee Journey. 2007. (Illus.). 288p. (YA). pap. 6.95 (978-0-15-205845-6(1), Harcourt Paperbacks) Harcourt Children's Bks.

—White Lilacs. 2007. (Illus.). 256p. (YA). pap. 6.95 (978-0-15-205851-7(6), Harcourt Paperbacks) Harcourt Children's Bks.

Michael, Todd. Texas State Bird Beauty Pageant. Randall, Lee Brandt, illus. 2005. 32p. (J). (ps-3). 16.95 (978-1-893062-75-7(9)) Quail Ridge Pr., Inc.

Michaels, Vaughn. Dodi's Prince. Rogers, Jacqueline, illus. 2003. 96p. (J). (gr. 2-5). 15.99 (978-0-525-47034-2(4), Dutton Juvenile) Penguin Group (USA) Inc.

Moore, Martha A. Angels on the Roof. 1999. (J). 11.64 (978-0-606-17346-9(3)) Tandem Library Bks.

—Matchit. 2003. (Illus.). 208p. (J). (gr. 3-7). pap. 4.99 (978-0-440-41716-3(3), Yearling) Random Hse. Children's Bks.

Mora, Pat. Rainbow Tulip. 2003. (gr. k-3). lib. bdg. 15.30 (978-0-613-61653-9(7)) Tandem Library Bks.

Morris, Joyce. Sweet Annie. 2006. pap. 14.99 (***978-1-4259-7159-5(8)***) AuthorHouse.

Myers, Anna. Stolen by the Sea. 2006. 144p. (J). pap. 6.95 (978-0-8027-8976-1(5)) Walker & Co.

Naylor, Phyllis Reynolds. The Healing of Texas Jake. Daniel, Alan, illus. 1998. 128p. (J). (gr. 3-7). pap. 4.50 (978-0-689-82243-8(X), Aladdin) Simon & Schuster Children's Publishing.

Nielson, Ane O. The Lone Star G Brand on My Behind. 2004. (Illus.). 96p. (J). per. 9.95 (978-1-930580-56-5(8), Luminary Media Group) Pine Orchard, Inc.

Nixon, Joan Lowery. Laugh till You Cry. 2004. 112p. (J). (gr. 5). lib. bdg. 17.99 (978-0-385-90186-4(0), Delacorte Bks. for Young Readers) Random Hse. Children's Bks.

—The Trap. 2004. 176p. (J). (gr. 5). pap. 5.50 (978-0-440-22870-7(0), Yearling) Random Hse. Children's Bks.

O'Flatharta, Antoine. Hurry & the Monarch. So, Meilo, illus. 2005. 40p. (J). (gr. k-3). 14.95 (978-0-375-83003-7(0), Knopf Bks. for Young Readers) Random Hse. Children's Bks.

O'Kane, George & McEntee, Bill, illus. Hook Em's Colorful Campus Tour - University of Texas A-Z: Forty Acres (A-Z) 2004. (J). 9.99 (978-1-933069-01-2(5)) Odd Duck Ink, Inc.

Old Yeller. 1999. (J). 9.95 (978-1-56137-081-8(9)) Novel Units, Inc.

Pascal, Francine. The Ruling Class. (YA). 2006. 208p. pap. 8.99 (978-0-689-87333-1(6), Simon Pulse); 2004. 192p. 14.95 (978-0-689-87332-4(8), Simon & Schuster/Paula Wiseman Bks.) Simon & Schuster Children's Publishing.

Paulsen, Gary. The Legend of Bass Reeves. 2006. 160p. (YA). (gr. 7). 15.95 (978-0-385-74661-8(X)); lib. bdg. 17.99 (978-0-385-90898-6(9)) Random Hse. Children's Bks. (Lamb, Wendy).

Pearson, Mary E. A Room on Lorelei Street. rev. ed. 2005. 272p. (YA). 16.95 (978-0-8050-7667-7(0)) Holt, Henry & Co.

Penson, Mary. Billy Bardin & the Witness Tree. 2003. 140p. (J). 11.95 (978-0-87565-283-2(2)) Texas Christian Univ. Pr.

Penson, Mary. Martha Mary Overstreet, M. D. 2007. (Chaparral Book for Young Readers Ser.). 142p. (J). pap. 11.95 (***978-0-87565-345-7(6)***) Texas Christian Univ. Pr.

Perez, L. King. Remember As You Pass Me By. 2007. 224p. (J). (gr. 4-8). 16.95 (***978-1-57131-677-6(9)***) Milkweed Editions.

—Remember as You Pass Me By. 2007. 184p. (J). (gr. 2-7). per. 6.95 (***978-1-57131-678-3(7)***) Milkweed Editions.

Pierotti, Jr. Toward the Setting Sun. 2007. 268p. per. 17.95 (***978-0-595-45469-3(0)***) iUniverse, Inc.

Powers, J. L. The Confessional. 2007. 304p. (gr. 9). (J). 16.99 (***978-0-375-83872-9(4)***); (YA). lib. bdg. 19.99 (***978-0-375-93872-6(9)***) Random Hse. Children's Bks. (Knopf Bks. for Young Readers).

Reynolds, Patrick M. Texas Lore, Vols. 1-4. 2000. (gr. 7-12). lib. bdg. 24.55 (978-0-613-77643-1(7)) Tandem Library Bks.

Rice, David Talbot. Crazy Loco: Stories about Growing up Chicano in Southern Texas. 2003. (gr. 7-12). lib. bdg. 14.15 (978-0-613-67142-2(2)) Tandem Library Bks.

Rice, James. Victor Lopez at the Alamo. 2001. (Illus.). 128p. (J). (gr. 3-7). pap. 12.95 (978-1-56554-866-4(3)) Pelican Publishing Co., Inc.

Rice, Mel. Fire on the Hillside. 2001. (gr. 3-6). lib. bdg. 17.60 (978-0-613-86878-5(1)) Tandem Library Bks.

—Messenger on the Battlefield. 2001. (gr. 3-6). lib. bdg. 17.60 (978-0-613-87964-4(3)) Tandem Library Bks.

—Messenger on the Battlefield. 2001. (Lone Star Heroine Ser.). (Illus.). 106p. (gr. 4-7). pap. 8.95 (978-1-55622-788-2(4), Republic of Texas Pr.) Wordware Publishing, Inc.

—Secrets in the Sky. 2001. (gr. 3-6). lib. bdg. 17.60 (978-0-613-86877-8(3)) Tandem Library Bks.

—Secrets in the Sky. 2001. (Lone Star Heroine Ser.). (Illus.). 116p. (gr. 4-7). pap. 8.95 (978-1-55622-787-5(6), Republic of Texas Pr.) Wordware Publishing, Inc.

Rice, Melinda. Fire on the Hillside. 2001. (Lone Star Heroine Ser.). (Illus.). 108p. (gr. 4-7). pap. 8.95 (978-1-55622-789-9(2), Republic of Texas Pr.) Wordware Publishing, Inc.

—Marooned on the Pirate Coast. 2002. (Lone Star Heroine Ser.: No. 4). 123p. (gr. 4-7). pap. 8.95 (978-1-55622-935-0(6), Republic of Texas Pr.) Wordware Publishing, Inc.

Rinaldi, Ann. Come Juneteenth. 2007. (Great Episodes Ser.). (Illus.). 256p. (YA). 17.00 (978-0-15-205947-7(4)) Harcourt Children's Bks.

Rizzo, Cynthia Marie. Julie & the Unicorn. 2003. 49p. pap. 9.95 (978-1-4137-0785-4(8)) PublishAmerica, Inc.

Roach, Joyce Gibson, tr. Cowgirl of the Rocking R. 2003. (J). (978-0-9726573-0-3(4)) Crosswinds Bks.

Roberts, Diane. Puppet Pandemonium. 128p. (J). (gr. 3-7). 2007. 5.99 (***978-0-440-42096-5(2)***, Yearling); 2006. 15.95 (978-0-385-73309-0(7), Delacorte Bks. for Young Readers); 2006. lib. bdg. 17.99 (978-0-385-90328-8(6), Delacorte Bks. for Young Readers) Random Hse. Children's Bks.

Roberts, Sally A. The Legend of Crystal Lake. (Illus.). 2001. vi, 135p. (J). pap. 10.95 (978-1-57168-557-5(X), Eakin Pr.); 2000. 136p. 16.95 (978-1-57168-369-4(0)) Eakin Pr.

Rogers, Lisa Waller. The Great Storm: The Hurricane Diary of J. T. King, Galveston, Texas, 1900. 2002. (Lone Star Journals). (Illus.). 192p. (J). 14.50 (978-0-89672-478-5(6)) Texas Tech Univ. Pr.

—Remember the Alamo! The Runaway Scrape Diary of Belle Wood. 2003. (Lone Star Journals: Bk. 3). 208p. (J). 15.95 (978-0-89672-497-6(2)) Texas Tech Univ. Pr.

Ruby, Lois. The Moxie Kid. 2002. 218p. 17.95 (978-1-57168-677-0(0)); 2001. iv, 214p. (J). pap. 15.95 (978-1-57168-608-4(8), Eakin Pr.) Eakin Pr.

—Swindletop. 2000. (Illus.). 128p. (J). 15.95 (978-1-57168-393-9(3)) Eakin Pr.

Rumbley, Rose-Mary. What? No Chili? Rowden, Susan, illus. rev. ed. 2000. 144p. (J). (gr. 6-8). pap. 16.95 (978-0-89015-992-7(0)) Eakin Pr.

Sachar, Louis. Holes. 1998. 240p. (J). (gr. 4-7). 17.00 (978-0-374-33265-5(7), Farrar, Straus & Giroux (BYR)) Farrar, Straus & Giroux.

—Holes. 240p. (J). (gr. 4-6). pap. 5.99 (978-0-8072-8073-7(9), Listening Library) Random Hse. Audio Publishing Group.

—Holes. 2000. (Newbery Ser.). (Illus.). 240p. (J). (gr. 5-6). reprint ed. pap. 6.50 (978-0-440-41480-3(6), Yearling) Random Hse. Children's Bks.

—Hoyos. (SPA.). 236p. (YA). (gr. 5-8). (978-84-348-6793-2(1), SM7975) SM Ediciones ESP. *Dist:* Lectorum Pubns., Inc.

—Hoyos. Abos, Elena, tr. 2nd ed. 2005. (Barco de Vapor Ser.). (SPA., Illus.). 240p. (J). (gr. 4-8). 8.95 (978-84-348-7860-0(7), SM5090) SM Ediciones ESP. *Dist:* AIMS International Bks., Inc., Lectorum Pubns., Inc., Iaconi, Mariuccia Bk. Imports.

—Hoyos. 2001. (SPA.). (gr. 5-8). lib. bdg. 16.40 (978-0-613-64523-2(5)) Tandem Library Bks.

Saldana, Rene, Jr. The Jumping Tree. 2002. (Illus.). 192p. (YA). (gr. 5). pap. 5.99 (978-0-440-22881-3(6), Laurel Leaf) Random Hse. Children's Bks.

—Jumping Tree. 2002. (gr. 5-8). lib. bdg. 13.55 (978-0-613-72279-7(5)) Tandem Library Bks.

Sargent, Dave & Sargent, Pat. Grady: (Dappled Grey) Proud to Be an American, 30 vols., Vol. 30. Lenoir, Jane, illus. 2003. (Saddle Up Ser.: Vol. 30). 42p. (J). lib. bdg. 22.60 (978-1-56763-813-4(9)) Ozark Publishing.

—Grady: Proud to Be an American, 30 vols. Lenoir, Jane, illus. 2003. (Saddle Up Ser.: Vol. 30). 42p. (J). pap. 6.95 (978-1-56763-814-1(7)) Ozark Publishing.

Saunders, Susan. Lucky Lady. 2000. 128p. (J). (gr. 4-7). 14.95 (978-0-380-97784-0(2)) HarperCollins Pubs.

Savage, Derek. Cool Cat Goes to Texas. Bustamante, Denny, illus. 2001. (Cool Cat Ser.: Vol. 3). 32p. (J). pap. 9.95 (978-0-9673000-5-4(3)) Savage Bks.

Seals, Hollie. When You Can't Find the Words. 2007. 144p. per. 11.95 (***978-0-595-45023-7(7)***) iUniverse, Inc.

Shefelman, Janice J., et al. Comanche Song. 2000. (Illus.). 256p. (J). (gr. 4-7). 17.95 (978-1-57168-397-7(6)) Eakin Pr.

Simmons, Marc. Jose's Buffalo Hunt: A Story from History. Kil, Ronald R., tr. Kil, Ronald R., illus. 2004. 64p. 17.95 (978-0-8263-3315-5(X)) Univ. of New Mexico Pr.

Smith, Cynthia Leitich. Tantalize. 2007. (Illus.). 336p. (YA). (gr. 9). 16.99 (978-0-7636-2791-1(7)) Candlewick Pr.

Smith, Debra. Hattie Marshall & the Dangerous Fire. 2007. 144p. (J). pap. 7.95 (***978-1-58980-492-0(9)***) Pelican Publishing Co., Inc.

Smith, Debra West. Hattie Marshall & the Prowling Panther. 2005. 144p. (J). 6.95 (978-1-56554-940-1(6)) Pelican Publishing Co., Inc.

Stem, Jacqueline. The Borrowed Grave. Laronde, Gary, illus. 2001. v, 153p. (J). pap. 11.95 (978-1-57168-556-8(1), Eakin Pr.) Eakin Pr.

—The Borrowed Grave, Vol. 3. 2001. (Hollow Tree Mystery Ser.). (Illus.). 160p. 16.95 (978-1-57168-451-6(4)) Eakin Pr.

—Dangerous Games, Vol. 4. Eckhardt, Jason C., illus. 2002. (Hollow Tree Mystery Ser.). 160p. 16.95 (978-1-57168-701-2(7)); 12.95 (978-1-57168-702-9(5)) Eakin Pr.

—The Ghosts of Goliad. 2003. iii, 165p. (J). 17.95 (978-1-57168-785-2(8), Eakin Pr.) Eakin Pr.

—The Haunted Tunnel. 96p. 8.95 (978-1-57168-310-6(0)) Eakin Pr.

—The Secret of Little Creek Farm, Vol. 2. 1999. (Hollow Tree Mystery Ser.). (Illus.). 136p. 14.95 (978-1-57168-293-2(7)) Eakin Pr.

Stephenson, Lynda. Dancing with Elvis. 331p. (YA). 2006. pap. 8.00 (978-0-8028-5300-4(5)); 2005. (gr. 7). 17.00 (978-0-8028-5293-9(9)) Eerdmans, William B. Publishing Co. (Eerdmans Bks For Young Readers).

Stone, B. J. Girl on the Bluff. (Illus.). 160p. 8.95 (978-1-57168-297-0(X)); 1999. 124p. (J). (gr. 4-6). 14.95 (978-1-57168-280-2(5)) Eakin Pr.

Stork, Francisco X. Behind the Eyes. 2006. 256p. (YA). (gr. 9). 16.99 (978-0-525-47735-8(7), Dutton Adult) Penguin Group (USA) Inc.

Tex. 1999. 17p. (YA). (gr. 7-12). 9.95 (978-1-56137-146-4(7), BK8619) Novel Units, Inc.

Tingle, Tim & Moore. Spooky Texas Tales. Miller, Gina, illus. 2005. x, 85p. (J). pap. (978-0-89672-566-9(9)) Texas Tech Univ. Pr.

Tolliver, Ruby C. Sarita, Be Brave. 1999. 144p. (gr. 3-6). 14.95 (978-1-57168-184-3(1)) Eakin Pr.

Torres, David M. A Whooper Named Frank. 1999. (Illus.). 96p. 14.95 (978-1-57168-329-8(1)) Eakin Pr.

Townsend, Tom. Powderhorn Passage. 112p. 9.95 (978-1-57168-433-2(6)) Eakin Pr.

Wallace, Bill. Eye of the Great Bear. 1999. 176p. (J). (gr. 3-6). pap. 9.95 (978-0-671-02502-1(3), Aladdin) Simon & Schuster Children's Publishing.

—Eye of the Great Bear. 1999. (J). 11.64 (978-0-606-19050-3(3)); (gr. 3-6). lib. bdg. 13.00 (978-0-613-21509-1(5)) Tandem Library Bks.

Weihrich, Carroll. On Jim Street. 2003. 144p. 24.50 (978-1-932621-19-8(9)); per. 15.00 (978-1-932621-18-1(0)) Open Bk. Publishing.

White, Tom. Lost in the Texas Desert. 2004. (Illus.). 132p. per. 7.95 (978-0-9753611-0-8(4)) Arlington Pubns.

Whitehead, Kathy. Looking for Uncle Louie on the Fourth of July. Torrecilla, Pablo, illus. 2004. 32p. (J). 15.95 (978-1-59078-061-9(2)) Boyds Mills Pr.

Wilburn, Garlyn Webb. The Donkey Boy. Eckhardt, Jason C., illus. 2002. 207p. (J). 17.95 (978-1-57168-697-8(5), Eakin Pr.); 218p. 12.95 (978-1-57168-698-5(3)) Eakin Pr.

Williams, Lori Aurelia. When Kambia Elaine Flew in from Neptune. unabr. ed. 2004. 246p. (J). (gr. 7 up). pap. 50.00 incl. audio (978-0-8072-8851-1(9), Listening Library) Random Hse. Audio Publishing Group.

—When Kambia Elaine Flew in from Neptune. Louth, Jack, illus. 2001. 256p. (YA). pap. 10.00 (978-0-689-84593-2(6), Simon Pulse) Simon & Schuster Children's Publishing.

—When Kambia Elaine Flew in from Neptune. 2002. (978-0-606-22109-2(3)); 2001. (gr. 7-12). lib. bdg. 18.80 (978-0-613-73307-6(X)) Tandem Library Bks.

Wilsdon, Christina. A Wild Ride in Texas. Jaekel, Susan, illus. 2006. 26p. (J). 7.99 (978-1-59939-011-6(6), Reader's Digest Young Families, Inc.) Reader's Digest Children's Publishing, Inc.

Wilson, Linda Miller. A Few Days Journey. 1998. 124p. (YA). (gr. 4-8). 9.99 (978-0-88092-402-3(0), 4020) Royal Fireworks Publishing Co.

Wilton, Jene, Jr. Little Blue Blessings. 2004. 120p. (J). pap. 11.95 (978-1-58736-295-8(3), Starbound Bks.) Wheatmark.

Wisler, G. Clifton. All for Texas: A Story of Texas Liberation. 2001. (American Portraits Ser.). 140p. (gr. 5-8). 15.32 (978-0-8092-0588-2(2), 9780809205882) Jamestown.

—All for Texas: A Story of Texas Liberation. 2004. (Jamestown's American Portraits Ser.). (Illus.). 144p. (J). (gr. 5-7). pap. 4.95 (978-0-7696-3428-9(1), Waterbird Bks.) School Specialty Publishing.

—All for Texas: A Story of Texas Liberation. 2000. (gr. 5-8). lib. bdg. 15.70 (978-0-613-36169-9(5)) Tandem Library Bks.

Wisler, G. Clifton & McGraw-Hill Staff. All for Texas: A Story of Texas Liberation. 2001. (Jamestown Classics Ser.). 140p. (C). (gr. 5-8). pap. 10.00 (978-0-8092-0629-2(3), 9780809206292) Jamestown.

Woolley, Bryan. Mr. Green's Magnificent Machine. Arbuckle, Scott, illus. 2003. 32p. 15.95 (978-1-57168-606-0(1)) Eakin Pr.

Young, K. A. Man in the Moon. 2001. (Illus.). 120p. (J). per. 10.00 (978-0-9708999-5-8(5)) Whyte Dove Pr.

Ziegler, Jennifer. Alpha Dog. 2006. 336p. (YA). (gr. 7). pap. 7.95 (978-0-385-73285-7(6)); lib. bdg. 9.99 (978-0-385-90302-8(2)) Random Hse. Children's Bks. (Delacorte Bks. for Young Readers).

TEXAS—HISTORY

Alter, Judy. Martin de Leon: Tejano Empresario. Messersmith, Patrick, illus. 2007. 64p. (J). 17.95 (***978-1-933337-08-1(7)***) State Hse. Pr.

—Mirabeau B. Lamar: Second President of Texas. Messersmith, Patrick, illus. 2005. (Stars of Texas Ser.). 72p. (J). (gr. 3-7). 17.95 (978-1-880510-97-1(9)) State Hse. Pr.

—Miriam Ma Ferguson: First Woman Governor of Texas. Messersmith, Patrick, illus. 2006. (Stars of Texas Ser.). 72p. (J). 17.95 (978-1-933337-01-2(X)) State Hse. Pr.

Amberson, Mary Margaret McAllen. A Brave Boy & a Good Soldier: John C. C. Hill & the Texas Expedition to Mier. 2006. (Illus.). 100p. (J). 24.95 (978-0-87611-214-4(9)); pap. 12.95 (978-0-87611-230-4(0)) Texas State Historical Assn.

—A Brave Boy & a Good Soldier: John C. C. Hill & the Texas Expedition to Mier, Educator's Guide. 2006. (Illus.). 24p. tchr.'s training gde. ed. 19.95 (978-0-87611-229-8(7)) Texas State Historical Assn.

Asherman, Robyn. I Lived in Texas Before It Was Texas: A Child's Life at Mission Espada, San Antonio, Texas, 1756. Rizopatron, Marina, ed. 1999. (ENG & SPA., Illus.). 32p. (J). (gr. 1-6). per. 20.00 (978-0-9700418-0-7(2)) Missions & Forts Pr., Inc.

Baker, Karle Wilson. Texas Flag Primer. 2005. reprint ed. pap. 20.95 (978-0-7661-9572-1(4)) Kessinger Publishing, LLC.

Baldridge, Carol. Texas Missions Fact Cards. Tamminga, Jean, illus. 1998. 86p. (J). (gr. 4-8). ring bd. 34.00 (978-1-884925-58-0(8)) Toucan Valley Pubns., Inc.

—Texas Trails Fact Cards. Tamminga, Jean, illus. 2001. 70p. (J). ring bd. 32.00 (978-1-884925-79-5(0)) Toucan Valley Pubns., Inc.

Boraas, Tracey. Sam Houston: Soldier & Statesman. 2002. (Let Freedom Ring Ser.). (Illus.). 48p. (J). (gr. 3-4). lib. bdg. 22.60 (978-0-7368-1350-1(0), Bridgestone Bks.) Capstone Pr., Inc.

Bredeson, Carmen & Dodson Wade, Mary. Texas. 2005. (Celebrate the States Ser.). (Illus.). 144p. (J). (gr. 1-2). lib. bdg. 37.07 (978-0-7614-1736-1(2), Benchmark Bks.) Cavendish, Marshall Corp.

Brennan, Kristine. The Galveston Hurricane. 2002. (Great Disasters, Reforms & Ramifications Ser.). (Illus.). 112p. (J). 30.00 (978-0-7910-6740-6(8), Chelsea Hse.) Facts On File, Inc.

Brown, Jonatha A. Texas. 2005. (Portraits of the States Ser.). (Illus.). 32p. (J). pap. (978-0-8368-4654-6(0)); lib. bdg. 23.33 (978-0-8368-4635-5(4)) Stevens, Gareth Inc.

Bruun, Erik & Peterson, Rick. Texas. 2000. (Illus.). 48p. (J). (gr. 3-7). 9.95 (978-1-57912-102-0(0), 81102) Black Dog & Leventhal Pubs., Inc.

Caravantes, Peggy. American in Texas: The Story of Sam Houston. 2004. (Notable Americans Ser.). (Illus.). 144p. (YA). (gr. 6-12). 23.95 (978-1-931798-19-8(2)) Reynolds, Morgan Inc.

Chipman, Donald & Joseph, Harriett Denise. Explorers & Settlers of Spanish Texas: Men & Women of Spanish Texas. 2001. (Illus.). 272p. (J). (gr. 7-12). pap. 19.95 (978-0-292-71231-7(6)) Univ. of Texas Pr.

Colley, Betty Bailey & Monday, Jane Clements. Tales of the Wild Horse Desert. 2001. (Jack & Doris Smothers Series in Texas History, Life, & Culture: Vol.4). (Illus.). 138p. (J). pap. 19.95 (978-0-292-71241-6(3)) Univ. of Texas Pr.

Dorling Kindersley Publishing Staff. Texas. 2003. (Eyewitness Bks.). (SPA., Illus.). 64p. (J). pap. 15.99 (978-0-7894-9744-4(1)) Dorling Kindersley Publishing, Inc.

Durden-Nelson, Mae. I Just Called Her Momma. 2003. (Illus.). xii, 162p. (J). 18.95 (978-1-57168-714-2(9)) Eakin Pr.

Egan, Tracie. Francisca Alavez, the Angel of Goliad. 2003. (Famous People in American History Ser.). (Illus.). 32p. (J). pap. (978-0-8239-4181-0(7)) Rosen Publishing Group, Inc., The.

Espinosa, Chris & Rawlett, Robert. Rocket Megabyte's Texas Adventure. Espinosa, Chris, illus. (Illus.). 68p. (J). 2004. 14.00 (978-0-9724637-1-3(2)); 2002. per. 10.00 (978-0-9724637-0-6(4)) Sky Rocket Pr.

Eyewitness Staff & Dorling Kindersley Publishing Staff. Texas. 2003. (Eyewitness Bks.). (Illus.). 64p. (J). lib. bdg. 19.99 (978-0-7894-9835-9(9)) Dorling Kindersley Publishing, Inc.

Fehrenbach, T. R. Lone Star: The Story of Texas. 2003. (Illus.). xxxii, 600p. (J). 60.00 (978-0-13-058625-4(0)) Prentice Hall PTR.

Flynn, Jean. Henry B. Gonzalez: Rebel with a Cause. 2003. (Illus.). v, 140p. (J). 16.95 (978-1-57168-780-7(7), Eakin Pr.) Eakin Pr.

Fradin, Dennis B. The Alamo. 2006. (Turning Points in U. S. History Ser.). (Illus.). 48p. (J). (gr. 3-6). lib. bdg. 29.93 (978-0-7614-2127-6(0), Benchmark Bks.) Cavendish, Marshall Corp.

Garland, Sherry. Voices of the Alamo. Himler, Ronald, illus. 2004. 40p. (J). pap. 15.95 (978-1-58980-222-3(5)) Pelican Publishing Co., Inc.

Garza, Carmen Lomas. In My Family. 2000. Tr. of En Mi Familia. (SPA.). (gr. 3-6). lib. bdg. 16.40 (978-0-613-28536-0(0)) Tandem Library Bks.

George, Linda & George, Charles. Texas. 2001. (Seeds of a Nation Ser.). (Illus.). 48p. (J). (gr. 3-5). 26.20 (978-0-7377-0648-2(1), LML00902-178558, Kidhaven) Thomson Gale.

Glass, Andrew, illus. The Legend of Strap Buckner: A Texas Tale. 2001. 32p. (J). (gr. k-3). tchr. ed. 16.95 (978-0-8234-1536-6(8)) Holiday Hse., Inc.

Gregson, Susan R. Sam Houston: Texas Hero. 2005. (Signature Lives Ser.). (Illus.). 112p. (J). (gr. 5-7). (978-0-7565-1004-6(X)) Compass Point Bks.

Guzzetti, Paula. An American Hero: Sam Houston. 1998. (YA). (978-0-7614-0791-1(X), Benchmark Bks.) Cavendish, Marshall Corp.

Haley, James L. Stephen F. Austin & the Founding of Texas. 2005. (Library of American Lives & Times). (Illus.). 112p. (YA). (gr. 4-8). lib. bdg. 31.95 (978-0-8239-5738-5(1)) Rosen Publishing Group, Inc., The.

Hall, M. C. Big Bend National Park. 2005. (Symbols of Freedom Ser.). (Illus.). 32p. (J). (gr. k-2). lib. bdg. 25.36 (978-1-4034-6697-6(1)) Heinemann Library.

Hall, Margaret. Big Bend National Park. 2005. (Heinemann First Library). (Illus.). 32p. (J). pap. (978-1-4034-6704-1(8)) Heinemann Library.

Harcourt School Publishers Staff. TIME for Kids: Texas. 3rd ed. 2002. (Horizontes (Social Studies) Ser.). (SPA., Illus.). Bk. 1. pap. 7.00 (978-0-15-333819-9(9)); Bk. 2. pap. 7.00 (978-0-15-333821-2(0)) Harcourt Schl. Pubs.

Herold, Vickey. Discover a Cattle Town: Forth Worth. 2006. pap. 39.00 (***978-1-4108-6430-7(8)***) Benchmark Education Co.

Holt, Rinehart and Winston Staff. Holt Texas! 3rd ed. 2003. (SPA., Illus.). 83.00 (978-0-03-073767-1(2)) Holt, Rinehart & Winston.

Hughes, Bill. Texas History Coloring Book & Punch Out Playset. 2004. (Illus.). 16p. (J). 4.95 (978-0-9746784-0-5(6)) Hughes, Bill.

Jackson, Jack, text. New Texas History Movies. 2007. (Illus.). 50p. (J). pap. 9.95 (***978-0-87611-223-6(8)***) Texas State Historical Assn.

Jackson, Sarah. A Child's History of Texas. Arbuckle, Scott, illus. 2nd ed. 1999. 56p. 16.95 (978-1-57168-347-2(X)); 11.95 (978-1-57168-356-4(9)) Eakin Pr.

Jackson, Sarah. Preep II: More Tales of Early Texas. Jenkins, Delores, illus. 2007. 48p. (J). 19.95 (***978-1-931823-52-4(9)***) Halcyon Pr., Ltd.

Kelly, Amy. Albany, the Coolest Small Town in Texas: Historic Coloring Book. 2004. (Illus.). 32p. 5.95 (978-1-931721-35-6(1)) Bright Sky Pr.

Kiely Miller, Barbara. Sam Houston. 2007. (J). pap. (***978-0-8368-8323-7(3)***, Weekly Reader Early Learning Library) Stevens, Gareth Inc.

Larson, Erik. Isaac's Storm: A Man, a Time, & the Deadliest Hurricane in History. 2000. 323p. (gr. 7-12). per. 22.25 (978-0-613-29271-9(5)) Tandem Library Bks.

Marsh, Carole. Cowboy Christmas Ball. 2002. (Carole Marsh Bks.). (Illus.). 32p. (gr. 2-6). pap. 6.95 (978-0-635-01355-2(X), 1355X) Gallopade International.

—My First Pocket Guide Texas. 2000. (Texas Experience! Ser.). (Illus.). 96p. (J). (gr. 3-8). 12.95 (978-0-635-01333-0(9), 13339) Gallopade International.

—The Survivor: A Class Challenge. 2001. (Texas Experience! Ser.). (J). lib. bdg. 29.95 (978-0-635-00689-9(8)) Gallopade International.

—Texas History Projects: 30 Cool, Activities, Crafts, Experiments & More for Kids to Do to Learn about Your State! 2003. (Texas Experience Ser.). 32p. (gr. k-5). pap. 5.95 (978-0-635-01812-0(8), Marsh, Carole Bks.) Gallopade International.

—Texas Millionaire. 2001. (GameBook Ser.). 32p. (J). (gr. 3-8). pap., act. bk. ed. 9.95 (978-0-635-00102-3(0)) Gallopade International.

—Texas Survivor. 2001. (GameBook Ser.). 32p. (J). (gr. 3-8). pap., act. bk. ed. 9.95 (978-0-635-00564-9(6)) Gallopade International.

—Wheel of Fortune. 2001. (Texas Experience! Ser.). (J). lib. bdg. 29.95 (978-0-635-00003-3(2)) Gallopade International.

—Who Wants to Be a Millionaire? 2001. (Texas Experience! Ser.). (J). lib. bdg. 29.95 (978-0-635-00103-0(9)) Gallopade International.

Maxwell, Margaret M. Let's Visit Texas Missions. 1998. (Illus.). 64p. (gr. 4-5). 14.95 (978-1-57168-197-3(3)) Eakin Pr.

McAuliffe, Emily. Texas: Facts & Symbols. 1998. (States & Their Symbols Ser.). 24p. (J). lib. bdg. 13.75 (978-0-531-11553-4(4), Watts, Franklin) Scholastic Library Publishing.

McGowen, Tom. The Alamo. (Cornerstones of Freedomtrade;, Second Ser.). 48p. (J). (gr. 4-6). 2007. pap. 5.95 (***978-0-531-18684-8(9)***); 2003. (Illus.). 26.00 (978-0-516-24208-8(3)) Scholastic Library Publishing. (Children's Pr.).

McKinley, Fred B. Chinqua Where? The Spirit of Rural America, 1947-1955. Blassingame, Calvin, illus. 2003. 319p. 24.95 (978-0-9729655-0-7(5)) Willow Creel Publishing Co.

McNeese, Tim. Alamo. 2003. (Sieges That Changed the World Ser.). (Illus.). 112p. (gr. 6-12). 30.00 (978-0-7910-7101-4(4), Chelsea Hse.) Facts On File, Inc.

Miller, Barbara Kiely. Sam Houston. 2007. (Great Americans Ser.). 24p. (J). (gr. 2-4). lib. bdg. 19.93 (***978-0-8368-8316-9(0)***, Weekly Reader Early Learning Library) Stevens, Gareth Inc.

Miller, William & Boyette, Pat. Texas Days of Glory. Boyette, Pat, illus. 1998. (Illus.). 64p. (YA). (gr. 6 up). pap. 9.95 (978-1-57168-228-4(7)) Eakin Pr.

Mitchell, Mark. Raising la Belle. Mitchell, Mark, illus. (Professor Wigglestix & the Weather Ser.). (Illus.). 112p. 10.95 (978-1-57168-703-6(3)) Eakin Pr.

Munro, Roxie. The Inside-Outside Book of Texas. 2001. (Illus.). 48p. (J). (ps-4). 17.50 (978-1-58717-051-5(5), SeaStar Bks.) Chronicle Bks. LLC.

Nelson, Kristin L. The Alamo. 2004. (Pull Ahead Bks.). (Illus.). 32p. (J). (gr. k-3). lib. bdg. 22.60 (978-0-8225-3599-7(8)) Lerner Publishing Group.

Nelson, Sheila. A Proud & Isolated Nation. 2005. (How America Became America Ser.). (Illus.). 96p. (J). lib. bdg. (978-1-59084-906-4(X)) Mason Crest Pubs.

Obregon, José María. Texas. 2005. (Bilingual Library of the United States of America). (ENG & SPA.). (J). lib. bdg. (978-1-4042-3136-8(6), PowerKids Pr.) Rosen Publishing Group, Inc., The.

O'Hern, Kerri & Riehecky, Janet. The Battle of the Alamo. 2006. (Graphic Histories Ser.). (Illus.). (J). pap. (978-0-8368-6253-9(8)); 32p. lib. bdg. 26.00 (978-0-8368-6201-0(5)) Stevens, Gareth Inc. (World Almanac Library).

Petrick, Neila Skinner. Jane Wilkinson Long: Texas Pioneer. Haynes, Joyce, illus. 2004. 32p. (J). pap. 15.95 (978-1-58980-147-9(4)) Pelican Publishing Co., Inc.

Preszler, June. Juneteenth: Jubilee for Freedom. 2007. (First Facts Ser.). (Illus.). 24p. (J). 21.26 (978-0-7368-6396-4(6), 1258818) Capstone Pr., Inc.

Roberts, Russell. The Life & Times of Stephen F. Austin. 2007. (Profiles in American History Ser.). (Illus.). 48p. (J). lib. bdg. 29.95 (***978-1-58415-531-7(0)***) Mitchell Lane Pubs., Inc.

—Texas Joins the United States. 2007. (Building America Ser.). (Illus.). 48p. (J). lib. bdg. 29.95 (***978-1-58415-550-8(7)***) Mitchell Lane Pubs., Inc.

Ruffin, Frances E. The Alamo. 2006. (Illus.). 24p. (J). pap. (978-0-8368-6414-4(X)); lib. bdg. 19.33 (978-0-8368-6407-6(7)) Stevens, Gareth Inc.

Rumbley, Rose-Mary. What? No Chili? Rowden, Susan, illus. rev. ed. 2000. 144p. (J). (gr. 6-8). pap. 16.95 (978-0-89015-992-7(0)) Eakin Pr.

Schaefer, Ted & Schaefer, Lola M. The Alamo. 2005. (Symbols of Freedom Ser.). (Illus.). 32p. (J). pap. (978-1-4034-6671-6(8)); lib. bdg. 25.36 (978-1-4034-6662-4(9)) Heinemann Library.

Scher, Linda. The Texas City Disaster. 2007. (Code Red Ser.). (Illus.). 32p. (J). (gr. 3-7). lib. bdg. 25.27 (978-1-59716-363-7(5)) Bearport Publishing Co., Inc.

Spradlin, Mike. Texas Rangers: Legendary Lawmen. Munro, Roxie, illus. 2008. 32p. (J). 17.85 (***978-0-8027-8097-3(0)***); 16.95 (***978-0-8027-8096-6(2)***) Walker & Co.

Steele, Christy. Texas Joins the United States. 2005. (Illus.). 48p. (J). pap. (978-0-8368-5798-6(4)); lib. bdg. 30.00 (978-0-8368-5791-7(7)) Stevens, Gareth Inc. (World Almanac Library).

Stone, Lynn M. Texas Longhorn. 2003. (Animals in U.S. History Ser.). (Illus.). 24p. (J). 25.64 (978-1-58952-702-7(X)) Rourke Publishing, LLC.

Teitelbaum, Michael. Texas 1527 - 1836. 2006. (Voices from Colonial America Ser.). (Illus.). 112p. (J). (gr. 5-9). 32.90 (978-0-7922-6682-2(X), National Geographic Children's Bks.) National Geographic Society.

Temple, Teri & Temple, Bob. Remember the Alamo. 2007. (Illus.). 48p. (J). (978-1-60044-125-7(4)) Rourke Publishing, LLC.

Texas, 6 bks., Set. 2003. (Heinemann State Studies). (Illus.). (J). lib. bdg. 162.42 (978-1-4034-0692-7(8)) Heinemann Library.

Texas. 2003. (World Almanac Biblioteca de los Estados). (SPA., Illus.). 48p. (J). (gr. 5 up). pap. 11.95 (978-0-8368-5554-8(X), World Almanac Library) Stevens, Gareth Inc.

Torres, John Albert. The Texas Fight for Independence[97]from the Alamo to San Jacinto. 2006. (Wild History of the American West Ser.). (Illus.). 128p. (J). lib. bdg. 33.27 (978-1-59845-011-8(5), MyReportLinks.com Bks.) Enslow Pubs., Inc.

Tracy, Kathleen. Lorenzo de Zavala. 2002. (Latinos in American History). (Illus.). 56p. (gr. 4-8). lib. bdg. 29.95 (978-1-58415-154-8(4)) Mitchell Lane Pubs., Inc.

Wade, Mary. Texas History. 2003. (Heinemann State Studies). (Illus.). 48p. (J). pap. 8.50 (978-1-4034-2696-3(1)) Heinemann Library.

Wade, Mary Dodson. Fun Facts & Games: Texas. Roeder, Virginia M., illus. 2000. (Fun Facts & Games Ser.). 64p. (J). (ps-3). pap. 5.95 (978-1-892920-23-2(9)) GHB Publishers, LLC.

—People of Texas. 2003. (Heinemann State Studies). (Illus.). 48p. (J). 8.50 (978-1-4034-2695-6(3)); lib. bdg. 27.07 (978-1-4034-0689-7(8)) Heinemann Library.

—People of Texas. 2003. (gr. 3-6). lib. bdg. 17.05 (978-0-613-88567-6(8)) Tandem Library Bks.

—Texas History. 2003. (Heinemann State Studies). (Illus.). 48p. (J). lib. bdg. 27.07 (978-1-4034-0687-3(1)) Heinemann Library.

—Texas History. 2003. (gr. 3-6). lib. bdg. 17.05 (978-0-613-89943-7(1)) Tandem Library Bks.

—Texas Plants & Animals. 2003. (Heinemann State Studies). (Illus.). 48p. (J). lib. bdg. 27.07 (978-1-4034-0690-3(1)) Heinemann Library.

—Texas Plants & Animals. 2003. (gr. 3-6). lib. bdg. 17.05 (978-0-613-88569-0(4)) Tandem Library Bks.

We the People - Expansion & Reform, 11 bks. Incl. Alamo. Burgan, Michael. 2001. lib. bdg. 22.60 (978-0-7565-0097-9(4)); Battle of the Little Bighorn. Nobleman, Marc Tyler. 2001. lib. bdg. 22.60 (978-0-7565-0150-1(4)); California Gold Rush. Blashfield, Jean F. 2000. lib. bdg. 22.60 (978-0-7565-0041-2(9)); Great Women of the Old West. Alter, Judy. 2001. lib. bdg. 22.60 (978-0-7565-0099-3(0)); Lewis & Clark Expedition. Quiri, Patricia Ryon. 2000. lib. bdg. 22.60 (978-0-7565-0044-3(3)); Louisiana Purchase. Burgan, Michael. 2002. lib. bdg. 22.60 (978-0-7565-0210-2(1)); Oregon Trail. Blashfield, Jean F. 2000. lib. bdg. 22.60 (978-0-7565-0045-0(1)); Pony Express. Williams, Jean Kinney. 2002. lib. bdg. 22.60 (978-0-7565-0301-7(9)); Santa Fe Trail. Blashfield, Jean F. 2000. lib. bdg. 22.60 (978-0-7565-0047-4(8)); Trail of Tears. Burgan, Michael. 2001. lib. bdg. 22.60 (978-0-7565-0101-3(6)); Transcontinental Railroad. Blashfield, Jean F. 2001. lib. bdg. 22.60 (978-0-7565-0153-2(9)); 48p. (J). (gr. 4 up). (Illus.). Set lib. bdg. 248.60 (978-0-7565-0777-0(4)) Compass Point Bks.

Woodward, Walter M. Sam Houston: For Texas & the Union. 2005. (Library of American Lives & Times). (Illus.). 112p. (YA). (gr. 4-8). lib. bdg. 31.95 (978-0-8239-5739-2(X)) Rosen Publishing Group, Inc., The.

TEXAS RANGERS

Spradlin, Mike. Texas Rangers: Legendary Lawmen. Munro, Roxie, illus. 2008. 32p. (J). 17.85 (***978-0-8027-8097-3(0)***); 16.95 (***978-0-8027-8096-6(2)***) Walker & Co.

TEXAS RANGERS—FICTION

Flanagan, John. Oakleaf Bearers. 2008. (Ranger's Apprentice Ser.: Bk. 4). 272p. (YA). (gr. 4). 16.99 (978-0-399-24457-5(3), Philomel) Penguin Group (USA) Inc.

Patchin, Gee Frank. The Pony Rider Boys with the Texas Rangers. 2006. 78.99 (***978-1-4280-0012-4(7)***); pap. 72.99 (***978-1-4280-0014-8(3)***) IndyPublish.com.

TEXTILE FABRICS

see Textile Industry

TEXTILE INDUSTRY

see also Cotton Manufacture; Dyes and Dyeing; Tapestry; Textile Printing; Weaving

also names of special textile fabrics, (e.g. Silk); and names of articles manufactured, e.g. Carpets

Doney, Meryl. Textiles. 1998. (World Crafts Ppbk Ser.). (Illus.). 32p. (J). (gr. 3-5). pap. 6.95 (978-0-531-15331-4(2), Watts, Franklin) Scholastic Library Publishing.

Doyle, Alfreda C. Posie Meets the Fabric Farm Story & Education Pages, Vol. 10. 1998. (Illus.). 25p. pap. 8.95 (978-1-56820-284-6(9)) Story Time Stories That Rhyme.

Isaacs, Sally Senzell. Life in a New England Mill Town. 2003. (Picture the Past Ser.). (Illus.). 32p. (J). (gr. 2-4). lib. bdg. (978-1-58810-693-3(4)); pap. 6.95 (978-1-4034-0525-8(5)) Heinemann Library.

James, Diane. What We Wear: A First Look at Fabric. Lynn, Sara, illus. rev. ed. 2000. (Play & Discover Ser.). (J). (ps). 32p. pap. 4.95 (978-1-58728-047-4(7)); 9.95 (978-1-58728-043-6(4)) T&N Children's Publishing. (Two Can Publishing).

Janes, Susan Niner. Textiles. 1999. (Arts & Crafts Skills Ser.). (Illus.). 32p. (J). (gr. 3-6). pap. 6.95 (978-0-516-26216-1(5), Children's Pr.) Scholastic Library Publishing.

—Textiles. 2005. (Illus.). 32p. (J). (gr. 3-7). lib. bdg. 27.10 (978-1-932889-86-4(8)) Sea-To-Sea Pubns.

Kinsner, Kathy. Fabric Around the World. ed. 2004. (Shared Connections Ser.). (J). pap. 27.00 (978-1-4108-1646-7(X)) Benchmark Education Co.

—Fabric Around the World (Big Book) ed. 2004. (Shared Connections Ser.). (J). pap., instr.'s gde. ed. 27.00 (978-1-4108-1622-1(2)) Benchmark Education Co.

Llimos Plomer, Anna. Easy Cloth Crafts in 5 Steps. 2008. (Easy Crafts in 5 Steps Ser.). 32p. (J). (gr. 3-4). lib. bdg. 22.60 (***978-0-7660-3084-8(9)***) Enslow Pubs., Inc.

McArthur, Alex & Shepard, Tristram. Textiles Technology for Key Stage 3. 2000. (Design & Make It Ser.). (Illus.). 144p. (J). (gr. 6-9). pap., stu. ed. 22.50 (978-0-7487-4431-2(2)) Nelson Thornes Ltd. GBR. *Dist:* Trans-Atlantic Pubns., Inc.

Mitchell, Melanie S. Cloth. 2003. (First Step Nonfiction Ser.). (Illus.). 24p. (J). (gr. k-2). lib. bdg. 18.60 (978-0-8225-4616-0(7)) Lerner Publishing Group.

Parker, Steve. Textiles. 2002. (Science Files Ser.). (Illus.). 32p. (J). (gr. 3 up). lib. bdg. 24.67 (978-0-8368-3086-6(5)) Stevens, Gareth Inc.

Poratto, Maria Laura. Costura para Ninos. 2004. (SPA., Illus.). 48p. (J). pap. 7.95 (978-987-550-297-0(9)) Longseller S.A. ARG. *Dist:* Libros Sin Fronteras.

Richardson, Adele D. Silk. 1999. (Let's Investigate Ser.). (Illus.). 32p. (J). (gr. 1-4). lib. bdg. 19.95 (978-0-88682-963-6(1), Creative Education) Creative Co., The.

Shepard, Tristram, et al. Design & Make It! Food & Textiles. 1998. (Illus.). 128p. pap. 115.00 (978-0-7487-3512-9(7)) Nelson Thornes Ltd. GBR. *Dist:* Trans-Atlantic Pubns., Inc.

Stokoe, Suzie. Inspirations: Fabrics. 2000. (Inspirations Ser.). (Illus.). 96p. pap. 12.95 (978-1-84215-038-2(3), Southwater) Anness Publishing GBR. *Dist:* National Bk. Network.

Stoppleman, Monica & Crowe, Carol. Fabric. 1998. (Craft Workshop Ser.). (Illus.). 32p. (J). (gr. 3). lib. bdg. (978-0-86505-779-1(6)) Crabtree Publishing Co.

Storey, Rita. Wool & Cotton. 2007. (***978-1-59920-001-9(5)***) Smart Apple Media.

Thompson, Ruth. What Are Textiles? 2005. (Illus.). 30p. (J). (gr. 3-7). lib. bdg. 27.10 (978-1-932889-90-1(6)) Sea-To-Sea Pubns.

Thomson, Ruth. Clothes. 2006. (Illus.). 29p. (978-1-58340-939-8(4)) Smart Apple Media.

Tiner, John Hudson. Cloth. 2003. (Matter & Materials Ser.). (J). (978-1-58417-162-1(6)); (978-1-58417-168-3(5)) Lake Street Pubs.

Top That Publishing Staff, ed. Funky Fabrics. 2004. (Creative Studios Ser.). (Illus.). 48p. (J). (978-1-84510-249-4(5)) Top That! Publishing PLC.

Warwick, Ellen. Injeanuity. Lum, Bernice, illus. 2006. 80p. 12.95 (978-1-55337-681-1(1)) Kids Can Pr., Ltd. CAN. *Dist:* Wybel Marketing Group.

TEXTILE PAINTING

Boase, Petra & Beak, Nick Huckleberry. Crafty T-Shirts. Freeman, John, photos by. 1999. (Crafty Kids Ser.). (Illus.). 64p. (J). (gr. 3 up). lib. bdg. 26.00 (978-0-8368-2483-4(0)) Stevens, Gareth Inc.

Klutz Press Staff, ed. T-Shirt Art: Make Your Own Iron-on Designs. 2004. (Illus.). 60p. (J). spiral bd. 19.95 (978-1-57054-850-5(1)) Klutz.

Schreiber, Anne. Fabric Painting for Fun! 2006. (For Fun! Ser.). (Illus.). 48p. (J). (gr. 3-5). 22.60 (978-0-7565-1690-1(0)) Compass Point Bks.

Stoppleman, Monica & Crowe, Carol. Fabric. 1998. (Craft Workshop Ser.). (Illus.). 32p. (J). (gr. 3). lib. bdg. (978-0-86505-779-1(6)) Crabtree Publishing Co.

Stoppleman, Monica, et al. Fabric. 1998. (Craft Workshop Ser.). (Illus.). 32p. (J). (gr. 3). pap. (978-0-86505-789-0(3)) Crabtree Publishing Co.

TEXTILE PRINTING

Stoppleman, Monica & Crowe, Carol. Fabric. 1998. (Craft Workshop Ser.). (Illus.). 32p. (J). (gr. 3). lib. bdg. (978-0-86505-779-1(6)) Crabtree Publishing Co.

Stoppleman, Monica, et al. Fabric. 1998. (Craft Workshop Ser.). (Illus.). 32p. (J). (gr. 3). pap. (978-0-86505-789-0(3)) Crabtree Publishing Co.

THAILAND

Boraas, Tracey. Thailand. 2002. (Countries & Cultures Ser.). (Illus.). 64p. (J). (gr. 3-4). lib. bdg. 23.93 (978-0-7368-0940-5(6), Bridgestone Bks.) Capstone Pr., Inc.

Campbell, Geoffrey A. Thailand. 2001. (Modern Nations of the World Ser.). (Illus.). 96p. (YA). (gr. 7-10). 29.95 (978-1-56006-866-2(3), Lucent Bks.) Thomson Gale.

Clayton, Terry. Thailand. 2004. (Changing Face Of... Ser.). (Illus.). 48p. (J). (ps-7). lib. bdg. 28.56 (978-0-7398-6831-7(4)) Harcourt Schl. Pubs.

Darling, Kathy. The Elephant Hospital. Darling, Tara, illus. 2000. 40p. (gr. 4-6). lib. bdg. 23.90 (978-0-7613-1723-4(6), Millbrook Pr.) Lerner Publishing Group.

Ericson, Alex. Thailand. 2001. (Countries: Faces & Places Ser.). (Illus.). 32p. (J). (gr. 1-5). 25.64 (978-1-56766-913-8(1)) Child's World, Inc.

Furstinger, Nancy. Bangkok. 2005. (Checkerboard Geography Library). (Illus.). 32p. (J). (gr. k-6). lib. bdg. 22.78 (978-1-59197-852-7(1)) ABDO Publishing Co.

Goodman, Jim. Thailand. 2nd ed. 2002. (Cultures of the World Ser.). (Illus.). 144p. (gr. 5 up). lib. bdg. 37.07 (978-0-7614-1478-0(9), Cavendish, Marshall Reference Bks.) Cavendish, Marshall Corp.

Grolier Educational Staff, contrib. by. Thailand. 2003. (Illus.). 32p. (J). (978-0-7172-5803-1(3), Grolier) Scholastic Library Publishing.

Hill, Valerie. Thailand. 2002. (Ask about Asia Ser.). (Illus.). 48p. (J). (gr. 4 up). lib. bdg. (978-1-59084-205-8(7)) Mason Crest Pubs.

Leonowens, Anna. English Governess at the Siamese Court. 1999. (gr. 7-12). lib. bdg. 13.00 (978-0-613-29233-7(2)) Tandem Library Bks.

McNair, Sylvia. Bangkok. 2000. (Cities of the World Ser.). (Illus.). 64p. (J). (gr. 4-9). pap. 9.95 (978-0-516-26531-5(8), Children's Pr.) Scholastic Library Publishing.

—Bangkok. 1999. (gr. 5-8). lib. bdg. 18.75 (978-0-613-51479-8(3)) Tandem Library Bks.

Peterson, David. Thailand. 2001. (gr. 3-6). lib. bdg. 15.25 (978-0-613-51683-9(4)) Tandem Library Bks.

Phillips, Douglas A. Thailand. 2007. (Modern World Nations Ser.). (Illus.). 112p. (J). (gr. 6-12). 30.00 (***978-0-7910-9250-7(X)***, Chelsea Hse.) Facts On File, Inc.

Rau, Dana Meachen. Thailand. 2006. (Discovering Cultures Ser.). (Illus.). 48p. (J). lib. bdg. 28.50 (978-0-7614-1989-1(6), Benchmark Bks.) Cavendish, Marshall Corp.

Sapre, Reshma. Thailand. 2003. (World Tour Ser.). (Illus.). 48p. (J). lib. bdg. 25.70 (978-0-7398-6818-8(7)) Raintree.

Sheen, Barbara. Foods of Thailand. 2006. (Taste of Culture Ser.). 64p. (J). (gr. 3-6). 27.45 (978-0-7377-3037-1(4) , Greenhaven Pr., Inc.) Thomson Gale.

Sobol, Richard. An Elephant in the Backyard. 2004. (Illus.). 32p. (J). (gr. 1). 17.99 (978-0-525-47288-9(6) , Dutton Juvenile) Penguin Group (USA) Inc.

Sobol, Richard, photos by. An Elephant in the Backyard. 2004. (Illus.). (J). (978-0-525-46970-4(2) , Dutton Juvenile) Penguin Group (USA) Inc.

Taus-Bolstad, Stacy. Thailand in Pictures. 2nd ed. 2004. (Visual Geography Series, Second Ser.). (Illus.). 80p. (J). (gr. 5-12). 27.93 (978-0-8225-0939-4(3)) Lerner Publishing Group.

Thoennes, Kristin. Thailand. 1999. (Countries of the World Ser.). (Illus.). 126p. (J). (gr. 2-3). 18.60 (978-0-7368-0157-7(X) , Bridgestone Bks.) Capstone Pr., Inc.

Wilkens, Frances. Thailand. 1999. (Major World Nations Ser.). (Illus.). 103p. (J). (gr. 4-7). 29.95 (978-0-7910-5400-0(4) , Chelsea Hse.) Facts On File, Inc.

Wynaden, Jo & Cherry, Ronald. Welcome to Thailand. 2001. (Welcome to My Country Ser.). (Illus.). 48p. (J). (gr. 2 up). lib. bdg. 26.00 (978-0-8368-2527-5(6)) Stevens, Gareth Inc.

THAILAND—BIOGRAPHY

Landon, Margaret. Anna & the King. 1999. (Illus.). (J). 11.60 (978-0-606-21838-2(6)); 2000. (gr. 3-6). lib. bdg. 12.95 (978-0-613-24213-4(0)) Tandem Library Bks.

THAILAND—FICTION

Bridges, Shirin Yim. The Umbrella Queen. Yoo, Tae-Eun, illus. 2008. 32p. (J). 16.99 (978-0-06-075040-4(5)); lib. bdg. 17.89 (978-0-06-075041-1(3)) HarperCollins Pubs.

Fleischman, Sid. The White Elephant. McGuire, Robert, illus. 2006. 112p. (J). (gr. 3-6). 15.99 (978-0-06-113136-3(9) , Greenwillow Bks.); lib. bdg. 16.89 (978-0-06-113137-0(7)) HarperCollins Pubs.

Gilligan, Shannon. The Case of the Silk King. 2005. 116p. (J). pap. (***978-0-7608-9702-7(6)***) Sundance/Newbridge Educational Publishing.

Gilligan, Shannon. The Case of the Silk King No. 14: Choose Your Own Adventure. 2006. (Choose Your Own Adventure Ser.). (Illus.). 144p. (J). mass mkt. 5.99 (978-1-933390-14-7(X) , CHCL14) Chooseco LLC.

Ho, Minfong. Peek! A Thai Hide-and-Seek. Ho, Minfong & Meade, Holly, illus. 2004. 40p. (J). (ps-1). 16.99 (978-0-7636-2041-7(6)) Candlewick Pr.

Jordan, Lana. The Sleepytime Ponies Trick a Trickster. Allen, Kd & Giraud, Teresa, illus. 2004. 32p. (J). 12.95 (978-0-9710696-1-9(1)) Jorlan Publishing, Inc.

Marsden, Carolyn. Silk Umbrellas. 2007. (Illus.). 144p. (J). (gr. 3-7). 5.99 (***978-0-7636-3376-9(3)***) Candlewick Pr.

—Silk Umbrellas. Swiatkowska, Gabi, illus. 2004. 144p. (J). (gr. 3-7). 15.99 (978-0-7636-2257-2(5)) Candlewick Pr.

Oliviero, Jamie. Som See & the Magic Elephant. Kelly, Jo'Anne, illus. 2005. 27p. (J). (ps-2). reprint ed. 17.00 (978-0-7567-8929-9(X)) DIANE Publishing Co.

Thompson, Lisa. Taste of Thailand. Cantell, Brenda, illus. 2006. (Read-It! Chapter Books). 80p. (J). (gr. 2-4). 19.95 (978-1-4048-1677-0(1)) Picture Window Bks.

THAMES RIVER AND VALLEY

Bowden, Rob. Settlements of the River Thames. 2005. (Rivers Through Time Ser.). 48p. (J). pap. 8.50 (978-1-4034-5726-4(3)) Heinemann Library.

Burgess, Melvin. The Copper Treasure. Williams, Richard, illus. rev. ed. 2000. 112p. (YA). (gr. 4-7). 15.95 (978-0-8050-6381-3(1) , Holt, Henry & Co. Bks. For Young Readers) Holt, Henry & Co.

THANKSGIVING DAY

Anderson, Laurie Halse. Thank You, Sarah: The Woman Who Saved Thanksgiving. Faulkner, Matt, illus. 40p. (J). 2005. 6.99 (978-0-689-85143-8(X) , Aladdin); 2002. 16.95 (978-0-689-84787-5(4)) Simon & Schuster Children's Publishing.

Ansary, Mir Tamim. El Día de Accion de Gracias. 2003. (SPA.). 32p. (J). pap. 6.95 (978-1-4034-3030-4(6)) Heinemann Library.

—El Día de Accion de Gracias. 2003. (Historias de Fiestas Ser.).Tr. of Thanksgiving. (SPA., Illus.). 32p. (J). lib. bdg. 22.79 (978-1-4034-3007-6(1)) Heinemann Library.

—El Día de Accion de Gracias. 2003. Tr. of Thanksgiving. (SPA.). (gr. k-3). lib. bdg. 14.75 (978-0-613-87970-5(8)) Tandem Library Bks.

—Thanksgiving Day. 2001. (Holiday Histories Ser.). (Illus.). 32p. (J). (gr. k-2). lib. bdg. 21.36 (978-1-58810-224-9(6)) Heinemann Library.

Ansary, Tamim. Thanksgiving Day. 2002. (Illus.). 32p. (J). (gr. k-2). pap. 6.95 (978-1-58810-574-5(1) , 91689) Heinemann Library.

Balfour, Barbara. Thanksgiving Day. 2006. (J). (978-1-59036-405-5(8)); (978-1-59036-408-6(2)) Weigl Pubs., Inc.

Barnett, Michelle Noble, et al. Theme Pockets - November: The First Thanksgiving; Native Americans; the Food Pyramid. Evans, Marilyn, ed. Larsen, Jo, illus. 1999. (Making Books with Pockets). 96p. (J). pap., tchr. ed. 12.99 (978-1-55799-708-1(X) , EMC 594) Evan-Moor Educational Pubs.

Barth, Edna. Turkeys, Pilgrims, & Indian Corn: The Story of Thanksgiving Symbols. Arndt, Ursula, illus. 2000. 96p. (J). (ps-7). lib. bdg. 16.40 (978-0-613-30168-8(4)) Tandem Library Bks.

—Turkeys, Pilgrims, & Indian Corn: The Story of the Thanksgiving Symbols. Arndt, Ursula, illus. 2000. 96p. (J). (gr. 4-6). tchr. ed. 16.00 (978-0-618-06783-1(3)); pap. 7.95 (978-0-618-06785-5(X)) Houghton Mifflin Co. Trade & Reference Div. (Clarion Bks.).

Bartlett, Robert Merrill. The Story of Thanksgiving. Comport, Sally Wern, illus. rev. ed. 2004. 30p. (J). (gr. k-4). reprint ed. (978-0-7567-7757-9(7)) DIANE Publishing Co.

—The Story of Thanksgiving. Comport, Sally Wern, illus. Date not set. 40p. (J). (gr. 2-5). 5.99 (978-0-06-446238-9(2)) HarperCollins Pubs.

Beylon, Cathy. Invisible Thanksgiving Magic Picture Book. 1998. (Illus.). 16p. (J). pap. 1.50 (978-0-486-40527-8(3)) Dover Pubns., Inc.

Bodden, Valerie. Thanksgiving. 2005. (My First Look at Holidays Ser.). (Illus.). 24p. (gr. k-3). 15.95 (978-1-58341-370-8(7) , Creative Education) Creative Co., The.

Borden, Louise. Thanksgiving Is . . . Bjorkman, Steve, illus. 2002. (J). 11.91 (978-0-7587-1733-7(4)) Book Wholesalers, Inc.

Brighter Vision Publishing Staff. Halloween & Thanksgiving. 2000. (Make It Now Crafts Ser.). (Illus.). (J). (ps-3). pap. 3.95 (978-1-55254-178-4(9)) Brighter Vision Pubns.

Bruchac, Margaret M. & Grace, Catherine O'Neill. 1621: A New Look at Thanksgiving. Coulson, Cotton & Brimberg, Sisse, photos by. 2004. (I Am American Ser.). (Illus.). 48p. (J). (gr. 3-7). pap. 7.95 (978-0-7922-6139-1(9) , National Geographic Children's Bks.) National Geographic Society.

Court, Rob. How to Draw Thanksgiving Things. 2008. (Doodle Bks.). 32p. (J). 21.36 (***978-1-59296-957-9(7)***) Child's World, Inc.

Crane, Carol. P Is for Pilgrim: A Thanksgiving Alphabet. Urban, Helle, illus. 2003. 40p. (J). 14.95 (978-1-58536-134-2(8)) Sleeping Bear Pr.

—P Is for Pilgrim: A Thanksgiving Alphabet. rev. ed. 2007. (Holiday Ser.). 40p. pap. 7.95 (***978-1-58536-353-7(7)***) Sleeping Bear Pr.

Crawford, Laura. The Pilgrims' Thanksgiving from A to Z. Hierstein, Judith, illus. 2005. 32p. (J). (ps-k). pap. 7.95 (978-1-58980-238-4(1)) Pelican Publishing Co., Inc.

Dean, Sheri. Thanksgiving. 2006. (Illus.). 24p. (J). 19.33 (978-0-8368-6509-7(X)); (SPA., 19.33 (978-0-8368-6523-3(5)); pap. 5.95 (978-0-8368-6516-5(2)); (SPA., pap. 5.95 (978-0-8368-6530-1(8)) Stevens, Gareth Inc.

Dear Santa: Individual Title Six-Packs. (Literatura 2000 Ser.). (gr. k-1). 28.00 (978-0-7635-0048-1(8)) Rigby Education.

Doering, Amanda. Thanksgiving: A Day of Thanks. 2007. (First Facts Ser.). (Illus.). 24p. (J). 21.26 (978-0-7368-6399-5(0)) Capstone Pr., Inc.

Douglas, Punchye. Safari Oklahoma Presents: Thanksgiving History Coloring Book. (Illus.). 16p. (J). (gr. k-6). 5.00 (978-0-9703183-3-6(2)) Douglas, Bettye Forum, Inc., The.

Englar, Mary. The Pilgrims & the First Thanksgiving. 2007. (Graphic Library). (Illus.). 32p. (J). (978-0-7368-5492-4(4)) Capstone Pr., Inc.

—The Pilgrims & the First Thanksgiving. McDonnell, Peter, illus. 2007. (Graphic Library). 32p. (J). (***978-0-7368-9656-6(2)***) Capstone Pr., Inc.

Erlbach, Arlene & Erlbach, Herbert. Thanksgiving Day Crafts. 2005. (Fun Holiday Crafts Kids Can Do Ser.). (Illus.). 32p. (J). lib. bdg. 22.60 (978-0-7660-2345-1(1) , Enslow Elementary) Enslow Pubs., Inc.

Everything for Thanksgiving. (100+ Seriestm Ser.). 48p. (gr. 2-5). 4.99 (978-1-56822-459-6(1) , IF8870) School Specialty Publishing.

Flanagan, Alice K. Thanksgiving. Kelleher, Kathie, illus. 2001. (Holidays & Festivals Ser.). 32p. (J). (gr. 3 up). lib. bdg. 22.60 (978-0-7565-0087-0(7)) Compass Point Bks.

George, Jean Craighead. The First Thanksgiving. Locker, Thomas, illus. 2001. 32p. (J). (ps-3). pap. 6.99 (978-0-698-11392-3(6) , Putnam Juvenile) Penguin Group (USA) Inc.

Gibbons, Gail. Thanksgiving Is... (Illus.). 32p. (J). pap. 6.95 (978-0-8234-1979-1(7)); tchr. ed. 17.95 (978-0-8234-1849-7(9)) Holiday Hse., Inc.

Gillis, Jennifer Blizin. My Thanksgiving. 2005. (Illus.). 24p. (J). (ps-k). lib. bdg. 20.64 (978-1-4109-1402-6(X)); pap. 5.75 (978-1-4109-1403-3(8)) Steck-Vaughn.

Grace, Catherine O'Neill, et al. 1621: A New Look at Thanksgiving. Brimberg, Sisse & Coulson, Cotton, photos by. 2001. (Illus.). 48p. (J). (gr. 3-7). 17.95 (978-0-7922-7027-0(4) , National Geographic Children's Bks.) National Geographic Society.

Greene, Rhonda Gowler. The Very First Thanksgiving Day. Gaber, Susan, illus. 2002. 32p. (J). (gr. k-3). 15.95 (978-0-689-83301-4(6) , Atheneum) Simon & Schuster Children's Publishing.

Greenwood, Barbara. Pioneer Thanksgiving. 1999. (978-0-606-17230-1(0)) Tandem Library Bks.

—A Pioneer thanksgiving: A story of harvest celebrations in 1841. Collins, Heather, illus. 1999. (History Comes Alive Ser.). 48p. (J). (gr. 4-6). (978-1-55074-574-0(3)); (978-1-55074-744-7(4)) Kids Can Pr., Ltd.

Hall, Katy, pseud & Eisenberg, Lisa. Turkey Riddles. Sorra, Kristin, illus. 2005. (Easy-to-Read, Puffin Ser.). 40p. (J). pap. 3.99 (978-0-14-240369-3(5) , Puffin) Penguin Group (USA) Inc.

Happy Thanksgiving. 32p. (J). 2.69 (978-0-7847-1128-6(3)) Standard Publishing.

Happy Thanksgiving Coloring Book. 2006. 16p. (J). pap. 1.99 (978-0-7847-1744-8(3) , 04370) Standard Publishing.

Haugen, Brenda. Thanksgiving. Ouren, Todd, illus. 2004. (Holidays & Celebrations Ser.). 24p. (gr. k-3). 22.60 (978-1-4048-0191-2(X)) Picture Window Bks.

Hayes, Dan, illus. The Thanksgiving. 24p. (J). pap., act. bk. ed. 7.95 (978-0-8249-5324-9(X)) Ideals Pubns.

Heiligman, Deborah. Celebrate Thanksgiving: With Turkey, Family, & Counting Blessings. 2006. (Holidays Around the World Ser.). (Illus.). 32p. (J). (gr. 1-4). 15.95 (978-0-7922-5928-2(9)); 23.90 (978-0-7922-5929-9(7)) National Geographic Society. (National Geographic Children's Bks.).

Heinrichs, Ann. Thanksgiving. Jordan, Charles, illus. 2006. (Holidays, Festivals, & Celebrations Ser.). 32p. (J). (gr. k-4). 22.79 (978-1-59296-582-3(2)) Child's World, Inc.

Herman, Debbie & Koffsky, Ann D. Beyond Turkey: A Thankgiving Feast of Fun, Facts, & Activities. 2005. (Let's Celebrate Ser.). (Illus.). 48p. (J). pap. 8.99 (978-0-7641-3063-2(3)) Barron's Educational Series, Inc.

Jackson, Garnet N. First Thanksgiving. 2000. (gr. k-3). lib. bdg. 11.80 (978-0-613-35508-7(3)) Tandem Library Bks.

—The First Thanksgiving: Level 3. Croll, Carolyn, illus. 2001. (Hello Reader! Ser.). 40p. (J). (gr. 1-3). pap. 3.99 (978-0-439-20628-0(6) , Cartwheel Bks.) Scholastic, Inc.

—El Primer Dia de Accion de Gracias. Croll, Carolyn, illus. 2002. (Coleccion "Hola, Lector" Ser.). (SPA.). 40p. (J). (gr. 1-3). pap. 3.99 (978-0-439-31733-7(9) , SO30895, Scholastic en Espanol) Scholastic, Inc.

Kamma, Anne. First Thanksgiving. Dodson, Bert, illus. 2001. (If You Ser.). 64p. (J). pap. 5.99 (978-0-439-10566-8(8)) Scholastic, Inc.

—If You Were at the First Thanksgiving. 2001. (gr. k-3). lib. bdg. 14.15 (978-0-613-89056-4(6)); 12.79 (978-0-606-22213-6(8)) Tandem Library Bks.

Kessel, Joyce K. Squanto & the First Thanksgiving. Donze, Lisa, illus. rev. ed. 2004. (On My Own Holidays Ser.). 48p. (J). (gr. 2-4). lib. bdg. 25.26 (978-0-87614-941-6(7)) Lerner Publishing Group.

—Squanto & the First Thanksgiving. 2004. (gr. k-3). lib. bdg. 14.10 (978-0-613-63654-4(6)) Tandem Library Bks.

Kessel Joyce K. Squanto y el primer Día de Accion de Gracias (Squanto & the First Thanksgiving) Donze, Lisa, illus. 2007. (Yo solo Festividades (on My Own Holidays) Ser.). (J). pap. 6.95 (***978-0-8225-7795-9(X)*** , Ediciones Lerner) Lerner Publishing Group.

Kessel, Joyce K. Squanto y el Primer Día de Accion de Gracias (Squanto & the First Thanksgiving) Donze, Lisa, illus. 2007. (Yo Solo Festividades (On My Own Holidays) Ser.). (SPA.). 48p. (J). (gr. 2-4). lib. bdg. 25.26 (***978-0-8225-7792-8(5)*** , Ediciones Lerner) Lerner Publishing Group.

Klingel, Cynthia Fitterer & Noyed, Robert B. Thanksgiving. 2002. (Wonder Books Level 2: Holidays Ser.). (Illus.). 24p. (J). (ps-3). 22.79 (978-1-56766-956-5(5)) Child's World, Inc.

Kreiswirth, Kinny & Fink, Deborah F. It's a Family Thanksgiving! A Celebration of an American Tradition for Children. 2000. mass mkt. 5.95 net. (978-0-9678871-0-4(0)) Harmony Hearth, LLC.

Kule, Elaine A. Celebrate Thanksgiving Day. 2006. (Celebrate Holidays Ser.). (Illus.). 112p. (J). lib. bdg. 31.93 (978-0-7660-2578-3(0)) Enslow Pubs., Inc.

Kupperstein, Joel. Celebrating Thanksgiving No. 4531: Giving Thanks. Burris, Priscilla, illus. 1999. 16p. (J). (ps-2). pap. 2.99 (978-1-57471-576-7(3)) Creative Teaching Pr., Inc.

Landau, Elaine. Celebrate the First Thanksgiving with Elaine Landau. 2006. (Explore Colonial America with Elaine Landau Ser.). (Illus.). 48p. (J). lib. bdg. 23.93 (978-0-7660-2556-1(X) , Enslow Elementary) Enslow Pubs., Inc.

—Thanksgiving Day: A Time to Be Thankful. 2001. (Finding Out about Holidays Ser.). (Illus.). 48p. (J). (gr. 1-4). lib. bdg. 23.93 (978-0-7660-1572-2(6)) Enslow Pubs., Inc.

Let's Celebrate God's Blessings on Thanksgiving. 2006. 16p. (J). pap. 1.99 (978-0-7847-1536-9(X) , 04361) Standard Publishing.

Lilly, Melinda. Pilgrims in America. 2002. (Rourke Discovery Library). (Illus.). 24p. (J). lib. bdg. 20.64 (978-1-58952-360-9(1)) Rourke Publishing, LLC.

Mackall, Dandi Daley. Off to Plymouth Rock. 2006. 26p. (J). bds. 9.99 (978-1-4003-0822-4(4)) Nelson, Thomas Inc.

—Off to Plymouth Rock. Barretta, Gene, illus. 2004. 32p. (J). 12.99 (978-1-4003-0473-8(3)) Nelson, Thomas Inc.

Marx, David F. Thanksgiving. 2000. (Rookie Read-About Holidays Ser.). (Illus.). 32p. (J). (gr. 1-2). 19.50 (978-0-516-22208-0(2)); pap. 5.95 (978-0-516-27157-6(1)) Scholastic Library Publishing. (Children's Pr.).

—Thanksgiving. 2000. (gr. k-3). lib. bdg. 14.10 (978-0-613-62322-3(3)) Tandem Library Bks.

Metaxas, Eric. Squanto & the First Thanksgiving. Donato, Michael A., illus. 2005. (Rabbit Ears-A Classic Tale Ser.). 40p. (J). (gr. k-5). 25.65 (978-1-59197-771-1(1)) Spotlight.

—Squanto & the First Thanksgiving: The Legendary American Tale. Donato, Michael A., illus. 2004. 36p. (J). (gr. 3-8). reprint ed. 19.00 (978-0-7567-7123-2(4)) DIANE Publishing Co.

Miller, Marilyn. Thanksgiving. 1998. (World of Holidays Ser.). (Illus.). 32p. (J). (gr. 2-5). lib. bdg. 25.69 (978-0-8172-4612-9(6)) Raintree.

—Thanksgiving. 1998. (World of Holidays Ser.). (Illus.). 32p. (J). (gr. 2-5). pap. 7.95 (978-0-8172-8106-9(1)) Steck-Vaughn.

Monin, Margie. The Story of Thanksgiving. 2007. (Illus.). 128p. 4.95 (***978-0-7624-3099-4(0)*** , Running Pr. Minature Editions) Running Pr. Bk. Pubs.

Murray, Julie. Thanksgiving. 2005. (Holidays Ser.). (Illus.). 24p. (J). (gr. k-4). lib. bdg. 21.35 (978-1-57765-956-3(2)) ABDO Publishing Co.

O'Neal, Bill. Long Before the Pilgrims: The First Thanksgiving, el Paso del Norte, 1598. Martinez, Lynn O'Neal, tr. Morgan, Polsky, illus. 2000. (ENG & SPA.). 48p. (J). 15.95 (978-1-57168-448-6(4)) Eakin Pr.

Pingry, Patricia A. & Skarmeas, Nancy J. La Historia del Dia de Accion de Gracias. Venturi-Pickett, Stacy, illus. 2000. (SPA.). 26p. (J). (ps-k). 6.95 (978-0-8249-4195-6(0)) Ideals Pubns.

Potts, Steve. Thanksgiving. 2001. (Holiday Ser.). (Illus.). 24p. (J). 21.35 (978-1-58340-117-0(2)) Smart Apple Media.

Raabe, Emily. A Thanksgiving Holiday Cookbook. 2002. (Festive Foods for the Holidays Ser.). (Illus.). 24p. (J). lib. bdg. 19.95 (978-0-8239-5628-9(8) , PowerKids Pr.) Rosen Publishing Group, Inc., The.

Rader, Laura & Utt, Mary Ann, illus. A Child's Story of Thanksgiving. 24p. (J). 7.95 (978-0-8249-5327-0(4) , Ideals Children's Bks.) Ideals Pubns.

Rau, Dana Meachen. Thanksgiving. 2000. (Illus.). 47p. (J). (gr. 3-5). lib. bdg. 15.25 (978-0-613-51684-6(2)) Tandem Library Bks.

Roop, Connie. Let's Celebrate Thanksgiving. 1999. (Let's Celebrate Ser.). (Illus.). 32p. (gr. k-3). lib. bdg. 22.90 (978-0-7613-0973-4(X) , Millbrook Pr.) Lerner Publishing Group.

Roop, Connie, et al. Let's Celebrate Thanksgiving. 1999. (Let's Celebrate Ser.). (Illus.). 32p. (gr. k-3). pap. 7.95 (978-0-7613-0429-6(0) , Millbrook Pr.) Lerner Publishing Group.

Roop, Peter. Let's Celebrate Thanksgiving. 1999. (Illus.). (J). (978-0-606-18293-5(4)) Tandem Library Bks.

Rosinsky, Natalie M. Thanksgiving. 2002. (Let's See Library). (Illus.). 24p. (J). (gr. 1 up). lib. bdg. 19.93 (978-0-7565-0391-8(4)) Compass Point Bks.

Ross, Kathy. All New Crafts for Thanksgiving. Holm, Sharon Lane, illus. (J). (gr. k-2). 2005. 48p. pap. 7.95 (978-0-7613-2394-5(5) , First Avenue Editions); 2004. lib. bdg. 25.26 (978-0-7613-2922-0(6) , Millbrook Pr.) Lerner Publishing Group.

Santella, Andrew. The First Thanksgiving. 2003. (Cornerstones of Freedom). (Illus.). 48p. (J). (gr. 4-6). 26.00 (978-0-516-24204-0(0) , Children's Pr.) Scholastic Library Publishing.

Schuh, Mari C. Thanksgiving. Saunders-Smith, Gail, ed. 2001. (Holidays & Celebrations Ser.). (Illus.). 24p. (J). (gr. k-1). lib. bdg. 15.93 (978-0-7368-0981-8(3) , Pebble Bks.) Capstone Pr., Inc.

—Thanksgiving, Vol. 2. 2005. (Holidays & Celebrations Ser.). (Illus.). 24p. (YA). (gr. k-3). pap. (978-0-7368-9438-8(1) , Pebble Bks.) Capstone Pr., Inc.

—Thanksgiving Day. 2003. (National Holidays Ser.). (Illus.). 24p. (J). (gr. k-1). lib. bdg. 15.93 (978-0-7368-1654-0(2) , Pebble Bks.) Capstone Pr., Inc.

Sechrist, Elizabeth Hough, et al. It's Time for Thanksgiving. 1999. 251p. (J). lib. bdg. 40.00 (978-0-7808-0307-7(8)) Omnigraphics, Inc.

Silver, Donald M. & Wynne, Patricia J. Easy Make & Learn Projects: The Pilgrims, the Mayflower, & More. 2001. (Illus.). 72p. pap. 10.95 (978-0-439-15277-8(1)) Scholastic, Inc.

Skarmeas, Nancy J. La Historia del Dia de Accion de Gracias. Venturi-Pickett, Stacy, illus. 2000. 24p. (J). (gr. 1-3). reprint ed. 7.00 (978-0-7567-5846-2(7)) DIANE Publishing Co.

—The Story of Thanksgiving. Venturi-Pickett, Stacy, illus. 1999. 24p. (J). (ps-k). bds. 6.95 (978-0-8249-4164-2(0)) Ideals Pubns.

Standard Publishing Staff. Standard Christmas Program BK. 2006. 48p. pap. 6.99 (978-0-7847-1647-2(1)) Standard Publishing.

Stewart, Pat. Learning about Thanksgiving. 2001. (Illus.). 16p. (J). (ps up). pap. 1.50 (978-0-486-41644-1(5)) Dover Pubns., Inc.

Stiegemeyer, Julie. Thanksgiving: A Harvest Celebration. Benoit, Renne, illus. 2003. (ENG.). 32p. (J). 12.99 (978-0-7586-0530-6(7)) Concordia Publishing Hse.

The Thanksgiving. 2001. (J). act. bk. ed. 8.95 (978-0-439-24119-9(7)) Scholastic, Inc.

Thanksgiving Fun. 2002. (Holiday Fun Bks.). 32p. pap. 2.99 (978-0-88724-790-3(3) , CD-0182) Carson-Dellosa Publishing Co., Inc.

Trueit, Trudi Strain. Thanksgiving. 2006. (Rookie Read-About Holidays Ser.). (Illus.). 31p. (J). (978-0-531-12460-4(6)) Children's Pr., Ltd.

—Thanksgiving. rev. ed. 2006. (Rookie Read-About Holidays Ser.). (Illus.). 32p. (J). (gr. 1-2). pap. 5.95 (978-0-531-11841-2(X) , Children's Pr.) Scholastic Library Publishing.

Vidrine, Beverly. Thanksgiving Day Alphabet. 2006. (Illus.). 32p. (J). pap. 7.95 (978-1-58980-338-1(8)) Pelican Publishing Co., Inc.

Wesemann, Tim. Tassel-Free Living for Grads: God's Grace for Grads. 2003. 64p. (YA). 9.99 (978-0-9718985-8-5(0)) C T A, Inc.

Whitehurst, Susan. The First Thanksgiving. 2002. (Library of the Pilgrims). (Illus.). 24p. (J). (gr. 3). lib. bdg. 19.95 (978-0-8239-5807-8(8) , PowerKids Pr.) Rosen Publishing Group, Inc., The.

Williams, Colleen Madonna Flood. My Adventure on Thanksgiving Day. 2006. 44p. (J). 8.99 (978-1-59092-557-7(2) , Orchard Academy Pr.) Windstorm Creative.

Winne, Joanne. Let's Get Ready for Thanksgiving. 2001. (gr. k-3). lib. bdg. 12.95 (978-0-613-51086-8(0)) Tandem Library Bks.

Yero, Judith Lloyd. American Documents: Mayflower Compact. 2006. (Illus.). 40p. (J). (gr. 5-9). 15.95 (978-0-7922-5891-9(6) , National Geographic Children's Bks.) National Geographic Society.

—American Documents: The Mayflower Compact. 2006. (Illus.). 40p. (J). (gr. 5-9). 23.90 (978-0-7922-5892-6(4) , National Geographic Children's Bks.) National Geographic Society.

Zocchi, Judy. On Thanksgiving Day. Wallis, Rebbeca, illus. 2005. (Holiday Happenings Ser.). 32p. (J). pap. 9.95 (978-1-59646-212-0(4)) Dingles & Co.

—On Thanksgiving Day. Wallis, Rebecca, illus. 2005. (Holiday Happenings Ser.). 32p. (J). per. 9.95 (978-1-59646-213-7(2)) Dingles & Co.

—On Thanksgiving Day/el Día de Accion de Gracias. Wallis, Rebecca, illus. 2005. (Holiday Happenings Ser.).Tr. of Día de Accion de Gracias. (ENG & SPA.). 32p. (J). pap. 9.95 (978-1-59646-214-4(0)); lib. bdg. 20.65 (978-1-891997-75-4(0)); per. 9.95 (978-1-59646-215-1(9)) Dingles & Co.

THANKSGIVING DAY—FICTION

Ada, Alma Flor. Pavo para la Cena de Accion de Gracias? No Gracias! (Cuentos para Todo el Ano Ser.). (SPA., Illus.). 16p. (J). (gr. k-3). pap. 8.95 (978-1-58105-180-3(8)) Santillana USA Publishing Co., Inc.

—Pavo para la Cena de Accion de Gracias? No Gracias! 2000. (SPA.). (gr. k-3). lib. bdg. 17.60 (978-0-613-79371-1(4)) Tandem Library Bks.

—Turkey for Thanksgiving Dinner? No Thanks! (Stories the Year 'Round Ser.). (Illus.). 16p. (J). (gr. k-3). pap. 8.95 (978-1-58105-224-4(3)) Santillana USA Publishing Co., Inc.

Alcott, Louisa May. An Old-Fashioned Thanksgiving. Bernardin, James, illus. 2005. 32p. (J). (ps-3). 15.99 (978-0-06-000450-7(9)); lib. bdg. 16.89 (978-0-06-000451-4(7)) HarperCollins Pubs.

Alley, R. W., illus. The Know-Nothings Talk Turkey. 2002. (Know-Nothings Ser.). (J). 12.30 (978-0-7587-6906-0(7)) Book Wholesalers, Inc.

Anderson, Derek & Child, Lydia Maria. Over the River: A Turkey's Tale. 2005. (Illus.). 40p. (J). 14.95 (978-0-689-87635-6(1)) Simon & Schuster Children's Publishing.

Anderson, Laurie Halse. Fear of Falling. 2003. (Wild at Heart Ser.). (Illus.). 105p. (J). (gr. 4 up). lib. bdg. 23.33 (978-0-8368-3255-6(8)) Stevens, Gareth Inc.

—Thank You, Sarah: The Woman Who Saved Thanksgiving. 2003. mass mkt. 6.99 (978-0-689-84902-2(8) , Aladdin) Simon & Schuster Children's Publishing.

Archer, Peggy. Turkey Surprise. Wickstrom, Thor, illus. 32p. (J). (gr. k). 2007. pap. 5.99 (978-0-14-240852-0(2) , Puffin); 2005. 10.99 (978-0-8037-2969-8(3) , Dial) Penguin Group (USA) Inc.

Atwell, Debby. The Thanksgiving Door. (Illus.). 32p. (J). (gr. k-3). 2006. pap. 5.95 (978-0-618-77124-0(7)); 2003. 16.00 (978-0-618-24036-4(5)) Houghton Mifflin Co. Trade & Reference Div. (Walter Lorraine).

Auch, Mary Jane & Auch, Herm, illus. Beauty & the Beaks: A Turkey's Cautionary Tale. 2007. 32p. (J). (ps-3). 16.95 (978-0-8234-1990-6(8)) Holiday Hse., Inc.

Banks, Steven. Thanks a Lot, Robo-Turkey! LaPadula, Tom, illus. ed. 2005. (Adventures of Jimmy Neutron Ser.: 10). 24p. (J). lib. bdg. 15.00 (978-1-59054-787-8(X)) Fitzgerald Bks.

Berenstain, Stan & Berenstain, Jan. The Berenstain Bears & the Prize Pumpkin. Berenstain, Stan & Berenstain, Jan, illus. 2002. (Berenstain Bears First Time Bks.). (Illus.). (J). 11.19 (978-0-7587-0959-2(5)) Book Wholesalers, Inc.

Bildner, Phil. Turkey Bowl. Payne, C. F., illus. 2006. (J). 16.99 (978-0-689-87896-1(6) , Simon & Schuster Children's Publishing) Simon & Schuster Children's Publishing.

Boelts, Maribeth. The Firefighters' Thanksgiving. Widener, Terry, illus. 32p. (J). (ps). 2006. pap. 6.99 (978-0-14-240631-1(7) , Puffin); 2004. 15.99 (978-0-399-23600-6(7) , Putnam Juvenile) Penguin Group (USA) Inc.

Boniface, William. Five Little Turkeys. Adams, Lynn, illus. 2003. 12p. (J). (ps). 5.99 (978-0-8431-0464-6(3) , Price Stern Sloan) Penguin Group (USA) Inc.

Bourgeois, Paulette. Franklin y el Dia de Accion de Gracias. Varela, Alejandra Lopez, tr. Clark, Brenda, illus. (SPA.). pap. 5.95 (978-1-930332-06-5(8) , LC30183); (J). ring bd. 10.95 (978-1-930332-07-2(6) , LC30184) Lectorum Pubns., Inc.

—Franklin y el Dia de Accion de Gracias. 2001. (978-0-606-22645-5(1)) Tandem Library Bks.

—Franklin's Thanksgiving. Clark, Brenda, illus. 2001. (Franklin Ser.). 32p. (J). (gr. 3-6). pap. 4.99 (978-0-439-23820-5(X)) Scholastic, Inc.

—Franklin's Thanksgiving. 2001. (Franklin Ser.). (Illus.). (J). 11.30 (978-0-606-22045-3(3)) Tandem Library Bks.

Bourgeois, Paulette & Jennings, Sharon. Franklin's Thanksgiving. Clark, Brenda, illus. 2004. (Franklin the Turtle Ser.). 32p. (J). (gr. k-3). (978-1-55074-798-0(3)) Kids Can Pr., Ltd.

Brown, Marc. Arturo y el Dia de Accion de Gracias. 2000. (Arthur Adventure Ser.). (SPA., Illus.). (J). (gr. k-2). pap. 6.95 (978-1-880507-79-7(X) , LC7610) Lectorum Pubns., Inc.

—Arturo y el Dia de Accion de Gracias. 2000. (J). 13.75 (978-0-606-20186-5(6)) Tandem Library Bks.

Bunting, Eve. A Turkey for Thanksgiving. 2002. (Illus.). (J). 13.79 (978-0-7587-3875-2(7)) Book Wholesalers, Inc.

Caldwell, Lise. Let's Celebrate God's Blessings on Thanksgiving. Burris, Priscilla, illus. 2006. (Holiday Discovery Ser.). 24p. (J). (ps-3). bds. 6.99 (978-0-7847-1383-9(9) , 04048) Standard Publishing.

Capucilli, Alyssa Satin. Happy Thanksgiving, Biscuit! Schories, Pat, illus. 1999. (Biscuit Ser.). 20p. (J). (ps-1). pap. 6.99 (978-0-694-01221-3(1) , Harper Festival) HarperCollins Pubs.

Cazet, Denys. Minnie & Moo: Minnie & Moo & the Thanksgiving Tree. Cazet, Denys, illus. 2002. (Live Oak Readalong Ser.). (Illus.). (J). pap. 18.95 incl. audio compact disk (978-1-59112-386-6(0)) Live Oak Media.

—Minnie & Moo & the Thanksgiving Tree. Cazet, Denys, illus. 2002. (Minnie & Moo Ser.). (Illus.). (J). 11.45 (978-0-7587-6206-1(2)) Book Wholesalers, Inc.

—Minnie & Moo & the Thanksgiving Tree. Cazet, Denys, illus. 2002. (Live Oak Readalong Ser.). (Illus.). (J). pap. 16.95 incl. audio (978-0-87499-914-3(6)); 28.95 incl. audio compact disk (978-1-59112-587-7(1)); pap. 31.95 incl. audio compact disk (978-1-59112-586-0(3)) Live Oak Media.

—Minnie & Moo & the Thanksgiving Tree. 2000. (ps-2). lib. bdg. 11.80 (978-0-613-32839-5(6)) Tandem Library Bks.

Cazet, Denys & Dorling Kindersley Publishing Staff. Minnie & Moo & the Thanksgiving Tree. Cazet, Denys, illus. 2000. (Illus.). 48p. (J). (gr. 1-3). 12.99 (978-0-7894-2654-3(4)); pap. 3.99 (978-0-7894-2655-0(2)) Dorling Kindersley Publishing, Inc.

Chavez, Michael A., Jr. The Adventures of Tom Turkey: Thanksgiving in the White House. 2001. (J). 8.00 (978-0-8059-5079-3(6)) Dorrance Publishing Co., Inc.

Child, Lydia Maria, contrib. by. Over the River: A Turkey's Tale. 2007. (Classic Board Bks.). (Illus.). 38p. (J). (ps-3). bds. 7.99 (***978-1-4169-3803-3(6)*** , Little Simon) Simon & Schuster Children's Publishing.

Clark, Brenda, illus. Franklin's Thanksgiving. 2002. (Franklin Ser.). 12.40 (978-1-4046-0329-5(8)) Book Wholesalers, Inc.

Cohen, Barbara. Molly's Pilgrim. Duffy, Daniel M. & Deraney, Michael J., illus. rev. ed. 1998. 32p. (J). (ps-3). 16.99 (978-0-688-16279-5(7)) HarperCollins Pubs.

—Molly's Pilgrim. Duffy, Daniel Mark & Deraney, Michael J., illus. 97th rev. ed. 1998. 32p. (J). (gr. 1-4). pap. 3.99 (978-0-688-16280-1(0) , Harper Trophy) HarperCollins Pubs.

—Molly's Pilgrim. (Literature to Go Ser.). pap., tchr. ed. incl. VHS (978-0-7919-2685-7(0)) Phoenix Films & Video.

Cole, Grace. The Donkey's Thanksgiving. Miller, Leila, illus. 1998. 16p. (J). pap. 4.99 (978-1-893181-06-9(5) , Lagesse Stevens) Martell Publishing Co.

—The Donkey's Thanksgiving. Miller, Lelia, illus. 2002. (J). 4.95 (978-0-9712923-1-4(0)) Taylor-Dth Publishing.

Cowley, Joy. Gracias the Thanksgiving Turkey. Cepeda, Joe, illus. 2005. 32p. (J). (ps-ps). pap. 5.99 (978-0-439-76987-7(6) , Scholastic Paperbacks) Scholastic, Inc.

Cowley, Joy & Pasternac, Susana. Gracias, el Pavo de Thanksgiving. Cepeda, Joe & Abdullah, Maryam Muhammad, illus. 1998. (SPA.). 32p. (J). (gr. 1-3). pap. 5.99 (978-0-590-39964-7(0) , SO8202, Scholastic en Espanol) Scholastic, Inc.

Cox, Judy. One Is a Feast for Mouse. Ebbeler, Jeffrey, illus. 2008. (J). (***978-0-8234-1977-7(0)***) Holiday Hse., Inc.

deGroat, Diane. Annie Pitts, Burger Kid. (Illus.). (J). 2001. 112p. (gr. 3-7). pap. 3.95 (978-1-58717-110-9(4)); 2000. 75p. pap. 14.95 (978-1-58717-016-4(7)) Chronicle Bks. LLC. (SeaStar Bks.).

—Annie Pitts, Burger Kid. 2001. (gr. 3-6). lib. bdg. 11.80 (978-0-613-43671-7(7)) Tandem Library Bks.

—We Gather Together... Now Please Get Lost! 2005. (Illus.). 32p. (J). pap. 6.95 (978-0-8118-5055-1(2) , SeaStar Bks.) Chronicle Bks. LLC.

dePaola, Tomie. My First Thanksgiving. 2008. 14p. (J). (ps-k). bds. 5.99 (***978-0-448-44857-2(2)*** , Grosset & Dunlap) Penguin Group (USA) Inc.

Devlin, Wende & Devlin, Harry. Cranberry Thanksgiving. unabr. ed. 2001. (J). (gr. k-3). pap. 16.95 incl. audio (978-0-8045-6658-2(5) , 6552-B) Spoken Arts, Inc.

Dickinson, Asa Don. Good Cheer Stories Every Child Should Know. 2005. 339p. (J). (***978-1-59605-692-3(4)*** , Cosimo Classics) Cosimo, Inc.

Dower, Laura. Thanks for Nothing with Tattoos. 2001. (gr. 3-6). lib. bdg. 13.00 (978-0-613-91011-8(7)) Tandem Library Bks.

Follen, Eliza Lee. The Talkative Wig. 2006. (ENG.). pap. (***978-1-4250-3316-3(4)***) Assistedreadingbooks.com Inc.

Geisert, Arthur. Nursery Crimes. (Illus.). 32p. (J). (ps-3). 2007. 6.95 (***978-0-618-95671-5(9));*** 2001. tchr. ed. 16.00 (978-0-618-06487-8(7) , Walter Lorraine) Houghton Mifflin Co. Trade & Reference Div.

Goode, Diane. Thanksgiving Is Here! Goode, Diane, illus. 2003. (Illus.). 32p. (J). (ps-3). 17.99 (978-0-06-051588-1(0)); lib. bdg. 16.89 (978-0-06-051589-8(9)) HarperCollins Pubs.

Goodspeed, Judy. Perky Turkey's Perfect Plan. 2006. (Illus.). 22p. (J). lib. bdg. 24.95 (978-0-9778651-1-6(8)) Dragonfly Publishing, Inc.

—Perky Turkey's Perfect Plan. Taylor, Chet, illus. 2005. 22p. (J). 18.99 (978-0-9765786-0-4(3)) Dragonfly Publishing, Inc.

Greene, Rhonda Gowler. The Very First Thanksgiving Day. Gaber, Susan, illus. 2006. 32p. (J). 6.99 (978-1-4169-1916-2(3) , Aladdin) Simon & Schuster Children's Publishing.

Gutman, Dan. Dr. Carbles Is Losing His Marbles! Paillot, Jim, illus. 2007. (My Weird School Ser.: No.19). 112p. (J). lib. bdg. 15.89 (***978-0-06-123478-1(8));*** pap. 3.99 (***978-0-06-123477-4(X)*** , Harper Trophy) HarperCollins Pubs.

Hallinan, P. K. Thanksgiving at Our House. 2006. (Illus.). 32p. (J). (gr. k). 8.95 (978-0-8249-5534-2(X) , 1262730, Ideals Children's Bks.) Ideals Pubns.

Halperin, Wendy Anderson, tr. & illus. The Peterkins' Thanksgiving. Halperin, Wendy Anderson, illus. 2005. 32p. (J). (gr. 2-4). 17.95 (978-0-689-84142-2(6) , Atheneum) Simon & Schuster Children's Publishing.

Harrison, Emma, et al. Slipping Away. 2005. 163p. (YA). (978-1-4155-8181-0(9) , Simon Spotlight) Simon & Schuster Children's Publishing.

Haston, Meg. The Thanksgiving Gift. Fletcher, Lyn, illus. 2007. (My Little Pony Ser.). 24p. (J). (ps-2). pap. 4.99 (***978-0-06-123446-0(X)*** , Harper Festival) HarperCollins Pubs.

Hawley, Mabel C. Four Little Blossoms Through the Holidays. 2005. pap. 22.95 (978-1-4179-9003-0(1)) Kessinger Publishing, LLC.

Hennessy, B. G. My Book of Thanks. Nakata, Hiroe, illus. 2005. 32p. (J). (gr. k-2). 6.99 (978-0-7636-2864-2(6)) Candlewick Pr.

Herman, Charlotte. The Memory Cupboard: A Thanksgiving Story. Stahl, Ben F., illus. 2003. 32p. (J). (gr. 1-4). 16.95 (978-0-8075-5055-7(8)) Whitman, Albert & Co.

Herman, Gail. Thanksgiving Mystery. 2006. (Hello Reader! Ser.: No. 17). (Illus.). 32p. (J). pap. 3.99 (978-0-439-78359-0(3)) Scholastic, Inc.

Hill, Eric. Spot's Thanksgiving. Hill, Eric, illus. 2003. (Spot Ser.). (Illus.). 10p. (J). (ps-1). bds. 5.99 (978-0-399-24186-4(8) , Putnam Juvenile) Penguin Group (USA) Inc.

Hillert, Margaret. Why We Have Thanksgiving. Siculan, Dan, illus. rev. exp. ed. 2007. (Beginning to Read Ser.). (J). lib. bdg. (978-1-59953-049-9(X)) Norwood Hse. Pr.

Hines, Gary. Thanksgiving in the White House. Wallner, Alexandra, illus. rev. ed. 2003. 32p. (J). 15.95 (978-0-8050-6530-5(X) , Holt, Henry & Co. Bks. For Young Readers) Holt, Henry & Co.

Holub, Joan. More Snacks! A Thanksgiving Play. Terry, Will, illus. 2006. (Ant Hill Ser.). 24p. (J). pap. 3.99 (978-1-4169-0954-5(0) , Aladdin); lib. bdg. 11.89 (978-1-4169-2559-0(7) , Aladdin Library) Simon & Schuster Children's Publishing.

Horowitz, Dave. The Ugly Pumpkin: A Thanksgiving Story. Horowitz, Dave, illus. 2005. (Illus.). 40p. (J). (ps-2). 16.99 (978-0-399-24267-0(8) , Putnam Juvenile) Penguin Group (USA) Inc.

Huelin, Jodi. Countdown to Thanksgiving. Motoyama, Keiko, illus. 2002. 24p. (J). pap. 3.99 (978-0-8431-4880-0(2) , Price Stern Sloan) Penguin Group (USA) Inc.

Jackson, Alison. I Know an Old Lady Who Swallowed a Pie. Schachner, Judith B., illus. 2002. 32p. (J). (ps-3). pap. 6.99 (978-0-14-056595-9(7) , Puffin) Penguin Group (USA) Inc.

—I Know an Old Lady Who Swallowed a Pie. Schachner, Judith Byron, illus. 2002. (J). (ps-ps). lib. bdg. 15.30 (978-0-613-55215-8(6)) Tandem Library Bks.

Kroll, Virginia. The Thanksgiving Bowl. O'Neill, Philomena, illus. 2007. 32p. (J). (gr. k-3). 15.95 (***978-1-58980-365-7(5)***) Pelican Publishing Co., Inc.

Kupperstein, Joel. Celebrating Thanksgiving: Giving Thanks. 1999. (ps-2). lib. bdg. 10.65 (978-0-613-34125-7(2)) Tandem Library Bks.

Lakin, Patricia. Fat Chance Thanksgiving. Schuett, Stacey, illus. 2001. 32p. (J). (gr. 2-5). 15.95 (978-0-8075-2288-2(0)) Whitman, Albert & Co.

Levine, Abby. This Is the Turkey. Billin-Frye, Paige, illus. 2000. 32p. (J). (ps-1). pap. 6.95 (978-0-8075-7889-6(4)) Whitman, Albert & Co.

Lissy, Jessica. Blue's Thanksgiving Feast. Cutting, David, illus. 2001. (Blue's Clues Ser.: Vol. 8). 24p. (J). (ps-k). pap. 3.50 (978-0-689-84185-9(X) , Simon Spotlight/Nickelodeon) Simon & Schuster Children's Publishing.

—Blue's Thanksgiving Feast. 2001. (gr. k-3). lib. bdg. 11.25 (978-0-613-43919-0(8)) Tandem Library Bks.

Longstreet, Barbara, et al. Woodsey School Kids Thanksgiving Feast. 2004. 28p. pap. 14.95 (978-1-4137-1992-5(9)) PublishAmerica, Inc.

Lowry, Lois. Gooney Bird & the Room Mother. Thomas, Middy Chilman, illus. 2005. 80p. (J). (gr. 3-5). 15.00 (978-0-618-53230-8(7) , Walter Lorraine) Houghton Mifflin Co. Trade & Reference Div.

—Gooney Bird & the Room Mother. 2006. 80p. (J). (gr. 2-5). 5.50 (978-0-440-42133-7(0) , Yearling) Random Hse. Children's Bks.

Markes, Julie. Thanks for Thanksgiving. Barrette, Doris, illus. 2004. 32p. (J). (ps-2). 12.99 (978-0-06-051096-1(X)) HarperCollins Pubs.

Martin, Ann M. Needle & Thread. 2007. (Main Street Ser.: No. 2). 224p. (J). (gr. 4-6). pap. 6.99 (***978-0-439-86880-8(7)***) Scholastic, Inc.

Marzollo, Jean. Thanksgiving Cats. 1999. (978-0-606-17282-0(3)) Tandem Library Bks.

Masurel, Claire. Happy Thanksgiving, Emily! Calitri, Susan, illus. 2004. (Emily Ser.). 16p. (J). pap. 6.99 (978-0-14-240201-6(X) , Puffin) Penguin Group (USA) Inc.

Mathews, Cornelius. Chanticleer: A Thanksgiving Story of the. 2006. pap. (***978-1-4250-1905-1(6)***) Assistedreadingbooks.com Inc.

Mayr, Diane. Run, Turkey Run. Rader, Laura, illus. 2007. 32p. (J). (ps-2). 15.95 (***978-0-8027-9630-1(3)***) Walker & Co.

Mayr, Diane & Rader, Laura. Run, Turkey Run. 2007. (Illus.). 32p. (J). 16.85 (***978-0-8027-9631-8(1)***) Walker & Co.

McCourt, Lisa. The Most Thankful Thing. Moore, Cyd, illus. 2004. 32p. (J). (gr. k). pap. 15.95 (978-0-439-65083-0(6) , Cartwheel Bks.) Scholastic, Inc.

McCue, Lisa, illus. Corduroy's Thanksgiving. 2006. 16p. (J). (ps). bds. 5.99 (978-0-670-06108-2(5) , Viking Juvenile) Penguin Group (USA) Inc.

McGrath, Barbara Barbieri. The M&M's Thanksgiving Feast. Tagel, Peggy, illus. 2002. 12p. (J). (ps-k). bds. 6.95 (978-1-57091-433-1(8)) Charlesbridge Publishing, Inc.

McMullan, Kate. Fluffy's Thanksgiving. Smith, Mavis, illus. 2000. (Fluffy the Classroom Guinea Pig Ser.). 40p. (J). (ps-3). pap. 3.99 (978-0-590-37215-2(7)) Scholastic, Inc.

McNamara, Margaret. Happy Thanksgiving. Gordon, Mike, illus. 2005. 32p. (J). lib. bdg. 15.00 (***978-1-4242-0953-8(6)***) Fitzgerald Bks.

—Happy Thanksgiving. Gordon, Mike, illus. 2005. (Ready-To-Read Ser.). 32p. (J). (ps-3). lib. bdg. 11.89 (978-1-4169-0506-6(5) , Aladdin) Simon & Schuster Children's Publishing.

McNamara, Margaret & Gordon, Mike. Happy Thanksgiving: Robin Hill School. 2005. (Ready-To-Read Ser.). (Illus.). 32p. (J). (ps-3). pap. 3.99 (978-1-4169-0505-9(7) , Aladdin) Simon & Schuster Children's Publishing.

Melmed, Laura. This First Thanksgiving Day: A Counting Story. Buehner, Mark, illus. 2003. 32p. (J). (ps-3). pap. 6.99 (978-0-06-054184-2(9)) HarperCollins Pubs.

Metzger, Steve. It's Thanksgiving! Wilhelm, Hans, illus. 2001. (Dinofours Ser.). (J). (ps-1). 3.25 (978-0-439-29570-3(X)) Scholastic, Inc.

Milgrim, David. Thank You, Thanksgiving. 2006. (Illus.). 32p. (J). (ps-k). 5.95 (978-0-618-75243-0(9) , Clarion Bks.) Houghton Mifflin Co. Trade & Reference Div.

—Thank You, Thanksgiving. Milgrim, David, illus. 2003. (Illus.). 32p. (J). (gr. k-ps). 9.95 (978-0-618-27466-6(9) , Clarion Bks.) Houghton Mifflin Co. Trade & Reference Div.

Moon, Alice. Lucky's Special Thanksgiving. 2007. (Illus.). (J). pap. 9.95 (***978-0-9795831-2-4(8)***) PeachMoon Publishing.

Myra, Harold Lawrence. Thanksgiving: What Makes It Special? Kurisu, Jane, illus. 2002. 32p. (J). (ps-3). 7.99 (978-1-4003-0006-8(1)) Nelson, Thomas Inc.

Nikola-Lisa, W. Setting the Turkeys Free. Wilson-Max, Ken, illus. 2004. 32p. (ps-1). 15.99 (978-0-7868-1952-2(9) , Jump at the Sun) Hyperion Bks. for Children.

Osborne, Mary Pope. Thanksgiving on Thursday. Murdocca, Sal, illus. 2002. (Magic Tree House Ser.: No. 27). 96p. (J). (gr. k-3). lib. bdg. 11.99 (978-0-375-90615-2(0)); mass mkt. 3.99 (978-0-375-80615-5(6)) Random Hse. Children's Bks. (Random Hse. Bks. for Young Readers).

—Thanksgiving on Thursday. 2002. (Magic Tree House Ser.: No. 27). (J). (gr. k-3). lib. bdg. 11.80 (978-0-613-56853-1(2)) Tandem Library Bks.

Packard, Mary. It's Thanksgiving Day! Ewing, C. S., illus. 2001. (Hello Reader! Ser.). (J). pap. (978-0-439-32101-3(8)) Scholastic, Inc.

Pease, Pamela. Macy's on Parade: A Pop-Up Celebration of the Macy's Thanksgiving Day Parade. Pease, Pamela, illus. 2002. (Illus.). 16p. (J). 36.00 (978-0-9669433-2-0(5)) Paintbox Pr.

Pinkwater, Daniel M. Big Bob & the Thanksgiving Potatoes. Pinkwater, Jill, illus. 1999. (Hello Reader! Ser.). 32p. (J). (gr. 1-3). pap. 3.99 (978-0-590-64095-4(X)) Scholastic, Inc.

Piper, Watty. The Little Engine That Could Saves the Thanksgiving Day Parade. Ong, Cristina, illus. 2002. (Reading Railroad Bks.). 32p. (J). pap. 3.49 (978-0-448-42861-1(X) , Grosset & Dunlap) Penguin Group (USA) Inc.

Preller, James. Case of the Runaway Dog. 1999. (gr. 3-6). lib. bdg. 11.80 (978-0-613-21301-1(7)) Tandem Library Bks.

Rael, Elsa Okon. Rivka's First Thanksgiving. Kovalski, Maryann, illus. 2004. 32p. (J). pap. 6.99 (978-0-689-84105-7(1) , Aladdin) Simon & Schuster Children's Publishing.

Richards, Kitty. Thornberry Thanksgiving. 2001. (gr. k-3). lib. bdg. 14.15 (978-0-613-43963-3(5)) Tandem Library Bks.

Robbins, Sandra. Tobias Turkey: A Thanksgiving Tale. Oseki, Iku, illus. 1998. (See-More's Stories Ser.). 32p. (J). (ps-3). pap. 6.95 (978-1-882601-26-4(2)); pap. 11.95 incl. audio (978-1-882601-28-8(9)) See-More's Workshop.

Roberts, Bethany. Thanksgiving Mice! Cushman, Doug, illus. 32p. (J). (ps-k). 2005. 5.95 (978-0-618-60486-9(3)); 2001. tchr. ed. 13.00 (978-0-618-12040-6(8)) Houghton Mifflin Co. Trade & Reference Div. (Clarion Bks.).

Rockwell, Anne F. Thanksgiving Day. Rockwell, Lizzy, illus. 2002. 40p. (J). (ps-k). pap. 6.99 (978-0-06-443789-9(2)) HarperCollins Pubs.

—Thanksgiving Day. Rockwell, Lizzy, illus. 2002. (J). (ps-ps). lib. bdg. 14.15 (978-0-613-65362-6(9)) Tandem Library Bks.

Roe, E. P. Three Thanksgiving Kisses. 2004. reprint ed. pap. 15.95 (978-1-4191-8991-3(3)) Kessinger Publishing, LLC.

Ruelle, Karen Gray. The Thanksgiving Beast Feast. (Holiday House Readers Ser.). (Illus.). 32p. (J). (gr. k-3). pap. 4.95 (978-0-8234-1802-2(2)) Holiday Hse., Inc.

—The Thanksgiving Beast Feast Level 2: A Holiday House Reader. Ruelle, Karen Gray, illus. (Illus.). 32p. (J). (gr. k-3). tchr. ed. 15.95 (978-0-8234-1511-3(2)) Holiday Hse., Inc.

Santa's Thanksgiving. 2005. (J). 5.95 (978-0-9769321-0-9(5)) Steingart, Nathan Publishing.

Scheer, Julian. A Thanksgiving Turkey. Himler, Ronald, illus. 2001. 32p. (J). (gr. k-3). tchr. ed. 16.95 (978-0-8234-1674-5(7)) Holiday Hse., Inc.

Schoberle, Cecile. The Thanksgiving Parade Surprise. Stephenson, Kristina, illus. 2000. (Sparkle 'n' Twinkle Ser.). 16p. (J). (ps-2). pap. 4.99 (978-0-689-83357-1(1) , Little Simon) Simon & Schuster Children's Publishing.

Schulz, Charles M. A Charlie Brown Thanksgiving. 2006. (Illus.). 128p. 4.95 (978-0-7624-2753-6(1)) Running Pr. Bk. Pubs.

Slater, Teddy. The BEST THANKSGIVING EVER. 2007. 32p. (J). pap. 5.99 (***978-0-439-87390-1(8)*** , Cartwheel Bks.) Scholastic, Inc.

Smalls, Irene. A Strawbeater's Thanksgiving. Rosales, Meodye, illus. 1998. 32p. (J). (gr. 2-5). 15.95 (978-0-316-79866-2(5)) Little Brown & Co.

Smith, Anne Warren. Turkey Monster Thanksgiving. 2003. 112p. (J). (gr. 2-5). 14.95 (978-0-8075-8125-4(9)) Whitman, Albert & Co.

Spinelli, Eileen. The Perfect Thanksgiving. Adinolfi, JoAnn, illus. rev. ed. 2003. 32p. (J). 16.95 (978-0-8050-6531-2(8) , Holt, Henry & Co. Bks. For Young Readers) Holt, Henry & Co.

—The Perfect Thanksgiving. Adinolfi, JoAnn, illus. 2007. 32p. (J). pap. 6.99 (***978-0-312-37505-8(0)*** Square Fish.

Spinelli, Eileen. Thanksgiving at the Tappletons' Lloyd, Megan, illus. 32p. (J). (ps-3). 2003. 16.99 (978-0-06-008670-1(X)); 2004. pap. 6.99 (978-0-06-008672-5(6) , Harper Trophy) HarperCollins Pubs.

Spirn, Michele. The Know-Nothings Talk Turkey. Alley, R. W., illus. 2001. 48p. (J). (gr. k-3). lib. bdg. 11.80 (978-0-613-62145-8(X)) Tandem Library Bks.

Spirn, Michele Sobel. The Know-Nothings Talk Turkey. Alley, R. W., illus. (I Can Read Bks.). 48p. (J). (ps-3). 2001. pap. 3.99 (978-0-06-444251-0(9) , Harper Trophy); 2000. 14.95 (978-0-06-028183-0(9)); 2000. 14.89 (978-0-06-028184-7(7)) HarperCollins Pubs.

—The Know-Nothings Talk Turkey. Alley, Robert W., illus. 2000. 48p. (J). (gr. k-3). lib. bdg. 11.19 (978-0-606-22291-4(X)) Tandem Library Bks.

Stanley, Diane. Thanksgiving on Plymouth Plantation. Berry, Holly, illus. 2004. (Time-Traveling Twins Ser.). 48p. (J). (gr. k-5). 15.99 (978-0-06-027069-8(1)); lib. bdg. 16.89 (978-0-06-027076-6(4)) HarperCollins Pubs. (Cotler, Joanna Books).

Star, Nancy. The Case of the Thanksgiving Thief. Bernardin, James, illus. 2004. 79p. (J). (978-0-439-67261-0(9)) Scholastic, Inc.

Steinberg, David. Theo's Thanksgiving. Woolf, Julia, illus. 2006. 10p. (J). (ps-k). bds. 6.99 (978-0-8431-2024-0(X) , Price Stern Sloan) Penguin Group (USA) Inc.

Stern, Ricki. Mission Impossible. Date not set. (Beryl E. Bean Ser.: Vol. 3). (Illus.). (J). lib. bdg. 15.89 (978-0-06-028773-3(X) , Harper Trophy) HarperCollins Pubs.

Stern, Ricki & Worcester, Heidi P. Beryl E. Bean: Mission Impossible Friendship. Bates, Amy June, illus. 2002. (J). pap. 5.99 (978-0-06-442122-5(8) , Harper Trophy) HarperCollins Pubs.

Suhay, Lisa. Pardon Me, It's Ham, Not Turkey. Cindy, Huffman, ed. Barcita, Pamela, illus. 2007. (J). (ps-3). lib. bdg. 17.95 (***978-1-933982-01-4(2))*** Bumble Bee Publishing.

Sutherland, Margaret. Thanksgiving Is for Giving Thanks. 2000. (gr. k-3). lib. bdg. 11.25 (978-0-613-31796-2(3)) Tandem Library Bks.

Sutherland, Margaret & Lamut, Sonja. Thanksgiving Is for Giving Thanks. Lamut, Sonja, illus. 2000. (Reading Railroad Bks.). (Illus.). 32p. (J). (ps-3). pap. 3.99 (978-0-448-42286-2(7) , Grosset & Dunlap) Penguin Group (USA) Inc.

Taylor, Helen. Little Pilgrim's Progress: From John Bunyan's Classic. 2006. 336p. pap. 7.99 (978-0-8024-4924-5(7)) Moody Pubs.

Tripp, Valerie. Kit Learns a Lesson: A School Story, Bk. 2. Rane, Walter, illus. 2000. (American Girls Collection: Bk. 2). 80p. (J). (gr. 2 up). 6.95 (978-1-58485-018-2(3)); 12.95 (978-1-58485-121-9(X)) American Girl Publishing, Inc.

—Kit Learns a Lesson: A School Story. 2000. (gr. 3-6). lib. bdg. 14.10 (978-0-613-28917-7(X)); (American Girls Collection: Bk. 2). (YA). (gr. 2 up). (978-0-606-18943-9(2)) Tandem Library Bks.

Wargin, Kathy-Jo. The Legend of Thanksgiving. Papp, Robert, illus. 2008. (J). (978-0-310-71179-7(7)) Zonderkidz.

Warner, Sally. Best Friend Emma. Harper, Jamie, illus. 2007. 112p. (J). (gr. 2-4). 14.99 (978-0-670-06173-0(5) , Viking Juvenile) Penguin Group (USA) Inc.

Wax, Wendy. Runaway Turkey. 2003. (ps-2). lib. bdg. 11.80 (978-0-613-73407-3(6)) Tandem Library Bks.

Weinberger, Kimberly. Our Thanksgiving. deGroat, Diane, illus. 2000. (My First Hello Reader! Ser.). 32p. (J). (ps-3). pap. 3.99 (978-0-439-09908-0(0)) Scholastic, Inc.

—Our Thanksgiving. 2000. (Hello Reader! Ser.). (J). (978-0-606-19586-7(6)) Tandem Library Bks.

Wheeler, Lisa. Turk & Runt: A Thanksgiving Comedy. Ansley, Frank, illus. 2005. 32p. (J). 6.99 (978-1-4169-0714-5(9) , Aladdin) Simon & Schuster Children's Publishing.

Willever, Lisa Funari & Funari, Lorraine. Chumpkin. Overman, Emma, illus. 2001. 32p. (ps-3). 9.95 (978-0-9679227-9-9(8) , 329-001) Franklin Mason Pr.

Willey, Margaret. Thanksgiving with Me. Bloom, Lloyd, illus. 1998. 32p. (J). (ps-3). 15.95 (978-0-06-027113-8(2) , Geringer, Laura Book) HarperCollins Pubs.

Williams, Jacklyn. Happy Thanksgiving, Gus! Cushman, Doug, illus. 2005. (Read-It! Readers Ser.). 32p. (J). (gr. k-3). 18.60 (978-1-4048-0961-1(9)) Picture Window Bks.

Willson. Dora's Thanksgiving. Roper, Robert, illus. ed. 2005. (Dora the Explorer Ser.: No. 5). 22p. (J). lib. bdg. 15.00 (978-1-59054-797-7(7)) Fitzgerald Bks.

Willson, Sarah. Dora's Thanksgiving. Roper, Robert, illus. 2003. (Dora the Explorer Ser.). 24p. (J). pap. 3.99 (978-0-689-85842-0(6) , Simon Spotlight/Nickelodeon) Simon & Schuster Children's Publishing.

Wing, Natasha. The Night Before Thanksgiving. Lyon, Tammie, illus. 2002. (J). 11.06 (978-0-7587-6890-2(7)) Book Wholesalers, Inc.

—The Night Before Thanksgiving. Lyon, Tammie Speer, illus. 2001. (Reading Railroad Bks.). 24p. (J). pap. 3.99 (978-0-448-42529-0(7) , Grosset & Dunlap) Penguin Group (USA) Inc.

—The Night Before Thanksgiving. 2001. (gr. k-3). lib. bdg. 11.25 (978-0-613-72389-3(9)) Tandem Library Bks.

Wood, Francis Eugene. Autumn's Reunion: A Story of Thanksgiving. Dean, Tina & Marken, Jon, eds. McDermott, Robert W., illus. 2006. 47p. pap. 8.00 (978-0-9746372-2-8(X)) Tip-Of-The-Moon Publishing Co.

Ziefert, Harriet. This Is Thanksgiving. Zemke, Deborah, illus. 2004. 40p. (J). 8.95 (978-1-59354-065-4(5)) Blue Apple Bks.

THEATER

see also Acting; Actors and Actresses; Ballet; Mysteries and Miracle Plays; Opera; Puppets; Shadow Shows; Theaters

Alexander, Martha, et al. Teatro para Ninos. Tenorio, Miguel A., ed. 2005. (SPA.). 246p. (gr. 4-7). pap. 14.95 (978-968-860-739-8(8)) Editorial Pax MEX. *Dist:* Independent Pubs. Group.

Bingham, Jane. Look Around a Roman Amphitheater. 2007. (***978-1-84193-721-2(5))*** Smart Apple Media.

Branch, Muriel M. Film & Theater: America in the King Years 1963-65. 2003. (African-American Arts Ser.). 80p. (J). lib. bdg. (978-0-7613-1867-5(4) , Twenty-First Century Bks.) Lerner Publishing Group.

Burdett, Lois. Much Ado about Nothing for Kids. 2002. (Shakespeare Can Be Fun Ser.). (Illus.). 64p. (J). (gr. 2-3). lib. bdg. 19.95 (978-1-55209-411-2(1)); pap. 8.95 (978-1-55209-413-6(8)) Firefly Bks., Ltd.

Chambers, Catherine. Theater. 2001. (Behind Media Ser.). (Illus.). 48p. (J). (gr. 5-8). lib. bdg. 24.22 (978-1-58810-036-8(7)) Heinemann Library.

Chrisp, Peter & Hook, Adam. A Greek Theater. 2000. (Look Inside Ser.). (Illus.). 32p. (J). (gr. 4-7). lib. bdg. 25.69 (978-0-7398-2379-8(5)) Raintree.

Cobb, Lisa Kaniut. Literary Ideas & Scripts for Young Playwrights. 2004. (Illus.). 192p. (J). pap. 30.00 (978-1-59158-071-3(4) , LU0714, Teacher Ideas Pr.) Libraries Unlimited, Inc.

DK Publishing. A Trip to the Theater. 2008. (Dk Readers Ser.). 32p. (J). 14.99 (***978-0-7566-3491-9(1));*** pap. 3.99 (***978-0-7566-3490-2(3))*** Dorling Kindersley Publishing, Inc.

DK Publishing Staff. Drama School. 2005. 48p. (J). 12.99 (978-0-7566-1138-5(5)) Dorling Kindersley Publishing, Inc.

Dunleavy, Deborah. The Jumbo Book of Drama. Kurisu, Jane, tr. Kurisu, Jane, illus. 2004. (Jumbo Bks.). 208p. (J). (gr. 4-6). (978-1-55337-008-6(2)) Kids Can Pr., Ltd.

Gallegos, Manuel. Mi Primer Teatro. 2003. (J). (978-956-240-371-9(8)) Arrayan Editores S.A.

Glencoe McGraw-Hill Staff. The Stage & the School. 9th ed. 2004. 660p. (C). stu. ed. 74.60 (978-0-07-861627-3(1) , 9780078616273) Glencoe/McGraw-Hill.

Harcourt School Publishers Staff. Behind the Scenes. 3rd ed. 2002. (Trophies English Language Learners Ser.). (Illus.). pap. 5.10 (978-0-15-327883-9(8)) Harcourt Schl. Pubs.

—Sight, Sound, Celebration. 3rd ed. 2002. (Horizons Ser.). (Illus.). (J). pap. 5.50 (978-0-15-333310-1(3)) Harcourt Schl. Pubs.

Hill, Mary. Let's Go to a Play. 2004. (Welcome Bks.). (J). (ps-2). pap. 4.95 (978-0-516-25919-2(9)); (Illus.). 24p. 18.00 (978-0-516-23995-8(3)) Scholastic Library Publishing. (Children's Pr.).

In the Movies, 6 vols. (Book2WebTM Ser.). (gr. 4-8). 36.50 (978-0-322-02982-8(1)) Wright Group, The.

Introduction to Theatre Arts 2 Student Handbook: An action handbook for middle grade & high school students & Teachers. 2007. pap., stu. ed. 24.95 (***978-1-56608-148-1(3))*** Meriwether Publishing, Ltd.

Kemper, Bitsy. Out & about at the Theater. Trover, Zachary, illus. 2006. (Field Trips Ser.). 24p. (J). (gr. 2-4). lib. bdg. 25.26 (978-1-4048-2281-8(X)) Picture Window Bks.

Madl-Palfi, L. & Tujner-Marko, B. Kaspertheater Rund ums Jahr. (Illus.). 144p. pap. (978-3-12-675640-2(9)) Klett, Ernst, Verlag GmbH DEU. *Dist:* International Bk. Import Service, Inc.

Malam, John. Theater: From First Rehearsal to Opening Night! a Building Works Book. Malam, John, illus. 2006. (Illus.). 32p. (J). (gr. k-4). 17.00 (978-1-4223-5179-6(3)) DIANE Publishing Co.

Miller, Kimberly M. Backstage at a Play. 2003. (Backstage Pass Ser.). (Illus.). 48p. (J). 24.00 (978-0-516-24327-6(6)); (YA). (gr. 7-12). pap. 6.95 (978-0-516-24389-4(6)) Scholastic Library Publishing. (Children's Pr.).

Roca, Nuria. Que Es el Arte? Teatro. 2004. (Libros Que Es el Arte? Ser.).Tr. of What Is Art? Theatre. (SPA.). 36p. (J). pap. 6.95 (978-0-7641-2705-2(5)) Barron's Educational Series, Inc.

—What Is Art? Theater. 2004. (What Is Art? Bks.). (Illus.). 36p. (J). pap. 6.95 (978-0-7641-2701-4(2)) Barron's Educational Series, Inc.

Schumacher, Thomas & Kurtti, Jeff. How Does the Show Go On: An Introduction to the Theatre. 2007. (Illus.). 128p. (J). (ps-17). 19.95 (***978-1-4231-0088-1(3)*** , Disney Editions) Disney Pr.

Sondheim, Stephen & Lapine, James. Into the Woods. Talbot, Hudson, illus. 2002. 96p. pap. 20.00 (978-0-7432-3290-6(9) , Touchstone) Simon & Schuster.

Tyre, Travis. Introduction to Drama: Discovering Theatre in Christian Education. 2001. (Illus.). 256p. (YA). (gr. 7-12). pap. 18.50 (978-1-887710-20-6(5) , ArtCan Drama Resources) Promise Productions, Inc.

VBS-Fiesta-Chadder's Theater: Preschool Leader Manual (Silly Chilies Preschool) 2006. pap. 6.99 (978-0-7644-3126-5(9)) Group Publishing, Inc.

Williams, Bill. Stage Door Workshop. Morrison, Cathy, illus. 2002. 16p. (J). (978-0-439-35085-3(9)) Scholastic, Inc.

THEATER—FICTION

Adler, David A. Cam Jansen & the School Play Mystery. Natti, Susanna, illus. 2001. (Cam Jansen Ser.: No. 21). 64p. (J). (gr. 2-6). 14.99 (978-0-670-89280-8(7) , Viking Juvenile) Penguin Group (USA) Inc.

Alexander, Lloyd. The Rope Trick. 2002. 192p. (J). (gr. 3-6). 16.99 (978-0-525-47020-5(4) , Dutton Juvenile) Penguin Group (USA) Inc.

Alexander, Lloyd, contrib. by. The Rope Trick. 2004. 195p. (J). (gr. 5). lib. bdg. 13.64 (978-0-606-30794-9(X)) Tandem Library Bks.

Aliki. Play's the Thing. Aliki, illus. 2005. (Illus.). 32p. (J). 16.99 (978-0-06-074355-0(7)); lib. bdg. 17.89 (978-0-06-074356-7(5)) HarperCollins Pubs.

Bauer, Marion Dane. The Secret of the Painted House. Gore, Leonid, illus. 2007. (Stepping Stone Bks.). 112p. (J). (gr. 1-4). lib. bdg. 14.99 (***978-0-375-94079-8(0)*** , Random Hse. Bks. for Young Readers) Random Hse. Children's Bks.

Best, Cari. Shrinking Violet. Potter, Giselle, illus. 2002. (J). 25.45 (978-0-7587-9811-4(3)) Book Wholesalers, Inc.

—Shrinking Violet. Potter, Giselle, illus. 2000. (J). (978-0-7894-6531-3(0)) Dorling Kindersley Publishing, Inc.

—Shrinking Violet. Potter, Giselle, illus. 2001. 40p. (J). (gr. 9-13). 16.50 (978-0-374-36882-1(1) , Farrar, Straus & Giroux (BYR)) Farrar, Straus & Giroux.

Blackwood, Gary L. The Shakespeare Stealer. 2000. (ps-7). 216p. (J). lib. bdg. 14.15 (978-0-613-28638-1(3)); (978-0-606-17870-9(8)) Tandem Library Bks.

Blackwood, Gary L. & Alcorn, Stephen. The Shakespeare Stealer. 1998. 208p. (J). (gr. 4-6). 16.99 (978-0-525-45863-0(8) , Dutton Juvenile) Penguin Group (USA) Inc.

Bonk, John J. Dustin Grubbs: One Man Show. 2006. 272p. (J). (gr. 3-7). pap. 5.99 (978-0-316-15408-6(3)) Little Brown & Co.

—Dustin Grubbs: Take Two! 2006. 256p. (J). (gr. 3-7). 15.99 (978-0-316-15637-0(X)) Little Brown & Co.

Brown, Marc. Arturo y el Dia de Accion de Gracias. 2000. (Arthur Adventure Ser.). (SPA., Illus.). (J). (gr. k-2). pap. 6.95 (978-1-880507-79-7(X) , LC7610) Lectorum Pubns., Inc.

—Arturo y el Dia de Accion de Gracias. 2000. (J). 13.75 (978-0-606-20186-5(6)) Tandem Library Bks.

—Francine the Superstar. Brown, Marc, illus. 22nd ed. 2000. (Arthur Chapter Bks. : Bk. 22). (Illus.). 64p. (J). (gr. 2-4). 13.95 (978-0-316-12227-6(0)) Little, Brown Bks. for Young Readers.

—Francine the Superstar. Krensky, Stephen, tr. Brown, Marc, illus. 22nd ed. 2000. (Arthur Chapter Bks. : Bk. 22). (Illus.). 64p. (J). (gr. 2-4). pap. 4.25 (978-0-316-12250-4(5)) Little, Brown Bks. for Young Readers.

—Francine the Superstar. 2000. (Arthur Chapter Bks.: Bk. 22). (Illus.). (J). 57p. (ps). lib. bdg. 11.80 (978-0-613-25249-2(7)); (gr. 3-6). 10.75 (978-0-606-18253-9(5)) Tandem Library Bks.

Byars, Betsy. Me Tarzan. Cigliano, Bill, illus. 2000. 96p. (J). (ps-3). lib. bdg. 15.89 (978-0-06-028707-8(1)) HarperCollins Pubs.

—Me Tarzan. 2002. (gr. 3-6). lib. bdg. 13.00 (978-0-613-61917-2(X)) Tandem Library Bks.

Cheaney, J. B. The True Prince. 2004. 352p. (J). (gr. 5). reprint ed. pap. 6.50 (978-0-440-41940-2(9) , Yearling) Random Hse. Children's Bks.

—The True Prince. 2004. (gr. 5-8). lib. bdg. 14.15 (978-0-613-89784-6(6)) Tandem Library Bks.

The Christmas Eve Caper. 1999. (SmartReader Ser.). (J). pap., tchr. ed. 19.95 incl. audio (978-0-7887-0118-4(5) , 79306T3) Recorded Bks., LLC.

Chute, Marchette. The Wonderful Winter. 2002. 256p. 12.95 (978-0-9714612-1-5(X)) Green Mansion Pr. LLC.

Clark, Brenda, illus. Franklin's School Play. 2002. (Franklin Ser.). 12.40 (978-1-4046-0328-8(X)) Book Wholesalers, Inc.

Cocca-Leffler, Maryann, illus. Spotlight on Stacey. 2007. (Social Studies Connects). 32p. (J). (***978-1-4287-1948-4(2));*** (gr. 2-4). pap. 4.99 (***978-1-57565-236-8(6))*** Kane Pr., The.

Conford, Ellen. Hound of the Barkervilles. Andriani, Renee W., illus. 2002. (Annabel the Actress Ser.). 96p. (J). (gr. 2-5). 15.00 (978-0-689-84734-9(3)) Simon & Schuster Children's Publishing.

Cookson, Catherine. The Cultured Handmaiden. 2000. 319p. (J). mass mkt. 10.95 (978-0-552-12476-8(1) , Corgi) Transworld Publishers Ltd. GBR. *Dist:* Trafalgar Square Publishing.

Craig, Helen. Angelina on Stage. 2006. 32p. (J). 12.99 (978-0-670-06058-0(5) , Viking Juvenile) Penguin Group (USA) Inc.

Creech, Sharon. Replay. 240p. (J). (gr. 3-7). 2007. pap. 5.99 (978-0-06-054021-0(4) , Harper Trophy); 2005. 15.99 (978-0-06-054019-7(2) , Cotler, Joanna Books); 2005. lib. bdg. 16.89 (978-0-06-054020-3(6) , Cotler, Joanna Books) HarperCollins Pubs.

de Paola, Tomie. Stagestruck. 2005. (Illus.). 32p. (J). (ps-2). 16.99 (978-0-399-24338-7(0) , Putnam Juvenile) Penguin Group (USA) Inc.

deGroat, Diane. Annie Pitts, Artichoke. 2001. 10.75 (978-0-606-22330-0(4)) Tandem Library Bks.

—Liar, Liar, Pants on Fire. deGroat, Diane, illus. 2006. (Illus.). 27p. (J). (gr. k-4). reprint ed. 16.00 (978-0-7567-9987-8(2)) DIANE Publishing Co.

dePaola, Tomie. Stagestruck. 2007. 32p. (J). (ps). pap. 6.99 (***978-0-14-240899-5(9)*** , Puffin) Penguin Group (USA) Inc.

Doudna, Kelly. Jellyfish Role. Chawla, Neena, illus. (Fact & Fiction Ser.). 24p. (J). 2007. 21.35 (978-1-59928-446-0(4)); 2006. (978-1-59928-447-7(2)) ABDO Publishing Co.

Edwards, Julie Andrews. The Great American Mousical. Walton, Tony, illus. 2007. 160p. (J). pap. 5.99 (***978-0-06-057920-3(X)*** , Harper Trophy) HarperCollins Pubs.

Edwards, Julie Andrews & Hamilton, Emma Walton. The Great American Mousical. Walton, Tony, illus. 2006. (Julie Andrews Collection). 160p. (J). 15.99 (978-0-06-057918-0(8) , Julie Andrews Collection); lib. bdg. 16.89 (978-0-06-057919-7(6)) HarperCollins Pubs.

Engelbreit, Mary. Queen of the Class. Engelbreit, Mary, illus. 2004. (Ann Estelle Stories Ser.). (Illus.). 32p. (J). (ps-3). 15.99 (978-0-06-008178-2(3)) HarperCollins Pubs.

Engelbreit, Mary. Queen of the Class. Engelbreit, Mary, illus. 2007. (Ann Estelle Stories Ser.). 32p. (J). pap. 6.99 (***978-0-06-008180-5(5)*** , Harper Trophy) HarperCollins Pubs.

Fine, Anne. Only a Show. (Illus.). 44p. (J). 11.95 (978-0-241-12906-7(0) , Hamilton, Hamish) Penguin Bks., Ltd. GBR. *Dist:* Trafalgar Square Publishing.

Forward, Toby. Shakespeare's Globe: An Interactive Pop-Up Theatre. Wijngaard, Juan, illus. 2005. 14p. (J). (gr. 3). 19.99 (978-0-7636-2694-5(5)) Candlewick Pr.

Fox, Mem. Wombat Divine. 1999. (gr. k-3). lib. bdg. 14.15 (978-0-613-22962-3(2)) Tandem Library Bks.

Fredericks, Mariah. Fame. Watkins, Liselotte, illus. 2008. (In the Cards Ser.). 288p. (J). 15.99 (978-0-689-87656-1(4)) Simon & Schuster Children's Publishing.

Gardner, Sally. Boolar's Big Day Out. 2003. (Tales from the Box Ser.: Vol. 2). (Illus.). 128p. (J). 14.95 (978-1-58234-833-9(2) , Bloomsbury Children) Bloomsbury Publishing.

Geras, Adèle. Happy Endings. 2006. 182p. (J). (***978-1-4156-6767-5(5))*** Harcourt Trade Pubs.

Geras, Adele. Happy Endings. 2006. (Illus.). 192p. (YA). reprint ed. pap. 6.95 (978-0-15-205773-2(0) , Harcourt Paperbacks) Harcourt Children's Bks.

Geras, Adèle. Like a Real Ballerina. McNicholas, Shelagh, illus. 2008. 32p. (J). (ps). 16.99 (***978-0-8037-3237-7(6)*** , Dial) Penguin Group (USA) Inc.

Guest, Elissa Haden. Iris & Walter: The School Play. Davenier, Christine, illus. 2003. (Iris & Walter Ser.). 44p. (J). 15.00 (978-0-15-216481-2(2)) Harcourt Children's Bks.

—Iris & Walter: The School Play. Davenier, Christine, illus. 2004. 44p. (J). (gr. 1-4). lib. bdg. 13.15 (978-0-606-30392-7(8)) Tandem Library Bks.

—The School Play. Davenier, Christine, illus. 2006. (Iris & Walter Ser.). 44p. (J). pap. 5.95 (978-0-15-205668-1(8) , Harcourt Paperbacks) Harcourt Children's Bks.

Harcourt School Publishers Staff. Quiet Backstage! On Level. 3rd ed. 2002. (Trophies Reading Program Ser.). (Illus.). pap. 5.10 (978-0-15-323357-9(5)) Harcourt Schl. Pubs.

Hartman, Bob. Granny Mae's Christmas Play. Cravath, Lynne W., illus. 2004. 40p. (gr. k-5). 16.99 (978-0-8066-4063-1(4) , Augsburg Bks.) Augsburg Fortress, Pubs.

Higginson, Hadley. Keeker & Springtime Surprise. Parrett, Lisa, illus. 2007. (Sneaky Pony Ser.: No. 4). 56p. (J). 15.50 (978-0-8118-5598-3(8)) Chronicle Bks. LLC.

—Keeker & Springtime Surprise. Perrett, Lisa, illus. 2007. (Sneaky Pony Ser.: No. 4). 56p. (J). pap. 3.95 (978-0-8118-5599-0(6)) Chronicle Bks. LLC.

Hirsch, Odo. Antonio S. & the Mysterious Theodore Guzman. 2001. (Illus.). 224p. (J). lib. bdg. 16.49 (978-0-7868-2605-6(3)) Hyperion Bks. for Children.

—Antonio S. & the Mysterious Theodore Guzman. Hall, August, illus. 2001. 208p. (gr. 3-7). 15.99 (978-0-7868-0747-5(4)) Hyperion Bks. for Children.

Hobbie, Nathaniel. Priscilla, Superstar. Hobbie, Jocelyn, illus. 2007. 36p. (J). (ps-1). 16.99 (978-0-316-01386-4(2)) Little Brown & Co.

Hoeye, Michael. No Time Like Show Time. 2007. 304p. (J). pap. 7.99 (***978-0-14-240982-4(0)*** , Puffin) Penguin Group (USA) Inc.

Hoeye, Michael. No Time Like Show Time: A Hermux Tantamoq Adventure. 2004. (Illus.). 288p. (J). (ps). 14.99 (978-0-399-23880-2(8) , Putnam Juvenile) Penguin Group (USA) Inc.

Hoffman, Mary. Amazing Grace. (Illus.). 32p. (J). (ARA & ENG.). (978-1-85430-334-9(1) , 93433); (ENG & VIE.). (978-1-85430-340-0(6) , 93435) Magi Pubns.

—Amazing Grace. Binch, Caroline, illus. 1998. (ENG & TUR.). 32p. (J). (ps-3). (978-1-85430-338-7(4)) Magi Pubns.

—Amazing Grace. 1999. (YA). pap. 32.99 incl. audio (978-0-7887-4097-8(0) , 41103) Recorded Bks., LLC.

—Encore, Grace! Allan, June & Binch, Caroline, illus. 2003. 112p. (J). (gr. 2-6). 14.99 (978-0-8037-2951-3(0) , Dial) Penguin Group (USA) Inc.

Hoffman, Mary & Youngblood, Shay. Amazing Grace. 1998. 44p. pap. 6.25 (978-0-87129-809-6(0) , A64) Dramatic Publishing Co.

Hoobler, Dorothy & Hoobler, Thomas. The First Decade: Curtain Going Up. Hoffman, Robin, illus. 2000. (Century Kids Ser.). 160p. (gr. 5-8). lib. bdg. 22.90 (978-0-7613-1600-8(0) , Twenty-First Century Bks.) Lerner Publishing Group.

—The Second Decade: Voyages. Hoffman, Robin, illus. 2000. (Century Kids Ser.). 160p. (gr. 5-8). lib. bdg. 22.90 (978-0-7613-1601-5(9) , Twenty-First Century Bks.) Lerner Publishing Group.

Horowitz, Anthony. The Devil & His Boy. 2007. 192p. (J). 6.99 (978-0-14-240797-4(6) , Puffin); 2000. 1p. (YA). (gr. 5-9). 17.99 (978-0-399-23432-3(2) , Philomel) Penguin Group (USA) Inc.

—The Devil & His Boy. 2001. (978-0-606-22508-3(0)); (gr. 5-8). lib. bdg. 14.15 (978-0-613-44387-6(X)) Tandem Library Bks.

Howe, James. Pinky & Rex & the School Play. 1999. (Pinky & Rex Ser.). (J). (gr. 1-4). pap., stu. ed. 22.24 incl. audio (978-0-7887-2984-3(5) , 40866) Recorded Bks., LLC.

—Pinky & Rex & the School Play. Sweet, Melissa, illus. 1998. (Pinky & Rex Ser.). (J). (gr. 1-4). (978-0-606-13707-2(6)) Tandem Library Bks.

—Pinky & Rex & the School Play. 2006. (J). (gr. 1-4). 24.21 (978-1-59961-078-8(7)) Spotlight.

Isadora, Rachel. Lili on Stage. Isadora, Rachel, illus. 2002. (Illus.). (J). 14.04 (978-0-7587-2988-0(X)) Book Wholesalers, Inc.

T U V

Jackson, Melanie. The Man in the Moonstone. 2003. (Dinah Galloway Mystery Ser.). 192p. (J). (gr. 3-7). pap. 6.95 (978-1-55143-264-9(1)) Orca Bk. Pubs. USA.

Jellen, Michelle. Spain or Shine. 2005. (S. A. S. S. (Students Across the Seven Seas) Ser.). (Illus.). 224p. (YA). (gr. 7). pap. 6.99 (978-0-14-240368-6(7) , Puffin) Penguin Group (USA) Inc.

Kimmel, Elizabeth Cody. Spin the Bottle. 2008. 240p. (J). (gr. 5). 16.99 (***978-0-8037-3191-2(4)*** , Dial) Penguin Group (USA) Inc.

Klam, Cheryl. The Pretty One. 2008. 288p. (YA). (gr. 7). pap. 9.99 (***978-0-385-73373-1(9)***); lib. bdg. 12.99 (***978-0-385-90388-2(X)***) Random Hse. Children's Bks. (Delacorte Bks. for Young Readers).

Kline, Suzy. Horrible Harry Bugs the Three Bears. Remkiewicz, Frank, illus. 2008. (J). (gr. 2). 13.99 (***978-0-670-06293-5(6)*** , Viking Juvenile) Penguin Group (USA) Inc.

Koja, Kathe. Talk. 2005. 144p. (YA). 16.00 (978-0-374-37382-5(5) , Farrar, Straus & Giroux (BYR)) Farrar, Straus & Giroux.

—Talk. 2008. 160p. (YA). pap. 6.99 (***978-0-312-37605-5(7)***) Square Fish.

—Talk. Lt. ed. 2006. 183p. (YA). 21.95 (978-0-7862-8811-3(6)) Thorndike Pr.

Korman, Gordon. No More Dead Dogs. Orig. Title: Touchdown Stage Left. 192p. (gr. 5-9). 2002. (J). pap. 5.99 (978-0-7868-1601-9(5)); 2000. (Illus.). 15.99 (978-0-7868-0531-0(5)) Hyperion Bks. for Children.

—No More Dead Dogs. 2002. Orig. Title: Touchdown Stage Left. (gr. 5-8). lib. bdg. 14.15 (978-0-613-61850-2(5)) Tandem Library Bks.

Krishnaswami, Uma. The Happiest Tree: A Yoga Story. Jeyaveeran, Ruth, illus. 2005. 32p. (J). 16.95 (978-1-58430-237-7(2)) Lee & Low Bks., Inc.

Krulik, Nancy E. No Biz Like Show Biz, No. 24. John and Wendy Staff, illus. 2007. (Katie Kazoo, Switcheroo Ser.: No. 24). 80p. (J). pap. 3.99 (978-0-448-44440-6(2) , Grosset & Dunlap) Penguin Group (USA) Inc.

—No Matzoh for Me. Hendrix, Bryan, illus. 2003. (Reading Railroad Bks.). 32p. (J). (ps-4). pap. 3.49 (978-0-448-43119-2(X) , Grosset & Dunlap) Penguin Group (USA) Inc.

—No Matzoh for Me! 2003. (ps-2). lib. bdg. 11.25 (978-0-613-61648-5(0)) Tandem Library Bks.

Landon, Kristen. Life in the Pit. Johnson, Regan, illus. 2007. 192p. (YA). (gr. 8-12). 16.95 (***978-1-933831-08-4(1)***) Blooming Tree Pr.

L'Engle, Madeleine. The Joys of Love. 2008. 272p. (YA). 16.95 (***978-0-374-33870-1(1)***) Farrar, Straus & Giroux.

Lin, Grace. The Year of the Dog. (Illus.). (J). (gr. 3-7). 2007. 162p. pap. 5.99 (978-0-316-06002-8(X)); 2005. 144p. 14.99 (978-0-316-06000-4(3)) Little Brown & Co.

Lithgow, John & Davis, Jack E. Marsupial Sue Presents the Runaway Pancake. 2005. (Illus.). 40p. (J). (ps-3). 17.95 (978-0-689-87847-3(8) , Simon & Schuster Children's Publishing) Simon & Schuster Children's Publishing.

Lorimer, Janet. The Bad Luck Play: Set 3. 2002. 32p. (YA). 2.95 (978-1-56254-425-6(X) , SP 425X) Saddleback Educational Publishing.

Maclean, Christine. Mary Margaret, Center Stage. Vicky, Lowe, illus. 2007. 176p. (J). (gr. 3). pap. 5.99 (978-0-14-240768-4(2) , Puffin) Penguin Group (USA) Inc.

—Mary Margaret, Center Stage. 2006. (Illus.). 160p. (J). (gr. 3). 15.99 (978-0-525-47597-2(4) , Dutton Juvenile) Penguin Group (USA) Inc.

Matlin, Marlee & Cooney, Doug. Leading Ladies. 2007. 288p. (J). (gr. 3-7). 15.99 (***978-0-689-86987-7(8)*** , Simon & Schuster Children's Publishing) Simon & Schuster Children's Publishing.

Mcgaffey, Kenneth. The Sorrows of a Show Girl. 2005. 144p. pap. 10.95 (978-1-4218-1579-4(6) , 1st World Library - Literary Society) 1st World Publishing, Inc.

—The Sorrows of a Show Girl. 2004. reprint ed. pap. 15.95 (978-1-4191-8297-6(8)) Kessinger Publishing, LLC.

McGaffey, Kenneth. The Sorrows of A Show Girl. 2004. reprint ed. pap. 1.99 (978-1-4192-8297-3(2)) Kessinger Publishing, LLC.

McKenna, Colleen O'Shaughnessy. Third Grade Wedding Bells. Roth, Stéphanie, illus. 2006. 160p. (J). (gr. 2-5). 15.95 (978-0-8234-1943-2(6)) Holiday Hse., Inc.

McMullan, Kate. Help! It's Parent's Day at DSA. 2006. (Dragon Slayers' Academy Ser.: No. 10). (J). (gr. 1-6). 24.21 (978-1-59961-125-9(2)) Spotlight.

Metzger, Steve. Dinofours, Our Holiday Show! Wilhelm, Hans, illus. 2002. (J). 3.50 (978-0-439-38218-2(1)) Scholastic, Inc.

Millman, Isaac. Moses Sees a Play. Millman, Isaac, illus. 2004. (Moses Goes To Ser.). (Illus.). 32p. (J). 16.00 (978-0-374-35066-6(3) , Farrar, Straus & Giroux (BYR)) Farrar, Straus & Giroux.

Moore, Peter G. Caught in the Act. 2005. 274p. (J). (gr. 7). 16.99 (978-0-670-05990-4(0) , Viking Juvenile) Penguin Group (USA) Inc.

Mullins, Julie. School Play Stars. Maddock, Monika, illus. 2005. (Girlz Rock! Ser.). (J). pap. (978-1-59336-706-0(6)) Mondo Publishing.

Naylor, Phyllis Reynolds. Simply Alice. (Alice Ser.). 240p. (YA). 2003. (Illus.). mass mkt. 5.99 (978-0-689-85965-6(1) , Simon Pulse); 2002. (gr. 6-9). 16.00 (978-0-689-82635-1(4) , Atheneum) Simon & Schuster Children's Publishing.

—Simply Alice. 2003. (Alice Ser.). (gr. 7-12). lib. bdg. 13.00 (978-0-613-73415-8(7)) Tandem Library Bks.

Oden, Fay G. Calvin's Curtain Call. 1999. 170p. (J). (gr. 4-10). per. 14.95 (978-0-9638946-2-5(5)) Tennedo Pubs.

Osborne, Mary Pope. Stage Fright on a Summer Night. Murdocca, Sal, illus. 2002. (Magic Tree House Ser.: No. 25). 96p. (J). (gr. k-3). lib. bdg. 11.99 (978-0-375-90611-4(8)); 25. pap. 3.99 (978-0-375-80611-7(3)) Random Hse. Children's Bks. (Random Hse. Bks. for Young Readers).

—Stage Fright on a Summer Night. Murdocca, Salvatore, illus. 2002. (Magic Tree House Ser. : No. 25). 70p. (J). (gr. k-3). lib. bdg. 10.79 (978-0-606-24092-5(6)) Tandem Library Bks.

—Stage Fright on a Summer Night. 2002. (Magic Tree House Ser. : No. 25). (J). (gr. k-3). lib. bdg. 11.80 (978-0-613-50506-2(9)) Tandem Library Bks.

Osborne, Mary Pope, et al. A Time to Dance Bk. 3: Virginia's Civil War Diary. 2003. (My America Ser.). 112p. (J). pap. 12.95 (978-0-439-44341-8(5)) Scholastic, Inc.

Paratore, Coleen Murtagh. Willa by Heart. 2008. (Wedding Planner's Daughter Ser.). 240p. (J). 15.99 (***978-1-4169-4076-0(6)***) Simon & Schuster Children's Publishing.

Park, Barbara. Junie B., First Grader: Shipwrecked. Brunkus, Denise, illus. 2004. 88p. (J). lib. bdg. 18.46 (***978-1-4242-0360-4(0)***) Fitzgerald Bks.

—Junie B., 1st Grader: Shipwrecked. Brunkus, Denise, illus. 2004. (Junie B. Jones Ser.: No. 23). 96p. (J). (gr. 1-4). 11.95 (978-0-375-82804-1(4) , Random Hse. Bks. for Young Readers) Random Hse. Children's Bks.

—Junie B., First Grader: Shipwrecked. Brunkus, Denise, illus. (Junie B. Jones Ser.: No. 23). 96p. (J). (gr. k-3). 2005. mass mkt. 3.99 (978-0-375-82805-8(2)); 2004. lib. bdg. 13.99 (978-0-375-92804-8(9)) Random Hse. Children's Bks. (Random Hse. Bks. for Young Readers).

Patterson, Nancy Ruth. A Simple Gift. 2003. 128p. (J). 16.00 (978-0-374-36924-8(0) , Farrar, Straus & Giroux (BYR)) Farrar, Straus & Giroux.

Pinkwater, Daniel M. Big Bob & the Winter Holiday Potato. 1999. (gr. k-3). lib. bdg. 11.80 (978-0-613-17985-0(4)) Tandem Library Bks.

Plante, Raymond. Marilou on Stage. Cummins, Sarah, tr. Favreau, Marie-Claude, illus. 1999. 59p. (gr. 1-5). (Early Readers Ser.). 4.95 (978-0-88780-480-9(2)); (First Novels Ser.: Vol. 30). (J). (978-0-88780-481-6(0)) Formac Publishing Co., Ltd. CAN. *Dist:* Casemate Pubs. & Bk. Distributors, LLC.

Poydar, Nancy. Bunny Business. 2003. (Illus.). 32p. (J). (gr. k-3). tchr. ed. 16.95 (978-0-8234-1771-1(9)) Holiday Hse., Inc.

Rallison, Janette. Fame, Glory & Other Things on My to Do List. 2005. 192p. (YA). 16.95 (978-0-8027-8991-4(9)) Walker & Co.

Rallison, Janette. Fame, Glory, & Other Things on My to Do List. 2007. 208p. (YA). pap. 6.95 (***978-0-8027-9682-0(6)***) Walker & Co.

Rau, Dana Meachen. Ladies & Gentlemen, Level C. Caputo, Jim, illus. 2001. (Compass Point Early Reader Ser.). 32p. (J). (gr. k up). lib. bdg. 18.60 (978-0-7565-0120-4(2)) Compass Point Bks.

Reich, Susanna. Penelope Bailey Takes the Stage. 2006. 208p. (J). 16.95 (978-0-7614-5287-4(7)) Cavendish, Marshall Corp.

The Reluctant Heart: A Penny Parrish Story. 2001. (Penny Parrish Story). 192p. (YA). pap. 12.95 (978-1-930009-31-8(3)) Image Cascade Publishing.

Roberts, Bethany. Thanksgiving Mice! Cushman, Doug, illus. 32p. (J). (ps-k). 2005. 5.95 (978-0-618-60486-9(3)); 2001. tchr. ed. 13.00 (978-0-618-12040-6(8)) Houghton Mifflin Co. Trade & Reference Div. (Clarion Bks.).

Roberts, Diane. Puppet Pandemonium. 128p. (J). (gr. 3-7). 2007. 5.99 (***978-0-440-42096-5(2)*** , Yearling); 2006. 15.95 (978-0-385-73309-0(7) , Delacorte Bks. for Young Readers); 2006. lib. bdg. 17.99 (978-0-385-90328-8(6) , Delacorte Bks. for Young Readers) Random Hse. Children's Bks.

Ross, Andrea. To Touch the Sun. Davenport, May, ed. l.t. ed. 2000. 195p. (YA). (gr. 9-12). pap. 15.95 (978-0-943864-99-0(2)) Davenport, May Pubs.

Sathre, Vivian. Stage Invader. l.t. ed. 2000. (Wishbone Mysteries Ser.: No. 15). (Illus.). 140p. (J). (gr. 4 up). lib. bdg. 23.33 (978-0-8368-2698-2(1)) Stevens, Gareth Inc.

—Stage Invader. 1999. (Wishbone Mysteries Ser.: No. 15). (J). (gr. 2-5). 10.04 (978-0-606-15826-8(X)) Tandem Library Bks.

Schreiber, Elisheva. The Miniature Puppet Theater Book. Pollack, Gadi & Markovitch, Evegeny, illus. (J). 14.95 (978-1-58330-617-8(X)) Feldheim Pubs.

Schwartz, Amy. Starring Miss Darlene. 2007. (Illus.). 32p. (J). (ps-3). 16.95 (***978-1-59643-230-7(6)***) Roaring Brook Pr.

Scott, Kieran. Geek Magnet. 2008. 256p. (YA). (gr. 7). 16.99 (***978-0-399-24760-6(2)*** , Putnam Juvenile) Penguin Group (USA) Inc.

Scrimger, Richard. Of Mice & Nutcrackers: A Peeler Christmas. 2001. lib. bdg. 16.40 (978-0-613-53630-1(4)) Tandem Library Bks.

—Of Mice & Nutcrackers: A Peeler Christmas. Hendry, Linda, illus. 2001. 232p. (J). (gr. 3-7). pap. 7.95 (978-0-88776-498-1(3)) Tundra Bks., Inc./Livres Toundra, Inc. CAN. *Dist:* Random Hse., Inc.

Selfors, Suzanne. Saving Juliet. 2008. 256p. (YA). 16.95 (***978-0-8027-9740-7(7)***) Walker & Co.

Shanahan, Lisa. The Sweet, Terrible, Glorious Year I Truly, Completely Lost It. 2007. 304p. (YA). (gr. 7-10). 15.99 (***978-0-385-73516-2(2)***); lib. bdg. 18.99 (***978-0-385-90505-3(X)***) Random Hse. Children's Bks. (Delacorte Bks. for Young Readers).

Shrinking Violet. 2004. 29.95 incl. cd-rom (978-1-55592-497-3(2)) Weston Woods Studios, Inc.

Sloan, Brian. Tale of Two Summers. 2006. 256p. (YA). 15.95 (978-0-689-87439-0(1) , Simon & Schuster Children's Publishing) Simon & Schuster Children's Publishing.

Smith, Michael T. Farley's Nabisco: I Want to Be in the Show. Norden, Carolyn, illus. 2001. 8p. (J). mass mkt. 0.06 (978-0-689-84484-3(0) , Simon Spotlight/ Nickelodeon) Simon & Schuster Children's Publishing.

Spirn, Michele Sobel. I Am the Turkey. Allen, Joy, illus. (I Can Read Bks.). 48p. (J). 2006. pap. 3.99 (978-0-06-053232-1(7)); 2004. 16.89 (978-0-06-053231-4(9)); 2004. 15.99 (978-0-06-053230-7(0)) HarperCollins Pubs.

Stewart, Shawn. Donny & the Doorman's Nightmare. 2004. 54p. pap. 8.11 (978-1-4116-2188-6(3)) Lulu.com.

Sumpolec, Sarah Anne. The Alliance. 2004. (Becoming Beka Ser.). 256p. (YA). pap. 12.99 (978-0-8024-6452-1(1)) Moody Pubs.

Sutherland, Tui. This Must Be Love. 256p. (J). 2005. pap. 7.99 (978-0-06-056477-3(6) , Harper Trophy); 2004. (gr. 7 up). 15.99 (978-0-06-056475-9(X)); 2004. (gr. 7 up). lib. bdg. 16.89 (978-0-06-056476-6(8)) HarperCollins Pubs.

Thomson, Sarah L. The Secret of the Rose. 2006. 304p. (J). 16.99 (978-0-06-087250-2(0)); lib. bdg. 17.89 (978-0-06-087251-9(9)) HarperCollins Pubs.

Tirabassi, Maren. Footlights & Fairy Dust: Matt & Maria Go to the Theatre. Miller, Brandie, illus. 2007. (J). pap. 14.95 (978-1-933002-26-2(3)) PublishingWorks.

Tolan, Stephanie S. The Face in the Mirror. 2000. (J). (978-0-606-19968-1(3)) Tandem Library Bks.

Trimble, Marcia. Malinda Martha Meets Mariposa: A Star Is Born. Lund, John, illus. 32p. (J). (gr. k-5). 2000. pap. 7.95 (978-1-891577-58-1(1)); 1999. 15.95 (978-1-891577-57-4(3)) Images Pr.

Understudies: Individual Title Six-Packs. (Bookweb Ser.). 32p. (gr. 4 up). 34.00 (978-0-7635-3724-1(1)) Rigby Education.

Up Goes the Curtain: A Penny Parrish Story. 2001. (Penny Parrish Story). 189p. (YA). pap. 12.95 (978-1-930009-29-5(1)) Image Cascade Publishing.

Vail, Rachel. Do-Over. 2005. 176p. (J). (gr. 7 up). pap. 7.99 (978-0-06-058749-9(0) , Harper Trophy) HarperCollins Pubs.

Vinopol, Corinne & Bednarczyk, Angela. ASL Tales & Games for Kids - Biscuit Blvd: Computer Software in American Sign Language. 2004. (J). cd-rom 34.95 (978-0-9667589-9-3(4)) Institute for Disabilities Research & Training, Inc.

Waber, Bernard. Evie & Margie. Waber, Bernard, illus. 2003. (Illus.). 32p. (J). (gr. k-3). 15.00 (978-0-618-34124-5(2) , Walter Lorraine) Houghton Mifflin Co. Trade & Reference Div.

Wells, Rosemary. The School Play. Wheeler, Jody, illus. 2001. (Yoko & Friends School Days Ser.: No. 2). 32p. (gr. k-2). 9.99 (978-0-7868-0721-5(0)); pap. 3.99 (978-0-7868-1527-2(2)) Hyperion Bks. for Children. (Volo).

—The School Play. 2001. (J). (978-0-606-22547-2(1)); lib. bdg. 11.80 (978-0-613-53555-7(3)) Tandem Library Bks.

Wesley, Valerie Wilson. How to (Almost) Ruin Your School Play. Roos, Maryn, illus. 2005. 105p. (J). (978-1-4155-7357-0(3) , Jump at the Sun) Hyperion Bks. for Children.

Wesley, Valerie Wilson. How to Almost Ruin Your School Play. 2005. (Illus.). 105p. (J). lib. bdg. 15.00 (***978-1-4242-0645-2(6)***) Fitzgerald Bks.

Weston, Martha. Act I, Act II, Act Normal. rev. ed. 2003. (Roman Mysteries Ser.). 160p. (J). (gr. 5-9). 22.90 (978-0-7613-2859-9(9)) Roaring Brook Pr.

Willner-Pardo, Gina. My Mom & Other Mysteries of the Universe. 2004. 176p. (YA). (gr. 4-6). tchr. ed. 15.00 (978-0-618-43020-8(2) , Clarion Bks.) Houghton Mifflin Co. Trade & Reference Div.

Wilson, Sarah. George Hogglesberry, Grade School Alien. Cameron, Chad, illus. 2004. 38p. (J). 14.95 (978-1-58246-063-5(9) , Tricycle Pr.) Ten Speed Pr.

Winkler, Henry & Oliver, Lin. The Curtain Went Up, My Pants Fell Down. Watson, Jesse Joshua, illus. 2007. (Hank Zipzer Ser.: No. 11). 160p. (J). 13.99 (978-0-448-44268-6(X)); pap. 4.99 (978-0-448-44267-9(1)) Penguin Group (USA) Inc. (Grosset & Dunlap).

Wood, Maryrose. My Life, the Musical. 2008. (YA). (***978-0-385-90297-7(2)***); 240p. (gr. 9). 15.99 (***978-0-385-73278-9(3)***) Dell Publishing. (Delacorte Pr.).

THEATER—HISTORY

Agate, James. The Contemporary Theatre, 1923-45, 5 Vols., Set. 2001. (YA). reprint ed. 625.00 (978-0-7222-6298-6(1)) Library Reprints, Inc.

Aliki. William Shakespeare & the Globe. Aliki, illus. 2000. (Illus.). 48p. (J). (gr. 4-7). pap. 6.99 (978-0-06-443722-6(1) , Harper Trophy) HarperCollins Pubs.

—William Shakespeare & the Globe. 2000. (gr. 3-6). lib. bdg. 15.25 (978-0-613-30192-3(7)) Tandem Library Bks.

Allison, Amy. Shakespeare's Globe. 1999. (Building History Ser.). (Illus.). 96p. (YA). (gr. 6-9). 27.45 (978-1-56006-526-5(5) , Lucent Bks.) Thomson Gale.

Childs, Alan. Tudor Theatre. (Illus.). 32p. pap. (978-0-7502-3738-3(4) , Hodder Wayland) Hodder Children's Division.

Chrisp, Peter. Welcome to the Globe! the Story of Shakespeare's Theater. 2000. (gr. k-3). lib. bdg. 11.80 (978-0-613-33212-5(1)) Tandem Library Bks.

Currie, Stephen. An Actor on the Elizabethan Stage. 2002. (Working Life Ser.). (Illus.). 112p. (J). 29.95 (978-1-59018-174-4(3) , Lucent Bks.) Thomson Gale.

Dunlap, Richard. Stars of a Summer Night: A Seventy-Year History of the Berkshire Theatre Festival, Stockbridge, Massachusetts. 2001. (Illus.). 135p. (Orig.). (YA). (gr. 6-12). pap. 15.95 (978-1-58157-023-6(6) , Berkshire Hse.) Countryman Pr.

Elgin, Kathy. Theater & Entertainment. 2004. (Changing Times Ser.). (Illus.). 32p. 26.60 (978-0-7565-0888-3(6)) Compass Point Bks.

Greenhill, Wendy, contrib. by. Shakespeare's Theater. 2000. (Illus.). 32p. (J). lib. bdg. 21.36 (978-1-57572-286-3(0)) Heinemann Library.

Greenhill, Wendy & Wignall, Paul. Shakespeare: Man of the Theater. 2000. (Illus.). 196p. (J). (gr. 8 up). lib. bdg. 28.50 (978-1-57572-282-5(8)) Heinemann Library.

Harcourt School Publishers Staff. Early Days in the American Theater Advanced Level. 3rd ed. 2002. (Trophies Reading Program Ser.). (Illus.). pap. 5.10 (978-0-15-323387-6(7)) Harcourt Schl. Pubs.

Hilliam, David. William Shakespeare: England's Greatest Playwright & Poet. 2004. (Rulers, Scholars, & Artists of Renaissance Europe Ser.). (Illus.). 112p. lib. bdg. 31.95 (978-1-4042-0318-1(4)) Rosen Publishing Group, Inc., The.

McDonnell, Kathleen. Putting on a Show: Theater for Young People. 2005. (Illus.). 199p. (J). pap. 11.95 (978-1-896764-89-4(4)) Second Story Pr. CAN. *Dist:* Orca Bk. Pubs. USA, Univ. of Toronto Pr.

Nardo, Don. Great Elizabethan Playwrights. 2002. (Lucent Library of Historical Eras). (Illus.). 112p. (J). 32.45 (978-1-59018-017-4(8) , Lucent Bks.) Thomson Gale.

Rosen, Michael. Shakespeare: His Work & His World. Ingpen, Robert R., illus. 2006. 96p. (J). (gr. 7-11). pap. 9.99 (978-0-7636-3201-4(5)) Candlewick Pr.

Sitarz, Paula Gaj. The Curtain Rises Vol. 1: A History of Theatre from Its Origins in Greek & Roman Times Through the English Restoration. Landes, William-Alan, ed. 2003. (Illus.). 144p. (YA). (gr. 5-12). pap. 28.00 (978-0-88734-685-9(5)) Players Pr., Inc.

Woollard, Mary. An Illustrated Guide to Staging History. unabr. ed. 2003. (Illus.). 302p. (YA). (gr. 4-12). pap. 30.00 (978-0-85343-624-9(X)) Miller, J. Garnet Ltd. GBR. *Dist:* Empire Publishing Service.

THEATER—PRODUCTION AND DIRECTION

Ahart, John. The Director's Eye: A Comprehensive Textbook for Directors & Actors. 2001. (Illus.). 376p. pap. 24.95 (978-1-56608-071-2(1) , N-B246) Meriwether Publishing, Ltd.

Burkholder, Kelly. Plays. 2000. (Artistic Adventures Ser.). (Illus.). 24p. (J). (gr. 2-6). lib. bdg. 23.93 (978-1-57103-357-4(2)) Rourke Publishing, LLC.

Butterfield, Moira. Little Red Riding Hood. 1998. (Playtales Ser.). 24p. (J). lib. bdg. 19.92 (978-1-57572-650-2(5)) Heinemann Library.

—Puss-in-Boots. 1998. (Playtales Ser.). 24p. (J). lib. bdg. 19.92 (978-1-57572-649-6(1)) Heinemann Library.

—Sleeping Beauty. 1998. (Playtales Ser.). 24p. (J). lib. bdg. 19.92 (978-1-57572-651-9(3)) Heinemann Library.

Domenico, Gino & Amendola, Dana. A Day at the New Amsterdam Theatre. 2004. (Illus.). 128p. (gr. 4 up). 24.95 (978-0-7868-5438-7(3) , Disney Editions) Disney Pr.

Emmer, Rae. Drama Club. 2002. (Reading Power Ser.). (Illus.). (J). (gr. 1). lib. bdg. 17.25 (978-0-8239-5968-6(6) , PowerKids Pr.) Rosen Publishing Group, Inc., The.

Friedman, Lise & Dowdle, Mary. Break a Leg! The Kids' Guide to Acting & Stagecraft. Dowdle, Mary, photos by. 2001. (Illus.). 256p. (J). (gr. 4-7). pap. 14.95 (978-0-7611-2208-1(7) , 12208) Workman Publishing Co., Inc.

Garrett, Dan, ed. Masks & Faces. 5th ed. 2003. (Drama Workshop Plays Ser.). (Illus.). 96p. (Orig.). (YA). (gr. 6-12). pap. 15.00 (978-0-333-36056-9(7)) Macmillan Education, Ltd. GBR. *Dist:* Players Pr., Inc.

—Scapegoats. 3rd ed. 2003. (Drama Workshop Plays Ser.). (Illus.). 96p. (Orig.). (YA). (gr. 6-12). pap. 15.00 (978-0-333-36055-2(9)) Macmillan Education, Ltd. GBR. *Dist:* Players Pr., Inc.

Jacobs, Paul DuBois & Swender, Jennifer. Putting on a Play: Drama Activities for Kids. Dixon, Debra, illus. 2005. 64p. pap. 9.95 (978-1-58685-767-7(3)) Gibbs Smith, Publisher.

Miller, Kimberly M. Backstage at a Play. 2003. (Backstage Pass Ser.). (Illus.). 48p. (J). 24.00 (978-0-516-24327-6(6)); (YA). (gr. 7-12). pap. 6.95 (978-0-516-24389-4(6)) Scholastic Library Publishing. (Children's Pr.).

Williamson, W. Behind the Scenes. 30.90 (978-0-8027-6704-2(4)) Walker & Co.

THEATERS

Drinkard, Lawson. Hiding in a Fort. 1999. (J). (978-0-606-17088-8(X)) Tandem Library Bks.

Fitzgerald, J. A. The Story of the Savoy Opera. 2001. (YA). reprint ed. 150.00 (978-0-7222-5540-7(3)) Library Reprints, Inc.

Greenhill, Wendy. Shakespeare's Theater. 2006. (Illus.). 32p. (978-1-4034-8610-3(7)) Heinemann Library.

Halfmann, Janet. Theaters. 1999. (Designing the Future Ser.). (Illus.). 32p. (YA). (gr. 4-7). lib. bdg. (978-0-88682-720-5(5) , Creative Education) Creative Co., The.

Haskins, James. Black Theatre in America. 1999. 160p. (YA). (gr. 7 up). pap. 6.95 (978-0-06-446159-7(9) , Harper Trophy) HarperCollins Pubs.

Peggy Parks. The Sydney Opera House. 2004. (Building World Landmarks Ser.). (Illus.). 48p. (J). 24.95 (978-1-4103-0447-6(7) , Blackbirch Pr., Inc.) Thomson Gale.

Ross, Stewart. Look Around a Shakespearean Theater. 2007. (***978-1-84193-722-9(3)***) Smart Apple Media.

Shofner, Shawndra. Sydney Opera House. 2006. (Modern Wonders of the World Ser.). (Illus.). 32p. 18.95 (***978-1-58341-442-2(8)*** , Creative Education) Creative Co., The.

THEATERS—STAGE SETTING AND SCENERY

Cobb, Vicki. On Stage. Gold, Michael, photos by. 2006. (Where's the Science Here? Ser.). (Illus.). 48p. (J). (gr. 3-7). 23.93 (978-0-7613-2774-5(6) , Millbrook Pr.) Lerner Publishing Group.

Woollard, Mary. An Illustrated Guide to Staging History. unabr. ed. 2003. (Illus.). 302p. (YA). (gr. 4-12). pap. 30.00 (978-0-85343-624-9(X)) Miller, J. Garnet Ltd. GBR. *Dist:* Empire Publishing Service.

THEATRICAL COSTUME
see Costume

THEATRICAL MAKEUP
see Make-Up, Theatrical

THEATRICAL SCENERY
see Theaters—Stage Setting and Scenery

THEFT

Amos, Janine. Thief. 2007. (Good & Bad Ser.). (Illus.). 32p. (J). (ps-2). pap. 9.95 (***978-1-84234-398-2(X)*** , Evans Brothers, Limited) Evans Publishing Group GBR. *Dist:* Independent Pubs. Group.

Berry, Joy Wilt. A Book about Stealing. 2005. (Illus.). (J). (978-0-7172-8585-3(5)) Scholastic, Inc.

Howard, Amanda. Robbery File: The Museum Heist. 2008. (J). lib. bdg. (***978-1-59716-550-1(6)***) Bearport Publishing Co., Inc.

Page, Katherine Hall. Bon Voyage, Christie & Company. (Christie & Company Ser.). (YA). (gr. 6-8). 1999. (Illus.). 10p. pap. 3.99 (978-0-380-78035-8(6)); 1998. 288p. 14.00 (978-0-380-97398-9(7)) HarperCollins Pubs.

THEFT—FICTION

Adler, David A. Bones & the Big Yellow Mystery. Newman, Barbara, illus. 2008. (Jeffrey Bones Mystery Ser.: No. 1). 32p. (J). (gr. k). pap. 3.99 (***978-0-14-241042-4(X)*** , Puffin) Penguin Group (USA) Inc.

Adler, David A. The Valentine Baby Mystery. Natti, Susanna, illus. 2006. (Cam Jansen Ser.: No. 25). 80p. (J). (gr. 2). pap. 3.99 (978-0-14-240694-6(5) , Puffin) Penguin Group (USA) Inc.

Aldridge, Janet. The Meadow-Brook Girls by the Sea, or Th. 2006. pap. (***978-1-4065-0693-8(1)***) Dodo Pr.

Ashby, Freya Katrina. Summer at the Dunes: A Deirdre Carlisle Mystery. 2007. 108p. per. 9.95 (***978-0-595-43663-7(3)***) iUniverse, Inc.

Ashworth, Sherry. Something Wicked. 2004. 222p. (J). pap. 9.99 (978-0-00-712335-3(3)) HarperCollins Pubs. Ltd. GBR. *Dist:* Independent Pubs. Group.

Atkins, Ron. Abby & the Bicycle Caper. 2004. 48p. pap. 8.95 (978-0-595-30565-0(2)) iUniverse, Inc.

Bellingham, Brenda. Lilly's Special Gift. 2005. (Illus.). 59p. (J). lib. bdg. 12.00 (***978-1-4242-1204-0(9)***) Fitzgerald Bks.

Brimner, Larry Dane. The Sparkle Thing. Tripp, Christine, illus. (Rookie Choices Ser.). 32p. (J). (gr. 1-2). 2002. pap. 5.95 (978-0-516-25978-9(4)); 2001. 19.50 (978-0-516-22159-5(0)) Scholastic Library Publishing. (Children's Pr.).

—The Sparkle Thing. 2001. (gr. k-3). lib. bdg. 14.10 (978-0-613-54360-6(2)) Tandem Library Bks.

Brooke, Samantha. Oopsy Does It. 2007. (Care Bears 8x8 Ser.). 24p. (J). pap. 3.99 (***978-0-439-02676-5(8)***) Scholastic, Inc.

Buchanan, Paul & Randall, Rod. Face the Music, Vol. 18. 2001. (Misadventures of Willie Plummett Ser.: Vol. 18). (Illus.). 128p. (J). (gr. 3-7). 5.99 (978-0-570-07126-6(7)) Concordia Publishing Hse.

Cooney, Caroline B. Mummy. 2000. (Illus.). 176p. (J). (gr. 7-12). pap. 4.50 (978-0-590-67450-8(1)) Scholastic, Inc.

—Mummy. 2000. (978-0-606-18881-4(9)) Tandem Library Bks.

Couloumbis, Audrey. Say Yes. 2003. 208p. (J). pap. 6.99 (978-0-14-250186-3(7) , Puffin) Penguin Group (USA) Inc.

Dhami, Narinder. Samosa Thief. Blundell, Tony, illus. 2005. 24p. (J). lib. bdg. 22.65 (***978-1-59646-708-8(8)***) Dingles & Co.

Diamond Hunter: MainSails Individual Title Six-Packs. (Sails Literacy Ser.). (gr. 5 up). 37.00 (978-0-7578-8063-6(0)) Rigby Education.

Dixon, Franklin W. Boardwalk Bust. 2005. 164p. (J). lib. bdg. 16.92 (***978-1-4242-0385-7(6)***) Fitzgerald Bks.

Doder, Joshua. Grk & the Hotdog Trail. 2008. (J). (***978-0-385-73361-8(5)***); (***978-0-385-90376-9(6)***); pap. (***978-0-440-42150-4(0)***) Dell Publishing. (Delacorte Pr.).

Douglas, Erin. Get That Pest! 2000. (gr. k-3). lib. bdg. 11.80 (978-0-613-63287-4(7)); (Illus.). (J). (978-0-606-18174-7(1)) Tandem Library Bks.

—Get That Pest! Yee, Wong Herbert, illus. 2003. (Green Light Readers Level 2 Ser.). 24p. (J). 11.95 (978-0-15-204873-0(1)); pap. 3.95 (978-0-15-204833-4(2)) Harcourt Children's Bks. (Green Light Readers).

Duey, Kathleen. Summer MacCleary: Virginia, 1749. 1998. (American Diaries Ser.: Vol. 10). (J). (gr. 3-7). (978-0-606-13120-9(5)) Tandem Library Bks.

Elkins, Stephen. God Is in Control. Colton, Ellie, illus. 2002. (Dove Award Signature Ser.). 32p. (J). (gr. k up). 14.99 (978-0-8054-2402-7(4)) B&H Publishing Grp.

Fertig, Dennis. Something Rotten at Village Market. McMahon, Bob, tr. McMahon, Bob, illus. 2003. 60p. (978-0-7398-5170-8(5)) Steck-Vaughn.

Friedman, Michael Jan. The Stolen Trophy. l.t. ed. 1999. (Wishbone Mysteries Ser.: No. 5). 144p. (J). (gr. 4 up). lib. bdg. 23.33 (978-0-8368-2386-8(9)) Stevens, Gareth Inc.

—The Stolen Trophy. 1998. (Wishbone Mysteries Ser.: No. 5). (J). (gr. 2-5). (978-0-606-12859-9(X)) Tandem Library Bks.

Gutman, Dan. Babe Ruth & the Ice Cream Mess. Garvin, Elaine, illus. 2004. (Ready-to-Read Cofa Ser.). 32p. (J). pap. 3.99 (978-0-689-85529-0(X) , Aladdin) Simon & Schuster Children's Publishing.

Hood, Susan. Pup & Hound Catch a Thief. Hendry, Linda, illus. 2007. (Kids Can Read Ser.). 32p. (J). (gr. k-1). (***978-1-55337-972-0(1)***); (***978-1-55337-973-7(X)***) Kids Can Pr., Ltd.

Hopkins, Lee Bennett. Mama. Marchesi, Stephen, illus. 2003. 80p. (YA). (gr. 4-6). pap. 8.95 (978-1-56397-813-5(X)) Boyds Mills Pr.

—Mama. 2000. (gr. 3-6). lib. bdg. 17.60 (978-0-613-78895-3(8)) Tandem Library Bks.

—Mama & Her Boys. Marchesi, Stephen, illus. 2003. 80p. (YA). (gr. 4-6). pap. 8.95 (978-1-56397-814-2(8)) Boyds Mills Pr.

—Mama & Her Boys. 2000. 130p. (J). (gr. 4-7). per. 17.60 (978-0-613-78896-0(6)) Tandem Library Bks.

Hunt, Elizabeth Singer. The Caper of the Crowned Jewels. 2008. (Secret Agent Jack Stalwart Ser.). 128p. (J). (gr. 1-4). pap. 4.99 (***978-1-60286-013-1(0)***) Weinstein Bks.

—The Mystery of the Mona Lisa. 2007. (Secret Agent Jack Stalwart Ser.). 128p. (J). (gr. 1-4). pap. 4.99 (***978-1-60286-001-8(7)***) Weinstein Bks.

Jackson, Melanie. Man in the Moonstone. 2003. (gr. 3-6). lib. bdg. 15.25 (978-0-613-87473-1(0)) Tandem Library Bks.

Jacobson, Rick. The Mona Lisa Caper. Jacobson, Rick & Fernandez, Laura, illus. 2005. 24p. (J). (gr. k-2). 15.95 (978-0-88776-726-5(5)) Tundra Bks., Inc./Livres Toundra, Inc. CAN. *Dist:* Random Hse., Inc.

Jewel Cases: Five Classic Mysteries of Theft. 2002. (gr. 7-12). lib. bdg. 14.70 (978-0-613-79334-6(X)) Tandem Library Bks.

Jones, Allan Frewin. Blood Stone, Vol. 6. 2003. 176p. (J). mass mkt. (978-0-330-37476-7(1) , Pan) Pan Macmillan.

Joyce, Graham. T. W. O. C. Taken Without Owner's Consent. 2007. 224p. (YA). (gr. 8 up). 16.99 (978-0-670-06090-0(9) , Viking Juvenile) Penguin Group (USA) Inc.

Keene, Carolyn. The Apple Bandit. Jones, Jan Naimo, illus. 2005. 74p. (J). lib. bdg. 15.00 (***978-1-4242-0917-0(X)***) Fitzgerald Bks.

—The Cinderella Ballet Mystery. 2007. (Nancy Drew & the Clue Crew Ser.). 96p. (J). (gr. 2-4). 24.21 (***978-1-59961-345-1(X)***) Spotlight.

—The Orchid Thief. 2006. (Nancy Drew Ser.: No. 19). 144p. (J). pap. 4.99 (978-1-4169-0980-4(X) , Aladdin) Simon & Schuster Children's Publishing.

—Scream for Ice Cream. 2007. (Nancy Drew & the Clue Crew Ser.). 96p. (J). (gr. 2-4). 24.21 (***978-1-59961-347-5(6)***) Spotlight.

—Sleepover Sleuths. 2007. (Nancy Drew & the Clue Crew Ser.). 96p. (J). (gr. 2-4). 24.21 (***978-1-59961-348-2(4)***) Spotlight.

Kline, Suzy. Horrible Harry Takes the Cake. Remkiewicz, Frank, illus. 2007. (Horrible Harry Ser.). 64p. (J). (gr. 2). 3.99 (***978-0-14-240939-8(1)*** , Puffin) Penguin Group (USA) Inc.

Lewis, J. Patrick. The Stolen Smile. Kelley, Gary, illus. 2004. 40p. 17.95 (978-1-56846-192-2(5) , Creative Editions) Creative Co., The.

Marshall, Catherine. Stage Fright/Goodbye, Sweet Prince/ Brotherly Love. 2005. (Christy Juvenile Ser.). 368p. (J). (gr. 4-7). pap. 9.99 (978-1-4003-0775-3(9)) Nelson, Thomas Inc.

Matheson, Shirlee Smith. Fastback Beach. 2006. (Orca Soundings Ser.). 112p. (YA). lib. bdg. 14.95 (978-1-55143-580-0(2)) Orca Bk. Pubs. USA.

—FastBack Beach. 2003. (gr. 7-12). lib. bdg. 16.40 (978-0-613-83711-8(8)) Tandem Library Bks.

Mazer, Anne. Now You See It, Now You Don't. 2005. (Amazing Days of Abby Hayes Ser.: No. 15). 126p. (J). lib. bdg. 16.92 (***978-1-4242-0751-0(7)***) Fitzgerald Bks.

—Now You See It, Now You Don't. 2005. (Amazing Days of Abby Hayes Ser.: No. 15). (Illus.). 126p. (J). (978-1-4156-0511-0(4)) Scholastic, Inc.

Meadows, Daisy. Amy the Amethyst Fairy. 2007. (Jewel Fairies Ser.). 80p. (Orig.). (J). pap. 4.99 (***978-0-439-93532-6(6)*** , Scholastic Paperbacks) Scholastic, Inc.

Messina, Noreen E. State House Hostage. 2002. 108p. pap. 16.95 (978-1-59286-243-6(8)) PublishAmerica, Inc.

Muhawi, Ibrahim & Kananah, Sharif. Tunjur! Tunjur! Tunjur! A Palestinian Folktale. Arzoumanian, Alik, illus. 2006. 32p. (J). (ps-3). 16.95 (978-0-7614-5225-6(7)) Cavendish, Marshall Corp.

Nostlinger. Filo Entra en Accion. 1999. Tr. of Filo Gets into the Action. 15.60 (978-0-606-17656-9(X)) Tandem Library Bks.

Oldfield, Jenny. Silver Mist 2. 2007. (Illus.). 144p. pap. 6.95 (***978-0-340-90324-7(4)***) Hodder Children's Division GBR. *Dist:* Independent Pubs. Group.

Oliver, Andrew. Scrambled. 2007. 288p. (J). per. 12.95 (***978-0-9661009-8-3(0)***) Adams-Pomeroy Pr.

Park, Barbara. Junie B. Jones Is Not a Crook. unabr. ed. 2004. (Junie B. Jones Ser.: No. 9). 67p. (J). (gr. k-3). pap. 17.00 incl. audio (978-0-8072-0530-3(3) , Listening Library) Random Hse. Audio Publishing Group.

Peck, Robert Newton. Horse Thief: A Novel. 2003. (gr. 7-12). lib. bdg. 14.15 (978-0-613-65695-5(4)) Tandem Library Bks.

Peters, Julie Anne. A Snitch in the Snob Squad. 2001. 24p. (J). 5.95 (978-0-316-54561-7(9) , Tingley, Megan Bks.) Little, Brown Bks. for Young Readers.

Pollack, Jenny. Klepto (Splashproof Edition) 2007. 1p. (J). (gr. 7). pap. 7.99 (978-0-14-240835-3(2) , Puffin) Penguin Group (USA) Inc.

Preller, James. Case of the Bicycle Bandit. 2001. (gr. 3-6). lib. bdg. 11.80 (978-0-613-35680-0(2)) Tandem Library Bks.

Prineas, Sarah. Stolen. 2008. (Magic Thief Ser.). 416p. (J). 16.99 (***978-0-06-137587-3(X)***) HarperCollins Pubs.

Roy, Ron. Mystery at the Washington Monument. Bush, Timothy, illus. 2007. 87p. (J). (***978-1-4287-4577-3(7)***) Random Hse. Children's Bks.

—The Orange Outlaw. Gurney, John Steven, illus. 2001. (A to Z Mysteries Ser.: No. 15). (J). (gr. k-3). lib. bdg. 11.80 (978-0-613-36856-8(8)) Tandem Library Bks.

—A Thief at the National Zoo. 2007. 96p. (J). lib. bdg. (***978-0-375-94804-6(X)***); pap. 3.99 (***978-0-375-84804-9(5)***) Random Hse., Inc.

Roy, Ron. Trouble at the Treasury. Bush, Timothy, illus. 2006. (Capital Mysteries Ser.: No. 7). 96p. (J). (gr. 2-4). pap. 3.99 (978-0-375-83969-6(0) , Random Hse. Bks. for Young Readers) Random Hse. Children's Bks.

Sander, Sonia. Oopsy Saves the Day. 2007. (Care Bears Movie Reader Ser.). 32p. (J). pap. 3.99 (***978-0-439-02675-8(X)***) Scholastic, Inc.

Skead, Robert. Elves Can't Kick. 2005. 84p. per. 7.99 (978-1-929478-66-8(6)) Cross Training Publishing.

Smith, D. James. The Boys of San Joaquin. 2005. (Illus.). 240p. (J). (gr. 3-7). 16.99 (978-0-689-87606-6(8) , Atheneum) Simon & Schuster Children's Publishing.

Tang, Charles, illus. The Mystery in New York, Vol. 13. 2004. (Boxcar Children Special Ser.: No. 13). 121p. (J). (gr. 2-5). 14.95 (978-0-8075-5459-3(6)); pap. 4.50 (978-0-8075-5460-9(X)) Whitman, Albert & Co.

Tosten, S. Kennedy. Troy's Amazing Universe Bk. 2: T for Toy. 2004. (Illus.). 149p. (YA). (gr. 2 up). pap. 13.95 (978-0-9743185-1-6(5)) Brite Pr.

Umansky, Kaye. Solomon Snow & the Stolen Jewel. Nash, Scott, illus. 2007. 256p. (J). (gr. 2-7). 12.99 (978-0-7636-2793-5(3)) Candlewick Pr.

Wallace, Karen. The Diamond Takers. 2007. (Lady Violet's Casebook Ser.). 224p. (J). (gr. 4-7). pap. 9.95 (***978-1-4169-0100-6(0)***) Simon & Schuster, Ltd. GBR. *Dist:* Independent Pubs. Group.

Warner, Gertrude Chandler. Mystery at Skeleton Point. 2002. (gr. 3-6). lib. bdg. 11.80 (978-0-613-65047-2(6)) Tandem Library Bks.

—The Mystery in New York. 1999. (Boxcar Children Special Ser.: No.13). (Illus.). (J). (gr. 2-5). (978-0-606-18771-8(5)) Tandem Library Bks.

Woodbury, Mary. The International Polly McDoodle. 2004. (Polly Mcdoodle Mystery Ser.). 200p. (J). (gr. 4-7). pap. 7.95 (978-1-55050-293-0(X)) Coteau Bks. CAN. *Dist:* Fitzhenry & Whiteside, Ltd.

Woodson, Marion. Dinosaur Fever. 2007. 168p. (YA). pap. 11.99 (***978-1-55002-690-0(9)*** , Sandcastle Bks.) Dundurn Group, The CAN. *Dist:* Univ. of Toronto Pr.

THEOLOGY

see also Baptism; Christianity; Church; Ethics; Faith; God; Jesus Christ; Religion; Religion and Science; Spiritual Life; Worship

Amodei, Michael. Questions of Faith: A Workbook Companion to the Catechism of the Catholic Church. 2003. 96p. wbk. ed. 6.95 (978-0-87793-689-3(7)) Ave Maria Pr.

Bridges, Jerry, et al. The Chase: Pursuing Holiness in Your Everyday Life. 2004. 128p. pap. 9.99 (978-1-57683-468-8(9)) NavPress Publishing Group.

Butt, Kyle. How Do You Know the Bible Is from God? 2002. (Illus.). 40p. 10.95 (978-0-932859-46-4(1)) Apologetics Pr., Inc.

Carroll, Michael W. & Carroll, Caroline, illus. People of the World. 2005. (God's Creation Ser.). (J). 7.99 (978-0-310-70583-3(5)) Zonderkidz.

Colkmire, Lance. Know It, Live It: Helping Kids Embrace Pentecostal Teachings. 2004. (Illus.). (J). per. 9.99 (978-0-87148-468-0(4)) Pathway Pr.

Crompton, Samuel Willard. Emanuel Swedenborg. 2004. (Spiritual Leaders & Thinkers Ser.). (Illus.). 120p. (gr. 9-13). 30.00 (978-0-7910-8102-0(8) , Chelsea Hse.) Facts On File, Inc.

Discover 1 John. (Discover Your Bible Ser.). (KOR.). (J). pap., stu. ed. 2.75 (978-1-55883-240-4(8) , 600220) C R C World Literature Ministries/Libros Desafio.

Greenwald, Zev. Stories My Grandfather Told Me: Memorable Tales based on the Weekly Sidrah. 2001. 84.99 (978-1-57819-535-0(7) , SGSH) Mesorah Pubns., Ltd.

Una Historia Que no Cesa, 2 vols. 2003. (SPA., Illus.). 240p. (YA). 24.95 (978-0-915741-18-2(0)) Stampley, C.D. Enterprises, Inc.

Is There Really a God? 2003. (BUL.). (YA). 0.75 (978-1-893345-14-0(9)) Answers in Genesis Ministries.

Kaska, Mary Jo & Bulaoro, Arnel A. Journey Through the New Testament. 2000. 84p. (YA). pap., stu. ed. 4.95 (978-0-15-901088-4(8)) Harcourt Religion Pubs.

—Journey Through the Old Testament. 2000. 84p. (YA). pap., stu. ed. 4.95 (978-0-15-900758-7(5)) Harcourt Religion Pubs.

Mitchell, Joan. Giver of Life. 2002. 24p. (YA). (gr. 6-9). pap., stu. ed. 4.00 (978-1-885996-11-4(X)) Good Ground Pr.

—Giver of Life: Confirmation Journal. 2002. 40p. (YA). (gr. 6-9). 3.25 (978-1-885996-12-1(8)) Good Ground Pr.

Pierce, Seth J. What We Believe for Teens. 2007. (J). pap. (***978-0-8163-2213-8(9)***) Pacific Pr. Publishing Assn.

Reynolds, Ralph V. The Cry of the Unborn: Understanding the Spiritual Birth Process. 125p. (Orig.). (YA). pap. 5.95 (978-1-877917-09-7(5)) Alpha Bible Pubns.

—Dividing the Word of Truth. 193p. (YA). (gr. 9). pap. 14.95 (978-1-877917-08-0(7)) Alpha Bible Pubns.

—Usando Bien la Palabra de Verdad. Geissler, Darry & Geissler, Kimberly, eds. Crossley, Darry, tr. (SPA.). 220p. (Orig.). (YA). pap. 14.95 (978-1-877917-12-7(5)) Alpha Bible Pubns.

Shewan, Edward. Manual of Christian Doctrine, Answer Key. 2004. pap. 3.95 (978-1-930367-99-9(6) , CLP10091) Christian Liberty Pr.

Shewan, Edward J. & Bristley, Eric D. God's Wonderful Works: The Creation in Six Days. 1999. (God's Creation Ser.: Vol. 3). (Illus.). 144p. (J). (gr. 2-3). pap. 9.95 (978-1-930092-08-2(3)) Christian Liberty Pr.

Smith, JoAnn Dejoria & Smith, Stan. Prayers of Blessing. 2002. 36p. 12.95 (978-0-9715405-0-7(0)) Sonrose Pubs.

Through Christ Our Lord. (YA). (gr. 9-12). 19.00 (978-1-931555-42-5(7)) Our Lady of Victory Schl.

Williams, Stephen L., Sr. The Black Heritage Bible Lessons: 14 Powerful Lessons Teaching the History of the African Race Directly from the Bible. 2002. 94p. (YA). per. 5.99 (978-1-59196-003-4(7)) Instantpublisher.com.

THEOLOGY, DEVOTIONAL
see Prayers

THEORETICAL CHEMISTRY
see Chemistry, Physical and Theoretical

THEORY OF NUMBERS
see Number Theory

THEORY OF SETS
see Set Theory

THERESE, DE LISIEUX, SAINT, 1873-1897

Baudouin-Croix, Marie. Saint Therese of Lisieux: And the "Little Way" of Love. Keefe, Maryellen, tr. from FRE. Bienfait, Andree, illus. 1999. (Along the Paths of the Gospel Ser.). 74p. (J). (gr. 2-5). 6.95 (978-0-8198-7021-6(8) , 332-339) Pauline Bks. & Media.

Glavich, Mary Kathleen. Saint Therese of Lisieux: The Way of Love. Esquinaldo, Virginia, tr. Esquinaldo, Virginia, illus. 2003. (Encounter the Saints Ser.). 132p. (J). pap. 5.95 (978-0-8198-7074-2(9) , 332-370) Pauline Bks. & Media.

Julita, Sister. The Little Flower of Jesus. 2005. (J). 15.95 (978-1-930873-98-8(0)) Neumann Pr., The.

Monahan, Joan. St. Therese of Lisieux: Missionary of Love. 2003. (Illus.). 144p. 9.95 (978-0-8091-6710-4(7) , 6710-7) Paulist Pr.

THERMODYNAMICS

see also Heat; Quantum Theory

Fleisher, Paul & Seeley, Tim. Matter & Energy: Principles of Matter & Thermodynamics. 2005. (Secrets of the Universe Ser.). (Illus.). 80p. (gr. 6-12). 25.26 (978-0-8225-2986-6(6)) Lerner Publishing Group.

Moran, Jeffrey B. How Do We Know the Laws of Thermodynamics? 2001. (Great Scientific Questions & the Scientists Who Answered Them Ser.). (Illus.). 112p. (YA). (gr. 4-6). lib. bdg. 26.50 (978-0-8239-3384-6(9)) Rosen Publishing Group, Inc., The.

Richards, Julie. Geothermal Energy & Bio-Energy. 2003. 32p. (J). lib. bdg. 24.25 (978-1-58340-336-5(1)) Smart Apple Media.

Rivera, Sheila. Heating. 2007. (First Step Nonfiction Ser.). (Illus.). 8p. (J). pap. (978-0-8225-6415-7(7)) Lerner Publishing Group.

Stefan, V. Thermonuclear Fusion Energy. 2002. (Series on HIGH SCHOOL SCIENCE). (YA). per. (978-1-889545-52-3(X)) Stefan Univ. Pr., The.

Winholtz, Wallie, et al. Thermodynamic Thrills. Hixson, Bryce, illus. 2002. (J). per. 14.95 (978-0-9660965-2-1(5)) Loose In The Lab.

THERMOMETERS AND THERMOMETRY

see also Temperature

Doudna, Kelly. If You Prefer, I'll Use a Thermometer. 2007. (Illus.). 24p. (J). 19.93 (978-1-59928-594-8(0) , Sandcastle) ABDO Publishing Co.

—If You Prefer, I'll Use a Thermometer! 2006. (Illus.). 24p. (J). pap. (978-1-59928-595-5(9)) ABDO Publishing Co.

Richardson, Adele D. Thermometers. 2004. (First Facts Ser.). (Illus.). 24p. (J). 15.95 (978-0-7368-2519-1(3)) Capstone Pr., Inc.

Rivera, Sheila. Thermometer. 2006. (First Step Nonfiction Ser.). (Illus.). 8p. (J). pap. (***978-0-8225-5711-1(8)*** , Lerner Pubns.) Lerner Publishing Group.

Royston, Angela. Hot & Cold. (My World of Science Ser.). (Illus.). 32p. (J). (gr. k-2). 2002. pap. 6.95 (978-1-4034-0040-6(7) , 91484); 2001. lib. bdg. 21.36 (978-1-58810-241-6(6)) Heinemann Library.

—Hot & Cold. 2002. (gr. k-3). lib. bdg. 14.75 (978-0-613-86991-1(5)) Tandem Library Bks.

Sargent, Brian. Hot Numbers, Cool Math. 2006. (Rookie Read-About Math Ser.). (Illus.). 31p. (J). (978-0-516-29918-1(2)) Children's Pr., Ltd.

Sullivan, Navin. Temperature. 2006. (Measure Up! Ser.). (Illus.). 48p. (J). (gr. 4-7). lib. bdg. 29.93 (978-0-7614-2322-5(2) , Benchmark Bks.) Cavendish, Marshall Corp.

Turnbauer, Lisa. What Is a Thermometer? 2004. (Rookie Read-About Science Ser.). (Illus.). 31p. (J). (gr. 1-2). pap. 4.95 (978-0-516-24611-6(9) , Children's Pr.) Scholastic Library Publishing.

THESEUS (GREEK MYTHOLOGY)

Ford, James Evelyn. Theseus & the Minotaur. Andrews, Gary, illus. 2004. (Ancient Myths Ser.). (J). (978-0-7565-0662-9(X)) Compass Point Bks.

—Theseus & the Minotaur. Andrews, Gary, illus. 2004. (Ancient Myths Ser.). 24p. (gr. 3-5). 23.93 (978-1-4048-0903-1(1)) Picture Window Bks.

Limke, Jeff. Theseus: Battling the Minotaur. McCrea, John, illus. 2007. (Graphic Myths & Legends Ser.). 48p. (J). (gr. 4-8). 26.60 (***978-0-8225-6756-1(3)*** , Graphic Universe) Lerner Publishing Group.

McCaughrean, Geraldine, retold by. Theseus. 2005. (Heroes Ser.). (Illus.). 120p. (J). (gr. 3-7). 15.95 (978-0-8126-2739-8(3)) Cricket Bks.

Tracy, Kathleen. Theseus. 2007. (Profiles in Greek & Roman Mythology Ser.). (Illus.). 48p. (J). (gr. 4-9). lib. bdg. 29.95 (***978-1-58415-554-6(X)***) Mitchell Lane Pubs., Inc.

Welvaert, Scott R. & Bowman, Laurel. Theseus & the Minotaur. 2004. (World Mythology Ser.). (Illus.). 24p. (J). lib. bdg. 21.26 (978-0-7368-2663-1(7) , Bridgestone Bks.) Capstone Pr., Inc.

THIEVES
see Robbers and Outlaws

T U V

THINKING

see Thought and Thinking

THOMAS, THE TANK ENGINE (FICTITIOUS CHARACTER)—FICTION

Allcroft, Britt. Little Engines Can Do Big Things. Coatimundi Studios, illus. 2000. (Thomas & the Magic Railroad Ser.). 24p. (J). (ps-1). pap. 3.25 (978-0-375-80553-0(2) , Random Hse. Bks. for Young Readers) Random Hse. Children's Bks.

Awdry, Christopher, ed. Thomas the Really Useful Engine. Stubbs, Tommy, illus. 1999. (Thomas the Tank Engine & Friends Ser.). 48p. (J). (gr. k-3). 11.99 (978-0-375-80242-3(8) , Random Hse. Bks. for Young Readers) Random Hse. Children's Bks.

Awdry, W. Thomas & Friends: Lift-the-Flap Freight. Courtney, Richard, illus. 2008. (Thomas & Friends Ser.). 10p. (J). (gr. k-k). bds. 6.99 (***978-0-375-84301-3(9)*** , Random Hse. Bks. for Young Readers) Random Hse. Children's Bks.

—Thomas & Friends: Thomas' Read along Storybook. Stubbs, Tommy, illus. 2007. 112p. (J). (ps-2). 15.99 (***978-0-375-84182-8(2)*** , Random Hse. Bks. for Young Readers) Random Hse. Children's Bks.

—Thomas & the Hide & Seek Animals. Bell, Owain, illus. 2007. (Thomas & Friends Ser.). 24p. (J). (ps-1). pap. 5.99 (***978-0-375-84173-6(3)*** , Random Hse. Bks. for Young Readers) Random Hse. Children's Bks.

Awdry, Wilbert V. Blue Train, Green Train. Stubbs, Tommy, illus. 2007. 24p. (J). (gr. k-ps). bds. 4.99 (***978-0-375-83984-9(4)*** , Random Hse. Bks. for Young Readers) Random Hse. Children's Bks.

—Calling All Engines! Courtney, Richard, illus. 2005. (Thomas & Friends Ser.). (J). (***978-1-4156-2388-6(0)*** Random Hse. Children's Bks.

—The Cranky Day & Other Thomas the Tank Engine Stories. 2000. (Random House Picturebacks Ser.). (Illus.). 24p. (J). (gr. k-3). pap. 3.25 (978-0-375-80246-1(0) , Random Hse. Bks. for Young Readers) Random Hse. Children's Bks.

—Para, Trencito, Para! Un Cuento de Thomas the Tank Engine. Marquez, Desiree, tr. 2001. (SPA., Illus.). 24p. (gr. k-ps). bds. 4.99 (978-0-375-81502-7(3) , RH Para Niños) Random Hse. Children's Bks.

—Thomas & Friends: On the Track. . . There & Back. Red Giraffe, illus. 2004. 16p. (J). (gr. k-ps). bds. 4.99 (978-0-375-82774-7(9) , Random Hse. Bks. for Young Readers) Random Hse. Children's Bks.

—Thomas & Friends: Henry & the Elephant. Courtney, Richard, illus. 2007. 32p. (J). (ps-1). pap. 3.99 (978-0-375-83976-4(3)); lib. bdg. 11.99 (978-0-375-93976-1(8)) Random Hse. Children's Bks. (Random Hse. Bks. for Young Readers).

—Thomas & Friends Movie Theater Storybook & Movie Projector. 2007. (RD Innovative Book & Player Format Ser.). 48p. (J). 24.99 (***978-0-7944-1362-0(5)***) Reader's Digest Assn., Inc., The.

—Thomas & the School Trip. Bell, Owain, illus. 2003. (Step into Reading Step 1 Bks.). 32p. (J). (ps-1). 11.99 (978-0-679-94365-5(X) , Random Hse. Bks. for Young Readers) Random Hse. Children's Bks.

—Thomas the Tank Engine's Hidden Surprises. Yee, Josie, illus. 1999. (Let's Go Lift & Peek Bks.). 14p. (J). (gr. k-ps). bds. 4.99 (978-0-679-89482-7(9) , Random Hse. Bks. for Young Readers) Random Hse. Children's Bks.

—Track Stars! Three Thomas & Friends Stories. 2007. (Thomas & Friends Ser.). (Illus.). 24p. (J). (ps-2). 9.99 incl. audio compact disk (978-0-375-83924-5(0) , Random Hse. Bks. for Young Readers) Random Hse. Children's Bks.

Awdry, Wilbert V. Track Stars! Three Thomas & Friends Stories. Permane, Terry, illus. Palone, Terry & Permane, Terry, photos by. 2006. (Thomas & Friends Ser.). (J). (***978-1-4156-5364-7(X)***) Random Hse. Children's Bks.

Awdry, Wilbert V. & Gerver, Jane E. A Crack in the Track: A Thomas the Tank Engine Story. Stubbs, Tommy & Nelson, Mary Beth, illus. 2001. (Beginner Bks.). 48p. (J). (gr. k-3). 8.99 (978-0-375-81246-0(6) , Random Hse. Bks. for Young Readers) Random Hse. Children's Bks.

Awdry, Wilbert V. & Random House Staff. Thomas & the Shooting Star. Stubbs, Tommy, illus. 2002. (Thomas & Friends Ser.). 32p. (J). (ps-2). 8.99 (978-0-375-81523-2(6) , Random Hse. Bks. for Young Readers) Random Hse. Children's Bks.

Awdry, Wilbert Vere. Thomas the Tank Engine 26 Volume Boxed Set: The Classic Library. 2007. (Thomas & Friends Ser.). (Illus.). 1904p. (J). (ps-2). 175.00 (***978-0-375-84183-5(0)*** , Random Hse. Bks. for Young Readers) Random Hse. Children's Bks.

Courtney, Richard, illus. The Special Delivery. 2002. (Jellybean Bks.). 24p. (J). (gr. k-k). pap. 3.25 (978-0-375-81494-5(9) , Random Hse. Bks. for Young Readers) Random Hse. Children's Bks.

—Thomas Comes to Breakfast. 2004. (Step into Reading Ser.). 32p. (J). (ps-1). pap. 3.99 (978-0-375-82892-8(3) , Random Hse. Bks. for Young Readers) Random Hse. Children's Bks.

Gerver, Jane E. A Crack in the Track: A Thomas the Tank Engine Story. Stubbs, Tommy, illus. 2001. (Beginner Bks. Ser.). 48p. (J). (ps-3). lib. bdg. 11.99 (978-0-375-91246-7(0) , Random Hse. Bks. for Young Readers) Random Hse. Children's Bks.

Golden Books Staff. All Aboard! Red Giraffe (Firm) Staff, illus. 2004. (Thomas the Tank Engine Ser.). 32p. (J). (ps-2). pap. 4.99 (978-0-375-82652-8(1) , Golden Bks.) Random Hse. Children's Bks.

—Count along with Thomas. 2000. (Thomas the Tank Engine Ser.). (J). (ps-3). bds. 12.99 (978-0-307-71308-7(3) , Golden Bks.) Random Hse., Inc.

—Thomas & Friends. 2007. (Fun Kit Ser.). (Illus.). 48p. (J). (ps-2). pap. 9.99 (***978-0-375-84693-9(X)*** , Golden Bks.) Random Hse. Children's Bks.

—Thomas & Friends Book Bag. 2007. (Bookbag Ser.). 32p. (J). (ps-2). pap. 4.99 (978-0-375-84160-6(1) , Golden Bks.) Random Hse. Children's Bks.

—Travel with Thomas. 2007. (Deluxe Coloring Book Ser.). (Illus.). 96p. (J). (ps-2). pap. 3.99 (978-0-375-83953-5(4) , Golden Bks.) Random Hse. Children's Bks.

John Brown Publishing Ltd. Games with James: Follow the Reader Level I. 2007. (Thomas & Friends Ser.). 24p. (J). (ps-1). 24.99 (***978-1-4169-4988-6(7)*** , Simon Scribbles) Simon & Schuster Children's Publishing.

—Thomas on Track: Follow the Reader Level I. 2007. (Thomas & Friends Ser.). 24p. (J). (ps-1). 24.99 (***978-1-4169-4991-6(7)*** , Simon Scribbles) Simon & Schuster Children's Publishing.

Random House Staff. Thomas' Milkshake Muddle. 2007. (Pictureback(R) Ser.). (Illus.). 24p. (J). (ps-1). pap. 3.99 (978-0-375-83979-5(8) , Random Hse. Bks. for Young Readers) Random Hse. Children's Bks.

Random House Staff. Thomas' Milkshake Muddle Book & CD. 2008. (Book & CD Ser.). (Illus.). 24p. (J). (ps-2). 9.99 (***978-0-375-84227-6(6)*** , Random Hse. Bks. for Young Readers) Random Hse. Children's Bks.

Stubbs, Tommy, illus. A Crack in the Track: A Thomas the Tank Engine Story. 2004. (Bright & Early Board Bks.). 24p. (J). (gr. k-ps). bds. 4.99 (978-0-375-82755-6(2) , Random Hse. Bks. for Young Readers) Random Hse. Children's Bks.

Thomas & Friends Picture Day. 2001. (Illus.). (J). 7.98 (978-0-7853-4782-8(8)) Publications International, Ltd.

Thomas the Tank Engine & Friends. 1999. (Thomas the Tank Engine Ser.). pap. 1.49 (978-0-307-28901-8(X) , Golden Bks.) Random Hse. Children's Bks.

THOMAS, A BECKET, SAINT, 1118?-1170—FICTION

Willard, Barbara. If All the Swords in England. Sax, Robert M., illus. 2000. (Living History Library). x, 181p. (J). (gr. 8-12). reprint ed. pap. 12.95 (978-1-883937-49-2(3) , 49-3) Bethlehem Bks.

THOMAS MORE, SAINT, 1478-1535

see More, Thomas, Sir, Saint, 1478-1535

THOMSON, J. J. (JOSEPH JOHN), SIR, 1856-1940

Sherman, Josepha. J. J. Thomson & the Discovery of Electrons. 2005. (Uncharted, Unexplored, & Unexplained Ser.). (Illus.). 48p. (J). (gr. 4-8). lib. bdg. 29.95 (978-1-58415-370-2(9)) Mitchell Lane Pubs., Inc.

THOREAU, HENRY DAVID, 1817-1862

Johnson, D. B. Henry Builds a Cabin. 2002. (Illus.). 32p. (J). (gr. k-3). 15.00 (978-0-618-13201-0(5)) Houghton Mifflin Co. Trade & Reference Div.

Locker, Thomas. Walking with Henry: Based on the Life & Works of Henry David Thoreau. (Illus.). 32p. (gr. 4). 17.95 (978-1-55591-355-7(5)) Fulcrum Publishing.

McCarthy, Pat. Henry David Thoreau: Writer, Thinker, Naturalist. 2003. (Historical American Biographies Ser.). (Illus.). 128p. (J). (gr. 6-12). lib. bdg. 26.60 (978-0-7660-1978-2(0)) Enslow Pubs., Inc.

Meltzer, Milton. Henry David Thoreau: A Biography. 2007. (J). spiral bd. 31.93 (978-0-8225-5893-4(9) , Twenty-First Century Bks.) Lerner Publishing Group.

Miller, Douglas T. Henry David Thoreau: A Man for All Seasons. 1999. 228p. (J). lib. bdg. 24.95 (978-0-7351-0220-0(1)) Replica Bks.

O'Neal, Deborah & Westengard, Angela. The Trouble with Henry: A Tale of Walden Pond. Schindler, S. D., illus. 2005. 40p. (J). (gr. k-3). 16.99 (978-0-7636-1828-5(4)) Candlewick Pr.

Thoreau, Henry David. Henry David's House. Schnur, Steven, ed. Fiore, Peter, illus. 2007. (J). pap. 7.95 (***978-0-88106-117-8(4)***) Charlesbridge Publishing, Inc.

Thoreau, Henry David, et al. Henry David's House. Schnur, Steven, ed. Fiore, Peter A., illus. 2002. (Writing & Thinking Ser.). 32p. (J). (ps-2). 16.95 (978-0-88106-116-1(6)) Charlesbridge Publishing, Inc.

THOROUGHFARES

see Roads; Streets

THORPE, JIM, 1888-1953

Brown, Don. Bright Path: Young Jim Thorpe. Brown, Don, illus. 2006. (Illus.). 40p. (J). 17.95 (978-1-59643-041-9(9)) Roaring Brook Pr.

—Bright Path: Young Jim Thorpe. 2008. (Illus.). 40p. (J). pap. 6.99 (***978-0-312-37748-9(7)***) Square Fish.

Bruchac, Joseph. Jim Thorpe, Original All-American. 2006. (Illus.). 288p. (J). (gr. 5). 16.99 (978-0-8037-3118-9(3) , Dial) Penguin Group (USA) Inc.

Fandel, Jennifer. Jim Thorpe: Greatest Athlete in the World. Whigham, Rod, illus. 2008. (J). (***978-1-4296-0152-8(3)***) Capstone Pr., Inc.

Jim Thorpe, Mejor Atleta del Mundo. 2003. (Notas Biograficas Ser.). (SPA., Illus.). pap. 48.95 (978-0-8136-5916-9(7)) Modern Curriculum Pr.

McLeese, Don. Jim Thorpe. 2003. (Rourke Discovery Library). (Illus.). 24p. (gr. 2-5). 14.95 (978-1-58952-305-0(9)) Rourke Publishing, LLC.

THOUGHT AND THINKING

see also Intellect; Logic; Perception; Reasoning

Baker, Michael. Mind Benders Beginning Bk. 1: Deductive Thinking Skills. 2005. (J). pap. 9.99 (978-0-89455-872-6(2)) Critical Thinking Bks. & Software.

—Mind Benders Beginning Bk. 2: Deductive Thinking Skills. 2005. (J). pap. 9.99 (978-0-89455-873-3(0)) Critical Thinking Bks. & Software.

Baker, Michael & Block, Cheryl. Can You Find Me? K Book: Building Thinking Skills in Reading, Math, Science, & Social Studies. 2003. (J). 14.99 (978-0-89455-794-1(7)) Critical Thinking Bks. & Software.

—Can You Find Me? PreK Book: Building Thinking Skills in Reading, Math, Science, & Social Studies. 2003. (J). 14.99 (978-0-89455-793-4(9)) Critical Thinking Bks. & Software.

Barbie Kindergarten Learning Pads: Basic Thinking Skills. 2004. (Illus.). 48p. (J). (978-0-7666-0611-1(2) , 49870) Modern Publishing.

Black, Howard & Parks, Sandra. Building Thinking Skills Level 1. 2006. 29.99 (***978-1-60144-149-2(5)***) Critical Thinking Bks. & Software.

—Building Thinking Skills Level 2. 2006. 29.99 (***978-1-60144-150-8(9)***) Critical Thinking Bks. & Software.

Bluedorn, Nathaniel & Bluedorn, Hans. The Thinking Toolbox. 2005. (Illus.). 234p. (J). per. 22.00 (978-0-9745315-1-9(0) , 4000) Christian Logic.

Bright & Beyond - Thinking. 2004. (J). (978-0-9763648-1-8(6)) Pal Toys, LLC.

Carr, Mary. Great Chocolate Caper: Mystery That Teaches Logic Skills. 2005. 64p. 11.95 (978-1-59363-035-5(2)) Prufrock Pr.

Critical Thinking-What's Wrong with This Picture? (Gr. 1-3) 2003. (J). (978-1-58232-066-3(7)) Bryan Hse. Pubs., Inc.

DiSpezio, Michael A. How Bright Is Your Brain? Amazing Games to Play with Your Mind. Leary, Catherine, illus. 2006. 80p. pap. 7.95 (978-1-4027-3463-2(8)) Sterling Publishing Co., Inc.

Donahue, Jill L. Being Considerate. Previn, Stacey, illus. 2007. (J). lib. bdg. (***978-1-4048-3777-5(9)***) Picture Window Bks.

Draze, Dianne. First Time Analogies. 2005. 48p. 10.95 (978-1-59363-073-7(5)) Prufrock Pr.

Halley. Think Before You Blink. 2002. (J). 12.95 (978-1-58728-668-1(8) , Two Can Publishing) T&N Children's Publishing.

Hubbard, L. Ron. The Thinking Book. 2002. (Illus.). 380p. (YA). (gr. 5-9). pap. 29.50 (978-0-89739-011-8(3)) Heron Bks.

Imagine That! Celebrating God's Gift of Creative Thinking. (Imagine That! Activity Bks.). (Illus.). 48p. (J). (gr. k-3). pap. 5.95 (978-0-87162-832-9(5) , E2300); (gr. 3-7). pap. 5.95 (978-0-87162-834-3(1) , E2301) Warner Pr. Pubs.

Jerome, Kate Boehm. Thinking It Through. 2004. (National Geographic Reading Expeditions Ser.). (Illus.). 24p. (J). pap. (978-0-7922-4593-3(8)) National Geographic Society.

Koumpouras, Sally. Quick Pick Activities for Critical Thinking. Rogers, Kathy, ed. 2001. (Illus.). 120p. (J). Level 1. (ps-2). 14.99 (978-1-56472-397-0(6)); Level 2. (gr. 2-4). 14.99 (978-1-56472-398-7(4)); Level 3. (gr. 4-6). 14.99 (978-1-56472-399-4(2)) Edupress, Inc.

Lanza, Janet & Flahive, Lynn. Blooming Category Activities. 2006. (ACE., Illus.). 190p. (J). per. 37.95 (978-0-7606-0654-4(4)) LinguiSystems, Inc.

Levine, Melvin D., contrib. by. Developing Minds Library, 22 cass.; set. 2004. (ps up). stu. ed. 499.95 incl. VHS (978-1-57807-643-7(9) , WG1166) WGBH Boston Video.

The Library of Higher Order of Thinking Skills. (YA). (gr. 5-8). 143.70 (978-1-4042-0624-3(8) , Rosen Central) Rosen Publishing Group, Inc., The.

Metzroth, Rupert A. Think for Yourself. 2004. (Illus.). 170p. per. 18.95 (978-1-931934-30-5(4)) Back Yard Pub.

Meyer, Joyce & Hafer, Todd. Battlefield of the Mind for Teens: Winning the Battle in Your Mind. 2006. 176p. pap. 10.99 (978-0-446-69764-4(8)) FaithWords.

Meyer, Joyce & Moore, Karen. Battlefield of the Mind for Kids. 2006. (Illus.). 192p. pap. 10.99 (978-0-446-69125-3(9)) FaithWords.

Michie, Sue. Thought Seeds: Plant Them & They Will Grow. 2005. 66p. (J). pap. (978-1-56825-098-4(3)) Rainbow Bks., Inc.

Nettleton, Pamela Hill. You First! Kids Talk about Consideration. Muehlenhardt, Amy Bailey, illus. 2004. (Kids Talk Ser.). 32p. (C). (gr. 2-5). 23.93 (978-1-4048-0624-5(5)) Picture Window Bks.

Nicholaus, Bret & Lowrie, Paul. Kidchat: 222 Creative Questions to Spark Conversations. 2007. (KidChat Ser.). (Illus.). 128p. (J). pap. 6.99 (***978-1-59643-314-4(0)***) Roaring Brook Pr.

—KidChat Too! All-New Questions to Fuel Young Minds & Mouths. 2nd rev. ed. 2007. (KidChat Ser.). (Illus.). 128p. (J). (gr. 3 up). pap. 6.99 (***978-1-59643-315-1(9)***) Roaring Brook Pr.

Powell, Jillian. Thinking & Feeling. 2004. (J). pap. (978-1-58340-439-3(2)) Smart Apple Media.

Price, Joan. Ancient & Hellenistic Thought. 2008. (Understanding Philosophy Ser.). 160p. (gr. 9). 35.00 (***978-0-7910-8739-8(5)*** , Chelsea Hse.) Facts On File, Inc.

—Contemporary Thought. 2008. (Understanding Philosophy Ser.). 160p. (gr. 9). 35.00 (***978-0-7910-8792-3(1)*** , Chelsea Hse.) Facts On File, Inc.

Risby, Bonnie. Logic Countdown. 2005. 64p. (Orig.). 11.95 (978-1-59363-087-4(5)) Prufrock Pr.

—Logic Liftoff. 2005. 64p. (Orig.). 11.95 (978-1-59363-088-1(3)) Prufrock Pr.

—Logic Safari. 2005. 32p. Bk. 1. 8.95 (978-1-59363-089-8(1)); Vol. 2. 8.95 (978-1-59363-090-4(5)); Vol. 3. 8.95 (978-1-59363-091-1(3)) Prufrock Pr.

—Lollipop Logic: Critical Thinking Activities. 2005. 64p. 11.95 (978-1-59363-092-8(1)) Prufrock Pr.

Rodríguez, Ana María. A Day in the Life of the Brain. 2006. (Brain Works). (Illus.). 112p. (J). (gr. 5-8). 32.95 (978-0-7910-8947-7(9) , Chelsea Hse.) Facts On File, Inc.

Rogers, George L. The Seven C's of Thinking Clearly Grades 5-9: Character Based Learning Activities for Developing Emotional. Social & Thinking Skills. Rogers, Gerald R., illus. 2002. 192p. (YA). (gr. 5-9). 24.95 (978-0-938399-13-1(6)) ChoiceSkills, Inc.

Rogers, Karen M. Who Can I Be? Bulat, Getty, illus. 1998. (Think-Kids Book Collection). 16p. (J). (gr. 1-4). pap. 2.95 (978-1-58237-004-0(4)) Creative Thinkers, Inc.

Roy, Jennifer Rozines & Roy, Gregory. Graphing in the Desert. 2006. (Math All Around Ser.). (Illus.). 32p. (J). lib. bdg. 28.50 (978-0-7614-2262-4(5) , Benchmark Bks.) Cavendish, Marshall Corp.

—Multiplication on the Farm. 2006. (Math All Around Ser.). (Illus.). 32p. (J). lib. bdg. 28.50 (978-0-7614-2268-6(4) , Benchmark Bks.) Cavendish, Marshall Corp.

School Specialty Publishing. Memory. 2006. (Brighter Child Flash Cards Ser.). 54p. (J). 2.99 (978-0-7696-4729-6(4) , Brighter Child) School Specialty Publishing.

School Specialty Publishing. Pentomino Pattern Cards. 1999. (C). 4.99 (***978-1-56451-862-0(0)*** , Ideal School Supply) Schaffer, Frank Pubns.

School Zone Publishing Company Staff. Thinking Skills Bilingual: Get Ready! 2004. 64p. (J). pap. 3.79 (978-1-58947-975-3(0)) School Zone Publishing Co.

Schuette, Sarah L. Consideration. 2005. (First Facts Ser.). (Illus.). 24p. (J). 21.26 (978-0-7368-3677-7(2)) Capstone Pr., Inc.

Schwartz, Linda. Brain Stretchers: Using Deductive Reasoning to Problem Solving. Larson, Eric, ed. Kennedy, Kelly, illus. 2002. 48p. (J). (gr. 4-6). pap. 7.99 (978-0-88160-329-3(5) , LW-403, Learning Works, The) Creative Teaching Pr., Inc.

Spiegel, Al. Ideas. Mortimer, Mitch, illus. 2003. 32p. (J). lib. bdg. 13.99 (978-0-9743553-0-6(5)) Crazy Man Press, LLC.

Spon, Rogie A. Truthought Bugs of Doodle Forest Activity Guide: A Companion to the Corrective Thinking Reader. Pendergrass, Mark, illus. 2001. (J). per. (978-0-9653376-5-6(0) , Truthought Pubns.) Truthought Group.

—Truthought Bugs of Doodle Forest Corrective Thinking Reader: Corrective Thinking Reader. Pendergrass, Mark, illus. 2001. (J). per. (978-0-9653376-4-9(2) , Truthought Pubns.) Truthought Group.

Walker, Pam & Wood, Elaine. Crime Scene Investigations: Real-Life Science Activities for the Elementary Grades. 1999. 272p. pap. 29.95 (978-0-7879-6687-4(8) , Jossey-Bass) Wiley, John & Sons, Inc.

Wesley, Sonya L. Game Plan Learning: A Discussion & Activity Tool. 2000. (Sport Ser.). (Illus.). (YA). spiral bd. 30.00 (978-1-931377-03-4(0)) Game Plan Pubns.

THOUGHT TRANSFERENCE

see also Extrasensory Perception

Brunke, Dawn Baumann. Awakening to Animal Voices: A Teen Guide to Telepathic Communication with All Life. 2004. (Illus.). 272p. (J). 14.95 (978-0-89281-136-6(6) , Healing Arts Pr.) Inner Traditions International, Ltd.

THREATENED PLANTS

see Endangered Plants

THREATENED SPECIES

see Endangered Species

THREE MUSKETEERS (FICTITIOUS CHARACTERS)—FICTION

Dumas, Alexandre. The Man in the Iron Mask. 1998. (978-0-606-13594-8(4)) Tandem Library Bks.

—The Three Musketeers. Nino, Alex, illus. 2nd ed. 1998. (Illustrated Classic Book Ser.). 61p. (J). (gr. 3 up). reprint ed. pap. 4.95 (978-1-56767-251-0(5)) Educational Insights, Inc.

—The Three Musketeers. Bair, Lowell, tr. Kidd, Thomas, illus. 1998. (Books of Wonder). 656p. (J). (gr. 4-7). 25.00 (978-0-688-14583-5(3)) HarperCollins Pubs.

—The Three Musketeers. (Classics Ser.). (Illus.). 56p. (J). 3.50 (978-0-7214-1753-0(1) , Dutton Juvenile) Penguin Group (USA) Inc.

—The Three Musketeers. Le Clercq, Jacques, tr. from ENG. 1999. (Modern Library Ser.). 624p. (J). (gr. 4-11). 24.95 (978-0-679-60332-0(8) , Modern Library) Random House Publishing Group.

—Los Tres Mosqueteros. (SPA.). (J). 2.49 (978-968-890-125-0(3)) Edivision Compania Editorial, S.A. de C.V. MEX. *Dist:* Continental Bk. Co., Inc., Giron Bks.

Dumas, Alexandre & Mantell, Paul. The Man in the Iron Mask. abr. ed. 1998. (Stepping Stone Book Classic Ser.). (Illus.). 128p. (J). (gr. 2-4). pap. 3.99 (978-0-679-89433-9(0) , Random Hse. Bks. for Young Readers) Random Hse. Children's Bks.

Mantell, Paul. The Man in the Iron Mask. 1998. (Bullseye Step into Classics Ser.). (J). (978-0-606-13965-6(6)) Tandem Library Bks.

THUNDERSTORMS

see also Lightning

Branley, Franklyn M. Flash, Crash, Rumble, & Roll. Kelley, True, illus. 1999. (Let's-Read-and-Find-Out Science Ser.). 32p. (J). (gr. k-4). 15.89 (978-0-06-027859-5(5)); pap. 5.99 (978-0-06-445179-6(8) , Harper Trophy) HarperCollins Pubs.

Bryan, Ashley. Story of Lightning & Thunder. 1999. (978-0-606-16282-1(8)) Tandem Library Bks.

Burby, Liza N. Electrical Storms. 1999. (Extreme Weather Ser.). 24p. (J). (gr. k-4). lib. bdg. 18.75 (978-0-8239-5294-6(0) , PowerKids Pr.) Rosen Publishing Group, Inc., The.

Chambers, Catherine. Thunderstorm. (Illus.). 32p. (J). 2007. (***978-1-4034-9580-8(7)***); 2002. lib. bdg. 21.36 (978-1-58810-653-7(5)) Heinemann Library.

Doeden, Matt. Thunderstorms. 2008. (Pull Ahead Books-Forces of Nature Ser.). (J). lib. bdg. 22.60 (***978-0-8225-7908-3(1)*** , Lerner Pubns.) Lerner Publishing Group.

Galiano, Dean. Thunderstorms & Lightning. 2003. (Weather Watchers' Library). (Illus.). 48p. (YA). (gr. 5-8). lib. bdg. 23.95 (978-0-8239-3093-7(9) , WETHLI, Rosen Central) Rosen Publishing Group, Inc., The.

Mezzanotte, Jim. Thunderstorms. 2006. (J). pap. ***978-0-8368-7922-3(8));*** lib. bdg. ***(978-0-8368-7915-5(5))*** Stevens, Gareth Inc. (Weekly Reader Early Learning Library).

Pfeffer, Wendy. Thunder & Lightning. (Science Readers Ser.). 32p. (J). 2003. mass mkt. 3.99 (978-0-439-42504-9(2)); 2002. (Illus.). pap. (978-0-439-26988-9(1)) Scholastic, Inc. (Scholastic Reference).

Redmond, Jim & Redmond, Ronda. Thunderstorms. 2001. (Nature on the Rampage Ser.). (Illus.). 32p. (J). lib. bdg. 22.83 (978-0-7398-4705-3(8)) Raintree.

Sipiera, Paul P. Thunderstorms. 1999. (978-0-606-22892-3(6)) Tandem Library Bks.

Sipiera, Paul P. & Sipiera, Diane M. Thunderstorms. 1999. (True Bks.). (Illus.). 48p. (J). (gr. 3-5). pap. 6.95 (978-0-516-26442-4(7) , Children's Pr.) Scholastic Library Publishing.

Thomas, Rick. Rumble, Boom! A Book about Thunderstorms. Shea, Denise, illus. 2005. (Amazing Science Ser.). 24p. (J). (gr. k-3). 22.60 (978-1-4048-0929-1(5)) Picture Window Bks.

Watt, Fiona. Thunder & Lightning. (Information Ser.). (Illus.). 32p. (J). 3.50 (978-0-7214-1749-3(3) , Dutton Juvenile) Penguin Group (USA) Inc.

World Book, Inc Staff, contrib. by. Thunderstorms. 2007. (J). ***(978-0-7166-9812-8(9))*** World Bk., Inc.

THUNDERSTORMS—FICTION

Adams, William J. Hate that Thunder. Stiglich, Tom, illus. 2005. 24p. (J). pap. 8.95 (978-0-9772757-0-0(1)) Mandy & Andy Bks., Inc.

Adams, William J. Hate That Thunder/Odio Ese Trueno, 1 vol. Stiglich, Tom, illus. 2006. (ENG & SPA.). 50p. (J). pap. 10.95 ***(978-0-9772757-1-7(X))*** Mandy & Andy Bks., Inc.

Beeke, Joel & Kleyn, Diana. How God Used a Thunderstorm. Anderson, Jeff, illus. (Building on the Rock Ser.). 176p. (J). pap. (978-1-85792-815-0(6) , Christian Focus) Christian Focus Pubns. GBR. *Dist:* Riverside.

Bourgeois, Paulette. Franklin & the Thunderstorm. Clark, Brenda, illus. 1998. (Franklin the Turtle Ser.). 32p. (J). (gr. k-3). (978-1-55074-403-3(8)) Kids Can Pr., Ltd.

—Franklin & the Thunderstorm. Clark, Brenda, illus. 1998. (Franklin Ser.). 32p. (J). (ps-3). pap. 4.99 (978-0-590-02635-2(6) , Cartwheel Bks.) Scholastic, Inc.

—Franklin & the Thunderstorm. Clark, Brenda, illus. 1998. (Franklin Ser.). (J). (ps-3). 11.30 (978-0-606-13403-3(4)); lib. bdg. 12.40 (978-0-613-07814-6(4)) Tandem Library Bks.

Bowdish, Lynea. Thunder Doesn't Scare Me! Wallace, John, illus. 2001. (Rookie Reader Espanol Ser.). 32p. (J). (gr. k-2). pap. 4.95 (978-0-516-27291-7(8) , Children's Pr.) Scholastic Library Publishing.

—Thunder Doesn't Scare Me! 2001. (gr. k-3). lib. bdg. 12.95 (978-0-613-54706-2(3)) Tandem Library Bks.

—Los Truenos No Me Asustan! Wallace, John, illus. 2001. (Rookie Espanol Ser.). (SPA.). 32p. (J). (gr. k-2). 19.50 (978-0-516-22354-4(2) , Children's Pr.) Scholastic Library Publishing.

—Truenos No Me Asustan! 2001. (SPA.). (gr. k-3). lib. bdg. 12.95 (978-0-613-54434-4(X)) Tandem Library Bks.

Brown, Peter. The Flight of the Dodo. 2005. (Illus.). 32p. (J). (ps-1). 15.99 (978-0-316-11038-9(8)) Little Brown & Co.

Capeci, Anne. Electric Storm. 2002. (gr. 3-6). lib. bdg. 11.80 (978-0-613-63280-5(X)) Tandem Library Bks.

Capeci, Anne & Moore, Eva. Electric Storm. Gangloff, Hope, illus. 2003. (Magic School Bus Chapter Bks.: No. 14). 96p. (J). pap. 4.99 (978-0-439-31434-3(8)) Scholastic, Inc.

Cazet, Denys. Minnie & Moo Meet Frankenswine. Cazet, Denys, illus. 2002. (Minnie & Moo Ser.). (Illus.). 12.34 (978-1-4046-1308-9(0)) Book Wholesalers, Inc.

—Minnie & Moo Meet Frankenswine. Cazet, Denys, illus. (I Can Read Bks.: Bk. 3). (Illus.). 48p. (J). 2002. pap. 3.99 (978-0-06-444311-1(6)); 2001. 15.89 (978-0-06-623749-7(1)); 2001. 14.95 (978-0-06-623748-0(3)) HarperCollins Pubs.

Minnie & Moo Meet Frankenswine. Cazet, Denys, illus. (Readalongs for Beginning Readers Ser.). (Illus.). 2005. (J). pap. 16.95 incl. audio (978-1-59112-261-6(9)); 2005. (J). pap. 18.95 incl. audio compact disk (978-1-59112-875-5(7)); 2004. 28.95 incl. audio compact disk (978-1-59112-876-2(5)); 2004. (J). 25.95 incl. audio (978-1-59112-262-3(7)); 2004. (J). pap. 29.95 incl. audio (978-1-59112-263-0(5)); 2004. (J). pap. 31.95 incl. audio compact disk (978-1-59112-877-9(3)) Live Oak Media.

—Minnie & Moo Meet Frankenswine. 2002. (gr. k-3). lib. bdg. 11.80 (978-0-613-62183-0(2)) Tandem Library Bks.

Clark, Brenda, illus. Franklin & the Thunderstorm. 2002. (Franklin Ser.). 12.40 (978-1-4046-0310-3(7)) Book Wholesalers, Inc.

D'Agata, Tabatha. Storm Tunes. Lineberger, Judy, illus. 2006. (Yes, I Can Read! Ser.: Bk. 2). 30p. (J). 6.95 ***(978-1-934138-02-1(9))*** Bouncing Ball Bks., Inc.

Dunrea, Olivier, illus. Goslings on the Prowl! 2005. (J). (978-0-618-53241-4(2)) Houghton Mifflin Co.

Fisher, Leonard Everett. Sky, Sea, the Jetty, & Me. 2001. (Illus.). 32p. (J). (gr. k-3). 15.95 (978-0-7614-5082-5(3) , Cavendish Children's Bks.) Cavendish, Marshall Corp.

Gorbachev, Valeri. Dragon Is Coming! 2008. (J). ***(978-0-15-205196-9(1))*** Harcourt Trade Pubs.

Griessman, Annette. Like a Hundred Drums. Monks, Julie, illus. 2006. 32p. (J). (gr. k-3). 15.00 (978-0-618-55878-0(0)) Houghton Mifflin Co.

Harshman, Terry Webb. Bessie's Bed. Vargo, Sharon Hawkins, illus. 2003. (Silly Millies Ser.). 32p. lib. bdg. 17.90 (978-0-7613-2742-4(8) , Millbrook Pr.) Lerner Publishing Group.

High, Gracia. I am not going to sleep Now. 2004. 21p. pap. 14.95 (978-1-4137-3000-5(0)) PublishAmerica, Inc.

Hip Hip Hooray, It's Monsoon Day! 2007. (ENG & SPA.). (YA). pap. 15.95 ***(978-1-886679-36-8(3))*** Arizona Sonora Desert Museum Pr.

Lignell, Kirk. Listen to the Raindrops W/cd. 2007. 32p. 17.95 ***(978-1-932399-15-8(1))*** Huron River Pr.

Mortensen, Denise Dowling. Ohio Thunder. Kiesler, Kate, illus. 2006. 32p. (J). (gr. k-3). 16.00 (978-0-618-59542-6(2) , Clarion Bks.) Houghton Mifflin Co. Trade & Reference Div.

Moss, Miriam. Wiley & Jasper. Bucker, Jutta, tr. Bucker, Jutta, illus. 2003. (J). 25p. pap. (978-1-59336-061-0(4)); 32p. 15.95 (978-1-59336-060-3(6)) Mondo Publishing.

Norton, Jack, Jr., as told by. Brave from Thunders. 2003. pap. 15.00 (978-0-9740071-3-7(7)) Ctr. for the Affirmation of Responsible Education.

Rumble & Bolt. 2007. 14p. pap. 10.95 ***(978-1-59125-913-8(4)*** , Penton Kids) Penton Overseas, Inc.

TIBET (CHINA)

Dolphin, Laurie. Our Journey from Tibet. Johnson, Nancy Jo, photos by. 2006. (Illus.). 40p. (J). (gr. k-4). 16.00 (978-0-7567-9812-3(4)) DIANE Publishing Co.

Gibb, Christopher. The Dalai Lama: Peacemaker from Tibet. 2002. (Famous Lives Ser.). (Illus.). 48p. (J). lib. bdg. 27.12 (978-0-7398-5520-1(4)) Raintree.

Kummer, Patricia K. Tibet. 2003. (Enchantment of the World, Second Ser.). (Illus.). 144p. (YA). (gr. 5-9). 36.00 (978-0-516-22693-4(2) , Children's Pr.) Scholastic Library Publishing.

Levy, Patricia & Bosco, Don. Tibet. 2nd ed. 2007. (Cultures of the World Ser.). 144p. (J). lib. bdg. 39.93 (978-0-7614-2076-7(2) , Benchmark Bks.) Cavendish, Marshall Corp.

Rice, Earle. Alexandra David-Neel: Explorer at the Roof of the World. 2004. (Women in Explorers Ser.). 30.00 (978-0-7910-7715-3(2) , Chelsea Hse.) Facts On File, Inc.

Sis, Peter. Tibet Through the Red Box: Through the Red Box. Sis, Peter, illus. 1998. (Illus.). 64p. (J). (gr. 4-7). 25.00 (978-0-374-37552-2(6) , Farrar, Straus & Giroux (BYR)) Farrar, Straus & Giroux.

Worth, Richard. Dalai Lama (Tenzin Gyatso) 2004. (Spiritual Leaders & Thinkers Ser.). (Illus.). 120p. (gr. 9-13). 30.00 (978-0-7910-7868-6(X) , Chelsea Hse.) Facts On File, Inc.

TIBET (CHINA)—FICTION

Carlson, Dale Bick. The Mountain of Truth. Nicklaus, Carol, illus. 2nd ed. 2005. 169p. (gr. 8-12). reprint ed. pap. 14.95 (978-1-884158-30-8(7)) Bick Publishing Hse.

Gecko Gathering. 2005. (Soundprints' Amazing Animal Adventures! Ser.). (Illus.). 36p. (J). (ps-2). 8.95 incl. reel tape (978-1-59249-322-7(X) , SC7107) Soundprints.

Giancamilli, Vanessa. Gecko Gathering. 2005. (Soundprints' Amazing Animal Adventures! Ser.). (Illus.). 32p. (J). (ps-2). 19.95 incl. audio (978-1-59249-321-0(1) , BC7107) Soundprints.

—Gecko Gathering. Kest, Kristin, illus. 2005. (Amazing Animal Adventures Ser.). 32p. (J). (ps-2). 2.95 (978-1-59249-289-3(4) , S7157); 9.95 (978-1-59249-323-4(8) , PS7157); 15.95 (978-1-59249-288-6(6) , B7107); pap. 6.95 (978-1-59249-290-9(8) , S7107) Soundprints.

The Goat & the Rock: a Tale from Tibet: Fifth Grade Guided Comprehension Level O. (On Our Way to English Ser.). (gr. 5 up). 34.50 (978-0-7578-6604-3(2)) Rigby Education.

Hergé. Tintin au Tibet. 1999. (Tintin Ser.).Tr. of Tintin in Tibet. (FRE.). (J). (gr. 4-7). pap. 21.95 (978-2-203-00119-0(4)) Casterman, Editions FRA. *Dist:* Distribooks, Inc.

—Tintin au Tibet.Tr. of Tintin in Tibet. (J). (gr. 7-9). ring bd. 24.95 (978-0-8288-5092-6(5)) French & European Pubns., Inc.

—Tintin en Tibet. (SPA., Illus.). 62p. (J). 24.95 (978-0-8288-4996-8(X)) French & European Pubns., Inc.

—Tintin en Tibet. (Tintin Ser.). (SPA.). 64p. (J). 14.95 (978-84-261-1403-7(2)) Juventud, Editorial ESP. *Dist:* Distribooks, Inc.

—Tintin in Tibet. Orig. Title: Tintin au Tibet. (Illus.). 62p. (J). 24.95 (978-0-8288-5001-8(1)) French & European Pubns., Inc.

Moffett, Rodney. The Eighth Crest. 2006. (ENG.). 228p. per. 19.95 ***(978-1-4241-3907-1(4))*** PublishAmerica, Inc.

Montgomery, R. A. Caravan. 2007. (Choose Your Own Adventure - Dragonlarks Ser.). (Illus.). 64p. (J). pap. 5.99 ***(978-1-933390-54-3(9))*** Chooseco LLC.

Rose, Naomi. Tibetan Tales for Little Buddhas. 2003. (Illus.). 64p. (J). pap. 16.95 (978-1-57416-081-9(8)) Clear Light Pubs.

Trottier, Maxine. Little Dog Moon. Fernandez, Laura & Jacobson, Rick, illus. 2000. 20p. (J). (ps-3). 14.95 (978-0-7737-3220-9(9)) Stoddart Kids CAN. *Dist:* Fitzhenry & Whiteside, Ltd.

Whitesel, Cheryl Aylward. Rebel: A Tibetan Odyssey. 2000. 208p. (J). (gr. 5 up). 16.99 (978-0-688-16735-6(7)) HarperCollins Pubs.

TIDAL WAVES

see Ocean Waves

TIDES

Declus, Jennifer. What Might I Find in a Tidepool. Kalasea, illus. 2004. (J). (978-0-9743690-4-4(7)) Britt Allcroft Productions.

Halfmann, Janet. Life in a Tide Pool. 2000. (Lifeviews Ser.). (Illus.). 32p. (J). lib. bdg. (978-1-58341-076-9(7) , Creative Education) Creative Co., The.

Jacobs, Marian B. Why Does the Ocean Have Tides? 1999. (Library of Why). (Illus.). 24p. (J). (gr. k-4). lib. bdg. 18.75 (978-0-8239-5272-4(X) , PowerKids Pr.) Rosen Publishing Group, Inc., The.

Kudlinski, Kathleen V. The Seaside Switch. Burnett, Lindy, illus. 2007. 32p. (gr. k-3). 16.95 (978-1-55971-964-3(8) , NorthWord Bks. for Young Readers) T&N Children's Publishing.

Llewellyn, Claire. Seashore & Tides. 2007. (Illus.). 24p. (J). ***(978-1-59771-019-0(9))*** Sea-To-Sea Pubns.

O'Daley, Anne. Gravity. 2003. (Illus.). 24p. (J). 22.45 (978-1-4103-0081-2(1) , Blackbirch Pr., Inc.) Thomson Gale.

Richter, Al. Ocean Tides. 2006. (Reading Room Collection. Science). (Illus.). 16p. (J). lib. bdg. (978-1-4042-3343-0(1) , PowerKids Pr.) Rosen Publishing Group, Inc., The.

Stone, Lynn M. High Tide, Low Tide. 2007. (Illus.). 24p. (J). (978-1-60044-178-3(5)) Rourke Publishing, LLC.

TIDES—FICTION

Herman, Gail. The Creeping Tide. Nez, John, illus. 2003. (Science Solves It! Ser.). 32p. (J). 4.99 (978-1-57565-128-6(9)) Kane Pr., The.

—Creeping Tide. 2003. (gr. k-3). lib. bdg. 13.00 (978-0-613-79276-9(9)) Tandem Library Bks.

TIGERS

Aaseng, Nathan. Tigers. 2005. (Animals Attack Ser.). (Illus.). 48p. (J). (gr. 4-8). lib. bdg. 26.20 (978-0-7377-1545-3(6) , Greenhaven Pr., Inc.) Thomson Gale.

Adams, Richard & Bayley, Nicola. El Viaje de los Tigres. (SPA.). 32p. (J). (gr. 3). (978-84-264-3587-3(4) , LM0669) Editorial Lumen ESP. *Dist:* Lectorum Pubns., Inc.

Animal Lives: Tigers. 2006. pap. 4.99 (978-1-4206-8161-1(3)) Teacher Created Materials, Inc.

Baker, David G. & Stewart, Margaret Taylor. Tales of Mike the Tiger: Facts & Fun for Everyone. 2006. (Illus.). 144p. (J). 19.95 (978-0-8071-3118-3(0)) Louisiana State Univ. Pr.

Barnes, Julia. The Secret Lives of Tigers. 2006. (Illus.). 32p. (J). lib. bdg. ***(978-0-8368-7659-8(8))*** Stevens, Gareth Inc.

Barnes, Julia. 101 Facts about Tigers. 2004. (One Hundred One Facts about Predators Ser.). (Illus.). 32p. (J). (gr. 3 up). lib. bdg. 23.33 (978-0-8368-4041-4(0)) Stevens, Gareth Inc.

Biel, Timothy Levi. Tigers. 2001. (Zoobooks Ser.). (Illus.). 24p. (J). (gr. 1-6). 15.95 (978-1-888153-43-9(1)) Wildlife Education, Ltd.

Big Cats. 2004. (Explorasaws Ser.). (Illus.). 48p. (J). pap. (978-1-84229-758-2(9)) Top That! Publishing PLC.

Books Are Fun 8 Title Animal Lives Set: Tigers. 2006. (J). (978-1-59566-312-2(6)) QEB Publishing Inc.

Bortolotti, Dan. Tiger Rescue: Changing the Future for Endangered Wildlife. 2003. (Firefly Animal Rescue Ser.). (Illus.). 64p. (J). (gr. 5). pap. 9.95 (978-1-55297-558-9(4)); lib. bdg. 19.95 (978-1-55297-599-2(1)) Firefly Bks., Ltd.

—Tiger Rescue: Changing the Future for Endangered Wildlife. 2003. (gr. 5-8). lib. bdg. 18.75 (978-0-613-78596-9(7)) Tandem Library Bks.

Buettner, Debi. Discover Siberian Tigers Vol. 1: Cubs First Hunt. Karecki, Jason & Williams, Sandra, illus. 1998. 24p. (J). (gr. k-5). (978-1-890716-04-2(9)) K&M International.

Chancellor, Deborah. Tiger Tales. 2000. (Eyewitness Readers Ser.). (J). (978-0-606-19391-7(X)) Tandem Library Bks.

Cole & Leeson. El Tigre. 2002. (Gatos Salvajes del Mundo Serie).Tr. of Wild Cats Of The World: The Tiger. (SPA.). 24p. (J). (gr. 3-5). 24.94 (978-1-4103-0002-7(1) , Blackbirch Pr., Inc.) Thomson Gale.

Cole, Melissa S. Tigers. 2001. (Wild Cats of the World Ser.). (Illus.). 24p. (J). (gr. 3-6). 22.45 (978-1-56711-446-1(6) , Blackbirch Pr., Inc.) Thomson Gale.

Cooper, Jason. Kitten to Tiger. 2003. (Illus.). 24p. (J). 20.64 (978-1-58952-695-2(3)) Rourke Publishing, LLC.

—Tigers. 2002. (Illus.). 24p. (J). lib. bdg. 20.64 (978-1-58952-406-4(3)) Rourke Publishing, LLC.

Corrigan, Patricia, et al. Big Cats! Exploring the Fascinating Worlds of Cougars, Leopards, Lions, & Tigers. McGee, John F., illus. 2002. (Our Wild World Ser.). 192p. (J). (gr. 2-5). 16.95 (978-1-55971-798-4(X) , NorthWord Bks. for Young Readers) T&N Children's Publishing.

Costain, Meredith. Tigers. 2000. (gr. k-3). lib. bdg. 11.80 (978-0-613-30792-5(5)) Tandem Library Bks.

Eckart, Edana. Bengal Tiger. 2003. (Welcome Book Ser.). (Illus.). 24p. (J). 17.00 (978-0-516-24294-1(6)); pap. 4.95 (978-0-516-27881-0(9)) Scholastic Library Publishing. (Children's Pr.).

—Bengal Tiger. 2003. (gr. k-3). lib. bdg. 12.95 (978-0-613-67693-9(9)) Tandem Library Bks.

Frost, Helen. Sabertooth Cat. 2005. (Dinosaurs & Prehistoric Animals Ser.). (Illus.). 24p. (J). (ps). lib. bdg. 19.93 (978-0-7368-3648-7(9)) Capstone Pr., Inc.

—Tigers. Saunders-Smith, Gail, ed. 2002. (Rain Forest Animals Ser.). (Illus.). 24p. (J). (gr. k-1). lib. bdg. 15.93 (978-0-7368-1458-4(2) , Pebble Bks.) Capstone Pr., Inc.

Gaines, Richard Marshall. When Tigers Attack! 2006. (When Wild Animals Attack! Ser.). (Illus.). 48p. (J). (gr. 6-10). lib. bdg. 23.93 (978-0-7660-2665-0(5)) Enslow Pubs., Inc.

Galvin, Laura Gates. Tiger Cub See & So. Cohen, Jessie, photos by. 2005. (Let's Go to the Zoo! Ser.). (Illus.). 16p. (J). (ps-k). bds. 5.95 (978-1-56899-856-5(2) , B9006) Soundprints.

Gareth Stevens Publishing Staff, contrib. by. Tigers. 2004. (All about Wild Animals Ser.). (Illus.). 32p. (J). lib. bdg. 23.33 (978-0-8368-4189-3(1)) Stevens, Gareth Inc.

Gentle, Victor & Perry, Janet. Tigers. 2002. (Big Cats Ser.). (Illus.). 24p. (J). (gr. 2 up). lib. bdg. 22.00 (978-0-8368-3029-3(6)) Stevens, Gareth Inc.

Goecke, Michael P. Saber-Toothed Cat. 2003. (Prehistoric Animals Ser.). (Illus.). 24p. (J). (gr. k-4). lib. bdg. 21.35 (978-1-57765-970-9(8)) ABDO Publishing Co.

Goodman, Susan E. Saber-Toothed Cats. Maguire, Kerry, illus. 2006. (On My Own Science Ser.). 48p. (J). pap. 5.95 (978-1-57505-851-1(0) , First Avenue Editions); (gr. 2-4). lib. bdg. 25.26 (978-1-57505-759-0(X)) Lerner Publishing Group.

Green, Carl R. The Tiger: A MyReportLinks.com Book. 2003. (Endangered & Threatened Animals Ser.). (Illus.). 48p. (J). (gr. 4-10). lib. bdg. 25.26 (978-0-7660-5059-4(9) , MyReportLinks.com Bks.) Enslow Pubs., Inc.

Guarnotta, Lucia, illus. We Are Tigers. 2002. 40p. bds. (978-2-7641-1456-8(7)) Tormont Pubns.

Hall, Margaret. Tigers & Their Cubs. 2003. (Animal Offspring Ser.). (Illus.). 24p. (J). lib. bdg. 17.26 (978-0-7368-2110-0(4) , Pebble Bks.) Capstone Pr., Inc.

Hanel, Rachael. Tigers. 2008. (J). ***(978-1-58341-660-0(9)*** , Creative Education) Creative Co., The.

Hewett, Joan. A Tiger Cub Grows Up. Hewett, Richard, photos by. (Baby Animals Ser.). (Illus.). 32p. (gr. k-3). 2005. lib. bdg. 21.27 (978-1-57505-163-5(X)); 2001. (J). pap. 6.95 (978-0-8225-0089-6(2) , Lerner Pubns.) Lerner Publishing Group.

—Tiger Cub Grows Up. 2002. (gr. k-3). lib. bdg. 15.25 (978-0-613-56655-1(6)) Tandem Library Bks.

Hoff, Mary King. Tigers. 2005. (Illus.). 32p. (gr. 2-5). 18.95 (978-1-58341-355-5(3) , Creative Education) Creative Co., The.

Hughes, Monica. Tiger Cub. 2006. (I Love Reading Ser.). (Illus.). 24p. (J). lib. bdg. 19.96 (978-1-59716-155-8(1)) Bearport Publishing Co., Inc.

Johnson, Jinny. Tiger. Woods, Michael, illus. 2005. 32p. (J). (gr. 2-5). lib. bdg. 27.10 (978-1-58340-640-3(9)) Smart Apple Media.

—Tiger. Ch'en-Ling, illus. Price, Susanna, photos by. 2001. (Busy Baby Animals Ser.). 16p. (J). (ps up). lib. bdg. 19.33 (978-0-8368-2928-0(X)) Stevens, Gareth Inc.

Kalman, Bobbie. Endangered Tigers. 2003. (Earth's Endangered Animals Ser.). (Illus.). 32p. (J). (978-0-7787-1850-5(6)); pap. (978-0-7787-1896-3(4)) Crabtree Publishing Co.

Kendell, Patricia. Tigers. 2002. (In the Wild Ser.). (Illus.). 32p. (J). lib. bdg. 25.69 (978-0-7398-4909-5(3)) Raintree.

Landau, Elaine. Fierce Cats. 2003. (Fearsome, Scary, & Creepy Animals Ser.). (Illus.). 48p. (J). (gr. 1-4). lib. bdg. 23.93 (978-0-7660-2062-7(0)) Enslow Pubs., Inc.

Latta, Jan. Timba the Tiger. 2006. (Illus.). 24p. (J). pap. ***(978-0-8368-7779-3(9));*** lib. bdg. ***(978-0-8368-7772-4(1))*** Stevens, Gareth Inc.

Ledu-Frattini, Stephanie. The Tiger. Uhlig, Elizabeth, tr. from FRE. Sah, Anup, photos by. 2004. (Animal Close-Ups Ser.). (Illus.). 28p. (J). pap. 6.95 (978-1-57091-373-0(0)) Charlesbridge Publishing, Inc.

Levine, Stuart P. The Tiger. 1998. (Endangered Animals & Habitats Ser.). (Illus.). 96p. (YA). (gr. 4-12). 28.70 (978-1-56006-465-7(X) , Lucent Bks.) Thomson Gale.

Lions & Tigers. 2007. 24p. pap. 2.99 ***(978-1-4037-3433-4(X))*** Dalmatian Pr.

Macken, JoAnn Early. Tigers. 2002. (Weekly Reader Early Learning Library). (Illus.). 24p. (J). (ps up). pap. 5.95 (978-0-8368-3289-1(2)); lib. bdg. 19.33 (978-0-8368-3276-1(0)) Stevens, Gareth Inc. (Weekly Reader Early Learning Library).

—Tigers: Los Tigres. 2004. (ENG & SPA., Illus.). 24p. (J). pap. (978-0-8368-4391-0(6)); lib. bdg. 19.33 (978-0-8368-4386-6(X)) Stevens, Gareth Inc.

Markert, Jenny. Tigers. 2007. (New Naturebooks Ser.). 32p. (J). (gr. 1-5). 27.07 ***(978-1-59296-853-4(8))*** Child's World, Inc.

Matthews, Rupert. Sabre Tooth. 2003. (Gone Forever Ser.). (Illus.). 32p. pap. 6.50 (978-1-4034-3419-7(0)) Heinemann Library.

—Sabretooth Tiger. 2003. (Gone Forever Ser.). (Illus.). 32p. (J). lib. bdg. 22.79 (978-1-4034-0791-7(6)) Heinemann Library.

McClanahan. Tiger. 1999. (Wild Baby Animals Ser.). (Illus.). 16p. (J). (ps-k). 4.99 (978-0-7681-0190-4(5) , McClanahan Bk.) Learning Horizons, Inc.

Middleton, Don. Tigers. 1999. (PowerKids Readers Ser.). 24p. (J). (gr. k-4). lib. bdg. 18.75 (978-0-8239-5213-7(4) , PowerKids Pr.) Rosen Publishing Group, Inc., The.

Miller-Schroeder, Patricia. Tigers. 2002. (Untamed World Ser.). (Illus.). 64p. (J). lib. bdg. 28.54 (978-0-7398-4973-6(5)) Raintree.

Montgomery, Sy. The Man-Eating Tigers of Sundarbans. Briggs, Eleanor, photos by. (Illus.). 64p. (J). (gr. 4-6). 2004. pap. 6.95 (978-0-618-49490-3(1)); 2001. tchr. ed. 16.00 (978-0-618-07704-5(9)) Houghton Mifflin Co. Trade & Reference Div.

Moore, Sharon. Tiger Talk. 2002. (PowerPhonics Ser.). (Illus.). 23p. (J). lib. bdg. (978-0-8239-8259-2(9)) Rosen Publishing Group, Inc., The.

—Tiger Talk: Learning the T Sound. 2002. (PowerPhonics Ser.). (Illus.). 24p. (J). (gr. 1). lib. bdg. 18.50 (978-0-8239-5914-3(7) , PowerKids Pr.) Rosen Publishing Group, Inc., The.

Morgan, Sally. Tigers. 2004. (QEB Animal Lives Ser.). (Illus.). 32p. (J). lib. bdg. 18.95 (978-1-59566-035-0(6)) QEB Publishing Inc.

Murdico, Suzanne J. Tiger Attacks. 2000. (High Interest Bks.). (Illus.). 48p. (YA). (gr. 7-12). pap. 6.95 (978-0-516-23519-6(2) , Children's Pr.) Scholastic Library Publishing.

—Tiger Attacks. 2000. (gr. 7-12). lib. bdg. 15.25 (978-0-613-52199-4(4)) Tandem Library Bks.

Murdico, Suzanne J., contrib. by. Tiger Attacks. 2000. (Animal Attack! Ser.). (J). (978-0-531-12107-8(0) , Watts, Franklin) Scholastic Library Publishing.

Murray, Julie. Tigers. 2002. (Animal Kingdom Ser.). (Illus.). 24p. (J). (gr. k-4). lib. bdg. 21.35 (978-1-57765-646-3(6)) ABDO Publishing Co.

T U V

Murray, Peter. Tigers. 2005. (World of Mammals Ser.). 40p. (J). (gr. 2-6). 29.93 (978-1-59296-498-7(2)) Child's World, Inc.

Nagda, Ann Whitehead. Tiger Territory: A Story of the Chitwan Valley. Kratter, Paul, illus. 1999. (Habitat Ser.: Vol. 11). (J). 36p. (gr. 1-4). pap. 10.95 incl. audio (978-1-56899-723-0(X)); 32p. (ps-3). 15.95 (978-1-56899-720-9(5)); 32p. (ps-3). pap. 5.95 (978-1-56899-721-6(3)); Incl. toy. 36p. (gr. 1-4). 26.95 (978-1-56899-724-7(8)); Incl. toy. 36p. (gr. 1-4). 31.95 incl. audio (978-1-56899-726-1(4)); Incl. toy. 32p. (gr. 1-4). pap. 16.95 (978-1-56899-725-4(6)); Incl. toy. 36p. (gr. 1-4). pap. 19.95 incl. audio (978-1-56899-727-8(2)) Soundprints.

Pingry, Patricia A. & Sharp, Chris. Baby Tiger. 2003. (San Diego Zoo Animal Library). (Illus.). 24p. (J). bds. 6.95 (978-0-8249-6527-3(2)) Ideals Pubns.

¿Por Que los Tigres Tienen Rayas? (Coleccion Primeros Pasos en la Ciencia). (SPA., Illus.). (J). (gr. 1-3). pap. (978-950-724-494-0(8) , LMA8229) Lumen ARG. *Dist:* Lectorum Pubns., Inc.

Quality Productions Staff. Tigres. Rountree, Monica, tr. 2003. (Zoobooks). Orig. Title: Tigers. (SPA., Illus.). 24p. (J). (gr. k-6). lib. bdg. 15.95 (978-1-888153-75-0(X)) Wildlife Education, Ltd.

Richardson, Adele. Tigers. 2006. (Illus.). 24p. (J). (978-0-7368-5417-7(7) , Bridgestone Bks.) Capstone Pr., Inc.

Richardson, Adele D. Tigers: Striped Stalkers. 2002. (Wild World of Animals Ser.). (Illus.). 24p. (J). (gr. 1-2). lib. bdg. 18.60 (978-0-7368-1140-8(0) , Bridgestone Bks.) Capstone Pr., Inc.

Ring, Susan. Project Tiger. Marshall, Diana & Nault, Jennifer, eds. 2003. (Zoo Life Ser.). (Illus.). 24p. (J). pap. 6.95 (978-1-59036-061-3(3)) Weigl Pubs., Inc.

—Project Tiger. 2002. (Zoo Babies Ser.). (Illus.). 24p. (J). lib. bdg. 15.15 (978-1-59036-015-6(X)) Weigl Pubs., Inc.

Ryan, Marla Felkins & Corwin, Jeff. Into Wild India 2. 2004. (Jeff Corwin Experience Ser.). (Illus.). 48p. (J). 11.20 (978-1-4103-0234-2(2)); (gr. 4-7). 24.95 (978-1-4103-0233-5(4)) Thomson Gale. (Blackbirch Pr., Inc.).

Saber-Toothed Tigers. 2004. 25.70 (978-1-4109-1062-2(8)); pap. 7.50 (978-1-4109-1230-5(2)) Raintree.

Schafer, Susan. Tigers. 2000. (Animals Animals Ser.). (Illus.). 48p. (J). (gr. 3-5). lib. bdg. 25.64 (978-0-7614-1170-3(4)) Cavendish, Marshall Corp.

Spilsbury, Louise & Spilsbury, Richard. Bengal Tiger. (Illus.). (J). 2006. 32p. pap. (978-1-4034-7811-5(2)); 2004. 48p. lib. bdg. 27.07 (978-1-4034-4858-3(2)) Heinemann Library.

—The Bengal Tiger. 2004. (Animals under Threat Ser.). (Illus.). 48p. (J). pap. 8.50 (978-1-4034-5432-4(9)) Heinemann Library.

—Save the Bengal Tiger. 2006. (Illus.). 32p. (J). 25.36 (978-1-4034-7803-0(1)) Heinemann Library.

Squire, Ann O. Tigers. 2005. (True Bks.). (Illus.). (J). (gr. 3-5). 47p. pap. 6.95 (978-0-516-27937-4(8)); 48p. 25.00 (978-0-516-22796-2(3)) Scholastic Library Publishing. (Children's Pr.).

St. Pierre, Stephanie. Siberian Tigers. 2002. (In the Wild Ser.). (Illus.). 24p. (J). (gr. k-2). pap. 6.95 (978-1-58810-384-0(6) , 91104) Heinemann Library.

Stanley, Elizabeth. Tyger! Tyger! Stanley, Elizabeth, illus. 2007. (Illus.). 32p. (J). (ps-3). 16.95 (978-1-59270-068-4(3)) Enchanted Lion Bks., LLC.

—Tyger! Tyger! Stanley, Elizabeth, illus. 2007. (Illus.). 32p. 21.50 (***978-1-920694-84-5(6)*** , Cygnet Bks.) Univ. of Western Australia Pr. AUS. *Dist:* International Specialized Bk. Services.

Steele. Bengal Tigers. 2002. pap. (978-0-7398-5807-3(6)) Steck-Vaughn.

Steele, Christy. Bengal Tigers. 2002. (Animals of the Rain Forest Ser.). (Illus.). 32p. (J). lib. bdg. 22.83 (978-0-7398-5369-6(4)) Raintree.

Stefoff, Rebecca. Tigers. 2002. (Animalways Ser.). (J). 31.36 (978-0-7614-1391-2(X) , Benchmark Bks.) Cavendish, Marshall Corp.

Stephanie, St Pierre. Siberian Tigers. 2001. (In the Wild Ser.). (Illus.). 24p. (J). (ps-3). lib. bdg. 21.36 (978-1-58810-110-5(X)) Heinemann Library.

Stone, Lynn M. Tigers. 2005. (Nature Watch Ser.). (J). 25.26 (978-1-57505-578-7(3) , Carolrhoda Bks.) Lerner Publishing Group.

—Tigers. 2001. (Wildlife in Danger Ser.). (Illus.). 24p. (gr. 1-4). 14.95 (978-1-58952-023-3(8)) Rourke Publishing, LLC.

Stone, Tanya Lee. Tigers. 2003. (Wild Wild World Ser.). 24p. (YA). 24.94 (978-1-56711-826-1(7) , Blackbirch Pr., Inc.) Thomson Gale.

Suen, Anastasia. A Tiger Grows Up. Denman, Michael L. & Huiett, William J., illus. 2005. (Wild Animals Ser.). 24p. (J). (ps). lib. bdg. 23.93 (978-1-4048-0987-1(2)) Picture Window Bks.

Swain, Gwenyth. Tigers. McGee, John F., illus. 2004. (Our Wild World Ser.). 48p. (J). (gr. 2-5). ring bd. 10.95 (978-1-55971-808-0(0)); pap. 7.95 (978-1-55971-797-7(1)) T&N Children's Publishing. (NorthWord Bks. for Young Readers).

—Tigers. 2002. (gr. 3-6). lib. bdg. 16.40 (978-0-613-55909-6(6)) Tandem Library Bks.

Swanson, Diane. Wild Cats. 1998. (Welcome to the World of Animals Ser.). (Illus.). 32p. (J). (gr. 3 up). lib. bdg. 23.33 (978-0-8368-2217-5(X)) Stevens, Gareth Inc.

Taylor, Barbara. Why Don't Tigers Eat Bananas? 2004. (Animal Puzzlers Ser.). (Illus.). 32p. (J). 12.95 (978-1-57768-947-8(X) , Waterbird Bks.) School Specialty Publishing.

Thapar, Valmik. The Tiger. 1999. (Natural World Ser.). (Illus.). 48p. (J). (gr. 4-7). pap. 7.95 (978-0-7398-0946-4(6)) Steck-Vaughn.

Theodorou, Rod. Bengal Tiger. (Animals in Danger Ser.). (Illus.). 32p. (J). (gr. k-2). 2002. pap. 6.95 (978-1-58810-441-0(9) , 91149); 2000. lib. bdg. 21.36 (978-1-57572-267-2(4)) Heinemann Library.

Thomas, Isabel. Lion vs. Tiger. 2006. (Illus.). 32p. (J). (978-1-4109-2391-2(6)); pap. (978-1-4109-2398-1(3)) Steck-Vaughn.

Thomson, Sarah L. Amazing Tigers! 2004. (Illus.). 32p. (J). lib. bdg. 13.85 (***978-1-4242-0511-0(5)***) Fitzgerald Bks.

—Amazing Tigers! 2005. (I Can Read Bks.). (Illus.). 32p. (J). pap. 3.99 (978-0-06-054452-2(X) , Harper Trophy) HarperCollins Pubs.

Tigers. 2003. (J). per. (978-1-57657-946-6(8)) Paradise Pr., Inc.

Tigers, 6, Pack. (Sails Literacy Ser.). (gr. 1-2). 36.00 (978-0-7578-6743-9(X)) Rigby Education.

Tigers: Level R, 6 vols. (Wonder Worldtm Ser.). 48p. 44.95 (978-0-7802-7068-8(1)) Wright Group, The.

Tiger's Tail. Date not set. (Touch & Feel Ser.). (J). 4.98 (978-0-7525-9570-2(9)) Parragon, Inc.

Unwin, Mike. Why Do Tigers Have Stripes? 2006. 24p. (J). pap. 4.99 (978-0-7945-1408-2(1) , Usborne) EDC Publishing.

Vogel, Elizabeth. Tigers. 2002. (PowerKids Readers Ser.). (Illus.). 24p. (J). (gr. 1). lib. bdg. 16.00 (978-0-8239-6020-0(X) , PowerKids Pr.) Rosen Publishing Group, Inc., The.

Ward, Rebecca. Tiger. 1999. (J). (978-1-84100-212-5(7)) Quadrillion Publishing.

Welsbacher, Anne. Tigers. 2000. (Wild Cats Ser.). (Illus.). 24p. (J). (gr. k-6). lib. bdg. 21.35 (978-1-57765-089-8(1) , Checkerboard Library) ABDO Publishing Co.

Whitehouse, Patricia. Tiger. 2003. (Zoo Animals Ser.). (Illus.). 24p. (ps-1). (J). lib. bdg. 17.08 (978-1-58810-904-0(6)); pap. 5.25 (978-1-4034-0648-4(0)) Heinemann Library.

—El Tigre. 2003. (Animales del Zoologico (Zoo Animals) Ser.). (SPA., Illus.). 24p. (ps-1). (J). lib. bdg. 17.08 (978-1-4034-0408-4(9)); pap. 5.25 (978-1-4034-0656-9(1)) Heinemann Library.

Wildlife Education, contrib. by. Tigers. 2005. (Zootles Ser.). (Illus.). 23p. (J). (ps-k). lib. bdg. 10.95 (978-1-932396-10-2(1)) Wildlife Education, Ltd.

Wilsdon, Christina. Tigers. 2007. (J). (***978-1-59939-117-5(1)*** , Reader's Digest Young Families, Inc.) Reader's Digest Children's Publishing, Inc.

Yoyo Books. We are Tigers. 2005. 40p. bds. 12.95 (978-90-5843-818-8(X)) YoYo Bks. BEL. *Dist:* National Bk. Network.

Zumbusch, Amelie von. Tigers: World's Largest Cats. 2007. (Dangerous Cats Ser.). (Illus.). 24p. (J). (gr. k-5). lib. bdg. 21.25 (978-1-4042-3632-5(5)) Rosen Publishing Group, Inc., The.

TIGERS—FICTION

Adams, Pam. Tiger. 2005. (Illus.). 8p. (J). (ps). bds. 5.99 (978-1-904550-28-0(2)) Child's Play-International.

Amazing Mallika - Evaluation Guide: Evaluation Guide. 2006. (J). (978-1-55942-398-4(6)) Marsh Media.

Annaud, Jean-Jacques & Ellison, James. Two Brothers: The Tale of Kumal & Sangha. novel ed. 2005. (Novelization for Young Readers Ser.). (Illus.). 192p. (YA). pap. 7.95 (978-1-55704-632-1(8)) Newmarket Pr.

Arnett, Paul. Yoo Hoo! Tiger! Dial, Thornton, illus. 2001. 32p. (J). (ps-1). 16.95 (978-0-9653766-2-4(1)) Tinwood Bks.

Aryal, Aimee. Hello Tiger! Graybill, Joni, illus. 2004. (J). 19.95 (978-1-932888-25-6(X)) Mascot Bks., Inc.

Ayers, Linda. Tiger Does the Write Thing. Hunt, Jane, illus. l.t. ed. 2005. 35p. (J). per. 7.95 (978-0-9760505-4-4(4)) Blue Thistle Pr.

—Tiger Goes Collecting. Hunt, Jane, illus. l.t. ed. 2004. 55p. (J). per. 7.95 (978-0-9760505-2-0(8)) Blue Thistle Pr.

Baby Tiger's Blanket. 2005. (J). (978-1-932570-44-1(6)) Literacy Footprints Inc.

Baker, Keith. Quien es la Bestia? Ada, Alma Flor, tr. 2005. (SPA., Illus.). 28p. (J). bds. 6.95 (978-0-15-205596-7(7) , Red Wagon Bks.) Harcourt Children's Bks.

—Who Is the Beast? 2003. (Illus.). 28p. (J). bds. 6.95 (978-0-15-204752-8(2) , Red Wagon Bks.) Harcourt Children's Bks.

Banks, Kate. Close Your Eyes. Hallensleben, Georg, illus. 2002. 40p. (J). (ps-1). 16.95 (978-0-374-31382-1(2) , Farrar, Straus & Giroux (BYR)) Farrar, Straus & Giroux.

Banks, Lynne Reid. Tiger, Tiger. 208p. (gr. 7-11). 2007. (YA). mass mkt. 5.99 (978-0-440-42044-6(X) , Laurel Leaf); 2005. (J). 15.95 (978-0-385-73240-6(6) , Delacorte Bks. for Young Readers); 2005. (YA). lib. bdg. 17.99 (978-0-385-90264-9(6) , Delacorte Bks. for Young Readers) Random Hse. Children's Bks.

Bannerman, Helen. The Boy & the Tigers. Petrone, Valeria, illus. 2004. (Little Golden Book Ser.). 24p. (J). (gr. k-k). 2.99 (978-0-375-82719-8(6) , Golden Bks.) Random Hse. Children's Bks.

—La Historia del Pequeno Babachi. 2001. Tr. of Story of Little Babaji. (SPA.). (J). (gr. 2-4). 16.76 (978-84-261-3064-8(X)) Juventud, Editorial ESP. *Dist:* Lectorum Pubns., Inc.

—The Story of Little Babaji. Marcellino, Fred, illus. 2002. 72p. (J). (ps up). pap. 7.99 (978-0-06-008093-8(0) , Harper Trophy) HarperCollins Pubs.

—Story of Little Babaji. 2002. (gr. k-3). lib. bdg. 16.40 (978-0-613-85154-1(4)) Tandem Library Bks.

—The Story of Little Babaji. ed. 2004. (Illus.). (J). (ps up). spiral bd. (978-0-616-14615-6(9)) Canadian National Institute for the Blind/Institut National Canadien pour les Aveugles.

—The Story of Little Black Sambo. 2004. (Wee Books for Wee Folks). (Illus.). 61p. (J). (gr. 1-3). reprint ed. 6.95 (978-1-55709-414-8(4)) Applewood Bks.

—The Story of Little Black Sambo. 2007. pap. 7.99 (***978-1-59986-912-4(8)*** , FQ Classics) Filiquarian Publishing, LLC.

—The Story of Little Black Sambo. Bing, Christopher H., illus. 2003. 40p. (J). (ps up). 17.95 (978-1-929766-55-0(6)) Handprint Bks.

—The Story of Little Black Sambo. Bannerman, Helen, illus. 2003. (Illus.). 64p. (J). (gr. k-3). 15.99 (978-0-397-30006-8(9)) HarperCollins Pubs.

—Tigers for Supper. Pollema-Cahill, Phyllis, illus. 1998. (Domino Readers Ser.). 24p. (J). (ps-1). pap. 5.95 (978-1-887734-36-3(8)) Star Bright Bks., Inc.

Barkow, Henriette & Finlay, Lizzie, illus. Buri & the Marrow: An Indian Folk Tale: Un Conte Traditionnel Indien = Buri et la Courge. 2004. (TAM, VIE, SPA, GUJ & PER.). 24p. (J). pap. (978-1-85269-583-5(8)) Mantra Publishing, Ltd.

Bee, William. Whatever. 2005. (Illus.). 40p. (J). (gr. k-1). 12.99 (978-0-7636-2886-4(7)) Candlewick Pr.

—Whatever: Mini Edition. Bee, William, illus. 2007. (Illus.). 32p. (J). (gr. k). 5.99 (978-0-7636-3431-5(X)) Candlewick Pr.

Berkeley, Jon. The Palace of Laughter: The Wednesday Tales No. 1. Dorman, Brandon, illus. (J). 2007. 464p. (gr. 3-7). pap. 7.99 (***978-0-06-075509-6(1)*** , Harper Trophy); 2006. 448p. 16.99 (978-0-06-075507-2(5) , Julie Andrews Collection); 2006. 448p. lib. bdg. 17.89 (978-0-06-075508-9(3) , Julie Andrews Collection) HarperCollins Pubs.

—The Tiger's Egg. Dorman, Brandon, illus. 2007. 416p. (J). (gr. 3-7). lib. bdg. 17.89 (***978-0-06-075511-9(3));*** (Wednesday Tales Ser.: No. 2). 16.99 (***978-0-06-075510-2(5)***) HarperCollins Pubs. (Julie Andrews Collection).

Blackford, Harriet. Tiger's Story. Stojic, Manya, illus. 2007. 32p. (J). 12.95 (978-1-905417-39-1(X)) Boxer Bks., Ltd. GBR. *Dist:* Sterling Publishing Co., Inc.

Blue Lantern Studio Staff, ed. The Green Tiger's Mother Goose. 2003. (Illus.). 144p. (J). (ps-k). 24.95 (978-1-883211-85-1(9) , Green Tiger Pr.) Laughing Elephant.

Bonnell, Kris. What Tigers Do. 2006. (J). 3.95 (***978-1-933727-41-7(1)***) Reading Reading Bks., LLC.

Boucher, Carter. Tiger Dave. Dunbar, Leo, illus. 1999. (Books for Young Learners). 8p. (J). (gr. k-2). pap. 5.00 (978-1-57274-151-5(1)) Owen, Richard C. Pubs., Inc.

Brooks, John. The Sundarbans Tiger. 2006. 115p. (J). pap. 13.58 (978-0-9661789-4-4(7)) Lulu.com.

Bunting, Eve. Jin Woo. Soentpiet, Chris K., illus. 2001. 32p. (J). (gr. k-3). tchr. ed. 16.00 (978-0-395-93872-0(4) , Clarion Bks.) Houghton Mifflin Co. Trade & Reference Div.

—Riding the Tiger. Frampton, David, illus. 2001. 32p. (J). (gr. 4-6). tchr. ed. 16.00 (978-0-395-79731-0(4) , Clarion Bks.) Houghton Mifflin Co. Trade & Reference Div.

Caffrey-Kira, Albina. The White Tiger, & Other Children's Stories. 2006. 21.00 (978-0-8059-9023-2(2)) Dorrance Publishing Co., Inc.

Carey, Keelin. A Princess, a Tiger, & Other Deaf Tales. 2005. (Illus.). 50p. (J). pap. 7.95 (978-1-896764-90-0(8)) Second Story Pr. CAN. *Dist:* Orca Bk. Pubs. USA.

Chancellor, Deborah. Tiger Tales. 2000. (gr. k-3). lib. bdg. 11.80 (978-0-613-27251-3(X)) Tandem Library Bks.

Chancellor, Deborah & Dorling Kindersley Publishing Staff. Tiger Tales. 2000. (Readers Ser.). (Illus.). 48p. (J). (gr. 2-3). 14.99 (978-0-7894-5424-9(6)); Vol. 3. pap. 3.99 (978-0-7894-5423-2(8)) Dorling Kindersley Publishing, Inc.

Cheripko, Jan. Imitate the Tiger. 2003. (Illus.). 224p. (YA). (gr. 6-9). pap. 9.95 (978-1-56397-705-3(2)) Boyds Mills Pr.

Christie, Jacky. Roger's Big Adventure. 2005. (J). pap. 8.00 (978-0-8059-6889-7(X)) Dorrance Publishing Co., Inc.

Cleveland, Robert. How Tiger Got His Stripes. Hoffmire, Baird, illus. 2006. 32p. pap. 3.95 (978-0-87483-799-5(5)) August Hse. Pubs., Inc.

Cook, Sherry & Johnson, Terri. Timothy Tornado, 26. Kuhn, Jesse, illus. l.t. ed. 2006. (Quirkles—Exploring Phonics through Science Ser.: 20). 32p. 7.99 (978-1-933815-19-0(1) , Quirkles, The) Creative 3, LLC.

Cowcher, Helen. Tigress. 2001. (Illus.). 40p. (YA). (BEN, ENG, URD, TUR & VIE.). 16.95 (978-1-84059-024-1(6)); (GRE, ENG, URD, TUR & VIE., 16.95 (978-1-84059-026-5(2)); (GUJ, ENG, URD, TUR & VIE., 16.95 (978-1-84059-027-2(0)); (TUR, ENG, URD, VIE & CHI., 16.95 (978-1-84059-028-9(9)); (URD, ENG, TUR, VIE & CHI., 16.95 (978-1-84059-029-6(7)) Milet Publishing.

De Armellada, Fray C. El Tigre y el Rayo. Ocante, Aracelis, illus. Tr. of Jaguar & the Lightning Bolt. (SPA.). 24p. (J). (gr. 1-4). pap. 6.99 (978-980-257-008-9(7)) Ekare, Ediciones VEN. *Dist:* Kane/Miller Bk. Pubs., Inc., Lectorum Pubns., Inc.

de Beer, Hans. Llevame a Casa, Osito Polar! Gambolini, Gerardo, tr. from GER. 2001. (SPA & ENG., Illus.). 32p. (J). (gr. k-3). pap. 6.95 (978-0-7358-1500-1(3) , NS30711) North-South Bks., Inc.

—Llevame a Casa, Osito Polar! 2001. (gr. k-3). (SPA.). lib. bdg. 15.25 (978-0-613-73576-6(5)); (978-0-606-22735-3(0)) Tandem Library Bks.

DeGrazia, John. The Three Little Tigers & Their Birthday Party. Spirin, Ilya, illus. 1999. (Three Little Tigers Ser.: Vol. 1). 20p. (J). (gr. 1-8). pap. 6.00 (978-0-9670522-0-5(3)) Big Cats Publishing.

—The Three Little Tigers Go Fishing. Spirin, Ilya, illus. 1999. (Three Little Tigers Ser.: Vol. 2). 15p. (J). (gr. 1-8). pap. 5.00 (978-0-9670522-1-2(1)) Big Cats Publishing.

—The Three Little Tigers Go to College. Spirin, Ilya, illus. 1999. (Three Little Tigers Ser.: Vol. 4). 25p. (J). (gr. 1-8). pap. 6.00 (978-0-9670522-3-6(8)) Big Cats Publishing.

Delval, Marie-Helene. A Tigreton le gusta Moverse. Courtin, Thierry, illus. 2004. (Palabras menudas Ser.). (SPA.). 14p. 5.95 (978-84-7864-709-5(0)) Combel Editorial, S.A. ESP. *Dist:* Independent Pubs. Group.

Desrosiers, Sylvie. Qui a Deja Touche a un Vrai Tigre? Sylvestre, Daniel, illus. 2002. (Roman Jeunesse Ser.). (FRE.). 96p. (YA). (gr. 4-7). pap. (978-2-89021-335-7(8)) Diffusion du livre Mirabel.

DiCamillo, Kate. The Tiger Rising. Sheban, Chris, illus. 2006. 144p. (J). (gr. 5). pap. 5.99 (978-0-7636-2916-8(2)) Candlewick Pr.

—The Tiger Rising. 128p. (gr. 5-12). 2002. (YA). pap. 5.99 (978-0-7636-1898-8(5)); 2001. (Illus.). (J). 15.99 (978-0-7636-0911-5(0)) Candlewick Pr.

—The Tiger Rising. 2002. (gr. 5-8). lib. bdg. 14.15 (978-0-613-66924-5(X)) Tandem Library Bks.

Dietl, Erhard. A Veces Quisiera Ser un Tigre. (Torre de Papel Ser.). (SPA., Illus.). (J). 7.95 (978-958-04-5040-5(4)) Norma S.A. COL. *Dist:* Distribuidora Norma, Inc.

Dowson, Nick. Tigress. Chapman, Jane, tr. Chapman, Jane, illus. 2004. 32p. (J). (gr. k-3). 15.99 (978-0-7636-2325-8(3)) Candlewick Pr.

Dowson, Nick. Tigress: Read & Wonder. Chapman, Jane, illus. 2007. (Read & Wonder Ser.). 32p. (J). (gr. k-3). pap. 6.99 (***978-0-7636-3314-1(3)***) Candlewick Pr.

Doyle, Malachy. Dancing Tiger. 2005. 32p. (J). (ps-3). 15.99 (978-0-670-06020-7(8) , Viking Juvenile) Penguin Group (USA) Inc.

—Dancing Tiger. Fancher, Lou & Johnson, Steve, illus. 2005. 32p. (978-0-689-87309-6(3)) Simon & Schuster.

Durant, Alan. If You Go Walking in Tiger Wood. Boon, Debbie, illus. 2005. 24p. (J). pap. 9.99 (978-0-00-710390-4(5) , HarperSport) HarperCollins Pubs. Ltd. GBR. *Dist:* Trafalgar Square Publishing.

Ellie. Bengal & Sengal. 2006. (J). pap. 8.00 (***978-0-8059-7273-3(0)***) Dorrance Publishing Co., Inc.

Fenner Williams, Carol. 2 Picture Books: Tigers in the Cellar & Gorilla Gorilla. 2001. 112p. (J). pap. 14.95 (978-0-595-17555-0(4) , Backinprint.com) iUniverse, Inc.

Flood, Pansie Hart. Tiger Turcotte Takes on the Know-It-All. Wummer, Amy, illus. 2005. 72p. (J). (gr. 1-4). pap. 6.95 (978-1-57505-900-6(2)) Lerner Publishing Group.

Fore, S. J. Tiger Can't Sleep. Alley, R. W., illus. 2006. 32p. (J). 15.99 (978-0-670-06078-8(X) , Viking Juvenile) Penguin Group (USA) Inc.

Franzese, Philip C. The Baseball Heroes of Tiger Park. 2000. (Illus.). 32p. (J). (gr. 2-6). 11.95 (978-0-9675551-0-2(8)) Marketing Magic, Inc.

Gaines, Isabel. Bounce, Tigger, Bounce. 1999. 40p. (J). pap. 3.99 (978-0-7868-4409-8(4)) Hyperion Pr.

—Bounce, Tigger, Bounce. 2001. (Illus.). (J). (978-0-606-21886-3(6)) Tandem Library Bks.

—Pooh's Family Tree, Vol. 20. 2000. (Winnie the Pooh Ser.). (Illus.). 34p. (J). (gr. k-3). pap. 3.99 (978-0-7868-4367-1(5)) Disney Pr.

—Tiggers Hate to Lose. 1999. 40p. (J). pap. 3.99 (978-0-7868-4389-3(6)) Disney Pr.

Gleeson, Brian. The Tiger & the Brahmin. Vargo, Kurt, illus. 2006. (J). (gr. 2-6). 25.65 (978-1-59679-347-7(3)) Spotlight.

Golden Books Family Entertainment Staff. Tigger Movie. 2000. (Golden Look-Look Bks.). (Illus.). 24p. (J). (ps-2). pap. 3.29 (978-0-307-13268-0(4) , Golden Bks.) Random Hse. Children's Bks.

Goode, Diane. Tiger Trouble! Goode, Diane, illus. 2001. (Illus.). 40p. (J). (ps up). pap. 15.95 (978-0-439-20866-6(1) , Blue Sky Pr., The) Scholastic, Inc.

Greenburg, Dan. Claws. 2007. 208p. (YA). (gr. 3-7). 5.99 (978-0-375-83411-0(7) , Yearling) Random Hse. Children's Bks.

Hamilton, Linda. Smile & Say Cheetah! Brown, Kevin, illus. 2005. (978-1-933248-00-4(9)) World Quest Learning.

Harcourt School Publishers Staff. Collections: Leo the Late Bloomer: Grade Level Library. 1999. (Illus.). (J). pap. 4.70 (978-0-15-315204-7(4)) Harcourt Schl. Pubs.

Hinnen, Brandy & Kahn, Karen, illus. The Adventures of Travel Tiger. 2002. 34p. per. 16.99 (978-1-931540-85-8(3)) SynergEbks.

Hoffman, Eric. No Fair to Tigers, 1. 2004. (Anti-Bias Books for Kids). (SPA., Illus.). 32p. (J). (ps-3). pap. 11.95 (978-1-884834-62-2(0)) Redleaf Pr.

Hogan, Mary. Tigger's Family. 2000. (Winnie the Pooh Ser.). (Illus.). 10p. (J). (ps-k). bds. 4.99 (978-0-7364-1062-5(7)) Mouse Works.

Hogrogian, Nonny. The Tiger of Turkestan. Hogrogian, Nonny, illus. 2002. (Illus.). 32p. (J). (gr. k-3). 16.95 (978-1-57174-308-4(1)) Hampton Roads Publishing Co., Inc.

Hom, Nancy, illus. Nine-in-One Grr! Grr! Cuaj Tug-Ih-Xyoos Mlaug! Mlaug! 2001. 32p. (J). (ps-4). pap. 6.95 (978-1-931016-10-0(0) , MHC-0-0) Minnesota Humanities Commission.

Horowitz, Dave. Beware of Tigers. Horowitz, Dave, illus. 2006. (Illus.). 40p. (J). (ps-3). 12.99 (978-0-399-24508-4(1)) Penguin Group (USA) Inc.

Inkpen, Mick. The Thing. 2001. (978-0-606-22350-8(9)) Tandem Library Bks.

Janosch. Ich Mach Dich Gesund Sagte der Bar. 2000. Tr. of I'll Make You Well Tiger, Said the Bear. (GER.). (J). pap. 14.95 (978-3-257-25103-6(3)) Diogenes Verlag AG CHE. *Dist:* Distribooks, Inc.

—Riesenparty fuer den Tiger: Die Geschichte, wie der Kleine Tiger einmal Geburtstag Hatte. 1999. (Taschenbuecher Ser.). (GER., Illus.). 48p. (J). pap. (978-3-257-25108-1(4)) Diogenes Verlag AG CHE. *Dist:* International Bk. Import Service, Inc.

T U V

Johnson, Julia. Cheetah's Tale. Keeble, Suzie, illus. 2004. 56p. pap. 16.95 (978-1-900988-87-2(9)) Stacey International Pubs. GBR. *Dist:* Interlink Publishing Group, Inc.

Kako, Satoshi. Little Daruma & Little Tiger: A Japanese Children's Tale. 2003. (Illus.). 32p. 10.95 (978-0-8048-3350-9(8)) Tuttle Publishing.

Kasza, Keiko. The Rat & the Tiger. 2007. 32p. (J). (ps). pap. 6.99 (*978-0-14-240900-8(6) , Puffin) Penguin Group (USA) Inc.

Kasza, Keiko. El Tigre y el Raton. (SPA.). (J). pap. 7.16 (978-958-04-2583-0(3)) Norma S.A. COL. *Dist:* Lectorum Pubns., Inc.

Kchodl, Joseph 'PaleoJoe' & Caszatt-Allen, Wendy. Secret Sabertooth. 2007. (PaleoJoe's Dinosaur Detective Club Ser.: 3). (Illus.). 140p. (J). pap. 6.95 (*978-1-934133-10-1(8)) Mackinac Island Pr., Inc.

Kenrick, Joanna & Weir, Doffy. Moondance. 2004. (Illus.). 32p. (J). 19.99 (978-1-84270-324-3(2)) Andersen GBR. *Dist:* Independent Pubs. Group.

Kerr, Judith. Tiger Who Came to Tea. 2006. pap. (978-0-06-052468-5(5)) HarperCollins Canada, Ltd.

Kinney, Kendall. Tiger Tails. 2004. 68p. (J). per. 10.95 (978-1-932196-21-4(8)) WordWright.biz, Inc.

Kraus, Robert. Leo, el Retono Tardio. Mlawer, Teresa, tr. Aruego, Jose, illus. (SPA.). (J). (gr. k-1). pap. 7.95 (978-1-930332-02-7(5) , LC30358) Lectorum Pubns., Inc.

—Leo the Late Bloomer. Aruego, Jose, illus. 1999. (Share a Story Ser.). (J). (ps up). 9.95 incl. reel tape (978-0-694-70098-1(3) , Harper Festival) HarperCollins Pubs.

—Leo the Late Bloomer. 1998. (Illus.). 17p. (J). (ps up). 7.95 (978-0-694-00980-0(6)) HarperCollins Pubs.

—Leo the Late Bloomer. Aruego, Jose, illus. 2000. 32p. (J). (ps-3). pap. 6.95 (978-1-931016-02-5(X) , MHC-2-X) Minnesota Humanities Commission.

—Little Louie the Baby Bloomer. Aruego, Jose, illus. 1998. 32p. (J). (ps-3). 15.89 (978-0-06-026294-5(X)) HarperCollins Pubs.

—Little Louie the Baby Bloomer. 2000. (Illus.). (J). (978-0-606-18702-2(2)) Tandem Library Bks.

—Little Louie the Baby Bloomer. Aruego, Jose & Dewey, Ariane, illus. 2000. 32p. (J). (ps-3). pap. 5.95 (978-0-06-443656-4(X) , Harper Trophy) HarperCollins Pubs.

Kraus, Robert, et al. Leo the Late Bloomer, 3 vols. Aruego, Jose, illus. 1998. (My Little Library Board Book Ser.). (J). bds. 19.95 (978-0-694-01183-4(5) , Harper Festival) HarperCollins Pubs.

Lagonegro, Melissa. A Pet for a Princess. Harchy, Atelier Philippe, illus. 2005. (Step into Reading Ser.). 32p. (J). (ps-2). pap. 3.99 (978-0-7364-2280-2(3) , RH/Disney) Random Hse. Children's Bks.

Lagonegro, Melissa & Random House Disney Staff. A Pet for Princess. 2005. (Step into Reading Ser.). (Illus.). 32p. (J). (ps-2). lib. bdg. 11.99 (978-0-7364-8037-6(4) , RH/Disney) Random Hse. Children's Bks.

Lee, Lucas Taekwondo. The Legend of Baeoh: How Baeoh Got His Stripes. Forward, Max, illus. 2007. 36p. (J). 17.95 (*978-1-931741-88-0(3)) Reed, Robert D. Pubs.

Lester, Julius. Sam & the Tigers. 2000. (978-0-606-18845-6(2)); lib. bdg. 15.30 (978-0-613-28630-5(8)) Tandem Library Bks.

—Sam & the Tigers: A New Telling of Little Black Sambo. Pinkney, Jerry, illus. 2002. (J). 14.04 (978-0-7587-0141-1(1)) Book Wholesalers, Inc.

Lester, Julius & Isadora, Rachel. Sam & the Tigers: A Retelling of 'Little Black Sambo' Pinkney, Jerry & Christiansen, Hans, illus. 2000. (Picture Puffin Ser.). 40p. (J). (ps-3). pap. 6.99 (978-0-14-056288-0(5) , Puffin) Penguin Group (USA) Inc.

Lillegard, Dee. Tiger, Tiger. Guevara, Susan, illus. 2002. 32p. (J). 16.99 (978-0-399-22633-5(8) , Putnam Juvenile) Penguin Group (USA) Inc.

Little Tiger Goes to School. 1999. (Illus.). 8p. (J). 9.99 (978-1-58048-083-3(7)) Sandvik Publishing.

Little Tiger's Big Surprise. 1999. (Illus.). 28p. (J). 9.99 (978-1-58048-082-6(9)) Sandvik Publishing.

Lorenz, Jinye. Ryong's Story: Extended Version of Grandfather, the Tiger & Ryong. Lorenz, Virginia O., ed. 2006. (Illus.). 135p. (YA). per. 14.95 (978-1-888350-11-1(3)) Lighted Lamp Pr.

Lourie, Peter. Everglades: Buffalo Tiger & the River of Grass. 2003. (River Ser.). (Illus.). 48p. (YA). (gr. 4-6). pap. 11.95 (978-1-56397-702-2(8)) Boyds Mills Pr.

Lumry, Amanda & Hurwitz, Laura. Tigers in Terai. McIntyre, Sarah, illus. 2nd rev. ed. 2007. 36p. 15.95 (*978-1-60040-003-2(5)) Centro Bks., LLC.

—Tigers in Terai. McIntyre, Sarah, illus. (Adventures of Riley Ser.). 36p. 2003. 15.95 (978-0-9662257-7-8(5)); 2nd ed. 2007. (*978-0-9748411-6-8(1)) Eaglemont Pr.

Mahr, Juli. Mama Tiger, Baba Tiger. 2001. (Illus.). (J). (978-0-606-21314-1(7)) Tandem Library Bks.

Mallett, Victor. Trouble with Tigers. (Illus.). xvii, 332p. 35.00 (978-0-00-255860-0(2)) Zondervan.

Malone, Geoffrey. Tiger. 2007. 304p. pap. 10.95 (*978-0-340-89358-6(3)) Hodder Children's Division GBR. *Dist:* Independent Pubs. Group.

Marlow, Herb. The Tiger's Den. Head, Pat, illus. 2003. 22p. (J). 19.95 (978-1-893595-37-8(4)) Four Seasons Bks., Inc.

Martel, Yann. Life of Pi: A Novel. 2003. (gr. 7-12). lib. bdg. 23.45 (978-0-613-59907-8(1)) Tandem Library Bks.

Mason, Jane B. & Hines Stephens, Sarah. Jungle Book. 2004. 128p. (J). pap. 3.99 (978-0-439-57424-2(2) , Scholastic Paperbacks) Scholastic, Inc.

Mayer, Mercer. Tiger's Birthday. Mayer, Mercer, illus. 2003. (Little Critter Ser.). (Illus.). 24p. (J). (ps-2). 10.95 (978-1-57768-645-3(4)) School Specialty Publishing.

—Tiger's Birthday. 2002. (Little Critter First Readers Ser.). (Illus.). 24p. (J). (gr. k-1). pap. 3.95 (978-1-57768-828-0(7)) School Specialty Publishing.

—Tiger's Birthday. 2001. (gr. k-3). lib. bdg. 11.80 (978-0-613-67675-5(0)) Tandem Library Bks.

McCafferty, Catherine, et al. Tigger's Bouncy Easter. Kleven, Dean, illus. 2002. (Disney's Winnie the Pooh Ser.). (J). (978-0-7853-6672-0(5)) Publications International, Ltd.

Medearis, Angela Shelf. On the Way to the Pond. Cauley, Lorinda Bryan, illus. 2006. (Green Light Readers Level 2 Ser.). 32p. (J). 12.95 (978-0-15-205599-8(1)); pap. 3.95 (978-0-15-205623-0(8)) Harcourt Trade Pubs.

Millhouse, Jackie. The Tiger & the General. Girouard, Patrick, illus. 2007. (J). (*978-1-932911-32-9(4)) World Tribune Pr.

Milne, A. A. In Which It Is Shown That Tiggers Don't Climb Trees. Shepard, Ernest H., illus. unabr. ed. (Classic Pooh Treasury Ser.). (J). incl. audio (978-1-57375-529-0(X) , 71414) Audioscope.

—Pu Baut ein Haus.Tr. of Pooh Builds a House. (GER.). (J). pap. 12.95 (978-3-423-07395-0(0)) Deutscher Taschenbuch Verlag GmbH & Co KG DEU. *Dist:* Distribooks, Inc.

—Tigger Tales. Shepard, Ernest H., illus. 2006. 36p. (J). (gr. k-4). reprint ed. 15.00 (978-1-4223-5453-7(9)) DIANE Publishing Co.

Milne, A. A. & Krensky, Stephen. Tigger Comes to the Forest. Shepard, Ernest H., illus. 2002. (Easy-to-Read, Puffin Ser.). 48p. (J). pap. 3.99 (978-0-14-230185-2(X) , Puffin) Penguin Group (USA) Inc.

Montgomery, Rutherford G. Yellow Eyes. 2004. (Classic Ser.). (Illus.). 358p. (gr. 4-7). pap. 15.95 (978-0-87004-417-5(6)) Caxton Pr.

Morris, Gilbert. Dixie & Stripes. 1998. (Dixie Morris Animal Adventure Ser.: No. 2). 128p. (J). (gr. 4-7). pap. 5.99 (978-0-8024-3364-0(2)) Moody Pubs.

Mouse Works Staff. Pooh: Tigger Friendly Tales. 1998. 10p. (J). 6.99 (978-0-7364-0020-6(6)) Mouse Works.

—Tigger. 1999. (My Very First Cloth Book Ser.). (J). 6.99 (978-0-7364-0178-4(4)) Disney Pr.

Much Ado at the Zoo. 2001. (gr. k-3). lib. bdg. 11.80 (978-0-613-32851-7(5)) Tandem Library Bks.

Murakami, Jon & Yeh, Phil. The Winged Tiger & the Dragons of Hawaii. 2005. 48p. pap. 11.95 (978-0-9755635-0-2(5)) Eastland Studios.

Murphy, Frank. Charlie Harte & His Two-Wheeled Tiger. 1998. (Illus.). 96p. pap. 6.95 (978-0-86278-532-1(4)) O'Brien Pr., Ltd., The IRL. *Dist:* Irish American Bk. Co.

Nagda, Ann Whitehead. Tiger Math: Learning to Graph from a Baby Tiger. Bickel, Cindy, illus. rev. ed. 2000. 32p. (J). (gr. 2-5). 16.95 (978-0-8050-6248-9(3) , Holt, Henry & Co. Bks. For Young Readers) Holt, Henry & Co.

—A Tiger Tale. 2005. (Soundprints' Amazing Animal Adventures! Ser.). (Illus.). 36p. (J). (ps-2). 8.95 incl. audio (978-1-59249-389-0(0) , SC7101) Soundprints.

—A Tiger Tale. Kratter, Paul, illus. 2005. (Amazing Animal Adventures Ser.). 36p. (J). (ps-2). 15.95 (978-1-59249-042-4(5) , B7101); pap. 6.95 (978-1-59249-043-1(3) , S7101) Soundprints.

—Tiger Tale. 2003. (gr. k-3). lib. bdg. 15.25 (978-0-613-71029-9(0)) Tandem Library Bks.

—A Tiger Tale. Kratter, Paul, illus. 2005. (Soundprints' Amazing Animal Adventures! Ser.). 32p. (J). (ps-2). 2.95 (978-1-59249-044-8(1) , S7151) Soundprints.

Nagda, Ann Whitehead & Bickel, Cindy. Tiger Math: Learning to Graph from a Baby Tiger. rev. ed. 2002. (Illus.). 32p. (J). (gr. 2-5). pap. 7.95 (978-0-8050-7161-0(X)) Holt, Henry & Co.

Oramas, Rafael. El Hojarasquerito del Monte. 2001. Tr. of Leaf Pile of the Mountain. (SPA., Illus.). 24p. (J). pap. 2.95 (978-980-257-011-9(7)) Ekare, Ediciones VEN. *Dist:* AIMS International Bks., Inc.

Oramas, Rafael Rivero. El Hombre, el Tigre, y la Luna. Areco, Amelie, illus. (SPA.). (J). pap. 7.96 (978-980-01-0482-8(8)) Monte Avila Editores Latinoamericana CA VEN. *Dist:* Lectorum Pubns., Inc.

Osborne, Mary Pope. Tigers at Twilight, Vol. 19. unabr. ed. 2004. (Magic Tree House Ser. : No. 19). 72p. (J). (gr. k 3). pap. 17.00 incl. audio (978-0-8072-0928-8(7) , S FTR 251 SP, Listening Library) Random Hse. Audio Publishing Group.

—Tigers at Twilight. Murdocca, Sal, illus. 1999. (Magic Tree House Ser.: No. 19). 96p. (J). (gr. k-3). lib. bdg. 11.99 (978-0-679-99065-9(8)); mass mkt. 3.99 (978-0-679-89065-2(3)) Random Hse. Children's Bks. (Random Hse. Bks. for Young Readers).

—Tigers at Twilight. 1999. (Magic Tree House Ser. : No. 19). (J). (gr. k-3). (Illus.). 71p. lib. bdg. 10.79 (978-0-606-16957-8(1)); lib. bdg. 11.80 (978-0-613-16224-1(2)) Tandem Library Bks.

Parish, Scott. Tigre a la Mesa. 2005. 14p. (J). 10.00 (978-1-4116-6003-8(X)) Lulu.com.

Partis, Joanne. Stripe. Partis, Joanne, illus. (Carolrhoda Picture Books Ser.). 32p. (J). 2004. pap. 6.95 (978-1-57505-667-8(4)); 2003. (Illus.). 14.95 (978-1-57505-450-6(7)) Lerner Publishing Group.

—Stripe. Partis, Joanne, illus. 2004. (Illus.). 32p. (J). (ps-ps). lib. bdg. 14.15 (978-0-606-30383-5(9)) Tandem Library Bks.

—Stripe's Naughty Sister. 2003. (Picture Bks.). (Illus.). 32p. (J). (ps-3). 15.95 (978-0-87614-466-4(0) , Carolrhoda Bks.) Lerner Publishing Group.

Peters, Andrew Fusek. The Tiger & the Wise Man. Mayo, Diana, illus. 2005. 32p. (J). 7.99 (978-1-904550-07-5(X)) Child's Play-International.

Petty. Little Tiger's Birthday. 1999. (Illus.). 14p. (J). pap. 9.99 (978-0-09-176772-3(5)) Random Hse. GBR. *Dist:* Independent Pubs. Group.

Pitcher, Caroline. Lord of the Forest. Morris, Jackie, illus. 2004. 32p. (J). 16.95 (978-1-84507-058-8(5)) Lincoln, Frances Ltd. GBR. *Dist:* Perseus Distribution.

Pogo the Clown. The Littlest Tiger: Harley's Great Adventures. Miller, Richard, illus. 2004. (J). 12.95 (978-0-9755253-2-6(8)) Chiliric Pubns.

Potter, Tony. Look Out Tiger. 1998. (Illus.). 32p. (J). (ps-3). 7.95 (978-1-902553-04-7(7)) Grimond FRA. *Dist:* Continental Enterprises Group, Inc. (CEG).

Powell, Richard. Big Tiger. Martín Larrañaga, Ana, illus. 2001. 10p. bds. 5.95 (978-1-58925-661-3(1) , tiger tales) ME Media LLC.

—Timmy Tiger. Rhodes, Katie, illus. 2004. (Fuzzy Friends Ser.). 10p. (J). 7.95 (978-1-58925-722-1(7) , tiger tales) ME Media LLC.

Prebeg, Rick. You've Got Cheetah Mail. Prebeg, Rick, photos by. 2005. (J). (978-1-933248-11-0(4)) World Quest Learning.

Ravishankar, Anushka. Tiger on a Tree. Biswas, Pulak, illus. 2004. 48p. (J). 15.00 (978-0-374-37555-3(0) , Farrar, Straus & Giroux (BYR)) Farrar, Straus & Giroux.

Rayner, Catherine. Augustus & His Smile. 2006. (Illus.). 28p. (J). (ps-2). 16.00 (978-1-56148-510-9(1)) Good Bks.

Rigby Education Staff. Sleepy Tiger. (Sails Literacy Ser.). (Illus.). 16p. (gr. k-1). 27.00 (978-0-7635-9860-0(7) , 698607C99) Rigby Education.

Rohmann, Eric. Cinder-Eyed Cat. 2001. (gr. k-3). lib. bdg. 15.30 (978-0-613-36797-4(9)) Tandem Library Bks.

Roy, Ron. A Thief at the National Zoo. 2007. 96p. (J). lib. bdg. (*978-0-375-94804-6(X)); pap. 3.99 (*978-0-375-84804-9(5)) Random Hse., Inc.

Rubio, Gabriela. Se Acabo! 2004. (SPA., Illus.). 30p. (J). 6.50 (978-84-348-7875-4(5)) SM Ediciones ESP. *Dist:* Lectorum Pubns., Inc.

—Terrible Terrible. 2006. (SPA., Illus.). 32p. (J). (978-84-933060-7-6(X)) Ekare, Ediciones.

Safari Press Staff, ed. Book Buddy - Tiger with Story Book. (Illus.). 10p. (J). (ps-3). reprint ed. pap. (978-1-881469-85-8(9)) Safari, Ltd.

Samore, Sam, photos by & text. The Adventure. Samore, Sam, text. 2005. (Illus.). 140p. pap. 35.00 (978-1-57687-095-2(2) , powerHouse Bks.) powerHouse Cultural Entertainment, Inc.

Sanner, Jennifer Jackson, ed. The Three Little Jayhawks. Pearson, Larry Leroy, illus. 2006. 40p. (J). per. 20.00 (*978-0-9742918-1-9(1)) Kansas Alumni Assoc.

Sargent, Dave & Sargent, Pat. Tiggy Tiger: Strong Points, 56 vols., 58. Lenoir, Jane, illus. 2001. (Animal Pride Ser.: Vol. 58). 36p. (J). lib. bdg. 19.95 (978-1-56763-557-7(1)) Ozark Publishing.

Scelsa, Greg. Rhyme Time. Faulkner, Stacey, ed. Hanke, Karen, illus. 2006. (J). pap. 2.99 (*978-1-59198-323-1(1)) Creative Teaching Pr., Inc.

Schulz, Charles M. Alle Achtung. Herbst, Gabriele & Rolle, Ekkehard, trs. from ENG. (Snoopy & die Peanuts Ser.: Vol. 5). (GER., Illus.). 128p. (J). pap. (978-3-8105-1818-7(2)) Kruger, Wolfgang Verlag, GmbH DEU. *Dist:* International Bk. Import Service, Inc.

Shaky Tiger. alt. ed. 2002. (J). (978-1-931312-98-1(2)) Soft-Play, Inc.

Shepard, Ernest H., illus. Tigger: Giant Shaped Board Book. 1999. 10p. (J). (ps-k). bds. 7.99 (978-0-525-46233-0(3) , Dutton Juvenile) Penguin Group (USA) Inc.

Silver Dolphin en Español Editors. Caritas felices: Winnie the Pooh: Happy Faces: Winnie the Pooh, Spanish-Language Edition. 2007. (Illus.). 8p. (J). bds. 7.95 (*978-970-718-393-3(4) , Silver Dolphin en Español) Advanced Marketing, S. de R. L. de C. V. MEX. *Dist:* Perseus Distribution.

Simon, Mary Manz. Tiger Forgives. Clearwater, Linda & Couri, Kathy, illus. 2006. (First Virtues for Toddlers Ser.). 20p. (J). 5.99 (978-0-7847-1413-3(4) , 04065) Standard Publishing.

So-Un, Kim. Tigers of the Kumgang Mountains. 2005. (Illus.). 32p. (J). 16.95 (978-0-8048-3653-1(1)) Tuttle Publishing.

Stewart, Celeste. The White Jade Tiger. Talley-Jones, Kathy, ed. Miller, Sara Swan, illus. 2001. 56p. (J). (gr. 3-5). 15.00 (978-0-9710165-0-7(X)) Dickason, Linda.

Stockton, Frank Richard. The Lady or the Tiger. Carlson, Claudia & DeNieff, Jacqueline S., illus. (J). (gr. 1-8). reprint ed. pap. 4.95 (978-0-934254-11-3(7)) Claymont Communications.

Sykes, Julie. A Dormir, Tigrito. Warnes, Tim, illus. 2002. (Little Tiger Board Book Ser.). (SPA.). 88p. 8.95 (978-84-488-0928-7(9) , BS7936) Beascoa, Ediciones S.A. ESP. *Dist:* Lectorum Pubns., Inc.

—Despierta, Tigrito. 2002. (Little Tiger Board Book Ser.). (SPA., Illus.). 76p. 8.95 (978-84-488-0929-4(7) , BS7937) Beascoa, Ediciones S.A. ESP. *Dist:* Lectorum Pubns., Inc.

—I Don't Want to Go to Bed! Warnes, Tim, illus. 1998. 14p. (J). (ps-2). bds. 6.95 (978-1-888444-33-9(9) , 21301) Little Tiger Pr.

—I Don't Want to Go to Bed! Warnes, Tim, illus. 2001. (J). 32p. 5.95 (978-1-58925-350-6(7)); 26p. tchr. ed. 14.95 (978-1-58925-001-7(X)) ME Media LLC. (tiger tales).

—I Don't Want to Go to Bed! Warnes, Tim, illus. 1998. (ENG, URD, SPA, VIE & CHI.). 32p. (J). (978-1-85430-535-0(2)); (978-1-85430-537-4(9)); (978-1-85430-539-8(5)); (978-1-85430-538-1(7)); (978-1-85430-536-7(0)) Magi Pubns.

—I Don't Want to Take a Bath! Warnes, Tim, illus. 1998. (J). (ps-2). 32p. pap. 5.95 (978-1-888444-36-0(3) , 21036); 14p. bds. 6.95 (978-1-888444-34-6(7) , 21300) Little Tiger Pr.

—Little Tiger Goes to School. Warnes, Tim, illus. 1998. (Lift-The-Flap Book Ser.). 5p. (J). (ps-1). bds. 11.95 (978-1-888444-49-0(5)) Little Tiger Pr.

—Little Tiger's Big Surprise! Warnes, Tim, illus. 2001. 32p. (J). (ps-2). tchr. ed. 14.95 (978-1-58925-002-4(8) , tiger tales) ME Media LLC.

—Little Tiger's Big Surprise! Warnes, Tim, illus. 1999. 32p. (J). (ps-2). 14.95 (978-1-888444-52-0(5)) Little Tiger Pr.

—Rainy Day Adventure. 2001. (gr. k-3). lib. bdg. 11.25 (978-0-613-53545-8(6)) Tandem Library Bks.

—Tigrito Va a la Escuela. Warnes, Tim, illus. 2002. (SPA.). 12p. (J). 12.95 (978-84-488-0934-8(3) , BS7979) Beascoa, Ediciones S.A. ESP. *Dist:* Lectorum Pubns., Inc.

—Time for Bed, Little Tiger. Warnes, Tim, illus. 2001. (Little Tiger Lift-the-Flap Ser.). 14p. (J). (ps-k). bds. 5.95 (978-1-58925-654-5(9) , tiger tales) ME Media LLC.

—Wait for Me, Little Tiger! Warnes, Tim, illus. 2001. 28p. (J). (ps-k). tchr. ed. 14.95 (978-1-58925-009-3(5) , tiger tales) ME Media LLC.

—Wake up, Little Tiger. Warnes, Tim, illus. 2000. (J). (ps-k). 5.95 (978-1-58431-019-8(7)) Little Tiger Pr.

—Wake up, Little Tiger! Warnes, Tim, illus. 2001. (Little Tiger Lift-the-Flap Ser.). 12p. (J). (ps-k). bds. 5.95 (978-1-58925-655-2(7) , tiger tales) ME Media LLC.

Sykes, Julie & Warnes, Tim. Little Tiger's Big Surprise! 2001. (Illus.). 32p. (J). (ps-2). 5.95 (978-1-58925-352-0(3) , tiger tales) ME Media LLC.

Taylor, Maxine Susie. Tygger O Tiger O'Toole: The Tiger Who Went to School. 2004. (ENG.). 36p. per. 15.99 (978-1-4141-0120-0(1)) Pleasant Word.

Taylor, Thomas. The Loudest Roar. 2003. (Illus.). (J). pap. (978-0-439-50131-6(8) , Levine, Arthur A. Bks.) Scholastic, Inc.

Taylor, Thomas, illus. The Loudest Roar. 2003. 32p. (J). 15.95 (978-0-439-50130-9(X) , Levine, Arthur A. Bks.) Scholastic, Inc.

Temple, Frances. Tiger Soup: An Anansi Story from Jamaica. 1998. (Illus.). 32p. (J). (ps-2). pap. 6.95 (978-0-531-07097-0(2) , Orchard Bks.) Scholastic, Inc.

Tiger & Monkey: Early Level Satellite Individual Title Six-Packs. (Sails Literacy Ser.). 16p. (gr. 1-2). 27.00 (978-0-7578-2923-9(6)) Rigby Education.

A Tiger Tale. 2005. (Soundprints' Amazing Animal Adventures! Ser.). (Illus.). 36p. (J). (ps-2). 19.95 incl. reel tape (978-1-59249-388-3(2) , BC7101) Soundprints.

Tiger's Tale. 2002. (Animal's Around the World Mini Bks.). (Illus.). 32p. (J). (978-1-59069-174-8(1) , H4010) Studio Mouse LLC.

Tigger's Bouncy Day. 2000. (Giant Pooh Book Ends Ser.). (Illus.). 10p. (J). (ps). (978-1-57584-808-2(2)) Reader's Digest Children's Publishing, Inc.

Tigre se Escapa, 6, Pack. (Coleccion Pm Ser.).Tr. of Tiger runs away. (SPA.). 16p. (gr. 1 up). 26.00 (978-0-7578-3021-1(8)) Rigby Education.

Tigre, Tigre, 6, Pack. (Coleccion Pm Ser.).Tr. of Tiger, Tiger. (SPA.). 16p. (gr. 1 up). 26.00 (978-0-7578-2963-5(5)) Rigby Education.

Tommy's Tummy Ache: Individual Title Six-Packs. (Literatura 2000 Ser.). (ps-1). 28.00 (978-0-7635-0015-3(1)) Rigby Education.

Twinn, Michael. Tiger. Adams, Pam, illus. 2001. (Pocket Pals Ser.). 12p. (J). (ps). per. 1.99 (978-0-85953-871-8(0)) Child's Play-International.

Umansky, Kaye. Tiger & Me. 2001. (Illus.). 32p. (J). pap. 9.99 (978-0-09-972210-6(0)) Random Hse. GBR. *Dist:* Independent Pubs. Group.

Urdaneta, Josefina. Pequeno Zambo. 2000. 7.95 (978-980-6437-13-5(6)) Baker & Taylor Bks.

Walt Disney Records Staff. Tigger Mania, 1. 1998. 22.50 (978-0-7634-0433-8(0)); 5.72 (978-0-7634-0432-1(2)) Walt Disney Records.

Walters, Eric. Tiger by the Tail. 2006. 176p. (J). (gr. 3-8). pap. 5.95 (978-0-88878-396-7(5) , Sandcastle Bks.) Dundurn Group, The CAN. *Dist:* Univ. of Toronto Pr.

—Tiger in Trouble. 2006. 192p. (J). pap. 5.95 (978-0-88878-420-9(1) , Sandcastle Bks.) Dundurn Group, The CAN. *Dist:* Univ. of Toronto Pr.

Wang, Eva, illus. Auntie Tigress & Other Favorite Chinese Folk-Tales. 2006. 48p. (J). 16.50 (978-1-933327-29-7(4)); 15.95 (978-1-933327-28-0(6)) Purple Bear Bks., Inc.

Warnes, Tim. Little Tiger's Funtime 123. 2001. (J). bds. 8.95 (978-1-58925-660-6(3) , tiger tales) ME Media LLC.

—Little Tiger's Funtime ABC. 2001. (J). 8.95 (978-1-58925-659-0(X) , tiger tales) ME Media LLC.

Warnes, Tim & Sykes, Julie. Bathtime, Little Tiger! Warnes, Tim, illus. 2003. (Little Tiger Lift-the-Flap Ser.). (Illus.). 12p. (J). 5.95 (978-1-58925-693-4(X) , tiger tales) ME Media LLC.

—Hide & Seek, Little Tiger. Warnes, Tim, illus. 2003. (Little Tiger Lift-the-Flap Ser.). (Illus.). 14p. (J). 5.95 (978-1-58925-694-1(8) , tiger tales) ME Media LLC.

Waterson, Bill. Jetzt geht's Rund. Goetting, Waltraud, tr. from ENG. (Calvin & Hobbes Ser.: Vol. 1). (GER., Illus.). 64p. (J). pap. (978-3-8105-0328-2(2)) Kruger, Wolfgang Verlag, GmbH DEU. *Dist:* International Bk. Import Service, Inc.

Watterson, Bill. Achtung, Fertig, Los! Goetting, Waltraud, tr. from ENG. (Calvin & Hobbes Ser.: Vol. 8). (GER., Illus.). 64p. (J). pap. (978-3-8105-0336-7(3)) Kruger, Wolfgang Verlag, GmbH DEU. *Dist:* International Bk. Import Service, Inc.

—Alles unter Kontrolle. Goetting, Waltraud, tr. from ENG. (Calvin & Hobbes Ser.: Vol. 3). (GER., Illus.). 64p. (J). pap. (978-3-8105-0330-5(4)) Kruger, Wolfgang Verlag, GmbH DEU. *Dist:* International Bk. Import Service, Inc.

—Auf dem Sprung. Goetting, Waltraud, tr. from ENG. (Calvin & Hobbes Ser.: Bk. 1). (GER., Illus.). 96p. (J). pap. (978-3-8105-0320-6(7)) Kruger, Wolfgang Verlag, GmbH DEU. *Dist:* International Bk. Import Service, Inc.

T U V

—Bloss nicht Aergern. Goetting, Waltraud, tr. from ENG. (Calvin & Hobbes Ser.: Bk. 3). (GER., Illus.). 96p. (J). pap. (978-3-8105-0322-0(3)) Kruger, Wolfgang Verlag, GmbH DEU. *Dist:* International Bk. Import Service, Inc.

—Calvin & Hobbes: Das Jubilaumsalbum, 10 vols. Bartoszko, Alexandra, tr. from ENG. (Calvin & Hobbes Ser.). (GER., Illus.). 208p. (J). (978-3-8105-0370-1(3)) Kruger, Wolfgang Verlag, GmbH DEU. *Dist:* International Bk. Import Service, Inc.

—Einfach Umwerfend. Goetting, Waltraud, tr. from ENG. (Calvin & Hobbes Ser.: Vol. 13). (GER., Illus.). 48p. (J). pap. (978-3-8105-0350-3(9)) Kruger, Wolfgang Verlag, GmbH DEU. *Dist:* International Bk. Import Service, Inc.

—Enorm in Form. Goetting, Waltraud, tr. from ENG. (Calvin & Hobbes Ser.: Vol. 9). (GER., Illus.). 64p. (J). pap. (978-3-8105-0340-4(1)) Kruger, Wolfgang Verlag, GmbH DEU. *Dist:* International Bk. Import Service, Inc.

—Feine Freunde. Goetting, Waltraud, tr. from ENG. (Calvin & Hobbes Ser.: Vol. 15). (GER., Illus.). 80p. (J). pap. (978-3-8105-0353-4(3)) Kruger, Wolfgang Verlag, GmbH DEU. *Dist:* International Bk. Import Service, Inc.

—Fix & Fertig. Goetting, Waltraud, tr. from ENG. (Calvin & Hobbes Ser.: Bk. 2). (GER., Illus.). 96p. (J). pap. (978-3-8105-0321-3(5)) Kruger, Wolfgang Verlag, GmbH DEU. *Dist:* International Bk. Import Service, Inc.

—Ganz schoen Daneben. Goetting, Waltraud, tr. from ENG. (Calvin & Hobbes Ser.: Vol. 7). (GER., Illus.). 64p. (J). pap. (978-3-8105-0335-0(5)) Kruger, Wolfgang Verlag, GmbH DEU. *Dist:* International Bk. Import Service, Inc.

—Immer mit der Ruhe. Goetting, Waltraud, tr. from ENG. (Calvin & Hobbes Ser.: Vol. 4). (GER., Illus.). 64p. (J). pap. (978-3-8105-0331-2(2)) Kruger, Wolfgang Verlag, GmbH DEU. *Dist:* International Bk. Import Service, Inc.

—Immer Voll Drauf. Goetting, Waltraud, tr. from ENG. (Calvin & Hobbes Ser.: Vol. 5). (GER., Illus.). 64p. (J). pap. (978-3-8105-0332-9(0)) Kruger, Wolfgang Verlag, GmbH DEU. *Dist:* International Bk. Import Service, Inc.

—Jetzt Erst Recht. Goetting, Waltraud, tr. from ENG. (Calvin & Hobbes Ser.: Vol. 10). (GER., Illus.). 64p. (J). pap. (978-3-8105-0339-8(8)) Kruger, Wolfgang Verlag, GmbH DEU. *Dist:* International Bk. Import Service, Inc.

—Mach mir den Tiger. Goetting, Waltraud, tr. from ENG. (Calvin & Hobbes Ser.: Vol. 11). (GER., Illus.). 64p. (J). pap. (978-3-8105-0341-1(X)) Kruger, Wolfgang Verlag, GmbH DEU. *Dist:* International Bk. Import Service, Inc.

—Die Phantastischen Zwei. Goetting, Waltraud, tr. from ENG. (Calvin & Hobbes Ser.: Vol. 14). (GER., Illus.). 80p. (J). pap. (978-3-8105-0351-0(7)) Kruger, Wolfgang Verlag, GmbH DEU. *Dist:* International Bk. Import Service, Inc.

—Steil nach Oben. Goetting, Waltraud, tr. from ENG. (Calvin & Hobbes Ser.: Vol. 6). (GER., Illus.). 64p. (J). pap. (978-3-8105-0333-6(9)) Kruger, Wolfgang Verlag, GmbH DEU. *Dist:* International Bk. Import Service, Inc.

—Tierisch Lyrisch. Goetting, Waltraud, tr. from ENG. (Calvin & Hobbes Ser.: Vol. 12). (GER., Illus.). 64p. (J). pap. (978-3-8105-0349-7(5)) Kruger, Wolfgang Verlag, GmbH DEU. *Dist:* International Bk. Import Service, Inc.

Williams, Laura E. The Mystery of the Missing Tiger. 2002. (Mystic Lighthouse Mysteries Ser.). 112p. (J). pap. 4.50 (978-0-439-21728-6(8)) Scholastic, Inc.

—Mystery of the Missing Tiger. 2002. (gr. 3-6). lib. bdg. 12.40 (978-0-613-83241-0(8)) Tandem Library Bks.

Yep, Laurence. Lee, Insu, illus. 2008. (J). ***(978-0-06-029551-6(1));*** lib. bdg. ***(*978-0-06-029552-3(X))*** HarperCollins Pubs.

Youngberg, Norma. The Tiger of Bitter Valley. 2004. (Illus.). 251p. (J). (gr. 3-6). reprint ed. per. 13.95 (978-1-57258-186-9(7) , 945-6048) TEACH Services, Inc.

Zahradka, Miroslav. The Un-Terrible Tiger. Zahradka, Miroslav, illus. (Illus.). 32p. (J). (ps-3). 12.95 (978-0-87592-056-6(X)) Scroll Pr., Inc.

Zocchi, Judy. Paulie & Sasha: The Rescue. Vannozzi, Don, illus. 2001. (Paulie & Sasha Ser.). 32p. (J). lib. bdg. 23.00 (978-1-891997-15-0(7)) Dingles & Co.

TIGRIS RIVER VALLEY

Mountjoy, Shane. The Tigris & Euphrates Rivers. 2004. (Rivers in World History Ser.). (Illus.). 120p. (J). (gr. 9-13). 30.00 (978-0-7910-8246-1(6) , Chelsea Hse.) Facts On File, Inc.

Whitcraft, Melissa. The Tigris & Euphrates River. 2000. (Watts Library Ser.). (Illus.). 64p. (J). (gr. 5-7). pap. 8.95 (978-0-531-16432-7(2) , Watts, Franklin) Scholastic Library Publishing.

—The Tigris & Euphrates Rivers. 1999. (Watts Library). (Illus.). 64p. (J). (gr. 5-7). 25.50 (978-0-531-11741-5(3) , Watts, Franklin) Scholastic Library Publishing.

—Tigris & Euphrates Rivers. 1999. (gr. 3-6). lib. bdg. 17.60 (978-0-613-37561-0(0)) Tandem Library Bks.

TIMBER

see Forests and Forestry; Lumber and Lumbering; Trees; Wood

TIME

see also Calendars; Clocks and Watches

Adam, Winky. Telling Time. 1999. 32p. (J). (ps-2). pap. 3.50 (978-0-486-40794-4(2)) Dover Pubns., Inc.

Adams, Colleen. A Weekend in the City: Adding & Subtracting Times to the Nearest Minute. 2004. (PowerMath Ser.). (Illus.). 24p. (J). lib. bdg. (978-0-8239-8897-6(X)); lib. bdg. 21.25 (978-0-8239-8974-4(7)) Rosen Publishing Group, Inc., The. (PowerKids Pr.).

Akaishi, Shinobu & Sarris, Eno, eds. My Book of Easy Telling Time: Learning about Hours & Half-Hours. 2006. (Illus.). 80p. (J). per. 6.95 (978-1-933241-26-5(8)) Kumon Publishing North America, Inc.

Akaisihi, Shinobu & Sarris, Eno, eds. My Book of Telling Time: Learning about Minutes. 2006. (J). per. 6.95 (978-1-933241-27-2(6)) Kumon Publishing North America, Inc.

Algonzzine, Kate. Time & Money. 1998. (Basic Skills Ser.). (Illus.). 32p. (J). (gr. k-1). pap. 4.95 (978-0-88724-466-7(1) , CD-2134) Carson-Dellosa Publishing Co., Inc.

American Education Publishing Staff. Time & Money. 2003. (Brighter Child Learning Flash Cards Ser.). (Illus.). 36p. (J). 2.99 (978-1-56189-467-3(2) , 31050, American Education Publishing) School Specialty Publishing.

American Education Publishing Staff & Douglas, Vincent. Time & Money: Grade 2. 2001. (Together We Learn Ser.). (Illus.). 32p. (C). (gr. 2). pap. 2.99 (978-1-56189-629-5(2) , 31325-629, American Education Publishing) School Specialty Publishing.

American Education Publishing Staff, et al. The Complete Book of Time & Money. 2000. (Complete Book Ser.). (Illus.). 352p. (J). (gr. k-6). pap. 14.95 (978-1-56189-500-7(8) , 31133, American Education Publishing) School Specialty Publishing.

Amery, H. Telling the Time. 2004. (Treasury of Farmyard Tales Ser.). (SPA.). 24p. (J). (ps up). 8.95 (978-0-7945-0146-4(X) , Usborne) EDC Publishing.

Amery, Heather. Telling the Time. 2007. 24p. (J). bds. 12.99 (978-0-7945-1519-5(3) , Usborne) EDC Publishing.

Attwood, Jilly. Talking about Time: Days of the Week. 2005. (Illus.). 24p. (J). (978-1-4109-1638-9(3)); pap. (978-1-4109-1644-0(8)) Heinemann Library.

—Talking about Time: How Long Does It Take? 2005. (Illus.). 24p. (J). (978-1-4109-1639-6(1)); pap. (978-1-4109-1645-7(6)) Heinemann Library.

—Talking about Time: Times of the Day. 2005. (Illus.). 24p. (J). (978-1-4109-1641-9(3)); pap. (978-1-4109-1647-1(2)) Heinemann Library.

Awdry, Wilbert V. Thomas 'Right on Time' 2003. (Illus.). 10p. (J). bds. 16.98 (978-0-7853-8810-4(9) , 7192400) Publications International, Ltd.

Beers, Jack. Time & Measurement. 2000. (Metro Math Readers Yellow Level Ser.). (J). (gr. 12-2). 52.95 (978-1-58120-558-9(9)) Metropolitan Teaching & Learning Co.

—Ya Es Hora: Metro Math Readers Yellow Level. 2000. (Metro Math Readers Yellow Level Ser.). (J). (gr. 1-2). 3.75 (978-1-58120-475-9(2)) Metropolitan Teaching & Learning Co.

Benchmark Education Staff, compiled by. Measuring Time. 2006. spiral bd. 249.00 ***(*978-1-4108-7074-2(X))*** Benchmark Education Co.

—Telling Time. 2006. spiral bd. 229.00 ***(*978-1-4108-7050-6(2))*** Benchmark Education Co.

Bernardi, Philip & Havens, Diane. Twice upon a Time. 2003. (Theater for Young Audiences Ser.). (Illus.). 24p. (J). (gr. k-6). pap. 6.00 (978-0-88734-425-1(9)) Players Pr., Inc.

Brallier, Jess M. Y2kids: A Guide to the Millennium. 1999. (gr. 3-6). lib. bdg. 11.80 (978-0-613-22662-2(3)) Tandem Library Bks.

Brimner, Larry Dane. The Official "M&M's" Book of the Millennium. 1999. (gr. k-3). lib. bdg. 15.25 (978-0-613-88704-5(2)) Tandem Library Bks.

Burkett, Larry. All about Time: Discovering How the Calendar Affects You. Locke, Gary, illus. 2003. (All about Ser.). 32p. (J). pap., pap. 7.99 (978-0-7814-3788-2(1) , 0781437881) Cook, David C. Publishing Co.

—All about Time: Discovering How the Calendar Affects You. 2003. (gr. 3-6). lib. bdg. 16.45 (978-0-613-74880-3(8)) Tandem Library Bks.

Burstein, John. Keeping Track of Time: Go Fly a Kite! Destiny Images Staff, illus. 2003. (Math Monsters Ser.). 24p. (YA). (gr. 1 up). lib. bdg. 19.33 (978-0-8368-3810-7(6) , Weekly Reader Early Learning Library) Stevens, Gareth Inc.

—Keeping Track of Time: Go Fly a Kite! 2003. (Weekly Reader Early Learning Library). (Illus.). 24p. (J). (gr. 1 up). pap. 7.93 (978-0-8368-3825-1(4) , Weekly Reader Early Learning Library) Stevens, Gareth Inc.

Burton, Margie, et al. Measuring Time. Evento, Susan, ed. 1998. (Early Connections Ser.). 16p. (J). (gr. k-2). pap. 4.25 (978-1-892393-42-5(5)) Benchmark Education Co.

Cernek, Kim. Build-a-Skill Instant Books Time & Money. Faulkner, Stacey, ed. Campbell, Jenny & Tom, Darcy, illus. 2007. (J). 4.99 ***(*978-1-59198-417-7(3))*** Creative Teaching Pr., Inc.

Cipriano, Jeri S. It's Time! 2003. (Yellow Umbrella Books for Early Readers). (Illus.). 17p. (J). 15.93 (978-0-7368-2916-8(4)); pap. (978-0-7368-2875-8(3)) Yellow Umbrella Pr.

Clock & Time Workbook. 2002. (J). pap. 8.95 (978-1-56911-043-0(3)) Learning Resources, Inc.

Clockwise Time Workbook. 2001. (J). pap. (978-1-56911-723-1(3)) Learning Resources, Inc.

Dalmatian Press Staff. Money, Time & Fractions: Chalkboard Book. 2003. (Home Learning Tools Ser.). 10p. (J). (gr. 2 up). pap. 3.99 (978-1-4037-0331-6(0)) Dalmatian Pr.

—Same or Different. 1998. (Precious Moments Workbooks Ser.). (Illus.). (J). (ps-3). pap. 2.99 (978-1-57759-115-3(1)) Dalmatian Pr.

Dash, Joan. The Longitude Prize: The Race Between the Moon & the Watch-Machine. Petricic, Dusan, illus. 2000. 208p. (J). (gr. 4-7). 17.00 (978-0-374-34636-2(4) , Farrar, Straus & Giroux (BYR)) Farrar, Straus & Giroux.

Davies & Ne, Harriet. What Time Is It? Asks Elephant. (Illus.). 10p. (J). pap. 15.95 (978-1-85479-262-4(8)) O'Mara, Michael Bks., Ltd. GBR. *Dist:* Trans-Atlantic Pubns., Inc.

DK Publishing Staff. Telling Time. 2007. 32p. (J). 14.99 (978-0-7566-2949-6(7)); pap. 3.99 (978-0-7566-2948-9(9)) Dorling Kindersley Publishing, Inc.

—Time. 2007. (Eye Know Ser.). (Illus.). 24p. (J). 8.99 (978-0-7566-2530-6(0)) Dorling Kindersley Publishing, Inc.

Dolan, Graham. The Greenwich Guide to Measuring Time. 2001. (Illus.). 32p. (J). (gr. 2-4). lib. bdg. 22.79 (978-1-58810-043-6(X)) Heinemann Library.

—The Greenwich Guide to Time & the Millenium. 1999. (Illus.). 48p. (gr. 7-9). (978-1-57572-802-5(8)) Heinemann Library.

—Greenwich Guides to... How Do We Measure Time?, 3 bks., Set. 2001. (Illus.). 32p. (J). (gr. 2-4). lib. bdg. 68.37 (978-1-58810-008-5(1)) Heinemann Library.

Dorling Kindersley Publishing Staff. My First Time. 2nd ed. 2006. (Illus.). 36p. (J). (ps-3). bds. 5.99 (978-0-7566-0504-9(0)) Dorling Kindersley Publishing, Inc.

Dorling Kindersley Publishing Staff, ed. Future. 2004. (Dk Eyewitness Books Ser.). (Illus.). 72p. (J). 15.99 (978-0-7566-0684-8(5)) Dorling Kindersley Publishing, Inc.

Douglas, Vincent. Math, Time, & Money. 2004. (Flash Card Collection). 324p. (C). 16.95 (978-1-58845-663-2(3)) School Specialty Publishing.

Douglas, Vincent & School Specialty Publishing Staff. My Little Showcase of Getting Ready for School. 2005. (My Little Showcase Ser.). (Illus.). 100p. (J). bds. 14.95 (978-1-58845-652-6(8) , Brighter Child) School Specialty Publishing.

—My Own Little Judy Clock with Booklet. 2001. (Illus.). 16p. (C). pap. 8.99 (978-0-7682-0592-3(1) , Judy) Schaffer, Frank Pubns.

—Telling Time. 2000. (Spectrum Flash Cards Ser.). (Illus.). 50p. (J). (gr. k-3). 2.99 (978-1-57768-138-0(X) , Spectrum) School Specialty Publishing.

—Time. 2003. (Brighter Child Flash Cards Ser.). (Illus.). 54p. (J). (ps up). 2.99 (978-0-7696-2398-6(0) , Brighter Child) School Specialty Publishing.

DPWW. Mickey Mouse Telling Time: Book & Watch Set. 2020. 24p. (J). 12.99 (978-0-7868-3248-4(7)) Disney Pr.

Farndon, John. Time. 2002. (Science Experiments Ser.). (Illus.). 32p. (J). 25.64 (978-0-7614-1470-4(3) , Benchmark Bks.) Cavendish, Marshall Corp.

Fawcett, Linda, et al. It's about Time. Cordel, Betty & Pauls, Michelle, eds. Mason, Renee, illus. 2002. 141p. (J). pap. 18.95 (978-1-881431-97-8(5)) AIMS Education Foundation.

First Steps: Time. 2002. (First Steps Reading Ser.). 32p. (J). pap. 2.95 (978-0-7894-8485-7(4)) Dorling Kindersley Publishing, Inc.

Flikkema, Elizabeth. Time. Morris, Susan & Seltzer, Erin, eds. 2005. 48p. (J). per. 6.99 (978-1-59441-062-8(3) , CD-104026) Carson-Dellosa Publishing Co., Inc.

Forte, Imogene. Ready to Learn Time & Money. 2003. (Illus.). 64p. per. 7.95 (978-0-86530-592-2(7)) Incentive Pubns., Inc.

Fowler, Allan. Seconds, Minutes & Hours. 1999. (Rookie Read-About Science Ser.). (J). (978-0-516-21211-1(7) , Children's Pr.) Scholastic Library Publishing.

Ganeri, Anita. Day & Night. (Nature's Patterns Ser.). (Illus.). 32p. 2005. (978-1-4109-1327-2(9)); 2004. (J). pap. 7.25 (978-1-4034-5883-4(9)); 2004. (J). lib. bdg. 24.21 (978-1-4034-5877-3(4)) Heinemann Library.

Gerard, Franck J. Time Waits for No One! Prioritize to Change Your Life! 2005. (Illus.). 90p. per., training bk. ed. 14.99 net. (978-0-9772685-0-4(0)) ABC Pubs.

Gold, Kari Jenson. It's Time! Date not set. (Early Math Big Bks.). (Illus.). 16p. (J). (ps-2). pap. 16.95 (978-1-56784-430-6(8)) Sundance/Newbridge Educational Publishing.

Greenes, Carol, et al. Time & Money. 2003. (Illus.). 60p. (J). (ps-3). 16.95 (978-0-7690-0004-6(5)) Seymour, Dale Pubns.

Greenes, Carole, et al. Money & Time. 2003. (Illus.). (J). (gr. 3). 16.95 (978-0-7690-0834-9(8)) Seymour, Dale Pubns.

Gribbin, John R. Time & Space. 2000. (Eyewitness Bks.). (Illus.). 64p. (J). (gr. 3-7). 15.99 (978-0-7894-5578-9(1)) Dorling Kindersley Publishing, Inc.

Harcourt School Publishers Staff. The Caterpillar, 5 Pack, On Level. 3rd ed. 2002. (Trophies Reading Program Ser.). (Illus.). (J). pap. 20.10 (978-0-15-326835-9(2)) Harcourt Schl. Pubs.

—The Caterpillar: On Level. 3rd ed. 2002. (Trophies Reading Program Ser.). (Illus.). (J). pap. 4.10 (978-0-15-322985-5(3)) Harcourt Schl. Pubs.

—Time Keepers. 3rd ed. 2002. (Trophies English Language Learners Ser.). (Illus.). pap. 5.10 (978-0-15-327773-3(4)) Harcourt Schl. Pubs.

—Where Time Begins. 3rd ed. 2002. (Horizons Ser.). (Illus.). (J). pap. 7.30 (978-0-15-333602-7(1)) Harcourt Schl. Pubs.

Haslam, Andrew. Time. 2004. (Make It Work! Science Ser.). (Illus.). 48p. (gr. 3-6). (J). pap. 6.95 (978-1-58728-363-5(8)); 12.95 (978-1-58728-377-2(8)) T&N Children's Publishing. (Two Can Publishing).

Haslam, Andrew, et al. Time. (Make It Work! Ser.). (Illus.). 48p. (J). pap. 16.99 (978-0-590-24914-0(2)); pap. 7.99 (978-0-590-24915-7(0)) Scholastic, Inc.

Head, Honor. Times of Day. Stower, Adam, illus. 1998. (Ed Mouse Finds Out about Ser.). 32p. (J). (ps-2). pap. 5.95 (978-0-8172-8103-8(7)) Steck-Vaughn.

Hendra, Sue. Time for Lunch. 2003. (Illus.). 20p. (J). 6.99 (978-0-333-76288-2(6)) Macmillan Publishers Ltd. GBR. *Dist:* Trafalgar Square Publishing.

Heurtelou, Maude. Telling Time: Aprann Le. Vilsaint, Fequiere, illus. 1999. 28p. (J). (gr. k-2). pap. 5.50 (978-1-58432-021-0(4)) Educa Vision.

Hewitt, Sally. Time. 2000. (It's Science! Ser.). (Illus.). 32p. (J). (gr. k-3). 23.50 (978-0-516-21655-3(4) , Children's Pr.) Scholastic Library Publishing.

—Time. 2007. (J). ***(*978-1-59604-134-9(X))*** Stargazer Bks.

Holden, Arianne. Time. (Playschool Ser.). (Illus.). 2003. 32p. pap. 5.99 (978-1-84215-773-2(6) , Southwater); 1999. 48p. 7.95 (978-1-85967-683-7(9) , Lorenz Bks.) Anness Publishing GBR. *Dist:* National Bk. Network.

Holt, Rinehart and Winston Staff. Horizons: Time for Kids Collection, 18 vols. 2003. (Harcourt Horizons Ser.). (Illus.). (gr. k up). 63.70 (978-0-15-333097-1(X)) Harcourt Schl. Pubs.

Honey. What Time Is It?: a Visual Learning Tool for Telling Time. 2006. (ENG.). 48p. per. 20.50 ***(*978-1-4259-6999-8(2))*** AuthorHouse.

HSP. Time & Money, Bk. E. 2nd ed. 2002. (First-Place Math Ser.). (gr. 1 up). pap. 12.60 (978-0-15-334613-2(2)); (gr. 2 up). pap. 12.60 (978-0-15-334619-4(1)) Harcourt Schl. Pubs.

Hunt, Laura. Pooh Everyday Learn & Grow. 1999. (Disney's Winnie the Pooh Ser.). (Illus.). 20p. (J). (ps-4). bds. 4.99 (978-0-7364-0033-6(8) , RH/Disney) Random Hse. Children's Bks.

Hutchins, Hazel. A Second Is a Hiccup: A Child's Book of Time. Denton, Kady MacDonald, illus. (J). 2008. 16.99 (978-0-439-83110-9(5)); 2007. 40p. 16.99 (978-0-439-83106-2(7)) Scholastic, Inc. (Levine, Arthur A. Bks.).

Judy/Instructo. Telling Time. 2001. (Illus.). (J). (gr. 1-3). 3.99 (978-0-7682-1899-2(3) , J41009) School Specialty Publishing.

Kaufmann, Kelli. Party Time with Blue. Miller, Victoria, illus. 2003. (J). 16.98 (978-0-7853-8812-8(5)) Publications International, Ltd.

Keeping Time: Individual Title Six-Packs. (Rigby Infoquest Ser.). 32p. (gr. 4 up). 37.00 (978-0-7578-5731-7(0)) Rigby Education.

Kirkby, David. Measuring. 1998. (Mini Math Ser.). (Illus.). (J). (978-1-57572-004-3(3)) Heinemann Library.

Klutz Press Staff, creator. How to Tell Time. 2005. (Illus.). 24p. (J). (ps-3). spiral bd. 12.95 (978-1-59174-086-5(X)) Klutz.

Kompelien, Tracy. I Can Tell Time with a Rhyme! (Math Made Fun Ser.). (Illus.). 24p. (J). 2007. 19.93 (978-1-59928-525-2(8)); 2006. (978-1-59928-526-9(6)) ABDO Publishing Co.

Koscielniak, Bruce. About Time: A First Look at Time & Clocks. 2004. (Illus.). 32p. (J). (gr. 3-5). tchr. ed. 16.00 (978-0-618-39668-9(3)) Houghton Mifflin Co. Trade & Reference Div.

Kumon Publishing Staff, ed. Easy Telling Time Write & Wipe. 2007. 32p. 9.95 ***(*978-1-933241-45-6(4))*** Kumon Publishing North America, Inc.

LeapFrog Time Wipe off Book. 2007. (J). 4.99 ***(*978-1-59545-136-1(6))*** Learning Horizons, Inc.

Learn to Tell the Time. 2003. (Illus.). (J). bds. 4.98 (978-1-4054-1145-5(7)) Parragon, Inc.

Let's Tell Time. 2003. 16p. (J). 3.79 (978-1-58792-052-3(2)) Trend Enterprises, Inc.

Levy, Janey. Keeping Time Through the Ages: The History of Tools Used to Measure Time. 2004. (PowerMath Ser.). (Illus.). 32p. (J). lib. bdg. (978-0-8239-8917-1(8)); lib. bdg. 22.50 (978-0-8239-8993-5(3)) Rosen Publishing Group, Inc., The. (PowerKids Pr.).

Llewellyn, Claire. Day & Night. 2007. (Illus.). 24p. (J). ***(*978-1-59771-018-3(0))*** Sea-To-Sea Pubns.

Lorenz Books Staff. Time with Sticker. 1999. (Sticker Fun Ser.). (Illus.). 16p. (ps-k). pap. 4.95 (978-0-7548-0281-5(7) , Lorenz Bks.) Anness Publishing GBR. *Dist:* National Bk. Network.

Martin, W. Eric, et al. Tools of Timekeeping: A Kid's Guide to the History & Science of Telling Time. 2005. (Tools of Discovery Ser.). (Illus.). 144p. (J). pap. 16.95 (978-0-9722026-7-1(6)) Nomad Pr.

Massaro, Dom & Rothman, Don. Time to Learn about Time. Rowe, Bill, illus. 2002. 62p. (J). (gr. 1-3). per. 14.95 (978-0-9712714-2-5(9)) Fuzzy Bks.

McIntyre, Pat. It's about Time. 2002. (J). 5.95 (978-1-879260-44-3(1)) Chicago Spectrum Pr.

—It's about Time. 2005. (Illus.). 36p. pap. 3.95 (978-1-933148-49-6(7)) Tate Publishing & Enterprises, L.L.C.

Miglis, Jenny. My Talking Clock: Hannah's Busy Day. 2005. 12p. bds. 9.95 (978-1-932915-06-8(0)) Sandvik Publishing.

Millard, Anne. A Street Through Time: A 12,000 Year Walk Through History. Noon, Steve, illus. 1998. 32p. (J). (gr. 3-7). 17.99 (978-0-7894-3426-5(1)) Dorling Kindersley Publishing, Inc.

Moffatt, Judith, illus. Slide & Discover: It's Time! 2005. (Slide & Discover Ser.). 8p. (J). bds. 7.95 (978-1-58117-247-8(8) , Intervisual/Piggy Toes) Dalmatian Pr.

Murphy, Debbie & Murphy, Frank. Time & Money. 2002. (Best-Ever Activities for Grades 2-3 Ser.). (Illus.). 48p. (J). (gr. 2-3). 10.95 (978-0-439-29648-9(X)) Scholastic, Inc.

Murphy, Patricia J. Telling Time with Puppies & Kittens. 2007. (Puppy & Kitten Math Ser.). (Illus.). 32p. (J). lib. bdg. 22.60 (978-0-7660-2728-2(7) , Enslow Elementary) Enslow Pubs., Inc.

Murphy, Stuart J. It's about Time! Speirs, John, illus. 2005. (MathStart Ser.). 40p. (J). 15.99 (978-0-06-055768-3(0)); pap. 5.99 (978-0-06-055769-0(9)) HarperCollins Pubs.

—Rodeo Time. Wenzel, David T., illus. 2006. (MathStart Ser.). 40p. (J). 15.99 (978-0-06-055778-2(8)); pap. 5.99 (978-0-06-055779-9(6)) HarperCollins Pubs.

Nadeau, Isaac. Learning about Earth's Cycles with Graphic Organizers. 2005. (Graphic Organizers in Science Ser.). (Illus.). 24p. (J). 19.95 (978-1-4042-2807-8(1)); pap. (978-1-4042-5044-4(1)) Rosen Publishing Group, Inc., The. (PowerKids Pr.).

Nagda, Ann Whitehead & Bickel, Cindy. Chimp Math: Learning about Time from a Baby Chimpanzee. rev. ed. 2002. (Illus.). 32p. (J). (gr. 2-5). 17.95 (978-0-8050-6674-6(8) , Holt, Henry & Co. Bks. For Young Readers) Holt, Henry & Co.

Nayer, Judy. It's about Time. 2002. (Yellow Umbrella Books). (Illus.). 16p. (J). (gr. 1). lib. bdg. 14.60 (978-0-7368-1283-2(0) , Pebble Bks.) Capstone Pr., Inc.

Older, Jules. Telling Time. 2000. (978-0-606-18030-6(3)) Tandem Library Bks.

—Telling Time: How to Tell Time on Digital & Analog Clocks! Halsey, Megan, illus. 2000. 32p. (J). (gr. k-4). pap. 6.95 (978-0-88106-397-4(5)); 16.95 (978-0-88106-396-7(7)) Charlesbridge Publishing, Inc.

—Telling Time: How to Tell Time on Digital & Analog Clocks! Halsey, Megan, illus. 2000. (J). (ps-ps). lib. bdg. 15.25 (978-0-613-28318-2(X)) Tandem Library Bks.

Osen, Janet E. Mini Maestro Presents the Tic-Toc Clocks. Angermueller, Ivy & Boshart, Martha, illus. l.t. ed. 2000. 30p. (J). (ps-k). 16.95 incl. audio compact disk (978-0-9700489-0-5(4)) Little Fiddle Co., Inc., The.

Osofsky, Jill & Snyder, Spence. Me & My Watch. 2000. (Illus.). 23p. (J). (978-1-56451-343-4(2) , Ideal School Supply) Schaffer, Frank Pubns.

Patilla, Peter. Starting off with Time. 2001. (Starting Off Ser.). (Illus.). (J). (978-0-606-21463-6(1)) Tandem Library Bks.

—Time. 2001. (Illus.). 32p. (J). lib. bdg. 24.25 (978-1-930643-17-8(9)) Chrysalis Education.

—Time. 1999. (Math Links Ser.). 32p. (J). (gr. k-2). lib. bdg. 21.36 (978-1-57572-970-1(9)) Heinemann Library.

Peat, Ann. My World. 2005. (Heinemann Read & Learn Ser.). (Illus.). 24p. (J). pap. (978-1-4034-6469-9(3)); pap. (978-1-4034-6470-5(7)) Heinemann Library.

—Time. 2005. (My World Ser.). (Illus.). 24p. (J). lib. bdg. 20.64 (978-1-4034-6464-4(2)) Heinemann Library.

Petelinsek, Kathleen & Primm, E. Russell. Days & Times: Días y Horas. 2006. (Talking Hands Ser.). (ENG & SPA., Illus.). 24p. (J). 21.36 (978-1-59296-681-3(0)) Child's World, Inc.

Pistoia, Sara. Time. 2006. (MathBooks Ser.). (Illus.). 24p. (J). 24.21 (978-1-59296-692-9(6)) Child's World, Inc.

Pluckrose, Henry. My Day. 2001. (Let's Explore Ser.). (Illus.). 32p. (J). (gr. 1 up). lib. bdg. 23.33 (978-0-8368-2963-1(8)) Stevens, Gareth Inc.

Priddy, Roger. Telling Time: Let's Get Ready for School. rev. ed. 2005. (Wipe Clean Ser.). 20p. (J). spiral bd. 9.95 (978-0-312-49543-5(9) , Priddy Bks.) St. Martin's Pr.

—Wipe Clean Early Learning Activity Book - Time. 2007. 12p. (J). bds. 3.47 (978-0-312-49905-1(1) , Priddy Bks.) St. Martin's Pr.

Prior, Jennifer. Math Games to Master Basic Skills: Time & Money: 14 Reproducible Games That Help Struggling Learners Practice & Really Master Basic Time & Money Skills & Concepts. 2007. 48p. pap. 10.99 (978-0-439-55414-5(4) , Teaching Resources) Scholastic, Inc.

Procter, Alice. At School: Telling Time by the Half Hour. 2007. (I Can Tell Time Ser.). (Illus.). 24p. (J). (gr. k-2). lib. bdg. 19.93 (***978-0-8368-8390-9(X)***) Stevens, Gareth Inc.

—At the Beach: The Parts of a Day. 2007. (I Can Tell Time Ser.). 24p. (J). (gr. k-2). lib. bdg. 19.93 (***978-0-8368-8388-6(8)***) Stevens, Gareth Inc.

—At the Park: Telling Time by the Hour. 2007. (I Can Tell Time Ser.). 24p. (J). (gr. k-2). lib. bdg. 19.93 (***978-0-8368-8389-3(6)***) Stevens, Gareth Inc.

—At the Zoo: Telling Time by the Quarter Hour. 2007. (I Can Tell Time Ser.). 24p. (J). (gr. k-2). lib. bdg. 19.93 (***978-0-8368-8391-6(8)***) Stevens, Gareth Inc.

Proctor, Alice. At School: Telling Time by the Half Hour. 2007. (Illus.). pap. (***978-0-8368-8395-4(0)***) Stevens, Gareth Inc.

—At the Beach: The Parts of a Day. 2007. (J). pap. (***978-0-8368-8393-0(4)***) Stevens, Gareth Inc.

—At the Park: Telling Time by the Hour. 2007. (J). pap. (***978-0-8368-8394-7(2)***) Stevens, Gareth Inc.

—At the Zoo: Telling Time by the Quarter Hour. 2007. (J). pap. (***978-0-8368-8396-1(9)***) Stevens, Gareth Inc.

Race Against Time: Individual Title Six-Packs. (Bookweb Ser.). 32p. (gr. 4 up). 34.00 (978-0-7635-3745-6(4)) Rigby Education.

Randolph, Joanne. All about an Hour. 2007. (J). lib. bdg. (***978-1-4042-3766-7(6)*** , PowerKids Pr.) Rosen Publishing Group, Inc., The.

Realtime Associates and Mazer Corporation Staff & LeapFrog Staff, compiled by. Identify Measurements of Time. 2002. (J). (gr. 2). 66.75 (978-1-58605-341-3(8) , LeapFrog Schl. Hse.) LeapFrog Enterprises, Inc.

Ring, Susan. Es Tiempo. 2005. Tr. of It's Time!. (SPA., Illus.). 16p. (J). (gr. k-1). lib. bdg. 15.93 (978-0-7368-4152-8(0)) Capstone Pr., Inc.

Rosa-Mendoza, Gladys. What Time Is It? Cifuentes, Carolina, ed. 2004. (English-Spanish Foundations Ser.: Vol. 7). Tr. of ¿Que Hora Es?. (ENG & SPA., Illus.). 20p. (J). (ps-4). bds. 6.95 (978-0-9679748-9-7(5)) Me+Mi Publishing.

Sargent, Brian. A Busy Day. 2006. 32p. (gr. 1-2). (YA). pap. 5.95 (978-0-516-29811-5(9)); (Illus.). (J). 20.50 (978-0-516-24964-3(9)) Scholastic Library Publishing. (Children's Pr.).

School Specialty Publishing. I Can Tell Time & Count Money. 2006. (Brighter Child I Can... Ser.). 128p. (J). pap. 3.95 (978-0-7696-4907-8(6) , Brighter Child) School Specialty Publishing.

—Telling Time to the Hour & Half-Hour. 2003. (Modified Basic Skills Ser.). 48p. (J). (gr. k-4). pap. 6.99 (978-0-7424-1938-4(X) , LL90011) School Specialty Publishing.

—Time. 1999. (Flip Flashtmmath Ser.). 160p. (J). (gr. 1 up). pap. 7.99 (978-1-56451-348-9(3) , ID7872, Ideal School Supply) Schaffer, Frank Pubns.

—Time & Money. 2006. (Brighter Child Flash Cards Ser.). 54p. (J). 2.99 (978-0-7696-6480-4(6) , Brighter Child) School Specialty Publishing.

School Zone Interactive Staff. Time, Money & Fractions. rev. ed. 2003. (On-Track Software Ser.). 64p. (J). (gr. k-2). pap. 15.99 incl. cd-rom (978-1-58947-832-9(0)) School Zone Publishing Co.

School Zone Publishing Interactive Staff. Time, Money & Fractions. 2001. (On-Track Software Ser.). (Illus.). 32p. (J). pap. 13.99 incl. cd-rom (978-0-88743-954-4(3) , 08830) School Zone Publishing Co.

School Zone Staff. Time & Money. 2004. 56p. (J). 2.79 (978-1-58947-990-6(4)) School Zone Publishing Co.

School Zone Staff, ed. Time & Money. 2005. 26p. (J). (gr. 1-2). pap. 3.79 (978-1-58947-788-9(X)) School Zone Publishing Co.

—Time, Money & Fractions. 2003. (J). (gr. 1-2). cd-rom 19.99 (978-1-58947-930-2(0)) School Zone Publishing Co.

Scott, Janine. Time to Tell Time. 2003. (Spyglass Books). (Illus.). 24p. (J). (gr. 1 up). lib. bdg. 18.60 (978-0-7565-0455-7(4)) Compass Point Bks.

Seibert, Patricia. We Were Here: A Short History of Time Capsules. 2002. (Illus.). 48p. (J). (gr. 3-6). lib. bdg. 22.90 (978-0-7613-0423-4(1) , Millbrook Pr.) Lerner Publishing Group.

Sherman, Josepha. How Do We Know the Nature of Time. 2005. (Great Scientific Questions & the Scientists Who Answered Them Ser.). (Illus.). 112p. (J). (gr. 7-12). lib. bdg. 26.50 (978-1-4042-0073-9(8)) Rosen Publishing Group, Inc., The.

Skurzynski, Gloria. On Time: From Seasons to Split Seconds. 2000. (Illus.). 48p. (J). (ps-3). 17.95 (978-0-7922-7503-9(9) , National Geographic Children's Bks.) National Geographic Society.

Smart Kids Publishing Staff. Its Potty Time for Boys. 2000. (Time to... Board Books Ser.). 16p. (J). bds. 7.95 (978-1-56015-222-4(2)) Penton Overseas, Inc.

—Its Potty Time for Girls. 2000. (Time to... Board Books Ser.). 16p. (J). bds. 7.95 (978-1-56015-223-1(0)) Penton Overseas, Inc.

Smith, A. G. What Time Is It? (Illus.). 86p. (Orig.). (YA). (gr. 4-9). pap. 13.95 (978-0-7737-6219-0(1)) Stoddart Kids CAN. *Dist:* Fitzhenry & Whiteside, Ltd.

—What Time Is It? 2000. (Orig.). (gr. 3-6). lib. bdg. 23.40 (978-0-613-81886-5(5)) Tandem Library Bks.

Southwater Books Staff. Let's Stick & Learn. 2000. (Illus.). 64p. pap. 7.95 (978-1-84215-124-2(X) , Southwater) Anness Publishing GBR. *Dist:* National Bk. Network.

Steck-Vaughn Staff. At-Home Workbooks: Time. 2004. (Illus.). pap., wbk. ed. (978-0-7398-8538-3(3)) Steck-Vaughn.

—Early Math: Time I. 2005. pap. 2.99 (978-1-4190-0327-1(5)) Steck-Vaughn.

—Early Math: Time II. 2005. pap. 2.99 (978-1-4190-0337-0(2)) Steck-Vaughn.

—Time: Concepts & Problem Solving. 2000. (Illus.). (J). (gr. 1). pap. (978-0-7398-3428-2(2)); (gr. 2). pap. (978-0-7398-3429-9(0)); (gr. 3). pap. (978-0-7398-3430-5(4)); (gr. 4). pap. (978-0-7398-3431-2(2)) Steck-Vaughn.

—Times of Day: Go to Bed/What Time is It. 1998. (Illus.). (J). pap. (978-0-8172-8644-6(6)) Steck-Vaughn.

—The Untamed World Classroom Library. 2000. (Illus.). (J). pap. (978-0-7398-2894-6(0)) Steck-Vaughn.

Strawberry Shortcake Grow Better with Time. 2004. (J). pap. 2.95 (***978-1-58610-897-7(2)***) Learning Horizons, Inc.

Studio Mouse. Disney's Winnie the Pooh: Time to Learn: Learn & Carry 4 Books with CD. rev. ed. 2007. 4x20p. 14.99 (***978-1-59069-564-7(X)***) Studio Mouse LLC.

Sullivan, Navin. Time. 2006. (Measure Up! Ser.). (Illus.). 48p. (J). (gr. 4-7). lib. bdg. 29.93 (978-0-7614-2321-8(4) , Benchmark Bks.) Cavendish, Marshall Corp.

Sweeney, Joan. Me Counting Time. 2001. (gr. k-3). lib. bdg. 15.30 (978-0-613-36842-1(8)) Tandem Library Bks.

—Me Counting Time: From Seconds to Centuries. Cable, Annette, illus. 2001. 32p. (J). (gr. k-3). pap. 6.99 (978-0-440-41751-4(1) , Dragonfly Bks.) Random Hse. Children's Bks.

—Me Counting Time: From Seconds to Centuries. 2001. (978-0-606-22398-0(3)) Tandem Library Bks.

Taylor, Barbara & Walpole, Brenda. I Wonder Why the Sun Rises & Other Questions about Time & Seasons. 2006. (I Wonder Why Ser.). 32p. (J). (gr. k-3). pap. 6.95 (978-0-7534-5964-5(7) , Kingfisher) Houghton Mifflin Co. Trade & Reference Div.

Taylor, Thomas. Tick! Tock! Jungle Clock. 2007. (Illus.). 12p. (J). (ps-2). 9.99 (***978-1-4052-2307-2(3)***) Egmont Bks., Ltd. GBR. *Dist:* Independent Pubs. Group.

Tell Me the Time. (First Bks.: No. S808-3). (Illus.). (J). (ps). pap. 3.95 (978-0-7214-5054-4(7) , Dutton Juvenile) Penguin Group (USA) Inc.

Tell the Time. 2004. (Wall Charts Ser.). (J). 4.99 (978-1-904586-22-7(8)); 32p. wbk. ed. 3.99 (978-1-904586-16-6(3)) Byeway Bks.

Telling the Time: With Re-Usable Stickers. 1999. (Fun to Learn Ser.). (Illus.). 32p. (ps-3). 1.99 (978-1-58279-011-4(6) , 100) Trident Pr. International.

Telling Time. (Illus.). 24p. (J). (gr. k-2). pap. 6.95 (978-1-55254-045-9(6) , BV25003) Brighter Vision Pubns.

Telling Time. (Classroom Helpers Ser.). 24p. (gr. 1 up). 3.99 (978-0-7682-0813-9(0) , FS194112) Schaffer, Frank Pubns.

Telling Time. (Illus.). (J). pap. 2.79 (978-0-88743-714-4(1)) School Zone Publishing Co.

Telling Time. 48p. (gr. k-2). 8.99 (978-1-56451-372-4(6) , ID4904) School Specialty Publishing.

Telling Time, Grades K-2. 2006. 48p. (J). (gr. k-2). pap. 6.99 (***978-0-7682-3510-4(3)*** , Schaffer, Frank) Schaffer, Frank Pubns.

Telling Time to the Quarter-Hour & Minute. (Modified Basic Skills Ser.). 48p. (gr. k-4). 5.99 (978-0-7424-1939-1(8) , LL90012) School Specialty Publishing.

Time. (Make it Work Ser.). 42p. (J). (gr. 4-8). pap. (978-1-882210-40-4(9)) Action Publishing, Inc.

Time. 2002. (My First Sticker Bks.). 16p. (J). (ps-k). pap. 2.98 (978-1-84273-836-8(4) , Exclusive Editions) Parragon, Inc.

Time. 2001. (Let's Explore Ser.). (Illus.). 32p. (J). (gr. 1 up). lib. bdg. 23.33 (978-0-8368-2967-9(0)) Stevens, Gareth Inc.

Time - Set 1: What Time Is It. 2005. (J). spiral bd. 23.40 (978-0-9770248-6-5(5)) Sidedoor Publishing LLC.

Time & Money. (Basics First Ser.). 32p. (gr. k up). 4.99 (978-0-7647-0048-4(0) , FS30090); (gr. 1 up). 4.99 (978-0-7647-0049-1(9) , FS30091); (gr. 2 up). 4.99 (978-0-7647-0075-0(8) , FS30092); (gr. 3 up). 4.99 (978-0-7647-0076-7(6) , FS30093) Schaffer, Frank Pubns.

Time & Money. (Homework Booklets Ser.). 80p. (gr. 1 up). 2.99 (978-1-56822-834-1(1) , IF0357); (gr. 3 up). 2.99 (978-1-56822-836-5(8) , IF0359) School Specialty Publishing.

Time for a Party, 6, Pack. (Discovery World Ser.). 16p. (gr. 1-2). 28.00 (978-0-7635-8457-3(6)) Rigby Education.

Time Lines. (Poster Projects Ser.). (gr. 3-6). 9.99 (978-0-7424-0693-3(8) , IF22450) School Specialty Publishing.

TNT Stone and Associates Staff & Petertil Design Partners Staff, illus. Telling Time: Clocks, Calendars, Seasons. 1998. (Powertools for Kids Ser.: No. 11). 4p. (J). (gr. 1-3). pap., wbk. ed. 4.95 (978-1-58220-010-1(6) , 32501, PowerTools for Kids) Navigator Systems, Inc.

Top That Publishing Staff, ed. Lets Explore Time. 2004. (Fun Kits Ser.). (Illus.). 48p. (J). (978-1-84510-246-3(0)) Top That! Publishing PLC.

Tyler, Jenny & Gee, R. Time. Bryant-Mole, K., ed. rev. ed. 2004. (First Learning Ser.). (Illus.). 24p. (J). (ps-3). pap., act. bk. ed. 4.95 (978-0-7460-3806-2(2)) EDC Publishing.

Vorderman, Carol. Learn Your Times Tables Kit. 2006. 1p. (J). 15.99 (978-0-7566-1982-4(3)) Dorling Kindersley Publishing, Inc.

Wadsworth, Pamela. Golwg Gyntaf Ar Amser a Gofod. 2005. (WEL., Illus.). 24p. pap. (978-1-85596-248-4(9)) Dref Wen.

Walker, Jane. El Tiempo. 2001. (Coleccion Todas las Maneras De Ver...). (SPA., Illus.). (J). (gr. 3-5). 10.95 (978-84-263-3170-0(X) , LV7273) Vives, Luis Editorial (Edelvives) ESP. *Dist:* Lectorum Pubns., Inc.

Walsh, Kieran. Time Math. 2005. (Math & My World Ser.). (Illus.). 48p. (J). (gr. 4-6). 20.95 (978-1-59515-496-5(5)) Rourke Publishing, LLC.

What Time Is It Benchmark. 2002. (Illus.). (J). pap. (978-0-7398-5938-4(2)) Steck-Vaughn.

Whitehouse, Patricia. La Hora en el Zoologico. 2002. (Matematicas del Zoologico (Zoo Math) Ser.). 24p. (J). (ps-1). pap. 5.25 (978-1-58810-865-4(1) , 91626); (SPA.). lib. bdg. 18.50 (978-1-58810-806-7(6)) Heinemann Library.

—Zoo Time. 2002. (Zoo Math Ser.). 24p. (J). (ps-1). (Illus.). lib. bdg. 18.50 (978-1-58810-552-3(0)); pap. (978-1-58810-760-2(4) , 91414) Heinemann Library.

Williams, Brian. Latitude & Longitude. 2002. (Illus.). 32p. (J). lib. bdg. 24.25 (978-1-58340-209-2(8)) Smart Apple Media.

—Measuring Time. 2002. (Illus.). 32p. (J). lib. bdg. 24.25 (978-1-58340-208-5(X)) Smart Apple Media.

Williams, Gilbert A. Why Is Time Important? An Innovative Time Study Guide. 2002. (ENG., Illus.). 19p. (YA). (gr. 2-12). lib. bdg. 4.50 (978-0-9722724-2-1(9)) Blackfoot Burkino Cherokee Publishing.

Willis, Shirley. Dime Que Hora Es. 1999. (Coleccion los Estupendos). (SPA., Illus.). 32p. (J). (gr. 2-4). 20.00 (978-0-531-11846-7(0) , OD30037, Watts, Franklin) Scholastic Library Publishing.

—Dime Que Hora Es. 2000. (gr. k-3). (SPA.). lib. bdg. 14.10 (978-0-613-72668-9(5)); (J). 12.75 (978-0-606-20152-0(1)) Tandem Library Bks.

—Tell Me What the Time Is. 2000. (Whiz Kids Ser.). (Illus.). 32p. (J). (gr. 1-3). pap. 5.95 (978-0-531-15979-8(5) , Watts, Franklin) Scholastic Library Publishing.

Wilmes, Liz, et al. Circle Time Book: For Holiday & Seasons. Dane, Donna, illus. 2004. 128p. (J). pap. 12.95 (978-0-943452-00-5(7) , 20002) Building Blocks, LLC.

Wingate, Philippa. Tick Tock Time. Cooke, Andy, illus. 2007. (J). (ps-1). per. 8.95 (978-1-905158-12-6(2) , Buster Bks.) O'Mara, Michael Bks., Ltd. GBR. *Dist:* Ingram Pub. Services.

Woodford, Chris. Time. 2005. (J). 11.20 (978-1-4103-0519-0(8) , Blackbirch Pr., Inc.) Thomson Gale.

Work with Time & Money. 2004. (Math "How To" Ser.). (Illus.). 48p. (J). 7.99 (978-1-57690-967-6(0)) Teacher Created Materials, Inc.

Zelcer, Draizy. Once upon a Time. Romanenko, Vitaliy, illus. 2001. 32p. (J). (gr. k-2). 11.95 (978-1-929628-00-1(5)) Hachai Publishing.

TIME—FICTION

Bergen, Lara. Telling Time with Diego. Maher, Alex, illus. 2007. (Go, Diego, Go! Ser.). 14p. (J). bds. 7.99 (***978-1-4169-3369-4(7)*** , Simon Spotlight/Nickelodeon) Simon & Schuster Children's Publishing.

Butler, Dori. Late Again! 2005. 40.00 (***978-1-4108-4209-1(6)***) Benchmark Education Co.

Cobb, Annie. Long Wait. 2000. (gr. k-3). lib. bdg. 12.95 (978-0-613-27952-9(2)) Tandem Library Bks.

Cole, Bob. Power Reading: Chapter/Sci-Fi/Time Warp. Ford, David, illus. 2004. 25p. (J). (gr. 4 up). vinyl bd. 39.95 (978-1-883186-60-9(9) , PPSF3) National Reading Styles Institute, Inc.

Danziger, Paula. It's Justin Time, Amber Brown. Ross, Tony, illus. 9.95 (978-1-59112-294-4(5)); 2002. 28.95 incl. audio compact disk (978-1-59112-567-9(7)); 2002. pap. 31.95 incl. audio compact disk (978-1-59112-566-2(9)) Live Oak Media.

—It's Justin Time, Amber Brown. 2001. (gr. k-3). lib. bdg. 11.80 (978-0-613-44396-8(9)) Tandem Library Bks.

Degen, Bruce, illus. It's about Time, Jesse Bear: And Other Rhymes. 2002. (Jesse Bear Ser.). (J). 14.47 (978-0-7587-2875-3(1)) Book Wholesalers, Inc.

Derrick, Patricia. Mr Walrus & the Old School Bus. 2007. 32p. 18.95 (978-1-933818-13-9(1)) Animalations.

Dobson, Jill. Time to Go. 180p. pap. 11.95 (978-0-7022-2351-8(4)) Univ. of Queensland Pr. AUS. *Dist:* International Specialized Bk. Services.

Fraser, Mary Ann. I. Q., It's Time. Fraser, Mary Ann, illus. 2005. (Illus.). 32p. (J). (ps-3). 16.85 (978-0-8027-8980-8(3)); 15.95 (978-0-8027-8978-5(1)) Walker & Co.

Fun Around the Clock. 1998. (Fisher-Price Hideaway Hollow Padded Board Bks.). (Illus.). 16p. (J). (gr. 1). bds. (978-0-7666-0113-0(7) , Honey Bear Bks.) Modern Publishing.

Garrity, Jennifer Johnson. Calendar Quest: A 5,000 Year Trek Through Western History with Father Time. 2004. (J). per. 14.00 net. (978-0-9770704-0-4(9) , CQ-001, Tools For Young Historians) BrimWood Pr.

Gregory, Nan. Amber Waiting. Denton, Kady MacDonald, illus. 2004. (Northern Lights Books for Children). 32p. (J). (ps-1). 17.95 (978-0-88995-258-4(2)) Red Deer Pr. CAN. *Dist:* Fitzhenry & Whiteside, Ltd.

Harcourt School Publishers Staff. What Time Is It? Below Lewvel. 3rd ed. 2002. (Trophies Reading Program Ser.). (Illus.). pap. 5.10 (978-0-15-323042-4(8)) Harcourt Schl. Pubs.

Hawkins, Colin. What's the Time, Mr Wolf? 2004. (Illus.). 32p. (J). 9.95 (978-1-4052-0684-6(5)) Egmont Bks., Ltd. GBR. *Dist:* Trafalgar Square Publishing.

Hennessy, B. G. Mr. Ouchy's First Day. Meisel, Paul, illus. 2006. 32p. (J). (ps-3). 15.99 (978-0-399-24248-9(1) , Putnam Juvenile) Penguin Group (USA) Inc.

—Mr. Ouchy's First Day. Meisel, Paul, illus. 2007. 27.95 incl. audio (***978-0-8045-6946-0(0) ;*** 29.95 incl. audio compact disk (***978-0-8045-4160-2(4)***) Spoken Arts, Inc.

Herbauts, Anne. Monday. 2006. 36p. (J). (gr. 3-5). 16.95 (978-1-59270-057-8(8)) Enchanted Lion Bks., LLC.

Jocelyn, Marthe, ed. First Times. 2007. 200p. (J). (gr. 5-8). pap. 9.95 (***978-0-88776-777-7(X)***) Tundra Bks., Inc./Livres Toundra, Inc. CAN. *Dist:* Random Hse., Inc.

Johnson, Sarah. Time to Dance. Lew, Willie, illus. Lew, Willie, photos by. 2003. (J). 16.98 (978-0-7853-8811-1(7)) Publications International, Ltd.

Keenan, Sheila. What Time Is It? a Book of Math Riddles. 1999. (gr. k-3). lib. bdg. 11.80 (978-0-613-22609-7(7)) Tandem Library Bks.

Kubler, Annie. What's the Time Mr Wolf? 2003. (Illus.). 24p. (J). 9.99 (978-0-85953-944-9(X)) Child's Play-International.

Littler, Keith. Tell the Time with Merlin. 2002. (Illus.). 24p. (J). pap. 11.99 (978-1-84222-653-7(3)) Carlton Bks., Ltd. GBR. *Dist:* Independent Pubs. Group.

Lou Weber Staff, ed. Exploring Time with Dora Clock. 2004. 10p. (J). bds. 16.98 (978-1-4127-3050-1(3) , 7228800) Publications International, Ltd.

—Spongebob Clock It's Time Sound Book. 2004. 10p. (J). bds. 16.98 (978-1-4127-3030-3(9) , 7226500) Publications International, Ltd.

McNamee, Eoin. The Navigator. (gr. 4-7). 2008. 252p. (J). 6.99 (***978-0-385-73554-4(5)*** , Yearling); 2007. (Illus.). 352p. (YA). 15.99 (978-0-375-83910-8(0) , Lamb, Wendy) Random Hse. Children's Bks.

Millman, M. C. Time Will Tell. 2004. 272p. (YA). 19.95 (978-1-932443-25-7(8) , TWTH) Judaica Pr., Inc., The.

Mills, Elizabeth. Tick-Tock Sharks. Bettoli, Delana, illus. 2005. 40p. (J). (ps-ps). 9.99 (978-0-439-72308-4(6) , Cartwheel Bks.) Scholastic, Inc.

Moon, Nicola. Mouse Tells the Time. Morris, Tony, illus. 2002. 32p. (J). 18.00 (978-1-84365-000-3(2) , Pavilion Bks., Ltd.) Anova Bks. GBR. *Dist:* Independent Pubs. Group.

Moore, Ulysses. The Long-Lost Map. Bruno, Iacopo, illus. 2006. (Ulysses Moore Ser.: No. 2). 272p. (J). pap. 12.99 (978-0-439-77439-0(X) , Scholastic) Scholastic, Inc.

Mullican, Judy. Just in Time. Storch, Ellen N., illus. 2005. (J). pap. (978-1-57332-370-3(5)) HighReach Learning, Inc.

Murphy, Stuart J. Game Time! Jabar, Cynthia, illus. 2000. (Mathstart Ser.). (J). 11.79 (978-0-606-19984-1(5)) Tandem Library Bks.

My Time on Nantucket. 2005. (J). cd-rom 11.95 (978-0-9755078-2-7(6)) Sweet Punkin Pr.

Myers, Bill. Baseball for Breakfast: The Story of a Boy Who Hated to Wait. Riccio, Frank, illus. 2005. 29p. (J). (gr. 4-8). reprint ed. 15.00 (978-0-7567-9248-0(7)) DIANE Publishing Co.

Omololu, Cynthia Jaynes. Six O'clock in San Francisco. DuBurke, Randy, illus. 2008. (J). (***978-0-618-76827-1(0)*** , Clarion Bks.) Houghton Mifflin Co. Trade & Reference Div.

Peck, Dale. Drift House: The First Voyage. (J). 2006. 448p. pap. 7.95 (978-1-59990-005-6(X)); 2005. 420p. 16.95 (978-1-58234-969-5(X)) Bloomsbury Publishing. (Bloomsbury Children).

Pilegard, Virginia Walton. The Warlord's Alarm. Debon, Nicholas, illus. 2006. 32p. (J). 15.95 (978-1-58980-378-7(7)) Pelican Publishing Co., Inc.

Pinto, Sara. Clockwise. 2006. 32p. (J). 19.95 (978-1-58234-660-1(7)); 16.95 (978-1-58234-669-4(0)) Bloomsbury Publishing.

Ruffenach, Jessie, ed. Baby Learns about Time. Thomas, Peter, tr. from ENG. Blacksheep, Beverly, illus. 2005. (NAV & ENG.). 16p. (J). bds. 7.95 (978-1-893354-64-7(4)) Salina Bookshelf.

Rupp, Rebecca. Journey to the Blue Moon: In Which Time Is Lost & Then Found Again. 2006. 272p. (J). (gr. 5). 15.99 (978-0-7636-2544-3(2)) Candlewick Pr.

Savadier, Elivia. Time to Get Dressed! Savadier, Elivia, illus. 2006. (Illus.). 32p. (J). 14.95 (978-1-59643-161-4(X)) Roaring Brook Pr.

Schuepbach, Lynnette. Cat Time. 2006. 28p. pap. 12.95 (978-0-9759613-2-2(2)) Creative Sources.

Sharratt, Nick & Tucker, Stephen. The Time It Took Tom. Sharratt, Nick, illus. 2000. (Illus.). 32p. (J). (ps-2). pap. 14.95 (978-1-888444-63-6(0)) Little Tiger Pr.

Steck-Vaughn Staff. What Time Is It. 1999. (Illus.). pap. (978-0-8172-8721-4(3)) Steck-Vaughn.

Time Slime. 2003. 156p. (YA). (gr. 5-12). pap. 7.95 (978-0-9702176-3-9(3) , 0004) Night Howl Productions.

Turley, Sandy. The Clock & the Mouse: A Teaching Rhyme about Time. Peterson, Sara & Lindstrom, Brita, illus. 2006. (J). 16.95 (*978-0-9778548-0-6(9)) Turley, Sandy.

What Time Is It Jeanne-Marie. 2005. (Illus.), 34p. (J). mass mkt. 9.99 (978-0-9740599-7-6(8)) Omnibus Publishing.

Whybrow, Ian, et al. Owain A'r Cloc. 2005. (WEL., Illus.). 18p. 6.99 (978-1-84323-366-4(5)) Gomer Pr. GBR. *Dist:* Gomer Pr.

Williams, David. Tick Tock. Ovresat, Laura, illus. 2006. (Green Light Reader Ser.). 24p. (J). 12.95 (978-0-15-205581-3(9)); pap. 3.95 (978-0-15-205605-6(X)) Harcourt Trade Pubs.

Winterson, Jeanette. Tanglewreck. 2007. 416p. (J). (gr. 3-7). pap. 6.95 (*978-1-59990-081-0(5) , Bloomsbury Children) Bloomsbury Publishing.

Woodruff, Liza. What Time Is It? Woodruff, Liza, illus. 2005. (My First Reader Ser.). (Illus.). 32p. (J). (gr. k-1). 18.50 (978-0-516-25180-6(5) , Children's Pr.) Scholastic Library Publishing.

Woodruff, Liza, illus. What Time Is It? 2005. (My First Reader Ser.). 31p. (J). (gr. k-1). pap. 3.95 (978-0-516-25279-7(8) , Children's Pr.) Scholastic Library Publishing.

TIME—POETRY

Barner, Bob. To Everything. 2004. (Illus.). 38p. (J). pap. 6.95 (978-0-8118-4456-7(0)) Chronicle Bks. LLC.

Cookson, Paul. Staying Out Late, Playing Out Late. Baines, Nigel, illus. 2003. 96p. (J). pap. 8.99 (978-0-7459-4812-6(X) , Lion) Lion Hudson plc GBR. *Dist:* Independent Pubs. Group.

Pierce, Terry. Ticktock. 2007. (Mother Goose Rhymes Ser.). (Illus.). 32p. (J). (*978-1-4048-2354-9(9) , 1265753) Picture Window Bks.

Watkins, Dawn L. Nantucket Cats. Bonge, Lynn E., illus. 1998. 32p. (J). (ps-1). pap. 5.49 (978-0-89084-975-0(7)) Jones, Bob Univ. Pr.

Wright, Blanche Fisher, illus. Real Mother Goose Clock Book. 22p. (J). (ps-2). 6.95 (978-1-56288-095-8(0)) Checkerboard Pr., Inc.

TIME TRAVEL

Hamilton, John. Time Travel. 2007. (World of Science Fiction Ser.). (Illus.). 32p. (J). 24.21 (978-1-59679-996-7(X)) ABDO Publishing Co.

Korman, Susan. Horse Raid: An Arapaho Camp in the 1800s. Farnsworth, Bill, illus. 1998. (Smithsonian Odyssey Ser.: Vol. 10). 32p. (J). (gr. 2-5). 14.95 (978-1-56899-613-4(6) , B6011) Soundprints.

Masessa, Ed. The Time Traveler's Journal. 2007. (J). (gr. 2 up). 24.99 (*978-0-545-02211-8(8)) Scholastic, Inc.

Richardson, Hazel. How to Build a Time Machine. Rowe, Alan, illus. 2001. (How to Ser.). 96p. (J). (gr. 5-7). 16.00 (978-0-531-14644-6(8) , Watts, Franklin) Scholastic Library Publishing.

—How to Build a Time Machine. 2001. (gr. 5-8). lib. bdg. 12.95 (978-0-613-54545-7(1)) Tandem Library Bks.

Thompson, Caro, ed. Time Traveler: Research Guide. Brough, Holly, illus. 1998. 60p. spiral bd. 9.95 (978-1-929082-01-8(0)) Vermont Public Television.

Time Travelers: Individual Title Six-Packs. 32p. (gr. 5 up). 44.00 (978-0-7578-0989-7(8)) Rigby Education.

TIME TRAVEL—FICTION

Abbott, Tony. The Hawk Bandits of Tarkoom. 2001. (gr. 3-6). lib. bdg. 11.80 (978-0-613-32634-6(2)) Tandem Library Bks.

—The Magic Escapes. 2002. (gr. 3-6). lib. bdg. 13.00 (978-0-613-58158-5(X)) Tandem Library Bks.

Adams, Douglas. So Long, & Thanks for All the Fish. 1999. (gr. 7-12). lib. bdg. 15.30 (978-0-613-17519-7(0)) Tandem Library Bks.

Adone, Claudio. My Grandfather Jack the Ripper. 2000. Tr. of Mio Nonno Jack Lo Squartatore. (Illus.). 304p. (J). (gr. 7-10). 19.00 (978-1-928746-16-4(0)) Herodias.

Alfred Oscar Valentine: Tales from Spoon Creek. 2005. (J). (978-0-9766894-4-7(8)) Stanley, Donna Lacy.

Anderson, Scoular. The Mean Team from Mars. Anderson, Scoular, illus. 2005. (Read-It! Chapter Bks.). (Illus.). 52p. (J). (ps-k). lib. bdg. 19.95 (978-1-4048-1274-1(1)) Picture Window Bks.

Andrews, Jane. Ten Boys Who Lived on the Road from Long Ago to Now (Yesterday's Classics) 2006. (J). 9.95 (*978-1-59915-064-2(6)) Yesterday's Classics.

Anzalone, Karen. Time in a Bottle. 2003. 100p. (YA). pap. 9.00 (978-0-7599-3840-3(7)) Hard Shell Word Factory.

Apps, Roy. The Time Spinner. 2003. (Illus.). 128p. (J). pap. 9.99 (978-1-84270-231-4(9)) Andersen GBR. *Dist:* Independent Pubs. Group.

, Asah, Asah & , Kooma, Kooma. The 7 Big Secrets of Planet WU. 2006. 68p. (J). 22.73 (978-1-4116-9101-8(6)) Lulu.com.

Atwater-Rhodes, Amelia. In the Forests of the Night. 2000. (Illus.). 176p. (YA). (gr. 7-12). mass mkt. 5.99 (978-0-440-22816-5(6) , Laurel Leaf) Random Hse. Children's Bks.

—In the Forests of the Night. 2000. (gr. 7-12). lib. bdg. 13.55 (978-0-613-28537-7(9)); (Illus.). (J). 12.15 (978-0-606-17999-7(2)) Tandem Library Bks.

Ayasta, Ayasta. Star. 2007. 117p. 34.95 (*978-1-4303-1520-9(2)) Lulu.com.

Ayers, Linda. The Time Bridge Travelers, 3 bks., Bk. 1. Ayers, Ryan, illus. 56p. (J). 2006. 13.95 (978-0-9760505-8-2(7)); 2004. per. 7.95 (978-0-9760505-0-6(1)) Blue Thistle Pr.

—The Time Bridge Travelers & the Mysterious Map, 3 bks., Bk. 2. Ayers, Ryan, illus. l.t. ed. (Time Bridge Travelers Ser.: 2). 80p. (J). 2006. 13.95 (978-0-9760505-6-8(0)); 2005. per. 7.95 (978-0-9760505-3-7(6)) Blue Thistle Pr.

Ayers, Linda. The Time Bridge Travelers & the Time Travel Station, 3 bks., Bk. 3. Ayers, Ryan, illus. l.t. ed. 2007. (Time Bridge Travelers Ser.: 3). 140p. (J). lib. bdg. 16.95 (*978-0-9786302-8-7(9)); per. 7.95 (*978-0-9786302-7-0(0)) Blue Thistle Pr.

Bailer, Darice. The Pony Express. Antonishak, Tom, illus. 3rd ed. 2005. (Soundprints' Read-and-Discover Ser.). 48p. (J). (gr. 2-4). pap. 3.95 (978-1-59249-019-6(0) , S2008) Soundprints.

Bailey, Linda. Adventures with the Vikings. Slavin, Bill et al, illus. 2004. (Good Times Travel Agency Ser.). 48p. (J). (gr. 4-6). (978-1-55074-544-3(1)) Kids Can Pr., Ltd.

—Adventures with the Vikings, No. 3. Slavin, Bill et al, illus. 2004. (Good Times Travel Agency Ser.). 48p. (J). (gr. 4-6). (978-1-55074-542-9(5)) Kids Can Pr., Ltd.

—Adventures with the Vikings. 2003. (gr. 3-6). lib. bdg. 16.40 (978-0-613-70944-6(6)) Tandem Library Bks.

Baker, E. D. Once upon a Curse: The Sequel to the Frog Princess & Dragon's Breath. 2006. (Tales of the Frog Princess Ser.). (Illus.). 256p. (J). pap. 6.95 (978-1-58234-911-4(8) , Bloomsbury Children) Bloomsbury Publishing.

Baker, Kage. The Life of the World to Come. rev. ed. 2005. (Company Ser.). 416p. mass mkt. 6.99 (978-0-7653-5432-7(2) , Tor Bks.) Doherty, Tom Assocs., LLC.

Banks, Steven. In Search of Reptar: A Time Travel Adventure. Artful Doodlers Limited Staff, illus. 2002. (Rugrats Files: Bk. 5). 96p. (J). (gr. 3-7). pap. 3.99 (978-0-689-84609-0(6) , Simon Spotlight) Simon & Schuster Children's Publishing.

Banks, Steven. Lost in Time. The Artifact Group, illus. 2006. 22p. (J). lib. bdg. 15.00 (*978-1-4242-0977-4(3)) Fitzgerald Bks.

—Lost in Time. 2007. 24p. (J). 21.35 (*978-1-59961-367-3(0)) Spotlight.

Barkan, Joanne. A Pup in King Arthur's Court. l.t. ed. 1999. (Adventures of Wishbone Ser.: No. 15). (Illus.). 164p. (J). (gr. 2-5). lib. bdg. 22.60 (978-0-8368-2593-0(4)) Stevens, Gareth Inc.

Barnes, Susan. Kelly Karate: Discovers the Ice Princess. 2004. 138p. (J). (gr. 4-8). pap. 5.95 (978-0-9705777-3-3(7)) McBook Pubs., LLC.

Barrett, Tracy. On Etruscan Time. rev. ed. 2005. 176p. (J). 17.95 (978-0-8050-7569-4(0) , Holt, Henry & Co. Bks. For Young Readers) Holt, Henry & Co.

Barron, T. A. The Ancient One. 2003. 320p. (gr. 12). mass mkt. 6.99 (978-0-441-01032-5(6) , Ace Bks.) Penguin Group (USA) Inc.

Bauer, Christina. The Pirate Queen: A Timewalker Journey. 2005. 280p. (YA). pap. 14.99 (978-1-59092-224-8(7) , Blue Works) Windstorm Creative.

Bauer, Marion Dane. The Blue Ghost. Wang, Suling, illus. 2006. (Stepping Stones Ser.). 96p. (J). (gr. 3-7). pap. 3.99 (978-0-375-83339-7(0) , Random Hse. Bks. for Young Readers) Random Hse. Children's Bks.

—The Blue Ghost. 2005. (Illus.). 96p. (J). (gr. 3-7). 11.95 (978-0-375-83179-9(7)); lib. bdg. 13.99 (978-0-375-93179-6(1)) Random Hse. Children's Bks. (Random Hse. Bks. for Young Readers).

Beckman, Thea. Crusade in Jeans. 2004. 320p. (YA). 9.95 (978-1-886910-26-3(X) , Lemniscaat) Boyds Mills Pr.

Beechen, Adam. Blast from the Past. George, Chris, illus. 2004. (Fairly OddParents Ser.). 24p. (J). pap. 3.50 (978-0-689-86322-6(5) , Simon Spotlight/Nickelodeon) Simon & Schuster Children's Publishing.

Beecher, Adam. Blast from the Past. George, Chris, illus. ed. 2005. (Fairly Odd Parents Ser.: 1). 24p. (J). lib. bdg. 15.00 (978-1-59054-802-8(7)) Fitzgerald Bks.

Bellairs, John. The Ghost in the Mirror. 2002. (J). (gr. 3 up). 20.75 (978-0-8446-7205-2(X)) Smith, Peter Pub., Inc.

—The House with a Clock in Its Walls. Gorey, Edward, illus. 2004. (Lewis Barnavelt Ser.). 192p. (J). pap. 5.99 (978-0-14-240257-3(5) , Puffin) Penguin Group (USA) Inc.

—The House with a Clock in Its Walls. 179p. (J). (gr. 4-6). pap. 4.50 (978-0-8072-1423-7(X) , Listening Library) Random Hse. Audio Publishing Group.

Benderly, Beryl Lieff. Jason's Miracle: A Hanukkah Story. 2004. 114p. (J). (gr. 4-8). reprint ed. (978-0-7567-7792-0(5)) DIANE Publishing Co.

—Jason's Miracle: A Hanukkah Story. 2000. (Illus.). 120p. (J). (gr. 4-8). 14.95 (978-0-8075-3781-7(0)) Whitman, Albert & Co.

Bennett, Cherie & Gottesfeld, Jeff. Anne Frank & Me. 2002. 291p. (YA). pap. 6.99 (978-0-698-11973-4(8) , Putnam Juvenile) Penguin Group (USA) Inc.

Benton, Jim. The Fran That Time Forgot. Benton, Jim, illus. 2005. (Franny K. Stein, Mad Scientist Ser.: Bk. 4). (Illus.). 112p. (J). mass mkt. 3.99 (978-0-689-86298-4(9) , Aladdin); 14.95 (978-0-689-86294-6(6) , Simon & Schuster Children's Publishing) Simon & Schuster Children's Publishing.

Bernard, Virginia. Eliza & the Sacred Mountain. 2000. (Going to Ser.). (Illus.). 121p. (J). (gr. 4-8). pap. 6.95 (978-1-893577-05-3(8)) Four Corners Publishing Co., Inc.

Bessey, Sian Ann. Escape from Germany. 2004. 183p. (J). (978-1-59156-436-2(0)) Covenant Communications.

—Uprising in Samoa: A Novel. 2004. 178p. (J). (978-1-59156-890-2(0)) Covenant Communications.

Bethany: Adventures of the Mighty Mustard Seed. 2004. Orig. Title: Bethany in Beulah Land. (J). mass mkt. 12.95 (978-0-9745440-0-7(0)) McKatlib Pr.

Birdsall, Jeanne. The Penderwicks on Gardam Street. 2008. 320p. (J). (gr. 3-7). 15.99 (*978-0-375-84090-6(7) , Knopf Bks. for Young Readers) Random Hse. Children's Bks.

Bishop, Mary Harelkin. Tunnels of Treachery: Another Moose Jaw Adventure. 2003. (Tunnels of Moose Jaw Adventure Ser.: Vol. 3). (Illus.). 312p. (J). (gr. 5-7). pap. 7.95 (978-1-55050-270-1(0)) Coteau Bks. CAN. *Dist:* Fitzhenry & Whiteside, Ltd.

—Tunnels of Tyranny: A Fourth Moose Jaw Adventure. 2005. (Juvenile Novel, Ser.). 312p. (J). (gr. 4-6). pap. 7.95 (978-1-55050-316-6(2)) Coteau Bks. CAN. *Dist:* Fitzhenry & Whiteside, Ltd.

Blair, Margaret Whitman. House of Spies: Danger in the Civil War. 1999. (White Mane Kids Ser.: Vol. 7). (Illus.). 169p. (YA). (ps up). pap. 8.95 (978-1-57249-161-8(2) , White Mane Kids) White Mane Publishing Co., Inc.

—The Sand Castle: Blockade Running & the Battle of Fort Fisher. 2004. (White Mane Kids Ser.: 17). (Illus.). 200p. (J). pap. 8.95 (978-1-57249-346-9(1) , White Mane Kids) White Mane Publishing Co., Inc.

Bloor, Edward. London Calling. 304p. (gr. 5). 2008. (YA). pap. 8.99 (*978-0-375-84363-1(9)); 2006. (J). lib. bdg. 18.99 (978-0-375-93635-7(1)); 2006. (YA). 16.95 (978-0-375-83635-0(7)) Random Hse. Children's Bks. (Knopf Bks. for Young Readers).

Bond, Nancy. A String in the Harp. 2006. 384p. (J). pap. 6.99 (978-1-4169-2771-6(9) , Aladdin) Simon & Schuster Children's Publishing.

Borchard, Therese Johnson. Whitney Climbs the Tower of Babel & Learns What Happens to Snobs. VanNest, Wendy, illus. 2001. (Emerald Bible Collection). 80p. (J). (gr. 3-7). 5.95 (978-0-8091-6675-6(5) , 6675-5) Paulist Pr.

—Whitney Coaches David on Fighting Goliath: And Learns to Stand up for Herself. 2000. (Emerald Bible Collection). (Illus.). 80p. (gr. 3-7). 5.95 (978-0-8091-6669-5(0) , 6669-0) Paulist Pr.

—Whitney Rides the Whale with Jonah: And Learns She Can't Run Away. 1999. (Emerald Bible Collection). (Illus.). 80p. (gr. 3-7). 5.95 (978-0-8091-6663-3(1) , 6663-1) Paulist Pr.

—Whitney Sews Joseph's Many-Colored Coat: And Learns a Lesson about Jealousy. 1999. (Emerald Bible Collection). (Illus.). 80p. (gr. 3-7). 5.95 (978-0-8091-6664-0(X) , 6664-x) Paulist Pr.

—Whitney Solves a Dilemma with Solomon: And Learns the Importance of Honesty. 2000. (Emerald Bible Collection). (Illus.). 80p. (gr. 3-7). 5.95 (978-0-8091-6668-8(2) , 6668-2) Paulist Pr.

—Whitney Stows Away on Noah's Ark: And Learns How to Deal with Peer Pressure. VanNest, Wendy, illus. 2000. (Emerald Bible Collection). 80p. (gr. 3-7). 5.95 (978-0-8091-6674-9(7) , 6674-7) Paulist Pr.

Boston, L. M. The Stones of Green Knowe. Boston, Peter, illus. 2006. (Green Knowe Ser.). 144p. (J). 17.00 (978-0-15-205560-8(6)); pap. 5.95 (978-0-15-205566-0(5)) Harcourt Trade Pubs.

Bowman, Vicki. Julie Flies Back to the Past. 2005. 71p. pap. 14.95 (978-1-4137-7529-7(2)) PublishAmerica, Inc.

Bradford, Emma. Kat & the Missing Notebooks. Sano, Kazuhiko, illus. 1999. (Stardust Classics: No. 4). 119p. (J). (gr. 2-5). 12.95 (978-1-889514-27-7(6)); pap. 5.95 (978-1-889514-28-4(4)) Dolls Corp.

Breslin, Theresa. Dream Master Nightmare! l.t. ed. 2005. (Illus.). 216p. (J). pap. (978-0-7540-6144-1(2) , CLP 336) BBC Audio.

Broderick, Damien. Time Zones. 2000. (gr. 7-12). lib. bdg. 12.10 (978-0-613-29108-8(5)) Tandem Library Bks.

Brodland, Rita, ed. State Fair Time Warp. Freeman, Troy, illus. l.t. ed. 2002. (WeWrite Kids! Ser.). 64p. (J). (gr. k-3). pap. 8.95 (978-1-57635-059-1(2)) WeWrite LLC.

Buckley-Archer, Linda. Gideon the Cutpurse. 2006. (Gideon Trilogy Ser.). 416p. (J). (gr. 5 up). 17.95 (978-1-4169-1525-6(7)) Simon & Schuster Children's Publishing.

—The Time Thief. 2007. (Gideon Trilogy Ser.). 512p. (J). (gr. 5 up). 17.99 (*978-1-4169-1527-0(3)) Simon & Schuster Children's Publishing.

—The Time Travelers. 2007. (Gideon Trilogy Ser.). 416p. (J). (gr. 4-8). pap. 7.99 (*978-1-4169-1526-3(5) , Aladdin) Simon & Schuster Children's Publishing.

Buja, John E. Race to Freedom. Morrison, Melody, illus. 2002. 132p. pap. 7.95 (978-1-894303-24-8(5)) RRP Pubs.

Buja, John E. & Morrison, Melody. Ballcourt of Death: Novel. 2000. (Illus.). 128p. (J). (gr. 7-12). pap. (978-1-894303-23-1(7)) Raven Rock Publishing.

Bull, Angela. Time Traveler. 1999. (gr. k-3). lib. bdg. 11.80 (978-0-613-22497-0(3)) Tandem Library Bks.

Bull, Angela & Dorling Kindersley Publishing Staff. Time Traveler: Surfing the Centuries. Smith, Tony, illus. 1999. (Eyewitness Books). 48p. (J). (ps-3). 14.99 (978-0-7894-4763-0(0)); pap. 3.99 (978-0-7894-4762-3(2)) Dorling Kindersley Publishing, Inc.

Burge, Constance M. Whispers from the Past. 2000. (gr. 7-12). lib. bdg. 14.15 (978-0-613-28134-8(9)) Tandem Library Bks.

Burkhard, Daryl. Riddle in the Mountain. Riccio, Frank, illus. 2005. 240p. 16.95 (978-0-9668289-5-5(X)) Nomad Pr.

Butler, Dori. The Time Capsule. 2005. 22.00 (*978-1-4108-4198-8(7)) Benchmark Education Co.

Byng, Georgia. Molly Moon, Micky Minus, & the Mind Machine. 2007. 416p. (J). (gr. 3-7). 16.99 (*978-0-06-075036-7(7)); lib. bdg. 17.89 (*978-0-06-075037-4(5)) HarperCollins Pubs.

—Molly Moon Viaja a Traes del Tiempo. Crispin, Maria Dolores, tr. 2005. (SPA.). 350p. (978-84-675-0570-2(2)) SM Ediciones.

—Molly Moon's Hypnotic Time Travel Adventure. 400p. (J). 2007. (gr. 3-7). pap. 6.99 (978-0-06-075034-3(0) , Harper Trophy); 2005. (Illus.). 16.99 (978-0-06-075032-9(4)); 2005. (Illus.). lib. bdg. 17.89 (978-0-06-075033-6(2)) HarperCollins Pubs.

Cabot, Meg. Twilight. 2005. (Mediator Ser.: Bk. 6). 256p. (J). 15.99 (978-0-06-072467-2(6)); (gr. 7 up). lib. bdg. 16.89 (978-0-06-072468-9(4)) HarperCollins Pubs.

Cameron, Ian. Stirling Bridge. (Illus.). 32p. pap. 6.95 (978-1-899827-07-7(2)) Scottish Children's Pr. GBR. *Dist:* Wilson & Assocs.

Case, Cassandra. Run with Me, Nike! The Olympics in 420, B.C. Brown, Dan, illus. 1999. (Smithsonian Odyssey Ser.: No. 12). 32p. (J). (gr. 2-5). 14.95 (978-1-56899-604-2(7) , B6012); pap. 5.95 (978-1-56899-605-9(5)) Soundprints.

—Run with Me, Nike! The Olympics in Four Hundred Twenty. 1999. (gr. 3-6). lib. bdg. 14.10 (978-0-613-51585-6(4)) Tandem Library Bks.

Chapman, Bob. Visitors. 2006. 304p. pap. (*978-1-84401-693-8(5)) Athena Pr.

Cherrington, Janelle. Tale of Two Catdogs. 2000. (gr. 3-6). lib. bdg. 11.80 (978-0-613-27166-0(1)) Tandem Library Bks.

Ciencin, Scott. Beverly Hills Brontosaurus. Fredericks, Mike, illus. 2000. (Dinoverse Ser.: Vol. 5). (J). (978-0-606-19891-2(1)) Tandem Library Bks.

Citra, Becky. Jeremy & the Enchanted Theater. Milne, Jessica, illus. 2004. 64p. (J). lib. bdg. 20.00 (*978-1-4242-1258-3(8)) Fitzgerald Bks.

—Jeremy in the Underworld. Milne, Jessica, illus. 2006. 63p. (J). lib. bdg. 20.00 (*978-1-4242-1250-7(2)) Fitzgerald Bks.

Clark, Hattie Mae. It Happened at a Hanging. 2003. (Single Titles Ser.: up). 160p. (gr. 6 up). lib. bdg. 22.90 (978-0-7613-2521-5(2) , Millbrook Pr.) Lerner Publishing Group.

The Coin. 2000. 112p. (J). pap. 6.50 (978-0-9658730-1-7(3)) Drew Publishing Co.

Comerford, Kevin. Halcyon. 2003. 158p. pap. 19.95 (978-1-4137-0675-8(4)) PublishAmerica, Inc.

Condon, Bill. Time Travelers: The Jungle Goes Bananas, Sherwood Forest Goes to Pieces, the Wild West Goes Crazy. 2005. (Triple Play Ser.). (Illus.). 48p. (gr. 4-8). 41.85 (978-0-7910-9076-3(0)) Facts On File, Inc.

Coniglio, Michael. Two Times, One: Traveling the Time Fanta. 2005. 233p. pap. 19.95 (978-1-4137-6402-4(9)) PublishAmerica, Inc.

Cooney, Caroline B. For All Time. 2003. 272p. (YA). (gr. 7). pap. 5.99 (978-0-440-22931-5(6) , Laurel Leaf) Random Hse. Children's Bks.

—For All Time. 2003. (gr. 7-12). lib. bdg. 13.00 (978-0-613-72328-2(7)) Tandem Library Bks.

—Prisoner of Time. 1999. (gr. 7-12). lib. bdg. 13.00 (978-0-613-19425-9(X)) Tandem Library Bks.

—The Time Travelers. 2006. (Time Traveler Ser.: Vol. 2). (YA). (gr. 7). Vol. 2. 480p. pap. 7.50 (978-0-553-49481-5(3)); Vol. 5. 432p. pap. 7.50 (978-0-553-49480-8(5)) Random Hse. Children's Bks. (Laurel Leaf).

Cooper, Clare. Time Ball. 2003. 72p. pap. 11.95 (978-1-84323-255-1(3)) Beekman Bks., Inc.

Cooper, Susan. King of Shadows. 2005. 192p. (J). pap. 2.99 (978-1-4169-0532-5(4) , Aladdin) Simon & Schuster Children's Publishing.

—King of Shadows. l.t. ed. 2000. (Thorndike Press Large Print Juvenile Ser.). (Illus.). 246p. (J). (gr. 8-12). 21.95 (978-0-7862-2706-8(0)) Thorndike Pr.

Cote, Denis & Poulin, Stephane. Le Voyage dans le Temps. 2001. (Roman Jeunesse Ser.). (FRE., Illus.). 96p. (J). (gr. 4-7). pap. (978-2-89021-468-2(0)) Diffusion du livre Mirabel.

Crawford, Charlene E. Adventures with Granny in the Garden. 2006. (J). pap. 7.95 (978-1-882185-69-6(2)) Cornerstone Publishing, Inc.

Crawford, Quinton Douglass. Moochie the Soochie Visits the Peace People. 2007. 27p. 12.50 (*978-0-615-14879-3(4)) Crawford, Quinton Douglass.

Crichton, Michael. Timeline. 2000. xii, 496p. (gr. 7-12). lib. bdg. 16.45 (978-0-613-33633-8(X)) Tandem Library Bks.

Cuate, Melodie A. Journey to San Jacinto. 2007. (Illus.). 160p. (J). 17.95 (*978-0-89672-602-4(9)) Texas Tech Univ. Pr.

Cuate, Melodie A. Journey to the Alamo. 2006. 144p. (J). 17.95 (978-0-89672-592-8(8)) Texas Tech Univ. Pr.

Cunningham, Mary. The Magic Medallion. 2006. 160p. (YA). pap. 9.99 (978-1-59080-460-5(0)) Echelon Press Publishing.

Curry, Jane Louise. The Black Canary. 2005. (Illus.). 288p. (J). (gr. 5 up). 17.99 (978-0-689-86478-0(7) , McElderry, Margaret K.) Simon & Schuster Children's Publishing.

Dalton, Annie. Angels Unlimited: Losing the Plot. l.t. ed. 2005. 164p. (J). pap. (978-1-4056-6047-1(3)) BBC Audio.

—Flying High, No. 3. 2003. (Angels Unlimited Ser.). (Illus.). 144p. (J). pap. 4.99 (978-0-06-008817-0(6)) HarperCollins Pubs.

—Mel Beeby, Agent Angel - Flying High. 2008. 144p. (J). pap. 6.95 (*978-0-00-720473-1(6)) HarperCollins Pubs. Ltd. GBR. *Dist:* Independent Pubs. Group.

Laurence, Margaret. The Olden Days Coat. Wood, Muriel, illus. 2004. 32p. (J). (gr. 2-5). pap. 8.95 (978-0-88776-704-3(4)) Tundra Bks., Inc./Livres Toundra, Inc. CAN. *Dist:* Random Hse., Inc.

L'Engle, Madeleine. An Acceptable Time. 2007. 224p. (J). 6.99 (978-0-312-36862-3(3)); pap. 6.99 (978-0-312-36858-6(5)) Square Fish.

—Many Waters. 2002. (Illus.). (J). 15.00 (978-0-7587-9605-9(6)) Book Wholesalers, Inc.

—Many Waters. Sis, Peter & Nelson, Cliff, illus. anniv. rev. ed. 1998. 336p. (J). (gr. 5-8). pap. 5.99 (978-0-440-22770-0(4) , Laurel Leaf) Random Hse. Children's Bks.

—Many Waters. 2007. 224p. (J). 6.99 (978-0-312-36861-6(5)); pap. 6.99 (978-0-312-36857-9(7)) Square Fish.

—Many Waters. 1998. (J). (978-0-606-13596-2(0)); (gr. 5-8). lib. bdg. 14.15 (978-0-613-72320-6(1)) Tandem Library Bks.

Levitin, Sonia. The Cure. 1999. 192p. (YA). (gr. 5 up). 16.00 (978-0-15-201827-6(1) , Silver Whistle) Harcourt Trade Pubs.

—The Cure. 2000. 272p. (J). (gr. 7 up). pap. 6.99 (978-0-380-73298-2(X) , Harper Trophy) HarperCollins Pubs.

—The Cure. 2000. (J). 12.64 (978-0-606-19967-4(5)) Tandem Library Bks.

—Cure. 2000. (gr. 5-8). lib. bdg. 14.15 (978-0-613-29918-3(3)) Tandem Library Bks.

Lezaeta, Gabriela. Marcos y Andrea en el Olimpo. 1999. (J). (978-956-240-283-5(5)) Arrayan Editores S.A.

Lindbergh, Anne M. The Prisoner of Pineapple Place. 2003. (Illus.). 224p. (J). (gr. 2-7). 16.99 (978-0-7636-2132-2(3)); (gr. 3-7). pap. 5.99 (978-0-7636-1740-0(7)) Candlewick Pr.

—Prisoner of Pineapple Place. 2003. (gr. 3-6). lib. bdg. 14.15 (978-0-613-70999-6(3)) Tandem Library Bks.

Little, Kimberley Griffiths. The Last Snake Runner. 2004. 208p. (YA). (gr. 7). pap. 5.99 (978-0-440-23782-2(3) , Laurel Leaf) Random Hse. Children's Bks.

Little, Kimberley Griffiths. The Last Snake Runner: A Novel. 2006. 201p. (YA). (gr. 7-10). reprint ed. 16.00 (***978-1-4223-5838-2(0)***) DIANE Publishing Co.

Loesch, Joe. The Pony Express. Hutchinson, Cheryl, ed. Cox, Brian T., illus. unabr. ed. 2000. (Backyard Adventure Ser.). 56p. (J). (gr. k-5). reprint ed. 16.95 incl. audio compact disk (978-1-932332-04-9(9)) Toy Box Productions.

Lojeski, Lynne & O'Donnell, Thomas. Sneak Force, Mission Infinity: The Legend. 2004. (J). lib. bdg. 28.95 (978-1-932303-17-9(0)) Media Creations, Inc.

London, Victoria. Lucy & the Beauty Queen. 2002. (Gifted Girls Ser.). 64p. (J). (gr. 2-7). per. 6.95 (978-0-9714776-1-2(2)) Sparklesoup Studios, Inc.

Lopez, David Mark. Maddie's Magic Markers: Ride Like an Indian. 2006. (J). (gr. 3-7). (***978-0-9744097-1-9(5)***) Lopez, David.

—Run Like a Fugitive. 2006. (J). (gr. 4-8). (***978-0-9744097-2-6(3)***) Lopez, David.

—Walk Like an Egyptian. 2006. (J). (gr. 3-7). (***978-0-9744097-0-2(7)***) Lopez, David.

Lytle, Robert A. Three Rivers Crossing. 2000. 161p. (J). pap. 8.95 (978-0-938682-60-8(1)); (gr. 4-8). 15.95 (978-0-938682-55-4(5)) River Road Pubns., Inc.

MacDonald, Kimber. Time Travelers, Level 3. Sisk, Clay, illus. 2006. (Phonics Comics Ser.). 24p. (J). (gr. 1-17). pap. 3.99 (978-1-58476-472-4(4) , IKIDS) Innovative Kids.

MacHale, D. J. The Never War. 2003. (Pendragon Ser.: Bk. 3). (Illus.). 352p. (J). pap. 7.99 (978-0-7434-3733-2(0) , Aladdin) Simon & Schuster Children's Publishing.

Mahy, Margaret. Maddigan's Fantasia. 2007. 512p. (J). (gr. 5 up). 17.99 (978-1-4169-1812-7(4) , McElderry, Margaret K.) Simon & Schuster Children's Publishing.

Manzi, Edward Reynolds. The Time Trav-lrz: Tanya Takes Room 215. 2003. 156p. (YA). pap. 13.95 (978-1-58736-177-7(9) , Starbound Bks.) Wheatmark.

Marsden, John. Out of Time. 2007. 128p. (YA). 6.99 (978-0-7653-5303-0(2) , Tor Teen) Doherty, Tom Assocs., LLC.

Martin, Gayle. Gunfight at the O. K. Corral: Luke & Jenny Visit Tombstone. 2006. (J). per. 14.95 net. (978-1-58985-050-7(5)) Five Star Pubns., Inc.

Masters, Elaine. Kalani & the Night Marchers. Croci, Ronald, illus. 2002. pap. 3.49 (978-0-89610-359-7(5)) Island Heritage Publishing.

Maxson, H. A. & Young, Claudia H. Kalmar Nyckel & Fort Christina. Kosits, Andrew, illus. 2002. (J). per. 8.95 (978-0-9704692-6-7(8)) Bay Oak Pubs., Ltd.

—Lenapehoking: Land of the Delawares. Etherson, Lesley, illus. 2001. 64p. (J). per. 8.95 (978-0-9704692-1-2(7)) Bay Oak Pubs., Ltd.

—William Penn & the Lower Three Counties. Kosits, Andrew, illus. 2002. 64p. (J). per. 8.95 (978-0-9704692-8-1(4)) Bay Oak Pubs., Ltd.

—Zwaanendael: Resource Guide. Etherson, Lesley, illus. 2001. 13.95 (978-0-9704692-2-9(5)) Bay Oak Pubs., Ltd.

May, Scott. Sten Gizzle, Time Traveler: The Egyptian Adventure. Farkas, Josh, illus. 2000. 24p. (J). (gr. 1-3). pap. (978-0-9701450-4-8(7)) Long Hill Productions, Inc.

McBratney, Sam. Stranger from Somewhere in Time. Chatterton, Martin & Chatterton, Ann, illus. (Yellow Bananas Ser.). 48p. (J). (gr. 3-4). 2003. lib. bdg. (978-0-7787-0937-4(X)); 2002. pap. (978-0-7787-0983-1(3)) Crabtree Publishing Co.

—Stranger from Somewhere in Time. 2002. (gr. 3-6). lib. bdg. 12.95 (978-0-613-52917-4(0)) Tandem Library Bks.

McCann, Jesse Leon. The Case of the Stolen Stallion. 2000. (Ace Ventura Chapter Bk.: Vol. 2). (J). 10.79 (978-0-606-19526-3(2)) Tandem Library Bks.

McCusker, Paul. Strange Journey Back. 2006. (Adventures in Odyssey Ser.: No. 1). 304p. (J). pap. 13.99 (978-1-58997-325-1(9)) Focus on the Family Publishing.

McDonnell, Kathleen. The Shining World. 2005. 235p. (YA). pap. 6.95 (978-1-896764-79-5(7)) Second Story Pr. CAN. *Dist:* Orca Bk. Pubs. USA, Univ. of Toronto Pr.

McKee, David. Mr. Benn, Gladiator. 2002. (Illus.). 32p. (J). (ps-3). 17.99 (978-1-84270-024-2(3)) Andersen GBR. *Dist:* Trafalgar Square Publishing.

McKinty, Adrian. The Lighthouse Land. 2007. 416p. (YA). (gr. 7-17). pap. 7.95 (***978-0-8109-9361-7(9)***) Abrams, Harry N. , Inc.

McMasters, Gretchen. Aesock's Travels & Los Viajes de Aesock: Lights, Camera, Edison! & Luz, Camara, Edison. 2004. (Aesock's Travels & Los Viajes de Aesock Ser.: 1). (ENG & SPA., Illus.). 160p. (J). pap. 5.99 (978-0-9713756-9-7(0)) Stargazer Publishing Co.

McMullan, Kate. Countdown to the Year 1000. 2007. (Dragon Slayers' Academy Ser.: No. 8). 112p. (J). (gr. 1-6). 24.21 (***978-1-59961-376-5(X)***) Spotlight.

McPhail, David M. Edward in the Jungle. McPhail, David M., illus. 2002. (Illus.). 32p. (J). (ps-3). 16.99 (978-0-316-56391-8(9)) Little, Brown Bks. for Young Readers.

Meacham, Margaret. Quiet! You're Invisible. 2001. 120p. (J). (gr. 4-6). tchr. ed. 15.95 (978-0-8234-1651-6(8)) Holiday Hse., Inc.

Melnikoff, Pamela. Prisoner in Time. 2001. 144p. (gr. 5-8). pap. 9.95 (978-0-8276-0735-4(0)) Jewish Pubn. Society.

Mercer, Gary. Justin Flowers & the Orb of Time. 2003. 147p. pap. 16.95 (978-1-59286-530-7(5)) PublishAmerica, Inc.

Metz, Melinda. Ravens Point. 2005. pap. (978-0-06-052373-2(5)) HarperCollins Canada, Ltd.

Molloy, Michael. The Time Witches. 2002. (Illus.). 272p. (J). (gr. 5-8). 4.99 (978-0-439-42090-7(3) , Chicken Hse., The) Scholastic, Inc.

Montes, Marisa. A Circle of Time. 2002. (Time Travel Mystery Ser.). 272p. (YA). (gr. 6-10). 17.00 (978-0-15-202626-4(6)) Harcourt Children's Bks.

Moonshower, Candie. The Legend of Zoey. 2007. 224p. (J). (gr. 4-7). 5.99 (***978-0-440-23924-6(9)*** , Yearling) Random Hse. Children's Bks.

Moore, Ulysses. Isle of Masks. 2008. (Ulysses Moore Book Ser.). 256p. (J). 5.99 (***978-0-439-77671-4(6)*** , Scholastic Paperbacks) Scholastic, Inc.

Muir, Sabine. Matthew & the Highland Rescue: The Time Gate Series. 2005. 131p. pap. 16.95 (978-1-4137-5916-7(5)) PublishAmerica, Inc.

—Meeting Wolfie: A Story about Mozart. 2006. 129p. pap. 16.95 (978-1-4241-3968-2(6)) PublishAmerica, Inc.

Nesbit, E. The House of Arden. 2006. (New York Review Children's Collection). 248p. (J). (gr. 3). 17.95 (978-1-59017-202-5(7) , NYR Children's Collection) New York Review of Bks., Inc., The.

Nimmo, Jenny. Charlie Bone & the Time Twister. 2003. (Children of the Red King Ser.). 416p. (J). 9.95 (978-0-439-49687-2(X) , Orchard Bks.) Scholastic, Inc.

Niven, Larry. Rainbow Mars. 2000. (gr. 7-12). lib. bdg. 15.30 (978-0-613-28032-7(6)) Tandem Library Bks.

Norton, Andre. The Defiant Agents & Key Out of Time, 2 vols. 2001. (Time Traders II Ser.). 384p. (J). 19.00 (978-0-671-31968-7(X)) Baen Bks.

—Dragon Magic. 2006. (Magic Bks.: No. 4). 224p. (J). 5.99 (978-0-7653-5300-9(8) , Starscape) Doherty, Tom Assocs., LLC.

—Red Hart Magic. 2007. (Magic Bks.: Bk. 6). 224p. (J). 5.99 (978-0-7653-5302-3(4) , Starscape) Doherty, Tom Assocs., LLC.

Norton, Andre. Time Traders. 2007. 95.99 (***978-1-4280-5221-5(6)***); pap. 89.99 (***978-1-4280-5202-4(X)***) Indy-Publish.com.

Norton, Andre Alice. The Time Traders. 2006. pap. (***978-1-4068-3561-8(7)***) Echo Library.

O'Neill, Katrina & Thompson, Lisa. In Search of the Egyptian Queen. Cantell, Brenda, illus. 2005. (Treasure Trackers Ser.). 80p. (gr. 5-9). 19.00 (978-0-7910-8874-6(X)) Facts On File, Inc.

Osborne, Mary Pope. Blizzard of the Blue Moon. Murdocca, Sal, illus. 2007. (Magic Tree House Ser.: No. 36). 144p. (J). (gr. 2-5). pap. 4.99 (978-0-375-83038-9(3) , Random Hse. Bks. for Young Readers) Random Hse. Children's Bks.

—Blizzard of the Blue Moon. 2006. (Magic Tree House Ser.: No. 36). (Illus.). 128p. (J). (gr. k-3). lib. bdg. 13.99 (978-0-375-93037-9(X)); (gr. 2-5). 11.95 (978-0-375-83037-2(5)) Random Hse. Children's Bks. (Random Hse. Bks. for Young Readers).

—Buffalo Before Breakfast. 2004. (Magic Tree House Ser. : No. 18). 72p. (J). (gr. k-3). pap. 17.00 incl. audio (978-0-8072-0927-1(9) , Listening Library) Random Hse. Audio Publishing Group.

—Buffalo Before Breakfast. Murdocca, Sal, illus. 1999. (Magic Tree House Ser.: No. 18). (J). (gr. k-3). 20.00 (978-0-375-80041-2(7)); 96p. lib. bdg. 11.99 (978-0-679-99064-2(X)); Vol. 18. 96p. mass mkt. 3.99 (978-0-679-89064-5(5)) Random Hse. Children's Bks. (Random Hse. Bks. for Young Readers).

—Buffalo Before Breakfast. Murdocca, Salvatore, illus. 1999. (Magic Tree House Ser. : No. 18). 72p. (J). (gr. k-3). lib. bdg. 11.80 (978-0-613-16067-4(3)) Tandem Library Bks.

—Buffalo Before Breakfast. 1999. (Magic Tree House Ser. : No. 18). (J). (gr. k-3). lib. bdg. 10.79 (978-0-606-16841-0(9)) Tandem Library Bks.

—El Caballero del Alba. 2004. (Coleccion la Casa Del Arbol the Magic Tree House Ser.). (SPA.). (J). pap. 4.95 (978-1-930332-50-8(5)) Lectorum Pubns., Inc.

—Carnival at Candlelight. 2006. (Magic Tree House Ser.: No. 33). (Illus.). 144p. (J). (gr. 2-6). pap. 4.99 (978-0-375-83034-1(0) , Random Hse. Bks. for Young Readers) Random Hse. Children's Bks.

—Carnival at Candlelight. Murdocca, Sal, illus. 2005. (Magic Tree House Ser.: No. 33). 128p. (J). (gr. k-3). 11.95 (978-0-375-83033-4(2) , Random Hse. Bks. for Young Readers) Random Hse. Children's Bks.

—Christmas in Camelot. Murdocca, Sal, illus. 2001. (Magic Tree House Ser.: No. 29). 128p. (J). (gr. k-3). 11.95 (978-0-375-81373-3(X)); lib. bdg. 13.99 (978-0-375-91373-0(4)) Random Hse. Children's Bks. (Random Hse. Bks. for Young Readers).

—Civil War on Sunday, Vol. 21. unabr. ed. 2004. (Magic Tree House Ser. : No. 21). 76p. (J). (gr. k-3). pap. 17.00 incl. audio (978-0-8072-0930-1(9) , S FTR 253 SP, Listening Library) Random Hse. Audio Publishing Group.

—Civil War on Sunday. Murdocca, Sal, illus. 2000. (Magic Tree House Ser.: No. 21). 96p. (J). (gr. k-3). lib. bdg. 11.99 (978-0-679-99067-3(4)); mass mkt. 3.99 (978-0-679-89067-6(X)) Random Hse. Children's Bks. (Random Hse. Bks. for Young Readers).

—Civil War on Sunday. 2000. (Magic Tree House Ser. : No. 21). (J). (gr. k-3). lib. bdg. 11.80 (978-0-613-24596-8(2)); (Illus.). 10.79 (978-0-606-18852-4(5)) Tandem Library Bks.

—Dark Day in the Deep Sea. Murdocca, Sal, illus. 2008. (Stepping Stone Bks.). 128p. (J). (gr. 3-7). lib. bdg. 14.99 (***978-0-375-93731-6(5)*** , Random Hse. Bks. for Young Readers) Random Hse. Children's Bks.

—Day of the Dragon King, Vol. 14. unabr. ed. 2004. (Magic Tree House Ser. : No. 14). 68p. (J). (gr. k-3). pap. 17.00 incl. audio (978-0-8072-0783-3(7) , S FTR 242 SP, Listening Library) Random Hse. Audio Publishing Group.

—Day of the Dragon King. Murdocca, Sal, illus. 1998. (Magic Tree House Ser.: No. 14). 96p. (J). (gr. k-3). lib. bdg. 11.99 (978-0-679-99051-2(8)); 14th ed. pap. 3.99 (978-0-679-89051-5(3)) Random Hse. Children's Bks. (Random Hse. Bks. for Young Readers).

—Day of the Dragon King. Murdocca, Sal, illus. 1998. (Magic Tree House Ser.: No. 14). (J). (gr. k-3). 10.79 (978-0-606-13958-8(3)) Tandem Library Bks.

—Dinosaurios al Atardecer. 2004. (Coleccion la Casa Del Arbol the Magic Tree House Ser.). (SPA.). (J). pap. 4.95 (978-1-930332-49-2(1)) Lectorum Pubns., Inc.

—Dinosaurios al Atardecer. 2003. (SPA.). (gr. 3-6). lib. bdg. 12.95 (978-0-613-64486-0(7)) Tandem Library Bks.

—Dinosaurs Before Dark. unabr. ed. 2004. (Magic Tree House Ser. : No. 1). 68p. (J). (gr. k-5). pap. 17.00 incl. audio (978-0-8072-0330-9(0) , FTR208SP, Listening Library) Random Hse. Audio Publishing Group.

—Dragon of the Red Dawn. Murdocca, Sal, illus. 2007. (Magic Tree House Ser.: No. 37). 128p. (J). (gr. k-3). 11.99 (978-0-375-83727-2(2) , Random Hse. Bks. for Young Readers) Random Hse. Children's Bks.

—Dragon of the Red Dawn. Murdocca, Sal, illus. 2007. (Magic Tree House Ser.: No. 37). 108p. (J). (gr. k-3). pap. (978-0-375-83728-9(0)) Random Hse., Inc.

—Earthquake in the Early Morning, Vol. 24. unabr. ed. 2004. (Magic Tree House Ser. : No. 24). 71p. (J). (gr. k-3). pap. 17.00 incl. audio (978-0-8072-0933-2(3) , S FTR 256 SP, Listening Library) Random Hse. Audio Publishing Group.

—Earthquake in the Early Morning. Murdocca, Sal, illus. 2001. (Magic Tree House Ser.: No. 24). 96p. (J). (gr. k-3). 11.99 (978-0-679-99070-3(4)); mass mkt. 3.99 (978-0-679-89070-6(X)) Random Hse. Children's Bks. (Random Hse. Bks. for Young Readers).

—Earthquake in the Early Morning. 2001. (Magic Tree House Ser. : No. 24). (J). (gr. k-3). lib. bdg. 11.80 (978-0-613-35684-8(5)); (Illus.). 10.79 (978-0-606-21166-6(7)) Tandem Library Bks.

—Ghost Town at Sundown. unabr. ed. 2004. (Magic Tree House Ser. : No. 10). 73p. (J). (gr. k-3). pap. 17.00 incl. audio (978-0-8072-0535-8(4) , Listening Library) Random Hse. Audio Publishing Group.

—Haunted Castle on Hallows Eve. Murdocca, Sal, illus. 2003. (Magic Tree House Ser.: No. 30). 128p. (J). (gr. k-3). 11.95 (978-0-375-82521-7(5)); lib. bdg. 13.99 (978-0-375-92521-4(X)) Random Hse. Children's Bks. (Random Hse. Bks. for Young Readers).

—High Tide in Hawaii. Murdocca, Sal, illus. 2003. (Magic Tree House Ser.: No. 28). 96p. (J). (gr. k-3). lib. bdg. 11.99 (978-0-375-90616-9(9)); (gr. 1-4). pap. 3.99 (978-0-375-80616-2(4)) Random Hse. Children's Bks. (Random Hse. Bks. for Young Readers).

—High Tide in Hawaii. 2003. (Magic Tree House Ser. : No. 28). (J). (gr. k-3). lib. bdg. 11.80 (978-0-613-62386-5(X)) Tandem Library Bks.

—Hour of the Olympics. unabr. ed. 2004. (Magic Tree House Ser. : No. 16). 70p. (J). (gr. k-3). pap. 17.00 incl. audio (978-0-8072-0785-7(3) , LFTR 244 SP, Listening Library) Random Hse. Audio Publishing Group.

—Hour of the Olympics. Murdocca, Sal, illus. 1998. (Magic Tree House Ser.: No. 16). 96p. (J). (gr. k-3). lib. bdg. 11.99 (978-0-679-99062-8(3)); mass mkt. 3.99 (978-0-679-89062-1(9)) Random Hse. Children's Bks. (Random Hse. Bks. for Young Readers).

—The Knight at Dawn. unabr. ed. 2004. (Magic Tree House Ser. : No. 2). 66p. (J). (gr. k-3). pap. 17.00 incl. audio (978-0-8072-0331-6(9) , Listening Library) Random Hse. Audio Publishing Group.

—The Knight at Dawn Book & CD. Murdocca, Sal, illus. 2008. (Stepping Stone Book(TM) Ser.). (J). (gr. k-3). 9.99 (***978-0-375-84406-5(6)*** , Random Hse. Bks. for Young Readers) Random Hse. Children's Bks.

—Una Momia en la Manana. 2004. (Coleccion la Casa Del Arbol the Magic Tree House Ser.). (SPA.). (J). pap. 4.95 (978-1-930332-51-5(3)) Lectorum Pubns., Inc.

—Una Momia en la Manana. 2003. (SPA.). (gr. 3-6). lib. bdg. 12.95 (978-0-613-64609-3(6)) Tandem Library Bks.

—Monday with a Mad Genius. Murdocca, Sal, illus. 2007. (Stepping Stone Bks.). 128p. (J). (gr. 2-6). 11.99 (***978-0-375-83729-6(9)***); lib. bdg. 14.99 (***978-0-375-93729-3(3)***) Random Hse. Children's Bks. (Random Hse. Bks. for Young Readers).

—Monday with a Mad Genius. Murdocca, Sal, illus. 2007. (J). pap. (***978-0-375-83730-2(2)***) Random Hse., Inc.

—Night of the New Magicians. Murdocca, Sal, illus. (Magic Tree House Ser.: No. 35). (J). 2007. 144p. (gr. 2-5). pap. 4.99 (978-0-375-83036-5(7)); 2006. 128p. (gr. k-3). 11.95 (978-0-375-83035-8(9)); 2006. 128p. (gr. k-3). lib. bdg. 13.99 (978-0-375-93035-5(3)) Random Hse. Children's Bks. (Random Hse. Bks. for Young Readers).

—La Noche de los Ninjas. 2004. (Coleccion la Casa Del Arbol the Magic Tree House Ser.).Tr. of Night of the Ninjas. (SPA., Illus.). (J). pap. 4.95 (978-1-930332-66-9(1)) Lectorum Pubns., Inc.

—Piratas Despues del Mediodia. 2004. (Coleccion la Casa Del Arbol the Magic Tree House Ser.). (SPA.). (J). pap. 4.95 (978-1-930332-52-2(1)) Lectorum Pubns., Inc.

—Piratas Despues del Mediodia. 2003. (SPA.). (gr. 3-6). lib. bdg. 12.95 (978-0-613-64578-2(2)) Tandem Library Bks.

—Pirates Past Noon. unabr. ed. 2000. (Magic Tree House Ser. : No. 4). (J). (gr. k-3). pap. 17.00 incl. audio Random Hse. Audio Publishing Group.

—Revolutionary War on Wednesday, Vol. 22. unabr. ed. 2004. (Magic Tree House Ser. : No. 22). 69p. (J). (gr. k-3). pap. 17.00 incl. audio (978-0-8072-0931-8(7) , S FTR 254 SP, Listening Library) Random Hse. Audio Publishing Group.

—Revolutionary War on Wednesday. Loehr, Mallory, ed. Murdocca, Sal, illus. 2000. (Magic Tree House Ser.: No. 22). 96p. (J). (gr. k-3). lib. bdg. 11.99 (978-0-679-99068-0(2)); pap. 3.99 (978-0-679-89068-3(8)) Random Hse. Children's Bks. (Random Hse. Bks. for Young Readers).

—Revolutionary War on Wednesday. Murdocca, Salvatore, illus. 2000. (Magic Tree House Ser. : No. 22). 69p. (J). (gr. k-3). lib. bdg. 11.80 (978-0-613-28355-7(4)) Tandem Library Bks.

—Revolutionary War on Wednesday. Murdocca, Sal, illus. 2000. (Magic Tree House Ser. : No. 22). (J). (gr. k-3). (978-0-606-19907-0(1)) Tandem Library Bks.

—Season of the Sandstorms. 2006. (Magic Tree House Ser.: No. 34). 144p. (J). (gr. k-3). pap. 4.99 (978-0-375-83032-7(4) , Random Hse. Bks. for Young Readers) Random Hse. Children's Bks.

—Stage Fright on a Summer Night. Murdocca, Sal, illus. 2002. (Magic Tree House Ser.: No. 25). 96p. (J). (gr. k-3). lib. bdg. 11.99 (978-0-375-90611-4(8)); 25. pap. 3.99 (978-0-375-80611-7(3)) Random Hse. Children's Bks. (Random Hse. Bks. for Young Readers).

—Stage Fright on a Summer Night. Murdocca, Salvatore, illus. 2002. (Magic Tree House Ser. : No. 25). 70p. (J). (gr. k-3). lib. bdg. 10.79 (978-0-606-24092-5(6)) Tandem Library Bks.

—Stage Fright on a Summer Night. 2002. (Magic Tree House Ser. : No. 25). (J). (gr. k-3). lib. bdg. 11.80 (978-0-613-50506-2(9)) Tandem Library Bks.

—Summer of the Sea Serpent. Murdocca, Sal, tr. Murdocca, Sal, illus. 2004. (Magic Tree House Ser.: No. 31). 128p. (J). (gr. k-3). lib. bdg. 13.99 (978-0-375-92735-5(2)); (gr. 2-5). 11.95 (978-0-375-82735-8(8)) Random Hse. Children's Bks. (Random Hse. Bks. for Young Readers).

—Una Tarde en el Amazonas. 2004. (Coleccion la Casa Del Arbol the Magic Tree House Ser.).Tr. of Afternoon on the Amazon. (SPA., Illus.). (J). pap. 4.95 (978-1-930332-67-6(X)) Lectorum Pubns., Inc.

—Thanksgiving on Thursday. Murdocca, Sal, illus. 2002. (Magic Tree House Ser.: No. 27). 96p. (J). (gr. k-3). lib. bdg. 11.99 (978-0-375-90615-2(0)); mass mkt. 3.99 (978-0-375-80615-5(6)) Random Hse. Children's Bks. (Random Hse. Bks. for Young Readers).

—Thanksgiving on Thursday. 2002. (Magic Tree House Ser. : No. 27). (J). (gr. k-3). lib. bdg. 11.80 (978-0-613-56853-1(2)) Tandem Library Bks.

—Un Tigre Dientes de Sable en el Ocaso. 2004. (Coleccion la Casa Del Arbol the Magic Tree House Ser.).Tr. of Sunset of the Sabretooth. (SPA., Illus.). (J). pap. 4.95 (978-1-930332-68-3(8)) Lectorum Pubns., Inc.

—Tonight on the Titanic. unabr. ed. 2004. (Magic Tree House Ser. : No. 17). 71p. (J). (gr. k-3). pap. 17.00 incl. audio (978-0-8072-0926-4(0) , S FTR 249 SP, Listening Library) Random Hse. Audio Publishing Group.

—Tonight on the Titanic. Murdocca, Sal, illus. 1999. (Magic Tree House Ser.: No. 17). (J). (gr. k-3). 96p. lib. bdg. 11.99 (978-0-679-99063-5(1)); 71p. pap. 3.99 (978-0-679-89063-8(7)) Random Hse. Children's Bks. (Random Hse. Bks. for Young Readers).

—Tonight on the Titanic. Murdocca, Sal, illus. 1999. (Magic Tree House Ser. : No. 17). 70p. (J). (gr. k-3). lib. bdg. 11.19 (978-0-606-16894-6(X)) Tandem Library Bks.

—Tonight on the Titanic. 1999. (Magic Tree House Ser. : No. 17). (J). (gr. k-3). lib. bdg. 11.80 (978-0-613-16226-5(9)) Tandem Library Bks.

—Twister on Tuesday, Vol. 23. 2004. (Magic Tree House Ser. : No. 23). 70p. (J). (gr. k-3). pap. 17.00 incl. audio (978-0-8072-9932-6(4) , Listening Library) Random Hse. Audio Publishing Group.

—Twister on Tuesday, 23. Murdocca, Sal, illus. 2001. (Magic Tree House Ser.: No. 23). 96p. (J). (gr. k-3). pap. 3.99 (978-0-679-89069-0(6) , Random Hse. Bks. for Young Readers) Random Hse. Children's Bks.

—Twister on Tuesday. 2001. (Magic Tree House Ser. : No. 23). (J). (gr. k-3). lib. bdg. 11.80 (978-0-613-35706-7(X)); (Illus.). (978-0-606-21498-8(4)) Tandem Library Bks.

—Vacation under the Volcano, Vol. 13. unabr. ed. 2004. (Magic Tree House Ser.: No. 13). 74p. (J). (gr. k-3). pap. 17.00 incl. audio (978-0-8072-0782-6(9) , LFTR 241 SP, Listening Library) Random Hse. Audio Publishing Group.

—Vacation under the Volcano. Murdocca, Sal, illus. 1998. (Magic Tree House Ser.: No. 13). (J). (gr. k-3). 96p. lib. bdg. 11.99 (978-0-679-99050-5(X)); 80p. mass mkt. 3.99 (978-0-679-89050-8(5)) Random Hse. Children's Bks. (Random Hse. Bks. for Young Readers).

—Vacation under the Volcano, nO. 13. Murdocca, Sal, illus. 1998. (Magic Tree House Ser. : No. 13). (J). (gr. k-3). (978-0-606-13972-4(9)) Tandem Library Bks.

—Viking Ships at Sunrise, Vol. 15. unabr. ed. 2004. (Magic Tree House Ser. : No. 15). 71p. (J). (gr. k-3). pap. 17.00 incl. audio (978-0-8072-0784-0(5) , LFTR 243 SP, Listening Library) Random Hse. Audio Publishing Group.

—Viking Ships at Sunrise. Murdocca, Sal, illus. 1998. (Magic Tree House Ser.: No. 15). 96p. (J). (gr. k-3). lib. bdg. 11.99 (978-0-679-99061-1(5)); mass mkt. 3.99 (978-0-679-89061-4(0)) Random Hse. Children's Bks. (Random Hse. Bks. for Young Readers).

—Viking Ships at Sunrise. Murdocca, Salvatore, illus. 1998. (Magic Tree House Ser.: No. 15). 71p. (J). lib. bdg. 10.79 (978-0-606-15755-1(7)) Tandem Library Bks.

Owen, James A. Here, There Be Dragons. Owen, James A., illus. (Chronicles of the Imaginarium Geographica Ser.). (YA). 2007. 352p. pap. 9.99 (***978-1-4169-1228-6(2)*** , Simon Pulse); 2006. 336p. 17.95 (978-1-4169-1227-9(4)) Simon & Schuster Children's Publishing.

—The Search for the Red Dragon. Owen, James A., illus. 2008. (Chronicles of the Imaginarium Geographica Ser.). 384p. (YA). (gr. 7 up). 17.99 (***978-1-4169-4850-6(3)***) Simon & Schuster Children's Publishing.

Park, Linda Sue. Archer's Quest. 2006. (Illus.). 176p. (J). (gr. 5-9). 16.00 (978-0-618-59631-7(3) , Clarion Bks.) Houghton Mifflin Co. Trade & Reference Div.

Paulsen, Gary. The Transall Saga. 1998. (J). (978-0-385-43196-5(1)) Dell Distributing.

—The Transall Saga. 1999. 256p. (J). (gr. 5-7). mass mkt. 6.99 (978-0-440-21976-7(0) , Laurel Leaf) Random Hse. Children's Bks.

—The Transall Saga. 1999. 248p. lib. bdg. 12.64 (978-0-606-17349-0(8)) Tandem Library Bks.

—Transall Saga. 1999. (gr. 7-12). lib. bdg. 14.15 (978-0-613-22948-7(7)) Tandem Library Bks.

—The Transall Saga. l.t. ed. 1999. 312p. (YA). (gr. 7-12). 21.95 (978-0-7862-2187-5(9)) Thorndike Pr.

Paulsen, Gary & Roberts, Esyllt Nest. Plygu Amser. 2005. (WEL.). 77p. (978-0-86381-683-3(5)) Gwasg Carreg Gwalch.

Paulson Sternlight, Phyllis. Journey to the Dark Edge of Time. Anderson, Gunn, illus. 1999. 29p. (J). (gr. 4-7). 9.95 (978-0-9673505-0-9(6)) Sternlight, Phyllis Paulson.

Peck, Richard. The Dreadful Future of Blossom Culp. 2001. 192p. (J). (gr. 4-7). pap. 5.99 (978-0-14-131094-7(4) , Puffin) Penguin Group (USA) Inc.

—The Dreadful Future of Blossom Culp. 2001. 12.64 (978-0-606-21162-8(4)); (gr. 7-12). lib. bdg. 14.15 (978-0-613-35939-9(9)) Tandem Library Bks.

Pepper, Dennis. The Young Oxford Book of Timewarp Stories. 2002. (Illus.). 224p. (YA). (gr. 5). 15.95 (978-0-19-278167-3(7)) Oxford Univ. Pr., Inc.

Perrin, Randy, et al. Time Like a River. 2004. 144p. (gr. 5 up). 14.95 (978-1-57143-061-8(X)) RDR Bks.

Petti, Ken. Zenda 09 Trapped in Time. 2007. 144p. (J). pap. (***978-0-448-44343-0(0)*** , Grosset & Dunlap) Penguin Group (USA) Inc.

Phillips, Don. I, Tutus: Book One: the Son of Heaven. 2005. 263p. pap. 21.95 (978-1-4137-5932-7(7)) PublishAmerica, Inc.

Pierson, Jan. Goodbye God, I'm Going to Bodie (Bodie, California) 2002. (Ghostowners Ser.: Vol. 1). 112p. (gr. 4-8). pap. 10.00 (978-0-9721800-0-9(1)) WildWest Publishing.

Plante, Raymond. Le Monde de Xéros. Delezenne, Christine, illus. 2004. (Roman Jeunesse Ser.). (FRE.). 96p. (J). (gr. 4-7). pap. (978-2-89021-615-0(2)) Diffusion du livre Mirabel.

Pratchett, Terry. Johnny & the Bomb. 2007. 256p. (J). lib. bdg. 17.89 (978-0-06-054192-7(X)); (gr. 5-8). 16.99 (978-0-06-054191-0(1)) HarperCollins Pubs.

Prévost, Guillaume & Rodarmor, William. The Book of Time. 2007. (J). (***978-0-439-88379-5(2)***); 224p. (gr. 4-7). pap. 16.99 (***978-0-439-88375-7(X)***) Scholastic, Inc. (Levine, Arthur A. Bks.).

Price, Susan. The Sterkarm Handshake. 2000. 448p. (J). (gr. 4-7). 17.95 (978-0-06-028959-1(7)); 18.89 (978-0-06-029392-5(6)) HarperCollins Pubs.

—The Sterkarm Handshake. 2000. (978-0-606-21707-1(X)) Tandem Library Bks.

—A Sterkarm Kiss. 2004. 288p. (J). (gr. 7 up). 16.99 (978-0-06-072197-8(9)) HarperCollins Pubs.

Prior, Natalie Jane. Lily Quench & the Treasure of Mote Ely, Vol. 3. 2004. (Illus.). 160p. (J). (gr. 3-7). pap. 4.99 (978-0-14-240022-7(X) , Puffin) Penguin Group (USA) Inc.

Quindlen, Anna. Happily Ever After. 1999. (gr. 3-6). lib. bdg. 13.00 (978-0-613-17806-8(3)) Tandem Library Bks.

Rabin, Staton. Black Powder. 2005. 256p. (J). (gr. 6-9). 16.95 (978-0-689-86876-4(6) , McElderry, Margaret K.) Simon & Schuster Children's Publishing.

—The Curse of the Romanovs. 2007. 288p. (J). (gr. 7 up). 17.99 (978-1-4169-0208-9(2) , McElderry, Margaret K.) Simon & Schuster Children's Publishing.

Raham, Gary, et al. The Deep Time Diaries: As Recorded by Neesha & Jon Olifee. 2000. (Illus.). 96p. (J). (gr. 3-4). pap. 17.95 (978-1-55591-415-8(2)) Fulcrum Publishing.

Ralph, Brian. Crum Bums. 2007. (Illus.). 208p. (YA). pap. 15.00 (***978-1-60309-002-5(9)***) Top Shelf Productions.

Ramsay, Elizabeth. The Burning Light. Katz, Avi, illus. 2005. 144p. (J). (gr. 4-9). 14.95 (978-1-930143-43-2(5)); pap. 9.95 (978-1-930143-44-9(3)) Pitspopany Pr. (Devora Publishing).

Ransom, Candice. Horses in the Wind: A Tale of Seabiscuit. 2007. 128p. (J). (gr. 1-5). pap. 4.99 (***978-0-7869-4355-5(6)*** , Mirrorstone) Wizards of the Coast.

Ransom, Candice. Signals in the Sky. 2007. 128p. (J). 4.99 (978-0-7869-4353-1(X) , Mirrorstone) Wizards of the Coast.

Reed, W. F. Andy & Mark & the Time Machine: Pickett's Charge at Gettysburg. 2000. 144p. (YA). pap. 10.95 (978-0-595-12885-3(8)) iUniverse, Inc.

Reed, Wilfred. Andy & Mark & the Time Machine: Custer's Last Stand. 2003. 240p. (YA). pap. 15.95 (978-0-595-26496-4(4) , Writers Club Pr.) iUniverse, Inc.

Reeve, Philip. Starcross: An Intergalactic Adventure of Spies & Time Travel. Wyatt, David, illus. 2007. 320p. (J). (gr. 5 up). 16.95 (***978-1-59990-121-3(8)*** , Bloomsbury Children) Bloomsbury Publishing.

Reiche, Dietlof. Freddy's Final Quest Book Five in Golden Hamster. 2008. 208p. pap. 5.99 (***978-0-439-87415-1(7)*** , Scholastic Paperbacks) Scholastic, Inc.

Reiche, Dietlof & Brownjohn, John. Freddy's Final Quest. Cepeda, Joe, illus. 2007. (Golden Hamster Saga Ser.: Bk. 5). 304p. (J). pap. 16.99 (978-0-439-87414-4(9) , Scholastic Pr.) Scholastic, Inc.

Reid, Kate. Operation Timewarp. 2003. 195p. pap. 9.99 (978-1-84255-203-2(1)) Orion Children's Bks. GBR. *Dist:* Trafalgar Square Publishing.

Reiss, Kathryn. Paint by Magic. 2003. (Time Travel Mystery Ser.). 288p. (J). (gr. 5 up). pap. 6.95 (978-0-15-204925-6(8) , Harcourt Paperbacks) Harcourt Children's Bks.

—Paint by Magic. 2002. (gr. 5-8). lib. bdg. 14.10 (978-0-613-70531-8(9)) Tandem Library Bks.

—Pale Phoenix. 2004. 326p. (J). (gr. k-17). lib. bdg. 12.60 (978-0-606-30243-2(3)); 2003. (gr. 7-12). lib. bdg. 14.10 (978-0-613-67837-7(0)) Tandem Library Bks.

Resnick, Mike. Lady with an Alien: An Encounter with Leonardo da Vinci. 2005. (Art Encounterstm Series- Ser.). 244p. pap. 6.99 (978-0-8230-0419-5(8)) Watson-Guptill Pubns., Inc.

—Lady with an Alien: An Encounter with Leonardo Da Vinci. 2005. (Art Encounters Ser.). (Illus.). 176p. (YA). (gr. 3-7). 15.95 (978-0-8230-0323-5(X)) Watson-Guptill Pubns., Inc.

Riding, John. Sean's World Cup Final Day Out - Wembley 1966. 2006. 97p. (YA). pap. (978-1-84685-059-2(2) , Exposure Publishing) Meadow Bks.

Riley, Lehman C. Meeting Dr. Martin Luther King. 2004. (Adventures of Papa Lemon's Little Wanderers Ser.: Bk. 1). 35p. (***978-0-9760523-0-2(X)***) Matter of Africa America Time.

Ritt, Wilma. The Country Club. 2003. 113p. (J). pap. 16.95 (978-1-59286-098-2(2)) PublishAmerica, Inc.

Rizzo, Cynthia Marie. Angela & the Princess. 2006. 89p. pap. 14.95 (978-1-4241-2599-9(5)) PublishAmerica, Inc.

Robertson, Barbara. Rosemary & the Island Treasure: Back to 1947. 2001. (Hourglass Adventures Ser.: Bk. 4). (Illus.). 128p. (J). (gr. 3-5). pap. 4.95 (978-1-890817-58-9(9)) Winslow Pr.

—Rosemary & the Mystery Down Under. 2002. (Illus.). 128p. (J). (gr. 4-6). pap. 4.95 (978-1-890817-64-0(3)) Winslow Pr.

—Rosemary at Sea: Back to 1919. 2001. (Hourglass Adventures Ser.: Bk. 3). (Illus.). 128p. (J). (gr. 4-6). pap. 4.95 (978-1-890817-57-2(0)) Winslow Pr.

—Rosemary in Paris: Back to 1889. 2001. (Hourglass Adventures Ser.: Bk. 2). (Illus.). 121p. (J). (gr. 4-7). pap. 4.95 (978-1-890817-56-5(2)) Winslow Pr.

—Rosemary Meets Rosemarie Bk. 1: Berlin in 1870. 2001. (Hourglass Adventures Ser.: Bk. 1). (Illus.). 128p. (J). (gr. 4-6). pap. 5.95 (978-1-890817-55-8(4)) Winslow Pr.

—Rosemary Rocks Spain. 2002. (Illus.). 128p. (J). (gr. 4-6). pap. 4.95 (978-1-890817-63-3(5)) Winslow Pr.

Rose, Simon. The Sorcerer's Letterbox. 2006. 116p. (J). 7.95 (978-1-896580-52-4(1)) Tradewind Bks. CAN. *Dist:* Orca Bk. Pubs. USA.

Ruby, Anne. Children of the Sea. Meier, Ty, illus. 2007. (YA). per. (978-0-9787881-0-0(9)) Seachild.

Sabuda, Robert. Uh-Oh Leonardo! 2003. (Illus.). 48p. (J). 16.95 (978-0-689-81160-9(8) , Atheneum) Simon & Schuster Children's Publishing.

Sage, Angie. Physik. Zug, Mark, illus. 2008. (Septimus Heap Ser.: Bk. 3). 560p. (J). (gr. 4-6). pap. 7.99 (***978-0-06-057739-1(8)*** , Harper Trophy) HarperCollins Pubs.

Sathre, Vivian. Digging up the Past. l.t. ed. 1999. (Adventures of Wishbone Ser.: No. 6). (Illus.). 144p. (J). (gr. 4 up). lib. bdg. 22.60 (978-0-8368-2302-8(8)) Stevens, Gareth Inc.

Saunders, Joanne. The Secret at the Winthrop House, Independence Day: Book 2. 2007. 208p. (YA). per. 13.99 (***978-1-59886-935-4(3)***) Tate Publishing & Enterprises, L.L.C.

Scieszka, Jon. Birdman or Birdbrain? 2007. (Time Warp Trio). 48p. (J). pap. 3.99 (***978-0-06-111647-6(5)*** , Harper Trophy) HarperCollins Pubs.

—Harem Scare'em. 2007. (Time Warp Trio). 80p. (J). pap. 4.99 (***978-0-06-111649-0(1)*** , Harper Trophy) HarperCollins Pubs.

—Knights of the Kitchen Table. unabr. ed. 1998. (Time Warp Trio Ser.: No. 1). 55p. (J). (gr. 2-5). pap. 17.00 incl. audio (978-0-8072-0391-0(2) , FTR193SP, Listening Library) Random Hse. Audio Publishing Group.

—Me Oh Maya. McCauley, Adam, illus. (Time Warp Trio Ser.: No. 13). (J). 2005. 96p. pap. 4.99 (978-0-14-240300-6(8) , Puffin); 2003. 80p. (gr. 2-6). 14.99 (978-0-670-03629-5(3) , Viking Juvenile) Penguin Group (USA) Inc.

—Meet You at Waterloo. 2007. (Time Warp Trio: Vol. 4). 96p. (J). pap. 6.99 (***978-0-06-111646-9(7)*** , Harper Trophy) HarperCollins Pubs.

—Nos Vemos, Gladiador.Tr. of See you later, gladiator. (SPA.). (J). 7.95 (978-958-04-6484-6(7)) Norma S.A. COL. *Dist:* Distribuidora Norma, Inc.

—Oh Say, I Can't See. McCauley, Adam, illus. 2007. (Time Warp Trio Ser.: No. 15). 80p. (J). (gr. 2-6). pap. 4.99 (978-0-14-240808-7(5) , Puffin) Penguin Group (USA) Inc.

—El Pirata Barbanegra. Smith, Lane, illus. (SPA.). (J). (gr. 5-8). 7.95 (978-958-04-3401-6(8) , NR8584) Norma S.A. COL. *Dist:* Distribuidora Norma, Inc., Lectorum Pubns., Inc.

—Sam Samurai, Vol. 10. McCauley, Adam, illus. (Time Warp Trio Ser.: No. 10). (J). 2004. 112p. (gr. 2-6). pap. 4.99 (978-0-14-240088-3(2) , Puffin); 2001. 80p. (gr. 1-5). 14.99 (978-0-670-89915-9(1) , Viking Juvenile) Penguin Group (USA) Inc.

—See You Later, Gladiator. McCauley, Adam, illus. (Time Warp Trio Ser.: No. 9). 96p. (J). (gr. 2-5). 2000. 14.99 (978-0-670-89340-9(4) , Viking Juvenile); Vol. 9. 2004. pap. 4.99 (978-0-14-240117-0(X) , Puffin) Penguin Group (USA) Inc.

—South Pole or Bust (an Egg) 2007. (Time Warp Trio). 48p. (J). pap. 3.99 (978-0-06-111640-7(8) , Harper Trophy) HarperCollins Pubs.

—Tut, Tut. Smith, Lane, illus. 2004. (Time Warp Trio Ser.: No. 6). 74p. (J). (ps-7). lib. bdg. 11.79 (978-0-606-30136-7(4)) Tandem Library Bks.

—Tut, Tut. 1998. (Time Warp Trio Ser.: No. 6). (978-0-606-13879-6(X)) Tandem Library Bks.

—Viking It & Liking It. McCauley, Adam, illus. (Time Warp Trio Ser.: No. 12). (J). 2002. 80p. 14.99 (978-0-670-89918-0(6) , Viking Juvenile); Vol. 12. 2004. 96p. (gr. 2 up). pap. 4.99 (978-0-14-240002-9(5) , Puffin) Penguin Group (USA) Inc.

—Wushu Were Here. 2007. (Time Warp Trio: No. 3). 80p. (J). pap. 4.99 (***978-0-06-111645-2(9)*** , Harper Trophy) HarperCollins Pubs.

—You Can't, but Genghis Khan. 2006. (Time Warp Trio). 80p. (J). (gr. 2-5). pap. 4.99 (978-0-06-111636-0(X) , Harper Trophy) HarperCollins Pubs.

—Your Mother Was a Neanderthal. Smith, Lane, illus. (Time Warp Trio Ser.: No. 4). (J). 2006. 78p. (***978-1-4176-3603-7(3)***); Vol. 4. 2004. 80p. (gr. 2-6). pap. 4.99 (978-0-14-240048-7(3)) Penguin Group (USA) Inc. (Puffin).

Scieszka, Jon. 2095. (Time Warp Trio Ser.: No. 5). (SPA.). (J). (gr. 2). 7.95 (978-958-04-5638-4(0) , NR31192) Norma S.A. COL. *Dist:* Distribuidora Norma, Inc., Lectorum Pubns., Inc.

—2095. Smith, Lane, illus. 2004. (Time Warp Trio Ser.: No. 5). 80p. (J). (gr. 2-6). pap. 4.99 (978-0-14-240044-9(0) , Puffin) Penguin Group (USA) Inc.

Scieszka, Jon & Kaemon, Amy Court. Plaid to the Bone. 2007. (Time Warp Trio: Vol. 3). 96p. (J). pap. 6.99 (978-0-06-111642-1(4) , Harper Trophy) HarperCollins Pubs.

Scieszka, Jon, et al. The High & the Flighty. Scieszka, Jon, illus. 2007. (Time Warp Trio). (Illus.). 48p. (J). (gr. k-2). 15.99 (***978-0-06-111644-5(0)***); pap. 3.99 (***978-0-06-111643-8(2)*** , Harper Trophy) HarperCollins Pubs.

Sescoe, Vincent E. Double Time. Helms, Clinton, illus. 2001. (gr. 6-12). 191p. (J). 17.95 (978-1-930093-00-3(4)); 192p. (YA). pap. 6.95 (978-1-930093-06-5(3)) Brookfield Reader, Inc., The.

Sheley, Kristen. No Time Like the Present. 2002. (Partners in Time Ser.). 262p. (YA). pap. 14.95 (978-0-595-24687-8(7) , Writer's Showcase Pr.) iUniverse, Inc.

Shipley, Jocelyn. Seraphina's Circle: A Young Adult Novel. 2006. 144p. (YA). (gr. 6-9). pap. 9.95 (978-1-894549-51-6(1)) Sumach Pr. CAN. *Dist:* Orca Bk. Pubs. USA.

Shire, Poppy. Brightheart the Knight's Pony. Berg, Ron, illus. 2007. (Magic Pony Carousel Ser.: No. 2). 96p. (J). pap. 3.99 (978-0-06-083782-2(9)); 14.99 (978-0-06-083780-8(2)) HarperCollins Pubs. (Harper Trophy).

Silverthorne, Judith. Dinosaur Breakout. 2004. (Dinosaur Adventure Ser.). 180p. (J). (gr. 4-6). pap. 6.95 (978-1-55050-294-7(8)) Coteau Bks. CAN. *Dist:* Fitzhenry & Whiteside, Ltd.

—The Secret of the Stone House. 2006. (From Many Peoples Ser.). (Illus.). 192p. (J). pap. 7.95 (978-1-55050-325-8(1)) Coteau Bks. CAN. *Dist:* F & W Pubns., Inc.

Simons, Jamie & Scollon, E. W. Double Trouble. Evans, Michael, illus. 1999. (Goners Ser.: No. 9). 160p. (J). (gr. 3-7). pap. 3.99 (978-0-380-80725-3(4)) HarperCollins Pubs.

Snider, Cindy Gay. Finding Anna Bee. Chambers, Mary, illus. 2007. (J). pap. (***978-0-8361-9392-3(X)***) Herald Pr.

Solice, Deborah. The Eye of the Undead: The Hidden Channel: an Adventure Series in Time. l.t. ed. 2005. (ENG., Illus.). 100p. (J). per. 7.59 (978-1-933300-01-6(9)) Wandering Sage Bookstore & More, LLC.

Something Upstairs. 2002. (Avi Ser.). (Illus.). (J). 13.40 (978-0-7587-9129-0(1)) Book Wholesalers, Inc.

Sommer, Carl. Time Remote! 2003. (Another Sommer-Time Story Ser.). (Illus.). 48p. (J). (gr. 1-4). 16.95 incl. audio compact disk (978-1-57537-512-0(5)); 16.95 incl. audio (978-1-57537-561-8(3)) Advance Publishing, Inc.

—Time Remote! Budwine, Greg, illus. 2000. (Another Summer-Time Story Ser.). 48p. (J). (gr. 1-4). 9.95 (978-1-57537-012-5(3)); lib. bdg. 16.95 (978-1-57537-064-4(6)) Advance Publishing, Inc.

Sorensen, Susan & Whims, Joette. Kit-Cat's Time-Travel Adventure: The Story of the National Day of Prayer. Young, Woody, illus. 2001. 152p. (J). (gr. 3-6). pap. 7.99 (978-0-939513-69-7(2)) Joy Publishing.

Stanley, Diane. Roughing It on the Oregon Trail. Berry, Holly, illus. 2001. (Time-Traveling Twins Ser.: No. 1). 48p. (J). (gr. k-5). pap. 6.99 (978-0-06-449006-1(8) , Harper Trophy) HarperCollins Pubs.

—Roughing It on the Oregon Trail. 2001. (gr. 3-6). lib. bdg. 14.10 (978-0-613-44250-3(4)) Tandem Library Bks.

—Thanksgiving on Plymouth Plantation. Berry, Holly, illus. 2004. (Time-Traveling Twins Ser.). 48p. (J). (gr. k-5). 15.99 (978-0-06-027069-8(1)); lib. bdg. 16.89 (978-0-06-027076-6(4)) HarperCollins Pubs. (Cotler, Joanna Books).

Stewart, Jennifer. If That Breathes Fire, We're Toast! 2001. (978-0-606-22151-1(4)); 2000. (gr. 3-6). lib. bdg. 12.40 (978-0-613-35730-2(2)) Tandem Library Bks.

Stier, Roy E. Son of Bunyon & the Swamp Angel. 2002. (J). pap. 11.95 (978-1-58151-082-9(9)) BookPartners, Inc.

Stoddard, Michael Eugene. The Porthole to Time. 1999. 176p. (YA). pap. 9.95 (978-0-9675924-0-4(2)) Stoddard, Michael Eugene.

Stohler, Dolores. The Land That Might Have Been. 2003. 168p. pap. 16.95 (978-1-4137-0047-3(0)) PublishAmerica, Inc.

Sullivan, Jenny. Magic Maldwyn. 2002. (WEL.). 72p. pap. 11.95 (978-1-84323-074-8(7)) Beekman Bks., Inc.

Sutherland, Tui. So This Is How It Ends. (Avatars Ser.: Bk. 1). (J). 2007. 512p. pap. 6.99 (***978-0-06-075029-9(4)***); 2006. 368p. 16.99 (978-0-06-075024-4(3)) HarperCollins Pubs. (Eos).

Swindells, Robert. Blitzed. 2008. 176p. (YA). pap. 9.95 (***978-0-552-55589-0(4)***) Transworld Publishers Ltd. GBR. *Dist:* Independent Pubs. Group.

—In the Nick of Time. 2008. 224p. (YA). pap. 9.95 (***978-0-552-55585-2(1)***) Transworld Publishers Ltd. GBR. *Dist:* Independent Pubs. Group.

Tauss, Marc. Superhero. Tauss, Marc, illus. 2005. (Illus.). 40p. (J). (gr. k-3). pap. 16.99 (978-0-439-62734-4(6) , Scholastic Pr.) Scholastic, Inc.

Taylor, Cora. The Deadly Dance. 2005. 160p. (J). (gr. 7-9). 7.95 (978-1-55050-272-5(7)) Coteau Bks. CAN. *Dist:* Fitzhenry & Whiteside, Ltd.

Teague, Bobbie T. Simon's Gold. Deppner, Charles, illus. 2001. 94p. (J). per. 13.00 (978-1-887774-09-3(2) , Wynden) Canmore Pr.

Tebbetts, Christopher. Viking Saga Three: Land of the Dead. 2003. (gr. 5-8). lib. bdg. 14.15 (978-0-613-67588-8(6)) Tandem Library Bks.

—Viking Saga Two: The Quest for Faith. 2003. (gr. 5-8). lib. bdg. 14.15 (978-0-613-67476-8(6)) Tandem Library Bks.

A Theft in Time: Timedetectors II, 6 Pack. (Action Packs Ser.). 120p. (gr. 3-5). 44.00 (978-0-7635-8425-2(8)) Rigby Education.

There's No Room for You, Maddie Morrison. 2006. (J). per. 6.99 (978-0-9786117-0-5(5)) Neal Morgan Publishing.

Tighe, Bridget M. Traveling Wildflower: Treasure in Time. 2006. 109p. pap. 16.95 (978-1-4137-7959-2(X)) PublishAmerica, Inc.

The Time Machine. 2006. (Saddleback's Illustrated Classics). (J). (978-1-56254-944-2(8)) Saddleback Educational Publishing.

Time Slime. 2003. 156p. (YA). (gr. 5-12). pap. 7.95 (978-0-9702176-3-9(3) , 0004) Night Howl Productions.

Townson, Hazel. The Secret Room. Salisbury, Martin, illus. 2006. (Pathway Books). 75p. (J). 21.26 (978-1-59889-003-7(4)) Stone Arch Bks.

Valentine, James. Don't Touch Anything. Koopman, Caia, illus. 2004. (Jump-Man Ser.: No. 1). 272p. (J). 14.95 (978-0-689-86872-6(3)) Simon & Schuster Children's Publishing.

—The Future Is Unknown. 2007. (TimeJumpers Ser.). 288p. (J). pap. 5.99 (***978-0-689-87354-6(9)*** , Aladdin) Simon & Schuster Children's Publishing.

—JumpMan Rule #2: Don't Even Think about It. 2005. (Illus.). 288p. (J). 14.95 (978-0-689-87353-9(0)) Simon & Schuster Children's Publishing.

Valentine, James. The Present Never Happens. 2007. (TimeJumpers Ser.). 304p. (J). pap. 5.99 (***978-1-4169-3956-6(3)*** , Aladdin) Simon & Schuster Children's Publishing.

Vande Velde, Vivian & Nielsen, Cliff. A Well-Timed Enchantment. 2006. (Illus.). 240p. (YA). pap. 6.95 (978-0-15-204919-5(3) , Magic Carpet Bks.) Harcourt Children's Bks.

Vaupel, Robin. The Rules of the Universe by Austin W. Hale. 2007. 192p. (YA). (gr. 5 up). 16.95 (978-0-8234-1811-4(1)) Holiday Hse., Inc.

Waring, Scott C. West's Time MacHine. 2007. 200p. 24.95 (***978-0-595-88775-0(9)***); per. 14.95 (***978-0-595-41887-9(2)***) iUniverse, Inc.

Warkentin, Karla. Mystery in Medieval Castle. 2004. (Time Stone Travelers Ser.). 144p. (J). pap. 6.99 (978-0-7814-4025-7(4) , 0781440254) Cook, David C. Publishing Co.

Wechter, Nell Wise & Tucker, Bruce. Teach's Light. 1999. (Chapel Hill Book Ser.). (Illus.). 160p. (gr. 4-7). pap. 10.95 (978-0-8078-4793-0(3)) Univ. of North Carolina Pr.

Wells, H. G. H. G. Wells: Graphic Classics. Steine, Kent, illus. 2005. 144p. (J). lib. bdg. 30.77 (***978-1-4242-1821-9(7)***) Fitzgerald Bks.

—The Time Machine. Lynch, Brendan, illus. 2002. (Great Illustrated Classics Ser.). 240p. (J). (gr. 3-8). 21.35 (978-1-57765-804-7(3) , ABDO & Daughters) ABDO Publishing Co.

—The Time Machine. 2004. (Scholastic Classics Ser.). 144p. (J). (ps-7). pap. 3.99 (978-0-439-43654-0(0) , Scholastic Paperbacks) Scholastic, Inc.

—The Time Machine. 2004. (Fast Track Classics Ser.). (Illus.). 48p. (J). pap. 8.99 (978-0-237-52406-7(6) , Evans Brothers, Limited) Evans Publishing Group GBR. *Dist:* Independent Pubs. Group.

—The Time Machine. Howell, Troy, illus. 2008. (Classic Starts Ser.). 160p. (J). 5.95 (***978-1-4027-4582-9(6)***) Sterling Publishing Co., Inc.

—Time Machine. abr. ed. 1999. (gr. 7-12). lib. bdg. 15.25 (978-0-613-33147-0(8)) Tandem Library Bks.
—The Time Machine. unabr. ed. 2002. (YA). pap. incl. audio compact disk (978-1-58472-338-7(6) , In Audio) Sound Room Pubs., Inc.
Wendel, Tim. My Man Stan. 2006. (J). 15.95 (978-0-9766104-7-2(7)) Arbutus Pr.
Wesley, Mary. Haphazard House. Date not set. (Sky Bks.). 200p. pap. 54.75 (978-0-582-08108-6(4)) Addison-Wesley Longman, Ltd. GBR. *Dist:* Trans-Atlantic Pubns., Inc.
West, Cathy. All Growed Up. 2001. (gr. k-3). lib. bdg. 14.15 (978-0-613-43915-2(5)) Tandem Library Bks.
West, Keith. Mirror World: A Science-Fiction Drama. Buckley, Harriet, illus. 2001. (Star Plays Ser.). 48p. (gr. 4-6). pap. 8.99 (978-0-237-52189-9(X) , Evans Brothers, Limited) Evans Publishing Group GBR. *Dist:* Independent Pubs. Group.
Weston, Joanna M. The Willow Tree Girl. 2003. (ENG.). 84p. pap. (***978-1-55352-073-3(4)***) Treeside Pr.
Weston, Martha. The Dinosaurs Meet Dr. Clock: A Holiday House Reader. 2002. (Reader Level 1 Ser.). (Illus.). 32p. (J). (gr. k-3). tchr. ed. 14.95 (978-0-8234-1661-5(5)) Holiday Hse., Inc.
—Dr. Clock-Sicle: A Holiday House Reader, Level 1. (Illus.). 32p. (J). (gr. k-3). tchr. ed. 14.95 (978-0-8234-1825-1(1)) Holiday Hse., Inc.
Whinnem, Reade Scott. Utten & Plumley. 2003. (gr. 3-6). lib. bdg. 21.05 (978-0-613-79189-2(4)) Tandem Library Bks.
Williams, Maiya. The Golden Hour. 2006. 288p. (J). (gr. 5-10). pap. 5.95 (978-0-8109-9216-0(7)) Abrams, Harry N. , Inc.
—The Hour of the Cobra. (YA). 2007. 320p. (gr. 2-7). pap. 5.95 (***978-0-8109-9362-4(7)***); 2006. 312p. (gr. 4-9). 16.95 (978-0-8109-5970-5(4) , Amulet Bks.) Abrams, Harry N. , Inc.
—The Hour of the Outlaw. 2007. 360p. (YA). (gr. 4-9). 16.95 (***978-0-8109-9355-6(4)***) Abrams, Harry N. , Inc.
Williams, Mark London. Ancient Fire. 2004. (Danger Boy Ser.: No. 1). (Illus.). 224p. (J). (gr. 4-8). 12.99 (978-0-7636-2152-0(8)) Candlewick Pr.
—Ancient Fire: Danger Boy Episode 1. 2006. 232p. (J). (gr. 4-8). pap. 4.99 (978-0-7636-3092-8(6)) Candlewick Pr.
—City of Ruins, No. 4. 2007. 288p. (J). (gr. 4-8). 12.99 (978-0-7636-2871-0(9)) Candlewick Pr.
—Dragon Sword. (Danger Boy Ser.: Vol. 2). (Illus.). 288p. (J). (gr. 4-8). 2007. 4.99 (978-0-7636-3290-8(2)); 2004. 12.99 (978-0-7636-2153-7(6)) Candlewick Pr.
—Trail of Bones. Koelsch, Michael, illus. 2005. (Danger Boy Ser.: No. 3). 320p. (J). (gr. 4-8). 12.99 (978-0-7636-2154-4(4)) Candlewick Pr.
Williams, Mark London. Trail of Bones: Danger Boy Episode 3. 2007. (Illus.). 320p. (J). (gr. 4-8). 5.99 (***978-0-7636-3410-0(7)***) Candlewick Pr.
Winterson, Jeanette. Tanglewreck. (J). 2007. 416p. (gr. 3-7). pap. 6.95 (***978-1-59990-081-0(5)***); 2006. 250p. 16.95 (978-1-58234-919-0(3)) Bloomsbury Publishing. (Bloomsbury Children).
Wiseman, David. Jeremy Visick. 2005. 176p. (YA). (gr. 5 up). 21.25 (978-0-8446-7271-7(8) , 3594) Smith, Peter Pub., Inc.
Wood, Beverley & Wood, Chris. Jack's Knife. 2006. (Sirius Mystery Ser.). 288p. (J). pap. 7.95 (978-1-55192-709-1(8)) Raincoast Bk. Distribution CAN. *Dist:* Perseus Distribution.
Woodfield, Gary. The Time Thief. 2004. (J). per. 19.95 (978-0-9761289-2-2(6)) Nightengale Pr.
Woodruff, Elvira. Orphan of Ellis Island. 2000. (gr. 5-8). lib. bdg. 12.40 (978-0-613-30079-7(3)) Tandem Library Bks.
Yamada, Debbie Leung. Striking It Rich: Treasures from Gold Mountain. Tang, You-shan, illus. l.t. ed. 2004. 128p. (J). (gr. 4-8). pap. 13.95 (978-1-879965-21-8(6)) Polychrome Publishing Corp.
Yolen, Jane. The Devil's Arithmetic. 2002. (J). 13.19 (978-0-7587-9594-6(7)) Book Wholesalers, Inc.
—The Devil's Arithmetic. 2004. (Puffin Modern Classics Ser.). 176p. (gr. 3). pap. 6.99 (978-0-14-240109-5(9) , Puffin) Penguin Group (USA) Inc.
—Pictish Child. 2002. (gr. 3-6). lib. bdg. 14.10 (978-0-613-53854-1(4)) Tandem Library Bks.
Young, Joseph R. Legend of the Lost Josephine Mine: A Fascinating Adventure. 2001. 221p. (J). pap. 13.95 (978-1-55517-550-4(3) , Bonneville Bks.) Cedar Fort, Inc./CFI Distribution.
Young, Steve. 15 Minutes. 2006. 176p. (J). 15.99 (978-0-06-072508-2(7)); lib. bdg. 16.89 (978-0-06-072509-9(5)) HarperCollins Pubs.

TIMOTHY (BIBLICAL CHARACTER)

Rottmann, Erik. Timothy Joins Paul. Snyder, Joel, illus. 2005. (ENG.). 16p. (J). 1.99 (978-0-7586-0506-1(4)) Concordia Publishing Hse.

TINTIN (FICTITIOUS CHARACTER)—FICTION

Hergé. The Adventures of Tintin in the Congo: Reporter for Le Petit Vingtieme. 2004. (Adventures of Tintin Ser.). (Illus.). 120p. (J). 24.95 (978-0-86719-902-4(4)) Last Gasp of San Francisco.
—L' Affaire Tournesol. 1999. (Tintin Ser.).Tr. of Calculus Affair. (FRE.). (J). (gr. 4-7). 21.95 (978-2-203-00117-6(8)) Casterman, Editions FRA. *Dist:* Distribooks, Inc.
—Aterrizaje en la Lune. (Tintin Ser.). (SPA.). 64p. (J). 14.95 (978-84-261-1412-9(1)) Juventud, Editorial ESP. *Dist:* Distribooks, Inc.
—Les Bijoux de la Castafiore. 1999. (Tintin Ser.).Tr. of Castafiore Emerald. (FRE.). (J). (gr. 4-7). 21.95 (978-2-203-00120-6(8)) Casterman, Editions FRA. *Dist:* Distribooks, Inc.
—The Black Island. (Illus.). 62p. (J). 19.95 (978-0-8288-5012-4(7)) French & European Pubns., Inc.
—The Blue Lotus. (Illus.). (J). 19.95 (978-0-8288-5480-1(7)) French & European Pubns., Inc.
—The Broken Ear. (Illus.). 62p. (J). 24.95 (978-0-8288-5086-5(0)) French & European Pubns., Inc.
—The Calculus Affair. (Illus.). 62p. (J). 19.95 (978-0-8288-5014-8(3)) French & European Pubns., Inc.
—Cangrejo de la Pinzas de Oro. (Tintin Ser.). (SPA.). 64p. (J). 14.95 (978-84-261-1414-3(8)) Juventud, Editorial ESP. *Dist:* Distribooks, Inc.
—The Castafiore Emerald. (Illus.). 62p. (J). 19.95 (978-0-8288-5016-2(X)) French & European Pubns., Inc.
—Les Cigares du Pharaon. 1999. (Tintin Ser.).Tr. of Cigars of the Pharaoh. (FRE., Illus.). 62p. (J). (gr. 4-7). 21.95 (978-2-203-00103-9(8)) Casterman, Editions FRA. *Dist:* Distribooks, Inc.
—Cigars of the Pharaoh.Tr. of Cigares du Pharoan. (Illus.). 62p. (J). 19.95 (978-0-8288-5021-6(6)) French & European Pubns., Inc.
—Coke en Stock. 1999. (Tintin Ser.). (FRE., Illus.). 62p. (J). (gr. 4-7). 21.95 (978-2-203-00118-3(6)) Casterman, Editions FRA. *Dist:* Distribooks, Inc.
—The Crab with the Golden Claws. (Illus.). 62p. (J). (gr. 3-8). 19.95 (978-0-8288-5023-0(2)) French & European Pubns., Inc.
—Le Crabe aux Pinces d'Or. 1999. (Tintin Ser.).Tr. of Crab with the Golden Claws. (FRE.). (J). (gr. 4-7). 21.95 (978-2-203-00108-4(9)) Casterman, Editions FRA. *Dist:* Distribooks, Inc.
—Le Crabe aux Pinces d'Or.Tr. of Crab with the Golden Claws. (FRE., Illus.). (J). (gr. 7-9). ring bd. 19.95 (978-0-8288-5025-4(9)) French & European Pubns., Inc.
—Destination Moon.Tr. of Objectif Lune. (J). (gr. 3-8). ring bd. 19.95 (978-0-8288-5026-1(7)); (Illus.). 62p. 19.95 (978-0-8288-5027-8(5)) French & European Pubns., Inc.
—L' Etoile Mysterieuse. 1999. (Tintin Ser.).Tr. of Mysterious Star. (FRE., Illus.). 62p. (J). (gr. 4-7). pap. 21.95 (978-2-203-00109-1(7)) Casterman, Editions FRA. *Dist:* Distribooks, Inc.
—Flight 714. (Illus.). 62p. (J). 19.95 (978-0-8288-5034-6(8)) French & European Pubns., Inc.
—L' Ile Noire. 1999. (Tintin Ser.).Tr. of Black Island. (FRE., Illus.). (J). (gr. 4-7). pap. 21.95 (978-2-203-00106-0(2)) Casterman, Editions FRA. *Dist:* Distribooks, Inc.
—L' Ile Noire.Tr. of Black Island. (FRE., Illus.). (J). (gr. 7-9). ring bd. 19.95 (978-0-8288-5039-1(9)) French & European Pubns., Inc.
—King Ottokars Sceptre. Orig. Title: Sceptre d'Ottokar. (Illus.). 62p. (J). 19.95 (978-0-8288-5044-5(5)) French & European Pubns., Inc.
—Land of Black Gold. Orig. Title: Tintin au Pays de l'Or Noir. (Illus.). 62p. (J). 19.95 (978-0-8288-5048-3(8)) French & European Pubns., Inc.
—El Loto Azul.Tr. of Blue Lotus. (SPA., Illus.). 62p. (J). 19.95 (978-0-8288-5049-0(6)) French & European Pubns., Inc.
—El Loto Azul. (Tintin Ser.).Tr. of Blue Lotus. (SPA.). 64p. (J). 14.95 (978-84-261-1418-1(0)) Juventud, Editorial ESP. *Dist:* Distribooks, Inc.
—Le Lotus Bleu. 1999. (Tintin Ser.).Tr. of Blue Lotus. (FRE.). (J). (gr. 4-7). 21.95 (978-2-203-00104-6(6)) Casterman, Editions FRA. *Dist:* Distribooks, Inc.
—Le Lotus Bleu.Tr. of Blue Lotus. (FRE.). (J). (gr. 2-9). 19.95 (978-0-8288-5050-6(X)) French & European Pubns., Inc.
—Objectif Lune. 1999. (Tintin Ser.).Tr. of Destination Moon. (FRE., Illus.). 62p. (J). (gr. 4-7). 21.95 (978-2-203-00115-2(1)) Casterman, Editions FRA. *Dist:* Distribooks, Inc.
—Objectif Lune.Tr. of Destination Moon. (FRE., Illus.). (J). (gr. 7-9). ring bd. 19.95 (978-0-8288-5051-3(8)) French & European Pubns., Inc.
—On a Marche sur la Lune. (Tintin Ser.).Tr. of Explorers on the Moon. (FRE.). (J). pap. 21.95 (978-2-203-00116-9(X)) Casterman, Editions FRA. *Dist:* Distribooks, Inc.
—On a Marche sur la Lune.Tr. of Explorers on the Moon. (FRE., Illus.). (J). (gr. 7-9). ring bd. 19.95 (978-0-8288-5053-7(4)) French & European Pubns., Inc.
—L' Oreille Cassee.Tr. of Broken Ear. (FRE., Illus.). 62p. (J). 19.95 (978-0-8288-5054-4(2)) French & European Pubns., Inc.
—Prisoners of the Sun. (Illus.). 62p. (J). 24.95 (978-0-8288-5056-8(9)) French & European Pubns., Inc.
—Red Rackham's Treasure. Orig. Title: Tresor de Rackham le Rouge. (Illus.). 62p. (J). 24.95 (978-0-8288-5057-5(7)) French & European Pubns., Inc.
—The Red Sea Sharks. (Illus.). (J). (gr. 3-8). 24.95 (978-0-8288-5058-2(5)) French & European Pubns., Inc.
—Le Sceptre d'Ottokar. 1999. (Tintin Ser.).Tr. of King Ottokar's Sceptre. (FRE., Illus.). (J). (gr. 4-7). 21.95 (978-2-203-00107-7(0)) Casterman, Editions FRA. *Dist:* Distribooks, Inc.
—Secret de la Licorne.Tr. of Secret of the Unicorn. (FRE., Illus.). (J). (gr. 7-9). 24.95 (978-0-8288-5065-0(8)) French & European Pubns., Inc.
—La Secret de la Licorne. 1999. (Tintin Ser.).Tr. of Secret of the Unicorn. (FRE., Illus.). (J). (gr. 4-7). 21.95 (978-2-203-00110-7(0)) Casterman, Editions FRA. *Dist:* Distribooks, Inc.
—The Secret of the Unicorn. Orig. Title: Secret de la Licorne. (Illus.). 62p. (J). 24.95 (978-0-8288-5066-7(6)) French & European Pubns., Inc.
—Sept Boules de Cristal. (FRE., Illus.). (J). (gr. 7-9). 24.95 (978-0-8288-5069-8(0)) French & European Pubns., Inc.
—Les Sept Boules de Cristal. 1999. (Tintin Ser.). (FRE., Illus.). (J). (gr. 4-7). 21.95 (978-2-203-00112-1(7)) Casterman, Editions FRA. *Dist:* Distribooks, Inc.
—The Seven Crystal Balls. (Illus.). 62p. (J). (gr. 3-8). 24.95 (978-0-8288-5071-1(2)) French & European Pubns., Inc.
—The Shooting Star. (Illus.). (J). (gr. 3-8). ring bd. 24.95 (978-0-8288-5073-5(9)) French & European Pubns., Inc.
—Le Temple du Soleil. 1999. (Tintin Ser.). (FRE.). (J). (gr. 4-7). 21.95 (978-2-203-00113-8(5)) Casterman, Editions FRA. *Dist:* Distribooks, Inc.
—Tintín: Descubro Las Letras. 2004. (SPA.). 24p. 19.95 (978-1-59497-066-5(1)) Public Square Bks.
—Tintín: El cangrejo de las pinzas de Oro. 2007. (SPA., Illus.). 64p. reprint ed. 22.95 (***978-1-59497-346-8(6)***) Public Square Bks.
—Tintín: El cetro de Ottokar. 2007. (SPA., Illus.). 64p. reprint ed. 22.95 (***978-1-59497-345-1(8)***) Public Square Bks.
—Tintín: La isla Negra. 2007. (SPA., Illus.). 64p. reprint ed. 22.95 (***978-1-59497-344-4(X)***) Public Square Bks.
Herge. Tintin & Alph-Art. 2007. (Adventures of Tintin Ser.). 64p. pap. 10.99 (***978-0-316-00375-9(1)***) Little, Brown Bks. for Young Readers.
Hergé. Tintin & the Golden Fleece. (J). (gr. 3-8). 24.95 (978-0-8288-5087-2(9)) French & European Pubns., Inc.
—Tintin & the Lake of Sharks. (Illus.). 62p. (J). 24.95 (978-0-416-78950-8(1)) French & European Pubns., Inc.
—Tintin & the Picaros. Orig. Title: Tintin et les Picaros. (Illus.). 62p. (J). 24.95 (978-0-8288-5089-6(5)) French & European Pubns., Inc.
—Tintin au Congo. 1999. (Tintin Ser.). (FRE., Illus.). 62p. (J). (gr. 4-7). 21.95 (978-2-203-00101-5(1)) Casterman, Editions FRA. *Dist:* Distribooks, Inc.
—Tintin au Congo. (FRE., Illus.). (J). (gr. 7-9). 24.95 (978-0-8288-5090-2(9)) French & European Pubns., Inc.
—Tintin au Pays de l'Or Noir. 1999. (Tintin Ser.).Tr. of Land of Black Gold. (FRE., Illus.). 62p. (J). (gr. 4-7). 21.95 (978-2-203-00114-5(3)) Casterman, Editions FRA. *Dist:* Distribooks, Inc.
—Tintin au Pays de l'Or Noir.Tr. of Land of Black Gold. (FRE.). (J). (gr. 7-9). 24.95 (978-0-8288-5091-9(7)) French & European Pubns., Inc.
—Tintin au Pays des Soviets. 1999. (Tintin Ser.). (FRE.). (J). (gr. 4-7). pap. 29.95 (978-2-203-01101-4(7)) Casterman, Editions FRA. *Dist:* Distribooks, Inc.
—Tintin au Tibet. 1999. (Tintin Ser.).Tr. of Tintin in Tibet. (FRE.). (J). (gr. 4-7). pap. 21.95 (978-2-203-00119-0(4)) Casterman, Editions FRA. *Dist:* Distribooks, Inc.
—Tintin au Tibet.Tr. of Tintin in Tibet. (J). (gr. 7-9). ring bd. 24.95 (978-0-8288-5092-6(5)) French & European Pubns., Inc.
Herge. Tintin Boxed Set Of 8. 2007. (ps-17). 150.00 (***978-0-316-00668-2(8)***) Little, Brown Bks. for Young Readers.
Hergé. Tintin el Pais del Oro Negro. (Tintin Ser.). (SPA., Illus.). 64p. (J). 14.95 (978-84-261-1402-0(4)) Juventud, Editorial ESP. *Dist:* Distribooks, Inc.
—Tintin en Amerique. 1999. (Tintin Ser.). Orig. Title: Tintin in America. (FRE., Illus.). 62p. (J). (gr. 4-7). pap. 21.95 (978-2-203-00102-2(X)) Casterman, Editions FRA. *Dist:* Distribooks, Inc.
—Tintin en Amerique. Orig. Title: Tintin in America. (Illus.). 62p. (J). (FRE.). 24.95 (978-0-8288-5093-3(3)); (SPA., 24.95 (978-0-8288-5094-0(1)) French & European Pubns., Inc.
—Tintin en Amerique. (Tintin Ser.). Orig. Title: Tintin in America. (SPA.). 64p. (J). 14.95 (978-84-261-1400-6(8)) Juventud, Editorial ESP. *Dist:* Distribooks, Inc.
—Tintin en el Congo. (SPA., Illus.). 62p. (J). 24.95 (978-0-8288-5095-7(X)) French & European Pubns., Inc.
—Tintin en el Congo. (Tintin Ser.). (SPA.). 64p. (J). 14.95 (978-84-261-1401-3(6)) Juventud, Editorial ESP. *Dist:* Distribooks, Inc.
—Tintin en el Pais del Oro Negro.Tr. of Land of Black Gold. (SPA., Illus.). 62p. (J). 24.95 (978-0-8288-4995-1(1)) French & European Pubns., Inc.
—Tintin en Tibet. (SPA., Illus.). 62p. (J). 24.95 (978-0-8288-4996-8(X)) French & European Pubns., Inc.
—Tintin en Tibet. (Tintin Ser.). (SPA.). 64p. (J). 14.95 (978-84-261-1403-7(2)) Juventud, Editorial ESP. *Dist:* Distribooks, Inc.
—Tintin et les Picaros. 1999. (Tintin Ser.).Tr. of Tintin & the Picaros. (FRE.). (J). (gr. 4-7). 21.95 (978-2-203-00123-7(2)) Casterman, Editions FRA. *Dist:* Distribooks, Inc.
—Tintin et les Picaros.Tr. of Tintin & the Picaros. (FRE., Illus.). 62p. (J). 24.95 (978-0-8288-4997-5(8)) French & European Pubns., Inc.
—Tintin im Amerika.Tr. of Tintin in America. (GER., Illus.). 62p. (J). pap. 24.95 (978-0-8288-4999-9(4)) French & European Pubns., Inc.
—Tintin im Kongo. (GER., Illus.). 62p. (J). pap. 24.95 (978-0-8288-4998-2(6)) French & European Pubns., Inc.
—Tintin in America. Orig. Title: Tintin en Amerique. (Illus.). 62p. (J). 24.95 (978-0-8288-5000-1(3)) French & European Pubns., Inc.
—Tintin in America. 2004. (Adventures of Tintin Ser.). Orig. Title: Tintin en Amerique. (Illus.). 124p. 24.95 (978-0-86719-904-8(0)) Last Gasp of San Francisco.
Herge. Tintin in the Land of the Soviets. 2007. (Adventures of Tintin Ser.). 144p. pap. 10.99 (***978-0-316-00374-2(3)***) Little, Brown Bks. for Young Readers.
Hergé. Tintin in the Land of the Soviets: Reporter for Le Petit Vingtieme. fac. ed. 2004. (Adventures of Tintin Ser.). (Illus.). 138p. (J). reprint ed. 24.95 (978-0-86719-903-1(2)) Last Gasp of San Francisco.
—Tintin in Tibet. Orig. Title: Tintin au Tibet. (Illus.). 62p. (J). 24.95 (978-0-8288-5001-8(1)) French & European Pubns., Inc.
—Tintin y el Lago de los Tiburones. (Tintin Ser.). (SPA.). 64p. (J). 14.95 (978-84-261-1390-0(7)) Juventud, Editorial ESP. *Dist:* Distribooks, Inc.
—Tintin y los Picaros. (SPA., Illus.). 62p. (J). 24.95 (978-0-8288-5002-5(X)) French & European Pubns., Inc.
—Tintin y los Picaros. (Tintin Ser.). (SPA.). 64p. (J). 14.95 (978-84-261-1389-4(3)) Juventud, Editorial ESP. *Dist:* Distribooks, Inc.
—Tresor de Rackham le Rouge.Tr. of Red Rackham's Treasure. (FRE., Illus.). 62p. (J). (gr. 7-9). 24.95 (978-0-8288-5003-2(8)) French & European Pubns., Inc.
—Le Tresor de Rackham le Rouge. (Tintin Ser.). (FRE., Illus.). 62p. (J). pap. 21.95 (978-2-203-00111-4(9)) Casterman, Editions FRA. *Dist:* Distribooks, Inc.
—Vol 714 Pour Sydney Vol. 714: Flight 714 for Sydney. (FRE., Illus.). 62p. 21.95 (978-2-203-00121-3(6)) Casterman, Editions FRA. *Dist:* Distribooks, Inc.

TIRES, RUBBER

Ridley, Sarah. A Rubber Tire. 2006. (Illus.). 32p. (J). lib. bdg. 23.33 (978-0-8368-6295-9(3)) Stevens, Gareth Inc.

TITANIC (STEAMSHIP)

Aaseng, Nathan. The Titanic. 1999. (Building History Ser.). (Illus.). 96p. (YA). (gr. 6-9). 28.70 (978-1-56006-569-2(9) , Lucent Bks.) Thomson Gale.
Adams, Simon & Dorling Kindersley Publishing Staff. Titanic. 2004. (Eyewitness Books). (Illus.). 72p. (J). lib. bdg. 19.99 (978-0-7566-0733-3(7)) Dorling Kindersley Publishing, Inc.
Ballard, Robert D. Finding the Titanic. Marshall, Ken, illus. 2002. (J). 11.91 (978-0-7587-1161-8(1)) Book Wholesalers, Inc.
—Finding the Titanic. 1998. (J). (gr. 3). pap. 3.95 (978-0-439-04454-7(5)) Scholastic, Inc.
—Finding the Titanic. 1999. (Illus.). (J). (gr. 3-6). lib. bdg. 11.80 (978-0-7857-2438-4(9)) Tandem Library Bks.
—Finding the Titanic. 2004. (Illus.). 48p. (J). lib. bdg. 15.00 (978-1-59054-520-1(6)) Fitzgerald Bks.
Brewster, Hugh. 882 1/2 Amazing Answers to Your Questions about the Titanic. Marshall, Ken, illus. 1999. 96p. (J). (gr. 3-7). pap. 9.99 (978-0-439-04296-3(8)) Scholastic, Inc.
Burgan, Michael. The Titanic. 2004. (We the People Ser.). (Illus.). 48p. (J). (gr. 4 up). lib. bdg. 22.60 (978-0-7565-0614-8(X)) Compass Point Bks.
Caper, William. Nightmare on the Titanic. 2007. (Code Red Ser.). (Illus.). 32p. (J). (gr. 3-7). lib. bdg. 25.27 (978-1-59716-362-0(7)) Bearport Publishing Co., Inc.
Capstone Press, contrib. by. The Sinking of the Titanic. (Graphic History Ser.). 32p. (YA). pap. 7.95 (978-0-7368-5247-0(6)) Capstone Pr., Inc.
Claybourne, Anna & Daynes, Katie. Titanic. 2006. 64p. (J). 8.99 (978-0-7945-1269-9(0) , Usborne) EDC Publishing.
Cole, Michael D. The Titanic: Disaster at Sea. 2001. (American Disasters Ser.). (Illus.). 48p. (YA). (gr. 4-10). lib. bdg. 23.93 (978-0-7660-1557-9(2)) Enslow Pubs., Inc.
Conklin, Thomas. The Titanic Sinks! 1999. (J). pap. (978-0-375-80920-0(1) , Random Hse. Bks. for Young Readers) Random Hse. Children's Bks.
Crosbie, Duncan. Titanic: The Ship of Dreams. Geist, Ken, ed. Moulder, Bob et al, illus. 2007. 30p. (J). 18.99 (978-0-439-89995-6(8) , Orchard Bks.) Scholastic, Inc.
Deady, Kathleen W. The Titanic: The Tragedy at Sea. 2002. (Disaster! Ser.). (Illus.). 32p. (J). (gr. 3-4). lib. bdg. 21.26 (978-0-7368-1323-5(3) , Capstone High-Interest Bks.) Capstone Pr., Inc.
Doeden, Matt. The Sinking of the Titanic. Barnett, Charles, III, illus. 2005. (Graphic Library). 32p. (J). 22.60 (978-0-7368-3834-4(1)) Capstone Pr., Inc.
Dorling Kindersley Publishing Staff, ed. Titanic. 2004. (Dk Eyewitness Books Ser.). (Illus.). 72p. (J). (ps-12). 15.99 (978-0-7566-0732-6(9)) Dorling Kindersley Publishing, Inc.
Dubowski, Mark. Titanic: The Disaster That Shocked the World. 1998. (Eyewitness Readers). (Illus.). 48p. (J). (gr. 2-4). pap. 3.99 (978-0-7894-3441-8(5)) Dorling Kindersley Publishing, Inc.
Dubowski, Mark & Dorling Kindersley Publishing Staff. Titanic: The Disaster That Shocked the World. 1998. (Eyewitness Readers). (Illus.). 48p. (J). (gr. 2-4). 14.99 (978-0-7894-3767-9(8)) Dorling Kindersley Publishing, Inc.
Dunn, Joeming W. & Dunn, Ben. The Titanic. Dunn, Joeming W. & Dunn, Ben, illus. 2007. (Graphic History Ser.). (Illus.). 32p. (J). (gr. 3-6). lib. bdg. 27.07 (***978-1-60270-079-6(6)*** , Graphic Planet) Magic Wagon.
Fitzgerald, Dawn. Robert Ballard: Discovering the Titanic & Beyond. 2004. (Gateway Biography Ser.). 48p. (J). lib. bdg. (978-0-7613-2836-0(X) , Millbrook Pr.) Lerner Publishing Group.
Hamilton, Sue. R. M. S. Titanic. Hamilton, John, ed. 1999. (Day of Disaster Ser.). (Illus.). 32p. (J). (gr. 4). lib. bdg. 20.95 (978-0-939179-42-8(3)) ABDO Publishing Co.
Harmon, Daniel E. The Titanic. 2000. (Great Disasters, Reforms & Ramifications Ser.). (Illus.). 112p. (J). (gr. 6-8). 30.00 (978-0-7910-5265-5(6) , Chelsea Hse.) Facts On File, Inc.
Higginson, Sheila Sweeny. Desastres de la tecnología & Disasters of Technology. 2005. spiral bd. 88.00 (***978-1-4108-5731-6(X)***) Benchmark Education Co.
Hill, Christine M. Robert Ballard: Oceanographer Who Discovered the Titanic. 1999. (People to Know Ser.). (Illus.). 128p. (YA). (gr. 6-12). lib. bdg. 26.60 (978-0-7660-1147-2(X)) Enslow Pubs., Inc.
Hoh, Diane. Remembering the Titanic. 1998. 72p. (YA). (gr. 6-10). pap. 4.99 (978-0-590-87585-1(X)) Scholastic, Inc.
Hughes, Susan. Science & Story of Titanic. 2000. (978-0-606-18449-6(X)) Tandem Library Bks.
Jenkins, Martin. Titanic. Sanders, Brian, illus. 2007. 32p. (J). (gr. 3). 29.99 (***978-0-7636-3468-1(9)***) Candlewick Pr.
Kentley, Eric. The Story of the Titanic. Thistlethwaite, Diane, ed. Noon, Steve, illus. 2001. 32p. (J). (gr. k-3). 17.99 (978-0-7894-7943-5(3)) Dorling Kindersley Publishing, Inc.

Kupperberg, Paul. The Tragedy of the Titanic: When Disaster Strikes! 2005. (When Disaster Strikes! Ser.). (Illus.). 48p. (YA). (gr. 5-8). lib. bdg. 23.95 (978-0-8239-3679-3(1)) Rosen Publishing Group, Inc., The.

Landau, Elaine. Heroine of the Titanic: The Real Unsinkable Molly Brown. 2001. (Illus.). 144p. (J). (gr. 5-9). tchr. ed. 19.00 (978-0-395-93912-3(7) , Clarion Bks.) Houghton Mifflin Co. Trade & Reference Div.

Lohse, Joyce B. Unsinkable: The Molly Brown Story. 2006. (Now You Know Bio Ser.). (J). pap. 8.95 (*978-0-86541-081-7(X)*) Filter Pr., LLC.

Majoor, Mireille. Titanic: Ghosts of the Abyss. Marschall, Ken, illus. 2004. 48p. (J). 20.00 (978-0-7567-8237-5(6)) DIANE Publishing Co.

Marsh, Carole. Gigantic Titanic Trivia for Kids! 1998. (Titanic for Kids! Ser.). (Illus.). pap. 19.95 (978-0-7933-8988-9(7) , Marsh, Carole Family CD-Rom) Gallopade International.

Matsen, Bradford. The Incredible Quest to Find the Titanic. 2003. (Incredible Deep-Sea Adventures Ser.). (Illus.). 48p. (J). lib. bdg. 23.93 (978-0-7660-2191-4(2)) Enslow Pubs., Inc.

Molony, Senan. Titanic: A Primary Source History. 2005. (Illus.). 48p. 26.00 (978-0-8368-5980-5(4)) Stevens, Gareth Inc.

Osborne, Mary Pope & Osborne, Will. Titanic: A Nonfiction Companion to Tonight on the Titanic. Murdocca, Sal, illus. 2002. (Magic Tree House Research Guide Ser.: No. 7). 144p. (J). (gr. k-3). lib. bdg. 11.99 (978-0-375-91357-0(2)); pap. 4.99 (978-0-375-81357-3(8)) Random Hse. Children's Bks. (Random Hse. Bks. for Young Readers).

Parker, Victoria. The Titanic, 1912. 2006. (When Disaster Struck Ser.). (Illus.). 56p. (J). lib. bdg. (978-1-4109-2282-3(0)) Steck-Vaughn.

Ruffin, Frances E. "Unsinkable" Molly Brown. 2002. (American Legends Ser.). (Illus.). 24p. (J). (gr. 3). lib. bdg. 18.75 (978-0-8239-5827-6(2) , PowerKids Pr.) Rosen Publishing Group, Inc., The.

Sherrow, Victoria. Titanic. 2002. (History Readers Ser.). (Illus.). 48p. (J). pap. 3.99 (978-0-439-26706-9(4) , Scholastic Reference) Scholastic, Inc.

—Titanic. 2002. (gr. k-3). lib. bdg. 11.80 (978-0-613-71985-8(9)) Tandem Library Bks.

Spangenburg, Ray & Moser, Diane Kit. Robert Ballard: Tbd. 2008. (Makers of Modern Science Ser.). 160p. (gr. 6-12). 29.95 (*978-0-8160-6173-0(4)* , Chelsea Hse.) Facts On File, Inc.

Stewart, David. You Wouldn't Want to Sail on the Titanic! 2001. (gr. 3-6). lib. bdg. 18.75 (978-0-613-44280-0(6)) Tandem Library Bks.

—You Wouldn't Want to Sail on the Titanic! One Voyage You'd Rather Not Make. Antram, David, illus. 2001. (You Wouldn't Want to Be Ser.). 32p. (J). (gr. 2-5). 28.50 (978-0-531-14604-0(9)); pap. 9.95 (978-0-531-16210-1(9)) Scholastic Library Publishing. (Watts, Franklin).

Tanaka, Shelley & Marschall, Ken. I Was There: On Board the Titanic - What It Was Like When the Great Liner Sank. (Illus.). 48p. (J). pap. 19.99 (978-0-590-24894-5(4)) Scholastic, Inc.

Temple, Bob. The Titanic: An Interactive History Adventure. 2008. (You Choose Bks.). 112p. (J). (gr. 3-7). lib. bdg. 27.23 (*978-1-4296-0163-4(9)*) Capstone Pr., Inc.

Whiting, Jim. The Sinking of the Titanic. 2006. (Monumental Milestones Ser.). (Illus.). 48p. (J). lib. bdg. 20.95 (978-1-58415-472-3(1)) Mitchell Lane Pubs., Inc.

TITANIC (STEAMSHIP)—FICTION

Crew, Gary. Pig on the Titanic: A True Story. Whatley, Bruce, illus. 2005. (J). 32p. 15.99 (978-0-06-052305-3(0)); 40p. lib. bdg. 17.89 (978-0-06-052306-0(9)) HarperCollins Pubs.

Crisp, Marty. White Star: A Dog on the Titanic. 2006. 160p. (J). pap. 4.99 (978-0-439-71265-1(3) , Scholastic Paperbacks) Scholastic, Inc.

Duey, K. & Bale, K. A. Salvados! Titanic. 2003. (Survival Ser.).Tr. of Survival! Titanic. (SPA.). (J). pap. 9.95 (978-0-9715256-4-1(1)) Planeta Publishing Corp.

Jenner, Caryn. Survivors: The Night the Titanic Sank. Martin, Linda, ed. 2001. (Readers Ser.). (Illus.). 32p. (J). (ps-3). pap. 3.99 (978-0-7894-7373-8(9)) Dorling Kindersley Publishing, Inc.

Jenner, Caryn & Dorling Kindersley Publishing Staff. Survivors: The Night the Titanic Sank. 2001. (Readers Ser.). (Illus.). 32p. (J). (ps-3). 14.99 (978-0-7894-7374-5(7)) Dorling Kindersley Publishing, Inc.

Kentley, Eric. Descubre el Titanic. 1998. (SPA.). lib. bdg. 22.25 (978-0-613-80912-2(2)) Tandem Library Bks.

Lawlor, Laurie. American Sisters: A Titanic Journey Across the Sea. 2000. (J). (978-0-606-20220-6(X)) Tandem Library Bks.

Osborne, Mary Pope. Tonight on the Titanic. unabr. ed. 2004. (Magic Tree House Ser. : No. 17). 71p. (J). (gr. k-3). pap. 17.00 incl. audio (978-0-8072-0926-4(0) , S FTR 249 SP, Listening Library) Random Hse. Audio Publishing Group.

—Tonight on the Titanic. Murdocca, Sal, illus. 1999. (Magic Tree House Ser.: No. 17). (J). (gr. k-3). 96p. lib. bdg. 11.99 (978-0-679-99063-5(1)); 71p. pap. 3.99 (978-0-679-89063-8(7)) Random Hse. Children's Bks. (Random Hse. Bks. for Young Readers).

—Tonight on the Titanic. Murdocca, Sal, illus. 1999. (Magic Tree House Ser. : No. 17). 70p. (J). (gr. k-3). lib. bdg. 11.19 (978-0-606-16894-6(X)) Tandem Library Bks.

—Tonight on the Titanic. 1999. (Magic Tree House Ser. : No. 17). (J). (gr. k-3). lib. bdg. 11.80 (978-0-613-16226-5(9)) Tandem Library Bks.

Peck, Richard. Amanda/Miranda. 2001. (gr. 7-12). lib. bdg. 14.15 (978-0-613-36046-3(X)) Tandem Library Bks.

Spedden, Daisy Corning Stone. Polar the Titanic Bear. 2001. (978-0-606-22559-5(5)) Tandem Library Bks.

Tanaka, Shelley. On Board the Titanic: What It Was Like When the Great Liner Sank. 1999. (Illus.). (J). (978-0-606-15659-2(3)) Tandem Library Bks.

Warner, Mike. The Titanic Game. Ordaz, Frank, illus. 2007. 201p. (J). pap. 9.95 (978-0-9744446-2-8(6)) All About Kids Publishing.

Wilson, Lynda. The Virtual Zone: Titanic's Race to Disaster. 2001. (On Time's Wing Ser.). (Illus.). 104p. (J). (gr. 3-7). pap. 6.95 (978-1-896184-96-8(0)) Roussan Pubs., Inc./Roussan Editeur, Inc. CAN. *Dist:* Orca Bk. Pubs. USA.

TITIAN, CA. 1488-1576

Venezia, Mike. Titian. Venezia, Mike, illus. 2003. (Getting to Know the World's Greatest Artists Ser.). (Illus.). (gr. 3-4). pap. 6.95 (978-0-516-26975-7(5) , Children's Pr.) Scholastic Library Publishing.

—Titian. 2003. (Getting to Know World Artists Ser.). (Illus.). 32p. (J). 27.00 (978-0-516-22575-3(8) , Children's Pr.) Scholastic Library Publishing.

—Titian. 2003. (gr. 3-6). lib. bdg. 15.25 (978-0-613-67938-1(5)) Tandem Library Bks.

TIZIANO, CA. 1488-1576

see Titian, ca. 1488-1576

TOADS

see Frogs

TOADSTOOLS

see Mushrooms

TOBACCO HABIT

Amos, Janine. Kate Smokes Cigarettes. 2002. (Body Matters Ser.). (Illus.). 32p. (YA). 19.99 (978-1-84234-108-7(1) , Cherrytree Books) Evans Publishing Group GBR. *Dist:* Independent Pubs. Group.

Carson-DeWitt, Rosalyn, ed. Drugs, Alcohol, & Tobacco: Learning about Addictive Behavior, 3 vols. 2002. (Illus.). (J). Vol. 1. (978-0-02-865757-8(8)); Vol. 2. (978-0-02-865758-5(6)); Vol. 3. (978-0-02-865759-2(4)) Thomson Gale. (Macmillan Reference USA).

Connolly, Sean. Tobacco. 2000. (Just the Facts Ser.). (Illus.). 56p. (YA). (gr. 6-8). lib. bdg. 24.22 (978-1-57572-260-3(7)) Heinemann Library.

—Tobacco. 2006. (Illus.). 46p. (J). (978-1-58340-649-6(2)) Smart Apple Media.

Constant. Tobacco. 2004. (Teen Issues Ser.). (Illus.). 56p. (J). pap. 8.95 (978-1-4109-0885-8(2)) Harcourt Schl. Pubs.

—Tobacco 6-Pack. 2004. (Teen Issues Ser.). (Illus.). (YA). pap. 48.30 (978-1-4109-0892-6(5)) Harcourt Schl. Pubs.

Esherick, Joan. Clearing the Haze: A Teen's Guide to Smoking-Related Health Issues. 2005. (Science of Health Ser.). (Illus.). 128p. (J). lib. bdg. 24.95 (978-1-59084-844-9(6)) Mason Crest Pubs.

Green, Carl R. Nicotine & Tobacco: A Myreportlinks. com Book. 2005. (Drugs Ser.). (Illus.). 48p. (J). (ps-10). lib. bdg. 25.26 (978-0-7660-5283-3(4) , MyReportLinks.com Bks.) Enslow Pubs., Inc.

Haughton, Emma. The Right to Smoke? 2005. (Illus.). 32p. (J). (gr. 5-8). lib. bdg. 27.10 (978-1-932889-62-8(0)) Sea-To-Sea Pubns.

Hirschfelder, Arlene B. Kick Butts! A Kid's Action Guide to a Tobacco-Free America. 2001. (Illus.). 160p. pap. 29.95 (978-0-8108-3913-7(X)) Scarecrow Pr., Inc.

Holt, Rinehart and Winston Staff. A Lifetime of Health Chptr. 11: Tobacco. 4th ed. Date not set. pap. 11.20 (978-0-03-068103-5(0)) Holt, Rinehart & Winston.

Huard, Donald V. Teen-Agers: What Will Cigarettes, Booze & Drugs Do for/to You? 1998. 50p. (J). (gr. 7-12). mass mkt. 3.95 (978-0-9661606-1-1(4)) Huard Pubns.

Hudson, David. Smoking Bans. 2004. (Point/Counterpoint Ser.). (Illus.). 120p. (gr. 9-13). 32.95 (978-0-7910-7974-4(0) , Chelsea Hse.) Facts On File, Inc.

Jaffe, Steven L., ed. Nicotine & Cigarettes. 1999. (Junior Drug Awareness Ser.). (Illus.). 80p. (J). (gr. 4-8). 32.00 (978-0-7910-5175-7(7) , Chelsea Hse.) Facts On File, Inc.

Jones, David C. One Person to Another: Smoking, Chewing Tobacco & Young Peopole. l.t. ed. 2003. 20p. (YA). 4.00 (978-1-878400-17-8(7)) Dolphin Publishing.

Keyishian, Elizabeth. Smoking. rev. ed. 2005. (Need to Know Library). (Illus.). 64p. (J). (gr. 7-12). lib. bdg. 25.25 (978-0-8239-4092-9(6)) Rosen Publishing Group, Inc., The.

Lynette, Rachel. Tobacco. 2007. (J). (*978-1-4034-9696-6(X)*); pap. (*978-1-4034-9703-1(6)*) Heinemann Library.

MacDonald, Joan Vos. Tobacco & Nicotine Drug Dangers. (Drug Dangers Ser.). (Illus.). 64p. (YA). (gr. 4-10). 2001. pap. 13.26 (978-0-7660-1966-9(7)); 2000. lib. bdg. 27.93 (978-0-7660-1317-9(0)) Enslow Pubs., Inc.

Nadelson, Carol C. & Reinburg, Claire E., eds. Smoke Screen: Psychological Disorders Related to Nicotine Use. 1999. (Encyclopedia of Psychological Disorders Ser.). (Illus.). 96p. (J). (gr. 6 up). lib. bdg. 42.55 (978-0-7910-4958-7(2) , Chelsea Hse.) Facts On File, Inc.

Perspectives on Physical Health, 8 bks. Incl. Alcohol Use & Abuse. Graves, Bonnie. lib. bdg. 23.93 (978-0-7368-0415-8(3)); Drug Use & Abuse. Graves, Bonnie. lib. bdg. 23.93 (978-0-7368-0416-5(1)); Fitness. Graves, Bonnie. lib. bdg. 23.93 (978-0-7368-0418-9(8)); Healthy Eating. Gregson, Susan R. lib. bdg. 23.93 (978-0-7368-0420-2(X)); Premenstrual Syndrome. Gregson, Susan R. lib. bdg. 23.93 (978-0-7368-0421-9(8)); Skin Care. Gregson, Susan R. lib. bdg. 23.93 (978-0-7368-0419-6(6)); Tattooing & Body Piercing. Graves, Bonnie. lib. bdg. 23.93 (978-0-7368-0417-2(X)); Tobacco Use. Graves, Bonnie. lib. bdg. 23.93 (978-0-7368-0414-1(5)); 64p. (J). (gr. 4-6). (Illus.). 2000. Set lib. bdg. 191.44 (978-0-7368-0438-7(2) , LifeMatters Bks.) Capstone Pr., Inc.

Pollard, Jim & Kent, Chloe. Tobacco. 2004. (Teen Issues Ser.). (Illus.). 56p. (J). (gr. 6-8). lib. bdg. 28.56 (978-1-4109-0614-4(0)) Harcourt Schl. Pubs.

Powell, Jillian. Why Do People Smoke? 2001. (Exploring Tough Issues Ser.). (Illus.). 48p. (J). (gr. 4-7). lib. bdg. 25.69 (978-0-7398-3234-9(4)) Raintree.

Price, Sean. Nicotine. 2008. (Junior Drug Awareness Ser.). 112p. (J). (gr. 5-8). 30.00 (*978-0-7910-9696-3(3)* , Chelsea Hse.) Facts On File, Inc.

Sanders, Bruce. Smoking. 2005. (Illus.). 32p. (J). (gr. 3-7). lib. bdg. 27.10 (978-1-59604-047-2(5)) Stargazer Bks.

Stewart, Gail B. Smoking. 2002. (Understanding Issues Ser.). (Illus.). 48p. (J). (gr. 3-5). 26.20 (978-0-7377-1026-7(8) , Kidhaven) Thomson Gale.

Tobacco: What about It? 2001. (Health & Human Development Resource Library). (J). (gr. 4-6). tchr. ed. 69.95 (978-1-55942-177-5(0) , 9228V9) Marsh Media.

Wagner, Heather Lehr. Nicotine. 2003. (Drugs, the Straight Facts Ser.). 112p. (J). (gr. 9-13). 30.00 (978-0-7910-7264-6(9) , Chelsea Hse.) Facts On File, Inc.

Williams, Mary E. Smoking. 2000. 96p. (YA). (gr. 8-12). lib. bdg. 27.45 (978-0-613-61335-4(X)) Tandem Library Bks.

—Smoking. 2000. (At Issue Ser.). (YA). (gr. 9-12). 80p. lib. bdg. 29.95 (978-0-7377-0157-9(9)); 2nd rev. ed. (Illus.). 128p. pap. 21.20 (978-0-7377-0156-2(0)) Thomson Gale. (Greenhaven Pr., Inc.).

—Teen Smoking. 2000. (Contemporary Issues Companion Ser.). 144p. (YA). (gr. 9-12). lib. bdg. 36.20 (978-0-7377-0169-2(2)); (Illus.). (gr. 10 up). lib. bdg. 24.95 (978-0-7377-0168-5(4)) Thomson Gale. (Greenhaven Pr., Inc.).

TOES

see Foot

TOILET

see Beauty, Personal

TOILET PREPARATIONS

see Cosmetics

TOILET TRAINING

Aaron-Barrada, prod. PottieStickers 3-pack Sports Equipment, Seashells & Butterflies: How to Toilet Train in 7 Days with Success with the #1 Portable Toilet Training Reward System for today's family-on-the-go-lifestyle... because consistency Counts!, 3 vols. 2004. (Illus.). 6p. (J). 9.99 (978-0-9768671-1-1(7)) Aaron-Barrada, Inc.

Aaron-Barrada, Tammie, creator. PottieStickers 3-Pack Fireflies, Kites & Fish Tank: How to Toilet Train in 7 Days with Success with the #1 Portable Toilet Training Reward System for Today's Family-on-the-Go-Lifestyle... Because Consistency Counts!, 3 vols. 2004. (Illus.). 6p. (J). 9.99 (978-0-9768671-2-8(5)) Aaron-Barrada, Inc.

—PottieStickers 3-Pack Tools, Sea Horses & Flowers: How to Toilet Train in 7 Days with Success! #1 Portable Toilet Training Reward System for today's family-on-the-go-lifestyle... because consistency Counts! 2004. Orig. Title: #1 Portable Toilet Training Reward System for today's family-on-the-go-lifestyle... because consistency Counts!. (Illus.). 6p. (J). 9.99 (978-0-615-12767-5(3)) Aaron-Barrada, Inc.

Allison, Alida. The Toddler's Potty Book. Parmentier, Henry, illus. 2003. 32p. (J). (ps-1). bds. 5.99 (978-0-8431-0509-4(7) , Price Stern Sloan) Penguin Group (USA) Inc.

Berry, Joy Wilt. Teach Me about Potty Training: A Growing up Book. Fitzpatrick, Roey, illus. rev. ed. 1999. (Teach Me about Ser.: Vol. 2). (J). (ps). bds. 5.95 (978-1-58634-005-6(0) , 01-0102-02) Goldstar Publishing, Inc.

Berry, Ron & Sharp, Chris. It's Potty Time: For Girls. Sharp, Chris & Currant, Gary, illus. rev. ed. 2000. (It's Time to Ser.). 18p. (J). (gr. 2-4). bds. 7.95 (978-1-891100-59-8(9) , Smart Kids) Penton Overseas, Inc.

—It's Potty Time for Boys. Sharp, Chris & Currant, Gary, illus. rev. ed. 2000. (It's Time to Ser.). 18p. (J). (gr. 2-4). bds. 7.95 (978-1-891100-60-4(2) , Smart Kids) Penton Overseas, Inc.

Brooks, Felicity. Baby's Potty. 2006. 10p. (J). bds. 8.99 (978-0-7945-1362-7(X) , Usborne) EDC Publishing.

Butler, Dori. Zach's Potty: A Learning to Go Book. 2006. (Illus.). 20p. (J). pap. 12.95 (978-0-7624-1939-5(3) , Running Pr. Kids) Running Pr. Bk. Pubs.

—Zoe's Potty: A Learning to Go Book. 2006. (Illus.). 20p. (J). pap. 12.95 (978-0-7624-2026-1(X) , Running Pr. Kids) Running Pr. Bk. Pubs.

Cole. My Big Boy Potty Book. 2000. (J). lib. bdg. 5.89 (978-0-06-029023-7(8)) HarperCollins Pubs.

Delittle, Cathy. It's My Potty... I'll Cry If I Want To. Delittle, Cathy, illus. 1998. (Illus.). 10p. (J). (ps-1). spiral bd. 7.95 (978-1-892633-09-5(4) , OOCD208) Delittle Storyteller Co.

Dorling Kindersley Publishing Staff, contrib. by. My Potty Book for Boys. 2001. (My First Bks.). (Illus.). 12p. (J). (ps-k). bds. 7.99 (978-0-7894-4889-7(0)) Dorling Kindersley Publishing, Inc.

—My Potty Book for Girls. 2001. (Potty Bks.). (Illus.). 12p. (J). (ps-k). bds. 7.99 (978-0-7894-4845-3(9)) Dorling Kindersley Publishing, Inc.

Foote, Tracy. My Potty Activity Book + 45 Toilet Training Tips: Potty Training Workbook with Parent / Child Interaction with Coloring & Creative Fun. 2nd ed. 2001. (Illus.). 64p. (J). (ps-k). act. bk. ed. 9.95 (978-0-9708226-0-4(X)) TracyTrends.

—My Potty Activity Book + 45 Training Tips: Aimed at Parent/Child Toilet Training Interaction. 2000. 40p. (J). spiral bd., act. bk. ed. 9.95 (978-0-615-11462-0(8)) TracyTrends.

—My Potty Reward Stickers for Boys: 126 Boy Potty Training Stickers & Chart to Motivate Toilet Training. 4th ed. 2006. (J). per. 7.95 (978-0-9708226-8-0(5)) TracyTrends.

—My Potty Reward Stickers for Boys: 126 Boy Stickers & Chart to Motivate Toilet Training. 2003. (J). 7.95 (978-0-9708226-6-6(9)) TracyTrends.

—My Potty Reward Stickers for Girls: 126 Girl Potty Training Stickers & Chart to Motivate Toilet Training. 4th ed. 2006. (Illus.). (J). 7.95 (978-0-9708226-7-3(7)) TracyTrends.

—My Potty Reward Stickers for Girls: 126 Girl Stickers & Chart to Motivate Toilet Training. 3rd rev. ed. 2003. (J). 7.95 (978-0-9708226-5-9(0)) TracyTrends.

Frankel, Alona. Once upon a Potty: Boy & Doll. 2000. (Illus.). (J). (ps up). 16.95 (978-0-694-01376-0(5)) HarperCollins Pubs.

—Once upon a Potty: Girl & Doll. 1999. (Illus.). (J). (ps up). 16.95 (978-0-694-01375-3(7)) HarperCollins Pubs.

—Once upon a Potty - Boy. Frankel, Alona, illus. 2007. (Illus.). 40p. (J). (gr. k-ps). 6.95 (*978-1-55407-283-5(2)*) Firefly Bks., Ltd. CAN. *Dist:* Firefly Bks., Ltd.

—Once upon a Potty - Boy. Frankel, Alona, illus. 1999. (Once upon a Potty Ser.). (Illus.). 48p. (J). (ps up). 5.99 (978-0-694-01387-6(0) , Harper Festival) HarperCollins Pubs.

Frankel, Alona. Once upon a Potty - Girl. Frankel, Alona, illus. 2007. (Illus.). 40p. (J). (gr. k-ps). 6.95 (*978-1-55407-284-2(0)*) Firefly Bks., Ltd. CAN. *Dist:* Firefly Bks., Ltd.

—Once upon a Potty - Girl. Frankel, Alona, illus. 1999. (Once upon a Potty Ser.). (Illus.). 48p. (J). (ps up). 5.99 (978-0-694-01388-3(9) , Harper Festival) HarperCollins Pubs.

The Girl Potty Book. 1999. (My First Bks.). (J). (978-0-7894-4730-2(4)) Dorling Kindersley Publishing, Inc.

Goodman, Susan E. The Truth about Poop. Smith, Elwood H., illus. 2004. 40p. (J). (gr. 1). 15.99 (978-0-670-03674-5(9) , Viking Juvenile) Penguin Group (USA) Inc.

Hochman, David & Kennison, Ruth. Potty Train. Anderson, Derek, illus. 2008. 32p. (J). 9.99 (978-1-4169-2833-1(2) , Simon & Schuster Children's Publishing) Simon & Schuster Children's Publishing.

Lansky, Bruce & Pottle, Robert. Tinkle, Tinkle, Little Tot: Songs & Rhymes for Toilet Training. Blake, Anne Catharine, illus. 2005. 32p. (J). 8.95 (978-0-88166-492-8(8) , 1182) Meadowbrook Pr.

—Tinkle, Tinkle, Little Tot: Songs & Rhymes for Toilet Training. 2005. (Illus.). 32p. (J). (gr. 2-2). 7.95 (978-0-689-04646-9(4)) Meadowbrook Pr.

Lansky, Vicki. Koko Bear's New Potty Package: Includes Koko Potty Doll. Prince, Jane, illus. 1999. (Lansky, Vicki Ser.). 17.95 (978-0-916773-69-4(8)) Book Peddlers.

—Toilet Training: A Guide to Daytime & Nighttime Training, 2 in 1. 3rd ed. 2002. (Lansky, Vicki Ser.). 112p. pap. 12.95 (978-0-916773-64-9(7)) Book Peddlers.

Lewis, Bisa. Let's Potty! Floyd, John, Jr., illus. 2006. (J). bds. 6.99 (*978-1-934214-12-1(4)*) OurRainbow Pr., LLC.

Morgan, Richard. Zoo Poo: A First Toilet Training Book. 2004. (Illus.). 24p. (J). pap. 5.95 (978-0-7641-2767-0(5)) Barron's Educational Series, Inc.

—Zoo Poo: A First Toilet Training Book. 2004. (ps-2). lib. bdg. 12.95 (978-0-613-81357-0(X)) Tandem Library Bks.

Murkoff, Heidi. What to Expect When You Use the Potty. Rader, Laura, illus. (What to Expect Kids Ser.). (J). (ps-k). 2004. 24p. pap. 3.50 (978-0-06-053801-9(5)); 2000. 32p. 8.99 (978-0-694-01322-7(6)) HarperCollins Pubs. (Harper Festival).

Patt, Benjamin. Potty Time for Erin. 2003. 42p. pap. 19.95 (978-1-4137-0909-4(5)) PublishAmerica, Inc.

Penton Overseas, Inc. Staff. Es Hora de Ir al Bano- para Ninas. 2005. (Time Toand Ser.). (SPA & ENG., Illus.). 18p. (J). (gr. 2-4). bds. 7.95 (978-1-59125-340-2(3) , Penton Kids) Penton Overseas, Inc.

—Es Hora de Ir al Bano- para Ninos. 2005. (Time Toand Ser.). (SPA & ENG., Illus.). 10p. (J). (gr. 2-4). 7.95 (978-1-59125-339-6(X) , Penton Kids) Penton Overseas, Inc.

Pinnington, Andrea. Big Boys Use the Potty. 2005. (Illus.). 12p. (J). bds. 6.99 (978-0-7566-1451-5(1)) Dorling Kindersley Publishing, Inc.

Pinnington, Andrea, text. Big Girls Use the Potty. 2005. (Illus.). 12p. (J). bds. 6.99 (978-0-7566-1452-2(X)) Dorling Kindersley Publishing, Inc.

Potty Hunt. 2002. (Lift the Flap Ser.). (J). bds. 4.98 (978-0-7525-8696-0(3)) Parragon, Inc.

Priddy, Roger. Potty Time Training Pack. 2007. 15p. (J). 12.95 (*978-0-312-49977-8(9)* , Priddy Bks.) St. Martin's Pr.

Priddy, Roger. 3 in 1: New Baby, Potty Time, Pre-School. 2005. (J). bds. 16.95 (978-0-312-49563-3(3) , Priddy Bks.) St. Martin's Pr.

Sawyer, Parker K. Potty Time! Moroney, Christopher, illus. 2006. (Sesame Beginnings Ser.). 12p. (J). (gr. k). bds. 5.99 (978-0-375-83695-4(0) , Random Hse. Bks. for Young Readers) Random Hse. Children's Bks.

Sears, William, et al. You Can Go to the Potty. Andriani, Renee W., illus. 2002. 32p. (J). (ps-ps). 12.99 (978-0-316-78888-5(0)) Little, Brown Bks. for Young Readers.

Smart Kids Publishing Staff. It's Potty Time for Boys: A Children's Book about Toilet Training. 2005. (Illus.). 16p. (J). (gr. 2-4). bds. 7.95 (978-1-59125-583-3(X)) Penton Overseas, Inc.

—It's Potty Time for Girls: A Children's Book about Toilet Training. 2005. (Illus.). 16p. (J). (gr. 2-4). bds. 7.95 (978-1-59125-597-0(X)) Penton Overseas, Inc.

Willems, Mo. Time to Pee! Willems, Mo, illus. 2003. (Illus.). 40p. (ps). 12.99 (978-0-7868-1868-6(9)) Hyperion Bks. for Children.

TOILET TRAINING—FICTION

Allison, Alida. Toddler's Potty Book. Parmentier, Henry, illus. 2003. Tr. of Libro de Basinica del Pequenito. (SPA.). 16p. (J). (ps-1). bds. 5.99 (978-0-8431-0502-5(X) , Price Stern Sloan) Penguin Group (USA) Inc.

TUV

Barrett, John E., photos by. Too Big for Diapers. 2000. (Sesame Street Babies Ser.). (Illus.). 12p. (J). (gr. k-ps). bds. 4.99 (978-0-375-81045-9(5) , Random Hse. Bks. for Young Readers) Random Hse. Children's Bks.

Bentley, Dawn. Fuzzy Bear's Potty Book. Nagy, Krisztina, illus. 2005. (Fuzzy Bear Ser.). 10p. (J). (ps). 11.95 (978-1-58117-161-7(7) , Intervisual/Piggy Toes) Dalmatian Pr.

Bolam, Emily, illus. Go Girl! Go Potty! 2006. 16p. (J). pap. 5.95 (978-1-4027-3736-7(X)) Sterling Publishing Co., Inc.

—No Potty! Yes Potty! 2006. 16p. (J). pap. 5.95 (978-1-4027-3737-4(8)) Sterling Publishing Co., Inc.

Capucilli, Alyssa Satin. The Potty Book & Doll Package for Boys: Henry Edition. Stott, Dorothy, illus. 2007. 32p. (J). 16.99 (***978-0-7641-9373-6(2)***) Barron's Educational Series, Inc.

—The Potty Book & Doll Package for Girls: Hannah Edition. Stott, Dorothy, illus. 2007. 32p. (J). (gr. k-k). 16.99 (***978-0-7641-9374-3(0)***) Barron's Educational Series, Inc.

—The Potty Book for Boys. Stott, Dorothy, illus. 2000. (Potty Book (for Boys & for Girls) Ser.). 32p. (J). 5.95 (978-0-7641-5232-0(7)) Barron's Educational Series, Inc.

—The Potty Book for Girls. Stott, Dorothy, illus. 2000. (Potty Book (for Boys & for Girls) Ser.). 32p. (J). 5.95 (978-0-7641-5231-3(9)) Barron's Educational Series, Inc.

Chambliss, Maxie, illus. My Big Boy Potty. 2002. (My Big Kid Potty Ser.). (J). 15.53 (978-0-7587-2396-3(2)) Book Wholesalers, Inc.

—My Big Girl Potty. 2002. (My Big Kid Potty Ser.). (J). 14.43 (978-0-7587-2623-0(6)) Book Wholesalers, Inc.

Cole, Joanna. My Big Boy Potty. Chambliss, Maxie, illus. 2000. 32p. (J). (ps up). 6.99 (978-0-688-17042-4(0)) HarperCollins Pubs.

—My Big Boy Potty Lap Edition. Chambliss, Maxie, illus. 2006. 28p. (J). 12.99 (978-0-06-085411-9(1) , Harper Festival) HarperCollins Pubs.

—My Big Girl Potty. Chambliss, Maxie, illus. 2000. 32p. (J). (ps up). 6.99 (978-0-688-17041-7(2)) HarperCollins Pubs.

—My Big Girl Potty Lap Edition. Chambliss, Maxie, illus. 2006. 28p. (J). 12.99 (978-0-06-085410-2(3) , Harper Festival) HarperCollins Pubs.

De Smet, Marian & Meijer, Marja. Encerrada: Anna's Tight Squeeze. Pacheco, Laura Emilia, tr. Uitgeverij, Clavis, illus. 2004. 28p. (J). 14.95 (978-970-29-0665-0(2)) Santillana USA Publishing Co., Inc.

DePrisco, Dorothea & McKendry, Sam. I'm a Big Kid Now. 2006. 12.95 (978-1-58117-523-3(X) , Intervisual/Piggy Toes) Dalmatian Pr.

Fanning, Tena & Friedlander, Tim. Island Potty Party. 2007. 32p. (ps-3). 14.95 (***978-1-933721-15-6(4)***) Playdate Kids Publishing.

Ford, Bernette. No More Diapers for Ducky! Williams, Sam, illus. 2007. 26p. (J). bds. 6.95 (***978-1-905417-38-4(1)***) Boxer Bks., Ltd. GBR. *Dist:* Sterling Publishing Co., Inc.

Frankel, Alona. Mi Bacinica y Yo: Para El. Frankel, Alona, illus. 2002. (Once upon a Potty Ser.). (SPA., Illus.). 48p. (J). (ps up). 6.95 (978-0-694-01649-5(7)) HarperCollins Pubs.

—Mi Bacinica y Yo (Para Ella) Frankel, Alona, illus. 2002. (Once upon a Potty Ser.). (SPA., Illus.). 48p. (J). (ps up). 6.95 (978-0-694-01648-8(9)) HarperCollins Pubs.

Fung, Karen & Butterfield, Moira. Let's Go Potty. Utton, Peter, illus. 2000. 10p. (J). (ps-k). 9.99 (978-0-7641-5288-7(2)) Barron's Educational Series, Inc.

Golden Books Staff. My Potty Book. 2005. (Precious Moments Ser.). (Illus.). 16p. (J). (gr. k-ps). pap. 3.99 (978-0-375-83254-3(8) , RH/Disney) Random Hse. Children's Bks.

Higgins, Kitty. I'm a Potty Champion! Nez, John, illus. 1999. 20p. (J). 9.95 (978-0-7641-0965-2(0)) Barron's Educational Series, Inc.

—I'm a Potty Champion: With Miniature Trophy. Nez, John, illus. 1999. 20p. (J). (ps). 9.95 (978-0-7641-7249-6(2)) Barron's Educational Series, Inc.

Ingle, Annie. Lift the Lid, Use the Potty. McCue, Lisa, illus. 2001. (Nifty Lift-and-Look Bks.). 12p. (J). (gr. k-ps). bds. 7.99 (978-0-375-81146-3(X) , Random Hse. Bks. for Young Readers) Random Hse. Children's Bks.

Jones, Lara. I Love My Potty. Jones, Lara, illus. 2002. (Illus.). 16p. (J). bds. 6.95 (978-0-439-36768-4(9) , Cartwheel Bks.) Scholastic, Inc.

Kelly, Mij. Have You Seen My Potty? McQuillan, Mary, illus. 2007. 32p. (J). (ps). 12.99 (***978-0-7641-6030-1(3)***) Barron's Educational Series, Inc.

Kriegman, Mitchell. When You've Got to Go. Mitter, Kathryn, illus. 2002. 24p. (J). mass mkt. 5.95 (978-0-689-85510-8(9) , Simon Spotlight) Simon & Schuster Children's Publishing.

Lewison, Wendy Cheyette. The Prince & the Potty. Motoyama, Keiko, illus. 2006. 40p. (J). (ps). 12.95 (978-0-689-87808-4(7) , Simon & Schuster Children's Publishing) Simon & Schuster Children's Publishing.

—The Princess & the Potty. Brown, Rick, illus. 2nd ed. 2005. (Stories to Go! Ser.). 40p. (J). 4.99 (978-0-689-87838-1(9) , Aladdin) Simon & Schuster Children's Publishing.

Lindgren, Barbro. Sam's Potty. Lindgren, Barbro, illus. 2002. Tr. of Max Potta. (Illus.). (J). 15.70 (978-0-7587-3556-0(1)) Book Wholesalers, Inc.

Markes, Julie. Where's the Poop? Hartung, Susan Kathleen, illus. 2004. 20p. (J). (ps up). pap. 8.99 (978-0-06-053089-1(8) , Harper Festival) HarperCollins Pubs.

Mayer, Mercer & Mayer, Gina. The New Potty. 2003. (Illus.). 24p. (J). (gr. k-ps). pap. 3.25 (978-0-375-82631-3(9) , Random Hse. Bks. for Young Readers) Random Hse. Children's Bks.

McNaughton, Colin. Potty Poo-Poo Wee-Wee! McNaughton, Colin, illus. 2005. (Illus.). 40p. (J). (gr. k-ps). 9.99 (978-0-7636-2781-2(X)) Candlewick Pr.

Miller, Virginia. On Your Potty. Miller, Virginia, illus. 1998. (George & Ba Ser.). (Illus.). 32p. (J). (gr. k-k). pap. 5.99 (978-0-7636-0694-7(4)) Candlewick Pr.

Neis, Izzy. I Want to Potty. Shakir, Susie, illus. 2005. 10p. (J). 9.95 (978-1-58117-422-9(5) , Intervisual/Piggy Toes) Dalmatian Pr.

Nussbaum, Dori. The Hungry Potty. 2004. 28p. per. 8.95 (978-1-932344-67-7(5)) Thornton Publishing.

Penton Overseas, Inc. Staff, contrib. by. Its Potty Time Boys. 2007. 14p. 7.95 (***978-1-59125-843-8(X)***) Penton Overseas, Inc.

—Its Potty Time Girls. 2007. 14p. 7.95 (***978-1-59125-842-1(1)***) Penton Overseas, Inc.

Ross, Tony. I Want My Potty. Ross, Tony, illus. 2007. (People Love Little Princess Books! Ser.). (Illus.). 28p. (J). pap. 4.95 (978-1-933605-23-4(5) , 05234) Kane/Miller Bk. Pubs., Inc.

Sanschagrin, Joceline. Caillou - Potty Time. Brignaud, Pierre, illus. rev. ed. 2005. (Hand in Hand Ser.).Tr. of Caillou - Le Pot. 24p. (J). (ps-1). pap. 5.95 (978-2-89450-367-6(9)) Chouette Publishing CAN. *Dist:* Independent Pubs. Group.

Slattery, Karen. Piper's Diapers. 2003. (J). pap. 9.00 (978-0-8059-5765-5(0)) Dorrance Publishing Co., Inc.

Smith, Dana C. Monkey Learns to Potty. 2005. (Illus.). 8p. pap. 7.95 (978-0-9762877-2-8(2) , 2500) PottyMD LLC.

Torres, Melissa & A&J Studios Staff. El entrenamiento de Dora (Dora's Potty Book) 2006. (Dora la Exploradora Ser.). (SPA.). 14p. (J). bds. 8.99 (978-1-4169-1565-2(6) , Libros Para Ninos) Simon & Schuster Children's Publishing.

Trotter, Stuart. Potties! 2007. (Illus.). 24p. (J). (gr. k). bds. 6.99 (***978-0-375-83933-7(X)*** , Random Hse. Bks. for Young Readers) Random Hse. Children's Bks.

Watt, Fiona & Wells, Rachel, eds. Potty Time. 2004. (Baby's World Ser.). (Illus.). 16p. (J). (ps up). pap. 4.95 (978-0-7460-3839-0(9)) EDC Publishing.

Wax, Wendy & Wax, Naomi. Even Firefighters Use the Potty. Sisk, Clay & Gilpin, Stephen, illus. 2008. 24p. (J). 7.99 (***978-1-4169-2720-4(4)*** , Little Simon) Simon & Schuster Children's Publishing.

Weiss, Ellen. Bye-Bye, Diapers. 1998. (Muppets Ser.). 14p. (J). (ps). bds. 3.49 (978-0-307-13467-7(9) , 13467, Golden Bks.) Random Hse. Children's Bks.

Worth, Bonnie & Prebenna, David. I Can Go Potty. Cooke, Tom, illus. 1998. (Muppets Ser.). 14p. (J). (ps). bds. 4.99 (978-0-307-13465-3(2) , 13465, Golden Bks.) Random Hse. Children's Bks.

TOKYO (JAPAN)

Barber, Nicola. Tokyo. Bowden, Rob, photos by. 2006. (Global Cities Ser.). 64p. (YA). (gr. 5-8). 30.00 (978-0-7910-8855-5(3) , Chelsea Hse.) Facts On File, Inc.

—Tokyo. 2004. (Great Cities of the World Ser.). (Illus.). 48p. (J). (gr. 5 up). pap. 11.95 (978-0-8368-5193-9(5)); lib. bdg. 30.00 (978-0-8368-5033-8(5)) Stevens, Gareth Inc. (World Almanac Library).

Kallen, Stuart A. Life in Tokyo. 2000. (Way People Live Ser.). (Illus.). 96p. (YA). (gr. 7-10). 29.95 (978-1-56006-797-9(7) , LML00902-178133, Lucent Bks.) Thomson Gale.

Takabayashi, Mari. I Live in Tokyo. 2004. (Illus.). 32p. (J). (gr. k-3). reprint ed. pap. 6.95 (978-0-618-49484-2(7)) Houghton Mifflin Co. Trade & Reference Div.

TOLERATION

see also Discrimination; Freedom of Religion

All about Us Interactive Packages: Here I Am. (Pebble Soup Explorations Ser.). (ps up). 52.00 (978-0-7578-5227-5(0)) Rigby Education.

Currie, Stephen. Religious Oppression. 2003. (Great Escapes Ser.). (Illus.). 112p. (J). 29.95 (978-1-59018-280-2(4) , Lucent Bks.) Thomson Gale.

Donahue, Jill L. Being Tolerant. Previn, Stacey, illus. 2007. (J). lib. bdg. (***978-1-4048-3776-8(0)***) Picture Window Bks.

Freedom Writers Staff. Freedom Writers Diary: How a Teacher & 150 Teens Used Writing to Change Themselves & the World. 1999. (Illus.). (YA). 20.60 (978-0-606-18104-4(0)) Tandem Library Bks.

—The Freedom Writers Diary: How a Teacher & 150 Teens Used Writing to Change Themselves & the World Around Them. 1999. (Illus.). 304p. pap. 13.95 (978-0-385-49422-9(X) , Main St. Bks.) Broadway Bks.

Gay, Kathlyn. Cultural Diversity: Conflicts & Challenges: The Ultimate Teen Guide. 2003. (It Happened to Me Ser.: No. 6). (Illus.). 144p. pap. 30.95 (978-0-8108-4805-4(8)) Scarecrow Pr., Inc.

Hanes, Richard Clay, et al. Prejudice in the Modern World. 2007. (J). (***978-1-4144-0205-5(8)); (978-1-4144-0206-2(6)***) Thomson Gale.

LaMachia, John. So What Is Tolerance Anyway? 2000. (Students Guide to American Civics Ser.). 48p. (YA). lib. bdg. 23.95 (978-0-8239-3449-2(7)); (Illus.). (gr. 5-8). lib. bdg. 23.95 (978-0-8239-3099-9(8) , CVTOLE) Rosen Publishing Group, Inc., The. (Rosen Central).

Lester, Julius. Let's Talk about Race. Barbour, Karen, illus. 2005. (Amistad Ser.). 32p. (J). (gr. 1-5). 16.99 (978-0-06-028596-8(6)); lib. bdg. 16.89 (978-0-06-028598-2(2)) HarperCollins Pubs. (Amistad).

Levy, Debbie. Bigotry. 2001. (Overview Ser.). (Illus.). 128p. (YA). (gr. 6-9). lib. bdg. 29.95 (978-1-56006-500-5(1) , Lucent Bks.) Thomson Gale.

Magliano, Tony. Moonlight Miracle. Brindle, Susan Andrews, illus. 2001. 32p. (ps-2). 9.95 (978-0-8091-6676-3(3) , 6676-3) Paulist Pr.

McCann, Joseph T. There's a Skunk in My Bunk: Helping Children Learn Tolerance. Gerlach, Thomas, illus. 2002. (Let's Talk Ser.). 48p. (J). (ps-4). pap. 12.95 (978-0-88282-214-3(4) , Small Horizons) New Horizon Pr. Pubs., Inc.

Meiners, Cheryl J. Accept & Value Each Person. 2006. (Learning to Get Along Ser.). (Illus.). 40p. (J). (ps-3). pap. 10.95 (978-1-57542-203-9(4)) Free Spirit Publishing, Inc.

Miller, Connie Colwell. Tolerance. 2005. (First Facts Ser.). (Illus.). 24p. (J). (ps-7). lib. bdg. 21.26 (978-0-7368-4282-2(9)) Capstone Pr., Inc.

Munson, Derek. Pastel para Enemigos. King, Tara Calahan, illus. 2004. Tr. of Enemy Pie. (SPA.). (J). pap. 8.99 (978-84-261-3378-6(9)) Juventud, Editorial ESP. *Dist:* Lectorum Pubns., Inc.

Nettleton, Pamela Hill. Let's Get Along! Kids Talk about Tolerance. Muehlenhardt, Amy Bailey, illus. 2004. (Kids Talk Ser.). 32p. (J). (gr. 2-5). 23.93 (978-1-4048-0622-1(9)) Picture Window Bks.

Penchina, Sharon. Dogs & Bugs Go Together, Really They Do! 2007. 28p. 12.95 (978-0-9740684-8-0(9)) 2 Imagine.

Sanders, Pete & Myers, Steve. Dealing with Racism. 2006. (Choices & Decisions Ser.). (Illus.). 32p. (J). (978-1-59604-097-7(1)) Stargazer Bks.

Scheunemann, Pam. Learning about Differences. 2004. (Keeping the Peace Ser.). (Illus.). 23p. (J). (ps-3). lib. bdg. 19.93 (978-1-59197-561-8(1)) ABDO Publishing Co.

—Tolerance. 2003. (United We Stand Ser.). (Illus.). 24p. (J). (ps-3). lib. bdg. 19.93 (978-1-57765-881-8(7)) ABDO Publishing Co.

Schuette, Sarah L. I Am Tolerant. 2004. (Character Values Ser.). (Illus.). 24p. (J). lib. bdg. 15.93 (978-0-7368-2573-3(8) , Pebble Bks.) Capstone Pr., Inc.

Thomson Gale Staff. Prejudice in the Modern World: Almanac, 2 vols. Hanes, Richard C. et al, eds. rev. ed. 2007. (Prejudice Throughout History Reference Library). 462p. (YA). 120.00 (978-1-4144-0204-8(X) , UXL) Thomson Gale.

—Prejudice in the Modern World: Biographies. Hanes, Richard C. & Rudd, Kelly, eds. rev. ed. 2007. (Prejudice Throughout History Reference Library). 920p. (YA). 67.00 (978-1-4144-0207-9(4) , UXL) Thomson Gale.

—Prejudice in the Modern World: Cumulative Index. Hermsen, Sarah, ed. rev. ed. 2007. (Prejudice Throughout History Reference Library). 34p. (YA). 5.00 (978-1-4144-0209-3(0) , UXL) Thomson Gale.

—Prejudice in the Modern World: Primary Sources. Hanes, Sharon M., ed. rev. ed. 2007. (Prejudice Throughout History Reference Library). 214p. (YA). 67.00 (978-1-4144-0208-6(2) , UXL) Thomson Gale.

Wandberg, Robert. Tolerance: Celebrating Differences. 2000. (Contemporary Issues Ser.). (Illus.). 64p. (J). (gr. 4-6). lib. bdg. 23.93 (978-0-7368-1021-0(8) , LifeMatters Bks.) Capstone Pr., Inc.

Watson, Susan. Respecting Cultural Differences. 2003. 32p. (J). lib. bdg. 24.25 (978-1-58340-400-3(7)) Smart Apple Media.

TOLERATION—FICTION

BAKER, E. D. Story of kitten Cuckoo. 2007. 32p. 15.95 (***978-1-933572-04-8(3)***) Centro Bks., LLC.

Behar, Joy. Sheetzucacapoopoo: My Kind of Dog. Barretta, Gene, illus. 2006. 32p. (J). (ps). 15.99 (978-0-525-47718-1(7) , Dutton Juvenile) Penguin Group (USA) Inc.

Bondoux, Anne-Laure. Vasco, Leader of the Tribe. Maudet, Y., tr. from FRE. 2007. (J). (gr. 3-7). 352p. 15.99 (***978-0-385-73363-2(1));*** 256p. lib. bdg. 18.99 (***978-0-385-90378-3(2)***) Random Hse. Children's Bks. (Delacorte Bks. for Young Readers).

Calhoun, Dia. White Midnight. 2003. 304p. (YA). 18.00 (978-0-374-38389-3(8) , Farrar, Straus & Giroux (BYR)) Farrar, Straus & Giroux.

Carvell, Marlene. Who Will Tell My Brother? 2004. 160p. (gr. 7-17). pap. 5.99 (978-0-7868-1657-6(0)) Hyperion Bks. for Children.

Defosse, Rosana Curiel. Santiago en el Pantano. Barradas, Leticia, illus. (Santiago Y Los Valores Ser.). (SPA.). 32p. (J). (gr. 3-5). pap. 7.95 (978-970-29-0133-4(2)) Santillana USA Publishing Co., Inc.

Dupasquier, Philippe. Quack, Quack! 2001. (Illus.). 32p. (J). 17.99 (978-1-84270-015-0(4)) Andersen GBR. *Dist:* Independent Pubs. Group.

—Quack Quack! 2002. (Illus.). 32p. (J). (gr. k-3). pap. 8.99 (978-1-84270-112-6(6)) Andersen GBR. *Dist:* Trafalgar Square Publishing.

Ellison, Laura. Hard Rock, Hard Times: Coming of Age in Butte Montana, 1911-1917. 2005. 195p. (YA). per. (978-0-9722217-7-1(8)) Horse Creek Pubns.

Erskine, Kathryn. Quaking. 2007. 272p. (YA). (gr. 6 up). 16.99 (***978-0-399-24774-3(2)*** , Philomel) Penguin Group (USA) Inc.

Flinn, Alex. Fade to Black. 2006. 208p. (J). pap. 7.99 (978-0-06-056842-9(9) , HarperTeen) HarperCollins Pubs.

Frost, Daniel, tr. from SPA. You, Them, & the Others. 2006. Orig. Title: Tu, ellos y los Otros. (Illus.). 111p. (J). per. 12.95 net. (978-0-9785270-8-2(9)) Pasiteles Publishing Co.

Hill, Janet Muirhead. Danny's Dragon: A Story of Wartime Loss. Lehmkuhl, Pat & Ore, Peter, illus. 2006. 192p. (J). per. 10.00 (978-0-9772525-0-3(7)) Raven Publishing Inc. of Montana.

Hockerman, Dennis, illus. The Country Mouse & the City Mouse: A Tale of Tolerance. 2006. (J). 6.99 (978-1-59939-003-1(5) , Reader's Digest Young Families, Inc.) Reader's Digest Children's Publishing, Inc.

Holwitz, Peter. Scribbleville. Holwitz, Peter, illus. 2005. (Illus.). 40p. (J). (ps-3). 15.99 (978-0-399-24303-5(8) , Philomel) Penguin Group (USA) Inc.

Hooray for Boys & Girls! ed. 2006. (J). 15.95 (978-0-9776837-0-3(2)) West Woods Pr.

Hughes, Pat. Seeing the Elephant: A Story of the Civil War. Stark, Ken, illus. 2007. 40p. (J). (gr. 3 up). 16.00 (978-0-374-38024-3(4)) Farrar, Straus & Giroux.

Job. Yakari & the Beavers. 2007. 48p. pap. 9.99 (***978-1-905460-09-0(0)***) CineBook GBR. *Dist:* Biblio Distribution.

Johnston, Tony. The Worm Family. Innerst, Stacy, tr. Innerst, Stacy, illus. 2004. 40p. (J). 16.00 (978-0-15-205011-5(6) , Harcourt Children's Bks) Harcourt Children's Bks.

Kelly, Clint. Escape Underground. 2001. (KidWitness Tales Ser.). 128p. (J). (gr. 3-8). pap. 5.99 (978-1-56179-964-0(5)) Bethany Hse. Pubs.

—Escape Underground. 2001. (gr. 5-8). lib. bdg. 14.15 (978-0-613-85882-3(4)) Tandem Library Bks.

Kenrick, Angela. The Quilt That Wouldn't Be Built. Hunt, Devin, illus. 2001. (J). (978-1-57102-177-9(9) , Ideals Children's Bks.) Ideals Pubns.

Luchsinger, Dena Fox. Sometimes Smart Is Good: A Veces Es Bueno Ser Listo. Jerome, Karen A., illus. 2007. 32p. (J). (ps). 16.00 (978-0-8028-5215-1(7) , Eerdmans Bks For Young Readers) Eerdmans, William B. Publishing Co.

Lutz, Norma Jean. Carrie's Courage: Battling the Powers of Bigotry. 2005. (Sisters in Time Ser.). 144p. (J). pap. 4.97 (978-1-59310-656-0(4)) Barbour Publishing, Inc.

McCann, Jesse Leon, et al. The Scrapyard Detectives: Collected Cases Volume 1. 2007. 106p. (J). pap. 5.00 (***978-0-9797193-0-1(5)***) Diversity Foundation, The.

Morris, Gilbert. Too Smart Jones & the Pool Party Thief: A Gilbert Morris Mystery. 1999. (Gilbert Morris Mysteries Ser.: Vol. 1). (Illus.). 115p. (J). (gr. 2-7). pap. 5.99 (978-0-8024-4025-9(8)) Moody Pubs.

Moulton, Mark Kimball. One Enchanted Evening. Crouch, Karen Hillard, illus. 2003. 32p. (J). 14.95 (978-0-8249-5480-2(7)) Ideals Pubns.

—One Enchanted Evening. Crouch, Karen Hillard, illus. 2000. 32p. (J). (gr. k-3). 18.00 (978-0-7412-0439-4(8)) Lang Graphics, Ltd.

Moulton, Mark Kimball. A Royal Wedding. Good, Karen Hillard, illus. 2007. 32p. (J). (gr. k-3). 14.99 (***978-0-8249-8677-3(6)***) Ideals Pubns.

Pelley, Kathleen. The Giant King. Manning, Maurie, tr. Manning, Maurie, illus. 2003. (New Child & Family Press Titles Ser.). 32p. (ps-4). 14.95 (978-0-87868-880-7(3) , 8803, Child & Family Pr.) Child Welfare League of America, Inc.

Sagar, Marie. Jimmy's Adventures: I'm Bored & Mr. Gray Bat. 2007. 20p. (J). 7.00 (***978-0-8059-7494-2(6)***) Dorrance Publishing Co., Inc.

Shelley, Mary Wollstonecraft. Frankenstein: With a Discussion of Tolerance. Clift, Eva, tr. Clift, Eva, illus. 2003. (Values in Action Illustrated Classics Ser.). (J). (978-1-59203-048-4(3)) Learning Challenge, Inc.

Stonecipher, Philip. Boudreau of de Bayou. Perez Sanchez, Delia, tr. from ENG. 1999. (SPA & ENG., Illus.). ii, 22p. (J). (gr. 2-3). 6.95 (978-0-943864-92-1(5)) Davenport, May Pubs.

Swift, Jonathan. Gulliver's Travels: And A Discussion of Tolerance. Clift, Eva, illus. 2003. (Values in Action Illustrated Classics Ser.). 191p. (J). (978-1-59203-029-3(7)) Learning Challenge, Inc.

Swope, Sam. The Araboolies of Liberty Street. Root, Barry, illus. 2001. (Sunburst Bks.). 32p. (J). (ps up). reprint ed. pap. 6.95 (978-0-374-30390-7(8) , Sunburst) Farrar, Straus & Giroux.

—The Araboolies of Liberty Street. 2001. (gr. 3-6). lib. bdg. 14.10 (978-0-613-49713-8(9)) Tandem Library Bks.

Uhlberg, Myron. Dad, Jackie, & Me. Bootman, Colin, illus. 2005. 32p. (J). (ps-3). 16.95 (978-1-56145-329-0(3)) Peachtree Pubs., Ltd.

Vanoosting, James. Walking Mary. 2005. 144p. (J). (gr. 7 up). lib. bdg. 16.89 (978-0-06-028472-5(2)) HarperCollins Pubs.

Wahl, Jan. Candy Shop. Wong, Nicole, illus. 2005. 32p. (J). (ps-ps). pap. 6.95 (978-1-57091-668-7(3)) Charlesbridge Publishing, Inc.

—Candy Shop. Wong, Nicole E., illus. 2004. 32p. (J). 15.95 (978-1-57091-508-6(3)) Charlesbridge Publishing, Inc.

Williams, Sam. Talk Peace. Moriuchi, Mique, illus. 2005. 32p. (J). 16.95 (978-0-8234-1936-4(3)) Holiday Hse., Inc.

Wood, Douglas. Old Turtle & the Broken Truth. Muth, Jon J., illus. 2003. 64p. (J). pap. 17.95 (978-0-439-32109-9(3)) Scholastic, Inc.

TOLKIEN, J, R. R. (JOHN RONALD RUEL), 1892-1973

Collins, David R. J. R. R. Tolkien. 2005. (Lighting Bolt Bios Ser.). (Illus.). 112p. (J). (gr. 6-12). lib. bdg. 27.93 (978-0-8225-2470-0(8)) Lerner Publishing Group.

Coren, Michael. J. R. R. Tolkien: The Man Who Created the Lord of the Rings. 2001. 11.64 (978-0-606-22238-9(3)) Tandem Library Bks.

Heims, Neil. J. R. R. Tolkien. 2004. (Great Writers Ser.). (Illus.). 128p. (YA). (gr. 9-13). 31.95 (978-0-7910-7847-1(7) , Chelsea Hse.) Facts On File, Inc.

Lynch, Doris. J. R. R. Tolkien: Creator of Languages & Legends. 2003. (Great Life Stories: Writers & Poets Ser.). (Illus.). 128p. (J). 30.50 (978-0-531-12253-2(0) , Watts, Franklin) Scholastic Library Publishing.

Neimark, Anne E. Myth Maker: J. R. R. Tolkien. Newbold, Greg, illus. 1998. 128p. (J). (gr. 5-9). pap. 4.95 (978-0-688-15741-8(6) , Harper Trophy) HarperCollins Pubs.

—Myth Maker: J. R. R. Tolkien. 1998. (J). (978-0-606-13639-6(8)) Tandem Library Bks.

Parker, Victoria. J.R.R. Tolkien. 2006. (Illus.). 48p. (J). pap. (978-1-4034-7338-7(2)); lib. bdg. (978-1-4034-7335-6(8)) Heinemann Library.

Repun, Graceiela. Master of the Rings: Inside the World of J. R. R. Tolkein. 2003. (Illus.). 176p. pap. 13.95 (978-1-84046-400-9(3)) Totem Bks. GBR. *Dist:* National Bk. Network.

TOLSTOY, LEO, GRAF, 1828-1910

Chapman, Lynne F. Leo Tolstoy. 1999. (Notebooks Ser.). 48p. 17.95 (978-1-56846-156-4(9) , Creative Editions) Creative Co., The.

Tolstoy, Leo. Death of Ivan Ilych & Other Stories. 2003. (gr. 7-12). lib. bdg. 15.25 (978-0-613-67240-5(2)) Tandem Library Bks.

TONGUE

Bonsignore, Joan. Stick Out Your Tongue! Fantastic Facts, Features, & Functions of Animal & Human Tongues. Ward, John T., illus. 2001. 32p. (J). (gr. k-3). 15.95 (978-1-56145-230-9(0)) Peachtree Pubs., Ltd.

Fernandez, A. & Fernandez, Q. Hooray for My Taste. (Hooray for My Senses Ser.). (Illus.). (J). 19.27 (978-1-58952-376-0(8)) Rourke Publishing, LLC.

Libra, Anna. Why Does That Taste Bad? An Inside Look at the Tongue. 2003. (J). pap. (978-1-58417-069-3(7)); lib. bdg. (978-1-58417-006-8(9)) Lake Street Pubs.

Olien, Rebecca. Tasting. 2005. (Illus.). 24p. (J). (ps-7). lib. bdg. 21.26 (978-0-7368-4304-1(3)) Capstone Pr., Inc.

Pryor, Kimberley Jane. Tasting. 2003. (Senses Ser.). (Illus.). 32p. (gr. 2-4). 23.00 (978-0-7910-7557-9(5) , Chelsea Hse.) Facts On File, Inc.

Rau, Dana Meachen. Yum! A Book about Your Sense of Taste. Peterson, Rick, illus. 2005. (Amazing Body Ser.). 24p. (C). (gr. k-3). 22.60 (978-1-4048-1021-1(8)) Picture Window Bks.

TOOLS

see also Agricultural Machinery; Carpentry—Tools; Machinery

Adams, Barbara. A World of Tools. Date not set. (Early Science Big Bks.). (Illus.). 16p. (J). (ps-2). pap. 16.95 (978-1-58273-115-5(2)) Sundance/Newbridge Educational Publishing.

Archer, Amanda. My Dad's Toolbox: Fabulous Pop-up Toolbox with Working Tools. Van Der Leijgraaf, Deborah, photos by. 2007. (Illus.). 12p. (J). 16.99 (978-0-7641-5971-8(2)) Barron's Educational Series, Inc.

Benchmark Education Staff, compiled by. Tools & Technology. 2006. spiral bd. 139.00 (***978-1-4108-7034-6(0)***) Benchmark Education Co.

Burton, Margie, et al. People Use Tools. Evento, Susan, ed. 1998. (Early Connections Ser.). 16p. (J). (gr. k-2). pap. 4.25 (978-1-892393-56-2(5)) Benchmark Education Co.

Canizares, Susan. Tools. 1999. (J). pap. 2.50 (978-0-439-08128-3(9)) Scholastic, Inc.

Clements, Andrew. Workshop. Wisniewski, David, illus. 1999. 32p. (J). (gr. k-3). tchr. ed. 16.00 (978-0-395-85579-9(9) , Clarion Bks.) Houghton Mifflin Co. Trade & Reference Div.

Cool Tools. 2002. (Illus.). (J). pap. 3.74 (978-0-7398-5840-0(8)) Steck-Vaughn.

Cooper, Sharon Katz. Whose Tools Are These? A Look at Tools Workers Use—Big, Sharp, & Smooth. Muehlenhardt, Amy Bailey, illus. 2006. (Whose Is It? Ser.). 24p. (J). (ps-2). 22.60 (978-1-4048-1602-2(X)) Picture Window Bks.

Dahl, Michael & Shea, Denise. Corta y Para: Un Libro Sobre Cunas. Shea, Denise, illus. 2007. (ENG & SPA.). (J). lib. bdg. (***978-1-4048-3210-7(6)***) Picture Window Bks.

Dalmatian Press Staff. Little Builder: Board Book Set, 4 bks., Set. 2003. (Illus.). 10p. (J). bds. 7.99 (978-1-57759-714-8(1)) Dalmatian Pr.

Davis, Nancy. Who Uses a Wrench? Popular Mechanics Staff, ed. 2004. (Popular Mechanics for Kids Ser.). (Illus.). 10p. (J). bds. 4.95 (978-1-58816-372-1(5)) Hearst Bks.

Douglas, Lloyd G. What Is a Screw? 2002. (Wel-Simple MaChines Ser.). (Illus.). 24p. (J). (ps-2). 18.00 (978-0-516-23966-8(X)); pap. 4.95 (978-0-516-24025-1(0)) Scholastic Library Publishing. (Children's Pr.).

Frost, Helen. What Are Screws? Saunders-Smith, Gail, ed. 2001. (Looking at Simple Machines Ser.). (Illus.). 24p. (J). (gr. k-1). lib. bdg. 15.93 (978-0-7368-0848-4(5) , Pebble Bks.) Capstone Pr., Inc.

Gallimard Jeunesse Publishing Staff & Delafosse, Claude. Tools. Barish, Wendy, tr. from FRE. Moignot, Daniel, illus. 1999. (First Discovery Book Ser.). 24p. (J). (ps-2). spiral bd. 12.95 (978-0-439-04404-2(9)) Scholastic, Inc.

The Go-cart Team: Individual Nonfiction Title Six-Packs. 24p. (gr. 3-4). 44.00 (978-0-7635-4484-3(1)) Rigby Education.

Guarnaccia, Steven. Bolts. 1999. 32p. (J). (978-0-7868-0030-8(5)) Hyperion Pr.

—The Bolts. 1999. 32p. (J). (978-0-7868-2025-2(X)) Hyperion Bks. for Children.

Harcourt School Publishers Staff. In the Classroom. 3rd ed. 2002. (Trophies English Language Learners Ser.). (Illus.). pap. 5.10 (978-0-15-327705-4(X)) Harcourt Schl. Pubs.

Hooker, Karen. My New Toolbox. McWilliams, Sean, illus. 1999. 8p. (J). (gr. k-2). pap. (978-1-880612-96-5(8) , Seedling Pubns.) Continental Pr., Inc.

Innovative Kids Staff & Bockol, Leslie. My Tool Box. Filipowich, Bob, illus. 2003. (Soft Shapes Ser.). (J). (ps-ps). 9.99 (978-1-58476-174-7(1)) Innovative Kids.

Keller-Mathers, Susan & Puccio, Kristin. Big Tools for Young Thinkers: Using Creative Problem Solving Tools with Primary Students. 2000. 70p. tchr. ed. 19.95 (978-1-882664-60-3(4)) Prufrock Pr.

Luder, George. Trabajando Con Mi Papito. Maval Publishing Inc. Staff, illus. 2001. Tr. of Working with Dad. (SPA.). 32p. (J). (gr. k-3). pap. 7.50 (978-1-59134-007-2(1)) Maval Publishing, Inc.

Miura, Taro. Tools. 2006. (Illus.). 52p. (J). 15.95 (978-0-8118-5519-8(8)) Chronicle Bks. LLC.

Monroe, Andrea. The Science of Tools. 2003. (Living Science Ser.). (Illus.). 32p. (J). (gr. 1-3). pap. 7.95 (978-1-930954-31-1(X)) Weigl Pubs., Inc.

Morris, Ann. Tools. Heyman, Ken, illus. 1998. 32p. (J). (ps-3). pap. 6.99 (978-0-688-16165-1(0) , Harper Trophy) HarperCollins Pubs.

Munro, Andrea. The Science of Tools. 2001. (Living Science Ser.). (Illus.). 32p. (J). (gr. 2 up). lib. bdg. 24.67 (978-0-8368-2793-4(7)) Stevens, Gareth Inc.

My Drill. 2001. (Home Depot Board Bks.). (Illus.). 10p. (J). (ps-1). bds. 6.95 (978-0-439-30934-9(4) , Cartwheel Bks.) Scholastic, Inc.

My Screwdriver. 2001. (Home Depot Board Bks.). (Illus.). 10p. (J). (ps-1). bds. 6.95 (978-0-439-30933-2(6) , Cartwheel Bks.) Scholastic, Inc.

Oxlade, Chris. Screws. 2003. (Useful Machines Ser.). (Illus.). 32p. (J). pap. (978-1-4034-3679-5(7)); lib. bdg. 22.79 (978-1-4034-3664-1(9)) Heinemann Library.

Popular Mechanics Staff, ed. Who Uses a Drill? Davis, Nancy, illus. 2004. (Popular Mechanics for Kids Ser.). 10p. (J). bds. 4.95 (978-1-58816-370-7(9)) Hearst Bks.

—Who Uses a Hammer? Davis, Nancy, illus. 2004. (Popular Mechanics for Kids Ser.). 10p. (J). bds. 4.95 (978-1-58816-371-4(7)) Hearst Bks.

—Who Uses a Saw? Davis, Nancy, illus. 2004. (Popular Mechanics for Kids Ser.). 10p. (J). bds. 4.95 (978-1-58816-373-8(3)) Hearst Bks.

Rau, Dana Meachen. Builders/Los Constructores. 2007. (Tools We Use/Instrumentos de Trabajo Ser.). (SPA & ENG.). 32p. (J). lib. bdg. 22.79 (***978-0-7614-2821-3(6)*** , Benchmark Bks.) Cavendish, Marshall Corp.

Robbins, Ken. Tools. 1999. (J). 24.99 (978-0-590-07881-8(X) , Blue Sky Pr., The) Scholastic, Inc.

Sloan, Peter. Tools at Home. 1999. (gr. k-3). lib. bdg. 11.80 (978-0-613-30798-7(4)) Tandem Library Bks.

Snyder, Inez. Gardening Tools. 2002. (Welcome Bks.). (Illus.). 24p. (J). (ps-2). pap. 4.95 (978-0-516-24037-4(4) , Children's Pr.) Scholastic Library Publishing.

—Tools, 6 vols., Set. 2004. (Illus.). 24p. (J). (ps-2). 87.00 (978-0-516-29313-4(3)) Scholastic Library Publishing.

Stickland, Paul. Tools. Stickland, Paul, illus. 1998. (Working Ser.). (Illus.). 16p. (J). (ps up). lib. bdg. 19.93 (978-0-8368-2159-8(9)) Stevens, Gareth Inc.

Tieck, Sarah. Screws. 2007. (Simple Machines Ser.). (Illus.). 24p. (J). (gr. k-4). lib. bdg. 21.35 (978-1-59679-817-5(3)) ABDO Publishing Co.

Tools Scientists Use Set F, 6 vols. (Phonics Readers Ser.). (gr. k-2). 28.95 (978-0-7368-4080-4(X)) Red Brick Learning.

Ward, Beck, et al. Tools: Pull the Tabs! Change the Pictures! 2004. (Magic Windows Ser.). (Illus.). 8p. (J). pap. 4.95 (978-0-7624-1845-9(1) , Running Pr. Kids) Running Pr. Bk. Pubs.

Weinberger, Kimberly. The Home Depot Big Book of Tools. LaPadula, Tom, illus. 2001. (Home Depot Ser.). 32p. (J). (ps-1). pap. 12.95 (978-0-439-28857-6(6) , Cartwheel Bks.) Scholastic, Inc.

—Home Depot Build-Your-Own Toolbox 1-2-3. Miller, Edward, illus. 2001. (Home Depot Ser.). 32p. (J). (ps-1). pap. 3.50 (978-0-439-28859-0(2) , Cartwheel Bks.) Scholastic, Inc.

—My Saw. Davis, Billy, illus. 2001. (Home Depot Board Bks.). 5p. (J). (ps-1). bds. 6.95 (978-0-439-29500-0(9) , Cartwheel Bks.) Scholastic, Inc.

Welsbacher, Anne. Screws. 2000. (Bridgestone Science Library). (Illus.). 24p. (J). (gr. 1-2). lib. bdg. 18.60 (978-0-7368-0613-8(X) , Bridgestone Bks.) Capstone Pr., Inc.

Whitehouse, Patricia. Make It Smooth. (Illus.). 24p. 2007. (J). (978-1-60044-208-7(0)); 2005. pap. 27.00 (***978-1-59515-562-7(7)***) Rourke Publishing, LLC.

—Plant & Prune. 2007. (Illus.). 24p. (J). (978-1-60044-210-0(2)) Rourke Publishing, LLC.

—Put It Together. 2007. 24p. (J). (978-1-60044-211-7(0)) Rourke Publishing, LLC.

Whitehouse, Patricia. Take It Apart. 2005. (Readers for Writers Emergent Ser.). (Illus.). 24p. pap. 18.00 (***978-1-59515-560-3(0)***) Rourke Publishing, LLC.

Whitehouse, Patty. Take It Apart: Took Kit. 2007. (Illus.). 24p. (J). (978-1-60044-212-4(9)) Rourke Publishing, LLC.

Williams, Linda D. Backhoes. 2004. (Pebble Plus: Mighty Machines Ser.). (Illus.). 24p. (J). lib. bdg. 19.93 (978-0-7368-2592-4(4) , Pebble Bks.) Capstone Pr., Inc.

A Worker's Tools: Individual Title Six-Packs. (Discovery World Ser.). 16p. (gr. 1-2). 28.00 (978-0-7635-8459-7(2)) Rigby Education.

TOOLS—FICTION

Capozzi, Suzy. Fix that Fence! 2006. (Illus.). 14p. (J). (ps-1). bds. 9.99 (978-0-375-83238-3(6) , Golden Bks.) Random Hse. Children's Bks.

Connor, Leslie. Miss Bridie Chose a Shovel. Azarian, Mary, tr. Azarian, Mary, illus. 2004. 32p. (J). (gr. k-3). tchr. ed. 16.00 (978-0-618-30564-3(5)) Houghton Mifflin Co. Trade & Reference Div.

—Miss Bridie Chose a Shovel. Azarian, Mary, illus. unabr. ed. 2005. (J). (gr. k-3). 27.95 incl. audio (978-0-8045-6936-1(3) , SAC6936); 29.95 incl. audio compact disk (978-0-8045-4135-0(3) , SACD4135) Spoken Arts, Inc.

Fry, Sonali. Talkin' Tools Take Charge. Goudreau, Roc, illus. 2002. (Tonka Talkin' Tools Ser.). 8p. (J). bds. 5.99 (978-0-439-40144-9(5)) Scholastic, Inc.

Golden Books Staff. Fix It With Bob: Scruffty Helps Out. 2002. (Illus.). 14p. (J). (ps-1). bds. 9.99 (978-0-307-20074-7(4) , Golden Bks.) Random Hse. Children's Bks.

—Fix It With Bob: The Very Busy Day. 2002. (Illus.). 14p. (J). (ps-1). bds. 9.99 (978-0-307-20075-4(2) , Golden Bks.) Random Hse. Children's Bks.

Harcourt School Publishers Staff. A Dinosaur for Middleville. 3rd ed. 2002. (Trophies English Language Learners Ser.). (Illus.). pap. 5.10 (978-0-15-327889-1(7)) Harcourt Schl. Pubs.

—Three Kite Tales On Level. 3rd ed. 2002. (Trophies Reading Program Ser.). (Illus.). pap. 5.10 (978-0-15-323257-2(9)) Harcourt Schl. Pubs.

Higginson, Sheila. Over the River & Through the Woods. Disney Storybook Artists Staff, illus. 2007. 24p. (J). (ps-k). pap. 3.99 (***978-1-4231-0649-4(0)***) Disney Pr.

Johnson, Stephen T. My Little Red Toolbox. 2000. (Illus.). 14p. (J). (ps-2). 19.95 (978-0-15-202154-2(X) , Silver Whistle) Harcourt Trade Pubs.

Klinting, Lars. Harvey the Carpenter. 2005. (Handy Harvey Ser.). (Illus.). 40p. (J). (ps-k). pap. 4.95 (978-0-7534-5912-6(4) , Kingfisher) Houghton Mifflin Co. Trade & Reference Div.

McNeil, Niki, et al. HOCPP 1070 Mike & Mary Anne the Steam Shovel. 2006. spiral bd. (***978-1-60308-070-5(8)***) In the Hands of a Child.

Monroe, Chris. Monkey with a Tool Belt. 2008. (J). lib. bdg. (***978-0-8225-7631-0(7)***) Univ. of Minnesota Pr.

Reed, Nathan, illus. My Little Toolbox. 2005. 10p. (J). bds. 6.99 (978-0-689-87706-3(4) , Little Simon) Simon & Schuster Children's Publishing.

Rockwell, Anne & Rockwell, Harlow. The Toolbox. Rockwell, Anne & Rockwell, Harlow, illus. 2006. (Illus.). 24p. (J). 6.95 (978-0-8027-9609-7(5)) Walker & Co.

Schaefer, Lola. Toolbox Twins. Iwai, Melissa, illus. rev. ed. 2006. 32p. (J). 16.95 (978-0-8050-7733-9(2)) Holt, Henry & Co.

Shulman, Lisa. Old MacDonald Had a Woodshop. Wolff, Ashley, illus. 2002. 32p. (J). 16.99 (978-0-399-23596-2(5) , Putnam Juvenile) Penguin Group (USA) Inc.

Shulman, Lisa & Wolff, Ashley. Old MacDonald Had a Woodshop. 2004. (Illus.). 32p. (J). reprint ed. pap. 6.99 (978-0-14-240186-6(2) , Puffin) Penguin Group (USA) Inc.

Singer, Marilyn. Let's Build a Clubhouse. Bush, Timothy, illus. 2006. 32p. (J). (gr. k-3). 16.00 (978-0-618-30670-1(6) , Clarion Bks.) Houghton Mifflin Co. Trade & Reference Div.

Slater, David Michael. The Sharpest Tool in the Shed. Reibeling, Brandon, illus. 2007. (Missy Swiss & More Ser.). 32p. (J). (ps-4). lib. bdg. 27.07 (***978-1-60270-013-0(3)*** , Looking Glass Library) Magic Wagon.

Sturges, Philemon. I Love Tools! Halpern, Shari, illus. 2006. 32p. (J). 12.99 (978-0-06-009287-0(4)); lib. bdg. 14.89 (978-0-06-009288-7(2)) HarperCollins Pubs.

Weinberger, Kimberly. My Surprise Toolbox. LaPadula, Tom, illus. 2002. (Home Depot Ser.). 5p. (J). bds. 10.95 (978-0-439-28861-3(4) , Cartwheel Bks.) Scholastic, Inc.

West, Tracey. Teeth Thief. 2002. (gr. k-3). lib. bdg. 11.25 (978-0-613-43941-1(4)) Tandem Library Bks.

TORNADOES

see also Storms

Allen, Jean. Tornadoes. 2000. (Natural Disasters Ser.). (Illus.). 48p. (J). (gr. 3-4). lib. bdg. 21.26 (978-0-7368-0588-9(5) , Capstone High-Interest Bks.) Capstone Pr., Inc.

Ball, Jacqueline A. Tornado! The 1974 Super Outbreak. 2005. (X-Treme Disasters That Changed America Ser.). (J). lib. bdg. 25.27 (978-1-59716-009-4(1)) Bearport Publishing Co., Inc.

Berger, Melvin. Do Tornadoes Really Twist? 2000. (gr. 3-6). lib. bdg. 14.10 (978-0-613-32476-2(5)) Tandem Library Bks.

Berger, Melvin & Berger, Gilda. Do Tornadoes Really Twist? Questions & Answers about Tornadoes & Hurricanes. Bond, Barbara Higgins, illus. 2000. (Question & Answer Ser.). 48p. (J). (gr. 2-5). pap. 14.95 (978-0-439-09584-6(0)) Scholastic, Inc.

—Do Tornadoes Really Twist? Questions & Answers about Tornadoes & Hurricanes. 2000. (Scholastic Question & Answer Ser.). (J). 10.01 (978-0-439-09585-3(9)) Scholastic Inc.

—Hurricanes Have Eyes but Can't See: And Other Amazing Facts about Wild Weather. 2003. (Illus.). 48p. (J). (978-0-439-54980-6(9)) Scholastic, Inc.

Bockhoff, P. M. & Kallen, Stuart A. Tornadoes. 2002. (Kidhaven Science Library). (Illus.). 48p. (J). (gr. 3-5). 26.20 (978-0-7377-1032-8(2) , Kidhaven) Thomson Gale.

Burby, Liza N. Tornadoes. 1999. (Extreme Weather Ser.). (Illus.). 24p. (J). lib. bdg. 18.75 (978-0-8239-5289-2(4)) Rosen Publishing Group, Inc., The.

Cassie, Brian. Tornadoes. (Science Readers Ser.). (Illus.). 32p. (J). pap. 3.99 (978-0-439-42505-6(0)); 2002. (978-0-439-26990-2(3) , Scholastic Reference) Scholastic, Inc.

Ceban, Bonnie. Tornadoes: Disaster & Survival. 2005. (Deadly Disasters Ser.). (Illus.). 48p. (J). lib. bdg. 23.93 (978-0-7660-2383-3(4)) Enslow Pubs., Inc.

Chambers, Catherine. Tornado. (Wild Weather Ser.). (Illus.). 32p. (J). 2007. (gr. 2-4). pap. 7.99 (***978-1-4034-9590-7(4)***); 2007. (gr. 2-4). lib. bdg. 25.36 (***978-1-4034-9581-5(5)***); 2002. (gr. k-2). lib. bdg. 21.36 (978-1-58810-652-0(7)) Heinemann Library.

Chambers, Catherine. Tornadoes. (Disasters in Nature Ser.). (Illus.). 48p. (J). (gr. 4-7). 2002. pap. 8.50 (978-1-58810-335-2(8) , 91081); 2000. lib. bdg. 24.22 (978-1-57572-430-0(8)) Heinemann Library.

Davies, Jon. Project Storm Chaser: A Kids' Guide to Safe Storm Chasing. 2007. (J). (***978-1-56037-407-7(1)***) Farcountry Pr.

Doeden, Matt. Tornadoes. 2008. (Pull Ahead Books-Forces of Nature Ser.). (J). lib. bdg. 22.60 (***978-0-8225-7910-6(3)*** , Lerner Pubns.) Lerner Publishing Group.

Donnelly, Karen J. Storms of the Past & the Future. 2003. (Earths Changing Weather & Climate Ser.). (Illus.). 24p. (J). lib. bdg. 18.75 (978-0-8239-6216-7(4) , PowerKids Pr.) Rosen Publishing Group, Inc., The.

Galiano, Dean. Tornadoes. 2005. (Weather Watchers' Library). (Illus.). 48p. (YA). (gr. 5-8). lib. bdg. 23.95 (978-0-8239-3094-4(7) , WETORN) Rosen Publishing Group, Inc., The.

Graf, Mike. Tornado! The Strongest Winds on Earth. 1999. (Cover-to-Cover Bks.). (Illus.). 56p. (J). pap. (978-0-7891-2871-3(3)); (gr. 4-7). lib. bdg. 17.95 (978-0-7807-7860-3(X)) Perfection Learning Corp.

Group/McGraw-Hill, Wright. Savage Storms: Tornadoes & Hurricanes, 6 vols. (Book2WebTM Ser.). (gr. 4-8). 36.50 (978-0-322-04424-1(3)) Wright Group, The.

Harris, Nancy. Tornadoes. 2003. (gr. 7-12). lib. bdg. 30.35 (978-0-613-73879-8(9)) Tandem Library Bks.

Hayden, Kate. Twisters!, Vol. 2. Dennis, Peter, illus. 2000. (Readers Ser.). 32p. (J). (ps-3). pap. 3.99 (978-0-7894-5709-7(1)) Dorling Kindersley Publishing, Inc.

—Twisters! 2000. (gr. k-3). lib. bdg. 11.80 (978-0-613-33171-5(0)) Tandem Library Bks.

Hayden, Kate & Dorling Kindersley Publishing Staff. Twisters! Dennis, Peter, illus. 2000. (Readers Ser.). 32p. (J). (ps-3). 12.99 (978-0-7894-5708-0(3)) Dorling Kindersley Publishing, Inc.

Jeffrey, Gary. Tornadoes & Superstorms. Riley, Terry, illus. 2007. 48p. (J). (***978-1-4042-1986-1(2)***); pap. (***978-1-4042-1985-4(4)***); (gr. 5-8). lib. bdg. 29.25 (978-1-4042-1993-9(5)) Rosen Publishing Group, Inc., The.

Jennings, Terry. Hurricanes & Tornadoes. 1999. (Natural Disasters Ser.). (Illus.). 32p. (J). lib. bdg. 16.95 (978-1-929298-47-1(1)) Chrysalis Education.

Kerrod, Robin. Shaking Earth: Volcanoes, Earthquakes, Hurricanes Etc. 2005. (Illus.). 128p. pap. 17.99 (978-1-84476-097-8(9) , Southwater) Anness Publishing GBR. *Dist:* National Bk. Network.

Leathers, Dan. The Year of the Tornadoes 1985. 2007. (Natural Disasters Ser.). (J). lib. bdg. 25.70 (***978-1-58415-571-3(X)***) Mitchell Lane Pubs., Inc.

Lindop, Laurie. Chasing Tornadoes. 2003. (Science on the Edge Ser.). (Illus.). 80p. (gr. 5 up). lib. bdg. 26.90 (978-0-7613-2703-5(7) , Twenty-First Century Bks.) Lerner Publishing Group.

Lock, Deborah. Tornados! 2006. (Dk Readers Ser.). 32p. (J). 14.99 (978-0-7566-2249-7(2)); pap. 3.99 (978-0-7566-2248-0(4)) Dorling Kindersley Publishing, Inc.

Meister, Cari. Tornadoes. 1999. (Nature's Fury Ser.). (Illus.). 32p. (J). (gr. 3-8). lib. bdg. 24.21 (978-1-57765-081-2(6) , ABDO & Daughters) ABDO Publishing Co.

Mezzanotte, Jim. Tornadoes. 2006. (J). pap. (***978-0-8368-7923-0(6)***); lib. bdg. (***978-0-8368-7916-2(3)***) Stevens, Gareth Inc. (Weekly Reader Early Learning Library).

Mogil, H. Michael. Tornadoes. 2003. (WorldLife Library). (Illus.). 72p. (J). (gr. 5 up). pap. 16.95 (978-0-89658-522-5(0)) Voyageur Pr., Inc.

Morris, Neil. Hurricanes & Tornadoes. 1999. (Natural Disasters Ser.). (Illus.). 31p. (J). (gr. 5 up). pap. 5.95 (978-0-7641-1060-3(8)) Barron's Educational Series, Inc.

—Hurricanes & Tornadoes. 1998. (Wonders of Our World Ser.). (Illus.). 32p. (J). (gr. 3-4). lib. bdg. (978-0-86505-831-6(8)) Crabtree Publishing Co.

—Inside Hurricanes & Tornadoes. 2006. (Inside Nature's Disasters Ser.). (Illus.). 36p. (J). lib. bdg. (978-0-8368-7249-1(5)) Stevens, Gareth Inc.

Nicolson, Cynthia Pratt. Tornado! 2003. (Disaster Ser.). (Illus.). 32p. (J). (gr. 4-6). (978-1-55074-972-4(2)); (978-1-55074-951-9(X)) Kids Can Pr., Ltd.

—Tornado! 2003. (gr. 3-6). lib. bdg. 15.25 (978-0-613-87155-6(3)) Tandem Library Bks.

Olson, Nathan. Tornadoes. 2005. (Weather Update Ser.). (Illus.). 24p. (J). (ps-7). lib. bdg. 21.26 (978-0-7368-4333-1(7) , Bridgestone Bks.) Capstone Pr., Inc.

Orme, David & Orme, Helen. Tornadoes. 2005. (What on Earth? Ser.). (Illus.). 32p. (J). 25.50 (978-0-516-25321-3(2) , Children's Pr.) Scholastic Library Publishing.

Oxlade, Chris. Storm Warning: Tornadoes. 2004. (Turbulent Planet Ser.). (Illus.). 48p. (J). 28.56 (978-1-4109-1099-8(7)); pap. 8.50 (978-1-4109-1206-0(X)) Harcourt Schl. Pubs.

—Storm Warning: Tornadoes. 2005. (Turbulent Planet Ser.). (Illus.). 48p. (J). (gr. 4-7). pap. 9.35 (978-1-4109-1750-8(9)); (978-1-4109-1740-9(1)) Steck-Vaughn.

Park, Louise. Tornadoes. 2007. (J). (***978-1-59920-114-6(3)***) Smart Apple Media.

Phelan, Glen. Extreme Weather. 2004. (National Geographic Reading Expeditions Ser.). (Illus.). 32p. (J). pap. (978-0-7922-4575-9(X)) National Geographic Society.

Richards, Julie. Terrifying Tornadoes. 2001. (Natural Disasters Ser.). (Illus.). 32p. (J). (gr. 5 up). 28.00 (978-0-7910-6579-2(0) , 010454, Chelsea Hse.) Facts On File, Inc.

Scavuzzo, Wendy. Tornado Alert! 2004. (Disaster Alert! Ser.). (Illus.). 32p. (J). pap. (978-0-7787-1603-7(1)); (978-0-7787-1571-9(X)) Crabtree Publishing Co.

Schreiber, Anne. Twister Trouble. (Magic School Bus Chapter Bks.). 2001. (Illus.). (J). (978-0-606-20780-5(5)); 2000. (gr. 3-6). lib. bdg. 11.80 (978-0-613-33170-8(2)) Tandem Library Bks.

Sherrow, Victoria. Plains Outbreak Tornadoes: Killer Twisters. 1998. (American Disasters Ser.). (Illus.). 48p. (YA). (gr. 4-10). lib. bdg. 23.93 (978-0-7660-1059-8(7)) Enslow Pubs., Inc.

Simon, Seymour. Tornadoes. Simon, Seymour, illus. 2001. (Illus.). 32p. (J). (gr. k-3). pap. 6.99 (978-0-06-443791-2(4) , Harper Trophy) HarperCollins Pubs.

—Tornadoes. 1999. (Illus.). 32p. (J). (gr. k-3). 16.89 (978-0-688-14647-4(3)) HarperCollins Pubs.

—Tornadoes. 2001. (Illus.). (J). (ps-3). lib. bdg. 15.30 (978-0-613-36023-4(0)) Tandem Library Bks.

T
U
V

Sood, Malini. Hurricanes & Tornadoes. 2008. (J). lib. bdg. (***978-1-4042-3900-5(6)*** , PowerKids Pr.) Rosen Publishing Group, Inc., The.

Spilsbury, Louise & Spilsbury, Richard. Terrifying Tornadoes. 2004. (Heinemann Infosearch Ser.). (Illus.). 32p. (J). pap. 7.50 (978-1-4034-5447-8(7)); lib. bdg. (978-1-4034-4787-6(X)) Heinemann Library.

Steele, Christy. Tornadoes. 2000. (Nature on the Rampage Ser.). (Illus.). 32p. (J). (gr. 4-7). lib. bdg. 22.83 (978-0-7398-1794-0(9)) Raintree.

Thomas, Rick. Twisters: A Book about Tornadoes. Shea, Denise, illus. 2005. (Amazing Science Ser.). 24p. (C). (gr. k-3). 22.60 (978-1-4048-0930-7(9)) Picture Window Bks.

Thoron, Joe. Tornadoes. 2006. (Kaleidoscope Natural Disasters Ser.). (Illus.). 48p. (J). lib. bdg. 28.50 (978-0-7614-2104-7(1) , Benchmark Bks.) Cavendish, Marshall Corp.

Trueit, Trudi Strain. Storm Chasers. 2002. (Watts Library). (Illus.). 64p. (J). (gr. 5-7). 25.50 (978-0-531-11971-6(8) , Watts, Franklin) Scholastic Library Publishing.

Twister. 1999. (SmartReader Ser.). (J). Level 1. pap., tchr. ed. 19.95 incl. audio (978-0-7887-0756-8(6) , 79344T3); Level 2. pap., tchr. ed. 19.95 incl. audio (978-0-7887-0762-9(0) , 79345T3) Recorded Bks., LLC.

Verkaik, Jerrine & Verkaik, Arjen. Under the Whirlwind: Everything You Need to Know about Tornadoes but Didn't Know Who to Ask. 2nd ed. 2001. (Illus.). 224p. pap. 21.95 (978-0-9681537-4-1(7)) Whirlwind Bks. CAN. *Dist:* Independent Pubs. Group.

Weather Wise: Terrifying Tornadoes! 2001. (J). pap. 5.95 (978-1-56911-727-9(6)) Learning Resources, Inc.

Weingartz, Jill. Tornadoes. 2001. (Natural Disasters Ser.). (Illus.). 24p. (J). 21.35 (978-1-58340-122-4(9)) Smart Apple Media.

White, Matt. Storm Chasers: On the Trail of Deadly Tornadoes. 2002. (High Five Reading Ser.). (Illus.). 48p. (J). (gr. 2-3). lib. bdg. 22.60 (978-0-7368-9552-1(3) , Capstone High-Interest Bks.); pap. (978-0-7368-9530-9(2)) Capstone Pr., Inc.

Woods, Michael & Woods, Mary B. Tornadoes. 2007. (Disasters up Close Ser.). (Illus.). 64p. (J). 27.93 (978-0-8225-4714-3(7) , Lerner Pubns.) Lerner Publishing Group.

World Book, Inc Staff, contrib. by. Tornadoes. 2007. (J). (***978-0-7166-9813-5(7)); (978-0-7166-9801-2(3))*** World Bk., Inc.

TORNADOES—FICTION

Arnold, Marsha D. The Bravest of Us All. Sneed, Brad, illus. 2000. 32p. (J). (ps-3). 16.99 (978-0-8037-2409-9(8) , Dial) Penguin Group (USA) Inc.

Beard, Darleen Bailey. Twister. Carpenter, Nancy, illus. 32p. (J). 2003. pap. 6.95 (978-0-374-48014-1(1) , Sunburst); 1999. 16.00 (978-0-374-37977-3(7) , Farrar, Straus & Giroux (BYR)) Farrar, Straus & Giroux.

—Twister. 2003. (gr. k-3). lib. bdg. 14.10 (978-0-613-59749-4(4)) Tandem Library Bks.

Bell, William. Death Wind. 2006. 112p. (YA). lib. bdg. 14.95 (978-1-55143-543-5(8)) Orca Bk. Pubs. USA.

Brooke, Lauren. Darkest Hour. 2003. (Heartland Ser.). 160p. mass mkt. 4.99 (978-0-439-42508-7(5) , Scholastic Paperbacks) Scholastic, Inc.

—Darkest Hour. 2003. (gr. 3-6). lib. bdg. 12.40 (978-0-613-72128-8(4)) Tandem Library Bks.

Clay, Shenise Tiana. The Kids Who Were Left Alone When There Was A Tornado. 2004. (J). 6.00 (978-0-9701482-6-1(7)) Changing Lives Publishing.

Cook, Sherry & Johnson, Terri. Timothy Tornado, 26. Kuhn, Jesse, illus. l.t. ed. 2006. (Quirkles—Exploring Phonics through Science Ser.: 20). 32p. 7.99 (978-1-933815-19-0(1) , Quirkles, The) Creative 3, LLC.

Fisher, Carolyn. A Twisted Tale. 2004. (Illus.). 33p. (J). (gr. k-4). reprint ed. 16.00 (978-0-7567-8412-6(3)) DIANE Publishing Co.

—A Twisted Tale. 2002. (Illus.). 40p. (J). (ps-3). 15.95 (978-0-375-81540-9(6) , Knopf Bks. for Young Readers) Random Hse. Children's Bks.

Golden, Christopher & Sniegoski, Thomas E. Force Majeure. 2002. mass mkt. 5.99 (978-0-7434-2671-8(1)); 400p. (YA). (gr. 11 up). pap. 5.99 (978-0-7434-2670-1(3)) Simon & Schuster Children's Publishing. (Simon Pulse).

Hanson, Ed. Tornado. 2003. (Barclay Family Adventure Ser.: Bk. 8). 64p. (J). (gr. k-6). per. 3.95 (978-1-56254-559-8(0) , SP 5590) Saddleback Educational Publishing.

Higman, Anita. Texas Twisters. 1999. (Illus.). 64p. 13.95 (978-1-57168-316-8(X)) Eakin Pr.

Jenkins, Amanda. Tornado! 2005. 22.00 (***978-1-4108-4212-1(6)***) Benchmark Education Co.

Jennings, Patrick. The Tornado Watches: An Ike & Mem Story. Alter, Anna, illus. 2002. 64p. (J). (gr. k-3). tchr. ed. 15.95 (978-0-8234-1672-1(0)) Holiday Hse., Inc.

Karas, G. Brian, illus. Carlita Ropes the Twister. 1999. (J). 27.84 (978-0-8172-7256-2(9)) Steck-Vaughn.

Leppard, Lois Gladys. Mandie & the Tornado!, Vol. 34. 2001. (Mandie Bks.: No. 34). 160p. (J). (gr. 4-7). mass mkt. 5.99 (978-1-55661-675-4(9)) Bethany Hse. Pubs.

—Mandie & the Tornado! 2001. (gr. 3-6). lib. bdg. 13.00 (978-0-613-53361-4(5)) Tandem Library Bks.

Lester, Helen. Batter up Wombat. Munsinger, Lynn, illus. 2006. 32p. (J). (***978-1-4287-0160-1(5)***) Houghton Mifflin Co.

—Batter up Wombat. Munsinger, Lynn M., illus. 2006. 32p. (J). (gr. k-3). 16.00 (978-0-618-73784-0(7) , Walter Lorraine) Houghton Mifflin Co. Trade & Reference Div.

Marsh, Carole. The Treacherous Tornado Mystery! 2007. 128p. pap. 5.99 (***978-0-635-06338-0(7)***) Gallopade International.

McMullan, Kate. A Fine Start Bk. 3: Meg's Prairie Diary. 2003. (My America Ser.: No. 3). 112p. (J). pap. 12.95 (978-0-439-37061-5(2)) Scholastic, Inc.

Osborne, Mary Pope. Twister on Tuesday, Vol. 23. 2004. (Magic Tree House Ser. : No. 23). 70p. (J). (gr. k-3). pap. 17.00 incl. audio (978-0-8072-9932-6(4) , Listening Library) Random Hse. Audio Publishing Group.

—Twister on Tuesday. Murdocca, Sal, illus. 2001. (Magic Tree House Ser.: No. 23). 96p. (J). (gr. k-3). 11.99 (978-0-679-99069-7(0)); 23. pap. 3.99 (978-0-679-89069-0(6)) Random Hse. Children's Bks. (Random Hse. Bks. for Young Readers).

—Twister on Tuesday. 2001. (Magic Tree House Ser. : No. 23). (J). (gr. k-3). lib. bdg. 11.80 (978-0-613-35706-7(X)); (Illus.). (978-0-606-21498-8(4)) Tandem Library Bks.

Prigger, Mary Skillings. Aunt Minnie & the Twister. Lewin, Betsy, illus. 2002. 40p. (J). (gr. k-3). 15.00 (978-0-618-11136-7(0) , Clarion Bks.) Houghton Mifflin Co. Trade & Reference Div.

Ross, Tim & Ross, Scott, illus. Twinkle Twinkle Little Twister, Vol. 2. 2001. (Professor Wigglestix & the Weather Ser.). 32p. 14.95 (978-1-57168-447-9(6)); 7.95 (978-1-57168-619-0(3)) Eakin Pr.

Schreiber, Anne. Twister Trouble. 2001. (Magic School Bus Chapter Bks.: No. 5). 80p. (J). (gr. 1-4). pap. 4.99 (978-0-439-20419-4(4)) Scholastic, Inc.

Scrimger, Richard. Into the Ravine. 2007. 144p. (YA). (gr. 6 up). pap. 9.95 (***978-0-88776-822-4(9)***) Tundra Bks., Inc./Livres Toundra, Inc. CAN. *Dist:* Random Hse., Inc.

Sloat, Teri. Farmer Brown Goes Round & Round. 2001. (978-0-606-22359-1(2)) Tandem Library Bks.

TORONTO (ONT.)

Comeau, Natalie Ann. The Lobster Kids' Guide to Exploring Toronto: 12 Months of Fun. Kirner, Bob, ed. Battuz, Christine, illus. 2000. (Lobster Kids' City Explorers Ser.). 272p. (J). pap. 12.95 (978-1-894222-07-5(5)) Lobster Pr. CAN. *Dist:* Univ. of Toronto Pr.

Kennerley, Sara Jane. Toronto. 1999. (Cities of the World Ser.). 26.00 (978-0-516-20786-5(5) , Children's Pr.) Scholastic Library Publishing.

Mackay, Claire. The Toronto Story. Wales, Johnny, illus. rev. ed. 2002. 176p. (J). (gr. 5 up). 34.95 (978-1-55037-763-7(9)) Annick Pr., Ltd. CAN. *Dist:* Firefly Bks., Ltd.

Moak, Allan. A Big City ABC. rev. ed. 2002. (Illus.). 32p. (J). (ps up). 16.95 (978-0-88776-587-2(4)) Tundra Bks., Inc./Livres Toundra, Inc. CAN. *Dist:* Random Hse., Inc.

Rogers, Barbara Radcliffe. Toronto. 2000. (gr. 5-8). lib. bdg. 18.75 (978-0-613-51518-4(8)) Tandem Library Bks.

Rowe, Percy. Toronto. 2003. (Great Cities of the World Ser.). (Illus.). 48p. (J). (gr. 5 up). pap. 11.95 (978-0-8368-5186-1(2)); lib. bdg. 30.00 (978-0-8368-5026-0(2)) Stevens, Gareth Inc. (World Almanac Library).

TORTOISES

see Turtles

TOTALITARIANISM—FICTION

Holt, Rinehart and Winston Staff. Animal Farm with Connections. 1999. pap. 14.60 (978-0-03-055417-9(9)) Holt, Rinehart & Winston.

TOTEMS AND TOTEMISM

Feldman, Richard D. Home Before the Raven Caws: The Mystery of the Totem Pole. 2003. (Illus.). 72p. (J). pap. 15.95 (978-1-57860-126-4(6)) Emmis Bks.

Feldmann, Susan. The Storytelling Stone: Traditional Native American Myths & Tales. 1999. 304p. (ps-3). pap. 16.00 (978-0-385-33402-0(8) , Delta) Dell Publishing.

Kramer, Pat. Totem Poles for Kids: A Kids Own Super-Guide. Kramer, Pat, photos by. (Illus.). 48p. (J). pap. (978-1-55153-626-2(9)) Altitude Publishing Canada Ltd.

TOTEMS AND TOTEMISM—FICTION

Sargent, Dave, et al. Once upon a Totem Pole Vol. 14: (Haida) Be Creative, 20 vols. Lenoir, Jane, illus. l.t. ed. 2003. (Story Keeper Ser.: 14). 42p. (J). pap. 6.95 (978-1-56763-930-8(5)); Vol. 14. lib. bdg. 22.60 (978-1-56763-929-2(1)) Ozark Publishing.

TOUCANS

Dollar. Toucans. 2001. (Animals of the Rain Forest Ser.). (SPA., Illus.). pap. (978-0-7398-3360-5(X)) Steck-Vaughn.

Dollar, Sam. Toucans. 2000. (Animals of the Rain Forest Ser.). (Illus.). 32p. (J). (gr. 4-7). lib. bdg. 22.83 (978-0-7398-3100-7(3)) Raintree.

McDonald, Mary Ann. Toucans. 2006. (New Naturebooks). (Illus.). 32p. (J). (gr. 1-5). 27.07 (978-1-59296-652-3(7)) Child's World, Inc.

Miller, Sara Swan. Woodpeckers, Toucans, & Their Kin. 2003. (Animals in Order Ser.). (Illus.). 48p. (J). 26.50 (978-0-531-12243-3(3) , Watts, Franklin) Scholastic Library Publishing.

TOUCANS—FICTION

Flemming, Paul. Toby Toucan & His Noisy Beak: Includes Toy. Goode, Jon, illus. 1998. (Snappy Head Books Ser.: Vol. 2). 12p. (J). (ps-k). bds. 4.99 (978-1-57584-172-4(X) , Reader's Digest Children's Bks.) Reader's Digest Children's Publishing, Inc.

Mayfield, Sue & Padua, Rochelle. I Can, You Can, Toucan! 2006. (Green Bananas Ser.). (Illus.). 47p. (J). (978-0-7787-1032-5(7)) Crabtree Publishing Co.

TOUCH

Adoff, Arnold. Touch the Poem. Desimini, Lisa, illus. 2000. 32p. (J). (ps-3). pap. 16.95 (978-0-590-47970-7(9) , Blue Sky Pr., The) Scholastic, Inc.

Barraclough, Sue. What Can I Feel? 2005. (Illus.). 24p. (J). (978-1-4109-2162-8(X)); pap. (978-1-4109-2168-0(9)) Heinemann Library.

—What Can I Feel? 2005. (J). (978-1-4034-7077-5(4)); pap. (978-1-4034-7083-6(9)) Steck-Vaughn.

Beaumont, Susanna. Touch. 2005. (Baby Senses Ser.). (Illus.). 12p. (ps-k). per., bds. 9.95 (978-1-905051-47-2(6)) Make Believe Ideas GBR. *Dist:* Ingram Pub. Services.

Cobb, Vicki. Feeling Your Way: Discover Your Sense of Touch. Lewis, Cynthia C., illus. 2001. (Five Senses Ser.: 4). 32p. (gr. 2-4). lib. bdg. 22.90 (978-0-7613-1657-2(4) , Millbrook Pr.) Lerner Publishing Group.

Cotta, Susan. I Can Show You I Care: Compassionate Touch for Children. Crawford, Gregory, illus. 2003. 32p. (gr. 1-5). 16.95 (978-1-55643-433-4(2)) North Atlantic Bks.

Frost, Helen. Touching. Saunders-Smith, Gail, ed. 1999. (Senses Ser.). (Illus.). 24p. (J). (gr. k-1). lib. bdg. 15.93 (978-0-7368-0386-1(6) , Pebble Bks.) Capstone Pr., Inc.

—Touching. 1999. pap. 13.25 (978-0-516-21913-4(8) , Children's Pr.) Scholastic Library Publishing.

Gordon, Sharon. Duro Blando. 2006. (Bookworms Ser.). (SPA & ENG., Illus.). 24p. (J). lib. bdg. 22.79 (978-0-7614-2368-3(0)) Cavendish, Marshall Corp.

—Hard Soft (Duro Blando) 2006. (Bookworms Ser.). (ENG & SPA., Illus.). 24p. (J). lib. bdg. 22.79 (978-0-7614-2448-2(2)) Cavendish, Marshall Corp.

—Touching. 2002. (Rookie Read-About Health Ser.). (Illus.). 32p. (J). (gr. k-2). pap. 5.95 (978-0-516-25993-2(8) , Children's Pr.) Scholastic Library Publishing.

—Touching. 2001. (gr. k-3). lib. bdg. 14.10 (978-0-613-50757-8(6)) Tandem Library Bks.

Hall, Kirsten. Animal Touch. 2005. (Illus.). 24p. (J). pap. (978-0-8368-4812-0(8)); lib. bdg. 14.50 (978-0-8368-4806-9(3)) Stevens, Gareth Inc.

—Animal Touch: El Tacto en Los Animales. 2005. (ENG & SPA., Illus.). 24p. pap. (978-0-8368-4824-3(1)); lib. bdg. 19.33 (978-0-8368-4818-2(7)) Stevens, Gareth Inc.

Hathon, Elizabeth. Oh, Baby! 1999. (Touch & Feel Ser.). (Illus.). 12p. (J). (ps-k). bds. 6.99 (978-0-448-41897-1(5) , Grosset & Dunlap) Penguin Group (USA) Inc.

Hidalgo, Maria. Touch. 2003. 24p. (J). lib. bdg. 21.35 (978-1-58340-307-5(8)) Smart Apple Media.

Llewellyn, Claire. Touching. 2005. (Illus.). 24p. (J). (gr. 1-4). lib. bdg. 22.80 (978-1-932889-50-5(7)) Sea-To-Sea Pubns.

Mackill, Mary. Touching. 2006. (Super Senses Ser.). (Illus.). 24p. (J). (978-1-4034-7380-6(3)); pap. (978-1-4034-7387-5(0)) Steck-Vaughn.

McKendry, Sam & Rescek, Sanja. Bless Everyone. 2006. (Illus.). (J). 8.95 (978-1-58117-445-8(4) , Intervisual/Piggy Toes) Dalmatian Pr.

Molter, Carey. Sense of Touch. l.t. ed. 2001. (Senses Ser.). (Illus.). 24p. (J). (ps-3). lib. bdg. 19.93 (978-1-57765-630-2(X) , SandCastle) ABDO Publishing Co.

Murphy, Patricia J. Touch. 2003. (True Bks.). (gr. 3-5). pap. 6.95 (978-0-516-26972-6(0) , Children's Pr.) Scholastic Library Publishing.

—Touch. 2003. (gr. 3-6). lib. bdg. 15.25 (978-0-613-67990-9(3)) Tandem Library Bks.

Nelson, Robin. Touching. 2005. (First Step Nonfiction Ser.). (Illus.). 24p. (J). (gr. k-2). lib. bdg. 17.27 (978-0-8225-1266-0(1)) Lerner Publishing Group.

Olien, Rebecca. Touching. 2005. (Illus.). 24p. (J). (ps-7). lib. bdg. 21.26 (978-0-7368-4305-8(1)) Capstone Pr., Inc.

Parker. Is It..., 4 vols., Set 1. 2004. (Illus.). 74.24 (978-1-4109-0768-4(6)); 19.80 (978-1-4109-0773-8(2)) Raintree.

—Is It Slippery or Sticky? 2004. (Illus.). 24p. (J). pap. 5.50 (978-1-4109-0772-1(4)) Raintree.

Parker, Vic. Rough or Smooth. 2004. (Raintree Sprouts Ser.). (Illus.). 24p. (J). (ps-ps). lib. bdg. 18.56 (978-1-4109-0764-6(3)) Raintree.

—Slippery or Sticky. 2004. (Illus.). 24p. (J). (ps-6). lib. bdg. 18.56 (978-1-4109-0767-7(8)) Raintree.

Parker, Victoria. Is It Rough or Smooth? 2004. (J). pap. (978-1-4109-0769-1(4)) Raintree.

Pringle, Laurence P. Touch. 2000. (Explore Your Senses Ser.). (Illus.). 32p. (J). (gr. 4-8). lib. bdg. 25.64 (978-0-7614-0738-6(3) , Benchmark Bks.) Cavendish, Marshall Corp.

Pryor, Kimberley Jane. Touching. 2003. (Senses Ser.). (Illus.). 32p. (gr. 2-4). 23.00 (978-0-7910-7558-6(3) , Chelsea Hse.) Facts On File, Inc.

Rau, Dana Meachen. Ouch! A Book about Your Sense of Touch. Peterson, Rick, illus. 2005. (Amazing Body Ser.). 24p. (C). (gr. k-3). 22.60 (978-1-4048-1022-8(6)) Picture Window Bks.

Rivera, Sheila. How Does It Feel? 2004. (First Step Nonfiction Ser.). (J). pap. (978-0-8225-5405-9(4)); lib. bdg. (978-0-8225-2863-0(0)) Lerner Publishing Group. (Lerner Pubns.).

Schuh, Mari. The Sense of Touch. 2007. (Illus.). 24p. (J). lib. bdg. 19.95 (978-1-60014-074-7(2)) Bellwether Media.

Sherman, Joanne. Because It's My Body! Keep 'Em Safe Series: Anxiety-Free Learning for Children. Gurney, John Steven, illus. 2006. 40p. (J). 18.95 (978-0-9711735-9-0(1)) S.A.F.E. for Children Publishing, LLC.

Shott, Steve & Gorton, Steve, photos by. Playtime. 2001. (Touch & Feel Ser.). (Illus.). 12p. (J). (ps-3). bds. 6.99 (978-0-7894-7419-3(0)) Dorling Kindersley Publishing, Inc.

Silverstein, Alvin, et al. Touching & Feeling. 2002. (Senses & Sensors Ser.). (Illus.). 64p. (gr. 5-8). lib. bdg. 25.90 (978-0-7613-1668-8(X) , Millbrook Pr.) Lerner Publishing Group.

Slippery or Sticky?, 6 pack. 2004. (Illus.). lib. bdg. 31.05 (978-1-4109-0777-6(5)) Raintree.

El Tacto (Touching) (J). 2007. pap. 4.25 (978-0-8225-6544-4(7)); 2006. (SPA.). 18.60 (978-0-8225-6225-2(1)) Lerner Publishing Group. (Ediciones Lerner).

Woodward, Kay. Touch. 2005. (Illus.). 24p. (J). lib. bdg. 22.00 (978-0-8368-4410-8(6)) Stevens, Gareth Inc.

Yates, Irene. Touch. 2002. (All about Ser.). (Illus.). 32p. (J). lib. bdg. 24.25 (978-1-931983-01-3(1)) Chrysalis Education.

TOUCH—FICTION

Aigner-Clark, Julie. Violet's House: A Giant Touch-and-Feel Book. Zaidi, Nadeem, illus. 2003. 10p. (ps-17). 9.99 (978-0-7868-1872-3(7)) Disney Pr.

Becker, Bonny. Tickly Prickly. Halpern, Shari, photos by. 1999. (Growing Tree Ser.). (Illus.). 24p. (J). (ps up). 9.95 (978-0-694-01239-8(4) , Harper Festival) HarperCollins Pubs.

Grossman, Linda Sky. Sam Speaks Out. Bockus, Petra, illus. 24p. pap. 4.95 (978-1-896764-57-3(6)); 2002. 11.95 (978-1-896764-59-7(2)) Second Story Pr. CAN. *Dist:* Orca Bk. Pubs. USA.

Oxenbury, Helen. Helen Oxenbury's Big Baby Book. Oxenbury, Helen, illus. 2003. 10p. (J). (gr. k-ps). bds. 7.99 (978-0-7636-2016-5(5)) Candlewick Pr.

Watt, Fiona. That's Not My Kitten. Wells, Rachel, illus. rev. ed. 2006. 10p. (J). bds. 7.99 (978-0-7945-1266-8(6) , Usborne) EDC Publishing.

TOULOUSE-LAUTREC, HENRI DE, 1864-1901

Burleigh, Robert. Toulouse-Lautrec: The Moulin Rouge & the City of Light. 2005. (Illus.). 32p. (J). (gr. k-4). 17.95 (978-0-8109-5867-8(8)) Abrams, Harry N. , Inc.

—Toulouse-Lautrec: The Moulin Rouge & the City of Light. 2006. (Illus.). 32p. (J). (gr. 4-8). 18.00 (978-1-4223-5493-3(8)) DIANE Publishing Co.

Cook, Diane. Henri Toulouse-Lautrec: 19th Century French Painter. 2002. (Great Names Ser.). (Illus.). 32p. (J). (gr. 3 up). lib. bdg. (978-1-59084-155-6(7)) Mason Crest Pubs.

Hart, Tony. Toulouse-Lautrec. Hellard, Susan, illus. 2002. (Ninos Famosos Ser.). (SPA & ENG.). 24p. (gr. 1-5). pap. 6.95 (978-85-7416-164-8(0)) Callis Editora Ltda BRA. *Dist:* Independent Pubs. Group.

Toulouse-Lautrec, Henri de. Color Your Own Toulouse-Lautrec Masterpieces. 2006. 32p. (J). pap. 3.95 (978-0-486-44714-8(6)) Dover Pubns., Inc.

TOURISM

see also Travel

Bowden, Rob. Tourism. 2004. (21st Century Debates Ser.). (Illus.). 64p. (J). lib. bdg. 28.56 (978-0-7398-6468-5(8)) Raintree.

Hospitality & Tourism Careers (AVA) 2001. (YA). pap. 6.00 (978-1-57078-018-9(8) , CEV00018); pap. 8.00 (978-1-57078-019-6(6) , CEV00019) C E V Multimedia, Ltd.

McAlpine, Margaret. Working in Travel & Tourism. 2004. (My Future Career Ser.). (Illus.). 64p. (J). lib. bdg. 26.00 (978-0-8368-4239-5(1)) Stevens, Gareth Inc.

Parks, Peggy J. Ecotourism. 2005. (Our Environment Ser.). (Illus.). 48p. (J). (gr. 4-8). lib. bdg. 26.20 (978-0-7377-3048-7(X) , Kidhaven) Thomson Gale.

Pasternak, Ceel. Cool Careers for Girls in Travel & Hospitality. 2003. (Illus.). 144p. pap. 13.95 (978-1-57023-192-6(3)) Impact Pubns.

Penta, Mark, creator. Cape Cod Invasion! 2007. 17.95 (***978-1-933212-49-4(7)***) Commonwealth Editions.

Randolph, Joanne. Dennis Tito, First Space Tourist. 2003. (Reading Room Collection). (Illus.). 24p. (J). lib. bdg. 18.75 (978-0-8239-3699-1(6)) Rosen Publishing Group, Inc., The.

Ward, John. An Introduction to Travel & Tourism. 2000. (Illus.). 240p. pap. 37.50 (978-0-582-41909-4(3)) Longman Publishing Group.

TOURISM—FICTION

Holm, Annika. Anton y los Dragones. Pardo, Jeses, tr. Hald, Fibben, illus. 2000. Tr. of Anton & the Dragons. (SPA.). 44p. (J). (gr. 4-7). 17.95 (978-84-95040-91-6(3)) Serres, Ediciones, S. L. ESP. *Dist:* Lectorum Pubns., Inc.

Holm, Annika & Hald, Fibben. Anton y los Dragones. 2nd ed. 2001. Tr. of Anton & the Dragons. (CAT., Illus.). 44p. (J). (gr. 4-7). 17.95 (978-84-8488-002-8(8)) Serres, Ediciones, S. L. ESP. *Dist:* Lectorum Pubns., Inc.

Ogden, Charles. Triple Threat Vols. 1-3, Set: Their First Three Misadventures: Rare Beasts, Tourist Trap, under Town. Carton, Rick, illus. 2007. (Edgar & Ellen Ser.). 464p. (J). 29.99 (978-1-4169-3462-2(6) , Aladdin) Simon & Schuster Children's Publishing.

Spalding, Andrea. An Island of My Own. 2007. 112p. (YA). pap. 11.99 (***978-1-55002-635-1(6)*** , Sandcastle Bks.) Dundurn Group, The CAN. *Dist:* Univ. of Toronto Pr.

Walton, Rick. Just Me & 6,000 Rats: A Tale of Conjunctions. Gordon, Mike & Gordon, Carl, illus. 2007. 32p. (J). (ps-3). 15.95 (***978-1-4236-0219-4(6)***) Gibbs Smith, Publisher.

Weston, Carol. Melanie in Manhattan. 288p. (J). (gr. 3-7). 2006. 5.99 (978-0-440-42040-8(7) , Yearling); 2005. (Illus.). 15.95 (978-0-375-83028-0(6) , Knopf Bks. for Young Readers) Random Hse. Children's Bks.

TOURIST TRADE

see Tourism

TOUSSAINT LOUVERTURE, 1743?-1803

Rockwell, Anne. Open the Door to Liberty! A Biography of Toussaint L'Ouverture. Christie, Gregory, illus. 2008. (J). (***978-0-618-60570-5(3)***) Houghton Mifflin Co.

TOWER OF LONDON (LONDON, ENGLAND)

Hynson, Colin. The Tower of London. 2005. (Places in History Ser.). (Illus.). 48p. (J). pap. (978-0-8368-5820-4(4)); lib. bdg. 30.00 (978-0-8368-5813-6(1)) Stevens, Gareth Inc. (World Almanac Library).

Riley, Gail Blasser. Tower of London: England's Ghostly Castle. 2006. (Illus.). 32p. (J). lib. bdg. 25.27 (978-1-59716-249-4(3)) Bearport Publishing Co., Inc.

TOWN OFFICERS

see Local Government

TOWN PLANNING

see City Planning

TOWNS

see Cities and Towns

TOXIC WASTES
see Hazardous Wastes

TOXICOLOGY
see Poisons

TOY AND MOVABLE BOOKS

Abel, Simone, illus. Where Is Caterpillar Look & Play. (Lamaze Ser.). bds. 8.99 (978-1-58663-731-6(2)) Friedman, Michael Publishing Group, Inc.

Aboff, Marcie & Funke, Cornelia. Shrek: Classic Shrek Halloween. 2006. (Shrek Ser.). (Illus.). 16p. (J). pap. 5.99 (978-0-439-82817-8(1) , Scholastic) Scholastic, Inc.

Accorsi, William. Apple, Apple, Alligator: A Picture-Puzzle Book. 2000. (Illus.). 20p. (J). (ps). bds. 14.95 (978-0-7611-1787-2(3)) Workman Publishing Co., Inc.

Accorsi, William. The 10 Color Book. 2007. (Illus.). 14p. bds. 15.95 ***(978-0-7611-4739-8(X))*** Workman Publishing Co., Inc.

Active Minds, 6 bks. (Illus.). (J). (ps-3). lib. bdg. 71.70 (978-1-56674-926-8(3)) Forest Hse. Publishing Co., Inc.

Adair, Amy. Fire Truck: Lift-a-Flap Fun. Wieland, Don, illus. 2000. (Active Minds Ser.). 12p. (J). bds. 15.98 (978-0-7853-4172-7(2) , 3996300) Publications International, Ltd.

—Jay Jay's Special Delivery. 2003. (Illus.). (J). 15.98 (978-0-7853-8625-4(4)) Publications International, Ltd.

—Space Adventure: Ligt-A-Flap Fun. Birmingham, Lloyd, tr. Birmingham, Lloyd, illus. 2002. (Leap Frog Ser.). 12p. (J). bds. 7.98 (978-0-7853-6347-7(5) , 7159300) Publications International, Ltd.

Adam, Winky. Musical Instruments Stickers. 1999. (Illus.). 4p. (J). (ps-5). pap. 1.50 (978-0-486-40739-5(X)) Dover Pubns., Inc.

—Toy Bugs Stickers. 1999. (Illus.). 4p. (J). pap. 1.50 (978-0-486-40738-8(1)) Dover Pubns., Inc.

Adams, Georgie. Three Bears on Vacation. Young, Selina, illus. 2003. 28p. (J). (gr. k-1). pap. 6.95 (978-0-7696-3154-7(1) , Gingham Dog Pr.) School Specialty Publishing.

Adams, Pam. There Was an Old Lady Who Swallowed a Fly. Adams, Pam, illus. 2002. (Illus.). (J). 22.72 (978-0-7587-0154-1(3)) Book Wholesalers, Inc.

—There Was an Old Lady Who Swallowed a Fly. Adams, Pam, illus. (Illus.). pap. 16.95 incl. audio (978-0-87499-778-1(X)); pap. incl. audio (978-0-87499-780-4(1)); pap. 18.95 incl. audio compact disk (978-1-59112-408-5(5)); pap. incl. audio compact disk (978-1-59112-607-2(X)); 2001. (J). 28.95 incl. audio compact disk (978-1-59112-409-2(3)) Live Oak Media.

—There Was an Old Lady Who Swallowed a Fly. unabr. ed. 2001. (Live Oak Readalong Ser.). (Illus.). (J). (ps-2). 25.95 incl. audio (978-0-87499-779-8(8)) Live Oak Media.

Adams, Pam, illus. Old Macdonald Had a Farm. 2000. 16p. (J). (ps-k). bds. 5.99 (978-0-85953-662-2(9)) Child's Play-International.

—There Was an Old Lady Who Swallowed a Fly. 2000. 16p. (J). (ps-k). bds. 5.99 (978-0-85953-727-8(7)) Child's Play-International.

Adams, Pam, tr. & illus. Old Macdonald Had a Farm. Adams, Pam, illus. 2003. (Classic Books with Holes). (J). (978-0-85953-135-1(X)) Child's Play-International.

—There Was an Old Lady Who Swallowed a Fly. Adams, Pam, illus. 2003. (Classic Books with Holes). (J). 4.99 (978-0-85953-134-4(1)) Child's Play-International.

Ageledis, Ida. First Foil Poetry Seasons, 2 vols. Berg, Michelle, illus. 2005. (First Foil Poetry Haikus Ser.). 10p. (J). 6.95 (978-1-58117-188-4(9) , Intervisual/Piggy Toes) Dalmatian Pr.

Ahlberg, Allan. The Jolly Postman: Or, Other People's Letters. Ahlberg, Janet, illus. 2006. 28p. (J). (gr. k-3). 19.99 (978-0-316-01776-3(0)) Little Brown & Co.

Aigner-Clark, Julie. Baby Einstein: Las rimas de Bard : Bard4s Rhyme Time, Spanish-Language Edition. Zaidi, Nadeem, illus. 2005. (Baby Einstein: Libros de Carton Ser.). (SPA.). 16p. (J). 6.95 (978-970-718-304-9(7) , Silver Dolphin en Español) Advanced Marketing, S. de R. L. de C. V. MEX. *Dist:* Perseus Distribution.

—Baby Einstein: Puzzling Shapes, Spanish-Language Edition. Zaidi, Nadeem, illus. 2005. (Baby Einstein: Libros de Carton Ser.). (SPA.). 12p. (J). bds. 6.95 (978-970-718-303-2(9) , Silver Dolphin en Español) Advanced Marketing, S. de R. L. de C. V. MEX. *Dist:* Perseus Distribution.

—Baby Einstein: See How I Feel, Spanish-Language Edition. Zaidi, Nadeem, illus. 2005. (Baby Einstein: Libros de Carton Ser.). (SPA.). 14p. (J). bds. 7.95 (978-970-718-308-7(X) , Silver Dolphin en Español) Advanced Marketing, S. de R. L. de C. V. MEX. *Dist:* Perseus Distribution.

—Baby Einstein Poemas Preciosos: Pretty Poems & Wonderful Words. Zaidi, Nadeem, illus. 2004. (SPA.). 10p. (J). 9.95 (978-970-718-210-3(5) , Silver Dolphin Bks.) Advantage Pubs. Group.

—Baby Einstein: Shapes Flip Flap Book. Zaidi, Nadeem, illus. 2006. 12p. (J). (ps-17). bds. 6.99 (978-0-7868-4952-9(5)) Baby Einstein Co., LLC, The.

—Baby Einstein: Wrist Books. Zaidi, Nadeem, illus. 2006. 6p. (J). (ps-17). bds. 7.99 (978-0-7868-4953-6(3)) Baby Einstein Co., LLC, The.

—Baby MacDonald Magnetic Puzzle Book. 2008. 8p. (ps-17). 12.99 ***(978-1-4231-0205-2(3))*** Hyperion Bks. for Children.

—Circle Time: An Interactive Book to Engage & Delight Your Child. Zaidi, Nadeem, illus. 2000. 10p. (J). (978-1-892309-22-8(X)) Baby Einstein Co., LLC, The.

—Colors. Zaidi, Nadeem, illus. 2006. (Baby Einstein Ser.). 12p. (J). (ps-17). bds. 6.99 (978-0-7868-4950-5(9)) Baby Einstein Co., LLC, The.

—Mama & Me. Zaidi, Nadeem, illus. 2004. (Baby Einstein Ser.). 16p. (ps-ps). 5.99 (978-0-7868-5133-1(3)) Hyperion Bks. for Children.

—Master Pieces. Zaidi, Nadeem, illus. 2004. (SPA.). 10p. (J). 9.95 (978-970-718-211-0(3) , Silver Dolphin Bks.) Advantage Pubs. Group.

—Violet's House: A Giant Touch-and-Feel Book. Zaidi, Nadeem, illus. 2003. 10p. (ps-17). 9.99 (978-0-7868-1872-3(7)) Disney Pr.

—Water, Water Everywhere: A Splash & Giggle Bath Book. Zaidi, Nadeem, illus. 2003. (Baby Einstein Ser.: No. 3). 10p. (ps-17). 6.99 (978-0-7868-1911-9(1)) Hyperion Bks. for Children.

—What Does Violet See? Snowflakes & Icicles. Zaidi, Nadeem, illus. 2002. (Baby Einstein Ser.). 16p. (ps-ps). 5.99 (978-0-7868-0872-4(1)) Disney Pr.

—What Floats? Bk. 4: A Splash & Giggle Bath. 2003. (Baby Einstein Ser.: Bk. 4). 10p. (ps-17). pap. 6.99 (978-0-7868-1912-6(X)) Hyperion Bks. for Children.

—World Around Me: Oceans. 2003. (Baby Einstein Ser.). 12p. (ps-17). 15.99 (978-0-7868-1913-3(8)) Disney Pr.

Aignier-Clark, Julie. Nighttime Lullaby. 2008. 10p. 9.99 ***(978-1-4231-0861-0(2))*** Hyperion Bks. for Children.

—Peek-a-Boo Bard. 2008. 10p. 9.99 ***(978-1-4231-0860-3(4))*** Hyperion Bks. for Children.

Alborough, Jez. It's the Bear! Alborough, Jez, illus. 2002. (Illus.). (J). 13.83 (978-0-7587-2879-1(4)) Book Wholesalers, Inc.

—It's the Bear! Alborough, Jez, illus. 2004. (Illus.). 30p. (J). (gr. k-ps). bds. 6.99 (978-0-7636-2316-6(4)) Candlewick Pr.

Alex Toys. Bunny's Easter Basket. Silver-Thompson, Pattie, illus. rev. ed. 2008. 10p. (J). (ps-1). 5.99 ***(978-0-316-15404-8(0))*** Little, Brown Bks. for Young Readers.

Aliens Sticker Book. (Weird & Wacky Ser.). 16p. (J). (978-2-89393-870-7(1)) Phidal Publishing, Inc./Editions Phidal, Inc.

All Things Bright & Beautiful. 2006. 16p. (J). pap. 1.99 (978-0-7847-1588-8(2) , 22135) Standard Publishing.

Allen, J. J. Hello Kitty's Fun Friend Day! 2003. (Illus.). 32p. (J). pap. (978-0-439-44917-5(0)) Scholastic, Inc.

Allen, Jonathan. Chicken Licken: A Wickedly Funny Flap Book. 2000. (Illus.). 17p. (J). 15.95 (978-0-385-40669-7(X)) Transworld Publishers Ltd. GBR. *Dist:* Trafalgar Square Publishing.

—Little Red Hen. 2003. (Illus.). 24p. (J). pap., bds. 9.99 (978-0-552-54812-0(X) , Corgi) Transworld Publishers Ltd. GBR. *Dist:* Trafalgar Square Publishing.

Amery, H. Where's Curly? Cartwright, Stephen, illus. 2004. (Treasury of Farmyard Tales Ser.). 16p. (J). (gr. 1 up). pap. 7.95 (978-0-7945-0514-1(7)) EDC Publishing.

—Where's Woolly? Cartwright, Stephen, illus. 2004. (Treasury of Farmyard Tales Ser.). 16p. (J). (gr. 1 up). pap. 7.95 (978-0-7945-0405-2(1)) EDC Publishing.

Amery, H. & Cartwright, S. Where's Rusty? 2004. (Treasury of Farmyard Tales Ser.). 10p. (J). 7.95 (978-0-7945-0545-5(7)) EDC Publishing.

Amery, Heather. Farmyard Tales Christmas Flap Bk And. 2006. 24p. 12.99 (978-0-7945-0556-1(2) , Usborne) EDC Publishing.

—Farmyard Tales Christmas Flap Book. 2000. (Farmyard Tales Flap Bks.). (Illus.). 24p. (YA). (ps-3). 9.95 (978-0-7460-4138-3(1)) EDC Publishing.

—Red Tractor Board Book. Cartwright, Stephen, illus. 2004. (Young Farmyard Tales Board Books Ser.). 10p. (J). bds. 3.95 (978-0-7945-0469-4(8) , Usborne) EDC Publishing.

—Where's Woolly? Cartwright, Stephen, illus. 1998. (Farmyard Tales Ser.). 16p. (J). (ps-2). pap. 7.95 (978-0-7460-3012-7(6)); lib. bdg. 15.95 (978-1-58086-127-4(X)) EDC Publishing.

Anastas, Margaret. Mommy's Best Kisses Board Book. Winter, Susan, illus. 2008. 34p. (J). 6.99 ***(978-0-06-124130-7(X)*** , Harper Festival) HarperCollins Pubs.

Andersen, Hans Christian. The Ugly Duckling. Furukawa, Masumi et al, illus. 2006. 24p. pap. 5.99 (978-1-84643-022-0(4)) Child's Play-International.

Anderson, Airlie. A Very Furry Flap Book. 2004. (Illus.). 10p. (J). bds. 5.95 (978-1-58925-701-6(4) , tiger tales) ME Media LLC.

Anderson, Airlie, illus. A Very Patchy Flap Book. 2004. 10p. (J). bds. 5.95 (978-1-58925-702-3(2) , tiger tales) ME Media LLC.

—A Very Spotty Flap Book. 2004. 10p. (J). bds. 5.95 (978-1-58925-703-0(0) , tiger tales) ME Media LLC.

—A Very Stripy Flap Book. 2004. 10p. (J). bds. 5.95 (978-1-58925-704-7(9) , tiger tales) ME Media LLC.

Anderson, Sara. Numbers. Anderson, Sara, illus. 2007. 11p. (J). bds. 10.95 (978-1-59354-185-9(6)) Chronicle Bks. LLC.

Andreae, Giles. The Pop-Up Commotion in the Ocean. Wojtowycz, David, illus. 2002. 12p. (J). tchr. ed. 14.95 (978-1-58925-680-4(8) , tiger tales) ME Media LLC.

Andrews, Jan. The Twelve Days of Summer. Jolliffe, Susan Rennick, illus. 2007. 32p. (J). (ps-3). ***(978-1-55143-735-4(X))*** Orca Bk. Pubs.

—The Twelve Days of Summer. Jolliffe, Susan Rennick, illus. 2005. 112p. (J). (gr. 4-10). 16.95 (978-1-55143-365-3(6)) Orca Bk. Pubs. USA.

Angus Plush. 2000. (What to Expect Kids Ser.). (Illus.). 16p. (J). (ps-1). 7.99 (978-0-694-01511-5(3) , Harper Festival) HarperCollins Pubs.

Anholt, Catherine & Anholt, Laurence. Can You Guess? A Lift-the-Flap Birthday Party Book. 2003. (Illus.). 16p. pap. 7.95 (978-0-7112-2214-4(2)) Lincoln, Frances Ltd. GBR. *Dist:* Transition Vendor.

—Chimp & Zee's Clothes. 2007. (Chimp & Zee Ser.). (Illus.). 22p. (J). bds. 3.95 ***(978-1-84507-729-7(6))*** Lincoln, Frances Ltd. GBR. *Dist:* Perseus Distribution.

—Chimp & Zee's Noisy Book. 2008. (Chimp & Zee Ser.). (Illus.). 8p. (J). 5.95 ***(978-1-84507-804-1(7))*** Lincoln, Frances Ltd. GBR. *Dist:* Perseus Distribution.

—Play. 2007. (Chimp & Zee Ser.). (Illus.). 22p. (J). bds. 3.95 ***(978-1-84507-746-4(6))*** Lincoln, Frances Ltd. GBR. *Dist:* Perseus Distribution.

Animal Treasury. 2001. 190p. (J). 19.95 (978-0-7525-3835-8(7)) Parragon, Inc.

Animals: Lift-a-Flap Fun. 2000. (Active Minds Ser.). (Illus.). 12p. (J). bds. 7.98 (978-0-7853-4256-4(7) , 3998500) Publications International, Ltd.

Anthony, Mary. Noisy Workbench: My Electronic Sound & Lift-the-Flap Storybook. Giles, Mike, illus. 2004. (Little Tikes Ser.). 5p. (J). bds. 14.99 (978-0-7944-0364-5(6) , Reader's Digest Children's Bks.) Reader's Digest Children's Publishing, Inc.

Aptekar, Devan. Webslinger! Mada Design Staff, illus. 2004. (Spider Man Ser.). 32p. (J). 4.99 (978-0-439-35452-3(8) , Scholastic Paperbacks) Scholastic, Inc.

Archambault, John & Martin, Bill. Chicka Chicka ABC Magnet Book. Ehlert, Lois, illus. 2002. 22p. (J). (ps-3). 15.95 (978-0-689-85026-4(3) , Little Simon) Simon & Schuster Children's Publishing.

Archer, Amanda. My Dad's Toolbox: Fabulous Pop-up Toolbox with Working Tools. Van Der Leijgraaf, Deborah, photos by. 2007. (Illus.). 12p. (J). 16.99 (978-0-7641-5971-8(2)) Barron's Educational Series, Inc.

Arnold, Tedd. Huggly & the Toy Monster. 1999. (Huggly Ser.). (Illus.). 32p. (J). (ps-3). pap. 3.25 (978-0-439-10270-4(7)) Scholastic, Inc.

Arps, Melissa. Shapes. 2006. (Illus.). (J). ***(978-0-7364-2383-0(4))*** Random Hse., Inc.

Ashbe, Jeanne. And after That. Ashbe, Jeanne, illus. 2002. (Illus.). 12p. (J). 9.95 (978-1-929132-24-9(7)) Kane/Miller Bk. Pubs., Inc.

Asquith, Ros. My Do It! 2000. (Toddlers Storybook Ser.). (Illus.). 24p. (J). (ps-k). pap. 5.95 (978-0-7894-5648-9(6) , D K Ink) Dorling Kindersley Publishing, Inc.

—Pass the Parcel. 2005. (Illus.). 32p. (J). pap. 11.95 (978-0-00-711269-2(6)); 19.99 (978-0-00-711268-5(8)) HarperCollins Pubs. Ltd. GBR. *Dist:* Trafalgar Square Publishing, Independent Pubs. Group.

Aston, Dianna Hutts. Bless This Mouse: A Soft-to-Touch Book. 2004. (Illus.). 24p. (J). 14.95 (978-1-59354-050-0(7)) Handprint Bks.

Auerbach, Annie. Cindy Big Hair: A Twisted (and Teased & Braided) Cinderella Story. Maxey, David, illus. 2005. 16p. (J). 12.95 (978-1-58117-387-1(3) , Intervisual/Piggy Toes) Dalmatian Pr.

Augarde, Steve. Big Nose, Small Nose. 2004. (Silly Monsters Ser.). (Illus.). 8p. (J). 5.95 (978-0-7696-3337-4(4) , Gingham Dog Pr.) School Specialty Publishing.

—Garage: A Pop-up Book. Augarde, Steve, illus. 2005. (Illus.). 10p. (J). (gr. k-4). reprint ed. 15.00 (978-0-7567-9299-2(1)) DIANE Publishing Co.

—Hello, Moon. 2004. (Silly Monsters Ser.). (Illus.). 8p. (J). 5.95 (978-0-7696-3338-1(2) , Gingham Dog Pr.) School Specialty Publishing.

—One Paper Hat. 2004. (Silly Monsters Ser.). (Illus.). 8p. (J). 5.95 (978-0-7696-3339-8(0) , Gingham Dog Pr.) School Specialty Publishing.

Awdry, Wilbert V. Keeping Track of Thomas. 2003. (Thomas & Friends Ser.). (Illus.). 12p. (J). (ps-2). pap. 6.99 (978-0-375-82594-1(0) , Random Hse. Bks. for Young Readers) Random Hse. Children's Bks.

—Thomas the Tank Engine's Hidden Surprises. Yee, Josie, illus. 1999. (Let's Go Lift & Peek Bks.). 14p. (J). (gr. k-ps). bds. 4.99 (978-0-679-89482-7(9) , Random Hse. Bks. for Young Readers) Random Hse. Children's Bks.

Baby Einstein, creator. Baby Einstein Discover & Play. 2005. (Pop-up Songbook Ser.). (Illus.). 14p. (J). (ps-ps). per. 15.98 (978-1-4127-0578-3(9) , 7223100) Publications International, Ltd.

Baby Jesus Is Born: A Touch & Feel Book. 2003. (Illus.). 10p. (J). bds. 10.99 (978-0-8254-5507-0(3)) Kregel Pubns.

Baby Looney Tunes Visit a Haunted House. 2005. (Baby Looney Tunes Ser.). (Illus.). 14p. (J). (ps-3). bds. 9.95 (978-0-8249-6609-6(0)) Ideals Pubns.

Baby Strawberry Loves to Count. 2007. (Strawberry Shortcake Baby Ser.). 10p. (J). bds. 6.99 ***(978-0-448-44717-9(7)*** , Grosset & Dunlap) Penguin Group (USA) Inc.

Baby Strawberry's First Christmas. 2007. (Strawberry Shortcake Baby Ser.). 10p. (J). (ps). bds. 4.99 ***(978-0-448-44669-1(3)*** , Grosset & Dunlap) Penguin Group (USA) Inc.

Baby's Bathtime Kid Kit. (Illus.). 10p. (YA). (ps up). 14.95 (978-1-58086-406-0(6)) EDC Publishing.

Bada, Kathleen. Ghosts: Glow in the Dark Sticker Book. 2001. (Ultimate Sticker Bks.). (Illus.). 16p. (J). pap. 6.99 (978-0-7894-7868-9(4)) Dorling Kindersley Publishing, Inc.

Bagley, Val. Gospel Truths from the Book of Mormon. 2004. (Seek & Ye Shall Find Flap Book Ser.). (Illus.). (J). bds. 13.95 (978-1-59156-279-5(1)) Covenant Communications, Inc.

Bagley, Val Chadwick & Mullins, Amy. My Favorite Stories from the Bible. 2006. (Illus.). 28p. (J). ***(978-1-59811-173-6(6))*** Covenant Communications.

Baglio, Ben M. Cat Crazy. 2000. (Animal Ark Pets Ser.: No. 13). (Illus.). 128p. (J). (gr. 2-5). pap. 3.99 (978-0-439-05170-5(3)) Scholastic, Inc.

Baker, Alan. Little Rabbit's Snacktime. 1998. (Little Rabbit Bks.). (Illus.). 24p. (J). (gr. k-ps). tchr. ed. 10.95 (978-0-7534-5144-1(1) , Kingfisher) Houghton Mifflin Co. Trade & Reference Div.

—White Rabbit's Color Book Set: Includes Plush Toy. Baker, Alan, illus. gif. ed. 2003. (Little Rabbit Bks.). (Illus.). 24p. (J). (ps-k). 9.95 (978-0-7534-5625-5(7) , Kingfisher) Houghton Mifflin Co. Trade & Reference Div.

Baker, Keith. Quack & Count. 2002. (Illus.). (J). 20.00 (978-0-7587-4193-6(6)) Book Wholesalers, Inc.

—Quack & Count. (Illus.). (J). 2004. 24p. pap. 6.00 (978-0-15-205025-2(6) , Voyager Bks./Libros Viajeros); 2003. 22p. bds. 6.95 (978-0-15-204751-1(4) , Red Wagon Bks.) Harcourt Children's Bks.

Baker, Liza. My First Purse. McBee, Scott, illus. 2003. 12p. (J). bds. 9.95 (978-0-439-46879-4(5) , Cartwheel Bks.) Scholastic, Inc.

Baker, Sue. Oh Baby!. Stockham, Jess, illus. 2006. (Blanket Babies Ser.). 12p. (J). 6.99 (978-1-904550-87-7(8)) Child's Play-International.

—Pass the Parcel. 2005. (Illus.). 24p. (J). pap. 9.99 (978-1-904550-29-7(0)) Child's Play-International.

—Sleep Tight! Stockham, Jess, illus. 2006. (Blanket Babies Ser.). 12p. (J). 6.99 (978-1-904550-90-7(8)) Child's Play-International.

Balducci, Rita. Disney Princess Storybook & Movie Projector: Season of Enchantment: Jeweled Collector's Edition. 2007. (RD Innovative Book & Player Format Ser.). 48p. (J). 24.99 ***(978-0-7944-1355-2(2))*** Reader's Digest Assn., Inc., The.

Balducci, Rita. Princess Treasury: A Collection of Special Moments from Your Favorite Princess Stories. 2003. (Disney Carryalong(R) Treasuries Ser.). (Illus.). 12p. (J). bds. 14.99 (978-1-57584-979-9(8) , Reader's Digest Children's Bks.) Reader's Digest Children's Publishing, Inc.

Balloon Books Staff, ed. Scout in the Woods: 85 Removable Stickers. 2003. (Sticker Story Bks.). (Illus.). 18p. (J). (ps-1). pap. 4.95 (978-1-4027-0101-6(2) , Balloon Bks.) Sterling Publishing Co., Inc.

—Scout Super Sticker Book: 180 Removable Stickers. 2003. (Sticker Story Bks.). (Illus.). 18p. (J). (ps-1). pap. 4.95 (978-1-4027-0102-3(0) , Balloon Bks.) Sterling Publishing Co., Inc.

Bampton, Claire. The Amazing Pop-up Pull-Out Mummy Book. Hawcock, David & Watton, Nick, illus. 2004. 15p. (gr. 4-10). reprint ed. 20.00 (978-0-7567-7290-1(7)) DIANE Publishing Co.

Barad, Alexis. World Around Me: Colors, Numbers & More. 2008. (Fisher-Price Ser.). 12p. (J). 7.99 ***(978-0-06-145039-6(1)*** , Harper Festival) HarperCollins Pubs.

Barbaresi, Nina. Funny Fruits & Vegetables Stickers. 2003. (Dover Little Activity Bks.). (Illus.). 4p. (J). pap. 1.50 (978-0-486-43004-1(9)) Dover Pubns., Inc.

Barbas, Keri., des. Travel Scratch & Sketch. 2005. (Activity Journal Ser.). (J). 12.99 (978-0-88088-486-0(X)) Peter Pauper Pr. Inc.

Barkan, Joanne. Good Night, Summer Lights. Bryant, Laura, illus. 2005. (Fiber Optic Book Ser.). 10p. (J). bds. 12.99 (978-0-7944-0671-4(8)) Reader's Digest Assn., Inc., The.

Barker, Cicely Mary. Flower Fairies Dress-Up for the Ball Boo. 2005. (Illus.). 8p. pap. 7.99 (978-0-7232-5376-1(5) , Warne) Penguin Group (USA) Inc.

—Flower Fairies Dress up Sticker Book. 2006. 16p. (J). 5.99 (978-0-7232-5728-8(0) , Warne) Penguin Group (USA) Inc.

Barlowe, Dot. Seashore Birds. 2003. (Dover Little Activity Bks.). (Illus.). 4p. (J). (ps-5). pap. 1.50 (978-0-486-43005-8(7)) Dover Pubns., Inc.

Bauer, Marion Dane. A Recipe for Valentine's Day: A Rebus Lift-the-Flap Story. Herbert, Jennifer, illus. 2004. (Lift-the-Flap Bks.). 16p. (J). 6.99 (978-0-689-85895-6(7) , Little Simon) Simon & Schuster Children's Publishing.

—Toes, Ears, & Nose! Katz, Karen, illus. 2003. (Lift-the-Flap Bks.). 16p. (J). (ps-3). 6.99 (978-0-689-84712-7(2) , Little Simon) Simon & Schuster Children's Publishing.

Baum, L. Frank. The Wonderful Wizard of Oz. Sabuda, Robert, illus. 2000. (Classic Collectible Pop-Up Ser.). 16p. (J). (ps-3). pap. 26.99 (978-0-689-81751-9(7) , Little Simon) Simon & Schuster Children's Publishing.

Baumann, Anne-Sophie. Where Does It Come From? Daigen, Al, tr. from FRE. Barborini, Robert & Chollat, Emilie, illus. 2006. (Explore Your World Ser.). 28p. (J). (ps-1). 15.95 (978-1-55407-009-1(0)) Firefly Bks., Ltd.

Bean Sprouts Editors. Favorite Bible Stories. Pepper, Bob, illus. 2000. (Place-a-Piece Bks.). 10p. (J). (ps-k). bds. 14.99 (978-0-7847-1212-2(3) , 04394, Bean Sprouts) Standard Publishing.

Beardshaw, Rosalind. I am a Spaceman! 2008. (Illus.). 12p. (J). bds. 12.95 ***(978-1-4052-2759-9(1))*** Egmont Bks., Ltd. GBR. *Dist:* Independent Pubs. Group.

Beardshaw, Rosalind, illus. I am a Princess! 2008. 12p. (J). bds. 12.95 ***(978-1-4052-2758-2(3))*** Egmont Bks., Ltd. GBR. *Dist:* Independent Pubs. Group.

Beck, Andrea, illus. Elliot's Great Big. 2003. (Elliot Moose Ser.). 12p. (J). (gr. k-3). (978-1-55337-373-5(1)) Kids Can Pr., Ltd.

Bedford, David. Toes. Worthington, Leonie, illus. 2007. 16p. (J). (ps-k). 9.95 ***(978-1-921049-64-4(2))*** Little Hare Bks. AUS. *Dist:* Independent Pubs. Group.

Bedford, David & Worthington, Leonie. Who's Laughing. 2007. (Illus.). 16p. (J). (ps-k). 9.95 ***(978-1-921049-40-8(5))*** Little Hare Bks. AUS. *Dist:* Independent Pubs. Group.

Beeler, Selby B. How Many Elephants? A Lift-the-Flap Counting Book. Saltzberg, Barney, illus. 2004. 20p. (J). (gr. k-k). 9.99 (978-0-7636-1583-3(8)) Candlewick Pr.

Beer, Barbara Vagnozzi. Jack & the Beanstalk. (Illus.). 24p. pap. (978-1-904550-20-4(7)); 2004. (J). 7.99 (978-0-85953-676-9(9)) Child's Play-International.

Bek, et al. Rahab Saves Spies & Esther Rescues Her People. Bek et al, illus. 2006. (Upside down Bible Stories Ser.). 62p. (J). pap. 7.99 (978-0-7814-4392-0(X)) Cook, David C. Publishing Co.

Bender and Bender Staff. Ribbit! Flip & See Who Froggy Can Be. 2007. 40p. (J). (ps-1). 16.99 ***(978-0-06-113820-1(7))*** HarperCollins Pubs.

Bentley, Dawn. Fuzzy Bear: A Getting Dressed Book. Nagy, Krisztina, illus. 1998. (Fuzzy Bear Ser.). 10p. (J). (ps-k). 10.95 (978-1-58117-011-5(4) , Intervisual/Piggy Toes) Dalmatian Pr.

—Fuzzy Bear's Potty Book. Nagy, Krisztina, illus. 2005. (Fuzzy Bear Ser.). 10p. (J). (ps). 11.95 (978-1-58117-161-7(7) , Intervisual/Piggy Toes) Dalmatian Pr.

—Goodnight Bear: A Book & Night Light. Couri, Kathryn A., illus. 2005. (Stories to Share Ser.). 12p. (J). 12.95 (978-1-58117-034-4(3) , Intervisual/Piggy Toes) Dalmatian Pr.

—I'm a Pink Piggy. Tom-Nellis, Susan, illus. 1998. (Baby Buddy Bks.: No. 4). 12p. (YA). (ps up). bds. 4.95 (978-1-888443-70-7(7) , Intervisual/Piggy Toes) Dalmatian Pr.

—Little Lost Duck. Tom-Nellis, Susan, illus. 1998. (Baby Buddy Bks.). 12p. (YA). (ps up). bds. 4.95 (978-1-888443-72-1(3) , Intervisual/Piggy Toes) Dalmatian Pr.

—Shapes. Rivoli Group Staff, illus. 2000. (Jay Jay the Jet Plane's Peek-a-Boo Board Bks.). 12p. (J). (ps-k). bds. 6.95 (978-1-58117-101-3(3) , Intervisual/Piggy Toes) Dalmatian Pr.

—Who's in the Jungle. Valderrama, Rosario, illus. 2001. (Sneak-A-Peek Board Book Ser.: Vol. 1). 10p. (ps-k). bds. 6.95 (978-1-58117-141-9(2) , Intervisual/Piggy Toes) Dalmatian Pr.

Bently, Dawn. Kirsty's Big Adventure. Kemly, Kathleen, illus. 2005. (Woodkins Ser.). 12p. (J). bds. 14.95 (978-1-59354-049-4(3)) Handprint Bks.

Berg, Michelle, illus. Noah's Ark: A Hand Puppet Board Book. 2007. 6p. (J). bds. 12.99 (***978-0-439-86396-4(1)***) Scholastic, Inc.

Bergen, Lara Rice. General Jar Jar. Thompson, Dana et al, illus. 1999. (Lucas Books). 32p. (J). (978-0-439-10160-8(3)) Scholastic, Inc.

Berger, Carin. All Mixed Up: A Mix-and-Match Book. 2006. (Illus.). 46p. (J). 8.95 (978-0-8118-4966-1(X)) Chronicle Bks. LLC.

Berger, Samantha & Viscardi, Lisa Huberman. Junior in the City: A Spinwheels Book. Moreton, Daniel, illus. 2002. (Spinwheels Bk.). 7p. (J). (ps-1). 10.95 (978-0-8109-3497-9(3)) Abrams, Harry N. , Inc.

Berleman, Sean & Salyards, Jeffrey. Camera Contest. Saunders, Zina, illus. 2004. 14p. (J). bds. (978-0-7853-9955-1(0) , 7210000) Publications International, Ltd.

Bernthal, Mark S. Barney's 12 Days of Christmas. 1998. (Barney Ser.). 26p. (J). (ps-k). bds. 13.95 (978-1-57064-241-8(9)) Scholastic, Inc.

Berry, Ron. Charlie the Can-Do Choo-Choo! Sharp, Chris, illus. 2006. 7p. (J). (ps). bds. 12.95 (978-0-8249-6678-2(3) , Candy Cane Pr.) Ideals Pubns.

Beylon, Cathy. Decorate a Snowman with 35 Stickers. 1998. (Dover Little Activity Bks.). (Illus.). 4p. (J). (ps-5). 1.50 (978-0-486-40507-0(9)) Dover Pubns., Inc.

—Kids Cuts: Sticker Activity Book. 2003. (Dover Little Activity Bks.). (Illus.). 4p. (J). act. bk. ed. 1.50 (978-0-486-43011-9(1)) Dover Pubns., Inc.

—Little Gas Station Sticker Activity Book. 1998. (Illus.). 4p. (J). pap. 1.50 (978-0-486-40311-3(4)) Dover Pubns., Inc.

—My School Sticker Activity Book. 1998. (Dover Little Activity Bks.). (Illus.). 4p. (J). pap. 1.50 (978-0-486-40510-0(9)) Dover Pubns., Inc.

—Twelve Bugs Bookmarks. 2004. (Bookmarks Ser.). (Illus.). 6p. (J). (gr. k). pap. 1.50 (978-0-486-43498-8(2)) Dover Pubns., Inc.

—Twelve Mother Goose Bookmarks. 2003. (Dover Little Activity Bks.). (Illus.). 6p. (J). (gr. k). pap. 1.50 (978-0-486-43020-1(0)) Dover Pubns., Inc.

Bicknell, Joanna. Funny Farm. 2007. (Googlies Ser.). (Illus.). 14p. (ps). per., bds. 6.95 (***978-1-84610-477-0(7)***) Make Believe Ideas GBR. *Dist:* Ingram Pub. Services.

—Tickle Monsters. 2007. (Finger Puppet Books Ser.). (Illus.). 12p. (ps). bds. 12.99 (***978-1-84610-427-5(0)***) Make Believe Ideas GBR. *Dist:* Ingram Pub. Services.

Biesty, Stephen. Stephen Biesty's Incredible Pop-up Cross-Sections. Biesty, Stephen, illus. 2004. (Illus.). 6p. (gr. 4-8). reprint ed. 17.00 (978-0-7567-7292-5(3)) DIANE Publishing Co.

Bilgrami, Shaheen. Icy Antics. Chambers, Sally & Ratie, Patricia, illus. 2003. (Curious Creatures Bks.). 12p. (J). bds. 12.95 (978-1-4027-0820-6(3) , Sterling/Pinwheel) Sterling Publishing Co., Inc.

—A Magic Color Book: Jungle Art Show. Girouard, Patrick, illus. 2002. (Pinwheel Ser.). 10p. (J). (ps-k). 5.95 (978-1-4027-0206-8(X)) Sterling Publishing Co., Inc.

—A Magic Skeleton Book: Amazing Dinosaur Discovery. Tamblin, Treve & Phillips, Mike, illus. 2002. (Magic Color Bks.). 24p. (J). (ps-2). 9.95 (978-0-8069-8591-6(7)) Sterling Publishing Co., Inc.

—Safari Animal Adventure. Kees, Chantal & Shields, Chris, illus. 2003. (Magic Color Bks.). 12p. (J). (gr. k-2). 9.95 (978-1-4027-0822-0(X)) Sterling Publishing Co., Inc.

The Birth of Jesus Bible Sticker Book. 2003. (Illus.). 16p. (J). 2.98 (978-1-4054-1559-0(2)) Parragon, Inc.

Black, Jessica L. Opposites. Cress, Michelle H., illus. 2001. (Board Bk.). (J). (ps-1). pap. 10.95 (978-1-57332-193-8(1)) HighReach Learning, Inc.

—Opposites Board Book & Felt Puppet Set. Cress, Michelle H., illus. 2005. (J). bds. (978-1-57332-363-5(2)) HighReach Learning, Inc.

—What Can Baby Do? Board Book & Felt Puppet Set. Metzger, Jeanne, illus. 2005. (J). bds. (978-1-57332-366-6(7)) HighReach Learning, Inc.

Blake, Michel. Baby's Day. Blake, Michel, illus. 2007. (Easy-Open Ser.). (Illus.). 16p. (J). (ps). bds. 5.99 (978-0-7636-3368-4(2)) Candlewick Pr.

—Let's Play: Easy-Open Board Book. 2007. (Easy-Open Ser.). (Illus.). 16p. (J). (ps). bds. 5.99 (978-0-7636-3369-1(0)) Candlewick Pr.

Bleck, Linda. Pepper Picks a Pumpkin. Bleck, Linda, illus. 2007. (Pepper plays, pulls, & Pops! Ser.). 18p. (J). 8.99 (***978-1-4169-1773-1(X)*** , Little Simon) Simon & Schuster Children's Publishing.

Bleck, Linda. Pepper's Valentine Surprise. 2007. (Pepper plays, pulls, & Pops! Ser.). 18p. (J). (ps-2). 8.99 (978-1-4169-1774-8(8) , Little Simon) Simon & Schuster Children's Publishing.

Bloomsbury Staff. Mr. Bean's Holiday. 2007. (Illus.). 40p. (J). pap., act. bk. ed. 7.95 (978-1-59990-101-5(3)) Bloomsbury Publishing.

Bockol, Leslie. Tie your shoes rocket Style. 2007. 10p. (J). 9.95 (***978-1-59764-292-7(4)***) New Line Bks.

Boey, Stephanie. Undersea Treasure Hunt: Find the Treasure with Little Fish & Friends. Boey, Stephanie, illus. 2005. (Illus.). 20p. (J). 15.95 (978-0-8118-4622-6(9)) Chronicle Bks. LLC.

Bolam, Emily. Bunny. 2003. (Chunky Pet Bks.). (Illus.). 14p. (J). bds. 4.95 (978-0-7641-5607-6(1)) Barron's Educational Series, Inc.

—Dog. 2003. (Chunky Pet Bks.). (Illus.). 14p. (J). bds. 5.99 (978-0-7641-5610-6(1)) Barron's Educational Series, Inc.

—Guinea Pig. 2003. (Chunky Pet Bks.). (Illus.). 14p. (J). bds. 4.95 (978-0-7641-5612-0(8)) Barron's Educational Series, Inc.

Bonforte, Lisa. Baby Animals Stickers. 2002. (Illus.). 4p. (J). (ps-5). 1.50 (978-0-486-42341-8(7)) Dover Pubns., Inc.

Boniface, William. Christmastime Is Cookie Time. Rooney, Ronnie, illus. 2001. (Top This! Ser.). 12p. (J). bds. 9.99 (978-0-8431-7678-0(4) , Price Stern Sloan) Penguin Group (USA) Inc.

—Trim the Tree for Christmas! Palen, Debbie, illus. 2000. 12p. (J). (ps-2). bds. 9.99 (978-0-8431-7558-5(3) , Price Stern Sloan) Penguin Group (USA) Inc.

Book Company Staff. Animal World. 2003. (Novelty Bks.). (Illus.). (J). bds. 9.95 (978-1-74047-366-8(3)) Book Co. Publishing Pty, Ltd., The AUS. *Dist:* Penton Overseas, Inc.

—Catch That Hat! 2002. (Magical World of Teddies Ser.). 14p. (J). bds. 12.95 (978-1-74047-162-6(8)) Book Co. Publishing Pty, Ltd., The AUS. *Dist:* Penton Overseas, Inc.

—Let's Play. 2003. (Novelty Bks.). (Illus.). (J). bds. 9.95 (978-1-74047-365-1(5)) Book Co. Publishing Pty, Ltd., The AUS. *Dist:* Penton Overseas, Inc.

—Lift & Learn Animals. 2004. (Novelty Bks.). (Illus.). 10p. (J). (gr. 3-5). bds. 7.95 (978-1-74047-555-6(0)) Book Co. Publishing Pty, Ltd., The AUS. *Dist:* Penton Overseas, Inc.

—Lift & Learn Colors. 2004. (Novelty Bks.). (Illus.). 10p. (J). (gr. 3-5). bds. 7.95 (978-1-74047-556-3(9)) Book Co. Publishing Pty, Ltd., The AUS. *Dist:* Penton Overseas, Inc.

—Lift & Learn First Words. 2004. (Novelty Bks.). (Illus.). 10p. (J). (gr. 3-5). bds. 7.95 (978-1-74047-558-7(5)) Book Co. Publishing Pty, Ltd., The AUS. *Dist:* Penton Overseas, Inc.

—Lift & Learn Numbers. 2004. (Novelty Bks.). (Illus.). 10p. (J). (gr. 3-5). bds. 7.95 (978-1-74047-557-0(7)) Book Co. Publishing Pty, Ltd., The AUS. *Dist:* Penton Overseas, Inc.

—Magic Planet. Schimmel, Schim, illus. 2002. (Pop-up Bks.). 14p. (J). 15.95 (978-1-74047-187-9(3)) Book Co. Publishing Pty, Ltd., The AUS. *Dist:* Penton Overseas, Inc.

—Teddy Mini Box Set. 2002. (Pop-up Books Mini Ser.). 14p. (J). 15.95 (978-1-74047-209-8(8)) Book Co. Publishing Pty, Ltd., The AUS. *Dist:* Penton Overseas, Inc.

Borgardt, Marianne. Peekaboo You! Voo, Rhonda, illus. 1999. 12p. (J). reprint ed. 5.95 (978-1-892374-15-8(3)) Weldon Owen, Inc.

Borgo, Deborah Colvin, illus. Baby Bunny. 1999. (J). (978-0-7853-3353-1(3)) Publications International, Ltd.

Bourgeois, Paulette. Franklin's Christmas: A Sticker Activity Book. Clark, Brenda, illus. 2004. (Franklin Sticker & Activity Bks.). 16p. (J). (gr. k-3). (978-1-55337-506-7(8)) Kids Can Pr., Ltd.

Bourgeois, Paulette & Clark, Brenda. Franklin's Big Search And-Solve Flap Book. Jeffrey, Sean et al, trs. Jeffrey, Sean et al, illus. 2005. 10p. (J). (ps-1). (978-1-55337-522-7(X)) Kids Can Pr., Ltd.

Boyle, Alison. Twinkle, Twinkle, Little Star. Pichon, Liz, illus. 2000. (Finger Puppet Bks.). 16p. (J). (ps-k). 10.95 (978-1-86233-111-2(1)) Sterling Publishing Co., Inc.

Boynton, Sandra. Fuzzy Fuzzy Fuzzy! A Touch, Skritch, & Tickle Book. Boynton, Sandra, illus. 2003. (Illus.). 12p. (J). bds. 12.95 (978-0-689-86363-9(2) , Little Simon) Simon & Schuster Children's Publishing.

—My Puppy Book. Boynton, Sandra, illus. 2005. (Illus.). 10p. (J). 16.95 (978-1-4169-0844-9(7) , Little Simon) Simon & Schuster Children's Publishing.

—What's Wrong, Little Pookie? 2007. (Illus.). 18p. (J). (ps). bds. 5.99 (***978-0-375-84552-9(6)*** , Robin Corey Bks.) Random Hse. Children's Bks.

Boynton, Sandra. Your Personal Penguin. 2006. (Illus.). 24p. (J). bds. 6.95 (978-0-7611-4372-7(6)) Workman Publishing Co., Inc.

Bracken, Carolyn. 1 2 3 Fun. Garcia, Segundo, illus. 2001. (Fisher-Price Little People Ser.). 16p. (J). spiral bd., bds. (978-0-7853-5190-0(6) , 7134600) Publications International, Ltd.

Bradman, Tony. Has Anyone Seen Jack. rev. ed. 2007. (Illus.). 24p. (J). 7.95 (***978-1-84507-706-8(7)***) Lincoln, Frances Ltd. GBR. *Dist:* Perseus Distribution.

Brainy Baby Animals. 2004. (978-1-59394-234-2(6)) Bendon Publishing International.

Brainy Baby Quad Book. 2005. (Brainy Baby Ser.). 40p. (J). bds. 10.39 (978-1-59394-240-3(0)) Bendon Publishing International.

Brett, Jan. Gingerbread Baby. Brett, Jan, illus. 2003. (Illus.). 36p. (J). bds. 7.99 (978-0-399-24166-6(3) , Putnam Juvenile) Penguin Group (USA) Inc.

Brett, Jane. Noisy Garage. Thatcher, Frances, illus. 2000. (Little Helpers Ser.). (J). (978-0-439-21516-9(1)) Scholastic, Inc.

Bright & Beyond - Age 1. 2004. (J). (978-0-9726170-5-5(1)) Pal Toys, LLC.

Bright & Beyond - Age 2. 2004. (J). (978-0-9726170-6-2(X)) Pal Toys, LLC.

Bright & Beyond - Baby. 2004. (J). (978-0-9726170-4-8(3)) Pal Toys, LLC.

Bright & Beyond - Math. 2004. (J). (978-0-9763648-0-1(8)) Pal Toys, LLC.

Bright & Beyond - Preschool. 2004. (J). (978-0-9726170-7-9(8)) Pal Toys, LLC.

Bright & Beyond - Reading. 2004. (J). (978-0-9726170-8-6(6)) Pal Toys, LLC.

Bright & Beyond - Thinking. 2004. (J). (978-0-9763648-1-8(6)) Pal Toys, LLC.

Bright & Beyond - Writing. 2004. (J). (978-0-9726170-9-3(4)) Pal Toys, LLC.

Bright, Michael. Sharks. Howard, Colin, illus. 2001. (Trackpack Ser.). 32p. (J). 4.99 (978-0-439-37480-4(4)) Scholastic, Inc.

Brilliant Beginnings Staff. Furry Friends & Merry Melodies Follow-Along Picture Book. 1999. (Illus.). (978-0-9665815-9-1(8)) Brilliant Beginnings, LLC.

Brooke, Susan Rich, adapted by. Finding Nemo. 2003. (Interactive Play-A-Sound Ser.). (Illus.). (J). (978-0-7853-8916-3(4)); 24p. 15.98 (978-0-7853-8420-5(0) , 7184400) Publications International, Ltd.

Brooklyn Public Library Staff. Brooklyn Pops Up: A Moveable Book of Brooklyn Landmarks. 2000. 16p. mass mkt. (978-1-891001-04-8(3) , Simon & Schuster) Simon & Schuster.

Brooklyn Public Library Staff, et al. Brooklyn Pops Up: A Moveable Book of Brooklyn Landmarks. 2000. (Illus.). 8p. (J). (gr. 4-7). 22.99 (978-0-689-84019-7(5) , Little Simon) Simon & Schuster Children's Publishing.

Brooks, F. & Litchfield, J. Nativity Lift-the-Flap. 2004. (First Stories Ser.). 24p. (J). 10.95 (978-0-7945-0529-5(5)) EDC Publishing.

Brooks, Felicity. Farms lift & Look. Litchfield, Jo, illus. 2005. 12p. (J). 9.95 (978-0-7945-0932-3(0) , Usborne) EDC Publishing.

—Tractors Chunky Jigsaw Book. 2005. (Chunky Jigsaw Books Ser.). 14p. (J). 7.95 (978-0-7945-0861-6(8) , Usborne) EDC Publishing.

—Trains Chunky Jigsaw Book. 2005. (Chunky Jigsaw Books Ser.). 14p. (J). 7.95 (978-0-7945-0859-3(6) , Usborne) EDC Publishing.

—Trenes. 2006. (Illus.). 12p. (J). bds. 9.99 (978-0-7460-7402-2(6) , Usborne) EDC Publishing.

—Trucks Lift-and-Look. 2005. (Illus.). 12p. (J). per. 9.95 (978-0-7945-1068-8(X) , Usborne) EDC Publishing.

Bros, Warner & Warner Brothers Staff. Harry Potter Sticker Book Bk. 1: Mysterious Halls of Hogwarts. 2001. (Illus.). (gr. 4-7). pap. 7.99 (978-0-439-28634-3(4)) Scholastic, Inc.

Brown, Janet Allison. Choo! Choo! A Squeak Me Book. Pirie, Janie, illus. 2005. 12p. (J). bds. 5.95 (978-0-7641-5825-4(2)) Barron's Educational Series, Inc.

—Puppy Backpack. O'Neill, Rachael, illus. 2007. 10p. (J). bds. 12.95 (978-1-4027-4480-8(3)) Sterling Publishing Co., Inc.

Brown, Margaret Wise. Goodnight Moon Board Book & Slippers. Hurd, Clement, illus. 2007. 34p. (J). 19.99 (***978-0-06-123902-1(X)*** , Harper Festival) HarperCollins Pubs.

Browne, Anthony, illus. Anthony Browne Presents the Animal Fair: A Spectacular Pop-up. 2004. 12p. (J). (gr. k-4). reprint ed. 15.00 (978-0-7567-8005-0(5)) DIANE Publishing Co.

Browning, Dave. Marvin Weighs In. 2000. (Illus.). 12p. (J). (ps-3). pap. 6.95 (978-0-688-17735-5(2) , Harper Festival) HarperCollins Pubs.

Broyles, Beverly Ashley, illus. Grandmother's Alligator/ Burukenge Wa Nyanya Activity Guide. 2005. (ENG & SWA.). (J). 12.95 (978-0-9703632-7-5(3)) Wakefield Connection, The.

Bruna, Dick. What Will I Do Today? Miffy's Big Flap Book. 2004. 10p. 9.99 (978-1-59226-178-9(7)) Big Tent Entertainment, Inc.

Buddy Bear's Feelings. 2000. (Illus.). (J). (978-1-56156-832-1(5)) Kidsbooks, Inc.

Buehner, Caralyn. The Snowmen Pop-up Book. Buehner, Mark, illus. 2006. 14p. (J). (ps). 21.99 (978-0-8037-3180-6(9) , Dial) Penguin Group (USA) Inc.

Bug Mania. (Flip Flap Fun Book Ser.). 10p. (J). bds. (978-2-7643-0183-8(9)) Phidal Publishing, Inc./Editions Phidal, Inc.

Bugs Life. 1998. (Flip Bks.). (J). 3.99 (978-0-7364-0103-6(2)) Mouse Works.

Burns, Kate. Blink Like an Owl! 1998. (Lift-the-Flap Bk.). (Illus.). 10p. 6.95 (978-1-899607-41-9(2)) Sterling Publishing Co., Inc.

—Waddle Like a Duck! 1998. (Lift-the-Flap Bk.). (Illus.). 10p. (J). 6.95 (978-1-899607-42-6(0)) Sterling Publishing Co., Inc.

Bushell, Isobel, illus. Rudolph the Red-Nosed Reindeer: Musical Board Book. 1999. 12p. (YA). (ps up). bds. 5.95 (978-0-694-00564-2(9)) HarperCollins Pubs.

Bussolati, Emanuela. If You Put . . . Pagnoni, Roberta, illus. 2001. (Open the Little Windows Ser.). 22p. (J). (ps-k). bds. 4.95 (978-0-7641-5339-6(0)) Barron's Educational Series, Inc.

Busy Builders. (Flip Flap Fun Book Ser.). 10p. (J). bds. (978-2-7643-0138-8(3)) Phidal Publishing, Inc./Editions Phidal, Inc.

Busy City. (Flip Flap Fun Book Ser.). 10p. (J). bds. (978-2-89393-820-2(5)) Phidal Publishing, Inc./Editions Phidal, Inc.

Butterfield, Moira. Do Frogs Fly? Canals, Sonia, illus. 2007. (Animal Flappers Bks.). 16p. (J). (gr. k-k). 7.99 (978-0-7641-6027-1(3)) Barron's Educational Series, Inc.

—Do Lions Like Lettuce? Canals, Sonia, illus. 2007. (Animal Flappers Bks.). 16p. (J). (gr. k-k). 7.99 (978-0-7641-6026-4(5)) Barron's Educational Series, Inc.

—Peek-a-Boo! 2007. 10p. (J). pap. 6.99 (978-0-439-87521-9(8) , Cartwheel Bks.) Scholastic, Inc.

—Peek-a-Who? 2006. 10p. (J). 6.99 (978-0-439-78534-1(0) , Cartwheel Bks.) Scholastic, Inc.

Butterworth, Nick. The Secret Path. 2003. (Illus.). 32p. (J). pap. 11.00 (978-0-00-715518-7(2)) HarperCollins Pubs. Ltd. GBR. *Dist:* Trafalgar Square Publishing.

Caldwell, Lise. Please & Thank You 1-2-3. 2001. (Threads Ser.). (Illus.). 16p. (J). (ps-1). 5.99 (978-0-7847-1010-4(4) , Bean Sprouts) Standard Publishing.

Cameron, Ken. Plant Atlas/Plantas alrededor del Mundo: English/Spanish Pair, 12 texts, 2 titles, Vol. 2. ed. 2004. (Navigators Ser.). (J). pap., instr.'s gde. ed. 84.00 (978-1-4108-1767-9(9) , 17679) Benchmark Education Co.

Campbell-Ernst, Lisa. Good Morning, Sun! 2006. (Illus.). 5p. (J). bds. 6.95 (978-1-59354-154-5(6)) Blue Apple Bks.

—Learn to Turn: Breakfast Time! 2006. (Illus.). 5p. (J). bds. 6.95 (978-1-59354-155-2(4)) Blue Apple Bks.

Campbell, Rod. Dear Zoo: A Lift-the-Flap Book. Campbell, Rod, illus. 2007. 18p. (J). 6.99 (***978-1-4169-4737-0(X)*** , Little Simon) Simon & Schuster Children's Publishing.

—Dear Zoo: A Pop-up Book. Campbell, Rod, illus. 2005. (Illus.). 20p. (J). 12.95 (978-0-689-87751-3(X) , Little Simon) Simon & Schuster Children's Publishing.

—Pop-Up Jungle. (Illus.). 24p. (J). bds. 9.99 (978-0-333-73350-9(9)) Pan Macmillan GBR. *Dist:* Trafalgar Square Publishing.

—The Pop-Up Jungle. 2000. (Illus.). 8p. (J). (ps-k). (978-1-85292-247-4(8) , Campbell Bks.) Pan Macmillan.

Candlewick Books Staff, Books. Old MacDonald Had a Farm. 2003. (gr. k-3). lib. bdg. 11.80 (978-0-613-74739-4(9)) Tandem Library Bks.

Canetti, Yanitzia, tr. Cha-Cha-Cha en la Selva (The Animal Boogie) Harter, Debbie, illus. 2003. (SPA.). 32p. (J). 6.99 (978-1-84148-265-1(X)) Barefoot Bks., Inc.

Cannon, Janell. Stellaluna. 2007. (Illus.). 42p. (J). (ps). bds. 7.95 (***978-0-15-206287-3(4)*** , Red Wagon Bks.) Harcourt Children's Bks.

Capucilli, Alyssa Satin. Happy Easter, Biscuit! Schories, Pat, illus. 2000. (Biscuit Ser.). 20p. (J). (ps-1). pap. 6.99 (978-0-694-01223-7(8) , Harper Festival) HarperCollins Pubs.

—Happy Easter, Biscuit! 2000. (gr. k-3). lib. bdg. 15.25 (978-0-613-70589-9(0)) Tandem Library Bks.

—Happy Halloween, Biscuit! Schories, Pat, illus. 1999. (Biscuit Ser.). 20p. (J). (ps-1). pap. 6.99 (978-0-694-01220-6(3) , Harper Festival) HarperCollins Pubs.

—Happy Thanksgiving, Biscuit! Schories, Pat, illus. 1999. (Biscuit Ser.). 20p. (J). (ps-1). pap. 6.99 (978-0-694-01221-3(1) , Harper Festival) HarperCollins Pubs.

Carle, Eric. Dream Snow. Gauch, Patricia Lee, ed. Carle, Eric, illus. 2000. (Illus.). 32p. (J). (ps-1). 21.99 (978-0-399-23579-5(5) , Philomel) Penguin Group (USA) Inc.

—Little Cloud. Carle, Eric, illus. 1998. (Illus.). 28p. (J). (ps-k). bds. 6.99 (978-0-399-23191-9(9) , Philomel) Penguin Group (USA) Inc.

—My Very First Book of Animal Homes. Carle, Eric, illus. 2007. 20p. (J). (ps-k). bds. 5.99 (978-0-399-24647-0(9) , Philomel) Penguin Group (USA) Inc.

—My Very First Book of Motion. Carle, Eric, illus. 2007. 10p. (J). bds. 5.99 (978-0-399-24748-4(3) , Philomel) Penguin Group (USA) Inc.

—The Very Busy Spider. 2006. (World of Eric Carle Ser.). (Illus.). 24p. (J). (ps-1). pap. 5.99 (978-0-448-44421-5(6) , Grosset & Dunlap) Penguin Group (USA) Inc.

—The Very Busy Spider's Favorite Words. 2007. 20p. (J). (ps-1). bds. 3.99 (***978-0-448-44703-2(7)*** , Grosset & Dunlap) Penguin Group (USA) Inc.

—The Very Hungry Caterpillar. ed. 2004. (J). (ps-2). spiral bd. (978-0-616-01610-7(7)); spiral bd. (978-0-616-01611-4(5)) Canadian National Institute for the Blind/ Institut National Canadien pour les Aveugles.

—The Very Hungry Caterpillar. 2004. (VIE, GUJ, URD, SOM & CHI., Illus.). 23p. (J). (978-1-85269-129-5(8)) Mantra Publishing, Ltd.

—The Very Hungry Caterpillar. 2004. (Illus.). (J). (BEN, ARA, VIE, GUJ & URD.). 23p. 10.95 (978-1-85269-125-7(5)); (GUJ, BEN, VIE, URD & SOM., 23p. 10.95 (978-1-85269-127-1(1)); (SOM., 19p. 10.95 (978-1-85269-128-8(X)) Mantra Publishing, Ltd. GBR. *Dist:* AIMS International Bks., Inc.

—The Very Hungry Caterpillar. Carle, Eric, illus. 2007. 10p. (J). bds. 14.99 incl. audio compact disk (978-0-399-24745-3(9) , Philomel) Penguin Group (USA) Inc.

—The Very Hungry Caterpillar: Board Book & Plush Set. Carle, Eric, illus. 2002. (Illus.). 24p. (J). (ps-1). 16.99 (978-0-399-24205-2(8) , Philomel) Penguin Group (USA) Inc.

—The Very Hungry Caterpillar: Giant Board Book & Plush Package. Carle, Eric, illus. 2001. (Illus.). 24p. (J). 25.99 (978-0-399-23772-0(0) , Philomel) Penguin Group (USA) Inc.

—The Very Hungry Caterpillar's Favorite Words. 2007. 20p. (J). (ps-1). bds. 3.99 (***978-0-448-44704-9(5)*** , Grosset & Dunlap) Penguin Group (USA) Inc.

Carle, Eric. 10 Little Rubber Ducks (Spanish Edition) 10 patitos de Goma. Carle, Eric, illus. 2007. (SPA.). 36p. (J). 19.99 (978-0-06-112623-9(3) , Rayo) HarperCollins Pubs.

Carney, Charles. Harley-Davidson Great Rides. Eberhart, Donald G., illus. 2002. (J). 15.98 (978-0-7853-7043-7(9)) Publications International, Ltd.

Carrier, Lark. Five Little Goblins. 2001. (Illus.). 18p. (J). (ps-1). 6.95 (978-0-694-01576-4(8) , Harper Festival) HarperCollins Pubs.

Carrier, Lark, et al. Boo! A Halloween Peek-a-Boo! Book. Carrier, Lark, illus. 2003. (Illus.). 28p. (J). pap. 5.95 (978-0-439-38222-9(X) , Cartwheel Bks.) Scholastic, Inc.

Carter, David A. Alpha Bugs: A Pop-Up Alphabet. Carter, David A., illus. ed. 2006. (Illus.). 28p. (J). (ps-2). 11.95 (978-1-4169-0973-6(7) , Little Simon) Simon & Schuster Children's Publishing.

—Birthday Bugs: A Pop-up Party. Carter, David A., illus. 2004. (Illus.). 16p. (J). 10.95 (978-0-689-81858-5(0) , Little Simon) Simon & Schuster Children's Publishing.

—Chanukah Bugs: A Pop-up Celebration. Carter, David A., illus. 2002. (Illus.). 16p. (J). (ps-2). 10.95 (978-0-689-81860-8(2) , Little Simon) Simon & Schuster Children's Publishing.

—Easter Bugs: A Springtime Pop-up by David A Carter. Carter, David A., illus. 2001. (Bugs in a Box Bks.). (Illus.). 14p. (J). (ps-2). 10.95 (978-0-689-81862-2(9) , Little Simon) Simon & Schuster Children's Publishing.

—Feely Bugs: To Touch & Feel. Carter, David A., illus. ed. 2005. (Illus.). 14p. (J). (ps-ps). pap. 9.99 (978-1-4169-0326-0(7) , Little Simon) Simon & Schuster Children's Publishing.

—Halloween Bugs: A Trick or Treat. Carter, David A., illus. 2003. (Illus.). 14p. (J). 10.95 (978-0-689-85916-8(3) , Little Simon) Simon & Schuster Children's Publishing.

—Jingle Bugs: A Merry Pop-up Book with Lights & Music! Carter, David A., illus. 2004. (Illus.). 22p. (J). pap. 10.95 (978-0-689-87416-1(2) , Little Simon) Simon & Schuster Children's Publishing.

—One Red Dot: A Pop-up Book for Children of All Ages. Carter, David A., illus. 2005. (Classic Collectible Pop-Up Ser.). (Illus.). 18p. (J). 19.95 (978-0-689-87769-8(2) , Little Simon) Simon & Schuster Children's Publishing.

Carter, David A. 600 Black Spots: A Pop-up Book for Children of All Ages. 2007. (Classic Collectible Pop-up Ser.). (Illus.). 20p. (J). (ps-3). 19.99 (***978-1-4169-4092-0(8)*** , Little Simon) Simon & Schuster Children's Publishing.

Carter, David A. & Diaz, James. Let's Make It Pop-Up. Carter, David A. & Diaz, James, illus. 2004. (Illus.). 10p. (J). 12.95 (978-0-689-86508-4(2) , Little Simon) Simon & Schuster Children's Publishing.

Carter, Nancy & Julien, Terry, illus. Jesus Loves Me. 2006. 16p. (J). pap. 1.99 (978-0-7847-1804-9(0) , 04186) Standard Publishing.

Carter, Noelle. Birthday Fun 1, 2, 3! A Counting Flap Book. Carter, Noelle, illus. 2005. (Illus.). 14p. (J). bds. 6.99 (978-0-689-86027-0(7) , Little Simon) Simon & Schuster Children's Publishing.

Cartlidge, Michelle. The Mouse Christmas House: A Press-Out Model Book. (Illus.). 32p. (J). (978-1-904613-67-1(5) , Buster Bks.) O'Mara, Michael Bks., Ltd.

Cartwheel Books Staff. Sleeping Beauty. Stevenson, Peter, illus. 2000. (Finger Puppet Theater Bks.). 16p. (J). (ps-1). bds. 14.95 (978-0-439-17680-4(8)) Scholastic, Inc.

Cartwright, Stephen. Where's Curly? Amery, Heather, illus. 1998. (Usborne Farmyard Tales Ser.). 16p. (J). (ps up). lib. bdg. 15.95 (978-1-58086-150-2(4)) EDC Publishing.

Cartwright, Stephen & Zeff, Claudia. Find the Kitten. 2000. (Kid Kits Ser.). (Illus.). 10p. (J). (ps). 10.95 (978-0-88110-802-6(2)) EDC Publishing.

—Find the Puppy. 2000. (Kid Kits Ser.). (Illus.). 10p. (J). (ps). 10.95 (978-0-88110-801-9(4)) EDC Publishing.

Castiglione, Janice, illus. The Musical Twinkle, Twinkle, Little Star. 2000. (Rub-a-Dub-Tub Musical Bks.). (J). vinyl bd. 7.00 (978-1-883043-18-6(2)) Straight Edge Pr., The.

Caterpillar Inc. Staff. Big Noisy Trucks & Diggers Demolition. 2004. (Illus.). 14p. (J). 12.95 (978-0-8118-4262-4(2)) Chronicle Bks. LLC.

Caterpillar Inc. Staff, contrib. by. Big Trucks & Diggers: Touch & Feel. 2004. (Illus.). 12p. (J). 9.95 (978-0-8118-4302-7(5)) Chronicle Bks. LLC.

Cats & Kittens Sticker Activity Book. 2003. (Illus.). 12p. (J). 2.98 (978-1-4054-1178-3(3)) Parragon, Inc.

Caviezel, Giovanni. Knights. 2007. (Little People Shape Bks.). 10p. (J). (ps-3). bds. 10.99 (***978-0-7641-6065-3(6)***) Barron's Educational Series, Inc.

—Mi Propio Cuerpo: Spanish Edition of My Own Human Body. Mesturini, Cristina, illus. 2004. (SPA.). 10p. (J). bds. 10.95 (978-0-7641-5773-8(6)) Barron's Educational Series, Inc.

—Policeman's Saftey Hints. 2007. (Illus.). 10p. (J). (gr. k-2). bds. 10.99 (978-0-7641-6019-6(2)) Barron's Educational Series, Inc.

CEDCO Publishing Staff. Austin Powers. 2000. (Illus.). 24p. (J). (ps-3). pap. 8.95 (978-0-7683-2225-5(1)) CEDCO Publishing.

—Big Dogs Sticker Book. 2000. (Illus.). (J). pap. 8.95 (978-0-7683-2173-9(5)) CEDCO Publishing.

—Bubblegum Sticker Book: An Alter-Ego Trip. 2000. (Illus.). (J). pap. 8.95 (978-0-7683-2172-2(7)) CEDCO Publishing.

—Girl Things: Big Sticker Book. 2000. (Illus.). 48p. (gr. 1-5). pap. 8.95 (978-0-7683-2168-5(9)) CEDCO Publishing.

—The PowerPuff Girls Sticker Book. 2000. (Illus.). 24p. (J). (ps-3). pap. 8.95 (978-0-7683-2227-9(8)) CEDCO Publishing.

—South Park Sticker Book. 2000. (Illus.). 24p. (J). (ps-3). pap. 8.95 (978-0-7683-2226-2(X)) CEDCO Publishing.

—WWJD Sticker Book. 2000. (Illus.). 48p. pap. 8.95 (978-0-7683-2169-2(7)) CEDCO Publishing.

—Xtreme Sticker Book. 2000. (Illus.). 48p. (ps-3). pap. 8.95 (978-0-7683-2158-6(1)) CEDCO Publishing.

Celebrating Cat. 2003. (Happy Birthday Pull-Out Card-Bks.). (Illus.). 4.99 (978-1-56148-385-3(0)) Good Bks.

Cerasini, Marc. Godzilla Saves America: A Monster Showdown In 3-D! Morgan, Tom & Mounts, Paul, illus. 2006. 20p. (J). (gr. k-4). reprint ed. 12.00 (978-1-4223-5409-4(1)) DIANE Publishing Co.

Chaffey, Samantha, illus. Who Lives Here? 2006. 8p. (J). bds. 8.99 (978-0-7641-5997-8(6)) Barron's Educational Series, Inc.

Chambers, Angela. Follow That Chicken! Abel, Simone, illus. 2001. (Pinwheel Ser.). 10p. (J). bds. 3.95 (978-0-8069-0310-1(4)) Sterling Publishing Co., Inc.

—How Now, Cow? Abel, Simone, illus. 2001. (Pinwheel Ser.). 10p. (J). bds. 3.95 (978-0-8069-0275-3(2)) Sterling Publishing Co., Inc.

Chambers, Mark, illus. Build Your Own Fairytale Castle: A Push-Out-and-Play Book. 2008. 12p. (J). bds. 8.95 (***978-0-385-61115-2(3)***) Transworld Publishers Ltd. GBR. *Dist:* Independent Pubs. Group.

Chambers, Sally. Zippy Dinosaur: Diplodocus. 2000. (Illus.). 10p. (J). (ps-k). 6.95 (978-1-86233-178-5(2)) David & Charles Children's Bks. GBR. *Dist:* Sterling Publishing Co., Inc.

—Zippy Dinosaur: Stegosaurus. 2000. (Illus.). 10p. (J). (ps-k). 6.95 (978-1-86233-188-4(X)) David & Charles Children's Bks. GBR. *Dist:* Sterling Publishing Co., Inc.

—Zippy Dinosaur: Triceratops. 2000. (Illus.). 10p. (J). (ps-k). 6.95 (978-1-86233-193-8(6)) David & Charles Children's Bks. GBR. *Dist:* Sterling Publishing Co., Inc.

—Zippy Dinosaur: Tyrannosaurus Rex. 2000. (Illus.). 10p. (J). (ps-k). 6.95 (978-1-86233-183-9(9)) David & Charles Children's Bks. GBR. *Dist:* Sterling Publishing Co., Inc.

Channell, Jim. Quien Vive en el Arbol? 2000. (SPA., Illus.). 10p. (J). (ps-k). 7.95 (978-84-392-8315-7(6)) Lectorum Pubns., Inc.

—Quien Vive en el Jardin? 2000. (SPA., Illus.). 10p. (J). (ps-k). 7.95 (978-84-392-8320-1(2)) Lectorum Pubns., Inc.

—Quien Vive en el Rio? 2000. (SPA., Illus.). (J). (ps-k). bds. 7.95 (978-84-392-8313-3(X)) Lectorum Pubns., Inc.

Chatelier, Ed. Can You Spot the Ball? 2002. (Illus.). 24p. (J). pap. 13.99 (978-0-233-05075-1(2)) Andre Deutsch GBR. *Dist:* Independent Pubs. Group.

Chatterton, Martin. Can Dogs Fly? Fido's Book of Pop-up Transportation Surprises. 2005. (Illus.). 12p. (J). (gr. k-4). reprint ed. 10.00 (978-0-7567-8838-4(2)) DIANE Publishing Co.

Chen, Tony, et al, illus. Animals Showing Off. 2004. 14p. (J). (gr. k-4). reprint ed. 16.00 (978-0-7567-7640-4(6)) DIANE Publishing Co.

Child, Lauren. La Cama de Tus Suenos. 2002. (Illus.). 16p. (J). (CAT.). 20.95 (978-84-8488-005-9(2)); (SPA., 20.95 (978-84-8488-004-2(4) , RR5225) Serres, Ediciones, S. L. ESP. *Dist:* Lectorum Pubns., Inc.

Child's Play Staff. There Was an Old Lady Who Swallowed a Fly. Adams, Pam, illus. 1999. (Books with Holes Ser.). 16p. (J). (ps-3). 19.99 (978-0-85953-635-6(1)) Child's Play-International.

Chipponeri, Kelli. Ouch! Bye Bye, Boo-Boos. Gott, Barry, illus. 2002. 14p. (J). pap. 5.99 (978-0-689-84931-2(1) , Little Simon) Simon & Schuster Children's Publishing.

Christelow, Eileen. Five Little Monkeys Sitting in a Tree. Christelow, Eileen, illus. 2002. (Illus.). (J). 13.79 (978-0-7587-2512-7(4)) Book Wholesalers, Inc.

—Five Little Monkeys Sitting in a Tree. Christelow, Eileen, illus. 1999. (Five Little Monkeys Ser.). (Illus.). 28p. (J). (gr. k-ps). bds. 5.95 (978-0-395-98033-0(X) , Clarion Bks.) Houghton Mifflin Co. Trade & Reference Div.

Christian, Cheryl. Cuantos Hay? 2001. (Photoflaps Ser.). Orig. Title: How Many?. (SPA., Illus.). 12p. (J). (ps-k). bds. 5.50 (978-1-887734-25-7(2)) Star Bright Bks., Inc.

—What Happens Next? Kisa Kap Rive Apre? Dwight, Laura, photos by. 2005. (Illus.). 12p. (J). (ps). per. 5.50 (978-1-59572-025-2(1)) Star Bright Bks., Inc.

—What Happens Next? (Traditional Chinese) Dwight, Laura, photos by. 2004. (CHI., Illus.). 12p. (J). bds. 5.50 (978-1-932065-63-3(6)) Star Bright Bks., Inc.

—Where Does It Go? (English/Haitian Creole) 2005. (CRP., Illus.). 12p. (J). bds. 5.50 (978-1-59572-026-9(X)) Star Bright Bks., Inc.

—Where Does It Go?/Dondé Va? Bilingual Edition. 2004. (Photoflaps Ser.). (ENG & SPA., Illus.). 12p. (J). bds. 5.50 (978-1-932065-59-6(8) , 7187849112) Star Bright Bks., Inc.

—Where's the Baby? (Traditional Chinese) Dwight, Laura, photos by. 2004. (CHI., Illus.). 12p. (J). bds. 5.50 (978-1-932065-62-6(8)) Star Bright Bks., Inc.

—Where's the Baby?/Kote Tibebe a Ye? Dwight, Laura, photos by. 2005. (CRP., Illus.). 12p. (J). (ps). per. 5.50 (978-1-59572-027-6(8)) Star Bright Bks., Inc.

—Where's the Kitten? (Traditional Chinese) Dwight, Laura, photos by. 2004. (CHI., Illus.). 12p. (J). bds. 5.50 (978-1-932065-60-2(1)) Star Bright Bks., Inc.

—Where's the Kitten?/Kote Ti Chat la Ye? Dwight, Laura, photos by. 2005. (CRP., Illus.). 12p. (J). (ps). per. 5.50 (978-1-59572-028-3(6)) Star Bright Bks., Inc.

—Where's the Puppy? (Traditional Chinese) Dwight, Laura, photos by. 2004. (CHI., Illus.). 12p. (J). bds. 5.50 (978-1-932065-61-9(X)) Star Bright Bks., Inc.

—Where's the Puppy?/Kote Ti Toutous la Ye? Dwight, Laura, photos by. 2005. (CRP., Illus.). 12p. (J). (ps). per. 5.50 (978-1-59572-029-0(4)) Star Bright Bks., Inc.

Christie, Jean. Charlie Crab: Inflatable Bath Book. Canals, Sonia, illus. 2003. 7p. (J). 6.95 (978-1-4027-0447-5(X)) Sterling Publishing Co., Inc.

—Danny Dolphin: Inflatable Bath Book. Canals, Sonia, illus. 2003. 7p. (J). 6.95 (978-1-4027-0446-8(1)) Sterling Publishing Co., Inc.

—Lester the Lazy Lion. 2000. (Felt Lift the Flap Bks.). (Illus.). (J). (ps-k). 4.95 (978-1-58646-007-5(2)) Polka Dot Pr.

—Stella Starfish. Canals, Sonia, illus. 2002. 8p. (J). 6.95 (978-0-8069-8229-8(2)) Sterling Publishing Co., Inc.

—Sylvia the Sleepy Elephant. 2000. (Felt Lift the Flap Bks.). (Illus.). (J). (ps-k). 4.95 (978-1-58646-006-8(4)) Polka Dot Pr.

Christmas. (Illus.). (gr. 1-4). 3.00 (978-0-570-05521-1(0) , 54-1031) Concordia Publishing Hse.

Christmas. 2001. (Illus.). 12p. (J). bds. 6.99 (978-0-88271-055-6(9)) Regina Pr., Malhame & Co.

The Christmas Carol Book. (Illus.). 10p. (J). bds. (978-2-89393-929-2(5)) Phidal Publishing, Inc./Editions Phidal, Inc.

Christmas Numbers. 2001. (Illus.). 13p. (J). pap. 2.95 (978-1-55254-274-3(2) , BV24017) Brighter Vision Pubns.

Christmas Tales: Night Before Christmas; The First Christmas; Christmas Angel; Christmas Kitten. (Lift-A-Flap Ser.). (Illus.). (J). (978-0-7853-2070-8(9)) Publications International, Ltd.

Chronicle Books LLC Staff. Castaway Pirates. 2008. (J). 19.99 (978-0-8118-5923-3(1)) Chronicle Bks. LLC.

—Nick Jr. Nursery Rhyme Time: A Touch-and-See Activity Book. (J). 15.95 (978-0-8118-4726-1(8)) Chronicle Bks. LLC.

—Santa Claus: Finger Puppet Book. 2006. (Illus.). 12p. (J). bds. 6.95 (978-0-8118-5458-0(2)) Chronicle Bks. LLC.

Chronicle Books Staff. Little Reindeer: Finger Puppet Book. 2006. (Illus.). 12p. (J). 6.95 (978-0-8118-5457-3(4)) Chronicle Bks. LLC.

Church, Caroline Jayne. Woof's Playtime: Woof Touch-and-Feel. Church, Caroline Jayne, illus. 2007. (Illus.). 10p. (J). (ps). 5.95 (***978-0-8027-9621-9(4)***) Walker & Co.

—Woof's Snacktime: Woof Touch-and-Feel. Church, Caroline Jayne, illus. 2007. (Illus.). 10p. (J). (ps). 5.95 (***978-0-8027-9622-6(2)***) Walker & Co.

Ciboul, Adele. The Five Senses. Bell, Anthea, tr. from FRE. Collinet, Clementine et al, illus. 2006. (Explore Your World Ser.). 28p. (J). (ps-1). 15.95 (978-1-55407-007-7(4)) Firefly Bks., Ltd.

Cimarusti, Marie. Peek-a-Boooo! Peterson, Stephanie, illus. 2005. 12p. (J). (ps). 9.99 (978-0-525-47435-7(8) , Dutton Juvenile) Penguin Group (USA) Inc.

Cimarusti, Marie Torres. Peek-a-Boo Christmas! Peterson, Stephanie, illus. 2006. 12p. (J). (ps). pap. 10.99 (978-0-525-47770-9(5) , Dutton Juvenile) Penguin Group (USA) Inc.

—Peek-a-Pet! Peterson, Stephanie, illus. 2004. 12p. (J). (ps). 9.99 (978-0-525-47352-7(1) , Dutton Juvenile) Penguin Group (USA) Inc.

Clara Cow Wraps up Warm. 2002. (J). 5.98 (978-0-7525-8905-3(9)) Parragon, Inc.

Clark, Neil & Lindsay, William. Dinosaurs. 2nd rev. ed. 2003. (DK Pockets Ser.). (Illus.). 160p. pap. 6.99 (978-0-7894-9589-1(9)) Dorling Kindersley Publishing, Inc.

Clarke, Phil. Sharks. 2005. (Illus.). 16p. (J). (gr. 1 up). 11.99 (978-0-7945-1109-8(0) , Usborne) EDC Publishing.

Clarke, Phillip & Furnival, Keith. Sharks. Scott, Peter David, illus. 2005. (J). (***978-0-439-86358-2(9)***) Scholastic, Inc.

Clements, Andrew. Snowden Activity Book: Snow Time Fun Sticker Book. 1998. (Illus.). 16p. (J). mass mkt. 1.99 (978-0-689-82362-6(2) , Little Simon) Simon & Schuster Children's Publishing.

Cohen, Santiago, illus. Play Ball! 2008. (J). (***978-0-7614-5451-9(9)***) Cavendish, Marshall Corp.

Cohn, Arlen. Firsts: Reflections of a 7-Year Old. Vasconsellos, Daniel, tr. Vasconsellos, Daniel, illus. gif. ed. 2004. 28p. bds. 9.99 (978-1-57939-168-3(0)) Accord Publishing, Ltd.

Cohn, Arlen D. Camp Wazoo. Cole, Jeff, illus. 2007. 28p. bds. 9.99 (***978-1-57939-353-3(5)***) Andrews McMeel Publishing.

Cole, Stephen & Gardner, Lousie. Alien Olympics. 1998. (Alien Pop-Ups Ser.). (Illus.). 10p. (J). 4.95 (978-1-899607-65-5(X)) Sterling Publishing Co., Inc.

Collings, Julie. Utterly Elegant Tea Parties: For Dolls, Daddies, & Other Guests. 2005. (Illus.). 22p. (J). (ps-3). pap. 12.95 (978-1-59174-092-6(4)) Klutz.

Collins, Elaine Banks. I Like Dressing Up. Floyd, John, Jr., illus. 2005. (J). bds. 5.95 (***978-0-9752860-5-0(6)***) OurRainbow Pr., LLC.

—See What I Can Do. Floyd, John, Jr., illus. 2005. (J). bds. 5.95 (***978-0-9752860-4-3(8)***) OurRainbow Pr., LLC.

Colorful Present with Book. 2000. (Pooh Learning Ser.). (J). (ps-3). pap. 6.98 incl. audio (978-0-7634-0474-1(8)) Walt Disney Records.

Colors & Shapes Fun Wipe-Off Book. 2001. (Illus.). 16p. (J). (gr. k-2). mass mkt. 3.79 (978-1-889319-99-5(6)) Trend Enterprises, Inc.

Comfort, Louise. Lily's Busy Day. 2003. (Fairy Phones Ser.). (Illus.). 10p. (J). bds. 4.95 (978-0-7641-5692-2(6)) Barron's Educational Series, Inc.

—Poppy's Party. 2003. (Fairy Phones Ser.). (Illus.). 10p. (J). bds. 4.95 (978-0-7641-5694-6(2)) Barron's Educational Series, Inc.

—Rosie's Surprise. 2003. (Fairy Phones Ser.). (Illus.). 10p. (J). bds. 4.95 (978-0-7641-5693-9(4)) Barron's Educational Series, Inc.

Corke, Estelle. Cheetah Tale. 2001. (Bendy Tales Ser.). 8p. (J). (ps). 4.95 (978-0-7641-5368-6(4)) Barron's Educational Series, Inc.

—Monkey Tale. 2001. (Bendy Tales Ser.). 8p. (J). (ps). bds. 4.95 (978-0-7641-5371-6(4)) Barron's Educational Series, Inc.

Corke, Estelle, et al, illus. The Gingerbread Man. 2007. 24p. pap. 5.99 (***978-1-84643-078-7(X)***) Child's Play International Ltd. GBR. *Dist:* Child's Play-International.

Corke, Estelle, illus. Goldilocks & the Three Bears. 2005. 24p. pap. (978-1-904550-19-8(3)) Child's Play-International.

Cort, Ben. Little Witch. 2007. (Illus.). 12p. (J). 8.99 (***978-1-4052-0745-4(0)***) Egmont Bks., Ltd. GBR. *Dist:* Independent Pubs. Group.

—Little Wizard. 2007. (Illus.). 12p. (J). 8.99 (***978-1-4052-0746-1(9)***) Egmont Bks., Ltd. GBR. *Dist:* Independent Pubs. Group.

Cort, Ben, illus. Adam Astronaut. 2005. (Fun Phones Ser.). 10p. (J). bds. 4.95 (978-0-7641-5792-9(2)) Barron's Educational Series, Inc.

—Cody Cowboy. 2005. (Fun Phones Ser.). 10p. (J). bds. 4.95 (978-0-7641-5793-6(0)) Barron's Educational Series, Inc.

—Pip Pirate. 2005. (Fun Phones Ser.). 10p. (J). bds. 4.95 (978-0-7641-5794-3(9)) Barron's Educational Series, Inc.

—Will Wizard. 2005. (Fun Phones Ser.). 10p. (J). bds. 4.95 (978-0-7641-5795-0(7)) Barron's Educational Series, Inc.

Count to Ten. (J). 26.20 (978-0-8136-8410-9(2)); 26.20 (978-0-8136-8411-6(0)); 59.50 (978-0-8136-7942-6(7)) Modern Curriculum Pr.

Counting 123. 2003. (Active Minds Ser.). (Illus.). (J). (978-0-7853-7827-3(8)) Publications International, Ltd.

Counting Cards Staff. Learning Wrap Ups Palette. 2004. 7.99 (978-1-59204-013-1(6)) Learning Wrap-Ups.

Counting Fun Wipe-Off Book. 2001. (Illus.). 16p. (J). (gr. k-2). mass mkt. 3.79 (978-1-889319-98-8(8)) Trend Enterprises, Inc.

Courtin, Thierry. Bebes Dinamicos. 2003. (Bebes Series Ser.). (ENG & SPA., Illus.). 8p. 8.95 (978-84-7864-689-0(2)) Combel Editorial, S.A. ESP. *Dist:* Independent Pubs. Group.

—Bebes Juguetones. 2003. (Bebes Series Ser.). (ENG & SPA., Illus.). 8p. 8.95 (978-84-7864-690-6(6)) Combel Editorial, S.A. ESP. *Dist:* Independent Pubs. Group.

Cousins, Lucy. Diviertete y Aprende con Maisy. 2002. (Illus.). 12p. (J). (CAT.). bds. 16.95 (978-84-8488-019-6(2)); (SPA., 16.95 (978-84-8488-018-9(4) , RR7668) Serres, Ediciones, S. L. ESP. *Dist:* Lectorum Pubns., Inc.

—Fun with Maisy. 2002. (ps-2). lib. bdg. 11.80 (978-0-613-74761-5(5)) Tandem Library Bks.

—La Granja de Maisy. 2001. (Illus.). (J). (SPA.). 8p. 26.95 (978-84-8488-007-3(9)); (CAT., 16p. 26.95 (978-84-8488-011-0(7)) Serres, Ediciones, S. L. ESP. *Dist:* Lectorum Pubns., Inc.

—Jazzy in the Jungle. Cousins, Lucy, illus. 2002. (Illus.). 32p. (J). (gr. k-k). 14.99 (978-0-7636-1903-9(5)) Candlewick Pr.

—Maisy's First Clock. Cousins, Lucy, illus. 2002. (Maisy Ser.). (Illus.). 8p. (J). (gr. k-1). bds. 14.99 (978-0-7636-1788-2(1)) Candlewick Pr.

—Maisy's Seasons. 2002. (Maisy Ser.). (Illus.). 12p. (J). (gr. k-k). bds. 8.99 (978-0-7636-1914-5(0)) Candlewick Pr.

—Merry Christmas Maisy. Cousins, Lucy, illus. ed. 2003. (Maisy Ser.). (Illus.). 16p. (J). (ps). 4.99 (978-0-7636-2241-1(9)) Candlewick Pr.

—Where Is Maisy? A Lift-the-Flap Book. Cousins, Lucy, illus. 1999. (Maisy Bks.). (Illus.). 12p. (J). (gr. k-k). bds. 4.99 (978-0-7636-0752-4(5)) Candlewick Pr.

—Where Is Maisy's Panda? A Lift-the-Flap Book. Cousins, Lucy, illus. 1999. (Maisy Bks.). (Illus.). 14p. (J). (gr. k-k). bds. 4.99 (978-0-7636-0753-1(3)) Candlewick Pr.

Cowell, Cressida. Little Bo Peep's Library Book. Cowell, Cressida, illus. 1999. (Illus.). 32p. (J). (ps-2). pap. 14.95 (978-0-531-30179-1(6) , Orchard Bks.) Scholastic, Inc.

—Super Sue. Ayto, Russell, illus. 2003. 14p. (J). (ps-k). 7.99 (978-0-7636-2063-9(7)) Candlewick Pr.

—Super Sue at Super School. Ayto, Russell, illus. 2005. 16p. (J). (ps-k). 8.99 (978-0-7636-2734-8(8)) Candlewick Pr.

Cox, Phil Roxbee. Big Pig on A Dig. Cartwright, Stephen, illus. rev. ed. 2006. 16p. (J). pap. 6.99 (978-0-7945-1501-0(0) , Usborne) EDC Publishing.

—Curly's Friends. Cartwright, Stephen, illus. rev. ed. 2005. 10p. (J). bds. 7.95 (978-0-7945-1180-7(5) , Usborne) EDC Publishing.

—Frog on A Log. Cartwright, Stephen, illus. rev. ed. 2006. 16p. (J). pap. 6.99 (978-0-7945-1504-1(5) , Usborne) EDC Publishing.

—Hen's Pens. Cartwright, Stephen, illus. rev. ed. 2006. 16p. (J). pap. 6.99 (978-0-7945-1506-5(1) , Usborne) EDC Publishing.

Cox, Phil Roxbee & Cartwright, S. Rusty's Bone. 2004. (Farmyard Tales Touchy Feely Board Bks.). (Illus.). 10p. (J). 7.95 (978-0-7945-0012-2(9) , Usborne) EDC Publishing.

—Wolly's Walk. 2004. (Farmyard Tales Touchy Feely Board Bks.). (Illus.). 10p. (J). 7.95 (978-0-7945-0039-9(0) , Usborne) EDC Publishing.

Cox, Phil Roxbee & Cartwright, Stephen. Frog on a Log. 2004. (Easy Words to Read Ser.). (Illus.). 16p. (J). (gr. 1 up). pap. 6.95 (978-0-7945-0114-3(1) , Usborne) EDC Publishing.

—Hen's Pens. 2004. (Easy Words to Read Ser.). (Illus.). 16p. (J). (gr. 1 up). pap. 6.95 (978-0-7945-0113-6(3) , Usborne) EDC Publishing.

—Shark in the Park. 2004. (Easy Words to Read Ser.). (Illus.). 16p. (J). (gr. 1 up). pap. 6.95 (978-0-7945-0171-6(0) , Usborne) EDC Publishing.

Cox, Phil Roxbee & Grant, Marlynne. Goose on the Loose. Tyler, Jenny, ed. Cartwright, Stephen, illus. 10p. (J). pap. 4.95 (978-0-7460-4486-5(0) , Usborne) EDC Publishing.

Cox, Phil Roxbee & Tyler, Jenny. Shark in the Park. Cartwright, Stephen, illus. 2002. (Easy Words to Read Ser.). 16p. (J). (978-0-439-52876-4(3)) Scholastic, Inc.

Coxon, Michele. Catch up, Little Cheetah: A Lift-the-Flap Book. 2000. (Illus.). 32p. (J). (ps). 13.95 (978-1-899248-23-0(4)) Happy Cat Bks. GBR. *Dist:* Star Bright Bks., Inc.

—Too Big! Coxon, Michele, illus. 2000. (Illus.). 20p. (ps-1). 13.95 (978-1-899248-64-3(1)) Happy Cat Bks. GBR. *Dist:* Star Bright Bks., Inc.

—Where's My Kitten? (Illus.). 16p. (J). pap. 5.95 (978-1-903285-02-2(X)) Happy Cat Bks. GBR. *Dist:* Star Bright Bks., Inc.

Crabtree, Sally & Mathieson, Roberta. Jungle Boogie. Jennings, Patti, illus. 2004. 12p. (J). bds. 7.99 (978-0-689-86184-0(2) , Little Simon) Simon & Schuster Children's Publishing.

Crabtree, Sally & Wallace, John. One Spinning Spider. 2000. (Finger Puppet Bks.). (Illus.). 24p. (J). (ps-k). 10.95 (978-1-86233-167-9(7)) Sterling Publishing Co., Inc.

—Ten Buzzy Bees. 2000. (Finger Puppet Bks.). (Illus.). 24p. (J). (ps-k). 10.95 (978-1-86233-162-4(6)) Sterling Publishing Co., Inc.

Cranium. Cranium Silly Stories. 2007. (Play It Again Book Ser.). (Illus.). 52p. (J). (gr. 1). 9.99 (*978-0-316-01206-5(8)*) Little, Brown Bks. for Young Readers.

Crazy Animals Sticker Book. (Weird & Wacky Ser.). 16p. (J). (978-2-89393-869-1(8)) Phidal Publishing, Inc./ Editions Phidal, Inc.

Creepy Crawlers Sticker Book. (Weird & Wacky Ser.). 16p. (J). (978-2-89393-872-1(8)) Phidal Publishing, Inc./ Editions Phidal, Inc.

Crews, Donald. Inside Freight Train. Crews, Donald, illus. 2001. (Illus.). 12p. (J). (ps-3). 9.99 (978-0-688-17087-5(0) , Harper Festival) HarperCollins Pubs.

Crisp, Dan. Let's Ride. 2006. (Illus.). 14p. 7.99 (978-1-904550-96-9(7)) Child's Play-International.

Crisp, Dan, illus. Five Little Men in a Flying Saucer. 2005. (Classic Books with Holes). 16p. (J). bds. 5.99 (978-1-904550-58-7(4)) Child's Play-International.

Crosbie, Duncan. Finn & the Celtic Cross. 2002. (Illus.). 12p. (J). 7.95 (978-0-7171-3392-5(3)) Gill & MacMillan, Ltd. IRL. *Dist:* Irish Bks. & Media, Inc.

Crowson, Andrew. Flip Flap Christmas. Crowson, Andrew, illus. 2003. (Illus.). 12p. (J). bds. (978-1-85602-476-1(8)) Chrysalis Children's Bks.

—Flip Flap Fairytale. 2003. (Illus.). 12p. bds. (978-1-85602-444-0(X)) Chrysalis Children's Bks.

—Flip Flap People. 2003. (Illus.). 12p. bds. (978-1-85602-443-3(1)) Chrysalis Children's Bks.

—Flip Flap Prehistoric. Crowson, Andrew, illus. 2003. (Illus.). 12p. (J). pap. (978-1-85602-474-7(1)) Chrysalis Children's Bks.

—Flip Flap Safari. Crowson, Andrew, illus. 2003. (Illus.). 12p. (J). bds. (978-1-85602-473-0(3)) Chrysalis Children's Bks.

—Flip Flap Spooky. Crowson, Andrew, illus. 2003. (Illus.). 12p. (J). bds. (978-1-85602-475-4(X)) Chrysalis Children's Bks.

Crowther, Robert. Colors. Crowther, Robert, illus. 2001. (Illus.). 16p. (J). (ps-1). 12.99 (978-0-7636-1404-1(1)) Candlewick Pr.

—Deep down under Ground: A Pop-up Book of Amazing Facts & Feats. Crowther, Robert, illus. 2004. (Illus.). 18p. (J). (gr. 3-8). reprint ed. pap. 22.00 (978-0-7567-7179-9(X)) DIANE Publishing Co.

—Let's Cook! A Press-Out-and-Play Book. Crowther, Robert, illus. 2004. (Illus.). 10p. (J). (gr. k-k). 10.99 (978-0-7636-2266-4(4)) Candlewick Pr.

—Shapes. Crowther, Robert, illus. 2002. (Illus.). 14p. (J). (ps-2). 12.99 (978-0-7636-1889-6(6)) Candlewick Pr.

—Trains: A Pop-Up Railroad Book. Crowther, Robert, illus. 2006. (Illus.). 10p. (J). (gr. 1). 17.99 (978-0-7636-3082-9(9)) Candlewick Pr.

Crozon, Alain. Adivinanzas de Navidad. Menendez-Ponte, Maria, tr. 1999. Tr. of Christmas Riddles. (SPA., Illus.). 12p. 13.95 (978-84-348-6637-9(4)) SM Ediciones ESP. *Dist:* Distribooks, Inc.

Crozon, Alain & Lanchais, Aurelie. Wild Animals Who Am I? 2002. (Illus.). 14p. (J). 7.95 (978-0-8118-3321-9(6)) Chronicle Bks. LLC.

Cryan, Michelle. Where Is Baby? A Lift-the-Flap Sign Language Book. 2007. (Illus.). 24p. 10.95 (*978-1-56368-353-4(9)*) Gallaudet Univ. Pr.

Crystal, Billy. I Already Know I Love You Board Book. Sayles, Elizabeth, illus. 2008. 32p. (J). 7.99 (*978-0-06-145057-0(X)* , Harper Festival) HarperCollins Pubs.

Curry, Don, ed. Shrek the Third Mix & Match Jigsaw Puzzle Book. 2007. 10p. (J). bds. 9.99 (*978-0-696-23476-7(9)*) Meredith Bks.

—Spider-Man 3 Board Game Book. 2007. 10p. (J). bds. 12.99 (*978-0-696-23411-8(4)*) Meredith Bks.

Curtis, Susan. Five Little Ducklings. Smith, Eric, illus. 2007. 24p. (J). 14.99 (978-1-4169-3835-4(4) , Little Simon) Simon & Schuster Children's Publishing.

Dakin, Glenn & Chapman, Keith. Can We Tell Time? Bob the Builder. 2003. (Illus.). (J). bds. 16.98 (978-0-7853-8809-8(5)) Publications International, Ltd.

Dale, Kim. What Am I? (Illus.). 32p. pap. (978-0-7344-0125-0(6) , Lothian Bks.) Hachette Livre Australia.

Dalmatian Press Staff. The Baby Jesus Pop-up Book. 2005. (Illus.). 9p. (J). 10.99 (978-1-4037-1504-3(1)) Dalmatian Pr.

—Little Chick: Soft Spot Board Book. 2002. (Soft Spot Bks.). (Illus.). 10p. (J). bds. 3.99 (978-1-57759-652-3(8)) Dalmatian Pr.

—M&M's Brand I'm Outta Here! Sticker Book. 2002. (Illus.). 48p. (J). (ps-4). 2.99 (978-1-57759-782-7(6)) Dalmatian Pr.

—Playful Puppy: Little Pups Board Book. 2003. (Little Pups Board Bks.). (Illus.). 20p. (J). bds. 2.99 (978-1-57759-661-5(7)) Dalmatian Pr.

—Strawberry Shortcake Sweet As Can Be! Book to Color with Iron-on Stickers. 2003. (Strawberry Shortcake Ser.). (Illus.). 32p. (J). pap. 2.99 (978-1-4037-0303-3(5)) Dalmatian Pr.

—Strawberry Shortcake Sweet Stuff: Book to Color with Stamper Markers. 2003. (Strawberry Shortcake Ser.). (Illus.). 32p. (J). mass mkt. 4.49 (978-1-4037-0341-5(8)) Dalmatian Pr.

—Strawberry Shortcake Sweet Surprises: Amazing Marker. 2004. (Strawberry Shortcake Ser.). (Illus.). 48p. (J). spiral bd. 4.99 (978-1-4037-0764-2(2)) Dalmatian Pr.

—Thanks You, God: Board Book with Plush Toy. rev. ed. 2007. 7p. 12.99 (*978-1-4037-3074-9(1)* , Spirit Pr.) Dalmatian Pr.

—Tub Time Zoo Bath Set. 2006. 4p. (J). 4.99 (978-1-4037-1206-6(9)) Dalmatian Pr.

—Ultimate Wipe off Book. rev. ed. 2006. 26p. (J). bds. 7.99 (978-1-4037-2076-4(2)) Dalmatian Pr.

Dalmatian Press Staff, ed. Bambi (Classic Board Book) rev. ed. 2006. 10p. (J). 5.99 (978-1-4037-2376-5(1)) Dalmatian Pr.

—Mother Goose: Board Book with Plush Toy. 2007. 11p. bds. 12.99 (*978-1-4037-2550-9(0)*) Dalmatian Pr.

Dalmatian Press Staff, ed. Three Little Pigs (Classic Board Book) 2006. 10p. (J). bds. 5.99 (978-1-4037-2377-2(X)) Dalmatian Pr.

DALP, ed. The Veleveteen Rabbit: Board Book with Plush Toy. 2007. 12p. 12.99 (*978-1-4037-2552-3(7)*) Dalmatian Pr.

D'Andrea, Deborah & Borlasca, Hector. Pretend & Play Superhero. 2005. (Illus.). (J). (*978-1-57151-751-7(0)*) Playhouse Publishing.

Dann, Penny. Five Little Ducks. 2003. (Illus.). 14p. (J). bds. 3.95 (978-0-7641-5663-2(2)) Barron's Educational Series, Inc.

—The Secret Fairy Boutique. Dann, Penny, illus. 2000. (Secret Fairy Ser.). (Illus.). 16p. (J). (ps-3). pap. 14.95 (978-0-531-30308-5(X) , Orchard Bks.) Scholastic, Inc.

Dann, Penny. The Secret Fairy Christmas. Dann, Penny, illus. 2007. (Secret Fairy Ser.). (Illus.). 20p. (J). (ps-3). 14.99 (*978-1-4169-4905-3(4)* , Little Simon) Simon & Schuster Children's Publishing.

Danson, Lesley, et al, illus. Snow White. 2006. 24p. pap. 5.99 (978-1-84643-023-7(2)) Child's Play-International.

David & Goliath Bible Sticker Book. 2003. (Illus.). 16p. (J). 2.98 (978-1-4054-1554-5(1)) Parragon, Inc.

Davidson, Susanna. Fairyland. Ligi, Raffaella, illus. 2007. (See Inside Board Bks). 16p. (J). bds. 12.99 (978-0-7945-1570-6(3) , Usborne) EDC Publishing.

Davies, C. & Ladybird Books Staff. Shiny Flower. 1999. (Touch & Feel Ser.). (Illus.). 10p. (J). 5.99 (978-0-7214-2969-4(6) , Dutton Juvenile) Penguin Group (USA) Inc.

Davis, Caroline, illus. My Babies. 2007. 12p. (J). (ps). bds. 6.95 (*978-1-58925-822-8(3)* , tiger tales) ME Media LLC.

—My Friends. 2007. 12p. (J). (ps). bds. 6.95 (*978-1-58925-823-5(1)* , tiger tales) ME Media LLC.

—My Pets. 2007. 12p. (J). (ps). bds. 6.95 (*978-1-58925-824-2(X)* , tiger tales) ME Media LLC.

—My Toys. 2007. 12p. (J). (ps). bds. 6.95 (*978-1-58925-825-9(8)* , tiger tales) ME Media LLC.

Davis, Guy. Witzy's Colors. Spafford, Suzy, illus. 2001. (Little Suzy's Zoo Ser.). 12p. (J). (ps-k). pap. 5.99 (978-1-58668-055-8(2)) Lyrick Studios.

Davis, Jennifer. Before You Were Big. Cornell, Laura, illus. 2003. 36p. (J). 11.95 (978-0-7611-2732-1(1) , 12732) Workman Publishing Co., Inc.

Davis, Kate. Hanukkah's Here! Filipowich, Bob, illus. ed. 2001. (Mini Soft Shapes Ser.). 8p. (J). (ps-ps). 6.99 (978-1-58476-081-8(8)) Innovative Kids.

Davis, Kate & Innovative Kids Staff. Rough Road. Filipowich, Bob, illus. 2000. (Textured Soft Shapes Ser.). 8p. (J). (ps-ps). 10.99 (978-1-58476-041-2(9)) Innovative Kids.

Daynes, Katie. (See Inside Castles) - Spanish. 2006. 16p. (J). bds. 12.99 (978-0-7460-7383-4(6) , Usborne) EDC Publishing.

—See Inside: Your Body. 2006. 16p. (J). bds. 12.99 (978-0-7945-1233-0(X) , Usborne) EDC Publishing.

de Beer, Hans. Where Is Mother? 2004. (Little Polar Bear Story Ser.). (Illus.). 22p. (J). pap. 3.95 (978-1-4027-1634-8(6)) Sterling Publishing Co., Inc.

de Paola, Tomie. Hide-and-Seek All Week. de Paola, Tomie, illus. 2001. (All Aboard Reading Ser.). (Illus.). 32p. (J). (ps-2). 13.89 (978-0-448-42617-4(X)); pap. 3.99 (978-0-448-42545-0(9)) Penguin Group (USA) Inc. (Grosset & Dunlap).

—Hide-and-Seek All Week. 2001. 10.79 (978-0-606-22475-8(0)) Tandem Library Bks.

DeBoer, Rondi & Rondi, Christine. A Boy & His Lunch. Conger, Holli, illus. 2007. (J). 5.99 (*978-0-7847-1949-7(7)*) Standard Publishing.

Decorate & Play House: Interactive Playhouse. 1998. (Illus.). 10p. (J). (ps). 19.99 (978-1-890647-04-9(7)) RC2 Corp.

Delafosse, Claude & Jeunesse, Gallimard. Caves Hidden World. Heliadore, illus. 2000. (First Discovery Book Ser.). 24p. (J). (ps-3). 12.95 (978-0-439-10680-1(X) , Scholastic Reference) Scholastic, Inc.

Delafosse, Claude, et al. Human Body. 2000. (Hidden World Ser.). (Illus.). 24p. (J). (ps-3). 12.95 (978-0-439-10681-8(8) , Scholastic Reference) Scholastic, Inc.

DePrisco, Dorothea. Apple. Taxali, Gary, illus. 2005. (Plush Learning Books Ser.). 10p. (J). bds. 6.95 (978-1-58117-191-4(9) , Intervisual/Piggy Toes) Dalmatian Pr.

—Lemon. Taxali, Gary, illus. 2005. (Plush Learning Books Ser.). 10p. (J). bds. 6.95 (978-1-58117-194-5(3) , Intervisual/Piggy Toes) Dalmatian Pr.

—Meet Gator: A Picture Clues Touch & Feel Book. Croft, James Lee, illus. 2005. (Learn to Read Ser.). 10p. (J). (ps up). 10.95 (978-1-58117-123-5(4) , Intervisual/Piggy Toes) Dalmatian Pr.

—Mini Whos in the Jungle. 2006. 10p. (J). 4.95 (978-1-58117-507-3(8) , Intervisual/Piggy Toes) Dalmatian Pr.

—Mini Whos in the Ocean. 2006. 10p. 4.95 (978-1-58117-509-7(4) , Intervisual/Piggy Toes) Dalmatian Pr.

—Mini Whos on the Farm. 2006. 10p. 4.95 (978-1-58117-508-0(6) , Intervisual/Piggy Toes) Dalmatian Pr.

—Pear. Taxali, Gary, illus. 2005. (Plush Learning Books Ser.). 10p. (J). bds. 6.95 (978-1-58117-193-8(5) , Intervisual/Piggy Toes) Dalmatian Pr.

—Who Lives Here? A Changing Picture Book. Lunsford, Annie, illus. 2002. (Learning Pictures Ser.). 10p. (J). (ps). 7.95 (978-1-58117-159-4(5) , Intervisual/Piggy Toes) Dalmatian Pr.

DePrisco, Dorothea & Burnett, Alex. Tub-a-Tub: A Bath Book. 2006. (Illus.). 10p. (J). pap. 9.95 (978-1-58117-463-2(2) , Intervisual/Piggy Toes) Dalmatian Pr.

DePrisco, Dorothea & Summers, Lesley. Back in My Arms. 2006. (Illus.). 12p. (J). 9.95 (978-1-58117-459-5(4) , Intervisual/Piggy Toes) Dalmatian Pr.

DePrisco, Dorothea & Williamson, Gwyneth. Pizza! Pizza! Pizza! 2006. 12p. 10.95 (978-1-58117-454-0(3) , Intervisual/Piggy Toes) Dalmatian Pr.

Derico, Laura. Jesus, God's Precious Gift. Beylon, Cathy, illus. 2000. (Snow Globe Book Ser.). 10p. (J). (ps up). bds. 9.99 (978-0-7847-1058-6(9) , 03536, Bean Sprouts) Standard Publishing.

D'Harcourt, Claire. Art up Close. 6th ed. 2006. 64p. (J). 22.95 (978-0-8118-5464-1(7)) Chronicle Bks. LLC.

Diaz, James, illus. Blue: A Touchy Feely First Words Color Book. 2000. (Touchy Feely First Words Bks.). 10p. (J). (ps up). 5.95 (978-1-58117-071-9(8) , Intervisual/Piggy Toes) Dalmatian Pr.

—Green: A Touchy Feely First Words Book. 2000. (Touchy Feely First Words Bks.). 10p. (J). (ps up). 5.95 (978-1-58117-072-6(6) , Intervisual/Piggy Toes) Dalmatian Pr.

—Red: A Touchy Feely First Words Color Book. 2000. (Touchy Feely First Words Bks.). 10p. (J). (ps up). 5.95 (978-1-58117-070-2(X) , Intervisual/Piggy Toes) Dalmatian Pr.

—Yellow: A Touchy Feely First Words Book. 2000. (Touchy Feely First Words Bks.: Vol. 4). 10p. (J). (ps up). 5.95 (978-1-58117-069-6(6) , Intervisual/Piggy Toes) Dalmatian Pr.

Diaz, James & Gerth, Melanie. My First Jumbo Book of Letters. 2003. (My First Jumbo Book Ser.). (Illus.). 10p. (J). pap. 9.95 (978-0-439-44325-8(3) , Cartwheel Bks.) Scholastic, Inc.

Diaz, James & Gerth, Melanie, illus. My First Jumbo Book of Numbers. 2002. (My First Jumbo Book Ser.). 10p. (J). pap. 9.95 (978-0-439-40353-5(7) , Cartwheel Bks.) Scholastic, Inc.

Diaz, James & Gerth, Melanie, illus. Numbers: Learning Fun for Little Ones! 2007. 10p. (J). reprint ed. (*978-1-4223-6683-7(9)*) DIANE Publishing Co.

DiCicco, Gil, illus. Pooh's Piano Book. 2002. (Disney's Winnie the Pooh Ser.). (J). 16.98 (978-0-7853-5233-4(3)) Publications International, Ltd.

Dietz, James M. African Animal Giants. Cremins, Robert & Morrison, Robert, illus. 2004. 12p. (J). (gr. k-4). reprint ed. 16.00 (978-0-7567-7641-1(4)) DIANE Publishing Co.

Dippold, Jane, illus. I Love My Baby. 1999. (Leap Frog Lift-a-Flap Ser.). (J). (978-0-7853-3367-8(3)) Publications International, Ltd.

Discovering Dinos. (Flip Flap Fun Book Ser.). 10p. (J). bds. (978-2-7643-0137-1(5)) Phidal Publishing, Inc./Editions Phidal, Inc.

Disney Press Staff, creator. Sticky Situations: A Sticker Activity Storybook. 2005. (Disney's Chicken Little Ser.). (Illus.). 12p. (ps-17). 14.99 (978-0-7868-3646-8(6)) Disney Pr.

Disney Press Staff, ed. Magical Wishes: A Deluxe Pop-up Storybook. Disney Storybook Artists Staff, illus. 2007. 12p. (ps-2). 14.99 (*978-1-4231-0537-4(0)*) Disney Pr.

Disney Press Staff & Board Books Staff. Book of Pooh Bk. 2: Hide & Seek. 2002. (Illus.). 10p. (ps-k). 5.99 (978-0-7868-3356-6(4)) Disney Pr.

Disney Staff. Big Things, Little Things. Disney Staff, illus. 1999. (Pooh's Learn & Grow Ser.: Vol. 9). (Illus.). 12p. (J). 3.49 (978-1-57973-043-7(4)) Advance Pubs. LLC.

—Fruity-Tooty Picnic. Disney Staff, illus. 1999. (Pooh's Learn & Grow Ser.: Vol. 5). (Illus.). 12p. (J). 3.49 (978-1-57973-039-0(6)) Advance Pubs. LLC.

—Pooh Can, Can You? 1999. (Learn & Grow Busy Book Ser.: Vol. 1). (Illus.). 12p. (J). (ps-k). 6.99 (978-0-7364-0135-7(0)) Mouse Works.

—Pooh's Noisy Book. 1999. (Learn & Grow Busy Book Ser.). (Illus.). 12p. (J). (ps-3). 6.99 (978-0-7364-0136-4(9)) Mouse Works.

—Ready, Set, Go! Disney Staff, illus. 1999. (Pooh's Learn & Grow Ser.: Vol. 8). (Illus.). 12p. (J). 3.49 (978-1-57973-042-0(6)) Advance Pubs. LLC.

—Sweet Dreams. Disney Staff, illus. 1999. (Pooh's Learn & Grow Ser.: Vol. 12). (Illus.). 12p. (J). 3.49 (978-1-57973-046-8(9)) Advance Pubs. LLC.

Dixon, Dougal. Dinosaur. 2003. (DK Revealed Ser.). (Illus.). 40p. (J). 12.99 (978-0-7894-9749-9(2)) Dorling Kindersley Publishing, Inc.

DK Publishing. All about Me! 2008. (Baby Fun Ser.). 14p. (J). 4.99 (*978-0-7566-3438-4(5)*) Dorling Kindersley Publishing, Inc.

—Amazing, Fuzzy, Furry Wild Baby Animals. 2008. (Touchables Ser.). 10p. (J). (ps-ps). bds. 8.99 (*978-0-7566-3792-7(9)*) Dorling Kindersley Publishing, Inc.

—Animals. 2008. 14p. (J). (ps-k). bds. 5.99 (*978-0-7566-3468-1(7)*) Dorling Kindersley Publishing, Inc.

—Beep! Beep! 2008. 12p. (J). (ps-3). bds. 6.99 (*978-0-7566-3487-2(3)*) Dorling Kindersley Publishing, Inc.

—Bible. 2007. (Touch & Feel Ser.). 16p. (J). 9.99 (*978-0-7566-3365-3(6)*) Dorling Kindersley Publishing, Inc.

—Don't Forget Spike about Manners: Plush Board Book. 2008. 10p. (J). bds. 8.99 (*978-0-7566-3445-2(8)*) Dorling Kindersley Publishing, Inc.

—Eyes, Nose, Toes. 2008. 12p. (J). (ps-ps). bds. 6.99 (*978-0-7566-3759-0(7)*) Dorling Kindersley Publishing, Inc.

—Farm 1-2-3. 2008. 12p. (J). 8.99 (*978-0-7566-3525-1(X)*) Dorling Kindersley Publishing, Inc.

—First Words. 2008. 16p. (J). (ps-k). bds. 9.99 (*978-0-7566-3844-3(5)*) Dorling Kindersley Publishing, Inc.

—Night Creatures. 2007. 48p. (J). pap. 3.99 (*978-0-7566-3510-7(1)*) Dorling Kindersley Publishing, Inc.

—Noisy Animals. 2008. 10p. (J). (ps-k). 6.99 (*978-0-7566-3854-2(2)*) Dorling Kindersley Publishing, Inc.

—Playful Little Fairy: Plush Board Book. 2008. 10p. (J). bds. 8.99 (*978-0-7566-3444-5(X)*) Dorling Kindersley Publishing, Inc.

—Puppies & Kittens. 2008. 14p. (J). (ps-k). bds. 5.99 (*978-0-7566-3835-1(6)*) Dorling Kindersley Publishing, Inc.

—Rainbow Colors. 2008. 12p. (J). (ps-ps). bds. 6.99 (*978-0-7566-3760-6(0)*) Dorling Kindersley Publishing, Inc.

—Soft, Fluffy, Playful Puppies. 2008. (Touchables Ser.). 10p. (J). (ps-ps). bds. 8.99 (*978-0-7566-3793-4(7)*) Dorling Kindersley Publishing, Inc.

—Tractor. 2008. (Ultimate Sticker Bks.). 16p. (J). (gr. 1-3). 6.99 (*978-0-7566-3876-4(3)*) Dorling Kindersley Publishing, Inc.

—Water Magic Baby Animals 123. 2007. 16p. (J). bds. 7.99 (*978-0-7566-3449-0(0)*) Dorling Kindersley Publishing, Inc.

—Water Magic Letters ABC. 2007. 16p. (J). bds. 7.99 (*978-0-7566-3452-0(0)*) Dorling Kindersley Publishing, Inc.

—Water Magic Ocean. 2008. 16p. (J). bds. 7.99 (*978-0-7566-3450-6(4)*) Dorling Kindersley Publishing, Inc.

—Wheels on the Bus. 2008. 10p. (J). (ps-k). 4.99 (*978-0-7566-3814-6(3)*) Dorling Kindersley Publishing, Inc.

DK Publishing Staff. Animals. 2007. 26p. (J). (ps-1). bds. 9.99 (978-0-7566-3029-4(0)) Dorling Kindersley Publishing, Inc.

—Bright, Shiny, Rainbow Colors. 2007. (Touchables Ser.). 10p. (J). (ps-1). bds. 8.99 (978-0-7566-2939-7(X)) Dorling Kindersley Publishing, Inc.

—Don't Worry Spike about the Something. 2007. 10p. (J). (ps-2). pap. 3.99 (*978-0-7566-3097-3(5)*) Dorling Kindersley Publishing, Inc.

—My First Things That Go Board Book. 2007. (My First Bks.). 36p. (J). 5.99 (978-0-7566-2591-7(2)) Dorling Kindersley Publishing, Inc.

—My First Word Lift-the-Flap Board Book. 1999. (My First Bks.). (Illus.). 12p. (J). (ps-k). bds. 9.99 (978-0-7894-4736-4(3)) Dorling Kindersley Publishing, Inc.

—Pop-Up Animal ABC. 2007. (DK Toys & Games Ser.). (Illus.). (J). (ps-1). 12.99 (978-0-7566-2588-7(2)) Dorling Kindersley Publishing, Inc.

—Splishy, Splashy, Sparkly Sea Life. 2007. (Touchables Ser.). 10p. (J). (ps-1). 8.99 (978-0-7566-2936-6(5)) Dorling Kindersley Publishing, Inc.

Donaher, D F. & Bibleco. Daniel & the Lions. 2004. (Illus.). (J). bds. (978-0-9746058-2-1(4) , Biblemania) Bibleco, Inc.

Donna, Gelsinger, ed. In My Father's Garden. 2007. 10p. pap. 6.99 (*978-1-4037-3625-3(1)* , Spirit Pr.) Dalmatian Pr.

Donoghue, Stella. Lift & Learn 123. Snaith, Andy, photos by. 2006. (Illus.). 24p. (ps). per., bds. 5.95 (978-1-84610-030-7(5)) Make Believe Ideas GBR. *Dist:* Ingram Pub. Services.

Dorling Kindersley Publishing Staff. All about Me. 2003. (Lift-the-Flap Books Ser.). (Illus.). 1p. (J). bds. 6.99 (978-0-7894-9236-4(9)) Dorling Kindersley Publishing, Inc.

—Animals Boxed Set, 3 bks., Set. 2003. (Touch & Feel Ser.). (Illus.). (J). bds. 19.99 (978-0-7894-8877-0(9)) Dorling Kindersley Publishing, Inc.

—Avengers. 2005. (Ultimate sticker Bks.). (Illus.). 16p. (J). (ps-7). pap. 6.99 (978-0-7566-1453-9(8)) Dorling Kindersley Publishing, Inc.

—Babies Love. 2003. (Baby's World Ser.). (Illus.). 12p. (J). bds. 6.99 (978-0-7894-9212-8(1)) Dorling Kindersley Publishing, Inc.

—Baby Talk. 2005. (Baby Fun Ser.). (Illus.). 20p. (J). (ps-3). bds. 4.99 (978-0-7566-0986-3(0)) Dorling Kindersley Publishing, Inc.

—Backyardigans. 2006. (Ultimate Sticker Bks.). 16p. (J). (ps-1). pap. 6.99 (978-0-7566-2028-6(7)) Dorling Kindersley Publishing, Inc.

—Barbie International Dolls. 2000. (Ultimate Sticker Bks.). (Illus.). 16p. (J). pap. 6.99 (978-0-7894-5450-8(5)) Dorling Kindersley Publishing, Inc.

—Barbie Sports Star. 2004. (Ultimate Sticker Bks.). 20p. (J). pap. 6.99 (978-0-7566-0332-8(3)) Dorling Kindersley Publishing, Inc.

—Barbie Summer Fun. 2004. (Ultimate Sticker Bks.). 20p. (J). pap. 6.99 (978-0-7566-0333-5(1)) Dorling Kindersley Publishing, Inc.

—Bathtime Peekaboo! 2005. (Illus.). 12p. (J). bds. 6.99 (978-0-7566-1145-3(8)) Dorling Kindersley Publishing, Inc.

—Batman. 2001. (Ultimate Sticker Bks.). 16p. (J). pap. 6.99 (978-0-7894-7866-5(8)) Dorling Kindersley Publishing, Inc.

—Bedtime Peekaboo! 2006. (Illus.). 12p. (J). bds. 6.99 (978-0-7566-1622-9(0)) Dorling Kindersley Publishing, Inc.

—Big Book of the Human Body. 2006. (Illus.). 12p. (J). pap. (*978-1-4053-1745-0(0)*) Dorling Kindersley Publishing, Inc.

—Big Dump Truck. 2003. (Wheelies Ser.). (Illus.). 12p. (J). bds. 6.99 (978-0-7894-9714-7(X)) Dorling Kindersley Publishing, Inc.
—Christmas. 2001. (Scratch & Sniff Ser.). (Illus.). 12p. (J). bds. 6.99 (978-0-7894-7891-7(9)) Dorling Kindersley Publishing, Inc.
—Dinosaurs. 2002. (Touch & Feel Ser.). (Illus.). 12p. (J). bds. 6.99 (978-0-7894-8854-1(X)) Dorling Kindersley Publishing, Inc.
—Discover & Play Book. 2003. (My First Bks.). (Illus.). 80p. (J). 12.99 (978-0-7894-9847-2(2)) Dorling Kindersley Publishing, Inc.
—Dog. 2005. (Ultimate sticker Bks.). 16p. (J). pap. 6.99 (978-0-7566-1457-7(0)) Dorling Kindersley Publishing, Inc.
—Dress-Up. 2003. (Barbie Ser.). (Illus.). 12p. (J). bds. 6.99 (978-0-7894-9233-3(4)) Dorling Kindersley Publishing, Inc.
—Farm Tractor. 2003. (Wheelies Ser.). (Illus.). 12p. (J). bds. 6.99 (978-0-7894-9713-0(1)) Dorling Kindersley Publishing, Inc.
—Glow in the Dark: Dinosaur. Parsons, Jayne, ed. 2002. (Ultimate Sticker Bks.). (Illus.). 16p. (J). (gr. k-3). pap. 6.99 (978-0-7894-8458-1(7)) Dorling Kindersley Publishing, Inc.
—Glow in the Dark Night Creatures. 2004. (Ultimate Sticker Bks.). 16p. (J). pap. 6.99 (978-0-7566-0218-5(1)) Dorling Kindersley Publishing, Inc.
—Halloween. 2001. (Touch & Feel Ser.). (Illus.). 12p. (J). (ps-k). bds. 6.99 (978-0-7894-6511-5(6)) Dorling Kindersley Publishing, Inc.
—Look & Explore: Splish, Splash. 2002. (Babys World Touch & Explore Ser.). (Illus.). 12p. (J). bds. 6.99 (978-0-7894-8829-9(9)) Dorling Kindersley Publishing, Inc.
—Look at Me: I Can Clap. 2002. (Baby's World Board Books Ser.). (Illus.). 12p. (J). bds. 6.99 (978-0-7894-8827-5(2)) Dorling Kindersley Publishing, Inc.
—My Basketball. 2005. (Lift-the-Flap Bks.). (Illus.). 12p. (J). bds. 9.99 (978-0-7566-1222-1(5)) Dorling Kindersley Publishing, Inc.
—My Big Noisy Book: Use 8 Fun Sounds to Complete the Story! 2001. (DK Early Learners Ser.). (Illus.). 12p. (J). pap. (978-0-7513-1419-9(6)) Dorling Kindersley Publishing, Inc.
—My First Farm Sticker Book. 2003. (My First Sticker Board Bks.). (Illus.). 12p. (J). pap. 6.99 (978-0-7894-9542-6(2)) Dorling Kindersley Publishing, Inc.
—My First Puppy Touch & Feel. 2003. (My First Touch & Feel Ser.). (Illus.). 12p. (J). bds. 9.99 (978-0-7894-9625-6(9)) Dorling Kindersley Publishing, Inc.
—My First Truck. 2003. (My First Sticker Board Bks.). (Illus.). 12p. (J). pap. 6.99 (978-0-7894-9246-3(6)) Dorling Kindersley Publishing, Inc.
—My Little Baby Animals Carrying Case, 4 bks., Set. 2002. (Illus.). (J). bds. 9.99 (978-0-7894-8839-8(6)) Dorling Kindersley Publishing, Inc.
—My Little Farm Carrying Case, 4 vols. 2003. (Illus.). 22p. (J). bds. 9.99 (978-0-7894-9159-6(1)) Dorling Kindersley Publishing, Inc.
—My Pets: A Barbie Touch-and-Feel Book. 2003. (Barbie Ser.). (Illus.). 12p. (J). bds. 6.99 (978-0-7894-9232-6(6)) Dorling Kindersley Publishing, Inc.
—Night Sky. Parsons, Jayne, ed. 2002. (Ultimate Sticker Bks.). (Illus.). 16p. (J). (gr. k-3). pap. 6.99 (978-0-7894-8459-8(5)) Dorling Kindersley Publishing, Inc.
—Pajama Bedtime Bear Touch-and-Feel: Meet My Friends. 2002. (Touch & Feel Ser.). (Illus.). 12p. (J). bds. 6.95 (978-0-7894-6277-0(X) , D K Ink) Dorling Kindersley Publishing, Inc.
—Pajama Bedtime Bear's Magic Surprise: A Lift-the-Flap Book. 2002. (Lift-the-Flap Books Ser.). (Illus.). 12p. (J). pap. 6.95 (978-0-7894-6276-3(1) , D K Ink) Dorling Kindersley Publishing, Inc.
—Pirate. 2004. (Ultimate Sticker Books Glow in the Dark). 16p. (J). pap. 6.99 (978-0-7566-0219-2(X)) Dorling Kindersley Publishing, Inc.
—Playtime Peekaboo! 2005. (Illus.). 12p. (J). (ps-3). bds. 6.99 (978-0-7566-1144-6(X)) Dorling Kindersley Publishing, Inc.
—Shapes. 2000. (Touch & Feel Ser.). (Illus.). 12p. (J). (ps). bds. 6.99 (978-0-7894-5222-1(7)) Dorling Kindersley Publishing, Inc.
—Shapes. 2001. (ps-2). lib. bdg. 11.80 (978-0-613-75083-7(7)) Tandem Library Bks.
—SpongeBob SquarePants Glow-in-the-Dark Sticker Book. 2005. (Ultimate sticker Bks.). 16p. (J). (ps-12). pap. 6.99 (978-0-7566-1558-1(5)) Dorling Kindersley Publishing, Inc.
—Sports Car. 2003. (Wheelies Ser.). (Illus.). 12p. (J). bds. 6.99 (978-0-7894-9711-6(5)) Dorling Kindersley Publishing, Inc.
—Tacto y Textura Gatito. 2003. (Touch & Feel Bilingual Board Bks.). (SPA & ENG., Illus.). 12p. (J). (ps-k). bds. 6.99 (978-0-7894-9523-5(6)) Dorling Kindersley Publishing, Inc.
—Tacto y Textura Perrito. 2003. (Touch & Feel Bilingual Board Bks.). (SPA & ENG., Illus.). 12p. (J). bds. 6.99 (978-0-7894-9525-9(2)) Dorling Kindersley Publishing, Inc.
—Things That Go. (Let's Look Ser.). (Illus.). 36p. (J). (ps-3). 2006. bds. 4.99 (978-0-7566-1748-6(0)); 2003. bds. 6.99 (978-0-7894-8577-9(X)) Dorling Kindersley Publishing, Inc.
—Wild Animals. 2001. (Soft-to-Touch Bk.). (Illus.). 18p. (J). (ps-3). bds. 4.95 (978-0-7894-7402-5(6)) Dorling Kindersley Publishing, Inc.
Dorling Kindersley Publishing Staff, contrib. by. C Is for Cat: A Touch-and-Say ABC Book. 2002. (DK Ladybird Ser.). 16p. (J). bds. 6.95 (978-0-7894-8471-0(4)) Dorling Kindersley Publishing, Inc.
Dorling Kindersley Publishing Staff, ed. Fairy. 2005. (Make-Believe Ser.). (Illus.). 12p. (J). bds. 6.99 (978-0-7566-1016-6(8)) Dorling Kindersley Publishing, Inc.
—Farm. (Baby Fun Ser.). (J). (ps-3). 2005. (Illus.). 14p. bds. 4.99 (978-0-7566-0987-0(9)); 2004. 16p. pap. 6.99 (978-0-7566-0236-9(X)) Dorling Kindersley Publishing, Inc.
—Farm. 2002. (J). 4.98 (978-0-7525-5236-1(8)) Parragon, Inc.
—The Incredibles. 2004. (Ultimate Sticker Bks.). (Illus.). 16p. (J). pap. 6.99 (978-0-7566-0588-9(1)) Dorling Kindersley Publishing, Inc.
—Princess. 2005. (Make-Believe Ser.). (Illus.). 12p. (J). bds. 6.99 (978-0-7566-1017-3(6)) Dorling Kindersley Publishing, Inc.
Dorling Kindersley Publishing Staff & Millard, Anne. Birthday. 2002. (Touch & Feel Ser.). (Illus.). 12p. (J). (ps-3). bds. 6.99 (978-0-7894-8536-6(2)) Dorling Kindersley Publishing, Inc.
—The Puppy. 2000. (Stroller Bks.). (Illus.). 16p. (J). (ps-k). bds. 4.95 (978-0-7894-6656-3(2)) Dorling Kindersley Publishing, Inc.
—Things That Go. 2002. (Lift-the-Flap Books Ser.). (Illus.). 16p. (J). (ps). 6.99 (978-0-7894-8896-1(5)) Dorling Kindersley Publishing, Inc.
Dorling Kindersley Publishing Staff, et al. Christmas. 2001. (Touch & Feel Ser.). (Illus.). 12p. (J). (ps-k). bds. 6.99 (978-0-7894-6512-2(4)) Dorling Kindersley Publishing, Inc.
Douglas, Lisa Jo. Active Animals A Thru Z. 2007. (J). per. 13.99 (***978-1-59879-311-6(X)***) Lifevest Publishing, Inc.
Douglass, Jo & Graham, Neville. Happy Baby Animals. rev. ed. 2002. (Priddy Bicknell Big Ideas for Little People Ser.). (Illus.). 28p. (J). bds. 5.95 (978-0-312-49061-4(5) , Priddy Bks.) St. Martin's Pr.
Dowley, Tim & Wyart, Peter. The Shepherd's Tale. Pierce, Martin, illus. 2002. 14p. (J). (gr. k-3). 5.99 (978-0-8254-7257-2(1)) Kregel Pubns.
—The Wise Men's Tale. Pierce, Martin, illus. 2002. 14p. (J). (gr. k-3). 5.99 (978-0-8254-7256-5(3)) Kregel Pubns.
Dowling, Paul. Sally's Amazing Colour Book. 1999. (Illus.). 32p. (J). 17.99 (978-0-86264-801-5(7)) Andersen GBR. *Dist:* Independent Pubs. Group.
Downing, Julie, illus. All the Ways I Love You (bilingual Edition) 2005. (SPA & ENG.). 10p. (J). 8.95 (978-1-58117-335-2(0) , Intervisual/Piggy Toes) Dalmatian Pr.
Doyle, Richard. Fairyland Stickers. Harper, Ellen, ed. 2001. 4p. 1.50 (978-0-486-41614-4(3)) Dover Pubns., Inc.
Drake, Ernest. The Dragonology Handbook: A Practical Course in Dragons. Steer, Dugald, ed. Anderson, Wayne et al, illus. ed. 2005. 80p. (J). (gr. 4 up). 12.99 (978-0-7636-2814-7(X)) Candlewick Pr.
Dress, Robert, illus. Mars, Here We Come! 2006. (Backyardigans Ser.). 16p. (J). bds. 7.99 (978-1-4169-1471-6(4) , Simon Spotlight/Nickelodeon) Simon & Schuster Children's Publishing.
Driscoll, Laura. All Aboard the Circus Train! A Foldout Book with Flaps! Roper, Robert, illus. 2004. (Dora the Explorer Ser.). 14p. (J). bds. 6.99 (978-0-689-86868-9(5) , Simon Spotlight/Nickelodeon) Simon & Schuster Children's Publishing.
Dubarle-Bossy, Philippe. Flutter the Bird. Rinaldo, Luana, illus. 2005. (Playful Puppet Bks.). 10p. (J). 6.95 (978-0-7641-3045-8(5)) Barron's Educational Series, Inc.
Dunn, Opal. El Gato Leo Goes to School: A First Spanish Story. Gale, Cathy, illus. 2006. (ENG & SPA.). 24p. (J). 15.95 (***978-1-84507-552-1(8)***) Lincoln, Frances Ltd. GBR. *Dist:* Perseus Distribution.
—Leo le Chat Comes to Play: A First French Story. Gale, Cathy, illus. (ENG & FRE.). 24p. (978-0-7112-1930-4(3)) Lincoln, Frances Ltd. GBR. *Dist:* Transition Vendor.
Dunn, Opal. Leo le Chat Goes to School: A First French Story. Gale, Cathy, illus. 2006. (ENG & FRE.). 24p. (J). 15.95 (***978-1-84507-403-6(3)***) Lincoln, Frances Ltd. GBR. *Dist:* Perseus Distribution.
Dunrea, Olivier. Gossie & Friends: A First Flap Book. 2006. (Illus.). 12p. (J). (ps-k). 11.99 (978-0-618-70786-7(7)) Houghton Mifflin Co.
Dunrea, Olivier. Gossie's Busy Day. 2007. (Illus.). 10p. (J). (ps-k). 11.99 (***978-0-618-82148-8(1)***) Houghton Mifflin Co. Trade & Reference Div.
Durant, Alan. Dear Santa Claus. Cabban, Vanessa, illus. 2005. 32p. (J). (ps-2). 14.99 (978-0-7636-2829-1(8)) Candlewick Pr.
—Dear Santa Claus: Mini Edition. Cabban, Vanessa, illus. 2007. 32p. (J). (ps-2). 6.99 (***978-0-7636-3465-0(4)***) Candlewick Pr.
—Dear Tooth Fairy. Cabban, Vanessa, illus. ed. 2006. 32p. (J). (ps-2). 6.99 (978-0-7636-2991-5(X)) Candlewick Pr.
—If You Go Walking in Tiger Wood. Boon, Debbie, illus. 2005. 24p. (J). pap. 9.99 (978-0-00-710390-4(5) , HarperSport) HarperCollins Pubs. Ltd. GBR. *Dist:* Trafalgar Square Publishing.
Eckold, David. The Ultimate Mars Rover Kit. 2004. (Illus.). 1p. (J). 29.99 (978-0-7566-0799-9(X)) Dorling Kindersley Publishing, Inc.
Edgson, Alison, et al, illus. The Emperor's New Clothes. 24p. pap. 5.99 (978-1-84643-020-6(8)) Child's Play-International.
Edgson, Alison, et al. Cinderella. 2006. (Flip up Fairy Tales Ser.). (Illus.). 24p. (J). 9.99 (978-1-904550-46-4(0)) Child's Play-International.
—Hansel & Gretel. 2006. (Illus.). 24p. pap. 5.99 (978-1-904550-73-0(8)); pap. 9.99 (978-1-904550-45-7(2)) Child's Play-International.
—The Little Red Hen. 2006. (Illus.). 24p. pap. 9.99 (978-1-904550-47-1(9)) Child's Play-International.
Editions Phidal Staff. Radical Rides Super Sticker Book. (Illus.). 64p. (J). pap. (978-2-7643-0024-4(7)) Phidal Publishing, Inc./Editions Phidal, Inc.
Ehlert, Lois. Hands: Growing up to be an Artist. 2004. (Illus.). 48p. (J). 14.95 (978-0-15-205107-5(4) , Harcourt Children's Bks) Harcourt Children's Bks.
Ehlert, Lois. Planting a Rainbow: Lap-Sized Board Book. 2008. (Illus.). 32p. (J). bds. 10.95 (***978-0-15-206304-7(8)*** , Red Wagon Bks.) Harcourt Children's Bks.
Elder, Jamie. Construction: Lift-A-Flap Fun. Wieland, Don, tr. Wieland, Don, illus. 2002. (Leap Frog Ser.). 12p. (J). bds. 12.98 (978-0-7853-6332-3(7) , 7162100) Publications International, Ltd.
Elgar, Rebecca. Where's My Dinner? With Flaps & a Pop-Up! 2003. (Illus.). 12p. (J). bds. 9.99 (978-1-4052-0451-4(6)) Egmont Bks., Ltd. GBR. *Dist:* Trafalgar Square Publishing.
Ellis, Belinda. Tractor. 2007. (Pull-Alongs Ser.). (Illus.). 12p. (ps). per. 6.95 (978-1-84610-443-5(2)) Make Believe Ideas GBR. *Dist:* Ingram Pub. Services.
Ellis, Libby. Say Moo! A Speak-and-Play Book. Castillon, Carly, illus. 2001. (Stories to Share Ser.). 10p. (J). (ps-k). act. bk. ed. 11.95 (978-1-58117-140-2(4) , Intervisual/Piggy Toes) Dalmatian Pr.
Ellward, David. Tickle Teddy: A Touch & Feel Book. 2002. (Illus.). 10p. (J). 12.95 (978-1-929766-57-4(2)) Handprint Bks.
Elmo's Talking Camera. 2002. (Illus.). 14p. (J). bds. 15.98 (978-0-7853-6069-8(7) , 7153400) Publications International, Ltd.
Emberley, Ed. Bye-Bye, Big Bad Bullybug. Emberley, Ed, illus. 2007. (Illus.). 32p. (J). (ps-1). 10.99 (978-0-316-01762-6(0)) Little Brown & Co.
Emberley, Edward R. Go Away, Big Green Monster! 2005. (Illus.). 32p. (J). (ps-1). reprint ed. 10.99 (978-0-316-23653-9(5)) Little Brown & Co.
Emmett, Jonathan. A Mouse in the Marmalade. Church, Caroline, illus. 2002. (J). tchr. ed. 14.95 (978-1-58925-687-3(5) , tiger tales) ME Media LLC.
—A Turtle in the Toilet. Jayne Church, Caroline, illus. 2002. 16p. (J). tchr. ed. 14.95 (978-1-58925-688-0(3) , tiger tales) ME Media LLC.
English Heritage Staff. My Life as a Knight. 2005. (Illus.). 32p. pap. 19.95 (978-1-85074-985-1(X)) English Heritage GBR. *Dist:* Brown, David Bk. Co., The.
—My Life as a Princess. 2005. (Illus.). 32p. pap. 19.95 (978-1-85074-984-4(1)) English Heritage GBR. *Dist:* Brown, David Bk. Co., The.
Epstein, Brad. Kansas State Univ 101: My first Text-Board-Book. l.t. ed. 2007. (101—My First Text-Board Books). (Illus.). 20p. (J). bds. 10.95 (***978-1-932530-57-5(6)*** , 101 Bk.) Michaelson Entertainment.
Epstein, Brad, ed. Iowa State University 101: My First Text-Board-Book. 2006. (101—My First Text-Board Books). (J). bds. 10.95 (978-1-932530-37-7(1) , 101 Bk.) Michaelson Entertainment.
—University of Kansas 101: My First Text-Board-Book. 2006. (101—My First Text-Board Books). (J). bds. 10.95 (978-1-932530-40-7(1) , 101 Bk.) Michaelson Entertainment.
—University of Kentucky 101: My First Text-Board-Book. 2006. (101—My First Text-Board Books). (J). bds. 10.95 (978-1-932530-23-0(1) , 101 Bk.) Michaelson Entertainment.
Epstein, Brad M. Los Angeles Dodgers 101: My first Team-board-book. l.t. ed. 2007. (101—My First Text-Board Books). (Illus.). 22p. (J). bds. 10.95 (***978-1-932530-80-3(0)*** , 101 Bk.) Michaelson Entertainment.
—Army 101: My First Text-Board-Book. l.t. ed. 2007. (101—My First Text-Board Books). (Illus.). 20p. (J). bds. 10.95 (***978-1-932530-42-1(8)*** , 101 Bk.) Michaelson Entertainment.
—Atlanta Braves 101: My first Team-board-book. l.t. ed. 2007. (Illus.). 22p. (J). bds. 10.95 (***978-1-932530-74-2(6)*** , 101 Bk.) Michaelson Entertainment.
—Boston Red Sox 101: My first Team-board-book. l.t. ed. 2007. (101—My First Text-Board Books). (Illus.). 22p. (J). bds. 10.95 (***978-1-932530-92-6(4)*** , 101 Bk.) Michaelson Entertainment.
—Chicago Cubs 101: My first Team-board-book. l.t. ed. 2007. (101—My First Text-Board Books). (Illus.). 22p. (J). bds. 10.95 (***978-1-932530-77-3(0)*** , 101 Bk.) Michaelson Entertainment.
—Chicago White Sox 101: My first Team-board-book. l.t. ed. 2007. (101—My First Text-Board Books). (Illus.). 22p. (J). bds. 10.95 (***978-1-932530-98-8(3)*** , 101 Bk.) Michaelson Entertainment.
—Detroit Tigers 101: My first Team-board-book. l.t. ed. 2007. (101—My First Text-Board Books). (Illus.). 22p. (J). bds. 10.95 (***978-1-932530-96-4(7)*** , 101 Bk.) Michaelson Entertainment.
—New York Mets 101: My first Team-board-book. l.t. ed. 2007. (101—My First Text-Board Books). (Illus.). 22p. (J). bds. 10.95 (***978-1-932530-85-8(1)*** , 101 Bk.) Michaelson Entertainment.
—New York Yankees 101: My first Team-board-book. l.t. ed. 2007. (101—My First Text-Board Books). (Illus.). 22p. (J). bds. 10.95 (***978-1-932530-99-5(1)*** , 101 Bk.) Michaelson Entertainment.
—Oklahoma State University 101: My First Text-Board-Book. l.t. ed. 2007. (101—My First Text-Board Books). (Illus.). 20p. (J). bds. 10.95 (***978-1-932530-27-8(4)*** , 101 Bk.) Michaelson Entertainment.
—University of Arkansas 101: My First Text-Board-Book. l.t. ed. 2007. (101—My First Text-Board Books). (Illus.). 20p. (J). bds. 10.95 (***978-1-932530-58-2(4)*** , 101 Bk.) Michaelson Entertainment.
—University of South Carolina 101: My First Text-Board-Book. l.t. ed. 2007. (101—My First Text-Board Books). (Illus.). 20p. (J). bds. 10.95 (***978-1-932530-41-4(X)*** , 101 Bk.) Michaelson Entertainment.
—University of Texas Longhorns 123: My first counting Book. l.t. ed. 2006. (Illus.). 22p. (J). bds. 14.95 (***978-1-932530-54-4(1)*** , 123 Bk.) Michaelson Entertainment.
Ernst, Lisa Campbell. The Turn-Around, Upside-down Alphabet Book. Ernst, Lisa Campbell, illus. 2004. (Illus.). 32p. (J). 15.95 (978-0-689-85685-3(7)) Simon & Schuster Children's Publishing.
Escondidos en el Cuarto de Juegos. 2001. (Peek & Find Ser.).Tr. of Hiding in the Playroom. (SPA., Illus.). 12p. (J). (ps-3). (978-968-5308-60-1(8) , Silver Dolphin en Español) Advanced Marketing, S. de R. L. de C. V.
Esquinaldo, Virginia. What Did Baby Jesus Do? Esquinaldo, Virginia, illus. 2006. (Illus.). 14p. (J). bds. 6.95 (978-0-8198-8310-0(7)) Pauline Bks. & Media.
Eubank, Patricia Reeder. Countdown to Christmas. 2003. (Illus.). 14p. (J). (ps-k). 9.95 (978-0-8249-6505-1(1)) Ideals Pubns.
Eubank, Patti Reeder. Count Your Blessings! 2004. (Illus.). 14p. (J). bds. 9.95 (978-0-8249-6544-0(2)) Ideals Pubns.
Eurpsville U. S. A. Inc. Staff. Alphabet Eurps on Parade. 1999. (Concept Bks.). (J). 7.95 (978-1-892522-01-6(2)) Eurpsville USA, Inc.
—Alphabet Eurps Visit the Zoo. 1999. (Concept Bks.). (J). 7.95 (978-1-892522-00-9(4)) Eurpsville USA, Inc.
Eurpsville U. S. A. Inc. Staff, ed. The Alphabet Eurps & the Birthday Surprise. 1999. (Illus.). (J). 19.95 (978-1-892522-13-9(6)) Eurpsville USA, Inc.
—The Alphabet Eurps on Parade. 1999. (Illus.). (J). 19.95 (978-1-892522-12-2(8)) Eurpsville USA, Inc.
—The Alphabet Eurps Visit the Zoo. 1999. (Illus.). (J). 19.95 (978-1-892522-11-5(X)) Eurpsville USA, Inc.
Evans, Alwyn. Old MacDonald's Farm: A Three-Dimensional Playset with Sound! Bell, Owen, illus. 2001. (J). (ps-k). act. bk. ed. 16.95 (978-1-58117-145-7(5) , Intervisual/Piggy Toes) Dalmatian Pr.
Exclaim Entertainment & Bernthal, Mark. BOZtrade;-Count Your Blessings! McKee, Darren, illus. 2007. (BOZ#8482; Ser.). 14p. (J). 4.99 (978-0-310-71395-1(1)) Zonderkidz.
Fabiny, Sarah. Rainforest Animal Adventure. Kees, Chantal & Shields, Chris, illus. 2003. (Magic Color Bks.). 12p. (J). (gr. k-2). 9.95 (978-1-4027-0823-7(8)) Sterling Publishing Co., Inc.
Faces. Date not set. (Illus.). 40p. (J). 3.98 (978-1-4054-0174-6(5)) Parragon, Inc.
Fact Families Staff. Learning Wrap Ups Palette. 2004. 7.99 (978-1-59204-016-2(0)) Learning Wrap-Ups.
Fair Ideal Instructional Staff. What Matches with Sammy Spider. 1999. (Lost-N-Found Book Ser.). (Illus.). (J). 7.95 (978-1-56451-294-9(0) , Ideal School Supply) Schaffer, Frank Pubns.
—What's Different with Freddy Frog, Vol. 1. 1999. (Lost-N-Found Book Ser.). (Illus.). (J). 7.95 (978-1-56451-293-2(2) , Ideal School Supply) Schaffer, Frank Pubns.
Farm Animals. 2003. (Illus.). 12p. (J). 2.98 (978-1-4054-1181-3(3)) Parragon, Inc.
Farmer, Karen, ed. If I Could Be Anything What Would I Be. 2007. 12p. pap. 8.95 (***978-1-59125-914-5(2)***) Penton Overseas, Inc.
Fashion Fun Sticker Book. (Girlfriend Gang Ser.). 16p. (J). (978-2-7643-0018-3(2)) Phidal Publishing, Inc./Editions Phidal, Inc.
Faulkner, Keith. Big Bugs! Giant Creepy Crawly Pop-Ups. Holmes, Stephen, illus. 2004. 14p. (J). pap. 10.95 (978-0-439-49905-7(4)) Scholastic, Inc.
—Charlie Chimp's Christmas: A Pop-up Extravaganza of Festive Friends. Lambert, Jonathan, illus. 2006. 12p. (J). (ps-3). reprint ed. 10.00 (978-1-4223-5446-9(6)) DIANE Publishing Co.
—The Five Senses. Lambert, Jonathan, illus. 2002. 14p. (J). pap. 9.95 (978-0-439-38882-5(1) , Scholastic Pr.) Scholastic, Inc.
—Flip-Flap Math: Flip the Flpas to Check Your Answers! Irish, Martin, illus. 2005. 12 p.p. (J). (***978-0-439-78578-5(2)***) Scholastic, Inc.
—Funny Farm. Lambert, Jonathan, illus. 2002. (Mixed-Up Pop-Up Bks.). 5p. (J). (ps-1). 7.95 (978-0-439-30904-2(2) , Cartwheel Bks.) Scholastic, Inc.
—The Long-Nosed Pig. Lambert, Jonathan, illus. 1998. (Pop-Up Bks.). 16p. (J). (ps-2). 13.99 (978-0-8037-2296-5(6) , Dial) Penguin Group (USA) Inc.
—Maths Machine: A Fun New Way to Do Maths! Tyger, Rory, illus. 2004. (J). (***978-0-439-72174-5(1)***) Scholastic, Inc.
—The Mixed-Up Tooth Fairy. Lambert, Jonathan, illus. 2002. 8p. (J). (ps-1). pap. 9.95 (978-0-439-35609-1(1) , Cartwheel Bks.) Scholastic, Inc.
—Rainbow's End. 2003. (Illus.). 10p. (J). 9.95 (978-0-7641-5641-0(1)) Barron's Educational Series, Inc.
—The Scared Little Bear: A Not Too Scary Pop up Book. Lambert, Jonathan, illus. 2000. 16p. (J). (ps-2). bds. 9.95 (978-0-531-30267-5(9) , Orchard Bks.) Scholastic, Inc.
—Spelling Machine. Teel, Gina, illus. 2006. 16p. (J). pap. 7.99 (978-0-439-82090-5(1) , Cartwheel Bks.) Scholastic, Inc.
—The Spooky Trail. Brown, Leo, illus. 2005. 16p. (J). (ps-2). bds. 9.99 (978-0-7641-5834-6(1)) Barron's Educational Series, Inc.
—Surprise on the Farm. Clucas, Philip, illus. 2000. (J). (978-0-439-21059-1(3)) Scholastic, Inc.
—Ten Little Monkeys: A Counting Story Book. Lambert, Jonathan, illus. 2004. 12p. (J). reprint ed. 20.00 (978-0-7567-8203-0(1)) DIANE Publishing Co.
Faulkner, Keith & Holmes, Stephen. Animal ? Math. Faulkner, Keith & Holmes, Stephen, illus. 2003. (Illus.). (J). (978-0-439-62755-9(9)) Scholastic, Inc.
Ferguson, Richard. Backyard Bugs. 2007. (Illus.). 14p. (J). (gr. k-3). 12.99 (978-0-7566-2538-2(6)) Dorling Kindersley Publishing, Inc.
Filipowich, Bob & Hoe, Susan. My Ducky. 2004. (Soft Shapestm Ser.). (Illus.). 8p. (J). (ps-ps). 8.99 (978-1-58476-215-7(2)) Innovative Kids.

Finale, Frank. A Gull's Story, Part 3: Colors at the Shore. Moore, Margie, illus. 2007. (J). 22.00 (***978-0-9777077-2-0(5)***) Jersey Shore Pubns.

Fiona, Simpson, ed. Harry Potter & the Goblet of Fire: Deluxe Sticker Book. 2005. (Harry Potter Ser.). (Illus.). 10p. (J). (gr. 2-5). pap. 6.99 (978-0-439-63299-7(4), Levine, Arthur A. Bks.) Scholastic, Inc.

The First Christmas. (Illus.). 12p. (J). 4.95 (978-1-58989-102-9(3)) Thurman Hse., LLC.

First Words. 2001. (Early Learning Ser.). (J). (gr. k-12). vinyl bd. 4.95 (978-1-58845-052-4(X)) School Specialty Publishing.

Fischer, Chuck. The White House. 2004. (Illus.). 10p. 35.00 (978-0-7893-1064-4(3)) Universe Publishing.

Fisher-Price Little People Write & Wipe Activity Books. 2004. (J). act. bk. ed. (978-0-7666-0871-9(9), 28100); act. bk. ed. (978-0-7666-0872-6(7), 28100); act. bk. ed. (978-0-7666-0873-3(5), 28100); act. bk. ed. (978-0-7666-0874-0(3), 28100) Modern Publishing.

Fleming, Maria. Mini-Book of the Week: 40 Easy-to-Read Mini-Books on Fiction & Nonfiction Topics for Every Week of the School Year. 2005. 96p. pap. 13.99 (978-0-439-05921-3(6), Teaching Resources) Scholastic, Inc.

Flip Quiz: 2nd-4th Grade. 2002. (Flip Quiz Ser.). (Illus.). 114p. (J). (gr. 2-4). spiral bd. 12.95 (978-1-57145-808-7(5), Silver Dolphin Bks.) Advantage Pubs. Group.

Flip Quiz: 4th-5th Grade. 2002. (Flip Quiz Ser.). (Illus.). 114p. (J). (gr. 4-5). spiral bd. 12.95 (978-1-57145-809-4(3), Silver Dolphin Bks.) Advantage Pubs. Group.

Flip Quiz: 6th-7th Grade. 2002. (Flip Quiz Ser.). (Illus.). 114p. (YA). (gr. 6-7). spiral bd. 12.95 (978-1-57145-811-7(5), Silver Dolphin Bks.) Advantage Pubs. Group.

Flying Rhinoceros Inc. Staff. Bug Book Adventure Pack. 2000. (Illus.). 24p. (J). (gr. k-2). pap. 5.00 (978-1-883772-71-0(0)) Flying Rhinoceros, Inc.

—I Am Hercules Adventure Pack. 2000. 24p. (J). (gr. k-2). pap. 5.00 (978-1-883772-67-3(2)) Flying Rhinoceros, Inc.

—I Am Jenny Adventure Pack. 2000. (Illus.). 24p. (J). (gr. k-2). pap. 5.00 (978-1-883772-69-7(9)) Flying Rhinoceros, Inc.

—I Am Porkchop Adventure Pack. 2000. (Illus.). 24p. (J). (gr. k-2). pap. 5.00 (978-1-883772-68-0(0)) Flying Rhinoceros, Inc.

—I Am Sam Adventure Pack. 2000. (Illus.). 24p. (J). (gr. k-2). pap., wbk. ed. 5.00 (978-1-883772-66-6(4)) Flying Rhinoceros, Inc.

—Today I Will Moo Adventure Pack. 2000. (Illus.). 24p. (J). (gr. k-2). pap. 5.00 (978-1-883772-70-3(2)) Flying Rhinoceros, Inc.

Folder, Alan. Paper Dinosaurs. Galvani, Maureen, illus. 2001. (Paper Magic Ser.). 48p. (J). (gr. 3-7). 7.95 (978-0-439-22762-9(3)) Scholastic, Inc.

Fontes, Justine. Hocus-Pocus Halloween. Regan, Dana, illus. 2003. (Magical Color Bks.). 10p. (J). 5.95 (978-1-4027-0992-0(7), Sterling/Pinwheel) Sterling Publishing Co., Inc.

Fordham, Kate. Me & My Kitten. 2006. (Illus.). 80p. (J). (***978-0-439-89293-3(7)***) Scholastic, Inc.

Formby, Caroline. Dragonberries. 2000. (Illus.). 24p. (J). (ps-3). 8.99 (978-0-85953-660-8(2)) Child's Play-International.

Forward, Toby. Shakespeare's Globe: An Interactive Pop-Up Theatre. Wijngaard, Juan, illus. 2005. 14p. (J). (gr. 3). 19.99 (978-0-7636-2694-5(5)) Candlewick Pr.

Fox, Christyan & Fox, Diane. Around the World Piggy-wiggy. 2002. (Illus.). 24p. (J). 14.95 (978-1-929766-58-1(0)) Handprint Bks.

Fox, Diane, et al. Goodnight PiggyWiggy: A Pull-the-Page Book. Fox, Christyan, illus. 2000. 24p. (J). (ps-k). 12.95 (978-1-929766-06-2(8)) Handprint Bks.

Fractions Cards Staff. Learning Wrap Ups Palette. 2004. 7.99 (978-1-59204-020-9(9)) Learning Wrap-Ups.

Frantz, Jennifer. My Little Pony Color & Iron-Ons Book. Middleton, Gayle, illus. 2005. (My Little Pony Ser.). 32p. (J). (ps-1). pap. 3.99 (978-0-06-074441-0(3), Harper Festival) HarperCollins Pubs.

Freeman, Don. Corduroy's Buttons. 2008. 12p. (J). (ps-1). bds. 7.99 (***978-0-448-44815-2(7)***, Grosset & Dunlap) Penguin Group (USA) Inc.

—Corduroy's Sweet Surprise. 2008. 12p. (J). (ps-k). bds. 7.99 (***978-0-448-44821-3(1)***, Grosset & Dunlap) Penguin Group (USA) Inc.

Freeman, Tina. Ten Little Monkeys: Jumping on the Bed. 2001. (gr. k-3). lib. bdg. 15.30 (978-0-613-77001-9(3)) Tandem Library Bks.

Frith, Alex. See Inside Science. 2007. 16p. (J). bds. 12.99 (978-0-7945-1549-2(5), Usborne) EDC Publishing.

—See Inside the World of Dinosaurs. Scott, Peter, illus. 2007. 16p. (J). bds. 12.99 (978-0-7945-1436-5(7), Usborne) EDC Publishing.

—See Inside under the Ground. 2007. 16p. (J). bds. 12.99 (978-0-7945-1600-0(9), Usborne) EDC Publishing.

Fry, Sonali. Clifford's Christmas Presents. Kurtz, John, illus. 2002. (Clifford, the Big Red Dog Ser.). 7p. (J). bds. 8.99 (978-0-439-39451-2(1), Cartwheel Bks.) Scholastic, Inc.

—Dora's Spooky Halloween. Style Guide Staff, illus. 2006. (Dora the Explorer Ser.). 16p. (J). bds. 5.99 (978-1-4169-2482-1(5), Simon Spotlight/Nickelodeon) Simon & Schuster Children's Publishing.

—My Busy Day: A First Word Book. 2006. (Baby Nick Jr Ser.). 12p. (J). bds. 8.99 (978-1-4169-1793-9(4), Simon Spotlight/Nickelodeon) Simon & Schuster Children's Publishing.

Fung, Karen & Butterfield, Moira. Let's Go Potty. Utton, Peter, illus. 2000. 10p. (J). (ps-k). 9.99 (978-0-7641-5288-7(2)) Barron's Educational Series, Inc.

Gabriel, Ashala. Night Night Toes: A Lift-the-Flap Story. Porter, Sue, illus. 2002. 24p. (J). (ps-k). 12.95 (978-0-689-85089-9(1), Little Simon) Simon & Schuster Children's Publishing.

Gaffney, Michael. Time-Life Programa de Aprendizaje Infantil (Time-Life Early Learning Program), 10 bks. Incl. Cuantos Hipopotamos Hay? 1963. 16.95 (978-0-7835-3512-8(0)); Cuentos para un Dia de Tormenta (Takes for a Stormy Day) 1996. 16.95 (978-0-7835-3533-3(3)); Dia en la Vida del Sr. Atolondron. 1996. 16.95 (978-0-7835-3525-8(2)); Relojes Magicos del Abuelo Roberto (Roberto's Magical Clocks) 1996. 16.95 (978-0-7835-3504-3(X)); Secretos del Bosque (The Secret Forest) 1996. 16.95 (978-0-7835-3500-5(7)); Tania y Sus Amigos (Tanya Thinker & the Gizmo Gang) 1996. 16.95 (978-0-7835-3516-6(3)); Tomasol, el Mago del Color (Balderdash the Brilliant) 1996. 16.95 (978-0-7835-3529-6(5)); Viaje de los "Micronautas" (Voyage of the Micronauts) 1996. 16.95 (978-0-7835-3537-1(6)); (Illus.). 64p. (J). (gr. k-2). 144.08 (978-0-7835-3541-8(4)) Time-Life, Inc.

Gaines, Simon Ludvigsen. Good Night, Sleep Tight. 2007. (Little Scholastic Ser.). (Illus.). 24p. (J). (ps). bds. 9.99 (***978-0-439-86726-9(6)***, Cartwheel Bks.) Scholastic, Inc.

Garfield, Valerie. So Big! Yaccarino, Dan, illus. 2001. (Playtime Rhymes Ser.). 12p. (J). (ps up). pap. 7.99 (978-0-694-01509-2(1), Harper Festival) HarperCollins Pubs.

Garofoli, Viviana. Pirates! 2008. (J). (***978-0-7614-5455-7(1)***) Cavendish, Marshall Corp.

—Princess! 2008. (J). (***978-0-7614-5450-2(0)***) Cavendish, Marshall Corp.

Gerstein, Sherry. My Great Aunt Phibian. Reader's Digest Editors, ed. Van Fleet, Mara, illus. 2005. 10p. (J). bds. 12.99 (978-0-7944-0506-9(1), Reader's Digest Children's Bks.) Reader's Digest Children's Publishing, Inc.

Gertein, Sherry & Fleet, Mara Van. My Great Aunt Phibian. 2007. 10p. (J). bds. 6.99 (978-0-7944-1281-4(5)) Reader's Digest Assn., Inc., The.

Gerth, Melanie. Ten Little Ladybugs. Huliska-Beith, Laura, illus. 22p. (ps-k). 2005. (J). 10.95 (978-1-58117-091-7(2)); 2000. (YA). lp 12.95 (978-1-58117-122-8(6)) Dalmatian Pr. (Intervisual/Piggy Toes).

Get a Grip on Life: What Every Teen Must Know to Have a Great Life. 2004. 240p. (YA). per. 14.00 (978-0-9748994-0-4(2)) Youth Quest Institute.

Get Dressed with Elmo. 2000. (Illus.). 8p. (J). (ps). 19.95 (978-1-56156-883-3(X)) Kidsbooks, Inc.

Get Dressed with Elmo. (J). 2003. (978-1-59292-030-3(6)); 2000. (978-1-931312-09-7(5)); 2000. (978-1-931312-04-2(4)) SoftPlay, Inc.

Gifford, Christopher. A Present for Santa! A Lift-the-Flap Book with 45 Flaps! Fruchter, Jason, illus. 2002. (Dora the Explorer Ser.). 12p. (J). bds. 11.95 (978-0-689-84935-0(4), Simon Spotlight/Nickelodeon) Simon & Schuster Children's Publishing.

Gifford, Christopher & Ricci, Christine. Valentines for Everyone! Savitsky, Steven, illus. 2003. (Dora the Explorer Ser.). 14p. (J). (gr. k-3). bds. 5.99 (978-0-689-85236-7(3), Simon Spotlight/Nickelodeon) Simon & Schuster Children's Publishing.

Gilbert, Laura, text. Dora the Explorer. 2005. (Ultimate sticker Bks.). (SPA & ENG., Illus.). 16p. (J). (ps-7). 6.99 (978-0-7566-1561-1(5)) Dorling Kindersley Publishing, Inc.

Gilbert, Laura & Beck, Jerry. Pink Panther. 2005. (Ultimate Sticker Books Ser.). (Illus.). 16p. (J). (ps-3). pap. 6.99 (978-0-7566-1032-6(X)) Dorling Kindersley Publishing, Inc.

Gili, Phillida. Cinderella: A Pop Up Book. 2006. (Illus.). 14p. (J). 17.95 (978-1-58234-712-7(3), Bloomsbury Children) Bloomsbury Publishing.

Gili, Phillida. Cinderella: A Pop-up Book. Gili, Phillida, illus. 2007. (Illus.). 12p. (J). 25.00 (***978-1-4223-9031-3(4)***) DIANE Publishing Co.

Girl Friends Super Sticker Book. (Illus.). 64p. (J). pap. (978-2-7643-0026-8(3)) Phidal Publishing, Inc./Editions Phidal, Inc.

Glow in the Dark Advent Sticker Book. (Illus.). 16p. (J). (ps-5). 6.99 (978-0-8254-7233 6(4)) Kregel Pubns.

God Made Funny Bugs. 2000. (978-1-893065-79-6(0), Family Christian Pr.) Family Christian Stores, Inc.

Godsey, Kallen & Calitri, Susan, trs. Learn about Alphabet. Godsey, Kallen & Calitri, Susan, illus. 2001. (My Wipe-Off Book Ser.). (Illus.). 10.98 (978-0-7853-4402-5(0)) Publications International, Ltd.

Going Shopping! Sticker Book. (Girlfriend Gang Ser.). 16p. (J). (978-2-7643-0020-6(4)) Phidal Publishing, Inc./Editions Phidal, Inc.

Goldberg, Howard A. Bugs: Pull the Tabs! Change the Pictures! 2004. (Magic Windows Ser.). (Illus.). 8p. (J). pap. 4.95 (978-0-7624-1578-6(9), Running Pr. Kids) Running Pr. Bk. Pubs.

Goldberg, Malky. What Do I Say. Argoff, Patti, illus. 2006. (J). 9.95 (978-1-929628-24-7(2)) Hachai Publishing.

Goldberg, Malky. What Else Do I Say? A Lift the Flap Book. Argoff, Patti, illus. 2007. (J). (ps-k). bds. 9.95 (***978-1-929628-34-6(X)***) Hachai Publishing.

Golden Books Staff. Barbie Fairytopia: Mermaidia Board Book. 2007. 24p. (J). (gr. k-k). bds. 4.99 (978-0-375-83851-4(1), Golden Bks.) Random Hse. Children's Bks.

—Bob's Handy Hammer. 2003. (Fix It with Bob Ser.). (Illus.). 14p. (J). (ps-1). bds. 9.99 (978-0-375-82645-0(9), Golden Bks.) Random Hse. Children's Bks.

—Bring on the Rock! Schigiel, Gregg, illus. 2004. 32p. (J). (ps). pap. 4.99 (978-0-375-82989-5(X), Golden Bks.) Random Hse. Children's Bks.

—Christmas Surprise! 2007. (Deluxe Coloring Book Ser.). (Illus.). 96p. (J). pap. 3.99 (***978-0-375-84101-9(6)***, Golden Bks.) Random Hse. Children's Bks.

—Fashion Show. 2000. (Illus.). 128p. (J). (ps-2). pap. 0.99 (978-0-307-44332-8(9), Golden Bks.) Random Hse. Children's Bks.

—Fix It With Bob: Scruffty Helps Out. 2002. (Illus.). 14p. (J). (ps-1). bds. 9.99 (978-0-307-20074-7(4), Golden Bks.) Random Hse. Children's Bks.

—Fix It With Bob: The Very Busy Day. 2002. (Illus.). 14p. (J). (ps-1). bds. 9.99 (978-0-307-20075-4(2), Golden Bks.) Random Hse. Children's Bks.

—I'm Ready! Schigiel, Gregg, illus. 2004. (Color Plus Growing Characters Ser.). 32p. (J). (ps). pap. 4.99 (978-0-375-82988-8(1), Golden Bks.) Random Hse. Children's Bks.

—Pat the Bunny Alphabet Book. LV Studio Staff, illus. 2006. (Pat the Bunny Ser.). 30p. (J). (gr. k-ps). 10.95 (978-0-375-83550-6(4), Golden Bks.) Random Hse. Children's Bks.

—The Powerpuff Girls: Sugar, Spice & Everything Nice. 2000. (Illus.). 16p. (J). (ps-3). pap. 2.99 (978-0-307-28328-3(3), Golden Bks.) Random Hse. Children's Bks.

—Shell City, Here We Come! 2004. (Illus.). 32p. (J). (ps). pap. 3.99 (978-0-375-82947-5(4), Golden Bks.) Random Hse. Children's Bks.

—SpongeBob. 2001. (Illus.). 16p. (J). (ps-2). 9.99 (978-0-307-20054-9(X), 20054, Golden Bks.) Random Hse. Children's Bks.

—Trick or Treat! 2006. (Illus.). 32p. (J). (ps-2). pap. 2.99 (978-0-375-83928-3(3), Golden Bks.) Random Hse. Children's Bks.

—Trick or Treat. Borlasca, Hector, illus. 2006. 12p. (J). (gr. k-1). bds. 3.99 (978-0-375-87490-1(9), Golden Bks.) Random Hse. Children's Bks.

Goldowsky, Jill. It's a Wedding. Mattel Studios Staff, illus. 2003. (Barbie Press on Stick & Stay Ser.). 10p. (J). bds. 9.99 (978-0-7944-0257-0(7), Reader's Digest Children's Bks.) Reader's Digest Children's Publishing, Inc.

Gondek, Heather. Who's in the Jungle? Lift-the-Flap 'n' Learn. Gilvan-Cartwright, Chris, illus. 2005. (Fun with Animals Ser.). 10p. (J). 9.95 (978-1-58117-075-7(0), Intervisual/Piggy Toes) Dalmatian Pr.

Gondek, Heather J. Who's on the Farm? Lift-the-Flap 'n' Learn Book. Gilvan-Cartwright, Chris, illus. 2005. (Fun with Animals Ser.). 10p. (J). (ps-k). act. bk. ed. 9.95 (978-1-58117-143-3(9), Intervisual/Piggy Toes) Dalmatian Pr.

Goodale, Rebecca, illus. Island Dog. 1999. 38p. (J). (ps up). 17.95 (978-1-891090-03-5(8)) Two Dog Pr.

Gordon, Bob & Holmen, Lene. Lift & Learn Opposites. Snaith, Andy, photos by. 2006. (Illus.). 24p. (ps-ps). per., bds. 5.95 (978-1-84610-031-4(3)) Make Believe Ideas GBR. *Dist:* Ingram Pub. Services.

Gormley, Greg. Daddy's Day at Work. 2007. (Fantastic Phones Ser.). (Illus.). 12p. (J). 9.99 (***978-0-7475-8378-3(1)***) Bloomsbury Publishing Plc GBR. *Dist:* Independent Pubs. Group.

Got, Yves. Sweet Dreams, Sam. 2000. (Illus.). 14p. (J). (ps). 9.95 (978-0-8118-2985-4(5)) Chronicle Bks. LLC.

Graham, Alistair. Full Moon Afloat. Graham, Alistair, illus. 2003. (Full Moon Soup & Full Moon Afloat Ser.). (Illus.). 32p. (YA). pap. (978-1-85602-217-0(X)) Chrysalis Children's Bks.

Grahame, Kenneth. The Wind in the Willows. (Great Classics for Children Ser.). (Illus.). 192p. (J). 5.99 (978-1-4037-0600-3(X)) Dalmatian Pr.

Gravett, Emily. Meerkat Mail. Gravett, Emily, illus. 2007. (Illus.). 24p. (J). (ps-3). 17.99 (***978-1-4169-3473-8(1)***) Simon & Schuster Children's Publishing.

Green, John. Horses Tattoos. 2003. (Dover Little Activity Bks.). (Illus.). 2p. (J). (gr. k-5). pap. 1.50 (978-0-486-43029-4(4)) Dover Pubns., Inc.

Green, John, illus. Who Lives on the Farm? 2004. (Who Lives... Ser.). 12p. (J). bds. 4.99 (978-1-85854-647-6(8)) Brimax Books Ltd. GBR. *Dist:* Byeway Bks.

Green, Yuko. Christina from Sweden Sticker Paper Doll. 2003. (Dover Little Activity Bks.). (Illus.). 4p. (J). pap. 1.50 (978-0-486-43015-7(4)) Dover Pubns., Inc.

—Tien from Indonesia Sticker Paper Doll. 2004. (Dover Little Activity Bks.). (Illus.). 4p. (J). pap. 1.50 (978-0-486-43016-4(2)) Dover Pubns., Inc.

Greene, Sefton. Space Painters. 2003. 18p. bds. (978-1-904502-30-2(X)) MediaWorld/BestBooks.

Grimes, Nikki. My Man Blue. Lagarrigue, Jerome, illus. 2002. 32p. (J). (ps-3). pap. 6.99 (978-0-14-230197-5(3), Puffin) Penguin Group (USA) Inc.

—My Man Blue. 2002. (gr. 3-6). lib. bdg. 15.30 (978-0-613-60823-7(2)) Tandem Library Bks.

Grossblatt, Ben. Keep Out! Door Alarm: Build Your Own Key-Card Security System! 2004. (Illus.). 24p. (J). (978-0-439-66835-4(2)) Scholastic, Inc.

Grosset and Dunlap Staff. Night-Night, Baby: A Touch & Feel Book. Hathon, Elizabeth, photos by. 2000. (Illus.). 12p. (J). (ps-k). bds. 6.99 (978-0-448-42296-1(4), Grosset & Dunlap) Penguin Group (USA) Inc.

Group/McGraw-Hill, Wright. The Magic Shoes: Level N, 6 vols. 128p. (gr. 3-6). 36.95 (978-0-322-05884-2(8)) Wright Group, The.

Gubacz, Margorie. Piglet's Big Day. Baker, Darrell, illus. 2005. (J). (***978-1-4127-3102-7(X)***) Publications International, Ltd.

Guettier, Benedicte. In the Jungle. 2002. (Illus.). 14p. (J). bds. 11.95 (978-1-929132-38-6(7)) Kane/Miller Bk. Pubs., Inc.

Guidoux, Valerie. By Day & by Night. Faller, Regis et al, illus. 2006. (Explore Your World Ser.). (ENG & FRE.). 28p. (J). (ps-1). 15.95 (978-1-55407-003-9(1)) Firefly Bks., Ltd.

—Hidden Animals. Caillou, Pierre & Eydoux, Anne, illus. 2006. (Explore Your World Ser.). (ENG & FRE.). 28p. (J). (ps-1). 15.95 (978-1-55407-008-4(2)) Firefly Bks., Ltd.

Gulbis, Stephen, illus. Old MacDonald Had a Barn. 2003. 22p. (YA). (978-1-85602-453-2(9)) Chrysalis Children's Bks.

Gunson, Christopher. Animal Surprise. 2003. (Illus.). 32p. (J). 19.99 (978-0-385-60223-5(5), Doubleday); pap. 11.95 (978-0-552-54741-3(7), Corgi) Transworld Publishers Ltd. GBR. *Dist:* Trafalgar Square Publishing, Independent Pubs. Group.

Gunzi, Christiane. Cuddly Puppies. 2005. (Feels Real Bks.). (Illus.). 10p. (J). bds. 4.95 (978-0-7641-5853-7(8)) Barron's Educational Series, Inc.

—Furry Kittens. 2005. (Feels Real Bks.). (Illus.). 10p. (J). bds. 4.95 (978-0-7641-5854-4(6)) Barron's Educational Series, Inc.

Gutman, Anne. Penelope at School. Hallensleben, Georg, illus. 2004. 12p. (J). (ps up). pap. 12.95 (978-0-439-67357-0(7), Cartwheel Bks.) Scholastic, Inc.

—Penelope in the Winter. Hallensleben, Georg, illus. 2005. 12p. (J). (ps-k). pap. 9.99 (978-0-439-67360-0(7), Cartwheel Bks.) Scholastic, Inc.

Halfmann, Janet. Ogre Hunter No. 2: With Stencils. Karl, Linda, illus. 2004. (Shrek 2 Ser.). 32p. (J). act. bk. ed. 3.99 (978-0-439-57633-8(4)) Scholastic, Inc.

Hall, Katy, pseud & Eisenberg, Lisa. Boo Who? And Other Wicked Halloween Knock-Knock Jokes. Carpenter, Stephen, illus. 2000. (Lift-the-Flap Knock-Knock Bk.). 16p. (J). (gr. k-3). pap. 6.99 (978-0-694-01359-3(5), Harper Festival) HarperCollins Pubs.

Hall, Pamela. ELEMENOPEE, the Day I, M, N, O & P Left the Abc's. Williamson, James, illus. 2005. 16p. (J). 12.95 (978-1-58117-209-6(5), Intervisual/Piggy Toes) Dalmatian Pr.

Halton, Melanie. The Ultimated Haunted House Glow in the Dark Sticker Book. Halton, Melanie, ed. Kavanagh, Peter, illus. 2002. (Ultimate Sticker Bks.). 16p. (J). pap. 6.99 (978-0-7894-8857-2(4)) Dorling Kindersley Publishing, Inc.

Hammer, JoAnne. My Little Flap Book of Colors, Vol. 1. Kennedy, Anne, illus. 1999. (J). 6.95 (978-1-56451-223-9(1), Ideal School Supply) Schaffer, Frank Pubns.

Handford, Martin. Where's Waldo in Hollywood? Handford, Martin, illus. (Big Bks.). (Illus.). 32p. (J). (gr. 1). 2003. 19.99 (978-0-7636-2238-1(9)); 2002. 5.99 (978-0-7636-1919-0(1)) Candlewick Pr.

Hanft, Joshua. The Miracles of Passover. Chwast, Seymour, illus. 2007. 28p. (ps-3). 15.95 (978-1-59354-600-7(9)) Blue Apple Bks.

Hanshaw. My Little Red Toolbox. 2000. (Illus.). (J). 18.95 (978-0-15-216753-0(6)) Harcourt Trade Pubs.

Happy Lemonade. 2003. (Happy Birthday Pull-Out Card-Bks.). (Illus.). 4.99 (978-1-56148-384-6(2)) Good Bks.

Harcourt School Publishers Staff. What Is in the Box? Decodable Book. 3rd ed. 2002. (Trophies Reading Program Ser.). (Illus.). (gr. k). pap. 2.90 (978-0-15-325424-6(6)) Harcourt Schl. Pubs.

Hardy, Caroline, et al. Busy Places: A Child Safety Book. 2006. (Through the Peephole Ser.). (Illus.). 48p. 9.95 (978-1-84560-015-0(0)) Mercury Bks. Ltd. GBR. *Dist:* International Publishers Marketing.

Hargreaves, Roger. Little Miss Helpful. rev. ed. 1999. (Little Miss Bks.). (Illus.). 32p. (J). (gr. k-3). pap. 3.99 (978-0-8431-7503-5(6), Price Stern Sloan) Penguin Group (USA) Inc.

—Mr Strong. 1999. (ps-2). lib. bdg. 10.65 (978-0-613-22023-1(4)) Tandem Library Bks.

Harrast, Tracy L., et al. Guess What? Story Bible. Sharp, Paul & Sharp, Alice, illus. 2004. (Bible Storybooks Ser.). 192p. (J). 16.99 (978-0-310-70701-1(3)) Zonderkidz.

Harris, Annmarie, ed. Firehouse Fun. 2006. (Firehouse Tales Ser.). (Illus.). 5p. (J). bds. 9.99 (978-0-439-83722-4(7), Scholastic) Scholastic, Inc.

Harris, Emma. Bedtime, Little Monsters! Cherrill, Paul, illus. 2002. 20p. (J). tchr. ed. 14.95 (978-1-58925-689-7(1), tiger tales) ME Media LLC.

Harris, John. Pop-Up Aesop. Brown, Calef, illus. 2005. (Getty Trust Publications: J. Paul Getty Museum Ser.). 10p. (ps-7). 19.95 (978-0-89236-814-3(4)) Getty Pubns.

Harrison, James. Amazing Vehicles. Smith, Jan, illus. 2004. (Magic Color Bks.). 12p. (J). 9.95 (978-1-4027-1215-9(4)) Sterling Publishing Co., Inc.

Harrison, James & Graham, Ian, eds. Amazing Vehicles Foldout Book. 2002. (Foldout Bks.). 6p. (J). (gr. 3-7). 9.95 (978-1-57145-756-1(9), Silver Dolphin Bks.) Advantage Pubs. Group.

Harry, Rebecca, illus. Little Chimp. 2007. (Noisy Jungle Babies Ser.). 8p. (J). bds. 5.99 (978-0-7641-6034-9(6)) Barron's Educational Series, Inc.

—Little Elephant. 2007. (Noisy Jungle Babies Ser.). 8p. (J). bds. 5.99 (978-0-7641-6035-6(4)) Barron's Educational Series, Inc.

—Little Lion. 2007. (Noisy Jungle Babies Ser.). 8p. (J). bds. 5.99 (978-0-7641-6036-3(2)) Barron's Educational Series, Inc.

—Little Zebra. 2007. (Noisy Jungle Babies Ser.). 8p. (J). bds. 5.99 (978-0-7641-6037-0(0)) Barron's Educational Series, Inc.

Harvey, Roger. Caillou, My First Vacation. CINAR Animation Staff & Sévigny, Eric, illus. adapted rev. ed. 2006. (Lift-the-Flap Cinar Ser.). 20p. (J). pap. 5.95 (978-2-89450-525-0(6)) Chouette Publishing CAN. *Dist:* Independent Pubs. Group.

Hawcock, David & Brampton, Clare. Dinosaurs: With Six Amazing Dinosaur Models. 2004. (Illus.). 16p. (J). bds. 24.95 (978-1-4052-0801-7(5)) Egmont Bks., Ltd. GBR. *Dist:* Trafalgar Square Publishing.

Hawkins, Colin. Mr. Wolf's Week: Mini Pop-Up. 2005. (Illus.). 12p. (J). pap. 8.99 (978-1-4052-0708-9(6)) Egmont Bks., Ltd. GBR. *Dist:* Trafalgar Square Publishing.

—Pirate Ship: A Pop-up Adventure. Hawkins, Colin et al, illus. 2006. 28p. (J). (gr. 4-8). reprint ed. 20.00 (978-0-7567-9827-7(2)) DIANE Publishing Co.

—What's the Time,Mr. Wolf? Mini Pop-Up. 2005. (Illus.). 14p. (J). bds. 8.99 (978-1-4052-0707-2(8)) Egmont Bks., Ltd. GBR. *Dist:* Trafalgar Square Publishing.

Hawkins, Colin & Hawkins, Jacqui. Here's a Happy Elephant. 2004. (Illus.). 8p. (J). 3.95 (978-1-56148-442-3(3)) Good Bks.

—Here's a Happy Kitten. 2004. (Illus.). 8p. (J). 3.95 (978-1-56148-440-9(7)) Good Bks.

—Here's a Happy Pig. 2004. (Illus.). 8p. (J). 3.95 (978-1-56148-441-6(5)) Good Bks.

—Here's a Happy Puppy. 2004. (Illus.). 8p. (J). 3.95 (978-1-56148-439-3(3)) Good Bks.

—Whose House? 1998. (Illus.). 16p. (J). (ps-1). 8.95 (978-0-7641-5144-6(4)) Barron's Educational Series, Inc.

Hawthorn, Phillip & Tyler, Jenny. There's A Monster in My House. 2007. 16p. (J). 9.99 (978-0-7945-1567-6(3) , Usborne) EDC Publishing.

Hawthorne, Philip & Tyler, Jenny. Who's Making That Noise? Cartwright, Stephen, illus. 2005. (Flap Books Ser.). 16p. (J). (gr. 1 up). pap. 7.95 (978-0-7945-0432-8(9) , Usborne) EDC Publishing.

Hay DeSimone, Corkey. Dinosaur Explore Board Book: Dinosaurs Designed for Their Littlest Fans. Hay DeSimone, Corkey, illus. 2006. (J). bds. 7.95 (978-0-9777394-1-7(4)) Gentle Giraffe Pr.

Hays, Anna Jane. Cookie See! Cookie Do! Goldberg, Barry, illus. 2002. (Sesame Beginnings Ser.). 24p. (J). (gr. k). bds. 7.99 (978-0-375-81542-3(2) , Random Hse. Bks. for Young Readers) Random Hse. Children's Bks.

Heath, Beverly C. A Bedtime Lullaby. Floyd, John, Jr., illus. 2005. (J). bds. 5.95 ***(978-0-9752860-1-2(3))*** OurRainbow Pr., LLC.

—Counting with Colors. Floyd, John, Jr., illus. 2005. (J). bds. 5.95 ***(978-0-9752860-0-5(5))*** OurRainbow Pr., LLC.

—Opposites. Floyd, John, Jr., illus. 2005. (J). bds. 5.95 ***(978-0-9752860-3-6(X))*** OurRainbow Pr., LLC.

Heimberg, Justin. Shrek Scratch n' Stink Storybook. 2002. (Illus.). pap. 7.99 (978-0-525-46937-7(0) , Dutton Juvenile) Penguin Group (USA) Inc.

Heinze, Monica Bacon. A Day with Shapes. Dow, S. B., illus. 2004. (J). ***(978-0-9761710-0-3(7))*** Paisley Publishing.

Held, Elissa. My Ballet Bag. Thornburgh, Bethann, illus. 2002. 14p. (J). (ps-1). 14.95 (978-0-689-84966-4(4) , Little Simon) Simon & Schuster Children's Publishing.

—My Sleepover Bag: More than 45 Play Pieces Inside! Smith, Tammy, illus. 2004. 14p. (J). pap. 14.95 (978-0-689-87337-9(9) , Little Simon) Simon & Schuster Children's Publishing.

Hellen, Nancy. My Magic House. 2003. (Illus.). 11p. (J). 9.99 (978-0-333-66000-3(5)) Macmillan Publishers Ltd. GBR. *Dist:* Trafalgar Square Publishing.

Heller, Sarah & Reader's Digest Staff. Disney Tinker Bell Music Player & Storybook. 2008. (RD Innovative Book & Player Format Ser.). 36p. (J). 24.99 ***(978-0-7944-1300-2(5))*** Reader's Digest Assn., Inc., The.

Hendra, Sue. Time for Lunch. 2003. (Illus.). 20p. (J). 6.99 (978-0-333-76288-2(6)) Macmillan Publishers Ltd. GBR. *Dist:* Trafalgar Square Publishing.

Henkes, Kevin. The Lilly Book & Toy Box. 1998. (Illus.). 160p. (J). 24.95 (978-0-688-16437-9(4) , Harper Festival) HarperCollins Pubs.

Hennessy, B. G. & Freeman, Don. Corduroy Goes to School. McCue, Lisa, illus. 2002. 20p. (J). 11.99 (978-0-670-03514-4(9) , Viking Juvenile) Penguin Group (USA) Inc.

Henning. God Sent a Baby King. 2006. (Illus.). 32p. 14.00 (978-0-687-49498-9(2)) Abingdon Pr.

Henning, Heather. Christmas. Chapman, Gillian, illus. 2007. (ENG.). 16p. (J). pap. 9.99 ***(978-0-7586-1383-7(0))*** Concordia Publishing Hse.

—Creation. Chapman, Gillian, illus. 2007. (ENG.). 16p. (J). pap. 9.99 ***(978-0-7586-1384-4(9))*** Concordia Publishing Hse.

Hensley, Sarah M. I Can Be ... Board Book & Felt Puppet Set. Teeple, Jackie, illus. 2005. (J). bds. (978-1-57332-362-8(4)) HighReach Learning, Inc.

Hergé. On a Marche sur la Lune. (Tintin Ser.).Tr. of Explorers on the Moon. (FRE.). (J). pap. 21.95 (978-2-203-00116-9(X)) Casterman, Editions FRA. *Dist:* Distribooks, Inc.

—On a Marche sur la Lune.Tr. of Explorers on the Moon. (FRE., Illus.). (J). (gr. 7-9). ring bd. 19.95 (978-0-8288-5053-7(4)) French & European Pubns., Inc.

Hess, Jared & Hess, Jerusha. Napoleon Dynamite: Flippin' Sweet! Simon and Schuster Children's Staff, ed. 2005. (Illus.). 176p. 3.99 (978-1-4169-1914-8(7)) Simon & Schuster Children's Publishing.

Hessel, Brooke. Clifford the Big Red Dog Telephone Book. 2002. (Illus.). (J). 16.98 (978-0-7853-6401-6(3)) Publications International, Ltd.

—Telephone Book. 2002. (Illus.). (J). (978-0-7853-7183-0(4)) Publications International, Ltd.

Hewitt, Sally. Bugs Pop-up: Creepy Crawlers Face to Face. Gilvan-Cartwright, Chris, illus. 2004. 12p. (J). (ps-1). 14.95 (978-0-8109-5032-0(4)) Abrams, Harry N. , Inc.

—Face to Face Safari: Dare You Face the Six Giant Pop-up Animals? Gilvan-Cartwright, Chris, illus. 2003. 12p. (J). (ps-1). 14.95 (978-0-8109-4261-5(5)) Abrams, Harry N. , Inc.

—Happy Dresser. Cameron, Craig, illus. 2003. 14p. (J). pap. 10.95 (978-1-57145-733-2(X) , Silver Dolphin Bks.) Advantage Pubs. Group.

Hickle, Victoria. Fire Trucks in Action. DePew, Bob, illus. 2003. (Tonka Ser.). 4p. (J). (ps-2). bds. 6.99 (978-0-439-43432-4(7)) Scholastic, Inc.

—Tonka Big Trucks in Action. Depew, Bob, illus. 2004. (Tonka Ser.). 4p. (J). bds. 7.99 (978-0-439-63920-0(4)) Scholastic, Inc.

Hide & Seek ABC. 2007. (Illus.). 10p. bds. 14.95 ***(978-1-59125-795-0(6)*** , Penton Kids) Penton Overseas, Inc.

Higginson, Sheila. Happy Birthday! A Lift-the-Flap Surprise Story. Disney Storybook Artists Staff, illus. 2007. 16p. (J). (ps-k). pap. 5.99 ***(978-1-4231-0652-4(0))*** Disney Pr.

Higginson, Sheila Sweeny. 5+1 Makes More Fun. rev. ed. 2007. 10p. (J). (ps-1). 12.99 ***(978-1-4231-0744-6(6))*** Disney Pr.

Hill, Eric. Spot Bakes a Cake. Hill, Eric, illus. 2005. 20p. (J). pap. 6.99 (978-0-14-240329-7(6) , Puffin) Penguin Group (USA) Inc.

—Spot Can Count. Hill, Eric, illus. 2005. (Illus.). 12p. (J). (ps-1). bds. 6.99 (978-0-399-24361-5(5) , Putnam Juvenile) Penguin Group (USA) Inc.

—Spot Goes to School. Hill, Eric, illus. 2004. (Illus.). (J). (ps-1). (SPA.). 12p. bds. 7.99 (978-0-399-24246-5(5) , Putnam Juvenile); 24p. pap. 6.99 (978-0-14-240167-5(6) , Puffin) Penguin Group (USA) Inc.

—Spot Goes to the Beach. Hill, Eric, illus. 2005. (Illus.). 22p. (J). (ps-1). bds. 6.99 (978-0-399-24362-2(3) , Putnam Juvenile) Penguin Group (USA) Inc.

—Spot Goes to the Farm. Hill, Eric, illus. 2003. (Illus.). 24p. (J). pap. 6.99 (978-0-14-250123-8(9) , Puffin) Penguin Group (USA) Inc.

—Spot Goes to the Farm. 2001. (Spot Ser.). (Illus.). 12p. (J). (ps-1). bds. 7.99 (978-0-399-23647-1(3) , Putnam Juvenile) Penguin Group (USA) Inc.

—Spot Goes to the Farm. 2003. (ps-2). lib. bdg. 15.30 (978-0-613-86708-5(4)) Tandem Library Bks.

—Spot Goes to the Park. Hill, Eric, illus. 2005. (Illus.). 22p. (J). (ps-1). bds. 6.99 (978-0-399-24363-9(1) , Putnam Juvenile) Penguin Group (USA) Inc.

—Spot Loves His Daddy. Hill, Eric, illus. 2005. (Illus.). 12p. (J). (ps-1). bds. 5.99 (978-0-399-24351-6(8) , Putnam Juvenile) Penguin Group (USA) Inc.

—Spot Loves School. Hill, Eric, illus. 2008. (Spot Ser.). 10p. (J). (ps-k). bds. 7.99 ***(978-0-399-25165-8(0)*** , Putnam Juvenile) Penguin Group (USA) Inc.

—Spot's Big Lift-the-flap Book. Hill, Eric, illus. 2004. (Illus.). 24p. (J). pap. 8.99 (978-0-14-240083-8(1) , Puffin) Penguin Group (USA) Inc.

—Spot's Birthday Party. Hill, Eric, illus. 2003. (Illus.). 24p. (J). pap. 6.99 (978-0-14-250125-2(5) , Puffin) Penguin Group (USA) Inc.

—Spot's Birthday Party. 2003. (gr. k-3). lib. bdg. 15.30 (978-0-613-87829-6(9)) Tandem Library Bks.

—Spot's First Walk. Hill, Eric, illus. 2005. (Illus.). 12p. (J). (ps-k). bds. 6.99 (978-0-399-24482-7(4) , Putnam Juvenile) Penguin Group (USA) Inc.

—Spot's Giant Treasury. 2005. (Spot Ser.). 192p. (J). (ps-2). 10.99 (978-0-448-43973-0(5) , Grosset & Dunlap) Penguin Group (USA) Inc.

—Spot's Noisy Tractor. Hill, Eric, illus. 2008. 12p. (J). (ps-k). bds. 12.99 ***(978-0-399-25166-5(9)*** , Putnam Juvenile) Penguin Group (USA) Inc.

—Spot's Playtime Pop-up. Hill, Eric, illus. 2007. (Spot (Hardcover) Ser.). (Illus.). 12p. (J). (ps-k). 14.99 ***(978-0-399-25019-4(0)*** , Putnam Juvenile) Penguin Group (USA) Inc.

Hill, Eric. Where's Spot? Hill, Eric, illus. 2003. (Illus.). (J). (ps-1). (SPA.). 22p. bds. 7.99 (978-0-399-24046-1(2) , 53517281, Putnam Juvenile); 24p. pap. 7.99 (978-0-14-250126-9(3) , Puffin) Penguin Group (USA) Inc.

Hills, Tad. My Fuzzy Farm Babies: A Book to Touch & Feel. Hills, Tad, illus. 2001. (My Fuzzy Friends Board Bks.). (Illus.). 12p. (J). bds. 6.99 (978-0-689-84165-1(5) , Little Simon) Simon & Schuster Children's Publishing.

—My Fuzzy Safari Babies: A Book to Touch & Feel. Hills, Tad, illus. 2001. (My Fuzzy Friends Board Bks.). (Illus.). 12p. (J). bds. 6.99 (978-0-689-84164-4(7) , Little Simon) Simon & Schuster Children's Publishing.

Hiner, Mark. Village Garage. Thatcher, Fran, illus. 2001. 3p. (J). 16.95 (978-1-902413-62-4(8)) Van der Meer, a Div. of PHPC GBR. *Dist:* Abbeville Pr., Inc.

Hines, Anna Grossnickle. Daddy Makes the Best Spaghetti. Hines, Anna Grossnickle, illus. 2002. (Illus.). (J). 13.79 (978-0-7587-2332-1(6)) Book Wholesalers, Inc.

—Daddy Makes the Best Spaghetti. 1999. (J). (ps-2). lib. bdg. 14.10 (978-0-8335-2786-8(X)) Tandem Library Bks.

Hines, Anna Grossnickle & Rey, Hans Augusto. Daddy Makes the Best Spaghetti. Hines, Anna Grossnickle, illus. 1999. (Illus.). 12p. (J). (gr. k-ps). bds. 5.95 (978-0-395-98036-1(4) , Clarion Bks.) Houghton Mifflin Co. Trade & Reference Div.

Hinkler Books. At the Farm. rev. ed. 2007. (Illus.). 8p. (J). (gr. 2-5). 9.95 ***(978-1-74181-321-0(2))*** Hinkler Bks. Pty, Ltd. AUS. *Dist:* Penton Overseas, Inc.

Hirsch, Ron. No, No Jack! 2003. (Illus.). (J). 10.99 (978-0-8037-2997-1(9) , Dial) Penguin Group (USA) Inc.

Hobbie, Holly. I'll Be Home for Christmas, Set. gif. ed. 2004. (Toot & Puddle Ser.). (Illus.). 32p. (J). (ps-3). 19.99 (978-0-316-73586-5(8)) Little, Brown Bks. for Young Readers.

Hobson, Sally, illus. All Aboard! 2000. 24p. (J). (978-1-86233-079-5(4) , Gullane Children's Bks.) Pinwheel.

Hofer, Charles. Construction Zone! Little People. Durk, Jim, illus. 10p. (J). bds. 7.98 (978-0-7853-4791-0(7)) Publications International, Ltd.

Hogan, Mary. Let's Play with Winnie the Pooh. 1999. (Disney's Winnie the Pooh Ser.). (Illus.). 10p. (J). (ps-3). 9.99 (978-0-7364-0185-2(7)) Mouse Works.

—Tigger's Family. 2000. (Winnie the Pooh Ser.). (Illus.). 10p. (J). (ps-k). bds. 4.99 (978-0-7364-1062-5(7)) Mouse Works.

Holabird, Katharine. The Silver Locket. Craig, Helen, illus. 2006. (Angelina Ballerina Ser.). 24p. (J). (ps-1). 3.99 (978-0-448-44472-7(0) , Grosset & Dunlap) Penguin Group (USA) Inc.

Holder, Jennifer. Colors & Shapes to Share. 2001. (Threads Ser.). (Illus.). 16p. (J). (ps-1). 5.99 (978-0-7847-1011-1(2) , Bean Sprouts) Standard Publishing.

Holly Has a Nose for Christmas: Scratch & Sniff Storybook. 2002. (Illus.). 5p. (J). (ps-1). bds. 6.99 (978-1-57759-957-9(8)) Dalmatian Pr.

Holtz, Lara Tankel & Sutinis, Beth, eds. My Lift-the-Flap Book. 2001. (Early Learners Ser.). (Illus.). 12p. (J). (ps). bds. 9.95 (978-0-7894-7408-7(5)) Dorling Kindersley Publishing, Inc.

Holub, Joan. Dragon Dance: A Chinese New Year Lift-the-Flap Book. Huang, Benrei, illus. 2003. (Lift-the-Flap, Puffin Ser.). 16p. (J). (gr. k-1). pap. 6.99 (978-0-14-240000-5(9) , Puffin) Penguin Group (USA) Inc.

—Eek-a-Boo! A Spooky Book. Holub, Joan, illus. 2000. (Illus.). 24p. (J). (ps-k). pap. 6.95 (978-0-439-17324-7(8)) Scholastic, Inc.

—Glorious Grandmas. Holub, Joan, illus. 2006. (Sparkle 'n' Shimmer Ser.). (Illus.). 14p. (J). 5.99 (978-1-4169-0623-0(1) , Little Simon) Simon & Schuster Children's Publishing.

Hooper, Ruth. Santa's Factory. Charbonnel, Olivier & Mostyn, David, illus. 2004. 6p. (J). (gr. k-4). reprint ed. 16.00 (978-0-7567-7585-8(X)) DIANE Publishing Co.

Horacek, Petr. Strawberries Are Red. Horacek, Petr, illus. 2001. (Illus.). 14p. (J). (gr. k-k). bds. 4.99 (978-0-7636-1461-4(0)) Candlewick Pr.

Horne, Jane. Busy Baby: Noisy Book. 2007. (Busy Baby Ser.). (Illus.). 12p. (ps). per., bds. 9.99 (978-1-84610-434-3(3)) Make Believe Ideas GBR. *Dist:* Ingram Pub. Services.

Houghton Mifflin Company Staff. Bigger & Smaller. 2009. (Illus.). 12p. (J). (ps-k). bds. 6.99 ***(978-0-618-73760-4(X))*** Houghton Mifflin Co. Trade & Reference Div.

—Curious George Finds a Friend. 2007. (Illus.). 16p. (J). (ps-k). 5.99 ***(978-0-618-72398-0(6))*** Houghton Mifflin Co. Trade & Reference Div.

Houghton Mifflin Company Staff. Zathura the Movie Sticker Book. 2005. (Illus.). 8p. (J). (ps-k). 6.99 (978-0-618-60582-8(7)) Houghton Mifflin Co. Trade & Reference Div.

Houghton Mifflin Company Staff & Rey, Margret. Curious George the Movie: Touch & Feel Book. 2006. (Illus.). 10p. (J). (ps-k). bds. 5.99 (978-0-618-60587-3(8)) Houghton Mifflin Co. Trade & Reference Div.

Houghton Mifflin Company Staff, et al. Before & After. 2007. (Curious George Ser.). (Illus.). 12p. (J). (ps-k). bds. 6.99 (978-0-618-72399-7(4)) Houghton Mifflin Co. Trade & Reference Div.

Houghton, Walter E., et al. Shadow Book: An Interactive Shadow-Casting Bedtime Story. 2004. (Illus.). 6p. (J). (gr. 3-5). 12.99 (978-0-618-47793-7(4)) Houghton Mifflin Co. Trade & Reference Div.

Howell, Theresa. I Don't See Any Bears. Do You? Jones, Larry, illus. 2004. 12p. (J). bds. 7.95 (978-0-87358-862-1(2) , Rising Moon Bks. for Young Readers) Northland Publishing.

Hubbell, Joan. Corvette Pop-Up. 1999. (Illus.). 8.99 (978-0-525-46037-4(3) , Dutton Juvenile) Penguin Group (USA) Inc.

—Mustang Pop-Up. 1999. (Illus.). 8.99 (978-0-525-46038-1(1) , Dutton Juvenile) Penguin Group (USA) Inc.

Hudson, Sue. I Love You. Watanabe, Kaori, illus. 2004. (My First Taggies Book Ser.). 3p. (J). 12.95 (978-0-439-64947-6(1) , Cartwheel Bks.) Scholastic, Inc.

Huelin, Jodi. The Reusable Sticker Book. 2006. (Ice Age 2 Ser.). 12p. (J). pap. 6.99 (978-0-06-083973-4(2)) HarperCollins Pubs.

Hugo, Pierre de. Lions. Hugo, Pierre de, illus. 2000. (First Discovery Book Ser.). (Illus.). 30p. (J). (ps-3). 12.95 (978-0-439-14825-2(1)) Scholastic, Inc.

Hulme, Joy N. Eerie Feary Feeling: A Hairy Scary Pop-up Book. Fly, Paul & Dudley, Dick, illus. 2006. 12p. (J). (gr. k-4). reprint ed. 14.00 (978-1-4223-5171-0(8)) DIANE Publishing Co.

Hurst, Valerie. The Giraffe That Wore a Necklace: Mister Giraffe Bow Tie & Long Gold Chain! One Flip-Flop Books. 2002. 48p. 19.99 (978-0-9716882-3-0(0) , 661-392-0867) Giraffe Family Pr.

Hurt-Newton, Tania. Yee-Ha Harvey. Hurt-Newton, Tania, illus. 2007. (Illus.). 14p. (J). 14.95 ***(978-0-00-724414-0(2))*** HarperCollins Pubs. Ltd. GBR. *Dist:* Independent Pubs. Group.

—Yo-Ho Harvey. Hurt-Newton, Tania, illus. 2007. (Illus.). 14p. (J). 14.95 ***(978-0-00-724413-3(4))*** HarperCollins Pubs. Ltd. GBR. *Dist:* Independent Pubs. Group.

Ideal Instructional Fair Staff. Find the Shapes with Lizzy Lizard. 1999. (J). 7.95 (978-1-56451-226-0(6) , Ideal School Supply) Schaffer, Frank Pubns.

ImageBooks. Little Spider: Finger Puppet Book. 2007. (Illus.). 12p. (J). (ps). 6.95 ***(978-0-8118-6104-5(X))*** Chronicle Bks. LLC.

ImageBooks Staff. Finger Puppet Friends: Little Duck, Little Ladybug, Little Lamb, & Little Bee. 2007. (Illus.). 48p. (J). (ps). bds. 22.95 (978-0-8118-5805-2(7)) Chronicle Bks. LLC.

Imperato, Teresa. Colors All Around: A Turn & Pop Book. Petrone, Valeria, illus. 2005. 10p. (J). bds. 5.95 (978-1-58117-277-5(X) , Intervisual/Piggy Toes) Dalmatian Pr.

—Fiona's Fairy Magic. Huang, Benrei, illus. 2005. 14p. (J). 10.95 (978-1-58117-322-2(9) , Intervisual/Piggy Toes) Dalmatian Pr.

—Good Morning, Good Night. Mitchell, Melanie, illus. 2005. 12p. (J). (ps up). 9.95 (978-1-58117-279-9(6) , Intervisual/Piggy Toes) Dalmatian Pr.

—How Many Ducks in a Row? A Turn & Pop Book. Petrone, Valeria, illus. 2005. 10p. (J). bds. 5.95 (978-1-58117-278-2(8) , Intervisual/Piggy Toes) Dalmatian Pr.

—On the Farm: A Barnyard Book. Rayner, Olivia, illus. 2005. 10p. (J). 7.95 (978-1-58117-270-6(2) , Intervisual/Piggy Toes) Dalmatian Pr.

—On the Go! A Transportation Book. Rayner, Olivia, illus. 2005. 10p. (J). 7.95 (978-1-58117-271-3(0) , Intervisual/Piggy Toes) Dalmatian Pr.

—Ten Christmas Lights: Count the Lights from One to Ten! Parry, Jo, illus. 2005. 20p. (J). 10.95 (978-1-58117-321-5(0) , Intervisual/Piggy Toes) Dalmatian Pr.

—This Little Piggy. Haskamp, Steve, illus. 2005. 22p. (J). 9.95 (978-1-58117-281-2(8) , Intervisual/Piggy Toes) Dalmatian Pr.

Inches, Alison. Learn with Dora!/¡A aprender con Dora! A Bilingual Adventure with Pull-tabs, Wheels, & Flaps! Ziegler, Argentina Palacios, tr. Aikins, Dave, illus. 2006. (Dora the Explorer Ser.). 12p. (J). 7.99 (978-1-4169-1210-1(X) , Simon Spotlight/Nickelodeon) Simon & Schuster Children's Publishing.

Inches, Alison. Let's Play Sports! A Lift-the-Flap Story. Aikins, Dave, illus. 2007. (Dora the Explorer Ser.). 16p. (J). pap. 6.99 ***(978-1-4169-3350-2(6)*** , Simon Spotlight/Nickelodeon) Simon & Schuster Children's Publishing.

Ingle, Annie. Lift the Lid, Use the Potty. McCue, Lisa, illus. 2001. (Nifty Lift-and-Look Bks.). 12p. (J). (gr. k-ps). bds. 7.99 (978-0-375-81146-3(X) , Random Hse. Bks. for Young Readers) Random Hse. Children's Bks.

Innovative Kids Staff. Big & Little. Filipowich, Bob, illus. 2000. (Soft Shapes Ser.). 8p. (J). (ps-ps). 8.99 (978-1-58476-021-4(4)) Innovative Kids.

—Bunny Jumps. Filipowich, Bob, illus. ed. 2000. (Mini Soft Shapes Ser.). 8p. (J). (ps-ps). 6.99 (978-1-58476-037-5(0)) Innovative Kids.

—Ducky Swims. Filipowich, Bob, illus. ed. 2000. (Mini Soft Shapes Ser.). 8p. (J). (ps-ps). 6.99 (978-1-58476-038-2(9)) Innovative Kids.

Innovative Kids Staff & Bockol, Leslie. My Tool Box. Filipowich, Bob, illus. 2003. (Soft Shapes Ser.). (J). (ps-ps). 9.99 (978-1-58476-174-7(1)) Innovative Kids.

Inteli, Nancy. Farm Faces. 2008. 10p. (J). (ps-k). bds. 8.99 ***(978-0-618-91959-8(7))*** Houghton Mifflin Co. Trade & Reference Div.

Intrater, Roberta Grobel. Peek-a-Boo, You! Intrater, Roberta Grobel, photos by. 2nd rev. l.t. ed. 2005. (Illus.). 14p. (J). 14.99 (978-0-9764985-0-6(2)) 1212 Pr.

—Peek-a-Boo, You! Intrater, Roberta Grobel, photos by. 2002. (Illus.). 7p. (J). pap. 9.95 (978-0-439-33961-2(8) , Cartwheel Bks.) Scholastic, Inc.

Ishida, Jui, illus. Who Says Moo? A Touch & Feel Board Book. 2005. 16p. (J). bds. 6.95 (978-1-58117-178-5(1) , Intervisual/Piggy Toes) Dalmatian Pr.

Ita, Sam. Moby-Dick: A Pop-up Book. 2007. (Illus.). 8p. (J). 24.95 ***(978-1-4027-4528-7(1))*** Sterling Publishing Co., Inc.

Jacobson, David, illus. The Big Red Blanket. 2005. (J). (ps-k). lib. bdg. 11.15 (978-0-606-33864-6(0)) Tandem Library Bks.

Jaffe, Nina. The Journey Begins. Caldwell, Ben, illus. 2004. (Wonder Woman Ser.). 64p. (J). pap. 4.99 (978-0-06-056521-3(7) , Harper Festival) HarperCollins Pubs.

—Wonder Woman: Amazon Princess. 2004. (gr. 3-6). lib. bdg. 13.00 (978-0-613-71471-6(7)) Tandem Library Bks.

—Wonder Woman: The Journey Begins. 2004. (gr. 3-6). lib. bdg. 13.00 (978-0-613-71470-9(9)) Tandem Library Bks.

James, Annabelle. Jack & the Beanstalk Story in a Box. Ackerman, Michele L., illus. 2003. (Story in a Box Ser.). 12p. (J). bds. 8.99 (978-1-883043-42-1(5)) Straight Edge Pr., The.

James, Diane. Tomato, Lettuce & Wriggly Worms! Bulloch, Ivan, illus. 2004. (My Turn Ser.). 12p. (J). (ps-k). bds. 6.95 (978-1-58728-339-0(5) , Two Can Publishing) T&N Children's Publishing.

Jarrell, Pamela R. Baby's Hands. Metzger, Jeanne, illus. l.t. ed. 2001. (Board Bk.). 12p. (J). (ps-1). 4.99 (978-1-57332-196-9(6)) HighReach Learning, Inc.

—Flitter, Flutter Butterfly Board Book & Felt Puppet Set. Middleton, Mikell, illus. 2005. (J). bds. (978-1-57332-361-1(6)) HighReach Learning, Inc.

—Planting a Seed Board Book & Felt Puppet Set. Teeple, Jackie, illus. 2005. (J). bds. (978-1-57332-365-9(9)) HighReach Learning, Inc.

—Where Is the Teddy Bear? Board Book & Felt Puppet Set. Metzger, Jeanne, illus. 2005. (J). bds. (978-1-57332-358-1(6)) HighReach Learning, Inc.

Jeffrey, Linda, tr. & illus. The Gingerbread Man. Jeffrey, Linda, illus. 2003. 24p. (J). 9.99 (978-0-85953-464-2(2)) Child's Play-International.

Jennings, Linda. This Little Piggy. 2000. (Illus.). 16p. (J). (ps-1). 6.95 (978-1-86233-101-3(4)) David & Charles Children's Bks. GBR. *Dist:* Sterling Publishing Co., Inc.

Jennings, Patti. El Abuelo Oso lo Arregla Todo. 2003. (Busy Bears Ser.).Tr. of Grandpa Bear Fixes It. (ENG & SPA., Illus.). 10p. 14.95 (978-84-7864-704-0(X)) Combel Editorial, S.A. ESP. *Dist:* Independent Pubs. Group.

—El Desayuno de los Osos. 2003. (Busy Bears Ser.). (SPA & ENG., Illus.). 10p. 14.95 (978-84-7864-703-3(1)) Combel Editorial, S.A. ESP. *Dist:* Independent Pubs. Group.

John Brown Publishing Ltd. Diego in Action! Follow the Reader Level II. 2007. (Go, Diego, Go! Ser.). 24p. (J). 24.99 ***(978-1-4169-4993-0(3)*** , Simon Scribbles) Simon & Schuster Children's Publishing.

—Games with James: Follow the Reader Level I. 2007. (Thomas & Friends Ser.). 24p. (J). (ps-1). 24.99 ***(978-1-4169-4988-6(7)*** , Simon Scribbles) Simon & Schuster Children's Publishing.

Johnson, Richard. The Three Little Pigs. 2004. (Illus.). 24p. (J). 7.99 (978-0-85953-535-9(5)) Child's Play-International.

Johnson, Richard, illus. Three Little Pigs. 24p. pap. (978-1-904550-21-1(5)) Child's Play-International.

Johnson, Robyn. The Enchanted Dolls' House. Johnson, Robyn, illus. 2006. (Illus.). 32p. (J). (gr. k-3). 24.95 (978-1-59354-182-8(1)) Handprint Bks.

Johnson, Sarah. Barbie: Princess Story. Lloyd, Jeremy, illus. Lloyd, Jeremy, photos by. 2003. 24p. (J). 15.98 (978-0-7853-8090-0(6) , 7181100) Publications International, Ltd.

—Time to Dance. Lew, Willie, illus. Lew, Willie, photos by. 2003. (J). 16.98 (978-0-7853-8811-1(7)) Publications International, Ltd.

Jonah Bible Sticker Book. 2003. (Illus.). 16p. (J). 2.98 (978-1-4054-1555-2(X)) Parragon, Inc.

Jones, Carol. The Gingerbread Man. 2002. (J). 15.00 (978-0-618-18823-9(1)); (Illus.). 32p. 16.00 (978-0-618-18822-2(3)) Houghton Mifflin Co. Trade & Reference Div. (Walter Lorraine).

Jones, Christianne C. Autumn Orange. 2007. (Know Your Colors Ser.). (Illus.). 24p. (J). **_*978-1-4048-3491-0(5)_** , 1265680) Picture Window Bks.

—Autumn Orange. Ouren, Todd, illus. 2006. (Know Your Colors Ser.). 24p. (J). (978-1-4048-3108-7(8) , 1265680) Picture Window Bks.

—Big Red Farm. 2007. (Know Your Colors Ser.). (Illus.). 24p. (J). (**_*978-1-4048-3493-4(1)_** , 1265686) Picture Window Bks.

—Big Red Farm. Ouren, Todd, illus. 2006. (Know Your Colors Ser.). 24p. (J). (978-1-4048-3110-0(X) , 1265686) Picture Window Bks.

—Camping in Green. 2007. (Know Your Colors Ser.). (Illus.). 24p. (J). (**_*978-1-4048-3490-3(7)_** , 1265677) Picture Window Bks.

—Camping in Green. Ouren, Todd, illus. 2006. (Know Your Colors Ser.). 24p. (J). (978-1-4048-3107-0(X) , 1265677) Picture Window Bks.

—Hello, Yellow! 2007. (Know Your Colors Ser.). (Illus.). 24p. (J). (**_*978-1-4048-3494-1(X)_** , 1265687) Picture Window Bks.

—Hello, Yellow! Ouren, Todd, illus. 2006. (Know Your Colors Ser.). 24p. (J). (978-1-4048-3111-7(8) , 1265687) Picture Window Bks.

—Purple Pride. 2007. (Know Your Colors Ser.). (Illus.). 24p. (J). (**_*978-1-4048-3492-7(3)_** , 1265682) Picture Window Bks.

—Purple Pride. Ouren, Todd, illus. 2006. (Know Your Colors Ser.). 24p. (J). (978-1-4048-3109-4(6) , 1265682) Picture Window Bks.

—Splish, Splash, & Blue. 2007. (Know Your Colors Ser.). (Illus.). 24p. (J). (**_*978-1-4048-3489-7(3)_** , 1265675) Picture Window Bks.

—Splish, Splash, & Blue. Ouren, Todd, illus. 2006. (Know Your Colors Ser.). 24p. (J). (978-1-4048-3106-3(1) , 1265675) Picture Window Bks.

Jones-Hughes, Karen, illus. Munch, Munch! Who's There? 2002. (Mini Movers Ser.). 14p. (J). bds. 3.99 (978-0-7641-5570-3(9)) Barron's Educational Series, Inc.

Jones, Karen, illus. Bang, Bang! Who's There? 2002. (Mini Movers Ser.). 14p. (J). bds. 3.99 (978-0-7641-5571-0(7)) Barron's Educational Series, Inc.

—Tap,Tap! Who's There? 2002. (Mini Movers Ser.). 14p. (J). bds. 2.95 (978-0-7641-5568-0(7)) Barron's Educational Series, Inc.

Jones, Lara. Fun at the Park. Jones, Lara, illus. 2003. (Lola & Binky Bks.). (Illus.). 8p. (J). bds. 5.95 (978-0-7641-5689-2(6)) Barron's Educational Series, Inc.

—Fun at the Zoo. Jones, Lara, illus. 2003. (Lola & Binky Bks.). (Illus.). 8p. (J). bds. 5.95 (978-0-7641-5686-1(1)) Barron's Educational Series, Inc.

—Fun on the Beach. Jones, Lara, illus. 2003. (Lola & Binky Bks.). (Illus.). 8p. (J). bds. 5.95 (978-0-7641-5685-4(3)) Barron's Educational Series, Inc.

—Fun on the Farm. Jones, Lara, illus. 2003. (Lola & Binky Bks.). (Illus.). 8p. (J). bds. 5.95 (978-0-7641-5688-5(8)) Barron's Educational Series, Inc.

—Me divierto en el Zoo. 2003. (Lola y Bony Ser.). (SPA., Illus.). 8p. 8.95 (978-84-7864-627-2(2)) Combel Editorial, S.A. ESP. *Dist:* Independent Pubs. Group.

—Me Divierto en la Playa. 2003. (Lola y Bony Ser.). (SPA., Illus.). 8p. 8.95 (978-84-7864-629-6(9)) Combel Editorial, S.A. ESP. *Dist:* Independent Pubs. Group.

Joseph Bible Sticker Book. 2003. (Illus.). 16p. (J). 2.98 (978-1-4054-1556-9(8)) Parragon, Inc.

Joseph Had a Little Overcoat. 2004. 29.95 incl. cd-rom (978-1-55592-109-5(4)); 24.95 incl. audio (978-1-55592-083-8(7)); pap. 18.95 incl. audio compact disk (978-0-7882-0325-1(8)); pap. 32.75 incl. audio (978-0-7882-0326-8(6)); pap. 14.95 incl. audio (978-0-7882-0324-4(X)) Weston Woods Studios, Inc.

Joyful Sunflower. 2003. (Illus.). 4.99 (978-1-56148-383-9(4)) Good Bks.

Jugran, Jan. On the Go. Larranaga, Ana Martin, illus. 2007. 12p. (J). (ps-ps). bds. 8.99 (**_*978-1-58476-620-9(4)_** , IKIDS) Innovative Kids.

Julian, Russell. Busy Dog. 2005. (Farm Board Book Ser.). (Illus.). 12p. (J). bds. 9.99 (978-1-4052-1031-7(1)) Egmont Bks., Ltd. GBR. *Dist:* Trafalgar Square Publishing.

—Happy Cockerel. 2005. (Farm Board Book Ser.). (Illus.). 12p. (J). bds. 9.99 (978-1-4052-1030-0(3)) Egmont Bks., Ltd. GBR. *Dist:* Trafalgar Square Publishing.

—Hungry Pig. 2005. (Farm Board Book Ser.). (Illus.). 12p. (J). bds. 9.99 (978-1-4052-1032-4(X)) Egmont Bks., Ltd. GBR. *Dist:* Trafalgar Square Publishing.

—Lost Calf. 2005. (Farm Board Book Ser.). (Illus.). 12p. (J). pap. 9.99 (978-1-4052-1029-4(X)) Egmont Bks., Ltd. GBR. *Dist:* Trafalgar Square Publishing.

Jungle. 2002. (Fuzzy Felts Ser.). (J). 4.98 (978-0-7525-5233-0(3)) Parragon, Inc.

Kaminsky, Jeff & Atwater, Martha. Cow. Kaminsky, Jeff, illus. 2002. (Stickamajigs Ser.: Vol. 3). (Illus.). 8p. (ps-1). 5.99 (978-0-7868-0712-3(1)) Hyperion Bks. for Children.

—Duck. Kaminsky, Jeff, illus. 2002. (Stickamajigs Ser.: Vol. 2). (Illus.). 8p. (ps-1). 5.99 (978-0-7868-0711-6(3)) Hyperion Bks. for Children.

—Pig. Kaminsky, Jeff, illus. 2002. (Stickamajigs Ser.: Vol. 1). (Illus.). 8p. (ps-1). 5.99 (978-0-7868-0710-9(5)) Hyperion Bks. for Children.

Kate, Maggie, ed. Glitter Roses Stickers. 2004. (Glitter Stickers Ser.). (Illus.). 2p. 1.50 (978-0-486-43534-3(2)) Dover Pubns., Inc.

Katschke, Judy. Beautiful Makeup Book. Chapmanworks Staff, illus. 2000. (Barbie Ser.). 12p. (J). (gr. k-3). bds. 12.99 (978-1-57584-650-7(0) , Reader's Digest Children's Bks.) Reader's Digest Children's Publishing, Inc.

Katschke, Judy & Pope, Liz. The Best Thing about Sisters. Pope, Kate, illus. 2007. 16p. (J). 14.99 (978-0-7944-1278-4(5)) Reader's Digest Assn., Inc., The.

Katz, Karen. Daddy & Me. Katz, Karen, illus. 2003. (Illus.). 14p. (J). bds. 6.99 (978-0-689-84906-0(0) , Little Simon) Simon & Schuster Children's Publishing.

—Donde Esta el Ombliguito? (Where Is Baby's Belly Button?) Ziegler, Argentina Palacios, tr. Katz, Karen, illus. 2004. (SPA., Illus.). 14p. (J). bds. 5.99 (978-0-689-86977-8(0) , Libros Para Ninos) Simon & Schuster Children's Publishing.

—Excuse Me: A Little Book of Manners. Katz, Karen, illus. 2002. (Lift-the-Flap Bks.). (Illus.). 14p. (J). (ps-1). 5.99 (978-0-448-42585-6(8) , Grosset & Dunlap) Penguin Group (USA) Inc.

—Grandma & Me. Katz, Karen, illus. 2002. (Illus.). 14p. (J). 6.99 (978-0-689-84905-3(2) , Little Simon) Simon & Schuster Children's Publishing.

—Grandpa & Me. Katz, Karen, illus. 2004. (Illus.). 14p. (J). 6.99 (978-0-689-86644-9(5) , Little Simon) Simon & Schuster Children's Publishing.

—No Biting. Katz, Karen, illus. 2002. (Illus.). 14p. (J). (ps-1). 5.99 (978-0-448-42584-9(X) , Grosset & Dunlap) Penguin Group (USA) Inc.

—No Hitting! Katz, Karen, illus. 2004. (Illus.). 14p. (J). (ps-k). 5.99 (978-0-448-43612-8(4) , Grosset & Dunlap) Penguin Group (USA) Inc.

—Peek-a-Baby. Katz, Karen, illus. 2007. 14p. (J). 6.99 (**_*978-1-4169-3622-0(X)_** , Little Simon) Simon & Schuster Children's Publishing.

—Where Is Baby's Belly Button? Katz, Karen, illus. 2000. (Lift-the-Flap Bks.). (Illus.). 14p. (J). bds. 5.99 (978-0-689-83560-5(4) , Little Simon) Simon & Schuster Children's Publishing.

—Where Is Baby's Mommy? Katz, Karen, illus. 2001. (Illus.). 14p. (J). (ps-k). bds. 5.99 (978-0-689-83561-2(2) , Little Simon) Simon & Schuster Children's Publishing.

—Where Is Baby's Valentine? A Lift-the-Flap Book. Katz, Karen, illus. 2006. (Illus.). 14p. (J). 6.99 (978-1-4169-0971-2(0) , Little Simon) Simon & Schuster Children's Publishing.

—Wiggle Your Toes. Katz, Karen, illus. 2006. (Illus.). 14p. (J). 8.99 (978-1-4169-0365-9(8) , Little Simon) Simon & Schuster Children's Publishing.

Katz, Karen & Bauer, Marion Dane. Baby's Box of Fun Set: Where Is Baby's Belly Button; Where Is Baby's Mommy?; Toes, Ears, & Nose. Katz, Karen, illus. gif. ed. 2004. (Illus.). 44p. (J). 15.99 (978-0-689-03862-4(3) , Little Simon) Simon & Schuster Children's Publishing.

Kavanagh, Terry. Batman: Tell-A-Riddle Telephone Book. Doescher, Erik et al, illus. 2002. (J). (978-0-7853-6402-3(1)) Publications International, Ltd.

Kelley, K. C. Tonka Busy Trucks: A Lift the Flap Book. 2006. (Tonka Giant Flap Book Ser.). (Illus.). 10p. (J). bds. 9.99 (978-0-7944-1147-3(9)) Reader's Digest Assn., Inc., The.

Kelly, Matt. Scooby-Doo! Camera Clues. Wanhala, Dwight, illus. 2004. 14p. (J). bds. (978-0-7853-9954-4(2) , 7209900) Publications International, Ltd.

—Start to Read. Pfeiffer, Judith, illus. 2004. (J). (978-1-4127-3186-7(0)) Publications International, Ltd.

Kennaway, Adrienne. Baby Giraffe: A Lift-the-Flap Book. 2000. (Illus.). 32p. (J). (ps-k). 13.95 (978-1-899248-13-1(7)) Happy Cat Bks. GBR. *Dist:* Star Bright Bks., Inc.

Kent, Lorna, illus. Baby's First Board Books: On the Move; Animals; My Home; Playtime. 2004. (Baby's First Board Books Gift Set Ser.). 12p. (J). bds. 12.99 (978-1-85854-694-0(X)) Brimax Books Ltd. GBR. *Dist:* Byeway Bks.

Kerr, Judith. Mog the Forgetful Cat: Book & Toy Gift Set. 2005. (Illus.). 40p. (J). (ps). 16.99 (978-0-00-721134-0(1) , HarperCollins Children's Bks.) HarperCollins Pubs. Ltd. GBR. *Dist:* Independent Pubs. Group.

Keylocke, Andrew, illus. Dashing Daisy. 2004. (Crazy Racers Ser.). 12p. (J). bds. 4.95 (978-0-7641-5745-5(0)) Barron's Educational Series, Inc.

—Hasty Hetty. 2004. (Crazy Racers Ser.). 12p. (J). bds. 4.95 (978-0-7641-5746-2(9)) Barron's Educational Series, Inc.

—Lazy Larry. 2004. (Crazy Racers Ser.). 12p. (J). bds. 4.95 (978-0-7641-5747-9(7)) Barron's Educational Series, Inc.

—Whizzy Woof. 2004. (Crazy Racers Ser.). 12p. (J). bds. 4.95 (978-0-7641-5748-6(5)) Barron's Educational Series, Inc.

Khan, Sarah. Pets Lift-the-Flap. 2005. (Luxury Lift-the-Flap Learners Ser.). 16p. (J). (gr. 1 up). 11.95 (978-0-7945-0914-9(2) , Usborne) EDC Publishing.

Kids Discovery Staff. Animal Sticker Adventures. 2001. (Illus.). mass mkt. 12.95 (978-0-525-46813-4(7) , Dutton Juvenile) Penguin Group (USA) Inc.

—More Animal Sticker Adventures. 2001. (Illus.). mass mkt. 12.95 (978-0-525-46814-1(5) , Dutton Juvenile) Penguin Group (USA) Inc.

Kilby, Janice Eaton. The Code Chronicles: A Time Traveling, Code-Cracking Adventure. Fields, Robert Edward, illus. 2008. 64p. (J). 12.95 (**_*978-1-57990-926-0(4)_**) Lark Bks.

Kilpatrick, Irene. Meet Tyrone! A Hand-Puppet Cloth Book. McGee, Warner, illus. 2007. (Backyardigans Ser.). 6p. (J). 10.99 (978-1-4169-3515-5(0) , Simon Spotlight/Nickelodeon) Simon & Schuster Children's Publishing.

King, Dave, photos by. My Christmas Scratch & Sniff Book. 2004. (First Holiday Bks.). (Illus.). 12p. (J). (gr. k-3). bds. 7.95 (978-0-7534-5731-3(8) , Kingfisher) Houghton Mifflin Co. Trade & Reference Div.

King, Sue. Wake Up. 2004. (Magic Picture Book Ser.). (Illus.). 10p. (J). bds. 5.95 (978-0-8118-4402-4(1)) Chronicle Bks. LLC.

Kingfisher Editors, creator. My Halloween Sound Book. 2004. (First Holiday Bks.). (Illus.). 12p. (J). (gr. k-3). bds. 7.95 (978-0-7534-5730-6(X) , Kingfisher) Houghton Mifflin Co. Trade & Reference Div.

Kingfisher Editors, ed. Puzzling Puzzles: What Shape Is This? Book + 2004. (J). pap. 7.95 (978-0-7534-5644-6(3)) Kingfisher Bks.

Kinkade, Thomas, illus. Away in a Manger Board Book. 2007. 28p. (J). bds. 6.99 (**_*978-0-06-078735-6(X)_** , Harper Festival) HarperCollins Pubs.

Kitamura, Satoshi. Hello, Who's There? 2008. (Illus.). 16p. (J). 12.95 (**_*978-1-84270-587-2(3)_**) Andersen GBR. *Dist:* Independent Pubs. Group.

—Play with Me! 2008. (Illus.). 12p. (J). 12.95 (**_*978-1-84270-639-8(X)_**) Andersen GBR. *Dist:* Independent Pubs. Group.

Kliebenstein, Shane & McCracken, Craig. The Powerpuff Girls Telephone Book. 2002. (Illus.). (J). (978-0-7853-6400-9(5)) Publications International, Ltd.

Klutz Editors. Klutz Chicken Socks Little Letters. Date not set. 24p. (J). spiral bd. 9.95 (978-1-59174-244-9(7) , Chicken Socks) Klutz.

Kneen, Maggie. Halloween Kittens. Kneen, Maggie, illus. 2004. (Illus.). 20p. (J). 15.95 (978-0-8118-4228-0(2)) Chronicle Bks. LLC.

Knight, K. R. Farm Friends: Cuddly Pups Board Book. rev. ed. 2003. (Cuddly Pups Board Bks.). (Illus.). 20p. (J). bds. 4.99 (978-1-4037-0187-9(3)) Dalmatian Pr.

—Kitty: Cuddly Pups Board Book. rev. ed. 2002. (Cuddly Pups Board Bks.). (Illus.). 18p. (J). 4.99 (978-1-57759-788-9(5)) Dalmatian Pr.

—Puppy. 2002. (Cuddly Pups Board Bks.). (Illus.). 18p. (J). bds. 4.99 (978-1-57759-787-2(7)) Dalmatian Pr.

—Where Do You Live? Lift-a-Flap Board Book. Santalucia, Francesco, illus. 2002. (Lift-a-Flap Board Bks.). 10p. (J). bds. 8.99 (978-1-57759-785-8(0)) Dalmatian Pr.

Koeppel, Ruth. Tonka Town: The Big Race (Movie Storybook) LaCoste, Gary, illus. 2003. (Tonka Ser.). 24p. (J). pap. 3.50 (978-0-439-51210-7(7)) Scholastic, Inc.

Koeppel, Ruth & Reader's Digest Staff. Dora's Special Memories: Storybook & Toy Camera. 2007. (RD Innovative Book & Player Format Ser.). 10p. (J). 21.99 (**_*978-0-7944-1294-4(7)_**) Reader's Digest Assn., Inc., The.

Kolaczek, Marie. Exploring Space. Latyk, Olivier & Mignon, Philippe, illus. 2006. (Explore Your World Ser.). 28p. (J). (ps-1). 15.95 (978-1-55407-006-0(6)) Firefly Bks., Ltd.

Kriegman, Mitchell. Bear in the Big Blue House Good Night Songs. Rillo, Cary, illus. 2003. (Musical Nightlight Bks.). (J). bds. 15.98 (978-0-7853-7962-1(2)) Publications International, Ltd.

Kubler, Annie. See You Later Alligator. 2004. (Illus.). 24p. (J). 9.99 (978-1-904550-05-1(3)) Child's Play-International.

Kunhardt, Dorothy. Pat the Bunny. Kunhardt, Dorothy, illus. 2001. (Touch & Feel Bks.). (Illus.). 20p. (J). (gr. k). pap. 9.99 (978-0-307-12000-7(7) , Golden Bks.) Random Hse. Children's Bks.

—Pat the Bunny. 2000. (Touch & Feel Bks.). (Illus.). 20p. (J). (ps-k). bds. 17.95 (978-0-307-16209-0(5) , 16209, Golden Bks.) Random Hse. Children's Bks.

Kwas, Susan Estelle. Learning Block Books: Shapes, Animals, Colors, Numbers, 26 vols. 2001. (Illus.). -1p. (J). bds. 24.95 (978-0-8118-3278-6(3)) Chronicle Bks. LLC.

Ladd, Frances Ann. All for You! Johnson, Jay, illus. 2004. (Care Bears Ser.). 16p. (J). 5.99 (978-0-439-62493-0(2)) Scholastic, Inc.

—Where Are You? Johnson, Jay, illus. 2004. (Care Bears Ser.). 16p. (J). 5.99 (978-0-439-62491-6(6)) Scholastic, Inc.

Laden, Nina. Who Loves You, Baby? 2007. (Illus.). 18p. (J). (ps). bds. 6.95 (978-0-8118-5724-6(7)) Chronicle Bks. LLC.

Lambert, Angela. Food. 2006. (All Change! Ser.). (Illus.). 10p. (YA). (ps). 6.99 (978-1-904550-18-1(5)) Child's Play-International.

Lambert, Angela, illus. Animals. 2006. (All Change! Ser.). 10p. (J). (ps). 6.99 (978-1-904550-16-7(9)) Child's Play-International.

—Jobs. 2006. (All Change! Ser.). 10p. (J). (ps). 6.99 (978-1-904550-17-4(7)) Child's Play-International.

—Party. 2005. (All Change! Ser.). 10p. (YA). (ps). 6.99 (978-1-904550-15-0(0)) Child's Play-International.

Lamere, Jill. Upside Down. Lamere, Jill, illus. 2005. (J). bds. 12.95 (978-0-9772320-0-0(X)) Minikin Pr.

Lammie, Karen J., illus. Oink! 2005. (On the Farm Ser.). 10p. (J). (ps-ps). bds. 4.95 (978-0-7641-5829-2(5)) Barron's Educational Series, Inc.

Landy, Sarah. Blue's Snack Party. Cardinali, Kevin, illus. 2000. (Blue's Clues Ser.). 16p. (J). (ps-k). 5.99 (978-0-689-83432-5(2) , Simon Spotlight/Nickelodeon) Simon & Schuster Children's Publishing.

Langen, Annette. Letters from Felix: A Little Rabbit on a World Tour. Droop, Constanza, illus. 2003. 47p. (J). 14.99 (978-1-59384-034-1(9)) Parklane Publishing.

Langlois, Florence. The Extraordinary Gift. Goodman, John, tr. from FRE. Langlois, Florence, illus. 2005. (Illus.). 48p. (J). (ps-2). reprint ed. 15.00 (978-0-7567-8942-8(7)) DIANE Publishing Co.

Larson, Beverly. Toca y Siente las Historias de la Biblia. Pineda, Nancy, tr. Dillard, Sarah, illus. 2003. (Touch & Feel Ser.). (SPA.). (J). (ps-k). bds. 8.99 (978-0-7899-1088-2(8)) Editorial Unilit.

Lassen, Christian Riese & Book Company Staff. Water World. 2002. (Pop-up Bks.). (Illus.). 14p. (J). 15.95 (978-1-74047-180-0(6)) Book Co. Publishing Pty, Ltd., The AUS. *Dist:* Penton Overseas, Inc.

Lassieur, Allison. Knights' Kingdom: Activity Book with Narrative. Mada Design Staff, illus. 2005. (Lego Knights' Kingdom Ser.). 32p. (J). pap. 5.99 (978-0-439-71828-8(7)) Scholastic, Inc.

—Welcome to the Kingdom of Morcia! A Knights Kingdom Sticker Book. Mada Design Staff, illus. 2005. (Lego Knights' Kingdom Ser.). 32p. (J). pap. 5.99 (978-0-439-70232-4(1)) Scholastic, Inc.

Lawler, Janet. A Mama Bug's Love. Peterson, Rick, illus. 2006. (Preschool Pop-Ups Ser.). 14p. (J). 7.99 (978-1-4169-1548-5(6) , Little Simon) Simon & Schuster Children's Publishing.

Lawson-Miller, Barb. I Love Daddy Because... 2004. (Illus.). 14p. bds. (978-0-9688553-0-0(X)) Barbamel Bks., Inc.

—I Love Mommy Because... 2004. (Illus.). 14p. bds. (978-0-9688553-1-7(8)) Barbamel Bks., Inc.

Layton, Neal. The Story of Everything: From the Big Bang Until Now in 11 Pop-up Spreads. 2007. (Illus.). 22p. (J). 18.99 (978-0-7641-5985-5(2)) Barron's Educational Series, Inc.

LeapFrog Staff, compiled by. My First LeapPad: Richard Scarry ABC. 2001. (J). (ps-2). spiral bd. 12.99 (978-1-58605-217-1(9)) LeapFrog Enterprises, Inc.

Learning Colors. 1999. (Illus.). (J). (978-1-56156-835-2(X)) Kidsbooks, Inc.

Learning Wrap Staff. Skip Counting Video & Cassette. 2004. 24.95 (978-0-943343-32-7(1)) Learning Wrap-Ups.

Learning Wrap-Ups Addition. 2004. 7.99 (978-0-943343-26-6(7)) Learning Wrap-Ups.

Learning Wrap-Ups All About. 2004. 7.99 (978-0-943343-20-4(8)) Learning Wrap-Ups.

Learning Wrap-Ups Division. 2004. 7.99 (978-0-943343-29-7(1)); 18.99 (978-0-943343-98-3(4)) Learning Wrap-Ups.

Learning Wrap-Ups Early Child. 2004. 29.99 (978-0-943343-18-1(6)) Learning Wrap-Ups.

Learning Wrap-Ups Fractions. 2004. 7.99 (978-0-943343-36-5(4)) Learning Wrap-Ups.

Learning Wrap-Ups Math in Tro. 2004. 34.99 (978-0-943343-80-8(1)) Learning Wrap-Ups.

Learning Wrap-Ups Multiplication. 2004. 18.99 (978-0-943343-00-6(3)); 7.99 (978-0-943343-28-0(3)) Learning Wrap-Ups.

Learning Wrap-Ups Music Theory. 2004. 34.99 (978-0-943343-56-3(9)) Learning Wrap-Ups.

Learning Wrap Ups Palette. 2004. 7.99 (978-1-59204-005-6(5)); 7.99 (978-1-59204-009-4(8)); 7.99 (978-1-59204-011-7(X)); 7.99 (978-1-59204-017-9(9)); 7.99 (978-1-59204-018-6(7)); 7.99 (978-1-59204-019-3(5)) Learning Wrap-Ups.

Learning Wrap Ups Palette Base. 2004. 11.99 (978-1-59204-000-1(4)) Learning Wrap-Ups.

Learning Wrap-Ups Pre Algebra. 2004. 34.99 (978-0-943343-52-5(6)) Learning Wrap-Ups.

Learning Wrap-Ups Sight Words. 2004. 34.99 (978-0-943343-75-4(5)) Learning Wrap-Ups.

Learning Wrap-Ups Spanish. 2004. (ENG & SPA.). 34.99 (978-0-943343-76-1(3)) Learning Wrap-Ups.

Learning Wrap-Ups States & Capitols. 2004. 7.99 (978-0-943343-30-3(5)) Learning Wrap-Ups.

Learning Wrap-Ups Subtraction. 2004. 7.99 (978-0-943343-27-3(5)); 18.99 (978-0-943343-99-0(2)) Learning Wrap-Ups.

Lee, Brian, illus. A Construction Site. 2005. (What's Inside Ser.). (J). (**_*978-0-7607-6570-8(7)_**) backpackbook.

—A Pirate Ship. 2005. (What's Inside? Ser.). (**_*978-0-7607-6809-9(9)_**) backpackbook.

Lee, Brian, illus. The World of Dinosaurs. 2005. (J). (978-0-7607-6569-2(3)) backpackbook.

Lee, Jeanie. Baby Farm Friends. 2006. (Flips & Flaps Book Ser.). (Illus.). 10p. (J). 12.95 (978-1-4169-0702-2(5) , Little Simon) Simon & Schuster Children's Publishing.

—When I Grow Up! Valerio, Geraldo, illus. 2007. (Flips & Flaps Book Ser.). 12p. (J). 9.99 (978-1-4169-0933-0(8) , Little Simon) Simon & Schuster Children's Publishing.

Lee, Quinlan B. Who's Who? A Lift-the-Flap Riddle Book. Carter, Tod & Tootelian, Katherine, illus. 2007. (VeggieTales Ser.). 14p. (J). 6.99 (978-1-4169-3349-6(2) , Little Simon Inspirations) Simon & Schuster Children's Publishing.

LeFleur, David, illus. Hide & Seek in the Jungle. 2007. 19p. (J). (ps-k). 16.99 (**_*978-1-58476-623-0(9)_** , IKIDS) Innovative Kids.

Lego Staff. Cool Cars. 2000. (LEGO Creator Brick Tricks Ser.). (Illus.). 24p. (J). spiral bd. 7.99 (978-1-903276-09-9(8)) Lego Media International, Inc.

LeLeu, Lisa. Diggity the Dog Puppet Show Play Set. ed. 2004. (Lisa Leleu Puppet Show Books Ser.). (J). 19.95 (**_*978-0-9710537-2-4(3)_** , LeLeu, Lisa Puppet Show Bks.) LeLeu, Lisa Studios! Inc.

—Percilla the Gorilla Gift Set: Puppet Book Gift Set with 2 Books. 2004. (J). bds. 19.99 (**_*978-0-9710537-3-1(1)_**) LeLeu, Lisa Studios! Inc.

Lemmens, Riske. A Box Full of Monsters. 2004. (URD, SOM, ALB, CHI & ARA., Illus.). 26p. (J). (978-1-85269-827-0(6)); (978-1-85269-832-4(2)); (978-1-85269-837-9(3)); (978-1-85269-842-3(X)); (978-1-85269-847-8(0)); (978-1-85269-852-2(7)); (978-1-85269-857-7(8)) Mantra Publishing, Ltd.

Lemmens, Riske & Dutta, Kunal, texts. A Box Full of Monsters: Kutia Plot Me Monstra. 2004. (URD, SOM, ALB, CHI & ARA, Illus.). 25p. (J). (978-1-85269-822-5(5)) Mantra Publishing, Ltd.

Lenz Mulligan Rights and Co. Staff & van der Put, Klaartje. Little Lamb: Finger Puppet Book. 2006. (Illus.). 12p. (J). bds. 6.95 (978-0-8118-5235-7(0)) Chronicle Bks. LLC.

Leon McCann, Jesse. Haunted Halloween: Sticker Storybook. del Sur, Duendes, illus. 2004. (Scooby-Doo Ser.). 24p. (J). pap. 5.99 (978-0-439-60699-8(3) , Scholastic Paperbacks) Scholastic, Inc.

Leonard, Marcia. Guess Who? 2000. (Hanna Bks.). (Illus.). 18p. (J). (ps up). 7.95 (978-0-694-01374-6(9) , Harper Festival) HarperCollins Pubs.

Leslie, Amanda. Babies' Day. 2002. (Illus.). 10p. (J). 5.95 (978-1-58925-671-2(9) , tiger tales) ME Media LLC.

—Babies Play. 2002. 10p. (J). 5.95 (978-1-58925-672-9(7) , tiger tales) ME Media LLC.

—Do Crocodiles Moo? 2000. (Illus.). 16p. (J). (ps). 5.95 (978-1-929766-08-6(4)) Handprint Bks.

—Do Crocodiles Moo? Two Lift-the-Flap Books. Leslie, Amanda, illus. 2000. (Illus.). 12p. (J). 5.99 (978-1-58048-087-1(X)) Sandvik Publishing.

—Flappy, Waggly, Wiggly. Leslie, Amanda, illus. 1999. (Illus.). (J). 9.99 (978-1-58048-089-5(6)) Sandvik Publishing.

Lester, Anna. Fairies. Gower, Teri, illus. 2006. 48p. (J). 8.99 (978-0-7945-1326-9(3) , Usborne) EDC Publishing.

Let's Put on a Show: Interactive Playbook. 1998. (Illus.). 10p. (J). (ps). 19.99 (978-1-890647-05-6(5)) RC2 Corp.

Letter Fun Wipe-Off Book. 2001. (Illus.). 16p. (J). (gr. k-2). mass mkt. 3.79 (978-1-889319-97-1(X)) Trend Enterprises, Inc.

Lewis, Anthony, illus. Little Jungle Explorers. 14p. bds. 4.99 (***978-1-84643-036-7(4)***) Child's Play International Ltd. GBR. *Dist:* Child's Play-International.

—Little Ocean Explorers. 2007. 14p. bds. 7.99 (***978-1-84643-039-8(9)***) Child's Play International Ltd. GBR. *Dist:* Child's Play-International.

—Little Snow Explorers. 2007. 14p. bds. 7.99 (***978-1-84643-037-4(2)***) Child's Play International Ltd. GBR. *Dist:* Child's Play-International.

—Little Space Explorers. 2007. 14p. bds. 7.99 (***978-1-84643-038-1(0)***) Child's Play International Ltd. GBR. *Dist:* Child's Play-International.

Lewis, Anthony, illus. So Much to Love. 1999. (Leap Frog Lift-a-Flap Ser.). (J). (978-0-7853-3368-5(1)) Publications International, Ltd.

Lewis, Edwina. Who Eats? Parker, Ant, illus. 2003. (Who. . . Ser.). 16p. (YA). (978-1-85602-470-9(9)) Chrysalis Children's Bks.

—Who Jumps? Parker, Ant, illus. 2003. (Who. . . Ser.). 16p. (YA). (978-1-85602-447-1(4)) Chrysalis Children's Bks.

—Who Plays? Parker, Ant, illus. 2003. (Who. . . Ser.). 16p. (J). (978-1-85602-469-3(5)) Chrysalis Children's Bks.

—Who Swims? Parker, Ant, illus. 2003. (Who. . . Ser.). 16p. (YA). (978-1-85602-448-8(2)) Chrysalis Children's Bks.

Lewison, Wendy Cheyette. Baby Faces. Moroney, Christopher, illus. 2002. 14p. (J). (gr. k). bds. 6.99 (978-0-375-81538-6(4) , Random Hse. Bks. for Young Readers) Random Hse. Children's Bks.

—Peekaboo! I See You! Moroney, Christopher, illus. 2002. (Sesame Beginnings Ser.). 14p. (J). (gr. k). bds. 7.99 (978-0-375-81512-6(0) , Random Hse. Bks. for Young Readers) Random Hse. Children's Bks.

Lewman, David. Bottoms Up! Jokes from Bikini Bottom. Meurer, Caleb, illus. 2002. (SpongeBob SquarePants Ser.). 16p. (J). pap. 5.99 (978-0-689-85181-0(2) , Simon Spotlight/Nickelodeon) Simon & Schuster Children's Publishing.

—The SpongeBob SquarePants Oracle: The Oracle. 2003. (Illus.). 288p. pap. 10.00 (978-0-7434-8316-2(2) , Pocket) Simon & Schuster.

L'Hommedieu, Arthur John. Butterfly Play Pack. 2000. (Illus.). 12p. (J). (ps up). 7.99 (978-0-85953-003-3(5)) Child's Play-International.

Lift-A-Flap. Book of Pooh: Beginning Sounds: Match the Flap. 2001. (Learn to Read Ser.). (Illus.). 10p. (ps-1). 7.99 (978-0-7868-3344-3(0)) Disney Pr.

Light, Steve. I Am Happy: A Touch & Feel Book of Feelings. Light, Steve, illus. 2003. (Illus.). 12p. (J). (ps-1). 12.99 (978-0-7636-1753-0(9)) Candlewick Pr.

—Rocking Horse: A Press-Out & Play Book. Hirashima, Jean, illus. 2002. (Hello Kitty, Hello Playtime! Ser.). 8p. (J). (ps-1). 8.95 (978-0-8109-1233-5(3)) Abrams, Harry N. , Inc.

—Uncle Sam: Press-Out & Play Book. 2002. (Illus.). 8p. (J). (ps-1). 7.95 (978-0-8109-3498-6(1)) Abrams, Harry N. , Inc.

Linke, Uwe. Princess Moving Book. 2007. (J). bds. 8.95 (978-0-7358-2125-5(9)) North-South Bks., Inc.

Lipkowitz, Daniel. Grand Tournament, No. 2. Mada Design Staff, illus. 2005. (Knights' Kingdom Reader Ser.: No. 2). 32p. (J). pap. 3.99 (978-0-439-70231-7(3)) Scholastic, Inc.

—Search for the King. 2005. (Lego Knights' Kingdom Ser.). (Illus.). 32p. (J). 3.99 (978-0-439-70230-0(5)) Scholastic, Inc.

Lippman, Peter. Mini Express. (J). 119.40 (978-0-7611-2876-2(X) , 22876); 2002. (Illus.). 20p. bds. 9.95 (978-0-7611-2852-6(2) , 12852) Workman Publishing Co., Inc.

Listen to Alaskas Animals. 2006. 10.95 (978-1-931353-25-0(5)) Saddle Pal Creations, Inc.

Litchfield, J. My Clothes. 2004. (Rattle Board Bks.). 16p. (J). 4.95 (978-0-7945-0052-8(8) , Usborne) EDC Publishing.

—My Toys. 2004. (Rattle Board Bks.). 16p. (J). 4.95 (978-0-7945-0054-2(4) , Usborne) EDC Publishing.

Litchfield, Jo. Vacation. Litchfield, Jo, illus. 2006. (Illus.). 12p. (J). bds. 7.99 (978-0-7945-1315-3(8) , Usborne) EDC Publishing.

Little Softy, 4 bks., Set. alt. ed. 2002. (J). (978-1-931312-86-8(9)) SoftPlay, Inc.

Little Softy Cow. 2002. (J). (978-1-931312-90-5(7)) SoftPlay, Inc.

Little Softy Pig. 2002. (J). (978-1-931312-91-2(5)) SoftPlay, Inc.

Little Softy Pony. 2002. (J). (978-1-931312-92-9(3)) SoftPlay, Inc.

Little Tikes Block Board Books. 2004. (J). bds. (978-0-7666-1277-8(5) , 39290); bds. (978-0-7666-1278-5(3) , 39290); bds. (978-0-7666-1279-2(1) , 39290); bds. (978-0-7666-1280-8(5) , 39290); bds. (978-0-7666-1281-5(3) , 39290); bds. (978-0-7666-1282-2(1) , 39290) Modern Publishing.

Littler, Keith. Tell the Time with Merlin. 2002. (Illus.). 24p. (J). pap. 11.99 (978-1-84222-653-7(3)) Carlton Bks., Ltd. GBR. *Dist:* Independent Pubs. Group.

Lloyd, Sam. Grumpy Gracie. 2006. (Illus.). 12p. (J). 8.95 (978-0-7624-2521-1(0) , Running Pr. Kids) Running Pr. Bk. Pubs.

Lo Raso, Carlo, illus. We Love a Luau! 2007. (Backyardigans Ser.). 16p. (J). pap. 6.99 (978-1-4169-3365-6(4) , Simon Spotlight) Simon & Schuster Children's Publishing.

Lodge, Jo. Pass the Parcel with Pig. 1998. (Illus.). 12p. (J). (ps-3). 5.95 (978-0-7641-5076-0(6)) Barron's Educational Series, Inc.

Lodge, Yvette. Baby's First Pop-up. Ali, Lodge, illus. gif. ed. 2006. 5p. (J). 19.95 (978-1-57791-217-0(9)) Brighter Minds Children's Publishing.

Lorenz Books Staff. Colours: With over 50 Reusable Stickers. 1998. (Sticker Fun Ser.). (Illus.). 16p. (ps-k). pap. 4.95 (978-1-85967-770-4(3)) Anness Publishing GBR. *Dist:* National Bk. Network.

—Time with Sticker. 1999. (Sticker Fun Ser.). (Illus.). 16p. (ps-k). pap. 4.95 (978-0-7548-0281-5(7) , Lorenz Bks.) Anness Publishing GBR. *Dist:* National Bk. Network.

Lou Weber. Dora the Explorer My First Look & Find. 18p. 7.98 (978-1-4127-3909-2(8) , PIL Kids) Publications International, Ltd.

—Strawberry Shortcake Look & Find. 24p. 7.98 (978-1-4127-3932-0(2) , PIL Kids) Publications International, Ltd.

Lubber, William. Pirateology: The Pirate Hunter's Companion. Steer, Dugald A., ed. Gilbert, Anne Yvonne et al, illus. 2006. (Ologies Ser.). 32p. (J). (gr. 3). 19.99 (978-0-7636-3143-7(4)) Candlewick Pr.

Lucado, Max. You Are Special. Martinez, Sergio, illus. 2005. (Wemmicks Ser.). 28p. (gr. 4-7). bds. 6.99 (978-1-58134-219-2(5) , Crossway Bibles) Crossway Bks.

Lukas, Catherine & Cosby, Bill. Super Detective Little Bill: A Dial-the-Answer Book. Mastrocinque, Andy, illus. 2002. (Little Bill Ser.). 14p. (J). 8.99 (978-0-689-84200-9(7) , Simon Spotlight/Nickelodeon) Simon & Schuster Children's Publishing.

Lund, John, illus. Sing-Along Songs. 2002. (J). 16.98 (978-0-7853-6403-0(X)) Publications International, Ltd.

Luther's Seal Sticker. 2004. (Illus.). pap. 7.99 (978-0-8066-3720-4(X)) Augsburg Fortress, Pubs.

Lyon, Tammie Speer, illus. Three Little Kittens. 1999. (J). (978-0-7853-3362-3(2)) Publications International, Ltd.

Mach, Steven, illus. The Wheels on the Bus: A Three-Dimensional Playset with Wind-Up Bus & Sound! 2001. (ps-3). act. bk. ed. 16.95 (978-1-58117-144-0(7) , Intervisual/Piggy Toes) Dalmatian Pr.

Mackall, Dandi Daley. God Made Me. Nakata, Hiroe, illus. 2006. 14p. (J). 6.99 (978-1-4169-1499-0(4) , Little Simon Inspirations) Simon & Schuster Children's Publishing.

—The Treetops Are Whispering. Nguyen, Vincent, illus. 2007. 16p. (J). 8.99 (978-1-4169-1496-9(X) , Little Simon Inspirations) Simon & Schuster Children's Publishing.

MacKinnon, Debbie. Eye Spy Shapes. Sieveking, Anthea, illus. 2000. 24p. (J). (ps-3). 6.95 (978-0-88106-135-2(2)) Charlesbridge Publishing, Inc.

Maggard, John & LaFever, Greg, illus. Name That Train. 1998. 10p. (J). (ps-3). 7.95 (978-1-929174-07-2(1)) Oshkosh B'Gosh, Inc.

Magloff, Lisa & Dorling Kindersley Publishing Staff. Puppy. 2005. (Watch me Grow Ser.). (Illus.). 24p. (J). 7.99 (978-0-7566-1273-3(X)) Dorling Kindersley Publishing, Inc.

Magsamen, Sandra. Love Bug. rev. ed. 2007. (Snuggle-Me Stories Ser.). 20p. (J). (ps-ps). 7.99 (***978-0-316-06596-2(X)***) Little, Brown Bks. for Young Readers.

—Messages from the Heart: Baby Love:Huggable, Lovable, Snuggable Books. 2nd ed. 2006. (Message from the Heart Ser.). (Illus.). 10p. (J). (ps-17). 10.99 (978-0-316-16633-1(2)) Little Brown & Co.

—My Blanket: Huggable, Lovable, Snuggable Books. 2006. (Message from the Heart Ser.). (Illus.). 6p. (J). (ps-17). 10.99 (978-0-316-01459-5(1)) Little Brown & Co.

Maizels, Jennie. Things to Do Book. Maizels, Jennie, illus. 2007. (Illus.). 20p. (J). (gr. k-3). 15.99 (978-0-7636-3371-4(2)) Candlewick Pr.

Make Believe Ideas Staff, creator. Tractors & Trucks: Sticker Activity Book. 2005. (Lift Stick & Learn Ser.). (Illus.). 12p. (J). (ps-3). 4.95 (978-1-905051-67-0(0)) Make Believe Ideas GBR. *Dist:* Ingram Pub. Services.

Malloy, Christine. The Solar System: Flip Out & Learn. Leighton, Aaron, illus. 2003. (Pull-Out Book Ser.). 8p. (J). 12.95 (978-0-8118-3488-9(3)) Chronicle Bks. LLC.

Man-Kong, Mary. Fairytopia. 2006. (Board Books). (Illus.). 22p. (J). (gr. k-ps). bds. 4.99 (978-0-375-83538-4(5) , Golden Bks.) Random Hse. Children's Bks.

Man-Kong, Mary & Golden Books Staff. Amazing Makeover. Wolcott, Karen, illus. 2006. 12p. (J). (ps-1). 10.95 (978-0-375-83552-0(0) , Golden Bks.) Random Hse. Children's Bks.

Mandy, et al. George's Garden. (Illus.). 16p. 2005. (URD, ENG, VIE, CHI & BEN.). 9.95 (978-1-84059-168-2(4)); 2000. (TUR, ENG, URD, VIE & CHI., (J). pap. 9.95 (978-1-84059-167-5(6)); 2000. (VIE, ENG, URD, TUR & CHI., (J). pap. 9.95 (978-1-84059-169-9(2)) Milet Publishing.

—George's Garden. Datta, Kanai, tr. from ENG. 2000. (Senses Ser.). (BEN, ENG, VIE, GUJ & URD., Illus.). 16p. (J). pap. 9.95 (978-1-84059-164-4(1)) Milet Publishing.

—George's Garden. Dave, Pratima, tr. Ford, Shaun, photos by. 2000. (Senses Ser.). (GUJ, ENG, VIE, CHI & BEN., Illus.). 16p. (J). pap. 9.95 (978-1-84059-166-8(8)) Milet Publishing.

—Peter's Party. (Illus.). 16p. 2005. (URD, ENG, VIE, CHI & BEN.). 9.95 (978-1-84059-150-7(1)); 2000. (GUJ, ENG, VIE, CHI & BEN., (J). pap. 9.95 (978-1-84059-148-4(X)); 2000. (TUR, ENG, URD, VIE & CHI., (J). pap. 9.95 (978-1-84059-149-1(8)); 2000. (BEN, ENG, VIE, GUJ & URD., (J). pap. 9.95 (978-1-84059-146-0(3)); 2000. (VIE, ENG, CHI, BEN & GUJ., (J). pap. 9.95 (978-1-84059-151-4(X)) Milet Publishing.

—Rosie's Room. (Illus.). 16p. (ps-1). 2005. (URD, ENG, TUR, VIE & CHI.). 9.95 (978-1-84059-162-0(5)); 2000. (VIE, ENG, URD, TUR & CHI., (J). pap. 9.95 (978-1-84059-163-7(3)); 2000. (GUJ, ENG, VIE, CHI & BEN., (J). pap. 9.95 (978-1-84059-160-6(9)); 2000. (TUR, ENG, URD, VIE & CHI., (J). pap. 9.95 (978-1-84059-161-3(7)) Milet Publishing.

—Rosie's Room. Datta, Kanai, tr. from ENG. 2000. (Senses Ser.). (BEN, ENG, VIE, CHI & GUJ., Illus.). 16p. (J). pap. 9.95 (978-1-84059-158-3(7)) Milet Publishing.

Mann, Holly, illus. Farm. 2005. 8p. pap. (978-0-7624-2362-0(5)) Running Pr. Bk. Pubs.

Mann, Holly & Running Press Staff. People: Pull the Tabs! Change the Pictures! 2004. (Illus.). 8p. pap. (978-0-7624-1906-7(7)) Running Pr. Bk. Pubs.

Manning, Mick. Under Your Skin: Your Amazing Body. Granstrom, Brita, illus. 2007. 24p. (J). (gr. 1-4). 16.95 (***978-0-8075-8313-5(8)***) Whitman, Albert & Co.

Markell, Denis. The Great Stroller Adventure. Iwai, Melissa, illus. 2004. 16p. (J). pap. 9.95 (978-0-439-54651-5(6) , Cartwheel Bks.) Scholastic, Inc.

Marks, Burton. Tanya Tinker & the Gizmo Gang. Smath, Jerry, illus. 2003. 20p. (J). (ps-3). reprint ed. 22.00 (978-0-7567-6760-0(1)) DIANE Publishing Co.

Marqina, Mignon. Shapes & Me: A Flip & Learn Book. l.t. ed. 2006. (Illus.). 32p. (J). lib. bdg. (***978-1-934190-05-0(5)***) Ocean Front Bk. Publishing, Inc.

Marsh, Carole. Alaska Wheel of Fortune: Game Book. (Orig.). pap. 9.95 (978-0-7933-9621-4(2)) Gallopade International.

Marsoli, Lisa Ann. Christmas Is Coming! Barnard, Lucy, illus. 2007. 10p. (J). (ps-3). 6.99 (***978-0-375-84573-4(9)***, Robin Corey Bks.) Random Hse. Children's Bks.

Marsoli, Lisa Ann. Harold Takes a Trip: Harold & the Purple Crayon. Chiang, Andy, illus. 2005. 10p. (J). 7.95 (978-1-58117-262-1(1) , Intervisual/Piggy Toes) Dalmatian Pr.

Massey, Jane, illus. Farm Animals. 2000. (Touch & Fit Ser.). 10p. (J). (ps-k). bds. 12.95 (978-1-57145-416-4(0) , Silver Dolphin Bks.) Advantage Pubs. Group.

—Jungle Animals. 2000. (Touch & Fit Ser.). 10p. (J). (ps-k). bds. 12.95 (978-1-57145-415-7(2) , Silver Dolphin Bks.) Advantage Pubs. Group.

Master Merlin & Steer, Dugald. Wizardology Handbook: A Course for Apprentices. Gilbert, Anne Young et al, illus. 2007. (Ologies Ser.). 80p. (J). (gr. 3 up). 12.99 (***978-0-7636-3401-8(8)***) Candlewick Pr.

Masurel, Claire. Emily & Her Daddy. Calitri, Susan, illus. 2003. (Lift-the-Flap Ser.). 16p. (J). (gr. k-1). pap. 6.99 (978-0-14-250080-4(1) , Puffin) Penguin Group (USA) Inc.

—Emily's Dance Class. Peskin, Joy, ed. Calitri, Susan, illus. 2001. (Picture Puffin Ser.). 16p. (J). (ps-k). pap. 6.99 (978-0-14-056758-8(5) , Puffin) Penguin Group (USA) Inc.

Matthews, Derek. Happy Snappy Easter Egg Hunt. 2006. (Happy Snappy Bks.). (Illus.). 10p. (J). 4.95 (978-1-59223-565-0(4) , Silver Dolphin Bks.) Advantage Pubs. Group.

—Moo! Noisy Pop-Up Fun, 5 Fun Animal Sounds. 2004. (Snappy Ser.). (Illus.). 10p. (ps-k). 12.95 (978-1-59223-214-7(0)) Advantage Pubs. Group.

—Noisy Pop-Up Fun: Snappy Sounds, Roar. 2004. (Snappy Sounds Ser.). (Illus.). 10p. 12.95 (978-1-59223-213-0(2)) Advantage Pubs. Group.

—Snappy Sounds Ho, Ho, Ho! 2005. (Snappy Sounds Ser.). (ACE., Illus.). 10p. 12.95 (978-1-59223-453-0(4) , Silver Dolphin Bks.) Advantage Pubs. Group.

Matthews, Derek, illus. Animales de la Selva. 2005. (Escucha y Aprende Ser.). (SPA.). 10p. (J). (ps-7). 12.95 (978-970-718-298-1(9) , Silver Dolphin en Español) Advanced Marketing, S. de R. L. de C. V. MEX. *Dist:* Perseus Distribution.

—Escucha y Aprende: Animales de la Granja. 2005. (Escucha y Aprende Ser.). (SPA.). 10p. (J). (ps-7). 12.95 (978-970-718-300-1(4) , Silver Dolphin en Español) Advanced Marketing, S. de R. L. de C. V. MEX. *Dist:* Perseus Distribution.

—Escucha y Aprende: Mascotas. 2005. (Escucha y Aprende Ser.). (SPA.). 10p. (J). (ps-7). 12.95 (978-970-718-299-8(7) , Silver Dolphin en Español) Advanced Marketing, S. de R. L. de C. V. MEX. *Dist:* Perseus Distribution.

—Escucha y Aprende: Trafico. 2005. (Escucha y Aprende Ser.). (SPA.). 10p. (J). (ps-7). 12.95 (978-970-718-297-4(0) , Silver Dolphin en Español) Advanced Marketing, S. de R. L. de C. V. MEX. *Dist:* Perseus Distribution.

—Snappy Sounds: Woof! Five Fun Animal Sounds. 2005. (Snappy Sounds Ser.). 10p. (J). 12.95 (978-1-59223-215-4(9) , Silver Dolphin Bks.) Advantage Pubs. Group.

Mawhinney, Art, illus. Eeyore's Cheerful Surprises. 2005. (***978-1-4127-3101-0(1)***) Publications International, Ltd.

Max Lucado's Hermie & Friends. The Straight Path. 2005. (Illus.). 14p. (J). (ps-ps). 9.99 (978-1-4003-0511-7(X)) Nelson, Thomas Inc.

Maxwell-Hyslop, Miranda. Fish Go Woof! 2005. (Illus.). 36p. (J). (978-0-340-87338-0(8) , Hodder & Stoughton) Hodder General Publishing Division.

—Fish Go Woof! 2005. (Illus.). (J). pap. 9.99 (978-0-340-87339-7(6) , Hodder & Stoughton) Hodder General Publishing Division GBR. *Dist:* Trafalgar Square Publishing.

May, Darcy. Glitter Fairies Stickers. 2004. (Glitter Stickers Ser.). (Illus.). 2p. (J). (ps-5). 1.50 (978-0-486-43530-5(X)) Dover Pubns., Inc.

Mayer, Mercer & Capozzi, Suzy. Bob Paints the Town. Mayer, Mercer, illus. 2003. (Little Critter Ser.). (Illus.). 10p. (J). (gr. k-1). 7.99 (978-0-307-10603-2(9) , 10603, Golden Bks.) Random Hse. Children's Bks.

McCafferty, Catherine. Picture Me as Dad's Little Helper. Rasmussen, Wendy, illus. 2001. (Picture Me Ser.). 10p. (J). (ps up). bds. 4.99 (978-1-57151-588-9(7)) Playhouse Publishing.

—Picture Me as Mom's Little Helper. Rasmussen, Wendy, illus. 2001. (Picture Me Ser.). 10p. (J). (ps up). bds. 4.99 (978-1-57151-587-2(9)) Playhouse Publishing.

—Picture Me with My Grandpa. Rasmussen, Wendy, illus. 2000. (Picture Me Ser.). 10p. (J). (ps up). bds. 4.99 (978-1-57151-579-7(8)) Playhouse Publishing.

McCafferty, Catherine, et al. Tigger's Bouncy Easter. Kleven, Dean, illus. 2002. (Disney's Winnie the Pooh Ser.). (J). (978-0-7853-6672-0(5)) Publications International, Ltd.

McCann, Jesse Leon. Dragon Ball Sticker Book. collector's ed. 2003. (Dragon Ball Z Ser.). (Illus.). 32p. (J). pap. 5.99 (978-0-439-46519-9(2)) Scholastic, Inc.

—Scooby Doo & the Halloween Hotel Haunt. 1999. (gr. k-3). lib. bdg. 14.15 (978-0-613-29739-4(3)) Tandem Library Bks.

McDonald, Jill, illus. Finger Puppet Storybook: Mother Goose Rhymes. rev. ed. 2007. (Alex Toys Ser.). 10p. (J). (ps-1). 11.99 (***978-0-316-06524-5(2)***) Little, Brown Bks. for Young Readers.

McGee, Fatty. Santa's Workshop. 2007. 6p. 16.95 (***978-1-58117-599-8(X)***, Intervisual/Piggy Toes) Dalmatian Pr.

McGrath, Barbara Barbieri. The Pepperidge Farm Goldfish Fun Book. Bolster, Rob & Mazzola, Frank, Jr., illus. 1999. 16p. (J). (ps up). 5.99 (978-0-694-01450-7(8) , Harper Festival) HarperCollins Pubs.

McGuire, Leslie. Circles at the Circus: My First Book of Shapes. Haskamp, Steven, illus. 1999. (Gymboree Book Ser.). 16p. (J). reprint ed. 5.95 (978-1-892374-20-2(X)) Weldon Owen, Inc.

—My Rattle Book. Bell, Fred, illus. 1999. 12p. (J). 5.95 (978-1-892374-14-1(5)) Weldon Owen, Inc.

McGuirk, Leslie. Ho, Ho, Ho, Tucker! McGuirk, Leslie, illus. 2007. (Illus.). 30p. (J). (gr. k-k). pap. 4.99 (***978-0-7636-3663-0(0)***) Candlewick Pr.

McKee, Darren, illus. Barney's Dreamtime Songs. 2003. (Musical Nightlight Bks.). (J). bds. (978-0-7853-7983-6(5)) Publications International, Ltd.

McKendry, Sam. Are You Ticklish? Bilingual Edition. 2006. 12p. 10.95 (978-1-58117-472-4(1) , Intervisual/Piggy Toes) Dalmatian Pr.

—Curious Kitties: A Colors Book. Mitchell, Melanie, illus. 2005. 16p. (J). 9.95 (978-1-58117-417-5(9) , Intervisual/Piggy Toes) Dalmatian Pr.

McKendry, Sam & Rescek, Sanja. Bless Everyone. 2006. (Illus.). (J). 8.95 (978-1-58117-445-8(4) , Intervisual/Piggy Toes) Dalmatian Pr.

McKenzie, Michelle. Ocean Pop & Pull. 2001. 12p. (J). 12.95 (978-1-878244-36-9(1)) Monterey Bay Aquarium.

McLaughlin, AnnMarie. Dinos! Filipowich, Bob, illus. 2001. (Textured Soft Shapes Ser.). 8p. (J). (ps-ps). 10.99 (978-1-58476-066-5(4)) Innovative Kids.

McMahon, Kara. Opposites. 2004. (Elmo's World Ser.). (Illus.). 22p. (J). (gr. k-ps). bds. 6.99 (978-0-375-82716-7(1) , Random Hse. Bks. for Young Readers) Random Hse. Children's Bks.

McMullan, Kate. If You Were My Bunny. McPhail, David M., illus. 2002. 15.70 (978-0-7587-2831-9(X)) Book Wholesalers, Inc.

—If You Were My Bunny. McPhail, David M., illus. 1998. (Hello Reader! Ser.). 26p. (J). reprint ed. bds. 6.99 (978-0-590-34126-4(X)) Scholastic, Inc.

—Supercat to the Rescue. (J). 55.60 (978-0-7611-3234-9(1) , 23234) Workman Publishing Co., Inc.

—Supercat to the Rescue. Lemaitre, Pascal, illus. 2003. 32p. (J). bds. 6.95 (978-0-7611-2734-5(8) , 12734) Workman Publishing Co., Inc.

McMylor, Phil. Trouble Brewing. Ward, Matt, illus. 2002. (Wizard! Bks.). 16p. (J). (ps-2). bds. 4.95 (978-0-7641-5566-6(0)) Barron's Educational Series, Inc.

—Twinkle's Treat. Ward, Matt, illus. 2002. (Wizard! Bks.). 16p. (J). (ps-2). bds. 4.95 (978-0-7641-5567-3(9)) Barron's Educational Series, Inc.

McQuade, Jacqueline. Touch the Kitty. 2002. (Baby Animals to Touch & Feel! Ser.). (Illus.). 10p. (J). bds. 6.99 (978-0-439-33942-1(1) , Cartwheel Bks.) Scholastic, Inc.

McQuinn, Anna. Wanda's Washing Machine. McCafferty, Jan, illus. 2005. 16p. (J). (ps-ps). 12.95 (978-1-58925-768-9(5) , tiger tales) ME Media LLC.

Meadows, Daisy. Sophie the Sapphire Fairy. 2007. (Jewel Fairies Ser.). 80p. (Orig.). (J). pap. 4.99 (***978-0-439-93533-3(4)***, Scholastic Paperbacks) Scholastic, Inc.

Meeuwissen, Tony. Remarkable Animals. 2007. (Illus.). 24p. (J). spiral bd. 15.95 (978-1-84507-741-9(5)) Lincoln, Frances Ltd. GBR. *Dist:* Perseus Distribution.

T U V

Melmed Corace. Little Hoot. 2008. 36p. (J). 12.99 (978-0-8118-6023-9(X)) Chronicle Bks. LLC.

Merer, Laura, illus. Fuzzy Ducky's Birthday: A Touch-and-Feel Pop-up Book. 2005. 10p. (J). 8.95 (978-1-58117-324-6(5) , Intervisual/Piggy Toes) Dalmatian Pr.

Meridith, Shelley, illus. Hide n' Seek at Home with Josh B'Gosh. 1998. 10p. (J). 6.99 (978-1-929174-10-2(1)) Oshkosh B'Gosh, Inc.

Merrell, Patrick, illus. Colors & Shapes: Fun Color & Shape Activities! 2001. (My Wipe-Off Book Ser.). (J). (978-0-7853-5861-9(7)) Publications International, Ltd.

Merritt, Kate, illus. My Family: My Sister. 2003. 10p. (J). bds. 3.95 (978-0-8069-8581-7(X)) Sterling Publishing Co., Inc.

—Peekaboo, Baby! A Rhyming Flap Book. 2002. (DK Ladybird Ser.). 12p. (J). bds. 6.95 (978-0-7894-8467-3(6)) Dorling Kindersley Publishing, Inc.

Metrobooks Staff. Funny Faces: A Spinning Ball Book. 2000. (Illus.). 8p. (J). (ps-k). 9.99 (978-1-58663-103-1(9)) Friedman, Michael Publishing Group, Inc.

—Spots & Stripes: A Baby Soft Book. 2000. (Illus.). 8p. (J). (ps-k). 8.99 (978-1-58663-105-5(5)) Friedman, Michael Publishing Group, Inc.

Michaels, Nina. Love from Woolly: A Lift-the-Flap Book of Woolly Gifts. Smee, Nicola, illus. 2007. 12p. (J). (ps). 9.95 (978-1-905417-21-6(7)) Boxer Bks., Ltd. GBR. *Dist:* Sterling Publishing Co., Inc.

Miglis, Jenny. Peekaboo, Blue! Pontillo, Jenine, illus. 2004. (Blue's Clues Ser.). 12p. (J). bds. 7.99 (978-0-689-85257-2(6) , Simon Spotlight/Nickelodeon) Simon & Schuster Children's Publishing.

Miglis Sandvik, Jenny. Midnight Mayhem No. 4: Color Activity Book with Iron-On Transfer. Karl, Linda, illus. 2004. (Shrek 2 Ser.). 32p. (J). act. bk. ed. 3.99 (978-0-439-57635-2(0)) Scholastic, Inc.

Milbourne, Anna. Under the Sea Lift-the-Flap. 2001. (1001 Things to Spot Ser.). 16p. (J). (gr. 1 up). 11.95 (978-0-7945-0509-7(0)) EDC Publishing.

Miles, Elizabeth & Montgomery, Lee. Horror Masks. 2001. (Big Book of... Ser.). (Illus.). 24p. (J). pap. 9.95 (978-1-901323-14-6(5)) Orpheus Bks., Ltd. GBR. *Dist:* CPG Publishing, Inc.

Miles, Elizabeth & Noon, Steve. Warrior Masks. 2001. (Big Book of... Ser.). (Illus.). 24p. (J). pap. 9.95 (978-1-901323-16-0(1)) Orpheus Bks., Ltd. GBR. *Dist:* CPG Publishing, Inc.

Miles, Elizabeth & Wright, David. Animals Masks. 2001. (Big Book of... Ser.). (Illus.). 24p. (J). pap. 9.95 (978-1-901323-15-3(3)) Orpheus Bks., Ltd. GBR. *Dist:* CPG Publishing, Inc.

Miles Kelly Staff. Mix-Ups. 2003. (Illus.). 14p. 9.95 (978-1-902947-83-9(5)) Miles Kelly Publishing, Ltd. GBR. *Dist:* Independent Pubs. Group.

—Noises: Let's Learn. Nilsen, Anna, ed. 2003. (Let's Learn Ser.). (Illus.). 20p. (J). 7.95 (978-1-84236-139-9(2)) Miles Kelly Publishing, Ltd. GBR. *Dist:* Independent Pubs. Group.

—Opposites: Let's Learn. Nilsen, Anna, ed. 2003. (Let's Learn Ser.). (Illus.). 20p. (J). 7.95 (978-1-84236-138-2(4)) Miles Kelly Publishing, Ltd. GBR. *Dist:* Independent Pubs. Group.

—Sizes: Let's Learn. Nilsen, Anna, ed. 2003. (Let's Learn Ser.). (Illus.). 20p. (J). 7.95 (978-1-84236-140-5(6)) Miles Kelly Publishing, Ltd. GBR. *Dist:* Independent Pubs. Group.

Miles Kelly Staff & Nilsen, Anna. Actions: Let's Learn. 2003. (Let's Learn Ser.). (Illus.). 20p. (J). 7.95 (978-1-84236-137-5(6)) Miles Kelly Publishing, Ltd. GBR. *Dist:* Independent Pubs. Group.

—Numbers: Let's Learn. 2003. (Let's Learn Ser.). (Illus.). 20p. (J). 7.95 (978-1-84236-018-7(3)) Miles Kelly Publishing, Ltd. GBR. *Dist:* Independent Pubs. Group.

—Shapes: Let's Learn. 2003. (Let's Learn Ser.). (Illus.). 20p. (J). 7.95 (978-1-84236-016-3(7)) Miles Kelly Publishing, Ltd. GBR. *Dist:* Independent Pubs. Group.

Millard, Anne, et al. My First Farm Touch & Feel. 2002. (My First Ser.). (Illus.). 12p. (J). (ps-k). bds. 9.99 (978-0-7894-8524-3(9)) Dorling Kindersley Publishing, Inc.

Miller, Eileen Rudisill. Princess Leonora Paper Doll. 2007. 16p. (J). pap. 4.95 (***978-0-486-45959-2(4)***) Dover Pubns., Inc.

Miller, Margaret, illus. Boo ! Baby. 2001. (Look Baby Bks.). 14p. (J). bds. 5.99 (978-0-689-84432-4(8) , Little Simon) Simon & Schuster Children's Publishing.

Miller, Sara Swan. Barbie Super Fun. O'Brien, Jeff & Yuh, Ramona, photos by. 2001. (Barbie Friendship Craft Kit Ser.). (Illus.). (J). (gr. 1-3). (978-1-57584-812-9(0)) Reader's Digest Children's Publishing, Inc.

Milne, A. A. The Magical Pop-Up World of Winnie-the-Pooh. Shepard, Ernest H., illus. deluxe ed. 2003. 5p. (J). (ps). 24.99 (978-0-525-47141-7(3) , Dutton Juvenile) Penguin Group (USA) Inc.

—Pooh's First Clock. Shepard, Ernest H., illus. 1998. 12p. (J). (ps-3). bds. 12.99 (978-0-525-45983-5(9) , Dutton Juvenile) Penguin Group (USA) Inc.

—Slide & Seek Alphabet: A Sliding Window Book. 1999. (Illus.). 8p. (J). bds. 10.99 (978-0-7868-3240-8(1)) Disney Pr.

—Slide & Seek Numbers: A Sliding Window Book. 1999. (Illus.). 8p. (J). 10.99 (978-0-7868-3241-5(X)) Disney Pr.

—Where Is Eeyore: Slide & Find Books. Shepard, Ernest H., illus. 2001. 8p. (J). (ps-k). bds. 6.99 (978-0-525-46540-9(5) , Dutton Juvenile) Penguin Group (USA) Inc.

Milne, A. A. & Shepard, Ernest H. Where Is Poohs Honey: Slide & Find Books. 2001. (Illus.). 8p. (J). (ps-k). 6.99 (978-0-525-46539-3(1) , Dutton Juvenile) Penguin Group (USA) Inc.

Milnes, Margaret. Dinosaur Alive. 2000. (Pull a Page Ser.). (Illus.). 14p. (J). (ps-1). 9.99 (978-0-7364-1039-7(2)) Mouse Works.

Milord, Susan. Love That Baby! 2005. (Illus.). 16p. (J). (gr. k-ps). pap. 7.95 (978-0-618-56323-4(7)) Houghton Mifflin Co. Trade & Reference Div.

Minarik, Else Holmelund. Little Bear Makes a Mask. 2003. (gr. k-3). lib. bdg. 11.80 (978-0-613-69140-6(7)) Tandem Library Bks.

Mischel, Jenny Ann. Animal Alphabet. Bell-Myers, Darcy, illus. 2006. (J). bds. (978-0-9769239-0-9(4)) Perfect 4 Preschool.

Mitchell, Anastasia, illus. Josh B'Gosh at School. 1998. 10p. (J). 6.99 (978-1-929174-08-9(X)) Oshkosh B'Gosh, Inc.

Mitchell, Melanie. Mommy & Baby: Pets. 2006. (Illus.). 8p. (J). bds. 6.95 (978-0-8027-8982-2(X)) Walker & Co.

Moerbeck, Kees, illus. & des. Cinderella. Moerbeck, Kees, des. 2006. 9.99 (978-1-84643-019-0(4)) Child's Play-International.

Moerbeek, Kees. Alfred Hitchcock: The Master of Suspense: A Pop-Up Book. 2006. (Illus.). 16p. 29.95 (978-0-689-87595-3(9) , Little Simon) Simon & Schuster Children's Publishing.

—Way Home. 1999. (Illus.). 20p. (J). (ps-1). 4.99 (978-0-85953-725-4(0)) Child's Play-International.

—What's for Dinner? 1999. (Illus.). 20p. (J). (ps-1). 4.99 (978-0-85953-726-1(9)) Child's Play-International.

Moerbeek, Kees, illus. Raggedy Ann & Andy & the Camel with the Wrinkled Knees. collector's ed. 2003. (Raggedy Ann Ser.). 14p. (J). 21.99 (978-0-689-85775-1(6) , Little Simon) Simon & Schuster Children's Publishing.

Moffatt, Judith. Trick-or-Treat Faces: A Glowing Book You Can Read in the Dark! Moffatt, Judith, illus. 2000. (Illus.). 12p. (J). (ps-k). 6.95 (978-0-439-18299-7(9) , Cartwheel Bks.) Scholastic, Inc.

Monsters Unleashed. Scooby Doo: The Ultimate Sticker Book. 2004. (Ultimate Sticker Bks.). (Illus.). 16p. (J). pap. 6.99 (978-0-7566-0302-1(1)) Dorling Kindersley Publishing, Inc.

Montgomery, R. A. Choose Your Own Adventure Four Book Boxed Set #2: Mystery of the Maya, House of Danger, Race Forever, Escape. 2006. 576p. (J). per. 19.95 (***978-1-933390-95-6(6)***) Chooseco LLC.

Moore, Clement C. The Night Before Christmas: A Trim-a-Tree Story. l.t. ed. 1999. (Illus.). 16p. (J). (ps-3). 6.99 (978-1-57866-076-6(9) , Galahad Bks.) BBS Publishing Corp.

Moore, Clement C. The Night Before Christmas: Board Book. Birmingham, Christian, tr. 2007. (Illus.). 26p. (J). pap. 5.95 (***978-0-7624-3014-7(1)*** , Running Pr. Kids) Running Pr. Bk. Pubs.

Moore, Clement C., ed. & illus. The Night Before Christmas. Moore, Clement C., illus. Porfirio, Guy, illus. 2004. 20p. (J). 9.95 (978-0-8249-6553-2(1)) Ideals Pubns.

Moore, Clement Clarke. Night Before Christmas. Pinkney, Debbie, illus. 2004. (J). (***978-0-7853-1892-7(5)***) Publications International, Ltd.

Morgan, Mary. Bunny's Nursery Rhymes. Morgan, Mary, illus. 2007. (Preschool Pop-Ups Ser.). 14p. (J). bds. 7.99 (978-1-4169-0978-1(8) , Little Simon) Simon & Schuster Children's Publishing.

Moriarty, Sinéad. From Here to Maternity. 2006. 304p. pap. (***978-1-84488-068-3(0)***) Penguin Ireland.

Morris, Rick. Stars & Planets. 2005. (Time for Learning Ser.). (Illus.). 96p. (J). (978-1-4127-1135-7(5) , 7255300) Publications International, Ltd.

Moseley, Keith. Dragons: A Pop-up Book of Fantastic Adventures. Robertson, M. P., illus. 2006. 10p. (J). (ps-7). 15.95 (978-0-8109-4900-3(8)) Abrams, Harry N. , Inc.

Moseley, Keith, et al. Dragon World: A Pop-up Guide to These Scaled Beasts. 2007. 12p. (J). (ps-17). 15.95 (***978-0-8109-9456-0(9)***) Abrams, Harry N. , Inc.

Moses Bible Sticker Book. 2003. (Illus.). 16p. (J). 2.98 (978-1-4054-1557-6(6)) Parragon, Inc.

Moss, Miriam & Andreae, Giles. The Pop-Up Rumble in the Jungle. Mockler, Joanna & Wojtowycz, David, illus. 2001. 12p. (J). (ps-1). 14.95 (978-1-58925-658-3(1) , tiger tales) ME Media LLC.

Mouse Works Staff. Bug's Life: Can You Find the Difference Seek & See. 1998. 24p. (J). 3.99 (978-0-7364-0069-5(9)) Mouse Works.

—Buzz Book Pal. 1999. (Book Pals Ser.). (Illus.). 18p. (J). (ps-3). 8.99 (978-0-7364-0117-3(2)) Disney Pr.

—Dumbo. 2000. (Read-Aloud Storybook Ser.). 64p. (J). 6.99 (978-0-7364-1052-6(X)) Hyperion Bks. for Children.

—Dumbo. 1999. (Disney's Friendly Tales Ser.). (Illus.). 10p. (J). (ps-k). 6.99 (978-0-7364-1012-0(0)) Mouse Works.

—Simba. 1999. (Disney's Friendly Tales Ser.). (Illus.). 10p. (J). (ps-k). 6.99 (978-0-7364-1011-3(2)) Mouse Works.

—Toy Story 2. 1999. (Toy Story 2 Ser.). (Illus.). 10p. (J). (ps-3). 9.99 (978-0-7364-0186-9(5)) Mouse Works.

—Where Are the Bugs? 1998. (Illus.). 10p. (J). bds. 4.99 (978-0-7364-0068-8(0)) Mouse Works.

—Who's Our Mommy Pooh? Discovery Lift the Flap. 2000. 14p. (J). 5.99 (978-0-7364-1059-5(7)) Little Brown & Co.

—Woody Book Pal. 1999. (Book Pals Ser.). (Illus.). 18p. (J). (ps-3). 8.99 (978-0-7364-0116-6(4)) Disney Pr.

Mudd, Maria M. The Butterfly. Smith-Griswold, Wendy, illus. 2001. 14p. (J). (ps-3). 12.95 (978-1-58117-096-2(3) , Intervisual/Piggy Toes) Dalmatian Pr.

Muench-Williams, Heather. I Want a Pet Board Book & Felt Puppet Set. Teeple, Jackie, illus. 2005. (J). bds. (978-1-57332-367-3(5)) HighReach Learning, Inc.

Muldrow, Diane. The Happy Book. 1999. (Illus.). 18p. (J). pap. 13.95 (978-0-590-10993-2(6)) Scholastic, Inc.

Mullican, Judy. Time to Eat! Board Book & Felt Puppet Set. Coates, Jennifer, illus. 2005. (J). bds. (978-1-57332-359-8(4)) HighReach Learning, Inc.

—Trucks, Trucks Board Book & Felt Puppet Set. Cress, Michelle H., illus. 2005. (J). bds. (978-1-57332-357-4(8)) HighReach Learning, Inc.

Mullins, Amy. I'm Reverent When- Bagley, Val Chadwick, illus. 2005. ("Move-About" Book Ser.). (J). (978-1-59156-951-0(6)) Covenant Communications.

Mummy Sticker Book. 2003. (Illus.). 16p. (J). 2.98 (978-1-84273-122-2(X)) Parragon, Inc.

Murphy, Chuck. Shapes. Murphy, Chuck, illus. 2001. (Slide 'n' Seek Ser.: Vol. 3). (Illus.). 12p. (J). bds. 5.99 (978-0-689-84477-5(8) , Little Simon) Simon & Schuster Children's Publishing.

Murphy, Harriet. Hello, Dora! Follow the Reader Level 1. 2007. (Dora the Explorer Ser.). 24p. (J). 24.99 (***978-1-4169-4990-9(9)*** , Simon Scribbles) Simon & Schuster Children's Publishing.

Murphy, Mary. Let's Go! 2005. (Illus.). 16p. (J). bds. 14.99 (978-1-4052-1115-4(6)) Egmont Bks., Ltd. GBR. *Dist:* Trafalgar Square Publishing.

My First Bible Sticker Dictionary. 2000. (Illus.). 48p. (J). (ps-3). pap. 4.99 (978-0-570-05580-8(6)) Concordia Publishing Hse.

My First BK Of: Animals. 2007. 12p. pap. 7.99 (***978-1-4037-3059-6(8)***) Dalmatian Pr.

My First BK Of: Colors. 2007. 12p. pap. 7.99 (***978-1-4037-3057-2(1)***) Dalmatian Pr.

My First BK Of: Shapes. 2007. 12p. pap. 7.99 (***978-1-4037-3056-5(3)***) Dalmatian Pr.

My Friends Around the World: Sticker Book. (Girlfriend Gang Ser.). 16p. (J). (978-2-7643-0016-9(6)) Phidal Publishing, Inc./Editions Phidal, Inc.

My Little Softplay Cube Books. 2002. (J). (978-1-931312-69-1(9)) SoftPlay, Inc.

My Pats Equal Me! 2005. (J). bds. 5.95 (***978-0-9752860-2-9(1)***) OurRainbow Pr., LLC.

My TakeAlong Li, ed. Farm Animals. 2007. (My Take-along Library). 120p. (J). (ps-k). bds. 14.95 (***978-0-7696-5559-8(9)***) School Specialty Publishing.

—Nursery Rhymes. 2007. (My Take-along Library). 120p. (J). (ps-k). bds. 14.95 (***978-0-7696-5569-7(6)***) School Specialty Publishing.

Nagy, Krisztina. Fuzzy Bear: A Getting Dressed Book. enl. ed. 2000. (Illus.). 10p. (J). 16.95 (978-1-58117-050-4(5) , Intervisual/Piggy Toes) Dalmatian Pr.

Nall, Andrea. Have You Ever... ? 04. Davis, Tim, illus. 2006. (J). (***978-1-58650-582-0(3)***) Super Duper Pubns.

—Have You Ever... ? 05. Davis, Tim, illus. 2006. (J). (***978-1-58650-583-7(1)***) Super Duper Pubns.

—Have You Ever... ? 06. Davis, Tim, illus. 2006. (J). (***978-1-58650-584-4(X)***) Super Duper Pubns.

—Have You Ever... ? 07. Davis, Tim, illus. 2006. (J). (***978-1-58650-585-1(8)***) Super Duper Pubns.

—Have You Ever... ? 08. Davis, Tim, illus. 2006. (J). (***978-1-58650-586-8(6)***) Super Duper Pubns.

—Have You Ever... ? Book Set. Davis, Tim, illus. 2006. (J). (***978-1-58650-587-5(4)***) Super Duper Pubns.

Nathan, Cheryl. Funny Monsters Activity Book. 2003. (Illus.). 48p. (J). (gr. 4-7). pap., act. bk. ed. 3.95 (978-0-486-43060-7(X)) Dover Pubns., Inc.

Neis, Izzy. I Want to Potty. Shakir, Susie, illus. 2005. 10p. (J). 9.95 (978-1-58117-422-9(5) , Intervisual/Piggy Toes) Dalmatian Pr.

Nelson, Ray & Mohr-Hansen, Julie. On the Farm, 5 bks. Holveck, Kyle & Peeples, Aaron, illus. 2000. (J). (gr. k-2). pap. 60.00 (978-1-883772-79-6(6)) Flying Rhinoceros, Inc.

Nelson, Ray, et al. El Almuerzo Raro de Eduardo Bichero. Palladian Language Servies Staff & Rassmussen, Kari, eds. Palladian Language Servies Staff & Rassmussen, Kari, trs. 2000. (SPA., Illus.). 48p. (J). (gr. 3-5). pap. 9.00 (978-1-883772-76-5(1)) Flying Rhinoceros, Inc.

—The Weather, 5 bks. Siegel, Joseph, ed. 2000. (Farmer Bob Weather Ser.: No. 1). (Illus.). 31p. (Orig.). (J). (gr. k-2). pap. 60.00 (978-1-883772-77-2(X)) Flying Rhinoceros, Inc.

Neusner, Dena Wallenstein. Clifford's Touch & Feel Day. Lloyd, Gita & Binder, Eric, illus. 2003. (Clifford Ser.). 5p. (J). bds. 9.99 (978-0-439-44936-6(7)) Scholastic, Inc.

Newgarden, Mark & Cash, Megan Montague. Bow-Wow attracts Opposites. 2008. (Illus.). 18p. (J). bds. 4.95 (***978-0-15-205847-0(8)*** , Red Wagon Bks.) Harcourt Children's Bks.

—Bow-Wow hears Things. 2008. (Illus.). 18p. (J). bds. 4.95 (***978-0-15-205841-8(9)*** , Red Wagon Bks.) Harcourt Children's Bks.

Newsom, Tom, illus. The First Noel. 2006. 14p. (J). (gr. k-4). reprint ed. 8.00 (978-1-4223-5413-1(X)) DIANE Publishing Co.

Newton, Jill. Peek-a-Boo, Papa! A Peek-under-the Flap Book. 2007. (Illus.). 20p. (J). (ps). bds. 8.95 (***978-1-59354-626-7(2)***) Blue Apple Bks.

Nicholls, Judith. Crawly Caterpillar. 2008. (Doodlebops Ser.). 32p. (J). bds. 7.99 (***978-0-545-03026-7(9)*** , Cartwheel Bks.) Scholastic, Inc.

Nilsen, Anna. I Can Spell Words with Four Letters. 1998. (I Can Spell Ser.). (Illus.). 26p. (J). (ps-k). tchr. ed. 9.95 (978-0-7534-5125-0(5) , Kingfisher) Houghton Mifflin Co. Trade & Reference Div.

Nister, Ernest. Moving Pictures. (Illus.). (J). (978-0-399-22390-7(8) , Philomel) Penguin Group (USA) Inc.

Nister, Ernest, illus. Merry Magic-Go-Round: An Antique Book of Changing Pictures. 2005. 14p. (J). (gr. k-4). reprint ed. 19.00 (978-0-7567-9156-8(1)) DIANE Publishing Co.

Noah's Ark Bible Sticker Book. 2003. (Illus.). 16p. (J). 2.98 (978-1-4054-1558-3(4)) Parragon, Inc.

Noah's Ark Pillow Book. 2003. (J). (978-1-59292-025-9(X)) SoftPlay, Inc.

Nolan, Allia Zobel. Let's Ride Bikes. Terry, Michael, illus. 2005. 10p. (J). bds. 10.99 (978-0-7944-0610-3(6)) Reader's Digest Assn., Inc., The.

Nolan, Allia Zobel & Mitter, Matt. Bible Animal Friends: A Fun Goggly Eyes Book. McGee, Warner, illus. 2007. 12p. bds. 7.99 (978-1-59052-964-5(2) , Multnomah) WaterBrook Pr.

North, Dawn. Pull-Alongs: Digger. 2007. 12p. (ps). per. 6.95 (978-1-84610-446-6(7)) Make Believe Ideas GBR. *Dist:* Ingram Pub. Services.

North, Merry. My Grandma & Me: A Picture, Play & Tote Book. 2004. 10p. (J). (ps up). bds. 5.99 (978-1-57151-724-1(3)) Playhouse Publishing.

North, Merry. Squeaky Clean. 2005. 9p. (***978-1-57151-752-4(9)***) Playhouse Publishing.

Norworth, Jack. Take Me Out to the Ball Game. Stadler, John, illus. 2005. 16p. (J). 12.95 (978-0-689-85917-5(1) , Little Simon) Simon & Schuster Children's Publishing.

Novick, Mary. The Big Book of Animals & Bugs. Hale, Jenny, illus. 32p. (J). pap. (978-1-877003-38-7(7)) Little Hare Bks.

Numeroff, Laura Joffe. If You Take a Mouse to the Movies. Bond, Felicia, illus. 2000. (Laura Geringer Bks.). (J). (ps-2). 9.95 (978-0-694-01531-3(8) , Harper Festival) HarperCollins Pubs.

—If You Take a Mouse to the Movies: Book & Doll. Bond, Felicia, illus. 2001. (J). (ps-2). 19.95 (978-0-694-01427-9(3)) HarperCollins Pubs.

Nurse Pig: New Heroes Backpack Story. 2002. (J). (978-1-931312-60-8(5)) SoftPlay, Inc.

O'Brien, Joan. Fashion Accessories Stickers. 2003. (Illus.). 4p. 1.50 (978-0-486-43071-3(5)) Dover Pubns., Inc.

—Littlest Angels Stickers. 2003. (Dover Little Activity Bks.). (Illus.). 4p. (J). (ps-5). pap. 1.50 (978-0-486-43007-2(3)) Dover Pubns., Inc.

—Lucky Ladybug Stickers. 2004. (Dover Little Activity Bks.). (Illus.). 4p. (J). pap. 1.50 (978-0-486-43008-9(1)) Dover Pubns., Inc.

O'Brien, Kristen. Little Red Riding Hood Story in a Box. Winter, Janet, illus. 2003. (Story in a Box Ser.). 12p. (J). (ps-1). bds. 8.99 (978-1-883043-41-4(7)) Straight Edge Pr., The.

Oesch, Brian, illus. Berry Fun Playhouse. 2005. (Strawberry Shortcake Ser.). 6p. (J). (gr. k-1). 14.99 (978-0-448-43644-9(2) , Grosset & Dunlap) Penguin Group (USA) Inc.

Olesen, Cecilie. My First Handy Bible. Mazali, Gustavo, illus. 2006. 64p. (J). bds. 12.99 (978-1-59052-608-8(2) , Multnomah) WaterBrook Pr.

Oliver, Narelle. Baby Bilby, Where Do You Sleep? Oliver, Narelle, illus. 2002. (Illus.). 32p. (J). (978-0-7344-0230-1(9) , Lothian Bks.) Hachette Livre Australia.

Onish, Liane. The Alphabet Eurps & the 4 Seasons. 1999. (Eurps Concept Bks.). (Illus.). (J). 7.95 (978-1-892522-08-5(X)) Eurpsville USA, Inc.

—The Alphabet Eurps Build Eurpsville. 1999. (Eurps Concept Bks.). (Illus.). (J). 7.95 (978-1-892522-05-4(5)) Eurpsville USA, Inc.

—The Alphabet Eurps on the Farm. 1999. (Illus.). (J). 7.95 (978-1-892522-07-8(1)) Eurpsville USA, Inc.

—The Alphabet Eurps Ride a Rainbow. 1999. (Eurps Concept Bks.). (Illus.). (J). 7.95 (978-1-892522-06-1(3)) Eurpsville USA, Inc.

—The Alphabet Eurps Visit School. 1999. (Eurps Concept Bks.). (Illus.). 32p. (J). 7.95 (978-1-892522-04-7(7)) Eurpsville USA, Inc.

Ormerod, Jan. Ben Goes Swimming. 2000. (Illus.). 14p. (YA). (ps-3). 6.95 (978-0-688-17714-0(X)) HarperCollins Pubs.

Ostrow, Kim. A Colorful Christmas. Regan, Dana, illus. 2003. (Magical Color Bks.). 10p. (J). 5.95 (978-1-4027-0991-3(9)) Sterling Publishing Co., Inc.

Other. Build Your Own Pirate Ship: A Push-Out-and-Play Book. 2008. 12p. (J). bds. 8.95 (***978-0-385-61114-5(5)***) Transworld Publishers Ltd. GBR. *Dist:* Independent Pubs. Group.

Otterman, Lynn. Fluffy Bunny. Fletcher, Rusty, illus. 2002. (Animal Snuggles Ser.). 8p. (J). bds. 7.95 (978-0-8069-8403-2(1)) Sterling Publishing Co., Inc.

Oxenbury, Helen. Helen Oxenbury's Big Baby Book. Oxenbury, Helen, illus. 2003. (Illus.). 10p. (J). (gr. k-ps). bds. 7.99 (978-0-7636-2016-5(5)) Candlewick Pr.

Packard, Mary. Chopsticks. Nichols, Cathy, ed. 2000. (Illus.). 16p. (J). (978-1-884270-19-2(0)) Hall, Nancy Inc.

Pacovska, Kveta. The Little Flower King. Pacovska, Kveta, illus. 2007. 40p. (J). 17.99 (978-0-698-40054-2(2) , Minedition) Penguin Group (USA) Inc.

Paes, Rob, illus. Mighty Machines. 2003. 12p. (J). (gr. k-3). 20.00 (978-0-7567-6652-8(4)) DIANE Publishing Co.

Page, Jason. Wham Bam Boozle: A Gnastly, Noisy, Stinky Pop-Up Book! Quigley, Sebastian, illus. 2003. 12p. (J). (gr. k-4). reprint ed. 12.00 (978-0-7567-6906-2(X)) DIANE Publishing Co.

Pandell, Karen. I Love You Baby from Head to Toe. Fletcher, Jane, illus. 2004. 16p. (J). (gr. k-ps). bds. 5.99 (978-0-7636-1588-8(9)) Candlewick Pr.

—Peekaboo, Stretch! Mcelmurry, Jill, illus. 2006. 18p. (J). (gr. k-k). 9.99 (978-0-7636-1593-2(5)) Candlewick Pr.

—Where's Stretch? McElmurry, Jill, illus. 2004. 18p. (J). (gr. k-k). 9.99 (978-0-7636-1594-9(3)) Candlewick Pr.

Parent, Nancy. Pooh Says Boo. 1998. (Pooh Ser.). (Illus.). 10p. (J). (ps). 4.99 (978-1-57082-752-5(4)) Mouse Works.

Parker, Ant. Ginger. 2000. (Illus.). 32p. (J). (ps-1). pap. 5.95 (978-1-57255-429-0(0)) Mondo Publishing.

—Wake up, Ginger. Parker, Ant, illus. 2001. (Illus.). 32p. (J). (ps-1). pap. 5.95 (978-1-58653-853-8(5)) Mondo Publishing.

Parr, Todd. ToddWorld: It's a Colorful World! 2006. (Illus.). 10p. (J). (ps-3). bds., bds. 8.99 (978-0-316-05708-0(8)) Little, Brown Bks. for Young Readers.

Parry, Linda & Parry, Alan. The Greatest Story Ever Told: A Pop-up Activity Book. 2004. 8p. act. bk. ed. 10.95 (978-0-8294-1701-2(X)) Loyola Pr.

Partis, Joanne. Try Counting Sheep. 2007. (Illus.). (J). (ps-k). bds. 12.95 (*978-0-7696-5342-6(1) , Gingham Dog Pr.) School Specialty Publishing.

Patricelli, Leslie. Big Little. Patricelli, Leslie, illus. 2003. (Leslie Patricelli board Bks.). (Illus.). 24p. (J). (gr. k-ps). bds. 6.99 (978-0-7636-1951-0(5)) Candlewick Pr.

—Quiet Loud. Patricelli, Leslie, illus. 2003. (Leslie Patricelli board Bks.). (Illus.). 24p. (J). (gr. k-ps). bds. 6.99 (978-0-7636-1952-7(3)) Candlewick Pr.

—Yummy Yucky. 2003. (Leslie Patricelli board Bks.). (Illus.). 24p. (J). (gr. k-ps). bds. 6.99 (978-0-7636-1950-3(7)) Candlewick Pr.

Pearlman, Bobby. Passover Is Here! Desmoinaux, Christel, illus. 2005. 16p. (J). pap. 6.99 (978-0-689-86587-9(2) , Little Simon) Simon & Schuster Children's Publishing.

Pelham, David. Applebee's Colors. 2006. (Illus.). 16p. (J). 12.95 (978-0-7624-2647-8(0) , Running Pr.) Running Pr. Bk. Pubs.

—Applebee's Shapes. 2006. (Illus.). 16p. (J). 12.95 (978-0-7624-2648-5(9) , Running Pr.) Running Pr. Bk. Pubs.

—A Is for Animals: An ABC Pop-Up. Pelham, David, illus. 10th anniv. ed. 2001. (Illus.). 14p. (J). 18.99 (978-0-689-84706-6(8) , Little Simon) Simon & Schuster Children's Publishing.

Penton Overseas, Inc. Staff. Diego Numbers Slide & Learn: Interactive Flash Cards. rev. ed. 2007. (J). (gr. 3-6). 9.95 (*978-1-74181-172-8(4)) Hinkler Bks. Pty, Ltd. AUS. *Dist:* Penton Overseas, Inc.

—My First Words: Early Language Development System. rev. ed. 2007. (Illus.). 12p. (J). (gr. k-5). 10.95 (*978-1-59125-810-0(3) , Smart Kids) Penton Overseas, Inc.

—Your Baby Can Read! Book 2: Early Language Development System. 2007. (Illus.). 20p. (J). (gr. k-5). pap. 8.95 (*978-1-59125-778-3(6) , Smart Kids) Penton Overseas, Inc.

—Your Baby Can Read! Book 3: Early Language Development System. 2007. (Illus.). 20p. (J). (gr. k-5). pap. 8.95 (*978-1-59125-779-0(4) , Smart Kids) Penton Overseas, Inc.

—Your Baby Can Read! Review Book: Early Language Development System. 2007. (Illus.). 20p. (J). (gr. k-5). pap. 8.95 (*978-1-59125-780-6(8) , Smart Kids) Penton Overseas, Inc.

—Your Baby Can Read! Starter Book: Early Language Development System. 2007. (Illus.). 20p. (J). (gr. k-5). pap. 8.95 (*978-1-59125-776-9(X) , Smart Kids) Penton Overseas, Inc.

Penton Overseas, Inc. Staff, contrib. by. Its Potty Time Boys. 2007. 14p. 7.95 (*978-1-59125-843-8(X)) Penton Overseas, Inc.

—Its Potty Time Girls. 2007. 14p. 7.95 (*978-1-59125-842-1(1)) Penton Overseas, Inc.

Penton Overseas, Inc. Staff & Titzer, Bob. Your Baby Can Read! Book 1: Early Language Development System. 2007. (Illus.). 20p. (J). (gr. k-5). pap. 8.95 (*978-1-59125-777-6(8) , Smart Kids) Penton Overseas, Inc.

People. Date not set. (I Can Draw Ser.). 32p. (J). 4.98 (978-1-4054-0020-6(X)) Parragon, Inc.

Perez, Jessica. Under Construction: A Moving Track Book. Schneider, Christine, illus. 2005. 12p. (J). 12.95 (978-1-58117-272-0(9) , Intervisual/Piggy Toes) Dalmatian Pr.

—Who's Hiding Inside? Dinosaurs. Lensch, Chris, illus. 2005. (Who's Hiding Inside Ser.). 12p. (J). bds. 7.95 (978-1-58117-246-1(X) , Intervisual/Piggy Toes) Dalmatian Pr.

Peter, Rutherford. Ready for Bed. 2006. (Illus.). 32p. (J). (ps). 12.95 (978-1-904613-95-4(0) , Buster Bks.) O'Mara, Michael Bks., Ltd. GBR. *Dist:* Independent Pubs. Group.

Peters, Stephanie True. A Princess Primer: A Fairy Godmother's Guide to Being a Princess. Oberdieck, Bernhard & Gordeev, Denis, illus. 2006. 32p. (J). (ps). 19.99 (978-0-525-47765-5(9) , Dutton Juvenile) Penguin Group (USA) Inc.

Petruccio, Steven James. Cowboy Tattoos. 2003. (Dover Little Activity Bks.). (Illus.). 2p. (J). (gr. k-5). pap. 1.50 (978-0-486-43028-7(6)) Dover Pubns., Inc.

—Emergency Vehicles Stickers. 2003. (Dover Little Activity Bks.). (Illus.). 4p. (J). (ps-5). pap. 1.50 (978-0-486-43009-6(X)) Dover Pubns., Inc.

—Police Station Sticker Activity Book. 1999. (Dover Little Activity Bks.). (Illus.). 4p. (J). pap. 1.50 (978-0-486-40748-7(9)) Dover Pubns., Inc.

Petty, Kate. The Amazing Pop-Up Geography Book. Maizels, Jennie, illus. 2000. 1p. (J). (gr. 3 up). 24.99 (978-0-525-46438-9(7) , Dutton Juvenile) Penguin Group (USA) Inc.

—The Perfect Pop-up Punctuation Book. Maizels, Jennie, illus. 2006. 12p. (J). (gr. 2). 14.99 (978-0-525-47772-3(1) , Dutton Juvenile) Penguin Group (USA) Inc.

Petty, Kate & Maizels, Jennie. Global Garden. 2007. (Illus.). 12p. (J). (gr. 2-3). 19.99 (*978-1-903919-16-3(9) , Eden Project Books) Transworld Publishers Ltd. GBR. *Dist:* Independent Pubs. Group.

Pfister, Marcus. Just the Way You Are. Pfister, Marcus, illus. 2002. (Illus.). 32p. (J). (gr. k-3). 15.95 (978-0-7358-1615-2(8)) North-South Bks., Inc.

—Rainbow Fish Undersea Fun Sticker Storybook. 2003. (Illus.). (J). pap. 6.95 (978-1-59014-147-2(4)) North-South Bks., Inc.

—Somos Como Somos. Almohar, Ariel, tr. Pfister, Marcus, illus. 2002. (SPA., Illus.). 32p. (J). (gr. k-3). 15.95 (978-0-7358-1654-1(9) , NS31596) North-South Bks., Inc.

Phidal Publishing Staff, ed. Totally Girls: Super Sticker Book. (Illus.). 64p. (J). pap. (978-2-7643-0190-6(1)) Phidal Publishing, Inc./Editions Phidal, Inc.

Phillips, Karen. Klutz Lettering. Date not set. 60p. (J). spiral bd. 16.95 (978-1-57054-428-6(X)) Klutz.

Phillips, Sara. Animals. 2003. (Illus.). 8p. (J). pap. 4.95 (978-0-7624-1650-9(5)) Running Pr. Bk. Pubs.

Phillips, Sarah. Lift & Learn ABC. Snaith, Andy, photos by. 2006. (Illus.). 24p. (ps). per., bds. 5.95 (978-1-84610-029-1(1)) Make Believe Ideas GBR. *Dist:* Ingram Pub. Services.

—Touch & Learn: 123. 2007. (Touch & Learn (Make Believe Ideas) Ser.). (Illus.). 12p. (ps). per., bds. 6.95 (978-1-84610-462-6(9)) Make Believe Ideas GBR. *Dist:* Ingram Pub. Services.

—Touch & Learn: ABC. 2007. (Touch & Learn (Make Believe Ideas) Ser.). (Illus.). 12p. (ps). per., bds. 6.95 (978-1-84610-461-9(0)) Make Believe Ideas GBR. *Dist:* Ingram Pub. Services.

Pienkowski, Jan. The First Noel: A Christmas Carousel. Pienkowski, Jan et al, illus. 2004. 10p. (J). 12.99 (978-0-7636-2190-2(0)) Candlewick Pr.

—Haunted House. Pienkowski, Jan, illus. 2005. (Illus.). 12p. (J). (ps up). 14.99 (978-0-7636-2818-5(2)) Candlewick Pr.

Pienkowski, Jan, illus. Dinner Time. 2000. (Monsterpops Ser.). 12p. (J). (ps-3). 5.95 (978-1-58117-024-5(6) , Intervisual/Piggy Toes) Dalmatian Pr.

—Monster Pops: Dinner Time; Oh My, a Fly!; Small Talk, 3 vols., Set. 2000. (J). (ps-3). 14.95 (978-1-58117-023-8(8) , Intervisual/Piggy Toes) Dalmatian Pr.

—Oh My, a Fly! 2000. (Monsterpops Ser.). 12p. (J). (ps-3). 5.95 (978-1-58117-026-9(2) , Intervisual/Piggy Toes) Dalmatian Pr.

—Small Talk. 2000. (Monsterpops Ser.). 12p. (J). (ps-3). 5.95 (978-1-58117-025-2(4) , Intervisual/Piggy Toes) Dalmatian Pr.

Piggy Toes Press. Our Ballet Recital. Maddocks, Maria, illus. 2005. 12p. (J). (ps-ps). 12.95 (978-1-58117-425-0(X) , Intervisual/Piggy Toes) Dalmatian Pr.

Piggy Toes Press Staff. Baby Bugs' Toys. 2000. (Lovable Huggable Baby Looney Tunes Cloth Bks.). (Illus.). 6p. (J). (ps up). 14.95 (978-1-58117-078-8(5) , Intervisual/Piggy Toes) Dalmatian Pr.

—Baby Tweety's Bedtime. 2000. (Lovable Huggable Baby Looney Tunes Cloth Bks.). (Illus.). 6p. (J). (ps up). 14.95 (978-1-58117-077-1(7) , Intervisual/Piggy Toes) Dalmatian Pr.

Piggy Toes Press Staff & Borlasca, Hector. The Alphabet Song. 2006. 12.95 (978-1-58117-444-1(6) , Intervisual/Piggy Toes) Dalmatian Pr.

Piggy Toes Press Staff & Embleton, Chris. Baby Says. 2006. (Illus.). 6p. (J). 12.95 (978-1-58117-458-8(6) , Intervisual/Piggy Toes) Dalmatian Pr.

Piggy Toes Press Staff & Haskamp, Steve. Five Silly Monkeys: With Handpuppet. 2006. (Illus.). 12p. (J). bds. 12.95 (978-1-58117-460-1(8) , Intervisual/Piggy Toes) Dalmatian Pr.

—Good Morning, Good Night! 2006. (Illus.). 12p. (J). 12.95 (978-1-58117-461-8(6) , Intervisual/Piggy Toes) Dalmatian Pr.

Pilkey, Dav. Ricky Ricotta Y el Poderoso Robot Contra Los Mecamonos de Marte. 2007. (Ricky Ricotta Ser.: No. 4). 144p. (J). pap. 3.99 (978-0-439-85105-3(X) , Scholastic en Espanol) Scholastic, Inc.

Pinkney, Debbie, illus. The First Christmas. 2004. (J). (*978-0-7853-1894-1(1)) Publications International, Ltd.

Pinto, Sara. The Alphabet Room. Pinto, Sara, illus. 2003. (Illus.). 56p. (J). 16.95 (978-1-58234-841-4(3) , Bloomsbury Children) Bloomsbury Publishing.

Piper, Watty. The Little Engine That Could. Long, Loren, illus. 2005. 48p. (J). (ps-3). 17.99 (978-0-399-24467-4(0) , Philomel) Penguin Group (USA) Inc.

Pirates. (Awesome Adventures Ser.). 16p. (J). (978-2-7643-0117-3(0)) Phidal Publishing, Inc./Editions Phidal, Inc.

Pirates of the Caribbean: The Black Pearl - a Pop-up Pirate Ship. 2007. 4p. (ps-3). 12.99 (*978-1-4231-0808-5(6)) Disney Pr.

Pirulino. On the Farm. Ferri, Francesca, illus. 2004. 10p. (J). 16.95 (978-0-7641-2947-6(3)) Barron's Educational Series, Inc.

Play & Learn Fo, ed. Farm Animals. 2007. (Play & Learn Foam Puzzle Bks.). 10p. (J). bds. 16.95 (*978-0-7696-5389-1(8) , Brighter Child) School Specialty Publishing.

—Shapes. 2007. (Play & Learn Foam Puzzle Bks.). 10p. (J). bds. 16.95 (*978-0-7696-5409-6(6) , Brighter Child) School Specialty Publishing.

—Wild Animals. 2007. (Play & Learn Foam Puzzle Bks.). 10p. (J). bds. 16.95 (*978-0-7696-5399-0(5) , Brighter Child) School Specialty Publishing.

Playskool Staff. Puppy Book & Ball. 1999. (Illus.). 7.99 (978-0-525-46021-3(7) , Dutton Juvenile) Penguin Group (USA) Inc.

Plush Book - Land Before Time (English) 2000. (J). (978-1-58805-103-5(X)) DS-Max USA, Inc.

Policeman Dog: New Heroes Backpack Story. 2002. (J). (978-1-931312-59-2(1)) SoftPlay, Inc.

Polk, Milbry. Egyptian Mummies. Stewart, Roger & Seminario, Jose R., illus. 2004. 8p. (J). (gr. k-4). reprint ed. 20.00 (978-0-7567-8329-7(1)) DIANE Publishing Co.

Pomaska, Anna. Sun, Moon & Stars Stickers. 1998. (Dover Little Activity Bks.). (Illus.). 4p. (J). (ps-5). pap. 1.50 (978-0-486-40504-9(4)) Dover Pubns., Inc.

Post, Jim & Post, Janet. Barnyard Boogie. Vasconsellos, Daniel, illus. gif. ed. 2003. 32p. (J). 15.99 (978-1-57939-130-0(3)) Accord Publishing, Ltd.

Potter, Beatrix. Jemima Puddle-Duck. (Potter Ser.). 12p. (J). (ps). 2008. bds. 7.99 (*978-0-7232-5955-8(0)); 2007. bds. 3.99 (978-0-7232-5856-8(2)) Penguin Group (USA) Inc. (Warne).

—Merry Christmas, Peter Rabbit! 2003. (Illus.). 12p. (J). (ps). bds. 6.99 (978-0-7232-4925-2(3) , Warne) Penguin Group (USA) Inc.

—Peter Rabbit & Friends. ed. 2008. (Potter Ser.). (Illus.). 12p. (J). (ps). pap. 4.99 (*978-0-7232-5888-9(0) , Warne) Penguin Group (USA) Inc.

—Peter Rabbit & Friends Classic Nursery Songs. 2003. (Illus.). (J). bds. (978-0-7853-8531-8(2)) Publications International, Ltd.

—Peter Rabbit Large Shaped Board Book. 2008. 12p. (J). (ps-1). bds. 7.99 (*978-0-7232-5956-5(9) , Warne) Penguin Group (USA) Inc.

—Peter Rabbit Lift-the-Flap Words, Colors, Numbers (R/I) 2007. 12p. (J). 14.99 (978-0-7232-5828-5(7) , Warne) Penguin Group (USA) Inc.

—Peter Rabbit Shaped Board Book. 2007. 12p. (J). bds. 3.99 (978-0-7232-5855-1(4) , Warne) Penguin Group (USA) Inc.

—Peter Rabbit's Hide & Seek. 2004. (Potter Ser.). (Illus.). 16p. (J). 12.99 (978-0-7232-5351-8(X) , Warne) Penguin Group (USA) Inc.

—Peter Rabbit's Touch & Feel Book. 1999. (Illus.). 12p. (J). (ps-3). 9.99 (978-0-7232-4518-6(5) , Warne) Penguin Group (USA) Inc.

—Tale of Peter Rabbit Book & Toy. 2006. (Illus.). 80p. (J). 14.99 (978-0-7232-5356-3(0) , Warne) Penguin Group (USA) Inc.

Potter, Beatrix, text. Jemima Puddle-Duck. 2003. (Play-A-Sound Ser.). (Illus.). (J). (978-0-7853-7970-6(3)); (978-0-7853-7969-0(X)) Publications International, Ltd.

—Peter Rabbit. 2003. (Play-A-Sound Ser.). (Illus.). (J). (978-0-7853-7972-0(X)); (978-0-7853-7971-3(1)) Publications International, Ltd.

Pountney, Beth. Farmyard Friends. 2007. (Lift & Count Ser.). (Illus.). 12p. (ps). per., bds. 5.95 (978-1-84610-458-9(0)) Make Believe Ideas GBR. *Dist:* Ingram Pub. Services.

—Ocean Buddies. 2007. (Touchy Feely Ser.). (Illus.). 12p. (ps). per., bds. 5.95 (978-1-84610-457-2(2)) Make Believe Ideas GBR. *Dist:* Ingram Pub. Services.

—Playful Pets. 2007. (Lift & Count Ser.). (Illus.). 12p. (ps). per., bds. 5.95 (978-1-84610-459-6(9)) Make Believe Ideas GBR. *Dist:* Ingram Pub. Services.

—Wacky Wild Animals. 2007. (Touchy Feely Ser.). (Illus.). 12p. (ps). per., bds. 5.95 (978-1-84610-456-5(4)) Make Believe Ideas GBR. *Dist:* Ingram Pub. Services.

Powell, R. This Little Doggy. Curry, Peter, illus. 2004. (Mini Movers Ser.). 14p. (J). bds. 3.50 (978-0-7641-5741-7(8)) Barron's Educational Series, Inc.

—This Little Fish. Curry, Peter, illus. 2004. (Mini Movers Ser.). 14p. (J). bds. 3.50 (978-0-7641-5738-7(8)) Barron's Educational Series, Inc.

Powell, Richard. Hoot! Hoot! Martín Larrañaga, Ana, illus. 2003. (Lift-the-Flap Bks.). 24p. (J). (gr. k-k). 8.99 (978-0-7636-2107-0(2)) Candlewick Pr.

—I See a Cow. Davis, Caroline, illus. 2003. (Plastic Shapes Ser.). 12p. (J). bds. 5.95 (978-0-7641-5647-2(0)) Barron's Educational Series, Inc.

—I See a Teddy. Davis, Caroline, illus. 2003. (Plastic Shapes Ser.). 12p. (J). bds. 5.95 (978-0-7641-5648-9(9)) Barron's Educational Series, Inc.

—I See a Tractor. Davis, Caroline, illus. 2003. (Plastic Shapes Ser.). 12p. (J). bds. 5.95 (978-0-7641-5646-5(2)) Barron's Educational Series, Inc.

—Quiet as a Mouse: A Moving Picture Storybook. Hendra, Sue, illus. 2003. 16p. (J). 7.95 (978-1-58925-678-1(6) , tiger tales) ME Media LLC.

—Whose Hat Is That? Martín Larrañaga, Ana, illus. 2004. (Ana's Mini Movers Ser.). 12p. (J). 5.95 (978-1-58925-740-5(5) , tiger tales) ME Media LLC.

Powell, Richard J. Who's Peeking at You? from the Pond. Clark, Debbie, illus. 2006. (Who's Peeking? Bks.). 12p. (J). bds. 4.99 (978-0-7641-5994-7(1)) Barron's Educational Series, Inc.

—Who's Peeking at You? in the Pet Store. Clark, Debbie, illus. 2006. (Who's Peeking Bks.). 12p. (J). bds. 4.99 (978-0-7641-5996-1(8)) Barron's Educational Series, Inc.

Powers, Amelia. Giant Pop-Out Shapes. 2007. (Illus.). 26p. (J). (ps). 10.95 (978-0-8118-5921-9(5)) Chronicle Bks. LLC.

—Giant Pop-Out Vehicles: A Pop-out Surprise Book. 2007. (Illus.). 26p. (J). (ps). 10.95 (978-0-8118-5953-0(3)) Chronicle Bks. LLC.

Powers, Christine. Love Is a Rainbow. 1999. (Leap Frog Lift-A-Flap Ser.). (Illus.). (J). (978-0-7853-3370-8(3)) Publications International, Ltd.

Prayer Bear Pillow Book. 2003. (J). (978-1-59292-026-6(8)) SoftPlay, Inc.

Price, Mathew. In the Snow. Augarde, Steve, illus. 2000. (Little Red Car Bks.). 10p. (J). (ps-1). pap. 6.95 (978-0-7892-0674-9(9) , Abbeville Kids) Abbeville Pr., Inc.

—Little Red Car Has an Accident. Augarde, Steve, illus. 2000. (Little Red Car Bks.). 10p. (J). (ps-1). pap. 6.95 (978-0-7892-0673-2(0) , Abbeville Kids) Abbeville Pr., Inc.

—Little Red Car Plays Taxi. Augarde, Steve, illus. 2000. (Little Red Car Bks.). 10p. (J). (ps-1). pap. 6.95 (978-0-7892-0675-6(7) , Abbeville Kids) Abbeville Pr., Inc.

—My Mommy. Claverie, Jean, illus. 2003. (Peekaboo Board Bks.). 10p. (J). bds. 4.99 (978-0-7696-3155-4(X) , Gingham Dog Pr.) School Specialty Publishing.

—Peekaboo Collection. 2004. 40p. (J). bds. 19.95 (978-0-7696-3459-3(1)) School Specialty Publishing.

Priddy, Roger. Animals. 2005. (Bright Baby Ser.). 12p. (J). bds. 0.97 (978-0-312-49610-4(9) , Priddy Bks.) St. Martin's Pr.

—Baby Gund Mirror Bathtime. rev. ed. 2006. 12p. (J). bds. 6.95 (978-0-312-49708-8(3) , Priddy Bks.) St. Martin's Pr.

—Baby Gund Mirror Book Playtime. 2006. 6p. (J). bds. 6.95 (978-0-312-49765-1(2) , Priddy Bks.) St. Martin's Pr.

—Baby Touch & Feel: Puppy Love. rev. ed. 2005. 14p. (J). bds. 8.95 (978-0-312-49536-7(6) , Priddy Bks.) St. Martin's Pr.

—Bright Baby Animals. 2006. 26p. (J). bds. 8.95 (978-0-312-49781-1(4) , Priddy Bks.) St. Martin's Pr.

—Bright Baby Soft-to-Touch Large: Words, Animals, Colors. 2005. (J). 22.95 (978-0-312-49555-8(2) , Priddy Bks.) St. Martin's Pr.

—Bright Baby Touch & Feel at the Zoo. 2006. (Bright Baby Ser.). (Illus.). 10p. (J). bds. 4.95 (978-0-312-49857-3(8) , Priddy Bks.) St. Martin's Pr.

—Bright Baby Touch & Feel Baby Animals. 2006. 10p. (J). bds. 4.95 (978-0-312-49858-0(6) , Priddy Bks.) St. Martin's Pr.

—Bright Baby Touch & Feel on the Farm. 2006. 10p. (J). bds. 4.95 (978-0-312-49859-7(4) , Priddy Bks.) St. Martin's Pr.

—Bright Baby Touch & Feel Perfect Pets. 2006. 10p. (J). bds. 4.95 (978-0-312-49860-3(8) , Priddy Bks.) St. Martin's Pr.

—Bright Baby Touch, Feel & Listen: Puppy & Friends. rev. ed. 2006. (Touch, Feel & Say Ser.). (Illus.). 10p. (J). bds. 8.95 (978-0-312-49675-3(3) , Priddy Bks.) St. Martin's Pr.

—Bunny & Friends. rev. ed. 2001. (Touch & Feel Ser.). (Illus.). 12p. (J). bds. 6.95 (978-0-312-49030-0(5) , Priddy Bks.) St. Martin's Pr.

—Cloth Shaker Teether Animals. rev. ed. 2006. 10p. (J). 6.95 (978-0-312-49669-2(9) , Priddy Bks.) St. Martin's Pr.

—Counting Colors (large Format) 2007. 20p. (J). 8.95 (*978-0-312-50137-2(4) , Priddy Bks.) St. Martin's Pr.

—Duckling & Friends: Bright Baby Touch Feel Listen Duckling. rev. ed. 2006. (Touch, Feel & Say Ser.). (Illus.). 10p. (J). bds. 8.95 (978-0-312-49673-9(7) , Priddy Bks.) St. Martin's Pr.

—Earth IQ. 2007. 24p. (J). bds. 14.95 (*978-0-312-50011-5(4) , Priddy Bks.) St. Martin's Pr.

—Funny Faces Rusty Robot. 2006. (Illus.). 10p. (J). bds. 9.95 (978-0-312-49693-7(1) , Priddy Bks.) St. Martin's Pr.

—Funny Faces Touch & Feel: Charlie Monkey. rev. ed. 2006. (Illus.). 10p. (J). bds. 9.95 (978-0-312-49692-0(3) , Priddy Bks.) St. Martin's Pr.

—Giant Sticker Activity First Words. rev. ed. 2005. 120p. (J). pap. 12.95 (978-0-312-49522-0(6) , Priddy Bks.) St. Martin's Pr.

—Happy Baby. rev. ed. 2001. (Baby Shakers Ser.). (Illus.). 24p. (J). bds. 5.95 (978-0-312-49021-8(6) , Priddy Bks.) St. Martin's Pr.

—Happy Baby Animals. (J). 2007. bds. 3.95 (*978-0-312-49956-3(6)); 2001. (Illus.). 24p. bds. 5.95 (978-0-312-49020-1(8)) St. Martin's Pr. (Priddy Bks.).

—Happy Baby Colors. 2007. (J). bds. 3.95 (*978-0-312-49955-6(8) , Priddy Bks.) St. Martin's Pr.

—Happy Dog Activity Cloth Book. rev. ed. 2007. 24p. (J). 9.95 (*978-0-312-49999-0(X) , Priddy Bks.) St. Martin's Pr.

—Happy Dog Activity Cloth Book in Bag. 2007. 24p. (J). 9.95 (*978-0-312-50076-4(9) , Priddy Bks.) St. Martin's Pr.

—Lift the Flap - Colors. 2005. (Priddy Books Big Ideas for Little People). (Illus.). 30p. (J). bds. 5.95 (978-0-312-49436-0(X) , Priddy Bks.) St. Martin's Pr.

—Millie Cow Large Format. 2007. 10p. (J). bds. 14.95 (*978-0-312-50115-0(3) , Priddy Bks.) St. Martin's Pr.

—Natural Baby Eat. 2008. (J). bds. 6.95 (*978-0-312-50199-0(4) , Priddy Bks.) St. Martin's Pr.

—Rainbow Rob. 2006. (Illus.). 20p. (J). bds. 12.95 (978-0-312-49791-0(1) , Priddy Bks.) St. Martin's Pr.

—Rainbow Trucks. 2006. (Priddy Books Big Ideas for Little People). (Illus.). 14p. (J). bds. 12.95 (978-0-312-49814-6(4) , Priddy Bks.) St. Martin's Pr.

—Rocky Dog Large Format. 2007. 10p. (J). bds. 14.95 (*978-0-312-50116-7(1) , Priddy Bks.) St. Martin's Pr.

Priddy, Roger. Sticker Fun: Dinosaurs. rev. ed. 2004. (Illus.). 20p. (J). 3.95 (978-0-312-49310-3(X) , Priddy Bks.) St. Martin's Pr.

Priddy, Roger & Priddy Books Staff. Dinosaurs. rev. ed. 2006. 48p. (J). bds. 3.47 (978-0-312-49797-2(0) , Priddy Bks.) St. Martin's Pr.

—Sticker Acivity Fun Animals: Play & Learn. rev. ed. 2006. 48p. (J). bds. 3.47 (978-0-312-49795-8(4) , Priddy Bks.) St. Martin's Pr.

—Sticker Activity Fun Busy Bugs: Play & Learn. rev. ed. 2006. 48p. (J). bds. 3.47 (978-0-312-49796-5(2) , Priddy Bks.) St. Martin's Pr.

—Sticker Activity Fun Tough Trucks: Play & Learn. rev. ed. 2006. 48p. (J). bds. 3.47 (978-0-312-49800-9(4) , Priddy Bks.) St. Martin's Pr.

Problem of the Day Flip Chart. 1999. (SPA.). (gr. 2 up). suppl. ed. 86.00 (978-0-201-36532-0(4)); (gr. 3 up). suppl. ed. 86.00 (978-0-201-36540-5(5)); (gr. 4 up). suppl. ed. 86.00 (978-0-201-36548-1(0)); (gr. 5 up). suppl. ed. 86.00 (978-0-201-36556-6(1)) Addison-Wesley Educational Pubs., Inc.

Problem of the Day Flip Chart & Blackline Masters. 1999. (SPA.). (gr. k up). suppl. ed. 78.75 (978-0-201-36517-7(0)) Addison-Wesley Educational Pubs., Inc.

Prudom, Sharla. Jambo! Elephants. Prudom, Sharla, photos by. 2002. (Jambo! Ser.). (SWA & ENG., Illus.). 11p. (J). cd-rom 12.50 (978-1-931792-23-3(2)) E-Digital Bks., LLC.

Publications International, Ltd Staff, contrib. by. Bob the Builder: Baby's First Sound Book. 2002. (Illus.). (J). 7.95 (978-0-7853-6641-6(5)) Publications International, Ltd.

Puppy. 2004. (J). per. (978-1-57657-397-6(4)) Paradise Pr., Inc.

Puppy. (Buggy Buddies Ser.). (Illus.). (J). (ps). bds. (978-1-56021-351-2(5) , 202) W.J. Fantasy, Inc.

Puzzle Track Staff, ed. Adv with Little Duck. 2007. (Puzzle Track Ser.). 20p. (J). bds. 18.95 (*978-0-7696-5619-9(6)) School Specialty Publishing.

—Around the World Adv. 2007. (Puzzle Track Ser.). 20p. (J). bds. 18.95 (*978-0-7696-5589-5(0)) School Specialty Publishing.

—Great Train Ride. 2007. (Puzzle Track Ser.). 20p. (J). bds. 18.95 (*978-0-7696-5599-4(8)) School Specialty Publishing.

—Hello Ladybug. 2007. (Puzzle Track Ser.). 20p. (J). bds. 18.95 (*978-0-7696-5629-8(3)) School Specialty Publishing.

—Our Family Vacation. 2007. (Puzzle Track Ser.). 20p. (J). bds. 18.95 (*978-0-7696-5609-0(9)) School Specialty Publishing.

—Red Car Ride. 2007. (Puzzle Track Ser.). 20p. (J). bds. 18.95 (*978-0-7696-5579-6(3)) School Specialty Publishing.

Quarto Children's Books Staff, contrib. by. Buildings: Pocket Tangrams. 2001. (Illus.). (J). (978-0-439-27310-7(2)) Scholastic, Inc.

Rabe, Tish. Spooky Night! Sexton, Brenda, illus. 2006. (Nose Knows Ser.). 10p. (J). (ps-17). bds. 9.99 (978-1-58476-483-0(X) , IKIDS) Innovative Kids.

Radevsky, Anton. The Wild West Pop-Up Book. 2007. (Illus.). 8p. (gr. 3-7). 24.95 (*978-1-4027-4628-4(8)) Sterling Publishing Co., Inc.

Randall, Ronne. Snuggle up, Little Penguin! Church, Caroline Jayne, illus. 2003. (Little Friends Ser.). 14p. (J). 12.95 (978-1-57145-919-0(7) , Silver Dolphin Bks.) Advantage Pubs. Group.

Randinelli, Tracy & Prokos, Anna. Secrets of Space. Snow, Alan, illus. 2002. (Crash Course Ser.). 68p. (J). (gr. 2-17). spiral bd. 16.99 (978-1-58476-137-2(7)) Innovative Kids.

Random House Disney Staff. Cars. 2006. (Read-Aloud Board Book Ser.). (Illus.). 24p. (J). (gr. k-k). bds. 4.99 (978-0-7364-2293-2(5) , RH/Disney) Random Hse. Children's Bks.

—Cars Reusable Sticker Book. 2006. (Reusable Sticker Book Ser.). (Illus.). 12p. (J). (ps-2). pap. 6.99 (978-0-7364-2342-7(7) , RH/Disney) Random Hse. Children's Bks.

—Heart to Heart. 2006. (Illus.). 32p. (J). (ps-2). pap. 3.99 (978-0-7364-2361-8(3) , Golden/Disney) Random Hse. Children's Bks.

Ranson, Erin. The Story of Noah's Ark. Petrlik, Andrea, illus. 2007. 10p. (J). (ps). 8.99 (*978-1-84666-359-8(8) , Tide Mill Pr.) Top That! Publishing PLC GBR. *Dist:* Random Hse., Inc.

Ratnett, Michael. Dracula Steps Out. Goulding, June & Smyth, Iain, illus. 2005. 12p. (J). (gr. k-4). reprint ed. 16.00 (978-0-7567-8585-7(5)) DIANE Publishing Co.

Rau, Dana, Rise & Shine. 2007. 12p. 10.95 (*978-1-58117-559-2(0)) Dalmatian Pr.

Rayles, Jason. Fair: An Artful Documentation of the Final Day of the 2002 Brockton Fair in Video Stills & Stereophonic Sound with Attention to the Dual Nature of the 12-Hour Event. 2002. (978-0-9725651-0-3(8)) Rayles, Jason.

Reader's Digest Children's Books, creator. Little Cricket & Friends 3 Volume Boxed Set. 2007. (Illus.). 36p. (J). (ps-k). bds., bds. 16.99 (*978-0-7944-1359-0(5)) Reader's Digest Assn., Inc., The.

—Little People Welcome to Our Town: A Look-Inside Book. 2007. (Fisher Price Lift the Flap Ser.). (Illus.). 20p. (J). (ps-k). bds. 9.99 (*978-0-7944-1360-6(9)) Reader's Digest Assn., Inc., The.

Reader's Digest Editors. Let's Go to the Zoo! 2006. (FP A-Lift-the-Flap Play Book Ser.). (Illus.). 10p. (J). pap. 8.99 (978-0-7944-1112-1(6)) Reader's Digest Assn., Inc., The.

Reader's Digest Editors, ed. Winnie the Pooh's: Movie Theater: Storybook & Movie Projector. 2005. (Diseny Winnie the Pooh Ser.). (Illus.). 48p. (J). bds. 24.99 (978-0-7944-0522-9(3) , Reader's Digest Children's Bks.) Reader's Digest Children's Publishing, Inc.

Reader's Digest Staff. Disney Fairies Tinker Bell & Friends Storybook & Kaleidoscope Viewer. 2007. (RD Innovative Book & Player Format Ser.). 40p. (J). bds. 24.99 (*978-0-7944-1350-7(1)) Reader's Digest Assn., Inc., The.

—Disney Princess My Pod Storybook & Music Player. Disney & Reader's Digest, illus. 2007. (RD Innovative Book & Player Format Ser.). 40p. 24.99 (*978-0-7944-1301-9(3)) Reader's Digest Assn., Inc., The.

—Disney's Little Einsteins Storybook & Viewer. 2007. (RD Innovative Book & Player Format Ser.). 40p. (J). 24.99 (*978-0-7944-1307-1(2)) Reader's Digest Assn., Inc., The.

—Dream Works Shrek Magnetic. 2007. 16p. (J). bds. 14.99 (*978-0-7944-1356-9(0)) Reader's Digest Assn., Inc., The.

—Shrek the Halls: Lift-the-Flap. 2007. 10p. (J). (ps-k). bds. 9.99 (*978-0-7944-1365-1(X)) Reader's Digest Assn., Inc., The.

Reasoner, Charles. I'm Just a Crab. Reasoner, Charles, illus. 2007. 12p. (J). (ps). bds. 7.99 (*978-1-84666-291-1(5) , Tide Mill Pr.) Top That! Publishing PLC GBR. *Dist:* Random Hse., Inc.

—Who's Hatching? Reasoner, Charles, illus. 2003. (Sliding Surprise Bks.). (Illus.). 12p. (J). (ps). bds. 7.99 (978-0-8431-0598-8(4) , Price Stern Sloan) Penguin Group (USA) Inc.

—Who's There? Reasoner, Charles, illus. 2003. (Sliding Surprise Bks.). (Illus.). 12p. (J). (ps). bds. 7.99 (978-0-8431-0600-8(X) , Price Stern Sloan) Penguin Group (USA) Inc.

—Whose Mommy Is This? Reasoner, Charles, illus. 2002. (Sliding Surprise Bks.). (Illus.). 12p. (J). bds. 7.99 (978-0-8431-4579-3(X) , Price Stern Sloan) Penguin Group (USA) Inc.

Reber, Deborah. Blue's Valentines Day. Pontillo, Jenine, illus. 2000. (Blue's Clues Ser.). 16p. (J). (ps-k). pap. 3.99 (978-0-689-83062-4(9) , Simon Spotlight/Nickelodeon) Simon & Schuster Children's Publishing.

Redenbaugh, Vicki. Skar's Picnic ... A Bear's Tale. Redenbaugh, Vicki, illus. 2005. (Illus.). (J). 14.95 (978-1-59091-034-4(6)) Eastern National.

Reed, Nathan, illus. My Little Handbag. 2005. 10p. (J). bds. 6.99 (978-0-689-87705-6(6) , Little Simon) Simon & Schuster Children's Publishing.

—My Little Toolbox. 2005. 10p. (J). bds. 6.99 (978-0-689-87706-3(4) , Little Simon) Simon & Schuster Children's Publishing.

Reeve, Tim. Action Robots: A Pop-up Book Showing How They Work. MacLeod, Gavin, illus. 2004. 14p. (YA). (gr. 4-10). reprint ed. 17.00 (978-0-7567-7284-0(2)) DIANE Publishing Co.

Regina Press Staff. All Things Bright & Beautiful. 1999. (J). (ps-3). 4.95 (978-0-88271-674-9(3)) Regina Pr., Malhame & Co.

—Thank You, God. 1999. 4.95 (978-0-88271-672-5(7)) Regina Pr., Malhame & Co.

Reid, Struan. Lift the Lid on Knights: Explore a Medieval World of Chivalry & Adventure, & Build Your Own Knight! 2001. (Quarto Children's Book Ser.). (Illus.). 32p. (J). 22.95 (978-0-7624-1125-2(2) , Running Pr. Kids) Running Pr. Bk. Pubs.

Reinhart, Matthew. Animal Popposites: A Pop-up Book of Opposites. Reinhart, Matthew, illus. 2002. (Illus.). 12p. (J). (ps-1). 13.95 (978-0-689-84423-2(9) , Little Simon) Simon & Schuster Children's Publishing.

—The Ark: A Pop-up Book. Reinhart, Matthew, illus. 2006. (Illus.). 12p. (J). (gr. k-4). reprint ed. 17.00 (978-1-4223-5673-9(6)) DIANE Publishing Co.

—Cinderella: A Pop-up Fairy Tale. Reinhart, Matthew, illus. 2005. (Illus.). 12p. (J). 25.99 (978-1-4169-0501-1(4) , Little Simon) Simon & Schuster Children's Publishing.

—The Jungle Book. Reinhart, Matthew, illus. ltd. ed. 2006. 12p. (J). 250.00 (978-1-4169-2543-9(0) , Little Simon) Simon & Schuster Children's Publishing.

—The Jungle Book: A Pop-up Adventure. Reinhart, Matthew, illus. 2006. 12p. (J). 26.95 (978-1-4169-1824-0(8) , Little Simon) Simon & Schuster Children's Publishing.

Reinhart, Matthew. Star Wars: A Pop-Up Guide to the Galaxy. 2007. (Illus.). 12p. (J). pap. 32.99 (*978-0-439-88282-8(6) , Orchard Bks.) Scholastic, Inc.

Reinhart, Matthew, illus. & adapted by. The Ark. Reinhart, Matthew, adapted by. 2005. 12p. (J). 16.95 (978-0-689-85909-0(0) , Little Simon) Simon & Schuster Children's Publishing.

Reinhart, Matthew & Sabuda, Robert. Encyclopedia Prehistorica Dinosaurs: The Definitive Pop-up. Reinhart, Matthew & Sabuda, Robert, illus. 2005. (Sabuda Encyclopedias Ser.). (Illus.). 12p. (J). (gr. k). 27.99 (978-0-7636-2228-2(1)) Candlewick Pr.

Reitman, Andrea. Mouse in the House: Pop-Up Playset. Bell, Karen, illus. 2001. 3p. (J). (ps-k). 16.95 (978-1-58117-156-3(0) , Intervisual/Piggy Toes) Dalmatian Pr.

Rentschler, Nancy, illus. Hand Puppet & Board Book Jumbo Set. 2006. (J). per. (978-1-57332-398-7(5)) HighReach Learning, Inc.

Repchuk, Caroline, ed. The Amazing Spiderman Pop-up. Marvel Comics Staff, illus. 2007. 16p. (J). (gr. k-12). 300.00 (978-0-7636-3267-0(8)) Candlewick Pr.

Rescue Vehicles. (Illus.). 24p. (J). 1.99 (978-1-59445-057-0(9)) Dogs in Hats Children's Publishing Co.

Rescue Vehicles. (Radical Rides Ser.). 16p. (J). (978-2-7643-0014-5(X)) Phidal Publishing, Inc./Editions Phidal, Inc.

Rettore, Kenny E. My Baby Goodnight. Lyly, Olivia, illus. 2006. 2p. (J). 12.99 (978-0-7641-7922-8(5)) Barron's Educational Series, Inc.

Rettore, Kenny E. & Rettore, A. S. Cow & Pig. Lyly, Olivia, illus. 2004. (Stroller Softies Ser.). 12p. (J). 11.95 (978-0-7641-7768-2(0)) Barron's Educational Series, Inc.

Rey, H. A., et al. Curious George's Color Fun Board Book. 2007. (Curious George Ser.). (Illus.). 14p. (J). (ps-k). bds. 6.99 (978-0-618-72400-0(1)) Houghton Mifflin Co. Trade & Reference Div.

Rey, H. A. and Margret. Curious George Hide-and-Seek CG TV shapedanimal tab Book. 2008. 10p. (J). (ps-k). bds. 6.99 (*978-0-618-89199-3(4)) Houghton Mifflin Co. Trade & Reference Div.

Rey, Margret. Curious George, the Movie: Sticker Fun Book. 2006. (Illus.). 8p. (J). (ps-k). 6.99 (978-0-618-60586-6(X)) Houghton Mifflin Co.

Rhoades, Heather. Picture Me in the Circus. 2000. (Picture Me Ser.). (Illus.). 10p. (J). (ps up). bds. 4.99 (978-1-57151-586-5(0)) Playhouse Publishing.

Rhyming Lions. 2001. 48p. 3.99 (978-0-307-10674-2(8) , 10674, Golden Bks.) Random Hse. Children's Bks.

Ricci, Christine. Good Night, Dora! A Lift-the-Flap Story. Hall, Susan, illus. 2002. (Dora the Explorer Ser.).Tr. of Good Night, Dora!. 16p. (J). (ps-1). pap. 5.99 (978-0-689-84774-5(2) , Simon Spotlight/Nickelodeon) Simon & Schuster Children's Publishing.

—The Little Duck. Hall, Susan T., illus. 2004. 24p. (J). 15.98 (978-0-7853-9959-9(3) , 7209800) Publications International, Ltd.

—Music Player Storybook. 2006. (Nick Jr. Dora the Explorer Ser.). (Illus.). 40p. (J). DVD 24.99 (978-0-7944-1004-9(9)) Reader's Digest Assn., Inc., The.

Richards, Julian. Amazing Pop-Up Stonehenge. 2005. (Illus.). 16p. (J). (*978-1-85074-926-4(4)) English Heritage.

Richards, Kitty. The Enchanted Castle. Disney Storybook Artists Staff, illus. rev. ed. 2007. (Disney Princess Ser.). 4p. (ps-1). 12.99 (*978-1-4231-0912-9(0)) Disney Pr.

Richter, Bernd C. & Richter, Susan E. Uncover Alaska's Wonders. Richter, Bernd C., illus. 1999. 24p. (ps-1). 10.95 (978-0-9663495-3-5(9)) Saddle Pal Creations, Inc.

Richter, Dana. Arthur's Road Trip. Moroney, Christopher, illus. 2001. (J). (978-0-7853-4859-7(X)) Publications International, Ltd.

—Barbie Picture Perfect Camera. 2002. (Illus.). (J). 16.98 (978-0-7853-6071-1(9)) Publications International, Ltd.

—Fisher Price Little People Busy Playtime. Nostrant, Judy, illus. 2003. (Busy Box Bks.). (J). bds. (978-0-7853-7978-2(9)) Publications International, Ltd.

Rights, Lenz-Mulligan & van der Put, Klaartje. Little Ladybug. 2005. (Illus.). 12p. (J). bds. 6.95 (978-0-8118-4848-0(5)) Chronicle Bks. LLC.

Rindone, Nancy. Cars, Trains, Planes, & Trucks. S. I. Artists Staff, illus. 2004. (Fisher-Price Little People Flip & Learn Ser.). 10p. (J). bds. 8.99 (978-0-7944-0443-7(X) , Reader's Digest Children's Bks.) Reader's Digest Children's Publishing, Inc.

Ring, Susan. Gross Anatomy. Snow, Alan, illus. 2002. (Crash Course Ser.). 68p. (J). (gr. 2-17). spiral bd. 16.99 (978-1-58476-136-5(9)) Innovative Kids.

Rinkel, Ken, illus. Giant Machines. 2003. 12p. (J). (gr. k-3). 20.00 (978-0-7567-6653-5(2)) DIANE Publishing Co.

Ristuccia, Christine & Ristuccia, James. The Entire World of WH? Questions. 2004. (J). 39.99 (978-0-9723457-9-8(5)) Say It Right.

—The Entire World of WH? Questions Flip Book. 2004. (Illus.). 9p. (J). spiral bd. 14.99 (978-0-9723457-8-1(7)) Say It Right.

Ritchie, Fern J. Alphabet Toys: Illuminated Alphabet: A Child's First Book. Ritchie, Fern J., illus. 2002. 26p. (J). 29.95 (978-0-939656-64-6(7)) Ritchie Unlimited Pubns.

Ritchie, Joseph R. Peek-a-Boo! Halverson, Lydia, illus. 2004. 14p. (J). bds. 7.95 (978-0-8249-6550-1(7)) Ideals Pubns.

—Peter Cottontail's Busy Day. Halverson, Lydia, illus. 2005. 16p. (J). bds. 9.95 (978-0-8249-6571-6(X)) Ideals Pubns.

—Peter Cottontail's Easter Egg Hunt. Thornburgh, Rebecca McKillip, illus. 2004. 12p. (J). (ps-k). bds. 9.95 (978-0-8249-6522-8(1)) Ideals Pubns.

—Peter Cottontail's Easter Surprise. Rasmussen, Wendy, illus. 2006. 18p. (J). bds. 9.95 (978-0-8249-6627-0(9) , Candy Cane Pr.) Ideals Pubns.

—Where's Santa? Halverson, Lydia, illus. 2006. 14p. (J). (ps). bds. 7.95 (978-0-8249-6673-7(2) , Candy Cane Pr.) Ideals Pubns.

Rives. If I Were a Polar Bear. Rives, illus. 2001. (Illus.). 12p. (J). (ps-k). 16.95 (978-1-58117-046-7(7) , Intervisual/Piggy Toes) Dalmatian Pr.

Rivoli Group Staff, illus. Hide & Seek Opposites. 2000. (Jay Jay the Jet Plane's Peek-a-Boo Board Bks.). 12p. (J). (ps-k). bds. 6.95 (978-1-58117-100-6(5) , Intervisual/Piggy Toes) Dalmatian Pr.

—Number Fun in Tarrytown. 2000. (Jay Jay the Jet Plane's Ready, Set, Let's Learn! Bks.). 10p. (J). (ps-k). 6.95 (978-1-58117-099-3(8) , Intervisual/Piggy Toes) Dalmatian Pr.

—Tarrytown's Rainbow of Colors. 2000. (Jay Jay the Jet Plane's Ready, Set, Let's Learn! Bks.). 10p. (J). (ps-k). 6.95 (978-1-58117-098-6(X) , Intervisual/Piggy Toes) Dalmatian Pr.

Roe, David & Reader's Digest Staff. Transformers Mix & Match. 2007. 12p. (J). bds. 14.99 (*978-0-7944-1286-9(6)) Reader's Digest Assn., Inc., The.

Rogers, Alan. Bon Voyage! 2003. (Little Giants Ser.). (FRE., Illus.). 16p. (J). (ps-k). 5.95 (978-1-58728-176-1(7) , Two Can Publishing) T&N Children's Publishing.

—En Forme de Bateau. 2003. (Little Giants Ser.). (FRE., Illus.). 16p. (J). (ps-k). 5.95 (978-1-58728-177-8(5) , Two Can Publishing) T&N Children's Publishing.

—Higher & Higher. 2004. (Little Giants Ser.). (Illus.). 16p. (J). (ps-k). 5.95 (978-1-58728-153-2(8)); pap. 3.95 (978-1-58728-396-3(4)) T&N Children's Publishing. (Two Can Publishing).

—Salta y Sube. 2004. (Pequenos Gigantes Ser.).Tr. of Higher & Higher. (SPA., Illus.). 16p. (ps-k). (J). pap. 3.95 (978-1-58728-961-3(X)); 5.95 (978-1-58728-296-6(8)) T&N Children's Publishing. (Two Can Publishing).

—Ship Shape. 2004. (Little Giants Ser.). (Illus.). 16p. (J). (ps-k). pap. 3.95 (978-1-58728-395-6(6) , Two Can Publishing) T&N Children's Publishing.

—Toujours Plus Haut! 2003. (Little Giants Ser.). (FRE., Illus.). 16p. (ps-k). 5.95 (978-1-58728-181-5(3) , Two Can Publishing) T&N Children's Publishing.

—Vacation Time. 2004. (Little Giants Ser.). (Illus.). 16p. (ps-k). (J). pap. 3.95 (978-1-58728-393-2(X)); 5.95 (978-1-58728-156-3(2)) T&N Children's Publishing. (Two Can Publishing).

Roitman, Tanya. Who Lives Here? Roitman, Tanya, illus. 2007. (Illus.). 32p. 12.95 (978-1-59354-599-4(1)) Blue Apple Bks.

Rooney, Anne. Wallace & Gromit's World of Mysteries. 2004. (Illus.). 30p. (gr. 5-9). reprint ed. 30.00 (978-0-7567-7410-3(1)) DIANE Publishing Co.

Root, Phyllis. The House That Jill Built. Durand, Delphine, illus. 2005. 20p. (J). (ps-1). 15.99 (978-0-7636-1008-1(9)) Candlewick Pr.

Root, Phyllis. The House That Jill Built: A Pop-up Book. Durand, Delphine, illus. 2007. 18p. (J). reprint ed. 16.00 (*978-1-4223-6756-8(8)) DIANE Publishing Co.

Rosario, Sherwin, illus. Meet the Letters. 2005. 26p. (J). 9.99 (978-0-9767008-0-7(8)) KRO Publishing.

—Meet the Numbers Lift the Flap Book. 2005. 12p. (J). bds. 9.99 (978-0-9767008-1-4(6)) KRO Publishing.

Rosen, Michael J. We're Going on a Bear Hunt. Oxenbury, Helen, illus. gif. ed. 2002. 40p. (J). 9.99 (978-0-7636-1979-4(5)) Candlewick Pr.

Rosenbaum, Andria Warmflash. A Grandma Like Yours: A Grandpa Like Yours. Bjornson, Barbara, illus. 2006. (J). 16.95 (978-1-58013-167-4(0)) Kar-Ben Publishing.

Ross, Odette. Counting. 2007. (Wordless Board Bks.). (Illus.). 12p. (J). (ps). bds. 5.95 (*978-1-894965-91-0(4)) Simply Read Bks. CAN. *Dist:* Perseus Distribution.

—Families. 2007. (Wordless Board Bks.). (Illus.). 12p. (J). (ps). bds. 5.95 (*978-1-894965-92-7(2)) Simply Read Bks. CAN. *Dist:* Perseus Distribution.

Rowling, J. K. Harry Potter & the Sorcerer's Stone. Smith, Rodger, illus. movie tie-in deluxe ed. 2001. (Harry Potter Ser.: Year 1). 12p. (J). (gr. 4-7). pap. 18.95 (978-0-439-29482-9(7)) Scholastic, Inc.

Roxbee-Cox, Phil. Ted's Shed. 2004. (Easy Words to Read Ser.). (Illus.). 16p. (J). (gr. 1 up). pap. 6.95 (978-0-7460-4210-6(8)) EDC Publishing.

Rueda, Claudia, illus. I Know an Old Lady Who Swallowed a Fly. 2005. 14p. (J). 12.95 (978-1-58117-267-6(2) , Intervisual/Piggy Toes) Dalmatian Pr.

Runnells, Treesha. Forest Friends: A Fold-Out Fun Book. Runnells, Treesha, illus. 2005. (Fold-Out Fun Ser.). (Illus.). 10p. (J). 4.95 (978-1-58117-275-1(3) , Intervisual/Piggy Toes) Dalmatian Pr.

Running Press Staff. Dress Up: Pull the Tabs! Change the Pictures! Bottled Lightning Staff, ed. 2004. (Magic Windows Ser.). (Illus.). 8p. (J). pap. 4.95 (978-0-7624-1703-2(X) , Running Pr. Kids) Running Pr. Bk. Pubs.

—Opposites. 2002. (First Discovery Look-Inside Board Bks.). (Illus.). 10p. (J). bds. 4.95 (978-0-439-35592-6(3) , Cartwheel Bks.) Scholastic, Inc.

—Trucks. 7th ed. 2000. (Fit-a-Shape Ser.). (Illus.). 10p. (J). (ps-k). pap. 6.95 (978-0-7624-0813-9(8) , Running Pr. Kids) Running Pr. Bk. Pubs.

Running Press Staff & Deere, John. The Biggest Pumpkin Ever. 2007. (Illus.). 10p. bds. 7.95 (*978-0-7624-3138-0(5) , Running Pr. Kids) Running Pr. Bk. Pubs.

Running Press Staff & Fitashape. Colors. 2000. (Fit-a-Shape Ser.). (Illus.). 10p. (J). (ps-k). pap. 6.95 (978-0-7624-0816-0(2) , Running Pr. Kids) Running Pr. Bk. Pubs.

Running Press Staff & Harry, Lou. It's Mini Slinky! 2001. (Pocket Packets Ser.). (Illus.). 32p. pap. 6.95 (978-0-7624-1135-1(X) , Running Pr. Miniature Editions) Running Pr. Bk. Pubs.

Running Press Staff & Mann, Holly. Dress Up: Pull the Tabs! Change the Pictures! 2004. (Magic Windows Ser.). (Illus.). 8p. (J). (ps-k). pap. 4.95 (978-0-7624-1702-5(1) , Running Pr. Kids) Running Pr. Bk. Pubs.

—Farm. 2005. (Illus.). 8p. (J). pap. 4.95 (978-0-7624-2345-3(5) , Running Pr. Kids) Running Pr. Bk. Pubs.

Rutman, Shereen Gertel. My First Amazing Game. Clough, Julie, illus. 2002. 36p. (J). (ps-1). bds. 19.99 (978-1-58476-094-8(X)) Innovative Kids.

Ryan, Lisa & Scholastic, Inc. Staff. The Wheels on Barney's Bus. Winslow, Becky, illus. 2002. (Barney Ser.). 6p. (J). (ps-1). pap. 9.99 (978-1-58668-292-7(X)) Scholastic, Inc.

Sabuda, Robert. America the Beautiful. Sabuda, Robert, illus. 2004. (Classic Collectible Pop-Up Ser.). (Illus.). 16p. (J). 26.95 (978-0-689-84744-8(0) , Little Simon) Simon & Schuster Children's Publishing.

—Christmas. 2006. (Illus.). 18p. (J). pap. 12.99 (978-0-439-84568-7(8) , Orchard Bks.) Scholastic, Inc.

—The Christmas Alphabet. 10th anniv. deluxe ed. 2004. (Illus.). 16p. (J). pap. 22.95 (978-0-439-67256-6(2) , Orchard Bks.) Scholastic, Inc.

—The Movable Mother Goose. Sabuda, Robert, illus. 1999. (Illus.). 12p. (J). (ps-3). 21.99 (978-0-689-81192-0(6) , Little Simon) Simon & Schuster Children's Publishing.

—Winter in White: A Mini Pop-up Treat. Sabuda, Robert, illus. 2007. 18p. (J). 12.99 (*978-0-689-85365-4(3) , Little Simon) Simon & Schuster Children's Publishing.

—Winter's Tale: An Original Pop-Up Journey. 2005. (Illus.). 12p. (J). 26.95 (978-0-689-85363-0(7) , Little Simon) Simon & Schuster Children's Publishing.

—The 12 Days of Christmas: A Pop-up Celebration. Sabuda, Robert, illus. 10th anniv. ed. 2006. (Illus.). 14p. (J). (ps-3). 26.95 (978-1-4169-2792-1(1) , Little Simon) Simon & Schuster Children's Publishing.

Sabuda, Robert & Olmon, Kyle. Castle: Medieval Days & Knights. Reinhart, Matthew & Sabin, Tracy, illus. 2006. 6p. (J). 19.99 (978-0-439-54324-8(X) , Orchard Bks.) Scholastic, Inc.

Sacks, Janet. Mini Magic Color Book: Bunny's Spring Day. Rinaldo, Luana, illus. 2007. 10p. (J). 3.95 (978-1-4027-4591-1(5) , Sterling/Pinwheel) Sterling Publishing Co., Inc.

—Mini Magic Color Book: Cars. Rinaldo, Luana, illus. 2007. 10p. (J). 3.95 (978-1-4027-4592-8(3) , Sterling/Pinwheel) Sterling Publishing Co., Inc.

Salmon, Michael. Dinosaur. 2006. (Illus.). 32p. (J). (*978-1-74178-213-4(9)) Five Mile Pr. Pty Ltd. The.

Saltzberg, Barney. Animal Kisses. 2000. (Touch & Feel Bks.). (Illus.). 14p. (J). (ps-k). bds. 8.95 (978-0-15-202340-9(2) , Red Wagon Bks.) Harcourt Children's Bks.

—Baby Animals Kisses. 2001. (Illus.). 14p. (J). (ps). bds. 8.95 (978-0-15-202635-6(5) , Red Wagon Bks.) Harcourt Children's Bks.

—Besos de Animales. Campoy, F. Isabel & Ada, Alma Flor, trs. 2004. Tr. of Animal Kisses. (SPA., Illus.). 14p. (J). bds. 8.95 (978-0-15-205448-9(0) , Red Wagon Bks.) Harcourt Children's Bks.

—Noisy Kisses. 2004. (Illus.). 14p. (J). bds. 8.95 (978-0-15-204929-4(0) , Red Wagon Bks.) Harcourt Children's Bks.

—Peekaboo Kisses. 2002. (Touch & Feel Bks.). (Illus.). 14p. (J). bds. 8.95 (978-0-15-216541-3(X) , Red Wagon Bks.) Harcourt Children's Bks.

SAMi. Woof-Woof. (J). bds. 8.95 (978-1-59354-137-8(6)) Blue Apple Bks.

—Yellow Red Blue. 2007. (Baby Flip-A Face Ser.). (Illus.). 12p. bds. 8.95 (978-1-59354-587-1(8)) Handprint Bks.

Sams, Ii Carl. Stranger in the Woods. 2004. 14.95 (978-0-9671748-7-7(2)) Sams, II, Carl R. Photography, Inc.

Samuel, Anna, ed. Glitter Butterflies Stickers. 2004. (Glitter Stickers Ser.). (Illus.). 2p. 1.50 (978-0-486-43537-4(7)) Dover Pubns., Inc.

Samuel, Catherine & Hartman, Butch. Timmy's Eggs-Ray Vision. Saunders, Zina, illus. 2005. (J). (*978-1-4155-8053-0(7) , Simon Spotlight/Nickelodeon) Simon & Schuster Children's Publishing.

Sander, Sonia. Care Bears: Find That Rainbow! Sticker Storybook. del Sur, Duendes, illus. 2003. (Care Bears Ser.). 16p. (J). (ps-2). pap. 5.99 (978-0-439-45176-5(0)) Scholastic, Inc.

—Care Bears: Find That Rainbow! Sticker Storybook. 2003. (ps-2). lib. bdg. 14.15 (978-0-613-72161-5(6)) Tandem Library Bks.

Sander, Sonia. Nintendogs Sticker Book. 2007. 16p. (J). pap. 5.99 (*978-0-439-84368-3(5)) Scholastic, Inc.

Sands, Emily. Egyptology: Search for the Tomb of Osiris. Andrew, Ian et al, illus. 2004. (Ologies Ser.). 32p. (J). (gr. 3). 19.99 (978-0-7636-2638-9(4)) Candlewick Pr.

Sanschagrin, Joceline. Caillou, Helps Mommy. CINAR Animation Staff & Sévigny, Eric, illus. adapted rev. ed. 2006. (Lift-the-Flap Cinar Ser.). 20p. (J). pap. 5.95 (978-2-89450-524-3(8)) Chouette Publishing CAN. *Dist:* Independent Pubs. Group.

Santomero, Angela C. Farley's Crayon World. Kim, illus. 2001. 8p. mass mkt. 0.06 (978-0-689-84796-7(3) , Simon Spotlight/Nickelodeon) Simon & Schuster Children's Publishing.

Scarry, Richard. Richard Scarry's Busiest Pop-up Ever! 2007. (Richard Scarry Ser.). 10p. (J). (ps-2). 19.99 (*978-0-375-84120-0(2) , Golden Bks.) Random Hse. Children's Bks.

Scarry's Best Band Ever. 2001. (Illus.). (J). 7.95 (978-0-7853-4753-8(4)) Publications International, Ltd.

Schneider, Judy. But Not Quite. Weeks, Mary, illus. 2004. (J). 19.95 (978-1-59404-005-4(2)) Peanut Butter Publishing.

Schoberle, Cecile. Sweetheart Fairies. Couri, Kathy, illus. 2003. 16p. (J). pap. 4.99 (978-0-689-85023-3(9) , Little Simon) Simon & Schuster Children's Publishing.

Scholastic, Inc. Staff. Adventures in Care-a-Lot Sticker Storybook. Swendsen, Silje, ed. 2004. (Care Bears Ser.). 16p. (J). pap. 5.99 (978-0-439-62489-3(4)) Scholastic, Inc.

—Five Little Ducks. 2007. (Little Scholastic Ser.). (Illus.). 12p. (J). bds. 7.99 (*978-0-439-02147-0(2)) Scholastic, Inc.

—Hand Puppet Board Book (Un Libro de Carton Con Titeres) 2007. (Noah's Ark Ser.). 6p. (J). bds. 12.99 (*978-0-439-92274-6(7) , Scholastic en Espanol) Scholastic, Inc.

—Humpty Dumpty Loop Rattle, 12 Pack. 2003. (Sidekicks Ser.). (J). 83.88 (978-0-439-55402-2(0) , Sidekicks TM) Scholastic, Inc.

—Let's Make Some Noise! 2008. (Doodlebops Ser.). 96p. (J). 9.99 (*978-0-545-01328-4(3)) Scholastic, Inc.

—Nativity Board Book. 2007. (J). bds. 5.99 (*978-0-545-00067-3(X) , Cartwheel Bks.) Scholastic, Inc.

—Old Macdonald Puppet Book. Berg, Michelle, illus. (Little Scholastic Ser.). 6p. (J). 2007. bds. 12.99 (*978-0-545-02603-1(2)); 2004. 12.95 (978-0-439-69392-9(6) , Cartwheel Bks.) Scholastic, Inc.

—Peek-a-Zoo. 2007. (Little Scholastic Ser.). (J). (ps). bds. 10.99 (*978-0-439-02154-8(5)) Scholastic, Inc.

—Rainbow Magic: Fairy Fashion Dress-Up Book. 2007. (Rainbow Magic Ser.). 16p. (J). pap. 5.99 (*978-0-439-93047-5(2)) Scholastic, Inc.

—Rainbow Magic: Fairy Friends Sticker Book. 2007. (Rainbow Magic Ser.). 12p. (J). pap. 5.99 (*978-0-439-93046-8(4)) Scholastic, Inc.

—Shrek Color & Activity: (Bilingual) Salas, Macarena, ed. 2004. (Shrek Ser.). (SPA.). 80p. (J). 2.99 (978-0-439-63201-0(3) , Scholastic en Espanol) Scholastic, Inc.

—The Small Red Puppy Teether Rattle, 12, Pack. 2003. (Clifford Ser.). (J). 83.88 (978-0-439-20131-5(4) , Sidekicks TM) Scholastic, Inc.

—The Springy Zingy Box. 2004. (Boohbah Ser.). (Illus.). 16p. (J). pap. 5.99 (978-0-439-59093-8(0)) Scholastic, Inc.

—Star. 2007. (Little Scholastic Ser.). 10p. (J). bds. 4.99 (*978-0-545-02070-1(0) , Cartwheel Bks.) Scholastic, Inc.

—Storyworld Stickers. 2004. (Boohbah Ser.). (Illus.). 16p. (J). 5.99 (978-0-439-62515-9(7)) Scholastic, Inc.

—What's the Weather? 2008. (Little Secrets Ser.). 28p. (J). 9.99 (*978-0-545-02599-7(0) , Cartwheel Bks.) Scholastic, Inc.

—Where's Moe? 2007. (Doodlebops Ser.). (J). bds. 5.99 (*978-0-545-01150-1(7)) Scholastic, Inc.

Scholastic, Inc. Staff. The Wobbly Bobbly Balls. 2004. (Boohbah Ser.). (Illus.). 16p. (J). pap. 5.99 (978-0-439-62512-8(2)) Scholastic, Inc.

Scholastic, Inc. Staff, ed. Harry Potter Hogwart's School: A Magical 3-D Carousel. 2001. (Harry Potter Ser.). (J). (gr. 4-7). 24.00 (978-0-439-28611-4(5)) Scholastic, Inc.

Scholastic, Inc. Staff & Berg, Michelle. This Little Piggy: A Hand-Puppet Board Book. 2007. (Little Scholastic Ser.). 6p. (J). bds. 12.99 (*978-0-545-03038-0(2)) Scholastic, Inc.

Scholastic, Inc. Staff, et al. Emily Elizabeth Playwear - Cheerleading Outfit. 2003. (Clifford Ser.). (J). 12.99 (978-0-439-20237-4(X) , Sidekicks TM) Scholastic, Inc.

Scholastic Teacher Editors. Musical Instruments. 1998. (J). 12.95 (978-0-590-78800-7(0)) Scholastic, Inc.

School Specialty Publishing. Flip-Flash Math Vocabulary. 2004. 160p. (J). (gr. 4-5). pap. 7.99 (978-0-7424-2768-6(4) , ID99073); (gr. k-1). pap. 7.99 (978-0-7424-2766-2(8) , ID99074); (gr. 2-3). pap. 7.99 (978-0-7424-2767-9(6) , ID99072) School Specialty Publishing.

—Flip-Flash Phonics & Vocabulary: Prefixes. 2004. 160p. (J). (gr. 3-6). pap. 7.99 (978-0-7424-2686-3(6) , ID99060) School Specialty Publishing.

—Flip-Flash Phonics & Vocabulary: Suffixes. 2004. 160p. (J). (gr. 3-6). pap. 7.99 (978-0-7424-2687-0(4) , ID99061) School Specialty Publishing.

—Flip-Flash Phonics & Vocabulary: Vocabulary. 2004. 160p. (J). (gr. k-1). pap. 7.99 (978-0-7424-2694-8(7) , ID99064); (gr. 2-3). pap. 7.99 (978-0-7424-2695-5(5) , ID99062) School Specialty Publishing.

—Flip-FlashTM Spanish Flash Cards: Level I. 2002. (SPA.). 160p. (J). (gr. 1-12). pap. 7.99 (978-1-56451-387-8(4) , ID2441) School Specialty Publishing.

—Flip-FlashTM Spanish Flash Cards: Level II. 2002. (SPA.). 160p. (J). (gr. 1-12). pap. 7.99 (978-1-56451-388-5(2) , ID2442) School Specialty Publishing.

School Zone Publishing Company Staff. Animal Match. 2000. (Game Cards Ser.). 56p. (J). 2.89 (978-0-88743-215-6(8) , 05038) School Zone Publishing Co.

Schories, Pat, illus. Biscuit's Fourth of July. 2005. (J). (*978-1-4156-0311-6(1) , Harper Festival) HarperCollins Pubs.

—Biscuit's Graduation Day. 2005. (J). (*978-1-4155-9660-9(3) , Harper Festival) HarperCollins Pubs.

Schwartz, Betty Ann. One to Ten... And back Again: An Amazing Pull-the-Ribbon Book. Shakir, Susie, illus. 2007. 24p. (J). (ps). 12.95 (*978-1-932403-27-5(2)) Handprint Bks.

—The Spinning Book of Colors, Shapes, & Numbers. Berg, Michelle, illus. 2007. 16p. (J). (ps-1). 9.99 (978-0-06-079974-8(9) , Harper Festival) HarperCollins Pubs.

—What Makes a Rainbow? A Magic Ribbon Book. Turner, Dona, illus. 2000. (Novelty Book Ser.). (J). (ps-k). 14p. 8.95 (978-1-58117-076-4(9)); 12p. 10.95 (978-1-58117-115-0(3)) Dalmatian Pr. (Intervisual/Piggy Toes).

Scruton, Clive, illus. I Love You! 1999. (Leap Frog Lift-A-Flap Ser.). (J). (978-0-7853-3369-2(X)) Publications International, Ltd.

Seeger, Laura Vaccaro. The Hidden Alphabet. Seeger, Laura Vaccaro, illus. rev. ed. 2003. (Single Titles Ser.). (Illus.). 32p. (J). (ps-1). 17.95 (978-0-7613-1941-2(7)) Roaring Brook Pr.

Seibold, J. Otto & Walsh, Vivian. Olive, the Other Reindeer. 10th deluxe anniv. ed. 2007. (Illus.). 40p. (J). (ps up). 19.95 (978-0-8118-5719-2(0)) Chronicle Bks. LLC.

Sesame Building Blocks: Cube Books. 2002. (J). (978-1-931312-81-3(8)) SoftPlay, Inc.

Sesame Workshop Staff & SoftPlay (Firm) Staff, contrib. by. Happy Families in Elmo's World. 2002. (Elmo's World Ser.). (Illus.). (J). (978-1-931312-47-9(8)) SoftPlay, Inc.

Seuss, Dr. All Aboard the Circus McGurkus. 2004. (Illus.). 8p. (J). (gr. k-ps). bds. 6.99 (978-0-375-83011-2(1) , Random Hse. Bks. for Young Readers) Random Hse. Children's Bks.

—Hop on Pop-Up! 2002. (Illus.). 12p. (J). 6.99 (978-0-375-81547-8(3) , Random Hse. Bks. for Young Readers) Random Hse. Children's Bks.

Seymour, Arlene. The Moon Book: A Lunar Pop-up Celebration. Seymour, Arlene, illus. 2004. (Illus.). 14p. (YA). (gr. k-4). reprint ed. 22.00 (978-0-7567-7645-9(7)) DIANE Publishing Co.

Shaffer, Christy. Glitter Unicorns Stickers. 2004. (Glitter Stickers Ser.). (Illus.). 2p. (J). (ps-5). 1.50 (978-0-486-43538-1(5)) Dover Pubns., Inc.

Shanklin, Sandra, told to. Tales of Cat Canyon. 2005. (Illus.). 143p. pap. 12.95 (978-0-9632459-2-2(9)) Great Plains Pr.

Sharp, Chris, illus. Noah's Park Songs. 2001. (Noahs Park Ser.). (J). (978-0-7853-5426-0(3) , 0785354263) Cook, David C. Publishing Co.

Sharratt, Nick. Come & Play: A Storybook & Activity Playmat in One. 1998. (Illus.). 8p. (J). pap. 14.95 (978-1-899607-55-6(2)) Sterling Publishing Co., Inc.

Shepherd, Jodi. Sesame Street When I Grow Up: Storybook & Magnetic Dress-up Dolls. Kwiat, Ernie, illus. 2007. 16p. (J). bds. 14.99 (*978-0-7944-1290-6(4)) Reader's Digest Assn., Inc., The.

Shepherd, Jodie. Ocean Friends. Ovresat, Laura, illus. 2007. 12p. (J). bds. 7.99 (978-0-7944-1122-0(3)) Reader's Digest Assn., Inc., The.

Sherman, Michael. Foam Gliders. 2006. 10p. (J). spiral bd. 9.95 (978-1-59174-315-6(X) , Chicken Socks) Klutz.

—Superhero Starter Kit. 2006. 20p. (J). spiral bd. 14.95 (978-1-59174-248-7(X) , Chicken Socks) Klutz.

Shields, Carol Diggory. Patterns. Junakovic, Svjetlan, illus. 2001. (Animagicals Ser.). 32p. (J). (ps-1). bds. 9.95 (978-1-929766-15-4(7)) Handprint Bks.

—Sports. Junakovic, Svjetlan, illus. 2001. (Animagicals Ser.). 32p. (J). 9.95 (978-1-929766-28-4(9)) Handprint Bks.

Shields, Carol Diggory & Junakovic, Svjetlan. On the Go. 2001. (Animagicals Ser.). (Illus.). 32p. (J). (ps-1). bds. 9.95 (978-1-929766-14-7(9)) Handprint Bks.

Shields, Carol Diggory, et al. Music. 2000. (Animagicals Ser.). (Illus.). 12p. (J). (ps-1). 9.95 (978-1-929766-05-5(X)) Handprint Bks.

Shulman, Mark. Big Cat. Chambers, Sally, illus. 2004. 8p. (J). bds. 6.95 (978-1-58925-737-5(5) , tiger tales) ME Media LLC.

—Enchanted Princess Castle. Wenzel, David T., illus. 2005. (Storytime Stickers Ser.). 16p. (J). (gr. k-2). pap. 4.95 (978-1-4027-2747-4(X)) Sterling Publishing Co., Inc.

—Flower Girls. Swanson, Maggie, illus. 2006. (Storytime Stickers Ser.). 16p. (J). pap. 4.95 (978-1-4027-3433-5(6)) Sterling Publishing Co., Inc.

—Foxy Fox. Chambers, Sally, illus. 2004. 8p. (J). bds. 6.95 (978-1-58925-738-2(3) , tiger tales) ME Media LLC.

—UFO Alien Invaders. Shems, Ed, illus. 2006. (Storytime Stickers Ser.). 16p. (J). pap. 4.95 (978-1-4027-3362-8(3)) Sterling Publishing Co., Inc.

Shultz, Lucy. Goodnight Faces. 2007. (Illus.). 12p. (J). (ps). bds. 5.99 (*978-1-58476-672-8(7) , IKIDS) Innovative Kids.

Siede, George & Press, Donna, photos by. Collections. 1998. (Active Minds Ser.). (Illus.). 40p. (J). bds. 12.98 (978-1-58048-032-1(2)) Sandvik Publishing.

—Counting. 1998. (Active Minds Ser.). (Illus.). 10p. (J). bds. 3.99 (978-1-58048-030-7(6)) Sandvik Publishing.

—First Words. 1998. (Active Minds Ser.). (Illus.). 10p. (J). bds. 3.99 (978-1-58048-031-4(4)) Sandvik Publishing.

Siede Preis Photography (Firm) Staff & Brian Warling Photography (Firm) Staff, contrib. by. Alphabet. 2003. (Active Minds Ser.). (Illus.). (J). (978-0-7853-7828-0(6)) Publications International, Ltd.

—First Words. 2003. (Lift-A-Flap Ser.). (Illus.). 12p. (J). bds. 12.98 (978-0-7853-8624-7(6) , 7188400) Publications International, Ltd.

—I Can Add. 2003. (Lift-A-Flap Ser.). (Illus.). 12p. (J). bds. (978-0-7853-8239-3(9) , 7190000) Publications International, Ltd.

—I Can Spell. 2003. (Lift-A-Flap Ser.). (Illus.). 12p. (J). bds. (978-0-7853-8238-6(0) , 7190100) Publications International, Ltd.

—Phonics for Fun. 2003. (Lift-A-Flap Ser.). (Illus.). 12p. (J). bds. (978-0-7853-8623-0(8) , 7188300) Publications International, Ltd.

Silver Dolphin en Español Editors. Seqorita Cmrculo: Miss Circle, Spanish-Language Edition. 2005. (Mis figuras Geometricas Ser.). (SPA., Illus.). 6p. (J). 9.95 (978-970-718-293-6(8) , Silver Dolphin en Español) Advanced Marketing, S. de R. L. de C. V. MEX. *Dist:* Perseus Distribution.

Silver Dolphin en Español Editors, creator. Mis Figuras Geometricas, Srita Estrella. 2005. (Mis figuras Geometricas Ser.). (SPA., Illus.). 6p. (J). (ps-k). 9.95 (978-970-718-295-0(4) , Silver Dolphin en Español) Advanced Marketing, S. de R. L. de C. V. MEX. *Dist:* Perseus Distribution.

Silverhardt, Lauryn. Blue's Fall Day: A Lift-the-Flap Story. Kanemoto, Dan, illus. 2007. (Blue's Clues Ser.). 16p. (J). pap. 6.99 (*978-1-4169-3436-3(7) , Simon Spotlight/Nickelodeon) Simon & Schuster Children's Publishing.

Simson, Dana. Sunny Days. 2002. (J). 12.95 (978-1-74047-212-8(8)) Book Co. Publishing Pty, Ltd., The AUS. *Dist:* Penton Overseas, Inc.

Sing & Learn, ed. Farm Animals. 2007. (Sing & Learn Padded Board Bks.). 53p. (J). bds. 16.95 (*978-0-7696-5429-4(0)) School Specialty Publishing.

—Nursery Rhymes. 2007. (Sing & Learn Padded Board Bks.). 53p. (J). bds. 16.95 (*978-0-7696-5469-0(X)) School Specialty Publishing.

Skeleton Sticker Book. 2003. (Illus.). 16p. (J). 2.98 (978-1-84273-121-5(1) , Exclusive Editions) Parragon, Inc.

Sladen, Louisa. Farm Animals. Rinaldo, Luana, illus. 2004. (Magic Color Bks.). 10p. (J). 3.95 (978-1-4027-1207-4(3)) Sterling Publishing Co., Inc.

Slater, Jean M. At the Fire Station: An Interactive Book. 2nd ed. 2003. (Illus.). 13p. (J). bds. (978-0-9743149-0-7(0)) Slater Software. Inc.

Slater, Nicola, illus. We're Bored. 2005. 12p. (J). 12.95 (978-1-58117-384-0(9) , Intervisual/Piggy Toes) Dalmatian Pr.

Slobodkina, Esphyr. Caps for Sale Board Book: A Tale of a Peddler, Some Monkeys & Their Monkey Business. Slobodkina, Esphyr, illus. 2008. 32p. (J). 8.99 (*978-0-06-147453-8(3) , Harper Festival) HarperCollins Pubs.

Smart Kids Publishing Staff. Play It Safe. (Illus.). 14p. (J). bds. 12.95 (978-0-8249-6593-8(0)) Ideals Pubns.

—Safe at Home! (Illus.). 14p. (J). bds. 12.95 (978-0-8249-6592-1(2)) Ideals Pubns.

Smee, Nicola. No Bed Without Ted. 2005. (Illus.). 24p. (J). (ps-ps). 14.95 (978-1-58234-963-3(0)) Bloomsbury Publishing.

Smith, A. & Tatchell, J. How are Babies Made? How do Your Senses Work? What Happens to Your Food? rev. ed. 2004. (Flip Flaps Ser.). 48p. (J). (gr. 2 up). 14.95 (978-0-7945-0618-6(6) , Usborne) EDC Publishing.

Smith, Alastair. Baby Animals. 2004. (Lift-the-Flap Learners Ser.). (SPA., Illus.). 16p. (J). (gr. 1 up). pap. 8.95 (978-0-7945-0133-4(8) , Usborne) EDC Publishing.

—Nighttime Lift-the-flap. Butler, John, illus. 2005. 16p. (J). (gr. 1 up). 11.95 (978-0-7945-0967-5(3) , Usborne) EDC Publishing.

—On the Farm Lift-the-Flap. Torode, Justine, illus. 2004. (Luxury Lift-the-Flap Ser.). 16p. (J). (gr. 1 up). 11.95 (978-0-7945-0508-0(2) , Usborne) EDC Publishing.

Smith, Alastair, ed. Homes & Houses Then & Now. 2004. (Then & Now Flip Flaps Ser.). (SPA., Illus.). 16p. (J). (gr. 2 up). pap. 7.95 (978-0-7460-3100-1(9)) EDC Publishing.

—Travel & Transport Then & Now. 2004. (Then & Now Flip Flaps Ser.). (Illus.). 16p. (J). (gr. 2 up). pap. 7.95 (978-0-7460-3102-5(5)) EDC Publishing.

Smith, Alastair & Furnival, Keith. Night-Time. Butler, John, illus. 2002. (Usborne Lift-The-Flap Book Ser.). (J). (978-0-439-66484-4(5)) Scholastic, Inc.

Smith, Alastair & Howell, Laura. On the Beach. 2004. (Lift-the-Flap Learners Ser.). (Illus.). 16p. (J). (gr. 1 up). pap. 8.95 (978-0-7945-0213-3(X) , Usborne) EDC Publishing.

Smith, Alastair & Tatchell, Judy. Dinosaurs. 2004. (Jumbo Lift-the-Flap Learners Ser.). (Illus.). 16p. (J). (gr. 1 up). 11.95 (978-0-7945-0418-2(3) , Usborne) EDC Publishing.

—Dinosaurs. Scott, Peter David, illus. 2005. (J). (*978-0-439-68903-8(1)) Scholastic, Inc.

Smith, Beth Esh. Red Bug Board Book & Felt Puppet Set. Coates, Jennifer, illus. 2005. (J). bds. (978-1-57332-368-0(3)) HighReach Learning, Inc.

Smith, Iain. Angel Fish: A Pull & Lift Book. Smith, Iain, illus. 2005. (Stories to Share Ser.). (Illus.). 12p. (J). 10.95 (978-1-58117-084-9(X) , Intervisual/Piggy Toes) Dalmatian Pr.

Smith, Kathryn. Little Donkey's Christmas Story. Wood, Amanda, illus. 2002. (Snuffleheads Puppet Book Ser.). (J). (ps-3). 14p. 7.99 (978-0-8254-7251-0(2)); 8p. 7.99 (978-1-85985-441-9(9)) Kregel Pubns.

—Little Lamb's Christmas Story. Wood, Amanda, illus. 2002. (Snuffleheads Ser.). 14p. (J). (gr. k-3). 7.99 (978-1-85985-442-6(7)); 7.99 (978-0-8254-7253-4(9)) Kregel Pubns.

Smith, Patty. Faces. Croft, James Lee, illus. 2001. (Busy Block Books). 12p. (J). (ps up). pap. 8.95 (978-0-7624-0933-4(9) , Running Pr. Kids) Running Pr. Bk. Pubs.

Snap! Snap! 2002. 10p. (J). 9.95 (978-0-7525-5580-5(4)) Parragon, Inc.

So-Big Whale. 2004. (Plush Pals Board Bks.). (Illus.). (J). (gr. k-1). bds. (978-0-7666-0558-9(2) , 39395) Modern Publishing.

Sommers, Joan. Rainbow Bird Tunnel Book: El Pajaro Del Arco Iris: un Libro Tunel. Shull, Valerie, tr. Spiess-Ferris, Eleanor, illus. 2007. (Take a Peek Ser.). 16p. (J). 14.95 (*978-0-9754150-5-4(0)) Tunnel Vision.

Souhami, Jessica. In the Dark, Dark Wood. 2007. (Illus.). 24p. (J). 7.95 (*978-1-84507-755-6(5)) Lincoln, Frances Ltd. GBR. *Dist:* Perseus Distribution.

Spafford, Suzy. Witzy Plays Hide & Seek. 2001. (Little Suzy's Zoo Ser.). (Illus.). 6p. (J). pap. 5.99 (978-0-439-34358-9(5)) Scholastic, Inc.

—Witzy's Backyard Easter Hunt. 2002. (Little Suzy's Zoo Ser.). (Illus.). 15p. (J). bds. 5.99 (978-0-439-36778-3(6)) Scholastic, Inc.

—Witzy's Block Party. 2001. (Little Suzy's Zoo Ser.). (Illus.). 16p. (J). (ps). pap. 9.99 (978-0-439-34356-5(9)) Scholastic, Inc.

—Witzy's Book of Words. 2001. (Little Suzy's Zoo Ser.). 12p. (J). (ps-1). bds. 9.99 (978-1-58668-054-1(4)) Lyrick Studios.

—Witzy's Book of Words. 2001. (Little Suzy's Zoo Ser.). (Illus.). 12p. (J). pap. 9.99 (978-0-439-34357-2(7)) Scholastic, Inc.

—Witzy's Shapes. 2002. (Little Suzy's Zoo Ser.). (Illus.). 12p. (J). bds. 4.99 (978-0-439-36632-8(1)) Scholastic, Inc.

Spence, Ann & Halifax, Guy. Bob's Busy Building Day. 2003. (Illus.). (J). (978-0-7853-8421-2(9)) Publications International, Ltd.

Sper, Emily. The Kids' Fun Book of Jewish Time. Sper, Emily, illus. 2006. (HEB & ENG., Illus.). 24p. (J). 16.99 (978-1-58023-311-8(2) , 1260461) Jewish Lights Publishing.

Spohn, Kate. Mommies! 2008. (Illus.). 14p. (J). (gr. k-ps). bds. 4.99 (*978-0-375-84277-1(2) , Random Hse. Bks. for Young Readers) Random Hse. Children's Bks.

Spurr, Elizabeth. Two Bears Beneath the Stairs. Westcott, Nadine Bernard, illus. 2002. 16p. (J). (ps-1). 8.99 (978-0-689-84759-2(9) , Little Simon) Simon & Schuster Children's Publishing.

Squillace, Elisa, illus. Down in the Jungle. 2005. (Classic Books with Holes). 16p. (J). bds. 5.99 (978-1-904550-61-7(4)) Child's Play-International.

Steadman, Barbara. Little Flower Girls Sticker Paper Dolls. 2003. (Dover Little Activity Bks.). (Illus.). 4p. (J). pap. 1.50 (978-0-486-43019-5(7)) Dover Pubns., Inc.

—Prince & Princess Sticker Paper Dolls. 2002. (Sticker Paper Dolls Ser.). (Illus.). 4p. (J). pap. 1.50 (978-0-486-42348-7(4)) Dover Pubns., Inc.

Steckel, Richard & Steckel, Michele, photos by. Happy Birthday. 2007. (Illus.). 20p. (J). bds. 6.95 (*978-1-58246-210-3(0) , Tricycle Pr.) Ten Speed Pr.

Steer, Dugald. Snappy Little Halloween. Matthews, Derek, illus. 2004. 20p. (J). (gr. k-4). reprint ed. 13.00 (978-0-7567-7403-5(9)) DIANE Publishing Co.

Steptoe, Javaka. Sweet, Sweet Baby! Fabric Petals with Fun Sounds & a Mylar Mirror! Steptoe, Javaka, illus. 2005. (Illus.). 4p. (J). bds. 12.95 (978-0-439-65086-1(0) , Cartwheel Bks.) Scholastic, Inc.

Sterling Publishing Company Staff. Katie Cat Super. abr. ed. 2000. (Balloon Ser.). (Illus.). 8p. (J). (ps-1). pap. 4.95 (978-0-8069-2765-7(8) , Balloon Bks.) Sterling Publishing Co., Inc.

Sterling Publishing Company Staff, ed. Make a Doll's Shop: Press Out & Play. 2000. (Press Out & Play Bks.). (Illus.). 16p. (J). (gr. k-2). pap. 5.95 (978-0-8069-2669-8(4)) Sterling Publishing Co., Inc.

Sterling/Balloon. Animals on the Farm Super Sticker Book. 2003. (Sticker Bks.). (Illus.). 16p. (J). (ps-1). pap. 4.95 (978-0-8069-2667-4(8) , Balloon Bks.) Sterling Publishing Co., Inc.

Stewart, Amber. Birthday Countdown. Marlow, Layn, illus. 2007. 20p. (J). (ps-k). bds. 12.95 (*978-0-7696-5352-5(9) , Gingham Dog Pr.) School Specialty Publishing.

Stewart, Ayoka. Dog of Steel. 2006. (Krypto Ser.). (Illus.). 6p. (J). bds. 7.99 (978-0-439-83004-1(4) , Scholastic) Scholastic, Inc.

Stewart, Pat L. Old Macdonald's Farm Stickers. 2003. (Dover Little Activity Bks.). (Illus.). 4p. (J). pap. 1.50 (978-0-486-43010-2(3)) Dover Pubns., Inc.

Stick & Stamp: Cats & Kittens. 2000. (Illus.). 36p. (J). (ps-3). pap. 9.95 (978-0-439-23585-3(5)) Scholastic, Inc.

Stick & Stamp: Dogs & Puppies. 2000. (Illus.). 36p. (J). (ps-3). pap. 9.95 (978-0-439-23586-0(3)) Scholastic, Inc.

Stickland, Henrietta. The Christmas Express: A Pop-Up Village, Toy Train, Light & Sound! Stickland, Paul, illus. 1999. (J). (ps up). 16.95 (978-1-58117-048-1(3) , Intervisual/Piggy Toes) Dalmatian Pr.

T
U
V

Stierle, Cynthia. Ratatouille Movie Theater Storybook & Movie Projector. Disney, Reader's Digest, Pixar, illus. 2007. (RD Innovative Book & Player Format Ser.). 48p. (J). (ps-4). bds. 24.99 (*978-0-7944-1284-5(X)) Reader's Digest Assn., Inc., The.

Stockham, Jess, et al, illus. Puss in Boots. 2007. 24p. pap. 5.99 (*978-1-84643-075-6(5)) Child's Play International Ltd. GBR. Dist: Child's Play-International.

Stockham, Jess, et al, illus. Stone Soup. 2006. 24p. pap. 5.00 (978-1-84643-021-3(6)) Child's Play-International.

Stockham, Jessica. Little Red Riding Hood. 2004. (Flip up Fairy Tales Ser.). (Illus.). 24p. (J). 7.99 (978-0-85953-675-2(0)) Child's Play-International.

—Runaway Train. 2004. (Illus.). 24p. (J). 9.99 (978-0-85953-144-3(9)) Child's Play-International.

Stockham, Jessica, illus. Down by the Station. 2002. 16p. (J). bds. 5.99 (978-0-85953-140-5(6)) Child's Play-International.

—Little Red Riding Hood. 2005. 24p. pap. (978-1-904550-22-8(3)) Child's Play-International.

Stockham, Jessica, tr. & illus. Down by the Station. Stockham, Jessica, illus. 2003. (Classic Books with Holes). (J). 6.99 (978-0-85953-132-0(5)) Child's Play-International.

—Ten Little Speckled Frogs. Stockham, Jessica, illus. 2003. 24p. (J). 9.99 (978-0-85953-959-3(8)) Child's Play-International.

Stories from the Bible: A Look Inside Flapbook. 2003. 18p. (J). bds. 10.99 (978-0-8254-7270-1(9)) Kregel Pubns.

Strawberry Shortcake Paint n' Play with Sticker Rolls. 2005. (J). spiral bd. (978-1-59487-146-7(9)) Artist Studios, Ltd.

Strawberry Shortcake Secret Diary with Pendant. 2005. (J). (978-1-59487-155-9(8)) Artist Studios, Ltd.

Stuart, Jon & Stuart, Page J. Whambamboozle. Quigley, Sebastian, illus. 2000. 16p. (J). (gr. 2-5). pap. 11.95 (978-0-688-17175-9(3) , Harper Festival) HarperCollins Pubs.

Studio Mouse. Disney's Winnie the Pooh: Time to Learn: Learn & Carry 4 Books with CD. rev. ed. 2007. 4x20p. 14.99 (*978-1-59069-564-7(X)) Studio Mouse LLC.

—Mother Goose Wheels on the Bus: Book & CD. rev. ed. 2007. 24p. 4.99 (*978-1-59069-562-3(3)) Studio Mouse LLC.

Studio Mouse, ed. Play, Laugh, & Learn All Year Long. 2007. (Illus.). 28p. 16.99 incl. audio compact disk (978-1-59069-503-6(8) , 1P1000) Studio Mouse LLC.

Suen, Anastasia. Toddler Two. Cheon, Winnie, illus. (J). 2002. 20p. bds. 6.95 (978-1-58430-052-6(3)); 2000. 22p. 6.95 (978-1-58430-015-1(9)) Lee & Low Bks., Inc.

Summer Fun. 2002. (Illus.). 32p. (J). 2.99 (978-0-88724-810-8(1) , CD-0189) Carson-Dellosa Publishing Co., Inc.

Super Sisters. 2001. (Powerpuff Girls Ser.). (Illus.). 32p. (J). (ps-3). pap. 4.99 (978-0-307-29950-5(3) , Golden Bks.) Random Hse. Children's Bks.

Sutinis, Beth, ed. Touch & Feel. 2001. (My First Word Books). (Illus.). 12p. (J). (ps). bds. 9.99 (978-0-7894-7931-0(1)) Dorling Kindersley Publishing, Inc.

Swan, Michelle. Old MacDonald Had a Farm. 2007. 12p. (J). bds. 5.99 (*978-0-439-85307-1(9)) Scholastic, Inc.

Sweeney, Alyse. Lift-the-Flap Timelines: American History. 2004. (Lift-the-flap Timelines Ser.). 72p. pap. 12.99 (978-0-439-47119-0(2) , Teaching Resources) Scholastic, Inc.

Sykes, Julie. Little Tiger Goes to School. Warnes, Tim, illus. 1998. (Lift-The-Flap Book Ser.). 5p. (J). (ps-1). bds. 11.95 (978-1-888444-49-0(5)) Little Tiger Pr.

Taback, Simms. Can You Smile? 2007. (Illus.). 12p. (ps). bds. 8.95 (*978-1-59354-611-3(4)) Blue Apple Bks.

Taback, Simms. Joseph Had a Little Overcoat. Taback, Simms, illus. (Illus.). pap. incl. audio compact disk (978-1-59112-608-9(8)); 2001. (J). 28.95 incl. audio compact disk (978-1-59112-412-2(3)) Live Oak Media.

Tabby, Abigail. Snap! Button! Zip! Moroney, Christopher, illus. 2003. (Sesame Beginnings Ser.). 14p. (J). (gr. k). bds. 7.99 (978-0-375-82369-5(7) , Random Hse. Bks. for Young Readers) Random Hse. Children's Bks.

Tagel, Peggy, illus. On the Go. 2003. (Squishy Shapes Ser.). 10p. (J). 12.95 (978-1-57145-739-4(9) , Silver Dolphin Bks.) Advantage Pubs. Group.

Tangvald, Christine Harder & DeBoer, Rondi. Listen, Live & Laugh Bible Stories. Neubecker, Robert, illus. 2006. 14p. (J). 9.99 (978-0-310-70892-6(3)) Zonderkidz.

Tatchell, Judy. Dragons Lift-the-flap. Scott, Peter, illus. 2005. 16p. (J). (gr. 1 up). 11.95 (978-0-7945-0968-2(1) , Usborne) EDC Publishing.

Tatcheva, Eva. Witch Zelda's Birthday Cake: A Wild & Wicked Pop-up, Pull-the-Tab Book. Tatcheva, Eva, illus. 2004. (Illus.). 12p. (J). (gr. k-3). reprint ed. 18.00 (978-0-7567-7225-3(7)) DIANE Publishing Co.

Tayback, Simms. Where Is My Friend? 2006. (Illus.). 6p. bds. 7.95 (978-1-59354-152-1(X)) Blue Apple Bks.

Taylor, Geraldine & Harker, Jillian. Twinkle, Twinkle, Little Star. Sharratt, Nick, illus. 1999. (Baby Touch & Count Ser.). 12p. (J). 7.99 (978-0-7214-2737-9(5) , Dutton Juvenile) Penguin Group (USA) Inc.

Teitelbaum, Michael. Spider-Man. Mada Design Staff, illus. 2004. (Spider Man Ser.). 32p. (J). 3.99 (978-0-439-32953-8(1) , Scholastic Paperbacks) Scholastic, Inc.

Thatcher, Fran. Tiger Cub's Jungle Home. 2006. 20p. (J). 7.95 (978-1-59764-191-3(X)) New Line Bks.

Things That Go! (Flip Flap Fun Book Ser.). 10p. (J). bds. (978-2-89393-933-9(3)) Phidal Publishing, Inc./Editions Phidal, Inc.

Thistlethwaite, Diane, ed. My First Lift-the-Flap ABC Book. 2001. (My First Word Books). (Illus.). 12p. (J). (ps-k). bds. 9.99 (978-0-7894-7413-1(1)) Dorling Kindersley Publishing, Inc.

Thompson-Alexander, Catherine. A Letteration Final & Middle Sounds: Phonemic Awareness Activity. 2002. (Illus.). 92p. (J). spiral bd. 18.95 (978-0-9725422-1-0(3)) Front Line Educ.

Thompson Brothers Staff, illus. Action Scenes: Tonka Joe's Machines Sticker Book. 2001. (Tonka Joe Action Scenes Ser.). 24p. (J). (gr. k-3). pap. 5.99 (978-0-439-25913-2(4)) Scholastic, Inc.

Thompson, Cornelia. My Very Own Horse Book. 2006. 70p. pap. 19.95 (978-1-57054-845-1(5)) Klutz.

Thompson, Kay & Cheshire, Marc. Here Comes Eloise! Bracken, Carolyn, illus. 2004. (Eloise Ser.). 16p. (J). (ps-1). pap. 6.99 (978-0-689-87154-2(6) , Little Simon) Simon & Schuster Children's Publishing.

Thompson, Lauren. Little Quack's Bath Book. Anderson, Derek, illus. 2006. 8p. (J). pap. 6.99 (978-1-4169-0803-6(X) , Little Simon) Simon & Schuster Children's Publishing.

—Sat on the Go. Anderson, Derek, illus. 2006. 12p. (J). 7.99 (978-1-4169-0932-3(X) , Little Simon) Simon & Schuster Children's Publishing.

Thornley, Rebecca Gundersen. I Know He Is There: A Lift-A-Flap Book about Faith. Dorman, Brandon, illus. 2006. (J). (*978-1-59038-550-0(0)) Deseret Bk. Co.

Thorpe, Kiki. Where Is Boots? A Lift-the-Flap Story. Savitsky, Steve, illus. 2002. (Dora the Explorer Ser.). 16p. (J). (ps-1). pap. 5.99 (978-0-689-84775-2(0) , Simon Spotlight/Nickelodeon) Simon & Schuster Children's Publishing.

Tierney, Tom. Kimberly the Little Ballerina Paper Doll. 1999. (J). pap. 3.50 (978-0-486-40577-3(X)) Dover Pubns., Inc.

Tiger Tales Staff. Little Bunny. Finn, Rebecca, illus. 2005. (Cuddly Cuffs Ser.). 6p. (J). 6.95 (978-1-58925-763-4(4) , tiger tales) ME Media LLC.

—Little Ducky. Finn, Rebecca, illus. 2005. (Cuddly Cuffs Ser.). 6p. (J). 6.95 (978-1-58925-762-7(6) , tiger tales) ME Media LLC.

—Little Kitty. Finn, Rebecca, illus. 2005. (Cuddly Cuffs Ser.). 6p. (J). 6.95 (978-1-58925-760-3(X) , tiger tales) ME Media LLC.

—Little Puppy. Finn, Rebecca, illus. 2005. (Cuddly Cuffs Ser.). 6p. (J). 6.95 (978-1-58925-761-0(8) , tiger tales) ME Media LLC.

Tiger's Tail. Date not set. (Touch & Feel Ser.). (J). 4.98 (978-0-7525-9570-2(9)) Parragon, Inc.

Tigger's Bouncy Day. 2000. (Giant Pooh Book Ends Ser.). (Illus.). 10p. (J). (ps). (978-1-57584-808-2(2)) Reader's Digest Children's Publishing, Inc.

Tildes, Phyllis Limbacher. Eye Guess: A Foldout Guessing Game. 2005. (Illus.). 36p. (J). (ps-ps). per. 9.95 (978-1-57091-650-2(0)) Charlesbridge Publishing, Inc.

Time for Toys! (Flip Flap Fun Book Ser.). 10p. (J). bds. (978-2-7643-0040-4(9)) Phidal Publishing, Inc./Editions Phidal, Inc.

Toast, Sarah & Milne, A. A. Piglet's Not So Small Snowball. Williams, Don, illus. 2002. (Disney's Winnie the Pooh Ser.). (J). (978-0-7853-7617-0(8)) Publications International, Ltd.

Tolkien, J. R. R. Letters from Father Christmas. Tolkien, Baillie, ed. 2004. (Illus.). 112p. pap. 15.00 (978-0-618-51265-2(9)) Houghton Mifflin Co. Trade & Reference Div.

Tomaselli, Doris. My Little People Farm. Thompson Brothers Staff, illus. 2003. (Fisher-Price Lift-The-Flap Playbook Ser.). (ENG & SPA.). 5p. (J). 8.99 (978-0-7944-0213-6(5) , Reader's Digest Children's Bks.) Reader's Digest Children's Publishing, Inc.

Toms, Kate. Baby Animals. 2006. (Funny Faces Ser.). (Illus.). 10p. (ps-k). per., bds. 9.95 (978-1-84610-118-2(2)) Make Believe Ideas GBR. Dist: Ingram Pub. Services.

—Farm Animals. 2006. (Funny Faces Ser.). (Illus.). 10p. (ps-k). bds. 9.95 (978-1-84610-117-5(4)) Make Believe Ideas GBR. Dist: Ingram Pub. Services.

Tong, Willabel L., illus. Baby Animals. 2001. (Cuddly Cloth Book Ser.). 6p. (ps). 14.95 (978-1-58117-149-5(8) , Intervisual/Piggy Toes) Dalmatian Pr.

—Merry Faces. 2001. (Cuddly Cloth Book Ser.). 6p. (J). 14.95 (978-1-58117-150-1(1) , Intervisual/Piggy Toes) Dalmatian Pr.

Top That!, ed. Alphabet Farm. Parry, Jo, illus. 2007. 10p. (J). (ps). 8.99 (*978-1-84666-272-0(9) , Tide Mill Pr.) Top That! Publishing PLC GBR. Dist: Random Hse., Inc.

—Counting on the Farm. Sapp, Karen, illus. 2007. 16p. (J). (ps). 14.99 (*978-1-84666-270-6(2) , Tide Mill Pr.) Top That! Publishing PLC GBR. Dist: Random Hse., Inc.

Touch & Feel Playtime. braille ed. 2004. (J). (ps up). bds. (978-0-616-14614-9(0)) Canadian National Institute for the Blind/Institut National Canadien pour les Aveugles.

Toy Box Innovations Staff, creator. Disney Pixar: Finding Nemo/A Bug's Life/Monsters, Inc. unabr. abr. ed. 2005. (Disney's Read along Collection). (J). audio compact disk 14.99 (978-0-7634-1151-0(5)) Walt Disney Records.

Tractors & Trucks Sticker Activity Book. 2003. (Illus.). 12p. (J). 2.98 (978-1-4054-1182-0(1)) Parragon, Inc.

Trivizas, Eugene. The Three Little Wolves & the Big Bad Pig: A Pop-Up Storybook with a Twist in the Tale! Oxenbury, Helen, illus. 2004. 16p. (J). 24.95 (978-1-4052-0669-3(1)) Egmont Bks., Ltd. GBR. Dist: Trafalgar Square Publishing.

Turn & Learn Busy Little Books. 2001. (J). bds. (978-0-9676292-5-4(X)) Manhattan Toy.

Twinkle, Twinkle, Little Star. 2002. (DK Ladybird Ser.). 12p. (J). bds. 6.95 (978-0-7894-8473-4(0)) Dorling Kindersley Publishing, Inc.

Two Piece Fun Flip Over Books - 123's. 2000. (Illus.). (J). (978-1-58805-113-4(7)) DS-Max USA, Inc.

Two Piece Math Flip Over Books - Adding. 2000. (Illus.). (J). (978-1-58805-114-1(5)) DS-Max USA, Inc.

Two Piece Math Flip Over Books - Times Tables. 2000. (Illus.). (J). (978-1-58805-115-8(3)) DS-Max USA, Inc.

Tyler, Jenny & Hawthorn, P. There's a Monster in My House. 2004. (Illus.). 16p. (J). (gr. 1 up). pap. 7.95 (978-0-7945-0624-7(0)) EDC Publishing.

—Who's Making That Mess? rev. ed. 2004. (Illus.). 16p. (J). (gr. 1 up). pap. 7.99 (978-0-7945-0431-1(0)) EDC Publishing.

—Who's Making That Smell? rev. ed. 2004. (Illus.). 16p. (J). (gr. 1 up). pap. 7.95 (978-0-7945-0523-3(6)) EDC Publishing.

Tyler, Jenny & Hawthorn, Phillip. Who's Making that Smell? 2007. (Luxury Flap Bks). 16p. (J). 9.99 (*978-0-7945-1696-3(3) , Usborne) EDC Publishing.

Tyminski, Lori, illus. The Jungle Book 2. 2003. (J). 15.98 (978-0-7853-7968-3(1)) Publications International, Ltd.

Tyrrell, Melissa. Busy Little Lamb. Tom-Nellis, Susan, illus. 1998. (Baby Buddy Bks.: Vol. 4). 12p. (YA). (ps up). bds. 4.95 (978-1-888443-71-4(5) , Intervisual/Piggy Toes) Dalmatian Pr.

Ultimate Boats Sticker Book. (Radical Rides Ser.). 16p. (J). (978-2-7643-0012-1(3)) Phidal Publishing, Inc./Editions Phidal, Inc.

Ultimate Cars Sticker Book. (Radical Rides Ser.). 16p. (J). (978-2-7643-0010-7(7)) Phidal Publishing, Inc./Editions Phidal, Inc.

Ultimate Planes Sticker Book, 4 vols. (Radical Rides Ser.). (Illus.). 16p. (J). (978-2-7643-0008-4(5)) Phidal Publishing, Inc./Editions Phidal, Inc.

University Games Staff. Very Hungrey Caterpillar. 2006. 24p. (J). (978-1-57528-891-8(5)) University Games.

Unknown 02. Franny's Frantabulous Shoes. 2008. 12p. (J). (ps-k). bds. 5.99 (*978-0-448-44838-1(6) , Grosset & Dunlap) Penguin Group (USA) Inc.

Up on the Housetop - Musical Book. 2007. 26p. (J). bds. 12.99 (*978-0-8249-6714-7(3) , Candy Cane Pr.) Ideals Pubns.

Upton, Deborah. Barbie: My First Telephone. Wolfson, Tom, illus. Wolfson, Tom, photos by. 2001. (Play-a-Sound Ser.). (J). 16.98 (978-0-7853-4800-9(X)) Publications International, Ltd.

—First Telephone Book. Kleven, Dean, illus. 2001. (J). 16.98 (978-0-7853-4794-1(1)) Publications International, Ltd.

—Scooby-Doo! Telephone Book. 2001. (Illus.). (J). 15.98 (978-0-7853-4755-2(0)) Publications International, Ltd.

—World of Words. 2001. (Illus.). (J). (978-0-7853-4798-9(4)) Publications International, Ltd.

Valat, Pierre-Marie. Things That Go. 2002. (First Discovery Look-Inside Board Bks.). (Illus.). 10p. (J). bds. 4.95 (978-0-439-35593-3(1) , Cartwheel Bks.) Scholastic, Inc.

Vampire Sticker Book. 2003. (Illus.). 16p. (J). 2.98 (978-1-84273-119-2(X) , Exclusive Editions) Parragon, Inc.

van der Put, Klaartje. Little Duck: Finger Puppet Book. 2005. (Illus.). 12p. (J). 6.95 (978-0-8118-4847-3(7)) Chronicle Bks. LLC.

Van Fleet, Matthew. Monday the Bullfrog. 2006. (J). (978-978-141-691-0(2) , Simon & Schuster Children's Publishing) Simon & Schuster Children's Publishing.

—Monday the Bullfrog. Van Fleet, Matthew, illus. 2006. (Illus.). 20p. (J). 17.99 (978-1-4169-1231-6(2)) Simon & Schuster Children's Publishing.

—Tails. 2003. (Illus.). 20p. (J). 13.95 (978-0-15-216773-8(0) , Red Wagon Bks.) Harcourt Children's Bks.

Van Per Put, Klaartje. Little Bee: Finger Puppet Book. 2006. (Illus.). 12p. (J). bds., bds. 6.95 (978-0-8118-5236-4(9)) Chronicle Bks. LLC.

Velasquez, Crystal. Maya & Miguel: Mi Hermana Gemela; Mi Hermano Gemelo. 2005. (Maya & Miguel Ser.). Orig. Title: My Twin Brother/My Twin Sister. (SPA., Illus.). 96p. (J). 3.99 (978-0-439-74915-2(8) , Scholastic en Espanol) Scholastic, Inc.

Vere, Ed. Everyone's Hungry. 2003. (Illus.). 12p. (J). 6.95 (978-0-333-78041-1(8)) Macmillan Publishers Ltd. GBR. Dist: Trafalgar Square Publishing.

—Everyones Hungry. Vere, Ed, illus. 2000. (Illus.). 12p. (J). (ps). bds. 6.95 (978-0-531-30299-6(7) , Orchard Bks.) Scholastic, Inc.

—Everyone's Little. 2003. (Illus.). 14p. (J). bds. 6.95 (978-0-333-78039-8(6)) Macmillan Publishers Ltd. GBR. Dist: Trafalgar Square Publishing.

—Everyone's Little. 2001. (Illus.). 12p. (J). (ps). 6.95 (978-0-531-30336-8(5) , Orchard Bks.) Scholastic, Inc.

—Everyone's Noisy. 2003. (Illus.). 14p. (J). 8.99 (978-0-333-78040-4(X)) Macmillan Publishers Ltd. GBR. Dist: Trafalgar Square Publishing.

—Everyone's Noisy. 2001. (Illus.). 12p. (J). (ps). 6.95 (978-0-531-30335-1(7) , Orchard Bks.) Scholastic, Inc.

—Everyone's Sleepy. 2003. (Illus.). 14p. (J). 8.99 (978-0-333-78038-1(8)) Macmillan Publishers Ltd. GBR. Dist: Trafalgar Square Publishing.

Vilcoq, Marianne. Espero un Hermanito. (SPA.). 24p. (J). (978-84-8470-013-5(5)) Corimbo, Editorial S.L. ESP. Dist: Lectorum Pubns., Inc.

Vize, Dania. Lift, Stick & Learn Baby Animals. 2006. (Illus.). 24p. (J). (ps-k). pap. 4.95 (978-1-84610-032-1(1)) Make Believe Ideas GBR. Dist: Ingram Pub. Services.

Vocabulary Flip Chart. 2004. (gr. 1 up). suppl. ed. 109.15 (978-0-673-62166-5(9)); (gr. 2 up). suppl. ed. 109.15 (978-0-673-62167-2(7)) Addison-Wesley Educational Pubs., Inc.

Volker, Kerstin. Suzie Goes to Sleep. 2003. (Funny Friends Lift-and-Learn Bks.). (Illus.). 14p. (J). 5.99 (978-1-59384-024-2(1)) Parklane Publishing.

Wade, Lee. Cheerios el Libro de Jugar. Wade, Lee, illus. 2000. (SPA., Illus.). 14p. (J). bds. 6.99 (978-0-689-84155-2(8) , Libros Para Ninos) Simon & Schuster Children's Publishing.

—The Cheerios Play Book. (Illus.). (J). (gr. k-3). 2000. 12p. mass mkt. 4.99 (978-0-689-82723-5(7) , Simon & Schuster Children's Publishing); 1998. 14p. bds. 7.99 (978-0-689-82280-3(4) , Little Simon) Simon & Schuster Children's Publishing.

Waite, Elsie, et al. Following Rules. Sparck, Carole C., illus. l.t. ed. 2001. 8p. (J). pap. 6.00 (978-1-58084-169-6(4)) Lower Kuskokwim Schl. District.

Wallace, B. L. Noisy Dinosaur. 2007. (Touch & Feel Ser.). (Illus.). 12p. (ps). per., bds. 6.95 (978-1-84610-444-2(0)) Make Believe Ideas GBR. Dist: Ingram Pub. Services.

Wallace, Bruce & Make Believe Ideas Staff. Farm Animals. 2005. (Touch & Sparkle Ser.). (Illus.). 12p. (ps-k). bds. 5.95 (978-1-905051-02-1(6)) Make Believe Ideas GBR. Dist: Ingram Pub. Services.

Wallace, Bruce, et al. Lift & Learn Colors. Snaith, Andy, photos by. 2006. (Illus.). 24p. (ps-ps). per., bds. 5.95 (978-1-84610-028-4(3)) Make Believe Ideas GBR. Dist: Ingram Pub. Services.

Wallace, Nancy Elizabeth, illus. Snow. 2007. 24p. (J). (ps-3). bds. 6.99 (*978-0-7614-5362-8(8)) Cavendish, Marshall Corp.

Walsh, Melanie. Ocean Animals. Walsh, Melanie, illus. 2002. (Tiny Teether Ser.). (Illus.). 14p. (J). (gr. k-ps). bds. 4.99 (978-0-7636-1807-0(1)) Candlewick Pr.

—Pets. Walsh, Melanie, illus. 2002. (Tiny Teether Ser.). (Illus.). 14p. (J). (gr. k-ps). bds. 4.99 (978-0-7636-1808-7(X)) Candlewick Pr.

—Wild Animals. Walsh, Melanie, illus. 2002. (Tiny Teether Ser.). (Illus.). 14p. (J). (gr. k-ps). bds. 4.99 (978-0-7636-1809-4(8)) Candlewick Pr.

Walt Disney Company Staff. Treasure Planet: A Pop-Up Adventure. 2002. 12p. (J). bds. 8.99 (978-0-7364-2014-3(2) , RH/Disney) Random Hse. Children's Bks.

Wang, Dorothea DePrisco & Imperato, Teresa. All the Ways I Love You. Downing, Julie, illus. 2005. 10p. (J). 8.95 (978-1-58117-190-7(0) , Intervisual/Piggy Toes) Dalmatian Pr.

Wang, Margaret. I Love You Every Little Bit. 2006. 10p. 9.95 (978-1-58117-482-3(9) , Intervisual/Piggy Toes) Dalmatian Pr.

Wang, Margaret C. When I Grow Up: A Touch & Feel Book. Gevry, Claudine, illus. 2005. 12p. (J). bds. 10.95 (978-1-58117-423-6(3) , Intervisual/Piggy Toes) Dalmatian Pr.

Ward, Beck & Bainbridge, Katie, eds. Life in the Jungle: Touch & Feel. 2004. (Magic Windows Ser.). (Illus.). 10p. (J). bds. 7.95 (978-0-7624-1843-5(5) , Running Pr. Kids) Running Pr. Bk. Pubs.

Ward, Beck, et al. People: Pull the Tabs! Change the Pictures! 2004. (Magic Windows Ser.). (Illus.). 8p. (J). pap. 4.95 (978-0-7624-1844-2(3) , Running Pr. Kids) Running Pr. Bk. Pubs.

—Tools: Pull the Tabs! Change the Pictures! 2004. (Magic Windows Ser.). (Illus.). 8p. (J). pap. 4.95 (978-0-7624-1845-9(1) , Running Pr. Kids) Running Pr. Bk. Pubs.

Warne, Frederick. Peter Rabbit's Easter. 2004. (Peter Rabbit Seedlings Ser.). (Illus.). 12p. (J). (ps). bds. 6.99 (978-0-7232-4953-5(9) , Warne) Penguin Group (USA) Inc.

Warner Brothers Staff. Harry Potter Sticker Book Bk. 2: Flying at Hogwarts, No. 2. 2001. (Illus.). (gr. 4-7). pap. 7.99 (978-0-439-28635-0(2)) Scholastic, Inc.

Warren, Jean. Buttons. Cubley, Kathleen, ed. 1998. (Sticker Book Ser.). (Illus.). 32p. (J). (ps). pap. 3.95 (978-1-57029-216-3(7) , WPH 3706, Totline Pubns.) Schaffer, Frank Pubns.

—Eggs. Cubley, Kathleen, ed. 1998. (Sticker Book Ser.). (Illus.). 32p. (J). (ps). pap. 3.95 (978-1-57029-217-0(5) , WPH 3707, Totline Pubns.) Schaffer, Frank Pubns.

—Flags. Cubley, Kathleen, ed. 1998. (Sticker Book Ser.). (Illus.). 32p. (J). (ps). pap. 3.95 (978-1-57029-218-7(3) , WPH 3708, Totline Pubns.) Schaffer, Frank Pubns.

—Flowers. Cubley, Kathleen, ed. 1998. (Sticker Book Ser.). (Illus.). 32p. (J). (ps). pap. 3.95 (978-1-57029-219-4(1) , WPH 3709, Totline Pubns.) Schaffer, Frank Pubns.

—Hearts. Cubley, Kathleen, ed. 1998. (Sticker Book Ser.). (Illus.). 32p. (J). (ps). pap. 3.95 (978-1-57029-220-0(5) , WPH 3710, Totline Pubns.) Schaffer, Frank Pubns.

—Leaves. Cubley, Kathleen, ed. 1998. (Sticker Book Ser.). (Illus.). 32p. (J). (ps). pap. 3.95 (978-1-57029-221-7(3) , WPH 3711, Totline Pubns.) Schaffer, Frank Pubns.

Watanabe, Etsuko. Oscar's Party. 2006. (Illus.). 12p. (J). 14.95 (978-1-58234-697-7(6) , Bloomsbury Children) Bloomsbury Publishing.

Watanabe, Kaori, illus. Sweet Dreams. 2003. (My First Taggies Book Ser.). 8p. (J). 12.95 (978-0-439-53771-1(1) , Cartwheel Bks.) Scholastic, Inc.

Watt, F. & Wells, R. That's Not My Dinosaur... It's Body Is Too Squashy. 2004. (Touchy-Feely Board Bks.). (SPA., Illus.). 10p. (J). pap. 7.95 (978-0-7945-0129-7(X) , Usborne) EDC Publishing.

—That's Not My Lion. 2004. (Touchy-Feely Board Bks.). (SPA.). 10p. (J). 7.99 (978-0-7945-0047-4(1) , Usborne) EDC Publishing.

Watt, Fiona. Christmas Eve Board Book. 2007. (Luxury Touchy-Feely Board Bks). 10p. (J). bds. 11.99 (*978-0-7945-1478-5(2) , Usborne) EDC Publishing.

—Este No Es Mi Tren. rev. ed. 2004. (Titles in Spanish Ser.).Tr. of That's Not My Train. 32p. (J). 12.99 (978-1-58086-585-2(2)) EDC Publishing.

—Fairies. Cartwright, Stephen & Bird, Glen, illus. 2004. 10p. (J). (ps-ps). per. 15.95 (978-0-7945-0811-1(1) , Usborne) EDC Publishing.

—(Fairies Luxury Touchy-Feely) - Spanish. 2006. 12p. (J). bds. 15.99 (978-0-7460-7405-3(0) , Usborne) EDC Publishing.

—Kittens. Wells, Rachel, illus. rev. ed. 2005. (Big Touchy Feely Board Books Ser.). 10p. (J). 11.95 (978-0-7945-0891-3(X) , Usborne) EDC Publishing.

—Nativity Touchy-feely. 2005. 10p. (J). 15.95 (978-0-7945-1172-2(4) , Usborne) EDC Publishing.

—Sleepy Baby Board Bk. Mackinnon, Catherine-Anne, illus. 2006. 10p. (J). bds. 8.99 (978-0-7945-1071-8(X) , Usborne) EDC Publishing.

—That's not My Pirate. Wells, Rachel, illus. 2007. (Touchy-Feely Board Bks). 10p. (J). bds. 7.99 (***978-0-7945-1702-1(1)*** , Usborne) EDC Publishing.

Watt, Fiona. That's Not My Snowman. 2006. 10p. (J). bds. 9.99 (978-0-7945-1414-3(6) , Usborne) EDC Publishing.

Watt, Fiona & Cartwright, Stephen. Tie-a-Bow Book. 2004. (Treasury of Farmyard Tales Ser.). (Illus.). 10p. (J). 7.95 (978-0-7945-0330-7(6) , Usborne) EDC Publishing.

Watt, Fiona & Wells, Rachel. Anifeiliaid y Fferm. 2005. (WEL., Illus.). 8p. (978-1-84512-000-9(0)) Cymdeithas Lyfrau Ceredigion.

—That's Not My Tractor. 2004. (Touchy-Feely Board Bks.). (SPA., Illus.). 10p. (J). 7.99 (978-0-7945-0011-5(0) , Usborne) EDC Publishing.

Wax, Wendy. Hippo Rules: A Tale of Good Manners. Terry, Michael, illus. 2007. 12p. (J). 12.99 (***978-0-7944-1289-0(0)*** Reader's Digest Assn., Inc., The.

Weare, Tim. Hide-and-Seek with Leo. 2001. (Hand Puppet Board Bks.). (Illus.). 10p. (J). (ps). pap., bds. 14.95 (978-0-439-29719-6(2) , Cartwheel Bks.) Scholastic, Inc.

—I'm a Little Sheep. 2005. (Illus.). 7p. (J). (ps-6). bds. 7.95 (978-1-904613-54-1(3) , Buster Bks.) O'Mara, Michael Bks., Ltd. GBR. *Dist:* Independent Pubs. Group.

Weatherill, Stephen. Shape up, Goz! 2003. (Baby Goz Ser.). (Illus.). 16p. (J). 12.95 (978-1-84507-005-2(4)) Lincoln, Frances Ltd. GBR. *Dist:* Perseus Distribution.

Weber, Lou. Little Sound Transformers. 12p. 9.98 (***978-1-4127-6802-3(0)***) Publications International, Ltd.

Weeks, Sarah. Ruff! Ruff! Where's Scruff? A Lift the Flap Adventure. Carter, David A., illus. 2006. 16p. (J). 13.95 (978-0-15-205575-2(4) , Red Wagon Bks.) Harcourt Children's Bks.

—Who's under That Hat? A Lift-the-Flap Pop-Up Adventure. Carter, David A., illus. 2005. 14p. (J). (ps). 6.98 (978-0-15-205467-0(7) , Red Wagon Bks.) Harcourt Children's Bks.

—Who's under That Hat? A Lift-the-Flap Pop-up Adventure. Carter, David A., illus. 2006. 14p. (J). (ps-2). 14.00 (978-1-4223-5440-7(7)) DIANE Publishing Co.

Wehr, Paul. The Animated Bunny's Tail. wehr, Julian, illus. 2005. 20p. (J). 18.95 (978-0-9748093-1-1(4)) Wehr Animations.

Weimer, Heidi R. I Love You More Than... Sharp, Chris, illus. 2006. 16p. (J). (ps). bds. 12.99 (978-0-8249-6679-9(1) , Candy Cane Pr.) Ideals Pubns.

Weinberger, Kimberly. A Dinosaur Named Sue. 2001. (Jurassic Park Ser.). (Illus.). 24p. (J). (ps-2). pap. 5.99 (978-0-439-28367-0(1)) Scholastic, Inc.

—My Surprise Toolbox. LaPadula, Tom, illus. 2002. (Home Depot Ser.). 5p. (J). bds. 10.95 (978-0-439-28861-3(4) , Cartwheel Bks.) Scholastic, Inc.

—Share-and-Be-Fair Sticker Book. 2001. (Clifford, the Big Red Dog Ser.). (J). pap. 5.99 (978-0-439-28681-7(6)) Scholastic, Inc.

—Spring Is Here, Hello, Kitty! 2003. (Illus.). 32p. (J). (978-0-439-45079-9(9)) Scholastic, Inc.

Weiss, David & Weiss, Bobbi J. G. Cat Attack! Storybook with Stickers. 2004. (Shrek 2 Ser.). (Illus.). 24p. (J). pap. 3.99 (978-0-439-53851-0(3)) Scholastic, Inc.

Weiss, Ellen. Fisher - Price Little People Christmas Is Here! S. I. International Staff, illus. 2002. (Fisher-Price Little People Mini-Flap PlayBooks Ser.). 10p. (J). (ps-k). bds. 9.99 (978-1-57584-997-3(6)) Reader's Digest Children's Publishing, Inc.

—Mickey's Neighborhood Discovery. 2000. (Lift the Flaps Bks.). 12p. (J). 6.99 (978-0-7364-1035-9(X)) Mouse Works.

Wells, Rosemary. Bunny Mail. 2004. (Max & Ruby Ser.). (Illus.). 32p. (J). (ps-3). 15.99 (978-0-670-03630-1(7) , Viking Juvenile) Penguin Group (USA) Inc.

—Goodnight Max. Wells, Rosemary, illus. 2000. (Max & Ruby Ser.). (Illus.). 14p. (J). (gr. k-2). pap. 11.99 (978-0-670-88707-1(2) , Viking Juvenile) Penguin Group (USA) Inc.

—Hide-and-Seek. 2008. (Max & Ruby Ser.). 12p. (J). (ps-k). bds. 7.99 (***978-0-448-44784-1(3)*** , Grosset & Dunlap) Penguin Group (USA) Inc.

—Max & Ruby's Show-and-Tell. 2006. (All Aboard Bks.). 24p. (J). (ps-ps). pap. 3.99 (978-0-448-43952-5(2) , Grosset & Dunlap) Penguin Group (USA) Inc.

—Max & Ruby's Snowy Day. 2004. (Max & Ruby Ser.). 10p. (J). (ps). bds. 6.99 (978-0-448-43567-1(5) , Grosset & Dunlap) Penguin Group (USA) Inc.

—McDuff's Favorite Things. Jeffers, Susan, illus. 2004. 16p. (J). (ps-k). 9.99 (978-0-7868-0893-9(4)) Hyperion Bks. for Children.

—McDuff's Hide-and-Seek. Jeffers, Susan, illus. 2004. 12p. (ps-ps). 9.99 (978-0-7868-1935-5(9)) Hyperion Bks. for Children.

Wen, Dref. Fy Llyfr Geiriau Croes Cyntaf. 2005. Tr. of My First Opposites. (WEL., Illus.). 32p. bds. (978-1-85596-671-0(9)) Dref Wen.

—Traeth Prysur. 2005. Tr. of Busy Beach. (WEL., Illus.). 10p. (978-1-85596-661-1(1)) Dref Wen.

What Makes a Rainbow? (J). 4.95 (978-1-58117-220-1(6) , Intervisual/Piggy Toes) Dalmatian Pr.

What Will I Be?, 4 vols. (Girlfriend Gang Ser.). (Illus.). 16p. (J). (978-2-7643-0022-0(0)) Phidal Publishing, Inc./ Editions Phidal, Inc.

The Wheels on the Bus: A Touch & Sing Book. 2002. (DK Ladybird Ser.). 12p. (J). bds. 6.95 (978-0-7894-8472-7(2)) Dorling Kindersley Publishing, Inc.

Where's Elmo? A Peek-a-boo Book. 1999. (Illus.). (J). (978-1-56156-833-8(3)) Kidsbooks, Inc.

Where's the Kitten? (English/Russian) 2004. (RUS., Illus.). 12p. (J). bds. 5.50 (978-1-932065-84-8(9)) Star Bright Bks., Inc.

Where's the Puppy? (English/Russian) 2005. (Photo Flap Bks.). (RUS., Illus.). 12p. (J). bds. 5.50 (978-1-932065-85-5(7)) Star Bright Bks., Inc.

Who Lives in the Garden? 2004. (Who Lives... Ser.). 12p. (J). bds. 4.99 (978-1-85854-643-8(5)) Brimax Books Ltd. GBR. *Dist:* Byeway Bks.

Whose Bottom? A Lift-the-Flap Book. 2002. (Lift-the-Flap Books Ser.). 16p. (J). pap. 5.95 (978-0-7894-8478-9(1)) Dorling Kindersley Publishing, Inc.

Whose Ears? A Lift-the-Flap Book. 2002. (Lift-the-Flap Books Ser.). 16p. (J). pap. 5.95 (978-0-7894-8479-6(X)) Dorling Kindersley Publishing, Inc.

Whybrow, Ian. Say Hello to the Snowy Animals! Touch & Feel Animals on Every Page. Eaves, Edward, illus. rev. ed. 2007. 20p. 22.95 (***978-0-230-01391-9(0)*** , Macmillan Children's Bks.) Pan Macmillan GBR. *Dist:* Trans-Atlantic Pubns., Inc.

Whybrow, Ian, et al. Owain A'r Cloc. 2005. (WEL., Illus.). 18p. 6.99 (978-1-84323-366-4(5)) Gomer Pr. GBR. *Dist:* Gomer Pr.

Wick, Walter. Can You See What I See? Trucks & Cars. 2007. (J). bds. 4.99 (978-0-439-86230-1(2) , Cartwheel Bks.) Scholastic, Inc.

Wick, Walter, photos by. I Spy: Interactive Sound Book of Picture Riddles. 2003. (Illus.). 30p. (J). 15.98 (978-0-7853-8424-3(3)) Publications International, Ltd.

Wickings, Ruth. Animals in the Desert. 2006. (First Fun Pop-ups Ser.). (Illus.). 12p. bds. 8.95 (978-1-84560-021-1(5)) Mercury Bks. Ltd. GBR. *Dist:* International Publishers Marketing.

—Animals in the Jungle. 2006. (First Fun Pop-ups Ser.). (Illus.). 12p. bds. 8.95 (978-1-84560-020-4(7)) Mercury Bks. Ltd. GBR. *Dist:* International Publishers Marketing.

—Animals in the Sea. 2006. (First Fun Pop-ups Ser.). (Illus.). 12p. bds. 8.95 (978-1-84560-023-5(1)) Mercury Bks. Ltd. GBR. *Dist:* International Publishers Marketing.

—Animals on the Ice. 2006. (First Fun Pop-ups Ser.). (Illus.). 12p. bds. 8.95 (978-1-84560-022-8(3)) Mercury Bks. Ltd. GBR. *Dist:* International Publishers Marketing.

—By the Seaside. 2006. (World at Your Feet Ser.). (Illus.). 10p. 9.95 (978-1-84560-024-2(X)) Mercury Bks. Ltd. GBR. *Dist:* International Publishers Marketing.

—Fairies. 2007. (Enchanted World Ser.). (Illus.). 10p. (J). (ps-3). 9.95 (***978-1-84560-030-3(4)***) Mercury Bks. Ltd. GBR. *Dist:* International Publishers Marketing.

—In the Pond. 2007. (World at Your Feet Ser.). (Illus.). 10p. (J). 9.95 (978-1-84560-026-6(6)) Mercury Bks. Ltd. GBR. *Dist:* International Publishers Marketing.

—Mermaids. 2007. (Enchanted World Ser.). (Illus.). 10p. (J). (ps-3). 9.95 (***978-1-84560-031-0(2)***) Mercury Bks. Ltd. GBR. *Dist:* International Publishers Marketing.

—On the Forest Floor. 2007. (World at Your Feet Ser.). (Illus.). 10p. (J). 9.95 (978-1-84560-027-3(4)) Mercury Bks. Ltd. GBR. *Dist:* International Publishers Marketing.

—Round the Garden. 2006. (World at Your Feet Ser.). (Illus.). 10p. 9.95 (978-1-84560-025-9(8)) Mercury Bks. Ltd. GBR. *Dist:* International Publishers Marketing.

—Witches. 2007. (Enchanted World Ser.). (Illus.). 10p. (J). (gr. 4-7). 9.95 (***978-1-84560-032-7(0)***) Mercury Bks. Ltd. GBR. *Dist:* International Publishers Marketing.

—Wizards. 2007. (Enchanted World Ser.). (Illus.). 12p. (J). (ps-3). 9.95 (***978-1-84560-033-4(9)***) Mercury Bks. Ltd. GBR. *Dist:* International Publishers Marketing.

Widdowson, Kay, illus. Please, Mr Crocodile... 2006. 24p. (J). (978-1-84643-025-1(9)) Child's Play-International.

Wild Animals Sticker Activity Book. 2003. (Illus.). 12p. (J). 2.98 (978-1-4054-1183-7(X)) Parragon, Inc.

Wilhelm, Hans. Friends Around the World. 2006. (Hans Wilhelm Lift-the-Flap Bks.). (Illus.). 16p. (J). 9.99 (978-0-7641-5891-9(0)) Barron's Educational Series, Inc.

Williams, Nancy. A Kwanzaa Celebration: Pop-up Book. Sabuda, Robert, illus. 2004. 14p. (J). reprint ed. 13.00 (978-0-7567-8229-0(5)) DIANE Publishing Co.

Willson, Sarah. Travis & Scoop's Big Race. Castellano, Giuseppe, illus. 2003. (Bob the Builder Ser.). 16p. (J). pap. 5.99 (978-0-689-85302-9(5) , Simon Spotlight) Simon & Schuster Children's Publishing.

Wingate, Philippa. Tick Tock Time. Cooke, Andy, illus. 2007. (J). (ps-1). per. 8.95 (978-1-905158-12-6(2) , Buster Bks.) O'Mara, Michael Bks., Ltd. GBR. *Dist:* Ingram Pub. Services.

Witch Sticker Book. 2003. (Illus.). 16p. (J). 2.98 (978-1-84273-117-8(3) , Exclusive Editions) Parragon, Inc.

Witzy's Very First Color & Activity Book. 2001. (Little Suzy's Zoo Ser.). 112p. (J). pap. 2.99 (978-1-58668-084-8(6)) Lyrick Studios.

Wizard Sticker Book. 2003. (Illus.). 16p. (J). 2.98 (978-1-84273-118-5(1) , Exclusive Editions) Parragon, Inc.

Wolf, Jackie. Campbell's Alphabet Soup Book. 2002. (Illus.). 10p. (J). bds. 5.99 (978-1-57151-639-8(5)) Playhouse Publishing.

Wolf, Jackie, et al. My Sparkle Egg Book. 2005. (Illus.). (J). (***978-1-57151-750-0(2)***) Playhouse Publishing.

Wood, Amanda. Amazing Baby Touch & Play! 2005. (Illus.). 12p. (J). 15.95 (978-1-59223-529-2(8) , Silver Dolphin Bks.) Advantage Pubs. Group.

—Baby's Day! Dodd, Emma, illus. 2006. (Amazing Baby Ser.). 16p. (J). bds. 5.95 (978-1-59223-588-9(3) , Silver Dolphin Bks.) Advantage Pubs. Group.

Wood, Tim & Wood, Jenny. Noah's Ark. Thatcher, Fran, illus. 1998. 10p. (J). (ps-2). 11.99 (978-0-8054-1797-5(4)) B&H Publishing Grp.

Wortzman, Ricki, et al. Red Riding Hood's Math Adventure. Mazille, Capucine, illus. 2001. 24p. (J). (ps-5). 14.95 (978-1-57091-477-5(X)) Charlesbridge Publishing, Inc.

Wright, Rachel. Pirates. (Illus.). 32p. (YA). (gr. 3 up). lib. bdg. 27.10 (978-1-932889-06-2(X)) Sea-To-Sea Pubns.

Yablonsky, Buster. Where Is Slippery Soap? A Bath Book with Magic Ink. Johnson, Traci Paige, illus. 2001. (Blue's Clues Ser.). 8p. (J). (ps-k). 5.99 (978-0-689-82948-2(5) , Simon Spotlight/Nickelodeon) Simon & Schuster Children's Publishing.

Yates, Gene, illus. The Chameleon Colors Book. 2006. (J). (***978-1-58865-361-1(7)***) Kidsbooks, Inc.

—The Giraffe Numbers Book. 2006. (J). (***978-1-58865-364-2(1)***) Kidsbooks, Inc.

Yoon, Salina. Easter Egg Surprise. Yoon, Salina, illus. 2005. (Illus.). 12p. (J). (ps-1). bds. 5.99 (978-0-8431-1364-8(2) , Price Stern Sloan) Penguin Group (USA) Inc.

—Good Night, Little One. 2005. (Illus.). 16p. (J). pap. 6.99 (978-0-439-66373-1(3) , Cartwheel Bks.) Scholastic, Inc.

—My Princess Essentials. 2007. 10p. (J). pap. 8.99 (978-0-8431-2180-3(7) , Price Stern Sloan) Penguin Group (USA) Inc.

—Santa. 2004. (Illus.). 10p. (J). (ps-1). bds. 5.99 (978-0-8431-1150-7(X) , Price Stern Sloan) Penguin Group (USA) Inc.

—School Bus. Yoon, Salina, illus. 2005. (Illus.). 10p. (J). (ps-1). bds. 5.99 (978-0-8431-1394-5(4) , Price Stern Sloan) Penguin Group (USA) Inc.

—Spring Fever! A Petal Tab Book. Yoon, Salina, illus. 2005. (Illus.). 12p. (J). bds. 6.99 (978-0-689-87424-6(3) , Little Simon) Simon & Schuster Children's Publishing.

Yoon, Salina, creator. Sea Creatures: A Sparkling Little Colors Book, 4 vols. 2005. (Illus.). 12p. (J). 5.95 (978-1-58117-169-3(2) , Intervisual/Piggy Toes) Dalmatian Pr.

Yoon, Salina, illus. Foil Fun Opposites. 2000. (Foil Fun Board Bks.). 10p. (J). (ps). bds. 4.95 (978-1-58117-063-4(7) , Intervisual/Piggy Toes) Dalmatian Pr.

—Peek-a-Boo Farm Animals. 2005. (Peek-a-Boo Guess Who Book Ser.: Vol. 2). 10p. (J). 7.95 (978-1-58117-158-7(7) , Intervisual/Piggy Toes) Dalmatian Pr.

—Peek-a-Boo Wild Animals. 2005. (Peek-a-Boo Guess Who Book Ser.: Vol. 1). 10p. (J). (ps-k). 7.95 (978-1-58117-157-0(9) , Intervisual/Piggy Toes) Dalmatian Pr.

Yorinks, Arthur. Mommy? Sendak, Maurice, illus. 2006. 32p. (J). pap. 24.95 (978-0-439-88050-3(5) , Di Capua, Michael) Scholastic, Inc.

Young, Jay. Magic World of Learning. Tucker, Sian, illus. 2003. 32p. (978-1-903174-42-5(2)) Chrysalis Children's Bks.

Yoyo Books Staff. Bedtime: Learning Words Series. 2004. 12p. bds. 12.95 (978-90-5843-607-8(1)) YoYo Bks. BEL. *Dist:* National Bk. Network.

—On the Farm: Learning Words Series. 2005. 12p. bds. 12.95 (978-90-5843-605-4(5)) YoYo Bks. BEL. *Dist:* National Bk. Network.

Zakiyyah. ChatterWorld: My Numbers in Spanish/French. 2006. 40p. 14.99 (978-0-9777085-0-5(0)) Little Linguists Press.

Zebra's Stripes. Date not set. (Touch & Feel Ser.). (Illus.). (J). 4.98 (978-0-7525-9571-9(7)) Parragon, Inc.

Zeifert, Harriet. Go! SAMi, illus. 2006. 24p. bds. 8.95 (978-1-59354-138-5(4)) Blue Apple Bks.

Zelinsky, Paul O. Knick-Knack Paddywhack: A Moving Parts Book. Zelinsky, Paul O., illus. 2002. (Illus.). 8p. (J). (ps-k). 18.99 (978-0-525-46908-7(7) , Dutton Juvenile) Penguin Group (USA) Inc.

Ziefert, Harriet. Baby Talk. Sami, illus. 2005. 24p. (ps). bds. 8.95 (978-1-59354-105-7(8)) Blue Apple Bks.

—Bear Gets Dressed: A Guessing Game Story. Lobel, Arnold & Capucilli, Alyssa, illus. 2004. 16p. (J). pap. 5.95 (978-1-4027-1795-6(4)) Sterling Publishing Co., Inc.

—Bear's Busy Morning: A Guessing Game Story. Lobel, Arnold & Capucilli, Alyssa, illus. 2004. 16p. (J). pap. 5.95 (978-1-4027-1796-3(2)) Sterling Publishing Co., Inc.

—The Best Smelling Christmas Book Ever: 9 Scents to Scratch & Sniff! Rader, Laura, illus. 2004. 18p. (J). (gr. k-4). reprint ed. 13.00 (978-0-7567-7600-8(7)) DIANE Publishing Co.

—Buzzy's Big Bedtime Book. Bolam, Emily, illus. 2004. 40p. 9.95 (978-1-59354-059-3(0)) Blue Apple Bks.

—Buzzy's Birthday. Bolam, Emily, illus. 2004. 24p. 9.95 (978-1-59354-062-3(0)) Blue Apple Bks.

—Monkey's Noisy Jungle. Newton, Jill, illus. 2007. bds. 7.95 (978-1-59354-598-7(3)) Blue Apple Bks.

—Nicky's Noisy Night. Brown, Richard, illus. 2003. 7p. (ps). bds. 6.95 (978-1-929766-79-6(3)) Blue Apple Bks.

—Oh No, Nicky! 2003. (Illus.). 14p. 6.95 (978-1-59354-012-8(4)) Blue Apple Bks.

—Rosie's Red String. Rader, Laura, illus. 2003. 15p. (J). reprint ed. pap. 15.00 (978-0-7567-6573-6(0)) DIANE Publishing Co.

—Thank You, Nicky! Brown, Richard, illus. 2002. 7p. (ps). bds. 6.95 (978-1-929766-73-4(4)) Blue Apple Bks.

—Two Little Witches 8x8 Stkr Bk. Taback, Simms, illus. 2007. 20p. (J). (gr. k-k). pap. 3.99 (***978-0-7636-3309-7(7)***) Candlewick Pr.

—What Happened to Jack & Jill? A Flip-and-Read Book. Rader, Laura, illus. 2004. 24p. (J). bds. 8.95 (978-1-4027-1784-0(9)) Sterling Publishing Co., Inc.

—What Is Mother's Day? Schumacher, Claire, illus. 2006. 16p. pap. 5.95 (978-1-4027-2398-8(9)) Sterling Publishing Co., Inc.

—Where Is Humpty Dumpty? A Flip-and-Read Book. Rader, Laura, illus. 2004. 24p. (J). bds. 8.95 (978-1-4027-1785-7(7)) Sterling Publishing Co., Inc.

—Where's Nicky's Easter Egg? Brown, Richard, illus. 2003. 7p. bds. 6.95 (978-1-929766-80-2(7)) Blue Apple Bks.

—Where's Nicky's Valentine? Brown, Richard, illus. 2002. 7p. (ps). bds. 6.95 (978-1-929766-72-7(6)) Blue Apple Bks.

Ziefert, Harriet & Taback, Simms. Where Is My Baby? 2002. (Lift-the-Flap Bks.). (Illus.). 8p. bds. 7.95 (978-1-929766-46-8(7)) Blue Apple Bks.

—Who Said Moo? 2002. (Lift-the-Flap Bks.). (Illus.). 8p. bds. 7.95 (978-1-929766-47-5(5)) Blue Apple Bks.

Zimmerman, Brooke. Trains: Lift-A-Flap Fun. Wieland, Don & Lovell, Mike, trs. Wieland, Don, illus. 2002. (Active Minds Ser.). 12p. (J). bds. 12.98 (978-0-7853-6303-3(3) , 7158300) Publications International, Ltd.

Zimmerman, Dottie, creator. Interactive Sing-along Big Books Five Little Ducks. 2007. (J). spiral bd. 12.95 (***978-1-58650-713-8(3)***) Super Duper Pubns.

—Interactive Sing-along Big Books Where Are My Crayons? 2007. (J). spiral bd. 12.95 (***978-1-58650-712-1(5)***) Super Duper Pubns.

Zimmermann, Dotte, creator. Interactive Sing-along Big Books Little Bo Peep. 2007. (J). spiral bd. 12.95 (***978-1-58650-718-3(4)***) Super Duper Pubns.

Zimmermann, Dottie, creator. Interactive Sing-along Big Books Cool Camping Fun. 2007. (J). spiral bd. 12.95 (***978-1-58650-721-3(4)***) Super Duper Pubns.

—Interactive Sing-along Big Books Dress Me Bear. 2007. (J). spiral bd. (***978-1-58650-716-9(8)***) Super Duper Pubns.

—Interactive Sing-along Big Books Funny Face. 2007. (J). spiral bd. 12.95 (***978-1-58650-715-2(X)***) Super Duper Pubns.

—Interactive Sing-along Big Books Old MacDonald. 2007. (J). spiral bd. 12.95 (***978-1-58650-722-0(2)***) Super Duper Pubns.

—Interactive Sing-along Big Books This Old Man. 2007. (J). spiral bd. 12.95 (***978-1-58650-720-6(6)***) Super Duper Pubns.

Zinsmeister, Elke, illus. Ten Fat Sausages. 2005. (Classic Books with Holes). 16p. (J). bds. 5.99 (978-1-904550-59-4(2)) Child's Play-International.

Zobel-Nolan, Allia. Jesus & the Children. MacLean, Moira, illus. 2000. (Mini Handle Bks.:). 5p. (J). (ps). bds. 7.99 (978-1-57584-669-9(1)) Reader's Digest Children's Publishing, Inc.

—The Secret Fairy Garden. Ember, Kathi, illus. 2005. 12p. (J). bds. 12.99 (978-0-7944-0513-7(4)) Reader's Digest Assn., Inc., The.

Zoehfeld, Kathleen Weidner. Who's Afraid of a Heffalump? 1999. (Learn & Grow Ser.). (Illus.). 14p. (J). (ps-k). 5.99 (978-0-7364-0111-1(3)) Mouse Works.

Zuravicky, Orli. Blue Says. Craig, Karen, illus. 2007. (Blue's Clues Ser.). 12p. (J). bds. 6.99 (978-1-4169-4127-9(4) , Simon Spotlight/Nickelodeon) Simon & Schuster Children's Publishing.

TOY MAKING

Aaseng, Nathan. Business Builders in Toys. 2003. (Business Builders Ser.). (Illus.). 160p. (gr. 5 up). lib. bdg. 22.95 (978-1-881508-81-6(1)) Oliver Pr., Inc.

Bulloch, Ivan & James, Diane. Les Jouets. 2000. (Let's Ser.). (FRE., Illus.). 24p. (J). (ps-1). pap. 5.95 (978-1-58728-211-9(9) , Two Can Publishing) T&N Children's Publishing.

Doney, Meryl. Toys. 2004. (Crafts from Many Cultures Ser.). (Illus.). 32p. (J). (gr. 3 up). lib. bdg. 23.33 (978-0-8368-4048-3(8)) Stevens, Gareth Inc.

Elton, Candice & Elton, Richard. Every Kid Needs a Marshmallow Launcher. 2005. (Illus.). 50p. (J). spiral bd. 19.95 (978-1-58685-708-0(8)) Gibbs Smith, Publisher.

Elton, Richard & Elton, Candice. Every Kid Needs a Rubber Band Launcher. 2007. (J). (***978-1-4236-0268-2(4)***) Gibbs Smith, Publisher.

Giacobello, John. Choosing a Career in the Toy Industry. 2005. (World of Work Ser.). (Illus.). 64p. (YA). (gr. 7-12). lib. bdg. 25.25 (978-0-8239-3438-6(1)) Rosen Publishing Group, Inc., The.

Greathead, Helen. Toys That Move. 2006. (Illus.). 32p. (J). (978 1 58340-951-0(3)) Smart Apple Media.

Heller, D. M. Let's Make a Bike with Everyday Materials. 2006. (Illus.). 24p. (J). lib. bdg. (978-1-4042-3064-4(5)) Rosen Publishing Group, Inc., The.

Hinkler Books Staff. Balloon Animals. 2004. (Illus.). 48p. (J). 6.95 (978-1-86515-644-6(2)) Hinkler Bks. Pty, Ltd. AUS. *Dist:* Penton Overseas, Inc.

Jaffke, Freya. Toymaking with Children. (Illus.). 1999. 96p. (J). reprint ed. pap. 12.95 (978-0-86315-069-2(1) , 20244); 2nd rev. ed. 2002. 160p. pap. 16.95 (978-0-86315-367-9(4)) Floris Bks. GBR. *Dist:* Gryphon Hse., Inc., SteinerBooks, Inc., SteinerBooks, Inc.

Khanna, Sudarshan, et al. Toys & Tales with Everyday Materials. 2003. (Illus.). 144p. 10.99 (978-81-86211-42-7(X)) Penguin Group (USA) Inc.

Klutz Press Staff, creator. How to Make Pompom Animals. 2005. (Illus.). 22p. (J). spiral bd. 9.95 (978-1-59174-095-7(9)) Klutz.

LaFosse, Michael. Making Origami Toys Step by Step. 2002. (Kid's Guide to Origami Ser.). (Illus.). 24p. (J). lib. bdg. 21.25 (978-0-8239-5876-4(0) , PowerKids Pr.) Rosen Publishing Group, Inc., The.

Oxlade, Chris. Toys Through Time: How Toys Were Designed, Developed, & Made. 2004. (Illus.). 45p. (J). (gr. 4-8). reprint ed. (978-0-7567-7848-4(4)) DIANE Publishing Co.

Pinchuk, Amy Ruth. Make Cool Gadgets for Your Room. Rodriques, Teco, illus. Boudreau, Ray, photos by. 2004. (Popular Mechanics for Kids Ser.). 64p. (J). (gr. 4-8). 21.95 (978-1-894379-11-3(X)) Maple Tree Pr. CAN. *Dist:* Firefly Bks., Ltd.

Pohl, Kathleen. What Happens at a Toy Factory?= ¿Qué Pasa en una Fabrica de Juguetes? 2006. (ENG & SPA., Illus.). 24p. (J). pap. (978-0-8368-7397-9(1)); lib. bdg. (978-0-8368-7390-0(4)) Stevens, Gareth Inc. (Weekly Reader Early Learning Library).

Sadler, Judy Ann. Beanbag Buddies: And Other Stuffed Toys. Bradford, June, illus. 1999. 40p. (J). (ps-7). lib. bdg. 14.10 (978-0-613-21180-2(4)) Tandem Library Bks.

Scott-Waters, Marilyn, creator. The Toymaker: Paper Toys That You Can Make Yourself, 1. 2004. (Illus.). 20p. (YA). 12.95 (978-0-9759884-0-4(9)) Scott-Waters, Marilyn.

Souter, Gillian. Terrific Toys. Watson, Clare, illus. Martin, Andre, photos by. 2002. (Handy Crafts Ser.). 48p. (J). (gr. 2 up). lib. bdg. 24.67 (978-0-8368-3053-8(9)) Stevens, Gareth Inc.

TOYS

see also Dollhouses; Dolls

Ackroyd, Dorothea. Playtime. 1999. 3.95 (978-1-58185-202-8(9)) Quadrillion Media LLC.

Animales Bebes. 2005. (Collection Abre Tus Ojos, Collection Eye Openers Ser.).Tr. of Animal Babies. (SPA.). (J). (gr. k-2). 6.95 (978-950-11-0964-1(X)) Sigmar ARG. *Dist:* Iaconi, Mariuccia Bk. Imports.

Anness Publishing Staff & Tuxworth, Nicola. Toys. 2000. (Very First Picture Board Bks.). (Illus.). 20p. bds. 5.00 (978-0-7548-0712-4(6)) Anness Publishing GBR. *Dist:* National Bk. Network.

Baby Einstein. 1998. (J). 15.98 (978-1-892309-00-6(9)) Baby Einstein Co., LLC, The.

Baby's First Toys. 2004. 10p. (J). bds. 4.99 (978-1-85854-922-4(1)) Brimax Books Ltd. GBR. *Dist:* Byeway Bks.

Beaton, Clare, illus. Toys: Los Juguetes. 2003. (Bilingual First Bks.). (ENG & SPA.). 24p. (J). pap. 4.95 (978-0-7641-2611-6(3)) Barron's Educational Series, Inc.

Bidder, Jane. Inventions We Use for Play. 2006. 32p. (J). lib. bdg. (978-0-8368-6900-2(1)) Stevens, Gareth Inc.

Black, Jessica L. The New Toys. Ruminski, Jeff, illus. 2003. 8p. (J). (ps-1). bds. 10.95 (978-1-57332-250-8(4)); bds. 10.95 (978-1-57332-243-0(1)) HighReach Learning, Inc.

Boase, Petra. Petra Boase's Terrifyingly Terrific Toys. 2002. (Illus.). 64p. pap. 6.95 (978-1-84215-615-5(2)) Anness Publishing GBR. *Dist:* National Bk. Network.

Bonkers, Izzy. Complete Crazy Bones Collector's Guide. 2000. (Illus.). 96p. (gr. 2-9). pap. 7.99 (978-0-439-15403-1(0)) Scholastic, Inc.

Burton, Margie, et al. Toy Models. Evento, Susan, ed. 1998. (Early Connections Ser.). 16p. (J). (gr. k-2). pap. 4.25 (978-1-892393-68-5(9)) Benchmark Education Co.

Butler, Steve. Hubley Toy Vehicles: 1946-1965. 2001. (Schiffer Book for Collectors Ser.). (Illus.). 160p. (gr. 10-13). pap. 29.95 (978-0-7643-1405-6(X)) Schiffer Publishing, Ltd.

La Casa. 2005. (Coleccion Primeras Imagenes). (SPA., Illus.). 86p. (J). (ps up). pap. 7.95 (978-950-11-0990-0(9) , SGM9909) Sigmar ARG. *Dist:* AIMS International Bks., Inc., Continental Bk. Co., Inc., Lectorum Pubns., Inc., Iaconi, Mariuccia Bk. Imports.

Cipriano, Jeri S. Toys Long Ago. 2006. (Yellow Umbrella Books for Early Readers). (Illus.). 18p. (J). (978-0-7368-5987-5(X)) Yellow Umbrella Pr.

—Toys Long Ago: Juguetes Del Pasado. 2006. (ENG & SPA., Illus.). 18p. (J). (978-0-7368-6023-9(1)) Yellow Umbrella Pr.

De Compreas. 2005. (Coleccion Primeras Imagenes). (SPA., Illus.). 86p. (J). (ps up). pap. 7.95 (978-950-11-0985-6(2) , SGM9852) Sigmar ARG. *Dist:* AIMS International Bks., Inc., Continental Bk. Co., Inc., Lectorum Pubns., Inc., Iaconi, Mariuccia Bk. Imports.

Doney, Meryl. Toys. 2004. (Crafts from Many Cultures Ser.). (Illus.). 32p. (J). (gr. 3 up). lib. bdg. 23.33 (978-0-8368-4048-3(8)) Stevens, Gareth Inc.

Dorling Kindersley Publishing Staff. The Ultimate Lego Book: Discover the Lego Universe. 1999. (Illus.). 128p. (J). (gr. 3-7). 24.99 (978-0-7894-4691-6(X)) Dorling Kindersley Publishing, Inc.

Dorling Kindersley Publishing Staff, ed. Toys That Go. 2004. (Baby Love Ser.). (Illus.). 16p. (J). bds. 4.99 (978-0-7566-0549-0(0)) Dorling Kindersley Publishing, Inc.

Dorling Kindersley Publishing Staff & Saunders, Catherine. Ultimate Barbie Winter Fun Sticker Book. 2003. (Ultimate Sticker Bks.). (Illus.). 1p. (J). pap. 6.99 (978-0-7894-9880-9(4)) Dorling Kindersley Publishing, Inc.

Dralle Wilson, Lynn. Unauthorized Beanie Baby Guide. 1998. (J). pap. 79.60 (978-0-590-63581-3(6)) Scholastic, Inc.

Eck, Kristin. Hide-and-Seek Toys. 2004. (Hide-And-Seek Books). (Illus.). (J). lib. bdg. 7.95 (978-1-4042-2704-0(0) , PowerKids Pr.) Rosen Publishing Group, Inc., The.

Emberley, Rebecca. Piñata. 2004. (Illus.). 32p. (J). (ps-3). 14.99 (978-0-316-17412-1(2)) Little, Brown Bks. for Young Readers.

Farshtey, Greg. Bionicle Encyclopedia (Updated) 2007. 160p. (J). pap. 6.99 (***978-0-439-91640-0(2)***) Scholastic, Inc.

Fuller, Jill. Toy Box Subtraction. (Rookie Read-About Math Ser.). (J). 2005. (Illus.). 32p. (gr. 1-2). pap. 5.95 (978-0-516-24673-4(9)); 2004. 20.50 (978-0-516-24423-5(X)) Scholastic Library Publishing. (Children's Pr.).

Furman, Simon. Transformers: The Movie Guide. 2007. 72p. (J). (gr. 5-8). 17.99 (978-0-7566-3013-3(4)) Dorling Kindersley Publishing, Inc.

—Transformers: the Ultimate Guide: The Ultimate Guide. 2007. 152p. (J). pap. 16.99 (978-0-7566-3012-6(6)) Dorling Kindersley Publishing, Inc.

Gardner, Robert. Science Projects about the Physics of Toys & Games. 2000. (Science Projects Ser.). (Illus.). 128p. (YA). (gr. 6-12). lib. bdg. 26.60 (978-0-7660-1165-6(8)) Enslow Pubs., Inc.

Gnojewski, Carol. Playtime Props for Toddlers. Burris, Priscilla, illus. 2001. (Time for Toddlers Ser.). 160p. (J). (ps). pap. 16.99 (978-1-57029-204-0(3) , WPH4701, Totline Pubns.) Schaffer, Frank Pubns.

Group/McGraw-Hill, Wright. Toys, Then & Now: Level E, 6 vols. (Take Twostm Ser.). 16p. 29.95 (978-0-322-08950-1(6)) Wright Group, The.

Grupos. 2005. (Coleccion Primeras Imagenes). (SPA., Illus.). 86p. (J). (ps up). pap. 7.95 (978-950-11-0986-3(0) , SGM9860) Sigmar ARG. *Dist:* AIMS International Bks., Inc., Continental Bk. Co., Inc., Lectorum Pubns., Inc., Iaconi, Mariuccia Bk. Imports.

Harcourt School Publishers Staff. Slinky for Sale Advanced Level. 3rd ed. 2002. (Trophies Reading Program Ser.). (Illus.). pap. 5.10 (978-0-15-323110-0(6)) Harcourt Schl. Pubs.

—What Children Play On Level. 3rd ed. 2002. (Trophies Reading Program Ser.). (Illus.). (gr. 2). pap. 5.10 (978-0-15-323078-3(9)) Harcourt Schl. Pubs.

Harris, Elizabeth. Mini-Scooter Mania with Toy. gif. ed. 2001. (Illus.). 24p. (J). (gr. 3-7). 7.95 (978-0-439-28247-5(0)) Scholastic, Inc.

Henderson, Meryl, illus. Things to Play With. (Picture Bks.: No. S8817-5). 28p. (J). (ps). pap. 3.95 (978-0-7214-5144-2(6) , Dutton Juvenile) Penguin Group (USA) Inc.

Hoena, B. A. Toys ABC: An Alphabet Book. 2004. (A+ Alphabet Books). (Illus.). 17p. (J). 22.60 (978-0-7368-2609-9(2) , Aplus Bks.) Capstone Pr., Inc.

Holloway, Zena. Water Babies Display. 1999. (J). 69.90 (978-0-439-07286-1(7) , Cartwheel Bks.) Scholastic, Inc.

La Hora. 2005. 102p. (J). spiral bd. 14.99 (978-1-59441-451-0(3) , K04002) Carson-Dellosa Publishing Co., Inc.

La Hora. 2005. (Coleccion Primeras Imagenes). (SPA., Illus.). 86p. (J). (ps up). pap. 7.95 (978-950-11-0987-0(9) , SGM9879) Sigmar ARG. *Dist:* AIMS International Bks., Inc., Continental Bk. Co., Inc., Lectorum Pubns., Inc., Iaconi, Mariuccia Bk. Imports.

Kent, Lorna, illus. Baby's First Toys Book. 2004. 10p. (J). bds. 7.99 (978-1-85854-882-1(9)) Brimax Books Ltd. GBR. *Dist:* Byeway Bks.

Khanna, Sudarshan, et al. Toys & Tales with Everyday Materials. 2003. (Illus.). 144p. 10.99 (978-81-86211-42-7(X)) Penguin Group (USA) Inc.

Klutz Press Staff. Icky Poo Toy. 1998. 48p. (gr. 4-7). 9.95 (978-1-57054-196-4(5)) Klutz.

Knapp, Pamela. Heartfelt Stories about Beannie Babies & Those Who Collect Them. 1999. (Illus.). 190p. (YA). (gr. 6-12). pap. 9.95 (978-0-9669923-9-7(3)) Beckett Publishing, Inc.

Ladybird Books Staff. First Picture Book: Toys. (First Picture Bks.: No. 832-2). (Illus.). 52p. (J). (ps). pap. 3.50 (978-0-7214-0750-0(1) , Dutton Juvenile) Penguin Group (USA) Inc.

Little Red School House. 2005. (Illus.). 18p. (978-0-7853-9162-3(2) , 3474800) Publications International, Ltd.

Lorenz Books Staff. Teddy Bears: With over 50 Reusable Stickers. 1999. (Sticker Fun Ser.). (Illus.). 16p. (ps-k). pap. 4.95 (978-0-7548-0049-1(0) , Lorenz Bks.) Anness Publishing GBR. *Dist:* National Bk. Network.

Mack, Charlie. The Encyclopedia of Matchbox Toys. 3rd rev. exp. ed. 2002. (Schiffer Book for Collectors Ser.). (Illus.). 352p. (gr. 10-13). pap. 29.95 (978-0-7643-1571-8(4)) Schiffer Publishing, Ltd.

Marks, Jenny L. Sorting Toys. 2007. (Sorting Ser.). (Illus.). 32p. (J). (gr. k-3). lib. bdg. 23.93 (978-0-7368-6737-5(6)) Capstone Pr., Inc.

McTague, Fiona. Knitted Toys: 21 Easy-to-Knit Patterns for Irresistible Soft Toys. 2004. (Illus.). 112p. 18.95 (978-0-7641-5766-0(3)) Barron's Educational Series, Inc.

Modern Publishing Staff, ed. First to the Finish Line. 2005. 12p. pap. 3.99 (978-0-7666-1911-1(7)) Modern Publishing.

—Lean Mean Screamin Machines. 2005. 12p. pap. 3.99 (978-0-7666-1910-4(9)) Modern Publishing.

Morrissey, Paulette. Greeting Bears for All Occasions: Send a Bear... Instead of a Card! Morrissey, Paulette, illus. 1999. (Illus.). (YA). (gr. 3 up). spiral bd. 8.95 (978-1-893502-12-3(0)) Adventures in Ceramics.

Murphy, Stuart J. Jack the Builder. Rex, Michael, illus. 2006. (MathStart Ser.). 40p. (J). 15.99 (978-0-06-055774-4(5)); pap. 5.99 (978-0-06-055775-1(3)) HarperCollins Pubs.

My Little Firehouse. (Illus.). 12p. (J). (ps-k). bds. (978-1-56021-354-3(X) , 205) W.J. Fantasy, Inc.

Nelson, Robin. Toys & Games. 2003. (First Step Nonfiction Ser.). (Illus.). 24p. (J). (gr. k-2). lib. bdg. 18.60 (978-0-8225-4644-3(2)) Lerner Publishing Group.

Nickelodeon Staff. Let's Go Yo-Yo! The Nick Guide to Yo-Yo Tricks. 2005. (Illus.). 48p. (J). pap. 9.95 (978-0-8118-4754-4(3)) Chronicle Bks. LLC.

Opuestos. (Coleccion Libritos Acordeon). (SPA., Illus.). (J). 10p. pap. 5.50 (978-950-11-0826-2(0) , SGM260); 2005. 86p. pap. 7.95 (978-950-11-0906-1(2) , SGM9062) Sigmar ARG. *Dist:* Continental Bk. Co., Inc., AIMS International Bks., Inc., Continental Bk. Co., Inc., Lectorum Pubns., Inc., Iaconi, Mariuccia Bk. Imports.

Pentland, Peter & Stoyles, Pennie. Toy & Game Science. 2003. (Science & Scientists Ser.). (Illus.). 32p. (gr. 4-8). lib. bdg. 27.00 (978-0-7910-7013-0(1) , Chelsea Hse.) Facts On File, Inc.

Pinchuk, Amy Ruth. Make Cool Gadgets for Your Room. Rodriques, Teco, illus. Boudreau, Ray, photos by. 2004. (Popular Mechanics for Kids Ser.). 64p. (J). (gr. 4-8). 21.95 (978-1-894379-11-3(X)) Maple Tree Pr. CAN. *Dist:* Firefly Bks., Ltd.

Pohl, Kathleen. What Happens at a Toy Factory? 2006. (Illus.). 24p. (J). pap. (978-0-8368-6896-8(X)); lib. bdg. (978-0-8368-6889-0(7)) Stevens, Gareth Inc.

Priddy, Roger. Baby Gund Mirror Book Playtime. 2006. 6p. (J). bds. 6.95 (978-0-312-49765-1(2) , Priddy Bks.) St. Martin's Pr.

Rathjen, Don. Lego Crazy Action Contraptions. Klutz Press Staff, ed. 1998. (Illus.). 68p. (J). (gr. 4-7). spiral bd. 19.95 (978-1-57054-157-5(4)) Klutz.

Rau, Dana Meachen. Spinning Toys. 2004. (Games Around the World Ser.). 32p. (J). (gr. 3 up). lib. bdg. 22.60 (978-0-7565-0676-6(X)) Compass Point Bks.

—Toys, Games, & Fun in American History. 2006. (Illus.). 24p. (J). pap. (978-0-8368-7216-3(9)); lib. bdg. (978-0-8368-7209-5(6)) Stevens, Gareth Inc.

Rice. Gaston Goes to Mardi Gras Ornament. 32p. 8.95 (978-1-56554-889-3(2)) Pelican Publishing Co., Inc.

Rigsby, Mike. Amazing Rubber Band Cars: Easy-To-Build Wind-Up Racers, Models, & Toys. 2007. 128p. (J). (gr. 4 up). pap. 12.95 (***978-1-55652-736-4(5)***) Chicago Review Pr., Inc.

La Ropa. 2005. (Coleccion Primeras Imagenes). (SPA., Illus.). 86p. (J). (ps up). pap. 7.95 (978-950-11-0988-7(7) , SGM9887) Sigmar ARG. *Dist:* AIMS International Bks., Inc., Continental Bk. Co., Inc., Lectorum Pubns., Inc., Iaconi, Mariuccia Bk. Imports.

Roper, Ingrid. Yo-Yos. Tiegreen, Alan, illus. 2001. 64p. (J). lib. bdg. 15.89 (978-0-688-14664-1(3)) HarperCollins Pubs.

—Yo-Yos: Tricks to Amaze Your Friends. Tiegreen, Alan, illus. 2001. 64p. (J). (gr. 3-7). 15.95 (978-0-688-14663-4(5)) HarperCollins Pubs.

—Yo-Yos: Tricks to Amaze Your Friends. 2001. (gr. 3-6). lib. bdg. 16.40 (978-0-613-89753-2(6)) Tandem Library Bks.

Rosen, Michael J. Balls! Margeson, John, illus. 2006. 72p. (J). (gr. 5 up). 18.95 (978-1-58196-030-3(1)) Darby Creek Publishing.

Rosie Raccoon & her Messy Room. 2004. (Play Pals Ser.). (Illus.). 12p. (J). bds. (978-1-84229-650-9(7)) Top That! Publishing PLC.

Sadler, Wendy. Construction Toys. 2005. (Heinemann First Library). (Illus.). 32p. (J). (ps). lib. bdg. 25.36 (978-1-4034-6826-0(5)); pap. (978-1-4034-6832-1(X)) Heinemann Library.

—Toy Cars. 2005. (Heinemann First Library). (Illus.). 32p. (J). (978-1-4034-6825-3(7)); pap. (978-1-4034-6831-4(1)) Heinemann Library.

Sanschagrin, Joceline. Caillou, Helps Mommy. CINAR Animation Staff & Sévigny, Eric, illus. adapted rev. ed. 2006. (Lift-the-Flap Cinar Ser.). 20p. (J). pap. 5.95 (978-2-89450-524-3(8)) Chouette Publishing CAN. *Dist:* Independent Pubs. Group.

Sharpe, Ben. The Ultimate Scooter Guide. 2001. 128p. (YA). (gr. 4-9). pap. 4.99 (978-0-439-28554-4(2)) Scholastic, Inc.

Shears, William. The Batman. Mawhinney, Art, illus. 2005. 18p. (J). (ps-ps). per. 7.98 (978-1-4127-3564-3(5) , 7265700) Publications International, Ltd.

Sloan, Peter. Car That Stopped. 2000. (gr. k-3). lib. bdg. 11.80 (978-0-613-30305-7(9)) Tandem Library Bks.

—Making a Car. 1999. (gr. k-3). lib. bdg. 11.55 (978-0-613-30583-9(3)) Tandem Library Bks.

—Making a Plane. 1999. (gr. k-3). lib. bdg. 11.80 (978-0-613-30584-6(1)) Tandem Library Bks.

—Making a Tape. 1999. (gr. k-3). lib. bdg. 11.80 (978-0-613-30586-0(8)) Tandem Library Bks.

—Making an Ooze Monster. 1999. (gr. k-3). lib. bdg. 11.80 (978-0-613-30587-7(6)) Tandem Library Bks.

SoftPlay Staff, contrib. by. Dinosaur Park. 2000. (SoftPlay Felt Playset Book Ser.). (Illus.). (J). (978-1-56156-937-3(2)) Kidsbooks, Inc.

Southwater Staff. Look & Learn: Toys. 2000. (Look & Learn Ser.). (Illus.). 32p. (ps). 7.95 (978-1-84215-046-7(4) , Southwater) Anness Publishing GBR. *Dist:* National Bk. Network.

Spinning Top: Level L, 6 vols. (Wonder Worldtm Ser.). 16p. 34.95 (978-0-7802-2908-2(8)) Wright Group, The.

Sterling/Balloon. My Toys. 1998. (Peek-a-Boo Bks.). (Illus.). 20p. (J). bds. 3.95 (978-0-8069-3762-5(9) , Balloon Bks.) Sterling Publishing Co., Inc.

Stevens, Beth Dvergsten. Toy Fads. 2001. (Cover-To-Cover Books). (Illus.). (J). 54p. pap. (978-0-7891-5452-1(8)); 56p. (gr. 1-4). lib. bdg. 16.95 (978-0-7569-0107-3(3)) Perfection Learning Corp.

Thomas, John E. & Thomas, Danita. The Ultimate Book of Kid Concoctions Vol. 2: More Than 65 New Wacky, Wild & Crazy Concoctions, 4 vols. Briller, Margaret, ed. Durr, Robb, illus. 2000. 80p. (J). (ps-9). per. 14.95 (978-0-9661088-1-1(7)) Kid Concoctions Co.

Time for Toys! (Flip Flap Fun Book Ser.). 10p. (J). bds. (978-2-7643-0040-4(9)) Phidal Publishing, Inc./Editions Phidal, Inc.

Tocando. (Coleccion Mil Preguntas). (SPA., Illus.). (J). 24p. pap. 5.50 (978-950-11-0657-2(8) , SGM625); 2005. 86p. pap. 7.95 (978-950-11-0902-3(X) , SGM902X) Sigmar ARG. *Dist:* Continental Bk. Co., Inc., AIMS International Bks., Inc., Continental Bk. Co., Inc., Lectorum Pubns., Inc., Iaconi, Mariuccia Bk. Imports.

Toys Long Ago. 2006. (Yellow Umbrella Social Studies). 8,16p. (J). 6.50 (978-0-7368-1721-9(2)) Red Brick Learning.

Toys with Wheels: Individual Title Six-Packs. (ps-2). 23.00 (978-0-7635-9006-2(1)) Rigby Education.

Tuxworth, Nicola. Toys, 12 vols. (Illus.). 2006. 12p. bds. 6.99 (978-0-7548-1367-5(3) , Lorenz Bks.); 2001. 20p. 5.95 (978-0-7548-0943-2(9)) Anness Publishing GBR. *Dist:* National Bk. Network.

Watt, Fiona. Al Agua Patos! 2000. (SPA.). (ps-2). lib. bdg. 12.95 (978-0-613-28273-4(6)) Tandem Library Bks.

Weber, Bruce. Advanced Yo-Yo Tricks. 1999. (Illus.). 84p. (J). (gr. 3-7). pap. 3.99 (978-0-439-12933-6(8)) Scholastic, Inc.

—You Can Yo-Yo! 25 Tricks to Try. 1999. (J). 7.95 (978-0-439-08828-2(3)) Scholastic, Inc.

—You Can Yo-Yo! Twenty-Five Tricks to Try. 1998. (Illus.). 48p. (J). (gr. 3-7). pap. 4.50 (978-0-590-81294-8(7)) Scholastic, Inc.

Weekly Reader Early Learning Library (Firm) Staff, contrib. by. Things I Play With. 2006. (Things in My World Ser.). (Illus.). 16p. (J). pap. (978-0-8368-6818-0(8)); lib. bdg. (978-0-8368-6811-1(0)) Stevens, Gareth Inc.

—Things I Play with: Las Cosas con Las Que Juego. 2006. (ENG & SPA.). (J). pap. (978-0-8368-7230-9(4) , Weekly Reader Early Learning Library) Stevens, Gareth Inc.

—Things I Play With (Las Cosas con las Que Juego) 2006. (ENG & SPA.). (J). lib. bdg. 17.27 (978-0-8368-7223-1(1) , Weekly Reader Early Learning Library) Stevens, Gareth Inc.

Which Toys? Individual Title Six-Packs. (ps-2). 23.00 (978-0-7635-9007-9(X)) Rigby Education.

Wilbur Plush. 2000. (J). 12.99 (978-0-439-14495-7(7)) Scholastic, Inc.

Wilkinson, Doris J. Toys. Wilkinson, Doris J., ed. Chipping, Oliver, illus. 2000. (Jacob's Magic Box Discovery Ser.). 20p. (J). (ps). pap. 4.95 (978-0-9700386-3-0(1)) Magic Box Pubns.

Wilson, Lynn D. & Dralle, Lee A. The Book of Beanie Babies Teenie Beanies: Pages for Twenty-Two Teenies from 1997 & 1998. 1998. (Illus.). 52p. 4.95 (978-0-9663077-4-0(7)) a.k.a. Publishing.

Wulffson, Don. Toys! Amazing Stories Behind Some Great Inventions. Keller, Laurie, illus. rev. ed. 2000. 144p. (J). (gr. 3-7). 16.95 (978-0-8050-6196-3(7) , Holt, Henry & Co. Bks. For Young Readers) Holt, Henry & Co.

Yo-Yos: Individual Nonfiction Title, 6 packs. 24p. (gr. 3-4). 44.00 (978-0-7635-4486-7(8)) Rigby Education.

Zak, Marc. Spin Pop Interactive Candy Toys. 2002. (Illus.). 160p. (gr. 10-13). pap. 16.95 (978-0-7643-1508-4(0)) Schiffer Publishing, Ltd.

TOYS—FICTION

Abruzzo, Nancy. Pop Flop's Great Balloon Ride. Chilton, Noel, illus. 2005. 32p. (J). (gr. k-17). pap. 12.95 (978-0-89013-475-7(8)) Museum of New Mexico Pr.

Ada, Alma Flor. The Empty Pinata. (Stories the Year 'Round Ser.). (SPA & ENG., Illus.). 18p. (J). (gr. k-3). pap. 8.95 (978-1-58105-202-2(2)) Santillana USA Publishing Co., Inc.

—La Jaula Dorada. (Cuentos para Todo el Ano Ser.). (SPA., Illus.). 16p. (J). (gr. k-3). pap. 8.95 (978-1-58105-182-7(4)) Santillana USA Publishing Co., Inc.

—La Pinata Vacia. (Cuentos para Todo el Ano Ser.). (SPA., Illus.). 18p. (J). (gr. k-3). pap. 8.95 (978-1-58105-188-9(3)) Santillana USA Publishing Co., Inc.

Alborough, Jez. Donde Esta Mi Osito? Alborough, Jez, illus. (Picture Books Collection). (SPA., Illus.). 30p. (J). (gr. k-3). pap. 9.95 (978-1-56014-582-0(X)) Santillana USA Publishing Co., Inc.

Alexander, Martha G. I'll Protect You from the Jungle Beasts. Alexander, Martha G., illus. 2006. (Illus.). 32p. (J). 9.95 (978-1-57091-677-9(2)) Charlesbridge Publishing, Inc.

Allison, Catherine & Scholastic, Inc. Staff. Brown Paper Teddy Bear. Reed, Neil & Harper, Piers, illus. 2004. 32p. (J). (ps-3). pap. 16.95 (978-0-439-63900-2(X) , Cartwheel Bks.) Scholastic, Inc.

Andersen, Hans Christian. The Steadfast Tin Soldier. Lemoine, Georges, illus. 2000. Tr. of Standhaftige Tinsoldat. 32p. (YA). lib. bdg. 13.95 (978-1-56846-132-8(1) , Creative Education) Creative Co., The.

—The Steadfast Tin Soldier. de Conno, Gianni, illus. 2006. Tr. of Standhaftige Tinsoldat. 44p. (J). 16.50 (978-1-933327-25-9(1)); 15.95 (978-1-933327-24-2(3)) Purple Bear Bks., Inc.

—The Steadfast Tin Soldier. Jorgensen, David, illus. 2006. Tr. of Standhaftige Tinsoldat. (J). (gr. 2-6). 25.65 (978-1-59679-346-0(5)) Spotlight.

Arkin, Alan. One Present from Flekman's. Egielski, Richard, illus. 1999. 32p. (J). (gr. k-3). 15.95 (978-0-06-024530-6(1)) HarperCollins Pubs.

Arnold, Shauna. Baa. Hines, Irene, illus. 2004. 19p. (J). (ps-3). 12.00 (978-0-9743669-0-6(0)) Trinity Bks.

Arnold, Tedd. Huggly & the Toy Monster. Arnold, Tedd, illus. 1999. (Monster under the Bed Ser.). (Illus.). 32p. (J). (ps-3). pap. 3.25 (978-0-590-91821-3(4) , Cartwheel Bks.) Scholastic, Inc.

—Huggly & the Toy Monster. 1998. (Monster under the Bed Ser.). (J). pap. 3.50 (978-0-590-11761-6(0)) Scholastic, Inc.

Atseriak, Liz. Ciumek Tungliakun. Brunk, Cara, illus. 1998. Tr. of Making Yo Yos. (ESK.). 16p. (J). (gr. k-3). pap. 6.00 (978-1-58084-033-0(7)) Lower Kuskokwim Schl. District.

Ayres, Katherine. Matthew's Truck. Takahashi, Hideko, tr. Takahashi, Hideko, illus. 2005. (Super Sturdy Picture Books Ser.). 24p. (J). (gr. k). 8.99 (978-0-7636-2269-5(9)) Candlewick Pr.

Baby Bear's Toys. (Early Intervention Levels Ser.). 21.30 (978-0-7362-0361-6(3)) Hampton-Brown Bks.

Baggott, Julianna & Bode, N. E. The Amazing Compendium. 2007. (Mr. Magorium's Wonder Emporium Ser.). 160p. (J). pap. 4.99 (***978-0-439-91636-3(4)***) Scholastic, Inc.

Bailey, Elinor Peace. Ducks in a Row. Bailey, Elinor Peace, illus. 2002. (J). 9.50 (978-0-9716586-2-2(5)) Fairfield Processing Corp.

—Effie Longnostril. 2002. (J). 9.50 (978-0-9716586-5-3(X)) Fairfield Processing Corp.

—Pickles Learns to Hide. Bailey, Elinor Peace, illus. 2002. (J). 9.50 (978-0-9716586-3-9(3)) Fairfield Processing Corp.

—What Wilhelmina Sees. 2002. (J). 9.50 (978-0-9716586-6-0(8)) Fairfield Processing Corp.

—Winifred Finds Her Shoes. Bailey, Elinor Peace, illus. 2002. (J). 9.50 (978-0-9716586-1-5(7)) Fairfield Processing Corp.

Ballou, Kathy. The Tracks Out Back. l.t. ed. 2005. (Illus.). 24p. (J). per. 10.00 (978-1-932338-50-8(0)) Lifevest Publishing, Inc.

Banks, Lynne Reid. The Indian in the Cupboard. (Indian in the Cupboard Ser.: No. 1). 44p. (J). (gr. 4-7). 1999. 9.95 (978-1-56137-225-6(0)); 1998. 11.95 (978-1-56137-693-3(0) , NU6930SP) Novel Units, Inc.

Banks, Steven. The Song That Never Ends. DePorter, Vince, illus. 2004. (Ready-to-Read Ser.: Vol. 4). 32p. (J). pap. 3.99 (978-0-689-86528-2(7) , Simon Spotlight/ Nickelodeon) Simon & Schuster Children's Publishing.

—Song That Never Ends. 2004. (gr. k-3). lib. bdg. 11.80 (978-0-613-73449-3(1)) Tandem Library Bks.

—Special Delivery. DePorter, Vince, illus. 2005. (Ready-to-Read Ser. Level 2). 32p. (J). lib. bdg. 15.00 (978-1-59054-986-5(4)) Fitzgerald Bks.

Barradel, Isabel. Toyshop Tales. 2006. 275p. pap. 21.95 (***978-1-4241-2798-6(X)***) PublishAmerica, Inc.

Be Nice to Pooh. 1999. (J). pap. 2.99 (978-0-307-08598-6(8) , 08598, Golden Bks.) Random Hse. Children's Bks.

Beach Ball. 2004. (J). 5.99 (978-0-7566-0250-5(5)) Dorling Kindersley Publishing, Inc.

The Bear Collection: Individual Chapter Book Title Six-Packs. Vol. 28. 32p. (gr. 4 up). 44.00 (978-0-7578-0600-1(7)) Rigby Education.

Beck, Ana. Elliot's Shipwreck. 2000. (gr. 3-6). lib. bdg. 14.10 (978-0-613-36328-0(0)) Tandem Library Bks.

Beck, Andrea. Elliot's Emergency. 2004. (Elliot Moose Ser.). (Illus.). 32p. (J). (gr. k-3). (978-1-55074-687-7(1)) Kids Can Pr., Ltd.

—Elliot's Emergency. Beck, Andrea, illus. 1998. (Elliot Moose Ser.). (Illus.). 32p. (J). (gr. k-3). (978-1-55074-441-5(0)) Kids Can Pr., Ltd.

—Elliot's Emergency. 1999. (J). (978-0-606-17371-1(4)) Tandem Library Bks.

Bell, Cece. Sock Monkey Boogie-Woogie: A Friend Is Made. Bell, Cece, illus. 2004. (Illus.). 32p. (J). (ps-2). 14.99 (978-0-7636-2392-0(X)) Candlewick Pr.

—Sock Monkey Goes to Hollywood: A Star Is Bathed. Bell, Cece, illus. 2003. (Illus.). 32p. (J). (ps). 13.99 (978-0-7636-1962-6(0)) Candlewick Pr.

—Sock Monkey Rides Again. Bell, Cece, illus. 2006. (Illus.). 32p. (J). (ps-2). 13.99 (978-0-7636-3089-8(6)) Candlewick Pr.

Bentley, Dawn. What's in the Toy Box? Valderrama, Rosario, illus. 2001. (Sneak-A-Peek Board Book Ser.: Vol. 2). 10p. (ps-k). bds. 6.95 (978-1-58117-142-6(0) , Intervisual/Piggy Toes) Dalmatian Pr.

Berenstain, Stan & Berenstain, Jan. The Berenstain Bears & the G-Rex Bones. 2001. (Berenstain Bears Big Chapter Bks.). (J). (gr. 2-6). lib. bdg. 11.99 (978-0-679-98949-3(8) , Random Hse. Bks. for Young Readers) Random Hse. Children's Bks.

Berlin, James, Sr. Cup'igtat Laanguarrutenka. Berlin, James & Nevak, Caroline, illus. l.t. ed. 1999. Tr. of My Yup'ik Eskimo Toys. (ESK.). 12p. (J). (gr. k-3). pap. 17.00 (978-1-58084-112-2(0)) Lower Kuskokwim Schl. District.

—My Yupik Eskimo Toys. Berlin, James & Nevak, Caroline, illus. l.t. ed. 1999. 12p. (J). (gr. k-3). pap. 17.00 (978-1-58084-074-3(4)) Lower Kuskokwim Schl. District.

—Yugtaat Naanguat. Berlin, James & Nevak, Caroline, illus. l.t. ed. 1999. Tr. of My Yup'ik Eskimo Toys. (ESK.). 12p. (J). (gr. k-3). pap. 17.00 (978-1-58084-075-0(2)) Lower Kuskokwim Schl. District.

Bernstein, Susan H. N. E. Pominonous Epstein Minds His Mind. (E. Pominonous Epstein Ser.). 18p. (J). (ps-3). pap. 8.95 (978-0-9706596-0-6(1)) Bernstein, Susan.

Birchall, Mark. Rabbit's Birthday Surprise. Birchall, Mark, illus. 2003. (Illus.). 32p. (J). (ps-3). 15.95 (978-0-87614-910-2(7) , Carolrhoda Bks.) Lerner Publishing Group.

—Rabbit's Wooly Sweater. Birchall, Mark, illus. 2003. (Picture Bks.). (Illus.). 32p. (J). (ps-3). 15.95 (978-1-57505-465-0(5) , Carolrhoda Bks.) Lerner Publishing Group.

Black, Jessica L. My Toys. Bicking, Judith, illus. l.t. ed. 2001. (Cuddle Bks.). (J). (ps-1). pap. 10.95 (978-1-57332-219-5(9)) HighReach Learning, Inc.

Blackaby, Susan. El Soldadito de Plomo: Version del Cuento de Hans Christian Andersen. Delage, Charlene, illus. 2006. (Read-It! Readers en Espanol Ser.).Tr. of Steadfast Tin Soldier: A Retelling of the Hans Christian Andersen Fairy Tale. (SPA.). 32p. (J). (ps-3). 19.95 (978-1-4048-1641-1(0)) Picture Window Bks.

—The Steadfast Tin Soldier: A Retelling of the Hans Christian Andersen Fairy Tale. DeLage, Charlene, illus. 2004. (Read-It! Readers Ser.). 32p. (C). (gr. k-3). 18.60 (978-1-4048-0226-1(6)) Picture Window Bks.

Blake, Quentin. Clown. 1998. (Illus.). 32p. (J). (ps-3). pap. 8.95 (978-0-8050-5933-5(4) , Holt, Henry & Co. Bks. For Young Readers) Holt, Henry & Co.

Boniface, William. Santa's Sleigh Is Full. Rooney, Ronnie, illus. 2002. (Top This! Ser.). 12p. (J). (ps-2). bds. 9.99 (978-0-8431-4543-4(9) , Price Stern Sloan) Penguin Group (USA) Inc.

Bonnell, Kris. Playtime. 2005. (J). 3.75 (978-1-933727-13-4(6)) Reading Reading Bks., LLC.

Braybrooks, Ann. Just Be Nice... & Help a Friend! 2000. (Disney Ser.). (Illus.). 24p. (J). (ps-k). pap. 3.29 (978-0-307-13312-0(5) , 13312, Golden Bks.) Random Hse. Children's Bks.

—King of the Beasties. Baker, Darrell, illus. 1998. (Little Golden Bks.). 24p. (J). (ps-k). bds. 2.99 (978-0-307-98820-1(1) , 98820, Golden Bks.) Random Hse. Children's Bks.

Braybrooks, Ann & Milne, A. A. Pooh, the Great Riddle Contest. 2000. (Illus.). pap. (978-0-307-98915-4(1) , Golden Bks.) Random Hse. Children's Bks.

Brown, Alan. Nikki & the Rocking Horse. Utton, Peter, illus. 1999. 30p. (J). (ps-3). pap. 9.95 (978-0-00-664517-7(8)) Zondervan.

Brown, Gwen. Clifford & His Bear. 2006. (Illus.). 48p. pap. (***978-1-84401-650-1(1)***) Athena Pr.

Buell, Janet. Sail Away, Little Boat. Ishida, Jui, illus. 2006. 32p. (J). 15.95 (978-1-57505-821-4(9) , Carolrhoda Bks.) Lerner Publishing Group.

Bunting, Eve. Ducky. Wisniewski, David, illus. 2004. 32p. (J). (gr. k-ps). 4.95 (978-0-618-43240-0(X) , Clarion Bks.) Houghton Mifflin Co. Trade & Reference Div.

—Reggie. Burkett, D. Brent, illus. 2006. 112p. 16.95 (978-0-8126-2746-6(6)) Cricket Bks.

Burroughs, Scott A. The Christmas Tail of Sampson the Silly-Looking Sock Monkey. 2005. (J). 12.99 (978-0-8254-2300-0(7)) Kregel Pubns.

Calhoun, Terry. The Muggwapps. 2007. (J). pap. 8.00 (***978-0-8059-7223-8(4)***) Dorrance Publishing Co., Inc.

Capalija, Ann Marie. Butterfly Hunt. LoRaso, Carlo, illus. 2005. (My Little Pony Ser.). 24p. (J). (ps-1). pap. 3.99 (978-0-06-074442-7(1) , Harper Festival) HarperCollins Pubs.

—Fashion Fun. Edwards, Ken, illus. 2005. (My Little Pony Ser.). 24p. (J). (ps-1). pap. 3.50 (978-0-06-074443-4(X) , Harper Festival) HarperCollins Pubs.

—Five Friends. Rodriguez, Angel & Antonio, Jose, illus. 2004. (My Little Pony Ser.). 20p. (J). (ps-1). pap. 8.99 (978-0-06-055406-4(1) , Harper Festival) HarperCollins Pubs.

—Rainbow Dash's Dress-Up Fun. Edwards, Ken, illus. 2004. (My Little Pony Ser.). 12p. (J). (ps-1). 5.99 (978-0-06-055404-0(5) , Harper Festival) HarperCollins Pubs.

—Rose Blossom's First Christmas. LoRaso, Carlo, illus. 2005. (My Little Pony Ser.). 24p. (J). (ps-2). pap. 4.99 (978-0-06-076182-0(2) , Harper Festival) HarperCollins Pubs.

Capalija, Ann Marie & Egan, Kate. My Little Pony: Three-in-One Book of Coloring & Activities. Middleton, Gayle, illus. 2004. (My Little Pony Ser.). 96p. (J). (ps-1). pap. 2.99 (978-0-06-054946-6(7) , Harper Festival) HarperCollins Pubs.

Carle, Eric. 10 Little Rubber Ducks. Carle, Eric, illus. 2005. (Illus.). 36p. (J). (ps-1). 19.99 (978-0-06-074075-7(2)) HarperCollins Pubs.

—10 Little Rubber Ducks (Spanish Edition) 10 patitos de Goma. Carle, Eric, illus. 2007. (SPA.). 36p. (J). 19.99 (978-0-06-112623-9(3) , Rayo) HarperCollins Pubs.

Carman, Patrick. Saving Mister Nibbles. 2008. (Elliot's Park Ser.). 80p. (J). 8.99 (***978-0-545-01930-9(3)*** , Orchard Bks.) Scholastic, Inc.

Carmichael, Clay. Osito Usado. 2000. (SPA.). (gr. k-3). lib. bdg. 14.10 (978-0-613-26503-4(3)) Tandem Library Bks.

Casado, Dami. Como Comes Tu? (SPA.). 8p. 9.95 (978-84-272-8325-1(3)) Molino, Editorial ESP. *Dist:* Distribooks, Inc.

—Como Te Lavas? (SPA.). 8p. 9.95 (978-84-272-8326-8(1)) Molino, Editorial ESP. *Dist:* Distribooks, Inc.

—Como Te Vistes? (SPA.). 8p. 9.95 (978-84-272-8328-2(8)) Molino, Editorial ESP. *Dist:* Distribooks, Inc.

Cave, Kathryn. Out for the Count: A Counting Adventure. Riddell, Chris, illus. 2006. 32p. pap. 7.95 (978-1-84507-539-2(0)) Lincoln, Frances Ltd. GBR. *Dist:* Perseus Distribution.

Changes, Changes. 2004. (J). 24.95 incl. audio (978-1-56008-176-0(7)); pap. 14.95 incl. audio (978-1-56008-177-7(5)) Weston Woods Studios, Inc.

Channell, Jim. Quien Vive en el Lago? 2000. (SPA.). 10p. (J). (ps-k). 7.95 (978-84-392-8317-1(2)) Lectorum Pubns., Inc.

—Quien Vive en el Mar? 2000. (SPA.). 10p. (J). (ps-k). 7.95 (978-84-392-8316-4(4)) Lectorum Pubns., Inc.

Choo! Choo! 2002. (Little Board Books Ser.). 24p. (J). bds. 3.95 (978-0-7894-8464-2(1)) Dorling Kindersley Publishing, Inc.

Clark, Emma Chichester. I Love You, Blue Kangaroo! Clark, Emma Chichester, illus. 2001. (Illus.). 32p. (J). (ps-3). pap. 6.99 (978-0-440-41549-7(7) , Dragonfly Bks.) Random Hse. Children's Bks.

—I Love You, Blue Kangaroo! 2001. (gr. k-3). lib. bdg. 15.30 (978-0-613-85711-6(9)); (Illus.). (J). 13.79 (978-0-606-20715-7(5)) Tandem Library Bks.

—It Was You, Blue Kangaroo! Clark, Emma Chichester, illus. 2004. 32p. (J). (gr. k-k). pap. 6.99 (978-0-553-11280-1(5) , Dragonfly Bks.) Random Hse. Children's Bks.

—It Was You, Blue Kangaroo. Clark, Emma Chichester, illus. 2002. (Illus.). 32p. (J). (gr. k-k). 15.95 (978-0-385-74623-6(7) , Doubleday Bks. for Young Readers) Random Hse. Children's Bks.

—What Shall We Do, Blue Kang? 2002. (Illus.). 32p. (J). (978-1-84270-185-0(1)) Andersen GBR. *Dist:* Random Hse. of Canada, Ltd.

—Where Are You, Blue Kangaroo? 2002. (ps-2). lib. bdg. 15.30 (978-0-613-89781-5(1)) Tandem Library Bks.

Cocca-Leffler, Maryann. Missing: One Stuffed Rabbit. 2000. (Illus.). (J). (978-0-606-21859-7(9)) Tandem Library Bks.

Cohen, Emma. It's Mine! His. Chambers, Sally, illus. 1998. (Nuk Bks.). 8p. (J). 6.95 (978-0-7641-7232-8(8)) Barron's Educational Series, Inc.

Collins, Heather, illus. Hey Diddle, Diddle. 2004. (Traditional Nursery Rhyme Board Bks.). 12p. (J). (ps-k). (978-1-55337-078-9(3)) Kids Can Pr., Ltd.

—Jack & Jill. 2004. (Traditional Nursery Rhyme Board Bks.). 12p. (J). (ps-k). (978-1-55337-075-8(9)) Kids Can Pr., Ltd.

—Little Miss Muffet. 2004. (Traditional Nursery Rhyme Board Bks.). 12p. (J). (ps-k). (978-1-55337-076-5(7)) Kids Can Pr., Ltd.

—Pat-a-Cake. 2004. (Traditional Nursery Rhyme Board Bks.). 12p. (J). (ps-k). (978-1-55337-077-2(5)) Kids Can Pr., Ltd.

Collodi, Carlo. Pinocchio. Ingpen, Robert R., illus. 2005. 136p. (J). (gr. 2-7). 19.95 (978-1-933327-00-6(6)) Purple Bear Bks., Inc.

Conrad, Liz, illus. Bedtime Bear. 1999. (J). (978-1-892374-26-4(9)) Weldon Owen, Inc.

—Bedtime Bear. 1999. 20p. (J). reprint ed. 16.95 (978-1-892374-28-8(5)) Weldon Owen, Inc.

Conrad, Pam. The Tub People. Egielski, Richard, illus. 1999. (Laura Geringer Bks.). 32p. (J). (ps-3). 15.95 (978-0-06-021340-4(X) , Geringer, Laura Book) HarperCollins Pubs.

—The Tub People's Christmas. Egielski, Richard, illus. 1999. 40p. (J). (ps-3). 15.89 (978-0-06-026029-3(7) , Geringer, Laura Book) HarperCollins Pubs.

Cooper, Helen. Historias de Juguetes. (SPA., Illus.). 80p. (J). (gr. k-2). 23.95 (978-84-261-3127-0(1) , JV1108) Juventud, Editorial ESP. *Dist:* Lectorum Pubns., Inc.

—Tatty Ratty. Cooper, Helen, illus. 2002. (Illus.). 32p. (J). (ps-3). 16.00 (978-0-374-37386-3(8) , Farrar, Straus & Giroux (BYR)) Farrar, Straus & Giroux.

—Tatty-Ratty. Cooper, Helen, illus. 2004. (Illus.). 28p. (J). (gr. k-3). reprint ed. 19.00 (978-0-7567-7214-7(1)) DIANE Publishing Co.

—Toy Tales. 2000. (gr. k-3). lib. bdg. 16.40 (978-0-613-30803-8(4)) Tandem Library Bks.

Cooper, James Thomas. The First Christmas Teddy Bear. Nardi, Cindy, illus. 1999. 32p. (J). pap. 6.95 (978-0-9675037-0-7(1)) Cooper Publishing Co.

Corduroy. 2004. (J). pap. 32.75 incl. audio (978-1-55592-210-8(4)); pap. 32.75 incl. audio (978-1-55592-211-5(2)); pap. 14.95 incl. audio (978-0-7882-0677-1(X)); pap. 14.95 incl. audio (978-1-55592-655-7(X)) Weston Woods Studios, Inc.

Corser-Gay, Joan. Jennifer Jane's Blanky. Corser-Gay, Joan, illus. 1999. 13p. (J). pap. 8.95 (978-0-7414-0233-2(5)) Infinity Publishing.

Cosby, Bill. Shipwreck Saturday. Honeywood, Varnette P., illus. 1998. (Little Bill Books for Beginning Readers Ser.). 40p. (J). (gr. k-3). pap. 13.95 (978-0-590-16400-9(7)); pap. 3.99 (978-0-590-95620-8(5)) Scholastic, Inc.

Coté, Geneviève, illus. The Magic Beads. 2007. 32p. (J). (gr. 2 up). 16.95 (***978-1-894965-47-7(7)***) Simply Read Bks. CAN. *Dist:* Perseus Distribution.

Coulton, Mia. Danny's New Toy. Coulton, Mia, photos by. 2002. (J). (978-0-9713518-8-2(0)) Maryruth Bks., Inc.

Cousins, Lucy. Maisy's Favorite Toys. Cousins, Lucy, illus. 2001. (Maisy Bks.). (Illus.). 22p. (J). (gr. k-k). bds. 3.99 (978-0-7636-1571-0(4)) Candlewick Pr.

Cowell, Cressida. That Rabbit Belongs to Emily Brown. Layton, Neal, illus. 2007. 40p. (ps-2). 16.99 (978-1-4231-0645-6(8)) Hyperion Bks. for Children.

Crews, Nina. Below. rev. ed. 2006. (Illus.). 32p. (J). 16.95 (978-0-8050-7728-5(6)) Holt, Henry & Co.

Crownover, Ashley, ed. The Velveteen Rabbit. Thompson, Pat, illus. 2002. 24p. (J). (gr. k-5). pap. 2.99 (978-1-57759-375-1(8)) Dalmatian Pr.

Cuantos Juguetes. 2000. (Mundo del Pequenin Ser.).Tr. of Baby's Toys. (SPA., Illus.). 16p. (YA). (ps up). pap. 4.95 (978-0-7460-3865-9(8)) EDC Publishing.

Custer, Jason. Everyday Monsters. 2005. (J). lib. bdg. 19.95 (***978-0-9754728-3-5(6)*** , Bear Hug Bks.) MidAmerica Publishing Co.

Dalmatian Press Staff. Two by Two Play Set with Toys. 2004. 64p. pap. 4.99 (978-1-4037-0713-0(8)) Dalmatian Pr.

—The Velveteen Rabbit. 2004. (Illus.). 14p. (J). (ps-1). bds. 5.99 (978-1-57759-611-0(0)) Dalmatian Pr.

Daniel, Chloe. Teddy's Toy Box. 1999. (Lamaze Ser.). (Illus.). 16p. (J). 6.99 (978-1-56799-892-4(5) , Friedman-Fairfax) Friedman, Michael Publishing Group, Inc.

David & Dog. 2004. (J). 24.95 incl. audio (978-0-89719-871-4(9)); pap. 14.95 incl. audio (978-0-7882-0657-3(5)) Weston Woods Studios, Inc.

Davis, Caroline, illus. My Toys. 2007. 12p. (J). (ps). bds. 6.95 (***978-1-58925-825-9(8)*** , tiger tales) ME Media LLC.

Davis, Lee. Spooky Game: Bear Read Alone. 2001. (Pajama Bedtime Bear Ser.). (Illus.). 24p. (J). (ps-1). pap. 6.95 (978-0-7894-4945-0(5) , D K Ink) Dorling Kindersley Publishing, Inc.

—Where Is P. B. Bear Going? 2001. (P. B. Bear Ser.). (Illus.). 24p. (J). (ps). pap. 4.95 (978-0-7894-2221-7(2) , D K Ink) Dorling Kindersley Publishing, Inc.

de Paola, Tomie. T-Rex Is Missing! 2002. (gr. k-3). lib. bdg. 11.80 (978-0-613-50544-4(1)) Tandem Library Bks.

—T-Rex Is Missing! A Barkers Book. 2002. (All Aboard Reading Ser.). (Illus.). 32p. (J). pap. 3.99 (978-0-448-42870-3(9) , Grosset & Dunlap) Penguin Group (USA) Inc.

de Seve, Randall. Toy Boat. Long, Loren, illus. 2007. 40p. (J). (ps-3). 16.99 (***978-0-399-24374-5(7)*** , Philomel) Penguin Group (USA) Inc.

Deacon, Alexis. While You Are Sleeping. 2006. (Illus.). 36p. (J). 16.50 (978-0-374-38330-5(8) , Farrar, Straus & Giroux (BYR)) Farrar, Straus & Giroux.

Dematons, Charlotte. Worry Bear. 1998. (Illus.). 32p. (J). 15.95 (978-1-886910-83-6(9) , Lemniscaat) Boyds Mills Pr.

Derolf, Shane. The Little Box of Crayons. 1998. (J). pap. 16.99 (978-0-679-85460-9(6) , Knopf Bks. for Young Readers) Random Hse. Children's Bks.

DiCamillo, Kate. The Miraculous Journey of Edward Tulane. Ibatoulline, Bagram, illus. 2006. 228p. (J). (gr. 2). 18.99 (978-0-7636-2589-4(2)) Candlewick Pr.

Dickens, Ned. By a Thread. Ross, Graham, illus. 2005. 32p. (J). (ps-2). 16.95 (978-1-55143-325-7(7)) Orca Bk. Pubs. USA.

Dierssen, A. & Sohr, D. Old Red Tractor. 2006. (Illus.). 32p. (J). 16.95 (978-0-7358-2088-3(0)) North-South Bks., Inc.

Disney-Pixar Toy Story 2. 2002. (J). spiral bd. (978-0-9720651-8-4(0)) Story Reader, Inc.

Disney Staff. Believe In Yourself. 2000. (Lessons from the Hundred-Acre Woods: Vol. 5). 32p. (J). (ps-4). 3.49 (978-1-57973-091-8(4)) Advance Pubs. LLC.

—Forgive & Forget. 2000. (Lessons from the Hundred-Acre Woods: Vol. 17). (Illus.). 32p. (J). (ps-3). 3.49 (978-1-57973-103-8(1)) Advance Pubs. LLC.

—Friendship Day. 2000. (Lessons from the Hundred-Acre Woods: Vol. 11). (Illus.). 32p. (J). (ps-4). 3.49 (978-1-57973-087-1(6)) Advance Pubs. LLC.

—Fruity-Tooty Picnic. Disney Staff, illus. 1999. (Pooh's Learn & Grow Ser.: Vol. 5). (Illus.). 12p. (J). 3.49 (978-1-57973-039-0(6)) Advance Pubs. LLC.

—Giving Is the Best Gift. 2000. (Lessons from the Hundred-Acre Woods: Vol. 14). (Illus.). 32p. (J). (ps-3). 3.49 (978-1-57973-100-7(7)) Advance Pubs. LLC.

—Home Sweet Home. 2000. (Lessons from the Hundred-Acre Woods: Vol. 4). 32p. (J). (ps-4). 3.49 (978-1-57973-090-1(6)) Advance Pubs. LLC.

—Just Say "Thank You" 2000. (Lessons from the Hundred-Acre Woods: Vol. 7). 32p. (J). (ps-4). 3.49 (978-1-57973-093-2(0)) Advance Pubs. LLC.

—Loyal Through & Through. 2000. (Lessons from the Hundred-Acre Woods: Vol. 13). (Illus.). 32p. (J). (ps-3). 3.49 (978-1-57973-099-4(X)) Advance Pubs. LLC.

—Make the Best of It. 2000. (Lessons from the Hundred-Acre Woods: 16). (Illus.). 32p. (J). 3.49 (978-1-57973-102-1(3)) Advance Pubs. LLC.

—Pooh's Noisy Book. 1999. (Learn & Grow Busy Book Ser.). (Illus.). 12p. (J). (ps-3). 6.99 (978-0-7364-0136-4(9)) Mouse Works.

—Ready, Set, Go! Disney Staff, illus. 1999. (Pooh's Learn & Grow Ser.: Vol. 8). (Illus.). 12p. (J). 3.49 (978-1-57973-042-0(6)) Advance Pubs. LLC.

—Sharing Can Be Fun. 2000. (Lessons from the Hundred-Acre Woods: Vol. 8). 32p. (J). (ps-4). 3.49 (978-1-57973-094-9(9)) Advance Pubs. LLC.

—Sweet Dreams. Disney Staff, illus. 1999. (Pooh's Learn & Grow Ser.: Vol. 12). (Illus.). 12p. (J). 3.49 (978-1-57973-046-8(9)) Advance Pubs. LLC.

—Try, Try Again. 2000. (Lessons from the Hundred-Acre Woods: Vol. 3). 32p. (J). (ps-4). 3.49 (978-1-57973-089-5(2)) Advance Pubs. LLC.

—You Can Count on Me. 2000. (Lessons from the Hundred-Acre Woods: Vol. 11). (Illus.). 32p. (J). (ps-3). 3.49 (978-1-57973-097-0(3)) Advance Pubs. LLC.

Disney Staff, ed. Toy Story 2: Buzz's Story. 1999. (Toy Story 2 Ser.). (Illus.). 48p. (J). (ps-3). 10.99 (978-0-7868-3233-0(9)) Disney Pr.

Disney Staff & Pixar Animation Studios Staff, contrib. by. Toy Story 2. 1999. (Disney's Wonderful World of Reading Ser.). (Illus.). (J). (978-0-7172-8988-2(5) , Grolier) Scholastic Library Publishing.

Disney Storybook Artists Staff. Disney Pixar Storybook Collection. 2006. 320p. (ps-17). 15.99 (978-0-7868-3602-4(4)) Disney Pr.

Disney/Pixar: Finding Nemo CD Read-Along. 2007. 48p. (ps-2). 12.99 (978-1-4231-0270-0(3)) Disney Pr.

Disney's Winnie the Pooh Collection Boxed Set. 1999. (Illus.). (J). (ps-3). pap. 1.09 (978-0-307-15894-9(2) , Golden Bks.) Random Hse. Children's Bks.

D'Lacey, Chris. Franklin's Bear. Taylor, Thomas, illus. 2005. (Red Go Bananas Ser.). 48p. (J). pap. (978-0-7787-2696-8(7)) Crabtree Publishing Co.

Dohaney, Rainy. My Best Sweet Potato. Dohaney, Rainy, illus. 2006. (Illus.). 40p. (J). (ps-2). 15.95 (978-0-689-86379-0(9)) Simon & Schuster Children's Publishing.

—My Best Sweet Potato. 2006. (Illus.). (J). (***978-1-4156-9211-0(4)***) Simon & Schuster Children's Publishing.

Droop, Constanza, illus. Felix's Cookbook. 2001. 72p. (J). pap. 24.95 (978-0-7892-0750-0(8) , Abbeville Kids) Abbeville Pr., Inc.

Egan, Kate. Fun at the Fair. Edwards, Ken, illus. 2004. (My Little Pony Ser.). 24p. (J). (ps-1). pap. 3.99 (978-0-06-055400-2(2) , Harper Festival) HarperCollins Pubs.

—Pinkie Pie's Pretty Hair Day. LoRaso, Carlo, illus. 2004. (My Little Pony Ser.). 12p. (J). (ps-1). 5.99 (978-0-06-055403-3(7) , Harper Festival) HarperCollins Pubs.

—Pony Parade. Middleton, Gayle, illus. 2004. (My Little Pony Ser.). 32p. (J). (ps-1). 3.99 (978-0-06-073841-9(3) , Harper Festival) HarperCollins Pubs.

—Pony Party. LoRaso, Carlo, illus. 2004. (My Little Pony Ser.). 24p. (J). (ps-1). pap. 3.99 (978-0-06-054950-3(5) , Harper Festival) HarperCollins Pubs.

Ehlenbeck, Stan. AllThumbs Mckringle by Stan Ehlenbeck & illustrated by Marilyn Martin. 2007. 29.00 (***978-0-8059-8957-1(9)***) Dorrance Publishing Co., Inc.

Ehrlich, H. M. Louie's Goose. Bolam, Emily, illus. 32p. (J). (gr. k-3). 2002. pap. 5.95 (978-0-618-26008-9(0)); 2000. tchr. ed. 15.00 (978-0-618-03023-1(9)) Houghton Mifflin Co. Trade & Reference Div. (Walter Lorraine).

—Louie's Goose. 2002. (gr. k-3). lib. bdg. 14.10 (978-0-613-72913-0(7)) Tandem Library Bks.

Elliott, D. T. Bobby's Toys. 2004. (Illus.). 22p. (J). pap. 12.95 (978-1-932373-11-0(X)) Cedar Hill Publishing.

Emberley, Rebecca. My Toys/Mis Juguetes. Emberley, Rebecca, illus. 2002. (SPA & ENG., Illus.). 10p. (J). (ps-ps). bds. 6.99 (978-0-316-17494-7(7)) Little, Brown Bks. for Young Readers.

Engelbrecht, Carla. Professor Dalrymple's Deluxe Patented Fairy Catching System. 2007. (Illus.). 32p. (J). (ps up). pap. 12.95 (***978-0-7624-2995-0(X)*** , Running Pr. Kids) Running Pr. Bk. Pubs.

Equipo Staff. El Vuelo de Igor. 2000. (Adventures of Winnie the Pooh! Ser.). (SPA., Illus.). 114p. (J). 12.95 (978-84-488-0733-7(2)) Beascoa, Ediciones S.A. ESP. *Dist:* Distribooks, Inc.

Falconer, Ian. Olivia & the Missing Toy. Falconer, Ian, illus. 2003. (Olivia Ser.). (Illus.). 42p. (J). (ps up). 16.95 (978-0-689-85291-6(6) , Atheneum) Simon & Schuster Children's Publishing.

—Olivia y el Juguete Desaparecido. Mlawer, Teresa, tr. from ENG. Falconer, Ian, illus. 2004. (Olivia Ser.). (SPA., Illus.). 30p. (J). 16.95 (978-1-930332-71-3(8)) Lectorum Pubns., Inc.

Farshtey, Greg. Bionicle World, Vol. 5. 2007. (Bionicle Ser.). 96p. (J). pap. 6.99 (978-0-439-78796-3(3)) Scholastic, Inc.

—Prisoners of the Pit. 2007. (Bionicle Legends Ser.: No. 7). 144p. (J). pap. 4.99 (*978-0-439-89034-2(9)) Scholastic, Inc.

—Shadows in the Sky. 2008. (Bionicle Legends Ser.). 128p. (J). 4.99 (*978-0-439-91641-7(0) , Scholastic) Scholastic, Inc.

—Time Trap. 2005. (Bionicle Adventures Ser.). (J). 144p. pap. 4.99 (978-0-439-74559-8(4)); 137p. (*978-1-4156-3150-8(6)) Scholastic, Inc.

—Web of Shadows. 2005. 139p. (J). (978-1-4156-0699-5(4)) Scholastic, Inc.

Feiffer, Jules. I Lost My Bear. Feiffer, Jules, illus. 2002. (Illus.). (J). 14.43 (978-0-7587-4249-0(5)) Book Wholesalers, Inc.

—I Lost My Bear. Feiffer, Jules, illus. 2000. (Illus.). 40p. (J). (ps-2). pap. 6.99 (978-0-688-17722-5(0) , Harper Trophy) HarperCollins Pubs.

—I Lost My Bear. 2000. (YA). pap. 34.25 incl. audio (978-0-7887-4095-4(4) , 41091) Recorded Bks., LLC.

—I Lost My Bear. 2000. (gr. k-3). lib. bdg. 14.15 (978-0-613-29984-8(1)) Tandem Library Bks.

Feldman, Jody. The Gollywhopper Games. Jamieson, Victoria, illus. 2008. 336p. (J). 16.99 (*978-0-06-121450-9(7)); lib. bdg. 17.89 (*978-0-06-121451-6(5)) HarperCollins Pubs. (Greenwillow Bks.).

Fellowes, Julian & Lewis, Shirley-Anne. The Curious Adventures of the Abandoned Toys. Schindler, S. D., illus. rev. ed. 2007. 64p. (J). (ps up). 17.95 (*978-0-8050-7526-7(7)) Holt, Henry & Co.

Ferreri, Della Ross. How Will I Ever Sleep in This Bed? Mazille, Capucine, illus. 2007. 24p. (J). bds. 5.95 (978-1-4027-4324-5(6)); 2005. 32p. 12.95 (978-1-4027-1492-4(0)) Sterling Publishing Co., Inc.

Field, Elaine. Toys (Cuddly Cuffs W/Hang Tag) Finn, Rebecca, illus. (Cuddly Cuffs Ser.). 12p. (J). tchr. ed. 5.95 (978-1-58925-709-2(X) , tiger tales) ME Media LLC.

Fine, Anne. The Jamie & Angus Stories. Dale, Penny, illus. 2002. 112p. (J). (ps-1). 15.99 (978-0-7636-1862-9(4)) Candlewick Pr.

Fine, Anne. Jamie & Angus Together. Dale, Penny, illus. 2007. 112p. (J). (ps-1). 15.99 (*978-0-7636-3374-5(7)) Candlewick Pr.

Finnegan, Evelyn M. My Little Friend Goes to a Baseball Game. Houghton, Diane R., illus. 2006. 32p. (J). (ps-3). reprint ed. pap. 7.00 (978-1-4223-5403-2(2)) DIANE Publishing Co.

Fontes, Justine. Toy Trouble. Hefferan, Rob, illus. 2003. 24p. (J). pap. (978-1-59034-447-7(2)); 14.95 (978-1-59034-446-0(4)) Mondo Publishing.

Fontes, Ron & Fontes, Justine. Rex to the Rescue! 1999. (Disney Chapters Ser.). (Illus.). 46p. (J). (gr. 2-4). pap. 3.99 (978-0-7868-4288-9(1)) Disney Pr.

Foreman, Michael. Scraps. (Illus.). 25p. (J). pap. 8.99 (978-1-84270-003-7(0)) Andersen GBR. *Dist:* Trafalgar Square Publishing.

Freedman, Claire. Night-Night, Emily! Massey, Jane, illus. 2005. 32p. (J). 6.95 (978-1-58925-390-2(6) , tiger tales) ME Media LLC.

—Night-Night, Emily! Massey, Jane, tr. Massey, Jane, illus. 2003. 32p. (J). (ps-1). tchr. ed. 15.95 (978-1-58925-032-1(X) , tiger tales) ME Media LLC.

Freeman, Don. Corduroy. Freeman, Don, illus. 2004. (Illus.). (J). pap. 18.95 incl. audio compact disk (978-1-59112-789-5(0)) Live Oak Media.

—Corduroy's Easter. McCue, Lisa, illus. 1999. (Corduroy Ser.). 8p. (J). (gr. k-1). 11.99 (978-0-670-88101-7(5) , Viking Juvenile) Penguin Group (USA) Inc.

—Corduroy's Easter Party. McCue, Lisa, illus. 2000. (Corduroy Ser.). 32p. (J). (gr. k-1). pap. 3.49 (978-0-448-42154-4(2) , Grosset & Dunlap) Penguin Group (USA) Inc.

—Corduroy's Easter Party. 2000. (ps-2). lib. bdg. 11.25 (978-0-613-24691-0(8)) Tandem Library Bks.

Fuge, Charles. I Know a Rhino. 2003. (Illus.). 32p. (J). bds. 5.95 (978-1-4027-0861-9(0)) Sterling Publishing Co., Inc.

—I Know a Rhino. Fuge, Charles, illus. 2002. (Illus.). 32p. (J). (ps-1). 12.95 (978-1-4027-0137-5(3)) Sterling Publishing Co., Inc.

Gaines, Isabel. Bounce, Tigger, Bounce. 1998. (Winnie the Pooh First Readers Ser.). (Illus.). 48p. (J). (ps-3). pap. 3.95 (978-0-7868-4255-1(5)) Disney Pr.

—Eeyore Finds Friends. 1999. (Winnie the Pooh First Readers Ser.: No. 11). (Illus.). 37p. (J). (gr. k-3). pap. 3.99 (978-0-7868-4269-8(5)) Disney Pr.

—Pooh's Easter Egg Hunt. 1999. (Winnie the Pooh First Readers Ser.: No. 10). (Illus.). 40p. (J). (gr. k-3). pap. 3.99 (978-0-7868-4268-1(7)) Disney Pr.

—Pooh's Family Tree, Vol. 20. 2000. (Winnie the Pooh Ser.). (Illus.). 34p. (J). (gr. k-3). pap. 3.99 (978-0-7868-4367-1(5)) Disney Pr.

—Pooh's Hero Party. 1999. (978-0-606-18111-2(3)) Tandem Library Bks.

—Pooh's Valentine. Marderosian, Mark & Lopez, Paul, illus. 2004. (Step into Reading Ser.). 32p. (J). (ps-1). pap. 3.99 (978-0-7364-2264-2(1) , RH/Disney) Random Hse. Children's Bks.

—Rabbit Gets Lost. 1998. (Winnie the Pooh First Readers Ser.). (Illus.). 48p. (J). (ps-3). pap. 3.95 (978-0-7868-4254-4(7)) Disney Pr.

Gaines, Isabel & Random House Disney Staff. Pooh's Halloween Pumpkin. Yee, Josie, illus. 2003. (Disney Winnie the Pooh Ser.). 32p. (J). (ps-1). pap. 3.99 (978-0-7364-2160-7(2) , RH/Disney) Random Hse. Children's Bks.

Gaines, Isabel, et al. The Giving Bear. Yee, Josie, illus. 1999. (Winnie the Pooh First Readers Ser.: No. 9). 37p. (J). (gr. k-3). pap. 3.99 (978-0-7868-4267-4(9)) Disney Pr.

—Pooh's Easter Egg Hunt. 2002. (Step into Reading Ser.). (Illus.). 32p. (J). (ps-1). pap. 3.99 (978-0-7364-1208-7(5) , RH/Disney) Random Hse. Children's Bks.

Garcia, Jerry & Grisman, David. The Teddy Bears' Picnic. Whatley, Bruce, illus. 1998. 18p. (J). (ps up). 7.99 (978-0-694-01182-7(7) , Harper Festival) HarperCollins Pubs.

Garvin, Sharon. Alexandra's Rag-Time Band. 2006. 28p. (J). per. 12.95 (978-1-56167-926-3(7)) American Literary Pr.

Gautier, Gary. Spaghetti & Peas. Bailey, Sheila, illus. 2007. (ENG.). 40p. (J). pap. 15.95 (978-0-9744446-1-1(8)) All About Kids Publishing.

Gavrilovskiy, Olga, illus. Elf Night: A Christmas Story. 2006. 52p. (J). 16.95 (*978-0-9788085-0-1(9)) Tetoca Pr.

Glaser, Byron & Higashi, Sandra. The Zolo A-B-Z: An Alphabet Book. Glaser, Byron & Higashi, Sandra, illus. 2003. (Illus.). 44p. (J). (ps-1). 15.95 (978-0-8109-4260-8(7)) Abrams, Harry N., Inc.

Golden Books Staff. Bounce Around, Tigger! 2000. (Disney Ser.). 24p. (J). (ps-3). pap. 3.29 (978-0-307-13173-7(4) , 13173, Golden Bks.) Random Hse. Children's Bks.

—Very Best Friends. 1999. (Disney Ser.). 24p. (J). (ps-3). pap. 3.29 (978-0-307-13142-3(4) , Golden Bks.) Random Hse. Children's Bks.

Golden Books Staff, ed. Best Buddies: Special Edition Coloring Book. 1999. (Disney Ser.). (Illus.). 84p. (J). (ps-3). pap. 2.99 (978-0-307-25728-4(2) , Golden Bks.) Random Hse. Children's Bks.

—Toy Story. 1999. (Super Coloring Book Ser.). (J). pap. 2.29 (978-0-307-08436-1(1) , 08436, Golden Bks.) Random Hse. Children's Bks.

Goldman, Leslie. Toy Story 2. 1999. (Toy Story 2 Ser.). (Illus.). 94p. (J). (gr. 3-7). pap. 4.99 (978-0-7868-4302-2(0)) Disney Pr.

—Toy Story 2: Junior Novel Book. 1999. (J). pap. 4.99 (978-0-7868-4394-7(2)) Disney Pr.

Goldsmith, Howard. The Twiddle Twins' Amusement Park Mystery. Jordan, Charles, illus. 1998. (Mondo Ser.). 40p. (J). (gr. 1-5). pap. 4.50 (978-1-57255-618-8(8)) Mondo Publishing.

Gordon, Dan. Davin. 1998. (978-0-606-13317-3(8)) Tandem Library Bks.

Gray, Kes. Duperball. Mould, Chris, illus. 2006. (Read-It! Chapter Books). 48p. (J). lib. bdg. (*978-1-4048-3118-6(5) , 1265805) Picture Window Bks.

Grey, Mini. Traction Man Is Here! 2005. (Illus.). 32p. (J). (ps-3). 15.95 (978-0-375-83191-1(6)); lib. bdg. 17.99 (978-0-375-93191-8(0)) Random Hse. Children's Bks. (Knopf Bks. for Young Readers).

Gruelle, Johnny & Palmer, Jan. Raggedy Ann & Andy & the Camel with the Wrinkled Knees. 2001. (My First Raggedy Ann Ser.). (Illus.). 32p. (J). pap. 6.99 (978-0-689-80888-3(7) , Aladdin) Simon & Schuster Children's Publishing.

Gutman, Anne & Hallensleben, Georg. Lisa's Airplane Trip. Schulman, Janet, ed. 2001. (Illus.). 32p. (J). (ps-1). 9.95 (978-0-375-81114-2(1) , Knopf Bks. for Young Readers) Random Hse. Children's Bks.

Hague, Michael. The Nutcracker. ed. 2005. (Illus.). 56p. (J). (ps-7). 7.95 (978-0-8118-5027-8(7)) Chronicle Bks. LLC.

Hague, Michael, illus. The Nutcracker. 2003. 48p. (J). 17.50 (978-1-58717-255-7(0)); 16.95 (978-1-58717-254-0(2)) Chronicle Bks. LLC. (SeaStar Bks.).

Hall, Patricia. Going to Grandma's. 2001. (gr. k-3). lib. bdg. 11.80 (978-0-613-90799-6(X)) Tandem Library Bks.

Hall, Patricia, et al. Going to Grandma's. 2001. (Classic Raggedy Ann & Andy Ser.). (Illus.). 32p. (J). pap. 3.99 (978-0-689-84702-8(5) , Little Simon) Simon & Schuster Children's Publishing.

Hapka, Catherine. Ballerina Bear. Valeri, Jim & Valeri, Kara, illus. 2004. (Build-A-Bear Workshop Ser.). 24p. (J). (ps-1). 3.50 (978-0-06-075284-2(X) , Harper Festival) HarperCollins Pubs.

Harcourt School Publishers Staff. One of My Bears: Take-Home Book. 1999. (Collections Ser.). (Illus.). (J). pap. 1.90 (978-0-15-317236-6(3)) Harcourt Schl. Pubs.

—What Is in the Box? Decodable Book. 3rd ed. 2002. (Trophies Reading Program Ser.). (Illus.). (gr. k). pap. 2.90 (978-0-15-325424-6(6)) Harcourt Schl. Pubs.

Hasquet, DeAnn. The Magic Palace Toy Shoppe. 2000th ed. 2000. 21p. (J). pap. 8.99 (978-1-930673-02-1(7)) Childhood Friends, Inc.

Hawksley, Gerald. Good Puppy. Stanley, Mandy, illus. 2005. (J). (978-1-890647-14-8(4)) RC2 Corp.

Henkes, Kevin. Owen's Marshmallow Chick. Henkes, Kevin, illus. 2002. (Illus.). 24p. (J). 6.99 (978-0-06-001012-6(6) , Harper Festival) HarperCollins Pubs.

—Owen's Marshmallow Chick Book & Finger Puppet. Henkes, Kevin, illus. 2003. (Illus.). 24p. (J). 10.99 (978-0-06-052769-3(2)) HarperCollins Pubs.

Hennessy, B. G. Claire & the Unicorn Happy Ever After. Mitchell, Susan, illus. 2005. 32p. (J). 12.95 (978-1-4169-0815-9(3)) Simon & Schuster Children's Publishing.

Here to Stay, Wah! Date not set. (Furby Storybooks Ser.). (Illus.). 24p. (J). pap. (978-0-7666-0436-0(5) , Honey Bear Bks.) Modern Publishing.

Herman, Gail. A Little Magic. 2007. (Mr. Magorium's Wonder Emporium Ser.). 32p. (J). pap. 3.99 (*978-0-439-91249-5(0)) Scholastic, Inc.

Hicks, Russell, illus. Winnie the Pooh & the Honey Tree. 2000. (Little Golden Bks.). (J). (ps-3). 3.99 (978-0-307-98267-4(X) , Golden Bks.) Random Hse. Children's Bks.

Hill, Eric. Buenas Noches Spot. (SPA.). pap. 4.95 (978-950-07-1964-3(9)) Editorial Sudamericana S.A. ARG. *Dist:* Distribooks, Inc.

—A Jugar Con Spot. (SPA.). pap. 4.95 (978-950-07-1961-2(4)) Editorial Sudamericana S.A. ARG. *Dist:* Distribooks, Inc.

Hillert, Margaret. The Ball Book. Brroks, Nan, illus. rev. ed. 2006. (Beginning to Read Ser.). 32p. (J). lib. bdg. 18.60 (978-1-59953-031-4(7)) Norwood Hse. Pr.

—The Birthday Car. Oechsli, Kelly, illus. rev. exp. ed. 2007. (Beginning to Read Ser.). 32p. (J). lib. bdg. (978-1-59953-043-7(0)) Norwood Hse. Pr.

—The Purple Pussycat. Stasiak, Krystyna, illus. rev. exp. ed. 2007. (Beginning to Read Ser.). 32p. (J). lib. bdg. (978-1-59953-044-4(9)) Norwood Hse. Pr.

Hissey, Jane. Donde Esta el Osito? 2001. (SPA., Illus.). 32p. (J). (gr. k-2). (978-84-89675-79-7(1)) Zendrera Zariquiey, Editorial ESP. *Dist:* Lectorum Pubns., Inc.

Hoban, Lillian. Arthur's Honey Bear. Hoban, Lillian, illus. 2002. (Arthur the Chimpanzee Ser.). (Illus.). (J). 11.91 (978-0-7587-5986-3(X)) Book Wholesalers, Inc.

Hoffman, Eric. No Fair to Tigers, 1. 2004. (Anti-Bias Books for Kids). (SPA., Illus.). 32p. (J). (ps-3). pap. 11.95 (978-1-884834-62-2(0)) Redleaf Pr.

Hogan, Mary. Tigger's Family. 2000. (Winnie the Pooh Ser.). (Illus.). 10p. (J). (ps-k). bds. 4.99 (978-0-7364-1062-5(7)) Mouse Works.

Hood, Sue. Monkey Business. Chapman, Susan, illus. 2005. (J). bds. (978-1-890647-17-9(9)) RC2 Corp.

Hope, Laura Lee. The Story of a China Cat. 2007. (ENG.). 72p. per. 87.99 (*978-1-4280-7317-3(5)) IndyPublish.com.

—The Story of a Nodding Donkey. rev. ed. 2006. 108p. 25.95 (978-1-4218-1794-1(2)); pap. 10.95 (978-1-4218-1894-8(9)) 1st World Publishing, Inc. (1st World Library - Literary Society).

Hope, Laura Lee. The Story of a Stuffed Elephant. 2007. (ENG.). 68p. per. 87.99 (*978-1-4280-7311-1(6)) IndyPublish.com.

Horse, Harry, illus. Little Rabbit Goes to School. 2004. 32p. (J). 15.95 (978-1-56145-320-7(X)) Peachtree Pubs., Ltd.

Howe, James. It Came from Beneath the Bed! 2003. (Tales from the House of Bunnicula Ser.). (gr. 3-6). lib. bdg. 11.80 (978-0-613-66415-8(9)) Tandem Library Bks.

—It Came from Beneath the Bed! 2004. (Tales from the House of Bunnicula Ser.). 112p. (J). (gr. 3-6). pap. 17.00 incl. audio (978-1-4000-8632-0(9) , Listening Library) Random Hse. Audio Publishing Group.

Hughes, Shirley. Dogger. 2007. (Illus.). 32p. (J). pap. 8.95 (*978-0-09-992790-7(X) , Red Fox) Random Hse. Children's Bks. GBR. *Dist:* Independent Pubs. Group.

Hutchins, Pat. Changes, Changes. Hutchins, Pat, illus. 2002. (Illus.). (J). 14.47 (978-0-7587-2213-3(3)) Book Wholesalers, Inc.

Huxman, K. D. Dragon Talk. Farrington, Teresa, illus. l.t. ed. 2006. 24p. (J). pap. 14.99 (978-0-9765786-7-3(0)) Dragonfly Publishing, Inc.

Huxman, Karin (K. D.). Dragon Talk. 2006. (Illus.). 24p. (J). lib. bdg. 24.95 (978-0-9778651-7-8(7)) Dragonfly Publishing, Inc.

I Can Say- Toys. 2005. (J). bds. (978-1-4194-0033-9(9)) Paradise Pr., Inc.

Ichikawa, Satomi. Come Fly with Me. Ichikawa, Satomi, illus. 2008. 40p. (J). (ps). 15.99 (*978-0-399-24679-1(7) , Philomel) Penguin Group (USA) Inc.

—I Am Pangoo the Penguin. Ichikawa, Satomi, illus. 2006. (Illus.). 40p. (J). (ps-4). 16.99 (978-0-399-23313-5(X) , Philomel) Penguin Group (USA) Inc.

—La-La Rose. Ichikawa, Satomi, illus. 2004. (Illus.). 40p. (J). (ps). 15.99 (978-0-399-24029-4(2) , Philomel) Penguin Group (USA) Inc.

In-House Staff. Meet Chuck the Dump Truck. Borer, Joe & Sinovcic, Miro, illus. 2001. (Chuck My Talking Truck Ser.). 5p. (J). (ps up). bds. 3.95 (978-0-439-31818-1(1) , Cartwheel Bks.) Scholastic, Inc.

Inches, Alison. Corduroy's Hike. Eitzen, Allan, illus. 2003. 32p. (J). (gr. k-2). pap. 3.99 (978-0-14-250164-1(6) , Puffin) Penguin Group (USA) Inc.

—Corduroy's Hike. 2003. (gr. k-3). lib. bdg. 11.80 (978-0-613-87823-4(X)) Tandem Library Bks.

—The Stuffed Animals Get Ready for Bed. Langdo, Bryan, illus. 2006. 32p. (J). 16.00 (978-0-15-216466-9(9)) Harcourt Children's Bks.

Inches, Alison & Freeman, Don. Corduroy's Garden. Eitzen, Allan, illus. 2002. (Viking Easy-to-Read Ser.). 32p. (J). (gr. k-3). 13.99 (978-0-670-03547-2(5) , Viking Juvenile) Penguin Group (USA) Inc.

—Corduroy's Hike. Eitzen, Allan, illus. 2001. (Corduroy Ser.). 32p. (J). (gr. k-1). 13.99 (978-0-670-88945-7(8) , Viking Juvenile) Penguin Group (USA) Inc.

The Indian in the Cupboard. 1998. (J). pap. 3.95 (978-0-439-04474-5(X)) Scholastic, Inc.

Inkpen, Mick. Kipper's Toybox. Inkpen, Mick, illus. 2002. (Kipper Ser.). (Illus.). (J). 13.15 (978-0-7587-6467-6(7)) Book Wholesalers, Inc.

—Kipper's Toybox. (Illus.). 25p. (J). (CHI, ENG, URD, VIE & FRE.). (978-1-85430-350-9(3) , 93452); (ENG, FRE, URD, VIE & CHI., (978-1-85430-351-6(1) , 93453) Magi Pubns.

—Kipper's Toybox. 2000. (Illus.). (J). (978-0-606-18182-2(2)) Tandem Library Bks.

—Nothing. 1998. (Illus.). 32p. (J). (ps-1). pap. 14.95 (978-0-531-30076-3(5) , Orchard Bks.) Scholastic, Inc.

—Rocket. 2001. (gr. k-3). lib. bdg. 12.95 (978-0-613-53550-2(2)) Tandem Library Bks.

Inns, Christopher. Help! (Illus.). 32p. 2006. pap. 7.95 (978-1-84507-123-3(9)); 2004. (J). 14.95 (978-1-84507-004-5(6)) Lincoln, Frances Ltd. GBR. *Dist:* Perseus Distribution.

Jack's New Skates. Date not set. (J). pap. (978-1-58453-039-8(1)) Pioneer Valley Educational Pr., Inc.

James, Mark S. Christopher's Little Airplane. Smelcer, Harold, illus. 2000. 32p. (J). (ps-3). 15.95 (978-0-9676960-0-3(3)) Chelonian Pr, Inc.

—Christopher's Little Airplane Coloring & Activity Fun Book. Smelcer, Harold, illus. 2001. 48p. (J). 3.95 (978-0-9676960-1-0(1)) Chelonian Pr, Inc.

Jandl, Ernst. Ser Quinto. Junge, Norman, illus. 2nd ed. 2002. (SPA.). 32p. (J). (978-84-89804-21-0(4)) Loguez Ediciones ESP. *Dist:* Lectorum Pubns., Inc.

Jane, Pamela. No Way, Winky Blue! Karas, G. Brian, illus. 1998. (Mondo Ser.). 56p. (J). (gr. 2-6). pap. 4.00 (978-1-57255-138-1(0)) Mondo Publishing.

Jeffers, Susan. The Nutcracker. Jeffers, Susan, illus. 2007. 40p. (J). (ps-3). lib. bdg. 17.89 (*978-0-06-074387-1(5)); (Illus.). 16.99 (*978-0-06-074386-4(7)) HarperCollins Pubs.

Jenkins, Emily. Toys Go Out: Being the Adventures of a Knowledgeable Stingray, a Toughy Little Buffalo, & Someone Called Plastic. Zelinsky, Paul O., illus. 2006. 128p. (J). (gr. 1-4). 16.95 (978-0-375-83604-6(7)); lib. bdg. 18.99 (978-0-375-93604-3(1)) Random Hse. Children's Bks. (Schwartz & Wade Bks.).

Jennings, Linda. Duna y Dan. Chapman, Jane, illus. (SPA.). 28p. (J). (gr. k-1). (978-84-8418-027-2(1) , ZZ4481) Zendrera Zariquiey, Editorial ESP. *Dist:* Lectorum Pubns., Inc.

Johnson, Crockett. Ellen's Lion: Twelve Stories by Crockett Johnson. 2003. (Illus.). 64p. (J). (gr. 1-5). 12.95 (978-0-375-82288-9(7)); lib. bdg. 14.99 (978-0-375-92288-6(1)) Random Hse. Children's Bks. (Knopf Bks. for Young Readers).

Johnson, Mildred D. Wait, Skates! Stromoski, Rick, illus. rev. ed. 2000. (Rookie Reader Skill Set Ser.). 32p. (J). (gr. k-2). pap. 4.95 (978-0-516-27002-9(8) , Children's Pr.) Scholastic Library Publishing.

Jones, Christianne C. Clinks the Robot. Trover, Zachary, illus. 2006. (Read-It! Readers Ser.). 24p. (J). (ps-3). 18.60 (978-1-4048-1579-7(1)) Picture Window Bks.

Jones, Sylvie. Go Back to Sleep. Constantin, Pascale, illus. 2006. 32p. 15.95 (978-1-59354-171-2(6)) Blue Apple Bks.

Kastner, Jill. Merry Christmas, Princess Dinosaur! 2002. (Illus.). 32p. (J). 17.89 (978-0-06-000472-9(X)) HarperCollins Pubs.

Katschke, Judy. Case of the Candy Cane Clue. 2002. (gr. 3-6). lib. bdg. 12.40 (978-0-613-64697-0(5)) Tandem Library Bks.

—Howdy, Sheriff Woody. 1999. (Toy Story 2 Ser.). (Illus.). 32p. (J). (gr. k-3). pap. 3.99 (978-0-7868-4358-9(6)) Disney Pr.

Kelly, Katherine, text. Albert Bear & the Big Celebration. 2005. (J). 12.95 (978-0-9773481-0-7(5)) Pink Hyacinth Pr.

Kemp, Jane & Walters, Clare. My Favorite Toys! Williams, Sam, illus. 2006. 24p. (J). 9.95 (978-1-58925-793-1(6) , tiger tales) ME Media LLC.

Kemp, Jane, et al. My First Toy Catalogue. (Illus.). 32p. (978-0-19-279147-4(8)) Oxford Univ. Pr., Inc.

Kennedy, Jimmy. The Teddy Bears' Picnic. Hague, Michael, illus. rev. ed. 2002. 30p. (J). (gr. k-2). bds. 6.95 (978-0-8050-6853-5(8) , Holt, Henry & Co. Bks. For Young Readers) Holt, Henry & Co.

—The Teddy Bears' Picnic. Day, Alexandra, illus. 2000. 32p. (J). (ps-1). 7.99 (978-0-689-83530-8(2) , Aladdin) Simon & Schuster Children's Publishing.

Kim, Sun-Min & Horvath, David. Ugly Guide to the Uglíverse. 2008. (Illus.). 64p. (J). (gr. 2-5). pap. 5.99 (*978-0-375-84275-7(6) , Random Hse. Bks. for Young Readers) Random Hse. Children's Bks.

Kleven, Elisa. Hooray, a Pinata! Kleven, Elisa, illus. 2002. (Illus.). (J). 25.45 (978-0-7587-2744-2(5)) Book Wholesalers, Inc.

—Hooray, a Pinata! Kleven, Elisa, illus. 2000. (Illus.). 32p. (J). (ps-3). pap. 6.99 (978-0-14-056764-9(X) , Puffin) Penguin Group (USA) Inc.

—Hooray, a Pinata! 2000. (gr. k-3). lib. bdg. 15.30 (978-0-613-33704-5(2)) Tandem Library Bks.

—The Paper Princess Finds Her Way. Kleven, Elisa, illus. 2003. (Illus.). 32p. (J). (gr. k). 16.99 (978-0-525-46911-7(7) , Dutton Juvenile) Penguin Group (USA) Inc.

—The Paper Princess Flies Again: With Her Dog! 2005. (Illus.). 32p. (J). (gr. k-2). 15.95 (978-1-58246-146-5(5) , Tricycle Pr.) Ten Speed Pr.

Klingel, Cynthia Fitterer & Noyed, Robert B. The Amazing Letter T. 2003. (Alphaphonics Ser.). (Illus.). 24p. (J). (ps-2). 21.36 (978-1-59296-110-8(X)) Child's World, Inc.

Knights, Harry B. The Boy with a Wish. (Nicholas Stories). (Illus.). 48p. (J). 16.95 (978-1-58980-059-5(1)) Pelican Publishing Co., Inc.

Koeppel, Ruth. Brought to You by the Number 1. 1999. (gr. k-3). lib. bdg. 10.95 (978-0-613-82501-6(2)) Tandem Library Bks.

Krensky, Stephen. Eeyore Has a Birthday. 2001. 10.79 (978-0-606-22514-4(5)) Tandem Library Bks.

—Winnie the Pooh & Some Bees. 2001. (978-0-606-22513-7(7)) Tandem Library Bks.

Kroll, Virginia L. Everybody Has a Teddy. Allsopp, Sophie, illus. 2007. 24p. (J). 12.95 (978-1-4027-3580-6(4)) Sterling Publishing Co., Inc.

Krul, Paige, ed. Pompom Pets. Green, Barry, illus. 2001. (M-m Ser.). 48p. (J). 7.95 (978-0-439-31764-1(9) , Tangerine Pr.) Scholastic, Inc.

Kulick Triscila, Verne. Joel & the Magic Toy Tree. 2005. 36p. (J). 11.99 (978-1-4116-6985-7(1)) Lulu.com.

Lagonegro, Melissa. Lots of Pots. 2005. (Pooh's Readables Ser.). (J). (978-0-7364-8035-2(8)) Random Hse., Inc.

Lagonegro, Melissa & Random House Disney Staff. Lots of Pots. 2005. (Pooh's Readables Ser.). (Illus.). 32p. (J). (ps-1). 4.99 (978-0-7364-2278-9(1) , RH/Disney) Random Hse. Children's Bks.

Lampl, Patricia Ryan. My Blankie: A Book to Touch & Feel. Petrone, Valeria, illus. 2005. 16p. (J). 8.99 (978-0-689-85589-4(3) , Little Simon) Simon & Schuster Children's Publishing.

LaReau, Kara. Rocko & Spanky Call It Quits. LaReau, Jenna, illus. 2008. (Rocko & Spanky Ser.). 40p. (J). 16.00 (978-0-15-216611-3(4)) Harcourt Children's Bks.

LaReau, Kara & LaReau, Jenna. Rocko & Spanky Have Company. LaReau, Kara & LaReau, Jenna, illus. 2006. (Rocko & Spanky Ser.). (Illus.). 40p. (J). 16.00 (978-0-15-216618-2(1)) Harcourt Trade Pubs.

Lassieur, Allison. Exo-force: Race to the Golden City. 2007. (Lego Ser.). 64p. (J). pap. 3.99 (***978-0-439-92328-6(X)***) Scholastic, Inc.

—Secret of the Golden Tower. 2007. (Lego Ser.). 48p. (J). pap. 3.99 (***978-0-439-92329-3(8)***) Scholastic, Inc.

Lee, Ingrid. George Most Wanted. Denis, Stephane, illus. 2005. 62p. (J). lib. bdg. 20.00 (***978-1-4242-1253-8(7)***) Fitzgerald Bks.

—George, the Best of All! Denis, Stephané, illus. 2006. 64p. (J). pap. 4.99 (978-1-55143-623-4(X)) Orca Bk. Pubs. USA.

Lee, Ingrid. The True Story of George. Denis, Stephane, illus. 2004. 62p. (J). lib. bdg. 20.00 (***978-1-4242-1262-0(6)***) Fitzgerald Bks.

Lego Staff. Rock Raiders Lego Game Books. 2000. (Illus.). 48p. 4.99 (978-1-903276-05-1(5)) Lego Media International, Inc.

Lehman, Barbara. Train Stop. 2008. 32p. (J). (ps-k). 16.00 (***978-0-618-75640-7(X)***) Houghton Mifflin Co.

LeLeu, Lisa. Miss Moo-Moo the Cow: Puppet Show Play Set with 2 books & Crayons. 2004. (Lisa Leleu Puppet Show Books Ser.). 30p. 19.95 (978-0-9710537-4-8(X)) LeLeu, Lisa Studios! Inc.

Leonard, Barry, ed. The Little Tin Soldier. 2003. (Illus.). 12p. (J). (gr. k-4). reprint ed. 17.00 (978-0-7567-6867-6(5)) DIANE Publishing Co.

Let's Pretend: Individual Title Six-Packs. (ps-2). 23.00 (978-0-7635-9001-7(0)) Rigby Education.

Lewis, Kevin. Chugga Chugga Choo Choo. Kirk, Daniel, illus. 1999. 32p. (ps-k). 12.99 (978-0-7868-0429-0(7)) Disney Pr.

—Chugga Chugga Choo-Choo Big Book. Kirk, Daniel, illus. 2001. 32p. (ps-k). 6.99 (978-0-7868-0760-4(1)) Hyperion Bks. for Children.

Lewis, Kim. Good Night Harry. Lewis, Kim, illus. 2004. (Illus.). 32p. (J). (ps-1). 15.99 (978-0-7636-2206-0(0)) Candlewick Pr.

—Here We Go, Harry. Lewis, Kim, illus. 2005. (Illus.). 32p. (J). (ps-1). 15.99 (978-0-7636-2549-8(3)) Candlewick Pr.

Lewis, Kim. Hooray for Harry. Lewis, Kim, illus. 2006. (Illus.). 32p. (J). (ps-1). 15.99 (978-0-7636-2962-5(6)) Candlewick Pr.

—Hooray for Harry. 2006. (Illus.). (J). (***978-1-4156-7111-5(7)***) Candlewick Pr.

Lewis, Naomi. Tales from Hans Christian Andersen. Clark, Emma Chicester, illus. 2005. 72p. (J). pap. 9.95 (978-1-84507-432-6(7)) Lincoln, Frances Ltd. GBR. *Dist:* Perseus Distribution.

Lewis, Paeony. No More Cookies. Granstrom, Brita, illus. 2005. 32p. (J). pap. 16.95 (978-0-439-68332-6(7) , Chicken Hse., The) Scholastic, Inc.

Lewis, Paeony. No More Yawning! Granstrom, Brita, illus. 2008. 32p. (J). pap. 16.99 (***978-0-545-02957-5(0)*** , Chicken Hse., The) Scholastic, Inc.

Lewison, Wendy Cheyette. Clang-Clang! Bang-Bang! Moroney, Christopher, illus. 2003. (Sesame Beginnings Ser.). 14p. (J). (gr. k). bds. 6.99 (978-0-375-81536-2(8) , Random Hse. Bks. for Young Readers) Random Hse. Children's Bks.

Liberts, Jennifer. Piglet Feels Small. Yee, Josie, illus. 2002. (Early Step into Reading Ser.). 32p. (J). (ps-1). pap. 3.99 (978-0-7364-1226-1(3) , RH/Disney) Random Hse. Children's Bks.

Lionni, Leo. Alexander & the Wind-up Mouse. 2002. (Illus.). (J). 13.83 (978-0-7587-0086-5(5)) Book Wholesalers, Inc.

Litchfield, J. My Toys. 2004. (Rattle Board Bks.). 16p. (J). 4.95 (978-0-7945-0054-2(4) , Usborne) EDC Publishing.

Lomack, Mary A. Atsiyalriit. Jacomet, Ida & Horesh, David, illus. l.t. ed. 1999. Tr. of People Who Are Going to Pick Berries. (ESK.). 12p. (J). (gr. 3-5). pap. 6.00 (978-1-58084-174-0(0)) Lower Kuskokwim Schl. District.

Lucado, Max. You Are Mine & Best of All, 2 vols. 2006. (Illus.). 64p. (J). 19.99 (978-1-58134-804-0(5)) Crossway Bks.

—You Are Mine & If Only I Had A Green Nose, vol. 2. 2006. (Illus.). 64p. (J). 19.99 (978-1-58134-805-7(3)) Crossway Bks.

—You Are Special. Martinez, Sergio, illus. rev. ed. 2007. 32p. 19.99 (***978-1-58134-894-1(0)***) Crossway Bks.

Lucado, Max. You Are Special: A Story for Everyone. Martinez, Sergio, illus. gif. ed. 2005. (Wemmicks Ser.). 46p. (ps-3). 10.99 (978-1-58134-405-9(8) , Crossway Bibles) Crossway Bks.

Making Waves. 2004. (J). per. (978-1-57657-460-7(1)) Paradise Pr., Inc.

Man-Kong, Mary. Rudolph's Bag of Toys. 2006. (Illus.). 10p. (J). (gr. k-ps). bds. 3.99 (978-0-375-84023-4(0) , Golden Bks.) Random Hse. Children's Bks.

The Marching Band. 1998. (P. B. Bear Ser.). (Illus.). 24p. (J). (ps). 6.95 (978-0-7894-3108-0(4)) Dorling Kindersley Publishing, Inc.

Marcus, Leonard S. & Schwartz, Amy. Oscar: The Big Adventure of a Little Sock Monkey. Schwartz, Amy, illus. 2006. (Illus.). 32p. (J). 16.99 (978-0-06-072622-5(9) , Tegen, Katherine Bks); lib. bdg. 17.89 (978-0-06-072623-2(7)) HarperCollins Pubs.

Marsoli, Lisa Ann. Let's Go to the Zoo. Smitherton, Jeb, illus. 2005. (J). bds. 14.99 (978-0-9767325-4-9(8)) Toy Quest.

Masurel, Claire. Christmas Is Coming! Henry, Marie H., illus. 2001. 24p. (J). bds. 6.95 (978-0-8118-3322-6(4)) Chronicle Bks. LLC.

Mattern, Joanne. The Pyramids: Make Your Own Egyptian Sandscape. 2007. (Illus.). 32p. (J). (gr. 1 up). pap. 12.95 (***978-0-7624-3143-4(1)*** , Running Pr. Kids) Running Pr. Bk. Pubs.

Maye, Beth. The Marble. Wise, Noreen, ed. 2000. (Lemonade Collection). 96p. (YA). (gr. 4 up). pap. 6.95 (978-1-58584-264-3(8)) Huckleberry Pr.

Mayfield, Sue. The Four Franks. Parsons, Garry, illus. 2005. (Blue Go Bananas Ser.). (J). 38p. (978-0-7787-2629-6(0)); 48p. pap. (978-0-7787-2651-7(7)) Crabtree Publishing Co.

McAllister, Angela. Brave Bitsy & the Bear. Beeke, Tiphanie, illus. 2006. 32p. (J). (ps-k). 16.00 (978-0-618-63994-6(2) , Clarion Bks.) Houghton Mifflin Co. Trade & Reference Div.

—The Little Blue Rabbit. Cockcroft, Jason, illus. 2003. 32p. (J). (gr. k-3). 16.95 (978-1-58234-834-6(0) , Bloomsbury Children) Bloomsbury Publishing.

—Mama & Little Joe. Milne, Terry, illus. 2007. 32p. (J). (ps-1). 15.99 (978-1-4169-1631-4(8) , McElderry, Margaret K.) Simon & Schuster Children's Publishing.

McCafferty, Catherine, et al. Tigger's Bouncy Easter. Kleven, Dean, illus. 2002. (Disney's Winnie the Pooh Ser.). (J). (978-0-7853-6672-0(5)) Publications International, Ltd.

McCallum, Ann. Beanstalk: The Measure of a Giant: A Math Adventure. Balkovek, James, illus. (Math Adventures Ser.). 32p. (J). 2006. pap. 6.95 (978-1-57091-894-0(5)); 2005. 16.95 (978-1-57091-893-3(7)) Charlesbridge Publishing, Inc.

McClintock, Barbara. Dahlia. McClintock, Barbara, illus. 2002. (Illus.). 32p. (J). (ps-3). 16.00 (978-0-374-31678-5(3) , Farrar, Straus & Giroux (BYR)) Farrar, Straus & Giroux.

McClure, Brian D. The Bubble. 2006. (Illus.). 64p. (J). 14.95 (978-1-933426-05-1(5)) Universal Flag Publishing.

McGuire, Leslie. My Rattle Book. Bell, Fred, illus. 1999. 12p. (J). 5.95 (978-1-892374-14-1(5)) Weldon Owen, Inc.

McKee, David. Elmer & the Lost Teddy. McKee, David, illus. 1999. (Illus.). 32p. (J). (ps-1). 15.99 (978-0-688-16912-1(0)) HarperCollins Pubs.

—The Monster & the Teddy Bear. 1998. (Illus.). 32p. (J). (ps-1). pap. 9.95 (978-0-86264-762-9(2)) Andersen GBR. *Dist:* Trafalgar Square Publishing.

McMenemy, Sarah. Jack's New Boat. McMenemy, Sarah, illus. 2005. (Illus.). 32p. (J). (ps-k). 15.99 (978-0-7636-2477-4(2)) Candlewick Pr.

McNease, Mitzy. Chester's Presents. Cox, Kim, illus. ed. 2006. 28p. (J). 10.96 (978-0-9779488-0-2(3)) Blancmange Publishing.

McPhail, David M. The Teddy Bear. McPhail, David M., illus. rev. ed. 2002. (Illus.). 32p. (J). (ps-2). 16.95 (978-0-8050-6414-8(1) , Holt, Henry & Co. Bks. For Young Readers) Holt, Henry & Co.

Meet Hook & Ladder. 2001. (Chuck My Talking Truck Ser.). (J). (ps up). bds. 3.95 (978-0-439-27196-7(7) , Cartwheel Bks.) Scholastic, Inc.

Meet the GiggleWings. 2005. (J). bds. 14.99 (978-1-890647-13-1(6)) RC2 Corp.

Miller, Shannon Terry & Warner, Timothy. Tub Toys. Calderon, Lee, illus. 2007. 32p. (J). pap. 6.95 (***978-1-58246-235-6(6)*** , Tricycle Pr.) Ten Speed Pr.

Mills, Elaine. Marinetta at the Ballet. Mills, Elaine, illus. 2001. (Illus.). 27p. (J). (gr. k-2). pap. 9.99 (978-1-84270-000-6(6)) Andersen GBR. *Dist:* Trafalgar Square Publishing.

Milne, A. A. The Complete Tales & Poems of Winnie the Pooh. Shepard, Ernest H., illus. 75th anniv. ed. 2001. 576p. (J). 40.00 (978-0-525-46726-7(2) , Dutton Juvenile) Penguin Group (USA) Inc.

—The Complete Tales of Winnie the Pooh. 70th ed. 1999. (Illus.). 368p. (J). (gr. 4-7). 40.00 (978-0-525-45060-3(2) , Dutton Juvenile) Penguin Group (USA) Inc.

—Disney's Pooh's Treasury of Special Days. Case, Cassandra, ed. 2000. (Illus.). 85p. (J). (978-0-7172-6413-1(0) , Grolier) Scholastic Library Publishing.

—Pooh's First Clock. Shepard, Ernest H., illus. 1998. 12p. (J). (ps-3). bds. 12.99 (978-0-525-45983-5(9) , Dutton Juvenile) Penguin Group (USA) Inc.

—Slide & Seek Alphabet: A Sliding Window Book. 1999. (Illus.). 8p. (J). bds. 10.99 (978-0-7868-3240-8(1)) Disney Pr.

—Slide & Seek Numbers: A Sliding Window Book. 1999. (Illus.). 8p. (J). 10.99 (978-0-7868-3241-5(X)) Disney Pr.

—Tigger Comes to the Forest. 2002. (gr. k-3). lib. bdg. 11.80 (978-0-613-62575-3(7)) Tandem Library Bks.

—Tigger Tales. Shepard, Ernest H., illus. 2006. 36p. (J). (gr. k-4). reprint ed. 15.00 (978-1-4223-5453-7(9)) DIANE Publishing Co.

Milne, A. A. & Krensky, Stephen. Pooh Goes Visiting, Vol. 2. Shepard, Ernest H., illus. 2002. (Puffin-Easy-to-Read Ser.). 48p. (J). pap. 3.99 (978-0-14-230184-5(1) , Puffin) Penguin Group (USA) Inc.

Milne, A.A. The House at Pooh Corner. Shepard, Ernest H., illus. 2007. 180p. (J). (gr. 4). 19.99 (978-0-525-47856-0(6) , Dutton Juvenile) Penguin Group (USA) Inc.

Mitchell, Anastasia, illus. Josh B'Gosh at School. 1998. 10p. (J). 6.99 (978-1-929174-08-9(X)) Oshkosh B'Gosh, Inc.

Mitton, Tony. Amazing Machines Book & Toy Box. Parker, Ant, illus. 2002. 24p. (J). (ps-k). 16.95 (978-0-7534-5563-0(3) , Kingfisher) Houghton Mifflin Co. Trade & Reference Div.

Moody, Betty G. Magical Wish. 1998. (Illus.). (J). 15.95 (978-0-9663522-1-4(1)) Character Lines Publishing.

Moray-Williams, Ursula & Williams, Ursula Moray. The Further Adventures of Gobbolino & the Little Wooden Horse. Howard, Paul, illus. 2002. (Kingfisher Modern Classics Ser.). 240p. (J). (gr. k-3). tchr. ed. 15.95 (978-0-7534-5495-4(5) , Kingfisher) Houghton Mifflin Co. Trade & Reference Div.

Morgan, Allen. Matthew & the Midnight Wrecker. ed. 2004. (Illus.). (J). (gr. k-3). spiral bd. (978-0-616-11123-9(1)) Canadian National Institute for the Blind/Institut National Canadien pour les Aveugles.

—Matthew & the Midnight Wrecker. Martchenko, Michael, illus. 2001. (Matthew's Midnight Adventures Ser.). 32p. (J). 6.99 (978-0-7737-3295-7(0)) Stoddart Kids CAN. *Dist:* Fitzhenry & Whiteside, Ltd.

Morrissey, Dean. The Christmas Ship. 2000. (Illus.). 40p. (J). (gr. k-4). 16.89 (978-0-06-028576-0(1)) HarperCollins Pubs.

—Christmas Ship. 2000. (gr. k-3). lib. bdg. 14.15 (978-0-613-68414-9(1)) Tandem Library Bks.

Morrow, Elizabeth. The Painted Pig: A Mexican Picture Book. D'Harnoncourt, Rene, illus. 2001. 1p. 13.95 (978-0-8263-2769-7(9)) Univ. of New Mexico Pr.

Morton, Lone & Risk, Mary. Goodnight Everyone. Bougard, Marie-Therese, tr. Wood, Jakki, photos by. 1998. (I Can Read Bks.).Tr. of Bonne Nuit a Tous. (ENG & FRE.). (J). (ps up). 9.95 incl. audio (978-0-7641-7188-8(7)) Barron's Educational Series, Inc.

Moscovich, Rotem & Lankford, Raye. Curious George Takes a Trip. 2007. (Illus.). 24p. (J). (ps-k). pap. 3.99 (***978-0-618-88403-2(3)***) Houghton Mifflin Co.

Mouse Works Staff. Disney's Winnie the Pooh's Feelings: Learn & Grow. 2000. (Winnie the Pooh Ser.). (Illus.). 20p. (J). (ps). bds. 4.99 (978-0-7364-1008-3(2) , RH/Disney) Random Hse. Children's Bks.

—Pinocchio - Toy Story, 2. 75th anniv. ed. 1998. 9.99 (978-0-7364-0088-6(5)) Mouse Works.

—Toy Story 2. 1999. (Toy Story 2 Ser.). (Illus.). 10p. (J). (ps-3). 9.99 (978-0-7364-0186-9(5)) Mouse Works.

—Toy Story 2: Find the Flag. 1999. (J). 4.99 (978-0-7364-1042-7(2)) Disney Pr.

—Toy Story 2: Flip. 1999. 96p. (J). 3.99 (978-0-7364-1044-1(9)) Disney Pr.

—Toy Story 2: Let's Play. 1999. 10p. (J). 11.99 (978-0-7364-1043-4(0)) Disney Pr.

—Toy Story 2: Punchout Play. 1999. (J). 8.99 (978-0-7364-0175-3(X)) Mouse Works.

—Toy Story II: Spanish Read. 1999. (SPA., Illus.). 64p. (978-0-7364-0128-9(8)) Mouse Works.

—Toy Story II Green Army Men. 1999. (J). 9.99 (978-0-7364-0174-6(1)) Mouse Works.

Muldrow, Diane. Woody's Round-Up. 1999. (Disney Ser.). (Illus.). 24p. (J). (ps-k). pap. 3.29 (978-0-307-13326-7(5) , Golden Bks.) Random Hse. Children's Bks.

Mullican, Judy. My Toys. Bicking, Judith, illus. l.t. ed. 2005. (Hrl Board Book Ser.). (J). (ps-k). pap. 10.95 (978-1-57332-307-9(1)) HighReach Learning, Inc.

Munoz, Isabel. Eric & Julieta: Now, What?/Ahora Que? Mazali, Gustavo, illus. 2006. (ENG & SPA.). 24p. (J). pap. 3.99 (978-0-439-78372-9(0)) Scholastic, Inc.

My Yo-Yo. Date not set. pap. 3.95 (978-0-89868-294-6(0)) ARO Publishing Co.

Napoli, Donna Jo. On Her Own. 1999. (Angelwings Ser.: No. 3). Orig. Title: Room to Grow. (Illus.). 96p. (J). (gr. 2-5). pap. 7.95 (978-0-689-82985-7(X) , Aladdin) Simon & Schuster Children's Publishing.

—On Her Own. 1999. (Angelwings Ser.: No. 3). Orig. Title: Room to Grow. (Illus.). (J). (978-0-606-17906-5(2)) Tandem Library Bks.

Nash, Scott. Tuff Fluff: The Case of Duckie's Missing Brain. Nash, Scott, illus. 2004. (Illus.). (J). 101.94 (978-0-7636-2503-0(5)) Candlewick Pr.

—Tuff Fluff: The Case of Duckie's Missing Brain. 2004. (Illus.). 40p. (J). (gr. 1-4). 16.99 (978-0-7636-1882-7(9)) Candlewick Pr.

Naylor, Phyllis Reynolds. Please Do Feed the Bears. Escriva, Ana Lopez, illus. 2002. 40p. (J). (ps-2). 16.00 (978-0-689-82561-3(7) , Atheneum) Simon & Schuster Children's Publishing.

Nelson, Delores Privette. Just a Minor Miracle: At the Uncommon Doll. Nelson, Delores Privette, photos by. 2002. (Illus.). 46p. (J). (gr. 1-7). 14.95 (978-0-9714344-0-0(9)) Enchanted Pen Publishing, LLC.

Német, Andreas. Five Little Sleepyheads. Schmidt, Hans-Christian, illus. 2007. 12p. (J). 8.95 (***978-0-7358-2138-5(0)***) North-South Bks., Inc.

Newman, Leslea. A Fire Engine for Ruthie. Moore, Cyd, illus. 2004. 32p. (J). (gr. k-3). tchr. ed. 16.00 (978-0-618-15989-5(4) , Clarion Bks.) Houghton Mifflin Co. Trade & Reference Div.

Nicholas, Christopher. Toy Story 2, Vol. 2. 2006. (Illus.). 24p. (J). (gr. k-k). 2.99 (978-0-7364-2394-6(X) , Golden/Disney) Random Hse. Children's Bks.

The Night Toys Came to Life. 2001. (J). (POL.). bds. (978-1-58805-156-1(0)); (FRE.). bds. (978-1-58805-157-8(9)) DS-Max USA, Inc.

Noisy Toys: Individual Title Six-Packs. (ps-2). 23.00 (978-0-7635-9002-4(9)) Rigby Education.

O'Brien, Sarah. Jacks O'Lantern. 2007. (Illus.). 32p. pap. 6.95 (***978-0-7624-3095-6(8)*** , Running Pr. Minature Editions) Running Pr. Bk. Pubs.

Ogilvy, Ian. Measle & the Dragodon. 2006. 352p. (J). pap. 6.99 (978-0-06-058690-4(7) , Harper Trophy) HarperCollins Pubs.

O'Malley, Kevin. Leo Cockroach... Toy Tester. 2001. (Illus.). (J). (978-0-606-20761-4(9)) Tandem Library Bks.

—Leo Cockroach... Toy Tester. O'Malley, Kevin, illus. 1999. (Illus.). 32p. (J). (gr. k-3). lib. bdg. 16.85 (978-0-8027-8690-6(1)) Walker & Co.

Ong, Christina. Little Engine That Could ABC Time. 2000. (ps-2). lib. bdg. 11.25 (978-0-613-26024-4(4)) Tandem Library Bks.

The Ooshes A Wish Comes True. 2005. (J). (978-1-932233-05-6(9)) Aurora Libris Corp.

The Ooshes the Night Before Christmas. 2004. (J). mass mkt. (978-1-932233-03-2(2)) Aurora Libris Corp.

Oppenheim, Shulamith Levey. I Love You, Bunny Rabbit. Moore, Cyd, illus. 2005. 32p. (J). pap. 7.95 (978-1-59078-337-5(9)) Boyds Mills Pr.

Orman, Roscoe, illus. Ricky & Mobo. 2007. (J). 14.95 (***978-1-59299-255-3(2)***) Inkwater Pr.

Orme, David. Boffin Boy & the Rock Men. 2007. (Boffin Boy Ser.). (Illus.). 36p. pap. 7.95 (***978-1-84167-624-1(1)***) Ransom Publishing Ltd. GBR. *Dist:* International Publishers Marketing.

Osborne, Mary Pope. Rocking Horse Christmas. Bittinger, Ned, illus. 2001. 32p. (J). (gr. 4). pap. 5.99 (978-0-439-30520-4(9)) Scholastic, Inc.

Packard, Mary. The Grand & Wonderful Day. Baker, Darrell, illus. 2000. (Little Golden Bks.). 24p. (J). (ps-2). bds. 2.99 (978-0-307-30263-2(6) , 98737, Golden Bks.) Random Hse. Children's Bks.

The Pajama Party. 1998. (P. B. Bear Ser.). (Illus.). 24p. (J). (ps). 6.95 (978-0-7894-3107-3(6)) Dorling Kindersley Publishing, Inc.

Paradine, Mike. King of Toys. 2006. 83p. pap. 14.95 (978-1-4241-2694-1(0)) PublishAmerica, Inc.

Parent, Nancy. Pooh Says Boo. 1998. (Pooh Ser.). (Illus.). 10p. (J). (ps). 4.99 (978-1-57082-752-5(4)) Mouse Works.

Paxton, Tom. The Marvelous Toy. 2000. (Metro Reading Program Ser.). (J). (gr. k). 7.98 (978-1-58120-970-9(3)); 45.95 (978-1-58830-028-7(5)) Metropolitan Teaching & Learning Co.

Pearlman, Bobby & Gruelle, Johnny. Leaf Dance. Mitter, Kathryn & Winfield, Alison, illus. 2001. (Classic Raggedy Ann & Andy Ser.). 32p. (J). pap. 3.99 (978-0-689-84679-3(7) , Little Simon) Simon & Schuster Children's Publishing.

Pegg, Laura Wittman. The Patch Quilt Pony. 2006. 17.00 (978-0-8059-7346-4(X)) Dorrance Publishing Co., Inc.

Pelletier, Andrew. The Amazing Adventures of Bathman. Elwell, Peter, illus. 2007. 32p. (J). (ps). pap. 5.99 (978-0-14-240776-9(3) , Puffin) Penguin Group (USA) Inc.

Pelletier, Andrew T. The Toy Farmer. Nash, Scott, illus. 2007. 32p. (J). (ps). 16.99 (978-0-525-47649-8(0) , Dutton Juvenile) Penguin Group (USA) Inc.

Piggy Toes Press. Our Ballet Recital. Maddocks, Maria, illus. 2005. 12p. (J). (ps-1). pap. 12.95 (978-1-58117-425-0(X) , Intervisual/Piggy Toes) Dalmatian Pr.

Piggy Toes Press Staff. Baby Bugs' Toys. 2000. (Lovable Huggable Baby Looney Tunes Cloth Bks.). (Illus.). 6p. (J). (ps up). 14.95 (978-1-58117-078-8(5) , Intervisual/Piggy Toes) Dalmatian Pr.

Piper, Watty. The Little Engine That Could. Long, Loren, illus. (J). (ps-3). 2005. 48p. 17.99 (978-0-399-24467-4(0)); 4th ltd. ed. 2006. 32p. 85.00 (978-0-399-24710-1(6)) Penguin Group (USA) Inc. (Philomel).

—The Little Engine That Could: Giant signed Edition. Long, Loren, illus. 2007. 48p. (J) (ps). 250.00 (***978-0-399-25084-2(0)*** , Philomel) Penguin Group (USA) Inc.

Piper, Watty. Meet the Little Engine That Could. 2001. (First Friends, First Readers Ser.). (Illus.). (J). (978-0-606-21324-0(4)) Tandem Library Bks.

Poulsen, Allan. Freezy Breezy Fun. Raymond, Kim, illus. 2000. (Look-Look Bks.). 24p. (J). (ps-3). pap. 3.29 (978-0-307-12891-1(1) , 12891, Golden Bks.) Random Hse. Children's Bks.

Powell, Richard. Puff & the Long Train. Hawksley, Gerald, illus. 2004. (Softy Wheels Ser.). 18p. (J). bds. 8.95 (978-0-7641-7790-3(7)) Barron's Educational Series, Inc.

—Zoom's Finest Hour. Hawksley, Gerald, illus. 2004. (Softy Wheels Ser.). 18p. (J). bds. 8.95 (978-0-7641-7789-7(3)) Barron's Educational Series, Inc.

Poyner, James R. Toy-Maker's Apprentice. 2006. 68p. (YA). per. 12.00 (***978-1-60002-282-1(0)*** , 4145, Airleaf Publishing) Airleaf Publishing & Bookselling.

Prater, John. On Top of the World. 1998. (Illus.). 32p. (J). (ps-2). 15.95 (978-1-57255-649-2(8)) Mondo Publishing.

Price, John. Quest. 2005. 37p. pap. 15.00 (978-1-4116-5649-9(0)) Lulu.com.

Price, Mathew. Tic, Tac Toc. (SPA.). pap. 3.95 (978-950-07-2059-5(0)) Editorial Sudamericana S.A. ARG. *Dist:* Distribooks, Inc.

Rainey, L. E. Sad Sam, Glad Sam. 2006. (Illus.). 32p. (J). 16.95 (978-0-9785521-0-7(5)) Shoetree Publishers, Inc.

Random House Disney Staff. Dream Dance. 2003. (Disney Princess Ser.). (Illus.). 32p. (J). (ps-3). pap. 4.99 (978-0-7364-2118-8(1) , Golden/Disney) Random Hse. Children's Bks.

—Fish in a Box. 2003. (Illus.). 10p. (J). (ps-3). bds. 9.99 (978-0-7364-2154-6(8) , RH/Disney) Random Hse. Children's Bks.

T
U
V

—Ka-Choww!/Blue Ramone. Harchy, Atelier Philippe, illus. 2008. (Pictureback(R) Ser.). 32p. (J). (ps-2). pap. 3.99 (978-0-7364-2404-2(0) , RH/Disney) Random Hse. Children's Bks.

Random House Disney Staff & Muldrow, Diane. Toy Story 2. 2003. (Random House Pictureback Book Ser.). (Illus.). 24p. (J). (gr. k-3). pap. 3.25 (978-0-7364-2129-4(7) , RH/Disney) Random Hse. Children's Bks.

Rau, Dana Meachen. Rubber Duck, Level C. Girouard, Patrick, illus. 2001. (Early Reader Ser.). 32p. (J). (gr. k up). lib. bdg. 18.60 (978-0-7565-0121-1(0)) Compass Point Bks.

Ray, Mary Lyn. All Aboard! Hirao, Amiko & Goodwin-Sturges, illus. 2002. 32p. (J). (ps-3). 14.95 (978-0-316-73507-0(8)) Little, Brown Bks. for Young Readers.

Reader's Digest Staff. Dress-up Fun. 2004. (Barbie Press-on Stick & Stay Ser.). (Illus.). 10p. (J). bds. 9.99 (978-0-7944-0355-3(7) , Reader's Digest Children's Bks.) Reader's Digest Children's Publishing, Inc.

Reed, Patrick. Theodore Elijah Bear Explores the United States. 1998. (Illus.). 40p. (J). pap. 12.00 (978-1-891989-02-5(2)) Fundbuilder$, U.S.A.

Reese, Della. God Inside of Me. Buchanan, Yvonne, illus. 2005. 30p. (J). (gr. 4-8). reprint ed. 16.00 (978-0-7567-9366-1(1)) DIANE Publishing Co.

—God Inside of Me. Buchanan, Yvonne, illus. 1999. 32p. (J). lib. bdg. 16.49 (978-0-7868-2395-6(X) , Jump at the Sun) Hyperion Bks. for Children.

Rey, Margret & Rey, H. A. Curious George Visits a Toy Store. Weston, Martha, illus. 2002. 24p. (J). (gr. k-3). tchr. ed. 12.00 (978-0-618-06398-7(6)) Houghton Mifflin Co. Trade & Reference Div.

Reynolds, Adrian. Pete & Polo's Farmyard Adventure. Reynolds, Adrian, illus. 2002. (Illus.). 32p. (J). (ps-1). pap. 16.95 (978-0-439-30913-4(1) , Orchard Bks.) Scholastic, Inc.

Rickards, Lynne. Jack's Bed. Beardshaw, Rosalind, illus. 2006. (Green Bananas Ser.). 48p. (J). (gr. k-2). pap. (978-0-7787-1044-8(0)) Crabtree Publishing Co.

Riddell, Chris. Platypus & the Birthday Party. 2003. (Platypus Ser.). (Illus.). 32p. (J). 16.00 (978-0-15-204753-5(0)) Harcourt Children's Bks.

Robinson, Sue. Bear in the Barnyard. Morris, Tony, illus. 2004. 28p. (J). 16.00 (978-1-56148-430-0(X)) Good Bks.

Rogers, Kenny & Junkerman, Kelly. Kenny Rogers Presents the Toy Shoppe. 2004. (Illus.). 30p. (J). (gr. 4-8). reprint ed. 16.00 (978-0-7567-7758-6(5)) DIANE Publishing Co.

Romano, Ralph & Burke, Joe. Elbo Elf: The Package Master of Christmas. l.t. ed. 2000. (Illus.). 29p. (J). (gr. 1-5). 19.95 (978-0-9704125-0-8(9)) Elbo Elf, Inc.

Roper, Robert, illus. Dolls of Danger. 2005. (Ready-To-Read Ser.). 32p. (J). pap. 3.99 (978-0-689-87722-3(6) , Simon Spotlight) Simon & Schuster Children's Publishing.

Rowe, Jeannette, illus. YoYo's Toys. 2002. 10p. (J). 3.95 (978-1-58925-684-2(0) , tiger tales) ME Media LLC.

Ryherd, Tim. My Hurricane Book. 2006. (J). 12.95 (978-0-9749974-1-4(2)) Ryherd, Tim Publishing.

Rylant, Cynthia. Little Whistle. Bowers, Tim, illus. 2007. (J). 96.84 ***(*978-1-59961-252-2(6));*** 32p. 24.21 ***(*978-1-59961-253-9(4))*** Spotlight.

—Little Whistle's Christmas. Bowers, Tim, illus. 2003. (Little Whistle Ser.). 32p. (J). 16.00 (978-0-15-204590-6(2)) Harcourt Children's Bks.

—Little Whistle's Christmas. Bowers, Tim, illus. 2007. 32p. (J). 24.21 ***(*978-1-59961-254-6(2))*** Spotlight.

—Little Whistle's Dinner Party. Bowers, Tim, illus. 2004. 32p. (J). pap. 6.00 (978-0-15-205062-7(0) , Voyager Bks./Libros Viajeros) Harcourt Children's Bks.

—Little Whistle's Dinner Party. Bowers, Tim, illus. 2007. 32p. (J). 24.21 ***(*978-1-59961-255-3(0))*** Spotlight.

—Little Whistle's Medicine. Bowers, Tim, illus. 2002. (Little Whistle Ser.). 32p. (J). (ps-2). 15.00 (978-0-15-201086-7(6)) Harcourt Children's Bks.

—Little Whistle's Medicine. Bowers, Tim, illus. 2007. 32p. (J). 24.21 ***(*978-1-59961-256-0(9))*** Spotlight.

Rylant, Cynthia. Mr. Putter & Tabby Fly the Plane. Howard, Arthur, illus. 2002. (Mr. Putter & Tabby Ser.). (J). 13.15 (978-0-7587-0681-2(2)) Book Wholesalers, Inc.

Safari Playset. 2007. 48p. pap. 3.99 ***(*978-1-4037-2202-7(1))*** Dalmatian Pr.

Salzmann, Mary Elizabeth. Here Are Toys! (First Words Ser.). (Illus.). 23p. (J). (ps-3). 2006. 19.93 (978-1-59679-374-3(0) , SandCastle); 2005. pap. (978-1-59679-375-0(9)) ABDO Publishing Co.

Samarrippas, Gloria. In Search for Lucky's Lost Toys. 2006. 17.00 ***(*978-0-8059-7329-7(X))*** Dorrance Publishing Co., Inc.

San Souci, Robert D. Zigzag. Czernecki, Stefan, illus. 2005. 32p. (gr. 9). 16.95 (978-0-87483-764-3(2)) August Hse. Pubs., Inc.

Sanschagrin, Joceline. El Osito de Peluche. 2004. (Caillou Osa Menor Sr.).Tr. of Where's Teddy?. (SPA., Illus.). 24p. (J). (ps up). bds. 5.95 (978-1-58728-404-5(9) , Creative Publishing International) Quayside.

Santillo, LuAnn. The Ball. Santillo, LuAnn, ed. 2003. (Half-Pint Kids Readers Ser.). (Illus.). 7p. (J). (ps-1). pap. (978-1-59256-081-3(4)) Half-Pint Kids, Inc.

Saxon, Victoria. Tigger's Tall Tales: Chuncky Roly Poly Book. 1999. (Learn & Grow Ser.). (Illus.). 16p. (J). (ps-k). 3.50 (978-0-7364-0153-1(9)) Mouse Works.

Schneider, Christine. I'm Bored. Pinel, Herve, illus. 2006. 40p. (J). (ps-k). 15.00 (978-0-618-65760-5(6) , Clarion Bks.) Houghton Mifflin Co. Trade & Reference Div.

Scholastic, Inc. Staff. Clifford the Big Red Dog with Cleo & T-Bone Finger Puppets. 2002. (Sidekicks Ser.). (Illus.). (J). 12.99 (978-0-439-38814-6(7) , Sidekicks TM) Scholastic, Inc.

—Clifford with Emily Elizabeth on His Back. 2002. (Sidekicks Ser.). (J). 24.99 (978-0-439-38815-3(5) , Sidekicks TM) Scholastic, Inc.

—Emily Elizabeth Playwear: Back-to-School Outfit. 2002. (Sidekicks Ser.). (J). 12.99 (978-0-439-38811-5(2) , Sidekicks TM) Scholastic, Inc.

—Emily Elizabeth Playwear: Ballerina Outfit. 2002. (Sidekicks Ser.). (J). 12.99 (978-0-439-38812-2(0) , Sidekicks TM) Scholastic, Inc.

—Emily Elizabeth Playwear - Jogging Outfit. 2002. (Sidekicks Ser.). (J). 12.99 (978-0-439-36577-2(5) , Sidekicks TM) Scholastic, Inc.

—Emily Elizabeth Wardrobe Box. 2003. (Sidekicks Ser.). (J). 24.99 (978-0-439-46688-2(1) , Sidekicks TM) Scholastic, Inc.

—Gingerbread Man Activity Developmental Toy. 2004. (Sidekicks Ser.). (J). 16.99 (978-0-439-62729-0(X) , Sidekicks TM) Scholastic, Inc.

—Gingerbread Man Attachable Toy. 2004. (Sidekicks Ser.). (J). 7.99 (978-0-439-63535-6(7) , Sidekicks TM) Scholastic, Inc.

—Gingerbread Man Security Blanket. 2004. (Sidekicks Ser.). (J). 14.99 (978-0-439-62337-7(5) , Sidekicks TM) Scholastic, Inc.

—Hudson Beanbag. 2003. (J). 8.99 (978-0-439-29695-3(1) , Sidekicks TM) Scholastic, Inc.

—Humpty Dumpty Activity Developmental Toy. 2004. (Sidekicks Ser.). (J). 16.99 (978-0-439-64495-2(X) , Sidekicks TM) Scholastic, Inc.

—Humpty Dumpty Attachable Toy. 2004. (Sidekicks Ser.). (J). 8.99 (978-0-439-64281-1(7) , Sidekicks TM) Scholastic, Inc.

—Humpty Dumpty Plush. 1998. (Sidekicks Ser.). (J). 16.99 (978-0-590-03421-0(9) , Sidekicks TM) Scholastic, Inc.

—Humpty Dumpty Ring Rattle (12 Count) 2004. (Sidekicks Ser.). (J). 83.88 (978-0-439-63153-2(X) , Sidekicks TM) Scholastic, Inc.

—I Spy Animals Wooden Shape Sorter. 2003. (Sidekicks Ser.). (J). 24.99 (978-0-439-46134-4(0) , Sidekicks TM) Scholastic, Inc.

—Liz Beanbag. 2003. (Sidekicks Ser.). (J). 8.99 (978-0-590-11852-1(8) , Sidekicks TM) Scholastic, Inc.

—Liz Plush. 2003. (J). 14.99 (978-0-590-10984-0(7) , Sidekicks TM) Scholastic, Inc.

—Mr Magorium's Wonder Emporium: Movie Reader. 2007. (Mr. Magorium's Wonder Emporium Ser.). 32p. (J). pap. 3.99 ***(*978-0-545-00516-6(7)*** , Scholastic en Espanol) Scholastic, Inc.

—Poppleton Plush. 2004. (J). 14.99 (978-0-439-29620-5(X) , Sidekicks TM) Scholastic, Inc.

—Poseable Emily Elizabeth. 2002. (Sidekicks Ser.). (J). 19.99 (978-0-439-38813-9(9) , Sidekicks TM) Scholastic, Inc.

—Stellaluna Backpack. 1999. (J). 29.99 (978-0-439-09819-9(X) , Sidekicks TM) Scholastic, Inc.

—Stellaluna Beanbag. 1999. (J). 8.99 (978-0-439-09818-2(1)) Scholastic, Inc.

—Stellaluna Large Hand Puppet. 1999. (J). 19.99 (978-0-439-09821-2(1) , Sidekicks TM) Scholastic, Inc.

Scholastic, Inc. Staff & Tonka Corporation Staff, contrib. by. Meet Pat the Patrol Car. 2001. (Tonka Ser.). (Illus.). 10p. (J). (ps up). pap. 3.95 (978-0-439-31820-4(3) , Cartwheel Bks.) Scholastic, Inc.

Schories, Pat. Jack & the Missing Piece. 2004. (Illus.). 32p. (J). 13.95 (978-1-932425-17-8(9) , Lemniscaat) Boyds Mills Pr.

Schotter, Roni. Missing Rabbit. Moore, Cyd, illus. 2002. 32p. (J). (gr. k-ps). 15.00 (978-0-618-03432-1(3) , Clarion Bks.) Houghton Mifflin Co. Trade & Reference Div.

—Room for Rabbit. Moore, Cyd, illus. 2003. 32p. (J). (gr. k-ps). tchr. ed. 15.00 (978-0-618-18183-4(0) , Clarion Bks.) Houghton Mifflin Co. Trade & Reference Div.

Scraper, Katherine. Tag Sale Today. 2005. 40.00 ***(*978-1-4108-4210-7(X))*** Benchmark Education Co.

Shannon, Terry Miller & Warner, Tim. Tub Toys. Calderon, Lee, illus. 2004. 30p. (J). (gr. k-2). 14.95 (978-1-58246-066-6(3) , Tricycle Pr.) Ten Speed Pr.

Shealy, Dennis R. & Random House Disney Staff. Going Buggy. Alvin and Associates, Inc. Staff, illus. 2002. 24p. (J). (gr. k-k). pap. 3.25 (978-0-7364-1173-8(9) , RH/Disney) Random Hse. Children's Bks.

Shepherd, Jodie. Merry Christmas, Rarity! Fletcher, Lyn, illus. 2006. (My Little Pony Ser.). 32p. (J). pap., act. bk. ed. 3.99 (978-0-06-079472-9(0) , Harper Festival) HarperCollins Pubs.

Si, Artists, illus. Playtime for Baby Strawberry. 2006. (Strawberry Shortcake Baby Ser.). 10p. (J). (ps-ps). bds. 5.99 (978-0-448-44358-4(9) , Grosset & Dunlap) Penguin Group (USA) Inc.

Silver Dolphin en Español Editors. Figuras Magicas: Disney Princesses Magical Magnets. 2005. (SPA., Illus.). 8p. (J). bds. 12.95 (978-970-718-241-7(5) , Silver Dolphin en Español) Advanced Marketing, S. de R. L. de C. V. MEX. *Dist:* Perseus Distribution.

—Figuras Magicas: Disney Winnie the Pooh Magical Magnets. 2005. (SPA., Illus.). 8p. (J). bds. 12.95 (978-970-718-243-1(1) , Silver Dolphin en Español) Advanced Marketing, S. de R. L. de C. V. MEX. *Dist:* Perseus Distribution.

Simmons, Andrew. Bad Bart Was Here. 2001. (Woody's Roundup Ser.: Bk. 8). 64p. (gr. 2-5). reprint ed. pap. 4.99 (978-0-7868-4459-3(0)) Disney Pr.

—Bullseye Express. 2001. (Woody's Roundup Ser.: Bk. 5). (Illus.). 64p. (gr. 2-5). reprint ed. pap. 4.99 (978-0-7868-4457-9(4)) Disney Pr.

Simonson, Audrey. Where Is Your Mousey? 2006. (ENG.). 40p. per. 22.65 ***(*978-1-4134-0270-4(4))*** Xlibris Corp.

Slonim, David. Oh, Ducky: A Chocolate Calamity. Slonim, David, illus. 2006. (Illus.). 36p. (J). pap. 6.95 (978-0-8118-5227-2(X)) Chronicle Bks. LLC.

—Oh, Ducky! A Chocolate Calamity. Slonim, David, illus. 2006. (Illus.). 28p. (J). (gr. k-4). 16.00 (978-1-4223-5259-5(5)) DIANE Publishing Co.

Smallman, Steve. Bumbletum. Warnes, Tim, illus. 2006. 32p. (J). 15.95 (978-1-58925-060-4(5) , tiger tales) ME Media LLC.

Smith, Maggie. Paisley. 2004. (Illus.). 40p. (J). (gr. k-3). 15.95 (978-0-375-82164-6(3)); lib. bdg. 17.99 (978-0-375-92164-3(8)) Random Hse. Children's Bks. (Knopf Bks. for Young Readers).

Spilny, Yuri. River of Fire. Schreiber, Catherine, ed. Balzhak, Anna & Balzhak, Nadezhda, illus. 1998. (Incredible Adventures of Kitto Ser.: Vol. 3). 52p. (J). (gr. 3-6). pap. 12.95 (978-1-892316-02-8(1)) Rama Pr., Inc.

—Sorceress's Spell. Schreiber, Catherine, ed. Balzhak, Anna & Balzhak, Nadezhda, illus. 1998. (Incredible Adventures of Kitto Ser.: Vol. 1). 48p. (J). (gr. 3-6). pap. 12.95 (978-1-892316-00-4(5)) Rama Pr., Inc.

—The Toynapers. Schreiber, Catherine, ed. Balzhak, Anna & Balzhak, Nadezhda, illus. 1998. (Incredible Adventures of Kitto Ser.: Vol. 2). 52p. (J). (gr. 3-6). pap. 12.95 (978-1-892316-01-1(3)) Rama Pr., Inc.

Spinelli, Eileen. Bath Time. Pedersen, Janet, illus. 2003. 32p. (J). 14.95 (978-0-7614-5117-4(X)) Cavendish, Marshall Corp.

Spohn, Kate. Mermaid Swim. 2002. (ps-2). lib. bdg. 14.15 (978-0-613-86240-0(6)) Tandem Library Bks.

Sprunger, Reed, photos by. The Velveteen Rabbit. 1998. (Illus.). 32p. (J). (ps-1). 12.99 (978-1-929174-01-0(2)) Oshkosh B'Gosh, Inc.

Steele, Michael Anthony. Mr. Magorium's Wonder Emporium: Magical Movie Storybook. 2007. (Mr. Magorium's Wonder Emporium Ser.). 48p. (J). pap. 8.99 ***(*978-0-439-91252-5(0))*** Scholastic, Inc.

Steinbrenner, Jessica. My Messy Room. 2007. (Illus.). 32p. pap. 14.95 ***(*978-1-59687-854-9(1)*** , Milk & Cookies) ibooks, Inc.

Stevenson, James. Night after Christmas. 2003. (J). pap. 2.95 (978-0-590-41600-9(6)) Scholastic, Inc.

Straight, Susan. The Friskative Dog. 2007. 160p. (J). (gr. 3-7). 14.99 (978-0-375-83777-7(9)); lib. bdg. 17.99 (978-0-375-93777-4(3)) Random Hse. Children's Bks. (Knopf Bks. for Young Readers).

Suben, Eric. Toy Story 2. 1999. (Disney Ser.). (Illus.). 24p. (J). (ps-3). pap. 3.29 (978-0-307-13254-3(4) , Golden Bks.) Random Hse. Children's Bks.

Talkington, Bruce. Winnie the Pooh's Valentine Mini. 1998. (Illus.). 32p. (J). 11.95 (978-0-7868-3201-9(0)) Disney Pr.

Taylor, Marshall, illus. & photos by. Adventures of Cow, Too. Taylor, Marshall, photos by. 2007. 32p. (J). (ps-1). 12.95 (978-1-58246-189-2(9) , Tricycle Pr.) Ten Speed Pr.

Teitelbaum, Michael. If I Could Drive a Crane! Klavins, Uldis & Walker, Jeff, illus. 2002. (Tonka Ser.). 24p. (J). (ps-3). pap. 3.50 (978-0-439-34174-5(4) , Cartwheel Bks.) Scholastic, Inc.

Thompson, Lisa. Game Plan. Thompson, Lisa & Stapleton, Matthew, illus. 2005. (Read-It! Chapter Bks.). 48p. (J). (ps-k). lib. bdg. 19.95 (978-1-4048-1344-1(6)) Picture Window Bks.

Thorpe, Kiki. No Cowgirls Allowed! 2001. (Woody's Roundup Ser.: Bk. 7). (Illus.). 64p. (gr. 2-5). reprint ed. pap. 4.99 (978-0-7868-4460-9(4)) Disney Pr.

Tigger's Bouncy Day. 2000. (Giant Pooh Book Ends Ser.). (Illus.). 10p. (J). (ps). (978-1-57584-808-2(2)) Reader's Digest Children's Publishing, Inc.

Tina's Toys: Big Book. 2005. (Emergent Library: Vol. 1). (YA). (ps-1). 23.94 (978-0-8215-8903-8(2)) Sadlier, William H. Inc.

Toast, Sarah & Milne, A. A. Piglet's Not So Small Snowball. Williams, Don, illus. 2002. (Disney's Winnie the Pooh Ser.). (J). (978-0-7853-7617-0(8)) Publications International, Ltd.

Tootin' Around Town. (Magnets on the Move Ser.). 8p. (J). bds. (978-2-7643-0101-2(4)) Phidal Publishing, Inc./ Editions Phidal, Inc.

Tosten, S. Kennedy. Troy's Amazing Universe Bk. 2: T for Toy. 2004. (Illus.). 149p. (YA). (gr. 2 up). pap. 13.95 (978-0-9743185-1-6(5)) Brite Pr.

Toy Box Innovations, creator. Disney/Pixar 2: Volume 2. abr. ed. 2006. (Disney's Read along Collection Ser.). (J). (ps-3). pap. 14.99 incl. audio compact disk (978-0-7634-2181-6(2)) Walt Disney Records.

Toy Story 2: Seek & See General Mills. 1999. (Toy Story 2 Ser.). (J). 3.99 (978-0-7364-0914-8(9)) Mouse Works.

Toy Story 2 Read Along. 1999. (J). (ps-3). pap. 6.98 incl. audio (978-0-7634-0535-9(3)) Walt Disney Records.

Toy Town: Individual Title Six-Packs. (ps-2). 23.00 (978-0-7635-9003-1(7)) Rigby Education.

Toybox Innovations. Disney Pixar's Toy Story. 2006. (Disney's Read Along Ser.). (Illus.). (J). (ps-3). audio compact disk 7.99 (978-0-7634-2179-3(0)) Walt Disney Records.

Tripathi, Namrata. Eight Little Ponies. LoRaso, Carlo, illus. 2003. (My Little Pony Ser.). 18p. (J). (ps-1). 6.99 (978-0-06-055401-9(0) , Harper Festival) HarperCollins Pubs.

—Meet the Ponies. LoRaso, Carlo, illus. 2003. (My Little Pony Ser.). 18p. (J). (ps-1). bds. 6.99 (978-0-06-055402-6(9) , Harper Festival) HarperCollins Pubs.

Try Again, Emma: Individual Title Six-Pack Pouch - Level J. (Lighthouse Ser.). 16p. (gr. 2 up). 28.00 (978-0-7578-0859-3(X)) Rigby Education.

The Velveteen Rabbit. 2002. (Puppy Tales Ser.). (Illus.). 24p. (J). (gr. k-3). 1.49 (978-1-57759-257-0(3)) Dalmatian Pr.

The Velveteen Rabbit. 2003. (J). 9.99 (978-0-9740847-3-2(5)) GiGi Bks.

Vulliamy, Clara. Small. 2002. (Illus.). 32p. (J). (gr. k-ps). 15.00 (978-0-618-19459-9(2) , Clarion Bks.) Houghton Mifflin Co. Trade & Reference Div.

Vv. Las Cosas Del Cuarto de Baño. (SPA.). 24p. 7.95 (978-84-488-1110-5(0)) Beascoa, Ediciones S.A. ESP. *Dist:* Distribooks, Inc.

Waddell, Martin. Tom Rabbit. Firth, Barbara, illus. 2006. 32p. (J). (ps-1). pap. 6.99 (978-0-7636-2879-6(4)) Candlewick Pr.

—When the Teddy Bears Came. 1998. (J). (978-0-606-13908-3(7)) Tandem Library Bks.

Wahl, Jan. Mabel Ran Away with the Toys. Woodruff, Liza, illus. 2000. 32p. (J). (ps-3). 16.95 (978-1-58089-059-5(8)); pap. 6.95 (978-1-58089-067-0(9)) Charlesbridge Publishing, Inc.

—Mabel Ran Away with the Toys. 2000. (gr. k-3). lib. bdg. 15.25 (978-0-613-35177-5(0)) Tandem Library Bks.

Wang, Adria. My World: My Playtimes Toys. Nicholls, Paul, illus. 2005. 10p. (J). 4.95 (978-1-58117-250-8(8) , Intervisual/Piggy Toes) Dalmatian Pr.

Ward, Helen. Twenty-five December Lane. Anderson, Wayne, illus. 2007. 17p. (J). ***(*978-1-74178-722-1(X))*** Five Mile Pr. Pty Ltd. The.

Watt, F. & Wells, R. That's Not My Dolly. 2004. 10p. (J). 7.95 (978-0-7945-0635-3(6)) EDC Publishing.

Wax, Wendy. Valentine for Tommy. 2003. (gr. k-3). lib. bdg. 11.80 (978-0-613-57563-8(6)) Tandem Library Bks.

Wells, Rosemary. Bunny Party. 2003. (Max & Ruby Ser.). (Illus.). 24p. (J). (ps-k). pap. 5.99 (978-0-14-250162-7(X) , Puffin) Penguin Group (USA) Inc.

—Bunny Party. Wells, Rosemary, illus. 2001. (Max & Ruby Ser.). (Illus.). 32p. (J). (gr. k-2). 15.99 (978-0-670-03501-4(7) , Viking Juvenile) Penguin Group (USA) Inc.

—Play with Max & Ruby. 2002. (ps-2). lib. bdg. 11.80 (978-0-613-64094-7(2)) Tandem Library Bks.

Weninger, Brigitte. Good Night, Nori. Bishop, Kathryn, tr. from GER. Yonezu, Yusuke, illus. 2007. 32p. (J). (ps-2). 15.99 ***(*978-0-698-40065-8(8)*** , Minedition) Penguin Group (USA) Inc.

Weston, Martha, illus. Curious George Visits a Toy Store. 2002. 24p. (J). (gr. k-3). pap. 3.95 (978-0-618-06570-7(9)) Houghton Mifflin Co. Trade & Reference Div.

Whybrow, Ian. Harry & the Bucketful of Dinosaurs. Reynolds, Adrian, illus. 2003. (Harry & the Dinosaurs Ser.). 32p. (J). (ps-3). 14.95 (978-0-375-82541-5(X) , Random Hse. Bks. for Young Readers) Random Hse. Children's Bks.

—Harry & the Dinosaurs at the Museum. Reynolds, Adrian, illus. 2005. 32p. (J). (ps-2). 15.95 (978-0-375-83338-0(2) , Random Hse. Bks. for Young Readers) Random Hse. Children's Bks.

—Harry & the Dinosaurs Go to School. Reynolds, Adrian, illus. 2007. 32p. (J). (ps-2). 15.99 (978-0-375-84180-4(6) , Random Hse. Bks. for Young Readers) Random Hse. Children's Bks.

—Harry & the Dinosaurs Say "Raahh!" Reynolds, Adrian, illus. 2004. 32p. (J). (ps-3). 14.95 (978-0-375-82542-2(8) , Random Hse. Bks. for Young Readers) Random Hse. Children's Bks.

—Sammy & the Dinosaurs. Reynolds, Adrian, illus. 1999. 32p. (J). (ps-1). pap. 15.95 (978-0-531-30207-1(5) , Orchard Bks.) Scholastic, Inc.

—Sammy & the Dinosaurs: Deluxe Gift Set. Reynolds, Adrian, illus. 2000. (J). (ps-3). 14.95 (978-0-531-30337-5(3) , Orchard Bks.) Scholastic, Inc.

—Sammy & the Robots. Reynolds, Adrian, illus. 2001. 32p. (J). (ps-1). pap. 15.95 (978-0-531-30327-6(6) , Orchard Bks.) Scholastic, Inc.

Wick, Walter. Seymour Makes New Friends. Wick, Walter, illus. 2006. (Can You See What I See Ser.). (Illus.). 32p. (J). (ps-k). pap. 8.99 (978-0-439-61780-2(4)) Scholastic, Inc.

Willems, Mo. Knuffle Bunny Too: A Case of Mistaken Identity. Willems, Mo, illus. rev. ed. 2007. (Illus.). 48p. (J). (ps-1). 16.99 ***(*978-1-4231-0299-1(1))*** Hyperion Pr.

Williams, Karen Lynn. Galimoto. Stock, Catherine, illus. unabr. ed. 2001. (J). (gr. k-3). pap. 16.90 incl. audio (978-0-8045-6845-6(6) , 6845) Spoken Arts, Inc.

Williams, Margery. The Velveteen Rabbit. Felix, Monique, illus. 2005. 40p. pap. 8.95 (978-0-89812-383-8(6)) Creative Co., The.

—The Velveteen Rabbit. Kliros, Thea, illus. 2004. 22p. (J). (ps-1). bds. 5.99 (978-0-06-052746-4(3) , Harper Festival) HarperCollins Pubs.

—The Velveteen Rabbit. (J). 2006. 32p. pap. 3.95 (978-0-8249-5530-4(7) , Ideals Children's Bks.); 2000. (Illus.). bds. 6.95 (978-0-8249-4173-4(5)) Ideals Pubns.

—The Velveteen Rabbit. Nicholson, William, illus. 44p. (J). (gr. 2-3). pap. 3.50 (978-0-8072-1346-9(2) , Listening Library) Random Hse. Audio Publishing Group.

—The Velveteen Rabbit. Daily, Don, illus. 2007. 28p. (J). pap. 5.95 (978-0-7624-2935-6(6) , Running Pr. Kids) Running Pr. Bk. Pubs.

—The Velveteen Rabbit. 2007. (J). 18.95 ***(*978-0-545-00512-8(4))*** Scholastic, Inc.

—The Velveteen Rabbit. Johnson, Steve & Fancher, Lou, illus. 2002. 32p. (J). (ps-2). reprint ed. 17.99 (978-0-689-84134-7(5) , Atheneum/Anne Schwartz Bks.) Simon & Schuster Children's Publishing.

—The Velveteen Rabbit. Jorgensen, David, illus. 2006. (J). (gr. 2-6). 25.65 (978-1-59197-757-5(6)) Spotlight.

—The Velveteen Rabbit. Hague, Michael, illus. 2008. 48p. (J). pap. 7.99 ***(*978-0-312-37750-2(9))*** Square Fish.

Williams, Margery & Daily, Don. The Classic Tale of the Velveteen Rabbit. 2007. 56p. 9.98 ***(*978-0-7624-3023-9(0)*** , Courage Bks.) Running Pr. Bk. Pubs.

Williams, Sam. Santa's Toys. Gill, Tim, illus. 2003. 14p. bds. (978-1-85602-274-3(9)) Chrysalis Children's Bks.

Wilson, Karma. Princess Me. Unzner-Fischer, Christa, illus. 2007. 32p. (J). (ps-2). 16.99 (978-1-4169-4098-2(7) , McElderry, Margaret K.) Simon & Schuster Children's Publishing.

Winnie the Pooh & a Day for Eeyore, (Read-Along Ser.). (J). 7.99 incl. audio (978-1-55723-176-5(1)) Walt Disney Records.

Wojtowycz, David, illus. Whatever the Weather, Clavde! 2004. 10p. (J). (ps-2). reprint ed. 8.00 (978-0-7567-8257-3(0)) DIANE Publishing Co.

Wynne-Jones, Tim. Architect of the Moon. Wallace, Ian, illus. 1998. (J). (ps-2). pap. 5.95 (978-0-88899-150-8(9) , Libros Tigrillo) Groundwood Bks. CAN. *Dist:* Transition Vendor.

—Architect of the Moon. 1998. (ps-2). lib. bdg. 14.10 (978-0-613-88548-5(1)) Tandem Library Bks.

Yoon, Salina. Toys. 2005. 6p. (J). (ps-1). bds. 3.99 (978-0-8431-1367-9(7) , Price Stern Sloan) Penguin Group (USA) Inc.

Yorinks, Arthur. Harry & Lulu. braille ed. 2004. (Illus.). (J). (gr. k-3). spiral bd. (978-0-616-07249-3(X)); spiral bd. (978-0-616-07250-9(3)) Canadian National Institute for the Blind/Institut National Canadien pour les Aveugles.

—Harry & Lulu. Matje, Martin, illus. 2020. 32p. (J). pap. 4.99 (978-0-7868-1221-9(4)) Hyperion Paperbacks for Children.

Young, James. My Bunny. 1999. (Read with Me Paperback Ser.). (Illus.). 32p. (J). (ps-1). pap. 3.25 (978-0-590-18375-8(3)) Scholastic, Inc.

Ziefert, Harriet. Clara Ann Cookie, Go to Bed! Bolam, Emily, illus. 2000. 32p. (J). (gr. k-3). tchr. ed. 15.00 (978-0-395-97381-3(3) , Walter Lorraine) Houghton Mifflin Co. Trade & Reference Div.

Zoehfeld, Kathleen Weidner. Don't Talk to Strangers, Pooh! 2000. (My Very First Winnie the Pooh Ser.). (Illus.). 32p. (J). (ps-k). pap. 4.99 (978-0-7868-4378-7(0)) Disney Pr.

—Pooh's Favorite Things about Spring. 2000. (My Very First Winnie the Pooh Ser.). (Illus.). 32p. (J). (ps-k). 12.99 (978-0-7868-3251-4(7)) Disney Pr.

—Pooh's Jingle Bells. (Illus.). 32p. (J). (ps-k). 2000. pap. 4.99 (978-0-7868-4419-7(1)); 1998. 11.95 (978-0-7868-3204-0(5)) Disney Pr.

—Roo's New Babysitter. 1999. (My Very First Winnie the Pooh Ser.). (Illus.). 32p. (J). (ps-k). 11.99 (978-0-7868-3215-6(0)) Disney Pr.

—Tigger's Moving Day. 1999. (My Very First Winnie the Pooh Ser.). (Illus.). 32p. (J). (ps-k). 11.99 (978-0-7868-3225-5(8)) Disney Pr.

—Toy Story 2: Buzz's Book Club Edition. 1999. 48p. (J). 10.99 (978-0-7868-4391-6(8)) Disney Pr.

—Who's Afraid of a Heffalump? 1999. (Learn & Grow Ser.). (Illus.). 14p. (J). (ps-k). 5.99 (978-0-7364-0111-1(3)) Mouse Works.

Zoehfeld, Kathleen Weidner & Milne, A. A. Don't Talk to Strangers, Pooh! Cuddy, Robbin, illus. 1998. (My Very First Winnie the Pooh Ser.). 32p. (J). (ps). pap. 11.95 (978-0-7868-3145-6(6)) Disney Pr.

Zolotow, Charlotte. Growing up Stories for 5-6 Year Olds. 2020. 114p. (J). (ps-17). 19.99 (978-0-7868-0519-8(6)) Disney Pr.

Zuber, Diane. The Broken Doll. Firtle, Mary, illus. 2006. 32p. (J). 17.95 (978-0-9785551-1-5(2)) Zuber Publishing.

TOYS—POETRY

Stevenson, Robert Louis. Block City. Kirk, Daniel, illus. 2005. (J). (***978-1-4156-2160-8(8)*** , Simon & Schuster Children's Publishing) Simon & Schuster Children's Publishing.

TRACK ATHLETICS

see also Walking

Boast, Clare. Field. 1998. (Olympic Library). (J). pap. (978-1-57572-038-8(8)) Heinemann Library.

Christopher, Matt. Run for It. 2002. (#1 Sports Series for Kids). 128p. (J). (gr. 2-4). pap. 4.50 (978-0-316-34914-7(3)) Little, Brown Bks. for Young Readers.

—Run for It. 2002. (gr. 3-6). lib. bdg. 12.40 (978-0-613-50638-0(3)) Tandem Library Bks.

Cox, Vicki. Marion Jones. 2001. (Women Who Win Ser.). (J). pap. (978-0-7910-6534-1(0)); (Illus.). 64p. (gr. 3 up). 25.00 (978-0-7910-6533-4(2)) Facts On File, Inc. (Chelsea Hse.).

Crossingham, John & Kalman, Bobbie. Track Events in Action. Rouse, Bonna, illus. 2004. (Sports in Action Ser.). 32p. (J). (978-0-7787-0339-6(8)) Crabtree Publishing Co.

—Track Events in Action. 2004. (Sports in Action Ser.). (Illus.). 32p. (J). pap. (978-0-7787-0359-4(2)) Crabtree Publishing Co.

Feldman, Heather. Marion Jones: World-Class Runner. 2001. (Reading Power Ser.). (Illus.). 24p. (J). (gr. 1). lib. bdg. 17.25 (978-0-8239-5718-7(7) , PKMAJO, PowerKids Pr.) Rosen Publishing Group, Inc., The.

—Marion Jones, Atleta de Categoria Internacional. 2002. (Coleccion Power Kids). (SPA & ENG., Illus.). 24p. (J). (gr. k-2). lib. bdg. 17.25 (978-0-8239-6141-2(9) , RN31310, Buenas Letra) Rosen Publishing Group, Inc., The.

Fleming, Sally. Rapid Runners. Underwood, Kay Povelite, illus. 2004. (It's Nature! Ser.). 32p. (J). (gr. 3-6). pap. 7.95 (978-1-55971-789-2(0) , NorthWord Bks. for Young Readers) T&N Children's Publishing.

—Rapid Runners. 2001. (gr. 3-6). lib. bdg. 16.40 (978-0-613-55886-0(3)) Tandem Library Bks.

Gifford, Clive. A World-Class Sprinter. 2004. (Making of a Champion Ser.). (J). pap. 8.50 (978-1-4034-5537-6(6)); lib. bdg. 27.07 (978-1-4034-4669-5(5)) Heinemann Library.

Griffis, Molly Levite. Great American Bunion Derby. 2003. (Illus.). viii, 87p. (J). 15.95 (978-1-57168-801-9(3) , Eakin Pr.) Eakin Pr.

Hayhurst, Chris. Ultra Marathon Running. 2002. (Ultra Sports Ser.). (Illus.). 64p. (YA). (gr. 5-8). lib. bdg. 26.50 (978-0-8239-3557-4(4) , Rosen Central) Rosen Publishing Group, Inc., The.

Housewright, Ed. Winning Track & Field for Girls. 2003. (Winning Sports for Girls Ser.). (Illus.). 208p. (YA). (gr. 9-12). pap. 16.95 (978-0-8160-5232-5(8) , Checkmark Bks.); (gr. 6-12). 35.00 (978-0-8160-5231-8(X)) Facts On File, Inc.

Hughes, Morgan. The Jumps. 1999. (Illus.). 48p. (J). (gr. 4-8). lib. bdg. 27.93 (978-1-57103-290-4(8)) Rourke Publishing, LLC.

—Training & Fitness. 1999. (Illus.). 48p. (J). lib. bdg. 27.93 (978-1-57103-293-5(2)) Rourke Publishing, LLC.

Kalman, Bobbie. Field Events in Action. Crabtree, Marc & Rouse, Bonna, illus. Crabtree, Marc, photos by. 2004. (Sports in Action Ser.). 32p. (J). (978-0-7787-0340-2(1)) Crabtree Publishing Co.

—Field Events in Action. 2004. (Sports in Action Ser.). (Illus.). 32p. (J). pap. (978-0-7787-0360-0(6)) Crabtree Publishing Co.

Knotts, Bob. Track & Field. 2000. (True Bks.). (Illus.). 48p. (J). (gr. 3-5). 25.00 (978-0-516-21066-7(1)); pap. 6.95 (978-0-516-27031-9(1)) Scholastic Library Publishing. (Children's Pr.).

Los ninos pueden Correr: Individual Title Six-Packs. (Coleccion Pm Ser.: Vol. 2). Tr. of We can run. (SPA.). 16p. (gr. k-1). 26.00 (978-0-7578-0684-1(8)) Rigby Education.

Macht, Norman L. Track & Field. 1999. (Composite Guide Ser.). (Illus.). 64p. (J). (gr. 4-7). 28.00 (978-0-7910-4720-0(2) , Chelsea Hse.) Facts On File, Inc.

MacNab, Chris. Field. 2003. (Sports Injuries Ser.). (Illus.). 64p. (J). lib. bdg. (978-1-59084-639-1(7)) Mason Crest Pubs.

Manley, Claudia B. Competitive Track & Field for Girls. 2005. (SportsGirl Ser.). (Illus.). 64p. (YA). (gr. 5-8). lib. bdg. 26.50 (978-0-8239-3408-9(X)) Rosen Publishing Group, Inc., The.

Mayer, Cassie. On Foot. 2006. (Illus.). 24p. (J). (978-1-4034-8393-5(0)); pap. (978-1-4034-8400-0(7)) Heinemann Library.

McNab, Chris. Track. 2003. (Sports Injuries Ser.). (Illus.). 64p. (J). lib. bdg. (978-1-59084-638-4(9)) Mason Crest Pubs.

Middleton, Haydn. A World-Class Marathon Runner. 2004. (Making of a Champion Ser.). (J). pap. 8.50 (978-1-4034-5535-2(X)); lib. bdg. 27.07 (978-1-4034-4670-1(9)) Heinemann Library.

Monroe, Judy. Jesse Owens: Track-and-Field Champion. 2005. (Fact Finders Ser.). (Illus.). 32p. (J). (ps-7). lib. bdg. 22.60 (978-0-7368-3744-6(2)) Capstone Pr., Inc.

Naden, Corinne J. Wilma Rudolph. 2003. (gr. 3-6). lib. bdg. 18.20 (978-0-613-78294-4(1)) Tandem Library Bks.

Naden, Corinne J. & Blue, Rose. Wilma Rudolph. 2003. (African-American Biographies Ser.). (Illus.). 64p. (J). pap. 8.95 (978-1-4109-0321-1(4)); lib. bdg. 28.56 (978-0-7398-7033-4(5)) Raintree.

Nitz, Kristin Wolden. Play-by-Play Field Events. King, Andy, illus. King, Andy, photos by. 2004. (Play-by-Play Ser.). 80p. (J). (gr. 4-8). lib. bdg. 23.93 (978-0-8225-3933-9(0)) Lerner Publishing Group.

Otten, Jack. Track. 2002. (Reading Power Ser.). (Illus.). 24p. (J). (gr. 1). lib. bdg. 17.25 (978-0-8239-5973-0(2) , PowerKids Pr.) Rosen Publishing Group, Inc., The.

A Robbie Reader-Extreme Sports, 4 vols., Set. Incl. Exteme Skateboarding with Paul Rodriguez. Smalley, Carol. lib. bdg. (978-1-58415-489-1(6)); Extreme Cycling with Dale Holmes. Smalley, Carol. lib. bdg. (978-1-58415-487-7(X)); Ride the Giant Waves with Garrett Mcnamara. Smalley, Carol. lib. bdg. (978-1-58415-486-0(1)); Ultra Running with Scott Jurek. Whiting, Jim. lib. bdg. (978-1-58415-484-6(5)); 32p. (J). (gr. 1-4). (Illus.). 2006. lib. bdg. (978-1-58415-485-3(3)) Mitchell Lane Pubs., Inc.

Running, 6 vols. (Multicultural Programs Ser.). 16p. (gr. 1-3). 24.95 (978-0-7802-9215-4(4)) Wright Group, The.

Schraff, Anne. Wilma Rudolph: The Greatest Woman Sprinter in History. 2004. (African-American Biographies Ser.). (Illus.). 112p. (J). lib. bdg. 26.60 (978-0-7660-2291-1(9)) Enslow Pubs., Inc.

Thom, Kara Douglass & Golden, Lilly. See Mom Run. 2003. 32p. 15.00 (978-1-891369-40-7(7)) Breakaway Bks.

Thompson, Luke. Track & Field: Field Events. 2001. (Sports Clinic Ser.). (Illus.). 48p. (YA). (gr. 7-12). 23.00 (978-0-516-23169-3(3)); pap. 6.95 (978-0-516-29565-7(9)) Scholastic Library Publishing. (Children's Pr.).

—Track & Field: Field Events. 2001. (gr. 7-12). lib. bdg. 15.25 (978-0-613-58806-5(1)) Tandem Library Bks.

—Track & Field: Track Events. 2001. (Sports Clinic Ser.). (Illus.). 48p. (YA). (gr. 7-12). 23.00 (978-0-516-23168-6(5)); pap. 6.95 (978-0-516-29564-0(0)) Scholastic Library Publishing. (Children's Pr.).

Track: Individual Title Six-Packs. (On Deck Ser.). 24p. (gr. 4-5). 35.00 (978-0-7578-1005-3(5)) Rigby Education.

Wade, Alison. The Female Distance Runner's Training Log. 2003. 6.00 (978-0-9701566-3-1(4)) Idea, Inc.

Ward, Tony. Track. 1998. (Olympic Library). (J). pap. (978-1-57572-037-1(X)) Heinemann Library.

—Track & Field. 1998. (Successful Sports Ser.). 32p. (J). lib. bdg. 21.36 (978-1-57572-201-6(1)) Heinemann Library.

Whitehouse, Patricia. What Can Run? 2003. (Heinemann Read & Learn Ser.). (Illus.). 24p. (J). pap. 5.25 (978-1-4034-4374-8(2)) Heinemann Library.

Worth, Richard. Gail Devers. 2001. (Overcoming Adversity Ser.). (Illus.). 112p. (J). 30.00 (978-0-7910-6305-7(4) , Chelsea Hse.) Facts On File, Inc.

TRACK ATHLETICS—BIOGRAPHY

Conrad, David. Stick to It! The Story of Wilma Rudolph. 2002. (Spyglass Books). (Illus.). 24p. (J). (gr. 1 up). lib. bdg. 18.60 (978-0-7565-0384-0(1)) Compass Point Bks.

Gutman, Bill. Dan O'Brien. 1998. (Overcoming the Odds Ser.). (Illus.). 48p. (J). (gr. 3-8). (978-0-8172-4129-2(9)) Raintree.

Knapp, Ron. Top 10 American Men Sprinters. 1999. (Sports Top 10 Ser.). (Illus.). 48p. (YA). (gr. 4-10). lib. bdg. 23.93 (978-0-7660-1074-1(0)) Enslow Pubs., Inc.

Krull, Kathleen. Wilma Unlimited: How Wilma Rudolph Became the World's Fastest Woman. Diaz, David, illus. 2000. 44p. (J). (gr. 2-7). pap. 7.00 (978-0-15-202098-9(5) , Harcourt Paperbacks) Harcourt Children's Bks.

—Wilma Unlimited: How Wilma Rudolph Became the World's Fastest Woman. 2000. (gr. 3-6). lib. bdg. 14.15 (978-0-613-37687-7(0)) Tandem Library Bks.

McMane, Fred. Superstars of Men's Track & Field. 1999. (Male Sports Stars Ser.). (Illus.). 64p. (YA). (gr. 4-7). 12.95 (978-0-7910-4591-6(9) , Chelsea Hse.) Facts On File, Inc.

Molzahn, Arlene Bourgeois. Top 10 American Women Sprinters. 1998. (Sports Top 10 Ser.). (Illus.). 48p. (YA). (gr. 4-10). lib. bdg. 23.93 (978-0-7660-1011-6(2)) Enslow Pubs., Inc.

Rambeck, Richard & Klingel, Cynthia Fitterer. Hockey. 2003. (Wonder Books Level 2: Sports Ser.). (Illus.). 24p. (J). (ps-2). 22.79 (978-1-56766-460-7(1)) Child's World, Inc.

Rutledge, Rachel. The Best of the Best in Track & Field. 1999. (Women of Sports Ser.). (Illus.). 64p. (gr. 5 up). lib. bdg. 24.90 (978-0-7613-1300-7(1)); pap. 7.95 (978-0-7613-0446-3(0)) Lerner Publishing Group. (Twenty-First Century Bks.).

—The Best of the Best in Track & Field. 1999. (gr. k-8). (Illus.). 64p. (J). lib. bdg. 16.40 (978-0-613-16603-4(5)); (978-0-606-17030-7(8)) Tandem Library Bks.

Steele, Philip. Jesse Owens. 2001. (Profiles Ser.). (Illus.). 56p. (J). (gr. 4-6). lib. bdg. (978-1-58810-059-7(6)) Heinemann Library.

Stewart, Mark. Marion Jones: Fast & Fearless. 2000. (New Wave Ser.). (Illus.). 48p. (gr. 4 up). lib. bdg. 22.90 (978-0-7613-1870-5(4) , Millbrook Pr.) Lerner Publishing Group.

Stewart, Mark Alan. Marion Jones: Sprinting Sensation. 2000. (Sports Stars Ser.). (Illus.). 48p. (J). (gr. 3-4). pap. 5.95 (978-0-516-27004-3(4) , Children's Pr.) Scholastic Library Publishing.

TRACK ATHLETICS—FICTION

Cartier, Wesley. Marco's Run. Ruffins, Reynold, illus. 2003. (Green Light Readers Level 2 Ser.). 24p. (J). 11.95 (978-0-15-204868-6(5)); pap. 3.95 (978-0-15-204828-0(6)) Harcourt Children's Bks. (Green Light Readers).

—Marco's Run. 2001. (gr. k-3). lib. bdg. 11.80 (978-0-613-64442-6(5)); (Illus.). (J). (978-0-606-21315-8(5)) Tandem Library Bks.

Cross-country Race: Individual Title Six-Packs. (gr. 1-2). 22.00 (978-0-7635-9169-4(6)) Rigby Education.

Driscoll, Laura. Slow down, Sara! O'Rourke, Page Eastburn, illus. 2003. (Science Solves It! Ser.). 32p. (J). 4.99 (978-1-57565-125-5(4)) Kane Pr., The.

Korman, Gordon. Need for Speed. 2001. (Jersey Ser.: 8). (Illus.). 128p. (gr. 3-7). reprint ed. pap. 4.99 (978-0-7868-4467-8(1)) Disney Pr.

McPhee, Peter. Runner. 1999. (SideStreets Ser.). 151p. (YA). (gr. 7-12). (***978-1-55028-675-5(7)*** Lorimer, James & Co., Ltd., Pubs. CAN. *Dist:* Casemate Pubs. & Bk. Distributors, LLC.

—Runner. 2000. (gr. 7-12). lib. bdg. 15.25 (978-0-613-89010-6(8)) Tandem Library Bks.

Mills, Claudia. Ziggy's Blue-Ribbon Day. Alley, R. W. & Alley, Robert W., illus. 2005. 32p. (J). (ps-ps). 16.00 (978-0-374-32352-3(6) , Farrar, Straus & Giroux (BYR)) Farrar, Straus & Giroux.

Nakajo, Hisaya. Hana-Kimi. 2007. (Hana-Kimi Ser.). 184p. (YA). Vol. 16. pap. 9.99 (978-1-4215-0991-4(1)); Vol. 17. pap. 9.99 (978-1-4215-0992-1(X)) Viz Media.

Neumann, Peter J. Playing a Virginia Moon. 1999. 248p. (YA). (gr. 11-12). reprint ed. 15.00 (978-0-7881-6636-5(0)) DIANE Publishing Co.

Rayner, Robert. Walker's Runners. 2002. (Sports Stories Ser.). 96p. (J). (gr. 3-8). (***978-1-55028-763-9(X)***); 7.95 (978-1-55028-762-2(1)) Lorimer, James & Co., Ltd., Pubs. CAN. *Dist:* Casemate Pubs. & Bk. Distributors, LLC.

Rayner, Robert J. Walker's Runners. 2002. (gr. 3-6). lib. bdg. 13.55 (978-0-613-78323-1(9)) Tandem Library Bks.

Scudamore, Beverly. Ready to Run. 2006. (Sports Stories Ser.). 96p. (J). (gr. 3-8). (***978-1-55028-915-2(2)***); 7.95 (978-1-55028-914-5(4)) Lorimer, James & Co., Ltd., Pubs. CAN. *Dist:* Casemate Pubs. & Bk. Distributors, LLC.

Stewart, Toni D., illus. Ron's Jog. 1999. 13p. (Orig.). (J). (gr. k-2). pap. 2.50 (978-1-889658-05-6(7)) New Canaan Publishing Co. LLC.

TRACKING AND TRAILING

Dendy, Leslie A. Tracks, Scats & Signs. 2004. (Take-Along Guide Ser.). (Illus.). 48p. (J). (gr. 2-5). pap. 7.95 (978-1-55971-599-7(5) , NorthWord Bks. for Young Readers) T&N Children's Publishing.

Hall, Kirsten. Tracking Animals: A Chapter Book. (True Tales Ser.). (Illus.). 48p. (J). 2006. (gr. 2-4). pap. 4.95 (978-0-516-25459-3(6)); 2005. (ps-ps). 22.50 (978-0-516-25186-8(4)) Scholastic Library Publishing. (Children's Pr.).

Johnson, Rebecca L. Tracking Animal Migrators. 2003. (National Geographic Reading Expeditions Ser.). (Illus.). 32p. (J). pap. (978-0-7922-8449-9(6)) National Geographic Society.

Kavanagh, James. African Animal Tracks: An Introduction to the Tracks & Dung of Familiar Species. Leung, Raymond, illus. 2001. (Pocket Traveller Ser.). 12p. pap. 5.95 (978-1-58355-037-3(2)) Waterford Pr., Ltd.

Mauro, Paul & Melton, H. Keith. Tracking & Surveillance. 2004. (Detective Academy Ser.). (Illus.). 48p. (J). (978-0-439-57180-7(4)) Scholastic, Inc.

Robson, Gary D. Who Pooped in the Park? Rath, Robert, illus. 2006. 48p. (J). (978-1-56037-339-1(3)) Farcountry Pr.

—Who Pooped in the Park: Yellowstone. 2004. (Illus.). 48p. (J). pap. 9.95 (978-1-56037-273-8(7)) Farcountry Pr.

—Who Pooped in the Park? Red Rock Canyon National Conservation Area. Rath, Robert, illus. 2005. 48p. (J). pap. 9.95 (978-1-56037-371-1(7)) Farcountry Pr.

—Who Pooped in the Sonoran Desert? Scat & Tracks for Kids. Rath, Robert, illus. 2006. 48p. (J). (978-1-56037-349-0(0)) Farcountry Pr.

Selsam, Millicent E. Big Tracks, Little Tracks Stage 1: Following Animal Prints. Hill Donnelly, Marlene, illus. rev. ed. 1999. (Let's-Read-and-Find-Out Science Ser.). 32p. (J). (ps-1). pap. 5.99 (978-0-06-445194-9(1) , Harper Trophy) HarperCollins Pubs.

Selsam, Millicent Ellis. Big Tracks, Little Tracks: Following Animal Prints. Donnelly, Marlene Hill, illus. 1999. 31p. (J). (ps-ps). lib. bdg. 14.15 (978-0-613-11333-5(0)) Tandem Library Bks.

TRACTION ENGINES

see Tractors

TRACTORS

Bender, Lionel. Diggers & Tractors. 2006. (J). (978-1-59389-267-8(5)) Chrysalis Education.

Bingham, Caroline & Dorling Kindersley Publishing Staff. Tractor. 2004. (Machines at Work Ser.). (Illus.). 32p. (J). 8.99 (978-0-7566-0217-8(3)) Dorling Kindersley Publishing, Inc.

Bridges, Sarah. I Drive a Tractor. 2006. (Illus.). 24p. (J). (ps-2). 22.60 (978-1-4048-1609-1(7)) Picture Window Bks.

Brooks, Felicity. Tractors. 2007. 12p. (J). bds. 9.99 (978-0-7945-1597-3(5) , Usborne) EDC Publishing.

Burch, Lynda S. Wicky Wacky Things that Go! Tractors. Burch, Lynda S., photos by. 2004. (Illus.). 28p. (J). E-Book 9.95 incl. cd-rom (978-1-933090-09-2(X)) Guardian Angel Publishing, Inc.

Chandler, Gil. Tractors. 2000. (Cruisin' Ser.). (Illus.). 48p. (J). (gr. 3-6). lib. bdg. 19.00 (978-0-516-35254-1(7) , Children's Pr.) Scholastic Library Publishing.

Chronicle Books Staff, contrib. by. Big Farm Machines. 2002. (Illus.). 24p. (J). bds. 6.95 (978-0-8118-3565-7(0)) Chronicle Bks. LLC.

Coppendale, Jean. Tractors & Farm Vehicles. 2007. (J). lib. bdg. 16.95 (***978-1-59566-340-5(1)***) QEB Publishing Inc.

DK Publishing. Touch & Feel Tractor. 2008. (Touch & Feel Ser.). 12p. (J). 6.99 (***978-0-7566-3524-4(1)***) Dorling Kindersley Publishing, Inc.

—Tractor. 2008. (Ultimate Sticker Bks.). 16p. (J). (gr. 1-3). 6.99 (***978-0-7566-3876-4(3)***) Dorling Kindersley Publishing, Inc.

DK Publishing Staff. Big Book of Tractors. 2007. 48p. (J). (gr. k-3). pap. 12.99 (***978-0-7566-3213-7(7)***) Dorling Kindersley Publishing, Inc.

—My Big Machine Book. 1999. (Big Tab Board Books Ser.). (Illus.). 8p. (J). (ps-3). bds. 9.99 (978-0-7894-4326-7(0)) Dorling Kindersley Publishing, Inc.

—My Terrific Tractor Book. 2007. 12p. (J). 12.99 (978-0-7566-2582-5(3)) Dorling Kindersley Publishing, Inc.

—Tractor. 2007. 14p. (J). (ps-k). pap. 5.99 (978-0-7566-2979-3(9)) Dorling Kindersley Publishing, Inc.

—Tractor: Things That Go Board Books. 2004. (Things That Go Shaped Board Bks.). (Illus.). 10p. (J). (ps-k). bds. 3.99 (978-0-7894-1137-2(7)) Dorling Kindersley Publishing, Inc.

Doeden, Matt. Tractors. 2006. (Pebble Plus: Mighty Machines Ser.). (J). (978-0-7368-4268-6(3)) Capstone Pr., Inc.

Dorling Kindersley Publishing Staff. Action Tractor. 2006. 8p. (J). bds. 7.99 (978-0-7566-1115-6(6)) Dorling Kindersley Publishing, Inc.

—The Bulldozer. 1999. (Wheelies Ser.). (Illus.). 12p. (J). (ps-3). bds. 5.99 (978-0-7894-4308-3(2)) Dorling Kindersley Publishing, Inc.

—Drive a Tractor. 1999. (Illus.). 12p. (J). (ps-2). pap. 12.99 (978-0-7894-4743-2(6)) Dorling Kindersley Publishing, Inc.

—Farm Tractor. 2003. (Wheelies Ser.). (Illus.). 12p. (J). bds. 6.99 (978-0-7894-9713-0(1)) Dorling Kindersley Publishing, Inc.

—My First Tractor Board Book. 2006. 36p. (J). bds. 5.99 (978-0-7566-1969-5(6)) Dorling Kindersley Publishing, Inc.

—Tractor. (J). 2006. (Illus.). 12p. 6.99 (978-0-7566-2329-6(4)); 2006. 32p. pap. 6.99 (978-0-7566-1787-5(1)); 2003. (Illus.). 12p. bds. 6.99 (978-0-7894-9838-0(3)); 2000. (Illus.). 12p. bds. 6.99 (978-0-7894-6533-7(7)); 1999. (Illus.). 16p. pap. 6.99 (978-0-7894-4282-6(5)) Dorling Kindersley Publishing, Inc.

—Tractor. 2000. (978-0-606-17815-0(5)) Tandem Library Bks.

—The Tractor. 1999. (Wheelies Ser.). (Illus.). 12p. (J). (ps-12). bds. 5.99 (978-0-7894-4307-6(4)) Dorling Kindersley Publishing, Inc.

Ellis, Belinda. Tractor. 2007. (Pull-Alongs Ser.). (Illus.). 12p. (ps). per. 6.95 (978-1-84610-443-5(2)) Make Believe Ideas GBR. *Dist:* Ingram Pub. Services.

Gillis, Jennifer Blizin. Farm Machines. 2004. (Let's See Ser.). (Illus.). 24p. (J). (gr. 1 up). lib. bdg. 19.93 (978-0-7565-0672-8(7)) Compass Point Bks.

Gilpin, Rebecca. How to Draw Trucks & Tractors. 2005. 34p. (J). pap. 8.95 (978-0-7945-1134-0(1) , Usborne) EDC Publishing.

Glover, David & Glover, Penny. Tractors. 2005. (Big Machines Ser.). (Illus.). 30p. (J). (gr. 2-5). lib. bdg. 27.10 (978-1-58340-703-5(0)) Smart Apple Media.

Hall, Margaret. John Deere. 2004. (Illus.). 32p. (J). pap. 6.50 (978-1-4034-5335-8(7)); lib. bdg. 22.79 (978-1-4034-5327-3(6)) Heinemann Library.

Horne, Jane. Tractors & Trucks. 2006. (Touch & Learn (Make Believe Ideas) Ser.). (Illus.). 12p. (ps). per., bds. 6.95 (978-1-84610-279-0(0)); per., bds. 6.95 (978-1-84610-276-9(6)) Make Believe Ideas GBR. *Dist:* Ingram Pub. Services.

Lindeen, Mary. Tractors. 2007. (Blastoff! Readers Ser.). (Illus.). 24p. (J). (gr. k-3). lib. bdg. 16.95 (978-1-60014-061-7(0)) Bellwether Media.

Litchfield, J. & Brooks, F. Tractors. 2004. (Illus.). 10p. (J). 4.95 (978-0-7945-0588-2(0)) EDC Publishing.

Mead, Sue. Monster Trucks & Tractors. (Race Car Legends Ser.). (Illus.). 1999. 64p. (YA). (ps up). 28.00 (978-0-7910-5021-7(1)); 2005. 77p. (J). (gr. 4-8). lib. bdg. 25.00 (978-0-7910-8689-6(5)) Facts On File, Inc. (Chelsea Hse.).

Mezzanotte, Jim. Camiones Tractores. 2006. (Vehiculos Gigantes (Giant Vehicles) Ser.). (SPA.). 24p. (J). pap. 5.95 (978-0-8368-5993-5(6)); lib. bdg. 22.00 (978-0-8368-5986-7(3)) Stevens, Gareth Inc.

—Giant Tractors. 2005. (Illus.). 24p. (J). pap. (978-0-8368-4922-6(1)); lib. bdg. 22.00 (978-0-8368-4915-8(9)) Stevens, Gareth Inc.

Mitchell, Joyce Slayton. Tractor-Trailer Trucker: A Powerful Truck Book. Borns, Steven, photos by. 2004. (Illus.). 40p. (YA). (gr. 2-5). 14.95 (978-1-58246-010-9(8) , Tricycle Pr.) Ten Speed Pr.

Mitton, Tony. Tremendous Tractors. Parker, Ant, illus. 2003. (Amazing Machines Ser.). 24p. (J). (ps-k). tchr. ed. 9.95 (978-0-7534-5599-9(4) , Kingfisher) Houghton Mifflin Co. Trade & Reference Div.

My Tractor. 2002. (Chunky Vehicle Shaped Boards Ser.). (J). bds. 1.98 (978-0-7525-7048-8(X)); bds. 4.98 (978-0-7525-4771-8(2)) Parragon, Inc.

Oxlade, Chris. This Is My Tractor. 2007. ***978-1-59771-106-7(3))** Sea-To-Sea Pubns.

Pearcey, Alice. Tractors & Trucks Stencil Book. Tudor, Andy, illus. 2006. 14p. (J). bds. 12.99 (978-0-7945-1139-5(2) , Usborne) EDC Publishing.

Randolph, Joanne. Tractors. 2002. (PowerKids Readers Ser.). (Illus.). 24p. (J). (gr. 1). lib. bdg. 16.00 (978-0-8239-6028-6(5) , PowerKids Pr.) Rosen Publishing Group, Inc., The.

Ransom, Candice F. Camiones Grandes (Big Rigs) 2006. (Libros para Avanzar Ser.). (ENG & SPA.). (J). 22.60 (978-0-8225-6500-0(5) , Ediciones Lerner) Lerner Publishing Group.

Rogers, Hal. Tractors. 2008. (Machines at Work Ser.). 24p. (J). 22.79 ***978-1-59296-959-3(3))** Child's World, Inc.

Schaefer, Lola M. Tractor Trailers. 2000. (Transportation Library). (Illus.). 24p. (J). (gr. 1-2). lib. bdg. 18.60 (978-0-7368-0504-9(4) , Bridgestone Bks.) Capstone Pr., Inc.

Stickland, Paul. Tractors. 2004. (By Air, Sea, & Land Ser.). (Illus.). 24p. (J). pap. 3.99 (978-0-7696-3377-0(3) , Waterbird Bks.) School Specialty Publishing.

Stille, Darlene R. Tractors. 2002. (Illus.). 32p. (J). (gr. 1 up). lib. bdg. 19.93 (978-0-7565-0287-4(X)) Compass Point Bks.

Tieck, Sarah. Farm Tractors. 2005. (Buddy Book Ser.). (Illus.). 24p. (J). (gr. k-4). lib. bdg. 21.35 (978-1-59197-827-5(0)) ABDO Publishing Co.

Tractor. 1999. (Illus.). 12p. (J). (978-0-7547-0018-0(6)) Funfax, Ltd.

Tractores agrícolas (Farm Tractors) 2006. (J). 22.60 (978-0-8225-6231-3(6)); pap. 5.95 (978-0-8225-6645-8(1)) Lerner Publishing Group. (Ediciones Lerner).

Tractors & Diggers. 2003. (Illus.). 32p. 12.98 (978-1-4054-2005-1(7)) Parragon, Inc.

Tractors & Trucks Sticker Activity Book. 2003. (Illus.). 12p. (J). 2.98 (978-1-4054-1182-0(1)) Parragon, Inc.

Voyageur Press Staff, creator. The World's Greatest John Deere Tractor Poster Book. rev. ed. 2007. (Illus.). 88p. pap. 9.95 (978-0-7603-3016-6(6)) Voyageur Pr., Inc.

Williams, Michael. Power Tractors. 2006. (Cool Wheels Ser.). (Illus.). 32p. (J). lib. bdg. (978-0-8368-6828-9(5)) Stevens, Gareth Inc.

Young, C. Tractors. rev. ed. 2004. (Young MacHines Ser.). (Illus.). 32p. (J). pap. 6.95 (978-0-7945-0632-2(1)) EDC Publishing.

—Usborne Big Machines Tractors. 2004. (Young MacHines Ser.). 32p. (J). lib. bdg. 14.95 (978-1-58086-616-3(6) , Usborne) EDC Publishing.

TRACTORS—FICTION

Amery, Heather. Red Tractor Board Book. Cartwright, Stephen, illus. 2004. (Young Farmyard Tales Board Books Ser.). 10p. (J). bds. 3.95 (978-0-7945-0469-4(8) , Usborne) EDC Publishing.

Aumann, Jane & Ladage, Cindy. The Christmas Tractor. Freitag, Charles, illus. 2003. 30p. (J). (gr. k-4). pap. 8.95 (978-0-9703319-2-2(4)) Roots & Wings.

—Tucker's Surprise. Craig, Christy, illus. 2000. 16p. (J). (ps-7). pap. 8.00 (978-0-9703319-0-8(8)) Roots & Wings.

Avery, Heather & Cartwright, Stephen. The Runaway Tractor. 2004. (Farmyard Tales Ser.). (Illus.). 16p. (J). (ps up). pap. 6.95 (978-0-7945-0069-6(2) , Usborne) EDC Publishing.

Barron, Kirk W. Johnny Tractor & Friends: A New Kind of Job. Torgerson, Dell & Reyner, Mark, eds. Barron, Kirk W., illus. 1999. (John Deere Storybook for Little Folks Ser.). (Illus.). 14p. (J). (gr. 3 up). 6.95 (978-1-887327-26-8(6)) Ertl Co., Inc.

—Johnny Tractor & Friends: Afraid of Nothing. Torgerson, Dell & Reyner, Mark, eds. Barron, Kirk W., illus. 1999. (John Deere Storybook for Little Folks Ser.). (Illus.). 14p. (J). (gr. 3 up). 6.95 (978-1-887372-25-1(3)) Ertl Co., Inc.

Brave Blue Tractor. 2002. (Vehicle Lights Ser.). (J). (ps-k). 6.98 (978-0-7525-8887-2(7)) Parragon, Inc.

Carter, Don. Old MacDonald Drives a Tractor. 2007. (Illus.). 24p. (J). (ps-2). 14.95 (978-1-59643-023-5(0)) Roaring Brook Pr.

Cazet, Denys. Minnie & Moo: Minnie & Moo Go to the Moon. Cazet, Denys, illus. (Live Oak Readalong Ser.). (Illus.). (J). 18.95 incl. audio compact disk (978-1-59112-392-7(5)) Live Oak Media.

—Minnie & Moo Go to the Moon. Cazet, Denys, illus. 2001. (Illus.). 25.95 incl. audio (978-0-87499-718-7(6)); pap. 29.95 incl. audio (978-0-87499-719-4(4)); pap. 31.95 incl. audio compact disk (978-1-59112-592-1(8)); pap. 18.95 incl. audio compact disk (978-1-59112-593-8(6)) Live Oak Media.

Cowley, Joy. The Rusty, Trusty Tractor. Dunrea, Olivier, illus. 2003. 32p. (J). (gr. k-2). 15.95 (978-1-56397-565-3(3)); pap. 8.95 (978-1-56397-873-9(3)) Boyds Mills Pr.

—Rusty, Trusty Tractor. 1999. (gr. k-3). lib. bdg. 16.40 (978-0-613-29045-6(3)) Tandem Library Bks.

Dierssen, A. & Sohr, D. Old Red Tractor. 2006. (Illus.). 32p. (J). 16.95 (978-0-7358-2088-3(0)) North-South Bks., Inc.

Doherty, Paula. Going Places-Tractor. Doherty, Paula, illus. 2005. (Going Places Board Bks.). (Illus.). 10p. (J). bds. 4.99 (978-0-7641-5887-2(2)) Barron's Educational Series, Inc.

Dollin, Laura. Tractor Power. Giraffe, Red, illus. 2003. (Tough Stuff Ser.).Tr. of Tractor Superfuerte. 10p. (ps-17). 5.99 (978-0-7868-1979-9(0)) Hyperion Bks. for Children.

—Tractor Superfuerte. 2003. (Tough Stuff Ser.). (SPA.). 10p. (ps-17). 5.99 (978-0-7868-1975-1(8)) Hyperion Bks. for Children.

Evans, Alwyn. Old MacDonald's Farm: A Three-Dimensional Playset with Sound! Bell, Owen, illus. 2001. (J). (ps-k). act. bk. ed. 16.95 (978-1-58117-145-7(5) , Intervisual/Piggy Toes) Dalmatian Pr.

Gould, Robert. Tractors. 2004. (Big Stuff Ser.). (Illus.). 16p. (J). bds. 7.95 (978-1-929945-44-3(2)) Big Guy Bks., Inc.

Hill, Eric. Spot's Noisy Tractor. Hill, Eric, illus. 2008. 12p. (J). (ps-k). bds. 12.99 ***978-0-399-25166-5(9)** , Putnam Juvenile) Penguin Group (USA) Inc.

Katschke, Judy. Johnny Tractor & Big Surprise. 2006. (Illus.). 24p. (J). pap. 3.95 (978-0-7624-2628-7(4) , Running Pr. Kids) Running Pr. Bk. Pubs.

Mitton, Tony. Tremendous Tractors. Parker, Ant, illus. 2005. (Amazing Machines Ser.). 24p. (J). (ps-k). pap., pap. 3.95 (978-0-7534-5918-8(3) , Kingfisher) Houghton Mifflin Co. Trade & Reference Div.

Murphy, Bonnie. Can A Rooster Drive A Tractor? Richardson, Shelley, illus. 2001. 32p. (J). 14.95 (978-0-9714419-0-3(1)) Alabama Farmers Federation.

Oliver, Merlin. John Laughinghouse. 2007. 20.00 ***978-0-8059-7333-4(8))** Dorrance Publishing Co., Inc.

Powell, Richard. I See a Tractor. Davis, Caroline, illus. 2003. (Plastic Shapes Ser.). 12p. (J). bds. 5.95 (978-0-7641-5646-5(2)) Barron's Educational Series, Inc.

Ransom, Candice F. Tractor Day. Bryant, Laura J., illus. 2007. 32p. (J). (ps). 17.85 (978-0-8027-8091-1(1)) Walker & Co.

Ransom, Candice F. & Bryant, Laura. Tractor Day. Bryant, Laura, illus. 2007. (Illus.). 32p. (J). (ps). 16.95 (978-0-8027-8090-4(3)) Walker & Co.

Roberts, Margiad & Owen, Carys Eurwen. Tecwyn a Ffergi Lwyd. 2005. (WEL., Illus.). 35p. (978-0-86381-495-2(6)) Gwasg Carreg Gwalch.

—Tecwyn A'r Combein. 2005. (WEL., Illus.). 34p. (978-0-86381-368-9(2)) Gwasg Carreg Gwalch.

—Tecwyn A'r Moto-Beic. 2005. (WEL., Illus.). 34p. (978-0-86381-437-2(9)) Gwasg Carreg Gwalch.

—Tecwyn Yn Plannu Tatws. 2005. (WEL., Illus.). 34p. (978-0-86381-408-2(5)) Gwasg Carreg Gwalch.

—Tecwyn Yn Teilo. 2005. (WEL., Illus.). 34p. (978-0-86381-328-3(3)) Gwasg Carreg Gwalch.

Rucker, Mike. Terry & the Beaver Dam Fiasco. 2003. (Terry the Tractor Ser.: Vol. 11). (Illus.). 63p. (J). (ps-5). pap. 4.95 (978-0-9711659-2-2(0)) Univ. Editions.

—Terry & the Earthquake. 2006. (Terry the Tractor Ser.: Vol. 14). 72p. (J). (gr. k-4). pap. 4.95 (978-0-9711659-5-3(5)) Univ. Editions.

—Terry & the Elephant. pap. (978-1-56002-746-1(0)) Univ. Editions.

—Terry & The South Pole Breakdown. pap. (978-0-615-11379-1(6)) Univ. Editions.

—Terry & the Super Powerful Fuel. (978-1-56002-673-0(1)) Univ. Editions.

—Terry & the Wild Well Blowout. 2002. (Terry the Tractor Ser.: Vol. 10). (Illus.). 72p. (J). (gr. k-4). pap. 3.95 (978-0-9711659-1-5(2)) Univ. Editions.

—Terry the Smokejumper. 2001. (Terry the Tractor Ser.: Vol. 9). (Illus.). (J). (ps-5). pap. 3.95 (978-0-9711659-0-8(4)) Univ. Editions.

Runaway Tractor. (Kid Kits Ser.). (Illus.). 16p. (YA). 15.95 (978-1-58086-409-1(0)) EDC Publishing.

Running Press Staff & Neusner, Dena. Johnny Tractors Fun Farm Day. 2006. (Illus.). 8p. (J). pap. 5.95 (978-0-7624-2630-0(6) , Running Pr. Kids) Running Pr. Bk. Pubs.

Session, Garry. Odessa Bluegill - Out Shovels a Yellow Tractor. Warren, Pamela, ed. Redel, Nicole, illus. Gorman, Suzy, photos by. 2003. 42p. (J). pap. 21.95 (978-0-9658006-2-4(8)) Session Family.

Shalev, Meir & Abulafja, Jossi. Der Traktor im Sandkasten. 1999. (GER., Illus.). 32p. (J). pap. (978-3-257-00851-7(1)) Diogenes Verlag AG CHE. *Dist:* International Bk. Import Service, Inc.

Shaw, Gina. Follow the Tractor. Peterkin, Mike & Jacobs, Phil, illus. 1999. (Tonka Board Bks.). 14p. (J). (ps). 4.50 (978-0-439-08288-4(9) , Cartwheel Bks.) Scholastic, Inc.

Siy, Alexandra. Old Macdonald had a Farm. Rogers, Jacqueline, illus. 2008. (J). ***978-0-8234-1923-4(1))** Holiday Hse., Inc.

Spinelli, Jami. David's Tractor. Margolis, Lois, illus. l.t. ed. 2006. 32p. (J). 20.99 ***978-1-59879-242-3(3));** per. 11.99 ***978-1-59879-241-6(5))** Lifevest Publishing, Inc.

Steers, Billy. Tractor Mac Arrives at the Farm. Steers, Billy, illus. 2004. (Illus.). 24p. (J). (ps-ps). pap. 3.29 (978-1-59445-042-6(0)) Dogs in Hats Children's Publishing Co.

—Tractor Mac Builds a Barn. 2004. (Illus.). 24p. (J). (ps-ps). pap. 3.29 (978-1-59445-075-4(7)) Dogs in Hats Children's Publishing Co.

Swan, Michelle. Old MacDonald Had a Farm. 2007. 12p. (J). bds. 5.99 ***978-0-439-85307-1(9))** Scholastic, Inc.

Terry & the Ecological Disaster. pap. (978-1-56002-792-8(4)) Univ. Editions.

Watt, Fiona & Wells, Rachel. That's Not My Tractor. 2004. (Touchy-Feely Board Bks.). (SPA., Illus.). 10p. (J). 7.99 (978-0-7945-0011-5(0) , Usborne) EDC Publishing.

Wellington, Monica. Truck Driver Tom. 2007. 32p. (J). (ps). 15.99 ***978-0-525-47831-7(0)** , Dutton Juvenile) Penguin Group (USA) Inc.

TRADE FAIRS

see Fairs

TRADE-MARKS

see Trademarks

TRADE ROUTES

Franck, Irene M. & Brownstone, David M. Around Africa & Asia by Sea: Trade & Travel Routes. 1999. (Illus.). 114p. (J). (gr. 5-12). reprint ed. 18.00 (978-0-7881-6255-8(1)) DIANE Publishing Co.

Levy, Janey. The Silk Road: Using a Map Scale to Measure Distances. 2005. (PowerMath Ser.). (Illus.). 32p. (J). 22.50 (978-1-4042-2938-9(8) , PowerKids Pr.); pap. (978-1-4042-5140-3(5)) Rosen Publishing Group, Inc., The.

Reid, Struan, tr. Exploration by Sea. 2002. (World Issues Ser.). (Illus.). 45p. (J). lib. bdg. 28.50 (978-1-931983-31-0(3)) Chrysalis Education.

Sloan, Frank. Titanic. 1998. (Illus.). 128p. (YA). (gr. 3-7). 19.98 (978-0-8172-4091-2(8)) Raintree.

Strathern, Paul, tr. Exploration by Land. 2002. (World Issues Ser.). (Illus.). 45p. (J). lib. bdg. 28.50 (978-1-931983-32-7(1)) Chrysalis Education.

TRADE SCHOOLS

see Technical Education

TRADE-UNIONS

see Labor Unions

TRADE WASTE

see Waste Products

TRADEMARKS

Olson, Kay Melchisedech. Frank Zamboni & the Ice-Resurfacing Machine. Dominguez, Richard & Barnett, Charles, III, illus. 2008. (J). ***978-1-4296-0147-4(7))** Capstone Pr., Inc.

Skinner, Tina & Palecko-Schuck, Jenna. Trademarks of The 1950s. 2003. (Schiffer Design Book Ser.). (Illus.). 160p. (gr. 10-13). pap. 29.95 (978-0-7643-1828-3(4)) Schiffer Publishing, Ltd.

TRADING CARDS

Arnold, J. Douglas & Brokaw, Brian. Pokemon Trading Card Game Player's Guide. 1999. (Illus.). 144p. (J). pap. 12.95 (978-1-884364-50-1(0)) Sandwich Islands Publishing.

Arnold, J. Douglas, et al. Digimon Cards! Player's & Collector's Guide. 2000. (Illus.). 144p. (J). pap. 12.95 (978-1-884364-52-5(7)) Sandwich Islands Publishing.

Kirkpatrick, Rob. Trading Cards. 2000. (gr. 3-6). lib. bdg. 15.25 (978-0-613-90735-4(3)) Tandem Library Bks.

Kirkpatrick, Rob. Trading Cards. 2000. (High Interest Bks.). (Illus.). 48p. (YA). (gr. 7-12). 24.00 (978-0-516-23335-2(1) , Children's Pr.) Scholastic Library Publishing.

Nintendo of America Staff. Official Nintendo Power Pokemon Trading Card Game Player's Guide. 2000. (Illus.). 112p. (J). pap. 14.95 (978-1-930206-00-7(3) , NES B GD44) Nintendo of America, Inc.

TRADITIONS

see Folklore; Legends; Superstition

TRAFFIC ACCIDENTS

Pascoe, Elaine, ed. Crash: The Body in Crisis. 2003. (Body Story Ser.). (Illus.). 48p. (J). 24.95 (978-1-4103-0062-1(5)); 11.20 (978-1-4103-0183-3(4)) Thomson Gale. (Blackbirch Pr., Inc.).

Walker, Niki. Transportation Disaster Alert! 2005. (Disaster Alert! Ser.). (Illus.). 32p. (J). (978-0-7787-1584-9(1)) Crabtree Publishing Co.

TRAFFIC ACCIDENTS—FICTION

Arterburn, Stephen & Hunt, Angela Elwell. Taz. 2004. (Young Believer on Tour Ser.). (J). pap. 3.99 (978-0-8423-8340-0(9)) Tyndale Hse. Pubs.

Beech, Linda. Alive! Hollander, Wendy Born, illus. 2002. 16p. (J). (978-0-439-35177-5(4)) Scholastic, Inc.

Bruchac, Joseph. Whisper in the Dark. Comport, Sally Wern, illus. 2005. 192p. (J). (gr. 5 up). 15.99 (978-0-06-058087-2(9)); lib. bdg. 16.89 (978-0-06-058088-9(7)) HarperCollins Pubs.

Carlson, Melody. Burnt Orange: Color Me Wasted. 2005. 207p. (YA). pap. 12.99 (978-1-57683-533-3(2)) NavPress Publishing Group.

Charlton-Trujillo, E. E. Prizefighter en Mi Casa. (J). (gr. 5-7). 2007. 192p. 5.99 ***978-0-440-42117-7(9)** , Yearling); 2006. 224p. 15.95 (978-0-385-73325-0(9) , Delacorte Bks. for Young Readers); 2006. 224p. lib. bdg. 17.99 (978-0-385-90344-8(8) , Delacorte Bks. for Young Readers) Random Hse. Children's Bks.

Dobkin, Bonnie. Dream Spinner. 2006. 288p. pap. 8.95 (978-0-7387-0919-2(0) , Flux) Llewellyn Pubns.

Easton, Kelly. Aftershock. 176p. (YA). 2007. pap. 6.99 (***978-1-4169-0053-5(5)** , Simon Pulse); 2006. (gr. 7 up). 16.95 (978-1-4169-0052-8(7) , McElderry, Margaret K.) Simon & Schuster Children's Publishing.

Frank, E. R. Wrecked. 256p. (YA). (gr. 7 up). 2007. pap. 8.99 (978-0-689-87384-3(0) , Simon Pulse); 2005. (Illus.). 16.99 (978-0-689-87383-6(2) , Atheneum) Simon & Schuster Children's Publishing.

Grabenstein, Chris. The Crossroads. 2008. 368p. (J). (gr. 4-7). 16.99 ***978-0-375-84697-7(2)** , Random Hse. Bks. for Young Readers) Random Hse. Children's Bks.

Guest, Jacqueline. Racing Fear. 2004. (SideStreets Ser.). 160p. (gr. 7-12). 7.95 (978-1-55028-838-4(5)); ***978-1-55028-839-1(3))** Lorimer, James & Co., Ltd., Pubs. CAN. *Dist:* Casemate Pubs. & Bk. Distributors, LLC.

Jocelyn, Marthe. Would You? 2008. (YA). ***978-0-375-83703-6(5));** lib. bdg. ***978-0-375-93703-3(X))** Dell Publishing. (Delacorte Pr.).

Koertge, Ron. Strays. 2006. 176p. (YA). (gr. 9 up). 16.99 (978-0-7636-2705-8(4)) Candlewick Pr.

MacKall, Dandi Daley. Sierra's Story. 2004. (Degrees of Betrayal Ser.). 336p. (YA). pap. 9.99 (978-0-8423-8726-2(9)) Tyndale Hse. Pubs.

Mankell, Henning & Thompson, Laurie. Shadows in the Twilight. 2008. 176p. (J). ***978-0-385-73496-7(4));** (YA). (gr. 7). lib. bdg. 18.99 ***978-0-385-90490-2(8))** Dell Publishing. (Delacorte Pr.).

McDaniel, Lurlene. The Girl Death Left Behind. 1999. 192p. (YA). (gr. 7-12). pap. 5.50 (978-0-553-57091-5(9) , Laurel Leaf) Random Hse. Children's Bks.

—The Girl Death Left Behind. 1999. (J). 11.64 (978-0-606-16371-2(9)) Tandem Library Bks.

McGhee, Alison. All Rivers Flow to the Sea. 176p. (YA). (gr. 9 up). 2007. (Illus.). pap. 7.99 ***978-0-7636-3372-1(0));** 2005. 15.99 (978-0-7636-2591-7(4)) Candlewick Pr.

Messer, Celeste M. Three Miracles. 2004. (Adventures of Andi O'Malley Ser.). (Illus.). 82-92p. (J). (gr. 4-7). 4.95 (978-0-9702171-4-1(5)) AshleyAlan Enterprises.

Newbery, Linda. Lost Boy. 2008. (J). ***978-0-375-84574-1(7));** lib. bdg. ***978-0-375-93617-3(3))** Random Hse. Children's Bks. (Fickling, David Bks.).

Oates, Joyce Carol. After the Wreck, I Picked Myself up, Spread My Wings, & Flew Away. 2007. 320p. (J). (gr. 9 up). pap. 7.99 ***978-0-06-073527-2(9)** , HarperTeen) HarperCollins Pubs.

Orr, Wendy. Peeling the Onion. 1999. (Laurel-Leaf Bks.). 176p. (YA). (gr. 7-12). mass mkt. 5.50 (978-0-440-22773-1(9) , Laurel Leaf) Random Hse. Children's Bks.

—Peeling the Onion: A Gripping Story, Told with Honesty & Biting Humour. 1999. (978-0-606-15918-0(5)); (gr. 7-12). lib. bdg. 13.00 (978-0-613-15339-3(1)) Tandem Library Bks.

Pollet, Alison. The Pity Party: 8th Grade in the Life of Me, Cass. (Pity Party Ser.). 160p. (J). 2006. pap. 5.99 (978-0-439-68195-7(2) , Scholastic Paperbacks); 2005. (gr. 5-8). pap. 15.95 (978-0-439-68194-0(4) , Orchard Bks.) Scholastic, Inc.

Price, Mathew. Little Red Car Has an Accident. Augarde, Steve, illus. 2000. (Little Red Car Bks.). 10p. (J). (ps-1). pap. 6.95 (978-0-7892-0673-2(0) , Abbeville Kids) Abbeville Pr., Inc.

Shusterman, Neal. Everlost. 2007. 384p. (YA). mass mkt. 6.99 ***978-0-689-87238-9(0)** , Simon Pulse); 2006. 320p. (J). (gr. 7 up). 16.95 (978-0-689-87237-2(2)) Simon & Schuster Children's Publishing.

Willner-Pardo, Gina. My Mom & Other Mysteries of the Universe. 2004. 176p. (YA). (gr. 4-6). tchr. ed. 15.00 (978-0-618-43020-8(2) , Clarion Bks.) Houghton Mifflin Co. Trade & Reference Div.

Zitelman, Jem. Ventures Tested: One Teenager's Story . . . to Happiness. 2000. viii, 206p. (J). 24.95 (978-1-891612-00-8(X) , 9701); pap. 15.95 (978-1-891612-01-5(8) , 9701); lib. bdg. 24.95 (978-1-891612-02-2(6) , 9701) Celjon Bks.

TRAFFIC REGULATIONS

see also Traffic Accidents

Caviezel, Giovanni. Street Safety Hints. 2005. (Illus.). 10p. (J). bds. 10.99 (978-0-7641-5840-7(6)) Barron's Educational Series, Inc.

Crossing the Street: Individual Title Six-Packs. (ps-2). 27.00 (978-0-7635-9443-5(1)) Rigby Education.

Green Means Go. 2006. (Yellow Umbrella Social Studies). 8,16p. (J). 6.50 (978-0-7368-1716-5(6)) Red Brick Learning.

Harcourt School Publishers Staff. Traffic Jam. 3rd ed. 2002. (Trophies English Language Learners Ser.). (Illus.). (J). pap. 3.20 (978-0-15-327570-8(7)) Harcourt Schl. Pubs.

—Turn Left, Turn Right. 3rd ed. 2002. (Trophies English Language Learners Ser.). (Illus.). pap. 5.10 (978-0-15-327656-9(8)) Harcourt Schl. Pubs.

Hoban, Tana. I Read Symbols. 1999. (Illus.). 32p. (J). (ps-3). pap. 4.95 (978-0-688-16696-0(2)) HarperCollins Pubs.

—I Read Symbols. 1999. (Illus.). (J). (978-0-606-16745-1(5)) Tandem Library Bks.

Holub, Joan. Red, Yellow, Green: What Do Signs Mean? Holub, Joan, illus. 1998. (Illus.). 32p. (J). (ps-2). pap., stu. ed. 3.95 (978-0-590-13455-2(8) , Cartwheel Bks.) Scholastic, Inc.

Ring, Susan. Green Means Go. 2006. (ENG & SPA.). (J). (978-0-7368-6021-5(5)) Yellow Umbrella Pr.

Waters, Carrie. Traffic. Grover, Max, illus. 2001. (Doors to Discovery Ser.). 8p. (J). pap. 7.76 (978-0-322-04829-4(X)) Wright Group, The.

TRAGEDY

Greenhill, Wendy, contrib. by. Romeo & Juliet. 2000. (Shakespeare Library). (Illus.). 32p. (J). lib. bdg. 21.36 (978-1-57572-285-6(2)) Heinemann Library.

Nardo, Don. Readings on "Othello" 2000. (Literary Companion to American Literature Ser.). (Illus.). 190p. (YA). (gr. 9-12). pap. 22.45 (978-0-7377-0186-9(2) , Greenhaven Pr., Inc.) Thomson Gale.

TRAILERS

see Automobiles—Trailers

TRAILING

see Tracking and Trailing

TRAINED NURSES

see Nurses and Nursing

TRAINING OF ANIMALS

see Animals—Training

TRAINING OF CHILDREN

see Child Rearing

TRAINS, RAILROAD

see Railroads

TRAMPS—FICTION

Carville, James & McKissack, Patricia C. Lu & the Swamp Ghost. Catrow, David, tr. Catrow, David, illus. 2004. 40p. (J). 17.95 (978-0-689-86560-2(0) , Atheneum) Simon & Schuster Children's Publishing.

Copeland, Colene. My Favorite Hobo. 2001. (Priscilla Pig Ser.: 8). 172p. (J). per. 4.95 (978-0-939810-25-3(5) , M) Jordan Valley Heritage Hse.

DeFelice, Cynthia C. Nowhere to Call Home. 2000. (YA). pap., stu. ed. 60.00 incl. audio (978-0-7887-4179-1(9) , 41113) Recorded Bks., LLC.

—Nowhere to Call Home. 2001. (J). (978-0-606-21359-2(7)); (gr. 5-8). lib. bdg. 14.10 (978-0-613-35992-4(5)) Tandem Library Bks.

Guest, Jacqueline. Secret Signs. 2006. (Illus.). 144p. (J). pap. 5.95 (978-1-55143-599-2(3)) Orca Bk. Pubs. USA.

Mackall, Dandi Daley. Rudy Rides the Rails: A Depression Era Story. Ellison, Chris, illus. rev. ed. 2007. (Tales of Young Americans Ser.). 40p. (J). (gr. 3-6). 17.95 (***978-1-58536-286-8(7)***) Sleeping Bear Pr.

Stellinga, Mark. Buster Boogernose & the Tramp. 2007. (J). per. 9.95 (***978-0-9796421-9-7(1)***) Stellinga, Mark.

Sweet, Melissa, illus. Tupelo Rides the Rails. 2008. (J). (***978-0-618-71714-9(5)***) Houghton Mifflin Co.

Tripp, Valerie. Kit Saves the Day! A Summer Story, Bk. 5. Rane, Walter & McAliley, Susan, illus. 2001. (American Girls Collection: Bk. 5). 80p. (J). (gr. 2 up). 12.95 (978-1-58485-025-0(6)) American Girl Publishing, Inc.

—Kit Saves the Day! A Summer Story, Bk. 5. Rane, Walter, illus. 2001. (American Girls Collection: Bk. 5). 80p. (YA). (gr. 2 up). pap. 6.95 (978-1-58485-024-3(8)) American Girl Publishing, Inc.

—Kit Saves the Day! A Summer Story. 2001. (American Girls Collection). (Illus.). (J). (978-0-606-21283-0(3)) Tandem Library Bks.

—Kit Saves the Day: A Summer Story 1934. 2001. (gr. 3-6). lib. bdg. 14.10 (978-0-613-44682-2(8)) Tandem Library Bks.

TRANSATLANTIC FLIGHTS

see Aeronautics—Flights

TRANSCONTINENTAL JOURNEYS

see Overland Journeys to the Pacific

TRANSFORMERS (FICTITIOUS CHARACTERS)—FICTION

Auerbach, Annie. The Quest for Energon. 2007. (Transformers Ser.). 64p. (J). pap. 4.99 (***978-0-06-088834-3(2)*** , Harper Entertainment) HarperCollins Pubs.

Chesterfield, Sadie. Optimus Prime Versus Megatron. Staples, Val, illus. 2007. (Transformers Ser.). 24p. (J). pap. 3.99 (***978-0-06-088824-4(5)*** , Harper Entertainment) HarperCollins Pubs.

Egan, Kate. Transformers: The Movie Storybook. Matere, Marcelo, illus. 2007. (Transformers Ser.). 48p. (J). pap. 8.99 (***978-0-06-088836-7(9)*** , Harper Entertainment) HarperCollins Pubs.

Fox, Jennifer & Frantz, Jennifer. Meet the Autobots. Guidi, Guido, illus. 2007. (I Can Read Bks.). 32p. (J). pap. 3.99 (***978-0-06-088831-2(8)*** , Harper Trophy) HarperCollins Pubs.

—Transformers: Meet the Decepticons. Guidi, Guido, illus. 2007. (I Can Read Bks.). 32p. (J). pap. 3.99 (***978-0-06-088828-2(8)*** , Harper Trophy) HarperCollins Pubs.

Photo Novel. 2007. (Transformers Ser.). 96p. (J). (gr. 2-5). pap. 7.99 (***978-0-06-088805-3(9)*** , Harper Entertainment) HarperCollins Pubs.

Roe, David & Reader's Digest Staff. Transformers Mix & Match. 2007. 12p. (J). bds. 14.99 (***978-0-7944-1286-9(6)***) Reader's Digest Assn., Inc., The.

Stein, Erin K. Sam's New Car. Staples, Val, illus. 2007. (Transformers Ser.). 24p. (J). pap. 3.99 (***978-0-06-088823-7(7)*** , Harper Entertainment) HarperCollins Pubs.

Weber, Lou. Little Sound Transformers. 12p. 9.98 (***978-1-4127-6802-3(0)***) Publications International, Ltd.

Wilkens, S. G. Transformers: The Junior Novel. 2007. (Transformers Ser.). 144p. (J). pap. 4.99 (***978-0-06-088835-0(0)*** , Harper Entertainment) HarperCollins Pubs.

TRANSPLANTATION OF ORGANS, TISSUES, ETC.

Ballard, Carol. Organ Transplants. 2006. (Illus.). 64p. (J). lib. bdg. (***978-0-8368-7868-4(X)*** , World Almanac Library) Stevens, Gareth Inc.

Bankston, John. Christiaan Barnard & the Story of the First Heart Transplant. l.t. ed. 2002. (Unlocking the Secrets of Science Ser.). (Illus.). 56p. (gr. 4-10). lib. bdg. 25.70 (978-1-58415-120-3(X)) Mitchell Lane Pubs., Inc.

Barter, James. Organ Transplants. 2005. (Great Medical Discoveries Ser.). (Illus.). 96-128p. (J). (gr. 7-10). 29.95 (978-1-59018-684-8(2) , Lucent Bks.) Thomson Gale.

Farndon, John. From Laughing Gas to Face Transplants: Discovering Transplant Surgery. 2006. (Chain Reactions Ser.). (Illus.). 64p. (YA). (gr. 6-9). lib. bdg. 34.29 (978-1-4034-8840-4(1)) Heinemann Library.

Freeman, J. A., et al. Red's True Heart. 2001. (J). (978-0-929895-96-3(7)) Maupin Hse. Publishing.

Fullick, Ann. Rebuilding the Body: Organ Transplantation. (Science at the Edge Ser.). (Illus.). 64p. 8.95 (978-1-4034-4122-5(7)); 2002. (J). (gr. 6-8). lib. bdg. 27.86 (978-1-58810-700-8(0)) Heinemann Library.

Hoffman, Nancy. Heart Transplants. 2003. (Great Medical Discoveries Ser.). (Illus.). 128p. (J). 29.95 (978-1-56006-929-4(5) , Lucent Bks.) Thomson Gale.

Hunnicutt, Susan. Organ Transplants. 2007. (At Issue Ser.). (Illus.). 128p. (J). (gr. 10-12). 29.95 (***978-0-7377-3691-5(7)***); pap. 21.20 (***978-0-7377-3692-2(5)***) Thomson Gale. (Greenhaven Pr., Inc.).

Kittredge, Mary. Organ Transplants. 1999. (Twenty-First Century Health & Wellness Ser.). (Illus.). 107p. (YA). (gr. 7-12). 24.95 (978-0-7910-5522-9(1) , Chelsea Hse.) Facts On File, Inc.

McClellan, Marilyn. Organ & Tissue Transplants: Medical Miracles & Challenges. 2003. (Issues in Focus Ser.). (Illus.). 128p. (YA). (gr. 6-12). lib. bdg. 26.60 (978-0-7660-1943-0(8)) Enslow Pubs., Inc.

Morgan, Sally. From Microscopes to Stem Cell Research: Discovering Regenerative Medicine. 2006. (Chain Reactions Ser.). (Illus.). 64p. (YA). (gr. 6-9). lib. bdg. 34.29 (978-1-4034-8836-7(3)) Heinemann Library.

Pace, Jessica & Talbert, Jane H. A Will to Live: The Story of a Transplant Kid. 1998. 92p. (J). pap. 15.00 (978-0-9615704-9-1(0)) Fawn Grove Pr.

UNOS (Organization) Staff, contrib. by. Organ Transplants: What Every Kid Needs to Know. 2003. (Illus.). (J). (978-1-886651-43-2(4)) United Network for Organ Sharing.

Walton, Karen A. How Will They Get That Heart down Your Throat? A Child's View of Transplants. Peterson, Allison P., illus. 2nd ed. 1999. 56p. (J). (gr. k-6). pap. 17.50 (978-1-880664-98-8(4)) E. M. Productions.

Winters, Adam. Organ Transplant: The Debate over Who, How & Why. 2000. (Focus on Science & Society Ser.). (Illus.). 64p. (YA). (gr. 4-6). lib. bdg. 26.50 (978-0-8239-3209-2(5) , FSORTR) Rosen Publishing Group, Inc., The.

Wood, Ramona. Now Caitlin Can: A Donated Organ Helps a Child Get Well. 2004. (Illus.). 32p. (J). 16.00 (978-0-9758622-0-9(0)) ABC Pr.

TRANSPORTATION

see also Aeronautics, Commercial; Automobiles; Bridges; Buses; Canals; Commerce; Freight and Freightage; Harbors; Inland Navigation; Postal Service; Railroads; Roads; Steamboats; Streets; Subways; Trade Routes; Traffic Regulations; Trucks; Waterways

Abramson, Beverley. Off We Go! 2006. (Illus.). 24p. (J). (ps-k). 15.95 (978-0-88776-728-9(1)) Tundra Bks., Inc./Livres Toundra, Inc. CAN. *Dist:* Random Hse., Inc.

Animals at Work: Individual Title Six-Packs. (gr. k-1). 23.00 (978-0-7635-9060-4(6)) Rigby Education.

Ashley, Susan. Going Places, 4 bks. Incl. Going by Bus. lib. bdg. 19.33 (978-0-8368-3729-2(0)); Going by Car. lib. bdg. 19.33 (978-0-8368-3730-8(4)); Going by Plane. lib. bdg. 19.33 (978-0-8368-3731-5(2)); Going by Train. lib. bdg. 19.33 (978-0-8368-3732-2(0)); 24p. (YA). (gr. 2 up). (Illus.). 2003. Set lib. bdg. 77.32 (978-0-8368-3728-5(2)); pap. (978-0-8368-3833-6(5)) Stevens, Gareth Inc. (Weekly Reader Early Learning Library).

—¡Vamonos!, 4 bks. Coffey, Colleen & Carrillo, Consuelo, trs. Incl. En Autobus. lib. bdg. 19.33 (978-0-8368-3734-6(7) , Weekly Reader Early Learning Library); En Carro. lib. bdg. 19.33 (978-0-8368-3735-3(5) , Weekly Reader Early Learning Library); Por Avion. lib. bdg. 19.33 (978-0-8368-3736-0(3) , Weekly Reader Early Learning Library); Por Tren. lib. bdg. 19.33 (978-0-8368-3737-7(1)); 24p. (J). (gr. 2 up). (SPA., Illus.). 2003. Set lib. bdg. 77.32 (978-0-8368-3733-9(9) , Weekly Reader Early Learning Library) Stevens, Gareth Inc.

—¡Vamonos!, 4 bks. Incl. En Autobus. pap. 5.95 (978-0-8368-3839-8(4)); En Carro. pap. (978-0-8368-3840-4(8)); Por Avion. pap. 5.95 (978-0-8368-3841-1(6)); Por Tren. pap. (978-0-8368-3842-8(4)); 24p. (J). (gr. 2 up). (SPA., Illus.). 2003. pap. (978-0-8368-3838-1(6) , Weekly Reader Early Learning Library) Stevens, Gareth Inc.

Barnett, Michelle Noble, et al. Theme Pockets - July: America the Beautiful; Space; Transportation. Evans, Marilyn, ed. Larsen, Jo, illus. 1999. (Making Books with Pockets). 96p. (J). pap., tchr. ed. 12.99 (978-1-55799-704-3(7) , EMC 590) Evan-Moor Educational Pubs.

Beaton, Clare, illus. Transportation: English-French. 2002. (Bilingual First Bks.).Tr. of Transporte. (ENG & FRE.). 24p. (J). pap. 5.99 (978-0-7641-2212-5(6)) Barron's Educational Series, Inc.

—Transportation: English-Spanish. 2002. (Bilingual First Books/English-Spanish Ser.).Tr. of Transporte. (ENG & SPA.). 24p. (J). pap. 4.95 (978-0-7641-2211-8(8)) Barron's Educational Series, Inc.

Benchmark Education Staff, compiled by. Transportation. 2006. spiral bd. 85.00 (***978-1-4108-7043-8(X)***) Benchmark Education Co.

Beyer, Mark. Transportation Through the Ages, 6 bks. Incl. Bicycles of the Past. lib. bdg. 17.25 (978-0-8239-5985-3(6)); Boats of the Past. lib. bdg. 17.25 (978-0-8239-5988-4(0)); Cars of the Past. lib. bdg. 17.25 (978-0-8239-5983-9(X)); Motorcycles of the Past. lib. bdg. 17.25 (978-0-8239-5987-7(2)); Planes of the Past. lib. bdg. 17.25 (978-0-8239-5984-6(8)); Trains of the Past. lib. bdg. 17.25 (978-0-8239-5986-0(4)); 24p. (J). (gr. 1). 2002. (Illus.). 2001. Set lib. bdg. 96.00 (978-0-8239-7122-0(8) , PowerKids Pr.) Rosen Publishing Group, Inc., The.

Beylon, Cathy. Color Your Own Things That Go Stickers. 2006. 2p. (J). pap. 2.95 (978-0-486-44898-5(3)) Dover Pubns., Inc.

Bicknell, Joanna. Emergency. 2005. (Shimmer & Shine Bks.). 12p. (ps-k). per., bds. 5.95 (978-1-905051-32-8(8)) Make Believe Ideas GBR. *Dist:* Ingram Pub. Services.

—My Digger Book. 2005. (Shimmer & Shine Books Ser.). 12p. (ps-k). per., bds. 5.95 (978-1-905051-30-4(1)) Make Believe Ideas GBR. *Dist:* Ingram Pub. Services.

Birch, B. Science Museum Transport. (Illus.). 128p. pap. 8.99 (978-0-340-65698-3(0) , Hodder & Stoughton) Hodder General Publishing Division GBR. *Dist:* Trafalgar Square Publishing.

Boothroyd, Jennifer. Transportation. 2006. (First Step Nonfiction Ser.). (Illus.). (J). pap. (978-0-8225-5730-2(4) , Lerner Pubns.) Lerner Publishing Group.

Bowden, Rob. Transportation & the Environment. 2004. (21st Century Debates Ser.). (Illus.). 64p. (J). 28.56 (978-0-7398-5505-8(0)) Raintree.

Brooks, Philip. Transportation. Kingfisher Editors, ed. 2001. (Questions & Answers about... Ser.). 40p. (J). (gr. 4-6). pap. 7.95 (978-0-7534-5373-5(8) , Kingfisher) Houghton Mifflin Co. Trade & Reference Div.

Broyles, Matthew. U.S. Air Marshals. 2006. (Extreme Careers Ser.). (Illus.). 64p. (J). (gr. 5-8). lib. bdg. 26.50 (978-1-4042-0942-8(5)) Rosen Publishing Group, Inc., The.

Bull, Peter, illus. Transport. (Music about Us Ser.). 64p. 9.95 (978-1-85909-294-1(2) , Warner Bros. Pubns.) Alfred Publishing Co., Inc.

Bulloch, Ivan & James, Diane. Vamos de Paseo! 2004. (Me Toca a Mi Ser.). (SPA., Illus.). 12p. (J). (ps-k). bds. 6.95 (978-1-58728-494-6(4) , Two Can Publishing) T&N Children's Publishing.

Burton, Margie, et al. Going Places. Adams, Alison, ed. 1999. (Early Connections Ser.). 16p. (J). (gr. k-2). pap. 4.50 (978-1-58344-063-6(1)) Benchmark Education Co.

Carey, Craig Robert. Exact Action. Mones, Isidre, illus. 2006. (Tonka Ser.). 24p. (J). pap. 3.50 (978-0-439-78965-3(6)) Scholastic, Inc.

Carle, Eric. My Very First Book of Motion. Carle, Eric, illus. 2007. 10p. (J). bds. 5.99 (978-0-399-24748-4(3) , Philomel) Penguin Group (USA) Inc.

Casanellas, Antonio. Great Discoveries & Inventions That Improved Transportation. Garousi, Ali, illus. 2000. (Great Discoveries & Inventions Ser.). 32p. (J). (gr. 4 up). lib. bdg. 24.67 (978-0-8368-2587-9(X)) Stevens, Gareth Inc.

Català, Ellen. How Do You Move? 2005. (Illus.). 17p. (J). (978-0-7368-5259-3(X)); (978-0-7368-5295-1(6)) Capstone Pr., Inc. (Yellow Umbrella Bks.).

Chancellor, Deborah. Traveling on Land. 2004. (Discovery Guides Ser.). (SPA., Illus.). 32p. (gr. 2-5). (J). pap. 6.95 (978-1-58728-214-0(3)); 11.95 (978-1-58728-220-1(8)) T&N Children's Publishing. (Two Can Publishing).

Chappell, Jackie. When I Ride the Bus. 2007. (J). (978-1-59515-939-7(8)) Rourke Publishing, LLC.

Cleland, JoAnn. How Will It Get There? 2007. (Illus.). 24p. (J). (***978-1-59515-989-2(4)***); pap. (***978-1-59515-960-1(6)***) Rourke Publishing, LLC.

Complete Set. (Transportation Ser.). (gr 1-3). 297.64 (978-0-7565-0714-5(6)) Compass Point Bks.

Cubley, Kathleen. Things That Go. Barr, Marilynn G., illus. 1999. (Rhyme & Reason Workbook Ser.). 32p. (J). (ps-k). pap. 3.95 (978-1-57029-258-3(2) , WPH 01110, Totline Pubns.) Schaffer, Frank Pubns.

Cummins, Jeff, illus. Cars, Boats, Trains & Planes: A Pop-Up Book. 1998. 10p. (J). (ps-1). pap. 12.95 (978-0-531-30058-9(7) , Orchard Bks.) Scholastic, Inc.

Demarest, Chris L. & Mayer, Bill. All Aboard! A Traveling Alphabet. 2008. 32p. (J). 17.99 (***978-0-689-85249-7(5)*** , McElderry, Margaret K.) Simon & Schuster Children's Publishing.

DK Publishing. Beep! Beep! 2008. 12p. (J). (ps-3). bds. 6.99 (***978-0-7566-3487-2(3)***) Dorling Kindersley Publishing, Inc.

—Things That Go. 2008. 10p. (J). 8.99 (***978-0-7566-3378-3(8)***) Dorling Kindersley Publishing, Inc.

—Water Magic Things That Go. 2008. 16p. (J). bds. 7.99 (***978-0-7566-3451-3(2)***) Dorling Kindersley Publishing, Inc.

DK Publishing Staff. My First Things That Go Board Book. 2007. (My First Bks.). 36p. (J). 5.99 (978-0-7566-2591-7(2)) Dorling Kindersley Publishing, Inc.

Dorling Kindersley Publishing Staff. Big Book of Transportation. 2006. (Illus.). 96p. (J). pap. 12.99 (978-0-7566-1934-3(3)) Dorling Kindersley Publishing, Inc.

—Things That Go. (Baby Genius Ser.). (Illus.). (J). (ps-ps). 2005. 12p. bds. 6.99 (978-0-7566-1379-2(5)); 2003. 36p. bds. 6.99 (978-0-7894-8577-9(X)) Dorling Kindersley Publishing, Inc.

Dorling Kindersley Publishing Staff, ed. Toys That Go. 2004. (Baby Love Ser.). (Illus.). 16p. (J). bds. 4.99 (978-0-7566-0549-0(0)) Dorling Kindersley Publishing, Inc.

Dorling Kindersley Publishing Staff & Bos, Samone. Go! The Whole World of Transportation. 2006. (Illus.). 240p. (J). (gr. 5). 26.99 (978-0-7566-2224-4(7)) Dorling Kindersley Publishing, Inc.

Dorling Kindersley Publishing Staff & Millard, Anne. Things That Go. 2002. (Lift-the-Flap Books Ser.). (Illus.). 16p. (J). (ps). 6.99 (978-0-7894-8896-1(5)) Dorling Kindersley Publishing, Inc.

Einhorn, Kama. Sesame Subjects: My First Book about Things That Go. Mathieu, Joe, illus. 2006. 24p. (J). (gr. k). 7.99 (978-0-375-83515-5(6) , Random Hse. Bks. for Young Readers) Random Hse. Children's Bks.

Encyclopedia of Custom & Classic Transportation, 7 vols. Incl. Vol. 1. Great Trucks. Carroll, John. 1998. 31.95 (978-0-7910-4998-3(1)); Vol. 2. Classic Racing Cars. Hodges, David W. 1999. 31.95 (978-0-7910-4999-0(X)); Vol. 3. Classic Motorcycles. Henshaw, Peter. 1998. 31.95 (978-0-7910-5000-2(9)); Vol. 4. World's Strangest Automobiles. Kessel, Adrienne. (gr. 7 up). 1999. 35.00 (978-0-7910-5001-9(7)); Vol. 5. Pickup Trucks. Carroll, John. (gr. 5 up). 1998. 31.95 (978-0-7910-5002-6(5)); Vol. 6. World's Greatest Tractors. Carroll, John. 1998. 31.95 (978-0-7910-5003-3(3)); (YA). (Illus.). 112p. 1998. 174.65 (978-0-7910-4997-6(3) , Chelsea Hse.) Facts On File, Inc.

Encyclopedia of Custom & Classic Transportation. 2005. 80p. pap. 159.75 (978-0-7910-8454-0(X) , Chelsea Hse.) Facts On File, Inc.

Equipo Staff. El Tren. 1999. (Coleccion Mundo Maravilloso). (SPA., Illus.). 36p. (J). (gr. 2-4). 16.95 (978-84-348-4777-4(9) , SM2685) SM Ediciones ESP. *Dist:* Lectorum Pubns., Inc.

Famous People in Transportation Set. (gr. k-2). 114.95 (978-0-7368-9060-1(2)) Red Brick Learning.

Fecher, Sarah & Kespert, Deborah. On the Move. Evrard, Gaetan, illus. rev. ed. 2004. (Ladders Ser.). 32p. (J). (ps-3). pap. 6.95 (978-1-58728-620-9(3) , Two Can Publishing) T&N Children's Publishing.

Fecher, Sarah, et al. On the Move, 4 vols., Set. Evrard, Gaetan & Stuart, Jon, illus. 1999. (Ladders Ser.). 32p. (J). (gr. k-3). (978-0-7166-7711-6(3)) World Bk., Inc.

Flatt, Lizann. Let's Go! The Story of Getting from There to Here. Ritchie, Scot, illus. 2007. 40p. (J). (gr. k-3). 16.95 (***978-1-897349-02-1(5)***) Maple Tree Pr. CAN. *Dist:* Perseus Distribution.

Francis, Dorothy Brenner. Our Transportation Systems. 2001. (I Know America Ser.). 48p. (gr. 2-4). lib. bdg. 24.90 (978-0-7613-2366-2(X) , Millbrook Pr.) Lerner Publishing Group.

Freeman, Marcia S. Ambulances. 2005. (Transportation Ser.). 24p. (YA). (gr. k-3). pap. (978-0-7368-8101-2(8) , Pebble Bks.) Capstone Pr., Inc.

Freudenthal. Ways to Go. 3rd ed. 2002. (Math in Context Ser.). (Illus.). (J). stu. ed. (978-0-85229-889-3(7)) Encyclopedia Britannica, Inc.

—Ways to Go. 3rd ed. 2003. (Math in Context Ser.). (Illus.). 8.33 (978-0-03-071614-0(4)) Holt, Rinehart & Winston.

Freymann, Saxton & Elffers, Joost. Fast Food. 2006. (Illus.). 32p. (J). pap. 12.99 (978-0-439-11019-8(X) , Levine, Arthur A. Bks.) Scholastic, Inc.

From Wheels to Wings. 2002. (Illus.). (J). pap. 5.43 (978-0-7398-5928-5(5)) Steck-Vaughn.

Gakken Co. Ltd. Editors. Wheels & Wings. Time-Life Books Editors, tr. 1999. (Illus.). 88p. (J). (gr. 1-4). 14.95 (978-0-8094-4861-6(0)) Time-Life, Inc.

Gerth, Melanie. Mi Primer Gran Libro de los Vehiculos. 2004. (Mi primer gran libro de ... Ser.). (SPA., Illus.). 10p. 16.95 (978-84-7864-821-4(6)) Combel Editorial, S.A. ESP. *Dist:* Independent Pubs. Group.

Gibbs, Lynne. The Great Book of Transport. 2004. (Illus.). 160p. (YA). (978-1-904516-09-5(2)) Chrysalis Children's Bks.

Gilpin, Daniel. Transportation Solutions. 2005. (Action for the Environment Ser.). (Illus.). 32p. (J). (gr. 4-7). lib. bdg. 27.10 (978-1-58340-599-4(2)) Smart Apple Media.

Glover, David. Transportation, 5 vols., Set. World Book, Inc. Staff, ed. 1999. (Picture Reference Ser.). (Illus.). 48p. (J). (gr. 2-6). (978-0-7166-9906-4(0)) World Bk., Inc.

Glover, David & Glover, Penny. Moving. 2005. (Illus.). 30p. (J). (gr. 3-7). lib. bdg. 27.10 (978-1-58340-691-5(3)) Smart Apple Media.

Graham, Buck. My First Big Book of Questions & Answers: Things That Go. 2005. (Illus.). 10p. bds. 9.98 (978-0-7853-7227-1(X) , 7171500) Publications International, Ltd.

Graham, Ian. The Best Book of Speed Machines. (Best Book of... Ser.). (Illus.). 32p. (J). 2008. pap. 6.95 (***978-0-7534-6168-6(4)***); 2002. tchr. ed. 12.95 (978-0-7534-5436-7(X)) Houghton Mifflin Co. Trade & Reference Div. (Kingfisher).

Graham, Ian. Transportation. 1999. (Tomorrow's Technology Ser.). (Illus.). 32p. (J). lib. bdg. 16.95 (978-1-929298-40-2(4)) Chrysalis Education.

Guin, Valerie. On the Move. 2005. (Illus.). 30p. (J). (gr. 3-7). lib. bdg. 27.10 (978-1-58340-699-1(9)) Smart Apple Media.

Hall, Margaret. Transportation. (Around the World Ser.). 32p. pap. 6.95 (978-1-4034-4007-5(7)) Heinemann Library.

Hall, Margaret C. Transportation. 2001. (Around the World Ser.). (Illus.). 32p. (J). (gr. k-2). lib. bdg. 21.36 (978-1-58810-104-4(5)) Heinemann Library.

Halle. Brunnert and Partners, Flughafen Leipzig/Halle: Opus 52. 2004. (GER & ENG., Illus.). 72p. 39.00 (978-3-930698-52-3(8)) Edition Axel Menges GmbH DEU. *Dist:* National Bk. Network.

Harcourt School Publishers Staff. Getting Around the City. 3rd ed. 2002. (Trophies English Language Learners Ser.). (Illus.). pap. 5.10 (978-0-15-327650-7(9)) Harcourt Schl. Pubs.

TUV

—Going Places! 3rd ed. 2002. (Trophies English Language Learners Ser.). (Illus.). pap. 5.10 (978-0-15-327762-7(9)) Harcourt Schl. Pubs.

—Moving Goods. 3rd ed. 2002. (Horizons Ser.). (Illus.). (J). pap. 3.70 (978-0-15-333133-6(X)) Harcourt Schl. Pubs.

—Ticket, Please. 3rd ed. 2002. (Trophies English Language Learners Ser.). (Illus.). pap. 5.10 (978-0-15-327711-5(4)) Harcourt Schl. Pubs.

Harrier Jump Jet. 2004. (Press-Out & Build Ser.). (Illus.). 24p. (J). per. (978-1-84229-725-4(2)) Top That! Publishing PLC.

Harris, Michelle, et al. Transport: The Amazing Story of Ships, Trains, Aircraft & Cars, & How They Work. 2003. (Illustrated Science Encyclopedia Ser.). (Illus.). 264p. pap. 19.99 (978-0-7548-1252-4(9)) Anness Publishing GBR. *Dist:* National Bk. Network.

Harrison, James. Amazing Vehicles. Smith, Jan, illus. 2004. (Magic Color Bks.). 12p. (J). 9.95 (978-1-4027-1215-9(4)) Sterling Publishing Co., Inc.

Harrison, Peter. Transport: The Illustrated Science Encyclopedia. 2002. (gr. 3-6). lib. bdg. 30.35 (978-0-613-82093-6(2)) Tandem Library Bks.

Hart, Simon. Vamos, Vamos, Barcos! 2006. 10p. (J). (ps-ps). bds. 4.99 (978-0-8431-2109-4(2) , Price Stern Sloan) Penguin Group (USA) Inc.

Hemminger, Marcia. Transportation Early Learner Photo Fun Activities. Rogers, Kathy, ed. 2001. 8p. (J). pap. 6.95 (978-1-56472-376-5(3)) Edupress, Inc.

Hergé. Tintin: Descubro Los Transportes. 2004. (SPA., Illus.). 24p. 19.95 (978-1-59497-064-1(5)) Public Square Bks.

Hewitt, Sally. Routes & Journeys. 2006. (Science Starters Ser.). (Illus.). 32p. (J). (978-1-59604-083-0(1)) Stargazer Bks.

Hill, Lee Sullivan. Get Around in the City. 1999. (Get Around Bks.). (Illus.). 32p. (J). (gr. k-3). lib. bdg. 14.60 (978-1-57505-307-3(1) , Carolrhoda Bks.) Lerner Publishing Group.

—Get Around in the Country. 1999. (Get Around Bks.). (Illus.). 32p. (J). (gr. k-3). lib. bdg. 14.60 (978-1-57505-308-0(X) , Carolrhoda Bks.) Lerner Publishing Group.

Hoenecke, Karen. What Has Wheels? 2005. 8p. (J). pap. 4.25 (978-1-57874-085-7(1)) Kaeden Corp.

HOP, LLC. Hooked on Trains, Planes, & Cars Super Activity Kit. 2006. (J). (ps). 9.99 (978-1-933863-21-4(8)) HOP, LLC.

—Super Activity 3-pack - Hooked on Things That Go. 2006. (J). (ps). 24.99 (978-1-933863-96-2(X)) HOP, LLC.

Imperato, Teresa. On the Go! A Transportation Book. Rayner, Olivia, illus. 2005. 10p. (J). 7.95 (978-1-58117-271-3(0) , Intervisual/Piggy Toes) Dalmatian Pr.

—Speed Machines: A Pop-up Book with Moving Gears. Robinson, Keith, illus. 2005. 8p. (J). 14.95 (978-1-58117-323-9(7) , Intervisual/Piggy Toes) Dalmatian Pr.

James, Diane. Let's Go for a Ride! Bulloch, Ivan, illus. rev. ed. 2004. (My Turn Ser.). 12p. (J). (ps-k). bds. 6.95 (978-1-58728-005-4(1) , Two Can Publishing) T&N Children's Publishing.

Johnson, Marion. Caillou: The School Bus. 2003. (Clubhouse Ser.). (Illus.). 24p. (J). pap. 2.50 (978-2-89450-421-5(7)) Chouette Publishing CAN. *Dist:* Independent Pubs. Group.

Kappely, Sarah. Happy Baby: Things That Go. rev. ed. 2003. (Priddy Bicknell Big Ideas for Little People Ser.). (Illus.). 28p. (J). bds. 5.95 (978-0-312-49134-5(4) , Priddy Bks.) St. Martin's Pr.

Keller, Irene. The Thingumajig Book of Manners. Keller, Dick, illus. 2002. (J). (ps-3). 6.95 (978-0-8249-5430-7(0) , Ideals Children's Bks.) Ideals Pubns.

Kent, Lorna, illus. On the Move. 2004. 8p. (J). bds. 3.99 (978-1-85854-089-4(5)) Brimax Books Ltd. GBR. *Dist:* Byeway Bks.

Keoke, Emory Dean & Porterfield, Kay Marie. American Indian Contributions to the World. 2005. (American Indian Contributions to the World Ser.). (Illus.). 160p. (gr. 4-9). (J). 35.00 (978-0-8160-5395-7(2)); (YA). 35.00 (978-0-8160-5397-1(9)) Facts On File, Inc.

Kespert, Deborah & Fecher, Sarah. On the Move. Evrard, Gaetan, illus. rev. ed. 2003. (Ladders Ser.). 32p. (J). (ps-3). 12.95 (978-1-58728-605-6(X) , Two Can Publishing) T&N Children's Publishing.

Lacome, Susie. Big Shiny Sparkly Book of Things-That-Go. 2004. (Illus.). 10p. (J). pap. 9.98 (978-0-7624-2005-6(7) , Courage Bks.) Running Pr. Bk. Pubs.

Lassieur, Allison. Taxis. 2000. (Transportation Library). (Illus.). 24p. (J). (gr. 1-2). lib. bdg. 18.60 (978-0-7368-0365-6(3) , Bridgestone Bks.) Capstone Pr., Inc.

—Taxis. 1999. (Illus.). pap. 14.60 (978-0-516-21876-2(X) , Children's Pr.) Scholastic Library Publishing.

Lindeen, Carol K. Ambulancias. 2006. (ENG & SPA.). (J). (978-0-7368-5865-6(2)) Capstone Pr., Inc.

Lomberg, Michelle. Avoiding Gridlock. Schwartzenberger, Tina, ed. 2004. (Understanding Global Issues). (Illus.). 56p. (J). (gr. 10-12). lib. bdg. (978-1-58340-357-0(4)) Weigl Pubs., Inc.

Make Believe Ideas Staff & Gordon, Bob. Touch & Sparkle Emergency. 2005. (Illus.). 12p. (ps-ps). bds. 5.95 (978-1-905051-58-8(1)) Make Believe Ideas GBR. *Dist:* Ingram Pub. Services.

Mansir, A. Richard. Stagecoach: The Ride of a Century. 1999. (Building America Ser.). (Illus.). 32p. (J). (ps-3). 15.95 (978-1-57091-960-2(7)) Charlesbridge Publishing, Inc.

Maquinas Extremas Series, 5 bks., Set. 2003. (Maquinas Extremas Ser.). (SPA & ENG., Illus.). (J). 103.50 (978-0-8239-6911-1(8) , Buenas Letra) Rosen Publishing Group, Inc., The.

Mattern, Joanne. Safety on the Go. 1999. (Safety First Ser.). (Illus.). 24p. (J). (gr. k-6). lib. bdg. 21.35 (978-1-57765-075-1(1) , Checkerboard Library) ABDO Publishing Co.

Mattern, Joanne. Staying Safe in the Car. 2006. (J). (ENG & SPA.). pap. ***(978-0-8368-8065-6(X));*** (ENG & SPA.). lib. bdg. ***(978-0-8368-8058-8(7));*** (Illus.). 24p. pap. ***(978-0-8368-7800-4(0));*** (Illus.). 24p. lib. bdg. ***(978-0-8368-7793-9(4))*** Stevens, Gareth Inc. (Weekly Reader Early Learning Library).

Maynard, Christopher. I Wonder Why Planes Have Wings: And Other Questions about Transportation. 2003. (I Wonder Why Ser.). (Illus.). 32p. (J). (gr. k-3). 6.95 (978-0-7534-5662-0(1) , Kingfisher) Houghton Mifflin Co. Trade & Reference Div.

McMorrow, Annalisa. Terrific Transportation. 1999. (Illus.). 80p. (J). pap. 9.95 (978-1-57612-112-2(7)) Monday Morning Bks., Inc.

Miller, Heather. Camiones de Bombero. 2003. (Ruedas, Alas y Agua Ser.).Tr. of Fire Trucks. (ENG & SPA., Illus.). 24p. (J). (ps-1). lib. bdg. 18.50 (978-1-4034-0920-1(X)) Heinemann Library.

Miller-Schroeder, Patricia. Wings, Wheels & Keels: The Science of Transportation. 1999. (Science @ Work Ser.). (Illus.). 48p. (J). (gr. 4-6). lib. bdg. 27.12 (978-0-7398-0139-0(2)) Raintree.

Mintzer, Richard. The National Transportation Safety Board. 2002. (Your Government Ser.). (Illus.). 64p. (J). 25.00 (978-0-7910-6794-9(7) , Chelsea Hse.) Facts On File, Inc.

Mitzo Thompson, Kim. Trucks, Planes, & Trains / Caminos, aviones y Trenes. 2006. (Dual Language Readers Ser.). 32p. (J). pap. 4.99 (978-0-7696-4627-5(1)) School Specialty Publishing.

Morgan, Terry E. The How to Trucker's Rate Manual. 2001. pap. (978-0-9721289-0-2(5)) Commercial Transportation Consultants, LLC.

Morris, Mark. Transportation. 2006. (Illus.). 56p. (J). pap. (978-1-4034-7435-3(4)) Heinemann.

Nathan, Emma. Transportation. 2002. (Eyeopeners Ser.). (Illus.). 24p. (J). 22.45 (978-1-56711-654-0(X) , Blackbirch Pr., Inc.) Thomson Gale.

—El Transporte. 2002. (Abre los Ojos y Aprende Serie).Tr. of Eyeopeners: Transportation. (SPA.). 24p. (J). (-3). 22.45 (978-1-4103-0021-8(8) , Blackbirch Pr., Inc.) Thomson Gale.

Orr, Tamra. The Department of Transportation. 2005. (This Is Your Government Ser.). (Illus.). 64p. lib. bdg. (978-1-4042-0211-5(0)) Rosen Publishing Group, Inc., The.

Oxlade, Chris. Boats & Ships. (Transportation Around the World Ser.). 32p. pap. 6.95 (978-1-4034-4132-4(4)) Heinemann Library.

—Transport: 40 Great Science Experiments & Projects. 2004. (Hands-On Science Ser.). (Illus.). 64p. pap. 10.99 (978-1-84215-857-9(0) , Southwater) Anness Publishing GBR. *Dist:* National Bk. Network.

—Transportation Around the World: How Do We Get Where We're Going?, 8 bks. (Illus.). (gr. k-2). Set lib. bdg. 170.88 (978-1-57572-310-5(7)); Set 1. (J). lib. bdg. 85.44 (978-1-57572-304-4(2)); Set 2. lib. bdg. 85.44 (978-1-57572-309-9(3)) Heinemann Library.

—Traveling on Water. Peppe, Mark, illus. 1998. (Launch Pad Library). 32p. (J). (gr. k-4). 11.95 (978-1-58087-001-6(5)) Stampley, C.D. Enterprises, Inc.

—Traveling on Water. 2003. (Discovery Guides Ser.). 32p. (J). 11.95 (978-1-58728-227-0(5)); pap. 6.95 (978-1-58728-233-1(X)) T&N Children's Publishing. (Two Can Publishing).

Pascoe, Elaine, ed. London Underground. 2003. (Super Structures of the World Ser.). (Illus.). 48p. (J). 24.95 (978-1-56711-866-7(6)); 11.20 (978-1-4103-0190-1(7)) Thomson Gale. (Blackbirch Pr., Inc.).

Pebble Books: Transportation: Who, Where, & What. 2005. (YA). (gr. k-3). 475.20 (978-0-7368-4216-7(0) , Pebble Bks.) Capstone Pr., Inc.

Phillips, Sarah. Things That Go. 2007. (Trace, Stick & Learn Ser.). (Illus.). 12p. (J). (ps-3). pap. 4.99 ***(978-1-84610-428-2(9))*** Make Believe Ideas GBR. *Dist:* Ingram Pub. Services.

Pipe, Jim. Getting Around. 2004. (Earthwise Ser.). (J). lib. bdg. 27.10 (978-1-932799-52-1(4)) Stargazer Bks.

Priddy Books Staff & Priddy, Roger. Happy Baby: Things That Go. 2004. (Illus.). 28p. (J). bds. 8.95 (978-0-312-49198-7(0) , Priddy Bks.) St. Martin's Pr.

Rau, Dana Meachen. Travel in American History. 2006. (Illus.). 24p. (J). lib. bdg. (978-0-8368-7210-1(X)) Stevens, Gareth Inc.

—Ways to Go, Level A. Contch-Morgan, Jane, illus. 2001. (Early Reader Ser.). 24p. (J). (gr. k up). lib. bdg. 18.60 (978-0-7565-0071-9(0)) Compass Point Bks.

Rey, H. A. How Do You Get There? 1998. (Illus.). 20p. (J). (gr. k-ps). pap. 5.95 (978-0-395-90694-1(6)) Houghton Mifflin Co. Trade & Reference Div.

Richard, John. Big Book of Transport. Leeks, David, illus. 2004. 48p. (J). 7.99 (978-1-85854-550-9(1)) Brimax Books Ltd. GBR. *Dist:* Byeway Bks.

Richards, Jon. Transport. 2005. (Illus.). 32p. (J). (gr. 3 up). lib. bdg. 27.10 (978-1-59389-196-1(2)) Chrysalis Education.

Ring, Susan. De aqui a Alla. 2005. Tr. of From Here to There. (SPA., Illus.). 16p. (J). (gr. 1 up). lib. bdg. 15.93 (978-0-7368-4175-7(X)) Capstone Pr., Inc.

—From Here to There. 2003. (Illus.). 17p. (J). 15.93 (978-0-7368-2908-3(3)); pap. (978-0-7368-2867-3(2)) Yellow Umbrella Pr.

Roberts, Sheena. We All Go Travelling By. Bell, Siobhan, illus. 2005. 24p. (J). 17.99 incl. audio compact disk (978-1-84148-168-5(8)) Barefoot Bks., Inc.

Rogers, Alan. De Viaje. 2004. (Pequenos Gigantes Ser.). (SPA., Illus.). 16p. (ps-k). (J). pap. 3.95 (978-1-58728-960-6(1)); 5.95 (978-1-58728-295-9(X)) T&N Children's Publishing. (Two Can Publishing).

Rosenberg, Aaron. Kick Scooters: Techniques & Tricks. 2005. (Rad Sports Techniques & Tricks Ser.). (Illus.). 48p. (YA). (gr. 5-8). lib. bdg. 26.50 (978-0-8239-3846-9(8)) Rosen Publishing Group, Inc., The.

Roy, Jennifer Rozines & Roy, Gregory. Shapes in Transportation. 2006. (Math All Around Ser.). (Illus.). 32p. (J). lib. bdg. 28.50 (978-0-7614-2265-5(X) , Benchmark Bks.) Cavendish, Marshall Corp.

Royston, Angela. Transportation. 1999. (Environment Starts Here Ser.). (Illus.). 32 p. (J). (gr. 1-4). 17.98 (978-0-8172-5352-3(1)) Raintree.

Royston, Angela. Travel of the Future. 2007. (J). pap. ***(978-1-4329-0132-5(X));*** lib. bdg. ***(978-1-4329-0127-1(3))*** Heinemann Library.

Sandler, Martin W. Driving Around the USA: Automobiles in American Life. 2003. (Transportation in America Ser.). (Illus.). 64p. (YA). 21.95 (978-0-19-513230-4(0)) Oxford Univ. Pr., Inc.

Saunders-Smith, Gail. Transportation: Basic Vehicles, 4 vols., Set. 1998. (J). pap. 53.00 (978-0-516-29781-1(3) , Children's Pr.) Scholastic Library Publishing.

Schaefer, Lola M. Formas en Movimiento. 2003. (Ruedas, Alas y Agua Ser.).Tr. of Shapes to Go. (SPA & ENG., Illus.). 24p. (J). (ps-1). lib. bdg. 18.50 (978-1-4034-0923-2(4)) Heinemann Library.

—Wheels, Wings & Water. 2003. (Wheels, Wings, & Water Ser.). (Illus.). 24p. (J). pap. (978-1-4034-3625-2(8)) Heinemann Library.

—Wheels, Wings, & Water ABC. 2003. (Wheels, Wings, & Water Ser.). (Illus.). 24p. (J). lib. bdg. 18.50 (978-1-4034-0887-7(4)) Heinemann Library.

—Wheels, Wings, & Water ABC. 2003. (gr. k-3). lib. bdg. 13.30 (978-0-613-67441-6(3)) Tandem Library Bks.

Schaefer, Lola M. & Miller, Heather. Wheels, Wings, & Water Series, 10 bks., Set. 2003. (Illus.). (J). (ps-1). lib. bdg. 185.00 (978-1-4034-0888-4(2)) Heinemann Library.

Schiller, Pam. Let's Go! 2006. (NOODLEBUG Activities for Hands-on Learning Ser.). 32p. (J). (gr. k-k). pap. 4.99 (978-0-7696-4235-2(7)) School Specialty Publishing.

Scholastic, Inc. Staff. My First Jumbo Book on the Go. 2007. (Little Scholastic Ser.). 10p. (J). 9.99 ***(978-0-545-03039-7(0))*** Scholastic, Inc.

Schon, Isabel, ed. Transportes (Transportation), 2 bks. Ferrer, Martin Luis Guzman, tr. Incl. Autobuses Escolares. Ready, Dee. lib. bdg. 18.60 (978-1-56065-792-7(8) , CAP1073); Camiones de Bomberos. Brady, Peter. lib. bdg. 18.60 (978-1-56065-791-0(X) , CAP1078); 24p. (J). (gr. k-3). 1998. (SPA., Illus.). Set lib. bdg. 37.20 (978-0-7368-0148-5(0) , Bridgestone Bks.) Capstone Pr., Inc.

School Zone Publishing Company Staff. Beep, Beep! 1998. (Start to Read! Ser.). (Illus.). (J). tchr.'s training gde. ed. 360.00 incl. cd-rom (978-0-88743-641-3(2)); ring bd., lab manual ed., tchr.'s training gde. ed. 149.99 incl. audio compact disk (978-0-88743-588-1(2)); ring bd., tchr.'s training gde. ed. 49.99 incl. audio compact disk (978-0-88743-587-4(4) , 08501) School Zone Publishing Co.

School Zone Publishing Interactive Staff. Beep, Beep!/I Want a Pet. 2001. (On-Track Software Ser.). (Illus.). 32p. (J). pap. 13.99 incl. cd-rom (978-0-88743-945-2(4) , 08821) School Zone Publishing Co.

Schuette, Sarah L. 3, 2, 1 Go! A Transportation Countdown. 2003. (A+ Counting Books). (Illus.). 32p. (J). (gr. k-1). lib. bdg. 22.60 (978-0-7368-1678-6(X) , Aplus Bks.) Capstone Pr., Inc.

Sebastiani, Laura, creator. Penny & Drew's Penciltips: Transportation. 2006. 80p. (J). 4.95 (978-0-9766793-3-2(7)) ThoughtRockets, Inc.

Shuter. Travel Through Time, 6 vols., Set. 2004. (Illus.). (J). 154.20 (978-1-4109-0585-7(3)) Raintree.

Smith, Alastair, ed. Travel & Transport Then & Now. 2004. (Then & Now Flip Flaps Ser.). (Illus.). 16p. (J). (gr. 2 up). pap. 7.95 (978-0-7460-3102-5(5)) EDC Publishing.

Souter, Janet. Air Marshal & Careers in Transportation Security. 2006. (Homeland Security & Counterterrorism Careers Ser.). (Illus.). 128p. (J). lib. bdg. 31.93 (978-0-7660-2647-6(7)) Enslow Pubs., Inc.

Stanley, Mandy. On the Move. 2004. (All Aboard Ser.). Orig. Title: Vamos de Viaje. (Illus.). 12p. (J). (ps-k). bds. 3.95 (978-0-7534-5749-8(0) , Kingfisher) Houghton Mifflin Co. Trade & Reference Div.

—Vamos de Viaje/On the Move. 2004. (Todos A Bordo Ser.). (ENG & SPA., Illus.). 12p. (J). (ps-k). bds. 4.95 (978-0-7534-5812-9(8) , Kingfisher) Houghton Mifflin Co. Trade & Reference Div.

Starke, John. Speed Machines: Mission Xtreme 3D. 2004. (Mission Xtreme 3D Ser.). (Illus.). 18p. (J). pap. 5.95 (978-1-902626-50-5(8)) Red Bird Publishing GBR. *Dist:* Weatherhill, Inc.

Stickland, Paul. On the Move, 4 bks. Stickland, Paul, illus. Incl. Boats. lib. bdg. 19.93 (978-0-8368-2151-2(3)); Cars. lib. bdg. 19.93 (978-0-8368-2152-9(1)); Planes. lib. bdg. 19.93 (978-0-8368-2153-6(X)); Trains. lib. bdg. 19.93 (978-0-8368-2154-3(8)); 16p. (J). (ps up). (Illus.). 1998. Set lib. bdg. 79.73 (978-0-8368-2150-5(5)) Stevens, Gareth Inc.

Stille, Darlene R. Police Cars. 2002. (Illus.). 32p. (J). (gr. 1 up). lib. bdg. 19.93 (978-0-7565-0290-4(X)) Compass Point Bks.

Stoppard, Miriam. On the Move: Toddler Playskills. 2006. (Let's Play Ser.). (Illus.). 14p. (J). bds. 8.99 (978-0-7566-1700-4(6)) Dorling Kindersley Publishing, Inc.

Stringer, John. Machines, Transportation & Art Activities. (Arty Facts Ser.). (Illus.). 48p. (J). (gr. 3-4). 2003. lib. bdg. (978-0-7787-1116-2(1)); 2002. pap. (978-0-7787-1144-5(7)) Crabtree Publishing Co.

—Machines, Transportation & Art Activities. 2002. (gr. 3-6). lib. bdg. 17.60 (978-0-613-52874-0(3)) Tandem Library Bks.

Sundance, ed. Machines That Travel. 2000. (ps-2). lib. bdg. 11.65 (978-0-613-37624-2(2)) Tandem Library Bks.

TBC Staff. Cutting Edge Transportation: High Speed, Power & Performance. 2006. (Illus.). 56p. (J). (978-0-431-13270-9(4)) Heinemann.

Terrific Transportation. 2000. (Learning Fun for Little Ones Ser.). (Illus.). 64p. (ps-1). pap. 8.99 (978-0-88724-589-3(7) , CD-6416) Carson-Dellosa Publishing Co., Inc.

Townsend. Out There, 8 vols., Set 1. 2004. (J). 228.48 (978-1-4109-0568-0(3)) Raintree.

Traffic: Individual Title Six-Pack Pouch - Level B. (Lighthouse Ser.). 12p. (gr. k-1). 24.00 (978-0-7578-0810-4(7)) Rigby Education.

Transportacion. 2005. 100p. (J). spiral bd. 14.99 (978-1-59441-462-6(9) , K04013) Carson-Dellosa Publishing Co., Inc.

Transportation. (Butterfly Bks.). (Illus.). 15p. (J). 11.95 (978-0-86685-613-3(7)) International Bk. Ctr., Inc.

Transportation, 8 bks. Incl. Bulldozers. Brady, Peter. 1996. lib. bdg. 18.60 (978-1-56065-351-6(5)); Cars. Ready, Dee. 1997. lib. bdg. 18.60 (978-1-56065-610-4(7)); Fire Trucks. Brady, Peter. 1996. lib. bdg. 18.60 (978-1-56065-350-9(7)); Freight Trains. Brady, Peter. 1996. lib. bdg. 18.60 (978-1-56065-349-3(3)); Motorcycles. Ready, Dee. 1997. lib. bdg. 18.60 (978-1-56065-611-1(5)); School Buses. Ready, Dee. 1997. lib. bdg. 18.60 (978-1-56065-612-8(3)); Tractors. Brady, Peter. 1996. lib. bdg. 18.60 (978-1-56065-348-6(5)); Trucks. Ready, Dee. 1997. lib. bdg. 18.60 (978-1-56065-613-5(1)); 24p. (J). (gr. 1-2). (Illus.). Set lib. bdg. 148.80 (978-1-56065-635-7(2) , Bridgestone Bks.) Capstone Pr., Inc.

Transportation & Communication. (J). (gr. k-1). (978-84-342-2418-6(6) , PR30572) Parramon Ediciones S.A. ESP. *Dist:* Lectorum Pubns., Inc.

Transportation & Communication Series, 14 bks., Set. Incl. Bridges. Farbman, Melinda. 48p. lib. bdg. 23.93 (978-0-7660-1647-7(1)); Cars. Flammang, James M. 48p. lib. bdg. 23.93 (978-0-7660-1646-0(3)); Fire Engines. Molzahn, Arlene Bourgeois. 48p. lib. bdg. 23.93 (978-0-7660-1643-9(9)); Motorcycles. Stuart, Dee. 48p. lib. bdg. 23.93 (978-0-7660-1648-4(X)); Television. Feeney, Kathy. 48p. lib. bdg. 23.93 (978-0-7660-1644-6(7)); Trains. Perry, Phyllis J. 46p. lib. bdg. 23.93 (978-0-7660-1645-3(5)); (J). (gr. 1-4). 2001. (Illus.). Set lib. bdg. 284.25 (978-0-7660-1804-4(0)) Enslow Pubs., Inc.

The Transportation Library, 20 bks. Incl. Airplanes. Schaefer, Lola M. 2000. lib. bdg. 18.60 (978-0-7368-0358-8(0)); Ambulances. Hanson, Anne E. 2001. lib. bdg. 18.60 (978-0-7368-0841-5(8)); Barges. Schaefer, Lola M. 2000. lib. bdg. 18.60 (978-0-7368-0502-5(8)); Bicycles. Schaefer, Lola M. 2000. lib. bdg. 18.60 (978-0-7368-0359-5(9)); Buses. Lassieur, Allison. 2000. lib. bdg. 18.60 (978-0-7368-0360-1(2)); Cable Cars. Schaefer, Lola M. 2000. lib. bdg. 18.60 (978-0-7368-0361-8(0)); Cargo Ships. Richardson, Adele D. 2000. lib. bdg. 18.60 (978-0-7368-0606-0(7)); Delivery Trucks. Richardson, Adele D. 2000. lib. bdg. 18.60 (978-0-7368-0609-1(1)); Ferries. Schaefer, Lola M. 2000. lib. bdg. 18.60 (978-0-7368-0362-5(9)); Fire Engines. Hanson, Anne E. 2001. lib. bdg. 18.60 (978-0-7368-0842-2(6)); Freight Trains. Richardson, Adele D. 2000. lib. bdg. 18.60 (978-0-7368-0607-7(5)); Passenger Trains. Lassieur, Allison. 2000. lib. bdg. 18.60 (978-0-7368-0363-2(7)); Police Cars. Olien, Becky. 2001. lib. bdg. 18.60 (978-0-7368-0843-9(4)); Rescue Helicopters. Olien, Becky. 2001. lib. bdg. 18.60 (978-0-7368-0844-6(2)); Subways. Lassieur, Allison. 2000. lib. bdg. 18.60 (978-0-7368-0364-9(5)); Taxis. Lassieur, Allison. 2000. lib. bdg. 18.60 (978-0-7368-0365-6(3)); Tow Trucks. Schaefer, Lola M. 2000. lib. bdg. 18.60 (978-0-7368-0503-2(6)); Tractor Trailers. Schaefer, Lola M. 2000. lib. bdg. 18.60 (978-0-7368-0504-9(4)); Transport Helicopters. Richardson, Adele D. 2000. lib. bdg. 18.60 (978-0-7368-0608-4(3)); Tugboats. Schaefer, Lola M. 2000. lib. bdg. 18.60 (978-0-7368-0505-6(2)); 24p. (J). (gr. 1-2). (Illus.). Set lib. bdg. 372.00 (978-0-7368-0885-9(X) , Bridgestone Bks.) Capstone Pr., Inc.

Transportation Technology Systems. 2nd rev. ed. 2004. 55p. pap. (978-0-86657-514-0(6)) Lab-Volt Systems, Inc.

Transportation: Then & Now: Small Versions of Big Books. (On Our Way to English Ser.). (gr. 3 up). 35.50 (978-0-7578-7248-8(4)) Rigby Education.

Transportation: Then & Now: Third Grade Big Books. (On Our Way to English Ser.). (gr. 3 up). 29.95 (978-0-7578-4209-2(7)) Rigby Education.

Transtech: A Tour of Transportation Technology, 2 vols. (YA). cd-rom 129.95 (978-0-7365-9925-2(8)) Films Media Group.

Trumbauer, Lisa. On the Go! 2000. (Yellow Umbrella Books). (Illus.). 16p. (J). (gr. 1). lib. bdg. 14.60 (978-0-7368-0735-7(7) , Pebble Bks.) Capstone Pr., Inc.

Tuxworth, Nicola. Learn-a-Word Picture Book: Things That Go, 12 vols. 2006. (Learn-A-Word Picture Bks.). (Illus.). 12p. bds. 6.99 (978-0-7548-1462-7(9) , Lorenz Bks.) Anness Publishing GBR. *Dist:* National Bk. Network.

Tuxworth, Nicola & Lorenz Editors. Things That Go. 2001. (Let's Look at... Ser.). (Illus.). 20p. 5.95 (978-0-7548-0954-8(4)) Anness Publishing GBR. *Dist:* National Bk. Network.

Two-Can Publishing Ltd. Staff, contrib. by. Wings & Wheels. 2004. (Interfact Play & Discover Ser.). (Illus.). 48p. (J). (ps-2). 14.95 incl. cd-rom (978-1-58728-629-2(7) , Two Can Publishing) T&N Children's Publishing.

Ultimate Speed. 2005. (Ultimate Speed Ser.). (J). lib. bdg. 143.76 (978-1-59716-094-0(6)) Bearport Publishing Co., Inc.

Varonka, Steve. Hard Coal Times Vol. 3: Early Coal Transportation. 2004. (Illus.). 24p. (YA). 4.72 (978-0-9709630-5-5(X)) Coal Hole Productions.

Vehiculos de Alta Tecnologia Series, 6 bks., Set. 2003. (Vehiculos de Alta Tecnologia Ser.). (SPA & ENG., Illus.). (J). lib. bdg. 103.50 (978-0-8239-6919-7(3) , Buenas Letra) Rosen Publishing Group, Inc., The.

Walker, Niki. Transportation Disaster Alert! 2005. (Disaster Alert! Ser.). (Illus.). 32p. (J). (978-0-7787-1584-9(1)) Crabtree Publishing Co.

Ward, Beck. On the Go. 2005. (Illus.). 10p. (J). pap. 7.95 (978-0-7624-1986-9(5) , Running Pr. Kids) Running Pr. Bk. Pubs.

Waxman, Laura Hamilton. Ambulances. 2004. (Pull Ahead Bks.). (Illus.). 32p. (J). (gr. k-2). lib. bdg. 22.60 (978-0-8225-0769-7(2)) Lerner Publishing Group.

Weber, Rebecca. How We Travel. 2004. (Spyglass Books). (Illus.). 24p. (J). (gr. 1 up). lib. bdg. 19.93 (978-0-7565-0652-0(2)) Compass Point Bks.

Welvaert, Scott R. Follow That Crop: From the Farmer's Field to Our Grocery Store. 2003. (From Here to There Ser.). (J). (978-1-58417-194-2(4)); pap. (978-1-58417-195-9(2)) Lake Street Pubs.

Wheels & Rockets. (J). (gr. 4). 42.95 (978-0-673-72657-5(6) , Scott Foresman) Addison Wesley Schl.

Will, Sandra. Transportation Inventions: From Subways to Submarines. 2006. (Which Came First? Ser.). (Illus.). 32p. (J). lib. bdg. 25.27 (978-1-59716-133-6(0)) Bearport Publishing Co., Inc.

World Book, Inc Staff, contrib. by. On the Move. 2007. (***978-0-7166-7728-4(8)***) World Bk., Inc.

A World of Wheels, 8 vols., Set. (Illus.). 104,132p. (gr. 7 up). lib. bdg. (978-1-59084-483-0(1)) Mason Crest Pubs.

Ziegler, Mark. Wacky Wheelies: A Book of Transportation Jokes. Haberstroh, Anne, illus. 2005. (Read-It! Readers Ser.). 24p. (C). (gr. 1-3). 18.60 (978-1-4048-0966-6(X)) Picture Window Bks.

TRANSPORTATION, AUTOMOTIVE

see also Automobiles; Buses; Trucks

Beyer, Mark. Transportation of the Future. 2002. (gr. 7-12). lib. bdg. 15.25 (978-0-613-58742-6(1)) Tandem Library Bks.

Dorling Kindersley Publishing Staff. My Little Things That Go Carrying Case. 2003. (Illus.). (J). bds. 9.99 (978-0-7894-9907-3(X)) Dorling Kindersley Publishing, Inc.

Jefferis. Mean Machines, 4 vols., Set 1. 2004. (J). 114.24 (978-1-4109-0559-8(4)); (Illus.). pap. 32.20 (978-1-4109-0833-9(X)) Raintree.

—Monster Machines, 6 packs, 30 Bks., Set. 2004. (Illus.). pap. 214.65 (978-1-4109-1266-4(3)) Raintree.

Maynard, Christopher. I Wonder Why Planes Have Wings: And Other Questions about Transportation. 2003. (gr. k-3). lib. bdg. 14.10 (978-0-613-90897-9(X)) Tandem Library Bks.

Mean Machines Series, 4 bks., Set 2. 2004. (Illus.). (J). 262.32 (978-1-4109-1111-7(X)); pap. 32.20 (978-1-4109-1200-8(0)) Harcourt Schl. Pubs.

Shuter, Jane. On the Road: Travel by Road. 2004. (Technology Through Time Ser.). (Illus.). 32p. (J). lib. bdg. 25.70 (978-1-4109-0582-6(9)) Raintree.

Winget, Mary. Taxis. 2007. (Pull Ahead Books-Mighty Movers Ser.). (J). 22.60 (978-0-8225-6419-5(X) , Lerner Pubns.) Lerner Publishing Group.

TRANSPORTATION, AUTOMOTIVE—FICTION

Auerbach, Annie. Police on Patrol. 2003. (gr. k-3). lib. bdg. 11.25 (978-0-613-66533-9(3)) Tandem Library Bks.

—Three-Alarm Fire! Ewers, Joe & Mitchell, Steve, illus. 2003. (Matchbox Ser.). 24p. (J). pap. 3.50 (978-0-689-85897-0(3) , Little Simon) Simon & Schuster Children's Publishing.

Redmond, Diane. Wendy's Big Game. Hot Animation Staff, Animation, illus. 2003. (Bob the Builder Ser.: Vol. 6). 24p. (J). pap. 3.50 (978-0-689-85460-6(9) , Simon Spotlight) Simon & Schuster Children's Publishing.

Silverhardt, Lauryn. Muck's Muddy Day. 2003. (Illus.). 32p. (gr. k-3). lib. bdg. 11.25 (978-0-613-66368-7(3)) Tandem Library Bks.

Sycamore, Beth. Sweep with Street Sweeper. MacLeod, Lee, illus. 2003. (Matchbox Ser.). 16p. (J). 6.99 (978-0-689-86205-2(9) , Little Simon) Simon & Schuster Children's Publishing.

TRANSPORTATION—FICTION

Aigner-Clark, Julie. Things That Go! Zaidi, Nadeem, illus. 2006. (Baby Einstein Ser.). 16p. (J). (ps-17). bds. 5.99 (978-0-7868-4949-9(5)) Baby Einstein Co., LLC, The.

Awdry, Wilbert V. A Day Out with Thomas. Stubbs, Tommy, illus. 2003. (Thomas & Friends Ser.). 10p. (J). (gr. k-2). bds. 5.99 (978-0-375-82562-0(2) , Random Hse. Bks. for Young Readers) Random Hse. Children's Bks.

—Hooray for Thomas! And Other Thomas the Tank Engine Stories. 2005. (Random House Pictureback Book Ser.). (Illus.). 24p. (J). (ps-2). pap. 3.99 (978-0-375-82876-8(1) , Random Hse. Bks. for Young Readers) Random Hse. Children's Bks.

—Keeping Track of Thomas. 2003. (Thomas & Friends Ser.). (Illus.). 12p. (J). (ps-2). pap. 6.99 (978-0-375-82594-1(0) , Random Hse. Bks. for Young Readers) Random Hse. Children's Bks.

—Thomas & Friends: On the Track. . . There & Back. Red Giraffe, illus. 2004. 16p. (J). (gr. k-ps). bds. 4.99 (978-0-375-82774-7(9) , Random Hse. Bks. for Young Readers) Random Hse. Children's Bks.

Awdry, Wilbert V. & Dalby, C. Reginald. Thomas the Tank Engine. anniv. ed. 2005. (Illus.). 64p. (J). (ps-2). 9.95 (978-0-375-83373-1(0) , Random Hse. Bks. for Young Readers) Random Hse. Children's Bks.

Awdry, Wilbert V. & Terrill, Elizabeth. Thomas & Friends: Go, Train, Go! Stubbs, Tommy, illus. 2005. (I Can Read It All by Myself Ser.). 48p. (J). (ps-2). 8.99 (978-0-375-83177-5(0)); lib. bdg. 12.99 (978-0-375-93177-2(5)) Random Hse. Children's Bks. (Random Hse. Bks. for Young Readers).

Berger, Samantha. Honk! Toot! Beep! Elliott, Gloria, illus. 2001. (My First Hello Reader! Ser.). 32p. (J). (gr. k-2). pap. 3.99 (978-0-439-21037-9(2)) Scholastic, Inc.

Blackstone, Stella. I Wish I Were a Pilot. Grover, Max, illus. 2005. 32p. (J). (ps-ps). pap. 15.99 (978-1-84148-341-2(9)) Barefoot Bks., Inc.

—Oso en Bicicleta. 2003. (SPA.). (gr. k-3). lib. bdg. 14.15 (978-0-613-65705-1(5)) Tandem Library Bks.

Book Company Staff. Beep Beep. 2003. (Novelty Bks.). (Illus.). (J). 15.95 (978-1-74047-232-6(2)) Book Co. Publishing Pty, Ltd., The AUS. *Dist:* Penton Overseas, Inc.

Boulter, Steve, illus. Let's Go! 2007. (Rattle Bks.). 8p. (J). (ps). bds. 4.99 (***978-0-7641-6076-9(1)***) Barron's Educational Series, Inc.

Burton, Virginia Lee. Maybelle the Cable Car. Burton, Virginia Lee, illus. 2002. (Illus.). (J). 14.66 (978-0-7587-3114-2(0)) Book Wholesalers, Inc.

—Maybelle the Cable Car. 2001. (Illus.). 32p. (J). (gr. k-3). pap. 9.95 incl. audio (978-0-618-16440-0(5)) Houghton Mifflin Co. Trade & Reference Div.

Carlson, Melody. God Goes with Me. Banek, Yvette Santiago, illus. 2000. (God Is Here Ser.). 20p. (ps-k). 9.99 (978-1-58134-160-7(1) , Crossway Bibles) Crossway Bks.

Cimarusti, Marie Torres. Peek-A-Choo-Choo! Peterson, Stephanie, illus. 2007. 12p. (J). (ps). 10.99 (***978-0-525-47842-3(6)*** , Dutton Juvenile) Penguin Group (USA) Inc.

Cottrell, Janet L. Train Ride to Grandma's. 2000. 27p. (J). pap. 8.00 (978-0-8059-5065-6(6)) Dorrance Publishing Co., Inc.

Courtney, Richard, illus. Thomas, Percy, & the Dragon. 2003. (Step into Reading Ser.). 32p. (J). (ps-1). pap. 3.99 (978-0-375-82230-8(5) , Random Hse. Bks. for Young Readers) Random Hse. Children's Bks.

Crampton, Gertrude. Tootle. Gergely, Tibor, illus. deluxe ed. Date not set. (J). (ps-2). reprint ed. (978-1-929566-58-7(1)) Cronies.

—Tootle: Classic Edition. Gergely, Tibor, illus. Date not set. 21p. (J). (ps-1). (978-1-929566-53-2(0)) Cronies.

Disney's Cars, Boats, Planes & Trains: Book about Things That Go. 2020. 48p. (J). (ps-3). 12.99 (978-0-7868-3304-7(1)) Disney Pr.

DK Publishing. Wheels on the Bus. 2008. 10p. (J). (ps-k). 4.99 (***978-0-7566-3814-6(3)***) Dorling Kindersley Publishing, Inc.

Eastman, P. D. Ve, Perro, Ve! Go, Dog. Go! Perdomo, Adolfo Perez, tr. 2003. Tr. of Go, Dog, Go!. (SPA & ENG., Illus.). 24p. (J). (gr. k-ps). bds. 4.99 (978-0-375-82361-9(1) , RH Para Ninos) Random Hse. Children's Bks.

Franco, Betsy. Going to Grandma's Farm. 2004. (Rookie Reader Espanol Ser.). (Illus.). 23p. (J). (gr. k-2). pap. 4.95 (978-0-516-27787-5(1) , Children's Pr.) Scholastic Library Publishing.

—Going to Grandma's Farm. Rueda, Claudia, illus. 2003. (Rookie Reader Ser.). 24p. (J). 19.50 (978-0-516-22875-4(7) , Children's Pr.) Scholastic Library Publishing.

—Going to Grandma's Farm. Rueda, Claudia, illus. 2004. 24p. (ps-ps). lib. bdg. 11.75 (978-0-606-30159-6(3)) Tandem Library Bks.

Frantz, Jennifer. Zoom: A Book of Things That Go. Tate, Don, illus. 2008. 22p. (J). 13.99 (***978-0-06-112859-2(7)*** , Harper Festival) HarperCollins Pubs.

Freed, Shirley & Moon, Louise. I Like to Ride. Morelan, Bill, ed. Harrell, Rob, illus. 2003. 8p. (J). (-k). pap. 3.99 (978-1-58938-103-2(3)) Concerned Communications.

Friday, Stormy. Signal's Airport Adventure. Saroff, Phyllis, illus. 2006. (J). 14.95 (***978-0-9717047-5-6(9)***) Bay Media, Inc.

Gnojewski, Carol. Transportation Theme-a-Saurus. Mohrman, Gary, illus. 1999. (Theme-a-Saurus Ser.). 280p. (ps-k). 22.99 (978-1-57029-264-4(7) , WPH01009, Totline Pubns.) Schaffer, Frank Pubns.

Golden Books Staff. Traffic Trouble. 2004. (Illus.). 10p. (J). (ps-1). bds. 8.99 (978-0-375-82921-5(0) , Golden Bks.) Random Hse. Children's Bks.

Herman, Gail. Meet Tonka Joe. Courtney, Richard, illus. 2001. (Hello Reader! Ser.). 32p. (J). (ps-1). pap. 3.99 (978-0-439-25730-5(1)) Scholastic, Inc.

Hurwitz, Andy Bl. On Road. 2007. 16p. (J). bds. 7.99 (***978-0-8431-2208-4(0)*** , Price Stern Sloan) Penguin Group (USA) Inc.

Knopf, Susan. Barney Backhoe & the Big City Dig. 2006. (Illus.). 24p. (J). pap. 3.95 (978-0-7624-2659-1(4)) Running Pr. Bk. Pubs.

Kupperberg, Paul. Never Give Up! Nunn, Paul E. & Sliwinski, Chad, illus. 2006. (Firehouse Tales Ser.). 96p. (J). act. bk. ed. 2.99 (978-1-4169-1844-8(2) , Simon Scribbles) Simon & Schuster Children's Publishing.

Let's Go Downtown: Individual Title Six-Packs. (ps-2). 27.00 (978-0-7635-9458-9(X)) Rigby Education.

London, Jonathan. A Truck Goes Rattley-Bumpa. Roche, Denis, illus. rev. ed. 2005. 32p. (J). (ps-ps). 14.95 (978-0-8050-7233-4(0) , Holt, Henry & Co. Bks. For Young Readers) Holt, Henry & Co.

Lord, Janet. Here Comes Grandma! Paschkis, Julie, illus. rev. ed. 2005. 32p. (J). (ps-ps). 12.95 (978-0-8050-7666-0(2)) Holt, Henry & Co.

Luciani, Brigitte. How Will We Get Beach?/¿Como Iremos a la Playa? An English-Spanish Guessing-Game Story. Tharlet, Eve, illus. 2006. (ENG & SPA.). 36p. (J). (ps-1). 15.95 (978-0-7358-2037-1(6)) North-South Bks., Inc.

—How Will We Get to the Beach? Tharlet, Eve, illus. 2000. 36p. (J). (ps-1). 14.95 (978-0-7358-1268-0(3)) North-South Bks., Inc.

Markell, Denis. The Great Stroller Adventure. Iwai, Melissa, illus. 2004. 16p. (J). pap. 9.95 (978-0-439-54651-5(6) , Cartwheel Bks.) Scholastic, Inc.

Mayo, Margaret. Choo Choo Clickety-Clack! Ayliffe, Alex, illus. 2005. 32p. (J). (ps-2). 14.95 (978-1-57505-819-1(7)) Lerner Publishing Group.

McOmber, Rachel B., ed. McOmber Phonics Storybooks: The Tan Cab. rev. ed. (Illus.). (J). (978-0-944991-04-6(1)) Swift Learning Resources.

Miller, Edward. Trains. 1998. (Sticker Stories Ser.). (Illus.). 16p. (J). (ps-1). pap. 4.99 (978-0-448-41826-1(6) , Grosset & Dunlap) Penguin Group (USA) Inc.

Mitter, Matt. Going Places: A Book about Opposites. 2006. (Puzzle Playbook Ser.). 12p. (J). pap. 9.99 (978-0-7944-0915-9(6)) Reader's Digest Assn., Inc., The.

Mitton, Tony. Amazing Machines. Parker, Ant, illus. 2003. 98p. (J). (ps-k). pap. 10.95 (978-0-7534-5642-2(7) , Kingfisher) Houghton Mifflin Co. Trade & Reference Div.

Mortensen, Denise Dowling. Wake up Engines. Iwai, Melissa, illus. 2007. 32p. (J). (ps-k). 16.00 (978-0-618-51736-7(7) , Clarion Bks.) Houghton Mifflin Co. Trade & Reference Div.

Perlman, Rhea. Born to Drive. Santat, Dan, illus. 2006. (Otto Undercover Ser.). 128p. (J). 14.99 (978-0-06-075496-9(6)); pap. 3.99 (978-0-06-075495-2(8)) HarperCollins Pubs. (Tegen, Katherine Bks).

—Toxic Taffy Takeover. Santat, Dan, illus. 2006. (Otto Undercover Ser.). 128p. (J). 14.99 (978-0-06-075502-7(4) , Tegen, Katherine Bks); pap. 3.99 (978-0-06-075501-0(6) , Harper Trophy) HarperCollins Pubs.

—Water Balloon Doom. Santat, Dan, illus. 2006. (Otto Undercover Ser.: No. 3). 128p. (J). (gr. 3-5). 14.99 (978-0-06-075500-3(8) , Tegen, Katherine Bks); pap. 3.99 (978-0-06-075499-0(0) , Harper Trophy) HarperCollins Pubs.

Random House Books for Young Readers Staff & Awdry, Wilbert V. Thomas, Percy, & the Dragon. Courtney, Richard, illus. 2003. (Step into Reading Ser.). 32p. (J). (ps-1). lib. bdg. 11.99 (978-0-375-92230-5(X) , Random Hse. Bks. for Young Readers) Random Hse. Children's Bks.

Random House Disney Staff. Mater & the Ghost Light. 2006. (Little Golden Book Ser.). (Illus.). 24p. (J). (ps-k). 2.99 (978-0-7364-2416-5(4) , Golden/Disney) Random Hse. Children's Bks.

Random House Staff. Thomas Breaks a Promise. Courtney, Richard, illus. 2006. (Thomas & Friends Ser.). 24p. (J). (ps-1). lib. bdg. 2.99 (978-0-375-83671-8(3) , Golden Bks.) Random Hse. Children's Bks.

—Thomas's Stop & Go Day. 2002. (Illus.). 10p. (J). (ps-1). 8.99 (978-0-375-82214-8(3) , Random Hse. Bks. for Young Readers) Random Hse. Children's Bks.

Rau, Dana Meachen. Riding. 2006. (On the Move Ser.). (Illus.). 24p. (J). (ps-1). lib. bdg. 22.79 (978-0-7614-2317-1(6)) Cavendish, Marshall Corp.

Rex, Michael. Truck Duck. Rex, Michael, illus. 2004. (Illus.). 34p. (J). (ps-2). 9.99 (978-0-399-24009-6(8) , Putnam Juvenile) Penguin Group (USA) Inc.

Rosa-Mendoza, Gladys. Cars, Trucks & Planes/Carros, Camiones y Aviones. Tugeau, Jeremy, illus. 2004. (English-Spanish Foundations Ser.). (SPA & ENG.). 20p. (J). (ps). bds. 6.95 (978-1-931398-14-5(3)) Me+Mi Publishing.

Running Press Staff & Neusner, Dena. Danny Dozer Hits a Home Run. 2006. (Illus.). 24p. (J). pap. 3.95 (978-0-7624-2629-4(2) , Running Pr. Kids) Running Pr. Bk. Pubs.

Samuel, Quentin. Where's Everybody Going? Corr, Christopher, illus. 2003. 24p. (J). (978-1-84089-218-5(8) , Zero to Ten, Limited) Evans Publishing Group.

—Why Is Everybody So Excited. Corr, Christopher, illus. 2003. 24p. (J). (978-1-84089-219-2(6) , Zero to Ten, Limited) Evans Publishing Group.

Scarry, Richard. Cosas Que Se Mueven.Tr. of Things That Move. (SPA., Illus.). (J). pap. 6.95 (978-950-04-1042-7(7)) Emecé Editores S.A. ARG. *Dist:* Planeta Publishing Corp.

—Cosas Que Se Mueven. 2003. (Richard Scarry Ser.).Tr. of Things That Move. (SPA.). (J). pap. (978-970-690-847-6(1)) Planeta Mexicana Editorial S. A. de C. V.

Scholastic, Inc. Staff & Mills, Liz. Go, Clifford, Go! Bracken, Carolyn & Edwards, Ken, illus. 2002. (Clifford, the Big Red Dog Ser.). 10p. (J). bds. 9.99 (978-0-439-39447-5(3)) Scholastic, Inc.

Schulman, Elayne. This Year We Took a Special Trip. Bowser, Ken, illus. 2000. (This Year We... Ser.: Vol. 2). 32p. (J). (ps up). 14.95 (978-1-892780-04-1(6)) Giggles Group, Inc., The.

Schwartz, Amy. What James Likes Best. Schwartz, Amy, illus. 2003. (Illus.). 32p. (J). 16.95 (978-0-689-84059-3(4) , Atheneum/Richard Jackson Bks.) Simon & Schuster Children's Publishing.

Sharpe, Jeannie w. Once There Was an Orange Truck. 2005. 37p. (J). 15.95 (978-0-9763117-0-6(4)) Sharpe, Jeannie W.

Shuttle Buggy. 1999. (McGraw-Hill Junior Academic Ser.). (Illus.). 16p. (J). (gr. 1). pap. 2.99 (978-1-57768-531-9(8)) School Specialty Publishing.

Sims, Matt. Tug. 1999. (gr. 3-6). lib. bdg. 10.85 (978-0-613-30818-2(2)) Tandem Library Bks.

Snyder, Margaret. On the Go! deluxe ed. 1999. (Talking Pages Ser.). (J). 7.95 (978-1-58224-002-2(7)) Futech Interactive Products, Inc.

Spanyol, Jessica. Come on, Bugs! Let's Have Some Fun! Spanyol, Jessica, illus. 2006. (Illus.). 32p. (J). (gr. k-k). 15.99 (978-0-7636-3055-3(1)) Candlewick Pr.

Spinelli, Eileen. Six Hogs on a Scooter. Nash, Scott, illus. 2000. 40p. (J). (gr. k-4). 16.99 (978-0-531-33212-2(8)); pap. 15.95 (978-0-531-30212-5(1)) Scholastic, Inc. (Orchard Bks.).

Suen, Anastasia. Delivery. 2001. (978-0-606-22519-9(6)) Tandem Library Bks.

—Red Light, Green Light. Wilson-Max, Ken, illus. 2005. 40p. (J). (ps-k). 16.00 (978-0-15-202582-3(0) , Gulliver Bks.) Harcourt Children's Bks.

Thompson, Karen & Mitzo Thompson, Kim. Huge Machines. 2006. (Read & Sing along Board Books with CDs Ser.). (Illus.). 18p. (J). bds. 7.49 (978-0-7696-4584-1(4)) School Specialty Publishing.

Tibo, Gilles & Vaillancourt, Francois. El Senor Patapum. (Barril Sin Fondo Ser.). (SPA.). (J). (gr. 3-5). pap. (978-968-6465-58-7(8)) Casa de Estudios de Literatura y Talleres Artisticos Amaquemecan A.C. MEX. *Dist:* Lectorum Pubns., Inc.

Transportation Board Books 800618, 4. 2005. (J). bds. (978-1-59794-035-1(6)) Environments, Inc.

Walton, Rick. Bunnies on the Go: Getting from Place to Place, Miglio, Paige, illus. 2003. 32p. (J). 16.99 (978-0-06-029185-3(0)) HarperCollins Pubs.

Wellington, Monica. Truck Driver Tom. 2007. 32p. (J). (ps). 15.99 (***978-0-525-47831-7(0)*** , Dutton Juvenile) Penguin Group (USA) Inc.

Wells, Rosemary. Max Drives Away. 2003. 12p. (J). bds. 5.99 (978-0-670-03651-6(X) , Viking Juvenile) Penguin Group (USA) Inc.

Wilkes, Angela. Grandes Camiones. 2004. (Ladders Ser.).Tr. of Tough Trucks. (SPA., Illus.). 32p. (J). (ps-3). pap. 6.95 (978-1-58728-410-6(3) , Two Can Publishing) T&N Children's Publishing.

Willis, Jeanne & Ross, Tony. Dr Xargle's Book of Earth Mobiles. 2004. (Illus.). 32p. (J). pap. 8.99 (978-1-84270-369-4(2)) Andersen GBR. *Dist:* Independent Pubs. Group.

Ziefert, Harriet. From Kalamazoo to Timbuktu. Miller, Gustaf, illus. 2002. (J). (978-0-399-23730-0(5)) Penguin Group (USA) Inc.

—From Kalamazoo to Timbuktu! Roitman, Tanya, illus. 2005. 40p. (ps-ps). 15.95 (978-1-59354-091-3(4)) Blue Apple Bks.

TRANSPORTATION, HIGHWAY

see Transportation, Automotive

TRANSPORTATION—HISTORY

Barron's Educational Editorial Staff. Railways. 1998. (History Ser.). (Illus.). 32p. (J). (gr. 5). pap. 5.95 (978-0-7641-0538-8(8)) Barron's Educational Series, Inc.

Dowswell, Paul. Transportation. 2001. (Great Inventions Ser.). (Illus.). 48p. (YA). (gr. 6-8). lib. bdg. 25.64 (978-1-58810-216-4(5)) Heinemann Library.

From There to Here: a Transportation Time Line: Individual Title Six-Packs. (Discovery World Ser.). 24p. (gr. 1-2). 33.00 (978-0-7635-8484-9(3)) Rigby Education.

Galford, Ellen. Transportation by Land, Sea & Air: Exploring History Through Art. 2007. 64p. (***978-1-58728-590-5(8)*** , Two Can Publishing) T&N Children's Publishing.

Harcourt School Publishers Staff. Transportation of Yesterday & Today. 3rd ed. 2002. (Horizons Ser.). (Illus.). (J). pap. 5.50 (978-0-15-333312-5(X)) Harcourt Schl. Pubs.

—Transportation Yesterday & Today Advanced Level. 3rd ed. 2002. (Trophies Reading Program Ser.). (Illus.). pap. 5.10 (978-0-15-323128-5(9)) Harcourt Schl. Pubs.

—Traveling Around Alaska On Level. 3rd ed. 2002. (Trophies Reading Program Ser.). (Illus.). pap. 5.10 (978-0-15-323348-7(6)) Harcourt Schl. Pubs.

Harrison, Peter, et al. Car & Road, Train & Track: Discover How Modern Land-Based Vehicles Changed Our World, How They Have Evolved & How They Work. 2004. (Illus.). 128p. pap. 17.99 (978-1-84476-004-6(9) , Southwater) Anness Publishing GBR. *Dist:* National Bk. Network.

Isaacs, Sally Senzell. Stagecoaches & the Pony Express. 2004. (Illus.). 32p. (J). pap. 7.50 (978-1-4034-4793-7(4)); lib. bdg. (978-1-4034-2508-9(6)) Heinemann Library.

Kalman, Bobbie. Travel in the Early Days. 2001. (gr. 3-6). lib. bdg. 16.40 (978-0-613-33160-9(5)) Tandem Library Bks.

Kalman, Bobbie & Calder, Kate. Travel in the Early Days. 2000. (Historic Communities Ser.). (Illus.). 32p. (J). (gr. 3). pap. (978-0-86505-472-1(X)); lib. bdg. (978-0-86505-442-4(8)) Crabtree Publishing Co.

Knight, James E. A Journey to Monticello: Traveling in Colonial Times. 1999. (J). (978-0-606-16869-4(9)) Tandem Library Bks.

Leebrick, Kristal. Travel & Transportation in Colonial America. 2004. (Everyday Life Long Ago Ser.). (J). (978-0-7368-2164-3(3) , Blue Earth Bks.) Capstone Pr., Inc.

Mattern, Joanne. Transportation. 2004. (Yesterday & Today Ser.). (Illus.). 32p. (J). 23.70 (978-1-56711-835-3(6) , Blackbirch Pr., Inc.) Thomson Gale.

Morrison, Ian. Travelling Scotland: A Story of Transport. Whelan, Olwyn, illus. 1999. (Scottie Bks.). 40p. (J). (gr. 3-7). pap. 6.95 (978-0-11-494264-9(1)) Stationery Office, The GBR. *Dist:* Balogh International, Inc.

Murdico, Suzanne J. Railroads & Steamships: Important Developments in American Transportation. 2003. (America's Industrial Society in the Nineteenth Century Ser.). (Illus.). 32p. (J). (978-0-8239-4278-7(3)) Rosen Publishing Group, Inc., The.

Nelson, Robin. TransportationThen & Now. 2003. (Then & Now Ser.). (Illus.). 24p. (J). (gr. k-2). lib. bdg. 18.60 (978-0-8225-4636-8(1)) Lerner Publishing Group.

Orr, Tamra B. The Department of Transportation. 2005. (This Is Your Government Ser.). (Illus.). 64p. pap. 13.25 (978-1-4042-0664-9(7)) Rosen Publishing Group, Inc., The.

Rau, Dana Meachen. Travel in American History. 2006. (Illus.). 24p. (J). pap. (978-0-8368-7217-0(7)) Stevens, Gareth Inc.

Ray, Kurt. New Roads, Canals, & Railroads in Early 19th-Century America: The Transportation Revolution. 2003. (Life in the New American Nation Ser.). (Illus.). 32p. (YA). pap. (978-0-8239-4254-1(6)) Rosen Publishing Group, Inc., The.

Shuter. Cycle Power. 2004. (Technology Through Time Ser.). (Illus.). pap. 7.50 (978-1-4109-0979-4(4)) Raintree.

Shuter, Jane. Cycle Power: Two-Wheeled Travel. 2004. (Technology Through Time Ser.). (Illus.). 32p. (J). lib. bdg. 25.70 (978-1-4109-0580-2(2)) Raintree.

—Flying High: Travel by Air. 2004. (Technology Through Time Ser.). (Illus.). 32p. (J). lib. bdg. 25.70 (978-1-4109-0579-6(9)) Raintree.

—Making Waves: Travel by Sea. 2004. (Technology Through Time Ser.). (Illus.). 32p. (J). lib. bdg. 25.70 (978-1-4109-0581-9(0)) Raintree.

—On the Road: Travel by Road. 2004. (Technology Through Time Ser.). (Illus.). 32p. (J). lib. bdg. 25.70 (978-1-4109-0582-6(9)) Raintree.

—Riding the Rails: Travel by Rail. 2004. (Technology Through Time Ser.). (Illus.). 32p. (J). lib. bdg. 25.70 (978-1-4109-0584-0(5)) Raintree.

—War Machines: Military Transportation. 2004. (Technology Through Time Ser.). (Illus.). 31p. (J). lib. bdg. 25.70 (978-1-4109-0583-3(7)) Raintree.

Stott, Colin. Victorian Transport. (Illus.). 32p. pap. (978-0-7502-3752-9(X), Hodder Wayland) Hodder Children's Division.

El Transporte Ayer y Hoy Series, 6 bks., Set. 2003. (Transporte Ayer y Hoy Ser.). (SPA & ENG., Illus.). (J). lib. bdg. 103.50 (978-0-8239-6916-6(9), Buenas Letra) Rosen Publishing Group, Inc., The.

Williams, Harriet. Road & Rail Transportation. 2004. (History of Invention Ser.). (Illus.). 96p. (YA). (gr. 6-12). 35.00 (978-0-8160-5437-4(1)) Facts On File, Inc.

Wirkner, Linda. Learning about America's Industrial Growth with Graphic Organizers. 2005. (Graphic Organizers in Social Studies). (J). 19.95 (978-1-4042-2812-2(8), PowerKids Pr.) Rosen Publishing Group, Inc., The.

Woods, Michael & Woods, Mary B. Ancient Transportation: From Camels to Canals. 2005. (Ancient Technology Ser.). (Illus.). 96p. (gr. 6-12). 25.26 (978-0-8225-2993-4(9)) Lerner Publishing Group.

TRANSPORTATION—VOCATIONAL GUIDANCE

Ferguson. Careers in Focus: Transportation. 3rd rev. ed. 2007. (Careers in Focus Ser.). 224p. (YA). (gr. 6-12). 29.95 (*978-0-8160-6595-0(0), Ferguson Publishing Co.) Facts On File, Inc.

J. G. Ferguson Publishing Company Staff, contrib. by. Discovering Careers in Your Future/Transportation. 2002. (Discovering Careers for Your Future Ser.). (Illus.). 96p. (J). (gr. 4-9). 21.95 (978-0-89434-399-5(8), Ferguson Publishing Co.) Facts On File, Inc.

McGlothlin, Bruce. Choosing a Career in Transportation. rev. ed. 1999. (World of Work Ser.). (Illus.). 64p. (YA). (gr. 7-12). lib. bdg. 25.25 (978-0-8239-2998-6(1), WWT-RAN) Rosen Publishing Group, Inc., The.

TRAPP FAMILY SINGERS

Ransom, Candice F. Maria Von Trapp: Beyond the Sound of Music. 2005. (Trailblazers Biographies Ser.). (Illus.). 112p. (J). (gr. 5-9). lib. bdg. 27.93 (978-1-57505-444-5(2)) Lerner Publishing Group.

TRAPPING

see also Fur Trade; Hunting

Burger, James P. The Rocky Mountain Fur Trade. 2002. (Library of the Westward Expansion). (Illus.). 24p. (J). (gr. 3). lib. bdg. 19.95 (978-0-8239-5851-1(5), PowerKids Pr.) Rosen Publishing Group, Inc., The.

Gilsvik, Bob. The Complete Book of Trapping. Gilsvik, David, illus. 172p. (J). (gr. 7). reprint ed. 14.95 (978-0-936622-29-3(6)) Harding, A.R. Publishing Co.

TRAPPING—FICTION

Anderson, Laurie Halse. Trapped. 2003. (Wild at Heart Ser.). (Illus.). 113p. (J). (gr. 4 up). lib. bdg. 23.33 (978-0-8368-3263-1(9)) Stevens, Gareth Inc.

Hotta, Yumi. Hikaru No Go, Vol. 7. 2006. (Hikaru No Go Ser.). 208p. (YA). pap. 7.95 (978-1-4215-0641-8(6)) Viz Media.

Kehret, Peg. Trapped. 2006. 192p. (J). (gr. 5). 16.99 (978-0-525-47728-0(4), Dutton Juvenile) Penguin Group (USA) Inc.

Smelcer, John. The Trap. 2006. 176p. (YA). (gr. 4-7). 15.95 (978-0-8050-7939-5(4)) Holt, Henry & Co.

—The Trap. 2007. 192p. (YA). pap. 7.99 (*978-0-312-37755-7(X)) Square Fish.

TRAVEL

see also Automobile Travel; Games for Travelers; Tourism; Voyages and Travels; Voyages around the World

also names of countries, states, etc. with the subdivision Description and Travel, e.g. United States—Description and travel

AAA Staff. Here, There & Everywhere: A Guide to Fun & Safe Travel. 2004. (Illus.). 72p. (J). pap. 4.99 (978-1-56251-373-3(7)) AAA.

—Wheels, Wings & Other Things: A Guide to Fun & Safe Travel. 2004. (Illus.). 72p. (J). pap. 4.99 (978-1-56251-374-0(5)) AAA.

Adams, Colleen. Planes Go Places: Learning the Sound of PL. 2001. (PowerPhonics Ser.). (Illus.). 23p. (J). pap. 26.40 (978-0-8239-8296-7(3), PowerKids Pr.) Rosen Publishing Group, Inc., The.

Anderson, Jill, ed. Let's Go!/Vamos a Viajar! Evrard, Gaetan, illus. 2006. (ENG & SPA.). 20p. (J). (ps-2). bds. 6.95 (978-1-58728-513-4(4), Two Can Publishing) T&N Children's Publishing.

Barbas, Keri, des. Travel Scratch & Sketch. 2005. (Activity Journal Ser.). (J). 12.99 (978-0-88088-486-0(X)) Peter Pauper Pr. Inc.

Bellamy, David. The Roadside. Dow, Jill, illus. 1999. (Our Changing World Ser.). 32p. (J). (gr. 1-5). pap. 7.99 (978-0-7112-1383-8(6)) Lincoln, Frances Ltd. GBR. *Dist:* Antique Collectors' Club.

Bowers, Vivien. Wow, Canada! Exploring This Land from Coast to Coast. Hobbs, Dan, illus. 1999. (Wow Canada! Ser.). 160p. (J). (gr. 3-7). pap. 19.95 (978-1-895688-94-8(9), Owl Bks.) Maple Tree Pr. CAN. *Dist:* Firefly Bks., Ltd.

Bree, Loris & Bree, Marlin. Kid's Trip Diary: Kids! Write about Your Own Adventures & Experiences! 4th ed. 2007. (Kid's Travel Ser.). 96p. (J). pap. 6.95 (*978-1-892147-14-1(9)) Marlor Pr., Inc.

Bree, Marlin & Bree, Loris Theovin. Kids' Trip Diary: Kids! Write about Your Own Adventures & Experiences, Have Fun for Hours! 5th rev. ed. 2003. (Affordable Travel Ser.). (Illus.). 96p. (J). pap. 6.95 (978-0-943400-98-3(8)) Marlor Pr., Inc.

Brett, Jane. Going Places. 1999. (Illus.). 10p. (J). pap. 3.95 (978-1-57717-100-3(4)) New Line Bks.

Bronston, Barri. The Lobster Kids' Guide to Exploring New Orleans. Fischer, Alison, ed. Battuz, Christine, illus. 2002. (Lobster Kids' City Explorers Ser.). 256p. (J). (ps-3). pap. 14.95 (978-1-894222-51-8(2)) Lobster Pr. CAN. *Dist:* Univ. of Toronto Pr.

Buckie, Catherine. The Lobster Kids' Guide to Exploring Halifax. Fischer, Alison, ed. 2002. (Lobster Kids' City Explorers Ser.). (Illus.). 240p. (J). pap. 14.95 (978-1-894222-53-2(9)) Lobster Pr. CAN. *Dist:* Univ. of Toronto Pr.

Bumper Travel Fun. 2002. 576p. pap. 6.98 (978-0-7525-8923-7(7)) Parragon, Inc.

Burton, Margie, et al. Going Places. Adams, Alison, ed. 1999. (Early Connections Ser.). 16p. (J). (gr. k-2). pap. 4.50 (978-1-58344-063-6(1)) Benchmark Education Co.

—Travel Money, U. S. A. Adams, Alison, ed. 1999. (Early Connections Ser.). 16p. (J). (gr. k-2). pap. 4.50 (978-1-58344-083-4(6)) Benchmark Education Co.

Canetti, Yanitzia. Our World of Wonders. 2000. (Pair-It Books). (Illus.). 40p. (J). pap. (978-0-7398-0887-0(7)) Steck-Vaughn.

Chancellor, Deborah. Viajes Por la Tierra. 2004. (Discovery Guides Ser.).Tr. of Traveling on Land. (SPA., Illus.). 32p. (gr. 2-5). 11.95 (978-1-58728-646-9(7), Two Can Publishing) T&N Children's Publishing.

Crichton, Andrew. The History of Arabia, Ancient & Modern Volume I, Vol. 1. 2006. (Illus.). cd-rom (978-1-892824-43-1(4)) AFCHRON.

Demarest, Chris L. & Mayer, Bill. All Aboard! A Traveling Alphabet. 2008. 32p. (J). 17.99 (*978-0-689-85249-7(5), McElderry, Margaret K.) Simon & Schuster Children's Publishing.

Exploration of Wonderful Places: Includes: Great Journeys; Mapping the Unknown; The Wild, Wild, West; The World's Wild Places, 4 bks., Set. (Remarkable World Ser.). (Illus.). (J). (gr. 4-7). lib. bdg. 75.92 (978-0-8172-5154-3(5)) Raintree.

Feeney, Kathy. Marco Polo: Explorer of China. 2004. (Explorers! Ser.). (Illus.). 48p. (J). lib. bdg. 23.93 (978-0-7660-2145-7(9)) Enslow Pubs., Inc.

Fisher-Price Little People Toddler Sticker Workbooks. 2004. (J). wbk. ed. (978-0-7666-0451-3(9), 49200); wbk. ed. (978-0-7666-0452-0(7), 49200); wbk. ed. (978-0-7666-0453-7(5), 49200); wbk. ed. (978-0-7666-0454-4(3), 49200) Modern Publishing.

Gedatus, Gus. Travel Safety. 2000. (Perspectives on Violence Ser.). (Illus.). 64p. (J). (gr. 4-6). lib. bdg. 23.93 (978-0-7368-0426-4(9), LifeMatters Bks.) Capstone Pr., Inc.

Gefen, Keren. Marco Polo. 2001. (Great Explorers Ser.). (Illus.). 48p. (J). (gr. 5 up). lib. bdg. 30.00 (978-0-8368-5017-8(3), World Almanac Library) Stevens, Gareth Inc.

Givens, David. For the Kids: A Family-Friendly Guide to Outings & Activities. 2003. (Illus.). 220p. (YA). pap. 20.95 (978-1-904148-27-2(1)) Liffey Pr., The IRL. *Dist:* Dufour Editions, Inc.

Going Out: KinderWords Individual Title Six-Packs. (Kinderstarters Ser.). 8p. (ps-1). 21.00 (978-0-7635-8696-6(X)) Rigby Education.

Harcourt School Publishers Staff. World Landmarks. 3rd ed. 2002. (Horizons Ser.). (Illus.). (J). pap. 3.70 (978-0-15-333214-2(X)) Harcourt Schl. Pubs.

Harvey, Roger. Caillou, My First Vacation. CINAR Animation Staff & Sévigny, Eric, illus. adapted rev. ed. 2006. (Lift-the-Flap Cinar Ser.). 20p. (J). pap. 5.95 (978-2-89450-525-0(6)) Chouette Publishing CAN. *Dist:* Independent Pubs. Group.

Heinemann Educational Ltd. Publishing Staff. Let's Get Moving. 2004. 8 Pack. 410.40 (978-1-4109-1391-3(0)); Pack. pap. 124.20 (978-1-4109-1385-2(6)) Raintree.

Hewitt, Sally. Routes & Journeys. 2006. (Science Starters Ser.). (Illus.). 32p. (J). (978-1-59604-083-0(1)) Stargazer Bks.

Hughes, Monica. My First Vacation. 2003. (Raintree Sprouts Ser.). (Illus.). 24p. (J). pap. 5.50 (978-1-4109-0672-4(8)); lib. bdg. 18.56 (978-1-4109-0646-5(9)) Raintree.

Hyperion Staff, ed. Disney Cruise Travel Log, Vol. 1. 1998. (Illus.). (J). 14.95 (978-0-7868-6384-6(6)) Hyperion Pr.

Johnson. The Greater Flamingo. 2002. (Illus.). 250p. (978-0-85661-115-5(8), Academic Pr.) Elsevier Science & Technology Bks.

Johnson, Allen L. Kayaking Around Iceland: Adventures with Grandchildren. 2003. (Illus.). 196p. 15.00 (978-1-880675-07-6(2)) Creative Enterprises.

LeapFrog Staff, compiled by. Travel: (Blue Book) 2002. (J). (ps-2). 19.95 (978-1-58605-704-6(9)) LeapFrog Enterprises, Inc.

—Travel: (Green Book) 2002. (J). (ps-2). 19.95 (978-1-58605-702-2(2)) LeapFrog Enterprises, Inc.

—Travel: (Orange Book) 2002. (J). (ps-2). 19.95 (978-1-58605-703-9(0)) LeapFrog Enterprises, Inc.

—Travel: (Purple Book) 2002. (J). (ps-2). 19.95 (978-1-58605-701-5(4)) LeapFrog Enterprises, Inc.

Litten, Troy, illus. Wanderlust Travel Journal. 2004. 144p. 16.95 (978-0-8118-4206-8(1)) Chronicle Bks. LLC.

MacDonald, Fiona. Travel & Trade in the Middle Ages. 2005. (World Almanac Library of the Middle Ages). (Illus.). 48p. (J). pap. (978-0-8368-5908-9(1)); (gr. 10-12). lib. bdg. 30.00 (978-0-8368-5899-0(9)) Stevens, Gareth Inc. (World Almanac Library).

Madruga, Dina Jo. The Lobster Kids' Guide to Exploring San Diego. Fischer, Alison, ed. 2002. (Lobster Kids' City Explorers Ser.). (Illus.). 256p. (J). (ps-3). pap. 14.95 (978-1-894222-52-5(0)) Lobster Pr. CAN. *Dist:* Univ. of Toronto Pr.

Mansir, A. Richard. Stagecoach: The Ride of a Century. 1999. (Building America Ser.). (Illus.). 32p. (J). (ps-3). 15.95 (978-1-57091-960-2(7)) Charlesbridge Publishing, Inc.

Marsh, Carole. My First Pocket Guide. 2001. (J). pap., tchr.'s assessmt. gde. ed. (978-0-635-00379-9(1)) Gallopade International.

Mattern, Joanne. I Use Math on a Trip. 2005. (Illus.). 24p. (J). pap. (978-0-8368-4866-3(7)); lib. bdg. 19.33 (978-0-8368-4859-5(4)) Stevens, Gareth Inc.

—I Use Math on a Trip: Uno Las Matematicas en un Viaje. 2005. (Illus.). 24p. (J). (SPA.). pap. (978-0-8368-6011-5(X)); (ENG & SPA., lib. bdg. 19.33 (978-0-8368-6004-7(7)) Stevens, Gareth Inc.

Mayo Clinic Staff, contrib. by. Healthy Traveler: Answers on Staying Well While Away from Home. 2002. (Mayo Clinic on Health Ser.). (Illus.). 36,52p. (YA). (gr. 8 up). lib. bdg. (978-1-59084-253-9(7)) Mason Crest Pubs.

McCann, Michelle Roehm. Going Places: True Tales from Young Travelers. 2003. (gr. 3-6). lib. bdg. 18.75 (978-0-613-82286-2(3)) Tandem Library Bks.

McGee, Sherry. AppleJack "Everywhere I Go" Johnson, Richard M., illus. 1999. (Applekid's Chapter Bks.). 12p. (J). (gr. 1-6). pap. 4.99 (978-0-9673591-2-0(0)) Apple Bk. Ctr.

Meine Erste Reise Um die Welt. 1998. (Meyer Multimedia Ser.). (J). (ps-4). cd-rom 31.50 (978-3-411-06541-7(9)) Langenscheidt Pubs Inc.

Michel, June, illus. Going Places: True Tales from Young Travelers. 2003. 160p. (J). (gr. 4-12). pap. (978-1-58270-070-0(2)) Beyond Words Publishing, Inc.

Mitchell-Burnett, Carolyn. The Sites & Sounds of Texas. 2001. (J). 15.95 (978-1-57168-198-0(1)) Eakin Pr.

Newman-D'Amico, Fran. Fun on the Go Travel Activity Book. 2005. 64p. (J). (ps-2). pap. 1.50 (978-0-486-44456-7(2)) Dover Pubns., Inc.

—Travel Fun. 2004. (Illus.). 64p. (J). (ps-3). pap., act. bk. ed. 1.50 (978-0-486-43532-9(6)) Dover Pubns., Inc.

Nix, Nelleke. Out & about Portland with Kids: The Ultimate Guide for Fun & Learning. 2nd ed. 2002. 240p. (J). pap. 14.95 (978-0-9715644-0-4(X)) Northwest Parent Publishing.

Pipe, Jim. Getting Around. 2004. (Earthwise Ser.). (J). lib. bdg. 27.10 (978-1-932799-52-1(4)) Stargazer Bks.

Quan, Elizabeth. Once upon a Full Moon. Quan, Elizabeth, illus. 2007. (Illus.). 48p. (J). (gr. 1-3). 19.95 (978-0-88776-813-2(X)) Tundra Bks., Inc./Livres Toundra, Inc. CAN. *Dist:* Random Hse., Inc.

Raintree Steck-Vaughn Staff. Our World of Wonders. 1999. (Illus.). (J). pap. 35.60 (978-0-7398-0918-1(0)) Steck-Vaughn.

Rau, Dana Meachen. Travel in American History. 2006. (Illus.). 24p. (J). lib. bdg. (978-0-8368-7210-1(X)) Stevens, Gareth Inc.

Rinella, Heidi Knapp. The Lobster Kids' Guide to Exploring Las Vegas. 2001. (Lobster Kids' City Explorers Ser.). (Illus.). 225p. (J). (ps-3). pap. 12.95 (978-1-894222-29-7(6)) Lobster Pr. CAN. *Dist:* Univ. of Toronto Pr.

Safro, Jill & Birnbaum, Stephen, contrib. by. Birnbaum's Walt Disney World for Kids, by Kids: Real Kids Give Honest Advice for the Most Awesome Vacation in the World. rev. ed. 2000. (Birnbaum's Walt Disney World for Kids, by Kids Ser.). (Illus.). (J). (gr. 4-7). pap. 10.95 (978-0-7868-5315-1(8), Disney Editions) Disney Pr.

Sanchez, Gervasio. Cinco Anos Despues (Vidas Minadas) 2004. (SPA & ENG.). 80p. pap. 24.95 (978-84-95939-33-3(9)) Blume ESP. *Dist:* Independent Pubs. Group.

Scillian, Devin. P Is for Passport: A World Alphabet. 2003. (Illus.). 56p. (J). 19.95 (978-1-58536-157-1(7)) Sleeping Bear Pr.

Shuter. On the Road. 2004. (Illus.). pap. 7.50 (978-1-4109-0981-7(6)) Raintree.

Steck-Vaughn Staff. Taking Your Camera To... 1999. pap., tchr. ed. (978-0-7398-2208-1(5)); Set 1. 1999. (Illus.). pap. (978-0-7398-2209-8(8)); Set 2. 2001. pap., tchr. ed. (978-0-7398-3368-1(5)); Set 2. 2000. (Illus.). pap. (978-0-7398-4122-8(X)) Steck-Vaughn.

Taking Your Camera to... Collection. 2001. pap. (978-0-7398-4557-8(8)) Steck-Vaughn.

Third and Fourth Grade Classes of Ouray Schools Staff. Under the Shadow of Mount Abram. 1999. (Illus.). 81p. (J). (gr. 3-4). pap. 5.00 (978-1-890437-03-9(4)) Western Reflections Publishing Co.

Travel Fun. 2002. 192p. (J). pap. 3.98 (978-0-7525-7918-4(5)) Parragon, Inc.

Travel Time. (Illus.). (J). pap. 6.99 (978-1-55254-192-0(4), BV24021) Brighter Vision Pubns.

Walsh, Kieran. Travel Math. 2003. (Illus.). 48p. (J). 29.93 (978-1-58952-383-8(0)) Rourke Publishing, LLC.

Weber, Valerie & Baker, Patricia A. Traveling in Grandma's Day. Lafford, Stuart, illus. 1999. (In Grandma's Day Ser.). 32p. (J). (ps-3). lib. bdg. 21.27 (978-1-57505-326-4(8), Carolrhoda Bks.) Lerner Publishing Group.

Woodward, Kay. Journeys. 2004. (Starters Ser.). (Illus.). 24p. (J). lib. bdg. 22.80 (978-1-58340-566-6(6)) Smart Apple Media.

Yates, Vicki. Travel. 2007. (J). (*978-1-4034-9831-1(8)); pap. (*978-1-4034-9839-7(3)) Heinemann Library.

Zannos, Susan. The Life & Times of Marco Polo. 2004. (Biography from Ancient Civilizations Ser.). (Illus.). 48p. (J). (gr. 4-8). lib. bdg. 29.95 (978-1-58415-264-4(8)) Mitchell Lane Pubs., Inc.

Zavatsky, George A. & Zavatsky, Michele A. Kids Love Kentucky: A Parent's Guide to Exploring Fun Places in Kentucky with Children. . . Year Round! 2nd ed. 2004. 186p. (J). per. 13.95 (978-0-9726854-3-6(X)) Kids Love Pubns.

TRAVEL—FICTION

Ahern, Carolyn L. Tino Turtle Travels to Beijing, China. 2008. (J). 17.95 incl. audio compact disk (*978-0-9793158-4-8(0)) Tino Turtle Travels, LLC.

—Tino Turtle Travels to London, England. Burt Sullivan, Neallia, illus. 2007. 36p. (J). 17.95 incl. audio compact disk (*978-0-9793158-0-0(8)) Tino Turtle Travels, LLC.

—Tino Turtle Travels to London, England Book & Sing-along PlushToy Bundle. 2007. (J). 29.95 incl. audio compact disk (*978-0-9793158-5-5(9)) Tino Turtle Travels, LLC.

—Tino Turtle Travels to Mexico City, Mexico. 2007. (ENG & SPA., Illus.). 36p. (J). 17.95 incl. audio compact disk (*978-0-9793158-2-4(4)) Tino Turtle Travels, LLC.

—Tino Turtle Travels to Nairobi, Kenya. 2008. (Illus.). (J). 17.95 incl. audio compact disk (*978-0-9793158-3-1(2)) Tino Turtle Travels, LLC.

—Tino Turtle Travels to Paris, France. Burt Sullivan, Neallia, illus. 2007. 36p. (J). 17.95 incl. audio compact disk (*978-0-9793158-1-7(6)) Tino Turtle Travels, LLC.

—Tino Turtle Travels to Paris, France Book & Sing-along Plush Toy Bundle. 2007. (J). 29.95 incl. audio compact disk (*978-0-9793158-6-2(7)) Tino Turtle Travels, LLC.

Aigner-Clark, Julie. Jane's Animal Expedition. Zaidi, Nadeem, illus. 2002. (Baby Einstein Ser.). 16p. (J). bds. 6.99 (978-0-7868-0841-0(1)) Hyperion Bks. for Children.

Alonso, Manuel L. Rumbo Sur. 2005. (*978-84-263-5948-3(5)) Vives, Luis Editorial (Edelvives).

Alsenas, Linas. Mrs. Claus Takes a Vacation. 2006. (Illus.). 32p. (J). pap. 16.99 (978-0-439-77978-4(2), Scholastic Pr.) Scholastic, Inc.

Asher Penny. Mommy & Daddy Are Going on a Trip. 2006. 32p. 12.95 (978-0-9755902-1-8(9)) Change Is Strange, Inc.

Auerbach, Annie. My Race into Space! A Water Wonder Book. Garofoli, Viviana, illus. 2005. 18p. (J). 9.95 (978-1-58117-351-2(2), Intervisual/Piggy Toes) Dalmatian Pr.

Backer, Miles. Travels with Charlie: Travelin' the Northeast. Nitzberg, Chuck, illus. 2006. (gr. 1-4). 15.95 (978-1-59354-162-0(7)) Blue Apple Bks.

Bilik-Franklin, MidiAna & Griffith, Indigo, photos by. The Carseat Tourist. 2006. (Illus.). (J). bds. 7.95 (978-0-9772825-0-0(3)) Critter Camp Inc.

Blackstone, Stella. Cleo on the Move. Mockford, Caroline, illus. 2002. 24p. (J). (gr. k-2). 14.99 (978-1-84148-898-1(4)) Barefoot Bks., Inc.

Briggs, Martha Wren. Travels with Virginia Bk. 5: The Little Ferry & the Hiding Peanuts. Beale, Ella L., illus. 2000. 18p. (YA). (gr. 3 up). pap. 6.95 (978-0-9633240-7-8(1), LFHP-00) Dory Pr.

Brooks, Walter R. Freddy Goes to Florida. Wiese, Kurt, illus. 2001. 208p. (J). (gr. 4-7). pap. 7.99 (978-0-14-131233-0(5), Puffin) Penguin Group (USA) Inc.

—Freddy Goes to Florida. Wiese, Kurt, illus. 2001. 196p. (J). (gr. 4-7). per. 15.30 (978-0-613-36062-3(1)) Tandem Library Bks.

—Freddy Goes to the North Pole. Wiese, Kurt, illus. 2001. 306p. (J). 23.95 (978-1-58567-104-5(5)) Overlook Pr., The.

Brown, Sally. Alexandra's Travel Adventure: Making Friends in Mexico. Lyons, Deborah, illus. 2005. 32p. (J). pap. 9.95 (978-1-57860-232-2(7)) Emmis Bks.

Bruna, Dick. Miffy Loves New York City! 2004. 32p. (ps-3). 9.99 (978-1-59226-179-6(5)) Big Tent Entertainment, Inc.

Brunelle, Lynn. I Go Places: A Fun Sticker Book. Espinosa, Leo, illus. 1999. 20p. (J). reprint ed. 7.95 (978-1-892374-23-3(4)) Weldon Owen, Inc.

Buitrago, Alberto. De Viaje. 1998. (SPA.). (gr. 7-12). lib. bdg. 14.10 (978-0-613-80665-7(4)) Tandem Library Bks.

Bunting, Eve. Man with the Red Bag. 2007. 240p. (J). (gr. 5 up). 15.99 (*978-0-06-081828-9(X)); lib. bdg. 16.89 (*978-0-06-081835-7(2)) HarperCollins Pubs. (Cotler, Joanna Books).

Bury, Laurie D. The Adventures of Dalbert Juan: Passport. Gallo, Karen A., illus. 2000. (J). (ps-2). 12.95 (978-0-9702319-3-2(8)) Rhette Enterprises, Inc.

Campbell, Aileen. The Wee Scot Travels. 2003. 32p. pap. 7.95 (978-1-56554-873-2(6)) Pelican Publishing Co., Inc.

Canetti. The Around-the-World Lunch. 1999. (Illus.). (J). pap. (978-0-7398-2404-7(X)) Steck-Vaughn.

Cann, Kate. Spanish Holiday: Or, How I Transformed the Worst Vacation Ever into the Best Sum. 2004. (gr. 7-12). lib. bdg. 14.15 (978-0-613-71954-4(9)) Tandem Library Bks.

Carney, Charles. Harley-Davidson Great Rides. Eberhart, Donald G., illus. 2002. (J). 15.98 (978-0-7853-7043-7(9)) Publications International, Ltd.

Chapman, Nancy Kapp. Tripper's Travels: An International Scrapbook. Chapman, Lee, illus. 2005. 48p. (J). (gr. k-4). per. 16.95 (978-0-7614-5240-9(0)) Cavendish, Marshall Corp.

Chesne, Sabrina. Lillie's Treasures/Los tesoros de Lili. Capasso, Diana, tr. Patagonia School, illus. 2004. (ENG & SPA.). 32p. per. 15.00 (*978-0-9630310-9-9(0)) Will Hall Bks.

Cockley, David H. Over the Falls: A Child's Storybook Guide to Chagrin Falls. Ascherman, Herbert, Jr., tr. 2000. (Illus.). 24p. (J). (ps-10). pap. 5.95 (978-0-9700846-1-3(7)) Fireside Book Shop, Inc.

Cooper, Patrick. I Is Someone Else. 304p. (YA). 2007. (gr. 7-11). mass mkt. 6.50 (978-0-440-23919-2(2) , Laurel Leaf); 2006. (Illus.). (gr. 9). 16.95 (978-0-385-73269-7(4) , Delacorte Bks. for Young Readers); 2006. (Illus.). (gr. 9). lib. bdg. 18.99 (978-0-385-90286-1(7) , Delacorte Bks. for Young Readers) Random Hse. Children's Bks.

Cunningham, Mary. Cynthia's Attic: The Missing Locket. 2005. (J). pap. 9.99 (978-1-59080-441-4(4)) Echelon Press Publishing.

de Brunhoff, Laurent. Babar's World Tour. 2005. (Illus.). 48p. (J). (978-0-8109-5982-8(8)) Abrams, Harry N. , Inc.

Donaki & Rosenberry, Donald. Spectacular Journey. Rosenberry, Akiko & Rosenberry, Susan, illus. 2006. (J). per. 20.00 ***(*978-0-9771482-6-4(2)** , Ithaca Pr.) Authors & Artists Publishers of New York, Inc.

Doyle, Malachy. Antonio on the Other Side of the World, Getting Smaller. Cneut, Carll, illus. 2003. 32p. (J). (ps-3). 15.99 (978-0-7636-2173-5(0)) Candlewick Pr.

Dream Catchers - Evaluation Guide: Evaluation Guide. 2006. (J). (978-1-55942-403-5(6)) Marsh Media.

Dream Catchers - Teaching Guide. 2001. (J). 17.95 (978-1-55942-183-6(5)) Marsh Media.

Dreliozis-Abon, Fotini. Franchesca's Journey. 2000. 132p. (YA). (gr. 5-12). pap. 15.95 (978-1-930002-16-6(5)) I & L Publishing.

Du Bois, William Pene. Twenty-One Balloons. Du Bois, William Pene, illus. 2005. (Illus.). 180p. (J). lib. bdg. 15.00 ***(*978-1-4242-2270-4(2))*** Fitzgerald Bks.

DuPrau, Jeanne. Car Trouble. 288p. (J). 2006. pap. 6.99 (978-0-06-073675-0(5) , HarperTeen); 2005. 15.99 (978-0-06-073672-9(0)); 2005. lib. bdg. 16.89 (978-0-06-073674-3(7)) HarperCollins Pubs.

Duthaluru, Vidhya. Michael's Field Trip. 2007. (Illus.). 18p. (J). 3.99 ***(*978-0-9797657-0-4(6))*** Duthaluru, Vidhya.

Eastman, P. D. Ve, Perro, Ve! Go, Dog. Go! Perdomo, Adolfo Perez, tr. 2003. Tr. of Go, Dog, Go!. (SPA & ENG., Illus.). 24p. (J). (gr. k-ps). bds. 4.99 (978-0-375-82361-9(1) , RH Para Ninos) Random Hse. Children's Bks.

Edwards, Julie Andrews. Little Bo in France. Cole, Henry, illus. 2002. 128p. (gr. 2-17). 19.49 (978-0-7868-2540-0(5)) Hyperion Pr.

—Little Bo in France: The Further Adventures of Bonnie Boadicea. Cole, Henry, illus. 2004. 117p. (J). (gr. k-4). reprint ed. 19.00 (978-0-7567-8163-7(9)) DIANE Publishing Co.

Elya, Susan Middleton. Oh No, Gotta Go! Karas, G. Brian, illus. 32p. (J). 2006. pap. 5.99 (978-0-14-240334-1(2) , Puffin); 2003. (SPA.). 15.99 (978-0-399-23493-4(4) , Putnam Juvenile) Penguin Group (USA) Inc.

Enric, Larreula I. Vidal. Bruja Aburrida Viaja Pro el Mundo. 1998. (SPA.). 124p. (J). (gr. 2-4). (978-84-08-02574-0(0)) GeoPlaneta, Editorial, S. A.

Evans, Douglas. MVP: Magellan Voyage Project. Shelley, John, illus. 2004. 232p. (J). 16.95 (978-1-932425-13-0(6) , Lemniscaat) Boyds Mills Pr.

Finley, Martha. Elsie's Winter Trip, Vol. 26. (Elsie Bks.: Vol. 26). 320p. (gr. 4-7). pap. 5.95 (978-1-58182-181-9(6)) Cumberland Hse. Publishing.

—Elsie's Winter Trip. unabr. ed. 1999. (Elsie Dinsmore Collection: Vol. 26). (J). reprint ed. 15.00 (978-1-889128-26-9(0)) Mantle Ministries.

—Mildred at Home, Vol. 5. (Mildred Classics Ser.: Vol. 5). 288p. pap. 6.95 (978-1-58182-231-1(6)) Cumberland Hse. Publishing.

—Mildred at Roselands, Vol. 2. (Mildred Classics Ser.: Vol. 2). 288p. pap. 6.95 (978-1-58182-228-1(6)) Cumberland Hse. Publishing.

Fiol, Doreen. Pookha Moon. 2006. pap. 11.99 ***(*978-1-4259-6686-7(1))*** AuthorHouse.

Franco, Betsy. Going to Grandma's Farm. 2004. (Rookie Reader Espanol Ser.). (Illus.). 23p. (J). (gr. k-2). pap. 4.95 (978-0-516-27787-5(1) , Children's Pr.) Scholastic Library Publishing.

—Going to Grandma's Farm. Rueda, Claudia, illus. 2003. (Rookie Reader Ser.). 24p. (J). 19.50 (978-0-516-22875-4(7) , Children's Pr.) Scholastic Library Publishing.

—Going to Grandma's Farm. Rueda, Claudia, illus. 2004. 24p. (ps-ps). lib. bdg. 11.75 (978-0-606-30159-6(3)) Tandem Library Bks.

Freeman, Marilyn. Pasquale's Journey. 2003. 49p. pap. 8.95 (978-0-595-30311-3(0)) iUniverse, Inc.

Frienz, D. J. Where Will Nana Go Next: An Illustrated Tour of 19 Places to Go & Things to Do Across America & the World. Garber, Sean, illus. 1999. 32p. (J). (ps-3). 15.95 (978-0-9654333-0-3(7)) Howling at the Moon Pr.

George, Audra. Vagabonding. George, Audra, illus. 2006. (Illus.). 32p. (J). 17.95 (978-1-60108-010-3(7)) Red Cygnet Pr.

Golden Books Staff. Travel with Thomas. 2007. (Deluxe Coloring Book Ser.). (Illus.). 96p. (J). (ps-2). pap. 3.99 (978-0-375-83953-5(4) , Golden Bks.) Random Hse. Children's Bks.

Gorbachev, Valeri. The Big Trip. Gorbachev, Valeri, illus. 2004. (Illus.). 32p. (J). 15.99 (978-0-399-23965-6(0) , Philomel) Penguin Group (USA) Inc.

Harcourt School Publishers Staff. City Celebrations On Level. 3rd ed. 2002. (Trophies Reading Program Ser.). (Illus.). pap. 5.10 (978-0-15-323186-5(6)) Harcourt Schl. Pubs.

—Cross Country. 3rd ed. 2002. (Trophies English Language Learners Ser.). (Illus.). pap. 5.10 (978-0-15-327839-6(0)) Harcourt Schl. Pubs.

—A Day in the City. 3rd ed. 2002. (Trophies English Language Learners Ser.). (Illus.). pap. 5.10 (978-0-15-327654-5(1)) Harcourt Schl. Pubs.

—Down in the Grand Canyon Advanced Level. 3rd ed. 2002. (Trophies Reading Program Ser.). (Illus.). pap. 5.10 (978-0-15-323308-1(7)) Harcourt Schl. Pubs.

—How Will I Get There? 3rd ed. 2002. (Trophies English Language Learners Ser.). (Illus.). pap. 5.10 (978-0-15-327882-2(X)) Harcourt Schl. Pubs.

—I Can Go Anyplace: Take-Home Book. 1999. (Signatures Ser.). (Illus.). (J). (gr. 2). pap. 1.90 (978-0-15-313863-8(7)) Harcourt Schl. Pubs.

—Jesse & Trevor Take a Trip: Take-Home Book. 1999. (Collections Ser.). (Illus.). (J). pap. 1.90 (978-0-15-317259-5(2)) Harcourt Schl. Pubs.

—A Journey in Time Advanced Level. 3rd ed. 2002. (Trophies Reading Program Ser.). (Illus.). pap. 5.10 (978-0-15-323478-1(4)) Harcourt Schl. Pubs.

—Leo's Trip: Take-Home Book. 1999. (Signatures Ser.). (J). pap. 1.90 (978-0-15-313866-9(1)) Harcourt Schl. Pubs.

—My Surprising Vacation Below Level. 3rd ed. 2002. (Trophies Reading Program Ser.). (Illus.). pap. 5.10 (978-0-15-323339-5(7)) Harcourt Schl. Pubs.

—The Oregon Trail Days On Level. 3rd ed. 2002. (Trophies Reading Program Ser.). (Illus.). pap. 5.10 (978-0-15-323369-2(9)) Harcourt Schl. Pubs.

—This Land. 3rd ed. 2002. (Trophies English Language Learners Ser.). (Illus.). pap. 5.10 (978-0-15-327717-7(3)) Harcourt Schl. Pubs.

—Travels with Dad On Level. 3rd ed. 2002. (Trophies Reading Program Ser.). (Illus.). pap. 5.10 (978-0-15-323098-1(3)) Harcourt Schl. Pubs.

—Walking to Nebraska On Level. 3rd ed. 2002. (Trophies Reading Program Ser.). (Illus.). pap. 5.10 (978-0-15-323277-0(3)) Harcourt Schl. Pubs.

Harrington, Jane. Four Things My Geeky-Jock-of-a-Best Friend Must Do in Europe. 2006. 160p. (YA). (gr. 6-10). 15.95 (978-1-58196-041-9(7)) Darby Creek Publishing.

Harrison, Troon. Poetry & Potatoes. Hellard, Susan, illus. 2003. 32p. (YA). (978-1-84365-020-1(7)) Chrysalis Children's Bks.

Hobbie, Holly. Charming Opal. Hobbie, Holly, illus. 2003. (Toot & Puddle Ser.). (Illus.). 32p. (J). (ps-3). 16.99 (978-0-316-36633-5(1)) Little Brown & Co.

—I'll Be Home for Christmas. Hobbie, Holly, illus. 2001. (Toot & Puddle Ser.: Bk. 5). (Illus.). 32p. (J). (ps-3). 15.95 (978-0-316-36623-6(4) , Tingley, Megan Bks.) Little, Brown Bks. for Young Readers.

—Toot & Puddle. 2007. 32p. (J). (ps-3). 16.99 ***(*978-0-316-16702-4(9))*** Little, Brown Bks. for Young Readers.

Hobbie, Holly. Wish You Were Here. 2005. (Toot & Puddle Ser.). (Illus.). 32p. (J). (ps-3). 16.99 (978-0-316-36602-1(1)) Little Brown & Co.

Hobbs, Will. Changes in Latitudes. 2004. 176p. (YA). pap. 9.95 (978-0-689-87069-9(8) , Simon Pulse) Simon & Schuster Children's Publishing.

Hodges, Candri. Gold Nugget Trip. 1998. (Illus.). 128p. (J). (gr. 3-5). pap. 3.99 (978-0-87406-896-2(7) , Willowisp Pr.) Darby Creek Publishing.

Hoffman, Mary. Seven Wonders of the Ancient World. Robertson, M. P., illus. 2004. 36p. (YA). (978-0-7112-1986-1(9)); 32p. (J). pap. 7.95 (978-1-84507-156-1(5)) Lincoln, Frances Ltd. GBR. *Dist:* Transition Vendor, Perseus Distribution.

Hofmeister, Alan, et al. A Trip. (Reading for All Learners Ser.). (Illus.). (J). pap. (978-1-56861-130-3(7)) Swift Learning Resources.

Hood, Karen Jean Matsko. Adventure Travel International: A Daily Journal. 2003. (J). 15.95 (978-1-59434-596-8(1)) Whispering Pine Pr., Inc.

—Adventure Travel USA: A Daily Journal. 2003. (JPN & ENG.). (YA). (978-1-59434-599-9(6)) Whispering Pine Pr., Inc.

Hooray for Boys & Girls! ed. 2006. (J). 15.95 (978-0-9776837-0-3(2)) West Woods Pr.

Hubbell, Patricia. Sidewalk Trip. Takabayashi, Mari, photos by. 1999. (Illus.). 24p. (J). (ps up). 9.95 (978-0-694-01174-2(6) , Harper Festival) HarperCollins Pubs.

Jacquemain, Patti. Journey of the Great Bear: Through California's Golden Past. Jacquemain, Patti, illus. 2006. (J). (978-0-929702-10-0(7)) Mission Creek Studios.

Joy, Brenda. Kaweah's Journey to New Mexico. 2005. 57p. pap. 12.95 (978-1-4137-9549-3(8)) PublishAmerica, Inc.

Kidd, Richard. Almost Famous Daisy: Around the World in Famous Paintings. Kidd, Richard, illus. 2000. (Illus.). 32p. (J). (gr. k-4). pap. 9.99 (978-0-7112-1070-7(5)) Lincoln, Frances Ltd. GBR. *Dist:* Transition Vendor.

Knight, Grover. Ahzar's Travels & Life Lessons - Meet Ahzar: Book One. 2003. (Illus.). 40p. (J). 16.95 (978-0-9746130-0-0(2)) Ahzar's Bk. Co. Publishing.

Koeppel, Ruth. Little Tikes All Around the Town: Little Tikes Cozy Coupe. 2006. (Little Tikes Ser.). 10p. (J). bds. 5.99 (978-0-7944-1149-7(5)) Reader's Digest Assn., Inc., The.

Lambert, Ian. Lost & Gone Seeking. Lambert, Ian, illus. 2001. (Illus.). 32p. (J). (ps-3). pap. 7.50 (978-1-884083-73-0(0)) Maval Publishing, Inc.

Lamote, Lisa Edman. A Day Out for Opus. 2006. (J). 15.99 (978-1-933673-03-5(6) , BookMann Pr.) Mann Publishing Group.

Lang, George. Pixy's Holiday Journey. 2006. 33.99 ***(*978-1-4280-4243-8(1));*** pap. 26.99 ***(*978-1-4280-4261-2(X))*** IndyPublish.com.

Langen, Annette. Felix Explores Planet Earth. Droop, Constanza, illus. 2004. (Perfect for Earth Day Promotions! Ser.). 47p. (J). 14.99 (978-1-59384-030-3(6)) Parklane Publishing.

Le Guin, Ursula K. Tom Mouse. ed. 2004. (Illus.). (J). (gr. k-3). spiral bd. (978-0-616-14584-5(5)) Canadian National Institute for the Blind/Institut National Canadien pour les Aveugles.

Learning Company Books Staff, ed. Westward Bound! 2004. (Oregon Trail Adventures Ser.). (Illus.). 96p. (J). pap. 4.99 (978-0-7630-7724-2(0)) Learning Co. Bks.

Lee, Quinlan B. Going Places. Harris, Annmarie, ed. 2006. (Barney Ser.). (Illus.). 96p. (J). pap. 2.99 (978-0-439-82953-3(4)) Scholastic, Inc.

Less, Emma. Snail's Race Around the World. Moon, Jo, illus. 2006. (Snail#39;s Adventures Ser.). 10p. (J). bds. 15.95 (978-0-7696-4607-7(7) , Brighter Child) School Specialty Publishing.

Linke, Uwe. Princess Moving Book. 2007. (J). bds. 8.95 (978-0-7358-2125-5(9)) North-South Bks., Inc.

The Littles Take a Trip. 2002. (Littles Ser.). (Illus.). (J). 12.17 (978-0-7587-6978-7(4)) Book Wholesalers, Inc.

Loesch, Joe. The Tuskegee Airmen: Raiders of the Skies with Buffalo Biff & Farley's Raiders. Hutchinson, Cheryl, ed. 2004. (Backyard Adventure Ser.). (Illus.). 56p. (J). bds. 16.95 incl. audio compact disk (978-1-932332-27-8(8)) Toy Box Productions.

Lottridge, Celia Barker. Ticket to Curlew. 2001. (J). (gr. 4-7). pap. (978-0-88899-221-5(1)) Groundwood Bks.

Lund, Deborah. All Aboard the Dinotrain. Fine, Howard, illus. 2006. 40p. (J). 16.00 (978-0-15-205237-9(2)) Harcourt Trade Pubs.

Manzano, Sonia & Muth, Jon J. No Dogs Allowed! 2004. (Illus.). 32p. (J). (ps-3). 15.95 (978-0-689-83088-4(2) , Atheneum) Simon & Schuster Children's Publishing.

Martel, Yann. Life of Pi: A Novel. 2003. (gr. 7-12). lib. bdg. 23.45 (978-0-613-59907-8(1)) Tandem Library Bks.

Mazer, Anne. Have Wheels, Will Travel. 2001. (Amazing Days of Abby Hayes Ser.: No. 4). 144p. (gr. 4-7). mass mkt. 4.99 (978-0-439-17878-5(9)) Scholastic, Inc.

McCloskey, Erin, ed. In the Wild West on MacKenzie's Trail. Howard, Catherine, tr. 2007. (Alex & Penny Ser.). (Illus.). 75p. (J). (gr. 2-5). 14.95 ***(*978-88-544-0245-4(1))*** White Star ITA. *Dist:* Random Hse., Inc.

McPherson, Missie & O'Neill, Elizabeth. Alfred Visits Washington D. C. 2006. 24p. (J). pap. 12.00 (978-0-9771836-1-6(0)) Funny Bone Bks.

Michot, Fabienne, et al. I Love to Travel. Michot, Fabienne & Brasset, Doris, illus. 2000. (Maki Ser.). 14p. (J). (ps up). bds. (978-1-894363-33-4(7)) Dominique & Friends.

Miller, Sara Swan. Cat in the Bag. Mahan, Benton, illus. 2001. (Rookie Reader Espanol Ser.). (J). 32p. (gr. k-2). pap. 4.95 (978-0-516-27292-4(6)); 31p. (gr. 1-2). 19.50 (978-0-516-22014-7(4)) Scholastic Library Publishing. (Children's Pr.).

—Cat in the Bag. 2001. (gr. k-3). lib. bdg. 12.95 (978-0-613-54112-1(X)) Tandem Library Bks.

—La Gatita en la Maleta. Mahan, Benton, illus. 2001. (Rookie Espanol Ser.). (SPA.). 32p. (J). (gr. k-2). 19.50 (978-0-516-22355-1(0) , Children's Pr.) Scholastic Library Publishing.

Montes, Marisa. Get Ready for Gabi No. 5: All in the Familia. Cepeda, Joe, illus. 2004. 112p. (J). (gr. 2-5). (978-0-439-66156-0(0) , Scholastic Paperbacks) Scholastic, Inc.

Montgomery, R. A. Caravan. 2007. (Choose Your Own Adventure - Dragonlarks Ser.). (Illus.). 64p. (J). pap. 5.99 ***(*978-1-933390-54-3(9))*** Chooseco LLC.

Montt, Alberto & Vega, Claudia. Para Ver y No Creer. Montt, Alberto, illus. 2002. (SPA., Illus.). 27p. (J). (gr. k-3). pap. 7.95 (978-956-239-141-2(8)) Santillana USA Publishing Co., Inc.

Moss, Marissa. Amelia Hits the Road. 1999. (Amelia's Notebooks). (J). (gr. 3-5). 12.75 (978-0-606-19867-7(9)) Tandem Library Bks.

Mullican, Judy. Let's Take a Ride. Gillen, Lisa P., illus. l.t. ed. 2004. (Hrl Big Book Ser.). (J). (ps-k). pap. 10.95 (978-1-57332-318-5(7)); pap. 10.95 (978-1-57332-319-2(5)) HighReach Learning, Inc.

Newcomb, Kristene. Molly Q's Trash Travels Through the Water Cycle. Paschall, Patricia, ed. Newcomb, Kristene, illus. 2007. (Illus.). 32p. (J). per. 8.00 ***(*978-0-9760790-9-5(7))*** Folsom Fallies Pr.

Norelli, Sallianne & O'Neil, Amy. The Jazz Jamboree. Yeagle, Barbara, illus. 2002. (Read-To-Me Ser.). 24p. (J). (978-0-7665-1210-8(X)) Abrams, Harry N. , Inc.

North, Merry. My Vacation: Picture, Play, & Tote. 2003. (Picture, Play & Tote-Book Ser.). (Illus.). 10p. (J). (ps up). bds. 5.99 (978-1-57151-720-3(0)) Playhouse Publishing.

Ohi, Ruth. A Trip with Grandma. Ohi, Ruth, illus. 2007. (Ruth Ohi Picture Book Ser.). (Illus.). 32p. (J). (ps-2). pap. 5.95 ***(*978-1-55451-071-9(6));*** lib. bdg. 19.95 ***(*978-1-55451-072-6(4))*** Annick Pr., Ltd. CAN. *Dist:* Firefly Bks., Ltd.

Olsen, Mary-Kate. Two for the Road. 2001. (gr. 3-6). lib. bdg. 13.00 (978-0-613-43966-4(X)) Tandem Library Bks.

Parker, Sandy. What Month Is It? Hofher, Cathy, illus. l.t. ed. 2004. 32p. 15.95 (978-0-9643462-5-3(7) , Just Think Bks.) Canary Connect Pubns.

Pati, Geeta. Finny's Voyage Through the Universe: The. 2005. (ENG.). 64p. per. 10.95 ***(*978-1-59526-019-2(6))*** Media Creations, Inc.

Pattison, Darcy. The Journey of Oliver K. Woodman. Cepeda, Joe, illus. 2003. 56p. (J). (gr. k-3). 16.00 (978-0-15-202329-4(1)) Harcourt Children's Bks.

—Searching for Oliver K. Woodman. Cepeda, Joe, illus. 2005. 56p. (J). 16.00 (978-0-15-205184-6(8)) Harcourt Children's Bks.

Paulsen, Gary. The Car. 2006. (Illus.). 192p. (YA). pap. 5.95 (978-0-15-205827-2(3) , Harcourt Paperbacks) Harcourt Children's Bks.

Payne, Rachel. Summer of Circles & Sapphires: Iggy Colvin Adventure Series. 2003. 194p. 23.95 (978-0-595-74705-4(1)); pap. 13.95 (978-0-595-27915-9(5)) iUniverse, Inc.

Peck, Richard. A Long Way from Chicago. 2000. (gr. 3-6). lib. bdg. 14.15 (978-0-613-30011-7(4)) Tandem Library Bks.

Perry, Shelly. Duckling's First Adventure. Loebel, Bonnie, illus. 2006. (ENG.). 56p. (J). per. 9.95 (978-0-9787740-3-5(5)) Peppertree Pr., The.

Peterson, Doug & Kenney, Cindy. Lost in Place: A Lesson in Overcoming Fear. Big Idea Productions Staff, illus. 2005. (VeggieTown Values Ser.: Bk. 4). 32p. pap. 3.99 (978-0-310-70629-8(7)) Zonderkidz.

Peterson, John. The Littles Take a Trip. Clark, Roberta C., illus. 2007. (Littles Ser.). 96p. (J). (gr. 1-5). pap. 3.99 (978-0-590-46222-8(9)) Scholastic, Inc.

Point, Virginia. Molly's Metamorphosis in India. 2005. 193p. pap. 19.95 (978-1-4137-3729-5(3)) PublishAmerica, Inc.

Quattlebaum, Mary. Underground Train. Smith, Cat Bowman, illus. 1999. (J). (ps-ps). lib. bdg. 12.54 (978-0-606-20025-7(8)) Tandem Library Bks.

Rangel, Graciela. Anthony's Christmas Journey. 2006. pap. 9.95 ***(*978-1-59526-650-7(X)*** , Llumina Christian Bks.) Media Creations, Inc.

Ready Reader Staff. Mr. Fins' Trip: Short I, Level A. 2003. (J). (ps-3). 24.50 (978-0-8136-1959-0(9)) Modern Curriculum Pr.

Renov, Ruki D. Don't Burst My Bubble. Renov, Ruki D., illus. 2001. (Illus.). 32p. (J). (gr. k-4). 15.95 (978-0-9667483-2-1(8)) Priority Multimedia Group, Inc.

Richter, Dana. Arthur's Road Trip. Moroney, Christopher, illus. 2001. (J). (978-0-7853-4859-7(X)) Publications International, Ltd.

Rigby Education Staff. The Island of Wingo. (Sails Literacy Ser.). (Illus.). 16p. (gr. 2-3). 27.00 (978-0-7635-9946-1(8) , 699468C99) Rigby Education.

Rizzo, Kay D. Old Friends & New. 2003. 96p. (J). (978-0-8163-1975-6(8)) Pacific Pr. Publishing Assn.

Roberts, Sheena. We All Go Traveling. Bell, Siobhan, illus. 2005. 24p. (J). pap. 9.99 (978-1-84148-410-5(5)) Barefoot Bks., Inc.

Runholt, Susan. The Mystery of the Third Lucretia. 2008. (J). (gr. 6). 16.99 ***(*978-0-670-06252-2(9)*** , Viking Juvenile) Penguin Group (USA) Inc.

Saddleback Pub. Gulliver's Travels. 2006. (Illus.). 61p. (J). lib. bdg. 30.77 ***(*978-1-4242-1328-3(2))*** Fitzgerald Bks.

Samantha's Travel Adventure Starter Kit. 1998. (Illus.). 2p. (J). (ps-1). 30.00 (978-1-888074-83-3(3)) Pockets of Learning.

Santillo, LuAnn. The Trip. Santillo, LuAnn, ed. 2003. (Half-Pint Kids Readers Ser.). (Illus.). 7p. (J). (ps-1). pap. (978-1-59256-057-8(1)) Half-Pint Kids, Inc.

Scalpone, Joan Lundquist. "Cool" Capers: Children's Stories. l.t. ed. 2000. (Illus.). 32p. (J). pap. 12.00 (978-0-929198-21-7(2)) Mini DayTrip Bks.

Scherer, Catherine W. Simon & Barklee in China, Book 2 - the Mountains. 2008. (Another Country Calling Ser.). (J). per. 15.00 (978-0-9714502-7-1(7) , Explorer Media) Simon & Barklee, Inc./ExplorerMedia.

—Simon & Barklee in China, Book 3 - the North. 2008. (Another Country Calling Ser.). (J). per. 15.00 (978-0-9714502-8-8(5) , Explorer Media) Simon & Barklee, Inc./ExplorerMedia.

Scholastic, Inc. Staff. The Wobbly Bobbly Balls. 2004 (Boohbah Ser.). (Illus.). 16p. (J). pap. 5.99 (978-0-439-62512-8(2)) Scholastic, Inc.

Seidler, Tor. The Revenge of Randal Reese-Rat. Helquist, Brett, illus. 2004. 240p. (J). reprint ed. pap. 5.99 (978-0-06-050867-8(1) , Harper Trophy) HarperCollins Pubs.

Sempe, Goscinny. Las Vacaciones del Pequeno Nicolas. 2003. (SPA., Illus.). 150p. (J). (gr. 5-8). pap. 9.95 (978-84-204-4813-8(3)) Santillana USA Publishing Co., Inc.

Shreeve, Elizabeth. Hector Finds a Fortune. Levy, Pamela R., illus. 2004. 68p. (J). lib. bdg. 15.00 ***(*978-1-4242-0903-3(X))*** Fitzgerald Bks.

Silverstein, Shel. La Parte que Falta Conoce a la O Grande. 2000. (SPA., Illus.). 96p. (J). pap. 17.95 (978-84-7808-352-7(9) , SJ30291) Sirio, Editorial S.A. ESP. *Dist:* Lectorum Pubns., Inc.

Simmie, Lois. Mister Got to Go: The Cat That Wouldn't Leave. Nugent, Cynthia, illus. 1998. (Northern Lights Books for Children Ser.). 32p. (J). (ps-3). pap. 7.95 (978-0-88995-157-0(8)) Red Deer Pr. CAN. *Dist:* Fitzhenry & Whiteside, Ltd.

Slegers, Liesbet. Kevin Takes a Trip. 2002. (On My Way Ser.). (Illus.). 28p. (J). 7.95 (978-1-929132-30-0(1)) Kane/Miller Bk. Pubs., Inc.

Smith, Beth Esh. Off We Go! Linke, Don, Jr., illus. l.t. ed. 1998. (Little Bks.). 10p. (J). (ps-k). pap. 10.95 (978-1-57332-110-5(9)) HighReach Learning, Inc.

Smith, Dona. Cross Country with Lewis & Clark. 2004. (Tall Tails Ser.: No. 2). 144p. (J). pap. 3.99 (978-0-439-43441-6(6) , Scholastic Paperbacks) Scholastic, Inc.

Southall, Donna. The Bubble Trailer. 2004. (J). 15.00 (978-0-8059-6585-8(8)) Dorrance Publishing Co., Inc.

Stern, Leonard. The Mad Libs Worst-Case Scenario Survival Handbook: Travel. 2004. (Mad Libs Ser.). (Illus.). 48p. (J). (gr. 3). pap. 3.99 (978-0-8431-1033-3(3) , Price Stern Sloan) Penguin Group (USA) Inc.

Stilton, Geronimo. The Wild, Wild West. Keys, Larry & Rattonchi, Ratterto, illus. 2005. (Geronimo Stilton Ser.: No. 21). 100p. (J). (ps-k). lib. bdg. 13.94 (978-0-606-33824-0(1)) Tandem Library Bks.

Sturt, M. The Canterbury Pilgrims (Being Chaucer's. 2006. 94.99 ***(*978-1-4280-0313-2(4));*** pap. 88.99 ***(*978-1-4280-0309-5(6))*** IndyPublish.com.

Sweeney, Jacqueline. Aloha! 2002. (We Can Read! Ser.). (Illus.). 32p. (J). 21.36 (978-0-7614-1510-7(6) , Benchmark Bks.) Cavendish, Marshall Corp.

Tamura, Yumi. Basara. 2004. (gr. 7-12). lib. bdg. 18.75 (978-0-613-86370-4(4)) Tandem Library Bks.

Tanen, Sloane. Where Is Coco Going? Hagen, Stefan, photos by. 2004. (Illus.). 32p. (J). 14.95 (978-1-58234-951-0(7) , Bloomsbury Children) Bloomsbury Publishing.

T
U
V

Thorpe, Kiki. Let's Go, Little Bill! Oxley, Jennifer & Kanemoto, Dan, illus. 2002. (Little Bill Ser.). 14p. (J). (ps-2). bds. 12.95 (978-0-689-84776-9(9) , Simon Spotlight/Nickelodeon) Simon & Schuster Children's Publishing.

Tomlinson, Theresa & Browne, Jane. Little Stowaway. 1999. (Illus.). 32p. (J). 19.99 (***978-1-85681-691-5(5)***) Random Hse. GBR. *Dist:* Independent Pubs. Group.

Travels Around the World! Sticker Story Book. 2002. (Mr. Potato Head Ser.). (Illus.). 16p. (J). (ps). pap. 2.99 (978-1-57759-204-4(2)) Dalmatian Pr.

Uncle Markie. Piglettè & Bobo in Berkeley. 2003. (YA). ring bd. 9.95 (978-1-933129-07-5(7)) Studio 403.

—Piglettè & Bobo in Kansas City. 2003. (YA). ring bd. 9.95 (978-1-933129-08-2(5)) Studio 403.

—Piglettè & Bobo in Sud Africa. 2003. (YA). ring bd. 9.95 (978-1-933129-15-0(8)) Studio 403.

—Piglettè & Bobo Join the Manscouts. 2003. (YA). ring bd. 9.95 (978-1-933129-05-1(0)) Studio 403.

—Piglettè & Bobo on Safari. 2003. (YA). ring bd. 9.95 (978-1-933129-16-7(6)) Studio 403.

—Piglettè & Bobo Winter in Zagreb. 2003. (YA). ring bd. 9.95 (978-1-933129-11-2(5)) Studio 403.

—Piglettè & BoBoTrash Orange County. 2003. (YA). ring bd. 9.95 (978-1-933129-09-9(3)) Studio 403.

Upton, Deborah. World of Words. 2001. (Illus.). (J). (978-0-7853-4798-9(4)) Publications International, Ltd.

Van Straaten, Harmen. TIM & the FLYING MACHINE. 2008. 28p. 12.95 (***978-1-60136-003-8(7)***) Mars Media Pubs.

Verne, Jules. Cinco Semanas en Globo.Tr. of Around the World in Eighty Days. (SPA., Illus.). 142p. (YA). 14.95 (978-84-7281-102-7(6) , AF1102) Auriga, Ediciones S.A. ESP. *Dist:* Continental Bk. Co., Inc.

—Cinco Semanas en Globo. 2003. (Advanced Reading Ser.).Tr. of Around the World in Eighty Days. (SPA., Illus.). 240p. (J). 11.95 (978-84-239-5898-6(1)) Espasa Calpe, S.A. ESP. *Dist:* Planeta Publishing Corp.

—Cinco Semanas en Globo. 2000. (Coleccion "Clasicos Juveniles" Ser.).Tr. of Around the World in Eighty Days. (SPA., Illus.). 180p. (gr. 4-7). pap. 9.95 (978-1-58348-828-7(6)) iUniverse, Inc.

Walsh, Maria Elena. Manuelita, Donde Vas? Ink, Lancman, illus. 2003. (SPA.). 136p. (J). (gr. 3-5). pap. 11.95 (978-950-511-631-7(4)) Santillana USA Publishing Co., Inc.

Walter, Mildred Pitts. Suitcase. Flavin, Teresa, illus. 2006. 112p. (J). pap. 5.99 (978-0-380-73210-4(6)) HarperCollins Pubs.

Walters, Virginia. Are We There Yet, Daddy? Schindler, S. D., illus. 2002. 32p. (J). pap. 6.99 (978-0-14-230013-8(6) , Puffin) Penguin Group (USA) Inc.

Warden, Evelyn. Tommy's Travels. 2005. 122p. pap. 17.95 (978-1-4137-6307-2(3)) PublishAmerica, Inc.

Watson, James, Jr. Ticket to Prague. (Illus.). 192p. (J). 9.95 (978-0-14-130008-5(6)) Penguin Bks., Ltd. GBR. *Dist:* Trafalgar Square Publishing.

Wells, Rosemary. The Bear Went over the Mountain. Wells, Rosemary, illus. 2007. (Bruno & Boots Book Ser.). (Illus.). 18p. (J). bds. 5.99 (978-0-590-02910-0(X)) Scholastic, Inc.

The Wet Goodbye. 2001. 32p. (YA). (gr. 6-12). pap. (978-0-8224-1461-2(9)) Globe Fearon Educational Publishing.

Whint, Ana Lee. Espalemit. 2003. (ENG.). 112p. pap. 9.95 (***978-0-595-26259-5(7)*** , Writers Club Pr.) iUniverse, Inc.

Williams, Jennifer. Stringbean's Trip to the Shining Sea. Williams, Vera B., illus. 1999. 48p. (J). (ps-3). pap. 6.99 (978-0-688-16701-1(2) , Harper Trophy) HarperCollins Pubs.

Williams, Rozanne Lanczak. Captain Jack's Journal. Maio, Barbara, ed. Grayson, Rick, illus. 2006. (Learn to Write Ser.). (J). 16p. pap. 2.99 (978-1-59198-303-3(7) , 6197); per. 6.99 (***978-1-59198-361-3(4)***) Creative Teaching Pr., Inc.

—Postcards from Barney Bear. Maio, Barbara & Faulkner, Stacey, eds. Thelen, Mary, illus. 2006. (Learn to Write Ser.). 8p. (J). pap. 1.99 (978-1-59198-287-6(1) , 6181) Creative Teaching Pr., Inc.

Williams, Vera B. Stringbean's Trip to the Shining Sea. 1999. (978-0-606-16744-4(7)); lib. bdg. 14.10 (978-0-613-18280-5(4)) Tandem Library Bks.

Wood, David. There's a World in my House. 2005. 36p. (J). per. 13.95 (978-1-933290-90-4(0)) Tate Publishing & Enterprises, L.L.C.

Woods, Tonita. Mystical Forest of Wise. 2001. 120p. pap. 10.95 (978-0-595-19147-5(9) , Writers Club Pr.) iUniverse, Inc.

Worcester, Daryl D. The Story of the Famous Traves Travlslot. 2006. 48p. pap. 12.95 (978-1-4241-2417-6(4)) PublishAmerica, Inc.

Would, Nick. The Warrior & the Moon: Spirit of the Maasai. Safarewicz, Evie, illus. 2004. 48p. (J). pap. 9.95 (978-1-84507-141-7(7)) Lincoln, Frances Ltd. GBR. *Dist:* Perseus Distribution.

Yansky, Brian. My Road Trip to the Pretty Girl Capital of the World. 2003. 160p. 16.95 (978-0-8126-2691-9(5)) Cricket Bks.

YKids Staff. Gulliver's Travels. 2007. (Manga Literary Classics Ser.). 148p. (J). (gr. 4-7). pap. 14.95 (***978-981-05-4941-1(5)***) Youngjin (Singapore) Pte Ltd. SGP. *Dist:* Independent Pubs. Group.

Zachary, Ken. Missions of Big Zach. 2005. (Illus.). 36p. (J). per. 9.95 (978-1-59879-061-0(7)) Lifevest Publishing, Inc.

Ziefert, Harriet. From Kalamazoo to Timbuktu. Miller, Gustaf, illus. 2002. (J). (978-0-399-23730-0(5)) Penguin Group (USA) Inc.

—From Kalamazoo to Timbuktu! Roitman, Tanya, illus. 2005. 40p. (ps-ps). 15.95 (978-1-59354-091-3(4)) Blue Apple Bks.

—When Daddy Travels. Bolam, Emily, illus. 2007. 16p. (J). pap. 5.95 (***978-1-4027-4802-8(7)***) Sterling Publishing Co., Inc.

—When Mommy Travels. Bolam, Emily, illus. 2007. 16p. (J). pap. 5.95 (***978-1-4027-4803-5(5)***) Sterling Publishing Co., Inc.

TRAVEL GAMES

see Games for Travelers

TRAVELERS

see also Explorers

Chait, Baruch. The Incredible Voyage to Good Middos. Pollack, Gadi, illus. (Good Middos Ser.: Vol. 1). 68p. 25.99 (978-1-58330-441-9(X)) Feldheim Pubs.

Comerciantes Y Viajeros, 6 vols., Vol. 2. (Explorers. Exploradores Nonfiction Sets Ser.). (SPA.). 32p. (gr. 3-6). 44.95 (978-0-7699-0647-8(8)) Shortland Pubns. (U. S. A.) Inc.

Gallagher, Debbie. Portable Homes. 2007. (J). (***978-1-59920-150-4(X)***) Smart Apple Media.

Marcovitz, Hal. Marco Polo & the Wonders of the East. 1999. (Explorers of the New World Ser.). (Illus.). 63p. (J). (gr. 4 up). 31.00 (978-0-7910-5511-3(6) , Chelsea Hse.) Facts On File, Inc.

McLean, Jacqueline. Women of Adventure. 2003. (Profiles Ser.). (Illus.). 160p. (gr. 5 up). lib. bdg. 19.95 (978-1-881508-73-1(0)) Oliver Pr., Inc.

Wagner, Heather Lehr. Gertrude Bell: Explorer of the Middle East. 2004. (Women Explorers Ser.). (Illus.). 120p. 30.00 (978-0-7910-7711-5(X) , Chelsea Hse.) Facts On File, Inc.

TRAVELERS—FICTION

Christie, Amanda. Drive You Crazy. 2001. (7th Heaven Ser.). 128p. (J). (gr. 5-8). mass mkt. 4.99 (978-0-375-81159-3(1) , Random Hse. Bks. for Young Readers) Random Hse. Children's Bks.

Creech, Sharon. Entre Dos Lunas. 2003. (SPA., Illus.). 191p. (YA). (gr. 5-8). (978-84-279-3221-0(9) , NG7785) Noguer y Caralt Editores, S. A. ESP. *Dist:* Lectorum Pubns., Inc.

Garis, Howard Roger. Uncle Wiggily's Travels. Date not set. 192p. (J). 20.95 (978-0-8488-2278-1(1)) Amereon LTD.

Gentile, Joe. Noir: The Mysterious Traveller. 2003. (Illus.). 48p. (gr. 12 up). pap. 5.50 (978-0-9721668-5-0(8)) Moonstone.

Greene, Janice. Gulliver's Travels. abr. ed. 2001. (gr. 7-12). lib. bdg. 15.25 (978-0-613-36384-6(1)) Tandem Library Bks.

Gulliver's Travels Study Guide. 2000. (Illus.). 48p. (YA). per. 17.95 (978-1-56254-286-3(9) , SP2869) Saddleback Educational Publishing.

Joan, Marler. Secrets of the Wind. 2006. pap. (***978-1-888251-37-1(9)***) Voice & Vision Pubns.

Morel, Alicia. Los Viajeros Invisibles. 2002. (J). (978-956-240-360-3(2)) Arrayan Editores S.A.

Rand, Kathleen G. Marianne's Magical Journey. 1998. (Illus.). 15p. (J). (ps-8). pap. 6.95 (978-1-880710-18-0(8)) Monterey Pacific Pubs.

Shulevitz, Uri. The Travels of Benjamin of Tudela: Through Three Continents in the Twelfth Century. 2005. (Illus.). 48p. (J). 17.00 (978-0-374-37754-0(5) , Farrar, Straus & Giroux (BYR)) Farrar, Straus & Giroux.

Stokes, Katherine. Motor Maids in Fair Japan. 2006. pap. (***978-1-4068-3090-3(9)***) Echo Library.

Swift, Jonathan. Gulliver's Travels. 2003. (gr. k-3). lib. bdg. 14.10 (978-0-613-67626-7(2)) Tandem Library Bks.

Timothy Flies South. 2000. (Let's Start! Teacher's Pets Ser.). (Illus.). 32p. (J). (ps-1). 6.95 (978-1-57145-439-3(X) , Silver Dolphin Bks.) Advantage Pubs. Group.

Whitney, Kim Ablon. See You down the Road. 2005. 192p. (YA). (gr. 7-12). mass mkt. 5.99 (978-0-440-23809-6(9) , Laurel Leaf) Random Hse. Children's Bks.

Yolen, Jane. Mary Celeste: An Unsolved Mystery from History. 2002. (gr. 3-6). lib. bdg. 15.30 (978-0-613-46226-6(2)) Tandem Library Bks.

TRAVELERS—POETRY

Capildeo, Vahni. No Traveller Returns. 2004. (Salt Modern Poets). 184p. pap. 16.99 (978-1-876857-88-2(9)) Salt Publishing GBR. *Dist:* SPD-Small Pr. Distribution.

Soto, Gary. Worlds Apart: Traveling with Fernie & Me: Poems. Clarke, Greg, illus. 2005. 64p. (J). 14.99 (978-0-399-24218-2(X) , Putnam Juvenile) Penguin Group (USA) Inc.

TRAVELS

see Overland Journeys to the Pacific; Scientific Expeditions; Voyages and Travels; Voyages around the World

TRAVESTIES

see Parodies

TREASURE ISLAND (IMAGINARY PLACE)—FICTION

Burnett, Frances Hodgson. Treasure Island: Juvenile Classic. 2005. (Illus.). 192p. (J). 5.99 (978-1-4037-1387-2(1)) Dalmatian Pr.

Cole, Bob. Power Reading: Classics/Treasure Island. Lee, Joe, illus. 2004. 94p. (J). (gr. 5-6). vinyl bd. 39.95 (978-1-883186-59-3(5) , PPCL3) National Reading Styles Institute, Inc.

Eaton, Cathy. Curse of the Pirate's Treasure. 2002. (gr. 7-12). lib. bdg. 29.20 (978-0-613-74589-5(2)) Tandem Library Bks.

Inches, Alison. Dora's Treasure Hunt. Hall, Susan', illus. 2002. (Dora the Explorer Ser.). 12p. (J). 5.99 (978-0-689-84664-9(9) , Simon Spotlight/Nickelodeon) Simon & Schuster Children's Publishing.

Stevenson, Robert Louis. Kidnapped. 2002. (Scholastic Classics Ser.). 288p. (J). (gr. 5). pap. 3.99 (978-0-439-29578-9(5)) Scholastic, Inc.

—Treasure Island. Todd, Justin, illus. 1999. (Abbeville Classics Ser.). 176p. (J). 12.95 (978-0-7892-0561-2(0)); pap. 7.95 (978-0-7892-0551-3(3)) Abbeville Pr., Inc. (Abbeville Kids).

—Treasure Island. 2002. (YA). 12.34 (978-0-7587-7947-2(X)) Book Wholesalers, Inc.

—Treasure Island. (Great Classics for Children Ser.). (J). (Illus.). 192p. (978-1-4037-0599-0(2)); 2003. 182p. 4.99 (978-1-57759-557-1(2)) Dalmatian Pr.

—Treasure Island. 2001. (Fast Track Classics Ser.). (Illus.). 48p. pap. 9.99 (978-0-237-52282-7(9) , Evans Brothers, Limited) Evans Publishing Group GBR. *Dist:* Independent Pubs. Group.

—Treasure Island. 2001. (YA). (gr. 5-12). pap. 8.50 (978-0-8359-0234-2(X)) Globe Fearon Educational Publishing.

—Treasure Island. (Young Collector's Illustrated Classics Ser.). (Illus.). 192p. (J). (gr. 3-7). 9.95 (978-1-56156-456-9(7)) Kidsbooks, Inc.

—Treasure Island. 2007. (Oxford Children's Classics). (Illus.). 288p. (YA). 9.95 (***978-0-19-271998-0(X)***) Oxford Univ. Pr., Inc.

—Treasure Island. Seelye, John, ed. 1999. (Classics Ser.). (Illus.). 240p. (gr. 12). pap. 7.00 (978-0-14-043768-3(1) , Penguin Classics) Penguin Group (USA) Inc.

—Treasure Island. 1998. (Signet Classic Shakespeare Ser.). 224p. mass mkt. 3.95 (978-0-451-52704-2(6) , Signet Classics) Penguin Group (USA) Inc.

—Treasure Island. Wyeth, N. C., illus. 2000. (Aladdin Classics Ser.). 368p. (gr. 3-7). mass mkt. 5.99 (978-0-689-83212-3(5) , Aladdin) Simon & Schuster Children's Publishing.

—Treasure Island. 2006. (J). (gr. 4-8). 24.21 (978-1-59961-119-8(8)) Spotlight.

—Treasure Island. 1998. (Children's Classics). (ENG., Illus.). 224p. (J). (gr. 3-7). pap. (978-1-85326-103-9(3) , 1033WW) Wordsworth Editions, Ltd.

—Treasure Island. 2003. (More for Teens Ser.). 64p. (Orig.). (YA). (gr. 6-12). pap. 6.00 (978-0-88734-412-1(7)) Players Pr., Inc.

—Treasure Island. McKowen, Scott, illus. 2004. (Unabridged Classics Ser.). 232p. 9.95 (978-1-4027-1457-3(2)) Sterling Publishing Co., Inc.

—Treasure Island. Todd, Justin, illus. unabr. ed. 2003. (Chrysalis Children's Classics Ser.). 222p. (YA). pap. (978-1-84365-037-9(1)) Chrysalis Children's Bks.

—Treasure Island. Cruz, Nardo, illus. 2nd ed. 1998. (Illustrated Classic Book Ser.). 61p. (J). (gr. 3 up). reprint ed. pap. 4.95 (978-1-56767-239-8(6)) Educational Insights, Inc.

—Treasure Island. unabr. ed. 1998. (Wordsworth Classics Ser.). (YA). (gr. 6-12). 5.27 (978-0-89061-103-6(3) , R1033WW) Jamestown.

—Treasure Island. 1999. (Illus.). 240p. (YA). (gr. 3 up). reprint ed. 7.95 (978-1-56852-233-3(9) , Konecky & Konecky) Konecky, William S. Assocs., Inc.

—Treasure Island. 1998. (Twelve-Point Ser.). 204p. reprint ed. lib. bdg. 25.00 (978-1-58287-075-5(6)) North Bks.

—Treasure Island. unabr. ed. 2002. (YA). pap. incl. audio compact disk (978-1-58472-361-5(0) , In Audio) Sound Room Pubs., Inc.

—Treasure Island: A Classic Story about Responsibility. 2003. (Illus.). 32p. per. 3.95 (978-0-9747133-4-2(1) , Values to Live By Classic Stories) Thomas, Frederic Inc.

—Treasure Island: With Story of the Treasure of Normon Island. Date not set. (J). (gr. 5-6). reprint ed. lib. bdg. 22.95 (978-0-89190-236-2(8) , American Reprint Co.) Amereon LTD.

Stevenson, Robert Louis & Wyeth, N. C. Treasure Island. abr. ed. 2003. (Scribner Storybook Classic Ser.). (Illus.). 64p. (J). 19.99 (978-0-689-85468-2(4) , Atheneum) Simon & Schuster Children's Publishing.

Stilton, Geronimo. El Misterio Del Ojo Esmeralda. (SPA., Illus.). 128p. (J). (gr. 3-5). pap. 7.95 (978-1-59437-453-1(8)) Santillana USA Publishing Co., Inc.

Wilkes, Angela. Treasure Island. 2003. (gr. 3-6). lib. bdg. 14.10 (978-0-613-88963-6(0)) Tandem Library Bks.

Wilkes, Angela & Rawson, Christopher. Treasure Island. 2004. (Young Reading Ser.). (Illus.). 64p. (J). (gr. 2 up). pap. 5.95 (978-0-7945-0411-3(6) , Usborne) EDC Publishing.

TREASURE-TROVE

see Buried Treasure

TREE HOUSES—FICTION

Arena, Felice & Kettle, Phil. The Tree House. Vane, Mitch, illus. 2004. (J). pap. (978-1-59336-357-4(5)) Mondo Publishing.

Blyton, Enid. Hollow Tree House. (J). (gr. k-6). pap. 5.95 (978-0-09-947220-9(1)) Random Hse. GBR. *Dist:* Trafalgar Square Publishing.

Bowen, Debralee. The Tree House Club Journal. 2003. 47p. pap. 19.95 (978-1-4137-0154-8(X)) PublishAmerica, Inc.

Brown, Marc. Arthur's Tree House. 2007. (Arthur's 8 x 8 Bks.). (Illus.). (J). (***978-1-4287-1970-5(9)***) Little Brown & Co.

—Arthur's Tree House. 2007. (Arthur's 8 x 8 Bks.). (Illus.). 24p. (J). (ps-1). mass mkt. 3.99 (978-0-316-05776-9(2)) Little, Brown Bks. for Young Readers.

Carrasco, Ledo & Munoz, Norma. Los Cuentos de la Casa del Arbol. Olson, Johan, illus. rev. ed. 2004. (Castillo de la Lectura Blanca Ser.). (SPA.). 72p. (J). pap. 6.95 (978-970-20-0124-9(2)) Castillo, Ediciones, S. A. de C. V. MEX. *Dist:* Macmillan.

Cassidy, Anne. The Sassy Monkey. Smith, Lisa, illus. 2004. (Read-It! Readers Ser.). 32p. (C). (gr. k-3). 18.60 (978-1-4048-0058-8(1)) Picture Window Bks.

Dahlstrom, Halene. Raven Cove Mystery: A Rennie of Alaska Mystery. 2005. 12.95 (978-1-59433-001-8(8)) Publication Consultants.

Edwards, Pamela Duncan. Jack's Treehouse. 2008. (Illus.). 24p. (J). lib. bdg. 17.89 (***978-0-06-009078-4(2)*** , Tegen, Katherine Bks) HarperCollins Pubs.

Eliot, Ethel Cook. The House above the Trees. 2003. (Illus.). 140p. (J). 20.00 (978-0-9615961-7-0(1)); 2nd ed. pap. 12.00 (978-0-9615961-6-3(3)) Raven Rocks Pr.

Greene, Stephanie. Owen Foote, Frontiersman. Weston, Martha, illus. 1999. 96p. (J). (gr. k-3). tchr. ed. 14.00 (978-0-395-61578-2(X) , Clarion Bks.) Houghton Mifflin Co. Trade & Reference Div.

Harcourt School Publishers Staff. The Tree House: Take-Home Book. 1999. (Collections Ser.). (Illus.). (J). pap. 1.90 (978-0-15-317227-4(4)) Harcourt Schl. Pubs.

Herman, Gail. Chutes & Ladders: The Magical Tree House Adventure. 2003. (Illus.). 12p. (J). pap. 9.95 (978-0-7624-1565-6(7) , Running Pr. Kids) Running Pr. Bk. Pubs.

Hibbeler, Stephen Paul. A Wonderful, Magical World. 2006. 48p. pap. 12.95 (978-1-4241-2631-6(2)) PublishAmerica, Inc.

Hoenecke, Karen. Tree House. Graves, Dennis, illus. 2005. (J). pap. 4.95 (978-1-57874-090-1(8)) Kaeden Corp.

Hutchens, Paul. The Battle of the Bees. rev. ed. 1999. (Sugar Creek Gang Ser.: No. 32). (J). (gr. 4-7). 144p. 4.99 (978-0-8024-7035-5(1)); 112p. 4.99 (978-0-8024-7036-2(X)) Moody Pubs.

Lee, Shell. Teenie's Treehouse Adventures: The Magic Begins. 2004. 37p. pap. 17.95 (978-1-4137-2879-8(0)) PublishAmerica, Inc.

Lubbert, Constance. Killdeer. 2004. 81p. pap. 14.95 (978-1-4137-1138-7(3)) PublishAmerica, Inc.

Luke, Deanna. Treetop Clubhouse. Carnehl, Jeff, illus. 2002. 112p. (J). (gr. 2-6). 9.95 (978-1-928777-02-1(3) , BOW Bks.) Blessing Our World, Inc.

Mayer, Mercer. Our Tree House, Vol. 3. 2002. (Little Critter First Readers Ser.). (Illus.). 24p. (J). (gr. 1-2). pap. 3.95 (978-1-57768-833-4(3)) School Specialty Publishing.

—Our Tree House. 2001. (gr. k-3). lib. bdg. 11.80 (978-0-613-67657-1(2)) Tandem Library Bks.

Morrow, Bradford. Didn't Didn't Do It. Wilson, Gahan, illus. 2007. 32p. (J). (gr. k-2). 16.99 (978-0-399-24480-3(8) , Putnam Juvenile) Penguin Group (USA) Inc.

Moses, Lucinda J. The Most Amazing Tree House Ever!!! Carrozza, Kyle A., illus. 2001. 36p. (J). 9.95 (978-1-58284-007-9(5) , Thoughtful Education Pr., The) Silver Strong & Assocs.

Osborne, Mary Pope. Blizzard of the Blue Moon. Murdocca, Sal, illus. 2007. (Magic Tree House Ser.: No. 36). 144p. (J). (gr. 2-5). pap. 4.99 (978-0-375-83038-9(3) , Random Hse. Bks. for Young Readers) Random Hse. Children's Bks.

—Blizzard of the Blue Moon. 2006. (Magic Tree House Ser.: No. 36). (Illus.). 128p. (J). (gr. k-3). lib. bdg. 13.99 (978-0-375-93037-9(X)); (gr. 2-5). 11.95 (978-0-375-83037-2(5)) Random Hse. Children's Bks. (Random Hse. Bks. for Young Readers).

—Buffalo Before Breakfast. 2004. (Magic Tree House Ser. : No. 18). 72p. (J). (gr. k-3). pap. 17.00 incl. audio (978-0-8072-0927-1(9) , Listening Library) Random Hse. Audio Publishing Group.

—Buffalo Before Breakfast. Murdocca, Sal, illus. 1999. (Magic Tree House Ser.: No. 18). (J). (gr. k-3). 20.00 (978-0-375-80041-2(7)); 96p. lib. bdg. 11.99 (978-0-679-99064-2(X)); Vol. 18. 96p. mass mkt. 3.99 (978-0-679-89064-5(5)) Random Hse. Children's Bks. (Random Hse. Bks. for Young Readers).

—Buffalo Before Breakfast. Murdocca, Salvatore, illus. 1999. (Magic Tree House Ser. : No. 18). 72p. (J). (gr. k-3). lib. bdg. 11.80 (978-0-613-16067-4(3)) Tandem Library Bks.

—Buffalo Before Breakfast. 1999. (Magic Tree House Ser. : No. 18). (J). (gr. k-3). lib. bdg. 10.79 (978-0-606-16841-0(9)) Tandem Library Bks.

—El Caballero del Alba. 2004. (Coleccion la Casa Del Arbol the Magic Tree House Ser.). (SPA.). (J). pap. 4.95 (978-1-930332-50-8(5)) Lectorum Pubns., Inc.

—Carnival at Candlelight. 2006. (Magic Tree House Ser.: No. 33). (Illus.). 144p. (J). (gr. 2-6). pap. 4.99 (978-0-375-83034-1(0) , Random Hse. Bks. for Young Readers) Random Hse. Children's Bks.

—Carnival at Candlelight. Murdocca, Sal, illus. 2005. (Magic Tree House Ser.: No. 33). 128p. (J). (gr. k-3). 11.95 (978-0-375-83033-4(2) , Random Hse. Bks. for Young Readers) Random Hse. Children's Bks.

—Christmas in Camelot. Murdocca, Sal, illus. 2001. (Magic Tree House Ser.: No. 29). 128p. (J). (gr. k-3). 11.95 (978-0-375-81373-3(X)); lib. bdg. 13.99 (978-0-375-91373-0(4)) Random Hse. Children's Bks. (Random Hse. Bks. for Young Readers).

—Civil War on Sunday, Vol. 21. unabr. ed. 2004. (Magic Tree House Ser. : No. 21). 76p. (J). (gr. k-3). pap. 17.00 incl. audio (978-0-8072-0930-1(9) , S FTR 253 SP, Listening Library) Random Hse. Audio Publishing Group.

—Civil War on Sunday. Murdocca, Sal, illus. 2000. (Magic Tree House Ser.: No. 21). 96p. (J). (gr. k-3). lib. bdg. 11.99 (978-0-679-99067-3(4)); mass mkt. 3.99 (978-0-679-89067-6(X)) Random Hse. Children's Bks. (Random Hse. Bks. for Young Readers).

—Civil War on Sunday. 2000. (Magic Tree House Ser. : No. 21). (J). (gr. k-3). lib. bdg. 11.80 (978-0-613-24596-8(2)); (Illus.). 10.79 (978-0-606-18852-4(5)) Tandem Library Bks.

—Dark Day in the Deep Sea. Murdocca, Sal, illus. 2008. (Stepping Stone Bks.). 128p. (J). (gr. 3-7). lib. bdg. 14.99 (***978-0-375-93731-6(5)*** , Random Hse. Bks. for Young Readers) Random Hse. Children's Bks.

—Day of the Dragon King, Vol. 14. unabr. ed. 2004. (Magic Tree House Ser. : No. 14). 68p. (J). (gr. k-3). pap. 17.00 incl. audio (978-0-8072-0783-3(7) , S FTR 242 SP, Listening Library) Random Hse. Audio Publishing Group.

—Day of the Dragon King. Murdocca, Sal, illus. 1998. (Magic Tree House Ser.: No. 14). 96p. (J). (gr. k-3). lib. bdg. 11.99 (978-0-679-99051-2(8)); 14th ed. pap. 3.99 (978-0-679-89051-5(3)) Random Hse. Children's Bks. (Random Hse. Bks. for Young Readers).

—Day of the Dragon King. Murdocca, Sal, illus. 1998. (Magic Tree House Ser. : No. 14). (J). (gr. k-3). 10.79 (978-0-606-13958-8(3)) Tandem Library Bks.

—Dinosaurs Before Dark. unabr. ed. 2004. (Magic Tree House Ser. : No. 1). 68p. (J). (gr. k-5). pap. 17.00 incl. audio (978-0-8072-0330-9(0) , FTR208SP, Listening Library) Random Hse. Audio Publishing Group.

—Earthquake in the Early Morning, Vol. 24. unabr. ed. 2004. (Magic Tree House Ser. : No. 24). 71p. (J). (gr. k-3). pap. 17.00 incl. audio (978-0-8072-0933-2(3) , S FTR 256 SP, Listening Library) Random Hse. Audio Publishing Group.

—Earthquake in the Early Morning. Murdocca, Sal, illus. 2001. (Magic Tree House Ser.: No. 24). 96p. (J). (gr. k-3). 11.99 (978-0-679-99070-3(4)); mass mkt. 3.99 (978-0-679-89070-6(X)) Random Hse. Children's Bks. (Random Hse. Bks. for Young Readers).

—Earthquake in the Early Morning. 2001. (Magic Tree House Ser. : No. 24). (J). (gr. k-3). lib. bdg. 11.80 (978-0-613-35684-8(5)); (Illus.). 10.79 (978-0-606-21166-6(7)) Tandem Library Bks.

—Ghost Town at Sundown. unabr. ed. 2004. (Magic Tree House Ser. : No. 10). 73p. (J). (gr. k-3). pap. 17.00 incl. audio (978-0-8072-0535-8(4) , Listening Library) Random Hse. Audio Publishing Group.

—Haunted Castle on Hallows Eve. Murdocca, Sal, illus. 2003. (Magic Tree House Ser.: No. 30). 128p. (J). (gr. k-3). 11.95 (978-0-375-82521-7(5)); lib. bdg. 13.99 (978-0-375-92521-4(X)) Random Hse. Children's Bks. (Random Hse. Bks. for Young Readers).

—High Tide in Hawaii. Murdocca, Sal, illus. 2003. (Magic Tree House Ser.: No. 28). 96p. (J). (gr. k-3). lib. bdg. 11.99 (978-0-375-90616-9(9)); (gr. 1-4). pap. 3.99 (978-0-375-80616-2(4)) Random Hse. Children's Bks. (Random Hse. Bks. for Young Readers).

—High Tide in Hawaii. 2003. (Magic Tree House Ser. : No. 28). (J). (gr. k-3). lib. bdg. 11.80 (978-0-613-62386-5(X)) Tandem Library Bks.

—Hour of the Olympics. unabr. ed. 2004. (Magic Tree House Ser. : No. 16). 70p. (J). (gr. k-3). pap. 17.00 incl. audio (978-0-8072-0785-7(3) , LFTR 244 SP, Listening Library) Random Hse. Audio Publishing Group.

—Hour of the Olympics. Murdocca, Sal, illus. 1998. (Magic Tree House Ser.: No. 16). 96p. (J). (gr. k-3). lib. bdg. 11.99 (978-0-679-99062-8(3)); mass mkt. 3.99 (978-0-679-89062-1(9)) Random Hse. Children's Bks. (Random Hse. Bks. for Young Readers).

—The Knight at Dawn. unabr. ed. 2004. (Magic Tree House Ser. : No. 2). 66p. (J). (gr. k-3). pap. 17.00 incl. audio (978-0-8072-0331-6(9) , Listening Library) Random Hse. Audio Publishing Group.

—The Knight at Dawn Book & CD. Murdocca, Sal, illus. 2008. (Stepping Stone Book(TM) Ser.). (J). (gr. k-3). 9.99 (***978-0-375-84406-5(6)*** , Random Hse. Bks. for Young Readers) Random Hse. Children's Bks.

—Magic Tree House #1-4, 4 bks., Vol. 1-4. Murdocca, Sal, illus. 2001. (J). (gr. 1-3). pap. 15.96 (978-0-375-81365-8(9) , Random Hse. Bks. for Young Readers) Random Hse. Children's Bks.

—Magic Tree House #5-8, Bks. 5-8. 2002. (Illus.). (J). (ps-3). pap. 15.96 (978-0-375-82266-7(6) , Random Hse. Bks. for Young Readers) Random Hse. Children's Bks.

—Magische Baumhaus der Ruf. 18.95 (978-3-7855-4185-2(6)) Loewe Verlag GmbH DEU. *Dist:* Distribooks, Inc.

—Una Momia en la Manana. 2004. (Coleccion la Casa Del Arbol the Magic Tree House Ser.). (SPA.). (J). pap. 4.95 (978-1-930332-51-5(3)) Lectorum Pubns., Inc.

—Una Momia en la Manana. 2003. (SPA.). (gr. 3-6). lib. bdg. 12.95 (978-0-613-64609-3(6)) Tandem Library Bks.

—Piratas Despues del Mediodia. 2004. (Coleccion la Casa Del Arbol the Magic Tree House Ser.). (SPA.). (J). pap. 4.95 (978-1-930332-52-2(1)) Lectorum Pubns., Inc.

—Revolutionary War on Wednesday, Vol. 22. unabr. ed. 2004. (Magic Tree House Ser. : No. 22). 69p. (J). (gr. k-3). pap. 17.00 incl. audio (978-0-8072-0931-8(7) , S FTR 254 SP, Listening Library) Random Hse. Audio Publishing Group.

—Revolutionary War on Wednesday. Loehr, Mallory, ed. Murdocca, Sal, illus. 2000. (Magic Tree House Ser.: No. 22). 96p. (J). (gr. k-3). lib. bdg. 11.99 (978-0-679-99068-0(2)); pap. 3.99 (978-0-679-89068-3(8)) Random Hse. Children's Bks. (Random Hse. Bks. for Young Readers).

—Revolutionary War on Wednesday. Murdocca, Salvatore, illus. 2000. (Magic Tree House Ser. : No. 22). 69p. (J). (gr. k-3). lib. bdg. 11.80 (978-0-613-28355-7(4)) Tandem Library Bks.

—Revolutionary War on Wednesday. Murdocca, Sal, illus. 2000. (Magic Tree House Ser.: No. 22). (J). (gr. k-3). (978-0-606-19907-0(1)) Tandem Library Bks.

—Stage Fright on a Summer Night. Murdocca, Sal, illus. 2002. (Magic Tree House Ser.: No. 25). 96p. (J). (gr. k-3). lib. bdg. 11.99 (978-0-375-90611-4(8)); 25. pap. 3.99 (978-0-375-80611-7(3)) Random Hse. Children's Bks. (Random Hse. Bks. for Young Readers).

—Summer of the Sea Serpent. Murdocca, Sal, tr. Murdocca, Sal, illus. 2004. (Magic Tree House Ser.: No. 31). 128p. (J). (gr. 2-5). 11.95 (978-0-375-82735-8(8) , Random Hse. Bks. for Young Readers) Random Hse. Children's Bks.

—Twister on Tuesday, Vol. 23. 2004. (Magic Tree House Ser. : No. 23). 70p. (J). (gr. k-3). pap. 17.00 incl. audio (978-0-8072-9932-6(4) , Listening Library) Random Hse. Audio Publishing Group.

—Twister on Tuesday. Murdocca, Sal, illus. 2001. (Magic Tree House Ser.: No. 23). 96p. (J). (gr. k-3). 11.99 (978-0-679-99069-7(0)); 23. pap. 3.99 (978-0-679-89069-0(6)) Random Hse. Children's Bks. (Random Hse. Bks. for Young Readers).

—Twister on Tuesday. 2001. (Magic Tree House Ser. : No. 23). (J). (gr. k-3). lib. bdg. 11.80 (978-0-613-35706-7(X)); (Illus.). (978-0-606-21498-8(4)) Tandem Library Bks.

—Vacation under the Volcano, Vol. 13. unabr. ed. 2004. (Magic Tree House Ser. : No. 13). 74p. (J). (gr. k-3). pap. 17.00 incl. audio (978-0-8072-0782-6(9) , LFTR 241 SP, Listening Library) Random Hse. Audio Publishing Group.

—Vacation under the Volcano. Murdocca, Sal, illus. 1998. (Magic Tree House Ser.: No. 13). (J). (gr. k-3). 96p. lib. bdg. 11.99 (978-0-679-99050-5(X)); 80p. mass mkt. 3.99 (978-0-679-89050-8(5)) Random Hse. Children's Bks. (Random Hse. Bks. for Young Readers).

—Vacation under the Volcano, nO. 13. Murdocca, Sal, illus. 1998. (Magic Tree House Ser. : No. 13). (J). (gr. k-3). (978-0-606-13972-4(9)) Tandem Library Bks.

—Viking Ships at Sunrise, Vol. 15. unabr. ed. 2004. (Magic Tree House Ser. : No. 15). 71p. (J). (gr. k-3). pap. 17.00 incl. audio (978-0-8072-0784-0(5) , LFTR 243 SP, Listening Library) Random Hse. Audio Publishing Group.

—Viking Ships at Sunrise. Murdocca, Sal, illus. 1998. (Magic Tree House Ser.: No. 15). 96p. (J). (gr. k-3). lib. bdg. 11.99 (978-0-679-99061-1(5)); mass mkt. 3.99 (978-0-679-89061-4(0)) Random Hse. Children's Bks. (Random Hse. Bks. for Young Readers).

—Viking Ships at Sunrise. Murdocca, Salvatore, illus. 1998. (Magic Tree House Ser. : No. 15). 71p. (J). lib. bdg. 10.79 (978-0-606-15755-1(7)) Tandem Library Bks.

Pittar, Gill. Milly, Molly & the Tree Hut (book W/dolls) 2006. 28p. pap. (978-1-86972-096-4(2)) Milly Molly Bks.

Randall, Rod. Along Came a Spider. 2000. (Heebie Jeebies Ser.: Vol. 7). 138p. (J). (gr. 3-7). pap. 5.99 (978-0-8054-1981-8(0)) B&H Publishing Grp.

Ron, Kare. Clumsy Wally the Handyman: The Treehouse. 2000. mass mkt. 8.95 (978-1-931179-15-7(8)) Long Hill Productions, Inc.

Rylant, Cynthia. Henry & Mudge & the Tall Tree House. Bracken, Carolyn, illus. 2003. (Henry & Mudge Ser.). 40p. (J). pap. 3.99 (978-0-689-83445-5(4) , Aladdin) Simon & Schuster Children's Publishing.

—Henry & Mudge & the Tall Tree House. 2003. (Henry & Mudge Ser.). (gr. k-3). lib. bdg. 11.80 (978-0-613-90605-0(5)) Tandem Library Bks.

The Tree House Lab. 2003. (J). per. (978-1-57657-826-1(7)) Paradise Pr., Inc.

The Treehouse Club: Individual Title Six-Packs. (ps-2). 23.00 (978-0-7635-8821-2(0)) Rigby Education.

Volker, Kerstin. Henry Builds a Tree House. 2003. (Funny Friends Lift-and-Learn Bks.). (Illus.). 14p. (J). 5.99 (978-1-59384-023-5(3)) Parklane Publishing.

TREE PLANTING

see also Trees

Ayers, Patricia. A Kid's Guide to How Trees Grow. 2000. (Digging in the Dirt Ser.). 24p. (J). (gr. k-4). lib. bdg. 18.75 (978-0-8239-5463-6(3) , PowerKids Pr.) Rosen Publishing Group, Inc., The.

TREES

see also Forests and Forestry; Fruit Culture; Leaves; Lumber and Lumbering; Nuts; Shrubs; Tree Planting; Wood

Aldrich, William & Williamson, Don. Tree & Shrub Gardening for Illinois, Vol. 1. rev. ed. 2004. (Illus.). 352p. (gr. 4). pap. 18.95 (978-1-55105-404-9(3)) Lone Pine Publishing USA.

El Arbol del Olivo: Por Dentro y Por fuera. 2004. (SPA., Illus.). 32p. lib. bdg. 21.25 (978-1-4042-2865-8(9)) Rosen Publishing Group, Inc., The.

Bachmann, Elaine Rice. While a Tree Grew: The Story of Maryland's Wye Oak. Harrell, Kim, illus. 2006. (J). (***978-0-87033-577-8(4)*** , Tidewater Pubs.) Cornell Maritime Pr., Inc.

Baran, Robert J. A Bonsai Coloring Book: A Guide to Your First Dwarf Potted Trees. 1999. (Illus.). 40p. (J). (gr. 2-12). pap. 3.95 (978-0-9659913-4-6(2)) Pyramid Dancer Pubns.

Bash, Barbara. Tree of Life: The World of the African Baobab. Bash, Barbara, illus. 2002. (Illus.). 32p. (J). pap. 7.95 (978-1-57805-086-4(3)) Sierra Club Bks. for Children.

Baumbusch, Brigitte. Trees in Art. 2005. (Illus.). 32p. (J). lib. bdg. 22.00 (978-0-8368-4449-8(1)) Stevens, Gareth Inc.

Beaty, Sandy & Wilkerson, J. L. Champion of Arbor Day: J. Sterling Morton. Parkison, Jami, ed. 1999. (Great Heartlanders Ser.). (Illus.). 130p. (YA). (gr. 4-12). pap. 8.95 (978-0-9664470-1-9(8)) Acorn Bks.

Bernard, Robin. A Tree for All Seasons. 1999. (J). (978-0-7922-9427-6(0)); pap. (978-0-7922-9435-1(1)) National Geographic Society.

—Tree for All Seasons. 2001. (Illus.). 16p. (J). (gr. 3-7). pap. 5.95 (978-0-7922-6674-7(9) , National Geographic Children's Bks.) National Geographic Society.

Blackaby, Susan. The World's Largest Plants: A Book about Trees. DeLage, Charlene, illus. 2004. (Growing Things Ser.). 24p. (C). (gr. k-2). 22.60 (978-1-4048-0110-3(3)) Picture Window Bks.

Boothroyd, Jennifer. In a Tree. 2006. (First Step Nonfiction Ser.). (Illus.). 8p. (J). pap. (978-0-8225-5663-3(4) , Lerner Pubns.) Lerner Publishing Group.

Brenner, Barbara. The Tremendous Tree Book. 2003. (Illus.). 40p. (J). (ps up). pap. 8.95 (978-1-56397-718-3(4)) Boyds Mills Pr.

Brimner, Larry Dane. What Good Is a Tree? Landry, Leo, illus. 1999. (Rookie Reader Skill Set Ser.). 32p. (J). (gr. k-2). pap. 4.95 (978-0-516-26414-1(1) , Children's Pr.) Scholastic Library Publishing.

Broutin, Christian. El Arbol. (Coleccion Mundo Maravilloso). (SPA., Illus.). 40p. (J). (gr. 2-4). (978-84-348-4056-0(1) , AR9290) SM Ediciones ESP. *Dist:* Lectorum Pubns., Inc.

Buff, Mary Conrad. Big Tree. 2001. (J). per. 12.95 (978-1-892857-02-6(2)) Whole Spirit Pr.

Bulla, Clyde Robert. Tree Is a Plant. 2001. (gr. k-3). lib. bdg. 12.95 (978-0-613-45558-9(4)) Tandem Library Bks.

—A Tree Is a Plant. Schuett, Stacey, illus. rev. ed. 2001. (Let's-Read-and-Find-Out Science Ser.). 40p. (J). (ps-1). 15.89 (978-0-06-028172-4(3)); pap. 5.99 (978-0-06-445196-3(8) , Harper Trophy) HarperCollins Pubs.

—A Tree Is a Plant. Schuett, Stacey, illus. 2001. (J). (ps-ps). lib. bdg. 12.19 (978-0-606-22286-0(3)) Tandem Library Bks.

Burnie, David & Dorling Kindersley Publishing Staff. Tree. 2005. (Eyewitness Books). (Illus.). 72p. (J). (ps-7). lib. bdg. 19.99 (978-0-7566-1094-4(X) , 1241927) Dorling Kindersley Publishing, Inc.

Burton, Margie, et al. Trees. Adams, Alison, ed. 1999. (Early Connections Ser.). 16p. (J). (gr. k-2). pap. 4.50 (978-1-58344-084-1(4)) Benchmark Education Co.

Cassie, Brian & Burns, Marjorie. Trees. 1999. (National Audubon Society First Field Guides). (Illus.). (gr. 3-7). 160p. (J). pap. 8.95 (978-0-590-05490-4(2)); 159p. (YA). pap. 17.95 (978-0-590-05472-0(4)) Scholastic, Inc.

Charman, Andrew. I Wonder Why Trees Have Leaves: And Other Questions about Plants. 2003. (gr. k-3). lib. bdg. 14.10 (978-0-613-90898-6(8)) Tandem Library Bks.

Cipriano, Jeri. Los arboles son Impresionantes! 2005. Tr. of Trees are Terrific!. (SPA., Illus.). 16p. (J). (gr. 3 up). lib. bdg. 15.93 (978-0-7368-4168-9(7)) Capstone Pr., Inc.

Cooper, Jason. Oak Tree. 2003. (Life Cycles Ser.). (Illus.). 24p. (gr. 1-4). 17.95 (978-1-58952-350-0(4)) Rourke Publishing, LLC.

—Trees. 1998. (Guide to State Symbols Ser.). (Illus.). 48p. (J). (gr. 3-8). lib. bdg. 29.93 (978-1-57103-195-2(2)) Rourke Publishing, LLC.

Cope, E. A., rev. Know Your Trees. 2002. (J). pap. 6.35 (978-1-57753-301-6(1)) Resource Centre, The.

Court, Rob. How to Draw Things in Nature. 2007. (Doodle Bks.). 32p. (J). 21.36 (***978-1-59296-807-7(4)***) Child's World, Inc.

DePalma, Mary Newell. A Grand Old Tree. 2005. (Illus.). (J). (978-0-439-62335-3(9)); 32p. pap. 16.99 (978-0-439-62334-6(0)) Scholastic, Inc. (Levine, Arthur A. Bks.).

Dorling Kindersley Publishing Staff. Tree. (Eye Know Ser.). (Illus.). (J). 2006. 24p. 8.99 (978-0-7566-1773-8(1)); 2005. 72p. 15.99 (978-0-7566-1093-7(1) , 1241927) Dorling Kindersley Publishing, Inc.

—Trees & Leaves. 2006. (Ultimate Sticker Bks.). 16p. (J). pap. 6.99 (978-0-7566-2102-5(X)) Dorling Kindersley Publishing, Inc.

Dowden, Anne Ophelia Todd. The Blossom on the Bough: A Book of Trees. Dowden, Anne Ophelia Todd, illus. 1999. (Illus.). 71p. (YA). (gr. 6-8). 17.00 (978-0-7881-6658-7(1)) DIANE Publishing Co.

Dreyer, Ellen. Grow, Tree, Grow! Swanson, Maggie, tr. Swanson, Maggie, illus. 2003. (Hello Reader! Ser.). (J). (978-0-439-43964-0(7)) Scholastic, Inc.

Edwards, Nicola. Trees. 2007. (J). (978-1-4042-3571-7(X)) Rosen Publishing Group, Inc., The.

Feely, Jenny. Tree. 1999. (ps-2). lib. bdg. 11.80 (978-0-613-30811-3(5)) Tandem Library Bks.

Fowler, Allan. Pine Trees. (Rookie Read-About Science Ser.). (Illus.). 32p. (J). (gr. 1-2). 2002. pap. 4.95 (978-0-516-25987-1(3)); 2001. 20.50 (978-0-516-21685-0(6)) Scholastic Library Publishing. (Children's Pr.).

—Pine Trees. 2001. (gr. k-3). lib. bdg. 12.95 (978-0-613-54443-6(9)) Tandem Library Bks.

Freeman, Marcia S. Maple Trees. Saunders-Smith, Gail, ed. 1998. (Trees Ser.). (Illus.). 24p. (J). (gr. k-1). lib. bdg. 15.93 (978-0-7368-0092-1(1) , Pebble Bks.) Capstone Pr., Inc.

—Oak Trees. Saunders-Smith, Gail, ed. 1998. (Trees Ser.). (Illus.). 24p. (J). (gr. k-1). lib. bdg. 15.93 (978-0-7368-0093-8(X) , Pebble Bks.) Capstone Pr., Inc.

—Palm Trees. Saunders-Smith, Gail, ed. 1998. (Trees Ser.). (Illus.). 24p. (J). (gr. k-1). lib. bdg. 15.93 (978-0-7368-0094-5(8) , Pebble Bks.) Capstone Pr., Inc.

—Pine Trees. Saunders-Smith, Gail, ed. 1998. (Trees Ser.). (Illus.). 24p. (J). (gr. k-1). lib. bdg. 15.93 (978-0-7368-0095-2(6) , Pebble Bks.) Capstone Pr., Inc.

—Pine Trees. (Trees Ser.). 24p. (J). pap. 5.95 (978-0-7368-8096-1(8)) Capstone Pr., Inc.

—Trees, 4 bks., Set. 1998. pap. (978-0-516-29824-5(0) , Children's Pr.) Scholastic Library Publishing.

Gallup, Tracy. Tree Crazy. Gallup, Tracy, illus. 2007. (Crazy Little Ser.). (Illus.). 32p. (J). 9.95 (***978-1-934133-27-9(2)***) Mackinac Island Pr., Inc.

Gerber, Carole. Leaf Jumpers. Evans, Leslie, illus. 32p. (J). 2006. pap. 6.95 (978-1-57091-498-0(2)); 2004. 15.95 (978-1-57091-497-3(4)) Charlesbridge Publishing, Inc.

Gerber, Carole. Winter Trees. Evans, Leslie, illus. 2008. (J). (***978-1-58089-168-4(3)***) Charlesbridge Publishing, Inc.

Gierecke, Ernestine. Trees. 1999. (Outside My Window Ser.). (Illus.). 24p. (J). (gr. 1-3). lib. bdg. 21.36 (978-1-57572-684-7(X)) Heinemann Library.

Godwin, Sam. From Little Acorns- A First Look at the Life Cycle of a Tree. Abel, Simone, illus. 2004. (First Look Science Ser.). 32p. (C). (gr. k-3). 22.60 (978-1-4048-0658-0(X)) Picture Window Bks.

Green, Jen. Dead Log. 1999. (gr. 3-6). lib. bdg. 17.60 (978-0-613-19511-9(6)) Tandem Library Bks.

Grewell, Susan Y. "ABC - Learn Your Trees with the Leaf Critters" Grewell, Susan Y., illus. 2000. (Illus.). 60p. (J). (gr. 1-10). pap. 11.95 (978-0-9703241-0-8(3)) Leaf Critters.

Harcourt School Publishers Staff. The Most Advanced Level. 3rd ed. 2002. (Trophies Reading Program Ser.). (Illus.). pap. 5.10 (978-0-15-323303-6(6)) Harcourt Schl. Pubs.

—A Year-Round Tree On Level. 3rd ed. 2002. (Trophies Reading Program Ser.). (Illus.). pap. 5.10 (978-0-15-323083-7(5)) Harcourt Schl. Pubs.

Hazen, Barbara Shook. Secret Life of Trees. 1999. (Eyewitness Readers Ser.). (J). (978-0-606-19387-0(1)) Tandem Library Bks.

Hazen, Barbara Shook & Dorling Kindersley Publishing Staff. The Secret Life of Trees. 1999. (Eyewitness Readers). (Illus.). 32p. (J). (ps-3). 14.99 (978-0-7894-4761-6(4)) Dorling Kindersley Publishing, Inc.

Hazen, Barbara Shook, et al. The Secret Life of Trees. 1999. (Eyewitness Readers). (Illus.). 32p. (J). (ps-3). pap. 3.99 (978-0-7894-4760-9(6)) Dorling Kindersley Publishing, Inc.

Henderson, Dave, illus. A Story of Three Trees: And the miracle of Prayer. 2005. 12p. (J). 5.99 (978-1-4037-1197-7(6) , Spirit Pr.) Dalmatian Pr.

Henderson, Douglas. Dinosaur Tree. 1999. (J). (978-0-606-17194-6(0)) Tandem Library Bks.

Hibbert. Life of a Tree 6-Pack. 2004. (Life Cycles Ser.). pap. 40.50 (978-1-4109-0825-4(9)) Harcourt Schl. Pubs.

Hickman, Pamela. Starting with Nature Tree Book. Collins, Heather, illus. unabr. ed. 1999. (Starting with Nature Ser.). 32p. (J). (gr. 4-6). (978-1-55074-655-6(3)); (978-1-55074-485-9(2)) Kids Can Pr., Ltd.

—Tree Book. 1999. (Illus.). (J). (978-0-606-16551-8(7)) Tandem Library Bks.

Hipp, Andrew. Oak. 2004. (Getting into Nature Ser.). (Illus.). 32p. (J). lib. bdg. 21.25 (978-0-8239-4206-0(6)) Rosen Publishing Group, Inc., The.

—Olive Tree. 2004. (Getting into Nature Ser.). (Illus.). 32p. (J). lib. bdg. 21.25 (978-0-8239-4207-7(4)) Rosen Publishing Group, Inc., The.

Hiscock, Bruce. The Big Tree. Hiscock, Bruce, illus. 2003. (Illus.). 32p. (YA). (gr. 2-4). pap. 9.95 (978-1-56397-810-4(5)) Boyds Mills Pr.

—Big Tree. 1999. (gr. 3-6). lib. bdg. 18.75 (978-0-613-53963-0(X)) Tandem Library Bks.

Hower, Fred & Beck, Alison. Tree & Shrub Gardening for Ohio, Vol. 1. rev. ed. 2004. (Illus.). 360p. (gr. 4). pap. 18.95 (978-1-55105-402-5(7)) Lone Pine Publishing USA.

Hubbell, Patricia. Every Orchard Tree. Broxon, Janet, illus. 2008. (J). (***978-1-55971-986-5(9)*** , NorthWord Bks. for Young Readers) T&N Children's Publishing.

Hughes, Meredith Sayles. Hard to Crack: Nut Trees. 2005. (Plants We Eat Ser.). (Illus.). 104p. (gr. 6-9). 26.60 (978-0-8225-2838-8(X)) Lerner Publishing Group.

—Tall & Tasty: Fruit Trees. 2005. (Plants We Eat Ser.). (Illus.). 104p. (gr. 6-9). 26.60 (978-0-8225-2837-1(1)) Lerner Publishing Group.

Jacobs, Marian B. Why Do Leaves Change Color? 1999. (Library of Why). (Illus.). 24p. (J). (gr. k-4). lib. bdg. 18.75 (978-0-8239-5275-5(4) , PowerKids Pr.) Rosen Publishing Group, Inc., The.

Julivert, Maria Angeles. Trees. 2007. (Field Guides). (Illus.). 32p. (J). (gr. 4-6). 16.95 (978-1-59270-065-3(9)) Enchanted Lion Bks., LLC.

Kalman, Bobbie. El Ciclo de Vida del Arbol. 2005. (Serie Ciclos de Vida Ser.). (SPA., Illus.). 32p. (J). (978-0-7787-8665-8(X)) Crabtree Publishing Co.

—The Life Cycle of a Tree. 2002. (Life Cycle Ser.). (Illus.). 32p. (J). (gr. 2-3). (978-0-7787-0659-5(1)); pap. (978-0-7787-0689-2(3)) Crabtree Publishing Co.

—Life Cycle of a Tree. 2002. (gr. 3-6). lib. bdg. 14.10 (978-0-613-52976-1(6)) Tandem Library Bks.

Kalman, Bobbie, et al. Les Arbres. 2005. (FRE., Illus.). 32p. (J). pap. (978-2-89579-052-5(3)) Crabtree Publishing Co.

Kavanagh, James. British Columbia Trees & Wildflowers. Leung, Raymond, illus. 1999. (Pocket Naturalist Ser.). (J). 5.95 (978-1-58355-045-8(3)) Waterford Pr., Ltd.

Kirkland, Jane. Take a Tree Walk. Burke, Dorothy et al, eds. Easter, Dennis, illus. Kirkland, Jane, photos by. 2005. (Take a Walk Ser.). 32p. (J). pap. 9.95 (978-0-9709754-1-6(4) , Take a Walk Bk.) Stillwater Publishing.

Kite, Lorien. A Rain Forest Tree. 1999. (Small Worlds Ser.). (Illus.). 32p. (J). (gr. 3-4). pap. (978-0-7787-0146-0(8)) Crabtree Publishing Co.

Kosek, Jane Kelly. What's Inside Trees? 1999. (What's Inside Library). 24p. (J). (gr. k-4). lib. bdg. 18.75 (978-0-8239-5281-6(9) , PowerKids Pr.) Rosen Publishing Group, Inc., The.

Locker, Thomas. Sky Tree: Seeing Science Through Art. 2001. (978-0-606-22281-5(2)) Tandem Library Bks.

Loves, June. Trees. 2004. (Plants Ser.). (Illus.). 32p. (J). (gr. 2-4). 23.00 (978-0-7910-8268-3(7) , Chelsea Hse.) Facts On File, Inc.

Mattern, Joanne. How Pine Trees Grow. 2006. (ENG & SPA., Illus.). 24p. (J). 19.33 (978-0-8368-6464-9(6)) Stevens, Gareth Inc.

—How Pine Trees Grow: Como Crecen Los Pinos. 2006. (ENG & SPA., Illus.). 24p. (J). pap. (978-0-8368-6471-7(9) , Weekly Reader Early Learning Library) Stevens, Gareth Inc.

Maurer, Tracy. Growing Trees. 2000. (Green Thumb Guides Ser.). (Illus.). (J). (gr. 2-6). lib. bdg. 23.93 (978-1-55916-255-5(4)) Rourke Publishing, LLC.

McEvoy, Paul. Trees. 2003. (Plant Facts Ser.). (Illus.). 24p. (gr. 2-4). 23.00 (978-0-7910-7293-6(2) , Chelsea Hse.) Facts On File, Inc.

Mellett, Peter. Trees: Fantastic Facts. 2000. (Fantastic Facts Ser.). (Illus.). 64p. (gr. 2-7). pap. 6.95 (978-1-84215-094-8(4) , Southwater) Anness Publishing GBR. *Dist:* National Bk. Network.

Miller, Debbie S. Are Trees Alive? Schuett, Stacey, illus. (J). (ps-2). 2003. 32p. 16.95 (978-0-8027-8801-6(7)); 2002. 17.85 (978-0-8027-8802-3(5)) Walker & Co.

Mitchell, Melanie S. Oak Trees. (First Step Nonfiction Ser.). (Illus.). (gr. k-2). 2005. 24p. lib. bdg. 17.27 (978-0-8225-4610-8(8)); 2003. 23p. (J). pap. 5.95 (978-0-8225-4611-5(6) , Lerner Pubns.) Lerner Publishing Group.

Oliver, Clare. Life in a Tree: Clare Oliver. 2002. (Microhabitats Ser.). (Illus.). 32p. (J). 25.69 (978-0-7398-4334-5(6)) Raintree.

Owen, Andy, et al. Forests. 2002. (Geography Starts Ser.). (Illus.). 32p. (J). (gr. k-2). pap. 6.95 (978-1-58810-971-2(2) , 91454) Heinemann Library.

Palm Trees. (Trees Ser.). 24p. (J). 5.95 (978-0-7368-8095-4(X)) Capstone Pr., Inc.

Palm Trees, 6 vols. (gr. k-2). 28.95 (978-0-7368-8119-7(0)) Red Brick Learning.

Pascoe, Elaine. The Ecosystem of a Fallen Tree. Kuhn, Dwight, illus. 2003. (Library of Small Ecosystems Ser.). 24p. (J). lib. bdg. 21.25 (978-0-8239-6308-9(X) , PowerKids Pr.) Rosen Publishing Group, Inc., The.

—Leaves & Trees. Kuhn, Dwight, photos by. 2001. (Nature Close-Up Ser.). (Illus.). 48p. (J). (gr. 4-8). 23.70 (978-1-56711-474-4(1) , Blackbirch Pr., Inc.) Thomson Gale.

Patton, Christopher. Jack Pine. Young, Cybele, illus. 2007. 32p. (J). (gr. 2-7). 18.95 ***(978-0-88899-780-7(9))*** Groundwood Bks. CAN. *Dist:* Perseus Distribution.

Petrides, George A. Peterson First Guide to Trees. Petrides, Olivia & Wehr, Janet, illus. 2nd ed. 1998. (First Guides). 128p. pap. 5.95 (978-0-395-91183-9(4)) Houghton Mifflin Co. Trade & Reference Div.

Picture Window Books, contrib. by. The World's Largest Plants. (Growing Things Ser.). 24p. (J). pap. 7.95 (978-1-4048-0386-2(6)) Picture Window Bks.

Pine Trees, 6 vols. (gr. k-2). 28.95 (978-0-7368-8120-3(4)) Red Brick Learning.

Pugliano-Martin, Carol. Discover the Life Cycle of Pine Trees. 2006. (English Explorers Ser.). (J). pap. 39.00 ***(*978-1-4108-6473-4(1))*** Benchmark Education Co.

—The Life Cycle of Pine Trees. 2006. (English Explorers Ser.). (J). pap. 42.00 ***(*978-1-4108-6470-3(7))*** Benchmark Education Co.

Rechenbaeume-Terme-Texte. (Duden-Schuelerhilfen Ser.). (GER.). 96p. (J). (gr. 5-6). (978-3-411-02621-0(9)) Bibliographisches Institut & F. A. Brockhaus AG DEU. *Dist:* International Bk. Import Service, Inc.

Richardson, Joy. Trees. 2005. (Illus.). 32p. (J). lib. bdg. 23.33 (978-0-8368-4509-9(9)) Stevens, Gareth Inc.

El Roble: Por Dentro y Por Fuera. 2004. (SPA., Illus.). 32p. lib. bdg. 21.25 (978-1-4042-2864-1(0)) Rosen Publishing Group, Inc., The.

Rosenfeld, Richard & Dorling Kindersley Publishing Staff. Garden Trees. 2004. (Garden Guides Ser.). (Illus.). 320p. pap. 13.00 (978-0-7566-0357-1(9)) Dorling Kindersley Publishing, Inc.

Rushworth, Gary. The Life Cycle of Trees. 2006. (Navigators Ser.). (J). pap. 38.00 ***(*978-1-4108-6223-5(2))*** Benchmark Education Co.

Russell, Tony. Spotting Trees in Britain & Eur: An Illustrated Guide to the Top 100 Trees. 2005. (Illus.). 96p. (ps-17). 10.99 (978-0-7548-1372-9(X) , Lorenz Bks.) Anness Publishing GBR. *Dist:* National Bk. Network.

Saunders-Smith, Gail. Apple Trees. 1998. (Plants Ser.). pap. 13.25 (978-0-516-21237-1(0) , Children's Pr.) Scholastic Library Publishing.

Schaefer, Lola M. What Grows from a Tree? 2000. (Yellow Umbrella Books). (Illus.). 16p. (J). (gr. 1). lib. bdg. 14.60 (978-0-7368-0730-2(6) , Pebble Bks.) Capstone Pr., Inc.

Schwartz, David M. In a Tree. Kuhn, Dwight, photos by. 1999. (Springboards into Science Ser.). (Illus.). 24p. (J). (gr. 1 up). lib. bdg. 20.67 (978-0-8368-2245-8(5)) Stevens, Gareth Inc.

—Maple Tree. Kuhn, Dwight, photos by. (Life Cycles Ser.). (Illus.). 16p. (J). (gr. 1-3). pap. 2.99 (978-1-57471-556-9(9) , 3066) Creative Teaching Pr., Inc.

—Maple Tree. Kuhn, Dwight, photos by. 2001. (Springboards into Science Ser.). (Illus.). 24p. (J). (gr. 1 up). lib. bdg. 20.67 (978-0-8368-2978-5(6)) Stevens, Gareth Inc.

Sharp, Zoe. In the Tree. 2002. (Windows on Literacy Ser.). (Illus.). 12p. (J). (978-0-7922-8461-1(5)) National Geographic Society.

Sheehan, Thomas F. Trees Don't Freeze: A Book about Adaptations. 2008. (J). ***(*978-1-60044-537-8(3))*** Rourke Publishing, LLC.

Shook-Hazen, Barbara. Secret Life of Trees. 1999. (gr. k-3). lib. bdg. 11.80 (978-0-613-22356-0(X)) Tandem Library Bks.

Soltis, Nicki. We Need More Trees! 2001. (gr. k-3). lib. bdg. 11.95 (978-0-613-33453-2(1)) Tandem Library Bks.

Souza, Dorothy M. Wacky Trees. (Watts Library). (J). 2004. (gr. 5-7). pap. 8.95 (978-0-531-16246-0(X)); 2003. (Illus.). 64p. 25.50 (978-0-531-12210-5(7)) Scholastic Library Publishing. (Watts, Franklin).

Superlibro de el Arbol: Unit 1: el arbol (A Tree) 2000. (McGraw-Hill Ciencias Ser.). (ENG & SPA.). (gr. 1 up). (978-0-02-277164-5(6)) Macmillan/McGraw-Hill Schl. Div.

Tagliaferro, Linda. The Life Cycle of a Pine Tree. 2007. (Pebble Plus Ser.). (Illus.). 24p. (J). (978-0-7368-6712-2(0) , 1264879) Capstone Pr., Inc.

Tanem, Bob & Williamson, Don. Tree & Shrub Gardening for Northern California. rev. ed. 2003. (Illus.). 360p. (gr. 4). pap. 18.95 (978-1-55105-275-5(X)) Lone Pine Publishing USA.

Taus-Bolstad, Stacy. From Shoot to Apple. 2002. (From Start to Finish Ser.). (J). pap. 4.95 (978-0-8225-0670-6(X)) Lerner Publishing Group.

Time-Life Staff. Flowers & Trees. 1999. (Illus.). 88p. (J). (gr. 1-4). 14.95 (978-0-8094-4857-9(2)) Time-Life, Inc.

Tree. 2005. (J). (978-0-9767139-0-6(X)) Britt Allcroft Productions.

A Tree Is Nice. 2004. (J). 24.95 incl. audio (978-1-56008-234-7(8)); pap. 14.95 incl. audio (978-0-7882-0676-4(1)) Weston Woods Studios, Inc.

Trees: Individual Title Six-Packs. (Sails Literacy Ser.). (gr. 1-2). 36.00 (978-0-7578-6744-6(8)) Rigby Education.

Trees, Please! Level M, 6 vols. 128p. (gr. 2-3). 40.50 (978-0-7699-1034-5(3)) Shortland Pubns. (U. S. A.) Inc.

Trees Set. (gr. k-2). 114.95 (978-0-7368-9053-3(X)) Red Brick Learning.

Trumbauer, Lisa. Trees Are Terrific! 2003. (Illus.). 17p. (J). 15.93 (978-0-7368-2923-6(7)); pap. (978-0-7368-2882-6(6)) Yellow Umbrella Pr.

Udry, Janice May. Un Arbol Es Hermoso. Simont, Marc, illus. 2006. Tr. of Tree Is Nice. (SPA.). 32p. (J). pap. 6.99 (978-0-06-088708-7(7)) HarperCollins Pubs.

Vitosh, Mark A. & Vitosh, Ashley Lee. The Forest Where Ashley Lives. Smith, John L., illus. l.t. ed. 2000. (PM 1812 Ser.). 20p. (J). (gr. 1-4). pap. 3.00 (978-0-9700528-0-3(4)) Iowa State Univ. Extension.

Waldman, Neil. The Never-Ending Greenness: We Made Israel Bloom. Waldman, Neil, illus. 2003. (Illus.). 32p. (YA). (gr. k-2). 16.95 (978-1-59078-064-0(7)) Boyds Mills Pr.

Weiss, Ellen. From Pine Cone to Pine Tree. 2007. (Scholastic News Nonfiction Readers Ser.). (Illus.). 24p. (J). (gr. 1-2). lib. bdg. 20.00 ***(*978-0-531-18537-7(0)*** , Children's Pr.) Scholastic Library Publishing.

—From Pinecone to Pine Tree. 2007. (Scholastic News Nonfiction Readers: How Things Grow—NEW SUBSET Ser.). 24p. (J). pap. 6.95 ***(*978-0-531-18790-6(X)*** , Children's Pr.) Scholastic Library Publishing.

—From Pit to Peach Tree. 2007. (Scholastic News Nonfiction Readers: How Things Grow—NEW SUBSET Ser.). 24p. (J). pap. 6.95 ***(*978-0-531-18791-3(8)*** , Children's Pr.) Scholastic Library Publishing.

Windsor, Jo. Living in Trees: Emergent Level Satellite Individual Title Six-Packs. (Sails Literacy Ser.). (gr. k-1). 27.00 (978-0-7578-7906-7(3)) Rigby Education.

Wood, Timothy D. & Beck, Alison. Tree & Shrub Gardening for Michigan. rev. ed. 2003. (Illus.). 352p. (J). (gr. 4). pap. 18.95 (978-1-55105-347-9(0)) Lone Pine Publishing USA.

World Book, Inc. Staff, contrib. by. Trees of the United States & Canada. 2004. (World Book's Science & Nature Guides Ser.). (Illus.). 80p. (J). (978-0-7166-4219-0(0)) World Bk., Inc.

Worth, Bonnie. I Can Name 50 Trees Today! All about Trees. Ruiz, Aristides & Mathieu, Joe, illus. 2006. (Cat in the Hat's Learning Library). 48p. (J). (gr. k-3). 8.99 (978-0-375-82277-3(1) , Random Hse. Bks. for Young Readers) Random Hse. Children's Bks.

—I Can Name 50 Trees Today! All about Trees. Ruiz, Aristides & Mathieu, Joseph, illus. 2006. (Cat in the Hat's Learning Library). 48p. (J). (gr. k-3). lib. bdg. 12.99 (978-0-375-92277-0(6) , Random Hse. Bks. for Young Readers) Random Hse. Children's Bks.

Zim, Herbert S. Trees. 2001. (J). mass mkt. 6.96 net. (978-0-307-64056-7(6)) St. Martin's Pr.

TREES—FICTION

Aardema, Verna. Koi & the Kola Nuts: A Tale from Liberia. Cepeda, Joe, illus. 2003. (gr. k-3). lib. bdg. 15.30 (978-0-613-59127-0(5)) Tandem Library Bks.

Allamand, Maite. Alamito el Largo. (SPA.). (J). (gr. 2-3). pap. (978-956-13-1428-3(2) , AB3840) Bello, Andres CHL. *Dist:* Lectorum Pubns., Inc.

Alonso, Fernando. El Arbol de los Suenos. Urberuaga, Emilio, illus. 2003. Tr. of Dream Trees. (SPA.). 124p. (J). (gr. 5-8). pap. 10.95 (978-968-19-0978-9(X)) Santillana USA Publishing Co., Inc.

—El Arbol de los Suenos. 1998. Tr. of Dream Trees. (SPA., Illus.). 128p. (J). (gr. 4-7). 15.95 (978-84-204-4802-2(8)) Santillana USA Publishing Co., Inc.

—El Arbol Que No Tenia Hojas (The Tree Without Leaves) (Superbks./Superlibros). (J). (gr. k-1). (SPA.). pap. 6.95 (978-0-88272-469-0(X)); (Illus.). 16p. pap. 6.95 (978-0-88272-470-6(3)); Big Book. (SPA.). 21.95 (978-0-88272-459-1(2)); Big Book. 21.95 (978-0-88272-460-7(6)) Santillana USA Publishing Co., Inc.

Anna's Tree: Individual Title Six-Packs. (gr. 1-2). 25.00 (978-0-7635-9134-2(3)) Rigby Education.

Atwood, Margaret. Up in the Tree. ed. 2006. (Illus.). 32p. (J). 14.95 (978-0-88899-729-6(9)) Groundwood Bks. CAN. *Dist:* Perseus Distribution.

Barrick, Sheila. Frazier the Crooked Christmas Tree. Grillo, Donato, illus. 2001. 48p. (J). (ps-7). (978-0-9713414-0-1(0)) Barrick, Sheila.

Barron, T. A. Tree Girl. 2001. 128p. (J). (gr. 4-7). 14.99 (978-0-399-23457-6(8) , Philomel); 2002. 144p. reprint ed. mass mkt. 6.99 (978-0-441-00994-7(8) , Ace Bks.) Penguin Group (USA) Inc.

—Tree Girl. 2002. (gr. 3-6). lib. bdg. 14.15 (978-0-613-81179-8(8)) Tandem Library Bks.

Beamish, Diane. The Treefellows. 2006. 35p. (J). pap. 14.28 (978-1-4116-5967-4(8)) Lulu.com.

Below, Halina. Chestnut Dreams. 2002. (Illus.). 40p. pap. (978-1-55041-690-9(1)) Fitzhenry & Whiteside, Ltd.

—Chestnut Dreams. Below, Halina, illus. 2000. (Illus.). 40p. (J). (ps-1). (978-1-55041-545-2(X)) Fitzhenry & Whiteside, Ltd.

Bennett-Minnerly, Denise. The Color Tree. Bennett-Minnerly, Denise, illus. 2005. (J). 14.95 (978-1-56290-328-2(4)) Crystal Productions.

Blyton, Enid. Up the Faraway Tree. (Illus.). 96p. (J). pap. 5.95 (978-0-09-942720-9(6)) Random Hse. GBR. *Dist:* Trafalgar Square Publishing.

Boger-Bass, Vallerie. The Mustard Seed: A Christian Promise. Boger-Bass, Vallerie, illus. 2003. 40p. pap. 10.00 (978-0-8059-5640-5(9)) Dorrance Publishing Co., Inc.

Bond, Ruskin. Cherry Tree. Eitzen, Allan, illus. 2003. 32p. (J). (gr. 2-4). pap. 9.95 (978-1-56397-621-6(8)) Boyds Mills Pr.

Boniface, William. Trim the Tree for Christmas! Palen, Debbie, illus. 2000. 12p. (J). (ps-2). bds. 9.99 (978-0-8431-7558-5(3) , Price Stern Sloan) Penguin Group (USA) Inc.

Bourgeois, Paulette & Jennings, Sharon. Franklin Plants a Tree. Jeffrey, Sean et al, illus. 2003. (Franklin TV StoryBks.). 32p. (J). (gr. k-3). (978-1-55074-878-9(5)) Kids Can Pr., Ltd.

Brenner, Barbara. The Tremendous Tree Book. 2003. (Illus.). 40p. (J). (ps up). pap. 8.95 (978-1-56397-718-3(4)) Boyds Mills Pr.

Brown, Alan. Dreaming Tree. Fletcher, Claire, illus. 2000. 29p. (J). (gr. k-3). 17.95 (978-0-00-198321-2(0)) Zondervan.

Brown, Margaret Wise. The Little Fir Tree. Date not set. (Illus.). 32p. (J). (ps-1). pap. 5.99 (978-0-06-443529-1(6)) HarperCollins Pubs.

—The Little Fir Tree. LaMarche, Jim, illus. 2005. 32p. (J). (ps-1). 15.99 (978-0-06-028189-2(8)); lib. bdg. 16.89 (978-0-06-028190-8(1)) HarperCollins Pubs.

Bryant, Megan E. Welcome Spring! Nunn, Paul E., illus. 2008. 32p. (J). (gr. 1-4). 6.99 ***(*978-0-448-44778-0(9)*** , Grosset & Dunlap) Penguin Group (USA) Inc.

Bunting, Eve. I Have an Olive Tree. Bunting, Eve & Barbour, Karen, illus. 1999. (Joanna Cotler Bks.). 32p. (J). (ps-3). 16.99 (978-0-06-027573-0(1) , Cotler, Joanna Books) HarperCollins Pubs.

Caldwell, Walter, text. The Tree in the Field of Mathingamy Thame. ltd. ed. 2002. (Stories of Mathingamy Thame Ser.). 30p. 18.95 (978-1-930729-02-5(2)) What's Inside Pr.

Canady, Pat. Tippy the Holiday Tree, 1. Bartley, Michael, illus. 2000. 9p. (J). (ps-4). pap. 10.00 (978-1-929889-01-3(1)) Canady SW Publishing.

Candy, Wolf. The Tree, the House & the Hurricane. l.t. ed. 2005. (Illus.). 24p. (J). 7.00 (978-0-9762292-3-0(4)) New Global Publishing.

Cannon, K. L. Mr. Mortimer: The Grapevine That Wouldn't Die. 2005. (J). 4.95 (978-0-9675594-2-1(1)) Cannon, K. L.

Cano, Carles. El Arbol de las Hojas Din A-4. (SPA., Illus.). 28p. (J). (gr. k-2). (978-84-8464-027-1(2) , KA30310) Kalandraka Editora, S.L. ESP. *Dist:* Lectorum Pubns., Inc.

Caple, Kathy. The Friendship Tree. Caple, Kathy, illus. (House Readers Ser.). (Illus.). 32p. (J). (gr. k-3). tchr. ed. 15.95 (978-0-8234-1376-8(4)) Holiday Hse., Inc.

Carmody, Isobelle. The Legend Begins. 2006. (Illus.). 208p. (J). (gr. 1-7). 12.95 (978-0-375-83854-5(6)); (gr. 3-7). lib. bdg. 14.99 (978-0-375-93854-2(0)) Random Hse. Children's Bks. (Random Hse. Bks. for Young Readers).

—Little Fur: The Legend Begins. 2006. (Illus.). 272p. (J). (978-0-375-83855-2(4)) Random Hse., Inc.

Carr, Lawrence. Under the Peach Tree. 2006. pap. 8.00 (978-0-8059-7019-7(3)) Dorrance Publishing Co., Inc.

Carr, Richard Wallace. Dolly & Ike Cherry Blossom Time. Parrish, Mary, illus. 2006. 32p. (J). (gr. k-3). per. 15.95 (978-0-933165-09-0(9)) Dicmar Publishing Co.

Chase, et al. Angel in a Gum Tree. (Illus.). 32p. pap. 13.95 (978-1-86368-222-0(8)) Fremantle Pr. AUS. *Dist:* International Specialized Bk. Services.

Cherry, Lynne. The Great Kapok Tree: A Tale of the Amazon Rain Forest. 1998. (Illus.). 36p. (J). (ps-3). 26.95 (978-0-15-201818-4(2)) Harcourt Trade Pubs.

Child, Lauren. De Que Planeta Eres, Ana Tarambana? 2002. Tr. of What Planet Are You From, Clarice Bean?. (Illus.). 32p. (J). (SPA.). 17.95 (978-84-8488-036-3(2)); (CAT., 17.95 (978-84-8488-037-0(0)) Serres, Ediciones, S. L. ESP. *Dist:* Lectorum Pubns., Inc.

Christmas Book - Christmas Tree. 2005. (J). bds. (978-1-4194-0073-5(8)) Paradise Pr., Inc.

Cincotta, Wendy. Christopher's Adventures in Evergreen: The Story of a Boy & His Encounter with a Tree That Has Come to Life. Cincotta, Eva, illus. 2002. (Adventures in Evergreen Ser.). 128p. (J). (gr. 3-7). pap. 9.95 (978-0-9723010-0-8(5)) Evergreen Bks.

Clement, Maria. The Forever Christmas Tree. 2006. (ENG.). 44p. per. 17.99 ***(*978-1-4259-8639-1(0))*** AuthorHouse.

Cosgrove, Stephen. The Dream Tree. James, Robin, illus. rev. ed. 2002. (Serendipity Bks.). 32p. (J). pap. 4.99 (978-0-8431-4889-3(6) , Price Stern Sloan) Penguin Group (USA) Inc.

Cruikshank, Fran. The Tale of the Not-So-Perfect Christmas Tree. Olson, Tom, illus. 2005. 17p. (J). 9.95 (978-1-59971-055-6(2)) Aardvark Global Publishing.

Cuccia, Louis J. The Bottle Tree. 2003. (Illus.). 106p. (J). per. (978-0-9727415-1-4(8)) Cuccia, Louis.

Cuomo, Mario. The Blue Spruce. van Frankenhuyzen, Gijsbert, illus. 1999. 48p. (J). (gr. k-4). 17.95 (978-1-886947-76-4(7)) Sleeping Bear Pr.

Curry, Kenneth. The Legend of the Dancing Trees: An African American Folk Tale. 2007. 111p. (J). per. 14.95 ***(*978-0-9798364-0-4(9))*** Curry Brothers Publishing.

Curry, Kenneth, et al. The Legend of the Dancing Trees Teachers Resource: The Legend of the Dancing Trees. 2007. Tr. of Teachers Resource. per. 19.95 ***(*978-0-9798364-1-1(7))*** Curry Brothers Publishing.

Cyr, Joe. Magical Trees & Crayons: Great Stories. 2006. (Illus.). pap. 9.95 ***(*978-0-9778525-6-7(3))*** Peppertree Pr., The.

Cyr, Joe. Shawn the Hopping Christmas Tree. Cyr, Diane, ed. Henry, Diane, illus. l.t. ed. 2001. 32p. 5.95 (978-0-9713768-0-9(8)) Cyr, Joe.

Dalmatian Press Staff. A Story of Three Trees Storybook. 2004. (Illus.). 32p. (J). 8.99 (978-1-4037-0975-2(0)) Dalmatian Pr.

D'Ath, Justin. Terrors of Nature. 2005. (Thrillogy Ser.). (Illus.). 48p. (gr. 4-8). 17.50 (978-0-7910-8892-0(8)) Facts On File, Inc.

Del Amo, Montserrat. Montes, Pajaros y Amigos. (SPA.). 104p. (YA). (gr. 5-8). (978-84-207-2788-2(1) , GS6293) Grupo Anaya, S.A. ESP. *Dist:* Lectorum Pubns., Inc.

Derrick, Patricia. Farley the Ferret of Farkleberry Farm. 2007. 32p. 18.95 (978-1-933818-12-2(3)) Animalations.

Donahue, Michael. The Grandpa Tree. Dorsey, Susan, illus. 2001. 24p. (gr. 7 up). pap. 7.95 (978-0-911797-42-8(4)) Rinehart, Roberts Pubs.

Dumas, Kim Renay. The Magic Tree Whispers. 2001. (J). pap. 7.00 (978-0-8059-5072-4(9)) Dorrance Publishing Co., Inc.

Duryee, Lynn. My Treehouse. Wise, Noreen, ed. 2000. (Lemonade Collection). 160p. (YA). (gr. 5 up). pap. 8.95 (978-1-58584-283-4(4)) Huckleberry Pr.

Dychtwald, Ken, et al. Gideons Dream. Zaboski, Dave, illus. 2008. 40p. (J). (ps-3). 16.99 ***(*978-0-06-143497-6(3))*** HarperCollins Pubs.

Ehlert, Lois. Pie in the Sky. 2004. (Illus.). 40p. (J). (ps-2). 16.00 (978-0-15-216584-0(3)) Harcourt Children's Bks.

—Red Leaf, Yellow Leaf. Ehlert, Lois, illus. 2002. (Illus.). (J). 23.40 (978-0-7587-3505-8(7)) Book Wholesalers, Inc.

Emerson, Carl. Old Oak & the Autumn Leaf. Doerrfeld, Cori, illus. 2007. (J). (978-1-4048-2624-3(6)) Picture Window Bks.

—Old Oak & the Cold Winter Day. Doerrfeld, Cori, illus. 2007. (J). (978-1-4048-2627-4(0)) Picture Window Bks.

—Old Oak & the Summer Playground. Doerrfeld, Cori, illus. 2007. (J). (978-1-4048-2626-7(2)) Picture Window Bks.

Emma's Problem, 6, Pack. (Literatura 2000 Ser.). (gr. 1-2). 28.00 (978-0-7635-0131-0(X)) Rigby Education.

Evert, Jeffrey. The Tree That Didn't Want to Be. 2004. pap. 9.00 (978-0-8059-6189-8(5)) Dorrance Publishing Co., Inc.

Fernandes, Eugenie. The Tree That Grew to the Moon. Fernandes, Eugenie, illus. 1998. (Illus.). 32p. (J). (gr. k-3). 14.95 (978-1-55209-282-8(8)); pap. 4.95 (978-1-55209-006-0(X)) Firefly Bks., Ltd.

Fine, Edith Hope. Bajo la Luna de Limon. 1999. (SPA.). (gr. k-3). 17.55 (978-0-613-28392-2(9)) Tandem Library Bks.

Fisher, Phyllis Mae Richardson. Twiglet the Little Christmas Tree. Fisher, Phyllis Mae Richardson & Fisher, Douglas W., illus. 2003. (J). 30.00 (978-0-9745615-1-6(7) , Twiglet The Little Christmas Tree); 186p. 12.00 (978-0-9745615-4-7(1)) PJs Corner.

Fontes, Justine. Christmas Cub. 1999. (gr. k-3). lib. bdg. 11.80 (978-0-613-32403-8(X)) Tandem Library Bks.

—The Easter Cub. McQueen, Lucinda, illus. 2003. (Hello Reader! Ser.). 32p. (J). (gr. k-2). pap. 3.99 (978-0-439-44340-1(7) , Cartwheel Bks.) Scholastic, Inc.

Forbes, Chris. El Tronco de Arbol, Level 1. Ada, Alma Flor, tr. Sullivan, Don, illus. 2003. (Dejame Leer Ser.). (SPA.). 8p. (J). (ps-k). 6.50 (978-0-673-36300-8(7) , Good Year Bks.) Celebration Pr.

Fortuna, Lorna. When God Spoke to Trees. 2006. 17.00 (978-0-8059-9884-9(5)) Dorrance Publishing Co., Inc.

Fowles, Shelley. Climbing Rosa. 2006. (Illus.). 32p. (J). 15.95 (978-1-84507-079-3(8)) Lincoln, Frances Ltd. GBR. *Dist:* Perseus Distribution.

Fox, Dorothea Warren. Miss Twiggley's Tree. Fox, Dorothea Warren, illus. 2002. 17.95 (978-1-930900-17-2(1)) Purple Hse. Pr.

Freedman, Georgene. The Olive Tree. 2nd num. ed. 2006. (J). per. 12.95 (978-0-9771322-1-8(8)) Simpatico Bks.

French, Vivian. Morris in the Apple Tree. 2004. (Illus.). 63p. pap. 7.99 (978-0-00-718027-1(6)) HarperCollins Pubs. Ltd. GBR. *Dist:* Independent Pubs. Group.

Froberg, Dennis W. Anna Bristlecone. l.t. unabr. ed. 2000. (Illus.). 32p. (J). (gr. k-5). pap. 5.95 (978-1-928632-44-3(0)) Writers Marketplace:Consulting, Critiquing & Publishing.

Gabby & the Christmas Tree. 2000. (J). (978-1-58453-118-0(5)); (978-1-58453-131-9(2)) Pioneer Valley Educational Pr., Inc.

Galjanic, Lisa. When Leaves Die. Hope, Michelle, illus. 2007. (J). 9.95 (978-1-933532-00-4(9)) LSG Pubns.

Gardner, Yvonne. Scrawny the Tree. 2005. 12p. 11.33 (978-1-4116-6413-5(2)) Lulu.com.

Geisert, Arthur. Nursery Crimes. (Illus.). 32p. (J). (ps-3). 2007. 6.95 ***(*978-0-618-95671-5(9));*** 2001. tchr. ed. 16.00 (978-0-618-06487-6(7) , Walter Lorraine) Houghton Mifflin Co. Trade & Reference Div.

Gentner, Norma L. & Young, Steve. Save a Tree for Me. (Song Box(R) Ser.). (Illus.). 16p. (gr. 1-2). 31.50 (978-0-7802-2264-9(4)) Wright Group, The.

George, Olivia. The Weather. Fletcher, Rusty, illus. 2005. (My First Reader Ser.). 31p. (J). (ps-ps). 18.50 (978-0-516-24880-6(4) , Children's Pr.) Scholastic Library Publishing.

Gibbs, D. Renee. The Special Little Christmas Tree. 2003. (J). bds. 14.95 (978-0-9741406-0-5(0)) Cranberry Quill Publishing Co.

Gill, Janie S. The Little Tree. Wing, Lori, illus. 1999. 23p. (J). 5.95 (978-0-89868-489-6(7)); pap. 3.95 (978-0-89868-488-9(9)); lib. bdg. 10.95 (978-0-89868-487-2(0)) ARO Publishing Co.

—The Old Tired Giving Tree. Reese, Robert, illus. 1999. 23p. (J). 5.95 (978-0-89868-445-2(5)); lib. bdg. 10.95 (978-0-89868-443-8(9)) ARO Publishing Co.

Gillen, Lisa P. Spring Time. Gillen, Lisa P., illus. l.t. ed. 2006. (Illus.). 12p. (J). (ps-k). pap. 10.95 (978-1-57332-351-2(9)) HighReach Learning, Inc.

Giono, Jean. The Man Who Planted Trees. 2000. (Helen & Scott Nearing Titles Ser.). 8.95 (978-0-930031-78-7(4)) Chelsea Green Publishing.

—The Man Who Planted Trees. 2000. 74p. pap. 6.00 (978-1-57062-538-1(7)) Shambhala Pubns., Inc.

Givens, Ed. Molly Maple: The Wishing Star. 2004. (Illus.). 32p. (J). bds. 14.95 (978-1-59094-053-2(9) , Jawbreakers for Kids) Jawbone Publishing Corp.

Glickman, Joe. Treasures among the Trees. Burdick, David, photos by. 1998. (Illus.). 32p. (J). (gr. k-5). 14.95 (978-0-9655081-1-7(0)) Pamacheyon Publishing.

Gold-Vukson, Marji & Evans, Leslie. Grandpa & Me on Tu B'Shevat. 2004. (Illus.). 32p. (J). (ps-3). pap. (978-1-58013-122-3(0)) Kar-Ben Publishing.

Golling, Joe, illus. Jonathan's Red Apple Tree. 1999. 24p. (J). (gr. k-7). pap. 9.95 (978-0-9660053-3-2(3)) Stagecoach Publishing.

Gove, Doris. My Mother Talks to Trees. Mallory, Marilynn H., illus. 2005. 32p. (J). pap. 7.95 (978-1-56145-336-8(6) , Q31285) Peachtree Pubs., Ltd.

—My Mother Talks to Trees. Mallory, Marilynn, illus. 1999. 32p. (J). (ps-3). 15.95 (978-1-56145-166-1(5) , Q31285) Peachtree Pubs., Ltd.

Graham, Brandon. Perverts of the Unknown. Graham, Brandon, illus. 2003. (Illus.). 56p. 9.95 (978-1-56163-374-6(7) , Amerotica) NBM Publishing Co.

The Great Christmas Tree Adventure. 1998. 40p. (J). per. 14.99 (978-0-689-82607-8(9) , Little Simon) Simon & Schuster Children's Publishing.

Griffin, Saundra J. Which Should I Be? 2004. 21p. pap. 14.95 (978-1-4137-3167-5(8)) PublishAmerica, Inc.

Guarneri, Cristina. The Magic Tree. 2005. 50p. pap. 10.95 (978-0-7414-2336-8(7)) Infinity Publishing.

Gustafson, Kay. Aunt Gussie & Grandfather Tree. 2005. (Illus.). 48p. (J). (ps-7). 19.95 (978-1-59298-101-4(1)) Beaver's Pond Pr., Inc.

Hachler, Bruno. Hubert & the Apple Tree. 2006. (Illus.). (J). 15.95 (978-0-7358-2044-9(9)) North-South Bks., Inc.

Halstead, Brenda. A Tree Grows in the Silo. 2002. (J). pap. 9.00 (978-0-8059-5172-1(5)) Dorrance Publishing Co., Inc.

Harcourt School Publishers Staff. The Mystery Tree Advanced Level. 3rd ed. 2002. (Trophies Reading Program Ser.). (Illus.). pap. 5.10 (978-0-15-323281-7(1)) Harcourt Schl. Pubs.

—Under the Lemon Moon: Reader's Choice Book. 2001. (Collections Ser.). (Illus.). (J). (gr. 4). 4.70 (978-0-15-314361-8(4)) Harcourt Schl. Pubs.

—Zora & the Chinaberry Tree: Reader's Choice Book. 2001. (Collections Ser.). (Illus.). (J). (gr. 5). 4.70 (978-0-15-314388-5(6)) Harcourt Schl. Pubs.

Harvey, Harry. Bright Little Leaf. 2002. pap. (978-1-58909-103-0(5)) Bookstand Publishing.

Hemery, Kathleen Maresh. The Healing Tree. Teis, Kyra, illus. 2001. (J). (978-1-56123-153-9(3) , HTRC) Centering Corp.

Henrie, Tanya. The Shaping. MacKessy, Kristine, illus. 1998. 60p. (J). (gr. 2-7). 17.95 (978-0-9667096-0-5(8)) Keeping Track of Time.

Higgs, Liz Curtis. The Pine Tree Parable: Special Edition. 2006. 32p. (J). 7.99 (978-1-4003-0847-7(X)) Nelson, Thomas Inc.

—The Pine Tree Parable: The Parable Series. 2005. 32p. (J). pap. 3.99 (978-1-4003-0685-5(X)) Nelson, Thomas Inc.

Hill, David. Running Hot. 2006. 116p. (Orig.). (gr. 5-8). pap. 9.95 (978-1-894965-52-1(3)) Simply Read Bks. CAN. *Dist:* Perseus Distribution.

Hill, Karen. I Am Good at Being Me. Graef, Renee, illus. 2005. 24p. (J). 3.99 (978-1-4169-0319-2(4)) ; 9.99 (978-1-4169-0512-7(X)) Simon & Schuster Children's Publishing. (Little Simon).

Hodges, James. The Trail of Truth. 2004. 36p. (J). pap. 18.99 (978-1-4141-0284-9(4)) Pleasant Word.

Hoedl, Lee. Jesse the Wait of the Wood. Hoedl, Lee, photos by. 2006. (Illus.). 30p. (J). per. 12.95 (978-1-59879-139-6(7)) Lifevest Publishing, Inc.

Hofmeister, Alan, et al. Bud & the Tree. (Reading for All Learners Ser.). (Illus.). (J). pap. (978-1-56861-135-8(8)) Swift Learning Resources.

Holston-Holloway, Angela M. The Apple Pie Kids. 2006. (J). pap. 8.00 (***978-0-8059-6899-6(7)***) Dorrance Publishing Co., Inc.

Hopkinson, Deborah & Carpenter, Nancy. Apples to Oregon: Being the (Slightly) True Narrative of How a Brave Pioneer Father Brought Apples, Peaches, Pears, Plums, Grapes, & Cherries (And Children) Across the Plains. 2004. (Illus.). 40p. (J). 16.95 (978-0-689-84769-1(6) , Atheneum) Simon & Schuster Children's Publishing.

Houghton, Eric. The Crooked Apple Tree. Gold, Caroline, illus. 2000. 24p. (J). (ps-3). pap. 6.99 (978-1-84148-186-9(6)) Barefoot Bks., Inc.

—The Crooked Apple Tree. Gold, Caroline, illus. 2000. 32p. (J). (ps-3). lib. bdg. 13.79 (978-0-606-19698-7(6)) Tandem Library Bks.

Huang, Kathryn. A Guide Book to the Great Tree. 2007. (Guardians of Ga'Hoole Ser.). 208p. (J). pap. 7.99 (***978-0-439-93188-5(6)***) Scholastic, Inc.

Hubery, Julia. A Friend for All Seasons. Matsuoka, Mei, illus. 2007. 32p. (J). (ps-2). 15.99 (***978-1-4169-2685-6(2)***) Simon & Schuster Children's Publishing.

Hunt, Angela Elwell. The Tale of Three Trees. deluxe ed. 2003. (Tale of Three Trees Ser.). (Illus.). 32p. (J). (ps-7). 19.99 (978-0-7459-4082-3(X) , 074594082X) Cook, David C. Publishing Co.

Hunt, Zoe. Azarels Christmas Wish. 2007. (J). per. 10.95 (***978-1-934345-20-7(2)***) SouthWest Pubns.

Hunter, Billie J. Who's Hiding in My Tree? Hunter, Kirsten, illus. 1998. 24p. (J). (ps-3). pap. 9.00 (978-1-57579-104-3(8)) Pine Hill Pr., Inc.

I Want to Be Like the Mango Tree. 2002. (J). 16.00 (978-0-9710860-0-5(1)) Libros, Encouraging Cultural Literacy.

Ichikawa, Satomi. What the Little Fir Tree Wore to the Christmas Party. 2003. (gr. k-3). lib. bdg. 15.30 (978-0-613-86699-6(1)) Tandem Library Bks.

Iverson, Diane. My Favorite Tree: Terrific Trees of North America. 2004. (Sharing Nature with Children Book Ser.). (Illus.). 64p. (YA). (ps-3). pap. 9.95 (978-1-883220-93-8(9)) Dawn Pubns.

Jackson, Tyrone. Save Our Home. 2006. (ENG.). 88p. per. 14.95 (***978-1-4241-0875-6(6)***) PublishAmerica, Inc.

Jacobson, John. A Tree in Tappen Wood: A Musical Tale of Growing & Gratitude, Adventure & Peace. 2006. 48p. 19.95 incl. audio compact disk (978-1-4234-1263-2(X) , 142341263X) Leonard, Hal Corp.

Jamieson, Mark. Ico Island. 2007. (J). pap. 11.95 (***978-0-9792518-0-1(X)***) Gequalsa.

Jarrell, Pamela R. Planting a Seed Board Book & Felt Puppet Set. Teeple, Jackie, illus. 2005. (J). bds. (978-1-57332-365-9(9)) HighReach Learning, Inc.

Jenkins, Jane J. The Little Fir Tree. 2005. (Illus.). 32p. (J). per. 7.95 (978-1-59453-184-2(6) , Airleaf Publishing) Airleaf Publishing & Bookselling.

Johnson, Donna. The Story of the Little Red Leaf. Johnson, Emily, illus. l.t. ed. 2006. 22p. (J). 25.00 (***978-0-9778774-0-9(X)***) Choicepoint Editions.

Johnston, Tony. Isabel's House of Butterflies. Guevara, Susan, illus. 2003. 32p. (J). (ps-3). 15.95 (978-0-87156-409-2(2)) Sierra Club Bks. for Children.

—Isabel's House of Butterflies. Guevara, Susan, illus. 2005. 32p. pap. 6.95 (978-1-58685-844-5(0)) Gibbs Smith, Publisher.

Kathan, Christine. La Oracion de Ashford. Maval Publishing Inc. Staff, illus. 2001. Tr. of Ashford's Prayer. (SPA.). 32p. (J). (gr. k-3). pap. 7.50 (978-1-59134-013-3(6)) ; pap. 7.50 (978-1-884083-65-5(X)) Maval Publishing, Inc.

Keene, Carolyn. The Message in the Hollow Oak. Tandy, Russell H., illus. fac. ed. 2004. (Nancy Drew Mystery Stories Ser.: No. 12). 210p. (J). (gr. 4-7). 17.95 (978-1-55709-258-8(3)) Applewood Bks.

Kendall, Jack. The Magic Apple Tree. Bostrom, Sally, illus. l.t. ed. 2006. (ENG.). 48p. (J). per. 9.95 (978-0-9787740-4-2(3)) Peppertree Pr., The.

Kessler, Cristina. My Great-Grandmother's Gourd. Krudop, Walter Lyon, illus. 2000. 32p. (J). (gr. k-4). 17.99 (978-0-531-33284-9(5) , Orchard Bks.) Scholastic, Inc.

Kirwan, Debra Giampapa. Oh, Please Help Me Save the Tree! A Record-Your-Voice Book. Holodook, Joseph, illus. l.t. ed. 2002. (Adventures of Buford the Bull & Friends Ser.: Vol. 1). 16p. (J). 49.95 (978-0-9713153-7-2(X)) FunZone Co.

Klise, Kate & Klise, M. Sarah. Regarding the Trees: A Splintered Saga Rooted in Secrets. 2007. (Regarding The ... Ser.). (Illus.). 160p. (J). pap. 5.95 (***978-0-15-206090-9(1)*** , Harcourt Paperbacks) Harcourt Children's Bks.

Korten, Gerri. The Parakeets & the Ginkgo Tree at Hide Park. l.t. ed. 2006. (Illus.). 36p. (J). 18.85 (***978-0-9785609-7-3(3)***) New Global Publishing.

Landa, Norbert. Little Bear & the Wishing Tree. Mendez, Simon, illus. 2007. 28p. (J). (ps-2). 16.95 (***978-1-56148-566-6(7)***) Good Bks.

Lanqcaon, Jeff. Grandpa's Magic Banyan Tree. 2005. 32p. (J). 12.95 (978-1-56647-740-6(9)) Mutual Publishing LLC.

Lasky, Kathryn. River of Wind. 2007. (Guardians of Ga'Hoole Ser.: No. 13). 224p. (J). pap. 5.99 (***978-0-439-88807-3(7)***) Scholastic, Inc.

—The Shattering. 2004. (Guardians of Ga'Hoole Ser.: Bk. 5). (Illus.). 192p. (J). (gr. 3-7). pap. 4.99 (978-0-439-40561-4(0) , Scholastic Paperbacks) Scholastic, Inc.

—The Siege. 2004. (Guardians of Ga'Hoole Ser.: Bk. 4). (Illus.). 224p. (J). (gr. 3-7). mass mkt. 4.99 (978-0-439-40560-7(2) , Scholastic Paperbacks) Scholastic, Inc.

Lawless, Mary Ann. The Proud Christmas Tree. McCool, Arlene, illus. 2006. (J). 12.95 (***978-0-9772795-0-0(2)***) Tuesday's Child.

Le Tord, Bijou. Noah's Trees. 1999. 40p. (J). (ps-1). pap. 5.95 (978-0-06-443540-6(7)) ; (Illus.). 15.89 (978-0-06-028527-2(3)) ; (Illus.). 15.95 (978-0-06-028235-6(5)) HarperCollins Pubs.

Lears, Laurie. Megan's Birthday Tree: A Story about Open Adoption. Farnsworth, Bill, illus. 2005. 32p. (J). (ps-3). 15.95 (978-0-8075-5036-6(1)) Whitman, Albert & Co.

Leavell, Chuck & Crovotta, Nicholas. The Tree Farmer. Bleau, Rebecca, illus. 2005. 32p. (J). 16.95 (978-1-893622-16-6(9) , VSP Bks.) Vacation Spot Publishing.

Leavey, Peggy Dymond. The Path Through the Trees. 2005. (Illus.). 128p. (J). pap. 7.95 (978-1-894917-21-6(9)) Napoleon Publishing/Rendezvous Pr. CAN. *Dist:* Atlas-Books Distribution.

Leon, Georgina Lazaro. El Flamboyan Amarillo. Delacre, Lulu, illus. 2004. Tr. of Yellow Flame Tree. (SPA.). (J). 13.99 (978-1-930332-55-3(6)) Lectorum Pubns., Inc.

LeTord, Bijou. Noah's Trees. 2002. (ps-2). lib. bdg. 14.10 (978-0-613-57253-8(X)) Tandem Library Bks.

Linsley, Sonja Paschal. The Conifer Court Competition. Linsley, Paul Adam, illus. 2005. (J). per. 18.95 (978-0-9766062-1-5(6) , HGP 2005-2) Higher Ground Pr.

Lionni, Leo. The Alphabet Tree. 2004. (Illus.). 40p. (J). (ps-3). reprint ed. 15.95 (978-0-394-81016-4(3) , Knopf Bks. for Young Readers) Random Hse. Children's Bks.

—A Busy Year. 2004. (Illus.). 26p. (J). (gr. k-ps). bds. 6.99 (978-0-375-82737-2(4) , Knopf Bks. for Young Readers) Random Hse. Children's Bks.

Liput, Andrew L. Evie the Evergreen's Christmas Adventure. 2002. 31p. (J). pap. 9.95 (978-0-7414-1034-4(6)) Infinity Publishing.

Little Tree. Date not set. (978-0-517-80134-5(5)) Random Hse. Value Publishing.

The Littlest Christmas Tree. 2005. 45.00 (978-0-916773-85-4(X)) Book Peddlers.

Lobe, Mira & Kaufmann, Angelika. El Manzano. Martinez, Eduardo, tr. from GER. Lobe, Mira & Kaufmann, Angelika, illus. 2000. (SPA., Illus.). 32p. (J). (gr. 2-4). 15.95 (978-84-89804-26-5(5)) Loguez Ediciones ESP. *Dist:* Baker & Taylor Bks.

Locker, Thomas. Sky Tree: Seeing Science Through Art. Locker, Thomas, illus. 2001. (Illus.). 40p. (J). (gr. k-4). pap. 6.99 (978-0-06-443750-9(7) , Harper Trophy) HarperCollins Pubs.

Lucado, Max. Best of All. Martinez, Sergio, illus. 2005. (Wemmicks Ser.). 32p. 15.99 (978-1-58134-501-8(1) , Crossway Bibles) Crossway Bks.

Lunn, Janet. The Hollow Tree. 2001. 272p. mass mkt. (978-0-7704-2887-7(8) , Seal Bks) Knopf Canada CAN. *Dist:* Random Hse., Inc.

Lyons, Dana. The Tree. Danioth, David, illus. l.t. ed. 2002. 32p. 16.95 (978-0-9701907-1-0(9)) Illumination Arts Publishing Co., Inc.

Mamchur, Carolyn. The Popcorn Tree. McGaw, Laurie, illus. 1998. 29p. (J). (ps-3). 15.95 (978-0-7737-2896-7(1)) Stoddart Kids CAN. *Dist:* Fitzhenry & Whiteside, Ltd.

Markarian, Marianne. The Pesky Bird, Wasielewski, Margaret M., illus. l.t. ed. 2005. 32p. (J). 16.00 (978-0-9767377-0-4(1)) Pomegranate Publishing.

Martin, Bill, Jr. & Archambault, John. Chicka Chicka Boom Boom. Ehlert, Lois, illus. 2006. 40p. (J). pap. 9.99 incl. audio compact disk (978-1-4169-2718-1(2) , Little Simon) Simon & Schuster Children's Publishing.

Martin, Jacqueline Briggs. Button, Bucket, Sky. Redenbaugh, Vicki J., illus. 1998. (Picture Bks.). 32p. (J). (ps-3). 15.95 (978-1-57505-244-1(X)) Lerner Publishing Group.

Matsuura, Richard & Matsuura, Ruth. Fruit, the Tree & the Flower. (J). 8.95 (978-1-887916-02-8(4)) Orchid Isle Publishing Co.

Mazzola, Lori. Tales of the Tree People to Tree... or. 2006. 48p. pap. 12.95 (***978-1-4241-5065-6(5)***) PublishAmerica, Inc.

McCafferty, Catherine. The Legend of the Three Trees. 2001. (Illus.). 16p. (J). (ps-k). bds. 6.99 (978-0-8499-7618-6(9)) Nelson, Thomas Inc.

McCord, David. Every Time I Climb a Tree. 1999. (gr. k-3). lib. bdg. 14.95 (978-0-613-21504-6(4)) Tandem Library Bks.

McEvoy, Grace. The Tiniest Tepee. 2005. 9.00 (978-0-8059-8040-0(7)) Dorrance Publishing Co., Inc.

McGaw, Victoria. Old Tree, Old Friend. Wise, Noreen, ed. Favazzao, Keith, illus. 2001. (Lemonade Collection). 64p. (J). (gr. 1-5). pap. 7.50 (978-1-58584-260-5(5)) Huckleberry Pr.

McMillan, Bruce. How the Ladies Stopped the Wind. Gunnella, illus. 2007. 32p. (J). (gr. k-3). 16.00 (***978-0-618-77330-5(4)***) Houghton Mifflin Co.

McPhail, David. The Searcher & Old Tree. 2008. (J). (***978-1-58089-223-0(X)***) Charlesbridge Publishing, Inc.

McVay, Elizabeth. Baby Bun & the Littlest Tree. 2004. (Illus.). 31p. (J). pap. 9.95 (978-0-9759621-0-7(8)) Koenisha Pubns.

Meigs, Cornelia. The Crooked Apple Tree. Grose, Helen Mason, illus. 2004. reprint ed. pap. 28.95 (978-1-4179-3174-3(4)) Kessinger Publishing, LLC.

Meister, Cari. I Love Trees. Sirrell, Terry, illus. (Rookie Reader Espanol Ser.). (J). (gr. k-2). 2005. 32p. pap. 4.95 (978-0-516-26827-9(9)); 2004. 31p. 19.50 (978-0-516-25900-0(8)) Scholastic Library Publishing. (Children's Pr.).

—I Love Trees. Sirrell, Terry, illus. 2005. 32p. (J). (gr. 1-2). lib. bdg. 12.15 (978-0-606-33170-8(0)) Tandem Library Bks.

Meister, Cari & Sirrell, Terry. Me Fascinan Los Arboles. Sirrell, Terry, illus. 2005. (Rookie Reader Espaanol Ser.). (ENG & SPA., Illus.). 32p. (J). (gr. k-2). 19.50 (978-0-516-25253-7(4) , Children's Pr.) Scholastic Library Publishing.

Mills, Joyce C. Gentle Willow: A Story for Children about Dying. Pillo, Cary, illus. 2nd ed. 2004. 32p. (J). 14.95 (978-1-59147-071-7(4)) ; pap. 8.95 (978-1-59147-072-4(2)) American Psychological Assn. (Magination Pr.).

—Little Tree: A Story for Children with Serious Medical Illness. Sebern, Brian, illus. 2nd ed. 2003. 32p. (J). pap. 8.95 (978-1-59147-042-7(0)) ; 14.95 (978-1-59147-041-0(2)) American Psychological Assn. (Magination Pr.).

Milson, Matthew R. Young Arcan & the Garden of Loc. 2007. 240p. pap. 14.95 (***978-1-933770-03-1(1)***) Avari Press.

Moulton, Mark Kimball. Sadie McGee Who Lived in a Tree. Good, Karen Hillard, illus. 2006. 32p. (J). (ps). 16.95 (978-0-8249-5152-8(2) , Ideals Children's Bks.) Ideals Pubns.

Munsch, Robert. Up, up, Down. Martchenko, Michael, illus. 2001. 32p. (J). (ps-1). pap. 11.95 (978-0-439-18770-1(2)) Scholastic, Inc.

—Up, Up, Down! Martchenko, Michael, illus. 2002. 32p. (J). pap. 4.99 (978-0-439-31796-2(7)) Scholastic, Inc.

—Up, up, Down. ed. 2004. (Illus.). (J). (gr. k-3). spiral bd. (978-0-616-11126-0(6)) ; spiral bd. (978-0-616-11127-7(4)) Canadian National Institute for the Blind/Institut National Canadien pour les Aveugles.

Musariri, Blessing. Going Home: A Tree's Story. 2005. (Illus.). 29p. pap. 12.95 (978-1-77922-042-4(1)) Weaver Pr. ZWE. *Dist:* Michigan State Univ. Pr.

My Apple Tree. 2003. (J). per. (978-1-57657-899-5(2)) Paradise Pr., Inc.

Nelson, Betty. The Mystery of Vanishing Trees. 2004. 192p. (J). 12.95 (978-1-56315-319-8(X)) SterlingHouse Pubs., Inc.

Nelson, Holly. Ig's Apples. l.t. ed. 2003. (Illus.). (J). 28p. lib. bdg. 14.95 (978-1-932338-32-4(2)) ; 15p. per. 9.99 (978-1-932338-17-1(9)) Lifevest Publishing, Inc.

The Nevergreen. 2003. (J). 15.99 (978-0-9744565-9-1(4)) Heart-to-Heart Pubns.

Newman, C. Edward. The Enchanted Bat. 2007. pap. 0.01 net. (***978-1-60402-471-5(2)***) Independent Pub.

Nitzberg, Chuck, illus. Christmas Is Coming! 2007. (I'm Going to Read Ser.). 28p. (J). (ps-1). pap. 3.95 (***978-1-4027-4296-5(7)***) Sterling Publishing Co., Inc.

Noble, Trinka Hakes. Apple Tree Christmas. Noble, Trinka Hakes, illus. 2005. (Illus.). 32p. (J). (ps-3). 16.95 (978-1-58536-270-7(0)) Sleeping Bear Pr.

Oak Tree Controversy, 6 Packs. (Bookweb Ser.). 32p. (gr. 5 up). 34.00 (978-0-7635-3782-1(9)) Rigby Education.

Orliac, Catherine. Te Tumu o Rapa Nui: El Arbolito de Rapa Nui. the Little Tree of Rapa Nui. le Petit Arbre de Rapa Nui. Haoa Cardinali, Viki et al, trs. Willemin, Veronique, illus. 2005. (FRE, SPA & ENG.). 40p. (J). spiral bd. 12.00 (978-1-880636-02-2(6)) Easter Island Foundation.

Osborne, Mary Pope. Magic Treehouse Goes to America. 1999. (J). pap. (978-0-679-88608-2(7) , Random Hse. Bks. for Young Readers) Random Hse. Children's Bks.

Osu Library Fund Staff. Fati et l'Arbre a Miel (Fati & the Honey Tree) Keita, Fatou, tr. 2002. (Illus.). 28p. pap. (978-9988-550-42-4(1)) Sub-Saharan Pubs. & Traders.

Our Shinning Christmas Tree. 2003. (J). per. (978-1-57657-911-4(5)) Paradise Pr., Inc.

Page, Lawana. The Weeping Willow Tree. Amaya, Laura, tr. Heaton, Layce, illus. 2006. (SPA.). 32p. 10.95 (978-0-9761128-2-2(5)) Hafabanana Pr.

Parent, Nancy. A Tree for Me, 15 vols. Harchy, Atelier Philippe, illus. 2003. (It's Fun to Learn Ser.). 32p. (J). (ps-3). 3.99 (978-1-57973-138-0(4)) Advance Pubs. LLC.

Paul Ponderosa. 2005. 60p. (J). per. 9.95 (978-1-933290-91-1(9)) Tate Publishing & Enterprises, L.L.C.

Paulson, Rachael P. Sir Johnny's Recycling Adventure: Symbols for Paper Recycling. Hutto, Jackie, ed. Gerdes, Delton, illus. 1999. (Hands on the World Environmental Ser.: Vol. II). 42p. (Orig.). (J). (ps-3). pap. 9.95 (978-0-9642296-2-4(5)) Crestmont Publishing.

Pease, Elaine. I'll Never Leave. MacLean, Kerry Lee, illus. 2000. 32p. (J). (ps-2). 14.95 (978-0-9702275-0-8(7)) Peasepod Bks.

Peck, Robert Newton. Nine Man Tree. 2000. (978-0-606-17875-4(9)) Tandem Library Bks.

Penson, Mary. Billy Bardin & the Witness Tree. 2003. 140p. (J). 11.95 (978-0-87565-283-2(2)) Texas Christian Univ. Pr.

Perry, Sarah Catherine. The Tale of the Very Tall Tree. Boscariol, Karyn, illus. 2006. (J). (978-1-55452-014-5(2)) Essence Publishing.

Pikey, Mikey. The Diamond Tree, Episode I: Coronation Day. 2006. 96p. pap. 14.00 (978-1-4116-7798-2(6)) Lulu.com.

Pillsbury, Joseph Gardner. Joey & the Boojum Tree. 2002. 32p. (J). (gr. k-6). 6.95 (978-0-9605808-3-5(2) , BC 0960580824) Rancho Santa Ana Botanic Garden.

Pitt, Tamina & Terri, Janke. What Makes a Tree Smile? Francine Ngardab, Riches, illus. 2003. (Uupababa Ser.). 24p. (J). pap. 4.95 (978-1-875641-80-2(7)) Magabala Bks. AUS. *Dist:* International Specialized Bk. Services.

Poole, Nancy W. Christopher the Christmas Tree. Burghdorf, Christie Stahl, illus. 1999. 28p. (J). (ps-6). pap. 14.95 (978-0-9673359-0-2(6) , 07) Grass Lake Publishing.

Prap, Lila. Animals Speak. 2006. (ENG & MUL., Illus.). 40p. (J). 15.95 (978-0-7358-2058-6(9)) North-South Bks., Inc.

Pugliano-Martin, Carol. Ready for Fall! 2006. (Early Explorers Ser.). (J). 34.00 (***978-1-4108-6103-0(1)***) Benchmark Education Co.

Ransburg, Ashley, illus. Evie Finds Her Family Tree. 2006 (J). 14.95 (978-0-87195-187-8(8)) Indiana Historical Society.

Ravishankar, Anushka & Rao, Sirish. One, Two, Tree! Bai, Durga, illus. 2004. 48p. 16.95 (978-81-86211-80-9(2)) Tara Publishing IND. *Dist:* Consortium Bk. Sales & Distribution.

Rawlinson, Julia. Fletcher & the Falling Leaves. Beeke, Tiphanie, illus. 2006. 32p. (J). 16.99 (978-0-06-113401-2(5)) HarperCollins Pubs.

Reardon, John. The South Overlook Oaks. Youngbluth, Chris, illus. 2006. 138p. 16.95 (***978-1-931643-91-7(1)***) Seven Locks Pr.

Redwine, Connie. A Story from Graandfather Tree. Keithline, Brian, illus. 2005. 25p. (J). (gr. k-2). pap. 7.95 (978-0-88100-135-8(X)) National Writers Pr., The.

Reed, Jennifer. The Falling Flowers. Cole, Dick, illus. 2005. (J). 16.95 (978-1-885008-28-2(7)) Shen's Bks.

Reitz, Ric. The Journey of Sir Douglas Fir: A Reader's Musical. Bell, Suzanne, ed. Brewer, David, illus. 1999. 48p. (J). (gr. 2-6). per. 19.95 (978-0-9670160-0-9(2) , Sir Fir Bks. & Music) Sir Fir Enterprises, LLC.

Reynolds, Bill. Willy Woodchuck. 2002. 52p. pap. 9.95 (978-0-7414-1012-2(5)) Infinity Publishing.

Riddell, Chris. The Emperor of Absurdia. 2006. (Illus.). 32p. (J). (***978-1-4050-5061-6(6)*** , Macmillan Children's Bks.) Pan Macmillan.

Ringgold, Robyn. My Mom Hugs Trees. Vasudevan, Vidya, illus. 2006. 24p. (J). per. 15.95 (978-0-9785326-1-0(9)) Solar Publishing LLC.

Robinson, Tim. Tobias, the Quig & the Rumplenut Tree. Robinson, Tim, illus. 2000. (Illus.). 40p. (J). (ps-3). 16.95 (978-1-890817-20-6(1)) Winslow Pr.

Roche, Luane. The Proud Tree. Sharp, Chris, illus. 1999. 48p. (J). (gr. 1-5). pap. 11.95 (978-0-7648-0377-2(8)) Liguori Pubns.

Roll, Renee. A Crooked Christmas Tree. 2006. (J). per. 13.99 (*978-0-9727995-1-5(6)*) Roll, Renee.

Rouss, Sylvia. The Littlest Tree. Binus, Ari, illus. 2005. 32p. (J). 16.95 (978-1-932687-25-5(4) , Devora Publishing) Pitspopany Pr.

Rouss, Sylvia A. Sammy Spider's First Tu B'Shevat. Kahn, Katherine Janus, illus. 2000. 32p. (J). (ps-3). pap. 7.95 (978-1-58013-065-3(8)) Kar-Ben Publishing.

Ruben, Pamela. Lessons from the Bubbe & Zayde Tree. 2004. (Illus.). 33p. (J). 12.95 (978-0-9764813-2-4(4)) Peppery Pr.

—Lessons from the Grandma & Grandpa Tree. 2004. (J). 12.95 (978-0-9764813-3-1(2)) Peppery Pr.

Rucker, David. The Valley of the Christmas Trees: A Legend. Laster, Brenda, illus. 2007. 41p. (J). (ps-3). 14.95 (*978-1-931643-94-8(6)*) Seven Locks Pr.

Ruelle, Karen Gray. The Tree. 2007. (J). (978-0-8234-1904-3(5)) Holiday Hse., Inc.

Ruiz-Flores, Lupe. The Woodcutter's Gift/El Regalo del Leñador. Jerome, Elaine, illus. 2007. (SPA & ENG.). 32p. (J). (ps-2). 15.95 (*978-1-55885-489-5(4)* , Piñata Books) Arte Publico Pr.

Russell, Christina. Lichee Tree. Zhang, Christopher Zhong-Yuan, illus. 2003. 192p. (YA). (gr. 4-6). 15.95 (978-1-56397-629-2(3)) Boyds Mills Pr.

Scarry, Richard. Richard Scarry's Father Cat's Christmas Tree. 2003. (Illus.). 24p. (J). (ps-2). pap. 3.25 (978-0-375-82556-9(8) , Golden Bks.) Random Hse. Children's Bks.

—Richard Scarry's Father Cat's Christmas Tree. 2003. (gr. k-3). lib. bdg. 10.95 (978-0-613-71907-0(7)) Tandem Library Bks.

Schultz, Agnes Szenozicska. The Little Tree. 2007. 32p. (J). 14.00 (*978-0-8059-7211-5(0)*) Dorrance Publishing Co., Inc.

Schwartz, Suzanne & Schwartz, Robert. The Christmas Palm Tree: A Storybook to Color. Schwartz, Suzanne & Schwartz, Robert, illus. l.t. ed. 2005. (Illus.). 22p. (J). spiral bd. 3.99 (978-0-9764152-3-7(2)) Seascay Productions.

Sera, Lucia. Another Tree in the Yard. Lonergan Iorio, John, illus. 2004. 32p. (J). per. 16.95 (978-1-932653-36-6(8)) Vocalis, Ltd.

Seredy, Kate. A Tree for Peter. Seredy, Kate, illus. 2004. (Illus.). 112p. (J). reprint ed. 19.95 (978-1-930900-26-4(0)) Purple Hse. Pr.

Shetterly, Susan Hand. Shelterwood. 1999. (gr. 3-6). lib. bdg. 16.40 (978-0-613-63530-1(2)) Tandem Library Bks.

—Shelterwood. McCall, Rebecca H., illus. 40p. (J). 2005. (gr. 3-6). 7.95 (978-0-88448-256-7(1)); 1999. (gr. k-3). 16.95 (978-0-88448-210-9(3)) Tilbury Hse. Pubs.

Silsbe, Brenda. A Tree Is Just a Tree? Yayo, illus. 2001. 32p. (J). 12.95 (978-1-894222-35-8(0)) Lobster Pr. CAN. *Dist:* Univ. of Toronto Pr.

Silverstein, Shel. Arbre Genereux. (FRE.). 20.95 (978-2-211-09415-3(5)) Archimede Editions FRA. *Dist:* Distribooks, Inc.

—The Giving Tree. (Illus.). 95.94 (978-0-06-056897-9(6)); 2002. 15.95 (978-0-06-009940-4(2)) HarperCollins Pubs.

—The Giving Tree. Silverstein, Shel, illus. anniv. ed. 2004. (Illus.). 64p. (J). (ps-3). 16.99 (978-0-06-025665-4(6) , HC5567) HarperCollins Pubs.

—The Giving Tree. anniv. ed. 2004. (Illus.). 64p. (J). 18.99 incl. audio compact disk (978-0-06-058675-1(3)) HarperCollins Pubs.

—The Giving Tree. Silverstein, Shel, illus. gif. ed. 2007. 64p. 16.99 (*978-0-06-124001-0(X)*) HarperCollins Pubs.

—The Giving Tree. 35th anniv. ed. 1999. (Illus.). 64p. (J). (ps-3). 17.99 (978-0-06-028451-0(X)) HarperCollins Pubs.

Skevington, Andrea. The Little Christmas Tree. Hussey, Lorna, illus. 2002. 32p. (J). (gr. k-2). pap. 8.99 (978-0-7459-4588-0(0) , Lion) Lion Hudson plc GBR. *Dist:* Independent Pubs. Group.

Smith, Linda. The Inside Tree. Brown, Kathryn, illus. Date not set. 32p. (J). (ps-3). 5.99 (978-0-06-443542-0(3)) HarperCollins Pubs.

—The Inside Tree. 2002. 32p. (J). (ps-3). 14.95 (978-0-06-028241-7(X)) HarperCollins Pubs.

Souza, Iza R. The Tree That Ran Away...! Lima, Gabriel S., tr. from POR. Lima, M., illus. 1999. 32p. (J). (gr. 2-7). pap. 3.25 (978-0-9662298-2-0(7)) Alba Bk. Co.

Spalding, Andrea. Solomon's Tree. Wilson, Janet, illus. 2005. 32p. (J). (ps-2). 7.95 (978-1-55143-380-6(X)) Orca Bk. Pubs. USA.

Speed, Bryan W. Little Bent Cedar. 2007. 24p. (J). 9.95 (*978-1-933255-38-5(2)*) DNA Pr.

Staheli, Don H. The Story of the Walnut Tree. Barrett, Robert, illus. 2000. (J). 16.95 (978-1-57345-885-6(6)) Scribbulations LLC.

Stamfl, Barbara. The Jumping Tree. 2001. (Illus.). 32p. (J). (gr. 2-5). pap. 10.00 (978-0-9713219-2-2(2)) Jumping Jack Holidays.

Steck-Vaughn Staff. The Great Kapok Tree. 2000. (Illus.). (J). pap. (978-0-7398-3367-4(7)) Steck-Vaughn.

Stewart, Sarah. The Money Tree. Small, David, illus. 2004. (J). (ps-ps). lib. bdg. 14.15 (978-0-606-29981-7(5)) Tandem Library Bks.

The Talking Christmas Tree. 2003. (J). per. (978-1-57657-925-1(5)) Paradise Pr., Inc.

Tan, Shaun. The Red Tree. 2002. (Illus.). 32p. (978-0-7344-0172-4(8) , Lothian Bks.) Hachette Livre Australia.

—The Red Tree. Tan, Shaun, illus. 2003. (Illus.). 32p. 16.95 (978-0-9688768-3-1(8)) Simply Read Bks. CAN. *Dist:* Perseus Distribution.

Tawhara, Merito & Robinson, Nikki Slade. Puriri. 2000. (MAO., Illus.). 37p. (J). pap. 12.95 (978-1-877266-17-1(5)) Huia Pubs. NZL. *Dist:* Pacific Island Bks.

—The Puriri Tree. 2000. (Illus.). 36p. (J). pap. 12.95 (978-1-877266-27-0(2)) Huia Pubs. NZL. *Dist:* Pacific Island Bks.

Taylor, Mildred D. Song of the Trees. 2003. (Illus.). 64p. (J). pap. 5.99 (978-0-14-250075-0(5) , Puffin) Penguin Group (USA) Inc.

—Song of the Trees. 2003. (gr. 3-6). lib. bdg. 14.15 (978-0-613-67301-3(8)) Tandem Library Bks.

Thesman, Jean. The Ornament Tree. 1998. (978-0-606-13682-2(7)) Tandem Library Bks.

Thomas, John & Rowe, Susan. Mynydd y Brain. 2005. (WEL., Illus.). 32p. pap. (978-1-85596-221-7(7)) Dref Wen.

Thompson, Lauren. The Apple Pie That Papa Baked. Bean, Jonathan, illus. 2007. 32p. (J). (gr. k up). 15.99 (*978-1-4169-1240-8(1)*) Simon & Schuster Children's Publishing.

Townsend, Peter L. The Father of All Trees. Femrite, Gina, illus. l.t. ed. 1999. 28p. (J). (ps-3). 16.95 (978-1-892458-01-8(2)) Life's Footprints, Inc.

The Tree Fort. 2001. (J). (978-1-58453-137-1(1)) Pioneer Valley Educational Pr., Inc.

Trembley, Skip & Ochs, Susan A. You'll See, Little Tree. Hollis, Michael, illus. 2003. (J). pap. 7.95 (978-0-9643452-2-5(6)) Graphics North.

Udry, Janice. A Tree Is Nice. Simont, Marc, illus. 2002. (J). 15.53 (978-0-7587-5500-1(7)) Book Wholesalers, Inc.

Vance, L. K. Jennadi. 2006. 73p. pap. 14.95 (978-1-4241-1574-7(4)) PublishAmerica, Inc.

Vaughan, Christina. Magic Wigglenose & the Dancing Christmas Trees. 2000. (Illus.). (J). (gr. 2-6). spiral bd. 18.95 (978-0-9641697-2-2(X) , You-Draw-It Bks.) Castlebrook Pubns.

Walsh, Ann. Flower Power. 2005. (Orca Currents Ser.). 112p. (J). (gr. 4-10). pap. 7.95 (978-1-55143-386-8(9)) Orca Bk. Pubs. USA.

Watkins, Albert. The Brothers Three. l.t. ed. 2004. (Illus.). 48p. (J). pap. 22.95 (978-0-9629124-4-3(1)) Floppinfish Publishing Co., Ltd.

West, Jane. The Lonesome Pine. Lujan-Bakerink, Monique, illus. 2000. 64p. (J). (ps). 24.95 (978-0-9701025-7-7(7)) Haylett Publishing.

Williams, Karen Lynn. Circles of Hope. Saport, Linda, illus. 2005. 32p. (J). 16.00 (978-0-8028-5276-2(9)) Eerdmans, William B. Publishing Co.

Wilson, Wendy. The First Book of Red. 2005. 99p. pap. 14.95 (978-1-4137-5570-1(4)) PublishAmerica, Inc.

Zagwyn, Deborah Turney. Apple Batter. 2004. (Illus.). 32p. (J). (gr. 1-3). 14.95 (978-1-883672-92-8(9) , Tricycle Pr.) Ten Speed Pr.

Ziefert, Harriet. My Friend Grandpa. Wurzberg, Robert, illus. 2004. 40p. 15.95 (978-1-59354-063-0(9)) Blue Apple Bks.

Zweibel, Alan. Our Tree Named Steve. Catrow, David, illus. 2005. 32p. (J). (ps-3). 15.99 (978-0-399-23722-5(4) , Putnam Juvenile) Penguin Group (USA) Inc.

—Our Tree Named Steve. Catrow, David, illus. 2007. 32p. (J). pap. 5.99 (978-0-14-240743-1(7) , Puffin) Penguin Group (USA) Inc.

TREES—POETRY

Argueta, Jorge. Los Arboles Estan Colgando del Cielo. Yockteng, Rafael, illus. 2003. (SPA.). 32p. (J). 15.95 (978-0-88899-510-0(5)) Groundwood Bks. CAN. *Dist:* Perseus Distribution.

—Trees Are Hanging from the Sky. Yockteng, Rafael, illus. 2003. 32p. (J). (ps-1). 15.95 (978-0-88899-509-4(1)) Groundwood Bks. CAN. *Dist:* Perseus Distribution.

Frost, Robert. Birches. Young, Ed, illus. rev. ed. 2002. 32p. (J). (gr. 1-5). pap. 7.95 (978-0-8050-7230-3(6) , Holt, Henry & Co. Bks. For Young Readers) Holt, Henry & Co.

George, Kristine O'Connell. Old Elm Speaks: Tree Poems. Kiesler, Kate A., illus. 1998. 48p. (J). (gr. k-3). tchr. ed. 16.00 (978-0-395-87611-4(7) , Clarion Bks.) Houghton Mifflin Co. Trade & Reference Div.

—Old Elm Speaks: Tree Poems. Kiesler, Kate, illus. 2007. 48p. (J). (gr. k-3). 5.95 (978-0-618-75242-3(0) , Clarion Bks.) Houghton Mifflin Co. Trade & Reference Div.

Singh, Rina. A Forest of Stories: Magical Tree Tales from Around the World. Cann, Helen, illus. 2003. 64p. (J). 19.99 (978-1-84148-963-6(8)) Barefoot Bks., Inc.

TRENTON (N.J.)

Waldman, Scott P. The Battle of Trenton. 2003. (Atlas of Famous Battles of the American Revolution Ser.). (Illus.). 24p. (J). lib. bdg. 21.25 (978-0-8239-6333-1(0) , PowerKids Pr.) Rosen Publishing Group, Inc., The.

TRIAL BY JURY

see Jury

TRIALS

see also Crime and Criminals

Alonso, Karen. The Alger Hiss Communist Spy Trial: A Headline Court Case. 2001. (Headline Court Cases Ser.). (Illus.). 128p. (J). (gr. 6-12). lib. bdg. 26.60 (978-0-7660-1483-1(5)) Enslow Pubs., Inc.

Axelrod-Contrada, Joan. The Lizzie Borden "Axe Murder" Trial: A Headline Court Case. 2000. (Headline Court Cases Ser.). (Illus.). 128p. (J). (gr. 6-12). lib. bdg. 26.60 (978-0-7660-1422-0(3)) Enslow Pubs., Inc.

Boraas, Tracey. The Salem Witch Trials. 2004. (Let Freedom Ring Ser.). (Illus.). 48p. (J). lib. bdg. 23.93 (978-0-7368-2464-4(2) , Bridgestone Bks.) Capstone Pr., Inc.

Burgan, Michael. Miranda V. Arizona: The Rights of the Accused. 2006. (J). (978-0-7565-2008-3(8)) Compass Point Bks.

—The Salem Witch Trials. 2004. (We the People Ser.). (Illus.). 48p. (J). 22.60 (978-0-7565-0845-6(2)) Compass Point Bks.

Crewe, Sabrina & Uschan, Michael V. The Scottsboro Case. 2004. (Events That Shaped America Ser.). (Illus.). 32p. (J). lib. bdg. 24.67 (978-0-8368-3407-9(0)) Stevens, Gareth Inc.

DeVillers, David. The John Brown Slavery Revolt Trial: A Headline Court Case. 2000. (Headline Court Cases Ser.). (Illus.). 104p. (YA). (gr. 6-12). lib. bdg. 26.60 (978-0-7660-1385-8(5)) Enslow Pubs., Inc.

Dolan, Edward F., Jr. The Salem Witch Trials. 2001. (Kaleidoscope Ser.). (Illus.). 48p. (J). (gr. 3 up). lib. bdg. 25.64 (978-0-7614-1302-8(2) , Benchmark Bks.) Cavendish, Marshall Corp.

Don Nardo. The Trial of Galileo. 2004. (Famous Trials Ser.). (Illus.). 112p. (J). 29.95 (978-1-59018-423-3(8)) Thomson Gale.

Ferguson, Amanda. The Attack Against the U. S. Embassies in Kenya & Tanzania. 2005. (Terrorist Attacks Ser.). (Illus.). 64p. (J). (gr. 7-12). lib. bdg. 26.50 (978-0-8239-3652-6(X)) Rosen Publishing Group, Inc., The.

Fireside, Bryna J. The Haymarket Square Riot Trial: A Headline Court Case. 2002. (Headline Court Cases Ser.). (Illus.). 128p. (YA). (gr. 6-12). lib. bdg. 26.60 (978-0-7660-1761-0(3)) Enslow Pubs., Inc.

—The Trial of the Police Officers in the Shooting Death of Amadou Diallo: A Headline Court Case. 2004. (Headline Court Cases Ser.). (Illus.). 128p. (J). lib. bdg. 26.60 (978-0-7660-2166-2(1)) Enslow Pubs., Inc.

Fremon, David K. The Salem Witchcraft Trials in American History. 1999. (In American History Ser.). (Illus.). 128p. (YA). (gr. 5-12). lib. bdg. 26.60 (978-0-7660-1125-0(9)) Enslow Pubs., Inc.

Graves, Renee. The Scopes Trial. 2003. (Cornerstones of Freedom, 2ND Ser.). (Illus.). 48p. (J). 26.00 (978-0-516-24221-7(0) , Children's Pr.) Scholastic Library Publishing.

Gray, Valerie A. The Court-Martial Trial of West Point Cadet Johnson Whittaker: A Headline Court Case. 2001. (Headline Court Cases Ser.). (Illus.). 104p. (J). (gr. 6-12). lib. bdg. 26.60 (978-0-7660-1485-5(1)) Enslow Pubs., Inc.

Headline Court Cases, 21 bks. , Set. Incl. Alger Hiss Communist Spy Trial : A Headline Court Case. Alonso, Karen. 128p. (J). 2001. lib. bdg. 26.60 (978-0-7660-1483-1(5)); Andersonville Prison Civil War Crimes Trial : A Headline Court Case. Banfield, Susan. 112p. (J). 2000. lib. bdg. 26.60 (978-0-7660-1386-5(3)); Court-Martial Trial of West Point Cadet Johnson Whittaker : A Headline Court Case. Gray, Valerie A. 104p. (J). 2001. lib. bdg. 26.60 (978-0-7660-1485-5(1)); John Brown Slavery Revolt Trial : A Headline Court Case. DeVillers, David. 104p. (YA). 2000. lib. bdg. 26.60 (978-0-7660-1385-8(5)); Lindbergh Baby Kidnapping Trial : A Headline Court Case. Monroe, Judy. 128p. (YA). 2000. lib. bdg. 26.60 (978-0-7660-1389-6(8)); Lizzie Borden "Axe Murder" Trial : A Headline Court Case. Axelrod-Contrada, Joan. 128p. (J). 2000. lib. bdg. 26.60 (978-0-7660-1422-0(3)); Mary Surratt "Lincoln Assassination" Trial : A Headline Court Case. Fireside, Bryna J. 128p. (J). 2001. lib. bdg. 26.60 (978-0-7660-1481-7(9)); Nuremberg Nazi War Crimes Trials : A Headline Court Case. Fireside, Harvey. 128p. (YA). 2000. lib. bdg. 26.60 (978-0-7660-1384-1(7)); O. J. Simpson Murder Trial : A Headline Court Case. Pellowski, Michael J. 104p. (J). 2001. lib. bdg. 26.60 (978-0-7660-1480-0(0)); Rosenberg Cold War Spy Trial : A Headline Court Case. Monroe, Judy. 128p. (J). 2001. lib. bdg. 20.95 (978-0-7660-1479-4(7)); Sacco & Vanzetti Controversial Murder Trial : A Headline Court Case. Monroe, Judy. 112p. (YA). 2000. lib. bdg. 26.60 (978-0-7660-1387-2(1)); Salem Witchcraft Trials : A Headline Court Case. Woods, Geraldine. 104p. (YA). 2000. lib. bdg. 26.60 (978-0-7660-1383-4(9)); Scopes Monkey Trial : A Headline Court Case. Hanson, Freya Ottem. 128p. (YA). 2000. lib. bdg. 26.60 (978-0-7660-1388-9(X)); Teapot Dome Scandal : A Headline Court Case. Thorndike, Jonathan L. 104p. (J). 2001. lib. bdg. 26.60 (978-0-7660-1484-8(3)); Trial of Gangster Al Capone : A Headline Court Case. Trespacz, Karen L. 112p. (J). 2001. lib. bdg. 26.60 (978-0-7660-1482-4(7)); (gr. 6-12). (Illus.). Set lib. bdg. 439.95 (978-0-7660-1603-3(X)) Enslow Pubs., Inc.

Hitchcock, Susan Tyler & McNeese, Tim. Roe V. Wade: Protecting a Woman's Right to Choose. 2006. (Great Supreme Court Decisions Ser.). (Illus.). 128p. (J). (gr. 5-8). 30.00 (978-0-7910-9239-2(9) , Chelsea Hse.) Facts On File, Inc.

Hogrogian, John. Miranda vs. Arizona: The Rights of the Accused. 1999. (Famous Trials Ser.). (Illus.). 112p. (YA). (gr. 7-10). lib. bdg. 29.95 (978-1-56006-471-8(4) , LML00902-177836, Lucent Bks.) Thomson Gale.

Kallen, Stuart A. Figures of the Salem Witch Trials. 2004. (History Makers Ser.). (Illus.). 112p. (J). (gr. 7-10). 29.95 (978-1-59018-559-9(5) , Lucent Bks.) Thomson Gale.

Kelly, Zachary A. Trials & Sentences. (Law & Order Ser.). (J). 1999. (Illus.). 48p. (gr. 4-8). lib. bdg. 27.93 (978-0-86593-576-1(9)); 1998. lib. bdg. 27.93 (978-0-86625-660-5(1)) Rourke Publishing, LLC.

Koopmans, Andy. The Leopold & Loeb Case. 2003. (Famous Trials Ser.). (Illus.). 112p. (J). 29.95 (978-1-59018-227-7(8) , Lucent Bks.) Thomson Gale.

Kraft, Betsy Harvey. Sensational Trials of the 20th Century. 1998. (Illus.). 216p. (YA). (gr. 4-9). pap. 16.95 (978-0-590-37205-3(X) , Scholastic Pr.) Scholastic, Inc.

Landau, Elaine. Sacco & Vanzetti. 2004. (Cornerstones of Freedom Ser.). (Illus.). 48p. (J). 26.00 (978-0-516-24237-8(7) , Children's Pr.) Scholastic Library Publishing.

Lock, Joan. Famous Trials. 2003. (Crime & Detection Ser.). (Illus.). 96p. (J). (gr. 7 up). lib. bdg. (978-1-59084-381-9(9)) Mason Crest Pubs.

Lucas, Eileen. The Aaron Burr Treason Trial. 2003. (Headline Court Cases Ser.). (Illus.). 128p. (J). (gr. 6-12). lib. bdg. 26.60 (978-0-7660-1765-8(6)) Enslow Pubs., Inc.

Mayell, Mark. The Lindbergh Kidnapping. 2003. (Famous Trials Ser.). (Illus.). 112p. (J). 29.95 (978-1-59018-267-3(7) , Lucent Bks.) Thomson Gale.

—Saskatchewan. 2003. (Illus.). 128p. (J). 29.95 (978-1-59018-052-5(6) , Lucent Bks.) Thomson Gale.

McLane, William. Furman vs. Georgia. 2001. (Famous Trials Ser.). (Illus.). 112p. (J). (gr. 7-10). lib. bdg. 29.95 (978-1-56006-470-1(6) , LML00902-177835, Lucent Bks.) Thomson Gale.

McLaurin, Melton A. Celia, a Slave. 1999. (J). (978-0-606-16086-5(8)) Tandem Library Bks.

Monroe, Judy. The Rosenberg Cold War Spy Trial: A Headline Court Case. 2001. (Headline Court Cases Ser.). (Illus.). 128p. (J). (gr. 6-12). lib. bdg. 20.95 (978-0-7660-1479-4(7)) Enslow Pubs., Inc.

Morrison, Toni. Remember: The Journey to School Integration. 2004. (Illus.). 80p. (J). (gr. k-3). tchr. ed. 18.00 (978-0-618-39740-2(X)) Houghton Mifflin Co. Trade & Reference Div.

Morse, Scott. Visitations. 1998. (Illus.). 96p. (YA). (gr. 8 up). pap. 8.95 (978-1-929998-34-0(1)) Oni Pr., Inc.

Nardo, Don. The Salem Witch Trials. 2007. (American History Ser.). 128p. (J). (gr. 7-10). 32.45 (*978-1-59018-950-4(7)* , Lucent Bks.) Thomson Gale.

Orr, Tamra. The Salem Witch Trials. 2003. (People at the Center of Ser.). (Illus.). 48p. (J). 24.95 (978-1-56711-770-7(8) , Blackbirch Pr., Inc.) Thomson Gale.

Owens, L. L. American Justice II: Six Trials That Captivated the Nation. 2001. (Cover-To-Cover Books). (Illus.). 56p. (J). pap. (978-0-7891-5450-7(1)); (gr. 4-7). lib. bdg. 17.95 (978-0-7569-0100-4(6)) Perfection Learning Corp.

Pellowski, Michael J. The Charles Manson Murder Trial: A Headline Court Case. 2004. (Headline Court Cases Ser.). (Illus.). 128p. (J). lib. bdg. 26.60 (978-0-7660-2167-9(X)) Enslow Pubs., Inc.

—The O. J. Simpson Murder Trial: A Headline Court Case. 2001. (Headline Court Cases Ser.). (Illus.). 104p. (J). (gr. 6-12). lib. bdg. 26.60 (978-0-7660-1480-0(0)) Enslow Pubs., Inc.

Pettifor, Bonnie & Petit, Charles E. McCulloch V. Maryland: When State & Federal Powers Conflict. 2004. (Landmark Supreme Court Cases Ser.). (Illus.). 128p. (J). lib. bdg. 26.60 (978-0-7660-1887-7(3)) Enslow Pubs., Inc.

Randolph, Ryan P. Marbury V. Madison: The New Supreme Court Gets More Power. 2003. (Life in the New American Nation Ser.). (Illus.). 32p. (J). pap. (978-0-8239-4252-7(X)) Rosen Publishing Group, Inc., The.

Roach, Marilynne K. In the Days of the Salem Witchcraft Trials. 2003. 96p. (J). (gr. 5 up). pap. 5.95 (978-0-618-39196-7(7)) Houghton Mifflin Co. Trade & Reference Div.

—In the Days of the Salem Witchcraft Trials. 2003. (gr. 3-6). lib. bdg. 14.10 (978-0-613-86973-7(7)) Tandem Library Bks.

Thorndike, Jonathan L. The Teapot Dome Scandal: A Headline Court Case. 2001. (Headline Court Cases Ser.). (Illus.). 104p. (J). (gr. 6-12). lib. bdg. 26.60 (978-0-7660-1484-8(3)) Enslow Pubs., Inc.

Trespacz, Karen L. The Trial of Gangster Al Capone: A Headline Court Case. 2001. (Headline Court Cases Ser.). (Illus.). 112p. (J). (gr. 6-12). lib. bdg. 26.60 (978-0-7660-1482-4(7)) Enslow Pubs., Inc.

Uschan, Michael V. The Salem Witch Trials. 2004. (Landmark Events in American History Ser.). (Illus.). 48p. (J). (gr. 5 up). pap. 11.95 (978-0-8368-5415-2(2)); lib. bdg. 30.00 (978-0-8368-5387-2(3)) Stevens, Gareth Inc. (World Almanac Library).

—The Scottsboro Case. 2004. (Landmark Events in American History Ser.). (Illus.). 48p. (J). (gr. 5 up). pap. 11.95 (978-0-8368-5416-9(0)); lib. bdg. 30.00 (978-0-8368-5388-9(1)) Stevens, Gareth Inc. (World Almanac Library).

VanMeter, Larry A. & McNeese, Tim. Miranda v. Arizona: The Rights of the Accused. 2006. (Great Supreme Court Decisions Ser.). (Illus.). 112p. (YA). (gr. 5-8). 30.00 (978-0-7910-9259-0(3) , Chelsea Hse.) Facts On File, Inc.

Westermann, Karen T. John Peter Zenger: Free Press Advocate. 2000. (Colonial Leaders Ser.). (Illus.). 80p. (J). (gr. 8-12). 27.50 (978-0-7910-5966-1(9) , Chelsea Hse.) Facts On File, Inc.

—John Peter Zenger: Free Press Advocate. 2000. (Illus.). 80p. (J). (gr. 4-7). lib. bdg. 17.60 (978-0-613-32727-5(6)) Tandem Library Bks.

Woods, Geraldine. The Salem Witchcraft Trials: A Headline Court Case. 2000. (Headline Court Cases Ser.). (Illus.). 104p. (YA). (gr. 6-12). lib. bdg. 26.60 (978-0-7660-1383-4(9)) Enslow Pubs., Inc.

TRIALS—FICTION

Bryant, Jennifer. The Trial. (Illus.). 176p. (J). (gr. 3-7). 2005. pap. 5.99 (978-0-440-41986-0(7) , Yearling); 2004. lib. bdg. 16.99 (978-0-375-92752-2(2) , Knopf Bks. for Young Readers) Random Hse. Children's Bks.

Egan, Tim. The Trial of Cardigan Jones. 2004. (Illus.). 32p. (J). (gr. k-3). tchr. ed. 16.00 (978-0-618-40237-3(3)) Houghton Mifflin Co. Trade & Reference Div.

Farrell, Liam. The Trial of the Big Bad Wolf. Myler, Terry, illus. 2003. (Elephant Ser.). 64p. (YA). (gr. 1 up). pap. 8.95 (978-1-901737-40-0(3)) Anvil Bks., Ltd. IRL. *Dist:* Dufour Editions, Inc.

Giovanni, Nikki. Jimmy Grasshopper Versus the Ants. Raschka, Christopher, illus. 2007. (J). (*978-0-7636-3021-8(7)*) Candlewick Pr.

Hearn, Julie & Frost, Michael. The Minister's Daughter. 2005. 272p. (YA). (gr. 7 up). 17.99 (978-0-689-87690-5(4) , Atheneum) Simon & Schuster Children's Publishing.

Heiner, Garth Farr. Arty Puts the Bite on Hopper. Melander, Eric, illus. unabr. ed. 2001. (Fun-with-the-Law Ser.: No. 1). 32p. (J). (gr. k-7). pap. 5.95 (978-1-929905-01-0(7)) Fun With the Law, Inc.

—Finders Keepers. Melander, Eric, illus. l.t. unabr. ed. 2001. (Fun-with-the-Law Ser.: No. 4). 32p. (J). (gr. k-7). pap. 5.95 (978-1-929905-04-1(1)) Fun With the Law, Inc.

Jardine, Quintin. Skinner's Trail. 2001. (Bob Skinner Mysteries Ser.). 499p. mass mkt. 9.99 (978-0-7472-4141-6(4)) Headline Bk. Publishing GBR. *Dist:* Independent Pubs. Group.

Klise, Kate. Trial by Journal. Klise, M. Sarah, illus. 256p. (J). 2002. (gr. 3-6). pap. 6.99 (978-0-380-81672-9(5)); 2001. (gr. 4-6). 15.95 (978-0-380-97880-9(6)); 2001. (gr. 4-6). 16.89 (978-0-06-029541-7(4)) HarperCollins Pubs.

—Trial by Journal. 2002. (gr. 5-8). lib. bdg. 15.30 (978-0-613-60649-3(3)) Tandem Library Bks.

Moses, Shelia P. I, Dred Scott: A Fictional Slave Narrative Based on the Life & Legal Precedent of Dred Scott. Christensen, Bonnie, illus. 2005. 112p. (YA). (gr. 7 up). 16.95 (978-0-689-85975-5(9), McElderry, Margaret K.) Simon & Schuster Children's Publishing.

Myers, Walter Dean. Monster. Myers, Christopher A., illus. 1999. (Amistad Ser.). 288p. (J). (gr. 7 up). 16.99 (978-0-06-028077-2(8)) HarperCollins Pubs.

—Monster. Myers, Christopher, illus. (Newbery Honor Roll Ser.). (J). 1999. 288p. (gr. 7 up). lib. bdg. 17.89 (978-0-06-028078-9(6)); 2001. 304p. reprint ed. pap. 7.99 (978-0-06-440731-1(4), Amistad) HarperCollins Pubs.

Pearsall, Shelley. Crooked River. (J). (gr. 5-9). 2007. 272p. pap. 6.50 (978-0-440-42101-6(2), Yearling); 2005. 256p. 15.95 (978-0-375-82389-3(1), Knopf Bks. for Young Readers); 2005. 256p. lib. bdg. 17.99 (978-0-375-92389-0(6), Knopf Bks. for Young Readers) Random Hse. Children's Bks.

TRIBES AND TRIBAL SYSTEMS

Haywood, John. Tribes & Empires. 2004. (Illus.). 64p. pap. 8.99 (978-1-84215-957-6(7), Southwater) Anness Publishing GBR. *Dist:* National Bk. Network.

MacDonald, Fiona. Tribes, Empires & Civilizations. 2001. (Through the Ages Ser.). (Illus.). 64p. (gr. 3-7). 12.95 (978-0-7548-0851-0(3)) Anness Publishing GBR. *Dist:* National Bk. Network.

TRICKS

see also Card Tricks; Magic

Amazing Tricks: Level L, 6 vols. 128p. (gr. 2-3). 40.50 (978-0-7699-0996-7(5)) Shortland Pubns. (U. S. A.) Inc.

Brunelle, Lynn. Mama's Little Book of Tricks. Eckel, Jessie, illus. 2007. 144p. pap. 12.95 (978-0-8118-5571-6(6)) Chronicle Bks. LLC.

Colombo, Luann. World's Coolest Dog Tricks. McFarlane, James, illus. 2001. 24p. (J). 6.95 (978-0-9700346-6-3(0)) becker&mayer! books.

Crompton, Richmal. Just William's Tricks. 2003. (Illus.). 64p. (J). pap. 2.95 (978-0-333-62679-5(6)) Macmillan Publishers Ltd. GBR. *Dist:* Trafalgar Square Publishing.

Ransford, Sandy. Jokes & Pranks. 2003. (Wicked Wallets Ser.). (Illus.). 96p. (YA). pap. (978-1-84347-040-3(3)) Chrysalis Children's Bks.

Smith, Bruce. Great Rope & Ring Tricks. 2000. (Magic Library). (Illus.). 160p. (gr. 3-7). pap. 5.95 (978-0-8069-7179-7(7)) Sterling Publishing Co., Inc.

Smith, Dian G. World's Greatest Practical Jokes. Willms, Russ, illus. 2004. 96p. (J). pap. 4.95 (978-1-4027-1020-9(8)) Sterling Publishing Co., Inc.

Tait, Chris. How to Be a Kid. Paillot, Jim, illus. 2003. 96p. (J). pap. 6.95 (978-0-8069-8503-9(8)) Sterling Publishing Co., Inc.

Top That Publishing Editors, ed. Terrible Tricks. Dahl, Roald, illus. 2005. 24p. (J). (978-1-905359-56-1(X)) Top That! Publishing PLC.

TRICYCLES

see Bicycles and Bicycling

TRIGONOMETRY

Accelerated Math West Virginia State Tagged Pre-Calculus Library. 2004. cd-rom 1199.00 (978-1-59455-116-1(2)) Renaissance Learning, Inc.

Algebra & Trigonometry: Complete Solutions Guide. 6th ed. 2004. (gr. 11-12). (978-0-618-31785-1(6), 3-32723) McDougal Littell Inc.

Algebra & Trigonometry: Learning Tools. 6th ed. 2004. (gr. 11-12). stu. ed. incl. cd-rom (978-0-618-31794-3(5), 3-32732) McDougal Littell Inc.

Algebra & Trigonometry: Test Item File. 6th ed. 2004. (gr. 11-12). (978-0-618-31786-8(4), 3-32724) McDougal Littell Inc.

Algebra & Trigonometry: A Graphing Approach: Complete Solutions Guide. 3rd ed. 2001. (gr. 11-12). (978-0-618-07303-0(5), 3-32224) McDougal Littell Inc.

Algebra & Trigonometry Vol. 2: Structure & Method. 2000. (gr. 10-12). tchr. ed. (978-0-395-97726-2(6), 2-13330); stu. ed. (978-0-395-97725-5(8), 2-13329) McDougal Littell Inc.

Aufmann. Aufmann College Trigonometry Plus Study & Solutions Manual Plus Math Space CD-ROM Fifth Edition Plus Eduspace / Blackboard. 5th ed. 2004. (YA). pap. 126.36 incl. cd-rom (978-0-618-51488-5(0), 389249) Houghton Mifflin College Div.

—Aufmann College Trigonometry Plus Study Guide/ solutions Manual Fifth Edition. 5th ed. 2004. (YA). pap. 124.76 (978-0-618-51437-3(6), 389236) Houghton Mifflin College Div.

Blitzer, Robert F. Precalculus. 2003. (Homework Booklets Ser.). 72p. (YA). (gr. 8 up). pap. 2.99 (978-1-56822-418-3(4), Instructional Fair) Schaffer, Frank Pubns.

Blitzer, Robert F. & Bentley, Wayne J. Precalculus. 1999. (100+ Seriestm Ser.). 128p. (YA). (gr. 9-12). pap. 12.99 (978-1-56822-488-6(5), IF8768) School Specialty Publishing.

Gardner, Colin. Examples of Equations & Relationships Taken from "New Advances in Trigonometry: New Quadratic Equation Relationships to All-Integer Pythagorean Triangles, Vols. 1 & 2. 2002. (Illus.). (YA). (gr. 6-12). 80p. pap. 14.95 (978-0-9720348-1-4(1)); 4p. pap. 4.95 (978-0-9720348-0-7(3)) Gardner, Colin.

—New Advances in Trigonometry Vol. 2: Multiple Pythagorean Relationships to Trigonometric Functions. 2002. (Illus.). 250p. (YA). (gr. 6-12). pap. 19.95 (978-0-9720348-2-1(X)) Gardner, Colin.

Holt, Rinehart and Winston Staff. Precalculus: A Graphing Approach. 4th ed. 2004. 85.13 (978-0-03-069608-4(9)) Holt, Rinehart & Winston.

Hostetler, Robert & Larson, Ron. Interactive Trigonometry 3.0. 6th ed. 2003. (YA). cd-rom 59.96 (978-0-618-37393-2(4), 332774) Houghton Mifflin College Div.

—Precalculus. 6th ed. 2003. 781p. (YA). stu. ed. 144.36 incl. cd-rom (978-0-618-38653-6(X), 332757) Houghton Mifflin College Div.

Larson. Algebra & Trigonometry A Graphing Approach 4th Edition Plus Smarthinking. 4th ed. 2004. (YA). pap. 151.16 (978-0-618-52382-5(0), 389381) Houghton Mifflin College Div.

—Algebra & Trigonometry A Graphing Approach Eduspace Ebook Fourth Edition. 4th ed. 2005. (YA). pap. 27.56 (978-0-618-72511-3(3), 333023) Houghton Mifflin College Div.

—College Algebra: Concepts & Models Student Study Guide: Used with ... Larson-Precalculus with Limits: A Graphing Approach. 3rd ed. 2000. (YA). (gr. 11-12). stu. ed. 49.56 (978-0-618-07410-5(4), 332282) Houghton Mifflin College Div.

—Precalculus: Used with ... Larson-Precalculus. 5th ed. 2000. (YA). (gr. 11-12). stu. ed. 49.56 (978-0-618-07271-2(3), 330443) Houghton Mifflin College Div.

—Precalculus Interactive 2.0. 5th ed. 2001. (YA). cd-rom 61.56 (978-0-618-07276-7(4), 330448) Houghton Mifflin College Div.

—Precalculus with Limits: A Graphing Approach 3rd Edition Plus Learning CD 6th Edition. 3rd ed. 2003. (YA). (gr. 11-12). 144.36 incl. cd-rom (978-0-618-39802-7(3), 386344) Houghton Mifflin College Div.

—Precalculus with Limits: A Graphing Approach Plus Eduspace/Blackboard. 4th ed. 2004. (YA). pap. 144.36 (978-0-618-52373-3(1), 389380) Houghton Mifflin College Div.

—Student Success Organizer: Used with ... Larson-Algebra & Trigonometry. 6th ed. 2003. (YA). (gr. 11-12). stu. ed. 8.36 (978-0-618-31787-5(2), 332725) Houghton Mifflin College Div.

—Student Success Organizer: Used with ... Larson-Precalculus. 6th ed. 2003. (YA). (gr. 11-12). stu. ed. 8.36 (978-0-618-31440-9(7), 332746) Houghton Mifflin College Div.

—Study & Solutions Guide: Used with ... Larson-Algebra & Trigonometry. 6th ed. 2003. (YA). (gr. 11-12). stu. ed. 49.56 (978-0-618-31784-4(8), 332722) Houghton Mifflin College Div.

—Study & Solutions Guide: Used with ... Larson-Algebra & Trigonometry: A Graphing Approach. 4th ed. 2004. (YA). stu. ed. 49.56 (978-0-618-39457-9(5), 333027) Houghton Mifflin College Div.

—Study & Solutions Guide: Used with ... Larson-Precalculus. 6th ed. 2003. (YA). (gr. 11-12). stu. ed. 49.56 (978-0-618-31437-9(7), 332743) Houghton Mifflin College Div.

—Study & Solutions Guide: Used with ... Larson-Precalculus: A Graphing Approach. 4th ed. 2004. (YA). stu. ed. 49.56 (978-0-618-39468-5(0), 333032) Houghton Mifflin College Div.

—Study & Solutions Guide: Used with ... Larson-Precalculus with Limits: A Graphing Approach. 4th ed. 2004. (YA). 49.56 (978-0-618-39481-4(8), 333053) Houghton Mifflin College Div.

—Study & Solutions Guide: Used with ... Larson-Trigonometry. 6th ed. 2003. (YA). (gr. 11-12). stu. ed. 49.56 (978-0-618-31798-1(8), 332763) Houghton Mifflin College Div.

—Trigonometry: Used with ... Larson-Trigonometry. 6th ed. 2003. (YA). (gr. 11-12). stu. ed. 8.36 (978-0-618-31801-8(1), 332766) Houghton Mifflin College Div.

—Trigonometry Advanced Placement Version. 6th ed. 2003. (YA). (gr. 11-12). 122.76 (978-0-618-31797-4(X), 332762) Houghton Mifflin College Div.

—Trigonometry Ap Version with Audio Cd 6th Edition. 6th ed. 2003. (YA). (gr. 11-12). 122.76 incl. cd-rom (978-0-618-38599-7(1), 384979) Houghton Mifflin College Div.

—Trigonometry Computer Solutions. (J). 7.00 (978-0-669-12001-1(4)) Houghton Mifflin Co. (Schl. Div.).

—Trigonometry IG. (J). 2.00 (978-0-669-08612-6(6)) Houghton Mifflin Co. (Schl. Div.).

—Trigonometry with CD-ROM & Student Study Guide Sixth Edition. 6th ed. 2003. (YA). pap., stu. ed. 128.76 incl. cd-rom (978-0-618-40838-2(X), 386487) Houghton Mifflin College Div.

Larson, Ron & Hostetler, Robert. Algebra & Trigonometry: Text with Learning Tools. 6th ed. 2003. 885p. (YA). (gr. 11-12). 144.36 incl. cd-rom (978-0-618-38650-5(5), 332735) Houghton Mifflin College Div.

—Interactive Algebra & Trigonometry 3.0. 6th ed. 2003. (YA). cd-rom 59.96 (978-0-618-37586-8(4), 332733) Houghton Mifflin College Div.

Larson, Ron, et al. Precalculus: A Graphing Approach. 4th ed. 2004. 832p. (YA). 144.36 (978-0-618-39466-1(4), 333030) Houghton Mifflin College Div.

—Precalculus Functions & Graphs: A Graphing Approach. 4th ed. 2004. 704p. (YA). 144.36 (978-0-618-39476-0(1), 333045) Houghton Mifflin College Div.

—Precalculus with Limits: A Graphing Approach. 4th ed. 2004. 796p. (YA). 144.36 (978-0-618-39478-4(8), 333050) Houghton Mifflin College Div.

McGraw-Hill Staff. Contemporary Precalculus Through Applications. 1999. stu. ed. 78.64 (978-1-57039-775-2(9), 9781570397752) Glencoe/McGraw-Hill.

Nation, Richard D., et al. College Trigonometry. 5th ed. 2004. (Illus.). 524p. (YA). 124.76 (978-0-618-38804-2(4), 302420) Houghton Mifflin College Div.

Precalculus. 5th ed. 2001. (gr. 11-12). (978-0-618-07272-9(1), 3-30444); (978-0-618-07273-6(X), 3-30445); cd-rom (978-0-618-07277-4(2), 3-30448) McDougal Littell Inc.

Precalculus: Complete Solutions Guide. 6th ed. 2004. (gr. 11-12). (978-0-618-31438-6(5), 3-32744) McDougal Littell Inc.

Precalculus: HM MathSpace Technology Package. 3rd ed. 2004. (gr. 6-12). tchr. ed. (978-0-618-35699-7(1), 3-02981) McDougal Littell Inc.

Precalculus with Limits: a Graphing Approach: Complete Solutions Guide. 3rd ed. 2001. (gr. 11-12). (978-0-618-07412-9(0), 3-32284) McDougal Littell Inc.

Precalculus with Limits: a Graphing Approach: Learning Tools. 6th ed. 2004. (gr. 11-12). stu. ed. incl. cd-rom (978-0-618-31447-8(4), 3-32754) McDougal Littell Inc.

Reeves, Brian & Robinson, Craig. Pre-Calculus Student Activities Book. Matthews, Douglas L., ed. 2003. (Illus.). stu. ed., per., wbk. ed. (978-1-931680-24-0(8), Expert Systems for Teachers) Teaching Point, Inc.

Sadler, Robert. Pre-Calculus. 1999. (Illus.). 128p. (YA). (gr. 5). pap. 11.95 (978-1-58037-093-6(4)) Twain, Mark Media, Inc. Pubs.

School Mathematics Project Staff. SMP 16-19 Pure 3: Vectors & Applications of Calculus. rev. ed. 2002. (School Mathematics Project 16-19 Ser.). (Illus.). 158p. pap. 19.80 (978-0-521-78799-4(8)) Cambridge Univ. Pr.

Ssm Contmp Coll Alg/Trig. 2nd ed. 2004. (C). pap. 39.95 (978-0-534-46792-0(X)) Brooks/Cole.

Ssm Precalc: Func/Graphs. 10th ed. 2005. (C). pap. 37.95 (978-0-534-99995-7(6)) Brooks/Cole.

Trigonometrie. 2nd ed. (Duden-Schuelerhilfen Ser.). (GER.). 112p. (YA). (gr. 10). (978-3-411-70892-5(1)) Bibliographisches Institut & F. A. Brockhaus AG DEU. *Dist:* International Bk. Import Service, Inc.

Wingard-Nelson, Rebecca. Trigonometry. 2004. (Math Success Ser.). (Illus.). 64p. (J). lib. bdg. 22.60 (978-0-7660-2568-4(3)) Enslow Pubs., Inc.

TRINIDAD AND TOBAGO

Hernandez, Romel. Trinidad & Tobago. 2003. (Discovering Latin America Ser.). (Illus.). 64p. (J). (gr. 5 up). lib. bdg. (978-1-59084-304-8(5)) Mason Crest Pubs.

Sheehan, Sean. Trinidad & Tobago. 2001. (Cultures of the World Ser.). (Illus.). 128p. (J). (gr. 5-12). lib. bdg. 37.07 (978-0-7614-1194-9(1), Benchmark Bks.) Cavendish, Marshall Corp.

Urosevich, Patricia R. Trinidad & Tobago: Major World Nations. 1999. (Major World Nations Ser.). (Illus.). 144p. (YA). (gr. 4-7). 29.95 (978-0-7910-4769-9(5), Chelsea Hse.) Facts On File, Inc.

TRINIDAD AND TOBAGO—FICTION

Baptiste, Tracey. Angel's Grace. 2005. 176p. (J). 15.95 (978-0-689-86773-6(5), Simon & Schuster/Paula Wiseman Bks.) Simon & Schuster Children's Publishing.

Bootman, Colin. Fish for the Grand Lady. Bootman, Colin, illus. 2006. (Illus.). 32p. (J). 16.95 (978-0-8234-1898-5(7)) Holiday Hse., Inc.

TRIPLETS—FICTION

Ahlberg, Allan. The Children Who Smelled a Rat. McEwen, Katharine, illus. 2005. 80p. (J). (gr. 2-4). 15.99 (978-0-7636-2870-3(0)) Candlewick Pr.

Capdevila, Roser. El Lobo y los Siete Cabritos. 2002. (Cuentos Fantasticos de las Tres Mellizas Coleccion: Vol. 2). (SPA.). (J). (gr. k-2). pap. 5.95 (978-1-930332-36-2(X)) Lectorum Pubns., Inc.

—Tarzan. 2002. (Cuentos Fantasticos de las Tres Mellizas Coleccion: Vol. 3). (SPA.). (J). (gr. k-2). pap. 5.95 (978-1-930332-37-9(8), LC6643) Lectorum Pubns., Inc.

Carpenter, Donna. A Triple Treat. 2007. (Illus.). 20p. (J). 14.95 (***978-0-9793987-0-4(3)***) DFC Pubs.

Fishbone, Greg. The Penguins of Doom. 2007. (From the Desk of Septina Nash Ser.). (Illus.). 192p. (J). (gr. 3-9). 13.95 (***978-1-933831-03-9(0)***) Blooming Tree Pr.

Jenkins, Emily. Daffodil. Bogacki, Tomek, illus. 2004. 32p. (J). 16.00 (978-0-374-31676-1(7), Farrar, Straus & Giroux (BYR)) Farrar, Straus & Giroux.

—Daffodil, Crocodile. Bogacki, Tomek, illus. 2007. 32p. (J). (ps-3). 16.00 (978-0-374-39944-3(1), Farrar, Straus & Giroux (BYR)) Farrar, Straus & Giroux.

Pagliarulo, Antonio. The Celebutantes: In the Club. 2008. (YA). (***978-0-385-73473-8(5)***); 12.99 (***978-0-385-90472-8(X)***) Dell Publishing. (Delacorte Pr.).

Pagliarulo, Antonio. On the Avenue. 2007. (Celebutantes Ser.). 352p. (YA). (gr. 9 up). pap. 9.99 (978-0-385-73404-2(2)); lib. bdg. 12.99 (978-0-385-90415-5(0)) Random Hse. Children's Bks. (Delacorte Bks. for Young Readers).

Reiss, Kathryn. Paperquake: A Puzzle. 2002. (gr. 5-8). lib. bdg. 14.15 (978-0-613-53851-0(X)) Tandem Library Bks.

Rhoton, Lesa. Angus & the Triplets. Switzer, Bobby, illus. 2006. 28p. per. 13.95 (978-1-58939-852-8(1)) Virtualbookworm.com Publishing, Inc.

The T-Shirt Triplets: Individual Title Six-Packs. (Literatura 2000 Ser.). (gr. 2-3). 33.00 (978-0-7635-0187-7(5)) Rigby Education.

TROJAN WAR

Ambrus, Victor G., illus. The Iliad. 2000. 95p. (J). (ps-8). lib. bdg. 25.70 (978-0-613-90907-5(0)) Tandem Library Bks.

Church, Alfred John. The Story of the Iliad. 2005. reprint ed. pap. 31.95 (978-1-4191-5466-9(4)) Kessinger Publishing, LLC.

Claybourne, A. & Khanduri, K. Greek Myths: Ulysses & the Trojan War: Mini-Edition. 2004. (Spotter's Guides). 160p. (J). 8.95 (978-0-7945-0535-6(X)) EDC Publishing.

Clement, David D. Trojan Horse. 1999. (J). (978-0-606-18992-7(0)) Tandem Library Bks.

Colum, Padraic. Adventures of Odysseus & the Tale of T. 2006. pap. 35.99 (***978-1-4219-6450-8(3)***) IndyPublish.com.

—The Adventures of Odysseus & the Tale of Troy. Pogany, Willy, illus. 2004. 176p. (J). (gr. 4-7). pap. 4.95 (978-0-486-43455-1(9)) Dover Pubns., Inc.

—The Children's Homer: The Adventures of Odysseus & the Tale of Troy. Pogany, Willy, illus. 2004. 256p. (J). pap. 9.95 (978-0-689-86883-2(9), Aladdin) Simon & Schuster Children's Publishing.

Coolidge, Olivia E. The Trojan War. Sandoz, Edouard, illus. 2001. 272p. (YA). (gr. 5-9). pap. 6.95 (978-0-618-15428-9(0)); tchr. ed. 16.00 (978-0-618-15427-2(2)) Houghton Mifflin Co. Trade & Reference Div.

—The Trojan War. 2001. (978-0-606-22595-3(1)); (gr. 5-8). lib. bdg. 14.10 (978-0-613-35586-5(5)) Tandem Library Bks.

Davis, David C. Trojan Horse. 1999. (Eyewitness Bks.). (Illus.). 48p. (J). (ps-4). pap. 3.99 (978-0-7894-4474-5(7)) Dorling Kindersley Publishing, Inc.

Khanduri, Kamini, intro. & retold by. Tales of the Trojan War. Khanduri, Kamini, retold by. 2002. (Usborne Classics Ser.). (Illus.). 159p. (J). pap. (978-0-439-78708-6(4)) Scholastic, Inc.

Lang, Andrew. Tales of Troy: Ulysses, the Sacker of Cities. 2004. reprint ed. pap. 1.99 (978-1-4192-5072-9(8)) Kessinger Publishing, LLC.

—Tales of Troy & Greece. Ford, H. J., illus. 2006. (Dover Value Editions Ser.). 336p. pap. 9.95 (978-0-486-44917-3(3)) Dover Pubns., Inc.

Lee, Alan & Sutcliff, Rosemary. Black Ships Before Troy. 2005. (Illus.). 128p. (J). 19.95 (978-1-84507-359-6(2)) Lincoln, Frances Ltd. GBR. *Dist:* Perseus Distribution.

Lorenz, Albert & Schleh, Joy. The Trojan Horse. 2006. (Illus.). 34p. (J). (gr. k-4). 17.95 (978-0-8109-5986-6(0), Abrams Bks. for Young Readers) Abrams, Harry N., Inc.

Malam, John. The Wooden Horse of Troy. Rutherford, Peter, illus. 2004. (Ancient Myths Ser.). 32p. (gr. 3-5). 23.93 (978-1-4048-0906-2(6)) Picture Window Bks.

Marston, Trude. Iliad: A Teaching Unit. 2001. 116p. spiral bd. 50.00 (978-1-930443-48-8(X)) Logos Schl.

Mayhew, James. Can You See a Little Bear? Morris, Jackie, illus. 2006. 32p. (J). pap. 7.95 (978-1-84507-364-0(9)) Lincoln, Frances Ltd. GBR. *Dist:* Perseus Distribution.

Shanower, Eric. A Thousand Ships, Vol. 1. (Illus.). 224p. pap. 19.95 (978-1-58240-200-0(0)) Image Comics.

Sutcliff, Rosemary. Black Ships Before Troy. 2005. 160p. (YA). (gr. 7 up). mass mkt. 5.99 (978-0-553-49483-9(X), Laurel Leaf) Random Hse. Children's Bks.

Tracy, Kathleen. The Life & Times of Homer. 2004. (Biography from Ancient Civilizations Ser.). (Illus.). 48p. (J). (gr. 4-8). lib. bdg. 29.95 (978-1-58415-260-6(5)) Mitchell Lane Pubs., Inc.

TROLLS

see Fairies

TROPICAL DISEASES

see Tropics—Diseases and Hygiene

TROPICAL FISH

Barron's Educational Editorial Staff & Windsor, Steve. Tropical Fish Keeping. 2000. (All about Your Pet Ser.). (Illus.). 32p. pap. 3.95 (978-0-7641-1494-6(8)) Barron's Educational Series, Inc.

Landau, Elaine. Piranhas. 1999. (gr. 3-6). lib. bdg. 15.25 (978-0-613-37505-4(X)) Tandem Library Bks.

—Siamese Fighting Fish. 1999. (True Bks.). (Illus.). 48p. (J). (gr. 3-5). pap 6.95 (978 0 516-26504-9(0)); 25.00 (978-0-516-20678-3(8)) Scholastic Library Publishing. (Children's Pr.).

—Your Pet Tropical Fish. 1998. (True Bks.). (Illus.). 48p. (J). (gr. 3-5). pap. 6.95 (978-0-516-26278-9(5), Children's Pr.) Scholastic Library Publishing.

Pronek, Neal. Tropical Fish. 1999. (Fish). (Illus.). 64p. (YA). (gr. 4-7). 32.00 (978-0-7910-5094-1(7), Chelsea Hse.) Facts On File, Inc.

Sovak, Jan. Learning about Tropical Fish. 1998. (Learning about Ser.). (Illus.). 16p. (J). pap. 1.50 (978-0-486-40336-6(X), 40336-X) Dover Pubns., Inc.

Walker, Braz. Angelfish: Keeping & Breeding Them in Captivity. 1999. (Fish). (Illus.). 64p. (YA). (gr. 4-7). lib. bdg. 19.75 (978-0-7910-5095-8(5), Chelsea Hse.) Facts On File, Inc.

Williams, Sarah, et al. 101 Facts about Tropical Fish. 2001. (One Hundred One Facts about Pets Ser.). (Illus.). 32p. (J). (gr. 3 up). lib. bdg. 23.33 (978-0-8368-2892-4(5)) Stevens, Gareth Inc.

TROPICAL RAIN FOREST ECOLOGY

see Rain Forest Ecology

TROPICAL RAIN FORESTS

see Rain Forests

TROPICS

Benduhn, Tea. Living in Tropical Rain Forests. 2007. (J). pap. (***978-0-8368-8349-7(7)***); 24p. (gr. 2-4). lib. bdg. 19.93 (***978-0-8368-8344-2(6)***) Stevens, Gareth Inc. (Weekly Reader Early Learning Library).

Gritzner, Charles F. The Tropics. 2007. (Geography of Extreme Environments Ser.). (Illus.). 128p. (J). (gr. 6-12). 24.95 (978-0-7910-9233-0(X), Chelsea Hse.) Facts On File, Inc.

Heelas, Richard. Tropical Environments: Contrasting Regimes & Challenges. 2001. (Epics Ser.). (Illus.). 104p. (YA). (gr. 11 up). pap. 23.50 (978-0-7487-5820-3(8)) Nelson Thornes Ltd. GBR. *Dist:* Trans-Atlantic Pubns., Inc.

Pirotta, Saviour. Trees & Plants in the Rain Forest. 1999. (Deep in the Rain Forest Ser.). (Illus.). 32p. (J). (978-0-7502-2198-6(4)) Steck-Vaughn.

TROPICS—DISEASES AND HYGIENE

see also names of tropical diseases, e.g. Yellow Fever

Isle, Mick. Malaria. 2001. (Epidemics Ser.). (Illus.). 64p. (J). (gr. 4-6). lib. bdg. 26.50 (978-0-8239-3342-6(3)) Rosen Publishing Group, Inc., The.

Ramen, Fred. Sleeping Sickness & Other Parasitic Tropical Diseases. 2002. (Epidemics Ser.). (Illus.). 64p. (YA). (gr. 7-12). lib. bdg. 26.50 (978-0-8239-3499-7(3)) Rosen Publishing Group, Inc., The.

TROPICS—FICTION

Collins, Pat L. The Fattening Hut. 2003. 192p. (YA). (gr. 7 up). tchr. ed. 15.00 (978-0-618-30955-9(1)) Houghton Mifflin Co. Trade & Reference Div.

Collins, Pat Lowery. The Fattening Hut. 2005. 192p. (YA). (gr. 7). pap. 7.99 (978-0-618-55209-2(X) , Graphia) Houghton Mifflin Co. Trade & Reference Div.

TROUT

Winner, Cherie. Trout. Lehnhausen, Bud, photos by. 1998. (Nature Watch Ser.). (Illus.). 48p. (J). (gr. 3-6). lib. bdg. 25.26 (978-1-57505-245-8(8) , Carolrhoda Bks.) Lerner Publishing Group.

Woodward, John. Trout. 2004. (Nature's Children Ser.). (J). (978-0-7172-5976-2(5) , Grolier) Scholastic Library Publishing.

TROY (EXTINCT CITY)

Khanduri, Kamini, intro. & retold by. Tales of the Trojan War. Khanduri, Kamini, retold by. 2002. (Usborne Classics Ser.). (Illus.). 159p. (J). pap. (978-0-439-78708-6(4)) Scholastic, Inc.

Schlitz, Laura Amy. The Hero Schliemann: The Dreamer Who Dug up Troy. Byrd, Robert, illus. 2006. 80p. (J). (gr. 4-8). 17.99 (978-0-7636-2283-1(4)) Candlewick Pr.

TROY (EXTINCT CITY)—FICTION

Alexander, Lloyd. The Xanadu Adventure. 2007. (Vesper Holly Ser.). 160p. (YA). (gr. 5-9). 5.99 (978-0-14-240786-8(0) , Dutton Juvenile) Penguin Group (USA) Inc.

Colum, Padraic. Odysseus & the Tale of Troy. unabr. ed. 2002. (Classic Literature on CDs Ser.). (J). (gr. 4-8). pap. incl. audio compact disk (978-1-58472-298-4(3) , In Audio) Sound Room Pubs., Inc.

Gabrielson, Ernest & Gabrielson, Brian. Home in Ithaca: A novel of Ancient Greece & Troy. 2004. 120p. (YA). pap. 10.95 (978-0-595-30889-7(9)) iUniverse, Inc.

Geras, Adele. Troy. 2002. 376p. (YA). (gr. 9 up). pap. 6.95 (978-0-15-204570-8(8) , Harcourt Paperbacks) Harcourt Children's Bks.

—Troy. 2004. 368p. (J). (gr. 8 up). pap. 48.00 incl. audio (978-0-8072-2288-1(7) , Listening Library) Random Hse. Audio Publishing Group.

—Troy. 2002. (gr. 7-12). lib. bdg. 15.25 (978-0-613-55224-0(5)) Tandem Library Bks.

McLaren, Clemence. Inside the Walls of Troy: A Novel of the Women Who Lived the Trojan War. 2004. 199p. (YA). (gr. 6-10). reprint ed. 18.00 (978-0-7567-7986-3(3)) DIANE Publishing Co.

—Inside the Walls of Troy: A Novel of the Women Who Lived the Trojan War. 2004. 208p. (YA). pap. 5.99 (978-0-689-87397-3(2) , Simon Pulse) Simon & Schuster Children's Publishing.

—Inside the Walls of Troy: A Novel of the Women Who Lived the Trojan War. 1998. (J). 12.15 (978-0-606-13519-1(7)) Tandem Library Bks.

Tomlinson, Theresa. The Moon Riders. 2006. (Illus.). 400p. (J). 17.99 (978-0-06-084736-4(0)) ; lib. bdg. 18.89 (978-0-06-084737-1(9)) HarperCollins Pubs.

TRUANCY (SCHOOLS)

see School Attendance

TRUCK DRIVERS

Clinton, Susan. Tractor-Trailer-Truck Driver. 1998. (Careers Without College Ser.). (Illus.). 48p. (J). (gr. 3-7). pap. 19.00 (978-0-516-21289-0(3) , Children's Pr.) Scholastic Library Publishing.

Gibson, Karen Bush. Truck Drivers. 2000. (Community Helpers Ser.). (Illus.). 92p. (J). (gr. 1-2). 18.60 (978-0-7368-0625-1(3) , Bridgestone Bks.) Capstone Pr., Inc.

Liebman, Daniel. I Want to Be a Truck Driver. 2001. (I Want to Be Ser.). (Illus.). 24p. (J). (ps-2). pap. 3.99 (978-1-55209-574-4(6)) ; lib. bdg. 14.95 (978-1-55209-576-8(2)) Firefly Bks., Ltd.

—Quiero Ser Camionero. 2001. (Coleccion Quierno Ser.). (SPA., Illus.). 24p. (J). (ps-2). pap. 5.99 (978-1-55209-596-6(7) , AP30395) Firefly Bks., Ltd.

Miller, Heather. Camionero. 2003. (Esto es lo Que Quiero Ser (This Is What I Want to Be) Ser.).Tr. of Truck Driver. (SPA.). 24p. (J). pap. 5.25 (978-1-4034-3394-7(1)) ; (Illus.). lib. bdg. 18.50 (978-1-4034-0946-1(3)) Heinemann Library.

—Truck Driver. 2003. (This Is What I Want to Be Ser.). (Illus.). 24p. (J). lib. bdg. 18.50 (978-1-4034-0911-9(0)) ; pap. 5.25 (978-1-4034-3608-5(8)) Heinemann Library.

Schomp, Virginia. If You Were a Truck Driver. 2000. (If You Were A... Ser.). (Illus.). 32p. (J). (gr. 2-4). lib. bdg. 22.79 (978-0-7614-1003-4(1) , Benchmark Bks.) Cavendish, Marshall Corp.

Teitelbaum, Michael. If I Could Drive Tanker Truck. LaPadula, Tom & Courtney, Richard, illus. 2004. (Tonka Ser.). 24p. (J). pap. 3.50 (978-0-439-54835-9(7)) Scholastic, Inc.

Trumbauer, Lisa. What Does a Truck Driver Do? 2006. (What Does a Community Helper Do? Ser.). (Illus.). 24p. (J). lib. bdg. 21.26 (978-0-7660-2324-6(9) , Enslow Elementary) Enslow Pubs., Inc.

TRUCK DRIVERS—FICTION

Hamblen, Herbert A., III. Sewing the Rock upon the Path. 2002. 400p. (J). per. 12.95 (978-1-930648-33-3(2)) Goose River Pr.

London, Jonathan. My Big Rig. Garofoli, Viviana, illus. 2007. 32p. (J). (ps-3). 14.99 (***978-0-7614-5346-8(6)***) Cavendish, Marshall Corp.

—My Big Rig. Garofoli, Viviana, illus. 2007. (J). (***978-1-4287-3689-4(1)***) Cavendish, Marshall Corp.

Wellington, Monica. Truck Driver Tom. 2007. 32p. (J). (ps). 15.99 (***978-0-525-47831-7(0)*** , Dutton Juvenile) Penguin Group (USA) Inc.

TRUCK FARMING

see Vegetable Gardening

TRUCKS

Adair, Amy. Tonka Trucks. Kleven, Dean, illus. 2002. (J). (978-0-7853-7015-4(3)) Publications International, Ltd.

Alinas, Marv. Forklifts. 2008. (Machines at Work Ser.). 24p. (J). 22.79 (***978-1-59296-950-0(X)***) Child's World, Inc.

Anderson, Jenna. How It Happens at the Truck Plant. Wolfe, Bob & Wolfe, Diane, photos by. 2002. (How It Happens Ser.). (Illus.). 32p. (J). (gr. 2-5). lib. bdg. 19.95 (978-1-881508-93-9(5)) Oliver Pr., Inc.

Anderson, Jill, ed. Let's Get to Work!/Vamos a Trabajar! Evrard, Gaetan, illus. 2006. (ENG & SPA.). 20p. (J). (ps-k). bds. 6.95 (978-1-58728-512-7(6) , Two Can Publishing) T&N Children's Publishing.

Ardagh, Philip. All at Sea. (Mighty Machines Ser.). (Illus.). 32p. (J). lib. bdg. 24.25 (978-1-931983-04-4(6)) Chrysalis Education.

—On the Farm. (Mighty Machines Ser.). (Illus.). 32p. lib. bdg. 24.25 (978-1-931983-05-1(4)) Chrysalis Education.

Armentrout, David & Armentrout, Patricia, trs. Trucks. 2003. (Transportation Ser.). (Illus.). 24p. (J). 20.64 (978-1-58952-673-0(2)) Rourke Publishing, LLC.

Bailer, Darice. Demolish: (with demolition Machine) S. I. International Staff, illus. 2005. (Matchbox Ser.). 16p. (J). bds. 6.99 (978-0-689-87795-7(1) , Little Simon) Simon & Schuster Children's Publishing.

Baker, David. M1097 Humvee. 2007. (Fighting Forces on Land Ser.). (J). (978-1-60044-244-5(7)) Rourke Publishing, LLC.

Balaban, Mariah, ed. Trucks. 2007. (Tonka Ser.). (Illus.). 18p. (J). bds. 7.99 (978-0-439-89464-7(6)) Scholastic, Inc.

Balloon. Vroom Vroom: Work Vehicles. 1998. (J). 9.95 (978-0-8069-9557-1(2)) Sterling Publishing Co., Inc.

Barton, Byron. Trucks. Barton, Byron, illus. 1998. (Illus.). 16p. (J). (ps-k). bds. 6.99 (978-0-694-01164-3(9) , Harper Festival) HarperCollins Pubs.

Bender, Lionel. Trucks & Trailers. 2006. (J). (978-1-59389-270-8(5)) Chrysalis Education.

Bingham, Caroline. Truck-Mania! 2003. (Vehicle-Mania! Ser.). (Illus.). 32p. (J). (gr. 2 up). lib. bdg. 23.33 (978-0-8368-3785-8(1)) Stevens, Gareth Inc.

Bingham, Caroline & Dorling Kindersley Publishing Staff. Big Book of Trucks. 1999. (Illus.). 32p. (J). (gr. k-4). 14.95 (978-0-7894-4739-5(8)) Dorling Kindersley Publishing, Inc.

Bledsoe, Glen & Bledsoe, Karen. The World's Fastest Trucks. 2002. (Built for Speed Ser.). (Illus.). 48p. (J). (gr. 3-4). lib. bdg. 21.26 (978-0-7368-1062-3(5) , Capstone High-Interest Bks.) Capstone Pr., Inc.

Book Studio Staff. Cool Trucks. 2006. (Cool Kits Ser.). 1p. (J). 7.99 (978-0-7566-2430-9(4)) Dorling Kindersley Publishing, Inc.

Bradley, Michael. The Hummer. 2008. (J). (***978-0-7614-2981-4(6)***) Cavendish, Marshall Bks., Ltd.

Bridges, Sarah. I Drive a Dump Truck. Alderman, Derrick & Shea, Denise, illus. 2004. (Working Wheels Ser.). 24p. (C). (gr. k-2). 22.60 (978-1-4048-0614-6(8)) Picture Window Bks.

—I Drive a Garbage Truck. Alderman, Derrick & Shea, Denise, illus. 2004. (Working Wheels Ser.). 24p. (J). (gr. k-2). 22.60 (978-1-4048-0615-3(6)) Picture Window Bks.

—I Drive a Semitruck. Alderman, Derrick & Shea, Denise, illus. 2004. (Working Wheels Ser.). 24p. (C). (gr. k-2). 22.60 (978-1-4048-0616-0(4)) Picture Window Bks.

Brill, Marlene Targ. Garbage Trucks. 2005. (Pull Ahead Bks.). (Illus.). 32p. (J). (gr. k-2). lib. bdg. 22.60 (978-0-8225-1539-5(3)) Lerner Publishing Group.

Brooks, Felicity. Camiones. 2006. (Illus.). 12p. (J). bds. 9.99 (978-0-7460-7403-9(4) , Usborne) EDC Publishing.

Budd, E. S. Military Trucks. 2001. (Machines at Work Ser.). (Illus.). 24p. (J). (ps-3). 21.36 (978-1-56766-982-4(4)) Child's World, Inc.

Budd, E. S. Street Sweepers. 2008. (Machines at Work Ser.). 24p. (J). 22.79 (***978-1-59296-952-4(6)***) Child's World, Inc.

Burch, Lynda S. Wicky Wacky Things That Go! Trucks. Burch, Lynda S., photos by. 2004. (Illus.). 28p. (J). E-Book 9.95 incl. cd-rom (978-1-933090-11-5(1)) Guardian Angel Publishing, Inc.

Camiones Grandes (Big Rigs) 2006. (J). pap. 5.95 (978-0-8225-6647-2(8) , Ediciones Lerner) Lerner Publishing Group.

Camionetas Gigantes (Monster Trucks) 2006. (J). 22.60 (978-0-8225-6227-6(8)) ; pap. 5.95 (978-0-8225-6646-5(X)) Lerner Publishing Group. (Ediciones Lerner).

Camionetas (Pickup Trucks) 2006. (J). pap. 5.95 (978-0-8225-6642-7(7) , Ediciones Lerner) Lerner Publishing Group.

Cars & Trucks. Date not set. (Illus.). (J). bds. 9.98 (978-0-7525-9892-5(9)) Parragon, Inc.

Castor, Harriet. Trucks. rev. ed. 2004. 32p. (J). pap. 6.95 (978-0-7945-0839-5(1) , Usborne) EDC Publishing.

Caterpillar. Look at Me! My Photo Book of Big Trucks & Diggers. 2005. (Illus.). 20p. (J). 6.95 (978-0-8118-4751-3(9)) Chronicle Bks. LLC.

Caterpillar Inc. Staff. Big Noisy Trucks & Diggers Demolition. 2004. (Illus.). 14p. (J). 12.95 (978-0-8118-4262-4(2)) Chronicle Bks. LLC.

Caterpillar Inc. Staff, contrib. by. C Is for Construction: Big Trucks & Diggers from A to Z. 2003. (Illus.). 32p. (J). 12.95 (978-0-8118-4028-6(X)) Chronicle Bks. LLC.

—Drawing Trucks & Diggers: A Book of 10 Stencils. 2001. (Illus.). 30p. (J). (gr. k up). 9.95 (978-0-8118-3174-1(4)) Chronicle Bks. LLC.

Collicutt, Paul. This Truck. 2004. (Illus.). 32p. (J). 15.00 (978-0-374-37496-9(1) , Farrar, Straus & Giroux (BYR)) Farrar, Straus & Giroux.

Collings, Julie & Klutz Editors. Rescue Trucks. 2005. (Illus.). 22p. (J). (ps-3). spiral bd. 12.95 (978-1-59174-089-6(4)) Klutz.

Construction Trucks. 2004. (Mega MacHines Ser.). (Illus.). 16p. (J). (978-2-7643-0198-2(7)) Phidal Publishing, Inc./Editions Phidal, Inc.

Coppendale, Jean. Trucks. 2007. (J). lib. bdg. 16.95 (***978-1-59566-339-9(8)***) QEB Publishing Inc.

Dalmatian Press Staff. Disney Mickey's BK of Trucks. 2006. 10p. bds. 5.99 (978-1-4037-1938-6(1)) Dalmatian Pr.

Daynes, Katie. Trucks. 2004. (Beginners Ser.). 32p. (J). (gr. 1 up). pap. 4.95 (978-0-7945-0365-9(9)) ; lib. bdg. 12.95 (978-1-58086-511-1(9)) EDC Publishing.

Daynes, Katie. Trucks - Internet Referenced (Level 1) 2007. 32p. (J). 4.99 (***978-0-7945-1657-4(2)*** , Usborne) EDC Publishing.

DeGezelle, Terri. Street Sweepers. 2006. (Pebble Plus Ser.). (Illus.). 24p. (J). (978-0-7368-5358-3(8)) Capstone Pr., Inc.

DK Publishing. Trucks. 2008. 14p. (J). 5.99 (***978-0-7566-3465-0(2)***) Dorling Kindersley Publishing, Inc.

DK Publishing Staff. Construction Vehicles: Dump Truck. 2007. 10p. (J). bds. 9.99 (978-0-7566-2723-2(0)) Dorling Kindersley Publishing, Inc.

—My Big Machine Book. 1999. (Big Tab Board Books Ser.). (Illus.). 8p. (J). (ps-3). bds. 9.99 (978-0-7894-4326-7(0)) Dorling Kindersley Publishing, Inc.

—Trucks & Diggers. 2007. (Let's Look Ser.). (Illus.). 36p. (J). 4.99 (978-0-7566-2595-5(5)) Dorling Kindersley Publishing, Inc.

Doeden, Matt. Camiones con Trailer. 2007. (SPA & ENG.). (J). (***978-0-7368-7644-5(8)***) Capstone Publishing.

—Camionetas Monster Trucks. 2007. (ENG & SPA.). (978-0-7368-6636-1(1)) Capstone Pr., Inc.

—Humvees. 2008. (J). (***978-1-4296-0030-9(6)*** , Pebble Bks.) Capstone Pr., Inc.

Doeden, Matt. Monster Trucks. 2004. (Horsepower Ser.). (Illus.). 32p. (J). lib. bdg. 19.93 (978-0-7368-2732-4(3)) Capstone Pr., Inc.

—Monster Trucks. 2007. (J). lib. bdg. (978-0-8225-6567-3(6) , Lerner Pubs.) Lerner Publishing Group.

Dorling Kindersley Publishing Staff. Action Truck. 2006. 8p. (J). bds. 7.99 (978-0-7566-1116-3(4)) Dorling Kindersley Publishing, Inc.

—Airborne Ranger. 2003. (Wheelies Ser.). (Illus.). 12p. (J). pap. 6.99 (978-0-7894-9934-9(7)) Dorling Kindersley Publishing, Inc.

—Big Dump Truck. 2003. (Wheelies Ser.). (Illus.). 12p. (J). bds. 6.99 (978-0-7894-9714-7(X)) Dorling Kindersley Publishing, Inc.

—Big Rig. 2000. (978-0-606-17798-6(1)) Tandem Library Bks.

—Chunky, Bumpy, Dumpy Trucks. 2006. (Touchables Ser.). 14p. (J). bds. 8.99 (978-0-7566-2019-6(8)) Dorling Kindersley Publishing, Inc.

—Dump Truck. Deschamps, Nicola, ed. Leeney, Richard, photos by. 2000. (Jumbo Shaped Board Books Ser.). (Illus.). 12p. (J). (ps-k). bds. 6.99 (978-0-7894-6532-0(9)) Dorling Kindersley Publishing, Inc.

—Dump Truck. 1998. (Wheelies Ser.). (Illus.). 10p. (J). bds. 5.99 (978-0-7894-3710-5(4)) Dorling Kindersley Publishing, Inc.

—Fire Truck. 2006. (Machines at Work Ser.). 32p. (J). pap. 6.99 (978-0-7566-1908-4(4)) Dorling Kindersley Publishing, Inc.

—Maquinas Grandes. 2003. (DK Readers Ser.). (SPA., Illus.). 48p. (J). pap. 3.99 (978-0-7894-9518-1(X)) Dorling Kindersley Publishing, Inc.

—My First Spanish Truck Board Book / Mi Primer Libro de Camoines en Espanol. 2002. (ENG & SPA., Illus.). 36p. (J). (ps-1). bds. 6.99 (978-0-7894-8592-2(3)) Dorling Kindersley Publishing, Inc.

—My First Truck. 2003. (My First Sticker Board Bks.). (Illus.). 12p. (J). pap. 6.99 (978-0-7894-9246-3(6)) Dorling Kindersley Publishing, Inc.

—Noisy Trucks. 2005. (Baby Fun Ser.). (Illus.). 14p. (J). (ps-ps). bds. 4.99 (978-0-7566-0988-7(7)) Dorling Kindersley Publishing, Inc.

—Prowler. 2003. (Wheelies Ser.). (Illus.). 12p. (J). bds. 6.99 (978-0-7894-9873-1(1)) Dorling Kindersley Publishing, Inc.

—Reptoid. 2003. (Wheelies Ser.). (Illus.). 12p. (J). bds. 6.99 (978-0-7894-9875-5(8)) Dorling Kindersley Publishing, Inc.

—Truck. (Machines at Work Ser.). (J). 2006. (Illus.). 32p. (gr. 5). 6.99 (978-0-7566-2267-1(0)); 2004. 36p. bds. 5.99 (978-0-7894-9904-2(5)); 2000. (Illus.). 24p. (gr. k-3). pap. 5.99 (978-0-7894-6072-1(6)) Dorling Kindersley Publishing, Inc.

—Truck. 2000. (978-0-606-17816-7(3)) Tandem Library Bks.

—Trucks. 2003. (Dk Picture Stickers Ser.). (Illus.). 16p. (J). pap. 3.99 (978-0-7894-9827-4(8)) Dorling Kindersley Publishing, Inc.

—What's Inside Trucks? 1999. (978-0-606-18120-4(2)) Tandem Library Bks.

Dorling Kindersley Publishing Staff, ed. Truck. 2004. (Ultimate Sticker Bks.). 16p. (J). pap. 6.99 (978-0-7566-0239-0(4)) Dorling Kindersley Publishing, Inc.

Dorling Kindersley Publishing Staff & Millard, Anne. My First Truck Bath Book. 2002. (My First Ser.). (Illus.). 10p. (J). (ps-k). 5.95 (978-0-7894-8525-0(7)) Dorling Kindersley Publishing, Inc.

Dorling Kindersley Publishing Staff, et al. Monster Machines. 1998. (Illus.). 32p. (J). (ps-3). 14.99 (978-0-7894-2796-0(6)) Dorling Kindersley Publishing, Inc.

Draw 50 Boats, Ships, Trucks & Trains. 2002. (Draw 50 Ser.). (Illus.). (J). 17.60 (978-0-7587-6968-8(7)) Book Wholesalers, Inc.

Dussling, Jennifer. Construction Trucks. Courtney, illus. 1998. (All Aboard Bks.). 32p. (J). (ps-3). pap. 3.99 (978-0-448-41885-8(1) , Grosset & Dunlap) Penguin Group (USA) Inc.

—Construction Trucks. 1998. (gr. k-3). lib. bdg. 11.25 (978-0-613-72421-0(6)) Tandem Library Bks.

Emberley, Ed. Ed Emberley's Drawing Book of Trucks & Trains. Emberley, Ed, illus. 2005. (Illus.). 32p. (J). (gr. 2-17). pap. 6.99 (978-0-316-78967-7(4)) Little, Brown Bks. for Young Readers.

Foster, Walter, ed. Cars & Trucks: Step by Step Instructions for 28 Different Vehicles. Shelly, Jeff, illus. 2004. (Draw & Color Ser.). 40p. pap. 4.95 (978-1-56010-819-1(3)) Foster, Walter Publishing, Inc.

Franks, Pete. Ice Cream: (With Sundae Driver) S. I. International Staff, illus. 2005. (Matchbox Ser.). 16p. (J). bds. 6.99 (978-1-4169-0253-9(8) , Little Simon) Simon & Schuster Children's Publishing.

Gibbs, Lynne. Mega Book of Trucks: Discover the Most Amazing Trucks on Earth! 2003. (Illus.). 32p. (YA). pap. (978-1-904516-21-7(1)) Chrysalis Children's Bks.

Gilpin, Rebecca. How to Draw Trucks & Tractors. 2005. 34p. (J). pap. 8.95 (978-0-7945-1134-0(1) , Usborne) EDC Publishing.

Glover, David & Glover, Penny. Trucks. 2005. (Big Machines Ser.). (Illus.). 30p. (J). (gr. 2-5). lib. bdg. 27.10 (978-1-58340-702-8(2)) Smart Apple Media.

Goldsack, Gabby. Trucks & Earthmovers. 2003. (Busy Books). (Illus.). 32p. (J). 9.95 (978-1-57768-901-0(1) , Waterbird Bks.) School Specialty Publishing.

Graham, Ian. Super Trucks. Bergin, Mark & Hewetson, Nicholas, illus. 2001. (Fast Forward Ser.). 32p. (J). (gr. 4-8). 29.00 (978-0-531-14618-7(9)) ; pap. 9.95 (978-0-531-14810-5(6)) Scholastic Library Publishing. (Watts, Franklin).

—Super Trucks. 2001. (gr. 3-6). lib. bdg. 18.75 (978-0-613-54695-9(4)) Tandem Library Bks.

—Trucks. 2007. (J). (***978-1-59920-043-9(0)***) Smart Apple Media.

Graham, Ian. Trucks & Earthmovers. 2005. (World's Greatest Ser.). (Illus.). 32p. (978-1-4109-2088-1(7)) ; pap. (978-1-4109-2095-9(X)) Steck-Vaughn.

Griffin, Georgene. Monster Trucks. 2001. (How to Draw Ser.). (Illus.). 32p. (J). (gr. 2-5). lib. bdg. 25.27 (978-1-58952-155-1(2)) Rourke Publishing, LLC.

Haldane, Elizabeth. Truck. 2005. (Machines at Work Ser.). (Illus.). 32p. 8.99 (978-0-7566-1142-2(3) , 1241931) Dorling Kindersley Publishing, Inc.

Hall, Kirsten. Tonka. Redondo, Jesus, illus. 2002. (Tonka Ser.). 12p. (J). pap. 8.99 (978-0-439-42518-6(2)) Scholastic, Inc.

Hankin, Rosie. Cut & Paste Trucks, Trains, & Big Machines. 2006. (Illus.). 32p. lib. bdg. (***978-0-8368-7721-2(7)***) Stevens, Gareth Inc.

Hanson, Anders. Let's Go by Truck. 2007. (Let's Go! Ser.). (ENG., Illus.). 24p. (J). (ps-3). lib. bdg. 19.93 (***978-1-59928-904-5(0)*** , SandCastle) ABDO Publishing Co.

Hart, Simon. Vamos, Vamos, Camiones! 2006. 10p. (J). (ps-ps). bds. 4.99 (978-0-8431-2108-7(4) , Price Stern Sloan) Penguin Group (USA) Inc.

Healy, Nick. High Mobility Vehicles: The Humvees. 2005. (War Machines Ser.). (Illus.). 32p. (J). 22.60 (978-0-7368-3778-1(7)) Capstone Pr., Inc.

Helbrough, Emma & Brooks, Felicity. First Picture Trucks. 2007. 16p. (J). bds. 11.99 (978-0-7945-1454-9(5) , Usborne) EDC Publishing.

Hickle, Victoria. Construction Action. 2007. (Tonka Power Reading Ser.: No. 1). 32p. (J). pap. 3.99 (***978-0-439-88481-5(0)***) Scholastic, Inc.

—Tonka Big Trucks in Action. Depew, Bob, illus. 2004. (Tonka Ser.). 4p. (J). bds. 7.99 (978-0-439-63920-0(4)) Scholastic, Inc.

—Tonka Construction Time: Book & Magnet Fun. Klavins, Uldis, illus. 2002. (Tonka Ser.). 8p. (J). bds. 7.99 (978-0-439-33474-7(8)) Scholastic, Inc.

HOP, LLC. Hooked on Trucks Super Activity Kit. 2006. (J). (ps). 9.99 (978-1-933863-18-4(8)) HOP, LLC.

Horne, Jane. Tractors & Trucks. 2006. (Touch & Learn (Make Believe Ideas) Ser.). (Illus.). 12p. (ps). per., bds. 6.95 (978-1-84610-279-0(0)) ; per., bds. 6.95 (978-1-84610-276-9(6)) Make Believe Ideas GBR. *Dist:* Ingram Pub. Services.

Horowitz, Jordan, et al. Working Hard with Tonka Trucks! Petruccio, Steven James, illus. 2002. (J). (978-0-439-44528-3(0)) Scholastic, Inc.

Hot Animation Staff, Animation & Redmond, Diane. El Cumpleaños de Bob. Ziegler, Argentina Palacios, tr. 2004. (Bob the Builder Ser.).Tr. of Bob's Birthday. (SPA., Illus.). 24p. (J). 3.99 (978-0-689-86975-4(4)) Simon & Schuster Children's Publishing.

Hughes, Monica. Busy Trucks. 2006. (I Love Reading Ser.). (Illus.). 24p. (J). lib. bdg. 19.96 (978-1-59716-150-3(0)) Bearport Publishing Co., Inc.

Jango-Cohen, Judith. Dump Trucks. 2003. (Pull Ahead Bks.). (Illus.). 32p. (J). (gr. k-2). pap. 5.95 (978-0-8225-0602-7(5)); lib. bdg. 22.60 (978-0-8225-0688-1(2)) Lerner Publishing Group.

—Dump Trucks. Jango-Cohen, Judith & Cohen, Eliot, photos by. 2003. (Illus.). 32p. (J). (ps-3). lib. bdg. 14.10 (978-0-613-52362-2(8)) Tandem Library Bks.

Jefferis. Trucks. 2003. mass mkt. 48.30 (978-1-4109-0279-5(X)) Raintree.

Jefferis, David. Trucks. 2001. (Monster Machines Ser.). (Illus.). 32p. (J). (ps-3). lib. bdg. 25.69 (978-0-7398-2879-3(7)) Raintree.

—Trucks. 2003. (gr. 3-6). lib. bdg. 16.40 (978-0-613-78224-1(0)) Tandem Library Bks.

Jeffries. Trucks. 2003. (Monster Machines Ser.). (Illus.). 32p. (J). pap. 7.95 (978-1-4109-0060-9(6)) Raintree.

Johnson, Earl L. The World's Greatest Tow Trucks, Vol. 4. Hawkins, Grace M., ed. 1998. (Illus.). 118p. (J). pap. 19.95 (978-0-9649645-5-6(4)) Lotus Publications.

—The World's Greatest Tow Trucks Vol. 5: The Best of the Millennium. Hawkins, Grace M., ed. 2001. (Illus.). 108p. (gr. 9-12). pap. 19.95 (978-0-9649645-9-4(7)) Lotus Publications.

—The World's Greatest Working Trucks Vol. 4: The Best of the Pacific Northwest. Hawkins, Grace M., ed. 2002. (Illus.). 100p. (YA). (gr. 9-12). pap. 19.95 (978-0-9649645-8-7(9)) Lotus Publications.

Johnson, Earl L. & Hawkins, Grace. The World's Greatest Working Trucks Vol. 5: The Best of the Northeast. 2003. 100p. (Orig.). (YA). (gr. 8-12). pap. 19.95 (978-0-9649645-1-8(1)) Lotus Publications.

Johnstone, Michael. Monster Trucks. 2005. (Need for Speed Ser.). (Illus.). 32p. (gr. 3-5). lib. bdg. 23.93 (978-0-8225-0388-0(3)) Lerner Publishing Group.

—Monster Trucks. 2002. (gr. 5-8). lib. bdg. 16.40 (978-0-613-46153-5(3)) Tandem Library Bks.

Kaelberer, Angie Peterson. U.S. Army Humvees. 2007. (Blazers—Military Vehicles Ser.). (Illus.). 32p. (J). 19.93 (978-0-7368-6458-9(X)) Capstone Pr., Inc.

Kalman, Bobbie & Miller, Reagan. Tough Trucks. 2007. (Vehicles on the Move Ser.). (Illus.). 32p. (J). (gr. 1-5). (*978-0-7787-3044-6(1)); pap. (*978-0-7787-3058-3(1)) Crabtree Publishing Co.

Kilby, Don. At a Construction Site. 2003. (Wheels at Work Ser.). (Illus.). 24p. (J). (ps-k). (978-1-55337-378-0(2)); (978-1-55337-044-4(9)) Kids Can Pr., Ltd.

—At A Construction Site. Kilby, Don, illus. 2006. 24p. (978-1-55337-987-4(X)) Kids Can Pr., Ltd.

—In the City. Kilby, Don, illus. 2006. (Illus.). 24p. (978-1-55337-984-3(5)) Kids Can Pr., Ltd.

—In the City. 2005. (Wheels at Work Ser.). (Illus.). 24p. (J). (ps-2). (978-1-55337-471-8(1)) Kids Can Pr., Ltd.

—On the Road. Kilby, Don, illus. 2006. 24p. (978-1-55337-986-7(1)) Kids Can Pr., Ltd.

—On the Road. 2003. (Wheels at Work Ser.). (Illus.). 24p. (J). (ps-k). (978-1-55337-043-7(0)); (978-1-55337-379-7(0)) Kids Can Pr., Ltd.

Kirk, Ellen. My Truck Book. 2006. 16p. (J). 5.99 (978-0-06-089942-4(5)) HarperCollins Pubs.

Klove, Lars. Trucks That Build. 1999. (Ready-to-Read Ser.). (J). (978-0-606-19731-1(1)) Tandem Library Bks.

Korman, Justine. Tonka Building the Skyscraper. 1999. (ps-2). lib. bdg. 11.25 (978-0-613-72020-5(2)) Tandem Library Bks.

LaFontaine, Bruce. Construction Trucks Stickers. 2000. (Illus.). 4p. (J). (ps-5). 1.50 (978-0-486-40973-3(2)) Dover Pubns., Inc.

Latham, Donna. Superfast Trucks. 2006. (Ultimate Speed Ser.). (Illus.). 32p. (J). lib. bdg. 25.27 (978-1-59716-253-1(1)) Bearport Publishing Co., Inc.

Lego Staff. Cool Cars. 2000. (LEGO Creator Brick Tricks Ser.). (Illus.). 24p. (J). spiral bd. 7.99 (978-1-903276-09-9(8)) Lego Media International, Inc.

Leonard, Barry, ed. Drawing Trucks & Diggers: A Book of 10 Stencils. 2004. (Illus.). 34p. (J). (gr. k-4). reprint ed. ring bd. 10.00 (978-0-7567-8505-5(7)) DIANE Publishing Co.

Levete. Monster Trucks. 2004. (Mean Machines Ser.). (Illus.). 64p. (J). pap. 8.95 (978-1-4109-1197-1(7)) Harcourt Schl. Pubs.

—Monster Trucks 6-Pack. 2004. (Mean Machines Ser.). (Illus.). (J). pap. 48.30 (978-1-4109-1202-2(7)) Harcourt Schl. Pubs.

Levete, Sarah. Monster Trucks. 2004. (Mean Machines Ser.). (Illus.). 64p. (J). 32.79 (978-1-4109-1082-0(2)) Harcourt Schl. Pubs.

Lindeen, Mary. Garbage Trucks. 2007. (Illus.). 24p. (J). lib. bdg. 19.95 (978-1-60014-117-1(X)) Bellwether Media.

—Trucks. 2007. (Blastoff! Readers Ser.). (Illus.). 24p. (J). (gr. k-3). lib. bdg. 16.95 (978-1-60014-063-1(7)) Bellwether Media.

—Trucks. 2007. (Blastoff! Readers Ser.). 24p. (J). (gr. k-2). 18.50 (*978-0-531-17561-3(8) , Children's Pr.) Scholastic Library Publishing.

Litchfield, Jo & Brooks, F. Trucks. 2004. (Chunky Board Bks.). (Illus.). 10p. (J). 4.95 (978-0-7945-0349-9(7) , Usborne) EDC Publishing.

Longhurst, Terry. I Can Draw Cars & Trucks. 2002. (I Can Draw Ser.). 32p. (J). 9.95 (978-0-7525-7282-6(2)) Parragon, Inc.

Maass, Robert. Little Trucks with Big Jobs. rev. ed. 2007. (Illus.). 32p. (J). (ps-2). 16.95 (*978-0-8050-7748-3(0)) Holt, Henry & Co.

Make Believe Ideas Staff, creator. Tractors & Trucks: Sticker Activity Book. 2005. (Lift Stick & Learn Ser.). (Illus.). 12p. (J). (ps-3). 4.95 (978-1-905051-67-0(0)) Make Believe Ideas GBR. *Dist:* Ingram Pub. Services.

Maurer, Tracy. Hummer. 2007. (Illus.). 32p. (J). (978-1-60044-222-3(6)) Rourke Publishing, LLC.

—Land Rover. 2007. (J). (978-1-60044-225-4(0)) Rourke Publishing, LLC.

—Monster Trucks. 2002. (Roaring Rides Ser.). (Illus.). 48p. (gr. 1-4). 20.95 (978-1-58952-749-2(6)) Rourke Publishing, LLC.

—4 X 4 Desert Trucks. 2003. (Illus.). 48p. (J). 29.93 (978-1-58952-746-1(1)) Rourke Publishing, LLC.

McAuliffe, Bill. Off-Road Truck Racing. 1998. (MotorSports Ser.). (Illus.). 48p. (J). (gr. 3-4). lib. bdg. 21.26 (978-0-7368-0026-6(3) , Capstone High-Interest Bks.) Capstone Pr., Inc.

McClellan, Ray. Dump Trucks. 2006. (Blastoff! Readers Ser.). (Illus.). 24p. (J). lib. bdg. 16.95 (978-1-60014-046-4(7)) Bellwether Media.

Mead, Sue. Monster Trucks & Tractors. (Race Car Legends Ser.). (Illus.). 1999. 64p. (YA). (ps up). 28.00 (978-0-7910-5021-7(1)); 2005. 77p. (J). (gr. 4-8). lib. bdg. 25.00 (978-0-7910-8689-6(5)) Facts On File, Inc. (Chelsea Hse.).

Mezzanotte, Jim. Camiones Basculantes. 2006. (Vehiculos Gigantes (Giant Vehicles) Ser.). (SPA.). 24p. (J). pap. 5.95 (978-0-8368-5992-8(8)); lib. bdg. 22.00 (978-0-8368-5985-0(5)) Stevens, Gareth Inc.

—Giant Dump Trucks. 2005. (Illus.). 24p. (J). pap. (978-0-8368-4919-6(1)); lib. bdg. 22.00 (978-0-8368-4912-7(4)) Stevens, Gareth Inc.

Mighty Movers. 2005. (J). (gr. k-4). lib. bdg. 128.10 (978-1-59197-824-4(6)) ABDO Publishing Co.

Milton, Joyce. Heavy Duty Trucks. Courtney, Richard, illus. 2000. (Step into Reading Ser.: Vol. 3). 48p. (J). (gr. 1-3). pap. 3.99 (978-0-679-88130-8(1) , Random Hse. Bks. for Young Readers) Random Hse. Children's Bks.

—Heavy Duty Trucks. 2000. (Step into Reading Ser.). (Illus.). (J). 10.79 (978-0-606-18496-0(1)) Tandem Library Bks.

—Heavy-Duty Trucks. 2000. (gr. k-3). lib. bdg. 11.80 (978-0-613-21690-6(3)) Tandem Library Bks.

Mitchell, Joyce Slayton. Tractor-Trailer Trucker: A Powerful Truck Book. Borns, Steven, photos by. 2004. (Illus.). 40p. (YA). (gr. 2-5). 14.95 (978-1-58246-010-9(8) , Tricycle Pr.) Ten Speed Pr.

Mitton, Tony. Tough Trucks. Parker, Ant, illus. 2003. (Amazing Machines Ser.). 24p. (J). (ps-k). tchr. ed. 9.95 (978-0-7534-5600-2(1) , Kingfisher) Houghton Mifflin Co. Trade & Reference Div.

Molzahn, Arlene Bourgeois. Trucks & Big Rigs. 2003. (Transportation & Communication Ser.). (Illus.). 48p. (J). lib. bdg. 23.93 (978-0-7660-2024-5(X)) Enslow Pubs., Inc.

Monroe, Debra. Little Tikes (r) Trucks: Pretend Play Book. 2002. (Little Tikes Ser.). (Illus.). 10p. (J). (ps up). bds. 4.99 (978-1-57151-598-8(4)) Playhouse Publishing.

Monster Trucks. (Horsepower Ser.). 32p. (YA). 7.95 (978-0-7368-5218-0(2)) Capstone Pr., Inc.

Monster Trucks, 6 vols. (gr. 4 up). 39.95 (978-0-7368-9292-6(3)) Red Brick Learning.

Moore, Patrick. The Mighty Street Sweeper. 2006. (Illus.). 32p. (J). 15.95 (978-0-8050-7789-6(8)) Holt, Henry & Co.

Morganelli, Adrianna. Trucks: Pickups to Big Rigs. 2007. (Illus.). 32p. (J). (gr. 2-9). (*978-0-7787-3015-6(8)); pap. (*978-0-7787-3037-8(9)) Crabtree Publishing Co.

Nelson, Kristen. Monster Trucks. 2003. (gr. k-3). lib. bdg. 14.10 (978-0-613-52447-6(0)) Tandem Library Bks.

Oxlade, Chris. This Is My Dump Truck. 2007. (*978-1-59771-105-0(5)) Sea-To-Sea Pubns.

Oxlade, Chris. Trucks. (Transportation Around the World Ser.). 32p. pap. 6.95 (978-1-4034-4136-2(7)); 2001. (Illus.). (J). lib. bdg. 21.36 (978-1-57572-308-2(5)) Heinemann Library.

—Trucks. 2006. (Mighty Machines Ser.). (Illus.). 31p. (J). (978-1-58340-920-6(3) , 1262378) Smart Apple Media.

Page, Josephine. I Am a Dump Truck. Bryan, Beth, ed. 2007. (J). bds. 4.99 (978-0-439-91617-2(8) , Cartwheel Bks.) Scholastic, Inc.

Parker, Steve. The HMMWV Humvee. 2008. (J). (*978-1-4296-0093-4(4)) Capstone Pr., Inc.

Pearcey, Alice. Tractors & Trucks Stencil Book. Tudor, Andy, illus. 2006. 14p. (J). bds. 12.99 (978-0-7945-1139-5(2) , Usborne) EDC Publishing.

Pearson, Debora. Hard Working Wheels. McLeod, Chum, illus. 2000. (Mighty Wheels Ser.). 24p. (J). (gr. k-ps). pap. 5.95 (978-1-55037-614-2(4)); lib. bdg. 15.95 (978-1-55037-615-9(2)) Annick Pr., Ltd. CAN. *Dist:* Firefly Bks., Ltd.

—Hard Working Wheels. 2000. (Illus.). (J). (978-0-606-18137-2(7)) Tandem Library Bks.

—Load 'em up Trucks. McLeod, Chum, illus. 1999. (Mighty Wheels Ser.). 24p. (J). (gr. k-ps). pap. 5.95 (978-1-55037-592-3(X)) Annick Pr., Ltd. CAN. *Dist:* Firefly Bks., Ltd.

—Load 'Em up Trucks. McLeod, Chum, illus. 1999. (Mighty Wheels Ser.). 24p. (J). (gr. k-ps). lib. bdg. 15.95 (978-1-55037-593-0(8)) Annick Pr., Ltd. CAN. *Dist:* Firefly Bks., Ltd.

Perez, Jessica. Under Construction: A Moving Track Book. Schneider, Christine, illus. 2005. 12p. (J). 12.95 (978-1-58117-272-0(9) , Intervisual/Piggy Toes) Dalmatian Pr.

Piehl, Janet. Humvees. 2005. 32p. (J). pap. 5.95 (978-0-8225-2874-6(6) , Lerner Pubns.) Lerner Publishing Group.

Pipe, Jim. Trucks. 2006. (Illus.). 24p. (J). (978-1-59604-117-2(X)) Stargazer Bks.

Playskool Staff. My Big Truck Steering Wheel. 1999. (Illus.). 8p. pap. 8.99 (978-0-525-46016-9(0) , Dutton Juvenile) Penguin Group (USA) Inc.

Poolos, Jamie. Monster Trucks. 2008. (J). lib. bdg. (*978-1-4042-3791-9(7) , PowerKids Pr.) Rosen Publishing Group, Inc., The.

Priddy, Roger. I Love Trucks Sticker Book. 2007. 20p. (J). pap. 3.95 (*978-0-312-49961-7(2) , Priddy Bks.) St. Martin's Pr.

—My Big Truck Book. rev. ed. 2002. (Illus.). 12p. (J). bds. 5.95 (978-0-312-49085-0(2) , Priddy Bks.) St. Martin's Pr.

—Slide & Find - Trucks. 2007. 10p. (J). bds. 6.95 (978-0-312-49909-9(4) , Priddy Bks.) St. Martin's Pr.

—Tough Trucks. 2005. (Sticker Activity Fun Workbooks). (Illus.). 48p. (J). pap. 3.47 (978-0-312-49666-1(4) , Priddy Bks.) St. Martin's Pr.

—Trucks. 2005. (Bright Baby Ser.). 12p. (J). bds. 0.97 (978-0-312-49624-1(9) , Priddy Bks.) St. Martin's Pr.

—Trucks. rev. ed. 2004. (Bright Baby Ser.). (Illus.). 26p. (J). bds. 4.95 (978-0-312-49389-9(4) , Priddy Bks.) St. Martin's Pr.

—Trucks, Bugs, Dinosaurs. 2006. 132p. (J). act. bk. ed. 12.95 (978-0-312-49741-5(5) , Priddy Bks.) St. Martin's Pr.

—3 in 1: My Big Truck, Train, Rescue. 2005. (J). bds. 16.95 (978-0-312-49561-9(7) , Priddy Bks.) St. Martin's Pr.

Priddy, Roger & Millard, Anne. Baby's Book of Trucks. 2001. (Illus.). 24p. (J). (ps-k). bds. 9.95 (978-0-7894-6795-9(X)) Dorling Kindersley Publishing, Inc.

Priddy, Roger & Priddy Books Staff. Sticker Activity Fun Tough Trucks: Play & Learn. rev. ed. 2006. 48p. (J). bds. 3.47 (978-0-312-49800-9(4) , Priddy Bks.) St. Martin's Pr.

Ramsden, Julie & Ramsden, Michael. Autos with Attitude. 2005. (X-Zone Ser.). (Illus.). 30p. (gr. 4-8). 23.00 (978-0-7910-8977-4(0)) Facts On File, Inc.

Randolph, Joanne. Dump Trucks. 2002. (PowerKids Readers Ser.). (Illus.). 24p. (J). (gr. 1). lib. bdg. 16.00 (978-0-8239-6027-9(7) , PowerKids Pr.) Rosen Publishing Group, Inc., The.

Random House Staff. Trains, Cranes, & Troublesome Trucks. 2002. 32p. (J). pap. 3.99 (978-0-375-81249-1(0)) Random Hse. Children's Bks.

Relf, Patricia. Look Inside Trucks. LaPadula, Tom, illus. 1999. (Tonka Ser.). 5p. (J). (ps). pap. 9.95 (978-0-439-05020-3(0) , Cartwheel Bks.) Scholastic, Inc.

—Tonka Trucks Night & Day. LaPadula, Tom, illus. 2000. (Tonka Ser.). 35p. (J). (ps-2). pap. 12.95 (978-0-439-12196-5(5) , Cartwheel Bks.) Scholastic, Inc.

Richardson, Adele D. Delivery Trucks. 2000. (Transportation Library). (Illus.). 24p. (J). (gr. 1-2). lib. bdg. 18.60 (978-0-7368-0609-1(1) , Bridgestone Bks.) Capstone Pr., Inc.

Roberts, Cynthia. Dump Trucks. 2007. (Machines at Work Ser.). 24p. (J). 22.79 (978-1-59296-830-5(9)) Child's World, Inc.

—Tow Trucks. 2007. (Machines at Work Ser.). 24p. (J). (gr. 2-4). 22.79 (978-1-59296-836-7(8)) Child's World, Inc.

Royston, Angela. Truck Trouble. 1998. (Eyewitness Readers Ser.). (Illus.). 32p. (J). (gr. 5-1). pap. 3.99 (978-0-7894-2958-2(6)) Dorling Kindersley Publishing, Inc.

Running Press Staff. Trucks. 7th ed. 2000. (Fit-a-Shape Ser.). (Illus.). 10p. (J). (ps-k). pap. 6.95 (978-0-7624-0813-9(8) , Running Pr. Kids) Running Pr. Bk. Pubs.

Rustad, Martha E. H. Semitrucks. 2008. (J). (*978-1-4296-0827-5(7)) Capstone Publishing.

Saunders-Smith, Gail. Trucks. 1998. (J). pap. 13.25 (978-0-516-21227-2(3) , Children's Pr.) Scholastic Library Publishing.

Sautter, Aaron. How to Draw Monster Trucks. Bascle, Brian, illus. 2008. (J). (*978-1-4296-0079-8(9)) Capstone Pr., Inc.

Savage, Jeff. Monster Truck Wars. 2000. (Motorsports Ser.). (Illus.). 48p. (J). (gr. 3-6). lib. bdg. 19.00 (978-0-516-35258-9(X) , Children's Pr.) Scholastic Library Publishing.

—The World's Fastest Pro Stock Trucks. 2003. (Built for Speed Ser.). (Illus.). 48p. (J). (gr. 3-4). lib. bdg. 21.26 (978-0-7368-1502-4(3) , Capstone High-Interest Bks.) Capstone Pr., Inc.

Scarry, Richard. Cars & Trucks & Things That Go. 1998. (Richard Scarry's Ser.). (Illus.). 72p. (J). (ps-3). 14.99 (978-0-307-15785-0(7) , 15785, Golden Bks.) Random Hse. Children's Bks.

Schaefer, A. R. Monster Trucks. (Wild Rides! Ser.). 32p. (YA). pap. 7.95 (978-0-7368-9194-3(3)) Capstone Pr., Inc.

—Monster Trucks. 2001. (Wild Rides! Ser.). (Illus.). 32p. (J). (gr. 3-4). lib. bdg. 21.26 (978-0-7368-0929-0(5) , Capstone High-Interest Bks.) Capstone Pr., Inc.

Schaefer, Lola M. Tractor Trailers. 2000. (Transportation Library). (Illus.). 24p. (J). (gr. 1-2). lib. bdg. 18.60 (978-0-7368-0504-9(4) , Bridgestone Bks.) Capstone Pr., Inc.

Schmauss, Judy Kentor. A Truck Can Help. 2006. (Reader's Clubhouse Set A Ser.). (Illus.). 24p. (J). pap. 3.99 (978-0-7641-3290-2(3)) Barron's Educational Series, Inc.

Schuette, Sarah L. Pickup Trucks. 2006. (Blazers—Horsepower Ser.). (Illus.). 32p. (J). (978-0-7368-5474-0(6)) Capstone Pr., Inc.

Sessler, Peter. Stock Trucks. 1999. (Off to the Races Ser.). 24p. (J). lib. bdg. 25.64 (978-1-57103-285-0(1)) Rourke Publishing, LLC.

Shealy, Dennis. I'm a Truck. Staake, Bob, illus. 2006. (Little Golden Book Ser.). 24p. (J). (gr. k-k). 2.99 (978-0-375-83263-5(7) , Golden Bks.) Random Hse. Children's Bks.

Simon, Seymour. Seymour Simon's Book of Trucks. (J). (ps-1). 2002. 40p. pap. 6.99 (978-0-06-446224-2(2)); 2000. (Illus.). 40p. 16.89 (978-0-06-028481-7(1)); 2000. (Illus.). 32p. 16.99 (978-0-06-028473-2(0)) HarperCollins Pubs.

—Seymour Simon's Book of Trucks. 2002. (Illus.). (J). (ps-ps). lib. bdg. 15.25 (978-0-613-36658-8(1)) Tandem Library Bks.

Stickland, Paul. Special Engines. 2004. (By Air, Sea, & Land Ser.). (Illus.). 24p. (J). pap. 3.99 (978-0-7696-3376-3(5) , Waterbird Bks.) School Specialty Publishing.

—Trucks. 2004. (By Air, Sea, & Land Ser.). (Illus.). 24p. (J). pap. 3.99 (978-0-7696-3379-4(X) , Gingham Dog Pr.) School Specialty Publishing.

Stille, Darlene R. Big Rigs. 2001. (Transportation Ser.). (Illus.). 32p. (J). (gr. 1 up). lib. bdg. 19.93 (978-0-7565-0147-1(4)) Compass Point Bks.

Sturges, Philemon. I Love Trucks! Halpern, Shari, illus. (J). (ps-1). 2003. 34p. 6.99 (978-0-06-052666-5(1) , Harper Festival); 2001. 32p. pap. 6.99 (978-0-06-443758-5(2) , Harper Trophy); 1999. 32p. 16.99 (978-0-06-027819-9(6)) HarperCollins Pubs.

—I Love Trucks! 2001. (ps-2). lib. bdg. 14.15 (978-0-613-84143-6(3)) Tandem Library Bks.

Sundance, ed. All Kinds of Trucks. 2000. (ps-2). lib. bdg. 11.65 (978-0-613-37619-8(6)) Tandem Library Bks.

Tatge, Cathy. Trucks. 2007. (978-1-58341-530-6(0) , Creative Education) Creative Co., The.

Teitelbaum, Michael. Humvees: High Mobility in the Field. 2006. (Mighty Military Machines Ser.). (Illus.). 48p. (J). (gr. 4-10). lib. bdg. 23.93 (978-0-7660-2661-2(2)) Enslow Pubs., Inc.

—Pedal to the Metal. LaCoste, Gary, illus. 2003. (Tonka Ser.). 5p. (J). (ps-2). bds. 6.99 (978-0-439-43430-0(0)) Scholastic, Inc.

Thompson Brothers Staff, illus. Action Scenes: Tonka Joe's Machines Sticker Book. 2001. (Tonka Joe Action Scenes Ser.). 24p. (J). (gr. k-3). pap. 5.99 (978-0-439-25913-2(4)) Scholastic, Inc.

Tieck, Sarah. Dump Trucks. 2005. (Buddy Book Ser.). (Illus.). 24p. (J). (gr. k-4). lib. bdg. 21.35 (978-1-59197-825-1(4)) ABDO Publishing Co.

—Monster Trucks. 2005. (Buddy Book Ser.). (Illus.). 24p. (J). (gr. k-4). lib. bdg. 21.35 (978-1-59197-829-9(7)) ABDO Publishing Co.

Tiner, John Hudson. Trucks. (Illus.). 32p. 2004. pap. 8.95 (978-0-89812-392-0(5) , Creative Paperbacks); 2003. (J). lib. bdg. 18.95 (978-1-58341-259-6(X) , Creative Education) Creative Co., The.

Tonka Rescue. 2002. (Illus.). (J). 15.95 (978-0-7853-6041-4(7)) Publications International, Ltd.

Tractors & Trucks Sticker Activity Book. 2003. (Illus.). 12p. (J). 2.98 (978-1-4054-1182-0(1)) Parragon, Inc.

Truck. 2000. (ps-2). lib. bdg. 14.15 (978-0-613-28681-7(2)) Tandem Library Bks.

Trucks. 2004. (Illus.). 18p. (J). bds. 5.99 (978-1-85854-431-1(9)) Brimax Books Ltd. GBR. *Dist:* Byeway Bks.

Trucks. 2005. (Transportation Ser.). (YA). (gr. k-3). (978-1-56065-967-9(X) , Pebble Bks.) Capstone Pr., Inc.

Trucks. 2003. 8p. pap. 1.95 (978-0-7624-1947-0(4)) Running Pr. Bk. Pubs.

Trucks & Cars. 2003. 32p. 12.98 (978-1-4054-2006-8(5)) Parragon, Inc.

Trusty Yellow Truck. 2002. (Vehicle Lights Ser.). (J). (ps-k). 6.98 (978-0-7525-8890-2(7)) Parragon, Inc.

Tuxworth, Nicola. Diggers & Dumpers. (Illus.). (ps). 2005. 12p. bds. 6.99 (978-0-7548-1336-1(3) , Lorenz Bks.); 2001. 20p. 5.95 (978-0-7548-0940-1(4)) Anness Publishing GBR. *Dist:* National Bk. Network.

—Machines at Work: A Very First Picture Book. 1999. (Pictures & Words Ser.). (Illus.). 24p. (J). (ps up). lib. bdg. 22.00 (978-0-8368-2432-2(6)) Stevens, Gareth Inc.

Volquetes (Dump Trucks) 2006. (J). 22.60 (978-0-8225-6228-3(6)); pap. 5.95 (978-0-8225-6643-4(5)) Lerner Publishing Group. (Ediciones Lerner).

Vrato, Elizabeth & Mann, Holly. Trucks. 2003. (Magic Window Bks.). (Illus.). 8p. (J). pap. 4.95 (978-0-7624-1575-5(4) , Running Pr. Kids) Running Pr. Bk. Pubs.

Ward, Beck. Busy Truck. Sweeten, Sami, illus. 2005. 10p. (J). 14.95 (978-1-4169-0251-5(1) , Little Simon) Simon & Schuster Children's Publishing.

Watt, Fiona. Los Camiones. 2005. (SPA.). 10p. (J). 15.99 (978-0-7460-6634-8(1) , Usborne) EDC Publishing.

Watt, Fiona & Wells, Rachel. Trucks. 2004. (Ultimate Touchy-Feely Ser.). (Illus.). 10p. (J). 15.95 (978-0-7945-0228-7(8) , Usborne) EDC Publishing.

Werther, Scott P. Big Rigs. 2002. (Reading Power Ser.). (Illus.). 24p. (J). (gr. 1). lib. bdg. 17.25 (978-0-8239-5956-3(2) , PowerKids Pr.) Rosen Publishing Group, Inc., The.

—Camiones de 18 Ruedas. 2004. (Maquinas Extremas Ser.). (SPA & ENG., Illus.). 24p. (J). (gr. 3-6). lib. bdg. 17.25 (978-0-8239-6887-9(1) , Buenas Letra) Rosen Publishing Group, Inc., The.

—Camiones de 18 Ruedas: Individual Title Six-Packs. (On Deck en Espanol Ser.).Tr. of Big Rigs. (SPA.). 24p. (gr. 4-5). 35.00 (978-0-7578-6418-6(X)) Rigby Education.

—Camionetas Gigantes. 2004. (Maquinas Extremas Ser.). (SPA & ENG., Illus.). 24p. (J). (gr. 3-6). lib. bdg. 17.25 (978-0-8239-6891-6(X) , Buenas Letra) Rosen Publishing Group, Inc., The.

—Camionetas Gigantes: Individual Title Six-Packs. (On Deck en Espanol Ser.).Tr. of Monster Trucks. (SPA.). 24p. (gr. 4-5). 35.00 (978-0-7578-6417-9(1)) Rigby Education.

—Monster Trucks. 2002. (Reading Power Ser.). (Illus.). 24p. (J). (gr. 1). lib. bdg. 17.25 (978-0-8239-5955-6(4) , PowerKids Pr.) Rosen Publishing Group, Inc., The.

—Monster Trucks: Individual Title Six-Packs. (On Deck Ser.). 24p. (gr. 4-5). 35.00 (978-0-7578-1042-8(X)) Rigby Education.

Wilkes, Angela. Grandes Camiones. 2004. (Ladders Ser.).Tr. of Tough Trucks. (SPA., Illus.). 32p. (ps-3). 12.95 (978-1-58728-407-6(3) , Two Can Publishing) T&N Children's Publishing.

—Tough Tracks. 2000. (ps-2). lib. bdg. 15.25 (978-0-613-43510-9(9)) Tandem Library Bks.

—Tough Trucks. rev. ed. 2004. (Ladders Ser.). (Illus.). 32p. (J). (ps-3). pap. 6.95 (978-1-58728-617-9(3) , Two Can Publishing) T&N Children's Publishing.

—Tough Trucks. 1999. (Ladders Ser.). (Illus.). 32p. (J). (gr. k-3). (978-0-7166-7713-0(X)) World Bk., Inc.

T
U
V

Wilkes, Angela, et al. Tough Trucks. rev. ed. 2004. (Ladders Ser.). (Illus.). 30p. (ps-3). 12.95 (978-1-58728-604-9(1) , Two Can Publishing) T&N Children's Publishing.

Williams, Linda D. Camiones de Volteo. 2006. (ENG & SPA.). (J). (978-0-7368-5870-0(9)) Capstone Pr., Inc.

—Dump Trucks. (Mighty MacHines Ser.). 24p. (J). pap. 6.95 (978-0-7368-5134-3(8)) Capstone Pr., Inc.

Wingert, Amy. Tow Trucks. 2006. (Illus.). 32p. (J). pap. 5.95 (978-0-8225-5894-1(7) , First Avenue Editions) Lerner Publishing Group.

World Book, Inc Staff, contrib. by. Tough Trucks. 2007. (J). (***978-0-7166-7730-7(X)***) World Bk., Inc.

Yoon, Salina. Construction Trucks. 2007. 10p. (J). (ps-1). pap. 8.99 (978-0-8431-2181-0(5) , Price Stern Sloan) Penguin Group (USA) Inc.

Zobel, Derek. Monster Vehicles. 2008. (Illus.). 24p. (J). lib. bdg. 19.95 (***978-1-60014-151-5(X)***) Bellwether Media.

Zuehlke, Jeffrey. Camionetas (Pickup Trucks) 2006. (Libros para Avanzar Ser.). (ENG & SPA.). (J). 22.60 (978-0-8225-6499-7(8) , Ediciones Lerner) Lerner Publishing Group.

—Forklifts. (Pull Ahead Books). (Illus.). 32p. (J). 2007. 22.60 (978-0-8225-6008-1(9) , Lerner Pubns.); 2006. pap. 5.95 (978-0-8225-5896-5(3) , First Avenue Editions) Lerner Publishing Group.

—Pickup Trucks. (Motor Mania Ser.). (J). 2007. 48p. (gr. 4-7). 26.60 (978-0-8225-6564-2(1) , Lerner Pubns.); 2005. (Illus.). 32p. (gr. k-2). lib. bdg. 22.60 (978-0-8225-1542-5(3)) Lerner Publishing Group.

TRUCKS—FICTION

Alborough, Jez. Duck in the Truck. Alborough, Jez, illus. (Illus.). (J). 2008. 32p. pap. 7.95 (***978-1-933605-76-0(6)); 2005. 16p. per. 7.99 (978-1-929132-83-6(2)) Kane/Miller Bk. Pubs., Inc.

Allen, Francesca & Brooks, Felicity. Busy Truck. Crisp, Dan, illus. 2007. 10p. (J). bds. 10.99 (978-0-7945-1453-2(7) , Usborne) EDC Publishing.

Anderson, Peggy Perry. Chuck's Truck. 2006. (Illus.). 32p. (J). (gr. k-3). 16.00 (978-0-618-66836-6(5)) Houghton Mifflin Co.

Auerbach, Annie. Dizzy & Muck Work It Out. 2002. (gr. k-3). lib. bdg. 11.25 (978-0-613-51299-2(5)) Tandem Library Bks.

Ayres, Katherine. Matthew's Truck. Takahashi, Hideko, tr. Takahashi, Hideko, illus. 2005. (Super Sturdy Picture Books Ser.). 24p. (J). (gr. k). 8.99 (978-0-7636-2269-5(9)) Candlewick Pr.

Bailer, Darice. Tow! Lopez, Paul, illus. 2003. (Matchbox Ser.). 16p. (J). bds. 6.99 (978-0-689-85972-4(4) , Little Simon) Simon & Schuster Children's Publishing.

Barton, Byron. Trucks. Barton, Byron, illus. 2006. 34p. (J). 12.99 (978-0-06-115016-6(9) , Harper Festival) HarperCollins Pubs.

Beil, Karen Magnuson. Jack's House. Wohnoutka, Mike, illus. 2008. (J). (***978-0-8234-1913-5(4)***) Holiday Hse., Inc.

Bourgeois, Paulette. Police Workers. LaFave, Kim, illus. 2004. 32p. (J). lib. bdg. 15.38 (***978-1-4242-1191-3(3)***) Fitzgerald Bks.

Bright, J. E. Driving Through Tonka Town. LaCoste, Gary, illus. 2003. (Tonka Ser.). 5p. (J). bds. 7.99 (978-0-439-48757-3(9)) Scholastic, Inc.

Carr, Jan. Big Truck & Little Truck. Bates, Ivan, illus. 2000. 32p. (J). (ps-2). pap. 15.95 (978-0-439-07177-2(1)) Scholastic, Inc.

Carter, Don. Get to Work, Trucks! Carter, Don, illus. rev. ed. 2002. (Illus.). 24p. (J). (ps-1). 14.95 (978-0-7613-1543-8(8)) Roaring Brook Pr.

Cochran, Jean M. Farmer Brown & His Little Red Truck. Enos, Daryl, illus. 2008. 32p. (J). 16.95 (***978-0-9792035-0-3(3)***) Pleasant St. Pr.

Cooke, Frank E. The Ninth Avenue Truck Tailor & Occasional Timepiece Co. unabr. ed. 1998. 66p. (Orig.). (J). (gr. 6-10). pap. 24.95 (978-0-940076-09-9(8)) Fiesta City Pubs.

Diaz, T. Richard. Little Growler, Big Heart. l.t. ed. 2003. (Illus.). 12p. (J). lib. bdg. 11.95 (978-1-932338-21-8(7)) ; per. 8.95 (978-1-932338-15-7(2)) Lifevest Publishing, Inc.

DK Publishing Staff. Noisy Little Dump Truck. 2007. 10p. (J). (ps-2). bds. 9.99 (***978-0-7566-3095-9(9)***) Dorling Kindersley Publishing, Inc.

Edwards, Julie & Hamilton, Emma Walton. Dumpy's Extra-Busy Day. Walton, Tony & Boyd, Katherine H., illus. 2006. (I Can Read Bks.). 32p. (J). 15.99 (978-0-06-088576-2(9) , Julie Andrews Collection) HarperCollins Pubs.

—Dumpy's Valentine. Walton, Tony & Randig, Ruby, illus. 2006. (My First I Can Read Bks.). 24p. (J). 15.99 (978-0-06-088573-1(4) , Julie Andrews Collection) HarperCollins Pubs.

Edwards, Julie Andres & Hamilton, Emma Walton. Dumpy's Apple Shop. Walton, Tony, illus. 2004. 24p. (J). lib. bdg. 13.85 (***978-1-4242-0708-4(8)***) Fitzgerald Bks.

Edwards, Julie Andrews. Dumpy & the Firefighters. Walton, Tony, illus. 2005. 32p. (J). pap. 5.99 (978-0-06-052683-2(1) , Julie Andrews Collection) HarperCollins Pubs.

—Dumpy's Apple Shop. Walton, Tony, illus. 2004. (My First I Can Read Bks.). 32p. (J). (ps up). 14.99 (978-0-06-052692-4(0)); lib. bdg. 15.89 (978-0-06-052693-1(9)) HarperCollins Pubs.

—Dumpy's Extra-Busy Day. Walton, Tony, illus. 2006. (I Can Read Bks.). 32p. (J). pap. 3.99 (978-0-06-088578-6(5) , Harper Trophy) HarperCollins Pubs.

—Dumpy's Happy Holiday. Walton, Tony, illus. 2005. 32p. (J). lib. bdg. 16.89 (978-0-06-052685-6(8) , Julie Andrews Collection) HarperCollins Pubs.

—Dumpy's Valentine. Walton, Tony & Randig, Ruby, illus. 2006. (My First I Can Read Bks.). 24p. (J). pap. 3.99 (978-0-06-088575-5(0) , Harper Trophy) HarperCollins Pubs.

Edwards, Julie Andrews & Hamilton, Emma Walton. Dumpy & His Pals. Walton, Tony, illus. 2001. (Dumpy Ser.: No. 1). 20p. (J). (ps-k). 6.99 (978-0-7868-0749-9(0)) Hyperion Bks. for Children.

—Dumpy & the Firefighters. Walton, Tony, illus. 2003. 32p. (J). (ps-2). 15.99 (978-0-06-052681-8(5) , Julie Andrews Collection) HarperCollins Pubs.

—Dumpy at School. Walton, Tony, illus. 2000. (Dumpy Ser.). 32p. (ps-2). 15.99 (978-0-7868-0610-2(9)) Hyperion Bks. for Children.

—Dumpy the Dumptruck. Walton, Tony, illus. 2000. (Dumpy Ser.). 32p. (ps-2). 15.99 (978-0-7868-0609-6(5)) Hyperion Bks. for Children.

—Dumpy to the Rescue! Walton, Tony, illus. 2004. (My First I Can Read Bks.). 32p. (J). (ps up). 14.99 (978-0-06-052689-4(0)); pap. 3.99 (978-0-06-052691-7(2)); lib. bdg. 15.89 (978-0-06-052690-0(4)) HarperCollins Pubs.

—Dumpy to the Rescue. Walton, Tony, illus. 2004. 24p. (J). lib. bdg. 13.85 (***978-1-4242-0707-7(X)***) Fitzgerald Bks.

—Dumpy's Happy Holiday. Walton, Tony, illus. 2005. 32p. (J). 15.99 (978-0-06-052684-9(X) , Julie Andrews Collection) HarperCollins Pubs.

—Friends on the Farm. Walton, Tony, illus. 2001. (Dumpy Ser.: No. 2). 20p. (J). (ps-k). 6.99 (978-0-7868-0672-0(9)) Hyperion Bks. for Children.

Eggleton, Jill. The Truck: Emergent Level Satellite Individual Title Six-Packs. Taylor, Clive, illus. (Sails Literacy Ser.). (gr. k-1). 27.00 (978-0-7578-7922-7(5)) Rigby Education.

Fienberg, Anna. Minton Goes Trucking. Gamble, Kim, illus. 2001. (Minton Ser.). 32p. (J). (ps-1). pap. 6.95 (978-1-86448-595-0(7)) Allen & Unwin AUS. *Dist:* Independent Pubs. Group.

Floca, Brian. Five Trucks. 2001. (978-0-606-22360-7(6)) Tandem Library Bks.

Fontes, Justine. Working Hard with the Mighty Backhoe. Petruccio, Steven James, illus. 1998. (Tonka Ser.). 32p. (J). (ps-2). pap. 3.50 (978-0-590-02378-8(0) , Cartwheel Bks.) Scholastic, Inc.

Gordon, David. Hansel & Diesel. Gordon, David, illus. 2006. (Illus.). 32p. (J). 15.99 (978-0-06-058122-0(0) , Geringer, Laura Book) ; lib. bdg. 16.89 (978-0-06-058123-7(9)) HarperCollins Pubs.

—The Three Little Rigs. Gordon, David, illus. 2005. (Illus.). 32p. (J). (ps-2). 15.99 (978-0-06-058118-3(2)); lib. bdg. 16.89 (978-0-06-058119-0(0)) HarperCollins Pubs. (Geringer, Laura Book).

—The Ugly Truckling. Gordon, David, illus. 2004. (Illus.). 32p. (J). (ps-2). lib. bdg. 16.89 (978-0-06-054601-4(8) , Geringer, Laura Book) HarperCollins Pubs.

Gould, Robert. Monster Trucks. 2004. (Big Stuff Ser.). (Illus.). 16p. (J). bds. 7.95 (978-1-929945-43-6(4)) Big Guy Bks., Inc.

Hall, Kirsten. My Trucks. 2004. (My First Reader Ser.). (Illus.). 31p. (J). (gr. k-1). pap. 3.95 (978-0-516-24637-6(2) , Children's Pr.) Scholastic Library Publishing.

—My Trucks. Boyd, Patti, illus. 2003. (My First Reader Ser.). 32p. (J). 18.50 (978-0-516-22935-5(4) , Children's Pr.) Scholastic Library Publishing.

Hamilton, Kersten. Red Truck. Petrone, Valeria, illus. 2008. 32p. (J). (ps). 15.99 (***978-0-670-06275-1(8)***, Viking Juvenile) Penguin Group (USA) Inc.

Hardyment, Christina. Arthur Ransome & Captain Flint's Trunk. (Illus.). 224p. (J). (978-0-224-02989-6(4)) Random Hse.

Haskins, Lori. Ducks in Muck. Petrone, Valeria, illus. 2007. (For Baby Board Bks.). 24p. (J). (gr. k-ps). bds. 4.99 (978-0-375-84028-9(1) , Random Hse. Bks. for Young Readers) Random Hse. Children's Bks.

—Ducks in Muck. Petrone, Valeria, illus. 2000. 32p. (J). (ps-ps). lib. bdg. 11.80 (978-0-613-21470-4(6)) Tandem Library Bks.

Hayler, Kate. Super Camion Al Rescate. 2003. (Tough Stuff Ser.). (SPA.). 10p. (ps-17). 8.99 (978-0-7868-1977-5(4)) Hyperion Bks. for Children.

—Tough Truck Rescue. Giraffe, Red, illus. 2003. (Tough Stuff Ser.). 10p. (ps-17). 8.99 (978-0-7868-1981-2(2)) Hyperion Bks. for Children.

Herman, Gail. Drive That Truck! 2006. (Tonka Ser.). (Illus.). 12p. (J). pap. 8.99 (978-0-7944-1049-0(9)) Reader's Digest Assn., Inc., The.

Hickle, Victoria. Trucks Around Town. 2008. (Tonka Power Reading Ser.: No. 4). 32p. (J). pap. 3.99 (***978-0-439-88480-8(2)***) Scholastic, Inc.

Houghton Mifflin Company Staff. Fire Truck Fun with Curious George. 2005. (J). (ps-k). pap. (978-0-618-70499-6(X)) Houghton Mifflin Co. Trade & Reference Div.

Hubbell, Patricia. Trucks. Halsey, Megan, illus. 2006. 32p. 5.99 (978-0-7614-5328-4(8)) Cavendish, Marshall Corp.

—Trucks: Whizz! Zoom! Rumble! Halsey, Megan, illus. 2003. 32p. (J). 14.95 (978-0-7614-5124-2(2)) Cavendish, Marshall Corp.

Hundal, Nancy. Melted Star Journey. 1999. (Illus.). 32p. (J). (ps-3). 13.50 (978-0-00-224406-0(3)) HarperCollins Pubs.

—Number 21. Deines, Brian, illus. 32p. (J). 2004. (gr. 1-3). pap. (978-1-55041-905-4(6)); 2001. (ps-2). (978-1-55041-543-8(3)) Fitzhenry & Whiteside, Ltd.

Hunter, Jana Novotny. When Daddy Picks Me Up. Miller, Thomas O., illus. 2004. (J). (gr. k-3). 12.95 (978-0-7696-3169-1(X) , Gingham Dog Pr.) School Specialty Publishing.

—When Daddy's Truck Picks Me Up. Thompson, Carol, illus. 2006. 32p. (J). 15.95 (978-0-8075-8914-4(4)) Whitman, Albert & Co.

The ice cream Truck. 2004. (J). per. 15.95 (978-0-9778937-4-4(X)) Priceless Ink Publishing Co., Inc.

Inches, Alison. Dizzy's Bird Watch. 2001. 10.79 (978-0-606-22130-6(1)); lib. bdg. 11.80 (978-0-613-51300-5(2)) Tandem Library Bks.

—A Surprise for Wendy. Dubreuil, Diane, illus. 2002. (Bob the Builder Ready-to-Read Ser.: Vol. 4). 24p. (J). pap. 3.99 (978-0-689-84754-7(8) , Simon Spotlight) Simon & Schuster Children's Publishing.

—Wendy Helps Out. 2001. (978-0-606-22131-3(X)); lib. bdg. 11.80 (978-0-613-51329-6(0)) Tandem Library Bks.

Kelley, K. C. Tonka Busy Trucks: A Lift the Flap Book. 2006. (Tonka Giant Flap Book Ser.). (Illus.). 10p. (J). bds. 9.99 (978-0-7944-1147-3(9)) Reader's Digest Assn., Inc., The.

Korman, Justine. Highway Trucks. Petruccio, Steven James, illus. 1998. (Tonka Ser.). 32p. (J). (ps-2). pap. 3.50 (978-0-590-02381-8(0) , Cartwheel Bks.) Scholastic, Inc.

Koury, Jen. Tommy Truck Helps Build a Park. Torgerson, Dell & Reyner, Mark, eds. Koury, Jen, illus. 1999. (John Deere Kids Toybook Ser.). (Illus.). 10p. (J). (ps up). mass mkt. 9.99 (978-1-887327-30-5(4)) Ertl Co., Inc.

Lewis, Kevin. My Truck Is Stuck! Kirk, Daniel, illus. (ps-ps). 2006. 30p. 6.99 (978-0-7868-3739-7(X)); 2002. 40p. 14.99 (978-0-7868-0534-1(X)) Hyperion Bks. for Children.

Linder, Cori. Bobby the Blue Bus. 2005. 21p. 10.75 (978-1-4116-3564-7(7)) Lulu.com.

Lyon, George Ella. Trucks Roll! Frazier, Craig, illus. 2007. 40p. (J). (ps-2). 14.99 (978-1-4169-2435-7(3)) Simon & Schuster Children's Publishing.

Mayer, Mercer. Just a Dump Truck. Mayer, Mercer, illus. 2005. (Little Critter Ser.). (Illus.). 20p. (J). (ps up). bds. 5.99 (978-0-06-053968-9(2) , Harper Festival) HarperCollins Pubs.

McEwen, James. Westley, the Big Truck. 2004. 32p. (J). 10.99 (978-0-89051-410-8(0)) Master Bks.

Mitton, Tony. Tough Trucks. Parker, Ant, illus. 2005. (Amazing Machines Ser.). 24p. (J). (ps-k). pap., pap. 3.95 (978-0-7534-5917-1(5) , Kingfisher) Houghton Mifflin Co. Trade & Reference Div.

Mitton, Tony. Truckload of Fun. Parker, Ant, illus. 2007. (Amazing Machines Ser.). 24p. (J). (ps-1). 19.95 (***978-0-7534-6154-9(4)***, Kingfisher) Houghton Mifflin Co. Trade & Reference Div.

The Monster Truck. 2002. 32p. (J). (ps-2). 12.95 (978-1-930758-68-1(5) , Yeva Kids) Yeva Corp.

Morgan, Allen. Matthew & the Midnight Tow Truck. Martchenko, Michael, illus. 2003. 32p. (J). (ps-2). pap. 5.95 (978-0-920303-01-6(3)); (Annikins Ser.: Vol. 11). pap. 1.25 (978-1-55037-192-5(4)) Annick Pr., Ltd. CAN. *Dist:* Firefly Bks., Ltd.

Mr. Cheesehead Goes for a Ride... 2nd rev. ed. 2005. (Illus.). 32p. (J). 12.99 (978-0-9764463-1-6(6)) Vertigo Publishing.

Mullican, Judy. Trucks, Trucks Board Book & Felt Puppet Set. Cress, Michelle H., illus. 2005. (J). bds. (978-1-57332-357-4(8)) HighReach Learning, Inc.

Newman, Leslea. A Fire Engine for Ruthie. Moore, Cyd, illus. 2004. 32p. (J). (gr. k-3). tchr. ed. 16.00 (978-0-618-15989-5(4) , Clarion Bks.) Houghton Mifflin Co. Trade & Reference Div.

Nickel, Scott. Barney's World of Trucks. Full, Dennis, photos by. 2001. (Barney Ser.). (Illus.). 40p. (J). (ps-k). pap. 6.99 (978-1-58668-135-7(4)) Scholastic, Inc.

Ostrow, Kim. Rock-and-Roll Bob. Hot Animation Staff, Animation, illus. 2003. (Bob the Builder Ser.: Vol. 6). 24p. (J). pap. 3.99 (978-0-689-85832-1(9) , Simon Spotlight) Simon & Schuster Children's Publishing.

Packard, Mary. Rob's Shiny Dump Truck. SGA Graphics Staff, illus. 1999. (Fisher-Price All Around Town Playbooks Ser.). 18p. (J). (ps-k). bds. 5.99 Reader's Digest Children's Publishing, Inc.

Petrie, Catherine. A Jaime Josue le Gustan los Camiones. Snyder, Joel, illus. 2000. (Rookie Espanol Ser.). (SPA.). 24p. (J). (gr. k-2). 19.50 (978-0-516-21691-1(0) , Children's Pr.) Scholastic Library Publishing.

—Joshua James Likes Trucks. Snyder, Joel, illus. rev. ed. (Rookie Reader Espanol Ser.). 24p. (J). (gr. k-2). 2000. pap. 4.95 (978-0-516-27000-5(1)); 1999. 19.50 (978-0-516-21639-3(2)) Scholastic Library Publishing. (Children's Pr.).

—Joshua James Likes Trucks. rev. ed. 1999. (gr. k-3). lib. bdg. 12.95 (978-0-613-54593-8(1)) Tandem Library Bks.

Priddy, Roger. Rainbow Trucks. 2006. (Priddy Books Big Ideas for Little People). (Illus.). 14p. (J). bds. 12.95 (978-0-312-49814-6(4) , Priddy Bks.) St. Martin's Pr.

Randall, Rod. I Scream the Truck. 1999. (Heebie Jeebies Ser.: Bk. 5). 153p. pap. 5.99 (978-0-8054-1974-0(8)) B&H Publishing Grp.

Reece, Stephen. The Bear in the Air Scare. 1998. (Illus.). 12p. (J). (ps-3). pap. 2.95 (978-1-892388-00-1(6)) Little Trucker Bks.

—Little Trucker Books, Series One, 3 vols. 1998. (Illus.). 40p. (J). (ps-3). pap. 7.95 (978-1-892388-03-2(0)) Little Trucker Bks.

—Little Trucker Books, Series Two, 3 vols. 1998. (Illus.). 40p. (J). (ps-5). pap. 7.95 (978-1-892388-04-9(9)) Little Trucker Bks.

—My Dad Drives a Big Truck. 1998. (Illus.). 12p. (J). (ps-3). pap. 2.95 (978-1-892388-02-5(2)) Little Trucker Bks.

Rey, Margret. Curious George & the Dump Truck. 1999. (gr. k-3). lib. bdg. 11.80 (978-0-613-21389-9(0)) Tandem Library Bks.

Rey, Margret & Rey, H. A. Curious George & the Dumptruck. 1999. (Curious George Ser.). (Illus.). 24p. (J). (gr. k-3). tchr. ed. 12.95 (978-0-395-97832-0(7)) Houghton Mifflin Co. Trade & Reference Div.

—Curious George & the Dumptruck. Vipah Interactive Staff, illus. 1999. (Curious George Ser.). 24p. (J). (gr. k-3). pap. 3.95 (978-0-395-97836-8(X)) Houghton Mifflin Co. Trade & Reference Div.

Robertson, Ruth. The Truck That Wouldn't! 2004. pap. 9.00 (978-0-8059-6316-8(2)) Dorrance Publishing Co., Inc.

Royston, Angela. Truck Trouble. 1998. (Illus.). (J). (ps-ps). lib. bdg. 11.80 (978-0-613-08958-6(8)) Tandem Library Bks.

Scarry, Richard. Coches y Cacharros. 1998. (Zagadki Rossiiskoi Istorii Ser.). (SPA., Illus.). 76p. (J). (ps-1). (978-84-08-01683-0(0)) GeoPlaneta, Editorial, S. A.

Schertle, Alice. Little Blue Truck. McElmurry, Jill, illus. 2008. (J). (***978-0-15-205661-2(0)***) Harcourt Trade Pubs.

Schoberle, Cecile. Everyday Heroes. Lopez, Paul, illus. 2005. (Ready-to-Read Ser. Level 1). 32p. (J). lib. bdg. 15.00 (978-1-59054-925-4(2)) Fitzgerald Bks.

—Everyday Heroes. Ewers, Joe & Lopez, Paul, illus. 2003. (Matchbox Ser.). 32p. (J). pap. 3.99 (978-0-689-85899-4(X) , Little Simon) Simon & Schuster Children's Publishing.

—Everyday Heroes. 2003. (gr. k-3). lib. bdg. 11.80 (978-0-613-66498-1(1)) Tandem Library Bks.

Scholastic, Inc. Staff. Working at the Christmas Tree Farm. 2007. (Tonka Power Reading Ser.). 32p. (J). pap. 3.99 (***978-0-439-88479-2(9)***) Scholastic, Inc.

Scieszka, Jon. Smash! Crash! Shannon, David et al, illus. 2008. (Jon Scieszka's Trucktown Ser.). 42p. (J). 16.99 (***978-1-4169-4133-0(9)***) Simon & Schuster Children's Publishing.

Shaw, Gina. Follow the Dump Truck. Peterkin, Mike & Jacobs, Phil, illus. 1999. (Tonka Ser.). 14p. (J). (ps). 4.50 (978-0-439-08287-7(0) , Cartwheel Bks.) Scholastic, Inc.

—Follow the Fire Truck. Peterkin, Mike & Jacobs, Phil, illus. 1999. (Tonka Board Bks.). 14p. (J). (ps). 4.50 (978-0-439-08286-0(2) , Cartwheel Bks.) Scholastic, Inc.

—Follow the Tow Truck. Peterkin, Mike & Jacobs, Phil, illus. 1999. (Tonka Ser.). 14p. (J). (ps). 4.50 (978-0-439-08289-1(7) , Cartwheel Bks.) Scholastic, Inc.

Silver Dolphin en Español Editors, ed. Figuras Magicas: Tonka, Camiones a la Obra! Magical Magnets: Tonka, Trucks at Work! 2006. (Illus.). 8p. (J). bds. 12.95 (978-970-718-360-5(8) , Silver Dolphin en Español) Advanced Marketing, S. de R. L. de C. V. MEX. *Dist:* Perseus Distribution.

Silver Dolphin en Español Staff. Serie aprendizaje: Tonka, Vehiculos robustos y Sensacionales: Learning Series: Tonka, Tough Trucks. 2006. (Illus.). 22p. (J). bds. 16.95 (978-970-718-362-9(4) , Silver Dolphin en Español) Advanced Marketing, S. de R. L. de C. V. MEX. *Dist:* Perseus Distribution.

Sis, Peter. Trucks Trucks Trucks. Sis, Peter, illus. 1999. (Illus.). 26p. (J). (ps-1). 16.99 (978-0-688-16276-4(2)) HarperCollins Pubs.

—Trucks, Trucks, Trucks. Sis, Peter, illus. 2004. (Illus.). 28p. (J). (ps-1). 6.99 (978-0-06-056258-8(7) , Harper Festival) HarperCollins Pubs.

Steele, Michael Anthony. I'm a Great Big Eighteen-Wheeler! 2003. (gr. k-3). lib. bdg. 11.25 (978-0-613-67096-8(5)) Tandem Library Bks.

—I'm a Great Big Monster Truck! Mones, Marc & Mones, Isidre, illus. 2004. (Tonka Ser.). 24p. (J). pap. 3.50 (978-0-439-54836-6(5) , Cartwheel Bks.) Scholastic, Inc.

—I'm a Great Big Tow Truck. Primeau, Chuck, illus. 2003. (Tonka Ser.). 24p. (J). (ps-2). pap. 3.50 (978-0-439-43434-8(3)) Scholastic, Inc.

—Tonka. Courtney, Richard et al, illus. 2003. (Tonka Ser.). 24p. (J). 3.50 (978-0-439-48724-5(2)) Scholastic, Inc.

Stenger, Lisa. Trucks. 2005. (Illus.). (J). pap. 4.95 (978-1-57874-094-9(0)) Kaeden Corp.

Stoddard, Jeffery. Pete & Pillar - The Big Rain: A Story of Friendship Based on John 15:13. 2007. (Illus.). 32p. (J). (ps-2). 12.99 (***978-1-59317-203-9(6)***) Warner Pr. Pubs.

Stoeke, Janet Morgan. Minerva Louise & the Red Truck. Stoeke, Janet Morgan, illus. 2002. (Illus.). 32p. (J). (ps-1). 14.99 (978-0-525-46909-4(5) , Dutton Juvenile) Penguin Group (USA) Inc.

Teitelbaum, Michael. If I Could Drive a Car Hauler! 2003. (gr. k-3). lib. bdg. 11.25 (978-0-613-67092-0(2)) Tandem Library Bks.

—If I Could Drive a Dump Truck. Klavins, Uldis & Walker, Jeff, illus. 2001. (Tonka Ser.). 24p. (J). pap. 3.99 (978-0-439-31814-3(9) , Cartwheel Bks.) Scholastic, Inc.

—If I Could Drive a Dump Truck! 2001. (ps-2). lib. bdg. 11.25 (978-0-613-54565-5(6)) Tandem Library Bks.

—If I Could Drive a Fire Truck! 2001. (ps-2). lib. bdg. 11.25 (978-0-613-54566-2(4)) Tandem Library Bks.

—If I Could Drive a Hauler. LaPadula, Tom & Courtney, Richard, illus. 2003. (Tonka Ser.). 24p. (J). pap. 3.50 (978-0-439-48725-2(0)) Scholastic, Inc.

—If I Could Drive a Mixer! Klavins, Uldis & Walker, Jeff, illus. 2001. (Tonka Ser.). 24p. (J). pap. 3.50 (978-0-439-31817-4(3) , Cartwheel Bks.) Scholastic, Inc.

—Tonka Trucks on the Go. La Padula, Thomas, illus. 2005. (Tonka Ser.). 16p. (J). (ps-7). 7.99 (978-0-7944-0772-8(2)) Reader's Digest Assn., Inc., The.

Todd, Mark. Monster Trucks! Todd, Mark, illus. 2003. (Illus.). 32p. (J). (gr. k-ps). tchr. ed. 15.00 (978-0-618-18208-4(X)) Houghton Mifflin Co. Trade & Reference Div.

—Monster Trucks. 2005. 13p. (J). (gr. k-ps). bds. 8.95 (978-0-618-58119-1(7)) Houghton Mifflin Co. Trade & Reference Div.

The Truck Is Stuck. (Little Book Practice Reader). (J). (978-0-8136-5379-2(7)) Modern Curriculum Pr.

The Trucks: First Wave Satellite Individual Title Six-Packs. (Sails Literacy Ser.). 16p. (gr. k up). 27.00 (978-0-7578-6853-5(3)) Rigby Education.

Ward, Frank. Moville. 1999. (Illus.). 32p. (J). (ps). 11.95 (978-0-9667475-0-8(X)) Renaissance-Atlantic Films.

T U V

Watt, F. & Wells, R. That's Not My Truck: It's Too Squashy. 2004. (Touchy-Feely Board Bks.). (Illus.). 10p. (J). (ps up). 7.99 (978-0-7945-0210-2(5) , Usborne) EDC Publishing.

Weatherby, Brenda & Weatherby, Mark Alan. The Trucker. 2004. (Illus.). 32p. (J). pap. 15.95 (978-0-439-39877-0(0)) Scholastic, Inc.

Wheeler, Lisa. Farmer Dale's Red Pickup Truck. Bates, Ivan, illus. 2006. 40p. (J). pap. 6.00 (978-0-15-205912-5(1) , Voyager Bks./Libros Viajeros) Harcourt Children's Bks.

—Farmer Dale's Red Pickup Truck. Bates, Ivan, tr. Bates, Ivan, illus. 2004. 40p. (J). 16.00 (978-0-15-202319-5(4)) Harcourt Children's Bks.

Wildman, Dale. Big Rig Daddy: A Ride in the Truck of All Trucks. Dickson, Bill, illus. 2006. 24p. (J). per. 2.99 (978-1-59958-007-4(1)) Journey Stone Creations, LLC.

Wilkes, Angela. Grandes Camiones. 2004. (Ladders Ser.).Tr. of Tough Trucks. (SPA., Illus.). 32p. (J). (ps-3). pap. 6.95 (978-1-58728-410-6(3) , Two Can Publishing) T&N Children's Publishing.

Williamson, Jennifer. Timmy the Tow Truck, 6 vols. Williamson, Alan, 8th, illus. 2005. 28p. (J). pap. (978-0-9771678-1-4(X)) Theee Hole Punch Publishing.

Wolf, Sallie. Truck Stuck. Davies, Andrew Robert, illus. 2008. (J). (***978-1-58089-119-6(5)***) Charlesbridge Publishing, Inc.

Wyre, Yvonne. The Adventures of Cuthbert the Coal Lorry. 2005. 160p. pap. (***978-1-84401-500-9(9)***) Athena Pr.

TRUMAN, HARRY S., 1884-1972

Alter, Judy. Harry S. Truman: A MyReportLinks.com Book. 2002. (Presidents Ser.). (Illus.). 48p. (J). (gr. 4-10). lib. bdg. 25.26 (978-0-7660-5069-3(6) , MyReportLinks.com Bks.) Enslow Pubs., Inc.

Cannarella, Deborah. Harry S. Truman. 2002. (Profiles of the Presidents Ser.). (Illus.). 64p. (J). (gr. 4 up). lib. bdg. 23.93 (978-0-7565-0278-2(0)) Compass Point Bks.

Fitzgerald, Brian. The Korean War: America's Forgotten War. 2006. (Snapshots in History Ser.). (Illus.). 96p. (J). (gr. 5-7). 30.60 (978-0-7565-1625-3(0)) Compass Point Bks.

Foley, Michael. Harry Truman. 2003. (Great American Presidents Ser.). (Illus.). 100p. (J). (gr. 4-8). 30.00 (978-0-7910-7596-8(6) , Chelsea Hse.) Facts On File, Inc.

Joseph, Paul. Harry Truman. 1999. (United States Presidents Ser.). (Illus.). 32p. (J). (gr. k-6). lib. bdg. 22.78 (978-1-56239-743-2(5) , Checkerboard Library) ABDO Publishing Co.

Lazo, Caroline Evensen. Harry S. Truman. 2003. (Presidential Biography Ser.). (Illus.). 112p. (J). (gr. 6-12). lib. bdg. 29.27 (978-0-8225-0096-4(5)) Lerner Publishing Group.

Otfinoski, Steven. Harry S. Truman. 2005. (Encyc of Presidents, 2ND Ser.). (Illus.). 112p. (J). (gr. 6-8). 34.00 (978-0-516-22974-4(5) , Watts, Franklin) Scholastic Library Publishing.

Parker, Lewis K. How to Draw the Life & Times of Harry S. Truman. 2007. (Kid's Guide to Drawing the Presidents of the United States of America Ser.). (Illus.). 32p. (J). 25.25 (978-1-4042-3009-5(2) , PowerKids Pr.) Rosen Publishing Group, Inc., The.

Saffer, Barbara. Harry S. Truman. 2003. (Childhoods of the Presidents Ser.). (Illus.). 48p. (J). (gr. 4 up). lib. bdg. (978-1-59084-282-9(0)) Mason Crest Pubs.

Schuman, Michael A. Harry S. Truman. rev. ed. 2003. (United States Presidents Ser.). (Illus.). 112p. (J). (gr. 5-12). lib. bdg. 26.60 (978-0-7660-2010-8(X)) Enslow Pubs., Inc.

Stanley, George Edward. Harry S. Truman: Thirty-Third President of the United States. Henderson, Meryl, illus. 2004. (Childhood of Famous Americans Ser.). 256p. (J). pap. 4.99 (978-0-689-86247-2(4) , Aladdin) Simon & Schuster Children's Publishing.

Uebelhor, Tracy S. The Truman Years. 2005. (Presidential Profiles Ser.). (Illus.). 832p. (gr. 9). 85.00 (978-0-8160-5490-9(8)) Facts On File, Inc.

Venezia, Mike. Harry S. Truman. Venezia, Mike, illus. 2007. (Getting to Know the U. S. Presidents Ser.). 32p. (J). 7.95 (***978-0-531-17946-8(X)***); (Illus.). (gr. 3-4). 27.00 (978 0 516-22637-8(1)) Scholastic Library Publishing. (Children's Pr.).

TRUMPET—FICTION

Dorie & Me. 2003. (YA). per. (978-1-59431-071-3(8) , Ebks. On The Net) ebooksonthe.net.

Downs, Martin F. The Silver Trumpet. Steinman, Zara, illus. 1999. 24p. (J). (ps-6). 19.95 (978-0-9668215-0-5(5)) Alicubi Pubns.

Karlins, Mark. Music over Manhattan. 1999. (J). (978-0-606-16712-3(9)) Tandem Library Bks.

Polizzotto, Carolyn & Spinks, Sarah. Trumpet's Kittens. Duke, Marion, illus. 2003. 32p. (YA). 22.50 (978-1-86368-331-9(3)) Fremantle Pr. AUS. *Dist:* International Specialized Bk. Services.

Ritter, John H. Under the Baseball Moon. 2008. 320p. (J). (gr. 6). 6.99 (***978-0-14-241090-5(X)*** , Puffin); 2006. (Illus.). 224p. (YA). (gr. 5). 16.99 (978-0-399-23623-5(6) , Philomel) Penguin Group (USA) Inc.

TRUST IN GOD

see Faith

TRUTH, SOJOURNER, D. 1883

Bernard, Catherine J. Sojourner Truth: Abolitionist & Women's Rights Activist. 2001. (Historical American Biographies Ser.). (Illus.). 112p. (YA). (gr. 6-12). lib. bdg. 26.60 (978-0-7660-1257-8(3)) Enslow Pubs., Inc.

Brezina, Corona. Sojourner Truth's "Ain't I a Woman?" Speech: A Primary Source Investigation. 2004. (Great Historic Debates & Speeches Ser.). (Illus.). 64p. (J). lib. bdg. 29.95 (978-1-4042-0154-5(8)) Rosen Publishing Group, Inc., The.

Butler, Mary G. Sojourner Truth: From Slave to Activist for Freedom. 2005. (Library of American Lives & Times). (Illus.). 112p. (YA). (gr. 4-8). lib. bdg. 31.95 (978-0-8239-5736-1(5)) Rosen Publishing Group, Inc., The.

Clinton, Catherine. Underground Railroad. 2007. 32p. (J). lib. bdg. 17.89 (978-0-06-050426-7(9)) HarperCollins Pubs.

—When Harriet Met Sojourner. Evans, Shane, illus. 2007. 32p. (J). (gr. k-2). 16.99 (978-0-06-050425-0(0)) HarperCollins Pubs.

Collins, Kathleen. Sojourner Truth: Equal Rights Advocate. 2003. (Famous People in American History Ser.). (Illus.). 32p. (J). pap. 6.50 (978-0-8239-4193-3(0)) Rosen Publishing Group, Inc., The.

Compass Point Books, contrib. by, Sojourner Truth. (Compass Point Early Biographies Ser.). 32p. (J). pap. 7.95 (978-0-7565-1180-7(1)) Compass Point Bks.

Frost, Helen. Sojourner Truth. Saunders-Smith, Gail, ed. 2003. (Famous Americans Ser.). (Illus.). 24p. (J). (gr. k-1). lib. bdg. 15.93 (978-0-7368-1640-3(2) , Pebble Bks.) Capstone Pr., Inc.

Gillis, Jennifer Blizin. Sojourner Truth. 2005. (Illus.). 32p. (J). (978-1-4034-6981-6(4)); pap. (978-1-4034-6988-5(1)) Heinemann Library.

Jaffe, Elizabeth Dana. Sojourner Truth. 2001. (Compass Point Early Biographies Ser.). (Illus.). 32p. (J). (gr. 2 up). lib. bdg. 21.26 (978-0-7565-0068-9(0)) Compass Point Bks.

Krass, Peter. Sojourner Truth. 2004. (Black Americans of Achievement Ser.). (Illus.). 112p. (J). (gr. 6-12). 30.00 (978-0-7910-8165-5(6) , Chelsea Hse.) Facts On File, Inc.

—Sojourner Truth: Antislavery Activist. 2005. (Black Americans of Achievement Ser.). (Illus.). 112p. (J). (gr. 6-12). pap. 13.25 (978-0-7910-8339-0(X) , Chelsea Hse.) Facts On File, Inc.

Kudlinski, Kathleen. Sojourner Truth. 2003. (gr. 3-6). lib. bdg. 13.00 (978-0-613-61658-4(8)) Tandem Library Bks.

—Sojourner Truth: Voice for Freedom. Wooden, Lenny, illus. 2003. (Childhood of Famous Americans Ser.). 160p. (Orig.). mass mkt. 5.99 (978-0-689-85274-9(6) , Aladdin) Simon & Schuster Children's Publishing.

Leebrick, Kristal. Sojourner Truth. 2002. (Let Freedom Ring Ser.). (Illus.). 48p. (J). (gr. 3-4). lib. bdg. 22.60 (978-0-7368-1090-6(0) , Bridgestone Bks.) Capstone Pr., Inc.

Lutz, Norma Jean. Sojourner Truth. 2001. (gr. 5-8). lib. bdg. 17.60 (978-0-613-33074-9(9)) Tandem Library Bks.

—Sojourner Truth: Abolitionist, Suffragist, & Preacher. (Famous Figures of the Civil War Era Ser.). (Illus.). 80p. (J). (gr. 4-7). 2001. 25.00 (978-0-7910-6007-0(1)); 2000. pap. 25.00 (978-0-7910-6145-9(0)) Facts On File, Inc. (Chelsea Hse.).

Malam, John. Sojourner Truth. 2000. (Tell Me about Ser.). (Illus.). 22p. (J). 16.95 (978-0-237-51972-8(0) , Evans Brothers, Limited) Evans Publishing Group GBR. *Dist:* Independent Pubs. Group.

Mattern, Joanne. Sojourner Truth: Early Abolitionist. 2003. (Reading Power Ser.). (Illus.). 24p. (J). lib. bdg. 17.25 (978-0-8239-6502-1(3) , PowerKids Pr.) Rosen Publishing Group, Inc., The.

—Sojourner Truth: Early Abolitionist: Individual Title Six-Packs. (On Deck Ser.: Vol. 2). 24p. (gr. 4-5). 35.00 (978-0-7578-5846-8(5)) Rigby Education.

McKissack, Patricia C. & McKissack, Fredrick L. Sojourner Truth: A Voice for Freedom. rev. ed. 2002. (Great African Americans Ser.). (Illus.). 32p. (J). (gr. 1-4). lib. bdg. 18.60 (978-0-7660-1693-4(5)) Enslow Pubs., Inc.

Moore, Barbara R. Sojourner Truth. 2005. (Illus.). 16p. (J). (***978-0-618-56039-4(4)***) Houghton Mifflin Co.

Rockwell, Anne. Only Passing Through: The Story of Sojourner Truth. Christie, R. Gregory, illus. 2002. 40p. (J). (gr. 2-5). pap. 6.99 (978-0-440-41766-8(X) , Dragonfly Bks.) Random Hse. Children's Bks.

Rockwell, Anne F. Only Passing Through. 2002. (gr. 3-6). lib. bdg. 15.30 (978-0-613-86684-2(3)) Tandem Library Bks.

—Only Passing Through: The Story of Sojourner Truth. Siscoe, Nancy, ed. Christie, R. Gregory, illus. 2000. 40p. (J). (gr. 2-5). 16.95 (978-0-679-89186-4(2)); lib. bdg. 18.99 (978-0-679-99186-1(7)) Random Hse. Children's Bks. (Knopf Bks. for Young Readers).

Roop, Connie & Roop, Peter. Sojourner Truth. 2003. (In Their Own Words Ser.). (Illus.). 128p. (J). (gr. 2-5). 4.99 (978-0-439-26323-8(9) , Scholastic Nonfiction) Scholastic, Inc.

Roop, Peter. Sojourner Truth. 2002. (gr. 3-6). lib. bdg. 12.40 (978-0-613-66669-5(0)) Tandem Library Bks.

Ruffin, Frances E. Her Story, Her Words: The Narrative of Sojourner Truth. 2004. (Great Moments in American History Ser.). (Illus.). 32p. (J). (gr. 4-8). lib. bdg. 21.25 (978-0-8239-4387-6(9) , Rosen Central) Rosen Publishing Group, Inc., The.

—Sojourner Truth. 2002. (American Legends Ser.). (Illus.). 24p. (J). (gr. 3). lib. bdg. 18.75 (978-0-8239-5826-9(4) , PowerKids Pr.) Rosen Publishing Group, Inc., The.

Slade, Suzanne. Sojourner Truth: Preacher for Freedom & Equality. Blanks, Natascha Alex, illus. 2007. (J). lib. bdg. (***978-1-4048-3726-3(4)***) Picture Window Bks.

Sojourner Truth. (Civil War Biographies Ser.). 48p. (YA). 7.95 (978-0-7368-4527-4(5)) Capstone Pr., Inc.

Sojourner Truth, 6 vols. (gr. 2-5). 39.95 (978-0-7368-4607-3(7)) Red Brick Learning.

Swain, Gwenyth. Sojourner Truth. Archambault, Matthew, illus. 2005. (On My Own Biography Ser.). 48p. (J). (ps-ps). pap. 5.95 (978-1-57505-827-6(8)) Lerner Publishing Group.

—Sojourner Truth. 2005. (On My Own Biography Ser.). (Illus.). 48p. (J). 25.26 (978-1-57505-651-7(8) , Carolrhoda Bks.) Lerner Publishing Group.

Trumbauer, Lisa. Let's Meet Sojourner Truth. 2003. (Let's Meet Biographies Ser.). (Illus.). 32p. (gr. 2-4). 23.00 (978-0-7910-7323-0(8) , Chelsea Hse.) Facts On File, Inc.

Waxman, Laura Hamilton. Sojourner Truth. 2008. (History Maker Biographies Ser.). (J). lib. bdg. 26.60 (***978-0-8225-7172-8(2)*** , Lerner Pubns.) Lerner Publishing Group.

Whalin, W. Terry. Sojourner Truth: American Abolitionist. Landgraf, Ken, illus. 1999. (Young Reader's Christian Library). 222p. (J). (gr. 8-12). pap. 1.39 (978-1-57748-515-5(7)) Barbour Publishing, Inc.

—Sojourner Truth: American Abolitionist. 1999. (Heroes of the Faith Ser.). 208p. (YA). (gr. 4-7). 14.95 (978-0-7910-5034-7(3) , Chelsea Hse.) Facts On File, Inc.

TRUTHFULNESS AND FALSEHOOD

see also Honesty

Amos, Janine. Liar. 2007. (Good & Bad Ser.). (Illus.). 32p. (J). (ps-2). pap. 9.95 (***978-1-84234-395-1(5)*** , Evans Brothers, Limited) Evans Publishing Group GBR. *Dist:* Independent Pubs. Group.

Berry, Joy Wilt. A Book about Cheating. 2005. (Illus.). (J). (978-0-7172-8583-9(9)) Scholastic, Inc.

—A Book about Lying. 2005. (Illus.). (J). (978-0-7172-8576-1(6)) Scholastic, Inc.

Braithwaite, Althea. Telling the Truth. Jude, Conny, illus. Best, Charlie, photos by. 1998. (Exploring Emotions Ser.). 32p. (J). (gr. 3 up). lib. bdg. 22.60 (978-0-8368-2120-8(3)) Stevens, Gareth Inc.

Moore, Stephanie Perry. Seeing Truth. Clark, Marla R., illus. 2000. (Amber "Senses" Ser.: Vol. 1). 100p. (J). (gr. 3-6). pap. 8.00 (978-1-929606-25-2(7)) Soul Publishing, Inc.

Morris-Dobie, Claire. Slam: A New Way to Tell the Truth. Federhofer-Stark, Sherri, ed. Dundis, Greg, illus. 1998. 64p. (J). (gr. 5-10). pap. 6.95 (978-0-9668242-0-9(2)) Morris Communications.

Moser, Adolph J. Don't Tell a Whopper on Fridays! The Children's Truth-Control Book. Thatch, Nancy R., ed. Melton, David, illus. 1999. (Emotional Impact Ser.). 61p. (J). (gr. 2-7). lib. bdg. 19.95 (978-0-933849-76-1(1)) Landmark Editions, Inc.

Rondina, Catherine. Lying: Straight Up. Workman, Dan, illus. 2006. (Deal with It Ser.). 32p. (J). (gr. 4-8). pap. 12.95 (978-1-55028-906-0(3)) Lorimer, James & Co., Ltd., Pubs. CAN. *Dist:* Casemate Pubs. & Bk. Distributors, LLC.

Simon, Mary Manz. What Did Jesus Do? Stories about Honesty & Forgiveness. Kennedy, Anne, illus. 1998. (What Did Jesus Do? Ser.). (J). (ps-3). 7.99 (978-0-8499-5857-1(1)) Nelson, Thomas Inc.

Thomas, Pat. I'm Telling the Truth: A First Look at Honesty. Harker, Lesley, illus. 2006. (First Look At... Ser.). 32p. (J). pap. 6.99 (978-0-7641-3214-8(8)) Barron's Educational Series, Inc.

Tubbs, Janet. Cheating. 2000. (Spud Packs Ser.). 16p. (J). pap. 19.95 (978-1-881185-11-6(7)) Arcadia Pr.

—Lying. 2000. (Spud Packs Ser.). (Illus.). 16p. (J). (ps-4). pap. 19.95 (978-1-881185-20-8(6)) Arcadia Pr.

Wan, Guofang. Virtually True: Questioning Online Media. 2007. (Fact Finders Ser.). (Illus.). 32p. (J). (***978-0-7368-7863-0(7)*** , 1264914) Capstone Pr., Inc.

Wan, Guofang & Capstone Press Staff. Virtually True: Questioning Online Media. 2007. (Fact Finders Ser.). (Illus.). 32p. (J). (gr. 4-7). lib. bdg. 22.60 (978-0-7368-6767-2(8) , 1264914) Capstone Pr., Inc.

TRUTHFULNESS AND FALSEHOOD—FICTION

Amado, Elisa. Tricycle. Ruano, Alfonso, illus. 2007. 32p. (J). (gr. 1-4). 17.95 (***978-0-88899-614-5(4)***); (SPA.). (gr. 2-5). 17.95 (***978-0-88899-613-8(6)***) Groundwood Bks. CAN. *Dist:* Perseus Distribution.

Bourgeois, Paulette & Clark, Brenda. Franklin Fibs. 1999. (Franklin Ser.). (Illus.). 162p. (J). (ps-3). (978-1-55074-668-6(5)) Kids Can Pr., Ltd.

Callaway, Phil. Jake & the Big Hairy Lie. 2002. (Jake Ser.). (Illus.). 36p. (J). pap. 3.99 (978-1-55305-030-8(4)) Cygnet Publishing Group, Inc./Coolreading.com CAN. *Dist:* Orca Bk. Pubs. USA.

Carlson, Melody. Grover Tells a Whopper: A Scoozie Tale about Honesty. Fincher, Kathryn Andrews, illus. Date not set. 32p. (J). 9.99 (978-0-7369-0733-0(5)) Harvest Hse. Pubs.

Curry, Kenneth. Chuka & the Drum. 2007. (Illus.). 22p. (J). 10.95 (***978-0-9798364-4-2(1)***) Curry Brothers Publishing.

deGroat, Diane. Liar, Liar, Pants on Fire. 2006. (Illus.). 32p. (J). reprint ed. pap. 6.95 (978-0-8118-5453-5(1)) Chronicle Bks. LLC.

Disney Staff. Always Tell the Truth. 2000. (Lessons from the Hundred-Acre Woods: Vol. 15). (Illus.). 32p. (J). (ps-3). 3.49 (978-1-57973-101-4(5)) Advance Pubs. LLC.

Garrelts, Christopher. Squarey Head Tells a Lie. Mayabb, Darrell, ed. 2003. (Adventures of Squarey Head Ser.: Bk. 1). (Illus.). 30p. (J). (gr. k-6). 4.95 (978-0-9742003-0-9(1)) Squarey Head, Inc.

Greenburg, Dan. Tell a Lie & Your Butt Will Grow, Vol. 28. Davis, Jack E., illus. 2002. (Zack Files Ser.: Vol. 28). 64p. (J). mass mkt. 4.99 (978-0-448-42682-2(X) , Grosset & Dunlap) Penguin Group (USA) Inc.

—Tell a Lie & Your Butt Will Grow. 2002. (gr. 3-6). lib. bdg. 13.00 (978-0-613-61662-1(6)) Tandem Library Bks.

Hall, Kirsten. Little Lies: All about Math. 2004. (Beastieville Ser.). 30p. (J). (gr. k-1). pap. 3.95 (978-0-516-24656-7(9) , Children's Pr.) Scholastic Library Publishing.

Hennessy, B. G. The Boy Who Cried Wolf. Kulikov, Boris, illus. 2006. 40p. (J). (ps-2). 15.95 (978-0-689-87433-8(2)) Simon & Schuster Children's Publishing.

Holt, Rinehart and Winston Staff. Nothing but the Truth: With Connections. 1998. pap., stu. ed. 13.20 (978-0-03-054068-4(2)) Holt, Rinehart & Winston.

Hopkins, Cathy. Starstruck. 2005. (Truth or Dare Ser.). 208p. (YA). (gr. 7 up). pap. 5.99 (978-0-689-87130-6(9) , Simon Pulse) Simon & Schuster Children's Publishing.

Jaredo's Day Off. 2002. (J). pap. 9.00 (978-0-8059-5394-7(9)) Dorrance Publishing Co., Inc.

Kulick Triscila, Verne. Joel & the Magic Toy Tree. 2005. 36p. (J). 11.99 (978-1-4116-6985-7(1)) Lulu.com.

Lucado, Max. Hermie & Wormie in the Flood of Lies. 2004. (Max Lucado's Hermie & Friends Ser.). 24p. (J). bds. 6.99 (978-1-4003-0287-1(0)) Nelson, Thomas Inc.

—Hermie y Wormie en un Diluvio de Mentiras. 2004. (SPA.). 24p. (J). bds. 10.99 (978-0-88113-775-0(8)) Grupo Nelson.

Madonna. Las Manzanas Del Sr. Peabody. Long, Loren, illus. 2003. Tr. of Mr. Peabody's Apples. (SPA.). 32p. (J). 19.95 (978-0-439-62279-0(4) , Scholastic en Espanol) Scholastic, Inc.

Rayner, Robert. Suspended. 2004. (Sports Stories Ser.). 112p. (J). (gr. 4-8). (***978-1-55028-861-2(X)***); 7.95 (978-1-55028-860-5(1)) Lorimer, James & Co., Ltd., Pubs. CAN. *Dist:* Casemate Pubs. & Bk. Distributors, LLC.

Reinhardt, Dana. Harmless. 2007. 240p. (J). (gr. 7 up). 15.99 (978-0-385-74699-1(7)); lib. bdg. 18.99 (978-0-385-90941-9(1)) Random Hse. Children's Bks. (Lamb, Wendy).

Ritchie, Madonna. Mr. Peabody's Apples. Ritchie, Madonna & Long, Loren, illus. 2003. 40p. (J). 19.95 (978-0-670-05883-9(1)) Callaway Editions, Inc.

—Mr. Peabody's Apples. Ritchie, Madonna & Long, Loren, illus. 2003. 40p. (J). 19.95 (978-0-670-04492-4(X)) Penguin Group (USA) Inc.

Simon, Mary Manz. Piglet Tells the Truth. Stott, Dorothy, illus. 2006. (First Virtues for Toddlers Ser.). 20p. (J). 5.99 (978-0-7847-1407-2(X) , 04035) Standard Publishing.

Sommer, Carl. No One Will Ever Know. 2003. (Another Sommer-Time Story Ser.). (Illus.). 48p. (J). (gr. 1-4). 16.95 incl. audio compact disk (978-1-57537-506-9(0)) Advance Publishing, Inc.

—Tied up in Knots. 2003. (Another Sommer-Time Story Ser.). (Illus.). 48p. (J). 14.95 incl. audio compact disk (978-1-57537-503-8(6)); (gr. 1-4). 16.95 incl. audio (978-1-57537-552-6(4)) Advance Publishing, Inc.

Tell the Truth, Tyler. 2006. 16p. (J). pap. 1.99 (978-0-7847-1709-7(5) , 04170) Standard Publishing.

Undercuffler, Gary, illus. The Boy Who Cried Wolf: A Tale about Telling the Truth. 2006. (Famous Fables Ser.). (J). 6.99 (978-1-59939-026-0(4)) Reader's Digest Young Families, Inc.

TUAREGS

Barber, Nicola. Living in the Sahara. 2007. (J). (***978-1-4109-2816-0(0)***); pap. (***978-1-4109-2825-2(X)***) Steck-Vaughn.

Giraud, Hervé. Leila: A Tuareg Child. Rey, Jean-Charles, photos by. 2005. (Children of the World Ser.). (Illus.). 24p. (J). (gr. k-3). 22.45 (978-1-4103-0545-9(7) , Blackbirch Pr., Inc.) Thomson Gale.

Reynolds, Jan. Sahara: Vanishing Cultures. 2007. 32p. (J). (***978-1-60060-131-6(6)***); (***978-1-60060-146-0(4)***) Lee & Low Bks., Inc.

TUBA—FICTION

Bartlett, T. C. Tuba Lessons. Felix, Monique, illus. 2004. 32p. pap. 9.95 (978-0-89812-522-1(7) , Creative Paperbacks) Creative Co., The.

Tripp, Paul. Tubby the Tuba. Cole, Henry, illus. 2006. 32p. (J). (ps). pap. 16.99 (978-0-525-47717-4(9) , Dutton Juvenile) Penguin Group (USA) Inc.

TUBMAN, HARRIET, 1820?-1913

Abnett, Dan. Harriet Tubman & the Underground Railroad. 2007. (Jr. Graphic Biographies Ser.). (Illus.). 24p. (J). (978-1-4042-2336-3(3)); pap. (978-1-4042-2146-8(8)); (gr. 2-6). lib. bdg. 21.25 (978-1-4042-3393-5(8)) Rosen Publishing Group, Inc., The. (PowerKids Pr.).

Abraham, Philip. Harriet Tubman. 2002. (Wel-Real People Ser.). (Illus.). 24p. (J). (ps-2). 17.00 (978-0-516-23953-8(8)); pap. 4.95 (978-0-516-23604-9(0)) Scholastic Library Publishing. (Children's Pr.).

—Harriet Tubman. 2002. (gr. k-3). lib. bdg. 12.95 (978-0-613-58836-2(3)) Tandem Library Bks.

Adler, David A. A Picture Book of Harriet Tubman. Byrd, Samuel, illus. 2005. (Picture Book Readalong Ser.). (J). (gr. k-4). pap. 16.95 incl. audio (978-1-59519-380-3(4)); pap. 18.95 incl. audio compact disk (978-1-59519-384-1(7)); 28.95 incl. audio compact disk (978-1-59519-385-8(5)); 25.95 incl. audio (978-1-59519-381-0(2)); Set. pap. 37.95 incl. audio (978-1-59519-382-7(0)); Set. pap. 39.95 incl. audio compact disk (978-1-59519-386-5(3)) Live Oak Media.

Allen, Thomas B. Harriet Tubman, Secret Agent: How Daring Slaves & Free Blacks Spied for the Union During the Civil War. Bauer, Carla, illus. 2006. (National Geographic Ser.). 192p. (J). (gr. 5-8). 16.95 (978-0-7922-7889-4(5)); 25.90 (978-0-7922-7890-0(9)) National Geographic Society. (National Geographic Children's Bks.).

Anastasio, Dina. Harriet Tubman. Morgan, Jacqui, illus. 2002. 16p. (J). pap. (978-0-439-35163-8(4)) Scholastic, Inc.

Anderson, Jane. Harriet Tubman & the Underground Railroad. 2005. 22.00 (***978-1-4108-4202-2(9)***) Benchmark Education Co.

Auch, Allison. Mujeres que se atrevieron & Women Who Dared. 2005. spiral bd. 84.00 (***978-1-4108-5692-0(5)***) Benchmark Education Co.

Benge, Janet & Benge, Geoff. Harriet Tubman: Moses of the Slaves. 2002. (Illus.). 208p. pap. 8.99 (978-1-883002-90-9(7)) Emerald Bks.

T U V

Blue, Rose & Naden, Corinne J. Harriet Tubman: Riding the Freedom Train. 2003. (Gateway Biography Ser.: 4). (Illus.). 48p. lib. bdg. 23.90 (978-0-7613-2571-0(9) , Millbrook Pr.) Lerner Publishing Group.

Calkhoven, Laurie. Harriet Tubman: Leading the Way to Freedom. 2008. (Sterling Biographies Ser.). (Illus.). 128p. (J). pap. 5.95 ***(978-1-4027-4117-3(0))*** Sterling Publishing Co., Inc.

Clinton, Catherine. Underground Railroad. 2007. 32p. (J). lib. bdg. 17.89 (978-0-06-050426-7(9)) HarperCollins Pubs.

—When Harriet Met Sojourner. Evans, Shane, illus. 2007. 32p. (J). (gr. k-2). 16.99 (978-0-06-050425-0(0)) HarperCollins Pubs.

Cooper, Terry, ed. Harriet Tubman & the Underground Railroad. 2001. 6p. 3.95 (978-0-439-30953-0(0)) Scholastic, Inc.

Feinstein, Stephen. Read about Harriet Tubman. 2005. (I Like Biographies! Ser.). (Illus.). 24p. (J). lib. bdg. 21.26 (978-0-7660-2591-2(8) , Enslow Elementary) Enslow Pubs., Inc.

Findley, Violet. Easy Reader Biographies: Harriet Tubman: Follow the North Star. 2007. 16p. pap. 2.99 ***(978-0-439-92330-9(1)*** , Teaching Resources) Scholastic, Inc.

Gayle, Sharon. Harriet Tubman & the Freedom Train. Marshall, Felicia, illus. ed. 2005. (Ready-to-Read Ser. Level 3). 32p. (J). lib. bdg. 15.00 (978-1-59054-960-5(0)) Fitzgerald Bks.

—Harriet Tubman & the Freedom Train. Marshall, Felicia, illus. 2003. (Ready-to-Read Ser.). 32p. (J). pap. 3.99 (978-0-689-85480-4(3) , Aladdin) Simon & Schuster Children's Publishing.

Gosda, Randy T. Harriet Tubman. 2002. (First Biographies Ser.). (Illus.). 32p. (J). (gr. k-4). lib. bdg. 22.78 (978-1-57765-736-1(5) , Buddy Bks.) ABDO Publishing Co.

Grant, Callie Smith. Harriet Tubman. 1999. (Young Reader's Christian Library). (Illus.). 224p. (J). (ps-3). pap. 1.39 (978-1-57748-651-0(X)) Barbour Publishing, Inc.

Harriet Tubman, Vol. 2. 2005. (First Biographies Ser.). (YA). (gr. k-3). (978-0-7368-9446-3(2) , Pebble Bks.) Capstone Pr., Inc.

Harriet Tubman & the Underground Railroad. (Graphic History Ser.). 32p. (YA). 7.95 (978-0-7368-5245-6(X)) Capstone Pr., Inc.

Healy, Nick. Harriet Tubman. 2005. (Fact Finders Ser.). (Illus.). 32p. (J). 22.60 (978-0-7368-3743-9(4)) Capstone Pr., Inc.

Kernan, Elizabeth. Harriet Tubman: A Lesson in Bravery. 2002. (Reading Room Collection). (Illus.). 24p. (J). pap. (978-0-8239-8229-5(7)); lib. bdg. 18.75 (978-0-8239-3750-9(X)) Rosen Publishing Group, Inc., The.

—Harriet Tubman: Una Leccion de Coraje. Gonzalez, Tomas, tr. 2003. (Buenas Letras Reading Room Ser.). (SPA., Illus.). 24p. (J). (gr. 4-7). lib. bdg. 18.75 (978-0-8239-6517-5(1) , Buenas Letra) Rosen Publishing Group, Inc., The.

Klingel, Cynthia Fitterer. Harriet Tubman: Abolitionist & Underground Railroad Conductor. 2003. (Spirit of America). (Illus.). 32p. (J). (gr. 2-6). 27.07 (978-1-59296-004-0(9)) Child's World, Inc.

Koestler-Grack, Rachel A. The Story of Harriet Tubman. 2003. (Breakthrough Biographies Ser.). (Illus.). 32p. (gr. 3-5). 23.00 (978-0-7910-7314-8(9) , Chelsea Hse.) Facts On File, Inc.

Kudlinski, Kathleen. Harriet Tubman: Freedom's Trailblazer. Brown, Robert, illus. 2002. (Childhood of Famous Americans Ser.). 192p. (J). pap. 5.99 (978-0-689-84866-7(8) , Aladdin) Simon & Schuster Children's Publishing.

—Harriet Tubman: Freedom's Trailblazer. 2002. (gr. 3-6). lib. bdg. 13.00 (978-0-613-45054-6(X)) Tandem Library Bks.

Kulling, Monica. Escape North! The Story of Harriet Tubman. Corey, Shana, ed. Flavin, Teresa, illus. 2000. (Step into Reading Step 3 Bks.). 48p. (J). (gr. 2-4). pap. 3.99 (978-0-375-80154-9(5) , Random Hse. Bks. for Young Readers) Random Hse. Children's Bks.

—Escape North! The Story of Harriet Tubman. Flavin, Teresa, illus. 2000. (Step into Reading Ser.). (J). 10.79 (978-0-606-19895-0(4)) Tandem Library Bks.

—Escape North! the Story of Harriet Tubman. 2000. (gr. k-3). lib. bdg. 11.80 (978-0-613-32507-3(9)) Tandem Library Bks.

Leavitt, Amie. Harriet Tubman. 2007. (What's So Great About... ? Ser.). (J). lib. bdg. 25.70 ***(978-1-58415-577-5(9))*** Mitchell Lane Pubs., Inc.

Lilley, Stephen R. Fighters Against American Slavery. 1998. (History Makers Ser.). (Illus.). 128p. (YA). (gr. 7-10). 27.45 (978-1-56006-036-9(0) , Lucent Bks.) Thomson Gale.

Lutz, Norma Jean. Harriet Tubman: Leader of the Underground Railroad. (Famous Figures of the Civil War Era Ser.). (Illus.). 80p. (J). (gr. 4-7). 2001. 25.00 (978-0-7910-6008-7(X)); 2000. pap. 25.00 (978-0-7910-6146-6(9)) Facts On File, Inc. (Chelsea Hse.).

—Harriet Tubman: Leader of the Underground Railroad. (Famous Figures of the Civil War Era Ser.). (Illus.). (J). 2001. 15.75 (978-0-606-20691-4(4)); 2000. 80p. lib. bdg. 17.60 (978-0-613-37643-3(9)) Tandem Library Bks.

Lynch, Emma. Harriet Tubman. 2005. (J). pap. (978-1-4034-6367-8(0)); (Illus.). 32p. lib. bdg. 25.36 (978-1-4034-6353-1(0)) Heinemann Library.

Mara, Wil. Harriet Tubman. (Rookie Bios Ser.). (Illus.). 32p. (J). (gr. 1-2). 2003. pap. 4.95 (978-0-516-27337-2(X)); 2002. 20.50 (978-0-516-22521-0(9)) Scholastic Library Publishing. (Children's Pr.).

—Harriet Tubman. 2002. (gr. k-3). lib. bdg. 12.95 (978-0-613-59495-0(9)) Tandem Library Bks.

Marsh, Carole. Harriet Tubman. 2002. (One Thousand Readers Ser.). (Illus.). 12p. (J). (gr. k-4). 2.95 (978-0-635-01480-1(7) , 14807) Gallopade International.

—Harriet Tubman: An Ohio Experience Reader. 2001. (J). (gr. k-5). pap. 1.95 (978-0-635-00435-2(6)) Gallopade International.

—The Virginia Reader: Harriet Tubman. 2001. (Virginia Experience! Ser.). (Illus.). 12p. (J). (gr. k-5). pap. 2.95 (978-0-635-00351-5(1)) Gallopade International.

Martin, Michael. Harriet Tubman & the Underground Railroad. 2005. (Graphic Library). (Illus.). 31p. (J). 22.60 (978-0-7368-3829-0(5)) Capstone Pr., Inc.

Mayer, Cassie. Harriet Tubman. 2007. (J). ***(978-1-4034-9973-8(X))***; pap. ***(978-1-4034-9982-0(9))*** Heinemann Library.

McDonough, Yona Zeldis. Who Was Harriet Tubman? Harrison, Nancy, illus. 2002. (Who Was...? Ser.). 112p. (J). mass mkt. 4.99 (978-0-448-42889-5(X) , Grosset & Dunlap) Penguin Group (USA) Inc.

—Who Was Harriet Tubman? 2002. (gr. 3-6). lib. bdg. 13.00 (978-0-613-61668-3(5)) Tandem Library Bks.

Mortensen, Lori. Harriet Tubman: Hero of the Underground Railroad. Moore, Frances, illus. 2006. (Biographies Ser.). 24p. (J). (gr. k-3). lib. bdg. 23.93 ***(978-1-4048-3103-2(7))*** Picture Window Bks.

Nelson, Richard. Harriet Tubman. 2007. (Essential Lives Ser.). (ENG., Illus.). 112p. (YA). (gr. 8-12). lib. bdg. 32.79 ***(978-1-59928-842-0(7)*** , Essential Library) ABDO Publishing Co.

Nichols, Catherine. Harriet Tubman. Dennington, Brian, illus. 2002. (Hello Reader! Ser.). (J). 3.99 (978-0-439-32103-7(4)) Scholastic, Inc.

Nielsen, Nancy J. Harriet Tubman. 2002. (Let Freedom Ring Ser.). (Illus.). 48p. (J). (gr. 3-4). lib. bdg. 22.60 (978-0-7368-1087-6(0) , Bridgestone Bks.) Capstone Pr., Inc.

Petry, Ann. Harriet Tubman: Conductor on the Underground Railroad. 1999. (YA). pap. 59.20 incl. audio (978-0-7887-3011-5(8) , 40893) Recorded Bks., LLC.

Rau, Dana Meachen. Harriet Tubman. 2000. (Compass Point Early Biographies Ser.). (Illus.). 32p. (J). (gr. 2 up). lib. bdg. 21.26 (978-0-7565-0015-3(X)) Compass Point Bks.

Rausch, Monica. Hariet Tubman. 2006. (ENG & SPA.). (J). pap. ***(978-0-8368-7992-6(9))***; lib. bdg. ***(978-0-8368-7985-8(6))*** Stevens, Gareth Inc. (Weekly Reader Early Learning Library).

—Harriet Tubman. 2006. 24p. (J). pap. ***(978-0-8368-7693-2(8))***; lib. bdg. ***(978-0-8368-7686-4(5))*** Stevens, Gareth Inc. (Weekly Reader Early Learning Library).

Rowley, John. Harriet Tubman. 2002. (Lives & Times Ser.). (Illus.). 24p. (J). (gr. k-3). pap. 6.50 (978-1-4034-0029-1(6) , 91473) Heinemann Library.

Rustad, Martha E. H. Harriet Tubman. Saunders-Smith, Gail, ed. 2001. (First Biographies Ser.). (Illus.). 24p. (J). (gr. k-1). lib. bdg. 15.93 (978-0-7368-0997-9(X) , Pebble Bks.) Capstone Pr., Inc.

Schraff, Anne. Harriet Tubman: Moses of the Underground Railroad. 2001. (African-American Biographies Ser.). (Illus.). 128p. (J). (gr. 6-12). lib. bdg. 26.60 (978-0-7660-1548-7(3)) Enslow Pubs., Inc.

Schroeder, Alan. Minty: A Story of Young Harriet Tubman. Pinkney, Jerry, illus. 2002. (YA). 25.45 (978-0-7587-0382-8(1)) Book Wholesalers, Inc.

—Minty: A Story of Young Harriet Tubman. Pinkney, Jerry, illus. 2000. (J). (ps-ps). lib. bdg. 15.30 (978-0-613-33712-0(3)) Tandem Library Bks.

—Minty: A Story of Young Harriet Tubman. 2000. (978-0-606-20365-4(6)); (YA). (978-0-606-20246-6(3)) Tandem Library Bks.

Shone, Rob & Ganeri, Anita. Harriet Tubman: The Life of an African-American Abolitionist. 2005. (Graphic Nonfiction Ser.). (Illus.). 48p. (J). (gr. 4-6). lib. bdg. 26.50 (978-1-4042-0245-0(5)) Rosen Publishing Group, Inc., The.

Skelton, Renee. Harriet Tubman: A Woman of Courage. 2005. (Time for Kids Ser.). (Illus.). 48p. (J). pap. 3.99 (978-0-06-057607-3(3)) HarperCollins Pubs.

Skelton, Renee. Harriet Tubman A Woman of Courage. 2005. 2005p. (J). lib. bdg. 15.00 ***(978-1-4242-0849-4(1))*** Fitzgerald Bks.

Skelton, Renee & Time for Kids Editors. Harriet Tubman: A Woman of Courage. 2005. (Time for Kids Ser.). (Illus.). 48p. (J). 15.99 (978-0-06-057608-0(1)) HarperCollins Pubs.

Slavicek, Louise Chipley. Harriet Tubman & the Underground Railroad. 2006. (Lucent Library of Black History). 112p. (J). (gr. 7-10). 32.45 (978-1-59018-927-6(2) , Lucent Bks.) Thomson Gale.

Stearns, Dan. Harriet Tubman & the Underground Railroad. 2006. (In the Footsteps of American Heroes Ser.). (Illus.). 64p. (J). pap. 11.95 (978-0-8368-6433-5(6)); lib. bdg. 32.67 (978-0-8368-6428-1(X)) Stevens, Gareth Inc. (World Almanac Library).

Sterling, Dorothy. Freedom Train: The Story of Harriet Tubman. 1999. (J). (gr. 5-8). lib. bdg. 12.40 (978-0-8085-8034-8(5)) Tandem Library Bks.

Taylor, Marian. Harriet Tubman. (Black Americans of Achievement Ser.). (Illus.). 112p. (J). (gr. 6-12). 2005. pap. 13.25 (978-0-7910-8340-6(3)); 2004. 30.00 (978-0-7910-8166-2(4)) Facts On File, Inc. (Chelsea Hse.).

Troy, Don. Harriet Ross Tubman. 1999. (Journey to Freedom Ser.). (Illus.). 40p. (J). (gr. 3-7). 28.50 (978-1-56766-568-0(3)) Child's World, Inc.

Turner, Glennette Tilley. An Apple for Harriet Tubman. Keeter, Susan, illus. 2006. 24p. (J). 15.95 (978-0-8075-0395-9(9)) Whitman, Albert & Co.

Weatherford, Carole Boston. Moses: When Harriet Tubman Led Her People to Freedom. Nelson, Kadir, illus. 2006. 48p. (J). (gr. k-3). 15.99 (978-0-7868-5175-1(9) , Jump at the Sun) Hyperion Bks. for Children.

Weidt, Maryann N. Harriet Tubman. (History Maker Bios Ser.). (Illus.). (J). 2003. 47p. 26.60 (978-0-8225-4676-4(0)); 2002. 48p. pap. 6.95 (978-0-8225-4803-4(8)) Lerner Publishing Group. (Lerner Pubns.).

Wheeler, Jill C. Harriet Tubman. 2003. (Breaking Barriers Ser.). (Illus.). 64p. (J). (gr. 3-8). lib. bdg. 25.65 (978-1-57765-908-2(2)) ABDO Publishing Co.

TUBMAN, HARRIET, 1820?-1913—FICTION

Hedstrom-Page, Deborah. From Slavery to Freedom with Harriet Tubman. Martinez, Sergio, illus. 2007. 80p. (J). (gr. 3-8). 9.99 (978-0-8054-3268-8(X)) B&H Publishing Grp.

Lawrence. Harriet & the Promise Land. 1998. (J). pap. 5.99 (978-0-87628-392-9(X)) Ctr. for Applied Research in Education, The.

TUGBOATS

Doeden, Matt. Tugboats. 2007. 24p. (J). ***(978-0-7368-6720-7(1)*** , Pebble Bks.) Capstone Pr., Inc.

Kreisler, Ken. My Grandpa Is a Tugboat Captain. O'Connor, John P., ed. Kolb, Joe, illus. 1999. 34p. (J). (gr. k-2). spiral bd. 9.95 (978-1-892216-13-7(2) , No. 1892216132) Bristol Fashion Publishing Co.

Schaefer, Lola M. Tugboats. 2000. (Transportation Library). (Illus.). 24p. (J). (gr. 1-2). lib. bdg. 18.60 (978-0-7368-0505-6(2) , Bridgestone Bks.) Capstone Pr., Inc.

TUGBOATS—FICTION

Belle, Jennifer. Little Stalker: A Novel. 2007. 352p. (gr. 8). 24.95 (978-1-59448-946-4(7) , Riverhead Bks. (Hardcover)) Penguin Group (USA) Inc.

Brookes, Diane. The Tough Little Tugboat. Brookes, Diane, illus. 1999. (Illus.). 8p. (J). (ps-3). bds. (978-1-894303-16-3(4)) Raven Rock Publishing.

Golden Books Staff. Scuffy the Tugboat. 2001. (Little Golden Bks.). (Illus.). 24p. (J). (gr. k-k). 2.99 (978-0-307-02046-8(0) , 98282, Golden Bks.) Random Hse. Children's Bks.

Gramatky, Hardie. Little Toot. Gramatky, Hardie, illus. 2007. 104p. (J). (ps). 17.99 (978-0-399-24713-2(0) , Putnam Juvenile) Penguin Group (USA) Inc.

—Little Toot. Burgess, Mark, illus. abr. ed. 2000. (Reading Railroad Bks.). 32p. (J). (ps-3). pap. 3.99 (978-0-448-42297-8(2) , Grosset & Dunlap) Penguin Group (USA) Inc.

Harris-Davies, Dafydd, et al. Caleb a Tyg. 2005. (WEL., Illus.). 23p. (978-0-86381-854-7(4)) Gwasg Carreg Gwalch.

Little Toot. 2004. 24.95 incl. audio (978-1-56008-231-6(3)); pap. 14.95 incl. audio (978-0-7882-0598-9(6)) Weston Woods Studios, Inc.

McMullan, Kate. I'm Mighty! McMullan, Jim, illus. 2003. (J). (978-0-06-056882-5(8)); 40p. 16.99 (978-0-06-009290-0(4)) HarperCollins Pubs.

TUNISIA

Carew-Miller, Anna. Tunisia. 2003. (Modern Middle East Nations & Their Strategic Place in the World Ser.). (Illus.). 112,128p. (YA). (gr. 7 up). lib. bdg. (978-1-59084-518-9(8)) Mason Crest Pubs.

Grolier Educational Staff, contrib. by. Argentina. 2003. (Illus.). 32p. (J). (978-0-7172-5788-1(6) , Grolier) Scholastic Library Publishing.

—Tunisia. 2003. (Illus.). 32p. (J). (978-0-7172-5804-8(1) , Grolier) Scholastic Library Publishing.

TUNISIA—FICTION

Colfer, Eoin. Benny & Omar. 2007. 288p. (gr. 5-17). 18.95 ***(978-1-4231-0281-6(9))***; pap. 7.95 ***(978-1-4231-0282-3(7))*** Miramax Bks.

—Benny & Omar. 2003. 240p. (YA). (gr. 5 up). pap. 7.95 (978-0-86278-567-3(7)) O'Brien Pr., Ltd., The IRL. *Dist:* Independent Pubs. Group.

TUNNELS

see also Excavation; Subways

Borchelt, Kelly L. The Longest Tunnel. 2004. (Extreme Places Ser.). (Illus.). 48p. (J). 26.20 (978-0-7377-1882-9(X) , Greenhaven Pr., Inc.) Thomson Gale.

Crowther, Robert. Deep down under Ground: A Pop-up Book of Amazing Facts & Feats. Crowther, Robert, illus. 2004. (Illus.). 18p. (J). (gr. 3-8). reprint ed. pap. 22.00 (978-0-7567-7179-9(X)) DIANE Publishing Co.

Donovan, Sandy. The Channel Tunnel. 2003. (Great Building Feats Ser.). (Illus.). 96p. (J). (gr. 5-9). 27.93 (978-0-8225-4692-4(2)) Lerner Publishing Group.

Fine, Jil. The Chunnel: The Building of a 200-Year-Old Dream. 2004. (High Interest Bks.). 48p. (YA). (gr. 7-12). pap. 6.95 (978-0-516-25906-2(7) , Children's Pr.) Scholastic Library Publishing.

Hill, Lee Sullivan. Tunnels Go Underground. 2000. (Building Block Bks.). (Illus.). 32p. (J). (gr. k-3). lib. bdg. 14.60 (978-1-57505-429-2(9) , Carolrhoda Bks.) Lerner Publishing Group.

Hunter, Ryan Ann. Dig a Tunnel. Miller, Edward, illus. 1999. 32p. (J). (gr. k-3). tchr. ed. 15.95 (978-0-8234-1391-1(8)) Holiday Hse., Inc.

Landau, Elaine. Tunnels. 2001. (Buildings & Structures Ser.). (Illus.). 48p. (J). (gr. 3-5). 25.00 (978-0-516-22185-4(X) , Children's Pr.) Scholastic Library Publishing.

—Tunnels. 2001. (gr. 3-6). lib. bdg. 15.25 (978-0-613-53575-5(8)) Tandem Library Bks.

Macken, JoAnn Early. Digging Tunnels. 2008. (J). ***(978-1-4296-1234-0(7))*** Capstone Pr., Inc.

Marchant, Ian. Crypts, Caves, & Tunnels of London. 2004. (... . of London Ser.). (Illus.). 96p. 8.99 (978-1-904153-04-7(6)) Watling St., Ltd. GBR. *Dist:* Trafalgar Square Publishing.

Oxlade, Chris. Tunnels. (Illus.). 32p. (J). 2005. (978-1-4034-7906-8(2)); 2000. (gr. 3-5). lib. bdg. 22.79 (978-1-57572-280-1(1)) Heinemann Library.

Pearson, Debora. Hidden Worlds: Amazing Tunnel Stories. Holdcroft, Tina, illus. 2002. (Hidden! Ser.). 32p. (J). (gr. 1-6). pap. 6.95 (978-1-55037-744-6(2)); lib. bdg. 19.95 (978-1-55037-745-3(0)) Annick Pr., Ltd. CAN. *Dist:* Firefly Bks., Ltd.

Richards, Julie. Tunnels. 2003. 32p. (J). lib. bdg. 24.25 (978-1-58340-346-4(9)) Smart Apple Media.

The Seikan Railroad Tunnel, 6 Packs. (On Deck Ser.). 24p. (gr. 4-5). 35.00 (978-0-7578-1072-5(1)) Rigby Education.

Spangenburg, Ray & Moser, Diane. The Story of America's Tunnels. 1999. (Connecting a Continent Ser.). (Illus.). 96p. (YA). (gr. 5 up). lib. bdg. 23.95 (978-0-7351-0199-9(X)) Replica Bks.

Swanson, Diane. Tunnels! 2003. (True Stories from the Edge Ser.). (Illus.). 144p. (J). (gr. 3-7). 18.95 (978-1-55037-781-1(7)); pap. 6.95 (978-1-55037-780-4(9)) Annick Pr., Ltd. CAN. *Dist:* Firefly Bks., Ltd.

—Tunnels! 2003. (gr. 3-6). lib. bdg. 15.25 (978-0-613-67587-1(8)) Tandem Library Bks.

Thomas, Mark. The Seikan Railroad Tunnel: World's Longest Tunnel. 2002. (Reading Power Ser.). (Illus.). 24p. (J). (gr. 1). lib. bdg. 17.25 (978-0-8239-5991-4(0) , PowerKids Pr.) Rosen Publishing Group, Inc., The.

—El Tunel Ferroviario Seikan: El Tunel Mas Largo Del Mundo. 2004. (Estructuras Extraordinarias Ser.). (SPA & ENG., Illus.). 24p. (J). (gr. 3-6). lib. bdg. 17.25 (978-0-8239-6867-1(7) , Buenas Letra) Rosen Publishing Group, Inc., The.

Tunnels: Early Level Satellite Individual Title Six-Packs. (Sails Literacy Ser.). 16p. (gr. 1-2). 27.00 (978-0-7578-2942-0(2)) Rigby Education.

TURKEY

Blomquist, Christopher. Turkey, a Primary Source Guide. 2005. (Countries of the World, a Primary Source Journey Ser.). (Illus.). 24p. (J). 19.95 (978-1-4042-2759-0(8) , PowerKids Pr.) Rosen Publishing Group, Inc., The.

Cornell, Kari & Turkoglu, Nurcay. Cooking the Turkish Way. 2nd rev. ed. 2004. (Easy Menu Ethnic Cookbooks). (Illus.). 72p. (J). 25.26 (978-0-8225-4123-3(8) , Carolrhoda Bks.) Lerner Publishing Group.

Eboch, Chris. Turkey. 2003. (Modern Nations of the World Ser.). (Illus.). 112p. (J). 29.95 (978-1-59018-122-5(0) , Lucent Bks.) Thomson Gale.

Ganeri, Anita. Focus on Turkey. 2007. (J). pap. ***(978-0-8368-6760-2(2))***; 64p. (gr. 5-8). lib. bdg. 33.27 ***(978-0-8368-6753-4(X))*** Stevens, Gareth Inc. (World Almanac Library).

Harmon, Daniel E. Turkey. 2003. (Modern Middle East Nations & Their Strategic Place in the World Ser.). (Illus.). 112,128p. (YA). (gr. 7 up). lib. bdg. (978-1-59084-524-0(2)) Mason Crest Pubs.

Kemal, Neriman & Kuo, Selina. Turkey. 2001. (Countries of the World Ser.). (Illus.). 96p. (J). (gr. 6 up). lib. bdg. 30.00 (978-0-8368-2341-7(9)) Stevens, Gareth Inc.

Khanduri, Kamini, intro. & retold by. Tales of the Trojan War. Khanduri, Kamini, retold by. 2002. (Usborne Classics Ser.). (Illus.). 159p. (J). pap. (978-0-439-78708-6(4)) Scholastic, Inc.

McNeil, Niki, et al. HOCPP 1117 Turkey Time. 2006. spiral bd. 14.00 ***(978-1-60308-117-7(8))*** In the Hands of a Child.

Mitten, Christopher. Turkey. 2002. (Steadwell Books World Tour). (Illus.). 48p. (J). lib. bdg. 25.70 (978-0-7398-5757-1(6)) Raintree.

Orr, Tamra. Turkey. 2003. (Enchantment of the World, Second Ser.). (Illus.). 144p. (J). (gr. 5-9). 36.00 (978-0-516-22679-8(7) , Children's Pr.) Scholastic Library Publishing.

O'Shea, Maria. Turkey. 1999. (Festivals of the World Ser.). (Illus.). 32p. (J). (gr. 3 up). lib. bdg. 24.67 (978-0-8368-2037-9(1)) Stevens, Gareth Inc.

Pavlovic, Zoran. Turkey. 2004. (Modern World Nations Ser.). (Illus.). 120p. (gr. 6-12). 30.00 (978-0-7910-7916-4(3) , Chelsea Hse.) Facts On File, Inc.

Stefoff, Rebecca. Asian Empires. 2004. (Illus.). 48p. (J). 27.07 (978-0-7614-1643-2(9) , Benchmark Bks.) Cavendish, Marshall Corp.

Zocchi, Judy. In Turkey. Brodie, Neale, illus. 2005. (Global Adventures II Ser.). 32p. (J). per. 9.95 (978-1-59646-153-6(5)) Dingles & Co.

—In Turkey/en Turquía. Brodie, Neale, illus. 2005. (Global Adventures II Ser.).Tr. of En Turquía. (ENG & SPA.). 32p. (J). per. 9.95 (978-1-59646-155-0(1)) Dingles & Co.

TURKEY—BIOGRAPHY

Lashnits, Tom. Recep Tayyip Erdogan: Prime Minister of Turkey. Schlesinger, Arthur M., Jr., ed. 2005. (Major World Leaders Ser.). (Illus.). 112-144p. (gr. 6-12). 30.00 (978-0-7910-8263-8(6) , Chelsea Hse.) Facts On File, Inc.

TURKEY—FICTION

Alexander, Lloyd. The Xanadu Adventure. 2007. (Vesper Holly Ser.). 160p. (YA). (gr. 5-9). 5.99 (978-0-14-240786-8(0) , Dutton Juvenile) Penguin Group (USA) Inc.

Anderson, Derek & Child, Lydia Maria. Over the River: A Turkey's Tale. 2005. (Illus.). 40p. (J). 14.95 (978-0-689-87635-6(1)) Simon & Schuster Children's Publishing.

Bagdasarian, Adam. Forgotten Fire. 2002. (Illus.). 304p. (YA). (gr. 9 up). mass mkt. 6.99 (978-0-440-22917-9(0) , Laurel Leaf) Random Hse. Children's Bks.

—Forgotten Fire. 2002. (gr. 7-12). lib. bdg. 14.15 (978-0-613-49414-4(8)) Tandem Library Bks.

Bunting, Eve. A Turkey for Thanksgiving. 2002. (Illus.). (J). 13.79 (978-0-7587-3875-2(7)) Book Wholesalers, Inc.

Cowley, Joy. Gracias the Thanksgiving Turkey. Cepeda, Joe, illus. 2005. 32p. (J). (ps-ps). pap. 5.99 (978-0-439-76987-7(6) , Scholastic Paperbacks) Scholastic, Inc.

Durmush, F. Ayshe, an Anatolian Tale. 2007. (ENG.). 84p. per. ***(978-1-84747-171-0(4))*** Chipmunkapublishing.

Mein eigenes Auto. 2005. (GER.). 4.95 net. (978-0-929724-89-8(5)) Command Performance Language Institute.

Sargent, Dave & Sargent, David, Jr. Tom Turkey: Don't Bully, 19, 20. Lenoir, Jane, illus. 2003. (Feather Tales Ser.: 20). 42p. (J). pap. 6.95 (978-1-56763-758-8(2)) Ozark Publishing.

Whelan, Gloria. Parade of Shadows. 2007. 304p. (J). (gr. 5 up). 15.99 (*978-0-06-089028-5(2)); lib. bdg. 16.89 (*978-0-06-089029-2(0)) HarperCollins Pubs.

TURKEY—HISTORY

Ahmed, Akbar, intro. Turkey. 2002. (Creation of the Modern Middle East Ser.). (Illus.). 125p. (gr. 6-12). 35.00 (978-0-7910-6504-4(9) , Chelsea Hse.) Facts On File, Inc.

Carlyon, Patrick. The Gallipoli Story. 2004. (Illus.). 192p. pap. 9.99 (978-0-14-300143-0(4) , Penguin Global) Penguin Group (USA) Inc.

Coolidge, Olivia E. The Trojan War. 2001. (gr. 5-8). lib. bdg. 14.10 (978-0-613-35586-5(5)) Tandem Library Bks.

Davis, Lucile. The Ottoman Empire. 2004. (Life During the Great Civilizations Ser.). (Illus.). 48p. (J). (gr. 3-5). 24.95 (978-1-56711-739-4(2) , Blackbirch Pr., Inc.) Thomson Gale.

Greenblatt, Miriam. Suleyman the Magnificent & the Ottoman Empire. 2002. (Rulers & Their Times Ser.). (Illus.). 80p. (J). (gr. 8-12). 29.93 (978-0-7614-1489-6(4) , Benchmark Bks.) Cavendish, Marshall Corp.

Hammond, Paula. Greece & Turkey. 2002. (Cultures & Costumes Ser.). (Illus.). 64p. (J). (gr. 7 up). lib. bdg. (978-1-59084-437-3(8)) Mason Crest Pubs.

Hay, Jeff. Renaissance. 2001. (gr. 7-12). lib. bdg. 39.05 (978-0-613-73785-2(7)) Tandem Library Bks.

Kohler, Christine. Turkey in the News: Past, Present, & Future. 2006. (Middle East Nations in the News Ser.). (Illus.). 128p. (J). lib. bdg. 33.27 (978-1-59845-024-8(7) , MyReportLinks.com Bks.) Enslow Pubs., Inc.

Ruggiero, Adriane. The Ottoman Empire. 2002. (Cultures of the Past Ser.). (Illus.). 80p. (YA). (gr. 5). 29.93 (978-0-7614-1494-0(0) , Benchmark Bks.) Cavendish, Marshall Corp.

Schuh, Marl C. Turkeys on the Farm, 6 vols. (gr. k-2). 28.95 (978-0-7368-9385-5(7)) Red Brick Learning.

Van Cleaf, Kristin. Turkey. 2007. (Countries Set VI Ser.). (Illus.). 40p. (J). (gr. k-6). lib. bdg. 24.21 (*978-1-59928-787-4(0) , Checkerboard Library) ABDO Publishing Co.

Zocchi, Judy. In Turkey. Brodie, Neale, illus. 2005. (Global Adventures I Ser.). 32p. (J). pap. 9.95 (978-1-59646-152-9(7)); lib. bdg. 20.65 (978-1-59646-031-7(8)) Dingles & Co.

—In Turkey/en Turquía. Brodie, Neale, illus. 2005. (Global Adventures I Ser.).Tr. of En Turquía. (ENG & SPA.). 32p. (J). pap. 9.95 (978-1-59646-154-3(3)); lib. bdg. 20.65 (978-1-59646-032-4(6)) Dingles & Co.

TURKEYS

Arnosky, Jim. All about Turkeys. 1998. (All about Ser.). 32p. (J). (ps-5). (Illus.). pap. 15.95 (978-0-590-48147-2(9)); pap. 5.99 (978-0-590-69780-4(3)) Scholastic, Inc.

Endres, Hollie. Turkeys. 2007. (Illus.). 24p. (J). lib. bdg. 19.95 (978-1-60014-086-0(6)) Bellwether Media.

Grolier Educational Staff. Turkeys. 2001. (Nature's Children Ser.). (Illus.). 48p. (J). (978-0-7172-5550-4(6) , Grolier) Scholastic Library Publishing.

Murray, Julie. Turkeys. 2005. (Animal Kingdom Set Ii Ser.). (Illus.). 24p. (J). (gr. k-4). lib. bdg. 21.35 (978-1-59197-337-9(6)) ABDO Publishing Co.

Patent, Dorothy Hinshaw. Wild Turkeys. Munoz, William, photos by. 1999. (Early Bird Nature Bks.). (Illus.). 48p. (J). (gr. 2-4). lib. bdg. 25.26 (978-0-8225-3026-8(0) , Lerner Pubns.) Lerner Publishing Group.

Schuh, Mari C. Turkeys on the Farm. 2002. (On the Farm Ser.). (Illus.). 24p. (J). (gr. k-1). lib. bdg. 15.93 (978-0-7368-1190-3(7) , Pebble Bks.) Capstone Pr., Inc.

Stemple, David. High Ridge Gobbler. 2001. (gr. 3-6). lib. bdg. 19.90 (978-0-613-51839-0(X)) Tandem Library Bks.

TURKEYS—FICTION

Ada, Alma Flor. Pavo para la Cena de Accion de Gracias? No Gracias! 2000. (SPA.). (gr. k-3). lib. bdg. 17.60 (978-0-613-79371-1(4)) Tandem Library Bks.

—Turkey for Thanksgiving Dinner? No Thanks! 2000. (gr. k-3). lib. bdg. 17.60 (978-0-613-79397-1(8)) Tandem Library Bks.

Alley, R. W., illus. The Know-Nothings Talk Turkey. 2002. (Know-Nothings Ser.). (J). 12.30 (978-0-7587-6906-0(7)) Book Wholesalers, Inc.

Archer, Peggy. Turkey Surprise. Wickstrom, Thor, illus. 32p. (J). (gr. k). 2007. pap. 5.99 (978-0-14-240852-0(2) , Puffin); 2005. 10.99 (978-0-8037-2969-8(3) , Dial) Penguin Group (USA) Inc.

Auch, Mary Jane & Auch, Herm, illus. Beauty & the Beaks: A Turkey's Cautionary Tale. 2007. 32p. (J). (ps-3). 16.95 (978-0-8234-1990-6(8)) Holiday Hse., Inc.

Bateman, Teresa. A Plump & Perky Turkey. Shelly, Jeff, illus. 2005. 32p. (J). pap. 5.95 (978-0-7614-5188-4(9)) Cavendish, Marshall Corp.

—A Plump & Perky Turkey. Shelly, Jeff, illus. 2001. 40p. (J). (ps-3). 15.95 (978-1-890817-91-6(0)) Winslow Pr.

Crissey, Brian L. The Loneliest Christmas Tree. Crissey, Noah, illus. 2004. (J). (978-1-930724-12-9(8)); (978-1-930724-13-6(6)) Granite Publishing, LLC.

Goodspeed, Judy. Perky Turkey Finds a Friend. 2006. (Illus.). 24p. (J). lib. bdg. 24.95 (978-0-9778651-2-3(6)) Dragonfly Publishing, Inc.

—Perky Turkey's Perfect Plan. 2006. (Illus.). 22p. (J). lib. bdg. 24.95 (978-0-9778651-1-6(8)) Dragonfly Publishing, Inc.

—Perky Turkey's Perfect Plan. Taylor, Chet, illus. 2005. 22p. (J). 18.99 (978-0-9765786-0-4(3)) Dragonfly Publishing, Inc.

Heurtelou, Maude. Konpe Kabrit ak Konpe Kodenn. Louissaint, Louis, illus. 1999. Tr. of Turkey & Goat. (CRP.). 26p. (J). (gr. 3-5). pap. 19.00 incl. audio (978-1-881839-94-1(X)) Educa Vision.

Hines, Gary. Thanksgiving in the White House. Wallner, Alexandra, illus. rev. ed. 2003. 32p. (J). 15.95 (978-0-8050-6530-5(X) , Holt, Henry & Co. Bks. For Young Readers) Holt, Henry & Co.

Hunter, Helen W. Turkey Hunting with Grandpa. Rozeboom, Grant, illus. 2000. (Young American Hunting & Fishing Ser.: Vol. 2). (J). (gr. 2-7). pap. 9.99 (978-0-9662769-2-3(2)) Hunter Hse. Pubns.

Johnston, Tony. Ten Fat Turkeys. Deas, Richard F., illus. 2004. 32p. (J). (gr. k-ps). pap. 3.99 (978-0-439-45948-8(6) , Cartwheel Bks.) Scholastic, Inc.

Karr, Kathleen. The Great Turkey Walk. 208p. (J). 2000. (gr. 4-7). pap. 6.95 (978-0-374-42798-6(4) , Sunburst); 1998. (gr. 5-9). 17.00 (978-0-374-32773-6(4) , Farrar, Straus & Giroux (BYR)) Farrar, Straus & Giroux.

—The Great Turkey Walk. 2000. (J). (978-0-606-20132-2(7)) Tandem Library Bks.

—Great Turkey Walk. 2000. 199p. (J). (gr. 4-7). lib. bdg. 12.60 (978-0-606-20395-1(8)); (gr. 3-6). lib. bdg. 12.95 (978-0-613-30449-8(7)) Tandem Library Bks.

—The Great Turkey Walk. unabr. ed. 2000. (YA). (gr. 5 up). pap. 59.00 incl. audio (978-0-7887-3631-5(0) , 41006X4) Recorded Bks., LLC.

Langlois, Annie. L' Evasion d'Alfred le Dindon. Beaulieu, Jimmy, illus. 2004. (Roman Jeunesse Ser.). (FRE.). 96p. (J). (gr. 4-7). pap. (978-2-89021-687-7(X)) Diffusion du livre Mirabel.

Law, Felicia. Rumble Meets Chester the Chef. Pak, Yoon Mi, illus. 2006. (Read-It! Readers Ser.). 32p. (J). (gr. 2-4). 18.60 (978-1-4048-1335-9(7)) Picture Window Bks.

Martin, Ann M. Karen's Runaway Turkey. 1999. (Baby-Sitters Little Sister Ser.: No. 115). (Illus.). 112p. (J). (gr. 3-7). pap. 3.99 (978-0-590-52392-9(9)) Scholastic, Inc.

Mayr, Diane. Run, Turkey Run. Rader, Laura, illus. 2007. 32p. (J). (ps-2). 15.95 (*978-0-8027-9630-1(3)) Walker & Co.

Mayr, Diane & Rader, Laura. Run, Turkey Run. 2007. (Illus.). 32p. (J). 16.85 (*978-0-8027-9631-8(1)) Walker & Co.

Morgan, Allen. Matthew & the Midnight Turkeys. Martchenko, Michael, illus. 2003. 24p. (J). (ps-2). pap. 5.95 (978-0-920303-37-5(4)); (Annikins Ser.: Vol. 11). pap. 0.99 (978-1-55037-193-2(2)) Annick Pr., Ltd. CAN. *Dist:* Firefly Bks., Ltd.

Mullican, Judy. Mr. Turkey. Carroll, Ken, Jr., illus. l.t. ed. 1998. (Cuddle Bks.). 7p. (J). (ps-k). pap. 10.95 (978-1-57332-126-6(5)) HighReach Learning, Inc.

Nielsen, Gwyn English. Torey the Turkey Goes Skiing. 2003. (Illus.). 24p. (Orig.). (ps-4). pap. 5.99 (978-0-9660726-0-0(X)) C.G.S. Pr.

Nikola-Lisa, W. Setting the Turkeys Free. Wilson-Max, Ken, illus. 2004. 32p. (ps-1). 15.99 (978-0-7868-1952-2(9) , Jump at the Sun) Hyperion Bks. for Children.

Reed, Lynn Rowe. Thelonius Turkey Lives! 2005. (Illus.). 40p. (J). (gr. k-3). 15.95 (978-0-375-83126-3(6) , Knopf Bks. for Young Readers) Random Hse. Children's Bks.

Robbins, Sandra. Tobias Turkey: A Thanksgiving Tale. Oseki, Iku, illus. 1998. (See-More's Stories Ser.). 32p. (J). (ps-3). pap. 6.95 (978-1-882601-26-4(2)); pap. 11.95 incl. audio (978-1-882601-28-8(9)) See-More's Workshop.

Robinson, Anne. Tom Turkey. 2001. (J). cd-rom 9.95 (978-1-58338-357-5(3)) CrossroadsPub.com.

Scheer, Julian. A Thanksgiving Turkey. Himler, Ronald, illus. 2001. 32p. (J). (gr. k-3). tchr. ed. 16.95 (978-0-8234-1674-5(7)) Holiday Hse., Inc.

Sharmat, Marjorie Weinman & Sharmat, Mitchell. Nate the Great Talks Turkey. Wheeler, Jody, illus. 2007. (Nate the Great Ser.). 96p. (J). (gr. 1-4). pap. 4.50 (*978-0-440-42126-9(8) , Yearling) Random Hse. Children's Bks.

Sharmat, Mitchell & Sharmat, Marjorie Weinman. Nate the Great Talks Turkey. Wheeler, Jody, illus. 2006. 80p. (J). (gr. 1-4). 11.95 (978-0-385-73336-6(4)); lib. bdg. 13.99 (978-0-385-90353-0(7)) Random Hse. Children's Bks. (Delacorte Bks. for Young Readers).

Spirn, Michele. The Know-Nothings Talk Turkey. Alley, R. W., illus. 2001. 48p. (J). (gr. k-3). lib. bdg. 11.80 (978-0-613-62145-8(X)) Tandem Library Bks.

Spirn, Michele Sobel. The Know-Nothings Talk Turkey. Alley, R. W., illus. (I Can Read Bks.). 48p. (J). (ps-3). 2001. pap. 3.99 (978-0-06-444251-0(9) , Harper Trophy); 2000. 14.95 (978-0-06-028183-0(9)); 2000. 14.89 (978-0-06-028184-7(7)) HarperCollins Pubs.

—The Know-Nothings Talk Turkey. Alley, Robert W., illus. 2000. 48p. (J). (gr. k-3). lib. bdg. 11.19 (978-0-606-22291-4(X)) Tandem Library Bks.

Steinberg, David. The Turkey Ball. Conrad, Liz, illus. 2005. 10p. (J). (ps-2). bds. 6.99 (978-0-8431-1456-0(8) , Price Stern Sloan) Penguin Group (USA) Inc.

Suhay, Lisa. Pardon Me, It's Ham, Not Turkey. Cindy, Huffman, ed. Barcita, Pamela, illus. 2007. (J). (ps-3). lib. bdg. 17.95 (*978-1-933982-01-4(2)) Bumble Bee Publishing.

Turkey in the Straw. (J). (ps-1). pap. 7.50 (978-0-932970-93-0(1)) Prinit Pr.

Ure, Jean. Snow Kittens. 1999. (We Love Animals Bks.). (Illus.). 160p. (J). (gr. 4-7). pap. 3.95 (978-0-7641-0970-6(7)) Barron's Educational Series, Inc.

Wallace, Carol. Turkeys Together. Rogers, Jaqueline, illus. 40p. (J). (ps). 15.95 (978-0-8234-1895-4(2)) Holiday Hse., Inc.

Wheeler, Lisa. Turk & Runt: A Thanksgiving Comedy. Ansley, Frank, illus. 2005. 32p. (J). 6.99 (978-1-4169-0714-5(9) , Aladdin) Simon & Schuster Children's Publishing.

Williams, Jacklyn. Happy Thanksgiving, Gus! Cushman, Doug, illus. 2005. (Read-It! Readers Ser.). 32p. (J). (gr. k-3). 18.60 (978-1-4048-0961-1(9)) Picture Window Bks.

Yoon, Salina. Five Silly Turkeys. Yoon, Salina, illus. 2005. 10p. (J). (ps-1). bds. 5.99 (978-0-8431-1416-4(9) , Price Stern Sloan) Penguin Group (USA) Inc.

TURNER, J. M. W. (JOSEPH MALLORD WILLIAM), 1775-1851

Woodhouse, Jayne. Joseph Turner. 2000. (Life & Work of. . . Ser.). (Illus.). 32p. (J). (gr. k-2). lib. bdg. 21.36 (978-1-57572-345-7(X)) Heinemann Library.

TURNER, NAT, 1800-1831

Bisson, Terry. Nat Turner: Slave Revolt Leader. (Black Americans of Achievement Ser.). (Illus.). 112p. (J). (gr. 6-12). 2005. pap. 13.25 (978-0-7910-8341-3(1)); 2004. 30.00 (978-0-7910-8167-9(2)) Facts On File, Inc. (Chelsea Hse.).

Edwards, Judith. Nat Turner's Slave Rebellion in American History. 2000. (In American History Ser.). (Illus.). 112p. (YA). (gr. 5-12). lib. bdg. 26.60 (978-0-7660-1302-5(2)) Enslow Pubs., Inc.

Gregson, Susan R. Nat Turner: Rebellious Slave. 2003. (Let Freedom Ring Ser.). (Illus.). 48p. (J). (gr. 3-4). lib. bdg. 22.60 (978-0-7368-1555-0(4) , Bridgestone Bks.) Capstone Pr., Inc.

Lilley, Stephen R. Fighters Against American Slavery. 1998. (History Makers Ser.). (Illus.). 128p. (YA). (gr. 7-10). 27.45 (978-1-56006-036-9(0) , Lucent Bks.) Thomson Gale.

Marsh, Carole. Nat Turner. 2002. (One Thousand Readers Ser.). (Illus.). 12p. (J). (gr. k-4). 2.95 (978-0-635-01530-3(7) , 15307) Gallopade International.

—The Virginia Reader: Nat Turner. 2001. (Virginia Experience! Ser.). 12p. (J). (gr. k-4). pap. 2.95 (978-0-635-00363-8(5)) Gallopade International.

TURTLES

Arnosky, Jim. All about Turtles. 1999. (All About Ser.). 32p. (J). pap. 5.99 (978-0-590-69781-1(1)) Scholastic, Inc.

Ashton, Patricia. The Gopher Tortoise: A Life History. 2004. (Life History Ser.). (Illus.). 72p. (J). 19.95 (978-1-56164-303-5(3)); pap. 14.95 (978-1-56164-301-1(7)) Pineapple Pr., Inc.

Baskin-Salzberg, Anita & Salzberg, Allen. Turtles. 1998. (Illus.). 63p. (J). (ps-7). lib. bdg. 15.25 (978-0-613-14379-0(5)) Tandem Library Bks.

Becker, John E. Green Sea Turtles. 2003. (Returning Wildlife Ser.). (Illus.). 48p. (J). 26.20 (978-0-7377-1831-7(5) , Greenhaven Pr., Inc.) Thomson Gale.

Berger, Melvin & Berger, Gilda. Turtles. 2002. (Illus.). 16p. (J). (978-0-439-44535-1(3)) Scholastic, Inc.

Biel, Timothy Levi. Turtles. rev. ed. 2003. (Illus.). 24p. (J). (gr. 1-7). 10.95 (978-1-888153-99-6(7) , Zoo Bks.) Wildlife Education, Ltd.

Blomquist, Christopher. Box Turtles. 2004. (Library of Turtles & Tortoises). (Illus.). 24p. (J). lib. bdg. 18.75 (978-0-8239-6735-3(2) , PowerKids Pr.) Rosen Publishing Group, Inc., The.

—Desert Turtles. 2004. (Library of Turtles & Tortoises). (Illus.). 24p. (J). lib. bdg. 18.75 (978-0-8239-6739-1(5) , PowerKids Pr.) Rosen Publishing Group, Inc., The.

—Gopher Tortoises. 2004. (Library of Turtles & Tortoises). (Illus.). 24p. (J). lib. bdg. 18.75 (978-0-8239-6740-7(9) , PowerKids Pr.) Rosen Publishing Group, Inc., The.

—Snapping Turtles. 2004. (Library of Turtles & Tortoises). (Illus.). 24p. (J). lib. bdg. 18.75 (978-0-8239-6736-0(0) , PowerKids Pr.) Rosen Publishing Group, Inc., The.

—Spiny Soft Shell Turtles. 2004. (Library of Turtles & Tortoises). 24p. (J). lib. bdg. 18.75 (978-0-8239-6737-7(9) , PowerKids Pr.) Rosen Publishing Group, Inc., The.

Box Turtle, Earth & Time. 2007. (YA). (978-0-9763354-3-6(3)) Gold Angel Pr.

Bredeson, Carmen. Fun Facts about Turtles! 2007. (I Like Reptiles & Amphibians! Ser.). (Illus.). 24p. (J). (gr. 1-3). lib. bdg. 21.26 (*978-0-7660-2785-5(6) , Enslow Elementary) Enslow Pubs., Inc.

Brennan, Patricia. Sea Turtles & Other Shelled Reptiles. 2002. (World Book's Animals of the World Ser.). (Illus.). 63p. (J). (978-0-7166-1231-5(3)) World Bk., Inc.

Burns, Diane L. Frogs, Toads & Turtles. Garrow, Linda, illus. 1999. (Young Naturalist Field Guides Ser.). 40p. (J). (gr. 3 up). lib. bdg. 24.67 (978-0-8368-2145-1(9)) Stevens, Gareth Inc.

—Frogs, Toads & Turtles. Garrow, Linda, illus. 2004. (Take-Along Guide Ser.). 48p. (J). (gr. 2-5). pap. 7.95 (978-1-55971-593-5(6) , NorthWord Bks. for Young Readers) T&N Children's Publishing.

Carroll, D. Year of the Turtle. (Illus.). 160p. (J). 21.95 (978-0-8048-7036-8(5)) Tuttle Publishing.

Cerullo, Mary M. Sea Turtles: Ocean Nomads. Rotman, Jeffrey L., illus. Rotman, Jeffrey L., photos by. 2003. 48p. (J). (gr. 2-6). 17.99 (978-0-525-46649-9(5) , Dutton Juvenile) Penguin Group (USA) Inc.

Cooper, Jason. Loggerhead Turtle. 2003. (Life Cycles Ser.). (Illus.). 24p. (J). (gr. 1-4). 17.95 (978-1-58952-354-8(7)) Rourke Publishing, LLC.

Costain, Meredith. Sea Turtles. 2000. (gr. k-3). lib. bdg. 11.80 (978-0-613-30716-1(X)) Tandem Library Bks.

Cussen, Sarah. Those Terrific Turtles. Weaver, Steve, illus. Dennis, David M., photos by. 2006. 55p. (J). 14.95 (978-1-56164-363-9(7)); pap. 8.95 (978-1-56164-364-6(5)) Pineapple Pr., Inc.

Davies, Nicola. One Tiny Turtle. Chapman, Jane, illus. 32p. (J). (gr. k-3). 2001. 15.99 (978-0-7636-1549-9(8)); 2005. reprint ed. pap. 6.99 (978-0-7636-2311-1(3)) Candlewick Pr.

Dennard, Deborah. Turtles. Dewey, Jennifer Owings, illus. 2004. (Our Wild World Ser.). 48p. (J). (gr. 2-5). ring bd. 10.95 (978-1-55971-862-2(5)); pap. 7.95 (978-1-55971-861-5(7)) T&N Children's Publishing. (NorthWord Bks. for Young Readers).

Dorling Kindersley Publishing Staff. Turtle. 2006. (Watch Me Grow Ser.). (Illus.). 24p. (J). 7.99 (978-0-7566-1977-0(7)) Dorling Kindersley Publishing, Inc.

Edwards, Roberta. Best Friends: The True Story of Owen & Mzee. Schwartz, Carol, illus. 2007. (All Aboard Science Reader Ser.). 32p. (J). pap. 3.99 (978-0-448-44567-0(0) , Grosset & Dunlap) Penguin Group (USA) Inc.

Foley, Cate. My Turtle. 2001. (My Pets Ser.). (Illus.). 24p. (J). (ps-2). 17.00 (978-0-516-23188-4(X) , Children's Pr.) Scholastic Library Publishing.

Franks, Katie. Turtles up Close. 2008. (J). lib. bdg. (*978-1-4042-4139-8(6) , PowerKids Pr.) Rosen Publishing Group, Inc., The.

Fridell, Ron & Walsh, Patricia. Life Cycle of a Turtle. 2001. (Heinemann First Library). (Illus.). 32p. (J). (gr. k-2). lib. bdg. 21.36 (978-1-58810-096-2(0)) Heinemann Library.

Gareth Stevens Publishing Staff, contrib. by. Turtles. 2004. (All about Wild Animals Ser.). (Illus.). 32p. (J). (gr. 2 up). lib. bdg. 23.33 (978-0-8368-4123-7(9)) Stevens, Gareth Inc.

George, Jean Craighead. Galapagos Picture Book. Minor, Wendell, illus. 32p. (J). (gr. k-3). Date not set. 5.99 (978-0-06-443648-9(9)); 2001. 15.95 (978-0-06-028793-1(4)); 2001. lib. bdg. 15.89 (978-0-06-028794-8(2)) HarperCollins Pubs.

Gibbons, Gail. Sea Turtles. Gibbons, Gail, illus. unabr. ed. 1999. (Gail Gibbons' Creatures Great & Small Ser.). (Illus.). (J). (gr. 1-6). pap. 16.95 incl. audio (978-0-87499-583-1(3)) BBC Audiobooks America.

—Sea Turtles. Gibbons, Gail, illus. 1999. (Illus.). 28.95 incl. audio compact disk (978-1-59519-078-9(3)); pap. 39.95 incl. audio compact disk (978-1-59519-077-2(5)); (J). pap. 18.95 incl. audio compact disk (978-1-59519-076-5(7)); (J). (gr. 1-6). 25.95 incl. audio (978-0-87499-584-8(1)) Live Oak Media.

Gilkerson, Patricia. My Adventure with Sea Turtles. 2007. 44p. (J). 8.99 (978-1-59092-466-2(5) , Orchard Academy Pr.) Windstorm Creative.

Gill, Janie S. Why Turtles Have Shells. Reese, Robert, illus. 1999. 5.95 (978-0-89868-527-5(3)); 23p. (J). pap. 3.95 (978-0-89868-526-8(5)); 23p. (J). lib. bdg. 10.95 (978-0-89868-525-1(7)) ARO Publishing Co.

Gillis, Jennifer Blizin. Turtles. 2004. (Heinemann Read & Learn Ser.). 24p. (J). 18.50 (978-1-4034-5056-2(0)); pap. 5.75 (978-1-4034-6023-3(X)) Heinemann Library.

Glaser, Jason. Sea Turtles. 2006. (Illus.). 24p. (J). (978-0-7368-5423-8(1)) Capstone Pr., Inc.

Gordon, Sharon. Adivina Quién Se Esconde. 2006. (Bookworms Ser.). (SPA & ENG., Illus.). 32p. (J). lib. bdg. 22.79 (978-0-7614-2385-0(0)) Cavendish, Marshall Corp.

—Guess Who Hides (Adivina Quién Se Esconde) 2006. (Bookworms Ser.). (ENG & SPA., Illus.). 32p. (J). lib. bdg. 22.79 (978-0-7614-2465-9(2)) Cavendish, Marshall Corp.

Group/McGraw-Hill, Wright. The Turtle: Collection 2. (Storyteller Interactive Writing Cards Ser.). (gr. k-3). (978-0-322-09340-9(6)) Wright Group, The.

—Turtles, Tortoises & Terrapins: Level M, 6 vols. 128p. (gr. 3-6). 36.95 (978-0-322-06723-3(5)) Wright Group, The.

Guiberson, Brenda Z. Into the Sea. Berenzy, Alix, illus. rev. ed. 2000. 32p. (J). (ps-k). pap., pap. 7.95 (978-0-8050-6481-0(8) , Holt, Henry & Co. Bks. For Young Readers) Holt, Henry & Co.

—Into the Sea. Berenzy, Alix, illus. 2000. (J). (ps-k). lib. bdg. 15.25 (978-0-613-28538-4(7)) Tandem Library Bks.

Gutman, Bill. Becoming Best Friends with Your Iguana, Snake or Turtle. Green, Anne Canevari, illus. 2001. (Pet Friends Ser.). 64p. (gr. 4-6). lib. bdg. 24.90 (978-0-7613-1862-0(3) , Millbrook Pr.) Lerner Publishing Group.

Hall, Kirsten. Leatherback Turtle: The World's Heaviest Reptile. 2007. (SuperSized! Ser.). (Illus.). 24p. (J). (gr. k-2). lib. bdg. 21.28 (978-1-59716-393-4(7) , 1265938) Bearport Publishing Co., Inc.

Hamilton, Lynn. Caring for Your Turtle. 2004. (Caring for Your Pet Ser.). (J). pap. 7.95 (978-1-59036-153-5(9)); (Illus.). 32p. lib. bdg. 16.95 (978-1-59036-118-4(0)) Weigl Pubs., Inc.

Haney, Johannah. Turtles. 2007. (Great Pets Ser.). 48p. (J). lib. bdg. 28.50 (*978-0-7614-2709-4(0) , Benchmark Bks.) Cavendish, Marshall Corp.

Hanson, Anders. Terrific Turtles. Nobens, C. A., illus. 2007. (Perfect Pets Ser.). 24p. (J). (gr. k-3). lib. bdg. 19.93 (*978-1-59928-755-3(2) , SandCastle) ABDO Publishing Co.

Harcourt School Publishers Staff. Careful! Turtles Ahead Below Level. 3rd ed. 2002. (Trophies Reading Program Ser.). (Illus.). pap. 5.10 (978-0-15-323136-0(X)) Harcourt Schl. Pubs.

—Turtle Talk Advanced Level. 3rd ed. 2002. (Trophies Reading Program Ser.). (Illus.). pap. 5.10 (978-0-15-323196-4(3)) Harcourt Schl. Pubs.

Hatkoff, Craig & Hatkoff, Isabella. Owen & Mzee: A Day Together. 2008. (Fairy House Ser.). 112p. (J). bds. 6.99 (*978-0-545-03766-2(2)) Scholastic, Inc.

Hatkoff, Craig, et al. Owen & Mzee: The Language of Friendship. Greste, Peter, photos by. 2007. (Illus.). 40p. (J). (ps-3). pap. 16.99 (978-0-439-89959-8(1) , Scholastic Pr.) Scholastic, Inc.

Hawxhurst, Joan C. Turtles & Tortoises. 2000. (Endangered Animals & Habitats Ser.). (Illus.). 96p. (J). (gr. 4-12). 28.70 (978-1-56006-731-3(4) , Lucent Bks.) Thomson Gale.

Heller, Ruth. Galapagos Means Tortoises. Heller, Ruth, illus. 2003. (Illus.). 48p. (J). reprint ed. pap. 6.95 (978-1-57805-101-4(0)) Gibbs Smith, Publisher.

Herriges, Ann. Sea Turtles. 2006. (Blastoff! Readers Ser.). (Illus.). 24p. (J). lib. bdg. 16.95 (978-1-60014-022-8(X)) Bellwether Media.

Hibbert. Life of a Sea Turtle, 6, Pack. 2004. pap. 40.50 (978-1-4109-0828-5(3)) Harcourt Schl. Pubs.

Hibbert, Clare. The Life of a Turtle. 2004. (Raintree Perspectives Ser.). (Illus.). 32p. (J). pap. (978-1-4109-0821-6(6)) Harcourt Schl. Pubs.

—The Life of a Turtle. 2004. (Life Cycles (Perspectives) Ser.). (Illus.). 32p. (J). (gr. 3-5). lib. bdg. 19.25 (978-1-4109-0546-8(2)) Raintree.

Hickman, Pamela. Turtle Rescue: Changing the Future for Endangered Wildlife. 2005. (Firefly Animal Rescue Ser.). (Illus.). 64p. (J). (gr. 5-12). 19.95 (978-1-55297-916-7(4)); pap. 9.95 (978-1-55297-915-0(6)) Firefly Bks., Ltd.

Hipp, Andrew. The Life Cycle of a Painted Turtle. 2002. (Life Cycles Library). (Illus.). 24p. (J). lib. bdg. 18.75 (978-0-8239-5869-6(8) , PowerKids Pr.) Rosen Publishing Group, Inc., The.

Hirschmann, Kris. Sea Turtles. 2005. (Creatures of the Sea Ser.). (Illus.). 48p. (J). (gr. 4-8). 26.20 (978-0-7377-3011-1(0) , Greenhaven Pr., Inc.) Thomson Gale.

Houbre, Gilbert & Gallimard Jeunesse Publishing Staff. Turtles & Snails. 1998. (First Discovery Book Ser.). (Illus.). 24p. (J). (ps-2). 12.95 (978-0-590-11764-7(5) , Scholastic Reference) Scholastic, Inc.

Houghton, Gillian. Turtle. 2004. (Getting into Nature Ser.). (Illus.). 32p. (J). lib. bdg. 21.25 (978-0-8239-4211-4(2)) Rosen Publishing Group, Inc., The.

Huelin, Jodi. Turtles. Gonzalez, Pedro Julio, illus. 2003. (All Aboard Science Reader Station Stop Ser.). 32p. (J). (ps-2). pap. 3.99 (978-0-448-43117-8(3) , Grosset & Dunlap) Penguin Group (USA) Inc.

—Turtles. 2003. (gr. k-3). lib. bdg. 11.80 (978-0-613-64427-3(1)) Tandem Library Bks.

Jacobs, Lee. Turtle. 2003. (Wild America Ser.). (Illus.). 24p. (J). 24.94 (978-1-56711-571-0(3) , Blackbirch Pr., Inc.) Thomson Gale.

Jay, Lorraine A. Sea Turtles. McGee, John F., photos by. 2004. (Our Wild World Ser.). (Illus.). 48p. (J). (gr. 2-5). pap. 7.95 (978-1-55971-746-5(7) , NorthWord Bks. for Young Readers) T&N Children's Publishing.

—Sea Turtles. 2000. (gr. 3-6). lib. bdg. 16.40 (978-0-613-26865-3(2)) Tandem Library Bks.

Johnston, Marianne. Sea Turtles: Past & Present. 2000. (Prehistoric Animals & Their Modern-Day Relatives Ser.). 24p. (J). (gr. k-4). lib. bdg. 18.75 (978-0-8239-5205-2(3) , PowerKids Pr.) Rosen Publishing Group, Inc., The.

Kalman, Bobbie. Endangered Sea Turtles. 2004. (Earth's Endangered Animals Ser.). (Illus.). 32p. (J). (978-0-7787-1853-6(0)); pap. (978-0-7787-1899-4(9)) Crabtree Publishing Co.

—The Life Cycle of a Sea Turtle. (Life Cycle Ser.). (Illus.). 32p. (J). (gr. 2-3). 2002. pap. (978-0-7787-0682-3(6)); 2001. (978-0-7787-0652-6(4)) Crabtree Publishing Co.

—Life Cycle of a Sea Turtle. 2002. (gr. 3-6). lib. bdg. 14.10 (978-0-613-52974-7(X)) Tandem Library Bks.

Kalman, Bobbie. Les Tortues de Mer. 2007. (FRE.). 32p. pap. 8.95 (***978-2-89579-164-5(3)***) Editions Banjo CAN. *Dist:* Crabtree Publishing Co.

Kishel, Ann-Marie. Turtles & Hatchlings. 2006. (First Step Nonfiction Ser.). (Illus.). 8p. (J). pap. (978-0-8225-5647-3(2) , Lerner Pubns.) Lerner Publishing Group.

Korman, Susan. Box Turtle at Silver Pond Lane. Marchesi, Stephen, illus. 2005. (Smithsonian's Backyard Ser.). 32p. (J). (ps-2). 15.95 (978-1-56899-860-2(0) , B5020); 19.95 incl. reel tape (978-1-56899-862-6(7) , BC5020) Soundprints.

—Box Turtle at Silver Pond Lane: Including Toy. Marchesi, Stephen, illus. 2000. (Smithsonian's Backyard Ser.). 32p. (J). (ps-2). 32.95 (978-1-56899-864-0(3) , PB5020) Soundprints.

—Box Turtle at Silver Pond Lane: Micro Edition Including Toy. Marchesi, Stephen, illus. 2005. (Smithsonian's Backyard Ser.: No. 20). 32p. (J). (ps-2). 9.95 (978-1-56899-865-7(1) , PB5070) Soundprints.

—Box Turtle at Silver Pond Lane: Smithsonian Backyard. Marchesi, Stephen, illus. 2005. (Smithsonian's Backyard Ser.). 30p. (J). (ps-2). 4.95 (978-1-56899-861-9(9) , B5070) Soundprints.

Kuzio, Daisy Williams. All about Annie: (A True Story) 2006. 9.00 (978-0-8059-9118-5(2)) Dorrance Publishing Co., Inc.

Lang, Aubrey. Baby Sea Turtle. Lynch, Wayne, photos by. 2007. (Nature Babies Ser.). (Illus.). 32p. (J). (gr. k-3). pap. (***978-1-55041-746-3(0)***) Fitzhenry & Whiteside, Ltd.

Laskey, Elizabeth. Sea Turtles. 2003. (Sea Creatures Ser.). (Illus.). 32p. (J). pap. 6.95 (978-1-4034-3564-4(2)); lib. bdg. 22.79 (978-1-4034-0962-1(5)) Heinemann Library.

Lasky, Kathryn. Interrupted Journey: Saving Endangered Sea Turtles. Knight, Christopher G., photos by. 48p. (J). (gr. 1-5). 2006. pap. 6.99 (978-0-7636-2883-3(2)); 2001. (Illus.). 16.99 (978-0-7636-0635-0(9)) Candlewick Pr.

Lewis, David, contrib. by. Turtles. 1999. (Junior Pet Care Ser.). (Illus.). 48p. (J). (gr. 4-7). 18.65 (978-0-7910-4911-2(6) , Chelsea Hse.) Facts On File, Inc.

Lindeen, Carol K. Sea Turtles. 2004. (Under the Sea Ser.). (Illus.). 24p. (J). lib. bdg. 19.93 (978-0-7368-2601-3(7) , Pebble Bks.) Capstone Pr., Inc.

Lockwood, Sophie. Desert Tortoises. 2006. (World of Reptiles Ser.). (Illus.). 40p. (J). (gr. 2-6). 29.93 (978-1-59296-546-5(6)) Child's World, Inc.

—Sea Turtles. 2006. (World of Reptiles Ser.). (Illus.). 40p. (J). (gr. 2-6). 29.93 (978-1-59296-550-2(4)) Child's World, Inc.

Martin-James, Kathleen. Sturdy Turtles. (Pull Ahead Bks.). (Illus.). 32p. (J). (gr. k-2). 2003. pap. 5.95 (978-0-8225-3631-4(5)); 1999. lib. bdg. 22.60 (978-0-8225-3627-7(7) , Lerner Pubns.) Lerner Publishing Group.

—Sturdy Turtles. 2000. (gr. k-3). lib. bdg. 14.10 (978-0-613-43897-1(3)) Tandem Library Bks.

Mason, Janeen. Ocean Commotion: Sea Turtles. Mason, Janeen, illus. 2006. (Illus.). 32p. (J). 15.95 (978-1-58980-434-0(1)) Pelican Publishing Co., Inc.

Merrick, Patrick. Turtles. 2006. (New Naturebooks). (Illus.). 32p. (J). (gr. 1-5). 27.07 (978-1-59296-653-0(5)) Child's World, Inc.

Miller, Chuck. Tortoises. 2002. (Animals of the Rain Forest Ser.). (Illus.). 32p. (YA). lib. bdg. 22.83 (978-0-7398-5531-7(X)) Raintree.

Miller, Sara Swan. Turtles: Life in a Shell. 1999. (gr. 3-6). lib. bdg. 15.25 (978-0-613-35015-0(4)) Tandem Library Bks.

Monroe, Mary Alice. Turtle Summer: A Journal for My Daughter. Downey, Lisa, illus. Bergwerf, Barbara J., photos by. 2007. 1p. (J). (gr. k-4). 8.95 (***978-0-9777423-7-0(7)***) Sylvan Dell Pubng.

—Turtle Summer: A Journal for My Daughter. Downey, Lisa, illus. Bergwerf, Barbara, photos by. 2007. 32p. (J). (gr. 1-5). 15.95 (***978-0-9777423-5-6(0)***) Sylvan Dell Pubng.

Morgan, Sally. Turtles. 2006. (Illus.). 32p. (J). lib. bdg. 18.95 (978-1-59566-206-4(5)) QEB Publishing Inc.

Murray, Julie. Sea Turtles. 2007. (Life Cycles Ser.). (Illus.). 24p. (J). (gr. k-4). lib. bdg. 21.35 (***978-1-59928-711-9(0)*** , Buddy Bks.) ABDO Publishing Co.

Murray, Julie. Turtles. 2002. (Buddy Book Ser.). (Illus.). 24p. (J). (gr. k-4). lib. bdg. 21.35 (978-1-57765-720-0(9)) ABDO Publishing Co.

Noonan, Diana. The Green Turtle. 2002. (Life Cycle Ser.). (Illus.). 32p. (J). (gr. k-2). 23.00 (978-0-7910-6967-7(2) , Chelsea Hse.) Facts On File, Inc.

Orr, Katherine. Sea Turtles Hatching. Orr, Katherine, illus. 2002. (Illus.). 32p. (J). pap. 7.95 (978-0-89317-048-6(8) , WW-0488, Windward Publishing) Finney Co., Inc.

Patterson, Jordan. Box Turtles: Keeping & Breeding Them in Captivity. 1999. (Basic Domestic Reptile & Amphibian Library). (Illus.). 64p. (YA). (gr. 4-7). 32.00 (978-0-7910-5077-4(7) , Chelsea Hse.) Facts On File, Inc.

Pohl, Kathleen. Sea Turtles. 2006. (Illus.). 24p. (J). pap. (***978-0-8368-7827-1(2)***); lib. bdg. (***978-0-8368-7820-2(5)***) Stevens, Gareth Inc. (Weekly Reader Early Learning Library).

—Sea Turtles: Tortugas Marinas. 2006. (Illus.). 24p. (J). pap. (***978-0-8368-8016-8(1)***); lib. bdg. (***978-0-8368-8009-0(9)***) Stevens, Gareth Inc. (Weekly Reader Early Learning Library).

Randolph, Joanne. Turtles. 2007. (Classroom Pets Ser.). (Illus.). 24p. (J). (gr. k-5). lib. bdg. 21.25 (978-1-4042-3677-6(5) , 1266096, PowerKids Pr.) Rosen Publishing Group, Inc., The.

Reader's Clubhouse Staff. Land Turtles, Sea Turtles. 2007. (Reader's Clubhouse Ser.). 24p. (J). (gr. k-2). pap. 3.99 (978-0-7641-3727-3(1)) Barron's Educational Series, Inc.

Rebman, Renee C. Turtles & Tortoises. 2006. (Animals Animals Ser.). (Illus.). 48p. (J). lib. bdg. 28.50 (978-0-7614-2239-6(0) , Benchmark Bks.) Cavendish, Marshall Corp.

Rizzati, Lorella. Turtle. 1998. (Portable Pets Ser.). (Illus.). 12p. (J). (ps). bds. 6.95 (978-0-8109-5678-0(0)) Abrams, Harry N. , Inc.

Rustad, Martha E. Sea Turtles, Vol. 2. 2005. (Ocean Life Ser.). 24p. (YA). (gr. k-3). pap. (978-0-7368-9082-3(3) , Pebble Bks.) Capstone Pr., Inc.

Rustad, Martha E. H. Sea Turtles. Saunders-Smith, Gail, ed. 2001. (Ocean Life Ser.). (Illus.). 24p. (J). (gr. k-1). lib. bdg. 15.93 (978-0-7368-0859-0(0) , Pebble Bks.) Capstone Pr., Inc.

—Turtles. 2001. (All about Pets Ser.). (Illus.). 24p. (J). (gr. k-1). lib. bdg. 15.93 (978-0-7368-0978-8(3) , Pebble Bks.) Capstone Pr., Inc.

Salariya, Savid. The Journey of a Turtle. Sorace, Carolyn, photos by. 2000. (Lifecycles Ser.). (Illus.). 32p. (J). (gr. k-2). 25.50 (978-0-531-14520-3(4) , Watts, Franklin) Scholastic Library Publishing.

Schafer, Susan. Turtles. 1999. (Perfect Pets Ser.). (Illus.). 32p. (J). (gr. 3-5). lib. bdg. 25.64 (978-0-7614-0796-6(0) , Benchmark Bks.) Cavendish, Marshall Corp.

Schueler, Donald G. The Gopher Tortoise: A MyReportLinks.com Book. 2003. (Endangered & Threatened Animals Ser.). (Illus.). 48p. (J). (gr. 4-10). lib. bdg. 25.26 (978-0-7660-5053-2(X) , MyReportLinks.com Bks.) Enslow Pubs., Inc.

Sea Turtles. (Under the Sea Ser.). 24p. (J). 6.95 (978-0-7368-5113-8(5)) Capstone Pr., Inc.

Sea Turtles. 2001. (Animals of the Ocean Ser.). (Illus.). (J). lib. bdg. 15.95 (978-1-56674-302-0(8)) Forest Hse. Publishing Co., Inc.

Sea Turtles, 6 vols. (gr. k-2). 28.95 (978-0-7368-9103-5(X)) Red Brick Learning.

Sea Turtles Oceans Alive. 2006. (Illus.). 24p. (J). (gr. k-2). 18.50 (***978-0-531-17874-4(9)***) Scholastic Library Publishing.

Seaworld Photographers, photos by. Baby Sea Turtle. 2006. (SeaWorld Library: Vol. 8). (Illus.). 26p. (J). bds. 6.95 (978-0-8249-6645-4(7) , Candy Cane Pr.) Ideals Pubns.

Sorace, Carolyn. The Journey of a Turtle. 2000. (Life Cycles Ser.). pap. 3.99 (978-0-531-18601-5(6) , Watts, Franklin) Scholastic Library Publishing.

Sovak, Jan. Learning about Turtles. 2001. (Learning about Ser.). (Illus.). 16p. (J). (ps up). pap. 1.50 (978-0-486-41853-7(7)) Dover Pubns., Inc.

Stefoff, Rebecca. Turtles. 2007. (Animalways Ser.). 112p. (J). lib. bdg. 34.21 (***978-0-7614-2539-7(X)*** , Benchmark Bks.) Cavendish, Marshall Corp.

Stone, Lynn M. Box Turtles. 2001. (Weird Pets Ser.). (Illus.). 24p. (J). (gr. 1-4). lib. bdg. 20.64 (978-1-58952-037-0(8)) Rourke Publishing, LLC.

—Sea Turtles. 2006. (Rourke Discovery Library). (Illus.). 24p. (gr. 1-4). 14.95 (978-1-59515-443-9(4)) Rourke Publishing, LLC.

Stone, Lynn M., photos by. Box Turtles. 2007. (Nature Watch Ser.). (Illus.). 48p. (J). 25.26 (978-1-57505-869-6(3) , Lerner Pubns.) Lerner Publishing Group.

Stone, Tanya Lee. Turtles. 2003. (Wild Wild World Ser.). (Illus.). 24p. (J). 22.45 (978-1-56711-824-7(0) , Blackbirch Pr., Inc.) Thomson Gale.

Taylor, Barbara, et al. Turtles & Tortoises. 2004. (Illus.). 64p. 15.99 (978-0-7548-1349-1(5) , Lorenz Bks.) Anness Publishing GBR. *Dist:* National Bk. Network.

Theodorou, Rod. Leatherback Sea Turtle. (Animals in Danger Ser.). (Illus.). 32p. (J). (gr. k-2). 2002. pap. 6.95 (978-1-58810-447-2(8) , 91154); 2001. lib. bdg. 21.36 (978-1-57572-272-6(0)) Heinemann Library.

Tortugas: Por Dentro y Por Fuera. 2004. (SPA., Illus.). 32p. lib. bdg. 21.25 (978-1-4042-2869-6(1)) Rosen Publishing Group, Inc., The.

Trueit, Trudi Strain. Turtles. 2003. (True Book Ser.). (Illus.). 48p. (J). 25.00 (978-0-516-22652-1(5) , Children's Pr.) Scholastic Library Publishing.

—Turtles. 2003. (gr. 3-6). lib. bdg. 15.25 (978-0-613-67992-3(X)) Tandem Library Bks.

Trumbauer, Lisa. The Life Cycle of a Turtle. 2003. (Life Cycles Ser.). (Illus.). 24p. (J). (gr. k-1). lib. bdg. 15.93 (978-0-7368-2092-9(2) , Pebble Bks.) Capstone Pr., Inc.

Vue, Gerry & Vue, David. Life of a Turtle. Yang, Siri, tr. Yang, Leng, photos by. 2000. (Illus.). 32p. (J). (gr. 1-9). 19.00 (978-0-9707435-0-3(5)) Asia Pubn.

Wang, Margaret. Turtles Take Their Time. 2007. 6p. 14.95 (***978-1-58117-601-8(5)*** , Intervisual/Piggy Toes) Dalmatian Pr.

Watt, Melanie. Leatherback Turtles. 2001. (Untamed World Ser.). (Illus.). 64p. (J). lib. bdg. 28.54 (978-0-8172-4575-7(8)) Raintree.

Wildlife Education, Ltd. Staff & Levibiel, Timothy. Turtles. Bliss, Rebecca & Stuart, Walter, illus. 2001. (Zoobooks Ser.). 24p. (J). (gr. 5 up). 15.95 (978-0-937934-89-0(5)) Wildlife Education, Ltd.

Wilsdon, Christina. Turtles. 2007. (J). (***978-1-59939-112-0(0)*** , Reader's Digest Young Families, Inc.) Reader's Digest Children's Publishing, Inc.

World Book, Inc. Box Turtles & Other Pond & Marsh Turtles. 2007. (World Book's Animals of the World Ser.). (Illus.). 64p. (J). (978-0-7166-1326-8(3)) World Bk., Inc.

Yin, Robert, illus. & photos by. Sea Turtles. Yin, Robert, photos by. 1999. 24p. (J). 6.50 (978-0-7685-0353-1(1)) Dominie Pr., Inc.

Zollman, Pam. A Turtle Hatchling Grows Up. 2005. (Scholastic News Nonfiction Readers Ser.). (Illus.). 24p. (J). (gr. 1-2). 19.00 (978-0-516-24948-3(7) , Children's Pr.) Scholastic Library Publishing.

TURTLES—FICTION

Aesop. The Hare & the Tortoise. 2006. 132p. (J). 12.95 (978-1-59764-186-9(3)) New Line Bks.

—Hare & the Tortoise. 2006. (Illus.). 32p. (J). (ENG & SPA.). 14.95 (978-0-8118-5057-5(9)); pap. 6.95 (978-0-8118-5058-2(7)) Chronicle Bks. LLC.

Aesop & Miles, Betty. The Tortoise & the Hare. Meisel, Paul, illus. 1998. (Starting to Read Ser.). (J). (978-0-606-13858-1(7)) Tandem Library Bks.

Ahern, Carolyn L. Tino Turtle Travels to Beijing, China. 2008. (J). 17.95 incl. audio compact disk (***978-0-9793158-4-8(0)***) Tino Turtle Travels, LLC.

—Tino Turtle Travels to London, England. Burt Sullivan, Neallia, illus. 2007. 36p. (J). 17.95 incl. audio compact disk (***978-0-9793158-0-0(8)***) Tino Turtle Travels, LLC.

—Tino Turtle Travels to London, England Book & Singalong PlushToy Bundle. 2007. (J). 29.95 incl. audio compact disk (***978-0-9793158-5-5(9)***) Tino Turtle Travels, LLC.

—Tino Turtle Travels to Mexico City, Mexico. 2007. (ENG & SPA., Illus.). 36p. (J). 17.95 incl. audio compact disk (***978-0-9793158-2-4(4)***) Tino Turtle Travels, LLC.

—Tino Turtle Travels to Nairobi, Kenya. 2008. (Illus.). (J). 17.95 incl. audio compact disk (***978-0-9793158-3-1(2)***) Tino Turtle Travels, LLC.

—Tino Turtle Travels to Paris, France. Burt Sullivan, Neallia, illus. 2007. 36p. (J). 17.95 incl. audio compact disk (***978-0-9793158-1-7(6)***) Tino Turtle Travels, LLC.

—Tino Turtle Travels to Paris, France Book & Sing-along Plush Toy Bundle. 2007. (J). 29.95 incl. audio compact disk (***978-0-9793158-6-2(7)***) Tino Turtle Travels, LLC.

Anastasio, Dina. The la tortuga magica & Magic Turtle. 2005. spiral bd. 66.00 (***978-1-4108-5650-0(X)***) Benchmark Education Co.

Anastasio, Dina. The Magic Turtle. ed. 2003. (Early Connections Ser.). (J). pap. 33.00 (978-1-4108-1366-4(5)) Benchmark Education Co.

Armitage, Kimo. Limu: The Blue Turtle & His Hawaiian Garden. Kaneshiro, Scott, illus. 2004. 28p. (J). 8.99 (978-0-931548-64-2(0)) Island Heritage Publishing.

Arnosky, Jim. Turtle in the Sea. Arnosky, Jim, illus. 2002. (Illus.). 32p. (J). (ps-1). 16.99 (978-0-399-22757-8(1) , Putnam Juvenile) Penguin Group (USA) Inc.

Artful Doodlers. TMNT: Intense Action. 2008. (Teenage Mutant Ninja Turtles Ser.). 224p. (J). 4.99 (***978-1-4169-5102-5(4)*** , Simon Scribbles) Simon & Schuster Children's Publishing.

Auerbach, Annie. The Cookie Heist. 2006. (Over the Hedge Ser.: No. 1). (Illus.). 24p. (J). pap. 3.99 (978-0-439-80144-7(3)) Scholastic, Inc.

Austin, K. B. Old Mother Turtle & the Three Frogs. 2005. (J). lib. bdg. (978-0-9772027-0-6(4)) Dream Star Productions.

Barsy, Kalman. The Three Castaways. Perez-Moliere, Marnie, illus. 2004. (Orange Ser.). (SPA.). 40p. (J). (gr. 3-5). pap. 5.95 (978-1-57581-469-8(2)) Santillana USA Publishing Co., Inc.

Bauer, Marion Dane. A Mama for Owen. Butler, John, illus. 2007. 32p. (J). 15.99 (978-0-689-85787-4(X) , Simon & Schuster Children's Publishing) Simon & Schuster Children's Publishing.

Bernstein, Dan. The Tortoise & the Hare Race Again. Glass, Andrew, illus. (J). (ps-3). 36p. 6.95 (***978-0-8234-2070-4(1)***); 32p. 16.95 (978-0-8234-1867-1(7)) Holiday Hse., Inc.

Bikle, Edie. Kapono & the Turtle. Hennings-Chilton, Connie, illus. 2001. (J). 10.99 (978-0-89610-199-9(1)) Island Heritage Publishing.

Blotnick, Elihu. Blue Turtle Moon Queen. Robinson, Barbara J., illus. Date not set. 120p. (YA). (gr. 6-12). pap. 6.95 (978-0-915090-20-4(1)) California Street.

Bourgeois, Paulette. Adventures with Franklin. 2000. (Franklin Color & Activity Bks.). (Illus.). 32p. (J). (ps-3). pap. (978-0-7666-0492-6(6)) Modern Publishing.

—Benjamin et Sa Petite Soeur. ed. 2004. Tr. of Franklin's Baby Sister. (FRE., Illus.). (J). (gr. k-3). spiral bd. (978-0-616-14597-5(7)) Canadian National Institute for the Blind/Institut National Canadien pour les Aveugles.

—El Club Secreto de Franklin. Clark, Brenda, illus. 2001. (Franklin Ser.). (SPA.). (J). (ps-3). 10.95 (978-1-930332-14-0(9) , LC6913) Lectorum Pubns., Inc.

—El Club Secreto de Franklin. Varela, Alejandra Lopez, tr. from ENG. Clark, Brenda, illus. 1998. (Franklin Ser.). (SPA.). 32p. (J). (ps-3). pap. 5.95 (978-1-880507-50-6(1) , LC8146) Lectorum Pubns., Inc.

—El Diente de Franklin. Vareta, Alejandra Lopez, tr. Clark, Brenda, illus. 2001. (Franklin Ser.). (SPA.). (J). (ps-3). pap. 5.95 (978-1-880507-88-9(9) , LC1651); ring bd. 10.95 (978-1-880507-89-6(7) , LC1736) Lectorum Pubns., Inc.

—El Diente de Franklin. 2001. (SPA.). (gr. k-3). lib. bdg. 14.10 (978-0-613-35932-0(1)) Tandem Library Bks.

—Finders Keepers for Franklin. Clark, Brenda, illus. 1998. (Franklin the Turtle Ser.). 32p. (J). (gr. k-3). (978-1-55074-368-5(6)) Kids Can Pr., Ltd.

—Franklin & Friends. 2000. (Franklin Color & Activity Bks.). (Illus.). 96p. (J). (ps-3). pap. (978-0-7666-0495-7(0)) Modern Publishing.

—Franklin & Harriet. Clark, Brenda, illus. unabr. ed. 2004. (Franklin the Turtle Ser.). 32p. (J). (gr. k-3). (978-1-55074-874-1(2)) Kids Can Pr., Ltd.

—Franklin & Harriet. Clark, Brenda, illus. 2001. (Franklin Ser.). (J). (ps-3). 32p. pap. 4.50 (978-0-439-20381-4(3)); (978-0-439-26424-2(3)) Scholastic, Inc.

—Franklin & Harriet. 2001. (Franklin Ser.). (Illus.). (J). 11.30 (978-0-606-20664-8(7)) Tandem Library Bks.

—Franklin & the Hero. Clark, Brenda, illus. 2004. (Franklin TV StoryBks.). 32p. (J). (gr. k-3). (978-1-55074-827-7(0)) Kids Can Pr., Ltd.

—Franklin & the Hero. Clark, Brenda, illus. 2000. (Franklin TV-Tie In Ser.). 32p. (J). (ps-3). pap. 4.50 (978-0-439-20380-7(5)) Scholastic, Inc.

—Franklin & the Hero. 2000. (Franklin TV Storybook Ser.). (J). (ps-3). 11.30 (978-0-606-20057-8(6)) Tandem Library Bks.

—Franklin & the Thunderstorm. Clark, Brenda, illus. 1998. (Franklin the Turtle Ser.). 32p. (J). (gr. k-3). (978-1-55074-403-3(8)) Kids Can Pr., Ltd.

—Franklin & the Thunderstorm. Clark, Brenda, illus. 1998. (Franklin Ser.). 32p. (J). (ps-3). pap. 4.99 (978-0-590-02635-2(6) , Cartwheel Bks.) Scholastic, Inc.

—Franklin & the Thunderstorm. Clark, Brenda, illus. 1998. (Franklin Ser.). (J). (ps-3). 11.30 (978-0-606-13403-3(4)); lib. bdg. 12.40 (978-0-613-07814-6(4)) Tandem Library Bks.

—Franklin & the Tooth Fairy. Clark, Brenda, illus. 2002. (Franklin Ser.). 12.40 (978-1-4046-0311-0(5)) Book Wholesalers, Inc.

—Franklin & the Tooth Fairy. 1999. (Franklin Ser.). (Illus.). 180p. (J). (ps-3). (978-1-55074-793-5(2)) Kids Can Pr., Ltd.

—Franklin en el Museo. Varela, Alejandra Lopez, tr. Clark, Brenda, illus. (SPA.). (J). (gr. k-2). ring bd. 10.95 (978-1-930332-12-6(2) , LC30199) Lectorum Pubns., Inc.

—Franklin en el Museo. Clark, Brenda, illus. 1999. (Franklin Ser.). (SPA.). (J). (ps-3). pap. 5.95 (978-1-880507-57-5(9) , LC2801) Lectorum Pubns., Inc.

—Franklin en el Museo. 1999. (Franklin Ser.). (SPA.). (J). (ps-3). 12.75 (978-0-606-17007-9(3)) Tandem Library Bks.

—Franklin en la Oscuridad. Varela, Alejandra Lopez, tr. Clark, Brenda, illus. 2001. (SPA.). (J). ring bd. 10.95 (978-1-880507-87-2(0) , LC3565) Lectorum Pubns., Inc.

—Franklin Es un Mandon. Varela, Alejandra Lopez, tr. Clark, Brenda, illus. (SPA.). ring bd. 10.95 (978-1-930332-16-4(5) , LC6564) Lectorum Pubns., Inc.

—Franklin Es un Mandon. Lopez Varela, Alejandra, tr. from ENG. Clark, Brenda, illus. 1998. (Franklin Ser.). (SPA.). 32p. (J). (ps-3). pap. 5.95 (978-1-880507-42-1(0) , LC7795) Lectorum Pubns., Inc.

—Franklin Forgets. 2000. (Franklin TV Storybook Ser.). (J). (ps-3). 11.30 (978-0-606-20058-5(4)) Tandem Library Bks.

—Franklin Goes to Day Camp: A Story & Activity Book. Clark, Brenda, illus. (Franklin Ser.). 74p. (J). (ps-3). (978-1-55074-372-2(4)) Kids Can Pr., Ltd.

—Franklin Goes to Day Camp: A Story & Activity Book. Clark, Brenda, illus. 1998. (Franklin Ser.). (J). (ps-3). pap. 4.50 (978-0-590-06828-4(8) , Cartwheel Bks.) Scholastic, Inc.

—Franklin Goes to the Hospital. Clark, Brenda, illus. 2000. (Franklin Ser.). (J). (ps-3). 30p. (978-1-55074-734-8(7)); 32p. (978-1-55074-732-4(0)) Kids Can Pr., Ltd.

—Franklin Goes to the Hospital. Clark, Brenda, illus. 2000. (Franklin Ser.). 32p. (J). (ps-3). pap. 4.99 (978-0-439-08370-6(2)) Scholastic, Inc.

—Franklin Goes to the Hospital. 2000. (Franklin Ser.). (Illus.). (J). (ps-3). 11.30 (978-0-606-18547-9(X)) Tandem Library Bks.

—Franklin Helps Out. Clark, Brenda, illus. 2004. (Franklin TV StoryBks.). 32p. (J). (gr. k-3). (978-1-55074-823-9(8)) Kids Can Pr., Ltd.

—Franklin Helps Out. 2000. (Franklin TV Storybook Ser.). (J). (ps-3). 11.30 (978-0-606-20059-2(2)) Tandem Library Bks.

—Franklin in the Dark. ed. 2004. (Illus.). (J). (ps-2). spiral bd. (978-0-616-01574-2(7)); spiral bd. (978-0-616-01575-9(5)) Canadian National Institute for the Blind/Institut National Canadien pour les Aveugles.

—Franklin Is Bossy. Clark, Brenda, illus. 1998. (Franklin Ser.). 30p. (J). (ps-3). 19.95 (978-0-590-25764-0(1)) Scholastic, Inc.

—Franklin Juega al Futbol. Varela, Alejandra Lopez, tr. Clark, Brenda, illus. (SPA.). (J). (gr. k-2). ring bd. 10.95 (978-1-930332-17-1(3) , LC6563) Lectorum Pubns., Inc.

—Franklin Juega al Futbol. Lopez Varela, Alejandra, tr. from ENG. Clark, Brenda, illus. 1998. (Franklin Ser.). (SPA.). 32p. (J). (ps-3). pap. 5.95 (978-1-880507-44-5(7) , LC7851) Lectorum Pubns., Inc.

—Franklin Miente. Clark, Brenda, illus. 2000. (Franklin Ser.). (SPA.). (J). (ps-3). pap. 5.95 (978-1-880507-69-8(2) , LC4551) Lectorum Pubns., Inc.

—Franklin Miente. 2000. (Franklin Ser.). (SPA., Illus.). (J). (ps-3). 12.75 (978-0-606-18243-0(8)) Tandem Library Bks.

—Franklin Plants a Tree. 2001. (Franklin Ser.). (Illus.). (J). 11.30 (978-0-606-21196-3(9)) Tandem Library Bks.

—Franklin Quiere una Mascota. Varela, Alejandra Lopez, tr. from ENG. Clark, Brenda, illus. 1998. (Franklin Ser.). (SPA.). 32p. (J). (ps-3). pap. 5.95 (978-1-880507-49-0(8) , LC8143) Lectorum Pubns., Inc.

—Franklin Says I Love You. ed. 2004. (Illus.). (J). (gr. k-3). spiral bd. (978-0-616-14561-6(6)); spiral bd. (978-0-616-14562-3(4)) Canadian National Institute for the Blind/Institut National Canadien pour les Aveugles.

—Franklin Says I Love You. Clark, Brenda, illus. 2004. (Franklin the Turtle Ser.). 32p. (J). (gr. k-3). (978-1-55337-035-2(X)) Kids Can Pr., Ltd.

—Franklin Says Sorry. 2000. (Franklin TV Storybook Ser.). (J). (ps-3). 11.30 (978-0-606-20060-8(6)) Tandem Library Bks.

—Franklin Se Pierde. Clark, Brenda, illus. 2000. (Franklin Ser.). (SPA.). (J). (ps-3). pap. 5.95 (978-1-880507-70-4(6) , LC6163) Lectorum Pubns., Inc.

—Franklin Se Pierde. 2000. (SPA.). (gr. k-3). lib. bdg. 14.10 (978-0-613-28393-9(7)); (Illus.). (J). 12.75 (978-0-606-18244-7(6)) Tandem Library Bks.

—Franklin Tiene un Mal Dia. Varela, Alejandra Lopez, tr. Clark, Brenda, illus. (Franklin Ser.). (SPA.). (J). (ps-3). 2001. ring bd. 10.95 (978-1-880507-86-5(2) , LC4083); 1999. pap. 5.95 (978-1-880507-52-0(8) , LC8141) Lectorum Pubns., Inc.

—Franklin Tiene un Mal Dia. 1999. (Franklin Ser.). (SPA.). (J). (ps-3). 12.75 (978-0-606-17011-6(1)) Tandem Library Bks.

—Franklin Treasury. 2000. (Franklin Ser.). (Illus.). (J). (ps-3). (978-1-55337-018-5(X)) Kids Can Pr., Ltd.

—Franklin Va a la Escuela. Lopez Varela, Alejandra, tr. Clark, Brenda, illus. (Franklin Ser.). (SPA.). (J). (ps-3). 2001. ring bd. 10.95 (978-1-880507-85-8(4) , LC4919); 1998. 32p. pap. 5.95 (978-1-880507-41-4(2) , LC7792) Lectorum Pubns., Inc.

—Franklin Wants a Badge. Clark, Brenda, illus. 2004. (Franklin TV StoryBks.). 32p. (J). (gr. k-3). (978-1-55337-467-1(3)) Kids Can Pr., Ltd.

—Franklin Wants a Badge. Clark, Brenda, illus. 2003. (Franklin TV-Tie In Ser.: No. 7). 32p. (J). (gr. k-3). pap. 4.50 (978-0-439-43122-4(0) , Scholastic Pr.) Scholastic, Inc.

—Franklin Wants a Badge. 2003. (ps-2). lib. bdg. 12.40 (978-0-613-89577-4(0)) Tandem Library Bks.

—Franklin Wants a Pet. 2000. (Franklin Ser.). (Illus.). 180p. (J). (ps-3). (978-1-55074-795-9(9)) Kids Can Pr., Ltd.

—Franklin y el Regalo de Navidad. Clark, Brenda, illus. 1999. (Franklin Ser.). (SPA.). (J). (ps-3). pap. 5.95 (978-1-880507-56-8(0) , LC2911) Lectorum Pubns., Inc.

—Franklin y el Regalo de Navidad. Varela, Alejandra Lopez, tr. from ENG. Clark, Brenda, illus. 1999. (Franklin Ser.). (SPA.). (J). (ps-3). ring bd. 10.95 (978-1-880507-67-4(6) , LC6006) Lectorum Pubns., Inc.

—Franklin y Harriet. 2001. (SPA., Illus.). (J). pap. 5.95 (978-1-880507-96-4(X) , LC8512); ring bd. 10.95 (978-1-880507-97-1(8) , LC0630) Lectorum Pubns., Inc.

—Franklin y Harriet. 2001. (SPA.). (gr. k-3). lib. bdg. 14.10 (978-0-613-36038-8(9)); (Illus.). (J). 12.75 (978-0-606-21197-0(7)) Tandem Library Bks.

—Franklin's Baby Sister. Clark, Brenda, illus. (Franklin Ser.). (J). (ps-3). 96p. (978-1-55074-858-1(0)); 2000. 32p. (978-1-55074-794-2(0)) Kids Can Pr., Ltd.

—Franklin's Baby Sister. Clark, Brenda, illus. 2000. (Franklin Ser.). (J). (ps-3). 11.30 (978-0-606-19919-3(5)) Tandem Library Bks.

—Franklin's Bicycle Helmet. 2000. (Franklin TV Storybook Ser.). (J). (ps-3). 11.30 (978-0-606-20061-5(4)) Tandem Library Bks.

—Franklin's Birthday Party. 2001. (Franklin TV Storybook Ser.). (Illus.). (J). 11.30 (978-0-606-21198-7(5)) Tandem Library Bks.

—Franklin's Blanket. 2000. (Franklin Ser.). (Illus.). 180p. (J). (ps-3). (978-1-55074-686-0(3)) Kids Can Pr., Ltd.

—Franklin's Christmas Gift. Clark, Brenda, illus. 1998. (Franklin the Turtle Ser.). (J). (gr. k-3). 32p. (978-1-55074-466-8(6)); 96p. (978-1-55074-468-2(2)) Kids Can Pr., Ltd.

—Franklin's Christmas Gift. Clark, Brenda, illus. 1998. (Franklin Ser.). (J). (ps-3). pap. 54.00 (978-0-590-95169-2(6) , Cartwheel Bks.) Scholastic, Inc.

—Franklin's Class Trip. Clark, Brenda, illus. (Franklin Ser.). (J). (ps-3). 1999. 30p. (978-1-55074-472-9(0)); 2004. 32p. (978-1-55074-470-5(4)) Kids Can Pr., Ltd.

—Franklin's Class Trip. Clark, Brenda, illus. 1999. (Franklin Ser.). 32p. (J). (ps-3). pap. 4.50 (978-0-590-13002-8(1)) Scholastic, Inc.

—Franklin's Class Trip. 1999. (Franklin Ser.). (Illus.). (J). (ps-3). 11.30 (978-0-606-18548-6(8)) Tandem Library Bks.

—Franklin's Classic Treasury. Clark, Brenda, illus. (Franklin Treasuries Ser.). 128p. (J). (gr. k-3). 1999. (978-1-55074-742-3(8)); Vol. 2. 2000. (978-1-55074-813-0(0)) Kids Can Pr., Ltd.

—Franklin's Friendship Treasury. Clark, Brenda, illus. 2000. (Franklin Treasuries Ser.). 128p. (J). (gr. k-3). (978-1-55074-872-7(6)) Kids Can Pr., Ltd.

—Franklin's Fun Book. 2000. (Franklin Color & Activity Bks.). (Illus.). 96p. (J). (ps-3). pap. (978-0-7666-0494-0(2)) Modern Publishing.

—Franklin's Fun Day. Reiter, Cheryl & Reyner, Mark, eds. Clark, Brenda, illus. 2000. 12p. (J). (ps). mass mkt. 9.99 (978-1-887327-39-8(8)) Ertl Co., Inc.

—Franklin's Halloween. Clark, Brenda, illus. 2002. (Franklin Ser.). 12.40 (978-1-4046-0326-4(3)) Book Wholesalers, Inc.

—Franklin's Neighborhood. ed. 2004. (Illus.). (J). (gr. k-3). spiral bd. (978-0-616-01588-9(7)); spiral bd. (978-0-616-01589-6(5)) Canadian National Institute for the Blind/Institut National Canadien pour les Aveugles.

—Franklin's Neighborhood. Clark, Brenda, illus. 1999. (Franklin Ser.). (J). (ps-3). 32p. (978-1-55074-704-1(5)); 270p. (978-1-55074-702-7(9)) Kids Can Pr., Ltd.

—Franklin's Neighborhood. Clark, Brenda, illus. 1999. (Franklin Ser.). 32p. (J). (ps-3). pap. 4.50 (978-0-439-08369-0(9)) Scholastic, Inc.

—Franklin's Neighborhood. 1999. (Franklin Ser.). (J). (ps-3). 11.30 (978-0-606-17271-4(8)) Tandem Library Bks.

—Franklin's New Friend. ed. 2004. (Illus.). (J). (gr. k-3). spiral bd. (978-0-616-01590-2(9)); spiral bd. (978-0-616-01591-9(7)) Canadian National Institute for the Blind/Institut National Canadien pour les Aveugles.

—Franklin's New Friend. Clark, Brenda, illus. (Franklin Ser.). 96p. (J). (ps-3). (978-1-55074-363-0(5)) Kids Can Pr., Ltd.

—Franklin's School Treasury. Clark, Brenda, illus. unabr. ed. 2001. (Franklin Treasuries Ser.). 128p. (J). (gr. k-3). (978-1-55074-877-2(7)) Kids Can Pr., Ltd.

—Franklin's Secret Club. Clark, Brenda, illus. 1998. (Franklin the Turtle Ser.). (J). (gr. k-3). 32p. (978-1-55074-474-3(7)); 96p. (978-1-55074-476-7(3)) Kids Can Pr., Ltd.

—Franklin's Secret Club. Clark, Brenda, illus. 1998. (Franklin Ser.). 32p. (J). (ps-3). pap. 4.99 (978-0-590-13000-4(5) , Scholastic Paperbacks) Scholastic, Inc.

—Franklin's Secret Club. Clark, Brenda, illus. 1998. (Franklin Ser.). (J). (ps-3). 11.30 (978-0-606-13406-4(9)) Tandem Library Bks.

—Franklin's Thanksgiving. 2001. (Franklin Ser.). (Illus.). (J). 11.30 (978-0-606-22045-3(3)) Tandem Library Bks.

—Franklin's Valentine Cards. Clark, Brenda, illus. 1998. (Franklin Sticker & Activity Bks.). 32p. (J). (gr. k-3). (978-1-55074-625-9(1)) Kids Can Pr., Ltd.

—Franklin's Valentines. Clark, Brenda, illus. 2002. (Franklin Ser.). (J). 12.40 (978-0-7587-2534-9(5)) Book Wholesalers, Inc.

—Franklin's Valentines. Clark, Brenda, illus. 1998. (Franklin the Turtle Ser.). (J). (gr. k-3). 32p. (978-1-55074-480-4(1)); 96p. (978-1-55074-482-8(8)) Kids Can Pr., Ltd.

—Franklin's Valentines. Clark, Brenda, illus. 1999. (Franklin Ser.). (J). (ps-3). pap. 54.00 (978-0-439-04355-7(7)) Scholastic, Inc.

—Franklin's Valentines. 1999. (gr. k-3). lib. bdg. 12.40 (978-0-613-11557-5(0)) Tandem Library Bks.

—Franklin's Valentines. Clark, Brenda, illus. 1999. (Franklin Ser.). (J). (ps-3). 11.30 (978-0-606-15536-6(8)) Tandem Library Bks.

—Fun & Games with Franklin. 2000. (Franklin Color & Activity Bks.). (Illus.). 32p. (J). (ps-3). pap. (978-0-7666-0493-3(4)) Modern Publishing.

—Fun with Franklin: A Learning to Read Book. Clark, Brenda, illus. (Franklin Ser.). (J). (ps-3). (978-1-55074-646-4(4)) Kids Can Pr., Ltd.

—Fun with Franklin: Math Activity Book. Clark, Brenda, illus. 1998. (Franklin Ser.). 72p. (J). (ps-3). (978-1-55074-452-1(6)) Kids Can Pr., Ltd.

—El Hallazgo de Franklin. Varela, Alejandra Lopez, tr. Clark, Brenda, illus. (SPA.). (J). (gr. k-2). ring bd. 10.95 (978-1-930332-10-2(6) , LC1928); 1999. pap. 5.95 (978-1-880507-51-3(X) , LC8142) Lectorum Pubns., Inc.

—La Hermanita de Franklin. Clark, Brenda, illus. 2000. (Franklin Ser.). (SPA.). (J). (ps-3). pap. 5.95 (978-1-880507-83-4(8) , LC7611); ring bd. 10.95 (978-1-880507-84-1(6) , LC3577) Lectorum Pubns., Inc.

—La Hermanita de Franklin. 2000. (Franklin Ser.). (SPA.). (J). (ps-3). 12.75 (978-0-606-20188-9(2)) Tandem Library Bks.

—Manta de Franklin. 2001. Tr. of Franklin's Blanket. (SPA.). (gr. k-3). lib. bdg. 14.10 (978-0-613-35979-5(8)); (Illus.). (J). (978-0-606-21285-4(X)) Tandem Library Bks.

—Un Nouvel Ami pour Benjamin. ed. 2004. Tr. of Franklin's New Friend. (FRE., Illus.). (J). (ps-2). spiral bd. (978-0-616-01828-6(2)) Canadian National Institute for the Blind/Institut National Canadien pour les Aveugles.

—Time to Play with Franklin. 2000. (Franklin Color & Activity Bks.). (Illus.). 32p. (J). (ps-3). pap. (978-0-7666-0491-9(8)) Modern Publishing.

—Welcome to Franklin's World. 2000. (Franklin Color & Activity Bks.). (Illus.). 32p. (J). (ps-3). pap. (978-0-7666-0490-2(X)) Modern Publishing.

Bourgeois, Paulette & Clark, Brenda. Franklin Fibs. 1999. (Franklin Ser.). (Illus.). 162p. (J). (ps-3). (978-1-55074-668-6(5)) Kids Can Pr., Ltd.

—Franklin Forgets. (Franklin TV StoryBks.). (Illus.). 32p. (J). (ps-3). 2005. (978-1-55074-722-5(3)); 2000. (978-1-55074-726-3(6)) Kids Can Pr., Ltd.

—Franklin Has a Sleepover. 1999. (Franklin Ser.). (Illus.). 168p. (J). (ps-3). (978-1-55074-664-8(2)) Kids Can Pr., Ltd.

—Franklin Is Lost. 1999. (Franklin Ser.). (Illus.). 162p. (J). (ps-3). (978-1-55074-670-9(7)) Kids Can Pr., Ltd.

—Franklin Is Messy. 1999. (Franklin Ser.). (Illus.). 180p. (J). (ps-3). (978-1-55074-678-5(2)) Kids Can Pr., Ltd.

—Franklin Says Sorry. (Franklin TV StoryBks.). (Illus.). 32p. (J). (gr. k-3). 2004. (978-1-55074-712-6(6)); 1999. (978-1-55074-714-0(2)) Kids Can Pr., Ltd.

—Franklin's Bicycle Helmet. 2000. (Franklin TV StoryBks.). (Illus.). 32p. (J). (gr. k-3). (978-1-55074-730-0(4)); (978-1-55074-728-7(2)) Kids Can Pr., Ltd.

—Franklin's Big Search-And-Solve Flap Book. Jeffrey, Sean et al, trs. Jeffrey, Sean et al, illus. 2005. 10p. (J). (ps-1). (978-1-55337-522-7(X)) Kids Can Pr., Ltd.

—Franklin's Family Treasury. 2003. (Franklin Treasuries Ser.). (Illus.). 128p. (J). (gr. k-3). (978-1-55337-479-4(7)) Kids Can Pr., Ltd.

—Franklin's Neighborhood. 1999. (Franklin Ser.). (Illus.). 194p. (J). (ps-3). (978-1-55074-752-2(5)) Kids Can Pr., Ltd.

—Franklin's New Friend. 1999. (Franklin Ser.). (Illus.). 180p. (J). (ps-3). (978-1-55074-797-3(5)) Kids Can Pr., Ltd.

—Franklin's Secret Club. 1999. (Franklin Ser.). (Illus.). 194p. (J). (ps-3). (978-1-55074-672-3(3)) Kids Can Pr., Ltd.

Bourgeois, Paulette & Clark, Brenda, creators. Franklin & the Baby. 1999. (Illus.). (J). (978-0-439-12065-4(9)) Scholastic, Inc.

—Hurry up, Franklin. 2000. (Franklin Ser.). (Illus.). 180p. (J). (ps-3). (978-1-55074-682-2(0)) Kids Can Pr., Ltd.

Bourgeois, Paulette & Jennings, Sharon. Franklin Plants a Tree. Jeffrey, Sean et al, illus. 2003. (Franklin TV StoryBks.). 32p. (J). (gr. k-3). (978-1-55074-878-9(5)) Kids Can Pr., Ltd.

—Franklin's Thanksgiving. Clark, Brenda, illus. 2004. (Franklin the Turtle Ser.). 32p. (J). (gr. k-3). (978-1-55074-798-0(3)) Kids Can Pr., Ltd.

—Franklin's Valentines. Clark, Brenda, illus. 1999. (Franklin Ser.). 32p. (J). (ps-3). pap. 4.50 (978-0-590-13001-1(3) , Cartwheel Bks.) Scholastic, Inc.

Bourgeois, Paulette & Moore, Eva. Franklin's First Day of School. Clark, Brenda, illus. 2000. (Franklin Ser.). 12p. (J). (ps-3). bds. 5.99 (978-0-439-20298-5(1)) Scholastic, Inc.

Bourgeois, Paulette, et al. Franklin en la Oscuridad. Lopez Varela, Alejandra, tr. from ENG. Clark, Brenda, illus. 1998. (Franklin Ser.). (SPA.). 32p. (J). (ps-3). pap. 5.95 (978-1-880507-43-8(9) , LC7861) Lectorum Pubns., Inc.

—Franklin y el Día de Halloween. Clark, Brenda, illus. 1999. (SPA.). (J). pap. (978-1-880507-45-2(5)) Lectorum Pubns., Inc.

—Franklin's Neighborhood. Clark, Brenda, illus. 1999. (Franklin the Turtle Ser.). 32p. (J). (gr. k-3). (978-1-55074-729-4(0)) Kids Can Pr., Ltd.

Box Turtle's Big Search. 2002. (Backyard Mini Bks.). (Illus.). 32p. (J). (978-1-59069-017-8(6) , H2006) Studio Mouse LLC.

Brandon, Taylor. The Turtle Who Felt Boxed In! Sandow, Paris, illus. 1999. (World's Greatest Children's Bks.). 48p. (J). (gr. k-5). 14.99 (978-1-889945-54-5(4)) Imperius.

Brightwood, Laura, illus. Anansi & the Turtle. Brightwood, Laura, . 2006. (J). (978-0-9779290-0-9(0)) 3-C Institute for Social Development.

Bruchac, Joseph and James. Turtle's Race with Beaver: A Traditional Seneca Story. Dewey, Ariane & Aruego, Jose, illus. 2005. 32p. (J). pap. 5.99 (978-0-14-240466-9(7) , Puffin) Penguin Group (USA) Inc.

Bumpsie the Red-Footed Tortoise. 2005. (J). bds. 5.99 (978-0-9770957-0-4(3)) Turtle Time Bks.

Bumpsie's Neighborhood. 2006. (J). bds. 6.99 (978-0-9770957-2-8(X)) Turtle Time Bks.

Bunting, Eve. Emma's Turtle. Winborn, Marsha, illus. 2007. 32p. (J). (ps-2). 15.95 (***978-1-59078-350-4(6))** Boyds Mills Pr.

Bunting, Eve. I Like the Way You Are. O'Brien, John, illus. 2000. 48p. (J). (gr. k-3). tchr. ed. 16.00 (978-0-395-89066-0(7) , Clarion Bks.) Houghton Mifflin Co. Trade & Reference Div.

Burgess, Thornton W. The Adventures of Jerry Muskrat. 2004. reprint ed. pap. 15.95 (978-1-4191-5151-4(7)); pap. 1.99 (978-1-4192-5151-1(1)) Kessinger Publishing, LLC.

Butler, Dori. The Tortoise & the Hare: An Aesop's Fable. 2006. 42.00 (***978-1-4108-6167-2(8))** Benchmark Education Co.

Cain, Sheridan. Little Turtle & the Song of the Sea. Burgin, Norma, illus. 2000. 32p. (J). (ps-3). 15.95 (978-1-56656-355-0(0) , Crocodile Bks.) Interlink Publishing Group, Inc.

—La Pequena Tortuga y la Cancion del Mar. Burgin, Norma, illus. 2003. (SPA.). 24p. (J). (gr. k-2). (978-84-8418-037-1(9) , ZZ30445) Zendrera Zariquiey, Editorial ESP. *Dist:* Lectorum Pubns., Inc.

Caplin, Daniel. Grandfather Turtle. 2003. pap. 14.95 (978-0-9726781-0-0(7)) Evening Sun Pr.

Cerat, Marie Lily. Do Toti. Soto, Anna & Hippolyte, Johanne, illus. 1999. Tr. of Turtle's Back. 12p. (J). (gr. k-2). pap. 6.50 (978-1-58432-018-0(4)) Educa Vision.

Cérat, Marie Lily. Turtule's Back. 2002. (Illus.). 12p. (J). 6.50 (978-1-58432-096-8(6)) Educa Vision.

Chambers, Sally. The Tortoise. 1999. (Illus.). 24p. (J). 6.95 (978-1-86233-015-3(8)) David & Charles Children's Bks. GBR. *Dist:* Sterling Publishing Co., Inc.

Chanda, J-P. The Big Sewer Surprise. Spaziante, Patrick, illus. 2004. (Teenage Mutant Ninja Turtles Ser.). 14p. (J). bds. 5.99 (978-0-689-87366-9(2) , Simon Spotlight) Simon & Schuster Children's Publishing.

Charlotte Latin School Staff. Ann & the Tortoise. Sher, illus. 2001. 32p. (J). per. 4.95 (978-0-9707920-7-5(7)) Charlotte's Storybooks.

Chidebelu-Eze, Obi. The Tales of Tortoise: Inspirtional Words of Wisdom. 2005. (Illus.). 76p. (J). 16.00 (978-0-9766578-0-4(5)) Dove Publishing, Inc.

Chrustowski, Rick. Turtle Crossing. rev. ed. 2006. (Illus.). 32p. (J). 16.95 (978-0-8050-7498-7(8) , Holt, Henry & Co. Bks. For Young Readers) Holt, Henry & Co.

Clark, Brenda, illus. Finders Keepers for Franklin. 2002. (Franklin Ser.). (J). 12.40 (978-1-4046-0308-0(5)) Book Wholesalers, Inc.

—Franklin & the Baby. 2002. (Franklin Ser.). (J). 12.40 (978-0-7587-0012-4(1)) Book Wholesalers, Inc.

—Franklin & the Baby-Sitter. 2002. (Franklin Ser.). (J). 12.40 (978-1-4046-0124-6(4)) Book Wholesalers, Inc.

—Franklin & the Big Kid. 2002. (Franklin Ser.). (J). 12.40 (978-1-4046-2017-9(6)) Book Wholesalers, Inc.

—Franklin & the Hero. 2002. (Franklin Ser.). 12.40 (978-1-4046-0309-7(3)) Book Wholesalers, Inc.

—Franklin & the Magic Show. 2002. (Franklin Ser.). (J). 12.40 (978-1-4046-1980-7(1)) Book Wholesalers, Inc.

—Franklin & the Thunderstorm. 2002. (Franklin Ser.). 12.40 (978-1-4046-0310-3(7)) Book Wholesalers, Inc.

—Franklin Fibs. 2002. (Franklin Ser.). (J). 19.72 (978-0-7587-4202-5(9)) Book Wholesalers, Inc.

—Franklin Forgets. 2002. (Franklin Ser.). (J). 12.40 (978-0-7587-6588-8(6)) Book Wholesalers, Inc.

—Franklin Goes to School. 2002. (Franklin Ser.). 12.40 (978-1-4046-0312-7(3)) Book Wholesalers, Inc.

—Franklin Has a Sleepover. 2002. (Franklin Ser.). (J). 12.40 (978-1-4046-0313-4(1)) Book Wholesalers, Inc.

—Franklin Helps Out. 2002. (Franklin Ser.). 12.40 (978-1-4046-0314-1(X)) Book Wholesalers, Inc.

—Franklin Is Bossy. 2002. (Franklin Ser.). 12.40 (978-1-4046-0316-5(6)) Book Wholesalers, Inc.

—Franklin Is Lost. 2002. (Franklin Ser.). (J). 12.40 (978-0-7587-4206-3(1)) Book Wholesalers, Inc.

—Franklin Is Messy. 2002. (Franklin Ser.). (J). 12.40 (978-0-7587-8755-2(3)) Book Wholesalers, Inc.

—Franklin Plays the Game. 2002. (Franklin Ser.). 12.40 (978-1-4046-0317-2(4)) Book Wholesalers, Inc.

—Franklin Rides a Bike. 2002. (Franklin Ser.). 12.40 (978-1-4046-0318-9(2)) Book Wholesalers, Inc.

—Franklin Says Sorry. 2002. (Franklin Ser.). 12.40 (978-1-4046-0319-6(0)) Book Wholesalers, Inc.

—Franklin Wants a Pet. 2002. (Franklin Ser.). 12.40 (978-1-4046-0320-2(4)) Book Wholesalers, Inc.

—Franklin's Baby Sister. 2002. (Franklin Ser.). (J). 14.40 (978-0-7587-6436-2(7)) Book Wholesalers, Inc.

—Franklin's Bad Day. 2002. (Franklin Ser.). 12.40 (978-1-4046-0321-9(2)) Book Wholesalers, Inc.

—Franklin's Bicycle Helmet. 2002. (Franklin Ser.). (J). 12.40 (978-1-4046-0322-6(0)) Book Wholesalers, Inc.

—Franklin's Birthday Party. 2002. (Franklin Ser.). 12.40 (978-1-4046-0323-3(9)) Book Wholesalers, Inc.

—Franklin's Canoe Trip. 2002. (Franklin Ser.). 12.40 (978-1-4046-0324-0(7)) Book Wholesalers, Inc.

—Franklin's Christmas Gift. 2002. (Franklin Ser.). (J). 12.40 (978-0-7587-2532-5(9)) Book Wholesalers, Inc.

—Franklin's Class Trip. 2002. (Franklin Ser.). 12.40 (978-1-4046-0325-7(5)) Book Wholesalers, Inc.

—Franklin's Music Lessons. 2002. (Franklin Ser.). 12.40 (978-1-4046-1981-4(X)) Book Wholesalers, Inc.

—Franklin's New Friend. 2002. (Franklin Ser.). 12.40 (978-1-4046-0327-1(1)) Book Wholesalers, Inc.

—Franklin's School Play. 2002. (Franklin Ser.). 12.40 (978-1-4046-0328-8(X)) Book Wholesalers, Inc.

—Franklin's Secret Club. 2002. (Franklin Ser.). (J). 12.40 (978-0-7587-2533-2(7)) Book Wholesalers, Inc.

—Franklin's Thanksgiving. 2002. (Franklin Ser.). 12.40 (978-1-4046-0329-5(8)) Book Wholesalers, Inc.

—Hurry up, Franklin. 2002. (Franklin Ser.). (J). 12.40 (978-0-7587-4167-7(7)) Book Wholesalers, Inc.

Clarke, Catherine. Ninja Turtles: The Next Mutation. 1998. (J). 3.99 (978-0-679-89301-1(6) , Random Hse. Bks. for Young Readers) Random Hse. Children's Bks.

—Teenage Mutant Ninja Turtles: The Next Mutation. 1998. (J). 3.99 (978-0-679-89302-8(4) , Random Hse. Bks. for Young Readers) Random Hse. Children's Bks.

Cockburn, Gerrie L. Why Turtles Have Shells. Cockburn, Ian, ed. Cockburn, Gerrie L., illus. (Friendship Ser.). (Illus.). 31p. (Orig.). (J). (gr. k-4). pap. 5.95 (978-1-887461-00-9(0)) Cockburn Publishing.

Cole, Marjorie E. The Pond. 2000. (J). pap. 9.95 (978-0-7414-0498-5(2)) Infinity Publishing.

Collier, Kevin Scott. Esther's Channel. 2005. (Illus.). 160p. pap. 10.95 (978-0-9752880-6-1(7)) Baker Trittin Pr.

Conway, Aaron, illus. Alex the Sea Turtle: None. 2007. Tr. of None. 26p. (J). (***978-0-9777923-0-6(7))** Shiloh Group.

Cook, Sherry & Johnson, Terri. Timothy Tornado, 26. Kuhn, Jesse, illus. l.t. ed. 2006. (Quirkles—Exploring Phonics through Science Ser.: 20). 32p. 7.99 (978-1-933815-19-0(1) , Quirkles, The) Creative 3, LLC.

Cooper, Mary B. A Tale of Two Turtles. 2005. (ENG., Illus.). 36p. (J). (ps-7). per. 19.25 (978-1-4184-8943-4(3)) AuthorHouse.

Cosgrove, Stephen. Tee Tee. 2003. (gr. k-3). lib. bdg. 13.00 (978-0-613-64604-8(5)) Tandem Library Bks.

Crawford, Deborah. Tyler the Turtle Is Afraid of the Dark. Balzer, Jeremy, illus. 2006. 32p. (J). 14.95 (*978-0-9770516-1-8(7)) Laffin Minor Pr.

Crowe, Carole. Turtle Girl. Postier, Jim, illus. 2007. (J). (*978-1-59078-262-0(3)) Boyds Mills Pr.

Curriculum Corporation. Tai Hao Le! 2005. pap. 79.95 incl. audio compact disk (978-1-86366-402-8(5)) Curriculum Corporation AUS. *Dist:* Cheng & Tsui Co.

Curtis, Jennifer. Turtles in My Sandbox. 2006. (Illus.). 32p. (J). 15.95 (978-0-9768823-7-4(X)) Sylvan Dell Pubng.

Cuyler, Margery. Road Signs: A Harey Race with a Tortoise. Haskamp, Steven, illus. 2000. 40p. (J). (ps-1). 15.95 (978-1-890817-23-7(6)) Winslow Pr.

Cuyler, Margery. Roadsigns. Haskamp, Steve, illus. 2008. (J). (*978-0-7614-5306-2(7)) Cavendish, Marshall Corp.

Denson, Sara Ann. Christmas Turtles. McMillen, Tara, illus. 2006. 32p. (J). 16.95 (978-0-9769017-6-1(5)) Purple Sky Publishing.

Dillon-Butler, Marybeth. Myrtle the Hurdler & Her Pink & Purple, Polka-Dotted Girdle. Messing, David, illus. 2005. 32p. (J). pap. 11.95 (978-0-9785075-9-6(2), Ferne Pr.) Nelson Publishing & Marketing.

Discovery Turtle: A Play & Discover Book. 2002. (J). (978-1-931312-56-1(7)) SoftPlay, Inc.

Dodd, Lynley. The Smallest Turtle. Dodd, Lynley, illus. 2000. (Gold Star First Readers Ser.). (Illus.). 32p. (J). (gr. 1 up). lib. bdg. 22.00 (978-0-8368-2692-0(2)) Stevens, Gareth Inc.

Domm, Kristin. The Hatchling's Journey: A Blanding's Turtle Story. Domm, Jeff, illus. 2003. pap. 8.95 (978-1-55109-438-0(X)) Nimbus Publishing, Ltd. CAN. *Dist:* National Bk. Network.

Dub-u-el. Zoom-Zoom & Slo-Poke. 2005. (J). pap. 15.00 (978-0-8059-6808-8(3)) Dorrance Publishing Co., Inc.

Duracell and the National Center for Missing & Exploited Children (NCMEC), creator. The Great Tomato Adventure: A Story about Smart Safety Choices. 2007. 0.00 (*978-0-9795307-0-8(9)) Duracell & the National Ctr. for Missing & Exploited Children (NCMEC).

Durrell, Gerald. Toby the Tortoise. (Illus.). 32p. (J). 15.95 (978-1-85479-032-3(3)) O'Mara, Michael Bks., Ltd. GBR. *Dist:* Trans-Atlantic Pubns., Inc.

Ende, Michael. Tranquila Tragaleguas: La Tortuga Cabezota. Asensio, Agusti, illus. 2003. (SPA.). 42p. (J). (gr. k-3). pap. 8.95 (978-84-204-3709-5(3)) Santillana USA Publishing Co., Inc.

Enwonwu, Chio. Tortoise Returns to the Woods. 1999. (Illus.). 58p. pap. (978-978-129-258-3(X)) Heinemann Educational Bks. (Nigeria), Ltd.

Erdman & Perez. Mitos y Leyendas Indigenas. 2005. (SPA.). 72p. 13.99 (978-84-241-8013-3(5)) Everest de Ediciones y Distribucion, S.L. ESP. *Dist:* Lectorum Pubns., Inc.

Falwell, Cathryn. Scoot! 2008. 32p. (J). 16.99 (*978-0-06-128882-1(9)); lib. bdg. 17.89 (*978-0-06-128883-8(7)) HarperCollins Pubs. (Greenwillow Bks.).

—Turtle Splash! Countdown at the Pond. Falwell, Cathryn, illus. 2002. (Illus.). (J). 25.04 (978-0-7587-8827-6(4)) Book Wholesalers, Inc.

—Turtle Splash! Countdown at the Pond. Falwell, Cathryn, illus. 32p. (J). 2008. pap. 6.99 (*978-0-06-142927-9(9), Harper Trophy); 2001. (Illus.). (gr. 7 up). 16.99 (978-0-06-029462-5(0)); 2001. (Illus.). (gr. 7 up). lib. bdg. 17.89 (978-0-06-029463-2(9)) HarperCollins Pubs.

Finally, Lil Rose. Slowpoke the Turtle & Company. Drape, Kaitlin, illus. 2005. (J). pap. 8.00 (978-0-8059-6778-4(8)) Dorrance Publishing Co., Inc.

Fleming, Candace. Sunny Boy! The Life & Times of a Tortoise. Wilsdorf, Anne, illus. 2005. 40p. (J). 16.00 (978-0-374-37297-2(7), Farrar, Straus & Giroux (BYR)) Farrar, Straus & Giroux.

For the Love of Turtles: Six-Pack. (Greetings Ser.: Vol. 1). 24p. (gr. 2-3). 31.00 (978-0-7635-9423-7(7)) Rigby Education.

Ford, Carole S. Timothy Turtle & Sammy Scallop. Edwin, Kimberly, illus. 30p. (J). (ps-k). pap. 4.95 (978-1-891533-02-0(9)) Calvin Partnership, LLC.

Franklin TV Staff, ed. Franklin's Halloween Fun. 2005. (Franklin Sticker & Activity Bks.). (Illus.). 16p. (J). (ps-3). (978-1-55337-670-5(6)) Kids Can Pr., Ltd.

Franklin's Birthday Party. 2004. (Franklin Tv Storybooks Ser.). (Illus.). 32p. (J). (ps-ps). (978-1-55074-882-6(3)) Kids Can Pr., Ltd.

Galera Staff. La Liebre y la Tortuga. (SPA.). 24p. (J). 9.95 (978-84-246-1555-0(7), GL3096) La Galera, S.A. Editorial ESP. *Dist:* AIMS International Bks., Inc., Lectorum Pubns., Inc.

Gandolfi, Silvana & Schwartz, Lynne Sharon. Aldabra, or, the Tortoise Who Loved Shakespeare. 2004. 151p. (J). (978-0-439-49744-2(2), Levine, Arthur A. Bks.) Scholastic, Inc.

Gaona, Gloria. Dominic & His Turtle Michael Angelo. 2003. 32p. (J). pap. 9.00 (978-0-8059-5764-8(2)) Dorrance Publishing Co., Inc.

Garcia, R. M. The Steamer Trunk Adventures #1: The Trunk & the Tortoise. 2006. 76p. pap. 14.95 (978-1-4241-0614-1(1)) PublishAmerica, Inc.

George, Margaret & Murphy, Christopher John. Lucille Lost: A True Adventure. Dacey, Bob & Bandelin, Debra, illus. 2006. 32p. (J). (gr. 1). 16.99 (978-0-670-06093-1(3), Viking Adult) Penguin Group (USA) Inc.

Gerver, Jane E. The Santa Snatcher. Spaziante, Patrick, illus. 2004. 32p. (J). lib. bdg. 15.00 (*978-1-4242-0959-0(5)) Fitzgerald Bks.

—The Santa Snatcher. 2004. (Ready-to-Read Ser.). 32p. (J). pap. 3.99 (978-0-689-87018-7(3), Simon Spotlight) Simon & Schuster Children's Publishing.

Gill, Janie S. Timothy Turtle Travels. 2001. (Predictable Readers Ser.). (Illus.). (J). (gr. k-2). lib. bdg. 11.95 (978-0-89868-534-3(6)) ARO Publishing Co.

Glaser, Shirley. The Big Race. Glaser, Milton & Glaser, Shirley, illus. 2005. 32p. (ps-2). 16.99 (978-0-7868-1821-1(2)) Hyperion Bks. for Children.

Gorbachev, Valeri. Heron & Turtle. Gorbachev, Valeri, illus. 2006. (Illus.). 40p. (J). (gr. k). 15.99 (978-0-399-24321-9(6), Philomel) Penguin Group (USA) Inc.

—Miss Turtle the Babysitter. Gorbachev, Valeri, illus. 2006. (I Can Read Bks.). (J). pap. 3.99 (978-0-06-058075-9(5), Harper Trophy) HarperCollins Pubs.

—Ms. Turtle the Babysitter. Gorbachev, Valeri, illus. 2005. (I Can Read Bks.). (Illus.). 64p. (J). (gr. k-3). 15.99 (978-0-06-058073-5(9)); lib. bdg. 16.89 (978-0-06-058074-2(7)) HarperCollins Pubs.

—Red Red Red. Gorbachev, Valeri, illus. 2007. 40p. (J). (ps-3). 16.99 (978-0-399-24628-9(2), Philomel) Penguin Group (USA) Inc.

—Whose Hat Is It? 2004. 30p. (J). lib. bdg. 13.85 (*978-1-4242-0713-8(4)) Fitzgerald Bks.

—Whose Hat Is It? Gorbachev, Valeri, illus. (My First I Can Read Bks.). (Illus.). 32p. (J). (ps up). 2005. pap. 3.99 (978-0-06-053436-3(2), Harper Trophy); 2004. 14.99 (978-0-06-053434-9(6)); 2004. lib. bdg. 15.89 (978-0-06-053435-6(4)) HarperCollins Pubs.

Greene, Constance. Beat the Turtle Drum. 2002. (J). (gr. 4-8). 20.25 (978-0-8446-7208-3(4)) Smith, Peter Pub., Inc.

Greenfield Educational Center Staff. Little Turtle Changes Its House. 2000. (I Can Read Ser.: Bk. 1). (CHI & ENG., Illus.). 8p. (J). pap. 2.99 (978-962-563-094-6(5)); pap. 24.99 (978-962-563-134-9(8)) Greenfield Enterprises, Ltd. HKG. *Dist:* Cheng & Tsui Co.

Grimm, Jacob W. & Grimm, Wilhelm K. The Fisherman & the Turtle. Avilel[81]s Junco, Martha, illus. 2008. (J). (*978-0-7614-5387-1(3)) Cavendish, Marshall Corp.

Hamilton, Linda. The Wise Old Turtle. 2005. (J). (978-1-933248-06-6(8)) World Quest Learning.

Haney, Donald. My Name Is Snappy! 2006. 24p. (J). per. 11.99 (978-1-59886-584-4(6)) Tate Publishing & Enterprises, L.L.C.

Harcourt School Publishers Staff. There Is a Turtle Ahead: Take-Home Book. 1999. (Collections Ser.). (Illus.). (J). pap. 1.90 (978-0-15-317293-9(2)) Harcourt Schl. Pubs.

—Turtle at Home On Level. 3rd ed. 2002. (Trophies Reading Program Ser.). (Illus.). pap. 5.10 (978-0-15-323166-7(1)) Harcourt Schl. Pubs.

—Why Geese Fly in Teams Advanced Level. 3rd ed. 2002. (Trophies Reading Program Ser.). (Illus.). pap. 5.10 (978-0-15-323377-7(X)) Harcourt Schl. Pubs.

The Hare & the Tortoise: Individual Title Six-Packs. 32p. (gr. 2 up). 37.00 (978-0-7635-9219-6(6)) Rigby Education.

Harms, John, II. The Saving of Okee & Dokee Sea Turtle. Belizar, Denise H., ed. Makowski, Robin Lee, illus. 2001. 32p. (YA). (gr. 7-12). 14.95 (978-0-9653871-4-9(3)) Frederick Pr.

Harper, Benjamin. TMNT Underground Art Studio. 2007. (Teenage Mutant Ninja Turtles Ser.). (Illus.). 48p. (J). (ps-3). 9.99 (*978-1-4169-3856-9(7), Simon Scribbles) Simon & Schuster Children's Publishing.

Hatkoff, Craig & Hatkoff, Isabella. Best Friends. 2007. (Owen & Mzee Ser.). 12p. (J). bds. 6.99 (978-0-439-92872-4(9), Scholastic Pr.) Scholastic, Inc.

Hensley, Terri Anne. Tobias andrew Bartholomew. 2007. (J). per. 8.95 (*978-0-9789057-6-7(8)) Huntington Ludlow Media Group.

Heurtelou, Maude. Do Toti. Soto, Anna & Hippolyte, Johanne, illus. 1999. (Big Book Ser.).Tr. of Turtle's Back. (CRP.). 12p. (J). (gr. k-2). 19.50 (978-1-58432-074-6(5)) Educa Vision.

Hicks, Robert Z. Tommie Turtle's Secret. Rolseth, Ruthie, illus. 2007. 40p. (J). 16.95 (*978-0-9792031-0-7(4)) R.Z. Enterprises of Florida.

Himmelman, John. Tudley Didn't Know. Himmelman, John, illus. (Illus.). (J). 2007. 1p. 8.95 (*978-1-934359-04-4(1)); 2006. 32p. 15.95 (978-0-9764943-6-2(1)) Sylvan Dell Pubng.

Hodgson, Mona Gansberg. Goofy Glasses. 2000. (ps-2). lib. bdg. 13.00 (978-0-613-72834-8(3)) Tandem Library Bks.

Hodgson, Mona Gansberg & Sharp, Chris. Goofy Glasses. 2000. (Desert Critter Friends Ser.: Vol. 10). (Illus.). 48p. (J). (ps-2). 4.99 (978-0-570-07011-5(2)) Concordia Publishing Hse.

Hoobler, David. Zonk & the Secret Lagoon: The Further Adventures of Zonk the Dreaming Tortoise. l.t. ed. 2005. (Illus.). 32p. (J). lib. bdg. 16.95 (978-0-9706537-1-0(9)) Zonk Galleries.

—Zonk, the dreaming Tortoise. l.t. ed. 2001. (Illus.). 32p. (J). lib. bdg. 16.95 (978-0-9706537-0-3(0)) Zonk Galleries.

Hooray for Boys & Girls! ed. 2006. (J). 15.95 (978-0-9776837-0-3(2)) West Woods Pr.

Hoppes, Lyn L. Freefall. 1998. (J). 12.95 (978-1-58021-044-7(9)); pap. 5.95 (978-1-58021-039-3(2)) Benefactory, Inc., The.

Horn, Peter. The Best Father of All. James, J. Alison, tr. from GER. Kadmon, Cristina, illus. 32p. (J). (ps). 2005. pap. 6.95 (978-0-7358-1977-1(7)); 2003. 15.95 (978-0-7358-1679-4(4)) North-South Bks., Inc.

—Best Father of All Spanish Le. 2007. (J). 16.50 (978-0-7358-2116-3(X)) North-South Bks., Inc.

—Best Father of All Spanish PB. 2007. (J). pap. 6.95 (978-0-7358-2117-0(8)) North-South Bks., Inc.

—Cuando Sea Grande... Kadmon, Cristina, illus. 2001. (SPA.). 32p. (J). (gr. k-3). pap. 6.95 (978-0-7358-1435-6(X), NS30340) North-South Bks., Inc.

—Cuando Sea Grande. 2001. (SPA.). (gr. k-3). lib. bdg. 15.25 (978-0-613-35921-4(6)) Tandem Library Bks.

—When I Grow Up... 1999. (Illus.). (J). (978-0-606-20987-8(5)) Tandem Library Bks.

—When I Grow Up. 2001. (gr. k-3). lib. bdg. 15.25 (978-0-613-33860-8(X)) Tandem Library Bks.

—When I Grow Up... Cuando Sea Grande. Almohar, Ariel, tr. from GER. Kadmon, Cristina, illus. 2001. 32p. (J). (ps-3). pap. 6.95 (978-0-7358-1418-9(X)) North-South Bks., Inc.

Howard, Florence. Pepe the Little Turtle & Little Rachel. Rose, Tony, ed. 2001. (Illus.). 25p. (J). (gr. k-5). pap. 5.95 (978-0-9655064-6-5(0)) Amber Bks.

Howell, Gill. Tortoise & the Baboon. Woody, illus. 2004. 16p. (J). lib. bdg. 22.65 (*978-1-59646-686-9(3)) Dingles & Co.

Howells, Graham, illus. I Saw a Ship A-Sailing. 2001. 32p. pap. 12.95 (978-1-85902-908-4(6)) Beekman Bks., Inc.

Irvin-Marston, Hope. My Little Book of Painted Turtles. Magdalena-Brown, Maria, illus. 2nd ed. 2004. 32p. (J). pap. 7.95 (978-0-89317-055-4(0), WW-0550, Windward Publishing) Finney Co., Inc.

Itoh, Shimpei. Hyper Dolls, Vol. 5. 2003. (Illus.). 208p. pap. 15.95 (978-1-929090-67-9(6)) International Comics & Entertainment L.L.C.

Jay, Alison, illus. The Race. 2006. 32p. (J). reprint ed. pap. 6.95 (978-0-8118-5226-5(1)) Chronicle Bks. LLC.

Jenkins, Amanda. How the Turtle Cracked its Shell: A Tale from Guatemala. 2006. 23.00 (*978-1-4108-6171-9(6)) Benchmark Education Co.

Jenkins, Susan. Franklin & the Magic Show. 2004. (Kids Can Read Ser.). (Illus.). 32p. (J). (gr. k-3). (978-1-55074-990-8(0)) Kids Can Pr., Ltd.

Jennings, Sharon. Franklin & the Tin Flute. Gagnon, Celeste et al, illus. 2005. (Kids Can Read with Help Ser.). 32p. (J). (ps-ps). (978-1-55337-800-6(8)) Kids Can Pr., Ltd.

—Franklin Stays Up. Jeffrey, Sean et al, illus. 2003. 32p. (J). pap. (978-0-439-41815-7(1)) Scholastic, Inc.

—Franklin's Pond Phantom. McIntyre, Sasha et al, illus. 2005. (Kids Can Read with Help Ser.). 32p. (J). (ps-ps). (978-1-55337-718-4(4)) Kids Can Pr., Ltd.

Jennings, Sharon, et al. Franklin & the Baby-Sitter. Southern, Shelley et al, illus. 2001. (Franklin TV Storybook Ser.). 32p. (J). (ps-3). (978-1-55074-916-8(1)) Kids Can Pr., Ltd.

—Franklin & the Big Kid. Southern, Shelley et al, illus. 2002. (Franklin TV Storybook Ser.). 27p. (J). (ps-3). (978-1-55337-054-3(6)) Kids Can Pr., Ltd.

—Franklin & the Bubble Gum. Jeffrey, Sean et al, illus. 2006. 32p. (978-1-55337-817-4(2)); (978-1-55337-816-7(4)) Kids Can Pr., Ltd.

—Franklin & the Computer. Southern, Shelley et al, illus. 2003. (Franklin TV Storybook Ser.). 32p. (J). (ps-3). (978-1-55337-362-9(6)) Kids Can Pr., Ltd.

—Franklin & the Cookies. Gagnon, Celeste, illus. 2005. (Kids Can Read Ser.). 32p. (J). (gr. 1-2). (978-1-55337-717-7(6)); (978-1-55337-716-0(8)) Kids Can Pr., Ltd.

—Franklin & the New Teacher. Gagnon, Celeste, illus. 2005. 32p. (J). (gr. k-3). (978-1-55337-500-5(9)) Kids Can Pr., Ltd.

—Franklin Celebrates. Jeffrey, Sean et al, illus. 2005. (Franklin Tv Storybooks Ser.). 30p. (J). (gr. k-3). (978-1-55337-502-9(5)) Kids Can Pr., Ltd.

—Franklin Plays Hockey. Koren, Mark & Lei, John, illus. 2002. (Franklin TV Storybook Ser.). 32p. (J). (ps-3). (978-1-55337-056-7(2)) Kids Can Pr., Ltd.

—Franklin Runs Away. Jeffrey, Sean, illus. 2001. (Franklin TV Storybook Ser.). 32p. (J). (ps-3). (978-1-55074-912-0(9)) Kids Can Pr., Ltd.

—Franklin Stays Up. Southern, Shelley et al, illus. 2004. (Kids Can Read Ser.). 32p. (J). (gr. k-3). (978-1-55337-372-8(3)); (978-1-55337-371-1(5)) Kids Can Pr., Ltd.

—Franklin's Canoe Trip. Jeffrey, Sean et al, illus. 2003. (Franklin TV StoryBks.). 32p. (J). (gr. k-3). (978-1-55337-019-2(8)) Kids Can Pr., Ltd.

—Franklin's Music Lessons. Southern, Shelley et al, illus. 2004. (Kids Can Read Ser.). 32p. (J). (gr. k-3). (978-1-55337-171-7(2)) Kids Can Pr., Ltd.

—Franklin's Soapbox Derby. Jeffrey, Sean et al, illus. 2006. 32p. (978-1-55337-819-8(9)); (978-1-55337-818-1(0)) Kids Can Pr., Ltd.

—Franklin's Surprise. Jeffrey, Sean et al, illus. 2004. (Kids Can Read Ser.). 32p. (J). (gr. k-3). (978-1-55337-466-4(5)); (978-1-55337-465-7(7)) Kids Can Pr., Ltd.

Jones, Shelley V. & Sprick, Marilyn. Turtle in the Tuba: Read Well Level K Unit 8 Storybook. McDonnell, Kevin, illus. 2004. (Read Well Level K Ser.). 20p. (978-1-57035-672-8(6)) Sopris West Educational Services.

Jorento, Dane, illus. Turtles into Butterflies. 2002. (J). 15.95 (978-0-9643004-1-5(9)) Laughing Peaches Pubns.

Kaths, Kathy. The Soaring Feather. 1999. (Illus.). 80p. (J). pap. 8.95 (978-0-9672533-0-5(6)) Kichita Productions.

Kids Can Press Staff, Press Can, creator. Franklin & the Tin Flute. 2005. (Kids Can Read with Help Ser.). (Illus.). 32p. (J). (ps-ps). (978-1-55337-801-3(6)) Kids Can Pr., Ltd.

Kids Can Read Staff, ed. Franklin's Picnic. 2006. (Illus.). 32p. 3.95 (978-1-55337-715-3(X)) Kids Can Pr., Ltd. CAN. *Dist:* Wybel Marketing Group.

—Franklin's Pond Phantom. 2005. (Kids Can Read with Help Ser.). (Illus.). 32p. (J). (gr. 1-2). (978-1-55337-719-1(2)) Kids Can Pr., Ltd.

Kleemann, Linda. Larry the Turtle When Everyone Helps, Everyone Wins! Malkowski, Melissa, illus. 2005. (J). pap. 7.95 (978-0-9776487-0-2(2)) Fencepost Communications Inc.

Korman, Susan. Box Turtle at Silver Pond Lane: Smithsonians Backyard. Marchesi, Stephen, illus. 2005. (Smithsonian's Backyard Ser.). 32p. (J). (ps-2). pap. 6.95 (978-1-56899-935-7(6), S5020) Soundprints.

Kuchling, Guundie. Turtle-Taxi. Himsworth, Chris & Loux, Andrea, eds. 1998. (Illus.). 32p. (YA). 9.95 (978-1-876268-15-2(8)) Univ. of Western Australia Pr. AUS. *Dist:* International Specialized Bk. Services.

Labatt, Mary. Franklin Stays Up. 2003. (gr. k-3). lib. bdg. 11.80 (978-0-613-87146-4(4)) Tandem Library Bks.

—Franklin's Trading Cards. 2003. (gr. k-3). lib. bdg. 11.80 (978-0-613-86543-2(X)) Tandem Library Bks.

Lane, Barry. The Tortoise & the Hare Continued. Bodimeade, Miles, illus. 2001. (J). (gr. 1-6). 16.00 (978-1-931492-01-0(8)) Discover Writing Pr.

Larsen, Alison. My Turtle. 2006. 23p. (J). per. 11.95 (*978-1-60002-095-7(X), 3963, Airleaf Publishing) Airleaf Publishing & Bookselling.

—Thomas the Turtle. 2006. (Illus.). 21p. (J). per. 14.95 (978-1-60002-097-1(6), 3961, Airleaf Publishing) Airleaf Publishing & Bookselling.

—Thomas the Turtle's Adventures. 2006. (Illus.). 30p. (J). per. 14.95 (978-1-60002-096-4(8), 3962, Airleaf Publishing) Airleaf Publishing & Bookselling.

LeapFrog Staff, compiled by. Squire Hare & Sir Turtle. 2001. (J). (ps-2). spiral bd. 14.95 (978-1-58605-065-8(6)) LeapFrog Enterprises, Inc.

Learning Wrap-Ups: The Grasshopper & the Ants, The Turtle & the Rabbit. 2006. 66p. (J). 12.99 (978-1-59204-203-6(1)) Learning Wrap-Ups.

Leon, Georgina Lazaro. ¡Viva la Tortuga! Torres, Walter, illus. (SPA.). 30p. (J). (gr. 3-5). 12.95 (978-1-57581-605-0(9)) Santillana USA Publishing Co., Inc.

Leonhardt, Alice. Save the Sea Turtles. 1999. (Illus.). (J). pap. (978-0-7398-2407-8(4)) Steck-Vaughn.

—Turtle's Big Race. 1999. (Illus.). (J). pap. 4.93 (978-0-7398-2406-1(6)) Steck-Vaughn.

Lewin, Ted. Nilo & the Tortoise. 1999. (J). (978-0-590-73912-2(3)); 40p. pap. 16.95 (978-0-590-96004-5(0)) Scholastic, Inc.

Lewis, Sian. I Saw a Ship A-Sailing. Howells, Graham, illus. 2001. 32p. pap. 24.95 (978-1-85902-994-7(9)) Beekman Bks., Inc.

Lievre et la Tortue. pap. 7.95 (978-88-8148-779-0(9)) European Language Institute ITA. *Dist:* Distribooks, Inc.

Limu the Blue Turtle. 2003. (J). 10.99 (978-0-89610-549-2(0)) Island Heritage Publishing.

Lingard, Joan. Tortoise Trouble. 2002. (Illus.). 112p. (J). pap. 8.99 (978-0-340-80578-7(1), Hodder & Stoughton) Hodder General Publishing Division GBR. *Dist:* Trafalgar Square Publishing.

London, Jonathan. What Newt Could Do for Turtle. 1998. (J). (978-0-606-13902-1(8)) Tandem Library Bks.

Love, Pamela. A Loon Alone. Sycks, Shannon, illus. 2002. 30p. pap. 9.95 (978-0-89272-526-7(5), 1078); 29p. 14.95 (978-0-89272-571-7(0)) Down East Bks.

Lowe, Lana. The Three Little Girls & the Giant Sea Turtle. Beaumont, Peter, illus. 2006. (J). (978-0-9777274-0-7(8)) Lone Star Publishing Co.

Lowell, Susan. The Tortoise & the Jackrabbit. Harris, Jim, illus. 2004. (New Bilingual Picture Book Ser.). (ENG & SPA.). 32p. (J). 7.95 incl. 5.25 hd (978-0-87358-869-0(X), Rising Moon Bks. for Young Readers) Northland Publishing.

Lowery, Paul. Do You Know Where Sea Turtles Go? 2007. (J). 15.99 (*978-0-9792379-0-4(4)) PBL Stories LLC.

—Do You Know Where Sea Turtles Go? Thomas, Tim, illus. 2005. (J). lib. bdg. 15.99 (978-0-9771059-9-1(7)) Thomas Expressions, Inc.

Lucia, Ruth. Mitzi, the Amazing Mud Turtle. 2004. (Illus.). 32p. (J). pap. (978-1-932373-67-7(5), Cedar Hill Pr.) Cedar Hill Publishing.

Lue, Grammy. Tuffy Turtle. 2007. pap. 11.99 (*978-1-4259-4872-6(3)) AuthorHouse.

Mackinnon, Mairi. Hare & the Tortoise. Howarth, Daniel, illus. 2007. (First Reading Level 4 Ser.). 48p. (J). 8.99 (*978-0-7945-1612-3(2), Usborne) EDC Publishing.

Martin, Candice J. Theo's Special Gift. Bonavita, Madison M., illus. l.t. ed. 2006. 12p. (J). per. 12.99 (978-1-59879-190-7(7)) Lifevest Publishing, Inc.

Mason, Craig. Turtle Games. Mason, Bergetta, illus. 2003. 32p. (J). 4.99 (978-0-9729153-0-4(3)) 1 Sleeve Publishing.

Matsumoto, Lisa. The Adventures of Gary & Harry: A Tale of Two Turtles. Furuya, Michael, illus. 2006. (J). 16.95 (978-0-9647491-4-6(9)) Lehua, Inc.

Mau, Connie. Catch me if you Can. Lemus, Kristina, illus. l.t. ed. 2006. 28p. (J). 14.95 (978-0-9778843-0-8(9)) Mau, C. Publishing Co.

McDermott, Gerald. Jabuti the Tortoise: A Trickster Tale from the Amazon. 2005. (Illus.). 32p. (J). (ps-ps). pap., pap. 7.00 (978-0-15-205374-1(3), Voyager Bks./Libros Viajeros) Harcourt Children's Bks.

Miller, Mike. Joshua's Surprise: A Tomas the Tortoise Adventure. Miller, Mike, illus. 2003. 32p. (J). 15.95 (978-1-932173-23-9(4)) Stephens Pr. LLC.

—My Big Book of the Desert: A Tomas the Tortoise Adventure. 2004. pap. 15.95 (978-1-932173-38-3(2)) Stephens Pr. LLC.

—One Hot Day: A Tomas the Tortoise Adventure. Miller, Mike, illus. 2004. 32p. (J). 15.95 (978-1-932173-21-5(8), 702-387-5260) Stephens Pr. LLC.

—Tales for Tomas: A Tomas the Tortoise Adventure. 2004. 15.95 (978-1-932173-37-6(4)) Stephens Pr. LLC.

Miller, Mike, told to. Tomas & the Ghost Town: A Tomas the Tortoise Adventure. 2004. 15.95 (978-1-932173-36-9(6)) Stephens Pr. LLC.

Mitter, Matt. Seymour Sea Turtle Snaps up Lunch. Goode, Jon, illus. 2003. (Snappy Fun Bks.). 12p. (J). bds. 4.99 (978-0-7944-0124-5(4), Reader's Digest Children's Bks.) Reader's Digest Children's Publishing, Inc.

Moen Cabanting, Ruth & Jensen, Natalie Mahina. Happy Honu Makes a Friend. 2006. 7p. 6.95 (978-1-933067-15-5(2)) Beachhouse Publishing, LLC.

Moore, Eva. Franklin & the Baby. 2004. (Franklin TV Storybks.). (Illus.). 32p. (J). (gr. k-3). (978-1-55074-706-5(1)) Kids Can Pr., Ltd.

—Franklin & the Baby. 1999. (Franklin TV-Tie In Ser.). (Illus.). 32p. (J). (ps-3). pap. 4.50 (978-0-439-08365-2(6)) Scholastic, Inc.

—Franklin & the Baby. 1999. (Franklin TV Storybook Ser.). (J). (ps-3). 11.30 (978-0-606-20056-1(8)) Tandem Library Bks.

Moore, Eva & Nelvana Staff. Franklin & the Baby. 2000. (Franklin TV Storybook Ser.). (Illus.). 96p. (J). (ps-3). (978-1-55074-708-9(8)) Kids Can Pr., Ltd.

Moran, Martin, V, ed. The Town Turtles of Sandy Springs: The Stories Behind the Turtles by the Children Who Saw Them. 2006. (Illus.). 64p. (J). 24.00 (978-0-9742704-1-8(5)) Hardin Publishing, LLC.

Moriarty, John. Turtle Was Gone a Long Time, Vol. 3. 1999. 332p. 44.95 (978-1-901866-02-5(5)) Lilliput Pr., Ltd., The IRL. *Dist:* Dufour Editions, Inc.

Moss, Deborah M. Shelley, the Hyperactive Turtle. Schwartz, Carol, illus. 2nd ed. 2006. 20p. (J). pap. (978-1-890627-75-1(5)) Woodbine Hse.

Murdocca, Sal. Tuttle's Shell. Murdocca, Sal, illus. 1999. (Illus.). 32p. (J). (gr. 1-5). 15.95 (978-1-57255-643-0(9)) Mondo Publishing.

Murphy, Stephen & Murphy, Sonia. The Master's Book. Johnson, Shane L., illus. unabr. ed. 2006. (Teenage Mutant Ninja Turtles Ser.: 1). 64p. (J). pap. 4.99 (978-1-4169-0945-3(1) , Simon Spotlight) Simon & Schuster Children's Publishing.

Murphy, Stephen, et al. The Secret. S. I. International Staff & Ostrom, Bob, illus. 2004. (Teenage Mutant Ninja Turtles Ser.). 32p. (J). pap. 3.99 (978-0-689-86965-5(7) , Simon Spotlight) Simon & Schuster Children's Publishing.

Murphy, Steve. Lean, Green Smackdown Machine! Ruiz, Aristides & Giles, Mike, illus. 2004. (Teenage Mutant Ninja Turtles Ser.). 24p. (J). pap. 3.99 (978-0-689-87059-0(0) , Simon Spotlight) Simon & Schuster Children's Publishing.

—The Legend of Yaotl. Spaziante, Patrick, illus. 2007. (Teenage Mutant Ninja Turtles Ser.). 24p. (J). pap. 3.99 (978-1-4169-4108-8(8) , Simon Spotlight) Simon & Schuster Children's Publishing.

—Mikey's Nightwatcher Scrapbook. Jourdan, Diego, illus. 2007. (Teenage Mutant Ninja Turtles Ser.). 16p. (J). pap. 4.99 (978-1-4169-3345-8(X) , Simon Spotlight) Simon & Schuster Children's Publishing.

Murphy, Stuart J. Seaweed Soup. 2001. (ps-2). lib. bdg. 12.95 (978-0-613-50243-6(4)) Tandem Library Bks.

Navarro, Dawn E., et al. Chelonia: El Retorno de la Tortuga Marina. 2002. (SPA., Illus.). (J). (gr. 3-5). 16.95 (978-0-930118-35-8(9) , SCH31403) Sea Challengers, Inc.

Northrop, Nancy. Connie - the Three Legged Turtle. Duckworth, Jeff, illus. 2002. 41p. (J). (gr. k-3). 8.25 (978-0-9627894-5-8(3)) LNR Pubns.

O'Flatharta, Antoine. Hurry & the Monarch. So, Meilo, illus. 2005. 40p. (J). (gr. k-3). 14.95 (978-0-375-83003-7(0) , Knopf Bks. for Young Readers) Random Hse. Children's Bks.

Oke, Janette. The Impatient Turtle. Munger, Nancy, illus. rev. ed. 2000. (Animal Friends Ser.). 64p. (Orig.). (J). (gr. 1-5). pap. 6.99 (978-0-7642-2407-2(7)) Bethany Hse. Pubs.

—The Impatient Turtle. 2000. (Orig.). (gr. 3-6). lib. bdg. 14.15 (978-0-613-84503-8(X)) Tandem Library Bks.

Oliver, Oliver J. Hare & Tortoise Race to the Moon. Oliver, Oliver J., illus. 2002. (Illus.). 40p. (J). (ps-3). 14.95 (978-0-8109-0566-5(3)) Abrams, Harry N. , Inc.

Orr, Wendy. Nim's Island. Millard, Kerry, illus. 2008. 144p. (gr. 3-7). 5.50 (***978-0-385-73606-0(1)*** , Yearling) Random Hse. Children's Bks.

Ostrom, Bob, illus. Friends till the End! 2004. (Teenage Mutant Ninja Turtles Ser.). 24p. (J). pap. 3.99 (978-0-689-87006-4(X) , Simon Spotlight) Simon & Schuster Children's Publishing.

—Friends till the End! ed. 2005. (Teenage Mutant Ninja Turtles Ser.: No. 3). 24p. (J). lib. bdg. 15.00 (978-1-59054-833-2(7)) Fitzgerald Bks.

Parish, Steve, illus. Sea Turtle's Clever Plan. 2005. 24p. (J). lib. bdg. 20.67 (978-0-8368-5975-1(8)) Stevens, Gareth Inc.

Patt, Ben. The Turtle Who Needed Glasses. Bullington, Syd, illus. 2000. 38p. (J). (gr. k-6). pap. 5.95 (978-0-943599-34-2(2)) Optometric Extension Program Foundation.

Pellant, Terry. The Real Valentine's Story. 2004. 27p. (J). pap. 14.95 (978-1-4137-2146-1(X)) PublishAmerica, Inc.

Perks, Anne-Marie, illus. The Tortoise Who Bragged: A Trigram Tale. 1999. 32p. (J). (gr. 2-4). pap. 8.50 (978-0-914534-18-1(1) , 120) Stokes Publishing Co., Inc.

Peters, Andrew. Bear & Turtle & the Great Winter Race. Edgson, Alison, illus. 2006. 32p. pap. 7.99 (978-1-904550-91-4(6)) Child's Play-International.

Peterson, Kevan. Turtle Takes the Bus. ed. 2005. (Illus.). 32p. (J). 12.99 (978-0-9767661-0-0(8)) Red Giant Publishing.

Peterson, Scott. Blackout! Spaziante, Patrick, illus. ed. 2005. (Teenage Mutant Ninja Turtles Ser.: Garden & No. 6). 24p. (J). lib. bdg. 15.00 (978-1-59054-831-8(0)) Fitzgerald Bks.

Pinkwater, Daniel M. The Neddiad: How Neddie Took the Train, Went to Hollywood, & Saved Civilization. 2007. 320p. (J). (gr. 5). 16.00 (***978-0-618-59444-3(2)***) Houghton Mifflin Co. Trade & Reference Div.

Pirotta, Saviour. Turtle Bay. Mistry, Nilesh, illus. 2005. 32p. (J). pap. 7.95 (978-1-84507-411-1(4)) Lincoln, Frances Ltd. GBR. *Dist:* Perseus Distribution.

Plater, Inge & Pearson, S. Green Turtle. 2000. (Illus.). 32p. (gr. 1-3). 16.00 (978-0-207-19690-4(7)) HarperCollins Pubs. AUS. *Dist:* Consortium Bk. Sales & Distribution.

Plowden, Sally H. Turtle Tracks. Plowden, Tee, illus. 2002. 32p. (J). (gr. 4-6). 14.95 (978-0-9679016-6-4(9)) Palmetto Conservation Foundation.

Potter-Hall, Meslisande. Ptolemy Turtle. 2000. 40p. 4.99 (978-976-610-172-5(8)) Penguin Group (USA) Inc.

Powell, Pamela. La Patrulla de las Tortugas. 2003. (SPA., Illus.). 190p. (YA). (gr. 5-8). (978-84-236-3791-1(3) , ED1183) Edebé ESP. *Dist:* Lectorum Pubns., Inc.

Price, D. Michael. Across the River: Walter & Oliver's Amazing Adventure. Price, D. Michael, illus. 1998. (Illus.). 48p. (J). (ps-3). pap. 15.95 (978-0-86713-047-8(4)) Greenwich Workshop Pr.

Price, Michael D. Across the River: Walter & Oliver's Amazing Adventure: a Tale of Persistence. Price, Michael D., illus. 2003. (Illus.). 44p. (J). reprint ed. 16.00 (978-0-7567-6990-1(6)) DIANE Publishing Co.

Priddy, Roger. Squishy Turtle & Friends. rev. ed. 2003. (Cloth Book Ser.). (Illus.). 14p. (J). 8.95 (978-0-312-49184-0(0) , Priddy Bks.) St. Martin's Pr.

Rathmell, Donna. Carolina's Story: Sea Turtles Get Sick Too! Bergwerf, Barbara J., illus. 2007. 1p. (J). 8.95 (***978-1-934359-00-6(9)***) Sylvan Dell Pubng.

—Carolina's Story: Sea Turtles Get Sick Too! Bergwerf, Barbara J., photos by. 2005. (Illus.). 32p. 15.95 (978-0-9764943-0-0(2)) Sylvan Dell Pubng.

Reber, Deborah. My Pet Turtle. Cutting, David, illus. 2001. (Blues Clue's Ready to Read Ser.: Vol. 5). 24p. (J). pap. 3.99 (978-0-689-84186-6(8) , Simon Spotlight/ Nickelodeon) Simon & Schuster Children's Publishing.

—My Pet Turtle. Cutting, David, illus. 2001. 32p. (gr. k-3). lib. bdg. 11.80 (978-0-613-57427-3(3)) Tandem Library Bks.

Redondo, Jesus, illus. Turtle Rescue! 2004. (Ready-to-Read Ser.). 32p. (J). pap. 3.99 (978-0-689-87007-1(8) , Simon Spotlight) Simon & Schuster Children's Publishing.

Reimer, Ramon. Were There Dinosaurs in My Past? Kilgore, Jeannette Vrlin, illus. 2002. 32p. (J). (gr. k-6). 14.95 (978-1-931650-16-8(0)) Coastal Publishing Carolina, Inc.

Rider, Cynthia. Chatterbox Turtle. Petrlik, Andrea, illus. 2004. 24p. (J). lib. bdg. 22.65 (***978-1-59646-696-8(0)***) Dingles & Co.

Robertson, Allen. Timothy Tuttles Story Book. 2005. 27p. 11.58 (978-1-4116-6352-7(7)) Lulu.com.

—Timothy Tuttles Story Book 11. 2005. 32p. 13.83 (978-1-4116-8045-6(6)) Lulu.com.

Rogers, Alan. Blue Tortoise. 2004. (Little Giants Ser.). (Illus.). 16p. (ps-k). (J). pap. 3.95 (978-1-58728-158-7(9)); 5.95 (978-1-58728-150-1(3)) T&N Children's Publishing. (Two Can Publishing).

—En Forme de Bateau. 2003. (Little Giants Ser.). (FRE., Illus.). 16p. (J). (ps-k). 5.95 (978-1-58728-177-8(5) , Two Can Publishing) T&N Children's Publishing.

—Tortue Bleue. 2000. (Little Giants Ser.). (FRE., Illus.). 16p. (J). (ps-k). 5.95 (978-1-58728-175-4(9) , Two Can Publishing) T&N Children's Publishing.

—La Tortuga Azul. 2004. (Pequenos Gigantes Ser.). (SPA., Illus.). 16p. (ps-k). (J). pap. 3.95 (978-1-58728-959-0(8)); 5.95 (978-1-58728-145-7(7)) T&N Children's Publishing. (Two Can Publishing).

Rose, Gerald. The Tortoise & the Hare. 2002. (Illus.). 16p. pap. 0.40 (978-0-521-01539-4(1)) Cambridge Univ. Pr.

Rose, Gerald, et al. The Clever Tortoise: PRP English Version. 2002. (Illus.). 32p. pap. 0.40 (978-0-521-01505-9(7)) Cambridge Univ. Pr.

Ross, Andrea. Turtles Go Slow. Ross, Andrea, illus. 2003. (Illus.). 25p. (J). (gr. 1-3). pap. 7.95 (978-1-887683-45-6(3)) Storybook Pr. & Productions.

Rylant, Cynthia. The Case of the Troublesome Turtle. Karas, G. Brian, illus. (High-Rise Private Eyes Ser.: No. 4). 48p. (J). 2002. pap. 3.99 (978-0-06-001323-3(0) , Harper Trophy); 2001. (gr. 1 up). 14.89 (978-0-688-16311-2(4)) HarperCollins Pubs.

—The Case of the Troublesome Turtle. Karas, G. Brian, illus. 2003. (High-Rise Private Eyes Ser.: No. 4). (J). (gr. k-3). pap. 18.95 incl. audio compact disk (978-1-59112-622-5(3)) Live Oak Media.

—The Case of the Troublesome Turtle. 2002. (High-Rise Private Eyes Ser.: No. 4). (J). (gr. k-3). lib. bdg. 11.80 (978-0-613-46123-8(1)) Tandem Library Bks.

—The Turtle. McDaniels, Preston, illus. (Lighthouse Family Ser.). 48p. (J). 2006. pap. 3.99 (978-0-689-86312-7(8) , Aladdin); 2005. 14.95 (978-0-689-86244-1(X) , Simon & Schuster Children's Publishing) Simon & Schuster Children's Publishing.

Salley, Coleen. Epossumondas Saves the Day. Stevens, Janet, illus. 2006. 48p. (J). 16.00 (978-0-15-205701-5(3)) Harcourt Trade Pubs.

Salzmann, Mary Elizabeth. Turtle Shells. 2006. (Fact & Fiction Ser.). (Illus.). 24p. (J). 21.35 (978-1-59679-969-1(2) , SandCastle) ABDO Publishing Co.

—Turtle Shells. Nobens, C. A., illus. 2006. (Fact & Fiction Ser.). 24p. (J). pap. (978-1-59679-970-7(6)) ABDO Publishing Co.

Sangwine, Jean. A Turtle Called Friendly. Lau, Bernadette, illus. 2002. 32p. pap. 6.95 (978-0-921156-48-2(0)) Rubicon Publishing, Inc. CAN. *Dist:* International Publishers Marketing.

Sargent, Dave & Sargent, Pat. Tunnel King: I Work Hard, 15 bks., 11. Huff, Jeane, illus. 2nd rev. ed. 2003. (Animal Pride Ser.: No. 11). 42p. (J). pap. 6.95 (978-1-56763-780-9(9)); lib. bdg. 19.95 (978-1-56763-779-3(5)) Ozark Publishing.

Sayre, April Pulley. Turtle, Turtle, Watch Out! Christiansen, Lee, illus. 2000. 32p. (J). (ps-2). 17.99 (978-0-531-33285-6(3)); pap. 16.95 (978-0-531-30285-9(7)) Scholastic, Inc. (Orchard Bks.).

Scheunemann, Pam. Pelican's Pouch. Nobens, C. A., illus. 2007. (Fact & Fiction Ser.). 24p. (J). pap. (978-1-59928-463-7(4)); 21.35 (978-1-59928-462-0(6)) ABDO Publishing Co.

Sea Turtle Goes Home. 2002. (Oceanic Mini Bks.). (Illus.). 32p. (J). (978-1-59069-008-6(7) , H1009) Studio Mouse LLC.

Sheffer, Donnel Gloster. Seacil the Sea Turtle. 2003. (J). pap. 8.00 (978-0-8059-5288-9(8)) Dorrance Publishing Co., Inc.

Silvermetz, Marcia A. Gertrude the Albino Frog & Her Friend Rupert the Turtle. Doyel, Ginger, illus. 2003. 48p. (J). (gr. 2-3). 19.95 (978-0-9718724-0-0(6)) Hiccup Cottage Pubns.

Simon and Schuster Children's Staff, illus. Totally Amazing Tales! 2006. (Teenage Mutant Ninja Turtles Ser.). 144p. (J). pap. 7.99 (978-1-4169-0794-7(7) , Simon Spotlight) Simon & Schuster Children's Publishing.

Simont, Marc, illus. Nate the Great & the Tardy Tortoise. 2002. (Nate the Great Ser.). (J). 12.87 (978-0-7587-0711-6(8)) Book Wholesalers, Inc.

Simpson, Fiona. We Are Family: Animal Antics. 2006. (Over the Hedge Ser.: No. 2). (Illus.). 17p. (J). pap. 3.99 (978-0-439-80146-1(X)) Scholastic, Inc.

Smith, Mariza A. Monkey & Turtle. Calamug, Cynthia & Calamug, Christine, illus. 1999. 18p. (J). (gr. 2-5). pap. 7.95 (978-0-9674241-0-1(0)) IZA Publishing Co.

The Snappy Turtle. 2003. (J). per. (978-1-57657-938-1(7)) Paradise Pr., Inc.

So-Timid Turtle. 2004. (Plush Pals Board Bks.). (Illus.). (J). (gr. k-1). bds. (978-0-7666-0557-2(4) , 39395) Modern Publishing.

Spaziante, Patrick, illus. Super Slam Turtles! 2005. (Teenage Mutant Ninja Turtles Ser.). 24p. (J). pap. 3.99 (978-1-4169-0502-8(2) , Simon Spotlight) Simon & Schuster Children's Publishing.

Spohn. Turtle & Snake & the Christmas Tree. 2000. (Easy-to-Read Ser.). (J). (978-0-606-20262-6(5)) Tandem Library Bks.

Spohn, Kate. Turtle & Snake & the Christmas Tree. 2000. (Puffin Easy-to-Read Ser.). (978-0-606-20378-4(8)) Tandem Library Bks.

—Turtle & Snake at Work. 1999. (Puffin Easy-to-Read Ser.). (978-0-606-16823-6(0)) Tandem Library Bks.

—Turtle & Snake Go Camping. 2000. (Easy-to-Read Ser.). (Illus.). 32p. (J). (ps-2). pap. 3.99 (978-0-14-130670-4(X) , Puffin) Penguin Group (USA) Inc.

—Turtle & Snake Go Camping. 2000. (Puffin Easy-to-Read Ser.). (978-0-606-18460-1(0)); lib. bdg. 11.80 (978-0-613-27346-6(X)) Tandem Library Bks.

—Turtle & Snake's Day at the Beach. Spohn, Kate, illus. 2004. (Easy-to-Read, Puffin Ser.). (Illus.). 32p. (J). (ps up). pap. 3.99 (978-0-14-240157-6(9) , Puffin) Penguin Group (USA) Inc.

—Turtle & Snake's Happy-Spooky Halloween. 2003. (gr. k-3). lib. bdg. 11.80 (978-0-613-87830-2(2)) Tandem Library Bks.

—Turtle & Snake's Spooky Halloween. Spohn, Kate, illus. 2003. (Easy-to-Read Ser.). (Illus.). 32p. (J). (gr. k-1). pap. 3.99 (978-0-14-250078-1(X) , Puffin) Penguin Group (USA) Inc.

—Turtle & Snake's Spooky Halloween. 2002. (Viking Easy-to-Read Ser.). (Illus.). 32p. (J). 13.99 (978-0-670-03560-1(2) , Viking Juvenile) Penguin Group (USA) Inc.

—Turtle & Snake's Valentine's Day. 2003. (Viking Easy-To-Read Ser.). (Illus.). 32p. (J). (ps-3). 13.99 (978-0-670-03613-4(7) , Viking Juvenile) Penguin Group (USA) Inc.

Sprick, Marilyn & Lemieux, Aurora, adapted by. The Race: Read Well Level K Unit 13 Storybook. 2003. (Read Well Level K Ser.). (Illus.). 20p. (J). (978-1-57035-684-1(X) , 55538) Sopris West Educational Services.

Stark, Barbara. Blue Dinosaur's Friends. l.t. ed. 2006. (Illus.). 24p. (J). E-Book 9.95 incl. cd-rom (978-1-933090-20-7(0)) Guardian Angel Publishing, Inc.

Strelecky, John. The Why Are You Here Cafe. 2003. pap. 7.95 (978-0-9743620-0-7(X)) Aspen Light Publishing.

Stringer, Bruce. Earlihee the Turtle. 2005. 130p. pap. 14.95 (978-1-933148-65-6(9)) Tate Publishing & Enterprises, L.L.C.

Sweeney, Jacqueline. Little Honu. Hart, G. K. & Hart, Vikki, illus. Hart, G. K. & Hart, Vikki, photos by. 2002. (We Can Read! Ser.). 32p. (J). 21.36 (978-0-7614-1512-1(2) , Benchmark Bks.) Cavendish, Marshall Corp.

Swimpson, Alayne. Murphy & Scootie. 2006. pap. 17.99 (***978-1-4259-7251-6(9)***) AuthorHouse.

—Murphy's Big Dream. 2006. (ENG.). 36p. per. 19.49 (***978-1-4259-5188-7(0)***) AuthorHouse.

Talbot, Amy. Deer & Friends: A Folktale from India. 2006. 23.00 (***978-1-4108-6173-3(2)***) Benchmark Education Co.

Tate, Suzanne. Tammy Turtle: A Tale of Saving Sea Turtles. Melvin, James, illus. 2004. (Suzanne Tate's Nature Ser.). 32p. (J). per. 10.95 (978-1-878405-45-6(4)) Nags Head Art, Inc.

Teenage Mutant Ninja Turtles Stencil Book. 2004. (Teenage Mutant Ninja Turtles Ser.). 24p. (J). bds. 9.99 (978-1-4169-0051-1(9) , Simon Spotlight) Simon & Schuster Children's Publishing.

Teitelbaum, Michael. The Littlest Ninja, Vol. 3. Aikins, Dave, illus. 2005. (Teenage Mutant Ninja Turtles Ser.). 128p. (J). pap. 4.99 (978-1-4169-0217-1(1) , Simon Spotlight) Simon & Schuster Children's Publishing.

Tharp, Barbara, et al. Tillena Lou's Day in the Sun. Denk, James, ed. Lewis, T., illus. 2006. (My World & Me Ser.). 32p. (J). pap. (978-1-888997-44-6(3) , BioEd) Baylor College of Medicine.

The Thirsty Turtle. 2003. 32p. (J). per. 14.95 (978-1-59094-049-5(0)) Jawbone Publishing Corp.

Thomas, Jim. Comic Book Heroes. Ruiz, Aristides & Giles, Mike, illus. ed. 2005. 32p. (J). lib. bdg. 15.00 (978-1-59054-990-2(2)) Fitzgerald Bks.

—Turtle Power! A Scrapbook by Leonardo. George, Chris & Giles, Mike, illus. 2004. (Teenage Mutant Ninja Turtles Ser.). 24p. (J). 5.99 (978-0-689-86898-6(7) , Simon Spotlight) Simon & Schuster Children's Publishing.

Tikki Turtle's Quest. (J). 8.95 (978-0-9701528-0-0(9)) Ruwanga Trading.

Towle, Barbara. How Timbo & Trevor Got Together. Spellman, Susan, illus. 2007. (J). 19.95 (978-1-933002-21-7(2)) PublishingWorks.

Triti. Changes: A True Story about Oscar Turtle & Amazon Red. 2000. (Illus.). (J). (978-0-915180-36-3(7)) Harrowood Bks.

Turin, Adela. Arturo y Clementina. Bosnia, Nella, illus. (SPA.). (J). (gr. 3-5). 40p. (978-84-264-3801-0(6)); 2001. 36p. 12.76 (978-84-264-3569-9(6)) Editorial Lumen ESP. *Dist:* Lectorum Pubns., Inc.

The Turtle Race. 2003. (J). per. (978-1-57657-891-9(7)) Paradise Pr., Inc.

Turtles Z. . Up. 2006. (J). 7.95 (978-0-9748884-5-3(1)) Little Thoughts For Little Ones Publishing, Inc.

Waddell, Martin. Hi, Harry! The Moving Story of How One Slow Tortoise Slowly Made a Friend. Firth, Barbara, illus. 2003. 56p. (J). (ps-1). 14.99 (978-0-7636-1802-5(0)) Candlewick Pr.

Walker, E. G. Mario & the Desert Tortoise. Rios, Jose Arthur, illus. 2002. 50p. (J). (gr. 5-12). pap. 6.95 (978-0-9716071-2-5(5)) Walker, Esther.

Ward, Helen. The Hare & the Tortoise: A Fable from Aesop. 1999. (Illus.). 40p. (J). (gr. k up). 16.95 (978-0-7613-0988-8(8) , First Avenue Editions) Lerner Publishing Group.

—Hare & Tortoise. 2005. (Illus.). 32p. (J). (ENG & ALB.). pap. 12.95 (978-1-84444-779-4(0)); (ENG & ARA., pap. 12.95 (978-1-84444-780-0(4)); (ENG & BEN., pap. 12.95 (978-1-84444-781-7(2)); (ENG & CHI., pap. 12.95 (978-1-84444-783-1(9)); (ENG, PER & FAR., pap. 12.95 (978-1-84444-786-2(3)); (ENG & FRE., pap. 12.95 (978-1-84444-787-9(1)); (ENG & GUJ., pap. 12.95 (978-1-84444-789-3(8)); (ENG & HIN., pap. 12.95 (978-1-84444-790-9(1)); (ENG & PAN., pap. 12.95 (978-1-84444-793-0(6)); (ENG & POL., pap. 12.95 (978-1-84444-794-7(4)); (POR & ENG., pap. 12.95 (978-1-84444-795-4(2)); (ENG, RUM & ROM., pap. 12.95 (978-1-84444-796-1(0)); (RUS & ENG., pap. 12.95 (978-1-84444-797-8(9)); (ENG & SOM., pap. 12.95 (978-1-84444-799-2(5)); (ENG & SPA., pap. 12.95 (978-1-84444-800-5(2)); (ENG & TAG., pap. 12.95 (978-1-84444-801-2(0)); (ENG & TUR., pap. 12.95 (978-1-84444-803-6(7)); (ENG & URD., pap. 12.95 (978-1-84444-805-0(3)); (ENG & VIE., pap. 12.95 (978-1-84444-806-7(1)) Mantra Lingua GBR. *Dist:* Mantra Publishing, Ltd.

Ward, Helen & Aesop. Hare & Tortoise. 2005. (Illus.). 32p. (J). (ENG & CHI.). pap. 12.95 (978-1-84444-784-8(7)); (ENG & GRE., pap. 12.95 (978-1-84444-788-6(X)); (JPN & ENG., pap. 12.95 (978-1-84444-791-6(X)) Mantra Lingua GBR. *Dist:* Mantra Publishing, Ltd.

Ward, Jean Elizabeth. A Barbara Anne Bushy Tale: Book #2 in a Series. 2007. 188p. per. 16.95 (***978-0-595-45726-7(6)***) iUniverse, Inc.

Wax, Wendy. Meet Leatherhead. Spaziante, Patrick, illus. 2005. 22p. (J). lib. bdg. 15.00 (***978-1-4242-0972-9(2)***) Fitzgerald Bks.

Weare, Tim, illus. I'm a Little Giraffe: A Finger-Puppet Pal. 2002. (I'm A Little Ser.). 12p. (J). (ps-k). bds. 6.95 (978-0-439-40641-3(2) , Cartwheel Bks.) Scholastic, Inc.

Weber, Lou, ed. Teenage Mutant Ninja Turtles: Interactive Play-a-Sound. 24p. (J). 15.98 (978-1-4127-3240-6(9) , 7236000) Publications International, Ltd.

Weeks, Sarah. Follow the Moon. Duranceau, Suzanne, illus. 2003. 32p. (J). (ps-2). 17.99 incl. audio compact disk (978-0-06-055744-7(3) , Geringer, Laura Book) HarperCollins Pubs.

When Tilly Turtle Came to Tea. 2001. (ps-2). lib. bdg. 9.80 (978-0-613-33239-2(3)) Tandem Library Bks.

White, Mark. La Liebre y la Tortuga: Version de la Fabula de Esopo. Rojo, Sara, illus. 2006. (Read-It! Readers en Espanol Ser.).Tr. of Tortoise & the Hare: A Retelling of Aesop's Fable. (SPA.). 32p. (J). (ps-3). 19.95 (978-1-4048-1624-4(0)) Picture Window Bks.

Whitfield, Peter. Zen Tails up & Down. Bevington, Nancy, illus. 2005. (Zen Tails Ser.). 28p. (J). (gr. 1-17). 15.95 (978-1-894965-22-4(1)) Simply Read Bks. CAN. *Dist:* Perseus Distribution.

Williams, Barbara. Albert's Gift for Grandmother. Cushman, Doug, illus. 2006. 32p. (J). (ps-1). 16.99 (978-0-7636-2097-4(1)) Candlewick Pr.

Williams, Barbara A. Tilli's Tale. Lewis, Rebecca, illus. 2004. 48p. (J). per. (978-1-932077-52-0(9)) Athena Pr.

Wilson, Anna. The Foolish Turtle. Gordon, Mike, illus. 2005. (Lightning Readers Ser.). 32p. (J). (gr. k-1). pap. 3.95 (978-0-7696-4040-2(0) , Gingham Dog Pr.) School Specialty Publishing.

—The Foolish Turtle. Gordon, Mike, illus. 2005. 32p. (J). (gr. k-1). lib. bdg. 11.15 (978-0-606-33597-3(8)) Tandem Library Bks.

—La Tortuga Tonta. Gordon, Mike, illus. 2005. (Lightning Readers Ser.). 32p. (J). (gr. k-1). pap. 3.95 (978-0-7696-4080-8(X) , Gingham Dog Pr.) School Specialty Publishing.

—La Tortuga Tonta. Gordon, Mike, illus. 2005. 32p. (J). (ps-ps). lib. bdg. 11.15 (978-0-606-33598-0(6)) Tandem Library Bks.

Winderman, Jay B. Thunder on the Desert. Becker, LuAnne E. & Becker, Lisa E., illus. 2005. 152p. (J). (gr. 3-7). per. 13.95 (978-0-9761623-1-5(8)) Pill Bug Pr.

Winderman, Jay B. Thunder on the Reservation. Becker, LuAnne E., illus. 2007. 147p. (J). (gr. 3-7). per. 13.95 (***978-0-9761623-2-2(6)***) Pill Bug Pr.

Wood, Douglas. Old Turtle. Chee, Cheng-Khee, illus. 2001. 48p. (J). (gr. k up). anniv. ed. pap. 17.95 (978-0-439-30908-0(5)); 10th anniv. ed. 17.95 incl. cd-rom (978-0-439-32106-8(9)) Scholastic, Inc.

Wood, June Rae. Turtle on a Fence Post. 2001. 272p. (J). pap. 6.99 (978-0-698-11783-9(2) , Putnam Juvenile) Penguin Group (USA) Inc.

Young, Steve. Winchell Mink: The Misadventure Begins. 2004. 144p. (J). 16.89 (978-0-06-053500-1(8)) HarperCollins Pubs.

Zagwyn, Deborah Turney. Turtle Spring. 2004. (Illus.). 32p. (J). (gr. k-2). 6.95 (978-1-58246-052-9(3) , Tricycle Pr.) Ten Speed Pr.

—Turtle Spring. Zagwyn, Deborah Turney, illus. 2004. (Illus.). 32p. (J). (gr. k-3). 15.95 (978-1-883672-53-9(8) , Tricycle Pr.) Ten Speed Pr.

TUSKEGEE INSTITUTE

Stroud, Bettye. A Personal Tour of Tuskegee Institute. 2001. (How It Was Ser.). (Illus.). (J). (gr. 4-6). lib. bdg. 25.26 (978-0-8225-3585-0(8)) Lerner Publishing Group.

TUTANKHAMEN, KING OF EGYPT

Briscoe, Diana. King Tut: Tales from the Tomb. 2002. (High Five Reading Ser.). (Illus.). 48p. (J). (gr. 3-4). lib. bdg. 22.60 (978-0-7368-9553-8(1) , Capstone High-Interest Bks.); pap. (978-0-7368-9531-6(0)) Capstone Pr., Inc.

Burgan, Michael. The Curse of King Tut's Tomb. (Graphic History Ser.). 32p. (YA). pap. 7.95 (978-0-7368-5244-9(1)) Capstone Pr., Inc.

—The Curse of King Tut's Tomb. Lohse, Otha Zackariah Edward, illus. 2005. (Graphic Library). 32p. (J). 22.60 (978-0-7368-3833-7(3)) Capstone Pr., Inc.

—King Tut's Tomb: Ancient Treasures Uncovered. 2005. (Mummies Ser.). (Illus.). 31p. (J). (ps-4). lib. bdg. 22.60 (978-0-7368-3770-5(1)) Capstone Pr., Inc.

Gogerly, Liz. Look Around an Egyptian Tomb: By Liz Gogerly. 2007. (J). ***978-1-84193-719-9(3))** Smart Apple Media.

Green, Jen. Tutankhamen's Tomb: Uncover the Secrets & Treasures of Ancient Egypt. Slater, Gary, illus. 2006. 32p. (J). (gr. 4 up). 18.99 (978-0-7641-5999-2(2)) Barron's Educational Series, Inc.

Harcourt School Publishers Staff. Tutankhamen's Gift. 2001. (Reader's Choice Bks.). (Illus.). (J). pap. 7.20 (978-0-15-314423-3(8)) Harcourt Schl. Pubs.

Harvey, Gill. Tutankhamun. Tomlins, Karen, illus. 2006. 64p. (J). 8.99 (978-0-7945-1271-2(2) , Usborne) EDC Publishing.

Hawass, Zahi. Tutankhamun: The Mystery of the Boy King. 2005. (Crossroads America Ser.). (Illus.). 64p. (gr. 5-9). (J). 17.95 (978-0-7922-8354-6(6)); 27.90 (978-0-7922-8355-3(4)) National Geographic Society. (National Geographic Children's Bks.).

Lace, William W. The Curse of King Tut. 2007. (YA). lib. bdg. ***978-1-60152-024-1(7))** ReferencePoint Pr., Inc.

MacDonald, Fiona. Tutankhamen. 2000. (World in the Time of... Ser.). (Illus.). (J). (gr. 4-7). 17.95 (978-0-7910-6035-3(7) , Chelsea Hse.) Facts On File, Inc.

Morely, Jacqueline. Inside the Tomb of Tutankhamun. James, John, illus. 2005. 48p. (J). (gr. 3-7). 19.95 (978-1-59270-042-4(X)) Enchanted Lion Bks., LLC.

Nardo, Don. King Tut's Tomb. 2004. (Illus.). (J). (gr. 4-7). 26.20 (978-0-7377-2352-6(1) , Greenhaven Pr., Inc.) Thomson Gale.

Sabuda, Robert. Tutankhamen's Gift. 1998. (J). pap. 6.99 (978-0-87628-372-1(5)) Ctr. for Applied Research in Education, The.

Stewart, David. You Wouldn't Want to Be Tutankhamen! A Mummy Who Really Got Meddled With. Antram, David, illus. 2007. (You Wouldn't Want to Ser.). 32p. (J). (gr. 2-5). 28.50 ***978-0-531-18725-8(X));** pap. 9.95 ***978-0-531-18924-5(4))** Scholastic Library Publishing. (Watts, Franklin).

Theisen, Gordon. The Secrets of Tutankhamen. 2001. (Natural History Guides Ser.). (Illus.). 40p. (J). pap. 9.99 (978-0-86730-843-3(5)) Lebhar-Friedman Bks.

The Treasures of Tutankhamun. (Butterfly Bks.). (ARA.). 48p. (YA). (gr. 5-8). 9.95 (978-0-86685-485-6(1)) International Bk. Ctr., Inc.

Williams, Brian. Tutankhamen. (Historical Biographies Ser.). 32p. 2003. pap. 7.50 (978-1-4034-0102-1(0)); 2002. (Illus.). (J). (gr. 2-4). lib. bdg. 22.79 (978-1-58810-568-4(7)) Heinemann Library.

Woods, Michael & Woods, Mary B. The Tomb of King Tutankhamun. 2008. (J). lib. bdg. ***978-0-8225-7506-1(X))** Twenty First Century Bks.

Wynne, Patricia J. King Tut Coloring Book. 2005. (Illus.). 32p. (J). (gr. 3). pap. 3.95 (978-0-486-44444-4(9)) Dover Pubns., Inc.

Zoehfeld, Kathleen Weidner. The Curse of King Tut's Mummy. Nelson, James, illus. 2007. (Stepping Stones Ser.). 112p. (J). (gr. 1-4). 3.99 (978-0-375-83862-0(7) , Random Hse. Bks. for Young Readers) Random Hse. Children's Bks.

—Curse of King Tut's Mummy. Nelson, James, illus. 2007. (Stepping Stones Ser.). 112p. (J). (gr. 2-4). lib. bdg. 11.99 (978-0-375-93862-7(1) , Random Hse. Bks. for Young Readers) Random Hse. Children's Bks.

TUTU, DESMOND, 1931-

Crompton, Samuel Willard. Desmond Tutu: Fighting Apartheid. 2007. (Modern Peacemakers Ser.). (Illus.). 120p. (YA). (gr. 9 up). 30.00 (978-0-7910-9221-7(6) , Chelsea Hse.) Facts On File, Inc.

TV

see Television

TWAIN, MARK, 1835-1910

Aller, Susan Bivin. Mark Twain. (Just the Facts Biographies Ser.). (Illus.). 112p. (J). 2006. 27.93 (978-0-8225-3425-9(8) , Lerner Pubns.); 2006. pap. ***978-0-8225-5998-6(6)** , Lerner Pubns.); 2003. (gr. 6 up). pap. 7.95 (978-0-8225-9696-7(2)); 2001. (gr. 6-12). lib. bdg. 27.93 (978-0-8225-4994-9(8) , Lerner Pubns.) Lerner Publishing Group.

—Mark Twain. 2001. (gr. 7-12). lib. bdg. 16.40 (978-0-613-68363-0(3)) Tandem Library Bks.

Armentrout, David & Armentrout, Patricia. Mark Twain. 2004. (Discover the Life of an American Legend Ser.). (Illus.). 24p. (gr. 2-5). 14.95 (978-1-58952-660-0(0)) Rourke Publishing, LLC.

Bloom, Harold, ed. The Adventures of Huckleberry Finn - Mark Twain. 2nd rev. ed. 2007. (Bloom's Modern Critical Interpretations Ser.). 256p. (YA). (gr. 9 up). 45.00 ***978-0-7910-9426-6(X)** , Chelsea Hse.) Facts On File, Inc.

Brown, Don. American Boy: The Adventures of Mark Twain. 2006. (Illus.). 32p. (J). (gr. k-3). pap. 6.95 (978-0-618-68950-7(8)) Houghton Mifflin Co.

—American Boy: The Adventures of Mark Twain. 2003. (Illus.). 32p. (J). (gr. k-3). 16.00 (978-0-618-17997-8(6)) Houghton Mifflin Co. Trade & Reference Div.

Carew-Miller, Anna. Mark Twain. Di Gennaro, Andrea, illus. 2003. (Great Names Ser.). (J). (978-957-745-414-0(3)) Mason Crest Pubs.

—Mark Twain: Great American Fiction Writer. 2002. (Great Names Ser.). (Illus.). 32p. (J). (gr. 3 up). lib. bdg. (978-1-59084-158-7(1)) Mason Crest Pubs.

Collier, James Lincoln. The Mark Twain You Never Knew. 2004. (You Never Knew Ser.). (Illus.). 80p. (J). 25.50 (978-0-516-24430-3(2) , Children's Pr.) Scholastic Library Publishing.

Diorio, Mary Ann L. A Student's Guide to Mark Twain. 2007. (Understanding Literature Ser.). (Illus.). 160p. (YA). (gr. 7-9). lib. bdg. 27.93 (978-0-7660-2438-0(5)) Enslow Pubs., Inc.

Goldsmith, Howard. Mark Twain at Work! Habbas, Frank, illus. ed. 2005. 32p. (J). lib. bdg. 15.00 (978-1-59054-951-3(1)) Fitzgerald Bks.

—Mark Twain at Work! Habbas, Frank, illus. 2003. (Ready-to-Read Childhood of the Famous Americans Ser.). 32p. (J). pap. 3.99 (978-0-689-85399-9(8) , Aladdin) Simon & Schuster Children's Publishing.

—Mark Twain at Work! 2003. (gr. k-3). lib. bdg. 11.80 (978-0-613-66461-5(2)) Tandem Library Bks.

Heims, Neil. Reading the Adventures of Tom Sawyer. 2005. (Engaged Reader Ser.). (Illus.). 96p. (J). (gr. 4-8). 25.00 (978-0-7910-8828-9(6) , Chelsea Hse.) Facts On File, Inc.

Houle, Michelle M. Mark Twain: Banned, Challenged, & Censored. 2008. (Authors of Banned Books Ser.). (Illus.). 160p. (YA). (gr. 9-12). lib. bdg. 34.60 ***978-0-7660-2689-6(2))** Enslow Pubs., Inc.

Lasky, Kathryn. A Brilliant Streak: The Making of Mark Twain. Moser, Barry, illus. 1998. 48p. (J). (gr. 1-7). 18.00 (978-0-15-252110-3(0)) Harcourt Children's Bks.

MacLeod, Elizabeth. Mark Twain: An American Star. 2008. 32p. pap. ***978-1-55337-909-6(8))** Kids Can Pr., Ltd.

Middleton, Haydn. Mark Twain. 2001. (Creative Lives Ser.). (Illus.). 64p. (YA). (gr. 6-8). lib. bdg. 27.07 (978-1-58810-205-8(X)) Heinemann Library.

Pflueger, Lynda. Mark Twain: Legendary Writer & Humorist. 1999. (Historical American Biographies Ser.). (Illus.). 128p. (YA). (gr. 6-12). lib. bdg. 26.60 (978-0-7660-1093-2(7)) Enslow Pubs., Inc.

—Mark Twain: Legendary Writer & Humorist. 1999. (Historical American Biographies Ser.). (978-0-07-601093-6(7)) McGraw-Hill Cos., The.

Prince, April Jones. Who Was Mark Twain? O'Brien, John & Harrison, Nancy, illus. 2004. (Who Was...? Ser.). 112p. (J). (gr. 3-7). pap. 4.99 (978-0-448-43319-6(2) , Grosset & Dunlap) Penguin Group (USA) Inc.

Rasmussen, R. Kent. Bloom's How to Write about Mark Twain. 2007. (Bloom's How to Write about Literature Ser.). 256p. (YA). (gr. 9 up). 45.00 ***978-0-7910-9487-7(1)** , Chelsea Hse.) Facts On File, Inc.

Rasmussen, R. Kent. Mark Twain for Kids: His Life & Times, 21 Activities. 2004. (For Kids Ser.). (Illus.). 160p. (J). pap. 14.95 (978-1-55652-527-8(3)) Chicago Review Pr., Inc.

Sherman, Josepha. Mark Twain. 2005. (Classic Storytellers Ser.). (Illus.). 48p. (J). lib. bdg. 29.95 (978-1-58415-374-0(1)) Mitchell Lane Pubs., Inc.

Sickels, Amy. Mark Twain. 2nd rev. ed. 2006. (Bloom's Modern Critical Views Ser.). 272p. 45.00 (978-0-7910-8569-1(4) , Chelsea Hse.) Facts On File, Inc.

Skarmeas, Nancy J., ed. Mark Twain. 1998. (Great American Ser.). (Illus.). 96p. (J). 17.95 (978-0-8249-4085-0(7)) Ideals Pubns.

Vickers, Rebecca. The Story Behind Mark Twain's the Adventures of Huckleberry Finn. 2006. (History in Literature Ser.). (Illus.). 56p. (YA). (gr. 6-9). lib. bdg. 32.86 (978-1-4034-8206-8(3)) Heinemann Library.

Youngblood, Wayne. Mark Twain along the Mississippi. 2006. (In the Footsteps of American Heroes Ser.). (Illus.). 64p. (J). pap. (978-0-8368-6435-9(2)); lib. bdg. 32.67 (978-0-8368-6430-4(1)) Stevens, Gareth Inc. (World Almanac Library).

TWAIN, MARK, 1835-1910—FICTION

Lasky, Kathryn. Alice Rose & Sam. 1999. (J). (978-0-606-17380-3(3)) Tandem Library Bks.

Olshan, Matthew. Finn: A Novel. 2001. (gr. 7-12). lib. bdg. 24.55 (978-0-613-59806-4(7)) Tandem Library Bks.

Sargent, Dave & Sargent, Pat. Charcoal: (Charcoal Grey) Be Decisive, 25, 13. Lenoir, Jane, illus. 2001. (Saddle Up Ser.: 13). 36p. (J). pap. 6.95 (978-1-56763-606-2(3)); lib. bdg. 22.60 (978-1-56763-605-5(5)) Ozark Publishing.

TWENTIETH CENTURY

Blackman, Cally. The 20s & 30s: Flappers & Vamps. 1999. (Twentieth Century Fashion Ser.). (Illus.). 32p. (J). (gr. 5 up). lib. bdg. 26.00 (978-0-8368-2599-2(3)) Stevens, Gareth Inc.

Chapman, Victoria L. & Lindroth, David. The 20th Century, Vol. 4. 2nd ed. 2004. (World History on File Ser.). (Illus.). 232p. (J). (gr. 9-12). ring bd. 140.00 (978-0-8160-5765-8(6)) Facts On File, Inc.

Golson Books, Ltd. Staff & Carlisle, Rodney P. The Thirties, 2 vols., Set. 2006. (Day by Day Ser.). 1168p. (YA). (gr. 9 up). 214.50 (978-0-8160-6664-3(7)) Facts On File, Inc.

Hill, Laban Carrick. America Dreaming. 2007. (Illus.). 176p. (YA). (gr. 7-17). 19.99 ***978-0-316-00904-1(0))** Little Brown & Co.

Hunter, Rebecca. Growing up in the Forties. 2003. (Illus.). 32p. pap. (978-0-7502-3434-4(2) , Hodder Wayland) Hodder Children's Division.

—Growing up in the Thirties. 2003. (Illus.). 32p. pap. (978-0-7502-3433-7(4) , Hodder Wayland) Hodder Children's Division.

National Geographic Society Staff. Eyewitness to the 20th Century. 1998. (National Geographic Destinations Ser.). (Illus.). 400p. (J). (gr. 5-8). 40.00 (978-0-7922-7049-2(5) , National Geographic) National Geographic Society.

Ryan, James G. & Schlup, Leonard C., eds. Historical Dictionary of the 1940s. 2006. (Illus.). 648p. 159.00 (978-0-7656-0440-8(X) , Sharpe Reference) Sharpe, M.E. Inc.

Sharman, Margaret. 1950s. (Illus.). 47p. (J). pap. (978-0-237-51664-2(0) , Evans Brothers, Limited) Evans Publishing Group.

1900s: Decades of the 20th Century, 10 vols. 2005. (Illus.). 64p. (YA). 29.95 (978-1-932904-00-0(X)) Eldorado Ink.

1910s: Decades of the 20th Century, 10 vols. 2005. (Illus.). 64p. (YA). 29.95 (978-1-932904-01-7(8)) Eldorado Ink.

1920s: Decades of the 20th Century, 10 vols. 2005. (Illus.). 64p. (YA). 29.95 (978-1-932904-02-4(6)) Eldorado Ink.

1930s: Decades of the 20th Century, 10 vols. 2005. (Illus.). 64p. (YA). 29.95 (978-1-932904-03-1(4)) Eldorado Ink.

1940s: Decades of the 20th Century, 10 vols. 2005. (Illus.). 64p. (YA). 29.95 (978-1-932904-04-8(2)) Eldorado Ink.

1950s: Decades of the 20th Century, 10 vols. 2005. (Illus.). 64p. (YA). 29.95 (978-1-932904-05-5(0)) Eldorado Ink.

1960s: Decades of the 20th Century, 10 vols. 2005. (Illus.). 64p. (YA). 29.95 (978-1-932904-06-2(9)) Eldorado Ink.

1970s: Decades of the 20th Century, 10 vols. 2005. (Illus.). 64p. (YA). 29.95 (978-1-932904-07-9(7)) Eldorado Ink.

1980s: Decades of the 20th Century, 10 vols. 2005. (Illus.). 64p. (YA). 29.95 (978-1-932904-08-6(5)) Eldorado Ink.

1990s: Decades of the 20th Century, 10 vols. 2005. (Illus.). 64p. (YA). 29.95 (978-1-932904-09-3(3)) Eldorado Ink.

TWINS

Blackburn, Tammie. It Takes Two. Coffman, Dennis, illus. 2000. 16p. (J). pap. 5.95 (978-1-891846-16-8(7)) Business Word, The.

Britton, Tamara L., contrib. by. Mary-Kate & Ashley Olsen. 1999. (Young Profiles Ser.). (Illus.). 32p. (J). (gr. 3). lib. bdg. 21.35 (978-1-57765-351-6(3) , Checkerboard Library) ABDO Publishing Co.

Freeman, Arrin. Look A-likes Don't Act A-like. Freeman, Arrin, illus. 2006. (J). 12.95 (978-0-9776711-4-4(3) , Blue Marble Bks.) Indigo Custom Publishing.

Golden Books Staff. Meet the Twins! Hall, Susan', illus. 2005. 32p. (J). (ps-2). pap. 2.99 (978-0-375-83479-0(6) , Golden Bks.) Random Hse. Children's Bks.

Rubel, Nicole. Twice As Nice: What It's Like to Be a Twin. 2004. (Illus.). 32p. (J). 16.50 (978-0-374-31836-9(0) , Farrar, Straus & Giroux (BYR)) Farrar, Straus & Giroux.

TWINS—FICTION

Advantage Publishers Group & Rojany Buccieri, Lisa. Let's Make Noise at the Ballpark. 2007. (Illus.). 10p. (J). 12.95 (978-1-59223-642-8(1) , Silver Dolphin Bks.) Advantage Pubs. Group.

Adventures with Kat & Dex: The search for the key to Golden Gate Park. l.t. ed. 2004. (Illus.). 32p. (J). lib. bdg. 22.95 (978-0-9754853-0-9(X)) DeAngelis, Anthony.

Ahrens, Robin Isabel. Dee & Bee. Haley, Amanda, illus. 2000. 40p. (J). (ps-1). 14.95 (978-1-890817-26-8(0)) Winslow Pr.

Aikins, Dave, illus. At the Carnival. 2005. (J). ***978-1-4156-0769-5(9)** , Simon Spotlight/Nickelodeon) Simon & Schuster Children's Publishing.

Alexander, Nina. The Case of the 202 Clues. 1998. (New Adventures of Mary-Kate & Ashley Ser.). (Illus.). 87p. (J). (gr. 2-7). pap. 3.99 (978-0-590-29307-5(9)) Scholastic, Inc.

—The Case of the Haunted Camp. 1998. (New Adventures of Mary-Kate & Ashley Ser.). (Illus.). 85p. (J). (gr. 2-7). pap. 3.99 (978-0-590-29397-6(4)) Scholastic, Inc.

Annie Auerbach & MikeNorton. The Good, the Bad & the Gassy. 2006. (Illus.). 96p. pap. 4.99 (978-1-59816-049-9(4) , Tokyopop Kids) TOKYOPOP, Inc.

Arnold, Tedd. More Parts. 2003. (Illus.). 32p. pap. 5.99 (978-0-14-250149-8(2) , Puffin) Penguin Group (USA) Inc.

—More Parts. Arnold, Tedd, illus. 2001. (Illus.). 32p. (J). (ps-3). 16.99 (978-0-8037-1417-5(3) , Dial) Penguin Group (USA) Inc.

—The Twin Princes. Arnold, Tedd, illus. 2007. (Illus.). 32p. (J). (ps-2). 16.99 (978-0-8037-2696-3(1) , Dial) Penguin Group (USA) Inc.

—The Twin Princes. 2007. (Illus.). (J). ***978-1-4287-3971-0(8)** , Dial) Penguin Group (USA) Inc.

Austin, Alyssa. It Was an Accident. 2003. 80p. pap. 11.95 (978-1-4137-0102-9(7)) PublishAmerica, Inc.

Avi. Never Mind! A Twin Novel. 2004. 208p. (J). (gr. 5 up). lib. bdg. 16.89 (978-0-06-054315-0(9)) HarperCollins Pubs.

Avi & Vail, Rachel. Never Mind! A Twin Novel. 2004. 208p. (J). (gr. 5 up). 15.99 (978-0-06-054314-3(0)) HarperCollins Pubs.

—Never Mind! A Twin Novel. 2005. 200p. (J). (gr. k-9). per. 12.64 (978-0-606-33941-4(8)) Tandem Library Bks.

Baccalario, Pierdomenico. The Door to Time. Dunfey, Beth, ed. Janeczko, Leah, tr. from ITA. Bruno, Iacopo, illus. 2006. (Ulysses Moore Ser.: No. 1). 240p. (J). (gr. 4-7). pap. 12.99 (978-0-439-77438-3(1)) Scholastic, Inc.

Bailey, Linda. Adventures with the Vikings. Slavin, Bill et al, illus. 2004. (Good Times Travel Agency Ser.). 48p. (J). (gr. 4-6). (978-1-55074-544-3(1)) Kids Can Pr., Ltd.

—Adventures with the Vikings, No. 3. Slavin, Bill et al, illus. 2004. (Good Times Travel Agency Ser.). 48p. (J). (gr. 4-6). (978-1-55074-542-9(5)) Kids Can Pr., Ltd.

—Adventures with the Vikings. 2003. (gr. 3-6). lib. bdg. 16.40 (978-0-613-70944-6(6)) Tandem Library Bks.

Bair, Sheila. Rock, Brock, & the Savings Shock. Gott, Barry, illus. 2006. (Way I ACT Ser.). 32p. (J). 15.95 (978-0-8075-7094-4(X)) Whitman, Albert & Co.

Bajoria, Paul. The God of Mischief. Bertholf, Bret, illus. 2007. 400p. (J). (gr. 4-8). 16.99 (978-0-316-01091-7(X)) Little Brown & Co.

—The God of Mischief. Bertholf, Bret, illus. 2007. 400p. (J). (gr. 3-7). pap. 6.99 ***978-0-316-01628-5(4))** Little, Brown Bks. for Young Readers.

Baker, Sue. Snakes. 2002. (Illus.). 32p. (J). (ps-3). 12.99 (978-0-85953-404-8(9)) Child's Play-International.

Banim, Lisa, et al. Winner Take All. 2000. (Two of a Kind Ser.: No. 10). (Illus.). 112p. (gr. 3-7). mass mkt. 4.99 (978-0-06-106580-4(3) , Harper Entertainment) HarperCollins Pubs.

Banks, Jacqueline Turner. Egg-Drop Blues. 2003. 128p. (J). (gr. 4-6). pap. 4.95 (978-0-618-25080-6(8)); 15.00 (978-0-618-34885-5(9)) Houghton Mifflin Co. Trade & Reference Div.

Banks, Lynne Reid. Angela & Diabola. 163p. (J). (gr. 4-6). pap. 4.50 (978-0-8072-1515-9(5) , Listening Library) Random Hse. Audio Publishing Group.

—Angela & Diabola. 1998. (J). (978-0-606-13124-7(8)) Tandem Library Bks.

Bass, L. G. The Outlaws of Moonshadow Marsh No. 1, Bk.1: The Sign of Qin. 2004. (Illus.). 400p. (gr. 5-17). 17.99 (978-0-7868-1918-8(9)) Hyperion Bks. for Children.

—The Outlaws of Moonshadow Marsh the Sign of Qin, Bk. 1. 2006. 400p. (gr. 5-17). reprint ed. pap. 7.99 (978-0-7868-5566-7(5)) Hyperion Pr.

—Sign of the Qin. l.t. ed. 2004. 513p. 23.95 (978-0-7862-6772-9(0) , Large Print Pr.) Thorndike Pr.

Bateman, Anya. The Makeover of James Orville Wickenbee. 2007. 262p. (J). pap. ***978-1-59038-707-8(4))** Deseret Bk. Co.

Baxter, David. The Tournesol Twins. 2006. 68p. pap. ***978-1-84401-901-4(2))** Athena Pr.

BEEBE, Diane. School's Out. 2006. (J). (978-1-4276-0238-1(7)) Aardvark Global Publishing.

Bell, Michele Ashman. Dragon's Jaw: A Heart-Pounding Adventure. 2005. 241p. (J). (978-1-59156-880-3(3)) Covenant Communications.

—Spyhunt: A Heart-Pounding Adventure: A Novel. 2004. 187p. (J). (978-1-59156-457-7(3)) Covenant Communications.

Birch, Beverley. Twelfth Night. 2007. (Illus.). 80p. 13.95 ***978-0-7502-4964-5(1)** , Hodder Wayland) Hodder Children's Division GBR. *Dist:* Independent Pubs. Group.

Bjork, Linda. Salmon Cavern. 2006. 92p. pap. 10.95 (978-1-59800-546-2(4)) Outskirts Press, Inc.

Black, Holly & DiTerlizzi, Tony. Spiderwick Chronicles Set: The Field Guide, the Seeing Stone, Lucinda's Secret, the Ironwood Tree, the Wrath of Mulgarath. DiTerlizzi, Tony, illus. movie tie-in ed. 2008. (Spiderwick Chronicles). 672p. (J). 49.99 ***978-1-4169-5016-5(8))** Simon & Schuster Children's Publishing.

Blackaby, Susan. Tricky Twins. Epstein, Len, illus. 2006. (Read-It! Readers Ser.). (J). 19.93 (978-1-4048-2419-5(7)) Picture Window Bks.

Bo, Ben. Skullcrack. 2003. 168p. (J). pap. 6.95 (978-0-8225-3311-5(1)); (gr. 9-12). 14.95 (978-0-8225-3308-5(1)) Lerner Publishing Group.

—Skullcrack. 2000. (gr. 5-8). lib. bdg. 15.25 (978-0-613-58938-3(6)) Tandem Library Bks.

Bobbsey Twins. 2006. (J). (ps-2). 128.10 (978-1-59961-094-8(9)) Spotlight.

Bodeen, S. A. The Compound. 2008. 256p. (YA). 16.95 ***978-0-312-37015-2(6))** Feiwel & Friends.

Bogart, Jo Ellen. The Big Tree Gang. Griffiths, Dean, illus. 2005. (Orca Echoes Ser.). 64p. (J). (gr. 2-3). pap. 4.99 (978-1-55143-345-5(1)) Orca Bk. Pubs. USA.

Bogart, Mike. The Henderson Twins in Muckleball! 2006. 107p. pap. 14.95 (978-1-4241-3050-4(6)) PublishAmerica, Inc.

—Meet the Henderson Twins: Matt & Mike. 2005. 93p. pap. 14.95 (978-1-4137-8233-2(7)) PublishAmerica, Inc.

Boling, Katharine. January 1905. 2006. 192p. (YA). pap. 5.95 (978-0-15-205121-1(X) , Harcourt Paperbacks); 2004. 176p. (J). 16.00 (978-0-15-205119-8(8)) Harcourt Children's Bks.

Bollback, Anthony G. Rescue at Cripple Creek, Vol. 4. 1999. (Jack & Jill Mysteries Ser.). 135p. (J). pap. 7.95 (978-1-885729-18-7(9)) Toccoa Falls College Pr.

Booth, Martin. Doctor Illuminatus. 2006. (Alchemist's Son Ser.: Pt. 1). 192p. (J). (gr. 4-9). pap. 6.99 (978-0-316-01285-0(8)) Little Brown & Co.

—Soul Stealer. 2006. (Alchemist's Son Ser.: Pt. 2). 256p. (J). (gr. 5-9). pap. 6.99 (978-0-316-05993-0(5)) Little Brown & Co.

Bradman, Tony. Nicky & the Twins' Lost Rabbit. 1999. (Illus.). 32p. (J). pap. 9.99 (978-0-00-664511-5(9)) HarperCollins Pubs. Ltd. GBR. *Dist:* Independent Pubs. Group.

Brandreth, Gyles. Myrtle Mouse & the Naughty Twins. 2000. (Tales from Mouse Village Ser.). (Illus.). 32p. (J). 8.99 (978-0-233-99576-2(5)) Andre Deutsch GBR. *Dist:* Independent Pubs. Group.

Bright, J. E. The Trouble with Twins. 2006. (Follow Your Heart Ser.: No. 2). 240p. (J). pap. 8.99 (978-0-439-79141-0(3) , Scholastic Paperbacks) Scholastic, Inc.

Brooks, Linda Grace. The Asquinn Twins & Where the Trail Forks. 2005. 119p. pap. 16.95 (978-0-7414-2445-7(2)) Infinity Publishing.

Brown, Jim D. The Foster Twins in the Mystery of the House on Joiner Lane. 2003. 160p. pap. 11.95 (978-0-595-26504-6(9) , Writers Club Pr.) iUniverse, Inc.

Brown, Jim D. & Brown, Ina M. The Foster Twins in the Mystery of the House on Joiner Lane. 2003. (ENG.). 164p. 21.95 (*978-0-595-74653-8(5) , Writers Club Pr.) iUniverse, Inc.

Bunting, Eve. Twinnies. 2001. (Illus.). (J). (978-0-606-21497-1(6)) Tandem Library Bks.

Butcher, Nancy. It's Snow Problem. 2001. (gr. 3-6). lib. bdg. 13.00 (978-0-613-43934-3(1)) Tandem Library Bks.

Byars, Betsy. Keeper of the Doves. 2004. (gr. 3-6). lib. bdg. 14.15 (978-0-613-89805-8(2)) Tandem Library Bks.

Byng, Georgia. Molly Moon, Micky Minus, & the Mind Machine. 2007. 416p. (J). (gr. 3-7). 16.99 (*978-0-06-075036-7(7)); lib. bdg. 17.89 (*978-0-06-075037-4(5)) HarperCollins Pubs.

Carr, Jan. Ballet Party! 1998. (You're Invited to Mary-Kate & Ashley's Ser.). (Illus.). 48p. (J). (gr. 2-4). pap. 3.99 (978-0-590-29399-0(0)) Scholastic, Inc.

Chanke, Pamela & Chanko, Pamela. Word Family Tales: Lin & Min Are Twins. Pillo, Cary, illus. 2002. (Word Family Tales Ser.). 16p. (ps-2). pap. 2.95 (978-0-439-26270-5(4)) Scholastic, Inc.

Choo, Choo, Choo, Me & You & You! 2005. (J). bds. (978-0-9769910-5-2(5)) Terrific Twins LLC.

Clairmont, Patsy. Basil & Parsley. 2007. (Tails from the Pantry Ser.). 32p. (J). 9.99 (*978-1-4003-1039-5(3)) Nelson, Thomas Inc.

—5 Cheesy Stories: About Friendship, Bravery, Bullying, & More. 2007. (Tails from the Pantry Ser.). 144p. (J). 14.99 (*978-1-4003-1042-5(3)) Nelson, Thomas Inc.

Cleary, Beverly. Two Times the Fun. Thompson, Carol, illus. 2005. 96p. (J). (ps-2). lib. bdg. 14.89 (978-0-06-057922-7(6)) HarperCollins Pubs.

—Two Times the Fun. Taylor, Thomas, illus. ed. 2005. 96p. (J). (ps-2). 13.99 (978-0-06-057921-0(8)) HarperCollins Pubs.

Cooney, Barbara. Lost Treasures Bk. 1: The Kellyhorns. 2001. 256p. (J). 13.49 (978-0-7868-2596-7(0)) Hyperion Pr.

Creech, Sharon. Ruby Holler. (J). 2004. 336p. pap. 6.99 (978-0-06-056015-7(0) , Harper Trophy); 2002. 320p. (gr. 3-7). lib. bdg. 17.89 (978-0-06-027733-8(5) , Cotler, Joanna Books); 2002. 320p. (gr. 4-7). 16.99 (978-0-06-027732-1(7) , Cotler, Joanna Books) HarperCollins Pubs.

—Ruby Holler. 2004. (gr. 3-6). lib. bdg. 14.15 (978-0-613-86272-1(4)) Tandem Library Bks.

—Ruby Holler. l.t. ed. 2003. (Juvenile Ser.). 250p. (J). 22.95 (978-0-7862-5429-3(7)) Thorndike Pr.

Crowley, James. The Magic Hour. 2003. (Illus.). 280p. (J). pap. 17.95 (978-1-55517-713-3(1) , 77131) Cedar Fort, Inc./CFI Distribution.

Cry of the Falcon. 2006. 208p. (J). pap. 9.95 (978-0-9788541-0-2(1)) m.d. hughes.

Cussler, Clive. The Adventures of Vin Fiz. Farnsworth, William, illus. 2006. 144p. (J). (gr. 3). 15.99 (978-0-399-24474-2(3) , Philomel) Penguin Group (USA) Inc.

Daddy! 2005. (J). bds. (978-0-9769910-6-9(3)) Terrific Twins LLC.

David, Luke. Twin Trouble. 1999. (gr. k-3). lib. bdg. 11.25 (978-0-613-16023-0(1)) Tandem Library Bks.

De Armond, Elizabeth. Tiny Tired Twins. Kaylor, Lori, illus. 1998. 16p. (J). (ps). pap. 5.95 (978-0-9655442-5-2(7)) Business Word, The.

de Paola, Tomie. Meet the Barkers. 2003. (Barker Twins Ser.). (Illus.). 32p. (J). (gr. k-1). pap. 5.99 (978-0-14-250083-5(6) , Puffin) Penguin Group (USA) Inc.

—Meet the Barkers: Morgan & Moffat Go to School. de Paola, Tomie, illus. 2001. (Illus.). 1p. (J). (ps-1). 13.99 (978-0-399-23708-9(9) , Putnam Juvenile) Penguin Group (USA) Inc.

—Meet the Barkers: Morgan & Moffat Go to School. 2005. (J). (gr. k-3). pap. 17.95 incl. audio (978-0-8045-6934-7(7) , SAC6934); pap. 19.95 incl. audio compact disk (978-0-8045-4129-9(9) , SACD4129) Spoken Arts, Inc.

—Morgan & Moffat Go to School. 2003. (gr. k-3). lib. bdg. 14.15 (978-0-613-66367-0(5)) Tandem Library Bks.

—A New Barker in the House. (Illus.). 32p. (J). (ps up). 2004. pap. 5.99 (978-0-14-240141-5(2) , Puffin); 2002. (SPA., 13.99 (978-0-399-23865-9(4) , Putnam Juvenile) Penguin Group (USA) Inc.

—Trouble in the Barkers' Class. de Paola, Tomie, illus. 2003. (Barker Twins Ser.). (Illus.). 32p. (J). (ps-3). 14.99 (978-0-399-24164-2(7) , Putnam Juvenile) Penguin Group (USA) Inc.

Demarest, Chris L. Supertwins Meet the Bad Dogs from Space. 2003. (gr. k-3). lib. bdg. 11.80 (978-0-613-72178-3(0)) Tandem Library Bks.

Denenberg, Barry. Mirror Mirror on the Wall: The Diary of Bess Brennan. 2002. (Dear America Ser.). (Illus.). 144p. (J). (gr. 4-9). pap. 10.95 (978-0-439-19446-4(6)) Scholastic, Inc.

DePaola, Tomie. Trouble in the Barkers' Class. DePaola, Tomie, illus. 2006. (Barker Twins Ser.). (Illus.). 32p. (J). (ps). reprint ed. pap. 5.99 (978-0-14-240585-7(X) , Puffin) Penguin Group (USA) Inc.

Disney Press Staff & King, M. C. Zack Attack, Bk. 4. 4th rev. ed. 2006. 80p. (gr. 2-5). pap. 3.99 (978-0-7868-4938-3(X)) Disney Pr.

DiTerlizzi, Tony & Black, Holly. The Ironwood Tree. (Spiderwick Chronicles: Bk. 4). 128p. (J). 2004. (Illus.). (gr. 1-5). 10.99 (978-0-689-85939-7(2)); 2008. 10.99 (*978-1-4169-5020-2(6)) Simon & Schuster Children's Publishing.

—The Ironwood Tree. l.t. ed. 2006. (Spiderwick Chronicles: Bk. 4). 90p. (YA). (gr. 2 up). 23.95 (978-0-7862-8583-9(4)) Thorndike Pr.

Doyle, Charlotte. It's Twins! Gorton, Julia, illus. 2003. 32p. (J). (ps-1). 10.99 (978-0-399-23718-8(6) , Putnam Juvenile) Penguin Group (USA) Inc.

DuJardin, Rosamond. Double Wedding: A Pam & Penny Story. 2002. 187p. (YA). pap. 12.95 (978-1-930009-52-3(6) , 800-691-7779) Image Cascade Publishing.

—Showboat Summer: A Pam & Penny Story. 2002. 192p. (YA). pap. 12.95 (978-1-930009-51-6(8)) Image Cascade Publishing.

Duke-Barbara, Brenda. Granny Grimes Visits. 1998. 70p. (YA). (gr. 5 up). pap. 5.99 (978-1-57502-927-6(8) , PO2557) Morris Publishing.

Dumas, Alexandre. Man in the Iron Mask. Lynch, Brendan, illus. 2005. (Great Illustrated Classics Ser.). 238p. (J). (gr. 3-8). 21.35 (978-1-59679-247-0(7) , ABDO & Daughters) ABDO Publishing Co.

Dumas, Alexandre. The Man in the Iron Mask. Ho, Oliver & Howell, Troy, illus. 2008. (Classic Starts Ser.). 160p. (J). 5.95 (*978-1-4027-4579-9(6)) Sterling Publishing Co., Inc.

Durant, Alan. Doing the Double. 2004. (Shades Ser.). 64p. (J). pap. 7.99 (978-0-237-52846-1(0) , Evans Brothers, Limited) Evans Publishing Group GBR. *Dist:* Independent Pubs. Group.

Dye, Stacey. Twinship Is in Your Heart. Stubbs, Charles, illus. 2001. 16p. (J). pap. 5.95 (978-1-891846-24-3(8)) Business Word, The.

Dyer, Heather. The GIRL with the BROKEN WIND. 2007. 160p. (J). pap. 4.99 (*978-0-439-74828-5(3) , Scholastic Paperbacks) Scholastic, Inc.

Dyer, Heather. The Girl with the Broken Wing. Bailey, Peter, illus. 2005. 160p. (J). pap. 15.99 (978-0-439-74827-8(5) , Chicken Hse., The) Scholastic, Inc.

Eaton, Jason Carter. The Facttracker. Constantin, Pascale, illus. 2008. 272p. (J). 15.99 (*978-0-06-056434-6(2)); lib. bdg. 16.89 (*978-0-06-056435-3(0)) HarperCollins Pubs.

Edwards, Pamela Duncan. Gigi & Lulu's Gigantic Fight. Cole, Henry, tr. Cole, Henry, illus. 2004. 40p. (J). (ps-2). 14.99 (978-0-06-050752-7(7)) HarperCollins Pubs.

Ehrenhaft, Daniel. The After Life. 2006. 272p. (YA). (gr. 9-12). pap. 8.99 (978-1-59514-080-7(8) , Razorbill) Penguin Group (USA) Inc.

Eisenberg, Lisa. The Case of the Rock & Roll Mystery. 1998. (New Adventures of Mary-Kate & Ashley Ser.). 87p. (J). (gr. 2-7). pap. 3.99 (978-0-590-29402-7(4)) Scholastic, Inc.

Emerson, Alice B. Ruth Fielding at Snow Camp or Lost in the Backwoods. 2005. reprint ed. pap. 24.95 (978-1-4179-3132-3(9)) Kessinger Publishing, LLC.

Epstein, Robin. Sleepover Surprise: A Twin-Sational Birthday. 2004. 60p. (J). (978-0-439-65791-4(1)) Scholastic, Inc.

Farnsworth, Frances Joyce. Tike & Tiny in the Tetons. 2007. (Illus.). 172p. (J). pap. 14.95 (*978-0-943972-79-4(5)) Homestead Publishing.

Fedor, Janis M. Girl Lieutenant in Blue, Vol. 2. 2002. 166p. (YA). (gr. 5-6). pap. 9.95 (978-0-936369-38-9(8)) Son-Rise Pubns. & Distribution Co.

Fisher, Phyllis Mae Richardson. Twiglet the Little Christmas Tree. Fisher, Phyllis Mae Richardson & Fisher, Douglas W., illus. 2003. (J). 30.00 (978-0-9745615-1-6(7) , Twiglet The Little Christmas Tree); 186p. 12.00 (978-0-9745615-4-7(1)) PJs Corner.

Fontenot, Mary Alice & Landry, Julie Fontenot. Clovis Crawfish & the Twin Sister. 2007. 32p. (J). 15.95 (*978-1-58980-467-8(8)) Pelican Publishing Co., Inc.

Freeman, Martha. The Trouble with Twins. Smith, Cat Bowman, illus. 2007. 112p. (J). (gr. 2-6). 16.95 (978-0-8234-2025-4(6)) Holiday Hse., Inc.

Friedrich, Joachim. 4 1/2 Friends & the Secret Cave, Bk. 1. Crawford, Elizabeth D., tr. from GER. 2001. (Illus.). 160p. (gr. 3-7). 14.99 (978-0-7868-0648-5(6)) Hyperion Bks. for Children.

Gaffney, Linda. My Daddy Does GOOD Things, Too! Dabney, Undra & Goettling, Nickalas, illus. 2006. 55p. per. 10.99 (*978-0-9787501-0-7(1)) Gaffney, Linda.

Gallagher, Mary. Mulhern Twins. 2007. (Illus.). 126p. pap. 10.95 (*978-1-905172-17-7(6)) Collins Pr., The IRL. *Dist:* Dufour Editions, Inc.

Gantos, Jack. The Love Curse of the Rumbaughs. 2006. 192p. (YA). (gr. 7 up). 17.00 (978-0-374-33690-5(3) , Farrar, Straus & Giroux (BYR)) Farrar, Straus & Giroux.

—The Love Curse of the Rumbaughs. 2008. 208p. (YA). pap. 7.99 (*978-0-312-38052-6(6)) Square Fish.

Garcia, Maria. Las Aventuras de Connie y Diego. ed. 2004. (ENG & SPA., Illus.). (J). (gr. k-3). spiral bd. (978-0-616-14605-7(1)) Canadian National Institute for the Blind/Institut National Canadien pour les Aveugles.

Gauthier, Bertrand. Abracadabra, les Jumeaux Sont La! 2003. (Premier Roman Ser.). (FRE.). 64p. (J). (gr. 2-5). pap. (978-2-89021-144-5(4)) Diffusion du livre Mirabel.

Gavlas, Kathleen M. Eagle Mountain. 2002. 206p. pap. 19.95 (978-1-58851-321-2(1)) PublishAmerica, Inc.

Gifford, Peggy. Moxy Maxwell Does Not Love Stuart Little. Fisher, Valorie, photos by. 2007. 104p. (J). (gr. 2-6). 12.99 (978-0-375-83915-3(1)); lib. bdg. 15.99 (978-0-375-93915-0(6)) Random Hse. Children's Bks. (Schwartz & Wade Bks.).

Gifford, Peggy. Moxy Maxwell Does Not Love Stuart Little. Fisher, Valorie, photos by. 2008. (Illus.). 112p. (J). (gr. 2-6). 5.50 (*978-0-440-42230-3(2) , Yearling) Random Hse. Children's Bks.

Gifford, Peggy Elizabeth. Moxy Maxwell Does Not Love Writing Thank-You Notes. Fisher, Valorie, illus. Fisher, Valorie, photos by. 2008. (J). (*978-0-375-84270-2(5)); (*978-0-375-94552-6(0)) Random Hse. Children's Bks. (Schwartz & Wade Bks.).

Gill, Janie S. The Tricky Twins. 1999. 23p. (J). 5.95 (978-0-89868-498-6(6)); pap. 3.95 (978-0-89868-497-1(8)); lib. bdg. 10.95 (978-0-89868-496-4(X)) ARO Publishing Co.

Gilmour, H. B. Building a Mystery. 2001. (gr. 5-8). lib. bdg. 12.40 (978-0-613-43800-1(0)); No. 2. (Illus.). (J). (978-0-606-21477-3(1)) Tandem Library Bks.

—The Power of Two, No. 1. 2001. (T*Witches Ser.). (Illus.). (J). (978-0-606-21476-6(3)) Tandem Library Bks.

Givner, Joan. Ellen Fremedon: Journalist. 2006. 192p. pap. 6.95 (978-0-88899-691-6(8)) Groundwood Bks. CAN. *Dist:* Perseus Distribution.

Glover, Sandra. It Didn't Happen. 2006. 160p. (J). pap. 9.99 (*978-1-84270-077-8(4)) Andersen GBR. *Dist:* Independent Pubs. Group.

Godby, Ron. The King of Imperial Hill. 2006. 76p. pap. 14.95 (978-1-4241-1061-2(0)) PublishAmerica, Inc.

Gold, Becky. Phil & Lil Go to the Doctor. 2001. (gr. k-3). lib. bdg. 11.25 (978-0-613-43948-0(1)) Tandem Library Bks.

Goldsmith, Howard. The Twiddle Twins' Amusement Park Mystery. Jordan, Charles, illus. 1998. (Mondo Ser.). 40p. (J). (gr. 1-5). pap. 4.50 (978-1-57255-618-8(8)) Mondo Publishing.

—The Twiddle Twins' Single Footprint Mystery. Jordan, Charles, illus. 1998. (Mondo Ser.). 40p. (J). (gr. 1-5). pap. 4.50 (978-1-57255-619-5(6)) Mondo Publishing.

Gonzalez, Mary. The Ferry That Was. 2005. 48p. pap. 12.95 (978-1-4137-4758-4(2)) PublishAmerica, Inc.

Goobie, Beth. Fixed. 2005. 288p. (YA). (gr. 7-12). lib. bdg. 16.95 (978-1-55143-374-5(5)) Orca Bk. Pubs. USA.

Grace, N. B. Double Trouble, Bk. 2. 2nd rev. ed. 2006. (Suite Life of Zack & Cody Ser.: Vol. 2). (Illus.). 80p. (gr. 2-5). pap. 3.99 (978-0-7868-4936-9(3)) Disney Pr.

Graves, Damien. Midnight Library #7 I Can See You. 2007. (Midnight Library). 176p. (J). pap. 5.99 (*978-0-439-89394-7(1) , Scholastic Paperbacks) Scholastic, Inc.

Gray, Keith. Oe10,000. Edwards, Mark, illus. 2001. 73p. (J). pap. 7.50 (978-0-7497-4351-2(4)) Egmont Bks., Ltd. GBR. *Dist:* Independent Pubs. Group.

Gray, Luli. The Timespinners. 2003. 160p. (J). (gr. 5-9). tchr. ed. 15.00 (978-0-618-16412-7(X)) Houghton Mifflin Co. Trade & Reference Div.

Greenburg, Dan. Attack of the Giant Octopus. Fischer, Scott M., illus. 2007. (Secrets of Dripping Fang Ser.: Bk. 6). 160p. (J). 9.95 (978-0-15-206041-1(3)) Harcourt Children's Bks.

—Fall of the House of Mandible. Fischer, Scott M., illus. 2006. (Outrageously Funny Ser.: Bk. 4). 160p. (J). 9.95 (978-0-15-205475-5(8)) Harcourt Children's Bks.

—The Onts. Fischer, Scott M., illus. 2006. (Secrets of Dripping Fang Ser.: Bk. 1). 144p. (J). 2.99 (978-0-15-205995-8(4) , Harcourt Paperbacks) Harcourt Children's Bks.

—Please Don't Eat the Children. Fischer, Scott M., illus. 2007. (Secrets of Dripping Fang Ser.: Bk. 7). 160p. (J). 9.95 (978-0-15-206047-3(2)) Harcourt Children's Bks.

—Treachery & Betrayal at Jolly Days. Fischer, Scott M., illus. 2006. (Secrets of Dripping Fang Ser.: Bk. 2). 144p. (J). 9.95 (978-0-15-205463-2(4)) Harcourt Children's Bks.

—When Bad Snakes Attack Good Children. Fischer, Scott M., illus. 2007. (Secrets of Dripping Fang Ser.: Bk. 8). 144p. (J). 9.95 (978-0-15-206056-5(1)) Harcourt Children's Bks.

Greenburg, Dan & Diterlizzi, Angela. The Vampire's Curse. Fischer, Scott M., illus. 2006. (Secrets of Dripping Fang Ser.: Bk. 3). 144p. (J). 9.95 (978-0-15-205469-4(3)) Harcourt Children's Bks.

Gregory, Nan. I'll Sing You One-O. 2006. 224p. (J). (gr. 4-6). 16.00 (978-0-618-60708-2(0) , Clarion Bks.) Houghton Mifflin Co. Trade & Reference Div.

Griffin, Adele. Witch Twins & Melody Malady. Rogers, Jacqueline, illus. 2004. 144p. (gr. 2-6). pap. 5.99 (978-0-7868-0964-6(7)) Hyperion Pr.

—Witch Twins & the Ghost of Glenn Bly. Rogers, Jacqueline, illus. 2005. 128p. (gr. 2-6). pap. 5.99 (978-0-7868-5496-7(0)) Hyperion Bks. for Children.

—Witch Twins at Camp Bliss. Rogers, Jacqueline, illus. 2003. 144p. (gr. 2-6). pap. 5.99 (978-0-7868-1583-8(3)) Hyperion Bks. for Children.

—Witch Twins at Camp Bliss. 2003. (gr. 3-6). lib. bdg. 14.15 (978-0-613-63671-1(6)) Tandem Library Bks.

Griffin, W. Marooned on Earth: The Adventures of O-Boo & U-Boo. 2005. 109p. pap. 16.95 (978-1-4137-6814-5(8)) PublishAmerica, Inc.

Gutman, Dan. The Million Dollar Goal. 2nd ed. 2006. 176p. (J). (gr. 3-7). pap. 5.99 (978-1-4231-0083-6(2)) Hyperion Pr.

Haas, Jessie. Jigsaw Pony. Hu, Ying-Hwa, illus. 2005. 128p. (J). 15.99 (978-0-06-078245-0(5)); (gr. 2-4). lib. bdg. 16.89 (978-0-06-078250-4(1)) HarperCollins Pubs.

Hale, Bruce. Pirates of Underwhere. Hillman, Shane, illus. 2008. (Underwhere Ser.). 160p. (J). 15.99 (*978-0-06-085127-9(9)); lib. bdg. 16.89 (*978-0-06-085128-6(7)) HarperCollins Pubs.

—Prince of Underwhere. Hillman, Shane, illus. 2008. (Underwhere Ser.). 176p. (J). lib. bdg. 16.89 (*978-0-06-085125-5(2)); (gr. 3-7). 15.99 (*978-0-06-085124-8(4)) HarperCollins Pubs.

Hamilton, Elizabeth L. Lost on Superstition Mountain. 2004. (Character Mystery Ser.: No. 3). (Illus.). 144p. (J). per. 9.95 (978-0-9754629-5-9(4) , Character-in-Action) Quiet Impact, Inc.

—Mystery at Lake Cachuma. 2003. (Character Mystery Ser.: No. 1). (Illus.). 114p. (J). (gr. 3-6). per. 9.95 (978-0-9713749-4-2(5) , Character-in-Action) Quiet Impact, Inc.

—Surprise at Pearl Harbor. 2004. (Character Mystery Ser.: No. 2). (Illus.). 144p. (J). per. 9.95 (978-0-9754629-2-8(X) , Character-in-Action) Quiet Impact, Inc.

Hamilton Geller, Diana. Simon Says. Finger, Matthew, illus. 2000. 16p. (J). pap. 5.95 (978-1-891846-23-6(X)) Business Word, The.

Hargreaves, Roger. Little Miss Twins. Hargreaves, Roger, illus. rev. ed. 2000. (Mr. Men & Little Miss Ser.). (Illus.). 32p. (J). (ps-3). pap. 3.99 (978-0-8431-7602-5(4) , Price Stern Sloan) Penguin Group (USA) Inc.

—Little Miss Twins. 2000. (ps-2). lib. bdg. 10.65 (978-0-613-26031-2(7)) Tandem Library Bks.

Harper, Meg. My Mum & the Gruesome Twosome. 160p. pap. 9.99 (978-0-7459-4829-4(4)); 2001. 144p. pap. 7.50 (978-0-7459-4567-5(8)) Lion Hudson plc GBR. (Lion). *Dist:* Trafalgar Square Publishing.

HarperCollins Staff, ed. How to Flunk Your First Date. 1999. (gr. 3-6). lib. bdg. 12.10 (978-0-613-16126-8(2)) Tandem Library Bks.

—One Twin Too Many. 1999. (gr. 3-6). lib. bdg. 12.10 (978-0-613-16172-5(6)) Tandem Library Bks.

Harrison, Troon. Bushel of Light. 2001. (gr. 5-8). lib. bdg. 16.40 (978-0-613-44633-4(X)) Tandem Library Bks.

Hassler, Kurt. Diva V Poe. 2006. 32p. (J). 16.95 (978-1-933164-29-8(8)) Seven Seas Entertainment, LLC.

Heller, Andrew. A Fine Mess. 2003. (J). 7.99 (978-0-9722038-6-9(9)) Mr Do It All, Inc.

Hermes, Patricia. Everything Stinks. MacDonald, Patricia, ed. 1999. (Cousins' Club Ser.). 176p. (J). 14.00 (978-0-671-89653-9(9) , Simon & Schuster Children's Publishing) Simon & Schuster Children's Publishing.

Heuston, Kimberley Burton. Book of Jude. 2008. (J). (*978-1-932425-26-0(8) , Front Street) Boyds Mills Pr.

Higgins, B. T. The Master of Disaster. 2005. 103p. pap. 10.00 (978-1-4116-3121-2(8)) Lulu.com.

Higgins, Jack & Richards, Justin. Sure Fire. 2007. 256p. (YA). (gr. 7). 16.99 (*978-0-399-24784-2(X) , Putnam Juvenile) Penguin Group (USA) Inc.

Hope, Laura Lee. The Bobbsey Twins at Home. 2006. 134p. pap. 10.99 (*978-1-4264-5199-7(7)); 152p. pap. 14.99 (*978-1-4264-5500-1(3)) BiblioBazaar.

—The Bobbsey Twins at Home. 2006. pap. 89.99 (*978-1-4280-2884-5(6)) IndyPublish.com.

—The Bobbsey Twins at Meadow Brook. 2006. 128p. pap. 10.99 (*978-1-4264-4949-9(6)); 140p. pap. 13.99 (*978-1-4264-5250-5(0)) BiblioBazaar.

—The Bobbsey Twins at Meadow Brook. 2006. pap. 71.99 (*978-1-4280-0181-7(6)) IndyPublish.com.

—The Bobbsey Twins at Snow Lodge. 2005. 26.95 (978-1-4218-0973-1(7) , 1st World Library - Literary Society) 1st World Publishing, Inc.

—The Bobbsey Twins on a Houseboat, Vol. 6. 2004. (Bobbsey Twins Ser.: Vol. 6). (Illus.). 196p. (J). (gr. 3-8). 5.99 (978-0-448-43757-6(0) , Grosset & Dunlap) Penguin Group (USA) Inc.

—Freddie & Flossie. Pyle, Chuck, illus. 2005. (Bobbsey Twins Ser.). 32p. (J). (ps-ps). pap. 3.99 (978-1-4169-0270-6(8) , Aladdin) Simon & Schuster Children's Publishing.

—Freddie & Flossie. 2006. (Ready-To-Read Ser.). (J). (ps-2). 21.35 (978-1-59961-095-5(7)) Spotlight.

—Freddie & Flossie & Snap. Pyle, Chuck, illus. 2005. (Ready-To-Read Ser.). 32p. (J). pap. 3.99 (978-1-4169-0267-6(8) , Aladdin) Simon & Schuster Children's Publishing.

—Freddie & Flossie & Snap. 2006. (Ready-To-Read Ser.). (J). (ps-2). 21.35 (978-1-59961-096-2(5)) Spotlight.

—Freddie & Flossie & the Easter Egg Hunt. Downer, Maggie, illus. 2006. 32p. (J). lib. bdg. 15.00 (*978-1-4242-0966-8(8)) Fitzgerald Bks.

—Freddie & Flossie & the Easter Egg Hunt. Downer, Maggie, illus. 2006. (Bobbsey Twins Ser.). 32p. (J). pap. 3.99 (978-1-4169-1029-9(8) , Aladdin) Simon & Schuster Children's Publishing.

—Freddie & Flossie & the Easter Egg Hunt. 2006. (Ready-To-Read Ser.). (Illus.). 32p. (J). (ps-2). 21.35 (978-1-59961-100-6(7)) Spotlight.

—Freddie & Flossie & the Little Seed. Downer, Maggie, illus. 2006. (Bobbsey Twins Ser.). 32p. (J). (ps-k). pap. 3.99 (978-1-4169-1766-3(7) , Aladdin) Simon & Schuster Children's Publishing.

—Freddie & Flossie & the Train Ride. Pyle, Chuck, illus. 2005. (Ready-To-Read Ser.). 32p. (J). (ps-ps). pap. 3.99 (978-1-4169-0269-0(4) , Aladdin) Simon & Schuster Children's Publishing.

—Freddie & Flossie & the Train Ride. 2006. (Ready-To-Read Ser.). (J). (ps-2). 21.35 (978-1-59961-097-9(3)) Spotlight.

—Freddie & Flossie at the Beach. Pyle, Chuck, illus. 2005. (Ready-To-Read Ser.). 32p. (J). (ps-ps). pap. 3.99 (978-1-4169-0268-3(6) , Aladdin) Simon & Schuster Children's Publishing.

—Freddie & Flossie at the Beach. 2006. (Ready-To-Read Ser.). (J). (ps-2). 21.35 (978-1-59961-098-6(1)) Spotlight.

Horowitz, Anthony. Nightrise. 2007. (Gatekeepers Ser.: No. 3). 368p. (YA). pap. 17.99 (*978-0-439-68001-1(8)) Scholastic, Inc.

Hoving, Isabel. The Dream Merchant. Velmans, Hester, tr. from DUT. 2005. 640p. (YA). (gr. 7 up). 19.99 (978-0-7636-2880-2(8)) Candlewick Pr.

Hrdlitschka, Shelley. Tangled Web. 2000. 240p. (J). (gr. 5-10). pap. 6.95 (978-1-55143-178-9(5)) Orca Bk. Pubs. USA.

—Tangled Web. 2000. (gr. 5-8). lib. bdg. 15.25 (978-0-613-34994-9(6)) Tandem Library Bks.

Hughes, Laura. Second Twins. 1998. (J). pap. 19.95 (978-0-8464-4914-0(5)) Beekman Bks., Inc.

Hunt, Gene. Accidental Space Ship. 2006. 150p. (J). (gr. 4-6). 16.95 (978-1-59354-119-4(8)) Handprint Bks.

I'm Not a Rerun! 2005. (J). bds. (978-0-9769910-4-5(7)) Terrific Twins LLC.

Irvin, William. The Adventures of Winston & Hazel: Episode 1: the Silver Medallion. 2006. 11.00 (978-0-8059-8220-6(5)) Dorrance Publishing Co., Inc.

It's Dark! 2005. (J). bds. (978-0-9769910-1-4(2)) Terrific Twins LLC.

Jackson, Marianne Bell. The Swan Twins, No. 1. 1999. (Illus.). 22p. (YA). (gr. k up). pap. 5.00 (978-0-9669554-0-8(4)) ColorAnDraw.

James, B. J., et al. Supertwins Meet the Dangerous Dino-Robots, No. 3. Demarest, Chris L., illus. 2003. (Scholastic Reader Ser.). 32p. (J). pap. 3.99 (978-0-439-46625-7(3) , Cartwheel Bks.) Scholastic, Inc.

Jefferies, Cindy. Secret Ambition, No. 4. 2007. (Fame School Ser.: Vol. 3). 128p. (YA). 4.99 (978-0-14-240814-8(X) , Puffin) Penguin Group (USA) Inc.

Jenkins, Jerry B. & Fabry, Chris. Canyon Echoes. 2005. (Tyndale Kids Ser.). 240p. (J). pap. 5.99 (978-1-4143-0147-1(2)) Tyndale Hse. Pubs.

—Double Fault. 2005. (Tyndale Kids Ser.). 272p. (J). pap. 5.99 (978-1-4143-0146-4(4)) Tyndale Hse. Pubs.

—Grave Shadows. 2005. (Red Rock Mysteries Ser.). (Illus.). 240p. (J). pap. 5.99 (978-1-4143-0144-0(8)) Tyndale Hse. Pubs.

—Hollywood Holdup. 2006. (Red Rock Mysteries Ser.). 224p. (J). pap. 5.99 (978-1-4143-0151-8(0)) Tyndale Hse. Pubs.

—Instant Menace. 2006. (Tyndale Kids Ser.). 256p. (J). pap. 5.99 (978-1-4143-0148-8(0)) Tyndale Hse. Pubs.

—Phantom Writer. 2005. (Red Rock Mysteries Ser.). 256p. (J). pap. 5.99 (978-1-4143-0145-7(6)) Tyndale Hse. Pubs.

—Wind Chill. 2006. (Tyndale Kids Ser.). 240p. (J). pap. 5.99 (978-1-4143-0153-2(7) , Tyndale Kids) Tyndale Hse. Pubs.

—Windy City Danger. 2006. (Red Rock Mysteries Ser.). 246p. (J). pap. 5.99 (978-1-4143-0150-1(2)) Tyndale Hse. Pubs.

Johnson, Allen. My Brothers Story. 2006. 192p. pap. 7.95 (978-0-944353-17-2(7)) Rivendell Bk. Factory.

Johnson, Janet. Hallie & Grace- in the Beginning, God... 2007. (Illus.). 24p. (J). per. 6.99 (***978-1-59988-696-1(0)***) Tate Publishing & Enterprises, L.L.C.

Jordan, Taylor. Movin' on In. Wummer, Amy, illus. 2005. 32p. (J). lib. bdg. 20.00 (***978-1-4242-1108-1(5)***) Fitzgerald Bks.

—Movin' on In. Wummer, Amy, illus. 2005. (Social Studies Connects). 32p. (J). pap. 4.99 (978-1-57565-159-0(9)) Kane Pr., The.

Katschke, Judy. Bye-Bye Boyfriend. 2000. (gr. 3-6). lib. bdg. 13.00 (978-0-613-31037-6(3)) Tandem Library Bks.

—Case of the Candy Cane Clue. 2002. (gr. 3-6). lib. bdg. 12.40 (978-0-613-64697-0(5)) Tandem Library Bks.

—The Case of the Weird Science Mystery. 2002. (New Adventures of Mary-Kate & Ashley Ser.: 29). (Illus.). 96p. (gr. 1-5). mass mkt. 4.50 (978-0-06-106651-1(6)) HarperCollins Pubs.

—The Case of the Wild Wolf River. 1998. (New Adventures of Mary-Kate & Ashley Ser.). 87p. (J). (gr. 2-7). pap. 3.99 (978-0-590-29401-0(6)) Scholastic, Inc.

—The Facts about Flirting. 2003. (Two of a Kind Ser.: Vol. 27). (Illus.). 112p. mass mkt. 4.99 (978-0-06-009323-5(4) , Harper Entertainment) HarperCollins Pubs.

Katschke, Judy, et al. To Snoop or Not to Snoop? 1999. (Two of a Kind Ser.: No. 5). 112p. (gr. 3-7). mass mkt. 4.99 (978-0-06-106575-0(7) , Harper Entertainment) HarperCollins Pubs.

Keene, Carolyn. The Twin Dilemma. 2005. (Nancy Drew Mystery Stories: Vol. 63). (Illus.). 196p. (J). (gr. 3-8). pap. 6.99 (978-0-448-43694-4(9) , Grosset & Dunlap) Penguin Group (USA) Inc.

Kerr, P. B. The Akhenaten Adventure. 2004. (Children of the Lamp Ser.: Bk. 1). 368p. (J). (gr. 4-7). pap. 16.95 (978-0-439-67019-7(5) , Orchard Bks.) Scholastic, Inc.

—The Akhenaten Adventure No. 1: Children of the Lamp. l.t. ed. 2005. 430p. 23.95 (978-0-7862-7299-0(6) , Large Print Pr.) Thorndike Pr.

—Blue Djinn of Baby. 2006. (Children of the Lamp Ser.: No. 2). 384p. (J). pap. 6.99 (978-0-439-67022-7(5)) Scholastic, Inc.

—The Blue Djinn of Babylon. 2006. (Children of the Lamp Ser.: Bk. 2). 384p. (J). (gr. 4-7). pap. 16.99 (978-0-439-67021-0(7) , Orchard Bks.) Scholastic, Inc.

—Cobra King of Kathmandu. 2007. (Children of the Lamp Ser.: No. 3). 400p. (J). pap. 6.99 (***978-0-439-67024-1(1)*** , Scholastic Paperbacks) Scholastic, Inc.

—The Cobra King of Kathmandu. 2007. (Children of the Lamp Ser.: No. 3). (Illus.). 384p. (J). (gr. 4-7). pap. 16.99 (978-0-439-67023-4(3) , Orchard Bks.) Scholastic, Inc.

Kerr, P. B. The Day of the Djinn Warriors. 2008. (Scholastic First Discovery Ser.). 400p. (J). pap. 17.99 (***978-0-439-93214-1(9)*** , Orchard Bks.) Scholastic, Inc.

King, M. C. Room of Doom, Bk. 3. 3rd rev. ed. 2006. (Suite Life of Zack & Cody Ser.: Vol. 3). (Illus.). 80p. (gr. 2-5). pap. 3.99 (978-0-7868-4937-6(1)) Disney Pr.

King-Smith, Dick. The Twin Giants. Grey, Mini, illus. 2008. 80p. (J). (gr. 1-4). 16.99 (***978-0-7636-3529-9(4)***) Candlewick Pr.

Kraft, Erik P. Lenny & Mel's Summer Vacation. Kraft, Erik P., illus. 2004. (Ready-for-Chapters Ser.). (Illus.). 64p. (J). pap. 3.99 (978-0-689-86874-0(X) , Aladdin) Simon & Schuster Children's Publishing.

Lamb, Charles & Lamb, Mary. Tales from Shakespeare: "Twelfth Night" Strang, Kay, ed. Andrews, Gary, illus. rev. ed. 2005. 40p. pap. 4.95 (978-0-9542905-7-3(7)) Capercaillie Bks., Ltd GBR. *Dist:* Wilson & Assocs.

Langrish, Katherine. Troll Fell. (J). 2005. 368p. (gr. 7 up). pap. 6.99 (978-0-06-058306-4(1)); 2004. (Illus.). 272p. (gr. 5 up). 16.99 (978-0-06-058304-0(5)); 2004. (Illus.). 272p. (gr. 5 up). lib. bdg. 16.89 (978-0-06-058305-7(3)) HarperCollins Pubs.

Lantz, Francess L. The Case of the Missing Mummy. 1998. (New Adventures of Mary-Kate & Ashley Ser.). (Illus.). 82p. (J). (gr. 2-7). pap. 3.99 (978-0-590-29404-1(0)) Scholastic, Inc.

Lappin, Amber. My, You Have Your Hands Full! Galey, Chuck, illus. 2000. 16p. (J). pap. 5.95 (978-1-891846-21-2(3)) Business Word, The.

LaReau, Kara & LaReau, Jenna. Rocko & Spanky Have Company. LaReau, Kara & LaReau, Jenna, illus. 2006. (Rocko & Spanky Ser.). (Illus.). 40p. (J). 16.00 (978-0-15-216618-2(1)) Harcourt Trade Pubs.

LaVerne B, Shaw. Mesa Magic. 2006. 192p. per. 19.95 (***978-1-59879-238-6(5)***) Lifevest Publishing, Inc.

Lee Hope, Laura. The Bobbsey Twins in the Great West. 2005. 200p. pap. 12.95 (978-1-4218-0465-1(4) , 1st World Library - Literary Society) 1st World Publishing, Inc.

—The Bobbsey Twins in the Great West. 2004. reprint ed. pap. 20.95 (978-1-4191-5444-7(3)); pap. 1.99 (978-1-4192-5444-4(8)) Kessinger Publishing, LLC.

L'Engle, Madeleine. Many Waters. 2002. (Illus.). (J). 15.00 (978-0-7587-9605-9(6)) Book Wholesalers, Inc.

—Many Waters. Sis, Peter & Nelson, Cliff, illus. anniv. rev. ed. 1998. 336p. (J). (gr. 5-8). pap. 5.99 (978-0-440-22770-0(4) , Laurel Leaf) Random Hse. Children's Bks.

—Many Waters. 2007. 224p. (J). 6.99 (978-0-312-36861-6(5)); pap. 6.99 (978-0-312-36857-9(7)) Square Fish.

—Many Waters. 1998. (J). (978-0-606-13596-2(0)); (gr. 5-8). lib. bdg. 14.15 (978-0-613-72320-6(1)) Tandem Library Bks.

Leonard, Marcia. Get the Ball, Slim. Handelman, Dorothy, photos by. 1998. (Real Kids Readers Ser.). (Illus.). 32p. (gr. k-1). (J). pap. 4.99 (978-0-7613-2025-8(3)); lib. bdg. 18.90 (978-0-7613-2000-5(8)) Lerner Publishing Group. (Millbrook Pr.).

—Spots. Handelman, Dorothy, photos by. 1998. (Real Kids Readers Ser.). (Illus.). 32p. (ps-1). lib. bdg. 18.90 (978-0-7613-2016-6(4)); (J). pap. 4.99 (978-0-7613-2041-8(5)) Lerner Publishing Group. (Millbrook Pr.).

—Trae la Pelota, Tito. Handelman, Dorothy, photos by. 2005. (Lecturas para Niños de Verdad (Real Kids Readers) Ser.). (Illus.). 32p. (J). (ps-1). (SPA.). pap. 4.99 (978-0-8225-3292-7(1) , Ediciones Lerner); (ENG & SPA., pap. 4.99 (978-0-8225-3293-4(X)) Lerner Publishing Group.

Lerangis, Peter. Spy X: Hide & Seek. 2004. 142p. (J). (978-0-439-70282-9(8)) Scholastic, Inc.

Let's Celebrate!, 10 bks. 2005. (Illus.). (J). bds. (978-0-9769910-9-0(8)) Terrific Twins LLC.

Levy, Elizabeth. Big Trouble in Little Twinsville. Elliot, Mark, illus. 2001. 96p. (J). (gr. 2-5). 15.89 (978-0-06-028591-3(5)) HarperCollins Pubs.

Lewis, Beverly. Shadows Beyond the Gate. 2000. (Summerhill Secrets Ser.: Vol. 10). 144p. (J). (gr. 6-9). pap. 6.99 (978-1-55661-876-5(X)) Bethany Hse. Pubs.

Lewison, Wendy Cheyette. Two Is for Twins. Nakata, Hiroe, illus. 2006. 40p. (J). (ps). 16.99 (978-0-670-06128-0(X) , Viking Juvenile) Penguin Group (USA) Inc.

Liebenthal, Jean Z. Curiosity. 1999. 133p. (J). (978-1-57008-707-3(5)) Scribbulations LLC.

Lingard, Joan. The Same Only Different. Whelan, Olwyn, illus. 2001. 32p. (J). (ps-1). pap. (978-1-871512-64-9(6)) Glowworm Bks., Ltd.

Lochner, David. Twice As Funny. . , Twins: A Book of Cartoons. 1998. (Illus.). 104p. (Orig.). spiral bd. 10.95 (978-1-891846-04-5(3)) Business Word, The.

Love, D. Anne. The Secret Prince. 2005. 240p. (J). 16.95 (978-0-689-84426-3(3) , McElderry, Margaret K.) Simon & Schuster Children's Publishing.

Lynx Twins Together. 2002. (Wild Heritage Collection Mini Bks.). (Illus.). 32p. (J). (978-1-59069-240-0(3) , H3011) Studio Mouse LLC.

MacDonald, Alan. Contest Crazy. Brown, Judy, illus. 2006. (Read-It! Chapter Books). 48p. (J). lib. bdg. (***978-1-4048-3134-6(7)*** , 1265803) Picture Window Bks.

Macguire, Gregory. Missing Sisters. 1998. (J). (978-0-606-13612-9(6)) Tandem Library Bks.

MacKall, Dandi Daley. Kyra's Story. 2003. (Degrees of Guilt Ser.). (YA). pap. 9.99 (978-0-8423-8284-7(4)) Tyndale Hse. Pubs.

MacNeil, Joan & MacNeil, Robin. Twin Babies, Twin Babies. Sherrodd, Lisa, illus. 2000. 16p. (J). pap. 5.95 (978-1-891846-17-5(5)) Business Word, The.

Maddox, Jake. Speedway Switch. Tiffany, Sean, illus. 2007. (J). 72p. (***978-1-59889-321-2(1)***); 65p. pap. (***978-1-59889-416-5(1)***) Stone Arch Bks.

Madsen, Wayne. The Case of Stolen Time: The Misadventures of Inspector Moustachio. 2007. (Misadventures of Inspector Moustachio Ser.: Bk. 1). 156p. (J). per. 16.99 (***978-0-9790878-9-9(9)***) Community Pr.

Mancusi, Mari. Stake That! 2006. 288p. (YA). (gr. 12). pap. 9.99 (978-0-425-21210-3(6) , Berkley Trade) Penguin Group (USA) Inc.

Manson, Sheri. Bumpy & Boo Visit the Eye Doctor: Guess Who Needs Glasses? 2006. 32p. 15.95 (978-0-9744307-3-7(0)) Merry Lane Pr.

Margallo, Ramon. The MANGER, the CROSS, & the EMPTY TOMB Christian Apologetics for Young Readers: A Short Story. 2006. 108p. pap. 9.99 (978-1-4116-5751-9(9)) Lulu.com.

Massie, Elizabeth. House Divided. 2000. (Young Founders Ser.). (J). 11.64 (978-0-606-19659-8(5)) Tandem Library Bks.

Mayfield, Julie. The Magical First Day. Reis, Michael, illus. 1998. (J). pap. 5.95 (978-1-56763-337-5(4)); lib. bdg. 17.25 (978-1-56763-336-8(6)) Ozark Publishing.

McCloskey, Erin, ed. In the Wild West on MacKenzie's Trail. Howard, Catherine, tr. 2007. (Alex & Penny Ser.). (Illus.). 75p. (J). (gr. 2-5). 14.95 (***978-88-544-0245-4(1)***) White Star ITA. *Dist:* Random Hse., Inc.

McGee, D. M. The Jollys & the Cross. 2007. 164p. per. (***978-1-84685-674-7(4)*** , Exposure Publishing) Meadow Bks.

Menning, Lori. One Was Not Enough. Christy, Jana, illus. 2000. 16p. (J). pap. 5.95 (978-1-891846-18-2(3)) Business Word, The.

Mercer, Sienna. Fangtastic! 2007. (My Sister the Vampire Ser.: No. 2). 208p. (J). (gr. 3-7). pap. 5.99 (***978-0-06-087115-4(6)*** , Harper Trophy) HarperCollins Pubs.

—My Sister the Vampire #4: Vampalicious! 2008. (My Sister the Vampire Ser.). 208p. (J). pap. 5.99 (***978-0-06-087121-5(0)*** , Harper Trophy) HarperCollins Pubs.

Messer, Celeste M. The Ghost of Piper's Landing. Hoeffner, Deb, illus. 2004. 82-92p. 4.95 (978-0-9702171-7-2(X)) AshleyAlan Enterprises.

Metz, Melinda. The Case of the Golden Slipper. 2000. (New Adventures of Mary-Kate & Ashley Ser.). (Illus.). (J). 11.30 (978-0-606-21918-1(8)) Tandem Library Bks.

—The Case of the Surprise Call. 1999. (New Adventures of Mary-Kate & Ashley Ser.). 86p. (J). (gr. 2-7). pap. 3.99 (978-0-590-29403-4(2)) Scholastic, Inc.

Miller, Gary & Miller, Lynda. The Adventures of Bob & Betty. 2006. (J). spiral bd. (978-1-933594-92-7(6)) Faith Baptist Church Publns.

Miller, Mitzi & Millner, Denene. Hotlanta #1. 2008. 288p. (J). 8.99 (***978-0-545-00308-7(3)*** , Scholastic Paperbacks) Scholastic, Inc.

Mitchard, Jacquelyn. Now You See Her. 2007. 208p. (J). lib. bdg. 16.89 (978-0-06-111684-1(X)); (YA). (gr. 7 up). 15.99 (978-0-06-111683-4(1)) HarperCollins Pubs. (HarperTeen).

Mitchell, Dawn. Always Zany Abcs. Molnar, Albert, illus. 2001. 16p. (J). pap. 5.95 (978-1-891846-25-0(6)) Business Word, The.

Moore, Ulysses. The Long-Lost Map. Bruno, Iacopo, illus. 2006. (Ulysses Moore Ser.: No. 2). 272p. (J). pap. 12.99 (978-0-439-77439-0(X) , Scholastic) Scholastic, Inc.

Morgan, C. M. Silver Doorway #1: A Gnome Away from Home. 2003. 104p. (J). pap. 6.99 (978-0-9702189-2-6(3)) Sabledrake Enterprises.

Morgan, Melissa J. Fair to Remember, Vol. 13. 2007. (Camp Confidential Ser.). 160p. (J). pap. 4.99 (978-0-448-44451-2(8) , Grosset & Dunlap) Penguin Group (USA) Inc.

Morris, Paris. I am Having Twins. 2008. (Illus.). 24p. (J). pap. 14.95 (***978-0-9760095-4-2(4)***) New Year Publishing.

—My Twins are Coming Home. 2008. (Illus.). 24p. (J). pap. 14.95 (***978-0-9760095-5-9(2)***) New Year Publishing.

Moses, Shelia P. The Baptism. 2007. 144p. (YA). (gr. 7 up). 15.99 (978-1-4169-0671-1(1) , McElderry, Margaret K.) Simon & Schuster Children's Publishing.

Mourlevat, Jean-Claude. The Pull of the Ocean. Maudet, Y., tr. from FRE. 2006. 208p. (gr. 7). (J). 13.95 (978-0-385-73348-9(8)); (YA). lib. bdg. 15.99 (978-0-385-90364-6(2)) Random Hse. Children's Bks. (Delacorte Bks. for Young Readers).

Muldrow, Diane. Lights! Camera! Cook! Pollak, Barbara, illus. 2007. (Dish Ser.: No. 8). 160p. (J). pap. 4.99 (978-0-448-44533-5(6) , Grosset & Dunlap) Penguin Group (USA) Inc.

—Recipe for Trouble. Pollak, Barbara, illus. 2007. (Dish Ser.: No. 7). 160p. (J). pap. 4.99 (978-0-448-44532-8(8) , Grosset & Dunlap) Penguin Group (USA) Inc.

—Recipe for Trouble. 2003. (gr. 3-6). lib. bdg. 13.00 (978-0-613-72489-0(5)) Tandem Library Bks.

—Stirring It Up, No. 1. Pollak, Barbara, illus. 2007. (Dish Ser.). 160p. (J). pap. 4.99 (978-0-448-44526-7(3) , Grosset & Dunlap) Penguin Group (USA) Inc.

—Sweet-and-Sour Summer, No. 9. Pollack, Barbara, illus. 2007. (Dish Ser.). 160p. (J). (gr. 4-7). pap. 4.99 (***978-0-448-44661-5(8)*** , Grosset & Dunlap) Penguin Group (USA) Inc.

—Turning up the Heat. Pollak, Barbara, illus. 2007. (Dish! Ser.: Vol. 3). 160p. (J). (gr. 4-7). pap. 4.99 (978-0-448-44527-4(1) , Grosset & Dunlap) Penguin Group (USA) Inc.

Muldrow, Diane. Winner Takes the Cake. Pollack, Barbara, illus. 2007. (Dish Ser.: No. 11). 160p. (J). (gr. 4-7). pap. 4.99 (***978-0-448-44666-0(9)*** , Grosset & Dunlap) Penguin Group (USA) Inc.

Murphy, Marcia. The Twins & the Birthday Party. Fabian, Natalie, illus. 1999. 16p. (J). (ps). pap. 5.95 (978-1-891846-06-9(X)) Business Word, The.

My Day! 2005. (J). bds. (978-0-9769910-0-7(4)) Terrific Twins LLC.

Neasi, Barbara J. Como Yo. 2002. Tr. of Just Like Me. (gr. k-3). lib. bdg. 12.95 (978-0-613-59462-2(2)) Tandem Library Bks.

—Just Like Me. Hantel, Johanna, illus. rev. ed. 2003. (Rookie Reader Espanol Ser.). 32p. (J). (gr. k-2). pap. 4.95 (978-0-516-27495-9(3) , Children's Pr.) Scholastic Library Publishing.

—Just Like Me. rev. ed. 2002. (Rookie Readers Ser.). (J). lib. bdg. 19.00 (978-0-516-22564-7(2) , Children's Pr.) Scholastic Library Publishing.

—Just Like Me. Hantel, Johanna, illus. rev. ed. 2002. (Rookie Readers Ser.). 31p. (J). (gr. 1-2). 19.50 (978-0-516-22669-9(X) , Children's Pr.) Scholastic Library Publishing.

—Just Like Me. rev. ed. 2002. (ps-2). lib. bdg. 12.95 (978-0-613-59651-0(X)) Tandem Library Bks.

Nicholson, William. Slaves of the Mastery. Sis, Peter, illus. 2001. (Wind on Fire Trilogy: Bk. 2). 448p. (gr. 5-9). 17.99 (978-0-7868-0570-9(6)) Hyperion Bks. for Children.

—The Wind on Fire Trilogy, Bk.1. Sis, Peter, illus. 2004. (Wind on Fire Trilogy). 486p. (J). (gr. 5-17). mass mkt. 7.99 (978-0-7868-1826-6(3)) Hyperion Bks. for Children.

—The Wind Singer. 2000. (Wind on Fire Trilogy: Bk. 1). 368p. (gr. 5-9). 17.99 (978-0-7868-2494-6(8)) Hyperion Bks. for Children.

—The Wind Singer. 2003. (Wind on Fire Trilogy: Bk. 1). 384p. (gr. 5-17). pap. 11.99 (978-0-7868-1799-3(2)) Hyperion Pr.

—The Wind Singer. 2004. (Wind on Fire Trilogy: Bk. 1). (YA). (gr. 5 up). lib. bdg. 16.45 (978-0-613-75034-9(9)) Tandem Library Bks.

Norling, Beth. Sister Night & Sister Day. Norling, Beth, illus. 2001. (Illus.). 32p. (J). (ps). 14.95 (978-1-86448-863-0(8)) Allen & Unwin AUS. *Dist:* Independent Pubs. Group.

Nunes, Shiho S. The Power of the Stone. Kane, Herb Kawainui, illus. 2002. mass mkt. 4.99 (978-0-89610-283-5(1)) Island Heritage Publishing.

Ogden, Charles. High Wire. Carton, Rick, illus. 2006. (Edgar & Ellen Ser.). 208p. (J). 9.95 (978-1-4169-1500-3(1) , Aladdin) Simon & Schuster Children's Publishing.

—Mischief Manual. Carton, Rick, illus. 2007. (Edgar & Ellen Ser.). 112p. (J). pap. 7.99 (978-1-4169-3935-1(0) , Aladdin) Simon & Schuster Children's Publishing.

—Nod's Limbs. Carton, Rick, illus. 2007. (Edgar & Ellen Ser.). (J). 224p. 9.99 (978-1-4169-1501-0(X)); 210p. (***978-1-4287-3214-8(4)***) Simon & Schuster Children's Publishing. (Aladdin).

—Pet's Revenge. Carton, Rick, illus. 2006. (Edgar & Ellen Ser.). 192p. (J). (gr. 3-7). 9.95 (978-1-4169-1408-2(0) , Aladdin) Simon & Schuster Children's Publishing.

—Triple Threat Vols. 1-3, Set: Their First Three Misadventures: Rare Beasts, Tourist Trap, under Town. Carton, Rick, illus. 2007. (Edgar & Ellen Ser.). 464p. (J). 29.99 (978-1-4169-3462-2(6) , Aladdin) Simon & Schuster Children's Publishing.

O'Hair, Margaret. Twin to Twin. Courtin, Thierry, illus. 2003. 32p. (J). 16.99 (978-0-689-84494-2(8) , McElderry, Margaret K.) Simon & Schuster Children's Publishing.

Older, Effin. Birthday Party. 1998. (You're Invited to Mary-Kate & Ashley's Ser.). (Illus.). 48p. (J). (gr. 2-4). pap. 12.95 (978-0-590-22593-9(6)) Scholastic, Inc.

Oldfield, J. Skye Champion, Bk. 13. (Illus.). 122p. (J). pap. 7.99 (978-0-340-69985-0(X) , Hodder & Stoughton) Hodder General Publishing Division GBR. *Dist:* Trafalgar Square Publishing.

—Stanley Troublemaker. (Illus.). 120p. (J). pap. 8.99 (978-0-340-72675-4(X) , Hodder & Stoughton) Hodder General Publishing Division GBR. *Dist:* Trafalgar Square Publishing.

—Sultan Patient, Vol. 2. (Illus.). 119p. (J). pap. 7.99 (978-0-340-69983-6(3) , Hodder & Stoughton) Hodder General Publishing Division GBR. *Dist:* Trafalgar Square Publishing.

—Sunny the Hero. (Home Farm Twins Ser.: No. 7). (Illus.). 120p. (J). pap. 7.99 (978-0-340-68990-5(0) , Hodder & Stoughton) Hodder General Publishing Division GBR. *Dist:* Trafalgar Square Publishing.

Oldfield, Jenny. Sorrel Substitute, Bk. 12. (Illus.). 120p. (J). pap. 7.99 (978-0-340-69984-3(1) , Hodder & Stoughton) Hodder General Publishing Division GBR. *Dist:* Trafalgar Square Publishing.

—Stevie the Rebel. (Home Farm Twins Ser.: Vol. 9). (Illus.). 128p. (J). pap. 7.99 (978-0-340-68992-9(7) , Hodder & Stoughton) Hodder General Publishing Division GBR. *Dist:* Trafalgar Square Publishing.

Oliver, Lin. Attack of the Growling Eyeballs. 2008. (Who Shrunk Daniel Funk? Ser.). 112p. (J). 14.99 (***978-1-4169-0951-4(6)*** , Simon & Schuster Children's Publishing) Simon & Schuster Children's Publishing.

Olsen, Ashley. Dream Date Debate. 2003. (gr. 5-8). lib. bdg. 13.00 (978-0-613-64706-9(8)) Tandem Library Bks.

—Dream Team. 2002. (gr. k-3). lib. bdg. 12.40 (978-0-613-64707-6(6)) Tandem Library Bks.

—Getting There. 2002. (gr. 5-8). lib. bdg. 13.00 (978-0-613-64720-5(3)) Tandem Library Bks.

Olsen, Mary-Kate. Cool Club. 2000. (gr. 3-6). lib. bdg. 13.00 (978-0-613-24677-4(2)) Tandem Library Bks.

—My Best Friend's Boyfriend. 2002. (gr. 5-8). lib. bdg. 13.00 (978-0-613-64749-6(1)) Tandem Library Bks.

—Switching Goals. 2000. (gr. 3-6). lib. bdg. 13.00 (978-0-613-27146-2(7)) Tandem Library Bks.

—Too Good to Be True. 2002. (gr. 5-8). lib. bdg. 13.00 (978-0-613-64774-8(2)) Tandem Library Bks.

Olsen, Mary-Kate & Olsen, Ashley. The Case of the Icy Igloo Inn. 2002. (Illus.). (J). pap. 18.00 (978-0-06-052114-1(7) , Harper Entertainment) HarperCollins Pubs.

—Forget Me Not, Set. 2002. (J). pap. 19.96 (978-0-06-052112-7(0) , Harper Entertainment) HarperCollins Pubs.

—Mary-Kate & Ashley Starring in... 2002. (Illus.). (J). pap. 19.96 (978-0-06-052110-3(4) , Harper Entertainment) HarperCollins Pubs.

—Mary-Kate & Ashley Switching Goals. 2000. (Mary-Kate & Ashley Ser.). 128p. (gr. 2-4). mass mkt. 4.99 (978-0-06-107603-9(1) , Harper Entertainment) HarperCollins Pubs.

—Starring You & Me. 2002. (Mary-Kate & Ashley Sweet 16 Ser.: No. 5). (Illus.). 128p. 4.99 (978-0-06-052811-9(7) , Harper Entertainment) HarperCollins Pubs.

Olum, Adhiambo. Twins a Step Behind. 1999. (Illus.). 44p. (J). (gr. 1-4). pap. 7.95 (978-1-881524-56-4(6)) Milligan Bks., Inc.

O'Mahony, Carol. A Dee Dee & Clark Delay Magical Myster. 2006. 73p. pap. 14.95 (*978-1-4241-5119-6(8)) PublishAmerica, Inc.

Orenstein, Denise Gosliner. The Secret Twin. McCarthy, Dan, illus. 2007. 400p. (J). lib. bdg. 17.89 (978-0-06-078565-9(9)); (gr. 7 up). 16.99 (978-0-06-078564-2(0)) HarperCollins Pubs.

Orr, Wendy. Mokie & Bik. Bean, Jonathan, illus. 2007. 80p. (J). (gr. 2-5). 15.95 (978-0-8050-7979-1(3)) Holt, Henry & Co.

Pascal, Francine. Ajuste de Cuentas. 2001. (Sweet Valley Twins Ser.).Tr. of Lois Strikes Back. (SPA.). 128p. (YA). 6.95 (978-84-272-3599-1(2)) Molino, Editorial ESP. *Dist:* AIMS International Bks., Inc.

—Amigacho de Pluma del Amy. Orig. Title: Amy's Pen Pal. (SPA.). 144p. (YA). 6.95 (978-84-272-3596-0(8)) Molino, Editorial ESP. *Dist:* AIMS International Bks., Inc.

—El Autentico Ganador. 2001. (Gemelas de Sweet Valley Ser.: No. 16). Tr. of Second Best. (SPA.). 128p. (J). (gr. 3-7). 6.95 (978-84-272-3786-5(3)) Molino, Editorial ESP. *Dist:* AIMS International Bks., Inc.

—Centro de Atencion. (Gemelas de Sweet Valley Ser.: No. 18). Tr. of Center of Attention. (SPA.). (J). (gr. 3-7). 6.95 (978-84-272-3788-9(X)) Molino, Editorial ESP. *Dist:* AIMS International Bks., Inc.

—Chicos Contra Chicas. 2000. (Gemelas de Sweet Valley Ser.: No. 17). Tr. of Boys Against Girls. (SPA.). 136p. (J). (gr. 3-7). 7.50 (978-84-272-3787-2(1)) Molino, Editorial ESP. *Dist:* AIMS International Bks., Inc.

—Cita a Escondidas. 2002. (Sweet Valley High Ser.).Tr. of Deceptions. (SPA.). (YA). 7.95 (978-84-272-3884-8(3)) Molino, Editorial ESP. *Dist:* AIMS International Bks., Inc.

—Contra las Normas. 2002. (Sweet Valley Twins Ser.).Tr. of Against the Rules. (SPA.). 128p. (YA). 6.95 (978-84-272-3779-7(0)) Molino, Editorial ESP. *Dist:* AIMS International Bks., Inc.

—Demasiado Perfecta.Tr. of Too Good to be True. (SPA.). 160p. (J). 7.95 (978-84-272-3881-7(9)) Molino, Editorial ESP. *Dist:* AIMS International Bks., Inc.

—Esa Clase de Chica.Tr. of Wrong Kind of Girl. (SPA.). 168p. (J). 7.95 (978-84-272-3880-0(0)) Molino, Editorial ESP. *Dist:* AIMS International Bks., Inc.

—Estrella del Rock. Orig. Title: Jessica the Rock Star. (SPA.). (J). 6.95 (978-84-272-3595-3(X)) Molino, Editorial ESP. *Dist:* AIMS International Bks., Inc.

—Los Gemelos Consiguen Cogidos. Orig. Title: The Twins Get Caught. (SPA.). 136p. (J). 6.95 (978-84-272-4641-6(2)) Molino, Editorial ESP. *Dist:* AIMS International Bks., Inc.

—Una Gran Luchadora. (Gemelas de Sweet Valley Ser.: No. 10). Tr. of One of the Gang. (SPA.). 128p. (J). (gr. 3-7). 6.95 (978-84-272-3780-3(4)) Molino, Editorial ESP. *Dist:* AIMS International Bks., Inc.

—El Gran Secreto. 2002. (Sweet Valley Twins Ser.).Tr. of Keeping Secrets. (SPA.). 128p. (YA). 6.95 (978-84-272-3782-7(0)) Molino, Editorial ESP. *Dist:* AIMS International Bks., Inc.

—Jessica en Etapa. 2001. (Sweet Valley Twins Ser.).Tr. of Jessica on Stage. (SPA.). 120p. (YA). 6.95 (978-84-272-3592-2(5)) Molino, Editorial ESP. *Dist:* AIMS International Bks., Inc.

—Una Larga Noche.Tr. of All Night Long. (SPA.). 128p. (J). 7.95 (978-84-272-3875-6(4)) Molino, Editorial ESP. *Dist:* AIMS International Bks., Inc.

—Lo Que los Padres Ignoran.Tr. of What Your Parents Don't Know.... (SPA.). 224p. (J). 10.50 (978-84-272-3163-4(6)) Molino, Editorial ESP. *Dist:* AIMS International Bks., Inc.

—Lust. 2003. (Fearless Ser.: No. 29). lib. bdg. 14.15 (978-0-613-73387-8(8)) Tandem Library Bks.

—Mala Idea de Jessica.Tr. of Jessica's Bad Idea. (SPA.). 112p. (J). 6.95 (978-84-272-3593-9(3)) Molino, Editorial ESP. *Dist:* AIMS International Bks., Inc.

—Maria Falta. Orig. Title: Mary Is Missing. (SPA.). 128p. (YA). 6.95 (978-84-272-3597-7(6)) Molino, Editorial ESP. *Dist:* AIMS International Bks., Inc.

—One 2 Many. 1999. (Sweet Valley Jr. High Ser.: No. 27). (gr. 3-6). lib. bdg. 12.40 (978-0-613-16173-2(4)) Tandem Library Bks.

—Peligrosa Tentacion.Tr. of Dangerous Love. (SPA., Illus.). 136p. (J). 7.95 (978-84-272-3876-3(2)) Molino, Editorial ESP. *Dist:* AIMS International Bks., Inc.

—Querida Hermana.Tr. of Dear Sister. (SPA., Illus.). 168p. (J). 7.95 (978-84-272-3877-0(0)) Molino, Editorial ESP. *Dist:* AIMS International Bks., Inc.

—Un Tesoro Enterrado. 2001. (Gemelas de Sweet Valley Ser.: No. 11). Tr. of Buried Treasure. (SPA.). 128p. (J). (gr. 3-7). 6.95 (978-84-272-3781-0(2)) Molino, Editorial ESP. *Dist:* AIMS International Bks., Inc.

—Trabajo del Equipo. Orig. Title: Team Work. (SPA.). 120p. (J). 6.95 (978-84-272-3797-1(9)) Molino, Editorial ESP. *Dist:* AIMS International Bks., Inc.

—Tres Es Multitud. 2000. (Gemelas de Sweet Valley Ser.: No. 7). Tr. of Three's a Crowd. (SPA.). 144p. (J). (gr. 3-7). 7.50 (978-84-272-3777-3(4)) Molino, Editorial ESP. *Dist:* AIMS International Bks., Inc.

Pascal, Francine & Suzanne, Jamie. Señorita Jessica. (Sweet Valley Twins Ser.: No. 46). Orig. Title: Mademoiselle Jessica. (SPA.). 160p. (J). (gr. 3-7). 6.95 (978-84-272-4646-1(3)) Molino, Editorial ESP. *Dist:* AIMS International Bks., Inc.

Paterson, Katherine. Jacob Have I Loved. l.t. ed. 2000. (LRS Large Print Cornerstone Ser.). 266p. (J). (gr. 5-12). lib. bdg. 29.95 (978-1-58118-073-2(X) , 23658) LRS.

Payson, Dale. Almost Twins. 1999. 196p. (J). (ps-3). 5.95 (978-0-13-022780-5(3)) Prentice Hall PTR.

Pederson, Katie. The Point of No Return. 2006. 304p. pap. 24.95 (978-1-4137-9945-3(0)) PublishAmerica, Inc.

Peel, John. Suddenly Twins! 2001. (Magical States Ser.: Vol. 1). (Illus.). 176p. (J). (gr. 4-6). pap. 4.99 (978-0-7434-1762-4(3) , Aladdin) Simon & Schuster Children's Publishing.

Perkins, Lucy Fitch. The Belgian Twins. 2004. reprint ed. pap. 15.95 (978-1-4191-5388-4(9)); pap. 1.99 (978-1-4192-5388-1(3)) Kessinger Publishing, LLC.

—Dutch Twins. 2006. pap. 25.99 (*978-1-4280-2261-4(9)) IndyPublish.com.

—The Dutch Twins. 2004. reprint ed. pap. 1.99 (978-1-4192-6040-7(5)) Kessinger Publishing, LLC.

—Eskimo Twins. 2006. 62.99 (*978-1-4280-3721-2(7)); pap. 55.99 (*978-1-4280-3694-9(6)) IndyPublish.com.

—The Eskimo Twins. 2004. reprint ed. pap. 15.95 (978-1-4191-6126-1(1)); pap. 1.99 (978-1-4192-6126-8(6)) Kessinger Publishing, LLC.

—The Eskimo Twins (Yesterday's Classics) 2006. (J). per. 9.95 (*978-1-59915-059-8(X)) Yesterday's Classics.

—The French Twins. 2006. 18.99 (*978-1-4280-1689-7(9)); pap. 11.99 (*978-1-4280-1681-1(3)) IndyPublish.com.

—The Japanese Twins. 2005. 26.95 (978-1-4218-0369-2(0) , 1st World Library - Literary Society) 1st World Publishing, Inc.

—The Japanese Twins. 2004. reprint ed. pap. 15.95 (978-1-4191-6781-2(2)); pap. 1.99 (978-1-4192-6781-9(7)) Kessinger Publishing, LLC.

—The Japanese Twins (Yesterday's Classics) 2006. (J). per. 9.95 (*978-1-59915-058-1(1)) Yesterday's Classics.

—Rhe Japanese Twins. 2005. 96p. pap. 10.95 (978-1-4218-0469-9(7) , 1st World Library - Literary Society) 1st World Publishing, Inc.

—Scotch Twins. 2006. 62.99 (*978-1-4280-3717-5(9)); pap. 55.99 (*978-1-4280-3713-7(6)) IndyPublish.com.

—The Scotch Twins. 2004. reprint ed. pap. 15.95 (978-1-4191-8160-3(2)); pap. 1.99 (978-1-4192-8160-0(7)) Kessinger Publishing, LLC.

—The Swiss Twins. 2004. reprint ed. pap. 15.95 (978-1-4191-8467-3(9)); pap. 1.99 (978-1-4192-8467-0(3)) Kessinger Publishing, LLC.

Peschke, M. Dead Man's Map. Smith, Tod, illus. 2008. (J). pap. (*978-1-59889-921-4(X)); (YA). (gr. 5-9). lib. bdg. 17.95 (*978-1-59889-855-2(8)) Stone Arch Bks.

Phillips, Leigh Hope. Birthday Wishes. Fountain, John, illus. 2005. (J). pap. (978-1-933156-10-1(4)); per. (978-1-933156-03-3(1)) GSVQ Publishing. (VisionQuest Kids).

Pilkey, Dav. Captain Underpants & the Preposterous Plight of the Purple Potty People. 2006. (Captain Underpants Ser.: Bk. 8). 176p. (J). pap. 4.99 (978-0-439-37614-3(9)); (gr. 2-5). pap. 16.99 (978-0-439-37613-6(0)) Scholastic, Inc. (Blue Sky Pr., The).

Platt, Randall Beth. Honor Bright. 1998. (978-0-606-13486-6(7)) Tandem Library Bks.

Pollak, Dale. Velocity. 2008. 144p. pap. 22.95 (*978-0-9760095-7-3(9)) New Year Publishing.

Price, Margaret Evans. The Angora Twinnies. Price, Margaret Evans, illus. 2005. (Illus.). 16p. (J). (ps-3). 9.00 (978-1-59583-046-3(4)) Laughing Elephant.

Purwin, Patricia. Grampa's a Scientist. Purwin, Patricia, illus. Dawson, John, photos by. 1999. (Illus.). 24p. (J). (ps-6). pap. 12.95 (978-0-9673408-0-7(2)) Collage Storybook Pr.

Rallison, Janette. How to Take the Ex Out of Ex-Boyfriend. 2007. 272p. (YA). (gr. 7 up). 15.99 (978-0-399-24617-3(7) , Putnam Juvenile) Penguin Group (USA) Inc.

Roberts, Mark. The 12 Day Jinx. 2002. (Illus.). 160p. (J). pap. 9.99 (978-1-84270-074-7(X)) Andersen GBR. *Dist:* Independent Pubs. Group.

Roberts, Willo Davis. The One Left Behind. (J). 2007. 139p. (gr. 3-7). per. 5.99 (978-0-689-85083-7(2)); 2006. (Illus.). 144p. 16.95 (978-0-689-85075-2(1) , Atheneum) Simon & Schuster Children's Publishing.

Romansky, Sally Rosenberg. Invincible. Ott, Margot Janet, illus. 2006. (J). pap. 8.95 (978-0-9723729-4-7(6)) Imagination Stage, Inc.

Rose, Valerie. The Family Reunion Is Not A Real Vacation. 2003. 28p. (J). 9.95 (978-0-9703489-2-0(4) , Little Petals) Roses Are READ Productions.

Ross, Pat. M & M & the Bad News Babies. 1999. (Illus.). (J). (gr. 3-6). lib. bdg. 13.00 (978-0-8085-3696-3(6)) Tandem Library Bks.

Roy, Arundhati. Le Dieu des Petits Riens. pap. 19.95 (978-2-07-041172-6(9)) Gallimard, Editions FRA. *Dist:* Distribooks, Inc.

Rubel, Nicole. It's Hot & Cold in Miami. 2006. (Illus.). 208p. (J). 17.00 (978-0-374-33611-0(3)) Farrar, Straus & Giroux.

Salzmann, Mary Elizabeth. Hummingbird Hummer. Nobens, C. A., illus. (Fact & Fiction Ser.). 24p. (J). 2007. 21.35 (978-1-59928-442-2(1)); 2006. (978-1-59928-443-9(X)) ABDO Publishing Co.

Same Day, Different Way! 2005. (J). bds. (978-0-9769910-3-8(9)) Terrific Twins LLC.

Sander, Sonia. Twin Gifts. 2006. (Maya & Miguel Ser.: No. 1). 24p. (J). pap. 3.50 (978-0-439-83007-2(9)) Scholastic, Inc.

—Twin Gifts (Maya & Miguel: el Mejor Regalo) 2006. (Maya & Miguel Ser.). 24p. (J). pap. 3.50 (978-0-439-87385-7(1) , Scholastic en Espanol) Scholastic, Inc.

Scholastic, Inc. Staff. The Case of the Missing Mummy. 1998. (J). pap. 71.82 (978-0-590-63041-2(5)) Scholastic, Inc.

Scholastic, Inc. Staff. Long-lost Map. 2007. (Ulysses Moore Ser.). 272p. (J). pap. 5.99 (*978-0-439-77673-8(2)) Scholastic, Inc.

Schraff, Anne. The Twin. rev. ed. 1999. (Standing Tall Mysteries Ser.). 49p. (YA). (gr. 4-12). pap. 3.95 (978-1-58659-081-9(2)) Artesian Pr.

Schuster, Judith. The Eddie Brewster Adventures, Bk. 1. 2006. 142p. pap. 19.95 (*978-1-4241-4418-1(3)) PublishAmerica, Inc.

Scott, Michael. The Alchemyst. 2007. (Secrets Imrtl Nicholas Flamel Ser.). (Illus.). 400p. (YA). (gr. 7 up). 16.99 (978-0-385-73357-1(7)); lib. bdg. 19.99 (978-0-385-90372-1(3)) Random Hse. Children's Bks. (Delacorte Bks. for Young Readers).

Seif, Adam, creator. Tacos, Beans & Rice... the Episodes: From the Beginning. l.t. ed. 2006. (Illus.). 32p. (J). (978-0-9719518-0-8(2)) Doodle Publishing.

Sescoe, Vincent E. Double Time. Helms, Clinton, illus. 2001. (gr. 6-12). 191p. (J). 17.95 (978-1-930093-00-3(4)); 192p. (YA). pap. 6.95 (978-1-930093-06-5(3)) Brookfield Reader, Inc., The.

Shakespeare, William. Comedy of Errors. 1999. (gr. 7-12). lib. bdg. 14.15 (978-0-613-64226-2(0)) Tandem Library Bks.

Shearer, Alex. Sea Legs. 2006. 320p. (J). pap. 5.99 (978-0-689-87144-3(9) , Aladdin) Simon & Schuster Children's Publishing.

Sheffield, Charles. My Brother's Keeper. 2000. (gr. 3-6). lib. bdg. 14.15 (978-0-613-46259-4(9)) Tandem Library Bks.

Sherwood, Barbara B. Jan & Ann Are Twins. Campbell, Nancy T., illus. 1998. 16p. (J). (ps). pap. 5.95 (978-1-891846-02-1(7)) Business Word, The.

Shinn, Sharon. The Truth-Teller's Tale. 2007. (Firebird Ser.). 304p. (YA). pap. 7.99 (978-0-14-240784-4(4) , Puffin) Penguin Group (USA) Inc.

Sidell, Yvonne. The Fairy Twins: Land of New Friends. 2006. (ENG.). 48p. per. 23.99 (*978-1-4259-4840-5(5)) AuthorHouse.

Skelton, Vonda Skinner. Bitsy & the Mystery at Amelia Island. 2005. (Bitsy Burroughs Mysteries Ser.). 183p. (J). pap. 8.95 (978-1-57072-307-0(9) , Silver Dagger Mysteries) Overmountain Pr.

Smallcomb, Pam. Trimoni Twins & the Changing Coin. 2004. 175p. (J). 15.95 (978-1-58234-939-8(8) , Bloomsbury Children) Bloomsbury Publishing.

—The Trimoni Twins & the Shrunken Treasure. 2005. 225p. (J). (gr. 3-6). 16.95 (978-1-58234-656-4(9) , Bloomsbury Children) Bloomsbury Publishing.

Smith, Roland. Cryptid Hunters. 2005. 352p. (J). (gr. 5-17). 15.99 (978-0-7868-5161-4(9)) Hyperion Bks. for Children.

—Cryptid Hunters. 2006. 352p. (gr. 5-17). pap. 5.99 (978-0-7868-5162-1(7)) Hyperion Pr.

Snyder, Lavinia Branca. The Mystery of the Lost Bells: The Kyss Family Mysteries, 2002. 32p. (J). mass mkt. (978-1-932233-67-4(9)) Aurora Libris Corp.

Somper, Justin. Demons of the Ocean. 2006. 336p. (J). (gr. 3-7). 15.99 (978-0-316-01373-4(0)) Little Brown & Co.

—Demons of the Ocean. 2007. 352p. (J). (gr. 3-7). pap. 5.99 (*978-0-316-01444-1(3)) Little, Brown Bks. for Young Readers.

—Vampirates: Tide of Terror. 2nd rev. ed. 2007. 464p. (J). (gr. 3-7). 15.99 (*978-0-316-01374-1(9)) Little, Brown Bks. for Young Readers.

Spinner, Stephanie. Be First in the Universe. 2001. (J). 11.15 (978-0-606-21051-5(2)) Tandem Library Bks.

Stamper, Bauer. Breakfast at Danny's Diner: A Book about Multiplication. 2003. (gr. k-3). lib. bdg. 11.80 (978-0-613-72522-4(0)) Tandem Library Bks.

Stephen, Smith. Red Card. 2006. 128p. (J). pap. 5.99 (978-0-7847-1438-6(X) , 42143) Standard Publishing.

Sternick, Michele J. The Charged up Twins. 2005. 29p. 9.98 (978-1-4116-3475-6(6)) Lulu.com.

Stillerman, Robbie. Twin Sisters Sticker Paper Dolls. 2003. (Dover Little Activity Bks.). (Illus.). 4p. (J). pap. 1.50 (978-0-486-43018-8(9)) Dover Pubns., Inc.

Stine, R. L. Dangerous Girls. 2003. (J). 256p. 111.92 (978-0-06-056909-9(3)); 256p. 111.92 (978-0-06-056910-5(7)); (Illus.). (gr. 7 up). 13.99 (978-0-06-053080-8(4)) HarperCollins Pubs.

Stirnkorb, Patricia. All about Me! Inspirational Version, 1. 2005. (Illus.). 12p. (J). bds. 12.99 (978-0-9758709-7-6(1) , A.W.A. Gang) Journey Stone Creations, LLC.

Stoddard, Michael Eugene. The Porthole to Time. 1999. 176p. (YA). pap. 9.95 (978-0-9675924-0-4(2)) Stoddard, Michael Eugene.

Streib, Sally. Octopus Encounter. 2007. (J). (*978-0-8163-2210-7(4)) Pacific Pr. Publishing Assn.

Struble, Maegann M. Where Are the Twins? Barry, Rich, illus. 2000. 16p. (J). pap. 5.95 (978-1-891846-19-9(1)) Business Word, The.

Sweeney, Jacqueline. Just Call Me J. P. Hart, G. K. & Empey, Mark, illus. 2000. (We Can Read! Ser.). 32p. (J). (gr. 1-2). lib. bdg. 21.36 (978-0-7614-0922-9(X) , Benchmark Bks.) Cavendish, Marshall Corp.

Swobud, I. K. The Case of the Blue-Ribbon-Horse. 1998. (New Adventures of Mary-Kate & Ashley Ser.). 86p. (J). (gr. 2-7). pap. 3.99 (978-0-590-29309-9(5)) Scholastic, Inc.

Tamura, Yumi. Basara. 2006. (Basara Ser.). 208p. (YA). Vol. 18. pap. 9.99 (978-1-4215-0528-2(2)); Vol. 19. pap. 9.99 (978-1-4215-0529-9(0)) Viz Media.

Tashjian, Janet. Tru Confessions. 1999. (Illus.). 176p. (J). pap. 4.99 (978-0-590-96047-2(4)) Scholastic, Inc.

—Tru Confessions. 2007. 176p. (J). pap. 6.99 (*978-0-312-37273-6(6)) Square Fish.

—Tru Confessions. 1999. (978-0-606-16611-9(4)) Tandem Library Bks.

Tate & Tini's Learning Journey Five Storybook Set. 2001. (J). (978-0-9768948-0-3(7)) Broken Wing Enterprises, Inc.

Taylor, Cora. Adventure in Istanbul No. 1: The Spy Who Wasn't There. 2005. (Juvenile Novel, Ser.). (Illus.). 176p. (J). (gr. 4-6). pap. 7.95 (978-1-55050-315-9(4)) Coteau Bks. CAN. *Dist:* Fitzhenry & Whiteside, Ltd.

Taylor, Cora. Murder in Mexico. 2007. (Spy Who Wasn't There Ser.). (Illus.). 360p. (J). (gr. 4-7). pap. 7.95 (*978-1-55050-353-1(7)) Coteau Bks. CAN. *Dist:* Fitzhenry & Whiteside, Ltd.

Taylor, G. P. The Tizzle Sisters & Erik. 2007. 188p. (*978-1-905692-22-4(6)) Markosia Enterprises Ltd.

Terry, Gail Contreina. Twins. 2005. pap. 8.00 (978-0-8059-6818-7(0)) Dorrance Publishing Co., Inc.

Tiernan, Cate. A Circle of Ashes, No. 2. 2005. (Balefire Ser.). 224p. (YA). (gr. 7-12). mass mkt. 6.99 (978-1-59514-046-3(8) , Razorbill) Penguin Group (USA) Inc.

—A Necklace of Water, Vol. 4. 2006. (Balefire Ser.). 240p. (YA). (gr. 7-12). mass mkt. 5.99 (978-1-59514-048-7(4) , Razorbill) Penguin Group (USA) Inc.

Tobin, C. La Mascota de la Clase. DeMonico, Rick, illus. 2005. (Maya & Miguel Ser.). (SPA.). 80p. (J). (ps-ps). pap. 5.99 (978-0-439-78347-7(X) , Scholastic en Espanol) Scholastic, Inc.

—Teacher's Pet. DeMonico, Rick, illus. 2005. (Maya & Miguel Ser.). 80p. (J). (ps-ps). pap. 5.99 (978-0-439-73385-4(5)) Scholastic, Inc.

Trottier, Maxine. A Circle of Silver. 2000. (Circle of Silver Chronicles Ser.). 216p. (J). (gr. 7-12). pap. 7.95 (978-0-7737-6055-4(5)) Stoddart Kids CAN. *Dist:* Fitzhenry & Whiteside, Ltd.

Troulis, Jennifer. Penelope & Priscilla & the City of the Banished. 2007. (J). per. 14.95 (*978-0-9768602-1-1(X)) Twin Monkeys Pr.

Troulis, Jennifer. Penelope & Priscilla & the Enchanted House of Whispers. 2005. (Illus.). (J). pap. 13.95 (978-0-9768602-0-4(1)) Twin Monkeys Pr.

Twelfth Night Paperback Book. 2006. (YA). 7.95 (*978-1-56254-858-2(1)) Saddleback Educational Publishing.

Twelfth Night Study Guide. 2006. (YA). per. 17.95 (*978-1-56254-859-9(X)) Saddleback Educational Publishing.

The Twins. 2001. (J). (978-1-58453-138-8(X)) Pioneer Valley Educational Pr., Inc.

Upton, Joe. Runaways on the Inside Passage. 2005. (Illus.). 304p. (gr. 5 up). 17.95 (978-0-88240-564-3(0)); pap. 9.95 (978-0-88240-565-0(9)) Graphic Arts Ctr. Publishing Co.

Ure, Jean. Shrinking Violet. l.t. ed. 2005. (Illus.). 224p. (J). pap. (978-0-7540-7833-3(7) , CLP 424) BBC Audio.

—Shrinking Violet. 2002. (Diary Ser.). (Illus.). 172p. (J). pap. 11.95 (978-0-00-714390-0(7)) HarperCollins Pubs. Ltd. GBR. *Dist:* Independent Pubs. Group.

Vail, Rachel. Never Mind! A Twin Novel. 2005. 208p. (J). (gr. 5 up). reprint ed. pap. 5.99 (978-0-06-054316-7(7) , Harper Trophy) HarperCollins Pubs.

Valdes, Leslie. At the Carnival. Roper, Robert, illus. 2005. 24p. (J). lib. bdg. 9.00 (*978-1-4242-0982-8(X)) Fitzgerald Bks.

Van Sickle, Lisa. Twin Stories: Shhhh... It's Bertha. McLaughlin, Wanda, ed. Hagler, Josh, illus. l.t. ed. 1998. 48p. (J). (gr. k-3). 16.95 (978-0-9659001-5-7(0)) Write Team, The.

—Twin Stories - Kaos . . . Bad Dog! McLaughlin, Wanda J., ed. Hagler, Josh, illus. 1998. 48p. (J). (ps-3). 16.95 (978-0-9659001-6-4(9)) Write Team, The.

van Stockum, Hilda. A Day on Skates: 2007 Commemorative Edition. van Stockum, Hilda, illus. 2007. (Illus.). 44p. (J). 19.95 (*978-1-932350-18-0(7)) Bethlehem Bks.

Velasquez, Crystal. Maya & Miguel: Mi Hermana Gemela; Mi Hermano Gemelo. 2005. (Maya & Miguel Ser.). Orig. Title: My Twin Brother/My Twin Sister. (SPA., Illus.). 96p. (J). 3.99 (978-0-439-74915-2(8) , Scholastic en Espanol) Scholastic, Inc.

—Maya & Miguel: My Twin Brother; My Twin Sister. 2005. (Maya & Miguel Ser.). 96p. (J). 3.99 (978-0-439-69603-6(8)) Scholastic, Inc.

—Neighborhood Friends. 2005. (Maya & Miguel Ser.: No. 1). 96p. (J). (ps-ps). pap. 3.99 (978-0-439-73384-7(7)) Scholastic, Inc.

—Rain or Shine. 2006. (Maya & Miguel Ser.). (Illus.). 32p. (J). pap. 3.99 (978-0-439-80350-2(0) , Scholastic) Scholastic, Inc.

Voake, Charlotte. Hello Twins. Voake, Charlotte, illus. 2006. (Illus.). 32p. (J). (gr. k-k). 15.99 (978-0-7636-3003-4(9)) Candlewick Pr.

Vogiel, Eva. Facing the Music. 2003. 284p. 19.95 (978-1-880582-94-7(5)) Judaica Pr., Inc., The.

Wallace, Karen. King Cudgel's Challenge. Flook, Helen, illus. 2007. (J). lib. bdg. (*978-1-4048-3706-5(X)) Picture Window Bks.

Wallace, Karen. The Peanut Prankster. Brown, Judy, illus. 2007. (Read-It! Chapter Books). (J). 21.26 (978-1-4048-2724-0(2)) Picture Window Bks.

Weiss, Ellen. Twins Have a Fight. Williams, Sam, tr. Williams, Sam, illus. 2004. (Ready-to-Read Ser.). 24p. (J). pap. 3.99 (978-0-689-86515-2(5) , Aladdin) Simon & Schuster Children's Publishing.

—Twins in the Park. Williams, Sam, illus. ed. 2005. (Ready-to-Read Ser. PreLevel 1). 22p. (J). lib. bdg. 15.00 (978-1-59054-963-6(5)) Fitzgerald Bks.

—Twins in the Park. Williams, Sam, illus. 2003. (Ready-to-Read Ser.). 24p. (J). pap. 3.99 (978-0-689-85742-3(X) , Aladdin) Simon & Schuster Children's Publishing.

—Twins Take a Bath. Williams, Sam, illus. 2003. (Ready-to-Read Ser.). 24p. (J). pap. 3.99 (978-0-689-85740-9(3) , Aladdin) Simon & Schuster Children's Publishing.

—Twins Take a Bath. 2003. (ps-2). lib. bdg. 11.80 (978-0-613-90471-1(0)) Tandem Library Bks.

—Twins Take a Bath. Williams, Sam, illus. ed. 2005. (Ready-to-Read Ser. PreLevel 1). 22p. (J). lib. bdg. 15.00 (978-1-59054-964-3(3)) Fitzgerald Bks.

Weiss, Ellen & Weiss, Ellen. Twins Go to Bed. 2004. (Ready-to-Read Ser.). (Illus.). 24p. (J). pap. 3.99 (978-0-689-86517-6(1) , Aladdin) Simon & Schuster Children's Publishing.

Welch, Sheila Kelly. The Shadowed Unicorn. 2000. 192p. (J). (gr. 5-9). 15.95 (978-0-8126-2895-1(0)) Cricket Bks.

We're a Team! 2005. (J). bds. (978-0-9769910-7-6(1)) Terrific Twins LLC.

Werlin, Nancy. Are You Alone on Purpose? 2007. 208p. (YA). (gr. 7). pap. 7.99 (978-0-14-240777-6(1) , Puffin) Penguin Group (USA) Inc.

Wescott, Derek. Terry & Thomas the Tandem Twins. 2007. 160p. pap. (*978-1-84401-875-8(X)) Athena Pr.

West, Tracey. El Futbol en Todo el Mundo. Albrecht, Jeff, illus. 2005. (Maya & Miguel Ser.). (SPA.). 32p. (J). (ps-ps). pap. 3.99 (978-0-439-78348-4(8) , Scholastic en Espanol) Scholastic, Inc.

Whitmore, Benette. Shelter. 2006. 304p. (YA). 16.95 (978-0-8027-8884-9(X)) Walker & Co.

Wiggin, Kate Douglas. Marm Lisa. 2004. reprint ed. pap. 15.95 (978-1-4191-3278-0(4)) ; pap. 1.99 (978-1-4192-3278-7(9)) Kessinger Publishing, LLC.

Williams, Laura E. The Mystery of the Bad Luck Curse. 2002. (Mystic Lighthouse Mysteries Ser.). 128p. (J). (gr. 2-7). pap. 4.99 (978-0-439-21727-9(X)) Scholastic, Inc.

—The Mystery of the Missing Tiger. 2002. (Mystic Lighthouse Mysteries Ser.). 112p. (J). pap. 4.50 (978-0-439-21728-6(8)) Scholastic, Inc.

Williams, Maiya. The Hour of the Cobra. (YA). 2007. 320p. (gr. 2-7). pap. 5.95 (*978-0-8109-9362-4(7)); 2006. 312p. (gr. 4-9). 16.95 (978-0-8109-5970-5(4) , Amulet Bks.) Abrams, Harry N. , Inc.

—The Hour of the Outlaw. 2007. 360p. (YA). (gr. 4-9). 16.95 (*978-0-8109-9355-6(4)) Abrams, Harry N. , Inc.

Wilson. Double Act. 2000. (Illus.). 187p. (J). 16.95 (978-0-385-40537-9(5)) Transworld Publishers Ltd. GBR. *Dist:* Trafalgar Square Publishing.

Wilson, Jacqueline. Double Act. Sharrat, Nick & Heap, Sue, illus. 1999. 192p. (gr. 3-7). 5.50 (978-0-440-41374-5(5) , Yearling) Random Hse. Children's Bks.

—Double Act. 1999. (J). (978-0-606-16442-9(1)); (gr. 3-6). lib. bdg. 12.40 (978-0-613-16097-1(5)) Tandem Library Bks.

—Double Act. 2001. (Corgi Yearling Ser.). (Illus.). 32p. 9.99 (978-0-440-86334-2(1) , Corgi) Transworld Publishers Ltd. GBR. *Dist:* Trafalgar Square Publishing.

Windle, Jeanette. Captured in Colombia, Vol. 3. 2002. (Parker Twins Ser.: No. 3). 160p. (gr. 3-8). pap. 5.99 (978-0-8254-4147-9(1)) Kregel Pubns.

—Cave of the Inca Re. 2001. (Parker Twins Ser.: No. 1). 160p. pap. 5.99 (978-0-8254-4145-5(5)) Kregel Pubns.

—Jungle Hideout. 2001. (Parker Twins Ser.: No. 2). 160p. pap. 5.99 (978-0-8254-4146-2(3)) Kregel Pubns.

—Secret of the Dragon Mark, Vol. 5. 2002. (Parker Twins Ser.: No. 5). 160p. (gr. 3-8). pap. 5.99 (978-0-8254-4149-3(8)) Kregel Pubns.

Winston, Sherri. Acting: A Novel. 2004. 256p. (YA). 15.95 (978-0-7614-5173-0(0)) Cavendish, Marshall Corp.

Wolf, Joan. How the Selves Became Elves. Squassoni, Christine, illus. 2001. (J). (ps-2). 19.95 (978-0-9711445-1-4(6)) Cruzane Mountain Publishing.

Wood, Brian. The Cramp Twins. 2001. (J). pap. 9.95 (978-0-385-32714-5(5) , Random Hse. Bks. for Young Readers) Random Hse. Children's Bks.

—The Cramp Twins: Lucien's Little. 2005. (Illus.). 112p. 13.95 (978-1-904674-01-6(1)) Reynolds & Hearn GBR. *Dist:* Trafalgar Square Publishing.

—Swamp Fever. 2001. (Cramp Twins Ser.). (J). pap. (978-0-385-32717-6(X) , Dell Books for Young Readers) Random Hse. Children's Bks.

—A Trip to Twinsanity. 2005. (Illus.). 112p. (ps-7). pap., pap. 13.00 (978-1-904674-00-9(3)) Reynolds & Hearn GBR. *Dist:* Independent Pubs. Group.

Yang, Belle. Always Come Home to Me. Yang, Belle, illus. 2007. (Illus.). 32p. (J). (ps-3). 16.99 (*978-0-7636-2899-4(9)) Candlewick Pr.

Yang, Belle & Williams, Marcia. Archie's War. Williams, Marcia, illus. 2007. (Illus.). 48p. (J). (gr. 3-7). 17.99 (*978-0-7636-3532-9(4)) Candlewick Pr.

Yolen, Jane. The Bagpiper's Ghost. 2003. (Tartan Magic Ser.: Bk. 3). (Illus.). 144p. (J). pap. 5.95 (978-0-15-204913-3(4) , Magic Carpet Bks.) Harcourt Children's Bks.

—Bagpiper's Ghost. 2003. (gr. 3-6). lib. bdg. 6.95 (978-0-613-70524-0(6)) Tandem Library Bks.

—The Wizard's Map. 1999. (Tartan Magic Ser.: Bk. 1). 144p. (YA). (gr. 3-7). 16.00 (978-0-15-202067-5(5)) Harcourt Children's Bks.

—Wizard's Map. 2002. (gr. 3-6). lib. bdg. 14.10 (978-0-613-53882-4(X)) Tandem Library Bks.

Zaugg, Sandra L. Hidden Notes & High Seas. 2005. (Illus.). 95p. (J). (978-0-8163-2052-3(7)) Pacific Pr. Pubns.

Zimmer, Tracie Vaughn. Sketches from a Spy Tree. Glass, Andrew, illus. 2005. 64p. (J). (gr. 4-6). 16.00 (978-0-618-23479-0(9) , Clarion Bks.) Houghton Mifflin Co. Trade & Reference Div.

1. 2. 3 Happy Family. 2005. (J). bds. (978-0-9769910-2-1(0)) Terrific Twins LLC.

TWINS—POETRY

Blackburn, Tammie. It Takes Two. Coffman, Dennis, illus. 2000. 16p. (J). pap. 5.95 (978-1-891846-16-8(7)) Business Word, The.

TYLER, JOHN, 1790-1862

Doak, Robin S. John Tyler. 2003. (Profiles of the Presidents Ser.). (Illus.). 64p. (J). (gr. 4 up). lib. bdg. 23.93 (978-0-7565-0258-4(6)) Compass Point Bks.

Ferry, Steven. John Tyler: Our Tenth President. 2001. (Spirit of America: Our Presidents Ser.). (Illus.). 48p. (J). (gr. 2-6). 28.50 (978-1-56766-849-0(6)) Child's World, Inc.

Havelin, Kate. John Tyler. 2005. (Presidential Leaders Ser.). (Illus.). 112p. (J). (gr. 6-12). 29.27 (978-0-8225-1395-7(1)) Lerner Publishing Group.

Ochester, Betsy. John Tyler. 2003. (Encyclopedia of Presidents Ser.). (Illus.). 110p. (J). 34.00 (978-0-516-22850-1(1) , Children's Pr.) Scholastic Library Publishing.

O'Connell, Kim A. John Tyler: A MyReportLinks.com Book. 2002. (Presidents Ser.). (Illus.). 48p. (J). (gr. 4-10). lib. bdg. 25.26 (978-0-7660-5070-9(X) , MyReportLinks.com Bks.) Enslow Pubs., Inc.

Venezia, Mike. John Tyler: Tenth President, 1841-1845. Venezia, Mike, illus. 2005. (Getting to Know the U. S. Presidents Ser.). (Illus.). 32p. (J). (gr. 3-4). pap. 7.95 (978-0-516-27484-3(8) , Children's Pr.) Scholastic Library Publishing.

Venezia, Mike, illus. John Tyler. 2005. (Getting to Know the U. S. Presidents Ser.). 32p. (J). (gr. 3-4). 26.00 (978-0-516-22615-6(0) , Children's Pr.) Scholastic Library Publishing.

Welsbacher, Anne. John Tyler. 2000. (United States Presidents Ser.). (Illus.). 32p. (J). (gr. k-6). lib. bdg. 22.78 (978-1-57765-239-7(8) , Checkerboard Library) ABDO Publishing Co.

Zamora, Dulce. How to Draw the Life & Times of John Tyler. 2006. (Kid's Guide to Drawing the Presidents of the United States of America Ser.). (J). 25.25 (978-1-4042-2987-7(6) , PowerKids Pr.) Rosen Publishing Group, Inc., The.

TYPEWRITERS—FICTION

Click Clack Moo Cows That Type Spanish. 2004. (J). pap. 32.75 incl. audio (978-1-55592-652-6(5)); (SPA.). pap. 14.95 incl. audio (978-1-55592-653-3(3)) Weston Woods Studios, Inc.

Cronin, Doreen. Click, Clack, Moo: Cows That Type. Lewin, Betsy, illus. 2000. 32p. (J). (ps-3). 15.95 (978-0-689-83213-0(3)) Simon & Schuster Children's Publishing.

—Click, Clack, Moo: Cows That Type. 2004. 29.95 incl. cd-rom (978-1-55592-104-0(3)); (J). pap. 18.95 incl. audio compact disk (978-1-55592-139-2(6)); (J). pap. 38.75 incl. audio compact disk (978-1-55592-630-4(4)); (J). pap. 32.75 incl. audio (978-1-55592-183-5(3)); (J). pap. 32.75 incl. audio (978-1-55592-347-1(X)); (J). pap. 14.95 incl. audio (978-1-55592-171-2(X)) Weston Woods Studios, Inc.

—Click, Clack, Moo: Cows That Type. Lewin, Betsy, illus. 2004. (J). 24.95 incl. audio (978-1-55592-077-7(2)) Weston Woods Studios, Inc.

—Click, Clack, Moo: Cows that Type. 2006. (Illus.). (J). (ps-3). 22.78 (978-1-59961-088-7(4)) Spotlight.

Dorie & Me. 2003. (YA). per. (978-1-59431-071-3(8) , Ebks. On The Net) ebooksonthe.net.

Gould, Peter L. Write Naked. 2008. 256p. (YA). 16.95 (*978-0-374-38483-8(5)) Farrar, Straus & Giroux.

TYPEWRITING

Hoggatt, Jack, et al. Century 21 Computer Applications & Keyboarding. 7th rev. ed. 2001. (Illus.). 608p. (C). 76.95 (978-0-538-69152-9(2)) Thomson South-Western.

TYPOGRAPHY

see Printing

U

U BOATS

see Submarines (Ships)

UFOS

see Unidentified Flying Objects

U. N.

see United Nations

U. S. S. R.

see Soviet Union

UGANDA

Barlas, Robert. Uganda. 2000. (Cultures of the World Ser.). (Illus.). 128p. (J). (gr. 5-12). lib. bdg. 37.07 (978-0-7614-0981-6(5) , Benchmark Bks.) Cavendish, Marshall Corp.

Barter, James. Idi Amin. 2004. (Heroes & Villains Ser.). (Illus.). 112p. (J). (gr. 7-10). 29.95 (978-1-59018-553-7(6) , Lucent Bks.) Thomson Gale.

Braun, Eric. Uganda in Pictures. 2nd ed. 2006. (Visual Geography Series, Second Ser.). (Illus.). 80p. (J). (gr. 3-7). lib. bdg. 27.93 (978-0-8225-2397-0(3)) Lerner Publishing Group.

Kubuitsile, Lauri. Uganda. 2004. (Africa Ser.). (Illus.). 79p. (J). lib. bdg. (978-1-59084-816-6(0)) Mason Crest Pubs.

Oghojafor, Kingsley. Uganda. 2004. (Countries of the World Ser.). (Illus.). 96p. (J). (gr. 6 up). lib. bdg. 30.00 (978-0-8368-3112-2(8)) Stevens, Gareth Inc.

Pundyk, Grace. Welcome to Uganda. 2005. (Welcome to My Country Ser.). (Illus.). 48p. (J). lib. bdg. 26.00 (978-0-8368-3130-6(6)) Stevens, Gareth Inc.

Schemenauer, Elma. Uganda. 2003. (Countries: Faces & Places Ser.). (Illus.). 32p. (J). (gr. 1-5). 25.64 (978-1-56766-914-5(X)) Child's World, Inc.

UKRAINE

Abrams, Dennis. Viktor Yushchenko. 2007. (Modern World Leaders Ser.). 120p. (J). (gr. 6-12). 30.00 (*978-0-7910-9266-8(6) , Chelsea Hse.) Facts On File, Inc.

Bassis, Volodymyr & Dhilawala, Sakina. Ukraine. 2nd ed. 2007. (Cultures of the World Ser.). 144p. (J). lib. bdg. 39.93 (*978-0-7614-2090-3(8) , Benchmark Bks.) Cavendish, Marshall Corp.

Brown, Katharine Elizabeth & Zemliansky, Pavel. Welcome to Ukraine. 2003. (Welcome to My Country Ser.). (Illus.). 48p. (J). (gr. 2 up). lib. bdg. 26.00 (978-0-8368-2555-8(1)) Stevens, Gareth Inc.

Bryan, Nichol. Chernobyl: Nuclear Disaster. 2003. (Environmental Disasters Ser.). (Illus.). 48p. (gr. 5 up). (YA). lib. bdg. 30.00 (978-0-8368-5504-3(3)); (J). pap. 11.95 (978-0-8368-5511-1(6)) Stevens, Gareth Inc. (World Almanac Library).

Condon, Judith. Chernobyl & Other Nuclear Accidents. 1999. (New Perspectives Ser.). (Illus.). 48p. (J). (gr. 4-7). lib. bdg. 28.54 (978-0-8172-5018-8(2)) Raintree.

Cooper, Catherine W. Ukraine. Gritzner, Charles F., ed. 2002. (Modern World Nations Ser.). (Illus.). 150p. (gr. 6-12). 30.00 (978-0-7910-6783-3(1) , Chelsea Hse.) Facts On File, Inc.

Cooper, Catherine W. & Pavlovic, Zoran. Ukraine. 2nd rev. ed. 2006. (Modern World Nations Ser.). (Illus.). 120p. (J). (gr. 6-12). 30.00 (978-0-7910-9207-1(0) , Chelsea Hse.) Facts On File, Inc.

Corona, Laurel. Ukraine. 2001. (Former Soviet Republics Ser.). (Illus.). 112p. (J). (gr. 6-9). 29.95 (978-1-56006-737-5(3) , Lucent Bks.) Thomson Gale.

Cruise, Robin. The Nuclear Disaster at Chernobyl. Taylor, Marjorie, illus. rev. ed. 1999. (Take Ten Ser.). 46p. (YA). (gr. 4 up). pap. 3.95 (978-1-58659-022-2(7)) Artesian Pr.

Dowswell, Paul. The Chernobyl Disaster. 2003. (Days That Shook the World Ser.). (Illus.). 47p. (J). lib. bdg. 28.56 (978-0-7398-6049-6(6)) Raintree.

DuPont, Lonnie H. Oksana Baiul. 1998. (Female Figure Skating Legends Ser.). (Illus.). 64p. (J). (gr. 4-7). lib. bdg. 18.65 (978-0-7910-4201-4(4) , Chelsea Hse.) Facts On File, Inc.

Grimberg, Tina. Out of Line: Growing up Soviet. 2007. 128p. (J). (gr. 6). 22.95 (*978-0-88776-803-3(2)) Tundra Bks., Inc./Livres Toundra, Inc. CAN. *Dist:* Random Hse., Inc.

Kummer, Patricia K. Ukraine. 2001. (Enchantment of the World, Second Ser.). (Illus.). 144p. (J). (gr. 5-9). 36.00 (978-0-516-21101-5(3) , Children's Pr.) Scholastic Library Publishing.

Lustig, Michael M. Ukraine. 1999. (Nations in Transition Ser.). (Illus.). 122p. (YA). (gr. 7-12). 35.00 (978-0-8160-3757-5(4)) Facts On File, Inc.

Siegal, Aranka. Upon the Head of the Goat: A Childhood in Hungary, 1939-1944. 2003. (gr. 5-8). lib. bdg. 14.10 (978-0-613-59754-8(0)) Tandem Library Bks.

Taylor, Peter Lane & Nicola, Christos. The Secret of Priest's Grotto: A Holocaust Survival Story. 2007. 64p. (gr. 5 up). (YA). pap. 8.95 (*978-1-58013-261-9(8)); (J). 18.95 (978-1-58013-260-2(X)) Kar-Ben Publishing.

Toll, Nelly. Behind the Secret Window: A Memoir of a Hidden Childhood During World War II. 2003. 176p. (J). (gr. 3-6). pap. 5.99 (978-0-14-230241-5(4) , Puffin) Penguin Group (USA) Inc.

Van Cleaf, Kristin. Ukraine. 2007. (Countries Set VI Ser.). (Illus.). 40p. (J). (gr. k-6). lib. bdg. 24.21 (*978-1-59928-788-1(9) , Checkerboard Library) ABDO Publishing Co.

Weber, Valerie. I Come from Ukraine. 2006. (Illus.). 24p. (J). pap. (978-0-8368-7245-3(2)); lib. bdg. (978-0-8368-7238-5(X)) Stevens, Gareth Inc. (Weekly Reader Early Learning Library).

Zemliansky, Pavel. Ukraine. 2002. (Countries of the World Ser.). (Illus.). 96p. (J). (gr. 6 up). lib. bdg. 30.00 (978-0-8368-2355-4(9)) Stevens, Gareth Inc.

UKRAINE—FICTION

Cizmich, Marilyne. Sonia, the Church Cat. 2007. (Illus.). 28p. (J). per. 9.99 (*978-1-60247-096-5(0)) Tate Publishing & Enterprises, L.L.C.

DeSena, Bronwen & Zucker, Linda. Babu's Babushka. 2000. (Publish-a-Book Ser.). (Illus.). 24p. (J). (ps-3). 7.95 (978-0-7398-2368-2(X)) Steck-Vaughn.

Landau, Natasha, illus. Misha Loves to Sing. 2004. (J). (*978-0-615-12595-4(6)) Tikva Corp.

McClintock, Barbara, illus. The Mitten. 2008. (J). (*978-0-439-92544-0(4) , Scholastic Pr.) Scholastic, Inc.

Tal, Eve. Double Crossing: A Jewish Immigration Story. 2005. 216p. (gr. 3-7). 16.95 (978-0-938317-94-4(6)) Cinco Puntos Pr.

ULYSSES (GREEK MYTHOLOGY)

see Odysseus (Greek Mythology)

UMBRELLAS AND PARASOLS

Josephson, Judith Pinkerton. Umbrellas. 1998. (Household History Ser.). (Illus.). 48p. (J). (gr. 2-5). lib. bdg. (978-1-57505-098-0(6) , Carolrhoda Bks.) Lerner Publishing Group.

UMBRELLAS AND PARASOLS—FICTION

Brett, Jan. The Umbrella. 2004. (Illus.). 32p. (J). (ps-3). 16.99 (978-0-399-24215-1(5) , Putnam Juvenile) Penguin Group (USA) Inc.

—The Umbrella. 2005. (Illus.). (J). (gr. k-3). 27.95 incl. audio (978-0-8045-6931-6(2) , SAC6931); 29.95 incl. audio compact disk (978-0-8045-4126-8(4) , SACD4126) Spoken Arts, Inc.

Bridges, Shirin Yim. The Umbrella Queen. Yoo, Tae-Eun, illus. 2008. 32p. (J). 16.99 (978-0-06-075040-4(5)); lib. bdg. 17.89 (978-0-06-075041-1(3)) HarperCollins Pubs.

Franson, Scott E. Un-Brella. 2007. (Illus.). 40p. (J). (ps-3). 15.95 (978-1-59643-179-9(2)) Roaring Brook Pr.

Glasco, Eileen. Travels with Sir Brolly: The Magic Umbrella. 2006. 31p. pap. 12.95 (978-0-9774603-0-4(4) , 704-001) Pollyanna Publishing.

Liu, Jae Soo. Yellow Umbrella. Liu, Jae Soo, illus. 2002. (Illus.). 32p. (J). (gr. k-3). 19.95 incl. audio compact disk (978-1-929132-36-2(0)) Kane/Miller Bk. Pubs., Inc.

Lunn, Janet. The Umbrella Party. 1998. (Illus.). (J). (ps-k). 14.95 (978-0-88899-298-7(X)) Groundwood Bks. CAN. *Dist:* Transition Vendor.

Marsden, Carolyn. Silk Umbrellas. 2007. (Illus.). 144p. (J). (gr. 3-7). 5.99 (*978-0-7636-3376-9(3)) Candlewick Pr.

Peacock, Hilda V. Happy Umbrellas. Jones, Richard C., illus. 1999. 48p. (J). (gr. k-3). pap. 12.95 (978-1-878647-63-4(6)) APU Publishing Group.

Saenz, Benjamin Alire. Grandma Fina & Her Wonderful Umbrellas. 2001. (gr. k-3). lib. bdg. 16.40 (978-0-613-77727-8(1)) Tandem Library Bks.

—Grandma Fina & Her Wonderful Umbrellas: La Abuelita Fina y Sus Sombrillas Maravillosas. Garcia, Geronimo, illus. 2001. (SPA.). 32p. (J). pap. 7.95 (978-0-938317-61-6(X)) Cinco Puntos Pr.

Stevens, Terry. Tommy, the Wizard & the Magic Umbrella. 2006. 60p. pap. (*978-1-84401-752-2(4)) Athena Pr.

Umbrella. 2004. 24.95 incl. audio (978-0-7882-0554-5(4)); pap. 14.95 incl. audio (978-0-7882-0619-1(2)) Weston Woods Studios, Inc.

Under the Big Green Umbrella. 2008. (J). spiral bd. (*978-0-9793930-4-4(3)) Dandelion Publishing.

Weeks, Sarah. Ella, of Course! Cushman, Doug, illus. 2007. 32p. (J). (ps). 16.00 (978-0-15-204943-0(6)) Harcourt Trade Pubs.

Yashima, Taro. Umbrella. 2000. (J). pap. 19.97 incl. audio (978-0-7366-9216-8(9)) Books on Tape, Inc.

UNDERGROUND, ANTI-COMMUNIST

see Anti-Communist Movements

UNDERGROUND MOVEMENTS (WORLD WAR, 1939-1945)

see World War, 1939-1945—Underground Movements

UNDERGROUND RAILROAD

see also Slavery—United States

Abnett, Dan. Harriet Tubman & the Underground Railroad. 2007. (Jr. Graphic Biographies Ser.). (Illus.). 24p. (J). (978-1-4042-2336-3(3)); pap. (978-1-4042-2146-8(8)); (gr. 2-6). lib. bdg. 21.25 (978-1-4042-3393-5(8)) Rosen Publishing Group, Inc., The. (PowerKids Pr.).

Abraham, Philip. Harriet Tubman. 2002. (Wel-Real People Ser.). (Illus.). 24p. (J). (ps-2). 17.00 (978-0-516-23953-8(8)); pap. 4.95 (978-0-516-23604-9(0)) Scholastic Library Publishing. (Children's Pr.).

—Harriet Tubman. 2002. (gr. k-3). lib. bdg. 12.95 (978-0-613-58836-2(3)) Tandem Library Bks.

Anastasio, Dina. Harriet Tubman. Morgan, Jacqui, illus. 2002. 16p. (J). pap. (978-0-439-35163-8(4)) Scholastic, Inc.

Anderson, Jane. Harriet Tubman & the Underground Railroad. 2005. 22.00 (*978-1-4108-4202-2(9)) Benchmark Education Co.

Ashby, Ruth. The Underground Railroad. 2002. (Illus.). 48p. (J). lib. bdg. 28.50 (978-1-58340-181-1(4)) Smart Apple Media.

Benge, Janet & Benge, Geoff. Harriet Tubman: Moses of the Slaves. 2002. (Illus.). 208p. pap. 8.99 (978-1-883002-90-9(7)) Emerald Bks.

Bial, Raymond. The Underground Railroad. 1999. (Illus.). 48p. (J). (gr. 4-6). pap. 6.95 (978-0-395-97915-0(3)) Houghton Mifflin Co. Trade & Reference Div.

—The Underground Railroad. 1999. (978-0-606-22068-2(2)) Tandem Library Bks.

Blue, Rose & Naden, Corinne J. Harriet Tubman: Riding the Freedom Train. 2003. (Gateway Biography Ser.: 4). (Illus.). 48p. lib. bdg. 23.90 (978-0-7613-2571-0(9) , Millbrook Pr.) Lerner Publishing Group.

Brill, Marlene Targ. Allen Jay & the Underground Railroad. 2007. (Readalongs for Beginning Readers Ser.). (J). (gr. 1-3). pap. 18.95 incl. audio compact disk (*978-1-59519-949-2(7)) Live Oak Media.

Brooks Simons, Barbara. Escape to Freedom: The Underground Railroad. 2006. (Navigators Ser.). (J). pap. 42.00 (*978-1-4108-6261-7(5)) Benchmark Education Co.

Burgan, Michael. Escaping to Freedom: The Underground Railroad. 2006. (Slavery in the Americas Ser.). (Illus.). 112p. (J). (gr. 4-9). 35.00 (978-0-8160-6137-2(8)) Facts On File, Inc.

Burke, Henry & Croy, Dick. The River Jordan: A True Story of the Underground Railroad. unabr. ed. 2001. (Illus.). 208p. (YA). pap. 14.95 (978-0-9645252-2-1(4)) Watershed Bks.

Calkhoven, Laurie. Harriet Tubman: Leading the Way to Freedom. 2008. (Sterling Biographies Ser.). (Illus.). 128p. (J). pap. 5.95 (*978-1-4027-4117-3(0)) Sterling Publishing Co., Inc.

Capstone Press, contrib. by. Underground Railroad: Bringing Slaves North to Freedom. (Civil War Ser.). 48p. (YA). pap. 7.95 (978-0-7368-4521-2(6)) Capstone Pr., Inc.

Carson, Mary Kay. The Underground Railroad for Kids: From Slavery to Freedom with 21 Activities. 2005. (For Kids Ser.). (Illus.). 176p. (J). pap. 14.95 (978-1-55652-554-4(0)) Chicago Review Pr., Inc.

Connell, Kate. Tales from the Underground Railroad. 2001. (Nonfiction Bookbag Ser.). (J). (gr. 4-5). per. 8.45 (978-1-58830-204-5(0)) Metropolitan Teaching & Learning Co.

Cooper, Terry, ed. Harriet Tubman & the Underground Railroad. 2001. 6p. 3.95 (978-0-439-30953-0(0)) Scholastic, Inc.

Eskridge, Ann E. Slave Uprisings & Runaways: Fighting for Freedom & the Underground Railroad. 2004. (Slavery in American History Ser.). (Illus.). 128p. (J). lib. bdg. 26.60 (978-0-7660-2154-9(8)) Enslow Pubs., Inc.

Espinosa, Rod. Underground Railroad. 2007. (Graphic History Ser.). (Illus.). 32p. (J). (gr. 3-6). lib. bdg. 27.07 (*978-1-60270-080-2(X) , Graphic Planet) Magic Wagon.

Feinstein, Stephen. Read about Harriet Tubman. 2005. (I Like Biographies! Ser.). (Illus.). 24p. (J). lib. bdg. 21.26 (978-0-7660-2591-2(8) , Enslow Elementary) Enslow Pubs., Inc.

Findley, Violet. Easy Reader Biographies: Harriet Tubman: Follow the North Star. 2007. 16p. pap. 2.99 (*978-0-439-92330-9(1) , Teaching Resources) Scholastic, Inc.

Ford, Carin T. Slavery & the Underground Railroad: Bound for Freedom. 2004. (Civil War Library Ser.). (Illus.). 48p. (J). lib. bdg. 23.93 (978-0-7660-2251-5(X)) Enslow Pubs., Inc.

Fradin, Dennis Brindell. Bound for the North Star: True Stories of Fugitive Slaves. 2000. (Illus.). 224p. (J). (gr. 7-12). tchr. ed. 20.00 (978-0-395-97017-1(2) , Clarion Bks.) Houghton Mifflin Co. Trade & Reference Div.

Gayle, Sharon. Harriet Tubman & the Freedom Train. Marshall, Felicia, illus. 2003. (Ready-to-Read Ser.). 32p. (J). pap. 3.99 (978-0-689-85480-4(3) , Aladdin) Simon & Schuster Children's Publishing.

Gosda, Randy T. Harriet Tubman. 2002. (First Biographies Ser.). (Illus.). 32p. (J). (gr. k-4). lib. bdg. 22.78 (978-1-57765-736-1(5) , Buddy Bks.) ABDO Publishing Co.

Greenwood, Barbara. The Last Safe House: A Story of the Underground Railroad. Collins, Heather, illus. 1998. (History Comes Alive Ser.). 120p. (J). (gr. 4-6). (978-1-55074-509-2(3)); (978-1-55074-507-8(7)) Kids Can Pr., Ltd.

Hamilton, Virginia. Many Thousand Gone: African Americans from Slavery to Freedom. Dillon, Leo & Dillon, Diane, illus. 2002. 160p. (J). (gr. 3-9). pap. 12.95 (978-0-679-87936-7(6)); lib. bdg. 18.99 (978-0-394-92873-9(3)) Random Hse. Children's Bks. (Knopf Bks. for Young Readers).

Hansen, Joyce & McGowan, Gary. Freedom Roads: Searching for the Underground Railroad. Ransome, James E., illus. 2003. (Marcato Book Ser.). 166p. (J). (gr. 5-9). 18.95 (978-0-8126-2673-5(7)) Cricket Bks.

Harcourt School Publishers Staff. Freedom Quilts. 3rd ed. 2002. (Horizons Ser.). (Illus.). (J). pap. 7.30 (978-0-15-333579-2(3)) Harcourt Schl. Pubs.

Haskins, James, et al. Following Freedom's Star: The Story of the Underground Railroad. 2001. (Great Journeys Ser.). (Illus.). 112p. (J). (gr. 5 up). lib. bdg. 32.79 (978-0-7614-1229-8(8) , Benchmark Bks.) Cavendish, Marshall Corp.

Healy, Nick. Harriet Tubman. 2005. (Fact Finders Ser.). (Illus.). 32p. (J). 22.60 (978-0-7368-3743-9(4)) Capstone Pr., Inc.

Heinrichs, Ann. The Underground Railroad. 2001. (We the People Ser.). (Illus.). 48p. (J). (gr. 4 up). lib. bdg. 22.60 (978-0-7565-0102-0(4)) Compass Point Bks.

Hudson, Wade. The Underground Railroad. (Cornerstones of Freedomtrade;, Second Ser.). 48p. (J). 2007. pap. 5.95 (*978-0-531-18770-8(5)); 2005. (Illus.). (gr. 4-6). 26.00 (978-0-516-23630-8(X)) Scholastic Library Publishing. (Children's Pr.).

Isaacs, Sally Senzell. Life on the Underground Railroad. (Picture the Past Ser.). (Illus.). 32p. (J). 2002. (gr. k-3). pap. 7.50 (978-1-58810-418-2(4) , 91185); 2001. (gr. 2-4). lib. bdg. 21.36 (978-1-58810-253-9(X)) Heinemann Library.

Kernan, Elizabeth. Harriet Tubman: A Lesson in Bravery. 2002. (Reading Room Collection). (Illus.). 24p. (J). pap. (978-0-8239-8229-5(7)); lib. bdg. 18.75 (978-0-8239-3750-9(X)) Rosen Publishing Group, Inc., The.

Kudlinski, Kathleen. Harriet Tubman: Freedom's Trailblazer. Brown, Robert, illus. 2002. (Childhood of Famous Americans Ser.). 192p. (J). pap. 5.99 (978-0-689-84866-7(8) , Aladdin) Simon & Schuster Children's Publishing.

Kulling, Monica. Escape North! The Story of Harriet Tubman. Corey, Shana, ed. Flavin, Teresa, illus. 2000. (Step into Reading Step 3 Bks.). 48p. (J). (gr. 2-4). pap. 3.99 (978-0-375-80154-9(5) , Random Hse. Bks. for Young Readers) Random Hse. Children's Bks.

—Escape North! The Story of Harriet Tubman. Flavin, Teresa, illus. 2000. (Step into Reading Ser.). (J). 10.79 (978-0-606-19895-0(4)) Tandem Library Bks.

—Escape North! the Story of Harriet Tubman. 2000. (gr. k-3). lib. bdg. 11.80 (978-0-613-32507-3(9)) Tandem Library Bks.

Landau, Elaine. Fleeing to Freedom on the Underground Railroad: The Courageous Slaves, Agents, & Conductors. 2006. (People's History Ser.). (Illus.). 88p. (J). 29.27 (978-0-8225-3490-7(8) , Twenty-First Century Bks.) Lerner Publishing Group.

Lassieur, Allison. The Underground Railroad: An Interactive History Adventure. 2008. (You Choose Bks.). 112p. (J). (gr. 3-7). lib. bdg. 27.23 (*978-1-4296-0164-1(7)) Capstone Pr., Inc.

Leavitt, Amie. Harriet Tubman. 2007. (What's So Great About... ? Ser.). (J). lib. bdg. 25.70 (*978-1-58415-577-5(9)) Mitchell Lane Pubs., Inc.

Lilly, Melinda. From Slavery to Freedom. 2003. (Reading American History Ser.). (Illus.). 24p. (gr. 1-4). 14.95 (978-1-58952-363-0(6)) Rourke Publishing, LLC.

Lutz, Norma Jean. Harriet Tubman: Leader of the Underground Railroad. (Famous Figures of the Civil War Era Ser.). (Illus.). 80p. (J). (gr. 4-7). 2001. 25.00 (978-0-7910-6008-7(X)); 2000. pap. 25.00 (978-0-7910-6146-6(9)) Facts On File, Inc. (Chelsea Hse.).

—Harriet Tubman: Leader of the Underground Railroad. 2001. (Famous Figures of the Civil War Era Ser.). (Illus.). (J). 15.75 (978-0-606-20691-4(4)) Tandem Library Bks.

Mara, Wil. Harriet Tubman. (Rookie Bios Ser.). (Illus.). 32p. (J). (gr. 1-2). 2003. pap. 4.95 (978-0-516-27337-2(X)); 2002. 20.50 (978-0-516-22521-0(9)) Scholastic Library Publishing. (Children's Pr.).

—Harriet Tubman. 2002. (gr. k-3). lib. bdg. 12.95 (978-0-613-59495-0(9)) Tandem Library Bks.

Martin, Michael. Harriet Tubman & the Underground Railroad. 2005. (Graphic Library). (Illus.). 31p. (J). 22.60 (978-0-7368-3829-0(5)) Capstone Pr., Inc.

Mayer, Cassie. Harriet Tubman. 2007. (J). (*978-1-4034-9973-8(X)); pap. (*978-1-4034-9982-0(9)) Heinemann Library.

McDonough, Yona Zeldis. Who Was Harriet Tubman? Harrison, Nancy, illus. 2002. (Who Was...? Ser.). 112p. (J). mass mkt. 4.99 (978-0-448-42889-5(X) , Grosset & Dunlap) Penguin Group (USA) Inc.

—Who Was Harriet Tubman? 2002. (gr. 3-6). lib. bdg. 13.00 (978-0-613-61668-3(5)) Tandem Library Bks.

McGraw-Hill - Jamestown Education. American History Ink: Book 4, the Underground Railroad. 2007. pap. 9.28 (*978-0-07-878026-4(8) , 9780078780264) Glencoe/McGraw-Hill.

McNamara, Margaret. Discover the Underground Railroad. 2006. pap. 39.00 (*978-1-4108-6449-9(9)) Benchmark Education Co.

—The Underground Railroad. 2006. pap. 42.00 (*978-1-4108-6446-8(4)) Benchmark Education Co.

Monroe, Judy. The Underground Railroad: Bringing Slaves North to Freedom. 2002. (Let Freedom Ring Ser.). (Illus.). 48p. (J). (gr. 3-4). lib. bdg. 22.60 (978-0-7368-1344-0(6) , Bridgestone Bks.) Capstone Pr., Inc.

Mortensen, Lori. Harriet Tubman: Hero of the Underground Railroad. Moore, Frances, illus. 2006. (Biographies Ser.). 24p. (J). (gr. k-3). lib. bdg. 23.93 (*978-1-4048-3103-2(7)) Picture Window Bks.

Nelson, Richard. Harriet Tubman. 2007. (Essential Lives Ser.). (ENG., Illus.). 112p. (YA). (gr. 8-12). lib. bdg. 32.79 (*978-1-59928-842-0(7) , Essential Library) ABDO Publishing Co.

Nichols, Catherine. Harriet Tubman. Dennington, Brian, illus. 2002. (Hello Reader! Ser.). (J). 3.99 (978-0-439-32103-7(4)) Scholastic, Inc.

Nielsen, Nancy J. Harriet Tubman. 2002. (Let Freedom Ring Ser.). (Illus.). 48p. (J). (gr. 3-4). lib. bdg. 22.60 (978-0-7368-1087-6(0) , Bridgestone Bks.) Capstone Pr., Inc.

Nofi, Albert A. The Underground Railroad & the Civil War. 1999. (Untold History of the Civil War Ser.). (Illus.). 64p. (J). (gr. 3 up). 25.00 (978-0-7910-5434-5(9) , Chelsea Hse.) Facts On File, Inc.

Perrin, Pat, intro. The Underground Railroad: Life on the Road to Freedom. 1999. (Perspectives on History Ser.). (Illus.). 66p. (YA). (gr. 5-12). pap. 6.95 (978-1-57960-051-8(4)) History Compass, LLC.

Perrin, Pat & Coleman, Wim. The Mystery of the Vanishing Slaves. 2004. (Cover-To-Cover Books). (Illus.). 64p. (J). pap. (978-0-7891-5874-1(4)); (gr. 4-7). lib. bdg. 17.95 (978-0-7569-1041-9(2)) Perfection Learning Corp.

Petry, Ann. Harriet Tubman: Conductor on the Underground Railroad. 1999. (YA). pap. 59.20 incl. audio (978-0-7887-3011-5(8) , 40893) Recorded Bks., LLC.

Pferdehirt, Julia. Freedom Train North: Stories of the Underground Railroad in Wisconsin. Butler, Jerry, illus. Date not set. (J). (gr. 3-8). pap. 10.00 (978-0-9664925-0-7(1)) Living History Pr.

Pierce, Alan. The Underground Railroad. 2005. (American Moments Ser.). (Illus.). 48p. (J). (gr. 4-8). lib. bdg. 25.65 (978-1-59197-942-5(0)) ABDO Publishing Co.

Prince, Bryan. I Came As a Stranger: The Underground Railroad. 2004. (gr. 5-8). lib. bdg. 24.55 (978-0-613-77347-8(0)) Tandem Library Bks.

—I Came As a Stranger: The Underground Railroad. 2004. (Illus.). 168p. (J). (gr. 5). pap. 15.95 (978-0-88776-667-1(6)) Tundra Bks., Inc./Livres Toundra, Inc. CAN. *Dist:* Random Hse., Inc.

Rappaport, Doreen. Escape from Slavery. 1999. (J). 12.79 (978-0-606-15855-8(3)) Tandem Library Bks.

—Escape from Slavery: Five Journeys to Freedom. Lilly, Charles, illus. 1999. 128p. (J). (gr. 4-7). pap. 5.99 (978-0-06-446169-6(6) , Harper Trophy) HarperCollins Pubs.

—Escape from Slavery: Five Journeys to Freedom. 1999. (gr. 3-6). lib. bdg. 14.15 (978-0-613-11514-8(7)) Tandem Library Bks.

—Freedom River. Collier, Bryan, illus. 32p. (gr. k-4). 2000. 14.99 (978-0-7868-0350-7(9)); 2007. pap. 6.99 (*978-1-4231-0634-0(2)) Hyperion Bks. for Children. (Jump at the Sun).

Rau, Dana Meachen. Harriet Tubman. 2000. (Compass Point Early Biographies Ser.). (Illus.). 32p. (J). (gr. 2 up). lib. bdg. 21.26 (978-0-7565-0015-3(X)) Compass Point Bks.

Rausch, Monica. Hariet Tubman. 2006. (ENG & SPA.). (J). pap. (*978-0-8368-7992-6(9)); lib. bdg. (*978-0-8368-7985-8(6)) Stevens, Gareth Inc. (Weekly Reader Early Learning Library).

—Harriet Tubman. 2006. 24p. (J). pap. (*978-0-8368-7693-2(8)); lib. bdg. (*978-0-8368-7686-4(5)) Stevens, Gareth Inc. (Weekly Reader Early Learning Library).

Rustad, Martha E. H. Harriet Tubman. Saunders-Smith, Gail, ed. 2001. (First Biographies Ser.). (Illus.). 24p. (J). (gr. k-1). lib. bdg. 15.93 (978-0-7368-0997-9(X) , Pebble Bks.) Capstone Pr., Inc.

Schraff, Anne. Harriet Tubman: Moses of the Underground Railroad. 2001. (African-American Biographies Ser.). (Illus.). 128p. (J). (gr. 6-12). lib. bdg. 26.60 (978-0-7660-1548-7(3)) Enslow Pubs., Inc.

Schroeder, Alan. Minty: A Story of Young Harriet Tubman. Pinkney, Jerry, illus. 2002. (YA). 25.45 (978-0-7587-0382-8(1)) Book Wholesalers, Inc.

—Minty: A Story of Young Harriet Tubman. Pinkney, Jerry, illus. 2000. (J). (ps-ps). lib. bdg. 15.30 (978-0-613-33712-0(3)) Tandem Library Bks.

—Minty: A Story of Young Harriet Tubman. 2000. (978-0-606-20365-4(6)); (YA). (978-0-606-20246-6(3)) Tandem Library Bks.

Shone, Rob & Ganeri, Anita. Harriet Tubman: The Life of an African-American Abolitionist. 2005. (Graphic Nonfiction Ser.). (Illus.). 48p. (J). (gr. 4-6). lib. bdg. 26.50 (978-1-4042-0245-0(5)) Rosen Publishing Group, Inc., The.

Simon, Barbara Brooks. Escape to Freedom: The Underground Railroad Adventures of Callie & William. 2004. (I Am American Ser.). (Illus.). 40p. (J). (gr. 3-7). pap. 6.99 (978-0-7922-6551-1(3) , National Geographic Children's Bks.) National Geographic Society.

Skelton, Renee. Harriet Tubman: A Woman of Courage. 2005. (Time for Kids Ser.). (Illus.). 48p. (J). pap. 3.99 (978-0-06-057607-3(3)) HarperCollins Pubs.

Skelton, Renee. Harriet Tubman A Woman of Courage. 2005. 2005p. (J). lib. bdg. 15.00 (*978-1-4242-0849-4(1)) Fitzgerald Bks.

Skelton, Renee & Time for Kids Editors. Harriet Tubman: A Woman of Courage. 2005. (Time for Kids Ser.). (Illus.). 48p. (J). 15.99 (978-0-06-057608-0(1)) HarperCollins Pubs.

Slavicek, Louise Chipley. Harriet Tubman & the Underground Railroad. 2006. (Lucent Library of Black History). 112p. (J). (gr. 7-10). 32.45 (978-1-59018-927-6(2) , Lucent Bks.) Thomson Gale.

Stearns, Dan. Harriet Tubman & the Underground Railroad. 2006. (In the Footsteps of American Heroes Ser.). (Illus.). 64p. (J). pap. 11.95 (978-0-8368-6433-5(6)); lib. bdg. 32.67 (978-0-8368-6428-1(X)) Stevens, Gareth Inc. (World Almanac Library).

Steck-Vaughn Staff. Journeys of Courage on Underground Railroads. 2002. pap. (978-0-7398-6166-0(2)) Steck-Vaughn.

Stein, R. Conrad. Escaping Slavery on the Underground Railroad. 2008. (From Many Cultures, One History Ser.). (Illus.). 128p. (J). (gr. 5 up). lib. bdg. 31.93 (*978-0-7660-2799-2(6)) Enslow Pubs., Inc.

Sterling, Dorothy. Freedom Train: The Story of Harriet Tubman. 1999. (J). (gr. 5-8). lib. bdg. 12.40 (978-0-8085-8034-8(5)) Tandem Library Bks.

Swain, Gwenyth. President of the Underground Railroad: A Story about Levi Coffin. Ramstad, Ralph L., illus. (Creative Minds Biographies Ser.). 64p. (J). (gr. 3-6). 2003. 6.95 (978-1-57505-552-7(X)); 2001. lib. bdg. 22.60 (978-1-57505-551-0(1) , Carolrhoda Bks.) Lerner Publishing Group.

—President of the Underground Railroad: A Story of Levi Coffin. 2001. (gr. 3-6). lib. bdg. 15.25 (978-0-613-68377-7(3)) Tandem Library Bks.

Taylor, Marian. Harriet Tubman. (Black Americans of Achievement Ser.). (Illus.). 112p. (J). (gr. 6-12). 2005. pap. 13.25 (978-0-7910-8340-6(3)); 2004. 30.00 (978-0-7910-8166-2(4)) Facts On File, Inc. (Chelsea Hse.).

Troy, Don. Harriet Ross Tubman. 1999. (Journey to Freedom Ser.). (Illus.). 40p. (J). (gr. 3-7). 28.50 (978-1-56766-568-0(3)) Child's World, Inc.

Turner, Glennette Tilley. An Apple for Harriet Tubman. Keeter, Susan, illus. 2006. 24p. (J). 15.95 (978-0-8075-0395-9(9)) Whitman, Albert & Co.

—The Underground Railroad in Illinois. 1999. (Illus.). xvii, 200p. (J). pap. 16.95 (978-0-938990-05-5(5)) Newman Educational Publishing Co.

Weidt, Maryann N. Harriet Tubman. (History Maker Bios Ser.). (Illus.). (J). 2003. 47p. 26.60 (978-0-8225-4676-4(0)); 2002. 48p. pap. 6.95 (978-0-8225-4803-4(8)) Lerner Publishing Group. (Lerner Pubns.).

Weymouth Seguin, Marilyn. The Freedom Stairs: The Story of Adam Lowry Rankin, Underground Railroad Conductor. 2004. (Illus.). 93p. (J). (ps-7). per. 12.95 net. (978-0-8283-2084-9(5)) Branden Bks.

Wheeler, Jill C. Harriet Tubman. 2003. (Breaking Barriers Ser.). (Illus.). 64p. (J). (gr. 3-8). lib. bdg. 25.65 (978-1-57765-908-2(2)) ABDO Publishing Co.

UNDERGROUND RAILROAD—FICTION

Ayres, Katherine. North by Night. 2000. (gr. 3-6). lib. bdg. 12.40 (978-0-613-23020-9(5)) Tandem Library Bks.

—Stealing South: A Story of the Underground Railroad. l.t. ed. 2002. 231p. (J). 22.95 (978-0-7862-4422-5(4)) Thorndike Pr.

Bell, Albert A., Jr. The Secret of the Lonely Grave. 2007. 160p. pap. 8.95 (*978-1-932158-79-3(0) , Claystone Bks.) Ingalls Publishing Group, Inc.

Brill Marlene Targ. Allen Jay y el Ferrocarril Subterraneo (Allen Jay & the Undergound Railroad) Porter, Janice Lee, illus. 2007. (Yo solo Historia (on My Own History) Ser.). (J). pap. 6.95 (*978-0-8225-7787-4(9) , Ediciones Lerner) Lerner Publishing Group.

Brill, Marlene Targ. Allen Jay y el Ferrocarril Subterraneo (Allen Jay & the Undergound Railroad) Porter, Janice Lee, illus. 2007. (Yo Solo - Historia (on My Own - History) Ser.). (SPA.). 48p. (J). (gr. 2-4). lib. bdg. 25.26 (*978-0-8225-7784-3(4) , Ediciones Lerner) Lerner Publishing Group.

Carbone, Elisa. Stealing Freedom. 2002. (EMC Masterpiece Series Access Editions). (Illus.). xix, 284p. (J). 14.60 (978-0-8219-2507-2(5)) EMC/Paradigm Publishing.

—Stealing Freedom. 2001. (Illus.). 272p. (YA). (gr. 5-8). 5.99 (978-0-440-41707-1(4) , Yearling) Random Hse. Children's Bks.

—Stealing Freedom. 2001. (gr. 5-8). lib. bdg. 13.55 (978-0-613-33729-8(8)) Tandem Library Bks.

—Stealing Freedom. l.t. ed. 2005. 346p. pap. 10.95 (978-0-7862-7314-0(3) , Large Print Pr.) Thorndike Pr.

Connelly, Bernardine. Follow the Drinking Gourd. Buchanan, Yvonne, illus. 2005. (Rabbit Ears-A Classic Tale Ser.). 40p. (J). (gr. k-5). 25.65 (978-1-59197-763-6(0)) Spotlight.

Dahlberg, Maurine F. The Spirit & Gilly Bucket. 2002. 240p. (J). (gr. 3-7). 18.00 (978-0-374-31677-8(5) , Farrar, Straus & Giroux (BYR)) Farrar, Straus & Giroux.

Dell, Pamela. Aquila's Drinking Gourd: A Story of the Underground Railroad. 2002. (Scrapbooks of America Ser.). (Illus.). 48p. (J). (gr. 2-6). 28.50 (978-1-59187-013-5(5)) Child's World, Inc.

Draper, Sharon M. Lost in the Tunnel of Time. Watson, Jesse Joshua, illus. 2006. (Ziggy & the Black Dinosaurs Ser.: Vol. 2). 112p. (J). pap. 4.99 (978-0-689-87912-8(1) , Aladdin) Simon & Schuster Children's Publishing.

Falk, Elizabeth Sullivan. Lettie's North Star. Wolf, Elizabeth, illus. 2006. (J). (978-1-59336-694-0(9)) Mondo Publishing.

Ferris, Jean. Underground. 2007. (Illus.). 176p. (J). (gr. 7 up). 16.00 (*978-0-374-37243-9(8) , Farrar, Straus & Giroux (BYR)) Farrar, Straus & Giroux.

Gayle, Sharon Shavers. Emma's Escape: A Story of America's Underground Railroad. Velasquez, Eric, illus. 3rd ed. 2005. (Soundprints' Read-and-Discover Ser.). 48p. (J). (gr. 2-4). pap. 3.95 (978-1-59249-021-9(2) , S2009) Soundprints.

—Escape! A Story of the Underground Railroad. Velasquez, Eric, illus. 1999. (Smithsonian Odyssey Ser.: Vol. 11). 32p. (J). (gr. 2-5). 14.95 (978-1-56899-622-6(5) , B6009); (ps-3). pap. 5.95 (978-1-56899-623-3(3)) Soundprints.

Griffiths, Robert. Adventures of Clive. 2005. 89p. pap. 8.81 (978-1-4116-5191-3(X)) Lulu.com.

Hamilton, Virginia. The House of Dies Drear. 1998. 32p. (J). 9.95 (978-1-56137-516-5(0) , NU5168) Novel Units, Inc.

—The House of Dies Drear. 2001. (Assessment Packs Ser.). 15p. pap. 15.95 (978-1-58303-122-3(7)) Pathways Publishing.

—The House of Dies Drear. 8.97 (978-0-13-437491-8(6)) Prentice Hall PTR.

—The House of Dies Drear. 2006. 256p. (J). pap. 5.99 (978-1-4169-1405-1(6) , Aladdin) Simon & Schuster Children's Publishing.

Hedstrom-Page, Deborah. From Slavery to Freedom with Harriet Tubman. Martinez, Sergio, illus. 2007. 80p. (J). (gr. 3-8). 9.99 (978-0-8054-3268-8(X)) B&H Publishing Grp.

Hopkinson, Deborah. Under the Quilt of Night. Ransome, James E., illus. 40p. (J). 2002. 18.99 (978-0-689-82227-8(8) , Atheneum/Anne Schwartz Bks.); 2005. reprint ed. 7.99 (978-0-689-87700-1(5) , Aladdin) Simon & Schuster Children's Publishing.

Houston, Gloria M. Bright Freedom's Song: A Story of the Underground Railroad. 1998. (Illus.). 160p. (YA). (gr. 5 up). 17.00 (978-0-15-201812-2(3) , Silver Whistle) Harcourt Trade Pubs.

Hulme, Lucy V. Passages, 1 bk. Redpath, Dale, illus. 2005. 40p. (J). 7.95 (978-0-9769854-0-2(3) , 001) Combs-Hulme Publishing.

Johnson, P. Mysterious Signal. 1998. (Riverboat Adventures Ser.: Vol. 5). (Illus.). 176p. (J). (gr. 3-8). pap. 5.99 (978-1-55661-355-5(5)) Bethany Hse. Pubs.

Kay, Alan N. Send 'Em South. 2001. (Young Heroes of History Ser.: Vol. 1). (Illus.). 145p. (J). (gr. 3-6). pap. 7.95 (978-1-57249-208-0(2) , White Mane Kids) White Mane Publishing Co., Inc.

Lasky, Kathryn. True North: A Novel of the Underground Railroad. 1998. (J). (978-0-606-13874-1(9)) Tandem Library Bks.

Lawrence. Harriet & the Promise Land. 1998. (J). pap. 5.99 (978-0-87628-392-9(X)) Ctr. for Applied Research in Education, The.

Levine, Ellen. Henry's Freedom Box: A True Story. Nelson, Kadir, illus. 2007. 40p. (J). (ps-3). pap. 16.99 (978-0-439-77733-9(X) , Scholastic Pr.) Scholastic, Inc.

Loesch, Joe. The Underground Railroad: Featuring Harriet Tubman. Hutchinson, Cheryl, ed. Cox, Brian T., illus. unabr. ed. 1999. (Backyard Adventure Ser.). 60p. (J). (gr. k-5). reprint ed. 16.95 incl. audio compact disk (978-1-932332-05-6(7)) Toy Box Productions.

—The Underground Railroad: Featuring Harriet Tubman. Cox, Brian T., illus. unabr. ed. 1999. (Backyard Adventure Ser.: Vol. 5). (J). (gr. 1-5). pap. 16.95 incl. audio compact disk (978-1-887729-18-5(6)); pap. 14.95 incl. audio (978-1-887729-17-8(8)) Toy Box Productions.

McKissack, Patricia C. A Picture of Freedom: The Diary of Clotee, a Slave Girl, Belmont Plantation, Virginia, 1859. 1999. (Dear America Ser.). (J). 9.95 (978-0-439-15599-1(1)) Scholastic, Inc.

Meltzer, Milton. Underground Man. 2006. 288p. (YA). pap. 5.95 (978-0-15-205524-0(X) , Odyssey Classics); (Illus.). 17.00 (978-0-15-205518-9(5) , Harcourt Young Classics) Harcourt Children's Bks.

Monjo, F. N. The Drinking Gourd: A Story of the Underground Railroad. Brenner, Fred, illus. 2002. (J). 12.34 (978-0-7587-5177-5(X)) Book Wholesalers, Inc.

—La Osa Menor: Una Historia del Ferrocarril Subterraneo. Mlawer, Teresa, tr. Brenner, Fred, illus. 2001. (SPA.). (J). (gr. 3-10). pap. 6.95 (978-1-880507-90-2(0) , LC7973); ring bd. 15.95 (978-1-880507-91-9(9) , LC7976) Lectorum Pubns., Inc.

—La Osa Menor: Una Historia del Ferrocarril Subterraneo. 2001. (978-0-606-21286-1(8)) Tandem Library Bks.

Morrow, Barbara Olenyik. A Good Night for Freedom. Jenkins, Leonard, illus. 2003. 32p. (J). (gr. k-3). tchr. ed. 16.95 (978-0-8234-1709-4(3)) Holiday Hse., Inc.

Nelson, Vaunda Micheaux. Almost to Freedom. Bootman, Colin, illus. 2003. (Carolrhoda Picture Books Ser.). 40p. (J). (gr. 1-5). 15.95 (978-1-57505-342-4(X)) Lerner Publishing Group.

Orzechowski, Shaween. Midnight Journey: Running for Freedom on the Underground Railroad. 2006. (J). pap. 8.95 (978-1-57249-379-7(8) , White Mane Kids) White Mane Publishing Co., Inc.

Pearsall, Shelley. Trouble Don't Last. 256p. (gr. 4-8). 2002. (Illus.). 14.95 (978-0-375-81490-7(6) , Knopf Bks. for Young Readers); 2002. (Illus.). lib. bdg. 16.99 (978-0-375-91490-4(0) , Knopf Bks. for Young Readers); 2003. (J). reprint ed. pap. 5.99 (978-0-440-41811-5(9) , Yearling) Random Hse. Children's Bks.

—Trouble Don't Last. 2003. (gr. 3-6). lib. bdg. 13.55 (978-0-613-85706-2(2)) Tandem Library Bks.

Pinkney, Andrea Davis. Silent Thunder. 2001. 224p. (gr. 3-7). pap. 5.99 (978-0-7868-1569-2(8) , Jump at the Sun) Hyperion Bks. for Children.

—Silent Thunder: A Civil War Story. 2001. (J). (978-0-606-21434-6(8)); (gr. 5-8). lib. bdg. 14.15 (978-0-613-62425-1(4)) Tandem Library Bks.

Rappaport, Doreen. Freedom River. Collier, Bryan, illus. 2007. 23p. (J). 15.00 (***978-1-4223-6700-1(2)***) DIANE Publishing Co.

Reed, Stephanie. Across the Wide River: A Novel. 2004. 176p. (J). pap. 9.99 (978-0-8254-3576-8(5)) Kregel Pubns.

Riggio, Anita. Secret Signs: An Escape Through the Underground Railroad. Riggio, Anita, illus. 2003. (Illus.). 32p. (J). (gr. k-2). pap. 9.95 (978-1-59078-072-5(8)); 15.95 (978-1-56397-555-4(6)) Boyds Mills Pr.

—Secret Signs: An Escape Through the Underground Railroad. 2003. (gr. k-3). lib. bdg. 17.60 (978-0-613-59359-5(6)) Tandem Library Bks.

Ruby, Lois. Steal Away Home. 1999. 208p. (J). (gr. 3-7). pap. 5.99 (978-0-689-82435-7(1) , Aladdin) Simon & Schuster Children's Publishing.

—Steal Away Home. 1999. 192p. lib. bdg. 11.64 (978-0-606-15921-0(5)); (gr. 3-6). lib. bdg. 13.00 (978-0-613-12154-5(6)) Tandem Library Bks.

Sargent, Dave & Sargent, Pat. Nubbin: (Linebacked Apricot Dun) Freedom, 30, 43. Lenoir, Jane, illus. 2003. (Saddle Up Ser.: Vol. 43). 42p. (J). pap. 6.95 (978-1-56763-704-5(3)); lib. bdg. 22.60 (978-1-56763-703-8(5)) Ozark Publishing.

Schlabach, Janet. Riverboat Runaways. 1999. (Illus.). 138p. (J). (gr. 4-8). pap. 15.95 (978-0-936389-75-2(3)) Tudor Pubs., Inc.

Schotter, Roni & Dorling Kindersley Publishing Staff. F Is for Freedom. Mordan, C. B., illus. 2000. 96p. (J). (gr. 2-5). 15.99 (978-0-7894-2641-3(2)) Dorling Kindersley Publishing, Inc.

Schwartz, Virginia Frances. If I Just Had Two Wings. (Illus.). 221p. pap. 9.95 (978-0-7737-6192-6(6)); 2001. (J). (gr. 5 up). 15.95 (978-0-7737-3302-2(7)) Stoddart Kids CAN. *Dist:* Fitzhenry & Whiteside, Ltd.

Smucker, Barbara. Underground to Canada. 25th anniv. ed. 1999. (Illus.). 144p. (J). (gr. 3-9). (978-0-14-130686-5(6)) Penguin Group (USA) Inc.

Stengel, Joyce A. Mystery at Kittiwake Bay. 2001. 176p. (J). pap. 9.95 (978-0-689-84595-6(2) , Aladdin) Simon & Schuster Children's Publishing.

Stroud, Bettye. The Patchwork Path: A Quilt Map to Freedom. Bennett, Erin Susanne, illus. 2005. 32p. (J). (gr. k-3). 16.99 (978-0-7636-2423-1(3)) Candlewick Pr.

Turtleback Books, creator. Evvy's Civil War. 2004. 209p. (YA). (gr. 8-12). per. 13.64 (978-0-606-30114-5(3)) Tandem Library Bks.

Vande Velde, Vivian. There's a Dead Person Following My Sister Around. 2001. 160p. (J). pap. 5.99 (978-0-14-131281-1(5) , Puffin) Penguin Group (USA) Inc.

—There's a Dead Person Following My Sister Around. 2001. (gr. 5-8). lib. bdg. 13.00 (978-0-613-43899-5(X)) Tandem Library Bks.

Vaughan, Marcia. The Secret to Freedom. Johnson, Larry, illus. 32p. (J). 2001. (gr. 1-4). 16.95 (978-1-58430-021-2(3)); 2nd ed. 2005. (ps-ps). pap. 7.95 (978-1-58430-251-3(8)) Lee & Low Bks., Inc.

Warburton, Carol. Edge of Night: A Novel. 2004. (Illus.). 278p. pap. 14.95 (978-1-59156-013-5(6)) Covenant Communications, Inc.

Winter, Jeanette. Follow the Drinking Gourd. Winter, Jeanette, illus. 2002. (Illus.). (J). 15.74 (978-0-7587-2527-1(2)) Book Wholesalers, Inc.

Wisehart, Randall. A Winding Road to Freedom. 1999. 184p. (J). (gr. 5-8). pap. 13.00 (978-0-944350-47-8(X)) Friends United Pr.

Woodruff, Elvira. Dear Austin: Letters from the Underground Railroad. 2000. (gr. 5-8). lib. bdg. 13.00 (978-0-613-28463-9(1)); (Illus.). (J). 11.64 (978-0-606-18811-1(8)) Tandem Library Bks.

Wyeth, Sharon Dennis. Freedom's Wings: Corey's Underground Railroad Diary, Bk. 1. 2002. (My America Ser.). (Illus.). 112p. (J). (gr. 4-7). 4.99 (978-0-439-36907-7(X) , Scholastic Pr.) Scholastic, Inc.

—Freedom's Wings: Corey's Underground Railroad Diary. 2002. (gr. 3-6). lib. bdg. 13.00 (978-0-613-53813-8(7)); 2001. (J). (gr. 4-7). (978-0-606-22804-6(7)) Tandem Library Bks.

—Message in the Sky Bk. 3: Corey's Underground Railroad Diary. 2003. (My America Ser.). 112p. (J). pap. 10.95 (978-0-439-37057-8(4) , Scholastic Pr.) Scholastic, Inc.

UNDERGROUND RAILROADS

see Subways

UNDERSEA EXPLORATION

see Underwater Exploration

UNDERSEA TECHNOLOGY

see Oceanography

UNDERSTANDING

see Intellect; Knowledge, Theory of

UNDERWATER EXPLORATION

see also Marine Biology; Skin Diving

Bailey, Gerry. Underwater Machines. Boulter, Steve & Smith, Jan, illus. 2005. (Crafty Inventions Ser.). 48p. (C). (gr. 4-6). 26.60 (978-1-4048-1045-7(5)) Picture Window Bks.

Bathroom Readers' Institute Staff. Uncle John's under the Slimy Sea Bathroom Reader for Kids Only. 2007. (Illus.). 144p. pap. 8.95 (***978-1-59223-711-1(8)*** , Portable Pr.) Advantage Pubs. Group.

Bittinger, Gayle. Under the Sea. 1999. (Rhyme & Reason Workbook Ser.). (Illus.). 32p. (J). (ps-k). pap. 3.95 (978-1-57029-259-0(0) , WPH 01111, Totline Pubns.) Schaffer, Frank Pubns.

Chapman, Simon. Under the Sea. Chapman, Simon, illus. 2005. (Illus.). 112p. (J). lib. bdg. 20.00 (***978-1-4242-0631-5(6)***) Fitzgerald Bks.

Earle, Sylvia A. Dive: My Adventures in the Deep Frontier. 1999. (My Adventures Ser.). (Illus.). 64p. (J). (gr. 3-7). 18.95 (978-0-7922-7144-4(0) , National Geographic Children's Bks.) National Geographic Society.

Hall, Kirsten. Deep Sea Adventures: A Chapter Book. 2003. (True Tales Ser.). (Illus.). 48p. (J). 22.50 (978-0-516-22917-1(6) , Children's Pr.) Scholastic Library Publishing.

Hitchcock, Susan Tyler. Sylvia A. Earle: Deep Sea Explorer. 2004. (Women Explorers Ser.). (Illus.). 120p. 30.00 (978-0-7910-7712-2(8) , Chelsea Hse.) Facts On File, Inc.

Holdcroft, Tina. Hidden Depths: Amazing Underwater Discoveries. Holdcroft, Tina, illus. 2004. (Hidden! Ser.). (Illus.). 32p. (J). (gr. 1-6). pap. 7.95 (978-1-55037-862-7(7)); lib. bdg. 19.95 (978-1-55037-863-4(5)) Annick Pr., Ltd. CAN. *Dist:* Firefly Bks., Ltd.

Hopkins, Ellen H. Into the Abyss: A Tour of Inner Space. 2001. (Cover-to-Cover Bks.). (Illus.). 72p. (J). pap. 8.95 (978-0-7891-2847-8(0)); (gr. 4-7). lib. bdg. 17.95 (978-0-7807-9767-3(1)) Perfection Learning Corp.

Jefferis, David. Super Subs: Opening up Undersea Frontiers. 2002. (Megatech Ser.). (Illus.). 32p. (J). (gr. 4-5). pap. (978-0-7787-0063-0(1)); lib. bdg. (978-0-7787-0053-1(4)) Crabtree Publishing Co.

—Super Subs: Opening up Undersea Frontiers. 2002. (gr. 3-6). lib. bdg. 17.60 (978-0-613-52999-0(5)) Tandem Library Bks.

Klingel, Cynthia Fitterer & Court, Rob. Art of Early Greece. 2003. (Scribbles Institute : Art in Ancient Civilizations Ser.). 32p. (J). (gr. 1-5). 21.36 (978-1-56766-554-3(3)) Child's World, Inc.

LaFontaine, Bruce. Submarines & Underwater Exploration. 1999. (Illus.). 48p. (J). pap. 3.95 (978-0-486-40803-3(5)) Dover Pubns., Inc.

Markle, Sandra. Down, down, down in the Ocean. Marstall, Bob, illus. 1999. 32p. (J). (gr. k-3). 16.95 (978-0-8027-8654-8(5)); lib. bdg. 17.85 (978-0-8027-8655-5(3)) Walker & Co.

Matsen, Bradford. An Extreme Dive under the Antarctic Ice. 2003. (Incredible Deep-Sea Adventures Ser.). (Illus.). 48p. (J). lib. bdg. 23.93 (978-0-7660-2190-7(4)) Enslow Pubs., Inc.

—The Incredible Record-Setting Deep-Sea Dive of the Bathysphere. 2003. (Incredible Deep-Sea Adventures Ser.). (Illus.). 48p. (J). (gr. 4-10). lib. bdg. 23.93 (978-0-7660-2188-4(2)) Enslow Pubs., Inc.

—The Incredible Submersible Alvin Discovers a Strange Deep-Sea World. 2003. (Incredible Deep-Sea Adventures Ser.). (Illus.). 48p. (J). (gr. 4-10). lib. bdg. 23.93 (978-0-7660-2189-1(0)) Enslow Pubs., Inc.

Rhodes, Mary Jo & Hall, David. Undersea Encounters, 5 bks., Set. Hall, David, photos by. Incl. Life in a Kelp Forest. 27.00 (978-0-516-24396-2(9)); Octopuses & Squids. 27.00 (978-0-516-24394-8(2)); Partners in the Sea. 27.00 (978-0-516-24397-9(7)); Sea Turtles. 27.00 (978-0-516-24391-7(8)); Seahorses & Sea Dragons. 27.00 (978-0-516-24393-1(4)); (Illus.). 48p. (J). (ps-7). 2005. 125.00 (978-0-516-24439-6(6) , Children's Pr.) Scholastic Library Publishing.

Shulman, Mark. Storytime Stickers: Undersea Adventures. Chicko, Terri, illus. 2007. (Storytime Stickers Ser.). 16p. (J). pap. 4.95 (978-1-4027-3586-8(3)) Sterling Publishing Co., Inc.

Smith, K. C. Shipwrecks of the Explorers. 2000. (Watts Library). (Illus.). 64p. (J). (gr. 5-7). 25.50 (978-0-531-20378-1(6) , Watts, Franklin) Scholastic Library Publishing.

—Shipwrecks of the Explorers. 2000. (gr. 3-6). lib. bdg. 17.60 (978-0-613-36667-0(0)) Tandem Library Bks.

Tief im Meer. (GER.). 19.95 (978-3-411-09271-0(8)) Bibliographisches Institut & F. A. Brockhaus AG DEU. *Dist:* Distribooks, Inc., i.b.d., Ltd.

Vogel, Carole G. Underwater Exploration. 2003. (Restless Sea Ser.). (Illus.). 80p. (J). 30.50 (978-0-531-12327-0(8)); (gr. 5-8). pap. 12.95 (978-0-531-16684-0(8)) Scholastic Library Publishing. (Watts, Franklin).

—Underwater Exploration. 2003. (gr. 5-8). lib. bdg. 22.20 (978-0-613-67861-2(3)) Tandem Library Bks.

UNDERWATER EXPLORATION—FICTION

Altan. Timpa Goes to the Sea. 2007. 48p. (J). pap. 14.95 (***978-1-933372-32-7(X)***) Europa Editions, Inc.

Berardy, Lloyd, 1st. A Tropical Bear in Hawaii Goes Underwater. 2006. (J). 12.95 (978-1-4276-0212-1(3)) Aardvark Global Publishing.

Bonnell, Kris. Down in the Sea. 2006. (J). 3.95 (***978-1-933727-38-7(1)***) Reading Reading Bks., LLC.

Cookson, Jan. Ant on the Run. 2003. 84p. pap. 8.95 (978-0-595-29440-4(5)) iUniverse, Inc.

Greenburg, J. C. Under Water. Reed, Mike, illus. 2003. (Andrew Lost Ser.: Bk. 5). 96p. (J). (gr. 2-5). mass mkt. 3.99 (978-0-375-82523-1(1) , Random Hse. Bks. for Young Readers) Random Hse. Children's Bks.

Meomi. The Octonauts & the Only Lonely Monster. 2006. (Illus.). 36p. (J). (ps-3). 15.95 (978-1-59702-005-3(2)) Immedium.

Meomi (Firm) Staff, contrib. by. The Octonauts & the Sea of Shade. 2007. 36p. (J). (ps-3). 15.95 (***978-1-59702-010-7(9)***) Immedium.

Montgomery, R. A. Journey under the Sea. 2006. (Choose Your Own Adventure Ser.: No. 2). (Illus.). 144p. (J). mass mkt. 5.99 (978-1-933390-02-4(6) , CHCL02) Chooseco LLC.

Myers, Bill. My Life as a Torpedo Test Target. Mangiat, Jeff, illus. 2005. (Incredible Worlds of Wally McDoogle Ser.: Vol. 6). 128p. (J). (ps-7). 9.99 (978-1-4003-0638-1(8)) Nelson, Thomas Inc.

Thompson, Lisa. Saving Atlantis. Cantell, Brenda, illus. 2005. (Treasure Trackers Ser.). 80p. (J). (gr. 5-9). 19.00 (978-0-7910-8878-4(2)) Facts On File, Inc.

Treasures of the Barrier Reef. 2005. (J). audio, cd-rom 24.95 (978-0-9771381-7-3(8)) Williams, Geoffrey T.

Verne, Jules. Twenty Thousand Leagues under the Sea. l.t. ed. 2006. 592p. pap. (978-1-84702-222-6(7)) Echo Library.

—Twenty Thousand Leagues under the Sea. 2005. (Illus.). 32p. (C). pap. 9.00 (***978-0-582-85494-9(6)***) Pearson ESL.

Verne, Jules. 20,000 Leagues under the Sea. 2004. (Fast Track Classics Ser.). (Illus.). 48p. (J). pap. 9.99 (978-0-237-52688-7(3) , Evans Brothers, Limited) Evans Publishing Group GBR. *Dist:* Independent Pubs. Group.

Zindel, Paul. Loch. 2005. 224p. (gr. 5-9). pap. 5.99 (978-0-7868-5150-8(3)) Hyperion Bks. for Children.

UNDERWATER GEOLOGY

see Submarine Geology

UNDERWATER SWIMMING

see Skin Diving

UNDERWRITING

see Insurance

UNICORNS

Clarke, Phillip & Rogers, Kirsteen. Unicorns Jigsaw Bk. 2007. 14p. (J). bds. 14.99 (978-0-7945-1467-9(7) , Usborne) EDC Publishing.

Dudley, William. Unicorns. 2007. (YA). lib. bdg. (***978-1-60152-028-9(X)***) ReferencePoint Pr., Inc.

Gibbons, Gail. Behold... the Unicorns! Gibbons, Gail, illus. 2001. (Illus.). 32p. (J). 15.89 (978-0-688-17958-8(4)) HarperCollins Pubs.

Hamilton, John. Unicorns & Other Magical Creatures. 2005. (Fantasy & Folklore Ser.). (Illus.). 32p. (J). (gr. 4-8). lib. bdg. 24.21 (978-1-59197-715-5(0)) ABDO Publishing Co.

More Unicorns. 2007. (Illus.). 20p. (J). 10.00 (***978-0-9795206-2-5(5)***) Unseen Gallery.

Netzley, Patricia D. Unicorns. 2000. (Mystery Library). (Illus.). 96p. (YA). (gr. 4-12). 27.45 (978-1-56006-687-3(3) , Lucent Bks.) Thomson Gale.

Shaffer, Christy. Glitter Unicorns Stickers. 2004. (Glitter Stickers Ser.). (Illus.). 2p. (J). (ps-5). 1.50 (978-0-486-43538-1(5)) Dover Pubns., Inc.

—Magical Unicorns Stained Glass Coloring Book. 2004. (Illus.). 16p. pap. 5.95 (978-0-486-43705-7(1)) Dover Pubns., Inc.

Wonderland Unicorns: Coloring book by Darla Hallmark. 2007. (Illus.). 20p. (YA). 10.00 (***978-0-9795206-1-7(4)***) Unseen Gallery.

UNICORNS—FICTION

Barber, Shirley. The Enchanted Woods. 2002. (Illus.). 96p. (J). reprint ed. (978-1-86503-781-3(8)) Summit Pr.

Bateman, Teresa. The Eyes of the Unicorn. Rayevsky, Robert & Spalenka, Greg, illus. 2007. 32p. (J). (gr. 1-5). 17.95 (978-0-8234-1728-5(X)) Holiday Hse., Inc.

Bell, Hilari. The Prophecy. 208p. (J). 2007. pap. 6.50 (***978-0-06-059945-4(6)*** , Eos); 2006. lib. bdg. 16.89 (978-0-06-059944-7(8)); 2006. (Illus.). 15.99 (978-0-06-059943-0(X)) HarperCollins Pubs.

Benz, Derek & Lewis, J. S. Revenge of the Shadow King Audio (library Edition) 2006. (Grey Griffins Ser.). (J). 84.95 (978-0-439-87913-2(2)) Scholastic, Inc.

Bharadwaj, Meenakshi. Lonely Unicorn. 2004. (Illus.). 20p. (J). pap. (978-81-87649-89-2(5)) Katha.

Brody, Dylan. The Thought That Counts: A Unicorn Story. 2000. (J). (978-1-928767-06-0(0)) Silk Label Bks., Inc.

Brooks, Stephen J. Unicorn Races. Crockett, Linda, illus. 2007. 32p. (J). 16.95 (978-0-9769017-3-0(0)) Purple Sky Publishing.

Carpenter, Nancy Sippel. The Land of Unicorns. 1999. (Sticker Stories Ser.). (Illus.). 16p. (J). (ps-1). pap. 4.99 (978-0-448-41984-8(X) , Grosset & Dunlap) Penguin Group (USA) Inc.

Chapman, Linda. Dreams Come True. 2006. (My Secret Unicorn Ser.: No. 2). (Illus.). 128p. (J). pap. 4.99 (978-0-439-81383-9(2) , Scholastic Paperbacks) Scholastic, Inc.

—Dreams Come True. Hull, Biz, illus. 2002. 120p. (J). (978-0-439-60010-1(3)) Scholastic, Inc.

—Flying High. 2006. (My Secret Unicorn Ser.). 144p. (J). pap. 4.99 (978-0-439-81384-6(0) , Scholastic Paperbacks) Scholastic, Inc.

—The Magic Spell. Hull, Biz, illus. 2003. 136p. (J). (978-0-439-60009-5(X)) Scholastic, Inc.

—Magic Spell. 2006. (My Secret Unicorn Ser.: No. 1). (Illus.). 128p. (J). pap. 4.99 (978-0-439-81382-2(4) , Scholastic Paperbacks) Scholastic, Inc.

—Magic Spell. 2007. (My Secret Unicorn Ser.: No. 1). 128p. (J). pap. 2.99 (***978-0-545-01036-8(5)***) Scholastic, Inc.

Chapman, Linda. Starlight Surprise. 2007. (My Secret Unicorn Ser.: No. 4). (Illus.). 144p. (J). pap. 4.99 (978-0-439-81385-3(9) , Scholastic Paperbacks) Scholastic, Inc.

Cherry, Lynne. The Dragon & the Unicorn. 1998. (Illus.). 36p. (J). (gr. 1-5). pap. 7.00 (978-0-15-201888-7(3) , Harcourt Paperbacks) Harcourt Children's Bks.

—The Dragon & the Unicorn. 1998. 13.80 (978-0-606-13347-0(X)) Tandem Library Bks.

Clarke, Phillip. Unicorns. Scott, Peter, illus. 2006. 16p. (J). 11.99 (978-0-7945-1280-4(1) , Usborne) EDC Publishing.

Coville, Bruce. A Glory of Unicorns. 1998. (J). pap. (978-0-590-95582-9(9)) Scholastic, Inc.

—Into the Land of the Unicorns. rev. ed. 1999. (Unicorn Chronicles: Vol. 1). 176p. (J). (gr. 4-7). pap. 4.99 (978-0-439-10838-6(1)) Scholastic, Inc.

—Into the Land of the Unicorns. 1999. (Unicorn Chronicles: Bk. 1). (Illus.). (J). (gr. 4-7). 11.64 (978-0-606-21863-4(7)) Tandem Library Bks.

—Song of the Wanderer. unabr. ed. 2002. (Unicorn Chronicles: Bk. 2). (J). (gr. 4-7). lib. bdg. 29.00 incl. audio (978-0-9717540-1-0(2) , 02001A) Full Cast Audio.

—Song of the Wanderer, No. 2. 2001. (Unicorn Chronicles Ser.). 336p. (J). pap. 5.99 (978-0-590-45954-9(6)) Scholastic, Inc.

—Song of the Wanderer. 2001. (Unicorn Chronicles: Bk. 2). (978-0-606-22215-0(4)); 2000. (gr. 3-6). lib. bdg. 12.40 (978-0-613-44369-2(1)) Tandem Library Bks.

—The Unicorn Treasury: Stories, Poems, & Unicorn Lore. 2004. (Illus.). 216p. (J). pap. 5.95 (978-0-15-205216-4(X) , Magic Carpet Bks.) Harcourt Children's Bks.

Cross, Frances. Butternut Blobber & the Blue Jade. 2007. (Blobber Trilogy Ser.). 98p. pap. 7.95 (***978-1-84167-561-9(X)***) Ransom Publishing Ltd. GBR. *Dist:* International Publishers Marketing.

The Crystal Unicorn: Individual Chapter Book Title Six-Packs. Vol. 26. 32p. (gr. 3-4). 44.00 (978-0-7635-4479-9(5)) Rigby Education.

Dickins, Rosie. Unicorns. Lo Cascio, Maria Cristina, illus. 2006. 48p. (J). 8.99 (978-0-7945-1331-3(X) , Usborne) EDC Publishing.

Duey, Kathleen. The Journey Home. Rayyan, Omar, illus. 2003. (Unicorn's Secret Ser.). 80p. (J). pap. 3.99 (978-0-689-85374-6(2) , Aladdin) Simon & Schuster Children's Publishing.

—Moonsilver. Rayyan, Omar, illus. 2002. (J). 12.34 (978-0-7587-6929-9(6)) Book Wholesalers, Inc.

—Moonsilver. Rayyan, Omar, illus. 2001. (Unicorn's Secret Ser.: No. 1). 80p. (J). (gr. 2-4). pap. 3.99 (978-0-689-84269-6(4) , Aladdin) Simon & Schuster Children's Publishing.

—Moonsilver. 2001. (978-0-606-22093-4(3)); (gr. 3-6). lib. bdg. 11.80 (978-0-613-58374-9(4)) Tandem Library Bks.

—The Mountains of the Moon. Rayyan, Omar, illus. ed. 2005. 76p. (J). lib. bdg. 15.00 (978-1-59054-907-0(4)) Fitzgerald Bks.

—The Mountains of the Moon. Rayyan, Omar, illus. 2002. (Unicorn's Secret Ser.: No. 4). 80p. (J). (gr. 2-5). pap. 3.99 (978-0-689-84272-6(4) , Aladdin); No. 4. lib. bdg. 11.89 (978-0-689-85137-7(5) , Aladdin Library) Simon & Schuster Children's Publishing.

—The Silver Bracelet. Rayyan, Omar, illus. 2002. (Unicorn's Secret Ser.: No. 3). 96p. (J). pap. 3.99 (978-0-689-84271-9(6) , Aladdin) Simon & Schuster Children's Publishing.

—Silver Bracelet. 2002. (gr. 3-6). lib. bdg. 11.80 (978-0-613-58388-6(4)) Tandem Library Bks.

—The Silver Bracelet. Rayyan, Omar, illus. ed. 2005. 90p. (J). lib. bdg. 15.00 (978-1-59054-917-9(1)) Fitzgerald Bks.

—The Silver Bracelet, Vol. 3. Rayyan, Omar, illus. 2002. (Unicorn's Secret Ser.). 96p. (J). lib. bdg. 11.89 (978-0-689-85058-5(1) , Aladdin Library) Simon & Schuster Children's Publishing.

—Silver Thread. 2001. (gr. 3-6). lib. bdg. 11.80 (978-0-613-58389-3(2)) Tandem Library Bks.

—Sunset Gates. 2002. (gr. 3-6). lib. bdg. 11.80 (978-0-613-57584-3(9)) Tandem Library Bks.

Durant, Sybrina, et al. Blue Unicorn II: Return of the Dragons, 3 vols. Johnson, Britt, ed. l.t. ed. 2003. (Illus.). 25p. (J). (gr. k-5). spiral bd. 8.99 (978-1-929063-93-2(8) , 331) Moons & Stars Publishing For Children.

Fabrick, Harriett. Furello Journeys: Furello Questions, Bk. II. 1998. (Illus.). 88p. (J). (gr. 5-12). 18.95 (978-0-9646698-2-6(X)) Wild Flower USA.

French, Jackie. The Book of Unicorns. 1998. 184p. (ps-3). pap. 7.95 (978-0-207-19115-2(8)) HarperCollins Pubs.

Golden Books Staff. Unicorn Magic. 2008. (Color Plus Chunky Crayons Ser.). (Illus.). 48p. (J). (ps-2). pap. 3.99 (***978-0-375-84212-2(8)*** , Golden Bks.) Random Hse., Inc.

Hennessy, B. G. Claire & the Unicorn Happy Ever After. Mitchell, Susan, illus. 2005. 32p. (J). 12.95 (978-1-4169-0815-9(3)) Simon & Schuster Children's Publishing.

Keckeis, M. B. The Silver Unicorn. Steiner, Frank et al, trs. from FRE. Cassidy, Christophe et al, illus. 1998. (ENG, FRE, GER & SPA.). 256p. (J). (gr. 6-10). 23.50 (978-1-879870-60-4(6)) Pro Lingua Pr.

K.M. Mohr, John Kelley and. Waking Dalifi. 2005. 72p. pap. 9.95 (978-1-4116-6364-0(0)) Lulu.com.

Lasky, Kathryn. Unicorns? Get Real! 2007. (Camp Princess Ser.). (Illus.). 160p. (J). 15.99 (***978-0-06-058764-2(4)***); pap. 4.99 (***978-0-06-058766-6(0)*** , Harper Trophy) HarperCollins Pubs.

Lee, Tanith. Black Unicorn. 2005. (Illus.). 138p. pap. 12.00 (978-1-59687-162-5(8)) ibooks, Inc.

Loehr, Mallory. Unicorn Wings. Silin-Palmer, Pamela, illus. 2006. (Step into Reading Ser.). 32p. (J). (ps-2). lib. bdg. 11.99 (978-0-375-93117-8(1)); 3.99 (978-0-375-83117-1(7)) Random Hse. Children's Bks. (Random Hse. Bks. for Young Readers).

MacHado, Ana Maria. Un Monton de Unicornios (A Bunch of Unicorns) Vasco, Irene, tr. Coll, Ivar Da, illus. 2001. (SPA.). 48p. (J). 8.95 (978-958-04-6261-3(5)) Norma S.A. COL. *Dist:* AIMS International Bks., Inc., Distribuidora Norma, Inc.

Malcolm, Jahnna N. The Emerald Princess Follows a Unicorn. 1999. (Jewel Kingdom Ser.: No. 11). (Illus.). 80p. (J). (gr. 3-5). pap. 3.99 (978-0-590-97879-8(9)) Scholastic, Inc.

McCaffrey, Anne. Acorna: The Unicorn Girl. 2001. (Acorna Ser.). lib. bdg. 15.90 (978-0-613-55549-4(X)) Tandem Library Bks.

McCann, Jesse Leon. The Case of the Lost Unicorn. 2001. (Ace Ventura Chapter Bk.: Vol. 3). (J). (gr. 1-4). (978-0-606-19909-4(8)) Tandem Library Bks.

McCarty, Barbara. To Save a Unicorn. 2005. 54p. pap. 12.95 (978-1-4137-5428-5(7)) PublishAmerica, Inc.

McDonald, Ann-Eve. The Tale of the Black Square. 2004. (J). (978-0-9770158-2-5(3)) BeachWalk Bks. Inc.

Mitchell, Adrian. Nobody Rides the Unicorn. Lambert, Stephen, illus. 2000. (J). (ps-3). 32p. pap. 16.95 (978-0-439-11204-8(4) , Levine, Arthur A. Bks.); (978-0-439-11205-5(2)) Scholastic, Inc.

Morpurgo, Michael. I Believe in Unicorns. Blythe, Gary, illus. 2006. 80p. (J). (gr. 1-4). 12.99 (978-0-7636-3050-8(0)) Candlewick Pr.

Nimmo, Jenny. The Night of the Unicorn. l.t. ed. 2005. (J). pap. (978-0-7540-7939-2(2) , CLP 488) BBC Audio.

Once upon a Time- Lost Unicorn. 2005. (J). bds. (978-1-4194-0097-1(5)) Paradise Pr., Inc.

Osborne, Mary Pope. Blizzard of the Blue Moon. Murdocca, Sal, illus. 2007. (Magic Tree House Ser.: No. 36). 144p. (J). (gr. 2-5). pap. 4.99 (978-0-375-83038-9(3) , Random Hse. Bks. for Young Readers) Random Hse. Children's Bks.

—Blizzard of the Blue Moon. 2006. (Magic Tree House Ser.: No. 36). (Illus.). 128p. (J). (gr. k-3). lib. bdg. 13.99 (978-0-375-93037-9(X)); (gr. 2-5). 11.95 (978-0-375-83037-2(5)) Random Hse. Children's Bks. (Random Hse. Bks. for Young Readers).

Penner, Lucille Recht. Unicorns. 2005. (Illus.). 48p. (J). lib. bdg. 11.99 (978-0-375-93008-9(6) , Random Hse. Bks. for Young Readers) Random Hse. Children's Bks.

—Unicorns. Grant, Mel, illus. 2005. 48p. (J). (gr. 1-3). pap. 3.99 (978-0-375-83008-2(1) , Random Hse. Bks. for Young Readers) Random Hse. Children's Bks.

Pierce, Meredith Ann. The Birth of the Firebringer, Vol. 1. 2003. (Firebird Ser.). 208p. pap. 6.99 (978-0-14-250053-8(4) , Puffin) Penguin Group (USA) Inc.

—The Dark Moon. 2003. (Firebird Ser.). 256p. (YA). (gr. 7-11). pap. 6.99 (978-0-14-250057-6(7) , Puffin) Penguin Group (USA) Inc.

—Dark Moon. 2003. (gr. 7-12). lib. bdg. 15.30 (978-0-613-67448-5(0)) Tandem Library Bks.

—Son of Summer Stars. 2003. (gr. 7-12). lib. bdg. 15.30 (978-0-613-67474-4(X)) Tandem Library Bks.

—The Son of Summer Stars, Vol. 3. 2003. (Firebird Ser.). 256p. (YA). (gr. 7). pap. 6.99 (978-0-14-250074-3(7) , Puffin) Penguin Group (USA) Inc.

Rizzo, Cynthia Marie. Julie & the Unicorn. 2003. 49p. pap. 9.95 (978-1-4137-0785-4(8)) PublishAmerica, Inc.

Roberts, Rachel. Song of the Unicorns. 2003. (Avalon Ser.). 175p. (J). (gr. 3-7). pap. 4.99 (978-1-59315-002-0(4)) Perseus Bks. Group.

Rodda, Emily. The Unicorn. Vitale, Raoul, illus. 2004. (Fairy Realm Ser.: No. 6). 112p. (J). 8.99 (978-0-06-009598-7(9)); lib. bdg. 14.89 (978-0-06-009599-4(7)) HarperCollins Pubs.

—The Unicorn. Vitale, Raoul, illus. 2007. (Fairy Realm Ser.). 112p. (J). (gr. 3-6). 25.65 (978-1-59961-328-4(X)) Spotlight.

Romero, Astrid. Cuentos de Unicornios Para Ninos. 2000. Tr. of Stories of Unicorns for Kids. (SPA.). (gr. 3-6). lib. bdg. 15.30 (978-0-613-83021-8(0)) Tandem Library Bks.

Stanton, Mary. Shadows over Balinor. 2000. (gr. 3-6). lib. bdg. 12.40 (978-0-613-26902-5(0)) Tandem Library Bks.

—Unicorns of Balinor. 2006. 416p. (J). pap. 9.99 (978-0-439-80843-9(X) , Scholastic) Scholastic, Inc.

—Valley of Fear No.3. 1999. (gr. 5-8). lib. bdg. 12.40 (978-0-613-16870-0(4)) Tandem Library Bks.

Vance, Steve. Walpurgis Night. 2002. (Illus.). 474p. (J). pap. 9.99 (978-1-928767-07-7(9) , 079) Silk Label Bks., Inc.

Welch, Sheila Kelly. The Shadowed Unicorn. 2000. 192p. (J). (gr. 5-9). 15.95 (978-0-8126-2895-1(0)) Cricket Bks.

Yolen, Jane. Where Have the Unicorns Gone. Sanderson, Ruth, illus. 2003. 32p. (J). 6.99 (978-0-689-86359-2(4) , Aladdin) Simon & Schuster Children's Publishing.

—Where Have the Unicorns Gone. 2003. (gr. k-3). lib. bdg. 15.30 (978-0-613-90038-6(3)) Tandem Library Bks.

UNIDENTIFIED FLYING OBJECTS

Aliens & UFOs: Famous UFO Sightings & Incidents. (Critical Reading Ser.). (YA). (gr. 6-12). pap. (978-0-8092-1104-3(1)) Jamestown.

Asimov, Isaac & Hantula, Richard. UFOs. 2004. (Isaac Asimov's 21st Century Library of the Universe). (Illus.). 32p. (J). lib. bdg. 24.67 (978-0-8368-3954-8(4)) Stevens, Gareth Inc.

Blackwood, Gary L. Alien Astronauts. 1998. (Secrets of the Unexplained Ser.). (Illus.). 80p. (J). (gr. 5-9). lib. bdg. 29.93 (978-0-7614-0469-9(4) , Benchmark Bks.) Cavendish, Marshall Corp.

Brookes, Philip. Invaders from Outer Space. 1999. (gr. k-3). lib. bdg. 11.80 (978-0-613-17309-4(0)) Tandem Library Bks.

—Invaders from Outer Space: Real Life Stories of UFOs. 1999. (Eyewitness Readers Ser.). (J). 10.75 (978-0-606-16985-1(7)) Tandem Library Bks.

Costain, Meredith. It's True! Hauntings Happen & Ghosts Get Grumpy. Smith, Craig, illus. 2006. (It's True! Ser.). 96p. (J). (gr. 5-8). 19.95 (978-1-55451-022-1(8)); pap. 5.95 (978-1-55451-021-4(X)) Annick Pr., Ltd. CAN. *Dist:* Firefly Bks., Ltd.

Deary, Terry. Alien Landing. 2004. (Classified Ser.). 96p. (J). (gr. 5-8). pap. 4.95 (978-0-7534-5824-2(1) , Kingfisher) Houghton Mifflin Co. Trade & Reference Div.

DeMolay, Jack. UFOs: The Roswell Incident. 2007. (Graphic Mysteries Ser.). (J). (978-1-4042-2346-2(0)); (Illus.). 24p. pap. (978-1-4042-2156-7(5)); (Illus.). 24p. (gr. 2-6). lib. bdg. 21.25 (978-1-4042-3403-1(9)) Rosen Publishing Group, Inc., The. (PowerKids Pr.).

Duncan, John. UFOs. 2006. 36p. (J). lib. bdg. 24.67 (978-0-8368-6268-3(6)) Stevens, Gareth Inc.

Earth Cosmology: The Effects of the Giant Destroyer Comet. 2004. (UFO Fact Bks.). (YA). cd-rom 15.00 (978-0-934269-41-4(6)) UFO Photo Archives.

Gorman, Jacqueline Laks. UFOs. 2002. (X Science Ser.). (Illus.). 24p. (YA). (gr. 2 up). lib. bdg. 22.00 (978-0-8368-3201-3(9)) Stevens, Gareth Inc.

Grace, N. B. UFO Mysteries. 2006. (Boys Rock! Ser.). 32p. (J). (gr. 1-5). 24.21 (978-1-59296-738-4(8)) Child's World, Inc.

—UFOs. 2007. (24/7 - Science Behind the Scenes Ser.). (Illus.). 64p. (J). (gr. 8-12). 26.00 ***(978-0-531-12074-3(0)** , Watts, Franklin) Scholastic Library Publishing.

—UFOs: What Scientists Say May Shock You! 2008. (24/7: Science Behind the Scenes: Mystery Files Ser.). 64p. (J). pap. 7.95 ***(978-0-531-18741-8(1)** , Watts, Franklin) Scholastic Library Publishing.

Henderson, Bonnie. UFOS: Out of the Black. 2004. (Illus.). 240p. pap. 15.95 (978-0-910042-90-1(X)) Allegheny Pr.

Herbst, Judith. UFOs. (Unexplained Ser.). (Illus.). 48p. (J). 2005. (gr. 5-12). lib. bdg. 26.60 (978-0-8225-0961-5(X)); 2004. pap. 7.95 (978-0-8225-2409-0(0) , Lerner Pubns.) Lerner Publishing Group.

Innes. Unsolved Mysteries Series, 14 bks., Set. 2000. (Unsolved Mysteries Ser.). (Illus.). 359.66 (978-0-7398-4285-0(4)) Steck-Vaughn.

Innes, Brian. Alien Visitors & Abductions. 1998. (Unsolved Mysteries Ser.). (Illus.). 48p. (J). (gr. 3-7). pap. 8.05 (978-0-8172-4275-6(9)) Steck-Vaughn.

—Mysteries of UFO's. 1999. (Unsolved Mysteries Ser.). (Illus.). 48p. (YA). (gr. 3 up). lib. bdg. 25.69 (978-0-8172-5477-3(3)) Raintree.

—The Mysteries of UFO's. 1998. (Unsolved Mysteries Ser.). (Illus.). 48p. (J). (gr. 3-7). pap. 8.05 (978-0-8172-4274-9(0)) Steck-Vaughn.

Jeffrey, Gary. UFOs. 2005. (Graphic Mysteries Ser.). (J). (978-1-4042-0821-6(6)); (Illus.). 48p. pap. (978-1-4042-0808-7(9)) Rosen Publishing Group, Inc., The.

—UFOs: Alien Abduction & Close Encounters. 2005. (Graphic Mysteries Ser.). (Illus.). 48p. (J). (gr. 5-8). lib. bdg. 29.95 (978-1-4042-0797-4(X)) Rosen Publishing Group, Inc., The.

Krull, Kathleen. What Really Happened in Roswell? Just the Facts. 2003. (gr. 3-6). lib. bdg. 12.10 (978-0-613-66747-0(6)) Tandem Library Bks.

—What Really Happened in Roswell? Just the Facts (Plus the Rumors) about UFOs & Aliens. Santoro, Christopher, illus. 2003. 64p. (J). (gr. 3 up). lib. bdg. 16.89 (978-0-688-17249-7(0)) HarperCollins Pubs.

Levy, Janey. UFOs. 2006. (Tony Stead Nonfiction Independent Reading Collection). (J). pap. (978-1-4042-5671-2(7)) Rosen Publishing Group, Inc., The.

Lyne, William R. Pentagon Aliens. 3rd exp. ed. 1999. Orig. Title: Space Aliens from the Pentagon. (Illus.). 316p. (Orig.). (YA). pap. 25.00 (978-0-9637467-7-1(4)) Creatopia Productions - Lamy, New Mexico.

Mason, Paul. Investigating UFOs. 2004. (Forensic Files Ser.). (Illus.). 48p. (J). pap. 8.50 (978-1-4034-5474-4(4)) Heinemann Library.

—UFOs. 2004. (Forensic Files Ser.). (Illus.). 48p. (J). lib. bdg. (978-1-4034-4834-7(5)) Heinemann Library.

—UFOs & Crop Circles. 2005. (Illus.). 32p. (J). (gr. 4-7). lib. bdg. 27.10 (978-1-58340-787-5(1) , 1247417) Smart Apple Media.

Messages from the Pleiades Vol. 1: The Contact Notes of Eduard Billy Meier. 2004. (UFO Fact Bks.). (YA). cd-rom 15.00 (978-0-934269-49-0(1)) UFO Photo Archives.

The Mormon Gold Plates: Au Unusual Account. 2004. (YA). cd-rom 15.00 (978-0-934269-57-5(2)) UFO Photo Archives.

Netzley, Patricia D. Alien Abductions. 2000. (Mystery Library). (Illus.). 96p. (YA). (gr. 4-12). 27.45 (978-1-56006-767-2(5) , Lucent Bks.) Thomson Gale.

Nobleman, Marc Tyler. Aliens & UFOs. 2006. (Illus.). 32p. (J). pap. 7.99 (978-1-4109-2514-5(5)); lib. bdg. (978-1-4109-2509-1(9)) Steck-Vaughn.

O'Neill, Terry. UFOs. 2002. (gr. 7-12). lib. bdg. 30.35 (978-0-613-73767-8(9)) Tandem Library Bks.

O'Neill, Terry, ed. UFOs. 2003. (Opposing Viewpoints Series (Unnumbered)). (Illus.). 160p. (J). 27.45 (978-0-7377-1070-0(5)); pap. 23.70 (978-0-7377-1069-4(1)) Thomson Gale. (Greenhaven Pr., Inc.).

Orme, David. Ufos. 2007. (Trailblazers Ser.). (Illus.). 36p. pap. 7.95 ***(978-1-84167-423-0(0))** Ransom Publishing Ltd. GBR. *Dist:* International Publishers Marketing.

Oxlade, Chris. The Mystery of UFOs. 2006. (Can Science Solve? Ser.). (Illus.). 32p. (J). 29.29 (978-1-4034-8338-6(8)) Heinemann Library.

Roleff, Tamara L. Alien Abductions. 2003. (gr. 7-12). lib. bdg. 30.35 (978-0-613-73927-6(2)) Tandem Library Bks.

Roleff, Tamara L., ed. Alien Abductions. 2003. (Illus.). 160p. (J). pap. 23.70 (978-0-7377-1590-3(1)); lib. bdg. 32.45 (978-0-7377-1589-7(8)) Thomson Gale. (Greenhaven Pr., Inc.).

Sievert, Terri. UFOs. 2004. (Edge Books, the Unexplained). (Illus.). 32p. (J). lib. bdg. 22.60 (978-0-7368-2714-0(5)) Capstone Pr., Inc.

Silverstein, Janna. Close Encounters with Aliens. 2005. (Unsolved Mysteries Ser.). (Illus.). 48p. (YA). (gr. 5-8). lib. bdg. 25.25 (978-0-8239-3562-8(0)) Rosen Publishing Group, Inc., The.

Stirling, Janet. UFOs. 2005. (Unsolved Mysteries Ser.). (Illus.). 48p. (YA). (gr. 5-8). lib. bdg. 25.25 (978-0-8239-3566-6(3)) Rosen Publishing Group, Inc., The.

Townsend. Mysterious Encounters. 2004. (Out There Ser.). (Illus.). pap. 8.95 (978-1-4109-0964-0(6)) Raintree.

—Mysterious Encounters 6-Pack. 2004. (Out There Ser.). lib. bdg. 48.30 (978-1-4109-0973-2(5)) Raintree.

Townsend, John. Mysterious Encounters. 2004. (Out There Ser.). (Illus.). 56p. (J). lib. bdg. 28.56 (978-1-4109-0563-5(2)) Raintree.

UFO Abduction at Botucatu: A Preliminary Report. 2004. (UFO Fact Bks.). (YA). cd-rom 15.00 (978-0-934269-36-0(X)) UFO Photo Archives.

UFO... Art: In Full Color. 2004. (UFO Fact Bks.). (YA). cd-rom 25.00 (978-0-934269-54-4(8)) UFO Photo Archives.

UFO Capture of two f-14 Jets: Lost Navy Aircraft. 2004. (YA). cd-rom (978-0-934269-56-8(4)) UFO Photo Archives.

UFO contact from beyond Rigel: A cherokee girl's Oddesy. 2004. (UFO Fact Bks.). (YA). cd-rom 15.00 (978-0-934269-50-6(5)) UFO Photo Archives.

UFO Contact from COMA Berenesis. 2005. (YA). cd-rom (978-0-934269-62-9(9)) UFO Photo Archives.

UFO Contact from Plamet Itibi-RA. 2003. (UFO Fact Bks.). (YA). cd-rom 15.00 (978-0-934269-30-8(0)) UFO Photo Archives.

UFO Contact from Planet Acart: From Utopia to Reality. 2003. (UFO Fact Bks.). (YA). cd-rom 15.00 (978-0-934269-32-2(7)) UFO Photo Archives.

UFO Contact from Planet Alcyone: Falling Bodies Theory. 2004. (UFO Fact Bks.). (YA). cd-rom 15.00 (978-0-934269-47-6(5)) UFO Photo Archives.

UFO Contact from Planet Apu: 100 Hours with Extraterrestrials. 2004. (UFO Fact Bks.). (YA). cd-rom 15.00 (978-0-934269-38-4(6)) UFO Photo Archives.

UFO Contact from Planet ARIAN. 2004. (YA). cd-rom 15.00 (978-0-934269-33-9(5)) UFO Photo Archives.

UFO Contact from Planet Baavi: Proxima Centauri Group. 2004. (UFO Fact Bks.). (YA). cd-rom 15.00 (978-0-934269-46-9(7)) UFO Photo Archives.

UFO Contact from Planet Klermer: Possibilities of the Infinite. 2004. (UFO Fact Bks.). (YA). cd-rom 15.00 (978-0-934269-34-6(3)) UFO Photo Archives.

UFO Contact from Planet Korendor Vol. 1: Another Advanced Society. 2004. (YA). cd-rom 15.00 (978-0-934269-63-6(7)) UFO Photo Archives.

UFO Contact from Planet Korendor, Vol. 2. 2005. (YA). cd-rom 15.00 (978-0-934269-64-3(5)) UFO Photo Archives.

UFO Contact from Planet Nep-4: Earth Development. 2004. (UFO Fact Bks.). (YA). cd-rom 15.00 (978-0-934269-40-7(8)) UFO Photo Archives.

UFO Contact from Planet Norca: The Shocking Truth. 2004. Orig. Title: The Shocking Truth. (YA). cd-rom 15.00 (978-0-934269-59-9(9)) UFO Photo Archives.

UFO Contact from Planet Ummo, Vol. 3, Sesma: Daily Life on Ummo. 2004. (YA). cd-rom 15.00 (978-0-934269-28-5(9)) UFO Photo Archives.

UFO Contact from Planet Venus: We Are Not Alone. 2004. (YA). cd-rom 15.00 (978-0-934269-55-1(6)) UFO Photo Archives.

UFO Contact from Planet Zeti: Going Home? 2004. (UFO Fact Bks.). (YA). cd-rom 15.00 (978-0-934269-39-1(4)) UFO Photo Archives.

UFO contact from the DAL Universe: With asket of the timmers Society. 2004. (UFO Fact Bks.). (YA). cd-rom 15.00 (978-0-934269-48-3(3)) UFO Photo Archives.

UFO Contact of an Erotic Kind: Children of the Sun. 2002. (YA). cd-rom 15.00 (978-0-934269-31-5(9)) UFO Photo Archives.

UFO Contact of an Erotic Kind: The Assignment. 2003. (UFO Fact Bks.). (YA). cd-rom 15.00 (978-0-934269-29-2(7)) UFO Photo Archives.

UFO Photographs Around the World, Vol. 3 of Series, Vol. 3. 2003. (UFO Fact Bks.). (YA). cd-rom 15.00 (978-0-934269-35-3(1)) UFO Photo Archives.

UFO Photographs Around the World, Vol. 4 in Series, Vol. 4. 2003. (YA). cd-rom 15.00 (978-0-934269-37-7(8)) UFO Photo Archives.

UFO, the DULCE Story: An Incredible Deception. 2004. (UFO Fact Bks.). (YA). cd-rom 15.00 (978-0-934269-52-0(1)) UFO Photo Archives.

UmmoCat: The ummo Documents. 2004. (UFO Fact Bks.). (YA). cd-rom 25.00 (978-0-934269-53-7(X)) UFO Photo Archives.

Usborne Books Staff. Alienigenas. 2000. (SPA.). (gr. 3-6). lib. bdg. 14.10 (978-0-613-90701-9(9)) Tandem Library Bks.

63 Photographs in Color, Meier Vol. 5: The Meier Variation V. Photos. 2004. (UFO Fact Bks.). (YA). cd-rom 25.00 (978-0-934269-51-3(3)) UFO Photo Archives.

76 UFO Photographs in Color, Vol 3: Clower Collection. 2004. (UFO Fact Bks.). (YA). cd-rom 25.00 (978-0-934269-44-5(0)) UFO Photo Archives.

100 UFO Photographs in Color Vol, 2 Vol. 2 Series: Series in Sequence. 2004. (UFO Fact Bks.). (YA). cd-rom 25.00 (978-0-934269-43-8(2)) UFO Photo Archives.

100 UFO Photographs in Color, Vol,1 Vol. 1: The Best of the Best. 2004. (UFO Fact Bks.). (YA). cd-rom 25.00 (978-0-934269-42-1(4)) UFO Photo Archives.

135 UFO Photographs in Color, Vol. 4: Best of Meier Early UFO Photos. 2004. (UFO Fact Bks.). (YA). cd-rom 25.00 (978-0-934269-45-2(9)) UFO Photo Archives.

UNIDENTIFIED FLYING OBJECTS—FICTION

Adler, David A. Cam Jansen & the Mystery of the UFO. Natti, Susanna, illus. 2004. (Cam Jansen Ser.: No. 2). 64p. (J). (gr. 2-4). pap. 3.99 (978-0-14-240011-1(4) , Puffin) Penguin Group (USA) Inc.

—Cam Jansen Double Mystery: Cam Jansen & the Mystery of the Dinosaur Bones; Cam Jansen & the Mystery of the U.F.O. Natti, Susanna, illus. 2000. (Cam Jansen Ser.: Nos. 2-3). 128p. (J). (gr. 2-5). 5.99 (978-0-670-89365-2(X) , Viking Juvenile) Penguin Group (USA) Inc.

Beechen, Adam. Ufo! Saunders, Zina, illus. ed. 2005. 32p. (J). lib. bdg. 15.00 (978-1-59054-988-9(0)) Fitzgerald Bks.

Bradman, Tony. Midnight in Memphis. Chatterton, Martin & Chatterton, Ann, illus. 2001. (Blue Bananas Ser.). 48p. (J). (gr. 1-2). (978-0-7787-0848-3(9)); pap. (978-0-7787-0894-0(2)) Crabtree Publishing Co.

—Midnight in Memphis. 2002. (gr. k-3). lib. bdg. 12.95 (978-0-613-52881-8(6)) Tandem Library Bks.

Braun, Lilian Jackson. The Cat Who Saw Stars. 2000. lib. bdg. 15.30 (978-0-613-21306-6(8)) Tandem Library Bks.

Buchanan, Paul. Uncle from Another Planet. 1999. (Heebie Jeebies Ser.: Vol. 4). 144p. (YA). pap. 5.99 (978-0-8054-1650-3(1)) B&H Publishing Grp.

Coville, Bruce. Bruce Coville's UFOs. 2000. (Illus.). (J). 11.64 (978-0-606-18679-7(4)) Tandem Library Bks.

Daly, Joseph M. Strange Town Volume One: The Woods Behind Trevor Malone's House. 2007. 265p. (YA). pap. ***(978-0-9779921-0-2(1))** Wolfs Corner Publishing.

Friedman, Michael Jan. The Sirian Conspiracy. 1999. (Wishbone Mysteries Ser.: No. 16). (J). (gr. 2-5). (978-0-606-17768-9(X)) Tandem Library Bks.

Friedman, Michael Jan, et al. The Sirian Conspiracy. l.t. ed. 2000. (Wishbone Mysteries Ser.: No. 16). (Illus.). 141p. (J). (gr. 4 up). lib. bdg. 23.33 (978-0-8368-2699-9(X)) Stevens, Gareth Inc.

Higgins, B. T. The Master of Disaster. 2005. 103p. pap. 10.00 (978-1-4116-3121-2(8)) Lulu.com.

Horton, Randy. Great UFO Frame-up. 2000. (gr. 5-8). lib. bdg. 11.80 (978-0-613-51213-8(8)) Tandem Library Bks.

Hutchens, Paul. The Ghost Dog. 1998. (gr. 3-6). lib. bdg. 13.00 (978-0-613-90866-5(X)) Tandem Library Bks.

Keene, Carolyn. The Flying Saucer Mystery, Vol. 58. 2005. (Nancy Drew Mystery Stories). (Illus.). 176p. (J). (gr. 3-9). 6.99 (978-0-448-43689-0(2) , Grosset & Dunlap) Penguin Group (USA) Inc.

Kitamura, Satoshi. UFO Diary. 2007. (Illus.). 32p. (J). pap. 9.95 ***(978-1-84270-591-9(1))** Andersen GBR. *Dist:* Independent Pubs. Group.

Myers, Bill. The Encounter. 2002. (Forbidden Doors Ser.: Vol. 6). 160p. (J). mass mkt. 4.99 (978-0-8423-5738-8(6)) Tyndale Hse. Pubs.

Passen, Lisa. Attack of the 50-Foot Teacher. 2005. (Illus.). 28p. (J). (gr. k-4). reprint ed. 16.00 (978-0-7567-9665-5(2)) DIANE Publishing Co.

—The Attack of the 50-Foot Teacher. Passen, Lisa, illus. rev. ed. (Illus.). 32p. (J). 2003. (gr. 1-3). pap. 6.95 (978-0-8050-7260-0(8)); 2000. (gr. k-3). 16.00 (978-0-8050-6100-0(2)) Holt, Henry & Co. (Holt, Henry & Co. Bks. For Young Readers).

Pinkwater, Daniel M. Go West. Rash, Andy, illus. 2002. (Fat Camp Commandos Ser.). 96p. (J). (gr. 3-8). pap. 14.95 (978-0-439-29772-1(9) , Scholastic Pr.) Scholastic, Inc.

—Go West. 2003. (gr. 3-6). lib. bdg. 12.40 (978-0-613-62511-1(0)) Tandem Library Bks.

Robinson, Alise. U, F & O... Where Did They Go? An Alphabet Book. 2005. (Illus.). 16p. (J). per. 6.95 (978-1-58117-395-6(4) , Intervisual/Piggy Toes) Dalmatian Pr.

San Souci, Daniel. Space Station Mars. 2005. (Illus.). 40p. (J). (gr. 1-4). 15.95 (978-1-58246-142-7(2) , Tricycle Pr.) Ten Speed Pr.

Santillo, LuAnn. The UFO. Santillo, LuAnn, ed. 2003. (Half-Pint Kids Readers Ser.). (Illus.). 7p. (J). (ps-1). pap. (978-1-59256-045-5(8)) Half-Pint Kids, Inc.

UNIFORMS

McDonald, Fiona. Uniforms Through History. 2006. (Illus.). 32p. (J). lib. bdg. (978-0-8368-6858-6(7)) Stevens, Gareth Inc.

McNab, Chris. Everyday Dress. 2002. (Twentieth-Century Developments in Fashion & Costume Ser.). (Illus.). 64p. (J). (gr. 7 up). lib. bdg. (978-1-59084-427-4(0)) Mason Crest Pubs.

Tadano, Kazuko. Girls' Life Illustration File. Ozawa, Tadashi, illus. 2003. (How to Draw Manga Ser.: Vol. 15). 132p. (YA). pap. 21.99 (978-4-7661-1338-9(1)) Graphic-Sha JPN. *Dist:* Diamond Bk. Distributors.

UNIFORMS, MILITARY

Anderson, Christopher A. Screaming Eagles. 2001. (G. I. Ser.). (Illus.). 80p. (J). 27.50 (978-0-7910-6672-0(X) , Chelsea Hse.) Facts On File, Inc.

Carman, William. The Ackermann Military Prints: Uniforms of the British & Indian Armies, 1840-1855. 2002. (Schiffer Military History Book Ser.). (Illus.). 176p. (gr. 10-13). 59.95 (978-0-7643-1671-5(0)) Schiffer Publishing, Ltd.

Graziadio, Stephanie. Personal Fighting Gear. 2004. (Heinemann Know It Ser.). (Illus.). 48p. (J). pap. 7.95 (978-1-4034-4559-9(1)); lib. bdg. (978-1-4034-4553-7(2)) Heinemann Library.

Harris, Carol & Brown, Mike. Ceremonial Costumes. 2002. (Twentieth-Century Developments in Fashion & Costume Ser.). (Illus.). 64p. (J). (gr. 7 up). lib. bdg. (978-1-59084-424-3(6)) Mason Crest Pubs.

—Military Uniforms. 2003. (Twentieth-Century Developments in Fashion & Costume Ser.). (Illus.). 64p. (J). (gr. 7 up). lib. bdg. (978-1-59084-418-2(1)) Mason Crest Pubs.

Katcher, Philip R. N. Civil War Confederate Troops. 2003. (Battle Ready Ser.). 48p. (J). 28.56 (978-1-4109-0120-0(3)) Raintree.

—Civil War State Troops. 2003. (Battle Ready Ser.). (Illus.). 48p. (YA). 28.56 (978-1-4109-0121-7(1)) Raintree.

Keller, William & Keller, Kurt. United States Army Shoulder Patches & Related Insignia from WWI to Korea. 2002. (Schiffer Military History Ser.). (Illus.). 224p. (gr. 10-13). 49.95 (978-0-7643-1502-2(1)) Schiffer Publishing, Ltd.

Lloyd, Mark. Combat Uniforms of the Civil War, 4 vols. Codd, Mike, illus. 1998. (YA). (gr. 7 up). lib. bdg. 74.95 (978-0-7910-4992-1(2) , Chelsea Hse.) Facts On File, Inc.

—The Confederate Army, 4 vols., Set. 1998. (Illus.). 64p. 17.98 (978-0-7910-4995-2(7) , Chelsea Hse.) Facts On File, Inc.

—The Federal Army, 4 vols., Set. 1998. (Illus.). 64p. 17.98 (978-0-7910-4993-8(0)); 17.98 (978-0-7910-4994-5(9)) Facts On File, Inc. (Chelsea Hse.).

—Military Badges & Insignia. 1999. (Illus.). 46p. (gr. 8-12). 20.00 (978-0-7881-6443-9(0)) DIANE Publishing Co.

Taliadoros, Jenny, ed. Navy Scouts Paper Dolls. Mingo, Norman & Ernst, Clara, illus. 2007. 8p. (J). pap. 12.00 (***978-0-9790668-3-2(2)***) Paper Studio Pr.

Tucker, Louise, ed. The Visual Dictionary of Military Uniforms: Eyewitness Visual Dictionaries. 2004. (Illus.). 64p. (J). (gr. 4-8). reprint ed. 18.00 (978-0-7567-7820-0(4)) DIANE Publishing Co.

UNIFORMS, NAVAL

see Uniforms, Military

UNION OF SOUTH AFRICA

see South Africa

UNION PACIFIC RAILROAD COMPANY

Ambrose, Stephen E. Nothing Like It in the World: The Men Who Built the Transcontinental Railroad 1863-1869. 2001. (gr. 7-12). lib. bdg. 25.75 (978-0-613-50134-7(9)) Tandem Library Bks.

Burger, James P. The Transcontinental Railroad. 2002. (Library of the Westward Expansion). (Illus.). 24p. (J). (gr. 3). lib. bdg. 19.95 (978-0-8239-5852-8(3) , PowerKids Pr.) Rosen Publishing Group, Inc., The.

Halpern, Monica. Building the Transcontinental Railroad. 2002. (Reading Expeditions Ser.). (Illus.). 40p. (J). (978-0-7922-8690-5(1)) National Geographic Society.

Renehan, Edward J. The Transcontinental Railroad: The Gateway to the West. 2007. (Milestones in American History Ser.). 128p. (J). (gr. 6-12). 35.00 (***978-0-7910-9351-1(4)*** , Chelsea Hse.) Facts On File, Inc.

Shea, Therese. The Transcontinental Railroad: Using Proportions to Solve Problems. 2006. (Math for the Real World Ser.). (Illus.). 32p. (J). pap. (978-1-4042-6075-7(7)); (gr. 4-8). lib. bdg. 23.95 (978-1-4042-3361-4(X)) Rosen Publishing Group, Inc., The.

Uschan, Michael V. The Transcontinental Railroad. 2004. (Events That Shaped America Ser.). (Illus.). 32p. (J). (gr. 3 up). lib. bdg. 24.67 (978-0-8368-3401-7(1)) Stevens, Gareth Inc.

UNIONS, LABOR

see Labor Unions

UNISON SPEAKING

see Choral Speaking

UNITARIANISM

Dant, Jennifer. Unitarian Universalism Is a Really Long Name. 2006. (Illus.). 30p. (J). pap. (978-1-55896-508-9(4) , Skinner Hse. Bks.) Unitarian Universalist Assn.

UNITED KINGDOM

see Great Britain

UNITED NATIONS

Acker, Kerry. Madeleine Albright. 2004. (Women in Politics Ser.). (Illus.). 120p. 30.00 (978-0-7910-7734-4(9)); 116p. pap. 30.00 (978-0-7910-7998-0(8)) Facts On File, Inc. (Chelsea Hse.).

Burgan, Michael. Madeleine Albright. 1998. (Single Titles Ser.: up). (Illus.). 144p. (gr. 7-12). lib. bdg. 24.90 (978-0-7613-0367-1(7) , Millbrook Pr.) Lerner Publishing Group.

Byman, Jeremy. Madam Secretary: The Story of Madeleine Albright. (Notable Americans Ser.). (Illus.). 1998. 96p. (gr. 5 up). 21.95 (978-1-883846-23-7(4)); 2004. 128p. (YA). (gr. 6-12). 23.95 (978-1-931798-34-1(6)) Reynolds, Morgan Inc.

Connolly, Sean. United Nations - Keeping the Peace. 2002. (Troubled World Ser.). (Illus.). 64p. (J). (gr. 6 up). lib. bdg. 28.54 (978-0-7398-6342-8(8)) Raintree.

Docalavich, Heather. The History & Structure of the United Nations: Development & Function. 2007. (United Nations Ser.). (Illus.). 88p. (J). (gr. 5 up). lib. bdg. 21.95 (978-1-4222-0068-1(X)) Mason Crest Pubs.

— UN Action Against Terrorism: Fighting Fear. 2007. (United Nations Ser.). (Illus.). 88p. (J). (gr. 5 up). lib. bdg. 21.95 (978-1-4222-0067-4(1)) Mason Crest Pubs.

Gall, Timothy L. & Gall, Susan B. Junior Worldmark Encyclopedia of the Nations, 10 vols., Set. 5th rev. ed. 2007. 520.00 (978-1-4144-1095-1(6) , UXL) Thomson Gale.

Gall, Timothy L. & Gall, Susan B. Junior Worldmark Encyclopedia of the Nations/[edited By] Timothy L. Gall & Susan Bevan Gall. 5th ed. 2007. (***978-1-4144-1096-8(4)); (978-1-4144-1097-5(2)); (978-1-4144-1098-2(0)); (978-1-4144-1099-9(9)); (978-1-4144-1100-2(6)); (978-1-4144-1101-9(4)); (978-1-4144-1102-6(2)); (978-1-4144-1103-3(0)); (978-1-4144-1104-0(9)); (978-1-4144-1105-7(7)*** Thomson Gale.

Gall, Timothy L. & Gall, Susan B., eds. Junior Worldmark Encyclopedia of the Nations, 9 vols. 2nd ed. 1999. (Illus.). (J). (978-0-7876-3807-8(2)); (978-0-7876-3804-7(8)); (978-0-7876-3805-4(6)) Thomson Gale.

Gunderson, Cory Gideon. U. N. Weapons Inspectors. 2004. (World in Conflict-the Middle East Ser.). (Illus.). 48p. (J). (gr. 4-8). lib. bdg. 25.65 (978-1-59197-414-7(3)) ABDO Publishing Co.

Horner, Matina S., intro. Madeleine Albright: Stateswoman. 1999. (Women of Achievement Ser.). (Illus.). 134p. (YA). (gr. 4-7). pap. 30.00 (978-0-7910-4709-5(1) , Chelsea Hse.) Facts On File, Inc.

Howard, Megan. Madeleine Albright. 1998. (Biography Ser.). (Illus.). 128p. (YA). (gr. 6-12). lib. bdg. 25.26 (978-0-8225-4935-2(2) , Lerner Pubns.) Lerner Publishing Group.

Junior World Mark Encyclopedia of the Nations/States/ Canadian Provinces, 3 vols., Set. 3rd ed. 2001. 455.00 (978-0-7876-4811-4(6)) Thomson Gale.

Koestler-Grack, Rachel. Kofi Annan: Guiding the United Nations. 2007. (Modern Peacemakers Ser.). (Illus.). 128p. (YA). (gr. 9 up). 30.00 (978-0-7910-8996-5(7) , Chelsea Hse.) Facts On File, Inc.

Kramer, Barbara. Madeleine Albright: First Woman Secretary of State. 2000. (People to Know Ser.). (Illus.). 112p. (J). (gr. 6-12). lib. bdg. 26.60 (978-0-7660-1143-4(7)) Enslow Pubs., Inc.

Libal, Autumn. International Security: Peacekeeping & Peace-Building Around the World. 2007. (United Nations Ser.). 88p. (J). (gr. 5 up). lib. bdg. 21.95 (978-1-4222-0071-1(X)) Mason Crest Pubs.

Lowry, Michael, ed. What's Next for the UN? Understanding Global Issues. 2002. (Understanding Global Issues). (Illus.). 56p. (J). (gr. 10-12). lib. bdg. 19.95 (978-1-58340-167-5(9)) Weigl Pubs., Inc.

Melvern, Linda. United Nations. 2001. (World Organizations Ser.). (Illus.). 32p. (J). (gr. 6-8). 24.00 (978-0-531-14624-8(3) , Watts, Franklin) Scholastic Library Publishing.

—United Nations. 2001. (gr. 5-8). lib. bdg. 15.25 (978-0-613-54752-9(7)) Tandem Library Bks.

Nelson, Sheila. Decolonization: Dismantling Empires & Building Independence. 2007. (United Nations Ser.). (Illus.). 88p. (YA). (gr. 5 up). lib. bdg. 21.95 (978-1-4222-0066-7(3)) Mason Crest Pubs.

—The UN & Cultural Globalization: One World, Many People. 2007. (United Nations Ser.). (Illus.). 88p. (YA). (gr. 5 up). lib. bdg. 21.95 (978-1-4222-0072-8(8)) Mason Crest Pubs.

O'Kelley, Jeff. A Visit to the United Nations. 2006. (Early Explorers Ser.). (J). 36.00 (***978-1-4108-6126-9(0)***) Benchmark Education Co.

Prior, Katherine. UNICEF. 2001. (World Organizations Ser.). (Illus.). 32p. (YA). (gr. 6-8). 24.00 (978-0-531-14625-5(1) , Watts, Franklin) Scholastic Library Publishing.

Ross, Stewart. The United Nations. 2003. (20th Century Perspectives Ser.). 48p. pap. 7.95 (978-1-4034-4622-0(9)); (Illus.). (J). (gr. 5-7). lib. bdg. 27.07 (978-1-4034-0152-6(7)) Heinemann Library.

—The United Nations. 2004. (World Watch Ser.). (Illus.). 48p. (YA). (gr. 6-8). lib. bdg. 18.99 (978-0-7398-6616-0(8)) Raintree.

Secondary School Package. (J). 19.95 (978-92-1-100623-0(6)) United Nations Pubns.

Suen, Anastasia. UNICEF: United Nations Children's Fund. 2002. (Reading Power Ser.). (Illus.). 24p. (J). (gr. 2). lib. bdg. 17.25 (978-0-8239-6005-7(6) , PowerKids Pr.) Rosen Publishing Group, Inc., The.

Tarsitano, Frank. United Nations. 2003. (International Organizations Ser.). (Illus.). 48p. (J). (gr. 5 up). lib. bdg. 30.00 (978-0-8368-5523-4(X)); pap. 11.95 (978-0-8368-5532-6(9)) Stevens, Gareth Inc. (World Almanac Library).

The United Nations: Global Leadership, 10 vols., Set. Incl. Decolonization : Dismantling Empires & Building Independence. Nelson, Sheila. (Illus.). (YA). lib. bdg. 21.95 (978-1-4222-0066-7(3)); Five Permanent Members of the un Security Council : Responsibilities & Roles. Walker, Ida. (Illus.). (YA). lib. bdg. 21.95 (978-1-4222-0075-9(2)); History & Structure of the United Nations : Development & Function. Docalavich, Heather. (Illus.). (J). lib. bdg. 21.95 (978-1-4222-0068-1(X)); Humanitarian Relief Operations : Lending a Helping Hand. Smith, Roger. (YA). lib. bdg. 21.95 (978-1-4222-0070-4(1)); International Security : Peacekeeping & Peace-Building Around the World. Libal, Autumn. (J). lib. bdg. 21.95 (978-1-4222-0071-1(X)); Pioneering International Law : Conventions, Treaties, & Standards. Nelson, Sheila. (Illus.). (YA). lib. bdg. 21.95 (978-1-4222-0073-5(6)); UN Action Against Terrorism : Fighting Fear. Docalavich, Heather. (Illus.). (J). lib. bdg. 21.95 (978-1-4222-0067-4(1)); UN & Cultural Globalization : One World, Many People. Nelson, Sheila. (Illus.). (YA). lib. bdg. 21.95 (978-1-4222-0072-8(8)); UN & the Global Marketplace : Economic Developments. Docalavich, Heather. (YA). lib. bdg. 21.95 (978-1-4222-0074-2(4)); UNICEF & Other Human Rights Efforts : Protection & Promotion. Smith, Roger. (Illus.). (YA). lib. bdg. 21.95 (978-1-4222-0069-8(8)); 88p. (gr. 5 up). 2007. 2006. Set lib. bdg. 219.50 (***978-1-4222-0065-0(5)***) Mason Crest Pubs.

Wheeler, Jill C. Madeleine Albright. 2002. (Women of the World Ser.). (J). lib. bdg. 21.35 (978-1-57765-316-5(5)) ABDO Publishing Co.

UNITED NATIONS—ARMED FORCES

Beller, Susan Provost. Battling in the Pacific: Soldiering in World War II. 2007. (Soldiers on the Battlefront Ser.). (Illus.). 112p. (YA). (gr. 6-8). lib. bdg. 33.26 (***978-0-8225-6381-5(9)*** , Twenty-First Century Bks.) Lerner Publishing Group.

UNITED NATIONS—FICTION

Birmajer, Marcelo. Una Vida Mas: Noticias Extranas IV. 2004. (SPA.). 111p. (J). pap. 9.95 (978-958-04-7081-6(2)) Norma S.A. COL. *Dist:* Lectorum Pubns., Inc.

Bowen, Anne. How Did You Grow So Big, So Soon? Backer, Marni, illus. 2003. 32p. (J). (ps-1). 15.95 (978-0-87614-024-6(X) , Carolrhoda Bks.) Lerner Publishing Group.

Fidler, Mark. Blaze of the Great Cliff. 2003. 196p. pap. 14.95 (978-0-595-28748-2(4)) iUniverse, Inc.

Zerfing, Robert A. The Silencer: A U. N. Conspiracy Novel. 2nd ed. 2003. 326p. (YA). per. 14.95 (978-0-9747881-0-4(4)) Clawfoot Publishing.

UNITED NATIONS' CHILDREN'S FUND

Grahame, Deborah A. UNICEF. 2003. (International Organizations Ser.). (Illus.). 48p. (J). (gr. 5 up). pap. 11.95 (978-0-8368-5531-9(0) , World Almanac Library) Stevens, Gareth Inc.

—"UNICEF (International Organizations) (Library Binding) " 2003. (International Organizations Ser.). (Illus.). 48p. (J). (gr. 5 up). lib. bdg. 30.00 (978-0-8368-5522-7(1) , World Almanac Library) Stevens, Gareth Inc.

Maddocks, Steven. UNICEF. 2004. (World Watch Ser.). 48p. (J). (gr. 11-13). lib. bdg. 271.40 (978-0-7398-6617-7(6)) Raintree.

Prior, Katherine. UNICEF (World Organizations) 2001. (gr. 5-8). lib. bdg. 15.25 (978-0-613-54751-2(9)) Tandem Library Bks.

Suen, Anastasia. UNICEF. 2004. (Organizaciones de Ayuda Ser.). (SPA., Illus.). 24p. (J). (gr. 3-6). lib. bdg. 17.25 (978-0-8239-6858-9(8) , Buenas Letra) Rosen Publishing Group, Inc., The.

Unicef: Individual Title Six-Packs. (On Deck Ser.). 24p. (gr. 4-5). 35.00 (978-0-7578-1036-7(5)); (SPA.). 35.00 (978-0-7578-6415-5(5)) Rigby Education.

UNITED STATES

see also names of regions of the U. S. and groups of states e.g. Atlantic States; Middle West; Mississippi valley; Northwest, Old; Northwest, Pacific; Southern States; Southwest, New; Southwest, Old; The West

Alabama to Wyoming: State Fact Cards. 2003rd ed. 2003. (Illus.). 105p. (J). ring bd. 39.00 (978-1-884925-66-5(9)) Toucan Valley Pubns., Inc.

Allard, Denise. United States. 2000. (Postcards from...Ser.). (Illus.). 32p. (J). (gr. 2-4). pap. 6.95 (978-0-8172-6220-4(2)) Steck-Vaughn.

America the Beautiful. (Color & Learn Ser.). 36p. (J). (gr. 1-5). pap. (978-1-882210-12-1(3)) Action Publishing, Inc.

Barlowe, Dot. America the Beautiful to Paint or Color. 2006. 48p. pap. 4.95 (978-0-486-44811-4(8)) Dover Pubns., Inc.

Benchmark Education Staff, compiled by. Regions of the U. S. 2006. spiral bd. 330.00 (***978-1-4108-7006-3(5)***); 2006. spiral bd. 239.00 (***978-1-4108-7111-4(8)***); 2005. (J). spiral bd. 265.00 (***978-1-4108-5769-9(7)***) Benchmark Education Co.

—Social Studies Theme: Regions of the U. S. 2005. spiral bd. 115.00 (***978-1-4108-5330-1(6)***) Benchmark Education Co.

Berg, Elizabeth. U. S. A. 1999. (Countries of the World Ser.). (Illus.). 96p. (J). (gr. 6 up). lib. bdg. 30.00 (978-0-8368-2313-4(3)) Stevens, Gareth Inc.

Bial, Raymond. Building America, 5 bks., Set. Incl. Canals : Building America. 2001. lib. bdg. 27.07 (978-0-7614-1336-3(7)); Farms : Building America. 2002. lib. bdg. 27.07 (978-0-7614-1332-5(4)); Forts : Building America. 2001. lib. bdg. 27.07 (978-0-7614-1334-9(0)); Houses : Building America. 2001. lib. bdg. 27.07 (978-0-7614-1335-6(9)); Mills : Building America. 2001. lib. bdg. 27.07 (978-0-7614-1333-2(2)); 56p. (J). (gr. 4-7). (Illus.). 2001. 135.36 (978-0-7614-1331-8(6) , Benchmark Bks.) Cavendish, Marshall Corp.

The Bilingual Library of the United States of America, 26 bks., Set 1. Incl. Alabama. Brown, Vanessa. (ps-k). 2005. lib. bdg. 22.50 (978-1-4042-3065-1(3)); Alaska. Obregon, Jose M. (ps-k). 2005. lib. bdg. 22.50 (978-1-4042-3066-8(1)); Arizona. Brown, Vanessa. (ps-k). 2005. lib. bdg. 22.50 (978-1-4042-3067-5(X)); Arkansas. Brown, Vanessa. Brusca, Maria Cristina, tr. (gr. 2-5). 2005. lib. bdg. 22.50 (978-1-4042-3068-2(8)); California. Obregon, Jose M. (ps-k). 2005. lib. bdg. 22.50 (978-1-4042-3069-9(6)); Colorado. Obregon, Jose M. (ps-k). 2005. lib. bdg. 22.50 (978-1-4042-3070-5(X)); Connecticut. Brown, Vanessa. (ps-k). 2005. lib. bdg. 22.50 (978-1-4042-3071-2(8)); Delaware. Brown, Vanessa. (ps-k). 2005. lib. bdg. 22.50 (978-1-4042-3073-6(4)); District of Columbia/Distrito de Columbia. Brown, Vanessa. (ps-k). 2005. lib. bdg. 22.50 (978-1-4042-3072-9(6)); Florida. Obregon, Jose M. (ps-k). 2005. lib. bdg. 22.50 (978-1-4042-3074-3(2)); Georgia. Brown, Vanessa. (ps-k). 2005. lib. bdg. 22.50 (978-1-4042-3075-0(0)); Hawaii/Hawai. Obregon, Jose M. (ps-k). 2005. lib. bdg. 22.50 (978-1-4042-3076-7(9)); Idaho. Brown, Vanessa. Brusca, Maria Cristina, tr. (gr. 2-5). 2005. lib. bdg. 22.50 (978-1-4042-3077-4(7)); Illinois. Brown, Vanessa. (ps-k). 2005. lib. bdg. 22.50 (978-1-4042-3078-1(5)); Indiana. Brown, Vanessa. (gr. 2-5). 2005. lib. bdg. 22.50 (978-1-4042-3079-8(3)); Iowa. Brown, Vanessa. (ps-k). 2005. lib. bdg. 22.50 (978-1-4042-3080-4(7)); Kansas. Obregon, Jose M. (ps-k). 2005. lib. bdg. 22.50 (978-1-4042-3081-1(5)); Kentucky. Brown, Vanessa. Brusca, Maria Cristina, tr. (gr. 2-5). 2005. lib. bdg. 22.50 (978-1-4042-3082-8(3)); Louisiana/Luisiana. Brown, Vanessa. (gr. 2-5). 2005. lib. bdg. 22.50 (978-1-4042-3083-5(1)); Maine. Obregon, Jose M. Brusca, Maria Cristina, tr. (gr. 2-5). 2005. lib. bdg. 22.50 (978-1-4042-3084-2(X)); Maryland. Brown, Vanessa. (gr. 2-5). 2005. lib. bdg. 22.50 (978-1-4042-3085-9(8)); Massachusetts. Obregon, Jose M. Brusca, Maria Cristina, tr. (gr. 2-5). 2005. lib. bdg. 22.50 (978-1-4042-3086-6(6)); Michigan. Obregon, Jose Maria. Brusca, Maria Cristina, tr. (gr. 2-5). 2005. lib. bdg. 22.50 (978-1-4042-3087-3(4)); Minnesota. Brown, Vanessa. Brusca, Maria Cristina, tr. (gr. 2-5). 2005. lib. bdg. 22.50 (978-1-4042-3088-0(2)); Nueva York. Obregon, Jose Maria. Brusca, Maria Cristina, tr. (gr. 2-5). 2006. lib. bdg. 22.50 (978-1-4042-3097-2(1)); Texas. Obregon, Jose Maria. de Leon, Mauricio Velazquez, tr. (gr. 2-5). 2005. lib. bdg. 22.50 (978-1-4042-3109-2(9)); 32p. (J). (ENG & SPA., Illus.). 2005. Set lib. bdg. 585.00 (978-1-4042-7565-2(7)); Set lib. bdg. 585.00 (978-1-4042-7566-9(5)); Set lib. bdg. 1170.00 (978-1-4042-7567-6(3)) Rosen Publishing Group, Inc., The. (Buenas Letra).

Brooks, Clare & Garrington, Sally. Focus on the United States. 2006. (Illus.). 64p. (J). pap. (978-0-8368-6732-9(7)); lib. bdg. (978-0-8368-6725-1(4)) Stevens, Gareth Inc. (World Almanac Library).

Burgan, Michael. United States of America. 2007. (Enchantment of the World, Second Ser.). 144p. (J). spiral bd. 37.00 (***978-0-531-18488-2(9)*** , Children's Pr.) Scholastic Library Publishing.

Canizares, Susan & Daniel, Moreton. In Our Country. 1999. (ps-2). lib. bdg. 10.10 (978-0-613-21752-1(7)) Tandem Library Bks.

Canizares, Susan & Moreton, Daniel. In Our Country. 1999. (J). 2.50 (978-0-439-04562-9(2)) Scholastic, Inc.

Celebraciones de Estados Unidos, Unidad 6: Libros de la Biblioteca (Classroom Library) 2000. (Aventuras A Traves Del Tiempo Ser.). (ENG & SPA.). (gr. 1 up). (978-0-02-147844-6(9)) Macmillan/McGraw-Hill Schl. Div.

Celebrate Freedom: Songs, Symbols, & Sayings of the United States. 2003. (Illus.). 32p. (gr. k-2). (978-0-328-03672-1(2)); 48p. (gr. 3-6). (978-0-328-03674-5(9)) Addison-Wesley Educational Pubs., Inc. (Scott Foresman).

Celebrate the States - Group 4, 5 vols. Incl. Florida. Chang, Perry. lib. bdg. 37.07 (978-0-7614-0420-0(1)); Hawaii. Goldberg, Jake. lib. bdg. 37.07 (978-0-7614-0203-9(9)); Iowa. Morrice, Polly. lib. bdg. 37.07 (978-0-7614-0421-7(X)); Michigan. Brill, Marlene Targ. lib. bdg. 37.07 (978-0-7614-0418-7(X)); Washington, D. C. Elish, Dan. lib. bdg. 37.07 (978-0-7614-0423-1(6)); 144p. (gr. 4-8). 1998. (Illus.). 1998. 185.36 (978-0-7614-0416-3(3) , Benchmark Bks.) Cavendish, Marshall Corp.

Celebrate the States - Group 5, 5 vols. Incl. Ohio. Sherrow, Victoria. lib. bdg. 37.07 (978-0-7614-0656-3(5)); Rhode Island. Klein, T. lib. bdg. 37.07 (978-0-7614-0417-0(1)); Washington. Stefoff, Rebecca. lib. bdg. 37.07 (978-0-7614-0422-4(8)); West Virginia. Hoffman, Nancy. lib. bdg. 37.07 (978-0-7614-0665-5(4)); Wyoming. Baldwin, Guy. lib. bdg. 37.07 (978-0-7614-0662-4(X)); 144p. (gr. 4-8). (Illus.). 1998. 185.36 (978-0-7614-0654-9(9) , Benchmark Bks.) Cavendish, Marshall Corp.

Celebrate the States - Group 6, 5 vols. Incl. Kentucky. Barrett, T. 1998. lib. bdg. 37.07 (978-0-7614-0657-0(3)); Minnesota. Schwabacher, Martin. 1997. lib. bdg. 37.07 (978-0-7614-0658-7(1)); Mississippi. Shirley, David. 1999. lib. bdg. 37.07 (978-0-7614-0664-8(6)); New Hampshire. Otfinoski, Steven. 1999. lib. bdg. 37.07 (978-0-7614-0669-3(7)); New Mexico. McDaniel, Melissa. 1998. lib. bdg. 37.07 (978-0-7614-0659-4(X)); 144p. (gr. 4-8). (Illus.). 1999. 185.36 (978-0-7614-0661-7(1) , Benchmark Bks.) Cavendish, Marshall Corp.

Celebrate the States - Group 7, 5 vols. Incl. Arkansas. Altman, Linda Jacobs. lib. bdg. 37.07 (978-0-7614-0672-3(7)); Idaho. Stefoff, Rebecca. lib. bdg. 37.07 (978-0-7614-0663-1(8)); Maryland. Rauth, Leslie. lib. bdg. 37.07 (978-0-7614-0671-6(9)); Massachusetts. LeVert, Suzanne. lib. bdg. 37.07 (978-0-7614-0666-2(2)); New Jersey. Moragne, Wendy. lib. bdg. 37.07 (978-0-7614-0673-0(5)); 144p. (gr. 4-8). (Illus.). 2000. 185.36 (978-0-7614-0668-6(9) , Benchmark Bks.) Cavendish, Marshall Corp.

Celebrate the States - Group 8, 5 vols. Incl. Alabama. Shirley, David. lib. bdg. 37.07 (978-0-7614-0648-8(4)); Arizona. McDaniel, Melissa. (J). lib. bdg. 37.07 (978-0-7614-0647-1(6)); Delaware. Schuman, Michael A. lib. bdg. 37.07 (978-0-7614-0645-7(X)); Kansas. Bjorklund, Ruth. lib. bdg. 37.07 (978-0-7614-0646-4(8)); Pennsylvania. Peters, Stephen. lib. bdg. 37.07 (978-0-7614-0644-0(1)); 144p. (gr. 4-8). 2000. (Illus.). 2000. 185.36 (978-0-7614-0643-3(3) , Benchmark Bks.) Cavendish, Marshall Corp.

Celebrate the States Group 3, 5 bks., Set. 2nd ed. Incl. Alaska. Stefoff, Rebecca. lib. bdg. 39.93 (978-0-7614-2153-5(X)); Connecticut. Sherrow, Victoria. lib. bdg. 39.93 (978-0-7614-2155-9(6)); South Dakota. McDaniel, Melissa. lib. bdg. 39.93 (978-0-7614-2156-6(4)); Tennessee. Barrett, Tracy. lib. bdg. 39.93 (978-0-7614-2151-1(3)); Wisconsin. Hart, Joyce & Zeinert, Karen. lib. bdg. 39.93 (978-0-7614-2157-3(2)); (J). 2006. 2007. Set lib. bdg. 199.64 (***978-0-7614-2150-4(5)*** , Benchmark Bks.) Cavendish, Marshall Corp.

Celebrate the States Group 4, 5 bks., Set. 2nd ed. Incl. Florida. Hart, Joyce & Chang, Perry. lib. bdg. 39.93 (978-0-7614-2348-5(6)); Hawaii. Goldberg, Jake & Hart, Joyce. lib. bdg. 39.93 (978-0-7614-2349-2(4)); Iowa. Morrice, Polly Alison & Hart, Joyce. lib. bdg. 39.93 (978-0-7614-2350-8(8)); Michigan. Brill, Marlene Targ. lib. bdg. 39.93 (978-0-7614-2351-5(6)); Washington, D. C. Elish, Dan. lib. bdg. 39.93 (978-0-7614-2352-2(4)); (J). 2007. 2007. Set lib. bdg. 199.64 (***978-0-7614-2347-8(8)*** , Benchmark Bks.) Cavendish, Marshall Corp.

Cheney, Lynne. America: A Patriotic Primer. Glasser, Robin Preiss, illus. 2002. 40p. (J). 16.95 (978-0-689-85192-6(8)) Simon & Schuster Children's Publishing.

Childrens Press Staff. America the Beautiful, Set. 1999. (Illus.). (J). pap. 320.00 (978-0-516-21642-3(2) , Children's Pr.) Scholastic Library Publishing.

Colman, C. H. The Bald Eagle's View of American History. Friar, Joanne H., illus. 2006. (J). (gr. 1-4). pap. 5.95 (978-1-58089-301-5(5)) Charlesbridge Publishing, Inc.

Colonial America Complete Unit. (gr. 2-5). 286.95 (978-0-7368-4487-1(2)) Red Brick Learning.

Coloring Fun of the U. S. States Images & Facts. 2003. (Illus.). 40p. (J). 3.95 (978-0-9729026-3-2(5)) Midwest Cylinder Management, Inc.

Coming to the United States Set F, 6 vols. (Phonics Readers Ser.). (gr. k-2). 28.95 (978-0-7368-4078-1(8)) Red Brick Learning.

Country Books: Arkansas Edition. 2002. pap. (978-0-7398-6759-4(8)) Raintree.

CultureGrams 2005 World Edition - the Americas. 2004. (YA). per. 39.99 (978-1-931694-89-6(3)) ProQuest CSA.

Davis, Kenneth C. Don't Know Much about the 50 States. Andriani, Renee, illus. 2004. (Don't Know Much About Ser.). 64p. (J). (gr. 1-4). pap. 7.99 (978-0-06-446227-3(7)) HarperCollins Pubs.

Dillon, Christine J., ed. Eastern United States. rev. ed. 1998. (My First Report Ser.). (Illus.). 58p. (J). (gr. 1-3). ring bd. 5.95 (978-1-57896-020-0(7) , 1996) Hewitt Research Foundation, Inc.

—Middle United States. rev. ed. 1998. (My First Report Ser.). (Illus.). 62p. (J). (gr. 1-3). ring bd. 5.95 (978-1-57896-021-7(5) , 1998) Hewitt Research Foundation, Inc.

—Southern United States. rev. ed. 1998. (My First Report Ser.). (Illus.). 58p. (J). (gr. 1-3). ring bd. 5.95 (978-1-57896-022-4(3) , 1997) Hewitt Research Foundation, Inc.

—Western United States. rev. ed. 1999. (My First Report Ser.). (Illus.). 62p. (J). (gr. 1-3). ring bd. 5.95 (978-1-57896-023-1(1)) Hewitt Research Foundation, Inc.

Doak, Robin S. The United States. 2004. (First Reports). (Illus.). 48p. (J). (gr. 3 up). 22.60 (978-0-7565-0583-7(6)) Compass Point Bks.

Fink, Sam. Declaration of Independence. 2007. 160p. (J). pap. 11.99 (***978-0-439-70315-4(8)*** , Scholastic Nonfiction) Scholastic, Inc.

Fisher, Donna R. My Book of States. 1999. (Illus.). 54p. (J). (gr. 1). 5.00 (978-1-57896-054-5(1) , 2820, Hewitt Homeschooling Resources) Hewitt Research Foundation, Inc.

Frank, E. R. America. 2002. (Illus.). 224p. (YA). (gr. 8 up). 18.00 (978-0-689-84729-5(7) , Atheneum/Richard Jackson Bks.) Simon & Schuster Children's Publishing.

Frank, Nicole & Berg, Elizabeth. Welcome to U. S. A. 2000. (Welcome to My Country Ser.). (Illus.). 48p. (J). (gr. 2 up). lib. bdg. 26.00 (978-0-8368-2513-8(6)) Stevens, Gareth Inc.

Gall, Timothy L. & Gall, Susan B. Junior Worldmark Encyclopedia of the States. 5th ed. 2007. (J). (***978-1-4144-1107-1(3)); (*978-1-4144-1108-8(1)); (*978-1-4144-1109-5(X)); (*978-1-4144-1110-1(3));*** Set. 235.00 (978-1-4144-1106-4(5) , UXL) Thomson Gale.

Gall, Timothy L. & Gall, Susan B., eds. Junior Worldmark Encyclopedia of the States, 4 vols., Set. 3rd ed. Incl. Junior Worldmark Encyclopedia of the States Vol. 1 : Alabama to Illinois. (978-0-7876-5377-4(2)); Junior Worldmark Encyclopedia of the States Vol. 2 : Indiana to Nebraska. (978-0-7876-5378-1(0)); Junior Worldmark Encyclopedia of the States Vol. 3 : Nevada to South Dakota. (978-0-7876-5379-8(9)); Junior Worldmark Encyclopedia of the States Vol. 4 : Tennessee to Wyoming. (978-0-7876-5380-4(2)); (J). (Illus.). 900p. 2001. lib. bdg. (978-0-7876-5376-7(4) , GML00502-173569, UXL) Thomson Gale.

—Junior Worldmark Encyclopedia of the States Vol. 1: Alabama to Illinois, 4 vols. 3rd ed. 2001. (Illus.). (J). (978-0-7876-5377-4(2) , UXL) Thomson Gale.

—Junior Worldmark Encyclopedia of the States Vol. 2: Indiana to Nebraska, 4 vols. 3rd ed. 2001. (Illus.). (J). (978-0-7876-5378-1(0) , UXL) Thomson Gale.

—Junior Worldmark Encyclopedia of the States Vol. 3: Nevada to South Dakota, 4 vols. 3rd ed. 2001. (Illus.). (J). (978-0-7876-5379-8(9) , UXL) Thomson Gale.

—Junior Worldmark Encyclopedia of the States Vol. 4: Tennessee to Wyoming, 4 vols. 3rd ed. 2001. (Illus.). (J). (978-0-7876-5380-4(2) , UXL) Thomson Gale.

Garrison, Edward T., Jr. Short Stories about States & Capitals. (Illus.). (J). (gr. 5 up). (978-0-9634033-0-8(3)) EG Photoprint Co.

Gillis, Jennifer Blizin. The Southeast. 2006. (Regions of the USA Ser.). (Illus.). 56p. (J). (978-1-4109-2308-0(8)) Steck-Vaughn.

Golden, Nancy. Exploring the United States with the Five Themes of Geography. (Library of the Western Hemisphere). (J). 2005. (Illus.). 24p. 19.95 (978-1-4042-2670-8(2) , PowerKids Pr.); 2004. pap. (978-0-8239-4642-6(8)); 2004. (Illus.). 24p. lib. bdg. (978-0-8239-4630-3(4)) Rosen Publishing Group, Inc., The.

Green, Michael & Green, Gladys. Night Attack Gunships: The AC-130H Spectres. 2003. (War Planes Ser.). (Illus.). 32p. (J). (gr. 3-4). lib. bdg. 21.26 (978-0-7368-1509-3(0) , Capstone High-Interest Bks.) Capstone Pr., Inc.

Hablitzel, Marie & Stitzer, Kim H. Draw Write Now Bk. 5: The United States, from Sea to Sea, Moving Forward. 1998. (Draw Write Now Ser.). (Illus.). 64p. (J). (gr. k-5). pap. 10.95 (978-0-9639307-5-0(3)) Barker Creek Publishing, Inc.

Hardcastle, Stoney. True, Last Wild West Frontier. 1999. (True, Last Wild West Frontier Ser.). 200p. (J). pap. 8.95 (978-0-9653874-2-2(9)) Indian Nations Publishing Co.

Hauser, Jill Frankel. Little Hands Celebrate America! Learning about the U.S.A Through Crafts & Activities. 2004. (Williamson's Little Hands Book Ser.). (Illus.). 128p. (J). 12.95 (978-1-885593-93-1(7) , Williamson Bks.) Ideals Pubns.

Heinrichs, Ann. America the Beautiful Set. 1998. pap. 320.00 (978-0-516-21641-6(4) , Children's Pr.) Scholastic Library Publishing.

Hopkins, Lee Bennett, et al. My America: A Poetry Atlas of the United States. Alcorn, Stephen, illus. 2000. 96p. (J). (gr. 4-7). 22.99 (978-0-689-81247-7(7)) Simon & Schuster Children's Publishing.

Hudson, David L. Educational Standards. 2007. (Point/Counterpoint Ser.). 112p. (J). (gr. 9). 32.95 (***978-0-7910-9278-1(X)*** , Chelsea Hse.) Facts On File, Inc.

Italia, Bob. The United States. 2003. (Countries Ser.). (Illus.). 48p. (J). (gr. k-6). lib. bdg. 22.78 (978-1-57765-845-0(0)) ABDO Publishing Co.

It's My State Group 8, 6 bks., Set. Incl. Alabama. Hart, Joyce. 2006. lib. bdg. 29.93 (978-0-7614-1925-9(X)); Hawaii. Gaines, Ann. (Illus.). (gr. 3-6). 2006. lib. bdg. 29.93 (978-0-7614-1926-6(8)); Indiana. Derzipilski, Kathleen. (Illus.). (gr. 3-6). 2006. lib. bdg. 29.93 (978-0-7614-1927-3(6)); Iowa. King, David C. (Illus.). 2006. lib. bdg. 29.93 (978-0-7614-1928-0(4)); Washington, D. C. Hicks, Terry Allan. (Illus.). (gr. 3-6). 2006. lib. bdg. 29.93 (978-0-7614-1929-7(2)); Wyoming. Petreycik, Rick. (Illus.). 2007. lib. bdg. 29.93 (***978-0-7614-1930-3(6));*** 80p. (J). 2007. Set lib. bdg. 179.57 (***978-0-7614-1924-2(1)*** , Benchmark Bks.) Cavendish, Marshall Corp.

It's My State! Series - Group 1, 6 bks., Set. 162.43 (978-0-7614-1417-9(7) , Benchmark Bks.) Cavendish, Marshall Corp.

Kalman, Bobbie. United States from a to Z. 1999. (gr. k-3). lib. bdg. 16.40 (978-0-613-12228-3(3)) Tandem Library Bks.

Katcher, Philip R. N. Union Flags of the Civil War. 2003. (Battle Ready Ser.). (Illus.). 48p. (J). 28.56 (978-1-4109-0123-1(8)) Raintree.

Kuntz, Lynn & Fleming, Jan. American Grub: Eats for Kids from All Fifty States. Hicks, Mark A., illus. 2003. 80p. (YA). pap. 7.95 (978-1-58685-260-3(4)) Gibbs Smith, Publisher.

Land of Liberty, 26 bks. Incl. Alabama. Welsbacher, Anne. lib. bdg. 23.93 (978-0-7368-1569-7(4)); Alaska. Niz, Xavier. lib. bdg. 23.93 (978-0-7368-1570-3(8)); Arizona. Adamson, Thomas K. lib. bdg. 23.93 (978-0-7368-1571-0(6)); Arkansas. Olien, Rebecca. lib. bdg. 23.93 (978-0-7368-1572-7(4)); California. Glaser, Jason. lib. bdg. 23.93 (978-0-7368-1573-4(2)); Colorado. Christian, Sandra J. lib. bdg. 23.93 (978-0-7368-1574-1(0)); Connecticut. Pell, Ed. lib. bdg. 23.93 (978-0-7368-1575-8(9)); Delaware. Welsbacher, Anne. lib. bdg. 23.93 (978-0-7368-1576-5(7)); Florida. Christian, Sandra J. lib. bdg. 23.93 (978-0-7368-1577-2(5)); Georgia. Sullivan, Jody. lib. bdg. 23.93 (978-0-7368-1578-9(3)); Hawaii. Sullivan, Jody. lib. bdg. 23.93 (978-0-7368-1579-6(1)); Idaho. Hodgkins, Fran. lib. bdg. 23.93 (978-0-7368-1580-2(5)); Illinois. Sievert, Terri. lib. bdg. 23.93 (978-0-7368-1581-9(3)); Indiana. Pell, Ed. lib. bdg. 23.93 (978-0-7368-1582-6(1)); Iowa. Christian, Sandra J. lib. bdg. 23.93 (978-0-7368-1583-3(X)); Kansas. Olien, Rebecca. lib. bdg. 23.93 (978-0-7368-1584-0(8)); Kentucky. Niz, Xavier. 23.93 (978-0-7368-1585-7(6)); Louisiana. Glaser, Jason. lib. bdg. 23.93 (978-0-7368-1586-4(4)); Maine. Knox, Barbara. lib. bdg. 23.93 (978-0-7368-1587-1(2)); Maryland. Pell, Ed. lib. bdg. 23.93 (978-0-7368-1588-8(0)); Massachusetts. Hodgkins, Fran. lib. bdg. 23.93 (978-0-7368-1589-5(9)); Michigan. Knox, Barbara. lib. bdg. 23.93 (978-0-7368-1590-1(2)); Minnesota. Glaser, Rebecca Stromstad. lib. bdg. 23.93 (978-0-7368-1591-8(0)); New York. Sturm, Ellen. lib. bdg. 23.93 (978-0-7368-1592-5(9)); Ohio. Sturm, Ellen. lib. bdg. 23.93 (978-0-7368-1593-2(7)); Texas. Sievert, Terri. lib. bdg. 23.93 (978-0-7368-1594-9(5)); 64p. (J). (gr. 3-4). (Illus.). 2003. lib. bdg. (978-0-7368-1603-8(8) , Bridgestone Bks.) Capstone Pr., Inc.

Leedy, Loreen. Celebrate the 50 States. (Illus.). 32p. (J). (gr. k-3). tchr. ed. 17.95 (978-0-8234-1431-4(0)) Holiday Hse., Inc.

Long, Cathryn J. The 50 States. Nolte, Larry, illus. 1999. (Crossword America Ser.). 64p. (J). (gr. 3-7). pap. 5.95 (978-0-7373-0173-1(2) , 01732W) McGraw-Hill/Contemporary.

Low, Robert S., ed. My Guide to Our State. 2001. 40p. (J). (gr. 3-4). pap., wbk. ed. 3.50 (978-1-56762-143-3(0)) Modern Learning Pr.

—My Guide to the U. S. A. 2001. 56p. (J). (gr. 5-6). pap., wbk. ed. 3.75 (978-1-56762-144-0(9)) Modern Learning Pr.

Miller, Millie & Nelson, Cyndi. The United States of America. 1999. (Illus.). 64p. (J). (gr. 3-7). pap. 14.95 (978-0-590-04374-8(9) , Scholastic Reference) Scholastic, Inc.

My World of Neighbors. (YA). 22.00 (978-1-931555-46-3(X)) Our Lady of Victory Schl.

Nault, Jennifer. A Guide to American States: Fact Book. 2002. (Guide to American States Ser.). (Illus.). 32p. (J). lib. bdg. 24.25 (978-1-59036-031-6(1)) Weigl Pubs., Inc.

Nelson, Robin. Where Is My State? (First Step Nonfiction Ser.). (gr. k-2). 2005. (Illus.). 24p. lib. bdg. 17.27 (978-0-8225-0191-6(0)); 2001. (J). pap. 3.95 (978-0-8225-1980-5(1) , Lerner Pubns.) Lerner Publishing Group.

New York Public Library Staff & Sutcliffe, Andrea. The New York Public Library Amazing U. S. Geography: A Book of Answers for Kids. 2002. (New York Public Library Books for Kids: Vol. 12). (Illus.). 176p. pap. 12.95 (978-0-471-39294-1(4) , Wiley) Wiley, John & Sons, Inc.

Orange County Children's Directory. 2001. pap. (978-1-888771-11-4(9)) Riviera Pubns.

Ostrow, Kim. Mission Nuestra Senora de la Soledad. 2000. (Missions of California Ser.). (SPA., Illus.). 64p. (J). (gr. 4). lib. bdg. 25.50 (978-0-8239-5500-8(1) , PowerKids Pr.) Rosen Publishing Group, Inc., The.

Pearl, Norman. The Bald Eagle. Skeens, Matthew, illus. 2006. 24p. (J). (***978-1-4048-2642-7(4)***) Picture Window Bks.

Pearl, Norman. The Great Seal of the United States. Skeens, Matthew, illus. 2006. 24p. (J). (ps-2). lib. bdg. 23.93 (978-1-4048-2214-6(3)) Picture Window Bks.

People of the United States. (J). (gr. 5). (978-0-8374-1459-1(8) , 207) Weekly Reader Corp.

Phillipson, Olly. United States. 2001. (Country Studies). (Illus.). 64p. (J). (gr. 6-8). lib. bdg. 27.07 (978-1-57572-423-2(5)) Heinemann Library.

Popper, Garry. Billy Joe in the U. S. A. Johnson, Andi, illus. 2004. 36p. (ps-7). 4.00 (978-1-84161-053-5(4)) Ravette Publishing, Ltd. GBR. *Dist:* Parkwest Pubns., Inc.

Quasha, Jennifer. A Kid's Guide to Drawing America. 2002. (Kids Guide to Drawing America Ser.). (Illus.). 32p. (J). lib. bdg. 25.25 (978-0-8239-6057-6(9)); lib. bdg. 25.25 (978-0-8239-6058-3(7)); lib. bdg. 25.25 (978-0-8239-6091-0(9)) Rosen Publishing Group, Inc., The. (PowerKids Pr.).

Raintree Steck-Vaughn Staff. States: Arkansas Edition, 44 Bks., Set. 2003. 1130.80 (978-1-4109-0164-4(5)) Raintree.

Rappaport, Doreen. In the Promised Land: Lives of Jewish Americans. Van Wright, Cornelius, illus. 2005. 32p. (J). (gr. k-4). lib. bdg. 16.89 (978-0-06-059395-7(4)) HarperCollins Pubs.

Rasmussen, R. Kent. The 50 States. 2000. (Illus.). 992p. (gr. 9 up). lib. bdg. 142.00 (978-0-89356-999-0(2) , 73) Salem Pr., Inc.

Reichblum, Charles. Knowledge in a Nutshell on America. 2001. (Knowledge in a Nutshell Ser.). 192p. (Orig.). (J). pap. 9.50 (978-0-9660991-3-3(3)) arpr, inc.

Reynolds, Jeff E. United States of America. 2005. (to Z Ser.). (Illus.). 40p. (J). (gr. 2-4). pap. 6.95 (978-0-516-25074-8(4) , Children's Pr.) Scholastic Library Publishing.

Rookie Read-About Geography: States, 5 Bks. 2004. 95.00 (978-0-516-23747-3(0) , Children's Pr.) Scholastic Library Publishing.

Rubel, David. Scholastic Atlas of the United States. 2000. (Illus.). 144p. (J). (gr. 4-7). pap. 19.95 (978-0-590-72562-0(9) , Scholastic Reference) Scholastic, Inc.

Ruth, Angie. My Adventure in the United States of America. 2007. 44p. (J). 8.99 (978-1-59092-438-9(X) , Orchard Academy Pr.) Windstorm Creative.

Scholastic, Inc. Staff. The Kids' Book of the 50 Great States. 1998. (Illus.). 216p. (J). 14.95 (978-0-590-99621-1(5)) Scholastic, Inc.

—Wheel of the States Pack. 1998. (Wheel Ser.). (J). (gr. 4-7). 3.95 (978-0-590-02727-4(1) , 865555T, Scholastic Reference) Scholastic, Inc.

Schroeder, Holly. The United States ABCs: A Book about the People & Places of the United States. Yesh, Jeff, illus. 2004. (Country ABCs Ser.). 32p. (J). (gr. k-5). 23.93 (978-1-4048-0181-3(2) , 1229509) Picture Window Bks.

Schuh, Mari C. In My State. 2006. (J). (978-0-7368-4240-2(3)) Capstone Pr., Inc.

Simon, Seymour. Summer Across America. 1999. (J). (978-0-7868-0181-7(6)) Hyperion Pr.

Sis, Peter. The Train of States. Sis, Peter, illus. 64p. (J). 2007. (gr. k-5). pap. 6.99 (***978-0-06-057840-4(8));*** 2004. (Illus.). (gr. 1 up). 17.99 (978-0-06-057838-1(6)); 2004. (Illus.). (gr. 1 up). lib. bdg. 18.89 (978-0-06-057839-8(4)) HarperCollins Pubs.

Smolan, Rick & Cohen, David Elliot, creators. America 24/7: 24 Hours. 7 Days. Extraordinary Images of One American Week. 2003. (Illus.). 304p. 50.00 (978-0-7894-9975-2(4)) Dorling Kindersley Publishing, Inc.

Spengler, Kremena. The United States: A Question & Answer Book. 2007. 32p. (J). (***978-0-7368-6774-0(0)***) Capstone Pr., Inc.

States. 2006. (Illus.). (J). (***978-1-4127-1308-5(0)***) Publications International, Ltd.

Stevens, Kathryn. The United States. 1999. (Countries: Faces & Places Ser.). (Illus.). 32p. (J). (gr. 1-5). 25.64 (978-1-56766-602-1(7)) Child's World, Inc.

Stewart, Mark. The Southwest. 2006. (Regions of the USA Ser.). (Illus.). 56p. (J). (978-1-4109-2309-7(6)); pap. (978-1-4109-2317-2(7)) Steck-Vaughn.

Stewart, Mark. The United States & Canada. 2007. (J). pap. (***978-1-4034-9912-7(8));*** (Illus.). 64p. (gr. 4-7). lib. bdg. (***978-1-4034-9903-5(9)***) Raintree.

Talbott, Hudson. United Tweets of America. 2008. 64p. (J). (gr. 1-3). 17.99 (***978-0-399-24520-6(0)*** , Putnam Juvenile) Penguin Group (USA) Inc.

Teitelbaum, Michael. Why People Want to Come to America. 2004. (Our Government & Citizenship Ser.). (Illus.). 32p. (J). (gr. 2-6). 27.07 (978-1-59296-328-7(5)) Child's World, Inc.

TNT Stone and Associates Staff & Petertil Design Partners Staff, illus. Our Fifty States & Their Flags. 1998. (Powertools for Kids Ser.: No. 15). 4p. (J). (gr. 2-5). pap., wbk. ed. 4.95 (978-1-58220-014-9(9) , 32505, Power-Tools for Kids) Navigator Systems, Inc.

United States Geography. 2004. 128p. (J). per. 11.99 (978-0-88724-254-0(5) , CD-4346) Carson-Dellosa Publishing Co., Inc.

Wargin, Kathy-Jo. The American Reader. Darnell, K. L., illus. 2006. 96p. (J). (gr. 1-5). 12.95 (978-1-58536-095-6(3)) Sleeping Bear Pr.

We Salute the Stars & Stripes: A Children's Book That Puts Meaning into the Pledge of Allegiance to Our Flag. 2001. (Illus.). 16p. (J). (gr. k-6). pap. 10.00 (978-0-9709436-0-6(1)) Michelson, Bettie E.

Webb, Marcus. The United States. 1999. (Modern Nations of the World Ser.). (Illus.). 112p. (YA). (gr. 7-10). 29.95 (978-1-56006-663-7(6) , Lucent Bks.) Thomson Gale.

Williams, Colleen Madonna Flood. My Adventure in the Northeast: Advanced My Adventure. 2007. 44p. (J). pap. 8.99 (978-1-59092-565-2(3) , Orchard Academy Pr.) Windstorm Creative.

Zocchi, Judy. In the United States. Brodie, Neale, illus. 2005. (Global Adventures II Ser.). 32p. (J). per. 9.95 (978-1-59646-173-4(X)) Dingles & Co.

—In the United States/en los Estados Unidos. Brodie, Neale, illus. 2005. (Global Adventures II Ser.).Tr. of En los Estados Unidos. (ENG & SPA.). 32p. (J). per. 9.95 (978-1-59646-175-8(6)) Dingles & Co.

UNITED STATES—AIR FORCE

Anzuoni, Robert P. The All American: An Illustrated History of the 82nd Airborne Division 1917 - to the Present. 2001. (Schiffer Military History Ser.). (Illus.). 176p. (gr. 10-13). 45.00 (978-0-7643-1321-9(5)) Schiffer Publishing, Ltd.

Boraas, Tracey. U. S. Air Force Special Forces: Special Operations Wings. 1999. (Warfare & Weapons Ser.). (Illus.). 48p. (J). (gr. 3-7). pap. 20.00 (978-0-531-12008-8(2) , Watts, Franklin) Scholastic Library Publishing.

Braulick, Carrie A. U.S. Air Force Bombers. 2006. (Blazers—Military Vehicles Ser.). (Illus.). 32p. (J). (978-0-7368-5466-5(5)) Capstone Pr., Inc.

—U.S. Air Force Fighters. 2006. (Blazers—Military Vehicles Ser.). (Illus.). 32p. (J). (978-0-7368-5467-2(3)) Capstone Pr., Inc.

—The U.S. Air Force Space Command. 2008. (J). (***978-1-4296-0829-9(3)***) Capstone Pr., Inc.

Braulick, Carrie A. The U.S. Air Force Thunderbirds. 2006. (Blazers—The U.S. Armed Forces Ser.). (Illus.). 32p. (J). (978-0-7368-4392-8(2)) Capstone Pr., Inc.

Camelo, Wilson. The U. S. Air Force & Military Careers. 2006. (U.S. Armed Forces & Military Careers Ser.). (Illus.). 128p. (J). lib. bdg. 31.93 (978-0-7660-2524-0(1)) Enslow Pubs., Inc.

Coggins, Patrick C. The Tuskegee Airmen: Flying from the Ground Up. 2001. (Illus.). 165p. (YA). pap. (978-1-892558-03-9(3)) Kreyol Connection Pubns.

Cooper, Jason. U. S. Air Force. 2003. (Illus.). 32p. (J). 28.50 (978-1-58952-712-6(7)) Rourke Publishing, LLC.

Covert, Kim. U. S. Air Force Special Forces: Combat Controllers. 1999. (Illus.). 48p. (J). (gr. 3-7). pap. 20.00 (978-0-531-12012-5(0) , Watts, Franklin) Scholastic Library Publishing.

—U. S. Air Force Special Forces: Pararescue. 1999. (Illus.). 48p. (J). (gr. 3-7). pap. 20.00 (978-0-531-12013-2(9) , Watts, Franklin) Scholastic Library Publishing.

Doeden, Matt. The U. S. Air Force. 2004. (Edge Books, the U.S. Armed Forces). (Illus.). 32p. (J). lib. bdg. 19.93 (978-0-7368-2738-6(2)) Capstone Pr., Inc.

Donovan, Sandy. The U. S. Air Force. 2005. (U. S. Armed Forces Ser.). (Illus.). 64p. (J). (gr. 4-7). lib. bdg. 26.60 (978-0-8225-1436-7(2)) Lerner Publishing Group.

Dougherty, Terri. The U. S. Air Force at War. 2001. (On the Front Lines Ser.). (Illus.). 32p. (J). (gr. 3-4). lib. bdg. 21.26 (978-0-7368-0921-4(X) , Capstone High-Interest Bks.) Capstone Pr., Inc.

Green, Michael. The United States Air Force. 1998. (Serving Your Country Ser.). (Illus.). 48p. (J). (gr. 4-7). lib. bdg. 19.00 (978-0-516-21310-1(5) , Children's Pr.) Scholastic Library Publishing.

Greene, Meg. Careers in the National Guards' Search & Rescue Units. 2005. (Careers in Search & Rescue Operations Ser.). (Illus.). 64p. (YA). (gr. 5-8). lib. bdg. 26.50 (978-0-8239-3836-0(0)) Rosen Publishing Group, Inc., The.

Holden, Henry M. Air Force Aircraft. 2001. (Aircraft Ser.). (Illus.). 48p. (J). (gr. 4-10). lib. bdg. 23.93 (978-0-7660-1714-6(1)) Enslow Pubs., Inc.

Hopkins, Ellen H. The Thunderbirds: The U. S. Air Force Aerial Demonstration Squadron. 2001. (Serving Your Country Ser.). (Illus.). 48p. (J). (gr. 3-4). lib. bdg. 21.26 (978-0-7368-0776-0(4) , Capstone High-Interest Bks.) Capstone Pr., Inc.

—U. S. Air Force Fighting Vehicles. 2003. (Heinemann Know It Ser.). (Illus.). 48p. (J). pap. 7.95 (978-1-4034-0447-3(X)) Heinemann Library.

—United States Air Force. 2003. (U. S. Armed Forces Ser.). (Illus.). 48p. (J). pap. 7.95 (978-1-4034-0444-2(5)) Heinemann Library.

Jordan, David. The US Air Force. 2004. (America's Armed Forces Ser.). (J). pap. (978-0-8368-5686-6(4)); lib. bdg. 30.00 (978-0-8368-5679-8(1)) Stevens, Gareth Inc. (World Almanac Library).

Keeter, Hunter. American Air Forces in the Vietnam War. 2005. (American Experience in Vietnam Ser.). (Illus.). 48p. (J). pap. (978-0-8368-5780-1(1)); lib. bdg. (978-0-8368-5773-3(9)) Stevens, Gareth Inc. (World Almanac Library).

Kennedy, Robert C. Life As an Air Force Fighter Pilot. 2000. (High Interest Bks.). (Illus.). 48p. (YA). (gr. 7-12). pap. 6.95 (978-0-516-23545-5(1) , Children's Pr.) Scholastic Library Publishing.

—Life As an Air Force Fighter Pilot. 2000. (gr. 7-12). lib. bdg. 15.25 (978-0-613-52120-8(X)) Tandem Library Bks.

Langley, Wanda. The Air Force in Action. 2001. (U. S. Military Branches & Careers Ser.). (Illus.). 104p. (J). (gr. 6-12). lib. bdg. 26.60 (978-0-7660-1636-1(6)) Enslow Pubs., Inc.

McNab, Chris. Protecting the Nation with the U. S. Air Force. 2003. (Rescue & Prevention Ser.). (Illus.). 96p. (J). (gr. 7 up). lib. bdg. (978-1-59084-416-8(5)) Mason Crest Pubs.

Roberts, Jeremy. U. S. Air Force Special Forces. 2005. (U. S. Armed Forces Ser.). (Illus.). 64p. (J). (gr. 4-7). lib. bdg. 26.60 (978-0-8225-1644-6(6)) Lerner Publishing Group.

Sweetman, Bill. Combat Rescue Helicopters: The MH-53 Pave Lows. 2002. (War Planes Ser.). (Illus.). 32p. (J). (gr. 3-4). lib. bdg. 21.26 (978-0-7368-1067-8(6) , Capstone High-Interest Bks.) Capstone Pr., Inc.

TUV

Warfare & Weapons, 9 bks. Incl. SWAT Teams. Green, Michael. 2000. lib. bdg. 21.26 (978-1-56065-758-3(8)); U. S. Air Force Special Forces : Combat Controllers. Covert, Kim. 1999. lib. bdg. 21.26 (978-0-7368-0334-2(3)); U. S. Air Force Special Forces : Pararescue. Covert, Kim. 1999. lib. bdg. 21.26 (978-0-7368-0335-9(1)); U. S. Air Force Special Forces : Special Operations Wings. Boraas, Tracey. 1999. lib. bdg. 21.26 (978-0-7368-0336-6(X)); U. S. Army Special Operations Command : Night Stalkers-Special Operations Aviation. Weiser, Andrea L. 1999. lib. bdg. 21.26 (978-0-7368-0338-0(6)); U. S. Army Special Operations Forces : Airborne Rangers. Burgan, Michael. 1999. lib. bdg. 21.26 (978-0-7368-0337-3(8)); U. S. Marine Corps Special Forces : Recon Marines. Voeller, Edward A. 1999. lib. bdg. 21.26 (978-0-7368-0339-7(4)); U. S. Navy Special Forces : SEAL Teams. Burgan, Michael. 1999. lib. bdg. 21.26 (978-0-7368-0340-3(8)); U. S. Navy Special Forces : Special Boat Units. Burgan, Michael. 1999. lib. bdg. 21.26 (978-0-7368-0341-0(6)); 48p. (J). (gr. 3-4). (Illus.). 2001. Set lib. bdg. 170.08 (978-0-7368-0465-3(X) , Capstone High-Interest Bks.) Capstone Pr., Inc.

Zobel, Derek. United States Air Force. 2008. (Illus.). 24p. (J). lib. bdg. 19.95 (***978-1-60014-161-4(7)***) Bellwether Media.

UNITED STATES—AIR FORCE—BIOGRAPHY

Ancona, George. Mi Casa: My House. 2004. (Somos Latino (We Are Latinos) Ser.). (ENG & SPA., Illus.). 32p. (J). 20.00 (978-0-516-23688-9(1) , Children's Pr.) Scholastic Library Publishing.

O'Grady, Scott & French, Michael. Basher Five-Two. 1998. (Illus.). 144p. (J). (gr. 5 up). reprint ed. pap. 5.50 (978-0-440-41313-4(3) , Yearling) Random Hse. Children's Bks.

Price Hossell, Karen. Benedict Arnold. 2004. (American War Biographies Ser.). (J). pap. 8.50 (978-1-4034-5085-2(4)); lib. bdg. 29.93 (978-1-4034-5078-4(1)) Heinemann Library.

Rice, Earle, Jr. Claire Chennault. 2003. (Famous Flyers Ser.). (Illus.). 112p. (gr. 6-12). 30.00 (978-0-7910-7217-2(7)); pap. 30.00 (978-0-7910-7499-2(4)) Facts On File, Inc. (Chelsea Hse.).

UNITED STATES—AIR FORCE ACADEMY

Alagna, Magdalena. Life Inside the Air Force Academy. 2002. (Insider's Look Ser.). (Illus.). 48p. (gr. 7-12). (J). pap. 23.00 (978-0-516-23924-8(4)); (YA). pap. 6.95 (978-0-516-24001-5(3)) Scholastic Library Publishing. (Children's Pr.).

UNITED STATES—AIR FORCE ACADEMY—FICTION

Weisleder, Stanley. Wings of the Panther. 2004. 224p. 15.00 (978-0-936783-38-3(9)) Merril Pr.

UNITED STATES—ANTIQUITIES

see also Indians of North America—Antiquities

Benson, Sonia & Baker, Deborah J. Almanac, Early Civilizations, 2 vols. 2005. (Early Civilizations in the Americas Reference Library). (Illus.). xli, 551p. (J). lib. bdg. 67.00 (978-0-7876-7679-7(9) , UXL) Thomson Gale.

—Primary Sources, Early Americas, 2 vols. 2005. (Early Civilizations in the Americas Reference Library). (Illus.). xli, 551p. (J). lib. bdg. 67.00 (978-0-7876-7681-0(0) , UXL) Thomson Gale.

Hansen, Joyce & McGowan, Gary. Freedom Roads: Searching for the Underground Railroad. Ransome, James E., illus. 2003. (Marcato Book Ser.). 166p. (J). (gr. 5-9). 18.95 (978-0-8126-2673-5(7)) Cricket Bks.

Hawk, Frank. The Story of the H. L. Hunley & Queenie's Coin. Nance, Dan, illus. 2004. 40p. (J). 16.95 (978-1-58536-218-9(2)) Sleeping Bear Pr.

Kavasch, E. Barrie. The Mound Builders of Ancient America. 2003. (J). lib. bdg. (978-0-7613-2368-6(6) , Twenty-First Century Bks.) Lerner Publishing Group.

Pauketat, Timothy R. & Bernard, Nancy Stone. Cahokia Mounds. 2004. (Digging for the Past Ser.). (Illus.). 48p. (YA). 22.95 (978-0-19-515810-6(5)) Oxford Univ. Pr., Inc.

Walker, Sally M. Written in Bone. 2008. (J). lib. bdg. (***978-0-8225-7135-3(8)*** , Carolrhoda Bks.) Lerner Publishing Group.

UNITED STATES—ARMED FORCES

see also official names of branches of the Armed Forces, e.g. U. S. Army; U. S. Navy

America's Armed Forces. 180.00 (978-0-8368-5678-1(3)) Stevens, Gareth Inc.

Baker, David. Armored Personnel Vehicle. 2007. (Fighting Forces on Land Ser.). (Illus.). 32p. (J). (978-1-60044-247-6(1)) Rourke Publishing, LLC.

—M1097 Humvee. 2007. (Fighting Forces on Land Ser.). (J). (978-1-60044-244-5(7)) Rourke Publishing, LLC.

Bell-Rehwoldt, Sheri. Military. 2005. (Careers for the Twenty-First Century Ser.). (Illus.). 112p. (J). (gr. 5-8). lib. bdg. 29.95 (978-1-59018-398-4(3) , 1244513, Lucent Bks.) Thomson Gale.

DeGezelle, Terri. The Pentagon. 2004. (First Facts Ser.). (Illus.). 24p. (J). 15.95 (978-0-7368-2530-6(4)) Capstone Pr., Inc.

Demarest, Chris L. Alpha Bravo Charlie: The Military Alphabet. Demarest, Chris L., illus. 2005. (Illus.). 40p. (J). 16.95 (978-0-689-86928-0(2) , McElderry, Margaret K.) Simon & Schuster Children's Publishing.

Donovan, Sandy. Protecting America: A Look at the People Who Keep Our Country Safe. 2004. (How Government Works). (Illus.). 56p. (J). (gr. 4-8). lib. bdg. 25.26 (978-0-8225-1345-2(5)) Lerner Publishing Group.

Draper, Allison Stark. Fighter Pilots: Life at Mach Speed. 2001. (Extreme Careers Ser.). (Illus.). 64p. (YA). (gr. 5-8). lib. bdg. 26.50 (978-0-8239-3366-2(0) , Rosen Central) Rosen Publishing Group, Inc., The.

Fandel, Jennifer. The U. S. Government Military. 2003. (Let's Investigate Ser.). (Illus.). 32p. (J). lib. bdg. 18.95 (978-1-58341-264-0(6) , Creative Education) Creative Co., The.

Fitzgerald, Stephanie & Lurch, Bruno. U.S. Armed Forces, 5 bks., Set 2. 2004. (J). (gr. 3-5). lib. bdg. 142.50 (978-1-4034-4554-4(0)) Heinemann Library.

Graziadio, Stephanie. Personal Fighting Gear. 2004. (Heinemann Know It Ser.). (Illus.). 48p. (J). pap. 7.95 (978-1-4034-4559-9(1)); lib. bdg. (978-1-4034-4553-7(2)) Heinemann Library.

Hamilton, John. America's Military. 2004. (War in Iraq Ser.). (Illus.). 48p. (J). (gr. 4-8). lib. bdg. 25.65 (978-1-59197-492-5(5)) ABDO Publishing Co.

—Armed Forces. 2002. (War on Terrorism Ser.). (Illus.). 64p. (J). (gr. 4-8). lib. bdg. 25.65 (978-1-57765-674-6(1) , ABDO & Daughters) ABDO Publishing Co.

—Special Forces. 2007. (Defending the Nation Ser.). (Illus.). 32p. (J). (gr. 3-5). lib. bdg. 22.78 (978-1-59679-759-8(2) , Checkerboard Library) ABDO Publishing Co.

—Weapons of the Twenty-First Century. 2004. (War in Iraq Ser.). (Illus.). 48p. (J). (gr. 4-8). lib. bdg. 25.65 (978-1-59197-501-4(8)) ABDO Publishing Co.

Harmon, Daniel E. The U. S. Armed Forces. 2001. (Your Government Ser.). (Illus.). 64p. (J). (gr. 4-7). 25.00 (978-0-7910-5994-4(4) , Chelsea Hse.) Facts On File, Inc.

Horn, Geoffrey M. The Armed Forces. 2003. (World Almanac Library of American Government). (Illus.). 48p. (J). (gr. 5 up). pap. 14.95 (978-0-8368-5461-9(6)); lib. bdg. 30.00 (978-0-8368-5456-5(X)) Stevens, Gareth Inc. (World Almanac Library).

—World Almanac Library of American Government: The Armed Forces; Congress; The Presidency; The Supreme Court, 4 bks. 2002. (Illus.). (J). (gr. 5 up). pap. 59.80 (978-0-8368-5460-2(8) , World Almanac Library) Stevens, Gareth Inc.

Kaelberer, Angie Peterson. U.S. Army Humvees. 2007. (Blazers—Military Vehicles Ser.). (Illus.). 32p. (J). 19.93 (978-0-7368-6458-9(X)) Capstone Pr., Inc.

Langellier, John P. American Indians in the U. S. Armed Forces, 1866-1945, Vol. 20. 2006. (G. I. Ser.: Vol. 20). (Illus.). 72p. pap. 14.95 (978-1-85367-408-2(7)) Greenhill Bks./Lionel Leventhal, Ltd. GBR. *Dist:* MBI Distribution Services.

Libal, Joyce. Military & Elite Forces Officer. 2003. (Careers with Character Ser.). (Illus.). 96p. (YA). (gr. 7 up). lib. bdg. 22.95 (978-1-59084-318-5(5)) Mason Crest Pubs.

Lieurance, Suzanne. Weapons & Strategies of the Civil War: A MyReportLinks. com Book. 2004. (American Civil War Ser.). (Illus.). 48p. (J). lib. bdg. 25.26 (978-0-7660-5185-0(4) , MyReportLinks.com Bks.) Enslow Pubs., Inc.

Marsh, Carole. John Paul Jones. 2002. (One Thousand Readers Ser.). (Illus.). 12p. (J). (gr. k-4). 2.95 (978-0-635-01523-5(4) , 15234) Gallopade International.

Miller, Connie Colwell. The National Security Agency: Cracking Secret Codes. 2008. (J). (***978-1-4296-1274-6(6)***) Capstone Pr., Inc.

Piehl, Janet. Humvees. 2005. 32p. (J). pap. 5.95 (978-0-8225-2874-6(6) , Lerner Pubns.) Lerner Publishing Group.

Rice, Earle. Claire Chennault: Flying Tigers. 2003. (gr. 5-8). lib. bdg. 18.75 (978-0-613-65196-7(0)) Tandem Library Bks.

—Korea 1950: From Pusan to Chosin. 2003. (Great Battles Through the Ages Ser.). (Illus.). 112p. (gr. 6-12). 30.00 (978-0-7910-7436-7(6) , Chelsea Hse.) Facts On File, Inc.

Rice, Earle, Jr. Korea 1950: Pusan to Chosin. 2004. (Great Battles Through the Ages Ser.). (Illus.). 112p. (gr. 6-12). pap. 13.25 (978-0-7910-7795-5(0) , Chelsea Hse.) Facts On File, Inc.

Rolling Thunder: Poster Book. 2002. (Armed Forces Ser.). (Illus.). 32p. (J). (ps). pap. 1.49 (978-1-57759-482-6(7)) Dalmatian Pr.

Roza, Greg. Careers in the Military. 2005. (World of Work Ser.). (Illus.). 64p. (YA). (gr. 7-12). lib. bdg. 25.25 (978-0-8239-3331-0(8)) Rosen Publishing Group, Inc., The.

Scillian, Devin. H Is for Honor: A Military Family Alphabet. Juhasz, Victor, illus. 2006. 40p. (J). 17.95 (978-1-58536-292-9(1)) Sleeping Bear Pr.

Smolinski, Diane. Soldiers of the French & Indian War. 2003. (Americans at War Ser.). (Illus.). 32p. (J). (gr. 4-6). lib. bdg. 25.64 (978-1-4034-0172-4(1)) Heinemann Library.

—Soldiers of the French & Indian War. 2003. (gr. 3-6). lib. bdg. 15.25 (978-0-613-89119-6(8)) Tandem Library Bks.

—Soldiers of the War of 1812. 2003. (Americans at War Ser.). (Illus.). 32p. (J). (gr. 4-6). lib. bdg. 25.64 (978-1-4034-0174-8(8)) Heinemann Library.

Smolinski, Diane & Smolinski, Henry. Soldiers of the French & Indian War. (Americans at War Ser.). 32p. pap. 6.95 (978-1-4034-3154-7(X)) Heinemann Library.

—Soldiers of the War of 1812. (Americans at War Ser.). 32p. pap. 6.95 (978-1-4034-3158-5(2)) Heinemann Library.

Sonder, Ben. Militia Movement: Fighters of the Far Right. 2000. (J). (978-0-606-19786-1(9)) Tandem Library Bks.

Stapleton, Gerard. Air Assault Teams. 2000. (Serving Your Country Ser.). (Illus.). 48p. (J). (gr. 3-7). lib. bdg. 19.00 (978-0-516-35285-5(7) , Children's Pr.) Scholastic Library Publishing.

Teitelbaum, Michael. Humvees: High Mobility in the Field. 2006. (Mighty Military Machines Ser.). (Illus.). 48p. (J). (gr. 4-10). lib. bdg. 23.93 (978-0-7660-2661-2(2)) Enslow Pubs., Inc.

U. S. Military Branches & Careers, 5 bks., Set. Incl. Air Force in Action. Langley, Wanda. 104p. (J). lib. bdg. 26.60 (978-0-7660-1636-1(6)); Army in Action. Sawyer, Susan. 104p. (J). lib. bdg. 26.60 (978-0-7660-1635-4(8)); Coast Guard in Action. Gaines, Ann Graham. 104p. (J). lib. bdg. 26.60 (978-0-7660-1634-7(X)); Marine Corps in Action. Aaseng, Nathan. 104p. (J). lib. bdg. 26.60 (978-0-7660-1637-8(4)); Navy in Action. Gaines, Ann Graham. 128p. (YA). lib. bdg. 26.60 (978-0-7660-1633-0(1)); (gr. 6-12). 2001. (Illus.). Set lib. bdg. 104.75 (978-0-7660-1803-7(2)) Enslow Pubs., Inc.

The US Armed Forces. 2005. (Blazers Ser.). (Illus.). (J). (gr. 1-2). lib. bdg. 239.16 (978-0-7368-4434-5(1)) Capstone Pr., Inc.

Wings of Freedom: Sticker Book. 2002. (Armed Forces Ser.). (Illus.). 48p. (J). (ps). pap. 1.99 (978-1-57759-483-3(5)) Dalmatian Pr.

Wolny, Philip. American Troops in Afghanistan: Building a New Nation. 2004. (Frontline Coverage of Current Events Ser.). (Illus.). 48p. (J). lib. bdg. 26.50 (978-1-4042-0343-3(5)) Rosen Publishing Group, Inc., The.

Yancey, Diane. Life of an American Soldier in Afghanistan. 2003. (American War Library). (Illus.). 128p. (J). 29.95 (978-1-59018-329-8(0) , Lucent Bks.) Thomson Gale.

UNITED STATES—ARMED FORCES—FICTION

Boyd, Jones Veda. Laura's Victory: End of the Second World War. 2006. 144p. (J). pap. 4.97 (978-1-59789-103-5(7)) Barbour Publishing, Inc.

Cummings, Mary. And the Baker's Boy Went to Sea. 2006. (Illus.). 195p. (YA). 16.95 (978-0-9774855-0-5(1)) Sparkling Pr.

Durrant, Lynda. My Last Skirt: The Story of Jennie Hodgers, Union Soldier. 2006. 245p. (YA). 21.95 (978-0-7862-8880-9(9)) Thorndike Pr.

Karr, Kathleen. Exiled: Memoirs of a Camel. 240p. (J). 2006. pap. 6.95 (978-0-7614-5291-1(5)); 2004. 15.95 (978-0-7614-5164-8(1)) Cavendish, Marshall Corp.

Sargent, Dave & Sargent, Pat. Buckshot: (Blue Eyed Chestnut) Mind Your Manners, 25, 8. Lenoir, Jane, illus. 2001. (Saddle Up Ser.: 8). 36p. (J). pap. 6.95 (978-1-56763-674-1(8)); lib. bdg. 22.60 (978-1-56763-673-4(X)) Ozark Publishing.

Zeinert, Karen. To Touch the Stars: A Story of World War II. 2004. (Jamestown's American Portraits Ser.). (Illus.). 136p. (J). (gr. 5-7). pap. 4.95 (978-0-7696-3442-5(7) , Waterbird Bks.) School Specialty Publishing.

—To Touch the Stars: A Story of World War II. 2000. (978-0-606-21878-8(5)) Tandem Library Bks.

UNITED STATES—ARMED FORCES—WOMEN

Worth, Richard. Women in Combat: The Battle for Equality. 1999. (Issues in Focus Ser.). (Illus.). 112p. (YA). (gr. 6-12). lib. bdg. 26.60 (978-0-7660-1103-8(8)) Enslow Pubs., Inc.

Zeinert, Karen & Miller, Mary. The Brave Women of the Gulf Wars: Operation Desert Storm & Operation Iraqi Freedom. 2006. (Women at War Ser.). (Illus.). 112p. (J). (ps-7). 30.60 (978-0-7613-2705-9(3) , Millbrook Pr.) Lerner Publishing Group.

UNITED STATES—ARMY

Aldrich, Dale & Hipperson, Carol Edgemon. The Belly Gunner. 2001. (Single Titles Ser.). (Illus.). 160p. (gr. 6 up). lib. bdg. 27.90 (978-0-7613-1873-6(9) , Twenty-First Century Bks.) Lerner Publishing Group.

Aller, Susan Bivin. Ulysses S. Grant. 2005. (History Maker Bios Ser.). (Illus.). 48p. (J). 26.60 (978-0-8225-2438-0(4) , Lerner Pubns.) Lerner Publishing Group.

Alter, Judy. Audie Murphy: War Hero & Movie Star. 2007. 72p. (YA). 14.95 (***978-1-933337-19-7(2)***) State Hse. Pr.

Anderson, Christopher A. Hell on Wheels. 2001. (G. I. Ser.). (Illus.). 80p. (J). 27.50 (978-0-7910-6670-6(3) , Chelsea Hse.) Facts On File, Inc.

—Screaming Eagles. 2001. (G. I. Ser.). (Illus.). 80p. (J). 27.50 (978-0-7910-6672-0(X) , Chelsea Hse.) Facts On File, Inc.

Anderson, Christopher J. The U. S. Army Today: From the End of the Cold War to the Present Day. 1999. (G. I. Ser.). (Illus.). 80p. (YA). (gr. 5 up). 27.50 (978-0-7910-5372-0(5) , Chelsea Hse.) Facts On File, Inc.

Anderson, Dale. Soldiers & Sailors in the American Revolution. 2005. (World Almanac Library of the American Revolution). (J). pap. (978-0-8368-5938-6(3)); lib. bdg. 30.00 (978-0-8368-5929-4(4)) Stevens, Gareth Inc. (World Almanac Library).

Anderson, Jane. My Name Is Deborah Samson. 2005. 40.00 (***978-1-4108-4225-1(8)***) Benchmark Education Co.

Aronson, Billy. Ulysses S. Grant. 2007. (Presidents & Their Times Ser.). 96p. (J). lib. bdg. 32.79 (978-0-7614-2430-7(X) , Benchmark Bks.) Cavendish, Marshall Corp.

Barbier, Mary. The U. S. Army. 2004. (America's Armed Forces Ser.). (Illus.). 48p. (J). 30.00 (978-0-8368-5680-4(5)); pap. (978-0-8368-5687-3(2)) Stevens, Gareth Inc. (World Almanac Library).

Bartlett, Richard. U. S. Army Fighting Vehicles. (Heinemann Know It Ser.). (Illus.). 48p. (J). 2003. pap. 7.95 (978-1-4034-0446-6(1)); 2002. (gr. 3-5). lib. bdg. 25.64 (978-1-4034-0189-2(6)) Heinemann Library.

—United States Army. 2003. (Heinemann Know It Ser.). (Illus.). 48p. (J). pap. 7.95 (978-1-4034-0445-9(3)) Heinemann Library.

—United States Army. 2003. (gr. 3-6). lib. bdg. 17.60 (978-0-613-70760-2(5)) Tandem Library Bks.

Beller, Susan Provost. Billy Yank & Johnny Reb: Soldiering in the Civil War. (Soldiers on the Battlefront Ser.). (Illus.). 2007. 112p. (YA). (gr. 6-8). lib. bdg. 33.26 (978-0-8225-6803-2(9)); 2000. 96p. (gr. 5 up). lib. bdg. (978-0-7613-1869-9(0) , Millbrook Pr.) Lerner Publishing Group.

Benge, Janet & Benge, Geoff. Douglas MacArthur: What Greater Honor. 2005. (Illus.). 205p. (J). 6.99 (978-1-932096-15-6(9)) Emerald Bks.

Benson, Michael. The U. S. Army. 2005. (U. S. Armed Forces Ser.). (Illus.). 64p. (J). (gr. 4-7). lib. bdg. 26.60 (978-0-8225-1645-3(4)) Lerner Publishing Group.

Blashfield, Jean F. Horse Soldiers: Cavalry in the Civil War. 1998. (First Bks.). (Illus.). 64p. (J). (gr. 5-7). 22.00 (978-0-531-20300-2(X) , Watts, Franklin) Scholastic Library Publishing.

Bodie, Idella. Light-Horse Harry. 2004. (Illus.). 86p. (J). pap. 6.95 (978-0-87844-172-3(7)) Sandlapper Publishing Co., Inc.

Braulick, Carrie A. The U.S. Army Golden Knights. 2006. (Blazers—The U.S. Armed Forces Ser.). (Illus.). 32p. (J). (978-0-7368-4393-5(0)) Capstone Pr., Inc.

—U.S. Army Helicopters. 2006. (Blazers—Military Vehicles Ser.). (Illus.). 32p. (J). (978-0-7368-5468-9(1)) Capstone Pr., Inc.

—The U.S. Army Rangers. 2006. (Blazers—The U.S. Armed Forces Ser.). (Illus.). 32p. (J). (978-0-7368-4394-2(9)) Capstone Pr., Inc.

—U.S. Army Tanks. 2006. (Blazers—Military Vehicles Ser.). (Illus.). 32p. (J). (978-0-7368-5469-6(X)) Capstone Pr., Inc.

Brooks, Philip. The Tuskegee Airmen. 2004. (Illus.). 48p. (J). (gr. 4 up). lib. bdg. 22.60 (978-0-7565-0683-4(2)) Compass Point Bks.

Buffalo Soldiers & the Western Frontier Vol. 2: Individual Title Six-Packs. (On Deck Ser.: Vol. 2). 24p. (gr. 4-5). 35.00 (978-0-7578-5805-5(8)) Rigby Education.

Burgan, Michael. Benedict Arnold: American Hero & Traitor. 2007. (Graphic Library). (Illus.). 32p. (J). (gr. 3-5). pap. 7.95 (***978-0-7368-7906-4(4)***) Capstone Pr., Inc.

Burgan, Michael. U. S. Army Special Operations Forces: Airborne Rangers. 1999. (Illus.). 48p. (J). (gr. 3-7). pap. 20.00 (978-0-531-12014-9(7) , Watts, Franklin) Scholastic Library Publishing.

Chandler, Gil. The Green Berets. 2000. (Serving Your Country Ser.). (Illus.). 48p. (J). (gr. 3-7). lib. bdg. 19.00 (978-0-516-35283-1(0) , Children's Pr.) Scholastic Library Publishing.

Clancy, Tom. Special Forces: A Guided Tour of U. S. Army Special Forces. 2001. (gr. 7-12). lib. bdg. 25.75 (978-0-613-62846-4(2)) Tandem Library Bks.

Cooper, Jason. U. S. Army. 2003. (Fighting Forces Ser.). (Illus.). 32p. (J). 28.50 (978-1-58952-713-3(5)) Rourke Publishing, LLC.

Cox, Clinton. Undying Glory: The Story of the Massachusetts 54th Regiment. 2007. 196p. (YA). (gr. 4-7). per. 15.95 (***978-0-595-45116-6(0)*** , Backinprint.com) iUniverse, Inc.

Cox, Kurt Hamilton. Longknives: The U. S. Cavalry & Other Mounted Forces, 1845-1942. 1999. (G. I. Ser.). (Illus.). 80p. (YA). (gr. 5 up). 27.50 (978-0-7910-5367-6(9) , Chelsea Hse.) Facts On File, Inc.

Darby, Jean. Dwight D. Eisenhower. 2004. (Presidential Leaders Ser.). (Illus.). 112p. (J). (gr. 6-12). lib. bdg. 29.27 (978-0-8225-0813-7(3)) Lerner Publishing Group.

David, Jack. United States Army. 2008. (Illus.). 24p. (J). lib. bdg. 19.95 (***978-1-60014-162-1(5)***) Bellwether Media.

DeAngelis, Gina. The Massachusetts 54th: African American Soldiers of the Union. 2002. (Let Freedom Ring Ser.). (Illus.). 48p. (J). (gr. 3-4). lib. bdg. 22.60 (978-0-7368-1343-3(8) , Bridgestone Bks.) Capstone Pr., Inc.

Dell, Pamela. Benedict Arnold: From Patriot to Traitor. 2004. (Signature Lives Ser.). (Illus.). 112p. (J). 30.60 (978-0-7565-0825-8(8) , 1240127) Compass Point Bks.

Doeden, Matt. The U. S. Army. 2004. (Edge Books, the U.S. Armed Forces). (Illus.). 32p. (J). lib. bdg. 19.93 (978-0-7368-2736-2(6)) Capstone Pr., Inc.

Dougherty, Terri. The U. S. Army at War. 2001. (On the Front Lines Ser.). (Illus.). 32p. (J). (gr. 3-4). lib. bdg. 21.26 (978-0-7368-0922-1(8) , Capstone High-Interest Bks.) Capstone Pr., Inc.

Feinstein, Stephen. Colin Powell. 2007. (African-American Heroes Ser.). (Illus.). 24p. (J). (gr. 1-3). lib. bdg. 21.26 (978-0-7660-2761-9(9) , Enslow Elementary) Enslow Pubs., Inc.

Flanagan, Alice K. The Buffalo Soldiers. 2004. (We the People Ser.). (Illus.). 48p. (J). 22.60 (978-0-7565-0833-3(9)) Compass Point Bks.

Fleischman, John. Black & White Airmen: Their True History. 2007. (Illus.). 160p. (J). (gr. 5 up). 20.00 (978-0-618-56297-8(4)) Houghton Mifflin Co.

Gimpel, Lee. Fighting Wars, Planning for Peace: The Story of George C. Marshall. 2005. (World Leaders Ser.). (Illus.). 176p. (J). (gr. 8 up). lib. bdg. 26.95 (978-1-931798-66-2(4)) Reynolds, Morgan Inc.

Glaser, Jason. The Buffalo Soldiers & the American West. Smith, Tod & Barnett, Charles, illus. 2005. (Graphic Library). 32p. (J). (gr. 3-7). lib. bdg. 25.26 (978-0-7368-4966-1(1)) Capstone Pr., Inc.

Glaser, Jason. Green Berets. 2007. (Edge Books, Warriors of History). (Illus.). 32p. (J). (***978-0-7368-6430-5(X)***) Capstone Pr., Inc.

Goldberg, Jan. Green Berets: The U. S. Army Special Forces. 2003. (Inside Special Operations Ser.). (Illus.). 64p. (YA). (gr. 5-8). lib. bdg. 26.50 (978-0-8239-3808-7(5) , Rosen Central) Rosen Publishing Group, Inc., The.

Goodman, Susan E. Robert Henry Hendershot. Ettlinger, Doris, illus. ed. 2005. 56p. (J). lib. bdg. 15.00 (978-1-59054-914-8(7)) Fitzgerald Bks.

Green, Michael. U. S. Army Special Operations. 2000. (Serving Your Country Ser.). (Illus.). 48p. (J). (gr. 3-4). lib. bdg. 21.26 (978-0-7368-0471-4(4) , Capstone High-Interest Bks.) Capstone Pr., Inc.

—The United States Army. 1998. (Serving Your Country Ser.). (Illus.). 48p. (J). (gr. 4-7). lib. bdg. 19.00 (978-0-516-21311-8(3) , Children's Pr.) Scholastic Library Publishing.

Green, Michael & Green, Gladys. U. S. Army Green Berets at War. 2003. (On the Front Lines Ser.). (Illus.). 32p. (J). lib. bdg. 22.60 (978-0-7368-2156-8(2) , Capstone High/Low Bks.) Capstone Pr., Inc.

—U. S. Army Rangers at War. 2003. (On the Front Lines Ser.). (Illus.). 32p. (J). lib. bdg. 22.60 (978-0-7368-2158-2(9) , Capstone High/Low Bks.) Capstone Pr., Inc.

Greene, Meg. Careers in the National Guards' Search & Rescue Units. 2005. (Careers in Search & Rescue Operations Ser.). (Illus.). 64p. (YA). (gr. 5-8). lib. bdg. 26.50 (978-0-8239-3836-0(0)) Rosen Publishing Group, Inc., The.

—The Hunt for Osama Bin Laden. 2004. (Frontline Coverage of Current Events Ser.). (Illus.). 48p. (J). lib. bdg. 26.50 (978-1-4042-0279-5(X)) Rosen Publishing Group, Inc., The.

Haney, Eric. Inside Delta Force. 2007. 256p. (YA). (gr. 7). pap. 9.99 (978-0-385-73252-9(X) , Delacorte Bks. for Young Readers) Random Hse. Children's Bks.

Hansen, Ole Steen. The AH-64 Apache Helicopter. 2006. (Illus.). 32p. (J). (978-0-7368-5250-0(6) , 1244012) Capstone Pr., Inc.

Hatch, Alden. General George Patton: Old Blood & Guts. 2006. (Sterling Point Bks.). (Illus.). 208p. (J). pap. 6.95 (978-1-4027-3614-8(2)) Sterling Publishing Co., Inc.

Haugen, Brenda. Douglas MacArthur: America's General. 2005. (Illus.). 112p. (J). (gr. 5-7). (978-0-7565-0994-1(7)) Compass Point Bks.

—Ulysses S. Grant: Union General & U.S. President. 2004. (Signature Lives Ser.). (Illus.). 112p. (J). 30.60 (978-0-7565-0820-3(7) , 1240145) Compass Point Bks.

Hopkins, Ellen H. The Golden Knights: The U. S. Army Parachute Team. 2001. (Serving Your Country Ser.). (Illus.). 48p. (J). (gr. 3-4). lib. bdg. 21.26 (978-0-7368-0775-3(6) , Capstone High-Interest Bks.) Capstone Pr., Inc.

Hughes, Libby. Norman Schwartzkopf: Hero with a Heart. 2002. 148p. pap. 12.95 (978-0-595-25570-2(1) , Backinprint.com) iUniverse, Inc.

Kaelberer, Angie Peterson. U. S. Army Special Operations. 2005. (Blazers—The U.S. Armed Forces Ser.). (Illus.). 32p. (J). 19.93 (978-0-7368-3795-8(7)) Capstone Pr., Inc.

Kennedy, Robert C. Life As a Paratrooper. 2000. (gr. 7-12). lib. bdg. 15.25 (978-0-613-52119-2(6)) Tandem Library Bks.

—Life As an Army Demolitions Expert. 2000. (gr. 7-12). lib. bdg. 15.25 (978-0-613-52121-5(8)) Tandem Library Bks.

Langellier, J. Phillip. Bluecoats: The U. S. Army in the West, 1848-1897. 1999. (G. I. Ser.). (Illus.). 80p. (YA). (gr. 5-9). 27.50 (978-0-7910-5366-9(0) , Chelsea Hse.) Facts On File, Inc.

—Sound the Charge: The U. S. Cavalry in the American West, 1861-1916. 1999. (G. I. Ser.). (Illus.). 80p. (YA). (gr. 5 up). 27.50 (978-0-7910-5376-8(8) , Chelsea Hse.) Facts On File, Inc.

Langellier, John P. Terrible Swift Sword. 2001. (G. I. Ser.). (Illus.). 80p. (J). 27.50 (978-0-7910-6673-7(8) , Chelsea Hse.) Facts On File, Inc.

McCarthy, Pat. Famous Union Generals & Leaders of the North: A MyReportLinks. com Book. 2004. (American Civil War Ser.). (Illus.). 48p. (J). lib. bdg. 25.26 (978-0-7660-5188-1(9) , MyReportLinks.com Bks.) Enslow Pubs., Inc.

McGowen, Tom. The Battle of Cantigny. 2002. (Cornerstones of Freedom Ser.). (Illus.). 48p. (J). (gr. 4-6). 26.00 (978-0-516-22264-6(3) , Children's Pr.) Scholastic Library Publishing.

McLeese, Don. George Meade. 2005. (Civil War Military Leaders Ser.). (Illus.). 32p. (J). (ps-6). lib. bdg. 6.45 (978-1-59515-480-4(9)) Rourke Publishing, LLC.

Mcleese, Don. George Meade. 2005. 32p. pap. 6.45 (978-1-59515-794-2(8)) Rourke Publishing, LLC.

McLeese, Don. Ulysses S. Grant. 2006. (Civil War Military Leaders Ser.). (Illus.). 32p. (gr. 3-6). 19.95 (978-1-59515-475-0(2)) Rourke Publishing, LLC.

—William Tecumseh Sherman. 2006. (Civil War Military Leaders Ser.). (Illus.). 32p. (gr. 3-6). 19.95 (978-1-59515-478-1(7)) Rourke Publishing, LLC.

McNab, Chris. Protecting the Nation with the U. S. Army. 2003. (Rescue & Prevention Ser.). (Illus.). 96p. (J). (gr. 7 up). lib. bdg. (978-1-59084-414-4(9)) Mason Crest Pubs.

McPherson, Stephanie Sammartino. Douglas MacArthur. 2005. (History Maker Bios Ser.). (Illus.). 48p. (J). 26.60 (978-0-8225-2434-2(1)) Lerner Publishing Group.

Miller, Roger G. Billy Mitchell: Evangelist of Airpower. 2007. (Illus.). 152p. (YA). (gr. 10 up). lib. bdg. 25.95 (*978-1-59556-025-4(4)) OTTN Publishing.

Myers, Walter Dean. The Harlem Hellfighters: When Pride Met Courage. 2006. (Illus.). 160p. (J). 17.99 (978-0-06-001136-9(X) , Amistad) HarperCollins Pubs.

Myers, Walter Dean & Miles, Bill. The Harlem Hellfighters: When Pride Met Courage. 2006. (Illus.). 160p. (J). lib. bdg. 18.89 (978-0-06-001137-6(8) , Amistad) HarperCollins Pubs.

Nardo, Don. Weapons of War. 2002. (American War Library). (Illus.). 112p. (J). 29.95 (978-1-59018-226-0(X) , Lucent Bks.) Thomson Gale.

Pitt, Matthew. Apache Helicopter: The AH-64. 2000. (gr. 7-12). lib. bdg. 15.25 (978-0-613-58687-0(5)) Tandem Library Bks.

Poolos, J. Army Rangers: Surveillance & Reconnaissance for the U. S. Army. 2003. (Inside Special Operations Ser.). (Illus.). 64p. (YA). (gr. 5-8). lib. bdg. 26.50 (978-0-8239-3805-6(0) , Rosen Central) Rosen Publishing Group, Inc., The.

Raabe, Emily. Buffalo Soldiers & the Western Frontier. 2003. (Reading Power Ser.). (Illus.). 24p. (J). lib. bdg. 17.25 (978-0-8239-6495-6(7) , PowerKids Pr.) Rosen Publishing Group, Inc., The.

Remstein, Henna. William Sherman. 2001. (gr. 5-8). lib. bdg. 17.60 (978-0-613-33253-8(9)) Tandem Library Bks.

Rice, Earle, Jr. Robert E. Lee: First Soldier of the Confederacy. 2005. (Civil War Leaders Ser.). (Illus.). 176p. (J). (gr. 6-12). 26.95 (978-1-931798-47-1(8)) Reynolds, Morgan Inc.

Rice, Earle. The U S Army & Military Careers. 2006. (U.S. Armed Forces & Military Careers Ser.). (Illus.). 128p. (J). lib. bdg. 31.93 (978-0-7660-2699-5(X)) Enslow Pubs., Inc.

Roberts, Jeremy. U. S. Army Special Operations Forces. 2005. (U. S. Armed Forces Ser.). (Illus.). 64p. (J). (gr. 4-7). lib. bdg. 26.60 (978-0-8225-1646-0(2)) Lerner Publishing Group.

Sapp, Richard. Ulysses S. Grant & the Road to Appomattox. 2006. (In the Footsteps of American Heroes Ser.). (Illus.). 64p. (J). pap. (978-0-8368-6436-6(0)); lib. bdg. 32.67 (978-0-8368-6431-1(X)) Stevens, Gareth Inc. (World Almanac Library).

Should Women Be Allowed to Serve in Combat in the U. S. Armed Forces? [New Title]. 2007. (At Issue Ser.). (Illus.). 128p. (gr. 10-12). 29.95 (*978-0-7377-3938-1(X)); pap. 21.20 (*978-0-7377-3939-8(8)) Thomson Gale. (Greenhaven Pr., Inc.).

Sonneborn, Liz. Benedict Arnold: Hero & Traitor. 2005. (Leaders of the American Revolution Ser.). (Illus.). 130p. (J). (ps-8). lib. bdg. 30.00 (978-0-7910-8617-9(8) , Chelsea Hse.) Facts On File, Inc.

Stanley, George E. George S. Patton: War Hero. Henderson, Meryl, illus. 2007. (Childhood of Famous Americans Ser.). 192p. (J). pap. 5.99 (*978-1-4169-1547-8(8) , Aladdin) Simon & Schuster Children's Publishing.

Stewart, Gail B. Life of a Soldier in Washington's Army. 2002. (Illus.). 112p. (J). 29.95 (978-1-59018-215-4(4) , Lucent Bks.) Thomson Gale.

Strong, Mike. Colin Powell: It Can Be Done! 2002. (High Five Reading Ser.). (Illus.). 48p. (J). pap. (978-0-7368-9529-3(9)) Capstone Pr., Inc.

Sutcliffe, Jane. George S. Patton Jr. 2005. (History Maker Bios Ser.). (Illus.). 48p. (J). 26.60 (978-0-8225-2436-6(8) , Lerner Pubns.) Lerner Publishing Group.

Venezia, Mike, illus. Ulysses S. Grant. 2005. 32p. (J). 27.00 (978-0-516-22623-1(1) , Children's Pr.) Scholastic Library Publishing.

Waryncia, Lou. Ulysses S. Grant: Confident Leaders & Hero. Hale, Sarah Elder, ed. 2005. (Civil War Ser.). (Illus.). 48p. (J). 17.95 (978-0-8126-7906-9(7)) Cobblestone Publishing Co.

Waxman, Laura Hamilton. Colin Powell. 2005. (History Maker Bios Ser.). 48p. (J). pap. 6.95 (978-0-8225-5463-9(1)); (Illus.). 26.60 (978-0-8225-2433-5(3) , Lerner Pubns.) Lerner Publishing Group.

Weiser, Andrea L. U. S. Army Special Operations Command: Night Stalkers-Special Operations Aviation. 1999. (Warfare & Weapons Ser.). (Illus.). 48p. (J). (gr. 3-7). pap. 20.00 (978-0-531-12009-5(0) , Watts, Franklin) Scholastic Library Publishing.

Welch, Catherine A. George C. Marshall. 2005. (History Maker Bios Ser.). 48p. (J). pap. 6.95 (978-0-8225-5460-8(7)); (Illus.). 26.60 (978-0-8225-2435-9(X) , Lerner Pubns.) Lerner Publishing Group.

Williams, Jean Kinney. Ulysses S. Grant. 2002. (Profiles of the Presidents Ser.). (Illus.). 64p. (J). (gr. 4 up). lib. bdg. 23.93 (978-0-7565-0265-2(9)) Compass Point Bks.

Young, Jeff C. Dwight D. Eisenhower: Soldier & President. 2004. (Notable Americans Ser.). (Illus.). 128p. (YA). (gr. 6-12). 23.95 (978-1-883846-76-3(5) , First Biographies) Reynolds, Morgan Inc.

UNITED STATES—ARMY—ENLISTMENT

see United States—Army—Recruiting, Enlistment, etc.

UNITED STATES—ARMY—MILITARY LIFE

Ammon, Richard. Valley Forge. Farnsworth, Bill, illus. 2004. 32p. (J). (gr. 4-6). tchr. ed. 16.95 (978-0-8234-1746-9(8)) Holiday Hse., Inc.

Anderson, Dale. A Soldier's Life in the Civil War. 2004. (World Almanac Library of the Civil War). (Illus.). 48p. (J). (gr. 5 up). pap. 11.95 (978-0-8368-5595-1(7)); lib. bdg. 30.00 (978-0-8368-5586-9(8)) Stevens, Gareth Inc. (World Almanac Library).

Beller, Susan Provost. Billy Yank & Johnny Reb: Soldiering in the Civil War. 2000. (Single Titles Ser.). (Illus.). 96p. (gr. 5 up). lib. bdg. 27.90 (978-0-7613-1869-9(0) , Millbrook Pr.) Lerner Publishing Group.

—Yankee Doodle & the Redcoats: Soldiering in the Revolutionary War. rev. ed. 2007. (Soldiers on the Battlefront Ser.). (Illus.). 112p. (YA). (gr. 6-8). lib. bdg. 33.26 (978-0-8225-6655-7(9) , Twenty-First Century Bks.) Lerner Publishing Group.

Doeden, Matt. Winter at Valley Forge. Barnett, Charles & Frenz, Ron, illus. 2006. (Graphic Library). 32p. (J). 25.26 (978-0-7368-4975-3(0)) Capstone Pr., Inc.

Gartman, Gene. Life in Army Basic Training. 2000. (High Interest Bks.). (Illus.). 48p. (YA). (gr. 7-12). 24.00 (978-0-516-23347-5(5) , Children's Pr.) Scholastic Library Publishing.

Hooker, Forrestine C. Child of the Fighting Tenth: On the Frontier with the Buffalo Soldiers. Wilson, Steve, ed. 2003. (Illus.). 280p. (YA). 26.00 (978-0-19-516158-8(0)) Oxford Univ. Pr., Inc.

Hughes, Libby. Colin Powell: A Man of Quality. 2000. (Illus.). 188p. (gr. 4-7). pap. 12.95 (978-0-595-00734-9(1) , Backinprint.com) iUniverse, Inc.

Kehoe, Stasia Ward. I Live at a Military Post. 2000. (Kids in Their Communities Ser.). (Illus.). 24p. (J). (gr. 3). lib. bdg. 18.75 (978-0-8239-5441-4(2) , PowerKids Pr.) Rosen Publishing Group, Inc., The.

Kennedy, Robert C. Life As an Army Demolition Expert. 2000. (On Duty Ser.). (Illus.). 48p. (YA). (gr. 7-12). 24.00 (978-0-516-23346-8(7) , Children's Pr.) Scholastic Library Publishing.

—Life in the Army Special Forces. 2000. (gr. 7-12). lib. bdg. 15.25 (978-0-613-52123-9(4)) Tandem Library Bks.

Kennedy, Robert C. & Gartman, Gene. Life in Army Basic Training. 2000. (High Interest Bks.). (Illus.). 48p. (YA). (gr. 7-12). pap. 6.95 (978-0-516-23547-9(8) , Children's Pr.) Scholastic Library Publishing.

Ratliff, Thomas M. & Salariya, David. You Wouldn't Want to Be a Civil War Soldier! A War You'd Rather Not Fight. Antram, David, illus. 2004. (You Wouldn't Want To Ser.). 32p. (J). 28.50 (978-0-531-12350-8(2) , Watts, Franklin) Scholastic Library Publishing.

Rebman, Renée C. The Union Soldier. 2006. 48p. (J). (gr. 4-6). lib. bdg. (978-0-7565-2030-4(4)) Compass Point Bks.

Savage, Douglas J. Soldier's Life During the Civil War. 2000. (Untold History of the Civil War Ser.). (Illus.). 64p. (J). (gr. 3 up). 25.00 (978-0-7910-5710-0(0) , Chelsea Hse.) Facts On File, Inc.

Wukovits, John F. Life of an American Soldier in Europe. 1999. (American War Library). (Illus.). 112p. (YA). (gr. 4-12). 27.45 (978-1-56006-666-8(0) , LML00902-178018, Lucent Bks.) Thomson Gale.

UNITED STATES—ARMY—RECRUITING, ENLISTMENT, ETC.

Sawyer, Susan. The Army in Action. 2001. (U. S. Military Branches & Careers Ser.). (Illus.). 104p. (J). (gr. 6-12). lib. bdg. 26.60 (978-0-7660-1635-4(8)) Enslow Pubs., Inc.

UNITED STATES—ARMY—UNIFORMS

Graziadio, Stephanie. Personal Fighting Gear. 2004. (Heinemann Know It Ser.). (Illus.). 48p. (J). pap. 7.95 (978-1-4034-4559-9(1)); lib. bdg. (978-1-4034-4553-7(2)) Heinemann Library.

Katcher, Philip R. N. Civil War State Troops. 2003. (Battle Ready Ser.). (Illus.). 48p. (YA). 28.56 (978-1-4109-0121-7(1)) Raintree.

—Civil War Union Troops. 2003. (Battle Ready Ser.). (Illus.). 48p. (J). 28.56 (978-1-4109-0119-4(X)) Raintree.

Langellier, John P. & Loane, C. Paul. U. S. Army Headgear, 1812-1872. 2002. (Illus.). 160p. (gr. 10-13). 69.95 (978-0-7643-1672-2(9)) Schiffer Publishing, Ltd.

McAfee, Michael J. Billy Yank: The Uniform of the Union Army, 1861-1865. 1999. (G. I. Ser.). (Illus.). 80p. (YA). (gr. 5 up). 27.50 (978-0-7910-5368-3(7) , Chelsea Hse.) Facts On File, Inc.

UNITED STATES—ARTISTS

see Artists, American

UNITED STATES—AUTHORS

see Authors, American

UNITED STATES—BIOGRAPHY

Abbey, Cherie D., ed. Biography Today Annual Cumulation 2004: Profiles of People of Interest to Young Readers. 2004. (Biography Today General Series: Annual Cumulation Ser.). (YA). lib. bdg. (978-0-7808-0686-3(7)) Omnigraphics, Inc.

Abrams, Dennis. Gary Soto. 2008. (Who Wrote That? Ser.). 128p. (gr. 6-12). 30.00 (*978-0-7910-9529-4(0) , Chelsea Hse.) Facts On File, Inc.

—Jay-Z. 2008. (Hip-Hop Stars Ser.). 176p. (J). pap. 14.95 (*978-0-7910-9729-8(3) , Chelsea Hse.) Facts On File, Inc.

—Ty Cobb. 2007. (Baseball Superstars Ser.). 136p. (J). (gr. 6-12). 30.00 (*978-0-7910-9439-6(1) , Chelsea Hse.) Facts On File, Inc.

Adams, Colleen. Jake Gyllenhaal. 2006. (Stars in the Spotlight Ser.). (Illus.). 32p. (J). lib. bdg. (978-1-4042-3514-4(0) , PowerKids Pr.) Rosen Publishing Group, Inc., The.

—Johnny Depp. 2006. (Tony Stead Nonfiction Independent Reading Collection). pap. (978-1-4042-5667-5(9)) Rosen Publishing Group, Inc., The.

Adler, David A. A Picture Book of Patrick Henry. Wallner, John et al, illus. 2005. 32p. (J). (gr. k-3). pap. 6.95 (978-0-8234-1678-3(X)) Holiday Hse., Inc.

Adler, David A. & Adler, Michael S. A Picture Book of John & Abigail Adams. Himler, Ronald, illus. 2007. (J). (978-0-8234-2007-0(8)) Holiday Hse., Inc.

Albee, Jo. American Heroes. 2003. (Compass Point Phonics Readers Ser.). (Illus.). 16p. (J). (gr. 1 up). 13.26 (978-0-7565-0502-8(X)) Compass Point Bks.

Aldrin, Buzz, Jr. Reaching for the Moon. Minor, Wendell, illus. 2005. 40p. (J). 16.99 (978-0-06-055445-3(2)); lib. bdg. 17.89 (978-0-06-055446-0(0)) HarperCollins Pubs.

—Reaching for the Moon. Minor, Wendell, illus. unabr. ed. 2006. (Picture Book Readalong Ser.). (J). (gr. k-4). 25.95 incl. audio (978-1-59519-581-4(5)); 28.95 incl. audio compact disk (978-1-59519-582-1(3)) Live Oak Media.

Alexander, Lauren. Mad for Miley: An Unauthorized Biography. 2007. 128p. (J). pap. 4.99 (*978-0-8431-2684-6(1) , Price Stern Sloan) Penguin Group (USA) Inc.

Allen, Kenny. Kurt Busch. 2007. (NASCAR Champions Ser.). (Illus.). 24p. (J). lib. bdg. (978-1-4042-3457-4(8) , PowerKids Pr.) Rosen Publishing Group, Inc., The.

Aller, Susan Bivin. Living with the Senecas: A Story about Mary Jemison. Harden, Laurie, illus. 2007. (Creative Minds Biographies Ser.). (J). spiral bd. 22.60 (978-0-8225-5989-4(7)) Lerner Publishing Group.

Allyson, Jackie. Howard "The Professor" Lederer. 2008. (J). (*978-1-4222-0223-4(2)) Mason Crest Pubs.

—Phil "Unabomber" Laak. 2008. (J). (*978-1-4222-0222-7(4)) Mason Crest Pubs.

Alter, Judy. Martin de Leon: Tejano Empresario. Messersmith, Patrick, illus. 2007. 64p. (J). 17.95 (*978-1-933337-08-1(7)) State Hse. Pr.

Ambrosek, Renee. Shawn Fanning: The Founder of Napster. 2006. (Internet Career Biographies Ser.). (Illus.). 112p. (YA). (gr. 7-12). lib. bdg. 31.95 (978-1-4042-0720-2(1)) Rosen Publishing Group, Inc., The.

American Biographies Set. 2005. (American Biographies Ser.). 432-464p. (gr. 9). 390.00 (978-0-8160-6515-8(2)) Facts On File, Inc.

Anderson, Dale. Leaders of the American Revolution. 2005. (World Almanac Library of the American Revolution). (J). pap. (978-0-8368-5940-9(5)); lib. bdg. 30.00 (978-0-8368-5931-7(6)) Stevens, Gareth Inc. (World Almanac Library).

Anderson, Wayne A. Tony Stewart: NASCAR Driver. 2006. (Illus.). 48p. (J). (gr. 5-8). lib. bdg. 26.50 (978-1-4042-0984-8(0)) Rosen Publishing Group, Inc., The.

Armentrout, David & Armentrout, Patricia. Important & Famous People. 2002. (Guides to State Symbols). (Illus.). 48p. (J). (gr. 3-8). 20.95 (978-1-58952-086-8(6)) Rourke Publishing, LLC.

Aronson, Virginia. Dave Thomas. 1999. (Overcoming Adversity Ser.). (Illus.). 128p. (YA). pap. 9.95 (978-0-7910-5303-4(2) , Chelsea Hse.) Facts On File, Inc.

Ashby, Ruth. Abraham & Mary Todd Lincoln. 2004. (Illus.). 48p. (J). pap. 11.95 (978-0-8368-5701-6(1)); lib. bdg. 30.00 (978-0-8368-5695-8(3)) Stevens, Gareth Inc. (World Almanac Library).

Auster, Michael A. They Led the Way. 2005. (Yellow Umbrella Ser.). (J). (978-0-7368-5315-6(4)); (Illus.). 16p. (978-0-7368-5279-1(4)) Capstone Pr., Inc.

Bailey, Tom. Jennifer Chandler: Olympic Champion Diver. 2005. (Alabama Roots Biography Ser.). (Illus.). 112p. (J). (978-1-59421-014-3(4)) Seacoast Publishing, Inc.

Bair, Diane. Leyendas del Oeste & Western Legends. 2005. spiral bd. 88.00 (*978-1-4108-5735-4(2)) Benchmark Education Co.

Baldwin, James. Four Great Americans. 2006. pap. (*978-1-4065-0509-2(9)) Dodo Pr.

Banting, Erinn. Katie Couric. 2007. (J). (*978-1-59036-643-1(3)); (*978-1-59036-644-8(1)) Weigl Pubs., Inc.

Baptiste, Tracey. Jerry Spinelli. 2007. 128p. 30.00 (*978-0-7910-9572-0(X) , Chelsea Hse.) Facts On File, Inc.

—Madeleine L'Engle. 2007. 128p. 30.00 (*978-0-7910-9573-7(8) , Chelsea Hse.) Facts On File, Inc.

Barnes, Geoffrey. Jay-Z. 2006. (Hip-Hop Ser.). (Illus.). 64p. (J). (gr. 5 up). 22.95 (978-1-4222-0119-0(8)) Mason Crest Pubs.

Bartoletti, Susan Campbell. The Flag Maker. Nivola, Claire A., illus. 2004. 32p. (J). (gr. 3-5). tchr. ed. 16.00 (978-0-618-26757-6(3)) Houghton Mifflin Co. Trade & Reference Div.

Benge, Janet & Benge, Geoff. Daniel Boone: Frontiersman. 2004. pap. 8.99 (978-1-932096-09-5(4)) Emerald Bks.

Bennett, William J. Our Country's Founders: A Book of Advice for Young People. 2001. (Illus.). (J). (978-0-606-21369-1(4)) Tandem Library Bks.

—Our Country's Founders: Book of Advice for Young People Adapted From Our Sacred Honor. 2001. (Illus.). 320p. (YA). (gr. 7-12). pap. 11.99 (978-0-689-84469-0(7) , Simon Pulse) Simon & Schuster Children's Publishing.

—Our Country's Founders: Words of Advice from the Founders in Stories, Letters, Poems & Speeches. 1998. 17.00 (978-0-8054-1600-8(5)) B&H Publishing Grp.

Benson, Edmund F. & Benson, Susan. Your Ticket to Handling Grief: Bus Book Series. 2001. 31p. (J). pap. 1.95 (978-1-58614-252-0(6)) Arise Foundation.

Benson, Sonia. Korean War: Biographies. 2001. (Korean War Reference Library). (Illus.). 200p. (YA). (gr. 6-10). 67.00 (978-0-7876-5692-8(5) , GML00502-175534, UXL) Thomson Gale.

Bentley, Karen & Gluck, Jeff, texts. The Unsers. rev. collector's ed. 2005. (Race Car Legends Ser.). (Illus.). 72p. (J). (gr. 4-7). lib. bdg. 25.00 (978-0-7910-8764-0(6) , Chelsea Hse.) Facts On File, Inc.

Berman, Ron. Future Stars of America. 2005. (Illus.). 90p. (J). (*978-0-9741997-4-0(5)) Scobre Pr. Corp.

Berne, Emma Carlson. Snoop Dogg. 2006. (Hip-Hop Ser.). (Illus.). 64p. (YA). (gr. 5 up). 22.95 (978-1-4222-0129-9(5)) Mason Crest Pubs.

Berne, Stanley. Empire Sweets: How I Learned to Live & Love in the Greatest Empire on Earth. 2003. 160p. (YA). pap. 40.00 (978-0-913844-26-7(8)) Rising Tide Pr.

Bill Gates. rev. ed. 2007. (Biography Ser.). 112p. (J). (gr. 6-12). 29.27 (*978-0-8225-7363-0(6) , Twenty-First Century Bks.) Lerner Publishing Group.

Biografías Ilustradas con Fotografías (Photo-Illustrated Biographies), 4 bks. Incl. Abraham Lincoln. Usel, T. M. lib. bdg. 18.60 (978-1-56065-806-1(1) , CAP2789); Cesar Chavez. Davis, Lucile. Schon, Isabel, ed. Ferrer, Martín Luis Guzman, tr. lib. bdg. 18.60 (978-1-56065-808-5(8) , CAP2791); George Washington. Usel, T. M. Schon, Isabel, ed. Ferrer, Martín Luis Guzman, tr. lib. bdg. 18.60 (978-1-56065-805-4(3) , CAP2623); John F. Kennedy. Potts, Steve. Schon, Isabel, ed. Ferrer, Martín Luis Guzman, tr. lib. bdg. 18.60 (978-1-56065-807-8(X) , CAP2790); 24p. (J). (gr. 2-3). 1998. (SPA., Illus.). Set lib. bdg. 74.40 (978-0-7368-0149-2(9) , Bridgestone Bks.) Capstone Pr., Inc.

Bodden, Valerie & Gehry, Frank O. Frank Gehry. 2008. (J). (*978-1-58341-662-4(5) , Creative Education) Creative Co., The.

Bodie, Idella. Heroes & Heroines of the American Revolution. 2004. (J). pap., instr.'s gde. ed. (978-0-87844-173-0(5)) Sandlapper Publishing Co., Inc.

Bolden, Tonya. The Champ: The Story of Muhamad Ali. Gregory Christie, R. Gregory, illus. 2007. 40p. (J). (gr. k-3). pap. 6.99 (*978-0-440-41782-8(1) , Dragonfly Bks.) Random Hse. Children's Bks.

Boomhower, Ray E. The Soldier's Friend: A Life of Ernie Pyle. 2006. (Illus.). 134p. 17.95 (978-0-87195-200-4(9)) Indiana Historical Society.

Boothroyd, Jennifer. Robert Fulton: A Life of Innovation. 2007. (Pull Ahead Books-Biographies Ser.). (J). 22.60 (978-0-8225-6458-4(0) , Lerner Pubns.) Lerner Publishing Group.

Bradley, Michael. Alex Rodriguez. 2004. (Illus.). 48p. (J). 27.07 (978-0-7614-1757-6(5)) Cavendish, Marshall Corp.

Braidich, Victoria. Dale Earnhardt. 2007. (NASCAR Champions Ser.). (Illus.). 24p. (J). lib. bdg. (978-1-4042-3512-0(4) , PowerKids Pr.) Rosen Publishing Group, Inc., The.

Braun, Eric. Bessie Coleman. 2006. (Illus.). 24p. (J). 15.93 (978-0-7368-4229-7(2) , Pebble Bks.) Capstone Pr., Inc.

Bregoli, Jane. The Goat Lady. 2005. 32p. (J). (gr. 3-6). 16.95 (978-0-88448-260-4(X)) Tilbury Hse. Pubs.

Brennan, Kristine. Scott Hamilton. 1999. (Overcoming Adversity Ser.). (J). (978-0-606-19354-2(5)) Tandem Library Bks.

Brill, Marlene Targ. Barack Obama. 2006. (J). pap. 6.95 (978-0-8225-6056-2(9) , First Avenue Editions) Lerner Publishing Group.

—Barack Obama: Working to Make a Difference. 2006. (Gateway Biographies Ser.). (Illus.). 48p. (J). 23.93 (978-0-8225-3417-4(7)) Lerner Publishing Group.

Brinster, Dick & Huff, Richard. Jeff Gordon. rev. ed. 2007. (Race Car Legends: Ser.). 80p. (J). (gr. 5-8). 25.00 (978-0-7910-8760-2(3) , Chelsea Hse.) Facts On File, Inc.

Brooks, Aaron & Brown, Greg. Aaron Brooks: Rise Above. 2004. (Illus.). 48p. (J). 15.95 (978-0-9634650-9-2(0)) Positively for Kids, Inc.

Brown, Jonatha A. Steven Spielberg. 19.33 (978-0-8368-4585-3(4)) Stevens, Gareth Inc.

Brown, Terrell. Reverend Run (Run MDC) 2007. (Hip-Hop Ser.). (Illus.). 64p. (J). (gr. 5 up). 22.95 (978-1-4222-0127-5(9)) Mason Crest Pubs.

Buckley, Susan. 15 Easy to Read Biography Mini Books: Famous Americans: Grades K-2. 2000. 48p. pap. 9.95 (978-0-590-96718-1(5)) Scholastic, Inc.

Buckley, Susan & Leacock, Elspeth. Journeys for Freedom: A New Look at America's Story. Prato, Rodica, illus. 2006. 48p. (J). (gr. 4-6). 17.00 (978-0-618-22323-7(1)) Houghton Mifflin Co.

Buckley, Susan Washburn & Leacock, Elspeth. Kids Make History: A New Look at America's Story. Jones, Randy, illus. 2006. 48p. (J). (gr. 4-6). 17.00 (978-0-618-22329-9(0)) Houghton Mifflin Co.

Burgan, Michael. George Washington Carver: Scientist, Inventor, & Teacher. 2006. (Signature Lives Ser.). (Illus.). 112p. (J). (978-0-7565-1882-0(2) , 1265882) Compass Point Bks.

—J. Pierpont Morgan: Industrialist & Financier. 2006. (J). (978-0-7565-1890-5(3)) Compass Point Bks.

Burke, Rick. American Lives, 12 bks. 2003. (J). Set. (Illus.). (gr. 2-4). lib. bdg. 290.64 (978-1-4034-0732-0(0)); Set 1. (gr. 2-4). lib. bdg. 145.32 (978-1-4034-0161-8(6)); Set 2. (Illus.). lib. bdg. 145.32 (978-1-4034-0731-3(2)) Heinemann Library.

Burleigh, Robert. American Moments: Scenes from American History. Strachan, Bruce, tr. Strachan, Bruce, illus. rev. ed. 2004. 48p. (J). 18.95 (978-0-8050-7082-8(6) , Holt, Henry & Co. Bks. For Young Readers) Holt, Henry & Co.

Butts, Ellen R. & Schwartz, Joyce R. Carl Sagan. 2005. (Biography Ser.). (Illus.). 112p. (gr. 6-12). lib. bdg. 27.93 (978-0-8225-4986-4(7)) Lerner Publishing Group.

Byers, Ann. Jeff Bezos: The Founder of Amazon.com. 2006. (Internet Career Biographies Ser.). (Illus.). 112p. (YA). (gr. 7-12). lib. bdg. 31.95 (978-1-4042-0717-2(1)) Rosen Publishing Group, Inc., The.

Byman, Jeremy. Ted Turner: Cable Televison Tycoon. 1998. (Makers of the Media Ser.). (Illus.). 112p. (YA). (gr. 6-12). 23.95 (978-1-883846-25-1(0) , First Biographies) Reynolds, Morgan Inc.

Calvert, Patricia. Zebulon Pike: Lost in the Rockies. 2003. (Great Explorations Ser.). (J). (978-0-7614-1740-8(0)); 29.93 (978-0-7614-1612-8(9)) Cavendish, Marshall Corp. (Benchmark Bks.).

Campbell, Loraine, illus. A Pocketful of Passage. 2007. (Great Lakes Books). xi, 77p. (J). pap. (***978-0-8143-3341-9(9)***) Wayne State Univ. Pr.

Caravantes, Peggy. Writing Is My Business: The Story of O. Henry. 2006. (World Writers Ser.). (Illus.). 160p. (J). (gr. 6-12). lib. bdg. 27.95 (978-1-59935-031-8(9)) Reynolds, Morgan Inc.

Cardona, Rodolfo & Cockcroft, James D., eds. Hispanics of Achievement. 1999. (Illus.). 128p. (J). (gr. 5-12). 99.50 (978-0-7910-3762-1(2) , Chelsea Hse.) Facts On File, Inc.

Carole Marsh. Patriotic Biographies. 2004. (Patriotic Favorites Ser.). lib. bdg. 29.95 (978-0-635-02225-7(7)); 32p. (gr. 3-8). pap. 7.95 (978-0-635-02224-0(9)) Gallopade International.

Carroll, Cathryn. Clerc: The Story of His Early Years. 2002. (Orig.). (gr. 7-12). lib. bdg. 21.05 (978-0-613-88531-7(7)) Tandem Library Bks.

Casapulla, Louise. Ashlee Simpson. 2005. (Pop People Ser.). (Illus.). 137p. (J). (978-0-439-76581-7(1)) Scholastic, Inc.

Chanko, Pamela. Easy Reader Biographies: Betsy Ross: The Story of Our Flag. 2007. 16p. pap. 2.99 (***978-0-439-77421-5(7)*** , Teaching Resources) Scholastic, Inc.

Christopher, Matt. Dale Earnhardt Sr. 2007. (Matt Christopher Legends in Sports Ser.). (Illus.). 128p. (J). (gr. 3-7). pap. 4.99 (***978-0-316-01114-3(2)***) Little Brown & Co.

Cohen, Della. Eleanor Roosevelt: Proud & Tall. 2005. (Illus.). 16p. (J). pap. (***978-0-7367-2879-9(1)***) Zaner-Bloser, Inc.

Coleman, Wim & Perrin, Pat. What Made the Wild West Wild. 2006. (Wild History of the American West Ser.). (Illus.). 128p. (J). lib. bdg. 33.27 (978-1-59845-016-3(6) , MyReportLinks.com Bks.) Enslow Pubs., Inc.

Collard, Sneed B., III. David Crockett: Fearless Frontiersman. 2006. (American Heroes Ser.). (Illus.). 48p. (J). lib. bdg. 28.50 (978-0-7614-2160-3(2) , Benchmark Bks.) Cavendish, Marshall Corp.

Collier, James Lincoln. The Benjamin Franklin You Never Knew. 2004. (You Never Knew Ser.). (Illus.). 80p. (J). 25.50 (978-0-516-24427-3(2) , Children's Pr.) Scholastic Library Publishing.

Colonial America Biographies. (Let Freedom Ring Ser.). (Illus.). (J). (gr. 3-4). lib. bdg. 95.72 (978-0-7368-2554-2(1)) Capstone Pr., Inc.

Colonial Leaders. 2005. 80p. pap. 550.00 (978-0-7910-6279-1(1) , Chelsea Hse.) Facts On File, Inc.

Comic Book Creators. 2007. 145.26 (978-1-59928-296-1(8) , ABDO & Daughters) ABDO Publishing Co.

Compass Point Early Biographies, 22 bks. Incl. Abraham Lincoln. Raatma, Lucia. 2000. lib. bdg. 21.26 (978-0-7565-0012-2(5)); Albert Einstein. Rau, Dana Meachen. 2003. lib. bdg. 21.26 (978-0-7565-0416-8(3)); Alexander Graham Bell. Raatma, Lucia. 2004. lib. bdg. 21.26 (978-0-7565-0569-1(0)); Benjamin Franklin. Raatma, Lucia. 2001. lib. bdg. 21.26 (978-0-7565-0067-2(2)); Charles Lindbergh. Raatma, Lucia. 2000. lib. bdg. 21.26 (978-0-7565-0013-9(3)); Eleanor Roosevelt. Rosenberg, Pam. 2003. lib. bdg. 21.26 (978-0-7565-0417-5(1)); Frederick Douglass. Rau, Dana Meachen. 2003. lib. bdg. 21.26 (978-0-7565-0418-2(X)); George Armstrong Custer. Rau, Dana Meachen. 2003. lib. bdg. 21.26 (978-0-7565-0419-9(8)); George Washington. Santella, Andrew. 2000. lib. bdg. 21.26 (978-0-7565-0014-6(1)); George Washington Carver. Franchino, Vicky. 2001. lib. bdg. 21.26 (978-0-7565-0112-9(1)); Harriet Tubman. Rau, Dana Meachen. 2000. lib. bdg. 21.26 (978-0-7565-0015-3(X)); Jackie Robinson. Raatma, Lucia. 2000. lib. bdg. 21.26 (978-0-7565-0016-0(8)); Jane Addams. Raatma, Lucia. 2004. lib. bdg. 21.26 (978-0-7565-0566-0(6)); John F. Kennedy. Franchino, Vicky. 2001. lib. bdg. 21.26 (978-0-7565-0113-6(X)); Levi Strauss. Raatma, Lucia. 2004. lib. bdg. 21.26 (978-0-7565-0568-4(2)); Marie Curie. Rau, Dana Meachen. 2000. lib. bdg. 21.26 (978-0-7565-0017-7(6)); Martin Luther King, Jr. Raatma, Lucia. 2001. lib. bdg. 21.26 (978-0-7565-0114-3(8)); Pocahontas. Raatma, Lucia. 2001. lib. bdg. 21.26 (978-0-7565-0115-0(6)); Sojourner Truth. Jaffe, Elizabeth Dana. 2001. lib. bdg. 21.26 (978-0-7565-0068-9(0)); Susan B. Anthony. Raatma, Lucia. 2001. lib. bdg. 21.26 (978-0-7565-0069-6(9)); Thomas Edison. Raatma, Lucia. 2004. lib. bdg. 21.26 (978-0-7565-0567-7(4)); Thomas Jefferson. Raatma, Lucia. 2001. lib. bdg. 21.26 (978-0-7565-0070-2(2)); 32p. (J). (gr. 2 up). (Illus.). Set lib. bdg. 467.72 (978-0-7565-0705-3(7)) Compass Point Bks.

Corrigan, Jim. Will Smith. 2006. (Hip-Hop Ser.). (Illus.). 64p. (YA). (gr. 5 up). 22.95 (978-1-4222-0128-2(7)) Mason Crest Pubs.

Crewe, Sabrina & Anderson, Dale. The Seneca Falls Women's Rights Convention. 2004. (Events That Shaped America Ser.). (J). lib. bdg. 24.67 (978-0-8368-3408-6(9)) Stevens, Gareth Inc.

Crompton, Samuel Willard. Thomas Paine & the Fight for Liberty. 2005. (Leaders of the American Revolution Ser.). (Illus.). 132p. (J). (gr. 4-8). lib. bdg. 30.00 (978-0-7910-8625-4(9) , Chelsea Hse.) Facts On File, Inc.

—100 Famous Americans Who Changed History. 2005. (People Who Changed History Ser.). (Illus.). 112p. (J). lib. bdg. 30.00 (978-0-8368-5768-9(2) , World Almanac Library) Stevens, Gareth Inc.

Crowe, Chris. Up Close: Thurgood Marshall: Thurgood Marshall. 2008. 208p. (YA). (gr. 6). 16.99 (***978-0-670-06228-7(6)*** , Viking Juvenile) Penguin Group (USA) Inc.

Crum, Anna-Maria. Rastreadores de nuestra dinamica Tierra & Trackers of Dynamic Earth. 2005. spiral bd. 84.00 (***978-1-4108-5718-7(2)***) Benchmark Education Co.

Cunningham, Kevin. Canadian Americans. 2004. (Our Cultural Heritage Ser.). 32p. (J). (gr. 2-6). 27.07 (978-1-59296-178-8(9)) Child's World, Inc.

Darby, Jean. Dwight D. Eisenhower. 2004. (Presidential Leaders Ser.). (Illus.). 112p. (J). (gr. 6-12). lib. bdg. 29.27 (978-0-8225-0813-7(3)) Lerner Publishing Group.

Darraj, Susan Muaddi. Amy Tan. 2007. (Asian Americans of Achievement Ser.). 112p. (gr. 6-12). 30.00 (978-0-7910-9269-9(0) , Chelsea Hse.) Facts On File, Inc.

Davis, Lucile. R. J. Reynolds: He Saw the Future. 2000. (Community Builders Ser.). (J). (978-0-516-21600-3(7) , Children's Pr.) Scholastic Library Publishing.

De Capua, Sarah. J. C. Watts Jr. Character Counts. 1999. (Community Builders Ser.). (Illus.). 48p. (J). (gr. 3-5). pap. 6.95 (978-0-516-26346-5(3) , Children's Pr.) Scholastic Library Publishing.

De Capua, Sarah E. Andrew Carnegie. 2008. (J). lib. bdg. 26.00 (***978-1-60279-067-4(1)***) Cherry Lake Publishing.

de Paola, Tomie. On My Way: A 26 Fairmount Avenue Book. 2002. (gr. 3-6). lib. bdg. 14.15 (978-0-613-45300-4(X)) Tandem Library Bks.

—What a Year, Vol. 4. 2004. (26 Fairmount Avenue Ser.). 75p. (J). (gr. 2-5). pap. 17.00 incl. audio (978-0-8072-0657-7(1) , Listening Library) Random Hse. Audio Publishing Group.

Defining Moments. 2005. (Defining Moments Ser.). (J). lib. bdg. 143.76 (978-1-59716-093-3(8)) Bearport Publishing Co., Inc.

Dell, Pamela. Benedict Arnold: From Patriot to Traitor. 2004. (Signature Lives Ser.). (Illus.). 112p. (J). 30.60 (978-0-7565-0825-8(8) , 1240127) Compass Point Bks.

Denenberg, Dennis. 50 American Heroes Every Kid Should Meet. Roscoe, Lorraine, illus. 2002. 112p. (gr. 4 up). pap. (978-0-7613-1645-9(0) , Twenty-First Century Bks.) Lerner Publishing Group.

Denenberg, Dennis & Roscoe, Lorraine. 50 American Heroes Every Kid Should Meet. 2001. (Inspiring People Ser.). (Illus.). 128p. (J). (gr. 4 up). lib. bdg. 29.90 (978-0-7613-1612-1(4) , Twenty-First Century Bks.) Lerner Publishing Group.

—50 American Heroes Every Kid Should Meet! rev. ed. 2005. (Illus.). 128p. (J). (gr. 3-7). pap. 14.95 (978-0-7613-9548-5(2) , First Avenue Editions) Lerner Publishing Group.

DiConsiglio, John. Young Americans: Tales of Teenage Immigrants. 2005. (Illus.). 43p. (978-0-439-12405-8(0)) Scholastic, Inc.

Ditchfield, Christin. Condoleezza Rice: America's Leading Stateswoman. 2006. (Great Life Stories Ser.). (Illus.). 111p. (J). (gr. 5-8). 30.50 (978-0-531-13874-8(7) , Watts, Franklin) Scholastic Library Publishing.

Doeden, Matt. Lance Armstrong. 2006. (Sports Heroes & Legends Ser.). (J). 27.93 (978-0-8225-5959-7(5) , Lerner Pubns.) Lerner Publishing Group.

—NASCAR's Greatest Moments. 2008. (J). (***978-1-4296-0086-6(1)***) Capstone Pr., Inc.

—Shaun White. (Amazing Athletes Ser.). (Illus.). 32p. (J). 2007. (gr. 2-4). 23.93 (978-0-8225-6840-7(3) , Lerner Pubns.); 2006. pap. 5.95 (978-0-8225-6841-4(1) , First Avenue Editions) Lerner Publishing Group.

—Will Smith. 2007. (Just the Facts Biographies Ser.). (J). 27.93 (978-0-8225-6608-3(7) , Lerner Pubns.) Lerner Publishing Group.

Donlan, Leni. A Life Well Lived: Ben Franklin. 2007. (J). (***978-1-4109-2698-2(2)***); pap. (***978-1-4109-2709-5(1)***) Steck-Vaughn.

Donovan, Sandra. Will Rogers: Cowboy, Comedian, & Commentator. 2006. (Signature Lives Ser.). (Illus.). 112p. (J). (gr. 4-8). lib. bdg. 31.93 (978-0-7565-2463-0(6)) Compass Point Bks.

Dougherty, Terri. Ben Stiller. 2007. (People in the News Ser.). 128p. (J). (gr. 7-10). 31.20 (***978-1-59018-723-4(7)*** , Lucent Bks.) Thomson Gale.

Driscoll, Laura. Hillary Clinton: An American Journey. Wood, Judith V., illus. 2007. (All Aboard Reading Ser.). 48p. (J). (gr. 1-3). pap. 3.99 (***978-0-448-44787-2(8)*** , Grosset & Dunlap) Penguin Group (USA) Inc.

Dunn, Joeming W. The Wright Brothers. Dunn, Joeming W. & Dunn, Ben, illus. 2007. (Bio-Graphics Ser.). 32p. (J). (gr. 3-6). lib. bdg. 27.07 (***978-1-60270-071-0(0)*** , Graphic Planet) Magic Wagon.

Edwards, Karen. Christopher Reeve: A Real-Life Superhero. 2005. (Illus.). 32p. (J). (978-0-669-51411-7(X)) Great Source Education Group, Inc.

Eggleston, Edward. Stories of Great Americans for Little Am. 2006. 41.99 (***978-1-4280-4852-2(9)***); pap. 34.99 (***978-1-4280-4915-4(0)***) IndyPublish.com.

—Stories of Great Americans for Little Americans. 2004. reprint ed. pap. 1.99 (978-1-4192-4958-7(4)); pap. 15.95 (978-1-4191-4958-0(X)) Kessinger Publishing, LLC.

—Stories of Great Americans for Little Americans. 2006. 164p. pap. 14.45 (***978-1-59462-414-8(3)*** , 450, Book Jungle) Standard Pubns., Inc.

—Stories of Great Americans for Little Americans (Yesterday's Classics) 2007. (J). per. 9.95 (***978-1-59915-084-0(0)***) Yesterday's Classics.

Eklund, Emmet E. & Eklund, Marion L. The Difference He Made: A Biography of Emory K. Lindquist. Pearson, John, ed. 1999. (Illus.). 357p. (YA). 20.00 (978-0-916030-10-0(5)) Bethany College Pr.-Kansas.

Espinosa, Rod. Benjamin Franklin. 2007. (Bio-Graphics Ser.). (Illus.). 32p. (J). (gr. 3-6). lib. bdg. 27.07 (***978-1-60270-066-6(4)*** , Graphic Planet) Magic Wagon.

Famous Americans Set. (gr. k-2). 114.95 (978-0-7368-9055-7(6)) Red Brick Learning.

Famous Figures of the American Frontier. 2005. 64p. pap. 250.00 (978-0-7910-6501-3(4) , Chelsea Hse.) Facts On File, Inc.

Fandel, Jennifer. George Eastman & the Kodak Camera. 2007. 32p. (J). (***978-0-7368-6848-8(8)***) Capstone Pr., Inc.

Feinstein, Stephen. Muhammad Ali. 2007. (African-American Heroes Ser.). (Illus.). 24p. (J). (gr. 1-3). lib. bdg. 21.26 (978-0-7660-2763-3(5) , Enslow Elementary) Enslow Pubs., Inc.

—Read about Benjamin Franklin. 2006. (I Like Biographies! Ser.). (Illus.). 24p. (J). lib. bdg. 21.26 (978-0-7660-2596-7(9) , Enslow Elementary) Enslow Pubs., Inc.

Fighting the Monster. 2004. (YA). ring bd. 59.95 (***978-0-9661256-2-7(2)***) Youth Communication - New York Center.

Findley, Violet. Easy Reader Biographies: Abraham Lincoln: A Great President, A Great American. 2007. 16p. pap. 2.99 (***978-0-439-77418-5(7)*** , Teaching Resources) Scholastic, Inc.

First Biographies Set 5. 2007. 136.68 (978-1-59679-784-0(3) , Buddy Bks.) ABDO Publishing Co.

Fitzgerald, Stephanie. Mary-Kate & Ashley Olsen. 2005. (Star Files Ser.). (Illus.). 48p. (J). (ps-1). lib. bdg. 31.43 (978-1-4109-1662-4(6)) Harcourt Schl. Pubs.

Fitzpatrick, Jim. Tony Hawk. 2006. (World's Greatest Athletes Ser.). (Illus.). 32p. (J). (gr. 1-5). 27.07 (978-1-59296-760-5(4)) Child's World, Inc.

Fleischman, Sid. Escape! The Story of the Great Houdini. 2006. (Illus.). 224p. (J). (gr. 4-8). 18.99 (978-0-06-085094-4(9)); lib. bdg. 19.89 (978-0-06-085095-1(7)) HarperCollins Pubs.

Fleming, Thomas. Sterling Point Books: Ben Franklin: Inventing America. 2007. (Sterling Point Bks.). (Illus.). 192p. (J). 12.95 (978-1-4027-4523-2(0)); pap. 6.95 (978-1-4027-4143-2(X)) Sterling Publishing Co., Inc.

Flynn, Jean. Henry B. Gonzalez: Rebel with a Cause. 2004. (Illus.). v, 140p. (J). pap. 16.95 (978-1-57168-846-0(3)) Eakin Pr.

Ford, Carin T. Paul Robeson: I Want to Make Freedom Ring. 2007. (African-American Biography Library). (Illus.). 128p. (J). (gr. 6 up). lib. bdg. 31.93 (***978-0-7660-2703-9(1)***) Enslow Pubs., Inc.

Frisch, Aaron. Jesse James. 2005. (Illus.). 48p. (gr. 5-9). 21.95 (978-1-58341-338-8(3) , Creative Education) Creative Co., The.

Fritz, Jean. Who's Saying What in Jamestown, Thomas Savage? Comport, Sally Wern, illus. 2007. 64p. (J). (gr. 2 up). 18.99 (978-0-399-24644-9(4) , Putnam Juvenile) Penguin Group (USA) Inc.

Fry, Erin. Arthur Ashe Against the Odds. 2005. (Voices Reading Ser.). (Illus.). 16p. (J). (978-0-7367-2915-4(1)) Zaner-Bloser, Inc.

Gaines, Ann Graham. Kenny Irwin. 1999. (Race Car Legends Ser.). (Illus.). 64p. (YA). (gr. 4-7). 28.00 (978-0-7910-5413-0(6)); pap. 25.00 (978-0-7910-5679-0(1)) Facts On File, Inc. (Chelsea Hse.).

Galens, Judy. Queen Latifah. 2007. (People in the News Ser.). 128p. (J). (gr. 7-10). 31.20 (***978-1-59018-930-6(2)*** , Lucent Bks.) Thomson Gale.

Gallagher, Jim. Daniel Morgan: Fighting Frontiersman. 2006. (J). pap. (978-1-59556-020-9(3)); (Illus.). 88p. (gr. 5-11). lib. bdg. 23.95 (978-1-59556-015-5(7)) OTTN Publishing.

Gaskill, Rachel. Agnes Demille. 2005. (Library of American Choreographers). (Illus.). 48p. (J). (ps-ps). lib. bdg. 23.95 (978-1-4042-0444-7(X)) Rosen Publishing Group, Inc., The.

Gaunt, Michael G. A History of Us, Grades 7-8: Junior High Syllabus. 2000. 29p. (J). tchr. ed. 4.95 (978-1-57896-088-0(6) , 2852, Hewitt Homeschooling Resources) Hewitt Research Foundation, Inc.

Geoghegan, Bronwyn. Livewire Real Lives Michael Klim. 2000. (Livewires Ser.). (Illus.). 32p. pap. 7.00 (978-0-521-77613-4(9)) Cambridge Univ. Pr.

Georgia Biographies (PB) 2005. 36p. pap. 19.95 (***978-0-635-02615-6(5)***) Gallopade International.

Giblin, James. The Many Rides of Paul Revere. 2007. 96p. (J). pap. 17.99 (***978-0-439-57290-3(8)*** , Scholastic Pr.) Scholastic, Inc.

Giesecke, Ernestine. Frederic Remington. 2006. (Heinemann First Library). (Illus.). 32p. (J). (***978-1-4034-8490-1(2)***) Heinemann Library.

Giff, Patricia Reilly. Dias Sombrios.Tr. of Purple Climbing Days. (SPA.). (J). 3.95 (978-0-922852-50-5(2)); 2000. (YA). (gr. 1 up). 3.95 (978-0-922852-53-6(7)) AIMS International Bks., Inc.

Gigliotti, Jim. LaDainian Tomlinson. 2008. (World's Greatest Athletes Ser.). 32p. (J). (gr. 1-5). 27.07 (***978-1-59296-881-7(3)***) Child's World, Inc.

Gigliotti, Jim. Peyton Manning. 2006. (World's Greatest Athletes Ser.). (Illus.). 32p. (J). (gr. 1-5). 27.07 (978-1-59296-758-2(2)) Child's World, Inc.

Gilbert, Sara. Annie Oakley. 2005. (Illus.). 48p. (gr. 5-9). 21.95 (978-1-58341-334-0(0) , Creative Education) Creative Co., The.

Gilbreth, Frank B., Jr. Cheaper by the Dozen. 2000. (YA). (gr. 7 up). (978-0-606-19692-5(7)) Tandem Library Bks.

Gilbreth, Frank B., Jr. & Carey, Ernestine Gilbreth. Cheaper by the Dozen. 188p. (YA). (gr. 7 up). reprint ed. lib. bdg. 24.95 (978-0-88411-289-1(6)) Amereon LTD.

—Cheaper by the Dozen. 2002. (Perennial Classics Ser.). 224p. (gr. 7 up). pap. 11.95 (978-0-06-008460-8(X)) HarperCollins Pubs.

—Cheaper by the Dozen. 180p. (YA). (gr. 7 up). pap. 5.50 (978-0-8072-8308-0(8)); 2004. (J). (gr. 4-7). pap. 38.00 incl. audio (978-0-8072-8307-3(X) , YA157SP) Random Hse. Audio Publishing Group. (Listening Library).

Gillis, Jennifer Blizin. Patrick Henry. 2004. (Illus.). 32p. (J). lib. bdg. 24.22 (978-1-4034-5960-2(6)) Heinemann Library.

Gimpel, Les. Fighting Wars, Planning for Peace: The Story of George C. Marshall. 2005. (World Leaders Ser.). (Illus.). 176p. (J). (gr. 8 up). lib. bdg. 26.95 (978-1-931798-66-2(4)) Reynolds, Morgan Inc.

Glaser, Jason. Patrick Henry: Liberty or Death. McDonnell, Peter, illus, 2005. (Graphic Library). 32p. (J). (gr. 3-7). lib. bdg. 25.26 (978-0-7368-4970-8(X)) Capstone Pr., Inc.

Glassman, Bruce. John Paul Getty: Billionaire Oilman. 2001. (Giants of American Industry Ser.). (Illus.). 112p. (J). (gr. 5-8). 27.45 (978-1-56711-513-0(6) , Blackbirch Pr., Inc.) Thomson Gale.

Golus, Carrie. Enrico Fermi. 2006. (Giants of Science Ser.). (J). (978-1-4103-0578-7(3) , Blackbirch Pr., Inc.) Thomson Gale.

Golus, Carrie. Russell Simmons. 2007. (J). lib. bdg. (***978-0-8225-7158-2(7)***) Twenty First Century Bks.

Goodman, Michael E. Buffalo Bill. 2005. (Illus.). 48p. (gr. 5-9). 21.95 (978-1-58341-336-4(7) , Creative Education) Creative Co., The.

Gotsch, Patrice. Cesar Chavez: Changing Lives. Arreola, Gil, illus. 2005. 19p. (J). pap. (***978-1-55501-780-4(0)***) Ballard & Tighe Pubs.

Graham, Amy. Thomas Edison: Wizard of Light & Sound. 2007. (Inventors Who Changed the World Ser.). (Illus.). 128p. (J). lib. bdg. 33.27 (978-1-59845-052-1(2) , MyReportLinks.com Bks.) Enslow Pubs., Inc.

Gray, Peter Winslow. Who Was Who in America: Their Childhood Years. (Illus.). (J). Vol. I. 2002. 53p. spiral bd. 10.95 (978-1-889639-03-1(6)); Vol. III. 2003. 54p. spiral bd. 10.95 (978-1-889639-07-9(9)) AMSC, Adventures in Math & Social Studies for Children.

—Who Was Who in America Volume II: Their Childhood Years. 2003. (Illus.). (J). spiral bd. 10.95 (978-1-889639-02-4(8)) AMSC, Adventures in Math & Social Studies for Children.

Graziano, Jim. Johnny Depp. 2007. (J). (*978-1-4222-0200-5(3)) Mason Crest Pubs.

Gregson, Susan R. Benjamin Franklin. 2000. (Let Freedom Ring Ser.). (Illus.). 48p. (J). (gr. 3-4). lib. bdg. 22.60 (978-0-7368-1031-9(5) , Bridgestone Bks.) Capstone Pr., Inc.

Grolier Educational Staff. The American Scene, 12 vols., Set. 2001. (Illus.). (J). (978-0-7172-9584-5(2) , Grolier) Scholastic Library Publishing.

Grolier Educational Staff, contrib. by. The American Scene, 12 vols. 2001. (Illus.). (J). (978-0-7172-9573-9(7)); (978-0-7172-9574-6(5)); (978-0-7172-9575-3(3)); (978-0-7172-9576-0(1)); (978-0-7172-9577-7(X)); (978-0-7172-9578-4(8)); (978-0-7172-9579-1(6)); (978-0-7172-9580-7(X)); (978-0-7172-9581-4(8)); (978-0-7172-9582-1(6)); (978-0-7172-9583-8(4)) Scholastic Library Publishing. (Grolier).

—The American Scene: Lives, Dale Earnhardt-Newt Gringrich, 12 vols. 2001. (Illus.). (J). (gr. 6-9). 329.00 (978-0-7172-9572-2(9) , Grolier) Scholastic Library Publishing.

Guzman, Lila & Guzman, Rick. César Chavez: Fighting for Fairness. 2006. (Famous Latinos Ser.). (Illus.). 32p. (J). lib. bdg. 22.60 (978-0-7660-2370-3(2) , Enslow Elementary) Enslow Pubs., Inc.

—George Lopez: Comedian & TV Star. 2006. (Famous Latinos Ser.). (Illus.). 32p. (J). lib. bdg. 22.60 (978-0-7660-2644-5(2) , Enslow Elementary) Enslow Pubs., Inc.

Hamilton, Sue. Jack Kirby. 2007. (Comic Book Creators Ser.). (Illus.). 32p. (J). (gr. 3-5). lib. bdg. 24.21 (978-1-59928-298-5(4) , ABDO & Daughters) ABDO Publishing Co.

—Joe Simon. 2007. (Comic Book Creators Ser.). (Illus.). 32p. (J). (gr. 3-5). lib. bdg. 24.21 (978-1-59928-300-5(X) , ABDO & Daughters) ABDO Publishing Co.

—Joe Sinnott. 2007. 24.21 (978-1-59928-299-2(2) , ABDO & Daughters) ABDO Publishing Co.

—John Buscema. 2007. (Illus.). 32p. 24.21 (978-1-59928-297-8(6) , ABDO & Daughters) ABDO Publishing Co.

—John Romita, Sr. 2007. 24.21 (978-1-59928-302-9(6) , ABDO & Daughters) ABDO Publishing Co.

Hardin, Travis. The Young Writers Series: Called to Serve. 2007. (YA). pap. 5.99 (*978-1-58158-108-9(4)) McDougal Publishing Co.

Harkins, Susan and William. The Life & Times of Father Jacques Marquette. 2007. (Profiles in American History Ser.). (J). lib. bdg. (*978-1-58415-528-7(0)) Mitchell Lane Pubs., Inc.

Harness, Cheryl. The Tragic Tale of Narcissa Whitman & a Faithful History of the Oregon Trail. Harness, Cheryl, illus. 2006. (Illus.). 144p. (J). (gr. 5-9). 16.95 (978-0-7922-5920-6(3) , National Geographic Children's Bks.) National Geographic Society.

Harris, Laurie Lanzen, ed. Biography for Beginners Fall 1998. 1998. 102p. (J). lib. bdg. 20.00 (978-1-931360-07-4(3)) Favorable Impressions.

—Biography for Beginners Fall 1999: Sketches for Early Readers. 1999. 102p. (J). lib. bdg. 20.00 (978-1-931360-09-8(X)) Favorable Impressions.

—Biography for Beginners Fall 2000: Sketches for Early Readers. 2000. 102p. (J). lib. bdg. 20.00 (978-1-931360-11-1(1)) Favorable Impressions.

—Biography for Beginners Fall 2001: Sketches for Early Readers. 2001. 120p. (J). lib. bdg. 20.00 (978-1-931360-17-3(0)) Favorable Impressions.

—Biography for Beginners Spring 1998: Sketches for Early Readers. 1998. 102p. (J). lib. bdg. 20.00 (978-1-931360-06-7(5)) Favorable Impressions.

—Biography for Beginners Spring 1999: Sketches for Early Readers. 1999. 102p. (J). lib. bdg. 20.00 (978-1-931360-08-1(1)) Favorable Impressions.

—Biography for Beginners Spring 2000: Sketches for Early Readers. 2000. 102p. (J). lib. bdg. 20.00 (978-1-931360-10-4(3)) Favorable Impressions.

—Biography for Beginners Spring 2001: Sketches for Early Readers. 2001. 120p. (J). lib. bdg. 20.00 (978-1-931360-16-6(2)) Favorable Impressions.

—Biography Today, Annual Cumulation 1999: Profiles of People of Interest to Young Readers. annual 1999. (Biography Today General Series: Annual Cumulation Ser.). (Illus.). 390p. (YA). (gr. 4-12). lib. bdg. (978-0-7808-0370-1(1)) Omnigraphics, Inc.

Haugen, Brenda. Thurgood Marshall: Civil Rights Lawyer & Supreme Court Justice. 2006. (Illus.). 112p. (J). lib. bdg. (*978-0-7565-1877-6(6)) Compass Point Bks.

Haugen, Brenda & Santella, Andrew. Benjamin Franklin: Scientist & Statesman. 2004. (Signature Lives Ser.). (Illus.). 112p. (J). 30.60 (978-0-7565-0826-5(6) , 1240128) Compass Point Bks.

Hayhurst, Chris. Jerry Yang & David Filo: The Founders of Yahoo! 2006. (Internet Career Biographies Ser.). (Illus.). 112p. (YA). (gr. 7-12). lib. bdg. 31.95 (978-1-4042-0718-9(X)) Rosen Publishing Group, Inc., The.

Heinrichs, Ann. French Americans. 2004. (Our Cultural Heritage Ser.). 32p. (J). (gr. 2-6). 27.07 (978-1-59296-180-1(0)) Child's World, Inc.

Helenthal, Janet. Helen Keller. 2005. (Illus.). 16p. (J). (*978-0-7367-2853-9(8)) Zaner-Bloser, Inc.

Heroes of America. 2005. (J). (gr. 3-8). lib. bdg. 170.80 (978-1-59679-254-8(X)) ABDO Publishing Co.

Hicks, Kyra E. Martha Ann's Quilt for Queen Victoria. 2006. (J). 16.95 (978-1-933285-59-7(1)) Brown Bks. Publishing Group.

Hicks, Terry Allan. Uncle Sam. 2006. (Symbols of America Ser.). (Illus.). 40p. (J). lib. bdg. 28.50 (978-0-7614-2137-5(8) , Benchmark Bks.) Cavendish, Marshall Corp.

Hill, Anne E. Sasha Cohen. 2007. (J). lib. bdg. (*978-0-8225-7164-3(1)) Twenty First Century Bks.

Hill, Christine M. Lance Armstrong: Cycling, Surviving, Inspiring Hope. 2007. (People to Know Today Ser.). (Illus.). 128p. (J). (gr. 6). lib. bdg. 31.93 (*978-0-7660-2694-0(9)) Enslow Pubs., Inc.

Hilliard, Richard. Godspeed, John Glenn. 2006. (Illus.). (J). 16.95 (978-1-59078-384-9(0)) Boyds Mills Pr.

Hilliard, Richard, illus. Ham, the Astrochimp. 2007. 32p. (J). (gr. 4-7). 16.95 (*978-1-59078-459-4(6)) Boyds Mills Pr.

Himelstein, Abram Shalom. What the Hell Am I Doing Here? The 100 T-Shirt Project. 2005. (Illus.). 128p. pap. 12.00 (978-1-891053-98-6(1)) Garrett County Pr.

Historical American Biographies, 53 bks., Set. (Illus.). (YA). (gr. 6-12). lib. bdg. 1111.35 (978-0-89490-911-5(8)) Enslow Pubs., Inc.

Hodgman, Ann. The House of a Million Pets. Yelchin, Eugene, illus. 2007. 263p. (J). (gr. 3 up). 16.95 (*978-0-8050-7974-6(2)) Holt, Henry & Co.

Hoffman, Mary Ann. Alex Rodriguez: Baseball Star = Estrella Del Béisbol. 2007. (Illus.). 24p. (J). (*978-1-4042-7598-0(3) , PowerKids Pr.) Rosen Publishing Group, Inc., The.

—Dwyane Wade: Basketball Star. 2006. (Sports Superstars Ser.). (Illus.). 24p. (J). lib. bdg. (978-1-4042-3536-6(1) , PowerKids Pr.) Rosen Publishing Group, Inc., The.

—LeBron James: Basketball Star. 2006. (Sports Superstars Ser.). (J). lib. bdg. (978-1-4042-3535-9(3)) Rosen Publishing Group, Inc., The.

—Peyton Manning: Football Star. 2006. (Illus.). 24p. (J). lib. bdg. (978-1-4042-3531-1(0) , PowerKids Pr.) Rosen Publishing Group, Inc., The.

—Shaun Alexander: Football Star. 2006. (Sports Superstars Ser.). (Illus.). 24p. (J). lib. bdg. (978-1-4042-3532-8(9) , PowerKids Pr.) Rosen Publishing Group, Inc., The.

Holt, Julia. Johnny Depp. 2001. (Livewire Ser.). (Illus.). 32p. pap. (978-0-340-80099-7(2) , Hodder Arnold) Hodder Education.

Hoose, Phillip M. We Were There, Too! Young People in U. S. History. 2000. (J). 25.00 (978-0-7894-2587-4(4)) Dorling Kindersley Publishing, Inc.

Horn, Geoffrey M. Adam Sandler. 2005. (Today's Superstars). (Illus.). 32p. (J). (gr. 5 up). lib. bdg. 23.93 (978-0-8368-4234-0(0)) Stevens, Gareth Inc.

—Alicia Keyes. 2005. (Today's Superstars). (Illus.). 32p. (J). (gr. 5 up). lib. bdg. 23.93 (978-0-8368-4233-3(2)) Stevens, Gareth Inc.

—Beyonce. 2005. (Today's Superstars). (Illus.). 32p. (J). (gr. 5 up). lib. bdg. 23.93 (978-0-8368-4230-2(8)) Stevens, Gareth Inc.

—Cameron Diaz. 2005. (Today's Superstars). (Illus.). 32p. (J). (gr. 5 up). lib. bdg. 23.93 (978-0-8368-4231-9(6)) Stevens, Gareth Inc.

—Colin Powell. 2004. (Trailblazers of the Modern World Ser.). (Illus.). 48p. (J). pap. 11.95 (978-0-8368-5267-7(2)); (YA). lib. bdg. 30.00 (978-0-8368-5498-5(5)) Stevens, Gareth Inc. (World Almanac Library).

—Jamie Foxx. 2005. (Today's Superstars). (Illus.). 32p. (J). (gr. 5 up). lib. bdg. 23.93 (978-0-8368-4232-6(4)) Stevens, Gareth Inc.

—Today's Superstars: Entertainment. 32p. (YA). 139.98 (978-0-8368-4229-6(4)) Stevens, Gareth Inc.

Hort, Dawn. Livewire Real Lives Sir Donald Bradman. 2000. (Livewires Ser.). 32p. pap. 6.00 (978-0-521-77614-1(7)) Cambridge Univ. Pr.

Houle, Michelle. Lindsey Williams: Gardening for Impoverished Families. 2007. (Young Heroes Ser.). (Illus.). 64p. (J). (gr. 4-8). 24.95 (*978-0-7377-3867-4(7) , Kidhaven) Thomson Gale.

Howard, Helen, et al. Living As a Refugee in America: Mohammed's Story. 2005. (J). lib. bdg. 30.00 (978-0-8368-5959-1(6) , World Almanac Library) Stevens, Gareth Inc.

Huff, Richard. The Jarretts. rev. ed. 2007. (Race Car Legends: Ser.). 80p. (J). (gr. 5-8). 25.00 (978-0-7910-8762-6(X) , Chelsea Hse.) Facts On File, Inc.

Hurtig, Jennifer. Maurice Sendak. 2007. (My Favorite Writer Ser.). (J). (978-1-59036-485-7(6)); lib. bdg. (978-1-59036-484-0(8)) Weigl Pubs., Inc.

Hyman, Trina Schart. A Self Portrait: Trina. 12.95 (978-0-201-09308-7(1)) HarperCollins Pubs.

Irwin, Cait, et al. Monochrome Days: A First-Hand Account of One Teenager's Experience with Depression. 2007. (Adolescent Mental Health Initiative Ser.). (Illus.). 184p. (gr. 8 up). 30.00 (978-0-19-531004-7(7)); pap. 9.95 (978-0-19-531005-4(5)) Oxford Univ. Pr., Inc.

Jackson, Ian. Livewire Real Lives Shane Warne. 2000. (Livewires Ser.). (Illus.). 32p. pap. 6.00 (978-0-521-77612-7(0)) Cambridge Univ. Pr.

James, Lincoln. Dale Jarrett. 2007. (NASCAR Champions Ser.). (Illus.). 24p. (J). lib. bdg. (978-1-4042-3459-8(4) , PowerKids Pr.) Rosen Publishing Group, Inc., The.

Jarrow, Gail. Robert H. Jackson: Voice of Justice. 2008. (J). (*978-1-59078-511-9(8) , Calkins Creek) Boyds Mills Pr.

John Winthrop. (Colonial America Biographies Ser.). 48p. (YA). 7.95 (978-0-7368-4484-0(8)) Capstone Pr., Inc.

Johns, Linda. A Rocket Boy Grows Up. 2005. (Illus.). 16p. (J). (*978-0-7367-2904-8(6)) Zaner-Bloser, Inc.

Johns, Michael-Anne. Hangin' with Lindsay Lohan. 2004. (Illus.). 48p. (J). (978-0-439-72512-5(7)) Scholastic, Inc.

Jones, Charlotte Foltz. Westward Ho! Eleven Explorers of the American West. 2005. (Illus.). 240p. (J). (gr. 4-6). tchr. ed. 22.95 (978-0-8234-1586-1(4)) Holiday Hse., Inc.

Josephson, Judith Pinkerton. Walt Disney: Genius of Entertainment. 2006. (People to Know Today Ser.). (Illus.). 128p. (J). lib. bdg. 31.93 (978-0-7660-2624-7(8)) Enslow Pubs., Inc.

Kate Shelley & the Midnight Express. 9.95 (978-1-59112-169-5(8)) Live Oak Media.

Keenan, Sheila. Scholastic Book of Outstanding Americans. 2003. 256p. (J). pap. 19.95 (978-0-439-28358-8(2) , Scholastic Reference) Scholastic, Inc.

Keep the Lights Burning. 9.95 (978-1-59112-293-7(7)) Live Oak Media.

Kehret, Peg. Small Steps: The Year I Got Polio. 2006. (Illus.). 224p. (J). 15.95 (978-0-8075-7459-1(7)) Whitman, Albert & Co.

Keith, Ted. Shaun Alexander. 2008. (World's Greatest Athletes Ser.). 32p. (J). (gr. 1-5). 27.07 (*978-1-59296-880-0(5)) Child's World, Inc.

Kerley, Barbara. What to Do about Alice?! How Alice Roosevelt Broke the Rules, Charmed the World, & Drove Her Father Teddy Crazy. Fotheringham, Ed, illus. 2008. 48p. (J). pap. 16.99 (*978-0-439-92231-9(3) , Scholastic Pr.) Scholastic, Inc.

Kerns, Anne. Martha Stewart. 2007. (Biography Ser.). (Illus.). 112p. (J). (gr. 6-12). 29.27 (978-0-8225-6613-7(3) , Twenty-First Century Bks.) Lerner Publishing Group.

Kiely Miller, Barbara. John Muir. 2007. (J). pap. (*978-0-8368-8325-1(X) , Weekly Reader Early Learning Library) Stevens, Gareth Inc.

Kimmel, Eric A. A Horn for Louis. 2005. (Illus.). 96p. (J). (gr. 1-4). 11.95 (978-0-375-83252-9(1)); lib. bdg. 13.99 (978-0-375-93252-6(6)) Random Hse. Children's Bks. (Random Hse. Bks. for Young Readers).

King, David C. & American Heritage Magazine Staff. World Wars & the Modern Age. 2004. (American Heritage, American Voices Ser.). (Illus.). 144p. pap. 12.95 (978-0-471-44392-6(1) , Wiley) Wiley, John & Sons, Inc.

Kirkpatrick, Katherine. The Snow Baby: The Arctic Childhood of Robert E. Peary's Daring Daughter. 2006. (Illus.). 48p. (J). 16.95 (978-0-8234-1973-9(8)) Holiday Hse., Inc.

Klein, Adam G. & Rockwell, Norman. Norman Rockwell. 2007. (Illus.). 32p. (J). 22.78 (978-1-59679-738-3(X)) ABDO Publishing Co.

Koestler-Grack, Rachel A. Nathan Hale: Courageous Spy. 2005. (Leaders of the American Revolution Ser.). (Illus.). 124p. (J). (gr. 4-8). lib. bdg. 30.00 (978-0-7910-8623-0(2) , Chelsea Hse.) Facts On File, Inc.

Kramer, Barbara. Gloria Estefan: Never Give Up. 2005. (Awesome Values in Famous Lives Ser.). (Illus.). 48p. (J). (gr. 3-4). lib. bdg. 23.93 (978-0-7660-2380-2(X) , Enslow Elementary) Enslow Pubs., Inc.

Kramer, Sydelle. Who Was Daniel Boone? Ulrich, George, illus. 2006. (Who Was... ? Ser.). 112p. (J). (gr. 2-5). pap. 4.99 (978-0-448-43902-0(6) , Grosset & Dunlap) Penguin Group (USA) Inc.

Kramer, Sydelle A. Night Flight: Charles Lindbergh's Incredible Adventure. 2002. (gr. k-3). lib. bdg. 11.80 (978-0-613-43635-9(0)) Tandem Library Bks.

Krensky, Stephen. Casey Jones. Schroder, Mark, illus. 2007. (On My Own Folklore Ser.). 48p. (J). (gr. 2-5). lib. bdg. 25.26 (978-1-57505-890-0(1) , Millbrook Pr.) Lerner Publishing Group.

Krensky Stephen. Casey Jones. Schroder, Mark, illus. 2007. (On My Own Folklore Ser.). (J). pap. 6.95 (*978-0-8225-6476-8(9) , First Avenue Editions) Lerner Publishing Group.

Krohn, Katherine E. Gwen Stefani. 2007. (J). lib. bdg. (*978-0-8225-7157-5(9)) Twenty First Century Bks.

Kroll, Steven. When I Dream of Heaven: Angelina's Story. 2001. (American Portraits Ser.). (gr. 5-8). 15.32 (978-0-8092-0581-3(5) , 9780809205813) Jamestown.

Krull, Kathleen. Houdini: World's Greatest Mystery Man & Escape King. Velasquez, Eric, illus. 2007. 32p. (J). pap. 6.95 (*978-0-8027-9646-2(X)) Walker & Co.

Kudlinski, Kathleen. Christopher Reeve: Young Actor. Henderson, Meryl, illus. 2007. (Childhood of Famous Americans Ser.). 224p. (J). pap. 5.99 (*978-1-4169-1544-7(3) , Aladdin) Simon & Schuster Children's Publishing.

Kudlinski, Kathleen. Dr. Seuss: Young Author & Artist. Henderson, Meryl, illus. 2005. (Childhood of Famous Americans Ser.). 192p. pap. 5.99 (978-0-689-87347-8(6) , Aladdin) Simon & Schuster Children's Publishing.

—Dr. Seuss: Young Author & Artist. Henderson, Meryl, illus. 2005. 184p. (J). (gr. 3-7). per. 12.04 (978-0-606-33885-1(3)) Tandem Library Bks.

Kurtz, Jane. Jane Kurtz & You. 2007. (Author & YOU Ser.: No. 8). (Illus.). 204p. 35.00 (978-1-59158-295-3(4) , LU2954) Libraries Unlimited, Inc.

Landau, Elaine. Women's Right to Vote. 2007. (Cornerstones of Freedomtrade;, Second Ser.). 48p. (J). (gr. 4-6). pap. 5.95 (*978-0-531-18833-0(7) , Children's Pr.) Scholastic Library Publishing.

Lasky, Kathryn. John Muir: America's First Environmentalist. Fellows, Stan, illus. 2006. 48p. (J). (gr. 1-5). 16.99 (978-0-7636-1957-2(4)) Candlewick Pr.

—John Muir: America's First Environmentalist. Fellows, Stanley, illus. 2006. 41p. (J). (978-1-4156-7115-3(X)) Candlewick Pr.

Leavitt, Amie. Dylan & Cole Sprouse. 2007. (Robbie Reader Ser.). (Illus.). 32p. (J). (gr. 1-4). lib. bdg. 25.70 (*978-1-58415-591-1(4)) Mitchell Lane Pubs., Inc.

—Miley Cyrus. 2007. (Robbie Reader Ser.). (Illus.). 32p. (J). (gr. 1-4). lib. bdg. 25.70 (*978-1-58415-590-4(6)) Mitchell Lane Pubs., Inc.

—Raven-Symone. 2007. (Robbie Reader Ser.). (Illus.). 32p. (J). (gr. 1-4). lib. bdg. 25.70 (*978-1-58415-593-5(0)) Mitchell Lane Pubs., Inc.

Lebrecque, Ellen. Magic Johnson. 2008. (J). lib. bdg. 26.00 (*978-1-60279-071-1(X)) Cherry Lake Publishing.

Lee, Sally. Sam Walton: Business Genius of Wal-Mart. 2007. (People to Know Today Ser.). (Illus.). 112p. (J). (gr. 6). lib. bdg. 31.93 (*978-0-7660-2692-6(2)) Enslow Pubs., Inc.

Leonard, Tara. The Gift of Imagination: John Steinbeck's Childhood. Scott, Laura, illus. 2001. 32p. (J). (gr. 2-4). pap. 12.95 (978-1-57931-150-6(4)) ToucanEd Pubns.

Lesinski, Jeanne M. Bill Gates. 2007. (J). pap. 7.95 (*978-0-8225-7027-1(0) , Lerner Pubns.) Lerner Publishing Group.

LeTourneau, Anthony Alex, illus. Hanni & Beth: Safe & Sound. 2007. (J). (*978-0-9792918-0-7(1)) Blue Marlin Pubns.

Levy, Janey. Motocross Superstars. 2007. (Motocross Ser.). (Illus.). 32p. (J). (gr. 4-6). lib. bdg. 23.95 (*978-1-4042-3695-0(3) , PowerKids Pr.) Rosen Publishing Group, Inc., The.

Library in a Book Set. 2005. 208p. 1305.00 (978-0-8160-6517-2(9)) Facts On File, Inc.

Lindop, Edmund. Presidents Who Dared. (Biographies Ser.). (Illus.). 64p. (978-0-7613-3084-4(4) , Twenty-First Century Bks.) Lerner Publishing Group.

Lommel, Cookie. Russell Simmons. 2007. (Hip-Hop Stars Ser.). 104p. (J). (gr. 6-12). 30.00 (*978-0-7910-9467-9(7) , Chelsea Hse.) Facts On File, Inc.

Lord, Raymond. Usher. 2007. (Hip-Hop Ser.). (Illus.). 64p. (YA). (gr. 5 up). 22.95 (978-1-4222-0131-2(7)) Mason Crest Pubs.

Louie, Ai-Ling. Vera Wang Queen of Fashion; Amazing Chinese American: Biographies of Amazing Asian Americans. 2007. (Illus.). 48p. (J). pap. 12.99 (*978-0-9787465-3-7(8)) Dragoneagle Pr.

Lupo, Tamar. Warren Buffet. 2007. (J). (*978-1-59036-651-6(4)); (*978-1-59036-652-3(2)) Weigl Pubs., Inc.

Lutz, Norma Jean. Cotton Mather: Author, Clergyman & Scholar. 2000. (gr. 5-8). lib. bdg. 17.60 (978-0-613-43314-3(9)) Tandem Library Bks.

Lynch, Kelly Ann. He Said Yes: The Story of Father Mychal Judge. 2007. (Illus.). 32p. (J). (gr. k-7). 12.95 (*978-0-8091-6740-1(9) , 6740-1) Paulist Pr.

Lynetter, Rachel. Ashley Shuyler: AfricAid. 2007. (Young Heroes Ser.). 64p. (J). (gr. 4-8). 27.45 (*978-0-7377-3669-4(0) , Kidhaven) Thomson Gale.

MacDonald, James. Dale Earnhardt, Jr: Racing's Living Legacy. 2008. (Heroes of Racing Ser.). (Illus.). 128p. (J). (gr. 5-9). lib. bdg. 31.93 (*978-0-7660-2996-5(4)) Enslow Pubs., Inc.

MacLeod, Elizabeth. Harry Houdini: A Magical Life. (Illus.). 32p. (978-1-55337-769-6(9)); 2005. (J). (gr. 3-7). (978-1-55337-770-2(2)) Kids Can Pr., Ltd.

Madison, Taylor. Boys We Love: Today's Top 30 Hottest Stars. 2005. (Illus.). (J). (978-0-439-74864-3(X)) Scholastic, Inc.

Magocsi, Paul R. The Carpatho-Rusyn Americans. 2000. (Immigrant Experience Ser.). (Illus.). (J). 21.95 (978-0-7910-6284-5(8) , Chelsea Hse.) Facts On File, Inc.

Mahaney, Ian F. Dave Mirra: Bicycle Stunt Champ. 2005. (Extreme Sports Biographies Ser.). (Illus.). 24p. (J). 19.95 (978-1-4042-2744-6(X) , PowerKids Pr.) Rosen Publishing Group, Inc., The.

Main, Mary. Dr. Phil: Self-Help Guru & TV Superstar. 2007. (People to Know Today Ser.). (Illus.). 128p. (J). (gr. 6). lib. bdg. 31.93 (*978-0-7660-2696-4(5)) Enslow Pubs., Inc.

Mallin, Jay. Al Sharpton: Community Activist. 2007. (Great Life Stories Ser.). (Illus.). 111p. (J). (*978-0-531-13672-0(8) , Franklin Watts) Hodder Children's Division.

Manly Inc., et al. Student's Encyclopedia of Great American Characters Set, 4-Volumes. 2007. 1600p. (gr. 9). 340.00 (*978-0-8160-6498-4(9)) Facts On File, Inc.

Mannis, Celeste Davidson. Julia Morgan Built a Castle. Hyman, Miles, illus. 2006. 40p. (J). (ps). 17.99 (978-0-670-05964-5(1) , Viking Adult) Penguin Group (USA) Inc.

Marcovitz, Hal. Lawrence Yep. 2008. (Who Wrote That? Ser.). 128p. (gr. 6-12). 30.00 (*978-0-7910-9527-0(4) , Chelsea Hse.) Facts On File, Inc.

—Maurice Sendak. 2006. (Who Wrote That? Ser.). (Illus.). 136-144p. (J). 30.00 (978-0-7910-8796-1(4) , Chelsea Hse.) Facts On File, Inc.

—Scott O'Dell. 2007. (Who Wrote That? Ser.). 112p. (J). (gr. 6-12). 30.00 (*978-0-7910-9526-3(6) , Chelsea Hse.) Facts On File, Inc.

Marcovitz, Hal. Tupac. 2006. (Hip-Hop Ser.). (Illus.). 64p. (YA). (gr. 5 up). 22.95 (978-1-4222-0130-5(9)) Mason Crest Pubs.

Marolf, Stacey & Pessano, Laurie. Founding Fathers... & Mothers: A Field Trip to 18th Century America. Evans, Peter, illus. 1999. 128p. (J). (gr. 4-7). pap. 27.95 incl. audio (978-1-892405-12-8(1)) Good Co. Players Educational Div.

Marsh, Carole. The Alabama Experience Library State Resource Set. 2001. (Illus.). (J). lib. bdg. 100.20 incl. cd-rom (978-0-635-00453-6(4)) Gallopade International.

—The Alaska Experience Library State Resource Set. 2001. (Alaska Experience! Ser.). (Illus.). (J). lib. bdg. 100.20 incl. cd-rom (978-0-635-00454-3(2)) Gallopade International.

—The Arizona Experience Library State Resource Set. 2001. (Arizona Experience! Ser.). (Illus.). (J). lib. bdg. 100.20 incl. cd-rom (978-0-635-00455-0(0)) Gallopade International.

—The Arkansas Experience Library State Resource Set. 2001. (Arkansas Experience! Ser.). (Illus.). (J). lib. bdg. 100.20 incl. cd-rom (978-0-635-00456-7(9)) Gallopade International.

—The Colorado Experience Library State Resource Set. 2001. (Colorado Experience! Ser.). (Illus.). (J). lib. bdg. 100.20 incl. cd-rom (978-0-635-00458-1(5)) Gallopade International.

—The Connecticut Experience Library State Resource Set. 2001. (Connecticut Experience! Ser.). (Illus.). (J). lib. bdg. 100.20 incl. cd-rom (978-0-635-00459-8(3)) Gallopade International.

—The Delaware Experience Library State Resource Set. 2001. (Delaware Experience! Ser.). (Illus.). (J). lib. bdg. 100.20 incl. cd-rom (978-0-635-00460-4(7)) Gallopade International.

T U V

—The Florida Experience Library State Resource Set. 2001. (Florida Experience! Ser.). (Illus.). (J). lib. bdg. 100.20 incl. cd-rom (978-0-635-00462-8(3)) Gallopade International.

—The Georgia Experience Library State Resource Set. 2001. (Georgia Experience! Ser.). (Illus.). (J). lib. bdg. 100.20 incl. cd-rom (978-0-635-00463-5(1)) Gallopade International.

—The Hawaii Experience Library State Resource Set. 2001. (Hawaii Experience! Ser.). (Illus.). (J). lib. bdg. 100.20 incl. cd-rom (978-0-635-00464-2(X)) Gallopade International.

—The Idaho Experience Library State Resource Set. 2001. (Idaho Experience! Ser.). (Illus.). (J). lib. bdg. 100.20 incl. cd-rom (978-0-635-00465-9(8)) Gallopade International.

—The Illinois Experience Library State Resource Set. 2001. (Ilinois Experience! Ser.). (Illus.). (J). lib. bdg. 100.20 incl. cd-rom (978-0-635-00466-6(6)) Gallopade International.

—The Indiana Experience Library State Resource Set. 2001. (Indiana Experience! Ser.). (Illus.). (J). lib. bdg. 100.20 incl. cd-rom (978-0-635-00467-3(4)) Gallopade International.

—The Kansas Experience Library State Resource Set. 2001. (Kansas Experience! Ser.). (Illus.). (J). lib. bdg. 100.20 incl. cd-rom (978-0-635-00469-7(0)) Gallopade International.

—The Kentucky Experience Library State Resource Set. 2001. (Kentucky Experience! Ser.). (Illus.). (J). lib. bdg. 100.20 incl. cd-rom (978-0-635-00470-3(4)) Gallopade International.

—The Louisiana Experience Library State Resource Set. 2001. (Louisiana Experience! Ser.). (Illus.). (J). lib. bdg. 100.20 incl. cd-rom (978-0-635-00471-0(2)) Gallopade International.

—The Maine Experience Library State Resource Set. 2001. (Maine Experience! Ser.). (Illus.). (J). lib. bdg. 100.20 incl. cd-rom (978-0-635-00472-7(0)) Gallopade International.

—The Maryland Experience Library State Resource Set. 2001. (Maryland Experience! Ser.). (Illus.). (J). lib. bdg. 100.20 incl. cd-rom (978-0-635-00473-4(9)) Gallopade International.

—Massachusetts Experience Library State Resource Set. 2001. (Massachusetts Experience! Ser.). (Illus.). (J). lib. bdg. 100.20 incl. cd-rom (978-0-635-00474-1(7)) Gallopade International.

—The New York Experience Library State Resource Set. 2001. (New York Experience! Ser.). (Illus.). (J). lib. bdg. 100.20 incl. cd-rom (978-0-635-00485-7(2)) Gallopade International.

—The North Carolina Experience Library State Resource Set. 2001. (North Carolina Experience! Ser.). (Illus.). (J). lib. bdg. 100.20 incl. cd-rom (978-0-635-00486-4(0)) Gallopade International.

—The North Dakota Experience Library State Resource Set. 2001. (North Dakota Experience! Ser.). (Illus.). (J). lib. bdg. 100.20 incl. cd-rom (978-0-635-00487-1(9)) Gallopade International.

—The Oklahoma Experience Library State Resource Set. 2001. (Oklahoma Experience! Ser.). (Illus.). (J). lib. bdg. 100.20 incl. cd-rom (978-0-635-00489-5(5)) Gallopade International.

—The Oregon Experience Library State Resource Set. 2001. (Oregon Experience! Ser.). (Illus.). (J). lib. bdg. 100.20 incl. cd-rom (978-0-635-00490-1(9)) Gallopade International.

—The Pennsylvania Experience Library State Resource Set. 2001. (Pennsylvania Experience! Ser.). (Illus.). (J). lib. bdg. 100.20 incl. cd-rom (978-0-635-00491-8(7)) Gallopade International.

—The Rhode Island Experience Library State Resource Set. 2001. (Rhode Island Experience! Ser.). (Illus.). (J). lib. bdg. 100.20 incl. cd-rom (978-0-635-00492-5(5)) Gallopade International.

—The South Carolina Experience Library State Resource Set. 2001. (South Carolina Experience! Ser.). (Illus.). (J). lib. bdg. 100.20 incl. cd-rom (978-0-635-00493-2(3)) Gallopade International.

—The South Dakota Experience Library State Resource Set. 2001. (South Dakota Experience! Ser.). (Illus.). (J). lib. bdg. 100.20 incl. cd-rom (978-0-635-00494-9(1)) Gallopade International.

—The Tennessee Experience Library State Resource Set. 2001. (Tennessee Experience! Ser.). (Illus.). (J). lib. bdg. 100.20 incl. cd-rom (978-0-635-00495-6(X)) Gallopade International.

—The Texas Experience Library State Resource Set. 2001. (Texas Experience! Ser.). (Illus.). (J). lib. bdg. 100.20 incl. cd-rom (978-0-635-00496-3(8)) Gallopade International.

—The Utah Experience Library State Resource Set. 2001. (Utah Experience! Ser.). (Illus.). (J). lib. bdg. 100.20 incl. cd-rom (978-0-635-00497-0(6)) Gallopade International.

—The Vermont Experience Library State Resource Set. 2001. (Vermont Experience! Ser.). (Illus.). (J). lib. bdg. 100.20 incl. cd-rom (978-0-635-00498-7(4)) Gallopade International.

—The Virginia Experience Library State Resource Set. 2001. (Virginia Experience! Ser.). (Illus.). (J). lib. bdg. 100.20 incl. cd-rom (978-0-635-00499-4(2)) Gallopade International.

—The Washington Experience Library State Resource Set. 2001. (Washington Experience! Ser.). (Illus.). (J). lib. bdg. 100.20 incl. cd-rom (978-0-635-00500-7(X)) Gallopade International.

—The West Virginia Experience Library State Resource Set. 2001. (West Virginia Experience! Ser.). (Illus.). (J). lib. bdg. 100.20 incl. cd-rom (978-0-635-00501-4(8)) Gallopade International.

—The Wisconsin Experience Library State Resource Set. 2001. (Wisconsin Experience! Ser.). (Illus.). (J). lib. bdg. 100.20 incl. cd-rom (978-0-635-00502-1(6)) Gallopade International.

—The Wyoming Experience Library State Resource Set. 2001. (Wyoming Experience! Ser.). (Illus.). (J). lib. bdg. 100.20 incl. cd-rom (978-0-635-00503-8(4)) Gallopade International.

Martin, Justin. Easy Reader Biographies: George Washington: George Washington. 2007. 16p. pap. 2.99 (*978-0-439-92331-6(X) , Teaching Resources) Scholastic, Inc.

Masar, Brendan. Usher. 2006. (Illus.). 112p. (J). (gr. 7-10). 32.45 (978-1-59018-724-1(5) , Lucent Bks.) Thomson Gale.

Mattern, Joanne. Dakota Fanning. 2006. (Robbie Reader Ser.). (Illus.). 32p. (J). (gr. 1-4). lib. bdg. (978-1-58415-519-5(1)) Mitchell Lane Pubs., Inc.

—Life Stories of 100 American Heroes. 2001. (Values in Action Ser.). (Illus.). 573p. (J). (978-1-56156-978-6(X)) Kidsbooks, Inc.

Mayer, Cassie. Abigail Adams. 2007. (J). (*978-1-4034-9971-4(3)); pap. (*978-1-4034-9980-6(2)) Heinemann Library.

—Benjamin Franklin. 2007. (J). (*978-1-4034-9970-7(5)); pap. (*978-1-4034-9979-0(9)) Heinemann Library.

McCarthy, Meghan. Strong Man: The Story of Charles Atlas. McCarthy, Meghan, illus. 2007. (Illus.). 40p. (J). (gr. k-3). 15.99 (978-0-375-82940-6(7)); lib. bdg. 18.99 (978-0-375-92940-3(1)) Random Hse. Children's Bks. (Knopf Bks. for Young Readers).

McCarthy, Pat. Famous Union Generals & Leaders of the North: A MyReportLinks. com Book. 2004. (American Civil War Ser.). (Illus.). 48p. (J). lib. bdg. 25.26 (978-0-7660-5188-1(9) , MyReportLinks.com Bks.) Enslow Pubs., Inc.

McDonnell, Peter. A Soldier in Disguise. Tormey, Carlotta, illus. 2005. 16p. (J). pap. (*978-0-7367-2909-3(7)) Zaner-Bloser, Inc.

McDonough, Yona Zeldis. Hammerin' Hank: The Life of Hank Greenberg. Zeldis, Malcah, illus. 2006. 32p. (J). 17.85 (978-0-8027-8998-3(6)); 16.95 (978-0-8027-8997-6(8)) Walker & Co.

McElroy Lisa Tucker. Nancy Pelosi: First Woman Speaker of the House. 2007. (Gateway Biographies Ser.). 48p. (J). (gr. 4-8). lib. bdg. 23.93 (*978-0-8225-8685-2(1) , Lerner Pubns.) Lerner Publishing Group.

McKinley, Fred B. Chinqua Where? The Spirit of Rural America, 1947-1955. Blassingame, Calvin, illus. 2003. 319p. 24.95 (978-0-9729655-0-7(5)) Willow Creel Publishing Co.

McKissack, Lisa Beringer. Women of the Harlem Renaissance. 2006. 48p. (J). (978-0-7565-2034-2(7)) Compass Point Bks.

McLeese, Don. Jonas Salk. 2006. (Rourke Discovery Library). (Illus.). 24p. (gr. 2-5). 14.95 (978-1-59515-436-1(1)) Rourke Publishing, LLC.

—Robert Fulton. 2006. (Rourke Discovery Library). (Illus.). 24p. (gr. 2-5). 14.95 (978-1-59515-434-7(5) , 1244323) Rourke Publishing, LLC.

—Robert Goddard. 2006. (Rourke Discovery Library). (Illus.). 24p. (gr. 2-5). 14.95 (978-1-59515-435-4(3) , 1244322) Rourke Publishing, LLC.

McNeese, Tim. New Amsterdam. 2007. (Colonial Settlements in America Ser.). 112p. (J). (gr. 5-8). 30.00 (*978-0-7910-9334-4(4) , Chelsea Hse.) Facts On File, Inc.

McNeill, Allison & Hanes, Richard Clay. American Home Front in World War II Reference Library Cumulative Index. 2004. (American Home Front in World War II Reference Library). 32p. 5.00 (978-0-7876-9125-7(9) , UXL) Thomson Gale.

McPherson, Stephanie Sammartino. Levi Strauss. 2007. (History Maker Bios Ser.). (Illus.). 48p. (J). 26.60 (978-0-8225-6581-9(1) , Lerner Pubns.) Lerner Publishing Group.

—Susan B. Anthony. 2006. (History Maker Bios Ser.). (Illus.). 48p. (J). 26.60 (978-0-8225-5938-2(2) , Lerner Pubns.) Lerner Publishing Group.

McVey, James. Martha Maxwell: Natural History Pioneer. 2005. (Now You Know Bio Ser.: 4). (Illus.). 84p. (J). per. 8.95 (978-0-86541-075-6(5)) Filter Pr., LLC.

Mello, Tara Baukus. Mark Martin. rev. ed. 2007. (Race Car Legends: Ser.). 72p. (J). (gr. 5-8). 25.00 (978-0-7910-8664-3(X) , Chelsea Hse.) Facts On File, Inc.

—Tony Stewart. rev. collector's ed. 2005. (Race Car Legends Ser.). (Illus.). 64p. (J). (gr. 4-8). lib. bdg. 25.00 (978-0-7910-8670-4(4) , Chelsea Hse.) Facts On File, Inc.

Meltzer, Milton. Henry David Thoreau: A Biography. 2007. (J). spiral bd. 31.93 (978-0-8225-5893-4(9) , Twenty-First Century Bks.) Lerner Publishing Group.

Meltzer, Milton. Up Close: John Steinbeck: John Steinbeck. 2008. 208p. (YA). (gr. 6). 16.99 (*978-0-670-06139-6(5) , Viking Juvenile) Penguin Group (USA) Inc.

Mickle, Shelley Fraser. Barbaro: America's Horse. 2007. 160p. (J). (gr. 3-7). lib. bdg. 16.89 (*978-1-4169-4866-7(X) , Aladdin Library); pap. 8.99 (*978-1-4169-4865-0(1) , Aladdin) Simon & Schuster Children's Publishing.

Micklos, John, Jr. Jerry Spinelli: Master Teller of Teen Tales. 2007. (Authors Teens Love Ser.). (Illus.). 104p. (J). (gr. 6 up). lib. bdg. 31.93 (978-0-7660-2718-3(X)) Enslow Pubs., Inc.

Miller, Barbara Kiely. John Muir. 2007. (Great Americans Ser.). 24p. (J). (gr. 2-4). lib. bdg. 19.93 (*978-0-8368-8318-3(7) , Weekly Reader Early Learning Library) Stevens, Gareth Inc.

Miller, Calvin Craig. Roy Wilkins: Leader of the NAACP. 2005. (Civil Rights Leaders Ser.). (Illus.). 176p. (J). (gr. 6-12). 26.95 (978-1-931798-49-5(4)) Reynolds, Morgan Inc.

Miller, Connie Colwell. Rosa Parks & the Montgomery Bus Boycott. 2007. (Graphic Library). (Illus.). 32p. (J). 25.26 (978-0-7368-6495-4(4)) Capstone Pr., Inc.

Miller, Raymond H. Matt Groening. 2005. (Inventors & Creators Ser.). (Illus.). 48p. (gr. 4-8). 26.20 (978-0-7377-3158-3(3) , Greenhaven Pr., Inc.) Thomson Gale.

Mills, Cliff & Anderson, Wayne A. Tupac Shakur. 2nd rev. ed. 2008. (Hip-Hop Stars Ser.). 672p. (J). pap. 21.95 (*978-0-7910-9732-8(3) , Chelsea Hse.) Facts On File, Inc.

Mintzer, Richard. Latino Americans in Sports, Film, Music & Government: Trailblazers. 2005. (Illus.). 112p. (J). (ps-7). lib. bdg. (978-1-59084-936-1(1)) Mason Crest Pubs.

Mitchell Lane Publishers. Profiles in American History. 2007. (YA). lib. bdg. 460.90 (*978-1-58415-532-4(9)) Mitchell Lane Pubs., Inc.

Mitchell, Susan K. Will Smith. 2006. (Today's Superstars). (Illus.). 32p. (J). (gr. 5 up). lib. bdg. 23.93 (*978-0-8368-7653-6(9)) Stevens, Gareth Inc.

Montgomery, Sy. Tarantula Scientist. Bishop, Nic, photos by. 2007. (Illus.). 80p. (J). (gr. 4-7). pap. 7.95 (*978-0-618-91577-4(X)) Houghton Mifflin Co. Trade & Reference Div.

Monumental Milestones: Great Events of Modern Times, 16 vols., Set. 2006. (J). (gr. 4-8). lib. bdg. 319.20 (*978-1-58415-292-7(3)) Mitchell Lane Pubs., Inc.

Moore, Barbara R. Sojourner Truth. 2005. (Illus.). 16p. (J). (*978-0-618-56039-4(4)) Houghton Mifflin Co.

Moore, Bob. Drivers Series: Dale Earnhardt Sr. 2002. (NASCAR Wonder Boy Collector's Ser.). (Illus.). 48p. (J). pap. 7.99 (978-1-57243-526-1(7)) Triumph Bks.

Moore, Heidi. Luisa Moreno. 2005. 32p. (J). (978-1-4034-6978-6(4)); pap. (978-1-4034-6985-4(7)) Heinemann Library.

—Medgar Evers. 2005. (Illus.). (J). 32p. (978-1-4034-7272-4(6)); 64p. pap. (978-1-4034-7273-1(4)) Heinemann Library.

Morris, Roz. Hugo L. Black: Justice for All. 2001. (Alabama Roots Biography Ser.). (Illus.). 128p. (J). (978-1-878561-85-5(5)) Seacoast Publishing, Inc.

Morrison, Taylor. Mastodon Mystery. 2006. (Illus.). 32p. (J). (gr. k-3). pap. 6.95 (978-0-618-77130-1(1)) Houghton Mifflin Co.

Mortensen, Lori. George Washington Carver: Teacher, Scientist, & Inventor. O'Connor, Niamh, illus. 2007. (J). lib. bdg. (*978-1-4048-3725-6(6)) Picture Window Bks.

Moses, Will. Johnny Appleseed: The Story of a Legend. Moses, Will, illus. 2004. (Illus.). 48p. (J). pap. 6.99 (978-0-14-240138-5(2) , Puffin) Penguin Group (USA) Inc.

Mullin, Rita Thievon. Sterling Biographies: Harry Houdini: Death-Defying Showman. 2007. (Sterling Biographies Ser.). (Illus.). 128p. (J). 12.95 (*978-1-4027-4953-7(8)) Sterling Publishing Co., Inc.

Neimark, Anne E. Johnny Cash. 2007. (Up Close Ser.). (Illus.). 208p. (J). (gr. 8 up). 15.99 (978-0-670-06215-7(4) , Viking Juvenile) Penguin Group (USA) Inc.

Nelson, Ashley. The Combination. 2005. (Neighborhood Story Project Ser.). 128p. (J). pap. (978-1-933368-28-3(4)) Counterpoint.

Nelson, Robin. George Washington Carver: A Life of Devotion. 2007. (Pull Ahead Books-Biographies Ser.). (J). 22.60 (978-0-8225-6461-4(0) , Lerner Pubns.) Lerner Publishing Group.

Nichols, Catherine. Sally Ride. 2005. (Scholastic News Nonfiction Readers Ser.). (Illus.). 24p. (J). (gr. 1-2). 19.00 (978-0-516-24942-1(8) , Children's Pr.) Scholastic Library Publishing.

Norwich, Grace. Ashley Tisdale: Life Is Sweet! An Unauthorized Biography. 2006. 128p. (J). pap. 4.99 (978-0-8431-2183-4(1) , Price Stern Sloan) Penguin Group (USA) Inc.

—Vanessa Hudgens: Breaking Free: An Unauthorized Biography. 2007. (Illus.). 128p. (J). pap. 4.99 (*978-0-8431-2668-6(X) , Price Stern Sloan) Penguin Group (USA) Inc.

Norwich, Grace. Zac Attack: An Unauthorized Biography. 2006. (Illus.). 128p. (J). (gr. 3). pap. 4.99 (978-0-8431-2496-5(2) , Price Stern Sloan) Penguin Group (USA) Inc.

O'Hara, Megan, ed. A Colonial Quaker Girl: The Diary of Sally Wister, 1777-1778. 1999. (Diaries, Letters & Memoirs Ser.). (Illus.). 32p. (J). (gr. 2-7). pap. 21.00 (978-0-516-21852-6(2) , Children's Pr.) Scholastic Library Publishing.

O'Hearn, Michael. Jake Burton Carpenter & the Snowboard. Frenz, Ron & Barnett, Charles, illus. 2007. (Graphic Library). 32p. (J). (*978-0-7368-7516-5(6)) Capstone Pr., Inc.

Oliver-Miles, Zelda. Amelia Gayle Gorgas: First Woman of Position. 2005. (Alabama Roots Biography Ser.). (Illus.). 100p. (J). (*978-1-59421-017-4(9)) Seacoast Publishing, Inc.

Olmstead. I. M. Pei: A Biography. 2004. (Asian-American Biographies Ser.). (Illus.). 64p. (J). pap. 9.50 (978-1-4109-1129-2(2)) Raintree.

O'Neal, Bill & Martinez, Lynn. Long Before the Pilgrams: The First Thanksgiving. 2000. (SPA & ENG., Illus.). 40p. (J). pap. 8.95 (978-1-57168-498-1(0)) Eakin Pr.

Orr, Tamra B. Susan B. Anthony. 2006. (Profiles in American History Ser.). (Illus.). 48p. (J). (gr. 4-8). lib. bdg. 29.95 (*978-1-58415-445-7(4)) Mitchell Lane Pubs., Inc.

O'Shei, Tim. Philo T. Farnsworth: Visionary Inventor of Television. 2008. (Inventors Who Changed the World Ser.). 128p. (J). (gr. 6 up). lib. bdg. 33.27 (*978-1-59845-075-0(1) , MyReportLinks.com Bks.) Enslow Pubs., Inc.

Palmer, Rosemary Gudmundson. Jim Bridger: Trapper, Trader, & Guide. 2006. (J). (978-0-7565-1870-7(9)) Compass Point Bks.

Parker, Robert Andrew. Piano Starts Here: The Young Art Tatum. 2008. (J). (*978-0-375-83965-8(8) , Schwartz & Wade Bks.) Random Hse. Children's Bks.

Pasachoff, Naomi E. Barbara McClintock: Genius of Genetics. 2006. (Great Minds of Science Ser.). (Illus.). 128p. (J). lib. bdg. 31.93 (978-0-7660-2505-9(5)) Enslow Pubs., Inc.

Paulsen, Gary. Puppies, Dogs, & Blue Northers: Reflections on Being Raised by a Pack of Sled Dogs. 2007. (Illus.). 80p. (J). pap. 5.95 (*978-0-15-206103-6(7) , Harcourt Paperbacks) Harcourt Children's Bks.

—Woodsong. 2007. 144p. (J). pap. 5.99 (*978-1-4169-3939-9(3) , Aladdin) Simon & Schuster Children's Publishing.

Peacock, Nancy. Dave Thomas. 1999. (Overcoming Adversity Ser.). (Illus.). 128p. (YA). (gr. 5 up). 21.95 (978-0-7910-5302-7(4) , Chelsea Hse.) Facts On File, Inc.

Pearce, Q. L. James Quadrino: Wildlife Protector. 2006. (Young Heroes Ser.). 64p. (J). (gr. 4-8). lib. bdg. 27.45 (978-0-7377-3612-0(7) , Kidhaven) Thomson Gale.

Peckham, Howard. William Henry Harrison, Young Tippecanoe. Underdown, Harold, ed. Morrison, Cathy, illus. 2nd rev. ed. 2001. (Young Patriots Ser.: Vol. 2). 112p. (J). (gr. 3 up). 15.95 (978-1-882859-03-0(0)) Patria Pr., Inc.

People Who Changed American History. 120.00 (978-0-8368-5766-5(6)) Stevens, Gareth Inc.

Pericoli, Matteo. The True Story of Stellina. 2006. (Illus.). 40p. (J). (gr. k). 14.95 (978-0-375-83273-4(4)); lib. bdg. 17.99 (978-0-375-93273-1(9)) Random Hse. Children's Bks. (Knopf Bks. for Young Readers).

Pfeffer, Wendy. Many Ways to Be a Soldier. 2008. (On My Own History Ser.). (J). lib. bdg. 25.26 (*978-0-8225-7279-4(6) , Millbrook Pr.) Lerner Publishing Group.

Platt, Janet. Livewire Real Lives Luc Longley. 2000. (Livewires Ser.). 32p. pap. 6.00 (978-0-521-77616-5(3)) Cambridge Univ. Pr.

Poole, Rebecca. Jimi Hendrix. 2006. (Just the Facts Biographies Ser.). (Illus.). 112p. (J). pap. (*978-0-8225-5994-8(3) , Lerner Pubns.) Lerner Publishing Group.

Poolos, J. Travis Pastrana. 2005. (Illus.). 64p. (J). (gr. 5-8). lib. bdg. 26.50 (978-1-4042-0071-5(1)) Rosen Publishing Group, Inc., The.

Prentzas, S. Mario Andretti. rev. ed. 2007. (Race Car Legends Ser.). 80p. (J). (gr. 5-8). 25.00 (978-0-7910-8755-8(7) , Chelsea Hse.) Facts On File, Inc.

Price Hossell, Karen. I Have a Dream. 2005. (Illus.). 48p. (J). (978-1-4034-6811-6(7)); pap. (978-1-4034-6816-1(8)) Heinemann Library.

—John F. Kennedy's Inaugural Speech. 2005. (Illus.). 48p. (J). (978-1-4034-6810-9(9)); pap. (978-1-4034-6815-4(X)) Heinemann Library.

Price, Sean. Crooks, Cowboys, & Characters: The Wild West. 2007. (J). (*978-1-4109-2695-1(8)); pap. (*978-1-4109-2706-4(7)) Steck-Vaughn.

Pringle, Laurence P. American Slave, American Hero: York of the Lewis & Clark Expedition. Van Wright, Cornelius & Hu, Ying-Hwa, illus. 2006. 40p. (J). (gr. 3-5). 17.95 (978-1-59078-282-8(8)) Boyds Mills Pr.

Profiles in American History, 18 vols., Set. Incl. Alexander Hamilton. Roberts, Russell. lib. bdg. 20.95 (978-1-58415-436-5(5)); Benjamin Franklin. Whiting, Jim. lib. bdg. 20.95 (978-1-58415-435-8(7)); Betsy Ross. Harkins, Susan. lib. bdg. 20.95 (978-1-58415-446-4(2)); Eli Whitney. Gibson, Karen Bush. lib. bdg. 20.95 (978-1-58415-434-1(9)); George Rogers Clark. Roberts, Russell. lib. bdg. 20.95 (978-1-58415-448-8(9)); John Adams. Whiting, Jim. lib. bdg. 20.95 (978-1-58415-442-6(X)); John Cabot. Rice Jr., Earle. lib. bdg. 20.95 (978-1-58415-451-8(9)); John Hancock. Kjelle, Marylou Morano. lib. bdg. 20.95 (978-1-58415-443-3(8)); Life & Times of Hernando Cortes. Whiting, Jim. lib. bdg. 29.95 (978-1-58415-449-5(7)); Life & Times of John Peter Zenger. Gibson, Karen Bush. lib. bdg. 29.95 (978-1-58415-437-2(3)); Life & Times of Patrick Henry. Harkins, Susan & Harkins, William H. lib. bdg. 29.95 (978-1-58415-438-9(1)); Life & Times of William Penn. Hinman, Bonnie. lib. bdg. 29.95 (978-1-58415-433-4(0) , 1259521); Nathan Hale. Tracy, Kathleen. lib. bdg. 20.95 (978-1-58415-447-1(0)); Paul Revere. Whiting, Jim. lib. bdg. 20.95 (978-1-58415-441-9(1)); Samuel Adams. Gibson, Karen Bush. lib. bdg. 20.95 (978-1-58415-440-2(3)); Sir Walter Raleigh. Rice Jr., Earle. lib. bdg. 20.95 (978-1-58415-452-5(7)); Susan B. Anthony. Orr, Tamra B. lib. bdg. 29.95 (*978-1-58415-445-7(4)); Thomas Jefferson. Roberts, Russell. lib. bdg. 20.95 (978-1-58415-439-6(X)); (Illus.). 48p. (J). (gr. 4-8). 2006. Set lib. bdg. 359.10 (*978-1-58415-287-3(7)) Mitchell Lane Pubs., Inc.

Raatma, Lucia. Bill Gates: Computer Programmer & Entrepreneur. 2000. (Career Biographies Ser.). (Illus.). 128p. (YA). (gr. 6-12). 25.00 (978-0-89434-335-3(1) , F400, Ferguson Publishing Co.) Facts On File, Inc.

Raintree Steck-Vaughn Staff. Raintree Biographies Set, 6 bks., Set. 2003. (Illus.). (J). pap. 37.50 (978-1-4109-0148-4(3)) Raintree.

Randall, Tina. Luis Walter Alvarez. 2006. (Biografías Hispanoamericanas Ser.). (SPA.). 64p. (J). lib. bdg. 32.86 (*978-1-4109-2129-1(8)) Raintree.

Randolph, Ryan P. How to Draw the Life & Times of Dwight D. Eisenhower. 2006. (Kid's Guide to Drawing the Presidents of the United States of America Ser.). (Illus.). 32p. (J). lib. bdg. (*978-4-04-230106-6(1) , PowerKids Pr.) Rosen Publishing Group, Inc., The.

Ransom, Candice. Daniel Boone. 2006. (History Maker Bios Ser.). (Illus.). 48p. (J). (gr. 3-7). 26.60 (978-0-8225-2941-5(6) , Lerner Pubns.) Lerner Publishing Group.

Ransom, Candice F. Willie McLean & the Civil War Surrender. Reeves, Jeni, illus. 2005. (On My Own History Ser.). 48p. (J). 25.26 (978-1-57505-588-6(0)) Lerner Publishing Group.

Rappaport, Doreen. Eleanor's Big Words. 2006. (J). (978-0-7868-5141-6(4)) Hyperion Bks. for Children.

Rau, Dana Meachen. Bill & Melinda Gates. 2008. (J). lib. bdg. 26.00 (***978-1-60279-068-1(X)*** Cherry Lake Publishing.

Raum, Elizabeth. John Glenn. 2005. (American Lives Ser.). (Illus.). 32p. (J). (978-1-4034-6940-3(7)); pap. (978-1-4034-6947-2(4)) Heinemann Library.

—Neil Armstrong. 2005. (American Lives Ser.). (Illus.). 32p. (J). (978-1-4034-6938-0(5)); pap. (978-1-4034-6945-8(8)) Heinemann Library.

Raum, Elizabeth. Wild West Legends. 2007. (J). (***978-1-4109-2968-6(X));*** pap. (***978-1-4109-2989-1(2))*** Steck-Vaughn.

Rausch, Monica. Benjamin Franklin. 2006. (Illus.). 24p. (J). pap. (***978-0-8368-7689-5(X));*** lib. bdg. (***978-0-8368-7682-6(2))*** Stevens, Gareth Inc. (Weekly Reader Early Learning Library).

—Thomas Edison y la Bombilla Eléctrica. 2006. (J). pap. (***978-0-8368-8002-1(1));*** lib. bdg. (***978-0-8368-7997-1(X))*** Stevens, Gareth Inc. (Weekly Reader Early Learning Library).

Regis, Frankye. A Voice from the Civil Rights Era. 2004. (Voices of Twentieth-Century Conflict Ser.). (Illus.). 184p. 36.95 (978-0-313-32998-2(2) , GR2998, Praeger Pubs.) Greenwood Publishing Group, Inc.

Remstein, Henna. William Sherman. 2001. (gr. 5-8). lib. bdg. 17.60 (978-0-613-33253-8(9)) Tandem Library Bks.

Rivera, Sheila. Rachel Carson: A Life of Responsibility. 2007. (Pull Ahead Books-Biographies Ser.). (J). 22.60 (978-0-8225-6462-1(9) , Lerner Pubns.) Lerner Publishing Group.

Robbins, Trina. Hedy Lamarr & a Secret Communication System. Martin, Cynthia & Timmons, Anne, illus. 2007. (Graphic Library). 32p. (J). 25.26 (978-0-7368-6479-4(2)) Capstone Pr., Inc.

Robinson, J. Dennis. Lord Baltimore: Founders of Maryland. 2006. (Signature Lives Ser.). (Illus.). 112p. (J). (gr. 5-7). 30.60 (978-0-7565-1592-8(0)) Compass Point Bks.

Robinson Masters, Nancy. Extraordinary Patriots of the United States of America: Colonial Times to Pre-Civil War. 2005. (Extraordinary People Ser.). (Illus.). 288p. (J). 40.00 (978-0-516-24404-4(3) , Children's Pr.) Scholastic Library Publishing.

Rompella, Natalie. Famous Firsts: The Trendsetters, Groundbreakers, & Risk-Takers That Got America Moving! 2007. (My America Ser.). 48p. (J). (gr. 3-8). 18.95 (***978-1-897073-55-1(0))*** Lobster Pr. CAN. *Dist:* National Bk. Network.

Roop, Connie & Roop, Peter. Tales of Famous Americans. Powell, Charlie, illus. 2007. 112p. (J). pap. 17.99 (***978-0-439-64116-6(0)*** , Scholastic Reference) Scholastic, Inc.

Ross, Harriet. Great American Heroes. (J). (gr. 4-9). lib. bdg. 12.95 (978-0-87460-182-4(7)) Lion Bks.

Roycroft, Mitch. Johnny "Orient Express" Chan. 2008. (***978-1-4222-0224-1(0))*** Mason Crest Pubs.

—Phil "The Poker Brat" Hellmuth. 2008. (***978-1-4222-0220-3(8))*** Mason Crest Pubs.

—Phil "Tiger Woods of Poker" Ivey. 2008. (***978-1-4222-0221-0(6))*** Mason Crest Pubs.

Roza, Greg. Venus & Serena Williams: The Sisters of Tennis. 2006. (Tony Stead Nonfiction Independent Reading Collection). (J). pap. (978-1-4042-5537-1(0)) Rosen Publishing Group, Inc., The.

Ruffin, David C. The Duties & Responsibilities of the Secretary of State. 2005. (Your Government in Action Ser.). (Illus.). 32p. (J). 21.95 (978-1-4042-2688-3(5) , PowerKids Pr.) Rosen Publishing Group, Inc., The.

Rusch, Elizabeth. The Planet Hunter. Francis, Guy, illus. 2007. 32p. 15.95 (***978-0-87358-926-0(2)*** , Rising Moon Bks. for Young Readers) Northland Publishing.

Saari, Peggy & Carnagie, Julie L. Colonial America: Biographies, 2 vols. 1999. (U-X-L Colonial America Reference Library). (Illus.). (J). (978-0-7876-3762-0(9) , UXL) Thomson Gale.

Sabin, Louis & Macken, JoAnn Early. Thomas Edison: Incredible Inventor. 2006. (Illus.). 52p. (J). (***978-0-439-88006-0(8))*** Scholastic, Inc.

Sally Ride. (Biographies Ser.). 24p. (J). 7.95 (978-1-4048-0462-3(5)) Picture Window Bks.

San Souci, Robert D. Larger Than Life: The Adventures of American Legendary Heroes. Colon, Raul, illus. 2000. (978-0-15-200398-2(3)) Harcourt Trade Pubs.

Sandford, Chester M. Modern Americans: A Biographical School. 2005. reprint ed. pap. 26.95 (978-1-4179-9549-3(1)) Kessinger Publishing, LLC.

Sandler, Michael. Bethany Hamilton: Follow Your Dreams! 2007. (Defining Moments Ser.). (Illus.). 32p. (J). (gr. 3-6). lib. bdg. 25.27 (978-1-59716-270-8(1)) Bearport Publishing Co., Inc.

—Jean Driscoll: Dream Big, Work Hard! 2007. (Defining Moments Ser.). (Illus.). 32p. (J). lib. bdg. 25.27 (978-1-59716-268-5(X)) Bearport Publishing Co., Inc.

Sandra Day O'Connor. 2005. 12p. (gr. k-4). 2.95 (***978-0-635-02621-7(X))*** Gallopade International.

Savage, Jeff. Dave Mirra. 2007. (Amazing Athletes Ser.). (J). 23.93 (978-0-8225-6593-2(5) , Lerner Pubns.) Lerner Publishing Group.

—Dwyane Wade. 2006. (Illus.). 32p. (J). pap. 5.95 (978-0-8225-6013-5(5) , First Avenue Editions) Lerner Publishing Group.

—Jeff Gordon. 2007. (Amazing Athletes Ser.). (J). pap. 5.95 (978-0-8225-6802-5(0) , Lerner Pubns.) Lerner Publishing Group.

—Steve Nash. 2006. (Amazing Athletes Ser.). (Illus.). 32p. (J). pap. 5.95 (978-0-8225-6014-2(3) , First Avenue Editions) Lerner Publishing Group.

—Tiger Woods. 2007. (Amazing Athletes Ser.). (J). 23.93 (978-0-8225-6889-6(6) , Lerner Pubns.) Lerner Publishing Group.

—Tony Hawk: Skateboarding Legend. 2004. (Skateboarding Ser.). (Illus.). 32p. (J). lib. bdg. 22.60 (978-0-7368-2704-1(8)) Capstone Pr., Inc.

Schaefer, A. R. Dale Earnhardt. 2006. (Edge Books NASCAR Racing). (Illus.). 32p. (J). (978-0-7368-4377-5(9)) Capstone Pr., Inc.

Schaefer, Lola M. Famous Americans, 4 vols. 1998. (978-0-516-29823-8(2) , Children's Pr.) Scholastic Library Publishing.

Schanzer, Rosalyn. George vs. George: The Revolutionary War as Seen by Both Sides. 2004. (Illus.). 64p. (J). (gr. 4-9). 16.95 (978-0-7922-7349-3(4) , National Geographic Children's Bks.) National Geographic Society.

—John Smith Escapes Again! Schanzer, Rosalyn, illus. 2006. (Illus.). 64p. (J). (gr. 4-9). 16.95 (978-0-7922-5930-5(0)); lib. bdg. 25.90 (978-0-7922-5931-2(9)) National Geographic Society. (National Geographic Children's Bks.).

Scher, Linda. The Texas City Disaster. 2007. (Code Red Ser.). (Illus.). 32p. (J). (gr. 3-7). lib. bdg. 25.27 (978-1-59716-363-7(5)) Bearport Publishing Co., Inc.

Scherer, Glenn & Fletcher, Marty. J. Robert Oppenheimer: The Brain Behind the Bomb. 2007. (Inventors Who Changed the World Ser.). (Illus.). 128p. (J). lib. bdg. 33.27 (978-1-59845-050-7(6) , MyReportLinks.com Bks.) Enslow Pubs., Inc.

Schiffman, Jessica, illus. Sybil Ludington: Freedom's Brave Rider. 2005. 32p. (J). pap. (***978-0-7367-2931-4(3))*** Zaner-Bloser, Inc.

Schilling, Vincent. Native Athletes in Action! 2007. (Native Trailblazers Ser.). (Illus.). 128p. (J). (gr. 4-8). pap. 9.95 (***978-0-9779183-0-0(0))*** 7th Generation.

Schmittroth, Linda, et al, contrib. by. American Revolution: Biographies, 2 vols. 2000. (Illus.). (J). (978-0-7876-3793-4(9) , UXL) Thomson Gale.

Scholastic, Inc. Staff. High School Musical: 101+ Secrets, Facts, & Buzz about High School Musical. 2007. (High School Musical Ser.). 48p. (J). pap. 5.99 (***978-0-545-03475-3(2))*** Scholastic, Inc.

Schuman, Michael. Bill Gates: Computer Mogul & Philanthropist. 2007. (People to Know Today Ser.). (Illus.). 128p. (J). (gr. 6). lib. bdg. 31.93 (***978-0-7660-2693-3(0))*** Enslow Pubs., Inc.

Schuman, Michael. Louis Armstrong: Jazz Is Played from the Heart. 2007. (African-American Biography Library). (Illus.). 128p. (J). (gr. 6 up). lib. bdg. 31.93 (978-0-7660-2700-8(7)) Enslow Pubs., Inc.

Scott, John Anthony, ed. Makers of America, 9 vols., Set. Incl. A. Philip Randolph : Messenger for the Masses. Patterson, Lillie. 128p. 1995. 25.00 (978-0-8160-2827-6(3)); Chief Joseph & the Nez Perces. Scott, Robert A. 144p. 1993. 25.00 (978-0-8160-2475-9(8)); Huey Long : The Kingfish of Louisiana. Le Vert, Suzanne. 144p. 1995. 25.00 (978-0-8160-2880-1(X)); John F. Kennedy : Portrait of a President. Goldman, Martin S. 192p. 1995. 25.00 (978-0-8160-3243-3(2)); Richard M. Nixon : The Complex President. Goldman, Martin S. 160p. 1998. 25.00 (978-0-8160-3397-3(8)); (Illus.). (YA). (gr. 7-12). 1999. 125.00 (978-0-8160-3775-9(2)) Facts On File, Inc.

Seibert, Brian. George Balanchine. (Library of American Choreographers). (Illus.). 48p. (J). 2006. pap. (978-1-4042-0641-0(8) , Rosen Central); 2005. lib. bdg. 23.95 (978-1-4042-0447-8(4)) Rosen Publishing Group, Inc., The.

Seivert, Terri. James Stewart. 2005. (Illus.). 32p. (J). (gr. 2 up). lib. bdg. 22.60 (978-0-7368-4365-2(5)) Capstone Pr., Inc.

Sexton, Sean. Waldo's Mountain: A Brief History of a Small Elevation. 2000. (Illus.). 80p. (J). 19.00 (978-1-883114-13-8(6)) Waterview Pr., Inc.

Shea, Pegi Deitz. Patience Wright: America's First Sculptor, & Revolutionary Spy. Andersen, Bethanne, illus. 2007. (J). (***978-1-4287-3694-8(8))*** Holt, Henry & Co.

Shea, Pegi Deitz. Patience Wright: America's First Sculptor, Revolutionary Spy. Andersen, Bethanne, illus. rev. ed. 2007. 40p. (J). (gr. 1-7). 17.95 (978-0-8050-6770-5(1) , Holt, Henry & Co. Bks. For Young Readers) Holt, Henry & Co.

Sherrow, Victoria. Jonas Salk: Beyond the Microscope. 2nd rev. ed. 2008. (Makers of Modern Science Ser.). 160p. (J). (gr. 6-12). 29.95 (***978-0-8160-6180-8(7)*** , Chelsea Hse.) Facts On File, Inc.

Shetterly, Robert. Americans Who Tell the Truth. 2008. 48p. (J). (gr. 4-6). pap. 7.99 (***978-0-14-241108-7(6)*** , Puffin) Penguin Group (USA) Inc.

—Americans Who Tell the Truth. Shetterly, Robert, illus. 2005. (Illus.). 48p. (J). (gr. 5-9). 18.99 (978-0-525-47429-6(3) , Dutton Juvenile) Penguin Group (USA) Inc.

Shichtman, Sandra H. Colin Powell: Have a Vision. Be Demanding. 2005. (African-American Biography Library). (Illus.). 128p. (J). (gr. 6-12). lib. bdg. 31.93 (978-0-7660-2464-9(4)) Enslow Pubs., Inc.

Shone, Rob. Rosa Parks: The Life of a Civil Rights Heroine. Spender, Nik, illus. 2006. 48p. (J). (978-1-4042-0926-8(3)); pap. (978-1-4042-0927-5(1)) Rosen Publishing Group, Inc., The.

Shuter, Jane. Henry Ford. 2000. (Lives & Times Ser.). (Illus.). 24p. (J). lib. bdg. 19.92 (978-1-57572-229-0(1)) Heinemann Library.

Sievert, Terri. Travis Pastrana: Motocross Legend. 2006. (Edge Books, Dirt Bikes). (Illus.). 32p. (J). (978-0-7368-4367-6(1)) Capstone Pr., Inc.

Signature Lives, 66 vols. 112p. (YA). (gr. 5-7). 2019.60 (978-0-7565-1693-2(5)) Compass Point Bks.

Signature Lives: Colonial America Era. 2006. (Illus.). (YA). (gr. 5-7). 153.00 (978-0-7565-1710-6(9)) Compass Point Bks.

Signature Lives: Modern America. 2006. (Illus.). (YA). (gr. 5-7). 336.60 (978-0-7565-1713-7(3)) Compass Point Bks.

Signature Lives: Reformation Era. 2006. (Illus.). (YA). (gr. 5-7). 153.00 (978-0-7565-1712-0(5)) Compass Point Bks.

Signature Lives: Renaissance Era, 8 vols. 112p. (YA). (gr. 5-7). 244.80 (978-0-7565-1008-4(2)) Compass Point Bks.

Signature Lives Series: Revolutionary War Era, 13 bks. 2006. (Illus.). (YA). (gr. 5-7). 397.80 (978-0-7565-1711-3(7)) Compass Point Bks.

Silate, Jennifer. The Calhoun-Randolph Debate on the Eve of the War of 1812: A Primary Source Investigation. 2004. (Great Historic Debates & Speeches Ser.). (Illus.). 64p. (YA). lib. bdg. 29.25 (978-1-4042-0150-7(5)) Rosen Publishing Group, Inc., The.

Simons, Rae. Bruce Springsteen. 2008. (J). (***978-1-4222-0187-9(2))*** Mason Crest Pubs.

Singer, Flora M. Flora - I Was but A Child. 2007. (J). pap. 15.95 (***978-0-9760739-8-7(6))*** Holocaust Survivors' Memoirs Project.

Sis, Peter. The Wall: Growing up Behind the Iron Curtain. 2007. (Illus.). 56p. (J). (gr. 3 up). 18.00 (978-0-374-34701-7(8) , Farrar, Straus & Giroux (BYR)) Farrar, Straus & Giroux.

Skelton, Renee. Harriet Tubman: A Woman of Courage. 2005. (Time for Kids Ser.). (Illus.). 48p. (J). pap. 3.99 (978-0-06-057607-3(3)) HarperCollins Pubs.

Skelton, Renee & Time for Kids Editors. Harriet Tubman: A Woman of Courage. 2005. (Time for Kids Ser.). (Illus.). 48p. (J). 15.99 (978-0-06-057608-0(1)) HarperCollins Pubs.

Skog, Jason. Yellow Journalism. 2006. (J). lib. bdg. (978-0-7565-2456-2(3)) Compass Point Bks.

Slade, Suzanne. Susan B. Anthony: Fighter for Freedom & Equality. Orback, Craig, illus. 2006. (Biographies Ser.). 24p. (J). (gr. k-3). lib. bdg. 23.93 (***978-1-4048-3104-9(5))*** Picture Window Bks.

Sloate, Susan. Ray Charles: Find Another Way! 2007. (Defining Moments Ser.). (Illus.). 32p. (J). lib. bdg. 25.27 (978-1-59716-267-8(1)) Bearport Publishing Co., Inc.

Smith, Terri Smith. Tony Hawk: Flying High. 2003. (J). pap. (978-1-932724-01-1(X) , Bios for Kids) Panda Publishing, L.L.C.

Sneed, Dani. Ferris Wheel! George Ferris & His Amazing Invention. 2008. (Genius at Work! Great Inventor Biographies Ser.). (Illus.). 32p. (J). (gr. 3-4). lib. bdg. 22.60 (***978-0-7660-2834-0(8)*** , Enslow Elementary) Enslow Pubs., Inc.

Snyder, Gail. Queen Latifah. 2006. (Hip-Hop Ser.). (Illus.). 64p. (J). (gr. 5 up). 22.95 (978-1-4222-0126-8(0)) Mason Crest Pubs.

Somervill, Barbara A. Clara Barton: Founder of the American Red Cross. (Illus.). 112p. (J). 2007. pap. (***978-0-7565-2199-8(8));*** 2006. (978-0-7565-1888-2(1)) Compass Point Bks.

Sonneborn, Liz. Benedict Arnold: Hero & Traitor. 2005. (Leaders of the American Revolution Ser.). (Illus.). 130p. (J). (ps-8). lib. bdg. 30.00 (978-0-7910-8617-9(8) , Chelsea Hse.) Facts On File, Inc.

Spangenburg, Ray & Moser, Diane. Barbara McClintock: Pioneering Geneticist. 2008. (Makers of Modern Science Ser.). 160p. (J). (gr. 6-12). 29.95 (***978-0-8160-6172-3(6)*** , Chelsea Hse.) Facts On File, Inc.

Spangenburg, Ray & Moser, Diane Kit. Robert Ballard: Tbd. 2008. (Makers of Modern Science Ser.). 160p. (gr. 6-12). 29.95 (***978-0-8160-6173-0(4)*** , Chelsea Hse.) Facts On File, Inc.

—Wernher Von Braun: Out of the Fire, the Stars. 2nd rev. ed. 2008. (Makers of Modern Science Ser.). 160p. (gr. 6-12). 29.95 (***978-0-8160-6179-2(3)*** , Chelsea Hse.) Facts On File, Inc.

Spencer, Eve. Stories of America, 25 bks., Set. (J). (gr. 1-8). lib. bdg. 483.50 (978-0-7398-3295-0(6)) Raintree.

Stanley, George Edward. Mr. Rogers: Young Friend & Neighbor. Henderson, Meryl, illus. 2004. (Childhood of Famous Americans Ser.). 208p. (J). mass mkt. 4.99 (978-0-689-87186-3(4) , Aladdin) Simon & Schuster Children's Publishing.

Stansfield, John. Enos Mills, Rocky Mountain Naturalist. 2005. (Now You Know Bio Ser.). (Illus.). 103p. (J). pap. (978-0-86541-072-5(0)) Filter Pr., LLC.

Star Tracks, Set. 2002. (J). (gr. 3-8). lib. bdg. 153.90 (978-1-57765-530-5(3)) ABDO Publishing Co.

Stewart, Gail B. Larry Page & Sergey Brin: The Google Guys. 2007. (Innovators Ser.). (Illus.). 64p. (J). (gr. 4-8). 24.95 (***978-0-7377-3863-6(4)*** , Kidhaven) Thomson Gale.

Stone, Amy. Jim Carrey. 2007. (Today's Superstars). 32p. (J). (gr. 5 up). lib. bdg. 23.93 (***978-0-8368-8197-4(4))*** Stevens, Gareth Inc.

Stone, Tanya Lee. Elizabeth Leads the Way. 2008. (Illus.). 32p. (J). 16.95 (***978-0-8050-7903-6(3))*** Holt, Henry & Co.

—Up Close: Ella Fitzgerald: Ella Fitzgerald. 2008. 208p. (YA). (gr. 6). 16.99 (***978-0-670-06149-5(2)*** , Viking Juvenile) Penguin Group (USA) Inc.

Strom, Laura Layton. Racing on the Wind: Steve Fossett. 2007. (Shockwave: Life Stories Ser.). (Illus.). 36p. (J). (gr. 4-6). lib. bdg. 25.00 (***978-0-531-17774-7(2)*** , Children's Pr.) Scholastic Library Publishing.

Strother, Ruth. Bill Gates. 2007. (Essential Lives Ser.). (ENG., Illus.). 112p. (J). (gr. 6-8). lib. bdg. 32.79 (***978-1-59928-841-3(9)*** , Essential Library) ABDO Publishing Co.

Sullivan, George. Her Life in Pictures. 2007. (Helen Keller Ser.). 80p. (J). (gr. 2-5). 17.99 (***978-0-439-91815-2(4)*** , Scholastic Nonfiction) Scholastic, Inc.

Susi, Geraldine Lee. For My People: The Jennie Dean Story, 1. 2003. (Illus.). 128p. (J). per. 11.95 (978-1-886826-08-3(0)) Manassas Museum, The.

Sutcliffe, Jane. John Deere. 2007. (History Maker Biographies Ser.). (J). 26.60 (978-0-8225-6579-6(X) , Lerner Pubns.) Lerner Publishing Group.

Swain, Gwenyth. Wanda Ga'g: Storybook Artist. 2005. (Illus.). (J). 98p. 22.95 (978-0-87351-545-0(5)); 112p. (gr. 3-7). pap. 12.95 (978-0-87351-544-3(7)) Minnesota Historical Society Pr. (Borealis Bk.).

Taylor-Butler, Christine. Thurgood Marshall. 2006. (Rookie Biographies Ser.). (Illus.). 32p. (J). (gr. 1-2). 20.50 (978-0-516-25015-1(9) , Children's Pr.) Scholastic Library Publishing.

Taylor, Gail. Livewire Real Lives Pemulwuy. 2000. (Livewires Ser.). 32p. pap. 6.00 (978-0-521-77625-7(2)) Cambridge Univ. Pr.

Taylor, Marian. Harriet Tubman. 2004. (Black Americans of Achievement Ser.). (Illus.). 112p. (J). (gr. 6-12). 30.00 (978-0-7910-8166-2(4) , Chelsea Hse.) Facts On File, Inc.

Teitelbaum. Feel the Sting. 2000. (Eyewitness Readers Ser.). (J). 10.75 (978-0-606-20120-9(3)) Tandem Library Bks.

Teitelbaum, Michael. Tony Stewart. 2007. (World's Greatest Athletes Ser.). 32p. (J). (gr. 1-5). 27.07 (978-1-59296-792-6(2)) Child's World, Inc.

Thatcher Murcia, Rebecca. Thomas Edison: Great Inventor. 2004. (Uncharted, Unexplored, & Unexplained Ser.). (Illus.). 48p. (J). (gr. 4-8). lib. bdg. 29.95 (978-1-58415-306-1(7)) Mitchell Lane Pubs., Inc.

They Died Too Young. 2005. pap. 285.35 (978-0-7910-9158-6(9) , Chelsea Hse.) Facts On File, Inc.

Thrasher, Thomas E. Gunfighters. 1999. (History Makers Ser.). (Illus.). 96p. (YA). (gr. 7-10). 28.70 (978-1-56006-570-8(2) , Lucent Bks.) Thomson Gale.

Tieck, Sarah. Rosa Parks. 2007. (Buddy Book Ser.). (Illus.). 32p. (J). 22.78 (978-1-59679-788-8(6)) ABDO Publishing Co.

Time for Kids Editors. Benjamin Franklin: A Man of Many Talents. 2005. (Time for Kids Ser.). (Illus.). 48p. (J). 14.99 (978-0-06-057610-3(3)); pap. 3.99 (978-0-06-057609-7(X)) HarperCollins Pubs.

Timer: An American Story. 2003. 291p. (YA). per. (978-0-9740774-0-6(2)) J L Publishing Co.

Torres, John. Usher. 2005. (Blue Banner Biography Ser.). (Illus.). 32p. (J). (ps-8). lib. bdg. 25.70 (978-1-58415-379-5(2)) Mitchell Lane Pubs., Inc.

Towle, Mike. Walter Payton: Football's Sweetest Superstar. 2005. (Great American Sports Legends Ser.). (Illus.). 225p. (ps-7). pap. 12.95 (978-1-58182-476-6(9) , 1249190) Cumberland Hse. Publishing.

Tracy, Kathleen. Carrie Underwood. 2005. (Blue Banner Biography Ser.). (Illus.). 32p. (J). (gr. 3-8). lib. bdg. 25.70 (978-1-58415-425-9(X)) Mitchell Lane Pubs., Inc.

Tracy, Kathleen. Matt Christopher. 2007. (Classic Storytellers Ser.). (J). lib. bdg. (***978-1-58415-535-5(3))*** Mitchell Lane Pubs., Inc.

Trollinger, Patsi B. Perfect Timing: How Isaac Murphy Became One of the World's Greatest Jockeys. LaGarrigue, Jerome, illus. 2006. 32p. (J). (gr. 2-5). 15.99 (978-0-670-06083-2(6) , Viking Juvenile) Penguin Group (USA) Inc.

Trumbauer, Lisa. Life in the Time of Abraham Lincoln & the Civil War. 2007. (J). (***978-1-4034-9668-3(4));*** pap. (***978-1-4034-9676-8(5))*** Heinemann Library.

—Life in the Time of George Washington & the Revolutionary War. 2007. (J). (***978-1-4034-9667-6(6));*** pap. (***978-1-4034-9675-1(7))*** Heinemann Library.

Tukan, Jaytoe Anthony, Sr. John Reid Edwards: The People's Senator. 2003. per. 19.95 (978-0-9665909-4-4(5)) Kalawantis Publishing Services, Inc.

Uebelhor, Tracy S. The Truman Years. 2005. (Presidential Profiles Ser.). (Illus.). 832p. (gr. 9). 85.00 (978-0-8160-5490-9(8)) Facts On File, Inc.

Umhau, Jan Fleet. The Adventures of Henry Fleete: Potomac Captive. 1999. (Illus.). 162p. (J). pap. 17.95 (978-0-87517-108-1(7)) Dietz Pr.

Underwood, Larry. All the Presidents Children. 2002. 120p. (J). per. 15.95 (978-1-886225-85-5(0)) Day of Grace Publishing Services.

Uphill All the Way. 2004. (Illus.). 170p. per. 12.95 (978-0-9718333-0-9(4)) Goldenrod Pr.

Vallaly, Barbara, compiled by. Life on East 76th Street: Stories of an American Family. 2004. (Illus.). 194p. (YA). per. 18.50 (978-0-9755822-0-6(8)) Woodland Pr.

Venezia, Mike. Dwight D. Eisenhower. Venezia, Mike, illus. 2007. (Getting to Know the U. S. Presidents Ser.). (Illus.). 32p. (J). (gr. 3-4). 27.00 (978-0-516-22638-5(X) , Children's Pr.) Scholastic Library Publishing.

—Harry S. Truman. Venezia, Mike, illus. 2007. (Getting to Know the U. S. Presidents Ser.). (Illus.). 32p. (J). (gr. 3-4). 27.00 (978-0-516-22637-8(1) , Children's Pr.) Scholastic Library Publishing.

—John F. Kennedy. Venezia, Mike, illus. 2007. (Getting to Know the U. S. Presidents Ser.). (Illus.). 32p. (J). (gr. 3-4). 27.00 (978-0-516-22639-2(8) , Children's Pr.) Scholastic Library Publishing.

—Lyndon B. Johnson. Venezia, Mike, illus. 2007. (Getting to Know the U. S. Presidents Ser.). (Illus.). 32p. (J). (gr. 3-4). 27.00 (978-0-516-22640-8(1) , Children's Pr.) Scholastic Library Publishing.

—Richard M. Nixon. Venezia, Mike, illus. 2007. (Getting to Know the U. S. Presidents Ser.). (Illus.). 32p. (J). (gr. 3-4). 27.00 (978-0-516-22641-5(X) , Children's Pr.) Scholastic Library Publishing.

Venezia, Mike, illus. Benjamin Harrison. 2006. (Getting to Know the U. S. Presidents Ser.). 32p. (J). (gr. 3-4). 27.00 (978-0-516-22628-6(2) , Children's Pr.) Scholastic Library Publishing.

—Chester A. Arthur. 2006. (Getting to Know the U. S. Presidents Ser.). 32p. (J). (gr. 3-4). 27.00 (978-0-516-22626-2(6) , Children's Pr.) Scholastic Library Publishing.

—Grover Cleveland. 2006. (Getting to Know the U. S. Presidents Ser.). 32p. (J). (gr. 3-4). 27.00 (978-0-516-22627-9(4) , Children's Pr.) Scholastic Library Publishing.

—James A. Garfield. 2006. (Getting to Know the U. S. Presidents Ser.). 32p. (J). (gr. 3-4). 27.00 (978-0-516-22625-5(8) , Children's Pr.) Scholastic Library Publishing.

Viegas, Jennifer. Pierre Omidyar: The Founder of eBay. 2006. (Internet Career Biographies Ser.). (Illus.). 112p. (YA). (gr. 7-12). lib. bdg. 31.95 (978-1-4042-0715-8(5)) Rosen Publishing Group, Inc., The.

Walters, John. Tim Duncan. 2006. (World's Greatest Athletes Ser.). (Illus.). 32p. (J). (gr. 1-5). 27.07 (978-1-59296-759-9(0)) Child's World, Inc.

Wat's So Great About... ?, 10 vols., Set. Incl. Annie Oakley. Whiting, Jim. lib. bdg. (978-1-58415-477-8(2)); Daniel Boone. Roberts, Russell. lib. bdg. (978-1-58415-475-4(6)); Davy Crockett. Roberts, Russell. lib. bdg. (978-1-58415-476-1(4)); Ferdinand Magellan. Whiting, Jim. lib. bdg. (978-1-58415-480-8(2)); Francis Scott Key. Kjelle, Marylou Morano. lib. bdg. (978-1-58415-474-7(8)); Henry Hudson. Smalley, Carol. lib. bdg. (978-1-58415-479-2(9)); Jacques Cartier. Kjelle, Marylou Morano. lib. bdg. (978-1-58415-481-5(0)); Johnny Appleseed. Zarzycki, Daryl. lib. bdg. (978-1-58415-483-9(7)); Robert Fulton. Whiting, Jim. lib. bdg. (978-1-58415-478-5(0)); Sam Houston. Harkins, Susan Sales & Harkins, William H. lib. bdg. (978-1-58415-482-2(9)); (Illus.). 32p. (J). (gr. 1-4). 2006. 2006. Set lib. bdg. 169.50 (***978-1-58415-297-2(4)***) Mitchell Lane Pubs., Inc.

Waxman, Laura Hamilton. W. K. Kellogg. 2007. (History Maker Biographies Ser.). (J). 26.60 (978-0-8225-6578-9(1) , Lerner Pubns.) Lerner Publishing Group.

We the People: Civil War Era. 2006. (J). (gr. 4-6). 311.09 (978-0-7565-1703-8(6)) Compass Point Bks.

Weber, Terri Smith. Hilary Duff: Branching Out. 2003. (J). pap. (978-1-932724-03-5(6)); lib. bdg. (978-1-932724-02-8(8) , Bios for Kids) Panda Publishing, L.L.C.

—Jeff Gordon: Racing to Win. 2003. (J). pap. (978-0-9740180-2-7(3)); lib. bdg. (978-0-9740180-0-3(7)) Panda Publishing, L.L.C. (Bios for Kids).

—Tony Hawk: Flying High. 2003. (J). lib. bdg. (978-1-932724-00-4(1) , Bios for Kids) Panda Publishing, L.L.C.

Weihenmayer, Erik. Touch the Top of the World. 2002. (gr. 7-12). lib. bdg. 23.45 (978-0-613-56864-7(8)) Tandem Library Bks.

Welch, Catherine A. Rise of the Reaper: A Story about Cyrus Hall McCormick. Jones, Jan Naimo, illus. 2007. (Creative Minds Biography Ser.). (J). spiral bd. 22.60 (978-0-8225-5988-7(9)) Lerner Publishing Group.

West, Betsy. Corbin Bleu: To the Limit: An Unauthorized Biography. 2007. 128p. (J). pap. 4.99 (***978-0-8431-2685-3(X)*** , Price Stern Sloan) Penguin Group (USA) Inc.

—Jennifer Hudson: American Dream Girl: American Dream Girl An Unauthorized Biography. 2007. 128p. (J). (gr. 3). pap. 4.99 (***978-0-8431-2687-7(6)*** , Price Stern Sloan) Penguin Group (USA) Inc.

Wheeler, Jill C. Andy Roddick. 2007. (Awesome Athletes Ser.). (Illus.). 32p. (J). 22.78 (978-1-59928-307-4(7)) ABDO Publishing Co.

—Ezra Jack Keats. 2005. (Children's Illustrators Ser.). (Illus.). 24p. (J). (gr. k-6). lib. bdg. 21.35 (978-1-59197-718-6(5)) ABDO Publishing Co.

Whitcombe, Dan. Justin Timberlake. 2004. (Star Files Ser.). (Illus.). 48p. 29.93 (978-1-4109-1087-5(3)) Harcourt Schl. Pubs.

White, Joseph C. Forged in a Country Crucible. 2003. (Illus.). 278p. per. 19.95 (978-0-9726095-1-7(2) , FCC2003) Crossing Trails Pubns.

Whiting, Jim. The Maryland Colony: Lord Baltimore. 2007. (Illus.). 48p. (J). lib. bdg. 29.95 (***978-1-58415-547-8(7)***) Mitchell Lane Pubs., Inc.

Wilcoxson, Billy. The CB Cowboys: The Sage of the Legendary Christensen Family. 2003. (Illus.). 217p. pap. (978-1-57168-823-1(4)) Eakin Pr.

Willett, Edward. Jimi Hendrix: Kiss the Sky. 2006. (American Rebels Ser.). (Illus.). 160p. (J). lib. bdg. 34.60 (978-0-7660-2449-6(0)) Enslow Pubs., Inc.

William Dawes. 2006. (J). lib. bdg. (978-1-58415-444-0(6)) Mitchell Lane Pubs., Inc.

Winter, Jonah. Dizzy. Qualls, Sean, illus. 2006. (J). 16.99 (978-0-439-50736-3(7) , Levine, Arthur A. Bks.) Scholastic, Inc.

—Muhammad Ali: Champion of the World. Roca, Francois, illus. 2008. 40p. (J). (ps-3). 16.99 (978-0-375-83622-0(5)) Random Hse. Children's Bks.

Winter, Jonah. Muhammad Ali: Champion of the World. Roca, Francois, illus. 2008. 40p. (J). (ps-3). lib. bdg. 19.99 (***978-0-375-93787-3(0)*** , Schwartz & Wade Bks.) Random Hse. Children's Bks.

Winters, Kay. John Appleseed: A Trail of Trees. Pullen, Zachary, illus. 2007. (J). (978-1-4263-0101-8(4)) National Geographic Society.

Wise, Bill. Louis Sockalexis: Native American Baseball Pioneer. Farnsworth, Bill, illus. 2007. (J). (978-1-58430-269-8(0)) Lee & Low Bks., Inc.

Wittmann, Kelly. Sean "Diddy" Combs. 2006. (Hip-Hop Ser.). (Illus.). 64p. (J). (gr. 5 up). 22.95 (978-1-4222-0115-2(5)) Mason Crest Pubs.

Wong, Li Keng. Good Fortune: My Journey to Gold Mountain. 2006. (Illus.). 144p. (J). (gr. 3-7). 14.95 (978-1-56145-367-2(6)) Peachtree Pubs., Ltd.

Woods, Bob. Mat Hoffman. 2006. (World's Greatest Athletes Ser.). (Illus.). 32p. (J). (gr. 1-5). 27.07 (978-1-59296-755-1(8)) Child's World, Inc.

Woodside, Martin. Sterling Biographies: Thomas Edison; The Man Who Lit up the World. 2007. (Sterling Biographies Ser.). (Illus.). 128p. (J). pap. 5.95 (***978-1-4027-3229-4(5)***) Sterling Publishing Co., Inc.

Woog, Adam. Pierre M. Omidyar: Creator of Ebay. 2007. (Innovators Ser.). (Illus.). 64p. (J). (gr. 4-8). 24.95 (***978-0-7377-3864-3(2)*** , Kidhaven) Thomson Gale.

Wooldridge, Connie N. Thank You Very Much, Captain Ericsson! Glass, Andrew, photos by. 2004. (Illus.). 32p. (J). (gr. k-3). tchr. ed. 16.95 (978-0-8234-1626-4(7)) Holiday Hse., Inc.

Wukovits, John F. Generals of the Revolutionary War. 2003. (American War Library). (Illus.). 112p. 29.95 (978-1-59018-219-2(7) , Lucent Bks.) Thomson Gale.

Wyborny, Shelia. Frederick W. Smith: Founder of FedEx. 2007. (Innovators Ser.). (Illus.). 64p. (J). (gr. 4-8). 24.95 (***978-0-7377-3861-2(8)*** , Kidhaven) Thomson Gale.

Yancey, Diane. The Case of the Green River Killer. 2007. (Crime Scene Investigations Ser.). 128p. (J). (gr. 7-10). 32.45 (978-1-59018-955-9(8) , Lucent Bks.) Thomson Gale.

Yanuck, Debbie L. Uncle Sam. 2003. (First Facts Ser.). (Illus.). 24p. (J). lib. bdg. 19.93 (978-0-7368-2295-4(X)) Capstone Pr., Inc.

Younger, Barbara. Purple Mountain Majesty. 2002. (gr. k-3). lib. bdg. 15.30 (978-0-613-45305-9(0)) Tandem Library Bks.

Zaunders, Bo. The Great Bridge-Building Contest. Munro, Roxie, illus. 2006. 30p. (J). (gr. 4-8). reprint ed. 17.00 (978-1-4223-5239-7(0)) DIANE Publishing Co.

Zimmer, Kyle, frwd. Who Wrote That? Incl. Avi. Speaker-Yuan, Margaret. 112p. (J). lib. bdg. 30.00 (978-0-7910-8230-0(X)); Beatrix Potter. Yuan, Margaret Speaker. 114p. (J). lib. bdg. 30.00 (978-0-7910-8655-1(0)); Beverly Cleary. Peltak, Jennifer. 116p. (J). lib. bdg. 30.00 (978-0-7910-8231-7(8)); Bruce Coville. Marcovitz, Hal. 128p. (J). 30.00 (978-0-7910-8656-8(9)); Charles Dickens. Dailey, Donna. 122p. (YA). lib. bdg. 30.00 (978-0-7910-8233-1(4)); E. B. White. LaBrie, Aimie. 112p. (YA). 30.00 (978-0-7910-8235-5(0)); Jane Yolen. 126p. (J). lib. bdg. 30.00 (978-0-7910-8660-5(7)); L. M. Montgomery. Kjelle, Marylou Morano. 124p. (J). lib. bdg. 30.00 (978-0-7910-8234-8(2)); Phillip Pullman. Speaker-Yuan, Margaret & Yuan, Margaret Speaker. 118p. (J). lib. bdg. 30.00 (978-0-7910-8658-2(5)); R. L. Stine. Marcovitz, Hal. 134p. (YA). lib. bdg. 30.00 (978-0-7910-8659-9(3)); Robert Cormier. Hyde, Margaret O. 102p. (YA). lib. bdg. 30.00 (978-0-7910-8232-4(6)); Will Hobbs. Marcovitz, Hal. 124p. (J). lib. bdg. 30.00 (978-0-7910-8657-5(7)); (Illus.). (gr. 6-12). 2005. 2005. 720.00 (978-0-7910-9155-5(4) , Chelsea Hse.) Facts On File, Inc.

Zuehlke, Jeffrey. Ben Roethlisberger. 2007. (Amazing Athletes Ser.). (J). 23.93 (***978-0-8225-7660-0(0)*** , Lerner Pubns.) Lerner Publishing Group.

UNITED STATES—BIOGRAPHY—DICTIONARIES

Extraordinary Americans: Remarkable People Who Have Made a Difference. 2003. 128p. (YA). (gr. 5-8). pap. 12.99 (978-1-56822-903-4(8) , IF87040-E4, Instructional Fair) Schaffer, Frank Pubns.

Founding Fathers. (J). tchr. ed. 41.95 (978-0-382-40882-3(9)) Cobblestone Publishing Co.

Kallen, Stuart A. Founding Fathers, Set. Incl. Alexander Hamilton. lib. bdg. 25.65 (978-1-57765-006-5(9)); Benjamin Franklin. lib. bdg. 25.65 (978-1-57765-009-6(3)); George Washington. lib. bdg. 25.65 (978-1-57765-017-1(4)); James Madison. lib. bdg. 25.65 (978-1-57765-015-7(8)); James Monroe. lib. bdg. 25.65 (978-1-57765-230-4(4)); John Adams. lib. bdg. 25.65 (978-1-57765-007-2(7)); John Hancock. lib. bdg. 25.65 (978-1-57765-010-2(7)); John Jay. lib. bdg. 25.65 (978-1-57765-013-3(1)); John Marshall. lib. bdg. 25.65 (978-1-57765-016-4(6)); Patrick Henry. lib. bdg. 25.65 (978-1-57765-012-6(3)); Samuel Adams. lib. bdg. 25.65 (978-1-57765-008-9(5)); Thomas Jefferson. lib. bdg. 25.65 (978-1-57765-014-0(X)); 64p. (J). (gr. 3-8). (Illus.). 2001. Set lib. bdg. 307.80 (978-1-57765-516-9(8) , ABDO & Daughters) ABDO Publishing Co.

Let Freedom Ring: The New Nation Biographies, 6 bks. Incl. Dolley Madison : First Lady. Witteman, Barbara. lib. bdg. 22.60 (978-0-7368-1551-2(1)); Dorothea Dix : Social Reformer. Witteman, Barbara. lib. bdg. 22.60 (978-0-7368-1552-9(X)); Eli Whitney : American Inventor. Bagley, Katie. lib. bdg. 22.60 (978-0-7368-1553-6(8)); Francis Scott Key : Patriotic Poet. Gregson, Susan R. lib. bdg. 22.60 (978-0-7368-1554-3(6)); Nat Turner : Rebellious Slave. Gregson, Susan R. lib. bdg. 22.60 (978-0-7368-1555-0(4)); Tecumseh : Shawnee Leader. Gregson, Susan R. lib. bdg. 22.60 (978-0-7368-1556-7(2)); 48p. (J). (gr. 3-4). (Illus.). 2003. Set lib. bdg. 135.60 (978-0-7368-1600-7(3) , Bridgestone Bks.) Capstone Pr., Inc.

Ottaiano, Mela. Internet Made Easy. 2002. (Internet Scavenger Hunts Ser.). (Illus.). 64p. pap. 10.95 (978-0-439-35545-2(1)) Scholastic, Inc.

Rudin, Ronald. Founding Fathers: The Celebration of Champlain & Laval in the Streets of Quebec, 1878-1908. 2003. (Illus.). 304p. (978-0-8020-3645-2(7)); pap. (978-0-8020-8479-8(6)) Univ. of Toronto Pr.

U. S. History Little Books: Famous People. 2002. 144p. (J). (gr. k-3). 14.99 (978-0-7439-3260-8(9) , 3260) Teacher Created Materials, Inc.

Wilson, Hoyt R. They Never Gave Up. 2006. (Illus.). 112p. (J). (gr. 4-7). pap. (978-0-9706429-0-5(3)) Resource Publishing.

UNITED STATES—BIOGRAPHY—POETRY

Dunne, Agnes C. & Crocco, Rose M. Read, Sing, & Learn Mini-Books: 20 Reproducible Books with Mini-Bios, Fun Facts, Activities - And Super Songs Set to Familiar Tunes. 2002. (Sing, Read, & Learn Mini-Bks.). (Illus.). 80p. pap., act. bk. ed. 12.95 (978-0-439-37665-5(3) , Teaching Resources) Scholastic, Inc.

Hopkins, Lee Bennett. Lives: Poems about Famous Americans. Staub, Leslie, illus. 1999. 40p. (J). (gr. 3-6). lib. bdg. 17.89 (978-0-06-027768-0(8)); 16.99 (978-0-06-027767-3(X)) HarperCollins Pubs.

Nelson, Marilyn. A Wreath for Emmett Till. Lardy, Philippe, illus. 2005. 48p. (J). (gr. 7). 17.00 (978-0-618-39752-5(3)) Houghton Mifflin Co. Trade & Reference Div.

UNITED STATES—BUREAU OF CUSTOMS

Green, Michael. Customs Service. 2000. (Law Enforcement Ser.). (Illus.). 48p. (J). (gr. 3-4). lib. bdg. 21.26 (978-1-56065-756-9(1) , Capstone High-Interest Bks.) Capstone Pr., Inc.

—Customs Service. 1998. (Law Enforcement Ser.). 48p. (J). lib. bdg. 19.00 (978-0-531-11559-6(3) , Watts, Franklin) Scholastic Library Publishing.

UNITED STATES—CENSUS

Harcourt School Publishers Staff. Census 2000: Who We Are. 3rd ed. 2002. (Horizons Ser.). (Illus.). (J). pap. 5.50 (978-0-15-333423-8(1)) Harcourt Schl. Pubs.

Kassinger, Ruth. U. S. Census: A Mirror of America. 1999. 80p. (J). (gr. 4-7). 28.54 (978-0-7398-1217-4(3)) Raintree.

McCave, Marta E. Counting Heads & More. 1998. (Single Titles Ser.: 8). (Illus.). 64p. (gr. 5-8). lib. bdg. 24.90 (978-0-7613-3017-2(8) , Millbrook Pr.) Lerner Publishing Group.

Wilson, Natashya. The Census & America's People: Analyzing Data Using Line Graphs & Tables. 2004. (PowerMath Ser.). (Illus.). 32p. (J). lib. bdg. (978-0-8239-8903-4(8)); lib. bdg. 22.50 (978-0-8239-8990-4(9)) Rosen Publishing Group, Inc., The. (PowerKids Pr.).

World Book, Inc. Staff, ed. World Book Special Census Edition, 1 vols. 2001. (Illus.). 160p. (J). (978-0-7166-1294-0(1)) World Bk., Inc.

UNITED STATES—CENTRAL INTELLIGENCE AGENCY

Abraham, Philip. The CIA. 2003. (High-Top Secret Ser.). (Illus.). 48p. (J). 23.00 (978-0-516-24316-0(0) , Children's Pr.) Scholastic Library Publishing.

Baker, David. CIA & FBI. 2006. (Fighting Terrorism Ser.). (Illus.). 48p. (gr. 4-8). 20.95 (978-1-59515-482-8(5)) Rourke Publishing, LLC.

Binns, Tristan Boyer. The CIA: Central Intelligence Agency. 2002. (Government Agencies Ser.). 48p. (J). (gr. 3-5). pap. 7.95 (978-1-58810-980-4(1) , 91595) Heinemann Library.

—The CIA: Central Intelligence Agency. 2003. (Government Agencies Ser.). (Illus.). 48p. (J). (gr. 3-5). lib. bdg. 27.07 (978-1-58810-496-0(6)) Heinemann Library.

Fridell, Ron. Spying, Modern World of Espionage. 2002. (Single Titles Ser.). (Illus.). 144p. (gr. 7 up). lib. bdg. 24.90 (978-0-7613-1662-6(0) , Millbrook Pr.) Lerner Publishing Group.

Hamilton, John. The CIA. 2007. (Defending the Nation Ser.). (Illus.). 32p. (J). (gr. 3-5). lib. bdg. 22.78 (978-1-59679-756-7(8)) ABDO Publishing Co.

Hines, Janet. Inside America's CIA: The Central Intelligence Agency. 2005. (Inside the World's Most Famous Intelligence Agencies Ser.). (Illus.). 64p. (YA). (gr. 7-12). lib. bdg. 26.50 (978-0-8239-3811-7(5)) Rosen Publishing Group, Inc., The.

Miller, Connie Colwell. The CIA: Stopping Terrorists. 2008. (J). (***978-1-4296-1271-5(1)***) Capstone Pr., Inc.

Streissguth, Thomas. America's Security Agencies: The Department of Homeland Security, FBI, NSA, & CIA. 2008. (Federal Government Ser.). 128p. (J). (gr. 6 up). lib. bdg. 33.27 (***978-1-59845-058-3(1)*** , MyReportLinks.com Bks.) Enslow Pubs., Inc.

Wagner, Heather Lehr. The Central Intelligence Agency. 2007. (U. S. Government Ser.). 104p. (YA). (gr. 5-8). 30.00 (***978-0-7910-9282-8(8)*** , Chelsea Hse.) Facts On File, Inc.

Wright, John D. Counterterrorist Forces with the CIA. 2002. (Rescue & Prevention Ser.). (Illus.). 96p. (J). (gr. 7 up). lib. bdg. (978-1-59084-407-6(6)) Mason Crest Pubs.

UNITED STATES—CHURCH HISTORY

Gaustad, Edwin S. Church & State in America. 2nd rev. ed. 2003. (Religion in American Life Ser.). (Illus.). 176p. (YA). 30.00 (978-0-19-516738-2(4)) Oxford Univ. Pr., Inc.

Miller, Susan. George Whitefield: Clergyman & Scholar. 2001. (gr. 5-8). lib. bdg. 17.60 (978-0-613-32600-1(8)) Tandem Library Bks.

Wacker, Grant. Religion in Nineteenth Century America. 2000. (Religion in America Ser.). (Illus.). 192p. (YA). (gr. 8 up). 30.00 (978-0-19-511021-0(8)) Oxford Univ. Pr., Inc.

Young Writers Workshop Staff, contrib. by. Kids Explore America's Catholic Heritage. 2001. (Illus.). 192p. (J). pap. 9.95 (978-0-8198-4208-4(7) , 332-162) Pauline Bks. & Media.

UNITED STATES—CIVILIZATION

Albert, Michael. Artist's America. 2008. 48p. (J). 17.95 (***978-0-8050-7857-2(6)***) Holt, Henry & Co.

The Amazing U. S. A. 2001. (Illus.). 64p. (J). (ps-3). pap. 3.95 (978-1-55254-262-0(9)) Brighter Vision Pubns.

Ciment, James, ed. Postwar America: An Encyclopedia of Social, Political, Cultural, & Economic History, 4 vols., Set. 2006. (Illus.). xxxiv, 1574p. (YA). (gr. 7 up). 399.00 (978-0-7656-8067-9(X) , Sharpe Reference) Sharpe, M.E. Inc.

Costain, Meredith & Collins, Paul. Welcome to the United States of America. 2001. (Countries of the World Ser.). (Illus.). 32p. (J). (gr. 4 up). 28.00 (978-0-7910-6542-6(1) , 010212, Chelsea Hse.) Facts On File, Inc.

Davis, Kevin A. Look What Came from the United States. 2000. (Look What Came from Ser.). (Illus.). 32p. (J). (gr. 2-4). pap. 6.95 (978-0-531-16436-5(5) , Watts, Franklin) Scholastic Library Publishing.

—Look What Came from the United States. 2000. (Illus.). (J). (978-0-606-18155-6(5)) Tandem Library Bks.

Dosier, Susan. Civil War Cooking: The Union. 2000. (Blue Earth Books). (Illus.). 32p. (J). (gr. 3-4). lib. bdg. (978-0-7368-0351-9(3) , Bridgestone Bks.) Capstone Pr., Inc.

—Civil War Cooking: The Union. 1999. (Exploring History Through Simple Recipes Ser.). (Illus.). 32p. (J). (gr. 2-7). pap. 14.60 (978-0-516-21862-5(X) , Children's Pr.) Scholastic Library Publishing.

Feinstein, Stephen. The 1900s from Teddy Roosevelt to Flying Machines. (Decades of the 20th Century Ser.). (Illus.). 64p. (J). 2001. (gr. 5-12). lib. bdg. 22.60 (978-0-7660-1612-5(9)); 2006. lib. bdg. 27.93 (978-0-7660-2630-8(2)) Enslow Pubs., Inc.

—The 1910s from World War I to Ragtime Music. (Decades of the 20th Century Ser.). (Illus.). 64p. (J). 2001. (gr. 5-12). lib. bdg. 22.60 (978-0-7660-1611-8(0)); 2006. lib. bdg. 27.93 (978-0-7660-2631-5(0)) Enslow Pubs., Inc.

—The 1920s from Prohibition to Charles Lindbergh. 2001. (Decades of the 20th Century Ser.). (Illus.). 64p. (J). (gr. 5-12). lib. bdg. 22.60 (978-0-7660-1610-1(2)) Enslow Pubs., Inc.

—The 1930s from the Great Depression to the Wizard of Oz. rev. ed. 2006. (Decades of the 20th Century in Color Ser.). (Illus.). 64p. (J). lib. bdg. 27.93 (978-0-7660-2633-9(7)) Enslow Pubs., Inc.

—The 1940s from World War II to Jackie Robinson. rev. ed. 2006. (Decades of the 20th Century in Color Ser.). (Illus.). 64p. (J). lib. bdg. 27.93 (978-0-7660-2634-6(5)) Enslow Pubs., Inc.

—The 1950s from the Korean War to Elvis. rev. ed. 2006. (Decades of the 20th Century in Color Ser.). (Illus.). 64p. (J). lib. bdg. 27.93 (978-0-7660-2635-3(3)) Enslow Pubs., Inc.

—The 1960s from the Vietnam War to Flower Power. rev. ed. 2006. (Decades of the 20th Century in Color Ser.). (Illus.). 64p. (J). lib. bdg. 27.93 (978-0-7660-2636-0(1)) Enslow Pubs., Inc.

—The 1990s from the Persian Gulf War to Y2K. (Decades of the 20th Century Ser.). (Illus.). 64p. (J). 2001. (gr. 5-12). lib. bdg. 22.60 (978-0-7660-1613-2(7)); 2006. lib. bdg. 27.93 (978-0-7660-2639-1(6)) Enslow Pubs., Inc.

Gordon, Patricia & Snow, Reed C. Kids Learn America. 1999. (J). (978-0-606-17307-0(2)) Tandem Library Bks.

Grolier Educational Staff. U. S. A. Sixties, 6 vols. 2000. (Illus.). (J). (978-0-7172-9504-3(4)); (J). (978-0-7172-9505-0(2)); (J). (978-0-7172-9506-7(0)); (J). (978-0-7172-9507-4(9)); (J). (978-0-7172-9508-1(7)); (YA). (978-0-7172-9509-8(5)) Scholastic Library Publishing. (Grolier).

Grolier Educational Staff, contrib. by. U. S. A. Sixties, 6 vols. 2000. (Illus.). 1200p. (YA). (gr. 9 up). 429.00 (978-0-7172-9503-6(6) , Grolier) Scholastic Library Publishing.

—USA 1950s, 6 vols. 2005. (Illus.). (J). (978-0-7172-6083-6(6)); (J). (978-0-7172-6084-3(4)); (J). (978-0-7172-6085-0(2)); (J). (978-0-7172-6086-7(0)); (J). (978-0-7172-6087-4(9)); (J). (978-0-7172-6088-1(7)); Set. (YA). (gr. 9-12). lib. bdg. 379.00 (978-0-7172-6082-9(8)) Scholastic Library Publishing. (Grolier).

Lindop, Edmund. America in the 1950s. 2002. (Women at War Ser.). (Illus.). 128p. (gr. 7 up). lib. bdg. 25.90 (978-0-7613-2551-2(4) , Twenty-First Century Bks.) Lerner Publishing Group.

Nickles, Greg. Germans. 2001. (gr. 3-6). lib. bdg. 17.60 (978-0-613-43444-7(7)) Tandem Library Bks.

—The Hispanics. 2000. (We Came to North America Ser.). (Illus.). 32p. (J). (gr. 4). (978-0-7787-0186-6(7)); pap. (978-0-7787-0200-9(6)) Crabtree Publishing Co.

Olson, Kay Melchisedech. Africans in America, 1665-1865. 2002. (Blue Earth Books). (Illus.). 32p. (J). (gr. 4). lib. bdg. 22.60 (978-0-7368-1204-7(0) , Bridgestone Bks.) Capstone Pr., Inc.

—French Immigrants, 1840-1940. 2002. (Blue Earth Books). (Illus.). 32p. (J). (gr. 3-4). lib. bdg. 22.60 (978-0-7368-1205-4(9) , Bridgestone Bks.) Capstone Pr., Inc.

Robb, Don. This Is America: The American Spirit in Places & People. Pratt, Christine Joy, illus. 2005. 32p. (J). 16.95 (978-1-57091-604-5(7)); pap. 6.95 (978-1-57091-605-2(5)) Charlesbridge Publishing, Inc.

Saunders-Smith, Gail, ed. American Symbols. (First Facts Ser.). (Illus.). (J). (gr. 1-2). lib. bdg. 297.64 (978-0-7368-2569-6(X)) Capstone Pr., Inc.

Schwartz, Eric. What Makes America America? 2005. (How America Became America Ser.). (Illus.). 96p. (J). lib. bdg. (978-1-59084-913-2(2)) Mason Crest Pubs.

Schwartz, Richard A. The 1950s. 2002. (Eyewitness History Ser.). (Illus.). 512p. (gr. 9). 75.00 (978-0-8160-4597-6(6)) Facts On File, Inc.

Steck-Vaughn Staff. The Way We Live: Windows/Macintosh Labs. 2000. pap. 249.40 incl. cd-rom (978-0-8172-8539-5(3)) Steck-Vaughn.

Stefoff, Rebecca. The New Republic, 1783-1830. 2004. (American Voices From- Ser.). 116p. (J). 34.21 (978-0-7614-1695-1(1)) Benchmark Investigative Group.

Stewart, Gail B. The 1970's. 1998. (Cultural History of the United States Through the Decades Ser.). (Illus.). 128p. (YA). (gr. 4-12). 29.95 (978-1-56006-557-9(5) , LML00902-177914, Lucent Bks.) Thomson Gale.

Stone, Amy. Jewish Americans. 2006. (World Almanac Library of American Immigration). (Illus.). 48p. (J). pap. (978-0-8368-7327-6(0)); lib. bdg. (978-0-8368-7314-6(9)) Stevens, Gareth Inc. (World Almanac Library).

Wirkner, Linda. Learning about Life in the New American Nation with Graphic Organizers. 2005. (Graphic Organizers in Social Studies). (J). 19.95 (978-1-4042-2810-8(1) , PowerKids Pr.) Rosen Publishing Group, Inc., The.

UNITED STATES—COAST AND GEODETIC SURVEY

Morrison, Taylor. The Coast Mappers. 2004. (Illus.). 48p. (J). (gr. 3-5). tchr. ed. 16.00 (978-0-618-25408-8(0) , Walter Lorraine) Houghton Mifflin Co. Trade & Reference Div.

UNITED STATES—COAST GUARD

Benson, Michael. The U. S. Coast Guard. 2005. (U. S. Armed Forces Ser.). (Illus.). 64p. (J). (gr. 4-7). lib. bdg. 26.60 (978-0-8225-1647-7(0)) Lerner Publishing Group.

Braulick, Carrie A. The U. S. Coast Guard. 2005. (Blazers—The U.S. Armed Forces Ser.). (Illus.). 32p. (J). 19.93 (978-0-7368-3796-5(5)) Capstone Pr., Inc.

—U.S. Coast Guard Cutters. 2007. (Blazers—Military Vehicles Ser.). (Illus.). 32p. (J). 19.93 (978-0-7368-6455-8(5)) Capstone Pr., Inc.

Cooper, Jason. U. S. Coast Guard. 2003. (Illus.). 32p. (J). 28.50 (978-1-58952-714-0(3)) Rourke Publishing, LLC.

David, Jack. United States Coast Guard. 2008. (Illus.). 24p. (J). lib. bdg. 19.95 (***978-1-60014-163-8(3))** Bellwether Media.

Demarest, Chris L. Mayday! Mayday! A Coast Guard Rescue. Demarest, Chris L., illus. 2004. (Illus.). 40p. (J). 16.95 (978-0-689-85161-2(8) , McElderry, Margaret K.) Simon & Schuster Children's Publishing.

Gaines, Ann Graham. The Coast Guard in Action. 2001. (U. S. Military Branches & Careers Ser.). (Illus.). 104p. (J). (gr. 6-12). lib. bdg. 26.60 (978-0-7660-1634-7(X)) Enslow Pubs., Inc.

Gray, Judy Silverstein. The U. S. Coast Guard & Military Careers. 2007. (U.S. Armed Forces & Military Careers Ser.). (Illus.). 128p. (J). (gr. 5). lib. bdg. 31.93 (978-0-7660-2493-9(8)) Enslow Pubs., Inc.

Green, Michael. The United States Coast Guard. 2000. (Serving Your Country Ser.). (Illus.). 48p. (J). (gr. 3-4). lib. bdg. 21.26 (978-0-7368-0472-1(2) , Capstone High-Interest Bks.) Capstone Pr., Inc.

Hamilton, John. The Coast Guard. 2007. (Defending the Nation Ser.). (Illus.). 32p. (J). (gr. 3-5). lib. bdg. 22.78 (978-1-59679-755-0(X)) ABDO Publishing Co.

Harcourt School Publishers Staff. Always Ready. 3rd ed. 2002. (Trophies English Language Learners Ser.). (Illus.). pap. 5.10 (978-0-15-327879-2(X)) Harcourt Schl. Pubs.

Holden, Henry M. Coast Guard Rescue & Patrol Aircraft. 2002. (Aircraft Ser.). (Illus.). 48p. (J). (gr. 4-10). lib. bdg. 23.93 (978-0-7660-1715-3(X)) Enslow Pubs., Inc.

Lurch, Bruno. United States Coast Guard. 2004. (Heinemann Know It Ser.). (Illus.). 48p. (J). pap. 7.95 (978-1-4034-4556-8(7)); lib. bdg. (978-1-4034-4550-6(8)) Heinemann Library.

Lyons, Lewis. Rescue at Sea with the U. S. & Canadian Coast Guards. 2003. (Rescue & Prevention Ser.). (Illus.). 96p. (J). (gr. 7 up). lib. bdg. (978-1-59084-405-2(X)) Mason Crest Pubs.

Noble, Dennis L. The US Coast Guard. 2004. (America's Armed Forces Ser.). (J). pap. (978-0-8368-5688-0(0)); lib. bdg. 30.00 (978-0-8368-5681-1(3)) Stevens, Gareth Inc. (World Almanac Library).

Randolph, Joanne. Coast Guard Boats. 2008. (J). lib. bdg. (***978-1-4042-4152-7(3)*** , PowerKids Pr.) Rosen Publishing Group, Inc., The.

Roza, Greg. Careers in the Coast Guard's Search & Rescue Unit. 2005. (Careers in Search & Rescue Operations Ser.). (Illus.). 64p. (YA). (gr. 5-8). lib. bdg. 26.50 (978-0-8239-3835-3(2)) Rosen Publishing Group, Inc., The.

Stone, Lynn M. Coast Guard Cutters. 2006. (Fighting Forces Ser.). (Illus.). 32p. (J). (gr. 4-8). 19.95 (978-1-59515-462-0(0)) Rourke Publishing, LLC.

UNITED STATES—COAST GUARD ACADEMY, NEW LONDON, CONNECTICUT

Weintraub, Aileen. Life Inside the Coast Guard Academy. 2002. (Insider's Look Ser.). (Illus.). 48p. (J). (gr. 7-12). pap. 23.00 (978-0-516-23925-5(2) , Children's Pr.) Scholastic Library Publishing.

UNITED STATES—COLONIES

see United States—Territories and Possessions

UNITED STATES—COMMERCE

Currie, Stephen. Outsourcing America. 2007. (Ripped from the Headlines Ser.). 64p. (J). (gr. 5). 23.95 (***978-1-60217-008-7(8))*** Erickson Pr.

Goldberg, Jan. The Department of Commerce. 2005. (This Is Your Government Ser.). (Illus.). 64p. (J). lib. bdg. (978-1-4042-0207-8(2)) Rosen Publishing Group, Inc., The.

UNITED STATES—COMMERCIAL POLICY

Goldberg, Jan. The Department of Commerce. 2005. (This Is Your Government Ser.). (Illus.). 64p. (J). (gr. 3-7). pap. 13.25 (978-1-4042-0660-1(4)) Rosen Publishing Group, Inc., The.

UNITED STATES—CONGRESS

Allen, Charles F. David Crockett: Scout, Small Boy, Pilgrim, Mountaineer, Soldier, Bear-Hunter, & Congressman, Defender of the Alamo. (Illus.). 308p. reprint ed. lib. bdg. 98.00 (978-0-7222-4856-0(3)) Library Reprints, Inc.

—David Crockett, Scout: Small Boy, Pilgrim, Mountaineer, Soldier, Bear-Hunter & Congressman: Defender of the Alamo. McKernan, Frank, illus. 2000. (J). (978-0-89526-228-8(2)) Regnery Publishing, Inc., An Eagle Publishing Co.

Brexel, Bernadette. Congress. 2003. (Primary Source Library of American Citizenship). (Illus.). 32p. (J). pap. (978-1-4042-5084-0(0)) Rosen Publishing Group, Inc., The.

Collins, David R. Huey P. Long: Talker & Doer. Smith, Jack K., illus. 2003. 32p. (J). 15.95 (978-1-56554-913-5(9)) Pelican Publishing Co., Inc.

The Congress of the United States, 6 vols. (gr. 2-5). 39.95 (978-0-7368-8923-0(X)) Red Brick Learning.

Crawford, Ann Fears. Barbara Jordan: Breaking the Barriers. 2002. (J). (978-1-57168-570-4(7) , Eakin Pr.) Eakin Pr.

—Barbara Jordan: Breaking the Barriers. 2003. (Illus.). 90p. (J). (gr. 7-9). lib. bdg. 19.95 (978-1-931823-11-1(1)) Halcyon Pr., Ltd.

Dirck, Brian R. Waging War on Trial: A Handbook with Cases, Laws, & Documents. 2004. 368p. (C). reprint ed. pap. 12.95 (978-0-87220-739-4(0)) Hackett Publishing Co., Inc.

Dodge, Andrew. Exploring Capitol Hill: A Kid's Guide to the U. S. Capitol & Congress. Wasniewski, Matthew, ed. Gibson, Barbara, illus. 12p. (J). pap. 1.95 (978-0-916200-25-1(6)) U. S. Capitol Historical Society.

Driscoll, Laura. Hillary Clinton: An American Journey. Wood, Judith V., illus. 2007. (All Aboard Reading Ser.). 48p. (J). (gr. 1-3). pap. 3.99 (***978-0-448-44787-2(8)*** , Grosset & Dunlap) Penguin Group (USA) Inc.

Dubois, Muriel L. The U. S. House of Representatives. 2003. (First Facts Ser.). (Illus.). 24p. (J). lib. bdg. 21.26 (978-0-7368-2288-6(7)) Capstone Pr., Inc.

Egan, Tracie. How a Bill Becomes a Law. 2003. (Primary Source Library of American Citizenship). (J). pap. (978-1-4042-5085-7(9)) Rosen Publishing Group, Inc., The.

Feeney, Kathy. Davy Crockett. 2002. (Photo-Illustrated Biographies Ser.). (Illus.). 24p. (J). (gr. 2-3). lib. bdg. 18.60 (978-0-7368-1110-1(9) , Bridgestone Bks.) Capstone Pr., Inc.

Feldman, Ruth Tenzer. How Congress Works: A Look at the Legislative Branch. 2004. (How Government Works Ser.). (Illus.). 56p. (J). (gr. 4-8). lib. bdg. 25.26 (978-0-8225-1347-6(1)) Lerner Publishing Group.

Fish, Bruce. The Speaker of the House of Representatives. 2001. (Your Government Ser.). (Illus.). 64p. (J). (gr. 4-7). 25.00 (978-0-7910-5998-2(7) , Chelsea Hse.) Facts On File, Inc.

Fitzpatrick, Anne. The U. S. Government Congress. 2003. (Let's Investigate Ser.). (Illus.). 32p. (J). lib. bdg. 18.95 (978-1-58341-262-6(X) , Creative Education) Creative Co., The.

Giddens-White, Bryon. Congress & the Legislative Branch. 2005. (Illus.). 32p. (J). (gr. 3-7). lib. bdg. 8.30 (978-1-4034-6602-0(5)) Heinemann Library.

—Our Government: Congress & the Legislative Branch. 2005. (Illus.). 32p. (J). pap. (978-1-4034-6607-5(6)) Heinemann Library.

Gorman, Jacqueline Laks. Member of Congress. 2005. (Illus.). 24p. (J). pap. (978-0-8368-4577-8(3)); lib. bdg. 19.33 (978-0-8368-4570-9(6)) Stevens, Gareth Inc.

Gregson, Susan R. Sam Houston: Texas Hero. 2005. (Signature Lives Ser.). (Illus.). 112p. (J). (gr. 5-7). (978-0-7565-1004-6(X)) Compass Point Bks.

Gutner, Howard. The Speaker of the House. 2003. (America's Leaders Ser.). (Illus.). 32p. (J). 23.70 (978-1-56711-964-0(6) , Blackbirch Pr., Inc.) Thomson Gale.

Hamilton, John. How a Bill Becomes a Law. 2005. (Government in Action! Ser.). (Illus.). 32p. (J). (gr. k-6). lib. bdg. 22.78 (978-1-59197-646-2(4)) ABDO Publishing Co.

Harmon, Daniel E. Davy Crockett. 2001. (Famous Figures of the American Frontier Ser.). (Illus.). 64p. (J). pap. 25.00 (978-0-7910-6482-5(4)); 25.00 (978-0-7910-6481-8(6)) Facts On File, Inc. (Chelsea Hse.).

Harris, Nancy. What's Congress? 2007. (J). (***978-1-4034-9466-5(5));*** pap. (***978-1-4034-9472-6(X))*** Heinemann Library.

Haskins, Jim & Benson, Kathleen. John Lewis in the Lead: A Story of the Civil Rights Movement. Andrews, Benny, illus. 2006. 40p. (J). 17.95 (978-1-58430-250-6(X)) Lee & Low Bks., Inc.

Heath, David. The Congress of the United States. 1998. (American Civics Ser.). (Illus.). 48p. (J). (gr. 3-4). lib. bdg. 22.60 (978-0-7368-0001-3(8) , Bridgestone Bks.) Capstone Pr., Inc.

—The Congress of the United States. (American Civics Ser.). 48p. (YA). pap. 6.95 (978-0-7368-8854-7(3)) Capstone Pr., Inc.

Hill, Christine M. John Lewis: From Freedom Rider to Congressman. 2002. (African-American Biographies Ser.). (Illus.). 128p. (YA). (gr. 6-12). lib. bdg. 26.60 (978-0-7660-1768-9(0)) Enslow Pubs., Inc.

Horn, Geoffrey M. Congress. 2003. (World Almanac Library of American Government). (Illus.). 48p. (J). (gr. 5 up). pap. 14.95 (978-0-8368-5462-6(4)); lib. bdg. 30.00 (978-0-8368-5457-2(8)) Stevens, Gareth Inc. (World Almanac Library).

—World Almanac Library of American Government: The Armed Forces; Congress; The Presidency; The Supreme Court, 4 bks. 2002. (Illus.). (J). (gr. 5 up). pap. 59.80 (978-0-8368-5460-2(8) , World Almanac Library) Stevens, Gareth Inc.

Johnston, Marianne. Davy Crockett. 2001. (American Legends Ser.). (Illus.). 24p. (J). (gr. 3). lib. bdg. 18.75 (978-0-8239-5581-7(8) , PowerKids Pr.) Rosen Publishing Group, Inc., The.

Kennedy, Edward M. My Senator & Me: A Dog's Eye View of Washington, D. C. Small, David, illus. 2006. 56p. (J). (ps-3). pap. 16.99 (978-0-439-65077-9(1) , Scholastic) Scholastic, Inc.

Kennedy, Edward M. My Senator & Me: A Dog's-Eye View of Washington, D. C. Small, David, illus. 2007. 53p. (J). reprint ed. 17.00 (***978-1-4223-6791-9(6))*** DIANE Publishing Co.

Koestler-Grack, Rachel A. The House of Representatives. 2nd rev. ed. 2007. (U. S. Government Ser.). 104p. (YA). (gr. 5-8). 30.00 (***978-0-7910-9285-9(2)*** , Chelsea Hse.) Facts On File, Inc.

Kunstler, James Howard. Davy Crockett. Brodner, Steve, illus. 2005. (Rabbit Ears-A Classic Tale Ser.). 40p. (J). (gr. k-5). 25.65 (978-1-59197-762-9(2)) Spotlight.

Leavitt, Amie. Nancy Pelosi. 2007. (Blue Banner Biography Ser.). (Illus.). 32p. (J). (gr. 4-8). lib. bdg. 25.70 (***978-1-58415-613-0(9))*** Mitchell Lane Pubs., Inc.

LeVert, Suzanne. The Congress. 2002. (Kaleidoscope - Government Ser.). (Illus.). 48p. (J). 25.64 (978-0-7614-1451-3(7) , Benchmark Bks.) Cavendish, Marshall Corp.

—Congress. 2005. (Watts Library). (Illus.). 64p. (J). (gr. 5-7). pap. 8.95 (978-0-531-16605-5(8) , Watts, Franklin) Scholastic Library Publishing.

Lutz, Norma Jean. J. C. Watts: Politician. 2000. (Black Americans of Achievement Ser.). (Illus.). 112p. (J). (gr. 4-7). 30.00 (978-0-7910-5338-6(5) , Chelsea Hse.) Facts On File, Inc.

McElroy Lisa Tucker. Nancy Pelosi: First Woman Speaker of the House. 2007. (Gateway Biographies Ser.). 48p. (J). (gr. 4-8). lib. bdg. 23.93 (***978-0-8225-8685-2(1)*** , Lerner Pubns.) Lerner Publishing Group.

Mendelsohn, James. Barbara Jordan: Getting Things Done. 2000. (Single Titles Ser.: up). (Illus.). 192p. (J). (gr. 7 up). lib. bdg. (978-0-7613-1467-7(9) , Twenty-First Century Bks.) Lerner Publishing Group.

Murphy, Patricia J. The U. S. Congress. 2002. (Let's See Library). (Illus.). 24p. (J). (gr. 1 up). lib. bdg. 19.93 (978-0-7565-0196-9(2)) Compass Point Bks.

Ritchie, Donald A. The Congress of the United States: A Student Companion. 3rd rev. ed. 2006. (Oxford Student Companions to American Government Ser.). (Illus.). 272p. (YA). 60.00 (978-0-19-530924-9(3)) Oxford Univ. Pr., Inc.

Ryon Quiri, Patricia. The Congress. 1999. 13.75 (978-0-606-22906-7(X)) Tandem Library Bks.

Sanders. Congress. 1999. (American Government Today Ser.). (Illus.). pap. 7.20 (978-0-7398-2129-9(6)) Steck-Vaughn.

Schlesinger, Arthur M., Jr., ed. The House of Representatives. 2000. (Your Government Ser.). (Illus.). 64p. (YA). (gr. 4-7). 31.00 (978-0-7910-5535-9(3) , Chelsea Hse.) Facts On File, Inc.

Shichtman, Sandra H. Nancy Peolosi. 2007. (Political Profiles Ser.). (Illus.). 112p. (YA). (gr. 5 up). lib. bdg. 27.95 (***978-1-59935-049-3(1))*** Reynolds, Morgan Inc.

Steadwell Books Publishing Staff, ed. Congress. 1999. (American Government Today Ser.). (Illus.). 48p. (J). (gr. 4-7). lib. bdg. 22.83 (978-0-7398-1788-9(4)) Raintree.

Taylor-Butler, Christine. The Congress of the United States. (True Booktrade;: American History Ser.). 48p. (J). 2008. pap. 6.95 (***978-0-531-14778-8(9));*** 2007. (Illus.). (gr. 3-5). lib. bdg. 26.00 (***978-0-531-12628-8(5))*** Scholastic Library Publishing. (Children's Pr.).

Wellman, Sam. J. C. Watts: Politician. 1999. (Black Americans of Achievement Ser.). (Illus.). 110p. (J). (gr. 5 up). pap. 30.00 (978-0-7910-5339-3(3) , Chelsea Hse.) Facts On File, Inc.

Zurlo, Tony. The Legislative Branch: Creating America's Laws. 2008. (Federal Government Ser.). 128p. (J). (gr. 6 up). lib. bdg. 33.27 (978-1-59845-056-9(5) , MyReportLinks.com Bks.) Enslow Pubs., Inc.

UNITED STATES—CONGRESS—SENATE

Anderson, Janet. The Senate. 2007. (U. S. Government Ser.). 104p. (YA). (gr. 5-8). 30.00 (***978-0-7910-9291-0(7)*** , Chelsea Hse.) Facts On File, Inc.

Bonner, Mike. Stephen a Douglas: Champion of the Union. 2002. (gr. 5-8). lib. bdg. 17.60 (978-0-613-52728-6(3)) Tandem Library Bks.

Brill, Marlene Targ. Barack Obama. 2006. (J). pap. 6.95 (978-0-8225-6056-2(9) , First Avenue Editions) Lerner Publishing Group.

—Barack Obama: Working to Make a Difference. 2006. (Gateway Biographies Ser.). (Illus.). 48p. (J). 23.93 (978-0-8225-3417-4(7)) Lerner Publishing Group.

Dubois, Muriel L. The U. S. Senate. 2003. (First Facts Ser.). (Illus.). 24p. (J). lib. bdg. 21.26 (978-0-7368-2290-9(9)) Capstone Pr., Inc.

Rau, Dana Meachen. Elizabeth Dole: Public Servant & Senator. 2005. (J). (978-0-7565-1583-6(1)) Compass Point Bks.

Renehan, Edward. The Clintons. 2005. (J). (978-0-7910-8526-4(0) , Chelsea Hse.) Facts On File, Inc.

Schlesinger, Arthur M., Jr., ed. The Senate. 2000. (Your Government Ser.). (Illus.). 64p. (J). (gr. 3-7). 25.00 (978-0-7910-5534-2(5) , Chelsea Hse.) Facts On File, Inc.

UNITED STATES—CONGRESS—SENATE—BIOGRAPHY

Anderson, Dale. Elizabeth Dole. 2004. (Women in Politics Ser.). (Illus.). 120p. 30.00 (978-0-7910-7733-7(0)); 104p. pap. 30.00 (978-0-7910-7997-3(X)) Facts On File, Inc. (Chelsea Hse.).

Berger, Donna, illus. Davy Crockett. 2004. (Imagination Ser.). 32p. (J). (gr. 3 up). 22.60 (978-0-7565-0603-2(4)) Compass Point Bks.

Boraas, Tracey. Sam Houston: Soldier & Statesman. 2002. (Let Freedom Ring Ser.). (Illus.). 48p. (J). (gr. 3-4). lib. bdg. 22.60 (978-0-7368-1350-1(0) , Bridgestone Bks.) Capstone Pr., Inc.

Brager, Bruce L. John Kerry: Senator from Massachusetts. 2005. (Twentieth Century Leaders Ser.). (Illus.). 128p. (J). (gr. 6-12). lib. bdg. 23.95 (978-1-931798-64-8(8)) Reynolds, Morgan Inc.

Burgan, Michael. Hillary Rodham Clinton: First Lady & Senator. 2005. (J). (978-0-7565-1588-1(2)) Compass Point Bks.

—William Henry Seward: Senator & Statesman. 2001. (Famous Figures of the Civil War Era Ser.). (Illus.). 80p. (J). pap. (978-0-7910-6419-1(0)); (gr. 5 up). 25.00 (978-0-7910-6418-4(2)) Facts On File, Inc. (Chelsea Hse.).

Caravantes, Peggy. American in Texas: The Story of Sam Houston. 2004. (Notable Americans Ser.). (Illus.). 144p. (YA). (gr. 6-12). 23.95 (978-1-931798-19-8(2)) Reynolds, Morgan Inc.

Davis, William Michael. Barack Obama: The Politics of Hope. 2007. (Illus.). 168p. (YA). (gr. 10 up). lib. bdg. 25.95 (***978-1-59556-024-7(6))*** OTTN Publishing.

Devaney, Sherri. Barack Obama. 2006. (Illus.). 112p. (J). (gr. 7-10). 32.45 (978-1-59018-937-5(X) , Lucent Bks.) Thomson Gale.

D'Orio, Wayne. Carol Moseley-Braun. 2003. (African American Leaders Ser.). (Illus.). 112p. (gr. 6-12). 30.00 (978-0-7910-7684-2(9) , Chelsea Hse.) Facts On File, Inc.

Feinberg, Barbara Jane. John McCain: Serving His Country. 2000. (Gateway Biography Ser.). (Illus.). 48p. (J). (gr. 2-4). lib. bdg. 23.90 (978-0-7613-1974-0(3) , Millbrook Pr.) Lerner Publishing Group.

Feinberg, Barbara Silberdick. Joseph Lieberman: Keeping Faith. 2001. (Gateway Biography Ser.). (Illus.). 48p. (J). (gr. 2-4). lib. bdg. 23.90 (978-0-7613-2303-7(1) , Millbrook Pr.) Lerner Publishing Group.

Fitzgerald, Brian. McCarthyism: The Red Scare. 2006. 96p. (YA). (gr. 7 up). lib. bdg. (978-0-7565-2007-6(X)) Compass Point Bks.

Freedman, Jeri. Hillary Rodham Clinton: Profile of a Leading Democrat. 2007. (J). (***978-1-4042-1910-6(2))*** Rosen Publishing Group, Inc., The.

Green, Robert. John Glenn: Astronaut & U. S. Senator. 2000. (Career Biographies Ser.). (Illus.). 128p. (YA). (gr. 6-12). 25.00 (978-0-89434-341-4(6) , F403, Ferguson Publishing Co.) Facts On File, Inc.

Guernsey, JoAnn B. Hillary Rodham Clinton. 2005. (Biography ' Ser.). (Illus.). 112p. (J). 29.27 (978-0-8225-2372-7(8) , Lerner Pubns.); (gr. 6 up). pap. 7.95 (978-0-8225-9613-4(X)) Lerner Publishing Group.

Gullo, James. Hillary Rodham Clinton. 2003. (Importance of Ser.). (Illus.). 112p. (J). 32.45 (978-1-59018-310-6(X) , Lucent Bks.) Thomson Gale.

Kiely Miller, Barbara. Sam Houston. 2007. (J). pap. (***978-0-8368-8323-7(3)*** , Weekly Reader Early Learning Library) Stevens, Gareth Inc.

Kozar, Richard. John McCain. 2001. (Overcoming Adversity Ser.). (Illus.). (J). 116p. pap. (978-0-7910-6300-2(3)); 112p. 30.00 (978-0-7910-6299-9(6)) Facts On File, Inc. (Chelsea Hse.).

Marcovitz, Hal. Nancy Pelosi. 2004. (Women in Politics Ser.). (Illus.). 120p. 30.00 (978-0-7910-7737-5(3)); 112p. pap. 30.00 (978-0-7910-8001-6(3)) Facts On File, Inc. (Chelsea Hse.).

Marsh, Carole. John Kerry: Successful Senator & 2004 Presidential Candidate. 2004. (J). 24p. pap. 5.95 (978-0-635-02537-1(X)); 24.95 (978-0-635-02542-5(6)) Gallopade International.

—Robert M. LaFollette: A Wisconsin Experience Reader. 2002. (One Thousand Readers Ser.). (Illus.). 12p. (J). (gr. k-4). 2.95 (978-0-635-01521-1(8) , 15218) Gallopade International.

Mattern, Joanne. Hillary Rodham Clinton. 2007. (First Ladies Ser.). (Illus.). 32p. (J). (gr. k-6). lib. bdg. 24.21 (***978-1-59928-792-8(7)*** , Checkerboard Library) ABDO Publishing Co.

McCain, John. Faith of Our Fathers. 2000. (gr. 7-12). lib. bdg. 23.45 (978-0-613-27819-5(4)) Tandem Library Bks.

McElroy, Lisa Tucker & Feinstein Mariano, Eileen. Meet My Grandmother: She's a United States Senator. Benjamin, Joel, photos by. 2000. (Grandmothers at Work Ser.). (Illus.). 32p. (gr. 2-4). lib. bdg. 22.90 (978-0-7613-1721-0(X) , Millbrook Pr.) Lerner Publishing Group.

Miller, Barbara Kiely. Sam Houston. 2007. (Great Americans Ser.). 24p. (J). (gr. 2-4). lib. bdg. 19.93 (***978-0-8368-8316-9(0)*** , Weekly Reader Early Learning Library) Stevens, Gareth Inc.

Plourde, Lynn. What a President She Would Have Been: Margaret Chase Smith. 2008. (J). (***978-1-58089-234-6(5))*** Charlesbridge Publishing, Inc.

Ryan, Bernard. Hillary Rodham Clinton: First Lady & Senator. 2004. (Ferguson Career Biographies Ser.). (Illus.). 160p. (J). (gr. 6-12). 25.00 (978-0-8160-5544-9(0) , Ferguson Publishing Co.) Facts On File, Inc.

Santella, Andrew. John Kerry. 2004. (Profiles of the Presidents Ser.). (J). (978-0-7565-0858-6(4)) Compass Point Bks.

Sapet, Kerrily. Barack Obama. 2007. (Political Profiles Ser.). (Illus.). 128p. (YA). (gr. 5 up). lib. bdg. 27.95 (***978-1-59935-045-5(9))*** Reynolds, Morgan Inc.

Schuman, Michael. Barack Obama: We Are One People. 2008. (African-American Biography Library). (Illus.). 128p. (J). (gr. 6 up). lib. bdg. 31.93 (***978-0-7660-2891-3(7))*** Enslow Pubs., Inc.

Slavicek, Louise Chipley. Daniel Inouye. 2007. (Asian Americans of Achievement Ser.). 128p. (YA). (gr. 6-10). lib. bdg. 30.00 (978-0-7910-9271-2(2) , Chelsea Hse.) Facts On File, Inc.

Streissguth, Tom. John Glenn. 2005. (Bios for Challenged Readers Ser.). (Illus.). 112p. (J). (gr. 6-12). lib. bdg. 27.93 (978-0-8225-2274-4(8)) Lerner Publishing Group.

—John Glenn. 1999. (gr. 7-12). lib. bdg. 16.40 (978-0-613-81316-7(2)) Tandem Library Bks.

Tibbitts, Alison Davis. Henry Clay: From War Hawk to the Great Compromiser. 2003. (Historical American Biographies Ser.). (Illus.). 128p. (J). lib. bdg. 26.60 (978-0-7660-1980-5(2)) Enslow Pubs., Inc.

Tilton, Rafael. John Glenn. 2000. (Importance of Ser.). (Illus.). 120p. (J). (gr. 7-10). 27.45 (978-1-56006-689-7(X) , Lucent Bks.) Thomson Gale.

Trumbauer, Lisa. Sam Houston. Saunders-Smith, Gail, ed. 2004. (First Biographies Ser.). (Illus.). 24p. (J). (gr. k-1). lib. bdg. 15.93 (978-0-7368-2370-8(0) , Pebble Bks.) Capstone Pr., Inc.

Wagner, Heather Lehr. Hillary Rodham Clinton. 2004. (Women in Politics Ser.). (Illus.). 120p. 30.00 (978-0-7910-7735-1(7)); 110p. pap. 30.00 (978-0-7910-7999-7(6)) Facts On File, Inc. (Chelsea Hse.).

Watson, Marilyn Myrick. Barry Goldwater. 2007. (J). per. 6.95 (***978-0-9790826-0-3(9))*** Acacia Publishing, Inc.

—Barry M. Goldwater. 2006. (J). (*978-0-9788283-4-9(8)) Acacia Publishing, Inc.
Winget, Mary. Gerald R. Ford. 2007. (Presidential Leaders Ser.). 112p. (J). (gr. 6-12). 29.27 (978-0-8225-1509-8(1) , Twenty-First Century Bks.) Lerner Publishing Group.
Wizner, Kira. John McCain: Profile of a Leading Republican. 2007. (J). (*978-1-4042-1911-3(0)) Rosen Publishing Group, Inc., The.

UNITED STATES—CONSTITUTION

Allen, Kathy. The U.S. Constitution. 2007. (Illus.). 24p. (J). 19.93 (978-0-7368-9594-1(9)) Capstone Pr., Inc.
Armentrout, David & Armentrout, Patricia. The Bill of Rights. (Documents that Shaped the Nation Ser.). 48p. 2005. (Illus.). (gr. 4-6). 20.95 (978-1-59515-234-3(2)); 2004. pap. 7.95 (978-1-59515-329-6(2)) Rourke Publishing, LLC.
—La Carta de Derechos. 2005. (SPA.). (978-1-59515-646-4(1)) Rourke Publishing, LLC.
—La Constitucion. 2005. (SPA.). (J). (978-1-59515-643-3(7)) Rourke Publishing, LLC.
—The Constitution. (Documents that Shaped the Nation Ser.). 48p. 2005. (Illus.). (gr. 4-6). 20.95 (978-1-59515-231-2(8)); 2004. pap. 7.95 (978-1-59515-330-2(6)) Rourke Publishing, LLC.
Benchmark Education Staff, compiled by. Freedom's Trail & U. S. Constitution. 2005. spiral bd. 75.00 (*978-1-4108-5826-9(X)) Benchmark Education Co.
The Bill of Rights in Today's World. 2003. (Our National Heritage Ser.). 48p. (gr. 5 8). 5.99 (978-1-56822-919-5(4) , IF2591) School Specialty Publishing.
Bjornlund, Lydia D. The Constitution & the Founding of America. 1999. (World History Ser.). (Illus.). 128p. (YA). (gr. 8-11). 27.45 (978-1-56006-586-9(9) , LML00902-177941, Lucent Bks.) Thomson Gale.
Brinkman, Patricia. Discover Writing the Constitution. 2006. pap. 39.00 (*978-1-4108-6453-6(7)) Benchmark Education Co.
Burgan, Michael. The Reconstruction Amendments. 2006. (Illus.). 48p. (J). (gr. 4-6). 23.93 (978-0-7565-1636-9(6)) Compass Point Bks.
—The 19th Amendment. 2005. (We the People Ser.). (Illus.). 48p. (J). (gr. 4-6). 23.93 (978-0-7565-1260-6(3) , 1244104) Compass Point Bks.
Carson-Dellosa Publishing Staff. Jumpstarters for the U. S. Constitution Ages 4-8+ 2005. 48p. (J). pap. (978-1-58037-304-3(6)) Carson-Dellosa Publishing Co., Inc.
Catrow, David. We the Kids: The Preamble of the Constitution of the United States. Catrow, David, illus. 2004. (J). (gr. k-5). 27.90 incl. audio (978-0-8045-6914-9(2)) Spoken Arts, Inc.
The Constitution of the United States. l.t. ed. 1998. (Large Print Heritage Ser.). 103p. (YA). (gr. 7-12). lib. bdg. 19.95 (978-1-58118-037-4(3) , 22506) LRS.
Conway, John Richard. A Look at the Constitution: Creating a More Perfect Union. 2008. (J). (*978-1-59845-072-9(7) , MyReportLinks.com Bks.) Enslow Pubs., Inc.
Digital University Press Ltd, prod. Constitutional Amendm Win Lb. (YA). cd-rom 322.50 (978-0-7365-4342-2(2)) Films Media Group.
Eck, Kristin. Drafting the Constitution: Weighing Evidence to Draw Sound Conclusions. 2005. (Critical Thinking in American History Ser.). (Illus.). 48p. (YA). (gr. 5-8). lib. bdg. 25.25 (978-1-4042-0412-6(1)) Rosen Publishing Group, Inc., The.
The Evolution of the Bill of Rights (NCHS) (YA). (gr. 8-12). spiral bd., tchr.'s planning gde. ed. 13.50 (978-0-382-40938-7(8)) Cobblestone Publishing Co.
Field, Robert J. Our Constitution, Our Government. 3rd ed. 1998. (Illus.). 158p. (YA). (gr. 4-12). pap., wbk. ed. 10.95 (978-0-87594-378-7(0) , 7502) Book-Lab.
Fradin, Dennis Brindell. The Founders: The 39 Stories Behind the U. S. Constitution. McCurdy, Michael, illus. 2005. 144p. (J). (gr. 5-9). 23.85 (978-0-8027-8973-0(0)) ; 22.95 (978-0-8027-8972-3(2)) Walker & Co.
—The U. S. Constitution. 2007. (Turning Points in U. S. History Ser.). (Illus.). 47p. (J). (gr. 4-7). lib. bdg. (978-0-7614-2036-1(3) , Benchmark Bks.) Cavendish, Marshall Corp.
Gonzales, Doreen. A Look at the Second Amendment: To Keep & Bear Arms. 2007. (Constitution of the United States Ser.). (Illus.). 128p. (J). (gr. 5). lib. bdg. 33.27 (978-1-59845-061-3(1) , MyReportLinks.com Bks.) Enslow Pubs., Inc.
Graham, Amy. A Look at the Bill of Rights: Protecting the Rights of Americans. 2007. (Constitution of the United States Ser.). (Illus.). 128p. (J). (gr. 5). lib. bdg. 33.27 (*978-1-59845-064-4(6) , MyReportLinks.com Bks.) Enslow Pubs., Inc.
Hamilton, John. The Constitution. 2005. (Government in Action! Ser.). (J). (gr. k-6). lib. bdg. 22.78 (978-1-59197-645-5(6)) ABDO Publishing Co.
Horn, Geoffrey M. The Constitution. 2003. (World Almanac Library of American Government). (Illus.). 48p. (J). (gr. 5 up). pap. 14.95 (978-0-8368-5482-4(9)); lib. bdg. 30.00 (978-0-8368-5477-0(2)) Stevens, Gareth Inc. (World Almanac Library).
Ideal Instructional Fair Staff. The Constitution. 1998. (Middle School Mastery Ser.). 47p. (YA). (gr. 5-8). pap. 3.99 (978-1-56822-634-7(9) , Instructional Fair) Schaffer, Frank Pubns.
Jacobstein, Bennett. A Constitution for California. 1999. (California Government Ser.). (Illus.). 46p. (YA). (gr. 4-10). pap. 14.95 (978-1-884925-97-9(9)) Toucan Valley Pubns., Inc.
LeVert, Suzanne. The Constitution. 2002. (Kaleidoscope - Government Ser.). (Illus.). 48p. (J). 25.64 (978-0-7614-1452-0(5) , Benchmark Bks.) Cavendish, Marshall Corp.
Marcovitz, Hal. The Constitution. 2002. (American Symbols & Their Meanings Ser.). (Illus.). 48p. (J). (gr. 4 up). lib. bdg. (978-1-59084-041-2(0)) Mason Crest Pubs.
Medina, Loreta M. Creation of the US Constitution. 2003. (gr. 7-12). lib. bdg. 33.25 (978-0-613-73837-8(3)) Tandem Library Bks.
Micklos, John. From Thirteen Colonies to One Nation. 2008. (Revolutionary War Library). (Illus.). 48p. (J). (gr. 3-4). lib. bdg. 23.93 (*978-0-7660-3015-2(6)) Enslow Pubs., Inc.
Moehn, Heather. The U. S. Constitution: A Primary Source Investigation into the Fundamental Law of the United States. 2005. (Great American Political Documents Ser.). (Illus.). 112p. (YA). (gr. 7-12). lib. bdg. 26.50 (978-0-8239-3804-9(2)) Rosen Publishing Group, Inc., The.
Patrick, John J. The Bill of Rights: A History in Documents. 2002. (Pages from History Ser.). (Illus.). 208p. 36.95 (978-0-19-510354-0(8)) Oxford Univ. Pr., Inc.
Perrin, Pat & Coleman, Wim. The Constitution & the Bill of Rights. 2nd ed. 2005. (Researching American History Ser.). (Illus.). 54p. (J). pap. (978-1-932663-11-2(8)) History Compass, LLC.
Perrin, Pat & Coleman, Wim, eds. The Constitution & the Bill of Rights. 2000. (Researching American History Ser.). (Illus.). 56p. (J). 7.95 (978-1-57960-069-3(7)) History Compass, LLC.
Peterson, Christine. The U.S. Constitution. 2007. (First Facts Ser.). (Illus.). 24p. (J). 21.26 (978-0-7368-9595-8(7)) Capstone Pr., Inc.
Prolman, Marilyn. The Story of the Constitution: Cornerstones of Freedom. Glaubke, Robert, illus. 2002. 31p. (J). (gr. 4-6). reprint ed. 15.00 (978-0-7567-5307-8(4)) DIANE Publishing Co.
Ramsey, Sally. The Constitution for Kids. 2000. 35p. pap., wbk. ed. 9.95 (978-1-58532-096-7(X)) Basic Educational Materials, Pubs.
Taylor-Butler, Christine. The Constitution. 2008. (True Booktrade;: American History Ser.). 48p. (J). pap. 6.95 (*978-0-531-14779-5(7) , Children's Pr.) Scholastic Library Publishing.
Travis, Cathy. Constitution Translated For Kids. 2nd ed. 2001. (Illus.). 69p. (J). per. 14.95 (978-1-59165-000-3(3)) Oakwood Publishing.
—Constitution Translated for Kids. 3rd ed. 2006. (Illus.). 100p. (J). 16.95 (978-1-933538-01-3(5)) Synergy Bks.
The United States Constitution Student Workbook. 2nd ed. 2003. pap. (978-0-9635364-8-8(6)) Academic Solutions, Inc.
The US Constitution, 6 vols. (gr. 2-5). 39.95 (978-0-7368-4581-6(X)) Red Brick Learning.
Webster, Christine. The Pledge of Allegiance. 2003. (Cornerstones of Freedom). (Illus.). 48p. (J). (gr. 4-6). 26.00 (978-0-516-22674-3(6) , Children's Pr.) Scholastic Library Publishing.
Weidner, Daniel. Creating the Constitution: The People & Events That Formed the Nation. 2002. (Constitution Ser.). (Illus.). 112p. (YA). (gr. 6-12). lib. bdg. 26.60 (978-0-7660-1905-8(5)) Enslow Pubs., Inc.
Williams, Jean Kinney. The U. S. Constitution. 2003. (We the People Ser.). (Illus.). 48p. (J). (gr. 4 up). lib. bdg. 22.60 (978-0-7565-0493-9(7)) Compass Point Bks.
Yero, Judith Lloyd. The Bill of Rights. 2004. (National Geographic Reading Expeditions Ser.). (Illus.). 32p. (J). (978-0-7922-4552-0(0)) National Geographic Society.

UNITED STATES—CONSTITUTION—AMENDMENTS

see Constitutional Amendments—United States

UNITED STATES—CONSTITUTIONAL CONVENTION (1787)

Banks, Joan. The U. S. Constitution. 2001. (Your Government Ser.). (Illus.). 64p. (J). (gr. 4-7). 25.00 (978-0-7910-5991-3(X) , Chelsea Hse.) Facts On File, Inc.
Collier, Christopher & Collier, James Lincoln. Creating the Constitution: 1787. 1998. (Drama of American History Ser.). (Illus.). 96p. (J). (gr. 5-9). lib. bdg. 31.36 (978-0-7614-0776-8(6) , Benchmark Bks.) Cavendish, Marshall Corp.
Hughes, Chris. The Constitutional Convention. 2005. (People at the Center of Ser.). (Illus.). 48p. (J). (ps-7). lib. bdg. 24.95 (978-1-56711-918-3(2) , Blackbirch Pr., Inc.) Thomson Gale.
Price, Sean. Designing America: The Constitutional Convention. 2007. (J). (*978-1-4109-2693-7(1)); pap. (*978-1-4109-2704-0(0)) Steck-Vaughn.
Shh! We're Writing the Constitution. 2004. 24.95 incl. audio (978-1-56008-220-0(8)); 29.95 incl. cd-rom (978-1-55592-682-3(7)); 24.95 incl. audio (978-1-55592-680-9(0)); pap. 18.95 incl. audio compact disk (978-1-55592-681-6(9)); pap. 32.75 incl. audio (978-1-55592-353-2(4)); pap. 14.95 incl. audio (978-1-55592-679-3(7)) Weston Woods Studios, Inc.

UNITED STATES—CONSTITUTIONAL HISTORY

see Constitutional History—United States

UNITED STATES—CONSTITUTIONAL LAW

see Constitutional Law—United States

UNITED STATES—CONTINENTAL CONGRESS

Adler, David A. A Picture Book of Patrick Henry. Wallner, John et al, illus. 2005. 32p. (J). (gr. k-3). pap. 6.95 (978-0-8234-1678-3(X)) Holiday Hse., Inc.
Espinosa, Rod. Patrick Henry. 2007. (Bio-Graphics Ser.). (Illus.). 32p. (J). (gr. 3-6). lib. bdg. 27.07 (*978-1-60270-070-3(2) , Graphic Planet) Magic Wagon.
Gillis, Jennifer Blizin. Patrick Henry. 2004. (Illus.). 32p. (J). pap. 7.50 (978-1-4034-5968-8(1)) Heinemann Library.
Glaser, Jason & McDonnell, Peter. Patrick Henry: Muerte o Libertad. McDonnell, Peter, illus. 2007. (Graphic Library). (ENG & SPA.). (J). 25.26 (978-0-7368-6608-8(6)) Capstone Pr., Inc.
Jarnow, Jesse. Patrick Henry's Liberty or Death Speech: A Primary Source Investigation. 2004. (Great Historic Debates & Speeches Ser.). (Illus.). 64p. (J). lib. bdg. 29.25 (978-1-4042-0152-1(1)) Rosen Publishing Group, Inc., The.
Kukla, Amy & Kukla, Jon. Patrick Henry: Voice of the Revolution. 2002. (Library of American Lives & Times). (Illus.). 112p. (J). lib. bdg. 31.95 (978-0-8239-5725-5(X) , PowerKids Pr.) Rosen Publishing Group, Inc., The.
Oberle, Lora Polack. The Declaration of Independence. 2002. (Let Freedom Ring Ser.). (Illus.). 48p. (J). (gr. 3-4). lib. bdg. 22.60 (978-0-7368-1095-1(1) , Bridgestone Bks.) Capstone Pr., Inc.
Ransom, Candice F. John Hancock. 2005. (History Maker Bios Ser.). (Illus.). 48p. (J). (gr. 3-4). 26.60 (978-0-8225-1547-0(4) , Lerner Pubns.) Lerner Publishing Group.
Welch, Catherine A. Patrick Henry. 2006. (History Maker Bios Ser.). (Illus.). 48p. (J). 26.60 (978-0-8225-5941-2(2) , Lerner Pubns.) Lerner Publishing Group.

UNITED STATES—DEBTS, PUBLIC

see Debts, Public

UNITED STATES—DECLARATION OF INDEPENDENCE

Adler, David A. & Adler, Michael S. A Picture Book of Samuel Adams. Himler, Ronald, illus. 2005. 32p. (J). 16.95 (978-0-8234-1846-6(4)) Holiday Hse., Inc.
Armentrout, David & Armentrout, Patricia. La Declaracion de Independencia. 2005. (SPA & ENG., Illus.). 24p. (J). (978-1-59515-641-9(0)) Rourke Publishing, LLC.
—The Declaration of Independence. (Documents that Shaped the Nation Ser.). 48p. 2005. (Illus.). (gr. 4-6). 20.95 (978-1-59515-230-5(X)); 2004. pap. 7.95 (978-1-59515-331-9(4)) Rourke Publishing, LLC.
Burgan, Michael. The Declaration of Independence. 2000. (We the People Ser.). (Illus.). 48p. (J). (gr. 4 up). lib. bdg. 22.60 (978-0-7565-0042-9(7)) Compass Point Bks.
—Samuel Adams: Patriot & Statesman. 2004. (Signature Lives Ser.). (Illus.). 112p. (J). 30.60 (978-0-7565-0823-4(1) , 1240135) Compass Point Bks.
Capstone Press, contrib. by. Declaration of Independence. (American Revolution Ser.). 32p. (YA). pap. 7.95 (978-0-7368-4494-9(5)) Capstone Pr., Inc.
Cheripko, Jan. Caesar Rodney's Ride: The Story of an American Patriot. Lippincott, Gary, illus. 2004. 40p. (J). (gr. 4-6). 16.95 (978-1-59078-065-7(5)) Boyds Mills Pr.
Davis, Kate. Samuel Adams. 2002. (Triangle History of the American Revolution Ser.). (Illus.). 104p. (J). 28.70 (978-1-56711-612-0(4) , Blackbirch Pr., Inc.) Thomson Gale.
Doeden, Matt. Samuel Adams: Patriot & Statesman. 2007. (Graphic Library). 32p. (J). 25.26 (978-0-7368-6500-5(4)) Capstone Pr., Inc.
Fradin, Dennis B. The Declaration of Independence. 2006. (Turning Points in U. S. History Ser.). (Illus.). 48p. (J). (gr. 3-6). lib. bdg. 29.93 (978-0-7614-2129-0(7) , Benchmark Bks.) Cavendish, Marshall Corp.
Fradin, Dennis Brindell. The Signers: The 56 Stories Behind the Declaration of Independence. McCurdy, Michael, illus. 2003. (J). (gr. 5 up). 144p. 23.85 (978-0-8027-8850-4(5)); 160p. 22.95 (978-0-8027-8849-8(1)) Walker & Co.
Freedman, Russell. Give Me Liberty! The Story of the Declaration of Independence. (Illus.). 96p. (J). (gr. 4-6). tchr. ed. 24.95 (978-0-8234-1448-2(5)); pap. 12.95 (978-0-8234-1753-7(0)) Holiday Hse., Inc.
Furgang, Kathy. The Declaration of Independence & Benjamin Franklin of Pennsylvania. 2002. (Framers of the Declaration of Independence Ser.). (Illus.). 24p. (J). (gr. 3). lib. bdg. 18.75 (978-0-8239-5591-6(5) , PowerKids Pr.) Rosen Publishing Group, Inc., The.
—The Declaration of Independence & John Adams of Massachusetts. 2002. (Framers of the Declaration of Independence Ser.). (Illus.). 24p. (J). (gr. 3-4). lib. bdg. 18.75 (978-0-8239-5590-9(7) , PowerKids Pr.) Rosen Publishing Group, Inc., The.
—The Declaration of Independence & Richard Henry Lee of Virginia. 2002. (Framers of the Declaration of Independence Ser.). (Illus.). 24p. (J). (gr. 3-4). lib. bdg. 18.75 (978-0-8239-5588-6(5) , PowerKids Pr.) Rosen Publishing Group, Inc., The.
—The Declaration of Independence & Robert Livingston of New York. 2002. (Framers of the Declaration of Independence Ser.). (Illus.). 24p. (J). (gr. 3). lib. bdg. 18.75 (978-0-8239-5592-3(3) , PowerKids Pr.) Rosen Publishing Group, Inc., The.
—The Declaration of Independence & Roger Sherman of Connecticut. 2002. (Framers of the Declaration of Independence Ser.). (Illus.). 24p. (J). (gr. 3-4). lib. bdg. 18.75 (978-0-8239-5593-0(1) , PowerKids Pr.) Rosen Publishing Group, Inc., The.
—The Declaration of Independence & Thomas Jefferson of Virginia. 2002. (Framers of the Declaration of Independence Ser.). (Illus.). 24p. (J). (gr. 3). lib. bdg. 18.75 (978-0-8239-5589-3(3) , PowerKids Pr.) Rosen Publishing Group, Inc., The.
—Framers of the Declaration of Independence, 6 bks. Incl. Declaration of Independence & Benjamin Franklin of Pennsylvania. lib. bdg. 18.75 (978-0-8239-5591-6(5)); Declaration of Independence & John Adams of Massachusetts. lib. bdg. 18.75 (978-0-8239-5590-9(7)); Declaration of Independence & Richard Henry Lee of Virginia. lib. bdg. 18.75 (978-0-8239-5588-6(5)); Declaration of Independence & Robert Livingston of New York. lib. bdg. 18.75 (978-0-8239-5592-3(3)); Declaration of Independence & Roger Sherman of Connecticut. lib. bdg. 18.75 (978-0-8239-5593-0(1)); Declaration of Independence & Thomas Jefferson of Virginia. lib. bdg. 18.75 (978-0-8239-5589-3(3)); 24p. (J). (gr. 3). 2002. (Illus.). 2001. Set lib. bdg. 103.50 (978-0-8239-7135-0(X) , PowerKids Pr.) Rosen Publishing Group, Inc., The.
Gillis, Jennifer Blizin. Samuel Adams. 2004. (Illus.). 32p. (J). pap. 7.50 (978-1-4034-5970-1(3)); lib. bdg. 25.64 (978-1-4034-5962-6(2)) Heinemann Library.
Graves, Kerry A. The Declaration of Independence: The Story Behind America's Founding Document. 2003. (America in Words & Song Ser.). (Illus.). 32p. (gr. 3-5). 23.00 (978-0-7910-7334-6(3) , Chelsea Hse.) Facts On File, Inc.
Harcourt School Publishers Staff. Fourth of July. 3rd ed. 2002. (Horizons Ser.). (Illus.). (J). pap. 3.70 (978-0-15-333172-5(0)) Harcourt Schl. Pubs.
Hicks, Terry Allan. The Declaration of Independence. 2006. (Symbols of America Ser.). (Illus.). 40p. (J). lib. bdg. 28.50 (978-0-7614-2135-1(1) , Benchmark Bks.) Cavendish, Marshall Corp.
Hossell, Karen Price. The Declaration of Independence. 2003. (Heinemann Know It Ser.). (Illus.). 48p. (J). pap. 8.50 (978-1-4034-3431-9(X)); lib. bdg. 27.07 (978-1-4034-0802-0(5)) Heinemann Library.
Jess, Denise, et al. Roots of Freedom: Growing the American Liberty Tree (1750-1800) 1999. 205p. (YA). (gr. 5-8). ring bd. 79.95 (978-1-885360-18-2(5) , 171-0110) Demco, Inc.
Landau, Elaine. The Declaration of Independence. (True Booktrade;: American History Ser.). 48p. (J). 2008. pap. 6.95 (*978-0-531-14780-1(0)); 2007. (Illus.). (gr. 3-5). lib. bdg. 26.00 (*978-0-531-12630-1(7)) Scholastic Library Publishing. (Children's Pr.).
Lilly, Melinda. Independence Day. 2002. (Rourke Discovery Library). (Illus.). 24p. (J). lib. bdg. 20.64 (978-1-58952-359-3(8)) Rourke Publishing, LLC.
Marcovitz, Hal. The Declaration of Independence. 2002. (American Symbols & Their Meanings Ser.). (Illus.). 48p. (YA). (gr. 4 up). lib. bdg. (978-1-59084-038-2(0)) Mason Crest Pubs.
Mazer, Anne. Declaration of Independence, No. 2. Gesue, Monica, illus. 2000. (Amazing Days of Abby Hayes Ser.: No. 2). 128p. (gr. 4-7). mass mkt. 4.99 (978-0-439-17876-1(2)) Scholastic, Inc.
—Declaration of Independence. 2000. (Amazing Days of Abby Hayes Ser.: No. 2). (J). (gr. 3-6). lib. bdg. 12.40 (978-0-613-24800-6(7)) Tandem Library Bks.
Micklos, John. From Thirteen Colonies to One Nation. 2008. (Revolutionary War Library). (Illus.). 48p. (J). (gr. 3-4). lib. bdg. 23.93 (*978-0-7660-3015-2(6)) Enslow Pubs., Inc.
Nardo, Don. The Declaration of Independence. 2006. (Illus.). 48p. (J). (gr. 4-8). reprint ed. 17.80 (978-1-4223-5323-3(0)) DIANE Publishing Co.
—The Declaration of Independence. 2003. (World History Ser.). (Illus.). 112p. (J). 32.45 (978-1-59018-293-2(6) , Lucent Bks.) Thomson Gale.
Oberle, Lora Polack. The Declaration of Independence. 2002. (Let Freedom Ring Ser.). (Illus.). 48p. (J). (gr. 3-4). lib. bdg. 22.60 (978-0-7368-1095-1(1) , Bridgestone Bks.) Capstone Pr., Inc.
Perrin, Pat & Coleman, Wim, eds. The Declaration of Independence. 2000. (Researching American History Ser.). (Illus.). 56p. (J). 7.95 (978-1-57960-070-9(0)) History Compass, LLC.
Richards, Norman. The Story of the Declaration of Independence: Cornerstones of Freedom. Dunnington, Tom, illus. 2002. 31p. (J). (gr. 4-6). reprint ed. 15.00 (978-0-7567-5311-5(2)) DIANE Publishing Co.
Sargent, Dave & Sargent, Pat. Duke: (Dappled Palomino) Good Behavior, 30 vols., Vol. 23. Lenoir, Jane, illus. 2003. (Saddle Up Ser.: Vol. 23). 42p. (J). pap. 6.95 (978-1-56763-682-6(9)); lib. bdg. 22.60 (978-1-56763-681-9(0)) Ozark Publishing.
Schauffler, Robert Haven, ed. Independence Day: Its Celebration, Spirit, & Significance As Related in Prose & Verse. 1999. (Our American Holidays Ser.). 318p. (J). (gr. 3-6). reprint ed. lib. bdg. 42.00 (978-0-7808-0394-7(9)) Omnigraphics, Inc.
Somervill, Barbara A. John Hancock: Signer for Independence. 2004. (Signature Lives Ser.). (Illus.). 112p. (J). 30.60 (978-0-7565-0828-9(2) , 1240133) Compass Point Bks.
St. George, Judith. The Journey of the One & Only Declaration of Independence. Hillenbrand, Will, illus. 2005. 48p. (J). 16.99 (978-0-399-23738-6(0) , Philomel) Penguin Group (USA) Inc.
The Story of America's Birthday. 1999. (Illus.). 24p. (J). (ps-k). 6.95 (978-0-8249-4170-3(5)) Ideals Pubns.
Swain, Gwenyth. Declaring Freedom: A Look at the Declaration of Independence, the Bill of Rights, & the Constitution. 2004. (How Government Works Ser.). (Illus.). 56p. (J). (gr. 4-8). lib. bdg. 25.26 (978-0-8225-1348-3(X)) Lerner Publishing Group.
Walsh, Kieran. Samuel Adams. (Discover the Life of a Colonial American Ser.). 24p. 2005. (Illus.). (gr. 2-5). 14.95 (978-1-59515-135-3(4)); 2004. pap. 4.95 (978-1-59515-336-4(5)) Rourke Publishing, LLC.
Williams, Brian. The Declaration of American Independence: 4 July 1776. 2002. (Dates with History Ser.). (Illus.). 31p. (J). lib. bdg. 24.25 (978-1-58340-211-5(X)) Smart Apple Media.
Yero, Judith Lloyd. The Declaration of Independence. 2004. (National Geographic Reading Expeditions Ser.). (Illus.). 32p. (J). pap. (978-0-7922-4554-4(7)) National Geographic Society.

UNITED STATES—DEFENSES

Baker, David. Department of Defense & State Department. 2006. (Fighting Terrorism Ser.). (Illus.). 48p. (gr. 4-8). 20.95 (978-1-59515-483-5(3)) Rourke Publishing, LLC.

Beyer, Mark. Homeland Security & Weapons of Mass Destruction: How Prepared Are We? 2004. (Library of Weapons of Mass Destruction). (Illus.). 64p. (J). lib. bdg. 26.50 (978-1-4042-0289-4(7)) Rosen Publishing Group, Inc., The.

Campbell, Geoffrey A. A Vulnerable America: An Overview of National Security. 2003. (Lucent Library of Homeland Security). (Illus.). 112p. (J). 29.95 (978-1-59018-383-0(5) , Lucent Bks.) Thomson Gale.

Evans, Fred. Maritime & Port Security. 2003. (Securing the Nation Ser.). (Illus.). 112p. (J). (gr. 9-13). 30.00 (978-0-7910-7614-9(8) , Chelsea Hse.) Facts On File, Inc.

Hamilton, John. Operation Noble Eagle. 2002. (War on Terrorism Ser.). (Illus.). 64p. (J). (gr. 4-8). lib. bdg. 25.65 (978-1-57765-664-7(4) , ABDO & Daughters) ABDO Publishing Co.

Keeter, Hunter. The US Homeland Security Forces. 2004. (J). pap. 11.95 (978-0-8368-5689-7(9)); lib. bdg. 30.00 (978-0-8368-5682-8(1)) Stevens, Gareth Inc. (World Almanac Library).

Meyer, Jared. Working in a War Zone: Military Contractors. 2006. (Extreme Careers Ser.). (Illus.). 64p. (J). (gr. 5-8). lib. bdg. 26.50 (978-1-4042-0959-6(X)) Rosen Publishing Group, Inc., The.

UNITED STATES—DEPT. OF AGRICULTURE

Rosaler, Maxine. The Department of Agriculture. 2005. (This Is Your Government Ser.). (Illus.). 64p. (YA). lib. bdg. (978-1-4042-0206-1(4)); (J). pap. 13.25 (978-1-4042-0659-5(0)) Rosen Publishing Group, Inc., The.

UNITED STATES—DEPT. OF COMMERCE

Goldberg, Jan. The Department of Commerce. 2005. (This Is Your Government Ser.). (Illus.). 64p. (J). lib. bdg. (978-1-4042-0207-8(2)); (gr. 3-7). pap. 13.25 (978-1-4042-0660-1(4)) Rosen Publishing Group, Inc., The.

UNITED STATES—DEPT. OF DEFENSE

Baker, David. Department of Defense & State Department. 2006. (Fighting Terrorism Ser.). (Illus.). 48p. (gr. 4-8). 20.95 (978-1-59515-483-5(3)) Rourke Publishing, LLC.

Ingram, Scott. The Secretary of Defense. 2002. (American Leaders Ser.). (Illus.). 32p. (J). 23.70 (978-1-56711-666-3(3) , Blackbirch Pr., Inc.) Thomson Gale.

Richie, Jason. Secretaries of War, Navy & Defense: Ensuring National Security. Lerner, Mark, ed. 2002. (In the Cabinet Ser.: Vol. 2). (Illus.). 176p. (gr. 7 up). lib. bdg. 22.95 (978-1-881508-64-9(1)) Oliver Pr., Inc.

Ruffin, David C. The Duties & Responsibilities of the Secretary of Defense. 2005. (Your Government in Action Ser.). (J). 21.95 (978-1-4042-2689-0(3) , PowerKids Pr.) Rosen Publishing Group, Inc., The.

—The Duties & Responsibilities of the Secretary of Education. 2005. (Your Government in Action Ser.). (Illus.). 32p. (J). 21.95 (978-1-4042-2692-0(3) , PowerKids Pr.) Rosen Publishing Group, Inc., The.

UNITED STATES—DEPT. OF JUSTICE

Harmon, Daniel E. Attorney General's Office. 2001. (Your Government Ser.). (Illus.). 64p. (J). (gr. 4-7). 25.00 (978-0-7910-5995-1(2) , Chelsea Hse.) Facts On File, Inc.

Kids Going to Court: A Story & Activities That Prepare Children for Court. 2003. 16p. (J). 4.95 (978-1-55864-116-7(5) , KIDSRIGHTS) JIST Publishing.

Mattern, Joanne. Attorney General. 2003. (America's Leaders Ser.). (Illus.). 32p. (J). 24.94 (978-1-56711-278-8(1) , Blackbirch Pr., Inc.) Thomson Gale.

McElroy, Lisa Tucker. Alberto Gonzales: Attorney General. 2006. (Gateway Biographies Ser.). (Illus.). 48p. (J). 23.93 (978-0-8225-3418-1(5)) Lerner Publishing Group.

UNITED STATES—DEPT. OF LABOR

Casil, Amy Sterling. The Department of Labor. 2005. (This Is Your Government Ser.). (Illus.). 64p. (J). lib. bdg. (978-1-4042-0210-8(2)); pap. 13.25 (978-1-4042-0663-2(9)) Rosen Publishing Group, Inc., The.

Scott Ingram. The Secretary of Labor. 2004. (America's Leaders Ser.). (Illus.). 32p. 23.70 (978-1-56711-961-9(1) , Blackbirch Pr., Inc.) Thomson Gale.

UNITED STATES—DEPT. OF STATE

Baker, David. Department of Defense & State Department. 2006. (Fighting Terrorism Ser.). (Illus.). 48p. (gr. 4-8). 20.95 (978-1-59515-483-5(3)) Rourke Publishing, LLC.

Harmon, Daniel E. The Secretary of State. 2001. (Your Government Ser.). (Illus.). 64p. (J). (gr. 4-7). 25.00 (978-0-7910-5996-8(0) , Chelsea Hse.) Facts On File, Inc.

Lewis, Lois F. The Secretary of State. 2002. (American Leaders Ser.). (Illus.). 32p. (J). 23.70 (978-1-56711-665-6(5) , Blackbirch Pr., Inc.) Thomson Gale.

Naden, Corinne J. & Blue, Rose. Condoleeza Rice. 2004. (African-American Biographies Ser.). (Illus.). 64p. (J). 28.56 (978-1-4109-1039-4(3)) Raintree.

Richie, Jason. Secretaries of State: Making Foreign Policy. Lerner, Mark, ed. 2002. (In the Cabinet Ser.: Vol. 1). (Illus.). 176p. (gr. 7 up). lib. bdg. 22.95 (978-1-881508-65-6(X)) Oliver Pr., Inc.

Ruffin, David C. The Duties & Responsibilities of the Secretary of State. 2005. (Your Government in Action Ser.). (Illus.). 32p. (J). 21.95 (978-1-4042-2688-3(5) , PowerKids Pr.) Rosen Publishing Group, Inc., The.

UNITED STATES—DEPT. OF THE INTERIOR

Davis, Kate. The Secretary of the Interior. 2002. (American Leaders Ser.). (Illus.). 32p. (J). 23.70 (978-1-56711-664-9(7) , Blackbirch Pr., Inc.) Thomson Gale.

UNITED STATES—DESCRIPTION AND TRAVEL

ABC Travel Guides for Kids-Philadelphia. 2004. (J). per. 12.95 (978-0-9760047-0-7(4)) Rosenberger, Matthew.

America's Landmarks & Monuments, 6 vols., Set I. 2002. (Illus.). (J). (gr. k-6). lib. bdg. 136.68 (978-1-57765-847-4(7)) ABDO Publishing Co.

Andrews, Barbara. The Southeast Region. 2006. pap. 39.00 (***978-1-4108-6432-1(4)***) Benchmark Education Co.

Barter, James. San Francisco in the 1960s. 2003. (Illus.). 96p. (J). 29.95 (978-1-59018-359-5(2) , Lucent Bks.) Thomson Gale.

Beken, Robert A. Tijuana River Estuary & Border Field State Park: Land of diversity, land of Hope. l.t. ed. 2004. (Illus.). 260p. spiral bd. 34.95 (978-0-9761726-0-4(7)) Tritium Pr.

Benchmark Education Staff. The Northeast Region. 2005. 2.00 (***978-1-4108-4660-0(1)***) Benchmark Education Co.

Brown, Don. Alice Ramsey's Grand Adventure. 2000. (YA). 12.75 (978-0-606-19423-5(1)) Tandem Library Bks.

Burt, Barbara. The Eve of Revolution: The Colonial Adventures of Benjamin Wilcox. 2004. (Illus.). 40p. (J). (gr. 4-8). pap. 7.00 (978-0-7567-8215-3(5)) DIANE Publishing Co.

Carole Marsh. Atlanta Coloring. 2004. (City Bks.). 24p. (gr. k-5). pap., act. bk. ed. 3.95 (978-0-635-02230-1(3)) Gallopade International.

Clawson, Calvin C. A Ride to the Infernal Regions: Yellowstone's First Tourists. Silliman, Lee, ed. 2003. per. 19.95 (978-1-931832-18-2(8) , 8667872363) Riverbend Publishing.

Cohen, Stephanie. The Northeast. 2005. (Navigators Ser.). (J). pap. 42.00 (***978-1-4108-5102-4(8)***) Benchmark Education Co.

Colorado Coloring Book. 2003. (J). (978-0-9726022-0-4(8)) Mountain States Specialties.

Colorado Pocket Guide. 2003. (Illus.). 32p. (YA). 1.75 net. (978-0-9726022-5-9(9)) Mountain States Specialties.

Columbia in Pictures. 2004. (Illus.). lib. bdg. 27.93 (978-0-8225-1996-6(8)) Lerner Publishing Group.

Cornerstones of Freedom: Second Series, 6 bks., Set. 2005. (J). 150.00 (978-0-516-25200-1(3) , Children's Pr.) Scholastic Library Publishing.

De Capua, Sarah. The Wilderness Road. 2006. (We the People Ser.). (Illus.). 48p. (J). (gr. 4-6). 23.93 (978-0-7565-1637-6(4)) Compass Point Bks.

Dentro de Madagascar Salvaje. 2005. (Jeff Corwin Experience Ser.). (ENG & SPA., Illus.). 48p. (J). (ps-7). lib. bdg. 24.95 (978-1-4103-0683-8(6) , Blackbirch Pr., Inc.) Thomson Gale.

Ditchfield, Christin. The Lewis & Clark Expedition. 2006. 48p. (YA). (gr. 3-5). pap. 6.95 (978-0-516-25222-3(4) , Children's Pr.) Scholastic Library Publishing.

Egginton, Jane. Pick Your Brains about the USA. Williams, Caspar, illus. 2005. (Pick Your Brains Ser.). 128p. pap. 9.95 (978-1-86011-222-5(6)) Cadogan Guides GBR. *Dist:* Globe Pequot Pr., The.

Espinosa, Rod. Lewis & Clark. 2007. (Bio-Graphics Ser.). (Illus.). 32p. (J). (gr. 3-6). lib. bdg. 27.07 (***978-1-60270-069-7(9)*** , Graphic Planet) Magic Wagon.

Famous US Landmarks Set E, 6 vols. (Phonics Readers Ser.). (gr. k-2). 28.95 (978-0-7368-4067-5(2)) Red Brick Learning.

Gamble, Adam. Good Night America. Chan, Suwin, illus. 2006. (Good Night Our World Ser.). 28p. (J). bds. 7.95 (978-0-9777979-0-5(2)) Our World of Books.

Garrington, Sally. United States. 2003. (Countries of the World Ser.). (Illus.). 64p. (gr. 6-12). 30.00 (978-0-8160-5385-8(5)) Facts On File, Inc.

Group/McGraw-Hill, Wright. The United States Coast to Coast, 6 vols. (Book2WebTM Ser.). (gr. 4-8). 36.50 (978-0-322-04443-2(X)) Wright Group, The.

Halls, Kelly Milner. The Random House Dinosaur Travel Guide. Rey, Luis, illus. 2006. 224p. (J). (gr. 1). 10.99 (978-0-375-82715-0(3) , Random Hse. Bks. for Young Readers) Random Hse. Children's Bks.

Harcourt School Publishers Staff. Horizons: The Journey North. 3rd ed. 2002. (Illus.). pap. 5.60 (978-0-15-333537-2(8)) Harcourt Schl. Pubs.

Heinrichs, Ann. Alabama. 2005. (Welcome to the USA Ser.). 40p. (J). (gr. 1-5). 27.07 (978-1-59296-370-6(6)) Child's World, Inc.

—America the Beautiful Set. 1998. pap. 320.00 (978-0-516-21641-6(4) , Children's Pr.) Scholastic Library Publishing.

Horowitz, Joseph. Dvoerak in America. 2003. (Illus.). x, 158p. (J). pap. 8.95 (978-0-8126-2692-6(3)) Cricket Bks.

—Dvorak in America: In Search of the New World. 2003. (Marcato Book Ser.). (Illus.). 160p. (YA). 17.95 (978-0-8126-2681-0(8)) Cricket Bks.

Houghton, Raymond C. A Revolutionary War Road Trip on US Route 202: Spend a Revolutionary Day along One of America's Most Historic Routes. 2004. (Illus.). 154p. per. 12.99 (978-1-931373-13-5(2)) Cyber Haus.

—A Revolutionary War Road Trip on US Route 7: Spend a Revolutionary Day along One of America's Most Historic Routes. 2004. (Illus.). 150p. per. 12.99 (978-1-931373-10-4(8)) Cyber Haus.

—A Revolutionary War Road Trip on US Route 9W: Spend a Revolutionary Day along One of America's Most Historic Routes. 2004. (Illus.). 174p. per. 12.99 (978-1-931373-11-1(6)) Cyber Haus.

Isserman, Maurice. Across America: The Lewis & Clark Expedition. 2004. (Discovery & Exploration Ser.). (Illus.). 192p. (J). (gr. 6-12). 40.00 (978-0-8160-5256-1(5)) Facts On File, Inc.

It's My State: Group 2, 6 vols. 2003. (YA). (gr. 3). lib. bdg. 162.43 (978-0-7614-1521-3(1)) Cavendish, Marshall Corp.

Jackson, Elaine. America. 2004. (QEB Travel Through Ser.). (Illus.). 32p. (J). lib. bdg. 18.95 (978-1-59566-057-2(7)) QEB Publishing Inc.

Jackson, Robert B. The Remarkable Ride of the Abernathy Boys. 2003. (Land We Belong to Is Grand Ser.). (Illus.). 69p. (J). pap. (978-1-57168-798-2(X) , Eakin Pr.) Eakin Pr.

Juvik, James O., et al. Puke Palapala Aina o Hawaii na ka Haumana. Kawai'eaia, Keiki et al, trs. 2000. Orig. Title: Student Atlas of Hawai'i. (HAW., Illus.). 48p. 10.95 (978-1-57306-115-5(8)) Bess Pr., Inc.

Kalman, Bobbie & Calder, Kate. The United States from A to Z. 1999. (AlphaBasiCs Ser.). (Illus.). 32p. (J). (gr. 2-3). pap. (978-0-86505-410-3(X)); lib. bdg. (978-0-86505-380-9(4)) Crabtree Publishing Co.

Knight, James E. A Journey to Monticello: Traveling in Colonial Times. 1999. (J). (978-0-606-16869-4(9)) Tandem Library Bks.

Kozar, Richard. Lewis & Clark: Explorers of the Louisiana Purchase. 2000. (Explorers of the New World Ser.). (Illus.). 64p. (J). (gr. 4 up). 25.00 (978-0-7910-5513-7(2) , Chelsea Hse.) Facts On File, Inc.

Leonardo, Victoria. The Northeast Region. 2005. 42.00 (***978-1-4108-4612-9(1)***) Benchmark Education Co.

MacGregor, Carol Lynn. Lewis & Clark's Bittersweet Crossing. Hoopes, Gaye, tr. Hoopes, Gaye, illus. 2004. 32p. (J). 16.95 (978-0-87004-437-3(0) , 043700) Caxton Pr.

Mishler, Donna. Travel Through Chesapeake. Walker, Lyn, illus. 2000. 40p. (J). (ps-5). pap. 6.95 (978-1-893709-05-8(1)) Suthersky.

Morley, Jacqueline. You Wouldn't Want to Be an American Pioneer! Antram, David, illus. 2002. (You Wouldn't Want to Ser.). 32p. (J). (gr. 2-5). 28.50 (978-0-531-14608-8(1) , Watts, Franklin) Scholastic Library Publishing.

Murphy, Jim. Across America on an Emigrant Train. 2003. (Illus.). 168p. (J). (gr. 4-6). pap. 10.95 (978-0-395-76483-1(1) , Clarion Bks.) Houghton Mifflin Co. Trade & Reference Div.

—Across America on an Emigrant Train. unabr. ed. 1998. (YA). (gr. 7 up). Class Set. 198.80 incl. audio (978-0-7887-2559-3(9) , 46729); Homework Set. 44.95 incl. audio (978-0-7887-2272-1(7) , 40739) Recorded Bks., LLC.

Nelson, Ray & Nelson, Douglas. Greetings from America: Postcards from Donovan Willoughby. Tronslin, Andrea, ed. Nelson, Ray & Nelson, Douglas, illus. 2nd ed. (Illus.). 48p. (J). (gr. k-5). 14.95 (978-1-56977-409-0(9)) Flying Rhinoceros, Inc.

Neubecker, Robert. Wow! America! Neubecker, Robert, illus. 2006. (Illus.). 48p. (ps-2). 16.99 (978-0-7868-3816-5(7)) Hyperion Bks. for Children.

Nicholaus, Bret & Lowrie, Paul. KidChat Oh, the Places to Go! 204 Creative Questions to Let the Imagination Travel. 2007. (KidChat Ser.). (Illus.). 128p. (J). (gr. 3 up). pap. 6.99 (***978-1-59643-317-5(5)***) Roaring Brook Pr.

Nikola-Lisa, W. America: A Book of Opposites/Un Libro de Contrarios. 2001. (ENG & SPA., Illus.). 24p. (J). (ps). bds. 6.95 (978-1-58430-028-1(0)) Lee & Low Bks., Inc.

Osborne, Mary Pope. Magic Tree House Visits America. 1998. (J). lib. bdg. 14.99 (978-0-679-98542-6(5) , Random Hse. Bks. for Young Readers) Random Hse. Children's Bks.

Price, Sean. Route 66: America's Road. 2007. (J). (***978-1-4109-2697-5(4)***); pap. (***978-1-4109-2708-8(3)***) Steck-Vaughn.

Rau, Dana Meachen. Travel in American History. 2006. (Illus.). 24p. (J). pap. (978-0-8368-7217-0(7)) Stevens, Gareth Inc.

Redmond, Shirley-Raye. Lewis & Clark: A Prairie Dog for the President. Manders, John, illus. 2003. (Step into Reading Ser.: No. 3). 48p. (J). (gr. k-2). pap. 3.99 (978-0-375-81120-3(6) , Random Hse. Bks. for Young Readers) Random Hse. Children's Bks.

Rossi, Ann. The Southeast. 2005. (Navigators Ser.). (J). pap. 42.00 (***978-1-4108-5103-1(6)***) Benchmark Education Co.

Sabuda, Robert. America the Beautiful. Sabuda, Robert, illus. 2004. (Classic Collectible Pop-Up Ser.). (Illus.). 16p. (J). 26.95 (978-0-689-84744-8(0) , Little Simon) Simon & Schuster Children's Publishing.

Schlesinger, Arthur M., Jr. & Israel, Fred L., eds. Touring America Seventy-Five Years Ago. 1999. (Cultural & Geographical Exploration Ser.). (Illus.). x, 122p. (J). (gr. 4-7). lib. bdg. 21.95 (978-0-7910-5098-9(X) , Chelsea Hse.) Facts On File, Inc.

Scholastic, Inc. Staff. Usa Road Trip Bulletin Board& 2005. spiral bd. 10.99 (***978-0-439-74922-0(0)*** , Teaching Resources) Scholastic, Inc.

Southern Waterway Guide 2004: Florida, the Bahamas & the Gulf of Mexico. 2nd ed. 2003. (Illus.). 485p. spiral bd. 39.95 (978-0-9723131-4-8(1)) Waterway Guide.

St Louis Gold C 2005. 2004. 436p. (YA). pap. 15.00 (978-1-58553-966-6(X) , 05GC0005) Entertainment Publications, Inc.

Steck-Vaughn Staff. All Around the U. S. A Travel Adventure. 2002. (Illus.). (J). pap. (978-0-7398-6175-2(1)) Steck-Vaughn.

Streissguth, Thomas. United States in Pictures. 2007. (J). lib. bdg. (***978-0-8225-8567-1(7)***) Twenty First Century Bks.

Tallarico, Tony. Ultimate Hidden Pictures Across America. 2003. (Illus.). 48p. (J). (ps-4). mass mkt. 3.99 (978-0-8431-0265-9(9) , Price Stern Sloan) Penguin Group (USA) Inc.

Weber, Valerie & Baker, Patricia A. Traveling in Grandma's Day. Lafford, Stuart, illus. 1999. (In Grandma's Day Ser.). 32p. (J). (ps-3). lib. bdg. 21.27 (978-1-57505-326-4(8) , Carolrhoda Bks.) Lerner Publishing Group.

Webster, Christine. The Lewis & Clark Expedition. 2007. (Cornerstones of Freedomtrade;, Second Ser.). 48p. (J). pap. 5.95 (***978-0-531-18689-3(X)*** , Children's Pr.) Scholastic Library Publishing.

Wheeler. Field Guide to Eastern U. S. 2002. (Illus.). 240p. pap. (978-0-12-745525-9(6) , Academic Pr.) Elsevier Science & Technology Bks.

—Field Guide to Western U. S. 2002. (Illus.). 240p. pap. (978-0-12-745527-3(2) , Academic Pr.) Elsevier Science & Technology Bks.

Yaccarino, Dan. Go, Go America: Oodles of Oddities from the Fifty States. 2008. 80p. (J). 17.99 (***978-0-439-70338-3(7)*** , Scholastic Pr.) Scholastic, Inc.

Zimmerman, Jerry. Around America in 80 Mazes. 2000. (Illus.). 80p. (J). (gr. 3-7). pap. 6.95 (978-0-7373-0333-9(6) , 03336W) Lowell Hse.

UNITED STATES—DESCRIPTION AND TRAVEL—MAPS

see United States—Maps

UNITED STATES—DISCOVERY AND EXPLORATION

see America—Discovery and Exploration; United States—Exploring Expeditions

UNITED STATES—ECONOMIC CONDITIONS

Bagley, Katie. The Early American Industrial Revolution, 1793-1850. 2003. (Let Freedom Ring Ser.). (Illus.). 48p. (J). (gr. 3-4). lib. bdg. 22.60 (978-0-7368-1557-4(0) , Bridgestone Bks.) Capstone Pr., Inc.

Brezina, Corona. The Industrial Revolution in America. 2005. (Illus.). 64p. (J). (gr. 5-8). lib. bdg. 29.25 (978-1-4042-0179-8(3)) Rosen Publishing Group, Inc., The.

Buckley, Susan Washburn. The Industrial Revolution: 1790-1850. 2002. (Reading Expeditions Ser.). (Illus.). 40p. (J). (978-0-7922-8685-1(5)) National Geographic Society.

Coleman, Wim & Perrin, Pat. The Amazing Erie Canal & How a Big Ditch Opened up the West. 2006. (Wild History of the American West Ser.). (Illus.). 128p. (J). lib. bdg. 33.27 (978-1-59845-017-0(4) , MyReportLinks.com Bks.) Enslow Pubs., Inc.

DeGezelle, Terri. Franklin D. Roosevelt & the Great Depression. 2007. (J). (***978-1-4034-9670-6(6)***); pap. (***978-1-4034-9678-2(1)***) Heinemann Library.

Downing, David. The Great Depression. (20th Century Perspectives Ser.). (Illus.). 48p. (J). 2001. (gr. 4-7). lib. bdg. 25.64 (978-1-57572-435-5(9)); Set 1. 2002. (gr. 5-7). pap. 7.95 (978-1-58810-374-1(9) , 91126) Heinemann Library.

—The Great Depression. 2001. (YA). 15.30 (978-0-606-22492-5(0)) Tandem Library Bks.

Gedney, Mona K. The Story of the Great Depression. 2005. (Monumental Milestones Ser.). (Illus.). 48p. (YA). (ps-7). lib. bdg. (978-1-58415-403-7(9)) Mitchell Lane Pubs., Inc.

Gerdes, Louise I. The Crash of 1929. 2001. (At Issue in History Ser.). (Illus.). 104p. (YA). (gr. 7-10). lib. bdg. 27.45 (978-0-7377-0819-6(0) , GML12001-179091, Greenhaven Pr., Inc.) Thomson Gale.

Gow, Mary. The Stock Market Crash Of 1929: Dawn of the Great Depression. 2003. (American Disasters Ser.). (Illus.). 48p. (J). lib. bdg. 23.93 (978-0-7660-2111-2(4)) Enslow Pubs., Inc.

Grant, R. G. The Great Depression. 2005. (How Did It Happen? Ser.). (Illus.). 48p. (YA). (gr. 7-10). lib. bdg. 29.95 (978-1-59018-606-0(0) , Lucent Bks.) Thomson Gale.

Gunderson, Cory. Great Depression. 2005. (American Moments Ser.). (Illus.). 48p. (J). (gr. 4-8). lib. bdg. 25.65 (978-1-59197-286-0(8) , ABDO & Daughters) ABDO Publishing Co.

Hakim, Joy. A History of US Bk. 8: Age of Extremes. rev. ed. 2007. (History of US Ser.: Vol. 8). 224p. pap. 15.95 (***978-0-19-532722-9(5)***) Oxford Univ. Pr., Inc.

Hakim, Joy. A History of US Bk. 8: An Age of Extremes. rev. ed. 2006. (History of US Ser.). (Illus.). 210p. 19.95 (978-0-19-518236-1(7)) Oxford Univ. Pr., Inc.

Heinemann Library Staff. The Great Depression. 2003. (Illus.). 56p. (J). pap. 8.95 (978-1-4034-4576-6(1)) Heinemann Library.

Ingram, Scott. The Stock Market Crash of 1929. 2004. (Landmark Events in American History Ser.). (J). pap. 11.95 (978-0-8368-5425-1(X)); lib. bdg. 30.00 (978-0-8368-5397-1(0)) Stevens, Gareth Inc. (World Almanac Library).

Kallen, Stuart A. Are America's Wealthy Too Powerful? 2006. (Illus.). 128p. (gr. 10-12). 21.20 (978-0-7377-3430-0(2)); pap. 29.95 (978-0-7377-3429-4(9)) Thomson Gale. (Greenhaven Pr., Inc.).

—Are Chain Stores Ruining America? 2006. (At Issue Ser.). 128p. (J). (gr. 10-12). 21.20 (978-0-7377-3096-8(X)); (Illus.). pap. 29.95 (978-0-7377-3095-1(1)) Thomson Gale. (Greenhaven Pr., Inc.).

Kalman, Bobbie. Railroad. 1999. (978-0-606-16432-0(4)); (gr. 3-6). lib. bdg. 16.40 (978-0-613-12014-2(0)) Tandem Library Bks.

Landau, Elaine. The Great Depression. 2007. (Cornerstones of Freedomtrade;, Second Ser.). 48p. (J). pap. 5.95 (***978-0-531-18767-8(5)*** , Children's Pr.) Scholastic Library Publishing.

Landau, Elaine. The Pony Express. 2006. 48p. (YA). (gr. 3-5). pap. 6.95 (978-0-516-27905-3(X) , Children's Pr.) Scholastic Library Publishing.

Lange, Brenda. The Stock Market Crash of 1929: The End of Prosperity. 2007. (Milestones in American History Ser.). 120p. (J). (gr. 6-12). 35.00 (***978-0-7910-9354-2(9)*** , Chelsea Hse.) Facts On File, Inc.

Lawrence, Katherine. Labor Legislation: The Struggle to Gain Rights for America's Workforce. 2004. (Progressive Movement, 1900-1920 Ser.). (Illus.). 32p. (J). lib. bdg. (978-1-4042-0191-0(2)) Rosen Publishing Group, Inc., The.

Petersen, Christine & Petersen, David. United States of America. 2002. (Illus.). 47p. (J). (gr. 4-7). lib. bdg. 15.25 (978-0-613-54371-2(8)) Tandem Library Bks.

Ripped from the Headlines, 10 bks., Set. Incl. Downloading Music. Allman, Toney. 23.95 (***978-1-60217-006-3(1)***); Fat in America. Stewart, Gail. 23.95 (***978-1-60217-002-5(9)***); Gas Crisis. Kallan, Stuart A. 23.95 (***978-1-60217-001-8(0)***); Illegal Immigration. Stewart, Gail.

23.95 (*978-1-60217-003-2(7)); Internet Predators. Allman, Toney. 23.95 (*978-1-60217-000-1(2)); Nuclear Weapons. Sheen, Barbara. 23.95 (*978-1-60217-004-9(5)); Outsourcing America. Currie, Stephen. 23.95 (*978-1-60217-008-7(8)); Reality TV. Woog, Adam. 23.95 (*978-1-60217-005-6(3)); Street Crime. Parks, Peggy. 23.95 (*978-1-60217-007-0(X)); Your Sexuality. Hirschmann, Kris. 23.95 (*978-1-60217-009-4(6)); 64p. (J). (gr. 5). 2007. 214.95 (*978-1-60217-010-0(X)) Erickson Pr.

Robinson, Tom. The Development of the Industrial United States. 2007. (J). (*978-1-59036-745-2(6)); (*978-1-59036-746-9(4)) Weigl Pubs., Inc.

Roza, Greg. America's Transition from Agriculture to Industry: Drawing Inferences & Conclusions. 2005. (Critical Thinking in American History Ser.). (Illus.). 48p. (YA). (gr. 5-8). lib. bdg. 25.25 (978-1-4042-0410-2(5)) Rosen Publishing Group, Inc., The.

Ruggiero, Adriane. The Great Depression. 2004. (American Voices From Ser.). (Illus.). xxi, 116p. (J). 34.21 (978-0-7614-1696-8(X) , Benchmark Bks.) Cavendish, Marshall Corp.

Shea, Kitty. Industrial America. 2004. (We the People Ser.). (Illus.). 48p. (J). 22.60 (978-0-7565-0840-1(1)) Compass Point Bks.

Smith, Robert W. Industrial Revolution. 2006. (Illus.). 48p. (YA). 8.99 (978-1-4206-3220-0(5)) Teacher Created Resources, Inc.

Stein, R. Conrad. The Industrial Revolution: Manufacturing a Better America. 2006. (American Saga Ser.). (Illus.). 128p. (J). lib. bdg. 31.93 (978-0-7660-2571-4(3)) Enslow Pubs., Inc.

Stich, Paul & Habib, George. Economics STAReview: Crosscurrents of the American Dream. 2002. (ENG., Illus.). 256p. (YA). per. 14.95 (978-0-935487-80-0(8) , STAReviews) N&N Publishing Co., Inc.

Topping, Elizabeth A. What's a Poor Girl to Do? Prostitution in Mid-Nineteenth Century America. 2001. (Illus.). 72p. 8.95 (978-1-57747-072-4(9)) Thomas Pubns.

Wilcox, Charlotte. Work & Occupations in Colonial America. 2004. (Everyday Life Long Ago Ser.). (J). (978-0-7368-2165-0(1) , Blue Earth Bks.) Capstone Pr., Inc.

Woolf, Alex. The Wall Street Crash. 2002. (Days That Shook the World Ser.). (Illus.). 48p. (J). lib. bdg. (978-0-7398-5237-8(X)) Raintree.

UNITED STATES—ECONOMIC POLICY

Nardo, Don. The Great Depression. 2000. (Turning Points in World History Ser.). (Illus.). 220p. (YA). (gr. 9-12). lib. bdg. 32.45 (978-0-7377-0231-6(1) , Greenhaven Pr., Inc.) Thomson Gale.

UNITED STATES—EMIGRATION AND IMMIGRATION

see also United States—Foreign Population

American Voices - Group 2, 6 bks., Set. 205.29 (978-0-7614-1200-7(X) , Benchmark Bks.) Cavendish, Marshall Corp.

Anderson, Dale. Arriving at Ellis Island. 2002. (Landmark Events in American History Ser.). (Illus.). 48p. (J). (gr. 5 up). lib. bdg. 30.00 (978-0-8368-5337-7(7)); pap. 14.60 (978-0-8368-5351-3(2)) Stevens, Gareth Inc. (World Almanac Library).

—Chinese Americans. 2006. (World Almanac Library of American Immigration). (Illus.). 47p. (J). pap. (978-0-8368-7321-4(1)); lib. bdg. (978-0-8368-7308-5(4)) Stevens, Gareth Inc. (World Almanac Library).

—Cuban Americans. 2006. (World Almanac Library of American Immigration). (Illus.). 48p. (J). pap. (978-0-8368-7322-1(X)); lib. bdg. (978-0-8368-7309-2(2)) Stevens, Gareth Inc. (World Almanac Library).

—Italian Americans. 2006. (World Almanac Library of American Immigration). 48p. (J). pap. (978-0-8368-7325-2(4)); lib. bdg. (978-0-8368-7312-2(2)) Stevens, Gareth Inc. (World Almanac Library).

—Japanese Americans. 2006. (World Almanac Library of American Immigration). (Illus.). 48p. (J). pap. (978-0-8368-7326-9(2)); lib. bdg. (978-0-8368-7313-9(0)) Stevens, Gareth Inc. (World Almanac Library).

—Korean Americans. 2008. (J). (*978-1-60044-613-9(2)) Rourke Publishing, LLC.

Anderson, Dale. Polish Americans. 2006. (World Almanac Library of American Immigration). (Illus.). 48p. (J). pap. (978-0-8368-7330-6(0)); lib. bdg. (978-0-8368-7317-7(3)) Stevens, Gareth Inc. (World Almanac Library).

Anderson, Marilyn D. Arab Americans. 2006. (World Almanac Library of American Immigration). (Illus.). 48p. (J). pap. (978-0-8368-7320-7(3)); lib. bdg. (978-0-8368-7307-8(6)) Stevens, Gareth Inc. (World Almanac Library).

Anderson, Stuart, ed. The Changing Face of America: Immigration Since 1965, 16 vols., Set. 2003. (Illus.). 112p. (YA). lib. bdg. (978-1-59084-679-7(6)) Mason Crest Pubs.

Barnett, Tracy. Immigration from South America. 2004. (Changing Face of North America Ser.). (Illus.). 112p. (J). lib. bdg. (978-1-59084-687-2(7)) Mason Crest Pubs.

Barrie, Laurie. Immigrant Kids. 2000. 31p. (J). ring bd. 20.00 (978-1-930443-23-5(4)) Logos Schl.

Benson, Sonia. U.S. Immigration & Migration Almanac, 2 vols. 2004. (U. S. Immigration & Migration Reference Library). (Illus.). (J). (978-0-7876-7566-0(0)); (978-0-7876-7567-7(9)) Thomson Gale. (UXL).

Berger, Melvin & Berger, Gilda. Where Did Your Family Come From? A Book about Immigrants. Quackenbush, Robert, illus. 1999. (Discovery Readers Ser.). 48p. (J). (ps-3). lib. bdg. 15.95 (978-0-7910-5063-7(7) , Chelsea Hse.) Facts On File, Inc.

Binns, Tristan Boyer. Ellis Island. (Visiting the Past Ser.). (Illus.). 32p. (J). (gr. 5-7). 2002. pap. 6.95 (978-1-58810-412-0(5) , 91180); 2001. lib. bdg. 24.22 (978-1-58810-270-6(X)) Heinemann Library.

—Ellis Island. 2001. (gr. 5-8). lib. bdg. 15.90 (978-0-613-82114-8(9)) Tandem Library Bks.

Bode, Janet. The Colors of Freedom: Immigrant Stories. (Single Titles Social Studies Ser.). (Illus.). 144p. (YA). (gr. 8-12). 2000. pap. 9.95 (978-0-531-15961-3(2)); 1999. 26.00 (978-0-531-11530-5(5)) Scholastic Library Publishing. (Watts, Franklin).

—Colors of Freedom: Immigrant Stories. 2000. (Illus.). (J). (978-0-606-18146-4(6)); 1999. (gr. 7-12). lib. bdg. 18.75 (978-0-613-29211-5(1)) Tandem Library Bks.

Britton, Tamara L. Ellis Island. 2005. (Symbols, Landmarks, & Monuments Set Ii Ser.). (Illus.). 32p. (J). (gr. k-6). lib. bdg. 22.78 (978-1-59197-519-9(0)) ABDO Publishing Co.

Broida, Marian. Projects about Nineteenth-Century European Immigrants. 2005. (Hands-On History Ser.). (Illus.). 47p. (J). (978-0-7614-1980-8(2) , Benchmark Bks.) Cavendish, Marshall Corp.

Bryan, Nichol. Japanese Americans. 2004. (One Nation Set Ii Ser.). (Illus.). 32p. (J). (gr. k-6). lib. bdg. 22.78 (978-1-59197-529-8(8)) ABDO Publishing Co.

Burgan, Michael. A Changing Nation. 2006. (Making a New Nation Ser.). (Illus.). 48p. (J). (978-1-4034-7830-6(9)); pap. (978-1-4034-7837-5(6)) Heinemann Library.

Byers, Ann. The History of U. S. Immigration: Coming to America. 2006. (American Saga Ser.). (Illus.). 128p. (J). lib. bdg. 31.93 (978-0-7660-2574-5(8)) Enslow Pubs., Inc.

Campbell, Wallis. Angel Island. 2006. (Illus.). 48p. (J). pap. (978-1-59034-808-6(7)) Mondo Publishing.

Choi, Anne Soon. Korean Americans. 2007. (New Immigrants Ser.). (Illus.). 136p. (J). (gr. 6-12). 27.95 (978-0-7910-8788-6(3) , Chelsea Hse.) Facts On File, Inc.

Conley, Kate A. The Puerto Rican Americans. 2005. (Immigrants in America Ser.). (Illus.). 112p. (YA). (gr. 7-10). lib. bdg. 29.95 (978-1-59018-432-5(7) , Lucent Bks.) Thomson Gale.

Creative Media Applications Staff. The Newest Americans. 2003. Vol. 1. (978-0-313-32554-0(5)); Vol. 2. (978-0-313-32555-7(3)); Vol. 3. (978-0-313-32556-4(1)); Vol. 4. (978-0-313-32557-1(X)) Greenwood Publishing Group, Inc.

Cromwell, Sharon. Arab Americans. 2008. (J). (*978-1-60044-610-8(8)) Rourke Publishing, LLC.

Deitch, JoAnne Weisman, ed. Immigration. 2000. (Researching American History Ser.). (Illus.). 56p. (J). (978-1-57960-073-0(5)) History Compass, LLC.

DiConsiglio, John. Coming to America: Voices of Teenage Immigrants. 2002. (Read 180 Ser.). (Illus.). 76p. (J). (978-0-439-12339-6(9)) Scholastic, Inc.

—Young Americans: Tales of Teenage Immigrants. 2005. (Illus.). 43p. (978-0-439-12405-8(0)) Scholastic, Inc.

Doak, Robin S. Indian Americans. 2008. (J). (*978-1-60044-612-2(4)) Rourke Publishing, LLC.

Egendorf, Laura K. Illegal Immigration. 2006. (Writing the Critical Essay Ser.). (Illus.). 244p. (gr. 6-10). 29.95 (978-0-7377-3582-6(1) , Greenhaven Pr., Inc.) Thomson Gale.

Events That Shaped America: Arriving at Ellis Island; Battle of the Little Bighorn; California Missions; Plymouth Colony; Settling of Jamestown; Siege of the Alamo, 6 bks. 2002. (Illus.). (J). (gr. 3 up). lib. bdg. 143.60 (978-0-8368-3220-4(5)) Stevens, Gareth Inc.

Faria, Joseph D. The Statue of Liberty & Ellis Island: A MyReportLinks.com Book. 2005. (Virtual Field Trips Ser.). (Illus.). 48p. (J). (gr. 4-10). lib. bdg. 25.26 (978-0-7660-5226-0(5) , MyReportLinks.com Bks.) Enslow Pubs., Inc.

Ferry, Joseph. Vietnamese Immigration. 2003. (Changing Face of North America Ser.). (Illus.). 112p. (YA). lib. bdg. (978-1-59084-682-7(6)) Mason Crest Pubs.

Figorito, Marcus. Ellis Island: Welcome to America. 2006. (Rosen Publishing Group's Reading Room Collection). (Illus.). 16p. (J). lib. bdg. (978-1-4042-3347-8(4)) Rosen Publishing Group, Inc., The.

Flanagan, Alice K. Angel Island. 2005. (We the People Ser.). (Illus.). 48p. (J). (gr. 4-6). (978-0-7565-1261-3(1)) Compass Point Bks.

Gaines, Jena. Haitian Immigration. 2003. (Changing Face of North America Ser.). (Illus.). 112p. (J). lib. bdg. (978-1-59084-691-9(5)) Mason Crest Pubs.

Gallegos, Yuliana. Mi Sueño de América/My American Dream. 2007. (SPA & ENG.). (Illus.). (gr. 3-7). pap. 9.95 (*978-1-55885-485-7(1) , Piñata Books) Arte Publico Pr.

Gelletly, LeeAnne. Mexican Immigration. 2003. (Changing Face of North America Ser.). (Illus.). 112p. (YA). lib. bdg. (978-1-59084-680-3(X)) Mason Crest Pubs.

Gravois, Michael. Hands-On History: Civil War. 2004. (Hands-on History Ser.). (Illus.). 48p. pap. 10.99 (978-0-439-41125-7(4) , Teaching Resources) Scholastic, Inc.

—Immigration. 2004. (Hands-on History Ser.). 48p. pap. 10.99 (978-0-439-41124-0(6) , Teaching Resources) Scholastic, Inc.

—Pioneers. 2004. (Hands-on History Ser.). (Illus.). 48p. pap. 10.99 (978-0-439-41126-4(2) , Teaching Resources) Scholastic, Inc.

Grolier Educational Staff. American Immigration, 10 vols., Set. 1998. (Illus.). (J). lib. bdg. 335.00 (978-0-7172-9283-7(5) , Grolier) Scholastic Library Publishing.

Haberle, Susan E. Jewish Immigrants, 1880-1924. 2002. (Blue Earth Books). (Illus.). 32p. (J). (gr. 4). lib. bdg. 22.60 (978-0-7368-1207-8(5) , Bridgestone Bks.) Capstone Pr., Inc.

Haerens, Margaret. Illegal Immigration. 2006. (Opposing Viewpoints Ser.). 244p. (YA). (gr. 7 up). pap. 24.95 (978-0-7377-3357-0(8)); lib. bdg. 36.20 (978-0-7377-3356-3(X)) Thomson Gale. (Greenhaven Pr., Inc.).

Harcourt School Publishers Staff. I Am an American: Take-Home Book. 2001. (Collections Ser.). (Illus.). (J). pap. 1.90 (978-0-15-319504-4(5)) Harcourt Schl. Pubs.

—Today I Am an American: Independent Reader. 3rd ed. 2002. (Trophies Reading Program Ser.). (Illus.). (J). pap. 2.90 (978-0-15-325471-0(8)) Harcourt Schl. Pubs.

Hernandez, Roger E. Immigration. 2006. (Gallup Major Trends & Events Ser.). (Illus.). 112p. (J). (gr. 7 up). lib. bdg. (978-1-59084-965-1(5)) Mason Crest Pubs.

Hernandez, Romel. Immigration from Central America. 2004. (Changing Face of North America Ser.). (Illus.). 112p. (YA). lib. bdg. (978-1-59084-688-9(5)) Mason Crest Pubs.

Hicks, Terry Allan. Ellis Island. 2006. (Symbols of America Ser.). (Illus.). 40p. (J). lib. bdg. 28.50 (978-0-7614-2134-4(3) , Benchmark Bks.) Cavendish, Marshall Corp.

Honovich, Nancy. Immigration from the Former Yugoslavia. 2003. (Changing Face of North America Ser.). (Illus.). 112p. (YA). lib. bdg. (978-1-59084-690-2(7)) Mason Crest Pubs.

Horst, Heather A. & Garner, Andrew. Jamaican Americans. 2007. (New Immigrants Ser.). (Illus.). 144p. (J). (gr. 6-12). 27.95 (978-0-7910-8790-9(5) , Chelsea Hse.) Facts On File, Inc.

Horton, Casey. Jews. 2000. (gr. 3-6). lib. bdg. 17.60 (978-0-613-27915-4(8)) Tandem Library Bks.

Hossell, Karen Price. The Irish Americans. 2003. (Immigrants in America Ser.). (Illus.). 112p. (J). 29.95 (978-1-56006-752-8(7) , Lucent Bks.) Thomson Gale.

Ingram, Scott. Korean Americans. 2006. (World Almanac Library of American Immigration). (Illus.). 48p. (J). pap. (978-0-8368-7328-3(9)); lib. bdg. (978-0-8368-7315-3(7)) Stevens, Gareth Inc. (World Almanac Library).

—Mexican Americans. 2006. (World Almanac Library of American Immigration). (Illus.). 48p. (J). pap. (978-0-8368-7329-0(7)); lib. bdg. (978-0-8368-7316-0(5)) Stevens, Gareth Inc. (World Almanac Library).

—South Asian Americans. 2006. (World Almanac Library of American Immigration). (Illus.). 48p. (J). pap. (978-0-8368-7331-3(9)); lib. bdg. (978-0-8368-7318-4(1)) Stevens, Gareth Inc. (World Almanac Library).

Jango-Cohen, Judith. Ellis Island. 2005. (Cornerstones of Freedom Ser.). (Illus.). 48p. (J). (gr. 4-6). 26.00 (978-0-516-23625-4(3) , Children's Pr.) Scholastic Library Publishing.

Kallen, Stuart A. Twentieth-Century Immigration to the United States. 2007. (American History Ser.). 128p. (J). (gr. 7-10). 32.45 (*978-1-59018-186-7(7) , Lucent Bks.) Thomson Gale.

Kerrigan, Michael. Border & Immigration Control. 2003. (Rescue & Prevention Ser.). (Illus.). 96p. (J). (gr. 7 up). lib. bdg. (978-1-59084-408-3(4)) Mason Crest Pubs.

Klingel, Cynthia Fitterer & Noyed, Robert B. Ellis Island. 2000. (Wonder Books Level 3: Landmarks Ser.). (Illus.). 32p. (J). (ps-3). 22.79 (978-1-56766-823-0(2)) Child's World, Inc.

Knowlton, MaryLee & Anderson, Dale. Arriving at Ellis Island. 2002. (Events That Shaped America Ser.). (Illus.). 32p. (J). (gr. 3 up). lib. bdg. 24.67 (978-0-8368-3221-1(3)) Stevens, Gareth Inc.

Kule, Elaine A. Beginning Again: Immigrating to America. Thermes, Jennifer, illus. 2006. 40p. (978-1-59137-473-2(1)) Options Publishing.

Landau, Elaine. Ellis Island. 2008. (True Booktrade;: American History Ser.). 48p. (J). pap. 6.95 (*978-0-531-14781-8(9) , Children's Pr.) Scholastic Library Publishing.

Langley, Andrew. Should Immigration Be Restricted? 2007. (J). (*978-1-4329-0359-6(4)) Heinemann Library.

Lemke, Donald B. The Schoolchildren's Blizzard. Hoover, Dave & Barnett, Charles, illus. 2008. (J). (*978-1-4296-0157-3(4)) Capstone Pr., Inc.

Lingen, Marissa. Chinese Immigration. 2004. (Changing Face of North America Ser.). (Illus.). 112p. (YA). lib. bdg. (978-1-59084-694-0(X)) Mason Crest Pubs.

Martin, Jennifer C. The Korean Americans. 2005. (Immigrants in America Ser.). (Illus.). 112p. (YA). (gr. 7-10). lib. bdg. 29.95 (978-1-59018-079-2(8) , Lucent Bks.) Thomson Gale.

Maury, Rob. Immigration from the Middle East. 2004. (Changing Face of North America Ser.). (Illus.). 112p. (J). lib. bdg. (978-1-59084-695-7(8)) Mason Crest Pubs.

—Your Rights as a U. S. Citizen. 2002. (Welcome to America Ser.). (Illus.). 64p. (J). (gr. 4-7). lib. bdg. (978-1-59084-105-1(0)) Mason Crest Pubs.

McDaniel, Jan. Indian Immigration. 2004. (Changing Face of North America Ser.). (Illus.). 112p. (YA). lib. bdg. (978-1-59084-683-4(4)) Mason Crest Pubs.

Meltzer, Milton, et al. Bound for America: The Story of the European Immigrants. 2001. (Great Journeys Ser.). (Illus.). 112p. (J). (gr. 5 up). lib. bdg. 32.79 (978-0-7614-1227-4(1) , Benchmark Bks.) Cavendish, Marshall Corp.

Meyer, Jared. Frequently Asked Questions about Being an Immigrant Teen. 2007. (J). lib. bdg. (*978-1-4042-1079-0(2)) Rosen Publishing Group, Inc., The.

Miller, Debra. Illegal Immigration. 2007. (Current Controversies Ser.). (Illus.). 240p. (J). (gr. 10-12). 36.20 (*978-0-7377-3723-3(9)); pap. 24.95 (*978-0-7377-3724-0(7)) Thomson Gale. (Greenhaven Pr., Inc.).

Miller, Debra A. Illegal Immigration. 2007. (Compact Research Ser.). 112p. (YA). lib. bdg. (*978-1-60152-009-8(3)) ReferencePoint Pr., Inc.

Miller, Karen, ed. Immigration. 2006. 110p. (YA). (gr. 8 up). lib. bdg. 29.95 (*978-0-7377-2893-4(0) , Greenhaven Pr., Inc.) Thomson Gale.

Moynihan, Daniel Patrick, intro. Immigrants in America. 2005. (Illus.). 112p. (gr. 6-12). pap. 180.00 (978-0-7910-7125-0(1) , Chelsea Hse.) Facts On File, Inc.

Nichol, Bryan. Greek Americans. 2004. (One Nation Ser.). (Illus.). 32p. (J). (gr. k-6). lib. bdg. 22.78 (978-1-59197-527-4(1) , Checkerboard Library) ABDO Publishing Co.

—Irish Americans. 2004. (One Nation Ser.). (Illus.). 32p. (J). (gr. k-6). lib. bdg. 22.78 (978-1-59197-528-1(X) , Checkerboard Library) ABDO Publishing Co.

Noonan, Sheila Smith. Korean Immigration. 2003. (Changing Face of North America Ser.). (Illus.). 112p. (YA). lib. bdg. (978-1-59084-693-3(1)) Mason Crest Pubs.

Olson, Kay Melchisedech. French Immigrants, 1840-1940. 2002. (Blue Earth Books). (Illus.). 32p. (J). (gr. 3-4). lib. bdg. 22.60 (978-0-7368-1205-4(9) , Bridgestone Bks.) Capstone Pr., Inc.

Outman, James L., et al. U.S. Immigration & Migration, 2 vols. 2004. ([U.S. Immigration & Migration Reference Library]). (Illus.). (J). 110.00 (978-0-7876-7568-4(7)); (978-0-7876-7668-1(3)) Thomson Gale. (UXL).

Parker, Lewis K. Why Mexican Immigrants Came to America. 2003. (Reading Power Ser.). (Illus.). 24p. (J). lib. bdg. 17.25 (978-0-8239-6459-8(0) , PowerKids Pr.) Rosen Publishing Group, Inc., The.

Perl, Lila. To the Golden Mountain: The Chinese Who Built the Transcontinental Railroad. 2002. (Great Journeys Ser.). (Illus.). 112p. (J). 32.79 (978-0-7614-1324-0(3) , Benchmark Bks.) Cavendish, Marshall Corp.

Peterson, Tiffany. Japanese Americans. 2004. (We Are America Ser.). (Illus.). 32p. (J). lib. bdg. 24.22 (978-1-4034-5022-7(6)) Heinemann Library.

Petrini, Catherine M. The Italian-Americans. 2001. (Immigrants in America Ser.). (Illus.). 104p. (YA). (gr. 4-12). 29.95 (978-1-56006-882-2(5) , LML00902-178205, Lucent Bks.) Thomson Gale.

Pobst, Sandy. The Newest Americans, 5 vols. 2003. (Middle School Reference Ser.). (Illus.). 144p. (gr. 6-8). 209.95 (978-0-313-32553-3(7) , MS2553, Middle School Reference) Greenwood Publishing Group, Inc.

Powell, John. Immigration. 2006. (Library in a Book). (Illus.). 304p. (J). (gr. 9). 45.00 (978-0-8160-6234-8(X)) Facts On File, Inc.

Price Hossell, Karen. Dominican Americans. 2004. (We Are America Ser.). (Illus.). 32p. (J). lib. bdg. 24.22 (978-1-4034-5020-3(X)) Heinemann Library.

Price, Sean. Tenement Stories: Immigrant Life, 1835-1935. 2006. (American History Through Primary Sources Ser.). (Illus.). 32p. (J). (gr. 2-4). lib. bdg. 28.21 (978-1-4109-2412-4(2)) Raintree.

—Tenement Stories: Immigrant Life, 1835-1935. 2006. (American History Through Primary Sources Ser.). (Illus.). 32p. (J). pap. (978-1-4109-2423-0(8)) Steck-Vaughn.

Primary Sources of Immigration & Migration. (Primary Source Big Bookstm Ser.). 24p. (J). (gr. 4-8). 46.60 (978-0-8239-4594-8(4)) Rosen Publishing Group, Inc., The.

Raatma, Lucia. Ellis Island. 2002. (We the People Ser.). (Illus.). 48p. (J). (gr. 4 up). lib. bdg. 22.60 (978-0-7565-0302-4(7)) Compass Point Bks.

Raum, Elizabeth. Irish Immigrants in America: An Interactive History Adventure. 2008. (You Choose Bks.). 112p. (J). (gr. 3-7). lib. bdg. 27.23 (*978-1-4296-0161-0(2)) Capstone Pr., Inc.

Rinker, Kimberly. Immigration from the Dominican Republic. 2003. (Changing Face of North America Ser.). (Illus.). 112p. (J). lib. bdg. (978-1-59084-689-6(3)) Mason Crest Pubs.

Roberts, Jeremy. Benito Mussolini. 2005. (Pull Ahead Books). (J). lib. bdg. (978-978-082-252-1(6) , Lerner Pubns.) Lerner Publishing Group.

Ruffin, Frances E. Ellis Island. 2006. (Illus.). 24p. (J). pap. 5.95 (978-0-8368-6415-1(8)); lib. bdg. 19.33 (978-0-8368-6408-3(5)) Stevens, Gareth Inc.

Sandler, Martin. Immigrants: A Library of Congress Book. 2000. (gr. 3-6). lib. bdg. 19.95 (978-0-613-28531-5(X)) Tandem Library Bks.

Sandler, Martin W. Island of Hope: The Story of Ellis Island & the Journey to America. 2004. (Illus.). 144p. (J). pap. 18.95 (978-0-439-53082-8(2)) Scholastic, Inc.

Santos, Edward J. Everything You Need to Know If You & Your Parents Are New Americans. 2005. (Need to Know Library). (Illus.). 64p. (YA). (gr. 4-6). lib. bdg. 25.25 (978-0-8239-3547-5(7)) Rosen Publishing Group, Inc., The.

Saxon-Ford, Stephanie. The Czech Americans: The Immigrant Experience. 2006. (Illus.). 111p. (J). (gr. 4-8). reprint ed. 20.00 (978-1-4223-5547-3(0)) DIANE Publishing Co.

Schaefer, A. R. Modern Immigration & Expansion. 2006. (Making a New Nation Ser.). (Illus.). 48p. (J). (978-1-4034-7831-3(7)); pap. (978-1-4034-7838-2(4)) Heinemann Library.

Schur, Joan Brodsky. The Arab Americans. 2004. (Immigrants in America Ser.). (Illus.). 112p. (J). 29.95 (978-1-59018-075-4(5) , Lucent Bks.) Thomson Gale.

Sioux, Tracee. Immigrants, Migration, & the Industrial Revolution. 2004. (Primary Sources of Immigration & Migration in America Ser.). (Illus.). 24p. (J). lib. bdg. 19.95 (978-0-8239-6826-8(X) , PowerKids Pr.) Rosen Publishing Group, Inc., The.

—Immigration, Migration, & the Industrial Revolution. 2004. (Primary Sources of Immigration & Migration in America Ser.). (Illus.). 24p. (J). lib. bdg. (978-0-8239-8998-0(4) , PowerKids Pr.) Rosen Publishing Group, Inc., The.

Sonneborn, Liz. The Cuban-Americans. 2001. (Immigrants in America Ser.). (Illus.). 104p. (YA). (gr. 4-12). 29.95 (978-1-56006-902-7(3) , LML00902-178250, Lucent Bks.) Thomson Gale.

Steele, Christy, et al. Fighting for American Values. 2007. (Latino-American History Ser.). 112p. (J). (gr. 5-8). 35.00 (978-0-8160-6444-1(X) , Chelsea Hse.) Facts On File, Inc.

Stefoff, Rebecca. A Century of Immigration: 1820-1924. 2006. (American Voices Ser.). (Illus.). xxiii, 115p. (J). lib. bdg. 37.07 (978-0-7614-2172-6(6) , Benchmark Bks.) Cavendish, Marshall Corp.

Stewart, Gail. Illegal Immigration. 2007. (Ripped from the Headlines Ser.). 64p. (J). (gr. 5). 23.95 (***978-1-60217-003-2(7))*** Erickson Pr.

Teichmann, Iris. Immigration & the Law. 2006. (Understanding Immigration Ser.). (Illus.). 44p. (J). (gr. 5-8). lib. bdg. 31.35 (978-1-58340-970-1(X)) Smart Apple Media.

Thornton, Jeremy. Hard Times in Ireland: The Scotch-Irish Come to America (1603-1775) 2004. (Primary Sources of Immigration & Migration in America Ser.). (Illus.). 24p. (J). lib. bdg. 19.95 (978-0-8239-6830-5(8) , PowerKids Pr.) Rosen Publishing Group, Inc., The.

—New Industries, New Jobs: British Immigrants Come to America (1830s-1890s) 2004. (Primary Sources of Immigration & Migration in America Ser.). (Illus.). 24p. (J). lib. bdg. 19.95 (978-0-8239-6832-9(4) , PowerKids Pr.) Rosen Publishing Group, Inc., The.

Townsend, Dana E. Ellis Island. (Illus.). 32p. (J). (***978-0-7367-2944-4(5))*** Zaner-Bloser, Inc.

U. S. Immigration & Migration Reference Library: Includes Cumulative Index, 5 vols. Incl. U. S. Immigration & Migration : Almanac. Benson, Sonia. 400p. 120.00 (978-0-7876-7732-9(9)); U. S. Immigration & Migration : Biographies. Outman, James L. 400p. 120.00 (978-0-7876-7733-6(7)); U. S. Immigration & Migration : Primary Sources. Outman, James L. & Baker, Lawrence W. 200p. 67.00 (978-0-7876-7669-8(1)); (Illus.). (J). 1,327p. 2004. 290.00 (978-0-7876-7565-3(2) , UXL) Thomson Gale.

Uschan, Michael V. German Americans. 2006. (World Almanac Library of American Immigration). (Illus.). 48p. (J). pap. (978-0-8368-7323-8(8)); lib. bdg. (978-0-8368-7310-8(6)) Stevens, Gareth Inc. (World Almanac Library).

—Irish Americans. 2006. (World Almanac Library of American Immigration). (Illus.). 48p. (J). pap. (978-0-8368-7324-5(6)); lib. bdg. (978-0-8368-7311-5(4)) Stevens, Gareth Inc. (World Almanac Library).

Wallner, Rosemary. Greek Immigrants, 1890-1920. 2002. (Blue Earth Books). (Illus.). 32p. (J). (gr. 4). lib. bdg. 22.60 (978-0-7368-1206-1(7) , Bridgestone Bks.) Capstone Pr., Inc.

Weber, Valerie. I Come from Chile. 2006. (Illus.). 24p. (J). pap. (978-0-8368-7241-5(X)); lib. bdg. (978-0-8368-7234-7(7)) Stevens, Gareth Inc. (Weekly Reader Early Learning Library).

—I Come from Ivory Coast. 2006. (Illus.). 24p. (J). pap. (978-0-8368-7243-9(6)); lib. bdg. (978-0-8368-7236-1(3)) Stevens, Gareth Inc. (Weekly Reader Early Learning Library).

—I Come from South Korea. 2006. (Illus.). 24p. (J). pap. (978-0-8368-7244-6(4)); lib. bdg. (978-0-8368-7237-8(1)) Stevens, Gareth Inc. (Weekly Reader Early Learning Library).

—I Come from Ukraine. 2006. (Illus.). 24p. (J). pap. (978-0-8368-7245-3(2)); lib. bdg. (978-0-8368-7238-5(X)) Stevens, Gareth Inc. (Weekly Reader Early Learning Library).

Weber, Valerie J. I Come from Afghanistan. 2006. (This Is My Story Ser.). (Illus.). 24p. (J). (gr. k-2). pap. 5.95 (978-0-8368-7240-8(1)); lib. bdg. 19.93 (978-0-8368-7233-0(9)) Stevens, Gareth Inc. (Weekly Reader Early Learning Library).

—I Come from India. 2006. (This Is My Story Ser.). (Illus.). 24p. (J). (gr. k-2). pap. 5.95 (978-0-8368-7242-2(8)); lib. bdg. 19.93 (978-0-8368-7235-4(5)) Stevens, Gareth Inc. (Weekly Reader Early Learning Library).

Where Did Your Family Come From? (Discovery Readers Ser.). 48p. (J). pap. 3.95 (978-0-8249-5320-1(7) , Ideals Children's Bks.) Ideals Pubns.

Wong, Li Keng. Good Fortune: My Journey to Gold Mountain. 2006. (Illus.). 144p. (J). (gr. 3-7). 14.95 (978-1-56145-367-2(6)) Peachtree Pubs., Ltd.

Wood, Ethel, compiled by. The Immigrants. 2004. (Historical Reader Ser.). (Illus.). 240p. (gr. 6-12). 13.32 (978-0-618-04818-2(9) , 2-00150) McDougal Littell Inc.

Yancey, Diane. The German Americans. 2005. (Immigrants in America Ser.). (Illus.). 112p. (J). (gr. 4-7). lib. bdg. 29.95 (978-1-56006-962-1(7) , Lucent Bks.) Thomson Gale.

UNITED STATES—EMPLOYEES

see United States—Officials and Employees

UNITED STATES—EXECUTIVE POWER

see Executive Power

UNITED STATES—EXPLORING EXPEDITIONS

Here are entered works on exploration within the United States and for explorations in other countries which are sponsored by the United States. Works on early exploration in territory which became a part of the United States are entered under America—Discovery and Exploration.

see also names of expeditions, e.g. Lewis and Clark expedition

Benge, Janet & Benge, Geoff. Daniel Boone: Frontiersman. 2004. pap. 8.99 (978-1-932096-09-5(4)) Emerald Bks.

Blue. Exploring the Americas, 4 vols. Set 2. 2003. pap. 34.20 (978-1-4109-0431-7(8)); Set 3. 2004. (Illus.). 57.12 (978-1-4109-1033-2(4)); Set 3. 2004. (Illus.). pap. 17.10 (978-1-4109-1035-6(0)); Sets 1-3. 2004. (Illus.). 327.86 (978-1-4109-1034-9(2)); Sets 1-3. 2004. (Illus.). pap. 85.50 (978-1-4109-1036-3(9)) Raintree.

Blue, Rose. Exploring the Southeastern United States. 2003. (Exploring America Ser.). (Illus.). pap. 8.95 (978-1-4109-0045-6(2)) Raintree.

Levy, Janey. Mapping America's Westward Expansion: Applying Geographic Tools & Interpreting Maps. 2005. (Critical Thinking in American History Ser.). (Illus.). 48p. (J). (gr. 5-8). lib. bdg. 25.25 (978-1-4042-0416-4(4)) Rosen Publishing Group, Inc., The.

Lyne, William R. The Tanoan-Egyptian Djed Festival Stone: Thothmes III's Expedition to America, c. 1475 B.C. Michener-Rodin, Karl, photos by. 1999. (Illus.). 112p. (YA). pap. 10.00 (978-0-9637467-3-3(1)) Creatopia Productions - Lamy, New Mexico.

Philbrick, Nathaniel. Sea of Glory: America's Voyage of Discovery, the U. S. Exploring Expedition, 1838-1842. 2004. (Illus.). 452p. per. 22.65 (978-0-606-33469-3(6)) Tandem Library Bks.

Redmond, Shirley-Raye. Lewis & Clark: A Prairie Dog for the President. Manders, John, illus. 2003. (Step into Reading Ser.: No. 3). 48p. (J). (gr. k-2). pap. 3.99 (978-0-375-81120-3(6) , Random Hse. Bks. for Young Readers) Random Hse. Children's Bks.

UNITED STATES—FEDERAL BUREAU OF INVESTIGATION

Baker, David. CIA & FBI. 2006. (Fighting Terrorism Ser.). (Illus.). 48p. (gr. 4-8). 20.95 (978-1-59515-482-8(5)) Rourke Publishing, LLC.

Binns, Tristan Boyer. The FBI: Federal Bureau of Investigation. 2002. (US Government Agencies Ser.). (Illus.). 48p. (J). (gr. 3-5). lib. bdg. 27.07 (978-1-58810-499-1(0)) Heinemann Library.

Cunningham, Kevin. J. Edgar Hoover: Controversial FBI Director. 2005. (Signature Lives Ser.). (Illus.). 112p. (J). (gr. 5-7). (978-0-7565-0997-2(1)) Compass Point Bks.

De Capua, Sarah. The FBI. (Cornerstones of Freedomtrade;, Second Ser.). 48p. (J). (gr. 4-6). 2007. 5.95 (***978-0-531-18688-6(1));*** 2002. (Illus.). 26.00 (978-0-516-22691-0(6)) Scholastic Library Publishing. (Children's Pr.).

Fridell, Ron. Spying, Modern World of Espionage. 2002. (Single Titles Ser.). (Illus.). 144p. (gr. 7 up). lib. bdg. 24.90 (978-0-7613-1662-6(0) , Millbrook Pr.) Lerner Publishing Group.

Gaines, Ann. Special Agent & Careers in the FBI. 2006. (Homeland Security & Counterterrorism Careers Ser.). (Illus.). 128p. (J). lib. bdg. 31.93 (978-0-7660-2648-3(5)) Enslow Pubs., Inc.

Hamilton, John. The FBI. 2007. (Defending the Nation Ser.). (Illus.). 32p. (J). (gr. 3-5). lib. bdg. 22.78 (978-1-59679-757-4(6) , Checkerboard Library) ABDO Publishing Co.

Harmon, Daniel E. & Sarat, Austin. The FBI. 2001. (Crime, Justice & Punishment Ser.). (Illus.). 80p. (J). 30.00 (978-0-7910-4289-2(8) , Chelsea Hse.) Facts On File, Inc.

January, Brendan. The FBI. 2002. (gr. 3-6). lib. bdg. 17.60 (978-0-613-59477-6(0)) Tandem Library Bks.

Karlitz, Gail. Virtual Apprentice: FBI Agent. 2008. (Virtual Apprentice Ser.). 64p. (J). (gr. 6-12). 29.95 (***978-0-8160-6758-9(9)*** , Ferguson Publishing Co.) Facts On File, Inc.

Lewis, Brenda Ralph. Hostage Rescue with the FBI. 2002. (Rescue & Prevention Ser.). (Illus.). 96p. (J). (gr. 7 up). lib. bdg. (978-1-59084-403-8(3)) Mason Crest Pubs.

Miller, Connie Colwell. The FBI: Hunting Criminals. 2008. (J). (***978-1-4296-1273-9(8))*** Capstone Pr., Inc.

Poolos, Jamie. Hostage Rescuers. 2006. (Extreme Careers Ser.). (Illus.). 64p. (YA). (gr. 5-8). lib. bdg. 26.50 (978-1-4042-0941-1(7)) Rosen Publishing Group, Inc., The.

Ramaprian, Sheela. The FBI. 2003. (High-Top Secret Ser.). (Illus.). 48p. (J). 23.00 (978-0-516-24312-2(8)); (YA). (gr. 7-12). pap. 6.95 (978-0-516-24375-7(6)) Scholastic Library Publishing. (Children's Pr.).

Scott Ingram. The FBI Director. 2004. (America's Leaders Ser.). (Illus.). 32p. (J). 23.70 (978-1-4103-0090-4(0) , Blackbirch Pr., Inc.) Thomson Gale.

Streissguth, Thomas. America's Security Agencies: The Department of Homeland Security, FBI, NSA, & CIA. 2008. (Federal Government Ser.). 128p. (J). (gr. 6 up). lib. bdg. 33.27 (***978-1-59845-058-3(1)*** , MyReportLinks.com Bks.) Enslow Pubs., Inc.

Streissguth, Thomas. J. Edgar Hoover: Powerful FBI Director. 2002. (Historical American Biographies Ser.). (Illus.). 128p. (YA). (gr. 6-12). lib. bdg. 26.60 (978-0-7660-1623-1(4)) Enslow Pubs., Inc.

Wagner, Heather Lehr. The Federal Bureau of Investigation. 2007. (U. S. Government Ser.). 104p. (YA). (gr. 5-8). 30.00 (***978-0-7910-9281-1(X)*** , Chelsea Hse.) Facts On File, Inc.

UNITED STATES—FICTION

American Girl Magazine: Jan/Feb 2004. (J). 19.75 (978-1-58485-925-3(3)) American Girl Publishing, Inc.

American Girl Magazine: July/Aug 2004 Jumbo Issue. (J). 24.75 (978-1-58485-928-4(8)) American Girl Publishing, Inc.

American Girl Magazine: March/April 2004. (J). 19.75 (978-1-58485-926-0(1)) American Girl Publishing, Inc.

American Girl Magazine: May/June 2004. (J). 19.75 (978-1-58485-927-7(X)) American Girl Publishing, Inc.

American Girl Magazine: Sept/Oct 2004. (J). 19.75 (978-1-58485-929-1(6)) American Girl Publishing, Inc.

Ardagh, Philip. Terrible Times. Roberts, David, illus. 2004. (Eddie Dickens Trilogy: Bk. 3). 160p. (J). (gr. 4-7). mass mkt. 5.99 (978-0-439-53761-2(4) , Scholastic Paperbacks) Scholastic, Inc.

Barnes, Peter W. Little Miss Patriot: NFRW Edition. Barnes, Cheryl Shaw, illus. ed. 2007. 32p. (J). 17.95 (***978-1-893622-20-3(7)*** , VSP Bks.) Vacation Spot Publishing.

Bates, Katherine. America the Beautiful. 2005. (Illus.). 32p. pap. 7.95 (978-1-894997-10-2(7)) Fox Music Bks. CAN. *Dist:* SCB Distributors.

Bauer, Joan. Peeled. 2008. 256p. (YA). (gr. 7). 16.99 (***978-0-399-23475-0(6)*** , Putnam Juvenile) Penguin Group (USA) Inc.

Bauld, Jane Scoggins. Hector Saves the Moon, Vol. 2. Laronde, Gary, illus. 7.95 (978-1-57168-312-0(7)) Eakin Pr.

Baum, L. Frank. The Wonderful Wizard of Oz: The Authorized Anniversary Edition. Stout, William & Denslow, W. W., illus. 100th ed. 2001. 304p. pap. 15.00 (978-0-7567-5991-9(9)) DIANE Publishing Co.

Bourgeois, Paulette. Postal Workers. LaFave, Kim, illus. 2005. 32p. (J). lib. bdg. 15.38 (***978-1-4242-1192-0(1))*** Fitzgerald Bks.

Brandreth, Gyles. Bruno Bruin Discovers America. Dennis, Peter, illus. 1999. 48p. (J). 16.99 (978-0-233-99533-5(1)) Andre Deutsch GBR. *Dist:* Independent Pubs. Group.

Buckey, Sarah Masters. The Light in the Cellar: A Molly Mystery. 2007. 176p. (J). 10.95 (***978-1-59369-159-2(9));*** pap. 6.95 (***978-1-59369-158-5(0))*** American Girl Publishing, Inc.

Bunting, Eve. My Red Balloon. Life, Kay, illus. 2005. 32p. (J). 15.95 (978-1-59078-263-7(1)) Boyds Mills Pr.

Burg, Ann E. Rebekkah's Journey: A World War II Refugee Story. Iskowitz, Joel, illus. 2006. 48p. (J). (gr. 3-5). 17.95 (978-1-58536-275-2(1)) Sleeping Bear Pr.

Carney, Mary Lou. Dr Welch & the Great Grape Story. Meidell, Sherry, illus. 2004. 32p. (J). 16.95 (978-1-59078-039-8(6)) Boyds Mills Pr.

Chin-Lee, Cynthia, et al. A Is for the Americas. 1999. (Illus.). 32p. (J). (gr. k-4). 16.99 (978-0-531-33194-1(6) , Orchard Bks.) Scholastic, Inc.

Clack, Cynthia. Doodles the American Hero. 2007. (J). lib. bdg. 21.95 (***978-0-9787533-0-6(5))*** Tiger Tale Publishing Co.

Collier, Kevin Scott. Journeys of Hope, Pearl of Wisdom. Collier, Kevin Scott, illus. 2006. (Illus.). 28p. (J). E-Book 9.95 incl. cd-rom (978-1-933090-31-3(6)) Guardian Angel Publishing, Inc.

Cox, Stephen Angus. The Dare Boys of 1776. 2004. reprint ed. pap. 15.95 (978-1-4191-5856-8(2)); pap. 1.99 (978-1-4192-5856-5(7)) Kessinger Publishing, LLC.

Crabtree, Zona Mae. The Travelers. 2004. (Corn Cave Ser.: 2). (Illus.). 155p. (YA). per. 8.00 (978-0-9726826-1-9(9)) Owl Hollow Publishing.

Crew, Gary & Whatley, Bruce. Quetta. 2002. (Illus.). 32p. (YA). (978-0-7344-0240-0(6) , Lothian Bks.) Hachette Livre Australia.

Crocker, Nancy. Billie Standish Was Here. 2007. 288p. (YA). (gr. 9 up). 16.99 (978-1-4169-2423-4(X)) Simon & Schuster Children's Publishing.

Danziger, Paula. United Tates of America. 2002. (J). (gr. 4-7). lib. bdg. 20.00 incl. audio (978-0-9717540-5-8(5) , 02002) Full Cast Audio.

Danziger, Paula, et al. United Tates of America. 2003. (Illus.). 144p. (J). mass mkt. 5.99 (978-0-590-69222-9(4) , Scholastic Paperbacks) Scholastic, Inc.

Davies, Jacqueline. Where the Ground Meets the Sky. 2005. 224p. (YA). pap. 5.95 (978-0-7614-5187-7(0)) Cavendish, Marshall Corp.

Davis, Joyce. Can't Stop the Shine. 2007. 256p. pap. 9.99 (***978-0-373-83078-7(5))*** Harlequin Enterprises, Ltd. CAN. *Dist:* Simon & Schuster, Inc.

Deutsch, Stacia & Cohon, Rhody. Bell's Breakthrough. Wenzel, David, illus. 2005. 105p. (J). (***978-1-4156-2913-0(7)*** , Aladdin) Simon & Schuster Children's Publishing.

Deutsch, Stacia & Cohon, Rhody. Ben Franklin's Fame. Francis, Guy, illus. 2006. (Blast to the Past Ser.). 128p. (J). pap. 3.99 (978-1-4169-1804-2(3) , Aladdin) Simon & Schuster Children's Publishing.

Diggs, Dylan. The Palladium. ed. 2006. 112p. (YA). mass mkt. 3.80 (978-1-886366-12-1(8) , 10,000) Sights Productions.

Down, Heather. A Deadly Distance. 2005. (Illus.). 128p. (YA). pap. (978-0-88878-455-1(4) , Sandcastle Bks.) Dundurn Group, The.

England, Tamara, ed. Samantha - An American Girl Holiday: The Complete Script Book. 2004. (American Girls Collection). (Illus.). 140p. (J). pap. 9.95 (978-1-58485-968-0(7)) American Girl Publishing, Inc.

Epstein, Estelle Pottern. I Heard My Father's Voice. 2007. 124p. pap. 11.95 (***978-0-7414-4053-2(9))*** Infinity Publishing.

Farnsworth, Frances. Cubby in Wonderland. 2005. pap. 20.95 (978-1-4179-8778-8(2)) Kessinger Publishing, LLC.

Fidler, Mark. Blaze of the Great Cliff. 2003. 196p. 24.95 (978-0-595-65847-3(4)) iUniverse, Inc.

Fleury, Mike Stevenson. Natural Disaster 2222. 2003. (ENG.). 112p. 19.95 (***978-0-595-65436-9(3));*** 108p. (YA). pap. 9.95 (978-0-595-25921-2(9)) iUniverse, Inc. (Writers Club Pr.).

Flower, Jessie Graham. Grace Harlowe's Overland Riders on the Great American Desert. 2006. 132p. pap. 10.99 (978-1-4264-1676-7(8)) BiblioBazaar.

—Grace Harlowe's Overland Riders on the Great American Desert. 2004. reprint ed. pap. 20.95 (978-1-4191-2221-7(5)); pap. 1.99 (978-1-4192-2221-4(X)) Kessinger Publishing, LLC.

Frank, E. R. America. l.t. ed. 2004. 350p. 21.95 (978-0-7862-6484-1(5)) Thorndike Pr.

Frankel, Valerie. American Fringe. 2008. 272p. (gr. 12 up). 9.99 (***978-0-451-22292-3(X)*** , N A L Trade) Penguin Group (USA) Inc.

Gardner, Sheldon. Converso Legacy. 2005. 264p. (J). pap. 12.95 (978-1-932687-19-4(X) , Devora Publishing) Pitspopany Pr.

Gildea, Kathy. The Adventures of Baylee Beagle—Greenville. 2005. (Illus.). 20p. (J). 7.95 (978-0-9767096-0-2(0)) Maxim Pr.

Glaser, Higashi, illus. Hello Kitty, Hello USA! A Celebration of All Fifty States. 2006. 55p. (J). (gr. k-4). reprint ed. 13.00 (978-1-4223-5624-1(8)) DIANE Publishing Co.

Greenwell, Ivo. The Ancestor. 2003. 264p. (YA). pap. 16.95 (978-0-595-29494-7(4)) iUniverse, Inc.

Grote, JoAnn A. Emily Makes a Difference: A Time of Progress & Problems. 2004. (Sisters in Time Ser.). 144p. (J). pap. 4.97 (978-1-59310-206-7(2)) Barbour Publishing, Inc.

Hamilton, Virginia. The People Could Fly Picture. Dillon, Leo & Dillon, Diane, illus. 2007. 32p. (J). 17.99 incl. audio compact disk (***978-0-375-84553-6(4)*** , Knopf Bks. for Young Readers) Random Hse. Children's Bks.

Hancock, Irving H. Dave Darrin at Vera Cruz. 2006. 78.99 (***978-1-4219-9910-4(2));*** pap. 72.99 (***978-1-4219-9913-5(7))*** IndyPublish.com.

—Uncle Sam's Boys with Pershing's Troops. 2006. pap. 71.99 (***978-1-4219-9902-9(1))*** IndyPublish.com.

—Uncle Sams Boys with Pershings Troops or. 2006. 78.99 (***978-1-4219-9892-3(0))*** IndyPublish.com.

Harcourt School Publishers Staff. City Celebrations On Level. 3rd ed. 2002. (Trophies Reading Program Ser.). (Illus.). pap. 5.10 (978-0-15-323186-5(6)) Harcourt Schl. Pubs.

—The Stowaway: Take-Home Book. 2001. (Collections Ser.). (Illus.). (J). pap. 1.90 (978-0-15-319538-9(X)) Harcourt Schl. Pubs.

—The Stowaway Below Level. 3rd ed. 2002. (Trophies Reading Program Ser.). (Illus.). pap. 5.10 (978-0-15-323336-4(2)) Harcourt Schl. Pubs.

—This Land. 3rd ed. 2002. (Trophies English Language Learners Ser.). (Illus.). pap. 5.10 (978-0-15-327717-7(3)) Harcourt Schl. Pubs.

—Under One Roof. 3rd ed. 2002. (Trophies English Language Learners Ser.). (Illus.). pap. 5.10 (978-0-15-327760-3(2)) Harcourt Schl. Pubs.

Harris, Joel Chandle. Told by Uncle Remus: New Stories of the. 2006. (Illus.). pap. 31.95 (***978-1-4254-9964-8(3))*** Kessinger Publishing, LLC.

Hartman, Bob. The Littlest Camel. 2004. (Illus.). 64p. (J). pap. 6.99 (978-0-7459-4825-6(1) , Lion) Lion Hudson plc GBR. *Dist:* Independent Pubs. Group.

Hergé. Tintin en Amerique. 1999. (Tintin Ser.). Orig. Title: Tintin in America. (FRE., Illus.). 62p. (J). (gr. 4-7). pap. 21.95 (978-2-203-00102-2(X)) Casterman, Editions FRA. *Dist:* Distribooks, Inc.

—Tintin en Amerique. Orig. Title: Tintin in America. (Illus.). 62p. (J). (FRE.). 24.95 (978-0-8288-5093-3(3)); (SPA., 24.95 (978-0-8288-5094-0(1)) French & European Pubns., Inc.

—Tintin en Amerique. (Tintin Ser.). Orig. Title: Tintin in America. (SPA.). 64p. (J). 14.95 (978-84-261-1400-6(8)) Juventud, Editorial ESP. *Dist:* Distribooks, Inc.

—Tintin in America. Orig. Title: Tintin en Amerique. (Illus.). 62p. (J). 24.95 (978-0-8288-5000-1(3)) French & European Pubns., Inc.

Higashi/Glaser Design Inc. Staff. Hello Kitty, Hello USA! 2005. (Illus.). 56p. (J). (ps-3). 12.95 (978-0-8109-5772-5(8) , Abrams Bks. for Young Readers) Abrams, Harry N. , Inc.

Hobbs, Will. Beardance. 2004. (Illus.). 208p. (J). pap. 5.99 (978-0-689-87072-9(8) , Aladdin) Simon & Schuster Children's Publishing.

Holt, Kimberly Willis. Piper Reed, Navy Brat. Davenier, Christine, illus. 2008. 176p. (J). pap. 6.99 (***978-0-312-38020-5(8))*** Square Fish.

Howe, Kim, illus. American Life Series: Family, Teacher, Friend, 3 books. 2006. 80p. 19.95 (978-1-59971-554-4(6)) Aardvark Global Publishing.

Icenoggle, Jodi. America's Betrayal. 2001. (gr. 7-12). lib. bdg. 16.40 (978-0-613-83690-6(1)) Tandem Library Bks.

—America's Betrayal. 2001. 208p. (J). (gr. 7 up). 7.95 (978-1-57249-252-3(X) , White Mane Kids) White Mane Publishing Co., Inc.

Jesus, Eloisa D. de. Lakas & the Hotel Makibaka. Angel, Carl, illus. 2006. 32p. (J). 16.95 (978-0-89239-213-1(4)) Children's Bk. Pr.

Johnson, Angela. Those Building Men. Moser, Barry, illus. 2001. 32p. (J). (ps-3). pap. 16.95 (978-0-590-66521-6(9) , Blue Sky Pr., The) Scholastic, Inc.

Johnston, Annie Fellows. The Little Colonel. 2004. reprint ed. pap. 1.99 (978-1-4192-7020-8(6)) Kessinger Publishing, LLC.

Katzakian, Norma. Naomi - A First Generation American. Chidester, Ardis & Folchi, Robert A., eds. Heggie, Dolores, illus. l.t. ed. 2000. (J). (gr. 4-7). pap. 12.95 (978-0-9662228-1-4(4)) Dab Publishing Co.

Keep, Linda Lowery. Peace, Love, & Rock 'n' Roll. Field, Ann, illus. 2005. 144p. (J). 9.95 (978-0-307-10519-6(9) , Golden Bks.) Random Hse. Children's Bks.

Keller, Laurie. Scrambled States of America. 2002. (gr. k-3). lib. bdg. 15.25 (978-0-613-75400-2(X)) Tandem Library Bks.

—The Scrambled States of America. rev. ed. 2002. (Illus.). 40p. (J). (ps-4). pap. 7.95 (978-0-8050-6831-3(7) , Holt, Henry & Co. Bks. For Young Readers) Holt, Henry & Co.

Kelly, John & Simkins, Kate. Wagon Train Adventure. Inklink, illus. 2008. 48p. (J). (gr. 3-4). 14.99 (***978-0-7566-3852-8(6));*** pap. 3.99 (***978-0-7566-3851-1(8))*** Dorling Kindersley Publishing, Inc.

Krensky Stephen. John Henry. Oldroyd, Mark, illus. 2007. (On My Own Folklore Ser.). (J). pap. 6.95 (***978-0-8225-6477-5(7)*** , First Avenue Editions) Lerner Publishing Group.

Krensky, Stephen. Pecos Bill. Tong, Paul, illus. 2007. (On My Own Folklore Ser.). 48p. (J). (gr. 2-5). lib. bdg. 25.26 (978-1-57505-889-4(8) , Millbrook Pr.) Lerner Publishing Group, Inc.

Krulik, Nancy E. Dawn's Early Light. 2006. 208p. (YA). pap. 5.99 (978-1-4169-1465-5(X) , Simon Pulse) Simon & Schuster Children's Publishing.

Lachtman, Ofelia Dumas. The Truth about las Mariposas. 2007. 144p. (YA). (gr. 6 up). pap. 9.95 (*978-1-55885-494-9(0) , Piñata Books) Arte Publico Pr.

Lafaye, Alexandria. Edith Shay. 2001. (J). 11.64 (978-0-606-21170-3(5)) Tandem Library Bks.

Lester, Julius. Day of Tears. 2007. 192p. (gr. 7 up). pap. 7.99 (*978-1-4231-0409-4(9) , Jump at the Sun) Hyperion Bks. for Children.

Levitin, Sonia. Junkmans Girl. Porfirio, Guy, illus. rev. ed. 2007. (Tales of Young Americans Ser.). 40p. 17.95 (*978-1-58536-315-5(4)) Sleeping Bear Pr.

Lilly, Melinda. Mira y la Piedra. Fernandez, Queta, tr. Reasoner, Charles, illus. (Cuentos y Mitos de America Latina (Latin American Tales & Myths) Ser.).Tr. of Mira & the Stone Tortoise. (SPA.). 32p. 2002. mass mkt. 6.95 (978-1-58952-078-3(5) , RK31440); 2001. (J). (gr. 2-5). lib. bdg. 26.60 (978-1-58952-191-9(9) , RK7238) Rourke Publishing, LLC.

—La Serpiente y el Dolor de Muelas. Fernandez, Queta, tr. Reasoner, Charles, illus. (Cuentos y Mitos de America Latina (Latin American Tales & Myths) Ser.).Tr. of Snake's Toothache. (SPA.). 32p. 2002. mass mkt. 6.95 (978-1-58952-081-3(5) , RK31443); 2001. (J). lib. bdg. 26.60 (978-1-58952-194-0(3) , RK2055) Rourke Publishing, LLC.

—La Serpiente y el Dolor de Muelas. 2002. Tr. of Snake's Toothache. (SPA.). (gr. 3-6). lib. bdg. 15.25 (978-0-613-87421-2(8)) Tandem Library Bks.

Loomis, Christine. Across America, I Love You. Kiesler, Kate A., illus. 2000. 32p. (ps-3). 16.49 (978-0-7868-2314-7(3)) Hyperion Bks. for Children.

Lyford, Cabot. Arthur the Moose. Lyford, Cabot, illus. l.t. ed. 2004. (Illus.). 32p. (J). lib. bdg. (978-0-9748145-0-6(4)) Castlebay, Inc.

Lytle, Robert A. A Pitch in Time. Williams, Bill, illus. 2002. 368p. (YA). pap. 12.95 (978-0-9712692-5-5(4)) EDCO Publishing, Inc.

Merry Christmas USA. 2007. (J). bds. 21.95 (*978-0-9745191-3-5(8)) Lynn Tyner Mitchum & James Rogers.

Moonshower, Candie. The Legend of Zoey. 2006. 224p. (J). (gr. 4-7). 15.95 (978-0-385-73280-2(5)); lib. bdg. 17.99 (978-0-385-90298-4(9)) Random Hse. Children's Bks. (Delacorte Bks. for Young Readers).

Moss, Marissa. Rose's Journal: The Story of A Girl in the Great Depression. 2003. (gr. 3-6). lib. bdg. 15.30 (978-0-613-59923-8(3)) Tandem Library Bks.

Now We Live in the USA! Small Versions of Big Books. (On Our Way to English Ser.). (gr. 3 up). 35.50 (978-0-7578-7244-0(1)) Rigby Education.

Now We Live in the USA! Third Grade Big Books. (On Our Way to English Ser.). (gr. 3 up). 29.95 (978-0-7578-4207-8(0)) Rigby Education.

Obiadi, Boniface. The Good & the Bad Only in America: The Route from Nigeria to America. Strader, Jennifer, ed. Manser, Mark & Okoli, Gloria, illus. 1999. 154p. (YA). pap. 12.95 (978-0-9677864-0-7(1)) Bons Diversified Investment Co.

Orback, Craig, illus. Paul Bunyan. 2007. (On My Own Folklore Ser.). 48p. (J). (gr. 2-5). lib. bdg. 25.26 (978-1-57505-888-7(X) , Millbrook Pr.) Lerner Publishing Group.

Osa, Nancy. Cuba 15. 2005. 304p. (YA). (gr. 7). reprint ed. pap. 7.95 (978-0-385-73233-8(3) , Delacorte Bks. for Young Readers) Random Hse. Children's Bks.

Osborne, Mary Pope. Happy Birthday, America. Catalanotto, Peter, illus. rev. ed. 2005. 32p. (J). pap. 6.95 (978-1-59643-051-8(6)) Roaring Brook Pr.

Parkinson, Curtis. Death in Kingsport. 2007. 224p. (J). (gr. 5-9). pap. 11.95 (*978-0-88776-827-9(X)) Tundra Bks., Inc./Livres Toundra, Inc. CAN. *Dist:* Random Hse., Inc.

Percy, Graham, illus. La Bella Durmiente del Bosque. l.t. ed. 2001. (SPA.). 28p. (ps-3). incl. audio compact disk (978-84-8214-049-0(3) , 1620) Peralt Montagut.

Perkins, Mitali. The Not-So-Star-Spangled Life of Sunita Sen. 2nd ed. 2005. 192p. (J). (gr. 3-7). reprint ed. pap. 6.99 (978-0-316-73453-0(5)) Little Brown & Co.

Pintozzi, Nick. Bentley & the Cactus Rustlers. Pintozzi, Nick & Pintozzi, Connie, illus. 2006. per. 11.00 (*978-0-9749465-4-2(0)) BentDaiSha, LLC.

Ransom, Candice. Signals in the Sky. 2007. 128p. (J). 4.99 (978-0-7869-4353-1(X) , Mirrorstone) Wizards of the Coast.

Ray, Chapin Anna. Half a Dozen Girls. 2006. 64.99 (*978-1-4219-9731-5(2)); pap. 57.99 (*978-1-4219-9732-2(0)) IndyPublish.com.

Reed, Patrick. Theodore Elijah Bear Explores the United States. 1998. (Illus.). 40p. (J). pap. 12.00 (978-1-891989-02-5(2)) Fundbuilder$, U.S.A.

Reed, W. F. Andy & Mark & the Time Machine: Pickett's Charge at Gettysburg. 2000. 144p. (YA). pap. 10.95 (978-0-595-12885-3(8)) iUniverse, Inc.

Reisfeld, Randi. Starlet. 2007. 304p. (gr. 7 up). pap. 8.99 (*978-1-4231-0501-5(X)) Hyperion Pr.

Rexroth, Sharon. America from the Sky. 2006. (J). 9.95 (*978-1-57166-429-7(7)); per. 22.95 (*978-1-57166-430-3(0)) Quixote Pr.

Ricci, Christine. Hugs & Kisses. Aikins, Dave, illus. 2005. (Dora the Explorer Ser.). 10p. (J). (ps-k). bds. 9.99 (978-1-4169-0615-5(0) , Simon Spotlight/Nickelodeon) Simon & Schuster Children's Publishing.

Rinaldi, Ann. The Coffin Quilt: The Feud Between the Hatfields & the McCoys. 2nd ed. 2002. (J). 4.80 (978-0-03-073522-6(X)) Holt, Rinehart & Winston.

—The Coffin Quilt: The Feud Between the Hatfields & the McCoys. 2001. (J). 12.65 (978-0-606-20507-8(1)) Tandem Library Bks.

—The Last Silk Dress. 1999. (gr. 7-12). lib. bdg. 14.15 (978-0-613-72274-2(4)) Tandem Library Bks.

Rinaldi, Ann & Farnsworth, Bill. Sarah's Ground. 2005. (Illus.). 192p. (YA). mass mkt. 5.99 (978-0-689-85925-0(2) , Simon Pulse) Simon & Schuster Children's Publishing.

Robles, Tony. Joey Gonzales, Real American. 2007. (J). 12.95 (*978-0-9767269-3-7(9)) World Ahead Media.

Rolt-Wheeler, Francis. The Boy with the U. S. Census. 2007. 220p. pap. 12.99 (*978-1-4264-6792-9(3)); 242p. pap. 15.99 (*978-1-4264-6855-1(5)) BiblioBazaar.

Romain, Trevor. Jemma's Journey. Lopez, Pat, illus. 2003. 32p. (YA). (gr. k-2). 15.95 (978-1-56397-937-8(3)) Boyds Mills Pr.

Roy, Ron. A Thief at the National Zoo. 2007. 96p. (J). lib. bdg. (*978-0-375-94804-6(X)); pap. 3.99 (*978-0-375-84804-9(5)) Random Hse., Inc.

Rylant, Cynthia. Tulip Sees America. Desimini, Lisa, illus. 32p. (J). (ps up). 2002. pap. 6.99 (978-0-439-39978-4(5)); 1998. pap. 15.95 (978-0-590-84744-5(9) , Blue Sky Pr., The) Scholastic, Inc.

—Tulip Sees America. 2002. (gr. k-3). lib. bdg. 14.15 (978-0-613-53874-9(9)) Tandem Library Bks.

Sargent, Dave, et al. Counting Coup Vol. 4: (Cheyenne) Be Proud, 20. l.t. ed. 2003. (Story Keeper Ser.). (Illus.). 42p. (J). pap. 6.95 (978-1-56763-910-0(0)) Ozark Publishing.

Sfar, Joann. Klezmer, Collector's Edition: Tales of the Wild East. 2006. (Illus.). 144p. (YA). 25.00 (978-1-59643-210-9(1) , First Second Bks.) Roaring Brook Pr.

Sherrill, Ronda Scott. The Year of the New Barn. 2002. 132p. (J). pap. 19.95 (978-1-59129-140-4(2)) PublishAmerica, Inc.

Stilton, Geronimo. The Wild, Wild West. Keys, Larry & Rattonchi, Ratterto, illus. 2005. (Geronimo Stilton Ser.: No. 21). 100p. (J). (ps-k). lib. bdg. 13.94 (978-0-606-33824-0(1)) Tandem Library Bks.

Stowe, Harriet Beecher. Uncle Toms Cabin Young Folks Edition Ill. 2006. pap. (*978-1-4065-1077-5(7)) Dodo Pr.

Sula, Sondra. Traveling with the Witty's: An American Vacation. 2000. mass mkt. 4.50 (978-1-931179-20-1(4)); mass mkt. 8.95 incl. audio compact disk (978-1-931179-31-7(X)) Long Hill Productions, Inc.

Tales of O. Henry. 2004. (Classic Retelling Ser.). (gr. 6-12). (978-0-618-08596-5(3) , 2-00189) McDougal Littell Inc.

Taylor, Theodore. The Bomb. 2007. (Illus.). 208p. (YA). pap. 6.95 (*978-0-15-206165-4(7) , Harcourt Paperbacks) Harcourt Children's Bks.

To Keep Me SAFE! A Story for Children Affected by Military Deployments. 2003. (J). 12.00 (978-0-9740289-0-3(8)) State of Growth Publishing Co.

Tocher, Timothy. Chief Sunrise, John McGraw, & Me. 2004. 168p. (J). 16.95 (978-0-8126-2711-4(3)) Cricket Bks.

Tripp, Valerie. Felicity's Story Collection. Andreasen, Dan, illus. 2005. (American Girls Collection). 389p. (J). (gr. 3-17). 29.95 (978-1-59369-047-2(9) , American Girl) American Girl Publishing, Inc.

Tripp, Valerie. Molly's Short Story Collection. Bakces, Nick & Hood, Philip, illus. 2006. 232p. (J). 12.95 (*978-1-59369-123-3(8)) American Girl Publishing, Inc.

Tucker, Zekita. Don't Call Me N!gga. 2007. per. 0.01 net. (*978-1-60402-249-0(3)) Independent Pub.

Van Leeuwen, Jean. Hannah's Winter of Hope. 2001. (gr. 3-6). lib. bdg. 13.00 (978-0-613-33700-7(X)); (Illus.). (J). 11.79 (978-0-606-21780-4(0)) Tandem Library Bks.

Wakely, Carolrae. The History Nut. 2005. (Illus.). 81p. 17.95 (978-0-533-14985-8(1)) Vantage Pr., Inc.

Warner, Charles Dudley. Being A Boy. 2005. 124p. pap. 10.95 (978-1-4218-0414-9(X) , 1st World Library - Literary Society) 1st World Publishing, Inc.

—Being A Boy. 2004. reprint ed. pap. 15.95 (978-1-4191-0953-9(7)); pap. 1.99 (978-1-4192-0953-6(1)) Kessinger Publishing, LLC.

Watts, Guy L. Keepin' On. 2002. 156p. pap. 11.95 (978-0-595-23829-3(7) , Writer's Showcase Pr.) iUniverse, Inc.

Weston, Elise. The Coastwatcher. 2005. 160p. (J). (gr. 3-7). 14.95 (978-1-56145-350-4(1)) Peachtree Pubs., Ltd.

Wilder, Laura Ingalls. La Casa del Bosque. (SPA., Illus.). 160p. (YA). (gr. 5-8). 8.95 (978-84-279-3240-1(5) , NG8293) Noguer y Caralt Editores, S. A. ESP. *Dist:* Lectorum Pubns., Inc.

—La Casa del Bosque. 2001. (SPA.). (gr. 3-6). lib. bdg. 17.60 (978-0-613-80734-0(0)) Tandem Library Bks.

—Little House on the Prairie. 2007. (Little House Ser.). 336p. (J). pap. 6.99 (978-0-06-088539-7(4) , Harper Trophy) HarperCollins Pubs.

Williford, Lex. Scribner Anthology of Contemporary Short Fiction. 1999. (978-0-606-18627-8(1)) Tandem Library Bks.

Wishinsky, Frieda. Just Call Me Joe. 2003. (Orca Young Readers Ser.). (Illus.). 112p. (J). (gr. 3-6). pap. 4.99 (978-1-55143-249-6(8)) Orca Bk. Pubs. USA.

Wood, Jane R. Voices in St. Augustine. 2004. (Illus.). 144p. (J). per. 6.99 (978-0-9707267-6-6(7)) Bluefish Bay Publishing.

Yeh, Phil. Dinosaurs Across America. 2007. (Illus.). 32p. (J). (gr. 1-5). 12.95 (*978-1-56163-509-2(X)) NBM Publishing Co.

Youmans, Marly. Ingledove. 2006. 208p. (YA). (gr. 7). pap. 7.99 (978-0-14-240704-2(6) , Puffin) Penguin Group (USA) Inc.

UNITED STATES—FINANCE

see Finance—United States

UNITED STATES—FOLKLORE

see Folklore—United States

UNITED STATES—FOOD AND DRUG ADMINISTRATION

Esherick, Joan. The FDA & Psychiatric Drugs: How a Drug Is Approved. 2003. (Encyclopedia of Psychiatric Drugs & Their Disorders Ser.). (Illus.). 128p. (J). lib. bdg. (978-1-59084-578-3(1)) Mason Crest Pubs.

Stanley, Debbie. New Medications: The Debate over Approval & Access. 2000. (Focus on Science & Society Ser.). (Illus.). 64p. (YA). (gr. 4-6). lib. bdg. 26.50 (978-0-8239-3212-2(5) , FSNEME) Rosen Publishing Group, Inc., The.

UNITED STATES—FOREIGN POLICY

see United States—Foreign Relations

UNITED STATES—FOREIGN POPULATION

see also Minorities; United States—Emigration and Immigration

also Italians—United States; and similar headings

Horton, Casey. The French: From New France to Louisiana. 2000. (We Came to North America Ser.). (Illus.). 32p. (J). (gr. 4). (978-0-7787-0185-9(9)); pap. (978-0-7787-0199-6(9)) Crabtree Publishing Co.

We Came to North America, 10 bks. Incl. Africans. Green, Jen. 2000. (978-0-7787-0184-2(0)); Chinese. Kite, Lorien. 2000. (978-0-7787-0188-0(3)); French : From New France to Louisiana. Horton, Casey. 2000. (978-0-7787-0185-9(9)); Germans. Nickles, Greg. 2001. (978-0-7787-0191-0(3)); Hispanics. Nickles, Greg. 2000. (978-0-7787-0186-6(7)); Irish. Nickles, Greg. 2001. (978-0-7787-0190-3(5)); Italians. Fahey, Kathleen R. 2000. (978-0-7787-0189-7(1)); Japanese. Nickles, Greg. 2001. (978-0-7787-0193-4(X)); Jews. Horton, Casey. 2000. (978-0-7787-0187-3(5)); Poles. Nickles, Greg. 2001. (978-0-7787-0192-7(1)); 32p. (J). (gr. 4). (Illus.). 2001. o.p. (978-0-7787-0194-1(8)); Set pap. (978-0-7787-0195-8(6)) Crabtree Publishing Co.

UNITED STATES—FOREIGN RELATIONS

see also Monroe Doctrine

Alagna, Magdalena. The Monroe Doctrine: An End to European Colonies in America. 2003. (Life in the New American Nation Ser.). (Illus.). 32p. (YA). pap. 6.50 (978-0-8239-4258-9(9)) Rosen Publishing Group, Inc., The.

America's Battle Against Terrorism. 2005. (Current Controversies Ser.). 208p. (YA). (gr. 10-13). lib. bdg. 36.20 (978-0-7377-2783-8(7) , Greenhaven Pr., Inc.) Thomson Gale.

Baker, David. Department of Defense & State Department. 2006. (Fighting Terrorism Ser.). (Illus.). 48p. (gr. 4-8). 20.95 (978-1-59515-483-5(3)) Rourke Publishing, LLC.

Baker, Lawrence W. Cold War Reference Library Cumulative Index. 2003. (U-X-L Cold War Reference Library). 85p. (J). 5.00 (978-0-7876-7667-4(5) , UXL) Thomson Gale.

—Immigration & Migration Reference. 2003. (U-X-L Cold War Reference Library). (J). 5.00 (978-0-7876-7734-3(5)) Zagat Survey.

Brager, Bruce L. The Iron Curtain: The Cold War in Europe. 2004. (Arbitrary Borders Ser.). (Illus.). 112p. (gr. 9-13). 35.00 (978-0-7910-7832-7(9) , Chelsea Hse.) Facts On File, Inc.

Burgan, Michael. The Monroe Doctrine. 2006. (Illus.). 48p. (J). lib. bdg. (*978-0-7565-2028-1(2)) Compass Point Bks.

Burgan, Michael. The Vietnam War. 2006. (Wars That Changed American History Ser.). (Illus.). 48p. (J). pap. (978-0-8368-7304-7(1)); lib. bdg. (978-0-8368-7295-8(9)) Stevens, Gareth Inc. (World Almanac Library).

Campbell, Geoffrey A. The End of the Cold War: 1980 to the Present: The Cold War in the United States. 2002. (American War Library). 112p. (J). 29.95 (978-1-59018-213-0(8) , Lucent Bks.) Thomson Gale.

Carter, E. J. The Cuban Missile Crisis. 2003. (20th-Century Perspectives Ser.). (Illus.). 48p. (J). pap. (978-1-4034-4180-5(4)); lib. bdg. 27.07 (978-1-4034-3806-5(4)) Heinemann Library.

Chrisp, Peter. Cuban Missile Crisis. 2002. (gr. 7-12). lib. bdg. 24.15 (978-0-613-52355-4(5)) Tandem Library Bks.

Collier, Christopher & Collier, James Lincoln. The United States Enters the World: 1867-1919. 2000. (Drama of American History Ser.). (Illus.). 96p. (J). (gr. 5-9). lib. bdg. 31.36 (978-0-7614-1053-9(8) , Benchmark Bks.) Cavendish, Marshall Corp.

Corona, Laurel. War Within a War: Vietnam & the Cold War. 2004. (Lucent Library of Historical Eras). (Illus.). 112p. (J). 32.45 (978-1-59018-389-2(4) , Lucent Bks.) Thomson Gale.

Creative Media Applications Staff, contrib. by. American Presidents in World History, 5 vols. 2003. (Middle School Reference Ser.). (Illus.). 144p. (J). (gr. 6-8). 209.95 (978-0-313-32564-9(2) , MS2564, Middle School Reference) Greenwood Publishing Group, Inc.

Crewe, Sabrina & Uschan, Michael V. The Bombing of Pearl Harbor. 2003. (Events That Shaped America Ser.). (Illus.). 32p. (J). (gr. 3 up). lib. bdg. 24.67 (978-0-8368-3392-8(9)) Stevens, Gareth Inc.

Dolan, Edward F., Jr. America in the Korean War. 1998. (Illus.). 112p. (gr. 5-8). lib. bdg. 30.90 (978-0-7613-0361-9(8) , Millbrook Pr.) Lerner Publishing Group.

Feldman, Ruth Tenzer. World War I. 2004. (Chronicle of America's Wars Ser.). (Illus.). 96p. (J). (gr. 5-12). 27.93 (978-0-8225-0148-0(1)) Lerner Publishing Group.

Finkelstein, Norman H. Friends Indeed: The Special Relationship of Israel & the United States. 1998. (Single Titles Ser.: up). (Illus.). 176p. (gr. 7 up). lib. bdg. 24.90 (978-0-7613-0114-1(3) , Twenty-First Century Bks.) Lerner Publishing Group.

Gerdes, Louise, ed. Rogue Nations. 2006. (Opposing Viewpoints Ser.). (Illus.). 244p. (YA). (gr. 6 up). pap. 24.95 (978-0-7377-3422-5(1) , Greenhaven Pr., Inc.) Thomson Gale.

Greene, Meg. The Transcontinental Treaty, 1819: A Primary Source Examination of the Treaty Between the United States & Spain Over the American West. 2005. (Primary Sources of American Treaties Ser.). (J). lib. bdg. (978-1-4042-0439-3(3)) Rosen Publishing Group, Inc., The.

Hanes, Sharon M., et al. Cold War: Almanac, 2 vols. 2003. (Cold War Reference Library). (Illus.). (J). 200p. 55.00 (978-0-7876-7662-9(4)); (978-0-7876-9087-8(2)); lib. bdg. 120.00 (978-0-7876-9089-2(9)) Thomson Gale. (UXL).

Harmon, Daniel E. The Secretary of State. 2001. (Your Government Ser.). (Illus.). 64p. (J). (gr. 4-7). 25.00 (978-0-7910-5996-8(0) , Chelsea Hse.) Facts On File, Inc.

Harness, Cheryl. The Remarkable Rough-Riding Life of Theodore Roosevelt & the Rise of Empire America. 2007. (Illus.). 144p. (J). (gr. 3-7). lib. bdg. 25.90 (978-1-4263-0009-7(3) , National Geographic Children's Bks.) National Geographic Society.

Hasday, Judy L. Pearl Harbor. 2000. (Great Disasters, Reforms & Ramifications Ser.). (Illus.). 112p. (J). (gr. 4-7). 30.00 (978-0-7910-5271-6(0) , Chelsea Hse.) Facts On File, Inc.

Kallen, Stuart A. Primary Sources. 2003. (Illus.). 112p. (J). 29.95 (978-1-59018-243-7(X) , Lucent Bks.) Thomson Gale.

Katchur, Matthew & Sterngass, Jon. Spanish Settlement in North America. 2006. (Latino American History Ser.). (Illus.). 112p. (J). (gr. 5-8). 35.00 (978-0-8160-6442-7(3) , Chelsea Hse.) Facts On File, Inc.

Keeley, Jennifer. Containing the Communists: America's Foreign Entanglements. 2003. (American War Library). (Illus.). 112p. (J). 29.95 (978-1-59018-225-3(1) , Lucent Bks.) Thomson Gale.

Laxer, James. Empire. 2007. (Groundwork Guides). (Illus.). 144p. pap. 9.95 (*978-0-88899-707-4(8)) Groundwood Bks. CAN. *Dist:* Perseus Distribution.

Marquette, Scott. America at War. 2003. (America at War Ser.). (gr. 4-8). 167.60 (978-1-58952-385-2(7)) Rourke Publishing, LLC.

—America under Attack. 2003. (America at War Ser.). (Illus.). 48p. (gr. 4-8). 20.95 (978-1-58952-386-9(5)) Rourke Publishing, LLC.

McGowen, Tom. The Attack on Pearl Harbor. (Cornerstones of Freedomtrade;, Second Ser.). 48p. (J). 2007. pap. 5.95 (*978-0-531-18685-5(7)); 2002. (Illus.). (gr. 4-6). 26.00 (978-0-516-22586-9(3)) Scholastic Library Publishing. (Children's Pr.).

Miller, Debra A. U.S. Involvement in the Middle East: Inciting Conflict. 2004. (Lucent Library of Conflict in the Middle East). (Illus.). 112p. (J). (gr. 7-10). 29.95 (978-1-59018-494-3(7) , Lucent Bks.) Thomson Gale.

Nakaya, Andrea C. America's Battle Against Terrorism. 2005. (Current Controversies Ser.). 208p. (gr. 10-12). pap. 24.95 (978-0-7377-2784-5(5) , Greenhaven Pr., Inc.) Thomson Gale.

Paterson, Thomas, et al. Major Problems in American Foreign Relations, Vol. I. 6th ed. 2000. (Major Problems in American History Ser.). (Illus.). 463p. (YA). 55.56 (978-0-618-37038-2(2) , 343006) Houghton Mifflin College Div.

Richard Tames. Pearl Harbor. 2nd ed. 2006. (Point of Impact Ser.). (Illus.). 32p. (J). pap. (*978-1-4034-9151-0(8)) Heinemann Library.

Ruffin, David C. The Duties & Responsibilities of the Secretary of State. 2005. (Your Government in Action Ser.). (Illus.). 32p. (J). 21.95 (978-1-4042-2688-3(5) , PowerKids Pr.) Rosen Publishing Group, Inc., The.

Schlesinger, Arthur M., Jr., ed. The Central Intelligence Agency. 2000. (Your Government Ser.). (Illus.). 64p. (YA). (gr. 3 up). 31.00 (978-0-7910-5531-1(0) , Chelsea Hse.) Facts On File, Inc.

Schwartz, Eric. Crossing the Seas: Americans Form an Empire (1890-1899) 2004. (How America Became America Ser.). (Illus.). 91p. (J). (ps-7). lib. bdg. (978-1-59084-910-1(8)) Mason Crest Pubs.

—Super Power: Americans Today. 2004. (How America Became America Ser.). (Illus.). 89p. (J). (ps-7). lib. bdg. (978-1-59084-912-5(4)) Mason Crest Pubs.

—A World Contender. 2005. (How America Became America Ser.). (Illus.). 96p. (J). lib. bdg. (978-1-59084-911-8(6)) Mason Crest Pubs.

Stanley, George Edward. America in Today's World (1969-2004) 2005. (Illus.). 48p. (J). pap. (978-0-8368-5840-2(9)); lib. bdg. 30.00 (978-0-8368-5831-0(X)) Stevens, Gareth Inc. (World Almanac Library).

—An Emerging World Power (1900-1929) 2005. (Illus.). 48p. (J). pap. (978-0-8368-5837-2(9)); lib. bdg. 30.00 (978-0-8368-5828-0(X)) Stevens, Gareth Inc. (World Almanac Library).

Tames, Richard. Pearl Harbor: The U. S. Enters World War II. 2001. (gr. 5-8). lib. bdg. 15.90 (978-0-613-36122-4(9)) Tandem Library Bks.

Tames, Richard. Pearl Harbor: The U.S. Enters World War II. 2006. (Point of Impact Ser.). (Illus.). 32p. (YA). (gr. 5-8). lib. bdg. 29.29 (*978-1-4034-9142-8(9)) Heinemann Library.

Tapper, Suzanne Cloud. America as a World Power: From the Spanish-American War to Today. 2006. (American Saga Ser.). (Illus.). 128p. (J). lib. bdg. 31.93 (978-0-7660-2606-3(X)) Enslow Pubs., Inc.

Uschan, Michael V. Political Leaders. 2002. (American War Library). (Illus.). 112p. (J). 29.95 (978-1-59018-211-6(1) , Lucent Bks.) Thomson Gale.

Young, Mitch. Turning Points in World History Anthology. 2003. (Turning Points in World History Ser.). (Illus.). 224p. (YA). (gr. 9-12). pap. 24.95 (978-0-7377-1471-5(9) , Greenhaven Pr., Inc.) Thomson Gale.

—War on Terrorism. 2003. (Turning Points in World History Ser.). (Illus.). 224p. (YA). (gr. 9-12). lib. bdg. 37.45 (978-0-7377-1470-8(0) , Greenhaven Pr., Inc.) Thomson Gale.

UNITED STATES—FOREIGN RELATIONS—TREATIES

Primary Sources of American Treaties. (Illus.). (YA). (gr. 5-8). 175.50 (978-1-4042-0626-7(4)) Rosen Publishing Group, Inc., The.

UNITED STATES—FOREST SERVICE—FICTION

Rolt-Wheeler, Francis. Boy with the U S Foresters. 2006. 42.99 (***978-1-4280-4843-0(X)**); pap. 36.99 (***978-1-4280-4851-5(0)**) IndyPublish.com.

UNITED STATES—FURNITURE

see Furniture, American

UNITED STATES—GOVERNMENT

see United States—Politics and Government

UNITED STATES—GOVERNMENT EMPLOYEES

see United States—Officials and Employees

UNITED STATES—HISTORY

Abitz, Diana. Know-the-Facts Review Game: 100 Must-Know Facts in a Q&A Game Format to Help Kids Really Remember Standards-Based Social Studies Information. 2005. (American History Ser.). 48p. pap. 14.99 (978-0-439-37434-7(0)); (Illus.). pap. 14.99 (978-0-439-37431-6(6)) Scholastic, Inc. (Teaching Resources).

Abitz, Diana & LaRoy, Susan. Know-the-Facts Review Game: 100 Must-Know Facts in a Q&A Game Format to Help Kids Really Remember Standards-Based Social Studies Information. 2005. (Ancient Civilizations Ser.). 48p. pap. 14.99 (978-0-439-37432-3(4) , Teaching Resources) Scholastic, Inc.

Albert, Michael. Artist's America. 2008. 48p. (J). 17.95 (***978-0-8050-7857-2(6)**) Holt, Henry & Co.

Alcraft, Rob. Fort Laramie. 2002. (Visiting the Past Ser.). (Illus.). 32p. (J). (gr. 5-7). pap. 6.95 (978-1-58810-409-0(5) , 91181) Heinemann Library.

All Across America. (Guided Reading Levels Ser.). (Illus.). 4.76 (978-0-7362-0986-1(7)) Hampton-Brown Bks.

Altman, Linda Jacobs. The Politics of Slavery: Fiery National Debates Fueled by the Slave Economy. 2004. (Slavery in American History Ser.). (Illus.). 128p. (J). lib. bdg. 26.60 (978-0-7660-2150-1(5)) Enslow Pubs., Inc.

America Goes to War, 4 bks. Incl. Civil War. Graves, Kerry A. lib. bdg. 22.60 (978-0-7368-0582-7(6)); Revolutionary War. Todd, Anne M. lib. bdg. 22.60 (978-0-7368-0584-1(2)); Spanish-American War. Graves, Kerry A. lib. bdg. 22.60 (978-0-7368-0583-4(4)); War of 1812. Todd, Anne M. lib. bdg. 22.60 (978-0-7368-0585-8(0)); 48p. (J). (gr. 3-4). 2000. (Illus.). Set lib. bdg. 90.40 (978-0-7368-0676-3(8) , Bridgestone Bks.) Capstone Pr., Inc.

America the Beautiful: Third Series, Set. 2007. (J). (***978-0-531-16716-8(X)** , Children's Pr.) Scholastic Library Publishing.

American Community: History Comes to Life When You Travel to Sites Where Communities Once Thrived, 5 Bks, Set. 2004. (J). 140.00 (978-0-516-29808-5(9) , Children's Pr.) Scholastic Library Publishing.

American Education Publishing Staff & School Specialty Publishing Staff. U. S. States. 2001. (Brighter Child Fact Card Ser.). (Illus.). 54p. (J). (gr. 3-5). 2.99 (978-1-56189-691-2(8) , 31387, American Education Publishing) School Specialty Publishing.

American Education Publishing Staff, et al. The Complete Book of United States History. 2001. (Complete Book Ser.). (Illus.). 352p. (J). (gr. 3-5). pap. 14.95 (978-1-56189-679-0(9) , 31375, American Education Publishing) School Specialty Publishing.

American History. (YA). 20.00 (978-1-931555-47-0(8)) Our Lady of Victory Schl.

American History 2. 2003. pap. 5.95 (978-1-57222-765-1(6)) Barcharts, Inc.

American History Playhouse: Inspirational Classroom Plays about United States History. 80p. (gr. 4-8). 12.99 (978-0-7682-0659-3(6) , GA13092) School Specialty Publishing.

American History Playing Card Deck. 2004. (History Channel Ser.). (Illus.). 120p. pap. 12.00 (978-1-57281-440-0(3) , AMH55) U. S. Games Systems, Inc.

American Moments. 2004. (J). (gr. 4-8). lib. bdg. 307.80 (978-1-59197-276-1(0) , ABDO & Daughters) ABDO Publishing Co.

American Voices Group 3, 5 bks., Set. Incl. American Voices from the Women's Movement. Schomp, Virginia. xix, 138p. lib. bdg. 37.07 (978-0-7614-2171-9(8)); Century of Immigration : 1820-1924. Stefoff, Rebecca. xxiii, 115p. lib. bdg. 37.07 (978-0-7614-2172-6(6)); Time of Slavery. Sirimarco, Elizabeth. xxiii, 114p. lib. bdg. 37.07 (978-0-7614-2169-6(6)); Wild West. Stefoff, Rebecca. 111p. lib. bdg. 37.07 (978-0-7614-2170-2(X)); (Illus.). (J). 2006. 2007. Set lib. bdg. 185.36 (***978-0-7614-2167-2(X)** , Benchmark Bks.) Cavendish, Marshall Corp.

The Americans. 2005. (gr. 6-12). (978-0-618-17562-8(8) , 2-37930); (SPA.). (978-0-618-17566-6(0) , 2-37931); (978-0-618-17568-0(7) , 2-37933); (978-0-618-17615-1(2) , 2-37948); (978-0-618-17618-2(7) , 2-37951); (978-0-618-17619-9(5) , 2-37952); tchr. ed. (978-0-618-16260-4(7) , 2-37912); stu. ed. (978-0-618-10878-7(5) , 2-37910); wbk. ed. (978-0-618-17571-0(7) , 2-37934) McDougal Littell Inc.

The Americans: Reading Study Guide. 2002. (gr. 6-12). (978-0-395-95668-7(4) , 2-88562); (SPA.). (978-0-395-95669-4(2) , 2-88563) McDougal Littell Inc.

The Americans: Reading Study Guide Answer Key. 2002. (gr. 6-12). (978-0-395-95670-0(6) , 2-88564) McDougal Littell Inc.

The Americans: Reconstruction to the 21st Century. 2005. (gr. 6-12). stu. ed. (978-0-618-10879-4(3) , 2-37911) McDougal Littell Inc.

The Americans: The Americans Workbook. 2002. (gr. 6-12). (978-0-618-15632-0(1) , 2-01343) McDougal Littell Inc.

The Americans: The Americans Workbook Answer Key. 2002. (gr. 6-12). (978-0-618-15637-5(2) , 2-01345) McDougal Littell Inc.

Americans at War Series, 15 bks. 2003. (J). (gr. 4-6). Set 1-3. lib. bdg. 384.60 (978-1-4034-0175-5(6)); Set 3. lib. bdg. 153.84 (978-1-58810-874-6(0)) Heinemann Library.

The Americans: Reconstruction Through the 20th Century: Reading Study Guide Answer Key. 2002. (gr. 6-12). (978-0-395-92078-7(7) , 2-88550) McDougal Littell Inc.

America's Westward Expansion, 6 Vols. 180.00 (978-0-8368-5785-6(2)) Stevens, Gareth Inc.

Ancient Americas DBA. 2003. spiral bd. 16.95 (978-1-56004-156-6(0)) Social Studies Schl. Service.

Anderson, Dale. The Aftermath of the Civil War. 2004. (World Almanac Library of the Civil War). (Illus.). 48p. (J). (gr. 5 up). pap. 11.95 (978-0-8368-5597-5(3)); lib. bdg. 30.00 (978-0-8368-5588-3(4)) Stevens, Gareth Inc. (World Almanac Library).

—The Atom Bomb Project. 2004. (Landmark Events in American History Ser.). (Illus.). 48p. (J). (gr. 5 up). lib. bdg. 30.00 (978-0-8368-5385-8(7) , World Almanac Library) Stevens, Gareth Inc.

—World Almanac Library of the Civil War, 8 bks. Incl. Aftermath of the Civil War. (gr. 5 up). lib. bdg. 30.00 (978-0-8368-5588-3(4)); Causes of the Civil War. (gr. 5 up). lib. bdg. 30.00 (978-0-8368-5581-4(7)); Civil War at Sea. (gr. 5 up). lib. bdg. 30.00 (978-0-8368-5585-2(X)); Civil War in the East (1861-July 1863) (gr. 5 up). lib. bdg. 30.00 (978-0-8368-5582-1(5)); Civil War in the West (1861-July 1863) (gr. 5 up). lib. bdg. 30.00 (978-0-8368-5583-8(3)); Home Fronts in the Civil War. lib. bdg. 30.00 (978-0-8368-5587-6(6)); Soldier's Life in the Civil War. (gr. 5 up). lib. bdg. 30.00 (978-0-8368-5586-9(8)); Union Victory (July 1863-1865) (gr. 5 up). lib. bdg. 30.00 (978-0-8368-5584-5(1)); 48p. (J). (Illus.). 2004. Set lib. bdg. 240.00 (978-0-8368-5580-7(9) , World Almanac Library) Stevens, Gareth Inc.

Anderson, Mary Elizabeth. Link Across America: A Story of the Historic Lincoln Highway. 2000. (Illus.). 52p. (J). (gr. 1-8). reprint ed. 15.95 (978-1-877810-97-8(5) , LINK) Rayve Productions, Inc.

Andrews, Barbara. Discover the Southwest Region. 2006. pap. 39.00 (***978-1-4108-6436-9(7)**) Benchmark Education Co.

Andryszewski, Tricia. The Reform Party: Ross Perot, Pat Buchanan. 2000. (Headliners Ser.). (Illus.). 64p. (gr. 5-8). lib. bdg. 25.90 (978-0-7613-1906-1(9) , Millbrook Pr.) Lerner Publishing Group.

Ansary, Mir Tamim. Historias de Fiestas, 5 bks., Set. 2003. Tr. of Holiday Histories. (SPA & ENG., Illus.). (J). (gr. k-2). lib. bdg. 113.95 (978-1-4034-3002-1(0)) Heinemann Library.

Armentrout, David & Armentrout, Patricia. Historic & Famous Cities. 2002. (Guides to State Symbols). (Illus.). 48p. (gr. 3-8). 20.95 (978-1-58952-084-4(X)) Rourke Publishing, LLC.

Art, Suzanne Strauss. Ancient Times: The Story of the First Americans. Art, Suzanne Strauss, illus. 1999. (Illus.). 178p. (YA). (gr. 5-8). pap. 14.95 (978-0-9656557-7-4(6)) Pemblewick Pr.

Ashabranner, Brent. Great American Memorials, 5 vols. Incl. Badge of Valor : The National Law Enforcement Officers Memorial. Ashabranner, Jennifer, illus. 2000. lib. bdg. (978-0-7613-1522-3(5)); Date with Destiny : The Women in Military Service for America Memorial. Ashabranner, Jennifer, photos by. 2000. lib. bdg. (978-0-7613-1472-1(5)); No Better Hope : What the Lincoln Memorial Means to America. Ashabranner, Jennifer. (J). 2001. lib. bdg. 25.90 (978-0-7613-1523-0(3)); Remembering Korea : Korean War. Ashabranner, Jennifer, photos by. 2001. lib. bdg. 25.90 (978-0-7613-2156-9(X)); Their Names to Live : What the Vietnam Veterans Memorial Means to America. Ashabranner, Jennifer, photos by. 1998. lib. bdg. 24.90 (978-0-7613-3235-0(9)); Washington Monument : A Beacon for America. Ashabranner, Jennifer, photos by. 2002. lib. bdg. 25.90 (978-0-7613-1524-7(1)); 64p. (gr. 4-8). (Illus.). 2004. 155.40 (978-0-7613-3142-1(5) , Twenty-First Century Bks.) Lerner Publishing Group.

Bailey, Martha. New Mexico: Uno de muchos, de muchos Uno, 1. Bailey, Martha, illus. l.t. ed. 2006. (SPA., Illus.). 96p. (J). per. (978-0-9786448-0-2(8)) Bailey, Martha.

Baker, et al. Nueva Historia de los Estados Unidos. (SPA.). 350p. (J). 32.95 (978-0-8056-0124-4(4) , MI010) Minerva Bks., Ltd.

Baldwin, Peter C., et al. Major Problems in American Urban & Suburban History. 2nd ed. 2004. (Major Problems in American History Ser.). (Illus.). 514p. (YA). 55.56 (978-0-618-43276-9(0) , 309820) Houghton Mifflin College Div.

Ball, Lea. The Federalist—Anti-Federalist Debate over States' Rights: A Primary Source Investigation. 2004. (Great Historic Debates & Speeches Ser.). (Illus.). 64p. (J). lib. bdg. 29.25 (978-1-4042-0149-1(1)) Rosen Publishing Group, Inc., The.

Banks, James A. United States. 1999. (Adventures in Time & Place Ser.). (Illus.). (J). (978-0-02-147653-4(5) , Aladdin) Simon & Schuster Children's Publishing.

Barber, James. Presidents: Discover the Presidents Who Have Shaped American History, from the Founding Fathers to Today's Leaders. rev. ed. 2003. (Eyewitness Bks.). (Illus.). 64p. 15.99 (978-0-7894-8898-5(1)) Dorling Kindersley Publishing, Inc.

Barrie, Laurie. Writing Trails in American History. 2000. 42p. (J). spiral bd. 15.00 (978-1-930443-27-3(7)) Logos Schl.

Bartoletti, Susan Campbell. Kids on Strike! 1999. (Illus.). 208p. (J). (gr. 4-6). tchr. ed. 20.00 (978-0-395-88892-6(1)) Houghton Mifflin Co. Trade & Reference Div.

Beall, Pamela Conn & Nipp, Susan Hagen. Wee Sing America. 2005. (Wee Sing Ser.). (Illus.). 60p. (J). (gr. 1-3). pap. 9.99 incl. audio compact disk (978-0-8431-1279-5(4) , Price Stern Sloan) Penguin Group (USA) Inc.

Beautiful Feet U. S. & World History. 1999. 10p. (YA). ring bd. 1.00 (978-1-57896-068-2(1) , 2567, Hewitt Homeschooling Resources) Hewitt Research Foundation, Inc.

Benchmark Education Staff, compiled by. U. S. Hist. 2006. spiral bd. 159.00 (***978-1-4108-7113-8(4)**) Benchmark Education Co.

—United States HIST. 2006. spiral bd. 159.00 (***978-1-4108-7128-2(2)**) Benchmark Education Co.

Bennett, William J. The Children's Book of America. Hague, Michael, illus. 1998. 112p. (ps-3). 21.00 (978-0-684-84930-0(5)) Simon & Schuster.

—The Children's Treasury of Virtues. Hague, Michael, illus. 2000. 352p. (J). (ps-3). 29.95 (978-0-7432-1136-9(7) , Free Pr.) Simon & Schuster.

Bennett, William J., ed. The Children's Book of America. Hague, Michael, illus. 2000. 114p. (J). (gr. 4-7). reprint ed. 21.00 (978-0-7881-9358-3(9)) DIANE Publishing Co.

Berkin. Berkin, Making America, Volume 1, 4th Edition Plus Boyer, Enduring Vision, Document Set, Volume 1, 4/5 Edition Plus Norton, Student Research Passkey. 4th ed. 2005. (YA). pap., pap. 96.36 (978-0-618-64233-5(1) , 396096) Houghton Mifflin College Div.

—Berkin, Making America, Volume 2, 4th Edition Plus Boyer, Enduring Vision, Document Set, Volume 2, 4/5th Edition, Plus Norton, Student Research Passkey. 4th ed. 2005. (YA). pap., pap. 96.36 (978-0-618-64232-8(3) , 396095) Houghton Mifflin College Div.

—Berkin, Making America, Volume 2, 4th Edition Plus Norton, Student Research Passkey, 1st Edition Plus Atlas. 4th ed. 2005. (YA). pap., pap. 96.36 (978-0-618-64576-3(4) , 396123) Houghton Mifflin College Div.

—Making America V2 with Student Research Companion 4th Edition. 4th ed. 2005. (YA). pap. 96.36 (978-0-618-61273-4(4) , 304179) Houghton Mifflin College Div.

Bernstein, Vivian. America's Story. (J) 2006. (Illus.). xi, 390p. (***978-0-7398-9716-4(0)**); 2001. pap., tchr. ed. 10.50 (978-0-7398-2386-6(8)) Steck-Vaughn.

—America's Story: Before 1865. 2001. (gr. 5-8). lib. bdg. 26.65 (978-0-613-74073-9(4)) Tandem Library Bks.

—America's Story Bk. 2: After 1865. 2001. (Illus.). (J). pap. 17.40 (978-0-7398-2384-2(1)) Steck-Vaughn.

—America's Story Book: Before 1861. 2001. (Illus.). (J). pap. 17.40 (978-0-7398-2383-5(3)) Steck-Vaughn.

Bertrand, Nancy. Wakefield. 2000. (Images of America Ser.). (Illus.). 128p. pap. 18.99 (978-0-7385-0495-7(5)) Arcadia Publishing.

Bial, Raymond. The Long Walk: The Story of Navajo Captivity. 2002. (Great Journeys Ser.). (Illus.). 94p. (J). 32.79 (978-0-7614-1322-6(7) , Benchmark Bks.) Cavendish, Marshall Corp.

Binns, Tristan Boyer. Símbolos de Libertad, 5 bks., Set. 2003. Tr. of Symbols of Freedom. (SPA & ENG., Illus.). (J). (gr. k-2). lib. bdg. 113.95 (978-1-4034-2996-4(0)) Heinemann Library.

Binns, Tristan Boyer & Yoder, Carolyn. We Are America, 12 bks. 2003. (Illus.). (J). Set. lib. bdg. 290.64 (978-1-4034-0740-5(1)); Set 2. lib. bdg. 145.32 (978-1-4034-0739-9(8)) Heinemann Library.

Blattner, Don. U. S. History Maps. 1999. (Illus.). 96p. (YA). (gr. 5). pap. 10.95 (978-1-58037-109-4(4)) Twain, Mark Media, Inc. Pubs.

Blue Earth Books: Coming to America, 6 bks. Incl. Africans in America, 1665-1865. Olson, Kay Melchisedech. (gr. 4). 2002. lib. bdg. 22.60 (978-0-7368-1204-7(0)); Chinese Immigrants, 1850-1900. Olson, Kay Melchisedech. (gr. 3-4). 2001. lib. bdg. 22.60 (978-0-7368-0793-7(4)); French Immigrants, 1840-1940. Olson, Kay Melchisedech. (gr. 3-4). 2002. lib. bdg. 22.60 (978-0-7368-1205-4(9)); German Immigrants, 1820-1920. Frost, Helen. (gr. 3-4). 2001. lib. bdg. 22.60 (978-0-7368-0794-4(2)); Greek Immigrants, 1890-1920. Wallner, Rosemary. (gr. 4). 2002. lib. bdg. 22.60 (978-0-7368-1206-1(7)); Irish Immigrants, 1840-1920. O'Hara, Megan. (gr. 3-4). 2001. lib. bdg. 22.60 (978-0-7368-0795-1(0)); Italian Immigrants, 1880-1920. Todd, Anne M. (gr. 3-4). 2001. lib. bdg. 22.60 (978-0-7368-0796-8(9)); Japanese Immigrants, 1850-1950. Wallner, Rosemary. (gr. 3-4). 2001. lib. bdg. 22.60 (978-0-7368-0797-5(7)); Jewish Immigrants, 1880-1924. Haberle, Susan E. (gr. 4). 2002. lib. bdg. 22.60 (978-0-7368-1207-8(5)); Norwegian, Swedish, & Danish Immigrants, 1820-1920. Olson, Kay Melchisedech. (gr. 3-4). 2001. lib. bdg. 22.60 (978-0-7368-0798-2(5)); Polish Immigrants, 1890-1920. Wallner, Rosemary & Radzilowski, John. (gr. 4). 2002. lib. bdg. 22.60 (978-0-7368-1208-5(3)); Russian Immigrants, 1860-1915. Frost, Helen. (gr. 4-6). 2002. lib. bdg. 22.60 (978-0-7368-1209-2(1)); 32p. (J). (Illus.). Set lib. bdg. 271.20 (978-0-7368-1216-0(4) , Bridgestone Bks.) Capstone Pr., Inc.

Blue Earth Books: Exploring History Through Simple Recipes, 12 bks. Incl. American Indian Cooking Before 1500. Gunderson, Mary. lib. bdg. 22.60 (978-0-7368-0605-3(9)); California Gold Rush Cooking. Schroeder, Lisa Golden. lib. bdg. 22.60 (978-0-7368-0603-9(2)); Civil War Cooking : The Confederacy. Dosier, Susan. lib. bdg. 22.60 (978-0-7368-0350-2(5)); Civil War Cooking : The Union. Dosier, Susan. lib. bdg. (978-0-7368-0351-9(3)); Colonial Cooking. Dosier, Susan. lib. bdg. 22.60 (978-0-7368-0352-6(1)); Cooking on Nineteenth-Century Whaling Ships. Draper, Charla L. lib. bdg. 22.60 (978-0-7368-0602-2(4)); Cooking on the Lewis & Clark Expedition. Gunderson, Mary. lib. bdg. 22.60 (978-0-7368-0354-0(8)); Cowboy Cooking. Gunderson, Mary. lib. bdg. 22.60 (978-0-7368-0353-3(X)); Nineteenth-Century Lumber Camp Cooking. Fischer, Maureen M. lib. bdg. 22.60 (978-0-7368-0604-6(0)); Oregon Trail Cooking. Gunderson, Mary. lib. bdg. 22.60 (978-0-7368-0355-7(6)); Pioneer Farm Cooking. Gunderson, Mary. lib. bdg. 22.60 (978-0-7368-0356-4(4)); Southern Plantation Cooking. Gunderson, Mary. lib. bdg. 22.60 (978-0-7368-0357-1(2)); 32p. (J). (gr. 3-4). 2000. (Illus.). Set lib. bdg. 271.20 (978-0-7368-0680-0(6) , Bridgestone Bks.) Capstone Pr., Inc.

Bockenhauer, Mark H. & Cunha, Stephen F. National Geographic Our Fifty States. 2004. (Illus.). 240p. (J). (gr. 5). 24.95 (978-0-7922-6402-6(9) , National Geographic Children's Bks.) National Geographic Society.

Bodersteiner, Roberta. Our 50 States. 2000. (100+ Seriestm Ser.). 128p. (J). (gr. 5-8). pap., stu. ed. 12.99 (978-0-7424-0054-2(9) , IF87049) School Specialty Publishing.

Boehm, Richard G., et al. Game Time! Early United States. 1998. (Harcourt Brace Social Studies). (gr. k-7). pap. 9.40 (978-0-15-312361-0(3)) Harcourt Schl. Pubs.

—Reading Support & Test Preparation: Early United States. 1998. (Harcourt Brace Social Studies). (gr. k-7). pap. 32.70 (978-0-15-312384-9(2)) Harcourt Schl. Pubs.

Bonner, John. A Child's History of the United States, 2 vol., set. reprint ed. 250.00 (978-0-7222-7249-7(9)) Library Reprints, Inc.

Boorstin, Daniel J., et al. A History of the United States. 6th ed. 2005. (Illus.). (YA). (gr. 9-12). 85.20 (978-0-13-181542-1(3)) Prentice Hall Pr.

Borden, Louise. America Is... Schuett, Stacey, illus. 2005. 40p. (J). pap. 7.99 (978-1-4169-0286-7(4) , Aladdin) Simon & Schuster Children's Publishing.

Boyer. Enduring Vision Essentials. 1999. (J). pap. 22.47 net. (978-0-395-98233-4(2)); pap. 22.47 net. (978-0-395-98234-1(0)) Houghton Mifflin Co.

Boyer, Paul S. Holt American Nation: Online Edition Plus. 3rd ed. 2003. 17.26 (978-0-03-037432-6(4)) Holt, Rinehart & Winston.

Boyer's Staff. The American Nation: Modern Era: Online Edition. 5th ed. 2004. (gr. 1). 17.26 (978-0-03-038831-6(7)); (gr. 6). 77.26 (978-0-03-038832-3(5)) Holt, Rinehart & Winston.

Boyle, Donzella Cross. Quest of a Hemisphere. 2002. (Illus.). (YA). 24.95 (978-1-892647-02-3(8)) Robert Welch Univ.

Brannon, Barbara. Discover the Northeast Region. 2005. 39.00 (***978-1-4108-5152-9(4)**) Benchmark Education Co.

Branse, J. L. A Day in the Life of a Colonial Sea Captain. 2002. (Library of Living & Working in Colonial Times). (Illus.). 24p. (J). (gr. 3). lib. bdg. 18.75 (978-0-8239-5821-4(3) , PowerKids Pr.) Rosen Publishing Group, Inc., The.

Brill, Marlene Targ. Margaret Knight, Girl Inventor. Friar, Joanne, illus. 2001. 32p. (gr. 2-4). lib. bdg. 22.90 (978-0-7613-1756-2(2) , Twenty-First Century Bks.) Lerner Publishing Group.

Brinkley, Alan. The Unfinished Nation with PowerWeb. 4th rev. ed. 2003. (C). (gr. 6-12). (Illus.). pap. 65.00 (978-0-07-293522-6(7) , 9780072935226); Vol. 1. pap. 46.25 (978-0-07-293524-0(3) , 9780072935240); Vol. 2. pap. 46.25 (978-0-07-293525-7(1) , 9780072935257) Glencoe/McGraw-Hill.

Broida, Marian. Projects about American Immigrants from China. 2005. (Hands-On History Ser.). (Illus.). 48p. (J). (978-0-7614-1978-5(0) , Benchmark Bks.) Cavendish, Marshall Corp.

Brook, Henry. True Stories of D-Day. 2006. 160p. (J). pap. 4.99 (978-0-7945-1161-6(9) , Usborne) EDC Publishing.

Broyles, Angela. Heart of Dixie Alabama History. 2002. (Illus.). 251p. spiral bd. 49.95 (978-0-9719946-4-5(1)) Bluewater Pubns.

Bruchac, Margaret M. & Grace, Catherine O'Neill. 1621: A New Look at Thanksgiving. Coulson, Cotton & Brimberg, Sisse, photos by. 2004. (I Am American Ser.). (Illus.). 48p. (J). (gr. 3-7). pap. 7.95 (978-0-7922-6139-1(9) , National Geographic Children's Bks.) National Geographic Society.

Bruns, Roger. Almost History: Close Calls, Plan B's, & Twists of Fate in America's Past. 2001. (Illus.). 304p. pap. 19.95 (978-0-7868-8579-4(3)) Hyperion Pr.

Bryan, Nichol. One Nation Set I, 10 vols. 2004. (Illus.). (J). (gr. k-6). lib. bdg. 227.80 (978-1-57765-979-2(1) , Checkerboard Library) ABDO Publishing Co.

Buckley, Susan. Places in Time: A New Atlas of American History. 2001. (gr. 3-6). lib. bdg. 15.25 (978-0-613-60829-9(1)) Tandem Library Bks.

Buckley, Susan & Leacock, Elspeth. Journeys for Freedom: A New Look at America's Story. Prato, Rodica, illus. 2006. 48p. (J). (gr. 4-6). 17.00 (978-0-618-22323-7(1)) Houghton Mifflin Co.

—Places in Time: A New Atlas of American History. Jones, Randy, illus. 2003. 48p. (J). pap. 6.95 (978-0-618-31113-2(0)) Houghton Mifflin Co. Trade & Reference Div.

Buckley, Susan, et al. Journeys in Time: A New Atlas of American History. Prato, Rodica, illus. 2001. 48p. (J). (gr. 4-6). tchr. ed. 15.00 (978-0-395-97956-3(0)) Houghton Mifflin Co. Trade & Reference Div.

—Places in Time: A New Atlas of American History. Jones, Randy, illus. 2001. 48p. (J). (gr. 4-6). tchr. ed. 15.00 (978-0-395-97958-7(7)) Houghton Mifflin Co. Trade & Reference Div.

Building America, 7 vols., Set. Incl. Georgia : The Debtors Colony. Harkins, Susan Sales & Harkins, William H. lib. bdg. 20.95 (978-1-58415-465-5(9)); Holidays & Celebrations in Colonial America. Roberts, Russell. lib. bdg. 20.95 (978-1-58415-467-9(5)); Jamestown : The First English Colony. Harkins, Susan & Harkins, William H. lib. bdg. 20.95 (978-1-58415-458-7(6)); Massachusetts Bay Colony : The Puritans Arrive from England. Hinman, Bonnie. lib. bdg. 20.95 (978-1-58415-460-0(8)); New Netherland : The Dutch Settle the

Hudson Valley. Gibson, Karen Bush. lib. bdg. 20.95 (978-1-58415-461-7(6)); Pennsylvania : William Penn & the City of Brotherly Love. Hinman, Bonnie. lib. bdg. 20.95 (978-1-58415-463-1(2)); Plymouth Colony : The Pilgrims Settle in New England. Tracy, Kathleen. lib. bdg. 20.95 (978-1-58415-459-4(4)); (Illus.). 48p. (J). (gr. 4-8). 2006. 2007. Set lib. bdg. 139.65 (***978-1-58415-291-0(5)***) Mitchell Lane Pubs., Inc.

Buller, Jon. Smart about the Fifty States. 2003. (gr. 3-6). lib. bdg. 14.15 (978-0-613-64109-8(4)) Tandem Library Bks.

Buller, Jon, et al. The Fifty States. Buller, Jon et al, illus. 2003. (Smart about History Ser.). 64p. (J). (gr. 2-5). pap. 5.99 (978-0-448-43131-4(9) , Grosset & Dunlap) Penguin Group (USA) Inc.

Burgan, Michael. A Changing Nation. 2006. (Making a New Nation Ser.). (Illus.). 48p. (J). (978-1-4034-7830-6(9)); pap. (978-1-4034-7837-5(6)) Heinemann Library.

—Valley Forge. 2004. (We the People Ser.). (Illus.). 48p. (J). (gr. 4 up). lib. bdg. 22.60 (978-0-7565-0615-5(8)) Compass Point Bks.

Buy Sets 1, 2, 3 And 4. 2005. (Primary Sources in American History Ser.). (Illus.). 64p. (gr. 5-8). lib. bdg. (978-1-4042-0352-5(4)) Rosen Publishing Group, Inc., The.

C. Q. Press Staff. Landmark Events in U.S. History, 5 vols., Set. 2005. (Landmark Events in U. S. History Ser.). (gr. 9 up). 470.00 (978-1-933116-27-3(7)) CQ Pr.

Callan, Jim. America in the 1900s & 1910s. 2005. (Decades of American History Ser.). (Illus.). 128p. (J). (gr. 4-9). 35.00 (978-0-8160-5636-1(6)) Facts On File, Inc.

Callella, Trisha. Integrating American History with Reading Instruction. Walter, LaDawn, ed. Campbell, Jenny, illus. 2002. 72p. (J). (gr. 5-6). pap. 10.99 (978-1-57471-906-2(8) , 2831) Creative Teaching Pr., Inc.

Campbell, Ballard. Encyclopedia of Disasters, Accidents, & Crises in American History. 2008. 384p. (gr. 9). 95.00 (***978-0-8160-6603-2(5)***) Facts On File, Inc.

Campbell, Wallis. Angel Island. 2006. (Illus.). 48p. (J). pap. (978-1-59034-808-6(7)) Mondo Publishing.

Cassells, E. Steve. Tracing the Past: Archaeology along the Rocky Mountain Expansion Loop Pipeline, 1. 2003. (Illus.). 40p. 6.95 (978-0-9743137-0-2(X)) Alpine Archaeological Consultants, Inc.

Cayton, Andrew. America: Pathways to the Present. 2005. (YA). (gr. 9-12). 88.00 (978-0-13-181545-2(8)) Prentice Hall Pr.

—America: Pathways to the Present, Modern American History. 2005. (YA). (gr. 9-12). 85.90 (978-0-13-181547-6(4)) Prentice Hall Pr.

Celebrate the States - Group 10, 4 vols. Incl. Missouri. Bennett, M. lib. bdg. 37.07 (978-0-7614-1063-8(5)); Montana. Bennett, Clayton. (J). lib. bdg. 35.64 (978-0-7614-1068-3(6)); North Dakota. McDaniel, Melissa. (J). lib. bdg. 35.64 (978-0-7614-1069-0(4)); Puerto Rico. Schwabacher, Martin. (J). lib. bdg. 35.64 (978-0-7614-1070-6(8)); 144p. (gr. 4-8). (Illus.). 2001. 148.29 (978-0-7614-1066-9(X) , Benchmark Bks.) Cavendish, Marshall Corp.

Celebrate the States - Group 11, 4 vols. 2001. (gr. 4-8). 148.29 (978-0-7614-1310-3(3) , Benchmark Bks.) Cavendish, Marshall Corp.

Celebrate the States - Group 9, 4 vols. Incl. Georgia. Otfinoski, Steven, ed. 2000. lib. bdg. 37.07 (978-0-7614-1062-1(7)); Oklahoma. Baldwin, Guy. (J). 2000. lib. bdg. 37.07 (978-0-7614-1067-6(8)); South Carolina. Hoffman, Nancy. 2001. lib. bdg. 37.07 (978-0-7614-1065-2(1)); Utah. Steffof, R. 2001. lib. bdg. 37.07 (978-0-7614-1064-5(3)); 144p. (gr. 4-8). (Illus.). 2000. 148.29 (978-0-7614-1061-4(9) , Benchmark Bks.) Cavendish, Marshall Corp.

Center for Learning Network Staff. U. S. History & Geography 2 Bk. 2: Curriculum Unit, 2 vols. 2003. (Social Studies Ser.). 210p. tchr. ed., spiral bd. 29.95 (978-1-56077-655-0(2)) Ctr. for Learning, The.

Center for Learning Staff. The Age of Imperialism: 1895-1930 — Elementary U. S. History Series, 11 vols. 2003. (Social Studies Ser.). 143p. (J). tchr. ed., spiral bd. 29.95 (978-1-56077-748-9(6)) Ctr. for Learning, The.

—Using Literature to Teach U. S. History: Elementary U. S. History Series, 12 vols. 2003. (Social Studies Ser.). 227p. (J). tchr. ed., spiral bd. 37.95 (978-1-56077-736-6(2)) Ctr. for Learning, The.

Cheney, Lynne. A Is for Abigail: An Almanac of Amazing American Women. Glasser, Robin Preiss, illus. 2003. 48p. (J). 16.95 (978-0-689-85819-2(1)) Simon & Schuster Children's Publishing.

—Our 50 States: A Family Adventure Across America. Glasser, Robin Preiss, illus. 2006. 74p. (J). (gr. 2-5). 18.99 (978-0-689-86717-0(4)) Simon & Schuster Children's Publishing.

—A Time for Freedom: What Happened When in America. 2005. (Illus.). 304p. (J). (gr. 9 up). 15.95 (978-1-4169-0925-5(7) , Simon & Schuster/Paula Wiseman Bks.) Simon & Schuster Children's Publishing.

Child, Hamilton. Gazetteer & Business Directory of Sullivan County For 1872-73: Republished on CD-ROM by Between the Lakes Group, 2003. (Illus.). 380p. cd-rom 20.00 (978-0-9727403-4-0(1) , EJ03-03C) Between the Lakes Group, LLC.

Christopher, Tracy. Great Events. 1999. (Eyes on America Ser.). (Illus.). 29p. (J). (978-1-56156-712-6(4)) Kidsbooks, Inc.

Churchill, E. Richard & Churchill, Linda R. Short Lessons in U. S. History. rev. ed. 1999. 210p. (J). (gr. 6 up). act. bk. ed. 24.99 (978-0-8251-3940-6(6) , 0-39406) Walch Publishing.

Coco De Young, C. A Letter to Mrs. Roosevelt. 2000. (J). (978-0-606-20413-2(X)) Tandem Library Bks.

Coleman, Ronda, et al. My American GeoJourney. 2002. (Illus.). 32p. (J). (gr. 2-4). pap., wbk. ed. 2.50 (978-1-56762-167-9(8)) Modern Learning Pr.

Coletti, Sharon. Everything You Need to Supplement U. S. & State Studies. 2005. (YA). Pt. 1. ring bd. 249.95 (978-1-933558-08-0(3)); Pt. 2. ring bd. 249.95 (978-1-933558-09-7(1)) InspirEd Educators.

Coll Y Toste, Cayetano. Puerto Rican Tales: Legends of Spanish Colonial Times. 4th ed. 1999. (Illus.). 111p. reprint ed. pap. 9.95 (978-0-9601700-3-6(0)) Ediciones Libero.

Collier, Christopher & Collier, James Lincoln. The Drama of American History, 5 bks., Group 2, Set. Incl. Andrew Jackson's America : 1824-1850. lib. bdg. 29.93 (978-0-7614-0779-9(0)); Building a New Nation : 1789-1803. lib. bdg. 31.36 (978-0-7614-0777-5(4)); Creating the Constitution : 1787. lib. bdg. 31.36 (978-0-7614-0776-8(6)); Hispanic America, Texas & the Mexican War : 1835-1850. lib. bdg. 31.36 (978-0-7614-0780-5(4)); Jeffersonian Republicans : 1800-1823. lib. bdg. 29.93 (978-0-7614-0778-2(2)); 96p. (J). (gr. 5-9). 1998. (Illus.). 1998. Set lib. bdg. 149.65 (978-0-7614-0775-1(8)); Set lib. bdg. 149.65 (978-0-7614-0816-1(9)) Cavendish, Marshall Corp. (Benchmark Bks.).

—The Drama of American History - Group 4, 4 bks. Incl. Indians, Cowboys & Farmers : 1865-1910. lib. bdg. 31.36 (978-0-7614-1052-2(X)); Progressivism, the Great Depression & the New Deal : 1901-1941. lib. bdg. 31.36 (978-0-7614-1054-6(6)); Rise of the Cities : 1820-1920. lib. bdg. 31.36 (978-0-7614-1051-5(1)); United States Enters the World : 1867-1919. lib. bdg. 31.36 (978-0-7614-1053-9(8)); 96p. (J). (gr. 5-9). (Illus.). 2000. Set lib. bdg. 125.43 (978-0-7614-1050-8(3) , Benchmark Bks.) Cavendish, Marshall Corp.

—The Rise of the Cities: 1820-1920. 2000. (Drama of American History Ser.). (Illus.). 96p. (J). (gr. 5-9). lib. bdg. 31.36 (978-0-7614-1051-5(1) , Benchmark Bks.) Cavendish, Marshall Corp.

Colman, C. H. The Bald Eagle's View of American History. Friar, Joanne H., illus. 2006. (J). (gr. 1-4). 48p. 12.95 (978-1-58089-300-8(7)); pap. 5.95 (978-1-58089-301-5(5)) Charlesbridge Publishing, Inc.

Color All About: America: A Giant Coloring Book about the Birth of a Nation. 2004. (Illus.). (J). (978-0-9763307-3-8(3)) Food Marketing Consultants, Inc.

Color & Discover Activity Book: The Crabby Lady Gets Historical! 2001. (Suzanne Tate's History Ser.). 32p. (J). pap. 2.95 (978-1-878405-33-3(0)) Nags Head Art, Inc.

Compass Point Books, contrib. by. Expansion & Reform: The Trail of Tears. (We the People Ser.). 48p. (YA). pap. 8.95 (978-0-7565-0937-8(8)) Compass Point Bks.

Complete Set. (Compass Point Early Biographies Ser.). (gr. 2-4). 531.50 (978-0-7565-0794-7(4)); (gr. 4-6). 926.60 (978-0-7565-0734-3(0)) Compass Point Bks.

A Concise History of the Stanley Hotel. 2001. 80p. 5.99 (978-0-9643331-5-4(5)) Write On Pubns.

Cornerstones of Freedom, Second Series, 10 Bks. 2004. 240.00 (978-0-516-23714-5(4) , Children's Pr.) Scholastic Library Publishing.

Cornerstones of Freedom, Second Series, 4 bks., Set. Incl. Building the New York City Subway. Santella, Andrew. 26.00 (978-0-516-23638-4(5)); Gilded Age. Morrow, Ann. 26.00 (978-0-516-23641-4(5)); Manhattan Project. Elish, Dan. 26.00 (978-0-516-23299-7(1)); U. S. Supreme Court. Elish, Dan. 26.00 (978-0-516-23637-7(7)); (Illus.). 48p. (J). (gr. 4-6). 2007. 2007. 104.00 (***978-0-531-17731-0(9)*** , Children's Pr.) Scholastic Library Publishing.

Cornerstones of FreedomTM, Second Series. 2004. 504.00 (978-0-516-24710-6(7)); 504.00 (978-0-516-27712-7(X)) Scholastic Library Publishing.

Creating America: A History of the United States. 2005. (gr. 6-12). stu. ed. (978-0-395-92899-8(0) , 2-88557) McDougal Littell Inc.

Creating America: Beginnings Through Reconstruction. 2005. (gr. 6-12). stu. ed. (978-0-618-16254-3(2) , 2-81243) McDougal Littell Inc.

Creating America: Beginnings Through World War I. 2005. (gr. 6-12). stu. ed. (978-0-618-00767-7(9) , 2-81127); stu. ed. (978-0-618-16252-9(6) , 2-81241) McDougal Littell Inc.

Creating America: 1877 to the 21st Century: EEdition. 2005. (gr. 6-12). cd-rom (978-0-618-28489-4(3) , 2-90168) McDougal Littell Inc.

Creating America: A History of the United States: Creating America Workbook. 2005. (gr. 6-12). (978-0-618-16521-6(5) , 2-81244) McDougal Littell Inc.

Creating America: A History of the United States: Creating America Workbook Answer Key. 2005. (gr. 6-12). (978-0-618-15629-0(1) , 2-01341) McDougal Littell Inc.

Creating America: a History of the United States: EEdition. 2002. (gr. 6-12). cd-rom (978-0-618-28491-7(5) , 2-90170) McDougal Littell Inc.

Creating America: A History of the United States: EEdition. 2005. (gr. 6-12). cd-rom (978-0-618-42733-8(3) , 2-00717) McDougal Littell Inc.

Creating America: a History of the United States: EEdition Plus Online. 2002. (gr. 6-12). (978-0-618-03211-2(8) , 2-70898) McDougal Littell Inc.

Creating America: A History of the United States: EEdition Plus Online. 2005. (gr. 6-12). (978-0-618-42734-5(1) , 2-00718) McDougal Littell Inc.

Creating America: A History of the United States: EEdition Plus Online Parent Purchase. 2005. (gr. 6-12). (978-0-618-42903-5(4) , 2-00777); (978-0-618-18719-5(7) , 2-70029) McDougal Littell Inc.

Creating America: A History of the United States: EEdition Plus Online with purchase of print Pupil's Edition-1 Year. 2002. (gr. 6-12). (978-0-618-18694-5(8) , 2-70017) McDougal Littell Inc.

Creating America: A History of the United States: EEdition Plus Online with purchase of print Pupil's Edition-2 Year. 2002. (gr. 6-12). (978-0-618-18696-9(4) , 2-70019) McDougal Littell Inc.

Creating America: A History of the United States: EEdition Plus Online with purchase of print Pupil's Edition-3 Year. 2002. (gr. 6-12). (978-0-618-18697-6(2) , 2-70020) McDougal Littell Inc.

Creating America: A History of the United States: EEdition Plus Online with purchase of print Pupil's Edition-4 Year. 2002. (gr. 6-12). (978-0-618-18698-3(0) , 2-70021) McDougal Littell Inc.

Creating America: A History of the United States: EEdition Plus Online with purchase of print Pupil's Edition-5 Year. 2002. (gr. 6-12). (978-0-618-18717-1(0) , 2-70027) McDougal Littell Inc.

Creating America: A History of the United States: EEdition Plus Online with purchase of print Pupil's Edition-6 Year. 2002. (gr. 6-12). (978-0-618-34792-6(5) , 2-90231) McDougal Littell Inc.

Creating America: A History of the United States: EEdition Plus Online with purchase of print Pupil's Year. 2nd ed. 2005. (gr. 6-12). (978-0-618-42728-4(7) , 2-00712) McDougal Littell Inc.

Creating America: a History of the United States: EEdition Plus Online with purchase of print Pupil's Year. 2005. (gr. 6-12). 3rd ed. (978-0-618-42729-1(5) , 2-00713); 4th ed. (978-0-618-42730-7(9) , 2-00714); 5th ed. (978-0-618-42731-4(7) , 2-00715); 6th ed. (978-0-618-42732-1(5) , 2-00716) McDougal Littell Inc.

Creating America: A History of the United States: EEdition Plus Online with purchase of print Pupil'sYear. 2005. (gr. 6-12). (978-0-618-42727-7(9) , 2-00711) McDougal Littell Inc.

Creating America: A History of the United States: ETest Plus Online-1 year (per Student) 2005. (gr. 6-12). (978-0-618-28361-3(7) , 2-90117) McDougal Littell Inc.

Creating America: A History of the United States: ETest Plus Online-2 year (per Student) 2005. (gr. 6-12). (978-0-618-28362-0(5) , 2-90118) McDougal Littell Inc.

Creating America: A History of the United States: ETest Plus Online-3 year (per Student) 2005. (gr. 6-12). (978-0-618-28377-4(3) , 2-90119) McDougal Littell Inc.

Creating America: A History of the United States: ETest Plus Online-4 year (per Student) 2005. (gr. 6-12). (978-0-618-28379-8(X) , 2-90120) McDougal Littell Inc.

Creating America: A History of the United States: ETest Plus Online-5 year (per Student) 2005. (gr. 6-12). (978-0-618-28380-4(3) , 2-90121) McDougal Littell Inc.

Creating America: A History of the United States: ETest Plus Online-6 year (per Student) 2005. (gr. 6-12). (978-0-618-28382-8(X) , 2-90122) McDougal Littell Inc.

Creating America: A History of the United States: GeoQuest. 2005. (gr. 6-12). cd-rom (978-0-618-03712-4(8) , 2-81168) McDougal Littell Inc.

Creating America: a History of the United States: Power Presentations. 2002. (gr. 6-12). cd-rom (978-0-618-03709-4(8) , 2-81165) McDougal Littell Inc.

Creating America: A History of the United States: Power Presentations. 2005. (gr. 6-12). cd-rom (978-0-618-43740-5(1) , 2-00809) McDougal Littell Inc.

Creating America: A History of the United States: Presidential Elections Handbook. 2005. (gr. 6-12). (978-0-618-14616-1(4) , 2-81231) McDougal Littell Inc.

Creating America: a History of the United States: Primary Source Explorer. 2005. (gr. 6-12). cd-rom (978-0-618-05015-4(9) , 2-81184); cd-rom (978-0-618-05016-1(7) , 2-81185) McDougal Littell Inc.

Creating America: A History of the United States: Primary Source Explorer. 2005. (gr. 6-12). cd-rom (978-0-618-03708-7(X) , 2-81164) McDougal Littell Inc.

Creating America: Beginnings through Reconstruction: Creating America: Beginnings through Reconstruction Workbook. 2005. (gr. 6-12). (978-0-618-19420-9(7) , 2-70061) McDougal Littell Inc.

Creating America: Beginnings Through Reconstruction: EEdition. 2005. (gr. 6-12). cd-rom (978-0-618-28490-0(7) , 2-90169) McDougal Littell Inc.

Creating America: Beginnings Through Reconstruction: EEdition Plus Online. 2005. (gr. 6-12). (978-0-618-19411-7(8) , 2-70053) McDougal Littell Inc.

Creating America: Beginnings Through Reconstruction: EEdition Plus Online with purchase of print Pupil's Year. 2005. (gr. 6-12). (978-0-618-18720-1(0) , 2-70030); 2nd ed. (978-0-618-18729-4(4) , 2-70037); 3rd ed. (978-0-618-19390-5(1) , 2-70038) McDougal Littell Inc.

Creating America: Beginnings Through Reconstruction: EEdition Plus Online with purchase of print Pupil's year. 4th ed. 2005. (gr. 6-12). (978-0-618-19391-2(X) , 2-70039) McDougal Littell Inc.

Creating America: Beginnings Through Reconstruction: EEdition Plus Online with purchase of print Pupil's Year. 2005. (gr. 6-12). 5th ed. (978-0-618-19400-1(2) , 2-70045); 6th ed. (978-0-618-34793-3(3) , 2-90232) McDougal Littell Inc.

Creating America: Beginnings Through World War I. 2005. (gr. 6-12). (978-0-618-16522-3(3) , 2-81245); tchr. ed. (978-0-618-37710-7(7) , 2-00491) McDougal Littell Inc.

Creating America: Beginnings through World War I: EEdition. 2005. (gr. 6-12). cd-rom (978-0-618-42757-4(0) , 2-00741) McDougal Littell Inc.

Creating America: Beginnings Through World War I: EEdition. 2002. (gr. 6-12). cd-rom (978-0-618-30085-3(6) , 2-20191) McDougal Littell Inc.

Creating America: Beginnings through World War I: EEdition Plus Online. 2002. (gr. 6-12). (978-0-618-19412-4(6) , 2-70054) McDougal Littell Inc.

Creating America: Beginnings Through World War I: EEdition Plus Online. 2005. (gr. 6-12). (978-0-618-42758-1(9) , 2-00742) McDougal Littell Inc.

Creating America: Beginnings Through World War I: EEdition Plus Online with purchase of print Pupil's Edition-1 Year. 2002. (gr. 6-12). (978-0-618-25839-0(6) , 2-70081) McDougal Littell Inc.

Creating America: Beginnings Through World War I: EEdition Plus Online with purchase of print Pupil's Edition-2 Year. 2002. (gr. 6-12). (978-0-618-25840-6(X) , 2-70082) McDougal Littell Inc.

Creating America: Beginnings Through World War I: EEdition Plus Online with purchase of print Pupil's Edition-3 Year. 2002. (gr. 6-12). (978-0-618-25841-3(8) , 2-70083) McDougal Littell Inc.

Creating America: Beginnings Through World War I: EEdition Plus Online with purchase of print Pupil's Edition-4 Year. 2002. (gr. 6-12). (978-0-618-25842-0(6) , 2-70084) McDougal Littell Inc.

Creating America: Beginnings Through World War I: EEdition Plus Online with purchase of print Pupil's Edition-5 Year. 2002. (gr. 6-12). (978-0-618-25843-7(4) , 2-70085) McDougal Littell Inc.

Creating America: Beginnings Through World War I: EEdition Plus Online with purchase of print Pupil's Edition-6 Year. 2002. (gr. 6-12). (978-0-618-34795-7(X) , 2-90233) McDougal Littell Inc.

Creating America: Beginnings Through World War I: EEdition Plus Online with purchase of print Pupil's Year. 2005. (gr. 6-12). (978-0-618-42751-2(1) , 2-00735) McDougal Littell Inc.

Creating America: Beginnings through World War I: EEdition Plus Online with purchase of print Pupil's Year. 2005. (gr. 6-12). 2nd ed. (978-0-618-42752-9(X) , 2-00736); 3rd ed. (978-0-618-42753-6(8) , 2-00737); 5th ed. (978-0-618-42755-0(4) , 2-00739); 6th ed. (978-0-618-42756-7(2) , 2-00740) McDougal Littell Inc.

Creating America: Beginnings Through World War I: EEdition Plus Online with purchase of print Pupil'sear. 4th ed. 2005. (gr. 6-12). (978-0-618-42754-3(6) , 2-00738) McDougal Littell Inc.

Creative Media Applications Staff. How Geography Affects the United States: The Midwest, 5 vols., Vol. 3. 2002. (Illus.). (J). (978-0-313-32253-2(8)) Greenwood Publishing Group, Inc.

—How Geography Affects the United States: The Northeast, 5 vols., Vol. 1. 2002. (Illus.). (J). (978-0-313-32251-8(1)) Greenwood Publishing Group, Inc.

—How Geography Affects the United States: The Northwest, 5 vols., Vol. 4. 2002. (Illus.). (J). (978-0-313-32254-9(6)) Greenwood Publishing Group, Inc.

—How Geography Affects the United States: The Southeast, 5 vols. 2002. (Illus.). 720p. (gr. 6-8). 209.95 (978-0-313-32250-1(3) , MS2250, Middle School Reference); Vol. 2. (J). (978-0-313-32252-5(X)) Greenwood Publishing Group, Inc.

—How Geography Affects the United States: The Southwest, 5 vols., Vol. 5. 2002. (Illus.). (J). (978-0-313-32255-6(4)) Greenwood Publishing Group, Inc.

Creative Media Applications Staff, contrib. by. Debatable Issues in U. S. History, 5 vols. 2004. (Middle School Reference Ser.). (Illus.). (J). 720p. (gr. 6-8). 209.95 (978-0-313-32910-4(9) , MS2910); (978-0-313-32911-1(7)); (978-0-313-32912-8(5)); (978-0-313-32913-5(3)); (978-0-313-32914-2(1)); (978-0-313-32915-9(X)) Greenwood Publishing Group, Inc. (Greenwood Pr.).

Crewe, Sabrina. Events That Shaped America: Anasazi Culture at Mesa Verde; Battle of Gettysburg; Bombing of Pearl Harbor; California Gold Rush; Montgomery Bus Boycott; Settling of St. Augustine, 6 bks. 2002. (Illus.). (J). (gr. 3 up). lib. bdg. 143.60 (978-0-8368-3389-8(9)) Stevens, Gareth Inc.

Crewe, Sabrina & Anderson, Dale. The Atom Bomb Project. 2004. (Events That Shaped America Ser.). (Illus.). 32p. (J). lib. bdg. 24.67 (978-0-8368-3404-8(6)) Stevens, Gareth Inc.

—The Seneca Falls Women's Rights Convention. 2004. (Events That Shaped America Ser.). (J). lib. bdg. 24.67 (978-0-8368-3408-6(9)) Stevens, Gareth Inc.

Critical Anthologies of Nonfiction Writing. 2005. (gr. 7-12). lib. bdg. 183.60 (978-1-4042-0354-9(0)) Rosen Publishing Group, Inc., The.

Crompton, Samuel Willard. 100 Americans Who Shaped American History. 1999. (gr. 7-12). lib. bdg. 16.40 (978-0-613-88694-9(1)); (Illus.). (J). (978-0-606-20514-6(4)) Tandem Library Bks.

—100 Colonial Leaders Who Shaped North America. 1999. (gr. 7-12). lib. bdg. 16.40 (978-0-613-67507-9(X)); (Illus.). (J). (978-0-606-20519-1(5)) Tandem Library Bks.

Currie, Stephen. Expeditions in the Americas: 1492-1700. 2004. (National Geographic Reading Expeditions Ser.). (Illus.). 32p. (J). pap. (978-0-7922-4544-5(X)) National Geographic Society.

—The Quest for Freedom: The Abolitionist Movement. 2005. (Lucent Library of Black History). (Illus.). 112p. (YA). (gr. 7-10). lib. bdg. 32.45 (978-1-59018-703-6(2) , Lucent Bks.) Thomson Gale.

D'Amico, Joan & Drummond, Karen Eich. The U. S. History Cookbook: Delicious Recipes & Exciting Events from the Past. Cline, Jeff & Cash-Walsh, Tina, illus. 2003. 192p. pap. 14.95 (978-0-471-13602-6(6) , Howell Bk. Hse.) Wiley, John & Sons, Inc.

D'Amico, Joan & Drumond, Karen Eich. The US History Cook Book: Delicious Recipes & Exciting Events from the Past. 2006. (Illus.). 180p. (J). (gr. 4-8). reprint ed. pap. 15.00 (***978-1-4223-5809-2(7)***) DIANE Publishing Co.

Davenport, John. The Mason-Dixon Line. 2004. (Arbitrary Borders Ser.). (Illus.). 112p. (gr. 9-13). 35.00 (978-0-7910-7830-3(2) , Chelsea Hse.) Facts On File, Inc.

David Haugen. Colonists. 2004. (Voices from the Revolution Ser.). lib. bdg. 22.45 (978-1-4103-0413-1(2)) Thomson Gale.

—Leaders. 2004. lib. bdg. 22.45 (978-1-56711-958-9(1) , Blackbirch Pr., Inc.) Thomson Gale.

Davidson, James West & Lytle, Mark H. After the Fact Vol. I: With Primary Source Investigator. 5th ed. 2004. (C). pap., stu. ed. 43.75 (978-0-07-299610-4(2) , 9780072996104, McGraw-Hill Humanities, Social Sciences & World Languages) McGraw-Hill Higher Education.

—After the Fact Vol. II: With Primary Source Investigator CD. 5th rev. ed. 2004. (C). pap. 43.75 (978-0-07-299611-1(0) , 9780072996111, McGraw-Hill Humanities, Social Sciences & World Languages) McGraw-Hill Higher Education.

Davidson, James West, et al. The American Nation: Civil War to the Present. 2001. (Illus.). xxiii, 420p. (J). stu. ed. 78.10 (978-0-13-052270-2(8)) Prentice Hall PTR.

Davies, Gill. The Thirteen Colonies 1584 - 1776. 2005. (National Geographic Timelines Ser.). (Illus.). 64p. (J). 27.90 (978-0-7922-4171-3(1)) National Geographic Society.

Davis, Kenneth C. Don't Know Much about American History. 2004. (Don't Know Much about(R) Ser.). 224p. (J). (gr. 4-7). pap. 40.00 incl. audio (978-0-8072-2092-4(2) , Listening Library) Random Hse. Audio Publishing Group.

—Don't Know Much about American History. 2003. (gr. 3-6). lib. bdg. 30.40 (978-0-613-59234-5(4)) Tandem Library Bks.

—Don't Know Much about' American History. Faulkner, Matt, illus. 2003. (Don't Know Much About Ser.). 224p. (J). pap. 6.99 (978-0-06-440836-3(1) , Harper Trophy) HarperCollins Pubs.

Day, Nancy. Your Travel Guide to Colonial America. 2003. (Passport to History Ser.). (Illus.). 96p. (J). (gr. 5-8). pap. 7.95 (978-0-8225-9908-1(2)) Lerner Publishing Group.

—Your Travel Guide to Colonial America. 2001. (gr. 5-8). lib. bdg. 16.40 (978-0-613-33274-3(1)) Tandem Library Bks.

Day, Reed B. Two Families: A History of the Lives & Times of the Families of Isaac Newton Day & Lucilla Caroline Blachly 1640-1940. 2004. (Illus.). 285p. per. 29.95 (978-0-9760563-1-7(3) , 7796) Mechling Bookbindery.

DBQ Practice U. S. History. 2003. spiral bd. 19.95 (978-1-56004-144-3(7)) Social Studies Schl. Service.

Decade Days. 2002. 192p. (gr. 7-12). 16.99 (978-0-7682-0320-2(1) , GA13051) School Specialty Publishing.

Deitch, JoAnne Weisman, ed. Reconstruction. 2002. (Researching American History Ser.). (Illus.) (J). pap. 7.95 (978-1-57960-072-3(7)) History Compass, LLC.

Discover America State by State, 51 vols., Set. 2005. (Illus.). (J). (gr. k-5). 895.00 (978-1-58536-294-3(8)) Sleeping Bear Pr.

Dolan, Edward F., Jr. American History - Group 1, 4 bks., Set. Incl. Boston Tea Party. lib. bdg. 25.64 (978-0-7614-1303-5(0)); Lost Colony of Roanoke. lib. bdg. 25.64 (978-0-7614-1301-1(4)); Salem Witch Trials. lib. bdg. 25.64 (978-0-7614-1302-8(2)); Winter at Valley Forge. lib. bdg. 25.64 (978-0-7614-1304-2(9)); 48p. (J). (gr. 3 up). (Illus.). 2001. Set lib. bdg. 102.57 (978-0-7614-1300-4(6) , Benchmark Bks.) Cavendish, Marshall Corp.

Dooley, Tom. America's Lost Dream. Looney, Bill, illus. 2005. 80p. (J). 15.99 (978-0-89221-620-8(4) , 303-202, New Leaf Pr.) New Leaf Pr., Inc.

Dorling Kindersley Publishing Staff. Presidents. rev. ed. 2003. (Dk Eyewitness Books Ser.). 64p. (J). lib. bdg. 19.99 (978-0-7894-8899-2(X)) Dorling Kindersley Publishing, Inc.

—Texas. 2003. (Eyewitness Bks.). (Illus.). 64p. (J). pap. 15.99 (978-0-7894-9745-1(X)) Dorling Kindersley Publishing, Inc.

Douglas, Lloyd G. The Pledge of Allegiance. 2003. (Welcome Book Ser.). (Illus.). 24p. (J). 18.00 (978-0-516-25853-9(2)); pap. 4.95 (978-0-516-27876-6(2)) Scholastic Library Publishing. (Children's Pr.).

Douglas, Vincent & School Specialty Publishing Staff. All about the United States. 2001. (Brighter Child Activity Bks.). (Illus.). 32p. (J). pap. 2.99 (978-0-7696-3579-8(2) , American Education Publishing) School Specialty Publishing.

Downey, Matthew T. American History 1 (Before 1865) - Softcover Student Edition with CD-ROM. pap., stu. ed. 29.97 incl. cd-rom (978-0-07-704434-3(7)) McGraw-Hill/Contemporary.

—American History 1 (Before 1865) - Softcover Student Text Only. pap., stu. ed. 19.95 (978-0-07-704435-0(5)) McGraw-Hill/Contemporary.

—American History 2 (after 1865) - Softcover Student Edition with CD-ROM. pap., stu. ed. 29.97 incl. cd-rom (978-0-07-704437-4(1)) McGraw-Hill/Contemporary.

—American History 2 (after 1865) - Softcover Student Text Only. pap., stu. ed. 19.95 (978-0-07-704438-1(X)) McGraw-Hill/Contemporary.

Downing, Brian M. The Paths of Glory: Social Change in America from the Great War to Vietnam. 2003. 324p. (YA). per. 22.95 (978-1-877275-58-6(1)) Cybereditions Corp. Ltd. NZL. *Dist:* Ingram Bk. Co.

Draper, Allison Stark. Clothing, Costumes & Uniforms Throughout American History, 6 bks. Incl. What People Wore During the American Revolution. lib. bdg. 19.95 (978-0-8239-5666-1(0) , PKCLRE); What People Wore During the Civil War. lib. bdg. 19.95 (978-0-8239-5669-2(5) , PKCLCI); What People Wore During the Westward Expansion. lib. bdg. 19.95 (978-0-8239-5667-8(9) , PKCLPL); What People Wore in Colonial America. lib. bdg. 19.95 (978-0-8239-5665-4(2) , PKCLCO); What People Wore in Early America. lib. bdg. 19.95 (978-0-8239-5664-7(4) , PKCLEA); What People Wore on Southern Plantations. lib. bdg. 19.95 (978-0-8239-5668-5(7) , PKCLPL); 24p. (J). (gr. 3). 2001. (Illus.). Set lib. bdg. 117.00 (978-0-8239-7060-5(4) , PKCLAM, PowerKids Pr.) Rosen Publishing Group, Inc., The.

Duby, Marjorie. From Caravels to the Constitution: Puzzles Targeting Historical Themes That Reinforce Logic & Problem-Solving Skills. VanBlaricum, Pam, ed. Armstrong, Bev & Grayson, Rick, illus. 2006. 112p. pap. 13.99 (978-0-88160-385-9(6) , LW405, Learning Works, The) Creative Teaching Pr., Inc.

Dudley, William. From Colonial Times to Reconstruction. 2006. (Opposing Viewpoints in American History Ser.: Vol. 1). 224p. (J). (gr. 9 up). 59.95 (978-0-7377-3184-2(2)); pap. 39.95 (978-0-7377-3185-9(0)) Thomson Gale. (Greenhaven Pr., Inc.).

—From Reconstruction to the Present. 2006. (Opposing Viewpoints in American History Ser.: Vol. 2). 224p. (J). (gr. 9 up). 59.95 (978-0-7377-3186-6(9)); pap. 39.95 (978-0-7377-3187-3(7)) Thomson Gale. (Greenhaven Pr., Inc.).

Due Process DBA. 2003. spiral bd. 16.95 (978-1-56004-148-1(X)) Social Studies Schl. Service.

Dutch Colonies in the Americas, 6 Pks. (On Deck Ser.: Vol. 2). 24p. (gr. 4-5). 35.00 (978-0-7578-5800-0(7)) Rigby Education.

Egan, Lorraine Hopping. Great American History Games: More Than 20 Exciting, Ready-to-Go Games, Puzzles & Fun-Filled Activities. 2000. (Illus.). 80p. (J). 11.95 (978-0-439-11104-1(8)) Scholastic, Inc.

Elson, Henry W. Sidelights on American History I, 2 vols. 2001. (Sidelights on American History Ser.: Vol. 1). 272p. (gr. 7-12). (978-0-89526-295-0(9)) Regnery Publishing, Inc., An Eagle Publishing Co.

—Sidelights on American History II, 2 vols. 2001. (Sidelights on American History Ser.: Vol. 2). 272p. (gr. 7-12). (978-0-89526-294-3(0)) Regnery Publishing, Inc., An Eagle Publishing Co.

Encyclopedia Britannica's Annals of America 2003, 22 vols. 2003. 13000p. (YA). (gr. 5 up). 529.00 (978-0-85229-960-9(5)) Encyclopaedia Britannica, Inc.

English Colonies in the Americas: Individual Title, 6 pack. (On Deck Ser.: Vol. 2). 24p. (gr. 4-5). 35.00 (978-0-7578-5801-7(5)) Rigby Education.

English, June. Scholastic Encyclopedia of the United States at War: Updated Edition. 2003. (gr. 5-8). lib. bdg. 17.60 (978-0-613-72290-2(6)) Tandem Library Bks.

Ervin, Robert Edgar. The John Hunt Morgan Raid of 1863. 2003. (Illus.). 306p. lib. bdg. 29.95 net. (978-0-9746189-0-6(X)) Ervin, Robert E.

Expansion & Reform. (We the People Ser.). (gr. 4-6). 271.20 (978-0-7565-0796-1(0)) Compass Point Bks.

Exploration & Colonization. (We the People Ser.). (gr. 4-6). 180.80 (978-0-7565-0797-8(9)) Compass Point Bks.

Exquemelin, Alexander O. The Buccaneers of America. 2000. (Illus.). 231p. pap. 10.95 (978-0-486-40966-5(X)) Dover Pubns., Inc.

Eyewitness History Set. 2005. (Eyewitness History Ser.). 288p. (gr. 9). 1425.00 (978-0-8160-6343-7(5)) Facts On File, Inc.

Facts on File, Inc. Staff. Top Careers for History Graduates. 2004. (Top Careers Ser.). (Illus.). 384p. (gr. 9). pap. 14.95 (978-0-8160-5567-8(X) , Checkmark Bks.) Facts On File, Inc.

Feinberg, Barbara Silberdick. The Changing White House. 2001. (Cornerstones of Freedom Ser.). (Illus.). 32p. (J). (gr. 4-6). pap. 5.95 (978-0-516-27164-4(4) , Children's Pr.) Scholastic Library Publishing.

Feinstein. Rising of a New Nation. 2000. (Making of America Ser.). (J). (978-0-606-20306-7(0)) Tandem Library Bks.

Feinstein, Stephen. The 1950s from the Korean War to Elvis. 2000. (Decades of the 20th Century Ser.). (Illus.). 64p. (J). (gr. 5-12). lib. bdg. 22.60 (978-0-7660-1427-5(4)) Enslow Pubs., Inc.

Feinstein, Steve. Rising of a New Nation. 2000. (978-0-606-20383-8(4)) Tandem Library Bks.

Felder, Deborah G. 100 American Women Who Shaped American History. 2005. (Illus.). 112p. (J). (gr. 4-7). per. 15.90 (978-0-606-33775-5(X)) Tandem Library Bks.

Fetty, Maurice A. The Northeast Region of the United States. 1999. pap. (978-0-7398-1314-0(5)) Steck-Vaughn.

—The River & Lakes States. 1999. pap. (978-0-7398-1317-1(X)) Steck-Vaughn.

—The Southeast Region of the United States. 1999. pap. (978-0-7398-1315-7(3)) Steck-Vaughn.

—The West Region of the United States. 1999. pap. (978-0-7398-1316-4(1)) Steck-Vaughn.

Field, Robert J. History of the United States. 3rd rev. ed. 1998. (Illus.). (gr. 4-12). Vol. I. 106p. (J). pap., wbk. ed. 10.95 (978-0-87594-379-4(9) , 7576); Vol. 2. 152p. (YA). pap., wbk. ed. 10.95 (978-0-87594-374-9(8) , 7577) Book-Lab.

Findlay, Diane. Pages of the Past: Exploring U. S. History Through Children's Literature. 2002. 88p. (J). (gr. 4-8). pap. 16.95 (978-1-57950-043-6(9) , Upstart Bks.) Highsmith Inc.

First Americans, 6 bks., Set. Incl. Apache. Casey, Carolyn. lib. bdg. (978-0-7614-1894-8(6)); Cherokee. De Capua, Sarah E. lib. bdg. (978-0-7614-1895-5(4)); Iroquois. De Capua, Sarah E. lib. bdg. (978-0-7614-1896-2(2)); Navajo. King, David C. lib. bdg. (978-0-7614-1897-9(0)); Pueblo. Broida, Marian. lib. bdg. (978-0-7614-1898-6(9)); Sioux. King, David C. lib. bdg. (978-0-7614-1899-3(7)); (Illus.). 48p. (J). (gr. 3-7). 2005. (978-0-7614-1893-1(8) , Benchmark Bks.) Cavendish, Marshall Corp.

First Person America, 5 vols. 2004. (History & Social Studies Ser.). (Illus.). 64p. (YA). (gr. 5 up). (978-0-7613-3029-5(1) , Twenty-First Century Bks.) Lerner Publishing Group.

Fof. American Profiles, 26 vols., Set. 2002. (YA). (gr. 5-12). 300.00 (978-0-8160-4749-9(9)) Facts On File, Inc.

Fowler, Jennifer. Educate U. S. Achievement Book. 1999. (J). 10.95 (978-0-9673802-1-6(9) , Educate US); 2001. (Illus.). 114p. (YA). 8.00 (978-0-9673802-2-3(7)) Fowler Publishing.

Fradin, Dennis B. Turning Points in U. S. History, 6 bks., Set. Incl. Alamo. (gr. 3-6). lib. bdg. 29.93 (978-0-7614-2127-6(0)); Assassination of Abraham Lincoln. lib. bdg. 29.93 (978-0-7614-2123-8(8)); Custer's Last Stand. lib. bdg. 29.93 (978-0-7614-2124-5(6)); Declaration of Independence. (gr. 3-6). lib. bdg. 29.93 (978-0-7614-2129-0(7)); Jamestown, Virginia. (gr. 3-6). lib. bdg. 29.93 (978-0-7614-2122-1(X)); Mayflower Compact. lib. bdg. 29.93 (978-0-7614-2125-2(4)); (Illus.). 48p. (J). 2006. 2007. Set lib. bdg. 179.57 (***978-0-7614-2121-4(1)*** , Benchmark Bks.) Cavendish, Marshall Corp.

Fradin, Dennis Brindell. With a Little Luck: 11 Surprising Stories of Amazing Discoveries. Fradin, Dennis Brindell, illus. 2006. (Illus.). 144p. (J). (gr. 4). 17.99 (978-0-525-47196-7(0) , Dutton Juvenile) Penguin Group (USA) Inc.

Franck, Irene M. & Brownstone, David M. Frontier America, 10 vols. 2004. (Illus.). (J). 369.00 (978-0-7172-5990-8(0) , Grolier) Scholastic Library Publishing.

Frank, Sarah. Filipinos in America. 2006. (In America Ser.). (Illus.). 72p. (J). (ps-7). 27.93 (978-0-8225-4873-7(9) , Lerner Pubns.) Lerner Publishing Group.

French Colonies in the Americas: Individual Title Six-Packs. (On Deck Ser.: Vol. 2). 24p. (gr. 4-5). 35.00 (978-0-7578-5802-4(3)) Rigby Education.

Fridell, Ron. Prisoners of War. 2007. (Open for Debate Ser.). (J). lib. bdg. (***978-0-7614-2577-9(2)*** , Benchmark Bks.) Cavendish, Marshall Corp.

Friedman-Brunt, Elyse. Conflict Resolution in American History, Gr. 8: Lessons from the Past, Lessons for Today. Chandler, Terrence, illus. 2003. 48p. (YA). pap., wbk. ed. 19.95 (978-1-878227-89-8(0)) Peace Education Foundation.

—Conflict Resolution in American History, Grade 8: Lessons from the Past, Lessons for Today. Chandler, Terrence, illus. 2003. 200p. pap., instr.'s training gde. ed. 29.95 (978-1-878227-88-1(2)) Peace Education Foundation.

Friedman, Ian C. Freedom of Speech & the Press. 2005. (American Rights Ser.). (Illus.). 128p. (J). (gr. 4-9). per. 35.00 (978-0-8160-5662-0(5)) Facts On File, Inc.

Friedman, Michael & Friedman, Brett. Settlement Houses: Improving the Social Welfare of America's Immigrants. 2004. (Progressive Movement, 1900-1920 Ser.). (Illus.). 32p. (J). lib. bdg. (978-1-4042-0194-1(7)) Rosen Publishing Group, Inc., The.

Fritz, Jean. Why Not, Lafayette? Himler, Ronald, illus. 2001. 96p. (J). (gr. 3-7). pap. 5.99 (978-0-698-11882-9(0) , Putnam Juvenile) Penguin Group (USA) Inc.

Garcia, Jesus. Creating America: A History of the United States 1877 to the 21st Century, 2 vols. l.t. ed. 2005. (Illus.). (YA). (gr. 7-9). stu. ed. 77.32 (978-0-618-37684-1(4) , 2-00465) McDougal Littell Inc.

—Creating America: A History of the United States: Beginnings Through Reconstruction, 2 vols. l.t. ed. 2005. (Illus.). (YA). (gr. 7-9). stu. ed. 80.80 (978-0-618-37698-8(4) , 2-00479) McDougal Littell Inc.

—Creating America Set: A History of the United States, 11 vols. 2002. 3741p. (YA). (gr. 7-9). stu. ed. 1872.00 (978-0-618-16250-5(X) , 2-81239) McDougal Littell Inc.

—Creating America: A History of the United States. l.t. ed. 2005. (YA). (gr. 7-9). stu. ed. 78.64 (978-0-618-37690-2(9) , 2-00471) McDougal Littell Inc.

—Creating America: Beginnings Through World War I: Pupil's Edition (c)2005. l.t. ed. 2005. (Illus.). (YA). (gr. 7-9). (978-0-618-37708-4(5) , 2-00489) McDougal Littell Inc.

Gave, Marc. La historia de los Estados Unidos en Suma. ed. 2004. (SPA.). 32p. (J). pap. 6.00 (978-1-4108-2342-7(3) , A23423) Benchmark Education Co.

George, Linda & George, Charles. The Natchez Trace. 2002. (Cornerstones of Freedom Ser.). (Illus.). 32p. (J). (gr. 4-6). pap. 5.95 (978-0-516-25959-8(4) , Children's Pr.) Scholastic Library Publishing.

Gilchrist, Jan Spivey. My America. Gilchrist, Jan Spivey & Bryan, Ashley, illus. 2007. 40p. (J). (gr. k-4). 16.99 (***978-0-06-079104-9(7));*** lib. bdg. 17.89 (***978-0-06-079105-6(5)***) HarperCollins Pubs.

Gillon. American Experiment Complete with Student History Research Passkey Second Edition Plus Atlas. 2nd ed. 2005. (YA). pap. 65.16 (978-0-618-72362-1(5) , 397253) Houghton Mifflin College Div.

Glasthal, Jacqueline B. History Comes Alive Teaching Unit: The American Revolution. 2003. 72p. pap. 11.95 (978-0-590-31500-5(5)) Scholastic, Inc.

Globe Fearon American History Vol. 1: Prehistory Through Reconstruction. 2003. 542p. (YA). (gr. 6-12). 50.95 (978-0-13-024400-0(7)) Globe Fearon Educational Publishing.

Globe Fearon American History Vol. 2: Civil War to the Present. 2003. 524p. (YA). (gr. 6-12). 50.95 (978-0-13-024411-6(2)) Globe Fearon Educational Publishing.

Goldsmith, Marcia. Important Years: The 1980s. 2005. (Illus.). 16p. (J). (***978-0-618-56043-1(2)***) Houghton Mifflin Co.

Gonzalez, Libia. Geografia e Historia de los Estados Unidos. (SPA.). 376p. (J). pap. 52.50 (978-958-04-3011-7(X) , NOR011) Norma S.A. COL. *Dist:* AIMS International Bks., Inc., Continental Bk. Co., Inc., Distribuidora Norma, Inc.

Goodall, Barry, Jr. Glory Gone Forgotten: The Untold Story of the 12th Kentucky Cavalry. Embry, Eugene, ed. Brown, Stevi, illus. 2nd rev. ed. 2005. 182p. (978-0-9763932-1-4(2) , 500) Goodall, Barry.

Goodman, Susan E. Cora Frear: True Stories from America's Past. Ettlinger, Doris, illus. 2002. (Brave Kids Ready-for-Chapters Ser.). 64p. (J). lib. bdg. 11.89 (978-0-689-84330-3(5) , Aladdin Library) Simon & Schuster Children's Publishing.

—A Week in the 1800s, No. 4. 2001. (Ultimate Field Trip Ser.). (Illus.). (J). (978-0-606-21499-5(2)) Tandem Library Bks.

Goodrich, Samuel G. A Child's History of the United States. reprint ed. 150.00 (978-0-7222-7251-0(0)) Library Reprints, Inc.

Goodrich, Samuel Griswol. Peter Parleys Tales about America & Au. 2006. pap. (***978-1-4068-3320-1(7)***) Echo Library.

Gordy, F. Wilbur. Stories of Later American History. 2006. 96.99 (***978-1-4280-4034-2(X));*** pap. 89.99 (***978-1-4280-4021-2(8)***) IndyPublish.com.

Gould, Roberta. Kidtopia: 'Round the Country & Back Through Time in 60 Projects. 2000. (gr. 3-6). lib. bdg. 23.40 (978-0-613-85262-3(1)) Tandem Library Bks.

—Kidtopia: 'Round the Country & Back Through Time in 60 Projects. 2004. (Illus.). 160p. (gr. 1-7). 13.95 (978-1-58246-026-0(4) , Tricycle Pr.) Ten Speed Pr.

Graff, Jane. Nebraska Our Towns: East Southeast. 2002. per. 29.95 (978-0-934904-47-6(2)) Lee, J.& L. Co.

Grant, R. G. The Great Depression. 2005. (How Did It Happen? Ser.). (Illus.). 48p. (YA). (gr. 7-10). lib. bdg. 29.95 (978-1-59018-606-0(0) , Lucent Bks.) Thomson Gale.

Graphic History. 2005. (Graphic Library). (Illus.) (J). (gr. 3-4). lib. bdg. 505.20 (978-0-7368-4428-4(7)) Capstone Pr., Inc.

Graphic Organizers in Social Studies. (Illus.). (J). (gr. 3-5). 119.70 (978-1-4042-2956-3(6)) Rosen Publishing Group, Inc., The.

Great Depression & New Deal DBA. 2001. spiral bd. 16.95 (978-1-56004-119-1(6)) Social Studies Schl. Service.

Green, Carl R. The Gemini 4 Spacewalk Mission: A MyReportLinks. com Book. 2004. (Space Flight Adventures & Disasters Ser.). (Illus.). 48p. (J). lib. bdg. 25.26 (978-0-7660-5163-8(3) , MyReportLinks.com Bks.) Enslow Pubs., Inc.

Greenberg, Morrie. American Characters: They Marched to a Different Drummer, 1850 to 1950. 2000. (Illus.). (J). (978-0-9622652-4-2(1)) Brooke-Richards Pr.

Gregory, Kristiana. Five Smooth Stones: Hope's Revolutionary War Diary. 2002. (gr. 3-6). lib. bdg. 13.00 (978-0-613-53811-4(0)); 2001. (J). (gr. 4-7). (978-0-606-19581-2(5)) Tandem Library Bks.

Gregson, Susan R. Francis Scott Key: Patriotic Poet. 2003. (Let Freedom Ring Ser.). (Illus.). 48p. (J). (gr. 3-4). lib. bdg. 22.60 (978-0-7368-1554-3(6) , Bridgestone Bks.) Capstone Pr., Inc.

Gritzner, Charles F. The United States. 2007. (Modern World Nations Ser.). 144p. (J). (gr. 6-12). 30.00 (***978-0-7910-9511-9(8)*** , Chelsea Hse.) Facts On File, Inc.

Grodin, Elissa. Everyone Counts: A Citizen's Number Book. Juhasz, Victor, illus. rev. ed. 2006. 40p. (J). 17.95 (978-1-58536-295-0(6)) Sleeping Bear Pr.

Grote, JoAnn A. The American Victory: A New Nation Is Born. 1999. (American Adventure Ser.: No. 12). 144p. (J). (gr. 3-7). lib. bdg. 15.95 (978-0-7910-5586-1(8) , Chelsea Hse.) Facts On File, Inc.

—The Internal Revenue Service. 2001. (Your Government Ser.). (Illus.). 64p. (J). (gr. 4-7). 25.00 (978-0-7910-5989-0(8) , Chelsea Hse.) Facts On File, Inc.

Gustafson, R. W. York: The Slave Who Helped Explore America. 2001. (Illus.). 64p. (YA). (gr. 2 up). pap. 9.95 (978-0-912299-93-8(2)) Stoneydale Pr. Publishing Co.

Hablitzel, Marie & Stitzer, Kim H. Draw Write Now Bk. 5: The United States, from Sea to Sea, Moving Forward. 1998. (Draw Write Now Ser.). (Illus.). 64p. (J). (gr. k-5). pap. 10.95 (978-0-9639307-5-0(3)) Barker Creek Publishing, Inc.

Hakim, Joy. All the People. rev. ed. 2007. (History of US Ser.: Vol. 10). 272p. pap. 15.95 (***978-0-19-532724-3(1)***) Oxford Univ. Pr., Inc.

—First Americans. 2003. (gr. 5-8). lib. bdg. 23.40 (978-0-613-55164-9(8)) Tandem Library Bks.

—A History of the US Bk. 5: Liberty for All?, 1820-1860. 3rd rev. ed. 2002. (History of US Ser.: Vol. 5). (Illus.). 160p. pap. 15.95 (978-0-19-515328-6(6)) Oxford Univ. Pr., Inc.

—A History of the US Bk. 8: An Age of Extremes, 1880-1917. 3rd rev. ed. 2002. (History of US Ser.: Vol. 8). (Illus.). 160p. pap. 15.95 (978-0-19-515334-7(0)) Oxford Univ. Pr., Inc.

—A History of the US Bk. 11: Sourcebook & Index. 3rd rev. ed. 2002. (History of US Ser.: Vol. 11). (Illus.). 330p. pap. 15.95 (978-0-19-515340-8(5)) Oxford Univ. Pr., Inc.

—A History of U. S. War, Peace, & All That Jazz. rev. ed. 2007. (History of US Ser.: Vol. 9). 224p. pap. 15.95 (***978-0-19-532723-6(3)***) Oxford Univ. Pr., Inc.

—A History of US, 10 vols. 3rd ed. 2003. (Illus.). 186p. (J). 199.50 (978-0-19-515259-3(X)) Oxford Univ. Pr., Inc.

—A History of US: Ten-volume Set. rev. ed. 2006. (History of US Ser.). (Illus.). 199.50 (***978-0-19-531491-5(3)***) Oxford Univ. Pr., Inc.

—A History of US Bk. 1: The First Americans, Prehistory-1600. 3rd rev. ed. 2002. (History of US Ser.: Vol. 1). (Illus.). 160p. pap. 15.95 (978-0-19-515320-0(0)) Oxford Univ. Pr., Inc.

—A History of US Bk. 8: Age of Extremes. rev. ed. 2007. (History of US Ser.: Vol. 8). 224p. pap. 15.95 (***978-0-19-532722-9(5)***) Oxford Univ. Pr., Inc.

—A History of Us Bk. 8: An Age of Extremes. rev. ed. 2006. (History of US Ser.). (Illus.). 210p. 19.95 (978-0-19-518236-1(7)) Oxford Univ. Pr., Inc.

—A History of Us Bk. 11: Sourcebook & Index. rev. ed. 2005. (History of US Ser.). 160p. 21.95 (978-0-19-518903-2(5)) Oxford Univ. Pr., Inc.

—War, Peace, & All That Jazz 1918-1945 Teaching Guide, Bk. 9. 3rd ed. 2002. (History of US Ser.). (Illus.). 112p. pap., tchr. ed. 16.95 (978-0-19-515359-0(6)) Oxford Univ. Pr., Inc.

—War, Terrible War. 2003. (gr. 5-8). lib. bdg. 23.40 (978-0-613-55202-8(4)) Tandem Library Bks.

Hallan-Gibson, Pamela. Orange County the Golden Promise: An Illustrated History. 2002. 436p. 34.95 (978-1-892724-26-7(X)) American Historical Pr.

Hammond World Atlas Corporation Staff. American History Through Maps. 2004. (Atlas Ser.). (Illus.). 48p. (J). (gr. 5). pap. 8.95 (978-0-8437-7435-1(5) , 774355) Hammond World Atlas Corp.

Harcourt School Publishers Staff. Beginning Horizons: Test Prep: US History Indiana Edition. 2nd ed. 2002. (Illus.). (gr. 5). pap. 9.80 (978-0-15-335690-2(1)) Harcourt Schl. Pubs.

—Beginning Horizons: Test Prep: US History Virginia Edition. 2nd ed. 2002. (gr. 5). pap. 9.80 (978-0-15-335704-6(5)) Harcourt Schl. Pubs.

—Beginning Horizons: Time for Kids Readers: US History. 3rd ed. 2002. (Harcourt Horizons Ser.). (gr. k-7). pap., tchr. ed. 69.40 (978-0-15-334655-2(8)) Harcourt Schl. Pubs.

—Days of the Exodusters: Take-Home Book. 2001. (Collections Ser.). (Illus.). (J). pap. 1.90 (978-0-15-319508-2(8)) Harcourt Schl. Pubs.

—Diamond Cove Anthology. 99th ed. 1999. (Signatures Ser.). (Illus.). (gr. 2). 54.30 (978-0-15-310109-0(1)) Harcourt Schl. Pubs.

—Horizons. 3rd ed. 2003. (gr. 1). stu. ed. 46.20 (978-0-15-339615-1(6)); (gr. 2). stu. ed. 46.20 (978-0-15-339616-8(4)); (gr. 3). 53.20 (978-0-15-339617-5(2)) Harcourt Schl. Pubs.

—Horizons: Time for Kids Readers: State & Regions. 3rd ed. 2002. (Harcourt Horizons Ser.). (gr. k-7). pap., tchr. ed. 56.30 (978-0-15-334650-7(7)) Harcourt Schl. Pubs.

—Horizons: Time for Kids Readers: US History. 3rd ed. 2003. (Harcourt Horizons Ser.). (gr. k-7). tchr. ed. 57.40 (978-0-15-334654-5(X)) Harcourt Schl. Pubs.

—Horizons: US History. 3rd ed. (Harcourt Horizons Ser.). 2001. (Illus.). (gr. k-7). pap., act. bk. ed. 10.40 (978-0-15-322602-1(1)); Vol. 1. 2003. (gr. 4-7). tchr. ed. 143.40 (978-0-15-320189-9(4)); Vol. 2. 2002. (gr. 4-7). tchr. ed. 143.40 (978-0-15-321961-0(0)) Harcourt Schl. Pubs.

—Horizons: US History - Beginning-1877. 3rd ed. 2001. (Harcourt Horizons Ser.). (Illus.). (gr. k-7). pap., act. bk. ed. 10.40 (978-0-15-322603-8(X)) Harcourt Schl. Pubs.

—Horizons: US History Assessment Program. 3rd ed. 2002. (Harcourt Horizons Ser.). (gr. k-7). pap. 131.40 (978-0-15-322590-1(4)) Harcourt Schl. Pubs.

—Horizons: US History: Beginning-1877. 3rd ed. 2002. (Harcourt Horizons Ser.). (gr. 4-7). Vol. 1. (Illus.). tchr. ed. 143.40 (978-0-15-321964-1(5)); Vol. 2. tchr. ed. 143.40 (978-0-15-321965-8(3)) Harcourt Schl. Pubs.

—Horizons: US History: Beginning-1877 Assessment Program. 3rd ed. 2001. (Harcourt Horizons Ser.). (gr. k-7). pap. 107.20 (978-0-15-322591-8(2)) Harcourt Schl. Pubs.

—Horizons: US History: Civil War-Present. 3rd ed. 2002. (Harcourt Horizons Ser.). (gr. 4-7). Vol. 1. tchr. ed. 143.40 (978-0-15-321966-5(1)); Vol. 2. tchr. ed. 143.40 (978-0-15-321967-2(X)) Harcourt Schl. Pubs.

—Horizons: US History: Civil War-Present Assessment Program. 3rd ed. 2001. (Harcourt Horizons Ser.). (gr. k-7). pap. 107.20 (978-0-15-322592-5(0)) Harcourt Schl. Pubs.

—Horizons Bk. 6: Time for Kids Collections: US History 5 Pack. 3rd ed. 2002. (Harcourt Horizontes Ser.). (SPA.). (gr. 3 up). pap. 46.20 (978-0-15-333904-2(7)) Harcourt Schl. Pubs.

—Horizons Bk. 14: Time for Kids Collections: US History. 3rd ed. 2002. pap. 9.30 (978-0-15-333919-6(5)) Harcourt Schl. Pubs.

—Horizons Bk. 17: Time for Kids Collection: US History. 3rd ed. 2002. (Illus.). pap. 9.30 (978-0-15-333925-7(X)) Harcourt Schl. Pubs.

—Horizons Bk. 18: Time for Kids Collection: US History. 3rd ed. 2002. pap. 9.30 (978-0-15-333927-1(6)) Harcourt Schl. Pubs.

—Horizons Bk. 19: Time for Kids Collection: US History. 3rd ed. 2002. (Illus.). pap. 9.30 (978-0-15-333929-5(2)) Harcourt Schl. Pubs.

—Horizons Bk. 20: Time for Kids Collection: US History. 3rd ed. 2002. (Illus.). pap. 9.30 (978-0-15-333931-8(4)) Harcourt Schl. Pubs.

—Horizons Bk. 21: Time for Kids Collection: US History. 3rd ed. 2002. (Illus.). pap. 9.30 (978-0-15-333933-2(0)) Harcourt Schl. Pubs.

—Horizons Bk. 22: Time for Kids Collection: US History. 3rd ed. 2002. (Illus.). pap. 9.30 (978-0-15-333935-6(7)) Harcourt Schl. Pubs.

—Horizons Bk. 23: Time for Kids Collection: US History. 3rd ed. 2002. (Illus.). pap. 9.30 (978-0-15-333937-0(3)) Harcourt Schl. Pubs.

—Horizons Bk. 24: Time for Kids Collection: US History. 3rd ed. 2002. (Illus.). pap. 9.30 (978-0-15-333939-4(X)) Harcourt Schl. Pubs.

—Horizons Unit 5: Looking Back. 3rd ed. 2001. (Illus.). pap. 169.80 (978-0-15-322573-4(4)) Harcourt Schl. Pubs.

—Horizons Big Book. 3rd ed. 2003. (Horizons Ser.). (gr. k). 251.20 (978-0-15-339673-1(3)) Harcourt Schl. Pubs.

—Horizons, Grade 1. 3rd ed. 2003. Vol. 1. tchr. ed. 98.30 (978-0-15-339624-3(5)); Vol. 2. tchr. ed. 98.30 (978-0-15-339625-0(3)) Harcourt Schl. Pubs.

—Horizons, Grade 2. 3rd ed. 2003. Vol. 1. tchr. ed. 104.40 (978-0-15-339626-7(1)); Vol. 2. tchr. ed. 104.40 (978-0-15-339627-4(X)) Harcourt Schl. Pubs.

—Horizons, Grade 3. 3rd ed. 2004. Vol. 1. tchr. ed. 104.40 (978-0-15-339628-1(8)); Vol. 2. tchr. ed. 104.40 (978-0-15-339629-8(6)) Harcourt Schl. Pubs.

—Horizons, Grade K. 3rd ed. 2003. tchr. ed. 113.40 (978-0-15-339623-6(7)) Harcourt Schl. Pubs.

—Horizontes: States & Regions: Time for Kids Readers. 3rd ed. 2002. (Harcourt Horizontes Ser.). (SPA.). (gr. 3 up). pap., tchr. ed. 65.80 (978-0-15-334663-7(9)) Harcourt Schl. Pubs.

—Horizontes: US History. 3rd ed. (Harcourt Horizontes Ser.). (SPA., (gr. k-6). 2003. Illus.). act. bk. ed. 11.80 (978-0-15-324555-8(7)); 2002. pap., tchr. ed., act. bk. ed. 27.70 (978-0-15-324560-2(3)); Vol. 1. 2003. tchr. ed. 133.80 (978-0-15-321981-8(5)); Vol. 2. 2003. tchr. ed. 133.80 (978-0-15-321982-5(3)) Harcourt Schl. Pubs.

—Horizontes: US History: Time for Kids Readers. 3rd ed. 2002. (Harcourt Horizontes Ser.). (SPA.). (gr. 3 up). pap., tchr. ed. 81.10 (978-0-15-334664-4(7)) Harcourt Schl. Pubs.

—North of the Rio Grande Below Level. 3rd ed. 2002. (Trophies Reading Program Ser.). (Illus.). pap. 5.10 (978-0-15-323245-9(5)) Harcourt Schl. Pubs.

—Social Studies: States & Regions. 1999. (Harcourt Brace Social Studies). (Illus.). (gr. k-7). pupil's gde. ed. 65.90 (978-0-15-312099-2(1)) Harcourt Schl. Pubs.

—Social Studies: Stories in Time: Library Book Collection. 2003. (Harcourt Brace Social Studies). (Illus.). (gr. k-7). 130.90 (978-0-15-308394-5(8)) Harcourt Schl. Pubs.

—Social Studies: The U.S. in Modern Times. (Harcourt Brace Social Studies). (gr. k-7). 1999. (Illus.). pap., pupil's gde. ed. 72.20 (978-0-15-311398-7(7)); 1998. pap., tchr. ed. 166.20 (978-0-15-311399-4(5)) Harcourt Schl. Pubs.

—Social Studies: United States. 1999. (Harcourt Brace Social Studies). (Illus.). (gr. k-7). pupil's gde. ed. 73.10 (978-0-15-312101-2(7)) Harcourt Schl. Pubs.

—TIME for Kids: U. S. History. (Horizons Ser.). (gr. k-7). 2nd ed. 2003. 669.60 (978-0-15-336112-8(3)); Bk. 10. 3rd ed. 2002. (SPA., Illus.). pap. 9.30 (978-0-15-333911-0(X)); Bk. 11. 3rd ed. 2002. (SPA., Illus.). pap. 9.30 (978-0-15-333913-4(6)); Bk. 12. 3rd ed. 2002. (SPA., Illus.). pap. 9.30 (978-0-15-333915-8(2)) Harcourt Schl. Pubs.

—Time for Kids Collections: US History. 3rd ed. 2002. (Horizons Ser.). Bk. 1. pap. 9.30 (978-0-15-333893-9(8)); Bk. 2. pap. 9.30 (978-0-15-333895-3(4)); Bk. 3. pap. 9.30 (978-0-15-333897-7(0)); Bk. 5. pap. 9.30 (978-0-15-333901-1(2)); Bk. 6. pap. 9.30 (978-0-15-333903-5(9)); Bk. 9. pap. 9.30 (978-0-15-333909-7(8)); Bk. 16. pap. 9.30 (978-0-15-333923-3(3)) Harcourt Schl. Pubs.

—U. S. History. 3rd ed. 2003. (Horizons Ser.). stu. ed. 70.60 (978-0-15-339619-9(9)) Harcourt Schl. Pubs.

—U. S. History: Beginner's Level. 3rd ed. 2002. (Horizons Ser.: Vol. 3). (Illus.). pap. 6.70 (978-0-15-335269-0(8)) Harcourt Schl. Pubs.

—United States History, Vol. 1. 3rd ed. 2003. (Illus.). 52.90 (978-0-15-339681-6(4)) Harcourt Schl. Pubs.

—US History. 3rd ed. 2003. (Horizontes (Social Studies) Ser.). (SPA., Illus.). (gr. k-6). pupil's gde. ed. 71.90 (978-0-15-324536-7(0)) Harcourt Schl. Pubs.

—US History - Beginning to the Civil War. 3rd ed. 2003. (Harcourt Electronic Test Ser.). pap., tchr. ed. 10.70 (978-0-15-340792-5(1)) Harcourt Schl. Pubs.

—US History - Civil War to the Present. 3rd ed. 2003. (Harcourt Electronic Test Ser.). pap., tchr. ed. 10.70 (978-0-15-340790-1(5)) Harcourt Schl. Pubs.

—Walks in the Wilderness. 3rd ed. 2002. (Horizons Ser.). (Illus.). (J). pap. 5.50 (978-0-15-333388-0(X)) Harcourt Schl. Pubs.

Hardy, P. Stephen & Hardy, Sheila Jackson. Extraordinary People of the Harlem Renaissance. 2001. (Extraordinary People Ser.). (Illus.). 288p. (YA). (gr. 6 up). pap. 16.95 (978-0-516-27170-5(9) , Children's Pr.) Scholastic Library Publishing.

Harker, John B. Betsy Ross's Five Pointed Star: Elizabeth Claypoole, Quaker Flag Maker - A Historical Perspective. 2005. Orig. Title: Betsy Ross's Star Spangled Banner. (Illus.). 218p. per. 20.00 (978-1-887774-15-4(7)) Canmore Pr.

Harmon, Daniel E. The U. S. Armed Forces. 2001. (Your Government Ser.). (Illus.). 64p. (J). (gr. 4-7). 25.00 (978-0-7910-5994-4(4) , Chelsea Hse.) Facts On File, Inc.

Harness, Cheryl. Rabble Rousers: 20 Women Who Made a Difference. Harness, Cheryl, illus. 2003. (Illus.). 64p. (J). (gr. 2-6). 17.99 (978-0-525-47035-9(2) , Dutton Juvenile) Penguin Group (USA) Inc.

Harris, Nancy. The Bald Eagle. 2007. (J). pap. ***978-1-4034-9387-3(1))** Heinemann Library.

Hart, Diane. Discovery to the Civil War, Pt. 1. 1999. 128p. (YA). (gr. 7-9). pap. 17.95 (978-0-8359-4855-5(2)) Globe Fearon Educational Publishing.

—Industrialization to the Present, Pt. 2. 1999. 128p. (YA). (gr. 7-9). pap. 17.95 (978-0-8359-4854-8(4)) Globe Fearon Educational Publishing.

Hazen, Walter A. Everyday Life: Reform in America. 2004. (Illus.). iv, 100p. pap. (978-0-673-58898-2(X)) Good Year Bks.

Heeg, Berg Heeg. Voyage to Victory: The Voice of a Sailor in the Pacific 1943-1945. 2004. (YA). per. 9.95 (978-0-938682-79-0(2) , 682-79-2) River Road Pubns., Inc.

Hein, Connie L. Toliver in Time: For a Fourth of July Celebration. Theobald, Denise, illus. 2003. 40p. (J). lib. bdg. 19.95 (978-0-9740855-8-6(8)); per. 12.95 (978-0-9740855-9-3(6)) Still Water Publishing.

Heinrichs, Ann. Maine. 2005. (Welcome to the USA Ser.). (Illus.). 40p. (J). (gr. 1-5). 27.07 (978-1-59296-444-4(3)) Child's World, Inc.

—This Land Is Your Land, 52 bks. Incl. Alabama. 2003. lib. bdg. 22.60 (978-0-7565-0332-1(9)); Alaska. 2003. lib. bdg. 22.60 (978-0-7565-0337-6(X)); Arizona. 2003. lib. bdg. 22.60 (978-0-7565-0333-8(7)); Arkansas. 2003. lib. bdg. 22.60 (978-0-7565-0339-0(6)); California. 2002. lib. bdg. 22.60 (978-0-7565-0308-6(6)); Colorado. 2002. lib. bdg. 22.60 (978-0-7565-0331-4(0)); Connecticut. 2003. lib. bdg. 22.60 (978-0-7565-0340-6(X)); Delaware. 2003. lib. bdg. 22.60 (978-0-7565-0341-3(8)); Florida. 2002. lib. bdg. 22.60 (978-0-7565-0309-3(4)); Georgia. 2003. lib. bdg. 22.60 (978-0-7565-0321-5(3)); Hawaii. 2003. lib. bdg. 22.60 (978-0-7565-0346-8(9)); Idaho. 2003. lib. bdg. 22.60 (978-0-7565-0352-9(3)); Illinois. 2002. lib. bdg. 22.60 (978-0-7565-0313-0(2)); Indiana. 2003. lib. bdg. 22.60 (978-0-7565-0325-3(6)); Iowa. 2003. lib. bdg. 22.60 (978-0-7565-0342-0(6)); Kansas. 2003. lib. bdg. 22.60 (978-0-7565-0353-6(1)); Kentucky. 2003. lib. bdg. 22.60 (978-0-7565-0322-2(1)); Louisiana. 2003. lib. bdg. 22.60 (978-0-7565-0354-3(X)); Maine. 2003. lib. bdg. 22.60 (978-0-7565-0347-5(7)); Maryland. 2003. lib. bdg. 22.60 (978-0-7565-0348-2(5)); Massachusetts. 2003. lib. bdg. 22.60 (978-0-7565-0323-9(X)); Michigan. 2003. lib. bdg. 22.60 (978-0-7565-0314-7(0)); Minnesota. 2003. lib. bdg. 22.60 (978-0-7565-0315-4(9)); Mississippi. 2003. lib. bdg. 22.60 (978-0-7565-0355-0(8)); Missouri. 2003. lib. bdg. 22.60 (978-0-7565-0329-1(9)); Montana. 2003. lib. bdg. 22.60 (978-0-7565-0334-5(5)); Nebraska. 2003. lib. bdg. 22.60 (978-0-7565-0356-7(6)); Nevada. 2003. lib. bdg. 22.60 (978-0-7565-0327-7(2)); New Hampshire. 2003. lib. bdg. 22.60 (978-0-7565-0336-9(1)); New Jersey. 2003. lib. bdg. 22.60 (978-0-7565-0318-5(3)); New Mexico. 2003. lib. bdg. 22.60 (978-0-7565-0343-7(4)); New York. 2002. lib. bdg. 22.60 (978-0-7565-0311-6(6)); North Carolina. 2003. lib. bdg. 22.60 (978-0-7565-0324-6(8)); North Dakota. 2003. lib. bdg. 22.60 (978-0-7565-0349-9(3)); Ohio. 2003. lib. bdg. 22.60 (978-0-7565-0316-1(7)); Oklahoma. 2003. lib. bdg. 22.60 (978-0-7565-0330-7(2)); Oregon. 2003. lib. bdg. 22.60 (978-0-7565-0317-8(5)); Pennsylvania. 2003. lib. bdg. 22.60 (978-0-7565-0320-8(5)); Puerto Rico. Labbo, Linda D. 2003. lib. bdg. 22.60 (978-0-7565-0357-4(4)); Rhode Island. 2003. lib. bdg. 22.60 (978-0-7565-0358-1(2)); South Carolina. 2003. lib. bdg. 22.60 (978-0-7565-0326-0(4)); South Dakota. 2003. lib. bdg. 22.60 (978-0-7565-0286-7(1)); Tennessee. 2003. lib. bdg. 22.60 (978-0-7565-0319-2(1)); Texas. 2002. lib. bdg. 22.60 (978-0-7565-0312-3(4)); Utah. 2003. lib. bdg. 22.60 (978-0-7565-0344-4(2)); Vermont. 2003. lib. bdg. 22.60 (978-0-7565-0345-1(0)); Virginia. 2002. lib. bdg. 22.60 (978-0-7565-0310-9(8)); Washington. 2003. lib. bdg. 22.30 (978-0-7565-0350-5(7)); Washington, D. C. 2003. lib. bdg. 22.60 (978-0-7565-0335-2(3)); West Virginia. 2003. lib. bdg. 22.60 (978-0-7565-0351-2(5)); Wisconsin. 2003. lib. bdg. 22.60 (978-0-7565-0328-4(0)); Wyoming. 2003. lib. bdg. 22.60 (978-0-7565-0359-8(0)); 48p. (J). (gr. 3 up). (Illus.). Set lib. bdg. 1175.20 (978-0-7565-0475-5(9)) Compass Point Bks.

Hello U. S. A. 2004. (Illus.). lib. bdg. 7.95 (978-0-8225-3748-9(6)) Lerner Publishing Group.

Henretta, James A. America's History: High School Edition. 5th ed. 2004. 74.50 (978-0-312-44303-0(X)) Bedford/ Saint Martin's.

Herrick, Mark P., illus. Rock U. S. A. & the American Way CONNECT-IT: Fun Projects & Activity Pages. 2004. 128p. per. 29.95 (978-0-9749412-1-9(2)) EDCO Publishing, Inc.

Hewitt Staff. Activity Suggestions for Home Grown Kids: My America; Our America; Our American History; The History of the United States; Old World History; New World History. 1998. 136p. (J). (gr. 1-6). ring bd. 8.95 (978-1-57896-039-2(8) , 2491) Hewitt Research Foundation, Inc.

Hicks, Terry Allan. The Bald Eagle. 2006. (Symbols of America Ser.). (Illus.). 40p. (J). lib. bdg. 28.50 (978-0-7614-2133-7(5) , Benchmark Bks.) Cavendish, Marshall Corp.

Hillerman, Tony. The Great Taos Bank Robbery: And Other True Stories of the Southwest. 2001. (gr. 5-8). lib. bdg. 22.25 (978-0-613-59812-5(1)) Tandem Library Bks.

Hirsch, E. D., ed. The Age of Exploration, Level 5. 2003. tchr. ed. 9.95 (978-0-7690-5077-5(8)); stu. ed. 49.95 (978-0-7690-2852-1(7)) Pearson Learning.

—Americans Move West. 2003. tchr. ed. 9.95 (978-0-7690-5050-8(6)); stu. ed. 49.95 (978-0-7690-2955-9(8)) Pearson Learning.

—From Colonies to Independence. 2003. tchr. ed. 9.95 (978-0-7690-5042-3(5)); stu. ed. 49.95 (978-0-7690-2947-4(7)) Pearson Learning.

—Geography of the United States, Level 5. tchr. ed. 9.95 (978-0-7690-5084-3(0)); stu. ed. 49.95 (978-0-7690-2849-1(7)) Pearson Learning.

—Industrialization & Urbanization in America, Level 6. tchr. ed. 9.95 (978-0-7690-5092-8(1)); stu. ed. 49.95 (978-0-7690-2857-6(8)) Pearson Learning.

—Westward Expansion after the Civil War, Level 5. tchr. ed. 9.95 (978-0-7690-5082-9(4)); stu. ed. 49.95 (978-0-7690-2851-4(9)) Pearson Learning.

—Westward Expansion Before the Civil War, Level 5. tchr. ed. 9.95 (978-0-7690-5080-5(8)); 2003. stu. ed. 49.95 (978-0-7690-2850-7(0)) Pearson Learning.

Historia y Geografia de America. (SPA.). (J). 45.00 (978-958-04-5985-9(1)); (Illus.). wbk. ed. 15.00 (978-958-04-5986-6(X)) Norma S.A. COL. *Dist:* Distribuidora Norma, Inc.

A History of the US: Blackline Masters. 1999. (History of the United States Ser.: Vol. 10). 32p. 12.00 (978-0-19-512939-7(3)); Bk. 4. 12.00 (978-0-19-512933-5(4)); Bk. 5. 12.00 (978-0-19-512934-2(2)) Oxford Univ. Pr., Inc.

A History of the US Bk. 1: Blackline Masters. 1999. (History of the United States Ser.: Vol. 1). 32p. 12.00 (978-0-19-512930-4(X)) Oxford Univ. Pr., Inc.

A History of the US Bk. 2: Blackline Masters. 1999. (History of the United States Ser.: Vol. 2). 32p. 12.00 (978-0-19-512931-1(8)) Oxford Univ. Pr., Inc.

A History of the US Bk. 3: Blackline Masters. 1999. (History of the United States Ser.: Vol. 3). 32p. 12.00 (978-0-19-512932-8(6)) Oxford Univ. Pr., Inc.

A History of the US Bk. 7: Blackline Masters. 1999. (History of the United States Ser.: Vol. 7). 32p. 12.00 (978-0-19-512936-6(9)) Oxford Univ. Pr., Inc.

A History of US Bks. 1-10: Assessment Book. 3rd ed. 2002. (History of US Ser.). 164p. pap. 49.95 (978-0-19-515348-4(0)) Oxford Univ. Pr., Inc.

History Through Sources, 5 bks., Set. (YA). (gr. 6-8). lib. bdg. 128.20 (978-1-57572-222-1(4)) Heinemann Library.

Holt, Rinehart and Winston Staff. American History Political Cartoons Activities. 1998. pap. 44.73 (978-0-03-053668-7(5)) Holt, Rinehart & Winston.

—American Nation: Chapter & Unit Tests with Answer Key & Guide. 3rd ed. 2003. (SPA.). pap. 45.13 (978-0-03-070881-7(8)) Holt, Rinehart & Winston.

—The American Nation: Civil War: Literary & Primary Source. 2001. pap. 29.20 (978-0-03-055774-3(7)) Holt, Rinehart & Winston.

—American Nation: Standard Test Preparation Booklet: Arkansas Edition. 3rd ed. 2002. pap. 12.20 (978-0-03-068084-7(0)) Holt, Rinehart & Winston.

—The American Nation: Tennessee Edition. 3rd annot. ed. 2001. tchr. ed. 112.53 (978-0-03-067229-3(5)) Holt, Rinehart & Winston.

—The American Nation: Test Preparation: Missouri Edition. 2001. pap. 13.46 (978-0-03-067118-0(3)) Holt, Rinehart & Winston.

—Call to Freedom: 1865-Present: Daily Quizzes with Answer Key. 1999. pap. 45.60 (978-0-03-053617-5(0)) Holt, Rinehart & Winston.

—Call to Freedom: 1865-Present: Sheltered English Chapter Tests. 1999. pap. 45.60 (978-0-03-053639-7(1)) Holt, Rinehart & Winston.

—Call to Freedom: American History: Document-Based Activities. 3rd ed. 2001. pap. 25.80 (978-0-03-066534-9(5)) Holt, Rinehart & Winston.

—Call to Freedom: American History: Document-Based Activities Answer Key. 3rd ed. 2001. pap. 8.00 (978-0-03-066536-3(1)) Holt, Rinehart & Winston.

—Call to Freedom: Beginning-1914: Chapter Investigations. 1998. 22.26 (978-0-03-054491-0(2)) Holt, Rinehart & Winston.

—Call to Freedom: Beginning-1914: Chapter Study Guide with Answer Key. 1998. pap., stu. ed. 45.60 (978-0-03-054498-9(X)) Holt, Rinehart & Winston.

—Call to Freedom: Beginning-1914: Daily Quizzes with Answer Key. 1998. pap. 45.60 (978-0-03-054502-3(1)) Holt, Rinehart & Winston.

—Call to Freedom: Beginning-1914: Geography Activities - Answer Key. 3rd ed. 2001. pap. 8.00 (978-0-03-066679-7(1)) Holt, Rinehart & Winston.

—Call to Freedom: Beginning-1914: Graphic Organizer Activities. 1998. pap. 14.93 (978-0-03-054501-6(3)) Holt, Rinehart & Winston.

—Call to Freedom: Beginning-1914: Main Idea Activities for Reteaching. 1998. 28.13 (978-0-03-054496-5(3)) Holt, Rinehart & Winston.

—Call to Freedom: Beginning-1914: Sheltered English Chapter Tests. 1998. pap. 45.60 (978-0-03-054504-7(8)) Holt, Rinehart & Winston.

—Call to Freedom: Preparation Workbook. 3rd ed. 2002. (J). pap. 14.00 (978-0-03-069061-7(7)) Holt, Rinehart & Winston.

—Call to Freedom: Standardized Test Preparation: Missouri Edition. 2001. pap. 12.20 (978-0-03-066774-9(7)) Holt, Rinehart & Winston.

—Taks Every Day! Activities for American Nation. 3rd ed. 2002. (Illus.). pap. 45.60 (978-0-03-065408-4(4)) Holt, Rinehart & Winston.

—The United States: Change & Challenge. 3rd ed. 2001. (HRW Library). (Illus.). vi, 218p. (J). (gr. 8). 18.40 (978-0-03-065036-9(4) , 20020303.008) Holt, Rinehart & Winston.

—The United States, Grade 8: Change & Challenge: California Edition. 3rd ed. 2001. pap., tchr. ed. 16.00 (978-0-03-065044-4(5)) Holt, Rinehart & Winston.

—US History: Practice Test for High School: Oklahoma Edition. 2001. (YA). pap. 4.00 (978-0-03-066918-7(9)) Holt, Rinehart & Winston.

Holub, Joan & Buttler, Elizabeth. Yankee Doodle Riddles: American History Fun. 2003. (Illus.). 32p. (J). (gr. 2-5). 15.95 (978-0-8075-9260-1(9)) Whitman, Albert & Co.

Hoose, Phillip M. We Were There, Too! Young People in U. S. History. 2000. (J). 25.00 (978-0-7894-2587-4(4)) Dorling Kindersley Publishing, Inc.

—We Were There, Too! Young People in U. S. History. 2001. (Illus.). 276p. (J). (gr. 4-7). 28.00 (978-0-374-38252-0(2) , Farrar, Straus & Giroux (BYR)) Farrar, Straus & Giroux.

Horton, James Oliver. Landmarks of African American History. 2005. (American Landmarks Ser.). (Illus.). 208p. (YA). 30.00 (978-0-19-514118-4(0)) Oxford Univ. Pr., Inc.

How Our Nation Began. (YA). 15.00 (978-1-931555-45-6(1)) Our Lady of Victory Schl.

Howe, Randy. Speak to Me! Great American Texts Demystified for Today's Text-Messaging Students. 2007. 240p. pap. 9.99 (978-1-4195-9549-3(0)) Kaplan Publishing.

Hughes, Libby. West Point & Valley Forge. 2001. (Illus.). 148p. (YA). (gr. 4-7). pap. 19.95 (978-0-595-00636-6(1) , Backinprint.com) iUniverse, Inc.

Hughes, Morgan. History & Americana Hall of Fame. 2001. (Illus.). 24p. (J). (gr. 2-6). lib. bdg. 23.93 (978-1-55916-268-5(6)) Rourke Publishing, LLC.

Hults, Alaska, ed. American History Reader's Theater Vol. 2244: Develop Reading Fluency & Text Comprehension Skills. Hillam, Corbin & Vangsgard, Amy, illus. 2004. 96p. (J). pap. 12.99 (978-1-59198-039-1(9) , 2244) Creative Teaching Pr., Inc.

Ichord, Loretta Frances & Millbrook Press. Skillet Bread, Sourdough, & Vinegar Days: Cooking in Pioneer Days. Ellis, Jan Davey, illus. 2005. 64p. (J). (gr. 4-8). pap. 8.95 (978-0-7613-9521-8(0) , First Avenue Editions) Lerner Publishing Group.

In American History, 56 bks., Set. (Illus.). (YA). (gr. 5-12). lib. bdg. 1215.10 (978-0-89490-972-6(X)) Enslow Pubs., Inc.

In the Early Days: Southern Humboldt History 1853-1920, 1. 5th ed. 2006. (Illus.). 141p. per. 20.95 (978-0-9672162-3-2(0)) Hawk Mountaintop Publishing.

Ingraham, Joseph Holt. The Pillar of Fire: Or, Israel in Bondage. 2006. cd-rom (978-1-892824-42-4(6)) AFCHRON.

Isaacs, Sally Senzell. America in the Time of Lewis & Clark: 1801 to 1850. 2001. (Illus.). 48p. (J). (gr. 4-7). lib. bdg. 17.05 (978-0-613-83687-6(1)) Tandem Library Bks.

—America in the Time of Susan B. Anthony: 1845 to 1928. 2002. (America in the Time of... Ser.). (Illus.). 48p. (J). (gr. 4-7). pap. 8.50 (978-1-57572-941-1(5)) Heinemann Library.

—The American Adventure, 4 bks., Set 2. 2004. (J). (gr. 4-7). lib. bdg. 111.14 (978-1-4034-3053-3(5)) Heinemann Library.

—Life in America's First Cities. (Picture the Past Ser.). (Illus.). 32p. (J). 2002. (gr. k-3). pap. 7.50 (978-1-58810-299-7(8) , 91065); 2000. (gr. 2-4). lib. bdg. 21.36 (978-1-57572-315-0(8)) Heinemann Library.

—Life in America's First Cities. 2001. (Picture the Past Ser.). (Illus.). (J). (978-0-606-22005-7(4)) Tandem Library Bks.

It's My State: Group 5, 6 Bks, Set. 2004. (J). 162.43 (978-0-7614-1821-4(0)) Cavendish, Marshall Corp.

January, Brendan. The National Mall. 2001. (Cornerstones of Freedom Ser.). (Illus.). 32p. (J). (gr. 4-6). pap. 5.95 (978-0-516-27167-5(9) , Children's Pr.) Scholastic Library Publishing.

Jarrie, Martin, illus. ABC USA. 2005. 32p. 14.95 (978-1-4027-1619-5(2)) Sterling Publishing Co., Inc.

Jones, Charlotte Foltz. Westward Ho! Eleven Explorers of the American West. 2005. (Illus.). 240p. (J). (gr. 4-6). tchr. ed. 22.95 (978-0-8234-1586-1(4)) Holiday Hse., Inc.

Kaleidoscope - American History Series - Group 2, 4 bks., Set. 102.57 (978-0-7614-1459-9(2) , Benchmark Bks.) Cavendish, Marshall Corp.

Kallen, Stuart A. The 1980's. 1998. (Cultural History of the United States Through the Decades Ser.). (Illus.). 128p. (YA). (gr. 4-12). 29.95 (978-1-56006-558-6(3) , LML00902-177915, Lucent Bks.) Thomson Gale.

Kalman, Bobbie. The Blacksmith. Bedell, Barbara, illus. 2001. (Colonial People Ser.). 32p. (J). (gr. 3). (978-0-7787-0747-9(4)); pap. (978-0-7787-0793-6(8)) Crabtree Publishing Co.

—Travel in the Early Days. 2001. (gr. 3-6). lib. bdg. 16.40 (978-0-613-33160-9(5)) Tandem Library Bks.

Kalman, Bobbie & Calder, Kate. Travel in the Early Days. 2000. (Historic Communities Ser.). (Illus.). 32p. (J). (gr. 3). pap. (978-0-86505-472-1(X)); lib. bdg. (978-0-86505-442-4(8)) Crabtree Publishing Co.

Kalman, Bobbie & Crossingham, John. Colonial Home. 2000. (Historic Communities Ser.). (Illus.). 32p. (J). (gr. 3). pap. (978-0-86505-469-1(X)) Crabtree Publishing Co.

Kalman, Bobbie & Walker, Niki. Spotlight on the United States of America. 2007. (Spotlight on My Country Ser.). (Illus.). 32p. (J). (gr. 2-5). pap. (***978-0-7787-3478-9(1)***) Crabtree Publishing Co.

Kamma, Anne. If You Lived When There Was Slavery in America. 2004. (Illus.). 80p. (J). pap. 5.99 (978-0-439-56706 0(8)) Scholastic, Inc.

Karapetian, Marjam. Bilingual Content Dictionary: English to Spanish: Social Studies - American History Through 1776. 2004. (SPA & ENG.). 14.95 (978-0-9764829-3-2(2)) WizdomInc.

Karl, Jean. America Alive: A History. Schoenherr, Ian, illus. 1999. 120p. (J). reprint ed. 23.00 (978-0-7881-6822-2(3)) DIANE Publishing Co.

Kaserman & Haberkern, E. The United States of America, 50 vols. 2nd ed. 2003. (Illus.). 46p. (J). cd-rom (978-0-9714299-1-8(X)) I Save A Tree.

Keenan, Sheila. O, Say Can You See? America's Symbols, Landmarks, & Inspiring Words. Boyajian, Ann, illus. 2004. (Oh Say Can You See Ser.). 64p. (J). (ps-3). pap. 16.95 (978-0-439-42450-9(X) , Scholastic Reference) Scholastic, Inc.

Kelley, K. C. Hottest NASCAR Machines. 2007. (Wild Wheels! Ser.). (Illus.). 48p. (J). (gr. 4-10). lib. bdg. 23.93 (***978-0-7660-2869-2(0)***) Enslow Pubs., Inc.

Kennedy. American Pageant AP Test Preperations. 12th ed. 2001. (YA). 25.56 (978-0-618-25051-6(4) , 330017) Houghton Mifflin College Div.

—American Pageant Volume Two with Student History Research Passkey Thirteenth Edition Plus American Spirit Volume Two Eleventh Edition. 13th ed. 2005. (YA). pap., pap. 119.96 (978-0-618-72363-8(3) , 397254) Houghton Mifflin College Div.

Kim, Allen. American History, Vol. 1. Kim, Nicole, illus. 2005. 160p. (J). pap. 12.95 (978-981-05-2765-5(9)) Youngjin (Singapore) Pte Ltd. SGP. *Dist:* Independent Pubs. Group.

Knox, Barbara J. Hearst Castle: An American Palace. 2005. (Castles, Palaces, & Tombs Ser.). (Illus.). 32p. (J). lib. bdg. 25.27 (978-1-59716-069-8(5)) Bearport Publishing Co., Inc.

Kowalski, Kathiann M. Salvadorans in America. 2006. (In America Ser.). (Illus.). 80p. (J). (ps-7). 27.93 (978-0-8225-2424-3(4) , Lerner Pubns.) Lerner Publishing Group.

Kozleski, Lisa. The Pledge of Allegiance. 2002. (American Symbols & Their Meanings Ser.). (Illus.). 48p. (YA). (gr. 4 up). lib. bdg. (978-1-59084-040-5(2)) Mason Crest Pubs.

Krull, Kathleen. A Woman for President: The Story of Victoria Woodhull. Dyer, Jane, illus. 2004. 32p. (J). 16.95 (978-0-8027-8908-2(0)) Walker & Co.

Kuntz, Lynn. Celebrate the U. S. A. Hands-On History Activities for Kids. Hicks, Mark A., illus. 2007. 80p. (J). (gr. 3-5). pap. 7.95 (978-1-58685-846-9(7)) Gibbs Smith, Publisher.

Kurtz, Jane. What Columbus Found: It Was Orange, It Was Round. Billin-Frye, Paige, illus. 2007. (Ready-to-Reads Ser.). 32p. (J). pap. 3.99 (978-0-689-86762-0(X) , Aladdin) Simon & Schuster Children's Publishing.

Lader, Curt. Painless American History. 1999. (Painless Ser.). 272p. (gr. 7 up). pap. 8.95 (978-0-7641-0620-0(1)) Barron's Educational Series, Inc.

—Painless American History. 1999. (gr. 5-8). lib. bdg. 17.60 (978-0-613-52773-6(9)) Tandem Library Bks.

Land of Liberty. (Social Studies Collections). (Illus.). (J). (gr. 3-4). lib. bdg. 1313.52 (978-0-7368-3173-4(8)) Capstone Pr., Inc.

Landau, Elaine. The Bald Eagle. 2007. (True Bks.). (Illus.). 48p. (J). (gr. 3-5). lib. bdg. 26.00 (***978-0-531-12626-4(9)*** , Children's Pr.) Scholastic Library Publishing.

Landau, Elaine. The Wounded Knee Massacre. 2004. (Cornerstones of Freedom Ser.). (Illus.). 48p. (J). 26.00 (978-0-516-24244-6(X) , Children's Pr.) Scholastic Library Publishing.

Landmark Events in American History: Arriving at Ellis Island, The Battle of Little Bighorn, The California Missions, The Plymouth Colony, The Settling of Jamestown, The Siege of the Alamo, 6 bks. 2002. (Illus.). (J). (gr. 5 up). pap. 87.60 (978-0-8368-5350-6(4) , World Almanac Library) Stevens, Gareth Inc.

Landmark Events in American History: The Anasazi Culture at Mesa Verde; The Battle of Gettysburg; The Bombing of Pearl Harbor; The California Gold Rush; The Montgomery Bus Boycott; The Settling of St. Augustine, 6 bks. 2002. (Illus.). (J). (gr. 5 up). pap. 89.70 (978-0-8368-5398-8(9) , World Almanac Library) Stevens, Gareth Inc.

Lang, Robert. Old Glory: An American Treasure. Winget, Susan, illus. 1999. 32p. (J). (gr. k-3). 18.00 (978-0-7412-0435-6(5)) Lang Graphics, Ltd.

Lantos, Jeff, et al. Read-Draw-Remember American History Activities. 2003. 48p. pap. 10.95 (978-0-439-38519-0(9) , Teaching Resources) Scholastic, Inc.

Larkin, Tanya. Cooking Throughout American History Set 2, 6 bks. Incl. What Was Cooking in Abigail Adam's White House? lib. bdg. 19.95 (978-0-8239-5607-4(5)); What Was Cooking in Dolly Madison's White House? lib. bdg. 19.95 (978-0-8239-5608-1(3)); What Was Cooking in Edith Roosevelt's White House? lib. bdg. 19.95 (978-0-8239-5610-4(5)); What Was Cooking in Julia Grant's White House? lib. bdg. 19.95 (978-0-8239-5611-1(3)); What Was Cooking in Martha Washington's Presidential Mansions? lib. bdg. 19.95 (978-0-8239-5606-7(7)); What Was Cooking in Mary Todd Lincoln's White House? lib. bdg. 19.95 (978-0-8239-5609-8(1)); 24p. (J). (gr. 3). 2001. (Illus.). Set lib. bdg. 117.00 (978-0-8239-7062-9(0) , PowerKids Pr.) Rosen Publishing Group, Inc., The.

—What Was Cooking in Julia Grant's White House? 2001. (Cooking Throughout American History Ser.). (Illus.). 24p. (J). (gr. 3). lib. bdg. 19.95 (978-0-8239-5611-1(3) , PowerKids Pr.) Rosen Publishing Group, Inc., The.

Lassieur, Allison. The Navajo: A Proud People. 2005. (American Indians Ser.). (Illus.). 48p. (J). (gr. 4-7). lib. bdg. 23.93 (978-0-7660-2453-3(9) , Enslow Elementary) Enslow Pubs., Inc.

Latham, Donna. Hurricane! The 1900 Galveston Night of Terror. 2005. (X-Treme Disasters That Changed America Ser.). (Illus.). 32p. (J). (gr. 3-7). lib. bdg. 25.27 (978-1-59716-071-1(7)) Bearport Publishing Co., Inc.

Latinos in American History, 10 bks., Set. 2002. (Illus.). 56p. (J). (gr. 4-8). lib. bdg. 199.95 (978-1-58415-164-7(1)) Mitchell Lane Pubs., Inc.

Leacock, Elspeth. Journeys in Time: A New Atlas of American History. 2001. (gr. 3-6). lib. bdg. 15.25 (978-0-613-60811-4(9)) Tandem Library Bks.

Leacock, Elspeth & Buckley, Susan. Places in Time: A New Atlas of American History. Jones, Randy, illus. 2006. 48p. (J). (gr. 4-8). reprint ed. 15.00 (978-1-4223-5555-8(1)) DIANE Publishing Co.

Leebrick, Kristal. Travel & Transportation in Colonial America. 2004. (Everyday Life Long Ago Ser.). (J). (978-0-7368-2164-3(3) , Blue Earth Bks.) Capstone Pr., Inc.

Let's See Library - Our Nation, 16 bks. Incl. American Flag. Gray, Susan Heinrichs. 2001. lib. bdg. 19.93 (978-0-7565-0140-2(7)); Bald Eagle. Dell, Pamela. 2004. lib. bdg. 19.93 (978-0-7565-0616-2(6)); Liberty Bell. Nobleman, Marc Tyler. 2004. lib. bdg. 19.93 (978-0-7565-0617-9(4)); Lincoln Memorial. Nobleman, Marc Tyler. 2004. lib. bdg. 19.93 (978-0-7565-0618-6(2)); Mount Rushmore. Rau, Dana Meachen. 2002. lib. bdg. 19.93 (978-0-7565-0141-9(5)); National Anthem. Dell, Pamela. 2004. lib. bdg. 19.93 (978-0-7565-0619-3(0)); Our National Holidays. Murphy, Patricia J. 2002. lib. bdg. 19.93 (978-0-7565-0194-5(6)); Our National Parks. Raatma, Lucia. 2002. lib. bdg. 19.93 (978-0-7565-0195-2(4)); Pledge of Allegiance. Dell, Pamela. 2004. lib. bdg. 19.93 (978-0-7565-0620-9(4)); Presidency. Murphy, Patricia J. 2001. lib. bdg. 19.93 (978-0-7565-0142-6(3)); Statue of Liberty. Rau, Dana Meachen. 2001. lib. bdg. 19.93 (978-0-7565-0143-3(1)); U. S. Congress. Murphy, Patricia J. 2002. lib. bdg. 19.93 (978-0-7565-0196-9(2)); U. S. Supreme Court. Murphy, Patricia J. 2002. lib. bdg. 19.93 (978-0-7565-0197-6(0)); Voting & Elections. Murphy, Patricia J. 2001. lib. bdg. 19.93 (978-0-7565-0144-0(X)); Washington Monument. Nobleman, Marc Tyler. 2004. lib. bdg. 19.93 (978-0-7565-0621-6(2)); White House. Gray, Susan Heinrichs. 2001. lib. bdg. 19.93 (978-0-7565-0145-7(8)); 24p. (J). (gr. 1 up). (Illus.). Set lib. bdg. 318.88 (978-0-7565-0709-1(X)) Compass Point Bks.

Levy, Elizabeth. Revolting Revolutionaries. 2003. (America's Funny but True History Ser.). 160p. (J). 12.95 (978-0-439-30352-1(4) , Scholastic Pr.) Scholastic, Inc.

Levy, Nathan. American History. Kristensen, Renee & Sculthorp, Jeffrey A., eds. 2000. (Whose Clues? Ser.). 32p. (J). pap., tchr. ed. 5.99 (978-1-889319-39-1(2) , MindMotion) Trend Enterprises, Inc.

Liberman, Sherri. A Historical Atlas of the Industrial Age & the Growth of America's Cities. 2005. (United States, Historical Atlases of the Growth of a New Nation Ser.). (Illus.). 64p. (J). (gr. 7-12). lib. bdg. 30.60 (978-1-4042-0205-4(6)) Rosen Publishing Group, Inc., The.

Library in a Book Set. 2005. 208p. 1305.00 (978-0-8160-6517-2(9)); 208-320p. (gr. 9). 1080.00 (978-0-8160-6326-0(5)) Facts On File, Inc.

The Library of American Lives & Times, 12 vols., Set 3. 2005. (Illus.). (gr. 4-8). lib. bdg. 383.40 (978-0-8239-6657-8(7)) Rosen Publishing Group, Inc., The.

The Library of the Thirteen Colonies & the Lost Colony, 14 bks. Incl. Colony of Connecticut. Whitehurst, Susan. lib. bdg. 19.95 (978-0-8239-5479-7(X)); Colony of Delaware. Whitehurst, Susan. lib. bdg. 19.95 (978-0-8239-5482-7(X)); Colony of Georgia. Coleman, Brooke. lib. bdg. 19.95 (978-0-8239-5474-2(9)); Colony of Maryland. Coleman, Brooke. lib. bdg. 19.95 (978-0-8239-5483-4(8)); Colony of Massachusetts. Whitehurst, Susan. lib. bdg. 19.95 (978-0-8239-5475-9(7)); Colony of New Hampshire. Whitehurst, Susan. lib. bdg. 19.95 (978-0-8239-5477-3(3)); Colony of New Jersey. Whitehurst, Susan. lib. bdg. 19.95 (978-0-8239-5480-3(3)); Colony of New York. Whitehurst, Susan. lib. bdg. 19.95 (978-0-8239-5478-0(1)); Colony of North Carolina. Whitehurst, Susan. lib. bdg. 19.95 (978-0-8239-5485-8(4)); Colony of Pennsylvania. Whitehurst, Susan. lib. bdg. 19.95 (978-0-8239-5481-0(1)); Colony of Rhode Island. Whitehurst, Susan. lib. bdg. 19.95 (978-0-8239-5476-6(5)); Colony of South Carolina. Whitehurst, Susan. lib. bdg. 19.95 (978-0-8239-5486-5(2)); Colony of Virginia. Coleman, Brooke. lib. bdg. 19.95 (978-0-8239-5484-1(6)); Roanoke : The Lost Colony. Coleman, Brooke. lib. bdg. 19.95 (978-0-8239-5473-5(0)); 24p. (J). (gr. 3). 2000. (Illus.). Set lib. bdg. 273.00 (978-0-8239-7005-6(1) , PowerKids Pr.) Rosen Publishing Group, Inc., The.

Life in the Thirteen Colonies: The Ultimate Insight Into Life in Colonial America, 13 Bks, Set. 2004. (J). 455.00 (978-0-516-29807-8(0) , Children's Pr.) Scholastic Library Publishing.

Lloyd, Jon. A View of America's Future by America's. 2005. 51p. pap. 12.95 (978-1-4137-9110-5(7)) PublishAmerica, Inc.

Lockman, Vic, illus. History for Little Pilgrims. 1998. 38p. (J). (gr. 1-2). pap., wbk. ed. 2.00 (978-1-930092-86-0(5) , clp79904) Christian Liberty Pr.

Logiudice, Carolyn. US History Reading Comrehension Book. 2003. (Illus.). 167p. (J). per. 37.95 (978-0-7606-0449-6(5)) LinguiSystems, Inc.

Long, Cathryn J. American History to 1900. Nolte, Larry, illus. 1998. (Crossword America Ser.). 64p. (J). (gr. 3-7). pap. 5.95 (978-1-56565-934-6(1) , 09341W) Lowell Hse. Juvenile.

—Famous Places. 2001. (Crossword America Ser.). (Illus.). 64p. (J). (gr. 3-7). pap. 5.95 (978-0-7373-0582-1(7)) Lowell Hse. Juvenile.

Long, Cathryn J. & Douglas, Vincent. The Complete Book of American Facts & Games. 2002. (Complete Book Ser.). (Illus.). 352p. (J). (gr. k-6). pap. 14.95 (978-1-56189-208-2(4) , American Education Publishing) School Specialty Publishing.

A Look at American History. (J). (978-0-7613-3302-9(9) , Twenty-First Century Bks.) Lerner Publishing Group.

Lusted, Marcia Amidon. Revolution & the New Nation. 2007. (***978-1-59036-740-7(5)***) Weigl Pubs., Inc.

Lusted, Marcia Amidon, et al. The National Mall. 2005. (Building History Ser.). (Illus.). 112p. (YA). (gr. 7-10). lib. bdg. 32.45 (978-1-59018-665-7(6) , Lucent Bks.) Thomson Gale.

Maga, Timothy P. The 1960s. 2003. (Eyewitness History Ser.). (Illus.). 416p. (gr. 9). 75.00 (978-0-8160-4809-0(6)) Facts On File, Inc.

The Making of America, 4 vols. 2000. (Illus.). (J). 114.16 (978-0-7398-2846-5(0)) Raintree.

The Making of America, 12 bks., Set. Incl. America into a New Millennium. Anderson, Dale. Kossmann, Walter, ed. (J). (gr. 5-10). 2001. lib. bdg. 28.54 (978-0-8172-5712-5(8)); American Comes of Age. Wells, Donna. (J). (gr. 4-7). 2000. lib. bdg. 28.54 (978-0-8172-5708-8(X)); American Revolution. Weber, Michael. (J). (gr. 4-7). 2000. lib. bdg. 28.54 (978-0-8172-5702-6(0)); Civil War & Reconstruction. Weber, Michael. (J). (gr. 4-7). 2000. lib. bdg. 28.54 (978-0-8172-5707-1(1)); Cold War Years. Anderson, Dale. (J). (gr. 5-10). 2001. lib. bdg. 28.54 (978-0-8172-5711-8(X)); Colonial America. Steins, Richard. (J). (gr. 4-7). 2000. lib. bdg. 28.54 (978-0-8172-5701-9(2)); Exploration & Settlement. Steins, Richard. (J). (gr. 4-7). 2000. lib. bdg. 28.54 (978-0-8172-5700-2(4)); Great Depression & World War II. Stone, Tanya Lee. (J). (gr. 4-7). 2001. lib. bdg. 28.54 (978-0-8172-5710-1(1)); Growing & Dividing. Thro, Ellen. (J). (gr. 4-7). 2000. lib. bdg. 28.54 (978-0-8172-5704-0(7)); Progressive Era & World War I. Stone, Tanya Lee. (YA). (gr. 5-10). 2001. lib. bdg. 28.54 (978-0-8172-5709-5(8)); Westward Expansion. Anderson, Dale. (J). (gr. 4-7). 2000. lib. bdg. 28.54 (978-0-8172-5705-7(5)); Young Republic. Weber, Michael. (J). (gr. 4-7). 2000. lib. bdg. 28.54 (978-0-8172-5703-3(9)); 96p. (Illus.). 1998. Set lib. bdg. 342.48 (978-0-8172-5713-2(6)) Raintree.

The Making of America: Includes: Exploration & Settlement; Colonial America; The American Revolution; The Young Republic; Growing & Dividing; Westward Expansion; Civil War & Reconstruction; America Comes of Age, 8 bks., Set. 2000. (Illus.). (J). (gr. 4-7). 159.84 (978-0-7398-2847-2(9)) Raintree.

The Making of America: Includes: The Progressive Era & World War I; The Great Depression & World War II; The Cold War Years; America into a New Millennium, 4 bks., Set. 2001. (Illus.). (J). (gr. 4-7). lib. bdg. 79.92 (978-0-7398-4288-1(9)) Raintree.

The Making of America Series, 8 bks., Set. 2000. (Making of America Ser.). (Illus.). 228.32 (978-0-7398-4219-5(6)); 114.16 (978-0-7398-4220-1(X)) Steck-Vaughn.

Marcovitz, Hal. The Confederate Flag. 2002. (American Symbols & Their Meanings Ser.). (Illus.). 48p. (YA). (gr. 4 up). lib. bdg. (978-1-59084-035-1(6)) Mason Crest Pubs.

—The Liberty Bell. 2002. (American Symbols & Their Meanings Ser.). (Illus.). 48p. (YA). (gr. 4 up). lib. bdg. (978-1-59084-025-2(9)) Mason Crest Pubs.

Marolf, Stacey & Pessano, Laurie. Founding Fathers... & Mothers: A Field Trip to 18th Century America. Evans, Peter, illus. 1999. 128p. (J). (gr. 4-7). pap. 27.95 incl. audio (978-1-892405-12-8(1)) Good Co. Players Educational Div.

Marsh, Carole. The Young Patriot's Book of Puzzles, Games, Riddles, Stories, Poems, & Activities. 2004. (Patriotic Favorites Ser.). 48p. (gr. 1-4). pap. 5.95 (978-0-635-01032-2(1)) Gallopade International.

Marshall, H.E. This Country of Ours (Yesterday's Classics) 2006. (Illus.). 636p. (J). per. 19.95 (978-1-59915-010-9(7)) Yesterday's Classics.

Marshall, Peter, et al. Sounding Forth the Trumpet Children's Activity Book: Ages 5-8. 2001. (Illus.). 72p. pap. 10.99 (978-0-8007-5774-8(2) , Spire) Revell.

Marx, Trish. Jeannette Rankin: First Lady of Congress. Andreasen, Dan, illus. 2006. 48p. (J). (gr. 2-5). 18.95 (978-0-689-86290-8(3) , McElderry, Margaret K.) Simon & Schuster Children's Publishing.

Mattern, Joanne. Coming to America: The Story of Immigration. Sanfilippo, Margaret, illus. 2000. (Cover-to-Cover Informational Bks.). 64p. (J). (gr. 4-7). lib. bdg. 17.95 (978-0-7807-9715-4(9) , Covercraft); pap. 8.95 (978-0-7891-2851-5(9)) Perfection Learning Corp.

McCormick, Anita Louise. The Industrial Revolution in American History. 1998. (In American History Ser.). (Illus.). 128p. (YA). (gr. 5-12). lib. bdg. 26.60 (978-0-89490-985-6(1)) Enslow Pubs., Inc.

McGraw-Hill - Jamestown Education. American History Ink: Taming Horses on the Great Plains. 2007. (C). pap. 9.28 (***978-0-07-878023-3(3)*** , 9780078780233) Glencoe/McGraw-Hill.

McGraw-Hill Staff. American History: The Early Years. 3rd ed. 2000. stu. ed. 88.01 (978-0-07-821611-4(7) , 9780078216114) Glencoe/McGraw-Hill.

—American History: The Early Years, Interactive. 2001. stu. ed. 88.01 incl. cd-rom (978-0-07-827944-7(5) , 9780078279447) Glencoe/McGraw-Hill.

—American History: The Modern Era. 2000. stu. ed. 90.87 (978-0-07-821613-8(3) , 9780078216138) Glencoe/McGraw-Hill.

—American History: The Modern Era, Interactive. 2002. (C). stu. ed. 93.34 incl. cd-rom (978-0-07-827934-8(8) , 9780078279348) Glencoe/McGraw-Hill.

—American Issues: A Documentary Reader. 2001. (Illus.). xvii, 508p. (gr. 6-12). stu. ed. 34.00 (978-0-07-825814-5(6) , 9780078258145) Glencoe/McGraw-Hill.

—The American Journey. 2002. stu. ed. 89.84 incl. cd-rom (978-0-07-829589-8(0) , 9780078295898); 2002. pap., stu. ed., wbk. ed. 10.64 (978-0-07-825208-2(3) , 9780078252082); 2002. (Illus.). (C). stu. ed. 89.84 (978-0-07-824129-1(4) , 9780078241291); 4th ed. 2004. 87.32 (978-0-07-860980-0(1) , 9780078609800); 5th ed. 2006. stu. ed. 91.32 (978-0-07-874389-4(3) , 9780078743894) Glencoe/McGraw-Hill.

—The American Journey: Building a Nation. 2000. (C). stu. ed. 88.56 (978-0-02-821872-4(8) , 9780028218724) Glencoe/McGraw-Hill.

—The American Journey: Building a Nation, Chapter Challenger Interactive Review Software, Windows/ Macintsoh. 1999. 93.00 (978-0-02-821770-3(5) , 9780028217703) Glencoe/McGraw-Hill.

—The American Journey: Building a Nation, Standardized Test Practice Book. 2nd ed. 1999. pap., stu. ed. 21.81 (978-0-07-820645-0(6) , 9780078206450) Glencoe/ McGraw-Hill.

—American Journey: Standardized Test Practice. 2002. (C). pap., stu. ed., wbk. ed. 7.96 (978-0-07-825210-5(5) , 9780078252105) Glencoe/McGraw-Hill.

—The American Journey: StudentWorks. 5th ed. 2005. (C). 111.32 (978-0-07-866280-5(X) , 9780078662805) Glencoe/McGraw-Hill.

—The American Journey, Active Reading Note-Taking Guide, Student Edition. 2nd ed. 2004. (C). pap. 18.00 (978-0-07-867397-9(6) , 9780078673979) Glencoe/ McGraw-Hill.

—The American Journey & the American Journey: Reconstruction to the Present, Spanish Resources, Spanish Reading Essentials. 2nd ed. 2004. (SPA.). pap., stu. ed. 18.00 (978-0-07-865546-3(3) , 9780078655463) Glencoe/McGraw-Hill.

—The American Journey, Early Years, Reading Essentials & Note-Taking Guide Workbook. 2007. (C). pap. 18.00 (***978-0-07-880671-1(2)*** , 9780078806711) Glencoe/ McGraw-Hill.

T U V

—The American Journey Early Years, Student Edition. 2007. (C). 90.00 (*978-0-07-877715-8(1), 9780078777158) Glencoe/McGraw-Hill.

—The American Journey, Interactive Tutor Self Assessment CD-ROM. 5th ed. 2005. 93.32 (978-0-07-867794-6(7), 9780078677946) Glencoe/McGraw-Hill.

—The American Journey Modern Times, Reading Essentials & Note-Taking Guide. 2nd ed. 2007. (C). pap. 18.00 (*978-0-07-880638-4(0), 9780078806384) Glencoe/ McGraw-Hill.

—The American Journey Modern Times, Spanish Reading Essentials & Note-Taking Guide. 2nd ed. 2007. (C). pap. 18.00 (*978-0-07-880648-3(8), 9780078806483) Glencoe/McGraw-Hill.

—The American Journey Modern Times, Student Edition. 2nd ed. 2007. (C). 90.00 (*978-0-07-877718-9(6), 9780078777189) Glencoe/McGraw-Hill.

—The American Journey, Reading Essentials & Note-Taking Guide Workbook. 7th ed. 2007. (C). pap. 18.00 (*978-0-07-880608-7(9), 9780078806087) Glencoe/McGraw-Hill.

—The American Journey, Reconstruction to the Present. 2005. (C). stu. ed. 114.00 (978-0-07-867803-5(X), 9780078678035) Glencoe/McGraw-Hill.

—The American Journey Reconstruction to the Present: Reading Essentials Study & Guide. 2nd ed. 2004. pap., stu. ed., wbk. ed. 18.00 (978-0-07-865550-0(1), 9780078655500) Glencoe/McGraw-Hill.

—The American Journey, Reconstruction to the Present, Spanish Student Edition. 2005. (SPA.). 90.00 (978-0-07-868134-9(0), 9780078681349) Glencoe/McGraw-Hill.

—The American Journey, Reconstruction to the President: Active Reading Notetaking Guide. 2004. stu. ed. 18.00 (978-0-07-868547-7(8), 9780078685477) Glencoe/ McGraw-Hill.

—The American Journey, Spanish Reading Essentials & Note-Taking Guide Workbook. 7th ed. 2007. (C). pap. 18.00 (*978-0-07-880618-6(6), 9780078806186) Glencoe/McGraw-Hill.

—The American Journey, Spanish Student Edition. 2005. (SPA.). 91.32 (978-0-07-867380-1(1), 9780078673801) Glencoe/McGraw-Hill.

—The American Journey, Standardized Test Practice Workbook. 7th ed. 2007. (C). pap. 10.64 (*978-0-07-880612-4(7), 9780078806124) Glencoe/McGraw-Hill.

—The American Journey, Student Edition. 6th ed. 2007. (C). 91.32 (*978-0-07-877712-7(7), 9780078777127) Glencoe/McGraw-Hill.

—American Odyssey. 2nd ed. 2003. (gr. 6-12). stu. ed. 93.32 (978-0-07-860017-3(0), 9780078600173) Glencoe/ McGraw-Hill.

—American Odyssey, Interactive Student Edition. 2001. (gr. 6-12). stu. ed. 93.32 incl. cd-rom (978-0-07-828097-9(4), 9780078280979) Glencoe/McGraw-Hill.

—The American Repubic since 1877. 2nd ed. 2004. (C). stu. ed. 89.32 (978-0-07-860712-7(4), 9780078607127) Glencoe/McGraw-Hill.

—The American Republic since 1877. 2002. stu. ed. 91.33 incl. cd-rom (978-0-07-829251-4(4), 9780078292514); (C). stu. ed. 91.33 (978-0-07-828087-0(7), 9780078280870) Glencoe/McGraw-Hill.

—The American Republic since 1877: StudentWorks. 2nd ed. 2005. stu. ed. 113.32 (978-0-07-865416-9(5), 9780078654169) Glencoe/McGraw-Hill.

—The American Republic since 1877, Active Reading Note-Taking Guide. 2nd ed. 2004. (C). pap., stu. ed. 18.00 (978-0-07-867995-7(8), 9780078679957) Glencoe/ McGraw-Hill.

—The American Republic since 1877, Reading Essentials & Study Guide, Student Edition. 2nd ed. 2004. (C). pap. 21.32 (978-0-07-865405-3(X), 9780078654053) Glencoe/McGraw-Hill.

—The American Republic since 1877, Spanish Reading Essentials. 2nd ed. 2004. (SPA.). pap., stu. ed. 21.32 (978-0-07-865407-7(6), 9780078654077) Glencoe/McGraw-Hill.

—The American Republic to 1877. 2nd ed. 2005. stu. ed. 110.00 (978-0-07-866248-5(6), 9780078662485); 3rd ed. 2006. stu. ed. 90.00 (978-0-07-874675-8(2), 9780078746758) Glencoe/McGraw-Hill.

—The American Republic to 1877: Active Note-Taking Guide. 2nd ed. 2004. pap., stu. ed. 18.00 (978-0-07-866250-8(8), 9780078662508) Glencoe/McGraw-Hill.

—The American Republic to 1877, Spanish Student Edition. 2nd ed. 2005. (SPA.). 86.00 (978-0-07-867372-6(0), 9780078673726) Glencoe/McGraw-Hill.

—The American Vision. 2nd ed. 2004. (C). stu. ed. 90.64 (978-0-07-860719-6(1), 9780078607196) Glencoe/ McGraw-Hill.

—American Vision: Active Reading Note-Taking. 2nd ed. 2004. (C). pap., stu. ed. 18.00 (978-0-07-868002-1(6), 9780078680021) Glencoe/McGraw-Hill.

—The American Vision: Modern Times, Interactive Tutor Self-Assessment CD-ROM. 2007. (C). cd-rom 93.32 (*978-0-07-878527-6(8), 9780078785276) Glencoe/ McGraw-Hill.

—The American Vision: Modern Times, Reading Essentials & Note-Taking Guide. 2007. (C). pap. 18.00 (*978-0-07-878518-4(9), 9780078785184) Glencoe/McGraw-Hill.

—The American Vision: Modern Times, Spanish Reading Essentials & Note-Taking Guide. 2007. (C). pap. 9.00 (*978-0-07-878520-7(0), 9780078785207) Glencoe/ McGraw-Hill.

—The American Vision: Modern Times, Standardized Test Practice Workbook. 2007. (C). pap. 11.96 (*978-0-07-878510-8(3), 9780078785108) Glencoe/McGraw-Hill.

—The American Vision: Modern Times, StudentWorks Plus. 2005. cd-rom 117.32 (978-0-07-872733-7(2), 9780078727337) Glencoe/McGraw-Hill.

—American Vision, Interactive Student Edition. 2002. (C). 92.83 (978-0-07-829240-8(9), 9780078292408) Glencoe/McGraw-Hill.

—The American Vision, Interactive Tutor: Self-Assessment CD-ROM. 2007. (C). cd-rom 93.32 (*978-0-07-878450-7(6), 9780078784507) Glencoe/McGraw-Hill.

—The American Vision, Modern Times, Active Reading & Note-Taking Guide, Student Workbook. 2005. pap. 18.00 (978-0-07-872764-1(2), 9780078727641) Glencoe/McGraw-Hill.

—The American Vision, Modern Times, Reading Essentials. 2005. pap., stu. ed., wbk. ed. 18.00 (978-0-07-872768-9(5), 9780078727689) Glencoe/McGraw-Hill.

—The American Vision, Modern Times, Spanish Reading Essentials. 2005. pap., stu. ed., wbk. ed. 18.00 (978-0-07-872771-9(5), 9780078727719) Glencoe/McGraw-Hill.

—The American Vision, Reading Essentials & Study Guide, Student Edition. 2nd ed. 2004. pap. 22.64 (978-0-07-865439-8(4), 9780078654398) Glencoe/McGraw-Hill.

—American Vision, Spanish Reading Essentials & Study Guide, Student Edition. 2nd ed. 2004. (SPA.). pap. 22.64 (978-0-07-865441-1(6), 9780078654411) Glencoe/McGraw-Hill.

—The American Vision, Standardized Test Practice, Student Edition. 2007. (C). pap. 11.96 (*978-0-07-878431-6(X), 9780078784316) Glencoe/McGraw-Hill.

—The American Vision, StudentWorks Plus CD-ROM. 2nd ed. 2005. 114.64 (978-0-07-865456-5(4), 9780078654565) Glencoe/McGraw-Hill.

—Civics Today: Reading Essentials. 2003. pap., stu. ed. 19.17 (978-0-07-860531-4(8), 9780078605314) Glencoe/McGraw-Hill.

—Civics Today, Reading Essentials. 2003. (C). pap., stu. ed., wbk. ed. 18.00 (978-0-07-860532-1(6), 9780078605321) Glencoe/McGraw-Hill.

—Geography: The World & Its People, Reading Essentials. 2003. pap., stu. ed. 19.17 (978-0-07-860651-9(9), 9780078606519) Glencoe/McGraw-Hill.

McKissack, Patricia C. Run Away Home. 2001. 176p. (J). (ps-7). pap. 4.50 (978-0-590-46752-0(2)) Scholastic, Inc.

McLeese, Don. Benjamin Franklin. 2004. (Heroes of the American Revolution Ser.). 32p. pap. 5.95 (978-1-59515-316-6(0)) Rourke Publishing, LLC.

—Crispus Attucks. 2004. (Heroes of the American Revolution Ser.). 32p. pap. 5.95 (978-1-59515-315-9(2)) Rourke Publishing, LLC.

—Robert Fulton. 2006. (Rourke Discovery Library). (Illus.). 24p. (gr. 2-5). 14.95 (978-1-59515-434-7(5), 1244323) Rourke Publishing, LLC.

McNeese, Tim. Plessy V. Ferguson. 2006. (Great Supreme Court Decisions Ser.). (Illus.). 136p. (J). (gr. 5-8). 30.00 (978-0-7910-9237-8(2), Chelsea Hse.) Facts On File, Inc.

—The Rise & Fall of American Slavery: Freedom Denied, Freedom Gained. 2004. (Slavery in American History Ser.). (Illus.). 128p. (J). lib. bdg. 26.60 (978-0-7660-2156-3(4)) Enslow Pubs., Inc.

McNeese, Tim, ed. Rivers in American Life & Times. (Illus.). (gr. 9-13). pap. (978-0-7910-8059-7(5)); 2005. 120p. pap. 180.00 (978-0-7910-7722-1(5)) Facts On File, Inc. (Chelsea Hse.).

McPherson, Stephanie Sammartino. Coretta Scott King. 2007. (J). lib. bdg. (*978-0-8225-7156-8(0)) Twenty First Century Bks.

Millard, Catherine. Children's Companion Guide to America's History: History & Government. 2000. (gr. 5-8). lib. bdg. 21.10 (978-0-613-77338-6(1)) Tandem Library Bks.

Milone, Michael. LeapTrace Social Studies: American History. 2001. (J). (gr. k-5). spiral bd. 1.50 (978-1-58605-566-0(6)) LeapFrog Enterprises, Inc.

Mitchell Lane Publishers. Building America. 2007. (Building America Ser.). (J). lib. bdg. 329.45 (*978-1-58415-551-5(5)) Mitchell Lane Pubs., Inc.

—Profiles in American History. 2007. (YA). lib. bdg. 460.90 (*978-1-58415-532-4(9)) Mitchell Lane Pubs., Inc.

Mixon, Myrtis. Stories from American History. 2001. 96p. (J). tchr. ed. (978-0-8442-0444-4(7)) McGraw-Hill/ Contemporary.

Modern America. (We the People Ser.). (gr. 4-6). 180.80 (978-0-7565-0799-2(5)); Set. 2005. 244.80 (978-0-7565-1006-0(6)) Compass Point Bks.

Monumental Milestones: Great Events of Modern Times, 16 vols., Set. 2006. (J). (gr. 4-8). lib. bdg. 319.20 (*978-1-58415-292-7(3)) Mitchell Lane Pubs., Inc.

Moreno, Barry, intro. American Symbols & Their Meanings, 20 vols., Set. 2002. (Illus.). 48p. (YA). (gr. 4 up). lib. bdg. (978-1-59084-021-4(6)) Mason Crest Pubs.

Morley, Jacqueline & Langley, Andrew. You Woundn't Want to Be an American Colonist. Antram, David, illus. 2004. (You Wouldn't Want to Ser.). 32p. (J). (gr. 2-5). pap. 9.95 (978-0-531-16398-6(9), Watts, Franklin) Scholastic Library Publishing.

Morrow, Ann. The Gilded Age. 2007. (Cornerstones of Freedom). (Illus.). 48p. (J). (gr. 4-6). 26.00 (978-0-516-23641-4(5), Children's Pr.) Scholastic Library Publishing.

Moss, Marissa. Rachel's Journal: The Story of a Pioneer Girl. 2001. (Illus.). (J). (978-0-606-21394-3(5)) Tandem Library Bks.

Mullican, Judy. Horray for the U. S. A. Coates, Jennifer, illus. l.t. ed. 2000. (Big Bks.). (J). (ps-1). 10.95 (978-1-57332-183-9(4)) HighReach Learning, Inc.

Nash, Gary B. & Smith, Carter, eds. Atlas of American History. 4th rev. ed. 2007. (Illus.). 352p. (YA). (gr. 9 up). 95.00 (978-0-8160-5952-2(7)) Facts On File, Inc.

Nelson, Kristin L. Alamo. 2004. (ps-2). lib. bdg. 14.10 (978-0-613-76614-2(8)) Tandem Library Bks.

Nelson, Sheila. Thomas Jefferson's America: The Louisiana Purchase (1800-1811) 2005. (How America Became America Ser.). (Illus.). 96p. (J). lib. bdg. (978-1-59084-904-0(3)) Mason Crest Pubs.

New American History PTC Kit. 2002. (J). pap. 45.94 (978-0-14-270181-2(5), Puffin) Penguin Group (USA) Inc.

New Nation DBA. 2002. spiral bd. 16.95 (978-1-56004-127-6(7)) Social Studies Schl. Service.

Nichol, Bryan. One Nation Set II. 2004. (Series Title Ser.). (J). (gr. k-6). lib. bdg. 227.80 (978-1-59197-524-3(7), Checkerboard Library) ABDO Publishing Co.

Norton. A People & A Nation Complete 7th Edition Plus Oates Portrait of America Volume 1 & 2 8th Edition Plus Student Research Companion. 7th ed. 2004. (YA). pap., pap. 134.36 (978-0-618-53137-0(8), 390479) Houghton Mifflin College Div.

—A People & a Nation Complete Plus History Handbook, Vol. 1. 7th ed. 2004. (YA). pap., spiral bd. 99.96 (978-0-618-52930-8(6), 389449) Houghton Mifflin College Div.

—A People & A Nation Volume 1 7th Edition Plus Berkin History Handbook. 7th ed. 2004. (YA). pap., spiral bd. 99.96 (978-0-618-51653-7(0), 389272) Houghton Mifflin College Div.

Norton, Mary Beth, et al. A People & a Nation: A History of the United States. 7th ed. 2004. 948p. (YA). 125.96 (978-0-618-37589-9(9), 341890) Houghton Mifflin College Div.

Ochoa, George & Corey, Melinda, eds. American History on File. 2002. (YA). (978-0-8160-4661-4(1)); (978-0-8160-4662-1(X)) Facts On File, Inc.

Old Father's Long Journey. 2nd ed. 2001. 150p. (J). pap. 9.95 (978-1-930702-04-2(3), Wisdom Bks.) Literary Assocs. Pr.

One Nation: Revised & Updated, 52 bks. Incl. Alabama. Kummer, Patricia K. lib. bdg. 22.60 (978-0-7368-1225-2(3)); Alaska. Kummer, Patricia K. lib. bdg. 22.60 (978-0-7368-1226-9(1)); Arizona. Capstone Press Staff, contrib. by. lib. bdg. 22.60 (978-0-7368-1227-6(X)); Arkansas. Kummer, Patricia K. lib. bdg. 22.60 (978-0-7368-1228-3(8)); California. Capstone Press Staff, contrib. by. lib. bdg. 22.60 (978-0-7368-1229-0(6)); Colorado. Capstone Press, Geography Dept Staff, contrib. by. lib. bdg. 22.60 (978-0-7368-1230-6(X)); Connecticut. Capstone Press Staff, contrib. by. lib. bdg. 22.60 (978-0-7368-1231-3(8)); Delaware. Kummer, Patricia K. lib. bdg. 22.60 (978-0-7368-1232-0(6)); Florida. Capstone Press Staff, contrib. by. lib. bdg. 22.60 (978-0-7368-1233-7(4)); Georgia. Capstone Press Staff, contrib. by. lib. bdg. 22.60 (978-0-7368-1234-4(2)); Hawaii. Kummer, Patricia K. lib. bdg. 22.60 (978-0-7368-1235-1(0)); Idaho. Kummer, Patricia K. lib. bdg. 22.60 (978-0-7368-1236-8(9)); Illinois. Kummer, Patricia K. lib. bdg. 22.60 (978-0-7368-1237-5(7)); Indiana. Capstone Press Staff, contrib. by. lib. bdg. 22.60 (978-0-7368-1238-2(5)); Iowa. Kummer, Patricia K. lib. bdg. 22.60 (978-0-7368-1239-9(3)); Kansas. Kummer, Patricia K. lib. bdg. 22.60 (978-0-7368-1240-5(7)); Kentucky. Kummer, Patricia K. lib. bdg. 22.60 (978-0-7368-1241-2(5)); Louisiana. Capstone Press Staff, contrib. by. lib. bdg. 22.60 (978-0-7368-1242-9(3)); Maine. Kummer, Patricia K. lib. bdg. 22.60 (978-0-7368-1243-6(1)); Maryland. Kummer, Patricia K. lib. bdg. 22.60 (978-0-7368-1244-3(X)); Massachusetts. Capstone Press Staff, contrib. by. lib. bdg. 22.60 (978-0-7368-1245-0(8)); Michigan. Capstone Press Staff, contrib. by. lib. bdg. 22.60 (978-0-7368-1246-7(6)); Minnesota. Capstone Press Staff, contrib. by. lib. bdg. 22.60 (978-0-7368-1247-4(4)); Mississippi. Kummer, Patricia K. lib. bdg. 22.60 (978-0-7368-1248-1(2)); Missouri. Kummer, Patricia K. lib. bdg. 22.60 (978-0-7368-1249-8(0)); Montana. Kummer, Patricia K. lib. bdg. 22.60 (978-0-7368-1250-4(4)); Nebraska. Capstone Press Staff, contrib. by. lib. bdg. 22.60 (978-0-7368-1251-1(2)); Nevada. Kummer, Patricia K. lib. bdg. 22.60 (978-0-7368-1252-8(0)); New Hampshire. Kummer, Patricia K. lib. bdg. 22.60 (978-0-7368-1253-5(9)); New Jersey. Kummer, Patricia K. lib. bdg. 22.60 (978-0-7368-1254-2(7)); New Mexico. Kummer, Patricia K. lib. bdg. 22.60 (978-0-7368-1255-9(5)); New York. Capstone Press Staff, contrib. by. lib. bdg. 22.60 (978-0-7368-1256-6(3)); North Carolina. Kummer, Patricia K. lib. bdg. 22.60 (978-0-7368-1257-3(1)); North Dakota. Kummer, Patricia K. lib. bdg. 22.60 (978-0-7368-1258-0(X)); Ohio. Capstone Press Staff, contrib. by. lib. bdg. 22.60 (978-0-7368-1259-7(8)); Oklahoma. Kummer, Patricia K. lib. bdg. 22.60 (978-0-7368-1260-3(1)); Oregon. Capstone Press Staff, contrib. by. lib. bdg. 22.60 (978-0-7368-1261-0(X)); Pennsylvania. Capstone Press Staff, contrib. by. lib. bdg. 22.60 (978-0-7368-1262-7(8)); Puerto Rico. Kummer, Patricia K. lib. bdg. 22.60 (978-0-7368-1263-4(6)); Rhode Island. Kummer, Patricia K. lib. bdg. 22.60 (978-0-7368-1264-1(4)); South Carolina. Capstone Press Staff, contrib. by. lib. bdg. 22.60 (978-0-7368-1265-8(2)); South Dakota. Kummer, Patricia K. lib. bdg. 22.60 (978-0-7368-1266-5(0)); Tennessee. Kummer, Patricia K. lib. bdg. 22.60 (978-0-7368-1267-2(9)); Texas. Capstone Press Staff, contrib. by. lib. bdg. 22.60 (978-0-7368-1268-9(7)); Utah. Kummer, Patricia K. lib. bdg. 22.60 (978-0-7368-1269-6(5)); Vermont. Kummer, Patricia K. lib. bdg. 22.60 (978-0-7368-1270-2(9)); Virginia. Capstone Press Staff, contrib. by. lib. bdg. 22.60 (978-0-7368-1271-9(7)); Washington. Capstone Press Staff, contrib. by. lib. bdg. 22.60 (978-0-7368-1272-6(5)); Washington, D. C. Kummer, Patricia K. lib. bdg. 22.60 (978-0-7368-1273-3(3)); West Virginia. Kummer, Patricia K. lib. bdg. 22.60 (978-0-7368-1274-0(1)); Wisconsin. Capstone Press Staff, contrib. by. lib. bdg. 22.60 (978-0-7368-1275-7(X)); Wyoming. Kummer, Patricia K. lib. bdg. 22.60 (978-0-7368-1276-4(8)); 48p. (J). (gr. 3-4). 2002. (Illus.). 2002. Set lib. bdg. 1175.20 (978-0-7368-1277-1(6), Bridgestone Bks.) Capstone Pr., Inc.

O'Neal, Michael J. America in the 1920s. 2005. (Decades of American History Ser.). (Illus.). 128p. (J). (gr. 4-9). 35.00 (978-0-8160-5637-8(4)) Facts On File, Inc.

Open for Debate Group 3, 5 bks., Set. Incl. Affirmative Action. Kowalski, Kathiann M. 143p. (J). (gr. 6-9). lib. bdg. 39.93 (978-0-7614-2300-3(1)); Arab-Israeli Conflict. Worth, Richard. 127p. (J). (gr. 7 up). lib. bdg. 39.93 (978-0-7614-2295-2(1)); Marriage. Stefoff, Rebecca. 143p. (YA). (gr. 9 up). lib. bdg. 39.93 (978-0-7614-2299-0(4)); Media Bias. Streissguth, Thomas. 127p. (YA). (gr. 8 up). lib. bdg. 39.93 (978-0-7614-2296-9(X)); Racial Profiling. Kops, Deborah. 127p. (YA). (gr. 6-9). lib. bdg. 39.93 (978-0-7614-2298-3(6)); (Illus.). 2006. 2007. Set lib. bdg. 199.64 (*978-0-7614-2294-5(3), Benchmark Bks.) Cavendish, Marshall Corp.

Otfinoski, Steven. Major Disasters in U.S. History. 2005. (Illus.). 48p. (J). (*978-0-669-51416-2(0)) Great Source Education Group, Inc.

Paises del Mundo.Tr. of Lands & People. (SPA., Illus.). (YA). (gr. 5-8). 38.95 (978-84-241-9401-7(2)) Everest de Ediciones y Distribucion, S.L. ESP. *Dist:* Lectorum Pubns., Inc.

Paradigm Alternative Centers Staff, contrib. by. The Defining of America, 4 vols., Vol. 3. 2000. (Illus.). (J). per. 19.95 (978-1-928629-02-3(4)) Paradigm Accelerated Curriculum.

—The People, Places & Principles of America: The Defending of America (text), 4 Vols., Vol. 4. 2000. (Illus.). 284p. (J). per. 19.95 (978-1-928629-03-0(2)) Paradigm Accelerated Curriculum.

—The People, Places & Principles of America: The Designing of America (text), 4 vols., Vol. 2. 2000. (Illus.). 270p. (J). per. 19.95 (978-1-928629-01-6(6)) Paradigm Accelerated Curriculum.

—The People, Places & Principles of America: The Discovering of America (text), 4 vols., Vol. 1. 2000. (Illus.). 220p. (J). per. 19.95 (978-1-928629-00-9(8)) Paradigm Accelerated Curriculum.

Penton, ed. United States Flipper. 2003. (Smart Kids Flippers Ser.). (J). pap. 14.95 (978-1-59125-250-4(4)) Penton Overseas, Inc.

Perrin, Pat. Getting Started-America's Melting Pot. 2004. (Illus.). (J). (978-1-932663-04-4(5)) History Compass, LLC.

—Getting Started-Our 50 United States. 2004. (Illus.). (J). (978-1-932663-03-7(7)) History Compass, LLC.

—Getting Started-Our Government. 2004. (Illus.). (J). (978-1-932663-02-0(9)) History Compass, LLC.

Perrin, Pat, ed. America's Founders. 2003. (Researching American History Ser.). (J). pap. 7.95 (978-1-57960-097-6(2)) History Compass, LLC.

—The Civil Rights Movement. 2003. (Researching American History Ser.). (Illus.). 56p. (J). pap. 7.95 (978-1-57960-081-5(6)) History Compass, LLC.

—Communications. 2003. (Researching American History Ser.). (Illus.). 52p. (J). pap. 7.95 (978-1-57960-099-0(9)) History Compass, LLC.

—Spanish Explorers. 2003. (Researching American History Ser.). (Illus.). 56p. (J). pap. 7.95 (978-1-57960-088-4(3)) History Compass, LLC.

—Transportation Stories. 2003. (Researching American History Ser.). (Illus.). 52p. (J). pap. 7.95 (978-1-57960-098-3(0)) History Compass, LLC.

Petersen, Christine & Petersen, David. United States of America. 2002. (Illus.). 47p. (J). (gr. 4-7). lib. bdg. 15.25 (978-0-613-54371-2(8)) Tandem Library Bks.

Platt, D. D. & Conkling, Philip, eds. Island Journal: An Annual Publication of the Island Institute, 20. Ralston, Peter, photos by. 20th ed. 2003. (Island Journals: 20). (Illus.). 96p. pap. 9.95 (978-0-942719-33-8(6)) Island Institute.

Presidents: Discover the Presidents Who Have Shaped American History, from the Founding Fathers to Today's Leaders. rev. ed. 2001. (Eyewitness Books). (Illus.). 64p. (J). 15.95 (978-0-7894-6285-5(0)) Dorling Kindersley Publishing, Inc.

Price Hossell, Karen. The Nineteenth Amendment: Women Get the Vote. 2003. (Point of Impact Ser.). (Illus.). 32p. (J). (gr. 5-7). lib. bdg. 25.64 (978-1-58810-908-8(9)) Heinemann Library.

A Primary Source History of the United States, 8 Vols. 240.00 (978-0-8368-5823-5(9)) Stevens, Gareth Inc.

Primary Sources of American Wars. (J). (gr. 3-5). 119.70 (978-1-4042-3304-1(0)) Rosen Publishing Group, Inc., The.

Proctor, Allen. Multiple-Choice & Free-Response Questions with DBQ in Preparation for the AP United States History Examination. 4th ed. 2000. (Illus.). 128p. (YA). (gr. 9-12). pap. 18.95 (978-1-878621-61-0(0)) D&S Marketing Systems, Inc.

Question & Answer Library, 8 vols., Set. 2000. 256p. (J). 59.95 (978-0-7525-4640-7(6)) Parragon, Inc.

Raintree Steck-Vaughn Staff, ed. Making of America. 1999. (Illus.). (J). 114.20 (978-0-7398-2814-4(2)) Raintree.

Rakes, Celeste W. All-American History. 2005. (J). (978-1-892427-12-0(5)) Bright Ideas! Educational Resources.

Raymond, Clark. Living in the United States. 7th rev. ed. 1999. ("Living In" Ser.). 64p. pap. 9.95 (978-0-86647-153-4(7)) Pro Lingua Assocs., Inc.

Rebels & Revolutions: Individual Title Six-Packs. (Rigby Infoquest Ser.). (gr. 6 up). 37.00 (978-0-7578-8002-5(9)) Rigby Education.

Recorvits, Helen. Where Heroes Hide. 2002. (Illus.). 144p. (J). (gr. 4-6). 16.00 (978-0-374-33057-6(3), Farrar, Straus & Giroux (BYR)) Farrar, Straus & Giroux.

Remembering Medicine Creek: The Story of the First Treaty Signed in Washington. 2005. (YA). pap. 10.00 (978-0-9772528-0-0(9)) Fireweed Pr.

Research American History Series: Series Set. 2004. (Researching American History Ser.). (Illus.). (J). (978-1-932663-05-1(3)) History Compass, LLC.

The Rise & Fall of the United States of America. 2001. 30p. 4.95 (978-0-9707469-1-7(1) , DLS Bks.) Denney Literary Services.

Roberts, Paul M. Review Text in United States History. 2nd ed. 2002. (Illus.). 576p. (YA). (gr. 8-12). pap. 11.70 (978-0-87720-857-0(3) , R489P) AMSCO Schl. Pubns., Inc.

Robinette, Michelle. Internet Scavengr Hunt American History. 2002. (Internet Scavenger Hunts Ser.). (Illus.). 64p. (gr. 4-8). pap. 10.95 (978-0-439-31665-1(0)) Scholastic, Inc.

Robinson, Tom. The Development of the Industrial United States. 2007. (J). ***978-1-59036-745-2(6)); (*978-1-59036-746-9(4))** Weigl Pubs., Inc.

Roe, Chris. America: From Every Mountainside, 3 vols., Vol. 2 2001. (Illus.). 200p. (J). (gr. 3-7). pap. 34.99 (978-0-9707712-1-6(5)) Christian Novel Studies.

—America: Land of the Pilgrims' Pride, 3 vols., Vol. 1. 2001. (Illus.). 200p. (J). (gr. 3-6). pap. 34.99 (978-0-9707712-0-9(7)) Christian Novel Studies.

—America: Let Freedom Ring, 3 vols., Vol. 3. 2001. (Illus.). 200p. (J). (gr. 3-7). pap. 34.99 (978-0-9707712-2-3(3)) Christian Novel Studies.

Roop, Connie & Roop, Peter. The Declaration of Independence. 2005. (Illus.). 112p. (J). pap. 3.99 (978-0-689-86444-5(2) , Aladdin); lib. bdg. 11.89 (978-0-689-86446-9(9) , Aladdin Library) Simon & Schuster Children's Publishing.

Roop, Connie & Roop, Peter, eds. In My Own Words, 4 bks., Set. Incl. Diary of David R. Leeper : Rushing for Gold. 78p. lib. bdg. 27.07 (978-0-7614-1011-9(2)); Diary of John Wesley Powell : Exploring the Grand Canyon. Powell, John Wesley. 96p. lib. bdg. 24.21 (978-0-7614-1013-3(9)); Diary of Joseph Plumb Martin : A Revolutionary War Soldier. 96p. lib. bdg. 27.07 (978-0-7614-1014-0(7)); Diary of Mary Jemison : Captured by the Indians. Jemison, Mary. 64p. lib. bdg. 27.07 (978-0-7614-1010-2(4)); (J). (gr. 5 up). (Illus.). 2000. Set lib. bdg. 96.86 (978-0-7614-1012-6(0) , Benchmark Bks.) Cavendish, Marshall Corp.

Roop, Peter & Roop, Connie. Louisiana Purchase. Comport, Sally Wern, illus. 2004. (Milestone Ser.). 80p. (J). pap. 3.99 (978-0-689-86443-8(4) , Aladdin) Simon & Schuster Children's Publishing.

—Manten las Luces Encendidas, Abbie. Hanson, Peter E., illus. 2005. Tr. of Keep the Lights Burning, Abbie. (SPA.). 40p. (J). (gr. 2-5). pap. 5.95 (978-0-8225-3099-2(6)) Lerner Publishing Group.

Roop, Peter & Roop, Connie. River Roads West: America's First Highways. 2007. 64p. (J). (gr. 3 up). 19.95 **(*978-1-59078-430-3(8))** Boyds Mills Pr.

Rosen, Daniel. New Beginnings: Jamestown & the Virginia Colony 1607-1699. 2005. (Crossroads America Ser.). 40p. (J). (gr. 5-9). 12.95 (978-0-7922-8277-8(9)); (Illus.). lib. bdg. 21.90 (978-0-7922-8357-7(0)) National Geographic Society. (National Geographic Children's Bks.).

Rossi, Ann. Bright Ideas: The Age of Invention in America 1870-1910. 2005. (Crossroads America Ser.). (Illus.). 40p. (J). (gr. 5-9). 21.90 (978-0-7922-8356-0(2) , National Geographic Children's Bks.) National Geographic Society.

—Created Equal: Women Campaign for the Right to Vote 1840 - 1920. 2005. (Crossroads America Ser.). (Illus.). 40p. (gr. 5-9). 12.95 (978-0-7922-8275-4(2)); 21.90 (978-0-7922-8285-3(X)) National Geographic Society. (National Geographic Children's Bks.).

—Cultures Collide: Native American & Europeans 1492-1700. 2004. (Crossroads America Ser.). (Illus.). 40p. (J). (gr. 5-9). 12.95 (978-0-7922-7189-5(0) , National Geographic Children's Bks.) National Geographic Society.

Rous, Sheri, ed. United States History. 2004. (Illus.). 32p. (J). pap. 10.99 (978-1-59198-053-7(4) , CTP 2797) Creative Teaching Pr., Inc.

Rulers & Their Times - Group 3, 4 bks. 119.71 (978-0-7614-1486-5(X) , Benchmark Bks.) Cavendish, Marshall Corp.

Russian Colonies in the Americas, 6 Packs. (On Deck Ser.: Vol. 2). 24p. (gr. 4-5). 35.00 (978-0-7578-5803-1(1)) Rigby Education.

Ryan, Pam Muñoz. The Flag We Love. 2000. (J). 14.75 (978-0-606-19327-6(8)) Tandem Library Bks.

Sakolsky, Josh. Critical Perspectives on the Industrial Revolution. 2005. (Critical Anthologies of Nonfiction Writing Ser.). (Illus.). 176p. (gr. 7-12). lib. bdg. 30.60 (978-1-4042-0062-3(2)) Rosen Publishing Group, Inc., The.

Sanders, Jeff & Sanders, Nancy I. 15 Fun to Read American History Mini Books: Engaging Nonfiction Stories on Key Topics That Help Struggling Readers Learn the Content They Need to Know: Grades 4-8. 2001. (Illus.). 80p. (gr. 3-5). pap. 11.95 (978-0-439-11368-7(7)) Scholastic, Inc.

Sandifer, Kevin W., ed. History of the United States, Beginning-Civil War Pt. 1: Its Beginning Through the Civil War. I.t. ed. 2004. (Illus.). 400p. lib. bdg. 19.95 (978-0-910653-60-2(7) , 8201T, Red River Pr.) Red River Pr.

Sandler, Martin. Immigrants: A Library of Congress Book. 2000. (gr. 3-6). lib. bdg. 19.95 (978-0-613-28531-5(X)) Tandem Library Bks.

Sandler, Martin W. America's Great Disasters. Sandler, Martin W., illus. 2003. (Illus.). 96p. (J). (gr. 3 up). 17.99 (978-0-06-029107-5(9)) HarperCollins Pubs.

Savitz, Harriet May. YDear Daughters & Sons: Three Essays on the American Spirit... a Tribute. 2003. 40p. per. 4.95 (978-0-9639838-9-3(X)) Little Treasure Pubns., Inc.

Scenic Art Staff, compiled by. The American Revolution 1764-1784. 2002. (Illus.). 52p. per. 6.95 (978-0-9718567-2-1(9)) Scenic Art.

Schaefer, Lola M. The Pledge of Allegiance. 2002. (Symbols of Freedom Ser.). (Illus.). 32p. (J). (gr. k-2). pap. 6.95 (978-1-58810-398-7(6) , 91193) Heinemann Library.

Schaefer, Ted. Westward to the Pacific. 2006. (Making a New Nation Ser.). (Illus.). 48p. (J). (978-1-4034-7829-0(5)); pap. (978-1-4034-7836-8(8)) Heinemann Library.

Scholastic, Inc. Staff. Pledge of Allegiance. 2001. (J). (978-0-606-21382-0(1)) Tandem Library Bks.

—Pledge of Allegiance: Commemorative Edition. 2001. (Illus.). 32p. (J). pap. 3.99 (978-0-439-39962-3(9) , Scholastic Paperbacks) Scholastic, Inc.

Scillian, Devin. One Nation: America by the Numbers. Carroll, Pam, illus. 40p. (J). 2004. pap. 7.95 (978-1-58536-249-3(2)); 2002. 19.95 (978-1-58536-063-5(5)) Sleeping Bear Pr.

Scott Ingram. The FBI Director. 2004. (America's Leaders Ser.). (Illus.). 32p. (J). 23.70 (978-1-4103-0090-4(0) , Blackbirch Pr., Inc.) Thomson Gale.

—The National Security Advisor. 2004. (Illus.). 32p. (J). 23.70 (978-1-56711-962-6(X) , Blackbirch Pr., Inc.) Thomson Gale.

Seneca Falls, Grades 4-9: Achieving Women's Rights. (Teaching with Primary Sources Ser.). (J). tchr. ed. 32.95 (978-0-382-40975-2(2)) Cobblestone Publishing Co.

Settling the West. (History & Social Studies Ser.). (Illus.). 96p. (978-0-7613-3097-4(6) , Twenty-First Century Bks.) Lerner Publishing Group.

Shaw, Maura D. Owl's Journey: Four Centuries of an American County. Tantillo, Joe, illus. 2000. 152p. (J). (gr. 4-7). reprint ed. pap. 9.95 (978-1-885482-07-5(8)) Shawangunk Pr., Inc.

Shewan, Edward J. History for Little Pilgrims. 1998. 74p. (J). pap., tchr. ed. 5.00 (978-1-930092-85-3(7) , clp79901) Christian Liberty Pr.

Shields, Carol Diggory. Brainjuice: American History Fresh Squeezed! Thompson, Richard, illus. 2005. 80p. (J). (gr. 4-7). reprint ed. pap. 7.95 (978-1-59354-120-0(1)) Handprint Bks.

Shields, Charles J. Central America: Facts & Figures. 2002. (Let's Discover Central America Ser.). (Illus.). 64p. (J). (gr. 5-7). lib. bdg. (978-1-59084-099-3(2)) Mason Crest Pubs.

Shukin, Barbara. Renaissance History Portfolio: A History of Europe & the Americas from the 14th -18th Centuries. 2004. (J). spiral bd. 24.95 (978-0-9762918-2-4(7)) Homeschool Journey.

Shuter, Jane, et al. Picture the Past Series, Vol. 28. 2004. (gr. 2-4). 718.00 (978-1-4034-5834-6(0)) Heinemann Library.

Siebert, Anee & Clark, Raymond. All Around America Scripts/Workbook Package: The Time Traveler's Talk-show. 2004. pap. 30.00 (978-0-86647-192-3(8)) Pro Lingua Assocs., Inc.

Siebert, Anne & Clark, Raymond C. All Around America Activities Workbook: The Time Traveler's Talk Show. 2004. 76p. pap. 16.50 (978-0-86647-184-8(7)) Pro Lingua Assocs., Inc.

—All Around America Scripts/Workbook/2 CD's Package: The Time Traveler's Talk Show. 2004. pap. 39.00 (978-0-86647-186-2(3)) Pro Lingua Assocs., Inc.

Slovacek, Cindy. Trek Across America: A Game to Teach American History & Government. 2nd ed. 2001. 80p. (J). per. 15.95 net. (978-1-883055-39-4(3)) Dandy Lion Pubns.

Smith, A. G. Historic American Landmarks. 2005. (Illus.). 32p. (J). (gr. 3). pap. 3.95 (978-0-486-44489-5(9)) Dover Pubns., Inc.

Smith, Ruth J. Divine Providence: A Child's History of the United States. Mikler, Lisa M., illus. 2005. (J). per. 19.95 net. (978-0-9705618-5-5(7)) Bradford Pr.

—Liberty & Justice for All: A Child's History of the United States of America. Milker, Lisa, illus. 2003. (J). per. 19.95 (978-0-9705618-3-1(0)) Bradford Pr.

—Liberty & Justice for All Teacher's Guide: Liberty & Justice for All. 2003. (J). tchr. ed., per. 34.95 (978-0-9705618-4-8(9)) Bradford Pr.

—Self Government: A Child's History of the United States of America. Mikler, Lisa M., illus. 2002. 160p. (J). per. 17.95 (978-0-9705618-1-7(4)) Bradford Pr.

Smith, Shuford. ABC All-American Riddles. 2003. (Illus.). (J). (978-0-939217-56-4(2)) Peel Productions, Inc.

Sorensen, L. El Aguila Americana. Palacios, Argentina, tr. 2002. (Simbolos Americanos Ser.).Tr. of American Eagle. (SPA., Illus.). 24p. mass mkt. 5.95 (978-1-58952-267-1(2) , RK31480) Rourke Publishing, LLC.

Sorensen, Lynda. El Alamo. Palacios, Argentina, tr. 2002. (Simbolos Americanos Ser.). (SPA., Illus.). 24p. mass mkt. 5.95 (978-1-58952-268-8(0) , RK31481) Rourke Publishing, LLC.

Spanish Colonies in the Americas, 6 vols., Pack. (On Deck Ser.: Vol. 2). 24p. (gr. 4-5). 35.00 (978-0-7578-5804-8(X)) Rigby Education.

Stanley, George Edward. The Great Depression & World War II (1929-1949) 2005. (Illus.). 48p. (J). pap. (978-0-8368-5838-9(7)); lib. bdg. 30.00 (978-0-8368-5829-7(8)) Stevens, Gareth Inc. (World Almanac Library).

The Star-Spangled State Book: Have Fun Learning about All 50 States. 2006. (YA). per. (978-0-9787820-0-9(3)) King, Joel.

State History Syllabus. 1999. 4p. (YA). ring bd. 2.00 (978-1-57896-055-2(X) , 1035, Hewitt Homeschooling Resources) Hewitt Research Foundation, Inc.

States. (Smart Facts Ser.). (Illus.). 6p. (J). (978-1-4127-1091-6(X) , 7241200); 2005. 96p. 12.98 (978-0-7853-9600-0(4) , 7127301) Publications International, Ltd.

The States & Their Symbols. rev. ed. (Social Studies Collections). (Illus.). (J). (gr. 2-3). lib. bdg. 1105.52 (978-0-7368-2348-7(4)) Capstone Pr., Inc.

The States & Their Symbols Series. (Illus.). (gr. k-3). pap. 450.00 (978-0-531-19415-7(9) , Watts, Franklin) Scholastic Library Publishing.

Stckvagn. Americas Story Complete Book S. 2005. pap. (978-0-7398-9717-1(9)) Harcourt Schl. Pubs.

Steck-Vaughn Staff. Accelerated Reader Stage 2: Early Americans. 2000. (Pair-It Bks.). (J). pap. (978-0-7398-4125-9(4)); (Illus.). pap. (978-0-7398-4126-6(2)) Steck-Vaughn.

—American History: Answer Key - Level H. 2000. (Test Practice Success Ser.). (J). pap. 3.02 (978-0-7398-3130-4(5)) Steck-Vaughn.

—American History: Answer Key - Level HS. 2000. (Test Practice Success Ser.). (J). pap. 3.02 (978-0-7398-3132-8(1)) Steck-Vaughn.

—American History: Level H - Grade 8. 2000. (Test Practice Success Ser.). (J). pap. 14.56 (978-0-7398-3129-8(1)) Steck-Vaughn.

—American History Since 1865, Set. 2001. (Illus.). pap. 1051.40 (978-0-7398-6269-8(3)) Steck-Vaughn.

—Americas History. 2001. (J). pap., tchr. ed. (978-0-7398-3621-7(8)) Steck-Vaughn.

—Americas Story: Teacher's Resource Binder. 2001. (J). pap., tchr. ed. (978-0-7398-2388-0(4)) Steck-Vaughn.

—Social Studies Level E: History of Our Country. 2005. (Steck-Vaughn Social Studies). (Illus.). 208p. pap. 17.30 (978-0-7398-9222-0(3)) Steck-Vaughn.

—Step into History: Reading Group Packs. 2000. pap. 399.00 (978-1-58702-412-2(8)) Johnston, Don Inc.

—Step into History: Single User Pack. 2000. pap. 174.00 (978-1-58702-345-3(8)); pap. 174.00 (978-1-893376-77-9(X)) Johnston, Don Inc.

—Step into History: Single User Packs. 2000. pap 174.00 (978-1-58702-408-5(X)) Johnston, Don Inc.

—The United States: Region by Region. 2002. pap. (978-0-7398-6176-9(X)) Steck-Vaughn.

Stich, Paul, et al. U. S. History & Government: STAReview. Garnsey, Wayne, ed. 2000. (ENG., Illus.). 416p. (YA). (gr. 7-12). per. 15.95 (978-0-935487-69-5(7)) N&N Publishing Co., Inc.

—United States History & Government: Constitutional & Geopolitical Patterns. 2000. (ENG., Illus.). 416p. (YA). (gr. 9-12). per. 19.95 (978-0-935487-68-8(9) , STAReviews) N&N Publishing Co., Inc.

Stille, Darlene R. The Emergence of Modern America. 2007. (J). ***978-1-59036-747-6(2)); (*978-1-59036-748-3(0))** Weigl Pubs., Inc.

Stone, Lynn M. Land of Liberty. 2003. (Land of Liberty Ser.). (gr. 2-5). 89.75 (978-1-58952-308-1(3)) Rourke Publishing, LLC.

—Texas Longhorn. 2003. (Animals in U.S. History Ser.). (Illus.). 24p. (J). 25.64 (978-1-58952-702-7(X)) Rourke Publishing, LLC.

Stories of America, 20 bks. 2002. (Illus.). 542.80 (978-1-4109-0130-9(0)) Raintree.

The Story of Ulysses S. Grant. 2005. (Illus.). 26p. (J). 6.95 (978-0-8249-6565-5(5)) Ideals Pubns.

Streissguth, Thomas. United States in Pictures. 2007. (J). lib. bdg. **(*978-0-8225-8567-1(7))** Twenty First Century Bks.

Stuart Kallen. Political Activists of the 1960s. 2004. (History Makers Ser.). (Illus.). 96p. (J). 29.95 (978-1-59018-386-1(X)) Thomson Gale.

Stuckey. Call to Freedom. 3rd ed. 2003. (SPA., Illus.). 77.20 (978-0-03-073766-4(4)) Holt, Rinehart & Winston.

Sundling, Charles W. Frontier Land, Set. Incl. Cowboys of the Frontier. lib. bdg. 24.21 (978-1-57765-045-4(X)); Explorers of the Frontier. lib. bdg. 24.21 (978-1-57765-044-7(1)); Mountain Men of the Frontier. lib. bdg. 24.21 (978-1-57765-043-0(3)); Native Americans of the Frontier. lib. bdg. 24.21 (978-1-57765-042-3(5)); Pioneers of the Frontier. lib. bdg. 24.21 (978-1-57765-047-8(6)); Women of the Frontier. lib. bdg. 24.21 (978-1-57765-046-1(8)); 32p. (J). (gr. 3-8). 2000. (Illus.). 2000. Set lib. bdg. 145.26 (978-1-57765-271-7(1) , ABDO & Daughters) ABDO Publishing Co.

Swanson, June. I Pledge Allegiance. Hanson, Rick, illus. 2002. (On My Own History Ser.). 40p. lib. bdg. 23.93 (978-0-87614-925-6(5) , Carolrhoda Bks.) Lerner Publishing Group.

Tackach, James. Uncle Tom's Cabin: Indictment of Slavery. 2000. (Words That Changed History Ser.). (Illus.). 128p. (YA). (gr. 4-12). lib. bdg. 27.45 (978-1-56006-591-3(5) , LML00902-177946, Lucent Bks.) Thomson Gale.

Tate, Elfleda J. Legacy of Tragedy: American History Revisited. 2001. (Illus.). 256p. (YA). pap. 14.95 (978-1-881524-85-4(X)) Milligan Bks., Inc.

Tate, Suzanne. Color with the Wright Brothers: See How They Made History. Melvin, James, illus. 2003. (Suzanne Tate's History Ser.). 32p. (J). pap. 2.95 (978-1-878405-41-8(1)) Nags Head Art, Inc.

Thames, Susan. Nuestros Símbolos Americanos. 2007. (J). **(*978-1-60044-304-6(4))** Rourke Publishing, LLC.

Thayer, William M. From Log-Cabin to the White House. Life of James A. Garfield: 1881 James H. Earle, Publisher Edition. Exams Unlimited, Inc. Staff, ed. 2001. (Illus.). 392p. (YA). reprint ed. cd-rom 12.25 (978-1-885343-27-7(2)) Exams Unlimited, Inc.

Thompson, Carol & Thompson, Carol. America the Good: Stories of Goodwill by Good Americans. 2003. (Illus.). 95p. bds. 15.95 (978-0-9744111-0-1(8)) Wren's Nest Publishing, Inc.

Thompson, Kim Mitzo & Hilderbrand, Karen Mitzo. Celebrate America. 2005. 24p. (J). (gr. k-6). pap., act. bk. ed. 13.99 (978-1-57583-588-4(6) , Schaffer, Frank) Schaffer, Frank Pubns.

Thompson, Linda. First Settlements. 2005. 48p. pap. 7.45 (978-1-59515-825-3(1)) Rourke Publishing, LLC.

—Los Españoles en América. 2005. (ENG & SPA., Illus.). 48p. (J). (978-1-59515-657-0(7)) Rourke Publishing, LLC.

—Territorios de EE. UU. 2006. (Expansion de America II Ser.). (SPA.). 48p. (gr. 4-8). pap. 7.95 (978-1-59515-702-7(6)) Rourke Publishing, LLC.

Time for Kids Editors. Our 50 United States & Other U. S. Lands. 2007. (Time for Kids Ser.). (Illus.). 72p. (J). 17.99 (978-0-06-081557-8(4)); lib. bdg. 18.89 (978-0-06-081558-5(2)) HarperCollins Pubs.

A Time to Remember. 2001. (YA). (gr. 6-12). pap. incl. audio (978-0-8224-3296-8(X)) Globe Fearon Educational Publishing.

Timeless Voices, Timeless Themes: The American Experience. (YA). (gr. 11). 2000. stu. ed. 53.97 (978-0-13-050289-6(8)); 1999. stu. ed. 55.97 (978-0-13-434059-3(0)) Prentice Hall PTR.

Timeless Voices, Timeless Themes: The American Experience, Standardized Test Prep. Answers & Explanations. 2000. trans. 129.97 (978-0-13-050825-6(X)) Prentice Hall PTR.

Timeless Voices, Timeless Themes: The American Experience, Standardized Test Preparation Blackline Masters. 2000. (YA). (gr. 11). 19.97 (978-0-13-437471-0(1)) Prentice Hall PTR.

Timeless Voices, Timeless Themes: The American Experience, Strategies for Succeeding on Standardized Tests. 2000. (YA). (gr. 11). 24.47 (978-0-13-436133-8(4)) Prentice Hall PTR.

Tiner, John. The Story of the Pledge of Allegiance: Discovering Our Nations Heritage. 2003. (Discovering Our Nation's Heritage Ser.). (Illus.). 48p. (J). 9.99 (978-0-89051-393-4(7)) Master Bks.

Todd, Francine E. The Todds in America: 1741-2005: An American History/Genealogy Curriculum for Grades 3-5. 2006. (ENG., Illus.). 68p. per. **(*978-1-4120-7834-4(2))** Trafford Publishing.

Townsend, Dana E. Ellis Island. (Illus.). 32p. (J). **(*978-0-7367-2944-4(5))** Zaner-Bloser, Inc.

Tracy, Kathleen. Top Secret: The Story of the Manhattan Project. 2005. (Illus.). 48p. (YA). lib. bdg. (978-1-58415-399-3(7)) Mitchell Lane Pubs., Inc.

Travis, George. State Facts. 1999. (Rourke Guide to State Symbols Ser.). (Illus.). 48p. (J). (gr. 3-8). lib. bdg. 29.93 (978-1-57103-297-3(5)) Rourke Publishing, LLC.

A True Book - Westward Expansion, 6 bks., Set. Incl. Homestead Act. Landau, Elaine. 25.00 (978-0-516-25870-6(2)); Lewis & Clark Expedition. Ditchfield, Christin. 25.00 (978-0-516-22835-8(8)); Mormon Trail. Landau, Elaine. 25.00 (978-0-516-25872-0(9)); Oregon Trail. Landau, Elaine. 25.00 (978-0-516-25871-3(0)); Pony Express. Landau, Elaine. 25.00 (978-0-516-25873-7(7)); Spanish Missions. Ditchfield, Christin. 25.00 (978-0-516-22834-1(X)); 48p. (J). (gr. 3-5). 2006. (Illus.). 2006. 150.00 (978-0-516-25420-3(0) , Children's Pr.) Scholastic Library Publishing.

U. S. History. 2004. (Topic-Specific Brain Teasers Ser.). (Illus.). 80p. 9.99 (978-1-57690-639-2(6)) Teacher Created Materials, Inc.

U. S. History Little Books: Famous Events. 2002. 144p. (J). (gr. k-3). 14.99 (978-0-7439-3258-5(7) , 3258) Teacher Created Materials, Inc.

U. S. History Word (Re)Searches: From Colonial Times to the Present. 2003. 144p. (YA). (gr. 5-12). 14.99 (978-0-7439-3768-9(6)) Teacher Created Materials, Inc.

Uebelhor, Tracy S. The Truman Years. 2005. (Presidential Profiles Ser.). (Illus.). 832p. (gr. 9). 85.00 (978-0-8160-5490-9(8)) Facts On File, Inc.

The United States: Historical Atlases of the Growth of a New Nation. 2005. (Illus.). (gr. 7-12). lib. bdg. 183.60 (978-1-4042-0357-0(5)) Rosen Publishing Group, Inc., The.

United States, Army Junior ROTC Staff, et al, contrib. by. Army JROTC Leadership Education & Training. 2002. (Illus.). 416p. (J). (978-0-536-67808-9(1)) Pearson Custom Publishing.

United States History, 3 vols. 2004. 738p. (YA). (gr. 6-12). 43.95 (978-0-13-024410-9(4)) Globe Fearon Educational Publishing.

The United States Past to Present: Heath Social Studies. Incl. United States Past & Present. suppl. ed. (978-0-669-11382-2(4)); United States Past & Present. (978-0-669 11398 3(0)); The United States Past to Present. suppl. ed. (978-0-669-11424-9(3)); The United States Past to Present. pap., wbk. ed. (978-0-669-11404-1(9)); The United States Past to Present. tchr. ed., wbk. ed. (978-0-669-11409-6(X)); The United States Past to Present. suppl. ed. (978-0-669-11430-0(8)); The United States Past to Present. suppl. ed. (978-0-669-11725-7(0)); The United States Past to Present. suppl. ed. (J). (gr. 5-6). (978-0-669-11390-7(5)) Houghton Mifflin Co. (Schl. Div.).

US Facts & Fun. 2005. 192p. (gr. 1-3). 14.99 (978-1-59673-002-1(1) , EMC 6305); (gr. 4-6). 14.99 (978-1-59673-003-8(X) , EMC 6306) Evan-Moor Educational Pubs.

Uschan, Michael V. Reconstruction. 2007. (Lucent Library of Black History Ser.). (Illus.). 128p. (gr. 7-10). 28.70 **(*978-1-4205-0009-7(0)** , Lucent Bks.) Thomson Gale.

Uschan, Michael V. The 1940's. 1998. (Cultural History of the United States Through the Decades Ser.). (Illus.). 128p. (YA). (gr. 4-12). lib. bdg. 29.95 (978-1-56006-554-8(0) , LML00902-177911, Lucent Bks.) Thomson Gale.

Van Leeuwen, Jean. Hannah's Winter of Hope. Bonnell, J., ed. Diamond, Donna, illus. 2001. (Pioneer Daughters Ser.: Vol. 3). 96p. (J). (gr. 4-7). pap. 4.99 (978-0-14-130950-7(4) , Puffin) Penguin Group (USA) Inc.

Victor, Rae Anna. George Washington's Revolutionary Marshals. 2004. (Illus.). 62p. (J). pap. 9.95 (978-0-7414-2302-3(2)) Infinity Publishing.

Ward, Gail. Animals along the Lewis & Clark Trail. 2002. 32p. (978-1-886609-32-7(2)) Tamarack Bks., Inc.

Waryncia, Lou & Hale, Sarah Elder. Antietam: Day of Courage & Sacrifice. 2005. (Civil War Ser.). (Illus.). 48p. (J). 17.95 (978-0-8126-7904-5(0)) Cobblestone Publishing Co.

We Are America, 6 bks., Set 1. 2003. (J). (gr. 2-4). lib. bdg. 145.32 (978-1-4034-0168-7(3)) Heinemann Library.

T
U
V

We the People, 87 vols. 2006. 48p. (YA). (gr. 4-6). 2081.91 (978-0-7565-1715-1(X)) Compass Point Bks.

We the People - Revolution & the New Nation, 8 bks. Incl. Battles of Lexington & Concord. Raatma, Lucia. 2003. lib. bdg. 22.60 (978-0-7565-0490-8(2)); Bill of Rights. Burgan, Michael. 2001. lib. bdg. 21.26 (978-0-7565-0151-8(2)); Boston Tea Party. Burgan, Michael. 2000. lib. bdg. 22.60 (978-0-7565-0040-5(0)); Declaration of Independence. Burgan, Michael. 2000. lib. bdg. 22.60 (978-0-7565-0042-9(7)); Monticello. Burgan, Michael. 2003. lib. bdg. 22.60 (978-0-7565-0491-5(0)); Paul Revere's Ride. Raatma, Lucia. 2003. lib. bdg. 22.60 (978-0-7565-0492-2(9)); U. S. Constitution. Williams, Jean Kinney. 2003. lib. bdg. 22.60 (978-0-7565-0493-9(7)); Valley Forge. Burgan, Michael. 2004. lib. bdg. 22.60 (978-0-7565-0615-5(8)); 48p. (J). (gr. 4 up). (Illus.). Set lib. bdg. 180.80 (978-0-7565-0778-7(2)) Compass Point Bks.

We the People: Expansion & Reform. 2006. (J). (gr. 4-6). 717.90 (978-0-7565-1704-5(4)) Compass Point Bks.

We the People: Exploration & Colonization, 10 vols. 2006. 48p. (YA). (gr. 4-6). 239.30 (978-0-7565-0877-7(0)) Compass Point Bks.

We the People: Modern America, 10 vols. 2006. 48p. (YA). (gr. 4-6). 239.30 (978-0-7565-1576-8(9)) Compass Point Bks.

We the People: Revolution & the New Nation, 13 vols. 2006. 48p. (YA). (gr. 4-6). 311.09 (978-0-7565-1705-2(2)) Compass Point Bks.

Weintraub, Aileen. The Library of Pirates, 6 bks. Incl. Anne Bonny & Mary Read : Fearsome Female Pirates of the 18th-Century. lib. bdg. 18.75 (978-0-8239-5795-8(0)); Barbarossa Brothers : 16th-Century Pirates of the Barbary Coast. lib. bdg. 18.75 (978-0-8239-5799-6(3)); Blackbeard : 18th-Century Pirate of the Spanish Main & the Carolina Coast. lib. bdg. 18.75 (978-0-8239-5794-1(2)); Captain Kidd : 17th-Century Pirate of the Indian Ocean & African Coast. lib. bdg. 18.75 (978-0-8239-5797-2(7)); Henry Morgan : 17th-Century Buccaneer. lib. bdg. 18.75 (978-0-8239-5798-9(5)); Jean Lafitte : Pirate Hero of the War of 1812. lib. bdg. 18.75 (978-0-8239-5796-5(9)); 24p. (J). (gr. 3). 2002. (Illus.). 112.50 (978-0-8239-7133-6(3) , PowerKids Pr.) Rosen Publishing Group, Inc., The.

Weitzman, David L. Brown Paper School Book: My Backyard History Book. 2006. 128p. (J). pap. 12.99 (978-0-316-05981-7(1)) Little Brown & Co.

Wheeler, Ron. Our 50 States. 2001. (Homework Booklets Ser.). 80p. (J). (gr. 5-8). pap. 2.99 (978-0-7424-0153-2(7) , IF0237) School Specialty Publishing.

Whitmore, Arvella. Trapped Between the Lash & the Gun. Peskin, Joy, ed. 2001. 192p. (J). (gr. 3-7). pap. 6.99 (978-0-14-130319-2(0) , Puffin) Penguin Group (USA) Inc.

The Wilderness Road: Individual Title Six-Packs. (On Deck Ser.: Vol. 2). 24p. (gr. 4-5). 35.00 (978-0-7578-5816-1(3)) Rigby Education.

Wilkins, Jen. The Trucker That Saved the Day. Lt. ed. 2002. (Illus.). 16p. 3.95 (978-0-9651377-7-5(5)) Living Gold Pr.

Wilmore, Kathy. The Library of Living & Working in Colonial Times: Set 1, 6 bks. Incl. Day in the Life of a Colonial Blacksmith. lib. bdg. 18.75 (978-0-8239-5425-4(0)); Day in the Life of a Colonial Innkeeper. lib. bdg. 18.75 (978-0-8239-5430-8(7)); Day in the Life of a Colonial Printer. lib. bdg. 18.75 (978-0-8239-5428-5(5)); Day in the Life of a Colonial Schoolteacher. lib. bdg. 18.75 (978-0-8239-5429-2(3)); Day in the Life of a Colonial Silversmith. lib. bdg. 18.75 (978-0-8239-5427-8(7)); Day in the Life of a Colonial Wigmaker. lib. bdg. 18.75 (978-0-8239-5426-1(9)); 24p. (J). (gr. 3). 2000. (Illus.). Set lib. bdg. 103.50 (978-0-8239-7006-3(X) , PowerKids Pr.) Rosen Publishing Group, Inc., The.

Wingate, Katherine. Political Reforms: American Citizens Gain More Control over Their Government. 2004. (Progressive Movement, 1900-1920 Ser.). (Illus.). 32p. (J). lib. bdg. (978-1-4042-0192-7(0)) Rosen Publishing Group, Inc., The.

Wolfson, Evelyn. Wayland A-Z: A Dictionary of Then & Now. Wolfson, Evelyn, ed. 2004. per. 15.00 (978-0-9762756-0-2(0)) Wayland Historical Society.

Working Americans 1880-1999, 5 vols., 5. 2003. 675.00 (978-1-59237-034-4(9)) Grey Hse. Publishing.

Worth, Richard. Westward Expansion & Manifest Destiny in American History. 2001. (In American History Ser.). (Illus.). 112p. (YA). (gr. 5-12). lib. bdg. 26.60 (978-0-7660-1457-2(6)) Enslow Pubs., Inc.

Wynne, Patricia J. & Silver, Donald M. Easy Make & Learn Projects: 18 Fun-to-Create Reproducible Models That Bring the Colonial Period to Life. 2002. 80p. pap. 12.95 (978-0-439-16031-5(6)) Scholastic, Inc.

Zehnder, Christopher. History: Sea to Shining Sea. 2003. (Illus.). ix, 462p. (J). (gr. 5). 55.00 (978-0-89870-961-2(X)) Ignatius Pr.

Zinn, Howard. A Young People's History of the United States: Columbus to the Spanish-American War. 2007. (Illus.). 192p. (YA). (gr. 6-10). 16.95 (***978-1-58322-759-6(8)**) Seven Stories Pr.

—A Young People's History of the United States Vol. 2: Class Struggle to the War on Terror. 2007. (Illus.). 192p. (YA). (gr. 6-10). 17.95 (***978-1-58322-760-2(1)**) Seven Stories Pr.

Zocchi, Judy. In the United States. Brodie, Neale, illus. 2005. (Global Adventures II Ser.). 32p. (J). pap. 9.95 (978-1-59646-172-7(1)); lib. bdg. 20.65 (978-1-59646-085-0(7)) Dingles & Co.

—In the United States/en los Estados Unidos. Brodie, Neale, illus. 2005. (Global Adventures II Ser.).Tr. of En los Estados Unidos. (ENG & SPA.). 32p. (J). pap. 9.95 (978-1-59646-174-1(8)); lib. bdg. 20.65 (978-1-59646-086-7(5)) Dingles & Co.

The 50 States. Date not set. (Illus.). 32p. (J). 3.98 (978-0-7525-9870-3(8)) Parragon, Inc.

UNITED STATES—HISTORY—CHRONOLOGY

Cheney, Lynne. A Time for Freedom: What Happened When in America. 2007. 304p. (J). pap. 8.99 (***978-1-4169-4915-2(1)** , Aladdin) Simon & Schuster Children's Publishing.

Corey, Melinda. Chronology of 20th-Century America. 2005. (Decades of American History Ser.). (Illus.). 128p. (J). (gr. 4-9). 35.00 (978-0-8160-5646-0(3)) Facts On File, Inc.

Sweeney, Alyse. Lift-the-Flap Timelines: American History. 2004. (Lift-the-flap Timelines Ser.). 72p. pap. 12.99 (978-0-439-47119-0(2) , Teaching Resources) Scholastic, Inc.

UNITED STATES—HISTORY—DICTIONARIES

Brownstone, David M. & Franck, Irene M. Frontier America, 10 vols. 2004. (Illus.). (J). (978-0-7172-5991-5(9)); (978-0-7172-5992-2(7)); (978-0-7172-5993-9(5)); (978-0-7172-5994-6(3)); (978-0-7172-5995-3(1)); (978-0-7172-5996-0(X)); (978-0-7172-5997-7(8)); (978-0-7172-5998-4(6)); (978-0-7172-5999-1(4)); (978-0-7172-6000-3(3)) Scholastic Library Publishing. (Grolier).

Gale Encyclopedia US Hist: Bus, 2 Vol. 2007. 220.00 (***978-1-4144-3126-0(0)**) Thomson Gale.

Gale Encyclopedia US Hist: Fam, 2 Vol. 2007. 220.00 (***978-1-4144-3122-2(8)**) Thomson Gale.

Gale Encyclopedia US Hist: Sci Tech, 2 Vol. 2007. 220.00 (***978-1-4144-3110-9(4)**) Thomson Gale.

Gale Encyclopedia US Hist: War, 2 Vol. 2007. 220.00 (***978-1-4144-3114-7(7)**) Thomson Gale.

Kingfisher Editors, ed. The Student Encyclopedia of the United States. 2005. (Illus.). 808p. (J). (gr. 4-6). 29.95 (978-0-7534-5925-6(6) , Kingfisher) Houghton Mifflin Co. Trade & Reference Div.

Rubel, David. Scholastic Encyclopedia of the Presidents & Their Times. 2005. (Illus.). 256p. (J). pap. 19.95 (978-0-439-28323-6(X) , Scholastic Reference) Scholastic, Inc.

U-X-L Encyclopedia of US History, Vol. 10. 2007. 520.00 (***978-1-4144-3043-0(4)** , UXL) Thomson Gale.

World Almanac Library of the States, 52 bks. Incl. Alabama : The Heart of Dixie. Martin, Michael A. 2002. pap. 14.95 (978-0-8368-5297-4(4)); Alaska : The Last Frontier. Seder, Isaac. 2003. pap. 14.95 (978-0-8368-5318-6(0)); Arizona : The Grand Canyon State. Martin, Michael A. 2002. pap. 14.95 (978-0-8368-5298-1(2)); Arkansas : The Natural State. Bailer, Darice. 2002. pap. 14.95 (978-0-8368-5299-8(0)); California : The Golden State. Ingram, Scott. 2002. pap. 14.95 (978-0-8368-5282-0(6)); Colorado : The Centennial State. Elias, Megan. 2002. pap. 14.95 (978-0-8368-5300-1(8)); Connecticut : The Constitution State. Bailer, Darice. 2002. pap. 14.95 (978-0-8368-5301-8(6)); Delaware : The First State. Fontes, Justine & Fontes, Ron. 2003. pap. 14.95 (978-0-8368-5319-3(9)); Florida : The Sunshine State. Chui, Patricia. 2002. pap. 14.95 (978-0-8368-5283-7(4)); Georgia : Empire State of the South. Holtz, Eric Siegfried. 2002. pap. 14.95 (978-0-8368-5302-5(4)); Hawaii : The Aloha State. Doak, Robin S. 2003. pap. 14.95 (978-0-8368-5320-9(2)); Idaho : The Gem State. Edwards, Karen. 2003. pap. 14.95 (978-0-8368-5321-6(0)); Illinois : The Prairie State. Feeley, Kathleen. 2002. pap. 14.95 (978-0-8368-5284-4(2)); Indiana : The Hoosier State. Brunelle, Lynn. 2002. pap. 14.95 (978-0-8368-5285-1(0)); Iowa : The Hawkeye State. Martin, Michael A. 2002. pap. 14.95 (978-0-8368-5303-2(2)); Kansas : The Sunflower State. Ingram, W. Scott. 2002. pap. 14.95 (978-0-8368-5304-9(0)); Kentucky : The Blue Grass State. Ingram, Scott. 2002. pap. 14.95 (978-0-8368-5305-6(9)); Louisiana : The Pelican State. Gildart, Leslie S. 2002. pap. 14.95 (978-0-8368-5306-3(7)); Maine : The Pine Tree State. Craig, Janet. 2003. pap. 14.95 (978-0-8368-5322-3(9)); Maryland : The Old Line State. Martin, Michael A. 2002. pap. 14.95 (978-0-8368-5307-0(5)); Massachusetts : The Bay State. Barenblat, Rachel. 2002. pap. 14.95 (978-0-8368-5286-8(9)); Michigan : The Wolverine State. Barenblat, Rachel. 2002. pap. 14.95 (978-0-8368-5287-5(7)); Mississippi : The Magnolia State. Figueroa, Acton. 2003. pap. 14.95 (978-0-8368-5323-0(7)); Missouri : The Show Me State. Ingram, W. Scott. 2002. pap. 14.95 (978-0-8368-5309-4(1)); Montana : The Treasure State. Hirschmann, Kris. 2003. pap. 14.95 (978-0-8368-5324-7(5)); Nebraska : The Cornhusker State. Flocker, Michael. 2002. pap. 14.95 (978-0-8368-5310-0(5)); Nevada : The Silver State. Deford, Debra. 2003. pap. 14.95 (978-0-8368-5325-4(3)); New Hampshire : The Granite State. Mattern, Joanne. 2003. pap. 14.95 (978-0-8368-5326-1(1)); New Jersey : The Garden State. Holtz, Eric Siegfried. 2002. pap. 14.95 (978-0-8368-5311-7(3)); New Mexico : Land of Enchantment. Burgan, Michael. 2003. pap. 14.95 (978-0-8368-5327-8(X)); New York : The Empire State. Ball, Jacqueline A. 2002. pap. 14.95 (978-0-8368-5288-2(5)); North Carolina : The Tar Heel State. Rafle, Sarah. 2002. pap. 14.95 (978-0-8368-5289-9(3)); North Dakota : The Peace Garden State. Fontes, Justine & Fontes, Ron. 2003. pap. 14.95 (978-0-8368-5328-5(8)); Ohio : The Buckeye State. Martin, Michael A. 2002. pap. 14.95 (978-0-8368-5290-5(7)); Oklahoma : The Sooner State. Martin, Michael A. 2002. pap. 14.95 (978-0-8368-5312-4(1)); Oregon : The Beaver State. Ingram, Scott. 2002. pap. 14.95 (978-0-8368-5313-1(X)); Pennsylvania : The Keystone State. Ingram, Scott. 2002. pap. 14.95 (978-0-8368-5291-2(5)); Puerto Rico & Other Outlying Territories. Burgan, Michael. 2003. pap. 14.95 (978-0-8368-5329-2(6)); Rhode Island : The Ocean State. Mattern, Joanne. 2003. pap. 14.95 (978-0-8368-5330-8(X)); South Carolina : The Palmetto State. Volkwein, Ann. 2002. pap. 14.95 (978-0-8368-5314-8(8)); South Dakota : The Mount Rushmore State. Hirschmann, Kris. 2003. pap. 14.95 (978-0-8368-5331-5(8)); Tennessee : The Volunteer State. Peck, Barbara. 2002. pap. 14.95 (978-0-8368-5315-5(6)); Texas : The Lone Star State. Barenblat, Rachel. 2002. pap. 14.95 (978-0-8368-5292-9(3)); Utah : The Beehive State. Hirschmann, Kris. 2003. pap. 14.95 (978-0-8368-5332-2(6)); Vermont : The Green Mountain State. Flocker, Michael. 2002. pap. 14.95 (978-0-8368-5316-2(4)); Virginia : The Old Dominion. Pollack, Pamela. 2002. pap. 14.95 (978-0-8368-5293-6(1)); Washington : The Evergreen State. Barenblat, Rachel. 2002. pap. 14.95 (978-0-8368-5294-3(X)); Washington, D. C. Figueroa, Acton. 2003. pap. 14.95 (978-0-8368-5333-9(4)); West Virginia : The Mountain State. Fontes, Justine & Fontes, Ron. 2003. pap. 14.95 (978-0-8368-5334-6(2)); Wisconsin : The Badger State. Barenblat, Rachel. 2002. pap. 14.95 (978-0-8368-5295-0(8)); Wyoming : The Equality State. Fontes, Justine & Fontes, Ron. 2003. pap. 14.95 (978-0-8368-5335-3(0)); 48p. (J). (gr. 5 up). (Illus.). 2002. Set pap. 777.40 (978-0-8368-5168-7(4)); Set lib. bdg. 1560.00 (978-0-8368-5473-2(X)) Stevens, Gareth Inc. (World Almanac Library).

World Almanac Library of the States: Alaska; Delaware; Hawaii; Idaho; Maine; Mississippi; Montana; Nevada; New Hampshire; New Mexico; North Dakota; Puerto Rico & Other Outlying Areas; Rhode Island; South Dakota; Utah; Washington, D. C.; West Virginia; Wyoming, 18 bks. 2002. (Illus.). (J). (gr. 5 up). lib. bdg. 526.68 (978-0-8368-5167-0(6)); pap. 269.10 (978-0-8368-5317-9(2)) Stevens, Gareth Inc. (World Almanac Library).

World Almanac Library of the States New Releases: Alabama, Arizona, Arkansas, Colorado, Connecticut, Georgia, Iowa, Kansas, Kentucky, Louisiana, Maryland, Minnesota, Nebraska, New Jersey, Oklahoma, Oregon, South Carolina, Tennessee, Vermont, 20 bks. 2002. (Illus.). (J). (gr. 5 up). lib. bdg. 532.00 (978-0-8368-5166-3(8) , World Almanac Library) Stevens, Gareth Inc.

UNITED STATES—HISTORY—DRAMA

Burack, Sylvia K., ed. Great American Events on Stage. 2001. 232p. (J). (gr. 4-9). pap. 15.95 (978-0-8238-0305-7(8)) Kalmbach Publishing Co., Bks. Div.

Fincken, Hank. Three Midwestern History Plays & Then Some. 1998. (Illus.). 125p. (J). (gr. 3-6). pap. 9.00 (978-1-57860-053-7(3)) Emmis Bks.

UNITED STATES—HISTORY, ECONOMIC

see United States—Economic Conditions

UNITED STATES—HISTORY—FICTION

Adler, David A. Mama Played Baseball. O'Leary, Chris, illus. 2003. 32p. (J). 16.00 (978-0-15-202196-2(5) , Gulliver Bks.) Harcourt Children's Bks.

The Adventures of Tony & Little Britches. 2000. (J). pap. (978-0-9700756-4-2(2)) Pajo Publishing Co.

Alger, Horatio. Frank's Campaign: Or, What Boys Can Do on the Farm for the Camp. unabr. ed. 2002. (Polyglot Press Alger Ser.). (Illus.). (J). pap. 17.95 (978-1-4115-0000-6(8)) Polyglot Pr., Inc.

Alter, Judy. Sam Houston Is My Hero. 2003. (Chaparral Book for Young Readers Ser.). 140p. (J). pap. 15.95 (978-0-87565-277-1(8)) Texas Christian Univ. Pr.

Armistead, John. The Return of Gabriel. Gregory, Fran, illus. 2002. 240p. (J). (gr. 3-8). 17.95 (978-1-57131-637-0(X)); pap. 6.95 (978-1-57131-638-7(8)) Milkweed Editions.

Asim, Jabari. Road to Freedom: A Story of the Reconstruction. 2000. (978-0-606-21876-4(9)) Tandem Library Bks.

Atwell, Debby. Pearl. 2001. (Illus.). 32p. (J). (gr. k-3). tchr. ed. 16.00 (978-0-395-88416-4(0) , Walter Lorraine) Houghton Mifflin Co. Trade & Reference Div.

Avi. Lord Kirkle's Money. 1998. (Beyond the Western Sea Ser.: Vol. 2). 432p. (J). (gr. 5-9). reprint ed. pap. 7.99 (978-0-380-72876-3(1) , Harper Trophy) HarperCollins Pubs.

—The Secret School. 2003. (gr. 3-6). lib. bdg. 14.10 (978-0-613-70523-3(8)) Tandem Library Bks.

Babson, Jane F. A Story of Us: The Dolls' History of People of the United States. Babson, Jane F., illus. 2003. (Illus.). 56p. (J). (gr. 4-5). 10.95 (978-0-940787-03-2(2)) Winstead Pr., Ltd.

Barone, Michelle. Out of the Ordinary. 2004. (Adventures in History Ser.). (Illus.). 120p. (J). pap. (978-1-932663-08-2(8)) History Compass, LLC.

Blos, Joan W. Letters from the Corrugated Castle: A Novel of Gold Rush California, 1850-1852. 2007. 320p. (J). (gr. 5-9). 17.99 (978-0-689-87077-4(9) , Ginne Seo Bks) Simon & Schuster Children's Publishing.

Booth, A. Fran. Singing Violet: The Decade Between Georgia's Gold Rush & the Trail of Tears. 2002. 132p. (J). (gr. 4-7). pap. 16.95 (978-1-59129-299-9(9)) PublishAmerica, Inc.

Brooks, Nigel & Horner, Abigail. Town Mouse House: How We Lived One Hundred Years Ago. 2000. (Illus.). 32p. (J). (gr. k-3). 15.95 (978-0-8027-8732-3(0)) Walker & Co.

Bruce, Wendy, illus. Grandfather's Ship, The S. S. "United States" 2000. 50p. (J). (gr. 3-5). (978-0-9701870-0-0(9)) Fletcher, Elizabeth Byrd.

Bruchac, Joseph. Bowman's Store: A Journey to Myself. 2001. (Illus.). 328p. (YA). (gr. 7 up). pap. 6.95 (978-1-58430-027-4(2)) Lee & Low Bks., Inc.

—Bowman's Store: A Journey to Myself. 2001. (gr. 3-6). lib. bdg. 15.25 (978-0-613-84717-9(2)) Tandem Library Bks.

Cadnum, Michael. Blood Gold. 2004. 224p. (J). 16.99 (978-0-670-05884-6(X) , Viking Juvenile) Penguin Group (USA) Inc.

Call me. 2003. (J). pap. 2.25 (978-0-590-33766-3(1)) Scholastic, Inc.

Carbone, Elisa. Storm Warriors. 2002. 176p. (J). (gr. 5-8). pap. 5.99 (978-0-440-41879-5(8) , Yearling) Random Hse. Children's Bks.

Chambers, Veronica. Amistad Rising: A Story of Freedom. 1998. (Illus.). 40p. (J). (gr. 4-7). lib. bdg. (978-0-8172-5510-7(9)) Raintree.

Clark, Betsy Huhn. Lizzie's Extraordinary Adventure. 2006. (Illus.). 24p. (J). 9.99 (978-1-4276-0116-2(X)) Aardvark Global Publishing.

Coleman, Wim & Perrin, Pat. Sister Anna: A Story of Shaker Life. 2000. 232p. (J). (gr. 5-12). pap. 10.95 (978-1-57960-059-4(X)) History Compass, LLC.

Collier, James Lincoln. Who Is Carrie? 2001. (gr. 5-8). lib. bdg. 21.10 (978-0-613-86696-5(7)) Tandem Library Bks.

Collier, James Lincoln & Collier, Christopher. Who Is Carrie? 2001. 176p. (J). (gr. 5-7). 12.00 (978-0-375-89503-6(5) , Delacorte Bks. for Young Readers) Random Hse. Children's Bks.

Columbia River Stories. 2007. (J). per. 15.00 (***978-0-9792207-0-8(X)**) Earth Arts NW.

Connors, Faith Raymond. Love, Midgie. 2007. (J). pap. 14.95 (***978-0-9640138-1-0(9)**) BelleAire Pr.

Cook, Judy. Out of the Dust. 2001. 62p. (J). stu. ed., ring bd. 12.99 (978-1-58609-180-4(8)) Progeny Pr.

Cooney, Caroline B. The Ransom of Mercy Carter. 2002. 256p. (YA). (gr. 7 up). mass mkt. 5.99 (978-0-440-22775-5(5) , Laurel Leaf) Random Hse. Children's Bks.

Cox, Stephen Angus. The Dare Boys of 1776. 2006. 106p. pap. 10.99 (978-1-4264-3400-6(6)) BiblioBazaar.

Davis, Ossie. Just Like Martin. (J). 2002. 176p. 15.99 (978-0-7868-0812-0(8)); 2001. pap. (978-0-7868-1642-2(2)) Hyperion Bks. for Children. (Jump at the Sun).

De Angeli, Marguerite. Door in the Wall. 1998. (gr. 5-8). lib. bdg. 13.00 (978-0-613-72322-0(8)) Tandem Library Bks.

Denenberg, Barry. The Journal of Ben Uchida, Citizen 13559. 2003. (My Name Is America Ser.). 160p. (J). 12.95 (978-0-439-55530-2(2)) Scholastic, Inc.

—Mirror Mirror on the Wall: The Diary of Bess Brennan. 2002. (Dear America Ser.). (Illus.). 144p. (J). (gr. 4-9). pap. 10.95 (978-0-439-19446-4(6)) Scholastic, Inc.

—So Far from Home: The Diary of Mary Driscoll, an Irish Mill Girl. 2003. (Dear America Ser.). 144p. (J). 12.95 (978-0-439-55506-7(X)) Scholastic, Inc.

—When Will This Cruel War Be Over? The Civil War Diary of Emma Simpson. 2003. (Dear America Ser.). 160p. (J). 12.95 (978-0-439-55517-3(5)) Scholastic, Inc.

Deutsch, Stacia & Cohon, Rhody. Disney's Dream. Wenzel, David, illus. 2005. (Blast to the Past Ser.). 112p. (J). pap. 3.99 (978-0-689-87025-5(6) , Aladdin) Simon & Schuster Children's Publishing.

—Sacagawea's Strength. Wenzel, David, illus. 2006. (Blast to the Past Ser.). 128p. (J). pap. 3.99 (978-1-4169-1270-5(3) , Aladdin) Simon & Schuster Children's Publishing.

Deutsch, Stacia, et al. Washington's War. Francis, Guy & Lyon, Tammie, illus. 2007. (Blast to the Past Ser.). 128p. (J). pap. 3.99 (978-1-4169-3390-8(5) , Aladdin) Simon & Schuster Children's Publishing.

Doyle, Bill. Betrayed! The 1977 Journal of Zeke Moorie. 4th ed. 2006. (Crime Through Time Ser.: No. 4). 144p. (J). (gr. 3-7). pap. 5.99 (978-0-316-05741-7(X)) Little Brown & Co.

—ICED: The 2007 Journal of Nick Fitzmorgan. 5th ed. 2006. (Crime Through Time Ser.: No. 5). (Illus.). 144p. (J). (gr. 3-7). pap. 5.99 (978-0-316-05753-0(3)) Little Brown & Co.

—Trapped: The 2031 Journal of Otis Fitzmorgan. 6th ed. 2006. (Crime Through Time Ser.: No. 6). 144p. (J). (gr. 3-7). pap. 5.99 (978-0-316-05754-7(1)) Little Brown & Co.

Drexler, Sam & Shelby, Fay. Lost in Spillville. 2000. (Erika & Oz Adventures in American History Ser.: Vol. 1). (Illus.). 150p. (J). (gr. 5-9). pap. 6.99 (978-0-9669988-1-8(2)) Aunt Strawberry Bks.

Duey, Kathleen. Nell Dunne: New York City 1899. 2000. (American Diaries Ser.: No. 16). (J). (gr. 3-7). (978-0-606-17903-4(8)) Tandem Library Bks.

—Rosa Moreno: Hollywood, California, 1934. 1999. (American Diaries Ser.: No. 14). (J). (gr. 3-7). (978-0-606-17200-4(9)) Tandem Library Bks.

Durbin, William. El Lector. 2006. 208p. (J). (gr. 5). 15.95 (978-0-385-74651-9(2) , Lamb, Wendy) Random Hse. Children's Bks.

Eckert, Allan W. The Court-Martial of Daniel Boone. 2000. (Illus.). 324p. (gr. 7-12). pap. 19.95 (978-0-595-08990-1(9) , Backinprint.com) iUniverse, Inc.

Evernden, Margery. Wilderness Boy. 2001. 192p. (J). pap. 9.95 (978-0-8229-5754-6(X)) Univ. of Pittsburgh Pr.

Farhi, Roslyn. Molly's Century. White, Bobbie, illus. 1999. 32p. (J). (gr. k-4). pap. 9.95 (978-0-9660599-1-5(3)) Nostalgia Pubns.

Farrell, Mary Cronk. Fire in the Hole! 2004. 176p. (YA). (gr. 5-9). tchr. ed. 15.00 (978-0-618-44634-6(6) , Clarion Bks.) Houghton Mifflin Co. Trade & Reference Div.

Fennessey, Sharon. The Loom & the Lash. 1998. (J). (gr. 5-9). pap. 12.00 (978-1-57960-042-6(5)) History Compass, LLC.

Flaherty, Mildred. The Great Saint Patrick's Day Flood. 2004. (Illus.). 104p. (J). pap. (978-0-9711835-8-2(9)) Local History Co., The.

Fletcher, E. B. The Last American Star. 2005. 10.95 (978-0-533-15338-1(7)) Vantage Pr., Inc.

Furtney, Charles S. Tryconnel: An Antebellum Adventure along the C & O Canal. 2004. (Illus.). iii, 156p. (J). pap. (978-0-9711835-3-7(8)) Local History Co., The.

Giff, Patricia Reilly. Lily's Crossing. 2002. (Illus.). (J). 13.94 (978-0-7587-0287-6(6)) Book Wholesalers, Inc.

—Lily's Crossing. 1999. (Yearling Newbery Ser.). 208p. (J). (gr. 5-7). reprint ed. pap. 6.50 (978-0-440-41453-7(9) , Yearling) Random Hse. Children's Bks.

—Lily's Crossing. 1999. (gr. 5-8). lib. bdg. 13.55 (978-0-613-10350-3(5)); (Illus.). (J). (978-0-606-14423-0(4)) Tandem Library Bks.

—Lily's Crossing. l.t. ed. 2000. (Illus.). 200p. (J). (ps up). 22.95 (978-0-7862-2771-6(0)) Thorndike Pr.

Graafland, Monique Fijtje. 1774: Freedom Wanted. 2002. (ENG.). 96p. pap. (*978-1-55306-393-3(7)) Essence Publishing.

Haislip, Phyllis Hall. Divided Loyalties: A Revolutionary War Fifer's Story. 2005. (Illus.). 212p. (J). (ps-7). pap. 7.95 (978-1-57249-369-8(0) , White Mane Kids) White Mane Publishing Co., Inc.

Harcourt School Publishers Staff. Living History Day Advanced Level. 3rd ed. 2002. (Trophies Reading Program Ser.). (Illus.). pap. 5.10 (978-0-15-323397-5(4)) Harcourt Schl. Pubs.

—Prairie Fire On Level. 3rd ed. 2002. (Trophies Reading Program Ser.). (Illus.). pap. 5.10 (978-0-15-323352-4(4)) Harcourt Schl. Pubs.

—Prairie Neighbors Advanced Level. 3rd ed. 2002. (Trophies Reading Program Ser.). (Illus.). pap. 5.10 (978-0-15-323307-4(9)) Harcourt Schl. Pubs.

—The Star Spangled Banner. 3rd ed. 2002. (Horizons Ser.). (Illus.). (J). pap. 7.30 (978-0-15-333577-8(7)) Harcourt Schl. Pubs.

—Things Will Get Better On Level. 3rd ed. 2002. (Trophies Reading Program Ser.). (Illus.). pap. 5.10 (978-0-15-323262-6(5)) Harcourt Schl. Pubs.

Harlow, Joan Hiatt & Minor, Wendell. Midnight Rider. 2005. (Illus.). 416p. (J). 15.95 (978-0-689-87009-5(4) , McElderry, Margaret K.) Simon & Schuster Children's Publishing.

Hedstrom-Page, Deborah. From Settlement to City with Benjamin Franklin. Martinez, Sergio, illus. 2007. 80p. (J). (gr. 3-9). 9.99 (978-0-8054-3267-1(1)) B&H Publishing Grp.

Heibel, Dorothy. Message for a Spy. 2004. (Illus.). 94p. (J). pap. (978-1-932663-07-5(X)) History Compass, LLC.

Hermes, Patricia. The Brothers' War. 2005. (My Side of the Story Ser.). 192p. (J). (gr. 4-6). pap. 6.95 (978-0-7534-5795-5(4) , Kingfisher) Houghton Mifflin Co. Trade & Reference Div.

Hernandez, Natalie Nelson. Mapmakers of the Western Trails: Adventures with John Chrles Fremont, 3 bks. 2003. (Illus.). 130p. (J). per. 10.95 (978-1-885852-31-1(2)) James Stevenson Pub.

Hessong, Robert F. & Hessong, Katheryn. Ollie's Cabin in the Woods. Hickman, Carolyn Hessong, illus. 1999. 70p. (J). 14.95 (978-1-57860-045-8(6)); pap. 9.95 (978-1-57860-031-1(6)) Emmis Bks.

Hobbs, Valerie. Sonny's War. 2002. 224p. (YA). (gr. 7 up). 16.00 (978-0-374-37136-4(9) , Farrar, Straus & Giroux (BYR)) Farrar, Straus & Giroux.

Hoobler, Dorothy & Hoobler, Thomas. The Century Kids, 10 vols. Hoffman, Robin, illus. Incl. First Decade : Curtain Going Up. 2000. lib. bdg. 22.90 (978-0-7613-1600-8(0)); Second Decade : Voyages. 2000. lib. bdg. 22.90 (978-0-7613-1601-5(9)); 1920s : Luck. (J). 2000. lib. bdg. 22.90 (978-0-7613-1602-2(7)); 1930s : Directions. (J). 2000. lib. bdg. 22.90 (978-0-7613-1603-9(5)); 1940s : Secrets. (J). 2001. lib. bdg. 22.90 (978-0-7613-1604-6(3)); 1950's : Music. (J). 2001. lib. bdg. 22.90 (978-0-7613-1605-3(1)); 1960's : Rebels. (J). 2001. lib. bdg. 22.90 (978-0-7613-1606-0(X)); 1970's : Arguments. 2002. lib. bdg. 22.90 (978-0-7613-1607-7(8)); 1980s : Earthsong. 2002. lib. bdg. 22.90 (978-0-7613-1608-4(6)); 1990s : Families. 2002. lib. bdg. 22.90 (978-0-7613-1609-1(4)); 160p. (gr. 5-8). (Illus.). 2004. 229.00 (978-0-7613-2985-5(4) , Twenty-First Century Bks.) Lerner Publishing Group.

—The 1960's: Rebels. Hoffman, Robin, illus. 2001. (Century Kids Ser.). 160p. (J). (gr. 5-8). lib. bdg. 22.90 (978-0-7613-1606-0(X) , Twenty-First Century Bks.) Lerner Publishing Group.

Hopkinson, Deborah. Our Kansas Home. Faricy, Patrick, illus. 2003. (Prairie Skies Ser.: Bk. 3). 80p. (J). pap. 3.99 (978-0-689-84353-2(4) , Aladdin) Simon & Schuster Children's Publishing.

Hughes, Barbara. Then & Now. (Livewire Ser.). 192p. (YA). (gr. 6-9). pap. 8.95 (978-0-7043-4930-8(2)) Women's Pr., Ltd., The GBR. *Dist:* Trafalgar Square Publishing.

In One Day. 2002. (Illus.). 33p. (J). pap. 9.95 (978-0-9723826-0-1(7)) Tajiri Ventures LLC.

Ingold, Jeanette. The Big Burn. 2003. (gr. 5-8). lib. bdg. 15.25 (978-0-613-55148-9(6)) Tandem Library Bks.

—Hitch. 2006. (Illus.). 288p. (YA). pap. 6.95 (978-0-15-205619-3(X) , Harcourt Paperbacks) Harcourt Children's Bks.

Johnson, Dolores. Now Let Me Fly: The Story of a Slave Family. 1998. pap. 5.99 (978-0-87628-977-8(4)) Ctr. for Applied Research in Education, The.

Karr, Kathleen. Dwight D. Eisenhower: Letters from a New Jersey Schoolgirl. 2002. (Dear Mr. President Ser.). (Illus.). 128p. (YA). 9.95 (978-1-58837-007-5(0)) Winslow Pr.

Kinsey-Warnock, Natalie. Gifts from the Sea. Pederson, Judy, illus. 2005. 128p. (J). (gr. 3-7). 5.50 (978-0-440-41970-9(0) , Yearling) Random Hse. Children's Bks.

—Gifts from the Sea. Pedersen, Judy, illus. 2003. 128p. (J). (gr. 5). 14.95 (978-0-375-82257-5(7) , Knopf Bks. for Young Readers) Random Hse. Children's Bks.

Langton, Jane. The Fragile Flag. 2002. (Hall Family Chronicles). 272p. (J). (gr. 5 up). pap. 5.95 (978-0-06-440311-5(4) , Harper Trophy) HarperCollins Pubs.

Lasky, Kathryn. A Time for Courage: The Suffragette Diary of Kathleen Bowen, Washington D. C., 1917. (Dear America Ser.). 176p. (J). 2003. 12.95 (978-0-439-55542-5(6)); 2002. (Illus.). (gr. 4-9). pap. 10.95 (978-0-590-51141-4(6)) Scholastic, Inc.

Leininger, Tracy M. Alone, yet Not Alone: The Story of Barbara & Regina Leininger. Ingram, Charles, illus. 2001. 203p. (J). 16.00 (978-1-929241-36-1(4)) Vision Forum, Inc., The.

Levero, Diane. What So Proudly We Hail'd. Kemnitz, Myrna, ed. 1999. (Illus.). 302p. (YA). pap. 9.99 (978-0-88092-054-4(8) , 0548) Royal Fireworks Publishing Co.

Light, Steve. Uncle Sam: Press-Out & Play Book. 2002. (Illus.). 8p. (J). (ps-1). 7.95 (978-0-8109-3498-6(1)) Abrams, Harry N. , Inc.

Liles, Maurine W. Dona Maria, la Ranchera. 2000. (Illus.). 144p. 15.95 (978-1-57168-381-6(X)) Eakin Pr.

Loesch, Joe. The Pony Express: With Buffalo Biff & Farley's Raiders, 7 vols., Vol. 7. Cox, Brian T., illus. abr. ed. 2001. (Backyard Adventure Ser.: Vol. 7). 56p. (J). pap. 14.95 incl. audio (978-1-887729-79-6(8)); pap. 16.95 incl. audio compact disk (978-1-887729-80-2(1)) Toy Box Productions.

Lyons, Mary E. & Branch, Muriel M. Dear Ellen Bee: A Civil War Scrapbook of Two Union Spies. Tauss, Marc, illus. 2000. 176p. (J). (gr. 4 up). 21.99 (978-0-689-82379-4(7) , Atheneum) Simon & Schuster Children's Publishing.

MacBride, Roger Lea. Rose at Rocky Ridge. Graef, Renee, illus. 2000. (Little House Chapter Bks.: No. 2). 80p. (J). (gr. 2-5). 14.89 (978-0-06-028156-4(1)) HarperCollins Pubs.

—Rose at Rocky Ridge. 2000. (Little House Chapter Bks.: No. 2). (Illus.). (J). (gr. 3-6). (978-0-606-20478-1(4)) Tandem Library Bks.

Maxson, H. A. & Young, Claudia H. Tea Party at Chestertown. Kosits, Andrew, illus. 2003. 55p. (J). per. 8.95 (978-0-9741713-0-2(1)) Bay Oak Pubs., Ltd.

McKissack, Patricia C. A Picture of Freedom: The Diary of Clotee, a Slave Girl, Belmont Plantation, Virginia, 1859. 2003. (Dear America Ser.). 128p. (J). 12.95 (978-0-439-55501-2(9)) Scholastic, Inc.

Michaelson, Richard. Across the Alley. Lewis, E. B., illus. 2006. 32p. (J). (ps-3). 16.99 (978-0-399-23970-0(7) , Putnam Juvenile) Penguin Group (USA) Inc.

Nixon, Joan Lowery. David's Search. 2000. 11.15 (978-0-606-17831-0(7)) Tandem Library Bks.

Owens, Tom. Free to Learn. Pollema-Cahill, Phyllis, illus. 2000. (Cover-to-Cover Bks.). (J). 55p. pap. (978-0-7891-5164-3(2)); 56p. (gr. 1-4). lib. bdg. 16.95 (978-0-7807-9314-9(5)) Perfection Learning Corp.

Paprocki, Alice. Indian Boy's Story. 2001. (gr. 7-12). lib. bdg. 24.55 (978-0-613-74591-8(4)) Tandem Library Bks.

Pennington, Kate. Nightingale's Song. 2007. 284p. (YA). (gr. 7 up). pap. 9.95 (*978-0-340-87875-0(4)) Hodder Children's Division GBR. *Dist:* Independent Pubs. Group.

Pickford, Susan B. The Drama of la Amistad. 1998. (J). (gr. 5-9). pap. 12.00 (978-1-57960-034-1(4)) History Compass, LLC.

Polisar, Barry Louis. Stolen Man: The Story of the Amistad Rebellion. 2007. 32p. (J). (gr. 3-5). pap. 7.95 (*978-0-938663-50-8(X)) Rainbow Morning Music Alternatives.

r, Edward (Winf. Rover Boys at College. 2006. pap. (*978-1-4068-3128-3(X)) Echo Library.

—Rover Boys at School. 2006. pap. (*978-1-4068-3129-0(8)) Echo Library.

Recorvits, Helen. Where Heroes Hide. 2002. (Illus.). 144p. (J). (gr. 4-6). 16.00 (978-0-374-33057-6(3) , Farrar, Straus & Giroux (BYR)) Farrar, Straus & Giroux.

Reece, Colleen L. Plymouth Pioneers. 1998. (American Adventure Ser.: No. 2). (Illus.). 142p. (J). (gr. 3-7). lib. bdg. 15.95 (978-0-7910-5042-2(4) , Chelsea Hse.) Facts On File, Inc.

Reeder, Carolyn. Captain Kate. 2002. 210p. (J). (gr. 4-7). reprint ed. pap. 6.50 (978-1-890920-14-2(2)) Children's Literature.

—Captain Kate. 2000. 224p. (J). (gr. 3-7). pap. 4.99 (978-0-380-79668-7(6)) HarperCollins Pubs.

—Captain Kate. 1999. (Illus.). (J). (978-0-606-17963-8(1)) Tandem Library Bks.

Rees, Celia. Herencia de Bruja. Abos, Elena, tr. 2002. (Gran Angular Ser.). (SPA.). 222p. (978-84-348-9121-0(2)) SM Ediciones ESP. *Dist:* Lectorum Pubns., Inc.

Richards, J. Stuart. Hard Coal Times, Volume Two: Mules, Drivers & Spraggers, 2. 2003. (Illus.). 44p. (YA). 5.95 (978-0-9709630-3-1(3)) Coal Hole Productions.

Richardson, V. A. The Moneylender's Daughter. 2006. (Illus.). 300p. (YA). 17.95 (978-1-58234-885-8(5) , Bloomsbury Children) Bloomsbury Publishing.

Ruby, Lois. Journey to Jamestown. 2005. (My Side of the Story Ser.). 192p. (J). (gr. 4-6). pap. 7.95 (978-0-7534-5796-2(2) , Kingfisher) Houghton Mifflin Co. Trade & Reference Div.

Sargent, Dave & Sargent, Pat. Freckles: (Flea-bitten Grey) Be Proud of Old Glory, 30 vols., Vol. 26. Lenoir, Jane, illus. 2003. (Saddle Up Ser.: Vol. 26). 42p. (J). pap. 6.95 (978-1-56763-810-3(4)); lib. bdg. 22.60 (978-1-56763-809-7(0)) Ozark Publishing.

—Popcorn: (Blue Corn) Work Hard, 30, 47. Lenoir, Jane, illus. 2001. (Saddle Up Ser.). 36p. (J). lib. bdg. 22.60 (978-1-56763-659-8(4)); pap. 6.95 (978-1-56763-660-4(8)) Ozark Publishing.

Sescoe, Vincent E. After the Ashes. 2002. 208p. 17.95 (978-1-930093-11-9(X)); pap. 7.95 (978-1-930093-13-3(6)) Brookfield Reader, Inc., The.

Settle, Sally. In the Shadow of the Lone Cypress: One Man's Florida. 2003. 360p. (YA). per. 14.95 (978-0-9707267-3-5(2)) Bluefish Bay Publishing.

Smith, Samuel Francis. My Country 'Tis of Thee. 2004. 24p. (J). pap. 3.50 (978-0-439-39195-5(4) , Cartwheel Bks.) Scholastic, Inc.

Spooner, Michael. Last Child. rev. ed. 2005. 240p. (J). (gr. 3-7). 16.95 (978-0-8050-7739-1(1) , Holt, Henry & Co. Bks. For Young Readers) Holt, Henry & Co.

Stanley, George E. Dwight D. Eisenhower: Young Military Leader. Henderson, Meryl, illus. 2006. (Childhood of Famous Americans Ser.). 192p. (J). pap. 5.99 (978-1-4169-1257-6(6) , Aladdin) Simon & Schuster Children's Publishing.

Susi, Geraldine Lee. My Father, My Companion: Life at the Hollow, Chief Justice John Marshall's Boyhood Home in Virginia. 2001. (Illus.). 96p. (J). (gr. 4-9). pap. 10.95 (978-1-889324-22-7(1)) EPM Pubns., Inc.

Swager, Christine R. Black Crows & White Cockades. 1999. (gr. 7-12). lib. bdg. 22.20 (978-0-613-89131-8(7)) Tandem Library Bks.

Thomas, Carroll. Blue Creek Farm: A Matty Trescott Novel. 2000. (Illus.). 185p. (J). pap. 9.95 (978-1-57525-243-8(0)) Smith and Kraus Publishers, Incorporated.

—Blue Creek Farm: A Matty Trescott Novel. 2000. (gr. 3-6). lib. bdg. 18.75 (978-0-613-62668-2(0)) Tandem Library Bks.

Trent, J. P. Freedom's Fire. 2000. (Illus.). 160p. (J). (gr. 4-7). pap. 4.50 (978-0-439-18926-2(8)) Scholastic, Inc.

—Freedom's Fire. 2000. (Illus.). (J). (978-0-606-18874-6(6)) Tandem Library Bks.

Varonka, Steve. Hard Coal Times: Pennsylvania Anthracite Stories, Vol. 1. 2003. (Illus.). 40p. (J). 4.72 (978-0-9709630-2-4(5)) Coal Hole Productions.

Walters, Scott. Woman Too Young of Panther Cave. 2007. (YA). per. 16.95 (*978-1-934248-09-6(6)) Mill City Pr., Inc.

—Woman Too Young of Panther Cave. 2007. 20.95 (*978-1-934248-14-0(2)) Mill City Pr., Inc.

Weigman, Matthew. Liberty's Journey: The Story of Our Freedom. Eve, Lealand, illus. 2004. 31p. (J). 16.95 (978-0-9747981-0-3(X)) Fahnestock Pr.

Winthrop, Elizabeth. Counting on Grace. 2006. (Illus.). 240p. (J). (gr. 3-7). 15.95 (978-0-385-74644-1(X)); lib. bdg. 17.99 (978-0-385-90878-8(4)) Random Hse. Children's Bks. (Lamb, Wendy).

Wooderson, Philip. Trouble at the Mill. 2005. (My Side of the Story Ser.). 192p. (J). (gr. 4-6). pap. 6.95 (978-0-7534-5782-5(2) , Kingfisher) Houghton Mifflin Co. Trade & Reference Div.

Yolen, Jane. Naming Liberty. Burke, Jim, illus. 2008. 32p. (J). (gr. 1-4). 16.99 (*978-0-399-24250-2(3) , Philomel) Penguin Group (USA) Inc.

Young, Karen Romano. Outside In. 2002. (Illus.). 192p. (J). (gr. 5 up). 16.95 (978-0-688-17363-0(2)) HarperCollins Pubs.

UNITED STATES—HISTORY, LOCAL

Armentrout, David & Armentrout, Patricia. Historic Sites & Monuments. 2002. (Guides to State Symbols). (Illus.). 48p. (gr. 3-8). 20.95 (978-1-58952-085-1(8)) Rourke Publishing, LLC.

Benchmark Education Staff, compiled by. This State Is Mine & State HIST. 2005. spiral bd. 110.00 (*978-1-4108-5817-7(0)) Benchmark Education Co.

Bial, Raymond. The Forts: Building America. 2001. (Building America Ser.). (Illus.). 56p. (J). (gr. 4 up). lib. bdg. 27.07 (978-0-7614-1334-9(0) , Benchmark Bks.) Cavendish, Marshall Corp.

Gillis, Jennifer Blizin. Battlefields. 2008. (J). (*978-1-60044-559-0(4)) Rourke Publishing, LLC.

—Restored Villages. 2008. (J). (*978-1-60044-563-7(2)) Rourke Publishing, LLC.

Nash, Gary B. Landmarks of the American Revolution. 2003. (American Landmarks Ser.). (Illus.). 160p. (YA). 32.00 (978-0-19-512849-9(4)) Oxford Univ. Pr., Inc.

Putnam, Jeff. National Monuments: Events & Times. 2004. (Illus.). iii, 75p. (J). pap. (*978-0-7367-1787-8(0)) Zaner-Bloser, Inc.

Silber, Nina. Landmarks of the Civil War. 2003. (American Landmarks Ser.). (Illus.). 144p. (YA). 30.00 (978-0-19-512920-5(2)) Oxford Univ. Pr., Inc.

Stone, Lynn M. America's Monuments. 2003. (Land of Liberty Ser.). (Illus.). 24p. (gr. 2-5). 17.95 (978-1-58952-312-8(1)) Rourke Publishing, LLC.

Torpie, Kate. Our National Treasures. 2002. (Illus.). 32p. (J). pap. 6.00 (978-1-59034-042-4(6)); (gr. 1-5). 15.95 (978-1-59034-191-9(0)) Mondo Publishing.

U. S. History Little Books: Famous Places. 2002. 144p. (J). (gr. k-3). 14.99 (978-0-7439-3259-2(5) , 3259) Teacher Created Materials, Inc.

UNITED STATES—HISTORY, MILITARY

America in Conflict, 1941-1985. 2004. (Stories in History Ser.). (Illus.). 208p. (gr. 6-12). 9.99 (978-0-618-22197-4(2) , 2-00296) McDougal Littell Inc.

Ammon, Richard. Valley Forge. Farnsworth, Bill, illus. 2006. 32p. 6.95 (978-0-8234-2016-2(7)) Holiday Hse., Inc.

Anderson, Dale. The Civil War in the East (1861-July 1863) 2004. (World Almanac Library of the Civil War). (Illus.). 48p. (J). (gr. 5 up). pap. 11.95 (978-0-8368-5591-3(4)); lib. bdg. 30.00 (978-0-8368-5582-1(5)) Stevens, Gareth Inc. (World Almanac Library).

Ansary, Mir Tamim. Veteran's Day. 2002. (Holiday Histories Ser.). (Illus.). 32p. (J). (gr. k-2). pap. 6.95 (978-1-58810-435-9(4) , 91163) Heinemann Library.

Benge, Janet & Benge, Geoff. Douglas MacArthur: What Greater Honor. 2005. (Illus.). 205p. (J). 6.99 (978-1-932096-15-6(9)) Emerald Bks.

Bial, Raymond. The Forts: Building America. 2001. (Building America Ser.). (Illus.). 56p. (J). (gr. 4 up). lib. bdg. 27.07 (978-0-7614-1334-9(0) , Benchmark Bks.) Cavendish, Marshall Corp.

Bowman, John S. America at War Set. 2004. (America at War Ser.). 160-256p. (gr. 6-12). 455.00 (978-0-8160-6108-2(4)) Facts On File, Inc.

—Chronology of Wars. 2003. (America at War Ser.). (Illus.). 240p. (YA). (gr. 6-12). 35.00 (978-0-8160-4941-7(6)) Facts On File, Inc.

Brager, Bruce L. The Monitor vs. the Merrimack. 2004. (Great Battles Through the Ages Ser.). (Illus.). 112p. (gr. 6-12). pap. 13.25 (978-0-7910-7792-4(6) , Chelsea Hse.) Facts On File, Inc.

Britton, Tamara L. The Pentagon. 2005. (America's Landmarks & Monuments Ser.). (Illus.). 32p. (J). (gr. k-6). lib. bdg. 22.78 (978-1-57765-849-8(3)) ABDO Publishing Co.

Burgan, Michael. Valley Forge. 2004. (We the People Ser.). (Illus.). 48p. (J). (gr. 4 up). lib. bdg. 22.60 (978-0-7565-0615-5(8)) Compass Point Bks.

Crismon, Fred W. All American Wonder Vol. III: The Photographic History of the U. S. Military 1/4 Ton Truck. 2005. 605p. pap. 59.95 (978-0-9700567-4-0(5)) Victory WW 2 Publishing Ltd.

Dolan, Edward F., Jr. The Winter at Valley Forge. 2001. (Kaleidoscope Ser.). (Illus.). 48p. (J). (gr. 3 up). lib. bdg. 25.64 (978-0-7614-1304-2(9) , Benchmark Bks.) Cavendish, Marshall Corp.

The G. I. Series: The Illustrated History of the American Soldier, His Uniform, & His Equipment, 21. 2005. 76 - 84p. pap. 577.50 (978-0-7910-8077-1(3) , Chelsea Hse.) Facts On File, Inc.

Gillis, Jennifer Blizin. Battlefields. 2008. (J). (*978-1-60044-559-0(4)) Rourke Publishing, LLC.

Harmon, Daniel E. Fighting Units of the American Revolution. 1998. (Costume, Tradition & Culture). (Illus.). 64p. (J). 19.75 (978-0-7910-5162-7(5) , Chelsea Hse.) Facts On File, Inc.

Hatch, Alden. General George Patton: Old Blood & Guts. 2006. (Sterling Point Bks.). (Illus.). 208p. (J). 12.95 (978-1-4027-3186-0(8)); pap. 6.95 (978-1-4027-3614-8(2)) Sterling Publishing Co., Inc.

Haugen, Brenda. Douglas MacArthur: America's General. 2005. (Illus.). 112p. (J). (gr. 5-7). (978-0-7565-0994-1(7)) Compass Point Bks.

Hogue, Richard, Sr. We Were the Third Herd. 2003. per. 17.95 (978-0-9722264-0-0(0)) Richlyn Publishing.

Keeter, Hunter. American Ground Forces in the Vietnam War. 2005. (American Experience in Vietnam Ser.). (Illus.). 48p. (J). pap. (978-0-8368-5781-8(X)); lib. bdg. 30.00 (978-0-8368-5774-0(7)) Stevens, Gareth Inc. (World Almanac Library).

Langellier, John P. Uncle Sam's Little Wars: The Spanish-American War, Philippine Insurrection & Boxer Rebellion. 2001. (G. I. Ser.). (Illus.). 80p. (J). 27.50 (978-0-7910-6674-4(6) , Chelsea Hse.) Facts On File, Inc.

Lerch, Kathryn W., ed. Words of War: Wartime Memories from the Civil War Through the Gulf War. 2002. (Illus.). xii, 177p. (YA). pap. 24.95 (978-1-57860-108-0(8)) Emmis Bks.

Lloyd, Mark. The Confederate Army, 4 vols., Set. 1998. (Illus.). 64p. 17.98 (978-0-7910-4995-2(7) , Chelsea Hse.) Facts On File, Inc.

Maestro, Betsy. Struggle for a Continent: The French & Indian Wars, 1689-1763. Maestro, Giulio, illus. 2000. (American Story Ser.). 48p. (J). (gr. 2 up). 17.99 (978-0-688-13450-1(5)) HarperCollins Pubs.

Maynard, Charles W. Famous Forts Throughout American History, 6 bks. Incl. Castillo de San Marcos. lib. bdg. 18.75 (978-0-8239-5841-2(8)); Fort Clatsop. lib. bdg. 18.75 (978-0-8239-5837-5(X)); Fort Laramie. lib. bdg. 18.75 (978-0-8239-5839-9(6)); Fort McHenry. lib. bdg. 18.75 (978-0-8239-5838-2(8)); Fort Sumter. lib. bdg. 18.75 (978-0-8239-5840-5(X)); Fort Ticonderoga. lib. bdg. 18.75 (978-0-8239-5836-8(1)); 24p. (J). (gr. 3). 2002. (Illus.). 2001. Set lib. bdg. 112.50 (978-0-8239-7179-4(1) , PowerKids Pr.) Rosen Publishing Group, Inc., The.

McCormick, Anita Louise. The Vietnam Antiwar Movement in American History. 2000. (In American History Ser.). (Illus.). 128p. (YA). (gr. 5-12). lib. bdg. 26.60 (978-0-7660-1295-0(6)) Enslow Pubs., Inc.

McDermott, John D. Forlorn Hope: The Nez Perce Victory at White Bird Canyon. 2004. (Illus.). 246p. pap. 15.95 (978-0-87004-435-9(4) , 043540) Caxton Pr.

McPherson, Stephanie Sammartino. Douglas MacArthur. 2005. (History Maker Bios Ser.). (Illus.). 48p. (J). 26.60 (978-0-8225-2434-2(1)) Lerner Publishing Group.

Pollard, Josephine. Battles of America, Vol. 2. 1998. (Illus.). 256p. (J). reprint ed. 15.00 (978-1-889128-43-6(0)) Mantle Ministries.

Pugh, Harry F. & PERKOWSKI, Gary. U. S. Special Forces Group Insignia (Post 1975) 2004. (Elite Insignia Guides Ser.). (YA). pap. (978-0-9633231-8-7(0)) C&D Enterprises.

Ross, Thomas A. Privileges of War: A Good Story of American Service in South Vietnam. 2004. (Illus.). 356p. 24.95 (978-0-9754859-0-3(3) , 9005710) American Heritage Publishing.

Stanley, George E. George S. Patton: War Hero. Henderson, Meryl, illus. 2007. (Childhood of Famous Americans Ser.). 192p. (J). pap. 5.99 (*978-1-4169-1547-8(8) , Aladdin) Simon & Schuster Children's Publishing.

Stewart, Gail B. Fighting for Freedom: Blacks in the American Military. 2006. (Illus.). 112p. (J). (gr. 7-10). 32.45 (978-1-59018-952-8(3) , Lucent Bks.) Thomson Gale.

Sutcliffe, Jane. George S. Patton Jr. 2005. (History Maker Bios Ser.). (Illus.). 48p. (J). 26.60 (978-0-8225-2436-6(8) , Lerner Pubns.) Lerner Publishing Group.

Welch, Catherine A. George C. Marshall. 2005. (History Maker Bios Ser.). 48p. (J). pap. 6.95 (978-0-8225-5460-8(7)); (Illus.). 26.60 (978-0-8225-2435-9(X) , Lerner Pubns.) Lerner Publishing Group.

White, Matt. Cameras on the Battlefield: Photos of War. 2001. (High Five Reading Ser.). (Illus.). 64p. (J). pap. (978-0-7368-9504-0(3)); (gr. 4-5). lib. bdg. 22.60 (978-0-7368-4004-0(4) , Capstone High-Interest Bks.) Capstone Pr., Inc.

Women Soldiers in the Union Army. 2000. (Illus.). (J). pap. 4.95 (978-0-88388-221-4(3)) Bellerophon Bks.

UNITED STATES—HISTORY, NAVAL

Hobbs, Richard R. Naval Science 2: Maritime History & Nautical Sciences for the NJROTC Student. 2nd ed. 2006. (Illus.). 344p. 29.95 (978-1-59114-366-6(7)) Naval Institute Pr.

Smolinski, Diane. Naval Warfare of the Revolutionary War. 2001. (Americans at War Ser.). (Illus.). 32p. (J). (gr. 4-6). lib. bdg. (978-1-58810-275-1(0)) Heinemann Library.

Wizner, Kira. John McCain: Profile of a Leading Republican. 2007. (J). (***978-1-4042-1911-3(0)***) Rosen Publishing Group, Inc., The.

UNITED STATES—HISTORY—POETRY

Alcorn, Stephen. America at War: A Book of Poems. 2008. 96p. (J). 21.99 (978-1-4169-1832-5(9)) , McElderry, Margaret K.) Simon & Schuster Children's Publishing.

Bates, Katherine Lee. America the Beautiful. Minor, Wendell, illus. 2005. 48p. (J). (gr. k). reprint ed. pap. 5.99 (978-0-14-240321-1(0) , Puffin) Penguin Group (USA) Inc.

Katz, Bobbi. American History Poems: Make History Come Alive with 32 Original Poems with Background Information. 1998. (Illus.). 64p. (J). 9.95 (978-0-590-49973-6(4)) Scholastic, Inc.

—We the People: Poems. Crews, Nina, illus. 2000. 112p. (J). (gr. 3 up). 17.99 (978-0-688-16531-4(1)) HarperCollins Pubs.

Longfellow, Henry Wadsworth. Paul Revere's Ride. Vachula, Monica, illus. 2003. 32p. (J). (gr. 4-6). 16.95 (978-1-56397-799-2(0)) Boyds Mills Pr.

—Paul Revere's Ride: The Landlord's Tale. Santore, Charles, illus. 2003. 40p. (J). lib. bdg. 17.89 (978-0-06-623747-3(5)) HarperCollins Pubs.

Meltzer, Milton. Hour of Freedom: American History in Poetry. Nadel, Marc, illus. 2003. 96p. (YA). (gr. 6-9). 16.95 (978-1-59078-021-3(3)) Boyds Mills Pr.

Voorhees, Sue. I'm Your Very Own Flag. 2006. (J). per. 12.50 (***978-0-9764167-4-6(3)***) Old Soldier Publishing.

UNITED STATES—HISTORY, POLITICAL

see United States—Politics and Government

UNITED STATES—HISTORY—SOURCES

American Voices - Group 2, 5 Bks, Set. 2004. (J). 171.07 (978-0-7614-1692-0(7)) Cavendish, Marshall Corp.

Bennett, William J. Our Country's Founders: Book of Advice for Young People Adapted From Our Sacred Honor. 2001. (Illus.). 320p. (YA). (gr. 7-12). pap. 11.99 (978-0-689-84469-0(7) , Simon Pulse) Simon & Schuster Children's Publishing.

Colonial Life, 5 bks., Set. Incl. Cities & Towns. Stefoff, Rebecca. 37.95 (***978-0-7656-8109-6(9)***); Daily Living. Hinds, Kathryn. 37.95 (***978-0-7656-8110-2(2)***); Exploration & Settlement. Stefoff, Rebecca. 37.95 (***978-0-7656-8108-9(0)***); Government. Kelly, Martin & Kelly, Melissa. 37.95 (***978-0-7656-8112-6(9)***); Trade & Commerce. Altman, Linda Jacobs. 37.95 (***978-0-7656-8111-9(0)***); (Illus.). 96p. (gr. 6 up). (Colonial Life (Group 1) Ser.). 2007. 189.75 (***978-0-7656-8107-2(2)***) Sharpe, M.E. Inc.

Flanagan, Timothy. Reconstruction: A Primary Source History of the Struggle to Unite the North & South after the Civil War. 2005. (Illus.). 64p. (J). (gr. 5-8). lib. bdg. 29.25 (978-1-4042-0177-4(7)) Rosen Publishing Group, Inc., The.

Friedman, Margo R., ed. In Hope Freedom Rings. Mullett, Glenn C., illus. 2002. 96p. (J). per. 5.95 (978-0-9659488-4-5(6)) In Hope Freedom Rings, Inc.

Hakim, Joy. A History of U. S. Sourcebook & Index. rev. ed. 2007. (History of US Ser.). 352p. pap. 15.95 (***978-0-19-532725-0(X)***) Oxford Univ. Pr., Inc.

Hakim, Joy. Sourcebook & Index: Documents That Shaped the American Nation. (gr. 5-8). 2003. lib. bdg. 23.40 (978-0-613-66384-7(5)); 1999. lib. bdg. 23.40 (978-0-613-55191-5(5)) Tandem Library Bks.

King, David C. & American Heritage Magazine Staff. World Wars & the Modern Age. 2004. (American Heritage, American Voices Ser.). (Illus.). 144p. pap. 12.95 (978-0-471-44392-6(1) , Wiley) Wiley, John & Sons, Inc.

McIntire, Suzanne. American Heritage Book of Great American Speeches for Young People. 2001. (Illus.). 304p. (gr. 5 up). pap. 14.95 (978-0-471-38942-2(0) , Wiley) Wiley, John & Sons, Inc.

Miller, Marilyn. Words That Built a Nation: A Young Person's Collection of Historic American Documents. 1999. (Illus.). 176p. (YA). (gr. 4-9). pap. 18.95 (978-0-590-29881-0(X) , Scholastic Reference) Scholastic, Inc.

Miller, Marilyn, ed. Words That Built a Nation: A Young Person's Collection of Historic American Documents. 2001. (Illus.). 172p. (YA). (gr. 5-9). reprint ed. 19.00 (978-0-7881-9600-3(6)) DIANE Publishing Co.

National Archives Staff. Our Documents: 100 Milestone Documents from the National Archives. 2003. (Illus.). 256p. (YA). 40.00 (978-0-19-517206-5(X)) Oxford Univ. Pr., Inc.

Primary Sources in American History Set 4. 2005. (Illus.). 64p. (gr. 5-8). lib. bdg. 175.50 (978-1-4042-0351-8(6)) Rosen Publishing Group, Inc., The.

Primary Sources of Life in the New American Nation. (Primary Source Big Bookstm Ser.). 24p. (J). (gr. 4-8). 46.60 (978-0-8239-4602-0(9)) Rosen Publishing Group, Inc., The.

Scholastic, Inc. Staff & Keenan, Sheila. O, Say Can You See? America's Symbols, Landmarks, & Important Words. 2007. 64p. (J). pap. 5.99 (***978-0-439-59360-1(3)*** , Scholastic Nonfiction) Scholastic, Inc.

Stefoff, Rebecca. Colonial Life. 2002. (American Voices From Ser.). (Illus.). xxi, 119p. (J). 34.21 (978-0-7614-1205-2(0) , Benchmark Bks.) Cavendish, Marshall Corp.

Stites, Bill. Democracy: A Primary Source Analysis. 2003. (Primary Sources of Political Systems Ser.). (Illus.). 64p. (J). lib. bdg. 29.25 (978-0-8239-4518-4(9)) Rosen Publishing Group, Inc., The.

Tait, Leia. Primary Sources. 2007. (***978-1-59036-764-3(2)***); lib. bdg. (***978-1-59036-763-6(4)***) Weigl Pubs., Inc.

UNITED STATES—HISTORY—COLONIAL PERIOD, CA. 1600-1775

see also Pilgrims (New Plymouth Colony); United States—History—French and Indian War, 1755-1763

Allison, Amy. Roger Williams: Founder of Rhode Island. 2000. (Colonial Leaders Ser.). (Illus.). 80p. (J). (gr. 8-12). 27.50 (978-0-7910-5964-7(2) , Chelsea Hse.) Facts On File, Inc.

Allman, Melinda, ed. Primary Sources. 2001. (Thirteen Colonies Ser.). (Illus.). 104p. (J). (gr. 4-12). lib. bdg. 27.45 (978-1-59018-011-2(9) , LML00902-179659, Lucent Bks.) Thomson Gale.

Altman, Linda Jacobs. Trade & Commerce. 2007. (Colonial Life Ser.). (Illus.). 96p. (gr. 6 up). 37.95 (***978-0-7656-8111-9(0)***) Sharpe, M.E. Inc.

The American Colonies. 2005. (Fact Finders Ser.). (Illus.). (J). (gr. 3-4). lib. bdg. 293.80 (978-0-7368-2761-4(7)) Capstone Pr., Inc.

Amstel, Marsha. Sybil Ludington's Midnight Ride. Beier, Ellen, illus. 2003. (On My Own History Ser.). 48p. (J). (gr. 1-3). pap. 5.95 (978-1-57505-456-8(6)) Lerner Publishing Group.

—Sybil Ludington's Midnight Ride. 2000. (gr. k-3). lib. bdg. 14.10 (978-0-613-68293-0(9)) Tandem Library Bks.

Ansary, Mir Tamim. Independence Day. (Illus.). 32p. (J). 2006. (***978-1-4034-8887-9(8)***); 2001. lib. bdg. 21.36 (978-1-58810-223-2(8)) Heinemann Library.

—Independence Day. 2001. 13.75 (978-0-606-22385-0(1)) Tandem Library Bks.

Archaeology of Early Colonial Life: Grades 4-9. (Teaching with Primary Sources Ser.). (J). tchr. ed., ring bd. 28.95 (978-0-382-44366-4(7)) Cobblestone Publishing Co.

Aronson, Marc. Witch-Hunt: Mysteries of the Salem Witch Trials. Anderson, Stephanie, illus. 2005. 288p. (YA). reprint ed. pap. 8.99 (978-1-4169-0315-4(1) , Simon Pulse) Simon & Schuster Children's Publishing.

Axelrod-Contrada, Joan. A Historical Atlas of Colonial America. 2005. (United States, Historical Atlases of the Growth of a New Nation Ser.). (Illus.). 64p. (J). (gr. 7-12). lib. bdg. 30.60 (978-1-4042-0200-9(5)) Rosen Publishing Group, Inc., The.

—A Primary Source History of the Colony of Rhode Island. 2005. (Primary Sources of the Thirteen Colonies & the Lost Colony Ser.). (Illus.). 64p. (YA). (gr. 5-8). lib. bdg. 29.25 (978-1-4042-0434-8(2)) Rosen Publishing Group, Inc., The.

Benchmark Education Staff. The Thirteen Colonies. 2005. 2.00 (***978-1-4108-4667-9(9)***) Benchmark Education Co.

Bial, Raymond. The Houses: Building America. 2001. (Building America Ser.). (Illus.). 56p. (J). (gr. 4 up). lib. bdg. 27.07 (978-0-7614-1335-6(9) , Benchmark Bks.) Cavendish, Marshall Corp.

Bjornlund, Lydia D. Women in Colonial America. 2003. (Illus.). 112p. (J). 32.45 (978-1-59018-470-7(X) , Lucent Bks.) Thomson Gale.

Boraas, Tracey. The Salem Witch Trials. 2004. (Let Freedom Ring Ser.). (Illus.). 48p. (J). lib. bdg. 23.93 (978-0-7368-2464-4(2) , Bridgestone Bks.) Capstone Pr., Inc.

Bordessa, Kris. Great Colonial America Projects You Can Build Yourself: Learn Some Hands-on History. 2006. (Build It Yourself Ser.). (Illus.). 128p. (J). pap. 14.95 (978-0-9771294-0-9(3)) Nomad Pr.

Brannon, Barbara. Discover the Thirteen Colonies. 2005. 39.00 (***978-1-4108-5156-7(7)***) Benchmark Education Co.

Brenner, Barbara. If You Lived in Williamsburg in Colonial Days. 2000. (gr. 3-6). lib. bdg. 14.15 (978-0-613-32676-6(8)) Tandem Library Bks.

Britton, Tamara L. The Maryland Colony. 2001. (Colonies Ser.). (Illus.). 32p. (J). (gr. k-6). lib. bdg. 22.78 (978-1-57765-578-7(8) , Checkerboard Library) ABDO Publishing Co.

—The South Carolina Colony. 2001. (Colonies Ser.). (Illus.). 32p. (J). (gr. k-6). lib. bdg. 22.78 (978-1-57765-581-7(8) , Checkerboard Library) ABDO Publishing Co.

Burgan, Michael. Colonial America. 2006. (Making a New Nation Ser.). (Illus.). 48p. (J). (978-1-4034-7827-6(9)); pap. (978-1-4034-7834-4(1)) Heinemann Library.

Burt, Barbara. Colonial Life: The Adventures of Benjamin Wilcox. 2002. (Reading Expeditions Ser.). (Illus.). 40p. (J). (978-0-7922-8678-3(2)) National Geographic Society.

—The Eve of Revolution: The Colonial Adventures of Benjamin Wilcox. 2004. (Illus.). 40p. (J). (gr. 4-8). pap. 7.00 (978-0-7567-8215-3(5)) DIANE Publishing Co.

—Eve of Revolutuion: The Colonial Adventures of Benjamin Wilcox. 2003. (gr. 3-6). lib. bdg. 15.30 (978-0-613-67082-1(5)) Tandem Library Bks.

Capstone Press, contrib. by. Slave Trade in Early America. (Colonial America Ser.). 48p. (YA). pap. 7.95 (978-0-7368-4482-6(1)) Capstone Pr., Inc.

Carlisle, Rodney P. & Golson, J. Geoffrey, eds. Turning Points in History: Colonial America from Settlement to the Revolution. 2006. (Turning PointsÑActual & Alternate Histories Ser.). (Illus.). xix, 266p. lib. bdg. 85.00 (978-1-85109-827-9(5)) ABC-CLIO, Inc.

Carlson, Laurie M. Colonial Kids: An Activity Guide to Life in the New World. 2003. (Kid's Guide Ser.). (Illus.). 160p. (J). (gr. k-7). pap. 14.95 (978-1-55652-322-9(X)) Chicago Review Pr., Inc.

Carter, E. J. The Mayflower Compact. 2003. (Heinemann Know It Ser.). (Illus.). 48p. (J). pap. 8.50 (978-1-4034-3432-6(8)); lib. bdg. 27.07 (978-1-4034-0803-7(3)) Heinemann Library.

Cipriano, Jeri. Colonial Times/la época Colonial: English/Spanish Pair, 12 texts, 2 titles, Vol. 2. ed. 2004. (Navigators Ser.). (J). pap., instr.'s gde. ed. 84.00 (978-1-4108-1768-6(7) , 17687) Benchmark Education Co.

Cobb, Mary. A Sampler View of Colonial Life: With Projects Kids Can Make. Ellis, Jan Davey, illus. 1998. 64p. (gr. 2-4). lib. bdg. 24.90 (978-0-7613-0372-5(3) , Millbrook Pr.) Lerner Publishing Group.

Colonial America Biographies. (Let Freedom Ring Ser.). (Illus.). (J). (gr. 3-4). lib. bdg. 95.72 (978-0-7368-2554-2(1)) Capstone Pr., Inc.

Colonial Leaders. 2005. 80p. pap. 550.00 (978-0-7910-6279-1(1) , Chelsea Hse.) Facts On File, Inc.

Colonial Life, 5 bks., Set. Incl. Cities & Towns. Stefoff, Rebecca. 37.95 (***978-0-7656-8109-6(9)***); Daily Living. Hinds, Kathryn. 37.95 (***978-0-7656-8110-2(2)***); Exploration & Settlement. Stefoff, Rebecca. 37.95 (***978-0-7656-8108-9(0)***); Government. Kelly, Martin & Kelly, Melissa. 37.95 (***978-0-7656-8112-6(9)***); Trade & Commerce. Altman, Linda Jacobs. 37.95 (***978-0-7656-8111-9(0)***); (Illus.). 96p. (gr. 6 up). (Colonial Life (Group 1) Ser.). 2007. 189.75 (***978-0-7656-8107-2(2)***) Sharpe, M.E. Inc.

The Colonies, Set. Incl. Connecticut Colony. Italia, Bob. lib. bdg. 22.78 (978-1-57765-586-2(9)); Delaware Colony. Britton, Tamara L. lib. bdg. 22.78 (978-1-57765-577-0(X)); Georgia Colony. Britton, Tamara L. lib. bdg. 22.78 (978-1-57765-583-1(4)); Maryland Colony. Britton, Tamara L. lib. bdg. 22.78 (978-1-57765-578-7(8)); Massachusetts Colony. Italia, Bob. lib. bdg. 22.78 (978-1-57765-584-8(2)); New Hampshire Colony. Italia, Bob. lib. bdg. 22.78 (978-1-57765-585-5(0)); New Jersey Colony. Italia, Bob. lib. bdg. 22.78 (978-1-57765-590-9(7)); New York Colony. Italia, Bob. lib. bdg. 22.78 (978-1-57765-589-3(3)); North Carolina Colony. Britton, Tamara L. lib. bdg. 22.78 (978-1-57765-582-4(6)); Pennsylvania Colony. Italia, Bob. lib. bdg. 22.78 (978-1-57765-588-6(5)); Rhode Island Colony. Italia, Bob. lib. bdg. 22.78 (978-1-57765-587-9(7)); Roanoke: The Lost Colony. Italia, Bob. lib. bdg. 22.78 (978-1-57765-580-0(X)); South Carolina Colony. Britton, Tamara L. lib. bdg. 22.78 (978-1-57765-581-7(8)); Virginia Colony. Britton, Tamara L. lib. bdg. 22.78 (978-1-57765-579-4(6)); 32p. (J). (gr. k-6). 2001. (Illus.). 2001. Set lib. bdg. 318.92 (978-1-57765-503-9(6) , Checkerboard Library) ABDO Publishing Co.

Connelly, Elizabeth Russell. John Winthrop. 2000. (Colonial Leaders Ser.). (Illus.). 80p. (J). (gr. 4-7). pap. 27.50 (978-0-7910-6122-0(1)); (gr. 8-12). 27.50 (978-0-7910-5965-4(0)) Facts On File, Inc. (Chelsea Hse.).

David Haugen. Speechmakers & Writers. 2004. (Voices from the American Revolution Ser.). (Illus.). 32p. (J). 23.70 (978-1-4103-0415-5(9) , Blackbirch Pr., Inc.) Thomson Gale.

Dimartino, Catherine. Early American Alliances. 2005. (Illus.). 16p. (J). pap. (***978-0-328-14893-6(8)***) Pearson Education.

Doherty, Craig A. & Doherty, Katherine M. New Hampshire. 2005. (Thirteen Colonies Ser.). (Illus.). 144p. (J). (gr. 4-9). 35.00 (978-0-8160-5411-4(8)) Facts On File, Inc.

—New Jersey, 13 vols. 2005. (Thirteen Colonies Ser.). (Illus.). 128p. (J). (gr. 4-9). 35.00 (978-0-8160-5408-4(8)) Facts On File, Inc.

Dolan, Edward F., Jr. The Boston Tea Party. 2001. (Kaleidoscope Ser.). (Illus.). 48p. (J). (gr. 3). lib. bdg. 25.64 (978-0-7614-1303-5(0) , Benchmark Bks.) Cavendish, Marshall Corp.

Donlan, Leni. George Washington: Revolution & the New Nation. 2006. (American History Through Primary Sources Ser.). (Illus.). 32p. (J). (978-1-4109-2420-9(3)); pap. (978-1-4109-2431-5(9)) Steck-Vaughn.

Dosier, Susan. Colonial Cooking. 2000. (Blue Earth Books). (Illus.). 32p. (J). (gr. 3-4). lib. bdg. 22.60 (978-0-7368-0352-6(1) , Bridgestone Bks.) Capstone Pr., Inc.

—Colonial Cooking. 1999. (Exploring History Through Simple Recipes Ser.). (Illus.). 32p. (J). (gr. 2-7). pap. 14.60 (978-0-516-21863-2(8) , Children's Pr.) Scholastic Library Publishing.

Draper, Allison Stark. What People Wore in Colonial America. 2001. (Clothing, Costumes & Uniforms Thoughout American History Ser.). (Illus.). 24p. (J). (gr. 3). lib. bdg. 19.95 (978-0-8239-5665-4(2) , PKCLCO, PowerKids Pr.) Rosen Publishing Group, Inc., The.

DuPrau, Jeanne. The American Colonies. 2001. (Daily Life Ser.). (Illus.). 48p. (J). (gr. 3-5). 23.70 (978-0-7377-0936-0(7) , LML00902-17875, Kidhaven) Thomson Gale.

Eagan, Robynne. Early Settlers. Mitchell, Judy, ed. Hierstein, Judith, illus. 2001. (History - Hands On! Ser.). 32p. (J). (gr. 1-4). pap. 6.95 (978-1-57310-303-9(9)) Teaching & Learning Co.

Fisher, Leonard Everett. Colonial Craftsmen - Group 3, 5 bks., Set. Incl. Architects. lib. bdg. 21.36 (978-0-7614-0931-1(9)); Blacksmiths. lib. bdg. 24.21 (978-0-7614-0930-4(0)); Limners : America's Earliest Portrait Painters. lib. bdg. 24.21 (978-0-7614-0932-8(7)); Printers. lib. bdg. 24.21 (978-0-7614-0929-8(7)); Wigmakers. lib. bdg. 24.21 (978-0-7614-0933-5(5)); 48p. (J). (gr. 4-8). 1999. (Illus.). 1999. Set lib. bdg. 106.79 (978-0-7614-0928-1(9) , Benchmark Bks.) Cavendish, Marshall Corp.

—Colonial Craftsmen - Group 4, 4 bks., Set. Incl. Hatters. lib. bdg. 21.36 (978-0-7614-1146-8(1)); Papermakers. lib. bdg. 21.36 (978-0-7614-1147-5(X)); Potters. lib. bdg. 21.36 (978-0-7614-1149-9(6)); Tanners. lib. bdg. 24.21 (978-0-7614-1148-2(8)); 48p. (J). (gr. 4-8). (Illus.). 2000. Set lib. bdg. 85.43 (978-0-7614-1145-1(3) , Benchmark Bks.) Cavendish, Marshall Corp.

—The Hatters. 2000. (Colonial Craftsmen Ser.). (Illus.). 48p. (J). (gr. 4-8). lib. bdg. 21.36 (978-0-7614-1146-8(1) , Benchmark Bks.) Cavendish, Marshall Corp.

—The Papermakers. 2000. (Colonial Craftsmen Ser.). (Illus.). 48p. (J). (gr. 4-8). lib. bdg. 21.36 (978-0-7614-1147-5(X) , Benchmark Bks.) Cavendish, Marshall Corp.

—The Potters. 2000. (Colonial Craftsmen Ser.). (Illus.). 48p. (J). (gr. 4-8). lib. bdg. 21.36 (978-0-7614-1149-9(6) , Benchmark Bks.) Cavendish, Marshall Corp.

—The Tanners. 2000. (Colonial Craftsmen Ser.). (Illus.). 48p. (J). (gr. 4-8). lib. bdg. 24.21 (978-0-7614-1148-2(8) , Benchmark Bks.) Cavendish, Marshall Corp.

Fritz, Jean. The Lost Colony of Roanoke. Talbott, Hudson, illus. 2004. 64p. (J). (gr. 3-6). 16.99 (978-0-399-24027-0(6) , Putnam Juvenile) Penguin Group (USA) Inc.

Furbee, Mary Rodd. Of Colonial America. 2001. (gr. 5-8). lib. bdg. 22.20 (978-0-613-87292-8(4)) Tandem Library Bks.

George, Lynn. A Time Line of the American Revolutionary War. 2003. (Reading Room Collection). (Illus.). 24p. (J). lib. bdg. 18.75 (978-0-8239-3707-3(0)) Rosen Publishing Group, Inc., The.

Girod, Christina M. South Carolina. 2001. (Thirteen Colonies Ser.). (Illus.). 104p. (YA). (gr. 4-12). lib. bdg. 27.45 (978-1-56006-994-2(5) , LML00902-178232, Lucent Bks.) Thomson Gale.

Gourley, Catherine. Welcome to Felicity's World, 1774: Growing up in Colonial America. 1999. (American Girls Collection). (Illus.). 64p. (J). (gr. 2 up). 14.95 (978-1-56247-768-4(4) , American Girl) American Girl Publishing, Inc.

Gray, Edward G. Colonial America: A History in Documents. 2002. (Pages from History Ser.). (Illus.). 192p. 36.95 (978-0-19-513747-7(7)) Oxford Univ. Pr., Inc.

Greenhaven Staff. Colonial America. 2002. (gr. 7-12). lib. bdg. 33.25 (978-0-613-73862-0(4)) Tandem Library Bks.

Hakim, Joy. From Colonies to Country 1735-1791. 3rd ed. 2002. (History of US Ser.). (Illus.). 112p. pap., tchr. ed. 16.95 (978-0-19-515353-8(7)) Oxford Univ. Pr., Inc.

—A History of US Bk. 2: Making Thirteen Colonies. 3rd rev. ed. 2005. (History of US Ser.). (Illus.). 192p. 19.95 (978-0-19-518231-6(6)); 19.95 (978-0-19-518895-0(0)) Oxford Univ. Pr., Inc.

—A History of US Bk. 3: From Colonies to Country. 3rd rev. ed. 2005. (History of US Ser.). (Illus.). 224p. 19.95 (978-0-19-518232-3(4)); 19.95 (978-0-19-518896-7(9)) Oxford Univ. Pr., Inc.

—Making Thirteen Colonies. rev. ed. 2007. (History of US Ser.: Vol. 2). 192p. pap. 15.95 (***978-0-19-532716-8(0)***) Oxford Univ. Pr., Inc.

Hakim, Joy. Making Thirteen Colonies, 1600-1740. 3rd ed. 2002. (History of US Ser.: Bk. 2). 112p. pap., tchr. ed. 16.95 (978-0-19-515352-1(9)) Oxford Univ. Pr., Inc.

Hakin, Joy. From Colonies to Country. rev. ed. 2007. (History of US Ser.: Vol. 3). 224p. pap. 15.95 (***978-0-19-532717-5(9)***) Oxford Univ. Pr., Inc.

Hall, Margaret. Colonial Times. 2004. (Hands-On American History Ser.). (Illus.). 32p. (J). 27.07 (978-1-4034-6053-0(1)) Heinemann Library.

—First Days of the United States. 2004. (Hands-On American History Ser.). (Illus.). 32p. (J). 27.07 (978-1-4034-6051-6(5)) Heinemann Library.

—The History & Activities of the Colonies. 2006. (Hands-On American History Ser.). (Illus.). 32p. (J). pap. (978-1-4034-6060-8(4)) Heinemann Library.

—The History & Activities of the Revolutionary War. 2006. (Hands-On American History Ser.). (Illus.). 32p. (J). pap. (978-1-4034-6058-5(2)) Heinemann Library.

Hartwiger, Heidi. Tricorn Trivia: Colonial Facts & Fun for Kids. 2007. 5.00 (***978-1-59712-065-4(0)***) Catawba Publishing Co.

Harvey, Dan. The English Colonization of North America. 2002. (Exploration & Discovery Ser.). (Illus.). 64p. (J). (gr. 4-7). lib. bdg. (978-1-59084-051-1(8)) Mason Crest Pubs.

Haskins, James & Benson, Kathleen. Building a New Land: African Americans in Colonial America. Ransome, James E., illus. 2001. (Amistad Ser.). 48p. (J). (gr. 2-5). 17.89 (978-0-06-029361-1(6)); 17.95 (978-0-688-10266-1(2)) HarperCollins Pubs.

Holt, Rinehart and Winston Staff. Call to Freedom: Beginning 1877 - Texas Online Edition. 2003. cd-rom 77.60 (978-0-03-073346-8(4)) Holt, Rinehart & Winston.

—Call to Freedom: Beginning-1877: Geography Activities - Answer Key. 3rd ed. 2001. pap. 8.00 (978-0-03-066683-4(X)) Holt, Rinehart & Winston.

Hossell, Karen Price. Boston Tea Party: Rebellion in the Colonies. 2003. (gr. 5-8). lib. bdg. 15.25 (978-0-613-58195-0(4)) Tandem Library Bks.

How We Lived..., 5 bks., Set. Incl. In Colonial New England. Kent, Deborah. lib. bdg. 28.50 (978-0-7614-0905-2(X)); In the Middle Colonies. Kent, Deborah. lib. bdg. 28.50 (978-0-7614-0907-6(6)); In the Southern Colonies. Kent, Deborah. lib. bdg. 27.07 (978-0-7614-0908-3(4)); In the Spanish West. Stein, R. Conrad. lib. bdg. 27.07 (978-0-7614-0906-9(8)); On the Old Western Frontier. Stein, R. Conrad. lib. bdg. 28.50 (978-0-7614-0909-0(2)); 72p. (J). (gr. 4-8). 1999. (Illus.). 2000. 135.35 (978-0-7614-0904-5(1) , Benchmark Bks.) Cavendish, Marshall Corp.

Ichord, Loretta Frances. Hasty Pudding, Johnnycakes, & Other Good Stuff: Cooking in Colonial America. 2000. (Illus.). (J). 15.75 (978-0-606-18291-1(8)) Tandem Library Bks.

Isaacs, Sally Senzell. Life in a Colonial Town. (Picture the Past Ser.). (Illus.). 32p. (J). 2002. (gr. k-3). pap. 7.50 (978-1-58810-297-3(1) , 91063); 2000. (gr. 2-4). lib. bdg. 21.36 (978-1-57572-312-9(3)) Heinemann Library.

—Life in a Colonial Town. 2001. (Picture the Past Ser.). (Illus.). (J). (978-0-606-22003-3(8)) Tandem Library Bks.

Wiener. The 13 Colonies, 13 vols. 2004. (Illus.). (978-0-7398-6890-4(X)); 104.70 (978-1-4109-0427-0(X)); Set. pap. 666.90 (978-1-4109-1244-2(2)) Harcourt Schl. Pubs.

Wilcox, Charlotte. Games & Leisure in Colonial America. 2004. (Everyday Life Long Ago Ser.). (J). (978-0-7368-2162-9(7) , Blue Earth Bks.) Capstone Pr., Inc.

—Work & Occupations in Colonial America. 2004. (Everyday Life Long Ago Ser.). (J). (978-0-7368-2165-0(1) , Blue Earth Bks.) Capstone Pr., Inc.

Williams, Jean Kinney. African-Americans in the Colonies. 2002. (We the People Ser.). (Illus.). 48p. (J). (gr. 4 up). lib. bdg. 22.60 (978-0-7565-0303-1(5)) Compass Point Bks.

Wilmore, Kathy. A Day in the Life of a Colonial Blacksmith. 2000. (Library of Living & Working in Colonial Times). (Illus.). 24p. (J). (gr. 3). lib. bdg. 18.75 (978-0-8239-5425-4(0) , PowerKids Pr.) Rosen Publishing Group, Inc., The.

—A Day in the Life of a Colonial Printer. 2000. (Library of Living & Working in Colonial Times). (Illus.). 24p. (J). (gr. 3). lib. bdg. 18.75 (978-0-8239-5428-5(5) , PowerKids Pr.) Rosen Publishing Group, Inc., The.

—A Day in the Life of a Colonial Schoolteacher. 2000. (Library of Living & Working in Colonial Times). (Illus.). 24p. (J). (gr. 3). lib. bdg. 18.75 (978-0-8239-5429-2(3) , PowerKids Pr.) Rosen Publishing Group, Inc., The.

—A Day in the Life of a Colonial Silversmith. 2000. (Library of Living & Working in Colonial Times). (Illus.). 24p. (J). (gr. 3). lib. bdg. 18.75 (978-0-8239-5427-8(7) , PowerKids Pr.) Rosen Publishing Group, Inc., The.

—A Day in the Life of a Colonial Wigmaker. 2000. (Library of Living & Working in Colonial Times). (Illus.). 24p. (J). (gr. 3). lib. bdg. 18.75 (978-0-8239-5426-1(9) , PowerKids Pr.) Rosen Publishing Group, Inc., The.

Wirkner, Linda. Learning about America's Colonial Period with Graphic Organizers. 2005. (Graphic Organizers in Social Studies). (Illus.). 24p. (J). (gr. 3-5). lib. bdg. 19.95 (978-1-4042-2811-5(X) , PowerKids Pr.) Rosen Publishing Group, Inc., The.

Worland, Gayle. The Jamestown Colony. 2004. (Let Freedom Ring Ser.). (Illus.). 48p. (J). 17.95 (978-0-7368-2462-0(6) , Bridgestone Bks.) Capstone Pr., Inc.

Worth, Richard. Colonial America: Building Toward Independence. 2006. (American Saga Ser.). (Illus.). 128p. (YA). (gr. 5-8). lib. bdg. 31.93 (978-0-7660-2569-1(1)) Enslow Pubs., Inc.

Yero, Judith Lloyd. American Documents: Mayflower Compact. 2006. (Illus.). 40p. (J). (gr. 5-9). 15.95 (978-0-7922-5891-9(6) , National Geographic Children's Bks.) National Geographic Society.

—American Documents: The Mayflower Compact. 2006. (Illus.). 40p. (J). (gr. 5-9). 23.90 (978-0-7922-5892-6(4) , National Geographic Children's Bks.) National Geographic Society.

—The Bill of Rights. 2006. (American Documents Ser.). 40p. (J). (gr. 5-9). 15.95 (978-0-7922-5395-2(7)); 23.90 (978-0-7922-5396-9(5)) National Geographic Society. (National Geographic Children's Bks.).

—The Declaration of Independence. 2006. (American Documents Ser.). 40p. (J). (gr. 5-9). 15.95 (978-0-7922-5397-6(3)); 23.90 (978-0-7922-5398-3(1)) National Geographic Society. (National Geographic Children's Bks.).

Yorinks, Adrienne. Quilt of States: Piecing Together America. Larson, Jeanette, ed. 2005. (Illus.). 128p. (J). (gr. 5-8). 29.90 (978-0-7922-7285-4(4)); 19.95 (978-0-7922-7286-1(2)) National Geographic Society. (National Geographic Children's Bks.).

UNITED STATES—HISTORY—COLONIAL PERIOD, CA. 1600-1775—FICTION

Avi. Night Journeys. 2000. (Illus.). 160p. (J). (gr. 3-7). pap. 5.99 (978-0-380-73242-5(4) , Harper Trophy) HarperCollins Pubs.

—Night Journeys. 2000. (978-0-606-17978-2(X)); (gr. 5-8). lib. bdg. 14.15 (978-0-613-22094-1(3)) Tandem Library Bks.

Ayers, Linda. The Time Bridge Travelers & the Time Travel Station, 3 bks., Bk. 3. Ayers, Ryan, illus. l.t. ed. 2007. (Time Bridge Travelers Ser.: 3). 140p. (J). lib. bdg. 16.95 (***978-0-9786302-8-7(9)***); per. 7.95 (***978-0-9786302-7-0(0)***) Blue Thistle Pr.

Borden, Louise. Sleds on Boston Common: A Story from the American Revolution. Parker, Robert A., illus. 2000. 40p. (J). (gr. 3-7). 17.99 (978-0-689-82812-6(8) , McElderry, Margaret K.) Simon & Schuster Children's Publishing.

Burt, Barbara. The Eve of Revolution: The Colonial Adventures of Benjamin Wilcox. 2003. (I Am American Ser.). 40p. (J). (gr. 3-7). pap. 6.99 (978-0-7922-5211-5(X) , National Geographic Children's Bks.) National Geographic Society.

Cocca-Leffler, Maryann, illus. Spotlight on Stacey. 2007. (Social Studies Connects). 32p. (J). (***978-1-4287-1948-4(2)***); (gr. 2-4). pap. 4.99 (***978-1-57565-236-8(6)***) Kane Pr., The.

Cooney, Caroline B. The Ransom of Mercy Carter. 2002. (gr. 7-12). lib. bdg. 13.55 (978-0-613-60395-9(8)) Tandem Library Bks.

Deutsch, Stacia & Cohon, Rhody. Betsy Ross's Star. Francis, Guy, illus. 2007. (Blast to the Past Ser.). 80p. (J). pap. 3.99 (978-1-4169-3388-5(3) , Aladdin) Simon & Schuster Children's Publishing.

Draper, Sharon M. Copper Sun. 2006. 320p. (YA). (gr. 8 up). 16.95 (978-0-689-82181-3(6) , Atheneum) Simon & Schuster Children's Publishing.

Duey, Kathleen. Hoofbeats Silence & Lily 1773. 2007. 160p. (J). (gr. 5). 15.99 (***978-0-525-47852-2(3)*** , Dutton Juvenile) Penguin Group (USA) Inc.

Duey, Kathleen. Summer MacCleary: Virginia, 1749. 1998. (American Diaries Ser.: Vol. 10). (J). (gr. 3-7). (978-0-606-13120-9(5)) Tandem Library Bks.

Edmonds, Walter D. The Matchlock Gun. Lantz, Paul, illus. 1998. 64p. (J). (gr. 3-7). pap. 6.99 (978-0-698-11680-1(1) , Putnam Juvenile) Penguin Group (USA) Inc.

Forrester, Sandra. Wheel of the Moon. 2000. (Illus.). 176p. (J). (gr. 5-9). 15.95 (978-0-688-17149-0(4)) HarperCollins Pubs.

Gilberstadt, Debra Pack. Unmarked Grave: Remembering an American Patriot. 2005. (YA). lib. bdg. 29.95 (978-0-9763033-0-5(2)) Eslinger Hse. Publishing.

Grote, JoAnn A. Danger in the Harbor: Grain Riots Threaten Boston. 1999. (American Adventure Ser.: No. 6). (Illus.). 144p. (J). (gr. 3-7). lib. bdg. 15.95 (978-0-7910-5046-0(7) , Chelsea Hse.) Facts On File, Inc.

—Queen Anne's War. 1999. (American Adventure Ser.: No. 5). 144p. (J). (gr. 3-7). lib. bdg. 15.95 (978-0-7910-5045-3(9) , Chelsea Hse.) Facts On File, Inc.

Hamilton, Elizabeth L. Passport to Courage. 2002. (Character-in-Action Ser.: No. 1). (Illus.). 384p. (YA). per. 19.95 (978-0-9713749-3-5(7) , Character-in-Action) Quiet Impact, Inc.

Harmon, Lyn. Flight to Jewell Island. 2001. (Illus.). 148p. (gr. 4-7). pap. 10.95 (978-0-595-16337-3(8) , Backinprint.com) iUniverse, Inc.

Hemphill, Kris. A Secret Party in Boston Harbor. Martin, John F. & Van Pelt, Dan, illus. 1998. (Mysteries in Time Ser.: Vol. 6). 96p. (J). (gr. 4-7). 14.95 (978-1-881889-88-5(2)) Silver Moon Pr.

Hermes, Patricia. Our Strange New Land: Elizabeth's Jamestown Colony Diary. 2002. (gr. 3-6). lib. bdg. 13.00 (978-0-613-53849-7(8)) Tandem Library Bks.

—Season of Promise: Elizabeth's Jamestown Colony Diary. 2002. (My America Ser.: Bk. 3). (Illus.). 112p. (J). (gr. 2-5). pap. 10.95 (978-0-439-38898-6(8)); pap. 4.99 (978-0-439-27206-3(8)) Scholastic, Inc. (Scholastic Pr.).

—Season of Promise: Elizabeth's Jamestown Colony Diary. 2002. (gr. 3-6). lib. bdg. 13.00 (978-0-613-57130-2(4)) Tandem Library Bks.

—The Starving Time Bk. 2: Elizabeth's Jamestown Colony Diary. 2002. (My America Ser.: Bk. 2). (Illus.). 112p. (J). (gr. 2-5). pap. 4.99 (978-0-439-36902-2(9) , Scholastic Pr.) Scholastic, Inc.

Howard, Ginger. William's House. Day, Larry, illus. 2001. 32p. (gr. k-3). lib. bdg. 22.90 (978-0-7613-1674-9(4) , Millbrook Pr.) Lerner Publishing Group, Inc.

Kay, Verla. Tattered Sails. Andreasen, Dan, illus. 2001. 32p. (J). 15.99 (978-0-399-23345-6(8) , Putnam Juvenile) Penguin Group (USA) Inc.

Laird, Marnie. Water Rat. Shine, Andrea, illus. 1998. 196p. (J). (gr. 4-7). 15.95 (978-1-890817-08-4(2)) Winslow Pr.

Lawlor, Laurie. Horseback on the Boston Post Road 1704. Lyall, Dennis, illus. 2002. (American Sisters Ser.: Vol. 7). 208p. (J). pap. 4.99 (978-0-7434-3626-7(1) , Aladdin) Simon & Schuster Children's Publishing.

Leatherman, Diane. Abigail Before the Revolution. 2005. (Illus.). 64p. (J). (***978-0-9665861-2-1(3)***) Bounty Project, The.

Lutz, Norma Jean. Smallpox Strikes! Cotton Mather's Bold Experiment. 1999. (American Adventure Ser.: No. 7). (Illus.). 144p. (J). (gr. 3-7). lib. bdg. 15.95 (978-0-7910-5047-7(5) , Chelsea Hse.) Facts On File, Inc.

McDonald, Megan. Shadows in the Glasshouse. 2000. (American Girl Collection). (Illus.). (J). (978-0-606-20906-9(9)) Tandem Library Bks.

Nixon, Joan Lowery. Ann's Story, 1747. 2004. (J). (978-0-87935-198-4(5)) Colonial Williamsburg Foundation.

—Caesar's Story, 1759. 2004. (J). (978-0-87935-199-1(3)) Colonial Williamsburg Foundation.

—Maria's Story, 1773. 2004. (J). (978-0-87935-227-1(2)) Colonial Williamsburg Foundation.

—Nancy's Story, 1765. 2004. (J). (978-0-87935-225-7(6)) Colonial Williamsburg Foundation.

—Will's Story, 1771. 2004. (J). (978-0-87935-226-4(4)) Colonial Williamsburg Foundation.

Olasky, Susan. Will Northaway & the Gathering Storm. 2005. (Young American Patriots Ser.: No. 4). 96p. (J). (ps-7). pap. 5.99 (978-1-58134-478-3(3) , Crossway Bibles) Crossway Bks.

—Will Northaway & the Price of Loyalty. 2005. (Young American Patriots Ser.: #3). 93p. (J). (ps-7). pap. 5.99 (978-1-58134-477-6(5) , Crossway Bibles) Crossway Bks.

—Will Northaway & the Quest for Liberty. 2005. (Young American Patriots Ser.). 128p. pap. 5.99 (978-1-58134-475-2(9) , Crossway Bibles) Crossway Bks.

Otis, James. Neal the Miller. 2006. pap. (***978-1-4250-1390-5(2)***) Assistedreadingbooks.com Inc.

Paul Revere Play Set & Booklet: 15 Pieces Include 5" Figures, Horse, Steeple, Lanterns. 1999. (Illus.). 32p. (J). (gr. k-7). 28.00 (978-0-9677511-1-5(X)) Child Light.

Pfeffer, Susan Beth. Meg's Story. 2001. (Portraits of Little Women Ser.). (Illus.). (J). (978-0-606-21327-1(9)) Tandem Library Bks.

Prescott, Della. A Day in a Colonial Home. Dana, John Cotton, ed. 2006. 96p. (J). (gr. 4-7). per. 12.95 (978-1-55709-374-5(1)) Applewood Bks.

Richter, Conrad. The Light in the Forest. (YA). (gr. 7 up). 21.95 (978-0-89190-333-8(X)) Amereon LTD.

Rinaldi, Ann. The Fifth of March: A Story of the Boston Massacre. 2004. (Great Episodes Ser.). 352p. (YA). pap. 6.95 (978-0-15-205078-8(7) , Gulliver Bks.) Harcourt Children's Bks.

—The Journal of Jasper Jonathan Pierce: A Pilgrim Boy, Plymouth, 1620. 2000. (My Name Is America Ser.). (Illus.). 160p. (J). (gr. 4-8). pap. 10.95 (978-0-590-51078-3(9)) Scholastic, Inc.

—Time Enough for Drums. 2000. 256p. (YA). (gr. 7-12). pap. 5.99 (978-0-440-22850-9(6) , Laurel Leaf) Random Hse. Children's Bks.

—Time Enough for Drums. 2000. (978-0-606-18002-3(8)) Tandem Library Bks.

Rowe Fraustino, Lisa. I Walk in Dread, the Diary of Deliverance Trembley, Witness. 2004. (Dear America Ser.). (Illus.). 208p. (J). (gr. 4-7). pap. 10.95 (978-0-439-24973-7(2)) Scholastic, Inc.

Speare, Elizabeth George. Calico Captive. 2001. (gr. 5-8). lib. bdg. 15.25 (978-0-613-44381-4(0)) Tandem Library Bks.

Tripp, Valerie. Very Funny, Elizabeth! Andreasen, Dan, illus. 2005. (American Girls Collection). 81p. (J). (gr. 3). pap. 6.95 (978-1-59369-061-8(4) , American Girl) American Girl Publishing, Inc.

Trottier, Maxine. By the Standing Stone. 2001. (Circle of Silver Chronicles Ser.). (Illus.). 246p. (YA). (gr. 7-12). pap. 7.95 (978-0-7737-6138-4(1)) Stoddart Kids CAN. *Dist:* Fitzhenry & Whiteside, Ltd.

UNITED STATES—HISTORY—FRENCH AND INDIAN WAR, 1755-1763

Bruchac, Marge. Malian's Song. Maughan, William, illus. 2006. (Vermont Folklife Center Children's Book Ser.). 36p. 16.95 (978-0-916718-26-8(3)) Univ. Pr. of New England.

Green, Carl R. The French & Indian War: A MyReportLinks.com Book. 2002. (U. S. Wars Ser.). (Illus.). 48p. (J). (gr. 4-10). lib. bdg. 25.26 (978-0-7660-5090-7(4) , MyReportLinks.com Bks.) Enslow Pubs., Inc.

Hillstrom, Laurie Collier & Hillstrom, Kevin. French & Indian War. Baker, Lawrence W. & Carnagie, Julie, eds. 2003. (Illus.). xxviii, 206p. (J). lib. bdg. 67.00 (978-0-7876-6560-9(6) , UXL) Thomson Gale.

Kozar, Richard. Fort Duquesne & Fort Pitt. 2004. (American Forts & Their Strategic Importance Ser.). (J). (978-1-59084-719-0(9)) Mason Crest Pubs.

Laager, Hollie. The French & Indian War. 2007. (Events in American History Ser.). (Illus.). 48p. (J). (gr. 4-6). lib. bdg. 29.93 (978-1-60044-131-8(9)) Rourke Publishing, LLC.

Maestro, Betsy. Struggle for a Continent: The French & Indian Wars, 1689-1763. Maestro, Giulio, illus. 2000. (American Story Ser.). 48p. (J). (gr. 2 up). 17.99 (978-0-688-13450-1(5)) HarperCollins Pubs.

Maynard, Charles W. Fort Ticonderoga. 2002. (Famous Forts Throughout American History Ser.). (Illus.). 24p. (J). (gr. 3). lib. bdg. 18.75 (978-0-8239-5836-8(1) , PowerKids Pr.) Rosen Publishing Group, Inc., The.

Quasha, Jennifer. Robert Rogers: Rogers' Rangers & the French & Indian War. 2005. (Library of American Lives & Times). (Illus.). 112p. (J). (gr. 4-8). lib. bdg. 31.95 (978-0-8239-5731-6(4)) Rosen Publishing Group, Inc., The.

Santella, Andrew. The French & Indian War. 2004. (We the People Ser.). (Illus.). 48p. (J). (gr. 4 up). lib. bdg. 22.60 (978-0-7565-0613-1(1)) Compass Point Bks.

Smolinski, Diane. Battles of the French & Indian War. 2003. (Americans at War Ser.). (Illus.). 32p. (J). (gr. 4-6). lib. bdg. 25.64 (978-1-4034-0169-4(1)) Heinemann Library.

—Battles of the French & Indian War. 2003. (gr. 3-6). lib. bdg. 15.25 (978-0-613-84431-4(9)) Tandem Library Bks.

—Soldiers of the French & Indian War. 2003. (Americans at War Ser.). (Illus.). 32p. (J). (gr. 4-6). lib. bdg. 25.64 (978-1-4034-0172-4(1)) Heinemann Library.

—Soldiers of the French & Indian War. 2003. (gr. 3-6). lib. bdg. 15.25 (978-0-613-89119-6(8)) Tandem Library Bks.

Smolinski, Diane & Smolinski, Henry. Battles of the French & Indian War. (Americans at War Ser.). 32p. pap. 6.95 (978-1-4034-3155-4(8)) Heinemann Library.

—Soldiers of the French & Indian War. (Americans at War Ser.). 32p. pap. 6.95 (978-1-4034-3154-7(X)) Heinemann Library.

Thornton, Jeremy. The French & Indian War. 2003. (Building Americas Democracy Ser.). 24p. (J). lib. bdg. 19.95 (978-0-8239-6275-4(X) , PowerKids Pr.) Rosen Publishing Group, Inc., The.

UNITED STATES—HISTORY—FRENCH AND INDIAN WAR, 1755-1763—FICTION

Altsheler, Joseph A. The Lords of the Wild: A Story of the Ol. 2006. pap. (***978-1-4065-0816-1(0)***) Dodo Pr.

—The Masters of the Peaks: A Story of the. 2006. pap. (***978-1-4065-0817-8(9)***) Dodo Pr.

—The Shadow of the North: A Story of Old. 2006. pap. (***978-1-4065-0823-9(3)***) Dodo Pr.

Cooper, James Fenimore. The Last of the Mohicans. 2002. (Great Illustrated Classics Ser.). (Illus.). 240p. (J). (gr. 3-8). 21.35 (978-1-57765-692-0(X) , ABDO & Daughters) ABDO Publishing Co.

—The Last of the Mohicans. 2001. (Saddleback Classics). (Illus.). (J). (978-0-606-21559-6(X)) Tandem Library Bks.

—The Last of the Mohicans. Howell, Troy, illus. 2008. (Classic Starts Ser.). 160p. (J). 5.95 (***978-1-4027-4577-5(X)***) Sterling Publishing Co., Inc.

Cooper, James Fenimore. The Last of the Mohicans. Carrillo, Fred, illus. 2nd ed. 1998. (Illustrated Classic Book Ser.). 61p. (J). (gr. 3 up). reprint ed. pap. 4.95 (978-1-56767-249-7(3)) Educational Insights, Inc.

Hemphill, Kris. Ambush in the Wilderness. 2003. (Adventures in America Ser.). (Illus.). 90p. (J). 14.95 (978-1-893110-34-2(6)) Silver Moon Pr.

Henty, G. A. With Wolfe in Canada: The Winning of a Continent. 2001. (Illus.). 353p. (J). (978-0-921100-86-7(8)); pap. (978-0-921100-87-4(6)) Inheritance Pubns.

—With Wolfe in Canada: The Winning of a Continent. (Illus.). 353p. (J). 2000. (gr. 8-12). pap. 14.99 (978-1-887159-30-2(4)); 1998. lib. bdg. 20.99 (978-1-887159-18-0(5)) Preston-Speed Pubns.

—With Wolfe in Canada: The Winning of a Continent. 2006. per. 8.95 (978-1-57646-980-4(8)) Quiet Vision Publishing.

Hutchinson, Emily. Last of the Mohicans. abr. ed. 2001. (gr. 7-12). lib. bdg. 15.25 (978-0-613-36461-4(9)) Tandem Library Bks.

The Last of the Mohicans. 2000. (Illus.). (YA). 48p. stu. ed., per. 17.95 (978-1-56254-294-8(X) , SP294X); 80p. per. 6.95 (978-1-56254-293-1(1) , SP2931) Saddleback Educational Publishing.

McKissack, Patricia C. Look to the Hills: Diary of Lozette Moreau, a French Slave Girl, New York Colony 1763. 2004. (Dear America Ser.). (Illus.). 192p. (J). pap. 10.95 (978-0-439-21038-6(0)) Scholastic, Inc.

UNITED STATES—HISTORY—REVOLUTION, 1775-1783

Abnett, Dan. George Washington & the American Revolution. 2007. (Jr. Graphic Biographies Ser.). (Illus.). 24p. (J). (978-1-4042-2338-7(X)); pap. (978-1-4042-2148-2(4)); (gr. 2-6). lib. bdg. 21.25 (978-1-4042-3395-9(4)) Rosen Publishing Group, Inc., The. (PowerKids Pr.).

Adams, Colleen. Results of the American Revolution: Summarizing Information. 2005. (Critical Thinking in American History Ser.). (Illus.). 48p. (YA). (gr. 5-8). lib. bdg. 25.25 (978-1-4042-0417-1(2)) Rosen Publishing Group, Inc., The.

Adelson, Bruce. William Howe: British General. 2002. (gr. 5-8). lib. bdg. 17.60 (978-0-613-50852-0(1)) Tandem Library Bks.

Adler, David A. Heroes of the Revolution. Smith, Donald A., illus. 2006. 32p. (J). (gr. 1-5). 6.95 (978-0-8234-2017-9(5)) Holiday Hse., Inc.

Adler, David A. & Adler, Michael S. A Picture Book of John Hancock. Himler, Ronald, illus. 2007. 32p. (J). (ps-3). 16.95 (***978-0-8234-2005-6(1)***) Holiday Hse., Inc.

Adler, David A. & Adler, Michael S. A Picture Book of Samuel Adams. Himler, Ronald, illus. 2005. 32p. (J). 16.95 (978-0-8234-1846-6(4)) Holiday Hse., Inc.

Allen, Thomas B. George Washington, Spymaster: How the Americans Outspied the British & Won the Revolutionary War. 2007. (Illus.). 192p. (J). (gr. 5). pap. 5.95 (978-1-4263-0041-7(7) , National Geographic Children's Bks.) National Geographic Society.

The American Revolution Classroom Library. (gr. 2-5). lib. bdg. 74.95 (978-0-7368-4503-8(8)) Red Brick Learning.

The American Revolution Complete Unit. (gr. 2-5). 430.95 (978-0-7368-4502-1(X)) Red Brick Learning.

Anderson, Dale. The American Colonies Declare Independence. 2005. (World Almanac Library of the American Revolution). (J). pap. (978-0-8368-5935-5(9)); lib. bdg. 30.00 (978-0-8368-5926-3(X)) Stevens, Gareth Inc. (World Almanac Library).

—The American Revolution. 2002. (Events & Outcomes Ser.). (Illus.). 80p. (J). lib. bdg. 31.42 (978-0-7398-5797-7(5)) Raintree.

—The American Revolution: Events & Outcomes. 2006. (Illus.). 78p. (YA). (gr. 5-9). reprint ed. 17.00 (978-1-4223-5441-4(5)) DIANE Publishing Co.

—The Causes of the American Revolution. (World Almanac Library of the American Revolution). 2006. (Illus.). 48p. (YA). (gr. 7-10). lib. bdg. 30.00 (978-0-8368-5925-6(1)); 2005. (J). pap. (978-0-8368-5934-8(0)) Stevens, Gareth Inc. (World Almanac Library).

—Daily Life During the American Revolution. 2005. (World Almanac Library of the American Revolution). (J). pap. (978-0-8368-5939-3(1)); lib. bdg. 30.00 (978-0-8368-5930-0(8)) Stevens, Gareth Inc. (World Almanac Library).

—Leaders of the American Revolution. 2005. (World Almanac Library of the American Revolution). (J). pap. (978-0-8368-5940-9(5)); lib. bdg. 30.00 (978-0-8368-5931-7(6)) Stevens, Gareth Inc. (World Almanac Library).

—Soldiers & Sailors in the American Revolution. 2005. (World Almanac Library of the American Revolution). (J). pap. (978-0-8368-5938-6(3)); lib. bdg. 30.00 (978-0-8368-5929-4(4)) Stevens, Gareth Inc. (World Almanac Library).

—World Almanac Library of the American Revolution, 8 Vols. 240.00 (978-0-8368-5924-9(3)) Stevens, Gareth Inc.

Anonymous. Whig Against Tory or the Military Advent. 2004. reprint ed. pap. 15.95 (978-1-4191-9382-8(1)) Kessinger Publishing, LLC.

Ansary, Mir Tamim. Independence Day. (Illus.). 32p. (J). 2006. (***978-1-4034-8887-9(8)***); 2001. lib. bdg. 21.36 (978-1-58810-223-2(8)) Heinemann Library.

—Independence Day. 2001. 13.75 (978-0-606-22385-0(1)) Tandem Library Bks.

Armentrout, David & Armentrout, Patricia. The Gettysburg Address. 2004. (Documents That Shaped the Nation Ser.). 48p. pap. 7.95 (978-1-59515-333-3(0)) Rourke Publishing, LLC.

Aronson, Marc. The Real Revolution: The Global Story of American Independence. 2005. (Illus.). 256p. (J). (gr. 7-12). 21.00 (978-0-618-18179-7(2) , Clarion Bks.) Houghton Mifflin Co. Trade & Reference Div.

Aronson, Virginia. Ethan Allen: Revolutioinary Hero. 2001. (gr. 5-8). lib. bdg. 17.60 (978-0-613-32518-9(4)) Tandem Library Bks.

The Battle of Valcour Bay. 2003. (Triangle Histories of the American Revolution Ser.). (Illus.). 32p. (J). 22.45 (978-1-56711-778-3(3) , Blackbirch Pr., Inc.) Thomson Gale.

Beller, Susan Provost. The Revolutionary War. (American Voices From Ser.). (Illus.). (J). 2002. xxi, 104p. 34.21 (978-0-7614-1202-1(6)); 2001. 96p. (gr. 6 up). lib. bdg. 29.93 (978-0-7614-1094-2(5)) Cavendish, Marshall Corp. (Benchmark Bks.).

—Yankee Doodle & the Redcoats: Soldiering in the Revolutionary War. rev. ed. 2007. (Soldiers on the Battlefront Ser.). (Illus.). 112p. (YA). (gr. 6-8). lib. bdg. 33.26 (978-0-8225-6655-7(9) , Twenty-First Century Bks.) Lerner Publishing Group.

Benchmark Education Staff. George Washington & the AMER Revolution. 2005. 2.00 ***978-1-4108-4681-5(4))** Benchmark Education Co.

Benchmark Education Staff, compiled by. The AMER Revolution. 2006. spiral bd. 330.00 ***978-1-4108-7010-0(3));** 2005. (J). spiral bd. 265.00 **(*978-1-4108-5771-2(9))** Benchmark Education Co.

—The Amercian Revolution. 2006. spiral bd. 119.00 **(*978-1-4108-7125-1(8))** Benchmark Education Co.

—Freedom's Trail & AMER Revolution. 2005. spiral bd. 225.00 **(*978-1-4108-5825-2(1))** Benchmark Education Co.

—Social Studies Theme: The AMER Revolution. 2005. spiral bd. 115.00 **(*978-1-4108-5326-4(8))** Benchmark Education Co.

Bernstein, Richard B. Thomas Jefferson: The Revolution of Ideas. 2004. (Oxford Portraits Ser.). (Illus.). 256p. (YA). 28.00 (978-0-19-514368-3(X)) Oxford Univ. Pr., Inc.

Bobrick, Benson. Fight for Freedom: The American Revolutionary War. 2004. (Illus.). 96p. (J). 22.95 (978-0-689-86422-3(1) , Atheneum) Simon & Schuster Children's Publishing.

Bodie, Idella. Brave Black Patriots. 2002. (Illus.). 78p. (J). (978-0-87844-159-4(X)) Sandlapper Publishing Co., Inc.

—The Courageous Widow. 2001. 55p. (J). 5.95 (978-0-87844-157-0(3)) Sandlapper Publishing Co., Inc.

—Spunky Revolutionary War Heroine. 2000. (Heroes & Heroines of the American Revolution Ser.). (Illus.). 38p. (J). 5.95 (978-0-87844-154-9(9)) Sandlapper Publishing Co., Inc.

Bohannon, Lisa Frederiksen. The American Revolution. 2004. (Chronicles of American Wars Ser.). (Illus.). 96p. (J). (gr. 5-12). 27.93 (978-0-8225-4717-4(1)) Lerner Publishing Group.

Botones para el General Washington (Buttons for General Washington) 2006. (J). pap. 5.95 (978-0-8225-6617-5(6) , Ediciones Lerner) Lerner Publishing Group.

Branse, J. L. A Day in the Life of a Colonial Soldier. 2002. (Library of Living & Working in Colonial Times). (Illus.). 24p. (J). (gr. 3). lib. bdg. 18.75 (978-0-8239-5819-1(1) , PowerKids Pr.) Rosen Publishing Group, Inc., The.

Britton, Tamara L. Independence Hall. 2005. (Checkerboard History Library). (Illus.). 32p. (J). (gr. k-6). lib. bdg. 22.78 (978-1-57765-853-5(1)) ABDO Publishing Co.

Broida, Marian. Projects about the American Revolution. 2005. (Hands-On History Ser.). (Illus.). 48p. (J). (978-0-7614-1981-5(0) , Benchmark Bks.) Cavendish, Marshall Corp.

Burgan, Michael. Benedict Arnold: American Hero & Traitor. Beatty, Terry, illus. 2007. (Graphic Library). 32p. (J). (gr. 3-5). lib. bdg. 25.26 **(*978-0-7368-6854-9(2))** Capstone Pr., Inc.

—Benedict Arnold: American Hero & Traitor. 2007. (Graphic Library). (Illus.). 32p. (J). (gr. 3-5). pap. 7.95 **(*978-0-7368-7906-4(4))** Capstone Pr., Inc.

—Great Women of the American Revolution. 2004. (We the People Ser.). (Illus.). 48p. (J). 22.60 (978-0-7565-0838-8(X)) Compass Point Bks.

—John Adams. 2000. (Revolutionary War Leaders Ser.). (Illus.). 80p. (J). (gr. 4-7). pap. 27.50 (978-0-7910-6128-2(0)); (gr. 8-12). 31.00 (978-0-7910-5970-8(7)) Facts On File, Inc. (Chelsea Hse.).

—Samuel Adams: Patriot & Statesman. 2004. (Signature Lives Ser.). (Illus.). 112p. (J). 30.60 (978-0-7565-0823-4(1) , 1240135) Compass Point Bks.

—The Stamp ACT of 1765. 2004. (We the People Ser.). (Illus.). 48p. (J). 22.60 (978-0-7565-0846-3(0)) Compass Point Bks.

—Thomas Paine: Great Writer of the Revolution. 2004. (Signature Lives Ser.). (Illus.). 112p. (J). 30.60 (978-0-7565-0830-2(4)) Compass Point Bks.

—Valley Forge. 2004. (We the People Ser.). (Illus.). 48p. (J). (gr. 4 up). lib. bdg. 22.60 (978-0-7565-0615-5(8)) Compass Point Bks.

Burt, Barbara. Colonial Life: The Adventures of Benjamin Wilcox. 2002. (Reading Expeditions Ser.). (Illus.). 40p. (J). (978-0-7922-8678-3(2)) National Geographic Society.

—The Eve of Revolution: The Colonial Adventures of Benjamin Wilcox. 2004. (Illus.). 40p. (J). (gr. 4-8). pap. 7.00 (978-0-7567-8215-3(5)) DIANE Publishing Co.

Carole Marsh. How Our Nation Was Born: the American Revolution. 2004. (American Milestones Ser.). 32p. (gr. 3-8). pap. 5.95 (978-0-635-02348-3(2)); (gr. 4-12). 29.95 (978-0-635-02349-0(0)) Gallopade International.

Carr, Joaquin. The AMER Revolution. 2005. (Navigators Ser.). (J). pap. 42.00 **(*978-1-4108-5108-6(7))** Benchmark Education Co.

Causes of the American Revolution (NCHS) Grades 7-9. (J). tchr. ed., spiral bd. 13.50 (978-0-382-44448-7(5)) Cobblestone Publishing Co.

Chanko, Pamela. Easy Reader Biographies: Betsy Ross: The Story of Our Flag. 2007. 16p. pap. 2.99 **(*978-0-439-77421-5(7)** , Teaching Resources) Scholastic, Inc.

Cornelius, Kay. Francis Marion: Swamp Fox. 2000. (Revolutionary War Leaders Ser.). (Illus.). 80p. (J). (gr. 4-7). pap. 27.50 (978-0-7910-6134-3(5)); (gr. 8-12). 31.00 (978-0-7910-5976-0(6)) Facts On File, Inc. (Chelsea Hse.).

Cox, Vicki. Betsy Ross: Flag for a New Nation. 2005. (Leaders of the American Revolution Ser.). (Illus.). 148p. (J). (gr. 4-8). lib. bdg. 30.00 (978-0-7910-8618-6(6) , Chelsea Hse.) Facts On File, Inc.

Crompton, Samuel Willard. Thomas Paine & the Fight for Liberty. 2005. (Leaders of the American Revolution Ser.). (Illus.). 132p. (J). (gr. 4-8). lib. bdg. 30.00 (978-0-7910-8625-4(9) , Chelsea Hse.) Facts On File, Inc.

Davenport, John. The American Revolution. 2007. (American History Ser.). 128p. (J). (gr. 7-10). 32.45 (978-1-59018-939-9(6) , Lucent Bks.) Thomson Gale.

David Haugen. Speechmakers & Writers. 2004. (Voices from the American Revolution Ser.). (Illus.). 32p. (J). 23.70 (978-1-4103-0415-5(9) , Blackbirch Pr., Inc.) Thomson Gale.

Davis, Kate. Samuel Adams. 2002. (Triangle History of the American Revolution Ser.). (Illus.). 104p. (J). 28.70 (978-1-56711-612-0(4) , Blackbirch Pr., Inc.) Thomson Gale.

Deary, Terry. Esos Ruidosos Revolucionarios. 2001. Tr. of Rowdy Revolutionaries. (SPA.). (gr. 7-12). lib. bdg. 18.75 (978-0-613-86777-1(7)) Tandem Library Bks.

Deem, James M. Primary Source Accounts of the Revolutionary War. 2006. (America's Wars Through Primary Sources Ser.). (Illus.). 128p. (YA). (gr. 5-8). lib. bdg. 33.27 (978-1-59845-004-0(2) , MyReportLinks.com Bks.) Enslow Pubs., Inc.

DeFord, Deborah H. The American Revolution. 2006. (Wars That Changed American History Ser.). (Illus.). 48p. (J). pap. (978-0-8368-7298-9(3)); lib. bdg. (978-0-8368-7289-7(4)) Stevens, Gareth Inc. (World Almanac Library).

Dell, Pamela. Benedict Arnold: From Patriot to Traitor. 2004. (Signature Lives Ser.). (Illus.). 112p. (J). 30.60 (978-0-7565-0825-8(8) , 1240127) Compass Point Bks.

Denega, Danielle. Let's Read About— Betsy Ross. Graeff, Renee, illus. 2004. (Scholastic First Biographies Ser.). (J). pap. (978-0-439-56635-3(5)) Scholastic, Inc.

Doeden, Matt. Winter at Valley Forge. Barnett, Charles & Frenz, Ron, illus. 2006. (Graphic Library). 32p. (J). 25.26 (978-0-7368-4975-3(0)) Capstone Pr., Inc.

Donlan, Leni. George Washington: Revolution & the New Nation. 2006. (American History Through Primary Sources Ser.). (Illus.). 32p. (J). (978-1-4109-2420-9(3)); pap. (978-1-4109-2431-5(9)) Steck-Vaughn.

Dorling Kindersley Publishing Staff. American Revolution. 2005. (Eyewitness Bks.). 72p. (J). 15.99 (978-0-7566-1059-3(1)); (Illus.). lib. bdg. 19.99 (978-0-7566-1060-9(5)) Dorling Kindersley Publishing, Inc.

—American Revolution. 2004. (gr. 3-6). lib. bdg. 22.25 (978-0-613-75232-9(5)) Tandem Library Bks.

—American Revolution: Battles & Leaders. 2003. (Battles & Leaders Ser.). (Illus.). 96p. (J). pap. 9.99 (978-0-7894-9889-2(8)) Dorling Kindersley Publishing, Inc.

Draper, Allison Stark. The Boston Tea Party: Angry Colonists Dump British Tea. 2001. (Headlines from History Ser.). (Illus.). 24p. (J). (gr. 3). lib. bdg. 19.95 (978-0-8239-5671-5(7) , PKBOTE, PowerKids Pr.) Rosen Publishing Group, Inc., The.

—What People Wore During the American Revolution. 2001. (Clothing, Costumes & Uniforms Thoughout American History Ser.). (Illus.). 24p. (J). (gr. 3). lib. bdg. 19.95 (978-0-8239-5666-1(0) , PKCLRE, PowerKids Pr.) Rosen Publishing Group, Inc., The.

Duden, Jane. Betsy Ross. 2000. (Let Freedom Ring Ser.). (Illus.). 48p. (J). (gr. 3-4). lib. bdg. 22.60 (978-0-7368-1036-4(6) , Bridgestone Bks.) Capstone Pr., Inc.

Edwards, Pamela Duncan. Boston Tea Party. Cole, Henry, illus. 2001. 1p. (J). (gr. 1-3). 16.99 (978-0-399-23357-9(1) , Putnam Juvenile) Penguin Group (USA) Inc.

Farshtey, Greg. The American Revolution. 2003. (Daily Life Ser.). (Illus.). 48p. (J). (gr. 3-5). 26.20 (978-0-7377-1402-9(6) , Kidhaven) Thomson Gale.

Figley, Marty Rhodes. Prisoner for Liberty. Orback, Craig, illus. 2008. (On My Own History Ser.). (J). lib. bdg. 25.26 **(*978-0-8225-7280-0(X)** , Millbrook Pr.) Lerner Publishing Group.

—Salvar a la Campana de la Libertad. Lepp, Kevin, illus. 2005. (SPA.). 48p. (J). (gr. 2-5). pap. 5.95 (978-0-8225-3095-4(3)) Lerner Publishing Group.

—Saving the Liberty Bell. Lepp, Kevin, illus. 2004. 48p. (J). (ps-ps). lib. bdg. 12.75 (978-0-606-30522-8(X)) Tandem Library Bks.

Fleming, Thomas. Everybody's Revolution: A New Look at the People Who Won America's Freedom. 2006. (Illus.). 96p. (J). (gr. 4-7). pap. 19.99 (978-0-439-63404-5(0) , Scholastic Nonfiction) Scholastic, Inc.

Founding a Nation. 2004. (Historical Reader Ser.). (Illus.). 223p. (J). (gr. 6-12). (978-0-618-00366-2(5) , 2-00103) McDougal Littell Inc.

Founding Fathers. (J). tchr. ed. 41.95 (978-0-382-40882-3(9)) Cobblestone Publishing Co.

Fremont-Barnes, Gregory & Ryerson, Richard A., eds. American Revolutionary War: A Student Encyclopedia, 5 vols., Set. 2006. (Illus.). 1500p. (gr. 9 up). lib. bdg. 485.00 (978-1-85109-839-2(9)) ABC-CLIO, Inc.

Fritz, Jean. Why Don't You Get a Horse, Sam Adams? 2004. (J). (gr. 2-6). 24.95 incl. audio (978-1-55592-158-3(2)); 29.95 incl. cd-rom (978-1-55592-159-0(0)); pap. 14.95 incl. audio (978-1-55592-154-5(X)); pap. 18.95 incl. audio compact disk (978-1-55592-153-8(1)) Weston Woods Studios, Inc.

Frost, Helen. Betsy Ross. Saunders-Smith, Gail, ed. 2003. (Famous Americans Ser.). (Illus.). 24p. (J). (gr. k-1). lib. bdg. 15.93 (978-0-7368-1641-0(0) , Pebble Bks.) Capstone Pr., Inc.

Furbee, Mary Rodd. Women of the American Revolution. 1999. (History Makers Ser.). (Illus.). 112p. (YA). (gr. 7-10). 27.45 (978-1-56006-489-3(7) , Lucent Bks.) Thomson Gale.

Gaines, Ann Graham. John Hancock: President of the Continental Congress. 2000. (Revolutionary War Leaders Ser.). (Illus.). 80p. (J). (gr. 8-12). 27.50 (978-0-7910-5975-3(8) , Chelsea Hse.) Facts On File, Inc.

—King George III. 2000. (Revolutionary War Leaders Ser.). (Illus.). 80p. (J). (gr. 8-12). 27.50 (978-0-7910-5978-4(2) , Chelsea Hse.) Facts On File, Inc.

George, Lynn. A Time Line of the American Revolutionary War. 2003. (Reading Room Collection). (Illus.). 24p. (J). lib. bdg. 18.75 (978-0-8239-3707-3(0)) Rosen Publishing Group, Inc., The.

Giblin, James. The Many Rides of Paul Revere. 2007. 96p. (J). pap. 17.99 **(*978-0-439-57290-3(8)** , Scholastic Pr.) Scholastic, Inc.

Gillis, Jennifer Blizin. Mercy Otis Warren: Author & Historian. 2005. (Signature Lives Ser.). (Illus.). 112p. (J). (gr. 5-7). (978-0-7565-0982-8(3)) Compass Point Bks.

Green, Carl R. The Revolutionary War: A MyReportLinks.com Book. 2002. (U. S. Wars Ser.). (Illus.). 48p. (J). (gr. 4-10). lib. bdg. 25.26 (978-0-7660-5089-1(0) , MyReportLinks.com Bks.) Enslow Pubs., Inc.

Greene, Meg. Nathanael Greene. 2000. (Revolutionary War Leaders Ser.). (Illus.). 80p. (J). (gr. 8-12). 27.50 (978-0-7910-5977-7(4) , Chelsea Hse.) Facts On File, Inc.

Grolier Educational Staff. Colonial America, the Birth of the Nation, 10 vols., Set. 1998. (Illus.). (YA). lib. bdg. 309.00 (978-0-7172-9193-9(6) , Grolier) Scholastic Library Publishing.

Grolier Educational Staff, contrib. by. The American Cause in Peril, 10 vols., Vol. 8. 2001. (Illus.). (J). (978-0-7172-5561-0(1) , Grolier) Scholastic Library Publishing.

—An Independent Nation, 10 vols., Vol. 10. 2001. (Illus.). (J). (978-0-7172-5563-4(8) , Grolier) Scholastic Library Publishing.

—The Revolutionary War, 10 vols. Incl. Vol. 1. Road to Rebellion. (978-0-7172-5554-2(9)); Vol. 2. Shot Heard Around the World. (978-0-7172-5555-9(7)); Vol. 3. Taking up Arms. (978-0-7172-5556-6(5)); Vol. 4. Spirit of 1776. (978-0-7172-5557-3(3)); Vol. 5. 1777, Year of Decision. (978-0-7172-5558-0(1)); Vol. 6. Road to Valley Forge. (978-0-7172-5559-7(X)); Vol. 7. War of Attrition. (978-0-7172-5560-3(3)); Vol. 8. American Cause in Peril. (978-0-7172-5561-0(1)); Vol. 9. Turn of the Tide. (978-0-7172-5562-7(X)); Vol. 10. Independent Nation. (978-0-7172-5563-4(8)); (J). (Illus.). 800p. 2001. 269.00 (978-0-7172-5553-5(0) , Grolier) Scholastic Library Publishing.

—The Road to Rebellion, 10 vols., Vol. 1. 2001. (Illus.). (J). (978-0-7172-5554-2(9) , Grolier) Scholastic Library Publishing.

—The Road to Valley Forge, 10 vols., Vol. 6. 2001. (Illus.). (J). (978-0-7172-5559-7(X) , Grolier) Scholastic Library Publishing.

—The Shot Heard Around the World, 10 vols., Vol. 2. 2001. (Illus.). (J). (978-0-7172-5555-9(7) , Grolier) Scholastic Library Publishing.

—The Spirit of 1776, 10 vols., Vol. 4. 2001. (Illus.). (J). (978-0-7172-5557-3(3) , Grolier) Scholastic Library Publishing.

—Taking up Arms, 10 vols., Vol. 3. 2001. (Illus.). (J). (978-0-7172-5556-6(5) , Grolier) Scholastic Library Publishing.

—The Turn of the Tide, 10 vols., Vol. 9. 2001. (Illus.). (J). (978-0-7172-5562-7(X) , Grolier) Scholastic Library Publishing.

—War of Attrition, 10 vols., Vol. 7. 2001. (Illus.). (J). (978-0-7172-5560-3(3) , Grolier) Scholastic Library Publishing.

—1777, Year of Decision, 10 vols., Vol. 5. 2001. (Illus.). (J). (978-0-7172-5558-0(1) , Grolier) Scholastic Library Publishing.

Grote, JoAnn A. The American Revolution. 1999. (American Adventure Ser.: No. 11). 144p. (J). (gr. 3-7). lib. bdg. 15.95 (978-0-7910-5585-4(X) , Chelsea Hse.) Facts On File, Inc.

—Lafayette. 2000. (Revolutionary War Leaders Ser.). (Illus.). 80p. (J). pap. 27.50 (978-0-7910-6131-2(0)); (gr. 8-12). 27.50 (978-0-7910-5973-9(1)) Facts On File, Inc. (Chelsea Hse.).

Group/McGraw-Hill, Wright. History: Revolutionary War, 6 vols. (Book2WebTM Ser.). (gr. 4-8). 36.50 (978-0-322-04450-0(2)) Wright Group, The.

Gunderson, Cory. Boston Tea Party. 2005. (American Moments Ser.). (Illus.). 48p. (J). (gr. 4-8). lib. bdg. 25.65 (978-1-59197-280-8(9) , ABDO & Daughters) ABDO Publishing Co.

Hakim, Joy. From Colonies to Country 1735-1791. 3rd ed. 2002. (History of US Ser.). (Illus.). 112p. pap., tchr. ed. 16.95 (978-0-19-515353-8(7)) Oxford Univ. Pr., Inc.

—A History of US Bk. 3: From Colonies to Country. 3rd rev. ed. 2005. (History of US Ser.). (Illus.). 224p. 19.95 (978-0-19-518232-3(4)); 19.95 (978-0-19-518896-7(9)) Oxford Univ. Pr., Inc.

Hakin, Joy. From Colonies to Country. rev. ed. 2007. (History of US Ser.: Vol. 3). 224p. pap. 15.95 **(*978-0-19-532717-5(9))** Oxford Univ. Pr., Inc.

Hall, Margaret. First Days of the United States. 2004. (Hands-On American History Ser.). (Illus.). 32p. (J). 27.07 (978-1-4034-6051-6(5)) Heinemann Library.

—The History & Activities of the Revolutionary War. 2006. (Hands-On American History Ser.). (Illus.). 32p. (J). pap. (978-1-4034-6058-5(2)) Heinemann Library.

Harcourt School Publishers Staff. Paul Revere & the History of Boston. 3rd ed. 2002. (Horizons Ser.). (Illus.). (J). pap. 3.70 (978-0-15-333200-5(X)) Harcourt Schl. Pubs.

Hargrove, Julia. Bostons Trail to Freedom. 2003. (Historic Monuments Ser.). (Illus.). 48p. (J). (gr. 4-8). pap. 6.95 (978-1-57310-403-6(5)) Teaching & Learning Co.

Harmon, Daniel E. Fighting Units of the American Revolution. 1998. (Costume, Tradition & Culture). (Illus.). 64p. (J). 19.75 (978-0-7910-5162-7(5) , Chelsea Hse.) Facts On File, Inc.

—"Gentleman Johnny" Burgoyne. 2001. (Revolutionary War Leaders Ser.). (Illus.). 80p. (J). pap. 27.50 (978-0-7910-6391-0(7)); 27.50 (978-0-7910-6390-3(9)) Facts On File, Inc. (Chelsea Hse.).

Haugen, David M. Colonists. 2004. (Voices from the American Revolution Ser.). (Illus.). 32p. (J). 23.70 (978-1-4103-0448-3(5) , Blackbirch Pr., Inc.) Thomson Gale.

—Primary Sources. 2003. (American War Library). (Illus.). 112p. (J). 29.95 (978-1-59018-238-3(3) , Lucent Bks.) Thomson Gale.

Haugen, David M., ed. Leaders. 2004. (Voices from the American Revolution Ser.). (Illus.). 32p. (J). 23.70 (978-1-4103-0414-8(0) , Blackbirch Pr., Inc.) Thomson Gale.

Hazen, Walter A. The American Revolution. 1999. (Eye on History Ser.). 32p. (J). (gr. 5-12). pap. 5.99 (978-1-56822-778-8(7) , IF2671) School Specialty Publishing.

—Everyday Life: Revolutionary War. 2004. (Illus.). 104p. (J). pap. (978-0-673-58899-9(8)) Good Year Bks.

Heims, Neil. Reading Johnny Tremain. 2005. (Engaged Reader Ser.). (Illus.). 82p. (J). (ps-8). lib. bdg. 25.00 (978-0-7910-8831-9(6) , Chelsea Hse.) Facts On File, Inc.

Herbert, Janis. The American Revolution for Kids: A History with 21 Activities. 2002. (For Kids Ser.). (Illus.). 160p. (J). (gr. 4 up). pap. 14.95 (978-1-55652-456-1(0)) Chicago Review Pr., Inc.

Hinman, Bonnie. General Thomas Gage. 2001. (Revolutionary War Leaders Ser.). 80p. (J). pap. 27.50 (978-0-7910-6385-9(2)); 27.50 (978-0-7910-6384-2(4)) Facts On File, Inc. (Chelsea Hse.).

Hirsch, E. D., ed. The American Revolution, Level 4. 2003. stu. ed. 49.95 (978-0-7690-2845-3(4)); stu. ed. 9.95 (978-0-7690-5101-7(4)); tchr. ed. 9.95 (978-0-7690-5068-3(9)) Pearson Learning.

Holt, Rinehart and Winston Staff. Call to Freedom: Beginning-1877: Geography Activities - Answer Key. 3rd ed. 2001. pap. 8.00 (978-0-03-066683-4(X)) Holt, Rinehart & Winston.

Houghton, Raymond C. A Revolutionary War Road Trip on US Route 4: Spend a Revolutionary Day along One of America's Most Historic Routes, 2004. (Illus.). 162p. per. 12.99 (978-1-931373-09-8(4)) Cyber Haus.

—A Revolutionary War Road Trip on US Route 9: Spend a Revolutionary Day along One of America's Most Historic Routes. 2004. (Illus.). 166p. per. 12.99 (978-1-931373-12-8(4)) Cyber Haus.

Hull, Mary E. The Boston Tea Party in American History. 1999. (In American History Ser.). (Illus.). 128p. (YA). (gr. 5-12). lib. bdg. 26.60 (978-0-7660-1139-7(9)) Enslow Pubs., Inc.

Ingram, Scott. King George III. 2003. (Triangle History of the American Revolution Ser.). (Illus.). 104p. (J). 28.70 (978-1-56711-779-0(1) , Blackbirch Pr., Inc.) Thomson Gale.

January, Brendan. The Revolutionary War. 2001. (True Bks.). (Illus.). 48p. (J). (gr. 3-5). pap. 6.95 (978-0-516-27196-5(2) , Children's Pr.) Scholastic Library Publishing.

—The Revolutionary War. 2001. (978-0-606-22873-2(X)) Tandem Library Bks.

—Revolutionary War. 2000. (gr. 3-6). lib. bdg. 15.25 (978-0-613-51669-3(9)) Tandem Library Bks.

Jedson, Lee. The Treaty of Paris, 1783: A Primary Source Examination of the Treaty That Recognized American Independence. 2005. (Primary Sources of American Treaties Ser.). (J). lib. bdg. (978-1-4042-0441-6(5)) Rosen Publishing Group, Inc., The.

Jensen, Ann. The World Turned Upside Down: Children of 1776. Ramsey, Marcy Dunn, illus. 2001. 80p. (J). pap. 9.95 (978-0-87033-534-1(0) , Tidewater Pubs.) Cornell Maritime Pr., Inc.

Jensen, Dorothea. The Riddle of Penncroft Farm. 2001. (Great Episodes Ser.). 272p. (YA). (gr. 5-9). pap. 6.00 (978-0-15-216441-6(3) , Gulliver Bks.) Harcourt Children's Bks.

Kallen, Stuart A. John Hancock. 2001. (Founding Fathers Ser.). (Illus.). 64p. (J). (gr. 3-8). lib. bdg. 25.65 (978-1-57765-010-2(7) , ABDO & Daughters) ABDO Publishing Co.

—Samuel Adams. 2001. (Founding Fathers Ser.). (Illus.). 64p. (J). (gr. 3-8). lib. bdg. 25.65 (978-1-57765-008-9(5) , ABDO & Daughters) ABDO Publishing Co.

Kelley, Brent P. James Madison. 2000. (Revolutionary War Leaders Ser.). (Illus.). 80p. (J). pap. 27.50 (978-0-7910-6130-5(2)); (gr. 8-12). 27.50 (978-0-7910-5972-2(3)) Facts On File, Inc. (Chelsea Hse.).

—James Monroe. 2000. (Revolutionary War Leaders Ser.). (Illus.). 80p. (J). (gr. 4-7). pap. 8.95 (978-0-7910-6129-9(9)); (gr. 8-12). 27.50 (978-0-7910-5971-5(5)) Facts On File, Inc. (Chelsea Hse.).

Kemmerer, Susan. Revolution. 2002. per. 12.95 (978-0-9758543-4-1(8)) Schoolhouse Publishing.

Kent, Deborah. The American Revolution: "Give Me Liberty, or Give Me Death!" 2000. (American War Ser.). (Illus.). 128p. (YA). (gr. 5-12). pap. 13.26 (978-0-7660-1727-6(3)) Enslow Pubs., Inc.

—Lexington & Concord. 1998. (Cornerstones of Freedom Ser.). (Illus.). 32p. (J). (gr. 4-6). pap. 5.95 (978-0-516-26229-1(7) , Children's Pr.) Scholastic Library Publishing.

Kent, Jacqueline C. Molly Pitcher. 2003. (Women of the Revolution Ser.). (J). pap. (978-1-58417-088-4(3)); lib. bdg. (978-1-58417-025-9(5)) Lake Street Pubs.

Kent, Zachary. Alexander Hamilton: Creating a Nation. 2004. (America's Founding Fathers Ser.). (Illus.). 128p. (J). lib. bdg. 26.60 (978-0-7660-2181-5(5)) Enslow Pubs., Inc.

King, David C. American Heritage, American Voices: Colonies & Revolution. 2002. (American Heritage, American Voices Ser.). (Illus.). 144p. 22.95 (978-0-471-44391-9(3) , Wiley) Wiley, John & Sons, Inc.

—Revolutionary War Days: Discover the Past with Exciting Projects, Games, Activities, & Recipes. Noll, Cheryl Kirk, illus. 2001. 100p. (J). (ps-7). lib. bdg. 22.20 (978-0-613-82481-1(4)) Tandem Library Bks.

—Revolutionary War Days: Discover the Past with Exciting Projects, Games, Activities, & Recipes. 2001. (American Kids in History Ser.: Vol. 8). (Illus.). 112p. (gr. 7-12). pap. 12.95 (978-0-471-39308-5(8) , Wiley-Interscience) Wiley, John & Sons, Inc.

Klingel, Cynthia Fitterer & Noyed, Robert B. The Revolutionary War. 2001. (Wonder Books Level 3: U. S. History Ser.). (Illus.). 32p. (J). (ps-3). 22.79 (978-1-56766-961-9(1)) Child's World, Inc.

Kneib, Martha. A Historical Atlas of the American Revolution. 2005. (United States, Historical Atlases of the Growth of a New Nation Ser.). (Illus.). 64p. (J). (gr. 7-12). lib. bdg. 30.60 (978-1-4042-0204-7(8)) Rosen Publishing Group, Inc., The.

Koestler-Grack, Rachel A. Molly Pitcher: Heroine of the War for Independence. 2005. (Leaders of the American Revolution Ser.). (Illus.). 120p. (J). (gr. 4-8). lib. bdg. 30.00 (978-0-7910-8622-3(4) , Chelsea Hse.) Facts On File, Inc.

—Nathan Hale: Courageous Spy. 2005. (Leaders of the American Revolution Ser.). (Illus.). 124p. (J). (gr. 4-8). lib. bdg. 30.00 (978-0-7910-8623-0(2) , Chelsea Hse.) Facts On File, Inc.

Konstam, Angus. America Speaks, 10 vols. 2005. (Illus.). (J). (978-0-7172-6020-1(8)); (978-0-7172-6021-8(6)); (978-0-7172-6022-5(4)); (978-0-7172-6023-2(2)); (978-0-7172-6024-9(0)); (978-0-7172-6025-6(9)); (978-0-7172-6026-3(7)); (978-0-7172-6027-0(5)); (978-0-7172-6028-7(3)); (978-0-7172-6029-4(1)) Grolier, Ltd.

—America Speaks, 10 vols., Set. 2005. (Illus.). (J). (gr. 5-10). lib. bdg. 199.00 (978-0-7172-6030-0(5) , Grolier) Scholastic Library Publishing.

Kroll, Steven. The Boston Tea Party. Fiore, Peter, illus. 2000. 32p. (J). (ps-7). pap. 6.95 (978-0-8234-1557-1(0)) Holiday Hse., Inc.

Lakin, Patricia. Abigail Adams: First Lady of the American Revolution. Bandelin, Debra & Dacey, Bob, illus. 2006. 48p. (J). lib. bdg. 15.00 (***978-1-4242-1560-7(9)***) Fitzgerald Bks.

—Abigail Adams: First Lady of the American Revolution. Dacey, Bob & Bandelin, Debra, illus. 2006. (Ready-to-read SOFA Ser.). 48p. (J). (gr. 1-3). pap. 3.99 (978-0-689-87032-3(9)); lib. bdg. 11.89 (978-0-689-87033-0(7)) Simon & Schuster Children's Publishing. (Aladdin).

Landau, Elaine. Celebrate the Founding of America with Elaine Landau. 2006. (Explore Colonial America with Elaine Landau Ser.). (Illus.). 48p. (J). lib. bdg. 23.93 (978-0-7660-2557-8(8) , Enslow Elementary) Enslow Pubs., Inc.

Landau, Elaine. The Declaration of Independence. (True Booktrade: American History Ser.). 48p. (J). 2008. pap. 6.95 (***978-0-531-14780-1(0)***); 2007. (Illus.). (gr. 3-5). lib. bdg. 26.00 (***978-0-531-12630-1(7)***) Scholastic Library Publishing. (Children's Pr.).

The Library of Living & Working in Colonial Times: Set 2, 6 bks. Incl. Day in the Life of a Colonial Cabinetmaker. Merrill, Amy French. lib. bdg. 18.75 (978-0-8239-5822-1(1)); Day in the Life of a Colonial Dressmaker. Merrill, Amy French. lib. bdg. 18.75 (978-0-8239-5818-4(3)); Day in the Life of a Colonial Glassblower. Branse, J. L. lib. bdg. 18.75 (978-0-8239-5820-7(5)); Day in the Life of a Colonial Sea Captain. Branse, J. L. lib. bdg. 18.75 (978-0-8239-5821-4(3)); Day in the Life of a Colonial Soldier. Branse, J. L. lib. bdg. 18.75 (978-0-8239-5819-1(1)); Day in the Life of a Colonial Surveyor. Merrill, Amy French. lib. bdg. 18.75 (978-0-8239-5823-8(X)); 24p. (J). (gr. 3). 2002. (Illus.). 2001. Set lib. bdg. 103.50 (978-0-8239-7129-9(5) , PowerKids Pr.) Rosen Publishing Group, Inc., The.

Livesey, Robert. The Loyal Refugees. Smith, A. G., illus. 1999. (Discovering Canada Ser.). 90p. (J). (gr. 3-7). pap. 10.95 (978-0-7737-6043-1(1)) Stoddart Kids CAN. *Dist:* Fitzhenry & Whiteside, Ltd.

Lough, Loree. Nathan Hale. 1999. (Revolutionary War Leaders Ser.). (Illus.). 80p. (gr. 3 up). (J). 31.00 (978-0-7910-5361-4(X)); (YA). pap. 27.50 (978-0-7910-5704-9(6)) Facts On File, Inc. (Chelsea Hse.).

—Nathan Hale: Revolutionary Hero. 2000. (Illus.). 80p. (J). (gr. 3-17). lib. bdg. 17.60 (978-0-613-43357-0(2)) Tandem Library Bks.

Mader, Jan. Betsy Ross. 2007. (J). (978-0-7368-6702-3(3) , Pebble Bks.) Capstone Pr., Inc.

Maestro, Betsy. Liberty or Death: The American Revolution: 1763-1783. Maestro, Giulio, illus. 2005. 64p. (J). 16.99 (978-0-688-08802-6(3)); lib. bdg. 16.89 (978-0-688-08803-3(1)) HarperCollins Pubs.

Mara, Wil. Betsy Ross. 2005. (Rookie Biographies(R) Ser.). (Illus.). 31p. (J). (ps-ps). 20.50 (978-0-516-25268-1(2) , Children's Pr.) Scholastic Library Publishing.

Marcovitz, Hal. Independence Hall. 2002. (American Symbols & Their Meanings Ser.). (Illus.). 48p. (J). (gr. 4 up). lib. bdg. (978-1-59084-030-6(5)) Mason Crest Pubs.

Marolf, Stacey & Pessano, Laurie. Founding Fathers... & Mothers: A Field Trip to 18th Century America. Evans, Peter, illus. 1999. 128p. (J). (gr. 4-7). pap. 27.95 incl. audio (978-1-892405-12-8(1)) Good Co. Players Educational Div.

Marquette, Scott. Revolutionary War. 2003. (America at War Ser.). (Illus.). 48p. (gr. 4-8). 20.95 (978-1-58952-387-6(3)) Rourke Publishing, LLC.

McCarthy, Pat. The Thirteen Colonies from Founding to Revolution in American History. 2004. (In American History Ser.). (Illus.). 128p. (J). lib. bdg. 26.60 (978-0-7660-1990-4(X)) Enslow Pubs., Inc.

—Thomas Paine: Revolutionary Patriot & Writer. 2001. (Historical American Biographies Ser.). (Illus.). 128p. (J). (gr. 6-12). lib. bdg. 26.60 (978-0-7660-1446-6(0)) Enslow Pubs., Inc.

McConnell, Stacy A., ed. American Revolution: Primary Sources. 2000. (American Revolution Reference Library). (Illus.). xxxiii, 264p. (J). (gr. 5-9). 66.00 (978-0-7876-3790-3(4) , GML00502-113552, UXL) Thomson Gale.

McDonnell, Peter. A Soldier in Disguise. Tormey, Carlotta, illus. 2005. 16p. (J). pap. (***978-0-7367-2909-3(7)***) Zaner-Bloser, Inc.

McGraw-Hill Staff. American Republic to 1877. 2002. (C). pap., stu. ed., wbk. ed. 10.00 (978-0-07-829144-9(5) , 9780078291449) Glencoe/McGraw-Hill.

—The American Republic to 1877. 2nd ed. 2004. (C). stu. ed. 86.00 (978-0-07-860983-1(6) , 9780078609831) Glencoe/McGraw-Hill.

—The American Republic to 1877 Reading Essentials. 2nd ed. 2004. pap., stu. ed. 18.00 (978-0-07-865487-9(4) , 9780078654879) Glencoe/McGraw-Hill.

McLeese, Don. Alexander Hamilton. 2005. (Heroes of the American Revolution Ser.). (Illus.). 32p. (gr. 2-5). 19.95 (978-1-59515-219-0(9)) Rourke Publishing, LLC.

—Thomas Paine. 2005. (Heroes of the American Revolution Ser.). (Illus.). 32p. (gr. 2-5). 19.95 (978-1-59515-215-2(6)) Rourke Publishing, LLC.

McNeese, Tim. Alexander Hamilton: Framer of the Constitution. 2005. (Leaders of the American Revolution Ser.). (Illus.). 152p. (J). (gr. 4-8). lib. bdg. 30.00 (978-0-7910-8616-2(X) , Chelsea Hse.) Facts On File, Inc.

McNeil, Niki, et al. HOCPP 1061 American Revolution. 2006. spiral bd. 24.00 (***978-1-60308-061-3(9)***) In the Hands of a Child.

Melchiore, Susan McCarthy. Caesar Rodney. 2001. (gr. 3-6). lib. bdg. 17.60 (978-0-613-32357-4(2)) Tandem Library Bks.

Merrill, Amy French. A Day in the Life of a Colonial Cabinetmaker. 2002. (Library of Living & Working in Colonial Times). (Illus.). 24p. (J). (gr. 3). lib. bdg. 18.75 (978-0-8239-5822-1(1) , PowerKids Pr.) Rosen Publishing Group, Inc., The.

—A Day in the Life of a Colonial Dressmaker. 2002. (Library of Living & Working in Colonial Times). (Illus.). 24p. (J). (gr. 3). lib. bdg. 18.75 (978-0-8239-5818-4(3) , PowerKids Pr.) Rosen Publishing Group, Inc., The.

—A Day in the Life of a Colonial Surveyor. 2002. (Library of Living & Working in Colonial Times). (Illus.). 24p. (J). (gr. 3). lib. bdg. 18.75 (978-0-8239-5823-8(X) , PowerKids Pr.) Rosen Publishing Group, Inc., The.

Micklos, John. What Was the Revolutionary War All About? 2008. (Revolutionary War Library). (Illus.). 48p. (J). (gr. 3-4). lib. bdg. 23.93 (***978-0-7660-3014-5(8)***) Enslow Pubs., Inc.

Mierka, Gregg A. Nathanael Greene: The General Who Saved the Revolution. 2006. (J). pap. (978-1-59556-017-9(3)); (Illus.). 88p. (gr. 5-11). lib. bdg. 23.95 (978-1-59556-012-4(2)) OTTN Publishing.

Miller, Brandon Marie. Declaring Independence: Life During the American Revolution. 2005. (People's History Ser.). (Illus.). 112p. (J). 29.27 (978-0-8225-1275-2(0)) Lerner Publishing Group.

Miller, Susan Martins. Betsy Ross: American Patriot. 2000. (Revolutionary War Leaders Ser.). (J). 15.75 (978-0-606-19340-5(5)) Tandem Library Bks.

Minks, Benton & Minks, Louise. Revolutionary War. 2nd rev. ed. 2003. (America at War Ser.). (Illus.). 208p. (J). (gr. 6-12). 35.00 (978-0-8160-4936-3(X)) Facts On File, Inc.

Minor, Wendell. Yankee Doodle America: The Spirit of 1776 from A to Z. 2006. (Illus.). 48p. (J). (ps). 16.99 (978-0-399-24003-4(9) , Putnam Juvenile) Penguin Group (USA) Inc.

Mir Tamim Ansary. Independence Day. 2nd ed. 2006. (Illus.). 32p. (J). pap. (***978-1-4034-8900-5(9)***) Heinemann Library.

Moore, Kay. If You Lived at the Time of the American Revolution. 1998. (If You Ser.). (Illus.). 80p. (J). (gr. 2-6). pap. 5.99 (978-0-590-67444-7(7)) Scholastic, Inc.

—If You Lived at the Time of the American Revolution. 1998. 12.79 (978-0-606-13514-6(6)) Tandem Library Bks.

Murphy, Dallas. Revolutionary War. 2000. (Read Aloud Plays Ser.). (J). 10.95 (978-0-590-03325-1(5)) Scholastic, Inc.

Murphy, Jim. The Real Benedict Arnold. 2007. (Illus.). 272p. (YA). (gr. 5 up). 20.00 (***978-0-395-77609-4(0)*** , Clarion Bks.) Houghton Mifflin Co. Trade & Reference Div.

Nardo, Don. The American Revolution. 2003. (History of Weapons & Warfare Ser.). (Illus.). 112p. (J). 29.95 (978-1-59018-326-7(6) , Lucent Bks.) Thomson Gale.

—Weapons of War. 2002. (American War Library). (Illus.). 112p. (J). 29.95 (978-1-59018-226-0(X) , Lucent Bks.) Thomson Gale.

Nell, William C. Black Patriots of the American Revolution, with Sketches of Several Distinguished Black Persons to Which Is Added a Brief Survey of the Condition & Prospects of Black Americans. 2006. (Illus.). 396p. (YA). cd-rom (978-1-892824-87-5(6)) AFCHRON.

Nelson, Sheila. The Original United States of America. 2005. (How America Became America Ser.). (Illus.). 96p. (J). lib. bdg. (978-1-59084-903-3(5)) Mason Crest Pubs.

Nobleman, Marc Tyler. Independence Day. 2004. (Let's See Ser.). (Illus.). 24p. (J). (gr. 1 up). lib. bdg. 19.93 (978-0-7565-0769-5(3)) Compass Point Bks.

Olson, Kay Melchisedech. Betsy Ross & the American Flag. Cool, Anna-Maria et al, illus. 2005. (Graphic Library). 32p. (J). (gr. 3-7). lib. bdg. 25.26 (978-0-7368-4962-3(9)) Capstone Pr., Inc.

Olson, Nathan. Nathan Hale: Revolutionary Spy. Martin, Cynthia & Schoonover, Brent, illus. 2005. (Graphic Library). 32p. (J). (gr. 3-7). lib. bdg. 25.26 (978-0-7368-4968-5(8)) Capstone Pr., Inc.

Osborne, Mary Pope & Boyce, Natalie Pope. American Revolution: A Nonfiction Companion to Revolutionary War on Wednesday. Murdocca, Sal, illus. 2004. (Magic Tree House Research Guide Ser.: No. 11). 128p. (J). (gr. 1-5). lib. bdg. 11.99 (978-0-375-92379-1(9)); (gr. k-3). pap. 4.99 (978-0-375-82379-4(4)) Random Hse. Children's Bks. (Random Hse. Bks. for Young Readers).

Parker, Lewis K. Lord Charles Cornwallis. 2002. (Triangle History of the American Revolution Ser.). (Illus.). 104p. (J). 28.70 (978-1-56711-608-3(6) , Blackbirch Pr., Inc.) Thomson Gale.

Peacock, Judith. The Battles of Lexington & Concord. 2002. (Let Freedom Ring Ser.). (Illus.). 48p. (J). (gr. 3-4). lib. bdg. 22.60 (978-0-7368-1096-8(X) , Bridgestone Bks.) Capstone Pr., Inc.

Penner, Lucille Recht. Liberty! How the Revolutionary War Began. Wenzel, David, illus. 2002. 48p. (gr. 1). pap. 8.99 (978-0-375-82200-1(3) , Random Hse. Bks. for Young Readers) Random Hse. Children's Bks.

Pfeffer, Wendy. Many Ways to Be a Soldier. 2008. (On My Own History Ser.). (J). lib. bdg. 25.26 (***978-0-8225-7279-4(6)*** , Millbrook Pr.) Lerner Publishing Group.

Play Bac Publishing Staff, creator. American Revolution: From Colonies to Country. 2007. (Illus.). 10p. (J). pap. 6.95 (***978-1-60214-023-3(5)***) Play Bac Publishing, USA.

Poulakidas, Georgene. The American Revolutionary War. 2004. (Primary Sources of American Wars Ser.). (Illus.). 24p. (J). lib. bdg. (978-1-4042-2680-7(X)) Rosen Publishing Group, Inc., The.

Powell, Phelan. John Jay. 2000. (Revolutionary War Leaders Ser.). (Illus.). 80p. (J). (gr. 8-12). 27.50 (978-0-7910-5979-1(0) , Chelsea Hse.) Facts On File, Inc.

Price Hossell, Karen. Benedict Arnold. 2004. (American War Biographies Ser.). (J). pap. 8.50 (978-1-4034-5085-2(4)); lib. bdg. 29.93 (978-1-4034-5078-4(1)) Heinemann Library.

Raabe, Emily. Ethan Allen: The Green Mountain Boys & Vermont's Path to Statehood. 2005. (Library of American Lives & Times). (Illus.). 112p. (J). (gr. 4-8). lib. bdg. 31.95 (978-0-8239-5722-4(5)) Rosen Publishing Group, Inc., The.

Raatma, Lucia. The Minutemen. 2004. (We the People Ser.). (Illus.). 48p. (J). 22.60 (978-0-7565-0842-5(8)) Compass Point Bks.

Ransom, Candice F. John Hancock. 2005. (History Maker Bios Ser.). (Illus.). 48p. (J). (gr. 3-4). 26.60 (978-0-8225-1547-0(4) , Lerner Pubns.) Lerner Publishing Group.

Rappaport, Doreen & Verniero, Joan. Victory or Death! Stories of the American Revolution. Call, Greg, illus. 2003. 128p. (J). (ps-2). 16.99 (978-0-06-029515-8(5)) HarperCollins Pubs.

Ratliff, Thomas. How to Be a Revolutionary War Soldier. 2006. (Illus.). 32p. (J). (gr. 3-7). 14.95 (978-0-7922-7489-6(X)); 21.90 (978-0-7922-7546-6(2)) National Geographic Society. (National Geographic Children's Bks.).

Renehan, Edward J. The Treaty of Paris: The Precursor to a New Nation. 2007. (Milestones in American History Ser.). (Illus.). 128p. (J). (gr. 6-12). 35.00 (***978-0-7910-9352-8(2)*** , Chelsea Hse.) Facts On File, Inc.

Revolution & the New Nation. (We the People Ser.). (gr. 4-6). 203.40 (978-0-7565-0798-5(7)) Compass Point Bks.

Roop, Peter & Roop, Connie. Botones para el General Washington Hanson, Peter E., illus. 2006. (Yo Solo - Historia (on My Own - History) Ser.). (SPA.). 48p. (J). (gr. 2-4). lib. bdg. 25.26 (978-0-8225-6261-0(8) , Ediciones Lerner) Lerner Publishing Group.

—Let's Ride, Paul Revere! 2004. (Before I Made History Ser.). (Illus.). 60p. (J). pap. (978-0-439-67623-6(1)) Scholastic, Inc.

—Sew What, Betsy Ross? 2002. (Before I Made History Ser.). (Illus.). 57p. (J). (978-0-439-43925-1(6)) Scholastic, Inc.

Rosen, Daniel. Independence Now: The American Revolution 1763-1783. 2004. (Crossroads America Ser.). (Illus.). 40p. (J). (gr. 5-9). 21.90 (978-0-7922-6990-8(X)); 12.95 (978-0-7922-6766-9(4)) National Geographic Society. (National Geographic Children's Bks.).

Rothman, Cynthia. Our Flag. Baran, Esther, illus. 2002. 16p. (J). (978-0-439-35097-6(2)) Scholastic, Inc.

Rubin, Susan Goldman. Haym Salomon: American Patriot. Slonim, David, illus. 2007. 40p. (J). (ps-5). 16.95 (978-0-8109-1087-4(X) , Abrams Bks. for Young Readers) Abrams, Harry N., Inc.

Rudin, Ronald. Founding Fathers: The Celebration of Champlain & Laval in the Streets of Quebec, 1878-1908. 2003. (Illus.). 304p. (978-0-8020-3645-2(7)); pap. (978-0-8020-8479-8(6)) Univ. of Toronto Pr.

Schanzer, Rosalyn. George vs. George: The American Revolution As Seen from Both Sides. 2007. (Illus.). 64p. (J). (gr. 4-9). pap. 6.95 (978-1-4263-0042-4(5) , National Geographic Children's Bks.) National Geographic Society.

—George vs. George: The American Revolution as Seen from Both Sides. Schanzer, Rosalyn, illus. 2007. (Illus.). 60p. (J). reprint ed. 17.00 (***978-1-4223-6812-1(2)***) DIANE Publishing Co.

Schanzer, Rosalyn. George vs. George: The Revolutionary War as Seen by Both Sides. 2004. (Illus.). 64p. (J). (gr. 4-9). 16.95 (978-0-7922-7349-3(4)); 25.90 (978-0-7922-6999-1(3)) National Geographic Society. (National Geographic Children's Bks.).

Schauffler, Robert Haven, ed. Independence Day: Its Celebration, Spirit, & Significance As Related in Prose & Verse. 1999. (Our American Holidays Ser.). 318p. (J). (gr. 3-6). reprint ed. lib. bdg. 42.00 (978-0-7808-0394-7(9)) Omnigraphics, Inc.

Schiffman, Jessica, illus. Sybil Ludington: Freedom's Brave Rider. 2005. 32p. (J). pap. (***978-0-7367-2931-4(3)***) Zaner-Bloser, Inc.

Schmittroth, Linda. American Revolution: Almanac. McConnell, Stacy A., ed. 2000. (American Revolution Reference Library). (Illus.). xxxiii, 188p. (J). (gr. 5-9). 66.00 (978-0-7876-3795-8(5) , GML00502-113557, UXL) Thomson Gale.

Scholastic, Inc. Staff. American Revolution. 2002. (Super Social Studies Bulletin Board Set Ser.). pap. 8.95 (978-0-439-39600-4(X) , Teaching Resources) Scholastic, Inc.

Sheinkin, Steve. Storyteller's History: The American Revolution. 2005. (Storyteller's History Ser.). (Illus.). 144p. (J). (gr. 4-8). per. 10.95 (978-0-9766367-0-0(0)) Summer Street Pr.

Signature Lives: Revolutionary War Era, 8 titles, Set. 2005. (YA). (gr. 5-7). lib. bdg. 244.80 (978-0-7565-0873-9(8)); lib. bdg. 367.20 (978-0-7565-1009-1(0)) Compass Point Bks.

Smith, Robert. Spotlight on America: American Revolution. 2004. (Spotlight on America Ser.). (Illus.). 80p. (J). (gr. 4-8). pap. 10.99 (978-0-7439-3212-7(9)) Teacher Created Materials, Inc.

Smolinski, Diane. The Revolutionary War Home Front. (Americans at War Ser.). (Illus.). 32p. (J). (gr. 4-6). 2002. pap. 6.95 (978-1-58810-558-5(X) , 91693); 2001. lib. bdg. (978-1-58810-277-5(7)) Heinemann Library.

—Revolutionary War Soldiers. (Americans at War Ser.). (Illus.). 32p. (J). (gr. 4-6). 2002. pap. 6.95 (978-1-58810-562-2(8) , 91694); 2001. lib. bdg. (978-1-58810-276-8(9)) Heinemann Library.

Somervill, Barbara. The Life & Times of James Madison. 2007. (J). lib. bdg. (***978-1-58415-530-0(2)***) Mitchell Lane Pubs., Inc.

Somervill, Barbara A. John Hancock: Signer for Independence. 2004. (Signature Lives Ser.). (Illus.). 112p. (J). 30.60 (978-0-7565-0828-9(2) , 1240133) Compass Point Bks.

Sonneborn, Liz. Benedict Arnold: Hero & Traitor. 2005. (Leaders of the American Revolution Ser.). (Illus.). 130p. (J). (ps-8). lib. bdg. 30.00 (978-0-7910-8617-9(8) , Chelsea Hse.) Facts On File, Inc.

—John Paul Jones: American Naval Hero. 2005. (Leaders of the American Revolution Ser.). (Illus.). 123p. (J). (ps-8). lib. bdg. 30.00 (978-0-7910-8621-6(6) , Chelsea Hse.) Facts On File, Inc.

Stanley, George Edward. The New Republic (1763-1815) 2005. (Illus.). 48p. (J). pap. (978-0-8368-5834-1(4)); lib. bdg. 30.00 (978-0-8368-5825-9(5)) Stevens, Gareth Inc. (World Almanac Library).

Stewart, Gail B. Life of a Soldier in Washington's Army. 2002. (Illus.). 112p. (J). 29.95 (978-1-59018-215-4(4) , Lucent Bks.) Thomson Gale.

The Story of America's Birthday. 1999. (Illus.). 24p. (J). (ps-k). 6.95 (978-0-8249-4170-3(5)) Ideals Pubns.

Strum, Richard M. Causes of the American Revolution. 2005. (Road to War Ser.). (Illus.). 64p. (J). pap. 12.95 (978-1-59556-005-6(X)); (gr. 4 up). lib. bdg. 22.95 (978-1-59556-001-8(7)) OTTN Publishing.

Sullivan, George E. Paul Revere. 2000. (J). 11.15 (978-0-606-19925-4(X)) Tandem Library Bks.

Thornton, Jeremy. Famous Women of the American Revolution. 2003. (Building Americas Democracy Ser.). 24p. (J). lib. bdg. 19.95 (978-0-8239-6276-1(8) , PowerKids Pr.) Rosen Publishing Group, Inc., The.

—Foreign-Born Champions of the American Revolution. 2003. (Building Americas Democracy Ser.). (Illus.). 24p. (J). lib. bdg. 19.95 (978-0-8239-6277-8(6) , PowerKids Pr.) Rosen Publishing Group, Inc., The.

Todd, Anne M. The Revolutionary War. 2000. (America Goes to War Ser.). (Illus.). 48p. (J). (gr. 3-4). lib. bdg. 22.60 (978-0-7368-0584-1(2) , Bridgestone Bks.) Capstone Pr., Inc.

Tood, Anne M. Revolutionary War. (America Goes to War Ser.). 48p. (YA). pap. 6.95 (978-0-7368-8912-4(4)) Capstone Pr., Inc.

Tracy, Kathleen. Nathan Hale. 2006. (Profiles in American History Ser.). (Illus.). 48p. (J). (gr. 4-8). lib. bdg. 20.95 (978-1-58415-447-1(0)) Mitchell Lane Pubs., Inc.

Traugh, Steven. American Revolution: The Journey Toward Independence. Jennett, Pam, ed. Keely, John & Joyner, Eric, illus. rev. ed. 2002. (Voices of American History Ser.). 48p. (YA). (gr. 4-8). pap. 17.99 (978-1-57471-842-3(8) , CTP 2539) Creative Teaching Pr., Inc.

Tucker, Mary. Boston Tea Party. Mitchell, Judy, ed. Hierstein, Judith, illus. 2001. (History - Hands On! Ser.). 32p. (J). (gr. 1-4). pap. 6.95 (978-1-57310-302-2(0)) Teaching & Learning Co.

—Washington Crossing the Delaware. Mitchell, Judy, ed. Hierstein, Judith, illus. 2002. (History - Hands On! Ser.). 32p. (J). (gr. 1-4). pap. 6.95 (978-1-57310-352-7(7)) Teaching & Learning Co.

Wachter, Joanne. George Washington & the AMER Revolution. 2005. 42.00 (***978-1-4108-4633-4(4)***) Benchmark Education Co.

Wade, Linda R. Events Leading to the American Revolution. 2001. (American Revolution Ser.). (Illus.). 32p. (J). (gr. 3-8). lib. bdg. 24.21 (978-1-57765-153-6(7) , ABDO & Daughters) ABDO Publishing Co.

—Final Years of the American Revolution. 2001. (American Revolution Ser.). (Illus.). 32p. (J). (gr. 3-8). lib. bdg. 24.21 (978-1-57765-154-3(5) , ABDO & Daughters) ABDO Publishing Co.

—Life after the American Revolution. 2001. (American Revolution Ser.). (Illus.). 32p. (J). (gr. 3-8). lib. bdg. 24.21 (978-1-57765-079-9(4) , ABDO & Daughters) ABDO Publishing Co.

Wallis, Katherine. Quick & Easy Internet Activities for the One-Computer Classroom: 20 Fun, Web-Based Activities with Reproducible Graphic Organizers That Enable Kids to Research & Learn-on Their Own! 2002. 48p. pap., tchr. ed. 9.95 (978-0-439-30466-5(0)) Scholastic, Inc.

Wand, Kelly. The American Revolution. 2002. (Great Speeches in History Ser.). (Illus.). 208p. pap. 21.20 (978-0-7377-0866-0(2) , Greenhaven Pr., Inc.) Thomson Gale.

Warrick, Karen Clemens. Independence National Historical Park: A MyReportLinks.com Book. 2005. (Virtual Field Trips Ser.). (Illus.). 48p. (J). (gr. 4-10). lib. bdg. 25.26 (978-0-7660-5224-6(9) , MyReportLinks.com Bks.) Enslow Pubs., Inc.

Weber, Michael. The American Revolution. 2000. (Making of America Ser.). (Illus.). 96p. (J). (gr. 4-7). lib. bdg. 28.54 (978-0-8172-5702-6(0)) Raintree.

—The Young Republic. 2000. (Making of America Ser.). (Illus.). 96p. (J). (gr. 4-7). lib. bdg. 28.54 (978-0-8172-5703-3(9)) Raintree.

Whiting, Jim. The Life & Times of Abigail Adams. 2007. (Profiles in American History Ser.). (Illus.). 48p. (J). lib. bdg. 29.95 (***978-1-58415-527-0(2)*** Mitchell Lane Pubs., Inc.

Wiener, Roberta & Arnold, James R. New York. 2004. (13 Colonies Ser.). (Illus.). 64p. (J). 9.50 (978-1-4109-0308-2(7)) Harcourt Schl. Pubs.

Williams, Brian. The Declaration of American Independence: 4 July 1776. 2002. (Dates with History Ser.). (Illus.). 31p. (J). lib. bdg. 24.25 (978-1-58340-211-5(X)) Smart Apple Media.

Winter, Jonah. Paul Revere & the Bell Ringers. Dodson, Bert, illus. 2003. (Ready-to-Read Ser.). 32p. (J). pap. 3.99 (978-0-689-85635-8(0) , Aladdin) Simon & Schuster Children's Publishing.

—Paul Revere & the Bell Ringers. 2003. (gr. k-3). lib. bdg. 11.80 (978-0-613-89003-8(5)) Tandem Library Bks.

Wirkner, Linda. Learning about the American Revolutionary War with Graphic Organizers. 2005. (Graphic Organizers in Social Studies). (J). 19.95 (978-1-4042-2813-9(6) , PowerKids Pr.) Rosen Publishing Group, Inc., The.

Yero, Judith Lloyd. American Documents: Mayflower Compact. 2006. (Illus.). 40p. (J). (gr. 5-9). 15.95 (978-0-7922-5891-9(6) , National Geographic Children's Bks.) National Geographic Society.

—American Documents: The Mayflower Compact. 2006. (Illus.). 40p. (J). (gr. 5-9). 23.90 (978-0-7922-5892-6(4) , National Geographic Children's Bks.) National Geographic Society.

UNITED STATES—HISTORY—REVOLUTION, 1775-1783—BIOGRAPHY

Aaseng, Nathan. Strategic Battles. 2002. (American War Library). (Illus.). 112p. (J). 29.95 (978-1-59018-221-5(9) , Lucent Bks.) Thomson Gale.

Adelson, Bruce. British General William Howe. 2001. (Revolutionary War Leaders Ser.). (Illus.). 80p. (J). pap. 27.50 (978-0-7910-6389-7(5)); 27.50 (978-0-7910-6388-0(7)) Facts On File, Inc. (Chelsea Hse.).

Adler, David A. & Adler, Peter S. Heroes of the Revolution. 2003. (Illus.). 32p. (J). (gr. 1-5). tchr. ed. 16.95 (978-0-8234-1471-0(X)) Holiday Hse., Inc.

Anderson, Dale. The Patriots Win the American Revolution. 2005. (World Almanac Library of the American Revolution). (J). pap. (978-0-8368-5937-9(5)); lib. bdg. 30.00 (978-0-8368-5928-7(6)) Stevens, Gareth Inc. (World Almanac Library).

Anderson, Marcella Fisher. Young Patriots: Inspiring Stories of the American Revolution. 2004. (Illus.). 160p. (J). (gr. 4-6). 16.95 (978-1-59078-241-5(0)) Boyds Mills Pr.

Beller, Susan Provost. Yankee Doodle & the Redcoats: Soldiering in the Revolutionary War. Day, Larry, illus. 2003. (Single Titles Ser.). 96p. (gr. 5 up). lib. bdg. 26.90 (978-0-7613-2612-0(X) , Twenty-First Century Bks.) Lerner Publishing Group.

Ben Franklin. 2000. (McGraw-Hill Ciencias Ser.). (ENG & SPA.). (gr. 3 up). (978-0-02-279642-6(8)) Macmillan/McGraw-Hill Schl. Div.

Bertanzetti, Eileen Dunn. Molly Pitcher. 2001. (Revolutionary War Leaders Ser.). (Illus.). 80p. (J). 31.00 (978-0-7910-6400-9(X)); pap. 27.50 (978-0-7910-6401-6(8)) Facts On File, Inc. (Chelsea Hse.).

Bodie, Idella. Heroes & Heroines of the American Revolution. 2004. (J). pap., instr.'s gde. ed. (978-0-87844-173-0(5)) Sandlapper Publishing Co., Inc.

—Heroines of the American Revolution. 2003. (Illus.). 99p. (J). pap. 6.95 (978-0-87844-170-9(0)) Sandlapper Publishing Co., Inc.

—Quaker Commander. 2001. (Illus.). 89p. (J). 6.95 (978-0-87844-160-0(3)) Sandlapper Publishing Co., Inc.

—The Secret Message. 1998. (Heroes & Heroines of the American Revolution Ser.: Vol. 2). (Illus.). 45p. (J). (ps-3). pap. 5.95 (978-0-87844-145-7(X)) Sandlapper Publishing Co., Inc.

Castrovilla, Selene. By the Sword: A Young Man Meets War. 2007. (Illus.). 40p. (J). (gr. 4-6). 17.95 (978-1-59078-427-3(8)) Boyds Mills Pr.

Cheripko, Jan. Caesar Rodney's Ride: The Story of an American Patriot. Lippincott, Gary, illus. 2004. 40p. (J). (gr. 4-6). 16.95 (978-1-59078-065-7(5)) Boyds Mills Pr.

Clark, Charles. Patriots of the Revolutionary War. 2003. (American War Library). (Illus.). 112p. (J). 29.95 (978-1-59018-220-8(0) , Lucent Bks.) Thomson Gale.

Cornelius, Kay. Francis Marion: The Swamp Fox. 2001. (gr. 5-8). lib. bdg. 17.60 (978-0-613-32583-7(4)) Tandem Library Bks.

Crannell, Karl. John Stark: Live Free or Die. 2006. (Forgotten Heroes of the American Revolution Ser.). (Illus.). 80p. (J). (gr. 5-11). lib. bdg. 23.95 (978-1-59556-016-2(5)) OTTN Publishing.

—John Stark: Live Free or Die! 2006. (J). pap. (978-1-59556-021-6(1)) OTTN Publishing.

Davis, Kate. Samuel Adams. 2002. (Triangle History of the American Revolution Ser.). (Illus.). 104p. (J). 28.70 (978-1-56711-612-0(4) , Blackbirch Pr., Inc.) Thomson Gale.

Doeden, Matt. Samuel Adams: Patriot & Statesman. 2007. (Graphic Library). 32p. (J). 25.26 (978-0-7368-6500-5(4)) Capstone Pr., Inc.

Dolan, Edward F., Jr. The Winter at Valley Forge. 2001. (Kaleidoscope Ser.). (Illus.). 48p. (J). (gr. 3 up). lib. bdg. 25.64 (978-0-7614-1304-2(9) , Benchmark Bks.) Cavendish, Marshall Corp.

Draper, Allison Stark. America's First Traitor: Benedict Arnold Betrays the Colonies. 2001. (Headlines from History Ser.). (Illus.). 24p. (J). (gr. 3). lib. bdg. 19.95 (978-0-8239-5673-9(3) , PKTRAI, PowerKids Pr.) Rosen Publishing Group, Inc., The.

—The Start of the American Revolutionary War: Paul Revere Rides at Midnight. 2001. (Headlines from History Ser.). (Illus.). 24p. (J). (gr. 3). lib. bdg. 19.95 (978-0-8239-5672-2(5) , PKREWA, PowerKids Pr.) Rosen Publishing Group, Inc., The.

Fritz, Jean. Why Not, Lafayette? Himler, Ronald, illus. 1999. 1p. (J). (gr. 5-9). 17.99 (978-0-399-23411-8(X) , Putnam Juvenile) Penguin Group (USA) Inc.

Gillis, Jennifer Blizin. Samuel Adams. 2004. (Illus.). 32p. (J). pap. 7.50 (978-1-4034-5970-1(3)); lib. bdg. 25.64 (978-1-4034-5962-6(2)) Heinemann Library.

Glaser, Jason. Molly Pitcher: Young American Patriot. Smith, Tod et al, illus. 2006. (Graphic Library). 32p. (J). 25.26 (978-0-7368-5486-3(X)) Capstone Pr., Inc.

Greene, Meg. Thaddeus Kosciuszko. 2001. (Revolutionary War Leaders Ser.). (Illus.). 80p. (J). pap. 27.50 (978-0-7910-6399-6(2)); 27.50 (978-0-7910-6398-9(4)) Facts On File, Inc. (Chelsea Hse.).

Gregson, Susan R. Benedict Arnold. 2001. (Let Freedom Ring Ser.). (Illus.). 48p. (J). (gr. 3-4). lib. bdg. 22.60 (978-0-7368-1032-6(3) , Bridgestone Bks.) Capstone Pr., Inc.

Harness, Cheryl. The Revolutionary John Adams. 2003. (Illus.). 48p. (J). (gr. 3-7). 17.95 (978-0-7922-6970-0(5) , National Geographic Children's Bks.) National Geographic Society.

Haugen, David M. Colonists. 2004. (Voices from the American Revolution Ser.). (Illus.). 32p. (J). 23.70 (978-1-4103-0448-3(5) , Blackbirch Pr., Inc.) Thomson Gale.

Irvin, Benjamin H. Samuel Adams: Son of Liberty, Father of Revolution. 2002. (Oxford Portraits Ser.). (Illus.). 176p. (YA). 28.00 (978-0-19-513225-0(4)) Oxford Univ. Pr., Inc.

Jones, Veda Boyd. Samuel Adams. 2001. (Revolutionary War Leaders Ser.). (Illus.). 80p. (J). pap. 27.50 (978-0-7910-6387-3(9)); 27.50 (978-0-7910-6386-6(0)) Facts On File, Inc. (Chelsea Hse.).

Kauffman, Scott. Francis Marion: Swamp Fox of South Carolina. 2006. (Forgotten Heroes of the American Revolution Ser.). (Illus.). 88p. (YA). (gr. 5-11). lib. bdg. 23.95 (978-1-59556-014-8(9)) OTTN Publishing.

Krizner, L. J. & Sita, Lisa. Nathan Hale: Patriot & Martyr of the American Revolution. 2005. (Library of American Lives & Times). (Illus.). 112p. (J). (gr. 4-8). lib. bdg. 31.95 (978-0-8239-5724-8(1)) Rosen Publishing Group, Inc., The.

Leaders of the American Revolution. 2005. (Illus.). 100p. (gr. 4-8). 300.00 (978-0-7910-9019-0(1) , Chelsea Hse.) Facts On File, Inc.

Leaders of the American Revolution Set, 11-Volumes. 2006. (Leaders of the American Revolution Ser.). 100p. (gr. 5-8). 330.00 (978-0-7910-9320-7(4) , Chelsea Hse.) Facts On File, Inc.

The Legend of Jocko: Hero of the American Revolution. 2003. (YA). pap. 9.95 (978-0-9761778-0-7(3)) Lefall and Co., Inc.

Let Freedom Ring: American Revolution Biographies, 6 bks. Incl. Benedict Arnold. Gregson, Susan R. 2001. lib. bdg. 22.60 (978-0-7368-1032-6(3)); Benjamin Franklin. Gregson, Susan R. 2000. lib. bdg. 22.60 (978-0-7368-1031-9(5)); Betsy Ross. Duden, Jane. 2000. lib. bdg. 22.60 (978-0-7368-1036-4(6)); George Washington. Keller, Kristin Thoennes. 2000. lib. bdg. 22.60 (978-0-7368-1034-0(X)); Phillis Wheatley. Gregson, Susan R. 2000. lib. bdg. 22.60 (978-0-7368-1033-3(1)); Thomas Jefferson. Aldridge, Rebecca. 2001. lib. bdg. 22.60 (978-0-7368-1035-7(8)); 48p. (J). (gr. 3-4). (Illus.). 2001. Set lib. bdg. 135.60 (978-0-7368-1040-1(4) , Bridgestone Bks.) Capstone Pr., Inc.

Lewis, Noah & Graham, Loretta. Edward Ned Hector. 2005. (ENG., Illus.). 36p. (J). per. 19.99 (***978-1-4208-6817-3(9)*** AuthorHouse.

Libertson, Jody. Nathan Hale: Hero of the American Revolution. 2003. (Famous People in American History Ser.). (Illus.). 32p. (YA). pap. (978-0-8239-4189-6(2)) Rosen Publishing Group, Inc., The.

Mader, Jan. Molly Pitcher. 2007. (J). (978-0-7368-6703-0(1) , Pebble Bks.) Capstone Pr., Inc.

Marsh, Carole. Marquis de Lafayette. 2002. (One Thousand Readers Ser.). (Illus.). 12p. (J). (gr. k-4). 2.95 (978-0-635-01520-4(X) , 1520X) Gallopade International.

McLeese, Don. Thomas Paine. 2004. (Heroes of the American Revolution Ser.). 32p. pap. 5.95 (978-1-59515-319-7(5)) Rourke Publishing, LLC.

Otfinoski, Steven. People of the AMER Revolution. 2005. (Navigators Ser.). (J). pap. 42.00 (***978-1-4108-5110-9(9)*** Benchmark Education Co.

Redmond, Shirley-Raye. Patriots in Petticoats. 2005. (Illus.). 128p. (J). (gr. 3-7). lib. bdg. 13.04 (978-0-606-32535-6(2)) Tandem Library Bks.

—Patriots in Petticoats: Heroines of the American Revolution. 2004. (Landmark Bks.). (Illus.). 144p. (J). (gr. 3). lib. bdg. 16.99 (978-0-375-92357-9(8) , Random Hse. Bks. for Young Readers) Random Hse. Children's Bks.

Revolutionary War Leaders. 2005. pap. 495.00 (978-0-7910-9157-9(0) , Chelsea Hse.) Facts On File, Inc.

Riley, John B. John Paul Jones: A Photo Biography. l.t. ed. 2004. (First Biographies Ser.). (Illus.). 24p. (YA). (gr. 5 up). 16.95 (978-1-883846-63-3(3) , First Biographies) Reynolds, Morgan Inc.

Robinson Masters, Nancy. Extraordinary Patriots of the United States of America: Colonial Times to Pre-Civil War. 2005. (Extraordinary People Ser.). (Illus.). 288p. (J). 40.00 (978-0-516-24404-4(3) , Children's Pr.) Scholastic Library Publishing.

Rockwell, Anne F. They Called Her Molly Pitcher. von Buhler, Cynthia, illus. 2002. 40p. (J). (gr. 2-5). 16.95 (978-0-679-89187-1(0) , Knopf Bks. for Young Readers) Random Hse. Children's Bks.

Roop, Connie & Roop, Peter, eds. The Diary of Joseph Plumb Martin: A Revolutionary War Soldier. 2000. (In My Own Words Ser.). (Illus.). 96p. (J). (gr. 5 up). lib. bdg. 27.07 (978-0-7614-1014-0(7) , Benchmark Bks.) Cavendish, Marshall Corp.

Rose, Drew, illus. Molly Pitcher. 2004. (Imagination Ser.). 32p. (J). (gr. 3 up). 22.60 (978-0-7565-0604-9(2)) Compass Point Bks.

Rosen, Daniel. Fight for Freedom. 2003. (People Who Changed America Ser.). (Illus.). 40p. (J). (978-0-7922-8620-2(0)) National Geographic Society.

Ruffin, Frances E. Molly Pitcher. 2002. (American Legends Ser.). (Illus.). 24p. (J). (gr. 3). lib. bdg. 18.75 (978-0-8239-5829-0(9) , PowerKids Pr.) Rosen Publishing Group, Inc., The.

Schmittroth, Linda, et al, contrib. by. American Revolution: Biographies, 2 vols. 2000. (Illus.). (J). (978-0-7876-3793-4(9)); (978-0-7876-3794-1(7)) Thomson Gale. (UXL).

Schmittroth, Linda & Rosteck, Mary Kay. American Revolution: Biographies, 2 vols. McConnell, Stacy A., ed. 2000. (Illus.). 506p. (J). lib. bdg. 120.00 (978-0-7876-3792-7(0) , GML00502-113554, UXL) Thomson Gale.

Silate, Jennifer. Betsy Ross. 2003. (Famous People in American History Ser.). (Illus.). 32p. (J). pap. (978-0-8239-4176-6(0)) Rosen Publishing Group, Inc., The.

Silcox-Jarrett, Diane. Heroines of the American Revolution: America's Founding Mothers. Seiden, Art, illus. 1998. (Heroines of History Ser.: Vol. 1). 92p. (J). (gr. 3-8). per. 19.95 (978-0-9658065-2-7(9)) Green Angel Pr.

Smolinski, Diane. Important People of the Revolutionary War. 2001. (Illus.). 32p. (J). (gr. 4-6). lib. bdg. (978-1-58810-278-2(5)) Heinemann Library.

Stewart, Gail B. The Revolutionary War. 2003. (People at the Center of Ser.). (Illus.). 48p. (J). 26.20 (978-1-56711-769-1(4) , Blackbirch Pr., Inc.) Thomson Gale.

Sullivan, George E. Paul Revere. 2000. (In Their Own Words Ser.). (Illus.). 128p. (J). (gr. 3-7). pap. 12.95 (978-0-439-14748-4(4)) Scholastic, Inc.

Thornton, Jeremy. Foreign-Born Champions of the American Revolution. 2003. (Building Americas Democracy Ser.). (Illus.). 24p. (J). lib. bdg. 19.95 (978-0-8239-6277-8(6) , PowerKids Pr.) Rosen Publishing Group, Inc., The.

—Tories & Patriots: Neighbors at War. 2003. (Building Americas Democracy Ser.). (Illus.). 24p. (J). lib. bdg. 19.95 (978-0-8239-6279-2(2) , PowerKids Pr.) Rosen Publishing Group, Inc., The.

Towles, Louis P. Francis Marion: The Swamp Fox of the American Revolution. 2005. (Library of American Lives & Times). (Illus.). 112p. (J). (gr. 4-8). lib. bdg. 31.95 (978-0-8239-5728-6(4)) Rosen Publishing Group, Inc., The.

Wales, Dirk. Twice A Hero: Polish American Heroes of the American Revolution. Ihsen Peterson, Lynn, illus. 2007. (J). 18.95 (***978-0-9632459-4-6(5)*** Great Plains Pr.

Walsh, Kieran. Samuel Adams. (Discover the Life of a Colonial American Ser.). 24p. 2005. (Illus.). (gr. 2-5). 14.95 (978-1-59515-135-3(4)); 2004. pap. 4.95 (978-1-59515-336-4(5)) Rourke Publishing, LLC.

Women of the American Revolution (NCHS) (YA). (gr. 5-8). spiral bd., tchr.'s planning gde. ed. 11.50 (978-0-382-40933-2(7)) Cobblestone Publishing Co.

Women of the American Revolution (NCHS) Grades 5-8. 58p. (J). tchr. ed. 29.45 (978-0-382-40934-9(5)) Cobblestone Publishing Co.

UNITED STATES—HISTORY—REVOLUTION, 1775-1783—CAMPAIGNS

see also Yorktown (Va.)—History—Siege, 1781

Adelson, Bruce. Baron Von Steuben. 2001. (Revolutionary War Leaders Ser.). (Illus.). 80p. (J). pap. 27.50 (978-0-7910-6393-4(3)); 27.50 (978-0-7910-6392-7(5)) Facts On File, Inc. (Chelsea Hse.).

Ammon, Richard. Valley Forge. Farnsworth, Bill, illus. 2004. 32p. (J). (gr. 4-6). tchr. ed. 16.95 (978-0-8234-1746-9(8)) Holiday Hse., Inc.

Anderson, Dale. Key Battles of the American Revolution, 1776-1778. 2005. (World Almanac Library of the American Revolution). (J). pap. (978-0-8368-5936-2(7)); lib. bdg. 30.00 (978-0-8368-5927-0(8)) Stevens, Gareth Inc. (World Almanac Library).

—The Patriots Win the American Revolution. 2005. (World Almanac Library of the American Revolution). (J). pap. (978-0-8368-5937-9(5)); lib. bdg. 30.00 (978-0-8368-5928-7(6)) Stevens, Gareth Inc. (World Almanac Library).

Aronson, Virginia. Ethan Allen: Revolutionary Hero. 2000. (Revolutionary War Leaders Ser.). (Illus.). 80p. (J). (gr. 4-7). pap. 27.50 (978-0-7910-6132-9(9)); (gr. 8-12). 27.50 (978-0-7910-5974-6(X)) Facts On File, Inc. (Chelsea Hse.).

Battles of Lexington & Concord. (American Revolution Ser.). 32p. (YA). 7.95 (978-0-7368-4491-8(0)) Capstone Pr., Inc.

Bodie, Idella. Light-Horse Harry. 2004. (Illus.). 86p. (J). pap. 6.95 (978-0-87844-172-3(7)) Sandlapper Publishing Co., Inc.

Burgan, Michael. George Rogers Clark. 2001. (Revolutionary War Leaders Ser.). (Illus.). 80p. (J). pap. 27.50 (978-0-7910-6395-8(X)); 27.50 (978-0-7910-6394-1(1)) Facts On File, Inc. (Chelsea Hse.).

—Valley Forge. 2004. (We the People Ser.). (Illus.). 48p. (J). (gr. 4 up). lib. bdg. 22.60 (978-0-7565-0615-5(8)) Compass Point Bks.

Cheney, Lynne V. When Washington Crossed the Delaware: A Wintertime Story for Young Patriots. Fiore, Peter M., illus. 2004. 40p. (J). 16.95 (978-0-689-87043-9(4)) Simon & Schuster Children's Publishing.

Crannell, Karl. John Stark: Live Free or Die. 2006. (Forgotten Heroes of the American Revolution Ser.). (Illus.). 80p. (J). (gr. 5-11). lib. bdg. 23.95 (978-1-59556-016-2(5)) OTTN Publishing.

—John Stark: Live Free or Die! 2006. (J). pap. (978-1-59556-021-6(1)) OTTN Publishing.

Crewe, Sabrina & Uschan, Michael V. Lexington & Concord. 2004. (Events That Shaped America Ser.). (Illus.). 32p. (J). (gr. 3 up). lib. bdg. 24.67 (978-0-8368-3398-0(8)) Stevens, Gareth Inc.

Draper, Allison Stark. The End of the American Revolutionary War: The Colonists Defeat the British at Yorktown. 2001. (Headlines from History Ser.). (Illus.). 24p. (J). (gr. 3). lib. bdg. 19.95 (978-0-8239-5674-6(1) , PKENRE, PowerKids Pr.) Rosen Publishing Group, Inc., The.

Gallagher, Jim. Daniel Morgan: Fighting Frontiersman. 2006. (J). pap. (978-1-59556-020-9(3)); (Illus.). 88p. (gr. 5-11). lib. bdg. 23.95 (978-1-59556-015-5(7)) OTTN Publishing.

Grabowski, Patricia A. General "Mad" Anthony Wayne. 2001. (Revolutionary War Leaders Ser.). (Illus.). 80p. (J). pap. 27.50 (978-0-7910-6383-5(6)); 27.50 (978-0-7910-6382-8(8)) Facts On File, Inc. (Chelsea Hse.).

Haugen, Brenda & Santella, Andrew. Ethan Allen: Green Mountain Rebel. 2004. (Signature Lives Ser.). (Illus.). 112p. (J). 30.60 (978-0-7565-0824-1(X) , 1240131) Compass Point Bks.

Kimmel, Heidi. The Battles of Lexington & Concord. 2007. (Cornerstones of Freedomtrade;, Second Ser.). 48p. (J). pap. 5.95 (***978-0-531-18763-0(2)*** , Children's Pr.) Scholastic Library Publishing.

King, David C. Saratoga. 1998. (Battlefields Across America Ser.: 8). (Illus.). 64p. (gr. 5-8). lib. bdg. 26.90 (978-0-7613-3011-0(9) , Twenty-First Century Bks.) Lerner Publishing Group.

McGowen, Tom. The Revolutionary War & George Washington's Army in American History. 2004. (In American History Ser.). (Illus.). 128p. (J). lib. bdg. 26.60 (978-0-7660-2143-3(2)) Enslow Pubs., Inc.

Murray, Aaron R. & Dorling Kindersley Publishing Staff. American Revolution Battles & Leaders. 2003. (Illus.). 96p. (J). 16.99 (978-0-7894-9888-5(X)) Dorling Kindersley Publishing, Inc.

Ready, Dee. The Battle of Yorktown. 2002. (Let Freedom Ring Ser.). (Illus.). 48p. (J). (gr. 3-4). lib. bdg. 22.60 (978-0-7368-1097-5(8) , Bridgestone Bks.) Capstone Pr., Inc.

Rushworth, Victoria. Battles of the AMER Revolution: Saratoga. 2005. (Navigators Ser.). (J). pap. 42.00 (***978-1-4108-5109-3(5)*** Benchmark Education Co.

Scarbrough, Mary Hertz. The Battle of Harlem Heights. 2003. (Triangle Histories of the American Revolution Ser.). (Illus.). 32p. (J). 22.45 (978-1-56711-777-6(5) , Blackbirch Pr., Inc.) Thomson Gale.

Smolinski, Diane. Land Battles of the Revolutionary War. (Americans at War Ser.). (Illus.). 32p. (J). (gr. 4-6). 2002. pap. 6.95 (978-1-58810-560-8(1) , 91691); 2001. lib. bdg. (978-1-58810-274-4(2)) Heinemann Library.

—Land Battles of the Revolutionary War. 2002. (gr. 3-6). lib. bdg. 15.25 (978-0-613-55487-9(6)) Tandem Library Bks.

Stein, R. Conrad. Ethan Allen & the Green Mountain Boys. 2003. (Cornerstones of Freedom). (Illus.). 48p. (J). (gr. 4-6). 26.00 (978-0-516-24206-4(7) , Children's Pr.) Scholastic Library Publishing.

Strum, Richard. Henry Knox: Washington's Artilleryman. 2006. (Forgotten Heroes of the American Revolution Ser.). (Illus.). 88p. (J). (gr. 5-11). lib. bdg. 23.95 (978-1-59556-013-1(0)) OTTN Publishing.

Strum, Richard M. Henry Knox: Washington's Artilleryman. 2006. (J). pap. (978-1-59556-018-6(1)) OTTN Publishing.

Swager, Christine R. Come to the Cow Pens! The Story of the Battle of Cowpens, January 17, 1781. 2002. (Illus.). 120p. (J). per. (978-1-891885-31-0(6)) Hub City Writers Project.

Trumbauer, Lisa. Life in the Time of George Washington & the Revolutionary War. 2007. (J). (***978-1-4034-9667-6(6)*** ; pap. (***978-1-4034-9675-1(7)*** Heinemann Library.

Uschan, Michael V. Lexington & Concord. 2003. (Landmark Events in American History Ser.). (Illus.). 48p. (J). (gr. 5 up). lib. bdg. 30.00 (978-0-8368-5379-7(2)); pap. 11.95 (978-0-8368-5407-7(1)) Stevens, Gareth Inc. (World Almanac Library).

Wade, Linda R. Early Battles of the American Revolution. 2001. (American Revolution Ser.). (Illus.). 32p. (J). (gr. 3-8). lib. bdg. 24.21 (978-1-57765-155-0(3) , ABDO & Daughters) ABDO Publishing Co.

Waldman, Scott P. The Battle of Bunker Hill. 2003. (Atlas of Famous Battles of the American Revolution Ser.). (Illus.). 24p. (J). lib. bdg. 21.25 (978-0-8239-6329-4(2) , PowerKids Pr.) Rosen Publishing Group, Inc., The.

—The Battle of Lexington & Concord. 2003. (Atlas of Famous Battles of the American Revolution Ser.). (Illus.). 24p. (J). lib. bdg. 21.25 (978-0-8239-6328-7(4) , PowerKids Pr.) Rosen Publishing Group, Inc., The.

—The Battle of Monmouth. 2003. (Atlas of Famous Battles of the American Revolution Ser.). (Illus.). 24p. (J). lib. bdg. 21.25 (978-0-8239-6330-0(6) , PowerKids Pr.) Rosen Publishing Group, Inc., The.

—The Battle of Trenton. 2003. (Atlas of Famous Battles of the American Revolution Ser.). (Illus.). 24p. (J). lib. bdg. 21.25 (978-0-8239-6333-1(0) , PowerKids Pr.) Rosen Publishing Group, Inc., The.

—The Battle of Yorktown. 2003. (Atlas of Famous Battles of the American Revolution Ser.). (Illus.). 24p. (J). lib. bdg. 21.25 (978-0-8239-6331-7(4)) Rosen Publishing Group, Inc., The.

Whitcraft, Melissa. The Surrender at Yorktown. 2004. (Cornerstones of Freedom Ser.). (Illus.). 47p. (J). 26.00 (978-0-516-24234-7(2) , Children's Pr.) Scholastic Library Publishing.

Whitelaw, Nancy. The Shot Heard Round the World: The Battles of Lexington & Concord. 2004. (First Battles Ser.). (Illus.). 112p. (J). (gr. 6-12). 23.95 (978-1-883846-75-6(7) , First Biographies) Reynolds, Morgan Inc.

Worth, Richard. Saratoga. 2002. (Battles That Changed the World Ser.). (Illus.). 112p. (YA). (gr. 7-10). 30.00 (978-0-7910-6682-9(7) , Chelsea Hse.) Facts On File, Inc.

UNITED STATES—HISTORY—REVOLUTION, 1775-1783—DRAMA

McCaslin, Nellie. Brave New Banner. 2003. (Players Press Nellie McCaslin Ser.). (Illus.). 20p. (YA). (gr. 6-12). pap. 5.00 (978-0-88734-436-7(4)) Players Pr., Inc.

UNITED STATES—HISTORY—REVOLUTION, 1775-1783—FICTION

Anderson, M. T. The Astonishing Life of Octavian Nothing, Traitor to the Nation. 2006. (Pox Party Ser.: Vol. 1). (Illus.). 368p. (YA). (gr. 9). 17.99 (978-0-7636-2402-6(0)) Candlewick Pr.

Anderson, M. T. Astonishing Life of Octavian Nothing, Traitor to the Nation: The Pox Party. rev. l.t. ed. 2007. (Astonishing Life of Octavian Nothing Ser.). 500p. (YA). 23.95 ***978-0-7862-9552-4(X)*** Thorndike Pr.

Bjerregaard, Marcia. First Heroes for Freedom. Jones, Marty, illus. 2000. (Adventures in America Ser.). 92p. (J). (gr. 3-7). lib. bdg. 14.95 (978-1-893110-17-5(6)) Silver Moon Pr.

Blackwood, Gary L. The Year of the Hangman. 2004. 272p. (YA). pap. 6.99 (978-0-14-240078-4(5) , Puffin); 2002. 196p. (J). (gr. 9 up). 16.99 (978-0-525-46921-6(4) , Dutton Juvenile) Penguin Group (USA) Inc.

Bruchac, Joseph. The Arrow over the Door. Watling, James, illus. 2002. 96p. (J). pap. 4.99 (978-0-14-130571-4(1) , Puffin) Penguin Group (USA) Inc.

—The Arrow over the Door. 1998. (Illus.). 96p. (J). (gr. 2-4). 15.99 (978-0-8037-2078-7(5) , Dial) Penguin Group (USA) Inc.

Burt, Barbara. The Eve of Revolution: The Colonial Adventures of Benjamin Wilcox. 2003. (I Am American Ser.). 40p. (J). (gr. 3-7). pap. 6.99 (978-0-7922-5211-5(X) , National Geographic Children's Bks.) National Geographic Society.

Campbell, Donna. An Independent Spirit: The Tale of Betsy Dowdy & Black Bess. 2002. (Legends of the Carolinas Ser.). 200p. (J). 8.95 (978-1-928556-35-0(3)) Coastal Carolina Pr.

Carlson, Drew. Attack of the Turtle. Johnson, David A., illus. 2007. 160p. (J). (gr. 3-7). 16.00 (978-0-8028-5308-0(0) , Eerdmans Bks For Young Readers) Eerdmans, William B. Publishing Co.

Clark, Eleanor. Victoria Grace: Courageous Patriot. 2007. (Eleanor Jo Ser.). (J). 14.99 (978-0-9753036-8-9(6)) HonorNet.

Collier, James Lincoln. My Brother Sam Is Dead. 2005. 240p. (J). pap. 5.99 (978-0-439-78360-6(7) , Scholastic Paperbacks) Scholastic, Inc.

Collier, James Lincoln & Collier, Christopher. My Brother Sam Is Dead. rev. ed. 2003. (Illus.). 224p. (YA). (gr. 5-9). mass mkt. 5.99 (978-0-590-42792-0(X) , Scholastic Paperbacks) Scholastic, Inc.

Cox, Angus Stephen. The Dare Boys of 1776. 2006. 62.99 ***(978-1-4280-3047-3(6))*** IndyPublish.com.

Curtis, Alice Turner. A Little Maid of Massachusetts Bay Colony. Smith, Wuanita, illus. 2004. (Little Maid Ser.). 192p. (J). (gr. 4-7). reprint ed. per. 9.95 (978-1-55709-329-5(6)) Applewood Bks.

—A Little Maid of Narragansett Bay. 2004. (Little Maid Ser.). (Illus.). 192p. (J). (gr. 1-6). reprint ed. per. 12.95 (978-1-55709-334-9(2)) Applewood Bks.

—A Little Maid of Old Connecticut. Smith, Wuanita, illus. 2004. (Little Maid Ser.). 192p. (J). (gr. 4-7). reprint ed. per. 9.95 (978-1-55709-328-8(8)) Applewood Bks.

—A Little Maid of Ticonderoga. Smith, Wuanita, illus. 2004. (Little Maid Ser.). 192p. (J). (gr. 4-7). reprint ed. per. 12.95 (978-1-55709-330-1(X)) Applewood Bks.

—A Little Maid of Virginia. 2004. (Little Maid Ser.). (Illus.). 192p. (J). (gr. 1-3). reprint ed. per. 9.95 (978-1-55709-333-2(4)) Applewood Bks.

Dell, Pamela. Freedom's Light: A Story about Paul Revere's Midnight Ride. 2002. (Scrapbooks of America Ser.). (Illus.). 48p. (J). (gr. 2-6). 28.50 (978-1-59187-016-6(X)) Child's World, Inc.

Durrant, Lynda. Betsy Zane, the Rose of Fort Henry. 2000. 208p. (J). (gr. 5-9). tchr. ed. 15.00 (978-0-395-97899-3(8) , Clarion Bks.) Houghton Mifflin Co. Trade & Reference Div.

Elliott, L. M. Give Me Liberty. 2008. 384p. (J). pap. 6.99 ***(*978-0-06-074423-6(5)*** , Harper Trophy) HarperCollins Pubs.

Evan, Frances Y. The Forgotten Flag: Revolutionary Struggle in Connecticut. 2003. (Illus.). 92p. (J). 5.95 (978-1-57249-338-4(0) , White Mane Kids) White Mane Publishing Co., Inc.

Falk, Elizabeth Sullivan. Freedom's Fire. Wang, Qi Z., illus. 2004. (J). (978-1-59336-321-5(4)); pap. (978-1-59336-322-2(2)) Mondo Publishing.

Favole, Robert J. Through the Wormhole. 2001. (Illus.). 192p. (J). (gr. 5-10). 17.95 (978-1-930826-00-7(1)) Flywheel Publishing Co.

Fisher, Clavin. Three Spies for General Washington. 2000. 188p. (YA). (gr. 5 up). 9.99 (978-0-88092-459-7(4)) Royal Fireworks Publishing Co.

Fleming, Candace. The Hatmaker's Sign: A Story by Benjamin Franklin. Parker, Robert A., illus. 1998. 40p. (J). (gr. k-4). pap. 15.95 (978-0-531-30075-6(7) , Orchard Bks.) Scholastic, Inc.

—The Hatmaker's Sign: A Story by Benjamin Franklin. Parker, Robert, illus. 2000. (J). (978-0-606-19857-8(1)) Tandem Library Bks.

Forbes, Esther. Johnny Tremain. McCurdy, Michael, illus. 1998. (Illustrated American Classics Ser.). 304p. (YA). (gr. 5-9). tchr. ed. 22.00 (978-0-395-90011-6(5)) Houghton Mifflin Co. Trade & Reference Div.

—Johnny Tremain. Ward, Lynd, illus. 2002. (J). 15.00 (978-0-7587-0196-1(9)) Book Wholesalers, Inc.

—Johnny Tremain. 2002. (EMC Masterpiece Series Access Editions). (Illus.). xvi, 308p. (J). 10.95 (978-0-8219-2408-2(7)) EMC/Paradigm Publishing.

—Johnny Tremain. McCurdy, Michael, illus. l.t. ed. 412p. 2005. (YA). pap. 10.95 (978-0-7862-7178-8(7)); 2004. (J). 22.95 (978-0-7862-7066-8(7)) Thorndike Pr.

Forbes, Esther Hoskins. Johnny Tremain: Illustrated American Classics. Date not set. (J). lib. bdg. 22.95 (978-0-8488-1318-5(9)) Amereon LTD.

—Johnny Tremain: Illustrated American Classics. Dell Publishing.

—Johnny Tremain Set: Illustrated American Classics, 2 vols., l.t. ed. (J). reprint ed. (978-0-89064-029-6(7)) National Assn. for Visually Handicapped.

Garvie, Maureen McCallum, et al. George Johnson's War. (Illus.). (J). (gr. 7 up). 2003. 224p. pap. 8.95 (978-0-88899-468-4(0)); 2002. 15.95 (978-0-88899-465-3(6)) Groundwood Bks. CAN. *Dist:* Perseus Distribution, Transition Vendor.

Goodman, Joan Elizabeth. Hope's Crossing. 1998. (Illus.). 224p. (J). (gr. 4-6). tchr. ed. 16.00 (978-0-395-86195-0(0)) Houghton Mifflin Co. Trade & Reference Div.

—Hope's Crossing. 1999. (Illus.). 224p. (J). (gr. 3-7). pap. 6.99 (978-0-698-11807-2(3) , Putnam Juvenile) Penguin Group (USA) Inc.

—Hope's Crossing. 1999. (J). 12.64 (978-0-606-19068-8(6)); (gr. 3-6). lib. bdg. 14.15 (978-0-613-21719-4(5)) Tandem Library Bks.

Gregory, Kristiana. Five Smooth Stones: Hope's Revolutionary War Diary. 2001. (My America Ser.). (Illus.). 112p. (J). (gr. 4-7). pap. 10.95 (978-0-439-14827-6(8) , Scholastic Pr.) Scholastic, Inc.

—Five Smooth Stones Bk. 1: Hope's Revolutionary War Diary. 2002. (My America Ser.). (Illus.). 112p. (J). (gr. 2-5). pap. 4.99 (978-0-439-36905-3(3) , Scholastic Pr.) Scholastic, Inc.

—We Are Patriots: Hope's Revolutionary War Diary. 2002. (gr. 3-6). lib. bdg. 13.00 (978-0-613-45633-3(5)) Tandem Library Bks.

—We Are Patriots Bk. 2: Hope's Revolutionary War Diary. 2002. (My America Ser.). (Illus.). 112p. (J). (gr. 2-5). pap. 10.95 (978-0-439-21039-3(9)); pap. 4.99 (978-0-439-36906-0(1)) Scholastic, Inc. (Scholastic Pr.).

—When Freedom Comes: Hope's Revolutionary War Diary, Bk. 3. 2004. (My America Ser.). (Illus.). 112p. (J). pap. 4.99 (978-0-439-37054-7(X)) Scholastic, Inc.

—When Freedom Comes Bk. 3: Hope's Revolutionary War Diary. 2004. (My America Ser.). (Illus.). 112p. (J). pap. 12.95 (978-0-439-37053-0(1)) Scholastic, Inc.

—The Winter of Red Snow: The Revolutionary War Story of Abigail Jane Stewart, Valley Forge, Pa, 1777. 2000. (Dear America Ser.). (J). 9.95 (978-0-439-17969-0(6)) Scholastic, Inc.

Griffin, A. J. Asa's Choice. 2002. 156p. (YA). (gr. 7 up). 9.99 (978-0-88092-566-2(3) , 566-3) Royal Fireworks Publishing Co.

Griffin, Judith Berry. Phoebe, the Spy. Tomes, Margot, illus. 2002. 48p. (J). pap. 6.99 (978-0-698-11956-7(8) , Putnam Juvenile) Penguin Group (USA) Inc.

Gutman, Dan. Qwerty Stevens Stuck in Time with Benjamin Franklin. 2002. (Illus.). 192p. (J). (gr. 5-8). 17.95 (978-0-689-84553-6(7)) Simon & Schuster Children's Publishing.

Guzman, Lila. Lorenzo's Revolutionary Quest. 2003. (gr. 7-12). lib. bdg. 18.75 (978-0-613-84279-2(0)) Tandem Library Bks.

—Lorenzo's Secret Mission. 2001. (gr. 3-6). lib. bdg. 18.75 (978-0-613-84747-6(4)) Tandem Library Bks.

Guzman, Lila & Guzman, Rick. Lorenzo & the Turncoat. 183p. (J). pap. 9.95 (978-1-55885-471-0(1) , Piñata Books) Arte Publico Pr.

Guzman, Lila & Guzman, Rick. Lorenzo's Revolutionary Quest. 176p. (YA). pap. 9.95 (978-1-55885-392-8(8) , Piñata Books) Arte Publico Pr.

—Lorenzo's Secret Mission. 160p. (YA). pap. 9.95 (978-1-55885-341-6(3) , Piñata Books) Arte Publico Pr.

Harcourt School Publishers Staff. Downstream Crossing On Level. 3rd ed. 2002. (Trophies Reading Program Ser.). (Illus.). pap. 5.10 (978-0-15-323345-6(1)) Harcourt Schl. Pubs.

Harlow, Joan Hiatt. Midnight Rider. 2006. 384p. (J). pap. 5.99 (978-0-689-87010-1(8) , Aladdin) Simon & Schuster Children's Publishing.

Hedstrom-Page, Deborah. From Colonies to Country with George Washington. Martinez, Sergio, illus. 2007. 80p. (J). (gr. 3-9). 9.99 (978-0-8054-3265-7(5)) B&H Publishing Grp.

Helmer, Diana Star. We're Behind You, George Washington. Schneider, Rex, illus. 2000. (Cover-to-Cover Bks.). 56p. (J). pap. (978-0-7891-5081-3(6)); (gr. 1-4). lib. bdg. 16.95 (978-0-7807-9050-6(2)) Perfection Learning Corp.

Hilbtecht, Sharron. The Drummer Boy. 2005. 30p. pap. 6.95 (978-1-889658-35-3(9)) New Canaan Publishing Co. LLC.

Hogan, Stephen. Johnny Lynch: Patriot Drummerboy. rev. ed. 2007. (J). ***(*978-0-9795474-0-9(7))*** KAM Publishing.

—Johnny Lynch: Road to Camden. 2007. (J). ***(*978-0-9795474-1-6(5))*** KAM Publishing.

Hominick, Judy & Spreier, Jeanne. Ride for Freedom: The Story of Sybil Ludington. 2001. (Heroes to Remember Ser.). (Illus.). 52p. (J). 14.95 (978-1-893110-24-3(9)) Silver Moon Pr.

Hunter, John P. Red Thunder: Secrets, Spies, & Scoundrels at Yorktown. 2006. (J). ***(*978-0-87935-231-8(0))*** Colonial Williamsburg Foundation.

Ingle, Sheila C. Courageous Kate: A Daughter of the American Revolution. 2006. (J). ***(*978-1-891885-52-5(9))*** Hub City Writers Project.

Jensen, Dorothea. Riddle of Penncroft Farm. 2001. (gr. 3-6). lib. bdg. 14.15 (978-0-613-59249-9(2)) Tandem Library Bks.

Kirkpatrick, Katherine. Redcoats & Petticoats. Himler, Ronald, illus. 1999. 32p. (J). (gr. 4-6). tchr. ed. 16.95 (978-0-8234-1416-1(7)) Holiday Hse., Inc.

Krensky, Stephen. Dangerous Crossing: The Revolutionary Voyage of John & John Quincy Adams. Harlin, Greg, tr. Harlin, Greg, illus. 2004. 32p. (J). (gr. k). 16.99 (978-0-525-46966-7(4) , Dutton Juvenile) Penguin Group (USA) Inc.

—Hanukkah at Valley Forge. Harlin, Greg, illus. 2006. 32p. (J). (gr. k). 17.99 (978-0-525-47738-9(1) , Dutton Juvenile) Penguin Group (USA) Inc.

Lavender, William. Just Jane: A Daughter of England Caught in the Struggle of the American Revolution. (Great Episodes Ser.). (YA). 2005. 336p. pap. 6.95 (978-0-15-205472-4(3)); 2002. 288p. 17.00 (978-0-15-202587-8(1)) Harcourt Children's Bks. (Gulliver Bks.).

Lee Gauch, Patricia. Aaron & the Green Mountain Boys. Tomes, Margot, illus. 2004. 64p. (YA). 9.95 (978-1-59078-354-2(9)); pap. 16.95 (978-1-59078-335-1(2)) Boyds Mills Pr.

Lunn, Janet. Hollow Tree. 1998. 272p. (J). mass mkt. (978-0-676-97143-9(1) , Knopf Canada) Knopf Canada CAN. *Dist:* Random Hse., Inc.

Marshall, Peter, et al. Nate Donovan: Revolutionary Spy. 2007. 208p. (J). pap. 9.99 ***(*978-0-8054-4394-3(0)*** , B&H Bks.) B&H Publishing Grp.

Massie, Elizabeth. Son of Liberty: 1776. 2000. (gr. 5-8). lib. bdg. 13.00 (978-0-613-28077-8(6)) Tandem Library Bks.

—1776: Son of Liberty: A Novel of the American Revolution. 2007. (Young Founders Ser.). 192p. (YA). 5.99 (978-0-7653-5273-6(7) , Tor Bks.) Doherty, Tom Associates, LLC.

McGahan, Mary. Raid at Red Mill. Butterfield, Ned, illus. 2001. (Adventures in America Ser.). 96p. (J). (gr. 3-7). lib. bdg. 14.95 (978-1-893110-11-3(7)) Silver Moon Pr.

McIntyre, John T. Fighting King George. 2006. (Illus.). pap. 33.95 ***(*978-1-4286-1853-4(8))*** Kessinger Publishing, LLC.

Miller, Susan Martins. The Boston Massacre. 1999. (American Adventure Ser.: No. 10). 144p. (J). (gr. 3-7). lib. bdg. 15.95 (978-0-7910-5584-7(1) , Chelsea Hse.) Facts On File, Inc.

—Boston Revolts! 1999. (American Adventure Ser.: No. 9). (Illus.). 144p. (J). (gr. 3-7). lib. bdg. 15.95 (978-0-7910-5583-0(3) , Chelsea Hse.) Facts On File, Inc.

Moss, Marissa. Emma's Journal: The Story of a Colonial Girl. Moss, Marissa, illus. 2001. (Young American Voices Ser.: Bk. 2). (Illus.). 56p. (YA). (gr. 3-7). pap. 7.00 (978-0-15-216325-9(5) , Silver Whistle) Harcourt Trade Pubs.

Murphy, Jim. A Young Patriot: The American Revolution as Experienced by One Boy. 1998. (J). (978-0-606-13941-0(9)) Tandem Library Bks.

Myers, Anna. The Keeping Room. 1999. (Illus.). 128p. (J). (gr. 3-7). pap. 5.99 (978-0-14-130468-7(5) , Puffin) Penguin Group (USA) Inc.

—The Keeping Room. 1999. (J). (978-0-606-16786-4(2)) Tandem Library Bks.

—Keeping Room. 1999. (gr. 3-6). lib. bdg. 14.15 (978-0-613-19519-5(1)) Tandem Library Bks.

Nixon, Joan Lowery. John's Story, 1775. 2004. (J). (978-0-87935-228-8(0)) Colonial Williamsburg Foundation.

Noble, Trinka Hakes. The Scarlet Stockings Spy. Papp, Robert, illus. 2004. 48p. (J). (gr. 1-7). 16.95 (978-1-58536-230-1(1)) Sleeping Bear Pr.

Olasky, Susan. Annie Henry: Adventures in the American Revolution. 2005. (Illus.). 528p. (J). pap. 16.99 (978-1-58134-521-6(6) , Crossway Bibles) Crossway Bks.

Osborne, Mary Pope. Revolutionary War on Wednesday, Vol. 22. unabr. ed. 2004. (Magic Tree House Ser. : No. 22). 69p. (J). (gr. k-3). pap. 17.00 incl. audio (978-0-8072-0931-8(7) , S FTR 254 SP, Listening Library) Random Hse. Audio Publishing Group.

—Revolutionary War on Wednesday. Loehr, Mallory, ed. Murdocca, Sal, illus. 2000. (Magic Tree House Ser.: No. 22). 96p. (J). (gr. k-3). lib. bdg. 11.99 (978-0-679-99068-0(2)); pap. 3.99 (978-0-679-89068-3(8)) Random Hse. Children's Bks. (Random Hse. Bks. for Young Readers).

—Revolutionary War on Wednesday. Murdocca, Salvatore, illus. 2000. (Magic Tree House Ser. : No. 22). 69p. (J). (gr. k-3). lib. bdg. 11.80 (978-0-613-28355-7(4)) Tandem Library Bks.

—Revolutionary War on Wednesday. Murdocca, Sal, illus. 2000. (Magic Tree House Ser. : No. 22). (J). (gr. k-3). (978-0-606-19907-0(1)) Tandem Library Bks.

Owens, Tom. The Bravest Blacksmith. Hatala, Dan, illus. 2000. (Cover-to-Cover Bks.). 56p. (J). (gr. 1-4). lib. bdg. 16.95 (978-0-7807-9266-1(1)) Perfection Learning Corp.

—Flames of Freedom. Muchmore, Pat, illus. 2001. (Cover-to-Cover Bks.). 56p. (J). (gr. 1-4). lib. bdg. 16.95 (978-0-7807-9040-7(5)) Perfection Learning Corp.

Paulsen, Gary. The Rifle. 2006. 112p. (J). pap. 5.95 (978-0-15-205839-5(7)) Harcourt Trade Pubs.

Pettinato, Laura. Thirteen Americas: American Revolution & Constitution. Tiwari, Saral, illus. 2004. (J). 18.95 (978-0-9742502-7-4(9)) Gossamer Bks., LLC.

—Thirteen Americas: The Declaration of Independence. Tiwari, Saral, illus. 2nd ed. 2004. (J). lib. bdg. (978-0-9742502-6-7(0)) Gossamer Bks., LLC.

Prentice-Hall Staff. J. Tremain. 2nd ed. (J). stu. ed. (978-0-13-717174-3(9)) Prentice Hall (Schl. Div.).

Pryor, Bonnie. Hannah Pritchard: Girl Pirate of the Revolution. 2008. (Historical Fiction Adventures (HFA) Ser.). (Illus.). 160p. (J). (gr. 3-6). lib. bdg. 27.93 ***(*978-0-7660-2851-7(8))*** Enslow Pubs., Inc.

—Thomas: 1778, Patriots on the Run. 2000. (American Adventures Ser.). (978-0-606-17981-2(X)) Tandem Library Bks.

—Thomas in Danger, 1779. Dodson, Bert, illus. 2000. (American Adventures Ser.). 176p. (J). (gr. 3-7). pap. 4.95 (978-0-380-73212-8(2)) HarperCollins Pubs.

Quackenbush, Robert. Daughter of Liberty. 1999. (J). 11.79 (978-0-606-16661-4(0)) Tandem Library Bks.

—Daughter of Liberty: A True Story of the American Revolution. 1999. (gr. 3-6). lib. bdg. 13.00 (978-0-613-16485-6(7)) Tandem Library Bks.

Reit, Seymour V. Guns for General Washington: A Story of the American Revolution. 2001. (Great Episodes Ser.). 160p. (YA). (gr. 5-9). pap. 6.00 (978-0-15-216435-5(9) , Gulliver Bks.) Harcourt Children's Bks.

Rinaldi, Ann. The Fifth of March: A Story of the Boston Massacre. 2nd ed. 2002. (J). 4.80 (978-0-03-073524-0(6)) Holt, Rinehart & Winston.

—Finishing Becca: A Story about Peggy Shippen & Benedict Arnold. 2004. (Great Episodes Ser.). 384p. (YA). pap. 6.95 (978-0-15-205079-5(5) , Gulliver Bks.) Harcourt Children's Bks.

—Or Give Me Death: A Novel of Patrick Henry's Family. (Great Episodes Ser.). 240p. (YA). 2004. pap. 6.95 (978-0-15-205076-4(0)); 2003. 17.00 (978-0-15-216687-8(4)) Harcourt Children's Bks. (Gulliver Bks.).

—A Ride into Morning: The Story of Tempe Wick. 2003. (Great Episodes Ser.). 368p. (YA). pap. 6.95 (978-0-15-204683-5(6) , Gulliver Bks.) Harcourt Children's Bks.

—A Ride into Morning: The Story of Tempe Wick. l.t. ed. 2005. 383p. (YA). 21.95 (978-0-7862-7957-9(5) , Large Print Pr.) Thorndike Pr.

—The Secret of Sarah Revere. 2003. (Great Episodes Ser.). 336p. (YA). pap. 6.95 (978-0-15-204684-2(4) , Gulliver Bks.) Harcourt Children's Bks.

Roop, Peter. Eye for an Eye: A Story of the Revolutionary War. 2000. (gr. 5-8). lib. bdg. 15.70 (978-0-613-36805-6(3)) Tandem Library Bks.

Roop, Peter & Roop, Connie. An Eye for an Eye: A Story of the American Revolution. 2001. (Jamestown Classics Ser.). (Illus.). 168p. (J). (gr. 5-8). 15.32 (978-0-8092-0587-5(4) , 9780809205875) Jamestown.

—An Eye for an Eye: A Story of the Revolutionary War. 2004. (Jamestown's American Portraits Ser.). (Illus.). 176p. (J). (gr. 5-7). pap. 4.95 (978-0-7696-3422-7(2) , Waterbird Bks.) School Specialty Publishing.

Roop, Peter and Connie. An Eye for an Eye. 2004. 168p. (J). lib. bdg. 16.92 ***(*978-1-4242-0772-5(X))*** Fitzgerald Bks.

Rosenburg, John M. First in War: George Washington in the American Revolution. 1998. (Single Titles Ser.: up). (Illus.). 256p. (gr. 7-12). lib. bdg. 25.90 (978-0-7613-0311-4(1) , Millbrook Pr.) Lerner Publishing Group.

Rue, Nancy N. The Invasion. 1998. (Christian Heritage Ser.). 192p. (J). (gr. 3-7). pap. (978-1-56179-541-3(0)) Focus on the Family Publishing.

—Invasion. 1998. (gr. 3-6). lib. bdg. 14.15 (978-0-613-85284-5(2)) Tandem Library Bks.

—The Thief. 1998. (Christian Heritage Ser.). 192p. (J). (gr. 3-7). pap. (978-1-56179-479-9(1)) Focus on the Family Publishing.

Sargent, Dave & Sargent, Pat. Dan: (Dappled Mahogany Bay) Determination, 25, 21. Lenoir, Jane, illus. 2001. (Saddle Up Ser.: 21). 36p. (J). pap. 6.95 (978-1-56763-652-9(7)); lib. bdg. 22.60 (978-1-56763-651-2(9)) Ozark Publishing.

Schurfranz, Vivian. A Message for General Washington. 1998. (Stories of the States Ser.: Vol. 10). 92p. (J). (gr. 4-7). lib. bdg. 14.95 (978-1-881889-89-2(0)) Silver Moon Pr.

Scieszka, Jon. Oh Say, I Can't See. McCauley, Adam, illus. 2007. (Time Warp Trio Ser.: No. 15). 80p. (J). (gr. 2-6). pap. 4.99 (978-0-14-240808-7(5) , Puffin) Penguin Group (USA) Inc.

Singmaster, Elsie. Rifles for Washington. 2005. pap. 30.95 (978-1-4191-0108-3(0)) Kessinger Publishing, LLC.

Skinner, Constance Lindsay. Becky Landers: Frontier Warrior. 2006. (Living History Library). 200p. (J). pap. 13.95 (978-1-932350-06-7(3)) Bethlehem Bks.

Smith, Donna Campbell. An Independent Spirit: The Tale of Betsy Dowdy & Black Bess. 2006. (Illus.). 182p. (J). per. 11.95 (978-0-9779889-0-7(2)) Faithful Publishing.

Smith, Lane. John, Paul, George & Ben. 2006. (Illus.). 40p. (J). (ps-k). 16.99 (978-0-7868-4893-5(6)) Hyperion Pr.

Stratemeyer, Edward. The Minute Boys of Bunker Hill. Kennedy, J. W., illus. rev. ed. 1998. 316p. (J). (gr. 4-8). per. 14.95 (978-1-890623-05-0(9)) Lost Classics Bk. Co.

Sweetzer, Anna Leah, et al. Treason Stops at Oyster Bay. 1999. (Mysteries in Time Ser.: Vol. 7). (Illus.). 90p. (J). (gr. 3-7). lib. bdg. 14.95 (978-1-893110-03-8(6)) Silver Moon Pr.

TUV

Switzer-Clarke, Eileen. Blossom: A Girl's Adventures in Revolutionary Rockland. Carney, Barbara J., illus. 1998. 108p. (J). (gr. 3-6). pap. 8.00 (978-0-911183-44-3(2)) Historical Society of Rockland County, The.

Turner, Ann Warren. When Mr. Jefferson Came to Philadelphia: What I Learned of Freedom 1776. Hess, Mark, illus. 2004. 32p. (J). (ps-3). 15.99 (978-0-06-027579-2(0)) HarperCollins Pubs.

Turner Curtis, Alice. Little Maid of Mohawk Valley. 2004. (Little Maid Ser.). 192p. (J). (gr. 1-3). per. 9.95 (978-1-55709-337-0(7)) Applewood Bks.

Walker, Sally. 18 Penny Goose. 1999. (gr. k-3). lib. bdg. 11.80 (978-0-613-15776-6(1)) Tandem Library Bks.

Walker, Sally M. The 18 Penny Goose. Beier, Ellen, illus. 1998. (I Can Read Bks.). 64p. (J). (gr. k-3). 15.89 (978-0-06-027557-0(X)) HarperCollins Pubs.

Washington, Ida H. Brave Enough: The Story of Rob Sanford, Vermont Pioneer Boy. Smoak, I. W. & Washington, C. E., illus. 2003. vii, 128p. (J). (gr. 4-6). pap. 12.95 (978-0-9666832-7-1(7)) Cherry Tree Bks.

Waters, Kate. Mary Geddy's Day: A Colonial Girl in Williamsburg. 2002. (gr. k-3). lib. bdg. 14.15 (978-0-613-57317-7(X)) Tandem Library Bks.

White, Capers. The British Are Coming! McNeely, Tom, illus. 2002. 16p. (J). (978-0-439-35161-4(8)) Scholastic, Inc.

UNITED STATES—HISTORY—REVOLUTION, 1775-1783—NAVAL OPERATIONS

Abbot, Willis J. Blue Jackets of 1876: A History of the Naval Battles of the American Revolution Together with a Narrative of the War with Tripoli. 2006. (Illus.). pap. 30.95 (***978-1-4286-1609-7(8)***) Kessinger Publishing, LLC.

Alphin, Elaine Marie & Alphin, Arthur B. I Have Not Yet Begun to Fight: A Story about John Paul Jones. Casale, Paul, tr. Casale, Paul, illus. 2004. (Creative Minds Biography Ser.). 64p. (J). 22.60 (978-1-57505-601-2(1), Carolrhoda Bks.) Lerner Publishing Group.

Brager, Bruce L. John Paul Jones: America's Sailor. 2006. (Illus.). 160p. (J). lib. bdg. 26.95 (978-1-931798-84-6(2)) Reynolds, Morgan Inc.

Cooper, Michael. Hero of the High Seas: John Paul Jones & the American Revolution. 2006. (Illus.). 128p. (J). (gr. 5). 32.90 (978-0-7922-5548-2(8)); pap. 21.95 (978-0-7922-5547-5(X)) National Geographic Society. (National Geographic Children's Bks.).

Harkins, Susan and William. The Life & Times of John Paul Jones. 2007. (Profiles in American History Ser.). (Illus.). 48p. (J). lib. bdg. 22.95 (***978-1-58415-529-4(9)***) Mitchell Lane Pubs., Inc.

Haugen, Brenda & Santella, Andrew. John Paul Jones: Father of the American Navy. 2004. (Signature Lives Ser.). (Illus.). 112p. (J). 30.60 (978-0-7565-0829-6(0)) Compass Point Bks.

Price Hossell, Karen. John Paul Jones. 2004. (American War Biographies Ser.). (J). pap. 8.50 (978-1-4034-5086-9(2)); lib. bdg. 29.93 (978-1-4034-5079-1(X)) Heinemann Library.

Riley, John B. John Paul Jones: A Photo Biography. l.t. ed. 2004. (First Biographies Ser.). (Illus.). 24p. (YA). (gr. 5 up). 16.95 (978-1-883846-63-3(3), First Biographies) Reynolds, Morgan Inc.

Smolinski, Diane. Naval Warfare of the Revolutionary War. (Americans at War Ser.). (Illus.). 32p. (J). (gr. 4-6). 2002. pap. 6.95 (978-1-58810-561-5(X), 91692); 2001. lib. bdg. (978-1-58810-275-1(0)) Heinemann Library.

Sperry, Armstrong. John Paul Jones: The Pirate Patriot. 2006. (Sterling Point Bks.). (Illus.). 176p. (J). 12.95 (978-1-4027-3185-3(X)); pap. 6.95 (978-1-4027-3615-5(0)) Sterling Publishing Co., Inc.

UNITED STATES—HISTORY—1783-1809

see also Constitutional History United States; Lewis and Clark Expedition (1804-1806); Louisiana Purchase

Clifton, Chuck & Clifton, Joyce. A Daily Walk with Lewis & Clark - 1805. 2003. 390p. (J). spiral bd. 14.95 (978-0-9669760-4-5(5)) Maple Canyon Co.

—A Daily Walk with Lewis & Clark - 1806. 2003. 292p. (J). spiral bd. 14.95 (978-0-9669760-5-2(3)) Maple Canyon Co.

Collier, Christopher & Collier, James Lincoln. Building a New Nation: 1789-1803. 1998. (Drama of American History Ser.). (Illus.). 96p. (J). (gr. 5-9). lib. bdg. 31.36 (978-0-7614-0777-5(4), Benchmark Bks.) Cavendish, Marshall Corp.

—Creating the Constitution: 1787. 1998. (Drama of American History Ser.). (Illus.). 96p. (J). (gr. 5-9). lib. bdg. 31.36 (978-0-7614-0776-8(6), Benchmark Bks.) Cavendish, Marshall Corp.

Fritz, Jean. Shh! We're Writing the Constitution. de Paola, Tomie, illus. 2004. (J). pap. 14.95 incl. audio (978-1-56008-226-2(7)) Weston Woods Studios, Inc.

Hakim, Joy. From Colonies to Country 1735-1791. 3rd ed. 2002. (History of US Ser.). (Illus.). 112p. pap., tchr. ed. 16.95 (978-0-19-515353-8(7)) Oxford Univ. Pr., Inc.

Konstam, Angus. America Speaks, 10 vols. 2005. (Illus.). (J). (978-0-7172-6020-1(8)); (978-0-7172-6021-8(6)); (978-0-7172-6022-5(4)); (978-0-7172-6023-2(2)); (978-0-7172-6024-9(0)); (978-0-7172-6025-6(9)); (978-0-7172-6026-3(7)); (978-0-7172-6027-0(5)); (978-0-7172-6028-7(3)); (978-0-7172-6029-4(1)) Grolier, Ltd.

—America Speaks, 10 vols., Set. 2005. (Illus.). (J). (gr. 5-10). lib. bdg. 199.00 (978-0-7172-6030-0(5), Grolier) Scholastic Library Publishing.

Schlaepfer, Gloria G. The Louisiana Purchase. 2005. (Watts Library). (Illus.). 63p. (J). (gr. 5-8). 25.50 (978-0-531-12300-3(6), Watts, Franklin) Scholastic Library Publishing.

UNITED STATES—HISTORY—1783-1809—BIOGRAPHY

Marrin, Albert. George Washington & the Founding of a Nation. Brooks, Donna, ed. 2001. (Illus.). 256p. (J). (gr. 7 up). 30.00 (978-0-525-46481-5(6), Dutton Juvenile) Penguin Group (USA) Inc.

UNITED STATES—HISTORY—1783-1809—FICTION

McCully, Emily Arnold. The Escape of Oney Judge: Martha Washington's Slave Finds Freedom. 2007. (Illus.). 32p. (J). (gr. 1). 16.00 (978-0-374-32225-0(2), Farrar, Straus & Giroux (BYR)) Farrar, Straus & Giroux.

Wood, Frances M. Becoming Rosemary. 1998. (J). (978-0-606-13186-5(8)) Tandem Library Bks.

UNITED STATES—HISTORY—1783-1865

Bagley, Katie. The Early American Industrial Revolution, 1793-1850. 2003. (Let Freedom Ring Ser.). (Illus.). 48p. (J). (gr. 3-4). lib. bdg. 22.60 (978-0-7368-1557-4(0), Bridgestone Bks.) Capstone Pr., Inc.

Brownstone, David M. & Franck, Irene M. The Young Nation: America 1787-1861, 10 vols. 2002. (Illus.). 960p. (J). 339.00 (978-0-7172-5645-7(6), Grolier) Scholastic Library Publishing.

Center for Learning Network Staff. Antebellum America & Civil War: 1840-1865 — Primary Sources in U. S. History Series. 2000. (Social Studies Ser.). 104p. (YA). (gr. 9-12). tchr. ed., spiral bd. 29.95 (978-1-56077-614-7(5)) Ctr. for Learning, The.

Cloud Tapper, Suzanne. The Abolition of Slavery: Fighting for a Free America. 2006. (American Saga Ser.). (Illus.). 128p. (J). (gr. 5 up). lib. bdg. 31.93 (978-0-7660-2605-6(1)) Enslow Pubs., Inc.

Hakim, Joy. A History of US: Vol 4, the New Nation. rev. ed. 2007. (History of US Ser.). 208p. pap. 15.95 (***978-0-19-532718-2(7)***) Oxford Univ. Pr., Inc.

—A History of US Bk. 4: The New Nation. 3rd rev. ed. 2005. (History of US Ser.). (Illus.). 208p. 19.95 (978-0-19-518897-4(5)) Oxford Univ. Pr., Inc.

—A History of US Bk. 6: War, Terrible War 1855-1865. 3rd ed. 2002. (History of US Ser.). (Illus.). 112p. pap., tchr. ed. 16.95 (978-0-19-515356-9(1)) Oxford Univ. Pr., Inc.

—Liberty for All? 1820-1860 Teaching Guide. 3rd ed. 2002. (History of US Ser.). 112p. pap., tchr. ed. 16.95 (978-0-19-515355-2(3)) Oxford Univ. Pr., Inc.

—The New Nation 1789-1850, Bk. 4. 3rd ed. 2002. (History of US Ser.). (Illus.). 112p. pap., tchr. ed. 16.95 (978-0-19-515354-5(5)) Oxford Univ. Pr., Inc.

Hanes, Richard Clay, et al. Shaping of America, 1783-1815, Reference Library, 5 vols. 2005. (Illus.). (J). (978-1-4144-0184-3(1)); (978-1-4144-0185-0(X)) Thomson Gale. (UXL).

Holt, Rinehart and Winston Staff. Call to Freedom: Beginning-1877: Geography Activities - Answer Key. 3rd ed. 2001. pap. 8.00 (978-0-03-066683-4(X)) Holt, Rinehart & Winston.

Lusted, Marcia Amidon. Revolution & the New Nation. 2007. (***978-1-59036-739-1(1)***) Weigl Pubs., Inc.

McGraw-Hill Staff. American Republic to 1877. 2002. (C). pap., stu. ed., wbk. ed. 10.00 (978-0-07-829144-9(5), 9780078291449) Glencoe/McGraw-Hill.

—The American Republic to 1877. 2nd ed. 2004. (C). stu. ed. 86.00 (978-0-07-860983-1(6), 9780078609831) Glencoe/McGraw-Hill.

Porterfield, Jason. The Lincoln-Douglas Senatorial Debates of 1858: A Primary Source Investigation. 2004. (Great Historic Debates & Speeches Ser.). (Illus.). 64p. (YA). lib. bdg. 29.25 (978-1-4042-0153-8(X)) Rosen Publishing Group, Inc., The.

Stanley, George Edward. The New Republic (1763-1815) 2005. (Illus.). 48p. (J). pap. (978-0-8368-5834-1(4)); lib. bdg. 30.00 (978-0-8368-5825-9(5)) Stevens, Gareth Inc. (World Almanac Library).

UNITED STATES—HISTORY—1783-1865—BIOGRAPHY

Robinson Masters, Nancy. Extraordinary Patriots of the United States of America: Colonial Times to Pre-Civil War. 2005. (Extraordinary People Ser.). (Illus.). 288p. (J). 40.00 (978-0-516-24404-4(3), Children's Pr.) Scholastic Library Publishing.

UNITED STATES—HISTORY—1783-1865—FICTION

Armstrong, Jennifer. Thomas Jefferson: Letters from a Philadelphia Bookworm. 2001. (Dear Mr. President Ser.: Vol. 2). (Illus.). 117p. (J). (gr. 5-7). 8.95 (978-1-890817-30-5(9)) Winslow Pr.

Beaudouin, Frank, et al, illus. Cleared for Action: Four Tales of the Sea. 2002. (Bethlehem Budget Books). 600p. (J). 19.95 (978-1-883937-55-3(8)) Bethlehem Bks.

Hopkinson, Deborah. Under the Quilt of Night. Ransome, James E., illus. 40p. (J). 2002. 18.99 (978-0-689-82227-8(8), Atheneum/Anne Schwartz Bks.); 2005. reprint ed. 7.99 (978-0-689-87700-1(5), Aladdin) Simon & Schuster Children's Publishing.

Lyons, Mary E. Poison Place. 1999. (978-0-606-16334-7(4)) Tandem Library Bks.

Mosley, Walter. 47. 240p. (gr. 7-17). 2005. (YA). 16.99 (978-0-316-11035-8(3)); 2006. (J). reprint ed. pap. 7.99 (978-0-316-01635-3(7)) Little Brown & Co.

Yep, Laurence. My Name Is America: The Journal of Wongming-chun, A Chinese Miner. 2000. (My Name Is America Ser.). (Illus.). 224p. (J). (gr. 4-8). pap. 10.95 (978-0-590-38607-4(7)) Scholastic, Inc.

UNITED STATES—HISTORY—19TH CENTURY

Anderson, Dale. A Soldier's Life in the Civil War. 2004. (World Almanac Library of the Civil War). (Illus.). 48p. (J). (gr. 5 up). pap. 11.95 (978-0-8368-5595-1(7)); lib. bdg. 30.00 (978-0-8368-5586-9(8)) Stevens, Gareth Inc. (World Almanac Library).

Bolden, Tonya. Cause: Reconstruction America 1863-1877. 2005. (Illus.). 144p. (J). (gr. 3-7). 19.95 (978-0-375-82795-2(1)); lib. bdg. 21.99 (978-0-375-92795-9(6)) Random Hse. Children's Bks. (Knopf Bks. for Young Readers).

Burgan, Michael. Escaping to Freedom: The Underground Railroad. 2006. (Slavery in the Americas Ser.). (Illus.). 112p. (J). (gr. 4-9). 35.00 (978-0-8160-6137-2(8)) Facts On File, Inc.

Bussey, Jennifer. Events That Changed the World - 1820-1840. 2004. (Events That Changed the World Ser.). (Illus.). 143p. (gr. 10-12). 36.20 (978-0-7377-2031-0(X), Greenhaven Pr., Inc.) Thomson Gale.

—1820-1840 (Events That Changed the World) 2004. (gr. 10-12). 22.45 (978-0-7377-2032-7(8), Greenhaven Pr., Inc.) Thomson Gale.

Carson, Mary Kay. The Underground Railroad for Kids: From Slavery to Freedom with 21 Activities. 2005. (For Kids Ser.). (Illus.). 176p. (J). pap. 14.95 (978-1-55652-554-4(0)) Chicago Review Pr., Inc.

Connell, Kate & Feresten, Nancy. Servant to Abigail Adams: The Early Colonial Adventures of Hannah Cooper. 2003. (I Am American Ser.). (Illus.). 40p. (J). (gr. 3-7). pap. 6.99 (978-0-7922-5828-5(2), National Geographic Children's Bks.) National Geographic Society.

Depew, Lanette. A Bridge Spanning Time. 2003. 128p. (J). pap. 9.95 (978-1-57072-236-3(6)) Overmountain Pr.

Dickens, Charles. Martin Chuzzlewit. 2000. (gr. 7-12). lib. bdg. 19.90 (978-0-613-70856-2(3)) Tandem Library Bks.

Doyle, Kelly. 1880-1900 (Events That Changed the World) 2004. (Illus.). (gr. 10-12). 22.45 (978-0-7377-2036-5(0), Greenhaven Pr., Inc.) Thomson Gale.

Fisanick, Christina. Events that Changed the World - 1800-1820. 2004. (Events That Changed the World Ser.). (Illus.). 173p. (gr. 10-12). 36.20 (978-0-7377-2029-7(8), Greenhaven Pr., Inc.) Thomson Gale.

—1800-1820 (Events That Changed the World) 2004. (gr. 10-12). 22.45 (978-0-7377-2030-3(1), Greenhaven Pr., Inc.) Thomson Gale.

Haskins, Jim. The Geography of Hope: Black Exodus from the South after Reconstruction. 1999. (Single Titles Ser.: up). (Illus.). 144p. (gr. 7 up). lib. bdg. 31.90 (978-0-7613-0323-7(5), Millbrook Pr.) Lerner Publishing Group.

Hudson, Wade. The Underground Railroad. 2007. (Cornerstones of Freedomtrade:, Second Ser.). 48p. (J). pap. 5.95 (***978-0-531-18770-8(5)***, Children's Pr.) Scholastic Library Publishing.

Jacobs, Harriet A. Incidents in the Life of a Slave Girl. 2000. (gr. 7-12). lib. bdg. 14.10 (978-0-613-21756-9(X)) Tandem Library Bks.

Moore, Heidi. Elizabeth Cady Stanton. 2004. (American Lives (Heinemann Library (Firm))). (Illus.). 32p. (J). pap. 6.95 (978-1-4034-5705-9(0)); lib. bdg. (978-1-4034-4994-8(5)) Heinemann Library.

Morrison, Taylor. The Coast Mappers. 2004. (Illus.). 48p. (J). (gr. 3-5). tchr. ed. 16.00 (978-0-618-25408-8(0), Walter Lorraine) Houghton Mifflin Co. Trade & Reference Div.

Page, Mary S. & Metzger, Larry. Voices & Masks: The Experience of Nineteenth Century Mill Girls & Enslaved Women from Primary Sources. 2000. 223p. (YA). (gr. 10-12). 12.67 (978-1-877653-67-4(5)) Wayside Publishing.

Pierce, Alan. Lincoln-Douglas Debates. 2005. (American Moments Set Ii Ser.). (Illus.). 48p. (J). (gr. 4-8). lib. bdg. 25.65 (978-1-59197-734-6(7), ABDO & Daughters) ABDO Publishing Co.

Primary Sources of America's Industrial Society in the 19th Century. (Primary Source Big Bookssm Ser.). 24p. (J). (gr. 4-8). 46.60 (978-0-8239-4598-6(7)) Rosen Publishing Group, Inc., The.

Schaffer, David. The Louisiana Purchase—the Deal of the Century That Doubled the Nation. 2006. (Wild History of the American West Ser.). (Illus.). 128p. (J). lib. bdg. 33.27 (978-1-59845-018-7(2), MyReportLinks.com Bks.) Enslow Pubs., Inc.

Simms, Patsy Ford. Harriet's Freedom Train. 2000. (J). stu. ed. 12.50 (978-0-7692-9377-6(8)); tchr. ed. 24.95 (978-0-7692-9376-9(X)) Alfred Publishing Co., Inc. (Warner Bros. Pubns.).

Swanson, Wayne. Why the West Was Wild. 2004. (Illus.). 48p. (J). (gr. 5). 24.95 (978-1-55037-837-5(6)); pap. 12.95 (978-1-55037-836-8(8)) Annick Pr., Ltd. CAN. *Dist:* Firefly Bks., Ltd.

Thoennes Keller, Kristin. The Slave Trade in Early America. 2004. (Let Freedom Ring Ser.). (Illus.). 48p. (J). 17.95 (978-0-7368-2465-1(0), Bridgestone Bks.) Capstone Pr., Inc.

Zdrok, Jodie L. 1840-1860- The 19th Century. 2004. (Events That Changed the World Ser.). (Illus.). 175p. (gr. 10-12). 36.20 (978-0-7377-2033-4(6), Greenhaven Pr., Inc.) Thomson Gale.

—1840-1860 (Events That Changed the World) 2004. (Events That Changed the World Ser.). (Illus.). 175p. (gr. 10-12). 22.45 (978-0-7377-2034-1(4), Greenhaven Pr., Inc.) Thomson Gale.

UNITED STATES—HISTORY—19TH CENTURY—FICTION

Alger, Horatio. The Young Musician. reprint ed. pap. 79.00 (978-1-4047-3629-0(8)) Classic Textbooks.

—The Young Musician. 2006. pap. (***978-1-4068-0673-1(0)***) Echo Library.

Ambrose, Stephen E. This Vast Land: A Young Man's Journal of the Lewis & Clark Expedition. l.t. ed. 2004. 265p. (J). 22.95 (978-0-7862-6139-0(0)) Thorndike Pr.

Burkhard, Daryl. Riddle in the Mountain. Riccio, Frank, illus. 2005. 240p. 16.95 (978-0-9668289-5-5(X)) Nomad Pr.

Durrant, Lynda. My Last Skirt: The Story of Jennie Hodgers, Union Soldier. 2006. 192p. (J). (gr. 5). 16.00 (978-0-618-57490-2(5), Clarion Bks.) Houghton Mifflin Co. Trade & Reference Div.

Fletcher, Susan. Walk Across the Sea. Jakesevic, Nenad, illus. 2003. 224p. (J). pap. 11.95 (978-0-689-85707-2(1), Aladdin) Simon & Schuster Children's Publishing.

—Walk Across the Sea. 2003. (gr. 3-6). lib. bdg. 13.00 (978-0-613-62227-1(8)) Tandem Library Bks.

Golden, Christopher & Gilmore, Ford Lytle. Enemies, No. 4. 2006. (Hollow Ser.: No. 4). 240p. (YA). (gr. 7-12). mass mkt. 6.99 (978-1-59514-027-2(1), Razorbill) Penguin Group (USA) Inc.

Greenwood, Barbara. Pioneer Thanksgiving: A Story of Harvest Celebrations In 1841. 1999. (gr. 3-6). lib. bdg. 14.10 (978-0-613-22181-8(8)) Tandem Library Bks.

Hart, Alison. Fires of Jubilee. 2003. (Aladdin Historical Fiction Ser.). (Illus.). 192p. (J). pap. 4.99 (978-0-689-85528-3(1), Aladdin) Simon & Schuster Children's Publishing.

—Fires of Jubilee. 2003. (gr. 5-8). lib. bdg. 13.00 (978-0-613-90183-3(5)) Tandem Library Bks.

Hedstrom-Page, Deborah. From Log Cabin to White House with Abraham Lincoln. Martinez, Sergio, illus. 2007. 80p. (J). (gr. 3-9). 9.99 (978-0-8054-3269-5(8)) B&H Publishing Grp.

Holt, Rinehart and Winston Staff. Slave Dancer. 3rd ed. 2003. (Illus.). 16.75 (978-0-03-035274-4(6)) Holt, Rinehart & Winston.

Hughes, Lynn Gordon. To Live a Truer Life: A Story of the Hopedale Community. Lindro, illus. 2003. 32p. (J). 20.00 (978-0-9725017-2-9(X)) Blackstone Editions.

Ingold, Jeanette. Hitch. 2005. 288p. (YA). (gr. 7-12). 17.00 (978-0-15-204747-4(6)) Harcourt Children's Bks.

Kimmel, Elizabeth Cody. One Sky above Us. Snow, Scott, illus. 2004. (Adventures of Young Buffalo Bill Ser.). 192p. (J). pap. 5.99 (978-0-06-440895-0(7), Harper Trophy) HarperCollins Pubs.

Kroll, Steven. When I Dream of Heaven: Angelina's Story. 2004. (Jamestown's American Portraits Ser.). (Illus.). 160p. (J). (gr. 5-7). pap. 4.95 (978-0-7696-3424-1(9), Waterbird Bks.) School Specialty Publishing.

Mazer, Harry. A Boy No More. 2004. (Illus.). 144p. (J). 16.95 (978-0-689-85533-7(8)) Simon & Schuster Children's Publishing.

Reed, Wilfred. Andy & Mark & the Time Machine: Custer's Last Stand. 2003. 240p. (YA). pap. 15.95 (978-0-595-26496-4(4), Writers Club Pr.) iUniverse, Inc.

Rees, Shirley. Hannah Stands Tall. 2002. 130p. (J). pap. 10.95 (978-1-55517-652-5(6), 76526, Bonneville Bks.) Cedar Fort, Inc./CFI Distribution.

Rinaldi, Ann. An Unlikely Friendship: A Novel of Mary Todd Lincoln & Elizabeth Keckley. 2007. (Harcourt Great Episodes Ser.). (Illus.). 256p. (YA). (gr. 6-9). 17.00 (978-0-15-205597-4(5)) Harcourt Children's Bks.

Stratemeyer, Edward. The Rover Boys at College: The Right Road & the Wrong. l.t. ed. 2006. 180p. pap. 11.99 (***978-1-4264-4042-7(1)***); 202p. pap. 15.99 (***978-1-4264-4101-1(0)***) BiblioBazaar.

Tripp, Valerie. Josefina's Boxed Set: Meet Josefina; Josefina Learns a Lesson; Josefina's Surprise; Happy Birthday, Josefina; Josefina Saves the Day; Changes for Josefina, 6 bks. Tibbles, Jean-Paul & McAliley, Susan, illus. 1998. (American Girls Collection: Bks. 1-6). 432p. (J). (gr. 2-7). 74.95 (978-1-56247-676-2(9)) American Girl Publishing, Inc.

Wilson, Jane G. Pair of Winners. 2000. (gr. 7-12). lib. bdg. 21.60 (978-0-613-74528-4(0)) Tandem Library Bks.

Winfield, Arthur M. Rover Boys at College or the Right Road. 2006. pap. 30.95 (***978-1-4286-4106-8(8)***) Kessinger Publishing, LLC.

Winfield, M. Arthur. The Rover Boys at College or the Right R. 2006. 96.99 (***978-1-4219-7415-6(0)***); pap. 90.99 (***978-1-4219-7402-6(9)***) IndyPublish.com.

Wood, Frances M. Daughter of Madrugada. l.t. ed. 2004. 170p. 20.95 (978-0-7862-6142-0(0)) Thorndike Pr.

Yep, Laurence. The Traitor: Golden Mountain Chronicles: 1885. 2004. (Golden Mountain Chronicles). 320p. (J). (gr. 5 up). pap. 6.99 (978-0-06-000831-4(8), Harper Trophy) HarperCollins Pubs.

UNITED STATES—HISTORY—TRIPOLITAN WAR, 1801-1805

Abbot, Willis J. Blue Jackets of 1876: A History of the Naval Battles of the American Revolution Together with a Narrative of the War with Tripoli. 2006. (Illus.). pap. 30.95 (***978-1-4286-1609-7(8)***) Kessinger Publishing, LLC.

Forester, C. S. Sterling Point Books: the Barbary Pirates. 2007. (Sterling Point Bks.). (Illus.). 176p. (J). 12.95 (978-1-4027-4522-5(2)); pap. 6.95 (978-1-4027-4142-5(1)) Sterling Publishing Co., Inc.

UNITED STATES—HISTORY—WAR OF 1812

Bartoletti, Susan Campbell. The Flag Maker. Nivola, Claire A., illus. 2007. 32p. (J). (gr. 3-5). 6.95 (***978-0-618-80911-0(2)***) Houghton Mifflin Co. Trade & Reference Div.

Beyer, Mark. The War of 1812: The New American Nation Goes to War with England. 2003. (Life in the New American Nation Ser.). (Illus.). 32p. (YA). pap. (978-0-8239-4261-9(9)) Rosen Publishing Group, Inc., The.

Bowdish, Lynea. Francis Scott Key & "The Star Spangled Banner" 2002. (Illus.). 32p. (J). 15.95 (978-1-59034-195-7(3)) Mondo Publishing.

Bozonelis, Helen Koutras. Primary Source Accounts of the War of 1812. 2006. (America's Wars Through Primary Sources Ser.). (Illus.). 128p. (YA). (gr. 5-8). lib. bdg. 33.27 (978-1-59845-006-4(9), MyReportLinks.com Bks.) Enslow Pubs., Inc.

Childress, Diana. The War of 1812. 2004. (Chronicle of America's Wars Ser.). (Illus.). 96p. (J). (gr. 5-12). 27.93 (978-0-8225-0800-7(1)) Lerner Publishing Group.

TUV

Crewe, Sabrina & Ingram, Scott. The Writing of "The Star-Spangled Banner" 2004. (Events That Shaped America Ser.). (Illus.). 32p. lib. bdg. 24.67 (978-0-8368-3409-3(7)) Stevens, Gareth Inc.

Cunningham, Alvin Robert. Washington Is Burning! The War of 1812. 2003. (Reading Essentials in Social Studies). (Illus.). 48p. (J). (978-0-7891-5896-3(5)) Perfection Learning Corp.

Dell, Pamela. The National Anthem. 2004. (Let's See Library). (Illus.). 24p. (J). (gr. 1 up). lib. bdg. 19.93 (978-0-7565-0619-3(0)) Compass Point Bks.

Edelman, Rob & Kupferberg, Audrey. The War of 1812. 2005. (People at the Center of Ser.). (Illus.). 48p. (J). (ps-7). lib. bdg. 24.95 (978-1-56711-926-8(3) , Blackbirch Pr., Inc.) Thomson Gale.

Figley, Marty Rhodes. Washington Is Burning. Orback, Craig, illus. 2006. (On My Own History Ser.). 48p. (J). 25.26 (978-1-57505-875-7(8)) Lerner Publishing Group.

Green, Carl R. The War of 1812: A MyReportLinks.com Book. 2002. (U. S. Wars Ser.). (Illus.). 48p. (J). (gr. 4-10). lib. bdg. 25.26 (978-0-7660-5092-1(0)) Enslow Pubs., Inc.

Greenblatt, Miriam. War of 1812. 2nd ed. 2003. (America at War Ser.). (Illus.). 176p. (J). (gr. 6-12). 35.00 (978-0-8160-4933-2(5)) Facts On File, Inc.

Haberle, Susan E. The War of 1812. 2003. (Let Freedom Ring Ser.). (Illus.). 48p. (J). (gr. 3-4). lib. bdg. 22.60 (978-0-7368-1560-4(0) , Bridgestone Bks.) Capstone Pr., Inc.

Harcourt School Publishers Staff. Horizons: The Battle of Tippecanoe. 3rd ed. 2002. pap. 5.60 (978-0-15-333517-4(3)) Harcourt Schl. Pubs.

Ingram, Scott. The Writing of "The Star-Spangled Banner" 2004. (Landmark Events in American History Ser.). (Illus.). 48p. (J). (gr. 5 up). pap. 11.95 (978-0-8368-5418-3(7)); lib. bdg. 30.00 (978-0-8368-5390-2(3)) Stevens, Gareth Inc. (World Almanac Library).

Jacobson, Ryan. The Story of the Star-Spangled Banner. Martin, Cynthia, illus. 2006. (Graphic Library). 32p. (J). (978-0-7368-5493-1(2)) Capstone Pr., Inc.

Kjelle, Marylou Morano. Francis Scott Key. 2006. (What's So Great About... ? Ser.). (Illus.). 32p. (J). (gr. 1-4). lib. bdg. (978-1-58415-474-7(8)) Mitchell Lane Pubs., Inc.

Kroll, Steven. By the Dawn's Early Light: The Story of the Star Spangled Banner. Andreasen, Dan, illus. 2000. 40p. (J). (ps-3). pap. 5.99 (978-0-590-45055-3(7)) Scholastic, Inc.

—By the Dawn's Early Light: The Story of the Star-Spangled Banner. 2000. (Illus.). (J). 12.79 (978-0-606-18522-6(4)) Tandem Library Bks.

Kroll, Steven & Kroll, Steven. By the Dawn's Early Light: The Story of the Star-Spangled Banner. Andreasen, Dan, illus. 2000. 40p. (J). (ps-ps). lib. bdg. 14.15 (978-0-613-28433-2(X)) Tandem Library Bks.

Lilly, Melinda. The Star Spangled Banner. 2003. (Rourke Discovery Library). (Illus.). 24p. (gr. 1-4). 14.95 (978-1-58952-365-4(2)) Rourke Publishing, LLC.

Marquette, Scott. War of 1812. 2003. (America at War Ser.). (Illus.). 48p. (gr. 4-8). 20.95 (978-1-58952-389-0(X)) Rourke Publishing, LLC.

Nobleman, Marc Tyler. The Star-Spangled Banner. 2003. (First Facts Ser.). (Illus.). 24p. (J). lib. bdg. 19.93 (978-0-7368-2293-0(3)) Capstone Pr., Inc.

Poulakidas, Georgene. The War of 1812. 2004. (Primary Sources of American Wars Ser.). (Illus.). 24p. (J). lib. bdg. (978-1-4042-2681-4(8)) Rosen Publishing Group, Inc., The.

Santella, Andrew. War of Eighteen Twelve. 2001. (gr. 3-6). lib. bdg. 14.10 (978-0-613-52225-0(7)) Tandem Library Bks.

Schultz, Randy. Washington Ablaze: The War of 1812. 2007. (Events in American History Ser.). (Illus.). 48p. (J). (gr. 4-6). lib. bdg. 29.93 (978-1-60044-137-0(8)) Rourke Publishing, LLC.

Silate, Jennifer. The Calhoun-Randolph Debate on the Eve of the War of 1812: A Primary Source Investigation. 2004. (Great Historic Debates & Speeches Ser.). (Illus.). 64p. (YA). lib. bdg. 29.25 (978-1-4042-0150-7(5)) Rosen Publishing Group, Inc., The.

Smalley, Roger. Dolley Madison Saves History. Cool, Anna-Maria et al, illus. 2005. (Graphic Library). 32p. (J). (gr. 3-7). lib. bdg. 25.26 (978-0-7368-4972-2(6)) Capstone Pr., Inc.

Smolinski, Diane. Soldiers of the War of 1812. 2003. (Americans at War Ser.). (Illus.). 32p. (J). (gr. 4-6). lib. bdg. 25.64 (978-1-4034-0174-8(8)) Heinemann Library.

Smolinski, Diane & Smolinski, Henry. Soldiers of the War of 1812. (Americans at War Ser.). 32p. pap. 6.95 (978-1-4034-3158-5(2)) Heinemann Library.

Stefoff, Rebecca. The War of 1812. Mavrikis, Peter, ed. 2000. (North American Historical Atlases Ser.). (Illus.). 48p. (J). (gr. 4-8). lib. bdg. 27.07 (978-0-7614-1060-7(0) , Benchmark Bks.) Cavendish, Marshall Corp.

Tayac, Gabrielle & Bowes, John P. Black Hawk & the War of 1832: Removal in the North. 2007. (Landmark Events in Native American History Ser.). 136p. (gr. 9). 35.00 (***978-0-7910-9342-9(5)*** , Chelsea Hse.) Facts On File, Inc.

Todd, Anne M. Chief Tecumseh. 2004. (Illus.). 32p. (J). pap. 7.50 (978-1-4034-5009-8(9)); lib. bdg. 24.22 (978-1-4034-5002-9(1)) Heinemann Library.

—Sequoyah. 2004. (Illus.). 32p. (J). pap. 7.50 (978-1-4034-5012-8(9)); lib. bdg. 24.22 (978-1-4034-5005-0(6)) Heinemann Library.

—The War of 1812. 2000. (America Goes to War Ser.). (Illus.). 48p. (J). (gr. 3-4). lib. bdg. 22.60 (978-0-7368-0585-8(0) , Bridgestone Bks.) Capstone Pr., Inc.

The War of 1812, 6 vols. (gr. 2-5). 39.95 (978-0-7368-8932-2(9)) Red Brick Learning.

War Of 1812. (America Goes to War Ser.). 48p. (YA). 6.95 (978-0-7368-8860-8(8)) Capstone Pr., Inc.

Warrick, Karen Clemens. The War of 1812: We Have Met the Enemy & They Are Ours. 2002. (American War Ser.). (Illus.). 128p. (YA). (gr. 5-12). lib. bdg. 26.60 (978-0-7660-1854-9(7)) Enslow Pubs., Inc.

Washington Is Burning. 2007. (J). pap. 5.95 (***978-0-8225-6050-0(X)*** , First Avenue Editions) Lerner Publishing Group.

Welch, Catherine A. The Star-Spangled Banner. Warwick, Carrie, illus. 2005. (On My Own History Ser.). 48p. (J). 25.26 (978-1-57505-590-9(2)) Lerner Publishing Group.

UNITED STATES—HISTORY—WAR OF 1812—CAMPAIGNS

see also New Orleans, Battle of, New Orleans, La., 1815

King, David C. New Orleans. 1998. (Battlefields Across America Ser.: 8). (Illus.). 64p. (gr. 5-8). lib. bdg. 26.90 (978-0-7613-3010-3(0) , Twenty-First Century Bks.) Lerner Publishing Group.

Maynard, Charles W. Fort McHenry. 2002. (Famous Forts Throughout American History Ser.). (Illus.). 24p. (J). (gr. 3). lib. bdg. 18.75 (978-0-8239-5838-2(8) , PowerKids Pr.) Rosen Publishing Group, Inc., The.

Smolinski, Diane. Battles of the War of 1812. 2003. (Americans at War Ser.). (Illus.). 32p. (J). (gr. 4-6). lib. bdg. 25.64 (978-1-4034-0171-7(3)) Heinemann Library.

—Battles of the War of 1812. 2003. (gr. 3-6). lib. bdg. 15.25 (978-0-613-87167-9(7)) Tandem Library Bks.

Smolinski, Diane & Smolinski, Henry. Battles of the War of 1812. (Americans at War Ser.). 32p. pap. 6.95 (978-1-4034-3157-8(4)) Heinemann Library.

UNITED STATES—HISTORY—WAR OF 1812—FICTION

Alder, Elizabeth. Crossing the Panther's Path. 2002. (Illus.). 240p. (J). 18.00 (978-0-374-31662-4(7) , Farrar, Straus & Giroux (BYR)) Farrar, Straus & Giroux.

—Crossing the Panther's Path. 2003. (YA). 24.95 (978-0-7862-5013-4(5)) Thorndike Pr.

Beaudouin, Frank, et al, illus. Cleared for Action: Four Tales of the Sea. 2002. (Bethlehem Budget Books). 600p. (J). 19.95 (978-1-883937-55-3(8)) Bethlehem Bks.

Benton, Amanda. Silent Stranger. 1998. pap. 3.99 (978-0-380-79222-1(2)) HarperCollins Pubs.

Crook, Connie Brummel. Laura Secord's Brave Walk. Lawrason, June, illus. 2005. 24p. (J). (gr. 1-4). 14.95 (978-1-896764-34-4(7)) Second Story Pr. CAN. *Dist:* Orca Bk. Pubs. USA.

Greeson, Janet. An American Army of Two. 1999. (On My Own Biography Ser.). (Illus.). (J). 12.75 (978-0-606-21902-0(1)) Tandem Library Bks.

Hall, Marjory. The Gold-Lined Box. 2003. 224p. 11.95 (978-0-9714612-6-0(0)) Green Mansion Pr. LLC.

Ibbitson, John. Jeremy's War of 1812. 2000. 182p. (J). (gr. 5-9). (978-1-55074-988-5(9)) Kids Can Pr., Ltd.

Kimball, K. M. The Star-Spangled Secret. 2001. 234p. (J). (gr. 4-7). lib. bdg. 11.64 (978-0-606-22096-5(8)) Tandem Library Bks.

Kramer, Alan & Kramer, Candice. The Star-Spangled Banner Story. 2005. 40.00 (***978-1-4108-4203-9(7)***) Benchmark Education Co.

McCully, Emily Arnold. The Battle for St. Michaels. McCully, Emily Arnold, illus. 2004. (Illus.). 64p. (J). (ps-17). lib. bdg. 11.80 (978-0-613-82525-2(X)) Tandem Library Bks.

Meader, Stephen W. Clear for Action. 2000. 27.95 (978-0-8488-2831-8(3)) Amereon LTD.

Perkins, Lucy Fitch. American Twins of 1812. (J). (gr. 2-5). 20.95 (978-0-89190-473-1(5)) Amereon LTD.

Sargent, Dave & Sargent, Pat. Snow: (White) Be Truthful, 25, 53. Lenoir, Jane, illus. 2001. (Saddle Up Ser.: 53). 36p. (J). pap. 6.95 (978-1-56763-624-6(1)); lib. bdg. 22.60 (978-1-56763-623-9(3)) Ozark Publishing.

Simmons, Marc. Millie Cooper's Ride: A True Story from History. Kil, Ronald R., illus. 2002. 56p. (J). 16.95 (978-0-8263-2925-7(X)) Univ. of New Mexico Pr.

The Star-Spangled Banner. 2003. (Illus.). 32p. (J). 16.95 (978-0-8249-5462-8(9)) Ideals Pubns.

Sutherland, Robert. A River Apart. 2002. 178p. pap. (978-1-55041-646-6(4)) Fitzhenry & Whiteside, Ltd.

—Son of the Hounds. 2004. 196p. pap. (978-1-55041-906-1(4)) Fitzhenry & Whiteside, Ltd.

Wanttaja, Ronald. The Price of Command: Nate Lawton's War of 1812. Kemnitz, Myrna, ed. Wanttaja, Ronald, illus. 1998. (Illus.). 330p. (YA). (gr. 7 up). 9.99 (978-0-88092-286-9(9) , 2869) Royal Fireworks Publishing Co.

Wiley, Melissa. Little House by Boston Bay. 2007. (Little House Ser.). 160p. (J). pap. 5.99 (***978-0-06-114828-6(8)*** , Harper Trophy) HarperCollins Pubs.

—Little House by Boston Bay. Andreasen, Dan, illus. 1999. (Little House Ser.). 208p. (J). (ps-3). 16.89 (978-0-06-028201-1(0)) HarperCollins Pubs.

—Little House by Boston Bay. Andreasen, Dan, illus. 1999. (Little House Ser.). 195p. lib. bdg. 13.04 (978-0-606-16684-3(X)) Tandem Library Bks.

—Little House by Boston Bay. 1999. (gr. 3-6). lib. bdg. 14.15 (978-0-613-15882-4(2)) Tandem Library Bks.

Wiley, Melissa. On Tide Mill Lane. 2007. (Little House Ser.). 176p. (J). pap. 5.99 (***978-0-06-114829-3(6)*** , Harper Trophy) HarperCollins Pubs.

—On Tide Mill Lane, No. 2. Andreasen, Dan, illus. 2001. (Little House Ser.). 272p. (J). (gr. k-4). 16.95 (978-0-06-027013-1(6)); (gr. 3-7). 16.89 (978-0-06-027014-8(4)) HarperCollins Pubs.

UNITED STATES—HISTORY—1815-1861

The Antebellum Women's Movement, 1820-1860. (YA). (gr. 6-9). spiral bd., tchr.'s planning gde. ed. 12.00 (978-0-382-44465-4(5)) Cobblestone Publishing Co.

Casciato, Daniel. Expansion & Reform. 2007. (J). (***978-1-59036-741-4(3)***); (***978-1-59036-742-1(1)***) Weigl Pubs., Inc.

Collier, Christopher & Collier, James Lincoln. Slavery & the Coming of the Civil War: 1831-1861. 1998. (Drama of American History Ser.). (Illus.). 96p. (J). (gr. 5-9). lib. bdg. 29.93 (978-0-7614-0817-8(7) , Benchmark Bks.) Cavendish, Marshall Corp.

Hakim, Joy. A History of U. S. Liberty for All? rev. ed. 2007. (History of US Ser.: Vol. 5). 224p. pap. 15.95 (***978-0-19-532719-9(5)***) Oxford Univ. Pr., Inc.

—A History of US Bk. 5: Liberty for All? (1820-1860) 3rd rev. ed. 2005. (History of US Ser.). (Illus.). 224p. 19.95 (978-0-19-518898-1(5)) Oxford Univ. Pr., Inc.

—Liberty for All. 2003. (gr. 5-8). lib. bdg. 23.40 (978-0-613-55172-4(9)) Tandem Library Bks.

—Liberty for All Bk. 5. 3rd rev. ed. 2005. (History of US Ser.). (Illus.). 224p. 19.95 (978-0-19-518234-7(0)) Oxford Univ. Pr., Inc.

Isaacs, Sally Senzell. Life in St. Augustine. 2003. (J). (gr. k-3). lib. bdg. 15.25 (978-0-613-67337-2(9)) Tandem Library Bks.

Langellier, J. Phillip. Bluecoats: The U. S. Army in the West, 1848-1897. 1999. (G. I. Ser.). (Illus.). 80p. (YA). (gr. 5-9). 27.50 (978-0-7910-5366-9(0) , Chelsea Hse.) Facts On File, Inc.

McDougal, Littell Staff, contrib. by. A Nation Dividing 1800-1860. 2004. (Stories in History Ser.). (Illus.). 176p. (gr. 6-12). 13.32 (978-0-618-14222-4(3) , 2-00242) McDougal Littell Inc.

Thro, Ellen. Growing & Dividing. 2000. (Making of America Ser.). (Illus.). 96p. (J). (gr. 4-7). lib. bdg. 28.54 (978-0-8172-5704-0(7)) Raintree.

Yancey, Diane. Civil War Generals of the Union. 1998. (History Makers Ser.). (Illus.). 128p. (YA). (gr. 7-10). 28.70 (978-1-56006-022-2(0) , Lucent Bks.) Thomson Gale.

UNITED STATES—HISTORY—1815-1861—FICTION

Broyles, Anne. Priscilla & the Hollyhocks. Alter, Anna, illus. 2008. (J). (***978-1-57091-675-5(6)***) Charlesbridge Publishing, Inc.

Crawford, Neil. The Journeyers. 2006. (J). pap. (***978-0-9778205-4-2(8)***) Helm Publishing.

Kroll, Steven. John Quincy Adams: Letters from a Southern Planter's Son. 2001. (Dear Mr. President Ser.). (Illus.). 128p. (J). (gr. 4-6). 9.95 (978-1-890817-93-0(7)) Winslow Pr.

Paterson, Katherine. Jip, His Story. 1998. (Puffin Novel Ser.). 208p. (J). (gr. 5-9). pap. 6.99 (978-0-14-038674-5(2) , Puffin) Penguin Group (USA) Inc.

Wilson, Diane Lee. Black Storm Comin' (J). 2006. 240p. pap. 5.99 (978-0-689-87138-2(4) , Aladdin); 2005. 304p. (gr. 5-9). 17.99 (978-0-689-87137-5(6) , McElderry, Margaret K.) Simon & Schuster Children's Publishing.

UNITED STATES—HISTORY—WAR WITH MEXICO, 1845-1848

see Mexican War, 1846-1848

UNITED STATES—HISTORY—CIVIL WAR, 1861-1865

see also Slavery—United States

Abnett, Dan. Abraham Lincoln & the Civil War. 2007. (Jr. Graphic Biographies Ser.). (Illus.). 24p. (J). (978-1-4042-2335-6(5)); pap. (978-1-4042-2145-1(X)); (gr. 2-6). lib. bdg. 21.25 (978-1-4042-3392-8(X)) Rosen Publishing Group, Inc., The. (PowerKids Pr.).

Adler, David A. A Picture Book of Harriet Beecher Stowe. Bootman, Colin, illus. 2003. 32p. (J). (gr. k-3). 6.95 (978-0-8234-1878-7(2)); tchr. ed. 16.95 (978-0-8234-1646-2(1)) Holiday Hse., Inc.

The American Civil War. 1999. (Illus.). 64p. (YA). (gr. 6 up). pap. 8.00 (978-1-890541-15-6(X)) Americana Souvenirs & Gifts.

American Civil War Stereoviews 3D Anaglyphs, 3 vols., Vol. 1. 2001. cd-rom 11.99 (978-0-9710633-0-3(3)) Genesis Biotech.

Anderson, Dale. The Aftermath of the Civil War. 2004. (World Almanac Library of the Civil War). (Illus.). 48p. (J). (gr. 5 up). pap. 11.95 (978-0-8368-5597-5(3)); lib. bdg. 30.00 (978-0-8368-5588-3(4)) Stevens, Gareth Inc. (World Almanac Library).

—The Causes of the Civil War. 2004. (World Almanac Library of the Civil War). (Illus.). 48p. (J). (gr. 5 up). pap. 11.95 (978-0-8368-5590-6(6)); lib. bdg. 30.00 (978-0-8368-5581-4(7)) Stevens, Gareth Inc. (World Almanac Library).

—The Civil War in the West (1861-July 1863) 2004. (World Almanac Library of the Civil War). (Illus.). 48p. (J). (gr. 5 up). pap. 11.95 (978-0-8368-5592-0(2)); lib. bdg. 30.00 (978-0-8368-5583-8(3)) Stevens, Gareth Inc. (World Almanac Library).

—The Home Fronts in the Civil War. 2004. (World Almanac Library of the Civil War). (Illus.). 48p. (J). lib. bdg. 30.00 (978-0-8368-5587-6(6)); (gr. 5 up). pap. 11.95 (978-0-8368-5596-8(5)) Stevens, Gareth Inc. (World Almanac Library).

—A Soldier's Life in the Civil War. 2004. (World Almanac Library of the Civil War). (Illus.). 48p. (J). (gr. 5 up). pap. 11.95 (978-0-8368-5595-1(7)); lib. bdg. 30.00 (978-0-8368-5586-9(8)) Stevens, Gareth Inc. (World Almanac Library).

—World Almanac Library of the Civil War, 8 bks. Incl. Aftermath of the Civil War. pap. 11.95 (978-0-8368-5597-5(3)); Causes of the Civil War. pap. 11.95 (978-0-8368-5590-6(6)); Civil War at Sea. pap. 11.95 (978-0-8368-5594-4(9)); Civil War in the East (1861-July 1863) pap. 11.95 (978-0-8368-5591-3(4)); Civil War in the West (1861-July 1863) pap. 11.95 (978-0-8368-5592-0(2)); Home Fronts in the Civil War. pap. 11.95 (978-0-8368-5596-8(5)); Soldier's Life in the Civil War. pap. 11.95 (978-0-8368-5595-1(7)); Union Victory (July 1863-1865) pap. 11.95 (978-0-8368-5593-7(0)); 48p. (J). (gr. 5 up). (Illus.). 2004. pap. (978-0-8368-5589-0(2)) ; Set lib. bdg. 240.00 (978-0-8368-5580-7(9)) Stevens, Gareth Inc. (World Almanac Library).

Anderson, Maxine. Great Civil War Projects You Can Build Yourself. 2005. (Build It Yourself Ser.). (Illus.). 144p. (J). (ps-17). pap. 14.95 (978-0-9749344-1-9(0)) Nomad Pr.

Ansary, Mir Tamim. El Día de los Caídos. 2003. Tr. of Flag Day. (SPA.). 32p. (J). pap. 6.95 (978-1-4034-3028-1(4)) Heinemann Library.

Ansary, Mir Tamim. Memorial Day. 2006. (Illus.). 32p. (J). (***978-1-4034-8890-9(8)***) Heinemann Library.

Armentrout, David, et al. El Discurso de Gettysburg. 2005. (SPA.). (J). (978-1-59515-647-1(X)) Rourke Publishing, LLC.

—The Gettysburg Address. 2005. (Documents that Shaped the Nation Ser.). (Illus.). 48p. (gr. 4-6). 20.95 (978-1-59515-232-9(6)) Rourke Publishing, LLC.

Arnold, James R. The Civil War. 2005. (Chronicle of America's Wars Ser.). (Illus.). 96p. (J). (gr. 5-12). 27.93 (978-0-8225-0140-4(6)) Lerner Publishing Group.

Arnold, James R. & Wiener, Roberta. Divided in Two: The Road to Civil War, 1861. 2005. (Civil War Ser.). (Illus.). 72p. (J). (gr. 5-12). lib. bdg. 25.26 (978-0-8225-2312-3(4)) Lerner Publishing Group.

—Life Goes On: The Civil War at Home, 1861-1865. 2005. (Civil War Ser.). (Illus.). 72p. (gr. 5-12). lib. bdg. 25.26 (978-0-8225-2315-4(9)) Lerner Publishing Group.

Aronson, Billy. Abraham Lincoln. 2008. (J). (***978-0-7614-2839-8(9)***) Cavendish, Marshall Bks., Ltd.

Baker, Lawrence W., ed. Experiencing the American Civil War: Novels, Nonfiction Books, Short Stories, Poems, Plays, Films & Songs, 2 vols. Hillstrom, Kevin & Hillstrom, Laurie Collier, trs. 2002. (Experiencing Eras & Events Ser.). (Illus.). xl, 406p. (J). (978-0-7876-5413-9(2)); (978-0-7876-5586-0(4)) Thomson Gale. (UXL).

Banfield, Susan. The Andersonville Prison Civil War Crimes Trial: A Headline Court Case. 2000. (Headline Court Cases Ser.). (Illus.). 112p. (J). (gr. 6-12). lib. bdg. 26.60 (978-0-7660-1386-5(3)) Enslow Pubs., Inc.

Barr, Gary. Slavery in the Civil War Era. 2004. (Illus.). 56p. (J). pap. 8.95 (978-1-4034-4578-0(8)); lib. bdg. (978-1-4034-4570-4(2)) Heinemann Library.

Battlefields Across America. (History & Social Studies Ser.). (Illus.). 64p. (978-0-7613-1148-5(3) , Twenty-First Century Bks.) Lerner Publishing Group.

Bednarz, Robert, et al. Horizons: US History: Civil War-Present. 3rd ed. 2003. (Harcourt Horizons Ser.). (Illus.). (gr. 4-7). pupil's gde. ed. 69.10 (978-0-15-321350-2(7)) Harcourt Schl. Pubs.

Beller, Susan Provost. Billy Yank & Johnny Reb: Soldiering in the Civil War. (Soldiers on the Battlefront Ser.). (Illus.). 2007. 112p. (YA). (gr. 6-8). lib. bdg. 33.26 (978-0-8225-6803-2(9)); 2000. 96p. (gr. 5 up). lib. bdg. (978-0-7613-1869-9(0) , Millbrook Pr.) Lerner Publishing Group.

—The Civil War. 2002. (American Voices From Ser.). (Illus.). xxii, 103p. (J). 34.21 (978-0-7614-1204-5(2) , Benchmark Bks.) Cavendish, Marshall Corp.

—The Confederate Ladies of Richmond. 1999. (Single Titles Ser.). (Illus.). 96p. (gr. 4-7). lib. bdg. 26.90 (978-0-7613-1470-7(9) , Millbrook Pr.) Lerner Publishing Group.

Benchmark Education Staff, compiled by. The Civil War. 2006. spiral bd. 159.00 (***978-1-4108-7127-5(4)***) Benchmark Education Co.

Benson, Michael, ed. Civil War Tech Journal, No. 5. 1999. (Starlog Movie Ser.). (Illus.). (YA). pap. 5.99 (978-0-934551-54-0(5)) Profile Entertainment, Inc.

The Big Book of the Civil War (Scholastic HC Edition) 2006. (***978-0-7624-3124-3(5)*** , Running Pr.) Running Pr. Bk. Pubs.

The Big Book of the Civil War (Scholastic PBK Edition) 2006. 56p. pap. (***978-0-7624-3122-9(9)*** , Running Pr.) Running Pr. Bk. Pubs.

Black, Wallace B. Slaves to Soldiers: African-American Fighting Men in the Civil War. 1998. (First Bks.). (Illus.). 64p. (J). (gr. 5-7). 22.00 (978-0-531-20252-4(6) , Watts, Franklin) Scholastic Library Publishing.

Blashfield, Jean F. Horse Soldiers: Cavalry in the Civil War. 1998. (First Bks.). (Illus.). 64p. (J). (gr. 5-7). 22.00 (978-0-531-20300-2(X) , Watts, Franklin) Scholastic Library Publishing.

Bollich, James J. Innocents at War. Turner, Bruce et al, eds. 2001. 270p. (YA). pap. 20.00 (978-0-9643275-5-9(4)) Bollich, James J.

Bolotin, Norman. Civil War A to Z: A Young Person's Guide to over 100 People, Places, & Points of Importance. 2002. (Illus.). 160p. (J). (gr. 4-7). 19.99 (978-0-525-46268-2(6) , Dutton Juvenile) Penguin Group (USA) Inc.

Book Studio Staff. Blast from the Past Kit: Civil War. 2007. (Cool Kits Ser.). 32p. (J). 7.99 (978-0-7566-2667-9(6)) Dorling Kindersley Publishing, Inc.

Borges, Antonion. Cocoa & Company: A Civil War Classic. 2007. (ENG.). 124p. per. 17.95 (***978-1-4241-4829-5(4)***) PublishAmerica, Inc.

Bowers, Arden C., ed. The Civil War. 2001. (Researching American History Ser.). (Illus.). 56p. (J). 7.95 (978-1-57960-071-6(9)) History Compass, LLC.

Brager, Bruce. Petersburg. 2003. (gr. 7-12). lib. bdg. 18.75 (978-0-613-85628-7(7)) Tandem Library Bks.

Brocker, Susan. Voces de la Guerra Civil & Voices from the Civil War. 2005. spiral bd. 84.00 (***978-1-4108-5714-9(X)***) Benchmark Education Co.

Brooks, Victor D. African-Americans in the Civil War. 2000. (Untold History of the Civil War Ser.). (Illus.). 64p. (J). (gr. 3 up). 25.00 (978-0-7910-5435-2(7) , Chelsea Hse.) Facts On File, Inc.

—Civil War Forts. 1999. (Untold History of the Civil War Ser.). (Illus.). 64p. (YA). (gr. 3 up). 25.00 (978-0-7910-5438-3(1) , Chelsea Hse.) Facts On File, Inc.

Brown, Susan Taylor. Robert Smalls Sails to Freedom. Marshall, Felicia, illus. 2006. (On My Own History Ser.). 48p. (J). 25.26 (978-1-57505-872-6(3)) Lerner Publishing Group.

Brownell, Richard. The Civil War: The Fall of the Confederacy & the End of Slavery. 2005. (History's Great Defeats Ser.). (Illus.). 109p. (YA). (gr. 7-10). lib. bdg. 29.95 (978-1-59018-429-5(7) , Lucent Bks.) Thomson Gale.

Bunting, Eve. The Blue & the Gray. 2001. (J). (978-0-606-21073-7(3)) Tandem Library Bks.

Burgan, Michael. Fort Sumter. 2006. (We the People Ser.). (Illus.). 48p. (J). (gr. 4-6). 23.93 (978-0-7565-1629-1(3)) Compass Point Bks.

—The Gettysburg Address. 2005. (We the People Ser.). (Illus.). 48p. (J). (gr. 4-6). (978-0-7565-1271-2(9) , 1244089) Compass Point Bks.

Calkins, Chris. Auto Tour of Civil War Petersburg: 1861-1865, 1 vol. 2003. (Illus.). 80p. per. 7.66 (978-0-9744824-0-8(4)) Petersburg Museums, The.

Caravantes, Peggy. Petticoat Spies: Six Women Spies of the US Civil War. 2004. (Notable Americans Ser.). (Illus.). 112p. (YA). (gr. 6-12). 23.95 (978-1-883846-88-6(9) , First Biographies) Reynolds, Morgan Inc.

Carole Marsh. When Brother Fought Brother: the American Civil War. 2004. (American Milestones Ser.). 32p. (gr. 3-8). pap. 5.95 (978-0-635-02346-9(6)); (gr. 4-12). 29.95 (978-0-635-02347-6(4)) Gallopade International.

Carter, E. J. Robert E. Lee. 2004. (American War Biographies Ser.). (Illus.). 48p. (J). pap. 8.50 (978-1-4034-5088-3(9)); lib. bdg. 27.07 (978-1-4034-5081-4(1)) Heinemann Library.

Center for Learning Network Staff. Civil War & Reconstruction: 1860-1877 — Elementary U. S. History Series — Teacher Guide. 2001. (Social Studies Ser.). 135p. (J). tchr. ed., spiral bd. 29.95 (978-1-56077-680-2(3)) Ctr. for Learning, The.

Chelsea House Publishing Staff. Untold History of the Civil War. 1999. (Illus.). (J). 215.40 (978-0-7910-5439-0(X) , Chelsea Hse.) Facts On File, Inc.

Civil War. (Color & Learn Ser.). 36p. (J). (gr. 1-5). pap. (978-1-882210-07-7(7)) Action Publishing, Inc.

The Civil War Classroom Library. (gr. 2-5). lib. bdg. 74.95 (978-0-7368-4529-8(1)) Red Brick Learning.

The Civil War Complete Unit. (gr. 2-5). 430.95 (978-0-7368-4528-1(3)) Red Brick Learning.

Civil War DBA. 2002. spiral bd. 16.95 (978-1-56004-129-0(3)) Social Studies Schl. Service.

Civil War Era. (We the People Ser.). (gr. 4-6). 90.40 (978-0-7565-0795-4(2)) Compass Point Bks.

Civil War Tales of the Tennessee Valley, 2003. (Illus.). 241p. per. 17.95 (978-0-9719946-7-6(6)) Bluewater Pubns.

Clayton, Nancy L. Strange but True Civil War Stories. 1999. (Illus.). 128p. (J). (gr. 3-7). pap. 7.95 (978-0-7373-0110-6(4) , 01104W) McGraw-Hill/Contemporary.

Clinton, Catherine. Hold the Flag High. Evans, Shane W., illus. 2005. 32p. (J). (ps-2). 15.99 (978-0-06-050428-1(5) , Amistad); lib. bdg. 17.89 (978-0-06-050429-8(3)) HarperCollins Pubs.

—Scholastic Encyclopedia of the Civil War. 1999. (Illus.). 112p. (YA). (gr. 4-9). pap. 18.95 (978-0-590-37227-5(0) , RZB37227, Scholastic Reference) Scholastic, Inc.

Coddon, Karin. Civil War. 2003. (gr. 7-12). lib. bdg. 33.25 (978-0-613-73845-3(4)) Tandem Library Bks.

Cohen, Daniel. Civil War Ghosts. 1999. (Illus.). 105p. (J). (gr. 3-7). pap. 4.50 (978-0-439-05387-7(0)) Scholastic, Inc.

—Civil War Ghosts. 1999. (Illus.). (J). (gr. 3-7). (978-0-606-18532-5(1)) Tandem Library Bks.

Colbert, Nancy A. The Firing on Fort Sumter: A Splintered Nation Goes to War. 2004. (First Battles Ser.). (Illus.). 112p. (J). (gr. 6-12). 23.95 (978-1-883846-51-0(X) , First Biographies) Reynolds, Morgan Inc.

Collier, Christopher & Collier, James Lincoln. The Civil War: 1860-1865. 1999. (Drama of American History Ser.). (Illus.). 96p. (J). (gr. 5-9). lib. bdg. 31.36 (978-0-7614-0818-5(5) , Benchmark Bks.) Cavendish, Marshall Corp.

—The Rise of Industry: 1860-1900. 1999. (Drama of American History Ser.). (Illus.). 96p. (J). (gr. 5-9). lib. bdg. 31.36 (978-0-7614-0820-8(7) , Benchmark Bks.) Cavendish, Marshall Corp.

Corrick, James. The Civil War & Emancipation. 2007. (Lucent Library of Black History Ser.). (Illus.). 128p. (J). (gr. 7-10). 28.70 (*978-1-4205-0008-0(2) , Lucent Bks.) Thomson Gale.

Corrick, James A. The Civil War. 2003. (World History Ser.). (Illus.). 128p. (J). (gr. 8-11). 32.45 (978-1-59018-181-2(6) , Lucent Bks.) Thomson Gale.

Cosson, Jody. Civil War & Reconstruction. 2007. (J). (*978-1-59036-743-8(X)); (*978-1-59036-744-5(8)) Weigl Pubs., Inc.

Crewe, Sabrina & Uschan, Michael V. Fort Sumter: The Civil War Begins. 2005. (Events That Shaped America Ser.). (Illus.). 32p. (J). lib. bdg. 24.67 (978-0-8368-3414-7(3)) Stevens, Gareth Inc.

Cromwell Productions Limited, prod. The American Civil War: 1861-1865. (YA). cd-rom 149.95 (978-0-7365-0360-0(9)) Films Media Group.

Crozier, A. J. Technology & the Civil War. 2006. (Navigators Ser.). (J). pap. 42.00 (*978-1-4108-6260-0(7)) Benchmark Education Co.

Currie, Stephen. Women of the Civil War. 2002. (Women in History Ser.). (Illus.). 112p. (J). 32.45 (978-1-59018-170-6(0) , Lucent Bks.) Thomson Gale.

Day, Nancy. Your Travel Guide to Civil War America. (Passport to History Ser.). (Illus.). 96p. (gr. 5-8). 2005. lib. bdg. 26.50 (978-0-8225-3078-7(3)); 2003. (J). pap. 7.95 (978-0-8225-9909-8(0)) Lerner Publishing Group.

—Your Travel Guide to Civil War America. 2001. (gr. 5-8). lib. bdg. 16.40 (978-0-613-33277-4(6)) Tandem Library Bks.

DeAngelis, Gina. The Massachusetts 54th: African American Soldiers of the Union. 2002. (Let Freedom Ring Ser.). (Illus.). 48p. (J). (gr. 3-4). lib. bdg. 22.60 (978-0-7368-1343-3(8) , Bridgestone Bks.) Capstone Pr., Inc.

DeFord, Deborah H. The Civil War. 2006. (Wars That Changed American History Ser.). 48p. (J). pap. (978-0-8368-7300-9(9)); lib. bdg. (978-0-8368-7291-0(6)) Stevens, Gareth Inc. (World Almanac Library).

DK Publishing Staff. Abraham Lincoln & the Civil War. 2006. 16p. (J). pap. 6.99 (978-0-7566-2662-4(5)) Dorling Kindersley Publishing, Inc.

Dosier, Susan. Civil War Cooking: The Confederacy. 2000. (Blue Earth Books). (Illus.). 32p. (J). (gr. 3-4). lib. bdg. 22.60 (978-0-7368-0350-2(5) , Bridgestone Bks.) Capstone Pr., Inc.

—Civil War Cooking: The Confederacy. 1999. (Exploring History Through Simple Recipes Ser.). (Illus.). 32p. (J). (gr. 2-7). pap. 14.60 (978-0-516-21933-2(2) , Children's Pr.) Scholastic Library Publishing.

Downs, Sandra. Florida in the Civil War: A State in Turmoil. 2001. (Single Titles Ser.). (Illus.). 80p. (J). (gr. 8 up). lib. bdg. 25.90 (978-0-7613-1973-3(5) , Millbrook Pr.) Lerner Publishing Group.

Drama of African-American History, 5 bks., Set. Incl. Africa : A Look Back. Haskins, James & Benson, Kathleen. lib. bdg. 34.21 (978-0-7614-2148-1(3)); Civil War. Jordan, Anne Devereaux & Schomp, Virginia. lib. bdg. 34.21 (978-0-7614-2179-5(3)); Reconstruction ERA. Stroud, Bettye & Schomp, Virginia. lib. bdg. 34.21 (978-0-7614-2181-8(5)); Slave Trade & the Middle Passage. Sharp, S. Pearl & Schomp, Virginia. lib. bdg. 34.21 (978-0-7614-2176-4(9)); Slavery & Resistance. Jordan, Anne Devereaux & Schomp, Virginia. lib. bdg. 34.21 (978-0-7614-2178-8(5)); (Illus.). 80p. (J). 2006. 2007. Set lib. bdg. 171.07 (*978-0-7614-2174-0(2) , Benchmark Bks.) Cavendish, Marshall Corp.

Draper, Allison Stark. What People Wore During the Civil War. 2001. (Clothing, Costumes & Uniforms Thoughout American History Ser.). (Illus.). 24p. (J). (gr. 3). lib. bdg. 19.95 (978-0-8239-5669-2(5) , PKCLCI, PowerKids Pr.) Rosen Publishing Group, Inc., The.

Edwards, Judith. Abolitionists & Slave Resistance: Breaking the Chains of Slavery. 2004. (Slavery in American History Ser.). (Illus.). 128p. (J). lib. bdg. 26.60 (978-0-7660-2155-6(6)) Enslow Pubs., Inc.

Egger-Bovet, Howard, et al. Book of the American Civil War. Simison, D. J., illus. 1998. (Brown Paper School Uskids History Ser.). 96p. (J). (gr. 3-7). 22.95 (978-0-316-22239-6(9)) Little Brown & Co.

Epperson, James F. Causes of the Civil War. 2005. (Road to War Ser.). (Illus.). 64p. (J). pap. 12.95 (978-1-59556-006-3(8)); (gr. 4 up). lib. bdg. 22.95 (978-1-59556-002-5(5)) OTTN Publishing.

Farmer, Alan. The American Civil War, 1861-65. 2nd ed. 2002. (Illus.). 176p. pap. 13.99 (978-0-340-84889-0(8) , Hodder Murray) Hodder Education GBR. *Dist:* Trafalgar Square Publishing.

Fiore, C. A. Young Heros of the Civil War. (J). pap. 9.99 (978-0-88092-486-3(1)) Royal Fireworks Publishing Co.

Fiore, Carmen Anthony. Young Heroes of the Civil War. 2006. (J). pap. (978-0-88092-639-3(2)); lib. bdg. (978-0-88092-638-6(4)) Royal Fireworks Publishing Co.

Fluharty, Linda Cunningham. Civil War - West Virginia: Union Lives Lost. 2004. (Illus.). 175p. lib. bdg. 35.00 (978-0-9759097-1-3(1)) Fluharty, Linda Cunningham.

Ford, Carin T. African-American Soldiers in the Civil War: Fighting for Freedom. 2004. (Civil War Library Ser.). (Illus.). 48p. (J). lib. bdg. 23.93 (978-0-7660-2254-6(4)) Enslow Pubs., Inc.

—The American Civil War: An Overview. 2004. (Civil War Library Ser.). (Illus.). 48p. (J). lib. bdg. 23.93 (978-0-7660-2255-3(2)) Enslow Pubs., Inc.

Foreign Volunteers for the Confederacy. 1999. (Untold History of the Civil War Ser.). (gr. 4-7). 19.95 (978-0-7910-5431-4(4) , Chelsea Hse.) Facts On File, Inc.

Foreign Volunteers for the Union. 1999. (Untold History of the Civil War Ser.). (gr. 4-7). 19.95 (978-0-7910-5432-1(2) , Chelsea Hse.) Facts On File, Inc.

Fox, Arthur B. Pittsburgh During the American Civil War 1860-1865. ed. 2004. (Illus.). 236p. per. 29.95 (978-0-9760563-0-0(5) , 7526S) Mechling Bookbindery.

Frazier, Joey. Jefferson Davis: Confederate President. (Famous Figures of the Civil War Era Ser.). (Illus.). 80p. (J). (gr. 4-7). 2001. 25.00 (978-0-7910-6006-3(3)); 2000. pap. 25.00 (978-0-7910-6144-2(2)) Facts On File, Inc. (Chelsea Hse.).

Fredriksen, John C. Civil War Almanac. Facts on File, Inc. Staff, ed. 2007. (Almanacs of American Wars Ser.). 864p. (gr. 9). 85.00 (978-0-8160-6459-5(8)) Facts On File, Inc.

Furbee, Mary Rodd. Outrageous Women of Civil War Times. 2003. (gr. 5-8). lib. bdg. 22.20 (978-0-613-81400-3(2)) Tandem Library Bks.

—Outrageous Women of Civil War Times. 2003. (Outrageous Women Ser.). (Illus.). 124p. pap. 12.95 (978-0-471-22926-1(1) , Jossey-Bass) Wiley, John & Sons, Inc.

Gaines, Ann Graham. The Confederacy & the Civil War in American History. 2000. (In American History Ser.). (Illus.). 128p. (YA). (gr. 5-12). lib. bdg. 26.60 (978-0-7660-1417-6(7)) Enslow Pubs., Inc.

Gillis, Jennifer Blizin. The Confederate Soldier. 2006. 48p. (J). (gr. 4-6). lib. bdg. (978-0-7565-2025-0(8)) Compass Point Bks.

Goodman, Susan E. Robert Henry Hendershot. Ettlinger, Doris, illus. 2003. (Brave Kids Ser.). 64p. (J). pap. 3.99 (978-0-689-84980-0(X) , Aladdin) Simon & Schuster Children's Publishing.

Gottfried, Bradley M. Stopping Pickett: The History of the Philadelphia Brigade. 1999. (Illus.). 282p. 29.95 (978-1-57249-164-9(7)) White Mane Publishing Co., Inc.

Grabowski, John F. Abraham Lincoln: Civil War President. 2001. (Famous Figures of the Civil War Era Ser.). (Illus.). 80p. (J). (gr. 8-12). 25.00 (978-0-7910-6004-9(7) , Chelsea Hse.) Facts On File, Inc.

Grabowski, Patricia A. Robert E. Lee: Confederate General. (Famous Figures of the Civil War Era Ser.). (Illus.). 80p. (J). (gr. 4-7). 2001. 25.00 (978-0-7910-6000-1(4)); 2000. pap. 25.00 (978-0-7910-6138-1(8)) Facts On File, Inc. (Chelsea Hse.).

Graves, Kerry A. The Civil War. 2000. (America Goes to War Ser.). (Illus.). 48p. (J). (gr. 3-4). lib. bdg. 22.60 (978-0-7368-0582-7(6) , Bridgestone Bks.) Capstone Pr., Inc.

—Going to School During the Civil War: The Confederacy. 2001. (Blue Earth Books). (Illus.). 32p. (J). (gr. 3-4). lib. bdg. 22.60 (978-0-7368-0802-6(7) , Bridgestone Bks.) Capstone Pr., Inc.

—Going to School During the Civil War: The Union. 2001. (Blue Earth Books). (Illus.). 32p. (J). (gr. 3-4). lib. bdg. 22.60 (978-0-7368-0801-9(9) , Bridgestone Bks.) Capstone Pr., Inc.

Gravois, Michael. Hands-On History: Civil War. 2004. (Hands-on History Ser.). (Illus.). 48p. pap. 10.99 (978-0-439-41125-7(4) , Teaching Resources) Scholastic, Inc.

—Immigration. 2004. (Hands-on History Ser.). 48p. pap. 10.99 (978-0-439-41124-0(6) , Teaching Resources) Scholastic, Inc.

—Pioneers. 2004. (Hands-on History Ser.). (Illus.). 48p. pap. 10.99 (978-0-439-41126-4(2) , Teaching Resources) Scholastic, Inc.

Griskey, Michele. Harriet Beecher Stowe. 2005. (Classic Storytellers Ser.). (Illus.). 48p. (J). lib. bdg. 29.95 (978-1-58415-375-7(X)) Mitchell Lane Pubs., Inc.

Grolier Educational Staff, contrib. by. The Civil War, 10 Vols. 2004. (Illus.). (J). 259.00 (978-0-7172-5883-3(1)); (978-0-7172-5884-0(X)); (978-0-7172-5885-7(8)); (978-0-7172-5886-4(6)); (978-0-7172-5887-1(4)); (978-0-7172-5888-8(2)); (978-0-7172-5889-5(0)); (978-0-7172-5890-1(4)); (978-0-7172-5891-8(2)); (978-0-7172-5892-5(0)); (978-0-7172-5893-2(9)) Scholastic Library Publishing. (Grolier).

Hakim, Joy. A History of US Vol. 6: War, Terrible War. rev. ed. 2007. (History of US Ser.: Vol. 6). 176p. pap. 15.95 (*978-0-19-532720-5(9)) Oxford Univ. Pr., Inc.

Hakim, Joy. War, Terrible War Bk. 6: 1855-1865. 3rd rev. ed. (History of US Ser.). (Illus.). 2006. 178p. (J). 19.95 (978-0-19-518235-4(9)); 2005. 176p. 19.95 (978-0-19-518899-8(3)) Oxford Univ. Pr., Inc.

Hale, Sarah Elder & Waryncia, Lou. Nation at War: Soldiers, Saints, & Spies. 2005. (Civil War Ser.). (Illus.). 48p. (J). 17.95 (978-0-8126-7900-7(8)) Cobblestone Publishing Co.

Hall, Margaret. Civil War. 2004. (Hands-On American History Ser.). (Illus.). 32p. (J). 27.07 (978-1-4034-6052-3(3)) Heinemann Library.

—The History & Activities of the Civil War. 2006. (Hands-On American History Ser.). (Illus.). 32p. (J). pap. (978-1-4034-6059-2(0)) Heinemann Library.

Hama, Larry. The War Is On! Battle of First Bull Run. Verma, Dheeraj, illus. 2007. (Graphic History Ser.). 48p. (J). (gr. 3-7). pap. 9.95 (978-1-84603-054-3(4)) Osprey Publishing, Ltd. GBR. *Dist:* Random Hse., Inc.

Harcourt School Publishers Staff. Horizons: Time for Kids Reader: US History - Civil War to Present. 3rd ed. 2002. (Harcourt Horizons Ser.). (gr. k-7). pap., tchr. ed. 69.40 (978-0-15-334656-9(6)) Harcourt Schl. Pubs.

—Horizons: US History: Civil War-Present. 3rd ed. 2002. (Harcourt Horizons Ser.). (gr. 4-7). Vol. 1. tchr. ed. 143.40 (978-0-15-321966-5(1)); Vol. 2. tchr. ed. 143.40 (978-0-15-321967-2(X)) Harcourt Schl. Pubs.

—State & Regional Sites of the Civil War. 3rd ed. 2002. (Horizons Ser.). (Illus.). (J). pap. 5.50 (978-0-15-333409-2(6)) Harcourt Schl. Pubs.

Hargrove, Julia. Antietam National Battlefield (1862) Mitchell, Judy, ed. Mohrman, Gary, illus. 2004. 48p. (J). pap. 6.95 (978-1-57310-429-6(9)) Teaching & Learning Co.

Harkrader, Lisa. Reconstruction & Aftermath of the Civil War: A MyReportLinks. com Book. 2004. (American Civil War Ser.). (Illus.). 48p. (J). lib. bdg. 25.26 (978-0-7660-5265-9(6) , MyReportLinks.com Bks.) Enslow Pubs., Inc.

Harness, Cheryl. Abe Lincoln Goes to Washington 1837-1865. 2003. (Illus.). 48p. (J). (gr. 3-7). pap. 7.95 (978-0-7922-6906-9(3) , National Geographic Children's Bks.) National Geographic Society.

Haugen, Brenda. Harriet Beecher Stowe: Author & Advocate. 2004. (Signature Lives Ser.). (Illus.). 112p. (J). 30.60 (978-0-7565-0822-7(3) , 1240140) Compass Point Bks.

Herbert, Janis. The Civil War for Kids: A History with 21 Activities. 1999. (For Kids Ser.). (Illus.). 160p. (J). (gr. 4-7). pap. 14.95 (978-1-55652-355-7(6)) Chicago Review Pr., Inc.

Hewson, Martha S. Stonewall Jackson: Confederate General. (Famous Figures of the Civil War Era Ser.). (Illus.). 80p. (J). 2001. (gr. 8-12). 25.00 (978-0-7910-6002-5(0)); 2000. (gr. 4-7). pap. 25.00 (978-0-7910-6140-4(X)) Facts On File, Inc. (Chelsea Hse.).

Hill, Mary. Harriet Beecher Stowe. 2003. (Welcome Book Ser.). (Illus.). 24p. (J). 18.00 (978-0-516-25865-2(6) , Children's Pr.) Scholastic Library Publishing.

Hillstrom, Kevin & Hillstrom, Laurie Collier. American Civil War: Primary Sources. Baker, Lawrence W., ed. 2000. (American Civil War Reference Library). (Illus.). xxxi, 176p. (J). 67.00 (978-0-7876-3824-5(2) , GML00502-113587, UXL) Thomson Gale.

Hillstrom, Kevin, et al. American Civil War: Almanac. Baker, Lawrence W., ed. 2000. (American Civil War Reference Library). (Illus.). xlvi, 251p. (J). (gr. 4-7). 67.00 (978-0-7876-3823-8(4) , GML00502-113586, UXL) Thomson Gale.

Hirsch, E. D., ed. The Civil War, Level 5. tchr. ed. 9.95 (978-0-7690-5081-2(6)); stu. ed. 49.95 (978-0-7690-2848-4(9)) Pearson Learning.

Holt, Rinehart and Winston Staff. American Nation: Civil War: Chapter Tutorials. 2001. pap. 29.20 (978-0-03-056577-9(4)) Holt, Rinehart & Winston.

—American Nation: Civil War: Hands-on History Activities. 2001. pap. 23.73 (978-0-03-056576-2(6)) Holt, Rinehart & Winston.

Hull, Mary E. The Union & the Civil War in American History. 2000. (In American History Ser.). (Illus.). 128p. (YA). (gr. 5-12). lib. bdg. 26.60 (978-0-7660-1416-9(9)) Enslow Pubs., Inc.

Imbriaco, Alison. Causes of the Civil War: A MyReportLinks. com Book. 2004. (American Civil War Ser.). (Illus.). 48p. (J). lib. bdg. 25.26 (978-0-7660-5186-7(2) , MyReportLinks.com Bks.) Enslow Pubs., Inc.

Jerome, Kate Boehm. Civil War Sub Vol. 3: The Mystery of the Hunley. Sofo, Frank & Farnsworth, Bill, illus. 2002. (All Aboard Reading Ser.). 48p. (J). pap. 3.99 (978-0-448-42597-9(1) , Grosset & Dunlap) Penguin Group (USA) Inc.

—Civil War Sub Vol. 3: The Mystery of the Hunley. 2002. (gr. k-3). lib. bdg. 11.80 (978-0-613-64032-9(2)) Tandem Library Bks.

Jordan, Anne Devereaux & Schomp, Virginia. The Civil War. 2006. (Drama of African-American History Ser.). (Illus.). 80p. (J). lib. bdg. 34.21 (978-0-7614-2179-5(3) , Benchmark Bks.) Cavendish, Marshall Corp.

Jordan, Shirley. The Civil War: Moments in History. 1999. (Cover-to-Cover Bks.). (Illus.). 56p. (J). pap. 8.95 (978-0-7891-2903-1(5)); (gr. 4-7). lib. bdg. 17.95 (978-0-7807-8049-1(3)) Perfection Learning Corp.

Kallen, Stuart A. The Civil War & Reconstruction. 2001. (Black History Ser.). (Illus.). 48p. (J). (gr. 3-8). lib. bdg. 25.65 (978-1-57765-469-8(2) , ABDO & Daughters) ABDO Publishing Co.

Kantor, MacKinlay. Sterling Point Books: Lee & Grant at Appomattox. 2007. (Sterling Point Bks.). 144p. (J). pap. 6.95 (*978-1-4027-5124-0(9)) Sterling Publishing Co., Inc.

Katz, William Loren. Breaking the Chains: African-American Slave Resistance, Class Set. unabr. ed. 1998. (YA). 155.80 incl. audio (978-0-7887-2556-2(4) , 46726) Recorded Bks., LLC.

—Breaking the Chains Homework Set: African-American Slave Resistance. unabr. ed. 1998. (YA). 53.25 incl. audio (978-0-7887-2252-3(2) , 40736) Recorded Bks., LLC.

Kay, Alan N. Off to Fight: Young Heroes of History. 2001. (Young Heroes of History: Vol. 3). (Illus.). 175p. (J). (gr. 4-7). pap. 5.95 (978-1-57249-240-0(6) , 1572492406, Burd Street Pr.) White Mane Publishing Co., Inc.

Kennedy, Robert F. Robert F. Kennedy, Jr.'s American Heroes: Joshua Chamberlain & the American Civil War. Andreev, Nikita, illus. rev. ed. 2007. 48p. (gr. 3-7). 16.99 (*978-1-4231-0771-2(3)) Hyperion Pr.

Kent, Deborah. The Great Civil War Draft Riots. 2005. (Cornerstones of Freedom Ser.). (Illus.). 48p. (J). 26.00 (978-0-516-23632-2(6) , Children's Pr.) Scholastic Library Publishing.

Kent, Zachary. The Civil War: "A House Divided" 2000. (American War Ser.). (Illus.). 128p. (YA). (gr. 5-12). pap. 13.26 (978-0-7660-1728-3(1)) Enslow Pubs., Inc.

—George Armstrong Custer: Civil War General & Western Legend. 2000. (Historical American Biographies Ser.). (Illus.). 128p. (YA). (gr. 6-12). lib. bdg. 26.60 (978-0-7660-1255-4(7)) Enslow Pubs., Inc.

Kerley, Barbara. Walt Whitman: Words for America. Selznick, Brian, illus. 2004. 56p. (J). (gr. 2-5). pap. 16.95 (978-0-439-35791-3(8) , Scholastic Pr.) Scholastic, Inc.

King, David C. Civil War Days: Discover the Past with Exciting Projects, Games, Activities, & Recipes. 1999. (Illus.). 98p. (J). (ps-7). lib. bdg. 22.20 (978-0-613-16481-8(4)) Tandem Library Bks.

Kunstler, Mort, illus. The Civil War 1861-1865. 2002. 48p. per. 6.95 (978-0-9718567-5-2(3)) Scenic Art.

Landers, Eli P. Weep Not for Me, Dear Mother. Roberson, Elizabeth Whitley, ed. 1998. 168p. (J). (gr. 3-7). pap. 14.95 (978-1-56554-390-4(4)) Pelican Publishing Co., Inc.

Langellier, J. Phillip. Redlegs: The U. S. Artillery from the Civil War to the Spanish-American War, 1861-1898. 1999. (G. I. Ser.: Vol. 11). (Illus.). 80p. (YA). (gr. 5-9). 27.50 (978-0-7910-5375-1(X) , Chelsea Hse.) Facts On File, Inc.

Langellier, John P. American Indians in the U. S. Armed Forces, 1866-1945, Vol. 20. 2006. (G. I. Ser.: Vol. 20). (Illus.). 72p. pap. 14.95 (978-1-85367-408-2(7)) Greenhill Bks./Lionel Leventhal, Ltd. GBR. *Dist:* MBI Distribution Services.

—Terrible Swift Sword. 2001. (G. I. Ser.). (Illus.). 80p. (J). 27.50 (978-0-7910-6673-7(8) , Chelsea Hse.) Facts On File, Inc.

Let Freedom Ring: The Civil War, 6 bks. Incl. Battle of Gettysburg : Turning Point of the Civil War. De Angelis, Gina. lib. bdg. 22.60 (978-0-7368-1340-2(3)); Emancipation Proclamation : Hope of Freedom for the Slaves. Martin, Michael J. lib. bdg. 22.60 (978-0-7368-1339-6(X)); Massachusetts 54th : African American Soldiers of the Union. DeAngelis, Gina. lib. bdg. 22.60 (978-0-7368-1343-3(8)); Reconstruction : Rebuilding after the Civil War. Peacock, Judith. lib. bdg. 22.60 (978-0-7368-1341-9(1)); Secession : The Southern States Leave the Union. Peacock, Judith. lib. bdg. 22.60 (978-0-7368-

1342-6(X)); Underground Railroad : Bringing Slaves North to Freedom. Monroe, Judy. lib. bdg. 22.60 (978-0-7368-1344-0(6)); 48p. (J). (gr. 3-4). 2002. (Illus.). 2002. Set lib. bdg. 135.60 (978-0-7368-1345-7(4) , Bridgestone Bks.) Capstone Pr., Inc.

Lieurance, Suzanne. Weapons & Strategies of the Civil War: A MyReportLinks. com Book. 2004. (American Civil War Ser.). (Illus.). 48p. (J). lib. bdg. 25.26 (978-0-7660-5185-0(4) , MyReportLinks.com Bks.) Enslow Pubs., Inc.

Lloyd, Mark. Combat Uniforms of the Civil War, 4 vols. Codd, Mike, illus. 1998. (YA). (gr. 7 up). lib. bdg. 74.95 (978-0-7910-4992-1(2) , Chelsea Hse.) Facts On File, Inc.

—The Confederate Army, 4 vols., Set. 1998. (Illus.). 64p. 17.98 (978-0-7910-4995-2(7) , Chelsea Hse.) Facts On File, Inc.

—The Federal Army, 4 vols., Set. 1998. (Illus.). 64p. 17.98 (978-0-7910-4993-8(0)); 17.98 (978-0-7910-4994-5(9)) Facts On File, Inc. (Chelsea Hse.).

Marinelli, Deborah A. The Assassination of Abraham Lincoln. 2003. (Library of Political Assassinations). (Illus.). 64p. (J). (gr. 4-6). lib. bdg. 26.50 (978-0-8239-3539-0(6)) Rosen Publishing Group, Inc., The.

Marquette, Scott. The Civil War. 2003. (America at War Ser.). (Illus.). 48p. (gr. 4-8). 20.95 (978-1-58952-388-3(1)) Rourke Publishing, LLC.

Marrin, Albert. Commander in Chief: Abraham Lincoln & the Civil War. 2003. (Illus.). 256p. (J). (gr. 7). pap. 14.99 (978-0-525-47069-4(7) , Dutton Juvenile) Penguin Group (USA) Inc.

—Commander in Chief Abraham Lincoln & the Civil War. 2003. (Illus.). 246p. (YA). (gr. 8-12). lib. bdg. 24.60 (978-0-613-59800-2(8)) Tandem Library Bks.

Marsh, Carole. Louis & Cordelia Harvey. 2002. (One Thousand Readers Ser.). (Illus.). 12p. (J). (gr. k-4). 2.95 (978-0-635-01526-6(9) , 15269) Gallopade International.

Martin, Michael J. Emancipation Proclamation: Hope of Freedom for the Slaves. 2002. (Let Freedom Ring Ser.). (Illus.). 48p. (J). (gr. 3-4). lib. bdg. 22.60 (978-0-7368-1339-6(X) , Bridgestone Bks.) Capstone Pr., Inc.

Massachusetts 54th: African American Soldiers of the Union. (Civil War Ser.). 48p. (YA). 7.95 (978-0-7368-4518-2(6)) Capstone Pr., Inc.

Mattern, Joanne. The Big Book of the Civil War. 2007. 56p. (J). 9.98 (978-0-7624-2856-4(2) , Running Pr.) Running Pr. Bk. Pubs.

Matthews, Sherrie Voss, ed. A House Divided: America's Civil War. 2000. (Literature & Thought Ser.). (Illus.). 143p. (J). (978-0-7807-9320-0(X)); pap. (978-0-7891-5152-0(9)) Perfection Learning Corp.

McAfee, Michael J. Billy Yank: The Uniform of the Union Army, 1861-1865. 1999. (G. I. Ser.). (Illus.). 80p. (YA). (gr. 5 up). 27.50 (978-0-7910-5368-3(7) , Chelsea Hse.) Facts On File, Inc.

McCarthy, Pat. Famous Confederate Generals & Leaders of the South: A Myreportlinks. com Book. 2004. (American Civil War Ser.). (Illus.). 48p. (J). lib. bdg. 25.26 (978-0-7660-5189-8(7) , MyReportLinks.com Bks.) Enslow Pubs., Inc.

—Famous Union Generals & Leaders of the North: A MyReportLinks. com Book. 2004. (American Civil War Ser.). (Illus.). 48p. (J). lib. bdg. 25.26 (978-0-7660-5188-1(9) , MyReportLinks.com Bks.) Enslow Pubs., Inc.

McDonald, Archie P. Primary Source Accounts of the Civil War. 2006. (America's Wars Through Primary Sources Ser.). (Illus.). 128p. (J). lib. bdg. 33.27 (978-1-59845-000-2(X) , MyReportLinks.com Bks.) Enslow Pubs., Inc.

McDougal, Littell Staff, contrib. by. The Civil War 1860-1865. 2004. (Stories in History Ser.). (Illus.). 205p. (gr. 6-12). 13.32 (978-0-618-14214-9(2) , 2-00234) McDougal Littell Inc.

Mcleese, Don. Jeb Stuart. 2005. 32p. pap. 6.45 (978-1-59515-793-5(X)) Rourke Publishing, LLC.

McLeese, Don. William Tecumseh Sherman. 2006. (Civil War Military Leaders Ser.). (Illus.). 32p. (gr. 3-6). 19.95 (978-1-59515-478-1(7)) Rourke Publishing, LLC.

McNamara, Margaret. Discover the North & the South. 2006. pap. 39.00 (*978-1-4108-6447-5(2)) Benchmark Education Co.

—The North & the South. 2006. pap. 39.00 (*978-1-4108-6444-4(8)) Benchmark Education Co.

Mir Tamim Ansary. Memorial Day. 2nd ed. 2006. (Illus.). 32p. (J). pap. (*978-1-4034-8903-6(3)) Heinemann Library.

Morrison, Taylor. Civil War Artist. 2004. (Illus.). 32p. (J). (gr. k-3). pap. 5.95 (978-0-618-49538-2(X) , Walter Lorraine) Houghton Mifflin Co. Trade & Reference Div.

Murphy, Jim. The Long Road to Gettysburg. 2000. (J). (978-0-606-19362-7(6)) Tandem Library Bks.

Naden, Corinne J. & Blue, Rose. The Bloodiest Days: The Battles of 1861 & 1862. 1999. (House Divided Ser.). (Illus.). 112p. (J). (gr. 5-10). lib. bdg. 31.40 (978-0-8172-5581-7(8)) Raintree.

Nardo, Don. The Civil War. 2002. (History of Weapons & Warfare Ser.). (Illus.). 112p. (J). 29.95 (978-1-59018-068-6(2) , Lucent Bks.) Thomson Gale.

Nelson, Sheila. Americans Divided: The Civil War. 2005. (How America Became America Ser.). (Illus.). 96p. (J). lib. bdg. (978-1-59084-908-8(6)) Mason Crest Pubs.

Netzley, Patricia D., tr. The Civil War. 2004. (Greenhaven Encyclopedia of Ser.). (Illus.). 336p. (J). lib. bdg. 77.45 (978-0-7377-0438-9(1) , Greenhaven Pr., Inc.) Thomson Gale.

Newman, Marc. Potomac Diary: A Soldier's Account of the Capital in Crisis, 1864-1865. 2000. (Civil War History Ser.). (Illus.). 128p. pap. 18.99 (978-0-7385-0471-1(8)) Arcadia Publishing.

Nofi, Albert A. The Underground Railroad & the Civil War. 1999. (Untold History of the Civil War Ser.). (Illus.). 64p. (J). (gr. 3 up). 25.00 (978-0-7910-5434-5(9) , Chelsea Hse.) Facts On File, Inc.

O'Connell, Kim A. The Civil War: A MyReportLinks. Com Book. 2003. (U. S. Wars Ser.). (Illus.). 48p. (J). lib. bdg. 25.26 (978-0-7660-5130-0(7) , MyReportLinks.com Bks.) Enslow Pubs., Inc.

—Slavery, Emancipation, & the Civil War: A MyReportLinks. com Book. 2004. (American Civil War Ser.). (Illus.). 48p. (J). lib. bdg. 25.26 (978-0-7660-5190-4(0) , MyReportLinks.com Bks.) Enslow Pubs., Inc.

Ojeda, Auriana. The Civil War: 1850-1895, Vol. 5. 2003. (American History by Era Ser.: Vol. 5). (Illus.). 301p. (YA). pap. 33.70 (978-0-7377-1139-4(6)); lib. bdg. 52.45 (978-0-7377-1140-0(X)) Thomson Gale. (Greenhaven Pr., Inc.).

Olson, Steven P. Lincoln's Gettysburg Address: A Primary Source Investigation. 2004. (Great Historic Debates & Speeches Ser.). (Illus.). 64p. (J). lib. bdg. 29.25 (978-1-4042-0151-4(3)) Rosen Publishing Group, Inc., The.

Optic, Oliver. Stand by the Union. Bridgman, L. & Fitterling, Michael A., illus. 2002. (Blue & Gray Ser.). 362p. (J). (gr. 4-12). reprint ed. per. 14.95 (978-1-890623-11-1(3)) Lost Classics Bk. Co.

O'Shei, Tim. Ulysses S. Grant: Military Leader & President. (Famous Figures of the Civil War Era Ser.). (Illus.). 80p. (J). 2001. (gr. 8-12). 25.00 (978-0-7910-6001-8(2)); 2000. (gr. 4-7). pap. 25.00 (978-0-7910-6139-8(6)) Facts On File, Inc. (Chelsea Hse.).

Ouren, Todd, illus. When Johnny Comes Marching Home. 2004. (Patriotic Songs Ser.). 24p. (J). (ps-4). 22.60 (978-1-4048-0171-4(5)) Picture Window Bks.

Owens, L. L. America's Civil War. 2000. (Cover-to-Cover Bks.). (Illus.). 56p. (J). pap. (978-0-7891-5300-5(9)); (gr. 1-4). lib. bdg. 16.95 (978-0-7807-9647-8(0)) Perfection Learning Corp.

Page, Thomas Nelson. A Captured Santa Claus. reprint ed. pap. 28.00 (978-1-4047-4699-2(4)) Classic Textbooks.

—A Captured Santa Claus. 1999. (Notable American Authors Ser.). reprint ed. lib. bdg. 125.00 (978-0-7812-4699-6(7)) Reprint Services Co.

Peacock, Judith. Secession: The Southern States Leave the Union. 2002. (Let Freedom Ring Ser.). (Illus.). 48p. (J). (gr. 3-4). lib. bdg. 22.60 (978-0-7368-1342-6(X) , Bridgestone Bks.) Capstone Pr., Inc.

Penny, Morris M. & Laine, J. Gary. Struggle for the Round Tops: Law's Alabama Brigade at the Battle of Gettysburg, July 2-3, 1863. 1999. (Illus.). xvii, 254p. 24.95 (978-1-57249-063-5(2) , Burd Street Pr.) White Mane Publishing Co., Inc.

Pflueger, Lynda. Jeb Stuart: Confederate Cavalry General. 1998. (Historical American Biographies Ser.). (Illus.). 128p. (YA). (gr. 6-12). lib. bdg. 20.95 (978-0-7660-1013-0(9)) Enslow Pubs., Inc.

—Mathew Brady: Photographer of the Civil War. 2001. (Historical American Biographies Ser.). (Illus.). 128p. (J). (gr. 6-12). lib. bdg. 26.60 (978-0-7660-1444-2(4)) Enslow Pubs., Inc.

Pingry, Patricia A. Meet Robert E. Lee. Johnson, Meredith, illus. 2004. (J). 9.95 (978-0-8249-5465-9(3) , Ideals Pr.) Ideals Pubns.

—The Story of Robert E. Lee. Johnson, Meredith, illus. 2004. 26p. (J). (ps-k). bds. 6.95 (978-0-8249-6501-3(9)) Ideals Pubns.

Play Bac Edu-Team, creator. Civil War: From Divided to United. 2007. (Illus.). 10p. (J). pap. 6.95 (*978-1-60214-022-6(7)) Play Bac Publishing, USA.

Poulakidas, Georgene. The Civil War. 2005. (Primary Sources of American Wars Ser.). (Illus.). 24p. (J). lib. bdg. (978-1-4042-2684-5(2)) Rosen Publishing Group, Inc., The.

Randolph, Ryan P. Harriet Beecher Stowe: Author & Abolitionist. 2005. (Library of American Lives & Times). (Illus.). 112p. (J). (gr. 4-8). lib. bdg. 31.95 (978-0-8239-6623-3(2)) Rosen Publishing Group, Inc., The.

Ransom, Candice F. Children of the Civil War. 1998. (Picture the American Past Ser.). (Illus.). 48p. (gr. 2-5). lib. bdg. 22.60 (978-1-57505-241-0(5)) Lerner Publishing Group.

—Willie McLean & the Civil War Surrender. Reeves, Jeni, illus. 2005. (On My Own History Ser.). 48p. (J). 25.26 (978-1-57505-588-6(0)) Lerner Publishing Group.

Rappaport, Doreen & Verniero, Joan. United No More! Stories of the Civil War. Reeves, Rick, illus. 2006. 144p. (J). 15.99 (978-0-06-050599-8(0)); lib. bdg. 16.89 (978-0-06-050600-1(8)) HarperCollins Pubs.

Ratliff, Thomas. You Wouldn't Want to Be a Civil War Soldier! 2004. (You Wouldn't Want to Ser.). (Illus.). 32p. (J). (gr. 2-5). pap. 9.95 (978-0-531-16393-1(8) , Watts, Franklin) Scholastic Library Publishing.

Ratliff, Thomas M. & Salariya, David. You Wouldn't Want to Be a Civil War Soldier! A War You'd Rather Not Fight. Antram, David, illus. 2004. (You Wouldn't Want To Ser.). 32p. (J). 28.50 (978-0-531-12350-8(2) , Watts, Franklin) Scholastic Library Publishing.

Rebman, Renée C. The Union Soldier. 2006. 48p. (J). (gr. 4-6). lib. bdg. (978-0-7565-2030-4(4)) Compass Point Bks.

Remstein, Henna. William Sherman: Union Military Leader. (Famous Figures of the Civil War Era Ser.). (Illus.). 80p. (J). 2001. (gr. 8-12). 25.00 (978-0-7910-6005-6(5)); 2000. (gr. 4-7). pap. 25.00 (978-0-7910-6143-5(4)) Facts On File, Inc. (Chelsea Hse.).

Richardson, George C. Drummer. 2001. 108p. (YA). (gr. 6-9). pap. 9.95 (978-0-595-15359-6(3) , Writer's Showcase Pr.) iUniverse, Inc.

Riehecky, Janet. The Emancipation Proclamation: The Abolition of Slavery. 2002. (Point of Impact Ser.). (Illus.). 32p. (J). (gr. 5-7). lib. bdg. 25.64 (978-1-58810-556-1(3)) Heinemann Library.

Rivera, Sheila. The Gettysburg Address. 2005. (American Moments Ser.). (Illus.). 48p. (J). (gr. 4-8). lib. bdg. 25.65 (978-1-59197-285-3(X)) ABDO Publishing Co.

Robert Smalls Sails to Freedom. 2007. (J). pap. 5.95 (*978-0-8225-6051-7(8) , First Avenue Editions) Lerner Publishing Group.

Robinson, Robin. The Civil War Handbook: How to Dress, Talk, Eat & Command Like a Rebel Lieutenant. 2007. (Civil War Handbooks Ser.). (Illus.). 64p. (J). pap. 12.95 (978-1-933317-72-4(8)) Silverleaf Pr.

—The Civil War Handbook: How to Dress, Talk, Eat, & Command Like a Union Soldier. 2007. (Civil War Handbooks Ser.). (Illus.). 64p. (J). pap. 12.95 (978-1-933317-71-7(X)) Silverleaf Pr.

Sandler, Martin. Civil War. 2001. (gr. 5-8). lib. bdg. 19.95 (978-0-613-33686-4(0)) Tandem Library Bks.

Sandler, Martin W. Civil War. 2001. (Library of Congress Classics). (Illus.). 96p. (J). (gr. 3 up). pap. 12.99 (978-0-06-446264-8(1) , Harper Trophy) HarperCollins Pubs.

—Civil War: A Library of Congress Book. 2001. (Illus.). (J). 18.54 (978-0-606-20609-9(4)) Tandem Library Bks.

Santella, Andrew. Surrender at Appomattox. 2006. (Illus.). 48p. (J). (gr. 4-6). 23.93 (978-0-7565-1626-0(9)) Compass Point Bks.

Sateren, Shelley Swanson. A Civil War Drummer Boy: The Diary of William Bircher, 1861-1865. 1999. (Diaries, Letters & Memoirs Ser.). (Illus.). 32p. (J). (gr. 2-7). pap. 21.00 (978-0-516-21850-2(6) , Children's Pr.) Scholastic Library Publishing.

Savage, Douglas J. Civil War Medicine. 2000. (Untold History of the Civil War Ser.). (Illus.). 64p. (J). (gr. 3 up). 25.00 (978-0-7910-5709-4(7) , Chelsea Hse.) Facts On File, Inc.

—Far West in the Civil War. 2000. (Untold History of the Civil War Ser.). (Illus.). 64p. (J). (gr. 3 up). 25.00 (978-0-7910-5437-6(3) , Chelsea Hse.) Facts On File, Inc.

—Prison Camps in the Civil War. 2000. (Untold History of the Civil War Ser.). (Illus.). 64p. (J). (gr. 3-7). 25.00 (978-0-7910-5428-4(4) , Chelsea Hse.) Facts On File, Inc.

—Soldier's Life During the Civil War. 2000. (Untold History of the Civil War Ser.). (Illus.). 64p. (J). (gr. 3 up). 25.00 (978-0-7910-5710-0(0) , Chelsea Hse.) Facts On File, Inc.

—Women in the Civil War. 2000. (Untold History of the Civil War Ser.). (Illus.). 64p. (J). (gr. 3 up). 25.00 (978-0-7910-5436-9(5) , Chelsea Hse.) Facts On File, Inc.

Schomp, Virginia. The Civil War. 2001. (Letters from the Home Front Ser.). (Illus.). 96p. (J). (gr. 6 up). lib. bdg. 29.93 (978-0-7614-1095-9(3) , Benchmark Bks.) Cavendish, Marshall Corp.

Schoof, Heidi. Elizabeth Van Lew: Civil War Spy. 2005. (Signature Lives Ser.). (Illus.). 112p. (J). (gr. 5-7). (978-0-7565-0985-9(8)) Compass Point Bks.

Schroeder-Lein, Glenna R. The Encyclopedia of Civil War Medicine. 2007. 368p. 95.00 (*978-0-7656-1171-0(6)) Sharpe, M.E. Inc.

Schroeder, Patrick A. Thirty Myths about Lee's Surrender. 8th rev. ed. 2000. (Illus.). 32p. (YA). (gr. 7 up). pap. 4.00 (978-1-889246-05-5(0)) Schroeder Pubns.: Civil War Bks.

Seguin, Marilyn Weymouth. Knothole in the Closet: A Story about Belle Boyd, a Confederate Spy. 2002. 30p. (J). pap. 35.00 incl. audio compact disk (978-1-58472-277-9(0) , In Audio) Sound Room Pubs., Inc.

Shah, Ruchir, ed. The Civil War. 2007. (YA). 6.95 (*978-0-9795887-1-6(5)) EZ Comics.

Shea, Therese. Interpreting America's Civil War: Organizing & Interpreting Information in Outlines, Graphs, Timelines, Maps, & Charts. 2005. (Critical Thinking in American History Ser.). (Illus.). 48p. (YA). (gr. 5-8). lib. bdg. 25.25 (978-1-4042-0415-7(6)) Rosen Publishing Group, Inc., The.

Sheffield, Sarah. Life During the American Civil War. 2002. (Reading Room Collection). (Illus.). 24p. (J). lib. bdg. 18.75 (978-0-8239-3735-6(6)) Rosen Publishing Group, Inc., The.

Shipwreck Search: Discovery of the H. L. Hunley. 2007. (J). pap. 5.95 (*978-0-8225-6449-2(1) , First Avenue Editions) Lerner Publishing Group.

Silber, Nina. Landmarks of the Civil War. 2003. (American Landmarks Ser.). (Illus.). 144p. (YA). 30.00 (978-0-19-512920-5(2)) Oxford Univ. Pr., Inc.

Silverman, Jerry & Swan, Susan. Songs & Stories of the Civil War. 2002. (Single Titles Ser.). (Illus.). 96p. (gr. 5 up). lib. bdg. 29.90 (978-0-7613-2305-1(8) , Twenty-First Century Bks.) Lerner Publishing Group.

Sinnott, Susan. Welcome to Addy's World, 1864: Growing up During America's Civil War. 1999. (American Girls Collection). (Illus.). 64p. (J). (gr. 2 up). 16.95 (978-1-56247-771-4(4)) American Girl Publishing, Inc.

Smolinski, Diane. Americans at War Series: The Civil War, 4 bks., Set 1. 2001. (Illus.). (J). (gr. 4-6). lib. bdg. 96.88 (978-1-58810-018-4(9)) Heinemann Library.

—The Home Front in the North. (Americans at War Ser.). (Illus.). 32p. (J). (gr. 4-7). 2002. pap. 6.95 (978-1-58810-393-2(5) , 91133); 2001. lib. bdg. (978-1-58810-099-3(5)) Heinemann Library.

—The Home Front in the South. 2002. (Americans at War Ser.). (Illus.). 32p. (J). (gr. 4-7). pap. 6.95 (978-1-58810-394-9(3) , 91134) Heinemann Library.

—Soldiers of the Civil War. 2002. (Americans at War Ser.). (Illus.). 32p. (J). (gr. 4-6). lib. bdg. (978-1-58810-098-6(7)); pap. 6.95 (978-1-58810-392-5(7) , 91132) Heinemann Library.

Somervill, Barbara A. Great Women of the Confederacy. 2006. 48p. (J). (gr. 4-6). lib. bdg. (978-0-7565-2033-5(9)) Compass Point Bks.

Stanchak, John E. Civil War. 2000. (Eyewitness Bks.). (Illus.). 64p. (J). (gr. 4-7). 15.99 (978-0-7894-6302-9(4)) Dorling Kindersley Publishing, Inc.

Stanchak, John E. & Dorling Kindersley Publishing Staff. Civil War. 2000. (Eyewitness Bks.: Vol. 114). (Illus.). 64p. (J). (gr. 4-7). lib. bdg. 19.99 (978-0-7894-6988-5(X)) Dorling Kindersley Publishing, Inc.

Stanley, George Edward. The Crisis of the Union (1815-1865) 2005. (Illus.). 48p. (J). pap. (978-0-8368-5835-8(2)); lib. bdg. 30.00 (978-0-8368-5826-6(3)) Stevens, Gareth Inc. (World Almanac Library).

Steele, Christy & Todd, Anne M. A Confederate Girl: The Diary of Carrie Berry, 1864. 1999. (Diaries, Letters & Memoirs Ser.). (Illus.). 32p. (J). (gr. 2-7). pap. 21.00 (978-0-516-21338-5(5) , Children's Pr.) Scholastic Library Publishing.

Stefoff, Rebecca. The Civil War, 1861-1863. 2002. (North American Historical Atlases Ser.). (Illus.). 48p. (J). 27.07 (978-0-7614-1346-2(4) , Benchmark Bks.) Cavendish, Marshall Corp.

—The Civil War & Reconstruction 1863-1877. 2002. (North American Historical Atlases Ser.). (Illus.). 48p. (J). 27.07 (978-0-7614-1347-9(2) , Benchmark Bks.) Cavendish, Marshall Corp.

Sullivan, George E. The Civil War at Sea. 2001. (Single Titles Ser.: 8). (Illus.). 80p. (J). (gr. 5-8). lib. bdg. (978-0-7613-1553-7(5) , Twenty-First Century Bks.) Lerner Publishing Group.

—Portraits of War: Civil War Photographers & Their Work. 1998. (Single Titles Ser.). (Illus.). 80p. (gr. 5-8). lib. bdg. 26.90 (978-0-7613-3019-6(4) , Twenty-First Century Bks.) Lerner Publishing Group.

Thomson Gale Staff. Civil War: 1850-1895. 2002. (gr. 7-12). lib. bdg. 39.05 (978-0-613-73611-4(7)) Tandem Library Bks.

Thro, Ellen. Growing & Dividing. 2000. (Making of America Ser.). (Illus.). 96p. (J). (gr. 4-7). lib. bdg. 28.54 (978-0-8172-5704-0(7)) Raintree.

Trumbauer, Lisa. Life in the Time of Abraham Lincoln & the Civil War. 2007. (J). (*978-1-4034-9668-3(4)); pap. (*978-1-4034-9676-8(5)) Heinemann Library.

Untold History of the Civil War. 2005. pap. 275.00 (978-0-7910-9181-4(3) , Chelsea Hse.) Facts On File, Inc.

Uschan, Michael V. The Cavalry During the Civil War. 2002. (Working Life Ser.). (Illus.). 112p. (J). 29.95 (978-1-59018-175-1(1) , Lucent Bks.) Thomson Gale.

—A Civil War Doctor. 2005. (Working Life Ser.). (Illus.). 112p. (YA). (gr. 7-10). lib. bdg. 29.95 (978-1-59018-578-0(1) , Lucent Bks.) Thomson Gale.

—Fort Sumter: The Civil War Begins. 2004. (Landmark Events in American History Ser.). (Illus.). 48p. (J). pap. 15.93 (978-0-8368-5423-7(3)); lib. bdg. 30.00 (978-0-8368-5395-7(4)) Stevens, Gareth Inc. (World Almanac Library).

Vierow, Wendy. The Assault on Fort Wagner: Black Union Soldiers Make a Stand in South Carolina Battle. 2004. (Headlines from History Ser.). (Illus.). 24p. (J). lib. bdg. 19.95 (978-0-8239-6223-5(7) , PowerKids Pr.) Rosen Publishing Group, Inc., The.

—Shots Fired at Fort Sumter. 2004. (Headlines from History Ser.). (Illus.). 24p. (J). lib. bdg. 19.95 (978-0-8239-6220-4(2)) Rosen Publishing Group, Inc., The.

Walbridge, Mike. African-American Heroes of the Civil War. 2000. 144p. (gr. 6-12). tchr. ed. 21.99 (978-0-8251-4145-4(1) , 0-41451) Walch Publishing.

Walker, Gary C. A General History of the Civil War, the Southern Point of View. 2004. (Illus.). 510p. (J). (gr. 4-8). 34.95 (978-0-9617898-6-2(7)) A&W Enterprises.

Waryncia, Lou. Robert E. Lee: Duty & Honor. Hale, Sarah Elder, ed. 2005. (Civil War Ser.). (Illus.). 48p. (J). 17.95 (978-0-8126-7905-2(9)) Cobblestone Publishing Co.

—Ulysses S. Grant: Confident Leaders & Hero. Hale, Sarah Elder, ed. 2005. (Civil War Ser.). (Illus.). 48p. (J). 17.95 (978-0-8126-7906-9(7)) Cobblestone Publishing Co.

Waryncia, Lou & Hale, Sarah Elder. Abraham Lincoln: Defender of the Union. 2005. (Civil War Ser.). (Illus.). 48p. (J). 17.95 (978-0-8126-7902-1(4)) Cobblestone Publishing Co.

—Young Heroes of the North & South. 2005. (Civil War Ser.). (Illus.). 48p. (J). 17.95 (978-0-8126-7901-4(6)) Cobblestone Publishing Co.

Watson, Diane E. Strike the Tents. 1999. (Illus.). 20p. (YA). (gr. 6 up). pap. 3.00 (978-1-890541-18-7(4)) Americana Souvenirs & Gifts.

We the People: Civil War Era. 2006. (J). (gr. 4-6). 311.09 (978-0-7565-1703-8(6)) Compass Point Bks.

We the People- Civil War Era, 3 bks. Incl. Battle of Gettysburg. Burgan, Michael. 2001. lib. bdg. 22.60 (978-0-7565-0098-6(2)); Emancipation Proclamation. Heinrichs, Ann. 2002. lib. bdg. 22.60 (978-0-7565-0209-6(8)); Underground Railroad. Heinrichs, Ann. 2001. lib. bdg. 22.60 (978-0-7565-0102-0(4)); 48p. (J). (gr. 4 up). (Illus.). Set lib. bdg. 67.80 (978-0-7565-0776-3(6)) Compass Point Bks.

Weber, Michael. Civil War & Reconstruction. 2000. (Making of America Ser.). (Illus.). 96p. (J). (gr. 4-7). lib. bdg. 28.54 (978-0-8172-5707-1(1)) Raintree.

Wilbur, C. Keith. Civil War Medicine. 1999. (Illustrated Living History Ser.). (Illus.). 119p. (J). (gr. 5-9). 14.95 (978-0-7910-5207-5(9) , Chelsea Hse.) Facts On File, Inc.

—Civil War Medicine. 1998. (Illustrated Living History Ser.). (Illus.). 128p. pap. 14.95 (978-0-7627-0341-8(5)) Globe Pequot Pr., The.

Women Soldiers in the Union Army. 2000. (Illus.). (J). pap. 4.95 (978-0-88388-221-4(3)) Bellerophon Bks.

Wood, Ira. Fort Sumter: Where the Civil War Began. 2006. (Rosen Publishing Group's Reading Room Collection). (Illus.). 16p. (J). lib. bdg. (978-1-4042-3349-2(0) , PowerKids Pr.) Rosen Publishing Group, Inc., The.

Zeinert, Karen. Those Courageous Women of the Civil War. 1998. (Women at War Ser.). (Illus.). 96p. (gr. 5 up). lib. bdg. 29.90 (978-0-7613-0212-4(3) , Twenty-First Century Bks.) Lerner Publishing Group.

UNITED STATES—HISTORY—CIVIL WAR, 1861-1865—BIOGRAPHY

Adelson, Bruce. George Meade: Union General. 2001. (Famous Figures of the Civil War Era Ser.). (Illus.). (J). 79p. pap. (978-0-7910-6411-5(5)); 80p. (gr. 5 up). 25.00 (978-0-7910-6410-8(7)) Facts On File, Inc. (Chelsea Hse.).

Allison, Amy. Edwin Stanton, Union War Secretary. 2001. (Famous Figures of the Civil War Era Ser.). (Illus.). 80p. (J). pap. (978-0-7910-6421-4(2)); (gr. 5 up). 25.00 (978-0-7910-6420-7(4)) Facts On File, Inc. (Chelsea Hse.).

Ashby, Ruth. Ordinary Heroes. 2002. (Illus.). 48p. (J). lib. bdg. 28.50 (978-1-58340-182-8(2)) Smart Apple Media.

Baker, Lawrence W., contrib. by. American Civil War Reference Library: Cumulative Index. 2000. (Illus.). 17p. (J). lib. bdg. 5.00 (978-0-7876-3819-1(6)) Thomson Gale.

Balcavage, Dynise. Philip Sheridan. 2001. (Famous Figures of the Civil War Era Ser.). (Illus.). 80p. (J). pap. (978-0-7910-6407-8(7) , Chelsea Hse.) Facts On File, Inc.

—Philip Sheridan: Union General. 2001. (Famous Figures of the Civil War Era Ser.). (Illus.). 80p. (J). (gr. 5 up). 25.00 (978-0-7910-6406-1(9) , Chelsea Hse.) Facts On File, Inc.

Carter, E.J. & Price Hossell, Karen. American War Biographies, 6 bks. 2004. (J). (gr. 4-6). lib. bdg. 179.57 (978-1-4034-5083-8(8)) Heinemann Library.

Civil War Generals. 1998. (Illus.). 32p. (YA). (gr. 6 up). pap. 4.00 (978-1-890541-11-8(7)) Americana Souvenirs & Gifts.

Donlan, Leni. Mathew Brady: Photographing the Civil War. 2007. (J). (***978-1-4109-2699-9(0));*** pap. (***978-1-4109-2710-1(5)***) Steck-Vaughn.

Famous Figures of the Civil War Era. 2005. 80p. pap. 500.00 (978-0-7910-6725-3(4) , Chelsea Hse.) Facts On File, Inc.

Fiore, Carmen Anthony. Young Heroes of the Civil War. 2006. (J). pap. (978-0-88092-639-3(2)); lib. bdg. (978-0-88092-638-6(4)) Royal Fireworks Publishing Co.

Flanagan, Alice K. Great Women of the Union. 2006. 48p. (J). (gr. 4-6). lib. bdg. (978-0-7565-2035-9(5)) Compass Point Bks.

Friedman, Robin. The Silent Witness. Nivola, Claire A., illus. 2005. 32p. (J). (gr. k-3). 16.00 (978-0-618-44230-0(8)) Houghton Mifflin Co. Trade & Reference Div.

Green, Carl R. & Sanford, William R. Confederate Generals of the Civil War. 1998. (Collective Biographies Ser.). (Illus.). 112p. (YA). (gr. 6-12). lib. bdg. 26.60 (978-0-7660-1029-1(5)) Enslow Pubs., Inc.

—Union Generals of the Civil War. 1998. (Collective Biographies Ser.). (Illus.). 112p. (YA). (gr. 6-12). lib. bdg. 26.60 (978-0-7660-1028-4(7)) Enslow Pubs., Inc.

Greene, Meg. Jeb Stuart: Confederate General. 2001. (Famous Figures of the Civil War Era Ser.). (Illus.). 80p. (J). (gr. 5 up). pap. 25.00 (978-0-7910-6415-3(8)); 25.00 (978-0-7910-6414-6(X)) Facts On File, Inc. (Chelsea Hse.).

Haines, J. D. Put the Boys In: The Story of the Virginia Military Institute Cadets at the Battle of New Market. 2004. (Illus.). 76p. (J). pap. (978-1-57168-816-3(1)) Eakin Pr.

Hale, Sarah Elder & Waryncia, Lou. Nation at War: Soldiers, Saints, & Spies. 2005. (Civil War Ser.). (Illus.). 48p. (J). 17.95 (978-0-8126-7900-7(8)) Cobblestone Publishing Co.

Harmon, Daniel E. Civil War Generals. 1999. (Looking Into the Past Ser.). (Illus.). 64p. (YA). (gr. 5 up). 14.00 (978-0-7910-4675-3(3) , Chelsea Hse.) Facts On File, Inc.

Haskins, Jim. Black Stars of Civil War Times. 2003. (Black Stars Ser.). (Illus.). 122p. pap. 12.95 (978-0-471-22069-5(8) , Wiley-Interscience) Wiley, John & Sons, Inc.

Hirschhorn, Vera. America's Young Heroes: A Journal for You: Learn about Yourself, Learn the Lessons of the Civil War. 2nd rev. ed. 2002. 117p. (YA). (gr. 5-10). pap. 24.95 (978-0-9718197-0-2(X)) America's Young Heroes Pubns.

Hughes, Christopher. The Civil War. 2003. (People at the Center of Ser.). (Illus.). 48p. (J). 24.95 (978-1-56711-764-6(3) , Blackbirch Pr., Inc.) Thomson Gale.

Kelley, Brent P. George McClellan. 2001. (Famous Figures of the Civil War Era Ser.). (Illus.). 80p. (J). pap. (978-0-7910-6405-4(0) , Chelsea Hse.) Facts On File, Inc.

—George McClellan: Union General. 2001. (Famous Figures of the Civil War Era Ser.). (Illus.). 80p. (YA). (gr. 5-8). 25.00 (978-0-7910-6404-7(2) , Chelsea Hse.) Facts On File, Inc.

Lakin, Patricia. Clara Barton: Spirit of the American Red Cross. Sullivan, Simon, illus. 2004. (Ready-to-Read Stories of Famous Americans Ser.). 48p. (J). pap. 3.99 (978-0-689-86513-8(9) , Aladdin) Simon & Schuster Children's Publishing.

Let Freedom Ring: Civil War Biographies, 6 bks. Incl. Abraham Lincoln. Oberle, Lora Polack. lib. bdg. 22.60 (978-0-7368-1086-9(2)); Harriet Tubman. Nielsen, Nancy J. lib. bdg. 22.60 (978-0-7368-1087-6(0)); Jefferson Davis. Gunderson, Cory Gideon. lib. bdg. 22.60 (978-0-7368-1088-3(9)); Robert E. Lee. Monroe, Judy. lib. bdg. 22.60 (978-0-7368-1089-0(7)); Sojourner Truth. Leebrick, Kristal. lib. bdg. 22.60 (978-0-7368-1090-6(0)); Ulysses S. Grant. Gregson, Susan R. lib. bdg. 22.60 (978-0-7368-1091-3(9)); 48p. (J). (gr. 3-4). 2002. (Illus.). 2001. Set lib. bdg. 135.60 (978-0-7368-1152-1(4) , Bridgestone Bks.) Capstone Pr., Inc.

Murray, Aaron R. & Dorling Kindersley Publishing Staff. Civil War Battles & Leaders. 2003. (Illus.). 96p. (J). 16.99 (978-0-7894-9890-8(1)) Dorling Kindersley Publishing, Inc.

Nichols, Joan Kane. Civil War Heroines. 2005. (Illus.). 16p. (J). (***978-0-328-14901-8(2)*** , Scott Foresman) Addison-Wesley Educational Pubs., Inc.

—The Civil War Sisterhood: Women Who Made a Difference. 2005. (Illus.). 16p. (J). (***978-0-328-14902-5(0)*** , Scott Foresman) Addison-Wesley Educational Pubs., Inc.

—Women of the Civil War. 2005. (Illus.). 16p. (J). (***978-0-328-14900-1(4)*** , Scott Foresman) Addison-Wesley Educational Pubs., Inc.

Raatma, Lucia. Great Women of the Civil War. 2004. (We the People Ser.). (Illus.). 48p. (J). 22.60 (978-0-7565-0839-5(8)) Compass Point Bks.

Reger, James P. Civil War Generals of the Confederacy. 1998. (History Makers Ser.). (Illus.). 144p. (YA). (gr. 7-10). 27.45 (978-1-56006-359-9(9) , Lucent Bks.) Thomson Gale.

Reit, Seymour V. Behind Rebel Lines: The Incredible Story of Emma Edmonds, Civil War Spy. 2001. (Great Episodes Ser.). 144p. (YA). (gr. 5-9). pap. 6.95 (978-0-15-216427-0(8) , Gulliver Bks.) Harcourt Children's Bks.

Ross, Margie Dover. Emma Sansom: Confederate Heroine. 2001. (Alabama Roots Biography Ser.). (Illus.). 104p. (J). (978-1-878561-83-1(9)) Seacoast Publishing, Inc.

Signature Lives: Civil War Era, 9 vols. (YA). (gr. 5-7). 112p. 275.40 (978-0-7565-1007-7(4)); Set. 2005. lib. bdg. 183.60 (978-0-7565-0874-6(6)) Compass Point Bks.

Waryncia, Lou & Hale, Sarah Elder. Young Heroes of the North & South. 2005. (Civil War Ser.). (Illus.). 48p. (J). 17.95 (978-0-8126-7901-4(6)) Cobblestone Publishing Co.

A Woman Officer in the Confederate Army. (J). pap. 9.95 (978-0-88388-211-5(6)) Bellerophon Bks.

Yancey, Diane. Leaders of the North & South. 1999. (American War Library). (Illus.). 128p. (YA). (gr. 4-12). 27.45 (978-1-56006-497-8(8) , LML00902-177860, Lucent Bks.) Thomson Gale.

UNITED STATES—HISTORY—CIVIL WAR, 1861-1865—CAMPAIGNS

see also Bull Run, 1st Battle of, Va., 1861; Gettysburg, Battle of, Gettysburg, Pa., 1863; New Market (Va.), Battle of, 1864; Sherman's March to the Sea

Anderson, Dale. The Battle of Gettysburg. 2003. (Landmark Events in American History Ser.). (Illus.). 48p. (J). (gr. 5 up). pap. 14.95 (978-0-8368-5400-8(4)); lib. bdg. 30.00 (978-0-8368-5372-8(5)) Stevens, Gareth Inc. (World Almanac Library).

—The Civil War in the East (1861-July 1863) 2004. (World Almanac Library of the Civil War). (Illus.). 48p. (J). (gr. 5 up). pap. 11.95 (978-0-8368-5591-3(4)); lib. bdg. 30.00 (978-0-8368-5582-1(5)) Stevens, Gareth Inc. (World Almanac Library).

—The Union Victory (July 1863-1865) 2004. (World Almanac Library of the Civil War). (Illus.). 48p. (J). (gr. 5 up). pap. 11.95 (978-0-8368-5593-7(0)); lib. bdg. 30.00 (978-0-8368-5584-5(1)) Stevens, Gareth Inc. (World Almanac Library).

Anderson, Paul Christopher. Robert E. Lee: Legendary Commander of the Confederacy. 2005. (Library of American Lives & Times). (Illus.). 112p. (YA). (gr. 4-8). lib. bdg. 31.95 (978-0-8239-5748-4(9)) Rosen Publishing Group, Inc., The.

Arnold, James R. & Wiener, Roberta. Lost Cause: The End of the Civil War, 1864-1865. 2005. (Civil War Ser.). (Illus.). 72p. (gr. 5-12). lib. bdg. 25.26 (978-0-8225-2317-8(5)) Lerner Publishing Group.

—On to Richmond: The Civil War in the East, 1861-1862. 2005. (Civil War Ser.). (Illus.). 72p. (J). (gr. 5-12). lib. bdg. 25.26 (978-0-8225-2313-0(2)) Lerner Publishing Group.

—River to Victory: The Civil War in the West, 1861-1863. 2005. (Civil War Ser.). (Illus.). 72p. (J). (gr. 5-12). lib. bdg. 25.26 (978-0-8225-2314-7(0)) Lerner Publishing Group.

—This Unhappy Country: The Turn of the Civil War, 1863. 2005. (Civil War Ser.). (Illus.). 72p. (gr. 5-12). lib. bdg. 25.26 (978-0-8225-2316-1(7)) Lerner Publishing Group.

Ashby, Ruth. Gettysburg. 2002. (Illus.). 48p. (J). lib. bdg. 28.50 (978-1-58340-186-6(5)) Smart Apple Media.

—Lee vs. Grant: The Major Battles. 2002. (Illus.). 48p. (J). lib. bdg. 28.50 (978-1-58340-184-2(9)) Smart Apple Media.

Beller, Susan Provost. Cadets at War: The True Story of Teenage Heroism at the Battle of New Market. 2000. (gr. 3-6). lib. bdg. 18.75 (978-0-613-85694-2(5)) Tandem Library Bks.

—Cadets at War: The True Story of Teenage Heroism at the Battle of New Market. 2000. (Illus.). 108p. (gr. 4-7). pap. 9.95 (978-0-595-00787-5(2) , Backinprint.com) iUniverse, Inc.

Brager, Bruce L. There He Stands: The Story of Stonewall Jackson. 2005. (Civil War Leaders Ser.). (Illus.). 176p. (J). (gr. 6-12). 26.95 (978-1-931798-44-0(3)) Reynolds, Morgan Inc.

Burgan, Michael. The Battle of Gettysburg. 2001. (We the People Ser.). (Illus.). 48p. (J). (gr. 4 up). lib. bdg. 22.60 (978-0-7565-0098-6(2)) Compass Point Bks.

Capstone Press, contrib. by. Battle of Gettysburg: Turning Point of the Civil War. (Civil War Ser.). 48p. (YA). pap. 7.95 (978-0-7368-4516-8(X)) Capstone Pr., Inc.

Connell, Kate. Yankee Blue or Rebel Gray? The Civil War Adventures of Sam Shaw. 2003. (gr. 3-6). lib. bdg. 15.30 (978-0-613-67133-0(3)) Tandem Library Bks.

Corrigan, Jim. Civil War in the West. 2002. (History of the Old West Ser.). (Illus.). 64p. (J). (gr. 5 up). lib. bdg. (978-1-59084-067-2(4)) Mason Crest Pubs.

Crewe, Sabrina & Anderson, Dale. The Battle of Gettysburg. 2003. (Events That Shaped America Ser.). (Illus.). 32p. (J). (gr. 3 up). lib. bdg. 24.67 (978-0-8368-3391-1(0)) Stevens, Gareth Inc.

De Angelis, Gina. The Battle of Gettysburg: Turning Point of the Civil War. 2002. (Let Freedom Ring Ser.). (Illus.). 48p. (J). (gr. 3-4). lib. bdg. 22.60 (978-0-7368-1340-2(3) , Bridgestone Bks.) Capstone Pr., Inc.

Ditchfield, Christin. Joseph E. Johnston: Confederate General. 2001. (Famous Figures of the Civil War Era Ser.). (Illus.). (J). 79p. pap. (978-0-7910-6413-9(1)); 80p. (gr. 5 up). 25.00 (978-0-7910-6412-2(3)) Facts On File, Inc. (Chelsea Hse.).

Doak, Robin S. Thomas "Stonewall" Jackson: Confederate General. 2005. (Signature Lives Ser.). (Illus.). 112p. (J). (gr. 5-7). (978-0-7565-0987-3(4)) Compass Point Bks.

Dorling Kindersley Publishing Staff. Civil War. 2004. (gr. 3-6). lib. bdg. 22.25 (978-0-613-75237-4(6)) Tandem Library Bks.

—Civil War: Battles & Leaders. 2003. (Battles & Leaders Ser.). (Illus.). 96p. (J). pap. 9.99 (978-0-7894-9891-5(X)) Dorling Kindersley Publishing, Inc.

Ford, Carin T. The Battle of Gettysburg & Lincoln's Gettysburg Address. 2004. (Civil War Library Ser.). (Illus.). 48p. (J). lib. bdg. 23.93 (978-0-7660-2253-9(6)) Enslow Pubs., Inc.

Generals at Gettysburg. 2000. (Illus.). 32p. (YA). (gr. 5 up). pap. 5.00 (978-1-890541-24-8(9)) Americana Souvenirs & Gifts.

Hale, Sarah Elder, ed. Stonewall Jackson: Spirit of the South. 2005. (Cobblestone the Civil War Ser.). (Illus.). 48p. (J). 17.95 (978-0-8126-7907-6(5)) Cobblestone Publishing Co.

Hargrove, Julia. The Civil War's 54th Massachusetts Regiment: The Shaw Memorial. Mitchell, Judy, ed. Mohrman, Gary, illus. abr. ed. 2001. (Historic Monuments Ser.). 32p. (J). (gr. 4-8). pap. 5.95 (978-1-57310-282-7(2)) Teaching & Learning Co.

High, Linda Oatman. The Cemetery Keepers of Gettysburg. Filippucci, Laura Francesca, illus. 2007. 32p. (J). 17.85 (978-0-8027-8095-9(4)); 16.95 (978-0-8027-8094-2(6)) Walker & Co.

Hughes, Christopher. Antietam. 1998. (Battlefields Across America Ser.: 8). (Illus.). 64p. (gr. 5-8). lib. bdg. 26.90 (978-0-7613-3009-7(7) , Twenty-First Century Bks.) Lerner Publishing Group.

—Gettysburg. 1998. (Battlefields Across America Ser.: 8). (Illus.). 64p. (gr. 5-8). lib. bdg. 26.90 (978-0-7613-3012-7(7) , Twenty-First Century Bks.) Lerner Publishing Group.

January, Brendan. Gettysburg: July 1-3 1863. 2004. (American Battlefields Ser.). (Illus.). 32p. (J). 14.95 (978-1-59270-025-7(X)) Enchanted Lion Bks., LLC.

Katcher, Philip R. N. Confederate Artillerymen of the Civil War. 2003. (Soldier's Life Ser.). (Illus.). 64p. (J). 31.42 (978-1-4109-0113-2(0)) Raintree.

—Confederate Cavalrymen of the Civil War. 2003. (Soldier's Life Ser.). (Illus.). 64p. (J). 31.42 (978-1-4109-0114-9(9)) Raintree.

—Sharpshooters of the Civil War. 2003. (Soldier's Life Ser.). (Illus.). 64p. (J). 31.42 (978-1-4109-0111-8(4)) Raintree.

King, David C. The Battle of Chattanooga. 2002. (Triangle Histories of the Civil War Ser.). (Illus.). 32p. (J). (gr. 4-8). 22.45 (978-1-56711-561-1(6) , LML00902-182709, Blackbirch Pr., Inc.) Thomson Gale.

Langellier. Union Infantrymen of the Civil War. 2003. (Soldier's Life Ser.). (Illus.). 64p. (J). 31.42 (978-1-4109-0116-3(5)) Raintree.

Lieurance, Suzanne. Weapons & Strategies of the Civil War: A MyReportLinks. com Book. 2004. (American Civil War Ser.). (Illus.). 48p. (J). lib. bdg. 25.26 (978-0-7660-5185-0(4) , MyReportLinks.com Bks.) Enslow Pubs., Inc.

Marrin, Albert. Virginia's General: Robert E. Lee & the Civil War. 2003. (Illus.). 201p. (YA). pap. 14.95 (978-1-893103-14-6(5)) Beautiful Feet Bks.

Maynard, Charles W. Fort Sumter. 2002. (Famous Forts Throughout American History Ser.). (Illus.). 24p. (J). (gr. 3). lib. bdg. 18.75 (978-0-8239-5840-5(X) , PowerKids Pr.) Rosen Publishing Group, Inc., The.

McGowen, Tom. The Surrender at Appomattox. 2004. (Cornerstones of Freedom Ser.). (Illus.). 48p. (J). 26.00 (978-0-516-24231-6(8) , Children's Pr.) Scholastic Library Publishing.

McLeese, Don. George Meade. 2005. (Civil War Military Leaders Ser.). (Illus.). 32p. (J). (ps-6). lib. bdg. 6.45 (978-1-59515-480-4(9)) Rourke Publishing, LLC.

—Jeb Stuart. 2006. (Civil War Military Leaders Ser.). (Illus.). 32p. (gr. 3-6). 19.95 (978-1-59515-479-8(5)) Rourke Publishing, LLC.

—Robert E. Lee. 2006. (Civil War Military Leaders Ser.). (Illus.). 32p. (gr. 3-6). 19.95 (978-1-59515-476-7(0)) Rourke Publishing, LLC.

—Stonewall Jackson. 2006. (Civil War Military Leaders Ser.). (Illus.). 32p. (gr. 3-6). 19.95 (978-1-59515-477-4(9)) Rourke Publishing, LLC.

—Ulysses S. Grant. 2006. (Civil War Military Leaders Ser.). (Illus.). 32p. (gr. 3-6). 19.95 (978-1-59515-475-0(2)) Rourke Publishing, LLC.

—William Tecumseh Sherman. 2006. (Civil War Military Leaders Ser.). (Illus.). 32p. (gr. 3-6). 19.95 (978-1-59515-478-1(7)) Rourke Publishing, LLC.

Murphy, Jim. The Long Road to Gettysburg. 2000. (Illus.). 128p. (J). (gr. 4-6). pap. 8.95 (978-0-618-05157-1(0) , Clarion Bks.) Houghton Mifflin Co. Trade & Reference Div.

Murray, Aaron R. & Dorling Kindersley Publishing Staff. Civil War Battles & Leaders. 2003. (Illus.). 96p. (J). 16.99 (978-0-7894-9890-8(1)) Dorling Kindersley Publishing, Inc.

O'Connell, Kim A. Major Battles of the Civil War: A MyReportLinks. com Book. 2004. (American Civil War Ser.). (Illus.). 48p. (J). lib. bdg. 25.26 (978-0-7660-5187-4(0) , MyReportLinks.com Bks.) Enslow Pubs., Inc.

Remstein, Henna. William Sherman. 2001. (gr. 5-8). lib. bdg. 17.60 (978-0-613-33253-8(9)) Tandem Library Bks.

Rice, Earle. The Battle of Gettysburg. 2002. (Battles That Changed the World Ser.). (Illus.). (J). 118p. pap. 30.00 (978-0-7910-7108-3(1)); 112p. 30.00 (978-0-7910-6684-3(3)) Facts On File, Inc. (Chelsea Hse.).

Rice, Earle, Jr. Robert E. Lee: First Soldier of the Confederacy. 2005. (Civil War Leaders Ser.). (Illus.). 176p. (J). (gr. 6-12). 26.95 (978-1-931798-47-1(8)) Reynolds, Morgan Inc.

Robertson, James I., Jr. Robert E. Lee: Virginian Soldier, American Citizen. 2005. (Illus.). 176p. (YA). (gr. 7 up). 21.95 (978-0-689-85731-7(4) , Atheneum) Simon & Schuster Children's Publishing.

Rosen, Daniel. Battles of the Civil War: Antietam. 2006. (Navigators Ser.). (J). pap. 42.00 (***978-1-4108-6259-4(3)***) Benchmark Education Co.

Smolinski, Diane. Key Battles of the Civil War. (Americans at War Ser.). (Illus.). 32p. (J). (gr. 4-7). 2002. pap. 6.95 (978-1-58810-391-8(9) , 91131); 2001. lib. bdg. (978-1-58810-097-9(9)) Heinemann Library.

The Story of Gettysburg. 2003. (Illus.). 26p. (J). (ps-k). 6.95 (978-0-8249-6503-7(5)) Ideals Pubns.

Tackach, James, ed. The Battle of Gettysburg. 2002. (At Issue in History Ser.). (Illus.). 122p. (YA). (gr. 7-10). lib. bdg. 33.70 (978-0-7377-0817-2(4) , Greenhaven Pr., Inc.) Thomson Gale.

Vierow, Wendy. The Battle of Bull Run. 2004. (Headlines from History Ser.). (Illus.). 24p. (J). lib. bdg. 19.95 (978-0-8239-6221-1(0)) Rosen Publishing Group, Inc., The.

—The Battle of Saratoga. 2003. (Atlas of Famous Battles of the American Revolution Ser.). (Illus.). 24p. (J). lib. bdg. 21.25 (978-0-8239-6332-4(2) , PowerKids Pr.) Rosen Publishing Group, Inc., The.

—The Capture of New Orleans: Union Fleet Takes Control of the Lower Mississippi River. 2004. (Headlines from History Ser.). (Illus.). 24p. (J). lib. bdg. 19.95 (978-0-8239-6222-8(9) , PowerKids Pr.) Rosen Publishing Group, Inc., The.

UNITED STATES—HISTORY—CIVIL WAR, 1861-1865—FICTION

Alcorn, Anita C. Caught in the Crossfire: A Boy's View of the Battle of Mill Springs, KY. 2006. 48p. pap. 8.95 (***978-0-7414-3581-1(0)***) Infinity Publishing.

Alger, Horatio. Frank's Campaign: Or, The Farm & the Camp. 2006. 196p. pap. 11.99 (978-1-4264-0484-9(0)); 188p. pap. 14.99 (978-1-4264-0527-3(8)) BiblioBazaar.

—Frank's Campaign: Or, The Farm & the Camp. 2006. pap. (***978-1-4065-0705-8(9)***) Dodo Pr.

Alger Jr. Horatio Staff. Frank's Campaign. rev. ed. 2006. 300p. 29.95 (978-1-4218-1761-3(6)); pap. 14.95 (978-1-4218-1861-0(2)) 1st World Publishing, Inc. (1st World Library - Literary Society).

Altsheler, Joseph A. The Rock of Chickamauga: A Story of the. 2006. pap. (***978-1-4065-0818-5(7)***) Dodo Pr.

—The Shades of the Wilderness: A Story of. 2006. pap. (***978-1-4065-0822-2(5)***) Dodo Pr.

—The Star of Gettysburg: A Story of South. 2006. pap. (***978-1-4065-0824-6(1)***) Dodo Pr.

—The Sword of Antietam: A Story of the Na. 2006. pap. (***978-1-4065-0825-3(X)***) Dodo Pr.

Bahr, Howard. Black Flower: A Novel of the Civil War. 2000. (gr. 7-12). lib. bdg. 22.25 (978-0-613-36938-1(6)) Tandem Library Bks.

Beaudouin, Frank, et al, illus. Cleared for Action: Four Tales of the Sea. 2002. (Bethlehem Budget Books). 600p. (J). 19.95 (978-1-883937-55-3(8)) Bethlehem Bks.

Bell, Albert A., Jr. The Secret of the Lonely Grave. 2007. 160p. pap. 8.95 (***978-1-932158-79-3(0)*** , Claystone Bks.) Ingalls Publishing Group, Inc.

Biros, Florence W. Dog Jack: Heart-Warming Story of a Slave Boy & His Best Friend. 2nd rev. ed. 2001. (Illus.). (YA). (gr. 5 up). pap. 9.95 (978-0-936369-47-1(7)) Son-Rise Pubns. & Distribution Co.

Blackwood, Gary. Second Sight. 2007. 288p. (J). pap. 6.99 (978-0-14-240747-9(X) , Puffin) Penguin Group (USA) Inc.

Blair, Margaret Whitman. House of Spies: Danger in the Civil War. 1999. (White Mane Kids Ser.: Vol. 7). (Illus.). 169p. (YA). (ps up). pap. 8.95 (978-1-57249-161-8(2) , White Mane Kids) White Mane Publishing Co., Inc.

—The Sand Castle: Blockade Running & the Battle of Fort Fisher. 2004. (White Mane Kids Ser.: 17). (Illus.). 200p. (J). pap. 8.95 (978-1-57249-346-9(1) , White Mane Kids) White Mane Publishing Co., Inc.

Brill, Marlene Targ. Diary of A Drummer Boy. Garland, Michael, illus. 1998. 48p. (gr. 4-6). lib. bdg. 23.90 (978-0-7613-0118-9(6) , Millbrook Pr.) Lerner Publishing Group.

—The Diary of A Drummer Boy. Garland, Michael, illus. 2000. (I Know America Ser.: 6). 48p. (gr. 4-6). pap. (978-0-7613-1388-5(5) , Millbrook Pr.) Lerner Publishing Group.

Bunting, Eve. The Blue & the Gray. Bittinger, Ned, illus. 2001. 32p. (J). (gr. k-2). pap. 5.99 (978-0-590-60200-6(4)) Scholastic, Inc.

Burgan, Michael. Hot Iron: The Adventures of a Civil War Powder Boy. Rodríguez, Pedro, illus. 2007. (J). pap. (***978-1-59889-406-6(4));*** 56p. (gr. 3-6). 23.93 (***978-1-59889-311-3(4)***) Stone Arch Bks.

Chass, Vikentia. The Visiting Angels. 1999. 16p. (J). (gr. k-6). pap. 8.00 (978-0-8059-4713-7(2)) Dorrance Publishing Co., Inc.

Chickasaw Adventures: The Civil War. 2005. (J). (978-1-4265-0000-8(9)) Layne Morgan Media, Inc.

Clary, Margie Willis. Make It Three: The Story of the CSS H. L. Hunley, Civil War Submarine. Rickenbaker, Becky, illus. 2001. 110p. (J). 9.95 (978-0-87844-158-7(1)) Sandlapper Publishing Co., Inc.

Connell, Kate. Yankee Blue or Rebel Grey: A Family Divided by the Civil War. 2003. (I Am American Ser.). (Illus.). 40p. (J). (gr. 3-7). pap. 6.99 (978-0-7922-5179-8(2) , National Geographic Children's Bks.) National Geographic Society.

T U V

Crane, Stephen. The Red Badge of Courage. Cruz, Ernesto R, illus. 2002. (Great Illustrated Classics Ser.). 240p. (J). (gr. 3-8). 21.35 (978-1-57765-699-9(7) , ABDO & Daughters) ABDO Publishing Co.

—The Red Badge of Courage. 2004. (Dover Evergreen Classics Ser.). 160p. (YA). pap. 2.50 (978-0-486-43422-3(2)) Dover Pubns., Inc.

—The Red Badge of Courage. (YA). (gr. 6-12). pap. 9.50 (978-0-8359-0462-9(8)) Globe Fearon Educational Publishing.

—The Red Badge of Courage. 1999. (Masterpiece Series Access Editions). (J). 10.95 (978-0-8219-1981-1(4)) Paradigm Publishing, Inc.

—The Red Badge of Courage. 2005. (Aladdin Classics Ser.). 256p. pap. 4.99 (978-0-689-87835-0(4) , Aladdin) Simon & Schuster Children's Publishing.

—The Red Badge of Courage. 1999. (Saddleback Classics). (Illus.). (J). (978-0-606-21565-7(4)) Tandem Library Bks.

—The Red Badge of Courage. Hegarty, Carol, ed. 1998. (Classics Ser.: Set I). (Illus.). 79p. (YA). (gr. 5-12). pap. 6.95 (978-1-56254-270-2(2) , SP2702) Saddleback Educational Publishing.

—Red Badge of Courage. Akib, Jamel, illus. 2006. (Classic Starts Ser.). 160p. 4.95 (978-1-4027-2663-7(5)) Sterling Publishing Co., Inc.

—The Red Badge of Courage. unabr. ed. 2002. (YA). pap. incl. audio compact disk (978-1-58472-313-4(0) , In Audio) Sound Room Pubs., Inc.

—The Red Badge of Courage. abr. ed. 1999. (gr. 7-12). lib. bdg. 15.25 (978-0-613-32992-7(9)) Tandem Library Bks.

—The Red Badge of Courage: With a Discussion of Self-Esteem. Clift, Eva, illus. 2003. (Values in Action Illustrated Classics Ser.). 190p. (J). (978-1-59203-034-7(3)) Learning Challenge, Inc.

—La Roja Insignia del Valor. 2002. (Clover Ser.). (SPA., Illus.). 224p. (YA). 11.50 (978-84-392-8013-2(0) , EV4334) Lectorum Pubns., Inc.

—Stephen Crane/the Red Badge of Courage. Carrillo, Fred, illus. 2005. 48p. (gr. 5-8). 25.50 (978-0-7910-9103-6(1)) Facts On File, Inc.

Crist-Evans, Craig. Moon over Tennessee: A Boy's Civil War Journal. Christensen, Bonnie, illus. 64p. (J). (gr. 4-6). 2003. pap. 6.95 (978-0-618-31107-1(6)); 1999. tchr. ed. 15.00 (978-0-395-91208-9(3)) Houghton Mifflin Co. Trade & Reference Div.

—Moon over Tennessee: A Boy's Civil War Journal. 1999. (gr. 3-6). lib. bdg. 15.25 (978-0-613-60819-0(4)) Tandem Library Bks.

Curtis, Alice Turner. Yankee Girl at Fort Sumter. Caley, Isabel & Calley, Isabel W., illus. 2004. (Yankee Girl Ser.). 204p. (J). (gr. 4-7). per. 9.95 (978-1-55709-525-1(6)) Applewood Bks.

—A Yankee Girl at Fort Sumter. 2005. 26.95 (978-1-4218-0301-2(1) , 1st World Library - Literary Society) 1st World Publishing, Inc.

—Yankee Girl at Fort Sumter. 2004. reprint ed. pap. 19.95 (978-1-4191-9516-7(6)); pap. 1.99 (978-1-4192-9516-4(0)) Kessinger Publishing, LLC.

Curtis, Turner Alice. Yankee Girl at Fort Sumter. 2006. 62.99 (*978-1-4280-2477-9(8)) IndyPublish.com.

Dahl, Candy. Emma & the Civil Warrior. 2001. 158p. (J). 12.95 (978-0-9706358-3-9(4)); per. 6.95 (978-0-9706358-4-6(2)) Carolina Moon Publishing.

Denslow, Sharon Phillips. All Their Names Were Courage. 2003. 144p. (J). (gr. 2 up). 15.99 (978-0-06-623810-4(2)) HarperCollins Pubs.

DeRegnier, Elaine. The Leather Pouch, 4 vols. 2003. 125p. (YA). 9.95 (978-1-59453-022-7(X) , 1604) Airleaf Publishing & Bookselling.

Duey, Kathleen. Amelina Carrett: Thibodeau, Louisiana 1870. 1999. (American Diaries Ser.: No. 12). (J). (gr. 3-7). 10.64 (978-0-606-16281-4(X)) Tandem Library Bks.

—Maddie Retta Lauren: Sandersville, Georgia, 1864. 2000. (American Diaries Ser.: No. 15). (J). (gr. 3-7). (978-0-606-17902-7(X)) Tandem Library Bks.

Durrant, Lynda. My Last Skirt: The Story of Jennie Hodgers, Union Soldier. 2006. 192p. (J). (gr. 5). 16.00 (978-0-618-57490-2(5) , Clarion Bks.) Houghton Mifflin Co. Trade & Reference Div.

—My Last Skirt: The Story of Jennie Hodgers, Union Soldier. 2006. 245p. (YA). 21.95 (978-0-7862-8880-9(9)) Thorndike Pr.

Ekberg, Nancy. What Kind of War Was It, Anyhow? Reynolds, Rhonda, tr. Reynolds, Rhonda, illus. 2003. 45p. (J). pap. 8.95 (978-1-58838-085-2(8) , Junebug Bks.) NewSouth, Inc.

Elliott, L. M. Annie, Between the States. 2006. 544p. (J). pap. 6.99 (978-0-06-001213-7(7) , Harper Trophy) HarperCollins Pubs.

Elliott, Laura Malone. Annie, Between the States. 2004. (Illus.). 496p. (J). (gr. 7 up). 16.99 (978-0-06-001211-3(0)); lib. bdg. 16.89 (978-0-06-001212-0(9)) HarperCollins Pubs.

Ernst, Kathleen. Ghosts of Vicksburg. 2003. (White Main Kids Ser.: 13). (Illus.). 180p. (J). pap. 8.95 (978-1-57249-322-3(4) , White Mane Kids) White Mane Publishing Co., Inc.

—Hearts of Stone. 2006. 240p. (J). (gr. 7). 16.99 (978-0-525-47686-3(5) , Dutton Juvenile) Penguin Group (USA) Inc.

Fedor, Janis M. Girl Lieutenant in Blue, Vol. 2. 2002. 166p. (YA). (gr. 5-6). pap. 9.95 (978-0-936369-38-9(8)) Son-Rise Pubns. & Distribution Co.

Filegar, James. Fathers, Sons, & Brothers, Bk. 1. 2003. 191p. (J). pap. 19.95 (978-1-59129-908-0(X)) PublishAmerica, Inc.

Finley, Martha. Elsie's Troubled Times, Vol. 6. 2006. (Life of Faith': Elsie Dinsmore Ser.). 224p. (J). pap. 7.99 (978-1-928749-88-2(7)) Zonderkidz.

—Mildred's Boys & Girls, Vol. 6. (Mildred Classics Ser.: Vol. 6). 288p. pap. 6.95 (978-1-58182-232-8(4)) Cumberland Hse. Publishing.

Fireside, Bryna J. Private Joel & the Sewell Mountain Seder. Costello, Shawn, illus. 2008. (Passover Ser.). (J). lib. bdg. 16.95 (*978-0-8225-7240-4(0)) Kar-Ben Publishing.

Garrity, Jennifer Johnson. Bushwhackers: A Civil War Adventure. 1999. (gr. 3-6). lib. bdg. 17.60 (978-0-613-24444-2(3)) Tandem Library Bks.

Gayle, Sharon Shavers. Harriet Tubman & the Freedom Train. 2003. (gr. 3-6). lib. bdg. 11.80 (978-0-613-61560-0(3)) Tandem Library Bks.

Gibboney, Douglas Lee. Stonewall Jackson at Gettysburg. 2002. (Illus.). 132p. pap. 12.95 (978-1-57249-317-9(8) , Burd Street Pr.) White Mane Publishing Co., Inc.

Gutman, Dan. Abner & Me. (Baseball Card Adventures Ser.). 176p. (J). 2007. pap. 5.99 (978-0-06-053445-5(1) , Harper Trophy); 2005. (Illus.). 16.99 (978-0-06-053443-1(5)); 2005. (Illus.). lib. bdg. 17.89 (978-0-06-053444-8(3)) HarperCollins Pubs.

Hahn, Mary Downing. Hear the Wind Blow. 2003. (Illus.). 224p. (J). (gr. 5-9). tchr. ed. 16.00 (978-0-618-18190-2(3) , Clarion Bks.) Houghton Mifflin Co. Trade & Reference Div.

—Promises to the Dead. 2000. 208p. (J). (gr. 5-9). tchr. ed. 15.00 (978-0-395-96394-4(X) , Clarion Bks.) Houghton Mifflin Co. Trade & Reference Div.

Hahn, Stephen. Pike McCallister. 1998. 253p. (YA). (gr. 6 up). per. 14.95 (978-1-888125-29-0(2)) Publication Consultants.

Haislip, Phyllis Hall. Anybody's Hero: The Battle of Old Men & Young Boys. 2004. (Illus.). 220p. (J). pap. 8.95 (978-1-57249-343-8(7) , White Mane Kids) White Mane Publishing Co., Inc.

—Lili's Gift: A Civil War Healer's Story. 2007. (Illus.). (J). pap. 8.95 (*978-1-57249-392-6(5) , White Mane Kids) White Mane Publishing Co., Inc.

Haislip, Phyllis Hall. Lottie's Courage: A Contraband Slave's Story. 2003. (Illus.). 120p. (J). pap. 7.95 (978-1-57249-311-7(9) , White Mane Kids) White Mane Publishing Co., Inc.

Hall, Peg. Tales of the Civil War: Retold Timeless Classics. Hargreaves, Greg & Aspengren, Michael A., illus. 2000. (Cover-to-Cover Bks.). 72p. (J). (gr. 1-4). lib. bdg. 13.95 (978-0-7807-9676-8(4) , Covercraft); (gr. 4-8). pap. 5.60 (978-0-7891-5222-0(3)) Perfection Learning Corp.

Harness, Cheryl. Ghosts of the Civil War. Harness, Cheryl, illus. 2004. (Illus.). 48p. (J). 7.99 (978-0-689-86992-1(4) , Aladdin) Simon & Schuster Children's Publishing.

Harris, Dorthy. Taylor's Dream Ends Summer School Nightm. 2006. 95p. pap. 14.95 (978-1-4241-3574-5(5)) PublishAmerica, Inc.

Harrison, Harry. Stars & Stripes Forever. 1999. (gr. 7-12). lib. bdg. 15.30 (978-0-613-22443-7(4)) Tandem Library Bks.

Hart, Alison. Gabriel's Horses. 2007. 224p. (J). (gr. 3-7). 14.95 (*978-1-56145-398-6(6) , Peachtree Junior) Peachtree Pubs., Ltd.

—Gabriel's Triumph. 2007. 160p. (J). (gr. 3-7). 14.95 (*978-1-56145-410-5(9) , Peachtree Junior) Peachtree Pubs., Ltd.

Hemingway, Edith M. & Shields, Jacqueline C. Rebel Hart. 2000. (White Mane Kids Ser.: Vol. 8). (Illus.). xi, 173p. (J). (gr. 3-12). pap. 8.95 (978-1-57249-186-1(8) , White Mane Kids) White Mane Publishing Co., Inc.

Hill, Pamela Smith. A Voice from the Border. 2000. (J). (978-0-606-20004-2(5)) Tandem Library Bks.

Hite, Sid. Stick & Whittle. 2001. 208p. (J). (gr. 5 up). pap. 4.99 (978-0-439-09829-8(7)) Scholastic, Inc.

—Stick & Whittle. 2001. (gr. 5-8). lib. bdg. 13.00 (978-0-613-53868-8(4)) Tandem Library Bks.

Holt, Rinehart and Winston Staff. The Red Badge of Courage: With Connections. 2000. 14.64 (978-0-03-056462-8(X)) Holt, Rinehart & Winston.

Hopkinson, Deborah. A Band of Angels: A Story Inspired by the Jubilee Singers. Colon, Raul, illus. 1999. (Anne Schwartz Bks.). 40p. (J). (gr. 1-4). 16.95 (978-0-689-81062-6(8) , Atheneum/Anne Schwartz Bks.) Simon & Schuster Children's Publishing.

—Billy & the Rebel. Floca, Brian, illus. 2005. 44p. (J). lib. bdg. 15.00 (*978-1-4242-1148-7(4)) Fitzgerald Bks.

—Billy & the Rebel: Based on a True Civil War Story. Floca, Brian, illus. 2006. (Ready-to-Reads Ser.). 48p. (J). pap. 3.99 (978-0-689-83396-0(2) , Aladdin) Simon & Schuster Children's Publishing.

—Billy & the Rebel: Based on a True Civil War Story. Anderson, Bethanne & Floca, Brian, illus. 2005. (Ready-to-Read Ser.). 48p. (J). 14.95 (978-0-689-83964-1(2) , Atheneum) Simon & Schuster Children's Publishing.

—From Slave to Soldier: Based on a True Civil War Story. Floca, Brian, illus. 2007. (Ready-to-Reads Ser.). 48p. (J). pap. 3.99 (978-0-689-83966-5(9) , Aladdin) Simon & Schuster Children's Publishing.

Hughes, Pat. Guerrilla Season. 2003. 336p. (J). 18.00 (978-0-374-32811-5(0) , Farrar, Straus & Giroux (BYR)) Farrar, Straus & Giroux.

—Seeing the Elephant: A Story of the Civil War. Stark, Ken, illus. 2007. 40p. (J). (gr. 3 up). 16.00 (978-0-374-38024-3(4)) Farrar, Straus & Giroux.

Hunt, Irene. Across Five Aprils. 2002. 224p. (gr. 12). pap. 4.99 (978-0-425-18278-9(9) , Berkley) Penguin Group (USA) Inc.

—Across Five Aprils. 1999. (J). pap. 1.95 (978-0-590-05178-1(4)) Scholastic, Inc.

Immel, Mary Blair. Captured: A Boy Trapped in the Civil War. 2005. (Illus.). xi, 153p. (J). (978-0-87195-184-7(3)); pap. 6.95 (978-0-87195-188-5(6)) Indiana Historical Society.

Jiles, Paulette. Enemy Women: A Novel. 2003. (gr. 7-12). lib. bdg. 23.40 (978-0-613-62139-7(5)) Tandem Library Bks.

Johnson, Nancy. A Sweet-Sounding Place: A Civil War Story. 2007. 160p. (gr. 5-9). 14.95 (*978-0-89272-757-5(8)) Down East Bks.

Johnston, Annie Fell. The Little Colonel. 2005. reprint ed. pap. 21.95 (978-0-7661-9402-1(7)) Kessinger Publishing, LLC.

—The Little Colonel (Illustrated Edition) 2006. pap. (*978-1-4065-1132-1(3)) Dodo Pr.

—The Little Colonel's Chum: Mary Ware (il. 2006. (Illus.). pap. (*978-1-4065-1125-3(0)) Dodo Pr.

Johnston, Annie Fellows. The Little Colonel. Barry, Etheldred B., illus. 2004. (Little Colonel Ser.). 128p. (J). (gr. 4-7). reprint ed. per. 12.95 (978-1-55709-315-8(6)) Applewood Bks.

Johnston, Fellows Annie. Little Colonel. 2006. pap. 18.99 (*978-1-4280-3283-5(5)) IndyPublish.com.

Johnston, Tony. The Wagon. 1999. (Illus.). 40p. (J). (ps-3). pap. 5.95 (978-0-688-16694-6(6)) HarperCollins Pubs.

—Wagon. 1999. (978-0-606-16677-5(7)) Tandem Library Bks.

Jones, Elizabeth McDavid. Watcher in the Piney Woods. 2000. (American Girl Collection). (Illus.). (J). (978-0-606-20981-6(6)) Tandem Library Bks.

Joslyn, Mauriel Phillips. Shenandoah Autumn: Courage under Fire. 1999. (WM Kids Ser.). 164p. (YA). (gr. 4-7). pap. 8.95 (978-1-57249-137-3(X) , White Mane Kids) White Mane Publishing Co., Inc.

Kay, Alan. Breaking the Rules. 2007. (Young Heroes of History: 7). (J). pap. 7.95 (*978-1-57249-389-6(5) , White Mane Kids) White Mane Publishing Co., Inc.

Kay, Alan N. Crossroads at Gettysburg. 2005. (Young Heroes of History: 6). (Illus.). 166p. (J). (gr. 3-7). pap. 7.95 (978-1-57249-359-9(3) , White Mane Kids) White Mane Publishing Co., Inc.

—No Girls Allowed. 2003. (Young Heroes of History: Vol. 5). (Illus.). 140p. (J). pap. 6.95 (978-1-57249-324-7(0) , White Mane Kids) White Mane Publishing Co., Inc.

—Nowhere to Turn. 2002. (Young Heroes of History: 4). (Illus.). 164p. (J). pap. 6.95 (978-1-57249-297-4(X) , White Mane Kids) White Mane Publishing Co., Inc.

Keehn, Sally M. Anna Sunday. 2002. 272p. (YA). (gr. 5-9). 18.99 (978-0-399-23875-8(1) , Philomel) Penguin Group (USA) Inc.

Killgore, James. The Passage. 2006. (Illus.). 256p. (J). (gr. 7-10). 15.95 (978-1-56145-384-9(6) , Peachtree Junior) Peachtree Pubs., Ltd.

Kirkland, Joseph. The Captain of Company K. (Americans in Fiction Ser.). (Illus.). (J). reprint ed. lib. bdg. 27.00 (978-0-8398-1057-5(1)) Irvington Pubs.

Lambil, Willy & Raoul, Cauvin. The Blues in Black & White. 2004. (Blue Tunics Ser.: Vol. 1). (Illus.). (J). 12.45 (978-0-9752688-0-3(5)) Reney Editions, Inc.

Lawlor, Laurie. Wind on the River. 2004. 156p. (J). lib. bdg. 16.92 (*978-1-4242-0771-8(1)) Fitzgerald Bks.

Lawlor, Laurie. Wind on the River: A Story of the Civil War. 2001. (American Portraits Ser.). (Illus.). iv, 156p. (J). (gr. 5-8). 15.32 (978-0-8092-0582-0(3) , 9780809205820) Jamestown.

—Wind on the River: A Story of the Civil War. 2004. (Jamestown's American Portraits Ser.). (Illus.). 160p. (J). (gr. 5-7). pap. 4.95 (978-0-7696-3425-8(7) , Waterbird Bks.) School Specialty Publishing.

—Wind on the River: A Story of the Civil War. 2000. (978-0-606-21880-1(7).); (gr. 5-8). lib. bdg. 15.70 (978-0-613-36904-6(1)) Tandem Library Bks.

Lawlor, Laurie & McGraw-Hill Staff. Wind on the River: A Story of the Civil War. 2001. (Jamestown Classics Ser.). (Illus.). iv, 156p. (J). (gr. 5-8). pap. 10.00 (978-0-8092-0624-7(2) , 9780809206247) Jamestown.

LeSourd, Nancy. Liberty Letters: The Personal Correspondence of Emma Edmonds & Mollie Turner, Civil War Spies, 1862. 2004. (Liberty Letters Ser.). 224p. (J). 9.99 (978-0-310-70352-5(2)) Zonderkidz.

Love, D. Anne. Three Against the Tide. 2000. (978-0-606-18909-5(2)) Tandem Library Bks.

Lutz, Norma Jean. Elise the Actress: Climax of the Civil War. 2005. (Sisters in Time Ser.). (J). 144p. pap. 4.97 (978-1-59310-657-7(2)); 141p. (*978-1-4156-0075-7(9)) Barbour Publishing, Inc.

Lynch, Marcia. United in Freedom. Cornelison, Sue F., illus. 2000. (Cover-to-Cover Bks.). 92p. (J). pap. (978-0-7891-5102-5(2)); (gr. 2-5). lib. bdg. 13.95 (978-0-7807-9068-1(5)) Perfection Learning Corp.

Macatee, Susan. Under the Guns. 2002. (gr. 7-12). lib. bdg. 30.35 (978-0-613-85842-7(5)) Tandem Library Bks.

Massie, Elizabeth. House Divided. 2000. (Young Founders Ser.). (J). 11.64 (978-0-606-19659-8(5)) Tandem Library Bks.

Masters, Susan Rowan. Night Journey to Vicksburg. Killcoyne, Hope L., ed. Smith, Duane A., illus. 2003. (Adventures in America Ser.). 74p. (J). 14.95 (978-1-893110-30-4(3)) Silver Moon Pr.

Matas, Carol. The War Within: A Novel of the Civil War. l.t. ed. 2003. (J). 22.95 (978-0-7862-5499-6(8)) Thorndike Pr.

McDivitt, Barry. The Youngest Spy. 2007. 176p. (J). (gr. 3-9). pap. 10.95 (*978-1-897235-17-1(8)) Thistledown Pr., Ltd. CAN. *Dist:* Fitzhenry & Whiteside, Ltd.

McGowen, Tom. Jesse Bowman: A Union Boy's War Story. 2008. (Historical Fiction Adventures (HFA) Ser.). (Illus.). 160p. (J). (gr. 3-6). lib. bdg. 27.93 (*978-0-7660-2929-3(8)) Enslow Pubs., Inc.

McKissack, Patricia C. A Picture of Freedom: The Diary of Clotee, a Slave Girl, Belmont Plantation, Virginia, 1859. 1999. (Dear America Ser.). (J). 9.95 (978-0-439-15599-1(1)) Scholastic, Inc.

McMullan, Margaret. How I Found the Strong. 2004. 144p. (J). (gr. 5-9). tchr. ed. 15.00 (978-0-618-35008-7(X)) Houghton Mifflin Co. Trade & Reference Div.

—How I Found the Strong. 2006. 144p. (YA). (gr. 7). reprint ed. mass mkt. 5.50 (978-0-553-49492-1(9) , Laurel Leaf) Random Hse. Children's Bks.

McPherson, James M. Fields of Fury: The American Civil War. 2002. (Illus.). 96p. (J). (gr. 5-8). 22.95 (978-0-689-84833-9(1) , Atheneum) Simon & Schuster Children's Publishing.

Mickles Sr., Robert T. S. Blood Kin, a Savannah Story. 2007. 108p. per. 9.95 (*978-0-595-45129-6(2)) iUniverse, Inc.

Mills, Claudia. The Totally Made-Up Civil War Diary of Amanda MacLeish. 2008. 208p. (J). 16.00 (*978-0-374-37696-3(4)) Farrar, Straus & Giroux.

Monjo, F. N. La Osa Menor: Una Historia del Ferrocarril Subterraneo. Mlawer, Teresa, tr. Brenner, Fred, illus. 2001. (SPA.). (J). (gr. 3-10). pap. 6.95 (978-1-880507-90-2(0) , LC7973); ring bd. 15.95 (978-1-880507-91-9(9) , LC7976) Lectorum Pubns., Inc.

—La Osa Menor: Una Historia del Ferrocarril Subterraneo. 2001. (978-0-606-21286-1(8)) Tandem Library Bks.

Monte, Emily C. The Lost Sword of the Confederate Ghost: A Mystery in Two Centuries. 1999. 116p. (J). (gr. 4-7). 5.99 (978-1-57249-132-8(9)) White Mane Publishing Co., Inc.

Morris, Joyce. Sweet Annie. 2006. pap. 14.99 (*978-1-4259-7159-5(8)) AuthorHouse.

Mrazek, Robert J. Stonewall's Gold: A Novel of the Civil War. 2000. (Illus.). 223p. (gr. 7-12). per. 22.20 (978-0-613-28198-0(5)) Tandem Library Bks.

Myers, Anna. Assassin. 2007. 224p. (YA). pap. 6.95 (*978-0-8027-9643-1(5)); 2005. (J). (978-0-8027-8989-1(7)) Walker & Co.

Noble, Trinka Hakes. The Last Brother: A Civil War Tale. Papp, Robert, illus. 2006. 48p. (J). (gr. k-5). 17.95 (978-1-58536-253-0(0)) Sleeping Bear Pr.

Optic, Oliver. Fighting for the Right. 2006. 96.99 (*978-1-4280-4400-5(0)); pap. 90.99 (*978-1-4280-4378-7(0)) IndyPublish.com.

—On the Blockade. Bridgeman, L. & Fitterling, Michael A., illus. 1999. (Blue & the Gray Ser.). 351p. (J). (gr. 4-8). reprint ed. per. 14.95 (978-1-890623-10-4(5)) Lost Classics Bk. Co.

—Stand by the Union. 2006. 96.99 (*978-1-4280-4413-5(2)); pap. 90.99 (*978-1-4280-4406-7(X)) IndyPublish.com.

—Taken by the Enemy. 2006. 96.99 (*978-1-4280-3960-5(0)); pap. 89.99 (*978-1-4280-3988-9(0)) IndyPublish.com.

—Within the Enemy's Line. Fitterling, Michael A., illus. 1998. (Blue & the Gray Ser.). 351p. (J). (gr. 4-7). reprint ed. per. 14.95 (978-1-890623-09-8(1)) Lost Classics Bk. Co.

Optic, Oliver. Within the Enemys Lines. 2006. 20.99 (*978-1-4280-2613-1(4)); pap. 13.99 (*978-1-4280-2631-5(2)) IndyPublish.com.

Osborne, Mary Pope. After the Rain Bk. 2: Virginia's Civil War Diary. 2002. (My America Ser.). 112p. (J). (gr. 2-5). pap. 10.95 (978-0-439-20138-4(1)); (Illus.). pap. 4.99 (978-0-439-36904-6(5)) Scholastic, Inc. (Scholastic Pr.).

—Civil War on Sunday, Vol. 21. unabr. ed. 2004. (Magic Tree House Ser. : No. 21). 76p. (J). (gr. k-3). pap. 17.00 incl. audio (978-0-8072-0930-1(9) , S FTR 253 SP, Listening Library) Random Hse. Audio Publishing Group.

—Civil War on Sunday. Murdocca, Sal, illus. 2000. (Magic Tree House Ser.: No. 21). 96p. (J). (gr. k-3). lib. bdg. 11.99 (978-0-679-99067-3(4)); mass mkt. 3.99 (978-0-679-89067-6(X)) Random Hse. Children's Bks. (Random Hse. Bks. for Young Readers).

—Civil War on Sunday. 2000. (Magic Tree House Ser. : No. 21). (J). (gr. k-3). lib. bdg. 11.80 (978-0-613-24596-8(2)); (Illus.). 10.79 (978-0-606-18852-4(5)) Tandem Library Bks.

Oughton, Jerrie. The War in Georgia. 1999. (978-0-606-16444-3(8)) Tandem Library Bks.

Paulsen, Gary. Soldier's Heart. 2000. (gr. 7-12). lib. bdg. 13.55 (978-0-613-28375-5(9)) Tandem Library Bks.

—Soldier's Heart: eing the Story of the Enlistment & Due Service of the Boy Charley Goddard in the First Minnesota Volunteers. 1998. 128p. (YA). (gr. 7-12). 15.95 (978-0-385-32498-4(7) , Delacorte Bks. for Young Readers) Random Hse. Children's Bks.

Peck, Richard. The River Between Us. 176p. (J). 2003. (gr. 7). 16.99 (978-0-8037-2735-9(6) , Dial); 2005. (gr. 5-7). reprint ed. pap. 6.99 (978-0-14-240310-5(5) , Puffin) Penguin Group (USA) Inc.

—The River Between Us. 2005. 164p. (J). (ps-7). lib. bdg. 12.64 (978-0-606-33120-3(4)) Tandem Library Bks.

Pfeffer, Susan Beth. Devil's Den. 1998. 115p. (J). (gr. 3-7). 15.95 (978-0-8027-8650-0(2)) Walker & Co.

Pink & Say. 1998. (J). (gr. 4). pap. 3.95 (978-0-439-04467-7(7)) Scholastic, Inc.

Pinkney, Andrea Davis. Silent Thunder. 2001. 224p. (gr. 3-7). pap. 5.99 (978-0-7868-1569-2(8) , Jump at the Sun) Hyperion Bks. for Children.

—Silent Thunder: A Civil War Story. 2001. (J). (978-0-606-21434-6(8)); (gr. 5-8). lib. bdg. 14.15 (978-0-613-62425-1(4)) Tandem Library Bks.

Plunkett, N. Geraldine. Nathan's Secret. Gallo, Beth, illus. 2000. 87p. (J). pap. 7.95 (978-0-87178-029-4(1)) Brethren Pr.

Polacco, Patricia. Pink & Say. Polacco, Patricia, illus. 2002. (Illus.). (J). 23.64 (978-0-7587-3418-1(2)) Book Wholesalers, Inc.

—Pink & Say. (Illus.). (J). (gr. 3-4). pap. 6.36 net. (978-1-930332-54-6(8)) Lectorum Pubns., Inc.

—Pink & Say. 2001. (J). 27.95 incl. audio (978-0-8045-6835-7(9) , 6835) Spoken Arts, Inc.

Pryor, Bonnie. Joseph: 1861 - A Rumble of War. Dodson, Bert, illus. 1999. (American Adventures Ser.). 176p. (J). (gr. 3-7). 14.95 (978-0-688-15671-8(1)) HarperCollins Pubs.

—Joseph: 1861 - A Rumble of War. 2000. (Illus.). (J). (978-0-606-17975-1(5)) Tandem Library Bks.

—Joseph: 1861—A Rumble of War. 2000. (American Adventures Ser.). (Illus.). 176p. (J). (gr. 3-7). pap. 4.50 (978-0-380-73103-9(7) , Harper Trophy) HarperCollins Pubs.

—Joseph's Choice 1861. Dodson, Bert, illus. 2000. (American Adventures Ser.). 176p. (J). (gr. 3 up). 14.89 (978-0-06-029226-3(1)) HarperCollins Pubs.

Ransom, Candice. Signals in the Sky. 2007. 128p. (J). 4.99 (978-0-7869-4353-1(X) , Mirrorstone) Wizards of the Coast.

Ransom, Candice F. Promise Quilt. 2002. (gr. k-3). lib. bdg. 15.25 (978-0-613-75492-7(1)) Tandem Library Bks.

Reeder, Carolyn. Across the Lines. 1998. 224p. (J). (gr. 4-7). pap. 5.99 (978-0-380-73073-5(1) , Harper Trophy) HarperCollins Pubs.

—Before the Creeks Ran Red. 2003. 384p. (J). (gr. 5 up). 16.99 (978-0-06-623615-5(0)) HarperCollins Pubs.

—Captain Kate. 1999. (Avon Camelot Bks.). 224p. (J). (gr. 4-7). 15.00 (978-0-380-97628-7(5)) HarperCollins Pubs.

—Shade of Gray. 1999. (978-0-606-16311-8(5)) Tandem Library Bks.

—Shades of Gray. O'Brien, Tim, illus. 1999. 160p. (J). (gr. 3-7). pap. 4.99 (978-0-689-82696-2(6) , 076714004993, Aladdin) Simon & Schuster Children's Publishing.

Reisberg, Joanne A. Save the Colors: A Civil War Battle Cry. 2001. (Young Americans Ser.: Vol. 5). (Illus.). 92p. (J). 5.95 (978-1-57249-247-9(3) , White Mane Kids) White Mane Publishing Co., Inc.

Rifles for Watie. 1999. (YA). 9.95 (978-1-56137-598-1(5)) Novel Units, Inc.

Rinaldi, Ann. An Acquaintance with Darkness. 2005. (Great Episodes Ser.). 384p. (YA). pap. 6.95 (978-0-15-205387-1(5) , Gulliver Bks.) Harcourt Children's Bks.

—An Acquaintance with Darkness. 1999. (J). 12.65 (978-0-606-16525-9(8)) Tandem Library Bks.

—Amelia's War. 2002. 272p. (J). pap. 5.99 (978-0-439-32666-7(4) , Scholastic Paperbacks) Scholastic, Inc.

—Girl in Blue. 2005. 320p. (J). pap. 5.99 (978-0-439-67646-5(0) , Scholastic Paperbacks) Scholastic, Inc.

—The Last Silk Dress. 1999. 352p. (YA). (gr. 7). mass mkt. 6.50 (978-0-440-22861-5(1) , Laurel Leaf) Random Hse. Children's Bks.

—Sarah's Ground. 2004. (Illus.). 192p. (YA). 15.95 (978-0-689-85924-3(4)) Simon & Schuster Children's Publishing.

Robertson, William & Rimer, David. The Bucktails' Antietam Trials. 2004. (White Mane Kids Ser.: No.14). (J). pap. 7.95 (978-1-57249-337-7(2) , White Mane Kids) White Mane Publishing Co., Inc.

Robertson, William P. & Rimer, David. The Battling Bucktails at Fredericksburg. 2004. (WM Kids Ser.: Vol. 16). (Illus.). 164p. (J). 7.95 (978-1-57249-345-2(3) , White Mane Kids) White Mane Publishing Co., Inc.

—The Bucktails' Shenandoah March. 2002. (WM Kids Ser.: Vol. 12). (Illus.). 170p. (J). pap. 7.95 (978-1-57249-293-6(7) , White Mane Kids) White Mane Publishing Co., Inc.

—Hayfoot, Strawfoot: The Bucktail Recruits. 2001. (Illus.). 170p. (J). pap. 7.95 (978-1-57249-250-9(3) , White Mane Kids) White Mane Publishing Co., Inc.

Roddy, Lee. Cry of Courage. l.t. ed. 1999. (Paperback Ser.). 213p. (gr. 6-9). pap. 22.95 (978-0-7838-8611-4(X)) Thorndike Pr.

—Risking the Dream. 2000. (Between Two Flags Ser.: Vol. 6). (Illus.). 176p. (J). (gr. 6-9). pap. 5.99 (978-0-7642-2030-2(6)) Bethany Hse. Pubs.

Sappey, Maureen. Letters from Vinnie. 2007. 248p. (J). (gr. 4-6). pap. 10.95 (***978-1-59078-538-6(X)***) Boyds Mills Pr.

Sappey, Maureen S. Dreams of Ships, Dreams of Julia: At Sea with the Monitor & the Merrimack-Virginia, 1862. 1998. (Young American Ser.: Vol. 2). (Illus.). 140p. (YA). (gr. 4-7). 5.99 (978-1-57249-134-2(5)) White Mane Publishing Co., Inc.

Savage, Bridgette Z. Fly Like the Wind. Savage, Bridgette Z., illus. 2005. (Illus.). 112p. (J). per. 16.99 (978-0-9771494-0-7(4)) Buckbeech Studios.

Scott, Kathy. Beacon Hill. 2005. 85p. pap. 14.95 (978-1-4137-8423-7(2)) PublishAmerica, Inc.

Secrets at Pine Haven: Civil War Comes to Florida. 2006. (Illus.). 180p. (J). per. 12.95 (978-1-878398-75-8(X) , Blue Note Bks.) Blue Note Pubns.

Sescoe, Vincent E. Double Time. Helms, Clinton, illus. 2001. (gr. 6-12). 191p. (J). 17.95 (978-1-930093-00-3(4)); 192p. (YA). pap. 6.95 (978-1-930093-06-5(3)) Brookfield Reader, Inc., The.

Severance, John B. Braving the Fire. 2002. (Illus.). 160p. (YA). (gr. 5-9). tchr. ed. 15.00 (978-0-618-22999-4(X) , Clarion Bks.) Houghton Mifflin Co. Trade & Reference Div.

Seymour, Tres. We Played Marbles. Andreasen, Dan, illus. 1998. 32p. (J). (gr. k-4). 16.99 (978-0-531-33074-6(5)); pap. 15.95 (978-0-531-30074-9(9)) Scholastic, Inc. (Orchard Bks.).

Shaffer, Elizabeth N. Hannah & the Indian King, Vol. 2. Pratt, Fran, ed. 2002. (Historical Novel Ser.). pap. 9.95 (978-0-936369-35-8(3)) Son-Rise Pubns. & Distribution Co.

Simpson, Kathleen & Reynolds, Phyllis N. Shiloh. 2002. (Literature Circle Guides Ser.). 32p. pap. 5.95 (978-0-439-35539-1(7)) Scholastic, Inc.

Smith, Debra West. Yankees on the Doorstep: The Story of Sarah Morgan. 2001. (Illus.). 176p. (J). (gr. 3-7). pap. 10.95 (978-1-56554-872-5(8)) Pelican Publishing Co., Inc.

Spain, Susan Rosson. The Deep Cut. 2006. (Illus.). 224p. (J). 16.99 (978-0-7614-5316-1(4)) Cavendish, Marshall Corp.

Spier, Peter. The Star-Spangled Banner. 2004. (J). (ps-6). pap. 14.95 incl. audio (978-1-55592-160-6(4)); pap. 18.95 incl. audio compact disk (978-1-55592-144-6(2)); pap. 14.95 incl. audio (978-1-55592-161-3(2)); pap. 18.95 incl. audio compact disk (978-1-55592-143-9(4)) Weston Woods Studios, Inc.

Steele, William O. The Perilous Road. 2004. (Illus.). 176p. (J). 17.00 (978-0-15-205203-4(8) , Harcourt Young Classics); pap. 5.95 (978-0-15-205204-1(6) , Odyssey Classics) Harcourt Children's Bks.

—The Perilous Road. 2004. 156p. (J). (gr. 4-7). per. 13.00 (978-0-606-31268-4(4)) Tandem Library Bks.

Stites, Clara. Naming the Stones. Davis, Cindy, illus. 2002. 46p. (J). (978-0-932027-72-6(5)) Spinner Pubns., Inc.

Stolz, Mary. A Ballad of the Civil War. Martinez, Sergio, illus. 1998. (Trophy Chapter Bks.). 64p. (J). (gr. 2-5). pap. 4.99 (978-0-06-442088-4(4)) HarperCollins Pubs.

Susi, Geraldine Lee. Looking Back: A Boy's Civil War Memories. 2001. (Illus.). 128p. (J). (gr. 3-7). pap. 11.95 (978-1-880664-34-6(8)) E. M. Productions.

—Looking for Pa: A Civil War Journey from Catlett to Manassas, 1861. French, Douglas P., illus. 2nd ed. 2001. 127p. (J). (gr. 4-7). pap. 10.95 (978-1-880664-33-9(X)) E. M. Productions.

Sykes, Shelley & Szymanski, Lois. A Whisper of War. 2003. (J). 5.95 (978-1-57249-327-8(5) , White Mane Kids) White Mane Publishing Co., Inc.

Tate, Suzanne. Burnside & Sidebums: A Tale of Civil War Days. Melvin, James, illus. 2000. (Suzanne Tate's History Ser.). 32p. (J). (gr. k-4). pap. 4.95 (978-1-878405-28-9(4)) Nags Head Art, Inc.

Thomas, Carroll. Matty's War. Howard, Larry, illus. 1999. 164p. (J). (gr. 4-7). pap. 9.95 (978-1-57525-206-3(6)) Smith and Kraus Publishers, Incorporated.

—Matty's War. 1999. (J). (978-1-57525-205-6(8)) Smith and Kraus Publishers, Incorporated.

—Matty's War. 1999. (gr. 3-6). lib. bdg. 18.75 (978-0-613-62686-6(9)) Tandem Library Bks.

Trout, Robert J. Drumbeat: The Story of a Civil War Drummer Boy. 2007. (J). pap. 12.95 (***978-1-57249-390-2(9)*** , White Mane Kids) White Mane Publishing Co., Inc.

Turner, Ann Warren. Drummer Boy: Marching to the Civil War. Hess, Mark, illus. 1998. 32p. (J). (ps-3). 16.95 (978-0-06-027696-6(7)); lib. bdg. 17.89 (978-0-06-027697-3(5)) HarperCollins Pubs.

Turtleback Books, creator. Evvy's Civil War. 2004. 209p. (YA). (gr. 8-12). per. 13.64 (978-0-606-30114-5(3)) Tandem Library Bks.

Venner, Thomas. Young Heroes of Gettysburg. 2000. (White Mane Kids Ser.: Vol. 10). (Illus.). vi, 172p. (J). (gr. 4-7). pap. 8.95 (978-1-57249-200-4(7) , White Mane Kids) White Mane Publishing Co., Inc.

Walker, Margaret. Jubilee. 1999. (gr. 7-12). lib. bdg. 17.60 (978-0-613-29273-3(1)) Tandem Library Bks.

Walker, Robert W. Gideon Tell & the Siege of Vicksburg. 2000. 190p. (YA). (gr. 8 up). 9.99 (978-0-88092-555-6(8)) Royal Fireworks Publishing Co.

Wargin, Kathy-Jo. The Legend of Old Abe: A Civil War Eagle. Caple, Laurie, illus. 2006. 40p. (J). (gr. k-5). 17.95 (978-1-58536-232-5(8)) Sleeping Bear Pr.

Weiss, Ellen. Hitty's Travels: Civil War Days. 2001. 10.79 (978-0-606-22091-0(7)) Tandem Library Bks.

Wells, Rosemary. Red Moon at Sharpsburg. 2007. 256p. (YA). (gr. 7 up). 16.99 (978-0-670-03638-7(2) , Viking Juvenile) Penguin Group (USA) Inc.

Wilson, John. Battle scars. 2005. (Illus.). 168p. (YA). (gr. 5-9). (978-1-55337-703-0(6)); (978-1-55337-702-3(8)) Kids Can Pr., Ltd.

—Flags of War. 2005. 168p. (YA). (gr. 5-9). (978-1-55337-567-8(X)) Kids Can Pr., Ltd.

—Who'll Be a Soldier? 2006. 168p. (J). 6.95 (978-1-55337-568-5(8)) Kids Can Pr., Ltd. CAN. *Dist:* Wybel Marketing Group.

Winnick, Karen B. Cassie's Sweet Berry Pie: A Civil War Story. 2004. (Illus.). 32p. (J). 16.95 (978-1-56397-984-2(5)) Boyds Mills Pr.

Wisler, G. Clifton. The Drummer Boy of Vicksburg. 1999. (J). 12.64 (978-0-606-16768-0(4)) Tandem Library Bks.

—Red Cap, unabr. ed. 2000. (YA). pap., stu. ed. 41.24 incl. audio (978-0-7887-3629-2(9) , 41018X4) Recorded Bks., LLC.

—Red Cap. 2001. (YA). 20.25 (978-0-8446-7196-3(7)) Smith, Peter Pub., Inc.

—Run the Blockade. 2000. (Illus.). 122p. (J). (gr. 5-9). 15.95 (978-0-688-16538-3(9)) HarperCollins Pubs.

UNITED STATES—HISTORY—CIVIL WAR, 1861-1865—NAVAL OPERATIONS

Abnett, Dan. Ironclads at War: The Monitor vs the Merrimac. 2007. (Graphic History Ser.). (Illus.). 48p. (J). (gr. 3). pap. 9.95 (978-1-84603-053-6(6)) Osprey Publishing, Ltd. GBR. *Dist:* Random Hse., Inc.

—The Monitor vs. the Merrimac: Ironclads at War! 2007. (Graphic Battles of the Civil War Ser.). (Illus.). 48p. (J). lib. bdg. (978-1-4042-0778-3(3)) Rosen Publishing Group, Inc., The.

Anderson, Dale. The Civil War at Sea. 2004. (World Almanac Library of the Civil War). (Illus.). 48p. (J). (gr. 5 up). pap. 11.95 (978-0-8368-5594-4(9)); lib. bdg. 30.00 (978-0-8368-5585-2(X)) Stevens, Gareth Inc. (World Almanac Library).

Brager, Bruce L. The Monitor vs. the Merrimack. 2003. (Great Battles Through the Ages Ser.). (Illus.). 112p. (gr. 6-12). 30.00 (978-0-7910-7439-8(0) , Chelsea Hse.) Facts On File, Inc.

Burgan, Michael. The Battle of the Ironclads. 2006. (Illus.). 48p. (J). (gr. 4-6). 23.93 (978-0-7565-1628-4(5)) Compass Point Bks.

Hawk, Frank. The Story of the H. L. Hunley & Queenie's Coin. Nance, Dan, illus. 2004. 40p. (J). 16.95 (978-1-58536-218-9(2)) Sleeping Bear Pr.

O'Brien, Patrick. Duel of the Ironclads: The Monitor vs. the Virginia. O'Brien, Patrick, illus. 2007. (Illus.). 32p. (J). pap. 8.95 (978-0-8027-9562-5(5)) Walker & Co.

—Duel of the Ironclads: The Monitor vs. the Virginia. 2003. (Illus.). 40p. (J). (gr. 1-5). 18.85 (978-0-8027-8843-6(2)); 17.95 (978-0-8027-8842-9(4)) Walker & Co.

Thompson, Gare. Monitor: The Iron Warship That Changed the World. Day, Larry, illus. 2003. (All Aboard Reading Ser.). 48p. (J). (gr. 4-4). pap. 3.99 (978-0-448-43245-8(5) , Grosset & Dunlap) Penguin Group (USA) Inc.

—The Monitor: The Iron Warship That Changed the World. Day, Larry, illus. 2003. (All Aboard Reading Ser.). 48p. (J). 13.89 (978-0-448-43283-0(8) , Grosset & Dunlap) Penguin Group (USA) Inc.

Walker, Sally M. Secrets of a Civil War Submarine: Solving the Mysteries of the H.L. Hunley. 2005. (Illus.). 112p. (J). (gr. 6-8). 18.95 (978-1-57505-830-6(8) , Carolrhoda Bks.) Lerner Publishing Group.

—Shipwreck Search: Discovery of the H. L. Hunley. Verstraete, Elaine, illus. 2006. (On My Own Science Ser.). 48p. (J). (gr. 2-4). lib. bdg. 25.26 (978-1-57505-878-8(2) , Millbrook Pr.) Lerner Publishing Group.

UNITED STATES—HISTORY—CIVIL WAR, 1861-1865—POETRY

Gustafson, Joseph. Gettysburg Voices: Civil War Poems. 1998. vii, 45 p. (YA). (gr. 6-12). 6.95 (978-0-9620313-5-9(6)) Leicester Hill Bks.

Lewis, J. Patrick. The Brothers' War: Civil War Voices in Verses. 2007. (Illus.). 48p. (gr. 5-9). (J). 17.95 (***978-1-4263-0036-3(0)***); lib. bdg. 25.90 (***978-1-4263-0037-0(9)***) National Geographic Society. (National Geographic Children's Bks.).

UNITED STATES—HISTORY—1865-1898

see also Reconstruction (U.S. History, 1865-1877)

Collier, Christopher & Collier, James Lincoln. A Century of Immigration: 1820-1924. 1999. (Drama of American History Ser.). (Illus.). 96p. (J). (gr. 5-9). lib. bdg. 31.36 (978-0-7614-0821-5(5) , Benchmark Bks.) Cavendish, Marshall Corp.

—Reconstruction & the Rise of Jim Crow: 1864-1896. 1999. (Drama of American History Ser.). (Illus.). 96p. (YA). (gr. 5-9). lib. bdg. 31.36 (978-0-7614-0819-2(3) , Benchmark Bks.) Cavendish, Marshall Corp.

—The Rise of Industry: 1860-1900. 1999. (Drama of American History Ser.). (Illus.). 96p. (J). (gr. 5-9). lib. bdg. 31.36 (978-0-7614-0820-8(7) , Benchmark Bks.) Cavendish, Marshall Corp.

—The United States Enters the World: 1867-1919. 2000. (Drama of American History Ser.). (Illus.). 96p. (J). (gr. 5-9). lib. bdg. 31.36 (978-0-7614-1053-9(8) , Benchmark Bks.) Cavendish, Marshall Corp.

Espejo, Roman. The Age of Reform & Industrialization: 1896-1920. 2002. (American History by Era Ser.: Vol. 6). (Illus.). 272p. (J). pap. 33.70 (978-0-7377-1141-7(8) , Greenhaven Pr., Inc.) Thomson Gale.

Flanagan, Timothy. Reconstruction: A Primary Source History of the Struggle to Unite the North & South after the Civil War. 2005. (Illus.). 64p. (J). (gr. 5-8). lib. bdg. 29.25 (978-1-4042-0177-4(7)) Rosen Publishing Group, Inc., The.

Greenwood, Janette Thomas. The Gilded Age: A History in Documents. 2000. (Pages from History Ser.). (Illus.). 192p. (gr. 7 up). 36.95 (978-0-19-510523-0(0)) Oxford Univ. Pr., Inc.

Hakim, Joy. An Age of Extremes 1880-1917. 3rd ed. 2002. (History of US Ser.). (Illus.). 112p. (Orig.). pap., tchr. ed. 16.95 (978-0-19-515358-3(8)) Oxford Univ. Pr., Inc.

—A History of the US Bk. 7: Reconstructing America, 1865-1890. 3rd rev. ed. 2002. (History of US Ser.). (Illus.). 160p. pap. 15.95 (978-0-19-515332-3(4)) Oxford Univ. Pr., Inc.

—A History of U. S. Vol. 7: Reconstruction & Reform. rev. ed. 2007. (History of US Ser.). 208p. pap. 15.95 (***978-0-19-532721-2(7)***) Oxford Univ. Pr., Inc.

—A History of US Bk. 7: Reconstructing America. 3rd rev. ed. 2005. (History of US Ser.). (Illus.). 208p. 19.95 (978-0-19-518900-1(0)) Oxford Univ. Pr., Inc.

—Reconstructing America 1865-1890, Bk. 7. 3rd ed. 2002. (History of US Ser.). 112p. (Orig.). pap., tchr. ed. 16.95 (978-0-19-515357-6(X)) Oxford Univ. Pr., Inc.

—Reconstruction & Reform. 2003. (gr. 5-8). lib. bdg. 23.40 (978-0-613-55187-8(7)) Tandem Library Bks.

Hale, Sarah Elder, ed. Rebuilding a Nation: Picking up the Pieces. 2005. (Cobblestone the Civil War Ser.). (Illus.). 48p. (J). 17.95 (978-0-8126-7909-0(1)) Cobblestone Publishing Co.

Harkrader, Lisa. Reconstruction & Aftermath of the Civil War: A MyReportLinks. com Book. 2004. (American Civil War Ser.). (Illus.). 48p. (J). lib. bdg. 25.26 (978-0-7660-5265-9(6) , MyReportLinks.com Bks.) Enslow Pubs., Inc.

Holt, Rinehart and Winston Staff. Call to Freedom: 1865-Present: Standard Test Preparation - Virginia Edition. 3rd ed. 2003. (YA). pap., wbk. ed. 10.60 (978-0-03-070167-2(8)) Holt, Rinehart & Winston.

—Call to Freedom: 1865-Present: Virginia Edition. 3rd annot. ed. 2003. (J). tchr. ed. 107.60 (978-0-03-070139-9(2)) Holt, Rinehart & Winston.

Langellier, J. Phillip. Redlegs: The U. S. Artillery from the Civil War to the Spanish-American War, 1861-1898. 1999. (G. I. Ser.: Vol. 11). (Illus.). 80p. (YA). (gr. 5-9). 27.50 (978-0-7910-5375-1(X) , Chelsea Hse.) Facts On File, Inc.

McPherson, James M. Into the West: From Reconstruction to the Final Days of the American Frontier. 2006. 96p. (J). (gr. 4-9). 22.95 (978-0-689-86543-5(0) , Atheneum) Simon & Schuster Children's Publishing.

Naden, Corinne J. & Blue, Rose. Civil War Ends: Assassination, Reconstruction & the Aftermath. 1999. (House Divided Ser.). (Illus.). 112p. (J). (gr. 5-10). lib. bdg. 31.40 (978-0-8172-5583-1(4)) Raintree.

Ojeda, Auriana. The Civil War: 1850-1895, Vol. 5. 2003. (American History by Era Ser.: Vol. 5). (Illus.). 301p. (YA). pap. 33.70 (978-0-7377-1139-4(6)); lib. bdg. 52.45 (978-0-7377-1140-0(X)) Thomson Gale. (Greenhaven Pr., Inc.).

Pierce, Alan. Reconstruction. 2005. (American Moments Ser.). (Illus.). 48p. (J). (gr. 4-8). lib. bdg. 25.65 (978-1-59197-939-5(0)) ABDO Publishing Co.

Raatma, Lucia. The Carpetbaggers. 2004. (We the People Ser.). (Illus.). 48p. (J). 22.60 (978-0-7565-0834-0(7)) Compass Point Bks.

Spaeth, Lisa. Reconstruction. 2003. (gr. 7-12). lib. bdg. 28.90 (978-0-613-57377-1(3)) Tandem Library Bks.

Stanley, George Edward. The ERA of Reconstruction & Expansion, 1865-1900. 2005. (Illus.). 48p. (J). pap. (978-0-8368-5836-5(0)); lib. bdg. 30.00 (978-0-8368-5827-3(1)) Stevens, Gareth Inc. (World Almanac Library).

Stuckey. Call to Freedom: 1877-Present: Online Edition Plus. 3rd ed. 2003. 17.26 (978-0-03-037427-2(8)); 17.26 (978-0-03-037431-9(6)) Holt, Rinehart & Winston.

—Call to Freedom: Beginning-1877: Online Edition Plus. 3rd ed. 2003. 17.26 (978-0-03-037428-9(6)); 17.26 (978-0-03-037429-6(4)) Holt, Rinehart & Winston.

Wells, Donna. American Comes of Age. 2000. (Making of America Ser.). (Illus.). 96p. (J). (gr. 4-7). lib. bdg. 28.54 (978-0-8172-5708-8(X)) Raintree.

Ziff, Marsha. Reconstruction Following the Civil War in American History. 1999. (In American History Ser.). (Illus.). 128p. (YA). (gr. 5-12). lib. bdg. 26.60 (978-0-7660-1140-3(2)) Enslow Pubs., Inc.

UNITED STATES—HISTORY—1865-1898—FICTION

Bradbury, Bianca. Flight into Spring. 2005. 184p. (YA). pap. (***978-1-932350-01-2(2)***) Bethlehem Bks.

Finley, Martha. Elsie's Great Hope, Vol. 8. 2006. (Life of Faith': Elsie Dinsmore Ser.). 224p. (J). pap. 7.99 (978-1-928749-87-5(9)) Zonderkidz.

Hansen, Joyce. The Heart Calls Home. 1999. viii, 175p. (J). (gr. 7-12). 16.95 (978-0-8027-8636-4(7)) Walker & Co.

Lawlor, Laurie. He Will Go Fearless. 2006. 224p. (J). 15.95 (978-0-689-86579-4(1)) Simon & Schuster Children's Publishing.

MacBride, Roger Lea. Bachelor Girl. Gilleece, David, illus. 1999. (Little House). 256p. (J). (gr. 3-6). 15.89 (978-0-06-028434-3(X)) HarperCollins Pubs.

—Bachelor Girl. Andreasen, Dan, illus. 1999. (Little House Ser.). 256p. (J). (gr. 3-6). 15.95 (978-0-06-027755-0(6)); (gr. 5 up). pap. 6.99 (978-0-06-440691-8(1) , Harper Trophy) HarperCollins Pubs.

—Bachelor Girl. 1999. (gr. 3-6). lib. bdg. 14.15 (978-0-613-21154-3(5)); (Illus.). (J). 12.64 (978-0-606-18676-6(X)) Tandem Library Bks.

Porter, Connie. Addy's Short Story Collection. Dellosso, Gabriella & Graef, Renee, illus. 2006. 248p. (J). 12.95 (***978-1-59369-122-6(X)***) American Girl Publishing, Inc.

Robinet, Harriette Gillem. Forty Acres & Maybe a Mule. 2000. (YA). (gr. 3 up). pap. 52.00 incl. audio (978-0-7887-4332-0(5) , 41127) Recorded Bks., LLC.

—Forty Acres & Maybe a Mule. Nickens, Bessie, illus. 1998. (Jean Karl Ser.). 144p. (J). (gr. 3-7). 17.99 (978-0-689-82078-6(X) , Atheneum) Simon & Schuster Children's Publishing.

—Forty Acres & Maybe a Mule. 2000. 11.64 (978-0-606-17824-2(4)); (gr. 3-6). lib. bdg. 13.00 (978-0-613-22986-9(X)) Tandem Library Bks.

Robinet, Harriette Gillem & Minor, Wendell. Forty Acres & Maybe a Mule. 2000. (Jean Karl Ser.). 144p. (J). (gr. 3-7). reprint ed. pap. 4.99 (978-0-689-83317-5(2) , Aladdin) Simon & Schuster Children's Publishing.

Walsh, Alice. Pomiuk, Prince of the North. Whitehead, Jerry, illus. 2006. 64p. (J). pap., tchr. ed. 6.95 (978-0-88878-447-6(3) , Sandcastle Bks.) Dundurn Group, The CAN. *Dist:* Univ. of Toronto Pr.

UNITED STATES—HISTORY—1898-

Boyer, Paul. Holt American Nation: Modern Era: Online Edition Plus. 3rd ed. 2003. 17.26 (978-0-03-037433-3(2)) Holt, Rinehart & Winston.

Collier, Christopher & Collier, James Lincoln. The United States Enters the World: 1867-1919. 2000. (Drama of American History Ser.). (Illus.). 96p. (J). (gr. 5-9). lib. bdg. 31.36 (978-0-7614-1053-9(8) , Benchmark Bks.) Cavendish, Marshall Corp.

Espejo, Roman. The Age of Reform & Industrialization: 1896-1920. 2002. (American History by Era Ser.: Vol. 6). (Illus.). 272p. (J). pap. 33.70 (978-0-7377-1141-7(8) , Greenhaven Pr., Inc.) Thomson Gale.

Holt, Rinehart and Winston Staff. Call to Freedom: 1865-Present: Standard Test Preparation - Virginia Edition. 3rd ed. 2003. (YA). pap., wbk. ed. 10.60 (978-0-03-070167-2(8)) Holt, Rinehart & Winston.

—Call to Freedom: 1865-Present: Virginia Edition. 3rd annot. ed. 2003. (J). tchr. ed. 107.60 (978-0-03-070139-9(2)) Holt, Rinehart & Winston.

Stuckey. Call to Freedom: 1877-Present: Online Edition Plus. 3rd ed. 2003. 17.26 (978-0-03-037427-2(8)); 17.26 (978-0-03-037431-9(6)) Holt, Rinehart & Winston.

—Call to Freedom: Beginning-1877: Online Edition Plus. 3rd ed. 2003. 17.26 (978-0-03-037428-9(6)); 17.26 (978-0-03-037429-6(4)) Holt, Rinehart & Winston.

TUV

UNITED STATES—HISTORY—1898-1919

Hakim, Joy. An Age of Extremes 1880-1917. 3rd ed. 2002. (History of US Ser.). (Illus.). 112p. (Orig.). pap., tchr. ed. 16.95 (978-0-19-515358-3(8)) Oxford Univ. Pr., Inc.

Thomson Gale Staff. Age of Reform & Industrialization: 1896-1920. 2002. (gr. 7-12). lib. bdg. 39.05 (978-0-613-73612-1(5)) Tandem Library Bks.

Uschan, Michael V. The 1910's. 1998. (Cultural History of the United States Through the Decades Ser.). (Illus.). 128p. (YA). (gr. 4-12). 29.95 (978-1-56006-551-7(6) , LML00902-177908, Lucent Bks.) Thomson Gale.

UNITED STATES—HISTORY—WAR OF 1898

see Spanish-American War, 1898

UNITED STATES—HISTORY—20TH CENTURY

Anderson, Dale. The Atom Bomb Project. 2004. (Landmark Events in American History Ser.). (Illus.). 48p. (J). (gr. 5 up). pap. 11.95 (978-0-8368-5413-8(6) , World Almanac Library) Stevens, Gareth Inc.

Bednarz, Robert, et al. TIME for Kids Readers: On the Home Front. 3rd ed. 2002. (Harcourt Horizons Ser.). (gr. k-7). pap. 38.10 (978-0-15-335301-7(5)) Harcourt Schl. Pubs.

Blohm, Craig E. Strategic Battles. 2003. (American War Library). (Illus.). 128p. (J). 29.95 (978-1-59018-261-1(8) , Lucent Bks.) Thomson Gale.

Boyer, Paul S. Promises to Keep: The United States since World War II. 3rd ed. 2004. (Illus.). 560p. (YA). 59.96 (978-0-618-43383-4(X) , 305248) Houghton Mifflin College Div.

Burns, Bree. America in The 1970s. 2005. (Decades of American History Ser.). (Illus.). 128p. (J). (gr. 4-9). 35.00 (978-0-8160-5643-9(9)) Facts On File, Inc.

Campbell, Ian. The USA, 1917-1941. 1998. (History Programme Ser.). (Illus.). 66p. pap. 19.00 (978-0-521-56864-7(1)) Cambridge Univ. Pr.

Coates, Tim. The Shooting of John F. Kennedy 1963: The Warren Commission. 2003. (Moments of History Ser.). (Illus.). 320p. (978-1-84381-025-4(5)) Coates, Tim.

Collier, Christopher & Collier, James Lincoln. The Changing Face of America, 1945-2000. 2001. (Drama of American History Ser.). (Illus.). 96p. (J). (gr. 5-9). lib. bdg. 31.36 (978-0-7614-1319-6(7) , Benchmark Bks.) Cavendish, Marshall Corp.

—Progressivism, the Great Depression & the New Deal: 1901-1941. 2000. (Drama of American History Ser.). (Illus.). 96p. (J). (gr. 5-9). lib. bdg. 31.36 (978-0-7614-1054-6(6) , Benchmark Bks.) Cavendish, Marshall Corp.

Corey, Melinda. Chronology of 20th-Century America. 2005. (Decades of American History Ser.). (Illus.). 128p. (J). (gr. 4-9). 35.00 (978-0-8160-5646-0(3)) Facts On File, Inc.

Craats, Rennay. 1900s: America Through the Decades, 10 vols. 2001. (America Through the Decades). (Illus.). 48p. (J). lib. bdg. 24.95 (978-1-930954-42-7(5)) Weigl Pubs., Inc.

—1910s: America Through the Decades, 10 vols. 2001. (America Through the Decades). (Illus.). 48p. (J). lib. bdg. 24.95 (978-1-930954-47-2(6)) Weigl Pubs., Inc.

—1920s: America Through the Decades, 10 vols. 2001. (America Through the Decades). (Illus.). 48p. (J). lib. bdg. 24.95 (978-1-930954-09-0(3)) Weigl Pubs., Inc.

—1930s: America Through the Decades, 10 vols. 2001. (America Through the Decades). (Illus.). 48p. (J). lib. bdg. 24.95 (978-1-930954-14-4(X)) Weigl Pubs., Inc.

—1940s: America Through the Decades, 10 vols. 2001. (America Through the Decades). (Illus.). 48p. (J). lib. bdg. 24.95 (978-1-930954-19-9(0)) Weigl Pubs., Inc.

—1950s: America Through the Decades, 10 vols. 2001. (America Through the Decades). (Illus.). 48p. (J). lib. bdg. 24.95 (978-1-930954-24-3(7)) Weigl Pubs., Inc.

—1990s: America Through the Decades, 10 vols. 2001. (America Through the Decades). (Illus.). 48p. (J). lib. bdg. 24.95 (978-1-930954-44-1(1)) Weigl Pubs., Inc.

Craats, Rennay, told to. 1960s: America Through the Decades, 10 vols. 2001. (America Through the Decades). (Illus.). 48p. (J). lib. bdg. 24.95 (978-1-930954-29-8(8)) Weigl Pubs., Inc.

—1970s, 10 vols. 2001. (America Through the Decades). (Illus.). 48p. (J). lib. bdg. 24.95 (978-1-930954-34-2(4)) Weigl Pubs., Inc.

—1980s: America Through the Decades, 10 vols. 2001. (America Through the Decades). (Illus.). 48p. (J). lib. bdg. 24.95 (978-1-930954-39-7(5)) Weigl Pubs., Inc.

Davis, Barbara J. The Teapot Dome Scandal: Corruption Rocks 1920s America. 2007. (J). lib. bdg. ***(978-0-7565-3336-6(8))*** Compass Point Bks.

Events That Shaped America New Releases: The First Moon Landing; Lexington & Concord; The Terrorist Attacks of September11, 2001; The Trail of Tears; The Transcontinental Railroad; The Triangle Shirtwaist Factory Fire, 6 bks. 2004. (Illus.). (J). (gr. 3 up). lib. bdg. 143.60 (978-0-8368-3388-1(0)) Stevens, Gareth Inc.

Fandel, Jennifer. Martin Luther King, Jr. 2005. (Genius Ser.). (Illus.). 48p. (gr. 5-9). 21.95 (978-1-58341-329-6(4) , Creative Education) Creative Co., The.

Feinstein, Stephen. Decades of the 20th Century, 10 bks., Set. Incl. 1900s from Teddy Roosevelt to Flying Machines. (J). 2001. lib. bdg. 22.60 (978-0-7660-1612-5(9)); 1910s from World War I to Ragtime Music. (J). 2001. lib. bdg. 22.60 (978-0-7660-1611-8(0)); 1920s from Prohibition to Charles Lindbergh. (J). 2001. lib. bdg. 22.60 (978-0-7660-1610-1(2)); 1930s from the Great Depression to the Wizard of Oz. (J). 2001. lib. bdg. 22.60 (978-0-7660-1609-5(9)); 1940s from World War II to Jackie Robinson. (YA). 2000. lib. bdg. 22.60 (978-0-7660-1428-2(2)); 1950s from the Korean War to Elvis. (J). 2000. lib. bdg. 22.60 (978-0-7660-1427-5(4)); 1960s from the Vietnam War to Flower Power. (YA). 2000. lib. bdg. 22.60 (978-0-7660-1426-8(6)); 1970s from Watergate to Disco. (YA). 2000. lib. bdg. 22.60 (978-0-7660-1425-1(8)); 1980s from Ronald Reagan to MTV. (YA). 2000. lib. bdg. 22.60 (978-0-7660-1424-4(X)); 1990s from the Persian Gulf War to Y2K. (J). 2001. lib. bdg. 22.60 (978-0-7660-1613-2(7)); 64p. (gr. 5-12). (Illus.). Set lib. bdg. 179.50 (978-0-7660-1605-7(6)) Enslow Pubs., Inc.

—The 1930s from the Great Depression to the Wizard of Oz. 2001. (Decades of the 20th Century Ser.). (Illus.). 64p. (J). (gr. 5-12). lib. bdg. 22.60 (978-0-7660-1609-5(9)) Enslow Pubs., Inc.

—The 1970s from Watergate to Disco. rev. ed. 2006. (Decades of the 20th Century in Color Ser.). (Illus.). 64p. (J). lib. bdg. 27.93 (978-0-7660-2637-7(X)) Enslow Pubs., Inc.

—The 1980s from Ronald Reagan to MTV. rev. ed. 2006. (Decades of the 20th Century in Color Ser.). (Illus.). 64p. (J). lib. bdg. 27.93 (978-0-7660-2638-4(8)) Enslow Pubs., Inc.

Fiorelli, June Estep. Fannie Lou Hamer: A Voice for Freedom. 2004. (Avisson Young Adult Ser.). (Illus.). 117p. (J). pap. 19.95 (978-1-888105-62-9(3)) Avisson Pr., Inc.

Freedman, Russell. Children of the Great Depression. 2005. (Illus.). 128p. (J). (gr. 5-8). 20.00 (978-0-618-44630-8(3) , Clarion Bks.) Houghton Mifflin Co. Trade & Reference Div.

Gaines, Jena. Haitian Immigration. 2003. (Changing Face of North America Ser.). (Illus.). 112p. (J). lib. bdg. (978-1-59084-691-9(5)) Mason Crest Pubs.

Gershenson, Harold P. America the Musical 1900-2000: A Nation's History Through Music. Chesworth, Michael, illus. 2006. (J). ***(978-1-58987-201-1(0))*** Kindermusik International.

The Gilded Age. 2003. (Eye on History Ser.). 32p. (gr. 5-12). 5.99 (978-1-56822-943-0(7) , IF2676) School Specialty Publishing.

Hakim, Joy. An Age of Extremes. 2003. (gr. 5-8). lib. bdg. 23.40 (978-0-613-55139-7(7)) Tandem Library Bks.

—All the People. 2003. (gr. 5-8). lib. bdg. 23.40 (978-0-613-55140-3(0)) Tandem Library Bks.

—All the People 1945-2001, Bk. 10. 3rd ed. 2002. (History of US Ser.:). 112p. (Orig.). pap., tchr. ed. 16.95 (978-0-19-515360-6(X)) Oxford Univ. Pr., Inc.

—All the People since 1945. 3rd rev. ed. 2005. (History of US Ser.). (Illus.). 270p. 19.95 (978-0-19-530737-5(2)) Oxford Univ. Pr., Inc.

—War, Peace, & All That Jazz. 3rd rev. ed. 2005. (History of US Ser.). (Illus.). 224p. 19.95 (978-0-19-530738-2(0)) Oxford Univ. Pr., Inc.

Hamilton, Neil. The 1970s. 2006. (Eyewitness History Ser.). (Illus.). 512p. (J). (gr. 9). 75.00 (978-0-8160-5778-8(8)) Facts On File, Inc.

Hanson, Erica. The 1920's. 1998. (Cultural History of the United States Through the Decades Ser.). (Illus.). 128p. (YA). (gr. 4-12). 29.95 (978-1-56006-552-4(4) , LML00902-177909, Lucent Bks.) Thomson Gale.

Hardy, P. Stephen & Hardy, Sheila Jackson. Extraordinary People of the Civil Rights Movement. 2006. (Extraordinary People Ser.). (Illus.). 288p. (YA). (gr. 9 up). (978-0-516-25461-6(8)) Children's Pr., Ltd.

Haskins, James & Benson, Kathleen. Out of the Darkness: The Story of Blacks Moving North, 1890-1940. 2000. (Great Journeys Ser.). (Illus.). 112p. (J). (gr. 5 up). lib. bdg. 32.79 (978-0-7614-0970-0(X) , Benchmark Bks.) Cavendish, Marshall Corp.

Hatt, Christine. Martin Luther King, Jr. 2004. (Judge for Yourself Ser.). (Illus.). 64p. (J). pap. (978-0-8368-5565-4(5)); (gr. 5 up). lib. bdg. 30.00 (978-0-8368-5562-3(0)) Stevens, Gareth Inc. (World Almanac Library).

Hill, Laban Carrick. America Dreaming. 2007. (Illus.). 176p. (YA). (gr. 7-17). 19.99 ***(978-0-316-00904-1(0))*** Little Brown & Co.

Holland, Gini. The 1960's. 1998. (Cultural History of the United States Through the Decades Ser.). (Illus.). 128p. (YA). (gr. 4-12). 29.95 (978-1-56006-556-2(7) , LML00902-177913, Lucent Bks.) Thomson Gale.

Honovich, Nancy. Immigration from the Former Yugoslavia. 2003. (Changing Face of North America Ser.). (Illus.). 112p. (YA). lib. bdg. (978-1-59084-690-2(7)) Mason Crest Pubs.

Isaacs, Sally Senzell. America in the Time of Martin Luther King Jr. 1948 to 1976. (Illus.). 48p. (J). (gr. 4-7). 2002. pap. 8.50 (978-1-57572-939-8(3)); 1999. lib. bdg. (978-1-57572-780-6(3)) Heinemann Library.

Jackson, Robert B. The Remarkable Ride of the Abernathy Boys. 2003. (Land We Belong to Is Grand Ser.). (Illus.). 69p. (J). pap. (978-1-57168-798-2(X) , Eakin Pr.) Eakin Pr.

Jennings, Peter, et al. The Century for Young People. 1999. (Illus.). 256p. (J). (gr. 3-7). 29.95 (978-0-385-32708-4(0) , Doubleday Bks. for Young Readers) Random Hse. Children's Bks.

Karolides, Nicholas J. Literature Suppressed on Political Grounds. rev. ed. 2006. (Banned Books Ser.). 640p. (gr. 9). 50.00 (978-0-8160-6270-6(6)) Facts On File, Inc.

Kops, Deborah. Racial Profiling. 2006. (Open for Debate Ser.). (Illus.). 127p. (YA). (gr. 6-9). lib. bdg. 39.93 (978-0-7614-2298-3(6) , Benchmark Bks.) Cavendish, Marshall Corp.

Landau, Elaine. The Great Depression. 2006. (Cornerstones of Freedom Ser.: Vol. 2). (Illus.). 48p. (J). (gr. 4-6). 26.00 ***(978-0-516-23622-3(9))*** Scholastic Library Publishing.

Long, Cathryn J. Crossword America: American History 1900 to 2000. Nolte, Larry, illus. 2000. 64p. (J). (gr. 3-7). pap. 5.95 (978-0-7373-0366-7(2) , 03662W, Roxbury Park Juvenile) Lowell Hse. Juvenile.

Lynne, Douglas. Contemporary United States. 2007. (J). ***(978-1-59036-753-7(7)); (978-1-59036-754-4(5))*** Weigl Pubs., Inc.

Matthews, Sherrie Voss, ed. Free at Last: The Struggle for Civil Rights. 2000. (Literature & Thought Ser.). (Illus.). 144p. (J). (978-0-7807-9633-1(0)); (978-0-7891-5213-8(4)); pap. (978-0-7891-5212-1(6)) Perfection Learning Corp.

McDougal, Littell Staff & Nextext Staff, contrib. by. World War, Boom & Bust. 2004. (Stories in History Ser.). (Illus.). 224p. (J). (gr. 6-12). (978-0-618-22202-5(2) , 2-00308) McDougal Littell Inc.

Noonan, Sheila Smith. Korean Immigration. 2003. (Changing Face of North America Ser.). (Illus.). 112p. (YA). lib. bdg. (978-1-59084-693-3(1)) Mason Crest Pubs.

Ochoa, George. America in the 1990s. 2005. (Decades of American History Ser.). (Illus.). 128p. (J). (gr. 4-9). 35.00 (978-0-8160-5645-3(5)) Facts On File, Inc.

Pendergast, Tom & Pendergast, Sara. The Sixties in America, 3 vols. 2004. 600p. 181.00 (978-0-7876-9249-0(2) , UXL) Thomson Gale.

Perrin, Pat, ed. World War I. 2001. (Researching American History Ser.). (Illus.). 56p. (J). pap. 7.95 (978-1-57960-075-4(1)) History Compass, LLC.

Petersen, Christine. The Iran-Contra Scandal. 2004. (Cornerstones of Freedom Ser.). (Illus.). 48p. (J). 26.00 (978-0-516-24228-6(8) , Children's Pr.) Scholastic Library Publishing.

Potter, Tony, prod. Plantation Home Model. 2005. 3p. (J). pap. 19.95 (978-1-58980-274-2(8)) Pelican Publishing Co., Inc.

Press, Petra. The 1930's. 1998. (Cultural History of the United States Through the Decades Ser.). (Illus.). 128p. (YA). (gr. 4-12). 29.95 (978-1-56006-553-1(2) , LML00902-177910, Lucent Bks.) Thomson Gale.

Pringle, Laurence P. One Room School. 2003. (Illus.). 32p. (J). (gr. 2-4). 16.95 (978-1-56397-583-7(1)) Boyds Mills Pr.

Sandifer, Kevin W., ed. History of the United States, Reconstruction-Clinton Era Pt. 2. l.t. ed. 2007. (Illus.). 432p. lib. bdg. (978-0-910653-61-9(5) , 8202U, Red River Pr.) Red River Pr.

Schaefer, Adam. The Harlem Renaissance. 2003. (20th Century Perspectives Ser.). 48p. pap. 7.95 (978-1-4034-3858-4(7)) Heinemann Library.

Sitkoff, Harvard. Postwar America: A Student Companion. 1999. (Student Companions to American History Ser.). (Illus.). 296p. (YA). (gr. 7 up). 60.00 (978-0-19-510300-7(9)) Oxford Univ. Pr., Inc.

Skog, Jason. The Civil Rights Act of 1964. 2006. 48p. (J). 25.26 (978-0-7565-2459-3(8)) Compass Point Bks.

Smith, Robert W. Spotlight on America: 20th Century Wars. 2006. pap. 12.99 (978-1-4206-3219-4(1)) Teacher Created Resources, Inc.

Southwell, David & Twist, Sean. Unsolved Political Mysteries. 2007. (J). ***(978-1-4042-1083-7(0))*** Rosen Publishing Group, Inc., The.

Streissguth, Thomas. Clay V. United States & How Muhammad Ali Fought the Draft: Debating Supreme Court Decisions. 2006. (Debating Supreme Court Decisions Ser.). (Illus.). 112p. (J). lib. bdg. 26.60 (978-0-7660-2393-2(1)) Enslow Pubs., Inc.

Supples, Kevin. The Civil Rights Movement. 2003. (People Who Changed America Ser.). (Illus.). 40p. (J). (978-0-7922-8628-8(6)) National Geographic Society.

Tembo, Limbiko & Venable, Rose. The Civil Rights Movement. 2001. (Journey to Freedom Ser.). (Illus.). 40p. (J). (gr. 3-7). 28.50 (978-1-56766-917-6(4)) Child's World, Inc.

Thomson Gale Staff. Cold War Period: 1945-1992. 2002. (gr. 7-12). lib. bdg. 39.05 (978-0-613-73607-7(9)) Tandem Library Bks.

Uschan, Michael V. Life on the Front Lines: The Fight for Civil Rights. 2004. (Illus.). 112p. (J). 32.45 (978-1-59018-387-8(8) , Lucent Bks.) Thomson Gale.

Woog, Adam. The Fight Renewed: the Civil Rights Movement. 2005. (Lucent Library of Black History). (Illus.). 112p. (YA). (gr. 7-10). lib. bdg. 32.45 (978-1-59018-701-2(6) , Lucent Bks.) Thomson Gale.

Wright, John & Waugh, Steven. The USA 1929-1980. 2005. (Illus.). 144p. pap. 38.50 ***(978-0-340-88903-9(9)*** , Hodder Murray) Hodder Education GBR. *Dist:* Trans-Atlantic Pubns., Inc.

1920's Dba. 2001. spiral bd. 16.95 (978-1-56004-117-7(X)) Social Studies Schl. Service.

UNITED STATES—HISTORY—20TH CENTURY—FICTION

Birtha, Becky. Grandmama's Pride. Bootman, Colin, illus. 2005. 32p. (J). (gr. 7-10). 16.95 (978-0-8075-3028-3(X)) Whitman, Albert & Co.

Boling, Katharine. January 1905. 2004. 176p. (J). 16.00 (978-0-15-205119-8(8)) Harcourt Children's Bks.

Bradley, Kimberly Brubaker. The President's Daughter. 2004. (Illus.). 176p. (gr. 3-7). 15.95 (978-0-385-73147-8(7) , Delacorte Bks. for Young Readers) Random Hse. Children's Bks.

Brink, Carol Ryrie. Caddie Woodlawn. Hyman, Trina Schart, illus. 2002. (J). 13.94 (978-0-7587-0174-9(8)) Book Wholesalers, Inc.

Chaconas, Dori. Pennies in a Jar. Lewin, Ted, illus. 2007. 32p. (J). (ps-3). 16.95 ***(978-1-56145-422-8(2)*** , Peachtree Junior) Peachtree Pubs., Ltd.

Dastin, Lizy. December First: A Story of the Century. 2000. (gr. 7-12). lib. bdg. 18.75 (978-0-613-84088-0(7)) Tandem Library Bks.

Doyle, Bill. Betrayed! The 1977 Journal of Zeke Moorie. Hoskins, Brian, illus. 2006. 139p. (J). lib. bdg. 18.46 ***(978-1-4242-1733-5(4))*** Fitzgerald Bks.

Gwaltney, Doris. Homefront. 2006. 320p. (J). 17.99 (978-0-689-86842-9(1)) Simon & Schuster Children's Publishing.

Harrison, Marie Joseph. Mosanna & Me. 2003. 160p. pap. 12.95 (978-0-916251-62-8(4)) Sunbelt Pubns., Inc.

—Mosanna & Me. 2003. (gr. 7-12). lib. bdg. 22.20 (978-0-613-89684-9(X)) Tandem Library Bks.

Hobbs, Valerie. Sonny's War. 2006. 224p. (YA). pap. 7.95 (978-0-374-46970-2(9)) Macmillan.

Holubitsky, Katherine. Hippie House. 2004. 224p. (YA). (gr. 7-12). lib. bdg. 16.95 (978-1-55143-316-5(8)) Orca Bk. Pubs. USA.

Johnson, Angela. A Sweet Smell of Roses. Velasquez, Eric, illus. 2007. 32p. (J). 6.99 ***(978-1-4169-5361-6(2)*** , Aladdin) Simon & Schuster Children's Publishing.

Klages, Ellen. The Green Glass Sea. 2006. 272p. (YA). (gr. 5). 16.99 (978-0-670-06134-1(4) , Viking Juvenile) Penguin Group (USA) Inc.

Mazer, Harry. A Boy No More. 2004. (Illus.). 144p. (J). 16.95 (978-0-689-85533-7(8)) Simon & Schuster Children's Publishing.

McDonald, Megan. Julie's Journey, Bk. 5. McAliley, Susan, illus. 2007. 88p. (YA). (gr. 3 up). 12.95 ***(978-1-59369-353-4(2))*** American Girl Publishing, Inc.

Myers, Edward. Duck & Cover. 2004. 200p. (J). per. 11.95 (978-0-9674477-8-0(X)) Montemayor Pr.

Myers, Walter Dean. Patrol: An American Soldier in Vietnam. Grifalconi, Ann, illus. 2005. 40p. (J). pap. 6.99 (978-0-06-073159-5(1) , Harper Trophy) HarperCollins Pubs.

Noonan, Brandon. Plenty Porter. 2006. 240p. (YA). (gr. 7-17). 16.95 (978-0-8109-5996-5(8)) Abrams, Harry N. , Inc.

O'Dell, Kathleen. Bad Tickets. 2007. 240p. (YA). (gr. 7). 15.99 (978-0-375-83801-9(5)); lib. bdg. 18.99 (978-0-375-93801-6(X)) Random Hse. Children's Bks. (Knopf Bks. for Young Readers).

Shaw, Deirdre. Fair Play. 2005. (American Dreams Ser.). 176p. (YA). mass mkt. 5.99 (978-0-689-87850-3(8) , Simon Spotlight Entertainment) Simon & Schuster.

Shephard, Esther. Paul Bunyan. Kent, Rockwell, illus. 2006. 256p. (J). pap. 5.95 (978-0-15-205857-9(5) , Odyssey Classics) Harcourt Children's Bks.

UNITED STATES—HISTORY—1919-1933

Beyer, Mark. Temperance & Prohibition: The Movement to Pass Anti-Liquor Laws in America. 2006. (Progressive Movement, 1900-1920—Efforts to Reform America's New Industrial Society Ser.). (Illus.). 32p. (J). (978-1-4042-0861-2(5)); lib. bdg. (978-1-4042-0195-8(5)) Rosen Publishing Group, Inc., The.

Burg, David F. The Great Depression. 2nd rev. ed. 2005. (Eyewitness History Ser.). (Illus.). 464p. (J). (gr. 9). 75.00 (978-0-8160-5709-2(5)) Facts On File, Inc.

Callan, Jim. America in the 1930s. 2005. (Decades of American History Ser.). (Illus.). 128p. (J). (gr. 4-9). 35.00 (978-0-8160-5638-5(2)) Facts On File, Inc.

Clements, Peter. Prosperity, Depression & the New Deal. 2nd ed. 2001. (Illus.). vi, 168p. pap. 13.99 (978-0-340-80429-2(7)) Hodder Education GBR. *Dist:* Trafalgar Square Publishing.

Cooper, Michael L. Dust to Eat: Drought & Depression in the 1930s. 2004. (Illus.). 96p. (J). (gr. 7-9). tchr. ed. 17.00 (978-0-618-15449-4(3) , Clarion Bks.) Houghton Mifflin Co. Trade & Reference Div.

Egendorf, Laura K. Prosperity, Depression, & War, 1920-1945. 2002. (gr. 7-12). lib. bdg. 39.05 (978-0-613-73613-8(3)) Tandem Library Bks.

Feinstein, Stephen. The 1900s from Teddy Roosevelt to Flying Machines. 2001. (Decades of the 20th Century Ser.). (Illus.). 64p. (J). (gr. 5-12). lib. bdg. 22.60 (978-0-7660-1612-5(9)) Enslow Pubs., Inc.

—The 1910s from World War I to Ragtime Music. 2001. (Decades of the 20th Century Ser.). (Illus.). 64p. (J). (gr. 5-12). lib. bdg. 22.60 (978-0-7660-1611-8(0)) Enslow Pubs., Inc.

—The 1920s from Prohibition to Charles Lindbergh. (Decades of the 20th Century Ser.). (Illus.). 64p. (J). 2001. (gr. 5-12). lib. bdg. 22.60 (978-0-7660-1610-1(2)); 2006. lib. bdg. 27.93 (978-0-7660-2632-2(9)) Enslow Pubs., Inc.

—The 1990s from the Persian Gulf War to Y2K. 2001. (Decades of the 20th Century Ser.). (Illus.). 64p. (J). (gr. 5-12). lib. bdg. 22.60 (978-0-7660-1613-2(7)) Enslow Pubs., Inc.

Fitzgerald, Stephanie. The New Deal: FDR's Plan for Recovery. 2006. (J). (978-0-7565-2096-0(7)) Compass Point Bks.

Gale Research Staff. Great Depression & New Deal: Primary Sources, 3 vols., Vol. III. 2002. (U-X-L Great Depression & New Deal Reference Library). (Illus.). 225p. (J). lib. bdg. 67.00 (978-0-7876-6535-7(5) , GML00502-182437, UXL) Thomson Gale.

Gedney, Mona K. The Story of the Great Depression. 2005. (Monumental Milestones Ser.). (Illus.). 48p. (YA). (ps-7). lib. bdg. (978-1-58415-403-7(9)) Mitchell Lane Pubs., Inc.

Hensley, Laura. The Story Behind F. Scott Fitzgerald's the Great Gatsby. 2006. (History in Literature Ser.). (Illus.). 56p. (J). lib. bdg. (978-1-4034-8205-1(5)) Heinemann Library.

Howes, Kelly King. Roaring 20s Reference Library Biography. 2005. (Illus.). xlvi, 249p. (J). 67.00 (978-1-4144-0211-6(2) , UXL) Thomson Gale.

Howes, Kelly King & Carnagie, Julie. The Roaring Twenties Almanac & Primary Sources. 2005. (Illus.). liv, 286p. (J). 67.00 (978-1-4144-0212-3(0) , UXL) Thomson Gale.

King, David C. The Great Depression. Deitch, JoAnne Weisman, ed. 2000. (Researching American History Ser.). (Illus.). 56p. (J). 7.95 (978-1-57960-067-9(0)) History Compass, LLC.

Kupperberg, Paul. Critical Perspectives on the Great Depression. 2005. (Critical Anthologies of Nonfiction Writing Ser.). 176p. (gr. 7-12). lib. bdg. 30.60 (978-1-4042-0061-6(4)) Rosen Publishing Group, Inc., The.

Lieurance, Suzanne. The Prohibition Era in American History. 2003. (In American History Ser.). (Illus.). 112p. (J). (gr. 5-12). lib. bdg. 26.60 (978-0-7660-1840-2(7)) Enslow Pubs., Inc.

Lindop, Edmund. America in the 1920s. 2004. (20th-Century America Ser.). (Illus.). 112p. (YA). (gr. 7 up). lib. bdg. (978-0-7613-2831-5(9) , Twenty-First Century Bks.) Lerner Publishing Group.

McDougal, Littell Staff & Nextext Staff, contrib. by. World War, Boom & Bust. 2004. (Stories in History Ser.). (Illus.). 224p. (J). (gr. 6-12). (978-0-618-22202-5(2) , 2-00308) McDougal Littell Inc.

McNeill, Allison & Hanes, Sharon M. Great Depression & New Deal. 2002. 48p. (J). 5.00 (978-0-7876-6536-4(3) , UXL) Thomson Gale.

Orr, Tamra. Prohibition. 2003. (People at the Center of Ser.). (Illus.). 48p. (J). 24.95 (978-1-56711-768-4(6) , Blackbirch Pr., Inc.) Thomson Gale.

Ruggiero, Adriane. The Great Depression. 2004. (American Voices From Ser.). (Illus.). xxi, 116p. (J). 34.21 (978-0-7614-1696-8(X) , Benchmark Bks.) Cavendish, Marshall Corp.

Ruth, Amy. Growing up in the Great Depression, 1929 to 1941. 2003. (Our America Ser.). (Illus.). 64p. (J). (gr. 4-7). lib. bdg. 26.60 (978-0-8225-0655-3(6)) Lerner Publishing Group.

Schultz, Stanley. The Great Depression: A Primary Source History. 2005. lib. bdg. 26.00 (978-0-8368-5978-2(2)) Stevens, Gareth Inc.

Stein, R. Conrad. The New Deal: Pulling America Out of the Great Depression. 2006. (American Saga Ser.). (Illus.). 128p. (J). (gr. 6-9). lib. bdg. 31.93 (978-0-7660-2570-7(5)) Enslow Pubs., Inc.

Turck, Mary. The Dirty Thirties: The United States from 1929-1941. 2002. (Cover-To-Cover Books). (Illus.). 72p. (J). pap. (978-0-7891-5673-0(3)); (gr. 4-7). lib. bdg. 17.95 (978-0-7569-0637-5(7)) Perfection Learning Corp.

Uschan, Michael V. The 1910's. 1998. (Cultural History of the United States Through the Decades Ser.). (Illus.). 128p. (YA). (gr. 4-12). 29.95 (978-1-56006-551-7(6) , LML00902-177908, Lucent Bks.) Thomson Gale.

Wroble, Lisa A. Kids During the Great Depression. 1999. (Kids Throughout History Ser.). (Illus.). 24p. (J). (gr. 3). lib. bdg. 18.75 (978-0-8239-5255-7(X) , PowerKids Pr.) Rosen Publishing Group, Inc., The.

UNITED STATES—HISTORY—1933-1945

America in Conflict, 1941-1985. 2004. (Stories in History Ser.). (Illus.). 208p. (gr. 6-12). 9.99 (978-0-618-22197-4(2) , 2-00296) McDougal Littell Inc.

Barr, Gary. World War II Home Front. 2004. (Illus.). 56p. (J). pap. 8.95 (978-1-4034-4579-7(6)); lib. bdg. (978-1-4034-4571-1(0)) Heinemann Library.

Burg, David F. The Great Depression. 2nd rev. ed. 2005. (Eyewitness History Ser.). (Illus.). 464p. (J). (gr. 9). 75.00 (978-0-8160-5709-2(5)) Facts On File, Inc.

Callan, Jim. America in the 1930s. 2005. (Decades of American History Ser.). (Illus.). 128p. (J). (gr. 4-9). 35.00 (978-0-8160-5638-5(2)) Facts On File, Inc.

Campbell, Geoffrey A. The End of the Cold War: 1980 to the Present: The Cold War in the United States. 2002. (American War Library). 112p. (J). 29.95 (978-1-59018-213-0(8) , Lucent Bks.) Thomson Gale.

Ciment, James, ed. Encyclopedia of the Great Depression & the New Deal, 2 vols., Set. 2001. (Illus.). 942p. 199.00 (978-0-7656-8033-4(5) , Sharpe Reference) Sharpe, M.E. Inc.

Clements, Peter. Prosperity, Depression & the New Deal. 2nd ed. 2001. (Illus.). vi, 168p. pap. 13.99 (978-0-340-80429-2(7)) Hodder Education GBR. *Dist:* Trafalgar Square Publishing.

Cooper, Michael L. Dust to Eat: Drought & Depression in the 1930s. 2004. (Illus.). 96p. (J). (gr. 7-9). tchr. ed. 17.00 (978-0-618-15449-4(3) , Clarion Bks.) Houghton Mifflin Co. Trade & Reference Div.

Egendorf, Laura K. Prosperity, Depression, & War, 1920-1945. 2002. (gr. 7-12). lib. bdg. 39.05 (978-0-613-73613-8(3)) Tandem Library Bks.

Fitzgerald, Stephanie. The New Deal: FDR's Plan for Recovery. 2006. (J). (978-0-7565-2096-0(7)) Compass Point Bks.

Gale Research Staff. Great Depression & New Deal: Primary Sources, 3 vols., Vol. III. 2002. (U-X-L Great Depression & New Deal Reference Library). (Illus.). 225p. (J). lib. bdg. 67.00 (978-0-7876-6535-7(5) , GML00502-182437, UXL) Thomson Gale.

Gitlin, Marty. The Great Depression & World War II. 2007. (J). ***(978-1-59036-749-0(9)); (*978-1-59036-750-6(2))*** Weigl Pubs., Inc.

Halpern, Monica. The Home Front During World War II. 2004. (Reading Expeditions Ser.). (Illus.). 40p. (978-0-7922-4558-2(X)) National Geographic Society.

Harris, Nathaniel. The Great Depression. 2003. (Illus.). 56p. (J). lib. bdg. (978-1-4034-4568-1(0)) Heinemann Library.

Kallen, Stuart A. The 1950's. 1998. (Cultural History of the United States Through the Decades Ser.). (Illus.). 128p. (YA). (gr. 4-12). 29.95 (978-1-56006-555-5(9) , LML00902-177912, Lucent Bks.) Thomson Gale.

King, David C. The Great Depression. Deitch, JoAnne Weisman, ed. 2000. (Researching American History Ser.). (Illus.). 56p. (J). 7.95 (978-1-57960-067-9(0)) History Compass, LLC.

Klam, Julie. The War at Home. 2002. (Illus.). 48p. (J). lib. bdg. 28.50 (978-1-58340-190-3(3)) Smart Apple Media.

Kupperberg, Paul. Critical Perspectives on the Great Depression. 2005. (Critical Anthologies of Nonfiction Writing Ser.). 176p. (gr. 7-12). lib. bdg. 30.60 (978-1-4042-0061-6(4)) Rosen Publishing Group, Inc., The.

Landau, Elaine. The Great Depression. 2007. (Cornerstones of Freedomtrade;, Second Ser.). 48p. (J). pap. 5.95 ***(*978-0-531-18767-8(5)*** , Children's Pr.) Scholastic Library Publishing.

Lindop, Edmund. America in the 1940s. 2004. (20th-Century America Ser.). (J). lib. bdg. 27.90 (978-0-7613-2945-9(5) , Twenty-First Century Bks.) Lerner Publishing Group.

McNeill, Allison & Hanes, Richard Clay. American Home Front in World War II Reference Library Cumulative Index. 2004. (American Home Front in World War II Reference Library). 32p. 5.00 (978-0-7876-9125-7(9) , UXL) Thomson Gale.

McNeill, Allison & Hanes, Sharon M. Great Depression & New Deal. 2002. 48p. (J). 5.00 (978-0-7876-6536-4(3) , UXL) Thomson Gale.

Ruggiero, Adriane. The Great Depression. 2004. (American Voices From Ser.). (Illus.). xxi, 116p. (J). 34.21 (978-0-7614-1696-8(X) , Benchmark Bks.) Cavendish, Marshall Corp.

Ruth, Amy. Growing up in the Great Depression, 1929 to 1941. 2003. (Our America Ser.). (Illus.). 64p. (J). (gr. 4-7). lib. bdg. 26.60 (978-0-8225-0655-3(6)) Lerner Publishing Group.

Schultz, Stanley. The Great Depression: A Primary Source History. 2005. lib. bdg. 26.00 (978-0-8368-5978-2(2)) Stevens, Gareth Inc.

Stein, R. Conrad. The New Deal: Pulling America Out of the Great Depression. 2006. (American Saga Ser.). (Illus.). 128p. (J). (gr. 6-9). lib. bdg. 31.93 (978-0-7660-2570-7(5)) Enslow Pubs., Inc.

Turck, Mary. The Dirty Thirties: The United States from 1929-1941. 2002. (Cover-To-Cover Books). (Illus.). 72p. (J). pap. (978-0-7891-5673-0(3)); (gr. 4-7). lib. bdg. 17.95 (978-0-7569-0637-5(7)) Perfection Learning Corp.

Wills, Charles. America in the 1940s. 2005. (Decades of American History Ser.). (Illus.). 128p. (J). (gr. 4-9). 35.00 (978-0-8160-5639-2(0)) Facts On File, Inc.

Wroble, Lisa A. Kids During the Great Depression. 1999. (Kids Throughout History Ser.). (Illus.). 24p. (J). (gr. 3). lib. bdg. 18.75 (978-0-8239-5255-7(X) , PowerKids Pr.) Rosen Publishing Group, Inc., The.

Yancey, Diane. Life During the Dust Bowl. 2004. (Way People Live Ser.). (J). 29.95 (978-1-59018-265-9(0) , Lucent Bks.) Thomson Gale.

UNITED STATES—HISTORY—WORLD WAR, 1939-1945

see World War, 1939-1945—United States

UNITED STATES—HISTORY—1945-1953

Collier, Christopher & Collier, James Lincoln. The United States in the Cold War. 2001. (Drama of American History Ser.). (Illus.). 96p. (J). (gr. 5-9). lib. bdg. 31.36 (978-0-7614-1317-2(0) , Benchmark Bks.) Cavendish, Marshall Corp.

Fitzgerald, Brian. The Korean War: America's Forgotten War. 2006. (Snapshots in History Ser.). (Illus.). 96p. (J). (gr. 5-7). 30.60 (978-0-7565-1625-3(0)) Compass Point Bks.

Gitlin, Marty. Postwar United States. 2007. (J). ***(*978-1-59036-751-3(0)); (*978-1-59036-752-0(9))*** Weigl Pubs., Inc.

Lindop, Edmund. America in the 1940s. 2004. (20th-Century America Ser.). (J). lib. bdg. 27.90 (978-0-7613-2945-9(5) , Twenty-First Century Bks.) Lerner Publishing Group.

—America in the 1950s. 2002. (Women at War Ser.). (Illus.). 128p. (gr. 7 up). lib. bdg. 25.90 (978-0-7613-2551-2(4) , Twenty-First Century Bks.) Lerner Publishing Group.

Stanley, George Edward. America & the Cold War (1949-1969) 2005. (Illus.). 48p. (J). pap. (978-0-8368-5839-6(5)); lib. bdg. 30.00 (978-0-8368-5830-3(1)) Stevens, Gareth Inc. (World Almanac Library).

Wills, Charles. America in the 1940s. 2005. (Decades of American History Ser.). (Illus.). 128p. (J). (gr. 4-9). 35.00 (978-0-8160-5639-2(0)) Facts On File, Inc.

Wills, Charles A. America in The 1950s. 2005. (Decades of American History Ser.). (Illus.). 128p. (J). (gr. 4-9). per. 35.00 (978-0-8160-5640-8(4)) Facts On File, Inc.

UNITED STATES—HISTORY—1961-

Anderson, Dale. America into a New Millennium. Kossmann, Walter, ed. 2001. (Making of America Ser.). (Illus.). 96p. (J). (gr. 5-10). lib. bdg. 28.54 (978-0-8172-5712-5(8)) Raintree.

Callan, Jim. America in The 1960s. 2005. (Decades of American History Ser.). (Illus.). 128p. (J). (gr. 4-9). 35.00 (978-0-8160-5642-2(0)) Facts On File, Inc.

Feinstein, Stephen. The 1960s from the Vietnam War to Flower Power. 2000. (Decades of the 20th Century Ser.). (Illus.). 64p. (YA). (gr. 5-12). lib. bdg. 22.60 (978-0-7660-1426-8(6)) Enslow Pubs., Inc.

—The 1970s from Watergate to Disco. 2000. (Decades of the 20th Century Ser.). (Illus.). 64p. (YA). (gr. 5-12). lib. bdg. 22.60 (978-0-7660-1425-1(8)) Enslow Pubs., Inc.

—The 1980s from Ronald Reagan to MTV. 2000. (Decades of the Twentieth Century Ser.). (Illus.). 64p. (YA). (gr. 5-12). lib. bdg. 22.60 (978-0-7660-1424-4(X)) Enslow Pubs., Inc.

Greenhaven Staff. 1960s. 2002. (gr. 7-12). lib. bdg. 33.25 (978-0-613-73846-0(2)) Tandem Library Bks.

Kallen, Stuart A. Life in America During the 1960s. 2001. (Way People Live Ser.). (Illus.). 112p. (J). (gr. 7-10). 28.70 (978-1-56006-790-0(X) , LML00902-178128, Lucent Bks.) Thomson Gale.

—The 1990's. 1998. (Cultural History of the United States Through the Decades Ser.). (Illus.). 128p. (YA). (gr. 4-12). 29.95 (978-1-56006-559-3(1) , LML00902-177916, Lucent Bks.) Thomson Gale.

Levy, Debbie. The Vietnam War. 2004. (Chronicle of America's Wars Ser.). (Illus.). 96p. (J). (gr. 5-12). 27.93 (978-0-8225-0421-4(9)) Lerner Publishing Group.

Pendergast, Tom & Pendergast, Sara. Primary Sources, Sixties in America. 2004. (U-X-L the Sixties in America Reference Library). (Illus.). xxxviii, 240p. (J). lib. bdg. 67.00 (978-0-7876-9248-3(4) , UXL) Thomson Gale.

Ruffin, Frances E. Martin Luther King & the March on Washington. 2001. (gr. k-3). lib. bdg. 11.80 (978-0-613-31457-2(3)) Tandem Library Bks.

Schomp, Virginia. The Vietnam ERA. 2003. (American Voices From Ser.). (Illus.). xxiii, 134p. (J). 34.21 (978-0-7614-1693-7(5) , Benchmark Bks.) Cavendish, Marshall Corp.

Schwartz, Richard Alan. The 1990s. 2006. (Eyewitness History Ser.). (Illus.). 496p. (J). (gr. 9). 75.00 (978-0-8160-5696-5(X)) Facts On File, Inc.

United We Stand, Set. 2002. (J). (ps-3). lib. bdg. 119.58 (978-1-57765-876-4(0)) ABDO Publishing Co.

United We Stand. 2001. (Illus.). 16p. 6.95 (978-0-9727833-5-4(0)) Really Big Coloring Bks., Inc.

UNITED STATES—INDUSTRIES

Bagley, Katie. The Early American Industrial Revolution, 1793-1850. 2003. (Let Freedom Ring Ser.). (Illus.). 48p. (J). (gr. 3-4). lib. bdg. 22.60 (978-0-7368-1557-4(0) , Bridgestone Bks.) Capstone Pr., Inc.

Bodden, Valerie. The Story of Coca-Cola. 2008. (J). ***(*978-1-58341-602-0(1)*** , Creative Education) Creative Co., The.

Fandel, Jennifer. George Eastman & the Kodak Camera. 2007. 32p. (J). ***(*978-0-7368-6848-8(8))*** Capstone Pr., Inc.

Frisch, Aaron. The Story of Nike. 2008. (Built for Success Ser.). (J). ***(*978-1-58341-608-2(0)*** , Creative Education) Creative Co., The.

Gilbert, Sara. The Story of Google. 2008. (J). ***(*978-1-58341-605-1(6)*** , Creative Education) Creative Co., The.

—The Story of Starbucks. 2008. (J). ***(*978-1-58341-609-9(9)*** , Creative Education) Creative Co., The.

Greene, Jacqueline Dembar. The Triangle Shirtwaist Factory Fire. 2007. (Code Red Ser.). (Illus.). 32p. (J). (gr. 3-7). lib. bdg. 25.27 (978-1-59716-359-0(7)) Bearport Publishing Co., Inc.

Hall, Margaret. William Wrigley, Jr. & the Beginning of Wrigley's Chewing Gum. 2005. (Illus.). 32p. (J). pap. (978-1-4034-6361-6(1)) Heinemann Library.

Hall, Margaret & Hall, M. C. William Wrigley JR: The Founder of Wrigley's Gum. 2005. (Illus.). 32p. (J). (gr. k-2). lib. bdg. 24.21 (978-1-4034-6347-0(6)) Heinemann Library.

Hillstrom, Kevin & Hillstrom, Laurie Collier. Automobiles, Mining & Petroleum, Textiles, 3 vols.; set. 2006. (Industrial Revolution in America Ser.). (Illus.). 900p. lib. bdg. 185.00 (978-1-85109-749-4(X)) ABC-CLIO, Inc.

—Communications, Agriculture & Meatpacking: Overview/Comparison, 9 vols. 2007. (Industrial Revolution in America Ser.). (Illus.). lib. bdg. 185.00 (978-1-85109-719-7(8)) ABC-CLIO, Inc.

Kovatch, Sarah, text. Giving up Grapes. 2005. (Illus.). 16p. (J). pap. (978-0-7367-2924-6(0)) Zaner-Bloser, Inc.

Meyer, Jared. Working in a War Zone: Military Contractors. 2006. (Extreme Careers Ser.). (Illus.). 64p. (J). (gr. 5-8). lib. bdg. 26.50 (978-1-4042-0959-6(X)) Rosen Publishing Group, Inc., The.

Musolf, Nell. The Story of Ford. 2008. (J). ***(*978-1-58341-604-4(8)*** , Creative Education) Creative Co., The.

—The Story of Microsoft. 2008. (J). ***(*978-1-58341-607-5(2)*** , Creative Education) Creative Co., The.

Primary Sources of America's Industrial Society in the 19th Century. (Primary Source Big Bookstm Ser.). 24p. (J). (gr. 4-8). 46.60 (978-0-8239-4598-6(7)) Rosen Publishing Group, Inc., The.

Sakolsky, Josh. Critical Perspectives on the Industrial Revolution. 2005. (Critical Anthologies of Nonfiction Writing Ser.). (Illus.). 176p. (gr. 7-12). lib. bdg. 30.60 (978-1-4042-0062-3(2)) Rosen Publishing Group, Inc., The.

Waxman, Laura Hamilton. W. K. Kellogg. 2007. (History Maker Biographies Ser.). (J). 26.60 (978-0-8225-6578-9(1) , Lerner Pubns.) Lerner Publishing Group.

We the People: Industrial America, 11 vols. 2006. 48p. (YA). (gr. 4-6). 263.23 (978-0-7565-1702-1(8)) Compass Point Bks.

UNITED STATES—INSULAR POSSESSIONS

see United States—Territories and Possessions

UNITED STATES—LABOR AND LABORING CLASSES

see Labor and Laboring Classes—United States

UNITED STATES—LAW

see Law—United States

UNITED STATES—LEGENDS

see Legends—United States

UNITED STATES—LIBRARY OF CONGRESS

Sandler, Martin W. Library of Congress Activity Brochure. 2000. (J). pap. (978-0-06-449263-8(X) , Harper Trophy) HarperCollins Pubs.

Santella, Andrew. The Library of Congress. 2006. (Illus.). 48p. (J). (gr. 4-6). 23.93 (978-0-7565-1631-4(5)) Compass Point Bks.

UNITED STATES—MAIL

see Postal Service

UNITED STATES—MANNERS AND CUSTOMS

see United States—Social Life and Customs

UNITED STATES—MANUFACTURES

see United States—Industries

UNITED STATES—MAPS

Blattner, Don. U. S. History Maps. 1999. (Illus.). 96p. (YA). (gr. 5). pap. 10.95 (978-1-58037-109-4(4)) Twain, Mark Media, Inc. Pubs.

Buckley, Susan & Leacock, Elspeth. Journeys for Freedom: A New Look at America's Story. Prato, Rodica, illus. 2006. 48p. (J). (gr. 4-6). 17.00 (978-0-618-22323-7(1)) Houghton Mifflin Co.

Chadow, Alysa. US States. 2003. pap. 14.00 (978-0-8059-6054-9(6)) Dorrance Publishing Co., Inc.

Ciovacco, Justine, et al. State-by-State Atlas. 128p. (J). 2006. pap. 9.99 (978-0-7566-1828-5(2)); 2003. (Illus.). pap. 19.99 (978-0-7894-9257-9(1)) Dorling Kindersley Publishing, Inc.

Creative Media Applications. The 50 States Book & Magnetic Puzzle Map. Allen, Jessica, illus. 2007. 48p. (J). 14.99 ***(*978-0-7944-1288-3(2))*** Reader's Digest Assn., Inc., The.

Equipo Staff. Atlas Enciclopedico Paises de America. (SPA., Illus.). 224p. (YA). (gr. 5-8). (978-84-241-2522-6(3) , EV5866) Everest de Ediciones y Distribucion, S.L. ESP. *Dist:* Lectorum Pubns., Inc.

Finch, Spencer. Instant Map Skills: United States. 2004. (Instant Map Skills Ser.). 32p. pap. 9.99 (978-0-439-54047-6(X) , Teaching Resources) Scholastic, Inc.

—Maps for the Overhead: United States Geography. 2004. 32p. pap. 14.99 (978-0-439-55310-0(5) , Teaching Resources) Scholastic, Inc.

Fonda, Suzanne Patrick, ed. National Geographic United States Atlas for Young Explorers. rev. ed. 2004. (Illus.). 176p. (J). (gr. 3-7). 24.95 (978-0-7922-6840-6(7) , National Geographic Children's Bks.) National Geographic Society.

Gifford, Clive, et al. The Kingfisher Student Atlas of North America. Kingfisher Editors, ed. 2005. (Illus.). 192p. (J). (gr. 4-6). 24.95 (978-0-7534-5924-9(8) , Kingfisher) Houghton Mifflin Co. Trade & Reference Div.

Going Places Reader: 96 Lessons Focus on USA Destinations. 2005. 203p. (gr. 7-12). spiral bd. 49.00 incl. audio compact disk (978-1-57861-547-6(X) , IEP RESOURCES) Attainment Co., Inc.

Hammond World Atlas Corporation Staff. U. S. Flip View Map LL. 2003. pap. 3.95 (978-0-8437-1862-1(5)) Langenscheidt Pubs Inc.

—US Flip View Map. 2003. 12p. pap. 47.40 (978-0-8437-1869-0(2)) Langenscheidt Pubs Inc.

In the United States. (J). (gr. 4). 3.80 (978-0-8374-1453-9(9) , 404) Weekly Reader Corp.

The Little Man in the Map: With Clues to Remember All 50 States. 2007. (J). 19.95 ***(*978-0-9785100-4-6(6))*** Schoolside Pr.

Map - United States. 2004. (Wall Charts Ser.). (J). 4.99 (978-1-85997-987-7(4)) Byeway Bks.

Maps of the USA. 2004. (J). per. 14.99 (978-1-55799-955-9(4) , EMC 3721) Evan-Moor Educational Pubs.

McGowan, Kristy. Rand Mcnally Kids' Road Atlas. 2003. (gr. 3-6). lib. bdg. 11.80 (978-0-613-90398-1(6)) Tandem Library Bks.

Miller, Millie & Nelson, Cyndi. State-by-State Guide. 2006. (United States of America Ser.). 64p. (J). pap. 7.99 (978-0-439-82765-2(5) , Scholastic Reference) Scholastic, Inc.

Morrison, Taylor. The Coast Mappers. 2004. (Illus.). 48p. (J). (gr. 3-5). tchr. ed. 16.00 (978-0-618-25408-8(0) , Walter Lorraine) Houghton Mifflin Co. Trade & Reference Div.

National Geographic Society Staff. National Geographic United States Atlas for Young Explorers. rev. ed. 2004. (Illus.). 176p. (J). (gr. 3-7). 45.90 (978-0-7922-6981-6(0) , National Geographic Children's Bks.) National Geographic Society.

Rand McNally Staff. Atlas Schoolhouse Illustrated United States Atlas. 2005. 112p. (J). 9.95 (978-0-528-93459-9(7)) Rand McNally.

—Kids' Road Atlas. (Backseat Bks.). 80p. (J). pap. 3.95 (978-0-528-96544-9(1)) Rand McNally.

Scholastic, Inc. Staff. Scholastic Pocket U. S. Atlas. 2007. 176p. (J). pap. 8.99 ***(*978-0-439-85215-9(3)*** , Scholastic Reference) Scholastic, Inc.

Scholastic, Inc. Staff. U. S. Outline Maps: Reproducible Outline Maps of the 50 States to Use for Teaching Geography, Map Skills, History & More. 2000. (Ready-to-Go Ser.). (Illus.). 64p. (J). 10.95 (978-0-439-11762-3(3)) Scholastic, Inc.

School Atlas of Texas. 2001. 48p. (J). (gr. 1-12). pap. 9.95 (978-0-87443-129-2(8)) Benson, W. S. & Co., Inc.

School Specialty Publishing. U. S. A Map. 2004. (On-File Ser.). 4p. (J). (gr. 2-4). ring bd. 4.99 (978-0-7424-2927-7(X) , Instructional Fair) Schaffer, Frank Pubns.

Stefoff, Rebecca. North American Historical Atlases, 5 bks., Set. Incl. Colonies. Mavrikis, Peter, ed. lib. bdg. 27.07 (978-0-7614-1057-7(0)); Exploring the New World. lib. bdg. 27.07 (978-0-7614-1056-0(2)); First Frontier. Mavrikis, Peter, ed. lib. bdg. 24.21 (978-0-7614-1059-1(7)); Revolutionary War. Mavrikis, Peter, ed. lib. bdg. 27.07 (978-0-7614-1058-4(9)); War of 1812. Mavrikis, Peter, ed. lib. bdg. 27.07 (978-0-7614-1060-7(0)); 48p. (J). (gr. 4-8). (Illus.). 2000. 121.05 (978-0-7614-1055-3(4) , Benchmark Bks.) Cavendish, Marshall Corp.

TNI Stone and Associates Staff & Peteric Design Partners Staff. Quik View Map of the United States & World. 1998. (Illus.). 2p. pap. 2.95 (978-1-58220-018-7(1) , 21213, PowerTools for Kids) Navigator Systems, Inc.

Treasure Maps of Clarion County. 2004. per. 19.95 (978-0-9743881-1-3(4)) Hufnagel Software.

U. S. A. History Map. 2004. (J). (978-0-9759433-3-5(2)) Maps For Kids Inc.

U. S. A. History Notebook Map. 2004. (J). (978-0-9759433-5-9(9)) Maps For Kids Inc.

U. S. A. History Poster Map. 2004. (J). (978-0-9759433-4-2(0)) Maps For Kids Inc.

Womack, Randy L. U. S. Geography. 1998. (Illus.). 80p. (J). (gr. 4 up). stu. ed. 9.95 (978-1-56500-020-9(X)) Golden Educational Ctr.

UNITED STATES—MARINE CORPS

Abramovitz, Melissa. The U. S. Marine Corps at War. 2001. (On the Front Lines Ser.). (Illus.). 32p. (J). (gr. 3-4). lib. bdg. 21.26 (978-0-7368-0923-8(6) , Capstone High-Interest Bks.) Capstone Pr., Inc.

Anderson, Christopher A. The Marines in World War II. 2001. (G. I. Ser.). (Illus.). 80p. (J). 27.50 (978-0-7910-6671-3(1) , Chelsea Hse.) Facts On File, Inc.

Benson, Michael. The U. S. Marines. 2005. (U. S. Armed Forces Ser.). (Illus.). 64p. (J). (gr. 4-7). lib. bdg. 26.60 (978-0-8225-1648-4(9)) Lerner Publishing Group.

Braulick, Carrie A. U.S. Marine Expeditionary Units. 2006. (Blazers—The U.S. Armed Forces Ser.). (Illus.). 32p. (J). (978-0-7368-4395-9(7)) Capstone Pr., Inc.

Cooper, Jason. U. S. Marine Corps. 2003. (Fighting Forces Ser.). (Illus.). 32p. (J). 28.50 (978-1-58952-715-7(1)) Rourke Publishing, LLC.

Cureton, Charles H. The United States Marine Corps: From 1775 to Modern Day. 1999. (G. I. Ser.). (Illus.). 80p. (YA). (gr. 5 up). 27.50 (978-0-7910-5373-7(3)) , Chelsea Hse.) Facts On File, Inc.

David, Jack. United States Marine Corps. 2008. (Illus.). 24p. (J). lib. bdg. 19.95 (*978-1-60014-164-5(1)) Bellwether Media.

Doeden, Matt. La Infantería de Marina de EE.UU. 2007. (J). (978-0-7368-7744-2(4)) Capstone Pr., Inc.

—The U. S. Marine Corps. 2004. (Edge Books, the U.S. Armed Forces). (Illus.). 32p. (J). lib. bdg. 19.93 (978-0-7368-2739-3(0)) Capstone Pr., Inc.

Hamilton, John. The Marine Corps. 2007. (Defending the Nation Ser.). (Illus.). 32p. (J). (gr. 3-5). lib. bdg. 22.78 (978-1-59679-758-1(4) , Checkerboard Library) ABDO Publishing Co.

Kaelberer, Angie Peterson. U.S. Marine Corps Assault Vehicles. 2007. (Blazers—Military Vehicles Ser.). (Illus.). 32p. (J). 19.93 (978-0-7368-6456-5(3)) Capstone Pr., Inc.

Keeter, Hunter. American Ground Forces in the Vietnam War. 2005. (American Experience in Vietnam Ser.). (Illus.). 48p. (J). pap. (978-0-8368-5781-8(X)); lib. bdg. 30.00 (978-0-8368-5774-0(7)) Stevens, Gareth Inc. (World Almanac Library).

—The US Marine Corps. 2004. (America's Armed Forces Ser.). (J). pap. 11.95 (978-0-8368-5690-3(2)); lib. bdg. 30.00 (978-0-8368-5683-5(X)) Stevens, Gareth Inc. (World Almanac Library).

Lurch, Bruno. United States Marine Corps. 2004. (Heinemann Know It Ser.). (Illus.). 48p. (J). pap. 7.95 (978-1-4034-4557-5(5)); lib. bdg. (978-1-4034-4551-3(6)) Heinemann Library.

Payment, Simone. Frontline Marines: Fighting in the Marine Combat Arms Unit. 2006. (Extreme Careers Ser.). (Illus.). 64p. (J). (gr. 5-8). lib. bdg. 26.50 (978-1-4042-0946-6(8)) Rosen Publishing Group, Inc., The.

Rustad, Martha E. H. U.S. Marine Corps Combat Jets. 2007. (Blazers—Military Vehicles Ser.). (Illus.). 32p. (J). 19.93 (978-0-7368-6457-2(1)) Capstone Pr., Inc.

Santella, Andrew. Navajo Code Talkers. 2004. (We the People Ser.). (Illus.). 48p. (J). (gr. 4 up). lib. bdg. 22.60 (978-0-7565-0611-7(5)) Compass Point Bks.

Stein, R. Conrad. The U. S. Marine Corps & Military Careers. 2006. (U.S. Armed Forces & Military Careers Ser.). (Illus.). 128p. (YA). (gr. 5-8). lib. bdg. 31.93 (978-0-7660-2521-9(7)) Enslow Pubs., Inc.

Sweetman, Bill. Jump Jets: The AV-8B Harriers. 2002. (War Planes Ser.). (Illus.). 32p. (J). (gr. 3-4). lib. bdg. 21.26 (978-0-7368-1068-5(4) , Capstone High-Interest Bks.) Capstone Pr., Inc.

Voeller, Edward A. U. S. Marine Corps Special Forces: Recon Marines. 1999. (Warfare & Weapons Ser.). (Illus.). 48p. (J). (gr. 3-7). pap. 20.00 (978-0-531-12010-1(4) , Watts, Franklin) Scholastic Library Publishing.

UNITED STATES—MARINE CORPS—BIOGRAPHY

Bradley, James & Powers, Ron. Flags of Our Fathers: A Young People's Edition. 2005. (Illus.). 224p. (YA). (gr. 7). mass mkt. 5.99 (978-0-440-22920-9(0) , Laurel Leaf) Random Hse. Children's Bks.

—Flags of Our Fathers: Heroes of Iwo Jima. abr. ed. (Illus.). 224p. (YA). (gr. 7). 2001. lib. bdg. 17.99 (978-0-385-90009-6(0)); 2003. reprint ed. pap. 8.95 (978-0-385-73064-8(0)) Random Hse. Children's Bks. (Delacorte Bks. for Young Readers).

UNITED STATES—MARINE CORPS—VOCATIONAL GUIDANCE

Aaseng, Nathan. The Marine Corps in Action. 2001. (U. S. Military Branches & Careers Ser.). (Illus.). 104p. (J). (gr. 6-12). lib. bdg. 26.60 (978-0-7660-1637-8(4)) Enslow Pubs., Inc.

Green, Michael. The United States Marine Corps. 1998. (Serving Your Country Ser.). (Illus.). 48p. (J). (gr. 3-7). lib. bdg. 19.00 (978-0-516-21312-5(1) , Children's Pr.) Scholastic Library Publishing.

Kennedy, Robert C. Life in the Marines. 2000. (High Interest Bks.). (Illus.). 48p. (YA). (gr. 7-12). pap. 6.95 (978-0-516-23548-6(6) , Children's Pr.) Scholastic Library Publishing.

—Life in the Marines. 2000. (gr. 7-12). lib. bdg. 15.25 (978-0-613-52124-6(2)) Tandem Library Bks.

UNITED STATES MARSHALS

Goodman, Michael E. Wyatt Earp. 2005. (Legends of the West Ser.). (Illus.). 48p. (gr. 5-9). 21.95 (978-1-58341-339-5(1) , Creative Education) Creative Co., The.

Green, Michael. United States Marshals Service. 1999. (Law Enforcement Ser.). (Illus.). 48p. (J). (gr. 3-4). lib. bdg. 21.26 (978-0-7368-0189-8(8) , Capstone High-Interest Bks.) Capstone Pr., Inc.

Urban, William. Wyatt Earp: The OK Corral & the Law of the American West. 2005. (Library of American Lives & Times). (Illus.). 112p. (YA). (gr. 4-8). lib. bdg. 31.95 (978-0-8239-5740-8(3)) Rosen Publishing Group, Inc., The.

UNITED STATES—MERCHANT MARINE

see Merchant Marine—United States

UNITED STATES MILITARY ACADEMY

Epstein, Brad M. Army 101: My First Text-Board-Book. l.t. ed. 2007. (101—My First Text-Board Books). (Illus.). 20p. (J). bds. 10.95 (*978-1-932530-42-1(8) , 101 Bk.) Michaelson Entertainment.

Kimmel, Heidi. West Point. 2004. (Cornerstones of Freedom Ser.). (Illus.). 48p. (J). 26.00 (978-0-516-24230-9(X) , Children's Pr.) Scholastic Library Publishing.

Weintraub, Aileen. Life Inside the Military Academy. 2002. (gr. 7-12). lib. bdg. 15.25 (978-0-613-55863-1(4)) Tandem Library Bks.

UNITED STATES MILITARY ACADEMY—FICTION

Efaw, Amy. Battle Dress. (J). (gr. 7 up). 2003. 400p. pap. 6.99 (978-0-06-053520-9(2)); 2000. (Illus.). 304p. 16.99 (978-0-06-027943-1(5)) HarperCollins Pubs.

—Battle Dress. 2004. (Illus.). 382p. (YA). (gr. 8-12). per. 14.04 (978-0-606-30102-2(X)); 2000. (gr. 7-12). lib. bdg. 15.30 (978-0-613-68406-4(0)) Tandem Library Bks.

Hancock, H. Irving. Dick Prescott's Fourth Year at West Poin. rev. ed. 2006. 208p. 27.95 (978-1-4218-1735-4(7)); pap. 12.95 (978-1-4218-1835-1(3)) 1st World Publishing, Inc. (1st World Library - Literary Society).

—Dick Prescott's Second Year at West Poin. rev. ed. 2006. 208p. 27.95 (978-1-4218-1736-1(5)); pap. 12.95 (978-1-4218-1836-8(1)) 1st World Publishing, Inc. (1st World Library - Literary Society).

—Dick Prescott's Second Year at West Point: Finding the Glory of the Soldier's Life. 2007. 156p. pap. 11.99 (*978-1-4264-6424-9(X)); 174p. pap. 14.99 (*978-1-4264-6498-0(3)) BiblioBazaar.

Hancock, H. Irving. Dick Prescott's Third Year at West Point. rev. ed. 2006. 208p. 27.95 (978-1-4218-1737-8(3)); pap. 12.95 (978-1-4218-1837-5(X)) 1st World Publishing, Inc. (1st World Library - Literary Society).

Hancock, Irving H. Dick Prescott's First Year at West Point. 2006. 62.99 (*978-1-4219-9650-9(2)); pap. 56.99 (*978-1-4219-9662-2(6)) IndyPublish.com.

—Dick Prescott's Fourth Year at West Poin. 2006. 78.99 (*978-1-4219-9846-6(7)); pap. 71.99 (*978-1-4219-9852-7(1)) IndyPublish.com.

—Dick Prescott's Second Year at West Poin. 2006. 78.99 (*978-1-4219-9881-7(5)); pap. 72.99 (*978-1-4219-9883-1(1)) IndyPublish.com.

—Dick Prescott's Third Year at West Point. 2006. 78.99 (*978-1-4219-9897-8(1)); pap. 71.99 (*978-1-4219-9903-6(X)) IndyPublish.com.

UNITED STATES—MILITARY HISTORY

see United States—History, Military

UNITED STATES—MILITARY POLICY

Allport, Alan. American Military Policy. 2003. (Point/Counterpoint Ser.). (Illus.). 112p. (gr. 9-13). 32.95 (978-0-7910-7488-6(9) , Chelsea Hse.) Facts On File, Inc.

Egan, Tracie. Weapons of Mass Destruction & North Korea. 2004. (Library of Weapons of Mass Destruction). (Illus.). 64p. (J). lib. bdg. 26.50 (978-1-4042-0296-2(X)) Rosen Publishing Group, Inc., The.

Gerdes, Louise, ed. Rogue Nations. 2006. (Opposing Viewpoints Ser.). (Illus.). 244p. (YA). (gr. 6 up). pap. 24.95 (978-0-7377-3422-5(1) , Greenhaven Pr., Inc.) Thomson Gale.

Laxer, James. Empire. 2007. (Groundwork Guides). (Illus.). 144p. pap. 9.95 (*978-0-88899-707-4(8)) Groundwood Bks. CAN. *Dist:* Perseus Distribution.

UNITED STATES—MORAL CONDITIONS

Gourley, Catherine. Society's Sisters: Stories of Women Who Fought for Social Justice in America. 2003. (Single Titles Ser.). (Illus.). 96p. (gr. 7 up). lib. bdg. 25.90 (978-0-7613-2865-0(3) , Twenty-First Century Bks.) Lerner Publishing Group.

Hurley, Jennifer A. American Values. 2000. (Opposing Viewpoints Ser.). (Illus.). 224p. (YA). (gr. 10-12). pap. 21.20 (978-0-7377-0343-6(1) , Greenhaven Pr., Inc.) Thomson Gale.

UNITED STATES—NATIONAL AERONAUTICS AND SPACE ADMINISTRATION

Avera, Randy. The Truth about Challenger. 2003. (Illus.). 344p. 34.00 (978-1-932258-00-4(0) , SAN # 254-9522) Randolph Publishing.

Bitetto, Marco A. V., ed. NASA Case Studies. braille ed. 2000. (YA). (978-1-58578-082-2(0)) Institute of Cybernetics Research, Inc.

Britton, Tamara L. NASA. 2005. (Symbols, Landmarks & Monuments Ser.: Set III). (Illus.). 32p. (J). (gr. k-6). lib. bdg. 22.78 (978-1-59197-836-7(X)) ABDO Publishing Co.

Elish, Dan. Nasa. 2006. (Kaleidoscope Space Ser.). (Illus.). 48p. (J). lib. bdg. 28.50 (*978-0-7614-2046-0(0) , Benchmark Bks.) Cavendish, Marshall Corp.

Gibson, Diane. Hydroelectricity. 2001. (Sources of Energy Ser.). (Illus.). 24p. (J). (gr. 2-7). lib. bdg. 21.30 (978-1-887068-77-2(5)) Smart Apple Media.

Hakkila, Jon Eric & Richardson, Adele D. Nasa. 1999. (Above & Beyond Ser.). (Illus.). 32p. (J). (gr. 4 up). lib. bdg. 16.95 (978-1-58340-050-0(8)) Smart Apple Media.

Holden, Henry M. The Supersonic X-15 & High-Tech NASA Aircraft. 2002. (Aircraft Ser.). (Illus.). 48p. (J). (gr. 4-10). lib. bdg. 23.93 (978-0-7660-1717-7(6)) Enslow Pubs., Inc.

Kortenkamp, Steve. Nasa (The Solar System) 2008. (J). (*978-1-4296-0062-0(4)) Capstone Pr., Inc.

Spangenburg, Ray. The History of NASA. 2000. (978-0-606-20706-5(6)) Tandem Library Bks.

—History of NASA. 2000. (gr. 5-8). lib. bdg. 24.55 (978-0-613-54537-2(0)) Tandem Library Bks.

Spangenburg, Ray & Moser, Kit. The History of NASA. 2001. (Out of This World Ser.). (Illus.). 128p. (YA). (gr. 7-9). pap. 14.95 (978-0-531-16511-9(6) , Watts, Franklin) Scholastic Library Publishing.

Vogt, Gregory L. Space Mission Patches. 2001. (Enthusiastic Astronomy Ser.). (Illus.). 80p. (gr. 5-8). lib. bdg. (978-0-7613-1613-8(2) , Millbrook Pr.) Lerner Publishing Group.

UNITED STATES—NATIONAL GUARD

Braulick, Carrie A. The U.S. Army National Guard. 2008. (J). (*978-1-4296-0830-5(7)) Capstone Pr., Inc.

Bryan, Nichol. The National Guard. 2003. (Everyday Heroes (cb) Ser.). (Illus.). 32p. (J). (gr. k-6). lib. bdg. 22.78 (978-1-57765-858-0(2)) ABDO Publishing Co.

Greene, Meg. Careers in the National Guards' Search & Rescue Units. 2005. (Careers in Search & Rescue Operations Ser.). (Illus.). 64p. (YA). (gr. 5-8). lib. bdg. 26.50 (978-0-8239-3836-0(0)) Rosen Publishing Group, Inc., The.

Kerrigan, Michael. The National Guard. 2003. (Rescue & Prevention Ser.). (Illus.). 96p. (J). (gr. 7 up). lib. bdg. (978-1-59084-410-6(6)) Mason Crest Pubs.

UNITED STATES—NATIONAL PARKS AND RESERVES

see National Parks and Reserves—United States

UNITED STATES—NATURAL HISTORY

see Natural History—United States

UNITED STATES—NATURAL MONUMENTS

see Natural Monuments

UNITED STATES—NATURAL RESOURCES

see Natural Resources—United States; United States—Economic Conditions

UNITED STATES NAVAL ACADEMY, ANNAPOLIS

Fine, Jil. Life Inside the Naval Academy. 2002. (Insider's Look Ser.). (Illus.). 48p. (YA). (gr. 7-12). pap. 23.00 (978-0-516-23922-4(8) , Children's Pr.) Scholastic Library Publishing.

UNITED STATES NAVAL ACADEMY, ANNAPOLIS—FICTION

Hancock, H. Irving. Dave Darrin's First Year at Annapolis. rev. ed. 2006. 212p. 27.95 (978-1-4218-1739-2(X)); pap. 12.95 (978-1-4218-1839-9(6)) 1st World Publishing, Inc. (1st World Library - Literary Society).

—Dave Darrin's First Year at Annapolis. 2007. 160p. pap. 11.99 (*978-1-4264-6408-9(8)); 172p. pap. 14.99 (*978-1-4264-6482-9(7)) BiblioBazaar.

—Dave Darrin's Fourth Year at Annapolis. rev. ed. 2006. 216p. 27.95 (978-1-4218-1746-0(2)); pap. 12.95 (978-1-4218-1846-7(9)) 1st World Publishing, Inc. (1st World Library - Literary Society).

—Dave Darrin's Second Year at Annapolis. rev. ed. 2006. 184p. 26.95 (978-1-4218-1734-7(9)); pap. 11.95 (978-1-4218-1834-4(5)) 1st World Publishing, Inc. (1st World Library - Literary Society).

—Dave Darrin's Second Year at Annapolis: Or, Two Midshipmen as Naval Academy Youngsters. l.t. ed. 2006. 132p. pap. 10.99 (*978-1-4264-3913-1(X)) BiblioBazaar.

—Dave Darrin's Second Year at Annapolis: Or, Two Midshipmen As Naval Academy Youngsters. l.t. ed. 2006. 146p. pap. 13.99 (*978-1-4264-3971-1(7)) BiblioBazaar.

—Dave Darrin's Third Year at Annapolis. rev. ed. 2006. 216p. 27.95 (978-1-4218-1747-7(0)); pap. 12.95 (978-1-4218-1847-4(7)) 1st World Publishing, Inc. (1st World Library - Literary Society).

Hancock, H. Irving. Dave Darrin's Third Year at Annapolis: Leaders of the Second Class Midshipmen. l.t. ed. 2006. 160p. pap. 11.99 (*978-1-4264-4039-7(1)); 176p. pap. 14.99 (*978-1-4264-4098-4(7)) BiblioBazaar.

UNITED STATES—NAVAL HISTORY

see United States—History, Naval

UNITED STATES—NAVY

Abramovitz, Melissa. The U. S. Navy at War. 2001. (On the Front Lines Ser.). (Illus.). 32p. (J). (gr. 3-4). lib. bdg. 21.26 (978-0-7368-0924-5(4) , Capstone High-Interest Bks.) Capstone Pr., Inc.

Adelson, Bruce. David Farragut: Union Admiral. 2001. (Famous Figures of the Civil War Era Ser.). (Illus.). 80p. (J). (gr. 5 up). pap. 25.00 (978-0-7910-6417-7(4)); 25.00 (978-0-7910-6416-0(6)) Facts On File, Inc. (Chelsea Hse.).

—David Farragut: Union Admiral. 2002. (gr. 5-8). lib. bdg. 17.60 (978-0-613-52667-8(8)) Tandem Library Bks.

Anderson, Dale. Soldiers & Sailors in the American Revolution. 2005. (World Almanac Library of the American Revolution). (J). pap. (978-0-8368-5938-6(3)); lib. bdg. 30.00 (978-0-8368-5929-4(4)) Stevens, Gareth Inc. (World Almanac Library).

Bartlett, Richard. United States Navy. (Heinemann Know It Ser.). (Illus.). 48p. (J). 2003. pap. 7.95 (978-1-4034-0448-0(8)); 2002. (gr. 3-5). lib. bdg. 25.64 (978-1-4034-0191-5(8)) Heinemann Library.

Braulick, Carrie A. The Blue Angels. 2005. (Blazers—The U.S. Armed Forces Ser.). (Illus.). 32p. (J). 19.93 (978-0-7368-3793-4(0)) Capstone Pr., Inc.

—U.S. Navy Aircraft Carriers. 2006. (Blazers—Military Vehicles Ser.). (Illus.). 32p. (J). (978-0-7368-5470-2(3)) Capstone Pr., Inc.

Burgan, Michael. U. S. Navy Special Forces: SEAL Teams. 1999. (Warfare & Weapons Ser.). (Illus.). 48p. (J). (gr. 3-7). pap. 20.00 (978-0-531-12011-8(2) , Watts, Franklin) Scholastic Library Publishing.

—U. S. Navy Special Forces: Special Boat Units. 1999. (Illus.). 48p. (J). (gr. 3-7). pap. 20.00 (978-0-531-12015-6(5) , Watts, Franklin) Scholastic Library Publishing.

Cooper, Jason. U. S. Navy. 2003. (Illus.). 32p. (J). 28.50 (978-1-58952-716-4(X)) Rourke Publishing, LLC.

David, Jack. United States Navy. 2008. (Illus.). 24p. (J). lib. bdg. 19.95 (*978-1-60014-165-2(X)) Bellwether Media.

Doeden, Matt. The U. S. Navy. 2004. (Edge Books, the U.S. Armed Forces). (Illus.). 32p. (J). lib. bdg. 19.93 (978-0-7368-2737-9(4)) Capstone Pr., Inc.

Donovan, Sandy. U. S. Navy Special Forces. 2005. (U. S. Armed Forces Ser.). (Illus.). 64p. (J). (gr. 4-7). lib. bdg. 26.60 (978-0-8225-1650-7(0)) Lerner Publishing Group.

Foster, Linda. United States Naval Academy: Annapolis. Miller, Roger, photos by. 2006. 168p. 39.95 (978-0-911897-49-4(6)) Image Publishing, Ltd.

Gaines, Ann Graham. The Navy in Action. 2001. (U. S. Military Branches & Careers Ser.). (Illus.). 128p. (YA). (gr. 6-12). lib. bdg. 26.60 (978-0-7660-1633-0(1)) Enslow Pubs., Inc.

Garnett, Sammie & Pallotta, Jerry. U.S. Navy Alphabet Book. Bolster, Rob, illus. 2005. 32p. (J). 17.95 (978-1-57091-586-4(5)) Charlesbridge Publishing, Inc.

Green, Michael. The United States Navy. 1998. (Serving Your Country Ser.). (Illus.). 48p. (J). (gr. 3-7). lib. bdg. 19.00 (978-0-516-21313-2(X) , Children's Pr.) Scholastic Library Publishing.

Hamilton, John. The Navy. 2007. (Defending the Nation Ser.). (Illus.). 32p. (J). (gr. 3-5). lib. bdg. 22.78 (978-1-59679-760-4(6) , Checkerboard Library) ABDO Publishing Co.

Hodges, Tammy. Breakfast with the Blues. l.t. ed. 2006. (Illus.). 32p. (J). (978-1-934035-00-9(9)) Trent's Prints.

Holden, Henry M. Navy Combat Aircraft & Pilots. 2002. (Aircraft Ser.). (Illus.). 48p. (J). (gr. 4-10). lib. bdg. 23.93 (978-0-7660-1716-0(8)) Enslow Pubs., Inc.

Hollenbeck, Cliff. To Be a U. S. Navy Seal. rev. ed. 2003. (To Be A Ser.). (Illus.). 160p. 21.95 (978-0-7603-1404-3(7)) MBI Publishing Co. LLC.

Jordan, David. The US Navy. 2004. (America's Armed Forces Ser.). (J). pap. (978-0-8368-5691-0(0)); lib. bdg. 30.00 (978-0-8368-5684-2(8)) Stevens, Gareth Inc. (World Almanac Library).

Kaelberer, Angie Peterson. The Navy SEALs. 2005. (Blazers—The U.S. Armed Forces Ser.). (Illus.). 32p. (J). 19.93 (978-0-7368-3794-1(9)) Capstone Pr., Inc.

Kennedy, Robert C. Life with the Navy Seals. 2000. (On Duty Ser.). (Illus.). 48p. (YA). (gr. 7-12). 24.00 (978-0-516-23351-2(3)); pap. 6.95 (978-0-516-23551-6(6)) Scholastic Library Publishing. (Children's Pr.).

—Life with the Navy Seals. 2000. (gr. 7-12). lib. bdg. 15.25 (978-0-613-52127-7(7)) Tandem Library Bks.

Kennedy, Robert C. & Payan, Gregory. Life on a Submarine. 2000. (High Interest Bks.). (Illus.). 48p. (YA). (gr. 7-12). pap. 6.95 (978-0-516-23549-3(4) , Children's Pr.) Scholastic Library Publishing.

Kiland, Taylor Baldwin. The U. S. Navy & Military Careers. 2006. (U.S. Armed Forces & Military Careers Ser.). (Illus.). 128p. (YA). (gr. 5-8). lib. bdg. 31.93 (978-0-7660-2523-3(3)) Enslow Pubs., Inc.

McNab, Chris. Protecting the Nation with the U. S. Navy. 2003. (Rescue & Prevention Ser.). (Illus.). 96p. (J). (gr. 7 up). lib. bdg. (978-1-59084-415-1(7)) Mason Crest Pubs.

McNeil, Niki, et al. HOCPP 1106 the United States Navy. 2006. spiral bd. 23.50 (*978-1-60308-106-1(2)) In the Hands of a Child.

Murphy, Patricia J. Grace Hopper: Computer Pioneer. 2004. (Famous Inventors Ser.). (Illus.). 32p. (J). lib. bdg. 22.60 (978-0-7660-2273-7(0)) Enslow Pubs., Inc.

Payan, Gregory & Guelke, Alexander. Life on a Submarine. 2000. (On Duty Ser.). (Illus.). 48p. (YA). (gr. 7-12). 24.00 (978-0-516-23349-9(1) , Children's Pr.) Scholastic Library Publishing.

Payment, Simone. Navy SEALs: Special Operations for the U. S. Navy. 2003. (Inside Special Operations Ser.). (Illus.). 64p. (YA). (gr. 5-8). lib. bdg. 26.50 (978-0-8239-3809-4(3) , Rosen Central) Rosen Publishing Group, Inc., The.

Richie, Jason. Secretaries of War, Navy & Defense: Ensuring National Security. Lerner, Mark, ed. 2002. (In the Cabinet Ser.: Vol. 2). (Illus.). 176p. (gr. 7 up). lib. bdg. 22.95 (978-1-881508-64-9(1)) Oliver Pr., Inc.

Stein, R. Conrad. The United States Naval Academy. 2004. (Cornerstones of Freedom Ser.). (J). 26.00 (978-0-516-24229-3(6) , Children's Pr.) Scholastic Library Publishing.

Streissguth, Thomas. U. S. Navy SEALs. 2000. (Serving Your Country Ser.). (Illus.). 48p. (J). (gr. 3-7). lib. bdg. 19.00 (978-0-516-35282-4(2) , Children's Pr.) Scholastic Library Publishing.

Streissguth, Tom. The U. S. Navy. 2005. (U. S. Armed Forces Ser.). (Illus.). 64p. (J). (gr. 4-7). lib. bdg. 26.60 (978-0-8225-1649-1(7)) Lerner Publishing Group.

Thornton, Jeremy. The Birth of the American Navy. 2003. (Building Americas Democracy Ser.). (Illus.). 24p. (J). lib. bdg. 19.95 (978-0-8239-6274-7(1) , PowerKids Pr.) Rosen Publishing Group, Inc., The.

White Steve. Naval Warship. 2007. (High-Tech Military Weapons Ser.). (Illus.). 48p. (J). (978-0-531-12091-0(0)) Children's Pr., Ltd.

White, Steve. Naval Warship: FSF-1 Sea Fighter. 2007. (High-Tech Military Weapons Ser.). (Illus.). 48p. (J). pap. (978-0-531-18707-4(1)); (*978-1-4287-3127-1(X)) Children's Pr., Ltd.

UNITED STATES—NAVY—BIOGRAPHY

Alphin, Elaine Marie & Alphin, Arthur B. I Have Not Yet Begun to Fight: A Story about John Paul Jones. Casale, Paul, tr. Casale, Paul, illus. 2004. (Creative Minds Biography Ser.). 64p. (J). 22.60 (978-1-57505-601-2(1) , Carolrhoda Bks.) Lerner Publishing Group.

Bradford, James C. John Paul Jones: And the American Navy. 2005. (Library of American Lives & Times). (Illus.). 112p. (J). (gr. 4-8). lib. bdg. 31.95 (978-0-8239-5726-2(8)) Rosen Publishing Group, Inc., The.

Brager, Bruce L. John Paul Jones: America's Sailor. 2006. (Illus.). 160p. (J). lib. bdg. 26.95 (978-1-931798-84-6(2)) Reynolds, Morgan Inc.

Cooper, Michael. Hero of the High Seas: John Paul Jones & the American Revolution. 2006. (Illus.). 128p. (J). (gr. 5). 32.90 (978-0-7922-5548-2(8)); pap. 21.95 (978-0-7922-5547-5(X)) National Geographic Society. (National Geographic Children's Bks.).

Feinberg, Barbara Jane. John McCain: Serving His Country. 2000. (Gateway Biography Ser.). (Illus.). 48p. (J). (gr. 2-4). lib. bdg. 23.90 (978-0-7613-1974-0(3) , Millbrook Pr.) Lerner Publishing Group.

Greenfield, Eloise. How They Got Over: African Americans & the Call of the Sea. Gilchrist, Jan Spivey, illus. 2003. 128p. (J). (gr. 3-5). 16.99 (978-0-06-028991-1(0)) HarperCollins Pubs.

Grenga, Helen E., ed. Movies on the Fantail: A Sailor's Diary & Memories from Other Men of the USS Barr DE576/APD39 (World War II) 2001. (Illus.). xvi, 336p. (J). 27.95 (978-0-9709110-0-1(9)) Yeoman Pr.

Harkins, Susan and William. The Life & Times of John Paul Jones. 2007. (Profiles in American History Ser.). (Illus.). 48p. (J). lib. bdg. 22.95 (***978-1-58415-529-4(9)***) Mitchell Lane Pubs., Inc.

Haugen, Brenda & Santella, Andrew. John Paul Jones: Father of the American Navy. 2004. (Signature Lives Ser.). (Illus.). 112p. (J). 30.60 (978-0-7565-0829-6(0)) Compass Point Bks.

McCain, John. Faith of Our Fathers. 2000. (gr. 7-12). lib. bdg. 23.45 (978-0-613-27819-5(4)) Tandem Library Bks.

McDoniel, Estelle. Registered Nurse to Rear Admiral: A First for Navy Women. 2003. (Illus.). viii, 81p. (J). 16.95 (978-1-57168-766-1(1) , Eakin Pr.) Eakin Pr.

A Navy Medical Corpsman's Journey. 2003. 37p. (YA). lib. bdg. 20.00 net. (978-0-9747035-1-0(6)) Strickland, Wilton.

Osborn. Born to Fly. 2003. (gr. 5-8). lib. bdg. 13.55 (978-0-613-84567-0(6)) Tandem Library Bks.

Osborn, Shane & McConnell, Malcolm. Born to Fly: The Heroic Story of Downed U. S. Navy Pilot Lt. Shane Osborn. 2003. 192p. (gr. 5). 5.99 (978-0-440-23796-9(3) , Yearling) Random Hse. Children's Bks.

—Born to Fly: The Heroic Story of Downed U. S. Navy Pilot Lt. Shane Osborn. l.t. ed. 2002. 403p. 29.45 (978-0-7862-4101-9(2)) Thomson Gale.

Pollard, Josephine. Our Naval Heroes: Told in One Syllable Words, Vol. 4. 1998. (Illus.). 256p. (J). reprint ed. 15.00 (978-1-889128-45-0(7)) Mantle Ministries.

Price Hossell, Karen. John Paul Jones. 2004. (American War Biographies Ser.). (J). pap. 8.50 (978-1-4034-5086-9(2)); lib. bdg. 29.93 (978-1-4034-5079-1(X)) Heinemann Library.

Roop, Peter & Roop, Connie. Take Command, Captain Farragut! McCurdy, Michael, illus. 2002. 48p. (J). (gr. 3-5). 16.00 (978-0-689-83022-8(X) , Atheneum) Simon & Schuster Children's Publishing.

Sigler, George. Experiment in Survival. 2001. (Experiment in Survival). 200p. (C). per. (978-0-9711100-0-7(X)) Vero Technical Support, Inc.

Sonneborn, Liz. John Paul Jones: American Naval Hero. 2005. (Leaders of the American Revolution Ser.). (Illus.). 123p. (J). (ps-8). lib. bdg. 30.00 (978-0-7910-8621-6(6) , Chelsea Hse.) Facts On File, Inc.

Sperry, Armstrong. John Paul Jones: The Pirate Patriot. 2006. (Sterling Point Bks.). (Illus.). 176p. (J). 12.95 (978-1-4027-3185-3(X)); pap. 6.95 (978-1-4027-3615-5(0)) Sterling Publishing Co., Inc.

Van, Reinetta. Tiger Cruise: A Hampton Roads Adventure. Houlgrave, Michelle, illus. 2002. 200p. (YA). (gr. 9-12). pap. 9.95 (978-1-930211-30-8(9)) Maximilian Pr. Pubs.

UNITED STATES—NAVY—HISTORY

Abbot, Willis J. Blue Jackets of 1876: A History of the Naval Battles of the American Revolution Together with a Narrative of the War with Tripoli. 2006. (Illus.). pap. 30.95 (***978-1-4286-1609-7(8)***) Kessinger Publishing, LLC.

Baldwin, Carol & Baldwin, Ron. Navy Fighting Vessels. 2004. (Heinemann Know It Ser.). (Illus.). 48p. (J). pap. 7.95 (978-1-4034-4558-2(3)) Heinemann Library.

—U. S. Navy Fighting Vessels. 2004. (Heinemann Know It Ser.). (Illus.). 48p. (J). lib. bdg. (978-1-4034-4552-0(4)) Heinemann Library.

Giudici, Vittorio. The 20th Century, Vol. 5. 1999. (Bravo Ser.). (Illus.). 120p. (YA). (gr. 6 up). 8.95 (978-0-7641-0944-7(8)) Barron's Educational Series, Inc.

Gomez-Centurion, Carlos. Armada Invencible. (SPA.). 96p. (J). (978-84-207-3813-0(1)) Grupo Anaya, S.A.

Green, Michael & Green, Gladys. U. S. Navy Seals at War. 2003. (On the Front Lines Ser.). (Illus.). 32p. (J). lib. bdg. 22.60 (978-0-7368-2159-9(7) , Capstone High/Low Bks.) Capstone Pr., Inc.

Hemingway, Albert. American Naval Forces in the Vietnam War. 2005. (American Experience in Vietnam Ser.). (Illus.). 48p. (J). 30.00 (978-0-8368-5776-4(3)); pap. (978-0-8368-5783-2(6)) Stevens, Gareth Inc. (World Almanac Library).

McGowen, Tom. Carrier War: Aircraft Carriers of World War II. 2001. (Military Might Ser.: 8). (Illus.). 64p. (J). (gr. 5-8). lib. bdg. 26.90 (978-0-7613-1808-8(9) , Twenty-First Century Bks.) Lerner Publishing Group.

Presnall, Judith Janda. Navy Dolphins. 2001. (Animals with Jobs Ser.). (Illus.). 48p. (J). (gr. 3-5). 23.70 (978-0-7377-0675-8(9) , LML00902-178561, Kidhaven) Thomson Gale.

Sinking of the Maine. 2002. (History in the Headlines Ser.). 32p. (gr. 6-8). 6.99 (978-0-7682-0222-9(1) , GA13022) School Specialty Publishing.

Tibbitts, Alison Davis. John Paul Jones: Father of the American Navy. 2002. (Historical American Biographies Ser.). (Illus.). 128p. (J). (gr. 6-9). lib. bdg. 26.60 (978-0-7660-1448-0(7)) Enslow Pubs., Inc.

U. S. Navy Airships, 1915-1962. 2001. 190p. per. 22.00 (978-0-9639743-8-9(6)) Atlantis Productions.

USS Wisconsin: Hampton Roads Naval Historical Foundation Photo Museum Guide. 2003. per. 12.95 (978-1-930127-05-0(7)) Oxford Museum Pr.

UNITED STATES—OCCUPATIONS

Occupational Outlook Handbook 2004-2005. 2003. (gr. 7-12). lib. bdg. 29.20 (978-0-613-67572-7(X)) Tandem Library Bks.

UNITED STATES—OFFICIALS AND EMPLOYEES

Ferguson. Careers in Focus: Government. 2nd rev. ed. 2007. (Careers in Focus Ser.). 208p. (J). (gr. 6-12). 29.95 (***978-0-8160-6568-4(3)*** , Ferguson Publishing Co.) Facts On File, Inc.

Jacobstein, Bennett. Profiles of the California Governors. 1999. (California Government Ser.). (Illus.). 48p. (J). (gr. 4-10). pap. 14.95 (978-1-884925-98-6(7)) Toucan Valley Pubns., Inc.

UNITED STATES—PAINTERS

see Painters—United States

UNITED STATES—POETRY

Borden, Louise. America Is... Schuett, Stacey, illus. 2002. 40p. (J). (gr. k-3). 17.95 (978-0-689-83900-9(6) , McElderry, Margaret K.) Simon & Schuster Children's Publishing.

Gunning, Monica. America, My New Home. Condon, Ken, illus. 2004. 32p. (J). (gr. 2-4). 16.95 (978-1-59078-057-2(8)) Boyds Mills Pr.

Ha, Ha, It's Halloween! 2005. (Illus.). 30p. (J). (gr. k-5). 12.95 (978-0-8249-5508-3(0)) Ideals Pubns.

Hovey, Kate. Arachne Speaks. Drawson, Blair, illus. 2005. 33p. (gr. 4-8). reprint ed. 18.00 (978-0-7567-8718-9(1)) DIANE Publishing Co.

Lee Bates, Katharine & Gamwell, Calvert. America the Beautiful: A Pop-up Book about the Famous Song by Katharine Lee Bates. Jordan, Carrie, illus. 2006. 16p. (J). (gr. 4-8). reprint ed. 17.00 (978-1-4223-5447-6(4)) DIANE Publishing Co.

Myers, Walter. Tribute. 2008. 32p. (J). lib. bdg. 17.89 (***978-0-06-052309-1(3)***) HarperCollins Pubs.

National Museum of American Art Staff. Celebrate America in Poetry & Art. 1999. (J). 19.54 (978-0-606-16668-3(8)) Tandem Library Bks.

Perdomo, Willie. Visiting Langston. Collier, Bryan, illus. 2005. 32p. (J). reprint ed. pap. 6.95 (978-0-8050-7881-7(9) , Holt, Henry & Co. Bks. For Young Readers) Holt, Henry & Co.

Stockland, Patricia M., tr. The Free & the Brave: A Collection of Poems about the United States. 2004. (Poet's Toolbox Ser.). (Illus.). 32p. (J). (gr. 3 up). 22.60 (978-0-7565-0563-9(1)) Compass Point Bks.

Testa, Maria. Something about America. 2007. (Illus.). 96p. (YA). (gr. 7). pap. 6.99 (***978-0-7636-3415-5(8)***) Candlewick Pr.

Van Wassenhove, Sue. The Seldom-Ever-Shady Glades: Poems & Quilts. 2008. (J). (***978-1-59078-352-8(2)*** , Wordsong) Boyds Mills Pr.

UNITED STATES—POLITICS AND GOVERNMENT

Aaseng, Nathan. The Impeachment of Bill Clinton. 2000. (Famous Trials Ser.). (Illus.). 112p. (YA). (gr. 7-10). lib. bdg. 29.95 (978-1-56006-651-4(2) , LML00902-178005, Lucent Bks.) Thomson Gale.

Adams, Simon. The Presidents of the United States: Completely Revised & Updated to Include the 2004 Election. rev. ed. 2005. (Illus.). 96p. (978-1-58728-527-1(4) , Two Can Publishing) T&N Children's Publishing.

Adler, David A. A Picture Book of Patrick Henry. Wallner, John et al, illus. 2005. 32p. (J). (gr. k-3). pap. 6.95 (978-0-8234-1678-3(X)) Holiday Hse., Inc.

Altman, Linda Jacobs. The Politics of Slavery: Fiery National Debates Fueled by the Slave Economy. 2004. (Slavery in American History Ser.). (Illus.). 128p. (J). lib. bdg. 26.60 (978-0-7660-2150-1(5)) Enslow Pubs., Inc.

American Government Today Collection. 2001. (Illus.). (J). pap. (978-0-7398-4552-3(7)) Steck-Vaughn.

American Political Biographies, Set. 2005. (Political Biographies Ser.). 432-576p. (gr. 9-12). 275.00 (978-0-8160-6317-8(6)) Facts On File, Inc.

Anderson, Dale. The Aftermath of the Civil War. 2004. (World Almanac Library of the Civil War). (Illus.). 48p. (J). (gr. 5 up). pap. 11.95 (978-0-8368-5597-5(3)); lib. bdg. 30.00 (978-0-8368-5588-3(4)) Stevens, Gareth Inc. (World Almanac Library).

—The American Colonies Declare Independence. 2005. (World Almanac Library of the American Revolution). (J). pap. (978-0-8368-5935-5(9)); lib. bdg. 30.00 (978-0-8368-5926-3(X)) Stevens, Gareth Inc. (World Almanac Library).

—The Causes of the Civil War. 2004. (World Almanac Library of the Civil War). (Illus.). 48p. (J). (gr. 5 up). pap. 11.95 (978-0-8368-5590-6(6)); lib. bdg. 30.00 (978-0-8368-5581-4(7)) Stevens, Gareth Inc. (World Almanac Library).

—The Democratic Party: America's Oldest Party. 2007. (Illus.). 96p. (J). pap. (***978-0-7565-3169-0(1));*** (YA). (gr. 5-8). lib. bdg. 31.93 (***978-0-7565-2450-0(4)***) Compass Point Bks.

—Forming a New American Government. 2005. (World Almanac Library of the American Revolution). (J). pap. (978-0-8368-5941-6(3)); lib. bdg. 30.00 (978-0-8368-5932-4(4)) Stevens, Gareth Inc. (World Almanac Library).

—The Home Fronts in the Civil War. 2004. (World Almanac Library of the Civil War). (Illus.). 48p. (J). lib. bdg. 30.00 (978-0-8368-5587-6(6)); (gr. 5 up). pap. 11.95 (978-0-8368-5596-8(5)) Stevens, Gareth Inc. (World Almanac Library).

—Leaders of the American Revolution. 2005. (World Almanac Library of the American Revolution). (J). pap. (978-0-8368-5940-9(5)); lib. bdg. 30.00 (978-0-8368-5931-7(6)) Stevens, Gareth Inc. (World Almanac Library).

—The Republican Party: The Story of the Grand Old Party. 2007. (Snapshots in History Ser.). (Illus.). 96p. (YA). (gr. 5-8). lib. bdg. 31.93 (***978-0-7565-2449-4(0)***) Compass Point Bks.

—Watergate: Scandal in the White House. 2006. (J). (978-0-7565-2010-6(X)) Compass Point Bks.

—World Almanac Library of the Civil War, 8 bks. Incl. Aftermath of the Civil War. (gr. 5 up). lib. bdg. 30.00 (978-0-8368-5588-3(4)); Causes of the Civil War. (gr. 5 up). lib. bdg. 30.00 (978-0-8368-5581-4(7)); Civil War at Sea. (gr. 5 up). lib. bdg. 30.00 (978-0-8368-5585-2(X)); Civil War in the East (1861-July 1863) (gr. 5 up). lib. bdg. 30.00 (978-0-8368-5582-1(5)); Civil War in the West (1861-July 1863) (gr. 5 up). lib. bdg. 30.00 (978-0-8368-5583-8(3)); Home Fronts in the Civil War. lib. bdg. 30.00 (978-0-8368-5587-6(6)); Soldier's Life in the Civil War. (gr. 5 up). lib. bdg. 30.00 (978-0-8368-5586-9(8)); Union Victory (July 1863-1865) (gr. 5 up). lib. bdg. 30.00 (978-0-8368-5584-5(1)); 48p. (J). (Illus.). 2004. Set lib. bdg. 240.00 (978-0-8368-5580-7(9) , World Almanac Library) Stevens, Gareth Inc.

Anderson, Wayne. Fighting Racial Discrimination: Treating All Americans Fairly under the Law. 2004. (Progressive Movement, 1900-1920 Ser.). (Illus.). 32p. (J). lib. bdg. (978-1-4042-0189-7(0)) Rosen Publishing Group, Inc., The.

Ansary, Tamim. Election Day. 2002. (Holiday Histories Ser.). (Illus.). 32p. (J). (gr. k-2). pap. 6.95 (978-1-58810-571-4(7) , 91686) Heinemann Library.

Apel, Melanie Ann. The Federal Reserve ACT: Making the American Banking System Stronger. 2004. (Progressive Movement, 1900-1920 Ser.). (Illus.). 32p. (J). lib. bdg. (978-1-4042-0196-5(3)) Rosen Publishing Group, Inc., The.

Armentrout, David & Armentrout, Patricia. La Constitucion. 2005. (SPA.). (J). (978-1-59515-643-3(7)) Rourke Publishing, LLC.

—The Constitution. (Documents that Shaped the Nation Ser.). 48p. 2005. (Illus.). (gr. 4-6). 20.95 (978-1-59515-231-2(8)); 2004. pap. 7.95 (978-1-59515-330-2(6)) Rourke Publishing, LLC.

—La Declaracion de Independencia. 2005. (SPA & ENG., Illus.). 24p. (J). (978-1-59515-641-9(0)) Rourke Publishing, LLC.

—The Declaration of Independence. (Documents that Shaped the Nation Ser.). 48p. 2005. (Illus.). (gr. 4-6). 20.95 (978-1-59515-230-5(X)); 2004. pap. 7.95 (978-1-59515-331-9(4)) Rourke Publishing, LLC.

—The Emancipation Proclamation. (Documents that Shaped the Nation Ser.). 48p. 2005. (Illus.). (gr. 4-6). 20.95 (978-1-59515-233-6(4)); 2004. pap. 7.95 (978-1-59515-332-6(2)) Rourke Publishing, LLC.

—La Proclama de Emancipacion. 2005. (SPA.). (J). (978-1-59515-645-7(3)) Rourke Publishing, LLC.

Aronson, Billy. Richard M. Nixon. 2007. (Presidents & Their Times Ser.). 96p. (J). lib. bdg. 32.79 (978-0-7614-2428-4(8) , Benchmark Bks.) Cavendish, Marshall Corp.

Aronson, Marc. The Real Revolution: The Global Story of American Independence. 2005. (Illus.). 256p. (J). (gr. 7-12). 21.00 (978-0-618-18179-7(2) , Clarion Bks.) Houghton Mifflin Co. Trade & Reference Div.

Ball, Lea. The Federalist—Anti-Federalist Debate over States' Rights: A Primary Source Investigation. 2004. (Great Historic Debates & Speeches Ser.). (Illus.). 64p. (J). lib. bdg. 29.25 (978-1-4042-0149-1(1)) Rosen Publishing Group, Inc., The.

Barry, Michael. Civics in America. 2004. (Coursebooks Ser.). (Illus.). xiv, 386p. (gr. 6-12). (978-0-618-22198-1(0) , 2-00297) McDougal Littell Inc.

Bauder, Julia. Is the Political Divide Harming America? 2006. (Illus.). 128p. (gr. 10-12). 21.20 (978-0-7377-3522-2(8)); 29.95 (978-0-7377-3521-5(X)) Thomson Gale. (Greenhaven Pr., Inc.).

Bednarz, Robert, et al. TIME for Kids Readers: The Long Road to Statehood. 3rd ed. 2002. (Harcourt Horizons Ser.). (gr. k-7). pap. 38.10 (978-0-15-335291-1(4)) Harcourt Schl. Pubs.

Beier, Anne. The Importance of Being an Active Citizen. 2004. (Primary Source Library of American Citizenship). (Illus.). 32p. (J). lib. bdg. (978-1-4042-5089-5(1)) Rosen Publishing Group, Inc., The.

Benchmark Education Staff. The United States Government. 2005. 2.00 (***978-1-4108-4640-2(7)***) Benchmark Education Co.

Benchmark Education Staff, compiled by. GOVT & Citizenship. 2006. spiral bd. 330.00 (***978-1-4108-7007-0(3);*** 2006. spiral bd. 109.00 (***978-1-4108-7096-4(0));*** 2005. (J). spiral bd. 265.00 (***978-1-4108-5767-5(0)***) Benchmark Education Co.

Bennett, William. Our Country's Founders: Words of Advice from the Founders in Stories, Lteers, Po. 2001. (gr. 7-12). lib. bdg. 18.80 (978-0-613-37163-6(1)) Tandem Library Bks.

Bernstein, Richard B. Thomas Jefferson: The Revolution of Ideas. 2004. (Oxford Portraits Ser.). (Illus.). 256p. (YA). 28.00 (978-0-19-514368-3(X)) Oxford Univ. Pr., Inc.

Beyer, Mark. The Election of 1800: Congress Helps Settle a Three-Way Vote. 2004. (Life in the New American Nation Ser.). (Illus.). 32p. (YA). lib. bdg. (978-0-8239-4255-8(4)) Rosen Publishing Group, Inc., The.

Binns, Tristan Boyer. FEMA: Federal Emergency Management Agency. (Government Agencies Ser.). (Illus.). 48p. (J). (gr. 3-5). 2003. lib. bdg. 27.07 (978-1-58810-502-8(4)); 2002. pap. 7.95 (978-1-58810-984-2(4) , 91599) Heinemann Library.

Bishirjian, Richard J. The American Political Tradition & the Nature of Public Philosophy. 2004. (C). per. 12.50 (***978-1-58152-339-3(4)*** , Copley Custom Publishing Group) Copley Publishing Group.

Bjornlund, Lydia D. The Constitution & the Founding of America. 1999. (World History Ser.). (Illus.). 128p. (YA). (gr. 8-11). 27.45 (978-1-56006-586-9(9) , LML00902-177941, Lucent Bks.) Thomson Gale.

Bober, Natalie S. Thomas Jefferson: Draftsman of a Nation. 2007. 352p. (YA). (gr. 7 up). 22.95 (***978-0-8139-2632-2(7)***) Univ. Pr. of Virginia.

Bodersteiner, Roberta. U. S. Government. 2001. (Homework Booklets Ser.). 80p. (J). (gr. 5-8). pap. 2.99 (978-0-7424-0154-9(5) , IF0238) School Specialty Publishing.

Bonner, Mike. Stephen a Douglas: Champion of the Union. 2002. (gr. 5-8). lib. bdg. 17.60 (978-0-613-52728-6(3)) Tandem Library Bks.

Brannon, Barbara. Discover the United States GOVT. 2005. 39.00 (***978-1-4108-5146-8(X)***) Benchmark Education Co.

Brexel, Bernadette. The Populist Party: A Voice for the Farmers in the Industrialized Society. 2003. (America's Industrial Society in the 19th Century Ser.). (Illus.). 32p. (YA). pap. (978-0-8239-4284-8(8)) Rosen Publishing Group, Inc., The.

—Prosecuting Trusts. 2004. (Progressive Movement Ser.). (Illus.). 32p. (J). lib. bdg. (978-1-4042-0188-0(2)) Rosen Publishing Group, Inc., The.

Brown, Liz. Civics. 2007. (J). (***978-1-59036-766-7(9));*** lib. bdg. (***978-1-59036-765-0(0)***) Weigl Pubs., Inc.

Brownell, Richard. The Civil War: The Fall of the Confederacy & the End of Slavery. 2005. (History's Great Defeats Ser.). (Illus.). 109p. (YA). (gr. 7-10). lib. bdg. 29.95 (978-1-59018-429-5(7) , Lucent Bks.) Thomson Gale.

Buckwalter, Stephanie. Independent Government Agencies: Working for America. 2008. (Federal Government Ser.). 128p. (J). (gr. 6 up). lib. bdg. 33.27 (978-1-59845-057-6(3) , MyReportLinks.com Bks.) Enslow Pubs., Inc.

Burgan, Michael. The Creation of the U.S. Constitution. Purcell, Gordon & Beatty, Terry, illus. 2007. (Graphic Library). 32p. (J). 25.26 (978-0-7368-6491-6(1)) Capstone Pr., Inc.

—The Missouri Compromise. 2006. (We the People Ser.). (Illus.). 48p. (J). (gr. 4-6). 23.93 (978-0-7565-1634-5(X)) Compass Point Bks.

Callahan, Kerry P. The Articles of Confederation: A Primary Source Investigation into the Document That Preceded the U.S. Constitution. 2005. (Great American Political Documents Ser.). (Illus.). 112p. (YA). (gr. 7-12). lib. bdg. 26.50 (978-0-8239-3799-8(2)) Rosen Publishing Group, Inc., The.

Camardella, Michele L. America in The 1980s. 2005. (Decades of American History Ser.). (Illus.). 128p. (J). (gr. 4-9). per. 35.00 (978-0-8160-5644-6(7)) Facts On File, Inc.

Casciato, Daniel. Expansion & Reform. 2007. (J). (***978-1-59036-741-4(3)); (978-1-59036-742-1(1))*** Weigl Pubs., Inc.

Cheney, Lynne. America: A Patriotic Primer. Glasser, Robin Preiss, illus. 2002. 40p. (J). 16.95 (978-0-689-85192-6(8)) Simon & Schuster Children's Publishing.

Cohen, Daniel. The Impeachment of William Jefferson Clinton. 1999. (Single Titles Ser.). (Illus.). 112p. (gr. 7 up). lib. bdg. 23.90 (978-0-7613-1711-1(2) , Twenty-First Century Bks.) Lerner Publishing Group.

—Watergate: Deception in the White House. 1998. (Spotlight on American History Ser.). (Illus.). 64p. (gr. 4-6). lib. bdg. 24.90 (978-0-7613-0271-1(9) , Millbrook Pr.) Lerner Publishing Group.

Collier, Christopher & Collier, James Lincoln. Creating the Constitution: 1787. 1998. (Drama of American History Ser.). (Illus.). 96p. (J). (gr. 5-9). lib. bdg. 31.36 (978-0-7614-0776-8(6) , Benchmark Bks.) Cavendish, Marshall Corp.

—The Middle Road: American Politics, 1945 to 2000. 2001. (Drama of American History Ser.). (Illus.). 96p. (J). (gr. 5-9). lib. bdg. 31.36 (978-0-7614-1318-9(9) , Benchmark Bks.) Cavendish, Marshall Corp.

—Progressivism, the Great Depression & the New Deal: 1901-1941. 2000. (Drama of American History Ser.). (Illus.). 96p. (J). (gr. 5-9). lib. bdg. 31.36 (978-0-7614-1054-6(6) , Benchmark Bks.) Cavendish, Marshall Corp.

Connell, Kate. Servant to Abigail Adams: The Early American Adventures of Hannah Cooper. 2004. (Illus.). 40p. (J). (gr. 4-8). pap. 7.00 (978-0-7567-8216-0(3)) DIANE Publishing Co.

—The Spirit of a New Nation. 2002. (Voices from America's Past Ser.). (Illus.). 40p. (J). (978-0-7922-8684-4(7)) National Geographic Society.

Conway, John Richard. A Look at the Constitution: Creating a More Perfect Union. 2008. (J). (***978-1-59845-072-9(7)*** , MyReportLinks.com Bks.) Enslow Pubs., Inc.

Cosson, Jody. Civil War & Reconstruction. 2007. (J). (***978-1-59036-743-8(X)); (978-1-59036-744-5(8))*** Weigl Pubs., Inc.

Cox, Vicki. The History of the Third Parties. 2007. (U. S. Government: How It Works). 128p. (J). (gr. 5-8). 30.00 (***978-0-7910-9421-1(9)*** , Chelsea Hse.) Facts On File, Inc.

CQ Press Editors. Guide to Current American Government 2004. 2004. 160p. pap. 26.95 (978-1-56802-901-6(2)) CQ Pr.

Creative Media Applications Staff. American Presidents in World History, 5 vols. 2003. (Middle School Reference Ser.). (Illus.). (J). Vol. 2. (978-0-313-32566-3(9)); Vol. 3. (978-0-313-32567-0(7)); Vol. 4. (978-0-313-32568-7(5)); Vol. 5. (978-0-313-32569-4(3)) Greenwood Publishing Group, Inc.

Creative Media Applications Staff, contrib. by. American Presidents in World History, 5 vols. 2003. (Middle School Reference Ser.). (Illus.). 144p. (J). (gr. 6-8). 209.95 (978-0-313-32564-9(2) , MS2564, Middle School Reference) Greenwood Publishing Group, Inc.

—Debatable Issues in U. S. History, 5 vols. 2004. (Middle School Reference Ser.). (J). 720p. (gr. 6-8). 209.95 (978-0-313-32910-4(9) , MS2910); (978-0-313-32911-1(7)); (978-0-313-32912-8(5)); (978-0-313-32913-5(3)); (978-0-313-32914-2(1)); (978-0-313-32915-9(X)) Greenwood Publishing Group, Inc. (Greenwood Pr.).

Croddy, Marshall, et al. The Challenge of Governance. 2001. (W.M. Keck Foundation Ser.). (Illus.). 72p. (YA). pap. (978-1-886253-14-8(5)) Constitutional Rights Foundation.

Crompton, Samuel Willard. Gouverneur Morris: Creating a Nation. 2004. (America's Founding Fathers Ser.). (Illus.). 128p. (J). lib. bdg. 26.60 (978-0-7660-2213-3(7)) Enslow Pubs., Inc.

Darby, Jean. Dwight D. Eisenhower. 2004. (Presidential Leaders Ser.). (Illus.). 112p. (J). (gr. 6-12). lib. bdg. 29.27 (978-0-8225-0813-7(3)) Lerner Publishing Group.

Davis, Marc. George H. W. Bush. 2002. (Profiles of the Presidents Ser.). (Illus.). 64p. (J). (gr. 4 up). lib. bdg. 23.93 (978-0-7565-0285-0(3)) Compass Point Bks.

Doak, Robin S. Conflicts in Iraq & Afghanistan. 2006. (Wars That Changed American History Ser.). (Illus.). 48p. (J). pap. (978-0-8368-7305-4(X)); lib. bdg. (978-0-8368-7296-5(7)) Stevens, Gareth Inc. (World Almanac Library).

Draper, Allison Stark. George Washington Elected: How America's First President Was Chosen. 2001. (Headlines from History Ser.). (Illus.). 24p. (J). (gr. 3). lib. bdg. 19.95 (978-0-8239-5675-3(X) , PKFIPR, PowerKids Pr.) Rosen Publishing Group, Inc., The.

Dubois, Muriel L. The U. S. House of Representatives. 2003. (First Facts Ser.). (Illus.). 24p. (J). lib. bdg. 21.26 (978-0-7368-2288-6(7)) Capstone Pr., Inc.

—The U. S. Presidency. 2003. (First Facts Ser.). (Illus.). 24p. (J). lib. bdg. 21.26 (978-0-7368-2289-3(5)) Capstone Pr., Inc.

—The U. S. Senate. 2003. (First Facts Ser.). (Illus.). 24p. (J). lib. bdg. 21.26 (978-0-7368-2290-9(9)) Capstone Pr., Inc.

Eck, Kristin. Drafting the Constitution: Weighing Evidence to Draw Sound Conclusions. 2005. (Critical Thinking in American History Ser.). (Illus.). 48p. (YA). (gr. 5-8). lib. bdg. 25.25 (978-1-4042-0412-6(1)) Rosen Publishing Group, Inc., The.

Egan, Tracie. The President & the Executive Branch. 2003. (Primary Source Library of American Citizenship). (Illus.). 32p. (J). pap. (978-1-4042-5091-8(3)) Rosen Publishing Group, Inc., The.

Elish, Dan. The Watergate Scandal. (Cornerstones of Freedomtrade;, Second Ser.). 48p. (J). 2007. pap. 5.95 (*978-0-531-18771-5(3)); 2004. (Illus.). 26.00 (978-0-516-24239-2(3)) Scholastic Library Publishing. (Children's Pr.).

Emancipation Proclamation: Hope of Freedom for the Slaves. (Civil War Ser.). 48p. (YA). 7.95 (978-0-7368-4517-5(8)) Capstone Pr., Inc.

Epperson, James F. Causes of the Civil War. 2005. (Road to War Ser.). (Illus.). 64p. (J). pap. 12.95 (978-1-59556-006-3(8)); (gr. 4 up). lib. bdg. 22.95 (978-1-59556-002-5(5)) OTTN Publishing.

Espinosa, Rod. Patrick Henry. 2007. (Bio-Graphics Ser.). (Illus.). 32p. (J). (gr. 3-6). lib. bdg. 27.07 (*978-1-60270-070-3(2) , Graphic Planet) Magic Wagon.

Evans, Fred. Maritime & Port Security. 2003. (Securing the Nation Ser.). (Illus.). 112p. (J). (gr. 9-13). 30.00 (978-0-7910-7614-9(8) , Chelsea Hse.) Facts On File, Inc.

Feinstein, Steve. Rising of a New Nation. 2000. (978-0-606-20383-8(4)) Tandem Library Bks.

Fernandez, Justin. High Crimes & Misdemeanors. 2000. (Crime, Justice & Punishment Ser.). (Illus.). 80p. (J). 30.00 (978-0-7910-5450-5(0) , Chelsea Hse.) Facts On File, Inc.

Fink, Sam. Declaration of Independence. 2007. 160p. (J). pap. 11.99 (*978-0-439-70315-4(8) , Scholastic Nonfiction) Scholastic, Inc.

Firestone, Mary. The State Governor. 2004. (First Facts Ser.). (Illus.). 24p. (J). 15.95 (978-0-7368-2500-9(2)) Capstone Pr., Inc.

Ford, Carin T. Lincoln, Slavery, & the Emancipation Proclamation. 2004. (Civil War Library Ser.). (Illus.). 48p. (J). lib. bdg. 23.93 (978-0-7660-2252-2(8)) Enslow Pubs., Inc.

Fradin, Dennis B. The Declaration of Independence. 2006. (Turning Points in U. S. History Ser.). (Illus.). 48p. (J). (gr. 3-6). lib. bdg. 29.93 (978-0-7614-2129-0(7) , Benchmark Bks.) Cavendish, Marshall Corp.

—The Emancipation Proclamation. 2007. (Turning Points in U. S. History Ser.). (J). lib. bdg. (978-0-7614-2038-5(X) , Benchmark Bks.) Cavendish, Marshall Corp.

Fradin, Dennis Brindell. The Founders: The 39 Stories Behind the U. S. Constitution. McCurdy, Michael, illus. 2005. 144p. (J). (gr. 5-9). 23.85 (978-0-8027-8973-0(0)); 22.95 (978-0-8027-8972-3(2)) Walker & Co.

—The U. S. Constitution. 2007. (Turning Points in U. S. History Ser.). (Illus.). 47p. (J). (gr. 4-7). lib. bdg. (978-0-7614-2036-1(3) , Benchmark Bks.) Cavendish, Marshall Corp.

Freedman, Russell. Give Me Liberty! The Story of the Declaration of Independence. (Illus.). 96p. (J). (gr. 4-6). tchr. ed. 24.95 (978-0-8234-1448-2(5)); pap. 12.95 (978-0-8234-1753-7(0)) Holiday Hse., Inc.

Gale Encyclopedia US Hist: Gov Pol, 2 Vol. 2007. 220.00 (*978-1-4144-3118-5(X)) Thomson Gale.

Giddens-White, Bryon. Our Government: National Elections & the Political Process. 2005. (J). 28.21 (978-1-4034-6604-4(1)); pap. (978-1-4034-6609-9(2)) Heinemann Library.

Giesecke, Ernestine. National Government. 2000. (Kids' Guide Ser.). (Illus.). 32p. (J). (gr. 4-6). lib. bdg. 22.79 (978-1-57572-510-9(X)) Heinemann Library.

Gillis, Jennifer Blizin. Patrick Henry. 2004. (Illus.). 32p. (J). pap. 7.50 (978-1-4034-5968-8(1)); lib. bdg. 24.22 (978-1-4034-5960-2(6)) Heinemann Library.

—Samuel Adams. 2004. (Illus.). 32p. (J). pap. 7.50 (978-1-4034-5970-1(3)) Heinemann Library.

Gitelson, Alan R., et al. American Government. 7th ed. 2003. 485p. (YA). 90.76 (978-0-618-31194-1(7) , 317311) Houghton Mifflin College Div.

Gitlin, Marty. The Great Depression & World War II. 2007. (J). (*978-1-59036-749-0(9)); (*978-1-59036-750-6(2)) Weigl Pubs., Inc.

—Postwar United States. 2007. (J). (*978-1-59036-751-3(0)); (*978-1-59036-752-0(9)) Weigl Pubs., Inc.

Glaser, Jason. Patrick Henry: Liberty or Death. McDonnell, Peter, illus. 2005. (Graphic Library). 32p. (J). (gr. 3-7). lib. bdg. 25.26 (978-0-7368-4970-8(X)) Capstone Pr., Inc.

Glaser, Jason & McDonnell, Peter. Patrick Henry: Muerte o Libertad. McDonnell, Peter, illus. 2007. (Graphic Library). (ENG & SPA.). (J). 25.26 (978-0-7368-6608-8(6)) Capstone Pr., Inc.

Goldsmith, Marcia. Important Years: The 1980s. 2005. (Illus.). 16p. (J). (*978-0-618-56043-1(2)) Houghton Mifflin Co.

Gonzales, Doreen. A Look at the Second Amendment: To Keep & Bear Arms. 2007. (Constitution of the United States Ser.). (Illus.). 128p. (J). (gr. 5). lib. bdg. 33.27 (978-1-59845-061-3(1) , MyReportLinks.com Bks.) Enslow Pubs., Inc.

Gorman, R. F., et al. The Best Test Prep for the AP Examination for Both U. S. & Comparative Government & Politics. 8th ed. 2006. (Test Preps Ser.). 450p. pap. 18.95 (978-0-7386-0046-8(6)) Research & Education Assn.

Gottfried, Ted. Millard Fillmore. 2007. (Presidents & Their Times Ser.). 96p. (J). lib. bdg. 32.79 (978-0-7614-2431-4(8) , Benchmark Bks.) Cavendish, Marshall Corp.

Graves, Kerry A. The Constitution: The Story Behind America's Governing Document. 2004. (America in Words & Song Ser.). (Illus.). 32p. (gr. 3-5). 23.00 (978-0-7910-7333-9(5) , Chelsea Hse.) Facts On File, Inc.

Great American Political Documents. 2005. (Illus.). (gr. 7-12). lib. bdg. 159.00 (978-0-8239-4059-2(4)) Rosen Publishing Group, Inc., The.

Grodin, Elissa. D Is for Democracy: An American Citizen's Alphabet. Juhusz, Victor, illus. 2004. 40p. (J). 16.95 (978-1-58536-234-9(4)) Sleeping Bear Pr.

Grolier Educational Staff, contrib. by. Flash Focus. 2004. (Illus.). (J). Vol. 1. (978-0-7172-5934-2(X)); Vol. 2. (978-0-7172-5938-0(2)); Vol. 3. (978-0-7172-5937-3(4)); Vol. 4. (978-0-7172-5940-3(4)) Grolier, Ltd.

Gutman, Dan. Landslide! A Kid's Guide to the U. S. Elections. 2000. (gr. 3-6). lib. bdg. 11.80 (978-0-613-25923-1(8)) Tandem Library Bks.

Halpern, Monica. The Progressives. 2003. (People Who Changed America Ser.). (Illus.). 40p. (J). (978-0-7922-8624-0(3)) National Geographic Society.

Hamilton, John. Branches of Government. 2005. (Government in Action! Ser.). (J). (gr. k-6). lib. bdg. 22.78 (978-1-59197-644-8(8)) ABDO Publishing Co.

—Government in Action! 2005. (Government in Action! Ser.). (J). (gr. k-6). lib. bdg. 182.24 (978-1-59197-641-7(3) , Checkerboard Library) ABDO Publishing Co.

—Operation Noble Eagle. 2002. (War on Terrorism Ser.). (Illus.). 64p. (J). (gr. 4-8). lib. bdg. 25.65 (978-1-57765-664-7(4) , ABDO & Daughters) ABDO Publishing Co.

Harness, Cheryl. The Remarkable Rough-Riding Life of Theodore Roosevelt & the Rise of Empire America. 2007. (Illus.). 144p. (J). (gr. 3-7). lib. bdg. 25.90 (978-1-4263-0009-7(3) , National Geographic Children's Bks.) National Geographic Society.

Harris, Nancy. What's Government? 2007. (J). (*978-1-4034-9468-9(1)); pap. (*978-1-4034-9474-0(6)) Heinemann Library.

Hartley. Holt American Civics. 5th ed. 2004. (Illus.). 73.60 (978-0-03-037778-5(1)) Holt, Rinehart & Winston.

Haugen, Brenda & Santella, Andrew. Alexander Hamilton: Founding Father & Statesman. 2004. (Signature Lives Ser.). (Illus.). 112p. (J). 30.60 (978-0-7565-0827-2(4) , 1240126) Compass Point Bks.

Haugen, David M. America's Global Influence. 2007. (Opposing Viewpoints Ser.). 240p. (gr. 10-12). (J). 36.20 (978-0-7377-3423-2(X)); pap. 24.95 (978-0-7377-3424-9(8)) Thomson Gale. (Greenhaven Pr., Inc.).

Haulley, Fletcher. The Department of Homeland Security. 2005. (This Is Your Government Ser.). (Illus.). 64p. (J). lib. bdg. (978-1-4042-0209-2(9)) Rosen Publishing Group, Inc., The.

Hay, Jeff, ed. Richard M. Nixon. 2001. (Presidents & Their Decisions Ser.). (Illus.). 240p. (YA). (gr. 9 up). pap. 21.20 (978-0-7377-0404-4(7) , Greenhaven Pr., Inc.) Thomson Gale.

Heath, David. Elections in the United States. (American Civics Ser.). 48p. (YA). pap. 6.95 (978-0-7368-8857-8(8)) Capstone Pr., Inc.

Hiber, Amanda. Is the United States Ready for a Minority President? (New Title) 2007. (At Issue Ser.). (Illus.). 128p. (gr. 10-12). 28.70 (*978-0-7377-3878-0(2)); pap. 19.95 (*978-0-7377-3879-7(0)) Thomson Gale. (Greenhaven Pr., Inc.).

Hicks, Terry Allan. The Declaration of Independence. 2006. (Symbols of America Ser.). (Illus.). 40p. (J). lib. bdg. 28.50 (978-0-7614-2135-1(1) , Benchmark Bks.) Cavendish, Marshall Corp.

Hillstrom, Kevin. Watergate. 2004. (Defining Moments Ser.). (Illus.). 217p. (YA). lib. bdg. 49.00 (978-0-7808-0769-3(3)) Omnigraphics, Inc.

Holt, Rinehart and Winston Staff. American Civics: Online Edition Plus. 3rd ed. 2003. 17.26 (978-0-03-037434-0(0)) Holt, Rinehart & Winston.

—American Goverment: TAKS Review & Overhead Transparencies. 3rd ed. 2003. (Illus.). (J). pap. 211.00 incl. trans. (978-0-03-073586-8(6)) Holt, Rinehart & Winston.

—American History Political Cartoons Activities. 1998. pap. 44.73 (978-0-03-053668-7(5)) Holt, Rinehart & Winston.

—History on Hold: The 2000 Election. 2001. pap. 1.00 (978-0-03-066429-8(2)); pap., tchr. ed. 1.00 (978-0-03-066428-1(4)) Holt, Rinehart & Winston.

Horn, Geoffrey M. The Cabinet & Federal Agencies. 2003. (World Almanac Library of American Government). (Illus.). 48p. (J). (gr. 5 up). pap. 14.95 (978-0-8368-5481-7(0)); lib. bdg. 30.00 (978-0-8368-5476-3(4)) Stevens, Gareth Inc. (World Almanac Library).

—The Constitution. 2003. (World Almanac Library of American Government). (Illus.). 48p. (J). (gr. 5 up). pap. 14.95 (978-0-8368-5482-4(9)); lib. bdg. 30.00 (978-0-8368-5477-0(2)) Stevens, Gareth Inc. (World Almanac Library).

—The Presidency. 2003. (World Almanac Library of American Government). (Illus.). 48p. (J). (gr. 5 up). pap. 14.95 (978-0-8368-5463-3(2)); lib. bdg. 30.00 (978-0-8368-5458-9(6)) Stevens, Gareth Inc. (World Almanac Library).

—World Almanac Library of American Government, 8 bks. Incl. Armed Forces. lib. bdg. 30.00 (978-0-8368-5456-5(X)); Bill of Rights & Other Amendments. lib. bdg. 30.00 (978-0-8368-5475-6(6)); Cabinet & Federal Agencies. lib. bdg. 30.00 (978-0-8368-5476-3(4)); Congress. lib. bdg. 30.00 (978-0-8368-5457-2(8)); Constitution. lib. bdg. 30.00 (978-0-8368-5477-0(2)); Political Parties, Interest Groups & the Media. lib. bdg. 30.00 (978-0-8368-5478-7(0)); Presidency. lib. bdg. 30.00 (978-0-8368-5458-9(6)); Supreme Court. lib. bdg. 30.00 (978-0-8368-5459-6(4)); (J). (gr. 5 up). 2003. (Illus.). 48p. 2002. Set lib. bdg. 240.00 (978-0-8368-5555-5(8) , World Almanac Library) Stevens, Gareth Inc.

—World Almanac Library of American Government: The Armed Forces; Congress; The Presidency; The Supreme Court, 4 bks. 2002. (Illus.). (J). (gr. 5 up). pap. 59.80 (978-0-8368-5460-2(8) , World Almanac Library) Stevens, Gareth Inc.

Hubbard-Brown, Janet. How the Constitution Was Created. 2007. (U. S. Government: How It Works). 104p. (J). (gr. 5-8). 30.00 (*978-0-7910-9420-4(0) , Chelsea Hse.) Facts On File, Inc.

Hughes, Chris. The Constitutional Convention. 2005. (People at the Center of Ser.). (Illus.). 48p. (J). (ps-7). lib. bdg. 24.95 (978-1-56711-918-3(2) , Blackbirch Pr., Inc.) Thomson Gale.

It's My State! - Group 6. Incl. Georgia. Haywood, Karen Diane. 79p. 27.07 (978-0-7614-1862-7(8)); Louisiana. Bjorklund, Ruth & Santoro, Christopher. 80p. 27.07 (978-0-7614-1863-4(6)); Michigan. Haney, Johannah. 79p. 27.07 (978-0-7614-1861-0(X)); Nevada. Hicks, Terry Allan. 80p. 27.07 (978-0-7614-1860-3(1)); Rhode Island. Petreycik, Ryan. 80p. 27.07 (978-0-7614-1859-7(8)); Vermont. Dornfeld, Margaret. 80p. 27.07 (978-0-7614-1864-1(4)); (Illus.). (J). 2005. 2005. 162.43 (978-0-7614-1858-0(X) , Benchmark Bks.) Cavendish, Marshall Corp.

Jarnow, Jesse. Patrick Henry's Liberty or Death Speech: A Primary Source Investigation. 2004. (Great Historic Debates & Speeches Ser.). (Illus.). 64p. (J). lib. bdg. 29.25 (978-1-4042-0152-1(1)) Rosen Publishing Group, Inc., The.

Johnson, Darv. The Reagan Years. 1999. (World History Ser.). (Illus.). 111p. (YA). (gr. 8-11). 27.45 (978-1-56006-592-0(3) , LML00902-177947, Lucent Bks.) Thomson Gale.

Johnson, Etta. The United States Government. 2005. 42.00 (*978-1-4108-4592-4(3)) Benchmark Education Co.

Kaleidoscope - Government Series, 4 bks., Set. 102.57 (978-0-7614-1450-6(9) , Benchmark Bks.) Cavendish, Marshall Corp.

Kallen, Stuart A. Does Equality Exist in America? 2006. (Illus.). 128p. (gr. 10-12). 21.20 (978-0-7377-3434-8(5)); pap. 29.95 (978-0-7377-3433-1(7)) Thomson Gale. (Greenhaven Pr., Inc.).

—The Home Front: Americans Protest the War. 2001. (American War Library). (Illus.). 112p. (YA). (gr. 4-12). lib. bdg. 29.95 (978-1-56006-718-4(7) , LML00902-178070, Lucent Bks.) Thomson Gale.

Kelly, Martin & Kelly, Melissa. Government. 2007. (Colonial Life Ser.). (Illus.). 96p. (gr. 6 up). 37.95 (*978-0-7656-8112-6(9)) Sharpe, M.E. Inc.

Kent, Zachary. Alexander Hamilton: Creating a Nation. 2004. (America's Founding Fathers Ser.). (Illus.). 128p. (J). lib. bdg. 26.60 (978-0-7660-2181-5(5)) Enslow Pubs., Inc.

—William Seward: The Mastermind of the Alaska Purchase. 2001. (Historical American Biographies Ser.). (Illus.). 128p. (J). (gr. 6-12). lib. bdg. 26.60 (978-0-7660-1391-9(X)) Enslow Pubs., Inc.

Kishel, Ann-Marie. Government Services. 2007. (First Step Nonfiction Ser.). 24p. (J). (gr. k-2). 18.60 (978-0-8225-6397-6(5) , Lerner Pubns.) Lerner Publishing Group.

Klobuchar, Lisa. Third Parties: Influential Political Alternatives. 2007. (J). lib. bdg. (*978-0-7565-3324-3(4)) Compass Point Bks.

Koslow, Philip. Famous Presidents. 1999. (Eyes on America Ser.). (Illus.). 29p. (J). (978-1-56156-709-6(4)) Kidsbooks, Inc.

Kovach, John. Bob Ehrlich: His Historical Campaign for Governor & How a Young Girl Made a Difference. 2003. (Illus.). 52p. (J). pap. 9.95 (978-0-7414-1497-7(X)) Infinity Publishing.

Kowalski, Kathiann M. Separation of Powers: A Balancing Act. 2004. (How Government Works Ser.). (Illus.). 56p. (J). (gr. 4-8). lib. bdg. 25.26 (978-0-8225-1350-6(1)) Lerner Publishing Group.

Krakow, Kari. The Harvey Milk Story. Gardner, David, illus. 2002. 32p. (J). 17.95 (978-0-9674468-3-7(X)) Two Lives Publishing.

Landau, Elaine. The Declaration of Independence. (True Booktrade;: American History Ser.). 48p. (J). 2008. pap. 6.95 (*978-0-531-14780-1(0)); 2007. (Illus.). (gr. 3-5). lib. bdg. 26.00 (*978-0-531-12630-1(7)) Scholastic Library Publishing. (Children's Pr.).

—The Emancipation Proclamation: Would You Do What Lincoln Did? 2008. (What Would You Do? Ser.). (Illus.). 48p. (J). (gr. 3-4). lib. bdg. 23.93 (*978-0-7660-2899-9(2) , Enslow Elementary) Enslow Pubs., Inc.

—The President's Work: The Executive Branch. 2004. (How Government Works Ser.). (Illus.). 56p. (J). (gr. 4-8). lib. bdg. 25.26 (978-0-8225-0811-3(7)) Lerner Publishing Group.

—Women's Right to Vote. 2007. (Cornerstones of Freedomtrade;, Second Ser.). 48p. (J). (gr. 4-6). pap. 5.95 (*978-0-531-18833-0(7) , Children's Pr.) Scholastic Library Publishing.

Landau, Elaine. 2000 Presidential Election. 2002. (Cornerstones of Freedom). (Illus.). 48p. (J). (gr. 4-6). 26.00 (978-0-516-22527-2(8) , Children's Pr.) Scholastic Library Publishing.

Lee, Sally. Arnold Schwarzenegger: From Superstar to Governor. 2006. (People to Know Today Ser.). (Illus.). 128p. (J). lib. bdg. 31.93 (978-0-7660-2625-4(6)) Enslow Pubs., Inc.

Leonard, Barry, ed. Symbols of the US Government: Ben's Activity Book. 2005. (Illus.). 46p. (J). (gr. k-4). pap. 15.00 (978-0-7567-4540-0(3)) DIANE Publishing Co.

LeVert, Suzanne. The Constitution. 2002. (Kaleidoscope - Government Ser.). (Illus.). 48p. (J). 25.64 (978-0-7614-1452-0(5) , Benchmark Bks.) Cavendish, Marshall Corp.

Liljeblad, Fredrik. Democracy at Work. 2008. (J). lib. bdg. 25.26 (*978-1-60279-058-2(2)) Cherry Lake Publishing.

Lincoln's Cabinet / Sumter Crisis. 2001. spiral bd. 14.95 (978-1-56004-108-5(0)) Social Studies Schl. Service.

Lloyd, Jon. A View of America's Future by America's. 2005. 51p. pap. 12.95 (978-1-4137-9110-5(7)) PublishAmerica, Inc.

Lowi, Theodore J. American Government. 7th ed. 2002. (YA). pap. (978-0-393-97924-4(5)) Norton, W. W. & Co., Inc.

Lukes, Bonnie L. Woodrow Wilson & the Progressive Era. 2006. (World Leaders Ser.). (Illus.). 192p. (J). (gr. 6-10). lib. bdg. 26.95 (978-1-931798-79-2(6)) Reynolds, Morgan Inc.

Lusted, Marcia Amidon. Revolution & the New Nation. 2007. (*978-1-59036-739-1(1)); (*978-1-59036-740-7(5)) Weigl Pubs., Inc.

Lynne, Douglas. Contemporary United States. 2007. (J). (*978-1-59036-753-7(7)); (*978-1-59036-754-4(5)) Weigl Pubs., Inc.

Magoon, Kekla. Gun Control. 2007. (Essential Viewpoints Ser.). (Illus.). 112p. (YA). (gr. 7-9). lib. bdg. 32.79 (*978-1-59928-860-4(5) , Essential Library) ABDO Publishing Co.

Marcom Group Ltd, prod. History Hot off Press Win Lb. (YA). cd-rom 222.50 (978-0-7365-4348-4(1)) Films Media Group.

Margulies, Phillip. The Department of Energy. 2005. (This Is Your Government Ser.). (Illus.). 64p. (J). lib. bdg. (978-1-4042-0208-5(0)) Rosen Publishing Group, Inc., The.

Martin, Bill & Sampson, Michael. I Pledge Allegiance. Raschka, Chris, illus. 2004. 40p. (J). (gr. 1-4). reprint ed. pap. 6.99 (978-0-7636-2527-6(2)) Candlewick Pr.

McCarthy, Pat. Famous Union Generals & Leaders of the North: A MyReportLinks. com Book. 2004. (American Civil War Ser.). (Illus.). 48p. (J). lib. bdg. 25.26 (978-0-7660-5188-1(9) , MyReportLinks.com Bks.) Enslow Pubs., Inc.

McCormick, Anita Louise. The Vietnam Antiwar Movement in American History. 2000. (In American History Ser.). (Illus.). 128p. (YA). (gr. 5-12). lib. bdg. 26.60 (978-0-7660-1295-0(6)) Enslow Pubs., Inc.

McElroy, Lisa Tucker. Alberto Gonzalez. 2006. (J). pap. 6.95 (978-0-8225-6058-6(5) , First Avenue Editions) Lerner Publishing Group.

McGraw-Hill Staff. United States Government: Democracy in Action, Reading Essentials & Note Taking Guide. 2007. (C). pap. 18.00 (*978-0-07-878125-4(6) , 9780078781254) Glencoe/McGraw-Hill.

—United States Government: Democracy in Action, Spanish Reading Essentials & Note Taking Guide. 2007. pap. 18.00 (*978-0-07-878362-3(3) , 9780078783623) Glencoe/McGraw-Hill.

—United States Government: Democracy in Action, Student Edition. 2007. (C). 90.64 (*978-0-07-874762-5(7) , 9780078747625) Glencoe/McGraw-Hill.

—United States Government: Democracy in Action, Student-Works with Audio Summaries. 2007. (C). cd-rom 102.64 (*978-0-07-878365-4(8) , 9780078783654) Glencoe/McGraw-Hill.

T
U
V

Uebelhor, Tracy S. The Truman Years. 2005. (Presidential Profiles Ser.). (Illus.). 832p. (gr. 9). 85.00 (978-0-8160-5490-9(8)) Facts On File, Inc.

Vaughn, Wally G. & Davis, Mattie Campbell, eds. The Selma Campaign, 1963-1965: The Decisive Battle of the Civil Rights Movement. 2006. 261p. pap. 19.95 (978-0-912469-44-7(7)) Majority Pr., Inc., The.

Vickers, Roy & Bouchard, David. The Elders Are Watching. 5th rev. deluxe ed. 2003. (Illus.). 56p. 15.95 (978-1-55192-641-4(5)) Raincoast Bk. Distribution CAN. *Dist:* Perseus Distribution.

Waryncia, Lou & Hale, Sarah Elder. Abraham Lincoln: Defender of the Union. 2005. (Civil War Ser.). (Illus.). 48p. (J). 17.95 (978-0-8126-7902-1(4)) Cobblestone Publishing Co.

Watts, Duncan. Understanding American Government & Politics: A Comparative Guide. 2004. (Understanding Politics Ser.). 352p. pap. 21.95 (978-0-7190-6721-1(9)) Manchester Univ. Pr. GBR. *Dist:* Macmillan.

Weidner, Daniel. Creating the Constitution: The People & Events That Formed the Nation. 2002. (Constitution Ser.). (Illus.). 112p. (YA). (gr. 6-12). lib. bdg. 26.60 (978-0-7660-1905-8(5)) Enslow Pubs., Inc.

Welch, Catherine A. Patrick Henry. 2006. (History Maker Bios Ser.). (Illus.). 48p. (J). 26.60 (978-0-8225-5941-2(2) , Lerner Pubns.) Lerner Publishing Group.

Wellman, Sam. The Cabinet. 2001. (Your Government Ser.). (Illus.). 64p. (J). (gr. 4-7). 25.00 (978-0-7910-5993-7(6) , Chelsea Hse.) Facts On File, Inc.

Wheeler, Jill C. America's Leaders. 2002. (War on Terrorism Ser.). (Illus.). 64p. (J). (gr. 4-8). lib. bdg. 25.65 (978-1-57765-661-6(X) , ABDO & Daughters) ABDO Publishing Co.

Wheeler, Ron. U. S. Government. 2001. (100+ Seriestm Ser.). 128p. (J). (gr. 5-8). pap., stu. ed. 12.99 (978-0-7424-0055-9(7) , IF87050) School Specialty Publishing.

White, Casey. John Jay. 2005. (Library of American Thinkers). (Illus.). 112p. (J). (978-1-4042-0507-9(1)) Rosen Publishing Group, Inc., The.

Williams, Brian. The Declaration of American Independence: 4 July 1776. 2002. (Dates with History Ser.). (Illus.). 31p. (J). lib. bdg. 24.25 (978-1-58340-211-5(X)) Smart Apple Media.

Williams, Jean Kinney. The U. S. Constitution. 2003. (We the People Ser.). (Illus.). 48p. (J). (gr. 4 up). lib. bdg. 22.60 (978-0-7565-0493-9(7)) Compass Point Bks.

Williams, Robert F. & Williams, Mabel, as told by. Robert & Mabel Williams Resource Guide. 2005. (Illus.). 86p. 10.00 (978-0-9727422-7-6(1)) Freedom Archives, The.

Wilson, James & DiIulio, John. American Government Internet Guide. 7th ed. 1998. (YA). pap. 6.36 (978-0-395-85775-5(9) , 360529) Houghton Mifflin College Div.

Wilson, Richard L. American Political Leaders. 2002. (American Biographies Ser.). (Illus.). 464p. (gr. 9). 65.00 (978-0-8160-4536-5(4)) Facts On File, Inc.

Wingate, Katherine. Political Reforms: American Citizens Gain More Control over Their Government. (Progressive Movement, 1900-1920—Efforts to Reform America's New Industrial Society Ser.). (Illus.). 32p. (J). 2006. (978-1-4042-0853-7(4)); 2004. lib. bdg. (978-1-4042-0192-7(0)) Rosen Publishing Group, Inc., The.

Wirkner, Linda. Learning about Life in the New American Nation with Graphic Organizers. 2005. (Graphic Organizers in Social Studies). (J). 19.95 (978-1-4042-2810-8(1) , PowerKids Pr.) Rosen Publishing Group, Inc., The.

Wood, Ethel, compiled by. The Presidency. 2004. (Historical Reader Ser.). (Illus.). 240p. (gr. 6-12). 13.32 (978-0-618-04821-2(9) , 2-00153) McDougal Littell Inc.

World Book, Inc. Staff, contrib. by. The World Book of America's Presidents, 2 vols. 2005. (Illus.). (gr. 5-12). 99.00 (978-0-7166-3698-4(0)) World Bk., Inc.

Yero, Judith Lloyd. The Declaration of Independence. 2004. (National Geographic Reading Expeditions Ser.). (Illus.). 32p. (J). pap. (978-0-7922-4554-4(7)) National Geographic Society.

Your Government in Action. (Illus.). (J). (gr. 3-6). 127.50 (978-1-4042-2966-2(3)) Rosen Publishing Group, Inc., The.

Zimmerman, Bob. The American Challenge: Twenty-One Winning Strategies for the 21st Century. 2003. (Illus.). 303p. (gr. 8 up). bds. 25.00 (978-0-932555-04-5(7)) Uxor Pr., Inc.

UNITED STATES—POLITICS AND GOVERNMENT—DICTIONARIES

Charlesworth, Sylvia. 50 Great States Read-and-Solve Crossword Puzzles: Engaging Reproducible Nonfiction Passages about Each State with Fun Crosswords That Help Build Reading Comprehension & Teach Fascinating Facts about the Nifty Fifty, Grades 3-6. 2002. (Illus.). 112p. pap., tchr. ed. 14.95 (978-0-439-29707-3(9)) Scholastic, Inc.

Djupe, Paul A. & Olson, Laura R. Encyclopedia of American Religion & Politics. 2003. (Illus.). 528p. (gr. 9 up). 85.00 (978-0-8160-4582-2(8)) Facts On File, Inc.

Matuz, Roger. Complete American Presidents Sourcebook, 5 vols. Baker, Lawrence W., ed. (Illus.). (J). 2001. 1632p. (gr. 6-9). lib. bdg. 290.00 (978-0-7876-4837-4(X) , GML00502-114881); 2000. (978-0-7876-4838-1(8)); 2000. (978-0-7876-4839-8(6)); 2000. (978-0-7876-4840-4(X)); 2000. (978-0-7876-4841-1(8)) Thomson Gale. (UXL).

Matuz, Roger & Baker, Lawrence W. Complete American Presidents Sourcebook, 5 vols. 2000. (Illus.). (J). (978-0-7876-4842-8(6)) Thomson Gale.

UNITED STATES—POLITICS AND GOVERNMENT—FICTION

Cushman, Karen. The Loud Silence of Francine Green. 2006. 240p. (J). (gr. 5-9). 16.00 (978-0-618-50455-8(9) , Clarion Bks.) Houghton Mifflin Co. Trade & Reference Div.

Higgins, Helen Boyd. Alexander Hamilton: Young Statesman. Underdown, Harold, ed. Morrison, Cathy, illus. 2nd rev. ed. 2008. (Young Patriots Ser.: No. 14). 120p. (J). (gr. 2-7). 15.95 (***978-1-882859-61-0(8)*** , Young Patriots Series) Patria Pr., Inc.

Higgins, Helen Boyd & Morrison, Cathy. Alexander Hamilton: Young Statesman. Underdown, Harold, ed. 2nd rev. ed. 2008. (Young Patriots Ser.: No. 14). (Illus.). 120p. (J). (gr. 2-7). pap. 9.95 (***978-1-882859-62-7(6)*** , Young Patriots Series) Patria Pr., Inc.

Sargent, Dave & Sargent, Pat. Duke: (Dappled Palomino) Good Behavior, 30 vols., Vol. 23. Lenoir, Jane, illus. 2003. (Saddle Up Ser.: Vol. 23). 42p. (J). pap. 6.95 (978-1-56763-682-6(9)); lib. bdg. 22.60 (978-1-56763-681-9(0)) Ozark Publishing.

UNITED STATES—POST OFFICE DEPT.

Wales, Dirk. A Lucky Dog: Owney, U.S. Rail Mail Mascot. Kenna, Diane, illus. 2003. 32p. (J). 15.95 (978-0-9632459-0-8(2)) Great Plains Pr.

UNITED STATES—POSTAL SERVICE

see Postal Service

UNITED STATES—PRESIDENTS

see Presidents—United States

UNITED STATES—PUBLIC BUILDINGS

Binns, Tristan Boyer. Lincoln Memorial. 2001. (gr. 3-6). lib. bdg. 15.25 (978-0-613-43349-5(1)) Tandem Library Bks.

Silate, Jennifer. The Statue of Liberty. 2005. (Illus.). 24p. (J). lib. bdg. (978-1-4042-2696-8(6)) Rosen Publishing Group, Inc., The.

UNITED STATES—PUBLIC DEBTS

see Debts, Public

UNITED STATES—RACE RELATIONS

Aaseng, Nathan. Plessy vs. Ferguson. 2003. (Famous Trials Ser.). (Illus.). 112p. (J). 29.95 (978-1-59018-268-0(5) , Lucent Bks.) Thomson Gale.

Alderman, Bruce. Interracial Relationships. 2006. (Social Issues Firsthand Ser.). 224p. (YA). (gr. 7 up). 29.95 (978-0-7377-2895-8(7) , Greenhaven Pr., Inc.) Thomson Gale.

Altman, Linda Jacobs. The Politics of Slavery: Fiery National Debates Fueled by the Slave Economy. 2004. (Slavery in American History Ser.). (Illus.). 128p. (J). lib. bdg. 26.60 (978-0-7660-2150-1(5)) Enslow Pubs., Inc.

—Racism & Ethnic Bias: Everybody's Problem. 2001. (Teen Issues Ser.). (Illus.). 64p. (J). (gr. 6-12). lib. bdg. 22.60 (978-0-7660-1578-4(5)) Enslow Pubs., Inc.

Anderson, Wayne. Fighting Racial Discrimination: Treating All Americans Fairly under the Law. 2004. (Progressive Movement, 1900-1920 Ser.). (Illus.). 32p. (J). lib. bdg. (978-1-4042-0189-7(0)) Rosen Publishing Group, Inc., The.

Bauchner, Elizabeth. Teen Minorities in Rural North America: Growing up Different. 2008. (Youth in Rural North America Ser.). (J). (978-1-4222-0014-8(0)) Mason Crest Pubs.

Byers, Ann. African-American History from Emancipation to Today: Rising above the Ashes of Slavery. 2004. (Slavery in American History Ser.). (Illus.). 128p. (YA). lib. bdg. 26.60 (978-0-7660-2153-2(X)) Enslow Pubs., Inc.

Carnes, Jim. Us & Them: A History of Intolerance in America. 1999. (gr. 7-12). lib. bdg. 24.55 (978-0-613-89558-3(4)) Tandem Library Bks.

Clare, John D. The Black Peoples of America. 2001. (Illus.). 48p. pap. 23.50 (***978-0-340-79033-5(4)*** , Hodder Murray) Hodder Education GBR. *Dist:* Trans-Atlantic Pubns., Inc.

Connolly, Sean. Racial & Ethnic Equality. 2005. (Campaigns for Change Ser.). (Illus.). 48p. (J). (gr. 6-9). lib. bdg. 29.95 (978-1-58340-516-1(X)) Smart Apple Media.

Dray, Philip. Daughter of Freedom: The Life & Times of Ida B. Wells. Alcorn, Stephen, illus. 2007. (J). (***978-1-56145-417-4(6)***) Peachtree Pubs., Ltd.

Engelbert, Phillis. American Civil Rights: Biographies. 1999. (American Civil Rights Reference Library). (Illus.). xl, 203p. (J). (gr. 4-7). 67.00 (978-0-7876-3173-4(6) , GML00402-112774, UXL) Thomson Gale.

Featonby, Douglas & Whittock, Martyn. The Black Peoples of America. 2001. (Illus.). 48p. pap. 23.50 (***978-0-340-79034-2(2)*** , Hodder Murray) Hodder Education GBR. *Dist:* Trans-Atlantic Pubns., Inc.

Finlayson, Reggie. We Shall Overcome: The History of the American Civil Rights Movement. 2005. (People's History Ser.). (Illus.). 96p. (gr. 6-12). lib. bdg. 26.60 (978-0-8225-0647-8(5)) Lerner Publishing Group.

Fitzgerald, Stephanie. Struggling for Civil Rights. 2006. (On the Front Line Ser.). (Illus.). 48p. (J). (978-1-4109-2196-3(4)); pap. (978-1-4109-2203-8(0)) Steck-Vaughn.

Fradin, Dennis Brindell & Fradin, Judith Bloom. Ida B. Wells: Mother of the Civil Rights Movement. 2000. (Illus.). 192p. (J). (gr. 5-9). tchr. ed. 19.00 (978-0-395-89898-7(6) , Clarion Bks.) Houghton Mifflin Co. Trade & Reference Div.

Fradin, Judith Bloom & Fradin, Dennis Brindell. The Power of One: Daisy Bates & the Little Rock Nine. 2004. (Illus.). 192p. (YA). (gr. 5-9). tchr. ed. 19.00 (978-0-618-31556-7(X) , Clarion Bks.) Houghton Mifflin Co. Trade & Reference Div.

George, Charles. Racism. 2007. (Social Issues Firsthand Ser.). 192p. (gr. 10-12). 29.95 (978-0-7377-2901-6(5) , Greenhaven Pr., Inc.) Thomson Gale.

Giddens-White, Bryon. The Story Behind Harper Lee's to Kill a Mockingbird. 2006. (History in Literature Ser.). (Illus.). 56p. (YA). (gr. 7 up). lib. bdg. 32.86 (978-1-4034-8208-2(X)) Heinemann Library.

Hansen, Joyce. Bury Me Not in a Land of Slaves: African-Americans in the Time of Reconstruction. 2000. (J). 15.60 (978-0-606-19779-3(6)) Tandem Library Bks.

Hardy, P. Stephen & Hardy, Sheila Jackson. Extraordinary People of the Civil Rights Movement. 2006. (Extraordinary People Ser.). (Illus.). 288p. (YA). (gr. 9 up). (978-0-516-25461-6(8)) Children's Pr., Ltd.

Harmon, Rod. American Civil Rights Leaders. 2000. (Collective Biographies Ser.). (Illus.). 104p. (J). (gr. 6-12). lib. bdg. 26.60 (978-0-7660-1381-0(2)) Enslow Pubs., Inc.

Haugen, David M. Interracial Relationships. 2006. 128p. (YA). (gr. 7 up). 21.20 (978-0-7377-2391-5(2)); pap. 29.95 (978-0-7377-2390-8(4)) Thomson Gale. (Greenhaven Pr., Inc.).

Heberlein, Regine I. White Supremacists. 2002. (Contemporary Issues Companion Ser.). 155p. (J). 36.20 (978-0-7377-0847-9(6) , Greenhaven Pr., Inc.) Thomson Gale.

Hermann, Spring. The Struggle for Equality: Women & Minorities in America. 2006. (American Saga Ser.). (Illus.). 128p. (J). lib. bdg. 31.93 (978-0-7660-2573-8(X)) Enslow Pubs., Inc.

Hiber, Amanda. Is the United States Ready for a Minority President? (New Title) 2007. (At Issue Ser.). (Illus.). 128p. (gr. 10-12). 28.70 (***978-0-7377-3878-0(2)*** , Greenhaven Pr., Inc.) Thomson Gale.

Holliday, Laurel. Dreaming in Color, Living in Black & White. 2000. (gr. 3-6). lib. bdg. 13.00 (978-0-613-21468-1(4)) Tandem Library Bks.

—Dreaming in Color Living in Black & White: Our Own Stories of Growing up Black in America. 2000. (J). 12.15 (978-0-606-19494-5(0)) Tandem Library Bks.

Hopkinson, Deborah. Sweet Land of Liberty. Jenkins, Leonard, illus. 2007. 32p. (J). (gr. 1-5). 16.95 (978-1-56145-395-5(1) , Peachtree Junior) Peachtree Pubs., Ltd.

Howard, Melanie A. Civil Rights Marches. 2005. (American Moments Ser.). (Illus.). (J). (gr. 4-8). lib. bdg. 25.65 (978-1-59197-282-2(5) , ABDO & Daughters) ABDO Publishing Co.

Jakoubek, Robert E. Martin Luther King, Jr. Civil Rights Leader. (Black Americans of Achievement Ser.). (Illus.). 112p. (gr. 6-12). 2005. pap. 13.25 (978-0-7910-8335-2(7)); 2004. 30.00 (978-0-7910-8161-7(3)) Facts On File, Inc. (Chelsea Hse.).

Kallen, Stuart A. A History of Free Blacks in America. 2005. (Lucent Library of Black History). (Illus.). 112p. (YA). (gr. 7-10). lib. bdg. 32.45 (978-1-59018-776-0(8) , Lucent Bks.) Thomson Gale.

Lanier, Shannon & Feldman, Jane. Jefferson's Children: The Story of One American Family. 2004. (Illus.). 144p. (J). (gr. 4-8). reprint ed. 20.00 (978-0-7567-7418-9(7)) DIANE Publishing Co.

—Jefferson's Children: The Story of One American Family. Feldman, Jane, photos by. 2002. 160p. (gr. 5). pap. 16.95 (978-0-375-82168-4(6) , Random Hse. Bks. for Young Readers) Random Hse. Children's Bks.

—Jefferson's Children: The Story of One American Family. Feldman, Jane, photos by. 2002. (Illus.). 160p. (J). (ps-7). lib. bdg. 24.55 (978-0-613-57230-9(0)) Tandem Library Bks.

Lehman, Jeffrey, ed. Gale Encyclopedia of Multicultural America, 2 vols. 1999. (Illus.). xiv, 820p. (J). (978-0-7876-3991-4(5)) Thomson Gale.

—Gale Encyclopedia of Multicultural America Set: Primary Documents, 2 vols. 1999. (Illus.). xiv, 820p. (YA). (gr. 9 up). 225.00 (978-0-7876-3990-7(7) , GML00502-113793, Gale Research International, Ltd.) Thomson Gale.

Loonin, Meryl. Multicultural America. 2004. (Lucent Overview Ser.). (Illus.). 112p. (J). 29.95 (978-1-56006-766-5(7) , Lucent Bks.) Thomson Gale.

Lucas, Eileen. Cracking the Wall: The Story of the Little Rock Nine. Anthony, Mark, illus. 2007. pap. 16.95 incl. audio (***978-1-59519-937-9(3)***); pap. 18.95 incl. audio compact disk (***978-1-59519-941-6(1)***) Live Oak Media.

—Cracking the Wall (4 PB/1 Cass) Anthony, Mark, illus. 2007. pap. 37.95 incl. audio (***978-1-59519-939-3(X)***) Live Oak Media.

—Cracking the Wall (4 PB/1 CD) Anthony, Mark, illus. 2007. pap. 39.95 incl. audio compact disk (***978-1-59519-943-0(8)***) Live Oak Media.

Marcovitz, Hal. Race Relations. 2006. (Gallup Major Trends & Events Ser.). 112p. (J). (gr. 7 up). lib. bdg. (978-1-59084-968-2(X)) Mason Crest Pubs.

McNeese, Tim. Plessy V. Ferguson. 2006. (Great Supreme Court Decisions Ser.). (Illus.). 136p. (J). (gr. 5-8). 30.00 (978-0-7910-9237-8(2) , Chelsea Hse.) Facts On File, Inc.

Michelson, Richard. As Good as Anybody. 2008. 40p. (J). (gr. 1-5). lib. bdg. 19.99 (***978-0-375-93335-6(2)*** , Knopf Bks. for Young Readers) Random Hse. Children's Bks.

Miller, Jake. The Little Rock Nine: Young Champions for School Integration. 2004. (Library of the Civil Rights Movement Ser.). (Illus.). 24p. (J). lib. bdg. 19.95 (978-0-8239-6252-5(0) , PowerKids Pr.) Rosen Publishing Group, Inc., The.

—The March from Selma to Montgomery: African Americans Demand the Vote. 2004. (Library of the Civil Rights Movement Ser.). (Illus.). 24p. (J). lib. bdg. 19.95 (978-0-8239-6254-9(7) , PowerKids Pr.) Rosen Publishing Group, Inc., The.

Moore, Heidi. Ida B. Wells-Barnett. 2004. (Illus.). 32p. (J). pap. 6.95 (978-1-4034-5706-6(9)); lib. bdg. (978-1-4034-4997-9(X)) Heinemann Library.

O'Hern, Kerri & Walsh, Frank. The Montgomery Bus Boycott. 2006. (Graphic Histories Ser.). (Illus.). 32p. (J). lib. bdg. 26.00 (978-0-8368-6205-8(8) , World Almanac Library) Stevens, Gareth Inc.

Pinkney, Andrea Davis. Let It Shine: Stories of Black Women Freedom Fighters. 2000. (Illus.). 128p. (J). (ps-3). 22.98 (978-0-7398-3073-4(2)) Raintree.

Price, Sean. When Will I Get In? Segregation & Civil Rights. 2006. (American History Through Primary Sources Ser.). (Illus.). 32p. (J). (978-1-4109-2414-8(9)); pap. (978-1-4109-2425-4(4)) Steck-Vaughn.

Rappaport, Doreen. The Flight of Red Bird: The Life of Zitkala-sa. 1999. (J). (978-0-606-16777-2(3)) Tandem Library Bks.

—Nobody Gonna Turn Me 'Round: Stories & Songs of the Civil Rights Movement. Evans, Shane W., illus. 2006. 64p. (J). (gr. 4-7). 19.99 (978-0-7636-1927-5(2)) Candlewick Pr.

Regis, Frankye. A Voice from the Civil Rights Era. 2004. (Voices of Twentieth-Century Conflict Ser.). (Illus.). 184p. 36.95 (978-0-313-32998-2(2) , GR2998, Praeger Pubs.) Greenwood Publishing Group, Inc.

Robinson, Sharon. Promises to Keep: How Jackie Robinson Changed America. 2004. (Illus.). 64p. (YA). pap. 16.95 (978-0-439-42592-6(1)) Scholastic, Inc.

Schraff, Anne E. Ida B. Wells-Barnett: Strike a Blow Against Glaring Evil. 2008. (African-American Biography Library). (Illus.). 128p. (J). (gr. 6 up). lib. bdg. 31.93 (***978-0-7660-2704-6(X)***) Enslow Pubs., Inc.

Supples, Kevin. The Civil Rights Movement. 2003. (People Who Changed America Ser.). (Illus.). 40p. (J). (978-0-7922-8628-8(6)) National Geographic Society.

Tackach, James. Early Black Reformers. 2003. (gr. 7-12). lib. bdg. 33.25 (978-0-613-73930-6(2)) Tandem Library Bks.

—Early Black Reformers. 2003. (History Firsthand Ser.). (Illus.). (YA). 224p. pap. 24.95 (978-0-7377-1598-9(7)); 202p. lib. bdg. 36.20 (978-0-7377-1597-2(9)) Thomson Gale. (Greenhaven Pr., Inc.).

Tembo, Limbiko & Venable, Rose. The Civil Rights Movement. 2001. (Journey to Freedom Ser.). (Illus.). 40p. (J). (gr. 3-7). 28.50 (978-1-56766-917-6(4)) Child's World, Inc.

Turck, Mary. Civil Rights Movement for Kids: A History with 21 Activities. 2000. (For Kids Ser.). (Illus.). 208p. (J). (gr. 4-8). pap. 14.95 (978-1-55652-370-0(X)) Chicago Review Pr., Inc.

Wagner, Heather Lehr. Benjamin Hooks. 2003. (African American Leaders Ser.). (Illus.). 112p. (gr. 6-12). 30.00 (978-0-7910-7685-9(7) , Chelsea Hse.) Facts On File, Inc.

Weatherford, Carole Boston. The African-American Struggle for Legal Equality in American History. 2000. (In American History Ser.). (Illus.). 128p. (YA). (gr. 5-12). lib. bdg. 26.60 (978-0-7660-1415-2(0)) Enslow Pubs., Inc.

Welch, Catherine A. Ida B. Wells-Barnett: Powerhouse with a Pen. 2005. (Trailblazers Biographies Ser.). (Illus.). 112p. (gr. 5-9). 27.93 (978-1-57505-352-3(7)) Lerner Publishing Group.

Woog, Adam. The Fight Renewed: the Civil Rights Movement. 2005. (Lucent Library of Black History). (Illus.). 112p. (YA). (gr. 7-10). lib. bdg. 32.45 (978-1-59018-701-2(6) , Lucent Bks.) Thomson Gale.

UNITED STATES—RELIGION

Balmer, Randall H. Religion in Twentieth Century America. 2001. (Religion in America Ser.). (Illus.). 144p. (YA). (gr. 9 up). 30.00 (978-0-19-511295-5(4)) Oxford Univ. Pr., Inc.

Butler, Jon, ed. Religion in Colonial America. 2000. (Religion in America Ser.). (Illus.). 160p. (YA). 30.00 (978-0-19-511998-5(3)) Oxford Univ. Pr., Inc.

Crater, Timothy & Hunsicker, Ranelda. In God We Trust: Stories of Faith. 2003. (Illus.). 224p. (J). (gr. 10-7). pap. 12.99 (978-0-7814-3863-6(2) , 0781438632) Cook, David C. Publishing Co.

Djupe, Paul A. & Olson, Laura R. Encyclopedia of American Religion & Politics. 2003. (Illus.). 528p. (gr. 9 up). 85.00 (978-0-8160-4582-2(8)) Facts On File, Inc.

Harcourt School Publishers Staff. Social Studies: States & Regions. 1999. (Harcourt Brace Social Studies). (Illus.). (gr. k-7). pupil's gde. ed. 65.90 (978-0-15-312099-2(1)) Harcourt Schl. Pubs.

Head, Tom. Freedom of Religion. 2005. (American Rights Ser.). (Illus.). 160p. (J). (gr. 4-9). 35.00 (978-0-8160-5664-4(1)) Facts On File, Inc.

McHugh, Michael J. Our Nation under God. 2000. 16p. (J). pap. 1.95 (978-1-930092-89-1(X) , CLP79922) Christian Liberty Pr.

Tiner, John. The Story of the Pledge of Allegiance: Discovering Our Nations Heritage. 2003. (Discovering Our Nation's Heritage Ser.). (Illus.). 48p. (J). 9.99 (978-0-89051-393-4(7)) Master Bks.

Wacker, Grant. Religion in Nineteenth Century America. 2000. (Religion in America Ser.). (Illus.). 192p. (YA). (gr. 8 up). 30.00 (978-0-19-511021-0(8)) Oxford Univ. Pr., Inc.

UNITED STATES—SOCIAL CONDITIONS

Anderson, Dale. The Cold War Years. 2001. (Making of America Ser.). (Illus.). 96p. (J). (gr. 5-10). lib. bdg. 28.54 (978-0-8172-5711-8(X)) Raintree.

—The Home Fronts in the Civil War. 2004. (World Almanac Library of the Civil War). (Illus.). 48p. (J). lib. bdg. 30.00 (978-0-8368-5587-6(6)); (gr. 5 up). pap. 11.95 (978-0-8368-5596-8(5)) Stevens, Gareth Inc. (World Almanac Library).

Barr, Gary. World War II Home Front. 2004. (Illus.). 56p. (J). pap. 8.95 (978-1-4034-4579-7(6)); lib. bdg. (978-1-4034-4571-1(0)) Heinemann Library.

Bartoletti, Susan Campbell. Kids on Strike! 1999. (Illus.). 208p. (J). (gr. 4-6). tchr. ed. 20.00 (978-0-395-88892-6(1)) Houghton Mifflin Co. Trade & Reference Div.

Bauchner, Elizabeth. Teen Minorities in Rural North America: Growing up Different. 2008. (Youth in Rural North America Ser.). (J). (978-1-4222-0014-8(0)) Mason Crest Pubs.

Bausum, Ann. Muckrakers: How Writers Exposed Scandal, Inspired Reform, & Invented Investigative Journalism. 2007. (Illus.). 112p. (YA). (gr. 5 up). 21.95 (***978-1-4263-0137-7(5)*** , National Geographic Children's Bks.) National Geographic Society.

Boehm, Richard G., et al. Game Time! United States. 2003. (Harcourt Brace Social Studies). (gr. k-7). 7.80 (978-0-15-312367-2(2)) Harcourt Schl. Pubs.

—Game Time! United States in Modern Times. 1998. (Harcourt Brace Social Studies). (gr. k-7). pap. 9.40 (978-0-15-312364-1(8)) Harcourt Schl. Pubs.

—Reading Support & Test Preparation: United States. 2003. (Harcourt Brace Social Studies). (gr. k-7). 27.00 (978-0-15-312394-8(X)) Harcourt Schl. Pubs.

—Reading Support & Test Preparation: United States in Modern Times. 1998. (Harcourt Brace Social Studies). (gr. k-7). pap. 32.70 (978-0-15-312392-4(3)) Harcourt Schl. Pubs.

Buckley, Susan Washburn & Leacock, Elspeth. Kids Make History: A New Look at America's Story. Jones, Randy, illus. 2006. 48p. (J). (gr. 4-6). 17.00 (978-0-618-22329-9(0)) Houghton Mifflin Co.

Campbell, Geoffrey A. The End of the Cold War: 1980 to the Present: The Cold War in the United States. 2002. (American War Library). 112p. (J). 29.95 (978-1-59018-213-0(8) , Lucent Bks.) Thomson Gale.

Catalano, Angela. Community Plans: Making Choices about Money in Communities. 2005. (Communities at Work Ser.). (Illus.). 24p. (J). pap. (978-1-4042-5014-7(X) , PowerKids Pr.) Rosen Publishing Group, Inc., The.

—Community Resources: The Land & the People in Communities. 2005. (Communities at Work Ser.). (Illus.). 24p. (J). pap. (978-1-4042-5016-1(6) , PowerKids Pr.) Rosen Publishing Group, Inc., The.

Center for Learning Network Staff. Violence in America. 2005. (Social Studies Ser.). 83p. (YA). tchr. ed., spiral bd. 20.95 (978-1-56077-793-9(1)) Ctr. for Learning, The.

Coletti, Sharon. Everything You Need to Supplement U. S. & State Studies. 2005. (YA). Pt. 1. ring bd. 249.95 (978-1-933558-08-0(3)); Pt. 2. ring bd. 249.95 (978-1-933558-09-7(1)) InspirEd Educators.

Colman, Penny. Girls: History of Growing up Female in America. (Girls Ser.). (Illus.). 192p. (J). (gr. 3 up). 2003. pap. 12.95 (978-0-590-37130-8(4) , Scholastic Nonfiction); 2000. pap. 18.95 (978-0-590-37129-2(0) , Scholastic Reference) Scholastic, Inc.

Fighting the Monster. 2004. (YA). ring bd. 59.95 (***978-0-9661256-2-7(2))*** Youth Communication - New York Center.

Fleming, Thomas. Everybody's Revolution: A New Look at the People Who Won America's Freedom. 2006. (Illus.). 96p. (J). (gr. 4-7). pap. 19.99 (978-0-439-63404-5(0) , Scholastic Nonfiction) Scholastic, Inc.

Ford, Jean. Rural Crime & Poverty: Violence, Drugs, & Other Issues. 2008. (Youth in Rural North America Ser.). (J). (978-1-4222-0016-2(7)) Mason Crest Pubs.

Gourley, Catherine. Society's Sisters: Stories of Women Who Fought for Social Justice in America. 2003. (Single Titles Ser.). (Illus.). 96p. (gr. 7 up). lib. bdg. 25.90 (978-0-7613-2865-0(3) , Twenty-First Century Bks.) Lerner Publishing Group.

Hakim, Joy. A History of the US Bk. 7: Reconstructing America, 1865-1890. 3rd rev. ed. 2002. (History of US Ser.). (Illus.). 160p. pap. 15.95 (978-0-19-515332-3(4)) Oxford Univ. Pr., Inc.

—A History of U. S. Vol. 7: Reconstruction & Reform. rev. ed. 2007. (History of US Ser.). 208p. pap. 15.95 (***978-0-19-532721-2(7))*** Oxford Univ. Pr., Inc.

—A History of US Bk. 7: Reconstructing America. 3rd rev. ed. 2005. (History of US Ser.). (Illus.). 208p. 19.95 (978-0-19-518900-1(0)) Oxford Univ. Pr., Inc.

—A History of US Bk. 8: Age of Extremes. rev. ed. 2007. (History of US Ser.: Vol. 8). 224p. pap. 15.95 (***978-0-19-532722-9(5))*** Oxford Univ. Pr., Inc.

—A History of Us Bk. 8: An Age of Extremes. rev. ed. 2006. (History of US Ser.). (Illus.). 210p. 19.95 (978-0-19-518236-1(7)) Oxford Univ. Pr., Inc.

—Reconstruction & Reform. 2003. (gr. 5-8). lib. bdg. 23.40 (978-0-613-55187-8(7)) Tandem Library Bks.

Halpern, Monica. The Home Front During World War II. 2004. (Reading Expeditions Ser.). (Illus.). 40p. (978-0-7922-4558-2(X)) National Geographic Society.

Harcourt School Publishers Staff. TIME for Kids Bk. 12: State & Region, 5 Packs. 3rd ed. 2002. (Horizontes (Social Studies) Ser.). (SPA.). (gr. 3 up). pap. 34.90 (978-0-15-333879-3(2)) Harcourt Schl. Pubs.

Hazen, Walter. Everyday Life: Reform Movement. 2005. 112p. pap. (978-1-59647-085-9(2)) Good Year Bks.

Head, Judith. America's Daughters: 400 Years of American Women. 1999. 130p. (J). (gr. 4 up). pap. 16.95 (978-0-9622036-8-8(8)) Perspective Publishing, Inc.

—America's Daughters: 400 Years of American Women. 1999. (Illus.). 130p. (J). (ps-7). per. 26.85 (978-0-613-90517-6(2)) Tandem Library Bks.

Hermann, Spring. The Struggle for Equality: Women & Minorities in America. 2006. (American Saga Ser.). (Illus.). 128p. (J). lib. bdg. 31.93 (978-0-7660-2573-8(X)) Enslow Pubs., Inc.

Howard, Melanie A. Civil Rights Marches. 2005. (American Moments Ser.). (Illus.). (J). (gr. 4-8). lib. bdg. 25.65 (978-1-59197-282-2(5) , ABDO & Daughters) ABDO Publishing Co.

Hurley, Jennifer A. The 1960s. 2000. (Opposing Viewpoints Digests Ser.). (Illus.). 143p. (YA). (gr. 6-9). pap. 21.20 (978-0-7377-0210-1(9) , Greenhaven Pr., Inc.) Thomson Gale.

Josephson, Judith Pinkerton. Growing up in World War II, 1941-1945. 2003. (Our America Ser.). (Illus.). 64p. (J). (gr. 4-7). lib. bdg. 26.60 (978-0-8225-0660-7(2)) Lerner Publishing Group.

Kallen, Stuart A. Life in America During the 1960s. 2001. (Way People Live Ser.). (Illus.). 112p. (J). (gr. 7-10). 28.70 (978-1-56006-790-0(X) , LML00902-178128, Lucent Bks.) Thomson Gale.

Kamma, Anne. If You Lived When Women Won Their Rights. 2008. 64p. pap. 5.99 (***978-0-439-74869-8(0)*** , Scholastic Reference) Scholastic, Inc.

Konstam, Angus. America Speaks, 10 vols. 2005. (Illus.). (J). (978-0-7172-6020-1(8)); (978-0-7172-6021-8(6)); (978-0-7172-6022-5(4)); (978-0-7172-6023-2(2)); (978-0-7172-6024-9(0)); (978-0-7172-6025-6(9)); (978-0-7172-6026-3(7)); (978-0-7172-6027-0(5)); (978-0-7172-6028-7(3)); (978-0-7172-6029-4(1)) Grolier, Ltd.

—America Speaks, 10 vols., Set. 2005. (Illus.). (J). (gr. 5-10). lib. bdg. 199.00 (978-0-7172-6030-0(5) , Grolier) Scholastic Library Publishing.

Landau, Elaine. The Great Depression. 2007. (Cornerstones of Freedomtrade;, Second Ser.). 48p. (J). pap. 5.95 (***978-0-531-18767-8(5)*** , Children's Pr.) Scholastic Library Publishing.

Lauderdale, Kathie L., et al. Minefields in the Way: Growing up in America. Affleck, Eric & Weese, Peter, illus. 1998. 112p. (J). pap. 19.95 (978-1-879774-17-9(8)) ICA Publishing Co.

Levy, Debbie. Slaves on a Southern Plantation. 2004. (Daily Life Ser.). (Illus.). 48p. (J). 26.20 (978-0-7377-1827-0(7) , Greenhaven Pr., Inc.) Thomson Gale.

Loonin, Meryl. Multicultural America. 2004. (Lucent Overview Ser.). (Illus.). 112p. (J). 29.95 (978-1-56006-766-5(7) , Lucent Bks.) Thomson Gale.

Marcovitz, Hal. Race Relations. 2006. (Gallup Major Trends & Events Ser.). 112p. (J). (gr. 7 up). lib. bdg. (978-1-59084-968-2(X)) Mason Crest Pubs.

McIntosh, Kenneth & Livingston, Phyllis. Youth with Alcohol & Drug Addiction: Escape from Bondage. 2008. (J). (978-1-4222-0143-5(0)) Mason Crest Pubs.

McLaurin, Melton A. Celia, a Slave. 1999. (J). (978-0-606-16086-5(8)) Tandem Library Bks.

McNeill, Allison & Hanes, Richard Clay. American Home Front in World War II Reference Library Cumulative Index. 2004. (American Home Front in World War II Reference Library). 32p. 5.00 (978-0-7876-9125-7(9) , UXL) Thomson Gale.

Miller, Brandon Marie. Declaring Independence: Life During the American Revolution. 2005. (People's History Ser.). (Illus.). 112p. (J). 29.27 (978-0-8225-1275-2(0)) Lerner Publishing Group.

Miller, Debra. The Patriot Act. 2007. (Hot Topics Ser.). (Illus.). 128p. (J). (gr. 7-10). 32.45 (***978-1-59018-981-8(7)*** , Lucent Bks.) Thomson Gale.

Monk, Linda R. The Words We Live By: Your Annotated Guide to the Constitution. annot. ed. 2004. (Illus.). 288p. pap. 14.95 (978-0-7868-8620-3(X)) Hyperion Pr.

Multicultural America. 2004. (Anthologies Ser.). (Illus.). ix, 405p. (YA). (gr. 6-12). (978-0-618-22204-9(9) , 2-00309) McDougal Littell Inc.

Nardo, Don. The Atlantic Slave Trade. 2007. (Lucent Library of Black History Ser.). (Illus.). 128p. (J). (gr. 7-10). 28.70 (***978-1-4205-0007-3(4)*** , Lucent Bks.) Thomson Gale.

Nobleman, Marc Tyler. The Thirteen Colonies. 2002. (We the People Ser.). (Illus.). 48p. (J). (gr. 4 up). lib. bdg. 22.60 (978-0-7565-0211-9(X)) Compass Point Bks.

Rice, James. Vaqueros. 1998. (SPA & ENG., Illus.). 32p. (ps-3). 15.95 (978-1-56554-309-6(2)) Pelican Publishing Co., Inc.

Rossi, Ann. Immigrants Today. 2004. (National Geographic Reading Expeditions Ser.). (Illus.). 40p. (J). pap. (978-0-7922-4560-5(1)) National Geographic Society.

Sakany, Lois. The Platforms & Policies of America's Reform Politicians. 2004. (Progressive Movement, 1900-1920 Ser.). (Illus.). 32p. (J). lib. bdg. (978-1-4042-0193-4(9)) Rosen Publishing Group, Inc., The.

Sigerman, Harriet. Laborers for Liberty Vol. 6: American Women 1865-1890. 1998. (Young Oxford History of Women in the United States Ser.). (Illus.). 144p. (YA). reprint ed. pap. 12.95 (978-0-19-512404-0(9)) Oxford Univ. Pr., Inc.

Smolinski, Diane. The Home Front in the North. (Americans at War Ser.). (Illus.). 32p. (J). (gr. 4-7). 2002. pap. 6.95 (978-1-58810-393-2(5) , 91133); 2001. lib. bdg. (978-1-58810-099-3(5)) Heinemann Library.

—The Revolutionary War Home Front. 2001. (Americans at War Ser.). (Illus.). 32p. (J). (gr. 4-6). lib. bdg. (978-1-58810-277-5(7)) Heinemann Library.

Stauffer, Stacey & Koslow, Philip. Histories. 1998. (Asian American Experience Ser.). (YA). (gr. 5 up). (978-0-7910-4457-5(2) , Chelsea Hse.) Facts On File, Inc.

Steck-Vaughn Staff. Social Studies Level H-J: America Is... 2003. (Illus.). pap. (978-0-7398-7652-7(X)) Harcourt Schl. Pubs.

Stein, R. Conrad. The Home Front During World War II in American History. 2003. (In American History Ser.). (Illus.). 112p. (J). (gr. 5-12). lib. bdg. 26.60 (978-0-7660-1984-3(5)) Enslow Pubs., Inc.

Stone, Lynn M. America's People. 2002. (Illus.). 24p. (J). lib. bdg. 25.64 (978-1-58952-309-8(1)) Rourke Publishing, LLC.

Stuart Kallen. Political Activists of the 1960s. 2004. (History Makers Ser.). (Illus.). 96p. (J). 29.95 (978-1-59018-386-1(X)) Thomson Gale.

Wagner, Viqi. Poverty. 2007. (Opposing Viewpoints Ser.). (Illus.). 224p. (gr. 10-12). 36.20 (***978-0-7377-3747-9(6));*** pap. 24.95 (***978-0-7377-3748-6(4))*** Thomson Gale. (Greenhaven Pr., Inc.).

Wilcox, Charlotte. Work & Occupations in Colonial America. 2004. (Everyday Life Long Ago Ser.). (J). (978-0-7368-2165-0(1) , Blue Earth Bks.) Capstone Pr., Inc.

Williams, Mary, ed. Culture Wars. 1998. (Opposing Viewpoints Ser.). (Illus.). 208p. (YA). (gr. 8-12). lib. bdg. 32.45 (978-1-56510-939-1(2) , LML00501-177490, Greenhaven Pr., Inc.) Thomson Gale.

Wroble, Lisa A. Kids During the Industrial Revolution. 1999. (Kids Throughout History Ser.). (Illus.). 24p. (J). (gr. 3). lib. bdg. 18.75 (978-0-8239-5254-0(1) , PowerKids Pr.) Rosen Publishing Group, Inc., The.

UNITED STATES—SOCIAL LIFE AND CUSTOMS

Acker, Kerry. Everything You Need to Know about the Goth Scene. 2005. (Need to Know Library). (Illus.). 64p. (YA). (gr. 7-12). lib. bdg. 25.25 (978-0-8239-3223-8(0) , NTGOSC) Rosen Publishing Group, Inc., The.

The American Colonies. 2005. (Fact Finders Ser.). (Illus.). (J). (gr. 3-4). lib. bdg. 293.80 (978-0-7368-2761-4(7)) Capstone Pr., Inc.

Ancona, George. Mi Casa: My House. 2005. (Somos Latinos (We Are Latinos) Ser.). (SPA & ENG., Illus.). 32p. (J). (gr. 1-3). pap. 8.95 (978-0-516-25065-6(5) , Children's Pr.) Scholastic Library Publishing.

—Mi Familia: My Family. 2005. (Somos Latinos (We Are Latinos) Ser.). (SPA., Illus.). 32p. (J). (gr. 1-3). pap. 8.95 (978-0-516-25067-0(1) , Children's Pr.) Scholastic Library Publishing.

—Mis Amigos: My Friends. 2005. (Somos Latinos (We Are Latinos) Ser.). (SPA., Illus.). 32p. (J). (gr. 1-3). pap. 8.95 (978-0-516-25068-7(X) , Children's Pr.) Scholastic Library Publishing.

Anderson, Dale. Daily Life During the American Revolution. 2005. (World Almanac Library of the American Revolution). (J). pap. (978-0-8368-5939-3(1)); lib. bdg. 30.00 (978-0-8368-5930-0(8)) Stevens, Gareth Inc. (World Almanac Library).

Anderson, Laurie Halse. Thank You, Sarah: The Woman Who Saved Thanksgiving. Faulkner, Matt, illus. 2005. 40p. (J). 6.99 (978-0-689-85143-8(X) , Aladdin) Simon & Schuster Children's Publishing.

Arbelbide, C. L. The White House Easter Egg Roll. Gibson, Barbara Leonard, illus. 2005. 29p. (J). (gr. k-4). reprint ed. 17.00 (978-0-7567-4772-5(4)) DIANE Publishing Co.

Barter, James. San Francisco in the 1960s. 2003. (Illus.). 96p. (J). 29.95 (978-1-59018-359-5(2) , Lucent Bks.) Thomson Gale.

Berg, Elizabeth. USA (Festivals of the World) 1999. (Festivals of the World Ser.). (Illus.). 32p. (J). (gr. 3 up). lib. bdg. 24.67 (978-0-8368-2028-7(2)) Stevens, Gareth Inc.

Bial, Raymond. Frontier Settlements. 2004. (American Community Ser.). (Illus.). 48p. (J). (gr. 2-5). 29.00 (978-0-516-23705-3(5) , Children's Pr.) Scholastic Library Publishing.

Boehm, Richard G., et al. Activity Books: Early United States. 1998. (Harcourt Brace Social Studies). (gr. k-7). pap., act. bk. ed. 10.70 (978-0-15-310308-7(6)); pap., act. bk. ed. 20.00 (978-0-15-310312-4(4)) Harcourt Schl. Pubs.

—Activity Books: United States in Modern Times. 1998. (Harcourt Brace Social Studies). (gr. k-7). pap., act. bk. ed. 10.70 (978-0-15-311400-7(2)); pap., act. bk. ed. 20.00 (978-0-15-311401-4(0)) Harcourt Schl. Pubs.

—Early United States. 1999. (Harcourt Brace Social Studies). (gr. k-7). tchr. ed. 120.10 (978-0-15-315996-1(0)); tchr. ed. 120.10 (978-0-15-315997-8(9)) Harcourt Schl. Pubs.

Brenner, Barbara. If You Lived in Williamsburg in Colonial Days. 2000. (J). 12.79 (978-0-606-19569-0(6)) Tandem Library Bks.

Brode, Robyn. April. 2003. (Weekly Reader Early Learning Library). (Illus.). 24p. (J). (ps-2). pap. 7.93 (978-0-8368-3615-8(4)); lib. bdg. 19.33 (978-0-8368-3579-3(4)) Stevens, Gareth Inc. (Weekly Reader Early Learning Library).

—February. 2003. (Weekly Reader Early Learning Library). (Illus.). 24p. (J). (ps-2). pap. 7.93 (978-0-8368-3613-4(8)); lib. bdg. 19.33 (978-0-8368-3577-9(8)) Stevens, Gareth Inc. (Weekly Reader Early Learning Library).

—January. 2003. (Weekly Reader Early Learning Library). (Illus.). 24p. (J). (ps-2). pap. 7.93 (978-0-8368-3612-7(X)); lib. bdg. 19.33 (978-0-8368-3576-2(X)) Stevens, Gareth Inc. (Weekly Reader Early Learning Library).

—November. 2003. (Illus.). 24p. (J). pap. (978-0-8368-3622-6(7)); lib. bdg. 19.33 (978-0-8368-3586-1(7) , Weekly Reader Early Learning Library) Stevens, Gareth Inc.

—October. 2003. (Illus.). 24p. (J). pap. (978-0-8368-3621-9(9)); lib. bdg. 19.33 (978-0-8368-3585-4(9) , Weekly Reader Early Learning Library) Stevens, Gareth Inc.

Broida, Marian. Projects about the American Revolution. 2005. (Hands-On History Ser.). (Illus.). 48p. (J). (978-0-7614-1981-5(0) , Benchmark Bks.) Cavendish, Marshall Corp.

Brown, Harriet. Welcome to Kit's World, 1934: Growing up During America's Great Depression. Rane, Walter et al, illus. Young, Jamie, photos by. 2002. (American Girls Collection). 64p. (J). 16.95 (978-1-58485-359-6(X)) American Girl Publishing, Inc.

Buckley, Susan Washburn & Leacock, Elspeth. Kids Make History: A New Look at America's Story. Jones, Randy, illus. 2006. 48p. (J). (gr. 4-6). 17.00 (978-0-618-22329-9(0)) Houghton Mifflin Co.

Center for Learning Network Staff. Catch-22: Curriculum Unit. 2005. (Novel Ser.). 76p. (YA). tchr. ed., spiral bd. 19.95 (978-1-56077-792-2(3)) Ctr. for Learning, The.

Cfl. Everyday Life. 1999. (Illus.). 88p. (J). (ps-4). 14.95 (978-0-8094-4865-4(3)) Time-Life, Inc.

Cipriano, Jeri. Colonial Times/la época Colonial: English/Spanish Pair, 12 texts, 2 titles, Vol. 2. ed. 2004. (Navigators Ser.). (J). pap., instr.'s gde. ed. 84.00 (978-1-4108-1768-6(7) , 17687) Benchmark Education Co.

Cole, Sheila. To Be Young in America: Growing up with the Country, 1776-1940. 2005. (Illus.). 160p. (J). (gr. 8-17). 19.99 (978-0-316-15196-2(3)) Little Brown & Co.

Collier, Christopher & Collier, James Lincoln. The Changing Face of America, 1945-2000. 2001. (Drama of American History Ser.). (Illus.). 96p. (J). (gr. 5-9). lib. bdg. 31.36 (978-0-7614-1319-6(7) , Benchmark Bks.) Cavendish, Marshall Corp.

Colonial Life, 5 bks., Set. Incl. Cities & Towns. Stefoff, Rebecca. 37.95 (***978-0-7656-8109-6(9));*** Daily Living. Hinds, Kathryn. 37.95 (***978-0-7656-8110-2(2));*** Exploration & Settlement. Stefoff, Rebecca. 37.95 (***978-0-7656-8108-9(0));*** Government. Kelly, Martin & Kelly, Melissa. 37.95 (***978-0-7656-8112-6(9));*** Trade & Commerce. Altman, Linda Jacobs. 37.95 (***978-0-7656-8111-9(0));*** (Illus.). 96p. (gr. 6 up). (Colonial Life (Group 1) Ser.). 2007. 189.75 (***978-0-7656-8107-2(2))*** Sharpe, M.E. Inc.

Colonial People, 6 bks. Incl. Blacksmith. Kalman, Bobbie. Bedell, Barbara, illus. (gr. 3). 2001. pap. (978-0-7787-0793-6(8)); Colonial Cook. Kalman, Bobbie & Brown, Ellen. (gr. 3). 2001. pap. (978-0-7787-0794-3(6)); Colonial Women. Kalman, Bobbie. (gr. 3). 2002. pap. (978-0-7787-0795-0(4)); Milliner. Walker, Nicki. Bedell, Barbara, illus. (gr. 3). 2001. pap. (978-0-7787-0791-2(1)); Slave Family. Kalman, Bobbie. 2003. pap. (978-0-7787-0792-9(X)); Woodworkers. Kalman, Bobbie & Brady, Deanna. Rouse, Bonna, illus. (gr. 3). 2001. pap. (978-0-7787-0790-5(3)); 32p. (J). 2001. Set pap. (978-0-7787-0788-2(1)); (978-0-7787-0742-4(3)) Crabtree Publishing Co.

Connell, Kate. Servant to Abigail Adams: The Early American Adventures of Hannah Cooper. 2004. (Illus.). 40p. (J). (gr. 4-8). pap. 7.00 (978-0-7567-8216-0(3)) DIANE Publishing Co.

Costain, Meredith & Collins, Paul. Welcome to the United States of America. 2001. (Countries of the World Ser.). (Illus.). 32p. (J). (gr. 4 up). 28.00 (978-0-7910-6542-6(1) , 010212, Chelsea Hse.) Facts On File, Inc.

Cunningham, Robert G. Pearls of the Prairie: Life in Small Dakota Towns, 2002. (Illus.). 256p. lib. bdg. 17.95 (978-0-9717181-3-5(X)) Northern Lights, ND Pr.

Day, Nancy. Your Travel Guide to Civil War America. 2005. (Passport to History Ser.). (Illus.). 96p. (gr. 5-8). lib. bdg. 26.50 (978-0-8225-3078-7(3)) Lerner Publishing Group.

—Your Travel Guide to Colonial America. 2005. (Passport to History Ser.). (Illus.). 96p. (gr. 5-8). lib. bdg. 26.50 (978-0-8225-3079-4(1)) Lerner Publishing Group.

de Paola, Tomie. On My Way: A 26 Fairmount Avenue Book. 2002. (gr. 3-6). lib. bdg. 14.15 (978-0-613-45300-4(X)) Tandem Library Bks.

Doak, Robin. Struggling to Become American: 1899-1940. 2006. (Latino-American History Ser.). (Illus.). 112p. (YA). (gr. 5-8). 35.00 (978-0-8160-6443-4(1) , Chelsea Hse.) Facts On File, Inc.

Draper, Allison Stark. What People Wore During the American Revolution. 2001. (Clothing, Costumes & Uniforms Thoughout American History Ser.). (Illus.). 24p. (J). (gr. 3). lib. bdg. 19.95 (978-0-8239-5666-1(0) , PKCLRE, PowerKids Pr.) Rosen Publishing Group, Inc., The.

—What People Wore on Southern Plantations. 2001. (Clothing, Costumes & Uniforms Thoughout American History Ser.). (Illus.). 24p. (J). (gr. 3). lib. bdg. 19.95 (978-0-8239-5668-5(7) , PKCLSPL, PowerKids Pr.) Rosen Publishing Group, Inc., The.

Ehrlich, Amy, ed. When I Was Your Age Vol. 2: Original Stories about Growing Up. 2006. (Illus.). 187p. (YA). (gr. 8-11). reprint ed. 17.00 (978-1-4223-5199-4(8)) DIANE Publishing Co.

Epstein, Dan. The Eighties, 6 vols. 2000. (Illus.). 32p. (J). (gr. 7-10). 22.95 (978-0-7910-6088-9(8) , Chelsea Hse.) Facts On File, Inc.

—The Fifties, 6 vols. 2000. (Illus.). 32p. (J). (gr. 7-10). 22.95 (978-0-7910-6085-8(3) , Chelsea Hse.) Facts On File, Inc.

—The Nineties, 6 vols. 2000. (Illus.). 32p. (J). (gr. 7-12). 22.95 (978-0-7910-6089-6(6) , Chelsea Hse.) Facts On File, Inc.

—The Seventies, 6 vols. 2000. (Illus.). 32p. (J). (gr. 7-12). 22.95 (978-0-7910-6087-2(X) , Chelsea Hse.) Facts On File, Inc.

—20th Century Pop Culture: Early Years to 1949, 6 vols. 2000. (Illus.). 48p. (J). (gr. 7-12). 27.00 (978-0-7910-6084-1(5) , Chelsea Hse.) Facts On File, Inc.

—20th Century Pop Culture: The Sixties, 6 vols. 2000. (Illus.). 48p. (J). (gr. 7-10). 27.00 (978-0-7910-6086-5(1) , Chelsea Hse.) Facts On File, Inc.

Feinstein, Stephen. The 1920s from Prohibition to Charles Lindbergh. rev. ed. 2006. (Decades of the 20th Century in Color Ser.). (Illus.). 64p. (J). lib. bdg. 27.93 (978-0-7660-2632-2(9)) Enslow Pubs., Inc.

—The 1970s from Watergate to Disco. rev. ed. 2006. (Decades of the 20th Century in Color Ser.). (Illus.). 64p. (J). lib. bdg. 27.93 (978-0-7660-2637-7(X)) Enslow Pubs., Inc.

—The 1980s from Ronald Reagan to MTV. rev. ed. 2006. (Decades of the 20th Century in Color Ser.). (Illus.). 64p. (J). lib. bdg. 27.93 (978-0-7660-2638-4(8)) Enslow Pubs., Inc.

Gillis, Jennifer Blizin. Restored Villages. 2008. (J). (***978-1-60044-563-7(2))*** Rourke Publishing, LLC.

Gourley, Catherine. Welcome to Samantha's World, 1904: Growing up in America's New Century. 1999. (American Girls Collection). (Illus.). 64p. (J). (gr. 2 up). 14.95 (978-1-56247-772-1(2)) American Girl Publishing, Inc.

Gravelle, Karen. Soaring Spirits: Conversations with Native American Teens. 2001. (Illus.). 132p. (YA). (gr. 8-12). pap. 9.95 (978-0-595-16709-8(8) , Backinprint.com) iUniverse, Inc.

Greenlee, Carolyn Wing. Son of South Mountain & Dust. Wing, Thomas W. & Chin, Duncan, illus. 2001. vii, 149p. (J). (978-1-887400-30-5(3)) Earthen Vessel Publishing.

Hall, Margaret. Colonial Times. 2004. (Hands-On American History Ser.). (Illus.). 32p. (J). 27.07 (978-1-4034-6053-0(1)) Heinemann Library.

—The History & Activities of the Colonies. 2006. (Hands-On American History Ser.). (Illus.). 32p. (J). pap. (978-1-4034-6060-8(4)) Heinemann Library.

Hanauer, Jodi. A Child of the 80's Looks Back. 2004. 60p. pap. 12.95 (978-1-4137-2461-5(2)) PublishAmerica, Inc.

Hanson, Erica. The 1920's. 1998. (Cultural History of the United States Through the Decades Ser.). (Illus.). 128p. (YA). (gr. 4-12). 29.95 (978-1-56006-552-4(4) , LML00902-177909, Lucent Bks.) Thomson Gale.

Harcourt School Publishers Staff. Horizons Unit 4: All About People Big Book. 3rd ed. 2001. (Illus.). pap. 169.80 (978-0-15-322572-7(6)) Harcourt Schl. Pubs.

—North of the Rio Grande Below Level. 3rd ed. 2002. (Trophies Reading Program Ser.). (Illus.). pap. 5.10 (978-0-15-323245-9(5)) Harcourt Schl. Pubs.

Harness, Cheryl. Our Colonial Year. Harness, Cheryl, illus. 2005. (Illus.). 40p. (J). (ps-2). 16.95 (978-0-689-83479-0(9) , Simon & Schuster Children's Publishing) Simon & Schuster Children's Publishing.

Hart, Albert Bushnell & Chapman, Annie Bliss. How Our Grandfathers Lived. 1999. (Source-Readers in American History Ser.: No. 3). (Illus.). xiv, 371p. (J). (978-0-89526-297-4(5)) Regnery Publishing, Inc., An Eagle Publishing Co.

Heinz, Brian J. Nathan of Yesteryear & Michael of Today. Friar, Joanne H., illus. 2006. (Exceptional Social Studies Titles for Intermediate Grades). 32p. (J). lib. bdg. 22.60 (978-0-7613-2893-3(9) , Millbrook Pr.) Lerner Publishing Group.

Herrera, Juan Felipe. El Canto de las Palomas/Calling the Doves. ed. 2004. (ENG & SPA., Illus.). (J). (gr. 3-6). spiral bd. (978-0-616-14607-1(8)) Canadian National Institute for the Blind/Institut National Canadien pour les Aveugles.

Himelstein, Abram Shalom. What the Hell Am I Doing Here? The 100 T-Shirt Project. 2005. (Illus.). 128p. pap. 12.00 (978-1-891053-98-6(1)) Garrett County Pr.

Hinds, Kathryn. Daily Living. 2007. (Colonial Life Ser.). (Illus.). 96p. (gr. 6 up). 37.95 (***978-0-7656-8110-2(2)***) Sharpe, M.E. Inc.

Holland, Gini. The 1960's. 1998. (Cultural History of the United States Through the Decades Ser.). (Illus.). 128p. (YA). (gr. 4-12). 29.95 (978-1-56006-556-2(7) , LML00902-177913, Lucent Bks.) Thomson Gale.

Hoobler, Dorothy & Hoobler, Thomas. Vanity Rules: A History of American Fashion & Beauty. 2000. (Single Titles Ser.). (Illus.). 160p. (gr. 7 up). lib. bdg. 28.90 (978-0-7613-1258-1(7) , Millbrook Pr.) Lerner Publishing Group.

Hoyt-Goldsmith, Diane. Three Kings Day: A Celebration at Christmastime. Migdale, Lawrence, illus. 32p. (J). (gr. 4-6). tchr. ed. 16.95 (978-0-8234-1839-8(1)) Holiday Hse., Inc.

Isaacs, Sally Senzell. America in the Time of Martin Luther King Jr. 1948 to 1976, 2 vols. 1999. (America in the Time of... Ser.). (Illus.). 48p. (J). (gr. 4-7). lib. bdg. (978-1-57572-780-6(3)) Heinemann Library.

—Life in St. Augustine. 2003. (J). (gr. k-3). lib. bdg. 15.25 (978-0-613-67337-2(9)) Tandem Library Bks.

—Life on a Pioneer Homestead. (Picture the Past Ser.). (Illus.). 32p. (J). 2002. (gr. k-3). pap. 7.50 (978-1-58810-300-0(5) , 91066); 2000. (gr. 2-4). lib. bdg. 21.36 (978-1-57572-313-6(1)) Heinemann Library.

—Life on a Pioneer Homestead. 2001. (gr. k-3). lib. bdg. 15.90 (978-0-613-86820-4(X)) Tandem Library Bks.

Jackson, Ellen B. Turn of the Century. Ellis, Jan Davey, illus. 1998. 32p. (J). (gr. 2-7). 17.95 (978-0-88106-369-1(X)) Charlesbridge Publishing, Inc.

Kallen, Stuart A. Women of the American Frontier. 2004. (Illus.). 111p. (J). (gr. 7-10). 32.45 (978-1-59018-471-4(8) , Lucent Bks.) Thomson Gale.

—The 1950's. 1998. (Cultural History of the United States Through the Decades Ser.). (Illus.). 128p. (YA). (gr. 4-12). 29.95 (978-1-56006-555-5(9) , LML00902-177912, Lucent Bks.) Thomson Gale.

Kalman, Bobbie. Woodworkers. 2002. (gr. k-3). lib. bdg. 16.40 (978-0-613-82417-0(2)) Tandem Library Bks.

Klobuchar, Lisa. The History & Activities of the Wagon Trail. 2004. (Hands-On American History Ser.). (Illus.). 32p. (J). pap. (978-1-4034-6062-2(0)) Heinemann Library.

—History & Activities of the Wagon Trail. 2004. (Hands-On American History Ser.). (Illus.). 32p. (J). 27.07 (978-1-4034-6055-4(8)) Heinemann Library.

—Pioneer Days. 2004. (Hands-On American History Ser.). (Illus.). 32p. (J). 24.22 (978-1-4034-6056-1(6)) Heinemann Library.

Krebs, Laurie. A Day in the Life. 2004. (Library of Living & Working in Colonial Times). (Illus.). 24p. (J). lib. bdg. 18.75 (978-0-8239-6227-3(X)) Rosen Publishing Group, Inc., The.

Kuklin, Susan. How My Family Lives in America. Kuklin, Susan, illus. 1998. (Illus.). 40p. (J). (ps-2). 6.99 (978-0-689-82221-6(9) , Aladdin) Simon & Schuster Children's Publishing.

Landau, Elaine. El Dia de San Valentin: Caramelos, Amor y Corazones. 2005. (Días Festivos Ser.). (SPA., Illus.). 48p. (J). (ps-ps). lib. bdg. 23.93 (978-0-7660-2613-1(2) , Enslow Elementary) Enslow Pubs., Inc.

—Mardi Gras: Parades, Costumes, & Parties. 2002. (Finding Out about Holidays Ser.). (Illus.). 48p. (J). (gr. 1-4). lib. bdg. 23.93 (978-0-7660-1776-4(1)) Enslow Pubs., Inc.

Lankford, Mary D. Christmas USA. Dugan, Karen, illus. 2006. 48p. (J). lib. bdg. 16.89 (978-0-06-000861-1(X)) HarperCollins Pubs.

Lauderdale, Kathie L., et al. Minefields in the Way: Growing up in America. Affleck, Eric & Weese, Peter, illus. 1998. 112p. (J). pap. 19.95 (978-1-879774-17-9(8)) ICA Publishing Co.

Lieurance, Suzanne. The Prohibition Era in American History. 2003. (In American History Ser.). (Illus.). 112p. (J). (gr. 5-12). lib. bdg. 26.60 (978-0-7660-1840-2(7)) Enslow Pubs., Inc.

Lindop, Edmund. America in the 1930s. 2004. (J). lib. bdg. (978-0-7613-2832-2(7) , Twenty-First Century Bks.) Lerner Publishing Group.

Lisa Klobuchar. The History & Activities of the Frontier. 2006. (Hands-On American History Ser.). (Illus.). 32p. pap. (***978-1-4034-6063-9(9)***) Heinemann Library.

Lowery, Linda & Knutson, Barbara. El Día de los Muertos. Knutson, Barbara, illus. 2005. (Yo Solo Festividades (On My Own Holidays) Ser.). (SPA & ENG., Illus.). 48p. (J). (gr. 2-4). lib. bdg. 25.26 (978-0-8225-3122-7(4) , Ediciones Lerner) Lerner Publishing Group.

MacElroy, Mary H. Work & Play in Colonial Days. reprint ed. 150.00 (978-0-7222-6600-7(6)) Library Reprints, Inc.

McGovern, Ann. If You Lived 100 Years Ago. DiVito, Anna, illus. 1999. (If You Ser.). 80p. (J). (gr. 2-5). pap. 5.99 (978-0-590-96001-4(6)) Scholastic, Inc.

—If You Lived 100 Years Ago. 1999. 12.79 (978-0-606-17545-6(8)); (gr. 3-6). lib. bdg. 14.15 (978-0-613-17918-8(8)) Tandem Library Bks.

Miller, Brandon Marie. Good Women of a Well-Blessed Land: Women's Lives in Colonial America. 2003. (People's History Ser.). (Illus.). 96p. (J). 29.27 (978-0-8225-0032-2(9)) Lerner Publishing Group.

Moore, Kay. If You Lived at the Time of the American Revolution. 1998. (If You Ser.). (Illus.). 80p. (J). (gr. 2-6). pap. 5.99 (978-0-590-67444-7(7)) Scholastic, Inc.

Murray, Julie. Chinese New Year. 2005. (Buddy Book Ser.). (Illus.). 24p. (J). (gr. k-4). lib. bdg. 21.35 (978-1-59197-585-4(9)) ABDO Publishing Co.

Nobleman, Marc Tyler. Cinco de Mayo. 2004. (Let's See Ser.). 24p. (J). (gr. 1 up). lib. bdg. 19.93 (978-0-7565-0768-8(5)) Compass Point Bks.

Pelletier, Fran. Little Pine to King Spruce: A Franco-American Childhood. 2003. (Illus.). 192p. pap. 15.00 (978-0-88448-254-3(5)) Tilbury Hse. Pubs.

Petersen, Christine & Petersen, David. United States of America. 2002. (Illus.). 47p. (J). (gr. 4-7). lib. bdg. 15.25 (978-0-613-54371-2(8)) Tandem Library Bks.

Peterson, Tiffany. Greek Americans. 2004. (We Are America Ser.). (Illus.). 32p. (J). lib. bdg. 24.22 (978-1-4034-5021-0(8)) Heinemann Library.

Press, Petra. The 1930's. 1998. (Cultural History of the United States Through the Decades Ser.). (Illus.). 128p. (YA). (gr. 4-12). 29.95 (978-1-56006-553-1(2) , LML00902-177910, Lucent Bks.) Thomson Gale.

Rau, Dana Meachen. Clothing in American History. 2006. (Illus.). 24p. (J). pap. (978-0-8368-7212-5(6)); lib. bdg. (978-0-8368-7205-7(3)) Stevens, Gareth Inc.

Roberts, Russell. Holidays & Celebrations in Colonial America. 2006. (Building America Ser.). (Illus.). 48p. (J). (gr. 4-8). lib. bdg. 20.95 (978-1-58415-467-9(5)) Mitchell Lane Pubs., Inc.

Roberts, Russell. Life in Colonial America. 2007. (Building America Ser.). (Illus.). 48p. (J). lib. bdg. 29.95 (***978-1-58415-549-2(3)***) Mitchell Lane Pubs., Inc.

Roop, Peter & Roop, Connie. A Home Album. 1998. (Long Ago & Today Ser.). (Illus.). 24p. (J). (gr. 1-3). lib. bdg. 19.92 (978-1-57572-602-1(5)) Heinemann Library.

Samuel, Charlie. Entertainment in Colonial America. 2003. (Primary Sources of Everyday Life in Colonial America Ser.). (Illus.). 24p. (J). lib. bdg. 21.25 (978-0-8239-6600-4(3) , PowerKids Pr.) Rosen Publishing Group, Inc., The.

—Home Life in Colonial America. 2003. (Primary Sources of Everyday Life in Colonial America Ser.). (Illus.). 24p. (J). lib. bdg. 21.25 (978-0-8239-6599-1(6) , PowerKids Pr.) Rosen Publishing Group, Inc., The.

Schaefer, Lola M. Kwanzaa. Saunders-Smith, Gail, ed. 2000. (Holidays & Celebrations Ser.). (Illus.). 24p. (J). (gr. k-1). lib. bdg. 15.93 (978-0-7368-0663-3(6) , Pebble Bks.) Capstone Pr., Inc.

Schaun, George & Schaun, Virginia. American Holidays & Special Days. Wisniewski, David, illus. 3rd ed. 2002. 256p. (J). 20.00 (978-0-917882-54-8(7)) Maryland Historical Pr.

Scott, Janine. Life Long Ago. 2002. (Spyglass Books). (Illus.). 24p. (J). (gr. 1 up). lib. bdg. 18.60 (978-0-7565-0361-1(2)) Compass Point Bks.

Senker, Cath. The USA. 2007. (J). (***978-1-84234-464-4(1)***) Cherrytree Pubns., Inc.

Shea, Kitty. Industrial America. 2004. (We the People Ser.). (Illus.). 48p. (J). 22.60 (978-0-7565-0840-1(1)) Compass Point Bks.

Sheffield, Sarah. Life During the American Civil War. 2002. (Reading Room Collection). (Illus.). 24p. (J). lib. bdg. 18.75 (978-0-8239-3735-6(6)) Rosen Publishing Group, Inc., The.

Sonneborn, Liz. Women of the American West. 2005. (Watts Library). (Illus.). 63p. (J). (gr. k-7). 25.50 (978-0-531-12318-8(9) , Watts, Franklin) Scholastic Library Publishing.

Spangenburg, Ray & Moser, Kit. Teen Fads: Fun, Foolish, or Fatal? 2003. (Teen Issues Ser.). (Illus.). 64p. (J). (gr. 6-12). lib. bdg. 22.60 (978-0-7660-1665-1(X)) Enslow Pubs., Inc.

Stefoff, Rebecca. Colonial Life. 2002. (American Voices From Ser.). (Illus.). xxi, 119p. (J). 34.21 (978-0-7614-1205-2(0) , Benchmark Bks.) Cavendish, Marshall Corp.

Steins, Richard. Colonial America. 2000. (Making of America Ser.). (Illus.). 96p. (J). (gr. 4-7). lib. bdg. 28.54 (978-0-8172-5701-9(2)) Raintree.

Stewart, Gail B. The 1970's. 1998. (Cultural History of the United States Through the Decades Ser.). (Illus.). 128p. (YA). (gr. 4-12). 29.95 (978-1-56006-557-9(5) , LML00902-177914, Lucent Bks.) Thomson Gale.

Stone, Lynn M. America's People. 2002. (Illus.). 24p. (J). lib. bdg. 25.64 (978-1-58952-309-8(1)) Rourke Publishing, LLC.

Swanson, Wayne. Why the West Was Wild. 2004. (Illus.). 48p. (J). (gr. 5). 24.95 (978-1-55037-837-5(6)); pap. 12.95 (978-1-55037-836-8(8)) Annick Pr., Ltd. CAN. *Dist:* Firefly Bks., Ltd.

Tabor, Nancy Maria Grande. Celebrations/Celebraciones: Holidays of the United States of America & Mexico/Dias Feriados de los Estados Unidos y Mexico. Tabor, Nancy Maria Grande, illus. 2004. (SPA & ENG., Illus.). 32p. (J). pap. 7.95 (978-1-57091-550-5(4)) Charlesbridge Publishing, Inc.

Thompson, Gare. When the Mission Padre Came to the Rancho: The Early California Adventures of Rosalinda & Simon Delgado. 2004. (I Am American Ser.). (Illus.). 40p. (J). (gr. 3-7). pap. 6.99 (978-0-7922-6945-8(4) , National Geographic Children's Bks.) National Geographic Society.

Trumbauer, Lisa. About 100 Years Ago. 2000. (Yellow Umbrella Books). (Illus.). 16p. (J). (gr. 1). lib. bdg. 14.60 (978-0-7368-0736-4(5) , Pebble Bks.) Capstone Pr., Inc.

Urdahl, Dean. Lives Lived Large: Minnesotans in the Public Eye. 2001. 200p. pap. 15.00 (978-0-87839-164-6(9)) North Star Pr. of St. Cloud.

Wade, Linda R. Life in Colonial America. 2001. (American Revolution Ser.). (Illus.). 32p. (J). (gr. 3-8). lib. bdg. 24.21 (978-1-57765-152-9(9) , ABDO & Daughters) ABDO Publishing Co.

Warren, Andrea. Growing up on the Prairie. 2000. (978-0-606-17883-9(X)) Tandem Library Bks.

Weber, Valerie. I Come from Chile. 2006. (Illus.). 24p. (J). pap. (978-0-8368-7241-5(X)); lib. bdg. (978-0-8368-7234-7(7)) Stevens, Gareth Inc. (Weekly Reader Early Learning Library).

—I Come from Ivory Coast. 2006. (Illus.). 24p. (J). pap. (978-0-8368-7243-9(6)); lib. bdg. (978-0-8368-7236-1(3)) Stevens, Gareth Inc. (Weekly Reader Early Learning Library).

—I Come from South Korea. 2006. (Illus.). 24p. (J). pap. (978-0-8368-7244-6(4)); lib. bdg. (978-0-8368-7237-8(1)) Stevens, Gareth Inc. (Weekly Reader Early Learning Library).

—I Come from Ukraine. 2006. (Illus.). 24p. (J). pap. (978-0-8368-7245-3(2)); lib. bdg. (978-0-8368-7238-5(X)) Stevens, Gareth Inc. (Weekly Reader Early Learning Library).

Weber, Valerie J. I Come from Afghanistan. 2006. (This Is My Story Ser.). (Illus.). 24p. (J). (gr. k-2). pap. 5.95 (978-0-8368-7240-8(1)); lib. bdg. 19.93 (978-0-8368-7233-0(9)) Stevens, Gareth Inc. (Weekly Reader Early Learning Library).

—I Come from India. 2006. (This Is My Story Ser.). (Illus.). 24p. (J). (gr. k-2). pap. 5.95 (978-0-8368-7242-2(8)); lib. bdg. 19.93 (978-0-8368-7235-4(5)) Stevens, Gareth Inc. (Weekly Reader Early Learning Library).

Whitman, Sylvia. Children of the World War II Home Front. 2005. (Picture the American Past Ser.). (Illus.). 48p. (J). (gr. 2-5). lib. bdg. 22.60 (978-1-57505-484-1(1)) Lerner Publishing Group.

Whitney, Gleaves & Whitney, Louise. B Is for Buckaroo: A Cowboy Alphabet. Guy, Sue, illus. rev. ed. 2003. 40p. (J). 17.95 (978-1-58536-139-7(9)) Sleeping Bear Pr.

Williams, Mary, ed. Culture Wars. 1998. (Opposing Viewpoints Ser.). (Illus.). 208p. (YA). (gr. 8-12). lib. bdg. 32.45 (978-1-56510-939-1(2) , LML00501-177490, Greenhaven Pr., Inc.) Thomson Gale.

Williams, Nancy. A Kwanzaa Celebration: Pop-up Book. Sabuda, Robert, illus. 2004. 14p. (J). reprint ed. 13.00 (978-0-7567-8229-0(5)) DIANE Publishing Co.

Wilmore, Kathy. The Library of Living & Working in Colonial Times: Set 1, 6 bks. Incl. Day in the Life of a Colonial Blacksmith. lib. bdg. 18.75 (978-0-8239-5425-4(0)); Day in the Life of a Colonial Innkeeper. lib. bdg. 18.75 (978-0-8239-5430-8(7)); Day in the Life of a Colonial Printer. lib. bdg. 18.75 (978-0-8239-5428-5(5)); Day in the Life of a Colonial Schoolteacher. lib. bdg. 18.75 (978-0-8239-5429-2(3)); Day in the Life of a Colonial Silversmith. lib. bdg. 18.75 (978-0-8239-5427-8(7)); Day in the Life of a Colonial Wigmaker. lib. bdg. 18.75 (978-0-8239-5426-1(9)); 24p. (J). (gr. 3). 2000. (Illus.). Set lib. bdg. 103.50 (978-0-8239-7006-3(X) , PowerKids Pr.) Rosen Publishing Group, Inc., The.

Wroble, Lisa A. Kids During the Industrial Revolution. 1999. (Kids Throughout History Ser.). (Illus.). 24p. (J). (gr. 3). lib. bdg. 18.75 (978-0-8239-5254-0(1) , PowerKids Pr.) Rosen Publishing Group, Inc., The.

Zocchi, Judy. In the United States. Brodie, Neale, illus. 2005. (Global Adventures II Ser.). 32p. (J). pap. 9.95 (978-1-59646-172-7(1)); lib. bdg. 20.65 (978-1-59646-085-0(7)) Dingles & Co.

—In the United States/en los Estados Unidos. Brodie, Neale, illus. 2005. (Global Adventures II Ser.).Tr. of En los Estados Unidos. (ENG & SPA.). 32p. (J). pap. 9.95 (978-1-59646-174-1(8)); lib. bdg. 20.65 (978-1-59646-086-7(5)) Dingles & Co.

UNITED STATES—SOCIAL LIFE AND CUSTOMS—COLONIAL PERIOD, CA. 1600-1775

Appelbaum, Marci & Cantanese, Jeff. Colonial America. 2003. (Read-Aloud Plays Ser.). (Illus.). 64p. pap., tchr. ed. 11.99 (978-0-439-36602-1(X) , Teaching Resources) Scholastic, Inc.

Barter, James. Colonial New York. 2003. (Illus.). 112p. (J). 29.95 (978-1-59018-250-5(2) , Lucent Bks.) Thomson Gale.

Bial, Raymond. Early American Villages. 2004. (American Community Ser.). (Illus.). 48p. (J). 29.00 (978-0-516-23704-6(7) , Children's Pr.) Scholastic Library Publishing.

Carlson, Laurie M. Colonial Kids: An Activity Guide to Life in the New World. 2003. (Kid's Guide Ser.). (Illus.). 160p. (J). (gr. k-7). pap. 14.95 (978-1-55652-322-9(X)) Chicago Review Pr., Inc.

Cobb, Mary. A Sampler View of Colonial Life: With Projects Kids Can Make. Ellis, Jan Davey, illus. 1998. 64p. (gr. 2-4). lib. bdg. 24.90 (978-0-7613-0372-5(3) , Millbrook Pr.) Lerner Publishing Group.

Colonial Life. (J). tchr. ed. 41.95 (978-0-382-40663-8(X)) Cobblestone Publishing Co.

Colonial Life, 5 bks., Set. Incl. Cities & Towns. Stefoff, Rebecca. 37.95 (***978-0-7656-8109-6(9)***); Daily Living. Hinds, Kathryn. 37.95 (***978-0-7656-8110-2(2)***); Exploration & Settlement. Stefoff, Rebecca. 37.95 (***978-0-7656-8108-9(0)***); Government. Kelly, Martin & Kelly, Melissa. 37.95 (***978-0-7656-8112-6(9)***); Trade & Commerce. Altman, Linda Jacobs. 37.95 (***978-0-7656-8111-9(0)***); (Illus.). 96p. (gr. 6 up). (Colonial Life (Group 1) Ser.). 2007. 189.75 (***978-0-7656-8107-2(2)***) Sharpe, M.E. Inc.

Copeland, Peter F. Life in Colonial America. 2002. (Pictorial Archive Ser.). (Illus.). 48p. (J). pap. 3.95 (978-0-486-41861-2(8)) Dover Pubns., Inc.

Gravois, Michael. Hands-On History: Colonial America. 2003. 48p. pap., tchr. ed. 10.99 (978-0-590-66115-7(9) , Teaching Resources) Scholastic, Inc.

Levy, Elizabeth. Cranky Colonials: Pilgrims, Puritans, Even Pirates! Mc Feeley, Daniel, illus. 2003. (America's Funny but True History Ser.: No. 4). 160p. (J). (gr. 3-5). pap. 4.99 (978-0-590-12244-3(4) , Scholastic Paperbacks) Scholastic, Inc.

Maestro, Betsy. The New Americans: Colonial Times: 1620-1689. Maestro, Giulio, illus. 2004. (American Story Ser.). 48p. (J). (gr. 2 up). pap. 7.99 (978-0-06-057572-4(7) , Harper Trophy) HarperCollins Pubs.

Samuel, Charlie. Inventors & Inventions in Colonial America. 2003. (Primary Sources of Everyday Life in Colonial America Ser.). (Illus.). 24p. (J). lib. bdg. 21.25 (978-0-8239-6601-1(1) , PowerKids Pr.) Rosen Publishing Group, Inc., The.

Stefoff, Rebecca. Colonial Life. 2002. (American Voices From Ser.). (Illus.). xxi, 119p. (J). 34.21 (978-0-7614-1205-2(0) , Benchmark Bks.) Cavendish, Marshall Corp.

Sturm, Ellen. Clothing & Accessories in Colonial America. 2004. (Everyday Life Long Ago Ser.). (J). (978-0-7368-2160-5(0) , Blue Earth Bks.) Capstone Pr., Inc.

Thomas, Mark. Work in Colonial America. 2002. (Welcome Books: Colonial America Ser.). (Illus.). 24p. (J). (ps-2). 18.00 (978-0-516-23934-7(1)); pap. 4.95 (978-0-516-23495-3(1)) Scholastic Library Publishing. (Children's Pr.).

—Work in Colonial America. 2002. (gr. k-3). lib. bdg. 12.95 (978-0-613-58820-1(7)) Tandem Library Bks.

Zohorsky, Janet R. Colonial Craftsman. 2004. (Working Life Ser.). (Illus.). 112p. (J). (gr. 7-10). 29.95 (978-1-59018-176-8(X) , Lucent Bks.) Thomson Gale.

UNITED STATES—SOLDIERS

see Soldiers—United States

UNITED STATES—STATE GOVERNMENTS

see State Governments

UNITED STATES—STATISTICS

Bell, David C. & Italiano, Bob. New View Almanac. Glassman, Bruce, ed. 3rd ed. 2002. (Illus.). 608p. (J). 49.94 (978-1-56711-674-8(4) , Blackbirch Pr., Inc.) Thomson Gale.

World Almanac for Kids 2003. 2002. (gr. 3-6). lib. bdg. 21.05 (978-0-613-53787-2(4)) Tandem Library Bks.

UNITED STATES—SUPREME COURT

Aaseng, Nathan. You Are the Supreme Court Justice. rev. ed. 2000. (Great Decisions Ser.). (Illus.). 160p. (gr. 5 up). lib. bdg. 19.95 (978-1-881508-14-4(5)) Oliver Pr., Inc.

Bayer-Berenbaum, Linda. Ruth Bader Ginsburg: Supreme Court Justice. 2000. (Women of Achievement Ser.). (Illus.). 112p. (J). (gr. 4-7). 30.00 (978-0-7910-5287-7(7) , Chelsea Hse.) Facts On File, Inc.

Bayer, Linda N. Ruth Bader Ginsburg: Supreme Court Justice. 1999. (Illus.). 112p. (gr. 5-9). pap. 9.95 (978-0-7910-5288-4(5) , Chelsea Hse.) Facts On File, Inc.

Beier, Anne. The Supreme Court & the Judicial Branch. 2003. (Primary Source Library of American Citizenship). (Illus.). 32p. (J). pap. (978-1-4042-5092-5(1)) Rosen Publishing Group, Inc., The.

Benson, Michael. William Howard Taft. 2005. (Presidential Leaders Ser.). (Illus.). 112p. (J). 29.27 (978-0-8225-0849-6(4) , Lerner Pubns.) Lerner Publishing Group.

Billitteri, Thomas J. The Gault Case: Legal Rights for Young People. 2000. (Landmark Supreme Court Cases Ser.). (Illus.). 128p. (YA). (gr. 6-12). lib. bdg. 26.60 (978-0-7660-1340-7(5)) Enslow Pubs., Inc.

Boerst, William J. Galileo Galilei & the Science of Motion. 2004. (Profiles in Science Ser.). (Illus.). 144p. (YA). (gr. 6-12). lib. bdg. 26.95 (978-1-931798-00-6(1)) Reynolds, Morgan Inc.

Britton, Tamara L. The United States Supreme Court. 2005. (Symbols, Landmarks, & Monuments Set Ii Ser.). (Illus.). 32p. (J). (gr. k-6). lib. bdg. 22.78 (978-1-59197-522-9(0)) ABDO Publishing Co.

Compston, Christine L. Earl Warren: Justice for All. 2001. (Oxford Portraits Ser.). (Illus.). 160p. (YA). (gr. 9 up). 28.00 (978-0-19-513001-0(4)) Oxford Univ. Pr., Inc.

Conway, John Richard. A Look at the Constitution: Creating a More Perfect Union. 2008. (J). (***978-1-59845-072-9(7)*** , MyReportLinks.com Bks.) Enslow Pubs., Inc.

DeJohn, Heather. The Chief Justice of the Supreme Court. 2002. (American Leaders Ser.). (Illus.). 32p. (J). 23.70 (978-1-56711-663-2(9) , Blackbirch Pr., Inc.) Thomson Gale.

Dubois, Muriel L. & Smith, Steven S. The U. S. Supreme Court. 2003. (First Facts Ser.). (Illus.). 24p. (J). lib. bdg. 21.26 (978-0-7368-2291-6(7)) Capstone Pr., Inc.

Elish, Dan. The U. S. Supreme Court. 2007. (Cornerstones of Freedom). (Illus.). 48p. (J). (gr. 4-6). 26.00 (978-0-516-23637-7(7) , Children's Pr.) Scholastic Library Publishing.

Facts on File, Inc. Staff, ed. Great Supreme Court Decisions Set, 8 Vols. 2006. 240.00 (978-0-7910-9458-7(8) , Chelsea Hse.) Facts On File, Inc.

Farish, Leah. Lemon vs. Kurtzman: The Religion & Public Funds Case. 2000. (Landmark Supreme Court Cases Ser.). (Illus.). 128p. (YA). (gr. 6-12). lib. bdg. 26.60 (978-0-7660-1339-1(1)) Enslow Pubs., Inc.

Feldman, Ruth Tenzer. Thurgood Marshall. 2001. (Biography Ser.). (Illus.). 112p. (J). (gr. 6-12). lib. bdg. 27.93 (978-0-8225-4989-5(1) , Lerner Pubns.) Lerner Publishing Group.

Freedman, Suzanne. United States vs. Amistad: Rebellion on a Slave Ship. 2000. (Landmark Supreme Court Cases Ser.). (Illus.). 112p. (J). (gr. 6-12). lib. bdg. 26.60 (978-0-7660-1337-7(5)) Enslow Pubs., Inc.

Gibson, Karen Bush. Thurgood Marshall. 2002. (Photo-Illustrated Biographies Ser.). (Illus.). 24p. (J). (gr. 2-3). lib. bdg. 18.60 (978-0-7368-1113-2(3) , Bridgestone Bks.) Capstone Pr., Inc.

Giddens-White, Bryon. Our Government: The Supreme Court & the Judicial Branch. 2005. (Illus.). 32p. (J). 28.21 (978-1-4034-6603-7(3)); pap. (978-1-4034-6608-2(4)) Heinemann Library.

Goldish, Meish. Our Supreme Court. 2002. (I Know America Ser.: Vol. 4). 48p. (gr. 2). pap. 9.95 (978-0-7613-1847-7(X) , Millbrook Pr.) Lerner Publishing Group.

Hancock, Maryann. The Supreme Court. 2006. (Illus.). 32p. pap. (978-1-4034-7008-9(1)); (J). lib. bdg. 28.21 (978-1-4034-7001-0(4)) Heinemann Library.

Harris, Nancy. What's the Supreme Court? 2007. (J). ***978-1-4034-9467-2(3));** pap. **(*978-1-4034-9473-3(8))** Heinemann Library.

Heath, David. The Supreme Court of the United States. 1998. (American Civics Ser.). (Illus.). 48p. (J). (gr. 3-4). lib. bdg. 22.60 (978-0-7368-0003-7(4) , Bridgestone Bks.) Capstone Pr., Inc.

Horn, Geoffrey M. The Supreme Court. 2003. (World Almanac Library of American Government). (Illus.). 48p. (J). (gr. 5 up). pap. 14.95 (978-0-8368-5464-0(0)); lib. bdg. 30.00 (978-0-8368-5459-6(4)) Stevens, Gareth Inc. (World Almanac Library).

—Thurgood Marshall. 2004. (Trailblazers of the Modern World Ser.). (Illus.). 48p. (J). (gr. 5 up). pap. 11.95 (978-0-8368-5258-5(3)); lib. bdg. 30.00 (978-0-8368-5098-7(X)) Stevens, Gareth Inc. (World Almanac Library).

—World Almanac Library of American Government: The Armed Forces; Congress; The Presidency; The Supreme Court, 4 bks. 2002. (Illus.). (J). (gr. 5 up). pap. 59.80 (978-0-8368-5460-2(8) , World Almanac Library) Stevens, Gareth Inc.

Howse, Jennifer. Sandra Day O'Connor. 2007. (J). **(*978-1-59036-647-9(6)); (*978-1-59036-648-6(4))** Weigl Pubs., Inc.

Jarrow, Gail. Robert H. Jackson: Voice of Justice. 2008. (J). **(*978-1-59078-511-9(8)** , Calkins Creek) Boyds Mills Pr.

Jones, Brenn. Learning about Equal Rights from the Life of Ruth Bader Ginsburg. 2002. (Character Building Book Ser.). (Illus.). 24p. (J). (gr. 3). lib. bdg. 18.75 (978-0-8239-5781-1(0) , PowerKids Pr.) Rosen Publishing Group, Inc., The.

LeVert, Suzanne. The Supreme Court. 2002. (Kaleidoscope - Government Ser.). (Illus.). 48p. (J). 25.64 (978-0-7614-1453-7(3) , Benchmark Bks.) Cavendish, Marshall Corp.

Lewis, Thomas & Wilson, Richard L., eds. Encyclopedia of the U. S. Supreme Court, 3 vols., Vol. 3. 2000. (Illus.). 1200p. (gr. 9 up). lib. bdg. 331.00 (978 0 89356-097-3(9) , 208) Salem Pr., Inc.

Madani, Hamed. The Judicial Branch: Interpreting America's Laws. 2008. (Federal Government Ser.). 128p. (J). (gr. 6 up). lib. bdg. 33.27 (978-1-59845-059-0(X) , MyReportLinks.com Bks.) Enslow Pubs., Inc.

Marshall, Thurgood. Thurgood Marshall: Supreme Court Justice. (Black Americans of Achievement Ser.). (Illus.). 112p. (J). (gr. 6-12). 2005. pap. 13.25 (978-0-7910-8337-6(3)); 2004. 30.00 (978-0-7910-8163-1(X)) Facts On File, Inc. (Chelsea Hse.).

McElroy, Lisa Tucker. John G. Roberts, Jr: Chief Justice. 2007. (Gateway Biography Ser.). (J). 23.93 (978-0-8225-6389-1(4) , Lerner Pubns.) Lerner Publishing Group.

—Meet My Grandmother: She's a Supreme Court Justice. 1999. (978-0-606-18294-2(2)); (gr. 3-6). lib. bdg. 16.40 (978-0-613-26179-1(8)) Tandem Library Bks.

—Meeting Grandmother: She's a Supreme Court Justice. 2000. (Grandmothers at Work Ser.: 4). (Illus.). 32p. (J). (gr. 2-4). pap. 7.95 (978-0-7613-1386-1(9) , Millbrook Pr.) Lerner Publishing Group.

—Sandra Day O'Connor: Supreme Court Justice. 2003. (Gateway Biography Ser.). 48p. lib. bdg. 23.90 (978-0-7613-2502-4(6) , Millbrook Pr.) Lerner Publishing Group.

McPherson, Stephanie Sammartino. Lau vs. Nichols: Bilingual Education in Public Schools. 2000. (Landmark Supreme Court Cases Ser.). (Illus.). 128p. (YA). (gr. 6-12). lib. bdg. 26.60 (978-0-7660-1472-5(X)) Enslow Pubs., Inc.

Morris, Roz. Hugo L. Black: Justice for All. 2001. (Alabama Roots Biography Ser.). (Illus.). 128p. (J). (978-1-57864-851-5(5)) Seacoast Publishing, Inc.

Mountjoy, Shane & McNeese, Tim. Marbury V. Madison. 2006. (Great Supreme Court Decisions Ser.). (Illus.). 144p. (J). (gr. 5-8). 30.00 (978-0-7910-9240-8(2) , Chelsea Hse.) Facts On File, Inc.

Murphy, Patricia J. The U. S. Supreme Court. 2002. (Let's See Library). (Illus.). 24p. (J). (gr. 1 up). lib. bdg. 19.93 (978-0-7565-0197-6(0)) Compass Point Bks.

Naden, Corinne J. & Blue, Rose. Marbury V. Madison: The Court's Foundation. 2004. (Supreme Court Milestones Ser.). (Illus.). 128p. (J). 37.07 (978-0-7614-1840-5(7) , Benchmark Bks.) Cavendish, Marshall Corp.

Our Supreme Court: A History with 14 Activities. 2006. (For Kids Ser.). (Illus.). 196p. (YA). (gr. 7 up). pap. 16.95 (978-1-55652-607-7(5)) Chicago Review Pr., Inc.

Patrick, John J. The Supreme Court of the United States: A Student Companion. 3rd rev. ed. 2006. (Oxford Student Companions to American Government Ser.). (Illus.). 416p. (YA). (gr. 6 up). 60.00 (978-0-19-530925-6(1)) Oxford Univ. Pr., Inc.

Pettifor, Bonnie & Petit, Charles E. Weeks vs. United States: Illegal Search & Seizure. 2000. (Landmark Supreme Court Cases Ser.). (Illus.). 128p. (YA). (gr. 6-12). lib. bdg. 26.60 (978-0-7660-1341-4(3)) Enslow Pubs., Inc.

Prentzas, G. S. Gideon V. Wainwright: The Right to Free Legal Counsel. 2007. (Great Supreme Court Decisions Ser.). 120p. (J). (gr. 5-8). 30.00 (978-0-7910-9383-2(2) , Chelsea Hse.) Facts On File, Inc.

Randolph, Ryan P. How to Draw the Life & Times of William Howard Taft. 2007. (Kid's Guide to Drawing the Presidents of the United States of America Ser.). (Illus.). 32p. (J). 25.25 (978-1-4042-3003-3(3) , PowerKids Pr.) Rosen Publishing Group, Inc., The.

Rowh, Mark. Thurgood Marshall: Civil Rights Attorney & Supreme Court Justice. 2002. (African-American Biographies Ser.). (Illus.). 112p. (YA). (gr. 6-12). lib. bdg. 26.60 (978-0-7660-1547-0(5)) Enslow Pubs., Inc.

Sandra Day O'Connor. 2005. 12p. (gr. k-4). 2.95 **(*978-0-635-02621-7(X))** Gallopade International.

Savage, David. The Supreme Court & Individual Rights. 4th ed. 2004. (Illus.). 416p. 40.00 (978-1-56802-887-3(3)) CQ Pr.

Schlesinger, Arthur M., Jr., ed. The Supreme Court. 2000. (Your Government Ser.). (Illus.). 64p. (YA). (gr. 4-7). 25.00 (978-0-7910-5532-8(9) , Chelsea Hse.) Facts On File, Inc.

Sergis, Diana K. Cipollone vs. Liggett Group: Suing Tobacco Companies. 2001. (Landmark Supreme Court Cases Ser.). (Illus.). 128p. (J). (gr. 6-12). lib. bdg. 26.60 (978-0-7660-1343-8(X)) Enslow Pubs., Inc.

Steadwell Books Publishing Staff, ed. The Supreme Court. 1999. (American Government Today Ser.). (Illus.). 48p. (J). (gr. 4-7). lib. bdg. 22.83 (978-0-7398-1787-2(6)) Raintree.

Supreme Court DBQs: Exploring the Cases that Changed History. 2007. (YA). spiral bd. 29.95 **(*978-1-932785-28-9(0))** Bill of Rights Institute, The.

Supreme Court Milestones Group 3, 5 bks., Set. Incl. Gideon v. Wainwright : The Right to Free Counsel. Fridell, Ron. 144p. lib. bdg. 39.93 (978-0-7614-2146-7(7)); New York Times Co. v. Sullivan : Freedom of the Press or Libel? Gold, Susan Dudley. 144p. lib. bdg. 39.93 (978-0-7614-2145-0(9)); Reno v. ACLU : Internet Censorship. Axelrod-Contrada, Joan. 144p. lib. bdg. 39.93 (978-0-7614-2144-3(0)); Tinker v. Des Moines : Free Speech for Students. Gold, Susan Dudley. 143p. lib. bdg. 39.93 (978-0-7614-2142-9(4)); United States v. Amistad : Slave Ship Mutiny. Gold, Susan Dudley. 144p. lib. bdg. 39.93 (978-0-7614-2143-6(2)); (Illus.). (J). 2006. 2007. Set lib. bdg. 199.64 **(*978-0-7614-2140-5(8)** , Benchmark Bks.) Cavendish, Marshall Corp.

The Supreme Court of the United States. (American Civics Ser.). 48p. (YA). 6.95 (978-0-7368-8856-1(X)) Capstone Pr., Inc.

Taylor-Butler, Christine. The Supreme Court. (True Book-trade;: American History Ser.). 48p. (J). 2008. pap. 6.95 **(*978-0-531-14786-3(X));** 2007. (Illus.). (gr. 3-5). 26.00 **(*978 0 531-12636-3(6))** Scholastic Library Publishing. (Children's Pr.).

Taylor-Butler, Christine. Thurgood Marshall. 2006. 32p. (gr. 1-2). (YA). pap. 4.95 (978-0-516-27099-9(0)); (Illus.). (J). 20.50 (978-0-516-25015-1(9)) Scholastic Library Publishing. (Children's Pr.).

Wagner, Heather Lehr. The Supreme Court. 2nd rev. ed. 2007. (U. S. Government Ser.). 104p. (YA). (gr. 5-8). 30.00 **(*978-0-7910-9283-5(6)** , Chelsea Hse.) Facts On File, Inc.

Wetterer, Charles M. & Wetterer, Margaret K. Chief Justice. Walters, Kurt K. C., illus. 2005. 32p. (J). (978-1-59336-306-2(0)); pap. (978-1-59336-307-9(9)) Mondo Publishing.

Wheeler, Jill C. Thurgood Marshall. 2003. (Breaking Barriers Ser.). (Illus.). 64p. (J). (gr. 3-8). lib. bdg. 25.65 (978-1-57765-907-5(4)) ABDO Publishing Co.

Whitelaw, Nancy. Mr. Civil Rights: The Story of Thurgood Marshall. 2nd rev. exp. ed. 2004. (Notable Americans Ser.). (Illus.). 144p. (YA). (gr. 6-12). 23.95 (978-1-931798-02-0(8)) Reynolds, Morgan Inc.

Williams, Jean Kinney. Sandra Day O'Connor: Lawyer & Supreme Court Justice. 2000. (Career Biographies Ser.). (Illus.). 128p. (J). (gr. 6-12). 25.00 (978-0-89434-355-1(6) , F407, Ferguson Publishing Co.) Facts On File, Inc.

Young, Evan A. Lone Star Justice: A Biography of Justice Tom C. Clark. 1998. (Illus.). 160p. (YA). (gr. 7 up). 12.95 (978-1-885777-11-9(6)) Hendrick-Long Publishing Co.

UNITED STATES—TAXATION

see Taxation—United States

UNITED STATES—TERRITORIAL EXPANSION

Anderson, Dale. Westward Expansion. 2000. (Making of America Ser.). (Illus.). 96p. (J). (gr. 4-7). lib. bdg. 28.54 (978-0-8172-5705-7(5)) Raintree.

Burgan, Michael. A Changing Nation. 2006. (Making a New Nation Ser.). (Illus.). 48p. (J). (978-1-4034-7830-6(9)); pap. (978-1-4034-7837-5(6)) Heinemann Library.

—The Louisiana Purchase. 2002. (We the People Ser.). (Illus.). 48p. (J). (gr. 4 up). lib. bdg. 22.60 (978-0-7565-0210-2(1)) Compass Point Bks.

—The Louisiana Purchase. 2006. (Making a New Nation Ser.). (Illus.). 48p. (J). (978-1-4034-7828-3(7)); pap. (978-1-4034-7835-1(X)) Heinemann Library.

Casciato, Daniel. Expansion & Reform. 2007. (J). **(*978-1-59036-741-4(3)); (*978-1-59036-742-1(1))** Weigl Pubs., Inc.

Collier, Christopher & Collier, James Lincoln. The United States Enters the World: 1867-1919. 2000. (Drama of American History Ser.). (Illus.). 96p. (J). (gr. 5-9). lib. bdg. 31.36 (978-0-7614-1053-9(8) , Benchmark Bks.) Cavendish, Marshall Corp.

Deitch, JoAnne Weisman, ed. A Century of Westward Expansion. 2000. (Researching American History Ser.). (Illus.). 56p. (J). (978-1-57960-064-8(6)) History Compass, LLC.

Faber, Harold. John Charles Fremont: Pathfinder to the West. 2002. (Great Explorations Ser.). (Illus.). 79p. (J). 29.93 (978-0-7614-1481-0(9) , Benchmark Bks.) Cavendish, Marshall Corp.

Favor, Lesli J. A Historical Atlas of America's Manifest Destiny. 2005. (United States, Historical Atlases of the Growth of a New Nation Ser.). (Illus.). 64p. (J). (gr. 7-12). lib. bdg. 30.60 (978-1-4042-0201-6(3)) Rosen Publishing Group, Inc., The.

Harness, Cheryl. The Remarkable Rough-Riding Life of Theodore Roosevelt & the Rise of Empire America. 2007. (Illus.). 144p. (J). (gr. 3-7). lib. bdg. 25.90 (978-1-4263-0009-7(3) , National Geographic Children's Bks.) National Geographic Society.

Jaffe, Elizabeth Dana. The Louisiana Purchase. 2002. (Let Freedom Ring Ser.). (Illus.). 48p. (J). (gr. 3-4). lib. bdg. 22.60 (978-0-7368-1100-2(1) , Bridgestone Bks.) Capstone Pr., Inc.

Jarnow, Jesse. Manifest Destiny: A Primary Source History of the Settlement of the American Heartland in the Late 19th Century. 2005. (Illus.). 64p. (J). (gr. 5-8). lib. bdg. 29.25 (978-1-4042-0176-7(9)) Rosen Publishing Group, Inc., The.

Landau, Elaine. The Louisiana Purchase: Would You Close the Deal? 2008. (What Would You Do? Ser.). (Illus.). 48p. (J). (gr. 3-4). lib. bdg. 23.93 **(*978-0-7660-2902-6(6)** , Enslow Elementary) Enslow Pubs., Inc.

Marcovitz, Hal. John C. Fremont: Pathfinder of the West. 2001. (Explorers of New Worlds Ser.). (Illus.). (J). 63p. pap. 25.00 (978-0-7910-6431-3(X)); 64p. 25.00 (978-0-7910-6430-6(1)) Facts On File, Inc. (Chelsea Hse.).

Marsh, Carole. What a Deal! The Louisiana Purchase. 2003. 32p. (J). (gr. 3-8). pap. 5.95 (978-0-635-02123-6(4)) Gallopade International.

Maynard, Charles W. John Charles Fremont: The Pathfinder. 2003. (Famous Explorers of the American West Ser.). (Illus.). 24p. (J). lib. bdg. 18.75 (978-0-8239-6289-1(X) , PowerKids Pr.) Rosen Publishing Group, Inc., The.

Nelson, Sheila. From Sea to Shining Sea. 2005. (How America Became America Ser.). (Illus.). 96p. (J). lib. bdg. (978-1-59084-907-1(8)) Mason Crest Pubs.

—From Sea to Shining Sea: Americans Move West, 13 vols. 2005. (How America Became America Ser.). (Illus.). 96p. (J). lib. bdg. (978-1-59084-900-2(0)) Mason Crest Pubs.

—Thomas Jefferson's America: The Louisiana Purchase (1800-1811) 2005. (How America Became America Ser.). (Illus.). 96p. (J). lib. bdg. (978-1-59084-904-0(3)) Mason Crest Pubs.

Nextext Staff, contrib. by. How America Grew, 1775-1914. 2004. (Stories in History Ser.). (Illus.). 208p. (gr. 6-12). (978-0-618-22196-7(4) , 2-00295) McDougal Littell Inc.

Price Hossell, Karen. John C. Fremont. (Groundbreakers Ser.). (Illus.). 48p. (J). 2003. (gr. 5-7). lib. bdg. 27.07 (978-1-4034-0244-8(2)); 2002. pap. 8.50 (978-1-4034-0480-0(1)) Heinemann Library.

Sanna, Ellyn. The Expanding United States: The Rise of Nationalism 1812-1820. 2004. (How America Became America Ser.). (Illus.). 89p. (J). (ps-7). lib. bdg. (978-1-59084-905-7(1)) Mason Crest Pubs.

Schaefer, Ted. Westward to the Pacific. 2006. (Making a New Nation Ser.). (Illus.). 48p. (J). (978-1-4034-7829-0(5)); pap. (978-1-4034-7836-8(8)) Heinemann Library.

Schaffer, David. The Louisiana Purchase—the Deal of the Century That Doubled the Nation. 2006. (Wild History of the American West Ser.). (Illus.). 128p. (J). lib. bdg. 33.27 (978-1-59845-018-7(2) , MyReportLinks.com Bks.) Enslow Pubs., Inc.

Schlaepfer, Gloria G. The Louisiana Purchase. 2005. (Watts Library). (Illus.). 63p. (J). (gr. 5-8). 25.50 (978-0-531-12300-3(6) , Watts, Franklin) Scholastic Library Publishing.

Schwartz, Eric. Crossing the Seas: Americans Form an Empire (1890-1899) 2004. (How America Became America Ser.). (Illus.). 91p. (J). (ps-7). lib. bdg. (978-1-59084-910-1(8)) Mason Crest Pubs.

Smith, Robert W. Spotlight on America: Westward Movement. 2006. pap. 12.99 (978-1-4206-3216-3(7)) Teacher Created Resources, Inc.

Steele, Christy. California & the Southwest Join the United States. 2005. (Illus.). 48p. (J). pap. (978-0-8368-5793-1(3)); lib. bdg. 30.00 (978-0-8368-5786-3(0)) Stevens, Gareth Inc. (World Almanac Library).

—Pioneer Life in the American West. 2005. (Illus.). 48p. (J). pap. (978-0-8368-5797-9(6)); lib. bdg. 30.00 (978-0-8368-5790-0(9)) Stevens, Gareth Inc. (World Almanac Library).

—Texas Joins the United States. 2005. (Illus.). 48p. (J). pap. (978-0-8368-5798-6(4)); lib. bdg. 30.00 (978-0-8368-5791-7(7)) Stevens, Gareth Inc. (World Almanac Library).

Stefoff, Rebecca. The Opening of the West. 2002. (American Voices From Ser.). (Illus.). xxii, 105p. (J). 34.21 (978-0-7614-1201-4(8) , Benchmark Bks.) Cavendish, Marshall Corp.

—Texas & the Far West. 2002. (North American Historical Atlases Ser.). (Illus.). 48p. (J). 27.07 (978-0-7614-1345-5(6) , Benchmark Bks.) Cavendish, Marshall Corp.

Thompson, Linda. La Compra de Louisiana. 2005. (ENG & SPA., Illus.). 48p. (J). (978-1-59515-662-4(3)) Rourke Publishing, LLC.

—Los Grandes Lagos. 2005. (ENG & SPA., Illus.). 48p. (J). (978-1-59515-661-7(5)) Rourke Publishing, LLC.

—The Great Lakes. 2006. (Expansion of America II Ser.). (Illus.). 48p. (gr. 4-8). 20.95 (978-1-59515-512-2(0)) Rourke Publishing, LLC.

—The Louisiana Purchase. 2006. (Expansion of America II Ser.). (Illus.). 48p. (gr. 4-8). 20.95 (978-1-59515-513-9(9)) Rourke Publishing, LLC.

—The Mississippi & West. 2005. (Expansion of America Ser.). (Illus.). 48p. (gr. 4-8). 20.95 (978-1-59515-224-4(5)) Rourke Publishing, LLC.

—Territorios de Estados Unidos. 2005. (ENG & SPA., Illus.). 48p. (J). (978-1-59515-658-7(5)) Rourke Publishing, LLC.

Thro, Ellen. Growing & Dividing. 2000. (Making of America Ser.). (Illus.). 96p. (J). (gr. 4-7). lib. bdg. 28.54 (978-0-8172-5704-0(7)) Raintree.

Torr, James D. Westward Expansion. 2002. (gr. 7-12). lib. bdg. 33.25 (978-0-613-73610-7(9)) Tandem Library Bks.

Torr, James D., ed. Westward Expansion. 2003. (Interpreting American History Through Primary Documents Ser.x). (Illus.). 208p. (J). 32.45 (978-0-7377-1134-9(5) , Greenhaven Pr., Inc.) Thomson Gale.

Zurn, Jon. The Louisiana Purchase. 2007. (Essential Events Ser.). (ENG., Illus.). 112p. (YA). (gr. 8-12). lib. bdg. 32.79 **(*978-1-59928-853-6(2)** , Essential Library) ABDO Publishing Co.

UNITED STATES—TERRITORIES AND POSSESSIONS

Blackbirch Press Staff, contrib. by. Kid's Visual Reference of the USA. 2002. (Illus.). 320p. (J). 49.94 (978-1-56711-659-5(0) , Blackbirch Pr., Inc.) Thomson Gale.

Brown, Jonatha A. Puerto Rico & Other Outlying Areas. 2006. (Portraits of the States Ser.). (Illus.). 32p. (J). pap. (978-0-8368-4693-5(1)); lib. bdg. 23.33 (978-0-8368-4674-4(5)) Stevens, Gareth Inc.

Doherty, Craig A. & Doherty, Katherine M. The Thirteen Colonies Set. 2005. (Thirteen Colonies Ser.). 128-160p. (gr. 4-9). 350.00 (978-0-8160-6316-1(8)); 175.00 (978-0-8160-6109-9(2)); 455.00 (978-0-8160-5406-0(1)) Facts On File, Inc.

Thompson, Linda. Territorios de Estados Unidos. 2005. (ENG & SPA., Illus.). 48p. (J). (978-1-59515-658-7(5)) Rourke Publishing, LLC.

—United States Territories. 2006. (Expansion of America II Ser.). (Illus.). 48p. (gr. 4-8). 20.95 (978-1-59515-515-3(5)) Rourke Publishing, LLC.

—US Territories. 2005. 48p. pap. 7.45 (978-1-59515-829-1(4)) Rourke Publishing, LLC.

UNITED STATES—TREASURY DEPT.

Ruffin, David C. The Duties & Responsibilities of the Secretary of the Treasury. 2005. (Your Government in Action Ser.). (Illus.). 32p. (J). 21.95 (978-1-4042-2690-6(7) , PowerKids Pr.) Rosen Publishing Group, Inc., The.

UNITED STATES—TREATIES

see United States—Foreign Relations—Treaties

UNITED STATES—VICE-PRESIDENTS

see Vice-presidents—United States

UNITED STATES—WOMEN

see Women—United States

UNITED STATES—WORLD WAR, 1939-1945

see World War, 1939-1945—United States

UNITED STATES CAPITOL (WASHINGTON, D.C.)

Aikman, Lonnelle. We, the People: The Story of the United States Capitol. 15th ed. 2002. (Illus.). 144p. (YA). (gr. 7-12). pap. 9.95 (978-0-916200-27-5(2)) U. S. Capitol Historical Society.

Benchmark Education Staff, compiled by. Historical Communities. 2006. spiral bd. 109.00 **(*978-1-4108-7097-1(9))** Benchmark Education Co.

Britton, Tamara L. The Capitol. 2005. (Checkerboard History Library). (Illus.). 40p. (J). (gr. k-6). lib. bdg. 22.78 (978-1-57765-848-1(5)) ABDO Publishing Co.

Campodonica, Carol A. How Congress Works. Miller, Bondell, ed. Anderson, Bill, illus. Uni Photo Picture Agency Staff, photos by. Date not set. (J). (gr. 4-5). pap. (978-0-9648488-9-4(9)) Buzzard Pr. International.

Curlee, Lynn. Capital. Curlee, Lynn, illus. 2006. 48p. (J). pap. 7.99 (978-1-4169-1801-1(9) , Aladdin) Simon & Schuster Children's Publishing.

DeGezelle, Terri. The U. S. Capitol. 2003. (First Facts Ser.). (Illus.). 24p. (J). lib. bdg. 19.93 (978-0-7368-2294-7(1)) Capstone Pr., Inc.

Firestone, Mary. Our U.S. Capitol. Skeens, Matthew, illus. 2007. (J). lib. bdg. **(*978-1-4048-3719-5(1))** Picture Window Bks.

Hancock, Maryann. The U. S. Capitol. 2006. (Land of the Free Ser.). (Illus.). 32p. (J). lib. bdg. 28.21 (978-1-4034-7000-3(6)) Heinemann Library.

—The U.S. Capitol. 2006. (Illus.). 32p. (J). pap. (978-1-4034-7007-2(3)) Heinemann Library.

Hicks, Terry Allan. The Capitol. 2006. (Symbols of America Ser.). (Illus.). 40p. (J). lib. bdg. 28.50 (978-0-7614-2132-0(7) , Benchmark Bks.) Cavendish, Marshall Corp.

Schaefer, Lola M. El Capitolio. 2003. (Símbolos de Libertad Ser.). (SPA.). 32p. (J). pap. 6.95 (978-1-4034-3023-6(3)) Heinemann Library.

—The U. S. Capitol. (Symbols of Freedom Ser.). (Illus.). 32p. (J). (gr. k-2). 2002. pap. 6.95 (978-1-58810-399-4(4) , 91194); 2001. lib. bdg. (978-1-58810-178-5(9)) Heinemann Library.

—U S Capitol. 2002. (gr. k-3). lib. bdg. 14.75 (978-0-613-68180-3(0)) Tandem Library Bks.

Silate, Jennifer. The United States Capitol. 2004. (Illus.). 24p. (J). lib. bdg. (978-1-4042-2694-4(X)) Rosen Publishing Group, Inc., The.

UNITED STATES PEACE CORPS

see Peace Corps (U.S.)

UNIVERSAL HISTORY

see World History

UNIVERSE

Alex, Joanne DeFilipp. I Wonder What's Out There: A Vision of the Universe for Primary Classes. 2003. (Illus.). 64p. (J). spiral bd. (978-0-939195-32-9(1)) Parent Child Pr., Inc.

Allan, Jerry & Allan, Georgiana. The Horse & the Iron Ball: A Journey Through Time, Space & Technology. Allan, Jerry, illus. 2000. (Picture Bks.). (Illus.). 48p. (J). (ps-3). lib. bdg. (978-0-8225-2158-7(X) , Carolrhoda Bks.) Lerner Publishing Group.

Asimov, Isaac & Hantula, Richard. The Birth of Our Universe. 2005. (Isaac Asimov's 21st Century Library of the Universe). (Illus.). 32p. (J). lib. bdg. 24.67 (978-0-8368-3964-7(1)) Stevens, Gareth Inc.

—Black Holes, Pulsars, & Quasars. 2005. (Isaac Asimov's 21st Century Library of the Universe). (Illus.). 32p. (J). lib. bdg. 24.67 (978-0-8368-3965-4(X)) Stevens, Gareth Inc.

—Is There Life in Outer Space? 2004. (Isaac Asimov's 21st Century Library of the Universe). (Illus.). 32p. (J). lib. bdg. 24.67 (978-0-8368-3950-0(1)) Stevens, Gareth Inc.

—Isaac Asimov's Biblioteca del Universo del Siglo XXI, 12 bks. Porras, Carlos & D'Andrea, Patricia, trs. Incl. Asteroides. lib. bdg. 24.67 (978-0-8368-3853-4(X)); Jupiter. lib. bdg. 24.67 (978-0-8368-3854-1(8)); Luna. lib. bdg. 24.67 (978-0-8368-3855-8(6)); Marte : Nuestro Misteriosos Vecino. lib. bdg. 24.67 (978-0-8368-3856-5(4)); Mercurio : El Planeta Veloz. lib. bdg. 24.67 (978-0-8368-3857-2(2)); Neptuno : El Gigante Mas Lejano. lib. bdg. 24.67 (978-0-8368-3858-9(0)); Pluton y Caronte. lib. bdg. 24.67 (978-0-8368-3859-6(9)); Saturno : El Planeta de los Anillos. lib. bdg. 24.67 (978-0-8368-3860-2(2)); Sol. lib. bdg. 24.67 (978-0-8368-3861-9(0)); Tierra. lib. bdg. 24.67 (978-0-8368-3862-6(9)); Urano : El Planeta Inclinado. lib. bdg. 24.67 (978-0-8368-3863-3(7)); Venus : A Shrouded Mystery. lib. bdg. 24.67 (978-0-8368-3864-0(5)); 32p. (J). (gr. 3 up). (SPA., Illus.). 2003. Set lib. bdg. 296.04 (978-0-8368-3852-7(1)) Stevens, Gareth Inc.

Bankston, John. Stephen Hawking: Breaking the Boundaries of Time & Space. 2005. (Great Minds of Science Ser.). (Illus.). 128p. (J). lib. bdg. 26.60 (978-0-7660-2281-2(1)) Enslow Pubs., Inc.

Benchmark Education Staff, compiled by. The Universe. 2006. spiral bd. 125.00 (***978-1-4108-7149-7(5)***) Benchmark Education Co.

Bockus, William, Jr. The Universe: Theoretical Physics & Astronomy for the Young Adult. 1999. (Illus.). 212p. (J). (gr. 6-12). pap. 12.00 (978-0-9647151-1-0(2)) Print Place.

Bortz, Fred & Hammel, Heidi. Beyond Jupiter: The Story of Planetary Astronomer Heidi Hammet. 2006. (Women's Adventures in Science Ser.). 128p. pap. 9.95 (978-0-309-09552-5(2) , Joseph Henry Pr.) National Academies Pr.

Butt, Kyle. God Made the World. 2005. (Illus.). 32p. (J). pap. 3.00 (978-0-932859-69-3(0)) Apologetics Pr., Inc.

El Cosmos. (SPA.). (YA). (gr. 5-8). pap. (978-84-7131-925-8(X)) Editex, Editorial S.A. ESP. *Dist:* Lectorum Pubns., Inc.

Daly, Mary. The Universe in My Hands. 2002. 90p. (J). spiral bd. 14.00 (978-0-9723239-5-6(3)) Ye Hedge Schl.

DeCristofano, Carolyn Cinami. Big Bang! The Tongue-Tickling Tale of a Speck That Became Spectacular. Carroll, Michael, illus. 2005. 32p. (J). 16.95 (978-1-57091-618-2(7)); pap. 6.95 (978-1-57091-619-9(5)) Charlesbridge Publishing, Inc.

Discovery Channel School Science Set 3: Universes Large & Small, 10 bks. 2003. (Illus.). (J). (gr. 5 up). lib. bdg. 246.70 (978-0-8368-3365-2(1)) Stevens, Gareth Inc.

Dorling Kindersley Publishing Staff. Heroes of the DC Universe. 2005. (Ultimate Sticker Bks.). 16p. (J). pap. 6.99 (978-0-7566-1124-8(5)) Dorling Kindersley Publishing, Inc.

Earth Cosmology: The Destroyer Comet. 2004. (YA). cd-rom 15.00 (978-0-934269-61-2(0)) UFO Photo Archives.

Earth Cosmology: The Effects of the Giant Destroyer Comet. 2004. (UFO Fact Bks.). (YA). cd-rom 15.00 (978-0-934269-41-4(6)) UFO Photo Archives.

Farndon, John. From Ptolemy's Spheres to Dark Energy: Discovering the Universe. 2007. (Illus.). 64p. (J). (***978-1-4034-9553-2(X)***) Heinemann Library.

Fleisher, Paul. The Big Bang. 2006. (Great Ideas of Science Ser.). (Illus.). 80p. (J). (gr. 6-10). 27.93 (978-0-8225-2133-4(4) , Twenty-First Century Bks.) Lerner Publishing Group.

Ford, Harry & Barnham, Kay. Outer Space. 2003. (Knowledge Masters Ser.). (Illus.). 32p. (YA). pap. incl. cd-rom (978-1-903954-09-6(6)) Chrysalis Children's Bks.

Fredette, Nathalie & Lafleur, Claude. Exploring the Universe. 2001. (Twenty-First Century Science Ser.). (Illus.). 64p. (J). (gr. 5 up). lib. bdg. 32.67 (978-0-8368-5001-7(7) , World Almanac Library) Stevens, Gareth Inc.

Gaff, Jackie. Superman's Guide to the Universe. 2003. (Dk Readers Ser.). (Illus.). 48p. (J). pap. 3.99 (978-0-7894-9754-3(9)) Dorling Kindersley Publishing, Inc.

Gaff, Jackie & Dorling Kindersley Publishing Staff. Superman's Guide to the Universe. 2003. (Readers Ser.). (Illus.). 48p. (J). 12.99 (978-0-7894-9746-8(8)) Dorling Kindersley Publishing, Inc.

Gallant, Roy A. Earth's Place in Space. 2000. (Story of Science Ser.). (Illus.). 80p. (J). (gr. 5 up). lib. bdg. 28.50 (978-0-7614-0963-2(7) , Benchmark Bks.) Cavendish, Marshall Corp.

Garcia, Gloria. El Universo. (SPA.). 8p. 9.95 (978-84-272-7277-4(4)) Molino, Editorial ESP. *Dist:* Distribooks, Inc.

Germadnik, Mary Lynn. How Do We Know the Age of the Universe? 2001. (Great Scientific Questions & the Scientists Who Answered Them Ser.). (Illus.). 112p. (YA). (gr. 4-6). lib. bdg. 26.50 (978-0-8239-3382-2(2)) Rosen Publishing Group, Inc., The.

Graun, Ken & Maly, Suzanne. Our Galaxy & the Universe. 2002. (Twenty-First Century Astronomy Ser.: 2). (Illus.). 36p. (J). 15.95 (978-1-928771-08-1(4)) Ken Pr.

Hawking, Stephen W. A Brief History of Time. 1998. (Illus.). 212p. (gr. 7-12). per. 25.70 (978-0-613-07404-9(1)) Tandem Library Bks.

Hixson, Bryce. Galactic Cookie Dough. Hixson, Bryce, illus. 2003. (Illus.). (J). per. 14.95 (978-1-931801-06-5(1)) Loose In The Lab.

Holt, Rinehart and Winston Staff. Beyond the Planet Resources: Texas Edition. 2nd ed. 2001. (Holt Science & Technology Ser.: No. 7). (Illus.). pap. 26.00 (978-0-03-064856-4(4)) Holt, Rinehart & Winston.

—Holt Science & Technology Chapter 18: Earth Science: Studying Space. 5th ed. 2004. (Illus.). pap. 12.86 (978-0-03-030331-9(1)) Holt, Rinehart & Winston.

—Holt Science & Technology Chptr. 10: The Universe & Beyond: Chapter Resources - Tennessee Edition. 3rd ed. 2003. (J). pap. 11.40 (978-0-03-069117-1(6)) Holt, Rinehart & Winston.

Jedicke, Peter. Cosmology: Exploring the Universe. 2003. (Hot Science Ser.). (J). lib. bdg. 28.50 (978-1-58340-366-2(3)) Smart Apple Media.

Kerrod, Robin. Stars & Galaxies. 2001. (Illus.). 32p. (J). lib. bdg. 24.25 (978-1-930643-28-4(4)) Chrysalis Education.

Milner, Bryan. Cosmology. 2nd rev. ed. 2000. (Cambridge Advanced Sciences Ser.). (Illus.). 92p. pap. 15.00 (978-0-521-78722-2(X)) Cambridge Univ. Pr.

Miotto, Enrico. El Universo.Tr. of Universe. (SPA.). 40p. (YA). (gr. 5-8). 10.36 (978-84-207-5192-4(8)) Grupo Anaya, S.A. ESP. *Dist:* Lectorum Pubns., Inc.

Morgan, Jennifer. Born with a Bang: The Universe Tells Our Cosmic Story. Andersen, Dana Lynne, illus. 2004. (Sharing Nature with Children Book Ser.). 48p. (YA). (gr. 2 up). 19.95 (978-1-58469-033-7(X)); pap. 9.95 (978-1-58469-032-0(1)) Dawn Pubns.

—Born with a Bang: The Universe Tells Our Cosmic Story. 2002. (gr. 3-6). lib. bdg. 18.75 (978-0-613-59228-4(X)) Tandem Library Bks.

Nardo, Don. The Big Bang. 2005. (KidHaven Science Library). (Illus.). 48p. (J). (gr. 4-8). 26.20 (978-0-7377-2351-9(3) , Greenhaven Pr., Inc.) Thomson Gale.

Our Universe. 2004. (Illus.). lib. bdg. 7.95 (978-0-8225-4790-7(2)) Lerner Publishing Group.

Our Universe Collection. 2001. (Illus.). (J). pap. (978-0-7398-4555-4(1)) Steck-Vaughn.

Parsons, Jayne, ed. The Way the Universe Works. 2006. 160p. (J). pap. 14.99 (978-0-7566-1951-0(3)) Dorling Kindersley Publishing, Inc.

Perez, Miguel. The Earth & the Universe. Rius, María, illus. 1998. (Universe Ser.). 36p. (J). (ps-3). pap. 6.95 (978-0-7641-0687-3(2)) Barron's Educational Series, Inc.

—The Universe: The Solar System; Stars & Galaxies; The Earth & the Universe, 3 bks., Set. Rius, María, illus. 1998. 36p. (J). (ps-2). pap. 17.95 (978-0-7641-7203-8(4)) Barron's Educational Series, Inc.

Quadrillion Media Staff. The Universe (Unser Kosmos) To the Limits of Space & Time, Vol. 7. 1998. (Start Me Up Ser.: Vol. 7). 48p. (J). (gr. 3-8). mass mkt. 12.95 (978-1-58185-015-4(8) , Tessloff Publishing) Quadrillion Media LLC.

Raintree Steck-Vaughn Staff. The Universe. 1999. (Illus.). (J). pap. 35.60 (978-0-7398-0902-0(4)) Steck-Vaughn.

Saunders, W. B. Publishing Staff. The Universe. 1999. pap. (978-0-7398-0871-9(0)) Steck-Vaughn.

Scholastic, Inc. Staff. The Universe. 2007. (Scholastic First Discovery Ser.). 24p. (J). (ps-k). pap. 5.99 (***978-0-545-00146-5(3)*** , Scholastic Reference) Scholastic, Inc.

Silverstein, Alvin, et al. The Universe. 2003. (Science Concepts Ser.). (Illus.). 64p. (gr. 5-8). lib. bdg. 26.90 (978-0-7613-2255-9(8) , Twenty-First Century Bks.) Lerner Publishing Group.

Simon, Seymour. The Universe. 32p. (J). 2006. 16.99 (978-0-06-087724-8(3)); 2006. (Illus.). pap. 6.99 (978-0-06-087725-5(1)); 1998. (Illus.). lab manual ed. 17.89 (978-0-688-15302-1(X)) HarperCollins Pubs.

—The Universe. 2000. (J). (978-0-606-20290-9(0)) Tandem Library Bks.

—Universe. 2000. (978-0-606-20343-2(5)) Tandem Library Bks.

Solway, Andrew. What's Inside a Black Hole? Deep Space Objects & Mysteries. 2006. (Stargazers Guides Ser.). (Illus.). 48p. (J). (978-1-4034-7710-1(8)); pap. (978-1-4034-7717-0(5)) Heinemann Library.

Space & the Planets. gif. ed. (Illus.). (J). (ps-k). 6.95 (978-1-55254-260-6(2) , BV50003) Brighter Vision Pubns.

Sparrow, Giles. Probing Deep Space. 2006. (Illus.). 48p. (J). pap. (978-0-8368-7286-6(X)); lib. bdg. (978-0-8368-7279-8(7)) Stevens, Gareth Inc. (World Almanac Library).

Sumners, Carolyn. Earthling Guide to Deep Space. 1998. (gr. 3-6). lib. bdg. 22.20 (978-0-613-71539-3(X)) Tandem Library Bks.

Sweeney, Joan. Me & My Place in Space. 1999. (Dragonfly Bks.). (Illus.). 32p. (J). (gr. k-3). pap. 6.99 (978-0-517-88590-1(5) , Dragonfly Bks.) Random Hse. Children's Bks.

The Universe. (Jump Ser.). 36p. (J). (gr. 2-7). pap. (978-1-882210-21-3(2)) Action Publishing, Inc.

The Universe, 11 vols., Set. 2003. (Illus.). (J). (gr. 3-5). lib. bdg. 250.69 (978-1-58810-622-3(5)) Heinemann Library.

The Universe. 2002. (Questions & Answers Ser.). 32p. (J). 7.95 (978-0-7525-7247-5(4)) Parragon, Inc.

El Universo.Tr. of Universe. (SPA.). 96p. (YA). (gr. 5-8). 18.36 (978-84-241-1993-5(2)) Everest de Ediciones y Distribucion, S.L. ESP. *Dist:* Lectorum Pubns., Inc.

Vogt, Gregory L. High-Low Reading: Our Universe, 12 bks., Set. Incl. Asteroids, Comets, & Meteors. (YA). (gr. 5-12). lib. bdg. 22.83 (978-0-7398-3112-0(7)); Exploring Space. (J). (gr. 5-12). lib. bdg. 22.83 (978-0-7398-3113-7(5)); Jupiter, Saturn, Uranus & Neptune. (YA). (gr. 5-12). lib. bdg. 22.83 (978-0-7398-3109-0(7)); Living on Other Worlds. (YA). (gr. 5-12). lib. bdg. 22.83 (978-0-7398-3114-4(3)); Mars. (J). (gr. 4-7). lib. bdg. 22.83 (978-0-7398-3104-5(6)); Mercury, Venus, Earth & Mars. (J). (gr. 4-7). lib. bdg. 22.83 (978-0-7398-3110-6(0)); Milky Way & Other Galaxies. (YA). (gr. 5-12). lib. bdg. 22.83 (978-0-7398-3107-6(0)); Moons. (YA). (gr. 5-12). lib. bdg. 22.83 (978-0-7398-3106-9(2)); Nebulas. (YA). (gr. 5-12). lib. bdg. 22.83 (978-0-7398-3108-3(9)); Pluto & the Search for New Planets. (YA). (gr. 5-12). lib. bdg. 22.83 (978-0-7398-3111-3(9)); Stars & Constellations. (J). (gr. 5-12). lib. bdg. 22.83 (978-0-7398-3115-1(1)); Sun. (YA). (gr. 5-12). lib. bdg. 22.83 (978-0-7398-3105-2(4)); 48p. 2000. (Illus.). 2000. Set lib. bdg. 273.96 (978-0-7398-3116-8(X)) Raintree.

—Our Universe Series, Set. 2000. (Illus.). (J). pap. (978-0-7398-3355-1(3)) Steck-Vaughn.

Williams, Brian. Universe: Biggest & Best. 2004. (Biggest & Best Ser.). (Illus.). 40p. (J). pap. 7.95 (978-1-84236-025-5(6)) Miles Kelly Publishing, Ltd. GBR. *Dist:* Independent Pubs. Group.

Wolf, Aline D. How Big Is the Milky Way? Servello, Joe, illus. 2001. 24p. (J). spiral bd. 6.00 (978-0-939195-28-2(3) , 317) Parent Child Pr., Inc.

—I Know the Sun Does Not Set. Servello, Joe, illus. 2001. 24p. (J). spiral bd. 6.00 (978-0-939195-26-8(7)) Parent Child Pr., Inc.

—I Know What Gravity Does. 2000. 24p. (J). spiral bd. 6.00 (978-0-939195-24-4(0) , 314) Parent Child Pr., Inc.

—I Live in the Universe. Servello, Joe, illus. 2000. 24p. (J). spiral bd. (978-0-939195-22-0(4) , 313) Parent Child Pr., Inc.

—I Look Out at the Stars. Servello, Joe, illus. 2000. 24p. (J). spiral bd. 6.00 (978-0-939195-23-7(2) , 312) Parent Child Pr., Inc.

—I Travel on Planet Earth. Servello, Joe, illus. 2001. 24p. (J). spiral bd. 6.00 (978-0-939195-27-5(5) , 315) Parent Child Pr., Inc.

—I Want to Hear the Quiet. Servello, Joe, illus. 2001. 24p. (J). spiral bd. 6.00 (978-0-939195-25-1(9) , 318) Parent Child Pr., Inc.

UNIVERSITIES AND COLLEGES

see also Education, Higher; Scholarships; Students

also headings beginning with the word College and names of individual institutions

African-American Colleges & Universities. 2000. (My Ancestors—My Heroes Ser.: Vol. 37). (J). (gr. 3-4). (978-1-893091-36-8(8)) Parker Publishing Co.

Allshouse, Sara & Burns, Adam. University of San Francisco College Prowler off the Record. 2005. (College Prowler off the Record Guides: Vol. 181). 160p. (YA). (gr. 12 up). pap., stu. ed. 14.95 (978-1-59658-180-7(8)) College Prowler, Inc.

Alter, Austin & Lyon, Abby. Rhode Island School of Design College Prowler off the Record. 2005. (College Prowler off the Record Guides: Vol. 106). 160p. (YA). (gr. 12 up). pap., stu. ed. 14.95 (978-1-59658-105-0(0)) College Prowler, Inc.

Amboba, Ethan & Lyon, Abby. Occidental College College Prowler off the Record. 2nd ed. 2005. (College Prowler off the Record Guides: Vol. 94). 160p. (YA). (gr. 12 up). pap., stu. ed. 14.95 (978-1-59658-093-0(3)) College Prowler, Inc.

Amodeo, Jessica & Pecsenye, Jessica. University of Colorado College Prowler off the Record. 2nd ed. 2005. (College Prowler off the Record Guides: Vol. 151). 160p. (YA). (gr. 12 up). pap., stu. ed. 14.95 (978-1-59658-150-0(6)) College Prowler, Inc.

Andrew, Stacy & Davis, Cristine. Morehouse College College Prowler off the Record. 2005. (College Prowler off the Record Guides: Vol. 86). 160p. (YA). (gr. 12 up). pap., stu. ed. 14.95 (978-1-59658-085-5(2) , Off The Record) College Prowler, Inc.

Ayala, Anikka & Nash, Kevin. University of Notre Dame College Prowler off the Record. 2nd ed. 2005. (College Prowler off the Record Guides: Vol. 171). 160p. (YA). (gr. 12 up). pap., stu. ed. 14.95 (978-1-59658-170-8(0)) College Prowler, Inc.

Baier, Ellen & Skindzier, Jon. Franklin & Marshall College College Prowler off the Record. 2005. (College Prowler off the Record Guides: Vol. 52). 160p. (YA). (gr. 12 up). pap., stu. ed. 14.95 (978-1-59658-051-0(8)) College Prowler, Inc.

Ballow, Jonah & Gray, Kevan. University of Kansas College Prowler off the Record. 2nd ed. 2005. (College Prowler off the Record Guides: Vol. 159). 160p. (YA). (gr. 12 up). pap., stu. ed. 14.95 (978-1-59658-158-6(1)) College Prowler, Inc.

Barrish, Lily & Pecsenye, Jessice. University of Central Florida College Prowler off the Record. 2005. (College Prowler off the Record Guides: Vol. 149). 160p. (YA). (gr. 12 up). pap., stu. ed. 14.95 (978-1-59658-148-7(4)) College Prowler, Inc.

Beane, Abbie, et al. Middlebury College College Prowler off the Record. 2005. (College Prowler off the Record Guides: Vol. 85). 160p. (YA). (gr. 12 up). pap., stu. ed. 14.95 (978-1-59658-084-8(4)) College Prowler, Inc.

Bender, Abby & Weisgerber, Amy. Purdue University College Prowler off the Record. 2005. (College Prowler off the Record Guides: Vol. 103). 160p. (YA). (gr. 12 up). pap., stu. ed. 14.95 (978-1-59658-102-9(6)) College Prowler, Inc.

Benson, Elisa & Gohari, Omid. Colgate University College Prowler off the Record. 2005. (College Prowler off the Record Guides: Vol. 29). 160p. (YA). (gr. 12 up). pap., stu. ed. 14.95 (978-1-59658-028-2(3)) College Prowler, Inc.

Biggers, Nikki & Mason, Chris. Cal Poly College Prowler off the Record: Inside California Polytechnic State University. 2005. (College Prowler off the Record Guides: Vol. 21). 160p. (YA). (gr. 12 up). pap., stu. ed. 14.95 (978-1-59658-020-6(8)) College Prowler, Inc.

Bist, Richard & Skindzier, Jon. Florida State University College Prowler off the Record. 2005. (College Prowler off the Record Guides: Vol. 50). 160p. (YA). (gr. 12 up). pap., stu. ed. 14.95 (978-1-59658-049-7(6)) College Prowler, Inc.

Bohler, Victoria & Gray, Kevan. Loyola College in Maryland College Prowler off the Record. 2005. (College Prowler off the Record Guides: Vol. 76). 160p. (YA). (gr. 12 up). pap., stu. ed. 14.95 (978-1-59658-075-6(5)) College Prowler, Inc.

Brennan, Genevieve. Wellesley College College Prowler off the Record. 2005. (College Prowler off the Record Guides: Vol. 200). 160p. (YA). (gr. 12 up). pap., stu. ed. 14.95 (978-1-59658-199-9(9)) College Prowler, Inc.

Bretzius Matthew. West Virginia University College Prowler off the Record. 2005. (College Prowler off the Record Guides: Vol. 203). 160p. (YA). (gr. 12 up). pap., stu. ed. 14.95 (978-1-59658-202-6(2)) College Prowler, Inc.

Brown, Antoinette & Skindzier, Jon. St John's University NY College Prowler off the Record: Inside Saint Johns New York. 2nd ed. 2005. (College Prowler off the Record Guides: Vol. 122). 160p. (YA). (gr. 12 up). pap., stu. ed. 14.95 (978-1-59658-121-0(2)) College Prowler, Inc.

C. Ridley, Joi & Gray, Kevan. Howard University College Prowler off the Record. 2nd ed. 2005. (College Prowler off the Record Guides: Vol. 66). 160p. (YA). (gr. 12 up). pap., stu. ed. 14.95 (978-1-59658-065-7(8) , Off The Record) College Prowler, Inc.

Campbell, Margaret & Gohari, Omid. Duke University College Prowler off the Record. 2nd ed. 2005. (College Prowler off the Record Guides: Vol. 45). 160p. (YA). (gr. 12 up). pap., stu. ed. 14.95 (978-1-59658-044-2(5)) College Prowler, Inc.

Carlin, Daniel. Washington University in St Louis College Prowler off the Record. 2nd ed. 2005. (College Prowler off the Record Guides: Vol. 199). 160p. (YA). (gr. 12 up). pap., stu. ed. 14.95 (978-1-59658-198-2(0)) College Prowler, Inc.

Chadderdon, Andrea & Nash, Kevin. University of Oklahoma College Prowler off the Record. 2nd ed. 2005. (College Prowler off the Record Guides: Vol. 172). 160p. (YA). (gr. 12 up). pap., stu. ed. 14.95 (978-1-59658-171-5(9)) College Prowler, Inc.

Chang, Tristen & Pecsenye, Jessica. UC Davis College Prowler off the Record: Inside University of California Davis. 2nd ed. 2005. (College Prowler off the Record Guides: Vol. 142). 160p. (YA). (gr. 12 up). pap., stu. ed. 14.95 (978-1-59658-141-8(7)) College Prowler, Inc.

Chasan, Emily & Gray, Kevan. Tufts University College Prowler off the Record. 2nd ed. 2005. (College Prowler off the Record Guides: Vol. 136). 160p. (YA). (gr. 12 up). pap., stu. ed. 14.95 (978-1-59658-135-7(2)) College Prowler, Inc.

C.Laird, Elizabeth & Skindzier, Jon. Guilford College College Prowler off the Record. 2005. (College Prowler off the Record Guides: Vol. 59). 160p. (YA). (gr. 12 up). pap., stu. ed. 14.95 (978-1-59658-058-9(5)) College Prowler, Inc.

Clapp, Sarah & Varacalli, Lauren. Denison University College Prowler off the Record. 2005. (College Prowler off the Record Guides: Vol. 41). 160p. (YA). (gr. 12 up). pap., stu. ed. 14.95 (978-1-59658-040-4(2)) College Prowler, Inc.

Cloud, Megan & Nash, Kevin. Barnard College College Prowler off the Record. 2005. (College Prowler off the Record Guides: Vol. 8). 160p. (YA). (gr. 12 up). pap., stu. ed. 14.95 (978-1-59658-007-7(0)) College Prowler, Inc.

Cole, Kristin & Burns, Adam. Loyola Marymount University College Prowler off the Record. 2005. (College Prowler off the Record Guides: Vol. 77). 160p. (YA). (gr. 12 up). pap., stu. ed. 14.95 (978-1-59658-076-3(3)) College Prowler, Inc.

Coleman, Andrew & Mason, Chris. Clemson University College Prowler off the Record. 2nd ed. 2005. (College Prowler off the Record Guides: Vol. 27). 160p. (YA). (gr. 12 up). pap., stu. ed. 14.95 (978-1-59658-026-8(7)) College Prowler, Inc.

Collins, Elizabeth & Lyon, Abby. Swarthmore College College Prowler off the Record. 2nd ed. 2005. (College Prowler off the Record Guides: Vol. 129). 160p. (YA). (gr. 12 up). pap., stu. ed. 14.95 (978-1-59658-128-9(X)) College Prowler, Inc.

Connell, Sarah & Nash, Kevin. Bates College College Prowler off the Record. 2005. (College Prowler off the Record Guides: Vol. 9). 160p. (YA). (gr. 12 up). pap., stu. ed. 14.95 (978-1-59658-008-4(9)) College Prowler, Inc.

Cook, Peter & Nash, Kevin. Pomona College College Prowler off the Record. 2nd ed. 2005. (College Prowler off the Record Guides: Vol. 100). 160p. (YA). (gr. 12 up). pap., stu. ed. 14.95 (978-1-59658-099-2(2)) College Prowler, Inc.

Cooper, Amy & Keller, Carolyn. Rochester Institute of Technology College Prowler off the Record: Inside RIT. 2005. (College Prowler off the Record Guides: Vol. 109). 160p. (YA). (gr. 12 up). pap., stu ed. 14.95 (978-1-59658-108-1(5)) College Prowler, Inc.

Core, Sarah & Varacalli, Lauren. College of Wooster College Prowler off the Record. 2005. (College Prowler off the Record Guides: Vol. 33). 160p. (YA). (gr. 12 up). pap., stu. ed. 14.95 (978-1-59658-032-9(1)) College Prowler, Inc.

Cruttenden, Jamie & Pecsenye, Jessica. University of Pittsburgh College Prowler off the Record. 2nd ed. 2005. (College Prowler off the Record Guides: Vol. 175). 160p. (YA). (gr. 12 up). pap., stu. ed. 14.95 (978-1-59658-174-6(3)) College Prowler, Inc.

Cue, Carter B. & Davis, Lenwood G. Winston-Salem State University. 2000. (College History Ser.). 128p. (gr. 6 up). pap. 19.99 (978-0-7385-0617-3(6)) Arcadia Publishing.

Cusick, John. Wesleyan University College Prowler off the Record. 2005. (College Prowler off the Record Guides: Vol. 201). 160p. (YA). (gr. 12 up). pap., stu. ed. 14.95 (978-1-59658-200-2(6)) College Prowler, Inc.

Cyr, Jessica & Keller, Carolyn. Ohio University College Prowler off the Record. 2nd ed. 2005. (College Prowler off the Record Guides: Vol. 96). 160p. (YA). (gr. 12 up). pap., stu. ed. 14.95 (978-1-59658-095-4(X)) College Prowler, Inc.

Davis, Amy & Mandelbaum, Jolie. Michigan State University College Prowler off the Record. 2nd ed. 2005. (College Prowler off the Record Guides: Vol. 84). 160p. (YA). (gr. 12 up). pap., stu. ed. 14.95 (978-1-59658-083-1(6)) College Prowler, Inc.

Davis, Jenny & Skindzier, Jon. Indiana University College Prowler off the Record. 2nd ed. 2005. (College Prowler off the Record Guides: Vol. 67). 160p. (YA). (gr. 12 up). pap., stu. ed. 14.95 (978-1-59658-066-4(6)) College Prowler, Inc.

Davis, Lauren & Varacalli, Lauren. Bucknell University College Prowler off the Record. 2005. (College Prowler off the Record Guides: Vol. 20). 160p. (YA). (gr. 12 up). pap., stu. ed. 14.95 (978-1-59658-019-0(4)) College Prowler, Inc.

Dearing, Kate & Lyon, Abby. Tulane University College Prowler off the Record. 2nd ed. 2005. (College Prowler off the Record Guides: Vol. 137). 160p. (YA). (gr. 12 up). pap., stu. ed. 14.95 (978-1-59658-136-4(0)) College Prowler, Inc.

Dickson, Kristin & Pecsenye, Jessica. Trinity University Texas College Prowler off the Record. 2005. (College Prowler off the Record Guides: Vol. 135). 160p. (YA). (gr. 12 up). pap., stu. ed. 14.95 (978-1-59658-134-0(4)) College Prowler, Inc.

Doctorick, Jonathan & Gohari, Omid. Duquesne University College Prowler off the Record. 2005. (College Prowler off the Record Guides: Vol. 46). 160p. (YA). (gr. 12 up). pap., stu. ed. 14.95 (978-1-59658-045-9(3)) College Prowler, Inc.

Doscher, Melissa. Yale University College Prowler off the Record. 2nd ed. 2005. (College Prowler off the Record Guides: Vol. 208). 160p. (YA). (gr. 12 up). pap., stu. ed. 14.95 (978-1-59658-207-1(3)) College Prowler, Inc.

DuPree, Ben & Skindzier, Jon. Reed College College Prowler off the Record. 2nd ed. 2005. (College Prowler off the Record Guides: Vol. 104). 160p. (YA). (gr. 12 up). pap., stu. ed. 14.95 (978-1-59658-103-6(4)) College Prowler, Inc.

Dutt, Arjun & Varacalli, Lauren. Claremont Mckenna College College Prowler off the Record. 2005. (College Prowler off the Record Guides: Vol. 26). 160p. (YA). (gr. 12 up). pap., stu. ed. 14.95 (978-1-59658-025-1(9), Off The Record) College Prowler, Inc.

Eagan, Colin & Varacalli, Lauren. Davidson College College Prowler off the Record. 2005. (College Prowler off the Record Guides: Vol. 40). 160p. (YA). (gr. 12 up). pap., stu. ed. 14.95 (978-1-59658-039-8(9)) College Prowler, Inc.

Earl, Archie William, Sr. The Inside Scoop on American Colleges & Universities. 2004. (YA). pap. 6.99 (978-1-884169-32-8(5)) International Educational Improvement Ctr. Pr.

Easley, Michael F. Look Out, College, Here I Come! 2007. (J). ***(978-0-8106-2037-7(5))***; pap. ***(978-0-8106-2038-4(3))*** National Education Assn.

Epstein, Brad. Kansas State Univ 101: My first Text-Board-Book. l.t. ed. 2007. (101—My First Text-Board Books). (Illus.). 20p. (J). bds. 10.95 ***(978-1-932530-57-5(6)***, 101 Bk.) Michaelson Entertainment.

Epstein, Brad, ed. Iowa State University 101: My First Text-Board-Book. 2006. (101—My First Text-Board Books). (J). bds. 10.95 (978-1-932530-37-7(1), 101 Bk.) Michaelson Entertainment.

—University of Kansas 101: My First Text-Board-Book. 2006. (101—My First Text-Board Books). (J). bds. 10.95 (978-1-932530-40-7(1), 101 Bk.) Michaelson Entertainment.

—University of Kentucky 101: My First Text-Board-Book. 2006. (101—My First Text-Board Books). (J). bds. 10.95 (978-1-932530-23-0(1), 101 Bk.) Michaelson Entertainment.

Epstein, Brad M. Auburn Tigers 123: My first counting Book. l.t. ed. 2006. (Illus.). 22p. (J). bds. 14.95 ***(978-1-932530-44-5(4)***, 123 Bk.) Michaelson Entertainment.

—LSU Tigers 123: My first counting Book. l.t. ed. 2006. (Illus.). 22p. (J). bds. 14.95 ***(978-1-932530-49-0(5)***, 123 Bk.) Michaelson Entertainment.

—Michigan State University Spartans 123: My first counting Book. l.t. ed. 2006. (Illus.). 22p. (J). bds. 14.95 ***(978-1-932530-50-6(9)***, 123 Bk.) Michaelson Entertainment.

—The Ohio State University Buckeyes 123: My first counting Book. l.t. ed. 2006. (Illus.). 22p. (J). bds. 15.95 ***(978-1-932530-55-1(X)***, 123 Bk.) Michaelson Entertainment.

—Oklahoma State University 101: My First Text-Board-Book. l.t. ed. 2007. (101—My First Text-Board Books). (Illus.). 20p. (J). bds. 10.95 ***(978-1-932530-27-8(4)***, 101 Bk.) Michaelson Entertainment.

—Texas A&M Aggies 123: My first counting Book. l.t. ed. 2006. (Illus.). 22p. (J). bds. 14.95 ***(978-1-932530-53-7(3)***, 123 Bk.) Michaelson Entertainment.

—UCLA Bruins 123: My first counting Book. l.t. ed. 2006. (Illus.). 22p. (J). bds. 14.95 ***(978-1-932530-45-2(2)***, 123 Bk.) Michaelson Entertainment.

—University of Alabama Crimson Tide 123: My first counting Book. l.t. ed. 2006. (Illus.). 22p. (J). bds. 14.95 ***(978-1-932530-43-8(6)***, 123 Bk.) Michaelson Entertainment.

—University of Arkansas 101: My First Text-Board-Book. l.t. ed. 2007. (101—My First Text-Board Books). (Illus.). 20p. (J). bds. 10.95 ***(978-1-932530-58-2(4)***, 101 Bk.) Michaelson Entertainment.

—University of Georgia Bulldogs 123: My first counting Book. l.t. ed. 2006. (Illus.). 22p. (J). bds. 14.95 ***(978-1-932530-46-9(0)***, 123 Bk.) Michaelson Entertainment.

—University of Illinois Fighting Illini 123: My first counting Book. l.t. ed. 2006. (Illus.). 22p. (J). bds. 14.95 ***(978-1-932530-47-6(9)***, 123 Bk.) Michaelson Entertainment.

—University of Iowa Hawkeyes 123: My first counting Book. l.t. ed. 2006. (Illus.). 22p. (J). bds. 14.95 ***(978-1-932530-48-3(7)***, 123 Bk.) Michaelson Entertainment.

—University of Notre Dame Fighting Irish 123: My first counting Book. l.t. ed. 2006. (Illus.). 22p. (J). bds. 15.95 ***(978-1-932530-52-0(5)***, 123 Bk.) Michaelson Entertainment.

—University of South Carolina 101: My First Text-Board-Book. l.t. ed. 2007. (101—My First Text-Board Books). (Illus.). 20p. (J). bds. 10.95 ***(978-1-932530-41-4(X)***, 101 Bk.) Michaelson Entertainment.

—University of Texas Longhorns 123: My first counting Book. l.t. ed. 2006. (Illus.). 22p. (J). bds. 14.95 ***(978-1-932530-54-4(1)***, 123 Bk.) Michaelson Entertainment.

Epstein, Brad M., ed. Arizona State University 101: My First Text-Board-Book. l.t. ed. 2003. (101—My First Text-Board Books). (Illus.). 20p. (J). bds. 9.95 (978-0-9727702-3-1(2), 101 Bk.) Michaelson Entertainment.

—Clemson University 101: My First Text-Board-Book. l.t. ed. 2004. (101—My First Text-Board Books). (Illus.). 20p. (J). bds. 9.95 (978-1-932530-06-3(1)) Michaelson Entertainment.

—Florida State University 101: My First Text-Board-Book. l.t. ed. 2004. (My First Text Board Bks.). (Illus.). 20p. (J). bds. 9.95 (978-1-932530-07-0(X)) Michaelson Entertainment.

—Louisiana State University 101: My First Text-Board-Book. l.t. ed. 2004. (My First Text Board Bks.). (Illus.). 20p. (J). bds. 9.95 (978-1-932530-09-4(6)) Michaelson Entertainment.

—Michigan State University 101: My First Text-Board-Book. l.t. ed. 2004. (My First Text Board Bks.). (Illus.). 20p. (J). bds. 9.95 (978-1-932530-14-8(2)) Michaelson Entertainment.

—Purdue University 101: My First Text-Board-Book. l.t. ed. 2004. (101 My First Text-Board Books). (Illus.). 20p. (J). bds. 9.95 (978-1-932530-11-7(8)) Michaelson Entertainment.

—Texas A & M 101: My First Text. l.t. ed. 2003. (101—My First Text-Board Books). (Illus.). 20p. (J). bds. 9.95 (978-0-9727702-4-8(0)) Michaelson Entertainment.

—University of Florida 101: My First Text-Board-Book. l.t. ed. 2004. (101—My First Text-Board Books). (Illus.). 20p. (J). bds. 9.95 (978-1-932530-21-6(5)) Michaelson Entertainment.

—University of Georgia 101: My First Text-Board-Book. l.t. ed. 2004. (101—My First Text-Board Books). (Illus.). 20p. (J). bds. 9.95 (978-1-932530-08-7(8)) Michaelson Entertainment.

—University of Illinois 101: My First Text-Board-Book. l.t. ed. 2004. (101—My First Text-Board Books). (Illus.). 20p. (J). bds. 9.95 (978-1-932530-17-9(7)) Michaelson Entertainment.

—University of North Carolina 101: My First Text-Board-Book. l.t. ed. 2004. (My First Text Board Bks.). (Illus.). 20p. (J). bds. 9.95 (978-1-932530-12-4(6)) Michaelson Entertainment.

—University of Texas at Austin 101: My First Text-Board-Book. l.t. ed. 2004. (101—My First Text-Board Books). (Illus.). 20p. (J). bds. 9.95 (978-1-932530-13-1(4)) Michaelson Entertainment.

—University of Wisconsin 101: My First Text-Board-Book. l.t. ed. 2004. (101—My First Text-Board Books). (Illus.). 20p. (J). bds. 9.95 (978-1-932530-18-6(5)) Michaelson Entertainment.

—USC 101: My First Text-Board-Book. l.t. ed. 2004. (101—My First Text-Board Books). (Illus.). 20p. (J). bds. 9.95 (978-0-9727702-0-0(8)) Michaelson Entertainment.

—Yale 101: My First Text. l.t. ed. 2003. (101—My First Text-Board Books). (Illus.). 20p. (J). bds. 9.95 (978-0-9727702-2-4(4)) Michaelson Entertainment.

Eske, Aaron & Nash, Kevin. University of Nebraska College Prowler off the Record. 2nd ed. 2005. (College Prowler off the Record Guides: Vol. 168). 160p. (YA). (gr. 12 up). pap., stu. ed. 14.95 (978-1-59658-167-8(0)) College Prowler, Inc.

Evans, Moana & Pecsenye, Jessica. Harvey Mudd College College Prowler off the Record. 2005. (College Prowler off the Record Guides: Vol. 63). 160p. (YA). (gr. 12 up). pap., stu. ed. 14.95 (978-1-59658-062-6(3)) College Prowler, Inc.

Ewing, Drew & Burns, Adam. St Louis University College Prowler off the Record: Inside Saint Louis. 2nd ed. 2005. (College Prowler off the Record Guides: Vol. 123). 160p. (YA). (gr. 12 up). pap., stu. ed. 14.95 (978-1-59658-122-7(0)) College Prowler, Inc.

Fackrell, Caitlin & Lyon, Abby. Lewis & Clark College College Prowler off the Record. 2005. (College Prowler off the Record Guides: Vol. 75). 160p. (YA). (gr. 12 up). pap., stu. ed. 14.95 (978-1-59658-074-9(7)) College Prowler, Inc.

Fassio, Dan & Burns, Adam. Washington & Lee University College Prowler off the Record. 2005. (College Prowler off the Record Guides: Vol. 198). 160p. (YA). (gr. 12 up). pap., stu. ed. 14.95 (978-1-59658-197-5(2)) College Prowler, Inc.

Fitzgerald, Brendan & Burns, Adam. Hofstra University College Prowler off the Record. 2005. (College Prowler off the Record Guides: Vol. 65). 160p. (YA). (gr. 12 up). pap., stu. ed. 14.95 (978-1-59658-064-0(X)) College Prowler, Inc.

Flegal, Eric & Pecsenye, Jessica. UCLA College Prowler off the Record: Inside University of California Los Angeles. 2nd ed. 2005. (College Prowler off the Record Guides: Vol. 144). 160p. (YA). (gr. 12 up). pap., stu. ed. 14.95 (978-1-59658-143-2(3)) College Prowler, Inc.

Fleming, Jessica & Burns, Adam. Texas Christian University College Prowler off the Record. 2005. (College Prowler off the Record Guides: Vol. 133). 160p. (YA). (gr. 12 up). pap., stu. ed. 14.95 (978-1-59658-132-6(8)) College Prowler, Inc.

Florence, Sylvia & Keller, Carolyn. James Madison University College Prowler off the Record. 2nd ed. 2005. (College Prowler off the Record Guides: Vol. 70). 160p. (YA). (gr. 12 up). pap., stu. ed. 14.95 (978-1-59658-069-5(0)) College Prowler, Inc.

Foster, Jessica & Pecsenye, Jessice. University of South Carolina College Prowler off the Record. 2nd ed. 2005. (College Prowler off the Record Guides: Vol. 182). 160p. (YA). (gr. 12 up). pap., stu. ed. 14.95 (978-1-59658-181-4(6)) College Prowler, Inc.

Fosyth, Rebekah & Burns, Adam. Rose-Hulman Institute of Technology College Prowler off the Record. 2005. (College Prowler off the Record Guides: Vol. 111). 160p. (YA). (gr. 12 up). pap., stu. ed. 14.95 (978-1-59658-110-4(7), Off The Record) College Prowler, Inc.

Fraser, Alison & Lyon, Abby. Princeton University College Prowler off the Record. 2005. (College Prowler off the Record Guides: Vol. 101). 160p. (YA). (gr. 12 up). pap., stu. ed. 14.95 (978-1-59658-100-5(X)) College Prowler, Inc.

Fried, Alyssa & Seaman, Jim. Penn State College Prowler off the Record: Inside Pennsylvania State University. 2nd ed. 2005. (College Prowler off the Record Guides: Vol. 97). 160p. (YA). (gr. 12 up). pap., stu. ed. 14.95 (978-1-59658-096-1(8)) College Prowler, Inc.

Friedman, Sarah & Gohari, Omid. Bryn Mawr College College Prowler off the Record. 2005. (College Prowler off the Record Guides: Vol. 19). 160p. (YA). (gr. 12 up). pap., stu. ed. 14.95 (978-1-59658-018-3(6)) College Prowler, Inc.

G. de la Parra, John & Rahimi, Joey. The Cooper Union College Prowler off the Record. 2nd ed. 2005. (College Prowler off the Record Guides: Vol. 37). 160p. (YA). (gr. 12 up). pap., stu. ed. 14.95 (978-1-59658-036-7(4), Off The Record) College Prowler, Inc.

Garrett, Tiffany & Seaman, Jim. Miami University of Ohio College Prowler off the Record. 2005. (College Prowler off the Record Guides: Vol. 83). 160p. (YA). (gr. 12 up). pap., stu. ed. 14.95 (978-1-59658-082-4(8)) College Prowler, Inc.

Gatker, Anna & Varacalli, Lauren. Babson College College Prowler off the Record. 2005. (College Prowler off the Record Guides: Vol. 6). 160p. (YA). (gr. 12 up). pap., stu. ed. 14.95 (978-1-59658-005-3(4)) College Prowler, Inc.

Gilbert, Heather & Nash, Kevin. Virginia Tech College Prowler off the Record: Inside Virginia Polytechnic Institute. 2nd ed. 2005. (College Prowler off the Record Guides: Vol. 196). 160p. (YA). (gr. 12 up). pap., stu. ed. 14.95 (978-1-59658-195-1(6)) College Prowler, Inc.

Gilmore, David. Xavier University College Prowler off the Record. 2005. (College Prowler off the Record Guides: Vol. 207). 160p. (YA). (gr. 12 up). pap., stu. ed. 14.95 (978-1-59658-206-4(5)) College Prowler, Inc.

Glabe, Scott & Rahimi, Joey. Dartmouth College College Prowler off the Record. 2nd ed. 2005. (College Prowler off the Record Guides: Vol. 39). 160p. (YA). (gr. 12 up). pap., stu. ed. 14.95 (978-1-59658-038-1(0)) College Prowler, Inc.

Goldsmith, Emily & Nash, Kevin. Vassar College College Prowler off the Record. 2005. (College Prowler off the Record Guides: Vol. 194). 160p. (YA). (gr. 12 up). pap., stu. ed. 14.95 (978-1-59658-193-7(X)) College Prowler, Inc.

Gordon, Josh & Pecsenye, Jessica. Pitzer College College Prowler off the Record. 2005. (College Prowler off the Record Guides: Vol. 99). 160p. (YA). (gr. 12 up). pap., stu. ed. 14.95 (978-1-59658-098-5(4)) College Prowler, Inc.

Gordon, Julie & Skindzier, Jon. George Washington University College Prowler off the Record. 2nd ed. 2005. (College Prowler off the Record Guides: Vol. 54). 160p. (YA). (gr. 12 up). pap., stu. ed. 14.95 (978-1-59658-053-4(4)) College Prowler, Inc.

Gordon, Lily & Nash, Kevin. Union College College Prowler off the Record. 2nd ed. 2005. (College Prowler off the Record Guides: Vol. 138). 160p. (YA). (gr. 12 up). pap., stu. ed. 14.95 (978-1-59658-137-1(9)) College Prowler, Inc.

Goss, Nicole, et al. University of Georgia College Prowler off the Record. 2nd ed. 2005. (College Prowler off the Record Guides: Vol. 156). 160p. (YA). (gr. 12 up). pap., stu. ed. 14.95 (978-1-59658-155-5(7)) College Prowler, Inc.

Gossett, Kelley & Nash, Kevin. Boston College College Prowler off the Record. 2nd ed. 2005. (College Prowler off the Record Guides: Vol. 13). 160p. (YA). (gr. 12 up). pap., stu. ed. 14.95 (978-1-59658-012-1(7)) College Prowler, Inc.

Granberry, Debra & Skindzier, Jon. Furman University College Prowler off the Record. 2nd ed. 2005. (College Prowler off the Record Guides: Vol. 53). 160p. (YA). (gr. 12 up). pap., stu. ed. 14.95 (978-1-59658-052-7(6)) College Prowler, Inc.

Grashkina, Alexandra. Williams College College Prowler off the Record. 2005. (College Prowler off the Record Guides: Vol. 206). 160p. (YA). (gr. 12 up). pap., stu. ed. 14.95 (978-1-59658-205-7(7)) College Prowler, Inc.

Gray, Kevan. Spelman College College Prowler off the Record. 2005. (College Prowler off the Record Guides: Vol. 121). 160p. (YA). (gr. 12 up). pap., stu. ed. 14.95 (978-1-59658-120-3(4), Off The Record) College Prowler, Inc.

Greenfeld, Barbara C. The Kids' College Almanac: A First Look at College. 2001. (gr. 7-12). lib. bdg. 26.85 (978-0-613-50078-4(4)) Tandem Library Bks.

Greenfeld, Barbara C. & Weinstein, Robert A. The Kids College Almanac: A First Look at College. 3rd ed. 2005. (Illus.). 352p. (J). pap. 16.95 (978-1-59357-104-7(6), J1046, JIST Works) JIST Publishing.

Gunderman, Shelby & Burns, Adam. UC San Diego College Prowler off the Record: Inside University of California San Diego. 2005. (College Prowler off the Record Guides: Vol. 146). 160p. (YA). (gr. 12 up). pap., stu. ed. 14.95 (978-1-59658-145-6(X)) College Prowler, Inc.

Hall, Erin & Skindzier, Jon. University of Texas College Prowler off the Record. 2nd ed. 2005. (College Prowler off the Record Guides: Vol. 186). 160p. (YA). (gr. 12 up). pap., stu. ed. 14.95 (978-1-59658-185-2(9)) College Prowler, Inc.

Hansen, Peter & Skindzier, Jon. University of Richmond College Prowler off the Record. 2005. (College Prowler off the Record Guides: Vol. 178). 160p. (YA). (gr. 12 up). pap., stu. ed. 14.95 (978-1-59658-177-7(8)) College Prowler, Inc.

Hasslebeck, Kellie & Gohari, Omid. Depauw University College Prowler off the Record. 2005. (College Prowler off the Record Guides: Vol. 42). 160p. (YA). (gr. 12 up). pap., stu. ed. 14.95 (978-1-59658-041-1(0)) College Prowler, Inc.

Hayes, Matt & Nash, Kevin. College of the Holy Cross College Prowler off the Record. 2005. (College Prowler off the Record Guides: Vol. 31). 160p. (YA). (gr. 12 up). pap., stu. ed. 14.95 (978-1-59658-030-5(5)) College Prowler, Inc.

Hein, Michelle & Skindzier, Jon. Muhlenberg College College Prowler off the Record. 2005. (College Prowler off the Record Guides: Vol. 88). 160p. (YA). (gr. 12 up). pap., stu. ed. 14.95 (978-1-59658-087-9(9)) College Prowler, Inc.

Helmer, Jay & Skindzier, Jon. Kenyon College College Prowler off the Record. 2005. (College Prowler off the Record Guides: Vol. 72). 160p. (YA). (gr. 12 up). pap., stu. ed. 14.95 (978-1-59658-071-8(2)) College Prowler, Inc.

Hofius, Sarah & Skindzier, Jon. Ithaca College College Prowler off the Record. 2005. (College Prowler off the Record Guides: Vol. 69). 160p. (YA). (gr. 12 up). pap., stu. ed. 14.95 (978-1-59658-068-8(2)) College Prowler, Inc.

Hondorp, Michael & Nash, Kevin. University of Michigan College Prowler off the Record. 2nd ed. 2005. (College Prowler off the Record Guides: Vol. 164). 160p. (YA). (gr. 12 up). pap., stu. ed. 14.95 (978-1-59658-163-0(8)) College Prowler, Inc.

Hood, Dominic & Skindzier, Jon. Harvard University College Prowler off the Record. 2005. (College Prowler off the Record Guides: Vol. 62). 160p. (YA). (gr. 12 up). pap., stu. ed. 14.95 (978-1-59658-061-9(5)) College Prowler, Inc.

Hopkins, Adrianna & Lyon, Abby. University of North Carolina College Prowler off the Record. 2nd ed. 2005. (College Prowler off the Record Guides: Vol. 170). 160p. (YA). (gr. 12 up). pap., stu. ed. 14.95 (978-1-59658-169-2(7)) College Prowler, Inc.

Huang, Christine & Nash, Kevin. UC Berkeley College Prowler off the Record: Inside University of California Berkeley. 2nd ed. 2005. (College Prowler off the Record Guides: Vol. 141). 160p. (YA). (gr. 12 up). pap., stu. ed. 14.95 (978-1-59658-140-1(9)) College Prowler, Inc.

Intravia, Emily & Swope, Gretchen. Fordham University College Prowler off the Record. 2005. (College Prowler off the Record Guides: Vol. 51). 160p. (YA). (gr. 12 up). pap., stu. ed. 14.95 (978-1-59658-050-3(X)) College Prowler, Inc.

Jade, Torea, et al. Northwestern University College Prowler off the Record. 2005. (College Prowler off the Record Guides: Vol. 92). 160p. (YA). (gr. 12 up). pap., stu. ed. 14.95 (978-1-59658-091-6(7)) College Prowler, Inc.

Jardy, Adam & Pecsenye, Jessica. Ohio State University College Prowler off the Record. 2005. (College Prowler off the Record Guides: Vol. 95). 160p. (YA). (gr. 12 up). pap., stu. ed. 14.95 (978-1-59658-094-7(1)) College Prowler, Inc.

Jendrey, Julie. Loyola University New Orleans College Prowler off the Record. 2005. (College Prowler off the Record Guides: Vol. 79). 160p. (YA). (gr. 12 up). pap., stu. ed. 14.95 (978-1-59658-078-7(X)) College Prowler, Inc.

—San Diego State University College Prowler off the Record. 2005. (College Prowler off the Record Guides: Vol. 113). 160p. (YA). (gr. 12 up). pap., stu. ed. 14.95 (978-1-59658-112-8(3)) College Prowler, Inc.

Johnston, Cathy & Pecsenye, Jessica. Hamilton College College Prowler off the Record. 2005. (College Prowler off the Record Guides: Vol. 60). 160p. (YA). (gr. 12 up). pap., stu. ed. 14.95 (978-1-59658-059-6(3)) College Prowler, Inc.

Jordan, Keith. Don't Stress the Process: The College Plan. 2005. (J). lib. bdg. 18.95 (978-0-9761218-0-0(8)) Knowledge College Planning.

Joseph, Jessica, et al. Suny Albany College Prowler off the Record: Inside State University of New York. 2005. (College Prowler off the Record Guides: Vol. 126). 160p. (YA). (gr. 12 up). pap., stu. ed. 14.95 (978-1-59658-125-8(5)) College Prowler, Inc.

Joseph, Tiffani & Keller, Carolyn. Temple University College Prowler off the Record. 2nd ed. 2005. (College Prowler off the Record Guides: Vol. 131). 160p. (YA). (gr. 12 up). pap., stu. ed. 14.95 (978-1-59658-130-2(1)) College Prowler, Inc.

Katz, Andrew & Gohari, Omid. Brandeis University College Prowler off the Record. 2nd ed. 2005. (College Prowler off the Record Guides: Vol. 16). 160p. (YA). (gr. 12 up). pap., stu. ed. 14.95 (978-1-59658-015-2(1)) College Prowler, Inc.

Keller, Carolyn & Seaman, Jim. Allegheny College College Prowler off the Record. 2005. (College Prowler off the Record Guides: Vol. 1). 160p. (YA). (gr. 12 up). pap., stu. ed. 14.95 (978-1-59658-000-8(3)) College Prowler, Inc.

Kennedy, Lauren, et al. Arizona State University College Prowler off the Record. 2005. (College Prowler off the Record Guides: Vol. 4). 160p. (YA). (gr. 12 up). pap., stu. ed. 14.95 (978-1-59658-003-9(8)) College Prowler, Inc.

Killeen, Jared & Nash, Kevin. Bard College College Prowler off the Record. 2005. (College Prowler off the Record Guides: Vol. 7). 160p. (YA). (gr. 12 up). pap., stu. ed. 14.95 (978-1-59658-006-0(2)) College Prowler, Inc.

Kittay, Matthew & Mason, Chris. Brown University College Prowler off the Record. 2nd ed. 2005. (College Prowler off the Record Guides: Vol. 18). 160p. (YA). (gr. 12 up). pap., stu. ed. 14.95 (978-1-59658-017-6(8)) College Prowler, Inc.

Klein, Jennifer & Gray, Kevan. University of Pennsylvania College Prowler off the Record. 2nd ed. 2005. (College Prowler off the Record Guides: Vol. 174). 160p. (YA). (gr. 12 up). pap., stu. ed. 14.95 (978-1-59658-173-9(5)) College Prowler, Inc.

Klein, Nadav & Varacalli, Lauren. Amherst College College Prowler off the Record. 2005. (College Prowler off the Record Guides: Vol. 3). 160p. (YA). (gr. 12 up). pap., stu. ed. 14.95 (978-1-59658-002-2(X)) College Prowler, Inc.

Knight, Russell & Williams, Tim. University of Puget Sound College Prowler off the Record. 2005. (College Prowler off the Record Guides: Vol. 176). 160p. (YA). (gr. 12 up). pap., stu. ed. 14.95 (978-1-59658-175-3(1)) College Prowler, Inc.

Koestler-Grack, Rachel A. The Kent State Tragedy. 2005. (American Moments Ser.). (Illus.). 48p. (J). (gr. 4-8). lib. bdg. 25.65 (978-1-59197-934-0(X)) ABDO Publishing Co.

Koestler, Larry & Scheff, William. Lehigh University College Prowler off the Record. 2005. (College Prowler off the Record Guides: Vol. 74). 160p. (YA). (gr. 12 up). pap., stu. ed. 14.95 (978-1-59658-073-2(9)) College Prowler, Inc.

Krakauer, Steve & Skindzier, Jon. Syracuse University College Prowler off the Record. 2005. (College Prowler off the Record Guides: Vol. 130). 160p. (YA). (gr. 12 up). pap., stu. ed. 14.95 (978-1-59658-129-6(8)) College Prowler, Inc.

Kutscher, Scott & Lyon, Abby. Suny Binghamton College Prowler off the Record: Inside State University of New York. 2005. (College Prowler off the Record Guides: Vol. 125). 160p. (YA). (gr. 12 up). pap., stu. ed. 14.95 (978-1-59658-124-1(7)) College Prowler, Inc.

L. Brown, Stacia & Gray, Kevan. Sarah Lawrence College College Prowler off the Record. 2005. (College Prowler off the Record Guides: Vol. 114). 160p. (YA). (gr. 12 up). pap., stu. ed. 14.95 (978-1-59658-113-5(1)) College Prowler, Inc.

L, Jessica & Skindzier, Jon. Grove City College College Prowler off the Record. 2005. (College Prowler off the Record Guides: Vol. 58). 160p. (YA). (gr. 12 up). pap., stu. ed. 14.95 (978-1-59658-057-2(7)) College Prowler, Inc.

L. Wright, Sean & Nash, Kevin. Villanova University College Prowler off the Record. 2005. (College Prowler off the Record Guides: Vol. 195). 160p. (YA). (gr. 12 up). pap., stu. ed. 14.95 (978-1-59658-194-4(8)) College Prowler, Inc.

Lang, Alex & Burns, Adam. University of Iowa College Prowler off the Record. 2nd ed. 2005. (College Prowler off the Record Guides: Vol. 158). 160p. (YA). (gr. 12 up). pap., stu. ed. 14.95 (978-1-59658-157-9(3)) College Prowler, Inc.

Langlieb, David & Burns, Adam. Haverford College College Prowler off the Record. 2005. (College Prowler off the Record Guides: Vol. 64). 160p. (YA). (gr. 12 up). pap., stu. ed. 14.95 (978-1-59658-063-3(1)) College Prowler, Inc.

Langston, Mandy & Nash, Kevin. University of Kentucky College Prowler off the Record. 2nd ed. 2005. (College Prowler off the Record Guides: Vol. 160). 160p. (YA). (gr. 12 up). pap., stu. ed. 14.95 (978-1-59658-159-3(X)) College Prowler, Inc.

Leanoard, James & Nash, Kevin. University of San Diego College Prowler off the Record. 2nd ed. 2005. (College Prowler off the Record Guides: Vol. 180). 160p. (YA). (gr. 12 up). pap., stu. ed. 14.95 (978-1-59658-179-1(4)) College Prowler, Inc.

LeBaron, Sarah & Dawson, Kai. Oberlin College College Prowler off the Record. 2005. (College Prowler off the Record Guides: Vol. 93). 160p. (YA). (gr. 12 up). pap., stu. ed. 14.95 (978-1-59658-092-3(5)) College Prowler, Inc.

Lee, Brittany. Rollins College. Moore, Kim & Burns, Adam, eds. 2005. (College Prowler off the Record Guides: Vol. 110). (Illus.). 150p. (gr. 12 up). pap., stu. ed. 14.95 (978-1-59658-109-8(3)) College Prowler, Inc.

Lee, Danielle. JumpStart Your Future: A Guide for the College-Bound Christian. 2006. (Illus.). iii, 123p. (YA). per. 12.99 (978-0-9769298-9-5(9)) Olive Pr., The.

Lee, Susie & Skindzier, Jon. MIT College Prowler off the Record: Inside Massachusetts Institute of Technology. 2nd ed. 2005. (College Prowler off the Record Guides: Vol. 82). 160p. (YA). (gr. 12 up). pap., stu. ed. 14.95 (978-1-59658-081-7(X)) College Prowler, Inc.

Leitikow, Greg & Varacalli, Lauren. Colorado College College Prowler off the Record. 2005. (College Prowler off the Record Guides: Vol. 34). 160p. (YA). (gr. 12 up). pap., stu. ed. 14.95 (978-1-59658-033-6(X)) College Prowler, Inc.

Lenfest, Kevyn & Mandelbaum, Jolie. University of Vermont College Prowler off the Record. 2nd ed. 2005. (College Prowler off the Record Guides: Vol. 188). 160p. (YA). (gr. 12 up). pap., stu. ed. 14.95 (978-1-59658-187-6(5)) College Prowler, Inc.

Lewis, Brooke & Varacalli, Lauren. Dickinson College College Prowler off the Record. 2005. (College Prowler off the Record Guides: Vol. 43). 160p. (YA). (gr. 12 up). pap., stu. ed. 14.95 (978-1-59658-042-8(9)) College Prowler, Inc.

Lewis, Jeff & Burns, Adam. University of New Hampshire College Prowler off the Record. 2nd ed. 2005. (College Prowler off the Record Guides: Vol. 169). 160p. (YA). (gr. 12 up). pap., stu. ed. 14.95 (978-1-59658-168-5(9)) College Prowler, Inc.

Lewis, Jennifer & Williams, Tim. Mount Holyoke College College Prowler off the Record. 2005. (College Prowler off the Record Guides: Vol. 87). 160p. (YA). (gr. 12 up). pap., stu. ed. 14.95 (978-1-59658-086-2(0)) College Prowler, Inc.

Lexa, Katrina & Skindzier, Jon. Hampton University College Prowler off the Record. 2nd ed. 2005. (College Prowler off the Record Guides: Vol. 61). 160p. (YA). (gr. 12 up). pap., stu. ed. 14.95 (978-1-59658-060-2(7)) College Prowler, Inc.

Lieberman, Dan & Rahimi, Joey. Carnegie Mellon University College Prowler off the Record. 2nd ed. 2005. (College Prowler off the Record Guides: Vol. 24). 160p. (YA). (gr. 12 up). pap., stu. ed. 14.95 (978-1-59658-023-7(2)) College Prowler, Inc.

Lindin, Kerri & Pecsenye, Jessica. University of Rochester College Prowler off the Record. 2nd ed. 2005. (College Prowler off the Record Guides: Vol. 179). 160p. (YA). (gr. 12 up). pap., stu. ed. 14.95 (978-1-59658-178-4(6)) College Prowler, Inc.

Low, Jessica & Nash, Kevin. Bentley College College Prowler off the Record. 2005. (College Prowler off the Record Guides: Vol. 12). 160p. (YA). (gr. 12 up). pap., stu. ed. 14.95 (978-1-59658-011-4(9)) College Prowler, Inc.

Lynn Sauthoff, Taryn & Williams, Tim. Rutgers New Brunswick College Prowler off the Record. 2005. (College Prowler off the Record Guides: Vol. 112). 160p. (YA). (gr. 12 up). pap., stu. ed. 14.95 (978-1-59658-111-1(5)) College Prowler, Inc.

Maehl, Sarah & Nash, Kevin. Beloit College College Prowler off the Record. 2005. (College Prowler off the Record Guides: Vol. 11). 160p. (YA). (gr. 12 up). pap., stu. ed. 14.95 (978-1-59658-010-7(0)) College Prowler, Inc.

Mahon, Amy & Gohari, Omid. Elon University College Prowler off the Record. 2005. (College Prowler off the Record Guides: Vol. 47). 160p. (YA). (gr. 12 up). pap., stu. ed. 14.95 (978-1-59658-046-6(1)) College Prowler, Inc.

Marshall, Ashley & Keller, Carolyn. Texas a & M University College Prowler off the Record. 2nd ed. 2005. (College Prowler off the Record Guides: Vol. 132). 160p. (YA). (gr. 12 up). pap., stu. ed. 14.95 (978-1-59658-131-9(X)) College Prowler, Inc.

Mass, Aaron & Burns, Adam. Wake Forest University College Prowler off the Record. 2nd ed. 2005. (College Prowler off the Record Guides: Vol. 197). 160p. (YA). (gr. 12 up). pap., stu. ed. 14.95 (978-1-59658-196-8(4)) College Prowler, Inc.

McGregor, Tony L., illus. Victory Week. 1998. 40p. (J). lib. bdg. 22.95 (978-0-9634016-9-4(6) , Deaf Life Pr.) MSM Productions, Ltd.

McNeese, Tim. Regents of the University of California V. Bakke. 2007. (Great Supreme Court Decisions Ser.). (Illus.). 152p. (J). (gr. 5-8). 30.00 (978-0-7910-9260-6(7) , Chelsea Hse.) Facts On File, Inc.

McRobert, Megan & Skindzier, Jon. Smith College College Prowler off the Record. 2005. (College Prowler off the Record Guides: Vol. 119). 160p. (YA). (gr. 12 up). pap., stu. ed. 14.95 (978-1-59658-118-0(2)) College Prowler, Inc.

Meers, Whitney & Nash, Kevin. University of South Florida College Prowler off the Record. 2005. (College Prowler off the Record Guides: Vol. 183). 160p. (YA). (gr. 12 up). pap., stu. ed. 14.95 (978-1-59658-182-1(4)) College Prowler, Inc.

Megill, Colin & Davis, Cristine. University of Connecticut College Prowler off the Record. 2nd ed. 2005. (College Prowler off the Record Guides: Vol. 152). 160p. (YA). (gr. 12 up). pap., stu. ed. 14.95 (978-1-59658-151-7(4)) College Prowler, Inc.

Meyer, Jared & Jolis, Annie. University of Maryland College Prowler off the Record. 2nd ed. 2005. (College Prowler off the Record Guides: Vol. 161). 160p. (YA). (gr. 12 up). pap., stu. ed. 14.95 (978-1-59658-160-9(3)) College Prowler, Inc.

Miller, Kirystan & Burns, Adam. Iowa State University College Prowler off the Record. 2005. (College Prowler off the Record Guides: Vol. 68). 160p. (YA). (gr. 12 up). pap., stu. ed. 14.95 (978-1-59658-067-1(4)) College Prowler, Inc.

Mitchell, Kyra & Varacalli, Lauren. Baylor University College Prowler off the Record. 2005. (College Prowler off the Record Guides: Vol. 10). 160p. (YA). (gr. 12 up). pap., stu. ed. 14.95 (978-1-59658-009-1(7)) College Prowler, Inc.

Murphy, Ryan & Varacalli, Lauren. Drexel University College Prowler off the Record. 2nd ed. 2005. (College Prowler off the Record Guides: Vol. 44). 160p. (YA). (gr. 12 up). pap., stu. ed. 14.95 (978-1-59658-043-5(7)) College Prowler, Inc.

Murray, Melanie & Varacalli, Lauren. College of Charleston College Prowler off the Record. 2005. (College Prowler off the Record Guides: Vol. 30). 160p. (YA). (gr. 12 up). pap., stu. ed. 14.95 (978-1-59658-029-9(1)) College Prowler, Inc.

Nash, Kevin. Suny Stony Brook College Prowler off the Record: Inside State University of New York. 2005. (College Prowler off the Record Guides: Vol. 128). 160p. (YA). (gr. 12 up). pap., stu. ed. 14.95 (978-1-59658-127-2(1)) College Prowler, Inc.

—Valparaiso University College Prowler off the Record. 2005. (College Prowler off the Record Guides: Vol. 192). 160p. (YA). (gr. 12 up). pap., stu. ed. 14.95 (978-1-59658-191-3(3)) College Prowler, Inc.

Nicklin, Miriam & Pecsenye, Jessica. University of Virginia College Prowler off the Record. 2nd ed. 2005. (College Prowler off the Record Guides: Vol. 189). 160p. (YA). (gr. 12 up). pap., stu. ed. 14.95 (978-1-59658-188-3(3)) College Prowler, Inc.

Nicole, Bridget & Gray, Kevan. University of Illinois College Prowler off the Record. 2nd ed. 2005. (College Prowler off the Record Guides: Vol. 157). 160p. (YA). (gr. 12 up). pap., stu. ed. 14.95 (978-1-59658-156-2(5)) College Prowler, Inc.

Niekerk, Katie & Seaman, Jim. University of Denver College Prowler off the Record. 2nd ed. 2005. (College Prowler off the Record Guides: Vol. 154). 160p. (YA). (gr. 12 up). pap., stu. ed. 14.95 (978-1-59658-153-1(0)) College Prowler, Inc.

Nolan, Lindsey & Varacalli, Lauren. Auburn University College Prowler off the Record. 2nd ed. 2005. (College Prowler off the Record Guides: Vol. 5). 160p. (YA). (gr. 12 up). pap., stu. ed. 14.95 (978-1-59658-004-6(6)) College Prowler, Inc.

Olson, Remy & Mason, Chris. Case Western Reserve University College Prowler off the Record. 2nd ed. 2005. (College Prowler off the Record Guides: Vol. 25). 160p. (YA). (gr. 12 up). pap., stu. ed. 14.95 (978-1-59658-024-4(0)) College Prowler, Inc.

Paley, Briyah. Northeastern University. Belinsky, Robin et al, eds. 2nd ed. 2005. (College Prowler off the Record Guides: Vol. 91). (Illus.). 154p. (gr. 12 up). pap., stu. ed. 14.95 (978-1-59658-090-9(9)) College Prowler, Inc.

Palmer, Amy & Keller, Carolyn. University of Minnesota College Prowler off the Record. 2nd ed. 2005. (College Prowler off the Record Guides: Vol. 165). 160p. (YA). (gr. 12 up). pap., stu. ed. 14.95 (978-1-59658-164-7(6)) College Prowler, Inc.

Peckyno, Ryan. West Point Military Academy College Prowler off the Record. 2005. (College Prowler off the Record Guides: Vol. 202). 160p. (YA). (gr. 12 up). pap., stu. ed. 14.95 (978-1-59658-201-9(4)) College Prowler, Inc.

Peltak, Jennifer. History of African American Colleges & Universities. 2003. (American Mosaic Ser.). (Illus.). 112p. (gr. 6-12). 30.00 (978-0-7910-7269-1(X) , Chelsea Hse.) Facts On File, Inc.

Pinkerton, Steve & Pecsenye, Jessica. Pepperdine University College Prowler off the Record. 2005. (College Prowler off the Record Guides: Vol. 98). 160p. (YA). (gr. 12 up). pap., stu. ed. 14.95 (978-1-59658-097-8(6)) College Prowler, Inc.

Pommer, Christina & Skindzier, Jon. Johns Hopkins University College Prowler off the Record. 2005. (College Prowler off the Record Guides: Vol. 71). 160p. (YA). (gr. 12 up). pap., stu. ed. 14.95 (978-1-59658-070-1(4)) College Prowler, Inc.

Pope-Roush, Jordan & Skindzier, Jon. Emory University College Prowler off the Record. 2nd ed. 2005. (College Prowler off the Record Guides: Vol. 49). 160p. (YA). (gr. 12 up). pap., stu. ed. 14.95 (978-1-59658-048-0(8)) College Prowler, Inc.

Pouliot, Seth & Nash, Kevin. University of Massachusetts College Prowler off the Record. 2nd ed. 2005. (College Prowler off the Record Guides: Vol. 162). 160p. (YA). (gr. 12 up). pap., stu. ed. 14.95 (978-1-59658-161-6(1)) College Prowler, Inc.

R., Ben & Nash, Kevin. Suny Buffalo College Prowler off the Record: Inside State University of New York. 2005. (College Prowler off the Record Guides: Vol. 127). 160p. (YA). (gr. 12 up). pap., stu. ed. 14.95 (978-1-59658-126-5(3)) College Prowler, Inc.

R, Sarah & Seaman, Jim. Rhodes College College Prowler off the Record. 2nd ed. 2005. (College Prowler off the Record Guides: Vol. 107). 160p. (YA). (gr. 12 up). pap., stu. ed. 14.95 (978-1-59658-106-7(9)) College Prowler, Inc.

Rakovic, Robert & Pecsenye, Jessica. Seton Hall University College Prowler off the Record. 2005. (College Prowler off the Record Guides: Vol. 117). 160p. (YA). (gr. 12 up). pap., stu. ed. 14.95 (978-1-59658-116-6(6)) College Prowler, Inc.

Ramin, Nathan & Burns, Adam. Loyola University Chicago College Prowler off the Record. 2005. (College Prowler off the Record Guides: Vol. 78). 160p. (YA). (gr. 12 up). pap., stu. ed. 14.95 (978-1-59658-077-0(1)) College Prowler, Inc.

Renick, Ricki & Swope, Gretchen. University of Mississippi College Prowler off the Record. 2005. (College Prowler off the Record Guides: Vol. 166). 160p. (YA). (gr. 12 up). pap., stu. ed. 14.95 (978-1-59658-165-4(4)) College Prowler, Inc.

Richmond, Derek & Skindzier, Jon. Georgetown University College Prowler off the Record. 2nd ed. 2005. (College Prowler off the Record Guides: Vol. 55). 160p. (YA). (gr. 12 up). pap., stu. ed. 14.95 (978-1-59658-054-1(2)) College Prowler, Inc.

Robinson, Hadley & Seaman, Jim. UC Santa Cruz College Prowler off the Record: Inside University of California Santa Cruz. 2nd ed. 2005. (College Prowler off the Record Guides: Vol. 148). 160p. (YA). (gr. 12 up). pap., stu. ed. 14.95 (978-1-59658-147-0(6)) College Prowler, Inc.

Rosario, Nicole & Williams, Tim. University of Wisconsin College Prowler off the Record. 2nd ed. 2005. (College Prowler off the Record Guides: Vol. 191). 160p. (YA). (gr. 12 up). pap., stu. ed. 14.95 (978-1-59658-190-6(5)) College Prowler, Inc.

Rosenbaum, Jason & Weisgerber, Amy. University of Missouri College Prowler off the Record. 2nd ed. 2005. (College Prowler off the Record Guides: Vol. 167). 160p. (YA). (gr. 12 up). pap., stu. ed. 14.95 (978-1-59658-166-1(2)) College Prowler, Inc.

Ross, Jordan & Gohari, Omid. Emerson College College Prowler off the Record. 2nd ed. 2005. (College Prowler off the Record Guides: Vol. 48). 160p. (YA). (gr. 12 up). pap., stu. ed. 14.95 (978-1-59658-047-3(X)) College Prowler, Inc.

Rossi, Regine & Dawson, Kai. Rensselaer Polytechnic Institute College Prowler off the Record: Inside RPI. 2005. (College Prowler off the Record Guides: Vol. 105). 160p. (YA). (gr. 12 up). pap., stu. ed. 14.95 (978-1-59658-104-3(2)) College Prowler, Inc.

Rossi, Regine & Nash, Kevin. University of Florida College Prowler off the Record. 2nd ed. 2005. (College Prowler off the Record Guides: Vol. 155). 160p. (YA). (gr. 12 up). pap., stu. ed. 14.95 (978-1-59658-154-8(9)) College Prowler, Inc.

Roth, Pam & Williams, Tim. Lafayette College College Prowler off the Record. 2nd ed. 2005. (College Prowler off the Record Guides: Vol. 73). 160p. (YA). (gr. 12 up). pap., stu. ed. 14.95 (978-1-59658-072-5(0)) College Prowler, Inc.

Rudolph, Allyson & Gohari, Omid. Colby College College Prowler off the Record. 2005. (College Prowler off the Record Guides: Vol. 28). 160p. (YA). (gr. 12 up). pap., stu. ed. 14.95 (978-1-59658-027-5(5)) College Prowler, Inc.

Rugg, Frederick E. Rugg's Recommendations on the Colleges. (YA). 19th rev. ed. 2002. 216p. (gr. 11-12). pap. 22.95 (978-1-883062-43-9(8)); 20th rev. ed. 2003. 220p. (gr. 10-12). pap. 22.95 (978-1-883062-48-4(9)) Rugg's Recommendations.

—Twenty More Tips on the Colleges. (YA). 8th rev. ed. 2002. 5p. (gr. 11-12). pap. 8.95 (978-1-883062-44-6(6)); 9th rev. ed. 2003. 6p. (gr. 10-12). pap. 8.95 (978-1-883062-49-1(7)); 10th rev. ed. 2004. 6p. pap. 8.95 (978-1-883062-54-5(3)); 11th rev. ed. 2005. 6p. pap. 8.95 (978-1-883062-59-0(4)) Rugg's Recommendations.

S. Wong, Derrick & Varacalli, Lauren. Bowdoin College College Prowler off the Record. 2005. (College Prowler off the Record Guides: Vol. 15). 160p. (YA). (gr. 12 up). pap., stu. ed. 14.95 (978-1-59658-014-5(3)) College Prowler, Inc.

Salaver, Jillianne & Williams, Tim. UC Irvine College Prowler off the Record: Inside University of California Irvine. 2nd ed. 2005. (College Prowler off the Record Guides: Vol. 143). 160p. (YA). (gr. 12 up). pap., stu. ed. 14.95 (978-1-59658-142-5(5)) College Prowler, Inc.

Sanders, Carly. Whitman College College Prowler off the Record. 2005. (College Prowler off the Record Guides: Vol. 205). 160p. (YA). (gr. 12 up). pap., stu. ed. 14.95 (978-1-59658-204-0(9)) College Prowler, Inc.

Sandoval, Kate & Keller, Carolyn. UC Santa Barbara College Prowler off the Record: Inside University of California Santa Barbara. 2nd ed. 2005. (College Prowler off the Record Guides: Vol. 147). 160p. (YA). (gr. 12 up). pap., stu. ed. 14.95 (978-1-59658-146-3(8)) College Prowler, Inc.

Schubach, Alanna & Pecsenye, Jessica. American University College Prowler off the Record. 2nd ed. 2005. (College Prowler off the Record Guides: Vol. 2). 160p. (YA). (gr. 12 up). pap., stu. ed. 14.95 (978-1-59658-001-5(1)) College Prowler, Inc.

Schuvent, Julia & Skindzier, Jon. Rice University College Prowler off the Record. 2005. (College Prowler off the Record Guides: Vol. 108). 160p. (YA). (gr. 12 up). pap., stu. ed. 14.95 (978-1-59658-107-4(7)) College Prowler, Inc.

Sendrowski, Brian, Jr. & Gohari, Omid. Connecticut College Prowler off the Record. 2005. (College Prowler off the Record Guides: Vol. 36). 160p. (YA). (gr. 12 up). pap., stu. ed. 14.95 (978-1-59658-035-0(6)) College Prowler, Inc.

Shaw, Katie & Nash, Kevin. University of Washington College Prowler off the Record. 2nd ed. 2005. (College Prowler off the Record Guides: Vol. 190). 160p. (YA). (gr. 12 up). pap., stu. ed. 14.95 (978-1-59658-189-0(1)) College Prowler, Inc.

Sheik, Mayra & Varacalli, Lauren. Caltech College Prowler off the Record: Inside California Institute of Technology. 2nd ed. 2005. (College Prowler off the Record Guides: Vol. 22). 160p. (YA). (gr. 12 up). pap., stu. ed. 14.95 (978-1-59658-021-3(6)) College Prowler, Inc.

Singer, Jenny & Scheff, William. Marquette University College Prowler off the Record. 2nd ed. 2005. (College Prowler off the Record Guides: Vol. 81). 160p. (YA). (gr. 12 up). pap., stu. ed. 14.95 (978-1-59658-080-0(1)) College Prowler, Inc.

Skindzier, Jon. Southern Methodist University College Prowler off the Record. 2005. (College Prowler off the Record Guides: Vol. 120). 160p. (YA). (gr. 12 up). pap., stu. ed. 14.95 (978-1-59658-119-7(0)) College Prowler, Inc.

Smith, Stacy & Davis, Cristine. University of Rhode Island College Prowler off the Record. 2005. (College Prowler off the Record Guides: Vol. 177). 160p. (YA). (gr. 12 up). pap., stu. ed. 14.95 (978-1-59658-176-0(X)) College Prowler, Inc.

Spiro, Ian & Jendrey, Julie. Stanford University College Prowler off the Record. 2nd ed. 2005. (College Prowler off the Record Guides: Vol. 124). 160p. (YA). (gr. 12 up). pap., stu. ed. 14.95 (978-1-59658-123-4(9)) College Prowler, Inc.

Standifer, Lauren, et al. Grinnell College College Prowler off the Record. 2005. (College Prowler off the Record Guides: Vol. 57). 160p. (YA). (gr. 12 up). pap., stu. ed. 14.95 (978-1-59658-056-5(9)) College Prowler, Inc.

Steinman, Joshua & Nash, Kevin. University of Chicago College Prowler off the Record. 2nd ed. 2005. (College Prowler off the Record Guides: Vol. 150). 160p. (YA). (gr. 12 up). pap., stu. ed. 14.95 (978-1-59658-149-4(2)) College Prowler, Inc.

Stewart, Nicolette & Nash, Kevin. Skidmore College College Prowler off the Record. 2005. (College Prowler off the Record Guides: Vol. 118). 160p. (YA). (gr. 12 up). pap., stu. ed. 14.95 (978-1-59658-117-3(4)) College Prowler, Inc.

Striker, Oliver & Varacalli, Lauren. Cornell University College Prowler off the Record. 2005. (College Prowler off the Record Guides: Vol. 38). 160p. (YA). (gr. 12 up). pap., stu. ed. 14.95 (978-1-59658-037-4(2)) College Prowler, Inc.

Tafoya, Nathan & Nash, Kevin. University of Arizona College Prowler off the Record. 2nd ed. 2005. (College Prowler off the Record Guides: Vol. 140). 160p. (YA). (gr. 12 up). pap., stu. ed. 14.95 (978-1-59658-139-5(5)) College Prowler, Inc.

Takach, Jessica. Wheaton College Massachusetts College Prowler off the Record. 2005. (College Prowler off the Record Guides: Vol. 204). 160p. (YA). (gr. 12 up). pap., stu. ed. 14.95 (978-1-59658-203-3(0)) College Prowler, Inc.

Thomas, Jesse & Keller, Carolyn. University of Oregon College Prowler off the Record. 2nd ed. 2005. (College Prowler off the Record Guides: Vol. 173). 160p. (YA). (gr. 12 up). pap., stu. ed. 14.95 (978-1-59658-172-2(7)) College Prowler, Inc.

Thompson, Camille & Gohari, Omid. College of William & Mary College Prowler off the Record. 2nd ed. 2005. (College Prowler off the Record Guides: Vol. 32). 160p. (YA). (gr. 12 up). pap., stu. ed. 14.95 (978-1-59658-031-2(3)) College Prowler, Inc.

Todd, Danielle & Keller, Carolyn. University of Delaware College Prowler off the Record. 2nd ed. 2005. (College Prowler off the Record Guides: Vol. 153). 160p. (YA). (gr. 12 up). pap., stu. ed. 14.95 (978-1-59658-152-4(2)) College Prowler, Inc.

Tompkins, Michelle & Rahimi, Joey. Columbia University College Prowler off the Record. 2nd ed. 2005. (College Prowler off the Record Guides: Vol. 35). 160p. (YA). (gr. 12 up). pap., stu. ed. 14.95 (978-1-59658-034-3(8)) College Prowler, Inc.

Tran, Christine & Nash, Kevin. Scripps College College Prowler off the Record. 2005. (College Prowler off the Record Guides: Vol. 115). 160p. (YA). (gr. 12 up). pap., stu. ed. 14.95 (978-1-59658-114-2(X)) College Prowler, Inc.

Treadway, Kathryn & Seaman, Jim. Providence College College Prowler off the Record. 2nd ed. 2005. (College Prowler off the Record Guides: Vol. 102). 160p. (YA). (gr. 12 up). pap., stu. ed. 14.95 (978-1-59658-101-2(8)) College Prowler, Inc.

Trousdale, Jonathan & Skindzier, Jon. Georgia Tech College Prowler off the Record: Inside Georgia Institute of Technology. 2005. (College Prowler off the Record Guides: Vol. 56). 160p. (YA). (gr. 12 up). pap., stu. ed. 14.95 (978-1-59658-055-8(0)) College Prowler, Inc.

Turley, Meredith & Burns, Adam. New York University College Prowler off the Record: Inside NYU. 2005. (College Prowler off the Record Guides: Vol. 90). 160p. (YA). (gr. 12 up). pap., stu. ed. 14.95 (978-1-59658-089-3(5)) College Prowler, Inc.

Tylevich, Katherine & Skindzier, Jon. Macalester College College Prowler off the Record. 2nd ed. 2005. (College Prowler off the Record Guides: Vol. 80). 160p. (YA). (gr. 12 up). pap., stu. ed. 14.95 (978-1-59658-079-4(8)) College Prowler, Inc.

Ugarte, Julia & Jendrey, Julie. Seattle University College Prowler off the Record. 2nd ed. 2005. (College Prowler off the Record Guides: Vol. 116). 160p. (YA). (gr. 12 up). pap., stu. ed. 14.95 (978-1-59658-115-9(8)) College Prowler, Inc.

Unkovic, Rachel & Burns, Adam. Trinity College Connecticut College Prowler off the Record. 2005. (College Prowler off the Record Guides: Vol. 134). 160p. (YA). (gr. 12 up). pap., stu. ed. 14.95 (978-1-59658-133-3(6)) College Prowler, Inc.

Valhouli, Alex & Skindzier, Jon. University of Southern California College Prowler off the Record. 2nd ed. 2005. (College Prowler off the Record Guides: Vol. 184). 160p. (YA). (gr. 12 up). pap., stu. ed. 14.95 (978-1-59658-183-8(2)) College Prowler, Inc.

Vance, Ashley & Gohari, Omid. Brigham Young University College Prowler off the Record: Inside BYU. 2nd ed. 2005. (College Prowler off the Record Guides: Vol. 17). 160p. (YA). (gr. 12 up). pap., stu. ed. 14.95 (978-1-59658-016-9(X)) College Prowler, Inc.

Walker, Caren & Varacalli, Lauren. Boston University College Prowler off the Record. 2nd ed. 2005. (College Prowler off the Record Guides: Vol. 14). 160p. (YA). (gr. 12 up). pap., stu. ed. 14.95 (978-1-59658-013-8(5)) College Prowler, Inc.

Watkins, Boyce. Everything You Ever Wanted to Know about College: A Guide for Minority Students. 2004. xiii, 330p. (YA). per. 25.00 (978-0-9742632-0-5(6)) Blue Boy Publishing Co.

Whitley, Jared & Mandelbaum, Jolie. University of Utah College Prowler off the Record. 2nd ed. 2005. (College Prowler off the Record Guides: Vol. 187). 160p. (YA). (gr. 12 up). pap., stu. ed. 14.95 (978-1-59658-186-9(7)) College Prowler, Inc.

Wiedrich, Merrick & Scheff, William. University of Alabama College Prowler off the Record. 2nd ed. 2005. (College Prowler off the Record Guides: Vol. 139). 160p. (YA). (gr. 12 up). pap., stu. ed. 14.95 (978-1-59658-138-8(7)) College Prowler, Inc.

Wild, Cynthia & Nash, Kevin. UC Riverside College Prowler off the Record: Inside University of California Riverside. 2nd ed. 2005. (College Prowler off the Record Guides: Vol. 145). 160p. (YA). (gr. 12 up). pap., stu. ed. 14.95 (978-1-59658-144-9(1)) College Prowler, Inc.

Williams, Jacob & Burns, Adam. University of Tennessee College Prowler off the Record. 2nd ed. 2005. (College Prowler off the Record Guides: Vol. 185). 160p. (YA). (gr. 12 up). pap., stu. ed. 14.95 (978-1-59658-184-5(0)) College Prowler, Inc.

Williams, Rozalia. College FAQ Book: Over 5,000 Not Frequently Asked Questions about College! 2005. (Illus.). 494p. (YA). per. 24.95 (978-0-9755103-0-8(4)) Hidden Curriculum Education.

Williams, Tim. New School University College Prowler off the Record. 2nd ed. 2005. (College Prowler off the Record Guides: Vol. 89). 160p. (YA). (gr. 12 up). pap., stu. ed. 14.95 (978-1-59658-088-6(7) , Off The Record) College Prowler, Inc.

Wines, Shawn & Pecsenye, Jessica. University of Miami College Prowler off the Record. 2nd ed. 2005. (College Prowler off the Record Guides: Vol. 163). 160p. (YA). (gr. 12 up). pap., stu. ed. 14.95 (978-1-59658-162-3(X)) College Prowler, Inc.

Woolsey, Matthew & Keller, Carolyn. Vanderbilt University College Prowler off the Record. 2nd ed. 2005. (College Prowler off the Record Guides: Vol. 193). 160p. (YA). (gr. 12 up). pap., stu. ed. 14.95 (978-1-59658-192-0(1)) College Prowler, Inc.

Zang, Adam & Varacalli, Lauren. Carleton College College Prowler off the Record. 2005. (College Prowler off the Record Guides: Vol. 23). 160p. (YA). (gr. 12 up). pap., stu. ed. 14.95 (978-1-59658-022-0(4)) College Prowler, Inc.

UNIVERSITIES AND COLLEGES—DIRECTORIES

Kwapong, Ohene. 12 Steps to Getting Admitted into Colleges & Universities in the United States. 2003. 79p. (YA). pap. 10.95 (978-0-595-29647-7(5)) iUniverse, Inc.

Rugg, Frederick E. Rugg's Recommendations on the Colleges. 17th rev. ed. 2000. 178p. (J). (gr. 11-12). pap. 20.95 (978-1-883062-32-3(2)) Rugg's Recommendations.

—Thirty Questions & Answers. (gr. 11-12). 5th ed. 1999. 23p. pap. 9.95 (978-1-883062-30-9(6) , 4); 8th rev. ed. 2002. 19p. (YA). pap. 9.95 (978-1-883062-46-0(2)) Rugg's Recommendations.

—Thirty Questions & Answers on the Colleges. (YA). 7th ed. 2001. 20p. (gr. 11-12). pap. 9.95 (978-1-883062-31-6(4)); 9th rev. ed. 2003. 20p. pap. 9.95 (978-1-883062-52-1(7)); 10th rev. ed. 2004. 20p. pap. 9.95 (978-1-883062-56-9(X)); 11th rev. ed. 2005. 21p. pap. 9.95 (978-1-883062-61-3(6)) Rugg's Recommendations.

Viollt, Michael. The Best 201 Colleges for the Real World. 2000. (College Guides Ser.). 350p. (YA). (gr. 10 up). pap. 15.00 (978-1-57509-065-8(1)) Octameron Assocs.

UNIVERSITIES AND COLLEGES—ENTRANCE REQUIREMENTS

Martinson, Thomas H. Arco Teach Yourself the SAT in 30 Days. 4th ed. 1999. (Arco's Teach Yourself to Beat Ser.). (Illus.). xi, 638p. (YA). pap. 19.95 incl. cd-rom (978-0-02-862519-5(6) , Arco) Peterson's.

Wolf, Jonathan S. How to Prepare for the AP Physics B. 3rd ed. 2003. (Illus.). 480p. pap. 16.95 (978-0-7641-2359-7(9)) Barron's Educational Series, Inc.

UNIVERSITIES AND COLLEGES—FICTION

see also Schools—Fiction

Bee, Clair. Comeback Cagers, Vol. 21. 2001. (Chip Hilton Sports Ser.). 208p. (J). pap. 5.99 (978-0-8054-2100-2(9)) B&H Publishing Grp.

—Fence Busters, Vol. 11. 1999. (Chip Hilton Sports Ser.). x, 212p. (J). reprint ed. pap. 5.99 (978-0-8054-1993-1(4)) B&H Publishing Grp.

—Freshman Quarterback, Vol. 9. 1999. (Chip Hilton Sports Ser.). 208p. (J). reprint ed. pap. 5.99 (978-0-8054-1991-7(8)) B&H Publishing Grp.

—Home Run Feud, Vol. 22. 2002. (Chip Hilton Sports Ser.: Vol. 22). 208p. (J). pap. 5.99 (978-0-8054-2124-8(6)) B&H Publishing Grp.

Blumenthal, Bliss & Alarcon, Claudia. Wiley's Way: El Camino de Wiley. Gonzalez, Ricky & Gonzalez, Crysol, illus. 2004. (ENG & SPA.). 112p. pap. 9.95 (978-0-292-70615-6(4)) Univ. of Texas Pr.

Carlson, Melody. On My Own. 2002. (gr. 7-12). lib. bdg. 22.25 (978-0-613-85855-7(7)) Tandem Library Bks.

—On My Own: Diary Number 4. 2002. (Diary of a Teenage Girl Ser.: Bk. 4). 300p. (J). pap. 12.99 (978-1-59052-017-8(3) , Multnomah) WaterBrook Pr.

Choi, Sook Nyul. Gathering of Pearls. 2007. 176p. (YA). (gr. 7). pap. 6.95 (***978-0-618-80918-9(X)**) Houghton Mifflin Co. Trade & Reference Div.

Clark, Catherine. Wurst Case Scenario. 2001. 320p. (J). (gr. 8 up). 16.89 (978-0-06-029525-7(2)) HarperCollins Pubs.

Clement-Moore, Rosemary. Hell Week. 2008. 336p. (YA). 16.99 (***978-0-385-73414-1(X)**); lib. bdg. 19.99 (***978-0-385-90429-2(0)**) Dell Publishing. (Delacorte Pr.).

Coburn, Jake. LoveSick. 2005. 240p. (YA). (gr. 8-12). 16.99 (978-0-525-47383-1(1) , Dutton Juvenile) Penguin Group (USA) Inc.

Condie, Allyson. First Day. 2007. 304p. (YA). pap. 15.95 (***978-1-59038-775-7(9)**) Deseret Bk. Co.

Craft, Elizabeth & Fain, Sarah. Bass Ackwards & Belly Up. 2007. 404p. (J). (gr. 10 up). pap. 8.99 (***978-0-316-05794-3(0)** , Poppy) Little, Brown Bks. for Young Readers.

Ferrer, Caridad. It's Not about the Accent. 2007. 288p. (YA). (gr. 7 up). pap. 9.95 (***978-1-4165-2491-5(6)** , MTV) Simon & Schuster.

Flower, Jessie Graham. Grace Harlowe's Second Year at Overton College. 2004. reprint ed. pap. 20.95 (978-1-4191-2223-1(1)) Kessinger Publishing, LLC.

Frank, Hillary. Better Than Running at Night. Frank, Hillary, illus. 2002. (Illus.). 272p. (YA). (gr. 7 up). pap. 7.99 (978-0-618-25073-8(5)); (gr. 9 up). tchr. ed. 17.00 (978-0-618-10439-0(9)) Houghton Mifflin Co. Trade & Reference Div.

—Better Than Running at Night. 2002. (gr. 7-12). lib. bdg. 18.80 (978-0-613-90721-7(3)) Tandem Library Bks.

Golden, Christopher. Meets the Eye. 2000. (Body of Evidence Ser.: No. 4). 256p. (YA). (gr. 7 up). pap. 4.99 (978-0-671-03495-5(2) , Simon Pulse) Simon & Schuster Children's Publishing.

—Thief of Hearts. 1999. 245p. (YA). (gr. 8-12). per. 13.00 (978-0-613-73104-1(2)) Tandem Library Bks.

Grey, Zane. The Young Pitcher. Exams Unlimited, Inc. Staff, ed. 2002. (Illus.). 185p. (C). reprint ed. cd-rom 8.95 (978-1-59132-087-6(9)) Exams Unlimited, Inc.

Hobbs, Valerie. Anything but Ordinary. 2007. 176p. (YA). (gr. 7 up). 16.00 (978-0-374-30374-7(6)) Farrar, Straus & Giroux.

Johnson-Choong, Shelly. A Light to Come Home By. 2nd unabr. ed. 2004. 212p. (C). reprint ed. pap. 12.95 (978-1-932280-52-4(9) , 80529) Granite Publishing & Distribution.

Korman, Gordon. Hollywood Hustle. 2006. 272p. (gr. 7-17). reprint ed. pap. 5.99 (978-0-7868-0919-6(1)) Hyperion Pr.

Kornreich, Leron. Ivory Towers. 2001. (YA). 7.99 (978-0-9707509-0-7(0)) Banana Peel Bks.

Lithgow, John. Mahalia Mouse Goes to College. Oleynikov, Igor, illus. 2007. 40p. (J). 17.99 (978-1-4169-2715-0(8) , Simon & Schuster Children's Publishing) Simon & Schuster Children's Publishing.

Lovelace, Maud Hart. Carney's House Party. 2000. (gr. 3 6). lib. bdg. 15.25 (978-0-613-31046-8(2)) Tandem Library Bks.

MacPhee, Phoebe. Alphabetical Hook-up List A-J. 2002. (gr. 7-12). lib. bdg. 18.75 (978-0-613-60525-0(X)) Tandem Library Bks.

Mamet, David. Henrietta. Dahlie, Elizabeth, illus. 1999. 32p. (ps-3). tchr. ed. 16.00 (978-0-618-00416-4(5)) Houghton Mifflin Co. Trade & Reference Div.

McKendrick, Lisa. On a Whim. 2001. 156p. (J). (978-1-57734-896-2(6)) Covenant Communications.

Minter, J. Hold on Tight. 2006. (Insiders Novel Ser.: Bk. 5). 256p. (YA). pap. 8.95 (978-1-58234-719-6(0) , Bloomsbury Children) Bloomsbury Publishing.

Montgomery, L. M. Anne of the Island. Date not set. mass mkt. (978-0-8125-6563-8(0) , Tor Bks.) Doherty, Tom Assocs., LLC.

—Anne of the Island. 2006. (ENG.). pap. (***978-1-4068-2171-0(3)**); pap. (***978-1-4068-3175-7(1)**) Echo Library.

—Anne of the Island. 2006. (ENG.). 102.99 (***978-1-4219-3295-8(4)**) IndyPublish.com.

—Anne of the Island. 2004. reprint ed. pap. 1.99 (978-1-4192-0718-1(0)); pap. 30.95 (978-1-4179-0885-1(8)) Kessinger Publishing, LLC.

—Anne of the Island. (Twelve-Point Ser.). 2001. 240p. lib. bdg. 25.00 (978-1-58287-157-8(4)); 2004. 396p. 26.00 (978-1-58287-640-5(1)) North Bks.

—Anne of the Island. abr. ed. 1998. (Avonlea Ser.: No. 4). 304p. (J). (gr. 5-8). pap. 4.99 (978-0-14-036777-5(2) , Puffin) Penguin Group (USA) Inc.

—Anne of the Island. 2000. (Anne of Green Gables Ser.: Vol. No. 3). (gr. 5-8). 182p. 24.95 (978-1-57646-309-3(5)); 182p. pap. 14.99 (978-1-57646-308-6(7)); 336p. pap. 19.99 (978-1-57646-310-9(9)) Quiet Vision Publishing.

—Anne of the Island. 2001. (gr. 7-12). lib. bdg. 30.40 (978-0-613-79774-0(4)) Tandem Library Bks.

—Anne of the Island Book & Charm. 2005. (Charming Classics). 304p. (J). pap. 6.99 (978-0-06-075859-2(7) , Harper Festival) HarperCollins Pubs.

Moore, Stephanie Perry. Finally Sure, Vol. 5. 2004. (Laurel Shadrach Ser.). 208p. (YA). pap. 6.99 (978-0-8024-4039-6(8)) Moody Pubs.

Namioka, Lensey. An Ocean Apart, a World Away. 2003. (gr. 7-12). lib. bdg. 13.55 (978-0-613-72264-3(7)) Tandem Library Bks.

Oliver, Jasmine. Prada Princesses. 2007. (Project Fashion Ser.). 192p. (YA). pap. 8.99 (***978-1-4169-3812-5(5)** , Simon Pulse) Simon & Schuster Children's Publishing.

Pascal, Francine. Elizabeth. 2000. (Secret Love Diaries). (gr. 7-12). lib. bdg. 12.40 (978-0-613-33043-5(9)) Tandem Library Bks.

—Libertad Incondicional.Tr. of Love, Lies & Jessica Wakefield. (SPA.). 224p. (J). 8.95 (978-84-272-3162-7(8)) Molino, Editorial ESP. *Dist:* AIMS International Bks., Inc.

—Otra Oportunidad.Tr. of Love of Her Life. (SPA.). 200p. (J). 8.95 (978-84-272-3166-5(0)) Molino, Editorial ESP. *Dist:* AIMS International Bks., Inc.

Ransom, Jeanie Franz. Grandma U. Corvino, Lucy, illus. 2002. 32p. (J). 15.95 (978-1-56145-214-9(9)) Peachtree Pubs., Ltd.

Soileau, Hodges, illus. The Haunted Clock Tower Mystery, Vol. 84. 2004. (Boxcar Children Ser.: No. 84). 128p. (J). (gr. 2-7). pap. 3.95 (978-0-8075-5485-2(5)) Whitman, Albert & Co.

Soto, Gary. Jesse. 2006. (Illus.). 180p. (YA). pap. 6.95 (978-0-15-205425-0(1) , Harcourt Paperbacks) Harcourt Children's Bks.

Sparks, Beatrice, ed. Kim: Empty Inside: The Diary of an Anonymous Teenager. 2002. 176p. (YA). (gr. 7 up). pap. 5.99 (978-0-380-81460-2(9)) HarperCollins Pubs.

Thomas, Carroll. Ring Out Wild Bells: A Matty Trescott Novel. 2001. (Illus.). viii, 169p. (J). 9.95 (978-1-57525-291-9(0)) Smith and Kraus Publishers, Incorporated.

Voigt, Cynthia. The Vandemark Mummy. 2001. (978-0-606-20968-7(9)) Tandem Library Bks.

Webster, Jean. Daddy-Long-Legs. unabr. ed. 2002. (Dover Evergreen Classics Ser.). (Illus.). 144p. (J). (gr. 4-7). pap. 2.00 (978-0-486-42367-8(0)) Dover Pubns., Inc.

UNMARRIED MOTHERS—FICTION

Chambers, Aidan. Postcards from No Man's Land. 2007. 336p. (YA). (gr. 9). pap. 10.00 (978-0-14-240788-2(7) , Puffin) Penguin Group (USA) Inc.

Dessen, Sarah. Someone Like You. 1998. 272p. (J). (gr. 7-12). 17.99 (978-0-670-87778-2(6) , Viking Juvenile) Penguin Group (USA) Inc.

—Someone Like You. 2000. (978-0-606-18847-0(9)) Tandem Library Bks.

Ferris, Amy Schor. A Greater Goode. 2002. 192p. (YA). (gr. 5-9). 15.00 (978-0-618-13154-9(X)) Houghton Mifflin Co. Trade & Reference Div.

Grant, Cynthia D. White Horse. 2000. (978-0-606-17945-4(3)) Tandem Library Bks.

Lowry, Lois. The Silent Boy. 2003. (Illus.). 192p. (YA). (gr. 5-12). tchr. ed. 15.00 (978-0-618-28231-9(9) , Walter Lorraine) Houghton Mifflin Co. Trade & Reference Div.

Oughton, Jerrie. Perfect Family. 2000. 208p. (J). (gr. 5-9). tchr. ed. 15.00 (978-0-395-98668-4(0)) Houghton Mifflin Co. Trade & Reference Div.

Pennebaker, Ruth. Don't Think Twice. 2001. (gr. 7-12). lib. bdg. 15.25 (978-0-613-75497-2(2)); 2001. (YA). 13.60 (978-0-606-21159-8(4)); 1998. (978-0-606-13341-8(0)) Tandem Library Bks.

Reynolds, Marilyn. Detour for Emmy. 2003. 256p. (J). (gr. 7-12). pap. 8.95 (978-0-930934-76-7(8)) Morning Glory Pr., Inc.

Woodson, Jacqueline. The Dear One. 2004. 144p. (YA). pap. 6.99 (978-0-14-250190-0(5) , Puffin) Penguin Group (USA) Inc.

Wright, Julie. My Not-So-Fairytale Life. 2005. 256p. (YA). pap. 15.95 (978-1-59038-476-3(8)) Deseret Bk. Co.

UPPER ATMOSPHERE

see Atmosphere, Upper

UPPER CLASS—FICTION

Van Dyne, Edith. Aunt Jane's Nieces in Society. 2006. 144p. pap. 10.99 (***978-1-4264-4161-5(4)**); 156p. pap. 14.99 (***978-1-4264-4202-5(5)**) BiblioBazaar.

—Aunt Jane's Nieces in Society. 2004. reprint ed. pap. 20.95 (978-1-4191-0824-2(7)); pap. 1.99 (978-1-4192-0824-9(1)) Kessinger Publishing, LLC.

URANIUM

Saunders, N. Uranium & the Rare Earth Metals. 2003. (Periodic Table Ser.). (Illus.). 64p. (J). lib. bdg. (978-1-4034-1666-7(4)) Heinemann Library.

Tiner, John Hudson. Uranium & Plutonium Make Nuclear Power. 2003. (From Resource to Energy Source Ser.). (J). (978-1-58417-288-8(6)); pap. (978-1-58417-289-5(4)) Lake Street Pubs.

URANIUM—FICTION

Gilligan, Shannon. Struggle down Under. 2007. (Choose Your Own Adventure Ser.: No. 21). (Illus.). 144p. (J). (gr. 3-7). pap. 6.99 (***978-1-933390-21-5(2)**) Chooseco LLC.

URANUS (PLANET)

Adamson, Thomas K. Urano: Uranus. 2006. (ENG & SPA., Illus.). 24p. (J). (978-0-7368-5885-4(7)) Capstone Pr., Inc.

—Uranus. (J). 2008. (***978-1-4296-0730-8(0)**); 2008. (***978-1-4296-0734-6(3)**); 2005. (Illus.). 24p. lib. bdg. 21.26 (978-0-7368-3697-5(7)); 2003. (Illus.). 24p. lib. bdg. 17.26 (978-0-7368-2118-6(X) , Pebble Bks.) Capstone Pr., Inc.

Asimov, Isaac & Hantula, Richard. Urano: El Planeta Inclinado. Porras, Carlos & D'Andrea, Patricia, trs. 2003. (Isaac Asimov's Biblioteca del Universo del Siglo XXI). (SPA., Illus.). 32p. (J). (gr. 3 up). lib. bdg. 24.67 (978-0-8368-3863-3(7)); pap. 8.95 (978-0-8368-3876-3(9) , Weekly Reader Early Learning Library) Stevens, Gareth Inc.

—Uranus. rev. ed. 2003. (Isaac Asimov's 21st Century Library of the Universe). (Illus.). 32p. (YA). (gr. 3 up). lib. bdg. 24.67 (978-0-8368-3243-3(4)) Stevens, Gareth Inc.

—Uranus: The Sideways Planet. 2003. (Isaac Asimov's 21st Century Library of the Universe). (Illus.). 32p. (J). (gr. 3 up). pap. (978-0-8368-3947-0(1) , Weekly Reader Early Learning Library) Stevens, Gareth Inc.

Birch, Robin. Uranus. 2004. (Solar System Ser.). (Illus.). 32p. (gr. 3-5). 23.00 (978-0-7910-7935-5(X) , Chelsea Hse.) Facts On File, Inc.

Brimner, Larry Dane. Uranus. 1999. (True Bks.). (Illus.). 48p. (J). (gr. 3-5). 25.00 (978-0-516-21156-5(0) , Children's Pr.) Scholastic Library Publishing.

—Uranus. 1999. (gr. 3-6). lib. bdg. 15.25 (978-0-613-37571-9(8)) Tandem Library Bks.

Cole, Michael D. Uranus: The Seventh Planet. 2002. (Countdown to Space Ser.). (Illus.). 48p. (J). (gr. 4-10). lib. bdg. 23.93 (978-0-7660-1952-2(7)) Enslow Pubs., Inc.

Goldstein, Margaret J. Uranus. 2005. (Pull Ahead Bks.). (Illus.). 32p. (gr. 2-4). lib. bdg. 22.60 (978-0-8225-4654-2(X)) Lerner Publishing Group.

Goss, Tim. Uranus, Neptune & Pluto. 2003. (Universe Ser.). (Illus.). 32p. (J). (gr. 3-5). lib. bdg. 22.79 (978-1-58810-918-7(6)); pap. 7.50 (978-1-4034-0619-4(7)) Heinemann Library.

Howard, Fran. Uranus. 2007. (Planets Ser.). (ENG., Illus.). 32p. (J). (gr. k-4). lib. bdg. 24.21 ***978-1-59928-829-1(X)*** , Buddy Bks.) ABDO Publishing Co.

Landau, Elaine. Uranus. (True Booktrade;: Space Ser.). 48p. (J). 2008. pap. 6.95 ***978-0-531-14797-9(5));*** 2007. (Illus.). (gr. 3-5). lib. bdg. 26.00 ***978-0-531-12569-4(6))*** Scholastic Library Publishing. (Children's Pr.).

Orme, Helen & Orme, David. Let's Explore Uranus. 2006. (J). pap. ***978-0-8368-8134-9(6));*** lib. bdg. ***978-0-8368-7949-0(X))*** Stevens, Gareth Inc.

Potts, Steve. Uranus: Our Solar System. 2001. (Illus.). 24p. (J). lib. bdg. 21.35 (978-1-58340-099-9(0)) Smart Apple Media.

Rau, Dana Meachen. Uranus. 2002. (Illus.). 32p. (J). (gr. 3 up). lib. bdg. 21.26 (978-0-7565-0299-7(3)) Compass Point Bks.

Ring, Susan. Uranus. (Exploring Planets Ser.). (Illus.). (J). 2004. pap. (978-1-59036-224-2(1)); 2003. 24p. lib. bdg. 15.95 (978-1-59036-097-2(4)) Weigl Pubs., Inc.

Scherer, Glenn & Fletcher, Marty. Uranus: A MyReportLinks. com Book. 2005. (Solar System Ser.). (Illus.). 48p. (J). lib. bdg. 25.26 (978-0-7660-5307-6(5) , MyReportLinks.com Bks.) Enslow Pubs., Inc.

Sparrow, Giles. Uranus, Neptune & Pluto. (Exploring the Solar System Ser.). (Illus.). (J). (gr. 4-6). 2002. 40p. pap. 7.95 (978-1-58810-966-8(6) , 91449); 2001. 39p. lib. bdg. 24.22 (978-1-57572-397-6(2)) Heinemann Library.

Stefoff, Rebecca. Uranus. 2002. (Blastoff! Ser.). (Illus.). 64p. (J). 28.50 (978-0-7614-1401-8(0) , Benchmark Bks.) Cavendish, Marshall Corp.

Stille, Darlene R. Uranus. 2003. (Planets Ser.). (Illus.). 32p. (J). (gr. 2-6). 27.07 (978-1-59296-056-9(1)) Child's World, Inc.

Taylor-Butler, Christine. Uranus. (Scholastic News Nonfiction Readers: Space Science Ser.). 24p. (J). 2008. pap. 6.95 ***978-0-531-14769-6(X));*** 2007. (Illus.). (gr. 1-2). lib. bdg. 20.00 ***978-0-531-14754-2(1))*** Scholastic Library Publishing. (Children's Pr.).

Tocci, Salvatore. Look at Uranus. 2003. (gr. 7-12). lib. bdg. 24.55 (978-0-613-72690-0(1)) Tandem Library Bks.

Uranus. (Galaxy Ser.). 24p. (J). 6.95 (978-0-7368-8893-6(4)) Capstone Pr., Inc.

Uranus, 6 vols. (gr. 2-5). 36.95 (978-0-7368-8975-9(2)) Red Brick Learning.

Viegas, Jennifer. Uranus. 2004. (Library of the Nine Planets). (J). lib. bdg. 26.50 (978-1-4042-0174-3(2)) Rosen Publishing Group, Inc., The.

Vogt, Gregory L. Jupiter, Saturn, Uranus & Neptune. 2000. (Our Universe Ser.). (Illus.). 48p. (YA). (gr. 5-12). lib. bdg. 22.83 (978-0-7398-3109-0(7)) Raintree.

Wimmer, Teresa. Uranus. 2007. (J). (978-1-58341-523-8(8) , Creative Education) Creative Co., The.

World Book, contrib. by. Saturn & Uranus. 2nd ed. 2006. (World Book's Solar System & Space Exploration Library). (Illus.). 64p. (J). ***978-0-7166-9519-6(7))*** World Bk., Inc.

World Book, Inc. Staff, contrib. by. Saturn & Uranus. 2006. (World Book's Solar System & Space Exploration Library). (Illus.). 63p. (J). (978-0-7166-9506-6(5)) World Bk., Inc.

URBAN AREAS

see Metropolitan Areas

URBAN SOCIOLOGY

see Sociology, Urban

URUGUAY

Harcourt School Publishers Staff. Social Studies: Argentina, Chile, Paraguay & Uruguay. 2000. (Harcourt Brace Social Studies). (Illus.). (gr. k-7). pap. 33.90 (978-0-15-317433-9(1)) Harcourt Schl. Pubs.

Jermyn, Leslie. Uruguay. 1998. (Cultures of the World Ser.). (Illus.). 128p. (J). (gr. k-17). lib. bdg. 37.07 (978-0-7614-0873-4(8) , Benchmark Bks.) Cavendish, Marshall Corp.

Morrison, Marion. Uruguay. 2005. (Enchantment of the World, Second Ser.). (Illus.). 144p. (J). (gr. 5-9). 36.00 (978-0-516-23682-7(2) , Children's Pr.) Scholastic Library Publishing.

Shields, Charles J. Uruguay. 2003. (Discovering South America Ser.). (Illus.). 64p. (J). (gr. 5 up). lib. bdg. (978-1-59084-290-4(1)) Mason Crest Pubs.

USEFUL ARTS

see Technology

UTAH

Brown, Jonatha A. Utah. 2006. (Portraits of the States Ser.). (J). pap. (978-0-8368-4726-0(1)); lib. bdg. (978-0-8368-4709-3(1)) Stevens, Gareth Inc.

Deady, Kathleen W. Utah. 2003. (Land of Liberty Ser.). (Illus.). 64p. (J). lib. bdg. 25.26 (978-0-7368-2200-8(3)) Capstone Pr., Inc.

Dumas, Bianca. Uniquely Utah. 2003. (Heinemann State Studies). (Illus.). 48p. (J). 27.07 (978-1-4034-4663-3(6)) Heinemann.

Dumas, Bianca & Ross, D. J. Uniquely Utah. 2004. (Heinemann State Studies). (Illus.). 48p. (J). (gr. 3-5). pap. 8.50 (978-1-4034-4732-6(2)) Heinemann.

Feeney, Kathy. Utah Facts & Symbols. (States & Their Symbols Ser.). 24p. (J). 2000. (Illus.). (gr. 2-3). lib. bdg. 13.95 (978-0-7368-0526-1(5) , Bridgestone Bks.); 2003. lib. bdg. 19.93 (978-0-7368-2274-9(7)) Capstone Pr., Inc.

Fein, E. How to Draw Utahs Sights & Symbols. 2002. (Kids Guide to Drawing America Ser.). 32p. (J). lib. bdg. 25.25 (978-0-8239-6101-6(X) , PowerKids Pr.) Rosen Publishing Group, Inc., The.

Feinstein, Stephen. Utah: A MyReportLinks. Com Book. 2003. (States Ser.). (Illus.). 48p. (J). (gr. 4-10). lib. bdg. 25.26 (978-0-7660-5097-6(1) , MyReportLinks.com Bks.) Enslow Pubs., Inc.

Hall, Rebecca. A Is for Arches: A Utah Alphabet. Larson, Katherine, illus. 2003. 40p. (J). 17.95 (978-1-58536-096-3(1)) Sleeping Bear Pr.

Heinrichs, Ann. Utah. Kania, Matt, illus. 2005. (Welcome to the USA Ser.). 40p. (J). (gr. 1-5). 27.07 (978-1-59296-486-4(9)) Child's World, Inc.

—Utah. 2003. (This Land Is Your Land Ser.). (Illus.). 48p. (J). (gr. 3 up). lib. bdg. 22.60 (978-0-7565-0344-4(2)) Compass Point Bks.

Hirschmann, Kris. Utah: The Beehive State. 2003. (World Almanac Library of the States). (Illus.). 48p. (J). (gr. 5 up). pap. 14.95 (978-0-8368-5332-2(6)); lib. bdg. 30.00 (978-0-8368-5161-8(7)) Stevens, Gareth Inc. (World Almanac Library).

Kummer, Patricia K. Utah. rev. ed. 2002. (One Nation Ser.). (Illus.). 48p. (J). (gr. 3-4). lib. bdg. 22.60 (978-0-7368-1269-6(5) , Bridgestone Bks.) Capstone Pr., Inc.

Marsh, Carole. The Big Utah Reproducible Activity Book. 2001. (Carole Marsh Utah Bks.). 96p. (J). (gr. 2-6). pap. 9.95 (978-0-7933-9958-1(0)) Gallopade International.

—My First Book about Utah. Line Art Staff, illus. 2001. (Utah Experience! Ser.). 32p. (J). (gr. k-4). pap. 7.95 (978-0-7933-9900-0(9)) Gallopade International.

—The Survivor: A Class Challenge. 2001. (Carole Marsh Utah Bks.). lib. bdg. 29.95 (978-0-635-00690-5(1)) Gallopade International.

—Utah Classic Christmas Trivia. 2002. (Carole Marsh Utah Bks.). (Illus.). 32p. pap. 6.95 (978-0-635-01453-5(X) , 1453X); lib. bdg. 21.95 (978-0-635-01454-2(8) , 14548, Marsh, Carole Bks.) Gallopade International.

—Utah Current Events Projects: 30 Cool, Activities, Crafts, Experiments & More for Kids to Do to Learn about Your State! 2003. (Utah Experience Ser.). 32p. (gr. k-5). pap. 5.95 (978-0-635-02063-5(7) , Marsh, Carole Bks.) Gallopade International.

—The Utah Experience Pocket Guide. 2001. (Carole Marsh Utah Bks.). (Illus.). 96p. (J). (gr. 3-8). pap. 6.95 (978-0-7933-9929-1(7)) Gallopade International.

—Utah Geography Projects: 30 Cool, Activities, Crafts, Experiments & More for Kids to Do to Learn about Your State! 2003. (Utah Experience Ser.). 32p. (gr. k-5). pap. 5.95 (978-0-635-01862-5(4) , Marsh, Carole Bks.) Gallopade International.

—Utah Government Projects: 30 Cool, Activities, Crafts, Experiments & More for Kids to Do to Learn about Your State! 2003. (Utah Experience Ser.). 32p. (gr. k-5). pap. 5.95 (978-0-635-01963-9(9) , Marsh, Carole Bks.) Gallopade International.

—Utah Hot Zones! Viruses, Diseases, & Epidemics in Our State's History. 1998. (Hot Zones! Ser.). (Illus.). (J). (gr. 3-12). pap. 19.95 (978-0-7933-8961-2(5)); lib. bdg. 29.95 (978-0-7933-8960-5(7)) Gallopade International.

—Utah Jeopardy! Answers & Questions about Our State! Line Art Staff, illus. 2001. 32p. (J). (gr. 3-8). pap. 7.95 (978-0-7933-9813-3(4)) Gallopade International.

—Utah "Jography" A Fun Run Thru Our State! 2001. (Carole Marsh Utah Bks.). 32p. (J). (gr. 3-8). pap. 7.95 (978-0-7933-9842-3(8)) Gallopade International.

—Utah Symbols & Facts Projects: 30 Cool, Activities, Crafts, Experiments & More for Kids to Do to Learn about Your State! 2003. (Utah Experience Ser.). 32p. (gr. k-5). pap. 5.95 (978-0-635-01913-4(2) , Marsh, Carole Bks.) Gallopade International.

McCormick, John. The Utah Adventure. Myers, Susan, ed. 1998. (Illus.). 224p. (gr. 4). 28.95 (978-0-87905-719-0(X)) Gibbs Smith, Publisher.

Murray, Julie. Utah. 2006. (Illus.). 32p. (J). (gr. k-4). lib. bdg. 22.78 (978-1-59197-703-2(7) , Buddy Bks.) ABDO Publishing Co.

Neri, P. J. Utah. 2002. (From Sea to Shining Sea Ser.: 2). (Illus.). 80p. (J). (gr. 3-5). pap. 30.50 (978-0-516-22382-7(8) , Children's Pr.) Scholastic Library Publishing.

Obregon, José María. Utah. 2006. (Bilingual Library of the United States of America: Set 2). (ENG & SPA., Illus.). 32p. (J). (gr. 3-6). lib. bdg. 22.50 (978-1-4042-3110-8(2) , Buenas Letra) Rosen Publishing Group, Inc., The.

Parker, Janice. A Guide to Utah. 2001. (American States Ser.). (Illus.). 32p. (J). lib. bdg. 16.95 (978-1-930954-18-2(2)); per. (978-1-930954-61-8(1)) Weigl Pubs., Inc.

Schulte, Mary. Great Salt Lake. 2006. 32p. (YA). (gr. 1-2). pap. 5.95 (978-0-516-29703-3(1) , Children's Pr.) Scholastic Library Publishing.

Schulte, Mary Knudson. Great Salt Lake. 2006. (Rookie Read-About Geography Ser.). (Illus.). 32p. (J). (gr. 1-2). 20.50 (978-0-516-25034-2(5) , Children's Pr.) Scholastic Library Publishing.

Simon, Charnan. Brigham Young: Mormon & Pioneer. 1998. (Community Builders Ser.). (Illus.). 48p. (J). (gr. 3-5). 25.00 (978-0-516-20392-8(4) , Children's Pr.) Scholastic Library Publishing.

Sirvaitis, Karen. Utah. 2nd rev. exp. ed. 2002. (Hello U. S. A. Ser.). (Illus.). 84p. (J). (gr. 3-6). 25.26 (978-0-8225-4088-5(6) , Lerner Pubns.) Lerner Publishing Group.

—Utah. rev. ed. 2002. (gr. 3-6). lib. bdg. 15.25 (978-0-613-46111-5(8)) Tandem Library Bks.

Steffof, R. Utah. 2001. (Celebrate the States Ser.). (Illus.). 144p. (gr. 4-8). lib. bdg. 37.07 (978-0-7614-1064-5(3) , Benchmark Bks.) Cavendish, Marshall Corp.

Trueit, Trudi Strain. Utah. 2007. (Rookie Read-about' Geography: States Ser.). 32p. (J). pap. 5.95 ***978-0-531-16818-9(2));*** (Illus.). (gr. 1-2). 20.50 (978-0-531-12574-8(2)) Scholastic Library Publishing. (Children's Pr.).

Utah. 2000. (Switched on Schoolhouse Ser.). (Illus.). (YA). (gr. 7-12). pap. 24.95 incl. cd-rom (978-0-7403-0296-1(5) , SOSUT) Alpha Omega Pubns., Inc.

Utah Sold C 2005. 2004. 516p. (YA). pap. 15.00 (978-1-58553-967-3(8) , 05GC0027) Entertainment Publications, Inc.

UTAH—FICTION

Au, Steven T. Kid Posse & the Phantom Robber. 2003. (Illus.). pap. 24.95 (978-1-878044-89-1(3)) Mayhaven Publishing.

Brown, Marc. Buster Hunts for Dinosaurs. 2006. (Postcards from Buster Ser.). 32p. (J). (gr. 1-4). 14.99 (978-0-316-15914-2(X)) Little Brown & Co.

Carabine, Sue. The Night Before Christmas in Utah. Kawasaki, Shauna Mooney, illus. 2000. Vol. 17. 60p. 5.95 (978-0-87905-981-1(8)) Gibbs Smith, Publisher.

Crabtree, Dianne. On the Road to Royalty. 2005. 222p. (YA). pap. 14.95 (978-1-932898-32-3(8) , 98328) Spring Creek Bk. Co.

Durrant, George D. The Christmas Marble: A Christmas Story. 2004. 70p. (J). 4.95 (978-1-55517-824-6(3) , Bonneville Bks.) Cedar Fort, Inc./CFI Distribution.

Fitzgerald, John. Great Brain. 2006. 20.75 (978-0-8446-7293-9(9)) Smith, Peter Pub., Inc.

Fitzgerald, John D. More Adventures of the Great Brain. Mayer, Mercer, illus. (Great Brain Ser.). 160p. (J). 2004. (gr. 3-7). pap. 4.99 (978-0-14-240065-4(3) , Puffin); 2000. (ps-3). 9.99 (978-0-8037-2591-1(4) , Dial) Penguin Group (USA) Inc.

—More Adventures of the Great Brain. 2004. (Great Brain Ser.). 142p. (J). (gr. 3-7). pap., tchr.'s training gde. ed. 36.00 incl. audio (978-0-8072-0860-1(4) , Listening Library) Random Hse. Audio Publishing Group.

—More Adventures of the Great Brain. 2004. (gr. 3-6). lib. bdg. 14.15 (978-0-613-83003-4(2)) Tandem Library Bks.

Harrison, Mette Ivie. The Monster in Me. 2003. 160p. (J). (gr. 7 up). tchr. ed. 16.95 (978-0-8234-1713-1(1)) Holiday Hse., Inc.

Hobbs, Will. The Maze. 1999. 248p. (J). (gr. k-9). lib. bdg. 14.15 (978-0-613-19524-9(8)) Tandem Library Bks.

Hobbs, William. The Maze. (J). (gr. 5 up). 1999. (Illus.). 256p. pap. 5.99 (978-0-380-72913-5(X) , Harper Trophy); 1998. 208p. 17.99 (978-0-688-15092-1(6)) HarperCollins Pubs.

—The Maze. unabr. ed. 1999. (YA). pap., stu. ed. 59.00 incl. audio (978-0-7887-3990-3(5) , 41062X4) Recorded Bks., LLC.

—The Maze. 1999. (J). (978-0-606-16369-9(7)) Tandem Library Bks.

Jenkins, Jerry B. & Fabry, Chris. Canyon Echoes. 2005. (Tyndale Kids Ser.). 240p. (J). pap. 5.99 (978-1-4143-0147-1(2)) Tyndale Hse. Pubs.

Johnson, Annabel & Johnson, Edgar. Wilderness Bride. 2003. 232p. 12.95 (978-0-9714612-7-7(9)) Green Mansion Pr. LLC.

Kearns, Ann. Dell's Discovery. 2006. 108p. (YA). per. 9.95 (978-0-9710696-6-4(2)) Jorlan Publishing, Inc.

Mangum, Kay Lynn. A Love Like Lilly. 2006. 336p. (YA). pap. 15.95 (978-1-59038-580-7(2)) Deseret Bk. Co.

McKendrick, Lisa. On a Whim. 2001. 156p. (J). (978-1-57734-896-2(6)) Covenant Communications.

Nielsen, Gwyn English. Torey the Turkey Goes Skiing. 2003. (Illus.). 24p. (Orig.). (ps-4). pap. 5.99 (978-0-9660726-0-0(X)) C.G.S. Pr.

Plummer, Louise. Finding Daddy. 2007. 176p. (YA). (gr. 7). 15.99 (978-0-385-73092-1(6) , Delacorte Bks. for Young Readers) Random Hse. Children's Bks.

Preston, Douglas & Child, Lincoln. Thunderhead. 2000. (gr. 7-12). lib. bdg. 15.90 (978-0-613-28102-7(0)) Tandem Library Bks.

Rees, Shirley. Hannah Stands Tall. 2002. 130p. (J). pap. 10.95 (978-1-55517-652-5(6) , 76526, Bonneville Bks.) Cedar Fort, Inc./CFI Distribution.

Rowley, B. J. Missing Children. 2000. (Light Traveler Adventure Ser.: Vol. 3). 252p. (YA). (gr. 6-12). pap. 13.95 (978-0-9700103-3-9(8)) Golden Wings Enterprises.

—My Body Fell Off! 2000. (Light Traveler Adventure Ser.: Vol. 1). 206p. (YA). (gr. 6-12). pap. 11.95 (978-0-9700103-1-5(1)) Golden Wings Enterprises.

Sargent, Dave & Sargent, Pat. Bashful: (Dusty Dun) Be Brave. Lenoir, Jane, illus. 2003. (Saddle Up Ser.: Vol. 1). 42p. (J). pap. 6.95 (978-1-56763-684-0(5)); lib. bdg. 22.60 (978-1-56763-683-3(7)) Ozark Publishing.

Skurzynski, Gloria & Ferguson, Alane. Ghost Horses. 2000. (National Parks Mysteries Ser.: Vol. 6). (Illus.). 160p. (J). (gr. 3-7). 15.95 (978-0-7922-7055-3(X) , National Geographic Children's Bks.) National Geographic Society.

Stetson, Street Dog of Park City. 2002. (J). per. 18.95 (978-0-9717019-0-8(3)) Le Petit Chien.

Williams, Carol Lynch. A Mother to Embarrass Me. 2003. 144p. (J). (gr. 3-7). pap. 4.99 (978-0-440-41810-8(0) , Yearling) Random Hse. Children's Bks.

Young, Joseph R. Legend of the Lost Josephine Mine: A Fascinating Adventure. 2001. 221p. (J). pap. 13.95 (978-1-55517-550-4(3) , Bonneville Bks.) Cedar Fort, Inc./CFI Distribution.

Zindel, Paul. Raptor, No. 1. 1999. (Raptor Ser.: Vol. 1). 176p. (gr. 5-9). pap. 4.99 (978-0-7868-1224-0(9)) Disney Pr.

—Raptor. unabr. ed. 2000. (J). pap., stu. ed. 42.24 incl. audio (978-0-7887-4185-2(3) , 41098) Recorded Bks., LLC.

—Raptor. 1999. 170p. (J). (ps-7). per. 11.64 (978-0-606-17385-8(4)); (gr. 5-8). lib. bdg. 13.00 (978-0-613-22241-9(5)) Tandem Library Bks.

—Raptor Paperback Club. 1999. (Illus.). 176p. (J). pap. 4.99 (978-0-7868-1471-8(3)) Disney Pr.

UTAH—HISTORY

Boule, Mary Null. Native Americans of North America: Ute Tribe, 11 booklets. Liddell, Daniel & Basta, Mary, illus. 2002. (Native Americans of North America). (J). (gr. 3-6). pap. 7.95 (978-1-877599-60-6(3)) Merryant Pubs.

Hall, Carol S. & Hansen, T. J. This Is Utah. 257p. (J). (gr. 1-6). pap. 39.95 (978-1-56861-048-1(3)) Swift Learning Resources.

Marsh, Carole. My First Pocket Guide Utah. 2000. (Utah Experience! Ser.). (Illus.). 96p. (J). (gr. 3-8). 12.95 (978-0-635-01334-7(7) , 13347) Gallopade International.

—Utah History Projects: 30 Cool, Activities, Crafts, Experiments & More for Kids to Do to Learn about Your State! 2003. (Utah Experience Ser.). 32p. (gr. k-5). pap. 5.95 (978-0-635-01813-7(6) , Marsh, Carole Bks.) Gallopade International.

—Utah Millionaire. 2001. (GameBook Ser.). 32p. (J). (gr. 3-8). pap., act. bk. ed. 9.95 (978-0-635-00104-7(7)) Gallopade International.

—Utah Survivor. 2001. (GameBook Ser.). 32p. (J). (gr. 3-8). pap., act. bk. ed. 9.95 (978-0-635-00565-6(4)) Gallopade International.

—Utah Wheel of Fortune. 2001. (GameBook Ser.). 32p. (J). (gr. 3-8). pap., act. bk. ed. 9.95 (978-0-635-00004-0(0)) Gallopade International.

—Wheel of Fortune. 2001. (Utah Experience! Ser.). (J). lib. bdg. 29.95 (978-0-635-00005-7(9)) Gallopade International.

—Who Wants to Be a Millionaire? 2001. (Utah Experience! Ser.). (J). lib. bdg. 29.95 (978-0-635-00105-4(5)) Gallopade International.

UTENSILS, KITCHEN

see Household Equipment and Supplies

UTILITIES, PUBLIC

see Public Utilities

UTOPIAS

Marx, Paul. Utopia in America. 2002. (To Know the Land Ser.). (Illus.). 109p. (YA). 28.00 (978-0-934272-73-5(5)); pap. 16.00 (978-0-934272-72-8(7)) Burke, John Gordon Pub., Inc.

UTOPIAS—FICTION

Lowry, Lois. Messenger. 2004. 176p. (YA). (gr. 7 up). tchr. ed. 16.00 (978-0-618-40441-4(4) , Walter Lorraine) Houghton Mifflin Co. Trade & Reference Div.

—Messenger. 2006. 192p. (YA). (gr. 7). pap. 8.95 (978-0-385-73253-6(8) , Delacorte Bks. for Young Readers) Random Hse. Children's Bks.

—Messenger. l.t. ed. 2004. 184p. 23.95 (978-0-7862-6686-9(4) , Large Print Pr.) Thorndike Pr.

Metzger, Joanna. The Space Program. Elizalde, Marcelo, illus. 2006. 142p. (J). (978-1-59336-695-7(7)) Mondo Publishing.

More, Thomas. Utopia: A New Translation with an Introduction. 2003. (gr. 7-12). lib. bdg. 16.45 (978-0-613-64330-6(5)) Tandem Library Bks.

Thomas, John Ira. Zoo Force: Dear Eniko. Smith, Jeremy, illus. 2003. 68p. per. 6.95 (978-0-9743147-1-6(4)) Candle Light Pr.

Whelan, Gloria. Fruitlands: Louisa May Alcott Made Perfect. 2002. 128p. (J). (gr. 4-7). 15.99 (978-0-06-623815-9(3)) HarperCollins Pubs.

V

VACATIONS

Advantage Publishers Group. Clara's Fun Vacation. 2002. (Let's Start! Play Alongs Ser.). 32p. (J). (ps-1). 15.95 (978-1-57145-695-3(3) , Silver Dolphin Bks.) Advantage Pubs. Group.

Brode, Robyn. August. 2003. (Weekly Reader Early Learning Library). (Illus.). 24p. (J). (ps-2). pap. 7.93 (978-0-8368-3619-6(7)); lib. bdg. 19.33 (978-0-8368-3583-0(2)) Stevens, Gareth Inc. (Weekly Reader Early Learning Library).

Color All About: A Giant Coloring Book about Summer Vacation: Summer Vacation. 2004. (Illus.). 36p. (J). (978-1-59949-006-9(4)) Food Marketing Consultants, Inc.

de Jongh, Tim & Vandyck, William. How to Have the Best Holiday Ever. Rowe, Alan, illus. 96p. pap. 7.99 (978-0-340-66730-9(3) , Coronet) Hodder General Publishing Division GBR. *Dist:* Trafalgar Square Publishing.

Dorling Kindersley Publishing Staff. My First Vacation. 2004. (Barbie Sticker Books Ser.). 16p. (J). pap. 6.99 (978-0-7566-0336-6(6)) Dorling Kindersley Publishing, Inc.

Gibson, Ray. Little book of vacation Activities. 2005. 96p. (J). 7.95 (978-0-7945-1171-5(6) , Usborne) EDC Publishing.

Hanson, Anders. Let's Go by RV. 2007. (Let's Go! Ser.). (ENG., Illus.). 24p. (J). (ps-3). lib. bdg. 19.93 (***978-1-59928-902-1(4)*** , SandCastle) ABDO Publishing Co.

Hughes, Monica. First Vacation. 2003. (ps-2). lib. bdg. 13.55 (978-0-613-78208-1(9)) Tandem Library Bks.

—My First Vacation. 2003. (Raintree Sprouts Ser.). (Illus.). 24p. (J). pap. 5.50 (978-1-4109-0672-4(8)); lib. bdg. 18.56 (978-1-4109-0646-5(9)) Raintree.

Litchfield, Jo. Vacation. Litchfield, Jo, illus. 2006. (Illus.). 12p. (J). bds. 7.99 (978-0-7945-1315-3(8) , Usborne) EDC Publishing.

Muldrow, Diane. Dream Vacation. Cuddy, Robbin, illus. 2007. (Groovy Girls Ser.). 96p. (J). 2.99 (***978-1-4169-3508-7(8)*** , Simon Scribbles) Simon & Schuster Children's Publishing.

Ragland, Teresa B. My Vacation Diary. 2001. (Illus.). (J). (ps-3). pap. 9.95 (978-0-8249-5431-4(9) , Ideals Children's Bks.) Ideals Pubns.

Richards, Jon. On Holidays. 2005. (Illus.). 32p. (J). (gr. 3 up). lib. bdg. 27.10 (978-1-59389-197-8(0)) Chrysalis Education.

VACATIONS—FICTION

Adams, Georgie. Three Bears on Vacation. Young, Selina, illus. 2003. 28p. (J). (gr. k-1). pap. 6.95 (978-0-7696-3154-7(1) , Gingham Dog Pr.) School Specialty Publishing.

Adams, Sherred Willco. Five Little Friends. 2006. pap. 15.95 (***978-1-4304-4149-6(6)***) Kessinger Publishing, LLC.

Alapont, Pasqual. Un Verano Sin Francesas. Sola, Raquel, tr. from CAT. Molinero, David, illus. 2000. (Periscopio Ser.).Tr. of Summer Without French Girls. (SPA.). 112p. (YA). (gr. 9 up). (978-84-236-5512-0(1)) Edebé ESP. *Dist:* Baker & Taylor Bks.

Ameen, Judith. Harold & the Magic Books. 2005. 40p. pap. 8.95 (978-1-933265-42-1(6)) Wasteland Pr.

Andersen, C. B. The Forgotten Treasure. 2004. 215p. (J). pap. (978-1-59038-314-8(1)) Deseret Bk. Co.

Banks, Kate. Dillon Dillon. 160p. (J). 2002. (gr. 3-6). 16.00 (978-0-374-31786-7(0) , Farrar, Straus & Giroux (BYR)); 2005. reprint ed. pap. 5.95 (978-0-374-41715-4(6) , Sunburst) Farrar, Straus & Giroux.

Banscherus, Jurgen & Baron, Daniel C. The Secret of the Flying Cows. Butschkow, Ralf, illus. 2008. (J). pap. (***978-1-59889-913-9(9)***); lib. bdg. (***978-1-59889-877-4(9)***) Stone Arch Bks.

Barnett, Angela. Mystic Grove. 2006. pap. 10.00 (***978-1-4257-1912-8(0)***) Xlibris Corp.

Becker, Suzy. Manny's Cows: The Niagara Falls Tale. Becker, Suzy, illus. 2006. (Illus.). 40p. (J). 15.99 (978-0-06-054152-1(0)); lib. bdg. 16.89 (978-0-06-054153-8(9)) HarperCollins Pubs.

Berenstain, Stan & Berenstain, Jan. The Berenstain Bears & Too Much Vacation. Berenstain, Stan & Berenstain, Jan, illus. 2002. (Berenstain Bears First Time Bks.). (Illus.). (J). 11.19 (978-0-7587-0954-7(4)) Book Wholesalers, Inc.

—The Berenstain Bears Go on Vacation. 2006. (Berenstain Bears Ser.: No. 1). (Illus.). 32p. (J). 9.99 (978-0-06-057431-4(3)); Bk. 1. lib. bdg. 15.89 (978-0-06-057432-1(1)) HarperCollins Pubs.

—The Berenstain Bears Out West. Berenstain, Stan & Berenstain, Jan, illus. 2006. (Berenstain Bears Ser.). (Illus.). 32p. (J). 15.99 (978-0-06-058353-8(3)); pap. 3.99 (978-0-06-058354-5(1) , Harper Trophy) HarperCollins Pubs.

Bevin, Teresa. Tina Springs into Summer/Tina se Lanza al Verano. Rodríguez, Perfecto, illus. 2005. (ENG & SPA.). 114p. (J). pap. 21.00 (978-1-928589-28-0(6)) Gival Pr., LLC.

Billington, Rachel. There's More to Life. 2007. 240p. pap. 10.95 (***978-0-340-88247-4(6)***) Hodder Children's Division GBR. *Dist:* Independent Pubs. Group.

Birdsall, Jeanne. The Penderwicks. 2005. 272p. (J). (gr. 3-7). lib. bdg. 17.99 (978-0-375-93143-7(0) , Knopf Bks. for Young Readers) Random Hse. Children's Bks.

—The Penderwicks. 2006. 301p. (YA). 23.95 (978-0-7862-8897-7(3)) Thorndike Pr.

—The Penderwicks: A Summer Tale of Four Sisters, Two Rabbits, & a Very Interesting Boy. 272p. (J). 2007. (gr. 4-7). 6.50 (978-0-440-42047-7(4) , Yearling); 2005. (gr. 3-7). 15.95 (978-0-375-83143-0(6) , Knopf Bks. for Young Readers) Random Hse. Children's Bks.

Blume, Judy. Fudge-a-Mania. 2002. (Fudge Ser.). (Illus.). (J). 13.40 (978-0-7587-0013-1(X)) Book Wholesalers, Inc.

—Fudge-a-Mania. (Fudge Ser.). 160p. (J). 2007. (gr. 2). pap. 5.99 (978-0-14-240877-3(8) , Puffin); 2002. (Illus.). 15.99 (978-0-525-46927-8(3) , Dutton Juvenile) Penguin Group (USA) Inc.

—Fudge-a-Mania. (Fudge Ser.). (gr. 3-6). 2004. lib. bdg. 14.15 (978-0-613-87580-6(X)); 2003. lib. bdg. 14.15 (978-0-613-63936-1(7)) Tandem Library Bks.

—Otherwise Known As Sheila the Great. (Fudge Ser.). 2007. 144p. (J). 5.99 (978-0-14-240879-7(4) , Puffin); 2004. 160p. (gr. 12). mass mkt. 5.99 (978-0-425-19380-8(2) , Berkley) Penguin Group (USA) Inc.

Blumenthal, Deborah. The Pink House at the Seashore. Chayka, Doug, illus. 2005. 32p. (J). (gr. 3-5). 16.00 (978-0-618-37886-9(3) , Clarion Bks.) Houghton Mifflin Co. Trade & Reference Div.

Bridgman, C. A. Santa's Hawaiian Vacation. (J). 14.95 (978-0-681-32827-3(4)) Booklines Hawaii, Ltd.

Brown, Marc. Arthur in New York. 2008. (J). (***978-0-375-82976-5(8)***); (***978-0-375-92976-2(2)***) Random Hse., Inc.

—Arthur's Classroom Fib. 2007. (Illus.). 24p. (J). (gr. 1-3). pap. 3.99 (978-0-375-82975-8(X)); lib. bdg. 11.99 (978-0-375-92975-5(4)) Random Hse. Children's Bks. (Random Hse. Bks. for Young Readers).

—Arthur's Family Vacation. Brown, Marc, illus. 1998. (Arthur Adventure Ser.). (Illus.). (J). (gr. k-3). pap. 5.95 (978-0-316-11528-5(2)) Little, Brown Bks. for Young Readers.

—Buster Hits the Trail. 2005. (Postcards from Buster Ser.). (Illus.). 48p. (J). (gr. 1-4). 14.99 (978-0-316-15900-5(X)) Little, Brown Bks. for Young Readers.

Brown, Ruth Alberta. Tabitha's Vacation. 2005. reprint ed. pap. 27.95 (978-1-4191-1538-7(3)) Kessinger Publishing, LLC.

Bryant, Megan E. Have a Good Trip, Mr. Bean! The Junior Novelization. 2007. 96p. (J). (gr. 2-5). pap. 4.99 (978-0-8431-2521-4(7) , Price Stern Sloan) Penguin Group (USA) Inc.

Buffie, Margaret. Who Is Frances Rain? 20th ed. 2007. 184p. pap. (***978-1-55453-209-4(4)***) Kids Can Pr., Ltd.

Burn, Michael. Childhood at Oriol. 2005. 360p. pap. 16.95 (978-1-885586-32-2(9)) Turtle Point Pr.

Burshek, Edward & Burshek, Tonja. Explorers of the Word: Episode 1: the Creation. Peterson, Melanie, illus. 2007. (ENG.). 76p. per. 14.95 (***978-1-4241-6691-6(8)***) PublishAmerica, Inc.

Buske, Jody. Wilderness Awakening. 2006. 108p. pap. 16.95 (978-1-4241-2685-9(1)) PublishAmerica, Inc.

Byrum, R. T. The Phantom Bridge. 2002. 235p. pap. 14.95 (978-1-59113-173-1(1)) Booklocker.com, Inc.

Cann, Kate. Grecian Holiday: Or, How I Turned down the Best Possible Thing Only to Have The. 2002. (gr. 7-12). lib. bdg. 14.15 (978-0-613-71506-5(3)) Tandem Library Bks.

—Grecian Holiday: Or, How I Turned down the Best Possible Thing Only to Have the Time of My Life. 2002. 352p. (J). (gr. 8 up). pap. 5.99 (978-0-06-447302-6(3)) HarperCollins Pubs.

—Spanish Holiday: Or, How I Transformed the Worst Vacation Ever into the Best Sum. 2004. (gr. 7-12). lib. bdg. 14.15 (978-0-613-71954-4(9)) Tandem Library Bks.

—Spanish Holiday: Or, How I Transformed the Worst Vacation Ever into the Best Summer of My Life. 2004. (Illus.). 352p. pap. 5.99 (978-0-06-056160-4(2)) HarperCollins Pubs.

Carey, Rosa Nouchette. Uncle Max. 2007. pap. (***978-1-4065-1269-4(9)***) Dodo Pr.

Carman, Patrick. The Dark Hills Divide. 2005. (Land of Elyon Ser.: Bk. 1). (Illus.). 272p. (J). pap. 11.95 (978-0-439-70093-1(0) , Orchard Bks.) Scholastic, Inc.

Carr, Annie Roe. Nan Sherwoods Winter Holidays or Rescuin. 2007. pap. (***978-1-4065-1296-0(6)***) Dodo Pr.

Chittenden, Charlotte E. What Two Children Did. 2007. (ENG., Illus.). 132p. per. (***978-1-4065-1360-8(1)***) Dodo Pr.

Christopherson, Keven. Adventures of the Sky Kids: Lost Treasure of Kolob Canyon. 2005. 58p. pap. 12.95 (978-1-4137-6514-4(9)) PublishAmerica, Inc.

Coman, Carolyn. Sneaking Suspicions. Shepperson, Rob, illus. 2007. 204p. (J). (gr. 3-7). 16.95 (***978-1-59078-491-4(X)*** , Front Street) Boyds Mills Pr.

Culbertson, Jan E. The Legend of Dunsmoor Manor. 2006. 88p. pap. 13.95 (978-1-58909-348-5(8)) Bookstand Publishing.

—The Legend of the Lost Tiki. 2006. 95p. (YA). pap. 13.95 (978-1-58909-315-7(1)) Bookstand Publishing.

Danziger, Paula. What a Trip, Amber Brown. 2002. (Illus.). (J). pap. 16.95 incl. audio (978-0-87499-910-5(3)); pap. 18.95 incl. audio compact disk (978-1-59112-368-2(2)); pap., tchr.'s planning gde. ed. 29.95 incl. audio (978-0-87499-912-9(X)); 25.95 incl. audio (978-0-87499-911-2(1)) Live Oak Media.

—What a Trip, Amber Brown. Ross, Tony, illus. 2002. 28.95 incl. audio compact disk (978-1-59112-569-3(3)); pap. 31.95 incl. audio compact disk (978-1-59112-568-6(5)) Live Oak Media.

—What a Trip, Amber Brown. Ross, Tony, illus. 2001. (J). 48p. pap. 3.99 (978-0-698-11908-6(8)); (Amber Brown Ser.: No. 9). 1p. (gr. 3-6). 13.99 (978-0-399-23469-9(1)) Penguin Group (USA) Inc. (Putnam Juvenile).

—What a Trip, Amber Brown. 2001. (978-0-606-22523-6(4)); lib. bdg. 11.80 (978-0-613-44429-3(9)) Tandem Library Bks.

Davies, Jacqueline. The House Takes a Vacation. White, Lee, illus. 2006. (J). 16.99 (978-0-7614-5331-4(8)) Cavendish, Marshall Corp.

de Paola, Tomie. Strega Nona Takes a Vacation. (Illus.). 32p. (J). (gr. k-3). 2003. pap. 5.99 (978-0-14-250076-7(3) , Puffin); 2000. 16.99 (978-0-399-23562-7(0) , Putnam Juvenile) Penguin Group (USA) Inc.

—Strega Nona Takes a Vacation. 2003. (gr. k-3). lib. bdg. 14.15 (978-0-613-89803-4(6)) Tandem Library Bks.

Delhohne, Jean-Philippe. Visit to Another Planet. 2004. (Illus.). 31p. (J). (gr. k-4). reprint ed. (978-0-7567-7768-5(2)) DIANE Publishing Co.

Delton, Judy. Angel Spreads Her Wings. Weber, Jill, illus. 2002. 160p. (J). (gr. 2-5). pap. 4.95 (978-0-618-21617-8(0)) Houghton Mifflin Co. Trade & Reference Div.

—Angel Spreads Her Wings. 2002. (gr. 3-6). lib. bdg. 12.95 (978-0-613-90475-9(3)) Tandem Library Bks.

DeSio, Delores. Up a Tree with Mary Mcphee: A Mystery for Children. 2006. 86p. pap. 14.95 (978-1-4241-4309-2(8)) PublishAmerica, Inc.

Dewin, Howie. Sand Hassle. 2001. (gr. k-3). lib. bdg. 11.80 (978-0-613-43877-3(9)) Tandem Library Bks.

Dower, Laura. Give Me a Break. 2004. 166p. (J). lib. bdg. 16.92 (***978-1-4242-0649-0(9)***) Fitzgerald Bks.

—Give Me a Break. 2004. 166p. (J). (978-1-4155-7364-8(6) , Volo) Hyperion Bks. for Children.

Dowling, Paul. Sally's Amazing Colour Book. 1999. (Illus.). 32p. (J). 17.99 (978-0-86264-801-5(7)) Andersen GBR. *Dist:* Independent Pubs. Group.

Eady, Ellen. Pardon Me, Is That the Chattanooga Choo-Choo? Guhne, Kelly, illus. 2000. (J). pap. 9.95 (978-0-9679065-1-5(2)) Majestic Publishing.

Earls, Nick. After Summer. 2005. 240p. (YA). (gr. 7). pap. 6.99 (978-0-618-45781-6(X) , Graphia) Houghton Mifflin Co. Trade & Reference Div.

Edens, Cooper. Santa Cow Island. 1999. (J). (978-0-606-18952-1(1)) Tandem Library Bks.

Eggleton, Jill. Destination Planet Blobb: Individual Title Six-Packs. Gunson, Dave, illus. (Sails Literacy Ser.). 20p. (gr. 2-3). 27.00 (978-0-7578-0719-0(4)) Rigby Education.

Elkeles, Simone. How to Ruin a Summer Vacation. 2006. 240p. (J). pap. 9.95 (978-0-7387-0961-1(1) , Flux) Llewellyn Pubns.

Emzer, Counselor. The Day Before Summer Vacation. 2004. 31p. pap. 17.95 (978-1-4137-2680-0(1)) PublishAmerica, Inc.

En Vacances. 2000. (Collection des Mots pour Lire). (FRE.). 28p. (J). 15.95 (978-2-03-553019-6(9)) Librairie Larousse FRA. *Dist:* Distribooks, Inc.

Enright, Elizabeth. Gone-Away Lake. Krush, Beth & Krush, Joe, illus. 2006. 256p. (J). (gr. 4-8). reprint ed. pap. 6.00 (978-1-4223-5436-0(9)) DIANE Publishing Co.

—Gone-Away Lake. Krush, Beth & Krush, Joe, illus. 2000. (Gone-Away Lake Bks.). 272p. (YA). (gr. 3-7). pap. 6.00 (978-0-15-202272-3(4) , Odyssey Classics) Harcourt Children's Bks.

—Return to Gone Away Lake. 2000. (978-0-606-18741-1(3)) Tandem Library Bks.

Estes, Eleanor. The Moffat Museum. 2001. (gr. 3-6). lib. bdg. 14.15 (978-0-613-35463-9(X)) Tandem Library Bks.

Evans, Lezlie. The Bunnies' Trip. Chorao, Kay, illus. 2008. 32p. 16.99 (***978-0-7868-1898-3(0)***) Hyperion Bks. for Children.

Finley, Martha. Elsies Vacation & after Events. 2006. 42.99 (***978-1-4280-2122-8(1)***); pap. 35.99 (***978-1-4280-2125-9(6)***) IndyPublish.com.

Fitzhugh, Louise. The Long Secret. 2001. (Illus.). 288p. (J). (gr. 5 up). 15.95 (978-0-385-32784-8(6) , Delacorte Bks. for Young Readers) Random Hse. Children's Bks.

Fogelin, Adrian. My Brother's Hero. 2005. 224p. (J). reprint ed. pap. 6.95 (978-1-56145-352-8(8)) Peachtree Pubs., Ltd.

Frazee, Marla. A Couple of Boys Go to Antarctica (Sort Of) 2008. 40p. (J). 16.00 (***978-0-15-206020-6(0)***) Harcourt Trade Pubs.

Glass, June. Poker Fat: Takes a Vacation. 2005. (J). pap. 9.00 (978-0-8059-6150-8(X)) Dorrance Publishing Co., Inc.

Goldman, Leslie. Summer Vacation: The Ultimate Recess Junior Novel. 2001. 96p. (J). (gr. 3-7). pap. 4.99 (978-0-7868-4415-9(9)) Disney Pr.

Goode, Suzi. The Lost Wizard Series Bk 1. 2007. pap. 11.95 (***978-1-59374-817-3(5)***) Whiskey Creek Pr., LLC.

Goscinny, René. Nicholas on Vacation. Bell, Anthea, tr. from FRE. Sempé, Jean-Jacques, illus. rev. ed. 2006. 132p. (gr. 2-5). 19.95 (978-0-7148-4678-1(3)) Phaidon Pr., Inc.

Gutman, Anne & Hallensleben, Georg. Gaspard on Vacation. 2001. (Illus.). 32p. (J). (ps-1). 9.95 (978-0-375-81115-9(X) , Knopf Bks. for Young Readers) Random Hse. Children's Bks.

Gutman, Dan. The Get Rich Quick Club. 128p. (J). 2006. pap. 5.99 (978-0-06-053442-4(7) , Harper Trophy); 2004. 15.99 (978-0-06-053440-0(0)); 2004. lib. bdg. 16.89 (978-0-06-053441-7(9)) HarperCollins Pubs.

Hanson, Ed. Desert Ordeal. 2003. (Barclay Family Adventure Ser.: Bk. 3). 64p. (J). (gr. k-6). per. 3.95 (978-1-56254-552-9(3) , SP 5523) Saddleback Educational Publishing.

Harcourt School Publishers Staff. Are We Having Fun Yet? 3rd ed. 2002. (Trophies English Language Learners Ser.). (Illus.). (gr. 5). pap. 5.10 (978-0-15-327812-9(9)) Harcourt Schl. Pubs.

—A Vacation To... Take Home Book. 1999. (Signatures Ser.). (Illus.). (J). pap. 1.90 (978-0-15-313978-9(1)) Harcourt Schl. Pubs.

Harrison, Emma & SparkNotes Staff. Busted. 2004. (SAT Vocabulary Novels Ser.). (Illus.). 192p. pap. 7.95 (978-1-4114-0081-8(X)) Spark Publishing Group.

Hawthorne, Rachel. Island Girls & Boys. 2005. 336p. pap. 5.99 (978-0-06-075546-1(6)) HarperCollins Pubs.

Hendry, Diana. Harvey Angell & the Ghost Child. 2002. (gr. 3-6). lib. bdg. 13.00 (978-0-613-57904-9(6)) Tandem Library Bks.

Henning, Ann. Cow Patty Patti. 2004. 47p. pap. 19.95 (978-1-4137-3456-0(1)) PublishAmerica, Inc.

Herman, Gail. Dulcie's Taste of Magic. Clarke, Judith et al, illus. 2008. 128p. (J). (gr. 1-5). 5.99 (***978-0-7364-2454-7(7)***) Random Hse., Inc.

Higginson, Hadley. Keeker & the Not-So-Sleepy Hollow. Perrett, Lisa, illus. 2008. (J). (***978-0-8118-6073-4(6)***); 56p. pap. 3.99 (***978-0-8118-6074-1(4)***) Chronicle Bks. LLC.

Hobbs, Leigh, illus. Old Tom's Holiday. 2004. 32p. (J). 16.95 (978-1-56145-316-0(1)) Peachtree Pubs., Ltd.

Homel, David. Travels with My Family. Gay, Marie-Louise, illus. 2007. 120p. (J). pap. 7.95 (***978-0-88899-833-0(3)***) Groundwood Bks. CAN. *Dist:* Perseus Distribution.

Hortten, Jacqueline Faye. Pu Beach. Maximilian Press Staff, illus. l.t. unabr. ed. 2002. 48p. (J). (gr. k-5). pap. 12.50 (978-1-930211-42-1(2)) Maximilian Pr. Pubs.

Horvath, Polly. The Vacation. 2005. 208p. (J). 16.00 (978-0-374-38070-0(8) , Farrar, Straus & Giroux (BYR)) Farrar, Straus & Giroux.

—The Vacation. pap. 12.95 (978-0-88899-693-0(4)) Groundwood Bks. CAN. *Dist:* Transition Vendor.

Hurwitz, Johanna. Summer with Elisa. Maione, Heather Harms & Tilley, Debbie, illus. 2000. 96p. (J). (ps-2). 16.99 (978-0-688-17095-0(1)) HarperCollins Pubs.

Irwin, Inez Haynes. Maida's Little House. 2004. reprint ed. pap. 27.95 (978-1-4179-4236-7(3)) Kessinger Publishing, LLC.

James, Sara & Ruckdeschel, Liz. What If ... All the Boys Wanted You. 2006. 288p. (YA). (gr. 7). pap. 8.95 (978-0-385-73297-0(X) , Delacorte Bks. for Young Readers) Random Hse. Children's Bks.

Jarrell, Pamela R. Going on Vacation. Gillen, Lisa P., illus. l.t. ed. 1999. (Cuddle Bks.). 7p. (J). (ps-k). pap. 10.95 (978-1-57332-138-9(9)) HighReach Learning, Inc.

Jenck, Heidi Shelton. Pets on Vacation. 2007. (Illus.). 32p. (J). (***978-1-4048-1236-9(9)***) Picture Window Bks.

—Pets on Vacation. Blanks, Natascha Alex, illus. 2006. 32p. (J). lib. bdg. (***978-1-4048-3141-4(X)***) Picture Window Bks.

Jennings, Patrick. The Pup Tent: An Ike & Mem Story. O'Neill, Catharine, illus. 2005. (J). (978-0-8234-1938-8(X)) Holiday Hse., Inc.

Joan, Marler. Secrets of the Wind. 2006. pap. (***978-1-888251-37-1(9)***) Voice & Vision Pubns.

Johnston, Antony. Three Days in Europe, Vol. 1. 2003. (Illus.). 144p. pap. 14.95 (978-1-929998-72-2(4)) Oni Pr., Inc.

Johnston, Julie. The Only Outcast. 1999. (J). (978-0-606-19122-7(4)) Tandem Library Bks.

—Only Outcast. 1999. (gr. 7-12). lib. bdg. 15.25 (978-0-613-28008-2(3)) Tandem Library Bks.

—The Only Outcast. 1999. 248p. (J). (gr. 6-9). reprint ed. pap. 6.95 (978-0-88776-488-2(6)) Tundra Bks., Inc./Livres Toundra, Inc. CAN. *Dist:* Random Hse., Inc.

Khalsa, Dayal Kaur. My Family Vacation. 2003. (Illus.). 24p. (J). (gr. 1 up). pap. 6.95 (978-0-88776-629-9(3)) Tundra Bks., Inc./Livres Toundra, Inc. CAN. *Dist:* Random Hse., Inc.

Kimmelman, Leslie. In the Doghouse: An Emma & Bo Story. Kelley, True, illus. (Holiday House Reader Ser.: Level 2). 32p. (J). (gr. k-3). 14.95 (978-0-8234-1882-4(0)) Holiday Hse., Inc.

King, Dorothea. Teddybears' Vacation. King, Dorothea, illus. 1999. (Teddybears Ser.). (Illus.). 8p. (J). bds. 3.95 (978-1-57717-106-5(3)) New Line Bks.

Klingel, Cynthia Fitterer & Noyed, Robert B. Victoria's Vacation & the Letter V. 2003. (Alphaphonics Ser.). (Illus.). 24p. (J). (ps-2). 21.36 (978-1-59296-112-2(6)) Child's World, Inc.

Knowles, Kent. Lucius & the Storm. Knowles, Kent, illus. 2007. (Illus.). 32p. (J). 15.95 (978-1-60108-005-9(0)) Red Cygnet Pr.

Kraft, Erik P. Lenny & Mel's Summer Vacation. Kraft, Erik P., illus. 2004. (Ready-for-Chapters Ser.). (Illus.). 64p. (J). pap. 3.99 (978-0-689-86874-0(X) , Aladdin) Simon & Schuster Children's Publishing.

Lamba, Marie. What I Said- 2008. (J). (***978-0-375-84093-7(1)***); lib. bdg. (***978-0-375-94093-4(6)***) Random Hse., Inc.

Langlois, Annie. L' Evasion d'Alfred le Dindon. Beaulieu, Jimméy, illus. 2004. (Roman Jeunesse Ser.). (FRE.). 96p. (J). (gr 4-7). pap. (978-2-89021-687-7(X)) Diffusion du livre Mirabel.

Lewis, Beverly. Secret Summer Dreams. rev. ed. 2001. (Holly's Heart Ser.: Bk. 2). 144p. (YA). (gr. 6-9). pap. 6.99 (978-0-7642-2501-7(4)) Bethany Hse. Pubs.

Lewis, Rob. Grandpa at the Beach. Lewis, Rob, illus. 1998. (Mondo Ser.). (Illus.). 48p. (J). (gr. 1-5). pap. 4.50 (978-1-57255-552-5(1)) Mondo Publishing.

Lewis, Steven & Parker, Shelley. Return to Allapatria. 2006. 395p. (J). pap. 12.95 (978-0-9547092-9-7(2)) Accent Pr. GBR. *Dist:* Dufour Editions, Inc.

Little People on Vacation. 1998. (Fisher-Price Little People Toddler Skills Workbooks Ser.: Vol. 2). (Illus.). (J). pap. (978-0-7666-0183-3(8) , Honey Bear Bks.) Modern Publishing.

Littlefield, William. The Circus in the Woods. 2001. 208p. (J). (gr. 4-6). tchr. ed. 15.00 (978-0-618-06642-1(X)) Houghton Mifflin Co. Trade & Reference Div.

Lovelace, Maud Hart. Carney's House Party. 2000. (gr. 3-6). lib. bdg. 15.25 (978-0-613-31046-8(2)) Tandem Library Bks.

Man-Kong, Ann Marie & Forrester, Emma. The Greatest Vacation. Cutting, David A., illus. 2006. (Holly Hobbie & Friends Ser.). 96p. (J). act. bk. ed. 2.99 (978-1-4169-4104-0(5) , Simon Scribbles) Simon & Schuster Children's Publishing.

Marcum, Lance. The Cottonmouth Club. 2005. 336p. (J). 18.00 (978-0-374-31562-7(0) , Farrar, Straus & Giroux (BYR)) Farrar, Straus & Giroux.

Marsh, Carole. The Secret of Skullcracker Swamp. 2006. 128p. (gr. 3-5). pap. 5.99 (***978-0-635-06234-5(8)***); (gr. 7-14). 14.95 (***978-0-635-06238-3(0)***) Gallopade International.

Mayer, Mercer. Just a Snowy Vacation. 2001. (ps-2). lib. bdg. 11.00 (978-0-613-53269-3(4)) Tandem Library Bks.

Mayes-Stemple, Ellen. Where Are We Going. 2000. (gr. k-3). lib. bdg. 11.80 (978-0-613-29788-2(1)) Tandem Library Bks.

McGarrahan, Margaret. Nessie's Cape Cod Vacation. Wright, Kathleen, illus. 2000. 58p. (J). (gr. 1-3). pap. 12.50 (978-0-9672639-0-8(5)) Smith Lane Pubs.

McGirr, Randel W. Bible Camp. 2007. 176p. per. 13.95 (*978-0-595-44663-6(9)) iUniverse, Inc.

McLain, Tanya. A Different Kind of Summer. 2007. (ENG.). 72p. (J). per. 10.99 (*978-1-4141-0848-3(6)) Pleasant Word.

McLeod, Kate & Dorling Kindersley Publishing Staff. Outback Adventure. 2004. (Dk Readers Ser.). (Illus.). 32p. (J). 12.99 (978-0-7566-0544-5(X)); pap. 3.99 (978-0-7566-0545-2(8)) Dorling Kindersley Publishing, Inc.

McMullan, Kate. Fluffy's Silly Summer. 2000. (Hello Reader! Ser.). (Illus.). (J). 10.79 (978-0-606-18873-9(8)) Tandem Library Bks.

—Fluffy's Spring Vacation. Smith, Mavis, illus. 2004. 40p. (J). lib. bdg. 15.00 (978-1-59054-468-6(4)) Fitzgerald Bks.

—Fluffy's Spring Vacation. 2001. (Hello Reader! Ser.). (Illus.). (J). 10.79 (978-0-606-20661-7(2)) Tandem Library Bks.

Meadows, Daisy. Joy the Summer Vacation Fairy. 2007. (Rainbow Magic Ser.). 192p. (J). pap. 6.99 (*978-0-439-93442-8(7) , Scholastic Paperbacks) Scholastic, Inc.

Menefee, Angelo K. Billy's First Summer Vacation. 2007. (J). per. 16.95 (*978-1-60002-249-4(9) , Airleaf Publishing) Airleaf Publishing & Bookselling.

Mick Morris Myth Solver #3 Champ... A Wave of Terror! Five Ways to Finish. 2006. (J). mass mkt. 6.99 (*978-0-9774119-2-4(3) , Five Ways to Finish) Team B Creative LLC.

Miss O, Harlie, Justine, and Isabella, with Devra Newberger Speregen, Juliette. Miss O & Friends: Picture Perfecto! 2006. (Miss O & Friends Ser.). (Illus.). 128p. (J). pap. 5.99 (978-0-8230-2949-5(2)) Watson-Guptill Pubns., Inc.

Moscovich, Rotem & Lankford, Raye. Curious George Takes a Trip. 2007. (Illus.). 24p. (J). (ps-k). pap. 3.99 (*978-0-618-88403-2(3)) Houghton Mifflin Co.

Mostoller, Gordon. Randy Walter & Rex. 2006. pap. 12.95 (*978-1-4259-6498-6(2)) AuthorHouse.

Munsch, Robert N. The Sand Castle Contest. Martchenko, Michael, illus. 2005. 28p. (J). (ps). lib. bdg. 11.19 (978-0-606-33821-9(7)) Tandem Library Bks.

Murdocca, Sal. Lucy Takes a Holiday. Murdocca, Sal, illus. 1998. (Illus.). 32p. (J). (gr. 1-5). 15.95 (978-1-57255-560-0(2)) Mondo Publishing.

Napoli, Donna Jo & Johnston, Shelagh. Hotel Jungle. Spengler, Kenneth, tr. Spengler, Kenneth, illus. 2004. 33p. (J). 15.95 (978-1-59336-002-3(9)); pap. (978-1-59336-003-0(7)) Mondo Publishing.

Nelson, Blake. They Came from Below. 2007. 304p. (YA). (gr. 8 up). 17.95 (*978-0-7653-1423-9(1) , Tor Teen) Doherty, Tom Assocs., LLC.

Nixon, Joan Lowery. Gus & Gertie & the Missing Pearl. deGroat, Diane, illus. 2000. 48p. (J). (ps-3). 15.50 (978-1-58717-023-2(X) , SeaStar Bks.) Chronicle Bks. LLC.

Njeng, Pierre Yves. Vacation in the Village: A Story from West Africa. 2003. (Illus.). 24p. (J). (gr. 2-4). 14.95 (978-1-56397-768-8(0)); pap. 6.95 (978-1-56397-823-4(7)) Boyds Mills Pr.

North, Merry. My Vacation: Picture, Play, & Tote. 2003. (Picture, Play & Tote-Book Ser.). (Illus.). 10p. (J). (ps up). bds. 5.99 (978-1-57151-720-3(0)) Playhouse Publishing.

Oakley, Graham. Church Mice Take a Break. (Illus.). 25p. (J). 17.99 (978-0-340-73254-0(7) , Hodder & Stoughton) Hodder General Publishing Division GBR. *Dist:* Trafalgar Square Publishing.

O'Mahony, Carol. A Dee Dee & Clark Delay Magical Mystery Ser. 2006. 73p. pap. 14.95 (*978-1-4241-5119-6(8)) PublishAmerica, Inc.

Ostrow, Kim. M & Ms on Vacation. 1999. (Illus.). (J). mass mkt. 5.99 (978-0-689-84300-6(3) , Aladdin) Simon & Schuster Children's Publishing.

Page, Katherine Hall. Bon Voyage, Christie & Company. (Christie & Company Ser.). (YA). (gr. 6-8). 1999. (Illus.). 10p. pap. 3.99 (978-0-380-78035-8(6)); 1998. 288p. 14.00 (978-0-380-97398-9(7)) HarperCollins Pubs.

Papineau, Lucie. Bamboo at the Beach. Jolin, Dominique, illus. 2005. (Read-It! Readers Ser.). 32p. (C). (gr. k-3). 18.60 (978-1-4048-1035-8(8)) Picture Window Bks.

Papineau, Lucie, et al. Bamboo at the Beach. 2000. (Illus.). 32p. (J). (gr. 1-4). pap. (978-1-894363-38-9(8)) Dominique & Friends.

Park, Barbara. Junie B., First Grader: Aloha-Ha-Ha! Brunkus, Denise, illus. 2007. (Junie B. Jones Ser.: No. 26). 128p. (J). (gr. 1-4). 4.99 (978-0-375-83404-2(4) , Random Hse. Bks. for Young Readers) Random Hse. Children's Bks.

—Junie B., First Grader: Aloha-Ha-Ha! 2006. (Junie B. Jones Ser.: No. 26). (Illus.). 128p. (J). (gr. k-3). lib. bdg. 13.95 (978-0-375-93403-2(0)); (gr. 2-5). 11.95 (978-0-375-83403-5(6)) Random Hse. Children's Bks. (Random Hse. Bks. for Young Readers).

Paterson, Aileen. Maisie Bites the Big Apple. Paterson, Aileen, illus. 2002. (Illus.). 32p. (J). pap. (978-1-871512-69-4(7)) Glowworm Bks., Ltd.

Paton, Ian, illus. Margaret's Magnificent Colorado Adventure. 1999. 48p. (J). (gr. 4-7). 14.95 (978-1-56579-329-3(3) , A176) Westcliffe Pubs.

Payne, Helen. Vacation Paws. Youngblood, Carol, illus. 2006. 50p. per. 10.00 (*978-0-9786276-6-9(0)) Mentzer Printing Ink.

Perdew, Suzanne, et al. The Mystery of the Abandoned Lighthouse. 2001. (Shoebox Kids Ser.: Bk. 12). (Illus.). 93p. (J). (978-0-8163-1819-3(0)) Pacific Pr. Publishing Assn.

Perez, Angela J. Zack Attack! Hazard, Andrea, illus. 2007. 36p. (J). 17.95 (*978-0-9778328-9-7(9)) His Work Christian Publishing.

Perkins, Lynne Rae. Pictures from Our Vacation. Perkins, Lynne Rae, illus. 2007. (Illus.). (J). (gr. 2-5). 40p. 16.99 (*978-0-06-085097-5(3)); 32p. lib. bdg. 17.89 (*978-0-06-085098-2(1)) HarperCollins Pubs. (Greenwillow Bks.).

Peterson, Doug. Larryboy Versus the Volcano. 2004. (Illus.). 96p. pap. 4.99 (978-0-310-70728-8(5)) Zonderkidz.

Petrucha, Stefan. Snared. 2008. (Wicked Dead Ser.: No.3). 224p. (J). pap. 7.99 (*978-0-06-113851-5(7) , HarperTeen) HarperCollins Pubs.

Polacco, Patricia. The Graves Family Vacation. Polacco, Patricia, illus. 2008. 48p. (J). (gr. k). pap. 6.99 (*978-0-14-241175-9(2) , Puffin) Penguin Group (USA) Inc.

Prime, D. De Nuevo en Vacaciones. (Serie Sara y Pablo - Sarah & Paul Ser.: No. 6). Tr. of Go on Vacation. (SPA.). (J). 2.99 (978-0-7899-0495-9(0) , 498900) Editorial Unilit.

Pueppke. Fuzzy the Cat & his Vacation in Gatlinburg. 2000. (Illus.). 89p. (YA). per. 6.99 (978-0-9678352-2-8(4)) FUZZY DREAMS, Inc.

Puttock, Simon. Goat & Donkey in the Great Outdoors. Julian, Russell, illus. 2007. 28p. (J). (ps-2). 16.00 (*978-1-56148-573-4(X)) Good Bks.

Puzzle Track Staff, ed. Our Family Vacation. 2007. (Puzzle Track Ser.). 20p. (J). bds. 18.95 (*978-0-7696-5609-0(9)) School Specialty Publishing.

Ramblin' Rose: The Wire Forests of Peru. 2007. 200p. (YA). pap. 8.99 (*978-0-9776043-9-5(X)) Aspirations Media, Inc.

Rau, Dana Meachen. Bob's Vacation. 1999. (gr. k-3). lib. bdg. 12.95 (978-0-613-37294-7(8)) Tandem Library Bks.

Reberg, Evelyne. Vacances infernales Tom Tom. pap. 21.95 (978-2-227-73108-0(7)) Bayard Editions FRA. *Dist:* Distribooks, Inc.

Reynolds, Evan. My Vacation. 2004. (J). 12.95 (978-0-9759790-0-6(0)) Plant the Seed Publishing.

Rigby Education Staff. Mr. Merton's Vacation. (Sails Literacy Ser.). (Illus.). 16p. (gr. 2-3). 27.00 (978-0-7635-9948-5(4)) Rigby Education.

Rogers, Alan. Vacation Time. 2004. (Little Giants Ser.). (Illus.). 16p. (ps-k). (J). pap. 3.95 (978-1-58728-393-2(X)); 5.95 (978-1-58728-156-3(2)) T&N Children's Publishing. (Two Can Publishing).

Rose, Valerie. The Family Reunion Is Not A Real Vacation. 2003. 28p. (J). 9.95 (978-0-9703489-2-0(4) , Little Petals) Roses Are READ Productions.

Rylant, Cynthia. Henry & Mudge & the Tumbling Trip. Bracken, Carolyn, illus. 2006. (Henry & Mudge Ser.). 40p. (J). pap. 3.99 (978-0-689-83452-3(7) , Aladdin) Simon & Schuster Children's Publishing.

—Special Gifts. 2000. (Cobble Street Cousins Ser.: No. 4). (gr. 3-6). lib. bdg. 11.80 (978-0-613-30140-4(4)) Tandem Library Bks.

Sanchez, Alex. Rainbow Road. 2007. 272p. (YA). pap. 8.99 (978-1-4169-1191-3(X) , Simon Pulse) Simon & Schuster Children's Publishing.

Sanchez, Alex & Louth, Jack. Rainbow Road. 2005. 256p. (J). 16.95 (978-0-689-86565-7(1)) Simon & Schuster Children's Publishing.

Santa Takes A Vacation. 2005. (J). 5.95 (978-0-9769321-4-7(8)) Steingart, Nathan Publishing.

Santillo, LuAnn. At the Beach, 6 vols. Santillo, LuAnn, ed. 2003. (Half-Pint Kids Readers Ser.). (Illus.). 42p. (J). (ps-1). pap. 6.99 (978-1-59256-084-4(9)) Half-Pint Kids, Inc.

—A Fun Trip. Santillo, LuAnn, ed. 2003. (Half-Pint Kids Readers Ser.). (Illus.). 7p. (J). (ps-1). pap. (978-1-59256-085-1(7)) Half-Pint Kids, Inc.

—The Picnic. Santillo, LuAnn, ed. 2003. (Half-Pint Kids Readers Ser.). (Illus.). 7p. (J). (ps-1). pap. (978-1-59256-090-5(3)) Half-Pint Kids, Inc.

Schirripa, Steve & Fleming, Charles. Nicky Deuce: Welcome to the Family. 2006. 176p. (gr. 5-8). 5.99 (978-0-440-42053-8(9) , Yearling) Random Hse. Children's Bks.

Schulman, Elayne. This Year We Took a Special Trip. Bowser, Ken, illus. 2000. (This Year We... Ser.: Vol. 2). 32p. (J). (ps up). 14.95 (978-1-892780-04-1(6)) Giggles Group, Inc., The.

Sempe, Goscinny. Las Vacaciones del Pequeno Nicolas. 2003. (SPA., Illus.). 150p. (J). (gr. 5-8). pap. 9.95 (978-84-204-4813-8(3)) Santillana USA Publishing Co., Inc.

Sheldon, Dyan. Sophie Pitt-Turnbull Discovers America. 192p. (YA). (gr. 7). 2007. pap. 7.99 (*978-0-7636-3295-3(3)); 2005. 15.99 (978-0-7636-2740-9(2)) Candlewick Pr.

Smath, Jerry. Sammy Salami. 2007. (Illus.). 32p. (J). (gr. 1-3). 15.95 (*978-0-8109-9350-1(3) , Abrams Bks. for Young Readers) Abrams, Harry N. , Inc.

Smith, Anne Warren. Tails of Spring Break. 2005. 136p. (J). (gr. 2-5). 15.95 (978-0-8075-6358-8(7)) Whitman, Albert & Co.

Spalding, Andrea. Phoebe & the Gypsy. 1999. (Young Reader Ser.). (Illus.). 128p. (J). (gr. 3-6). pap. 4.99 (978-1-55143-135-2(1)) Orca Bk. Pubs. USA.

—Phoebe & the Gypsy. 1999. (Young Reader Ser.). (J). (978-0-606-19478-5(9)); (gr. 3-6). lib. bdg. 13.00 (978-0-8085-8430-8(8)) Tandem Library Bks.

St. Anthony, Jane. Grace above All. 2007. 176p. (J). (gr. 5-8). 16.00 (978-0-374-39940-5(9) , Farrar, Straus & Giroux (BYR)) Farrar, Straus & Giroux.

Standish, Burt L. Frank Merriwell's Vacation. Rudman, Jack, ed. 2003. (Frank Merriwell Ser.). (YA). (gr. 9 up). 29.95 (978-0-8373-9325-4(6)); pap. 9.95 (978-0-8373-9025-3(7) , FM-025) Merriwell, Frank Inc.

Stanley, Robin. Vacation Time. Fletcher, Rusty & Julien, Terry, illus. 2006. (Happy Day Summer Titles Ser.). 16p. (J). pap. 1.99 (978-0-7847-1828-5(8) , 04191) Standard Publishing.

Stem, Jacqueline. Mystery of the Whispering Walls. 2004. (J). 148p. pap. (978-1-57168-844-6(7)); (Hollow Tree Mystery Ser.: Bk. 6). (Illus.). v, 142p. (978-1-57168-850-7(1) , Eakin Pr.) Eakin Pr.

Stevenson, James. The Castaway. Stevenson, James, illus. 2002. (Illus.). 32p. (J). (gr. 2 up). 15.95 (978-0-688-16965-7(1)) HarperCollins Pubs.

Stilton, Geronimo. A Fabumouse Vacation for Geronimo. Keys, Larry, illus. 2004. (Geronimo Stilton Ser.: No. 9). 128p. (J). pap. 6.99 (978-0-439-55971-3(5) , Scholastic Paperbacks) Scholastic, Inc.

—A Fabumouse Vacation for Geronimo. 2004. (Geronimo Stilton Ser.: No. 9). (Illus.). 113p. (J). (gr. 2-5). lib. bdg. 13.94 (978-0-606-33272-9(3)) Tandem Library Bks.

—Surf's up Geronimo! 2005. (Geronimo Stilton Ser.: No. 20). (Illus.). 109p. (J). (gr. 2-5). per. 13.94 (978-0-606-33812-7(8)) Tandem Library Bks.

—Surf's up, Geronimo! 2005. (Geronimo Stilton Ser.: No. 20). (Illus.). 109p. (J). (978-1-4156-0622-3(6)) Scholastic, Inc.

Stinson, Kathy. Seven Clues. 2005. (Streetlights Ser.). 104p. (J). (gr. 2-5). 7.95 (978-1-55028-889-6(X)) Lorimer, James & Co., Ltd., Pubs. CAN. *Dist:* Casemate Pubs. & Bk. Distributors, LLC.

Stock, Catherine. A Porc in New York. Stock, Catherine, illus. 2007. (Illus.). 32p. (J). (ps-3). 16.95 (978-0-8234-1994-4(0)) Holiday Hse., Inc.

Swallow, Pamela Curtis. Melvil & Dewey Gone Fishing. Eliasen, Lorena, illus. 2004. 56p. (J). pap. 12.00 (978-1-59158-153-6(2) , LU1532) Libraries Unlimited, Inc.

Thomson, Sarah L. The Manny. 2007. 192p. (YA). pap. 6.99 (978-0-14-240803-2(4) , Puffin) Penguin Group (USA) Inc.

To-Do List. 2007. (J). 15.95 (*978-0-9741319-5-5(4)) 4N Publishing LLC.

Trimble, Marcia. Malinda Martha Meets Mariposa: A Star Is Born. Lund, John, illus. 32p. (J). (gr. k-5). 2000. pap. 7.95 (978-1-891577-58-1(1)); 1999. 15.95 (978-1-891577-57-4(3)) Images Pr.

—Serendipity Says to Know Me Is to Love Me. Grell, Susi, illus. 2000. 32p. (J). (ps-3). 15.95 (978-1-891577-77-2(8)) Images Pr.

Tuthill, Louisa C. Hurrah for New England! or the Virginia Boy's Vacation. 2004. reprint ed. pap. 15.95 (978-1-4191-2504-1(4)); pap. 1.99 (978-1-4192-2504-8(9)) Kessinger Publishing, LLC.

Vacations: Set B Individual Title Six-Packs. (Smart Start Ser.). (gr. k-1). 23.00 (978-0-7635-0418-2(1)) Rigby Education.

Van Dyne, Edith. Aunt Jane's Nieces. 2006. 96.99 (*978-1-4219-7428-6(2)); pap. 89.99 (*978-1-4219-7440-8(1)) IndyPublish.com.

—Aunt Jane's Nieces at Millville. 2006. 95.99 (*978-1-4219-7454-5(1)) IndyPublish.com.

—Aunt Jane's Nieces on Vacation. 2006. 95.99 (*978-1-4219-7507-8(6)) IndyPublish.com.

—Aunt Jane's Nieces on Vacation. 2004. reprint ed. pap. 21.95 (978-1-4191-0825-9(5)); pap. 1.99 (978-1-4192-0825-6(X)) Kessinger Publishing, LLC.

Voelkel, J&P. Middleworld. 2007. (Jaguar Stones Trilogy Ser.: Bk. 1). (Illus.). 400p. (J). (gr. 6-9). 17.95 (*978-1-57525-561-3(8)) Smith and Kraus Publishers, Incorporated.

Waldron, Ann. The Luckie Star. 2000. 180p. (YA). pap. 11.95 (978-0-595-00070-8(3)) iUniverse, Inc.

Waldron, Kathleen Cook. Five Stars for Emily. 2004. (Orca Young Readers Ser.). (Illus.). 144p. (J). (gr. 3-6). pap., tchr. ed. 4.99 (978-1-55143-296-0(X) , 1234541) Orca Bk. Pubs. USA.

Wallace, Sheila Ryan. Diving for the Gold. 2004. 142p. (YA). pap. 15.95 (978-0-7414-2269-9(7)) Infinity Publishing.

Weston, Carol. Melanie Martin Goes Dutch: The Private Diary of My Almost Bummer Summer with Cecily, Matt the Brat, & Vincent van Go Go Go. 2003. (Illus.). 240p. (J). (gr. 3-7). 5.99 (978-0-440-41899-3(2) , Yearling) Random Hse. Children's Bks.

—Melanie Martin Goes Dutch: The Private Diary of My Almost Bummer Summer with Cecily, Matt the Brat, & Vincent van Go Go Go. 2003. (gr. 3-6). lib. bdg. 25.70 (978-0-613-62527-2(7)) Tandem Library Bks.

—With Love from Spain, Melanie Martin. Roth, Marci, illus. 2005. 256p. (J). (gr. 3-7). 5.50 (978-0-440-41972-3(7) , Yearling) Random Hse. Children's Bks.

Whatley, Tom. James & Jessie (This Is Not A Mushy Romantic Novel) 2005. 70p. pap. 9.67 (978-1-4116-4370-3(4)) Lulu.com.

White, Steve. Family Vacations & Other Hazards of Growing Up. 2001. (Illus.). 206p. per. 14.95 (978-0-9679092-8-8(7)) Chloe Pr.

Whytock, Cherry. My Saucy Stuffed Ravioli: The Life of Angelica Cookson Potts. Whytock, Cherry, illus. 2005. (Illus.). 176p. (YA). 14.95 (978-0-689-86550-3(3)) Simon & Schuster Children's Publishing.

Wing, Natasha. The Night Before Summer Vacation. 2002. (gr. k-3). lib. bdg. 11.25 (978-0-613-72501-9(8)) Tandem Library Bks.

Wittlinger, Ellen. Zigzag. (Illus.). (YA). 2003. 272p. 16.95 (978-0-689-84996-1(6)); 2005. 288p. reprint ed. pap. 6.99 (978-0-689-84998-5(2) , Simon Pulse) Simon & Schuster Children's Publishing.

Wojciechowski, Susan. Beany Goes to Camp. Natti, Susanna, illus. ed. 2005. (Beany Ser.). 112p. (J). (gr. 1-4). pap. 4.99 (978-0-7636-2570-2(1)) Candlewick Pr.

Wright, Mary. Justice for All. 2004. 177p. pap. 19.95 (978-1-4137-4083-7(9)) PublishAmerica, Inc.

Yeager, Graham. Diablo: The Third Millersburg Novel. 2006. 145p. (YA). per. 7.99 (*978-0-9765478-4-6(8)) Stone Acres Publishing Co.

Young, Beryl. Wishing Star Summer. 2002. (Illus.). 144p. (J). (gr. 3-7). pap. 6.95 (978-1-55192-450-2(1)) Raincoast Bk. Distribution CAN. *Dist:* Perseus Distribution.

Ziefert, Harriet. What's a Vacation? Schumacher, Claire, illus. 2006. 16p. pap. 5.95 (978-1-4027-2400-8(4)) Sterling Publishing Co., Inc.

VACCINATION

see also Immunity

Ballard, Carol. From Cowpox to Antibiotics: Discovering Vaccines & Medicines. 2006. (Chain Reactions Ser.). (Illus.). 62p. (YA). (gr. 6-9). lib. bdg. 34.29 (978-1-4034-8839-8(8)) Heinemann Library.

De la Bédoyère, Guy. The First Polio Vaccine. 2005. (Milestones in Modern Science Ser.). (Illus.). 48p. (J). pap. (978-0-8368-5862-4(X)); lib. bdg. 30.00 (978-0-8368-5855-6(7)) Stevens, Gareth Inc. (World Almanac Library).

Gray, Shirley W. Prevention & Good Health. 2003. (Living Well). (Illus.). 32p. (J). (gr. 2-6). 27.07 (978-1-59296-083-5(9)) Child's World, Inc.

Hantula, Richard. Jonas Salk. 2004. (Trailblazers of the Modern World Ser.). (Illus.). 48p. (J). (gr. 5 up). pap. 11.95 (978-0-8368-5260-8(5)); lib. bdg. 30.00 (978-0-8368-5100-7(5)) Stevens, Gareth Inc. (World Almanac Library).

Nardo, Don. Vaccines. 2001. (Great Medical Discoveries Ser.). (Illus.). 120p. (YA). (gr. 4-12). 29.95 (978-1-56006-932-4(5) , Lucent Bks.) Thomson Gale.

Phelan, Glen. Killing Germs, Saving Lives: The Quest for the First Vaccines. 2006. (Science Quest Ser.). 64p. (J). (gr. 5-9). 17.95 (978-0-7922-5537-6(2) , National Geographic Children's Bks.) National Geographic Society.

—Science Quest: Killing Germs, Saving Lives: The Quest for the First Vaccines. 2006. 64p. (J). (gr. 5-9). 25.90 (978-0-7922-5538-3(0) , National Geographic Children's Bks.) National Geographic Society.

Shulman, Neil, et al. The Germ Patrol: All about Shots for Tots... & Big Kids, Too! 2004. (Illus.). 36p. (ps-3). pap. 14.95 (978-0-9639002-8-9(5)) Rx Humor.

Silverstein, Alvin, et al. Vaccinations. 2002. (My Health Ser.). (Illus.). 48p. (J). (gr. 3-5). pap. 6.95 (978-0-531-15564-6(1) , Watts, Franklin) Scholastic Library Publishing.

—Vaccinations. 2002. (Illus.). 48p. (J). (ps-7). lib. bdg. 15.25 (978-0-613-54374-3(2)) Tandem Library Bks.

Wells, Ken R. Vaccines. 2006. (Illus.). 224p. (gr. 10-12). 36.20 (978-0-7377-2857-6(4) , Greenhaven Pr., Inc.) Thomson Gale.

Williams, Mary E. Vaccinations. 2003. (gr. 3-6). lib. bdg. 28.90 (978-0-613-73882-8(9)) Tandem Library Bks.

VALENTINE'S DAY

Barnett, Michelle Noble, et al. Theme Pockets - February: Valentine's Day; President's Day; Fairy Tale Fantasy. Evans, Marilyn, ed. Larsen, Jo, illus. 1999. (Making Books with Pockets). 96p. (J). pap., tchr. ed. 12.99 (978-1-55799-699-2(7) , EMC 585) Evan-Moor Educational Pubs.

Barth, Edna. Hearts, Cupids, & Red Roses: The Story of the Valentine Symbols. Arndt, Ursula, illus. 2001. 64p. (J). (gr. 4-6). tchr. ed. 16.00 (978-0-618-06789-3(2)); pap. 7.95 (978-0-618-06791-6(4)) Houghton Mifflin Co. Trade & Reference Div. (Clarion Bks.).

—Hearts, Cupids, & Red Roses: The Story of the Valentine Symbols. 2001. (J). 14.75 (978-0-606-20696-9(5)); (gr. 3-6). lib. bdg. 16.40 (978-0-613-31303-2(8)) Tandem Library Bks.

Benton, Jim. I (Heart) Me Valentines. 2008. (It's Happy Bunny Ser.). 16p. (J). pap. 7.99 (*978-0-439-91547-2(3) , Scholastic Paperbacks) Scholastic, Inc.

Bodden, Valerie. Valentine's Day. 2005. (My First Look at Holidays Ser.). (Illus.). 24p. (gr. k-3). 15.95 (978-1-58341-371-5(5) , Creative Education) Creative Co., The.

Bond, Felicia. Make Your Own Valentines! 1999. (Illus.). 32p. (J). (ps-2). 9.95 (978-0-694-01259-6(9)) HarperCollins Pubs.

Bowman, Crystal. My Valentine Story: Giving My Heart to God. Gévry, Claudine, illus. 2007. 14p. (J). 6.99 (978-0-310-71163-6(0)) Zondervan.

Bulla, Clyde Robert. The Story of Valentine's Day. Kwas, Susan Estelle, illus. (Trophy Picture Bk.). 40p. (J). 2000. (gr. 2-5). pap. 6.99 (978-0-06-443626-7(8) , Harper Trophy); 1999. (gr. 4-7). 14.89 (978-0-06-027884-7(6)); 1999. (gr. 4-7). 14.95 (978-0-06-027883-0(8)) HarperCollins Pubs.

—The Story of Valentine's Day. 1999. (gr. 3-6). lib. bdg. 14.10 (978-0-613-22450-5(7)) Tandem Library Bks.

Carrick, Carol. Valentine. Bouma, Paddy, illus. 2001. 40p. (J). (gr. k-3). pap. 5.95 (978-0-618-05151-9(1) , Clarion Bks.) Houghton Mifflin Co. Trade & Reference Div.

Cooper, Jason. Valentine's Day. 2002. (Illus.). 24p. (J). lib. bdg. 20.64 (978-1-58952-222-0(2)) Rourke Publishing, LLC.

Disney Staff. Make Your Own Valentines. 1999. (Illus.). 40p. (J). (gr. k-3). 7.99 (978-0-7364-0100-5(8)) Mouse Works.

Douglas, Lloyd G. Let's Get Ready for Valentine's Day. 2003. (gr. k-3). lib. bdg. 12.95 (978-0-613-59665-7(X)) Tandem Library Bks.

Erlbach, Arlene & Erlbach, Herbert. Valentine's Day Crafts. 2004. (Fun Holiday Crafts Kids Can Do Ser.). (Illus.). 32p. (J). lib. bdg. 22.60 (978-0-7660-2237-9(4)) Enslow Pubs., Inc.

Flanagan, Alice K. Valentine's Day. Dieterichs, Shelley, illus. 2001. (Holidays & Festivals Ser.). 32p. (J). (gr. 3 up). lib. bdg. 22.60 (978-0-7565-0088-7(5)) Compass Point Bks.

Gibbons, Gail. Valentine's Day Is... Gibbons, Gail, illus. (Illus.). 32p. (J). 6.95 (978-0-8234-2036-0(1)); 17.95 (978-0-8234-1852-7(9)) Holiday Hse., Inc.

Gilpin, Rebecca. Valentine Things to Make & Do. 2006. (Usborne Activities Ser.). (Illus.). 31p. (J). (***978-0-439-78705-5(X)***) Scholastic, Inc.

Golden Books Staff. Vintage Valentines. 2005. (Illus.). 12p. (J). (ps-2). pap. 4.99 (978-0-375-87514-4(X) , Golden Bks.) Random Hse. Children's Bks.

Haugen, Brenda. Valentine's Day. Ouren, Todd, illus. 2004. (Holidays & Celebrations Ser.). 24p. (gr. k-3). 22.60 (978-1-4048-0193-6(6)) Picture Window Bks.

Heinrichs, Ann. Valentine's Day. Holm, Sharon Lane, illus. 2006. (Holidays, Festivals, & Celebrations Ser.). 32p. (J). (gr. k-4). 22.79 (978-1-59296-583-0(0)) Child's World, Inc.

Imler, Kathryn A. Valentines Day. 2003. (Holiday Histories Ser.). (Illus.). 32p. (J). 6.95 (978-1-4034-3687-0(8)) Heinemann Library.

—Valentine's Day. 2003. (Holiday Histories Ser.). (Illus.). 32p. (J). lib. bdg. 22.79 (978-1-4034-3502-6(2)) Heinemann Library.

Klingel, Cynthia Fitterer & Noyed, Robert B. Valentine's Day. 2002. (Wonder Books Level 2: Holidays Ser.). (Illus.). 24p. (J). (ps-3). 22.79 (978-1-56766-957-2(3)) Child's World, Inc.

Landau, Elaine. El Dia de San Valentin: Caramelos, Amor y Corazones. 2005. (Días Festivos Ser.). (SPA., Illus.). 48p. (J). (ps-ps). lib. bdg. 23.93 (978-0-7660-2613-1(2) , Enslow Elementary) Enslow Pubs., Inc.

—Valentine's Day: Candy, Love & Hearts. 2002. (Finding Out about Holidays Ser.). (Illus.). 48p. (J). (gr. 1-4). lib. bdg. 23.93 (978-0-7660-1779-5(6)) Enslow Pubs., Inc.

Let's Show God's Love on Valentine's Day. 2006. (J). 16p. pap. 1.99 (978-0-7847-1722-6(2) , 04183); 24p. bds. 7.99 (978-0-7847-1385-3(5) , 04050) Standard Publishing.

Marx, David F. Valentine's Day. 2001. (Rookie Read-About Holidays Ser.). (Illus.). 32p. (J). (gr. 1-2). pap. 5.95 (978-0-516-27179-8(2) , Children's Pr.) Scholastic Library Publishing.

—Valentine's Day: Holidays. 2001. (Rookie Read-About Holidays Ser.). (Illus.). 32p. (J). (gr. 1-2). 19.50 (978-0-516-22212-7(0) , Children's Pr.) Scholastic Library Publishing.

McGrath, Barbara Barbieri. The M & M's' Brand Valentine Book. Tagel, Peggy, illus. 2004. 12p. (J). (ps-k). bds. 6.95 (978-1-57091-422-5(2)) Charlesbridge Publishing, Inc.

McNeil, Niki, et al. HOCPP 1033 Valentine's Day. 2005. spiral bd. 20.00 (***978-1-60308-033-0(3)***) In the Hands of a Child.

—HOCPP 1145 Be My Valentine. 2007. spiral bd. 15.50 (***978-1-60308-145-0(3)***) In the Hands of a Child.

Mercier, Johanne. Caillou: Happy Valentine's Day! Tipeo, tr. from FRE. 2003. (Confetti Ser.). (Illus.). 24p. (J). pap. 5.95 (978-2-89450-467-3(5)) Chouette Publishing CAN. *Dist:* Perseus Distribution.

Moffatt, Judith. Valentines: A Read-and-Do Book. 1999. (gr. k-3). lib. bdg. 11.80 (978-0-613-64822-6(6)) Tandem Library Bks.

Murray, Julie. Valentine's Day. 2005. (Holidays Ser.). (Illus.). 24p. (J). (gr. k-4). lib. bdg. 21.35 (978-1-57765-954-9(6)) ABDO Publishing Co.

Potts, Steve. Valentine's Day. 2001. (Holiday Ser.). (Illus.). 24p. (J). 21.35 (978-1-58340-119-4(9)) Smart Apple Media.

Price, Roger & Stern, Leonard. Dear Valentine Letters Mad Libs. 2006. (Mad Libs Ser.). 48p. (J). (gr. 3). pap. 4.99 (978-0-8431-2088-2(6) , Price Stern Sloan) Penguin Group (USA) Inc.

Rau, Dana. Valentines Day. 2001. (gr. 3-6). lib. bdg. 15.25 (978-0-613-51688-4(5)) Tandem Library Bks.

Ripple, Wilhelminia. Valentine School Parties. Anderson, Heather, illus. 1998. (What Do I Do? Ser.). 192p. (J). pap. 19.95 (978-0-9649939-9-0(6)) Oakbrook Publishing Hse.

Roark, Kimberly. Celebrating Valentine's Day: My Special Valentines. 1999. (ps-2). lib. bdg. 10.65 (978-0-613-34126-4(0)) Tandem Library Bks.

—Celebrating Valentines Day No. 4525: My Special Valentines. Kupperstein, Joel, ed. Iwai, Melissa, illus. 1999. 16p. (J). (ps-2). pap. 2.99 (978-1-57471-570-5(4)) Creative Teaching Pr., Inc.

Roop, Connie. Let's Celebrate Valentine's Day. Arnsteen, Katy Keck, illus. 1999. (Let's Celebrate Ser.). 48p. (gr. k-3). lib. bdg. 22.90 (978-0-7613-0972-7(1) , Millbrook Pr.) Lerner Publishing Group.

Roop, Connie & Roop, Peter. Let's Celebrate Valentine's Day. Arnsteen, Katy Keck, illus. 1999. (Let's Celebrate Ser.). 32p. (J). (gr. 3-6). pap. 7.95 (978-0-7613-0428-9(2) , Millbrook Pr.) Lerner Publishing Group.

Roop, Peter. Let's Celebrate Valentine's Day. 1999. (gr. k-3). lib. bdg. 15.25 (978-0-613-16739-0(2)) Tandem Library Bks.

Rosinsky, Natalie M. Valentine's Day. 2002. (Let's See Library). (Illus.). 24p. (J). (gr. 1 up). lib. bdg. 19.93 (978-0-7565-0393-2(0)) Compass Point Bks.

Ross, Kathy. All New Crafts for Valentines. Leonard, Barbara, illus. 2002. (All New Holiday Crafts for Kids Ser.). 48p. (gr. k-3). lib. bdg. 23.90 (978-0-7613-2553-6(0) , Millbrook Pr.) Lerner Publishing Group.

—All New Crafts for Valentine's Day. Leonard, Barbara, illus. 2002. (All-New Holiday Crafts for Kids Ser.: Bk. 3). 48p. (J). (gr. k-3). pap. 7.95 (978-0-7613-1576-6(4) , Millbrook Pr.) Lerner Publishing Group.

—All-New Crafts for Valentine's Day. 2002. (gr. k-3). lib. bdg. 16.40 (978-0-613-91018-7(4)) Tandem Library Bks.

Sabuda, Robert. Saint Valentine. 1999. (Illus.). 32p. (J). (ps-2). pap. 7.99 (978-0-689-82429-6(7) , Aladdin) Simon & Schuster Children's Publishing.

—Saint Valentine. 1999. (978-0-606-16285-2(2)); lib. bdg. 15.30 (978-0-613-73243-7(X)) Tandem Library Bks.

Schuh, Mari C. Valentine's Day. Saunders-Smith, Gail, ed. 2001. (Holidays & Celebrations Ser.). (Illus.). 24p. (J). (gr. k-1). lib. bdg. 15.93 (978-0-7368-0982-5(1) , Pebble Bks.) Capstone Pr., Inc.

—Valentine's Day, Vol. 2. 2005. (One World, Many Cultures Ser.). 24p. (YA). (gr. k-3). pap. (978-0-7368-9440-1(3) , Pebble Bks.) Capstone Pr., Inc.

Sievert, Terri. Valentine's Day. 2006. (First Facts Ser.). (Illus.). 24p. (J). (978-0-7368-5393-4(6)) Capstone Pr., Inc.

Siewert, Pauline, illus. It's Valentine's Day! A Valentine Book & Activity Kit. 2005. 10p. (J). bds. 9.95 (978-1-58117-377-2(6) , Intervisual/Piggy Toes) Dalmatian Pr.

The Story of Valentine's Day. 1999. (Illus.). 24p. (J). (ps-k). 6.95 (978-0-8249-4184-0(5)) Ideals Pubns.

Tompert, Ann. Saint Valentine. Kasparaviecius, Knestutis, illus. 2004. 32p. (J). (gr. k-2). 15.95 (978-1-59078-181-4(3)) Boyds Mills Pr.

Trueit, Trudi Strain. Valentines Day. 2006. (Rookie Read-About Holidays Ser.). (Illus.). 31p. (J). (978-0-531-12461-1(4)) Children's Pr., Ltd.

—Valentine's Day. rev. ed. 2006. (Rookie Read-About Holidays Ser.). (Illus.). 32p. (J). (gr. 1-2). pap. 5.95 (978-0-531-11819-1(3) , Children's Pr.) Scholastic Library Publishing.

Valentine's Mini Counter 36-Copy Counter Display. 2004. No. 1. 178.20 (978-0-7624-1798-8(6)); No. 2. 178.20 (978-0-7624-1799-5(4)) Running Pr. Bk. Pubs.

Williams, Colleen Madonna Flood. My Adventure on Valentine's Day. 2007. 44p. (J). 8.99 (978-1-59092-558-4(0) , Orchard Academy Pr.) Windstorm Creative.

Zocchi, Judy. On Valentine's Day. Wallis, Rebecca, illus. 2005. (Holiday Happenings Ser.). 32p. (J). pap. 9.95 (978-1-59646-228-1(0)); lib. bdg. 20.65 (978-1-891997-79-2(3)); per. 9.95 (978-1-59646-229-8(9)) Dingles & Co.

—On Valentine's Day/el día de San Valentín. Wallis, Rebecca, illus. 2005. (Holiday Happenings Ser.).Tr. of Día de San Valentín. (ENG & SPA.). 32p. (J). pap. 9.95 (978-1-59646-230-4(2)); lib. bdg. 20.65 (978-1-891997-78-5(5)); per. 9.95 (978-1-59646-231-1(0)) Dingles & Co.

VALENTINE'S DAY—FICTION

Allan-Meyer, Kathleen. Little Bear's Surprise. Garvin, Elaine, illus. 1999. 32p. (J). (ps-1). pap. 6.49 (978-1-57924-066-0(6)) Jones, Bob Univ. Pr.

—Little Bear's Surprise. 1999. (ps-2). lib. bdg. 13.55 (978-0-613-83923-5(4)) Tandem Library Bks.

Arden, J. K. Be My Valenslime. 2001. (gr. k-3). lib. bdg. 15.30 (978-0-613-72595-8(6)) Tandem Library Bks.

Baglio, Ben M. Kitty in the Candy Hearts. 2007. (Illus.). 147p. (J). pap. (***978-0-439-87119-8(0)***) Scholastic, Inc.

Balian, Lorna. A Sweetheart for Valentine. Balian, Lorna, illus. 2005. (Illus.). 40p. (J). 15.95 (978-1-932065-14-5(8)) Star Bright Bks., Inc.

Bauer, Marion Dane. A Recipe for Valentine's Day: A Rebus Lift-the-Flap Story. Herbert, Jennifer, illus. 2004. (Lift-the-Flap Bks.). 16p. (J). 6.99 (978-0-689-85895-6(7) , Little Simon) Simon & Schuster Children's Publishing.

Beechen, Adam. Best Valentine. 2001. (gr. k-3). lib. bdg. 11.25 (978-0-613-43917-6(1)) Tandem Library Bks.

Benton, Jim. Attack of the 50-Ft. Cupid. Benton, Jim, illus. 2003. (Franny K. Stein, Mad Scientist Ser.: Bk. 2). (Illus.). 112p. (J). (gr. 2-5). 14.95 (978-0-689-86292-2(X)) Simon & Schuster Children's Publishing.

Berenstain, Stan & Berenstain, Jan. The Berenstain Bears' Funny Valentine. 2002. (Berenstain Bears First Time Bks.). (Illus.). 32p. (J). (gr. k-3). pap. 3.99 (978-0-375-81126-5(5) , Random Hse. Bks. for Young Readers) Random Hse. Children's Bks.

—The Berenstain Bears' Funny Valentine. 2003. (Berenstain Bears First Time Bks.). (J). (ps-2). lib. bdg. 10.95 (978-0-613-57494-5(X)) Tandem Library Bks.

Beylon, Cathy, illus. Queen of Hearts. 2002. (Sticker Styles Ser.). 20p. (J). mass mkt. 4.99 (978-0-448-42551-1(3) , Grosset & Dunlap) Penguin Group (USA) Inc.

Bickel, Karla. Fishnet Valentine. Bickel, Karla, illus. l.t. ed. 2004. (Illus.). 16p. (J). (ps-5). pap. 5.00 (978-1-891452-13-0(4) , 4) Heart Arbor Bks.

Bleck, Linda. Pepper's Valentine Surprise. 2007. (Pepper plays, pulls, & Pops! Ser.). 18p. (J). (ps-2). 8.99 (978-1-4169-1774-8(8) , Little Simon) Simon & Schuster Children's Publishing.

Bond, Felicia. The Day It Rained Hearts. Bond, Felicia, illus. 36p. (J). 2006. pap. 6.99 (978-0-06-073123-6(0) , Harper Trophy); 2001. (Illus.). 15.99 (978-0-06-623876-0(5) , Geringer, Laura Book); 2001. (Illus.). lib. bdg. 16.89 (978-0-06-001078-2(9) , Geringer, Laura Book) HarperCollins Pubs.

Bond, Katherine Grace. The Legend of the Valentine: An Inspirational Story of Love & Reconciliation. Tate, Don, illus. 2004. 28p. (J). 6.99 (978-0-310-70786-8(2)) Zonderkidz.

Bond, Katherine Grace & Tate, Don, II. The Legend of the Valentine: An Inspirational Story of Love & Reconciliation. 2002. (Illus.). 32p. (J). 15.99 (978-0-310-70039-5(6)) Zonderkidz.

Bourgeois, Paulette. Franklin's Valentine Cards. Clark, Brenda, illus. 1998. (Franklin Sticker & Activity Bks.). 32p. (J). (gr. k-3). (978-1-55074-625-9(1)) Kids Can Pr., Ltd.

—Franklin's Valentines. Clark, Brenda, illus. 1998. (Franklin the Turtle Ser.). (J). (gr. k-3). 32p. (978-1-55074-480-4(1)); 96p. (978-1-55074-482-8(8)) Kids Can Pr., Ltd.

Bourgeois, Paulette & Jennings, Sharon. Franklin's Valentines. Clark, Brenda, illus. 1999. (Franklin Ser.). 32p. (J). (ps-3). pap. 4.50 (978-0-590-13001-1(3) , Cartwheel Bks.) Scholastic, Inc.

Boynton, Sandra. Consider Love: Its Moods & Many Ways. Boynton, Sandra, illus. (Illus.). 32p. (J). 2003. 12.95 (978-0-689-85908-3(2)); 2004. 7.99 (978-0-689-87814-5(1)) Simon & Schuster Children's Publishing. (Little Simon).

Bridwell, Norman. Clifford's First Valentine's Day. Bridwell, Norman, illus. 2002. (Clifford, the Big Red Dog Ser.). (Illus.). (J). 11.45 (978-0-7587-6533-8(9)) Book Wholesalers, Inc.

—Clifford's Valentine. 2001. (ps-2). lib. bdg. 11.80 (978-0-613-50552-9(2)) Tandem Library Bks.

—Clifford's Valentines. 2004. 32p. (J). lib. bdg. 15.00 (978-1-59054-548-5(6)) Fitzgerald Bks.

—Clifford's Valentines. Bridwell, Norman, illus. 2002. (Hello Reader! Ser.). (Illus.). 32p. (J). (ps-3). pap. 3.99 (978-0-439-18300-0(6) , Cartwheel Bks.) Scholastic, Inc.

—Clifford's Valentines. 2001. 10.79 (978-0-606-22241-9(3)) Tandem Library Bks.

Brown, Marc. Arthur's Valentine. Brown, Marc, illus. 2002. (Arthur Adventure Ser.). (Illus.). (J). 13.15 (978-0-7587-1991-1(4)) Book Wholesalers, Inc.

—Arthur's Valentine. Brown, Marc, illus. 2000. (Arthur Adventure Ser.). 32p. (J). (ps-3). 9.95 (978-0-316-11866-8(4)) Little, Brown Bks. for Young Readers.

Bryant, Megan E. Be My Valentine! 2004. (Strawberry Shortcake Ser.). (Illus.). 32p. (J). (ps-2). pap. 3.99 (978-0-448-43641-8(8) , Grosset & Dunlap) Penguin Group (USA) Inc.

—The Great Valentine Mystery. Pierce, Mindy, illus. 2003. 24p. (J). (ps-1). pap. 4.99 (978-0-448-43281-6(1) , Grosset & Dunlap) Penguin Group (USA) Inc.

Capucilli, Alyssa Satin. Biscuit's Valentine's Day. Schories, Pat, illus. 2000. (Biscuit Ser.). 20p. (J). (ps-1). 6.99 (978-0-694-01222-0(X) , Harper Festival) HarperCollins Pubs.

Carlson, Nancy. Louanne Pig in the Mysterious Valentine. rev. ed. 2004. (Carolrhoda Picture Books Ser.). (Illus.). 32p. (J). (gr. k-2). 15.95 (978-1-57505-671-5(2)); pap. (978-1-57505-722-4(0)) Lerner Publishing Group.

Carr, Jan. Sweet Hearts. Donohue, Dorothy, illus. (gr. k-3). 28p. tchr. ed. 16.95 (978-0-8234-1732-2(8)); 32p. reprint ed. 6.95 (978-0-8234-1879-4(0)) Holiday Hse., Inc.

Carter, David A. Love Bugs. Carter, David A., illus. ed. 2003. (Illus.). 12p. (J). (gr. k-3). 6.99 (978-0-689-85815-4(9) , Little Simon) Simon & Schuster Children's Publishing.

Cazet, Denys. Minnie & Moo: Minnie & Moo: Will You Be My Valentine? Cazet, Denys, illus. 2005. (Live Oak Readalong Ser.). (Illus.). (J). pap. 16.95 incl. audio (978-1-59112-891-5(9)) Live Oak Media.

—Minnie & Moo: Will You Be My Valentine? Cazet, Denys, illus. 2002. (I Can Read Bks.). (Illus.). 48p. (J). (gr. k-3). 15.99 (978-0-06-623754-1(8)); lib. bdg. 16.89 (978-0-06-623755-8(6)) HarperCollins Pubs.

Cazet, Denys, reader. Minnie & Moo: Will You Be My Valentine? (Read-Alongs for Beginning Readers Ser.). (Illus.). (J). (ps-3). 2005. pap. 18.95 incl. audio compact disk (978-1-59112-895-3(1)); 2004. 25.95 incl. audio (978-1-59112-892-2(7)); 2004. pap. 31.95 incl. audio compact disk (978-1-59112-897-7(8)); 2004. pap. 29.95 incl. audio (978-1-59112-893-9(5)) Live Oak Media.

Ciminera, Siobhan. The Silliest Valentine EVER! Petrosino, Tamara, illus. 2007. 16p. (J). (ps-2). pap. 4.99 (***978-0-8431-2678-5(7)*** , Price Stern Sloan) Penguin Group (USA) Inc.

Cohen, Miriam. Bee My Valentine. Hoban, Lillian, illus. unabr. ed. 2001. (J). (gr. k-3). pap. 16.95 incl. audio Spoken Arts, Inc.

Collins, Terry. The World's Greatest Valentine. O'Hare, Mark, illus. 2001. (SpongeBob SquarePants Chapter Bks.: Vol. 4). 64p. (J). pap. 3.99 (978-0-689-84043-2(8) , Simon Spotlight) Simon & Schuster Children's Publishing.

Cooper, Mimi. Me Versus Cooties. 2006. 17p. 9.99 (978 1 4116-8256-6(4)) Lulu.com.

D'Andrea, Deborah, concept. Picture Me Bee My Honey. 2003. 10p. (J). (ps up). bds. 2.99 (978-1-57151-520-9(8)) Playhouse Publishing.

Demas, Corinne. Valentine Surprise. Alley, R. W., illus. (J). 2008. lib. bdg. (***978-0-8027-9665-3(6)***); 2007. 32p. 12.95 (***978-0-8027-9664-6(8)***) Walker & Co.

Denega, Danielle. Love & Friendship. 2007. (Littlest Pet Shop Ser.). 56p. (J). pap. 6.99 (978-0-439-89751-8(3)) Scholastic, Inc.

DK Publishing. If You Love Me: Fiberoptic Light. 2007. 16p. (J). pap. 4.99 (***978-0-7566-3448-3(2)***) Dorling Kindersley Publishing, Inc.

Dower, Laura. Powerpuff Girls & the Valentine's Day -up. 2002. (gr. k-3). lib. bdg. 14.15 (978-0-613-43951-0(1)) Tandem Library Bks.

—Powerpuff Girls Save Valentine's Day. 2001. (gr. k-3). lib. bdg. 14.15 (978-0-613-32965-1(1)) Tandem Library Bks.

—The Valentine's Day Mix-Up. Ruiz, Art, illus. 2002. (Powerpuff Girls Ser.). 32p. (J). (ps-3). pap. 5.99 (978-0-439-34431-9(X) , Cartwheel Bks.) Scholastic, Inc.

Duffey, Betsy. Cody's Secret Admirer. 1998. (Illus.). 80p. (J). (gr. 2-6). 13.99 (978-0-670-87400-2(0) , Viking Juvenile) Penguin Group (USA) Inc.

—Cody's Secret Admirer. 2000. (Illus.). (J). (978-0-606-18396-3(5)) Tandem Library Bks.

Edwards, Julie & Hamilton, Emma Walton. Dumpy's Valentine. Walton, Tony & Randig, Ruby, illus. 2006. (My First I Can Read Bks.). 24p. (J). 15.99 (978-0-06-088573-1(4) , Julie Andrews Collection) HarperCollins Pubs.

Edwards, Julie Andrews. Dumpy's Valentine. Walton, Tony & Randig, Ruby, illus. 2006. (My First I Can Read Bks.). 24p. (J). pap. 3.99 (978-0-06-088575-5(0) , Harper Trophy) HarperCollins Pubs.

Engelbreit, Mary. Queen of Hearts. Engelbreit, Mary, illus. 2004. (Ann Estelle Stories Ser.). (Illus.). 32p. (J). (ps-3). 15.99 (978-0-06-008181-2(3)) HarperCollins Pubs.

Erdogan, Buket & Thompson, Lauren. Mouse's First Valentine. 2004. (Classic Board Bks.). (Illus.). 34p. (J). 7.99 (978-0-689-85585-6(0) , Little Simon) Simon & Schuster Children's Publishing.

Frechette, Carole. Carmen. Ouriou, Susan, tr. 2005. (Illus.). 112p. (YA). 12.95 (978-0-88995-322-2(8)) Red Deer Pr. CAN. *Dist:* Fitzhenry & Whiteside, Ltd.

Friedman, Laurie. Heart to Heart with Mallory. Pollak, Barbara, illus. 2007. (Mallory Ser.). 160p. (J). (gr. 2-7). pap. 5.95 (***978-0-8225-7133-9(1)*** , First Avenue Editions) Lerner Publishing Group.

Friedman, Laurie. Love, Ruby Valentine. Cravath, Lynne Avril, illus. 2006. 32p. (J). 15.95 (978-1-57505-899-3(5) , Carolrhoda Bks.) Lerner Publishing Group.

Friedman, Laurie B. Heart to Heart with Mallory. Pollak, Barbara, illus. 2006. 160p. (J). (gr. 2-5). 15.95 (978-1-57505-932-7(0) , Twenty-First Century Bks.) Lerner Publishing Group.

Gaines, Isabel. Pooh's Valentine. Marderosian, Mark & Lopez, Paul, illus. 2004. (Step into Reading Ser.). 32p. (J). (ps-1). pap. 3.99 (978-0-7364-2264-2(1) , RH/Disney) Random Hse. Children's Bks.

Gantos, Jack. Rotten Ralph's Rotten Romance. Rubel, Nicole, illus. 2005. (Rotten Ralph Ser.). 32p. (J). (gr. k-3). pap. 5.95 (978-0-618-49486-6(3)) Houghton Mifflin Co. Trade & Reference Div.

Garcia, Mary. Play with Me: Togetherness Time for Your Preschooler & You: St. Valentine's Day. ed. 2007. (J). (***978-0-9790931-1-1(2)***) SMARTseeds Co., LLC, The.

Gerver, Jane E. Sweetest Valentines. 2003. (gr. k-3). lib. bdg. 11.80 (978-0-613-63569-1(8)) Tandem Library Bks.

Gifford, Christopher & Ricci, Christine. Valentines for Everyone! Savitsky, Steven, illus. 2003. (Dora the Explorer Ser.). 14p. (J). (gr. k-3). bds. 5.99 (978-0-689-85236-7(3) , Simon Spotlight/Nickelodeon) Simon & Schuster Children's Publishing.

Gradisher, Martha, illus. A Valentine for Ms. Vanilla. 2005. (I'm Going to Read Ser.). 32p. (J). (ps). pap. 3.95 (978-1-4027-2711-5(9)); 11.95 (978-1-4027-2712-2(7)) Sterling Publishing Co., Inc.

Gregory, Valiska. A Valentine for Norman Noggs. Winborn, Marsha, illus. 1999. 32p. (J). (gr. k-3). 14.95 (978-0-06-027656-0(8)); 15.89 (978-0-06-027657-7(6)) HarperCollins Pubs.

—Valentine for Norman Noggs. 1999. (978-0-606-18726-8(X)) Tandem Library Bks.

Gregory, Valiska & Winborn, Marsha L. A Valentine for Norman Noggs. 2000. (Trophy Picture Book Ser.). (Illus.). 32p. (J). (gr. k-3). pap. 5.95 (978-0-06-443623-6(3)) HarperCollins Pubs.

Gutman, Dan. Mr. Louie Is Screwy! Paillot, Jim, illus. 2007. (My Weird School Ser.: No. 20). 112p. (J). lib. bdg. 15.89 (***978-0-06-123480-4(X)***); pap. 3.99 (***978-0-06-123479-8(6)*** , Harper Trophy) HarperCollins Pubs.

Hallinan, P. K. Today Is Valentine's Day! Hallinan, P. K., illus. 2001. (Illus.). 24p. (J). 7.95 (978-0-8249-5356-0(8)); pap. 5.95 (978-0-8249-5357-7(6) , Ideals) Ideals Pubns.

Hannah, Montana. Hannah Montana Valentines. rev. ed. 2007. 32p. (gr. 2-7). pap. 5.99 (***978-1-4231-1061-3(7)***) Disney Pr.

Harcourt School Publishers Staff. Be My Valentine. 3rd ed. 2002. (Trophies English Language Learners Ser.). (Illus.). pap. 5.10 (978-0-15-327645-3(2)) Harcourt Schl. Pubs.

Hayes, Geoffrey. A Very Special Valentine: A Little Pop Book. Hayes, Geoffrey, illus. 2007. 16p. (J). (ps-1). 5.99 (***978-0-06-122756-1(0)*** , Harper Festival) HarperCollins Pubs.

Herman, Gail. Valentine's Day Dognapping. del Sur, Duendes, illus. 2002. (Scooby-Doo! Reader Ser.: No. 10). 32p. (J). (gr. k-2). pap. 3.99 (978-0-439-34113-4(2) , Cartwheel Bks.) Scholastic, Inc.

Herndon, Barbara & Gorey, Jill. Be My Valentine! del Carmen, Louis & Peters, James, illus. 2000. 30p. (J). (gr. k-3). per. 5.99 (978-0-671-77321-2(6) , Simon & Schuster Children's Publishing) Simon & Schuster Children's Publishing.

Higginson, Sheila Sweeny. Minnie's Valentine. rev. ed. 2007. 24p. (J). (ps-1). pap. 4.99 (***978-1-4231-0746-0(2)***) Disney Pr.

Hillert, Margaret. I Love You, Dear Dragon. Kock, Carl, illus. rev. ed. 2006. (Beginning to Read Ser.). 32p. (J). lib. bdg. 18.60 (978-1-59953-020-8(1)) Norwood Hse. Pr.

Hoban, Lillian. Silly Tilly's Valentine. Hoban, Lillian, illus. 1999. (I Can Read Bks.). (Illus.). 48p. (J). (gr. k-3). pap. 3.99 (978-0-06-444223-7(3) , Harper Trophy) HarperCollins Pubs.

—Silly Tilly's Valentine. 1999. (I Can Read Bks.). (978-0-606-15704-9(2)) Tandem Library Bks.

—Silly Tilly's Valentine. Hoban, Lillian, illus. 1999. (Illus.). 48p. (J). (ps-ps). lib. bdg. 11.80 (978-0-613-12109-5(0)) Tandem Library Bks.

Hoien, Ruth S. Ruthie's Four Hearts. (J). pap. 3.99 (978-0-88019-105-0(8)) Schmul Publishing Co., Inc.

Holabird, Katharine. Angelina Loves... Craig, Helen, illus. 2006. (Angelina Ballerina Ser.). 24p. (J). (ps-2). 5.99 (978-0-448-44270-9(1) , Grosset & Dunlap) Penguin Group (USA) Inc.

Holub, Joan. Big Heart! A Valentine's Day Tale. Terry, Will, illus. 2007. (Ant Hill Ser.). 24p. (J). lib. bdg. 13.89 (***978-1-4169-2562-0(7)***); pap. 3.99 (***978-1-4169-0957-6(5)***) Simon & Schuster Children's Publishing. (Aladdin).

Hudson, Eleanor. The Best Thing about Valentines. Melcher, Mary, tr. Melcher, Mary, illus. 2004. 32p. (J). pap. 3.50 (978-0-439-52109-3(2) , Cartwheel Bks.) Scholastic, Inc.

Huelin, Jodi. Countdown to Valentine's Day. Haskamp, Steve, illus. 2002. 24p. (J). pap. 3.99 (978-0-8431-4882-4(9) , Price Stern Sloan) Penguin Group (USA) Inc.

Inches, Alison. Dora quiere mucho a Boots. Saunders, Zina, illus. 2005. (Dora the Explorer Ser.).Tr. of Dora Loves Boots. (SPA.). 24p. (J). pap. 3.99 (978-1-4169-0620-9(7) , Libros Para Ninos) Simon & Schuster Children's Publishing.

Jackson, Alison. Ballad of Valentine. Tusa, Tricia, illus. 2002. 32p. (J). (gr. k-3). 16.99 (978-0-525-46720-5(3) , Dutton Juvenile) Penguin Group (USA) Inc.

—The Ballad of Valentine. Tusa, Tricia, illus. 2006. 32p. (J). (gr. 3). reprint ed. pap. 6.99 (978-0-14-240400-3(4) , Puffin) Penguin Group (USA) Inc.

Johnston, Antony. Three Days in Europe, Vol. 1. 2003. (Illus.). 144p. pap. 14.95 (978-1-929998-72-2(4)) Oni Pr., Inc.

Kent, Renee Holmes. Adventures in Misty Falls, Vol. 8. 2004. (Adventures in Misty Falls Ser.: Vol. 8). (Illus.). 100p. (gr. 4-7). pap. 4.99 (978-1-56309-456-9(8) , N017104) Woman's Missionary Union.

Killian, Beth. Everything She Wants. 2006. (310 Ser.). 240p. pap. 9.95 (978-1-4165-2168-6(2) , MTV) Simon & Schuster.

Kleinberg, Naomi. My Fuzzy Valentine. Womble, Louis, illus. 2005. (Board Books). 12p. (J). (gr. k-ps). bds. 4.99 (978-0-375-83392-2(7) , Random Hse. Bks. for Young Readers) Random Hse. Children's Bks.

Kline, Suzy. Horrible Harry & the Kickball Wedding. Remkiewicz, Frank, illus. 1999. (Horrible Harry Ser.: No. 6). 64p. (J). (gr. 2-4). pap. 3.99 (978-0-14-130316-1(6) , Puffin) Penguin Group (USA) Inc.

Kline, Suzy & Kline, Suzy. Horrible Harry & the Kickball Wedding. Remkiewicz, Frank, illus. 1999. 52p. (J). (ps-k). lib. bdg. 11.80 (978-0-7857-9249-9(X)) Tandem Library Bks.

Knudsen, Michelle. Hearts & Kisses. Trasler, Janee, illus. 2005. 12p. (J). 4.99 (978-0-689-87099-6(X) , Little Simon) Simon & Schuster Children's Publishing.

—Love. Haley, Amanda, illus. 2001. (Sparkle 'n' Shimmer Ser.). 14p. (J). (ps-k). bds. 5.99 (978-0-689-83783-8(6) , Little Simon) Simon & Schuster Children's Publishing.

Kroll, Steven. The Biggest Valentine Ever. Bassett, Jeni, illus. 2006. 32p. (J). pap. 3.99 (978-0-439-76419-3(X)) Scholastic, Inc.

Lee, Quilan B. Ositos Cariosos: Special Delivery. 2004. (Care Bears Ser.). 24p. (J). pap. 3.50 (978-0-439-61713-0(8) , Scholastic en Espanol) Scholastic, Inc.

Levithan, David. Marly's Ghost. Selznick, Brian, illus. 176p. 2007. (YA). (gr. 7). 6.99 (***978-0-14-240912-1(X)** , Puffin); 2005. (J). 14.99 (978-0-8037-3063-2(2) , Dial) Penguin Group (USA) Inc.

Lewman, David. Lovestruck! Fruchter, Jason, illus. ed. 2005. (Fairly Odd Parents Ser.: 2). 24p. (J). lib. bdg. 15.00 (978-1-59054-803-5(5)) Fitzgerald Bks.

—SpongeBob's Secret Valentine. Martinez, Heather, illus. 2003. (SpongeBob SquarePants Ser.). 24p. (J). pap. 3.99 (978-0-689-86326-4(8) , Simon Spotlight/Nickelodeon) Simon & Schuster Children's Publishing.

—Spongebob's Secret Valentine. Martinez, Heather, illus. ed. 2005. (SpongeBob Squarepants Ser.: No. 3). 22p. (J). lib. bdg. 15.00 (978-1-59054-828-8(0)) Fitzgerald Bks.

Lexau, Joan M. Don't Be My Valentine: A Classroom Mystery. Hoff, Syd, illus. 2002. (J). 12.30 (978-0-7587-6074-6(4)) Book Wholesalers, Inc.

—Don't Be My Valentine: A Classroom Mystery. Hoff, Syd, illus. rev. ed. 1999. (I Can Read Bks.). 64p. (J). (gr. k-3). 14.89 (978-0-06-028240-0(1)) HarperCollins Pubs.

—Don't Be My Valentine: A Classroom Mystery. 1999. (J). 10.75 (978-0-606-15848-0(0)) Tandem Library Bks.

Love Is. 2004. lib. bdg. 15.30 (978-0-613-86963-8(X)) Tandem Library Bks.

Lunsford, Susie. The Magical Wishing Well Forest Series. 2006. pap. 25.32 (***978-1-4134-9491-4(9)**) Xlibris Corp.

Mack, Lizzie. Give a Little Love. Gorton, Julia, illus. 2003. 16p. (J). 9.99 (978-0-689-85950-2(3) , Little Simon) Simon & Schuster Children's Publishing.

MacKall, Dandi Daley. My Secret Valentine. O'Neill, Rachael, illus. 2006. (Carry Me Along Ser.). 24p. (J). 6.99 (978-0-310-70941-1(5)) Zonderkidz.

Maguire, Gregory. Four Stupid Cupids. Clayton, Elaine, illus. 2001. 192p. (J). (gr. 4-6). tchr. ed. 16.00 (978-0-395-83895-2(9) , Clarion Bks.) Houghton Mifflin Co. Trade & Reference Div.

—Four Stupid Cupids. 2002. (gr. 3-6). lib. bdg. 12.95 (978-0-613-43035-7(2)) Tandem Library Bks.

—Four Stupid Cupids. l.t. ed. 2001. 225p. (J). 21.95 (978-0-7862-3547-6(0)) Thorndike Pr.

Maitland, Barbara. The Bookstore Valentine. LaRochelle, David, illus. 2002. (Easy-to-Read Ser.). 48p. (J). pap. 3.99 (978-0-14-230187-6(6) , Puffin) Penguin Group (USA) Inc.

—Bookstore Valentine. 2002. (gr. k-3). lib. bdg. 11.80 (978-0-613-64398-6(4)) Tandem Library Bks.

Marney, Dean. How to Drive Your Family Crazy on Valentine's Day. 2001. (gr. 3-6). lib. bdg. 12.40 (978-0-613-84121-4(2)) Tandem Library Bks.

Martin, Ann M. Abby's Un-Valentine. 1999. (Baby-Sitters Club Ser.: No. 127). 160p. (J). (gr. 3-7). pap. 4.50 (978-0-590-50350-1(2)) Scholastic, Inc.

Masurel, Claire. Emily's Valentine Party. Calitri, Susan, illus. 1999. (Picture Puffin Ser.). 16p. (J). (ps-k). pap. 6.99 (978-0-14-056452-5(7) , Puffin) Penguin Group (USA) Inc.

Mayer, Mercer. Happy Valentine's Day. Mayer, Mercer, illus. 2005. (Little Critter Ser.). (Illus.). 20p. (J). pap. 6.99 (978-0-06-053973-3(9) , Harper Festival) HarperCollins Pubs.

McCourt, Lisa. My Forever Valentine. Bryant, Laura J., illus. 2008. (J). (***978-0-439-75058-5(X)**) Scholastic, Inc.

McMullan, Kate. Fluffy's Valentine's Day. Smith, Mavis, illus. 2004. 40p. (J). lib. bdg. 15.00 (978-1-59054-470-9(6)) Fitzgerald Bks.

—Fluffy's Valentine's Day, Level 3. Smith, Mavis, illus. 2000. (Hello Reader! Ser.). 40p. (J). (gr. 1-3). pap. 3.99 (978-0-590-37216-9(5)) Scholastic, Inc.

McNamara, Margaret. Too Many Valentines. Gordon, Mike, illus. 2003. (Ready-to-Reads Ser.). 32p. (J). pap. 3.99 (978-0-689-85537-5(0) , Aladdin) Simon & Schuster Children's Publishing.

—Too Many Valentines. 2003. (gr. k-3). lib. bdg. 11.80 (978-0-613-61592-1(1)) Tandem Library Bks.

Modesitt, Jeanne. 1, 2, 3 Valentine's Day: A Counting Book. Spowart, Robin, illus. 2003. 32p. (J). (ps up). 15.95 (978-1-56397-868-5(7)) Boyds Mills Pr.

Morris, Elaine L. A Valentine Book for Honey Bee. Hell, Paula, illus. 2000. 12p. (J). (ps-5). pap. 3.98 (978-1-930977-00-6(X)) Cosmo Starr Bks.

My Crush Tacular Book of Valentines: Decorate Your Own Cards - Lizzie Style! 2003. (Lizzie McGuire Ser.). (Illus.). 32p. (ps-17). pap. 5.99 (978-0-7868-4613-9(5) , Disney Editions) Disney Pr.

My Little Love. 2003. (Illus.). 256p. (J). (ps-1). pap. 14.99 (978-0-06-051764-9(6)) HarperCollins Pubs.

Naylor, Phyllis Reynolds. A Spy among the Girls. 2002. (gr. 3-6). lib. bdg. 13.00 (978-0-613-88330-6(6)) Tandem Library Bks.

—A Spy among the Girls. l.t. ed. 2003. (Boys=Girls Battle Ser.). 145p. (J). 23.95 (978-0-7862-5821-5(7)) Thorndike Pr.

Novak, Matt. My Froggy Valentine. 2008. (Illus.). 16p. (J). (ps-1). 7.95 (***978-1-59643-204-8(7)**) Roaring Brook Pr.

Olsen, Mary-Kate & Olsen, Ashley. So Little Time No.13: Love Is in the Air. 2004. (gr. k-3). lib. bdg. 13.00 (978-0-613-71468-6(7)) Tandem Library Bks.

—Two of a Kind No. 33: Heart to Heart. 2004. (gr. 3-6). lib. bdg. 13.00 (978-0-613-71364-1(8)) Tandem Library Bks.

—Valentine's Day '04 Two of a Kind. 2004. mass mkt. 19.96 (978-0-06-059732-0(1) , Harper Entertainment) HarperCollins Pubs.

Park, Barbara. Junie B. Jones & the Mushy Gushy Valentime. unabr. ed. 2004. (Junie B. Jones Ser.: No. 14). 69p. (J). (gr. k-3). pap. 17.00 incl. audio (978-0-8072-0335-4(1) , Listening Library) Random Hse. Audio Publishing Group.

—Junie B. Jones & the Mushy Gushy Valentime. Brunkus, Denise, illus. 1999. (Junie B. Jones Ser.: No. 14). 80p. , (J). (gr. k-3). pap. 3.99 (978-0-375-80039-9(5)); lib. bdg. 11.99 (978-0-375-90039-6(X)) Random Hse. Children's Bks. (Random Hse. Bks. for Young Readers).

—Junie B. Jones & the Mushy Gushy Valentime. Brunkus, Denise, illus. 1999. (Junie B. Jones Ser.: No. 14). 69p. (J). (gr. k-3). lib. bdg. 11.80 (978-0-613-21832-0(9)) Tandem Library Bks.

—Junie B. Jones & the Mushy Gushy Valentime. 1999. (Junie B. Jones Ser.: No. 14). (J). (gr. k-3). 10.79 (978-0-606-19516-4(5)) Tandem Library Bks.

Perry, Naresha. Zora's Valentine. 2005. per. 17.00 (978-0-8059-9751-4(2)) Dorrance Publishing Co., Inc.

Pinkwater, Daniel M. Big Bob & the Magic Valentine's Day Potato. Pinkwater, Jill, illus. 2000. (Hello Reader! Ser.: Level 3). 32p. (J). (gr. 1-3). 3.99 (978-0-590-63275-1(2) , Cartwheel Bks.) Scholastic, Inc.

—Big Bob & the Magic Valentine's Day Potato. 2000. (Hello Reader! Ser.). (Illus.). (J). (978-0-606-18518-9(6)) Tandem Library Bks.

Poploff, Michelle. Roses Are Dread, Violets Are Boo! A Vampire Valentine Story. Basso, Bill, illus. 2002. 48p. (J). (gr. 2-4). pap. 3.99 (978-0-439-26076-3(0) , Scholastic Paperbacks) Scholastic, Inc.

Poydar, Nancy. Rhyme Time Valentine. Poydar, Nancy, illus. (Illus.). 32p. (J). (gr. k-3). tchr. ed. 16.95 (978-0-8234-1684-4(4)) Holiday Hse., Inc.

Preller, James. Case of the Kidnapped Candy. 2007. (Jigsaw Jones Ser.: No. 30). (Illus.). 80p. (J). pap. 3.99 (978-0-439-89618-4(5) , Scholastic Paperbacks) Scholastic, Inc.

—Case of the Secret Valentine. 1999. (gr. 3-6). lib. bdg. 11.80 (978-0-613-16906-6(9)) Tandem Library Bks.

Prince, April Jones. Valentine Friends. Schlossberg, Elisabeth, illus. 2007. 24p. (J). pap. 3.99 (978-0-439-79999-7(6)) Scholastic, Inc.

Reber, Deborah. Blue's Valentines Day. Pontillo, Jenine, illus. 2000. (Blue's Clues Ser.). 16p. (J). (ps-k). pap. 3.99 (978-0-689-83062-4(9) , Simon Spotlight/Nickelodeon) Simon & Schuster Children's Publishing.

Ricci, Christine. Music Player Storybook. 2006. (Nick Jr. Dora the Explorer Ser.). (Illus.). 40p. (J). DVD 24.99 (978-0-7944-1004-9(9)) Reader's Digest Assn., Inc., The.

Ricci, Christine & A&J Studios Staff. Dora's Valentine Adventure. 2006. (Dora the Explorer Ser.). 14p. (J). bds. 6.99 (978-1-4169-1754-0(3) , Simon Spotlight/ Nickelodeon) Simon & Schuster Children's Publishing.

Ritchie, Joseph R. Peek-a-Boo Valentine! Halverson, Lydia, illus. 2006. 14p. (J). (ps). bds. 7.95 (978-0-8249-6674-4(0) , Candy Cane Pr.) Ideals Pubns.

Roberts, Bethany. Valentine Mice! Cushman, Doug, illus. 2001. 32p. (J). (gr. k-3). pap. 5.95 (978-0-618-05152-6(X) , Clarion Bks.) Houghton Mifflin Co. Trade & Reference Div.

—Valentine Mice! 2001. (ps-2). lib. bdg. 14.10 (978-0-613-31854-9(4)); (Illus.). (J). (978-0-606-20967-0(0)) Tandem Library Bks.

Rockwell, Anne F. Valentine's Day. Rockwell, Lizzy, illus. 2000. 40p. (J). (ps-1). 14.95 (978-0-06-027794-9(7)) HarperCollins Pubs.

Rockwell, Anne F. & Rockwell, Lizzy. Valentine's Day. 2002. (Illus.). 40p. (J). (ps-1). pap. 5.99 (978-0-06-051183-8(4)) HarperCollins Pubs.

Ruckdeschel, Liz & James, Sara. What If... You Broke All the Rules. 2007. (What If... Ser.). 304p. (YA). (gr. 7). 11.99 (***978-0-385-90495-7(9)**); (Illus.). pap. 8.99 (***978-0-385-73501-8(4)**) Random Hse. Children's Bks. (Delacorte Bks. for Young Readers).

Ruelle, Karen Gray. Snow Valentines: A Holiday House Reader. Ruelle, Karen Gray, illus. (Illus.). 48p. (J). (gr. k-3). tchr. ed. 15.95 (978-0-8234-1533-5(3)) Holiday Hse., Inc.

Rylant, Cynthia. Henry & Mudge. Stevenson, Sucie, illus. 2002. (Henry & Mudge Ser.). (J). 11.91 (978-0-7587-1269-1(3)) Book Wholesalers, Inc.

—Henry & Mudge & Mrs. Hopper's House. Bracken, Carolyn, illus. 2003. (Henry & Mudge Ser.). 40p. (J). pap. 3.99 (978-0-689-83446-2(2) , Aladdin); 14.95 (978-0-689-81153-1(5)) Simon & Schuster Children's Publishing.

—Henry & Mudge & Mrs. Hopper's House. 2006. (Henry & Mudge Ser.). (J). (gr. 1-6). 24.21 (978-1-59961-084-9(1)) Spotlight.

—Henry & Mudge & Mrs. Hopper's House. Bracken, Carolyn, illus. 2004. (Henry & Mudge Ser.). 40p. (J). (gr. k-2). lib. bdg. 11.80 (978-0-613-90376-9(5)) Tandem Library Bks.

—If You'll Be My Valentine. Kosaka, Fumi, illus. 32p. (J). 2005. pap. 6.99 (978-0-06-009271-9(8)); 2004. 14.99 (978-0-06-009270-2(X)); 2004. lib. bdg. 16.89 (978-0-06-009269-6(6)) HarperCollins Pubs.

Samuels, Barbara. Happy Valentine's Day, Dolores. 2005. (Dolores Ser.). (Illus.). 32p. (J). 16.00 (978-0-374-32844-3(7) , Nelanie Kroupa Bks.) Farrar, Straus & Giroux.

Saunders, Zina. Dora Loves Boots. Saunders, Zina, illus. ed. 2005. (Dora the Explorer Ser.: No. 6). (Illus.). 22p. (J). lib. bdg. 15.00 (978-1-59054-792-2(6)) Fitzgerald Bks.

Schultz, Charles M. Be My Valentine, Charlie Brown. 2007. (Illus.). 128p. 4.95 (***978-0-7624-2754-3(X)** , Running Pr. Minature Editions) Running Pr. Bk. Pubs.

Schultz, Gwen. Blue Valentine. 1999. (Illus.). 64p. (J). 10.00 (978-0-915988-03-7(8)) Reading Gems.

Schulz. Buon San Valentino Dolce. pap. 19.95 (978-88-451-2996-4(9)) Fabbri - RCS Libri ITA. *Dist:* Distribooks, Inc.

Scull, Robert. Happy Valentine's Day! 2002. (gr. k-3). lib. bdg. 14.15 (978-0-613-50443-0(7)) Tandem Library Bks.

Setzer, Lee Ann. Sariah Mcduff: Book Three of the Sariah Mcduff Series: Valentine's Day Scrooge. Bonham, Bob, illus. 2005. (J). per. 5.95 (978-1-55517-841-3(3) , Bonneville Bks.) Cedar Fort, Inc./CFI Distribution.

Shulman, Mark & Less, Emma. Valentine Fun. Harpster, Steve, illus. 2005. (Little Scribbles Ser.). 12p. bds. 5.95 (978-1-4027-2255-4(9)) Sterling Publishing Co., Inc.

Simont, Marc, illus. Nate the Great & the Mushy Valentine. 2002. (Nate the Great Ser.). (J). 12.87 (978-0-7587-0707-9(X)) Book Wholesalers, Inc.

Snyder, Jackie. Secret Pal Surprises. 1999. (978-0-606-17743-6(4)) Tandem Library Bks.

Spinelli, Eileen. Somebody Loves You, Mr. Hatch. Yalowitz, Paul, illus. 2006. (Stories to Go! Ser.). 32p. (J). pap. 4.99 (978-1-4169-1235-4(5) , Aladdin) Simon & Schuster Children's Publishing.

Spohn, Kate. Turtle & Snake's Valentine's Day. 2003. (Viking Easy-To-Read Ser.). (Illus.). 32p. (J). (ps-3). 13.99 (978-0-670-03613-4(7) , Viking Juvenile) Penguin Group (USA) Inc.

Star, Nancy. Case of the Kidnapped Cupid. Bernardin, James, illus. 2005. (Calendar Club Mysteries Ser.). 79p. (J). (***978-0-439-67263-4(5)**) Scholastic, Inc.

Stephens, Monique. The Little Engine That Could's Valentine's Day Surprise. Ong, Cristina, illus. 2003. (Reading Railroad Bks.). 32p. (J). (ps-4). pap. 3.99 (978-0-448-43280-9(3) , Grosset & Dunlap) Penguin Group (USA) Inc.

Stilton, Geronimo. Valentine's Day Disaster. Keys, Larry et al, illus. 2006. (Geronimo Stilton Ser.: No. 23). 122p. (J). lib. bdg. 18.46 (***978-1-4242-0292-8(2)**) Fitzgerald Bks.

—Valentine's Day Disaster. 2006. (Geronimo Stilton Ser.: No. 23). (Illus.). (J). 91p. (978-1-4156-4780-6(1)); 128p. pap. 5.99 (978-0-439-69147-5(8) , Scholastic Paperbacks) Scholastic, Inc.

Sutherland, Margaret. Valentines Are for Saying I Love You. Wummer, Amy, illus. 2007. 24p. (J). (ps-k). pap. 4.99 (***978-0-448-44702-5(9)** , Grosset & Dunlap) Penguin Group (USA) Inc.

Tagg, Christine. A Very Special Valentine. Kneen, Maggie, illus. 2003. (J). 15.95 (978-0-8118-4073-6(5)) Chronicle Bks. LLC.

Talkington, Bruce. Winnie the Pooh's Valentine Mini. 1998. (Illus.). 32p. (J). 11.95 (978-0-7868-3201-9(0)) Disney Pr.

Thaler, Mike. Valentine's Day from the Black Lagoon. Lee, Jared D., illus. 2006. 64p. (J). lib. bdg. 15.00 (***978-1-4242-2263-6(X)**) Fitzgerald Bks.

Thompson, Kay. Love & Kisses, Eloise. Enik, Ted, illus. 2004. (Eloise Ser.). 24p. (J). pap. 3.99 (978-0-689-87156-6(2) , Little Simon) Simon & Schuster Children's Publishing.

Twyman, Gib. Stoneheart: The Real Valentine's Day Story. Cundiff, Meg, illus. 2002. 32p. (gr. 1-4). 14.95 (978-1-886110-13-7(1)) Addax Publishing Group, Inc.

Tym, Kate, et al. Choc n' Snogs Valentine Special. 1998. (Just Seventeen Ser.). (Illus.). 160p. pap. 6.99 (978-0-09-926374-6(2)) Random Hse. GBR. *Dist:* Independent Pubs. Group.

Vera Viper's Valentine. 2001. (ps-2). lib. bdg. 9.80 (978-0-613-33181-4(8)) Tandem Library Bks.

Wallace, Nancy Elizabeth, illus. The Valentine Express. 2004. 32p. (J). 16.95 (978-0-7614-5183-9(8)) Cavendish, Marshall Corp.

Waricha, Jean. Who Will Be My Valentine? 2004. (Full House Ser.: No. 3). (Illus.). 96p. mass mkt. 4.99 (978-0-06-054085-2(0) , Harper Entertainment) HarperCollins Pubs.

Warne, Frederick & Potter, Beatrix. Be My Valentine, Peter Rabbit: Surprise Sound Inside! 2002. (Illus.). 10p. (J). bds. 5.99 (978-0-7232-4864-4(8) , Warne) Penguin Group (USA) Inc.

Wasserman, Robin. Vanishing Valentines. del Sur, Duendes, illus. 2002. (Scooby-Doo! Picture Clue Book Ser.: No. 10). 32p. (J). (gr. k-2). pap. 3.99 (978-0-439-31846-4(7) , Cartwheel Bks.) Scholastic, Inc.

—Vanishing Valentines. 2002. (gr. k-3). lib. bdg. 11.80 (978-0-613-54718-5(7)) Tandem Library Bks.

Wax, Wendy. A Royal Valentine. Hall, Susan', illus. 2006. 24p. (J). lib. bdg. 9.00 (***978-1-4242-0951-4(X)**) Fitzgerald Bks.

Wax, Wendy. Valentine for Tommy. 2003. (gr. k-3). lib. bdg. 11.80 (978-0-613-57563-8(6)) Tandem Library Bks.

Weeks, Sarah. Be Mine, Be Mine, Sweet Valentine. Kosaka, Fumi, illus. 2005. 20p. (J). (ps-k). 9.99 (978-0-694-01514-6(8) , Geringer, Laura Book) HarperCollins Pubs.

Wells, Rosemary. Be My Valentine. Wheeler, Jody & Nez, John, illus. 2001. (Yoko & Friends School Days Ser.: No. 5). 32p. (gr. k-2). 9.99 (978-0-7868-0724-6(5)) Hyperion Bks. for Children.

—Be My Valentine. 2001. (J). (978-0-606-22549-6(8)) Tandem Library Bks.

—The Germ Busters. Wheeler, Jody, illus. 2002. (Yoko & Friends School Days Ser.: Bk. 6). 32p. (gr. k-2). pap. 3.99 (978-0-7868-1534-0(5) , Volo) Hyperion Bks. for Children.

—Max's Valentine. 2003. (Illus.). 32p. (J). (ps-ps). 5.99 (978-0-670-03668-4(4) , Viking Juvenile) Penguin Group (USA) Inc.

Wesley, Valerie Wilson. 23 Ways to Mess up Valentine's Day. Roos, Maryn, illus. 5th rev. ed. 2005. (Willimena Rules! Ser.: No. 5). 96p. (gr. 2-5). pap. 3.99 (978-0-7868-5524-7(X) , Jump at the Sun) Hyperion Bks. for Children.

Wesley, Valerie Wilson. 23 Ways to Miss up Valentine's Day. Roos, Maryn, illus. 2005. 89p. (J). lib. bdg. 15.00 (***978-1-4242-0646-9(4)**) Fitzgerald Bks.

Westcott, Nadine Bernard. Valentine's Day at the Zoo. Westcott, Nadine Bernard, illus. 2002. (Illus.). 16p. (J). pap. 5.99 (978-0-689-84567-3(7) , Little Simon) Simon & Schuster Children's Publishing.

Wigand, Molly. Be My Valentine! 2000. (gr. k-3). lib. bdg. 14.15 (978-0-613-21177-2(4)) Tandem Library Bks.

Willard, Eliza. Totally Crushed. 2008. (Candy Apple Ser.). 160p. (J). pap. 4.99 (***978-0-545-02814-1(0)** , Scholastic Paperbacks) Scholastic, Inc.

Williams, Jacklyn. Happy Valentine's Day, Gus! Cushman, Doug, illus. 2005. (Read-It! Readers Ser.). 32p. (J). (gr. k-3). 18.60 (978-1-4048-0962-8(7)) Picture Window Bks.

Willson, Sarah & Artful Doodlers Limited Staff. Valentine Villains. 2005. (Totally Spies! Ser.). (Illus.). 64p. (J). pap. 4.99 (978-1-4169-0283-6(X) , Simon Spotlight) Simon & Schuster Children's Publishing.

Wing, Natasha. The Night Before Valentine's Day. Petach, Heidi, illus. 2001. (Reading Rainbow Bks.). 32p. (J). (ps-3). mass mkt. 3.99 (978-0-448-42188-9(7) , Grosset & Dunlap) Penguin Group (USA) Inc.

—The Night Before Valentine's Day. 2000. (gr. k-3). lib. bdg. 11.25 (978-0-613-31527-2(8)) Tandem Library Bks.

Yoon, Salina. Be My Valentine. 2004. (Illus.). 10p. (J). (ps-1). bds. 5.99 (978-0-8431-1153-8(4) , Price Stern Sloan) Penguin Group (USA) Inc.

—Be My Valentine. Yoon, Salina, illus. 2005. (Illus.). 10p. (J). 5.99 (978-1-4169-0536-3(7) , Little Simon) Simon & Schuster Children's Publishing.

—A Purr-fect Valentine. 2006. (Illus.). 10p. (J). (ps-k). bds. 5.99 (978-0-8431-2006-6(1) , Price Stern Sloan) Penguin Group (USA) Inc.

Ziefert, Harriet. It's Valentine's Day! A Rosie Rabbit Book. Rader, Laura, illus. 2005. 12p. (J). (ps-ps). bds., bds. 7.95 (978-1-4027-2395-7(4)) Sterling Publishing Co., Inc.

—What Is Valentine's Day? Schumacher, Claire, illus. 2004. 16p. (ps-ps). pap. 5.95 (978-1-4027-2016-1(5)) Sterling Publishing Co., Inc.

—Where's Nicky's Valentine? Brown, Richard, illus. 2002. 7p. (ps). bds. 6.95 (978-1-929766-72-7(6)) Blue Apple Bks.

Ziefert, Harriet & Demarest, Chris L. I Need a Valentine! 1999. (Holiday Lift-the-Flap Ser.). (Illus.). 16p. (J). (ps-1). pap. 5.99 (978-0-689-81993-3(5) , Little Simon) Simon & Schuster Children's Publishing.

VALLEY FORGE (PA.)

Allen, Thomas B. Remember Valley Forge: Patriots, Tories, & Spies Tell Their Stories. 2007. (Illus.). 64p. (YA). (gr. 5 up). 17.95 (***978-1-4263-0149-0(9)**); lib. bdg. 27.90 (***978-1-4263-0150-6(2)**) National Geographic Society. (National Geographic Children's Bks.).

Burgan, Michael. Valley Forge. 2004. (We the People Ser.). (Illus.). 48p. (J). (gr. 4 up). lib. bdg. 22.60 (978-0-7565-0615-5(8)) Compass Point Bks.

Dolan, Edward F., Jr. The Winter at Valley Forge. 2001. (Kaleidoscope Ser.). (Illus.). 48p. (J). (gr. 3 up). lib. bdg. 25.64 (978-0-7614-1304-2(9) , Benchmark Bks.) Cavendish, Marshall Corp.

Stein, R. Conrad. Valley Forge. 1999. (Cornerstones of Freedom Ser.). (Illus.). 32p. (J). (gr. 4-6). pap. 5.95 (978-0-516-26510-0(5) , Children's Pr.) Scholastic Library Publishing.

VALUES

see also Ethics

Aguilera, Dana, et al. Character in Motion! Real Life Stories Series 5th Grade Student Workbook. 2006. 68p. (J). per. 5.95 (978-0-9765722-8-2(1)) Positively for Kids, Inc.

Arnett, Robert. Finders Keepers? A True Story. Turakhia, Smita, illus. 2003. 32p. (J). 16.95 (978-0-9652900-2-9(6)) Atman Pr.

Barron, T. A. The Hero's Trail: A Guide for a Heroic Life. 2007. 144p. (J). (gr. 3 up). pap. 6.99 (978-0-14-240760-8(7), Puffin) Penguin Group (USA) Inc.

Berry, Joy Wilt. Eating: A Good Manners Book About. Bartholomew & Pace, Don, illus. rev. ed. 2000. (Living Skills Ser.: Vol. 2). 48p. (J). (gr. 1-7). pap. 4.95 (978-1-58634-117-6(0)) Goldstar Publishing, Inc.

—Let's Talk about Accepting "No" An Early Social Skills Book. Fitzpatrick, Roey, illus. rev. ed. 2000. (Let's Talk about Ser.: Vol. 5). 36p. (J). (ps-3). pap. 3.95 (978-1-58634-058-2(1)) Goldstar Publishing, Inc.

—Let's Talk about Being Fair: An Early Social Skills Book. Fitzpatrick, Roey, illus. 2000. (Let's Talk about Ser.: Vol. 6). 36p. (J). (ps-2). 3.95 (978-1-58634-059-9(X)) Goldstar Publishing, Inc.

—Let's Talk about Being Good: An Early Social Skills Book. Fitzpatrick, Roey, illus. rev. ed. 1999. (Let's Talk about Ser.: Vol. 4). 36p. (J). (ps-2). pap. 3.95 (978-1-58634-057-5(3), 01-0204-04) Goldstar Publishing, Inc.

—Let's Talk about Being Patient: An Early Social Skills Book. Fitzpatrick, Roey, illus. rev. ed. 1999. (Let's Talk about Ser.: Vol. 2). 36p. (J). (ps-2). pap. 3.95 (978-1-58634-055-1(7), 01-0204-02) Goldstar Publishing, Inc.

—Let's Talk about Playing with Others: An Early Social Skills Book. Fitzpatrick, Roey, illus. rev. ed. 1999. (Let's Talk about Ser.: Vol. 7). 36p. (J). (ps-2). pap. 3.95 (978-1-58634-060-5(3), 01-0204-07) Goldstar Publishing, Inc.

Brimner, Larry Dane. Promise. 2002. (gr. k-3). lib. bdg. 14.10 (978-0-613-50231-3(0)) Tandem Library Bks.

Burch, Regina G. I Can Show I Care. Jarrett, Michael, photos by. 2004. (J). lib. bdg. 19.33 (978-0-8368-4247-0(2)) Stevens, Gareth Inc.

—I Can Show Respect. Ember, Kathi, illus. 2004. (J). lib. bdg. 19.33 (978-0-8368-4248-7(0)) Stevens, Gareth Inc.

Caring. (Character Education Ser.). 24p. (J). 6.95 (978-0-7368-9150-9(1)) Capstone Pr., Inc.

Character Concepts. 2007. (J). 159.44 (***978-1-59928-734-8(X)**, SandCastle) ABDO Publishing Co.

Colwell Miller, Connie. Tolerance. (Everyday Character Education Ser.). 24p. (J). pap. 6.95 (978-0-7368-6139-7(4)) Capstone Pr., Inc.

Consideration. (Everyday Character Education Ser.). 24p. (J). 6.95 (978-0-7368-5145-9(3)); 6.95 (978-0-7368-9151-6(X)) Capstone Pr., Inc.

Cooperation. (Everyday Character Education Ser.). 24p. (J). 6.95 (978-0-7368-5146-6(1)) Capstone Pr., Inc.

Covey, Sean. Los 7 Habitos de los Adolescentes Altamente Efectivos. 2003. (SPA., Illus.). 288p. pap. 16.95 (978-1-4000-5926-3(7)) Grijalbo Mondadori, S.A.-Junior ESP. *Dist:* Random Hse., Inc.

Dalmatian Press Staff. A Lesson In... Thankfulness: Book to Color with Stickers. 2003. (Big Idea's Veggie Tales Ser.). (Illus.). 32p. (J). pap. 2.99 (978-1-4037-0293-7(4), Spirit Pr.) Dalmatian Pr.

Dann, Penny, illus. Learn How to Share with Josh B'Gosh. 1998. 10p. (J). 5.99 (978-1-929174-06-5(3)) Oshkosh B'Gosh, Inc.

Day, Eileen. Soy Bueno para Ayudar. 2003. (SPA.). 24p. pap. 5.25 (978-1-4034-3575-0(8)) Heinemann Library.

Dennis, Jep & Dennis, Bill. It Really Was a Lovely Village: Auburn, Alabama. 2002. (Illus.). 244p. (YA). (gr. 11 up). pap. 16.95 (978-0-9632180-9-4(3)) Chinaberry Hse.

Deroche, Ed, et al. Character: A Guide for Middle Grade Students. 176p. pap. 9.95 (978-1-55864-152-5(1), JIST Life) JIST Publishing.

Doak, Robin S. Caring. 2003. (J). pap. 7.50 (978-1-4109-0328-0(1)) Raintree.

—Caring. 2003. (gr. k-3). lib. bdg. 15.90 (978-0-613-78301-9(8)) Tandem Library Bks.

Dougherty, Monica F. You're a Miracle. . .Pass It On! 2000. (Illus.). 160p. (gr. 4-7). pap. 9.95 (978-0-595-12401-5(1)) iUniverse, Inc.

Dylan, Matthew. Respect. (J). 2003. pap. 7.50 (978-1-4109-0331-0(1)); 2002. (Illus.). 32p. lib. bdg. 24.26 (978-0-7398-5780-9(0)) Raintree.

Edgar, Kathleen J., et al. Compassion. 2003. (J). (978-1-59203-055-2(6)) Learning Challenge, Inc.

—Courage. 2003. (J). (978-1-59203-056-9(4)) Learning Challenge, Inc.

—Determination. 2003. (J). (978-1-59203-057-6(2)) Learning Challenge, Inc.

—Imagination. 2003. (J). (978-1-59203-058-3(0)) Learning Challenge, Inc.

—Responsibility. 2003. (J). (978-1-59203-059-0(9)) Learning Challenge, Inc.

—Vision. 2003. (J). (978-1-59203-060-6(2)) Learning Challenge, Inc.

Endres, Hollie J. Fair Share. 2006. 16p. (J). (gr. k-2). 15.93 (978-0-7368-5852-6(0), Yellow Umbrella Bks.) Capstone Pr., Inc.

Espeland, Pamela & Verdick, Elizabeth. Knowing & Doing Whats Right. 2005. (Adding Assets Series for Kids). (Illus.). 80p. (J). (gr. 3-7). pap. 9.95 (978-1-57542-184-1(4)) Free Spirit Publishing, Inc.

Fulton, Ginger Adair. When I'm a Daddy. 2005. (J). 4.95 (978-0-9746505-9-3(5)) Zeezok Publishing.

—When I'm a Mommy. 2005. (J). 4.95 (978-0-9746505-8-6(7)) Zeezok Publishing.

Havergal, Frances Ridley. Little Pillows & Morning Bells: Good-Night Thoughts & Waking Thoughts for the Little Ones. 2004. 200p. (J). per. 14.95 (978-1-932474-25-1(0)) Solid Ground Christian Bks.

Hodge, Aleta S. The Value Book. 2002. 230p. 13.95 (978-0-9648316-3-6(5)) Money Counsel, Inc.

How Could You? (Kids Talk Ser.). 32p. (J). 8.95 (978-1-4048-0364-0(5)) Picture Window Bks.

Howard, Pam. Be Kind to Others. l.t. ed. 2003. (HRL Little Book Ser.). (Illus.). 8p. (Orig.). (J). (ps-k). pap. 10.95 (978-1-57332-254-6(7)) HighReach Learning, Inc.

—Be Kind to Others. Middleton, Mikell, illus. l.t. ed. 2003. (HRL Big Book Ser.). 8p. (Orig.). (J). (ps-k). pap. 10.95 (978-1-57332-253-9(9)) HighReach Learning, Inc.

Jordan, Denise. Fair Shares for You & Me. 2003. (You & Me Ser.). (Illus.). 24p. (J). lib. bdg. 18.50 (978-1-4034-4409-7(9)) Heinemann Library.

—Now It's Your Turn. 2003. (You & Me Ser.). (Illus.). 24p. (J). (ps-1). lib. bdg. 18.50 (978-1-4034-4405-9(6)) Heinemann Library.

Jordan, Denise M. Your Fair Share. 2004. (Heinemann Read & Learn Ser.). (Illus.). 24p. (J). (ps-1). pap. 5.25 (978-1-4034-4415-8(3)) Heinemann Library.

Keuss, Jeff & Sloth, Lia. Character in Motion! Athlete Series. 2006. (Illus.). 136p. (YA). per. 5.95 (978-0-9765722-0-6(6)) Positively for Kids, Inc.

—Rachel's Challenge: A Columbine Legacy. 2006. (YA). per. 10.95 (978-0-9765722-5-1(7)) Positively for Kids, Inc.

Kid's Kindness Adventure in Learning. 2005. (J). spiral bd. 19.95 (978-1-59808-758-1(4)); per. 19.95 (978-1-59808-757-4(6)) Whispering Pine Pr., Inc.

Kid's Kindness Adventures in Learning. 2005. (J). cd-rom 19.95 (978-1-59808-760-4(6)) Whispering Pine Pr., Inc.

Kid's Kindness Aventures in Learning. 2005. (J). 19.95 (978-1-59808-759-8(2)) Whispering Pine Pr., Inc.

Klingel, Cynthia Fitterer. Courage. 2007. (Learn about Values Ser.). 24p. (J). 21.36 (978-1-59296-667-7(5)) Child's World, Inc.

—Forgiveness. 2007. (Learn about Values Ser.). 24p. (J). 21.36 (978-1-59296-668-4(3)) Child's World, Inc.

—Friendliness. 2007. (Learn about Values Ser.). 24p. (J). 21.36 (978-1-59296-669-1(1)) Child's World, Inc.

—Generosity. 2007. (Learn about Values Ser.). 24p. (J). 21.36 (978-1-59296-670-7(5)) Child's World, Inc.

—Loyalty. 2007. (Learn about Values Ser.). 24p. (J). 21.36 (978-1-59296-672-1(1)) Child's World, Inc.

—Respect. 2007. (Learn about Values Ser.). 24p. (J). 21.36 (978-1-59296-675-2(6)) Child's World, Inc.

Kunjufu, Jawanza. A Culture of Respect. 2007. 24p. (J). pap. 9.95 (***978-1-934155-06-6(3)**) African American Images.

Lang, Carol, et al. Character in Motion! Real Life Stories Series 3rd Grade Student Workbook. 2006. 63p. (J). per. 5.95 (978-0-9765722-9-9(X)) Positively for Kids, Inc.

Lauren, Emily. Trustworthiness. (Illus.). (J). 2003. pap. 7.50 (978-1-4109-0333-4(8)); 2002. 32p. lib. bdg. 24.26 (978-0-7398-5782-3(7)) Raintree.

—Trustworthiness. 2003. (gr. k-3). lib. bdg. 15.90 (978-0-613-78300-2(X)) Tandem Library Bks.

Marcovitz, Hal. Teens, Religion, & Values. 2004. (Gallup Youth Survey, Major Issues & Trends Ser.). (Illus.). 112,128p. (J). (gr. 7-9). lib. bdg. 22.95 (978-1-59084-726-8(1)) Mason Crest Pubs.

Mead, David. Little Ben Franklin Learns a Lesson in Generosity: Generosity. Sharp, Chris, illus. 2003. (American Virtues for Kids Ser.). (J). bds. 6.95 (978-0-9746440-2-8(1)) Ideals Pubns.

Moses, Brian. I'll Do It. 2000. (gr. k-3). lib. bdg. 14.45 (978-0-613-30509-9(4)) Tandem Library Bks.

Munroe, Terri, et al. Rachel's Challenge: A Columbine Legacy Student Workbook. 2006. (YA). per. 5.95 (978-0-9765722-4-4(9)) Positively for Kids, Inc.

Nettleton, Pamela Hill. May I Help You? Kids Talk about Caring. Muehlenhardt, Amy Bailey, illus. 2004. (Kids Talk Ser.). 32p. (C). (gr. 2-5). 23.93 (978-1-4048-0620-7(2)) Picture Window Bks.

—Pitch In! Kids Talk about Cooperation. Muehlenhardt, Amy Bailey, illus. 2004. (Kids Talk Ser.). 32p. (C). (gr. 2-5). 23.93 (978-1-4048-0621-4(0)) Picture Window Bks.

No Fair! (Kids Talk Ser.). 32p. (J). 8.95 (978-1-4048-0366-4(1)) Picture Window Bks.

Peacefulness. (Character Education Ser.). 24p. (J). 6.95 (978-0-7368-9154-7(4)) Capstone Pr., Inc.

Perlyn, Marilyn B. The Biggest & Brightest Light: A True Story of the Heart. Perlyn, Amanda, illus. 2004. 48p. (J). 16.95 (978-1-931741-30-9(1)) Reed, Robert D. Pubs.

Pittau, Francesco & Gervais, Bernadette. That's Disgusting! 2004. (Illus.). 80p. (J). bds. 7.95 (978-1-57912-351-2(1), 81351) Black Dog & Leventhal Pubs., Inc.

—That's Mean! 2004. (Illus.). 80p. (J). bds. 7.95 (978-1-57912-352-9(X), 81352) Black Dog & Leventhal Pubs., Inc.

Roberts, Cynthia. Honesty. 2007. (Learn about Values Ser.). 24p. (J). 21.36 (978-1-59296-671-4(3)) Child's World, Inc.

—Patience. 2007. (Learn about Values Ser.). 24p. (J). 21.36 (978-1-59296-673-8(X)) Child's World, Inc.

—Responsibility. 2007. (Learn about Values Ser.). 24p. (J). 21.36 (978-1-59296-676-9(4)) Child's World, Inc.

—Thankfulness. 2007. (Learn about Values Ser.). 24p. (J). 21.36 (978-1-59296-677-6(2)) Child's World, Inc.

—Tolerance. 2007. (Learn about Values Ser.). 24p. (J). 21.36 (978-1-59296-678-3(0)) Child's World, Inc.

Scheunemann, Pam. Acting with Kindness. 2004. (Keeping the Peace Ser.). (Illus.). 23p. (J). (ps-3). lib. bdg. 19.93 (978-1-59197-557-1(3)) ABDO Publishing Co.

Schuette, Sarah L. Character Values. Saunders-Smith, Gail, ed. (Pebble Ser.). (Illus.). (J). (gr. k-1). lib. bdg. 159.30 (978-0-7368-2740-9(4)) Capstone Pr., Inc.

—Character Values, 6 bks. Saunders-Smith, Gail, ed. Incl. I Am Caring. lib. bdg. 15.93 (978-0-7368-1438-6(8)); I Am Cooperative. lib. bdg. 15.93 (978-0-7368-1439-3(6)); I Am Honest. lib. bdg. 14.60 (978-0-7368-1440-9(X)); I Am Patient. lib. bdg. 15.93 (978-0-7368-1441-6(8)); I Am Respectful. lib. bdg. 15.95 (978-0-7368-1442-3(6)); I Am Responsible. lib. bdg. 15.95 (978-0-7368-1443-0(4)); 24p. (J). (gr. k-1). 2002. (Illus.). 2002. Set lib. bdg. 95.58 (978-0-7368-1444-7(2), Pebble Bks.) Capstone Pr., Inc.

—Character Values Bilingual. Saunders-Smith, Gail, ed. (Pebble Ser.). (Illus.). (J). (gr. k-1). lib. bdg. 95.58 (978-0-7368-2353-1(0)) Capstone Pr., Inc.

Small, Mary. Respect Is. Ouren, Todd, illus. 2004. (J). (978-1-4048-0278-0(9)) Picture Window Bks.

Swainston, Jeani. Grandma Stuff: ... it's what love Is made Of. 2006. (J). (***978-0-9791384-0-9(X)**) Rock Cliff Media.

Tokarski, Steve, et al. Making Moral Decisions: A Guide for Catholic Teens. 1998. (Illus.). (J). tchr. ed., spiral bd. 13.95 (978-0-89837-162-8(7)) Pflaum Publishing Group.

Tolerance. (Character Education Ser.). 24p. (J). 6.95 (978-0-7368-9157-8(9)) Capstone Pr., Inc.

What Really Matters. 2007. (J). per. 10.00 (***978-1-930052-35-2(9)**) Cherokee Bks.

Willow Creek Association. 5-G Challenge Winter Quarter Kit: Doing Life with God in the Picture. 2003. (Promiseland Ser.). (J). 299.00 (978-0-7441-2369-2(0)) Zonderkidz.

—5-G Discovery Winter Quarter Kit: Doing Life with God in the Picture. 2003. (Promiseland Ser.). (Illus.). (J). (gr. 2-3). 299.00 (978-0-7441-2368-5(2)) Zonderkidz.

—5-G Impact Winter Quarter Kit: Doing Life with God in the Picture. 2003. (Promiseland Ser.). (J). 299.00 (978-0-7441-2370-8(4)) Zonderkidz.

VALUES—FICTION

Benton, Jim. Life Get One. 2nd ed. 2005. (It's Happy Bunny Ser.: No. 2). (Illus.). 72p. (J). 7.99 (978-0-439-69346-2(2)) Scholastic, Inc.

Blenkhorn, Les. The Adventures of Tracker. 2006. 26.99 (***978-1-4259-6605-8(5)**); pap. 16.99 (***978-1-4259-6604-1(7)**) AuthorHouse.

Bohlken, Robert L. Listening to the Mukies: And Their Character Building Adventures. Veasey, Michele, illus. 2003. (J). pap. 14.95 (978-0-930643-15-7(1)) Images Unlimited.

—Listening to the Mukies & Their Character Building Adventures. Veasey, Michele, illus. 2003. (J). 24.95 (978-0-930643-17-1(8)) Images Unlimited.

Bower, Gary. Wyatt's Wagon: Including Others. Velker, Kay, ed. Bower, Jan, illus. l.t. ed. 2001. (Thinking of Others: Vol. 2). 32p. (J). lib. bdg. 16.95 (978-0-9704621-1-4(5)) Storybook Meadow Publishing.

Clark, Emma Chichester. Amazing Mr Zooty! 2008. (Illus.). 32p. (J). pap. 9.95 (***978-1-84270-592-6(X)**) Andersen GBR. *Dist:* Independent Pubs. Group.

Cooper, Dolores Thome. Hands Are Not for Hitting. 2005. (Illus.). 32p. (J). 7.95 (978-1-881539-39-1(3)) Tabby Hse. Bks.

Cox, Phil Roxbee. Give That Back, Jack. 2004. (Cautionary Tales Ser.). 24p. (J). pap. 7.95 (978-0-7945-0466-3(3), Usborne) EDC Publishing.

Dalrymple, Marilyn. Bartholomew's Buttons. 2006. 18p. (J). 9.73 (978-1-4116-9200-8(4)) Lulu.com.

Davis, Holly. Thankful Together. Sokolova, Valerie, illus. 2006. 36p. (J). 5.99 (978-0-7847-1436-2(3), 04077) Standard Publishing.

Deckers, Amber. Ella Mental: And the Good Sense Guide. 2006. (Illus.). 240p. (YA). mass mkt. 6.99 (978-1-4169-1322-1(X), Simon Pulse) Simon & Schuster Children's Publishing.

Defosse, Rosana Curiel. Santiago & the Dobraks. Barradas, Leticia, illus. (SPA.). 32p. (J). (gr. 3-5). pap. 7.95 (978-970-29-0111-2(1)) Santillana USA Publishing Co., Inc.

—Santiago y el talisman de la Luz. Barradas, Leticia, illus. (Santiago Y Los Valores Ser.). (SPA.). 32p. (J). (gr. 3-5). pap. 7.95 (978-970-29-0131-0(6)) Santillana USA Publishing Co., Inc.

DeHeer, Jolene. 70 x 7: Learning to Forgive. ldr.'s ed. 2002. (LifeWise Ser.). 19.95 (978-1-56212-839-5(6), 131336, Faith Alive Christian Resources) CRC Pubns.

Duran, Maureen. Kids with Character III, 3 bks. 2001. (Illus.). 96p. (J). 22.95 (978-1-931636-07-0(9), Students Taking a Right Stand, (STARS)) National Center For Youth Issues.

Dureke, Jottn O. Z - the Goodluck Bird. Dureke, Jottn O., tr. 2004. (Illus.). 44p. (YA). pap. 6.95 (978-0-9701144-1-9(9)) Jahs Publishing Group.

Edgeworth, Maria. The Bracelets or Amiability & Industry Rewarded. 2004. reprint ed. pap. 15.95 (978-1-4191-5513-0(X)); pap. 1.99 (978-1-4192-5513-7(4)) Kessinger Publishing, LLC.

Esopo. El Leon y la Zorra. 2003. (SPA.). 24p. (978-84-246-1564-2(6), GL0475) La Galera, S.A. Editorial ESP. *Dist:* Lectorum Pubns., Inc.

Finkelstein, Ruth. Guess-the-Ending Mitzvah Book. Lazewnik, Sara, illus. 2004. 26p. (J). (gr. k-3). 9.95 (978-0-9628157-4-4(8)) Finkelstein, Ruth.

Frias, Miriam Rocio. Cuentos para Ninos Buenos - Relatos Reafirman Valores Humanos. (SPA.). (J). 7.98 (978-970-643-238-4(8)) Selector, S.A. de C.V. MEX. *Dist:* AIMS International Bks., Inc.

Fun Short Stories on Values & Morals of Life. 2003. (Illus.). 90p. (YA). per. (978-0-9742122-0-3(2)) Aunty Ems Boutique.

Gallegos, Patrick M. Meno's Gift. Russell, Ginger, illus. deluxe ed. 1999. 64p. (YA). (gr. 1-12). 19.95 (978-0-9675742-0-2(X)) Wiggly's Pubns.

Green, John. Terdellaline: A Free-Spirited, Energeti. 2005. 48p. pap. 12.95 (978-1-4137-9528-8(5)) PublishAmerica, Inc.

Grooms, Molly. We Are Puppies. 2005. 40p. bds. 12.95 (978-90-5843-815-7(5)) YoYo Bks. BEL. *Dist:* National Bk. Network.

Halliman, P. K. Heartprints. 2002. (gr. k-3). lib. bdg. 14.10 (978-0-613-76758-3(6)) Tandem Library Bks.

Harcourt School Publishers Staff. The Bird in the Plum Tree: On Level. 3rd ed. 2002. (Trophies Reading Program Ser.). (Illus.). pap. 5.10 (978-0-15-322999-2(3)) Harcourt Schl. Pubs.

—The Dog & His Shadow On Level. 3rd ed. 2002. (Trophies Reading Program Ser.). (Illus.). pap. 5.10 (978-0-15-323074-5(6)) Harcourt Schl. Pubs.

—The Edge of the Puddle: On Level. 3rd ed. 2002. (Trophies Reading Program Ser.). (Illus.). pap. 5.10 (978-0-15-323003-5(7)) Harcourt Schl. Pubs.

—The Emperor & the Peasant Boy: Take-Home Book. 2001. (Collections Ser.). (Illus.). (J). pap. 1.90 (978-0-15-319500-6(2)) Harcourt Schl. Pubs.

Harris, Rita & Long, Paul. The 19 Cats of Alabama. 2004. 35p. pap. 17.95 (978-1-4137-3006-7(X)) PublishAmerica, Inc.

Hofbauer, Michele Pace. Couldn't We Make a Difference? 2000. 40p. (J). (gr. k-2). 16.95 (978-1-880851-62-3(8)) Greene Bark Pr., Inc.

Hoose, Phillip & Hoose, Hannah. Oye, Hormiguita. 2004. (SPA., Illus.). 30p. (J). 6.95 (978-1-58246-089-5(2), Tricycle Pr.) Ten Speed Pr.

—Oye, Hormiguita. Tilley, Debbie, illus. 2003. (SPA.). 30p. (J). 14.95 (978-1-58246-088-8(4), Tricycle Pr.) Ten Speed Pr.

Hopkins, Ellen. Burned. 2006. (Illus.). 544p. (YA). 17.99 (978-1-4169-0354-3(2), McElderry, Margaret K.) Simon & Schuster Children's Publishing.

Jaysree. Drama. 2004. 134p. (YA). pap. 11.95 (978-0-595-29662-0(9)) iUniverse, Inc.

Katz, Karen. No Hitting! Katz, Karen, illus. 2004. (Illus.). 14p. (J). (ps-k). 5.99 (978-0-448-43612-8(4), Grosset & Dunlap) Penguin Group (USA) Inc.

Krulik, Nancy E. Dawn's Early Light. 2006. 208p. (YA). pap. 5.99 (978-1-4169-1465-5(X), Simon Pulse) Simon & Schuster Children's Publishing.

Langan, Paul. The Gun. Langan, Paul, ed. 2002. (Bluford Ser.: 6). 123p. (YA). mass mkt. 4.95 (978-0-944210-04-8(X)) Townsend Pr.

Langan, Paul. Payback. 2007. (Bluford Ser.: No. 6). 144p. (J). pap. 3.99 (***978-0-439-90487-2(0)**, Scholastic Paperbacks) Scholastic, Inc.

Langan, Paul & Blackwell, D. M. Blood Is Thicker. 2007. (Bluford Ser.: No. 8). (Illus.). 176p. (J). pap. 3.99 (***978-0-439-90489-6(7)**, Scholastic Paperbacks) Scholastic, Inc.

Lorenzo, Alejandro. Mateo's Progress/Jornadas de Mateo: Tales for Children of All Ages/Cuentos para Niños de Todas las Edades. 2004. (SPA & ENG., Illus.). 96p. (J). 20.00 (978-0-9714366-3-3(0)) Pureplay Pr.

Lucado, Max. Hermie y Wormie en un Diluvio de Mentiras. 2004. (SPA.). 24p. (J). bds. 10.99 (978-0-88113-775-0(8)) Grupo Nelson.

Maidment, Stella & Wilde, Oscar. The Star Child. Whelan, Olwyn, tr. Whelan, Olwyn, illus. gif. ed. 2003. 40p. (YA). (978-1-84365-012-6(6)) Chrysalis Children's Bks.

Matyas, Diane. The Terrible Captain Jack Visits the Museum: Or A Guide of Museum Manners for Incorrigible Pirates & the Like. ed. 2008. (Illus.). 24p. (J). (***978-0-9623017-2-8(8)**) Noble Maritime Collection, The.

McCann, Thomas P. "Tom". The Tree Nobody Wanted: A Christmas Story. 2007. 14.95 (***978-0-9797407-0-1(3)**) Exeter Pr.

Miller, Dennis. ABCs of Character. Wallace, Sam Amber, illus. 2003. 52p. (J). lib. bdg. 15.95 (978-0-9722259-1-5(9)) Twin Peaks Publishing, Inc.

Naylor, Phyllis Reynolds. The Grooming of Alice. 2001. (Alice Ser.). (gr. 5-8). lib. bdg. 13.00 (978-0-613-73309-0(6)) Tandem Library Bks.

Page, Shari. Little Master of Tall Tales. 2004. 17p. pap. 11.07 (978-1-4116-1568-7(9)) Lulu.com.

Parker, Daniel. February. 1999. (Count Down Ser.: No. 2). (YA). (gr. 5-8). (978-0-606-16236-4(4)) Tandem Library Bks.

Perez, Angela J. Zack Attack! Hazard, Andrea, illus. 2007. 36p. (J). 17.95 (***978-0-9778328-9-7(9)**) His Work Christian Publishing.

Pittau, Francesco & Gervais, Bernadette. That's Dangerous! 2004. (Illus.). 80p. (J). bds. 7.95 (978-1-57912-350-5(3), 81350) Black Dog & Leventhal Pubs., Inc.

Quigley's Village Staff. A Christmas Story: Joy of Giving. 1998. (Quigley's Village Ser.: Vol. 5). (J). (ps-2). 12.99 incl. VHS (978-0-310-58249-6(0), V5155) Zondervan.

Rawlings, John S. Sometimes Boxes Make the Best Forts. Espina, Vito, illus. 2006. (J). pap. 15.00 (***978-0-8059-7181-1(5)**) Dorrance Publishing Co., Inc.

Regan, Dana, illus. Messy Bessey. 2002. (Messy Bessey Ser.). (J). 12.83 (978-0-7587-7183-4(5)) Book Wholesalers, Inc.

—Messy Bessey & the Birthday Overnight. 2002. (Messy Bessey Ser.). (J). 12.83 (978-0-7587-7185-8(1)) Book Wholesalers, Inc.

—Messy Bessey's Holidays. 2002. (Messy Bessey Ser.). (J). 12.83 (978-0-7587-7188-9(6)) Book Wholesalers, Inc.

Richards, Arlene. That's Bingzy! Busy Building Self-Esteem. 2007. (J). per. 15.95 (***978-0-9794323-2-3(4)**) Bing Note, Inc.

Richardson, Beverly J. Timbs. Lilly & Me. (Illus.). 2006. (ENG.). 36p. per. 12.95 (978-1-59800-459-5(X)); 2005. 29p. 26.99 (978-1-59800-121-1(3)) Outskirts Press, Inc.

Rosenthal, Amy Krouse. It's Not Fair. Lichtenheld, Tom, illus. 2008. 40p. (J). 16.99 (***978-0-06-115257-3(9)**); lib. bdg. 17.89 (***978-0-06-115258-0(7)**) HarperCollins Pubs.

Rushford, Betty. Best Buddies: And the Fruit of the Spirit. 2003. 41p. pap. 16.95 (978-1-59286-746-2(4)) PublishAmerica, Inc.

Sapp, Brent. Teknon & the Champion Warriors. Cariello, Sergio, illus. 2003. 7.99 (978-1-57229-219-2(9)) FamilyLife.

T U V

Simon, Mary Manz. Tiger Forgives. Clearwater, Linda & Couri, Kathy, illus. 2006. (First Virtues for Toddlers Ser.). 20p. (J). 5.99 (978-0-7847-1413-3(4) , 04065) Standard Publishing.

Sinke, Janet. I Wanna Go to Grandma's House. 2003. (Illus.). 50p. (J). (978-0-9742732-0-4(1)) My Grandma & Me Pubs.

Sommer, Carl. If Only I Were... 2003. (Another Sommer-Time Story Ser.). (Illus.). 48p. (J). (gr. k-4). lib. bdg. 23.95 incl. audio compact disk (978-1-57537-702-5(0)); lib. bdg. 23.95 incl. audio (978-1-57537-752-0(7)) Advance Publishing, Inc.

—Mayor for A Day Read-along, 2003. (Another Sommer-Time Story Ser.). (Illus.). 48p. (J). lib. bdg. 23.95 incl. audio (978-1-57537-763-6(2)) Advance Publishing, Inc.

—No One Will Ever Know Read-Along, 1 bk. 2003. (Another Sommer-Time Story Ser.). (Illus.). 48p. (J). lib. bdg. 23.95 incl. audio compact disk (978-1-57537-706-3(3)); lib. bdg. 23.95 incl. audio (978-1-57537-756-8(X)) Advance Publishing, Inc.

—Noise! Noise! Noise! Read-Along, 2003. (Another Sommer-Time Story Ser.). (Illus.). 48p. (J). lib. bdg. 23.95 incl. audio compact disk (978-1-57537-719-3(5)) Advance Publishing, Inc.

—Proud Rooster & Little Hen Read-along, 1 bk. 2003. (Another Great Achiever Ser.). (Illus.). 48p. (J). lib. bdg. 23.95 incl. audio compact disk (978-1-57537-710-0(1)); lib. bdg. 23.95 incl. audio (978-1-57537-760-5(8)) Advance Publishing, Inc.

St. John, Patricia. Friska My Friend & the Other Kitten. 2003. (Illus.). 192p. 6.49 (978-1-85999-312-5(5)) Scripture Union GBR. *Dist:* Gabriel Resources.

Standish, Burt L. Frank Merriwell's Generosity. Rudman, Jack, ed. 2003. (Frank Merriwell Ser.). 29.95 (978-0-8373-9352-0(3)); pap. 9.95 (978-0-8373-9052-9(4)) Merriwell, Frank Inc.

Style Guide Staff, illus. It's Hug Day!, Vol. 19. 2005. (Blue's Clues Ser.: Vol. 19). 24p. (J). pap. 3.99 (978-1-4169-0222-5(8) , Simon Spotlight/Nickelodeon) Simon & Schuster Children's Publishing.

Tierno, Susan F. Otro Problema! Alvarado, Ana María, tr. Ramirez, Michael, illus. 2000. (Think-Kids Book Collection).Tr. of It Was Just Another Problem. (SPA.). 16p. (J). pap. 2.95 (978-1-58237-044-6(3)) Creative Thinkers, Inc.

Valeri, Maria Eulalia. El Leon y el Raton. 2003. (SPA.). 24p. (978-84-246-1925-1(0) , GL0474) La Galera, S.A. Editorial ESP. *Dist:* Lectorum Pubns., Inc.

Womack, Vernesia. What If... 2004. (J). pap. 7.00 (978-0-8059-6383-0(9)) Dorrance Publishing Co., Inc.

Wyatt, Cherokee, as told by. The Adventures of Margaret Mouse: Harvest Carnival. l.t. ed. 2006. (Illus.). 32p. (J). 6.95 (978-0-9761326-5-3(6)) www.margaretmouse.com publishing co.

Yang, John, Sr. You Can Eat Cheese but Don't Be Cheesy. 2003. (Illus.). 58p. (J). per. (978-0-9743080-0-5(5)) Painting With Words.

VAMPIRES

Besel, Jennifer M. Vampires. 2007. (Blazers Ser.). (Illus.). 32p. (J). 19.93 (978-0-7368-6443-5(1)) Capstone Pr., Inc.

Cybulski, Angela. Vampires. 2003. (gr. 7-12). lib. bdg. 30.35 (978-0-613-73888-0(8)) Tandem Library Bks.

Hamilton, John. Vampires. 2007. (ENG., Illus.). 32p. (J). lib. bdg. 24.21 (***978-1-59928-774-4(9)** , ABDO & Daughters) ABDO Publishing Co.

McMeans, Bonnie. Vampires. 2006. (Mysterious Encounters Ser.). 48p. (J). (gr. 4-8). 26.20 (978-0-7377-3476-8(0) , Greenhaven Pr., Inc.) Thomson Gale.

Oxlade, Chris. The Mystery of Vampires & Werewolves. 2002. (Can Science Solve? Ser.). 32p. (J). (gr. 4-7). (Illus.). lib. bdg. 22.79 (978-1-58810-668-1(3)); pap. 7.50 (978-1-58810-932-3(1) , 91568) Heinemann Library.

Pipe, Jim. Vampires. 2007. (Tales of Horror Ser.). (Illus.). 32p. (J). (gr. 3-6). lib. bdg. 25.27 (978-1-59716-205-0(1)) Bearport Publishing Co., Inc.

Roberts, Russell. Vampires. 2001. (Mystery Library). (Illus.). 96p. (YA). (gr. 4-12). 27.45 (978-1-56006-835-8(3) , Lucent Bks.) Thomson Gale.

Stefoff, Rebecca. Vampires, Zombies, & Shape-Shifters. 2007. (Secrets of the Supernatural Ser.). 96p. (J). lib. bdg. 32.79 (***978-0-7614-2635-6(3)** , Benchmark Bks.) Cavendish, Marshall Corp.

Streissguth, Thomas. Legends of Dracula. 1998. (Biography Ser.). (Illus.). 112p. (gr. 6-12). lib. bdg. 27.93 (978-0-8225-4942-0(5)) Lerner Publishing Group.

Streissguth, Thomas & Streissguth, Tom. Legends of Dracula. 2003. (Biography Ser.). (Illus.). 112p. (YA). (gr. 6 up). pap. 7.95 (978-0-8225-9682-0(2) , Carolrhoda Bks.) Lerner Publishing Group.

Vampire Sticker Book. 2003. (Illus.). 16p. (J). 2.98 (978-1-84273-119-2(X) , Exclusive Editions) Parragon, Inc.

VAMPIRES—FICTION

Anderson, M. T. Thirsty. ed. 2003. (Illus.). 256p. (YA). (gr. 9). pap. 7.99 (978-0-7636-2014-1(9)) Candlewick Pr.

Askegren, Pierce. Afterimage. 2006. (Buffy the Vampire Slayer Ser.). 272p. (YA). pap. 6.99 (978-1-4169-1181-4(2) , Simon Spotlight Entertainment) Simon & Schuster.

Asprin, Robert. M. Y. T. H. Inc. Link. 2006. 176p. (gr. 12). mass mkt. 6.99 (978-0-441-01449-1(6) , Ace Bks.) Penguin Group (USA) Inc.

Ataca el Gusano Vampiro. (Fantasmas de Fear Street Coleccion). (SPA.). (YA). (gr. 5-8). pap. 7.95 (978-950-04-2046-4(5) , EM4181) Emecé Editores S.A. ARG. *Dist:* Lectorum Pubns., Inc., Planeta Publishing Corp.

Atwater-Rhodes, Amelia. Demon in My View. 2001. 192p. (YA). (gr. 7). mass mkt. 5.99 (978-0-440-22884-4(0) , Laurel Leaf) Random Hse. Children's Bks.

—Demon in My View. 2000. (gr. 7-12). lib. bdg. 13.00 (978-0-613-69052-2(4)) Tandem Library Bks.

—In the Forests of the Night. 2000. (Illus.). 176p. (YA). (gr. 7-12). mass mkt. 5.99 (978-0-440-22816-5(6) , Laurel Leaf) Random Hse. Children's Bks.

—In the Forests of the Night. 2000. (gr. 7-12). lib. bdg. 13.55 (978-0-613-28537-7(9)); (Illus.). (J). 12.15 (978-0-606-17999-7(2)) Tandem Library Bks.

—Midnight Predator. l.t. ed. 2004. 195p. 20.95 (978-0-7862-6576-3(0)) Thorndike Pr.

—Shattered Mirror. 240p. (YA). (gr. 7). 2003. mass mkt. 5.99 (978-0-440-22940-7(5) , Laurel Leaf); 2001. 9.95 (978-0-385-32793-0(5) , Delacorte Bks. for Young Readers) Random Hse. Children's Bks.

—Shattered Mirror. 2003. (gr. 7-12). lib. bdg. 13.55 (978-0-613-72330-5(9)) Tandem Library Bks.

Barks, Carl, et al. Walt Disney's Comics & Stories #685. 2007. 64p. pap. 7.99 (***978-1-888472-96-7(0)**) Gemstone Publishing, Inc.

Baxter, Jason Matthew. To Become a Vampire: The Transformation. 2002. 188p. (YA). mass mkt. (978-0-9714841-0-8(4)) Morris Publishing.

Brereton, Dan. The Dust Waltz. 1998. (Buffy the Vampire Slayer Ser.). (Illus.). 80p. (YA). (gr. 7 up). pap. 9.95 (978-1-56971-342-6(1)) Dark Horse Comics.

Brewer, Heather. The Chronicles of Vladimir Tod: Eighth Grade Bites. 2008. 288p. (J). (gr. 4-6). pap. 7.99 (***978-0-14-241187-2(6)** , Puffin); 2007. 192p. (YA). (gr. 5 up). 16.99 (978-0-525-47811-9(6) , Dutton Juvenile) Penguin Group (USA) Inc.

Brush Creations & Holmes, A. M. X. Robbie Virtual vs. Vlad the Vampire: Book 1. 2007. 56p. pap. 9.95 (***978-0-7414-3621-4(3)**) Infinity Publishing.

Buffy the Vampire Slayer Vol. 1: Script Book, Season 1. 2000. (gr. 7-12). lib. bdg. 23.45 (978-0-613-63265-2(6)) Tandem Library Bks.

Buffy the Vampire Slayer Vol. 2: Script Book, Season 1. 2000. (gr. 7-12). lib. bdg. 23.45 (978-0-613-63261-4(3)) Tandem Library Bks.

Caine, Rachel. Midnight Alley: The Morganville Vampires, Book Three. 2007. 245p. (YA). (gr. 12). per. 5.99 (***978-0-451-22238-1(5)** , Signet) Penguin Group (USA) Inc.

Cary, Kate. Bloodline. 2006. 352p. (YA). (gr. 7-12). pap. 8.99 (978-1-59514-078-4(6) , Razorbill) Penguin Group (USA) Inc.

—Reckoning. 2007. (Bloodline Ser.: Bk. 2). 320p. (YA). (gr. 9 up). 16.99 (978-1-59514-013-5(1) , Razorbill) Penguin Group (USA) Inc.

Cast, P. C. & Cast, Kristin. Marked: A House of Night Novel. 2007. (House of Night Novels Ser.). 320p. (YA). (gr. 9 up). pap. 8.95 (***978-0-312-36026-9(6)** , St. Martin's Griffin) St. Martin's Pr.

Ciencin, Scott. Vengance. 2002. (gr. 7-12). lib. bdg. 14.15 (978-0-613-63240-9(0)) Tandem Library Bks.

Coffman, Patrick, tr. Vampire Game, Vol. 11. Judal, illus. rev. ed. 2005. 208p. pap. 9.99 (978-1-59532-441-2(0) , Tokyopop Adult) TOKYOPOP, Inc.

Cole, Joanna. The Magic School Bus Going Batty. 2002. (Magic School Bus Ser.). (Illus.). (J). 11.45 (978-0-7587-6478-2(2)) Book Wholesalers, Inc.

Collins, Craig, et al. Visitors. 1999. (Buffy the Vampire Slayer Ser.: No. 9). 176p. (YA). (gr. 7 up). pap. 5.99 (978-0-671-02628-8(3) , Simon Pulse) Simon & Schuster Children's Publishing.

Cooney, Caroline B. Deadly Offer. 2003. (gr. 7-12). lib. bdg. 13.00 (978-0-613-72155-4(1)) Tandem Library Bks.

Cooney, Caroline B., et al. Fatal Bargain. 2003. (Vampire's Promise Ser.). 176p. (J). pap. 4.99 (978-0-439-55397-1(0) , Scholastic Paperbacks) Scholastic, Inc.

Cox & Smedley. Invasion of the Sausage Snatchers. 2003. (Illus.). 128p. pap. (978-0-340-79592-7(1) , Hodder Children's Books) Hodder Children's Division.

Cox, Michael. Fall of the House of Blodvat. 2003. (Illus.). mass mkt. (978-0-340-79594-1(8) , Hodder Children's Books) Hodder Children's Division.

—Nightmare on Eck Street. Smedley, Chris, illus. 2003. 128p. pap. (978-0-340-79593-4(X) , Hodder Children's Books) Hodder Children's Division.

Crowson, Andrew. Flip Flap Spooky. Crowson, Andrew, illus. 2003. (Illus.). 12p. (J). bds. (978-1-85602-475-4(X)) Chrysalis Children's Bks.

Dadey, Debbie & Jones, Marcia Thornton. Mrs. Jeepers on Vampire Island. Gurney, John Steven, illus. 2002. (Bailey School Kids Ser.: No. 6). 128p. mass mkt. 3.99 (978-0-439-30641-6(8) , Scholastic Paperbacks) Scholastic, Inc.

de la Cruz, Melissa. Blue Bloods. (gr. 7 up). 2007. 336p. (YA). pap. 8.99 (***978-1-4231-0126-0(X));** 2006. 320p. 15.99 (978-0-7868-3892-9(2)) Hyperion Pr.

—Masquerade: A Blue Bloods Novel. 2007. 320p. (YA). (gr. 7 up). 15.99 (***978-0-7868-3893-6(0)**) Hyperion Pr.

Debrandt, Don. Shakedown. 2000. (Angel Ser.: No. 5). 320p. (YA). (gr. 7 up). pap. 5.99 (978-0-7434-0696-3(6) , Simon Pulse) Simon & Schuster Children's Publishing.

—Shakedown. 2000. (gr. 7-12). lib. bdg. 14.15 (978-0-613-63231-7(1)) Tandem Library Bks.

DeCandido, Keith R. A. The Deathless. 2007. (Buffy the Vampire Slayer Ser.). 224p. (YA). pap. 6.99 (978-1-4169-3630-5(0) , Simon Spotlight Entertainment) Simon & Schuster.

Dent, Sue. Never Ceese: Can Two Who Were Wronged Make It Right? 2006. 336p. (YA). lib. bdg. 17.99 (978-1-59958-017-3(9)) Journey Stone Creations, LLC.

Dole, D. Vampire's Daughter Vol. 1: Deadly Relations. 2004. 215p. pap. 19.95 (978-1-4137-4539-9(3)) PublishAmerica, Inc.

Dufaux, Jean. Rapaces. Marini, Enrico, illus. 2004. (SPA.). Vol. 1. 56p. pap. 17.95 (978-1-59497-003-0(3)); Vol. 2. 56p. pap. 17.95 (978-1-59497-004-7(1)); Vol. 3. 64p. pap. 17.95 (978-1-59497-005-4(X)) Public Square Bks.

Durgin, Doranna. Impressions. 2003. (gr. 7-12). lib. bdg. 14.15 (978-0-613-61777-2(0)) Tandem Library Bks.

Duval, Alex. Bloodlust. 2006. (Vampire Beach Ser.). 208p. (YA). (gr. 9 up). mass mkt. 5.99 (978-1-4169-1166-1(9) , Simon Pulse) Simon & Schuster Children's Publishing.

—Initiation. 2006. (Vampire Beach Ser.: Vol. 2). 192p. (YA). mass mkt. 5.99 (978-1-4169-1167-8(7) , Simon Pulse) Simon & Schuster Children's Publishing.

—Legacy. 2007. (Vampire Beach Ser.). 240p. (YA). mass mkt. 5.99 (***978-1-4169-1169-2(3)** , Simon Pulse) Simon & Schuster Children's Publishing.

Duval, Alex. Ritual. 2007. (Vampire Beach Ser.). 208p. (YA). mass mkt. 5.99 (978-1-4169-1168-5(5) , Simon Pulse) Simon & Schuster Children's Publishing.

Espenson, Jane. Haunted. 2002. (Buffy the Vampire Slayer Ser.). (Illus.). 96p. (YA). pap. 12.95 (978-1-56971-737-0(0)) Dark Horse Comics.

Fassbender, Tom, et al. Creatures of Habit. Allie, Scott, ed. Fassbender, Tom, tr. 2002. (Angel/Buffy the Vampire Slayer Ser.). (Illus.). 96p. (YA). pap. 17.95 (978-1-56971-563-5(7)) Dark Horse Comics.

Faulkner, Keith. The Spooky Trail. Brown, Leo, illus. 2005. 16p. (J). (ps-2). bds. 9.99 (978-0-7641-5834-6(1)) Barron's Educational Series, Inc.

Fort, Gloria. Vampirrisa. 2000. (Dulces Suenos Collection). (SPA., Illus.). 10p. (J). 7.95 (978-84-348-6260-9(3)) SM Ediciones ESP. *Dist:* Distribooks, Inc.

Gallagher, Diana G. Doomsday Deck. 2000. (gr. 7-12). lib. bdg. 14.15 (978-0-613-63278-2(8)) Tandem Library Bks.

—Prime Evil. 2000. (Buffy the Vampire Slayer Ser.: No. 10). 272p. (YA). pap. 5.99 (978-0-671-03930-1(X) , Simon Pulse) Simon & Schuster Children's Publishing.

—Prime Evil. 2000. (gr. 7-12). lib. bdg. 14.15 (978-0-613-63335-2(0)) Tandem Library Bks.

Gardiner, Lindsey. When Poppy & Max Grow Up. Gardiner, Lindsey, illus. 2001. (Illus.). 24p. (J). (gr. k-1). 12.95 (978-0-316-60342-3(2)) Little, Brown Bks. for Young Readers.

Garton, Ray. Resurrecting Ravana. 2000. (gr. 7-12). lib. bdg. 14.15 (978-0-613-22261-7(X)); 1999. (Buffy the Vampire Slayer Ser.: No. 9). (Illus.). (J). (978-0-606-18366-6(3)) Tandem Library Bks.

Gilman, Laura Anne. Deep Water. 2000. (Buffy the Vampire Slayer Ser.: No. 14). (Illus.). (YA). (gr. 7 up). (978-0-606-18365-9(5)) Tandem Library Bks.

Gloden, et al. Tales of the Slayer, Vol. 3. Simon and Schuster Children's Staff, ed. 2003. (Buffy the Vampire Slayer Ser.). (Illus.). 336p. (YA). pap. 9.99 (978-0-689-86436-0(1) , Simon Pulse) Simon & Schuster Children's Publishing.

Golden, Christopher. Ghost Roads. 1999. (gr. 7-12). lib. bdg. 15.30 (978-0-613-73059-4(3)) Tandem Library Bks.

—Immortal. 2000. (gr. 7-12). lib. bdg. 14.15 (978-0-613-63302-4(4)) Tandem Library Bks.

—Oz: Into the Wild. 2002. (Buffy the Vampire Slayer Ser.). 288p. (YA). pap. 6.99 (978-0-7434-0038-1(0) , Simon Pulse) Simon & Schuster Children's Publishing.

—Oz: Into the Wild. 2002. (gr. 7-12). lib. bdg. 15.30 (978-0-613-63328-4(8)) Tandem Library Bks.

—Spike & Dru: Pretty Maids All in a Row. 2001. (Buffy the Vampire Slayer Ser.: Vol. 2). 368p. (YA). (gr. 8-12). reprint ed. pap. 6.99 (978-0-7434-1892-8(1) , Simon Pulse) Simon & Schuster Children's Publishing.

—Spike & Dru: Pretty Maids All in a Row. 2001. (gr. 7-12). lib. bdg. 15.30 (978-0-613-74152-1(8)) Tandem Library Bks.

—The Wisdom of War. 2002. (Buffy the Vampire Slayer Ser.). 416p. (YA). pap. 6.99 (978-0-7434-2760-9(2) , Simon Pulse) Simon & Schuster Children's Publishing.

—Wisdom of War. 2002. (gr. 7-12). lib. bdg. 15.30 (978-0-613-63372-7(5)) Tandem Library Bks.

Golden, Christopher & Holder, Nancy. Ghost Roads, 3 vols. 1999. (Buffy the Vampire Slayer Ser.: No. 2). 384p. (YA). pap. 6.99 (978-0-671-02749-0(2) , Simon Pulse) Simon & Schuster Children's Publishing.

—The Watchers Guide Buffy the Vampire Slayer, Vol. 1. rev. ed. 1998. (Buffy the Vampire Slayer Ser.). (Illus.). 304p. (YA). pap. 17.95 (978-0-671-02433-8(7) , Simon Pulse) Simon & Schuster Children's Publishing.

Golden, Christopher & Sniegoski, Thomas E. Monster Island. 2004. (Buffy the Vampire Slayer & Angel Crossover Ser.). 448p. (YA). pap. 7.99 (978-0-689-86699-9(2) , Simon & Schuster Children's Publishing) Simon & Schuster Children's Publishing.

Golden, Christopher, et al. The Blood of Carthage. 2001. (Buffy the Vampire Slayer Ser.). 128p. (YA). pap. 12.95 (978-1-56971-534-5(3)) Dark Horse Comics.

—The Origin. 1999. (Buffy the Vampire Slayer Ser.). 80p. (YA). (gr. 7 up). pap. 9.95 (978-1-56971-429-4(0)) Dark Horse Comics.

Golightly, Holly, creator. School Bites. 2004. 64p. (YA). per. (978-0-9745367-2-9(5) , SB1A) BroadSword Comics/ Jim Balent Studios.

Greenburg, Dan. Fall of the House of Mandible. Fischer, Scott M., illus. 2006. (Outrageously Funny Ser.: Bk. 4). 160p. (J). 9.95 (978-0-15-205475-5(8)) Harcourt Children's Bks.

—The Onts. Fischer, Scott M., illus. 2006. (Secrets of Dripping Fang Ser.: Bk. 1). 144p. (J). 2.99 (978-0-15-205995-8(4) , Harcourt Paperbacks) Harcourt Children's Bks.

—Please Don't Eat the Children. Fischer, Scott M., illus. 2007. (Secrets of Dripping Fang Ser.: Bk. 7). 160p. (J). 9.95 (978-0-15-206047-3(2)) Harcourt Children's Bks.

Greenburg, Dan & Diterlizzi, Angela. The Vampire's Curse. Fischer, Scott M., illus. 2006. (Secrets of Dripping Fang Ser.: Bk. 3). 144p. (J). 9.95 (978-0-15-205469-4(3)) Harcourt Children's Bks.

Griffin, Adele. The Knaveheart's Curse: A Vampire Island Book: A Vampire Island Book. 2008. 128p. (J). (gr. 4-6). 14.99 (***978-0-399-25064-4(6)** , Putnam Juvenile) Penguin Group (USA) Inc.

Griffin, Adele. Vampire Island. 2007. 144p. (J). (gr. 3-6). 14.99 (978-0-399-23785-0(2) , Putnam Juvenile) Penguin Group (USA) Inc.

Hardcastle, Nick, illus. Vampire Stories. 2004. (Red Hot Reads Ser.). 224p. (J). (gr. k-3). pap. 6.95 (978-0-7534-5735-1(0) , Kingfisher) Houghton Mifflin Co. Trade & Reference Div.

Hautman, Pete. Sweetblood. 2003. (Illus.). 192p. (YA). 16.95 (978-0-689-85048-6(4)) Simon & Schuster Children's Publishing.

Henderson, Alice. Night Terrors. 2005. (Buffy the Vampire Slayer Ser.). 320p. (YA). pap. 6.99 (978-1-4169-0927-9(3) , Simon Spotlight Entertainment) Simon & Schuster.

—Portal Through Time. 2006. (Buffy the Vampire Slayer Ser.). 352p. (YA). pap. 6.99 (978-1-4169-1918-6(X) , Simon Spotlight Entertainment) Simon & Schuster.

Henson, Heather, et al. The Vampire Bunny. Mack, Jeff, tr. Mack, Jeff, illus. 2004. (Bunnicula & Friends Ser.: Vol. 1). 48p. (J). 14.95 (978-0-689-85724-9(1) , Atheneum) Simon & Schuster Children's Publishing.

Hill, William. The Vampire Hunters. 286p. (YA). (gr. 7-12). 2004. 19.95 (978-1-890611-05-7(0)); 1999. pap. 12.95 (978-1-890611-02-6(6)) Otter Creek Pr., Inc.

Hoffman, Mallory. Touched by a Vampire. 2005. 70p. pap. 14.95 (978-1-4137-6583-0(1)) PublishAmerica, Inc.

Holder, Nancy. The Angel Chronicles. (Buffy the Vampire Slayer Ser.: No. 6). (Illus.). (YA). (gr. 7 up). Vol. 1. 1998. 224p. pap. 5.99 (978-0-671-02133-7(8)); Vol. 3. 1999. 192p. pap. 5.99 (978-0-671-02631-8(3)) Simon & Schuster Children's Publishing. (Simon Pulse).

—Blood & Fog. 2003. (Buffy the Vampire Slayer Ser.: Vol. 16). 304p. (YA). mass mkt. 6.99 (978-0-7434-0039-8(9) , Simon Pulse) Simon & Schuster Children's Publishing.

—Book of Fours. 2002. (gr. 7-12). lib. bdg. 14.15 (978-0-613-63260-7(5)) Tandem Library Bks.

—The Evil That Men Do. 2000. (Buffy the Vampire Slayer Ser.: No. 6). 352p. (YA). pap. 6.99 (978-0-671-02635-6(6) , Simon Pulse) Simon & Schuster Children's Publishing.

—Journals of Rupert Giles. 2002. (gr. 7-12). lib. bdg. 14.15 (978-0-613-63306-2(7)) Tandem Library Bks.

—Not Forgotten. 2000. (Angel Ser.: No. 2). 256p. (YA). (gr. 7 up). pap. 5.99 (978-0-671-04145-8(2) , Simon Pulse) Simon & Schuster Children's Publishing.

—Not Forgotten. 2000. (gr. 7-12). lib. bdg. 14.15 (978-0-613-28001-3(6)) Tandem Library Bks.

Holder, Nancy, et al. Tales of the Slayer, Vol. 1. 2001. (Buffy the Vampire Slayer Ser.: Vol. 22). 288p. (YA). pap. 9.99 (978-0-7434-0045-9(3) , Simon Pulse) Simon & Schuster Children's Publishing.

Hopkins, Audrey. Vinny Drake Is One. Flook, Helen, illus. 2007. (Tiger Ser.). 64p. (J). 9.95 (***978-1-84270-437-0(0)**) Andersen GBR. *Dist:* Independent Pubs. Group.

Howe, Deborah & Howe, James. A Rabbit-Tale of Mystery. Daniel, Alan, illus. 2006. 128p. (J). pap. 4.99 (978-1-4169-2817-1(0) , Aladdin) Simon & Schuster Children's Publishing.

Howe, James. Bunnicula & Friends: Hot Fudge. Mack, Jeff, illus. 2004. 42p. (J). lib. bdg. 15.00 (***978-1-4242-1149-4(2)**) Fitzgerald Bks.

—Bunnicula Strikes Again! 2004. (Bunnicula Ser.). 116p. (J). (gr. 3-7). pap. 29.00 incl. audio (978-0-8072-8213-7(8) , Listening Library) Random Hse. Audio Publishing Group.

—Bunnicula Strikes Again! Daniel, Alan, illus. (Bunnicula Ser.). (J). 2007. 144p. pap. 5.99 (***978-1-4169-3968-9(7)** , Aladdin); 1999. 128p. (gr. 3-5). 16.00 (978-0-689-81463-1(1) , Atheneum) Simon & Schuster Children's Publishing.

—Bunnicula Strikes Again! 2001. (Bunnicula Ser.). (gr. 3-6). lib. bdg. 13.00 (978-0-613-49480-9(6)) Tandem Library Bks.

—The Celery Stalks at Midnight. unabr. ed. 2004. (Bunnicula Ser.). 111p. (J). (gr. 3-7). pap. 29.00 incl. audio (978-0-8072-8357-8(6) , YA173SP, Listening Library) Random Hse. Audio Publishing Group.

—The Celery Stalks at Midnight. Morrill, Leslie H., illus. 2006. (Bunnicula Ser.). 144p. (J). pap. 4.99 (978-1-4169-2814-0(6) , Aladdin) Simon & Schuster Children's Publishing.

—The Celery Stalks at Midnight. 2002. (Bunnicula Ser.). (gr. 3-6). lib. bdg. 13.00 (978-0-613-50190-3(X)) Tandem Library Bks.

—Hot Fudge. Mack, Jeff, tr. Mack, Jeff, illus. 2004. (Bunnicula & Friends Ser.). 48p. (J). 14.95 (978-0-689-85725-6(X) , Atheneum) Simon & Schuster Children's Publishing.

—Rabbit-Cadabra! Daniel, Alan, illus. 1999. (Bunnicula & Friends Ser.). 48p. (J). (gr. k-3). pap. 5.95 (978-0-688-16699-1(7)) HarperCollins Pubs.

Jezo & Jozev. Journal of the Vampire Hunter. 2006. (Illus.). 64p. (YA). pap. 5.95 (***978-1-59796-089-2(6));** pap. 5.95 (***978-1-59796-088-5(8)**) DrMaster Pubns. Inc.

Jones, Marcia Thornton & Dadey, Debbie. Vampire Baby. 1999. (Bailey City Monsters Ser.: No. 7). (Illus.). 80p. (J). (gr. 2-4). pap. 3.99 (978-0-439-05872-8(4)) Scholastic, Inc.

—Vampire Baby. 1999. (Bailey City Monsters Ser.: No. 7). (J). (gr. 2-4). (978-0-606-17059-8(6)) Tandem Library Bks.

—Vampire Trouble. 1998. (Bailey City Monsters Ser.: No. 3). (Illus.). 80p. (J). (gr. 2-4). pap. 3.99 (978-0-590-10846-1(8)) Scholastic, Inc.

Jozev. Journal of the Vampire Hunter. 2006. (Illus.). 64p. (YA). pap. 5.95 (978-1-59796-090-8(X)) DrMaster Pubns. Inc.

Judal. Vampire Game, 12, 5. Hiroe, Ikoi, tr. from JPN. rev. ed. 2004. (Graphic Novel-Manga Ser.). (Illus.). 192p. (YA). pap. 9.99 (978-1-59182-557-9(1) , Tokyopop Adult) TOKYOPOP, Inc.

—Vampire Game, 3 vols. rev. ed. 2003. (Graphic Novel-Manga Ser.). (Illus.). 192p. Vol. 2. (gr. 8 up). pap. 9.99 (978-1-59182-370-4(6)); Vol. 3. pap. 9.99 (978-1-59182-371-1(4)) TOKYOPOP, Inc. (Tokyopop Adult).

—Vampire Game, 12 vols. Hiroe, Ikoi, tr. from JPN. rev. ed. 2004. (Graphic Novel-Manga Ser.). (Illus.). 192p. Vol. 4. pap. 9.99 (978-1-59182-556-2(3)); Vol. 6. pap. 9.99 (978-1-59182-558-6(X)) TOKYOPOP, Inc. (Tokyopop Adult).

—Vampire Game, 12 vols., Vol. 7. Coffman, Patrick, tr. from JPN. rev. ed. 2004. (Graphic Novel-Manga Ser.). (Illus.). 192p. pap. 9.99 (978-1-59182-559-3(8) , Tokyopop Adult) TOKYOPOP, Inc.

Jungman, Ann. Vlad the Drac. 2006. (Vlad the Drac Ser.). (Illus.). 128p. (J). pap. 6.95 (978-1-903015-22-3(7)) Barn Owl Bks, London GBR. *Dist:* Independent Pubs. Group.

—Vlad the Drac Superstar. unabr. ed. 1998. (J). pap. 24.95 incl. audio (978-0-7540-6202-8(3)) BBC Audiobooks America.

—Vlad the Drac Superstar. 2006. (Vlad the Drac Ser.). (Illus.). 123p. (J). pap. 6.95 (978-1-903015-45-2(6)) Barn Owl Bks, London GBR. *Dist:* Independent Pubs. Group.

Keating, T. P. Bleeding Hearts: the Diary of a Country Vampire. 2005. 272p. (YA). pap. 12.48 (978-1-4116-4815-9(3)) Lulu.com.

Kenner, Julie. Good Ghouls Do. 2007. 320p. (YA). (gr. 12 up). pap. 9.99 (*978-0-425-21703-0(5) , Berkley Trade) Penguin Group (USA) Inc.

Kenner, Julie. The Good Ghouls' Guide to Getting Even. 2007. 256p. (YA). pap. 9.99 (978-0-425-21391-9(9) , Berkley Trade) Penguin Group (USA) Inc.

Klause, Annette Curtis. The Silver Kiss. 2007. 224p. (J). pap. 8.99 (*978-0-385-73422-6(0)); lib. bdg. 11.99 (*978-0-385-90435-3(5)) Random Hse. Children's Bks. (Delacorte Bks. for Young Readers).

—The Silver Kiss. 1999. (J). (gr. 7-12). lib. bdg. 13.55 (978-0-8335-9378-8(1)) Tandem Library Bks.

Knudsen, Michelle. Case of Vampire Vivian. 2003. (gr. k-3). lib. bdg. 13.00 (978-0-613-79275-2(0)) Tandem Library Bks.

Lane, Travis. Redhaze: Trilogy. 2004. 192p. pap. 19.95 (978-1-4137-6094-1(5)) PublishAmerica, Inc.

Laurence, James. Faith Trials. 2001. (gr. 7-12). lib. bdg. 14.15 (978-0-613-63284-3(2)) Tandem Library Bks.

Leblanc, Louise. Leo's Midnight Rescue. Prud'homme, Jules, illus. 2004. 62p. (J). lib. bdg. 12.00 (*978-1-4242-1217-0(0)) Fitzgerald Bks.

—Leo's Midnight Rescue. Cummins, Sarah, tr. from FRE. Prud'homme, Jules, illus. 2004. (First Novel Ser.). 64p. (J). (gr. 2-5). 4.95 (978-0-88780-640-7(6)); (*978-0-88780-641-4(4)) Formac Publishing Co., Ltd. CAN. *Dist:* Casemate Pubs. & Bk. Distributors, LLC.

Leblanc, Louise & Prud'Homme, Jules. Un Vampire en Detresse. 2000. (Premier Roman Ser.). (FRE.). 64p. (J). (gr. 2-5). pap. (978-2-89021-411-8(7)) Diffusion du livre Mirabel.

Leblanc, Louise & Prud'homme, Jules. Les Vampires Sortent de L'ombre. 2003. (Premier Roman Ser.). (FRE., Illus.). 64p. (J). (gr. 1-4). pap. (978-2-89021-609-9(8)) Diffusion du livre Mirabel.

Levy, Robert Joseph. Go Ask Malice: A Slayer's Diary. 2006. (Buffy the Vampire Slayer Ser.). 256p. (YA). pap. 9.99 (978-1-4169-1587-4(7) , Simon Spotlight Entertainment) Simon & Schuster.

Macdonald, Fiona & Stoker, Bram. Dracula. Gelev, Penko, illus. 2007. (Graphic Classics Ser.). 48p. (J). (gr. 3 up). 15.99 (*978-0-7641-6054-7(0)); pap. 8.99 (*978-0-7641-3778-5(6)) Barron's Educational Series, Inc.

Mancusi, Mari. Girls That Growl. 2007. 249p. (YA). (gr. 12-12). per. 9.99 (*978-0-425-21716-0(7) , Berkley Trade) Penguin Group (USA) Inc.

Mancusi, Mari. Stake That! 2006. 288p. (YA). (gr. 12). pap. 9.99 (978-0-425-21210-3(6) , Berkley Trade) Penguin Group (USA) Inc.

Mancusi, Marianne. Boys That Bite. 2006. 224p. (YA). (gr. 12). pap. 9.99 (978-0-425-20942-4(3) , Berkley Trade) Penguin Group (USA) Inc.

Marini, Enrico & Dufaux, Jean. Rapaces, Vol. 4. 2005. (SPA., Illus.). 56p. pap. 17.95 (978-1-59497-107-5(2)) Public Square Bks.

Mariotte, Jeff. Close to the Ground. 2000. (Angel Ser.: No. 4). 320p. (YA). (gr. 7 up). pap. 5.99 (978-0-671-04147-2(9) , Simon Pulse) Simon & Schuster Children's Publishing.

—Close to the Ground. 2002. (gr. 7-12). lib. bdg. 14.15 (978-0-613-63187-7(0)) Tandem Library Bks.

—Haunted. 2002. (Angel Ser.: Vol. 11). (Illus.). 336p. (YA). pap. 5.99 (978-0-7434-2748-7(3) , Simon Pulse) Simon & Schuster Children's Publishing.

—Haunted. 2002. (gr. 7-12). lib. bdg. 14.15 (978-0-613-63200-3(1)) Tandem Library Bks.

—Stranger to the Sun. 2002. (gr. 7-12). lib. bdg. 14.15 (978-0-613-63236-2(2)) Tandem Library Bks.

McAllister, Peter. Bites: Dracula Tooth: Beware Pains in the Neck! rev. ed. 2008. (Nibbles, Bites, & Chomps: Ser.). (Illus.). 112p. (J). pap. 3.95 (*978-0-7624-3055-0(9) , Running Pr. Kids) Running Pr. Bk. Pubs.

McCann, James. Pyre. 2007. 180p. (J). pap. 8.95 (978-1-894965-66-8(3)) Simply Read Bks. CAN. *Dist:* Perseus Distribution.

—Rancour. 2005. (Illus.). 240p. (J). (gr. 10). pap. 10.95 (978-1-894965-31-6(0)) Simply Read Bks. CAN. *Dist:* Perseus Distribution.

Mead, Richelle. Vampire Academy. 2007. 336p. (J). (gr. 7). pap. 8.99 (*978-1-59514-174-3(X) , Razorbill) Penguin Group (USA) Inc.

Mercer, Sienna. Fangtastic! 2007. (My Sister the Vampire Ser.: No. 2). 208p. (J). (gr. 3-7). pap. 5.99 (*978-0-06-087115-4(6) , Harper Trophy) HarperCollins Pubs.

—My Sister the Vampire #4: Vampalicious! 2008. (My Sister the Vampire Ser.). 208p. (J). pap. 5.99 (*978-0-06-087121-5(0) , Harper Trophy) HarperCollins Pubs.

—Re-Vamped! 2007. (My Sister the Vampire Ser.: No. 3). 208p. (J). (gr. 3-7). pap. 5.99 (*978-0-06-087118-5(0) , Harper Trophy) HarperCollins Pubs.

—Switched. 2007. (My Sister the Vampire Ser.). 208p. (J). 16.99 (*978-0-06-087111-6(3)); (gr. 3-7). pap. 5.99 (*978-0-06-087113-0(X) , Harper Trophy) HarperCollins Pubs.

Metz, Melinda & Burns, Laura J. Colony. 2005. (Buffy the Vampire Slayer Ser.). 256p. (YA). pap. 6.99 (978-1-4169-0057-3(8) , Simon Spotlight Entertainment) Simon & Schuster.

Meyer, Stephenie. Eclipse. rev. ed. 2007. (Twilight Saga Ser.). 640p. (YA). (gr. 7 up). 18.99 (*978-0-316-16020-9(2)) Little, Brown Bks. for Young Readers.

—New Moon. 2006. (Twilight Saga Ser.). 608p. (J). (gr. 7 up). 18.99 (978-0-316-16019-3(9) , Tingley, Megan Bks.) Little, Brown Bks. for Young Readers.

—Twilight. 2005. (Twilight Saga Ser.). 512p. (J). (gr. 9-17). 18.99 (978-0-316-16017-9(2)) Little Brown & Co.

—Twilight. 2006. (Twilight Saga Ser.). 544p. (J). (gr. 9-12). reprint ed. pap. 9.99 (978-0-316-01584-4(9) , Tingley, Megan Bks.) Little, Brown Bks. for Young Readers.

Meyer, Stephenie. The Twilight Collection. rev. ed. 2007. (YA). (gr. 7-17). 55.00 (*978-0-316-00372-8(7)) Little, Brown Bks. for Young Readers.

Myers, Bill. Undead. 2002. (gr. 3-6). lib. bdg. 13.00 (978-0-613-76882-5(5)) Tandem Library Bks.

Navarro, Yvonne. Paleo. 2000. (Buffy the Vampire Slayer Ser.: No. 11). 272p. (YA). pap. 6.99 (978-0-7434-0034-3(8) , Simon Pulse) Simon & Schuster Children's Publishing.

—Paleo. 2000. (gr. 7-12). lib. bdg. 15.30 (978-0-613-63329-1(6)) Tandem Library Bks.

—Shattered Twilight: Wicked Willow Two. 2004. (Buffy the Vampire Slayer Ser.). 272p. (YA). mass mkt. 13.95 (978-0-689-86953-2(3) , Simon Spotlight Entertainment) Simon & Schuster.

—Tempted Champions. 2001. (Buffy the Vampire Slayer Ser.: Vol. 13). (Illus.). 256p. (YA). pap. 6.99 (978-0-7434-0036-7(4) , Simon Pulse) Simon & Schuster Children's Publishing.

—Tempted Champions. 2002. (gr. 7-12). lib. bdg. 15.30 (978-0-613-63352-9(0)) Tandem Library Bks.

—The Willow Files, Vol. 1. 1999. (Buffy the Vampire Slayer Ser.: No. 13). (Illus.). (YA). (gr. 7 up). (978-0-606-18367-3(1)) Tandem Library Bks.

Niles, Steve. 30 Days of Night. 2003. (gr. 7-12). lib. bdg. 28.05 (978-0-613-66800-2(6)) Tandem Library Bks.

Odom, Mel. Cursed. 2003. (Buffy the Vampire Slayer & Angel Crossover Ser.). 448p. mass mkt. 7.99 (978-0-689-86437-7(X) , Simon Pulse) Simon & Schuster Children's Publishing.

—Image. 2002. (Angel Ser.: Bk. 12). (Illus.). 240p. (YA). pap. 5.99 (978-0-7434-2750-0(5) , Simon Pulse) Simon & Schuster Children's Publishing.

—Redemption. 2000. (gr. 7-12). lib. bdg. 14.15 (978-0-613-28038-9(5)) Tandem Library Bks.

—Revenant. 2001. (Buffy the Vampire Slayer Ser.: No. 12). 400p. (YA). pap. 6.99 (978-0-7434-0035-0(6) , Simon Pulse) Simon & Schuster Children's Publishing.

—Revenant. 2001. (gr. 7-12). lib. bdg. 15.30 (978-0-613-63340-6(7)) Tandem Library Bks.

—Tales of the Slayer. 2001. (gr. 7-12). lib. bdg. 17.65 (978-0-613-63351-2(2)) Tandem Library Bks.

Otomo, Katsuhiro. Hıpıra: The Little Vampire. 2005. (Illus.). 48p. 13.95 (978-1-59582-002-0(7)) DH Pr.

Pantin, Yolanda. Raton y Vampiro en el Castillo. Cabrera, Marcela, illus. (SPA.). (J). pap. 7.96 (978-980-01-0881-9(5)) Monte Avila Editores Latinoamericana CA VEN. *Dist:* Lectorum Pubns., Inc.

—Raton y Vampiro Se Concen. Cabrera, Marcela, illus. (SPA.). (J). pap. 6.00 (978-980-01-0480-4(1)) Monte Avila Editores Latinoamericana CA VEN. *Dist:* Lectorum Pubns., Inc.

Papineau, Lucie. Bebe-Vampire, Gloups! ed. 2004. (FRE., Illus.). (J). (gr. k-3). spiral bd. (978-0-616-07259-2(7)) Canadian National Institute for the Blind/Institut National Canadien pour les Aveugles.

Patrick, David. Nero Demare & the Legend of the Vampires. 2007. 284p. (YA). per. 17.95 (*978-0-595-42014-8(1)) iUniverse, Inc.

Petrie, Doug. Ring of Fire. 2000. (Buffy the Vampire Slayer Ser.). (Illus.). 80p. (YA). (gr. 7 up). pap. 9.95 (978-1-56971-482-9(7)) Dark Horse Comics.

Poploff, Michelle. Roses Are Dread, Violets Are Boo! A Vampire Valentine Story. Basso, Bill, illus. 2002. 48p. (J). (gr. 2-4). pap. 3.99 (978-0-439-26076-3(0) , Scholastic Paperbacks) Scholastic, Inc.

Poulsen, David A. The Book of Vampire. 4th rev. ed. 2007. (Salt & Pepper Chronicles). 160p. (gr. 3-7). pap. 6.95 (*978-1-55263-805-7(7)) Key Porter Bks. CAN. *Dist:* Perseus Distribution.

—The Vampire's Visit No. 1: The Salt & Pepper Chronicles. 2007. 168p. 6.95 (*978-1-55263-721-0(2)) Key Porter Bks. CAN. *Dist:* Perseus Distribution.

Ratnett, Michael. Dracula Steps Out. Goulding, June & Smyth, Iain, illus. 2005. 12p. (J). (gr. k-4). reprint ed. 16.00 (978-0-7567-8585-7(5)) DIANE Publishing Co.

Rees, Douglas. Vampire High. 2005. 240p. (YA). (gr. 7 up). mass mkt. 5.99 (978-0-440-23834-8(X) , Laurel Leaf) Random Hse. Children's Bks.

Rodgers, Frank. Eyetooth. l.t. ed. 2006. pap. 16.95 (978-1-4056-6041-9(4)) BBC Audio GBR. *Dist:* BBC Audiobooks America.

Rooke, Sebastian. The Vampire Plagues: Mexico 1850. 2005. (Apple Ser.: Vol. 3). 192p. (J). (gr. 4-7). pap. 5.99 (978-0-439-63394-9(X) , Scholastic Paperbacks) Scholastic, Inc.

—The Vampire Plagues II: Paris 1850. 2005. (Vampire Plagues II Ser.: Vol. 2). 208p. (J). pap. 5.99 (978-0-439-63393-2(1) , Scholastic Paperbacks) Scholastic, Inc.

Roy, Ron. The Vampire's Vacation. Gurney, John Steven, illus. 2004. (A to Z Mysteries Ser.: No. 22). 96p. (J). (gr. 1-4). pap. 3.99 (978-0-375-82479-1(0)); lib. bdg. 11.99 (978-0-375-92479-8(5)) Random Hse. Children's Bks. (Random Hse. Bks. for Young Readers).

Sanvoisin, Eric. Ink Drinker. 2002. (gr. 3-6). lib. bdg. 13.00 (978-0-613-59386-1(3)) Tandem Library Bks.

Schreiber, Ellen. Dance with a Vampire. 2007. (Vampire Kisses Ser.: Bk. 4). 192p. (J). lib. bdg. 16.89 (*978-0-06-113224-7(1)); (gr. 7 up). 15.99 (*978-0-06-113223-0(3)) HarperCollins Pubs. (HarperTeen).

—Kissing Coffins. (Vampire Kisses Ser.: Bk. 2). 2007. 240p. (J). pap. 5.99 (*978-0-06-077624-4(2) , HarperTeen); 2005. 176p. (J). (gr. 7 up). lib. bdg. 16.89 (978-0-06-077623-7(4) , Tegen, Katherine Bks); 2nd ed. 2005. 165p. (gr. 7 up). 16.99 (978-0-06-077622-0(6) , Tegen, Katherine Bks) HarperCollins Pubs.

—Vampire Kisses. (Vampire Kisses Ser.: Bk. 1). (gr. 7 up). 2003. 208p. (J). 16.99 (978-0-06-009334-1(X) , Tegen, Katherine Bks); 2003. 208p. (J). lib. bdg. 16.89 (978-0-06-009335-8(8) , Tegen, Katherine Bks); 2005. 272p. (YA). reprint ed. pap. 5.99 (978-0-06-009336-5(6) , Harper Trophy) HarperCollins Pubs.

—Vampireville. (Vampire Kisses Ser.: Bk. 3). (J). 2007. 208p. pap. 5.99 (*978-0-06-077627-5(7) , HarperTeen); 2006. 192p. 15.99 (978-0-06-077625-1(0) , Tegen, Katherine Bks); 2006. 192p. lib. bdg. 16.89 (978-0-06-077626-8(9)) HarperCollins Pubs.

Scott, Stefanie. Meet the Stars of Buffy the Vampire Slayer. 1998. (Illus.). 128p. (J). (gr. 6-8). pap. 4.99 (978-0-590-51477-4(6)) Scholastic, Inc.

Scroggs, Kirk Brandon. Dracula vs. Grampa at the Monster Truck Spectacular. 2006. (Wiley & Grampa's Creature Features Ser.: No. 1). (Illus.). 112p. (J). (gr. 3-7). pap. 2.99 (978-0-316-05941-1(2)) Little Brown & Co.

Sedgwick, Marcus. My Swordhand Is Singing. 2007. 208p. (YA). (gr. 7). 15.99 (*978-0-375-84689-2(1)); lib. bdg. 18.99 (*978-0-375-94689-9(6)) Random Hse. Children's Bks. (Lamb, Wendy).

Serra, Louis. The Reluctant Vampire. 2006. (YA). per. 12.00 (*978-0-9769132-5-2(9)) Capri Publishing.

Sfar, Joann. Little Vampire Does Kung Fu! Sfar, Joann, illus. 2003. (Illus.). 40p. (J). 12.95 (978-0-689-85769-0(1)) Simon & Schuster Children's Publishing.

Shan, Darren, pseud. Allies of the Night. (Cirque du Freak: Bk. 8). (J). (gr. 5-17). 2006. 224p. mass mkt. 6.99 (978-0-316-10653-5(4)); 2005. 256p. pap. 7.99 (978-0-316-11437-0(5)) Little Brown & Co.

—Allies of the Night. 2004. (Cirque du Freak: Bk. 8). (Illus.). 192p. (J). (gr. 5-17). 15.99 (978-0-316-15570-0(5)) Little, Brown Bks. for Young Readers.

—Cirque du Freak: Trials of Death; the Vampire Prince; Hunters of the Dusk; Allies of the Night. 2006. (Cirque du Freak: No. 2). (J). (gr. 7-17). pap. 27.99 (978-0-316-01684-1(5)) Little Brown & Co.

—Cirque du Freak Boxed Set: Killers of the Dawn; The Lake of Souls; Lord of the Shadows; Sons of Destiny, 3. 2007. (Cirque du Freak: Bks. 9-12). (J). (gr. 7-17). pap. 27.99 (*978-0-316-06697-6(4)) Little, Brown Bks. for Young Readers.

—Hunters of the Dusk. 2005. (Cirque du Freak: Bk. 7). (J). (gr. 5-17). 256p. mass mkt. 6.99 (978-0-316-00098-7(1)); (Illus.). 224p. pap. 7.99 (978-0-316-60211-2(6)) Little Brown & Co.

—Hunters of the Dusk. 2004. (Cirque du Freak: Bk. 7). (Illus.). 224p. (J). (gr. 5-17). 15.95 (978-0-316-60596-0(4)) Little, Brown Bks. for Young Readers.

—Killers of the Dawn. (Cirque du Freak: Bk. 9). 224p. (J). (gr. 5-17). 2006. mass mkt. 6.99 (978-0-316-01666-7(7)); 2006. pap. 7.99 (978-0-316-10654-2(2)); 2005. 15.99 (978-0-316-15626-4(4)) Little Brown & Co.

—The Lake of Souls. (Cirque du Freak: Bk. 10). (J). (gr. 5-17). 2006. 272p. pap. 7.99 (978-0-316-01665-0(9)); 2005. (Illus.). 302p. 16.99 (978-0-316-15627-1(2)) Little Brown & Co.

—The Lake of Souls. 2007. (Cirque du Freak: Bk. 10). 288p. (J). (gr. 5-17). mass mkt. 6.99 (978-0-316-15437-6(7)) Little, Brown Bks. for Young Readers.

—A Living Nightmare. 2001. (Cirque du Freak: Bk. 1). (J). 272p. (gr. k-3). 15.95 (978-0-316-60340-9(6)); (Illus.). viii, 279p. (gr. 3-6). pap. (978-0-316-64852-3(3)) Little, Brown Bks. for Young Readers.

—Lord of the Shadows. 2006. (Cirque du Freak: Bk. 11). (Illus.). 240p. (J). (gr. 3-7). 16.99 (978-0-316-15628-8(0)) Little Brown & Co.

—Lord of the Shadows. 2007. (Cirque du Freak: Bk. 11). (J). (gr. 3-7). 208p. mass mkt. 6.99 (*978-0-316-01662-9(4)); 256p. pap. 7.99 (*978-0-316-01661-2(6)) Little, Brown Bks. for Young Readers.

—Sons of Destiny. 2006. (Cirque du Freak: Bk. 12). 256p. (J). (gr. 3-7). 16.99 (978-0-316-15629-5(9)) Little Brown & Co.

—Sons of Destiny. 2007. (Cirque du Freak: Bk. 12). 272p. (J). (gr. 3-7). mass mkt. 6.99 (*978-0-316-01664-3(0)); (gr. 7-17). pap. 7.99 (*978-0-316-01663-6(2)) Little, Brown Bks. for Young Readers.

—Trials of Death. (Cirque du Freak: Bk. 5). 224p. (J). (gr. 5-17). 2005. mass mkt. 6.99 (978-0-316-00095-6(7)); 2004. pap. 7.99 (978-0-316-60395-9(3)); 2003. (Illus.). 16.99 (978-0-316-60367-6(8)) Little, Brown Bks. for Young Readers.

—Tunnels of Blood. 2004. (Cirque du Freak: Bk. 3). (Illus.). 240p. (J). (gr. 3-7). mass mkt. 6.99 (978-0-316-90573-2(9)) Little, Brown Bks. for Young Readers.

—Vampire Mountain. (Cirque du Freak: Bk. 4). (J). 2004. 208p. (gr. 3-7). mass mkt. 6.99 (978-0-316-90574-9(7)); 2003. (Illus.). 208p. (gr. 5-8). pap. 7.99 (978-0-316-60542-7(5)); 2003. (Illus.). 240p. (gr. 5-8). pap. 7.99 (978-0-316-60608-0(1)); 2002. (Illus.). 208p. (gr. 5-17). 15.95 (978-0-316-60806-0(8)); 2002. 240p. (gr. 5-17). 16.99 (978-0-316-60763-6(0)) Little, Brown Bks. for Young Readers.

—Vampire Mountain. 2003. (Cirque du Freak: Bk. 4). (gr. 5-8). lib. bdg. 14.75 (978-0-613-71781-6(3)); (J). (gr. 3-6). lib. bdg. 15.30 (978-0-613-71782-3(1)) Tandem Library Bks.

—The Vampire Prince. 2005. (Cirque du Freak: Bk. 6). 208p. (J). (gr. 5-17). mass mkt. 6.99 (978-0-316-00097-0(3)) Little Brown & Co.

—The Vampire Prince. (Cirque du Freak: Bk. 6). (J). (gr. 5-17). 2004. 208p. pap. 7.99 (978-0-316-60274-7(4)); 2003. 168p. 15.99 (978-0-316-60709-4(6)) Little, Brown Bks. for Young Readers.

—The Vampire's Assistant. (Cirque du Freak: Bk. 2). 256p. 2004. (Illus.). (gr. 3-7). mass mkt. 6.99 (978-0-316-90572-5(0)); 2002. (Illus.). (J). (gr. 5-17). pap. 7.99 (978-0-316-60684-4(7)); 2001. (J). (gr. 5-17). 15.95 (978-0-316-60610-3(3)) Little, Brown Bks. for Young Readers.

—The Vampire's Assistant. 2001. (Cirque du Freak: Bk. 2). (J). (gr. 3-6). lib. bdg. 14.45 (978-0-613-52640-1(6)) Tandem Library Bks.

—The Vampire's Assistant. l.t. ed. 2002. (Cirque du Freak: Bk. 2). 240p. (J). 24.95 (978-0-7862-3734-0(1)) Thomson Gale.

Smith, Cynthia Leitich. Tantalize. 2007. (Illus.). 336p. (YA). (gr. 9). 16.99 (978-0-7636-2791-1(7)) Candlewick Pr.

Smith, L. J. The Awakening. 1999. (Vampire Diaries: No. 1). 320p. (gr. 7-12). mass mkt. 5.99 (978-0-06-102000-1(1)) HarperCollins Pubs.

—The Vampire Diaries: the Fury & Dark Reunion. 2008. 528p. (J). pap. 8.99 (*978-0-06-114098-3(8) , HarperTeen) HarperCollins Pubs.

—The Vampire Diaries, Volumes I & II. 2007. 560p. (J). pap. 7.99 (*978-0-06-114097-6(X) , HarperTeen) HarperCollins Pubs.

Sommer-Bodenburg, Angela. The Little Vampire. 2005. (Illus.). 144p. (J). pap. 8.99 (*978-1-84270-444-8(3)) Transworld Publishers Ltd. GBR. *Dist:* Independent Pubs. Group.

—The Little Vampire Moves In. 2007. (Little Vampire Ser.). (Illus.). 144p. (J). 9.95 (*978-1-84270-596-4(2)) Andersen GBR. *Dist:* Independent Pubs. Group.

Sommer-Bodenburg, Angela. El Pequeno Vampiro. Glienke, Amelie, illus. 2003. (SPA.). 192p. (J). (gr. 3-5). pap. 11.95 (978-968-19-0673-3(X)) Santillana USA Publishing Co., Inc.

Somper, Justin. Demons of the Ocean. 2006. 336p. (J). (gr. 3-7). 15.99 (978-0-316-01373-4(0)) Little Brown & Co.

—Demons of the Ocean. 2007. 352p. (J). (gr. 3-7). pap. 5.99 (*978-0-316-01444-1(3)) Little, Brown Bks. for Young Readers.

—Vampirates: Tide of Terror. 2nd rev. ed. 2007. 464p. (J). (gr. 3-7). 15.99 (*978-0-316-01374-1(9)) Little, Brown Bks. for Young Readers.

Stafford, Nikki. Bite Me! An Unofficial Guide to the World of Buffy the Vampire Slayer. 1998. (Illus.). 250p. pap. 19.95 (978-1-55022-361-3(5)) ECW Pr. CAN. *Dist:* Independent Pubs. Group.

Stilton, Geronimo. Un granizado de moscas para el Conde. Wolf, Matt, illus. (SPA.). 128p. (J). (gr. 3-5). pap. 7.95 (978-1-59437-452-4(X)) Santillana USA Publishing Co., Inc.

—My Name Is Stilton, Geronimo Stilton. 2005. (Geronimo Stilton Ser.: No. 19). (Illus.). 128p. (J). pap. 5.99 (978-0-439-69142-0(7) , Scholastic Paperbacks) Scholastic, Inc.

—Red Pizzas for a Blue Count. Wolf, Matt & Keys, Larry, illus. 2004. (Geronimo Stilton Ser.: No. 7). 128p. (J). pap. 6.99 (978-0-439-55969-0(3)) Scholastic, Inc.

Stine, R. L. Dangerous Girls. 2003. (J). 256p. 111.92 (978-0-06-056909-9(3)); 256p. 111.92 (978-0-06-056910-5(7)); (Illus.). (gr. 7 up). 13.99 (978-0-06-053080-8(4)) HarperCollins Pubs.

—Vampire Breath. rev. ed. 2005. (Goosebumps Ser.). 128p. (J). (ps-7). pap. 4.99 (978-0-439-72406-7(6)) Scholastic, Inc.

Stoker, Bram. Bram Stoker/Dracula. Redondo, Nestor, illus. 2005. 48p. (gr. 5-8). 25.50 (978-0-7910-9109-8(0)) Facts On File, Inc.

—Bram Stoker's Dracula. Needle, Jan, ed. Blythe, Gary, illus. 2004. 336p. (J). (gr. 7 up). 18.99 (978-0-7636-2508-5(6)) Candlewick Pr.

—Count Dracula. 2004. (Fast Track Classics Ser.). (Illus.). 48p. (J). pap. 8.99 (978-0-237-52401-2(5) , Evans Brothers, Limited) Evans Publishing Group GBR. *Dist:* Independent Pubs. Group.

—Dracula. Redondo, Nestor, illus. 1998. (Illustrated Classic Book Ser.). 61p. (J). (gr. 3 up). pap. 4.95 (978-1-56767-261-9(2)) Educational Insights, Inc.

—Dracula. Moser, Barry, illus. 2000. (Books of Wonder). 430p. (J). (gr. 7-12). 21.95 (978-0-688-13921-6(3)) HarperCollins Pubs.

—Dracula. 2000. 502p. (gr. 4-7). pap. 4.99 (978-0-439-15411-6(1)) Scholastic, Inc.

—Dracula. 1999. (Saddleback Classics). (Illus.). (J). 13.75 (978-0-606-21550-3(6)) Tandem Library Bks.

Stoker, Bram. Dracula. Akib, Jamel, illus. 2007. (Classic Starts Ser.). 151p. (J). (*978-1-4287-4215-4(8)) Sterling Publishing Co., Inc.

Stoker, Bram, et al. Dracula. Marcos, Pablo, illus. 2005. (Great Illustrated Classics Ser.). 239p. (J). (gr. 3-8). 21.35 (978-1-59679-240-1(X) , ABDO & Daughters) ABDO Publishing Co.

Stone, David Lee. The Yowler Foul-Up. 2nd rev. ed. 2006. 304p. (gr. 5-9). pap. 6.99 (978-0-7868-5598-8(3)) Hyperion Pr.

Strasser, Todd. Help! I'm Trapped in a Vampire's Body. 2000. (Help! I'm Trapped Ser.). (J). (gr. 4-7). 11.64 (978-0-606-19565-2(3)) Tandem Library Bks.

Swift, John. Tea with a Vampire. 2007. pap. 9.00 (*978-0-8059-8963-2(3)) Dorrance Publishing Co., Inc.

Tales of the Slayer. 2003. (gr. 7-12). lib. bdg. 18.80 (978-0-613-61822-9(X)) Tandem Library Bks.

Taylor, Drew Hayden. The Night Wanderer: A Native Gothic Novel. 2007. 224p. (YA). (gr. 7-12). 21.95 (*978-1-55451-100-6(3)); pap. 10.95 (*978-1-55451-099-3(6)) Annick Pr., Ltd. CAN. *Dist:* Firefly Bks., Ltd.

Thompson, Kate. Midnight's Choice. unabr. ed. 2004. (Switchers Ser.: Vol. 2). 240p. (J). (gr. 5-9). pap. 38.00 incl. audio (978-0-8072-8769-9(5) , Listening Library) Random Hse. Audio Publishing Group.

—Midnight's Choice. 2000. (J). (978-0-606-20189-6(0)) Tandem Library Bks.

Trent, Tiffany. In the Serpent's Coils. 2007. (Hallowmere Ser.). 312p. (YA). (gr. 7-11). 8.95 (*978-0-7869-4229-9(0) , Mirrorstone) Wizards of the Coast.

Tyche & SparkNotes Staff. Vampire Dreams. 2004. (SAT Vocabulary Novels Ser.). (Illus.). 200p. pap. 7.95 (978-1-4114-0083-2(6)) Spark Publishing Group.

Van Helsing, Cornelius & De Wolff, Gustav. Vampyre: The Terrifying Lost Journal of Dr. Cornelius Van Helsing. 2007. 32p. (J). (gr. 5 up). 19.99 (*978-0-06-124780-4(4)) HarperCollins Pubs.

Vande Velde, Vivian. Companions of the Night. 2002. (gr. 7-12). lib. bdg. 14.10 (978-0-613-55209-7(1)) Tandem Library Bks.

Watson, Andi, et al. Bad Blood. 2000. (Buffy the Vampire Slayer Ser.). (Illus.). 88p. (YA). (gr. 7 up). pap. 9.95 (978-1-56971-445-4(2)) Dark Horse Comics.

—Crash Test Demons. 2000. (Buffy the Vampire Slayer Ser.). (Illus.). 80p. (YA). (gr. 7 up). pap. 9.95 (978-1-56971-461-4(4)) Dark Horse Comics.

—The Remaining Sunlight. 1999. (Buffy the Vampire Slayer Ser.). (Illus.). 88p. (YA). (gr. 7 up). pap. 9.95 (978-1-56971-354-9(5)) Dark Horse Comics.

—Uninvited Guests. 1999. (Buffy the Vampire Slayer Ser.). (Illus.). 96p. (YA). (gr. 7 up). pap. 10.95 (978-1-56971-436-2(3)) Dark Horse Comics.

West, Tracey. The Night Spies. 2007. (Yu-Gi-Oh Gx Ser.). 96p. (J). pap. 4.99 (*978-0-439-88832-5(8)) Scholastic, Inc.

Westerfeld, Scott. Peeps. (YA). (gr. 9-12). 2006. 336p. pap. 8.99 (978-1-59514-083-8(2)); 2005. 320p. 16.99 (978-1-59514-031-9(X)) Penguin Group (USA) Inc. (Razorbill).

Whedon, Joss & Others. Buffy the Vampire Slayer Omnibus Volume 1. 2007. (Illus.). 296p. (YA). pap. 24.95 (*978-1-59307-784-6(X)) Dark Horse Comics.

Wilde, Terry Lee. The Vampire ... in My Dreams. 2007. (YA). pap. (978-1-932815-38-2(4) , Bronze Medallion) Medallion Pr., Inc.

Williams, Tad & Hoffman, Nina Kiriki. Child of an Ancient City. 1999. (J). (978-0-606-16882-3(6)) Tandem Library Bks.

Wilson, Eric G. Vampires of Ottawa. 2001. (Liz Austen Mystery Ser.). (Illus.). 108p. (J). (gr. 3-7). pap. 4.99 (978-1-55143-228-1(5)) Orca Bk. Pubs. USA.

Wolf, P. Hiding in the Darkness. 2005. 362p. pap. 24.95 (978-1-4137-6247-1(6)) PublishAmerica, Inc.

Yamashita, Satsuki, et al, eds. Aquarian Age - Juvenile Orion Illustration Book: Realm of Light. Yamashita, Satsuki, tr. Gokurakuin, Sakurako et al, illus. 2006. (Aquarian Age - Juvenile Orion Ser.). 96p. 19.99 (978-1-59741-108-0(6) , Broccoli Bks.) Broccoli International USA, Inc.

Zornow, Jeff. Werewolf. Zornow, Jeff, illus. 2007. (Graphic Horror Ser.). (Illus.). 32p. (YA). (gr. 5-8). lib. bdg. 27.07 (*978-1-60270-062-8(1) , Graphic Planet) Magic Wagon.

VAN BUREN, MARTIN, 1782-1862

Doak, Robin S. Martin Van Buren. 2003. (Profiles of the Presidents Ser.). (Illus.). 64p. (J). (gr. 4 up). lib. bdg. 23.93 (978-0-7565-0256-0(X)) Compass Point Bks.

Favor, Lesli J. Martin Van Buren. 2003. (Encyclopedia of Presidents Ser.). (Illus.). 110p. (J). 34.00 (978-0-516-22770-2(X) , Children's Pr.) Scholastic Library Publishing.

Jankowski, Susan. Martin Van Buren: A MyReportLinks.com Book. 2002. (Presidents Ser.). (Illus.). 48p. (J). (gr. 4-10). lib. bdg. 25.26 (978-0-7660-5072-3(6) , MyReportLinks.com Bks.) Enslow Pubs., Inc.

Lazo, Caroline Evensen. Martin Van Buren. 2005. (Presidential Leaders Ser.). (Illus.). 112p. (J). (gr. 6-12). 29.27 (978-0-8225-1394-0(3)) Lerner Publishing Group.

Schmidt, Roderic. How to Draw the Life & Times of Martin Van Buren. 2006. (Kid's Guide to Drawing the Presidents of the United States of America Ser.). (J). 25.25 (978-1-4042-2985-3(X) , PowerKids Pr.) Rosen Publishing Group, Inc., The.

Venezia, Mike. Martin Van Buren: Eighth President, 1937-1841. Venezia, Mike, illus. 2005. (Getting to Know the U. S. Presidents Ser.). (Illus.). 32p. (J). (gr. 3-4). pap. 7.95 (978-0-516-27482-9(1) , Children's Pr.) Scholastic Library Publishing.

Venezia, Mike, illus. Martin Van Buren. 2005. (Getting to Know the U. S. Presidents Ser.). 32p. (J). (gr. 3-4). 27.00 (978-0-516-22613-2(4) , Children's Pr.) Scholastic Library Publishing.

Welsbacher, Anne. Martin Van Buren. 2001. (United States Presidents Ser.). (Illus.). 32p. (J). (gr. k-6). lib. bdg. 22.78 (978-1-57765-238-0(X) , Checkerboard Library) ABDO Publishing Co.

VANDALISM

see Crime and Criminals

VAN DIEMAN'S LAND

see Tasmania

VAN GOGH, VINCENT, 1853-1890

see Gogh, Vincent Van, 1853-1890

VANILLA

Karner, Julie. The Biography of Vanilla. 2006. (How Did That Get Here? Ser.). (Illus.). 32p. (J). (978-0-7787-2490-2(5)); (gr. 5). pap. (978-0-7787-2526-8(X)) Crabtree Publishing Co.

VAN LEW, ELIZABETH, 1818-1900

Schoof, Heidi. Elizabeth Van Lew: Civil War Spy. 2005. (Signature Lives Ser.). (Illus.). 112p. (J). (gr. 5-7). (978-0-7565-0985-9(8)) Compass Point Bks.

VAN WINKLE, RIP (FICTITIOUS CHARACTER)—FICTION

Irving, Washington & Busch, Jeffrey. Rip Van Winkle. (Classics Illustrated Ser.). (Illus.). 52p. (YA). pap. 4.95 (978-1-57209-009-5(X)) Classics International Entertainment, Inc.

Irving, Washington & Moses, Will. Rip Van Winkle. 1999. (Illus.). 1p. (J). (ps-3). 17.99 (978-0-399-23152-0(8) , Philomel) Penguin Group (USA) Inc.

VASQUEZ DE CORONADO, FRANCISCO, 1510-1549

see Coronado, Francisco Vasquez de, 1510-1554

VASSALS

see Feudalism

VATICAN CITY

Fox, Martha Capwell. Vatican City. 2005. (Modern Nations Ser.). (Illus.). 112p. (J). (gr. 4-7). lib. bdg. 29.95 (978-1-59018-733-3(4) , 1244593, Lucent Bks.) Thomson Gale.

Parker. The Vatican. 2003. (Holy Places Ser.). (Illus.). 32p. (J). pap. 6.95 (978-1-4109-0054-8(1)) Raintree.

Parker, Victoria. Vatican. 2003. (gr. k-3). lib. bdg. 15.25 (978-0-613-78219-7(4)) Tandem Library Bks.

Rebman, Renee C. The Sistine Chapel. 2000. (Building History Ser.). (Illus.). 96p. (YA). (gr. 6-9). 28.70 (978-1-56006-640-8(7) , Lucent Bks.) Thomson Gale.

Ross, Mandy. The Vatican. 2003. (Holy Places Ser.). (Illus.). 32p. (J). lib. bdg. 24.28 (978-0-7398-6081-6(X)) Raintree.

VEGETABLE ANATOMY

see Plant Anatomy

VEGETABLE GARDENING

see also Vegetables

Ayers, Patricia. A Kid's Guide to How Vegetables Grow. 2000. (Digging in the Dirt Ser.). 24p. (J). (gr. k-4). lib. bdg. 18.75 (978-0-8239-5461-2(7) , PowerKids Pr.) Rosen Publishing Group, Inc., The.

Blackstone, Stella. Making Minestrone. Brooks, Nan, illus. 2000. 32p. (J). (ps-3). 15.99 (978-1-84148-211-8(0)) Barefoot Bks., Inc.

Creasy, Rosalind. Blue Potatoes, Orange Tomatoes: How to Grow a Rainbow Garden. Heller, Ruth, illus. 2000. 40p. (J). (gr. 2-6). pap. 7.95 (978-0-87156-919-6(1)) Sierra Club Bks. for Children.

DK Publishing Staff & Buckingham, Alan. Vegetables. 2008. 352p. (gr. 12). pap. 19.95 (978-0-7566-2890-1(3)) Dorling Kindersley Publishing, Inc.

Kinstad-Pupeza, Lori. Vegetable Gardens. 2002. (Gardening Ser.). (Illus.). 32p. (J). (gr. k-6). lib. bdg. 22.78 (978-1-57765-030-0(1) , Checkerboard Library) ABDO Publishing Co.

Lerner, Carol. My Backyard Garden. 1998. (Illus.). 48p. (J). (ps-3). 16.00 (978-0-688-14755-6(0)) HarperCollins Pubs.

Minden, Cecilia. Gardening by the Numbers. 2008. (J). lib. bdg. 25.26 (*978-1-60279-008-7(6)) Cherry Lake Publishing.

O'Neil, Sarah. Growing Tomatoes. 1999. (ps-2). lib. bdg. 11.80 (978-0-613-19370-2(9)) Tandem Library Bks.

Rendon, Marcie R. & Bellville, Cheryl Walsh. Farmer's Market: Families Working Together. 2001. (Photo Bks.). (Illus.). 48p. (J). (gr. 3-5). lib. bdg. 23.93 (978-1-57505-462-9(0) , Carolrhoda Bks.) Lerner Publishing Group.

Rigby Education Staff. The Vegetable Garden. (Chiquilibros Ser.). (Illus.). (ps-1). 12.00 (978-0-7635-8538-9(6)) Rigby Education.

Sloan, Peter. Growing Beans. 1999. (gr. k-3). lib. bdg. 11.80 (978-0-613-30452-8(7)) Tandem Library Bks.

VEGETABLE GARDENING—FICTION

Cherry, Lynne. How Groundhog's Garden Grew. Cherry, Lynne, illus. 2003. (Illus.). 40p. (J). (ps up). pap. 15.95 (978-0-439-32371-0(1) , Blue Sky Pr., The) Scholastic, Inc.

Mayer, Mercer. Grandma's Garden. 2002. (Little Critter First Readers Ser.). (Illus.). 24p. (J). (gr. k-1). pap. 3.95 (978-1-57768-846-4(5)) School Specialty Publishing.

—Grandma's Garden. 2001. (gr. k-3). lib. bdg. 11.80 (978-0-613-67625-0(4)) Tandem Library Bks.

Roberts, Margiad & Owen, Carys Eurwen. Tecwyn Yn Plannu Tatws. 2005. (WEL., Illus.). 34p. (978-0-86381-408-2(5)) Gwasg Carreg Gwalch.

Tolstoy, Alexei. Enormous Turnip. 2003. (gr. k-3). lib. bdg. 11.80 (978-0-613-64495-2(6)) Tandem Library Bks.

VEGETABLE KINGDOM

see Botany; Plants

VEGETABLES

see also Vegetable Gardening; Vegetarianism

Anderson, Sara & Handprint Books Staff. Vegetables. 2007. 32p. (J). bds. 8.95 (*978-1-59354-189-7(9)) Handprint Bks.

Ayers, Patricia. A Kid's Guide to How Vegetables Grow. 2000. (Digging in the Dirt Ser.). 24p. (J). (gr. k-4). lib. bdg. 18.75 (978-0-8239-5461-2(7) , PowerKids Pr.) Rosen Publishing Group, Inc., The.

Barbaresi, Nina. Funny Fruits & Vegetables Stickers. 2003. (Dover Little Activity Bks.). (Illus.). 4p. (J). pap. 1.50 (978-0-486-43004-1(9)) Dover Pubns., Inc.

Basel, Roberta. From Tomato to Ketchup. 2005. (First Facts Ser.). (Illus.). 24p. (J). (ps-7). lib. bdg. 21.26 (978-0-7368-4286-0(1)) Capstone Pr., Inc.

Benduhn, Tea. Vegetables. 2007. (J). pap. (*978-0-8368-8262-9(8)); 24p. lib. bdg. 19.93 (*978-0-8368-8255-1(5)) Stevens, Gareth Inc. (Weekly Reader Early Learning Library).

—Vegetables: Vegetales. 2007. (SPA & ENG.). (J). pap. (*978-0-8368-8466-1(3) , Weekly Reader Early Learning Library) Stevens, Gareth Inc.

—Vegetables/Vegetales. 2007. (Find Out about Food/Conoce la Comida Ser.). (SPA & ENG.). 24p. (J). (gr. k-2). lib. bdg. 19.93 (*978-0-8368-8459-3(0) , Weekly Reader Early Learning Library) Stevens, Gareth Inc.

Bial, Raymond. The Super Soybean. Bial, Raymond, photos by. 2007. 40p. (J). (gr. 3-6). lib. bdg. 16.95 (*978-0-8075-7549-9(6)) Whitman, Albert & Co.

Branigan, Carrie & Dunne, Richard. Fruits & Vegetables. 2005. (World of Plants Ser.). (Illus.). 31p. (J). (gr. 2-5). lib. bdg. 27.10 (978-1-58340-613-7(1)) Smart Apple Media.

Chandler, Lynda E. Fruits & Vegetables Coloring Book. 2001. (Illus.). 48p. (J). pap. 3.95 (978-0-486-41543-7(0)) Dover Pubns., Inc.

Charney, Steve & Goldbeck, David. The ABC's of Fruits & Vegetables & Beyond: Delicious Alphabet Poems plus Food, Facts & Fun for Eveyrone. Goldbeck, Nikki, ed. Larson, Maria Burgaleta, illus. 2007. 112p. (J). (ps-7). per. 16.95 (978-1-886101-07-4(8)) Ceres Pr.

Dahl, Michael. From the Garden: A Counting Book about Growing Food. Ouren, Todd, illus. 2004. (Know Your Numbers Ser.). 24p. (C). (gr. k-3). 22.60 (978-1-4048-0578-1(8) , 1229520) Picture Window Bks.

Dawson, Susan H. & Norton, Susan R. Pyramid Pal - Vegetables: Eating Should Always Be Fun for a Kid. O'Hare, Mark, illus. 2000. (Adventures in Eating with the Nutrition Champion of Kids Ser.). 16p. (J). pap. 3.00 (978-1-58000-065-9(7)) Griffin Publishing Group.

de la Mare, Walter & Hawkes, Kevin. The Turnip. 2000. (Godine Storyteller Ser.). (Illus.). 32p. pap. 10.95 (978-1-56792-164-9(7)) Godine, David R. Pub.

Deal, Darlene. Play with Your Food & Learn How to Eat Right: Nutritional Book about Fruits & Vegetables. 2004. (ENG & SPA., Illus.). 22p. (J). (gr. 1-4). pap. 9.95 (978-0-9747299-0-9(6)) Deal, Darlene.

Derkazarian, Susan. Fruits & Vegetables. 2005. (Rookie Read-About Health Ser.). (Illus.). 32p. (J). 20.50 (978-0-516-23673-5(3) , Children's Pr.) Scholastic Library Publishing.

DerKazarian, Susan. Fruits & Vegetables. 2006. 32p. (J). (gr. k-2). pap. 5.95 (978-0-516-25926-0(1) , Children's Pr.) Scholastic Library Publishing.

Dwyer, Jacqueline, et al, contrib. by. Vegetables. 2001. (PowerKids Readers Ser.). (Illus.). 24p. (J). (gr. 1). lib. bdg. 16.00 (978-0-8239-5679-1(2) , PKVEGE, PowerKids Pr.) Rosen Publishing Group, Inc., The.

Edwards, Nicola. Vegetables. 2007. (J). lib. bdg. (978-1-4042-3700-1(3) , PowerKids Pr.) Rosen Publishing Group, Inc., The.

Ehlert, Lois. Eating the Alphabet: Fruits & Vegetables from A to Z Lap-Sized Board Book. 2006. (Illus.). 28p. (J). bds. 10.95 (978-0-15-205688-9(2) , Red Wagon Bks.) Harcourt Children's Bks.

Equipo Staff. La Zanahoria y Otras Hortalizas. (Coleccion Mundo Maravilloso). (SPA., Illus.). 48p. (J). (gr. 2-4). (978-84-348-4152-9(5) , SM6991) SM Ediciones ESP. *Dist:* Lectorum Pubns., Inc.

Flagg, Ann. Apples, Pumpkins & Harvest. 1998. (Illus.). 48p. pap. 9.95 (978-0-590-03316-9(6)) Scholastic, Inc.

Franck, Irene M. & Brownstone, David M. Potatoes. 2003. (Illus.). 32p. (J). (978-0-7172-5720-1(7) , Grolier) Scholastic Library Publishing.

Frost, Helen. The Vegetable Group. Saunders-Smith, Gail, ed. 2000. (Food Guide Pyramid Ser.). (Illus.). 24p. (J). (gr. k-1). lib. bdg. 15.93 (978-0-7368-0541-4(9) , Pebble Bks.) Capstone Pr., Inc.

Gibbons, Gail. The Vegetables We Eat. Gibbons, Gail, illus. 2007. (Illus.). 32p. (J). (ps-3). 16.95 (978-0-8234-2001-8(9)) Holiday Hse., Inc.

Graham, Pamela. Big Red Tomato. 2001. (Windows on Literacy Ser.). 32p. (J). (gr. k-2). (978-0-7922-9221-0(9)) National Geographic Society.

Green, Emily K. Vegetables. 2006. (Blastoff! Readers Ser.). (Illus.). 24p. (J). lib. bdg. 16.95 (978-1-60014-002-0(5)) Bellwether Media.

Harcourt School Publishers Staff. The Edible Pyramid: Library Edition. 1999. (Collections Ser.). (Illus.). (J). 4.70 (978-0-15-314348-9(7)) Harcourt Schl. Pubs.

Heurtelou, Maude. Mwen Pito Bwokoli. Hippolyte, Johanne & Corbett, Kecia, illus. 2001. Tr. of I Prefer Broccoli. 14p. (J). (gr. k-2). 19.50 (978-1-58432-080-7(X)); (CRP.). pap. 6.50 (978-1-58432-075-3(3)) Educa Vision.

Hibbert, Clare. The Life of a Broad Bean. 2004. (Raintree Perspectives Ser.). (Illus.). 32p. (J). pap. 7.50 (978-1-4109-0816-2(X)) Harcourt Schl. Pubs.

—The Life of a Broad Bean. 2004. (Life Cycles (Perspectives) Ser.). (Illus.). 32p. (J). (gr. 3-5). lib. bdg. 19.25 (978-1-4109-0541-3(1)) Raintree.

Hortalizas. 2003. (SPA.). (J). (978-84-246-0693-0(0) , GL30335) La Galera, S.A. Editorial ESP. *Dist:* Lectorum Pubns., Inc.

Hughes, Meredith Sayles. Green Power: Leaf & Flower Vegetables. 2005. (Plants We Eat Ser.). (Illus.). 104p. (gr. 6-9). 26.60 (978-0-8225-2839-5(8)) Lerner Publishing Group.

—Stinky & Stringy: Stem & Bulb Vegetables. 1998. (Plants We Eat Ser.). (Illus.). 104p. (gr. 6-9). 26.60 (978-0-8225-2833-3(9)) Lerner Publishing Group.

Hughes, Meredith Sayles & Hughes, E. Thomas. Cool as a Cucumber, Hot as a Pepper: Fruit Vegetables. 1998. (Plants We Eat Ser.). (Illus.). 80p. (J). (gr. 5-7). 26.60 (978-0-8225-2832-6(0) , Lerner Pubns.) Lerner Publishing Group.

Jeunesse, Gallimard. In the Garden. Heliadore, illus. 2003. (First Discovery Look-and-Learn Bks.). 24p. (J). bds. 6.95 (978-0-439-33637-6(6) , Cartwheel Bks.) Scholastic, Inc.

Julius, Jennifer. I Like Potatoes. 2001. (Welcome Bks.). (Illus.). 24p. (J). (ps-2). pap. 4.95 (978-0-516-23059-7(X) , Children's Pr.) Scholastic Library Publishing.

—I Like Potatoes. 2001. (gr. k-3). lib. bdg. 12.95 (978-0-613-52092-8(0)) Tandem Library Bks.

Kalz, Jill. Vegetables. 2003. 24p. (J). lib. bdg. 21.35 (978-1-58340-300-6(0)) Smart Apple Media.

Klingel, Cynthia Fitterer & Noyed, Robert B. Vegetables. Andersen, Gregg, photos by. 2002. (Weekly Reader Early Learning Library). (Illus.). 24p. (J). (ps up). pap. 7.93 (978-0-8368-3149-8(7)); lib. bdg. 19.33 (978-0-8368-3060-6(1)) Stevens, Gareth Inc. (Weekly Reader Early Learning Library).

Landau, Elaine. Tomatoes. 2000. (True Bks.). (Illus.). 48p. (J). (gr. 3-5). pap. 6.95 (978-0-516-26773-9(6) , Children's Pr.) Scholastic Library Publishing.

—Tomatoes. 1999. (gr. 3-6). lib. bdg. 15.25 (978-0-613-37562-7(9)) Tandem Library Bks.

Loves, June. Vegetables. 2004. (Plants Ser.). (Illus.). 32p. (J). (gr. 2-4). 23.00 (978-0-7910-8264-5(4) , Chelsea Hse.) Facts On File, Inc.

Martineau, Susan. Healthy Eating. 2006. (Illus.). 32p. (J). (978-1-58340-896-4(7)) Smart Apple Media.

Maurer, Tracy. Growing Vegetables. 2000. (Green Thumb Guides Ser.). (Illus.). 24p. (J). (gr. 2-6). lib. bdg. 23.93 (978-1-55916-256-2(2)) Rourke Publishing, LLC.

Mayo, Gretchen Will. Frozen Vegetables. 2004. (Weekly Reader Early Learning Library). (Illus.). 24p. (gr. 2 up). (J). pap. 5.95 (978-0-8368-4073-5(9)); (YA). lib. bdg. 19.33 (978-0-8368-4066-7(6)) Stevens, Gareth Inc. (Weekly Reader Early Learning Library).

McMillan, Bruce. Growing Colors. McMillan, Bruce, illus. 2002. (Illus.). (J). 14.43 (978-0-7587-2664-3(3)) Book Wholesalers, Inc.

Mitchell, Judy, ed. More Than One - Fruits & Vegetables. Rojas, Mary Galan, illus. 2001. (Pictures to Color Ser.). 32p. (J). (ps-k). pap. 4.95 (978-1-57310-264-3(4)) Teaching & Learning Co.

Mitchell, Melanie S. Potatoes. (First Step Nonfiction Ser.). (Illus.). (gr. k-2). 2005. 24p. lib. bdg. 17.27 (978-0-8225-4612-2(4)); 2003. 23p. (J). pap. 5.95 (978-0-8225-4613-9(2) , Lerner Pubns.) Lerner Publishing Group.

Moore, Sean. Veggies Smeggies. 2007. (Illus.). 32p. (ps-k). 16.95 (978-1-894965-41-5(8)) Simply Read Bks. CAN. *Dist:* Perseus Distribution.

Morganelli, Adrianna. The Biography of Tomatoes. 2007. (How Did That Get Here? Ser.). (Illus.). 32p. (J). (gr. 2-9). (*978-0-7787-2494-0(8)); pap. (*978-0-7787-2530-5(8)) Crabtree Publishing Co.

Nelson, Robin. Vegetables. 2003. (First Step Nonfiction Ser.). (Illus.). 24p. (J). (gr. k-2). lib. bdg. 18.60 (978-0-8225-4626-9(4)) Lerner Publishing Group.

—Las Verduras. 2003. (First Step Nonfiction Ser.). (SPA., Illus.). 24p. (J). (gr. k-2). lib. bdg. 18.60 (978-0-8225-5059-4(8)) Lerner Publishing Group.

Pickering, Robin. I Like Corn. 2000. (Welcome Bks.). (Illus.). 24p. (J). (ps-2). pap. 4.95 (978-0-516-23009-2(3) , Children's Pr.) Scholastic Library Publishing.

—I Like Corn. 2000. (gr. k-3). lib. bdg. 12.95 (978-0-613-52086-7(6)) Tandem Library Bks.

Potatoes, Potatoes: Level J, 6 vols. (Wonder Worldtm Ser.). 16p. 29.95 (978-0-7802-2904-4(5)) Wright Group, The.

Rodger, Ellen. The Biography of Potatoes. 2007. (How Did That Get Here? Ser.). (Illus.). 32p. (J). (gr. 2-9). (*978-0-7787-2492-6(1)); pap. (*978-0-7787-2528-2(6)) Crabtree Publishing Co.

Rondeau, Amanda. Vegetables Are Vital. 2003. (What Should I Eat? Ser.). (Illus.). 23p. (J). (ps-3). lib. bdg. 19.93 (978-1-57765-835-1(3) , SandCastle) ABDO Publishing Co.

Rosa-Mendoza, Gladys, creator. Fruits & Vegetables. 2004. (English-Spanish Foundations Ser.: Vol. 10). Tr. of Frutas y Vegetales. (SPA & ENG., Illus.). 22p. (J). bds. 6.95 (978-1-931398-10-7(0)) Me+Mi Publishing.

Schaefer, Lola M. Vegetables. 2007. (J). (*978-1-4329-0142-4(7)); pap. (*978-1-4329-0149-3(4)) Heinemann Library.

Schuette, Sarah L. Eating Pairs: Counting Fruits & Vegetables by Twos. 2003. (A+ Counting Books). (Illus.). 16p. (J). (gr. k-1). 22.60 (978-0-7368-1676-2(3) , Aplus Bks.) Capstone Pr., Inc.

Schuh, Mari C. The Vegetable Group. 2006. (Illus.). 24p. (J). (978-0-7368-5374-3(X) , Pebble Bks.) Capstone Pr., Inc.

Schwartz, David M. In the Garden. Kuhn, Dwight, photos by. 1999. (Springboards into Science Ser.). (Illus.). 24p. (J). (gr. 1 up). lib. bdg. 19.93 (978-0-8368-2242-7(0)) Stevens, Gareth Inc.

Shepard, Daniel. All Kinds of Farms. 2003. (Illus.). 17p. (J). 15.93 (978-0-7368-2912-0(1)); pap. (978-0-7368-2871-0(0)) Yellow Umbrella Pr.

Snyder, Inez. Carrots. 2004. (Harvesttime Ser.). (Illus.). 24p. (J). 18.00 (978-0-516-27591-8(7)); pap. 4.95 (978-0-516-25911-6(3)) Scholastic Library Publishing. (Children's Pr.).

VEGETABLES—CANNING

see Canning and Preserving

VEGETABLES—FICTION

VEGETABLES—MARKETING

see Farm Produce—Marketing

VEGETARIANISM

Watt, Fiona. Vegetarian Cooking for Beginners. 2001. (Cooking School Ser.). (Illus.). 48p. (YA). (gr. 5 up). lib. bdg. 15.95 (978-1-58086-203-5(9)) EDC Publishing.

Weiss, Stefanie Iris. Everything You Need to Know about Being a Vegan. 1999. (Need to Know Library). (Illus.). 64p. (J). (gr. 7-12). lib. bdg. 25.25 (978-0-8239-2958-0(2), NTVEGA) Rosen Publishing Group, Inc., The.

What Is a Vegetarian? 1999. (Illus.). 20p. (J). (ps-k). pap. 10.00 (978-0-9679561-2-1(9)) Debbie-Lou Productions.

Why Are People Vegetarian? 2002. (Exploring Tough Issues Ser.). 48p. (J). lib. bdg. 25.69 (978-0-7398-4960-6(3)) Raintree.

Winkler, Kathleen. Vegetarianism & Teens. 2001. (Hot Issues Ser.). (Illus.). 64p. (YA). (gr. 6-12). lib. bdg. 27.93 (978-0-7660-1375-9(8)) Enslow Pubs., Inc.

VEHICLES

Alinas, Marv. Garbage Trucks. 2007. (Machines at Work Ser.). 24p. (J). 22.79 (978-1-59296-832-9(5)) Child's World, Inc.

Anderson, Jill, ed. Let's Go!/Vamos a Viajar! Evrard, Gaetan, illus. 2006. (ENG & SPA.). 20p. (J). (ps-2). bds. 6.95 (978-1-58728-513-4(4), Two Can Publishing) T&N Children's Publishing.

Barlow, Amanda. Things That Go. 2004. (Baby Board Bks.). (Illus.). 10p. (J). (ps up). pap. 4.99 (978-0-7460-4101-7(2)) EDC Publishing.

Basic Vehicles. 2005. (Transportation Ser.). (YA). (gr. k-3). 118.80 (978-0-7368-4191-7(1), Pebble Bks.) Capstone Pr., Inc.

Basic Vehicles Set. (gr. k-2). 114.95 (978-0-7368-9059-5(9)) Red Brick Learning.

Beck, Isabel L., et al. Trophies Kindergarten: A Big, Big Van. 2003. (Trophies Ser.). (gr. k-6). 13.80 (978-0-15-329546-1(5)) Harcourt Schl. Pubs.

Bidder, Jane. Inventions We Use to Go Places. 2006. (Illus.). 32p. lib. bdg. (978-0-8368-6901-9(X)) Stevens, Gareth Inc.

Bingham, Caroline. Rescue-Mania! 2003. (Vehicle-Mania! Ser.). (Illus.). 32p. (J). (gr. 2 up). lib. bdg. 23.33 (978-0-8368-3784-1(3)) Stevens, Gareth Inc.

Braithwaite, Jill. Police Cars. 2004. (Pull Ahead Bks.). (Illus.). 32p. (J). (gr. k-2). pap. 5.95 (978-0-8225-9919-7(8)); lib. bdg. 22.60 (978-0-8225-0770-3(6)) Lerner Publishing Group.

Bridges, Sarah. I Drive a Snowplow. Alderman, Derrick & Shea, Denise, illus. 2004. (Working Wheels Ser.). 24p. (J). (gr. k-2). 22.60 (978-1-4048-0617-7(2)) Picture Window Bks.

Brooks, Felicity. Emergency Vehicles. 2007. 12p. (J). bds. 9.99 (978-0-7945-1596-6(7), Usborne) EDC Publishing.

Bryant, Raymond. Out at Work. 2003. (Funtime Rhymes Ser.). (Illus.). 10p. (J). bds. 4.95 (978-0-7641-2659-8(8)) Barron's Educational Series, Inc.

Burch, Lynda S. Wicky Wacky Things that Go! Emergency Vehicles. Burch, Lynda S., photos by. 2004. (Illus.). 30p. (J). E-Book 9.95 incl. cd-rom (978-1-933090-13-9(8)) Guardian Angel Publishing, Inc.

Campbell, Rod. On the Move. 2003. (Illus.). 10p. (J). 5.99 (978-1-85292-190-3(0), Campbell Bks.) Pan Macmillan GBR. *Dist:* Trafalgar Square Publishing.

Canizares, Susan. Where Does It Park? 1999. (J). pap. 2.50 (978-0-439-04583-4(5)) Scholastic, Inc.

Carroll, John. 4 x 4 Vehicles. 1999. (Encyclopedia of Custom & Classic Transportation Ser.). (Illus.). 112p. (YA). lib. bdg. 27.45 (978-0-7910-5004-0(1), Chelsea Hse.) Facts On File, Inc.

Chang, Lynn. Look at Me! Vehicles: My Own Photo Book. 2000. (Look at Me! Ser.). (Illus.). 20p. (J). (ps-3). 6.95 (978-0-8118-2278-7(8)) Chronicle Bks. LLC.

Chapman, Jane. Let's Go Novelty. Chapman, Jane, illus. 2003. (Illus.). 18p. (J). (gr. k-k). bds. 6.99 (978-0-7636-2040-0(8)) Candlewick Pr.

Community Vehicles. 2005. (Transportation Ser.). (YA). (gr. k-3). 118.80 (978-0-7368-4192-4(X), Pebble Bks.) Capstone Pr., Inc.

Community Vehicles, Set. (gr. k-2). 114.95 (978-0-7368-9058-8(0)) Red Brick Learning.

Coppendale, Jean. Fire Trucks & Rescue Vehicles. 2007. (J). lib. bdg. 16.95 (*978-1-59566-342-9(8)) QEB Publishing Inc.

David, Jack. ATVs. 2008. (Illus.). 24p. (J). lib. bdg. 19.95 (*978-1-60014-146-1(3)) Bellwether Media.

DK Publishing Staff. My First Things That Go Board Book. 2007. (My First Bks.). 36p. (J). 5.99 (978-0-7566-2591-7(2)) Dorling Kindersley Publishing, Inc.

—Things That Go. 2007. 26p. (J). (ps-1). bds. 9.99 (978-0-7566-3027-0(4)) Dorling Kindersley Publishing, Inc.

Dorling Kindersley Publishing Staff. Things That Go. 2006. (Let's Look Ser.). (Illus.). 36p. (J). (ps-3). bds. 4.99 (978-0-7566-1748-6(0)) Dorling Kindersley Publishing, Inc.

Ethan, Eric. Emergency Vehicles, 5 bks. Ethan, Eric, photos by. Incl. Ambulances. lib. bdg. 20.67 (978-0-8368-3044-6(X)); Fire Engines. lib. bdg. 20.67 (978-0-8368-3045-3(8)); Helicopters. lib. bdg. 20.67 (978-0-8368-3046-0(6)); Police Cars. lib. bdg. 20.67 (978-0-8368-3047-7(4)); Rescue Boats. lib. bdg. 20.67 (978-0-8368-3048-4(2)); 24p. (YA). (gr. 1 up). (Illus.). 2002. Set lib. bdg. 103.35 (978-0-8368-3043-9(1)) Stevens, Gareth Inc.

—Police Cars. Ethan, Eric, photos by. 2002. (Emergency Vehicles Ser.). (Illus.). 24p. (YA). (gr. 1 up). lib. bdg. 20.67 (978-0-8368-3047-7(4)) Stevens, Gareth Inc.

Freeman, Marcia S. Ambulances. Saunders-Smith, Gail, ed. 1999. (Community Vehicles Ser.). (Illus.). 24p. (J). (gr. k-1). lib. bdg. 15.93 (978-0-7368-0100-3(6), Pebble Bks.) Capstone Pr., Inc.

—Ambulances. 1998. (Community Vehicles Ser.). (J). lib. bdg. 13.25 (978-0-516-21488-7(8), Children's Pr.) Scholastic Library Publishing.

—Community Vehicles, 4 vols. 1998. (J). 53.00 (978-0-516-29820-7(8), Children's Pr.) Scholastic Library Publishing.

—Police Cars. Saunders-Smith, Gail, ed. 1999. (Community Vehicles Ser.). (Illus.). 24p. (J). (gr. k-1). lib. bdg. 15.93 (978-0-7368-0103-4(0), Pebble Bks.) Capstone Pr., Inc.

—Police Cars. 2005. (Transportation Ser.). 24p. (YA). (gr. k-3). pap. (978-0-7368-8104-3(2), Pebble Bks.) Capstone Pr., Inc.

Galford, Ellen. Transportation by Land, Sea & Air: Exploring History Through Art. 2007. 64p. (*978-1-58728-590-5(8), Two Can Publishing) T&N Children's Publishing.

Garcia, Emma. Tip Tip Dig Dig. 2007. (Illus.). 32p. (J). (ps). 14.95 (*978-1-905417-58-2(6)) Boxer Bks., Ltd. GBR. *Dist:* Sterling Publishing Co., Inc.

Gordon, Sharon. Fast Slow (Rapido Lento) 2006. (Bookworms Ser.). (ENG & SPA., Illus.). 24p. (J). lib. bdg. 22.79 (978-0-7614-2447-5(4)) Cavendish, Marshall Corp.

—¿Qué Hay Dentro de un Carro de Policía? 2006. (Bookworms Ser.). (SPA & ENG., Illus.). 32p. (J). lib. bdg. 22.79 (978-0-7614-2396-6(6)) Cavendish, Marshall Corp.

—Rapido Lento. 2006. (Bookworms Ser.). (SPA & ENG., Illus.). 24p. (J). lib. bdg. 22.79 (978-0-7614-2367-6(2)) Cavendish, Marshall Corp.

—What's Inside a Police Car? (¿Qué Hay Dentro de un Carro de Policía?) 2006. (Bookworms Ser.). (ENG & SPA., Illus.). 32p. (J). lib. bdg. 22.79 (978-0-7614-2475-8(X)) Cavendish, Marshall Corp.

Gould, Robert. Rescue Vehicles. Gould, Robert, photos by. 2005. (Big Stuff Ser.). (Illus.). 16p. (J). bds. 7.95 (978-1-929945-51-1(5)) Big Guy Bks., Inc.

Graham, Buck. My First Big Book of Questions & Answers: Things That Go. 2005. (Illus.). 10p. bds. 9.98 (978-0-7853-7227-1(X), 7171500) Publications International, Ltd.

Graham, Ian. Emergency Vehicles. 2006. (QEB Machines at Work Ser.). (Illus.). 36p. (J). lib. bdg. 16.95 (978-1-59566-188-3(3)) QEB Publishing Inc.

—Off-Road Vehicles. 2003. (Designed for Success Ser.). 32p. pap. 7.50 (978-1-4034-3358-9(5)); (Illus.). (J). 24.22 (978-1-4034-0770-2(3)) Heinemann Library.

Hanson, Anne E. Ambulances. 2001. (Transportation Library). (Illus.). 24p. (J). (gr. 1-2). lib. bdg. 18.60 (978-0-7368-0841-5(8), Bridgestone Bks.) Capstone Pr., Inc.

Harrison, James. Amazing Vehicles. Smith, Jan, illus. 2004. (Magic Color Bks.). 12p. (J). 9.95 (978-1-4027-1215-9(4)) Sterling Publishing Co., Inc.

Harrison, James & Graham, Ian, eds. Amazing Vehicles Foldout Book. 2002. (Foldout Bks.). 6p. (J). (gr. 3-7). 9.95 (978-1-57145-756-1(9), Silver Dolphin Bks.) Advantage Pubs. Group.

Horsepower. 2005. (Blazers Ser.). (Illus.). (J). (gr. 1-2). lib. bdg. 239.16 (978-0-7368-4433-8(3)) Capstone Pr., Inc.

Imperato, Teresa. Speed Machines: A Pop-up Book with Moving Gears. Robinson, Keith, illus. 2005. 8p. (J). 14.95 (978-1-58117-323-9(7), Intervisual/Piggy Toes) Dalmatian Pr.

Jefferis, David. Young Library - Monster Machines, 5 bks., Set. Incl. Jets. lib. bdg. 25.69 (978-0-7398-2878-6(9)); Racing Cars. lib. bdg. 25.69 (978-0-7398-2880-9(0)); Spacecraft. lib. bdg. 25.69 (978-0-7398-2881-6(9)); Super Bikes. lib. bdg. 25.69 (978-0-7398-2882-3(7)); Trucks. lib. bdg. 25.69 (978-0-7398-2879-3(7)); 32p. (J). (ps-3). 2001. (Illus.). 2001. Set lib. bdg. 128.45 (978-0-7398-2883-0(5)) Raintree.

Joachim, Jean. Rescue Vehicles Dot-to-Dot. 2005. 80p. (J). pap. 5.95 (978-1-4027-1080-3(1)) Sterling Publishing Co., Inc.

Johansen, Heidi Leigh. My Book of Things That Go. 2005. (J). lib. bdg. (978-1-4042-2799-6(7)) Rosen Publishing Group, Inc., The.

Jugran, Jan. On the Go. Larranaga, Ana Martin, illus. 2007. 12p. (J). (ps-ps). bds. 8.99 (*978-1-58476-620-9(4), IKIDS) Innovative Kids.

Kilby, Don. In the City. 2005. (Wheels at Work Ser.). (Illus.). 24p. (J). (ps-2). (978-1-55337-471-8(1)) Kids Can Pr., Ltd.

—In the Country. Kilby, Don, illus. 2006. (Illus.). 24p. (978-1-55337-985-0(3)) Kids Can Pr., Ltd.

—In the Country. 2005. (Wheels at Work Ser.). (Illus.). 24p. (J). (ps-2). (978-1-55337-472-5(X)) Kids Can Pr., Ltd.

Larousse Mexico Staff, ed. Los Vehiculos (Vehicles) 2006. (Mi Pequena Enciclopedia Ser.). (Illus.). 38p. (ps-k). pap. 3.95 (978-970-22-1189-1(1)) Larousse, Ediciones, S. A. de C. V. MEX. *Dist:* Houghton Mifflin Co. Trade & Reference Div.

Lindeen, Carol K. Patrullas de Policía: Police Cars. 2006. (ENG & SPA.). (J). (978-0-7368-5875-5(X)) Capstone Pr., Inc.

—Police Cars. 2005. (Pebble Plus: Mighty Machines Ser.). (Illus.). 24p. (J). 19.93 (978-0-7368-3654-8(3), Pebble Bks.) Capstone Pr., Inc.

Lindeen, Mary. Snowplows. 2007. (Illus.). 24p. (J). lib. bdg. 19.95 (978-1-60014-120-1(X)) Bellwether Media.

Lippman, Peter. Mini Fire Engine. 2001. (Illus.). 20p. (J). bds. 9.95 (978-0-7611-2498-6(5), 12498) Workman Publishing Co., Inc.

—School Bus. 2001. (Illus.). 20p. (J). bds. 9.95 (978-0-7611-2511-2(6), 12511) Workman Publishing Co., Inc.

Litchfield, J. & Brooks, F. Rescue Vehicles. 2004. (Illus.). 10p. (J). 4.99 (978-0-7945-0589-9(9)) EDC Publishing.

Marks, Jenny L. Dune Buggies. 2007. (Blazers—Horsepower Ser.). (Illus.). 32p. (J). 19.93 (978-0-7368-6447-3(4)) Capstone Pr., Inc.

Marx, Mandy. ATVs. 2006. (Blazers—Horsepower Ser.). 32p. (J). (978-0-7368-5473-3(8)) Capstone Pr., Inc.

Mason, Paul. The World's Fastest Machines. 2006. (Illus.). 32p. (J). (978-1-4109-2494-0(7)); pap. (978-1-4109-2499-5(8)) Steck-Vaughn.

Maurer, Tracy. ATV Riding. 2003. (Radsports Guides Ser.). (Illus.). 48p. (gr. 4-8). 20.95 (978-1-58952-276-3(1)) Rourke Publishing, LLC.

Maynard, Christopher. Extreme Machines, Vol. 4. 2000. (Eyewitness Readers). (Illus.). 48p. (J). (gr. 2-4). pap. 3.99 (978-0-7894-5417-1(3)) Dorling Kindersley Publishing, Inc.

—Extreme Machines. 2000. (Illus.). 48p. lib. bdg. 10.79 (978-0-606-18117-4(2)); lib. bdg. 11.80 (978-0-613-25102-0(4)) Tandem Library Bks.

—I Wonder Why Planes Have Wings: And Other Questions about Transportation. 2003. (I Wonder Why Ser.). (Illus.). 32p. (J). (gr. k-3). 6.95 (978-0-7534-5662-0(1), Kingfisher) Houghton Mifflin Co. Trade & Reference Div.

Maynard, Christopher & Dorling Kindersley Publishing Staff. Extreme Machines. 2000. (Eyewitness Readers). (Illus.). 48p. (J). (gr. 2-4). 12.95 (978-0-7894-5418-8(1)) Dorling Kindersley Publishing, Inc.

Mayo, Margaret. Dig Dig Digging. Ayliffe, Alex, illus. 2002. 32p. (J). (ps-k). 15.95 (978-0-8050-6840-5(6), Holt, Henry & Co. Bks. For Young Readers) Holt, Henry & Co.

McAuliffe, Bill. ATV Racing. 1998. (MotorSports Ser.). (Illus.). 48p. (J). (gr. 3-4). lib. bdg. 21.26 (978-0-7368-0024-2(7), Capstone High-Interest Bks.) Capstone Pr., Inc.

Mezzanotte, Jim. Giant Vehicles. 24p. (YA). 132.00 (978-0-8368-4909-7(4)) Stevens, Gareth Inc.

—Vehiculos gigantes (Giant Vehicles), 6 Vols. 132.00 (978-0-8368-5984-3(7)) Stevens, Gareth Inc.

Mighty Machines. 2000. (J). (ps). lib. bdg. 9.98 (978-0-7894-6797-3(6)) Dorling Kindersley Publishing, Inc.

Mighty Machines. (Illus.). (J). Date not set. 48p. 5.98 (978-1-4054-0207-1(5)); 2003. 256p. 12.98 (978-1-4054-1538-5(X)) Parragon, Inc.

Molzahn, Arlene Bourgeois. Police & Emergency Vehicles. 2002. (Transportation & Communication Ser.). (Illus.). 48p. (J). (gr. 1-4). lib. bdg. 23.93 (978-0-7660-1890-7(3)) Enslow Pubs., Inc.

Mott, Professor. Rescue Team: First Vehicles. Lenehan, Mary & Weber, Rich, illus. 1999. 8p. (J). (ps). 14.99 (978-1-890647-33-9(0)) RC2 Corp.

—Road Racers: First Vehicles. Lenehan, Mary & Weber, Rich, illus. 1999. 8p. (J). (ps). 14.99 (978-1-890647-35-3(7)) RC2 Corp.

—Work Crew: First Vehicles. Lenehan, Mary & Weber, Rich, illus. 1999. 8p. (J). (ps-3). 14.99 (978-1-890647-34-6(9)) RC2 Corp.

Mousetrap Powered Cars & Boats. 6th ed. 2001. 168p. pap. 14.00 (978-0-9656674-2-5(1)) Doc Fizzix.

My Big Book of Vehicles. 2004. 12p. (J). bds. 7.99 (978-1-85854-660-5(5)) Brimax Books Ltd. GBR. *Dist:* Byeway Bks.

Nelson, Angela, creator. Lang-O-Learn: Vehicle Cards. 2001. (SPA, FRE, GER, ITA & RUS.). (J). 9.95 (978-0-9668008-4-5(2)) Stages Learning Materials.

Off Road Vehicles. 2004. (Mega MacHines Ser.). (Illus.). 16p. (J). (978-2-7643-0200-2(2)) Phidal Publishing, Inc./Editions Phidal, Inc.

Oxlade, Chris. Emergency Vehicles. (Transportation Around the World Ser.). 32p. pap. 6.95 (978-1-4034-4133-1(2)); 2001. (Illus.). (J). lib. bdg. 21.36 (978-1-57572-306-8(9)) Heinemann Library.

Pearson, Debora. Alphabeep! A Zipping, Zooming ABC. Miller, Edward, illus. 36p. (J). (ps-1). 6.95 (*978-0-8234-2076-6(0)) Holiday Hse., Inc.

Penguin Books Staff. Vehicles. (Learners Ser.). (Illus.). 48p. (J). 3.50 (978-0-7214-1704-2(3), Dutton Juvenile) Penguin Group (USA) Inc.

Petruccio, Steven James. Emergency Vehicles Stickers. 2003. (Dover Little Activity Bks.). (Illus.). 4p. (J). (ps-5). pap. 1.50 (978-0-486-43009-6(X)) Dover Pubns., Inc.

Police Cars. (Mighty MacHines Ser.). 24p. (J). 6.95 (978-0-7368-5141-1(0)) Capstone Pr., Inc.

Powers, Amelia. Giant Pop-Out Vehicles: A Pop-out Surprise Book. 2007. (Illus.). 26p. (J). (ps). 10.95 (978-0-8118-5953-0(3)) Chronicle Bks. LLC.

Priddy, Roger. My Big Rescue Book. 2004. (Illus.). 10p. (J). (978-1-84332-215-3(3)) St. Martin's Pr.

Randolph, Joanne. Ambulances. 2008. (J). lib. bdg. (*978-1-4042-4150-3(7), PowerKids Pr.) Rosen Publishing Group, Inc., The.

—Police Cars. 2008. (J). lib. bdg. (*978-1-4042-4153-4(1), PowerKids Pr.) Rosen Publishing Group, Inc., The.

Rau, Dana Meachen, ed. ¡A Conducir! 2006. (En Movimiento Ser.). (SPA & ENG., Illus.). 24p. (J). lib. bdg. 22.79 (978-0-7614-2422-2(9), Benchmark Bks.) Cavendish, Marshall Corp.

Roberts, Cynthia. Police Cars. 2007. (Machines at Work Ser.). 24p. (J). (ps-2). 22.79 (*978-1-59296-834-3(1)) Child's World, Inc.

Rockwell, Anne F. Big Wheels. 2003. (Illus.). 24p. (J). (ps-1). 14.95 (978-0-8027-8882-5(3)) Walker & Co.

Rollin', 8 bks. Incl. Big Rigs. Schleifer, Jay. lib. bdg. 21.26 (978-1-56065-373-8(6)); BMX Bikes. Knox, Barbara. lib. bdg. 21.26 (978-1-56065-369-1(8)); Monster Trucks. Koons, James. lib. bdg. 21.26 (978-1-56065-371-4(X)); Motocross Cycles. Savage, Jeff. lib. bdg. 21.26 (978-1-56065-370-7(1)); Motorcycles. Jay, Jackson. lib. bdg. 21.26 (978-1-56065-366-0(3)); Pickup Trucks. Koons, James. lib. bdg. 21.26 (978-1-56065-372-1(8)); Racing Cars. Savage, Jeff. lib. bdg. 21.26 (978-1-56065-368-4(X)); Super Sports Cars. Jay, Jackson. lib. bdg. 21.26 (978-1-56065-367-7(1)); 48p. (J). (gr. 3-4). 1996. (Illus.). Set lib. bdg. 170.08 (978-1-56065-661-6(1), Capstone High-Interest Bks.) Capstone Pr., Inc.

Saunders-Smith, Gail. Transportation: Basic Vehicles, 4 vols., Set. 1998. (J). pap. 53.00 (978-0-516-29781-1(3), Children's Pr.) Scholastic Library Publishing.

Savage, Jeff. ATVs. 2004. (Wild Rides! Ser.). (Illus.). 32p. (J). lib. bdg. 16.95 (978-0-7368-2428-6(6)) Capstone Pr., Inc.

Schaefer, Lola M. Beep-Beep! Honk! 2007. (J). (978-1-59515-928-1(2)) Rourke Publishing, LLC.

—Tow Trucks. 2000. (Transportation Library). (Illus.). 24p. (J). (gr. 1-2). lib. bdg. 18.60 (978-0-7368-0503-2(6), Bridgestone Bks.) Capstone Pr., Inc.

Schoberle, Cecile. To the Rescue! 2003. (gr. k-3). lib. bdg. 11.80 (978-0-613-66550-6(3)) Tandem Library Bks.

Schuette, Sarah L. 3, 2, 1 Go! A Transportation Countdown. 2003. (A+ Counting Books). (Illus.). 32p. (J). (gr. k-1). lib. bdg. 22.60 (978-0-7368-1678-6(X), Aplus Bks.) Capstone Pr., Inc.

Simon, Seymour. Emergency Vehicles: SeeMore Readers Level 1. 2006. (Illus.). 32p. (J). pap. 3.95 (978-0-8118-5407-8(8)) Chronicle Bks. LLC.

Stanley, Mandy. On the Move. 2004. (All Aboard Ser.). Orig. Title: Vamos de Viaje. (Illus.). 12p. (J). (ps-k). bds. 3.95 (978-0-7534-5749-8(0), Kingfisher) Houghton Mifflin Co. Trade & Reference Div.

Swain, Cynthia. The Red Sled. 2003. (BuildUp Ser.). (J). pap. 22.00 (978-1-4108-0747-2(9)) Benchmark Education Co.

Tagel, Peggy, illus. On the Go. 2003. (Squishy Shapes Ser.). 10p. (J). 12.95 (978-1-57145-739-4(9), Silver Dolphin Bks.) Advantage Pubs. Group.

Tuxworth, Nicola. Learn-a-Word Picture Book: Things That Go, 12 vols. 2006. (Learn-A-Word Picture Bks.). (Illus.). 12p. bds. 6.99 (978-0-7548-1462-7(9), Lorenz Bks.) Anness Publishing GBR. *Dist:* National Bk. Network.

—Machines at Work: A Very First Picture Book. 1999. (Pictures & Words Ser.). (Illus.). 24p. (J). (ps up). lib. bdg. 22.00 (978-0-8368-2432-6(5)) Stevens, Gareth Inc.

Twist, Clint. The Inside & Out Guide to Mighty Machines. 2006. (Illus.). 32p. (J). (978-1-4034-9087-2(2)); pap. (978-1-4034-9094-0(5)) Heinemann Library.

Tyrrell, Melissa. Bulldozer: Little Vehicle Board Book. 1998. (Little Vehicle Board Bks.). (Illus.). 16p. (J). (ps). bds. 5.95 (978-1-888443-96-7(0), Intervisual/Piggy Toes) Dalmatian Pr.

—Dump Truck: Little Vehicle Board Book. 1998. (Little Vehicle Board Bks.). 16p. (J). (ps). bds. 5.95 (978-1-888443-97-4(9), Intervisual/Piggy Toes) Dalmatian Pr.

—Fire Engine: Little Vehicle Board Book. 1998. (Box Cars Ser.). 16p. (J). (ps). bds. 5.95 (978-1-888443-98-1(7), Intervisual/Piggy Toes) Dalmatian Pr.

—School Bus: Little Vehicle Board Book. 1998. (Little Vehicle Board Bks.). 16p. (J). (ps). bds. 5.95 (978-1-888443-99-8(5), Intervisual/Piggy Toes) Dalmatian Pr.

Vehicle-Mania!, 6 bks. Incl. Aero-Mania! Gunston, Bill. lib. bdg. 23.33 (978-0-8368-3780-3(0)); Auto-Mania! Kimber, David. lib. bdg. 23.33 (978-0-8368-3781-0(9)); Boat-Mania! Parker, Steve. lib. bdg. 23.33 (978-0-8368-3782-7(7)); Motorcycle-Mania! Kimber, David & Newland, Richard. lib. bdg. 23.33 (978-0-8368-3783-4(5)); Rescue-Mania! Bingham, Caroline. lib. bdg. 23.33 (978-0-8368-3784-1(3)); Truck-Mania! Bingham, Caroline. lib. bdg. 23.33 (978-0-8368-3785-8(1)); 32p. (J). (gr. 2 up). (Illus.). 2003. Set lib. bdg. 139.98 (978-0-8368-3779-7(7)) Stevens, Gareth Inc.

Vehicles. 2003. (First Concepts Book Ser.). 32p. (J). 3.98 (978-0-7525-8894-0(X)) Parragon, Inc.

Vehicles. (Cute & Cushy Ser.). 10p. (J). bds. (978-2-7643-0207-1(X)) Phidal Publishing, Inc./Editions Phidal, Inc.

Wheeler, Jill C. Alternative Cars. 2007. (Eye on Energy Ser.). (Illus.). 32p. (J). (gr. k-6). lib. bdg. 24.21 (*978-1-59928-803-1(6), Checkerboard Library) ABDO Publishing Co.

Wild Rides! (Illus.). (J). (gr. 3-4). lib. bdg. 452.00 (978-0-7368-2768-3(4)) Capstone Pr., Inc.

Will, Sandra. Transportation Inventions: From Subways to Submarines. 2006. (Which Came First? Ser.). (Illus.). 32p. (J). lib. bdg. 25.27 (978-1-59716-133-6(0)) Bearport Publishing Co., Inc.

VEHICLES, MILITARY

Baker, David. M126 Stryker. 2007. (Fighting Forces on Land Ser.). (Illus.). 32p. (J). (978-1-60044-246-9(3)) Rourke Publishing, LLC.

—M2A2 Bradley Fighting Vehicle. 2007. (Fighting Forces on Land Ser.). (Illus.). 32p. (J). (978-1-60044-249-0(8)) Rourke Publishing, LLC.

Bartlett, Richard. U. S. Army Fighting Vehicles. (Heinemann Know It Ser.). (Illus.). 48p. (J). 2003. pap. 7.95 (978-1-4034-0446-6(1)); 2002. (gr. 3-5). lib. bdg. 25.64 (978-1-4034-0189-2(6)) Heinemann Library.

Budd, E. S. Humvees. 2001. (Machines at Work Ser.). (Illus.). 24p. (J). (ps-3). 21.36 (978-1-56766-983-1(2)) Child's World, Inc.

Cain, Bill & Hama, Larry. Tank of Tomorrow: Stryker. 2007. (High-Tech Military Weapons Ser.). (Illus.). 48p. (J). pap. (*978-0-531-18710-4(1)) Children's Pr., Ltd.

Cornish, Geoff. Battleground Support. 2004. (Military Hardware in Action Ser.). (Illus.). 48p. (J). (gr. 4-9). lib. bdg. 25.26 (978-0-8225-4708-2(2)) Lerner Publishing Group.

—Tanks. 2004. (Military Hardware in Action Ser.). (Illus.). 48p. (J). (gr. 4-9). lib. bdg. 25.26 (978-0-8225-4701-3(5)) Lerner Publishing Group.

Ellis, Catherine. Mega Military Machines, 6 bks., Set. Incl. Cars & Trucks. lib. bdg. 21.25 (978-1-4042-3669-1(4)); Helicopters. lib. bdg. 21.25 (978-1-4042-3666-0(X)); Planes. lib. bdg. 21.25 (978-1-4042-3667-7(8)); Ships. lib. bdg. 21.25 (978-1-4042-3668-4(6)); Submarines. lib. bdg. 21.25 (978-1-4042-3665-3(1)); Tanks. lib. bdg. 21.25 (978-1-4042-3664-6(3)); (Illus.). 24p. (J). (gr. k-5). 2007. 2007. Set lib. bdg. 127.50 (*978-1-4042-3606-6(6)) Rosen Publishing Group, Inc., The.

Graham, Ian. Military Vehicles. 2003. (Designed for Success Ser.). (Illus.). 32p. pap. 7.50 (978-1-4034-3357-2(7)); (J). 24.22 (978-1-4034-2655-0(4)) Heinemann Library.

Green, Michael. Land & Sea, 16 bks. Incl. Aircraft Carriers. 1997. lib. bdg. 21.26 (978-1-56065-553-4(4)); Amphibious Ships. 1998. lib. bdg. 21.26 (978-0-7368-0040-2(9)); Amphibious Vehicles. 1997. lib. bdg. 21.26 (978-1-56065-460-5(0)); Battleships. 1997. lib. bdg. 21.26 (978-1-56065-554-1(2)); Cruisers. 1997. lib. bdg. 21.26 (978-1-56065-556-5(9)); Destroyers. 1998. lib. bdg. 21.26 (978-0-7368-0041-9(7)); Main Battle Tanks. 2001. lib. bdg. 21.26 (978-0-7368-0757-9(8)); Military Dune Buggies. 1997. lib. bdg. 21.26 (978-1-56065-461-2(9)); Military Motorcycles. 1997. lib. bdg. 21.26 (978-1-56065-462-9(7)); Military Trucks. 1997. lib. bdg. 21.26 (978-1-56065-463-6(5)); Mine Hunting Ships. 2001. lib. bdg. 21.26 (978-0-7368-0758-6(6)); Nuclear Submarines. 2001. lib. bdg. 21.26 (978-0-7368-0759-3(4)); PT Boats. 1998. lib. bdg. 21.26 (978-0-7368-0042-6(5)); River Patrol Boats. 1998. lib. bdg. 21.26 (978-0-7368-0043-3(3)); Submarines. 1997. lib. bdg. 21.26 (978-1-56065-555-8(0)); Supercarriers. 2001. lib. bdg. 21.26 (978-0-7368-0760-9(8)); 48p. (J). (gr. 3-4). (Illus.). Set lib. bdg. 340.16 (978-0-7368-0869-9(8) , Capstone High-Interest Bks.) Capstone Pr., Inc.

Green, Michael & Green, Gladys. Armored Personnel Carriers: The M113. 2005. (War Machines Ser.). (Illus.). 32p. (J). 22.60 (978-0-7368-3777-4(9)) Capstone Pr., Inc.

—Assault Amphibian Vehicles: The AAVs. 2004. (War Machines Ser.). (Illus.). 32p. (J). 16.95 (978-0-7368-2414-9(6)) Capstone Pr., Inc.

—Infantry Fighting Vehicles: The M2A2 Bradleys. 2004. (War Machines Ser.). (Illus.). 32p. (J). 16.95 (978-0-7368-2415-6(4)) Capstone Pr., Inc.

Hama, Larry. Tank of Tomorrow. 2006. (High-Tech Military Weapons Ser.). (Illus.). 48p. (J). (978-0-531-12094-1(5) , Children's Pr.) Scholastic Library Publishing.

Morse, Jenifer Corr. Military Vehicles. 2001. (Speed! Ser.). (Illus.). 24p. (J). (gr. 3-6). 21.20 (978-1-56711-471-3(7) , Blackbirch Pr., Inc.) Thomson Gale.

Parker, Steve. The M2 Bradley Infantry Fighting Vehicle. 2008. (J). (***978-1-4296-0092-7(6)***) Capstone Pr., Inc.

Rustad, Martha E. H. U.S. Army Infantry Fighting Vehicles. 2007. (Blazers—Military Vehicles Ser.). (Illus.). 32p. (J). 19.93 (978-0-7368-6454-1(7)) Capstone Pr., Inc.

Shuter, Jane. War Machines: Military Transportation. 2004. (Technology Through Time Ser.). (Illus.). 31p. (J). lib. bdg. 25.70 (978-1-4109-0583-3(7)) Raintree.

War Machines. 2005. (Illus.). (J). (gr. 3-4). lib. bdg. 271.20 (978-0-7368-3823-8(6)) Capstone Pr., Inc.

VELAZQUEZ, DIEGO, 1599-1660

Venezia, Mike. Diego Velazquez. Venezia, Mike, illus. 2004. (Getting to Know the World's Greatest Artists Ser.). (Illus.). 32p. (J). (gr. 3-4). pap. 6.95 (978-0-516-26980-1(1) , Children's Pr.) Scholastic Library Publishing.

Venezia, Mike, tr. & illus. Diego Velazquez. Venezia, Mike, illus. 2004. (Getting to Know World Artists Ser.). 32p. (J). 27.00 (978-0-516-22580-7(4) , Children's Pr.) Scholastic Library Publishing.

VELAZQUEZ, DIEGO, 1599-1660—FICTION

De Trevino, Elizabeth Borton. I, Juan de Pareja. 2008. 192p. (J). pap. 6.99 (***978-0-312-38005-2(4)***) Square Fish.

I, Juan de Pareja. 3rd ed. (J). pap., stu. ed. (978-0-13-667452-8(6)) Prentice Hall (Schl. Div.).

VELOCITY

see Speed

VENEREAL DISEASES

see Sexually Transmitted Diseases

VENEZUELA

Angel Falls: Individual Title Six-Packs. (On Deck Ser.). 24p. (gr. 4-5). 35.00 (978-0-7578-1078-7(0)) Rigby Education.

Cataratas Angel: Individual Title Six-Packs. (On Deck en Espanol Ser.).Tr. of Angel Falls. (SPA.). 24p. (gr. 4-5). 35.00 (978-0-7578-6449-0(X)) Rigby Education.

Conley, Kate A. Venezuela. 2004. (Countries Ser.). (Illus.). 40p. (J). (gr. k-6). lib. bdg. 22.78 (978-1-59197-298-3(1)) ABDO Publishing Co.

Crooker, Richard. Venezuela. 2006. (Modern World Nations Ser.). (Illus.). 120p. (J). (gr. 6-12). 30.00 (978-0-7910-8834-0(0) , Chelsea Hse.) Facts On File, Inc.

Gibson, Karen Bush. Venezuela: A Question & Answer Book. 2007. (Fact Finders Ser.). (Illus.). 32p. (J). 22.60 (978-0-7368-6413-8(X)) Capstone Pr., Inc.

Jones, Caryn Gracey. Teens in Venezuela. 2006. (Global Connections Ser.). (Illus.). 96p. (J). (gr. 5-7). 31.93 (978-0-7565-2447-0(4)) Compass Point Bks.

Jones, Helga. Venezuela. (Country Explorers Ser.). 2008. (J). lib. bdg. 27.93 (***978-0-8225-8663-0(0)*** , Lerner Pubns.); 2005. (Illus.). 48p. (gr. 2-4). lib. bdg. 22.60 (978-1-57505-146-8(X)); 2000. (Illus.). 48p. (J). (gr. 3-5). lib. bdg. 22.60 (978-1-57505-122-2(2) , Carolrhoda Bks.) Lerner Publishing Group.

Mattern, Joanne. Angel Falls: World's Highest Waterfall. 2002. (Reading Power Ser.). (Illus.). 24p. (J). (gr. 2). lib. bdg. 17.25 (978-0-8239-6016-3(1) , PowerKids Pr.) Rosen Publishing Group, Inc., The.

—Cataratas Angel. 2004. (Natures Greatest Hits Ser.). (SPA.). 24p. (J). (gr. 3-6). lib. bdg. 17.25 (978-0-8239-6878-7(2) , Buenas Letra) Rosen Publishing Group, Inc., The.

Morrison, Marion. Venezuela. 1999. (Major World Nations Ser.). (Illus.). 144p. (YA). (gr. 4-7). lib. bdg. 21.95 (978-0-7910-4972-3(8) , Chelsea Hse.) Facts On File, Inc.

Ng, Yumi. Welcome to Venezuela. 2004. (Welcome to My Country Ser.). (J). lib. bdg. 26.00 (978-0-8368-3123-8(3)) Stevens, Gareth Inc.

Rutten, Joshua & Merrick, Patrick. Venezuela. 2003. (Countries: Faces & Places Ser.). (Illus.). 32p. (J). (gr. 1-5). 25.64 (978-1-56766-915-2(8)) Child's World, Inc.

Shields, Charles J. Venezuela. 2003. (Discovering South America Ser.). (Illus.). 64p. (YA). (gr. 5 up). lib. bdg. (978-1-59084-289-8(8)) Mason Crest Pubs.

Wardrope, William. Venezuela. 2003. (Countries of the World Ser.). (Illus.). 96p. (J). (gr. 6 up). lib. bdg. 30.00 (978-0-8368-2369-1(9)) Stevens, Gareth Inc.

Watson, Galadriel Findlay. Angel Falls. 2005. (Natural Wonders of the U. S. A. Ser.). 32p. pap. 7.95 (978-1-59036-273-0(X)) Weigl Pubs., Inc.

—Angel Falls: The Largest Waterfall in the World. 2004. (Illus.). 32p. (J). lib. bdg. 18.20 (978-1-59036-267-9(5)) Weigl Pubs., Inc.

Willis, Terri. Venezuela. 2003. (Enchantment of the World, Second Ser.). (Illus.). 144p. (YA). (gr. 5-9). 36.00 (978-0-516-24214-9(8) , Children's Pr.) Scholastic Library Publishing.

Winter, J. Kohen & Baguley, K. Venezuela. 2nd ed. 2001. (Cultures of the World Ser.). (Illus.). 144p. (gr. 5 up). lib. bdg. 37.07 (978-0-7614-1362-2(6) , Cavendish, Marshall Reference Bks.) Cavendish, Marshall Corp.

VENEZUELA—FICTION

Cowcher, Helen. Jaguar. 2000. (SPA.). 32p. (J). pap. (978-980-257-248-9(9)) Ekare, Ediciones.

—Jaguar. 2001. (Illus.). 40p. (VIE, ENG, URD, TUR & CHI.). (J). 16.95 (978-1-84059-014-2(9)); (BEN, ENG, URD, TUR & VIE., (YA). 16.95 (978-1-84059-008-1(4)); (GRE, ENG, URD, TUR & VIE., (YA). 16.95 (978-1-84059-010-4(6)); (GUJ, ENG, URD, TUR & VIE., (YA). 16.95 (978-1-84059-011-1(4)); (TUR, ENG, URD, VIE & CHI., (YA). 16.95 (978-1-84059-012-8(2)); (URD, ENG, TUR, VIE & CHI., (YA). 16.95 (978-1-84059-013-5(0)); (TUR., (YA). 16.95 (978-1-84059-015-9(7)) Milet Publishing.

—Jaguar. (J). (gr. 1-2). (978-0-590-36037-1(X)); (SPA., Illus.). (gr. 1-3). pap. 3.96 net. (978-0-590-87599-8(X) , SO30738, Scholastic Pr.); 2002. 32p. pap. 5.99 (978-0-439-39470-3(8)) Scholastic, Inc.

Ficklin, Jonene H. Orinoco Intrigue. 2005. (YA). 14.95 (978-0-9761188-1-7(5)) Victor's Crown Publishing.

Johnson, Lissa Halls & Wierenga, Kathy. Croutons for Breakfast, Vol. 7. 2005. (Brio Girls Ser.). (Illus.). 192p. (YA). (gr. 6-11). pap. 7.99 (978-1-58997-080-9(2)) Focus on the Family Publishing.

Kurusa. The Streets Are Free. Doppert, Monika, illus. 2000. 50p. (J). (gr. k-5). reprint ed. pap. 7.95 (978-1-55037-370-7(6)) Annick Pr., Ltd. CAN. *Dist:* Firefly Bks., Ltd.

VENEZUELA—HISTORY

Cunill, Pedro. Venezuela II. (Biblioteca Iberoamericana Ser.). (SPA., Illus.). 128p. (978-84-207-3096-7(3) , BI-2036) Grupo Anaya, S.A.

Ganeri, Anita. Living in the Amazon Rainforest. 2007. (J). pap. (***978-1-4109-2826-9(8)***); lib. bdg. (***978-1-4109-2817-7(9)***) Steck-Vaughn.

VENICE (ITALY)

Kids Go Europe: Treasure Hunt Venice. 2006. (J). spiral bd. 9.95 (978-0-9772699-0-7(6)) Kids Go Europe, Inc.

Rossi, Renzo. Venice. 2003. (Great Cities Through the Ages Ser.). (Illus.). 44p. (J). 18.95 (978-1-59270-014-1(4)) Enchanted Lion Bks., LLC.

Sasek, M. This Is Venice. 2005. (Illus.). 64p. (J). (gr. k). 17.95 (978-0-7893-1223-5(9)) Universe Publishing.

Steele, Philip. Venetians Walk on Water. 2007. (I Wonder Why Ser.). (Illus.). 32p. (J). (gr. k-3). pap. 6.95 (978-0-7534-6083-2(1) , Kingfisher) Houghton Mifflin Co. Trade & Reference Div.

VENICE (ITALY)—FICTION

Bjork, Christina. Eugenia en Venecia. Eriksson, Inga-Karin, illus. 2000. (J). (gr. 3-5). (CAT.). 96p. 17.95 (978-84-95040-39-8(5)); (SPA.). 94p. 17.95 (978-84-95040-38-1(7) , RR2897) Serres, Ediciones, S. L. ESP. *Dist:* Lectorum Pubns., Inc.

Cowling, Douglas. Vivaldi's Ring of Mystery. Fernandez, Laura & Jacobson, Rick, illus. 2004. 44p. (J). pap. (***978-0-439-96904-8(2)*** , North Winds Pr) Scholastic Canada, Ltd.

Funke, Cornelia. The Thief Lord. 2004. 376p. (J). (gr. 5 up). pap. 44.00 incl. audio (978-0-8072-2278-2(X) , Listening Library) Random Hse. Audio Publishing Group.

—The Thief Lord. Burmingham, Christian, illus. 2005. (Thief Lord Ser.). 376p. (ps-7). mass mkt. 2.99 (978-0-439-77132-0(3)) Scholastic, Inc.

—The Thief Lord. Latsch, Oliver, tr. from GER. Burmingham, Christian, illus. (J). 2002. 352p. (gr. 4-7). pap. 16.95 (978-0-439-40437-2(1)); 2003. 376p. (gr. 3-6). reprint ed. 6.99 (978-0-439-42089-1(X)) Scholastic, Inc. (Chicken Hse., The).

—The Thief Lord. 2003. (gr. 3-6). lib. bdg. 15.30 (978-0-613-84572-4(2)) Tandem Library Bks.

—The Thief Lord. l.t. ed. 2005. 483p. (J). (gr. 4-7). pap. 10.95 (978-0-7862-8092-6(1)) Thorndike Pr.

Funke, Cornelia. Thief Lord ('el Senor de Los Ladrones) 2007. 352p. (J). pap. 7.99 (***978-0-545-00517-3(5)*** , Scholastic en Espanol) Scholastic, Inc.

Funke, Cornelia & Latsch, Oliver. The Thief Lord. l.t. ed. 2004. 422p. (J). 23.95 (978-0-7862-7084-2(5)) Thorndike Pr.

Gandolfi, Silvana & Schwartz, Lynne Sharon. Aldabra, or, the Tortoise Who Loved Shakespeare. 2004. 151p. (J). (978-0-439-49744-2(2) , Levine, Arthur A. Bks.) Scholastic, Inc.

Gavin, Jamila. The Blood Stone. 2005. (Illus.). 352p. (YA). (gr. 6-8). 18.00 (978-0-374-30846-9(2)) Farrar, Straus & Giroux.

Gutman, Anne & Hallensleben, Georg. Gaspard on Vacation. 2001. (Illus.). 32p. (J). (ps-1). 9.95 (978-0-375-81115-9(X) , Knopf Bks. for Young Readers) Random Hse. Children's Bks.

Marciano, John Bemelmans. There's a Dolphin in the Grand Canal! 2005. (Illus.). 40p. (J). (ps). 15.99 (978-0-670-05987-4(0) , Viking Juvenile) Penguin Group (USA) Inc.

Mauner, Claudia & Smalley, Elisa. Zoe Sophia's Scrapbook: An Adventure in Venice. Mauner, Claudia, illus. 2003. (Illus.). 40p. (J). (ps-1). 14.95 (978-0-8118-3606-7(1)) Chronicle Bks. LLC.

McKeown, Adam & Shakespeare, William. Othello. Hundley, Sterling, illus. 2005. (Young Reader's Shakespeare Ser.). 80p. (J). 14.95 (978-1-4027-1115-2(8)) Sterling Publishing Co., Inc.

Moore, Ulysses. Isle of Masks. 2008. (Ulysses Moore Book Ser.). 256p. (J). 5.99 (***978-0-439-77671-4(6)*** , Scholastic Paperbacks) Scholastic, Inc.

Morpurgo, Michael. Jo-Jo the Melon Donkey. Kerins, Tony, illus. 2002. (Yellow Bananas Ser.). 48p. (J). (gr. 3-4). pap. (978-0-7787-0988-6(4)); lib. bdg. (978-0-7787-0942-8(6)) Crabtree Publishing Co.

—Jo-Jo the Melon Donkey. 2002. (gr. 3-6). lib. bdg. 12.95 (978-0-613-52863-4(8)) Tandem Library Bks.

Morpurgo, Michael. The Mozart Question. Foreman, Michael, illus. 2008. (J). (gr. 1-4). 15.99 (***978-0-7636-3552-7(9)***) Candlewick Pr.

Napoli, Donna Jo. Daughter of Venice. 2003. 288p. (YA). (gr. 7). pap. 6.50 (978-0-440-22928-5(6) , Laurel Leaf) Random Hse. Children's Bks.

—Daughter of Venice. 2003. (gr. 7-12). lib. bdg. 13.55 (978-0-613-72327-5(9)) Tandem Library Bks.

—For the Love of Venice. 2000. (Illus.). (J). (978-0-606-17998-0(4)) Tandem Library Bks.

Osborne, Mary Pope. Carnival at Candlelight. 2006. (Magic Tree House Ser.: No. 33). (Illus.). 144p. (J). (gr. 2-6). pap. 4.99 (978-0-375-83034-1(0) , Random Hse. Bks. for Young Readers) Random Hse. Children's Bks.

—Carnival at Candlelight. Murdocca, Sal, illus. 2005. (Magic Tree House Ser.: No. 33). 128p. (J). (gr. k-3). 11.95 (978-0-375-83033-4(2) , Random Hse. Bks. for Young Readers) Random Hse. Children's Bks.

Papa Piccolo: Evaluation Guide. 2006. (J). 17.95 (978-1-55942-419-6(2)) Marsh Media.

Riva, Renee. Guido's Gondola. Bjorkman, Steve, illus. 2005. 40p. (J). 9.99 (978-1-4000-7060-2(0) , WaterBrook Pr.) WaterBrook Pr.

VENICE (ITALY)—HISTORY

Harcourt School Publishers Staff. Is Venice Sinking. 3rd ed. 2002. (Horizons Ser.). (Illus.). (J). pap. 7.30 (978-0-15-333620-1(X)) Harcourt Schl. Pubs.

Hinds, Kathryn. Venice & Its Merchant Empire. 1999. (Cultures of the Past Ser.). (Illus.). 80p. (J). (gr. 5 up). lib. bdg. 29.93 (978-0-7614-0305-0(1) , Benchmark Bks.) Cavendish, Marshall Corp.

Lusted, Marcia Amidon. The Canals of Venice. 2003. (Illus.). 112p. (J). 32.45 (978-1-59018-341-0(X) , Lucent Bks.) Thomson Gale.

VENOM

see Poisons

VENTRILOQUISM

Lucas, Ronn & Clobber, Chris. Talk to the Hand: Get Everything You Want with Ventriloquism. 2007. 32p. (J). pap. 9.95 (***978-0-7624-2634-8(9)*** , Running Pr. Kids) Running Pr. Bk. Pubs.

VENTURA, ACE (FICTITIOUS CHARACTER)—FICTION

McCann, Jesse Leon. The Case of the Stolen Stallion. 2000. (Ace Ventura Chapter Bk.: Vol. 2). (J). 10.79 (978-0-606-19526-3(2)) Tandem Library Bks.

VENUS (PLANET)

Adamson, Thomas K. Venus. (J). 2008. (***978-1-4296-0739-1(4)***); 2003. (Illus.). 24p. lib. bdg. 17.26 (978-0-7368-2119-3(8) , Pebble Bks.) Capstone Pr., Inc.

Adamson, Thomas K. Venus: Venus. 2006. (ENG & SPA., Illus.). 24p. (J). (978-0-7368-5886-1(5)) Capstone Pr., Inc.

Asimov, Isaac. The Solar System: Venus. 2004. (Illus.). 32p. 14.00 (978-1-59102-179-7(0)) Prometheus Bks., Pubs.

Asimov, Isaac & Hantula, Richard. Venus. rev. ed. 2003. (Isaac Asimov's 21st Century Library of the Universe). (Illus.). 32p. (YA). (gr. 3 up). lib. bdg. 24.67 (978-0-8368-3244-0(2)) Stevens, Gareth Inc.

—Venus: A Shrouded Mystery. Porras, Carlos & D'Andrea, Patricia, trs. 2003. (Isaac Asimov's Biblioteca del Universo del Siglo XXI). (SPA., Illus.). 32p. (J). (gr. 3 up). lib. bdg. 24.67 (978-0-8368-3864-0(5)) Stevens, Gareth Inc.

—Venus: A Shrouded Mystery. 2003. (Isaac Asimov's 21st Century Library of the Universe). (Illus.). 32p. (J). (gr. 3 up). pap. (978-0-8368-3948-7(X) , Weekly Reader Early Learning Library) Stevens, Gareth Inc.

—Venus: A Shrouded Mystery. Porras, Carlos & D'Andrea, Patricia, trs. 2003. (Isaac Asimov's Biblioteca del Universo del Siglo XXI). (SPA., Illus.). 32p. (J). (gr. 3 up). pap. 11.93 (978-0-8368-3877-0(7) , Weekly Reader Early Learning Library) Stevens, Gareth Inc.

Birch, Robin. Venus. 2004. (Solar System Ser.). (Illus.). 32p. (gr. 3-5). 23.00 (978-0-7910-7936-2(8) , Chelsea Hse.) Facts On File, Inc.

Chrismer, Melanie. Venus. (Scholastic News Nonfiction Readers: Space Science Ser.). 24p. (J). 2008. pap. 6.95 (***978-0-531-14770-2(3)***); 2007. (Illus.). (gr. 1-2). lib. bdg. 20.00 (***978-0-531-14755-9(X)***) Scholastic Library Publishing. (Children's Pr.).

Cole, Michael D. Venus: The Second Planet. 2001. (Countdown to Space Ser.). (Illus.). 48p. (YA). (gr. 4-10). lib. bdg. 23.93 (978-0-7660-1509-8(5)) Enslow Pubs., Inc.

Dunn, Mary R. A Look at Venus. 2008. (J). lib. bdg. (***978-1-4042-3826-8(3)*** , PowerKids Pr.) Rosen Publishing Group, Inc., The.

Feinstein, Stephen. Venus: A MyReportLinks. com Book. 2005. (Solar System Ser.). (Illus.). 48p. (J). lib. bdg. 25.26 (978-0-7660-5300-7(8) , MyReportLinks.com Bks.) Enslow Pubs., Inc.

Goldstein, Margaret J. Venus. 2005. (Pull Ahead Bks.). (Illus.). 32p. (gr. 2-4). lib. bdg. 22.60 (978-0-8225-4649-8(3)) Lerner Publishing Group.

Goss, Tim. Venus. 2003. (Universe Ser.). (Illus.). 32p. (J). (gr. 3-5). lib. bdg. 22.79 (978-1-58810-919-4(4)) Heinemann Library.

Haugen, David M. Venus. 2001. (Eyes on the Sky Ser.). (Illus.). 48p. (J). (gr. 3-5). 23.70 (978-0-7377-0940-7(5) , LML00902-178529, Kidhaven) Thomson Gale.

Howard, Fran. Venus. 2007. (Planets Ser.). (ENG., Illus.). 32p. (J). (gr. k-4). lib. bdg. 24.21 (***978-1-59928-824-6(9)*** , Buddy Bks.) ABDO Publishing Co.

Kipp, Steven L. Venus. 2000. (Galaxy Ser.). (Illus.). 24p. (J). (gr. 2-3). lib. bdg. 18.60 (978-0-7368-0519-3(2) , Bridgestone Bks.) Capstone Pr., Inc.

Landau, Elaine. Venus. (True Booktrade;: Space Ser.). 48p. (J). 2008. pap. 6.95 (***978-0-531-14798-6(3));*** 2007. (Illus.). (gr. 3-5). lib. bdg. 26.00 (***978-0-531-12564-9(5)***) Scholastic Library Publishing. (Children's Pr.).

Margaret, Amy. Venus. 2001. (Library of the Planets). (Illus.). 24p. (J). lib. bdg. 21.25 (978-0-8239-5643-2(1) , PowerKids Pr.) Rosen Publishing Group, Inc., The.

Miller, Ron. Venus. 2002. (Worlds Beyond Ser.). (Illus.). 64p. (gr. 7 up). lib. bdg. (978-0-7613-2359-4(7) , Twenty-First Century Bks.) Lerner Publishing Group.

Orme, Helen & Orme, David. Let's Explore Venus. 2006. (J). pap. (***978-0-8368-8135-6(4));*** lib. bdg. (***978-0-8368-7950-6(3)***) Stevens, Gareth Inc.

Potts, Steve. Venus. 2001. (Illus.). 24p. (J). 21.35 (978-1-58340-094-4(X)) Smart Apple Media.

Prinja, Raman. Venus. 2002. 32p. (J). (gr. 3-5). 7.50 (978-1-4034-0620-0(0)) Heinemann Library.

Rau, Dana Meachen. Venus. 2002. (Our Solar System Ser.). (Illus.). 32p. (J). (gr. 3 up). lib. bdg. 21.26 (978-0-7565-0201-0(2)) Compass Point Bks.

Renfield, R. K. Venus. 2006. (J). (***978-1-4042-1968-7(4)***) Rosen Publishing Group, Inc., The.

Richardson, Adele. Venus. (J). 2008. (***978-1-4296-0729-2(7));*** 2005. (Illus.). 24p. lib. bdg. 21.26 (978-0-7368-3698-2(5)) Capstone Pr., Inc.

Ring, Susan. Venus. (Exploring Planets Ser.). (Illus.). (J). 2004. pap. (978-1-59036-223-5(3)); 2003. 24p. lib. bdg. 15.95 (978-1-59036-096-5(6)) Weigl Pubs., Inc.

Romero, Libby. Discover Mars & Venus. 2006. pap. 39.00 (***978-1-4108-6507-6(X)***) Benchmark Education Co.

—Mars & Venus. 2006. pap. 39.00 (***978-1-4108-6504-5(5)***) Benchmark Education Co.

Simon, Charnan. Venus. 2003. (Planets Ser.). (Illus.). 32p. (J). (gr. 2-6). 27.07 (978-1-59296-057-6(X)) Child's World, Inc.

Simon, Seymour. Venus. 1998. (Illus.). 32p. (J). (ps-3). pap. 6.99 (978-0-688-16161-3(8) , Harper Trophy) HarperCollins Pubs.

Spangenburg, Ray. Look at Venus. 2001. (gr. 5-8). lib. bdg. 24.55 (978-0-613-54277-7(0)) Tandem Library Bks.

—Venus. 2001. (gr. 5-8). lib. bdg. 17.60 (978-0-613-37617-4(X)) Tandem Library Bks.

Spangenburg, Ray & Moser, Kit. Venus. 2001. (Watts Library). (Illus.). 64p. (J). (gr. 5-7). pap. 8.95 (978-0-531-13992-9(1)); 25.50 (978-0-531-11768-2(5)) Scholastic Library Publishing. (Watts, Franklin).

Sparrow, Giles. Venus. (Exploring the Solar System Ser.). (Illus.). 39p. (J). (gr. 4-7). 2002. pap. 7.95 (978-1-58810-967-5(4) , 91450); 2001. lib. bdg. 24.22 (978-1-57572-393-8(X)) Heinemann Library.

Stinson, Richard K. Venus. 2004. (Library of the Nine Planets). (J). lib. bdg. 26.50 (978-1-4042-0175-0(0)) Rosen Publishing Group, Inc., The.

Stone, Tanya Lee. Venus. 2002. (Blastoff! Ser.). (Illus.). 64p. (J). 28.50 (978-0-7614-1405-6(3) , Benchmark Bks.) Cavendish, Marshall Corp.

Teitelbaum, Michael. Mars & Venus Space Exploration. 2006. (Navigators Ser.). (J). pap. 44.00 (***978-1-4108-6243-3(7)***) Benchmark Education Co.

Vogt, Gregory L. Mercury, Venus, Earth & Mars. 2000. (Our Universe Ser.). (Illus.). 48p. (J). (gr. 4-7). lib. bdg. 22.83 (978-0-7398-3110-6(0)) Raintree.

Wimmer, Teresa. Venus. 2007. (J). (978-1-58341-524-5(6) , Creative Education) Creative Co., The.

World Book, contrib. by. Mercury & Venus. 2nd ed. 2006. (World Book's Solar System & Space Exploration Library). (Illus.). 64p. (J). (***978-0-7166-9517-2(0)***) World Bk., Inc.

World Book, Inc. Staff, contrib. by. Mercury & Venus. 2006. (World Book's Solar System & Space Exploration Library). (Illus.). 63p. (J). (978-0-7166-9502-8(2)) World Bk., Inc.

VERDI, GIUSEPPE, 1813-1901

Cencetti, Greta. Verdi. 2002. (Classic Composers Ser.). (Illus.). 40p. (J). incl. audio compact disk (978-1-59069-094-9(X) , T2104) Studio Mouse LLC.

—Verdi: Getting to Know Your Classical Composers. 2002. (Classic Composers Ser.). (Illus.). 32p. (978-1-59069-027-7(3) , T2004) Studio Mouse LLC.

Pougin, Arthur. Verdi: An Anecdotic History of His Life & Works. 2001. 308p. (YA). reprint ed. 98.00 (978-0-7222-5553-7(5)) Library Reprints, Inc.

Roosevelt, Blanche. Verdi: Milan & Othello. 2001. 249p. (YA). reprint ed. 98.00 (978-0-7222-5554-4(3)) Library Reprints, Inc.

Schoell, William. Giuseppe Verdi & Italian Opera. 2007. (Illus.). 128p. (J). (gr. 9 up). lib. bdg. 27.95 (978-1-59935-041-7(6)) Reynolds, Morgan Inc.

Vernon, Roland. Verdi: Introducing. 2000. (Introducing Composers Ser.). (Illus.). 32p. (J). (gr. 4-7). 21.95 (978-0-7910-6043-8(8) , Chelsea Hse.) Facts On File, Inc.

T U V

Whiting, Jim. The Life & Times of Guiseppe Verdi. 2004. (Masters of Music Ser.). (Illus.). 48p. (gr. 4-8). lib. bdg. 20.95 (978-1-58415-281-1(8)) Mitchell Lane Pubs., Inc.

VERMEER, JOHANNES, 1632-1675

Venezia, Mike. Johannes Vermeer. 2002. (Getting to Know the World's Greatest Artists Ser.). (Illus.). 32p. (J). (gr. 3-4). pap. 6.95 (978-0-516-26999-3(2), Children's Pr.) Scholastic Library Publishing.

—Johannes Vermeer. 2002. (gr. 3-6). lib. bdg. 15.25 (978-0-613-50710-3(X)) Tandem Library Bks.

Venezia, Mike & Vermeer, Johannes. Johannes Vermeer. 2002. (Getting to Know World Artists Ser.). (Illus.). 32p. (J). (gr. 3-4). 27.00 (978-0-516-22282-0(1), Children's Pr.) Scholastic Library Publishing.

VERMONT

Brown, Jonatha A. Vermont. 2006. (Portraits of the States Ser.). (J). pap. (978-0-8368-4727-7(X)); lib. bdg. (978-0-8368-4710-9(5)) Stevens, Gareth Inc.

Czech, Jan M. Vermont. 2002. (From Sea to Shining Sea Ser.: 2). (Illus.). 80p. (J). (gr. 3-5). pap. 30.50 (978-0-516-22480-0(8), Children's Pr.) Scholastic Library Publishing.

Dornfeld, Margaret. Vermont. 2005. (It's My State! Ser.). (Illus.). 80p. (J). 27.07 (978-0-7614-1864-1(4), Benchmark Bks.) Cavendish, Marshall Corp.

Elish, Dan. Vermont. 2nd ed. 2006. (Celebrate the States Ser.). (Illus.). 144p. (J). (gr. 6 up). lib. bdg. 37.07 (978-0-7614-2018-7(5), Benchmark Bks.) Cavendish, Marshall Corp.

Feeney, Kathy. Vermont Facts & Symbols. (States & Their Symbols Ser.). 24p. (J). 2000. (Illus.). (gr. 2-3). lib. bdg. 18.60 (978-0-7368-0647-3(4), Bridgestone Bks.); 2003. lib. bdg. 19.93 (978-0-7368-2275-6(5)) Capstone Pr., Inc.

Flocker, Michael. Vermont: The Green Mountain State. 2002. (World Almanac Library of the States). (Illus.). 48p. (J). (gr. 5 up). lib. bdg. 30.00 (978-0-8368-5146-5(3)); pap. 14.95 (978-0-8368-5316-2(4)) Stevens, Gareth Inc. (World Almanac Library).

Foran, Jill. A Guide to Vermont. 2001. (American States Ser.). (Illus.). 32p. (J). lib. bdg. 16.95 (978-1-930954-54-0(9)) Weigl Pubs., Inc.

Furlong Reynolds, Cynthia. M Is for Maple Syrup: A Vermont Alphabet. Joyner, Ginny, illus. 2002. 40p. (J). (ps-5). 17.95 (978-1-58536-030-7(9)) Sleeping Bear Pr.

Hassig, Susan M. Panama. 2nd ed. 2006. (Cultures of the World Ser.). (Illus.). 144p. (J). lib. bdg. 39.93 (978-0-7614-2028-6(2), Benchmark Bks.) Cavendish, Marshall Corp.

Haugen, Brenda & Santella, Andrew. Ethan Allen: Green Mountain Rebel. 2004. (Signature Lives Ser.). (Illus.). 112p. (J). 30.60 (978-0-7565-0824-1(X), 1240131) Compass Point Bks.

Heinrichs, Ann. Vermont. Kania, Matt, illus. 2005. (Welcome to the USA Ser.). 40p. (J). (gr. 1-5). 27.07 (978-1-59296-487-1(7)) Child's World, Inc.

—Vermont. 2003. (This Land Is Your Land Ser.). (Illus.). 48p. (J). (gr. 3 up). lib. bdg. 22.60 (978-0-7565-0345-1(0)) Compass Point Bks.

—Vermont. 2001. (America the Beautiful Ser.). (Illus.). 144p. (J). (gr. 5-8). 36.00 (978-0-516-21094-0(7), Children's Pr.) Scholastic Library Publishing.

Keizer, Garret, et al, contrib. by. The Twelve Seasons of Vermont: A Vermont Life Book. 2005. (Illus.). 112p. 34.95 (978-1-931389-07-5(1)) Vermont Life Magazine.

Knox, Barbara. Vermont. 2003. (Land of Liberty Ser.). (Illus.). 64p. (J). lib. bdg. 25.26 (978-0-7368-2201-5(1)) Capstone Pr., Inc.

Kummer, Patricia K. Vermont. rev. ed. 2002. (One Nation Ser.). (Illus.). 48p. (J). (gr. 3-4). lib. bdg. 22.60 (978-0-7368-1270-2(9), Bridgestone Bks.) Capstone Pr., Inc.

Marsh, Carole. The Big Vermont Reproducible Activity Book. 2001. (Carole Marsh Vermont Bks.). (Illus.). (J). (gr. 2-6). per., act. bk. ed. 9.95 (978-0-7933-9959-8(9)) Gallopade International.

—My First Book about Vermont. Line Art Staff, illus. 2001. (Vermont Experience! Ser.). 32p. (J). (gr. k-4). pap. 7.95 (978-0-7933-9901-7(7)) Gallopade International.

—The Survivor: A Class Challenge. 2001. (Carole Marsh Vermont Bks.). lib. bdg. 29.95 (978-0-635-00691-2(X)) Gallopade International.

—Vermont Classic Christmas Trivia. 2002. (Carole Marsh Vermont Bks.). (Illus.). 32p. pap. 14.95 (978-0-635-01455-9(6), 14556); lib. bdg. 21.95 (978-0-635-01456-6(4), 14564) Gallopade International. (Marsh, Carole Bks.).

—Vermont Current Events Projects: 30 Cool, Activities, Crafts, Experiments & More for Kids to Do to Learn about Your State! 2003. (Vermont Experience Ser.). 32p. (gr. k-5). pap. 5.95 (978-0-635-02065-9(3), Marsh, Carole Bks.) Gallopade International.

—The Vermont Experience Pocket Guide. 2001. (Carole Marsh Vermont Bks.). (Illus.). 96p. (J). (gr. 3-8). pap. 6.95 (978-0-7933-9930-7(0)) Gallopade International.

—Vermont Geography Projects: 30 Cool, Activities, Crafts, Experiments & More for Kids to Do to Learn about Your State! 2003. (Vermont Experience Ser.). 32p. (gr. k-5). pap. 5.95 (978-0-635-01863-2(2), Marsh, Carole Bks.) Gallopade International.

—Vermont Government Projects: 30 Cool, Activities, Crafts, Experiments & More for Kids to Do to Learn about Your State! 2003. (Vermont Experience Ser.). 32p. (gr. k-5). pap. 5.95 (978-0-635-01964-6(7), Marsh, Carole Bks.) Gallopade International.

—Vermont Hot Zones! Viruses, Disease, & Epidemics in Our State's History. 1998. (Hot Zones! Ser.). (Illus.). (J). (gr. 3-12). pap. 19.95 (978-0-7933-8964-3(X)); lib. bdg. 29.95 (978-0-7933-8963-6(1)) Gallopade International.

—Vermont Jeopardy! Answers & Questions about Our State! Line Art Staff, illus. 2001. 32p. (J). (gr. 3-8). pap. 7.95 (978-0-7933-9814-0(2)) Gallopade International.

—Vermont "Jography" A Fun Run Thru Our State! 2001. (Carole Marsh Vermont Bks.). 32p. (J). (gr. 3-8). pap. 7.95 (978-0-7933-9843-0(6)) Gallopade International.

—Vermont People Projects: 30 Cool, Activities, Crafts, Experiments & More for Kids to Do to Learn about Your State! 2003. (Vermont Experience Ser.). 32p. (gr. k-5). pap. 5.95 (978-0-635-02014-7(9), Marsh, Carole Bks.) Gallopade International.

—Vermont Symbols & Facts Projects: 30 Cool, Activities, Crafts, Experiments & More for Kids to Do to Learn about Your State! 2003. (Vermont Experience Ser.). 32p. (gr. k-5). pap. 5.95 (978-0-635-01914-1(0), Marsh, Carole Bks.) Gallopade International.

Murray, Julie. Vermont. 2006. (Buddy Book Ser.). (Illus.). 32p. (J). (gr. k-4). lib. bdg. 22.78 (978-1-59197-704-9(5), Buddy Bks.) ABDO Publishing Co.

Pelta, Kathy. Vermont. (Hello U. S. A. Ser.). (J). 2000. (Illus.). 72p. (gr. 3-6). pap. 5.95 (978-0-8225-9784-1(5), First Avenue Editions); 2nd ed. 2001. pap. (978-0-8225-4257-5(9), Lerner Pubns.); 2nd exp. rev. ed. 2002. (Illus.). 84p. (gr. 3-6). 25.26 (978-0-8225-4074-8(6), Lerner Pubns.); 2nd rev. exp. ed. 2003. (Illus.). 84p. (gr. 3-6). pap. 6.95 (978-0-8225-4135-6(1)) Lerner Publishing Group.

Peters, S. True. How to Draw Vermonts Sights & Symbols. 2002. (Kids Guide to Drawing America Ser.). 32p. (J). lib. bdg. 25.25 (978-0-8239-6102-3(8), PowerKids Pr.) Rosen Publishing Group, Inc., The.

Raabe, Emily. Uniquely Vermont. 2004. (Heinemann State Studies). (Illus.). 48p. (J). 31.36 (978-1-4034-4664-0(4)); pap. 9.00 (978-1-4034-4733-3(0)) Heinemann Library.

Schaffer, David. Vermont: A MyReportLinks.com Book. 2003. (States Ser.). (Illus.). 48p. (J). (gr. 4-10). lib. bdg. 25.26 (978-0-7660-5110-2(2), MyReportLinks.com Bks.) Enslow Pubs., Inc.

Taylor-Butler, Christine. Vermont. 2007. (Rookie Read-about' Geography: States Ser.). 32p. (J). pap. 5.95 (***978-0-531-16819-6(0)***); (Illus.). (gr. 1-2). 20.50 (978-0-531-12593-9(9)) Scholastic Library Publishing. (Children's Pr.).

Thompson, Kathleen. Vermont. 1998. (J). pap. 14.50 (978-0-8172-8459-6(1)) Steck-Vaughn.

Vermont. 2000. (Switched on Schoolhouse Ser.). (Illus.). (YA). (gr. 7-12). pap. 24.95 incl. cd-rom (978-0-7403-0297-8(3), SOSVT) Alpha Omega Pubns., Inc.

Way, Jennifer. Vermont. 2006. (Bilingual Library of the United States of America: Set 2). (ENG & SPA., Illus.). 32p. (J). (gr. 3-6). lib. bdg. 22.50 (978-1-4042-3111-5(0), Buenas Letra) Rosen Publishing Group, Inc., The.

VERMONT—FICTION

Alvarez, Julia. Cuando Tia Lola Vino (de Visita) a Quedarse. Valenzuela, Liliana, tr. 2004. Tr. of How Tia Lola Came to (Visit) Stay. (SPA.). 144p. (gr. 3-7). pap. 5.50 (978-0-375-81552-2(X), Yearling) Random Hse. Children's Bks.

—Cuando Tía Lola Vino (De Visita) a Quedarse. Valenzuela, Liliana, tr. 2004. (SPA.). 144p. (J). (gr. 3-7). lib. bdg. 17.99 (978-0-375-91552-9(4), Yearling) Random Hse. Children's Bks.

—How Tia Lola Came to Stay. 2002. (Illus.). 160p. (gr. 3-7). 5.99 (978-0-440-41870-2(4), Yearling) Random Hse. Children's Bks.

—How Tia Lola Came to (Visit) Stay. Cascardi, Andrea, ed. 2001. (Illus.). 160p. (J). (gr. 3-5). 15.95 (978-0-375-80215-7(0)); lib. bdg. 17.99 (978-0-375-90215-4(5)) Random Hse. Children's Bks. (Knopf Bks. for Young Readers).

—How Tia Lola Came to (Visit) Stay. 2002. (gr. 3-6). lib. bdg. 13.00 (978-0-613-57907-0(0)) Tandem Library Bks.

Anderson, M. T. The Game of Sunken Places. (J). 2004. 272p. pap. 16.95 (978-0-439-41660-3(4)); 2005. 288p. reprint ed. pap. 5.99 (978-0-439-41661-0(2), Scholastic Paperbacks) Scholastic, Inc.

—The Game of Sunken Places. l.t. ed. 2004. 331p. 23.95 (978-0-7862-7064-4(0), Large Print Pr.) Thorndike Pr.

Arnosky, Jim. Little Champ. Arnosky, Jim, illus. 2001. (J). pap. 6.95 (978-0-9657144-5-7(4)) Onion River Pr.

Baker, Carin Greenberg. Pride of the Green Mountains, No. 3. 1998. (Treasured Horses Ser.). (J). (978-0-606-13863-5(3)) Tandem Library Bks.

Blegvad, Lenore. Kitty & Mr. Kipling: Neighbors in Vermont. Blegvad, Erik, illus. 2005. 144p. (J). (gr. 3-5). 16.95 (978-0-689-87363-8(8), McElderry, Margaret K.) Simon & Schuster Children's Publishing.

Blier, Gloria. The Brook That Held Many Secrets. 2004. 144p. pap. 19.95 (978-1-4137-3639-7(4)) PublishAmerica, Inc.

Bohjalian, Chris. The Buffalo Soldier: A Novel. 2003. (gr. 7-12). lib. bdg. 23.40 (978-0-613-70910-1(1)) Tandem Library Bks.

Crist-Evans, Craig. North of Everything. 2004. (Illus.). 80p. (J). (gr. 5-9). 14.99 (978-0-7636-2098-1(X)) Candlewick Pr.

Curtis, Alice Turner. A Little Maid of Ticonderoga. Smith, Wuanita, illus. 2004. (Little Maid Ser.). 192p. (J). (gr. 4-7). reprint ed. per. 12.95 (978-1-55709-330-1(X)) Applewood Bks.

Doyle, Eugenie. Stray Voltage. 1998. 128p. (YA). (gr. 5-7). 16.95 (978-1-886910-86-7(3), Lemniscaat) Boyds Mills Pr.

Fairless, Caroline. Hambone. Edelson, Wendy, illus. 2001. 48p. (J). pap. 10.95 (978-0-89869-361-4(6)) Church Publishing, Inc.

Fisher, Dorothy Canfield. Understood Betsy. Root, Kimberly B., illus. rev. ed. 1999. 240p. (J). (gr. 4-6). 17.95 (978-0-8050-6073-7(1), Holt, Henry & Co. Bks. For Young Readers) Holt, Henry & Co.

—Understood Betsy. 2004. reprint ed. pap. 1.99 (978-1-4192-9201-9(3)); pap. 24.95 (978-1-4179-0955-1(2)) Kessinger Publishing, LLC.

—Understood Betsy. 1999. (Hardscrabble Bks.). 182p. (J). reprint ed. pap. 9.95 (978-0-87451-920-4(9)) Univ. Pr. of New England.

Gamble, Adam. Good Night Vermont. Kelly, Cooper, illus. 2007. (Good Night Our World Ser.). 20p. (J). bds. 9.95 (***978-1-60219-017-7(8)***) Our World of Books.

Gauthier, Gail. The Hero of Ticonderoga. 2002. 240p. (J). (gr. 5-9). pap. 6.99 (978-0-698-11968-0(1), Putnam Juvenile) Penguin Group (USA) Inc.

—Hero of Ticonderoga. 2002. lib. bdg. 15.30 (978-0-613-60807-7(0)) Tandem Library Bks.

Gould, Peter L. Write Naked. 2008. 256p. (YA). 16.95 (***978-0-374-38483-8(5)***) Farrar, Straus & Giroux.

Graff, Nancy Price. A Long Way Home. 2001. 208p. (J). (gr. 5-9). tchr. ed. 15.00 (978-0-618-12042-0(4), Clarion Bks.) Houghton Mifflin Co. Trade & Reference Div.

—Taking Wing. Minor, Wendell, illus. 2005. 224p. (YA). (gr. 5-9). 15.00 (978-0-618-53591-0(8), Clarion Bks.) Houghton Mifflin Co. Trade & Reference Div.

Henry, Marguerite. Justin Morgan Had a Horse. Dennis, Wesley, illus. 2006. 176p. (J). pap. 5.99 (978-1-4169-2785-3(9), Aladdin) Simon & Schuster Children's Publishing.

Hess, Karen. Witness. l.t. ed. 2005. 209p. pap. 10.95 (978-0-7862-7249-5(X), Large Print Pr.) Thorndike Pr.

Hesse, Karen. Witness. 2004. 168p. (J). (gr. 5-9). pap. 29.00 incl. audio (978-0-8072-2094-8(9), Listening Library) Random Hse. Audio Publishing Group.

—Witness. (J). (978-0-439-36634-2(8), Scholastic Pr.); 2003. (Illus.). 176p. (YA). pap. 5.99 (978-0-439-27200-1(9), Scholastic Paperbacks); 2001. (Illus.). 176p. (YA). (gr. 4-7). pap. 16.95 (978-0-439-27199-8(1)) Scholastic, Inc.

—Witness. 2001. (gr. 5-8). lib. bdg. 14.15 (978-0-613-62503-6(X)) Tandem Library Bks.

Higgenson, Hadley. Keeker & the Sugar Shack. Andersen, Maja, illus. 2006. (Sneaky Pony Ser.: Bk. 3). 48p. (J). pap. 3.95 (978-0-8118-5456-6(6)) Chronicle Bks. LLC.

Higginson, Hadley. Keeker & Springtime Surprise. Parrett, Lisa, illus. 2007. (Sneaky Pony Ser.: No. 4). 56p. (J). 15.50 (978-0-8118-5598-3(8)) Chronicle Bks. LLC.

—Keeker & Springtime Surprise. Perrett, Lisa, illus. 2007. (Sneaky Pony Ser.: No. 4). 56p. (J). pap. 3.95 (978-0-8118-5599-0(6)) Chronicle Bks. LLC.

—Keeker & the Crazy Upside-Down Day. Perrett, Lisa, illus. 2008. (J). (***978-0-8118-6255-4(0)***); pap. (***978-0-8118-6256-1(9)***) Chronicle Bks. LLC.

Higginson, Hadley. Keeker & the Sugar Shack, Bk. 3. Andersen, Maja, illus. 2006. 48p. (J). 15.50 (978-0-8118-5455-9(8)) Chronicle Bks. LLC.

Hurwitz, Johanna. Faraway Summer. Azarian, Mary, illus. 1998. 160p. (J). (gr. 3-7). 14.95 (978-0-688-15334-2(8)) HarperCollins Pubs.

—The Unsigned Valentine: And Other Events in the Life of Emma Meade. Azarian, Mary, illus. 2006. 176p. (J). 15.99 (978-0-06-056053-9(3)); lib. bdg. 16.89 (978-0-06-056054-6(1)) HarperCollins Pubs.

Isaacs, Anne & Bannerman, Helen. Pancakes for Supper! Teague, Mark, illus. 2006. 40p. (J). (gr. k-3). pap. 15.99 (978-0-439-64483-9(6), Scholastic Pr.) Scholastic, Inc.

Jacobs, E. Caroline. The S. W. F. Club. 2006. 77.99 (***978-1-4280-4783-9(2)***); pap. 71.99 (***978-1-4280-4779-2(4)***) IndyPublish.com.

Jaspersohn, William. The Two Brothers. Donato, Michael A., illus. 2005. (Family Heritage Ser.). 36p. (J). (gr. 1-5). 15.95 (978-0-916718-16-9(6)) Vermont Folklife Ctr.

Ketchum, Liza. Where the Great Hawk Flies. 2005. 272p. (J). (gr. 5-9). 16.00 (978-0-618-40085-0(0), Clarion Bks.) Houghton Mifflin Co. Trade & Reference Div.

Kinsey-Warnock, Natalie. As Long As There Are Mountains. 2001. (gr. 5-8). lib. bdg. 13.00 (978-0-613-35902-3(X)) Tandem Library Bks.

—A Christmas Like Helen's. Azarian, Mary, illus. 2004. 32p. (J). (gr. k-3). tchr. ed. 16.00 (978-0-618-23137-9(4)) Houghton Mifflin Co. Trade & Reference Div.

—A Doctor Like Papa. Bernardin, James, illus. 2002. 80p. (J). 14.99 (978-0-06-029319-2(5)) HarperCollins Pubs.

—A Doctor Like Papa. 2002. (gr. 3-6). lib. bdg. 13.00 (978-0-613-68417-0(6)) Tandem Library Bks.

—From Dawn till Dusk. Azarian, Mary, illus. 2002. 40p. (J). (gr. k-3). tchr. ed. 16.00 (978-0-618-18655-6(7)) Houghton Mifflin Co. Trade & Reference Div.

—From Dawn till Dusk. Azarian, Mary, illus. 2006. 40p. (J). (gr. k-3). reprint ed. pap. 6.95 (978-0-618-73750-5(2)) Houghton Mifflin Co. Trade & Reference Div.

—The Night the Bells Rang. 2001. (gr. 1-5). 20.50 (978-0-8446-7180-2(0)) Smith, Peter Pub., Inc.

—The Night the Bells Rang. 2000. (978-0-606-20367-8(2)) Tandem Library Bks.

—Night the Bells Rang. 2000. (gr. 3-6). lib. bdg. 13.00 (978-0-613-30071-1(8)) Tandem Library Bks.

Lange, Willem. John & Tom. Dodson, Bert, illus. 2001. (Family Heritage Ser.). 36p. (J). (ps-2). 15.95 (978-0-916718-17-6(4)) Vermont Folklife Ctr.

Lasky, Kathryn. Sugaring Time. 2003. (Illus.). 21.25 (978-0-8446-7248-9(3)) Smith, Peter Pub., Inc.

Littlefield, William. The Circus in the Woods. 2001. 208p. (J). (gr. 4-6). tchr. ed. 15.00 (978-0-618-06642-1(X)) Houghton Mifflin Co. Trade & Reference Div.

Mademann Vaughan, Kathryn. My Day at the Zoo. Martin, Don, illus. 2004. (J). per. 19.95 (978-0-9747447-1-1(9)) Chaser Media LLC.

Maguire, Gregory. Four Stupid Cupids. Clayton, Elaine, illus. 2001. 192p. (J). (gr. 4-6). tchr. ed. 16.00 (978-0-395-83895-2(9), Clarion Bks.) Houghton Mifflin Co. Trade & Reference Div.

—Four Stupid Cupids. 2002. (gr. 3-6). lib. bdg. 12.95 (978-0-613-43035-7(2)) Tandem Library Bks.

—Four Stupid Cupids. l.t. ed. 2001. 225p. (J). 21.95 (978-0-7862-3547-6(0)) Thorndike Pr.

—One Final Firecracker. 2007. (Hamlet Chronicles Ser.). 320p. (J). pap. 6.99 (***978-0-06-085284-9(4)***, Harper Trophy) HarperCollins Pubs.

—One Final Firecracker. Clayton, Elaine, illus. 2005. 240p. (J). (gr. 4-6). 17.00 (978-0-618-27480-2(4), Clarion Bks.) Houghton Mifflin Co. Trade & Reference Div.

—Six Haunted Hairdos. 1999. (978-0-606-17470-1(2)) Tandem Library Bks.

—Six Haunted Hairdos. l.t. ed. 2002. 178p. (J). 21.95 (978-0-7862-4421-8(6)) Thorndike Pr.

—Three Rotten Eggs. Clayton, Elaine, illus. 2002. 192p. (J). (gr. 4-6). 16.00 (978-0-618-09655-8(8), Clarion Bks.) Houghton Mifflin Co. Trade & Reference Div.

Mather, Melissa. One Summer in Between. 2000. 228p. (YA). pap. 14.95 (978-0-595-09384-7(1), Backinprint.com) iUniverse, Inc.

Medearis, Michael & Medearis, Angela Shelf. Daisy & the Doll. Johnson, Larry, illus. 2000. (Family Heritage Ser.). 32p. (J). (gr. 1-5). 14.95 (978-0-916718-15-2(8)) Vermont Folklife Ctr.

Page, Marion. The Printer's Devil. Dodge, Chris, illus. 2002. 171p. (YA). (gr. 6-9). 9.99 (978-0-88092-464-1(0), 4640) Royal Fireworks Publishing Co.

Paterson, Katherine. Preacher's Boy. 2001. 192p. (J). (gr. 5 up). pap. 5.99 (978-0-06-447233-3(7), Harper Trophy) HarperCollins Pubs.

—Preacher's Boy. 1999. (Illus.). 176p. (J). (gr. 5-9). tchr. ed. 15.00 (978-0-395-83897-6(5), Clarion Bks.) Houghton Mifflin Co. Trade & Reference Div.

—Preacher's Boy. 2001. (gr. 5-8). lib. bdg. 12.95 (978-0-613-34906-2(7)) Tandem Library Bks.

Pearson, Tracey Campbell. Where Does Joe Go? Pearson, Tracey Campbell, illus. 2002. (Illus.). 32p. (J). pap. 5.95 (978-0-374-48366-1(3), Sunburst) Farrar, Straus & Giroux.

Peck, Robert Newton. A Day No Pigs Would Die. 139p. (YA). (gr. 7 up). pap. 4.99 (978-0-8072-1384-1(5)); pap. 4.99 (978-0-8072-1357-5(8)) Random Hse. Audio Publishing Group. (Listening Library).

Porter, Eleanor H. Classic Starts: Pollyanna. Akib, Jamel, illus. 2007. (Classic Starts Ser.). 160p. (J). 4.95 (978-1-4027-3692-6(4)) Sterling Publishing Co., Inc.

Samantha's Vermont Adventure. 1998. (Illus.). 2p. (J). (ps-1). 15.00 (978-1-888074-89-5(2)) Pockets of Learning.

Schubert, Leda. Here Comes Darrell. Azarian, Mary, illus. 2005. 32p. (J). (gr. k-3). 16.00 (978-0-618-41605-9(6)) Houghton Mifflin Co. Trade & Reference Div.

Seidler, Tor. Brothers below Zero. McCarty, Peter, illus. 2003. 144p. (J). (gr. 5 up). pap. 5.99 (978-0-06-440936-0(8), Harper Trophy) HarperCollins Pubs.

—Brothers below Zero. 2002. (Illus.). 144p. (J). (gr. 3 up). 14.95 (978-0-06-029179-2(6), Geringer, Laura Book) HarperCollins Pubs.

—Brothers below Zero. McCarty, Peter, illus. 2002. 144p. (J). (gr. 5 up). lib. bdg. 15.89 (978-0-06-029180-8(X), Geringer, Laura Book) HarperCollins Pubs.

—Brothers below Zero. 2003. (gr. 3-6). lib. bdg. 14.15 (978-0-613-57705-2(1)) Tandem Library Bks.

Stahler, David, Jr. Gathering of Shades. 2006. pap. (978-0-06-052296-4(8)) HarperCollins Canada, Ltd.

—A Gathering of Shades. 2005. 304p. (J). 15.99 (978-0-06-052294-0(1)); lib. bdg. 16.89 (978-0-06-052295-7(X)) HarperCollins Pubs. (HarperTeen).

Walker, Mildred. A Piece of the World. 2001. (Illus.). 218p. pap. 12.95 (978-0-8032-9823-1(4), WALPIX, Bison Bks.) Univ. of Nebraska Pr.

Washington, Ida H. Brave Enough: The Story of Rob Sanford, Vermont Pioneer Boy. Smoak, I. W. & Washington, C. E., illus. 2003. vii, 128p. (J). (gr. 4-6). pap. 12.95 (978-0-9666832-7-1(7)) Cherry Tree Bks.

Wilhelm, Doug. Falling. 2007. 256p. (YA). (gr. 9 up). 17.00 (978-0-374-32251-9(1)) Farrar, Straus & Giroux.

Williams, G. Walton. The Beavers Build a Dam. Kollock, John, ed. unabr. ed. 2000. (Illus.). 64p. (Orig.). (J). pap. 6.95 (978-0-9703570-0-7(1)) Barksdale Hse. Pr.

Wilson, Nancy Hope. Mountain Pose. 2001. 240p. (J). (gr. 5 up). 17.00 (978-0-374-35078-9(7), Farrar, Straus & Giroux (BYR)) Farrar, Straus & Giroux.

Winthrop, Elizabeth. Counting on Grace. 240p. (J). (gr. 3-7). 2007. pap. 6.50 (***978-0-553-48783-1(3)***, Yearling); 2006. (Illus.). 15.95 (978-0-385-74644-1(X), Lamb, Wendy); 2006. (Illus.). lib. bdg. 17.99 (978-0-385-90878-8(4), Lamb, Wendy) Random Hse. Children's Bks.

VERMONT—HISTORY

Aronson, Virginia. Ethan Allen: Revolutionary Hero. 2000. (Revolutionary War Leaders Ser.). (Illus.). 80p. (J). (gr. 4-7). pap. 27.50 (978-0-7910-6132-9(9)); (gr. 8-12). 27.50 (978-0-7910-5974-6(X)) Facts On File, Inc. (Chelsea Hse.).

Carole Marsh. Vermont Indians. 2004. (Vermont Experience Ser.). 36p. (gr. 3-8). pap. 7.95 (978-0-635-02334-6(2)); lib. bdg. 29.95 (978-0-635-02335-3(0)) Gallopade International.

Davies, Jean S. Neighborly Notes: From Turn of the Century Small Town Vermont, 2004. (Illus.). 256p. per. 24.95 (978-0-9749151-9-7(X)) CoZi Publishing LLC.

Haugen, Brenda & Santella, Andrew. Ethan Allen: Green Mountain Rebel. 2004. (Signature Lives Ser.). (Illus.). 112p. (J). 30.60 (978-0-7565-0824-1(X), 1240131) Compass Point Bks.

Marsh, Carole. My First Pocket Guide Vermont. 2000. (Vermont Experience! Ser.). (Illus.). 96p. (J). (gr. 3-8). 12.95 (978-0-635-01335-4(5), 13355) Gallopade International.

TUV

—Vermont History Projects: 30 Cool, Activities, Crafts, Experiments & More for Kids to Do to Learn about Your State! 2003. (Vermont Experience Ser.). 32p. (gr. k-5). pap. 5.95 (978-0-635-01814-4(4) , Marsh, Carole Bks.) Gallopade International.

—Vermont Survivor. 2001. (GameBook Ser.). 32p. (J). (gr. 3-8). pap., act. bk. ed. 9.95 (978-0-635-00566-3(2)) Gallopade International.

—Vermont Wheel of Fortune. 2001. (GameBook Ser.). 32p. (J). (gr. 3-8). pap., act. bk. ed. 9.95 (978-0-635-00006-4(7)) Gallopade International.

—Wheel of Fortune. 2001. (Vermont Experience! Ser.). (J). lib. bdg. 29.95 (978-0-635-00007-1(5)) Gallopade International.

—Who Wants to Be a Millionaire? 2001. (Vermont Experience! Ser.). (J). lib. bdg. 29.95 (978-0-635-00107-8(1)) Gallopade International.

Price Hossell, Karen. Ethan Allen. 2004. (American War Biographies Ser.). (J). lib. bdg. 29.93 (978-1-4034-5077-7(3)); (Illus.). pap. 8.50 (978-1-4034-5084-5(6)) Heinemann Library.

Stein, R. Conrad. Ethan Allen & the Green Mountain Boys. 2003. (Cornerstones of Freedom). (Illus.). 48p. (J). (gr. 4-6). 26.00 (978-0-516-24206-4(7) , Children's Pr.) Scholastic Library Publishing.

VERNE, JULES, 1828-1905

Schoell, William. Remarkable Journeys: The Story of Jules Verne. 2004. (World Writers Ser.). (Illus.). 112p. (YA). (gr. 6-12). 23.95 (978-1-883846-92-3(7) , First Biographies) Reynolds, Morgan Inc.

Streissguth, Thomas. Science Fiction Pioneer: A Story about Jules Verne. Ramstad, Ralph L., illus. 2000. (Creative Minds Biographies Ser.). 64p. (J). (gr. 3-6). lib. bdg. 22.60 (978-1-57505-440-7(X) , Carolrhoda Bks.) Lerner Publishing Group.

VERRAZANO, GIOVANNI DA, 1485-1527

Healy, Nick. Giovanni Da Verrazano. 2003. (Explorers of the Unknown Ser.). (J). (978-1-58417-037-2(9)); pap. (978-1-58417-100-3(6)) Lake Street Pubs.

VERSIFICATION

see also Poetry

Fandel, Jennifer. Rhyme, Meter, & Other Word Music: Understanding Poetry. 2005. (Illus.). 48p. (gr. 5-9). 21.95 (978-1-58341-342-5(1) , Creative Education) Creative Co., The.

Roza, Greg. Patterns in Poetry: Recognizing & Analyzing Poetic Form & Meter. 2005. (PowerMath Ser.). 22.50 (978-1-4042-2941-9(8)); pap. 22.50 (978-1-4042-5146-5(4)) Rosen Publishing Group, Inc., The. (PowerKids Pr.).

VERTEBRATES

see also Amphibians; Birds; Fishes; Mammals; Reptiles

Bakker, Robert T. Prehistoric Monsters! 2008. (J). pap. (***978-0-375-83945-0(3)***); lib. bdg. (***978-0-375-93945-7(8)***) Random Hse., Inc.

Boothroyd, Jennifer. On the Ground. 2006. (First Step Nonfiction Ser.). (Illus.). 8p. (J). pap. (978-0-8225-5665-7(0) , Lerner Pubns.) Lerner Publishing Group.

Jakobsen, Laurie Mitchell. The Animals of Grandfather Mountain. 2001. (Illus.). xii, 66p. (J). 14.95 (978-1-887905-48-0(0)) Parkway Pubs., Inc.

Kalman, Bobbie. What Is a Vertebrate? 2007. (Big Science Ideas Ser.). (Illus.). 32p. (J). (gr. 1-5). pap. (***978-0-7787-3297-6(5)***) Crabtree Publishing Co.

McNeil, Niki, et al. HOCPP 1133 Vertebrates. 2006. spiral bd. 24.00 (***978-1-60308-133-7(X)***) In the Hands of a Child.

Ohare, Ted. Vertebrados. 2005. (Que Es un Animal? Biblioteca del Descubrimiento Ser.). (SPA.). 24p. pap. 5.45 (978-1-59515-692-1(5)) Rourke Publishing, LLC.

O'Hare, Ted. Vertebrates. 2006. (What Is an Animal Ser.). (Illus.). 24p. (gr. 1-4). 14.95 (978-1-59515-422-4(1)) Rourke Publishing, LLC.

Ohare, Ted. Vertebrates. 2005. 24p. pap. 5.45 (978-1-59515-736-2(0)) Rourke Publishing, LLC.

Pascoe, Elaine. Animals with Backbones. Kuhn, Dwight, illus. Kuhn, Dwight, photos by. 2003. (Kids Guide to the Classification of Living Things Ser.). 32p. (J). lib. bdg. 21.25 (978-0-8239-6310-2(1) , PowerKids Pr.) Rosen Publishing Group, Inc., The.

Pipe, Jim. Big Animals. 2007. (J). (***978-1-59604-161-5(7)***) Stargazer Bks.

So You Want to Dig Dinosaurs: A Field Manual on the Practice, Principles & Politics of Vertebrate Paleontology. l.t. ed. 2001. 280p. (YA). 59.99 (978-0-9716206-0-5(1)) Dragons Claw Pr.

Whitfield, Philip. Animals. 1999. (J). (978-0-02-865417-1(X)); (978-0-02-865418-8(8)) Thomson Gale. (Macmillan Reference USA).

Williams, Judith. The Discovery & Mystery of a Dinosaur Named Jane. 2007. (Prime Ser.). (Illus.). 48p. (J). (gr. 3-7). pap. 13.26 (***978-0-7660-2709-1(0)***) Enslow Pubs., Inc.

VESPUCCI, AMERIGO, 1451-1512

Donaldson-Forbes, Jeff. Amerigo Vespucci. 2002. (Famous Explorers Ser.). (Illus.). 24p. (J). (gr. 3). lib. bdg. 18.75 (978-0-8239-5833-7(7) , PowerKids Pr.) Rosen Publishing Group, Inc., The.

Hoogenboom, Lynn. Amerigo Vespucci: A Primary Source Biography. 2006. (Illus.). 24p. (J). lib. bdg. (978-1-4042-3037-8(8) , PowerKids Pr.) Rosen Publishing Group, Inc., The.

Lambert, Lorene. Who in the World Was the Forgotten Explorer? The Story of Amerigo Vespucci. Mickle, Jed, illus. 2005. 56p. (J). (gr. 2 up). pap. 9.50 (978-0-9728603-8-3(5)) Peace Hill Pr.

VESSELS (SHIPS)

see Ships

VETERINARIANS

Adamson, Heather. A Day in the Life of a Veterinarian. 2003. (First Facts Ser.). (Illus.). 24p. (J). lib. bdg. 21.26 (978-0-7368-2287-9(9)) Capstone Pr., Inc.

African-American Veterinarians. 2000. (My Ancestors—My Heroes Ser.: Vol. 33). (J). (gr. 3-4). (978-1-893091-32-0(5)) Parker Publishing Co.

Ask the Veterinarians: Fourth Grade Guided Comprehension Level O. (On Our Way to English Ser.). (gr. 4 up). 34.50 (978-0-7578-7169-6(0)) Rigby Education.

Aylmore, Angela. We Work at the Vet's. 2006. (Where We Work Ser.). (Illus.). 24p. (J). 21.36 (978-1-4109-2245-8(6)) Raintree.

—We Work at the Vet's. 2006. (Where We Work Ser.). (Illus.). 24p. (J). (978-1-4109-2250-2(2)) Steck-Vaughn.

Balliet, Gay. Touched by All Creatures: Doctoring Animals in the Pennsylvania Dutch Country. 1999. (Illus.). 368p. 25.95 (978-0-88282-169-6(5)) New Horizon Pr. Pubs., Inc.

Bennett, Leonie. A Day with Animal Doctors. 2006. (I Love Reading Ser.). (Illus.). 24p. (J). lib. bdg. 19.96 (978-1-59716-148-0(9)) Bearport Publishing Co., Inc.

Burgan, Michael. Veterinarian. 2000. (Career Exploration Ser.). (Illus.). 48p. (J). (gr. 3-4). lib. bdg. 21.26 (978-0-7368-0493-6(5) , LifeMatters Bks.) Capstone Pr., Inc.

Carson, Janet. Visiting the Vet: Learning the V Sound. (PowerPhonics Ser.). (Illus.). (J). 2002. 24p. (gr. 1). lib. bdg. 18.50 (978-0-8239-5934-1(1)); 2001. 23p. pap. 26.40 (978-0-8239-8279-0(3)) Rosen Publishing Group, Inc., The. (PowerKids Pr.).

Clemson, Wendy, et al. Using Math to Be a Zoo Vet. 2004. (Mathworks!). (Illus.). 31p. (J). lib. bdg. 24.67 (978-0-8368-4209-8(X)) Stevens, Gareth Inc.

Ermitage, Kathleen. Veterinarian. 2000. (Workers You Know Ser.). (Illus.). 32p. (J). (ps-3). lib. bdg. 25.70 (978-0-8172-5592-3(3)) Raintree.

Flanagan, Alice K. Dr. Friedman Helps Animals. 2000. (Our Neighborhood Ser.). 32p. (J). (gr. 1-2). pap. 6.95 (978-0-516-26538-4(5) , Children's Pr.) Scholastic Library Publishing.

—Dr. Friedman Helps Animals. Osinski, Christine, illus. 1999. (Our Neighborhood Ser.). 32p. (J). (gr. 1-2). 20.00 (978-0-516-21138-1(2) , Children's Pr.) Scholastic Library Publishing.

Hodge, Judith. Animal Hospital. 1999. (gr. k-3). lib. bdg. 11.80 (978-0-613-17084-0(9)) Tandem Library Bks.

Jackson, Donna M. ER Vets: Life in an Animal Emergency Room. 2005. (Illus.). 96p. (J). (gr. 5-7). 17.00 (978-0-618-43663-7(4)) Houghton Mifflin Co. Trade & Reference Div.

Kalman, Bobbie. Veterinarians Help Keep Animals Healthy. 2004. (My Community & Its Helpers Ser.). (Illus.). 32p. (J). (978-0-7787-2097-3(7)); pap. (978-0-7787-2125-3(6)) Crabtree Publishing Co.

—Los Veterinarios Cuidan la Salud de los Animales. 2006. (SPA., Illus.). 32p. pap. (978-0-7787-8443-2(6)) Crabtree Publishing Co.

Levin, Amy. The Vet. 2003. (Compass Point Phonics Readers Ser.). (Illus.). 16p. (J). (gr. 1 up). 13.26 (978-0-7565-0528-8(3)) Compass Point Bks.

Liebman, Dan. I Want to Be a Veterinarian. 2000. (Illus.). (J). 10.79 (978-0-606-18140-2(7)) Tandem Library Bks.

—Je veux etre Veterinaire. Lior, Tsipora, tr. from ENG. 2006. (Je veux Etre Ser.).Tr. of I Want to Be A Vet. (FRE., Illus.). 24p. (J). (ps-2). pap. 5.95 (978-1-55407-105-0(4)) Firefly Bks., Ltd.

—Quiero Ser Veterinario. 2000. Tr. of I Want to Be a Vet. (gr. k-3). (SPA.). lib. bdg. 14.15 (978-0-613-78550-1(9)); (Illus.). 24p. (J). lib. bdg. 12.79 (978-0-606-18145-7(8)) Tandem Library Bks.

Liebman, Daniel. I Want to Be a Vet. 2000. (I Want to Be Ser.). (Illus.). 24p. (J). (ps-2). pap. 3.99 (978-1-55209-469-3(3)); lib. bdg. 14.95 (978-1-55209-471-6(5)) Firefly Bks., Ltd.

—Quiero Ser un Veterinario. 2000. (Coleccion Quierno Ser.).Tr. of I Want to Be a Veterinarian. (SPA., Illus.). 24p. (J). (ps-2). pap. 5.99 (978-1-55209-477-8(4) , AP4988) Firefly Bks., Ltd.

Lowenstein, Felicia. What Does a Veterinarian Do? 2006. (What Does a Community Helper Do? Ser.). (Illus.). 24p. (J). lib. bdg. 21.26 (978-0-7660-2322-2(2) , Enslow Elementary) Enslow Pubs., Inc.

Macken, JoAnn Early. People in My Community: Crossing Guard; Mail Carrier; Nurse; Sanitation Worker; Teacher; Veterinarian, 6 bks. (Weekly Reader Early Learning Library). (Illus.). (J). (ps up). lib. bdg. 111.60 (978-0-8368-3588-5(3) , Weekly Reader Early Learning Library) Stevens, Gareth Inc.

—Veterinarian. 2003. (People in My Community Ser.). (Illus.). 24p. (J). (ps up). lib. bdg. 19.33 (978-0-8368-3594-6(8) , Weekly Reader Early Learning Library) Stevens, Gareth Inc.

—Veterinarian/El Veterinario. Coffey, Colleen & Carrillo, Consuelo, trs. 2003. (Weekly Reader Early Learning Library). (ENG & SPA., Illus.). 24p. (J). (ps up). lib. bdg. 19.33 (978-0-8368-3676-9(6) , Weekly Reader Early Learning Library) Stevens, Gareth Inc.

Macken, JoAnn Early & Gorman, Jacqueline Laks. Veterinarian. Andersen, Gregg, photos by. 2003. (Weekly Reader Early Learning Library). (Illus.). 24p. (J). (ps up). pap. 7.93 (978-0-8368-3601-1(4) , Weekly Reader Early Learning Library) Stevens, Gareth Inc.

—Veterinarian/El Veterinario. Carrillo, Consuelo & Coffey, Colleen, trs. Andersen, Gregg, photos by. 2003. (Weekly Reader Early Learning Library). (ENG & SPA., Illus.). 24p. (J). (ps up). pap. (978-0-8368-3690-5(1)) Stevens, Gareth Inc.

Maze, Stephanie. I Want to Be a Veterinarian. 1999. (I Want to Be Ser.). (Illus.). 48p. (J). (gr. 3-9). pap. 10.00 (978-0-15-201965-5(0) , Harcourt Paperbacks) Harcourt Children's Bks.

Miller, Heather. Esto es lo Que Quiero Ser, 14 bks., Set. 2003. Tr. of This Is What I Want to Be. (SPA & ENG., Illus.). (J). (ps-1). lib. bdg. 259.00 (978-1-4034-0987-4(0)) Heinemann Library.

—Veterinarian. 2003. (This Is What I Want to Be Ser.). (Illus.). 24p. (J). lib. bdg. 18.50 (978-1-4034-0905-8(6)); pap. 5.25 (978-1-4034-3609-2(6)) Heinemann Library.

—Veterinarian. 2003. (ps-2). lib. bdg. 13.30 (978-0-613-60993-7(X)) Tandem Library Bks.

—Veterinario. 2003. (Esto es lo Que Quiero Ser (This Is What I Want to Be) Ser.).Tr. of Veterinarian. (SPA.). 24p. (J). pap. 5.25 (978-1-4034-3396-1(8)) Heinemann Library.

—Veterinario (Veterinarian) 2003. (SPA & ENG., Illus.). 24p. (J). lib. bdg. 18.50 (978-1-4034-0988-1(9)) Heinemann Library.

Minden, Cecilia. Veterinarians. 2006. (Neighborhood Helpers Ser.). (Illus.). 32p. (J). (gr. k-4). 22.79 (978-1-59296-571-7(7)) Child's World, Inc.

Out & about at the Vet Clinic. (Field Trips Ser.). 24p. (J). 8.95 (978-1-4048-0201-8(0)) Picture Window Bks.

Owen, Ann. Caring for Your Pets: A Book about Veterinarians. Thomas, Eric, illus. 2004. (Community Workers Ser.). 24p. (C). (gr. k-3). 22.60 (978-1-4048-0087-8(5)) Picture Window Bks.

Parks, Peggy J. Veterinarian. 2004. (J). 26.20 (978-0-7377-2068-6(9) , Greenhaven Pr., Inc.) Thomson Gale.

Patrick, Jean L. S. Cows, Cats, & Kids: A Veterinarian's Family at Work. Upitis, Alvis, illus. 2003. 48p. (YA). (gr. 4-6). 17.95 (978-1-56397-111-2(9)) Boyds Mills Pr.

Raatma, Lucia. Veterinarians. 2002. (Community Workers Ser.). (Illus.). 32p. (J). (gr. 1 up). lib. bdg. 21.26 (978-0-7565-0304-8(3)) Compass Point Bks.

Rau, Dana Meachen. Veterinarian. 2007. (Jobs in Town Ser.). 24p. (J). lib. bdg. 22.79 (***978-0-7614-2622-6(1)*** , Benchmark Bks.) Cavendish, Marshall Corp.

Ready, Dee. Veterinarios y Veterinarias. Schon, Isabel, ed. Ferrer, Martín Luis Guzman, tr. from ENG. 1998. (Servidores Comunitarios Ser.). (SPA., Illus.). 24p. (J). (gr. 1-2). lib. bdg. 18.60 (978-1-56065-804-7(5) , Bridgestone Bks.) Capstone Pr., Inc.

Riddle, John. Veterinarian. 2002. (Careers with Character Ser.). (Illus.). 96p. (YA). (gr. 7 up). (978-1-59084-326-0(6)) Mason Crest Pubs.

Ring, Susan. Open Wide! Irvine, Tammy Kutsuma, illus. 2002. 16p. (J). (978-0-439-35117-1(0)) Scholastic, Inc.

Schaefer, Lola M. We Need Veterinarians. Saunders-Smith, Gail, ed. 2000. (Helpers in Our Community Ser.). (Illus.). 24p. (J). (gr. k-1). lib. bdg. 15.93 (978-0-7368-0395-3(5) , Pebble Bks.) Capstone Pr., Inc.

—We Need Veterinarians. 1999. pap. 13.25 (978-0-516-21908-0(1) , Children's Pr.) Scholastic Library Publishing.

Shea, Kitty. Out & About at the Vet Clinic. Shipe, Becky, illus. 2004. (Field Trips Ser.). 24p. (C). (gr. k-3). 23.93 (978-1-4048-0296-4(7)) Picture Window Bks.

Simon, Charnan. The Best Vet in the World. Schwartz, Carol, illus. 2006. (Magic Door to Learning Ser.). 24p. (J). (gr. k-2). 21.36 (978-1-59296-628-8(4)) Child's World, Inc.

—Veterinarians. 2003. (Wonder Books Level 3: Careers Ser.). (Illus.). 32p. (J). (ps-2). 22.79 (978-1-56766-492-8(X)) Child's World, Inc.

Sweeney, Alyse. Pets at the Vet. 2007. (Scholastic News Nonfiction Readers Ser.). (Illus.). 24p. (J). (gr. k-2). 19.00 (978-0-531-16811-0(5) , Watts, Franklin) Scholastic Library Publishing.

Turner, Pamela S. Gorilla Doctors: Saving Endangered Great Apes. 2005. (Scientists in the Field Ser.). (Illus.). 64p. (J). (gr. 4-6). 17.00 (978-0-618-44555-4(2)) Houghton Mifflin Co. Trade & Reference Div.

Veterinarians. (Community Helpers Ser.). 24p. (J). 6.95 (978-0-7368-8464-8(5)) Capstone Pr., Inc.

Veterinarians. (Community Workers Ser.). 32p. (J). 7.95 (978-0-7565-1198-2(4)) Compass Point Bks.

Veterinarians, 6 vols. (gr. 2-5). 36.95 (978-0-7368-8479-2(3)) Red Brick Learning.

Walker-Hodge, Judith. Animal Hospital. 1999. (Eyewitness Readers). (Illus.). 32p. (J). (gr. 5-4). pap. 3.99 (978-0-7894-3996-3(4) , 0-7894-4752-5) Dorling Kindersley Publishing, Inc.

—Animal Hospital. 1999. (J). 10.79 (978-0-606-18988-0(2)) Tandem Library Bks.

We Need Veterinarians, 6 vols. (gr. k-2). 28.95 (978-0-7368-8605-5(2)) Red Brick Learning.

VETERINARIANS—FICTION

Anderson, Laurie Halse. Fight for Life, Vol. 1. 2007. (Vet Volunteers Ser.). 144p. (J). (gr. 3). pap. 6.99 (978-0-14-240862-9(X) , Puffin) Penguin Group (USA) Inc.

—Fight for Life. 2003. (Wild at Heart Ser.). (Illus.). 127p. (J). (gr. 4 up). lib. bdg. 23.33 (978-0-8368-3256-3(6)) Stevens, Gareth Inc.

—Fight for Life. 2000. (American Girl Wild at Heart Ser.: Bk. 1). (YA). (978-0-606-18358-1(2)) Tandem Library Bks.

—Homeless, Vol. 2. 2007. (Vet Volunteers Ser.). 144p. (J). (gr. 3). pap. 6.99 (978-0-14-240863-6(8) , Puffin) Penguin Group (USA) Inc.

—Homeless. 2003. (Wild at Heart Ser.). (Illus.). 130p. (J). (gr. 4 up). lib. bdg. 23.33 (978-0-8368-3257-0(4)) Stevens, Gareth Inc.

—Say Good-Bye. 2003. (Wild at Heart Ser.). (Illus.). 129p. (J). (gr. 4 up). lib. bdg. 23.33 (978-0-8368-3259-4(0)) Stevens, Gareth Inc.

—Say Good-Bye. 2001. (American Girl Wild at Heart Ser.: Bk. 5). (Illus.). (YA). (978-0-606-21527-5(1)) Tandem Library Bks.

—Storm Rescue. 2003. (Wild at Heart Ser.). (Illus.). 105p. (J). (gr. 4 up). lib. bdg. 23.33 (978-0-8368-3260-0(4)) Stevens, Gareth Inc.

—Storm Rescue. 2001. (American Girl Wild at Heart Ser.: Bk. 6). (Illus.). (YA). (978-0-606-21528-2(X)) Tandem Library Bks.

—Teacher's Pet. 2003. (Wild at Heart Ser.). (Illus.). 132p. (J). (gr. 4 up). lib. bdg. 23.33 (978-0-8368-3261-7(2)) Stevens, Gareth Inc.

—Teacher's Pet. 2001. (American Girl Wild at Heart Ser.: Bk. 7). (Illus.). (YA). (978-0-606-21529-9(8)) Tandem Library Bks.

—Time to Fly. 2003. (Wild at Heart Ser.). (Illus.). 113p. (J). (gr. 4 up). lib. bdg. 23.33 (978-0-8368-3262-4(0)) Stevens, Gareth Inc.

—Trapped. 2003. (Wild at Heart Ser.). (Illus.). 113p. (J). (gr. 4 up). lib. bdg. 23.33 (978-0-8368-3263-1(9)) Stevens, Gareth Inc.

—Trickster. 2003. (Wild at Heart Ser.). (Illus.). 124p. (J). (gr. 4). lib. bdg. 23.33 (978-0-8368-3264-8(7)) Stevens, Gareth Inc.

—Trickster. 2000. (American Girl Wild at Heart Ser.: Bk. 3). (YA). (978-0-606-18360-4(4)) Tandem Library Bks.

Anderson, Laurie Halse. The Trickster, No. 3. 2008. (Vet Volunteers Ser.: No. 3). 144p. (J). (gr. 3). 6.99 (***978-0-14-241083-7(7)*** , Puffin) Penguin Group (USA) Inc.

Baglio, Ben M. Foals in the Field. 2001. (gr. 3-6). lib. bdg. 11.80 (978-0-613-58116-5(4)) Tandem Library Bks.

—Mare in the Meadow. Baum, Ann, tr. Baum, Ann, illus. 2003. (Animal Ark Hauntings Ser.). 144p. (J). 3.99 (978-0-439-34392-3(5) , Scholastic Paperbacks) Scholastic, Inc.

Brooke, Lauren. Beyond the Horizon. 2nd rev. ed. 2007. (Heartland Ser.). 208p. (J). pap. 5.99 (978-0-439-91610-3(0) , Scholastic Paperbacks) Scholastic, Inc.

Carris, Joan Davenport. Welcome to the Bed & Biscuit. Jones, Noah Z., illus. 2006. 128p. (J). (gr. 1-5). 15.99 (978-0-7636-2151-3(X)) Candlewick Pr.

Chukovskii, Kornei. Doctor Ouch. Seabaugh, Jan, tr. from RUS. Seabaugh, Jan, illus. 2004. (Children's International Ser.: 1). Orig. Title: Aibolit. 50p. (J). pap. 6.99 (978-0-9740551-0-7(7)) Smith, Viveca Publishing.

Daniels, Lucy. Cub in the Cupboard. 1999. (Animal Ark Ser.: No. 8). (J). (gr. 3-5). 10.64 (978-0-606-19087-9(2)) Tandem Library Bks.

—Hedgehogs in the Hall. l.t. ed. 2000. (Illus.). 214p. (J). pap. (978-0-7540-6109-0(4) , CLP 303) BBC Audio.

—Puppies in the Pantry. McNicholas, Shelagh, illus. l.t. ed. 1999. (Animal Ark Ser.: No. 3). 178p. (J). (gr. 3-5). pap. (978-0-7540-6058-1(6) , CLP 264) BBC Audio.

Dodd, Lynley. Hairy Maclary's Rumpus at the Vet. Dodd, Lynley, illus. 2000. (Gold Star First Readers Ser.). (Illus.). 32p. (J). (gr. 1 up). lib. bdg. 21.26 (978-0-8368-2691-3(4)) Stevens, Gareth Inc.

—Hairy Maclary's Rumpus at the Vet. 2005. (Illus.). 32p. (J). 5.95 (978-1-58246-094-9(9) , Tricycle Pr.) Ten Speed Pr.

Garcia, Randolph. The Steamer Trunk Adventures #2: The Ghosts of Machu Picchu. 2006. (ENG.). 88p. per. 14.95 (***978-1-4241-1843-4(3)***) PublishAmerica, Inc.

Henry, Heather French. Pepper's Purple Heart: A Veteran's Day Story. Henry, Heather French, illus. 2004. (Claire's Holiday Adventures Ser.: Vol. 1). (Illus.). 32p. (J). (gr. k-4). pap. 8.95 (978-0-9706341-1-5(0)) Cubbie Blue Publishing.

Hensley, Terri Anne. Henry visits the Veterinarian. 2007. (J). per. 6.95 (***978-0-9789057-2-9(5)***) Huntington Ludlow Media Group.

Huneck, Stephen. Sally Goes to the Vet. Huneck, Stephen, illus. 2004. (Illus.). 32p. (J). (ps-3). 17.95 (978-0-8109-4813-6(3)) Abrams, Harry N. , Inc.

Klein, Adria F. Max & Buddy Go to the Vet. Gallagher-Cole, Mernie, illus. 2007. (J). lib. bdg. (***978-1-4048-3679-2(9)***) Picture Window Bks.

Lee, Chinlun. Good Dog, Paw! Lee, Chinlun, illus. 2004. (Illus.). 40p. (J). (ps-1). 15.99 (978-0-7636-2178-0(1)) Candlewick Pr.

Leonard, Marcia. The Pet Vet. Handelman, Dorothy, photos by. 1999. (Real Kids Readers Ser.) (Illus.). 32p. (gr. k-1). (J). pap. 4.99 (978-0-7613-2075-3(X)); lib. bdg. 18.90 (978-0-7613-2050-0(4)) Lerner Publishing Group. (Millbrook Pr.).

—The Pet Vet. 1999. (J). (978-0-606-19168-5(2)) Tandem Library Bks.

—Pet Vet. 1999. (ps-2). lib. bdg. 13.00 (978-0-613-16795-6(3)) Tandem Library Bks.

Leonard, Marcia & Handelman, Dorothy. The Pet Vet. Handelman, Dorothy, illus. Leonard, Marcia, photos by. 2005. (ENG & SPA., Illus.). 32p. (J). (ps-1). pap. 4.99 (978-0-8225-3299-6(9)) Lerner Publishing Group.

Lofting, Hugh. The Story of Doctor Dolittle No. 3: Doctor Dolittle's Great Adventure. Kanzler, John, illus. 2007. (Easy Reader Classics Ser.). 32p. (J). pap. 3.95 (978-1-4027-4122-7(7)) Sterling Publishing Co., Inc.

—The Story of Doctor Dolittle No. 4: Doctor Dolittle's Magical Cure. Kanzler, John, illus. 2007. (Easy Reader Classics Ser.). 32p. (J). pap. 3.95 (978-1-4027-4123-4(5)) Sterling Publishing Co., Inc.

Miller, Sue. While I Was Gone. 2000. (gr. 3-6). lib. bdg. 23.45 (978-0-613-45855-9(9)) Tandem Library Bks.

Morris, Gilbert. Dixie & Stripes. 1998. (Dixie Morris Animal Adventure Ser.: No. 2). 128p. (J). (gr. 4-7). pap. 5.99 (978-0-8024-3364-0(2)) Moody Pubs.

Popper, Garry. The Beast of Didley Dale. Forshaw, John, illus. 2004. (Bret the Vet Ser.). 40p. 7.00 (978-1-84161-024-5(0)) Ravette Publishing, Ltd. GBR. *Dist:* Parkwest Pubns., Inc.

Santillo, LuAnn. The Vet. Santillo, LuAnn, ed. 2003. (Half-Pint Kids Readers Ser.). (Illus.). 7p. (J). (ps-1). pap. (978-1-59256-123-0(3)) Half-Pint Kids, Inc.

Smith, Maggie Caldwell. Tommy Wilson, Junior Veterinarian: The Case of the Orphaned Bobcat. Heyer, Carol & White, Charlotte L., illus. 2006. (J). per. 7.95 (978-0-9788391-1-6(0)) Magpie Pr., Pine Mtn Club, CA.

T
U
V

Thaler, Mike. My Cat Is Going to the Dogs. 1999. (gr. k-3). lib. bdg. 11.25 (978-0-613-76303-5(3)) Tandem Library Bks.

Viselman, Kenn. Li'l Pet Hospital: The Great Race. 2003. 32p. pap. 3.99 (978-0-06-054840-7(1) , Harper Entertainment) HarperCollins Pubs.

Wood, Jane Roberts. Mocha the Real Doctor. 2004. (Illus.). 32p. 14.95 (978-1-931721-30-1(0)) Bright Sky Pr.

VETERINARY MEDICINE

Allen, Connie. Ap Lab Manual with Fetal Pig Dissection Manual, Set. 2003. (Illus.). 724p. (YA). pap., lab manual ed. 25.00 net. (978-0-471-27068-3(7)) Wiley, John & Sons, Inc.

Aylmore, Angela. We Work at the Vet's. 2006. (Where We Work Ser.). (Illus.). 24p. (J). 21.36 (978-1-4109-2245-8(6)) Raintree.

—We Work at the Vet's. 2006. (Where We Work Ser.). (Illus.). 24p. (J). (978-1-4109-2250-2(2)) Steck-Vaughn.

Bennett, Leonie. A Day with Animal Doctors. 2006. (I Love Reading Ser.). (Illus.). 24p. (J). lib. bdg. 19.96 (978-1-59716-148-0(9)) Bearport Publishing Co., Inc.

Brownlee, Christen. Cute, Furry, & Deadly: Diseases You Can Catch from Your Pet! 2007. (24/7 - Science Behind the Scenes Ser.). 64p. (YA). (gr. 8-12). 26.00 (978-0-531-12072-9(4) , Watts, Franklin) Scholastic Library Publishing.

Carson, Janet. Visiting the Vet: Learning the V Sound. (PowerPhonics Ser.). (Illus.). (J). 2002. 24p. (gr. 1). lib. bdg. 18.50 (978-0-8239-5934-1(1)); 2001. 23p. pap. 26.40 (978-0-8239-8279-0(3)) Rosen Publishing Group, Inc., The. (PowerKids Pr.).

Devantier, Alecia T. & Turkington, Carol. Extraordinary Jobs with Animals. 2006. (Extraordinary Jobs Ser.). 160p. (J). (gr. 6-12). 35.00 (978-0-8160-5862-4(8) , Ferguson Publishing Co.) Facts On File, Inc.

DiConsiglio, John. When Birds Get Flu & Cows Go Mad! How Safe Are We? 2007. (24/7 - Science Behind the Scenes Ser.). 64p. (YA). (gr. 8-12). 26.00 (978-0-531-12069-9(4) , Watts, Franklin) Scholastic Library Publishing.

Ermitage, Kathleen. Veterinarian. 2000. (Workers You Know Ser.). (Illus.). 32p. (J). (ps-3). lib. bdg. 25.70 (978-0-8172-5592-3(3)) Raintree.

Kalman, Bobbie. Veterinarians Help Keep Animals Healthy. 2004. (My Community & Its Helpers Ser.). (Illus.). 32p. (J). (978-0-7787-2097-3(7)); pap. (978-0-7787-2125-3(6)) Crabtree Publishing Co.

Lauber, Patricia. The Tiger Has a Toothache: Helping Animals at the Zoo. Morgan, Mary, illus. 2002. 32p. (J). (gr. 1-4). pap. 7.95 (978-0-7922-8234-1(5) , National Geographic Children's Bks.) National Geographic Society.

—Tiger Has a Toothache: Helping Animals at the Zoo. 2002. (gr. k-3). lib. bdg. 16.40 (978-0-613-62654-5(0)) Tandem Library Bks.

Levin, Amy. The Vet. 2003. (Compass Point Phonics Readers Ser.). (Illus.). 16p. (J). (gr. 1 up). 13.26 (978-0-7565-0528-8(3)) Compass Point Bks.

Liebman, Dan. Quiero Ser Veterinario. 2000. Tr. of I Want to Be a Vet. (Illus.). 24p. (J). (ps-ps). lib. bdg. 12.79 (978-0-606-18145-7(8)) Tandem Library Bks.

Liebman, Daniel. I Want to Be a Vet. 2000. (I Want to Be Ser.). (Illus.). 24p. (J). (ps-2). lib. bdg. 14.95 (978-1-55209-471-6(5)) Firefly Bks., Ltd.

—Quiero Ser un Veterinario. 2000. (Coleccion Quierno Ser.).Tr. of I Want to Be a Veterinarian. (SPA., Illus.). 24p. (J). (ps-2). pap. 5.99 (978-1-55209-477-8(4) , AP4988) Firefly Bks., Ltd.

Macken, JoAnn Early. Veterinarian. 2003. (People in My Community Ser.). (Illus.). 24p. (J). (ps up). lib. bdg. 19.33 (978-0-8368-3594-6(8) , Weekly Reader Early Learning Library) Stevens, Gareth Inc.

Macken, JoAnn Early & Gorman, Jacqueline Laks. Veterinarian. Andersen, Gregg, photos by. 2003. (Weekly Reader Early Learning Library). (Illus.). 24p. (J). (ps up). pap. 7.93 (978-0-8368-3601-1(4) , Weekly Reader Early Learning Library) Stevens, Gareth Inc.

Meredith Books Staff, ed. Vet Emergencies 24/7. 2008. 48p. pap. 6.99 (***978-0-696-23979-3(5)***) Meredith Bks.

Minden, Cecilia. Veterinarians. 2006. (Neighborhood Helpers Ser.). (Illus.). 32p. (J). (gr. k-4). 22.79 (978-1-59296-571-7(7)) Child's World, Inc.

Owen, Ann. Caring for Your Pets: A Book about Veterinarians. Thomas, Eric, illus. 2004. (Community Workers Ser.). 24p. (C). (gr. k-3). 22.60 (978-1-4048-0087-8(5)) Picture Window Bks.

Raatma, Lucia. Veterinarians. 2002. (Community Workers Ser.). (Illus.). 32p. (J). (gr. 1 up). lib. bdg. 21.26 (978-0-7565-0304-8(3)) Compass Point Bks.

Ready, Dee. Veterinarios y Veterinarias. Schon, Isabel, ed. Ferrer, Martín Luis Guzman, tr. from ENG. 1998. (Servidores Comunitarios Ser.). (SPA., Illus.). 24p. (J). (gr. 1-2). lib. bdg. 18.60 (978-1-56065-804-7(5) , Bridgestone Bks.) Capstone Pr., Inc.

Ring, Susan. Open Wide! Irvine, Tammy Kutsuma, illus. 2002. 16p. (J). (978-0-439-35117-1(0)) Scholastic, Inc.

Simon, Charnan. The Best Vet in the World. Schwartz, Carol, illus. 2006. (Magic Door to Learning Ser.). 24p. (J). (gr. k-2). 21.36 (978-1-59296-628-8(4)) Child's World, Inc.

—Veterinarians. 2003. (Wonder Books Level 3: Careers Ser.). (Illus.). 32p. (J). (ps-2). 22.79 (978-1-56766-492-8(X)) Child's World, Inc.

VETERINARY MEDICINE—FICTION

Ahlberg, Allan. Mrs. Vole the Vet. Clark, Emma, illus. 24p. (J). pap. 6.95 (978-0-14-037880-1(4)) Penguin Bks., Ltd. GBR. *Dist:* Trafalgar Square Publishing.

Baglio, Ben M. Collie with a Card. Baum, Ann, illus. 2004. 136p. (J). pap. (***978-0-439-68760-7(8)***) Scholastic, Inc.

Baglio, Ben M. Mustang in the Mist. Baum, Ann, illus. 2007. (Animal Ark Hauntings Ser.: No. 48). 160p. (J). pap. 3.99 (978-0-439-77524-3(8)) Scholastic, Inc.

Carpenter, Christopher, illus. Lilly's Heart: The Veterinary Clinic Cases Series. 2006. 32p. (J). per. 9.95 (978-0-9766641-0-9(0)) Ichabod Ink.

Fletcher, Christine. Tallulah Falls. 2007. 400p. (YA). pap. 7.95 (***978-1-59990-095-7(5)*** , Bloomsbury Children) Bloomsbury Publishing.

Kerr, Judith. Mog & the Vet. (Illus.). 32p. (J). pap. 9.99 (978-0-00-664620-4(4)) HarperCollins Pubs. Ltd. GBR. *Dist:* Trafalgar Square Publishing.

Wilson, Diane Lee. Firehorse. 2006. 336p. (J). (gr. 7 up). 16.95 (978-1-4169-1551-5(6) , McElderry, Margaret K.) Simon & Schuster Children's Publishing.

VETERINARY MEDICINE—VOCATIONAL GUIDANCE

Adamson, Heather. A Day in the Life of a Veterinarian. 2003. (First Facts Ser.). (Illus.). 24p. (J). lib. bdg. 21.26 (978-0-7368-2287-9(9)) Capstone Pr., Inc.

Burgan, Michael. Veterinarian. 2000. (Career Exploration Ser.). (Illus.). 48p. (J). (gr. 3-4). lib. bdg. 21.26 (978-0-7368-0493-6(5) , LifeMatters Bks.) Capstone Pr., Inc.

Humane Society of the U. S. Staff & Sirch, Willow Ann. Careers with Animals. 2004. (Illus.). 128p. (gr. 4-6). 16.95 (978-1-55591-408-0(X)) Fulcrum Publishing.

Kalman, Bobbie. Veterinarians Help Keep Animals Healthy. 2004. (My Community & Its Helpers Ser.). (Illus.). 32p. (J). (978-0-7787-2097-3(7)); pap. (978-0-7787-2125-3(6)) Crabtree Publishing Co.

Lowenstein, Felicia. What Does a Veterinarian Do? 2006. (What Does a Community Helper Do? Ser.). (Illus.). 24p. (J). lib. bdg. 21.26 (978-0-7660-2322-2(2) , Enslow Elementary) Enslow Pubs., Inc.

Marinelli, Deborah A. Careers in Animal Care & Veterinary Science. 2005. (Careers Ser.). (Illus.). 192p. (YA). (gr. 7-12). lib. bdg. 26.50 (978-0-8239-3185-9(4)) Rosen Publishing Group, Inc., The.

Maze, Stephanie. I Want to Be a Veterinarian. 1999. (I Want to Be Ser.). (Illus.). 48p. (J). (gr. 3-9). pap. 10.00 (978-0-15-201965-5(0) , Harcourt Paperbacks) Harcourt Children's Bks.

—I Want to Be a Veterinarian. 1999. (I Want to Be Ser.). (Illus.). 48p. (YA). (gr. 4-9). pap. 18.98 (978-0-8172-6374-4(8)) Raintree.

Miller, Heather. Esto es lo Que Quiero Ser, 14 bks., Set. 2003. Tr. of This Is What I Want to Be. (SPA & ENG., Illus.). (J). (ps-1). lib. bdg. 259.00 (978-1-4034-0987-4(0)) Heinemann Library.

—Veterinarian. 2003. (This Is What I Want to Be Ser.). (Illus.). 24p. (J). lib. bdg. 18.50 (978-1-4034-0905-8(6)); pap. 5.25 (978-1-4034-3609-2(6)) Heinemann Library.

—Veterinarian. 2003. (ps-2). lib. bdg. 13.30 (978-0-613-60993-7(X)) Tandem Library Bks.

Parks, Peggy J. Veterinarian. 2004. (J). 26.20 (978-0-7377-2068-6(9) , Greenhaven Pr., Inc.) Thomson Gale.

Riddle, John. Veterinarian. 2002. (Careers with Character Ser.). (Illus.). 96p. (YA). (gr. 7 up). (978-1-59084-326-0(6)) Mason Crest Pubs.

Sweeney, Alyse. Pets at the Vet. 2007. (Scholastic News Nonfiction Readers Ser.). (Illus.). 24p. (J). (gr. k-2). 19.00 (978-0-531-16811-0(5) , Watts, Franklin) Scholastic Library Publishing.

VIADUCTS

see Bridges

VIBRATION

see also Light; Waves

Cambridge Educational, prod. Waves & Vibrations Hyb Lb D. (YA). cd-rom 222.50 (978-0-7365-4358-3(9)) Films Media Group.

Cheshire, Gerard. Sound & Vibrations. 2006. (Illus.). 48p. (J). (978-1-58340-997-8(1)) Smart Apple Media.

Claybourne, Anna. Feel the Noise! 2005. (Illus.). 32p. (J). (978-1-4109-1948-9(X)); lib. bdg. (978-1-4109-1917-5(X)) Steck-Vaughn.

Riley, Peter D. Sound & Vibrations. 2005. (Making Sense of Science Ser.). (Illus.). 32p. (J). (gr. 4-7). lib. bdg. 27.10 (978-1-58340-718-9(9)) Smart Apple Media.

Rothstein, Ruth S., et al. ARIES Exploring Waves: Ripple Tanks, Vibrations & Sound: Science Journal. 2000. (Aries Ser.). (Illus.). (J). pap. 3.80 (978-1-57091-254-2(8)) Charlesbridge Publishing, Inc.

Salway, Andrew. Waves, Vibration & Radiation. 2007. (J). lib. bdg. (***978-1-4042-3746-9(1)*** , Rosen Central) Rosen Publishing Group, Inc., The.

VICE

see Crime and Criminals

VICE-PRESIDENTS—UNITED STATES

Andrews, Elaine. Dick Cheney: A Life of Public Service. 2001. (Gateway Biography Ser.). (Illus.). 48p. (gr. 2-4). lib. bdg. 23.90 (978-0-7613-2306-8(6) , Millbrook Pr.) Lerner Publishing Group.

Gorman, Jacqueline Laks. Vice President. 2005. (Illus.). 24p. (J). pap. (978-0-8368-4579-2(X)); lib. bdg. 19.33 (978-0-8368-4572-3(2)) Stevens, Gareth Inc.

Harris, Nancy. What's a President & Vice President? 2007. (***978-1-4034-9465-8(7)***); pap. (***978-1-4034-9471-9(1)***) Heinemann Library.

Ingram, Scott. Aaron Burr: And the Young Nation. 2002. (Notorious Americans & Their Times Ser.). (Illus.). 112p. (J). (gr. 5-9). 28.70 (978-1-56711-250-4(1) , Blackbirch Pr., Inc.) Thomson Gale.

—The Vice President of the United States. 2002. (American Leaders Ser.). (Illus.). 32p. (J). 23.70 (978-1-56711-662-5(0) , Blackbirch Pr., Inc.) Thomson Gale.

Jeffrey, Laura S. Al Gore: Leader for the New Millennium. 1999. (People to Know Ser.). (Illus.). 112p. (YA). (gr. 6-12). lib. bdg. 26.60 (978-0-7660-1232-5(8)) Enslow Pubs., Inc.

Kramer, Barbara. Tipper Gore: Activist, Author, Photographer. 1999. (People to Know Ser.). (Illus.). 112p. (YA). (gr. 6-12). lib. bdg. 26.60 (978-0-7660-1142-7(9)) Enslow Pubs., Inc.

Lucas, Eileen. The Aaron Burr Treason Trial. 2003. (Headline Court Cases Ser.). (Illus.). 128p. (J). (gr. 6-12). lib. bdg. 26.60 (978-0-7660-1765-8(6)) Enslow Pubs., Inc.

—Al Gore: Vice President. rev. ed. 1999. (Gateway Biography Ser.: 4). (Illus.). 48p. (gr. 2-4). pap. 8.95 (978-0-7613-1329-8(X) , Millbrook Pr.) Lerner Publishing Group.

Pious, Richard M. The Presidency of the United States: A Student Companion. 2nd ed. 2001. (Student Companions to American History Ser.). (Illus.). 320p. (YA). stu. ed., suppl. ed. 60.00 (978-0-19-515006-3(6)) Oxford Univ. Pr., Inc.

Schnakenberg, Robert E. The Vice Presidency. 2001. (Your Government Ser.). (Illus.). 64p. (J). (gr. 4-7). 25.00 (978-0-7910-5997-5(9) , Chelsea Hse.) Facts On File, Inc.

Stefoff, Rebecca. Al Gore: Vice President. rev. ed. 1998. (Gateway Biography Ser.). (Illus.). 48p. (gr. 2-4). lib. bdg. 23.90 (978-1-56294-433-9(9) , Millbrook Pr.) Lerner Publishing Group.

—Al Gore: Vice President. 1999. 15.75 (978-0-606-17852-5(X)) Tandem Library Bks.

Winget, Mary. Gerald R. Ford. 2007. (Presidential Leaders Ser.). 112p. (J). (gr. 6-12). 29.27 (978-0-8225-1509-8(1) , Twenty-First Century Bks.) Lerner Publishing Group.

VICTORIA, QUEEN OF GREAT BRITAIN, 1819-1901

Ashworth, Leon. Queen Victoria. 1999. (British History Makers Ser.). (Illus.). 32p. pap. 11.99 (978-0-7540-9014-4(0) , Cherrytree Books) Evans Publishing Group GBR. *Dist:* Independent Pubs. Group.

Avp, prod. Victorian Britain. (YA). cd-rom 149.95 (978-1-56950-318-8(4)) Films Media Group.

Bernard, Catherine J. The British Empire & Queen Victoria in World History. 2003. (In World History Ser.). (Illus.). 128p. (J). (gr. 5-12). lib. bdg. 26.60 (978-0-7660-1824-2(5)) Enslow Pubs., Inc.

Fowke, Bob. Victorians. (Illus.). 128p. (J). pap. 9.99 (978-0-340-85184-5(8) , Hodder & Stoughton) Hodder General Publishing Division GBR. *Dist:* Independent Pubs. Group.

Green, Robert. Queen Victoria. 1998. (First Bks.). 64p. (J). (gr. 4-7). 23.00 (978-0-531-20330-9(1) , Watts, Franklin) Scholastic Library Publishing.

Guy, John. Victoria. 2004. (Illus.). 32p. (J). (gr. 4-7). pap. (978-1-86007-033-4(7)) Ticktock Media Ltd.

Hicks, Kyra E. Martha Ann's Quilt for Queen Victoria. 2006. (J). 16.95 (978-1-933285-59-7(1)) Brown Bks. Publishing Group.

Myers, Walter Dean. At Her Majesty's Request: An African Princess in Victorian England. (Illus.). (J). (978-0-439-07762-0(1)) Scholastic, Inc.

Price-Groff, Claire. Queen Victoria & Nineteenth-Century England. 2003. (Rulers & Their Times Ser.). (Illus.). 96p. (YA). (gr. 8-12). 29.93 (978-0-7614-1488-9(6) , Benchmark Bks.) Cavendish, Marshall Corp.

Whitelaw, Nancy. Queen Victoria & the British Empire. 2004. (World Leaders Ser.). (Illus.). 160p. (YA). (gr. 6-12). lib. bdg. 26.95 (978-1-931798-29-7(X)) Reynolds, Morgan Inc.

VIDEO GAMES

Andersen, Neil. At the Controls: Questioning Video & Computer Games. 2007. (Fact Finders Ser.). (Illus.). 32p. (J). (978-0-7368-6768-9(6) , 1264909, Fact Finders) Capstone Pr., Inc.

Andersen, Neil. At the Controls: Questioning Video & Computer Games. 2007. (Fact Finders Ser.). (Illus.). 32p. (J). (***978-0-7368-7864-7(5)*** , 1264909) Capstone Pr., Inc.

Brady Games Staff & Deats, Adam. Silent Hill 4: The Room Official Strategy Guide. 2004. (BradyGames Signature Ser.). (Illus.). 160p. pap. 14.99 (978-0-7440-0470-0(5)) Brady GAMES.

BradyGames Staff & Bogenn, Tim. Ghosthunter Official Strategy Guide. 2004. (Brady Games Ser.). (Illus.). 128p. pap. 14.99 (978-0-7440-0411-3(X)) Brady GAMES.

BradyGames Staff & Walsh, Doug. Street Racing Syndicate Official Strategy Guide. 2004. 144p. pap. 14.99 (978-0-7440-0412-0(8)) Brady GAMES.

Burns, Jan. Shigeru Miyamoto. 2006. (Inventors & Creators Ser.). 48p. (J). (gr. 4-8). 27.45 (978-0-7377-3534-5(1) , Greenhaven Pr., Inc.) Thomson Gale.

Capcom Japan Staff. Street Fighter Eternal Challenge. 2005. (Illus.). 304p. (YA). pap. 34.99 (***978-0-9738652-4-0(5)***) UDON Entertainment Corp. CAN. *Dist:* Diamond Bk. Distributors.

Cassady, David & Kolmos, Keith. ESPN NBA 2K5 Official Strategy Guide. 2004. (Illus.). 128p. pap. 9.99 (978-0-7440-0472-4(1)) Brady GAMES.

Cohen, Judith Love. You Can Be A Woman Video Game Producer. l.t. ed. 2005. (Illus.). 72p. (J). 17.95 (978-1-880599-74-7(0)); pap. 12.95 (978-1-880599-73-0(2)) Cascade Pass, Inc.

Croce, Nicholas. People Who Love Video Games. 2006. (Cool Careers Without College Ser.). (Illus.). 144p. (J). (gr. 5-8). lib. bdg. 33.25 (978-1-4042-0747-9(3)) Rosen Publishing Group, Inc., The.

Cuellar, Joey. King of Fighters(TM) Maximum Impact Official Fighters Guide. 2004. (Illus.). 128p. pap. 14.99 (978-0-7440-0465-6(9)) Brady GAMES.

Duffield, Katy. Ken Kutaragi: Playstation Developer. 2007. (Innovators Ser.). (Illus.). 64p. (J). (gr. 4-8). 24.95 (***978-0-7377-3862-9(6)*** , Kidhaven) Thomson Gale.

EDS Staff. Lost City of Gaxmoor. 2002. (Illus.). 134p. pap. 20.95 (978-1-931275-07-1(6) , 379660) Troll Lord Games/ Chenault & Gray.

Facts on File, Inc. Staff, ed. Aviation. 2005. (Careers in Focus Ser.). (Illus.). 192p. (YA). (gr. 6-12). 22.95 (978-0-8160-5850-1(4)) Facts On File, Inc.

Farkas, Bart. Psi-Ops(TM) The Mindgate Conspiracy Official Strategy Guide. 2004. (Illus.). 128p. pap. 14.99 (978-0-7440-0406-9(3)) Brady GAMES.

Farkas, Bart G. BloodRayne 2 Official Strategy Guide. 2004. (Illus.). 128p. pap. 14.99 (978-0-7440-0426-7(8)) Brady GAMES.

—Way of the Samurai 2(TM) Official Strategy Guide. 2004. (Illus.). 128p. pap. 14.99 (978-0-7440-0371-0(7)) Brady Publishing.

Galaxy, Billy. Collecting Classic Video Games. 2001. (Schiffer Book for Collectors Ser.). (Illus.). 144p. (gr. 10-13). pap. 29.95 (978-0-7643-1456-8(4)) Schiffer Publishing, Ltd.

Kolmos, Keith. Galactic Wrestling(TM) Featuring Ultimate Muscle(TM) Official Strategy Guide. 2004. 128p. pap. 14.99 (978-0-7440-0409-0(8)) Brady GAMES.

Long, Ben. Making Digital Videos. 2002. (CyberRookies). 320p. pap. 34.95 incl. cd-rom (978-1-58450-099-5(9)) Charles River Media.

Lummis, Michael. ShellShock(TM) Nam '67 Official Strategy Guide. 2004. (Illus.). 128p. pap. 14.99 (978-0-7440-0408-3(X)) Brady GAMES.

Olesky, Walter. Video Game Designer. 2000. (CoolCareers.com Ser.). (Illus.). 48p. (YA). (gr. 5-8). lib. bdg. 23.95 (978-0-8239-3117-0(X) , CCVIGA, Rosen Central) Rosen Publishing Group, Inc., The.

Parker, J. Guardian Universe Core Fuzion. 2004. (Illus.). 228p. (YA). per. 25.00 (978-0-9744698-0-5(7)) Dilly Green Bean Games.

Peterson, Tara & Hogan, Joyce W. Should We Play Video Games? A Persuasive Text. 2006. (Illus.). 30p. (J). pap. (978-1-59336-338-3(9)) Mondo Publishing.

Polette, Nancy. Improvisation & Theatre Games with Children's Literature. 2004. (J). pap. 10.95 (978-1-931334-41-9(2)) Pieces of Learning.

Prima Temp Authors Staff & Knight, David. SWAT 4: Urban Justice: Prima's Official Strategy Guide. 2005. (Illus.). 288p. pap. 19.99 (978-0-7615-3982-7(4) , Prima Games) Random Hse. Information Group.

Rubenstein, Glenn. Sports Gamer: The Best in Sports Video Games. (J). (gr. 3-9). pap. 3.99 (978-1-930623-22-4(4)) Sports Illustrated For Kids.

Sepelak, Greg. Mega Man X Command Mission(TM) Official Strategy Guide. 2004. (Brady Games Ser.). (Illus.). 128p. pap. 14.99 (978-0-7440-0399-4(7)) Brady GAMES.

Snyder, Jeffrey B., ed. Collecting Pokemon: An Unauthorized Handbook & Price Guide. 2000. (Schiffer Book for Collectors Ser.). (Illus.). 128p. pap. 9.95 (978-0-7643-1075-1(5)) Schiffer Publishing, Ltd.

Stolze, Greg. Rites of the Dragon. (Illus.). 120p. (YA). 24.99 (978-1-58846-254-1(4)) White Wolf Publishing, Inc.

Teitelbaum, Michael. How to Draw the Legend of Zelda. Zalme, Ron, illus. 2004. 32p. (J). pap. 4.99 (978-0-439-63581-3(0)) Scholastic, Inc.

Walsh, Doug. Viewtiful Joe(TM) Official Strategy Guide for PS2. 2004. (Illus.). 112p. pap. 14.99 (978-0-7440-0402-1(0)) Brady GAMES.

Wessel, Craig. Super Mario Advance. 2001. (Game Boy Ser.: No. 1). (Illus.). 96p. (J). (gr. 3-7). pap. 3.99 (978-0-439-36708-0(5)) Scholastic, Inc.

West, Tracey & Nolls, Katherine. Official Pokémon Pokédex. 2006. (Illus.). 111p. (J). (978-0-439-85586-0(1)) Scholastic, Inc.

VIENNA (AUSTRIA)—FICTION

Glatshteyn, Yankev. Emil & Karl. Shandler, Jeffrey, tr. 2008. 208p. (YA). pap. 6.99 (***978-0-312-37387-0(2)***) Square Fish.

Ibbotson, Eva. The Star of Kazan. 2006. (Illus.). 416p. (J). (gr. 3). reprint ed. 6.99 (978-0-14-240582-6(5) , Puffin) Penguin Group (USA) Inc.

Nostlinger, Christine. But Jasper Came Instead. 2000. 128p. (J). pap. 6.99 (978-0-86264-987-6(0)) Andersen GBR. *Dist:* Independent Pubs. Group.

Watts, Irene N. A Telling Time. Shoemaker, Kathryn E., illus. 2005. 32p. (J). (978-1-896580-39-5(4)) Tradewind Bks.

VIETNAM

Alberti, Theresa Jarosz. Vietnam ABCs: A Book about the People & Places of Vietnam. Blanks, Natascha Alex, illus. 2006. (Country ABCs Ser.). 32p. (J). (gr. k-5). lib. bdg. 25.26 (978-1-4048-2251-1(8)) Picture Window Bks.

Cha, Dia. Dia's Story Cloth: The Hmong People's Journey of Freedom. Cha, Chue & Cha, Nhia Thao, illus. 1998. 24p. (J). (gr. 1 up). 6.95 (978-1-880000-63-2(6)) Lee & Low Bks., Inc.

Cole, Wendy M. Vietnam. 1999. (Major World Nations Ser.). (Illus.). 144p. (YA). (gr. 4-7). 29.95 (978-0-7910-4751-4(2) , Chelsea Hse.) Facts On File, Inc.

Condra-Peters, Amy. Vietnam. 2002. (Countries of the World Ser.). (Illus.). 96p. (J). (gr. 6 up). lib. bdg. 30.00 (978-0-8368-2348-6(6)) Stevens, Gareth Inc.

Conley, Kate A. Vietnam. 2004. (Countries Ser.). (Illus.). 40p. (J). (gr. k-6). lib. bdg. 22.78 (978-1-59197-299-0(X)) ABDO Publishing Co.

De Capua, Sarah. Vietnam. 2003. (First Reports). (Illus.). 48p. (J). (gr. 3 up). lib. bdg. 22.60 (978-0-7565-0427-4(9)) Compass Point Bks.

Englar, Mary. Vietnam: A Question & Answer Book. 2007. (Fact Finders Ser.). (Illus.). 32p. (J). 22.60 (978-0-7368-6414-5(8)) Capstone Pr., Inc.

Ferro, Jennifer. Vietnamese Foods & Culture. 1999. (Festive Foods & Celebrations Ser.). (Illus.). 48p. (J). (gr. 3-6). lib. bdg. 27.93 (978-1-57103-306-2(8)) Rourke Publishing, LLC.

Frost, Helen. A Look at Vietnam. 2005. (One World, Many Cultures Ser.). (Illus.). 24p. (J). (gr. k-3). 15.93 (978-0-7368-9394-7(6) , Pebble Bks.) Capstone Pr., Inc.

—A Look at Vietnam. Saunders-Smith, Gail, ed. 2002. (Our World Ser.). (Illus.). 24p. (J). (gr. k-1). lib. bdg. 15.93 (978-0-7368-1431-7(0) , Pebble Bks.) Capstone Pr., Inc.

Giraud, Hervé. Basha: A Hmong Child. Rey, Jean-Charles, photos by. 2005. (Children of the World Ser.). (Illus.). 24p. (J). (gr. k-3). 22.45 (978-1-4103-0547-3(3) , Blackbirch Pr., Inc.) Thomson Gale.

Gray, Shirley W. Vietnam. 2003. (True Book Ser.). (Illus.). 48p. (J). 25.00 (978-0-516-24211-8(3) , Children's Pr.) Scholastic Library Publishing.

—Vietnam. 2003. (gr. 3-6). lib. bdg. 15.25 (978-0-613-67994-7(6)) Tandem Library Bks.

Harcourt School Publishers Staff. A Time for Peace: Take-Home Book. 2001. (Collections Ser.). (Illus.). (J). pap. 1.90 (978-0-15-319510-5(X)) Harcourt Schl. Pubs.

Heinemann Staff. Vietnam. (World Focus Ser.). (Illus.). 31p. (J). (gr. 3-7). pap. 3.99 (978-0-431-07264-7(7)) Oxfam Publishing GBR. *Dist:* Stylus Publishing, LLC.

Holmes, Jimmy, illus. & photos by. In a Vietnamese City. Holmes, Jimmy, photos by. Morgan, Tom, photos by. 2002. (Child's Day Ser.). 32p. (J). 25.64 (978-0-7614-1409-4(6) , Benchmark Bks.) Cavendish, Marshall Corp.

Huynh, Quang Nhuong. Water Buffalo Days: Growing up in Vietnam. 1999. (978-0-606-15859-6(6)) Tandem Library Bks.

Imbriaco, Alison. Vietnam: A MyReportLinks. com Book. 2004. (Top Ten Countries of Recent Immigrants Ser.). (Illus.). 48p. (J). lib. bdg. 25.26 (978-0-7660-5182-9(X) , MyReportLinks.com Bks.) Enslow Pubs., Inc.

Kalman, Bobbie. Vietnam: The Culture. 2002. (gr. 3-6). lib. bdg. 16.40 (978-0-613-53000-2(4)) Tandem Library Bks.

—Vietnam: The Land. 2002. (gr. 3-6). lib. bdg. 16.40 (978-0-613-53001-9(2)) Tandem Library Bks.

—Vietnam: The People. 2002. (gr. 3-6). lib. bdg. 16.40 (978-0-613-53002-6(0)) Tandem Library Bks.

—Vietnam - The Culture. rev. ed. 2002. (Lands, Peoples & Cultures Ser.). (Illus.). 32p. (J). (gr. 4-5). (978-0-7787-9357-1(5)); pap. (978-0-7787-9725-8(2)) Crabtree Publishing Co.

—Vietnam - The Land. rev. ed. 2002. (Lands, Peoples & Cultures Ser.). (Illus.). 32p. (J). (gr. 4-5). (978-0-7787-9355-7(9)); pap. (978-0-7787-9723-4(6)) Crabtree Publishing Co.

—Vietnam - The People. rev. ed. 2002. (Lands, Peoples & Cultures Ser.). (Illus.). 32p. (J). (gr. 4-5). (978-0-7787-9356-4(7)); pap. (978-0-7787-9724-1(4)) Crabtree Publishing Co.

A Look at Vietnam, 6 vols. (gr. k-2). 28.95 (978-0-7368-9395-4(4)) Red Brick Learning.

Moriarty, Aleta. Vietnam. 2006. (Destination Detectives Ser.). (Illus.). 48p. (J). (978-1-4109-2338-7(X)); pap. (978-1-4109-2349-3(5)) Steck-Vaughn.

Ng, Yumi & Condra-Peters, Amy. Welcome to Vietnam. 2003. (Welcome to My Country Ser.). (Illus.). 48p. (J). (gr. 2 up). lib. bdg. 26.00 (978-0-8368-2548-0(9)) Stevens, Gareth Inc.

Nhuong, Huynh Quang. Water Buffalo Days: Growing up in Vietnam. Tseng, Mou-Sien & Tseng, Jean, illus. 1999. 116p. (J). (ps-7). per. 13.00 (978-0-613-12252-8(6)) Tandem Library Bks.

O'Connor, Karen. Vietnam. 1999. (Ticket to Ser.). (Illus.). 48p. (gr. 2-4). lib. bdg. 22.60 (978-1-57505-142-0(7)); (J). (gr. 3-5). lib. bdg. 22.60 (978-1-57505-117-8(6) , Carolrhoda Bks.) Lerner Publishing Group.

Park. Taking Your Camera To..., 6 vols., Set 3. 2000. pap. (978-0-7398-4136-5(X)) Steck-Vaughn.

Park, Ted. Taking Your Camera To..., Set 3. 2000. pap., tchr. ed. (978-0-7398-4135-8(1)) Steck-Vaughn.

—Taking Your Camera to Vietnam. 2001. (Taking Your Camera to Ser.). (Illus.). 32p. (J). (gr. 4-7). lib. bdg. 22.83 (978-0-7398-3572-2(6)) Raintree.

—Taking Your Camera to Vietnam. 2000. (Illus.). pap. (978-0-7398-4134-1(3)) Steck-Vaughn.

Parker, Edward. Vietnam. 2005. (Countries of the World Ser.). (Illus.). 64p. (J). (gr. 6-12). 30.00 (978-0-8160-6007-8(X)) Facts On File, Inc.

Phillips, Doug. Vietnam. 2006. (Modern World Nations Ser.). (Illus.). 112p. (J). (gr. 6-12). 30.00 (978-0-7910-8835-7(9) , Chelsea Hse.) Facts On File, Inc.

Rose, Elizabeth. A Primary Source Guide to Vietnam. 2004. (Countries of the World : A Primary Source Journey Ser.). (Illus.). 24p. (J). lib. bdg. 19.95 (978-0-8239-6734-6(4) , PowerKids Pr.) Rosen Publishing Group, Inc., The.

Seah, Audrey & Nair, Charissa M. Vietnam. 2nd ed. 2004. (Illus.). 144p. (J). (ps-7). lib. bdg. 37.07 (978-0-7614-1789-7(3)) Benchmark Investigative Group.

Shea, Pegi Deitz & Weill, Cynthia. Ten Mice for Tet. Trang, Ngoc, illus. 2003. 36p. (J). 15.95 (978-0-8118-3496-4(4)) Chronicle Bks. LLC.

Simmons, Pat. Vietnam. 1998. (Worldfocus Ser.). (Illus.). 32p. (J). (gr. 4-7). (978-1-57572-026-5(4)) Heinemann Library.

Simpson, Judith. Vietnam. 2002. (Ask about Asia Ser.). (Illus.). 48p. (J). (gr. 4 up). lib. bdg. (978-1-59084-203-4(0)) Mason Crest Pubs.

Taking Your Camera To... Includes: Argentina, China, Germany, India, South Africa, Vietnam, 6 bks., Set. 2001. (Taking Your Camera to Ser.). (Illus.). (J). (gr. 4-7). 136.98 (978-0-7398-3573-9(4)) Raintree.

Taus-Bolstad, Stacy. Vietnam in Pictures. 2003. (Visual Geography Ser.). (Illus.). 80p. (J). (gr. 5-12). 27.93 (978-0-8225-4678-8(7)) Lerner Publishing Group.

Willis, Terri. Vietnam. 2002. (Enchantment of the World, Second Ser.). (Illus.). 144p. (YA). (gr. 5-9). pap. 36.00 (978-0-516-22150-2(7) , Children's Pr.) Scholastic Library Publishing.

Zocchi, Judy. In Vietnam. Brodie, Neale, illus. 2005. (Global Adventures II Ser.). 32p. (J). pap. 9.95 (978-1-59646-165-9(9)) Dingles & Co.

VIETNAM—FICTION

Acker, Rick. The Case of the Autumn Rose. 2003. (Davis Detective Mysteries Ser.). 192p. pap. 7.99 (978-0-8254-2004-7(0)) Kregel Pubns.

Cleveland, Robert. How Tiger Got His Stripes. Hoffmire, Baird, illus. 2006. 32p. pap. 3.95 (978-0-87483-799-5(5)) August Hse. Pubs., Inc.

Eisner, Will. The Last Day in Vietnam: A Memory. 2000. (Illus.). 80p. (gr. 11 up). pap. 10.95 (978-1-56971-500-0(9)) Dark Horse Comics.

Hanh, Thich Nhat. The Hermit & the Well. Mai, Vo-Dinh, illus. 2004. 36p. (J). 15.00 (978-1-888375-31-2(0)) Parallax Pr.

Himelblau, Linda. The Trouble Begins. 2005. 208p. (J). (gr. 3-7). 14.95 (978-0-385-73273-4(2) , Delacorte Bks. for Young Readers) Random Hse. Children's Bks.

Kenworthy, Sukalaya. Hmong Means Free. 2004. 49p. pap. 12.95 (978-1-4137-2364-9(0)) PublishAmerica, Inc.

Literature Connections English: Fallen Angels. 2004. (gr. 6-12). (978-0-395-83360-5(4) , 2-70783) McDougal Littell Inc.

Marsden, Carolyn. When Heaven Fell. 2007. (Illus.). 192p. (J). (gr. 3-7). 15.99 (978-0-7636-3175-8(2)) Candlewick Pr.

McAfee, Joan K. The Road to el Dorado. 2003. (Illus.). 186p. (YA). pap. 12.95 (978-0-89745-273-1(9)) Sunflower Univ. Pr.

McKay, Lawrence, Jr. Journey Home. Lee, Dom & Lee, Keunhee, illus. 2000. 32p. (J). (ps-5). 15.95 (978-1-880000-65-6(2)) Lee & Low Bks., Inc.

—Journey Home. Lee, Dom et al, illus. 2000. 32p. (J). (ps-5). 6.95 (978-1-58430-005-2(1)) Lee & Low Bks., Inc.

Minh Tang, Eric & Ifkovic, Ed. The Minh Man Rules. 2000. (J). (gr. 7-9). pap. 9.99 (978-0-88092-419-1(5)) Royal Fireworks Publishing Co.

Pevsner, Stella & Tang, Fay. Sing for Your Father, Su Phan. 1999. (978-0-606-16709-3(9)) Tandem Library Bks.

Pomerantz, Charlotte. The Princess & the Admiral. Chen, Tony, illus. 2004. 48p. (gr. 4-7). pap. 8.95 (978-1-55861-061-3(8)) Feminist Pr. at The City Univ. of New York.

Record, S. Leo. Not by Chance. 2002. (Illus.). 216p. lib. bdg. 19.95 (978-0-9725007-0-8(7)) Sonship Publishing.

Shafer, Audrey. The Mailbox. 2006. 192p. (J). (gr. 3-7). 15.95 (978-0-385-73344-1(5)); lib. bdg. 17.99 (978-0-385-90361-5(8)) Random Hse. Children's Bks. (Delacorte Bks. for Young Readers).

Sherlock, Patti. Letters from Wolfie. 2004. 256p. (J). (gr. 3-7). 16.99 (978-0-670-03694-3(3) , Viking Juvenile) Penguin Group (USA) Inc.

Tran, Truong. Going Home, Coming Home / Ve Nha Tham Que Hu'O'Ng. Phong, Ann, illus. 2003. Tr. of Ve Nha Tham Que Hu'O'Ng. (ENG & VIE.). 32p. (J). 16.95 (978-0-89239-179-0(0)) Children's Bk. Pr.

Vander Zee, Ruth. Always with You. Himler, Ronald, illus. 2008. (J). (***978-0-8028-5295-3(5)*** , Eerdmans Bks For Young Readers) Eerdmans, William B. Publishing Co.

VIETNAM—FOREIGN RELATIONS—UNITED STATES

Burgan, Michael. The Vietnam War. 2006. (Wars That Changed American History Ser.). (Illus.). 48p. (J). pap. (978-0-8368-7304-7(1) , World Almanac Library) Stevens, Gareth Inc.

VIETNAM—HISTORY

Cottrell, Robert C. Vietnam: The 17th Parallel. 2004. (Arbitrary Borders Ser.). (Illus.). 112p. (J). (gr. 9-13). 35.00 (978-0-7910-7834-1(5) , Chelsea Hse.) Facts On File, Inc.

D Clare, John. Hodder 20th Century History: Vietnam 1939-75 2nd Edition - Foundation Edition. 2nd rev. ed. 2004. (Illus.). 48p. pap. 26.50 (***978-0-340-81476-5(4)*** , Hodder Murray) Hodder Education GBR. *Dist:* Trans-Atlantic Pubns., Inc.

Demarco, Neil. Vietnam 1939-75. 2nd rev. ed. 2004. (Illus.). 48p. pap. 26.50 (***978-0-340-81475-8(6)*** , Hodder Murray) Hodder Education GBR. *Dist:* Trans-Atlantic Pubns., Inc.

Gavin, Philip. The Fall of Vietnam. 2003. (World History Ser.). (Illus.). 112p. (J). (gr. 8-11). 32.45 (978-1-59018-182-9(4) , Lucent Bks.) Thomson Gale.

Guile, Melanie. Culture in Vietnam. 2005. (Culture Insights Ser.). (Illus.). 32p. (J). (ps-7). lib. bdg. 25.70 (978-1-4109-1135-3(7)) Harcourt Schl. Pubs.

—Culture in Vietnam. 2004. (J). pap. (978-1-4034-6466-8(9)) Steck-Vaughn.

Harcourt School Publishers Staff. A Time for Peace Below Level. 3rd ed. 2002. (Trophies Reading Program Ser.). (Illus.). pap. 5.10 (978-0-15-323234-3(X)) Harcourt Schl. Pubs.

Kilbourne, Sarah S. Leaving Vietnam Class set: The True Story of Tuan Ngo. 1999. (J). (gr. 2 up). pap., stu. ed. 22.24 incl. audio (978-0-7887-3176-1(9) , 40911) Recorded Bks., LLC.

Nicolai, Gregory. Teens in Vietnam. 2006. (Global Connections Ser.). 96p. (J). (gr. 5-7). 31.93 (978-0-7565-2067-0(3)) Compass Point Bks.

Porterfield, Jason. Vietnam: A Primary Source Cultural Guide. 2005. (Primary Sources of World Cultures Ser.). (J). lib. bdg. (978-1-4042-0481-2(4)) Rosen Publishing Group, Inc., The.

Steele, Philip. Ho Chi Minh. 2003. (Leading Lives Ser.). (Illus.). 64p. (J). lib. bdg. 28.50 (978-1-4034-0836-5(X)) Heinemann Library.

Stibbens, Steve. Knights over the Delta: An Oral History of the 114th Aviation Company in Vietnam, 1963-72. Stibbens, Steve, ed. 2003. 60.00 (978-0-9742465-0-5(6)) 114th Aviation Co. Assn.

Uschan, Michael V. The Fall of Saigon: The End of the Vietnam War. 2002. (Point of Impact Ser.). 32p. (J). (gr. 5-7). (Illus.). lib. bdg. 25.64 (978-1-58810-555-4(5)); pap. 7.50 (978-1-4034-0072-7(5) , 91554) Heinemann Library.

Worth, Richard. Dien Bien Phu. 2003. (Sieges That Changed the World Ser.). (Illus.). 112p. (gr. 6-12). 30.00 (978-0-7910-7228-8(2) , Chelsea Hse.) Facts On File, Inc.

Zocchi, Judy. In Vietnam. Brodie, Neale, illus. 2005. (Global Adventures II Ser.). 32p. (J). pap. 9.95 (978-1-59646-164-2(0)); lib. bdg. 20.65 (978-1-59646-081-2(4)) Dingles & Co.

—In Vietnam/en Vietnam. Brodie, N. eale, illus. 2005. (Global Adventures II Ser.).Tr. of En Vietnam. (ENG & SPA.). 32p. (J). pap. 9.95 (978-1-59646-166-6(7)) Dingles & Co.

—In Vietnam/en Vietnam. Brodie, Neale, illus. 2005. (Global Adventures II Ser.).Tr. of En Vietnam. (ENG & SPA.). 32p. (J). lib. bdg. 20.65 (978-1-59646-082-9(2)); per. 9.95 (978-1-59646-167-3(5)) Dingles & Co.

VIETNAM WAR, 1961-1975

The American Experience In Vietnam. 180.00 (978-0-8368-5771-9(2)) Stevens, Gareth Inc.

Anderson, Dale. The Tet Offensive: Turning Point of the Vietnam War. 2006. (Snapshots in History Ser.). (Illus.). 96p. (J). (gr. 5-7). 30.60 (978-0-7565-1623-9(4)) Compass Point Bks.

Ashabranner, Brent. Their Names to Live: What the Vietnam Veterans Memorial Means to America. Ashabranner, Jennifer, photos by. 1998. (Great American Memorials Ser.). (Illus.). 64p. (gr. 4-8). lib. bdg. 24.90 (978-0-7613-3235-0(9) , Twenty-First Century Bks.) Lerner Publishing Group.

Barr, Linda. Long Road to Freedom: Journey of the Hmong. (High Five Reading Ser.). (J). (ps-k). 2005. (Illus.). 64p. lib. bdg. 23.93 (978-0-7368-3880-1(5)); 2004. pap. (978-0-7368-3852-8(X)) Capstone Pr., Inc.

Benson, Michael, ed. Vietnam the Untold Stories, No. 2. 1998. (YA). pap. 5.99 (978-0-934551-53-3(7)) Profile Entertainment, Inc.

Britton, Tamara L. The Vietnam Veterans Memorial. 2005. (Symbols, Landmarks, & Monuments Set Ii Ser.). (Illus.). 32p. (J). (gr. k-6). lib. bdg. 22.78 (978-1-59197-523-6(9)) ABDO Publishing Co.

Burgan, Michael. The Vietnam War. 2005. (Witness to History Ser.). 56p. (YA). pap. 8.95 (978-1-4034-6260-2(7)); (Illus.). (J). lib. bdg. 31.36 (978-1-4034-4873-6(6)) Heinemann Library.

—The Vietnam War. 2006. (Wars That Changed American History Ser.). (Illus.). 48p. (J). pap. (978-0-8368-7304-7(1)); lib. bdg. (978-0-8368-7295-8(9)) Stevens, Gareth Inc. (World Almanac Library).

Caputo, Philip. 10,000 Days of Thunder: A History of the Vietnam War. 2005. (Illus.). 128p. (J). (gr. 4-7). 23.99 (978-0-689-86231-1(8) , Atheneum) Simon & Schuster Children's Publishing.

Corona, Laurel. War Within a War: Vietnam & the Cold War. 2004. (Lucent Library of Historical Eras). (Illus.). 112p. (J). 32.45 (978-1-59018-389-2(4) , Lucent Bks.) Thomson Gale.

Cottrell, Robert C. Vietnam: The 17th Parallel. 2004. (Arbitrary Borders Ser.). (Illus.). 112p. (J). (gr. 9-13). 35.00 (978-0-7910-7834-1(5) , Chelsea Hse.) Facts On File, Inc.

D Clare, John. Hodder 20th Century History: Vietnam 1939-75 2nd Edition - Foundation Edition. 2nd rev. ed. 2004. (Illus.). 48p. pap. 26.50 (***978-0-340-81476-5(4)*** , Hodder Murray) Hodder Education GBR. *Dist:* Trans-Atlantic Pubns., Inc.

Dowswell, Paul. The Vietnam War. 2002. (Cold War Ser.). (Illus.). 64p. (YA). (gr. 7 up). pap. 14.60 (978-0-8368-5279-0(6)); lib. bdg. 32.67 (978-0-8368-5274-5(5)) Stevens, Gareth Inc. (World Almanac Library).

—Vietnam War. 2002. (gr. 7-12). lib. bdg. 24.15 (978-0-613-52520-6(5)) Tandem Library Bks.

Dubois, Muriel L. The Vietnam Veterans Memorial. 2002. (National Landmarks Ser.). (Illus.). 24p. (J). (gr. 2-3). lib. bdg. 18.60 (978-0-7368-1116-3(8) , Bridgestone Bks.) Capstone Pr., Inc.

Edelman, Rob. The Vietnam War. 2003. (People at the Center of Ser.). (Illus.). 48p. (J). 24.95 (978-1-56711-771-4(6) , Blackbirch Pr., Inc.) Thomson Gale.

Feinstein, Stephen. The 1960s from the Vietnam War to Flower Power. rev. ed. 2006. (Decades of the 20th Century in Color Ser.). (Illus.). 64p. (J). lib. bdg. 27.93 (978-0-7660-2636-0(1)) Enslow Pubs., Inc.

Ferry, Joseph. The Vietnam Veterans Memorial. 2002. (American Symbols & Their Meanings Ser.). (Illus.). 48p. (YA). (gr. 4 up). lib. bdg. (978-1-59084-039-9(9)) Mason Crest Pubs.

Fighting the Vietnam War 6-Pack. 2004. (Illus.). pap. 48.35 (978-1-4109-1477-4(1)) Raintree.

Fitzgerald, Brian. Fighting the Vietnam War. (On the Front Line Ser.). (Illus.). 48p. (J). 2005. (gr. 6-8). lib. bdg. 29.93 (978-1-4109-1463-7(1)); 2004. pap. 8.95 (978-1-4109-1470-5(4)) Raintree.

—Fighting the Vietnam War. 2006. (On the Front Line Ser.). (Illus.). 48p. pap. (978-1-4109-2200-7(6)); lib. bdg. (978-1-4109-2193-2(X)) Steck-Vaughn.

Galt, Margot Fortunato. Stop This War! American Protest of the Conflict in Vietnam. 2005. (People's History Ser.). (Illus.). 96p. (gr. 6-12). lib. bdg. 26.60 (978-0-8225-1740-5(X)) Lerner Publishing Group.

Gavin, Philip. The Fall of Vietnam. 2003. (World History Ser.). (Illus.). 112p. (J). (gr. 8-11). 32.45 (978-1-59018-182-9(4) , Lucent Bks.) Thomson Gale.

Gibson, Karen. The Vietnam War. 2007. (Monumental Milestones Ser.). (Illus.). 48p. (YA). lib. bdg. 29.95 (***978-1-58415-541-6(8)***) Mitchell Lane Pubs., Inc.

Gibson, Karen Bush. The Vietnam War. 2006. (J). lib. bdg. (978-1-58415-469-3(1)) Mitchell Lane Pubs., Inc.

Gifford, Clive. The Vietnam War. 2005. (How Did It Happen? Ser.). (Illus.). 48p. (J). (gr. 7-10). lib. bdg. 29.95 (978-1-59018-609-1(5) , Lucent Bks.) Thomson Gale.

Gold, Susan Dudley. The Pentagon Papers: National Security or the Right to Know. 2004. (Supreme Court Milestones Ser.). (Illus.). 144p. (J). 37.07 (978-0-7614-1843-6(1) , Benchmark Bks.) Cavendish, Marshall Corp.

Grant, R. G. The Vietnam War. 2004. (Atlas of Conflicts Ser.). (Illus.). 64p. (J). pap. 11.95 (978-0-8368-5674-3(0)); lib. bdg. 32.67 (978-0-8368-5667-5(8)) Stevens, Gareth Inc. (World Almanac Library).

Green, Carl R. The Vietnam War: A MyReportLinks. Com Book. 2003. (U.S. Wars Ser.). (Illus.). 48p. (J). lib. bdg. 25.26 (978-0-7660-5147-8(1) , MyReportLinks.com Bks.) Enslow Pubs., Inc.

Hay, Jeff, ed. Encyclopedia of the Vietnam War. 2004. (Greenhaven Encyclopedia of Ser.). (Illus.). 336p. (J). lib. bdg. 77.45 (978-0-7377-1149-3(3) , Greenhaven Pr., Inc.) Thomson Gale.

Hemingway, Albert. American Naval Forces in the Vietnam War. 2005. (American Experience in Vietnam Ser.). (Illus.). 48p. (J). 30.00 (978-0-8368-5776-4(3)); pap. (978-0-8368-5783-2(6)) Stevens, Gareth Inc. (World Almanac Library).

Hillstrom, Kevin & Hillstrom, Laurie Collier. Vietnam War: Biographies, 2 vols. Sawinski, Diane M., ed. 2000. (U-X-L Vietnam War Reference Library). (Illus.). (J). (978-0-7876-4885-5(X) , UXL) Thomson Gale.

Hogue, Richard, Sr. We Were the Third Herd. 2003. per. 17.95 (978-0-9722264-0-0(0)) Richlyn Publishing.

Kallen, Stuart A. The Home Front: Americans Protest the War. 2001. (American War Library). (Illus.). 112p. (YA). (gr. 4-12). lib. bdg. 29.95 (978-1-56006-718-4(7) , LML00902-178070, Lucent Bks.) Thomson Gale.

Keeter, Hunter. American Air Forces in the Vietnam War. 2005. (American Experience in Vietnam Ser.). (Illus.). 48p. (J). pap. (978-0-8368-5780-1(1)); lib. bdg. (978-0-8368-5773-3(9)) Stevens, Gareth Inc. (World Almanac Library).

—American Ground Forces in the Vietnam War. 2005. (American Experience in Vietnam Ser.). (Illus.). 48p. (J). pap. (978-0-8368-5781-8(X)); lib. bdg. 30.00 (978-0-8368-5774-0(7)) Stevens, Gareth Inc. (World Almanac Library).

Kent, Deborah. The Vietnam War: "What Are We Fighting For?" 2000. (American War Ser.). (Illus.). 128p. (YA). (gr. 5-12). pap. 13.26 (978-0-7660-1731-3(1)) Enslow Pubs., Inc.

Levy, Debbie. The Vietnam War. 2004. (Chronicle of America's Wars Ser.). (Illus.). 96p. (J). (gr. 5-12). 27.93 (978-0-8225-0421-4(9)) Lerner Publishing Group.

Marcovitz, Hal. Vietnam War. 2007. (World History Ser.). (Illus.). 128p. (gr. 7-10). 28.70 (***978-1-4205-0024-0(4)*** , Lucent Bks.) Thomson Gale.

Marquette, Scott. Vietnam War. 2003. (America at War Ser.). (Illus.). 48p. (gr. 4-8). 20.95 (978-1-58952-391-3(1)) Rourke Publishing, LLC.

Marrin, Albert. America & Vietnam: The Elephant & the Tiger. 2002. (Illus.). 277p. (J). pap. 13.95 (978-1-893103-08-5(0)) Beautiful Feet Bks.

Mason, Andrew. The Vietnam War: A Primary Source History. 2005. (Illus.). 48p. lib. bdg. 26.00 (978-0-8368-5981-2(2)) Stevens, Gareth Inc.

McCormick, Anita Louise. The Vietnam Antiwar Movement in American History. 2000. (In American History Ser.). (Illus.). 128p. (YA). (gr. 5-12). lib. bdg. 26.60 (978-0-7660-1295-0(6)) Enslow Pubs., Inc.

Murray, Stuart. Vietnam War Battles & Leaders. 2004. (Battles & Leaders Ser.). (Illus.). 96p. (J). 16.99 (978-0-7566-0770-8(1)); pap. 9.99 (978-0-7566-0771-5(X)) Dorling Kindersley Publishing, Inc.

Murray, Stuart & Dorling Kindersley Publishing Staff. Vietnam War. 2005. (Eyewitness Books). (Illus.). 72p. (J). 15.99 (978-0-7566-1166-8(0)); lib. bdg. 19.99 (978-0-7566-1165-1(2)) Dorling Kindersley Publishing, Inc.

Myers, Walter Dean. A Place Called Heartbreak: A Story of Vietnam. 2001. (Nonfiction Bookbag Ser.). (YA). (gr. 8-9). per. 8.45 (978-1-58830-212-0(1)) Metropolitan Teaching & Learning Co.

O'Brien, Tim. If I Die in a Combat Zone: Box Me up & Ship Me Home. 1999. (gr. 7-12). lib. bdg. 21.10 (978-0-613-08043-9(2)) Tandem Library Bks.

O'Connell, Kim A. Primary Source Accounts of the Vietnam War. 2006. (America's Wars Through Primary Sources Ser.). (Illus.). 128p. (J). lib. bdg. 33.27 (978-1-59845-001-9(8) , MyReportLinks.com Bks.) Enslow Pubs., Inc.

Olmstead. Le Ly Hayslip. 2004. (Asian-American Biographies Ser.). (Illus.). 64p. (J). pap. 9.50 (978-1-4109-1128-5(4)) Raintree.

Raffaelle, Gerda-Ann, ed. Vietnam War: Cumulative Index. 2000. (U-X-L Vietnam War Reference Library). 23p. (YA). (gr. 7 up). pap. 5.00 (978-0-7876-5576-1(7) , UXL) Thomson Gale.

Rice, Earle, Jr. Point of No Return: Tonkin Gulf & the Vietnam War. 2004. (First Battles Ser.). (Illus.). 144p. (YA). (gr. 6-12). 23.95 (978-1-931798-16-7(8)) Reynolds, Morgan Inc.

Ruane, Kevin. The Vietnam Wars. 2001. (Documents in Contemporary History Ser.). (Illus.). 256p. 79.95 (978-0-7190-5489-1(3)); 208p. pap. 26.95 (978-0-7190-5490-7(7)) Manchester Univ. Pr. GBR. *Dist:* Macmillan.

Schomp, Virginia. The Vietnam ERA. 2003. (American Voices From Ser.). (Illus.). xxiii, 134p. (J). 34.21 (978-0-7614-1693-7(5) , Benchmark Bks.) Cavendish, Marshall Corp.

—The Vietnam War. 2001. (Letters from the Home Front Ser.). (Illus.). 96p. (J). (gr. 6 up). lib. bdg. 29.93 (978-0-7614-1099-7(6) , Benchmark Bks.) Cavendish, Marshall Corp.

Schynert, Mark. Women of the Vietnam War. 2004. (Illus.). 112p. (J). (gr. 7-10). 32.45 (978-1-59018-474-5(2) , Lucent Bks.) Thomson Gale.

Sutherland, Jonathan & Canwell, Diane. American Women in the Vietnam War. 2005. (American Experience in Vietnam Ser.). (Illus.). 48p. (J). (978-0-8368-5784-9(4)); lib. bdg. 30.00 (978-0-8368-5777-1(1)) Stevens, Gareth Inc. (World Almanac Library).

Thomas, William. The Home Front in the Vietnam War. 2005. (American Experience in Vietnam Ser.). (Illus.). 48p. (J). pap. (978-0-8368-5782-5(8)); lib. bdg. 30.00 (978-0-8368-5775-7(5)) Stevens, Gareth Inc. (World Almanac Library).

Uschan, Michael V. The Fall of Saigon: The End of the Vietnam War. 2002. (Point of Impact Ser.). 32p. (J). (gr. 5-7). (Illus.). lib. bdg. 25.64 (978-1-58810-555-4(5)); pap. 7.50 (978-1-4034-0072-7(5) , 91554) Heinemann Library.

The Vietnam War. 2004. (Historical Reader Ser.). (Illus.). 288p. (J). (gr. 6-12). 13.32 (978-0-618-00369-3(X) , 2-00106) McDougal Littell Inc.

Warren, Andrea. Escape from Saigon: How a Vietnam War Orphan Became an American Boy. 2004. (Illus.). 128p. (J). 17.00 (978-0-374-32224-3(4) , Nelanie Kroupa Bks.) Farrar, Straus & Giroux.

Willoughby, Douglas. The Vietnam War. (20th Century Perspectives Ser.). (Illus.). 48p. (J). (gr. 5-7). 2001. lib. bdg. 25.64 (978-1-57572-439-3(1)); Set 1. 2002. pap. 7.95 (978-1-58810-378-9(1) , 91130) Heinemann Library.

—The Vietnam War. 2001. (J). (978-0-606-22494-9(7)) Tandem Library Bks.

Worth, Richard. Tet Offensive. 2002. (Battles That Changed the World Ser.). (Illus.). (J). 96p. pap. 13.25 (978-0-7910-7167-0(7)); 112p. 30.00 (978-0-7910-6688-1(6)) Facts On File, Inc. (Chelsea Hse.).

Young, Marilyn Blatt, et al. The Vietnam War: A History in Documents. 2002. (Pages from History Ser.). (Illus.). 176p. 36.95 (978-0-19-512278-7(X)) Oxford Univ. Pr., Inc.

VIETNAM WAR, 1961-1975—AFRICAN AMERICANS

Sutherland, Jonathan & Canwell, Diane. African Americans in the Vietnam War. 2005. (American Experience in Vietnam Ser.). (Illus.). 48p. (J). pap. (978-0-8368-5779-5(8)); lib. bdg. 30.00 (978-0-8368-5772-6(0)) Stevens, Gareth Inc. (World Almanac Library).

VIETNAM WAR, 1961-1975—FICTION

Arnold, Tedd. Rat Life. 2007. 208p. (YA). (gr. 7 up). 16.99 (978-0-8037-3020-5(9) , Dial) Penguin Group (USA) Inc.

Couloumbis, Audrey. Summer's End. 2007. 192p. (YA). (gr. 7 up). pap. 5.99 (978-0-14-240783-7(6) , Puffin) Penguin Group (USA) Inc.

Crist-Evans, Craig. Amaryllis. (YA). (gr. 9). 2006. 192p. pap. 7.99 (978-0-7636-2990-8(1)); 2003. 208p. 15.99 (978-0-7636-1863-6(2)) Candlewick Pr.

Dowell, Frances O'Roark. Shooting the Moon. 2008. 176p. (J). 16.99 (***978-1-4169-2690-0(9)***) Simon & Schuster Children's Publishing.

Easton, Kelly. The Life History of a Star. 2002. 208p. (YA). pap. 6.99 (978-0-689-85270-1(3) , Simon Pulse) Simon & Schuster Children's Publishing.

—The Life History of a Star. 2002. (gr. 7-12). lib. bdg. 15.30 (978-0-613-60641-7(8)) Tandem Library Bks.

—The Life History of a Star. l.t. ed. 2002. 200p. 22.95 (978-0-7862-4786-8(X)) Thorndike Pr.

Franklin, Kristine L. Dove Song. 2006. 192p. (J). (gr. 5-9). pap. 5.99 (978-0-7636-3219-9(8)) Candlewick Pr.

Hahn, Mary Downing. December Stillness. unabr. ed. 1998. (YA). Class Set. 102.80 incl. audio (978-0-7887-2561-6(0) , 46731); Homework Set. (gr. 7). 49.75 incl. audio (978-0-7887-2136-6(4) , 40710) Recorded Bks., LLC.

Hobbs, Valerie. Sonny's War. 2002. 224p. (YA). (gr. 7 up). 16.00 (978-0-374-37136-4(9) , Farrar, Straus & Giroux (BYR)) Farrar, Straus & Giroux.

—Sonny's War. 2006. 224p. (YA). pap. 7.95 (978-0-374-46970-2(9)) Macmillan.

Hoobler, Dorothy & Hoobler, Thomas. The 1970's: Arguments. Hoffman, Robin, illus. 2002. (Century Kids Ser.). 160p. (gr. 5-8). lib. bdg. 22.90 (978-0-7613-1607-7(8) , Twenty-First Century Bks.) Lerner Publishing Group.

Hughes, Dean. Search & Destroy. 224p. (YA). 2008. mass mkt. 5.99 (***978-1-4169-5371-5(X)*** , Simon Pulse); 2005. (Illus.). 16.95 (978-0-689-87023-1(X) , Atheneum) Simon & Schuster Children's Publishing.

Kadohata, Cynthia. Cracker! The Best Dog in Vietnam. 2007. 320p. (J). (gr. 5-8). 16.99 (978-1-4169-0637-7(1) , Atheneum) Simon & Schuster Children's Publishing.

Kerley, Barbara. Greetings from Planet Earth. 2007. (Illus.). 256p. (J). (gr. 4-7). pap. 16.99 (978-0-439-80203-1(2) , Scholastic Pr.) Scholastic, Inc.

Letts, Billie. The Honk & Holler Opening Soon. 1999. (gr. 7-12). lib. bdg. 23.40 (978-0-613-17283-7(3)) Tandem Library Bks.

Myers, Walter Dean. Fallen Angels. 2002. (Illus.). (J). 13.19 (978-0-7587-0353-8(8)) Book Wholesalers, Inc.

—Fallen Angels. 2003. (Illus.). 320p. (YA). (gr. 7-12). pap. 5.99 (978-0-590-40943-8(3) , Scholastic Paperbacks) Scholastic, Inc.

—Patrol: An American Soldier in Vietnam. Grifalconi, Ann, illus. 2005. 40p. (J). pap. 6.99 (978-0-06-073159-5(1) , Harper Trophy) HarperCollins Pubs.

Okimoto, Jean Davies. Jason's Women. 2000. 220p. (gr. 4-7). pap. 12.95 (978-0-595-00797-4(X) , Backinprint.com) iUniverse, Inc.

Paulsen, Gary. The Car. 2006. (Illus.). 192p. (YA). pap. 5.95 (978-0-15-205827-2(3) , Harcourt Paperbacks) Harcourt Children's Bks.

Pevsner, Stella & Tang, Fay. Sing for Your Father, Su Phan. 1999. (978-0-606-16709-3(9)) Tandem Library Bks.

Qualey, Marsha. Too Big a Storm. 2004. 256p. (J). (gr. 9). 16.99 (978-0-8037-2839-4(5) , Dial) Penguin Group (USA) Inc.

Ritter, John H. Over the Wall. 2002. (gr. 5-8). lib. bdg. 15.30 (978-0-613-67112-5(0)) Tandem Library Bks.

Santana, Patricia. Motorcycle Ride on the Sea of Tranquility. 2002. 270p. (YA). 19.95 (978-0-8263-2435-1(5)) Univ. of New Mexico Pr.

Schraff, Anne. The Greatest Heroes. 2000. 143p. (J). pap. (978-0-7891-5133-9(2)); (gr. 5-12). lib. bdg. 13.95 (978-0-7807-9271-5(8)) Perfection Learning Corp.

Sherlock, Patti. Letters from Wolfie. 2007. 240p. (YA). (gr. 5 up). pap. 6.99 (978-0-14-240358-7(X) , Puffin) Penguin Group (USA) Inc.

Testa, Maria. Almost Forever. 80p. (J). (gr. 4-8). 2007. pap. 5.99 (978-0-7636-3366-0(6)); 2003. (Illus.). 14.99 (978-0-7636-1996-1(5)) Candlewick Pr.

Trip to Freedom: Six-Pack. (Greetings Ser.: Vol. 3). (gr. 3-5). 31.00 (978-0-7635-1777-9(1)) Rigby Education.

Woodworth, Chris. Georgie's Moon. 2006. 176p. (J). 16.00 (978-0-374-33306-5(8)) Farrar, Straus & Giroux.

VIETNAMESE AMERICANS

Bryan, Nichol. Vietnamese Americans. 2004. (One Nation Set Ii Ser.). (Illus.). 32p. (J). (gr. k-6). lib. bdg. 22.78 (978-1-59197-534-2(4)) ABDO Publishing Co.

Coleman, Lori. Vietnamese in America. 2005. (In America Ser.). (Illus.). 80p. (J). (gr. 5-8). lib. bdg. 27.93 (978-0-8225-3951-3(9)) Lerner Publishing Group.

Englar, Mary. Le Ly Hayslip. 2006. (Asian-American Biographies Ser.). (Illus.). 64p. (J). 23.00 (978-1-4109-1055-4(5)) Raintree.

Ferry, Joseph. Vietnamese Immigration. 2003. (Changing Face of North America Ser.). (Illus.). 112p. (YA). lib. bdg. (978-1-59084-682-7(6)) Mason Crest Pubs.

Fitterer, C. Ann. Vietnamese Americans. 2002. (Spirit of America: Our Cultural Heritage Ser.). (Illus.). 32p. (J). (gr. 2-6). 27.07 (978-1-56766-160-6(2)) Child's World, Inc.

Hall, M. C. Vietnamese Americans. 2003. (We Are America Ser.). 32p. pap. 6.95 (978-1-4034-3139-4(6)) Heinemann Library.

Hall, Margaret. Vietnamese Americans. 2003. (We Are America Ser.). (Illus.). 32p. (J). lib. bdg. 24.22 (978-1-4034-0738-2(X)) Heinemann Library.

—Vietnamese Americans. 2003. (gr. 3-6). lib. bdg. 15.25 (978-0-613-67439-3(1)) Tandem Library Bks.

Imbriaco, Alison. Vietnam: A MyReportLinks. com Book. 2004. (Top Ten Countries of Recent Immigrants Ser.). (Illus.). 48p. (J). lib. bdg. 25.26 (978-0-7660-5182-9(X) , MyReportLinks.com Bks.) Enslow Pubs., Inc.

Olmstead. Le Ly Hayslip. 2004. (Asian-American Biographies Ser.). (Illus.). 64p. (J). pap. 9.50 (978-1-4109-1128-5(4)) Raintree.

Parker, Lewis K. Why Vietnamese Immigrants Came to America. 2003. (Reading Power Ser.). (Illus.). 24p. (J). lib. bdg. 17.25 (978-0-8239-6461-1(2) , PowerKids Pr.) Rosen Publishing Group, Inc., The.

Springstubb, Tricia. The Vietnamese-Americans. 2001. (Immigrants in America Ser.). (Illus.). 104p. (YA). (gr. 4-12). 29.95 (978-1-56006-964-5(3) , LML00902-179007, Lucent Bks.) Thomson Gale.

Warren, Andrea. Escape from Saigon: How a Vietnam War Orphan Became an American Boy. 2004. (Illus.). 128p. (J). 17.00 (978-0-374-32224-3(4) , Nelanie Kroupa Bks.) Farrar, Straus & Giroux.

VIETNAMESE AMERICANS—FICTION

Fleischman, Paul. Semillas. De Hernandez, Isaac, illus. 2000. (la Orilla Del Viento Ser.). (SPA.). 69p. (J). (ps-7). pap. 6.99 (978-968-16-6072-7(2) , 127) Fondo de Cultura Economica USA.

Good Morning, Vietnam, Good Afternoon, USA. 2000. (J). (978-0-9703585-0-9(4)) Hudson, Anna E.

Himelblau, Linda. The Trouble Begins. 2005. 208p. (J). (gr. 3-7). 14.95 (978-0-385-73273-4(2) , Delacorte Bks. for Young Readers) Random Hse. Children's Bks.

McKay, Lawrence, Jr. Journey Home. Lee, Dom & Lee, Keunhee, illus. 2000. 32p. (J). (ps-5). 15.95 (978-1-880000-65-6(2)) Lee & Low Bks., Inc.

—Journey Home. Lee, Dom et al, illus. 2000. 32p. (J). (ps-5). 6.95 (978-1-58430-005-2(1)) Lee & Low Bks., Inc.

Mosher, Richard. Zazoo. (YA). (gr. 7 up). 2001. 256p. tchr. ed. 16.00 (978-0-618-13534-9(0) , Clarion Bks.); 2004. 272p. reprint ed. pap. 6.99 (978-0-618-43904-1(8) , Graphia) Houghton Mifflin Co. Trade & Reference Div.

Perera, Hilda. MAI. (SPA.). 120p. (J). 7.95 (978-84-348-1149-2(9) , SM1210) SM Ediciones ESP. *Dist:* AIMS International Bks., Inc., Lectorum Pubns., Inc.

Schraff, Anne. Memories Are Forever. 1999. 135p. (J). pap. (978-0-7891-4924-4(9)); (gr. 5-12). lib. bdg. 13.95 (978-0-7807-8008-8(6)) Perfection Learning Corp.

Skurzynski, Gloria & Ferguson, Alane. Rage of Fire. (J). (gr. 3-7). 2001. (Mysteries in Our National Parks Ser.). 160p. pap. 5.95 (978-0-7922-7653-1(1)); 1999. (National Parks Mysteries Ser.: No. 2). (Illus.). 164p. 15.95 (978-0-7922-7035-5(5)) National Geographic Society. (National Geographic Children's Bks.).

Sugarman, Brynn Olenberg. Rebecca's Journey Home. Shapiro, Michelle, illus. 2006. 32p. (J). 17.95 (978-1-58013-157-5(3)) Kar-Ben Publishing.

Tran, Truong. Going Home, Coming Home / Ve Nha Tham Que Hu'O'Ng. Phong, Ann, illus. 2003. Tr. of Ve Nha Tham Que Hu'O'Ng. (ENG & VIE.). 32p. (J). 16.95 (978-0-89239-179-0(0)) Children's Bk. Pr.

Windle, Jeanette. Secret of the Dragon Mark, Vol. 5. 2002. (Parker Twins Ser.: No. 5). 160p. (gr. 3-8). pap. 5.99 (978-0-8254-4149-3(8)) Kregel Pubns.

VIETNAMESE CONFLICT, 1961-1975

see Vietnam War, 1961-1975

VIETNAMESE LANGUAGE

Hippocrene Books, ed. Children's Illustrated Vietnamese Dictionary: English-Vietnamese/Vietnamese-English. 2006. (ENG & VIE.). 112p. (J). pap. 14.95 (978-0-7818-1133-0(3)) Hippocrene Bks., Inc.

Hop Thi Nguyen & Yoon, Selina. Sing 'n Learn Vietnamese: Introduce Vietnamese with Favorite Children's Songs. 1998. (Sing 'n Learn Ser.). (ENG & VIE., Illus.). 24p. (J). (ps-6). pap. 14.95 incl. audio (978-1-888194-16-6(2)); pap. 17.95 incl. audio compact disk (978-1-888194-19-7(7)) Master Communications, Inc.

Lanchais, Aurelie, et al. I Have Wheels, What Am I? (Illus.). (ps-1). 2005. (RUS, ENG, TUR, VIE & CHI.). 14p. pap. 9.95 (978-1-84059-239-9(7)); 2000. (GUJ, ENG, VIE, CHI & RUS., 16p. (J). pap. 9.95 (978-1-84059-238-2(9)); 2000. (FRE, ENG, VIE, GUJ & CHI., 16p. (J). pap. 9.95 (978-1-84059-237-5(0)) Milet Publishing.

—I Have Wheels, What Am I? Erdogan, Faith, tr. 2000. (Who Am I? What Am I? Ser.). (TUR, ENG, RUS, VIE & CHI., Illus.). 16p. (J). (ps-1). pap. 9.95 (978-1-84059-240-5(0)) Milet Publishing.

—Who Am I? (Illus.). (ps-1). 2005. (CHI, ENG, VIE, GUJ & RUS.). 14p. pap. 9.95 (978-1-84059-229-0(X)); 2005. (RUS, ENG, TUR, VIE & CHI., 14p. pap. 9.95 (978-1-84059-232-0(X)); 2000. (FRE, ENG, VIE, GUJ & CHI., 16p. (J). pap. 9.95 (978-1-84059-230-6(3)); 2000. (GUJ, ENG, VIE, CHI & RUS., 16p. (J). pap. 9.95 (978-1-84059-231-3(1)) Milet Publishing.

Nguyen, An Mai. Let's Learn Animals in Vietnamese. 2006. (VIE & ENG., Illus.). (J). bds. 6.95 (978-0-9776482-3-8(0)) Viet Baby, LLC.

—Let's Learn Colors in Vietnamese. 2006. (VIE & ENG., Illus.). (J). bds. 6.95 (978-0-9776482-1-4(4)) Viet Baby, LLC.

—Let's Learn How to Count in Vietnamese. 2006. (VIE & ENG., Illus.). (J). bds. 6.95 (978-0-9776482-2-1(2)) Viet Baby, LLC.

—Let's Learn the Vietnamese Alphabet. 2006. (VIE & ENG., Illus.). (J). bds. 6.95 (978-0-9776482-0-7(6)) Viet Baby, LLC.

VIEWS

Countries - Set II, Set. Incl. Brazil. Furlong, Kate A. lib. bdg. 22.78 (978-1-57765-491-9(9)); China. Italia, Bob. lib. bdg. 22.78 (978-1-57765-492-6(7)); Egypt. Italia, Bob. lib. bdg. 22.78 (978-1-57765-493-3(5)); England. Britton, Tamara L. lib. bdg. 22.78 (978-1-57765-499-5(4)); France. Italia, Bob. lib. bdg. 22.78 (978-1-57765-494-0(3)); Iran. Italia, Bob. lib. bdg. 22.78 (978-1-57765-495-7(1)); Ireland. Italia, Bob. lib. bdg. 22.78 (978-1-57765-496-4(X)); Israel. Italia, Bob. lib. bdg. 22.78 (978-1-57765-497-1(8)); Poland. Furlong, Kate A. lib. bdg. 22.78 (978-1-57765-498-8(6)); Sweden. Furlong, Kate A. lib. bdg. 22.78 (978-1-57765-550-3(8)); 40p. (J). (gr. k-6). 2001. (Illus.). 2001. Set lib. bdg. 227.80 (978-1-57765-500-8(1) , Checkerboard Library) ABDO Publishing Co.

It's My State: Group 2, 6 vols. 2003. (YA). (gr. 3). lib. bdg. 162.43 (978-0-7614-1521-3(1)) Cavendish, Marshall Corp.

Priddy, Roger. My Big World Book. rev. ed. 2002. (Illus.). 12p. (J). bds. 5.95 (978-0-312-49122-2(0) , Priddy Bks.) St. Martin's Pr.

Yorinks, Arthur. The Alphabet Atlas. Yorinks, Adrienne, illus. 1999. 64p. (J). (ps-3). 19.95 (978-1-890817-14-5(7)) Winslow Pr.

VIKINGS

Here are entered works on the Scandinavian sea-warriors who plundered the northern and western coasts of Europe from the 8th to the 10th centuries. Works on the inhabitants of Scandinavia since the 10th century are entered under Scandinavians. Works on the inhabitants of Scandinavia prior to the 10th century are entered under Northmen.

see also Northmen

Binns, Tristan Boyer. On to Valhalla! Viking Beliefs. 2007. (J). (***978-1-4109-2893-1(4)***); pap. (***978-1-4109-2900-6(0)***) Steck-Vaughn.

Binns, Tristan Boyer. The Vikings. 2005. (Ancient Civilizations Ser.). (Illus.). 32p. (J). (gr. 4-6). 26.60 (978-0-7565-1678-9(1)) Compass Point Bks.

Burgan, Michael. Leif Eriksson. 2002. (Groundbreakers Ser.). (Illus.). 48p. (J). (gr. 5-7). lib. bdg. 27.07 (978-1-58810-596-7(2)) Heinemann Library.

Cando, Rich. Viking Dudes. Cando, Rich, illus. 2007. 64p. (J). (gr. 5-8). 12.99 (978-0-7566-2940-3(3)) Dorling Kindersley Publishing, Inc.

Charman, Andrew. The Viking World. 2007. (Life & Times In Ser.). (Illus.). 32p. (J). pap. 9.95 (***978-0-7534-6152-5(8)*** , Kingfisher) Houghton Mifflin Co. Trade & Reference Div.

Chrisp, Peter. Les Vikings. 2000. (Come & Discover My World Ser.). (Illus.). 32p. (J). (gr. 2-5). pap. 7.95 (978-1-58728-197-6(X) , Two Can Publishing) T&N Children's Publishing.

—The Vikings. 2003. (Strange Histories Ser.). (Illus.). 32p. (J). lib. bdg. 25.70 (978-0-7398-6443-2(2)) Raintree.

—Vikings: Come & Discover My World. 2002. (gr. 3-6). lib. bdg. 16.40 (978-0-613-43393-8(9)) Tandem Library Bks.

Civardi, Anne. Viking Raiders. 1998. (gr. 3-6). lib. bdg. 15.25 (978-0-613-74403-4(9)) Tandem Library Bks.

Cox, P. Roxbee. Who Were the Vikings? rev. ed. (Starting Point History Ser.). 32p. (J). (gr. 1 up). 4.95 (978-0-7945-0177-8(X)) EDC Publishing.

Cox, Phil Roxbee. Who Were the Vikings? rev. ed. 2004. (Starting Point History Ser.). (Illus.). 32p. (J). (gr. 1 up). lib. bdg. 12.95 (978-1-58086-397-1(3)) EDC Publishing.

Deary, Terry. Vicious Vikings. 1998. (Horrible Histories Ser.). (J). (gr. 7-12). pap. 4.50 (978-0-590-49849-4(5)) Scholastic, Inc.

Deem, James M. The Vikings: A MyReportLinks. com Book. 2004. (Civilizations of the Ancient World Ser.). (Illus.). 48p. (J). lib. bdg. 25.26 (978-0-7660-5198-0(6) , MyReportLinks.com Bks.) Enslow Pubs., Inc.

DK Publishing Staff. Viking. 2007. (Eye Wonder Ser.). 48p. (J). (gr. 1-3). 9.99 (978-0-7566-2906-9(3)); lib. bdg. 17.99 (978-0-7566-2907-6(1)) Dorling Kindersley Publishing, Inc.

Fowke, B. What They Don't Tell You about the Vikings. (Illus.). 128p. (J). pap. (978-0-340-68611-9(1) , Hodder & Stoughton) Hodder General Publishing Division.

Gallagher, Jim. Viking Explorers. 2000. (Explorers of the New World Ser.). (Illus.). (J). 63p. (gr. 4-7). pap. 8.95 (978-0-7910-6165-7(5)); 64p. (gr. 8-12). 25.00 (978-0-7910-5955-5(3)) Facts On File, Inc. (Chelsea Hse.).

Ganeri, Anita. Raiders & Traders. Studio Boni-Lalli-Critone-Pieri Staff et al, illus. 2001. (All in a Day's Work Ser.). 32p. (J). (gr. 3-9). 16.95 (978-0-87226-665-0(6) , Bedrick, Peter Bks.) School Specialty Publishing.

Gassos, Dolores. Vikings. 2005. (Ancient Civilizations Ser.). (Illus.). 32p. (J). (gr. 4-8). lib. bdg. 28.00 (978-0-7910-8490-8(6) , Chelsea Clubhouse) Facts On File, Inc.

Glaser, Jason. Leif Eriksson. 2004. (Fact Finders Ser.). (Illus.). 32p. (J). lib. bdg. 22.60 (978-0-7368-2664-8(5)) Capstone Pr., Inc.

Glencoe McGraw-Hill Staff & McGraw-Hill - Jamestown Education Staff. Jamestown's Early Civilizations: Viking Life. 2001. (gr. 5-12). pap. 11.96 (978-0-8092-9501-2(6) , 9780809295012) Jamestown.

Grant, Neil. Everyday Life of the Vikings. 2005. (Uncovering History Ser.). (Illus.). 46p. (J). (gr. 6-9). lib. bdg. 29.95 (978-1-58340-706-6(5)) Smart Apple Media.

Gravett, Christopher. Going to War in Viking Times. Bergin, Mark, illus. 2001. (Armies of the Past Ser.). 32p. (J). (gr. 3-6). pap. 6.95 (978-0-531-16353-5(9) , Watts, Franklin) Scholastic Library Publishing.

Green, Jen, et al. In the Daily Life of the Vikings. 2002. (Gods & Goddesses Ser.). (Illus.). 48p. (J). (gr. 4 up). 18.95 (978-0-87226-594-3(3) , Bedrick, Peter Bks.) School Specialty Publishing.

Hatt, Christine. The Viking World. 2004. (Excavating the Past Ser.). (J). pap. 8.50 (978-1-4034-5461-4(2)); lib. bdg. (978-1-4034-4841-5(8)) Heinemann Library.

Hewitt, Sally. The Vikings. 2007. (J). (***978-1-59920-047-7(3)***) Smart Apple Media.

Hopkins, Andrea. Viking Explorers & Settlers. 2002. (Viking Library). (Illus.). 24p. (J). (gr. 3). lib. bdg. 19.95 (978-0-8239-5816-0(7) , PowerKids Pr.) Rosen Publishing Group, Inc., The.

—Viking Families & Farms. 2002. (Viking Library). (Illus.). 24p. (J). (gr. 3). lib. bdg. 19.95 (978-0-8239-5815-3(9) , PowerKids Pr.) Rosen Publishing Group, Inc., The.

—The Viking Library, 6 bks. Incl. Viking Explorers & Settlers. 2002. lib. bdg. 19.95 (978-0-8239-5816-0(7)); Viking Families & Farms. 2002. lib. bdg. 19.95 (978-0-8239-5815-3(9)); Viking Gods & Legends. 2002. lib. bdg. 19.95 (978-0-8239-5814-6(0)); Viking Longships. 2002. lib. bdg. 19.95 (978-0-8239-5812-2(4)); Vikings : The Norse Discovery of America. 2011. lib. bdg. 19.50 (978-0-8239-5817-7(5)); Vikings Raiders & Traders. 2002. lib. bdg. 19.95 (978-0-8239-5813-9(2)); 24p. (J). (gr. 3). (Illus.). 2001. Set lib. bdg. 117.00 (978-0-8239-7132-9(5) , PowerKids Pr.) Rosen Publishing Group, Inc., The.

—Viking Longships. 2002. (Viking Library). (Illus.). 24p. (J). (gr. 3). lib. bdg. 19.95 (978-0-8239-5812-2(4) , PowerKids Pr.) Rosen Publishing Group, Inc., The.

—Vikings: The Norse Discovery of America. 2011. (Viking Library). (Illus.). 24p. (J). (gr. 3). lib. bdg. 19.50 (978-0-8239-5817-7(5) , PowerKids Pr.) Rosen Publishing Group, Inc., The.

—Vikings Raiders & Traders. 2002. (Viking Library). (Illus.). 24p. (J). (gr. 3). lib. bdg. 19.95 (978-0-8239-5813-9(2) , PowerKids Pr.) Rosen Publishing Group, Inc., The.

Jovinelly, Joann & Netelkos, Jason. The Crafts & Culture of the Vikings. 2002. (Crafts of the Ancient World Ser.). (Illus.). 48p. (YA). (gr. 5-8). lib. bdg. 29.25 (978-0-8239-3514-7(0) , Rosen Central) Rosen Publishing Group, Inc., The.

Kimmel, Elizabeth Cody. Before Columbus: The Leif Eriksson Expedition: A True Adventure. 2003. (Landmark Books Ser.). (Illus.). 112p. (J). (gr. 4). lib. bdg. 16.99 (978-0-375-91347-1(5) , Random Hse. Bks. for Young Readers) Random Hse. Children's Bks.

Knudsen, Shannon. Leif Eriksson. Oldroyd, Mark, illus. 2005. (On My Own Biography Ser.). 48p. (J). (gr. 3-7). pap. 5.95 (978-1-57505-828-3(6)); (ps-7). 25.26 (978-1-57505-649-4(6) , Carolrhoda Bks.) Lerner Publishing Group.

Landau, Elaine. Exploring the World of the Vikings. 2005. (Exploring Ancient Civilizations with Elaine Landau Ser.). (Illus.). 48p. (J). (ps-7). lib. bdg. 23.93 (978-0-7660-2340-6(0) , Enslow Elementary) Enslow Pubs., Inc.

Langley, Andrew. You Wouldn't Want to Be a Viking Explorer. 2000. (gr. 3-6). lib. bdg. 18.75 (978-0-613-44434-7(5)) Tandem Library Bks.

—You Wouldn't Want to Be a Viking Explorer! Voyages You'd Rather Not Make. Antram, David, illus. 2001. (You Wouldn't Want to Ser.). 32p. (J). (gr. 2-5). pap. 9.95 (978-0-531-16205-7(2) , Watts, Franklin) Scholastic Library Publishing.

Langley, Andrew & Antram, David. You Wouldn't Want to Be a Viking Explorer! Voyages You'd Rather Not Make. Salariya, David, illus. 2001. (You Wouldn't Want to Ser.). 32p. (J). (gr. 2-5). 28.50 (978-0-531-14599-9(9) , Watts, Franklin) Scholastic Library Publishing.

Lassieur, Allison. Lords of the Sea: The Vikings Explore the North Atlantic. Barnett, Charles, III & Frenz, Ron, illus. 2005. (Graphic Library). 32p. (J). (gr. 3-7). lib. bdg. 25.26 (978-0-7368-4974-6(2)) Capstone Pr., Inc.

Lassieur, Allison. The Vikings. 2007. (Illus.). 32p. (J). ***978-0-7368-6434-3(2))*** Capstone Pr., Inc.

—The Vikings. 2001. (Lost Civilizations Ser.). (Illus.). 112p. (J). (gr. 6-9). 29.95 (978-1-56006-816-7(7) , LML00902-178148, Lucent Bks.) Thomson Gale.

MacDonald, Fiona. Vikings. 2005. (First Look at History Ser.). (Illus.). 24p. (J). 22.00 (978-0-8368-4530-3(7)) Stevens, Gareth Inc.

MacDonald, Fiona. The Vikings. 2007. (J). lib. bdg. 19.95 ***(978-1-59566-354-2(1))*** QEB Publishing Inc.

Malam, John. Exploring the Vikings. 2000. (Illus.). 47p. (J). (978-0-237-52002-1(8) , Evans Brothers, Limited) Evans Publishing Group.

Manning, Mick & Granstrom, Brita. Viking Longship. 2006. (Fly on the Wall Ser.). (Illus.). 40p. (J). (gr. k-4). 15.95 (978-1-84507-465-4(3)) Lincoln, Frances Ltd. GBR. *Dist:* Perseus Distribution.

Margeson, Susan M. & Dorling Kindersley Publishing Staff. Viking. 2005. (Eyewitness Bks.). (Illus.). 72p. (J). (ps-7). 15.99 (978-0-7566-1095-1(8) , 1241928) Dorling Kindersley Publishing, Inc.

—Viking. Anderson, Peter, illus. Anderson, Peter, photos by. 2005. (Eyewitness Books). 72p. (J). lib. bdg. 19.99 (978-0-7566-1096-8(6) , 1241928) Dorling Kindersley Publishing, Inc.

Martell, Hazel Mary. Everyday Life in Viking Times. 2005. (Clues to the Past Ser.). (Illus.). 32p. (J). (gr. 4-7). lib. bdg. 27.10 (978-1-932889-80-2(9)) Sea-To-Sea Pubns.

—Vikings. Stalio, Ivan & D'Ottavi, Francesca, illus. 2001. (Myths & Civilization Ser.). 48p. (J). (gr. 3 up). 16.95 (978-0-87226-285-0(5) , 62855B, Bedrick, Peter Bks.) School Specialty Publishing.

Mattern, Joanne. Leif Eriksson: Viking Explorer. 2004. (Explorers! Ser.). (Illus.). 48p. (J). lib. bdg. 23.93 (978-0-7660-2146-4(7)) Enslow Pubs., Inc.

McNeil, Niki, et al. HOCPP 1082 Vikings. 2006. spiral bd. 24.00 ***(978-1-60308-082-8(1))*** In the Hands of a Child.

McRae, Anne & Agosta, Loredana. Who Were the Vikings. 2007. (J). ***(978-88-6098-051-9(8))*** McRae Bks. Srl.

Morley, Jacqueline. Viking Town. 2000. (Metropolis Ser.). (Illus.). 48p. (J). (gr. 5-7). pap. 8.95 (978-0-531-15380-2(0) , Watts, Franklin) Scholastic Library Publishing.

Mulvihill, Margaret. Viking Longboats. Smith, Tony, illus. 2006. (Hallmarks of History Ser.). 32p. (J). (gr. 4-6). lib. bdg. 27.10 (978-1-59604-120-2(X)) Stargazer Bks.

Murphy, Brian. Vikings. 2004. (Interfact Ser.). (SPA., Illus.). 48p. (J). (gr. 3-6). pap. 14.95 incl. cd-rom (978-1-58728-467-0(7) , Two Can Publishing) T&N Children's Publishing.

Nardo, Don. The Vikings. 2005. (Life During the Great Civilizations Ser.). (Illus.). 48p. (J). (gr. k-7). lib. bdg. 24.95 (978-1-4103-0584-8(8) , Blackbirch Pr., Inc.) Thomson Gale.

Nicholson, Sue & Ferris, Julie. Viking World: A Guide to 11th Century Scandinavia. 2000. (Sightseers Ser.). (Illus.). 38p. (J). (gr. 3-5). tchr. ed. 8.95 (978-0-7534-5237-0(5) , Kingfisher) Houghton Mifflin Co. Trade & Reference Div.

Rees, Rosemary. The Vikings. 2002. (Understanding People in the Past Ser.). (Illus.). 64p. (J). lib. bdg. 28.50 (978-1-58810-422-9(2)); (gr. 4-6). pap. 8.95 (978-1-4034-0100-7(4) , 91675) Heinemann Library.

Richardson, Hazel. Life of the Ancient Vikings. 2005. (Peoples of the Ancient World Ser.). (Illus.). 32p. (J). (ps-9). (978-0-7787-2044-7(6)); pap. (978-0-7787-2074-4(8)) Crabtree Publishing Co.

Schaffer, David. Viking Conquest. 2002. (World History Ser.). (Illus.). 112p. (YA). (gr. 8-11). lib. bdg. 32.45 (978-1-56006-322-3(X) , LML00902-177714, Lucent Bks.) Thomson Gale.

Schofield, Tracey Ann. Vikings. Mitchell, Judy, ed. Mohrman, Gary, illus. 2002. (Exploring Ancient Civilizations Ser.). 48p. (J). (gr. 3-6). pap. 7.95 (978-1-57310-356-5(X)) Teaching & Learning Co.

Schomp, Virginia. The Vikings. 2005. (People of the Ancient World Ser.). (Illus.). 112p. (J). (gr. 6-8). pap. 9.95 (978-0-531-16849-3(2)); 30.50 (978-0-531-12382-9(0)) Scholastic Library Publishing. (Watts, Franklin).

Shuter, Jane. Life in a Viking Town. 2005. (Picture the Past Ser.). (Illus.). 32p. (J). 25.64 (978-1-4034-6440-8(5)); pap. (978-1-4034-6447-7(2)) Heinemann Library.

—Life on a Viking Ship. 2005. (Picture the Past Ser.). (Illus.). 32p. (J). 25.64 (978-1-4034-6441-5(3)); pap. (978-1-4034-6448-4(0)) Heinemann Library.

—The Vikings. 2003. (History Opens Windows Ser.). (Illus.). 32p. (J). (gr. 2-4). lib. bdg. 22.79 (978-1-4034-0254-7(X)); pap. 7.50 (978-1-4034-0082-6(2)) Heinemann Library.

Smithee, Allan. The Vikings. rev. ed. 2004. (Come & Discover My World Ser.). (Illus.). 32p. (J). (gr. 2-5). 14.95 (978-1-58728-065-8(5)); pap. 7.95 (978-1-58728-071-9(X)) T&N Children's Publishing. (Two Can Publishing).

Steele. Find Out about Vikings. 2000. (Find Out about-...Ser.). (Illus.). 64p. (gr. 3-7). pap. 7.95 (978-1-84215-291-1(2) , Southwater) Anness Publishing GBR. *Dist:* National Bk. Network.

Steele, Phillip. Step Into: The Viking World. 2006. (Illus.). 64p. pap. 12.99 (978-1-84476-306-1(4) , Southwater) Anness Publishing GBR. *Dist:* National Bk. Network.

Weintraub, Aileen. Vikings: Raiders & Explorers. 2005. (Way of the Warrior Ser.). (Illus.). 48p. 24.00 (978-0-516-25118-6(X)); (YA). (gr. 7-12). pap. 6.95 (978-0-516-25087-8(6)) Scholastic Library Publishing. (Children's Pr.).

Williams, Colleen Madonna Flood. My Adventure with Vikings. 2007. 44p. (J). 8.99 (978-1-59092-474-7(6) , Orchard Academy Pr.) Windstorm Creative.

Wingate, P. & Millard, A. Viking World. 2004. (Illustrated World History Ser.). 64p. (J). lib. bdg. 19.95 (978-1-58086-628-6(X) , Usborne); (Illus.). pap. 11.95 (978-0-7945-0354-3(3)) EDC Publishing.

Wright, Rachel. The Viking News. 2001. (History News Ser.). (Illus.). 32p. (J). (gr. 4-9). pap. 6.99 (978-0-7636-1292-4(8)) Candlewick Pr.

—The Viking News. 2001. (History News Ser.). (Illus.). 32p. (J). (gr. 3 up). lib. bdg. 24.67 (978-0-8368-2779-8(1)) Stevens, Gareth Inc.

—The Viking News. 2001. (Illus.). (J). (ps-7). 32p. lib. bdg. 15.30 (978-0-613-43904-6(X)); (978-0-606-21503-9(4)) Tandem Library Bks.

VIKINGS—FICTION

Bailey, Linda. Adventures with the Vikings. Slavin, Bill et al, illus. 2004. (Good Times Travel Agency Ser.). 48p. (J). (gr. 4-6). (978-1-55074-544-3(1)) Kids Can Pr., Ltd.

—Adventures with the Vikings, No. 3. Slavin, Bill et al, illus. 2004. (Good Times Travel Agency Ser.). 48p. (J). (gr. 4-6). (978-1-55074-542-9(5)) Kids Can Pr., Ltd.

—Adventures with the Vikings. 2003. (gr. 3-6). lib. bdg. 16.40 (978-0-613-70944-6(6)) Tandem Library Bks.

Boyd, David. Beware the Vikings. Rooth, Mike, illus. 2007. 48p. (J). lib. bdg. 23.08 ***(978-1-4242-1624-6(9))*** Fitzgerald Bks.

Cadnum, Michael. Daughter of the Wind. 2003. 272p. (J). pap. 17.95 (978-0-439-35224-6(X) , Orchard Bks.) Scholastic, Inc.

—Raven of the Waves. 2004. 208p. (J). (gr. 7 up). pap. 5.99 (978-0-439-62661-3(7)); 2001. 224p. (YA). (gr. 9 up). pap. 17.95 (978-0-531-30334-4(9) , Orchard Bks.) Scholastic, Inc.

Ciddor, Anna. Runestone. 2007. (Viking Magic Ser.). (Illus.). 192p. (Orig.). (J). (gr. 4-7). pap. 7.95 ***(978-1-86508-689-7(4))*** Allen & Unwin AUS. *Dist:* Independent Pubs. Group.

—Stormriders. 2007. (Viking Magic Ser.). (Illus.). 192p. (J). (gr. 4-7). pap. 7.95 ***(978-1-74114-360-7(8))*** Allen & Unwin AUS. *Dist:* Independent Pubs. Group.

—Wolfspell. 2007. (Viking Magic Ser.). (Illus.). 192p. (J). (gr. 4-7). pap. 7.95 ***(978-1-74114-013-2(7))*** Allen & Unwin AUS. *Dist:* Independent Pubs. Group.

Cowell, Cressida. Heroic Misadventures of Hiccup the Viking, the: the First Collection Boxed Set. 2007. (gr. 3-7). 28.99 ***(978-0-316-00592-0(4))*** Little, Brown Bks. for Young Readers.

—How to Be a Pirate. 2005. (Illus.). 224p. (J). (gr. 3-7). 10.99 (978-0-316-15598-4(5)) Little Brown & Co.

—How to Cheat a Dragon's Curse. 2007. (Heroic Misadventures of Hiccup the Viking Ser.). 256p. (J). (gr. 3-7). 10.99 ***(978-0-316-11425-7(1))*** Little, Brown Bks. for Young Readers.

—How to Speak Dragonese. 2006. (Illus.). 240p. (J). (gr. 3-7). 10.99 (978-0-316-15600-4(0)) Little Brown & Co.

—How to Train Your Dragon. 2004. (Illus.). 224p. (J). (gr. 3-7). 10.99 (978-0-316-73737-1(2)) Little Brown & Co.

Cross, Gillian. Down with the Dirty Danes. (Illus.). 61p. (J). pap. 7.99 (978-0-00-675534-0(8) , HarperSport) HarperCollins Pubs. Ltd. GBR. *Dist:* Trafalgar Square Publishing.

Davis, Mike. Land of the Lost Mammoths: A Science Adventure. 2003. (Illus.). 174p. (J). 15.95 (978-0-9747078-0-8(5)) Perceval Pr.

Dinsdale, Christopher. Stolen Away. 2006. (Illus.). 229p. (YA). pap. 8.95 (978-1-894917-20-9(0)) Napoleon Publishing/Rendezvous Pr. CAN. *Dist:* AtlasBooks Distribution.

Farmer, Nancy. The Sea of Trolls. 480p. (J). (gr. 5-8). 2004. (Illus.). 17.95 (978-0-689-86744-6(1) , Atheneum); 2006. reprint ed. pap. 9.99 (978-0-689-86746-0(8) , Simon Pulse) Simon & Schuster Children's Publishing.

—The Sea of Trolls. l.t. ed. 2005. 554p. 23.95 (978-0-7862-7151-1(5)) Thorndike Pr.

French, Allen. The Story of Rolf: A Viking Adventure. 2005. 160p. (ps-7). pap. 8.95 (978-0-486-44133-7(4)) Dover Pubns., Inc.

Goscinny, René & Uderzo, Albert. Asterix & the Vikings. 2007. (Illus.). 72p. per. 9.95 ***(978-0-7528-8876-7(5))*** Orion Bks. Ltd. GBR. *Dist:* Sterling Publishing Co., Inc.

Hamel, Mike. Rylan the Renegade: Matterhorn, the Brave Series, 6. 2007. 192p. (J). pap. 12.99 ***(978-0-89957-838-5(1))*** AMG Pubs.

Hamme. Thorgal Child of the Stars. Rosinski, Grzegorz, illus. 2007. 96p. pap. 14.99 ***(978-1-905460-23-6(6))*** CineBook GBR. *Dist:* Biblio Distribution.

Harrison, Cora. The Viking at Drumshee. 2001. 128p. (J). pap. 7.95 (978-0-86327-788-7(8)) Interlink Publishing Group, Inc.

Hauger, Torill Thorstad. Escape from the Vikings. Hamnes, Lisa, ed. Born, Anne, tr. from NOR. Hauger, Torill Thorstad, illus. 2000. Orig. Title: Flukten Fra Vikingene. (Illus.). 175p. (J). (gr. 4-12). pap. (978-1-57534-013-5(5)) Skandisk, Inc.

Henighan, Tom. Viking Quest. 2005. 120p. (YA). pap., tchr. ed. (978-0-88878-421-6(X) , Sandcastle Bks.) Dundurn Group, The.

Henighan, Tom. Viking Terror. 2006. 180p. pap. 12.99 ***(978-1-55002-605-4(4)*** , Boardwalk Bks.) Dundurn Group, The CAN. *Dist:* Univ. of Toronto Pr.

Jacobsen, Annie. Ivar, the Short, but Brave Viking. Hanson, Susan Jo, illus. 2007. (J). lib. bdg. 16.95 ***(978-0-9778276-1-9(5))*** Pickled Herring Pr.

Johnson, Lois Walfrid. Raider's Promise. 2006. (Raiders from the Sea Ser.). (Illus.). 304p. (J). pap. 8.99 (978-0-8024-3116-5(X)) Moody Pubs.

Johnson, Vargie. Eric the Red the Fearless: What Made Them Famous? 2006. (J). per. 15.00 (978-1-931195-94-2(3)) KiwE Publishing, Ltd.

Langrish, Katherine. Troll Blood. Stevens, Tim, illus. 2008. 352p. (J). 16.99 ***(978-0-06-111674-2(2))***; lib. bdg. 17.89 ***(978-0-06-111675-9(0))*** HarperCollins Pubs. (Eos).

—Troll Fell. (J). 2005. 368p. (gr. 7 up). pap. 6.99 (978-0-06-058306-4(1)); 2004. (Illus.). 272p. (gr. 5 up). 16.99 (978-0-06-058304-0(5)); 2004. (Illus.). 272p. (gr. 5 up). lib. bdg. 16.89 (978-0-06-058305-7(3)) HarperCollins Pubs.

Langrish, Katherine. Troll Mill. 2008. 384p. (J). 7.99 ***(978-0-06-058309-5(6)*** , Eos) HarperCollins Pubs.

Osborne, Mary Pope. Viking Ships at Sunrise, Vol. 15. unabr. ed. 2004. (Magic Tree House Ser. : No. 15). 71p. (J). (gr. k-3). pap. 17.00 incl. audio (978-0-8072-0784-0(5) , LFTR 243 SP, Listening Library) Random Hse. Audio Publishing Group.

—Viking Ships at Sunrise. Murdocca, Sal, illus. 1998. (Magic Tree House Ser.: No. 15). 96p. (J). (gr. k-3). lib. bdg. 11.99 (978-0-679-99061-1(5)); mass mkt. 3.99 (978-0-679-89061-4(0)) Random Hse. Children's Bks. (Random Hse. Bks. for Young Readers).

—Viking Ships at Sunrise. Murdocca, Salvatore, illus. 1998. (Magic Tree House Ser. : No. 15). 71p. (J). lib. bdg. 10.79 (978-0-606-15755-1(7)) Tandem Library Bks.

Schachner, Judith B. Yo, Vikings! Schachner, Judith B., illus. 2002. (Illus.). 32p. (J). (gr. k-4). 16.99 (978-0-525-46889-9(7) , Dutton Juvenile) Penguin Group (USA) Inc.

Scieszka, Jon. Viking It & Liking It. McCauley, Adam, illus. (Time Warp Trio Ser.: No. 12). (J). 2002. 80p. 14.99 (978-0-670-89918-0(6) , Viking Juvenile); Vol. 12. 2004. 96p. (gr. 2 up). pap. 4.99 (978-0-14-240002-9(5) , Puffin) Penguin Group (USA) Inc.

Severin, Tim. King's Man: The Heroes of the North Live On. 3rd ed. 2005. (Viking Trilogy Ser.: Bk. 3). 319p. pap. 19.95 (978-1-4050-4117-1(X)) Macmillan Publishers Ltd. GBR. *Dist:* Independent Pubs. Group.

Strong, Jeremy. Viking at School. Levers, John, illus. l.t. ed. 2000. 96p. (J). pap. (978-0-7540-6093-2(4) , CLP 291) BBC Audio.

—Viking at School. Levers, John, illus. unabr. l.t. ed. 2003. (Read-Along Ser.). 104p. (J). pap. 24.95 incl. audio (978-0-7540-6230-1(9) , RA031, Galaxy Children's Large Print) BBC Audiobooks America.

Sutcliff, Rosemary. Sword Song. 2005. (Illus.). 288p. (J). pap. 6.95 (978-0-374-46984-9(9) , Farrar, Straus & Giroux (BYR)) Farrar, Straus & Giroux.

Tebbetts, Christopher. Viking Saga Three: Land of the Dead. 2003. (gr. 5-8). lib. bdg. 14.15 (978-0-613-67588-8(6)) Tandem Library Bks.

—Viking Saga Two: The Quest for Faith. 2003. (gr. 5-8). lib. bdg. 14.15 (978-0-613-67476-8(6)) Tandem Library Bks.

Tingle, Rebecca. The Edge on the Sword. 2003. (Sailing Mystery Ser.). 288p. (YA). (gr. 8-12). pap. 6.99 (978-0-14-250058-3(5) , Puffin) Penguin Group (USA) Inc.

Uderzo, Albert & Goscinny, René. Asterix & the Vikings. 2007. (Illus.). 64p. 12.95 (978-0-7528-8590-2(1)) Orion Bks. Ltd. GBR. *Dist:* Sterling Publishing Co., Inc.

Voigt, Cynthia. Elske: A Novel of the Kingdom. 2003. (Kingdom Ser.). (gr. 7-12). lib. bdg. 14.15 (978-0-613-73442-4(4)) Tandem Library Bks.

Wishinsky, Frieda. Yikes! Vikings! Griffiths, Dean, illus. 2007. (Canadian Flyer Adventures Ser.: No. 4). 96p. (gr. 1-4). (J). pap. 6.95 ***(978-1-897066-97-3(X))***; 16.95 ***(978-1-897066-96-6(1))*** Maple Tree Pr. CAN. *Dist:* Perseus Distribution.

VILLA, PANCHO, 1878-1923

Englar, Mary. Pancho Villa, Rebel of the Mexican Revolution. 2006. (Fact Finders Ser.). (Illus.). 32p. (J). (978-0-7368-5441-2(X)) Capstone Pr., Inc.

Marcovitz, Hal. Pancho Villa. 2003. (Great Hispanic Heritage Ser.). (Illus.). 112p. (gr. 6-12). 30.00 (978-0-7910-7257-8(6) , Chelsea Hse.) Facts On File, Inc.

Schumacher, Tyler. Junípero Serra: Explorer & Missionary. 2006. (Fact Finders Ser.). (Illus.). 32p. (J). (978-0-7368-5440-5(1)) Capstone Pr., Inc.

Stein, R. Conrad. Pancho Villa: Mexican Revolutionary Hero. 2004. (Proud Heritage: the Hispanic Library Ser.). 40p. (J). (gr. 3-7). 28.50 (978-1-59296-171-9(1)) Child's World, Inc.

VILLAGES

Anderson, Mercedes Padrino. Feudalism & Village Life in the Middle Ages. 2005. (World Almanac Library of the Middle Ages). (Illus.). 48p. (J). pap. (978-0-8368-5903-4(0) , World Almanac Library) Stevens, Gareth Inc.

Barber, Nicola. Village Home. 2007. 32p. (gr. 7-10). pap. ***(978-0-7787-3558-8(3))*** Crabtree Publishing Co.

Bial, Raymond. Early American Villages. 2004. (American Community Ser.). (Illus.). 48p. (J). 29.00 (978-0-516-23704-6(7) , Children's Pr.) Scholastic Library Publishing.

Campos, Maria de Fatima. A Child's Day in a Brazilian Village. 2001. (Child's Day Ser.). (Illus.). 32p. (J). (gr. k-2). lib. bdg. 25.64 (978-0-7614-1221-2(2) , Benchmark Bks.) Cavendish, Marshall Corp.

A Child's Day - Group 1, 5 bks., Set. Incl. Child's Day in a Brazilian Village. Campos, Maria de Fatima. lib. bdg. 25.64 (978-0-7614-1221-2(2)); Child's Day in a Chinese City. So, Sungwan. lib. bdg. 25.64 (978-0-7614-1224-3(7)); Child's Day in a Ghanaian City. Provencal, Francis & McNamara, Catherine. lib. bdg. 25.64 (978-0-7614-1223-6(9)); Child's Day in a Russian City. Ilyin, Andrey. lib. bdg. 25.64 (978-0-7614-1222-9(0)); Child's Day in an Indian Village. Das, Prodeepta. lib. bdg. 25.64 (978-0-7614-1220-5(4)); 32p. (J). (gr. k-2). (Illus.). 2001. 128.21 (978-0-7614-1219-9(0) , Benchmark Bks.) Cavendish, Marshall Corp.

Chrisp, Peter. Town & Country Life. 2004. (J). (gr. 7-10). 29.95 (978-1-59018-536-0(6) , Lucent Bks.) Thomson Gale.

Das, Prodeepta. A Child's Day in an Indian Village. 2001. (Child's Day Ser.). (Illus.). 32p. (J). (gr. k-2). lib. bdg. 25.64 (978-0-7614-1220-5(4) , Benchmark Bks.) Cavendish, Marshall Corp.

Gillis, Jennifer Blizin. Restored Villages. 2008. (J). ***(978-1-60044-563-7(2))*** Rourke Publishing, LLC.

Huebsch, Dave. Village Assignment: True Stories of Humor, Adventure, & Drama in Guatemala's Highland Villages. 2004. (Illus.). 268p. per. 16.95 (978-0-9741734-0-5(1)) Highlight Publishing.

Ilyin, Andrey. A Child's Day in a Russian City. 2001. (Child's Day Ser.). (Illus.). 32p. (J). (gr. k-2). lib. bdg. 25.64 (978-0-7614-1222-9(0) , Benchmark Bks.) Cavendish, Marshall Corp.

Padrino, Mercedes. Feudalism & Village Life in the Middle Ages. 2006. (World Almanac' Library of the Middle Ages). (Illus.). 48p. (YA). (gr. 7-10). lib. bdg. 30.00 (978-0-8368-5894-5(8) , World Almanac Library) Stevens, Gareth Inc.

Popper, Garry & Volke, Gordon. Big World Activity Sticker Book. Johnson, Andi, illus. 2004. 16p. 6.00 (978-1-84161-082-5(8)) Ravette Publishing, Ltd. GBR. *Dist:* Parkwest Pubns., Inc.

Provencal, Francis & McNamara, Catherine. A Child's Day in a Ghanaian City. 2001. (Child's Day Ser.). (Illus.). 32p. (J). (gr. k-2). lib. bdg. 25.64 (978-0-7614-1223-6(9) , Benchmark Bks.) Cavendish, Marshall Corp.

So, Sungwan. A Child's Day in a Chinese City. 2001. (Child's Day Ser.). (Illus.). 32p. (J). (gr. k-2). lib. bdg. 25.64 (978-0-7614-1224-3(7) , Benchmark Bks.) Cavendish, Marshall Corp.

VILLAGES—FICTION

Ackerman, Karen. Bean's Big Day. Mombourquette, Paul, tr. Mombourquette, Paul, illus. 2004. 32p. (J). (gr. k-3). (978-1-55337-444-2(4)) Kids Can Pr., Ltd.

Adams, H. J. The Song of the Blackbirds in the Reeds: In Which Great-Grandpa Nicholas Winslow Applewood Entertains Young Folk with Stories & Fables & Has Some Remarkable Betimes. Adams, Denise, illus. 1998. 168p. (J). lib. bdg. 20.00 (978-0-923687-48-9(3)) Celo Valley Bks.

Alfaro Sifontes, Manuel Guillermo. Alboroto en un Lugar Remoto. 2005. (Illus.). 32p. (J). (978-1-58018-052-8(3)) Versal Editorial Group.

Alger, Horatio. Fancy of Hers. 2006. pap. ***(978-1-4250-3505-1(1))***; pap. ***(978-1-4250-3545-7(0))***; pap. ***(978-1-4250-3583-9(3))*** Assistedreadingbooks.com Inc.

Baker, Barrie. The Village of a Hundred Smiles. Jorisch, Stephane, illus. 1998. 48p. (J). (gr. k-3). lib. bdg. 18.95 (978-1-55037-522-0(9)) Firefly Bks., Ltd.

Balian, Lorna. A Sweetheart for Valentine. Balian, Lorna, illus. 2005. (Illus.). 40p. (J). 15.95 (978-1-932065-14-5(8)) Star Bright Bks., Inc.

Bloom, Janice Stitziel. A Grateful Heart under My Bed. Woodcock, Marcy, illus. 2007. 36p. (J). per. 15.99 ***(978-1-934643-06-8(8))*** Villager Bk. Publishing.

—Wonderfully Made under My Bed. Woodcock, Marcy, illus. 2007. 36p. (J). per. 15.99 ***(978-1-934643-00-6(9))*** Villager Bk. Publishing.

Bynum, Eboni & Jackson, Roland. Jamari's Drum. Wagué Diakité, Baba, illus. 2004. 32p. (J). 16.95 (978-0-88899-531-5(8)) Groundwood Bks. CAN. *Dist:* Perseus Distribution.

Chandraratna, Bandula. Mirage. 2004. 224p. 24.95 (978-1-57423-196-0(0)) Godine, David R. Pub.

Coombs, Kate. The Secret-Keeper. Solomon, Heather M., illus. 2006. 32p. (J). (ps-3). 16.95 (978-0-689-83963-4(4) , Atheneum) Simon & Schuster Children's Publishing.

Cox, Judith. Daddy Bo Brown's Mysterious Village, Plus. 2005. 18.00 (978-0-8059-9869-6(1)) Dorrance Publishing Co., Inc.

Crabtree, Zona Mae. White Dove. 2005. (Corn Cave Ser.: 3). (Illus.). (YA). per. 8.00 (978-0-9726826-2-6(7)) Owl Hollow Publishing.

Crilley, Mark. Rogmasher Rampage. 2007. (Billy Clikk Ser.). 224p. (J). (gr. 4-7). 5.99 (978-0-440-41955-6(7) , Yearling) Random Hse. Children's Bks.

Deshpande, Shashi. 3 Novels. 2006. 379p. ***(978-0-14-333511-5(1)*** , Puffin) Penguin Group (USA) Inc.

Dorros, Arthur & Dorros, Alex. Numero Uno. Guevara, Susan, illus. 2007. 32p. (J). (ps-3). 16.95 ***(978-0-8109-5764-0(7))*** Abrams, Harry N. , Inc.

Foreman, Michael. Mia's Story: A Sketchbook of Hopes & Dreams. Foreman, Michael, illus. 2006. (Illus.). 32p. (J). (gr. k-3). 15.99 (978-0-7636-3063-8(2)) Candlewick Pr.

From the Hillside: Individual Chapter Book Title Six-Packs. Vol. 30. 32p. (gr. 5 up). 44.00 (978-0-7578-0980-4(4)) Rigby Education.

Gallagher, Mike. Sonic the Hedgehog Archives, Vol. 1. 2006. 112p. pap. 7.49 (978-1-879794-20-7(9)) Archie Comic Pubns., Inc.

Gallagher, Mike & DeCesare, Angelo. Sonic the Hedgehog Archives, Vol. 2. 2006. 112p. pap. 7.49 (978-1-879794-21-4(7)) Archie Comic Pubns., Inc.

Hiss, Jill. Peppeto's Magic Jelly Bean. 2005. 19.00 (978-0-8059-9893-1(4)) Dorrance Publishing Co., Inc.

James, Ian. Why the Sky Is Far Away: A Take from Nigeria. 2006. 42.00 ***(978-1-4108-6172-6(4))*** Benchmark Education Co.

Jones, T. Llew. Storïau Cwm-Pen-Llo. 2005. (WEL., Illus.). 100p. (978-0-86381-750-2(5)) Gwasg Carreg Gwalch.

Kanaan, Hanan S. The Curse of the Slaves. 2003. (Illus.). 96p. per. 11.95 (978-1-59405-013-8(9)) New Age World Publishing.

Kelleher, Victor. Dogboy. 2006. (YA). (gr. 9 up). 16.95 (978-1-932425-76-5(4) , Lemniscaat) Boyds Mills Pr.

Lai-Ma. The Monster of Palapala Mountain. 2006. (Illus.). 44p. (J). 17.95 (978-0-9762056-5-4(3)) Heryin Publishing Corp.

Lowry, Lois. Messenger. 2006. 176p. (YA). pap. 6.50 (978-0-440-23912-3(5) , Laurel Leaf) Random Hse. Children's Bks.

Matthews, T. J. The Village Safari. Rheburg, Judy, illus. 2005. (J). (978-0-938978-36-7(5)) Wycliffe Bible Translators.

McCaughrean, Geraldine. Smile! 128p. (J). (gr. 2-6). 2008. 5.50 (***978-0-440-23952-9(4)*** , Yearling); 2006. (Illus.). 14.95 (978-0-375-83640-4(3) , Random Hse. Bks. for Young Readers) Random Hse. Children's Bks.

McCaughrean, Geraldine. Smile. 2006. (Illus.). 128p. (J). (gr. 2-6). lib. bdg. 16.99 (978-0-375-93640-1(8) , Random Hse. Bks. for Young Readers) Random Hse. Children's Bks.

Moore, Baba Evans. While the Village Sleeps. 2003. 400p. (YA). pap. 14.95 (978-0-9709762-0-8(8)) Moore, Evans.

Mora, Pat. Dona Flor: Un Cuento de una Mujer Gigante con un Gran Corazon. Mora, Pat & Mlawer, Teresa, trs. Colon, Raul, illus. (J). 2005. 32p. (J). (ps-3). lib. bdg. 15.19 (978-0-606-33665-9(6)) Tandem Library Bks.

Nanami, Shingo & Tezuka, Kaname. Kamui, Vol. 7. Seto, Dietrich & Yamashita, Shizuki, eds. Yamashita, Satsuki, tr. O'Leary, Keiran & McDougall, Chris, illus. 2007. (Kamui Ser.). 224p. pap. 9.99 (***978-1-59741-054-0(3)***) Broccoli International USA, Inc.

Narsimhan, Mahtab. The Third Eye. 2007. 240p. (YA). pap. 11.99 (***978-1-55002-750-1(6)*** , Boardwalk Bks.) Dundurn Group, The CAN. *Dist:* Univ. of Toronto Pr.

Nettrour, Nelani. The Dragonlands Bk. 3: The Village. l.t. ed. 2004. (Illus.). 148p. (J). pap. 19.95 (978-1-932657-12-8(6)) Third Millennium Pubns.

Peterson, Elizabeth J. Christina & the Little Red Bird. Mcknight, C. D., illus. 1999. 23p. (J). (ps-5). reprint ed. spiral bd. 5.95 (978-0-938911-02-9(3)) Individualized Education Systems/Poppy Lane Publishing.

Revell, Cindy, illus. A Sack Full of Feathers. 2007. 32p. pap. (***978-1-55143-863-4(1)***) Orca Bk. Pubs.

Rymond, Lynda Gene. The Village of Basketeers. Ceccoli, Nicoletta, illus. 2005. 40p. (J). (gr. k-3). 16.00 (978-0-618-39671-9(3)) Houghton Mifflin Co. Trade & Reference Div.

Schott, Elizabeth, illus. Jake & Sam at the Empty Abbey. 2006. 96p. (J). per. 9.95 (978-0-9724421-1-4(1)) Fountain Square Publishing.

Shah, Idries. The Clever Boy & the Terrible, Dangerous Animal. Santiago, Rose Mary, illus. 2005. 32p. (J). (ps-ps). pap. 6.99 (978-1-883536-51-0(0) , Hoopoe Bks.) ISHK.

—The Clever Boy & the Terrible, Dangerous Animal/el Muchachito Listo y el Terrible y Peligroso Animal. Wirkala, Rita, tr. Santiago, Rose Mary, illus. 2005. 32p. (J). (ps-ps). 18.00 (978-1-883536-39-8(1)); pap. 6.95 (978-1-883536-40-4(5)) ISHK. (Hoopoe Bks.).

—The Silly Chicken. Jackson, Jeff, illus. 2005. 32p. (J). pap. 6.99 (978-1-883536-50-3(2) , Hoopoe Bks.) ISHK.

—The Silly Chicken/el Pollo Bobo. Wirkala, Rita, tr. Jackson, Jeff, illus. 2005. 32p. (J). (ps-ps). 18.00 (978-1-883536-37-4(5) , Hoopoe Bks.) ISHK.

Shinju, Mariko. A Pumpkin Story. Shinju, Mariko, illus. 1998. (Illus.). 32p. (J). (ps-4). 16.95 (978-1-880851-36-4(9)) Greene Bark Pr., Inc.

Shinn, Sharon. The Safe-Keeper's Secret. 2005. (Firebird Ser.). 240p. (YA). (gr. 7). pap. 6.99 (978-0-14-240357-0(1) , Puffin) Penguin Group (USA) Inc.

Watson, T. E. Glen Robbie: A Scottish Fairy Tale. Ferchaud, Steve, illus. ed. 2006. (J). lib. bdg. 22.95 (978-1-58478-013-7(4) , Highland Children's Pr.) Heather & Highlands Publishing.

VILLAS

see Architecture, Domestic

VINCENT DE PAUL, SAINT, 1581-1600

Ethievant, Catherine. St. Vincent de Paul: Servant of Charity. Morson, Caroline, tr. from FRE. Curelli, Augusta, illus. 1999. (Along the Paths of the Gospel Ser.). 74p. (J). (gr. 2-5). 6.95 (978-0-8198-7023-0(4) , 332-341) Pauline Bks. & Media.

VIOLENCE

Agassi, Martine. Hands Are Not for Hitting. Heinlen, Marieka, illus. 2000. (Best Behavior Ser.). 40p. (J). (ps-2). pap. 11.95 (978-1-57542-077-6(5)) Free Spirit Publishing, Inc.

Andryszewski, Tricia. Terrorism in America. (Headliners Ser.). 2003. (Illus.). 64p. (gr. 5-8). lib. bdg. 25.90 (978-0-7613-2803-2(3) , Millbrook Pr.); 1999. (J). lib. bdg. (978-0-8225-2629-2(8) , Lerner Pubns.) Lerner Publishing Group.

Armitage, Ronda. Family Violence. 1999. (Talking Points Ser.). (Illus.). 64p. (J). (gr. 4-7). lib. bdg. 27.12 (978-0-7398-1371-3(4)) Raintree.

—Violence in Society. 2004. (21st Century Debates Ser.). 112p. lib. bdg. 28.56 (978-0-7398-6469-2(6)) Raintree.

Barbour, Scott, ed. Teen Violence. 1998. (Opposing Viewpoints Digests Ser.). (Illus.). 144p. (YA). (gr. 6-9). lib. bdg. 31.20 (978-1-56510-865-3(5) , Greenhaven Pr., Inc.) Thomson Gale.

Biscontini, Tracey. Youth Violence. 2007. (History of Issues Ser.). (Illus.). 240p. (gr. 10-12). 36.20 (978-0-7377-2877-4(9) , Greenhaven Pr., Inc.) Thomson Gale.

Boduch, Jodie Lynn. Violence in the Media. 2007. (History of Issues Ser.). 240p. (gr. 10-12). 34.95 (***978-0-7377-2875-0(2)*** , Greenhaven Pr., Inc.) Thomson Gale.

Brown, Isobel. Domestic Crime. 2003. (Crime & Detection Ser.). (Illus.). 96p. (J). (gr. 7 up). lib. bdg. (978-1-59084-370-3(3)) Mason Crest Pubs.

Cefrey, Holly. Coping with Media Violence. 2005. (Coping Ser.). (Illus.). 192p. (YA). (gr. 7-12). lib. bdg. 26.50 (978-0-8239-2893-4(4)) Rosen Publishing Group, Inc., The.

Cruz, Barbara C. School Shootings & School Violence: A Hot Issue. 2002. (Hot Issues Ser.). (Illus.). 64p. (YA). (gr. 6-12). lib. bdg. 27.93 (978-0-7660-1813-6(X)) Enslow Pubs., Inc.

Dailey, D. C. Use Your Brains Stay Out of Gangs. Boudreau, Dawn, photos by. 1999. (Illus.). 37p. (J). (gr. 1-3). pap. 3.75 (978-1-929662-02-9(5)) Brighter Horizons Publishing.

Deaton, Wendy & Johnson, Kendall. GROW I Saw It Happen: A Child's Workbook about Witnessing Violence. 2002. (Grow Ser.). (Illus.). 32p. (J). pap., stu. ed., wbk. ed. 11.95 (978-0-89793-241-7(2)) Hunter Hse., Inc.

Edgar, Kathleen J. Everything You Need to Know about Media Violence. rev. ed. 2000. (Need to Know Library). (Illus.). 64p. (YA). (gr. 4-6). lib. bdg. 25.25 (978-0-8239-3108-8(0) , NTMEVI) Rosen Publishing Group, Inc., The.

Edwards, Nicola. Domestic Violence. (Illus.). 32p. (YA). (gr. 1 up). lib. bdg. 27.10 (978-1-932333-08-4(8)) Chrysalis Education.

Emanuele, Patricia. Coping with Aggression. 2005. (Coping Ser.). (Illus.). 192p. (YA). (gr. 7-12). lib. bdg. 26.50 (978-0-8239-3360-0(1)) Rosen Publishing Group, Inc., The.

Fernley, Fran. I Wrote on All Four Walls: Teens Speak Out on Violence. 2004. 144p. (YA). (gr. 8). 19.95 (978-1-55037-757-6(4)); pap. 9.95 (978-1-55037-756-9(6)) Annick Pr., Ltd. CAN. *Dist:* Firefly Bks., Ltd.

Fitzgerald, Sheila. Violence. 2007. (Opposing Viewpoints Ser.). 240p. (gr. 10-12). 36.20 (978-0-7377-3364-8(0)); pap. 24.95 (978-0-7377-3365-5(9)) Thomson Gale. (Greenhaven Pr., Inc.).

Fridell, Ron. Terrorism: Political Violence at Home & Abroad. 2001. (Issues in Focus Ser.). (Illus.). 128p. (J). (gr. 6-12). lib. bdg. 26.60 (978-0-7660-1671-2(4)) Enslow Pubs., Inc.

Gaines, Ann Graham. Terrorism. Sarat, Austin, ed. 1999. (Crime, Justice & Punishment Ser.). (Illus.). 80p. (J). (gr. 8). 30.00 (978-0-7910-4596-1(X) , Chelsea Hse.) Facts On File, Inc.

Gedatus, Gus. Violence at School. 2000. (Perspectives on Violence Ser.). (Illus.). 64p. (J). (gr. 4-6). lib. bdg. 23.93 (978-0-7368-0422-6(6) , LifeMatters Bks.) Capstone Pr., Inc.

—Violence in the Media. 2000. (Perspectives on Violence Ser.). (Illus.). 64p. (J). (gr. 4-6). lib. bdg. 23.93 (978-0-7368-0425-7(0) , LifeMatters Bks.) Capstone Pr., Inc.

Giacobello, John. You & Violence in Your Family. 2005. (Family Matters Ser.). (Illus.). 48p. (J). (gr. 5-8). lib. bdg. 23.95 (978-0-8239-3353-2(9)) Rosen Publishing Group, Inc., The.

Goldentyer, Debra. Street Violence. 1998. (Preteen Pressures Ser.). (Illus.). 48p. (J). (gr. 4-8). lib. bdg. 25.69 (978-0-8172-5028-7(X)) Raintree.

Grapes, Bryan J. Violence. 2001. (Teen Decisions Ser.). (Illus.). 142p. (YA). (gr. 10 up). lib. bdg. 36.20 (978-0-7377-0574-4(4) , Greenhaven Pr., Inc.) Thomson Gale.

—Violent Children. 2000. (At Issue Ser.). (Illus.). 78p. (YA). (gr. 5-12). pap. 17.45 (978-0-7377-0158-6(7) , Greenhaven Pr., Inc.) Thomson Gale.

Hacker, Caryn Sabes. A Bully Grows Up: Erik Meets the Wizard: Adult Guide Edition, 1. Boureau, Silvere, illus. 2006. 34p. (J). tchr. ed. 15.95 (***978-0-9791046-0-2(2)***) Caryn Solutions, LLC.

—A Bully Grows Up: Erik Meets the Wizard: Student Edition. Boureau, Silvere, illus. 2006. 52p. (J). stu. ed. 12.95 (***978-0-9791046-1-9(0)***) Caryn Solutions, LLC.

Hasday, Judy L. Columbine High School Shooting: Student Violence. 2002. (American Disasters Ser.). (Illus.). 48p. (J). (gr. 4-10). lib. bdg. 23.93 (978-0-7660-1782-5(6)) Enslow Pubs., Inc.

Hipp, Earl. Understanding the Human Volcano: What Teens Can Do about Violence. Hanson, L. K., illus. 2000. 190p. (gr. 8-12). pap. 16.00 (978-1-56838-359-0(2) , Z1613) Hazelden Publishing & Educational Services.

—Understanding the Human Volcano: What Teens Can Do about Violence. 2000. (gr. 7-12). lib. bdg. 25.75 (978-0-613-79022-2(7)) Tandem Library Bks.

Jackson, Ellen B. Sometimes Bad Things Happen. Rotner, Shelley, illus. 2002. 32p. (ps-1). pap. 7.95 (978-0-7613-1734-0(1) , Millbrook Pr.) Lerner Publishing Group.

Johnson, Loren G., et al. Change Starts Now! Your Child's SAY NO to Violence Kit - The Dreamers, Set. Carol Chambers-Benjamin Employee for Licensing by Loren Inc., Staff, ed. 1999. (Illus.). (J). (ps-8). 168p. pap. 24.99 (978-1-889151-00-7(9)); 192p. pap. 24.99 (978-1-889151-03-8(3)) Licensing by Loren, Inc.

—Charisse & Leah's - "I Feel Good about Me" Journal: The Dreamers, Set. 1999. (Change Starts Now! Your Child's SAY NO to Violence Kit Ser.). 200p. (J). (ps-8). pap. 3.99 (978-1-889151-01-4(7)) Licensing by Loren, Inc.

Jones, Jeffrey. School Violence. 2001. (Overview Ser.). (Illus.). 112p. (J). (gr. 6-9). lib. bdg. 29.95 (978-1-56006-710-8(1) , LML00902-178062, Lucent Bks.) Thomson Gale.

Katz, Samuel M. Global Counterstrike: International Counterterrorism. 2005. (Terrorist Dossiers Ser.). (Illus.). 72p. (J). (gr. 6-12). 26.60 (978-0-8225-1566-1(0)) Lerner Publishing Group.

Kent, Susan. Learning How to Stay Safe at School. 2001. (Violence Prevention Library). (Illus.). 24p. (J). (gr. 3). lib. bdg. 18.75 (978-0-8239-5616-6(4) , PowerKids Pr.) Rosen Publishing Group, Inc., The.

Kivel, Paul. I Can Make My World a Safer Place: A Kid's Book about Stopping Violence. Gorrell, Nancy, illus. 2001. 96p. (J). (gr. 4-7). pap. 11.95 (978-0-89793-291-2(9)) Hunter Hse., Inc.

Kreiner, Anna. La Violencia en la Escuela. 2002. (Todo lo Que Necesitas Saber Ser.). (SPA & ENG., Illus.). 64p. (YA). lib. bdg. 26.50 (978-0-8239-3582-6(5) , Buenas Letra) Rosen Publishing Group, Inc., The.

Landau, Elaine. Date Violence. (Life Balance Ser.). 80p. (J). 2005. (Illus.). (gr. 5-8). pap. 6.95 (978-0-531-16613-0(9)); 2004. 19.50 (978-0-531-12214-3(X)) Scholastic Library Publishing. (Watts, Franklin).

Larson, Karl & McCay, William. The Truth about Violence. 2005. (Truth About Ser.). (Illus.). 166p. (gr. 9). 35.00 (978-0-8160-5302-5(2)) Facts On File, Inc.

Loehfelm, Bill. Osama Bin Laden. 2003. (Heroes & Villains Ser.). (Illus.). 104p. (J). 29.95 (978-1-59018-294-9(4) , Lucent Bks.) Thomson Gale.

McGraw-Hill Staff. Teen Health Course 3, Modules, Violence Prevention. 5th ed. 2002. (Three-Level Middle School Health Ser.). (gr. 8 up). 15.32 (978-0-07-826215-9(1) , 9780078262159) Glencoe/McGraw-Hill.

McIntosh, Kenneth & Walker, Ida. Youth with Aggression Issues: Bullying & Violence. 2008. (J). (***978-1-4222-0136-7(8)***) Mason Crest Pubs.

Meggie, Mary, et al. Conflict Resolution: A Blueprint for Preventing School Violence. 2001. 121p. (YA). 19.95 (978-0-934623-74-2(0)) Solomon Pr., The.

Mintzer, Richard. Coping with Random Acts of Violence. 2005. (Coping Ser.). 192p. (YA). (gr. 7-12). lib. bdg. 26.50 (978-0-8239-4483-5(2)) Rosen Publishing Group, Inc., The.

Momma, Please Forgive Me! 2001. 195p. (YA). per. 13.95 (978-0-9713221-0-3(4)) TM Pubns.

Neri, Greg. Yummy: The Last Days of a Southside Shorty. DuBurke, Randy, illus. 2007. (J). (978-1-58430-266-7(6)); pap. (978-1-58430-267-4(4)) Lee & Low Bks., Inc.

Orr, Tamra. Violence in Our Schools: Halls of Hope, Halls of Fear. 2003. (Single Title: Social Studies Ser.). (Illus.). 192p. (YA). 30.50 (978-0-531-12268-6(9) , Watts, Franklin) Scholastic Library Publishing.

Piano, Doreen. Violence. 2007. (Social Issues Firsthand Ser.). 192p. (gr. 10-12). 29.95 (***978-0-7377-2909-2(0)*** , Greenhaven Pr., Inc.) Thomson Gale.

Pledge, Deanna S. When Something Feels Wrong: A Survival Guide about Abuse, for Young People. 2004. (Illus.). 224p. (YA). (gr. 8 up). pap. 14.95 (978-1-57542-115-5(1)) Free Spirit Publishing, Inc.

Radcliffe, Rebecca R. About to Burst: Handling Stress & Ending Violence—A Message for Youth. 1999. (Illus.). 208p. (YA). (gr. 7-12). pap. 15.00 (978-0-9636607-4-9(8)) EASE.

Roberts, Anita. Safe Teen: Powerful Alternatives to Violence. 2002. (Illus.). 312p. (gr. 10 up). pap. 14.95 (978-1-896095-99-8(2)) Raincoast Bk. Distribution CAN. *Dist:* Perseus Distribution.

Sanders, Pete & Myers, Steve. Violent Feelings. 2005. (Choices & Decisions Ser.). (Illus.). 32p. (J). (gr. 4-7). lib. bdg. 27.10 (978-1-59604-075-5(0)) Stargazer Bks.

Schmidt, April. Youth Violence. 2006. (Illus.). 244p. (gr. 10-12). 36.20 (978-0-7377-2490-5(0)); pap. 24.95 (978-0-7377-2491-2(9)) Thomson Gale. (Greenhaven Pr., Inc.).

Schwarz, Ted. Kids & Guns. 1999. (978-0-606-17536-4(9)); (gr. 7-12). lib. bdg. 18.75 (978-0-613-21854-2(X)) Tandem Library Bks.

Sperekas, Nicole B. But He Says He Loves Me: Girls Speak Out on Dating Abuse. 2002. viii, 162p. (J). 15.00 (978-1-884444-66-1(0)) Safer Society Pr.

Stewart, Gail B. Teens & Violence. 2001. (Other America Ser.). (Illus.). 112p. (YA). (gr. 4-12). lib. bdg. 29.95 (978-1-56006-883-9(3) , LML00902-178206, Lucent Bks.) Thomson Gale.

—Terrorism. 2002. (Understanding Issues Ser.). (Illus.). 48p. (J). (gr. 3-5). 26.20 (978-0-7377-1287-2(2) , LML00902-181530, Kidhaven) Thomson Gale.

The Violence Prevention Library, 6 bks. Incl. Learning How to Appreciate Differences. Kent, Susan. lib. bdg. 18.75 (978-0-8239-5617-3(2)); Learning How to Ask Someone for Help. Kent, Susan. lib. bdg. 18.75 (978-0-8239-5612-8(1)); Learning How to Be Kind to Others. Kent, Susan. lib. bdg. 18.75 (978-0-8239-5613-5(X)); Learning How to Feel Good about Yourself. Kent, Susan, contrib. by. lib. bdg. 18.75 (978-0-8239-5615-9(6)); Learning How to Say You Are Sorry. Kent, Susan. lib. bdg. 18.75 (978-0-8239-5614-2(8)); Learning How to Stay Safe at School. Kent, Susan. lib. bdg. 18.75 (978-0-8239-5616-6(4)); 24p. (J). (gr. 3). 2001. (Illus.). Set lib. bdg. 103.50 (978-0-8239-7080-3(9) , PowerKids Pr.) Rosen Publishing Group, Inc., The.

Wandberg, Robert. Conflict Resolution: Communication, Cooperation, Compromise. (Illus.). (J). 2001. 48p. pap. 8.95 (978-0-7368-8836-3(5)); 2000. 64p. (gr. 4-6). lib. bdg. 23.93 (978-0-7368-0695-4(4)) Capstone Pr., Inc. (LifeMatters Bks.).

Watkins, Christi. How Can Gang Violence Be Prevented? 2006. (Illus.). 128p. (J). (gr. 10-12). 21.20 (978-0-7377-2381-6(5)); pap. 29.95 (978-0-7377-2380-9(7)) Thomson Gale. (Greenhaven Pr., Inc.).

White, Katherine. Everything You Need to Know about Relationship Violence. 2001. (Need to Know Library). (Illus.). 64p. (YA). (gr. 4-6). lib. bdg. 25.25 (978-0-8239-3398-3(9)) Rosen Publishing Group, Inc., The.

Worth, Richard. Children, Violence & Murder. Sarat, Austin, ed. 2001. (Crime, Justice & Punishment Ser.). (Illus.). 80p. (J). (gr. 7-12). 30.00 (978-0-7910-5154-2(4) , Chelsea Hse.) Facts On File, Inc.

Worth, Richard. Massacre at Virginia Tech: Disaster & Survival. 2008. (Deadly Disasters Ser.). (Illus.). 48p. (gr. 5-9). lib. bdg. 23.93 (***978-0-7660-3274-3(4)***) Enslow Pubs., Inc.

VIOLENCE—FICTION

Athkins, D. E. Swans in the Mist. 2006. 256p. (YA). (gr. 9 up). pap. 5.99 (978-1-4169-0047-4(0) , Simon Pulse) Simon & Schuster Children's Publishing.

Berenstain, Stan & Berenstain, Jan. The Berenstain Bears & No Guns Allowed. 2000. (Berenstain Bears Big Chapter Bks.). (Illus.). (J). (gr. 3-6). 10.79 (978-0-606-18486-1(4)) Tandem Library Bks.

Blobel, Brigitte. Red Rage. Ward, Rachel, tr. from GER. 2007. 224p. (YA). (gr. 8-12). 21.95 (***978-1-55451-102-0(X)***); pap. 10.95 (***978-1-55451-101-3(1)***) Annick Pr., Ltd. CAN. *Dist:* Firefly Bks., Ltd.

Bonham, Frank. Durango Street. 1999. 192p. (YA). (gr. 7-12). pap. 5.99 (978-0-14-130309-3(3) , Puffin) Penguin Group (USA) Inc.

Byers, Reggie, illus. & creator. Kidz of the KING Bk. 1: There's No Egg Scuse for Doing Violence! Byers, Reggie, creator. 2002. 32p. (J). 4.95 (978-0-9721164-0-4(0)) Sheepdog Publishing.

Cadnum, Michael. Edge. 1999. (Illus.). 144p. (J). (gr. 7-12). 5.99 (978-0-14-038714-8(5) , Puffin) Penguin Group (USA) Inc.

—Edge. 1999. (gr. 7-12). lib. bdg. 14.15 (978-0-613-14695-1(6)) Tandem Library Bks.

Conly, Jane Leslie. What Happened on Planet Kid. rev. ed. 2000. (Illus.). 160p. (YA). (gr. 5-9). 16.95 (978-0-8050-6065-2(0) , Holt, Henry & Co. Bks. For Young Readers) Holt, Henry & Co.

Corrigan, Eireann. Splintering. 2004. 192p. (J). pap. 16.95 (978-0-439-53597-7(2)) Scholastic, Inc.

—Splintering. 2005. 184p. (YA). (gr. 8-12). lib. bdg. 15.04 (978-0-606-33304-7(5)) Tandem Library Bks.

Dessen, Sarah. Dreamland. 2000. 256p. (J). (gr. 7-12). 15.99 (978-0-670-89122-1(3) , Viking Juvenile) Penguin Group (USA) Inc.

Doucet, Sharon Arms. Fiddle Fever. 2007. 176p. (J). (gr. 5-9). pap. 6.95 (978-0-618-77682-5(6) , Clarion Bks.) Houghton Mifflin Co. Trade & Reference Div.

Favole, Robert. Monday Redux. 2003. 200p. (YA). 15.99 (978-1-930826-11-3(7)) Flywheel Publishing Co.

Flinn, Alex. Fade to Black. 2005. 192p. (J). (gr. 8-12). 16.99 (978-0-06-056839-9(9) , HarperTeen) HarperCollins Pubs.

Gerritsen, Tess. Bloodstream: A Novel of Medical Suspense. 1999. (gr. 7-12). lib. bdg. 16.45 (978-0-613-24020-8(0)) Tandem Library Bks.

Giles, Gail. Shattering Glass. 2004. 215p. (J). (gr. 7 up). pap. 37.00 incl. audio (978-1-4000-9013-6(X) , Listening Library) Random Hse. Audio Publishing Group.

—Shattering Glass. rev. ed. 2002. (Single Titles Ser.: 12). 224p. (YA). (gr. 7 up). 17.95 (978-0-7613-1581-0(0)) Roaring Brook Pr.

—Shattering Glass. 2003. 224p. (YA). pap. 7.99 (978-0-689-85800-0(0) , Simon Pulse) Simon & Schuster Children's Publishing.

—Shattering Glass. 2003. (gr. 7-12). lib. bdg. 15.30 (978-0-613-73394-6(0)) Tandem Library Bks.

Glover, Sandra. Crazy Games. 2002. (Illus.). 160p. (YA). 19.99 (978-1-84270-066-2(9)) Andersen GBR. *Dist:* Independent Pubs. Group.

Heneghan, James. Hit Squad. 2003. (Orca Soundings Ser.). 96p. (J). (gr. 7-12). pap. 7.95 (978-1-55143-269-4(2)) Orca Bk. Pubs. USA.

Herbert, James. The Fog. 2003. (Illus.). vi, 345p. (J). pap. 13.99 (978-0-330-37615-0(2) , Pan) Pan Macmillan GBR. *Dist:* Trafalgar Square Publishing.

Hobbs, Valerie. Letting Go of Bobby James: Or How I Found My Self of Steam. 2004. 144p. (YA). 16.00 (978-0-374-34384-2(5) , Frances Foster Bks.) Farrar, Straus & Giroux.

Houde, Monique. Blinded by Love. 2004. (YA). pap. 14.95 (978-0-9748689-0-5(6)) Choices For Tomorrow.

Jonsberg, Barry. Dreamrider. 2008. 256p. (J). (gr. 9). lib. bdg. 18.99 (***978-0-375-94457-4(5)*** , Knopf Bks. for Young Readers) Random Hse. Children's Bks.

Michaels, Rune. Genesis Alpha. 2007. 208p. (YA). (gr. 7-10). 14.99 (978-1-4169-1886-8(8) , Ginne Seo Bks) Simon & Schuster Children's Publishing.

Miller, Mary Beth. On the Head of a Pin. 2006. 256p. (YA). (gr. 6). 16.99 (978-0-525-47736-5(5) , Dutton Juvenile) Penguin Group (USA) Inc.

Moore, Monica A. Everyday Heroes. 2006. (ENG.). 52p. per. 12.95 (***978-1-59800-563-9(4)***) Outskirts Press, Inc.

Myers, Walter Dean. Shooter. 2004. (J). 224p. 15.99 (978-0-06-029519-6(8)); (Illus.). 240p. lib. bdg. 16.89 (978-0-06-029520-2(1)) HarperCollins Pubs. (HarperTeen).

Naidoo, Beverley. Web of Lies. 2006. 256p. (J). (gr. 6-8). 15.99 (978-0-06-076075-5(3)); lib. bdg. 16.89 (978-0-06-076077-9(X)) HarperCollins Pubs. (Amistad).

Ritter, John H. Over the Wall. 2002. (gr. 5-8). lib. bdg. 15.30 (978-0-613-67112-5(0)) Tandem Library Bks.

Saenz, Benjamin Alire. Sammy & Juliana in Hollywood. 2006. 368p. (J). pap. 7.99 (978-0-06-084374-8(8)) HarperCollins Pubs.

Schembri, Jim. Stullie the Great. 2002. 208p. pap. (978-0-7344-0281-3(3) , Lothian Bks.) Hachette Livre Australia.

Schmidt, C. A. Useful Fools. 2007. 272p. (YA). (gr. 8 up). 18.99 (***978-0-525-47814-0(0)*** , Dutton Juvenile) Penguin Group (USA) Inc.

Sitomer, Alan Lawrence. Hip-Hop High School. 2006. 368p. (J). (978-0-7868-3831-8(0) , Jump at the Sun) Hyperion Bks. for Children.

—The Hoopster. 2006. 224p. (gr. 7-17). pap. 5.99 (978-0-7868-4910-9(X) , Jump at the Sun) Hyperion Bks. for Children.

Soto, Gary. Buried Onions. 2006. (Illus.). 168p. (J). pap. 6.95 (978-0-15-206265-1(3) , Harcourt Paperbacks) Harcourt Children's Bks.

—Buried Onions. 10th ed. 1999. (Ageless Bks.). 160p. (J). (gr. 7-10). pap. 11.00 (978-0-06-440771-7(3)) , Harper Trophy) HarperCollins Pubs.

Spinelli, Jerry. Wringer. (J). 2004. 256p. (gr. 7 up). pap. 6.99 (978-0-06-059282-0(6)); 1998. 240p. (gr. 3-6). pap. 6.99 (978-0-06-440578-2(8)) HarperCollins Pubs. (Harper Trophy).

—Wringer. 2000. (J). tchr. ed. 9.95 (978-1-58130-676-7(8)) Novel Units, Inc.

—Wringer. 1999. 15p. (J). pap., tchr.'s training gde. ed. 15.95 (978-1-58303-099-8(9)) Pathways Publishing.

—Wringer. 1998. (J). (978-0-606-13930-4(3)) Tandem Library Bks.

—Wringer. l.t. ed. 2000. (Juvenile Ser.). 223p. (J). (gr. 4-7). 21.95 (978-0-7862-2774-7(5)) Thorndike Pr.

Walsh, Ann. By the Skin of His Teeth. 2005. (Illus.). 144p. (YA). pap., tchr. ed. 6.95 (978-0-88878-448-3(1)) Beach Holme Pubs., Ltd. CAN. *Dist:* Literary Pr. Group of Canada.

Walter, Virginia. Making up Megaboy. 1999. (978-0-606-17215-8(7)) Tandem Library Bks.

Wilde, Jerry. Peace in the Halls: Stories & Activities to Manage Anger & Prevent School Violence. 2003. 112p. (YA). (gr. 4-12). pap. 9.95 (978-0-9657610-4-8(5)) LGR Publishing, Inc.

VIOLIN

Abele, Hyacinth. The Violin: Its History & Construction Illustrated & Described. 2001. 151p. (YA). reprint ed. 88.00 (978-0-7222-5992-4(1)) Library Reprints, Inc.

Auh, Yoonil. Grand Concert Pieces. Auh, Yoonil, ed. (Illus.). (gr. k-12). 2001. 75p. pap. 19.00 (978-1-882858-53-8(0)); 2000. 62p. pap. 19.00 (978-1-882858-52-1(2)); 2000. 65p. pap. 17.00 (978-1-882858-50-7(6)); 2000. 68p. pap. 19.00 (978-1-882858-51-4(4)) Yoon-il Auh/Intrepid Pixels.

—A Guide to Practicing Repertoire: Level 1, 11 vols. Auh, Yoonil, ed. 2003. (Illus.). 85p. (gr. k-12). pap. 135.00 (978-1-882858-61-3(1)) Yoon-il Auh/Intrepid Pixels.

—A Guide to Practicing Repertoire: Level 2, 11 vols. Auh, Yoonil, ed. 2003. (Illus.). 85p. (gr. k-12). pap. 135.00 (978-1-882858-62-0(X)) Yoon-il Auh/Intrepid Pixels.

—A Guide to Practicing Repertoire Bk. 2: Virtuoso Concert Pieces, 11 vols. Auh, Yoonil, ed. 2001. (Illus.). 99p. (gr. k-12). pap. 225.00 (978-1-882858-71-2(9)) Yoon-il Auh/Intrepid Pixels.

—Musical Poet. Auh, Yoonil, ed. 2002. (Illus.). (gr. k-12). 60p. pap. 18.00 (978-1-882858-57-6(3)); 65p. pap. 18.00 (978-1-882858-56-9(5)) Yoon-il Auh/Intrepid Pixels.

—Picture Musical Diary. Auh, Yoonil, ed. 2002. (Illus.). 40p. (gr. k-12). pap. 12.00 (978-1-882858-58-3(1)) Yoon-il Auh/Intrepid Pixels.

—Representation Music. Auh, Yoonil, ed. 2003. (Illus.). 28p. (gr. k-12). pap., instr.'s gde. ed. 25.00 (978-1-882858-55-2(7)) Yoon-il Auh/Intrepid Pixels.

—Representation Music: A New Approch to Creating Sound & Representing Music. Auh, Yoonil, ed. 2003. (Illus.). 45p. (gr. k-12). pap. 17.00 (978-1-882858-54-5(9)) Yoon-il Auh/Intrepid Pixels.

—Singing Hand: Study of Vibrato. Auh, Yoonil, ed. 2003. (Illus.). (gr. k-12). 50p. pap. 16.00 (978-1-882858-59-0(X)); 45p. pap. 16.00 (978-1-882858-60-6(3)) Yoon-il Auh/Intrepid Pixels.

Bennett, Ned. New Tune Day Performance Piece. 2006. 48p. pap. 12.95 (978-0-8256-8217-9(7)); pap. 12.95 (978-0-8256-8218-6(5)); pap. 12.95 (978-0-8256-8219-3(3)); pap. 12.95 (978-0-8256-8220-9(7)) Music Sales Corp.

Candler, Pat. Testore: The Romance of an Italian Fiddle-Maker. 2001. 264p. (YA). reprint ed. 98.00 (978-0-7222-6048-7(2)) Library Reprints, Inc.

Chapin, Anna A. The Heart of Music: The Story of the Violin. 2001. 299p. (YA). reprint ed. 98.00 (978-0-7222-5994-8(8)) Library Reprints, Inc.

Davey, Peter. Abracadabra Violin, Bk. 1. Hussey, Christopher & Sebba, Jane, eds. Damerum, Kanako & Parks, Paul, illus. 2nd ed. 2004. (Abracadabra Strings Ser.). 64p. (J). pap. 10.95 (978-0-7136-6308-2(1)) A & C Black GBR. *Dist:* Consortium Bk. Sales & Distribution.

—Abracadabra Violin, Bk. 1. 2nd ed. 2003. (Abracadabra Strings Ser.). (Illus.). 64p. pap. 15.95 incl. audio compact disk (978-0-7136-6309-9(X)) A & C Black GBR. *Dist:* Consortium Bk. Sales & Distribution.

Doucet, Sharon Arms. Fiddle Fever. 2000. (Illus.). 176p. (J). (gr. 5-9). tchr. ed. 15.00 (978-0-618-04324-8(1) , Clarion Bks.) Houghton Mifflin Co. Trade & Reference Div.

Engel, Carl. Researches into the Early History of the Violin Family. 2001. 168p. (YA). reprint ed. 88.00 (978-0-7222-6049-4(0)) Library Reprints, Inc.

Farrell, W. J. The True-Tone Violin. 2001. (YA). reprint ed. 150.00 (978-0-7222-6001-2(6)) Library Reprints, Inc.

Hal Leonard Corp., creator. Disney Movie Hits: Violin. 2003. 20p. pap. 12.95 incl. audio compact disk (978-0-634-00099-7(3) , 0634000993) Leonard, Hal Corp.

Haweis, Hugh R. Old Violins. 2001. 293p. (YA). reprint ed. 98.00 (978-0-7222-6004-3(0)) Library Reprints, Inc.

Hill, William H. Antonio Stradivari: His Life & Work, 1644-1737. 2001. 303p. (YA). reprint ed. 98.00 (978-0-7222-6045-6(8)) Library Reprints, Inc.

McCabe, Larry. Easiest Fiddle Tunes for Children. 2007. 14.95 (***978-0-7866-7561-6(6))** Mel Bay Pubns., Inc.

Miles, Lucinda (Cindy). Old-Time Fiddling Gospel Favorites. 2005. (Illus.). 84p. (YA). audio compact disk 19.99 (978-0-9710446-6-1(X)) Miles Music.

Moss, Lloyd. Zin! Zin! Zin! A Violin. 2000. (gr. k-3). lib. bdg. 15.30 (978-0-613-28712-8(6)) Tandem Library Bks.

Petherick, Horace. The Repairing & Restoration of Violins. 2001. 199p. (YA). reprint ed. 88.00 (978-0-7222-6006-7(7)) Library Reprints, Inc.

Racster, Olga. Chats on Violins. 2001. 221p. (YA). reprint ed. 98.00 (978-0-7222-6007-4(5)) Library Reprints, Inc.

Roach-Langille, Nancy & Mitchell, Francis G. Fiddle Fantasy: A Selection of Fiddle Tunes by Maritime Composers. Mitchell, Francis G., ed. Roach-Langille, Nancy, illus. 2nd ed. 2004. (ENG., Illus.). 6p. pap. (978-1-895814-28-6(6) , NWP103) New World Publishing.

Smith, Melanie. Beginner Violin Theory for Children Book One. 2005. 84p. pap. 9.95 (978-0-7866-7087-1(8) , 20296) Mel Bay Pubns., Inc.

Spilsbury, Richard. Should I Learn to Play the Violin? 2006. (Learning Musical Instruments Ser.). (Illus.). 32p. (J). (gr. 3-5). lib. bdg. 28.21 (978-1-4034-8191-7(1)) Heinemann Library.

Turnbull, Elizabeth, ed. Teach Yourself Harmonica. 2004. (Step One Ser.). 32p. (J). (gr. 1-3). VHS, audio compact disk 19.95 (978-0-8256-1842-0(8)) Music Sales Corp.

VIOLIN—INSTRUCTION AND STUDY

Auh, Yoon-Il. Pre-School Virtuoso, Bk. IV. (Auh School of Violin Ser.). 40p. (J). (gr. k-5). stu. ed. 10.00 (978-1-882858-06-4(9)) Yoon-il Auh/Intrepid Pixels.

Auh, Yoonil. A Guide to Practicing Repertoire, 11 vols. Auh, Yoonil, ed. (Unaccompanied Work Ser.: Vol. 2). (Illus.). (gr. k-12). 2000. 95p. pap. 225.00 (978-1-882858-67-5(0)); 2000. 95p. pap. 185.00 (978-1-882858-66-8(2)); 1999. 100p. pap. 225.00 (978-1-882858-68-2(9)); 1999. 95p. pap. 225.00 (978-1-882858-69-9(7)) Yoon-il Auh/Intrepid Pixels.

—A Guide to Practicing Repertoire: Level 3, 11 vols. Auh, Yoonil, ed. 2000. (Concerto Ser.: Vol. 1). (Illus.). 88p. (gr. k-12). pap. 135.00 (978-1-882858-63-7(8)) Yoon-il Auh/Intrepid Pixels.

—A Guide to Practicing Repertoire: Level 4, 11 vols. Auh, Yoonil, ed. 2000. (Concerto Ser.: Vol. 2). (Illus.). 70p. (gr. k-12). pap. 135.00 (978-1-882858-64-4(6)) Yoon-il Auh/Intrepid Pixels.

—A Guide to Practicing Repertoire: Level 5, 11 vols. Auh, Yoonil, ed. 2000. (Concerto Ser.: Vol. 3). (Illus.). 75p. (gr. k-12). pap. 165.00 (978-1-882858-65-1(4)) Yoon-il Auh/Intrepid Pixels.

—A Guide to Practicing Repertoire Bk. 1: Virtuoso Concert Pieces, 11 vols. Auh, Yoonil, ed. 2000. (Illus.). 95p. (gr. k-12). pap. 225.00 (978-1-882858-70-5(0)) Yoon-il Auh/Intrepid Pixels.

—Teaching Auh Violin Method Level 1, 5 vols. Auh, Yoonil, ed. 2001. (Illus.). 70p. (gr. k-12). pap. 95.00 (978-1-882858-72-9(7)) Yoon-il Auh/Intrepid Pixels.

—Teaching Auh Violin Method Level 2, 5 vols. Auh, Yoonil, ed. 2002. (Illus.). 72p. (gr. k-12). pap., instr.'s gde. ed. 95.00 (978-1-882858-73-6(5)) Yoon-il Auh/Intrepid Pixels.

—Teaching Auh Violin Method Level 3, 5 vols. Auh, Yoonil, ed. 2002. (Illus.). 72p. (gr. k-12). pap., instr.'s gde. ed. 95.00 (978-1-882858-74-3(3)) Yoon-il Auh/Intrepid Pixels.

—Teaching Auh Violin Method Level 4, 5 vols. Auh, Yoonil, ed. 2002. (Illus.). 65p. (gr. k-12). pap., instr.'s gde. ed. 95.00 (978-1-882858-75-0(1)) Yoon-il Auh/Intrepid Pixels.

—Teaching Auh Violin Method Level 5, 5 vols. Auh, Yoonil, ed. 2002. (Illus.). 72p. (gr. k-12). pap., instr.'s gde. ed. 95.00 (978-1-882858-76-7(X)) Yoon-il Auh/Intrepid Pixels.

Grimson, Samuel B. Modern Violin-Playing. 2001. 98p. (YA). reprint ed. 88.00 (978-0-7222-6012-8(1)) Library Reprints, Inc.

Harris, P. Improve Your Sight Reading Violin. 1999. (Illus.). 26p. (YA). (gr. 7-8). 18.00 (978-0-571-51736-7(6)) Faber & Faber, Ltd. GBR. *Dist:* Leonard, Hal Corp.

Hunka, Alison & Bunting, Philippa. Playing the Violin & Stringed Instruments. 2004. (Young Musician Ser.). (J). lib. bdg. (978-1-932799-61-3(3)) Stargazer Bks.

Lehmann, George. Violinist's Lexicon. 2001. 156p. (YA). reprint ed. 88.00 (978-0-7222-5991-7(3)) Library Reprints, Inc.

Madden, Maxine A. & Spencer, Harry O. Sounds on Strings: Getting to Know Your Violin. Spencer, Harry O. et al, illus. 1998. 32p. (J). (gr. k-6). pap. 5.95 (978-1-893178-00-7(5)) AMSER.

Rivarde, Achille. The Violin & Its Technique As a Means to the Interpretation of Music. 2001. 51p. (YA). reprint ed. 88.00 (978-0-7222-6014-2(8)) Library Reprints, Inc.

Scott, Daniel. Classical Greats: Easy Playalong for Violin. 2004. (Illus.). 32p. 12.95 incl. audio compact disk (978-0-7119-9145-3(6)) Music Sales Corp.

Stoeving, Paul. Elements in Violin Playing. 2001. (YA). reprint ed. 150.00 (978-0-7222-6015-9(6)) Library Reprints, Inc.

Thistleton, Frank. Modern Violin Technique: How to Acquire It, How to Teach It. 2001. 135p. (YA). reprint ed. 88.00 (978-0-7222-6016-6(4)) Library Reprints, Inc.

Wohlfahrt, Franz. Easiest Elementary Method for Violin: Op. 38. (Carl Fischer Music Library: No. 1061). 56p. (J). pap. 10.95 (978-0-8258-0053-5(6) , L1061) Fischer, Carl LLC.

VIOLINISTS

Lahee, Henry Charles. Famous Violinists to Today & Yesterday. 2001. 384p. (YA). reprint ed. 98.00 (978-0-7222-6008-1(3)) Library Reprints, Inc.

Sutryn, Barbara M. Heartstrings: A Biography of Wilmos Csehy. l.t. ed. 2004. (Illus.). 160p. (YA). 21.00 (978-1-892135-33-9(7)) Lamp Post Publishing, Inc.

VIPERS

see Snakes

VIRGIN ISLANDS OF THE UNITED STATES

Puerto Rico y Otras Areas Perifericas. (World Almanac Ser.).Tr. of Puerto Rico & Other Outlying Areas. (SPA.). (J). (gr. 3-5). 30.00 (978-0-8368-5726-9(7) , GHS32693) Stevens, Gareth Inc.

Schrader, Richard A., Sr. Maute, Quelbe & Ting: A Calabash of Stories. 2001. (Illus.). 108p. (YA). (gr. 6-12). pap. 22.50 (978-0-9622987-4-5(3)) Schrader, Richard A.

VIRGIN ISLANDS OF THE UNITED STATES—FICTION

Gershator, Phillis. Someday Cyril. Lucas, Cedric, illus. 2000. (MONDO Chapter Books). 46p. (J). (978-1-57255-748-2(6)) Mondo Publishing.

Skurzynski, Gloria. Escape from Fear. 2002. (gr. 3-6). lib. bdg. 14.10 (978-0-613-62746-7(6)) Tandem Library Bks.

Skurzynski, Gloria & Ferguson, Alane. Escape from Fear. 2002. (Mysteries in Our National Parks Ser.: Vol. 9). 160p. (J). (gr. 3-7). 15.95 (978-0-7922-6780-5(X)); No. 9. pap. 5.95 (978-0-7922-6782-9(6)) National Geographic Society. (National Geographic Children's Bks.).

VIRGIN MARY

see Mary, Blessed Virgin, Saint

VIRGINIA

ADC, the Map People Staff. Virginia. 2000. (Switched on Schoolhouse Ser.). (YA). (gr. 7-12). pap. 24.95 incl. cd-rom (978-0-7403-0298-5(1) , SOSVA) Alpha Omega Pubns., Inc.

Anderson, Judy. Virginia. 2003. (Land of Liberty Ser.). (Illus.). 64p. (J). lib. bdg. 25.26 (978-0-7368-2202-2(X)) Capstone Pr., Inc.

Barrett, Tracy. Virginia. 2nd ed. 2005. (Celebrate the States Ser.). (Illus.). 142p. (J). (gr. 4-7). lib. bdg. 37.07 (978-0-7614-1734-7(6) , Benchmark Bks.) Cavendish, Marshall Corp.

Bennett, Kelly. Chesapeake Bay. 2006. (Rookie Read-About Geography Ser.). (Illus.). 32p. (J). (gr. 1-2). 20.50 (978-0-516-25032-8(9) , Children's Pr.) Scholastic Library Publishing.

Bruun, Erik. Virginia. Peterson, Rick, illus. 2000. 48p. (J). (gr. 3-7). 9.95 (978-1-57912-103-7(9) , 81103) Black Dog & Leventhal Pubs., Inc.

Capstone Press Staff, contrib. by. Virginia. rev. ed. 2002. (One Nation Ser.). (Illus.). 48p. (J). (gr. 3-4). lib. bdg. 22.60 (978-0-7368-1271-9(7) , Bridgestone Bks.) Capstone Pr., Inc.

Coleman, Brooke. Roanoke: The Lost Colony. 2000. (Library of the Thirteen Colonies & the Lost Colony). (Illus.). 24p. (J). (gr. 3). lib. bdg. 19.95 (978-0-8239-5473-5(0) , PowerKids Pr.) Rosen Publishing Group, Inc., The.

DeAngelis, Gina. Virginia. 2001. (From Sea to Shining Sea Ser.: 2). (Illus.). 80p. (J). (gr. 3-5). 30.50 (978-0-516-22313-1(5) , Children's Pr.) Scholastic Library Publishing.

Duncan Edwards, Pamela. O Is for Old Dominion: A Virginia Alphabet. Howell, Troy, illus. 2004. (State Ser.). 40p. (J). 17.95 (978-1-58536-161-8(5)) Sleeping Bear Pr.

Glaser, Jason & McDonnell, Peter. Patrick Henry: Muerte o Libertad. McDonnell, Peter, illus. 2007. (Graphic Library). (ENG & SPA.). (J). 25.26 (978-0-7368-6608-8(6)) Capstone Pr., Inc.

Harcourt School Publishers Staff. On Shirley Plantation. 3rd ed. 2002. (Horizons Ser.). (Illus.). (J). pap. 7.30 (978-0-15-333561-7(0)) Harcourt Schl. Pubs.

—Virginia. 2nd ed. 2002. (Horizons Ser.). (gr. 4). tchr. ed. 158.90 (978-0-15-336317-7(7)) Harcourt Schl. Pubs.

Heinrichs, Ann. Virginia. Kania, Matt, illus. 2005. (Welcome to the USA Ser.). 40p. (J). (gr. 1-5). 27.07 (978-1-59296-488-8(5)) Child's World, Inc.

—Virginia. 2002. (This Land Is Your Land Ser.). (Illus.). 48p. (J). (gr. 3 up). lib. bdg. 22.60 (978-0-7565-0310-9(8)) Compass Point Bks.

Kehoe, Stasia Ward. I Live at a Military Post. 2000. (Kids in Their Communities Ser.). (Illus.). 24p. (J). (gr. 3). lib. bdg. 18.75 (978-0-8239-5441-4(2) , PowerKids Pr.) Rosen Publishing Group, Inc., The.

King, David C. Virginia. 2004. (It's My State! Ser.). (Illus.). 80p. (J). 27.07 (978-0-7614-1827-6(X) , Benchmark Bks.) Cavendish, Marshall Corp.

Lederman, Marsha, illus. Virginia, an Alphabetical Journey. 2007. (J). 17.95 (978-1-893622-14-2(2) , VSP Bks.) Vacation Spot Publishing.

Mader, Jan. Virginia. 2003. (Rookie Read-About Geography Ser.). (gr. 1-2). pap. 5.95 (978-0-516-27780-6(4)); (Illus.). 32p. (J). 20.50 (978-0-516-22718-4(1)) Scholastic Library Publishing. (Children's Pr.).

Marsh, Carole. My First Book about Virginia. 2000. (Virginia Experience! Ser.). (Illus.). 32p. (J). (gr. k-4). pap. 7.95 (978-0-7933-9500-2(3)) Gallopade International.

—My First Pocket Guide to Virginia. 2000. (gr. 3-6). lib. bdg. 15.25 (978-0-613-75259-6(7)) Tandem Library Bks.

—The Survivor: A Class Challenge. 2001. (Virginia Experience! Ser.). lib. bdg. 29.95 (978-0-635-00692-9(8)) Gallopade International.

—The Very Virginia Coloring Book. 2000. (Virginia Experience! Ser.). (Illus.). 32p. (J). (gr. k-2). pap. 3.95 (978-0-7933-9476-0(7)) Gallopade International.

—Virginia Classic Christmas Trivia. 2002. (Carole Marsh Virginia Bks.). (Illus.). 32p. pap. 6.95 (978-0-635-01457-3(2) , 14572); lib. bdg. 21.95 (978-0-635-01458-0(0) , 14580) Gallopade International. (Marsh, Carole Bks.).

—Virginia Current Events Projects: 30 Cool, Activities, Crafts, Experiments & More for Kids to Do to Learn about Your State! 2003. (Virginia Experience Ser.). 32p. (gr. k-8). pap. 5.95 (978-0-635-02064-2(5) , Marsh, Carole Bks.) Gallopade International.

—The Virginia Experience! (Virginia Experience! Ser.). (Illus.). (J). (gr. k). 2000. pap., wbk. ed. 5.95 (978-0-7933-9445-6(7)); 1999. 48p. pap. 14.95 (978-0-7933-9413-5(9)); 1999. 32p. 24.95 (978-0-7933-9414-2(7)); 1999. pap., wbk. ed. 5.95 (978-0-7933-9415-9(5)) Gallopade International.

—The Virginia Experience! for Eleventh Graders Student Workbook. 1999. (Virginia Experience! Ser.). (Illus.). (YA). (gr. 11). pap., wbk. ed. 6.95 (978-0-7933-9421-0(X)) Gallopade International.

—The Virginia Experience! for First Graders Student Workbook. 1999. (Virginia Experience! Ser.). (Illus.). (J). (gr. 1). pap., wbk. ed. 5.95 (978-0-7933-9416-6(3)) Gallopade International.

—The Virginia Experience! for Fourth Graders Student Workbook. 1999. (Virginia Experience! Ser.). (Illus.). (J). (gr. 4). pap., wbk. ed. 10.95 (978-0-7933-9419-7(8)) Gallopade International.

—The Virginia Experience! for Second Graders Student Workbook. 1999. (Virginia Experience! Ser.). (Illus.). (J). (gr. 2). pap., wbk. ed. 5.95 (978-0-7933-9417-3(1)) Gallopade International.

—The Virginia Experience! for Seventh Graders Student Workbook. 1999. (Virginia Experience! Ser.). (Illus.). (YA). (gr. 7). pap., wbk. ed. 6.95 (978-0-7933-9420-3(1)) Gallopade International.

—The Virginia Experience! for Third Graders Student Workbook. 1999. (Virginia Experience! Ser.). (Illus.). (J). (gr. 3). pap., wbk. ed. 5.95 (978-0-7933-9418-0(X)) Gallopade International.

—The Virginia Experience! for Twelfth Graders Student Workbook. 1999. (Virginia Experience! Ser.). (Illus.). (YA). (gr. 12). pap., wbk. ed. 6.95 (978-0-7933-9422-7(8)) Gallopade International.

—The Virginia Experience Pocket Guide. 2002. (Virginia Experience! Ser.). (Illus.). 96p. (J). (gr. 3-8). pap. 6.95 (978-0-7933-9456-2(2)) Gallopade International.

—The Virginia Experience Sol Biographies. 2001. (Illus.). (J). (gr. 2-9). pap. 12.95 (978-0-635-00390-4(2)) Gallopade International.

—Virginia Geography Projects: 30 Cool, Activities, Crafts, Experiments & More for Kids to Do to Learn about Your State! 2003. (Virginia Experience Ser.). 32p. (gr. k-5). pap. 5.95 (978-0-635-01864-9(0) , Marsh, Carole Bks.) Gallopade International.

—Virginia Government Projects: 30 Cool, Activities, Crafts, Experiments & More for Kids to Do to Learn about Your State! 2003. (Virginia Experience Ser.). 32p. (gr. k-5). pap. 5.95 (978-0-635-01965-3(5) , Marsh, Carole Bks.) Gallopade International.

—Virginia Jeopardy! Answers & Questions about Our State! 2000. (Virginia Experience! Ser.). (Illus.). 32p. (J). (gr. 3-8). pap. 7.95 (978-0-7933-9501-9(1)) Gallopade International.

—Virginia People Projects: 30 Cool, Activities, Crafts, Experiments & More for Kids to Do to Learn about Your State! 2003. (Virginia Experience Ser.). 32p. (gr. k-5). pap. 5.95 (978-0-635-02015-4(7) , Marsh, Carole Bks.) Gallopade International.

—The Virginia Reader: Christopher Newport. 2001. (Virginia Experience! Ser.). (Illus.). 12p. (J). (gr. k-4). pap. 2.95 (978-0-635-00372-0(4)) Gallopade International.

—The Virginia Reader: Maggie Lena Walker. 2001. (Virginia Experience! Ser.). 12p. (J). (gr. k-4). pap. 2.95 (978-0-635-00366-9(X)) Gallopade International.

—Virginia Symbols & Facts Projects: 30 Cool, Activities, Crafts, Experiments & More for Kids to Do to Learn about Your State! 2003. (Virginia Experience Ser.). 32p. (gr. k-5). pap. 5.95 (978-0-635-01915-8(9) , Marsh, Carole Bks.) Gallopade International.

—Virginia Wheel of Fortune. 2001. (Carole Marsh Virginia Bks.). lib. bdg. 29.95 (978-0-635-00009-5(1) , Marsh, Carole Bks.) Gallopade International.

—Virginia's Big Activity Book. 2001. (Virginia Experience! Ser.). (Illus.). 128p. (J). (gr. 2-6). pap. 9.95 (978-0-7933-9466-1(X)) Gallopade International.

—Who Wants to Be a Millionaire? 2001. (Carole Marsh Virginia Bks.). lib. bdg. 29.95 (978-0-635-00109-2(8)) Gallopade International.

McAuliffe, Bill. Virginia: Facts & Symbols. 1999. (J). lib. bdg. 14.00 (978-0-531-11807-8(X)) Capstone Pr., Inc.

—Virginia Facts & Symbols. (States & Their Symbols Ser.). 24p. (J). 1999. (Illus.). (gr. 2-3). lib. bdg. 18.60 (978-0-7368-0221-5(5) , Bridgestone Bks.); 2003. lib. bdg. 19.93 (978-0-7368-2276-3(3)) Capstone Pr., Inc.

Melson, William G. Geology Explained: Virginia's Fort Valley & Massanutten Mountains. 2004. (Illus.). 170p. per. 15.95 (978-0-9744173-0-1(0) , Ft. Valley Geology Study Ctr.) InterPress.

Mis, Melody S. How to Draw Virginia's Sights & Symbols. 2002. (Kids Guide to Drawing America Ser.). 32p. (J). lib. bdg. 25.25 (978-0-8239-6103-0(6) , PowerKids Pr.) Rosen Publishing Group, Inc., The.

Mishler, Donna. Travel Through Chesapeake. Walker, Lyn, illus. 2000. 40p. (J). (ps-5). pap. 6.95 (978-1-893709-05-8(1)) Suthernsky.

—Travel Through Virginia. Melvin, James, illus. l.t. ed. 1999. 40p. (J). (gr. k-5). Bk. I. pap., stu. ed. 6.95 (978-1-893709-00-3(0)); Bk. II. pap., stu. ed. 5.95 (978-1-893709-01-0(9)) Suthernsky.

Murray, Julie. Virginia. 2006. (Buddy Book Ser.). (Illus.). 32p. (J). (gr. k-4). lib. bdg. 22.78 (978-1-59197-705-6(3) , Buddy Bks.) ABDO Publishing Co.

O'Connell, Kim A. Virginia: A MyReportLinks.com Book. 2003. (States Ser.). (Illus.). 48p. (J). (gr. 4-10). lib. bdg. 25.26 (978-0-7660-5122-5(6) , MyReportLinks.com Bks.) Enslow Pubs., Inc.

Parker, Janice. A Guide to Virginia. 2001. (American States Ser.). (Illus.). 32p. (J). lib. bdg. 16.95 (978-1-930954-94-6(8)) Weigl Pubs., Inc.

T U V

Pollack, Pamela. Virginia: The Old Dominion. 2002. (World Almanac Library of the States). (Illus.). 48p. (J). (gr. 5 up). pap. 14.95 (978-0-8368-5293-6(1)); lib. bdg. 30.00 (978-0-8368-5125-0(0)) Stevens, Gareth Inc. (World Almanac Library).

—Virginia: The Old Dominion. 2002. (gr. 5-8). lib. bdg. 24.15 (978-0-613-52522-0(1)) Tandem Library Bks.

Rose, Ruth. Norfolk, Virginia. 2000. (Black America Ser.). (Illus.). 128p. (YA). pap. 18.99 (978-0-7385-0564-0(1)) Arcadia Publishing.

Santella, Andrew. Mount Vernon. 2004. (Illus.). 48p. (J). (gr. 4 up). lib. bdg. 22.60 (978-0-7565-0682-7(4)) Compass Point Bks.

Sirvaitis, Karen. Virginia. 2nd rev. exp. ed. 2002. (Hello U. S. A. Ser.). (Illus.). 84p. (J). (gr. 3-6). 25.26 (978-0-8225-4084-7(3) , Lerner Pubns.) Lerner Publishing Group.

—Virginia. rev. ed. 2002. (Illus.). 84p. (J). (gr. 4-7). lib. bdg. 15.25 (978-0-613-46113-9(4)) Tandem Library Bks.

Smith, Karla. All Around Virginia. 2003. (gr. 3-6). lib. bdg. 17.05 (978-0-613-60951-7(4)) Tandem Library Bks.

—All Around Virginia: Regions & Resources. 2003. (Heinemann State Studies). (Illus.). 48p. (J). pap. 8.50 (978-1-4034-0580-7(8)); (gr. 3-5). lib. bdg. (978-1-4034-0358-2(9)) Heinemann Library.

—Uniquely Virginia. 2003. (Heinemann State Studies). (Illus.). 48p. (J). pap. 8.50 (978-1-4034-0583-8(2)); (gr. 3-5). lib. bdg. (978-1-4034-0361-2(9)) Heinemann Library.

—Virginia History. 2003. (Heinemann State Studies). (Illus.). 48p. (J). pap. 8.50 (978-1-4034-0584-5(0)); (gr. 3-5). lib. bdg. (978-1-4034-0362-9(7)) Heinemann Library.

Thompson, Gare. The Monitor: The Iron Warship That Changed the World. Day, Larry, illus. 2003. (All Aboard Reading Ser.). 48p. (J). 13.89 (978-0-448-43283-0(8) , Grosset & Dunlap) Penguin Group (USA) Inc.

Virginia Classic Christmas Trivia. 2005. 32p. pap. 6.95 (***978-0-635-03352-9(6)**) Gallopade International.

VIRGINIA—FICTION

Aryal, Aimee Sutter. Hello Hokie Bird! Meadows, Sarah, illus. 2003. (J). 18.95 (978-0-9743442-0-1(6)) Mascot Bks., Inc.

Beiler, Edna. Mattie Mae. Graber, Esther Rose, illus. 2nd ed. 2000. 112p. (J). (ps-4). pap. 6.99 (978-0-8361-9141-7(2)) Herald Pr.

Belle Prater's Boy. 1999. (Pathways to Critical Thinking Ser.). 32p. (YA). pap., stu. ed., tchr.'s training gde. ed. 19.95 (978-1-58303-081-3(9)) Pathways Publishing.

Bradby, Marie. Some Friend. 2007. 240p. (J). pap. 5.99 (978-1-4169-3452-3(9) , Aladdin) Simon & Schuster Children's Publishing.

Brantley, Steven & Brantley, Judi. Molly's Christmas Mystery. McDaniel-Clark, Carol, illus. l.t. ed. 2001. 40p. (J). 16.95 (978-1-892570-06-2(8)) Spring Hse. Bks.

Briggs, Martha Wren. Travels with Virginia, the Little Ferry Vol. 4: The Little Ferry Meets the Colonial Ships. Beale, Ella L., illus. 1999. 18p. (J). (gr. 3-8). pap. 6.95 (978-0-9633240-6-1(3)) Dory Pr.

Brooke, Lauren. After the Storm, No. 2. 2000. (Heartland Ser.: No. 2). 176p. (gr. 3-6). mass mkt. 4.99 (978-0-439-13022-6(0)) Scholastic, Inc.

—After the Storm. 2000. (gr. 3-6). lib. bdg. 12.40 (978-0-613-24101-4(0)) Tandem Library Bks.

—All or Nothing. 2007. (Chestnut Hill Ser.: No. 6). 184p. (J). lib. bdg. 15.38 (***978-1-4242-1719-9(9)**) Fitzgerald Bks.

—Chestnut Hill. 2006. (J). 192p. pap. 4.99 (978-0-439-85998-1(0)); 208p. pap. 4.99 (978-0-439-73857-6(1) , Scholastic Paperbacks) Scholastic, Inc.

—Coming Home. 2000. (Heartland Ser.: No. 1). 144p. (J). (gr. 3-6). 4.99 (978-0-439-13020-2(4)) Scholastic, Inc.

—Coming Home. 2000. (gr. 3-6). lib. bdg. 12.40 (978-0-613-24660-6(8)) Tandem Library Bks.

—From This Day On. 2005. 171p. (J). (978-1-4155-9728-6(6)) Scholastic, Inc.

Brown, Marc. Buster's Sugartime. 2006. (Postcards from Buster Ser.). 32p. (J). (gr. 1-4). 14.99 (978-0-316-15915-9(8)) Little Brown & Co.

Bryant, Bonnie. Conformation Faults. 1999. (Pine Hollow Ser.: No. 5). (YA). (gr. 7 up). (978-0-606-18958-3(0)) Tandem Library Bks.

—Stevie: The Inside Story. 1999. (978-0-606-17154-0(1)) Tandem Library Bks.

Burnham, Niki. Royally Jacked. 2004. (gr. 7-12). lib. bdg. 14.15 (978-0-613-73454-7(8)) Tandem Library Bks.

Burnham, Niki & Saidens, Amy. Royally Jacked. 2003. (Romantic Comedies Ser.). 208p. (YA). pap. 6.99 (978-0-689-86668-5(2) , Simon Pulse) Simon & Schuster Children's Publishing.

Butler, Amy. Virginia Bound. 2003. 192p. (J). (gr. 5-9). tchr. ed. 15.00 (978-0-618-24752-3(1) , Clarion Bks.) Houghton Mifflin Co. Trade & Reference Div.

Carbone, Elisa. Blood on the River: James Town, 1607. 2006. (Illus.). 256p. (YA). (gr. 7-8). 16.99 (978-0-670-06060-3(7) , Viking Adult) Penguin Group (USA) Inc.

Chapman, Cynthia. Dog Gone. 2008. 224p. (J). 16.95 (***978-0-312-37123-4(3)**) Feiwel & Friends.

Cowden, Christine. Mystical Christmas with Angels in Disguise: No Reward Needed. 2005. 48p. pap. 12.95 (978-1-4137-6759-9(1)) PublishAmerica, Inc.

Crane, Stephen. The Red Badge of Courage. 1999. (Masterpiece Series Access Editions). (J). 10.95 (978-0-8219-1981-1(4)) Paradigm Publishing, Inc.

Doyon, Stephanie. Buying Time. 1999. (On the Road Ser.: No. 2). (978-0-606-18898-2(3)) Tandem Library Bks.

Duey, Kathleen. Summer MacCleary: Virginia, 1749. 1998. (American Diaries Ser.: Vol. 10). (J). (gr. 3-7). (978-0-606-13120-9(5)) Tandem Library Bks.

Elliott, L. M. Annie, Between the States. 2006. 544p. (J). pap. 6.99 (978-0-06-001213-7(7) , Harper Trophy) HarperCollins Pubs.

Elliott, Laura Malone. Annie, Between the States. 2004. (Illus.). 496p. (J). (gr. 7 up). 16.99 (978-0-06-001211-3(0)); lib. bdg. 16.89 (978-0-06-001212-0(9)) HarperCollins Pubs.

Forrester, Sandra. Wheel of the Moon. 2000. (Illus.). 176p. (J). (gr. 5-9). 15.95 (978-0-688-17149-0(4)) HarperCollins Pubs.

Fuqua, Jonathon Scott. Willoughby Spit Wonder. 2004. (Illus.). 160p. (J). (gr. 5-8). 15.99 (978-0-7636-1776-9(8)) Candlewick Pr.

Griffin, Adele. Witch Twins at Camp Bliss. Rogers, Jacqueline, illus. 2003. 144p. (gr. 2-6). pap. 5.99 (978-0-7868-1583-8(3)) Hyperion Bks. for Children.

—Witch Twins at Camp Bliss. 2003. (gr. 3-6). lib. bdg. 14.15 (978-0-613-63671-1(6)) Tandem Library Bks.

Haislip, Phyllis Hall. Anybody's Hero: The Battle of Old Men & Young Boys. 2004. (Illus.). 220p. (J). pap. 8.95 (978-1-57249-343-8(7) , White Mane Kids) White Mane Publishing Co., Inc.

—Lili's Gift: A Civil War Healer's Story. 2007. (Illus.). (J). pap. 8.95 (***978-1-57249-392-6(5)** , White Mane Kids) White Mane Publishing Co., Inc.

Haislip, Phyllis Hall. Lottie's Courage: A Contraband Slave's Story. 2003. (Illus.). 120p. (J). pap. 7.95 (978-1-57249-311-7(9) , White Mane Kids) White Mane Publishing Co., Inc.

Hall, Lucy. From England to Jamestowne: A Journey to Find My Father. 2007. (J). (***978-0-9763706-5-9(4)**) Tendril Pr. LLC.

Hamilton, Virginia. M. C. Higgins, the Great. l.t. ed. 2005. 372p. (J). 22.95 (978-0-7862-7541-0(3)) Thorndike Pr.

Helmer, Diana Star. Give Me Liberty. Aspengren, Michael A. & Hatala, Dan, illus. 1999. (Cover-to-Cover Historical Moments Bks.). 56p. (J). (gr. 1-4). lib. bdg. 16.95 (978-0-7807-9042-1(1) , Covercraft) ; (gr. 3-6). pap. 8.95 (978-0-7891-5078-3(6)) Perfection Learning Corp.

Henry, Marguerite. Misty de Chincoteague. 2001. (978-0-606-22665-3(6)) Tandem Library Bks.

—Misty of Chincoteague. 2002. (Illus.). (J). 13.40 (978-0-7587-0291-3(4)) Book Wholesalers, Inc.

—Misty of Chincoteague. Dennis, Wesley, illus. 2006. 176p. (J). pap. 5.99 (978-1-4169-2783-9(2) , Aladdin) Simon & Schuster Children's Publishing.

—Stormy: Misty's Foal. 2002. (Illus.). (J). 13.40 (978-0-7587-6608-3(4)) Book Wholesalers, Inc.

Henry, Marguerite & Dennis, Wesley. Sea Star: Orphan of Chincoteague. 2007. 176p. (J). pap. 5.99 (978-1-4169-2784-6(0) , Aladdin) Simon & Schuster Children's Publishing.

—Stormy, Misty's Foal. 2007. 224p. (J). pap. 5.99 (978-1-4169-2788-4(3) , Aladdin) Simon & Schuster Children's Publishing.

Hermes, Patricia. Our Strange New Land: Elizabeth's Jamestown Colony Diary, Bk. 1. 2002. (My America Ser.: Bk. 1). 112p. (J). (gr. 2-5). 4.99 (978-0-439-36898-8(7) , Scholastic Pr.) Scholastic, Inc.

—Our Strange New Land: Elizabeth's Jamestown Colony Diary. 2002. (gr. 3-6). lib. bdg. 13.00 (978-0-613-53849-7(8)) Tandem Library Bks.

—Season of Promise: Elizabeth's Jamestown Colony Diary. 2002. (My America Ser.: Bk. 3). (Illus.). 112p. (J). (gr. 2-5). pap. 10.95 (978-0-439-38898-6(8)); pap. 4.99 (978-0-439-27206-3(8)) Scholastic, Inc. (Scholastic Pr.).

—Season of Promise: Elizabeth's Jamestown Colony Diary. 2002. (gr. 3-6). lib. bdg. 13.00 (978-0-613-57130-2(4)) Tandem Library Bks.

—The Starving Time Bk. 2: Elizabeth's Jamestown Colony Diary. 2002. (My America Ser.: Bk. 2). (Illus.). 112p. (J). (gr. 2-5). pap. 4.99 (978-0-439-36902-2(9) , Scholastic Pr.) Scholastic, Inc.

—The Starving Time Bk. 2: Elizabeth's Jamestown Colony Diary. 2002. (gr. 3-6). lib. bdg. 13.00 (978-0-613-53867-1(6)) Tandem Library Bks.

Hite, Sid. A Hole in the World. 208p. (J). 2001. (Illus.). pap. 16.95 (978-0-439-09830-4(0)); 2004. (gr. 5 up). reprint ed. pap. 5.99 (978-0-439-09831-1(9) , Scholastic Pr.) Scholastic, Inc.

Hollenbeck, Kathleen M. Dancing on the Sand: A Story of an Atlantic Blue Crab. 2005. (Illus.). 32p. (J). (ps-2). 8.95 incl. audio (978-1-59249-234-3(7) , SC4017) Soundprints.

—Dancing on the Sand: A Story of an Atlantic Blue Crab. Popeo, Joanie, illus. 1999. (Smithsonian Oceanic Collection: Vol. 17). 32p. (J). (ps-2). 19.95 incl. reel tape (978-1-56899-732-2(9) , BC4017) Soundprints.

Hunter, John P. Red Thunder: Secrets, Spies, & Scoundrels at Yorktown. 2006. (J). (***978-0-87935-231-8(0)**) Colonial Williamsburg Foundation.

Jones, Elizabeth McDavid. Watcher in the Piney Woods. 2000. (American Girl Collection). (Illus.). (J). (978-0-606-20981-6(6)) Tandem Library Bks.

Karwoski, Gail Langer. Surviving Jamestown: The Adventures of Young Sam Collier. 2001. (gr. 3-6). lib. bdg. 17.60 (978-0-613-51595-5(1)) Tandem Library Bks.

Kimmel, Eric A. Blackbeard's Last Fight. Fisher, Leonard Everett, illus. 2006. 32p. (J). 17.00 (978-0-374-30780-6(6) , Farrar, Straus & Giroux (BYR)) Farrar, Straus & Giroux.

Kudlinski, Kathleen V. My Lady, Pocahontas. 400th anniv. ed. 2006. 208p. (YA). (gr. 6-8). 16.95 (978-0-7614-5293-5(1)) Cavendish, Marshall Corp.

Lambert, Janet. Star Dream. 2002. (J). per. 9.95 (978-1-930009-53-0(4) , 800-691-7779) Image Cascade Publishing.

—Summer for Seven: A Dria Meredith Story. 2002. (J). per. 9.95 (978-1-930009-54-7(2) , 800-691-7779) Image Cascade Publishing.

Lester, Julius. Time's Memory. 2006. (Illus.). 240p. (YA). 17.00 (978-0-374-37178-4(4) , Farrar, Straus & Giroux (BYR)) Farrar, Straus & Giroux.

Marsh, Carole. Pocahontas. 2002. (One Thousand Readers Ser.). (Illus.). 12p. (J). (gr. k-4). 2.95 (978-0-635-01506-8(4) , 15064) Gallopade International.

—Pocahontas. (Read-Along Ser.). (J). 7.99 incl. audio (978-1-55723-739-2(5)) Walt Disney Records.

—The Virginia Experience! A Virginia Mystery Musical! 2000. (Virginia Experience! Ser.). (Illus.). (J). pap. 20.00 (978-0-7933-9496-8(1)) Gallopade International.

McDonald, Megan. Judy Moody Saves the World! Reynolds, Peter H., illus. (Judy Moody Ser.: No. 3). 160p. (J). (gr. 1-5). 2004. pap. 5.99 (978-0-7636-2087-5(4)); 2002. 15.99 (978-0-7636-1446-1(7)) Candlewick Pr.

—Shadows in the Glasshouse. 2000. (American Girl Collection). (Illus.). (J). (978-0-606-20906-9(9)) Tandem Library Bks.

McKissack, Patricia C. & McKissack, Fredrick L. Christmas in the Big House: Christmas in the Quarters. Thompson, John, illus. 2002. 80p. (J). pap. 6.99 (978-0-590-43028-9(9)) Scholastic, Inc.

McMahan, Stephanie K. The Mystery of the Golden Rings. 2007. 140p. 21.95 (***978-0-595-68451-9(3));** per. 11.95 (***978-0-595-43998-0(5)**) iUniverse, Inc.

McVicker, Mary. Secret of Belle Meadow. Ramsey, Marcy Dunn, illus. 2004. 152p. (J). per. 9.95 (978-0-87033-554-9(5) , Tidewater Pubs.) Cornell Maritime Pr., Inc.

Mills, Charles. The Secret of Scarlett Cove. 2004. (Honors Club Story Ser.: Bk. 3). 127p. (J). (978-0-8163-1999-2(5)) Pacific Pr. Publishing Assn.

Moore, Stephanie Perry. True Friends. 2005. (Carmen Browne Ser.). 128p. (YA). pap. 5.99 (978-0-8024-8172-6(8)) Moody Pubs.

Mrazek, Robert J. Stonewall's Gold: A Novel of the Civil War. 2000. (Illus.). 223p. (gr. 7-12). per. 22.20 (978-0-613-28198-0(5)) Tandem Library Bks.

Mullins, Norman D. Mountain Boy: The Adventures of Orion Saddler. 2004. 104p. (YA). per. 9.95 (978-0-9724867-4-3(7)) Woodland Pr. LLC.

Naylor, Phyllis Reynolds. Wrestle the Mountain. 2003. (gr. 5-8). lib. bdg. 18.75 (978-0-613-76649-4(0)) Tandem Library Bks.

—Wrestle the Mountain. 2003. 224p. (J). pap. 9.95 (978-0-8229-5790-4(6) , Golden Triangle Bks.) Univ. of Pittsburgh Pr.

Olasky, Susan. Annie Henry: Adventures in the American Revolution. 2005. (Illus.). 528p. (J). pap. 16.99 (978-1-58134-521-6(6) , Crossway Bibles) Crossway Bks.

—Annie Henry & the Mysterious Stranger. 2003. (Adventures of the American Revolution Ser.: Vol. 3). 144p. (YA). (gr. 3-7). pap. 5.99 (978-0-89107-907-1(6)) Crossway Bks.

Oneal, Elizabeth. Alfred Visits Virginia. 2006. 24p. pap. 12.00 (***978-0-9771836-8-5(8)**) Funny Bone Bks.

Paterson, Katherine. Bridge to Terabithia. Diamond, Donna, illus. movie tie-in ed. 2007. 176p. (J). pap. 6.99 (978-0-06-122728-8(5)) HarperCollins Pubs.

—Bridge to Terabithia Movie Tie-in Edition (rack) Diamond, Donna, illus. 2007. 208p. (J). pap. 6.99 (978-0-06-125370-6(7) , Harper Entertainment) HarperCollins Pubs.

Pinkney, Andrea Davis. Silent Thunder. 2001. 224p. (gr. 3-7). pap. 5.99 (978-0-7868-1569-2(8) , Jump at the Sun) Hyperion Bks. for Children.

—Silent Thunder: A Civil War Story. 2001. (gr. 5-8). lib. bdg. 14.15 (978-0-613-62425-1(4)) Tandem Library Bks.

Pistole, Katy. Flying High. 2003. (Illus.). 126p. (J). 7.99 (978-0-8163-1942-8(1)) Pacific Pr. Pubns.

—The Palomino. 2002. (Sonrise Farm Ser.). (Illus.). 128p. (J). 7.99 (978-0-8163-1863-6(8)) Pacific Pr. Publishing Assn.

—Stolen Gold, Vol. 2. 2002. (Illus.). 127p. (J). pap. 7.99 (978-0-8163-1882-7(4)) Pacific Pr. Publishing Assn.

Pyle, Howard. The Story of Jack Ballister's Fortunes. 2007. (YA). (***978-0-486-45467-2(3)**) Dover Pubns., Inc.

Quattlebaum, Mary. Sparks Fly High: The Legend of Dancing Point. Gore, Leonid, illus. 2006. 40p. (J). 16.00 (978-0-374-34452-8(3)) Farrar, Straus & Giroux.

Ransom, Candice. Signals in the Sky. 2007. 128p. (J). 4.99 (978-0-7869-4353-1(X) , Mirrorstone) Wizards of the Coast.

Ransom, Candice F. Finding Day's Bottom. 2006. 168p. (J). (gr. 4-6). 15.95 (978-1-57505-933-4(9) , Carolrhoda Bks.) Lerner Publishing Group.

—The Promise Quilt. Beier, Ellen, illus. 2002. 32p. (J). (gr. k-3). pap. 7.95 (978-0-8027-7648-8(5)) Walker & Co.

—Promise Quilt. 2002. (gr. k-3). lib. bdg. 15.25 (978-0-613-75492-7(1)) Tandem Library Bks.

Ray, Delia. Ghost Girl: A Blue Ridge Mountain Story. 2003. (Illus.). 224p. (YA). (gr. 5-9). tchr. ed. 15.00 (978-0-618-33377-6(0) , Clarion Bks.) Houghton Mifflin Co. Trade & Reference Div.

—Ghost Girl: A Blue Ridge Mountain Story. 2006. 236p. (YA). 22.95 (978-0-7862-8876-2(0)) Thorndike Pr.

Readler, Blaine C. Under the Radar: The Spy Drone Adventure. 2006. 248p. (J). pap. 14.95 (978-1-933255-18-7(8)) DNA Pr.

Reeder, Carolyn. Across the Lines. 1998. 224p. (J). (gr. 4-7). pap. 5.99 (978-0-380-73073-5(1) , Harper Trophy) HarperCollins Pubs.

—Moonshiner's Son. O'Brien, Tim, illus. 2003. 208p. (J). pap. 5.99 (978-0-689-85550-4(8) , Aladdin) Simon & Schuster Children's Publishing.

—Shade of Gray. 1999. (978-0-606-16311-8(5)) Tandem Library Bks.

—Shades of Gray. O'Brien, Tim, illus. 1999. 160p. (J). (gr. 3-7). pap. 4.99 (978-0-689-82696-2(6) , 076714004993, Aladdin) Simon & Schuster Children's Publishing.

Reid, Kathleen. Magical Mondays at the Art Museum. Reifsnider, Robin, illus. 2000. iii, 26p. (J). (978-0-9702653-0-2(1)); pap. (978-0-9702653-1-9(X)) Phoenix Color Corp.

Rinaldi, Ann. Or Give Me Death: A Novel of Patrick Henry's Family. (Great Episodes Ser.). 240p. (YA). 2004. pap. 6.95 (978-0-15-205076-4(0)); 2003. 17.00 (978-0-15-216687-8(4)) Harcourt Children's Bks. (Gulliver Bks.).

—Sarah's Ground. 2004. (Illus.). 192p. (YA). 15.95 (978-0-689-85924-3(4)) Simon & Schuster Children's Publishing.

Robertson, William & Rimer, David. The Bucktails' Antietam Trials. 2004. (White Mane Kids Ser.: No.14). (J). pap. 7.95 (978-1-57249-337-7(2) , White Mane Kids) White Mane Publishing Co., Inc.

Robertson, William P. & Rimer, David. The Battling Bucktails at Fredericksburg. 2004. (WM Kids Ser.: Vol. 16). (Illus.). 164p. (J). 7.95 (978-1-57249-345-2(3) , White Mane Kids) White Mane Publishing Co., Inc.

Roddy, Lee. Risking the Dream. 2000. (Between Two Flags Ser.: Vol. 6). (Illus.). 176p. (J). (gr. 6-9). pap. 5.99 (978-0-7642-2030-2(6)) Bethany Hse. Pubs.

Roop, Peter. Eye for an Eye: A Story of the Revolutionary War. 2000. (gr. 5-8). lib. bdg. 15.70 (978-0-613-36805-6(3)) Tandem Library Bks.

Roop, Peter & Roop, Connie. An Eye for an Eye: A Story of the American Revolution. 2001. (Jamestown Classics Ser.). (Illus.). 168p. (J). (gr. 5-8). 15.32 (978-0-8092-0587-5(4) , 9780809205875) Jamestown.

—An Eye for an Eye: A Story of the Revolutionary War. 2004. (Jamestown's American Portraits Ser.). (Illus.). 176p. (J). (gr. 5-7). pap. 4.95 (978-0-7696-3422-7(2) , Waterbird Bks.) School Specialty Publishing.

Roop, Peter and Connie. An Eye for an Eye. 2004. 168p. (J). lib. bdg. 16.92 (***978-1-4242-0772-5(X)**) Fitzgerald Bks.

Rue, Nancy. Sophie Tracks a Thief, Vol. 8. 2005. (Faithgirlz Ser.). (Illus.). 144p. (J). pap. 6.99 (978-0-310-71023-3(5)) Zonderkidz.

—Sophie's Encore, Vol. 12. 2006. (Faithgirlz! Ser.). (Illus.). 144p. (J). pap. 6.99 (978-0-310-71027-1(8)) Zonderkidz.

Rue, Nancy N. Sophie Breaks the Code, Vol. 7. 2005. (Faithgirlz Ser.). (Illus.). 144p. (J). pap. 6.99 (978-0-310-71022-6(7)) Zonderkidz.

Salisbury, Linda G. The Thief at Keswick Inn: A Bailey Fish Adventure. 2005. (Illus.). 192p. (J). per. 8.95 (978-1-881539-41-4(5)) Tabby Hse. Bks.

Scheer, Julian. A Thanksgiving Turkey. Himler, Ronald, illus. 2001. 32p. (J). (gr. k-3). tchr. ed. 16.95 (978-0-8234-1674-5(7)) Holiday Hse., Inc.

Schurfranz, Vivian. A Message for General Washington. 1998. (Stories of the States Ser.: Vol. 10). 92p. (J). (gr. 4-7). lib. bdg. 14.95 (978-1-881889-89-2(0)) Silver Moon Pr.

Seeley, Bonnie L. Chincoteague Daisy Chain. Lidard, Kelly & Seeley, Douglas A., illus. 2003. 32p. (J). bds. 12.95 (978-0-9728380-0-9(7)) Seelcraft Publishing.

Shaffer, Neal. Last Exit Before Toll. 2003. (Illus.). 96p. pap. 9.95 (978-1-929998-70-8(8)) Oni Pr., Inc.

Siwak, Brenda S. Counting on the Bay. Dodge, Barbara A., illus. 2006. (J). per. 14.95 (***978-0-9790906-0-8(1)**) Pleasant Plains Pr.

Smith, Eunice Geil. Treasure Hunt: A Shenandoah Valley Mystery. 2006. 119p. (J). pap. 9.99 (978-0-8361-9332-9(6)) Herald Pr.

Spain, Susan Rosson. The Deep Cut. 2006. (Illus.). 224p. (J). 16.99 (978-0-7614-5316-1(4)) Cavendish, Marshall Corp.

Stockton, Frank Richard. What Might Have Been Expected. 2006. 41.99 (***978-1-4280-4102-8(8));** pap. 35.99 (***978-1-4280-4103-5(6)**) IndyPublish.com.

Stone, Phoebe. Deep down Popular. 2008. (J). 288p. pap. 16.99 (***978-0-439-80245-1(8)); *978-0-439-80244-4(X)**) Scholastic, Inc. (Levine, Arthur A. Bks.).

Susi, Geraldine Lee. Looking Back: A Boy's Civil War Memories. 2001. (Illus.). 128p. (J). (gr. 3-7). pap. 11.95 (978-1-880664-34-6(8)) E. M. Productions.

—Looking for Pa: A Civil War Journey from Catlett to Manassas, 1861. French, Douglas P., illus. 2nd ed. 2001. 127p. (J). (gr. 4-7). pap. 10.95 (978-1-880664-33-9(X)) E. M. Productions.

—My Father, My Companion: Life at the Hollow, Chief Justice John Marshall's Boyhood Home in Virginia. 2001. (Illus.). 96p. (J). (gr. 4-9). pap. 10.95 (978-1-889324-22-7(1)) EPM Pubns., Inc.

Szymanski, Lois. Sea Feather. 1999. (Illus.). 80p. (J). (gr. 3-7). pap. 3.99 (978-0-380-80566-2(9)) HarperCollins Pubs.

Trent, Tiffany. In the Serpent's Coils. 2007. (Hallowmere Ser.). 312p. (YA). (gr. 7-11). 8.95 (***978-0-7869-4229-9(0)** , Mirrorstone) Wizards of the Coast.

Tripp, Valerie. Felicity's Short Story Collection. Andreasen, Dan & Hood, Philip, illus. 2006. 232p. (J). 12.95 (***978-1-59369-120-2(3)**) American Girl Publishing, Inc.

Tripp, Valerie. Very Funny, Elizabeth! Andreasen, Dan, illus. 2005. (American Girls Collection). 81p. (J). (gr. 3). pap. 6.95 (978-1-59369-061-8(4) , American Girl) American Girl Publishing, Inc.

Turner, Barbara F. Ghost Fire. 1998. (J). pap. 6.00 (978-1-892614-08-7(1)) Briarwood Pubns.

Turtleback Books, creator. Evvy's Civil War. 2004. 209p. (YA). (gr. 8-12). per. 13.64 (978-0-606-30114-5(3)) Tandem Library Bks.

Tuthill, Louisa C. Hurrah for New England! or the Virginia Boy's Vacation. 2004. reprint ed. pap. 15.95 (978-1-4191-2504-1(4)); pap. 1.99 (978-1-4192-2504-8(9)) Kessinger Publishing, LLC.

Walt Disney Company Staff. Pocahontas. 2005. (WEL., Illus.). 24p. (978-1-899877-04-1(5)) Y Ddraig Fach.

Warmuth, Donna Akers. Plumb Full of History: A Story of Abingdon, Virginia. Gobble, DeAnna Akers, illus. 2003. 64p. pap. 9.95 (978-1-932158-78-6(2)) Ingalls Publishing Group, Inc.

Watson, Sally. The Hornet's Nest. 2002. (J). pap. 12.95 (978-1-930009-66-0(6) , 800-691-7779) Image Cascade Publishing.

White, Ruth. Belle Prater's Boy. unabr. ed. 2004. 196p. (J). (gr. 5-9). pap. 38.00 incl. audio (978-0-8072-8682-1(6) , YA234SP, Listening Library) Random Hse. Audio Publishing Group.

—Belle Prater's Boy. 1998. (YA). 12.15 (978-0-606-12610-6(4)) Tandem Library Bks.

—Belle Prater's Boy. l.t. ed. 2000. (Illus.). 221p. (YA). (gr. 4-7). 21.95 (978-0-7862-2885-0(7)) Thorndike Pr.

—Memories of Summer. 2000. 144p. (J). (gr. 7-10). 17.00 (978-0-374-34945-5(2) , Farrar, Straus & Giroux (BYR)) Farrar, Straus & Giroux.

—The Search for Belle Prater. 2005. (Illus.). 176p. (J). (gr. 8-12). 16.00 (978-0-374-30853-7(5) , Farrar, Straus & Giroux (BYR)) Farrar, Straus & Giroux.

—The Search for Belle Prater. 2007. 176p. (J). (gr. 4-7). 6.50 (978-0-440-42164-1(0) , Yearling) Random Hse. Children's Bks.

—The Search for Belle Prater. l.t. ed. 2006. 205p. (J). 23.95 (978-0-7862-8278-4(9)) Thorndike Pr.

Wood, D. K. Nightmare at Indian Cave. 2006. pap. 10.00 (***978-1-4257-1640-0(7)***) Xlibris Corp.

Wood, Michael. Villains in Virginia Beach. 2004. 100p. (YA). per. (978-1-59196-534-3(9)) Instantpublisher.com.

VIRGINIA—HISTORY

Abnett, Dan. The Battle of the Wilderness: Deadly Inferno. 2007. (Graphic Battles of the Civil War Ser.). (Illus.). 48p. (J). lib. bdg. (978-1-4042-0780-6(5)) Rosen Publishing Group, Inc., The.

—Deadly Inferno: Battle of the Wilderness. Verma, Dheeraj, illus. 2007. (Graphic History Ser.). 48p. (J). pap. 9.95 (***978-1-84603-052-9(8)***) Osprey Publishing, Ltd. GBR. *Dist:* Random Hse., Inc.

—Ironclads at War: The Monitor vs the Merrimac. 2007. (Graphic History Ser.). (Illus.). 48p. (J). (gr. 3). pap. 9.95 (978-1-84603-053-6(6)) Osprey Publishing, Ltd. GBR. *Dist:* Random Hse., Inc.

—The Monitor vs. the Merrimac: Ironclads at War! 2007. (Graphic Battles of the Civil War Ser.). (Illus.). 48p. (J). lib. bdg. (978-1-4042-0778-3(3)) Rosen Publishing Group, Inc., The.

Adams, Colleen. Pocahontas: The Life on an Indian Princess. 2006. (Rosen Publishing Group's Reading Room Collection). (Illus.). 16p. (J). lib. bdg. (978-1-4042-3348-5(2) , PowerKids Pr.) Rosen Publishing Group, Inc., The.

Among These Ancient Mountains: The Story of Rockbridge County, Virginia. 2001. 220p. 45.00 (978-0-9675205-1-3(7)) Alone Mill Publishing.

Arlington Historical Society Staff. Arlington, Virginia. 2000. (Images of America Ser.). (Illus.). 128p. pap. 19.99 (978-0-7385-0619-7(2)) Arcadia Publishing.

Bauer, Brandy. The Virginia Colony. 2005. (Fact Finders Ser.). (Illus.). 32p. (J). (gr. 2-4). 22.60 (978-0-7368-2684-6(X) , Fact Finders) Capstone Pr., Inc.

Beller, Susan Provost. The Confederate Ladies of Richmond. 1999. (Single Titles Ser.). (Illus.). 96p. (gr. 4-7). lib. bdg. 26.90 (978-0-7613-1470-7(9) , Millbrook Pr.) Lerner Publishing Group.

Bennett, Kelly. Chesapeake Bay. 2006. 32p. (YA). (gr. 1-2). pap. 5.95 (978-0-516-29702-6(3) , Children's Pr.) Scholastic Library Publishing.

Brager, Bruce L. Petersburg. 2003. (Sieges That Changed the World Ser.). (Illus.). 112p. (gr. 6-12). 30.00 (978-0-7910-7100-7(6)); pap. 13.25 (978-0-7910-7530-2(3)) Facts On File, Inc. (Chelsea Hse.).

Britton, Tamara L. The Virginia Colony. 2001. (Colonies Ser.). (Illus.). 32p. (J). (gr. k-6). lib. bdg. 22.78 (978-1-57765-579-4(6) , Checkerboard Library) ABDO Publishing Co.

Bruchac, Joseph. Pocahontas. 2005. (Illus.). 192p. (YA). (gr. 6-8). pap. 5.95 (978-0-15-205465-6(0) , Harcourt Paperbacks) Harcourt Children's Bks.

Burgan, Michael. The Battle of the Ironclads. 2006. (Illus.). 48p. (J). (gr. 4-6). 23.93 (978-0-7565-1628-4(5)) Compass Point Bks.

Carole Marsh. Virginia Indians. 2004. (Virginia Experience Ser.). 36p. (gr. 3-8). 29.95 (978-0-635-02337-7(7)); pap. 7.95 (978-0-635-02336-0(9)) Gallopade International.

Coleman, Brooke. The Colony of Virginia. 2000. (Library of the Thirteen Colonies & the Lost Colony). (Illus.). 24p. (J). (gr. 3). lib. bdg. 19.95 (978-0-8239-5484-1(6) , PowerKids Pr.) Rosen Publishing Group, Inc., The.

Cooper, Michael L. Jamestown, 1607. 2006. (Illus.). 112p. (J). (gr. 3-7). 18.95 (978-0-8234-1948-7(7)) Holiday Hse., Inc.

Cressey, Pamela J. & Anderson, Margaret Jean. Alexandria, Virginia. 2006. (Digging for the Past Ser.). (Illus.). 48p. (YA). 22.95 (978-0-19-517334-5(1)) Oxford Univ. Pr., Inc.

Dantzlerward, Walter. This Is Virginia Set: The Virginia History & Social Science Standards of Learning Book. l.t. ed. 2002. 579p. lib. bdg. (978-0-9720535-2-5(2) , 0972053522) Academic Multimedia, Inc.

—This Is Virginia Vol. 2: The Virginia History & Social Science Standards of Learning Book Set. l.t. ed. 2002. 369p. lib. bdg. (978-0-9720535-1-8(4) , 0972053514) Academic Multimedia, Inc.

Dantzlerward, Walter, et al. This Is Virginia: The Virginia History & Social Science Standards of Learning Book Set, 2 vols. l.t. ed. 2002. 210p. lib. bdg. (978-0-9720535-0-1(6) , 0972053506) Academic Multimedia, Inc.

De Capua, Sarah. The Wilderness Road. 2006. (We the People Ser.). (Illus.). 48p. (J). (gr. 4-6). 23.93 (978-0-7565-1637-6(4)) Compass Point Bks.

De Capua, Sarah E. The Virginia Colony. 2003. (Spirit of America). (Illus.). 40p. (J). (gr. 2-6). 28.50 (978-1-56766-711-0(2)) Child's World, Inc.

Doherty, Craig A. & Doherty, Katherine M. Virginia. 2005. (Thirteen Colonies Ser.). (Illus.). 144p. (J). (gr. 4-9). 35.00 (978-0-8160-5416-9(9)) Facts On File, Inc.

Dubois, Muriel L. Virginia. 2005. (Portraits of the States Ser.). (Illus.). 32p. (J). pap. (978-0-8368-4655-3(9)) Stevens, Gareth Inc.

DuBois, Muriel L. Virginia. 2005. (Portraits of the States Ser.). (Illus.). 32p. (J). (ps). lib. bdg. 23.33 (978-0-8368-4636-2(2)) Stevens, Gareth Inc.

Edwards, Judith. Nat Turner's Slave Rebellion in American History. 2000. (In American History Ser.). (Illus.). 112p. (YA). (gr. 5-12). lib. bdg. 26.60 (978-0-7660-1302-5(2)) Enslow Pubs., Inc.

Espinosa, Rod. Patrick Henry. 2007. (Bio-Graphics Ser.). (Illus.). 32p. (J). (gr. 3-6). lib. bdg. 27.07 (***978-1-60270-070-3(2)*** , Graphic Planet) Magic Wagon.

Fountain, Clara. Danville in Vintage Postcards, Virginia. 2000. (Postcard History Ser.). (Illus.). 128p. (J). (gr. 5 up). pap. 19.99 (978-0-7385-0652-4(4)) Arcadia Publishing.

Fradin, Dennis B. Jamestown, Virginia. 2006. (Turning Points in U. S. History Ser.). (Illus.). 48p. (J). (gr. 3-6). lib. bdg. 29.93 (978-0-7614-2122-1(X) , Benchmark Bks.) Cavendish, Marshall Corp.

Frederick, Anne. Shenandoah: Its National Park & Neighbors. 2000. (Images of America Ser.). (Illus.). 128p. pap. 19.99 (978-0-7385-0645-6(1)) Arcadia Publishing.

Friedman, Robin. The Silent Witness. Nivola, Claire A., illus. 2005. 32p. (J). (gr. k-3). 16.00 (978-0-618-44230-0(8)) Houghton Mifflin Co. Trade & Reference Div.

Gillis, Jennifer Blizin. Patrick Henry. 2004. (Illus.). 32p. (J). pap. 7.50 (978-1-4034-5968-8(1)) Heinemann Library.

Gregson, Susan R. Nat Turner: Rebellious Slave. 2003. (Let Freedom Ring Ser.). (Illus.). 48p. (J). (gr. 3-4). lib. bdg. 22.60 (978-0-7368-1555-0(4) , Bridgestone Bks.) Capstone Pr., Inc.

Hall-Quest, Olga. Sterling Point Books: Jamestown: the Perilous Adventure. 2007. (Sterling Point Bks.). 192p. (J). pap. 6.95 (***978-1-4027-5122-6(2)***) Sterling Publishing Co., Inc.

Harkins, Susan and William. Colonial Virginia. 2007. (Building America Ser.). (Illus.). 48p. (J). lib. bdg. 29.95 (***978-1-58415-548-5(5)***) Mitchell Lane Pubs., Inc.

Krull, Kathleen. Pocahontas: Princess of the New World. Diaz, David, illus. 2007. 40p. (J). (gr. 1-6). 17.85 (978-0-8027-9555-7(2)); 16.95 (978-0-8027-9554-0(4)) Walker & Co.

Landau, Elaine. Explore Colonial Jamestown with Elaine Landau. 2006. (Explore Colonial America with Elaine Landau Ser.). (Illus.). 48p. (J). (gr. 1-3). lib. bdg. 23.93 (978-0-7660-2554-7(3) , Enslow Elementary) Enslow Pubs., Inc.

Lynette, Rachel. Virginia. 2004. (Seeds of a Nation Ser.). (Illus.). 48p. (J). 26.20 (978-0-7377-1566-8(9) , Greenhaven Pr., Inc.) Thomson Gale.

Marsh, Carole. My First Pocket Guide Virginia. 2000. (Virginia Experience! Ser.). (Illus.). 96p. (J). (gr. 3-8). 12.95 (978-0-635-01336-1(3) , 13363) Gallopade International.

—Virginia History Projects: 30 Cool, Activities, Crafts, Experiments & More for Kids to Do to Learn about Your State! 2003. (Virginia Experience Ser.). 32p. (gr. k-5). pap. 5.95 (978-0-635-01815-1(2) , Marsh, Carole Bks.) Gallopade International.

—Virginia Millionaire. 2001. (GameBook Ser.). 32p. (J). (gr. 3-8). pap., act. bk. ed. 9.95 (978-0-635-00108-5(X)) Gallopade International.

—The Virginia Reader: Chief Powhatan & the Powhatan. 2001. (Virginia Experience! Ser.). (Illus.). 12p. (J). (gr. k-5). pap. 2.95 (978-0-635-00373-7(2)) Gallopade International.

—Virginia Survivor. 2001. (GameBook Ser.). 32p. (J). (gr. 3-8). pap., act. bk. ed. 9.95 (978-0-635-00567-0(0)) Gallopade International.

—Virginia Wheel of Fortune. 2001. (GameBook Ser.). 32p. (J). (gr. 3-8). pap., act. bk. ed. 9.95 (978-0-635-00008-8(3)) Gallopade International.

McNeese, Tim. Jamestown. 2007. (Colonial Settlements in America Ser.). (Illus.). 112p. (YA). (gr. 5-8). 30.00 (***978-0-7910-9335-1(2)*** , Chelsea Hse.) Facts On File, Inc.

—Williamsburg. 2007. (Colonial Settlements in America Ser.). (Illus.). 112p. (YA). (gr. 5-8). 30.00 (***978-0-7910-9333-7(6)*** , Chelsea Hse.) Facts On File, Inc.

Miller, Jake. The Colony of Virginia: A Primary Source History. 2006. (Primary Source Library of the Thirteen Colonies & the Lost Colony). (Illus.). 24p. (J). lib. bdg. (978-1-4042-3029-3(7) , PowerKids Pr.) Rosen Publishing Group, Inc., The.

Morley, Jacqueline & Salariya, David. You Wouldn't Want to Be an American Colonist! A Settlement You'd Rather Not Start. Antram, David, illus. 2004. (You Wouldn't Want To Ser.). (J). 28.50 (978-0-531-12357-7(X) , Watts, Franklin) Scholastic Library Publishing.

Nelson, Sheila. The Southern Colonies: The Quest for Prosperity. 2005. (How America Became America Ser.). (Illus.). 96p. (J). lib. bdg. (978-1-59084-902-6(7)) Mason Crest Pubs.

O'Brien, Patrick. Duel of the Ironclads: The Monitor vs. the Virginia. O'Brien, Patrick, illus. 2007. (Illus.). 32p. (J). pap. 8.95 (978-0-8027-9562-5(5)) Walker & Co.

Osborne, Mary Pope. My Brother's Keeper Bk. 1: Virginia's Civil War Diary. 2002. (My America Ser.). (Illus.). 112p. (J). (gr. 4-7). pap. 4.99 (978-0-439-36903-9(7) , Scholastic Pr.) Scholastic, Inc.

Petrie, Kristin. John Smith. 2007. (Illus.). 32p. (J). 22.78 (978-1-59679-751-2(7)) ABDO Publishing Co.

Pobst, Sandra. Voices from Colonial America: Virginia: 1607 - 1776. 2005. (Voices from Colonial America Ser.). (Illus.). 109p. (J). (gr. 5-9). lib. bdg. 32.90 (978-0-7922-6771-3(0) , National Geographic Children's Bks.) National Geographic Society.

Pobst, Sandy & Roberts, Kevin D. Virginia: 1607-1776. 2005. (Voices from Colonial America Ser.). (Illus.). 112p. (J). (gr. 5-9). 21.95 (978-0-7922-6388-3(X) , National Geographic Children's Bks.) National Geographic Society.

Polette, Nancy. Pocahontas. 2003. (Rookie Biographies Ser.). (Illus.). 32p. (J). (gr. 1-2). 20.50 (978-0-516-22859-4(5) , Children's Pr.) Scholastic Library Publishing.

Quasha, Jennifer. Jamestown: Hands-On Projects about One of America's First Communities. 2001. (Great Social Studies Projects Ser.). (Illus.). 24p. (J). (gr. 3). lib. bdg. 19.95 (978-0-8239-5701-9(2) , PowerKids Pr.) Rosen Publishing Group, Inc., The.

Riehecky, Janet. The Settling of Jamestown. 2002. (Landmark Events in American History Ser.). (Illus.). 48p. (J). (gr. 5 up). pap. 14.60 (978-0-8368-5355-1(5)); lib. bdg. 30.00 (978-0-8368-5341-4(5)) Stevens, Gareth Inc. (World Almanac Library).

Rossi, Anne. Bright Ideas: The Age of Invention in America 1870-1910. 2005. (Crossroads America Ser.). (Illus.). 40p. (J). (gr. 5-9). 12.95 (978-0-7922-8276-1(0) , National Geographic Children's Bks.) National Geographic Society.

Ruffin, Frances E. Jamestown. 2006. (Illus.). 23p. (J). pap. (978-0-8368-6417-5(4)); lib. bdg. 19.33 (978-0-8368-6410-6(7)) Stevens, Gareth Inc.

Schaefer, Ted & Schaefer, Lola. The Pentagon. 2005. (Symbols of Freedom Ser.). (Illus.). 32p. (J). (gr. 1-3). lib. bdg. 25.36 (978-1-4034-6663-1(7)) Heinemann Library.

Schaefer, Ted & Schaefer, Lola M. Arlington National Cemetery. 2005. (Symbols of Freedom Ser.). (Illus.). 32p. (J). pap. (978-1-4034-6674-7(2)); (gr. 1-3). lib. bdg. 25.36 (978-1-4034-6665-5(3)) Heinemann Library.

—The Pentagon. 2005. (Symbols of Freedom Ser.). (Illus.). 32p. (J). pap. (978-1-4034-6672-3(6)) Heinemann Library.

Smith, Karla. People of Virginia. 2003. (Heinemann State Studies). (Illus.). 48p. (J). pap. 8.50 (978-1-4034-0581-4(6)); (gr. 3-5). lib. bdg. (978-1-4034-0359-9(7)) Heinemann Library.

—Virginia, 6 bks., Set. 2003. (Heinemann State Studies). (J). (gr. 3-5). lib. bdg. 162.42 (978-1-58810-614-8(4)) Heinemann Library.

—Virginia's Native Peoples. 2003. (Heinemann State Studies). (Illus.). 48p. (J). pap. 8.50 (978-1-4034-0585-2(9)) Heinemann Library.

Thomas, Peggy. Farmer George Plants a Nation. Johnson, Layne, illus. 2008. (J). (***978-1-59078-460-0(X)*** , Calkins Creek) Boyds Mills Pr.

Traylor, Waverley. Indian Legends of the Great Dismal Swamp. Traylor, Margaret, ed. Hancock, Stefanie, illus. 2004. 72p. (gr. 8 up). pap. 9.95 (978-0-9715068-3-1(3)) Traylor, Waverley Publishing.

Virginia Activity & Coloring Book. 2001. (978-0-9715160-1-4(4)) Coloring Bks. 'N Stuff.

Walker, Frank S., Jr. Remembering: A History of Orange County, Virginia. 2004. (Illus.). 314p. 30.00 (978-1-932547-00-9(2)) Orange Cty. Historical Society, Inc.

Way, Jennifer. Virginia. 2006. (Bilingual Library of the United States of America: Set 2). (ENG & SPA., Illus.). 32p. (J). (gr. 3-6). lib. bdg. 22.50 (978-1-4042-3112-2(9) , Buenas Letra) Rosen Publishing Group, Inc., The.

Whiteknact, Sandra. A Primary Source History of the Colony of Virginia. 2005. (Primary Sources of the Thirteen Colonies & the Lost Colony Ser.). (Illus.). 64p. (J). (gr. k-3). pap. 14.60 (978-1-4042-0678-6(7)); (YA). (gr. 5-8). lib. bdg. 29.25 (978-1-4042-0437-9(7)) Rosen Publishing Group, Inc., The.

Wiener. The 13 Colonies Pack: Virginia, 6. 2004. (Illus.). 48.30 (978-1-4109-0376-1(1)) Harcourt Schl. Pubs.

Wiener, Roberta & Arnold, James R. Virginia. 2004. (Thirteen Colonies Ser.). (Illus.). 64p. (J). 28.56 (978-0-7398-6889-8(6)); 9.50 (978-1-4109-0313-6(3)) Harcourt Schl. Pubs.

Wild, Wonderful West Virginia Activity & Coloring Book. 2001. (978-0-87012-654-3(7)) Coloring Bks. 'N Stuff.

Worland, Gayle. The Jamestown Colony. 2004. (Let Freedom Ring Ser.). (Illus.). 48p. (J). 17.95 (978-0-7368-2462-0(6) , Bridgestone Bks.) Capstone Pr., Inc.

Worth, Richard. Massacre at Virginia Tech: Disaster & Survival. 2008. (Deadly Disasters Ser.). (Illus.). 48p. (gr. 5-9). lib. bdg. 23.93 (***978-0-7660-3274-3(4)***) Enslow Pubs., Inc.

VIRGINIA CITY (NEV.)

Hopkins, Ellen H. Tarnished Legacy: The Story of the Comstock Lode. 2001. (Cover-to-Cover Bks.). (Illus.). 64p. (J). pap. (978-0-7891-1003-9(2)); (gr. 4-7). lib. bdg. 17.95 (978-0-7807-9702-4(7)) Perfection Learning Corp.

VIRGINIA CITY (NEV.)—FICTION

Lasky, Kathryn. Alice Rose & Sam. 1999. (J). (978-0-606-17380-3(3)) Tandem Library Bks.

VIRTUAL REALITY

Baker, Christopher W. A New World of Simulators: Training with Technology. 2001. (New Century Technology Ser.: 8). (Illus.). 48p. (gr. 5-8). lib. bdg. 23.90 (978-0-7613-1352-6(4) , Millbrook Pr.) Lerner Publishing Group.

Glassner, Andrew S. Interactive Storytelling: Techniques for 21st Century Fiction. 2004. (Illus.). 510p. pap. 39.00 (978-1-56881-221-2(3)) AK Peters, Ltd.

Grady, Sean M. Virtual Reality, New Edition: Simulating & Enhancing the World with Computers. 2nd ed. 2002. (Science & Technology in Focus Ser.). (Illus.). 240p. (J). (gr. 6-12). 35.00 (978-0-8160-4686-7(7)) Facts On File, Inc.

Greenberg, Keith Elliot. Virtual Reality. 2003. (Science on the Edge Ser.). (Illus.). 48p. (J). 24.95 (978-1-56711-789-9(9) , Blackbirch Pr., Inc.) Thomson Gale.

Jefferis, David. Cyberspace: Virtual Reality & the World Wide Web. 1999. (Megatech Ser.). (Illus.). 32p. (J). (gr. 4-5). pap. (978-0-7787-0057-9(7)); lib. bdg. (978-0-7787-0047-0(X)) Crabtree Publishing Co.

Virtual Reality: Individual Title Six-Packs. (Bookweb Ser.). 32p. (gr. 6 up). 34.00 (978-0-7578-0899-9(9)) Rigby Education.

Yount, Lisa. Virtual Reality. 2004. (Lucent Library of Science & Technology). (Illus.). 112p. (J). (gr. 7-10). 29.95 (978-1-59018-107-2(7) , Lucent Bks.) Thomson Gale.

VIRTUAL REALITY—FICTION

Blackman, Malorie. Dangerous Reality. l.t. ed. 2000. (Illus.). 208p. 18.99 (978-0-7089-9531-0(4)) Ulverscroft Large Print Bks. GBR. *Dist:* Ulverscroft Large Print Bks., Ltd.

Collins, Paul. Final Countdown. 2000. (gr. 7-12). lib. bdg. 12.25 (978-0-613-28841-5(6)) Tandem Library Bks.

—Knockout. 2000. (gr. 7-12). lib. bdg. 12.25 (978-0-613-28920-7(X)) Tandem Library Bks.

Henderson, J. A. Bunker 10. 2007. (Illus.). 272p. (YA). (gr. 7 up). 17.00 (***978-0-15-206240-8(8)***) Harcourt Children's Bks.

MacHale, D. J. Black Water. 2004. (Pendragon Ser.: Bk. 5). 200p. (J). (gr. k-9). lib. bdg. 14.30 (978-1-4176-2874-2(X)) Tandem Library Bks.

Sharpe, Gerald. What Lies Beneath the Bed: Parade of Lights. 2007. 496p. (YA). pap. 11.00 (***978-1-933894-01-0(6)***) IJN Publishing, Inc.

Vande Velde, Vivian. Heir Apparent. (Illus.). 336p. 2002. (YA). (gr. 3-7). 17.00 (978-0-15-204560-9(0)); 2004. (J). reprint ed. pap. 6.95 (978-0-15-205125-9(2) , Magic Carpet Bks.) Harcourt Children's Bks.

West, Tracey, adapted by. Jack in! MegaMan! 2006. 59p. (J). (***978-0-439-76837-5(3)***) Scholastic, Inc.

Whitman, John. The Nightmare Machine. l.t. ed. 1998. (Star Wars Ser.: No. 4). 144p. (J). (gr. 4 up). lib. bdg. 22.60 (978-0-8368-2238-0(2)) Stevens, Gareth Inc.

VIRUSES

Abramovitz, Melissa. West Nile Virus. 2003. (Illus.). 96p. (J). 32.45 (978-1-59018-343-4(6) , Lucent Bks.) Thomson Gale.

Baeuerle, Patrick A. & Landa, Norbert. Your Body's Heroes & Villains Vol. 4: Microexplorers. 1999. (Microexplorers Ser.). (Illus.). 42p. (J). (gr. k up). lib. bdg. 18.95 (978-1-56674-238-2(2)) Forest Hse. Publishing Co., Inc.

Balkwill, Frances R. & Rolph, Mic. You, Me & HIV: With Knowledge, We Have Hope! 2004. (J). pap. (978-0-87969-718-1(0)) Cold Spring Harbor Laboratory Pr.

Bueche, Shelley. The Ebola Virus. 2003. (Parasites Ser.). (Illus.). 32p. (J). 24.95 (978-0-7377-1780-8(7) , Greenhaven Pr., Inc.) Thomson Gale.

Casil, Amy Sterling. Hantavirus. 2004. (Epidemics Ser.). (Illus.). 64p. (J). lib. bdg. 26.50 (978-1-4042-0254-2(4)) Rosen Publishing Group, Inc., The.

Day, Nancy. Killer Superbugs: The Story of Drug-Resistant Diseases. 2001. (Issues in Focus Ser.). (Illus.). 128p. (YA). (gr. 6-12). lib. bdg. 26.60 (978-0-7660-1588-3(2)) Enslow Pubs., Inc.

Gareth Stevens Publishing Staff, contrib. by. Viruses. 2003. (Discovery Channel School Science Ser.). (Illus.). 32p. (J). (gr. 5 up). lib. bdg. 24.67 (978-0-8368-3375-1(9)) Stevens, Gareth Inc.

Hirschmann, Kris. The Ebola Virus. 2006. (Illus.). 112p. (J). (gr. 7-10). 32.45 (978-1-59018-672-5(9) , Lucent Bks.) Thomson Gale.

Holley, Dennis. Viruses & Bacteria: Hands-on & Minds-on Investigations for Middle to High School. 2000. (Illus.). 82p. (YA). (gr. 7-12). pap. 15.99 (978-0-89455-717-0(3) , MP6201) Critical Thinking Bks. & Software.

Holt, Rinehart and Winston Staff. Bacteria & Viruses: Chapter Resources: Tennessee Edition. 3rd ed. 2003. (Holt Science & Technology Ser.). pap. 11.40 (978-0-03-069134-8(6)) Holt, Rinehart & Winston.

—Holt Science & Technology Chapter 10: Life Science: Bacteria & Viruses. 5th ed. 2004. (Illus.). pap. 12.86 (978-0-03-030206-0(4)) Holt, Rinehart & Winston.

Leuenroth, Stephanie. Hantavirus Pulmonary Syndrome. 2006. (Deadly Diseases & Epidemics Ser.). (Illus.). 104p. (J). (gr. 9-12). 31.95 (978-0-7910-8676-6(3) , Chelsea Hse.) Facts On File, Inc.

Marsh, Carole. Utah Hot Zones! Viruses, Diseases, & Epidemics in Our State's History. 1998. (Hot Zones! Ser.). (Illus.). (J). (gr. 3-12). pap. 19.95 (978-0-7933-8961-2(5)); lib. bdg. 29.95 (978-0-7933-8960-5(7)) Gallopade International.

—Vermont Hot Zones! Viruses, Disease, & Epidemics in Our State's History. 1998. (Hot Zones! Ser.). (Illus.). (J). (gr. 3-12). pap. 19.95 (978-0-7933-8964-3(X)); lib. bdg. 29.95 (978-0-7933-8963-6(1)) Gallopade International.

—West Virginia Hot Zones! Viruses, Diseases, & Epidemics in Our State's History. 1998. (Hot Zones! Ser.). (Illus.). (J). (gr. 3-12). pap. 19.95 (978-0-7933-8973-5(9)); lib. bdg. 29.95 (978-0-7933-8972-8(0)) Gallopade International.

—Wyoming Hot Zones! Viruses, Diseases, & Epidemics in Our State's History. 1998. (Hot Zones! Ser.). (Illus.). (J). (gr. 3-12). pap. 19.95 (978-0-7933-8979-7(8)); lib. bdg. 29.95 (978-0-7933-8978-0(X)) Gallopade International.

May, Suellen. Invasive Microbes. 2007. (Invasive Species Ser.). (Illus.). 112p. (J). (gr. 6-12). 30.00 (978-0-7910-9131-9(7) , Chelsea Hse.) Facts On File, Inc.

Monroe, Judy. Influenza & Other Viruses. 2000. (Perspectives on Disease & Illness Ser.). (Illus.). 64p. (J). (gr. 4-6). lib. bdg. 23.93 (978-0-7368-1025-8(0) , LifeMatters Bks.) Capstone Pr., Inc.

Moore, Eva. The Giant Germ. 2001. (Magic School Bus Chapter Bks.). (Illus.). (J). 11.79 (978-0-606-21310-3(4)) Tandem Library Bks.

Nardo, Don. Human Papillomavirus (HPV) 2007. (Diseases & Disorders Ser.). (Illus.). 128p. (J). (gr. 7-10). 31.20 ***978-1-59018-998-6(1)** , Lucent Bks.) Thomson Gale.

Romanek, Trudee. Achoo! The Most Interesting Book You'll Ever Read about Germs. Cowles, Rose, illus. 2004. (Mysterious You Ser.). 40p. (J). (gr. 4-6). (978-1-55337-451-0(7)); (978-1-55337-450-3(9)) Kids Can Pr., Ltd.

Sfakianos, Jeffrey N. West Nile Virus. Alcamo, I. Edward, ed. (Deadly Diseases & Epidemics Ser.). (Illus.). 108p. (YA). (gr. 9-14). 2005. pap. 31.95 (978-0-7910-8381-9(0)); 2004. bds. 31.95 (978-0-7910-8185-3(0)) Facts On File, Inc. (Chelsea Hse.).

Silverstein, Alvin, et al. Chicken Pox & Shingles. 1998. (Diseases & People Ser.). (Illus.). 128p. (YA). (gr. 6-12). lib. bdg. 26.60 (978-0-89490-715-9(8)) Enslow Pubs., Inc.

—Common Colds. 2000. (Illus.). 48p. (J). (gr. 3-5). lib. bdg. 15.25 (978-0-613-31085-7(3)) Tandem Library Bks.

Sonenklar, Carol. Virus Hunters. 2004. (Twenty-First Century Medical Library). (Illus.). 144p. (J). (gr. 7 up). lib. bdg. (978-0-7613-2520-8(4) , Millbrook Pr.) Lerner Publishing Group.

Thomas, Peggy. Bacteria & Viruses. 2004. (Lucent Library of Science & Technology). (Illus.). 112p. (J). (gr. 7-10). 29.95 (978-1-59018-438-7(6) , Lucent Bks.) Thomson Gale.

VISION

see also Blind; Eye; Optical Illusions

Ballard, Carol. Eyes. 2003. (Body Focus Ser.). (Illus.). 48p. (J). lib. bdg. 27.07 (978-1-4034-0750-4(9)); pap. (978-1-4034-3298-8(8)) Heinemann Library.

Barraclough, Sue. What Can I See? 2005. (Illus.). 24p. (J). (978-1-4109-2165-9(4)); pap. (978-1-4109-2171-0(9)) Heinemann Library.

—What Can I See? 2005. (J). (978-1-4034-7080-5(4)); pap. (978-1-4034-7086-7(3)) Steck-Vaughn.

Beaumont, Susanna. Baby Senses Sight. 2005. (Baby Senses Ser.). (Illus.). 12p. (ps-k). per., bds. 5.95 (978-1-905051-48-9(4)) Make Believe Ideas GBR. *Dist:* Ingram Pub. Services.

Cobb, Vicki. Open Your Eyes: Discover Your Sense of Sight. 2003. (Five Senses Ser.). 32p. pap. 7.95 (978-0-7613-1982-5(4) , Millbrook Pr.) Lerner Publishing Group.

—Open Your Eyes: Discover Your Sense of Sight. Lewis, Cynthia C., illus. 2002. 32p. (gr. 2-4). lib. bdg. 22.90 (978-0-7613-1705-0(8) , Millbrook Pr.) Lerner Publishing Group.

—Open Your Eyes: Discover Your Sense of Sight. 2003. (gr. k-3). lib. bdg. 16.40 (978-0-613-91016-3(8)) Tandem Library Bks.

Daronco, Mickey. Can You See It, Too? 2003. (BuildUp Ser.). (J). pap. 22.00 (978-1-4108-0769-4(X)) Benchmark Education Co.

Douglas, Lloyd G. My Eyes. 2004. (Wel-My Body Ser.). (J). 18.00 (978-0-516-24060-2(9)); 24p. pap. 4.95 (978-0-516-22127-4(2)) Scholastic Library Publishing. (Children's Pr.).

Gordon, Sharon. Seeing. 2002. (Rookie Read-About Health Ser.). (Illus.). 32p. (J). (gr. k-2). pap. 5.95 (978-0-516-25990-1(3) , Children's Pr.) Scholastic Library Publishing.

—Seeing. 2001. (gr. k-3). lib. bdg. 14.10 (978-0-613-50742-4(8)) Tandem Library Bks.

Hall, Kirsten. Animal Sight. 2005. (Illus.). 24p. (J). pap. (978-0-8368-4809-0(8)); lib. bdg. 19.33 (978-0-8368-4803-8(9)) Stevens, Gareth Inc.

—Animal Sight: La Vista de Los Animales. 2006. (ENG & SPA., Illus.). 24p. (J). pap. (978-0-8368-4821-2(7)); lib. bdg. 19.33 (978-0-8368-4815-1(2)) Stevens, Gareth Inc.

Hidalgo, Maria. Sight. 2003. 24p. (J). lib. bdg. 21.35 (978-1-58340-303-7(5)) Smart Apple Media.

Klingel, Cynthia Fitterer & Noyed, Robert B. Eyes. Andersen, Gregg, photos by. 2002. (Weekly Reader Early Learning Library). (Illus.). 24p. (J). (ps up). pap. 5.95 (978-0-8368-3152-8(7)); lib. bdg. 19.33 (978-0-8368-3063-7(6)) Stevens, Gareth Inc. (Weekly Reader Early Learning Library).

—Eyes/Ojos. Acosta, Tatiana & Gutiérrez, Guillermo, trs. Andersen, Gregg, photos by. 2002. (Weekly Reader Early Learning Library). (ENG & SPA., Illus.). 24p. (J). (ps up). pap. (978-0-8368-3321-8(X)); lib. bdg. 19.33 (978-0-8368-3072-9(5)) Stevens, Gareth Inc. (Weekly Reader Early Learning Library).

Llewellyn, Claire. Seeing. 2005. (Illus.). 24p. (J). (gr. 1-4). lib. bdg. 22.80 (978-1-932889-48-2(5)) Sea-To-Sea Pubns.

—Seeing. 2004. (Body in Action Ser.). (J). pap. (978-1-58340-438-6(4)) Smart Apple Media.

Mackill, Mary. Seeing. 2006. (Heinemann Read & Learn Ser.). (Illus.). 24p. (J). (978-1-4034-7376-9(5)); pap. (978-1-4034-7383-7(8)) Steck-Vaughn.

Mandy, et al. Rosie's Room. (Illus.). 16p. (ps-1). 2005. (URD, ENG, TUR, VIE & CHI.). 9.95 (978-1-84059-162-0(5)); 2000. (VIE, ENG, URD, TUR & CHI., (J). pap. 9.95 (978-1-84059-163-7(3)); 2000. (TUR, ENG, URD, VIE & CHI., (J). pap. 9.95 (978-1-84059-161-3(7)); 2000. (GUJ, ENG, VIE, CHI & BEN., (J). pap. 9.95 (978-1-84059-160-6(9)) Milet Publishing.

Mayo Clinic on Vision & Eye Health: Practical Answers on Glaucoma, Cataracts, Macular Degeneration, & Other Conditions. 2005. (Mayo Clinic on Health Ser.). (Illus.). 178,248p. (YA). (gr. 8 up). lib. bdg. 34.95 (978-1-59084-243-0(X)) Mason Crest Pubs.

Molter, Carey. Sense of Sight. l.t. ed. 2001. (Senses Ser.). (Illus.). 24p. (J). (ps-3). lib. bdg. 19.93 (978-1-57765-626-5(1) , SandCastle) ABDO Publishing Co.

Murphy, Patricia J. Sight. 2003. (True Bks.). (gr. 3-5). pap. 6.95 (978-0-516-26968-9(2) , Children's Pr.) Scholastic Library Publishing.

—Sight. 2003. (gr. 3-6). lib. bdg. 15.25 (978-0-613-67983-1(0)) Tandem Library Bks.

Nelson, Robin. Seeing. 2005. (First Step Nonfiction Ser.). (Illus.). 24p. (J). (gr. k-2). lib. bdg. 17.27 (978-0-8225-1262-2(9)) Lerner Publishing Group.

Olien, Rebecca. Seeing. 2005. (Illus.). 24p. (J). (ps-7). lib. bdg. 21.26 (978-0-7368-4302-7(7)) Capstone Pr., Inc.

Pringle, Laurence P. Sight. 2000. (Explore Your Senses Ser.). (Illus.). 32p. (J). (gr. 4-8). lib. bdg. 25.64 (978-0-7614-0734-8(0) , Benchmark Bks.) Cavendish, Marshall Corp.

Pryor, Kimberley Jane. Seeing. 2003. (Senses Ser.). (Illus.). 32p. (gr. 2-4). 23.00 (978-0-7910-7555-5(9) , Chelsea Hse.) Facts On File, Inc.

Rau, Dana Meachen. Look Around! A Book about Your Sense of Sight. Peterson, Rick, illus. 2005. (Amazing Body Ser.). 24p. (C). (gr. k-3). 22.60 (978-1-4048-1019-8(6)) Picture Window Bks.

Riley, Peter D. Light & Seeing. 2007. (J). ***978-1-59920-028-6(7))** Smart Apple Media.

Royston, Angela. Sight. 2005. (Illus.). 32p. (J). (gr. 1 up). lib. bdg. 27.10 (978-1-59389-204-3(7)) Chrysalis Education.

Schuh, Mari. The Sense of Sight. 2007. (Illus.). 24p. (J). lib. bdg. 19.95 (978-1-60014-071-6(8)) Bellwether Media.

Sian Revision Vision & Hearing. 2004. (J). (978-1-59242-079-7(6)) Delta Education, LLC.

Sideri, Simona. Eyes. Noble, Sheilagh, tr. Noble, Sheilagh, illus. 2004. (J). lib. bdg. (978-1-58340-495-9(3)) Smart Apple Media.

Silverstein, Alvin, et al. Seeing. 2001. (Senses & Sensors Ser.). (Illus.). 64p. (gr. 5-8). lib. bdg. 25.90 (978-0-7613-1663-3(9) , Millbrook Pr.) Lerner Publishing Group.

Simon, Seymour. Out of Sight: Pictures of Hidden World. 2000. (gr. 3-6). lib. bdg. 15.25 (978-0-613-44470-5(1)) Tandem Library Bks.

—Out of Sight: Pictures of Hidden Worlds. 2002. (Illus.). 48p. (J). (gr. k up). 6.95 (978-1-58717-149-9(X) , SeaStar Bks.) Chronicle Bks. LLC.

Spilsbury, Louise. Why Should I Turn down the Volume? And Other Questions about Healthy Ears & Eyes. 2003. (Body Matters Ser.). (Illus.). 32p. (J). lib. bdg. 16.95 (978-1-4034-4683-1(0)) Heinemann Library.

Stanley, Debbie. Coping with Vision Disorders. 2005. (Coping Ser.). (Illus.). 192p. (YA). (gr. 7-12). lib. bdg. 26.50 (978-0-8239-3198-9(6)) Rosen Publishing Group, Inc., The.

—Everything You Need to Know about Vision Disorders. 2005. (Need to Know Library). (Illus.). 64p. (YA). (gr. 7-12). 25.25 (978-0-8239-3225-2(7)) Rosen Publishing Group, Inc., The.

Tabak, John. Look Through the Night. 2002. (J). (978-0-531-11891-7(6) , Watts, Franklin) Scholastic Library Publishing.

Viegas, Jennifer. The Eye: Learning How We See. 2002. (3-D Library of the Human Body). (Illus.). 48p. (YA). (gr. 5-8). lib. bdg. 26.50 (978-0-8239-3530-7(2) , Rosen Central) Rosen Publishing Group, Inc., The.

La Vista (Seeing) (J). 2007. pap. 4.25 (978-0-8225-6545-1(5)); 2006. (SPA.). 18.60 (978-0-8225-6222-1(7)) Lerner Publishing Group. (Ediciones Lerner).

Woodward, Kay. Sight. 2005. (Illus.). 24p. (J). lib. bdg. 22.00 (978-0-8368-4407-8(6)) Stevens, Gareth Inc.

VISTA

see Volunteers in Service to America

VISUAL INSTRUCTION

see Audio-Visual Education

VITAMINS

Dalton, Cindy Devine. Love My Vitamins. 2000. (Why Should I... Ser.). (Illus.). 24p. (J). lib. bdg. 19.27 (978-1-55916-306-4(2)) Rourke Publishing, LLC.

Kalbacken, Joan. Vitamins & Minerals. De Capua, Sarah, ed. 1998. (True Bks.). (Illus.). 48p. (J). (gr. 3-5). pap. 6.95 (978-0-516-26387-8(0) , Children's Pr.) Scholastic Library Publishing.

—Vitamins & Minerals. 1998. (Illus.). 47p. (J). (ps-ps). lib. bdg. 15.25 (978-0-613-37578-8(5)) Tandem Library Bks.

Petrie, Kristin. Vitamins Are Vital. 2004. (Nutrition Ser.). (Illus.). 32p. (J). (gr. k-6). lib. bdg. 22.78 (978-1-59197-406-2(2) , Checkerboard Library) ABDO Publishing Co.

Royston, Angela. Protein for a Healthy Body. 2003. (Body Needs Ser.). (Illus.). 48p. pap. 7.99 (978-1-4034-3312-1(7)); (J). (gr. 4-6). lib. bdg. 27.07 (978-1-4034-0759-7(2)) Heinemann Library.

—Protein for a Healthy Body. 2003. (gr. 3-6). lib. bdg. 16.40 (978-0-613-60982-1(4)) Tandem Library Bks.

—Vitamins & Minerals for a Healthy Body. 2003. (Illus.). 48p. (J). pap. 7.99 (978-1-4034-3313-8(5)); lib. bdg. 27.07 (978-1-4034-0758-0(4)) Heinemann Library.

Vitality: Individual Title Six-Packs. (Bookweb Ser.). 32p. (gr. 6 up). 34.00 (978-0-7578-0906-4(5)) Rigby Education.

Woodford, Chris. Potassium. 2002. (Elements Ser.). (Illus.). 32p. (J). 25.64 (978-0-7614-1463-6(0) , Benchmark Bks.) Cavendish, Marshall Corp.

VIVARIUMS

see Terrariums

VOCABULARY

see also Words, New

A Is for Apple. (Illus.). 10p. (J). bds. (978-1-57755-197-3(4)) Allied Publishing.

Abrams, Majella. Reading Pals: Short & Long Vowels Gr. K-1. Taylor, Jennifer, ed. Sexton, Brenda, illus. 2007. (J). per. 6.99 ***978-1-59198-436-8(X))** Creative Teaching Pr., Inc.

Ace Academics, ed. English Vocabulary: A Whole Course in a Box! 2007. (Exambusters Ser.). 384p. (gr. 7 up). (978-1-881374-85-5(8) , Exambusters) Ace Academics, Inc.

Acredolo, Linda & Goodwin, Susan. Animals. 2007. 12p. bds. 12.99 ***978-0-8249-6718-5(6)** , Ideals Children's Bks.) Ideals Pubns.

—Babies. 2007. (My first spoken Words Ser.). 12p. 12.99 ***978-0-8249-6719-2(4)** , Ideals Children's Bks.) Ideals Pubns.

Aigner-Clark, Julie. Circle Time: An Interactive Book to Engage & Delight Your Child. Zaidi, Nadeem, illus. 2000. 10p. (J). (978-1-892309-22-8(X)) Baby Einstein Co., LLC, The.

—Language Discovery Cards: Images & Words to Teach & Delight. 2003. (Baby Einstein Ser.). 29p. (ps-17). 9.99 (978-1-892309-20-4(3)) Hyperion Pr.

—Wordsworth's Book of Words: A Bilingual Book of Words. Zaidi, Nadeem, illus. 2002. (Baby Einstein Ser.). 64p. (ps-ps). 15.99 (978-0-7868-0883-0(7)) Disney Pr.

Akinyemi, Rowena. Under the Moon, Level 1. 2nd ed. 2000. (Bookworms Ser.). (Illus.). 64p. 6.50 (978-0-19-422955-5(6)) Oxford Univ. Pr., Inc.

Allen, Amy Meyer. Are There Ants in Your Pants? 2002. (Illus.). 30p. 4.99 (978-1-887169-21-9(0)) Wedding Solutions Publishing, Inc.

Allen, Margaret. Reading Pals: Rhyming Words Using Blends & DIgraphs Gr. K-1. Taylor, Jennifer, ed. Sexton, Brenda, illus. 2007. (J). per. 6.99 ***978-1-59198-437-5(8))** Creative Teaching Pr., Inc.

Allen, Molly. Reading Pals: Sight Words Gr. K-1. Taylor, Jennifer, ed. Sexton, Brenda, illus. 2007. (J). per. 6.99 ***978-1-59198-438-2(6))** Creative Teaching Pr., Inc.

Allen, William H., creator. TEH Learns to Read: Primary Words. 2004. (J). 34.95 (978-0-9745938-2-1(6)) LD Coach, LLC.

Alphasnaps & Snapphonics: Snapphonics Big Book: Eek! Squeak! A Leak! 2003. 36.95 (978-0-673-60206-0(0)) Celebration Pr.

Alphasnaps & Snapphonics: Snapphonics Big Book: Scat the Cat. 2003. 36.95 (978-0-673-60207-7(9)) Celebration Pr.

American Education Publishing Staff. First Words. 2003. (Brighter Child Preschool Flash Cards Ser.). (Illus.). 36p. (J). (ps). 2.99 (978-1-56189-461-1(3) , 31044, American Education Publishing) School Specialty Publishing.

American Heritage Dictionary Editors. The American Heritage Picture Word Book. Collier-Morales, Roberta, illus. 2001. (American Heritage Library). 48p. (J). (ps-k). 12.95 (978-0-618-12561-6(2)) Houghton Mifflin Co. Trade & Reference Div.

—How Can I Get There? (Como Puedo Llegar Alla?) Cote, Pamela & Zagarenski, Pamela, illus. 2001. (Good Beginnings/Un Buen Comienzo Ser.). (SPA & ENG.). 4p. (J). (gr. k-ps). bds. 3.95 (978-0-618-16934-4(2)) Houghton Mifflin Co. Trade & Reference Div.

—How Do I Feel? (Como Me Siento?) Cote, Pamela & Zagarenski, Pamela, illus. 2001. (Good Beginnings/Un Buen Comienzo Ser.). 4p. (J). (gr. k-ps). bds. 3.95 (978-0-618-16931-3(8)) Houghton Mifflin Co. Trade & Reference Div.

—What Color Is It? Cote, Pamela & Zagarenski, Pamela, illus. 2001. (Good Beginnings/Un Buen Comienzo Ser.). Orig. Title: Que Color Es Este?. (SPA & ENG.). 4p. (J). (gr. k-ps). bds. 3.95 (978-0-618-16932-0(6)) Houghton Mifflin Co. Trade & Reference Div.

—Where Can I Go? Cote, Pamela & Zagarenski, Pamela, illus. 2001. (Good Beginnings/Un Buen Comienzo Ser.). Orig. Title: Adonde Puedo Ir?. (SPA & ENG.). 4p. (J). (gr. k-ps). bds. 3.95 (978-0-618-16933-7(4)) Houghton Mifflin Co. Trade & Reference Div.

Amery, H. First Hundred Words. 2004. 32p. (J). pap. 6.95 (978-0-7945-0002-3(1)); lib. bdg. 14.95 (978-1-58086-505-0(4)) EDC Publishing.

—First Hundred Words French Sticker Book. rev. ed. 2004. (Picture Puzzles Ser.). (FRE.). 40p. (J). pap. 8.95 (978-0-7945-0191-4(5) , Usborne) EDC Publishing.

—First Thousand Words. 2004. (J). (SPA.). 70p. pap. 9.95 (978-0-7945-0463-2(9)); (HEB.). 64p. 12.99 (978-0-7945-0029-0(3)); (FRE.). 64p. 12.99 (978-0-7945-0283-6(0)); (FRE.). 64p. lib. bdg. 20.95 (978-1-58086-513-5(5)) EDC Publishing.

—First Thousand Words in Spanish IL. rev. ed. 2004. (First Thousand Words Ser.). (SPA.). 64p. (J). lib. bdg. 20.99 (978-1-58086-564-7(X)) EDC Publishing.

Amery, H. & Cartwright, S. First Hundred Words in German Sticker Book. 2004. (Computer Guide Ser.). (GER.). 40p. (J). pap. 8.95 (978-0-7945-0562-2(7)) EDC Publishing.

—First Spanish Word Book. 2004. (Treasury of Farmyard Tales Ser.). (SPA.). 48p. (J). 10.95 (978-0-7945-0476-2(0)) EDC Publishing.

Amery, Heather. Farmyard Tales First Word Book. 2004. (Farmyard Tales Bks.). (Illus.). 48p. (J). 10.95 (978-0-7460-4084-3(9)) EDC Publishing.

—First Thousand Words in French Sticker Book. Cartwright, Stephen, illus. rev. ed. 2004. (First Thousand Words Sticker Bks.). (FRE & ENG.). 70p. (J). (ps-6). pap. 9.95 (978-0-7945-0425-0(6) , Usborne) EDC Publishing.

—First Thousand Words in Italian. Cartwright, Stephen, illus. rev. ed. 2004. (First Thousand Words Ser.). (ITA & ENG.). 64p. (J). (ps-6). 12.99 (978-0-7945-0286-7(5)); lib. bdg. 20.99 (978-1-58086-560-9(7)) EDC Publishing. (Usborne).

—First Thousand Words in Japanese. Cartwright, Stephen, illus. rev. ed. 2004. (First Thousand Words Ser.). (JPN & ENG.). 64p. (J). (ps-6). 12.95 (978-0-7945-0480-9(9)); lib. bdg. 20.95 (978-1-58086-552-4(6)) EDC Publishing. (Usborne).

—First Thousand Words in Russian. MacKinnon, Mairi, ed. Cartwright, Stephen, illus. 2005. 63p. (J). 12.99 (978-0-7945-1001-5(9) , Usborne) EDC Publishing.

—On the Farm? rev. ed. 2006. 16p. (J). pap. 5.99 (978-0-7945-1288-0(7) , Usborne) EDC Publishing.

Amery, Heather & Cartwright, Stephen. First French Word Book. 2004. (Farmyard Tales First Words Ser.). (ENG & FRE., Illus.). 48p. (J). 10.95 (978-0-7945-0295-9(4) , Usborne) EDC Publishing.

—First Thousand Words. 2004. (First Thousand Words Ser.). (Illus.). 64p. (J). 12.99 (978-0-7945-0282-9(2) , Usborne) EDC Publishing.

Analogies 1 Grd 7-8 Quiz Book. 2004. pap. 8.20 (978-0-8388-2226-5(6)) Educators Publishing Service, Inc.

Analogies & Multiple Meanings (Gr. 2-3) 2003. (J). (978-1-58232-125-7(6)) Bryan Hse. Pubs., Inc.

Anderson, Jill, ed. Let's Dive in the Ocean! !Vamos a Bucear! Holmes, Steve, illus. 2005. (ENG & SPA.). 20p. (J). (gr. 3-7). bds. 6.95 (978-1-58728-524-0(X) , Two Can Publishing) T&N Children's Publishing.

—Let's Get to Work!/Vamos a Trabajar! Evrard, Gaetan, illus. 2006. (ENG & SPA.). 20p. (J). (ps-k). bds. 6.95 (978-1-58728-512-7(6) , Two Can Publishing) T&N Children's Publishing.

—Let's Go on Safari!/Vamos de Safari! Utton, Peter, illus. 2005. (ENG & SPA.). 20p. (J). (ps-k). bds. bds. 6.95 (978-1-58728-522-6(3) , Two Can Publishing) T&N Children's Publishing.

—Let's Go!/Vamos a Viajar! Evrard, Gaetan, illus. 2006. (ENG & SPA.). 20p. (J). (ps-2). bds. 6.95 (978-1-58728-513-4(4) , Two Can Publishing) T&N Children's Publishing.

—Let's Visit the Jungle! !Vamos a la Selva!, 5. Holmes, Steve, illus. 2005. (ENG & SPA.). 20p. (J). (gr. 3-7). bds. 6.95 (978-1-58728-523-3(1) , Two Can Publishing) T&N Children's Publishing.

Andrews, Becky, ed. High Frequency Booklets. 2005. 96p. 14.95 (978-1-56234-650-8(4) , Mailbox Bks., The) Education Ctr., Inc.

Animal Sight Words. 2006. (PBS Kids(R) Ser.). (J). 9.95 ***978-1-57791-310-8(8))** Brighter Minds Children's Publishing.

Animales. (Coleccion Libritos Acordeon). (SPA., Illus.). 10p. (J). pap. 5.50 (978-950-11-0790-6(6) , SGM906) Sigmar ARG. *Dist:* Continental Bk. Co., Inc.

Arco Staff. Get Wise! Mastering Vocabulary Skills. 2nd ed. 2003. (Get Wise! Ser.). (Illus.). 220p. pap. 12.95 (978-0-7689-1342-2(X)) Peterson's.

Armapalabras: Phonics/Vocabulary. 2001. (McGraw-Hill. Lectura Ser.). (ENG & SPA.). (gr. 2 up). (978-0-02-186613-7(9)); (gr. 3 up). (978-0-02-186614-4(7)); (gr. 4 up). (978-0-02-186615-1(5)); (gr. 5 up). (978-0-02-186616-8(3)); (gr. 6 up). (978-0-02-186617-5(1)) Macmillan/McGraw-Hill Schl. Div.

AstroWord. 2004. (gr. k up). cd-rom 69.00 (978-0-673-64439-8(1)); (gr. 1 up). cd-rom 69.00 (978-0-673-62235-8(5)); (gr. 2 up). cd-rom 69.00 (978-0-673-62236-5(3)); (gr. 3 up). cd-rom 69.00 (978-0-673-62237-2(1)); (gr. 4 up). cd-rom 69.00 (978-0-673-62238-9(X)); (gr. 5 up). cd-rom 69.00 (978-0-673-62239-6(8)); (gr. 6 up). cd-rom 69.00 (978-0-673-62240-2(1)) Addison-Wesley Educational Pubs., Inc.

At Home. 2005. (Look, Listen, & Speak Ser.). 80p. (gr. k-3). cd-rom 29.99 (978-1-55799-925-2(2) , EMC 2738) Evan-Moor Educational Pubs.

At School. 2005. (Look, Listen, & Speak Ser.). 80p. (gr. k-3). cd-rom 29.99 (978-1-55799-926-9(0) , EMC 2739) Evan-Moor Educational Pubs.

At the Park. 2005. (Look, Listen, & Speak Ser.). 80p. (gr. k-3). cd-rom 29.99 (978-1-55799-927-6(9) , EMC 2740) Evan-Moor Educational Pubs.

Austen, Jane & MacKay, Barbara. Dominoes: Level 2: 700 Headwords Emma. 2002. (Dominoes Ser.). (Illus.). 6.50 (978-0-19-424345-2(1)) Oxford Univ. Pr., Inc.

Baby's First Word Book. 2004. 10p. (J). bds. 4.99 (978-1-85854-925-5(6)) Brimax Books Ltd. GBR. *Dist:* Byeway Bks.

Baby's First Words. 2003. (Illus.). (J). bds. 7.98 (978-0-7525-8651-9(3)) Parragon, Inc.

Baker, Alan. Little Rabbits' First Word Book. 2001. (Little Rabbit Bks.). (Illus.). 40p. (J). (ps up). pap. 5.95 (978-0-7534-5355-1(X) , Kingfisher) Houghton Mifflin Co. Trade & Reference Div.

Balfour, Sandy & Dorling Kindersley Publishing Staff. My First Word Board Book. 2004. 36p. (J). (ps-3). bds. 5.99 (978-0-7894-9905-9(3)) Dorling Kindersley Publishing, Inc.

Balloon Books Staff, ed. Max Mouse Learns First Words. 2000. (Plush Learning Bks.). (Illus.). 12p. (J). bds. 4.95 (978-0-8069-2919-4(7) , Balloon Bks.) Sterling Publishing Co., Inc.

Barrett, Judi. Things That Are Most in the World. 2001. (978-0-606-21487-2(9)) Tandem Library Bks.

Bassett, Jennifer. One-Way Ticket Level 1: Short Stories. 2nd ed. 2000. (Bookworms Ser.). (Illus.). 64p. 6.50 (978-0-19-422950-0(5)) Oxford Univ. Pr., Inc.

Beech, Linda & Cooper, Terry, eds. Sight Word Readers, Box Set. 2003. pap., tchr. ed. 95.95 (978-0-439-51183-4(6)) Scholastic, Inc.

Beech, Linda Ward. 240 Vocabulary Words 5th Grade Kids Need to Know. 2003. 80p. pap. 12.95 (978-0-439-28045-7(1) , Teaching Resources) Scholastic, Inc.

Belle River Readers Staff. Colors. 2002. (Illus.). 12p. (J). (gr. k-1). pap. 2.00 (978-0-9703548-3-9(5) , 4) Belle River Readers, Inc.

Benchmark Education Staff, compiled by. High Frequency Word Component Set. 2005. spiral bd. 210.00 ***978-1-4108-4156-8(1))** Benchmark Education Co.

Beyond the Code Grd 2-3, Bk. 2. 2004. pap. 6.75 (978-0-8388-2402-3(1)) Educators Publishing Service, Inc.

Bicknell, Joanna. Cuddle Buddy: Baby Words. 2006. 10p. (ps). 9.95 (978-1-84610-094-9(1)) Make Believe Ideas GBR. *Dist:* Ingram Pub. Services.

T U V

Bicknell, Joanna, ed. Baby Fun Words. 2005. 12p. (978-1-905051-16-8(6)) Make Believe Ideas.

Biz Word Activity Set. 1998. (Illus.). (YA). stu. ed. 25.00 (978-1-893215-00-9(8)) Independent Means, Inc.

Black, Jessica L. & Mullican, Judy. Let's Build a Snowman: Cuddle Book. Crowell, Knox, illus. 6p. (J). (ps-1). bds. 10.95 (978-1-57332-222-5(9)) HighReach Learning, Inc.

Blanchard, Cherie. Word Roots Level A2: Learning the Building Blocks of Better Spelling & Vocabulary. 2005. (J). pap. 16.99 (978-0-89455-865-8(X)) Critical Thinking Bks. & Software.

—Word Roots Level B Bk. 2: Learning the Building Blocks of Better Spelling & Vocabulary. 2005. (YA). pap. 18.99 (978-0-89455-866-5(8)) Critical Thinking Bks. & Software.

Blasser-Riley, Gail. Building Reading Comprehension: High-Interest Selections for Critical Reading Skills. 2000. (100+ Seriestm Ser.). 128p. (J). (gr. 1-2). pap. 12.99 (978-1-56822-912-6(7) , IF8717, Instructional Fair) Schaffer, Frank Pubns.

Block, Cheryl. Think Analogies: Learning to Connect Words & Relationships. 2003. (J). pap. 13.99 (978-0-89455-791-0(2)) Critical Thinking Bks. & Software.

Bluedorn, Harvey. Vocabulary Bridges from English to Latin & Greek. 2001. 104p. per. 20.00 (978-0-9743616-0-4(7)) Trivium Pursuit.

Bobby Fling, 6 vols. 8p. (gr. k-1). 21.50 (978-0-322-02068-9(9)) Wright Group, The.

Body, Wendy. Minki's Day, 4 vols. 2005. (QEB Readers). (Illus.). 24p. (J). (ps-3). lib. bdg. 15.95 (978-1-59566-106-7(9)) QEB Publishing Inc.

—Mup's Days of the Week, 4 vols. 2005. (QEB Readers). (Illus.). 24p. (J). (ps-3). lib. bdg. 15.95 (978-1-59566-104-3(2)) QEB Publishing Inc.

Boehm, Gregory A. Big Big Book of Word Search. 2005. 224p. (YA). mass mkt. (978-1-59412-000-8(5)) Mud Puddle, Inc.

Book Company Staff. Lift & Learn First Words. 2004. (Novelty Bks.). (Illus.). 10p. (J). (gr. 3-5). bds. 7.95 (978-1-74047-558-7(5)) Book Co. Publishing Pty, Ltd., The AUS. *Dist:* Penton Overseas, Inc.

Bottino, Marlane. My Language Book for Spelling, Writing & Vocabulary: Level D. Bottino, Marlane, illus. 2000. (My Language Books for Spelling, Writing & Vocabulary Ser.: Vol. 4). (Illus.). (J). (gr. k-6). pap. 6.50 (978-1-893615-05-2(7)) Creative Enterprises.

—My Language Book for Spelling, Writing & Vocabulary: Level E. Bottino, Marlane, illus. 2000. (My Language Books for Spelling, Writing & Vocabulary Ser.: Vol. 5). (Illus.). (J). (gr. k-6). pap. 6.50 (978-1-893615-06-9(5)) Creative Enterprises.

—My Language Book for Spelling, Writing & Vocabulary: Level F. Bottino, Marlane, illus. 2000. (My Language Books for Spelling, Writing & Vocabulary Ser.: Vol. 6). (Illus.). (J). (gr. k-6). pap. 6.50 (978-1-893615-07-6(3)) Creative Enterprises.

Brantley, C. L. Word Smart Junior, No. 1. 2nd ed. 2002. (Smart Junior Guides). 352p. (J). pap. 12.00 (978-0-375-76257-4(4) , Princeton Review) Random Hse. Information Group.

—Word Smart Junior II. 2nd ed. 2002. (Smart Junior Guides). 384p. (J). pap. 12.00 (978-0-375-76258-1(2) , Princeton Review) Random Hse. Information Group.

Brennan, Murray. Vocabulary Development from Dictionary Skills, 3 vols., Vol. 3. 2000. 48p. (J). (gr. 4-5). pap. 7.95 (978-1-58324-063-2(2) , World Teachers Pr.) Didax Educational Resources, Inc.

Brinton, Margaret & Instructional Fair Staff. Vocabulary in Context: 1,500 Words Every Middle School Student Should Know. 2002. (100+ Seriestm Ser.). (Illus.). 128p. (J). (gr. 5-8). pap. 12.99 (978-0-7424-0225-6(8) , IF87022) School Specialty Publishing.

Brooks, F. & Litchfield, J. Mis Primeras Palabras. 2004. Tr. of Very First Words. (SPA., Illus.). 10p. (J). 6.95 (978-0-7460-4823-8(8)) EDC Publishing.

Brown, Susan. Spanish/English Sight Words. 2005. 80p. (J). per. 9.99 (978-1-59441-436-7(X) , FI-704007) Carson-Dellosa Publishing Co., Inc.

Brownell, Rick. Expressive & Receptive One-Word Picture Vocabulary Tests: EOWPVT-2000 Plates. 3rd rev. ed. (ENG & SPA.). spiral bd. (978-1-57128-136-4(3)) High Noon Bks.

—Expressive & Receptive One-Word Picture Vocabulary Tests: ROWPVT-2000 Plates. 2nd rev. ed. (ENG & SPA.). spiral bd. (978-1-57128-140-1(1)) High Noon Bks.

Bryant-Mole, Karen. Mortimer's Fun with Words, 6 bks. Incl. Beginning Letters. Mukhida, Zul, illus. lib. bdg. 22.00 (978-0-8368-2746-0(5)); Ending Letters. Mukhida, Zul, photos by. lib. bdg. 22.00 (978-0-8368-2747-7(3)); Letters Make Words. Mukhida, Zul, photos by. lib. bdg. 22.00 (978-0-8368-2748-4(1)); Mortimer Plays I-Spy. Mukhida, Zul, illus. lib. bdg. 22.00 (978-0-8368-2749-1(X)); Mortimer's ABC's. Mukhida, Zul, illus. lib. bdg. 22.00 (978-0-8368-2750-7(3)); Rhyming Words. Mukhida, Zul, illus. lib. bdg. 22.00 (978-0-8368-2751-4(1)); 24p. (J). (ps up). 2000. 2000. Set lib. bdg. 88.00 (978-0-8368-2745-3(7)) Stevens, Gareth Inc.

Budgell, Gill. Make Colors American English Edition. 2000. (Cambridge Reading Ser.). (Illus.). pap. 5.00 (978-0-521-79890-7(6)) Cambridge Univ. Pr.

—Make Colours. 2000. (Cambridge Reading Ser.). (Illus.). 10p. pap. 5.00 (978-0-521-77464-2(0)) Cambridge Univ. Pr.

Buen Viaje Pinguinos! (Coleccion Leo Con Figuras). (SPA., Illus.). 14p. (J). pap. 4.50 (978-950-11-0929-0(1) , SGM291) Sigmar ARG. *Dist:* Continental Bk. Co., Inc.

Build Vocabulary, Read, & Grow. 2006. (J). pap. (***978-1-57332-383-3(7)***) HighReach Learning, Inc.

Building an Enriched Vocabulary: Student Text. 4th ed. 2004. (YA). (gr. 9-12). pap., stu. ed. (978-0-8215-7571-0(6)) Sadlier, William H. Inc.

Building Vocabulary Skills & Strategies Level 3. 2003. (Illus.). 144p. (YA). per. 16.95 (978-1-56254-721-9(6)) Saddleback Educational Publishing.

Building Vocabulary Skills & Strategies Level 4. 2003. (Illus.). 144p. (YA). per. 16.95 (978-1-56254-722-6(4) , SP7224) Saddleback Educational Publishing.

Building Vocabulary Skills & Strategies Level 5. 2003. (Illus.). 144p. (YA). per. 16.95 (978-1-56254-723-3(2) , SP7232) Saddleback Educational Publishing.

Building Vocabulary Skills & Strategies Level 6. 2003. (Illus.). 144p. (YA). per. 16.95 (978-1-56254-724-0(0) , SP7240) Saddleback Educational Publishing.

Building Vocabulary Skills & Strategies Level 7. 2003. (Illus.). 144p. (YA). per. 16.95 (978-1-56254-725-7(9) , SP7259) Saddleback Educational Publishing.

Building Vocabulary Skills & Strategies Level 8. 2003. (Illus.). 144p. (YA). per. 16.95 (978-1-56254-726-4(7)) Saddleback Educational Publishing.

Bulloch, Ivan & James, Diane. Allons Faire un Tour. 2000. (My Turn Ser.). (Illus.). 12p. (J). (ps-k). bds. 6.95 (978-1-58728-167-9(8) , Two Can Publishing) T&N Children's Publishing.

Burchers, Sam, Jr., et al. Vocabulary Cartoons II: SAT Word Power. 2000. (Illus.). 344p. (YA). (gr. 5 up). pap. 12.95 (978-0-9652422-6-4(9)) New Monic Bks.

—Vocabulary Classic Series: The Call of the Wild. 2004. Orig. Title: The Call of the Wild. 216p. (YA). (gr. 6-12). pap. 7.95 (978-0-9652422-0-2(X)) New Monic Bks.

Burgess, Chris. English Skills: Vocabulary Module. 1999. (J). (gr. 4-8). pap. 35.00 (978-0-7217-0606-1(1)) Schofield & Sims Ltd. GBR. *Dist:* State Mutual Bk. & Periodical Service, Ltd.

Burt, Angela & Vandyck, William. Vocabulary Repair Kit. 2002. (Illus.). 128p. (J). pap. 9.99 (978-0-340-80499-5(8) , Hodder & Stoughton) Hodder General Publishing Division GBR. *Dist:* Trafalgar Square Publishing.

Caccamo, Pepe. A Cazar Palabras. Fernandez, Maria Xose, illus. (SPA.). 142p. (J). (gr. k-2). (978-84-95123-36-7(3) , KA1393) Kalandraka Editora, S.L. ESP. *Dist:* Lectorum Pubns., Inc.

Callella, Kim. Build-a-Skill Instant Books Short & Long Vowels. shiotsu, Vicky & Faulkner, Stacey, eds. Campbell, Jenny & Tom, Darcy, illus. 2007. (J). 4.99 (***978-1-59198-412-2(2)***) Creative Teaching Pr., Inc.

Callella, Trisha. Greek & Latin Roots: Teaching Vocabulary to Improve Reading Comprehension. Rous, Sheri, ed. Peterson, Barbara, illus. 2004. 144p. pap. 16.99 (978-0-88160-381-1(3) , LW-438) Creative Teaching Pr., Inc.

—More Greek & Latin Roots: Teaching Vocabulary to Improve Reading Comprehension. Faulkner, Stacey, ed. Hillam, Corbin, illus. 2006. (J). pap. 18.99 (***978-1-59198-328-6(2)***) Creative Teaching Pr., Inc.

Callella, Trisha. Prefixes & Suffixes: Teaching Vocabulary to Improve Reading Comprehension. Williams, Carolea & Rous, Sheri, eds. Peterson, Barbara, illus. 2004. 144p. pap. 16.99 (978-0-88160-380-4(5) , LW-437) Creative Teaching Pr., Inc.

Cameron, Alex J. Vocabulary Workshop: Interactive Audio Pronunciation Program. 1998. (Vocabulary Workshop Ser.). 2p. Level C. (J). (gr. 8-9). audio (978-0-8215-0688-2(9)); Level A. (J). (gr. 6-7). pap. incl. audio (978-0-8215-0686-8(2)); Level B. (J). (gr. 7-8). pap. incl. audio (978-0-8215-0687-5(0)); Level F. (YA). (gr. 11-12). pap. incl. audio (978-0-8215-0691-2(9)) Sadlier, William H. Inc. (Sadlier-Oxford).

Campbell Books Staff & Fry, Carolyn. Babies First Word. 2001. (Illus.). 10p. (J). bds. 9.95 (978-0-333-73343-1(6)) Macmillan Publishers Ltd. GBR. *Dist:* Independent Pubs. Group.

Campbell, Dorthina A. Step Forward Strategies for Struggling Readers: Student Resource Guide. 2005. 59p. (J). stu. ed., per. 8.99 (978-0-9768208-0-2(3)) Edutech Learning Resource Ctr.

Campbell, Rod. My Yellow Busy Book. 2003. (Illus.). 12p. (J). 6.99 (978-0-333-65972-4(4)) Macmillan Publishers Ltd. GBR. *Dist:* Independent Pubs. Group.

Carey Molter. Ate As in Skate. 2003. (Word Families Ser.: Vol. 8). (Illus.). 23p. (J). (ps-3). lib. bdg. 19.93 (978-1-59197-271-6(X) , SandCastle) ABDO Publishing Co.

Carle, Eric. My Very First Book of Words. Carle, Eric, illus. 2006. 20p. (J). (ps-1). bds. 5.99 (978-0-399-24510-7(3) , Philomel) Penguin Group (USA) Inc.

—The Very Busy Spider's Favorite Words. 2007. 20p. (J). (ps-1). bds. 3.99 (***978-0-448-44703-2(7)*** , Grosset & Dunlap) Penguin Group (USA) Inc.

—The Very Clumsy Click Beetle's Favorite Words. 2008. 22p. (J). (ps-1). bds. 3.99 (***978-0-448-44802-2(5)*** , Grosset & Dunlap) Penguin Group (USA) Inc.

—The Very Hungry Caterpillar's Favorite Words. 2007. 20p. (J). (ps-1). bds. 3.99 (***978-0-448-44704-9(5)*** , Grosset & Dunlap) Penguin Group (USA) Inc.

—The Very Quiet Cricket's Favorite Words. 2008. 22p. (J). (ps-1). bds. 3.99 (***978-0-448-44803-9(3)*** , Grosset & Dunlap) Penguin Group (USA) Inc.

Carroll, Joyce Armstrong, et al. Literature: Timeless Voices, Timeless Themes. 2001. Bronze Level. (YA). (gr. 7). pap., stu. ed., wbk. ed. 7.47 (978-0-13-043487-6(6)); Copper Level. (J). (gr. 6). pap., stu. ed., wbk. ed. 7.47 (978-0-13-043486-9(8)); Diamond Level. (YA). (gr. 12). pap., stu. ed., wbk. ed. 7.47 (978-0-13-043492-0(2)); Gold Level. (YA). (gr. 9). pap., stu. ed., wbk. ed. 7.47 (978-0-13-043489-0(2)); Platinum Level. (YA). (gr. 10). pap., stu. ed., wbk. ed. 7.47 (978-0-13-043490-6(6)); Ruby Level. (YA). (gr. 11). pap., stu. ed., wbk. ed. 7.47 (978-0-13-043491-3(4)) Prentice Hall PTR.

Cartwright, Stephen, illus. First Thousand Words in English. 2004. (First Thousand Words Ser.). 64p. (J). lib. bdg. 20.95 (978-1-58086-474-9(0)) EDC Publishing.

Cassie, Brian. Say It Again. Mooney, David A., illus. 2000. 32p. (J). (ps-3). 16.95 (978-0-88106-341-7(X)); pap. 6.95 (978-0-88106-342-4(8)) Charlesbridge Publishing, Inc.

—Say It Again. 2000. (978-0-606-18029-0(X)); lib. bdg. 15.25 (978-0-613-28310-6(4)) Tandem Library Bks.

Cernak, Kim. Build-a-Skill Instant Books Consonant Blends & Digraphs. shiotsu, Vicky & Faulkner, Stacey, eds. Campbell, Jenny & Tom, Darcy, illus. 2007. (J). 4.99 (***978-1-59198-410-8(6)***) Creative Teaching Pr., Inc.

Cernek, Kim & Williams, Rozanne Lanczak. Build-a-Skill Instant Books Color, Shape & Number Words. Shiotsu, Vicky & Faulkner, Stacey, eds. Campbell, Jenny & Tom, Darcy, illus. 2007. (J). 4.99 (***978-1-59198-411-5(4)***) Creative Teaching Pr., Inc.

Cestnik, Lisa & Cestnik, Jay. 100 Sight Word Mini-Books: Instant Fill-in Mini-Books That Teach 100 Essential Sight Words. 2005. 112p. pap. 15.99 (978-0-439-38780-4(9) , Teaching Resources) Scholastic, Inc.

Chanko, Pamela. Shoe Box Learning Centers: Word Families. 2006. 80p. pap. 12.99 (978-0-439-53795-7(9) , Teaching Resources) Scholastic, Inc.

Cheney, Martha C. Gifted & Talented Word Workbook for Preschoolers. Kaminski, Karol, illus. 1999. (Gifted & Talented Ser.). 48p. (J). (ps-k). pap., wbk. ed. 5.95 (978-1-56565-670-3(9) , 06709W) Lowell Hse. Juvenile.

Choosing the Right Word (Gr. 3+) 2003. (J). (978-1-58232-052-6(7)) Bryan Hse. Pubs., Inc.

Clamshell. Crazy Cats - Los Gatos Locos: Colors - Los Colores. 2000. (SPA & ENG., Illus.). 36p. (J). (ps-1). pap. 9.95 incl. audio (978-1-886972-30-8(3)) Emaginit.

—Crazy Cats - Los Gatos Locos: Numbers - Los Numeros. 2000. (ENG & SPA., Illus.). 36p. (J). (ps-1). pap. 9.95 incl. audio (978-1-886972-31-5(1)) Emaginit.

—Crazy Cats - Los Gatos Locos: Positions - Las Posiciones. 2000. (ENG & SPA., Illus.). 36p. (J). (ps-1). pap. 9.95 incl. audio (978-1-886972-32-2(X)) Emaginit.

Clark, Sarah Kartchner. How to Improve Your Vocabulary. Buehler, Stephanie J., ed. 1999. (How to Ser.). (Illus.). 48p. (J). (gr. 5-8). pap., act. bk. ed. 7.99 (978-1-57690-489-3(X) , TCA2489) Teacher Created Materials, Inc.

Clausen, Andrew. The Cricket in Times Square. 1998. 60p. (J). stu. ed., ring bd. 12.99 (978-1-58609-134-7(4)) Progeny Pr.

Clink! Clink! Clink!, 6 vols. 8p. (gr. k-1). 21.50 (978-0-322-02057-3(3)) Wright Group, The.

Clothing Language. 2001. (gr. 6-12). pap., tchr.'s training gde. ed. 1.95 (978-0-8359-1526-7(3)); 48p. (YA). pap. 16.95 (978-0-8359-1524-3(7)) Globe Fearon Educational Publishing.

Cole, Bob. Power Reading. Ford, David, illus. 2002. (J). (gr. 2-5). pap. 129.95 incl. audio (978-1-883186-18-0(8) , PP03C) National Reading Styles Institute, Inc.

Collins, S. H. Basic Signing Vocabulary Cards. 2001. (J). Set A. 7.95 (978-0-931993-23-7(7)); Set B. 7.95 (978-0-931993-24-4(5)) Garlic Pr.

Combining Categories, Inferences & Context Clues. 2000. 62p. spiral bd. 26.00 (978-1-886143-50-0(1)) Great Ideas for Teaching, Inc.

Come to My House: 6 Small Books. (Greetings Ser.: Vol. 3). 24p. (gr. 2-3). 31.00 (978-0-7635-9418-3(0)) Rigby Education.

Consonant Clusters, 20, Set. 2004. (Beastieville Ser.). 267.75 (978-0-516-25140-0(6) , Children's Pr.) Scholastic Library Publishing.

Cooper, Terry, ed. 100 Words Kids Need to Read by 1st Grade: Sight Word Practice to Build Strong Readers. 2002. 32p. (gr. 1). pap. 3.95 (978-0-439-39929-6(7)) Scholastic, Inc.

Cox, Phil Roxbee & Cartwright, S. Fox on a Box. 2004. (Easy Words to Read Ser.). 16p. (J). (gr. 1 up). pap. 6.95 (978-0-7945-0443-4(4)) EDC Publishing.

Cox, Phil Roxbee & Cartwright, Stephen. Frog on a Log. 2004. (Illus.). 10p. (J). 4.99 (978-0-7945-0302-4(0) , Usborne) EDC Publishing.

Crazy Cats - Los Gatos Locos: Colors, Numbers & Positions. 2000. (ENG & SPA., Illus.). 108p. (J). (ps-1). pap. 25.95 incl. audio (978-1-886972-40-7(0)) Emaginit.

Critters. 2007. (J). lib. bdg. 9.95 (***978-0-9768706-6-1(5)***) Learning Props.

Crosbie, Duncan. Find Out about Spain: Learn Spanish Words & Phrases & about Life in Spain. Hutchinson, Tim, illus. 2006. (Find Out about Ser.). (ENG & SPA.). 64p. (J). (gr. 3 up). spiral bd. 12.99 (978-0-7641-5955-8(0)) Barron's Educational Series, Inc.

Cunningham, Patricia M. Making More Words: Multilevel, Hands-on Phonics & Spelling Activities. 2001. (Illus.). 208p. (J). (gr. 1-3). pap. 18.99 (978-1-56417-900-5(1) , GA1588) Schaffer, Frank Pubns.

Daily Word Problems. 2001. (Illus.). 112p. (J). (gr. 2). pap. 14.99 (978-1-55799-814-9(0) , EMC 3002); (gr. 3). pap. 14.99 (978-1-55799-815-6(9) , EMC 3003); (gr. 4). pap. 14.99 (978-1-55799-816-3(7) , EMC 3004); (gr. 5). pap. 14.99 (978-1-55799-817-0(5) , EMC 3005); (gr. 6). pap. 14.99 (978-1-55799-818-7(3) , EMC 3006) Evan-Moor Educational Pubs.

Dainty, Peter & Hedge, Tricia. The Love of a King. 2nd ed. 2000. (Oxford Bookworms Ser.). (Illus.). 64p. 6.50 (978-0-19-422978-4(5)) Oxford Univ. Pr., Inc.

Data Notes Staff. Word Mapping for Literacy & Language. 2005. 14p. (gr. 11-12). stu. ed., wbk. ed. 25.95 (978-0-911569-18-6(9)) Prosperity & Profits Unlimited, Distribution Services.

Davis, Lee. What Does P. B. Bear Choose? 2001. (P. B. Bear Ser.). (Illus.). 24p. (J). (ps). pap. 4.95 (978-0-7894-2223-1(9) , D K Ink) Dorling Kindersley Publishing, Inc.

de Brunhoff, Laurent. Babar's ABC. 2001. (Babar Ser.). (Illus.). 38p. (J). (ps-3). 17.95 (978-0-8109-5707-7(8)) Abrams, Harry N. , Inc.

Diaz-Cubero, Jose H. Practicas de Ortografia: 3 Grado. (SPA & ENG.). (J). (gr. 3). 9.95 (978-84-357-0127-3(1) , CPR88) Ediciones y Distribuciones Codice, S.A. ESP. *Dist:* Continental Bk. Co., Inc.

—Practicas de Ortografia: 6 Grado. (SPA & ENG.). (J). (gr. 6). 9.95 (978-84-357-0124-2(7) , CPR94) Ediciones y Distribuciones Codice, S.A. ESP. *Dist:* Continental Bk. Co., Inc.

Diaz, James, illus. Blue: A Touchy Feely First Words Color Book. 2000. (Touchy Feely First Words Bks.). 10p. (J). (ps up). 5.95 (978-1-58117-071-9(8) , Intervisual/Piggy Toes) Dalmatian Pr.

—Green: A Touchy Feely First Words Book. 2000. (Touchy Feely First Words Bks.). 10p. (J). (ps up). 5.95 (978-1-58117-072-6(6) , Intervisual/Piggy Toes) Dalmatian Pr.

—Red: A Touchy Feely First Words Color Book. 2000. (Touchy Feely First Words Bks.). 10p. (J). (ps up). 5.95 (978-1-58117-070-2(X) , Intervisual/Piggy Toes) Dalmatian Pr.

—Yellow: A Touchy Feely First Words Book. 2000. (Touchy Feely First Words Bks.: Vol. 4). 10p. (J). (ps up). 5.95 (978-1-58117-069-6(6) , Intervisual/Piggy Toes) Dalmatian Pr.

Dickey, Laurel. Balloons. Dufresne, Michele, photos by. 1999. (Illus.). (J). pap. 3.75 (978-1-58453-028-2(6)) Pioneer Valley Educational Pr., Inc.

—Zack's House. Weinberg, Richard, photos by. 1999. (Illus.). (J). pap. 3.75 (978-1-58453-036-7(7)) Pioneer Valley Educational Pr., Inc.

Dickey, Laurel & Dufresne, Michele. Emergent Set 2: Classroom Collection. Dickey, Laurel et al, photos by. Dufresne, Robert et al, photos by. 1999. (Illus.). (J). pap. 90.00 (978-1-58453-074-9(X)) Pioneer Valley Educational Pr., Inc.

Diktattrainer 5. Klasse. (Duden-Schuelerhilfen Ser.). (GER.). 112p. (J). incl. cd-rom (978-3-411-71011-9(X)) Bibliographisches Institut & F. A. Brockhaus AG DEU. *Dist:* International Bk. Import Service, Inc.

Diktattrainer 6. Klasse. (Duden-Schuelerhilfen Ser.). (GER.). 112p. (J). incl. cd-rom (978-3-411-71021-8(7)) Bibliographisches Institut & F. A. Brockhaus AG DEU. *Dist:* International Bk. Import Service, Inc.

DK Publishing. First Words. 2008. (J). (ps-k). 16p. bds. 9.99 (***978-0-7566-3844-3(5));*** 14p. 5.99 (***978-0-7566-3466-7(0)***) Dorling Kindersley Publishing, Inc.

—Words: Let's Get Talking. 2008. 28p. (J). (ps-3). 9.99 (***978-0-7566-3431-5(8)***) Dorling Kindersley Publishing, Inc.

DK Publishing Staff. First Words. 2007. 24p. (J). (ps-1). 4.99 (978-0-7566-2922-9(5)) Dorling Kindersley Publishing, Inc.

—My First Word Board Book. 2007. (My First Bks.). 64p. (J). bds. 12.99 (978-0-7566-2589-4(0)) Dorling Kindersley Publishing, Inc.

—My First Word Lift-the-Flap Board Book. 1999. (My First Bks.). (Illus.). 12p. (J). (ps-k). bds. 9.99 (978-0-7894-4736-4(3)) Dorling Kindersley Publishing, Inc.

—Word: My First Activity Box. 2007. (My First Bks.). (J). (ps-1). 19.99 (978-0-7566-3022-5(3)) Dorling Kindersley Publishing, Inc.

Do you Like Rice?, 6 vols. 8p. (gr. k-1). 21.50 (978-0-322-02058-0(1)) Wright Group, The.

Dobkin, Bonnie. Go-with Words. rev. ed. 2000. (gr. k-3). lib. bdg. 12.95 (978-0-613-37364-7(2)) Tandem Library Bks.

Dora the Explorer Verbs- First Action Words. 2007. (J). pap. 2.95 (***978-1-59545-158-3(7)***) Learning Horizons, Inc.

Dorling Kindersley Publishing Staff. All about Me. 2003. (Lift-the-Flap Books Ser.). (Illus.). 1p. (J). bds. 6.99 (978-0-7894-9236-4(9)) Dorling Kindersley Publishing, Inc.

—Barbie My Picture Dictionary. 2005. (Illus.). 48p. (J). 12.99 (978-0-7566-1007-4(9)) Dorling Kindersley Publishing, Inc.

—Discover & Play Book. 2003. (My First Bks.). (Illus.). 80p. (J). 12.99 (978-0-7894-9847-2(2)) Dorling Kindersley Publishing, Inc.

—First Words. 2006. (Let's Look Ser.). (Illus.). 36p. (J). (ps-3). bds. 4.99 (978-0-7566-1749-3(9)) Dorling Kindersley Publishing, Inc.

—My Big Book. Langrish, Bob & Oliver, Stephen, illus. 1999. (Funfax Ser.). 8p. (J). (ps-3). bds. 9.95 (978-0-7894-4325-0(2)) Dorling Kindersley Publishing, Inc.

—My First Hanukkah. 2nd ed. 2005. (My First Word Books). (Illus.). 36p. (J). (ps-ps). per., bds. 5.99 (978-0-7566-1105-7(9)) Dorling Kindersley Publishing, Inc.

—My First Touch & Feel Picture Cards: First Words. 2005. (Baby Genius Ser.). 16p. (J). pap. 9.99 (978-0-7566-1518-5(6)) Dorling Kindersley Publishing, Inc.

—My First Word Bath Book. 1999. (My First Series Ser.). (Illus.). 10p. (J). (ps-k). 6.99 (978-0-7894-4297-0(3)) Dorling Kindersley Publishing, Inc.

—My First Word Book. 2002. (Illus.). 64p. (J). (ps). 16.99 (978-0-7894-8992-0(9)) Dorling Kindersley Publishing, Inc.

—My First Word Sticker Board Book. 2002. (Illus.). 16p. (J). pap. 6.99 (978-0-7894-8876-3(0)) Dorling Kindersley Publishing, Inc.

—Numbers Are Everywhere! 2006. (Fun Flaps Ser.). (Illus.). 14p. (J). bds. 4.99 (978-0-7566-1763-9(4)) Dorling Kindersley Publishing, Inc.

—Word Wizard. 2006. (DK Toys & Games Ser.). 1p. (J). pap. 9.99 (978-0-7566-1765-3(0)) Dorling Kindersley Publishing, Inc.

Dorling Kindersley Publishing Staff, ed. Dias Llenos de Color. 2004. (Dk Readers Ser.). 32p. (J). pap. 3.99 (978-0-7566-0640-4(3)) Dorling Kindersley Publishing, Inc.

—El Mundo Marino. 2004. (Dk Readers Ser.). 32p. (J). (gr. 5). pap. 3.99 (978-0-7566-0639-8(X)) Dorling Kindersley Publishing, Inc.

T U V

Dorling Kindersley Publishing Staff & Millard, Anne. My First Truck Bath Book. 2002. (My First Ser.). (Illus.). 10p. (J). (ps-k). 5.95 (978-0-7894-8525-0(7)) Dorling Kindersley Publishing, Inc.

Dorsey, Kathleen. Building Vocabulary with Familiar Songs. 2007. 64p. pap. 11.99 (***978-0-439-81311-2(5)***) Scholastic, Inc.

Doudna, Kelly. Any Day but Today! 2004. (Sight Words Ser.). (Illus.). 23p. (J). (ps-3). lib. bdg. 19.93 (978-1-59197-464-2(X)) ABDO Publishing Co.

—Are Buses Big? (Illus.). 23p. (J). (ps-3). 2006. 19.93 (978-1-59679-352-1(X) , SandCastle); 2005. (978-1-59679-353-8(8)) ABDO Publishing Co.

—The Balloons Go up, up, up! (Illus.). 23p. (J). (ps-3). 2006. 19.93 (978-1-59679-354-5(6) , SandCastle); 2005. pap. (978-1-59679-355-2(4)) ABDO Publishing Co.

—Can You Fly? (Illus.). 23p. (J). (ps-3). 2006. 19.93 (978-1-59679-358-3(9) , SandCastle); 2005. pap. (978-1-59679-359-0(7)) ABDO Publishing Co.

—Et As in Jet. 2003. (Word Families Ser.). 23p. (J). (ps-3). lib. bdg. 19.93 (978-1-59197-230-3(2) , SandCastle) ABDO Publishing Co.

—Give It a Try! 2004. (Sight Words Ser.). (Illus.). 23p. (J). (ps-3). lib. bdg. 19.93 (978-1-59197-469-7(0)) ABDO Publishing Co.

—Id As in Squid. 2003. (Word Families Ser.). (Illus.). 23p. (J). (ps-3). lib. bdg. 19.93 (978-1-59197-235-8(3) , SandCastle) ABDO Publishing Co.

—Ig As in Pig. Marx, Monica, ed. 2003. (Word Families Ser.). (Illus.). 23p. (J). (ps-3). lib. bdg. 19.93 (978-1-59197-236-5(1)) ABDO Publishing Co.

—Ill As in Grill. 2003. (Word Families Ser.). (Illus.). 23p. (J). (ps-3). lib. bdg. 19.93 (978-1-59197-237-2(X) , SandCastle) ABDO Publishing Co.

—In As in Twin. 2003. (Word Families Ser.). (Illus.). 23p. (J). (ps-3). lib. bdg. 19.93 (978-1-59197-238-9(8) , SandCastle) ABDO Publishing Co.

—Ip As in Ship. 2003. (Word Families Ser.). (Illus.). 23p. (J). (ps-3). lib. bdg. 19.93 (978-1-59197-239-6(6) , SandCastle) ABDO Publishing Co.

—Is It a Party? (Illus.). 23p. (J). (ps-3). 2006. 19.93 (978-1-59679-386-6(4) , SandCastle); 2005. pap. (978-1-59679-387-3(2)) ABDO Publishing Co.

—Is the TV On? (Illus.). 23p. (J). (ps-3). 2006. 19.93 (978-1-59679-388-0(0) , SandCastle); 2005. pap. (978-1-59679-389-7(9)) ABDO Publishing Co.

—It As in Sit. 2003. (See It, Say It, Hear It Ser.). (Illus.). 23p. (J). (ps-3). lib. bdg. 19.93 (978-1-59197-240-2(X) , SandCastle) ABDO Publishing Co.

—It Is My Hat. (Illus.). 23p. (J). (ps-3). 2006. 19.93 (978-1-59679-392-7(9) , SandCastle); 2005. pap. (978-1-59679-393-4(7)) ABDO Publishing Co.

—It's My Mission to Make a Definition! (Illus.). 24p. (J). 2007. 19.93 (978-1-59928-600-6(9)); 2006. (978-1-59928-601-3(7)) ABDO Publishing Co.

—Just Make Some Art! 2004. (Sight Words Ser.). (Illus.). 23p. (J). (ps-3). lib. bdg. 19.93 (978-1-59197-481-9(X)) ABDO Publishing Co.

—My Brother, My Sister. (Illus.). 23p. (J). (ps-3). 2006. 19.93 (978-1-59679-402-3(X) , SandCastle); 2005. (978-1-59679-403-0(8)) ABDO Publishing Co.

—My House Is Big! (Illus.). 23p. (J). (ps-3). 2006. 19.93 (978-1-59679-404-7(6) , SandCastle); 2005. (978-1-59679-405-4(4)) ABDO Publishing Co.

—Ow As in Crow. 2003. (Word Families Ser.). (Illus.). 23p. (J). (ps-3). lib. bdg. 19.93 (978-1-59197-265-5(5) , SandCastle) ABDO Publishing Co.

—Sound Words. 2004. (J). (ps-3). lib. bdg. 119.58 (978-1-59197-449-9(6) , SandCastle) ABDO Publishing Co.

—There Are Ants down There! 2004. (Sight Words Ser.). (Illus.). 23p. (J). (ps-3). lib. bdg. 19.93 (978-1-59197-473-4(9)) ABDO Publishing Co.

—To the Camp! 2005. (Illus.). (J). 23p. pap. (978-1-59679-421-4(6)); 24p. lib. bdg. 19.93 (978-1-59679-420-7(8) , SandCastle) ABDO Publishing Co.

—Up the Path. 2005. (Illus.). (J). 23p. pap. (978-1-59679-423-8(2)); 24p. lib. bdg. 19.93 (978-1-59679-422-1(4) , SandCastle) ABDO Publishing Co.

—Was That Fun? 2004. (Sight Words Ser.). (Illus.). 23p. (J). (ps-3). lib. bdg. 19.93 (978-1-59197-475-8(5)) ABDO Publishing Co.

—We Can Jump! 2005. (Illus.). (J). 23p. pap. (978-1-59679-429-0(1)); 24p. lib. bdg. 19.93 (978-1-59679-428-3(3) , SandCastle) ABDO Publishing Co.

—We Go to the Park. 2005. (Illus.). (J). 23p. pap. (978-1-59679-431-3(3)); 24p. lib. bdg. 19.93 (978-1-59679-430-6(5) , SandCastle) ABDO Publishing Co.

—When Can You Play Again? 2004. (Sight Words Ser.). (Illus.). 23p. (J). (ps-3). lib. bdg. 19.93 (978-1-59197-478-9(X)) ABDO Publishing Co.

Douglas, Vincent & School Specialty Publishing Staff. Challenge Word Searches. 2003. (Homework Helpers Ser.). (Illus.). 32p. (J). (gr. k-1). pap. 2.99 (978-0-7696-2938-4(5) , American Education Publishing) School Specialty Publishing.

—First Words. 2003. (Brighter Child Flash Cards Ser.). (Illus.). 54p. (J). (ps up). 2.99 (978-0-7696-2369-6(7) , Brighter Child) School Specialty Publishing.

—Sight Words. (Brighter Child Flash Cards Ser.). (Illus.). (J). (ps up). 2003. 54p. 2.99 (978-0-7696-2396-2(4) , Brighter Child); 2000. 50p. 2.99 (978-1-57768-160-1(6) , Spectrum) School Specialty Publishing.

—Word Search, Vol. 32. l.t. ed. 2004. (Large Print Word Searches Ser.). (Illus.). 120p. (J). pap. 2.99 (978-0-7696-3196-7(7) , Brighter Child) School Specialty Publishing.

Doyle, Arthur Conan. The Blue Diamond. 2002. (Illus.). 48p. 6.50 (978-0-19-424340-7(0)) Oxford Univ. Pr., Inc.

Doyle, Arthur Conan & Kingsley, Susan. The Lost World. 2002. 6.50 (978-0-19-424347-6(8)) Oxford Univ. Pr., Inc.

Draze, Dianne. Red Hot Root Words Bk. 1: Mastering Vocabulary with Prefixes, Suffixes & Root Words. 2003. (J). pap. 16.95 (978-1-883055-57-8(1)) Dandy Lion Pubns.

Dress Up. 2007. (J). lib. bdg. 9.95 (***978-0-9768706-4-7(9)***) Learning Props.

Drugstore Language. 2001. (YA). (gr. 6-12). pap. 16.95 (978-0-8359-1518-2(2)) Globe Fearon Educational Publishing.

Dufresne, Michele. Cooking Thanksgiving Dinner. Dufresne, Michele, photos by. 1999. (Illus.). (J). pap. 3.75 (978-1-58453-034-3(0)) Pioneer Valley Educational Pr., Inc.

—Emily Can't Sleep. Dufresne, Michele, photos by. 1999. (Illus.). (J). pap. 3.75 (978-1-58453-035-0(9)) Pioneer Valley Educational Pr., Inc.

—George's Show & Tell. Dufresne, Michele, photos by. 1999. (Illus.). (J). pap. 3.75 (978-1-58453-023-7(5)) Pioneer Valley Educational Pr., Inc.

—A Snack for Roberto. Dufresne, Michele, photos by. 1999. (Illus.). (J). pap. 3.75 (978-1-58453-024-4(3)) Pioneer Valley Educational Pr., Inc.

Dufresne, Michele & Dickey, Laurel. Emergent Set 1, Vol. 1. Dufresne, Michele et al, photos by. Dufresne, Robert et al, photos by. 1998. (Illus.). (J). pap. (978-1-58453-043-5(X)) Pioneer Valley Educational Pr., Inc.

—Emergent Set 2, Vol. 2. Dufresne, Michele et al, photos by. Dufresne, Robert et al, photos by. 1999. (Illus.). (J). pap. 16.50 (978-1-58453-033-6(2)) Pioneer Valley Educational Pr., Inc.

Duncan, Leonard C. Greek Roots J-Ology. Bigelow, Holly, illus. Date not set. 140p. (J). (gr. 6-12). spiral bd. 25.00 (978-0-941414-01-2(9)) L.C.D.

Dunham, Anne M. & O'Neal, Debbie M. Monopoly Junior Word Skills Grades K-1. 2002. 32p. (J). 3.99 (978-1-58792-024-0(7)) Trend Enterprises, Inc.

Dunn, Opal. Un, Deux, Trois. Aggs, Patrice, illus. 2006. (FRE.). 24p. (J). pap. 9.95 (978-1-84507-623-8(0)) Lincoln, Frances Ltd. GBR. *Dist:* Perseus Distribution.

Ebbers, Susan M. Vocabulary Through Morphemes: Suffixes, Prefixes, & Roots for Intermediate Grades. 2004. 240p. per. (978-1-59318-212-0(0)) Sopris West Educational Services.

Eck, Kristin. Colors in My House. 2004. (Look-And-Learn Books). (Illus.). (J). lib. bdg. 7.95 (978-1-4042-2698-2(2) , PowerKids Pr.) Rosen Publishing Group, Inc., The.

—Hide-and-Seek Clothes. 2004. (Hide-And-Seek Books). (Illus.). (J). lib. bdg. 7.95 (978-1-4042-2705-7(9) , PowerKids Pr.) Rosen Publishing Group, Inc., The.

—Shapes in My House. 2004. (Look-And-Learn Books). (Illus.). (J). lib. bdg. 7.95 (978-1-4042-2699-9(0) , PowerKids Pr.) Rosen Publishing Group, Inc., The.

Education Pub Staff. Code Cards. 2004. pap. 8.05 (978-0-8388-1788-9(2)) Educators Publishing Service, Inc.

Egan, Lorraine Hopping. The Best-Ever Vocabulary & Word Study Games: Engaging Games & Activities That Expand Students' Vocabulary to Help Them Read, Write, & Test Better. 2001. 64p. (gr. 4). pap. 11.95 (978-0-439-13844-4(2)) Scholastic, Inc.

Eichten, Philip. Baby's Early Words: A Picture Book For Exclamations, Sound-Words, & Other Early Words. Thornton, Andrew, illus. 2001. 32p. (J). spiral bd. 7.95 (978-0-9639415-4-1(2)) Pi Communication Materials, Inc.

Einhorn, Kama. 100 Vocabulary Words Kids Need to Know by 4th Grade. 2004. (100 Words Workbook Ser.). (Illus.). 256p. (J). wbk. ed. 12.95 (978-0-439-56676-6(2)) Scholastic, Inc.

Elliot. Vocabulary Workshop Course 4. 1998. (gr. 10). pap. 20.20 (978-0-03-043019-0(4)) Holt, Rinehart & Winston.

—Vocabulary Workshop Course 5. 1998. (gr. 11). pap. 20.20 (978-0-03-043022-0(4)) Holt, Rinehart & Winston.

Ellis, Libby. Buenos Dias Baby. 2004. (ENG & SPA., Illus.). 20p. (J). bds. 3.95 (978-0-8118-4270-9(3)) Chronicle Bks. LLC.

Emberley, Rebecca. My Day-Mia Dia: A Book in Two Languages. 2000. (978-0-606-18260-7(8)) Tandem Library Bks.

EMC-Paradigm Publishing Staff. Discovering Literature: Vocabulary Resource. 2002. (J). (gr. 6). (978-0-8219-2030-5(8)) EMC/Paradigm Publishing.

Enriquece tu Vocabulario: Student & Teacher Support Resources. 2003. (MacMillan/McGraw-Hill. Estudios Sociales Ser.). (ENG & SPA.). (gr. 1 up). (978-0-02-149765-2(6)); (gr. 2 up). (978-0-02-149766-9(4)); (gr. 3 up). (978-0-02-149767-6(2)); (gr. 4 up). (978-0-02-149976-2(4)); (gr. 5 up). (978-0-02-149769-0(9)) Macmillan/McGraw-Hill Schl. Div.

Entertainment Language. 2001. (gr. 6-12). pap., tchr.'s training gde. ed. 1.95 (978-0-8359-1506-9(9)); (YA). pap. 16.95 (978-0-8359-1505-2(0)) Globe Fearon Educational Publishing.

Escott, John. Dominoes: Level 1: 400 Headwords the Wild West. 2002. (Illus.). 48p. 6.50 (978-0-19-424341-4(9)) Oxford Univ. Pr., Inc.

—Dominoes: Starter Level: 250 Headwords William Tell & Other Stories. Stower, Adam, illus. 2002. 6.50 (978-0-19-424338-4(9)) Oxford Univ. Pr., Inc.

Escott, John & Hedge, Tricia. Dead Man's Island, Level 2. 2nd ed. 2000. (Bookworms Ser.). (Illus.). 64p. 6.50 (978-0-19-422968-5(8)) Oxford Univ. Pr., Inc.

Essential Words Reading & Language Arts Glossary (Elementary) Elementary School Series. 2006. (J). per. 19.95 (978-1-933655-00-0(3)) New Leaf Educ., Inc.

Falletta, Bernadette. We Love to Read Stories Coloring Book & Word Search Puzzles. 2005. 23p. (J). 10.95 (978-1-4116-6291-9(1)) Lulu.com.

Faulkner, Keith. Spelling Machine. Teel, Gina, illus. 2006. 16p. (J). pap. 7.99 (978-0-439-82090-5(1) , Cartwheel Bks.) Scholastic, Inc.

Fenske, Steve. Vocabulary Diary. 3rd ed. 2002. 108p. 14.95 (978-0-9726495-1-3(4)); 14.95 (978-0-9726495-2-0(2)); 14.95 (978-0-9726495-0-6(6)) Custom Curriculum & Design LLC.

Find It, Write It, Read It: Sentences. 2004. (J). pap. 7.95 (978-1-56911-179 6(0)) Learning Resources, Inc.

Find It, Write It, Read It: Words. 2004. (J). pap. 7.95 (978-1-56911-178-9(2)) Learning Resources, Inc.

Find That Word. 2002. (Interactive Book of Words). (J). 14.95 (978-1-74047-200-5(4)) Book Co. Publishing Pty, Ltd., The AUS. *Dist:* Penton Overseas, Inc.

First 100 Words: Busy Day. (Illus.). 12p. (J). (978-1-902272-36-8(6)) Tucker Slingsby, Ltd.

First Sight Words. 1998. (High Q Books Ser.). (J). (ps-6). bds. 2.99 (978-1-56293-599-3(2) , McClanahan Bk.) Learning Horizons, Inc.

First Steps: Everyday Words. 2002. (First Steps Reading Ser.). 32p. (J). pap. 2.95 (978-0-7894-8483-3(8)) Dorling Kindersley Publishing, Inc.

First Word Book. 2003. (J). per. (978-1-884907-29-6(6)); (SPA & ENG.). per. (978-1-884907-31-9(8)) Paradise Pr., Inc.

First Words. 2002. 48p. (J). bds. 15.95 (978-0-7525-5486-0(7)) Parragon, Inc.

First Words. 2001. (Early Learning Ser.). (J). (gr. k-12). vinyl bd. 4.95 (978-1-58845-052-4(X)) School Specialty Publishing.

Fisher, Ann. Vocabulary Mind Stretchers. 2003. (Illus.). 96p. (gr. 6-8). 9.99 (978-1-56822-624-8(1) , IF2529) School Specialty Publishing.

Fitzgibbon, Kathleen. 5-Min Daily Practice-Vocabulary. 2003. (5-Minute Daily Practice Ser.). (Illus.). 64p. pap., tchr. ed. 11.95 (978-0-439-46607-3(5) , Teaching Resources) Scholastic, Inc.

The Five Senses/Opposites & Position Words, 4 bks., Set. Incl. Let's Explore the Five Senses with City Dog & Country Dog. Falk, Laine. 18.00 (978-0-531-14873-0(4)); Let's Find Rain Forest Animals : Up, down, Around. Behrens, Janice. 18.00 (***978-0-531-14874-7(2)***); Let's Play a Five Senses Guessing Game. Miller, Amanda. 18.00 (978-0-531-14871-6(8)); Let's Talk about Opposites, Morning to Night. Falk, Laine. 18.00 (978-0-531-14872-3(6)); (Illus.). 24p. (J). (ps-k). (Let's Find Out Early Learning Bks.). 2007. 72.00 (***978-0-531-17574-3(X)*** , Children's Pr.) Scholastic Library Publishing.

Fleming, Sarah. Do the Lollipop Trick Pack of 6 American English Edition. 2000. (Cambridge Reading Ser.). (Illus.). 12p. pap. 28.00 (978-0-521-79897-6(3)) Cambridge Univ. Pr.

—Do the Lolly Trick. 2000. (Cambridge Reading Ser.). (Illus.). 14p. pap. 5.00 (978-0-521-77447-5(0)) Cambridge Univ. Pr.

—Do the Loops Trick. 2000. (Cambridge Reading Ser.). (Illus.). 10p. pap. 5.00 (978-0-521-77454-3(3)) Cambridge Univ. Pr.

—I Broke My Arm. 2000. (Cambridge Reading Ser.). (Illus.). 10p. pap. 5.00 (978-0-521-77462-8(4)) Cambridge Univ. Pr.

—Make a Paper Hat. 2000. (Cambridge Reading Ser.). (Illus.). 10p. pap. 5.00 (978-0-521-77458-1(6)) Cambridge Univ. Pr.

Fleming, Sarah, et al. Beginning to Read: Developing Sight Vocabulary Non-Fiction Strand Pack American Version. 2001. (Cambridge Reading Ser.). (Illus.). 8p. pap. 82.00 (978-0-521-01340-6(2)) Cambridge Univ. Pr.

Flora, Sherrill B. Building Essential Vocabulary Grades PK - Reproducible Photo Cards, Games, & Activities to Build Vocabulary in Any Language. 2005. 96p. pap. (978-1-933052-12-0(0)) Carson-Dellosa Publishing Co., Inc.

Fonetica/Conciencia Fonemica: Phonics/Vocabulary. 2001. (McGraw-Hill. Lectura Ser.). (ENG & SPA.). (gr. 3 up). (978-0-02-186117-0(X)); (gr. 4 up). (978-0-02-186540-6(X)) Macmillan/McGraw-Hill Schl. Div.

Fonetica/Conciencia fonemica (Phonics & Phonemic Awareness Practice Book: Phonics/Vocabulary. 2001. (McGraw-Hill. Lectura Ser.). (ENG & SPA.). (gr. 5 up). (978-0-02-186541-3(8)); (gr. 6 up). (978-0-02-186542-0(6)) Macmillan/McGraw-Hill Schl. Div.

Forte, Imogene. Ready to Learn: Words & Vocabulary. 2003. (Illus.). 64p. per. 7.95 (978-0-86530-591-5(9)) Incentive Pubns., Inc.

Foster, John. Barron's Junior Rhyming Dictionary. 2006. (Illus.). 160p. (J). pap. 12.99 (978-0-7641-3424-1(8)) Barron's Educational Series, Inc.

Foundations: Early Emergent-Upper Emergent - 1 Each of 25 Student Books: Level E. 124.95 (978-0-322-02722-0(5)) Wright Group, The.

Frazer, James George. Objetos & Palabras Tabu. 2000. (978-0-606-17724-5(8)) Tandem Library Bks.

Fried, Miriam. My Jelly Bean Book. 2005. (Illus.). (J). (978-1-57400-049-8(7)) Data Trace Publishing, Co.

Fry. Key Words for High Achievement. 2004. (Vocabulary Ser.). (Illus.). 304p. 24.99 (978-0-7439-3612-5(4)) Teacher Created Materials, Inc.

Fry, Sonali. My Busy Day: A First Word Book. 2006. (Baby Nick Jr Ser.). 12p. (J). bds. 8.99 (978-1-4169-1793-9(4) , Simon Spotlight/Nickelodeon) Simon & Schuster Children's Publishing.

Fun & Play. 2002. (First Words & Pictures Book Ser.). (J). bds. 7.95 (978-0-7525-7978-8(9)) Parragon, Inc.

Gerver, Jane, ed. First Words. 2003. (Scholastic Hands-on Learning Ser.). (Illus.). 99p. (J). 9.95 (978-0-439-55736-8(4) , Cartwheel Bks.) Scholastic, Inc.

Giglio, Judith & School Zone Publishing Company Staff. Vocabulary Puzzles. 1999. (I Know It! Workbooks Ser.). (Illus.). 32p. (J). (gr. 2). pap., wbk. ed. 2.49 (978-0-88743-751-9(6) , 02131); (gr. 1). pap., wbk. ed. 2.49 (978-0-88743-750-2(8) , 02130) School Zone Publishing Co.

Gilham, Bill & Pichon, Liz. Babies Start Here. 2004. (Illus.). 24p. (J). pap. 7.95 (978-1-84507-169-1(7)) Lincoln, Frances Ltd. GBR. *Dist:* Perseus Distribution.

Gillingham, Sarah. A Is for Astronaut: Space Exploration from A to Z. 2006. (Illus.). 40p. (J). 14.95 (978-0-8118-5462-7(0)) Chronicle Bks. LLC.

Girard, Franck. Baul de Palabras. de Monfreid, Dorothee, illus. 2005. (Baul de Palabras Ser.). (SPA.). 140p. (J). 18.95 (978-84-7864-789-7(9)) Combel Editorial, S.A. ESP. *Dist:* Independent Pubs. Group.

The Giver. 2000. (Novel Vocabulary Ser.). 40p. (J). pap., stu. ed., tchr.'s training gde. ed. 21.95 (978-1-58303-103-2(0)) Pathways Publishing.

Gobo Books Staff. My Magnetic First Words Book. 2006. 20p. 9.95 (978-1-932915-17-4(6)) National Bk. Network.

Gold, Ethel, illus. Outdoor Things. (Picture Bks.: No. S8817-3). 28p. (J). (ps). pap. 3.95 (978-0-7214-5142-8(X) , Dutton Juvenile) Penguin Group (USA) Inc.

—Things That Go. (Picture Bks.: No. S8817-1). 28p. (J). (ps). pap. 3.95 (978-0-7214-5140-4(3) , Dutton Juvenile) Penguin Group (USA) Inc.

Gold, Kimberley. Outer Space. (Puzzle Shapes Ser.). (Illus.). 10p. (J). bds. (978-2-89393-937-7(6)) Phidal Publishing, Inc./Editions Phidal, Inc.

Goldish, Meish. Content-Building Learning Songs: Dozens & Dozens of Songs-Set to Favorite Tunes-That Help Children Build Background Knowledge & Vocabulary. 2007. 96p. pap. 14.99 (***978-0-439-60964-7(X)*** , Teaching Resources) Scholastic, Inc.

Good Apple. Making Big Words & Making More Big Words. 2001. (Making More Big Words Ser.). 208p. (J). (gr. 3-6). pap. 34.98 (978-0-7682-2133-6(1) , KG1698) School Specialty Publishing.

Gordon, Jo Ann. Articulation Tales: Stories for Articulation Remediation. 2006. 136p. pap. 24.00 (978-1-57128-314-6(5)) Academic Therapy Pubns., Inc.

Got, Yves. Mi Gran Libro de Las Palabras: Las Vacaciones de Dodo. 2003. (SPA.). 28p. (978-84-233-3271-7(3) , DS3843) Ediciones Destino ESP. *Dist:* Lectorum Pubns., Inc.

—Sam's First Word Book. 2000. (Illus.). 144p. (J). (ps). 12.95 (978-0-8118-2615-0(5)) Chronicle Bks. LLC.

Gravois, Michael. Fill-in Flip Books for Grammar, Vocabulary, & More: Grades 3-5. 2005. (Illus.). 80p. (gr. 3-5). pap. 12.99 (978-0-439-67682-3(7) , Teaching Resources) Scholastic, Inc.

Grundwortschatz. (Duden-Schuelerhilfen Ser.). (GER.). 80p. (J). (gr. 3-4). (978-3-411-06342-0(4)) Bibliographisches Institut & F. A. Brockhaus AG DEU. *Dist:* International Bk. Import Service, Inc.

A Guide to Vocabulary: RUMGI A Guide to Vocabulary. 2005. 50p. 17.00 (978-1-932976-97-7(3)) National Ctr. on Education & The Economy.

Gunzi, Christiane. Clothes. (My Very First Look at Ser.). (SPA., Illus.). 24p. (ps-k). 2004. (J). pap. 5.95 (978-1-58728-686-5(6)); 2003. 9.95 (978-1-58728-672-8(6)) T&N Children's Publishing. (Two Can Publishing).

—Colors. 2004. (My Very First Look at Ser.). (SPA., Illus.). 24p. (ps-k). (J). pap. 5.95 (978-1-58728-276-8(3)); 9.95 (978-1-58728-236-2(4)) T&N Children's Publishing. (Two Can Publishing).

—My Home. (My Very First Look at Ser.). (SPA., Illus.). 24p. (ps-k). 2004. (J). pap. 5.95 (978-1-58728-685-8(8)); 2003. 9.95 (978-1-58728-671-1(8)) T&N Children's Publishing. (Two Can Publishing).

—My Very First Look at Opposites. 2007. (My Very First Look at Ser.). 22p. (J). (ps). bds. 6.95 (978-1-58728-591-2(6) , Two Can Publishing) T&N Children's Publishing.

—My Very First Look at Words. 2007. (My Very First Look at Ser.). 22p. (J). (ps). bds. 6.95 (978-1-58728-592-9(4) , Two Can Publishing) T&N Children's Publishing.

—Opposites. (My Very First Look at Ser.). (SPA., Illus.). 24p. (ps-k). 2004. (J). pap. 5.95 (978-1-58728-683-4(1)); 2003. 9.95 (978-1-58728-669-8(6)) T&N Children's Publishing. (Two Can Publishing).

—Words. (My Very First Look at Ser.). (SPA., Illus.). 24p. (ps-k). 2004. (J). pap. 5.95 (978-1-58728-684-1(X)); 2003. 9.95 (978-1-58728-670-4(X)) T&N Children's Publishing. (Two Can Publishing).

Haddon, Jean. Words: A Computer Lesson. Vargo, Sharon Hawkins, illus. 2003. (Silly Millies Ser.). 32p. (ps-1). (J). pap. 4.99 (978-0-7613-1797-5(X)); lib. bdg. 17.90 (978-0-7613-2870-4(X)) Lerner Publishing Group. (Millbrook Pr.).

Hahn, Marika, illus. Things to Wear. (Picture Bks.: No. S8817-4). 28p. (J). (ps). pap. 3.95 (978-0-7214-5143-5(8) , Dutton Juvenile) Penguin Group (USA) Inc.

Hall, Dorothy & Daniel, Marie. Guess the Covered Word for Seasons & Holidays. 2003. 48p. (J). per. 25.99 (978-0-88724-125-3(5)) Carson-Dellosa Publishing Co., Inc.

Hall, Nancy. Get Set for the Code Book B. 2004. pap. 5.95 (978-0-8388-1782-7(3)) Educators Publishing Service, Inc.

—Go for the Code Book C. 2004. pap. 5.95 (978-0-8388-1784-1(X)) Educators Publishing Service, Inc.

Hambleton, Laura & Turhan, Sedat. Strawberry Bullfrog: Fun with Compound Words. Hagin, Sally, illus. 2007. (Milet Wordwise Ser.). 28p. (J). pap. 6.95 (***978-1-84059-500-0(0)***) Milet Publishing.

—Telling Tails: Fun with Homonyms. Hambleton, Laura, illus. 2007. (Milet Wordwise Ser.). (Illus.). 28p. (J). pap. 6.95 (***978-1-84059-498-0(5)***) Milet Publishing.

Hamersky, Jean. Vocabulary Links: Helping Young Children Develop Word Knowledge. 1999. 172p. (J). (gr. 3-6). pap. 40.00 (978-1-888222-43-2(3)) Super Duper Pubns.

Haney Perez, Jessica. My First 100 Words Book: A Lift-the-Flap, Pull-Tab Learning Book. March, Chloe, illus. 2005. (Learn to Read Ser.). 10p. (J). 10.95 (978-1-58117-210-2(9) , Intervisual/Piggy Toes) Dalmatian Pr.

Hannam, Joyce. Dominoes: Level 1: 400 Headwords the Curse of the Mummy. Gicquel, Jocelyn, illus. 2002. 6.50 (978-0-19-424342-1(7)) Oxford Univ. Pr., Inc.

Hanson, Anders. Can You See Me? (Illus.). 23p. (J). (ps-3). 2006. 19.93 (978-1-59679-360-6(0) , SandCastle); 2005. pap. (978-1-59679-361-3(9)) ABDO Publishing Co.

—Come in & Swim! (Illus.). 23p. (J). (ps-3). 2006. 19.93 (978-1-59679-366-8(X) , SandCastle); 2005. pap. (978-1-59679-367-5(8)) ABDO Publishing Co.

—Go for It! (Illus.). 23p. (J). (ps-3). 2006. 19.93 (978-1-59679-372-9(4) , SandCastle); 2005. pap. (978-1-59679-373-6(2)) ABDO Publishing Co.

—Here Comes the Sun. (Illus.). 23p. (J). (ps-3). 2006. 19.93 (978-1-59679-376-7(7) , SandCastle); 2005. pap. (978-1-59679-377-4(5)) ABDO Publishing Co.

—I Like My Family! (Illus.). 23p. (J). (ps-3). 2006. 19.93 (978-1-59679-382-8(1) , SandCastle); 2005. pap. (978-1-59679-383-5(X)) ABDO Publishing Co.

—Little Like Me. (Illus.). 23p. (J). (ps-3). 2006. 19.93 (978-1-59679-394-1(5) , SandCastle); 2005. pap. (978-1-59679-395-8(3)) ABDO Publishing Co.

—Seasons Come & Go. 2005. (Illus.). (J). 23p. pap. (978-1-59679-413-9(5)); 24p. lib. bdg. 19.93 (978-1-59679-412-2(7) , SandCastle) ABDO Publishing Co.

—The Snowman's Clothes. 2005. (Illus.). (J). 23p. pap. (978-1-59679-417-7(8)); 24p. lib. bdg. 19.93 (978-1-59679-416-0(X) , SandCastle) ABDO Publishing Co.

—We Say Hooray! (Illus.). 23p. (J). (ps-3). 2006. 19.93 (978-1-59679-438-2(0) , SandCastle); 2005. pap. (978-1-59679-439-9(9)) ABDO Publishing Co.

—What Do I Look Like? (Illus.). 23p. (J). (ps-3). 2006. 19.93 (978-1-59679-442-9(9) , SandCastle); 2005. pap. (978-1-59679-443-6(7)) ABDO Publishing Co.

—You & I Can Read! (Illus.). 23p. (J). (ps-3). 2006. 19.93 (978-1-59679-444-3(5) , SandCastle); 2005. pap. (978-1-59679-445-0(3)) ABDO Publishing Co.

Harcourt School Publishers Staff. ADA Participa Below Level. 3rd ed. 2002. (Trofeos Ser.). (SPA., Illus.). pap. 6.80 (978-0-15-324043-0(1)) Harcourt Schl. Pubs.

—Aguila Calva Advanced Level. 3rd ed. 2002. (Trofeos Ser.). (SPA., Illus.). pap. 6.80 (978-0-15-324130-7(6)) Harcourt Schl. Pubs.

—Animal Adventures: Practice Book: California Edition. 3rd ed. 2002. (Trophies Reading Program Ser.). (Illus.). (J). pap. 2.00 (978-0-15-326630-0(9)) Harcourt Schl. Pubs.

—Cartas del Desierto On Level. 3rd ed. 2002. (Trofeos Ser.). (SPA., Illus.). (gr. 4). pap. 6.80 (978-0-15-324190-1(X)) Harcourt Schl. Pubs.

—Cinco Vecinos Honrados On Level. 3rd ed. 2002. (Trofeos Ser.).Tr. of Five Honest Neighbors. (SPA., Illus.). pap. 6.80 (978-0-15-324166-6(7)) Harcourt Schl. Pubs.

—Cloud Weaver: Take-Home Book. 1999. (Signatures Ser.). (Illus.). (J). pap. 1.90 (978-0-15-313864-5(5)) Harcourt Schl. Pubs.

—Como el Fuego... Below Level. 3rd ed. 2002. (Trofeos Ser.). (SPA., Illus.). pap. 6.80 (978-0-15-324050-8(4)) Harcourt Schl. Pubs.

—Como Escribir... On Level. 3rd ed. 2002. (Trofeos Ser.). (SPA., Illus.). pap. 6.80 (978-0-15-324179-6(9)) Harcourt Schl. Pubs.

—Como Hacer... Advanced Level. 3rd ed. 2002. (Trofeos Ser.). (SPA., Illus.). pap. 6.80 (978-0-15-324019-5(9)) Harcourt Schl. Pubs.

—Cowboy Talk: Take-Home Book. 2001. (Collections Ser.). (Illus.). (J). pap. 1.90 (978-0-15-319541-9(X)) Harcourt Schl. Pubs.

—Decoding & Word Recognition Assessment. 3rd ed. 2003. pap. 31.20 (978-0-15-340340-8(3)); pap. 31.20 (978-0-15-340341-5(1)) Harcourt Schl. Pubs.

—Exploring the Surroundings: Practice Book: California Edition. 3rd ed. 2002. (Trophies Reading Program Ser.). (Illus.). (J). pap. 2.00 (978-0-15-326633-1(3)) Harcourt Schl. Pubs.

—Family Ties: Practice Book: Califlornia Edition. 3rd ed. 2002. (Trophies Reading Program Ser.). (Illus.). (J). pap. 2.00 (978-0-15-326627-0(9)) Harcourt Schl. Pubs.

—Getting to Know You: Practice Book: Califlornia Edition. 3rd ed. 2002. (Trophies Reading Program Ser.). (Illus.). (J). pap. 2.00 (978-0-15-326623-2(6)) Harcourt Schl. Pubs.

—The Graceful Bull Is Full of Surprises: Take-Home Book. 2001. (Collections Ser.). (Illus.). (J). pap. 1.90 (978-0-15-319537-2(1)) Harcourt Schl. Pubs.

—Harcourt Language: Vocabulary Power. 2nd ed. 2003. (Harcourt Title I Reading Programs Ser.). (Illus.). (gr. 2 up). pupil's gde. ed. 5.90 (978-0-15-320608-5(X)); (gr. 3 up). 5.90 (978-0-15-320609-2(8)); (gr. 4 up). 5.90 (978-0-15-320610-8(1)); (gr. 5 up). 5.90 (978-0-15-320611-5(X)) Harcourt Schl. Pubs.

—A Hat I Like: Decodable Book. 3rd ed. 2002. (Trophies Reading Program Ser.). (Illus.). (gr. k). pap. 2.90 (978-0-15-325431-4(9)) Harcourt Schl. Pubs.

—I Am Special: Practice Book: California Edition. 3rd ed. 2002. (Trophies Reading Program Ser.). (Illus.). (J). pap. 2.00 (978-0-15-326624-9(4)) Harcourt Schl. Pubs.

—Lon's Secret Notebook: Take-Home Book. 1999. (Signatures Ser.). (Illus.). (J). pap. 1.90 (978-0-15-313887-4(4)) Harcourt Schl. Pubs.

—Look at That: Take-Home Book. 1999. (Collections Ser.). (Illus.). (J). pap. 1.90 (978-0-15-317148-2(0)) Harcourt Schl. Pubs.

—Mi Sombrero Below Level. 3rd ed. 2002. (Trophies Reading Program Ser.). (SPA., Illus.). (J). (gr. 1). pap. 3.50 (978-0-15-323850-5(X)) Harcourt Schl. Pubs.

—A Pie Hasta Nebraska On Level. 3rd ed. 2002. (Trofeos Ser.). (SPA., Illus.). pap. 6.80 (978-0-15-324187-1(X)) Harcourt Schl. Pubs.

—Vamos de Fiesta: Take-Home Book Collection, 30 vols. 2001. (SPA., Illus.). (gr. 5). pap. 105.60 (978-0-15-319963-9(6)) Harcourt Schl. Pubs.

Hargraves, Orin. Big Book of Spelling Test. 2007. 208p. pap. 9.95 (978-1-57912-696-4(0)) Black Dog & Leventhal Pubs., Inc.

Harpster, Steve, illus. Fun First Words. 2004. (First Word Search Ser.). 64p. (J). pap. 3.95 (978-1-4027-1320-0(7)) Sterling Publishing Co., Inc.

Harris, Valerie F. & Jones, Eula V. Shaping up for Sight Word Success. Date not set. 30p. (J). (gr. k-6). wbk. ed. (978-1-889654-03-4(5)) Enricharamics, Inc.

Hart, Chuck, illus. Artic Calendar Capers. 2004. (J). (978-1-58650-481-6(9)) Super Duper Pubns.

Harte, May. 1, 2, 3 in My House. 2004. (Look-And-Learn Books). (Illus.). (J). lib. bdg. 7.95 (978-1-4042-2823-8(3) , PowerKids Pr.) Rosen Publishing Group, Inc., The.

Haugen, Janie & Britt, Melissa. Name It Game. 1999. 16p. (J). pap., tchr. ed. 39.95 (978-1-884074-83-7(9)) PCI Educational Publishing.

Hayashi, Emiri & Mouton, Laurence, illus. Babys First Words. 2007. 32p. (J). 12.95 ***(978-0-7358-2165-1(8))*** North-South Bks., Inc.

Haydon, Julie. First 1000 Words. 2004. (Illus.). 95p. (J). (978-1-74121-402-4(5)) Hinkler Bks. Pty, Ltd.

Hayes, Larry E. My Name Starts with S (Library Version) Anderson, Airlie, illus. 2004. (My Name Starts With Ser.). 32p. (J). lib. bdg. 12.95 (978-0-9725292-8-0(4)) Inspire Pubns.

Hazan, Maurice. ESL Junior Book Michael's Friends. Hazan, Maurice, illus. 2002. (Illus.). 83p. spiral bd. 20.00 (978-1-932770-94-0(1) , EJRB-SM) Symtalk, Inc.

Hazan, Maurice, creator. El Camino: Practicing Everyday Vocabulary. 2000. (SPA.). (J). 90.00 (978-1-932770-44-5(5) , SG5) Symtalk, Inc.

Heidrich, Delana. Figuratively Speaking: Using Classic Literature to teach 40 Literary Terms, Vol. 1020. Clark, Kim, ed. Armstrong, Beverly & Grayson, Rick, illus. 2004. 136p. (J). (gr. 5-8). pap. 14.99 (978-0-88160-317-0(1) , LW-1020) Creative Teaching Pr., Inc.

Heinrichs, Ann. Sentences. 2005. (Magic of Language Ser.). (Illus.). 32p. (J). (gr. 1-5). 27.07 (978-1-59296-433-8(8)) Child's World, Inc.

Henderson, Meryl. Indoor Things. (Picture Bks.: No. S8817-2). (Illus.). 28p. (J). (ps). pap. 3.95 (978-0-7214-5141-1(1) , Dutton Juvenile) Penguin Group (USA) Inc.

Hentzell, Brittany, illus. Annie & Arnie's Arduous Afternoon. 2005. spiral bd. 12.95 (978-0-9773550-0-6(4)) Smartypants Bks.

Hepworth, Cathi. Bug Off! A Swarm of Insect Words. 1998. (Illus.). 1p. (J). (ps-3). 15.99 (978-0-399-22640-3(0) , Putnam Juvenile) Penguin Group (USA) Inc.

Hermes House Staff, ed. Having Fun: A First Word & Picture Book. 2000. (Point & Say Bks.). (Illus.). 96p. (ps-k). 9.95 (978-1-85967-801-5(7)) Anness Publishing GBR. *Dist:* National Bk. Network.

Herzog, Joyce. Excursion into Words: Student Activity Book. Sinclair, Angie & Sinclair, Dan, eds. 2005. (J). spiral bd. 15.00 ***(978-1-887225-46-5(3))*** JoyceHerzog.com, Inc.

Hicks, Diana & Littlejohn, Andrew. American English Primary Colors 2 Vocabulary Cards. 2004. 96p. 29.95 (978-0-521-60319-5(6)) Cambridge Univ. Pr.

Hiding: KinderWords Individual Title Six-Packs. (Kinderstarters Ser.). 8p. (ps-1). 21.00 (978-0-7635-8703-1(6)) Rigby Education.

Hill, Christopper T. If A Weren't for Apple. Hill, Christopper T., illus. l.t. ed. 1999. (Illus.). 90p. (YA). (gr. 2 up). pap. 12.95 (978-1-929136-00-1(5)) Topperhill Pubs.

Hill, Eric. Spot's Big Book of Words. Hill, Eric, illus. 2002. (Illus.). (J). 13.19 (978-0-7587-3685-7(1)) Book Wholesalers, Inc.

—Spot's First Words. Hill, Eric, illus. 2002. (Illus.). 12p. (J). (ps-1). bds. 3.99 (978-0-399-24045-4(4) , Putnam Juvenile) Penguin Group (USA) Inc.

Holden, Arianne. Words. 2002. (Playschool Ser.). (Illus.). 32p. pap. 5.99 (978-1-84215-727-5(2) , Southwater) Anness Publishing GBR. *Dist:* National Bk. Network.

Holes. 2000. (Assessment Packs Ser.). (J). pap., tchr.'s training gde. ed. 15.95 (978-1-58303-101-8(4)) Pathways Publishing.

Holt, Rinehart and Winston Staff. Allez Viens! Level 1: Grammar & Vocabulary Workbook. 1998. pap., tchr. ed. 21.86 (978-0-03-052642-8(6)) Holt, Rinehart & Winston.

—Allez Viens! Level 2: Grammar & Vocabulary Workbook. 1999. pap., tchr. ed. 21.86 (978-0-03-052764-7(3)) Holt, Rinehart & Winston.

—Elements of Literature: Assessment: Literature, Reading & Vocabulary. 2003. 4th ed. pap. 40.20 (978-0-03-068518-7(4)); 5th ed. pap. 40.20 (978-0-03-068517-0(6)); 5th ed. pap. 40.20 (978-0-03-068519-4(2)) Holt, Rinehart & Winston.

—Elements of Literature: Vocabulary Development. 5th ed. 2003. (Illus.). pap. 30.40 (978-0-03-073938-5(1)); pap. 30.40 (978-0-03-073939-2(X)); pap. 30.40 (978-0-03-073941-5(1)) Holt, Rinehart & Winston.

—Ven Conmigo! Level 3: Grammar & Vocabulary. 1999. pap., tchr. ed., wbk. ed. 21.86 (978-0-03-053958-9(7)) Holt, Rinehart & Winston.

—Vocabulary Workshop. (Elements of Language Ser.). 2003. (gr. 6 up). 19.20 (978-0-03-056023-1(3)); 2001. (YA). (gr. 12). pap. 18.40 (978-0-03-056296-9(1)); 2000. (YA). (gr. 10). pap. 18.40 (978-0-03-056029-3(2)); 2000. (YA). (gr. 7). pap. 18.40 (978-0-03-056024-8(1)); 2000. (YA). (gr. 8). pap. 18.40 (978-0-03-056027-9(6)); 2000. (Illus.). 700p. (YA). (gr. 11). pap. 18.40 (978-0-03-056214-3(7)); 2000. (YA). (gr. 9). pap. 18.40 (978-0-03-056028-6(4)) Holt, Rinehart & Winston.

Hop, Jog, & Tap: Consonants g, h, j; Short Vowel o word families: Level A, 6 vols. (Wright Skills Ser.). 12p. (gr. k-3). 17.95 (978-0-322-01449-7(2)) Wright Group, The.

Hop, L. L. C. Hooked on Kindergarten Super Workbook. 2006. 320p. 12.99 (978-1-931020-73-2(6)) HOP, LLC.

—Hooked on Pre-K Super Workbook. 2006. 320p. 12.99 (978-1-931020-72-5(8)) HOP, LLC.

Hoppner, Gabi. Backyard Fun. 2004. (What A Series of Fun! Ser.). (Illus.). 10p. (J). bds. 3.99 (978-1-59384-054-9(3)) Parklane Publishing.

—Fun on Wheels. 2004. (What A Series of Fun! Ser.). (Illus.). 10p. (J). bds. 3.99 (978-1-59384-055-6(1)) Parklane Publishing.

Las Horas. (Coleccion Libritos Acordeon). (SPA., Illus.). 10p. (J). pap. 5.50 (978-950-11-0827-9(9) , SGM279) Sigmar ARG. *Dist:* Continental Bk. Co., Inc.

How to Learn New Words, 5 Bks. (J). (gr. 2-6). (978-0-8374-1751-6(1) , 640); (978-0-8374-1752-3(X) , 641); (978-0-8374-1753-0(8) , 642); (978-0-8374-1754-7(6) , 643); (978-0-8374-1755-4(4) , 644) Weekly Reader Corp.

Howard, Linda & Dockray, Tracy Arah, illus. Mi Gran Libro de Palabras Play-Doh. 2006. (SPA.). 10p. (J). (ps-4). reprint ed. 10.00 (978-1-4223-5586-2(1)) DIANE Publishing Co.

Hudson, Cheryl Willis. Book of Opposites. Simpson, Howard, illus. (Afro-Bets Ser.). (J). pap. 4.95 (978-0-940975-11-8(4)) Just Us Bks., Inc.

Hughes, Linda. Dominie Vocabulary Builders. Peh, Sherlyne, illus. 1999. (J). (978-0-7685-0362-3(0)) Dominie Pr., Inc.

Hunsicker, Ranelda Mack. Faerie Gold: A Guide for Teachers & Students. 2005. (Classics for Young Readers Ser.). (Illus.). 64p. (J). 6.99 (978-0-87552-741-3(8)) P & R Publishing.

—Heidi: A Guide for Teachers & Students. 2006. (Classics for Young Readers Ser.). 64p. (J). per. 6.99 (978-0-87552-740-6(X)) P & R Publishing.

—Little Women: A Guide for Teachers & Students. 2003. (Classics for Young Readers Ser.). 64p. (J). 6.99 (978-0-87552-737-6(X)) P & R Publishing.

—Robinson Crusoe: A Guide for Teachers & Students. 2002. (Classics for Young Readers Ser.). 64p. (J). 6.99 (978-0-87552-736-9(1)) P & R Publishing.

Hunt, Sara, ed. Coconut's Words Around the World. 2007. 40p. (J). pap. 7.95 ***(978-1-59369-172-1(6)*** , Pleasant Co.) American Girl Publishing, Inc.

Huntley. Academic Vocabulary Plus Porter Read Write & Edit. 2006. (YA). pap. 57.56 (978-0-618-83655-0(1) , 363117) Houghton Mifflin College Div.

Icelandic Sheepdog Christian Adventures in Learning Book. 2005. (J). 19.95 (978-1-59210-425-3(8)) Whispering Pine Pr., Inc.

In My Home. 2002. (First Words & Pictures Book Ser.). 14p. (J). bds. 7.95 (978-0-7525-7980-1(0)) Parragon, Inc.

Inglés Basico para niños: Edad 7-12, Basic English for Children: ¡Aprenda las 250 Palabras Mas Importantes en Inglés!, Learn the 250 Most Important Words in English! 2005. 30.00 (978-0-9769266-2-7(8)) Weapons of Mass Instruction.

Inui, Tazuko & Yoon, Selina. Sing 'n Learn Japanese One Vol. 1: Introduce Japanese with Favorite Children's Songs. 1998. (Sing 'n Learn Ser.). (ENG & JPN., Illus.). 32p. (J). (ps-6). pap. 14.95 incl. audio (978-1-888194-21-0(9)); pap. 17.95 incl. audio compact disk (978-1-888194-22-7(7)) Master Communications, Inc.

James, Henry & Lindop, Christine. Turn of the Screw. 2002. (Dominoes Ser.). 6.50 (978-0-19-424344-5(3)) Oxford Univ. Pr., Inc.

Jay, Alison. Picture This. 2002. (Illus.). 30p. (J). bds. 8.99 (978-0-525-46828-6(5) , Dutton Juvenile) Penguin Group (USA) Inc.

Jensen, Frode. Jensen's Vocabulary. 2001. 264p. (YA). per. 30.00 (978-1-886061-27-9(0)) Wordsmiths.

Johnson. Building Sight Vocabulary: Reproducible, 3 vols. 1998. (Illus.). (J). pap. (978-0-8114-9667-4(8)) Steck-Vaughn.

Johnson, Kristin & Bayrd, Polly. Megawords 1: Multisyllabic Words for Reading, Spelling, & Vocabulary. 2004. 91p. (gr. 4 up). pap. 6.80 (978-0-8388-1825-1(0)) Educators Publishing Service, Inc.

Johnson, Paul F. & Halfman, Patti. 50 Quick Play Vocabulary Games. 2004. (YA). per. 34.95 (978-0-7606-0539-4(4)) LinguiSystems, Inc.

Johnsrud, Laura. Word Family Mini-Storybooks. 2002. (Illus.). 72p. (J). (gr. 4-6). pap. 11.95 (978-0-439-22248-8(6)) Scholastic, Inc.

Juguetes. (Coleccion Libritos Acordeon). (SPA., Illus.). 10p. (J). pap. 5.50 (978-950-11-0825-5(2) , SGM252) Sigmar ARG. *Dist:* Continental Bk. Co., Inc.

Just the Right Word! Classroom Set. (J). (gr. k-3). 109.22 (978-0-7362-2534-2(X)) Hampton-Brown Bks.

Kannas, C. Larousse Dictionnaire Mini Debutants. 2000. Tr. of Larousse Mini Beginners Dictionary. (FRE., Illus.). 512p. (J). 29.95 (978-2-03-532168-8(9)) Librairie Larousse FRA. *Dist:* Continental Bk. Co., Inc., Distribooks, Inc.

Kaplan Staff. The Adventures of Tom Sawyer: A Kaplan Vocabulary-Building Classic for Young Readers. 2006. 256p. pap. 4.95 (978-0-7432-6652-9(8)) Kaplan Publishing.

—Great Expectations: A Kaplan Vocabulary-Building Classic for Young Readers. 2006. (Vocabulary-Building Classics Ser.). 320p. pap. 4.95 (978-0-7432-8341-0(4)) Kaplan Publishing.

—Little Women: A Kaplan Vocabulary-Building Classic for Young Readers. 2006. 304p. pap. 4.95 (978-0-7432-6653-6(6)) Kaplan Publishing.

—Treasure Island: A Kaplan Vocabulary-Building Classic for Young Readers. 2006. 304p. pap. 4.95 (978-0-7432-8105-8(5)) Kaplan Publishing.

—Vocabulary Field Trip. 2006. 208p. pap. 4.99 (978-1-4195-9057-3(X)) Kaplan Publishing.

Kauffman, Dorothy. Content Readings. 2000. (gr. 3-6). lib. bdg. 23.40 (978-0-613-83265-6(5)) Tandem Library Bks.

Keenan, Sheila, ed. 100 Words Kids Need to Know by 1st Grade. 2004. 32p. (J). pap. 2.99 (978-0-439-66962-7(6)) Scholastic, Inc.

Kelley, Maria Felicia. Buz Words: Discovering Words in Pairs. l.t. ed. 2006. (Illus.). 32p. (J). per. 7.95 (978-0-9650918-2-4(1)) April Arts Press & Productions.

Kelley, Michelle. Different Places, Different Words. 2007. (World Around Me Ser.). (Illus.). 24p. (J). (gr. k-2). pap. 6.95 ***(978-1-59515-964-9(9));*** lib. bdg. 21.35 ***(978-1-59515-993-9(2))*** Rourke Publishing, LLC.

Kelley, Michelle & Lopetz, Craig. Diferentes Lugares, Diferentes Palabras. 2007. (ENG & SPA.). 24p. (J). ***(978-1-60044-298-8(6))*** Rourke Publishing, LLC.

Kennst du Das? Deine Welt. (Duden Ser.). (GER., Illus.). 16p. (J). (978-3-411-70431-6(4)) Bibliographisches Institut & F. A. Brockhaus AG DEU. *Dist:* International Bk. Import Service, Inc.

Kent, Lorna, illus. Baby's First Word Book. 2004. 12p. (J). bds. 7.99 (978-1-85854-478-6(5)) Brimax Books Ltd. GBR. *Dist:* Byeway Bks.

—Word Magic: Magnetic Sentence Builder. 8p. (J). bds. (978-1-58048-382-7(8)) Sandvik Publishing.

Kerrin, Jessica Scott. Martin Bridge Ready for Takeoff! Kelly, Joseph, illus. 2005. 120p. (J). (gr. 2-5). (978-1-55337-772-6(9)); (978-1-55337-688-0(9)) Kids Can Pr., Ltd.

Kido, Yukiko. Flip-a-Word. 2006. (Illus.). 32p. (J). pap. 5.95 (978-1-59354-178-1(3)) Blue Apple Bks.

—Flip-a-Word: Stop Pop. 2007. (Illus.). 32p. 12.95 ***(978-1-59354-620-5(3))*** Handprint Bks.

—Pig Wig. 2006. (Illus.). 32p. (J). 12.95 (978-1-59354-175-0(9)) Blue Apple Bks.

—Snow Bow: Flip-a-Word. 2007. (Flip-A-Word Ser.). (Illus.). 32p. (ps-2). pap. 5.95 ***(978-1-59354-623-6(8))*** Blue Apple Bks.

—Snow Bow: Flip-a-Word. 2007. (Illus.). 32p. 12.95 ***(978-1-59354-622-9(X))*** Handprint Bks.

—Stop Pop. 2007. (Illus.). 32p. (ps-2). pap. 5.95 ***(978-1-59354-621-2(1))*** Blue Apple Bks.

Kingfisher Editors, ed. The Kingfisher First Encyclopedia. 2005. (Kingfisher Encyclopedias Ser.). (Illus.). 160p. (J). (gr. k-3). pap. 9.95 (978-0-7534-5907-2(8) , Kingfisher) Houghton Mifflin Co. Trade & Reference Div.

Koizim, Jessica. Vocabulary Development. 2005. 48p. pap. 6.95 (978-1-4042-8563-7(6)) Rosen Publishing Group, Inc., The.

Krause, Claudia. Word Wheels. (Orig.). (J). pap. (978-0-9655689-0-6(3)) Krause, Claudia.

La Jars, David. Is Anyone Home? rev. ed. 2004. (Talk Together Ser.). (Illus.). 24p. (J). (ps-k). 9.95 (978-1-58728-014-6(0) , Two Can Publishing) T&N Children's Publishing.

Lacome, Susie. The Big Shiny Sparkly First Words Book. 2003. (Illus.). 10p. (J). pap. 9.98 (978-0-7624-1646-2(7) , Courage Bks.) Running Pr. Bk. Pubs.

Lakeshore Learning Materials, contrib. by. The Big Surprise: A Homophone Story, Set of 6 Student Books. 2007. (J). pap. 18.95 ***(978-1-59746-028-6(1))*** Lakeshore Learning Materials.

—The Big Surprise: A Homophone Story Big Book. 2007. (J). pap. 19.95 ***(978-1-59746-024-8(9))*** Lakeshore Learning Materials.

—The Game: A Multiple Meaning Story, Set of 6 Student Books. 2007. (J). pap. 18.95 ***(978-1-59746-029-3(X))*** Lakeshore Learning Materials.

—The Game: A Multiple Meaning Story Big Book. 2007. (J). pap. 19.95 ***(978-1-59746-025-5(7))*** Lakeshore Learning Materials.

—The Great Race: A Synonym Story Big Book. 2007. (J). pap. 19.95 ***(978-1-59746-022-4(2))*** Lakeshore Learning Materials.

—Partner Reading Book Set. 2007. (J). pap. 39.95 ***(978-1-59746-021-7(4))*** Lakeshore Learning Materials.

—Spanish Alphabet Big Book. 2006. (SPA.). (J). pap. 19.95 ***(978-1-59746-000-2(1))*** Lakeshore Learning Materials.

—A Special Gift: An Antonym Story, Set of 6 Student Books. 2007. (J). pap. 18.95 ***(978-1-59746-027-9(3))*** Lakeshore Learning Materials.

Lakeshore Learning Materials Staff, contrib. by. The Word Journal, 10 vols., Set. 2000. (J). pap. 19.95 (978-1-929255-35-1(7)) Lakeshore Learning Materials.

The Language of Literature: Vocabulary & Spelling Book. 2001. (gr. 7 up). (978-0-618-13668-1(1) , 2-04032) McDougal Littell Inc.

The Language of Literature: Vocabulary & Spelling Book Answer Key. 2001. (gr. 7 up). (978-0-618-15371-8(3) , 2-04128) McDougal Littell Inc.

Lapin, Gloria & Radtke, Becky. More Sight Word Stories: 57 Reproducible Books for Beginning Readers. 2001. (Illus.). 136p. (J). (gr. 1-3). pap. 15.99 (978-1-56417-969-2(9) , FE7954, Fearon Teacher Aids) Schaffer, Frank Pubns.

LaQuay, Kate & LoGiudice, Carolyn. Spotlight on Vocabulary Antonyms Level 1, 6 vols. 2005. (Illus.). (J). per. 11.95 (978-0-7606-0586-8(6)) LinguiSystems, Inc.

LaQuay, Kate & Logiudice, Carolyn. Spotlight on Vocabulary Associations Level 1, 6 vols. 2005. (Illus.). per. 11.95 (978-0-7606-0604-9(8)) LinguiSystems, Inc.

—Spotlight on Vocabulary Attributes Level 1, 6 vols. 2005. (Illus.). (J). per. 11.95 (978-0-7606-0588-2(2)) LinguiSystems, Inc.

LaQuay, Kate & LoGiudice, Carolyn. Spotlight on Vocabulary Categories, 6 vols. 2005. (Illus.). (J). per. 11.95 (978-0-7606-0589-9(0)) LinguiSystems, Inc.

—Spotlight on Vocabulary Concepts Level 1, 6 vols. 2005. (Illus.). (J). per. 11.95 (978-0-7606-0590-5(4)) LinguiSystems, Inc.

T U V

Lashley, Steven. E. The Buggouts: The Buggouts learning Club. Hunter, Laura, ed. 1.t. ed. 2005. (Illus.). 12p. (J). cd-rom 15.00 (978-1-59971-244-4(X)) Aardvark Global Publishing.

Latin Words Sticker Book. 2006. 16p. (J). pap. 8.99 (978-0-7945-1145-6(7) , Usborne) EDC Publishing.

Lazarri, Andrea. Vocabulary To Go. 2006. (J). per. 39.95 (978-0-7606-0663-6(3)) LinguiSystems, Inc.

LD COACH. TEH Learns to Read: Action Words, Volume Five. 2004. (Illus.). 40p. (J). 34.95 (978-0-9745938-5-2(0)) LD Coach, LLC.

—TEH Learns to Read: Basic Words, Volume Six. 2004. (Illus.). 40p. (J). 34.95 (978-0-9745938-6-9(9)) LD Coach, LLC.

—TEH Learns to Read: Elementary Words, Volume Seven. 2004. (Illus.). 40p. (J). 34.95 (978-0-9745938-7-6(7)) LD Coach, LLC.

—TEH Learns to Read: Mixed Sight Words—Group A, Volume Eight. 2004. (Illus.). 40p. (J). 34.95 (978-0-9745938-8-3(5)) LD Coach, LLC.

—TEH Learns to Read: More Action Words, Volume Nine. 2004. (Illus.). 40p. (J). 34.95 (978-0-9745938-9-0(3)) LD Coach, LLC.

Le Jars, David. Allons Voir Dehors! 2000. (Talk Together Ser.). (Illus.). 24p. (J). (ps-k). pap. 5.95 (978-1-58728-183-9(X) , Two Can Publishing) T&N Children's Publishing.

—Hay Alguien en Casa? 2004. (Hablemos Ser.).Tr. of Is Anyone Home?. (SPA., Illus.). (ps-k). 24p. (J). pap. 5.95 (978-1-58728-951-4(2)); 23p. 9.95 (978-1-58728-947-7(4)) T&N Children's Publishing. (Two Can Publishing).

—Hay Alguien en Casa? 2000. Tr. of Is Anyone Home?. (SPA.). 12.75 (978-0-606-20693-8(0)) Tandem Library Bks.

—Let's Go Out & About. rev. ed. 2004. (Talk Together Ser.). (Illus.). 24p. (J). (ps-k). 9.95 (978-1-58728-016-0(7)); pap. 5.95 (978-1-58728-020-7(5)) T&N Children's Publishing. (Two Can Publishing).

—Por Aqui y Por Alli. 2004. (Hablemos Ser.).Tr. of Here & There. (SPA., Illus.). 24p. (J). (ps-k). 9.95 (978-1-58728-949-1(0)); pap. 5.95 (978-1-58728-953-8(9)) T&N Children's Publishing. (Two Can Publishing).

LeapFrog Beginning Words Wipe Off. 2007. (J). 4.99 (***978-1-59545-137-8(4)***) Learning Horizons, Inc.

LeapFrog Staff. Thomas & the School Trip: Interactive Book & Cartridge. 2002. (J). pap. 12.99 (978-1-58605-805-0(3)) LeapFrog Enterprises, Inc.

LeapFrog Staff, compiled by. At the Shore. 2001. (J). (ps-2). spiral bd. 14.95 (978-1-58605-056-6(7)) LeapFrog Enterprises, Inc.

—Best Little Word Book Ever. 2001. (J). (ps-1). spiral bd. 14.99 (978-1-58605-003-0(6)) LeapFrog Enterprises, Inc.

—Learning Letter's with Leap. 2001. (YA). (ps up). spiral bd. 9.99 (978-1-58605-095-5(8)) LeapFrog Enterprises, Inc.

—Lil Can't Miss. 2001. (J). (ps-2). spiral bd. 13.95 (978-1-58605-027-6(3)) LeapFrog Enterprises, Inc.

—More Chores. 2001. (J). (ps-2). spiral bd. 14.95 (978-1-58605-064-1(8)) LeapFrog Enterprises, Inc.

—On My Street. 2001. (J). (ps-2). spiral bd. 14.95 (978-1-58605-060-3(5)) LeapFrog Enterprises, Inc.

—On the Go. 2001. (J). (ps-2). spiral bd. 10.95 (978-1-58605-023-8(0)) LeapFrog Enterprises, Inc.

—On the Train to Maine. 2001. (J). (ps-2). spiral bd. 14.95 (978-1-58605-059-7(1)) LeapFrog Enterprises, Inc.

—That Was That. 2001. (J). (ps-2). spiral bd. 14.95 (978-1-58605-057-3(5)) LeapFrog Enterprises, Inc.

—Things to Know. 2001. (J). (ps-1). spiral bd. 14.99 (978-1-58605-002-3(8)) LeapFrog Enterprises, Inc.

Learning Company Books Staff, ed. Reader Rabbit: Rhyming Words. 2003. (Illus.). 32p. (J). pap., wbk. ed. 3.99 (978-0-7630-7578-1(7)) Learning Co. Bks.

Learning New Words (Gr. K-1) 2003. (J). (978-1-58232-032-8(2)) Bryan Hse. Pubs., Inc.

Learning Wrap-Ups Sight Words. 2004. 34.99 (978-0-943343-75-4(5)) Learning Wrap-Ups.

Leber, Nancy Jolson & Onish, Liane B. We're Ready for Pre-K! Sounds & Letters. 2006. (Clear & Simple Workbooks Ser.). 64p. (J). pap. 4.99 (978-0-448-44305-8(8) , Grosset & Dunlap) Penguin Group (USA) Inc.

Lederer, Richard. The Circus of Words: Acrobatic Anagrams, Parading Palindromes, Wonderful Words on a Wire & More Lively Letter Play. Morice, Dave, illus. 2001. 144p. (J). (gr. 4 up). pap. 12.95 (978-1-55652-380-9(7)) Chicago Review Pr., Inc.

Lee, Betsy B. A Funny Dolch Word Book # 1: Un Libro Comico # 1 de la Palabra de Dolch. Davis, Pollyanna S., tr. 2006. (ENG & SPA.). pap. 5.95 (978-0-9720267-5-8(4)) Learning Abilities Bks.

Lee, Martin & Miller, Marcia. Vocabulary Word-of-the-day Writing Prompts. 2002. (Illus.). 96p. (gr. 3-6). pap. 13.95 (978-0-439-27603-0(9)) Scholastic, Inc.

Lengua Espanola: Cuarto Grado. (SPA & ENG.). (J). (gr. 4). 21.95 (978-84-357-0027-6(5) , CPR76) Ediciones y Distribuciones Codice, S.A. ESP. *Dist:* Continental Bk. Co., Inc.

Lengua Espanola: Quinto Grado. (SPA & ENG.). (J). (gr. 5). 22.00 (978-84-357-0171-6(9) , CPR78) Ediciones y Distribuciones Codice, S.A. ESP. *Dist:* Continental Bk. Co., Inc.

Lengua Espanola: Sexto Grado. (SPA & ENG.). (J). (gr. 6). 22.00 (978-84-357-0170-9(0) , CPR80) Ediciones y Distribuciones Codice, S.A. ESP. *Dist:* Continental Bk. Co., Inc.

Let's Read—Word Building. 2003. 16p. (J). 3.79 (978-1-58792-051-6(4)) Trend Enterprises, Inc.

Letters, Sounds, & Words 2, 16 vols. 2001. (Illus.). 8p. (J). pap. 120.00 net. (978-1-893986-22-0(5)) Keep Bks.

Lewis, Starin. Reading First Basics - Vocabulary. Gunzenhauser, Kelly, ed. 2005. 80p. (J). per. 10.99 (978-1-59441-050-5(X) , CD-104020); per. 10.99 (978-1-59441-051-2(8) , CD-104021) Carson-Dellosa Publishing Co., Inc.

—Vocabulary E-Book. 2005. 80p. (J). per. 10.99 (978-1-59441-567-8(6) , CD-104020-EB); per. 10.99 (978-1-59441-568-5(4) , CD-104021-EB) Carson-Dellosa Publishing Co., Inc.

Lindsay, Kristine. Basic Vocabulary - 1. 2005. (J). ring bd. 49.95 (978-1-58804-385-6(1)) PCI Educational Publishing.

—Basic Vocabulary 2. 2005. (J). ring bd. 49.95 (978-1-58804-386-3(X)) PCI Educational Publishing.

Litchfield & Allman. Los Animales (Animals) 2004. (First Words Board Bks.). (SPA., Illus.). 12p. (J). 4.95 (978-0-7460-4519-0(0)) EDC Publishing.

Litchfield, Jo. At Home. 2004. (First Words Board Bks.). (SPA., Illus.). 10p. (J). (ps up). bds. 4.95 (978-0-7460-4092-8(X)) EDC Publishing.

—Everyday Words. rev. ed. 2006. (Illus.). 48p. (J). pap. 9.99 (978-0-7945-0120-4(6) , Usborne) EDC Publishing.

—Everyday Words in French. 2006. 48p. (J). pap. 9.99 (978-0-7945-0882-1(0) , Usborne) EDC Publishing.

—Home. Litchfield, Jo, illus. 2006. 12p. (J). bds. 7.99 (978-0-7945-1425-9(1) , Usborne) EDC Publishing.

—Primeras Palabras. 2007. 18p. (J). bds. 14.99 (***978-0-7460-8570-7(2)*** , Usborne) EDC Publishing.

Litchfield, Jo. Things That Move. 2004. (First Words Board Bks.). (Illus.). 10p. (J). bds. 4.95 (978-0-7460-4149-9(7)) EDC Publishing.

Litchfield, Jo & Brooks, Felicity. Everyday Words Sticker Book. 2004. (Everyday Words Ser.). (Illus.). 32p. (J). (ps-3). (SPA.). pap. 8.95 (978-0-7460-4236-6(1)); (FRE., pap. 8.95 (978-0-7460-4237-3(X)) EDC Publishing.

Literature: Timeless Voices, Timeless Themes. 2001. (YA). (gr. 10). pap. 7.47 (978-0-13-053412-5(9)) Prentice Hall PTR.

Literature Guide for the Middle School Classroom. 2006. 48p. (YA). (gr. 6-8). 8.99 (978-1-4206-3078-7(4)) Teacher Created Resources, Inc.

Llewellyn, Claire. Going for a Ride. 2000. (Cambridge Reading Ser.). (Illus.). 10p. pap. 5.00 (978-0-521-77460-4(8)); Pack. 8p. pap. 28.00 (978-0-521-78759-8(9)) Cambridge Univ. Pr.

Lloyd, Sue & Wernham, Sara. Jolly Phonics Word Book (Print Letters) 2003. 48p. (J). (gr. k-2). 3.50 (978-1-84414-028-2(8)) Jolly Learning, Ltd. GBR. *Dist:* American International Distribution Corp.

LoGiudice, Carolyn & LaQuay, Kate. Spotlight on Vocabulary Antonyms Level 2, 6 vols. 2005. (Illus.). (J). per. 11.95 (978-0-7606-0598-1(X)) LinguiSystems, Inc.

Logiudice, Carolyn & LaQuay, Kate. Spotlight on Vocabulary Associations Level 2, 5 vols. 2005. (Illus.). (J). per. 11.95 (978-0-7606-0599-8(8)) LinguiSystems, Inc.

London, Jack & Escott, John. Dominoes Level 2: 700 Headwords White Fang. Frankland, David, illus. 2002. (Dominoes Ser.). 64p. 6.50 (978-0-19-424380-3(X)) Oxford Univ. Pr., Inc.

London, S. Keith & Osleeb, Rebecca. Defined Mind Vocabulary Accelerator: Music-Driven Vocabulary & Comprehension Tools for School / Test / SAT Prep, 1. 2004. 416p. (YA). pap. 25.00 (978-0-9763767-0-5(9)) Defined Mind, Inc.

Lonsdale, Mary, illus. First Words Sticker Book. 2003. 12p. (J). bds. (978-1-85854-658-2(3)) Autumn Publishing, Ltd.

Look, Listen, & Speak-at the Mall. 2005. 80p. (gr. k-3). cd-rom 29.99 (978-1-55799-951-1(1) , EMC 2745) Evan-Moor Educational Pubs.

Look, Listen, & Speak-at the Supermarket. 2005. 80p. (gr. k-3). cd-rom 29.99 (978-1-55799-950-4(3) , EMC 2744) Evan-Moor Educational Pubs.

Look, Listen, & Speak-from Farm to You. 2005. 80p. (gr. k-3). cd-rom 29.99 (978-1-55799-949-8(X) , EMC 2743) Evan-Moor Educational Pubs.

Look, Listen, & Speak-Keeping Healthy. 2005. 80p. (gr. k-3). cd-rom 29.99 (978-1-55799-948-1(1) , EMC 2742) Evan-Moor Educational Pubs.

Look, Listen, & Speak-Transportation. 2005. 80p. (gr. k-3). cd-rom 29.99 (978-1-55799-952-8(X) , EMC 2746) Evan-Moor Educational Pubs.

Lorbiecki, Marybeth. Going Places Book Set: That's Life! Literature Series, 4 vols. Gallop, Jim, photos by. 2004. (Illus.). 18p. (YA). 45.00 (978-0-9666667-4-8(7)) AbleNet, Inc.

Lorenz Books Staff, ed. Learning Fun: A First Word & Picture Book. 2000. (Point & Say Bks.). (Illus.). 96p. (ps-k). 9.95 (978-1-85967-802-2(5) , Lorenz Bks.) Anness Publishing GBR. *Dist:* National Bk. Network.

—Words. 2000. (Sticker Fun Ser.). (Illus.). 16p. (ps-k). pap. 4.95 (978-0-7548-0433-8(X)) Anness Publishing GBR. *Dist:* National Bk. Network.

Lorenz Books Staff & Llewellyn, Claire. Words. 1999. (Fun to Learn Ser.). (Illus.). 48p. (ps-k). 7.95 (978-0-7548-0032-3(6)) Anness Publishing, Inc.

Lorenz Books Staff & Royston, Angela. The World. 2000. (My Big Book of Ser.). (Illus.). 48p. (gr. k-4). pap. 7.95 (978-0-7548-0226-6(4) , Lorenz Bks.) Anness Publishing, Inc.

Lou Weber Staff, ed. Tonka Look & Find. 2004. 24p. (J). 7.98 (978-1-4127-0535-6(5) , 7219500) Publications International, Ltd.

Lowell House Juvenile Staff. My Big Book of Words. 2000. (My Big Board Books Ser.). (Illus.). 24p. (J). (ps-k). pap. 8.95 (978-0-7373-0407-7(3) , 04073W, Roxbury Park) Lowell Hse.

Lubben, Amy & Williams, Rozanne Lanczak. Build-a-Skill Instant Books Word Families-Long Vowels. Shiotsu, Vicky & Faulkner, Stacey, eds. Campbell, Jenny & Tom, Darcy, illus. 2007. (J). 4.99 (***978-1-59198-409-2(2)***) Creative Teaching Pr., Inc.

—Build-a-Skill Instant Books Word Families-Short Vowels. Shiotsu, Vicky & Faulkner, Stacey, eds. Campbell, Jenny & Tom, Darcy, illus. 2007. (J). 4.99 (***978-1-59198-408-5(4)***) Creative Teaching Pr., Inc.

Ludewig, Lizabeth L. 200 Words Your Child Will Read by the End of Grade 2. 2006. 256p. (J). 14.99 (978-0-7641-7915-0(2)) Barron's Educational Series, Inc.

Lundquist, Joegil K. & Lundquist, Jeanne L. English from the Roots Up: Help for Reading, Writing, Spelling, & S. A. T. Scores. 2003. 39.95 (978-1-885942-30-2(3)); II. (Illus.). 125p. 29.95 (978-1-885942-31-9(1)) Cune Pr., LLC.

Lunsford, Susan. Literature-Based Mini-Lessons: 15 Engaging Lessons That Use Your Favorite Picture Books to Help Every Student Become a More Fluent Reader. 2000. (Scholastic Teaching Strategies Ser.). (Illus.). 160p. (J). 16.95 (978-0-439-08682-0(5)) Scholastic, Inc.

Luther, Jacqui Moody. Word World: Dog Is Lost. 2005. (Illus.). 10p. (J). pap. 7.95 (978-0-7624-1992-0(X) , Running Pr. Kids) Running Pr. Bk. Pubs.

—Word World: Stop the Noise. 2005. (Word World Ser.). (Illus.). 12p. (J). pap. 12.95 (978-0-7624-2099-5(5) , Running Pr. Kids) Running Pr. Bk. Pubs.

Lynn, Sara. Jungle Friends. (Illus.). (J). bds. (978-0-7636-0042-6(3)) Candlewick Pr.

Maccarone, Grace, ed. Letters & Words. 2006. (Carry Wipe Clean Wheel Bks.). (Illus.). 26p. (J). 7.99 (978-0-439-85364-4(8) , Cartwheel Bks.) Scholastic, Inc.

MagneTalk' Match-up Adventure Kit (without Barrier) 2006. (J). 34.95 (***978-1-58650-616-2(1)***); 34.95 (***978-1-58650-653-7(6)***) Super Duper Pubns.

MagneTalk' Match-up Around the World. 2006. (J). 34.95 (***978-1-58650-644-5(7)***) Super Duper Pubns.

MagneTalk' Match-up Around the World (with Barrier) 2006. (J). 44.95 (***978-1-58650-610-0(2)***) Super Duper Pubns.

Make Words for Upper Grades from Month-by-Month Phonics Word Card Set. 2002. (Four-Blocks Ser.). (J). pap. 29.99 (978-0-88724-830-6(6) , CD-2816) Carson-Dellosa Publishing Co., Inc.

Making Word Cards: Classroom Letter. (gr. 1-3). 8.99 (978-0-7682-1798-8(9) , GA1676) School Specialty Publishing.

Maldonado, Premier, creator. House-Casa: English-Español. 2004. (SPA., Illus.). 20p. (J). bds. 6.00 (978-0-9727886-1-8(1)) Osmosis, LLC.

Marrow, Lesley Mandel & Vacca, Richard T. Sadlier Phonics, Level C. 2001st ed. 2004. (Sadlier Phonics Reading Program). (Illus.). 336p. (YA). (gr. 3 up). tchr. ed. 54.00 (978-0-8215-7013-5(7)) Sadlier, William H. Inc.

—Sadlier Word Study. 2001. (Sadlier Word Study (Level D-Level F) Ser.). (Illus.). (YA). (gr. 4-6). Level D. 2001st ed. 224p. stu. ed. 10.65 (978-0-8215-1039-1(8)); Level E. 2001st ed. 224p. stu. ed. 11.97 (978-0-8215-1040-7(1)); Level E. 2002nd ed. 320p. tchr. ed. 57.00 (978-0-8215-1043-8(6)); Level F. 2001st ed. 320p. tchr. ed. 57.00 (978-0-8215-1044-5(4)); Level F. 2001st ed. 224p. stu. ed. 11.97 (978-0-8215-1041-4(X)) Sadlier, William H. Inc.

Martin, Janet. Sight Words That Stick, 3 vols. 2001. (Sight Words That Stick Ser.). (Illus.). 170p. (J). (gr. 1-9). spiral bd. 85.00 (978-1-883186-33-3(1) , SWS04) National Reading Styles Institute, Inc.

Martin, John David. A Time to Plant: Workbook. 2005. (Rod & Staff's Readers Ser.). 145p. (gr. 5 up). 4.80 (978-0-7399-0402-2(7) , 11521) Rod & Staff Pubs., Inc.

Martin, Justin. Vocabulary Boosting Jokes & Riddles: Fast & Fun Rib-Ticklers That Teach Kids More Than 100 Great New Words. 2004. 64p. pap. 11.99 (978-0-439-54256-2(1) , Teaching Resources) Scholastic, Inc.

Mastering Sight Words (Gr. 1-2) 2003. (J). (978-1-58232-091-5(8)) Bryan Hse. Pubs., Inc.

Mayer, Mercer. Little Critter's. Picture Dictionary. Mayer, Mercer, illus. 2003. (Little Critter's(R) Picture Dictionary Ser.). (Illus.). 144p. (J). (ps up). pap. 8.95 (978-1-57768-839-6(2)) School Specialty Publishing.

McCarty, Diane Bischoff. Copywork for Children: For Grades 1-3. 2004. (Illus.). 63p. (J). (978-0-9712124-1-1(4)) Angel Heart Children's Pr.

McGrath, Barbara Barbieri. I Love Words. 2004. (Illus.). 32p. (J). 16.95 (978-1-57091-567-3(9)); pap. 6.95 (978-1-57091-568-0(7)) Charlesbridge Publishing, Inc.

McGraw-Hill Staff. Glencoe Language Arts Vocabulary Power. 2nd ed. 2001. Grade 7. pap., wbk. ed. 18.00 (978-0-07-826226-5(7) , 9780078262265); Grade 10. pap., wbk. ed. 18.00 (978-0-07-826232-6(1) , 9780078262326) Glencoe/McGraw-Hill.

—Glencoe Language Arts, Vocabulary Power. 2nd ed. 2001. Grade 11. (C). pap., wbk. ed. 18.00 (978-0-07-826234-0(8) , 9780078262340); Grade 12. pap., wbk. ed. 18.00 (978-0-07-826236-4(4) , 9780078262364) Glencoe/McGraw-Hill.

—Glencoe Language Arts Vocabulary Power Grade 6. 2nd ed. 2001. (C). pap., wbk. ed. 18.00 (978-0-07-826224-1(0) , 9780078262241) Glencoe/McGraw-Hill.

—Glencoe Language Arts, Vocabulary Power Grade 8. 2nd ed. 2001. pap., wbk. ed. 18.00 (978-0-07-826228-9(3) , 9780078262289) Glencoe/McGraw-Hill.

—Glencoe Language Arts Vocabulary Power Grade 9. 2nd ed. 2001. (C). pap., wbk. ed. 18.00 (978-0-07-826230-2(5) , 9780078262302) Glencoe/McGraw-Hill.

—Vocabulary Building with Word Puzzles. 2003. (Homework Booklets Ser.). (Illus.). 96p. (gr. 5-6). 2.99 (978-0-88012-787-5(2) , IF0159); (gr. 6-8). 2.99 (978-0-88012-788-2(0) , IF0169) School Specialty Publishing.

McGraw-Hill Staff & Schaffer, Frank. Word Skills. 2001. (Homework Helpers Activity Bks.). (Illus.). 56p. (J). (gr. k up). pap., act. bk. ed. 2.99 (978-0-7682-0699-9(5) , FS109028, Schaffer, Frank) Schaffer, Frank Pubns.

McLaughlin, Maureen, et al. Research-Based Reading Lessons for 4-6: Word Study, Fluency, Vocabulary, & Comprehension. 2006. 224p. pap. 25.99 (978-0-439-84381-2(2) , Teaching Resources) Scholastic, Inc.

McNamara, Connie. My First U of I Words Go Illini. 2004. (J). bds. 11.95 (978-0-9743244-1-8(8)) Shamrock Publishing, Inc.

McNaught, Harry, illus. ABC & 1,2,3: A Sesame Street Treasury of Words & Numbers. 1998. (Sesame Street Ser.). 80p. (J). (gr. k-ps). 9.99 (978-0-375-80042-9(5) , Random Hse. Bks. for Young Readers) Random Hse. Children's Bks.

Megawords 1 Student. 2004. (gr. 4 up). pap. 9.35 (978-0-8388-1826-8(9)) Educators Publishing Service, Inc.

Megawords 3 Student. 2004. (gr. 4 up). pap. 9.35 (978-0-8388-1830-5(7)) Educators Publishing Service, Inc.

Megawords 6 Student. 2004. (gr. 4 up). pap. 9.35 (978-0-8388-1836-7(6)) Educators Publishing Service, Inc.

Megawords 7 Student. 2004. (gr. 4 up). pap. 9.35 (978-0-8388-1838-1(2)) Educators Publishing Service, Inc.

Megawords 8 Student. 2004. (gr. 4 up). pap. 9.35 (978-0-8388-1840-4(4)) Educators Publishing Service, Inc.

Mein Erstes Woerterbuch: Auf dem Bauernhof. (Duden Ser.). (GER.). 48p. (J). (978-3-411-71071-3(3)) Bibliographisches Institut & F. A. Brockhaus AG DEU. *Dist:* International Bk. Import Service, Inc.

Mes 100 Premiers Mots. 2003. (First 100 Words Ser.).Tr. of My First 100 Words. (FRE.). 32p. 5.58 (978-1-4054-1139-4(2)) Parragon, Inc.

Meyer, Jan. 25 Nonfiction Passages with Vocabulary-Building Crosswords. 2006. 64p. pap. 11.99 (978-0-439-46857-2(4) , Teaching Resources) Scholastic, Inc.

Miles Kelly Staff. Mix-Ups. 2003. (Illus.). 14p. 9.95 (978-1-902947-83-9(5)) Miles Kelly Publishing, Ltd. GBR. *Dist:* Independent Pubs. Group.

Miles, Lisa. Escribo Palabras. 2004. (Sticker Learning Bks.).Tr. of Words to Write. (SPA., Illus.). 16p. (J). (ps-3). pap. 6.95 (978-0-7460-3903-8(4)) EDC Publishing.

Miller, Susan A. My First 1000 Words. 2005. (My First Ser.). (Illus.). 96p. (J). (978-1-4127-1182-1(7) , 1246993) Publications International, Ltd.

Mini My First Book of Words. 2004. (Early Learning Ser.). 18p. (J). bds. 2.99 (978-1-85854-831-9(4)) Brimax Books Ltd. GBR. *Dist:* Byeway Bks.

Minsky, Michael. Greenwood Word Lists: One-Syllable Words. 2003. 168p. spiral bd. (978-1-57035-770-1(6) , 206WORD1) Sopris West Educational Services.

Mis Primeras 100 Palabras. 2003. Tr. of My First 100 Words in Spanish. (FRE & SPA.). 32p. (J). 11.95 (978-0-7525-8380-8(8)) Parragon, Inc.

Molter, Carey. -Ain As in Train. 2003. (Word Families Ser.). (Illus.). 23p. (J). (ps-3). lib. bdg. 19.93 (978-1-59197-272-3(8) , SandCastle) ABDO Publishing Co.

—Ake As in Cake. 2003. (Word Families Ser.). (Illus.). 23p. (J). (ps-3). lib. bdg. 19.93 (978-1-59197-270-9(1) , SandCastle) ABDO Publishing Co.

—Eam As in Ice Cream. 2003. (Word Families Ser.). (Illus.). 23p. (J). (ps-3). lib. bdg. 19.93 (978-1-59197-273-0(6) , SandCastle) ABDO Publishing Co.

—En As in Pen. 2003. (Word Families Ser.). (Illus.). 23p. (J). (ps-3). lib. bdg. 19.93 (978-1-59197-229-7(9) , SandCastle) ABDO Publishing Co.

—Ide As in Tide. 2003. (Word Families Ser.). (Illus.). 23p. (J). (ps-3). lib. bdg. 19.93 (978-1-59197-275-4(2) , SandCastle) ABDO Publishing Co.

—One As in Stone. 2003. (Word Families Ser.). (Illus.). 23p. (J). (ps-3). lib. bdg. 19.93 (978-1-59197-274-7(4) , SandCastle) ABDO Publishing Co.

—Oon As in Spoon. 2003. (Word Families Ser.). (Illus.). 23p. (J). (ps-3). lib. bdg. 19.93 (978-1-59197-266-2(3) , SandCastle) ABDO Publishing Co.

Moncure, Jane Belk. My First Book. King, Colin, illus. 2000. (New Sound Box Library). 32p. (J). (ps-3). 22.79 (978-1-56766-765-3(1)) Child's World, Inc.

Moody-Luther, Jacqui. Bear & the Pizza Tree. Nicholls, Paul & Codor, Richard, illus. 2005. (Word World Ser.). 12p. (J). (ps-ps). pap. 12.95 (978-0-7624-2098-8(7) , Running Pr. Kids) Running Pr. Bk. Pubs.

—Frog's Jungle Adventure. Codor, Richard & Nicholls, Paul, illus. 2005. 12p. (J). (ps-ps). pap. 9.95 (978-0-7624-1995-1(4) , Running Pr. Kids) Running Pr. Bk. Pubs.

—Happy Word Day! Nicholls, Paul & Codor, Richard, illus. 2005. (Word World Ser.). 12p. (J). (ps-ps). pap. 11.95 (978-0-7624-1990-6(3) , Running Pr. Kids) Running Pr. Bk. Pubs.

—Meet the Word Things. Codor, Richard & Nicholls, Paul, illus. 2005. (Word World Ser.). 12p. (J). (ps-ps). pap. 9.95 (978-0-7624-1994-4(6) , Running Pr. Kids) Running Pr. Bk. Pubs.

—Sheep's Magic Hat. Nicholls, Paul & Codor, Richard, illus. 2005. (Word World Ser.). 12p. (J). (ps-ps). pap. 11.95 (978-0-7624-1991-3(1) , Running Pr. Kids) Running Pr. Bk. Pubs.

Mouse Works Staff. First Words. 1998. (J). 4.98 (978-1-57082-712-9(5)) Mouse Works.

The Moves Make the Man: Teaching Unit. 2003. 73p. (YA). ring bd. (978-1-58049-433-5(1) , TU4331) Prestwick Hse., Inc.

Multisyllabic Words, 19, Set. 2004. (Beastieville Ser.). (J). 257.60 (978-0-516-25142-4(2) , Children's Pr.) Scholastic Library Publishing.

Munton, Gill. How Crayons Are Made. 2000. (Cambridge Reading Ser.). (Illus.). 14p. pap. 5.00 (978-0-521-77452-9(7)) Cambridge Univ. Pr.

—Make a Banana Treat. 2000. (Cambridge Reading Ser.). (Illus.). 10p. pap. 5.00 (978-0-521-77463-5(2)) Cambridge Univ. Pr.

My Community. 2005. (Look, Listen, & Speak Ser.). 80p. (gr. k-3). cd-rom 29.99 (978-1-55799-928-3(7) , EMC 2741) Evan-Moor Educational Pubs.

My Day. 2002. (First Words & Pictures Book Ser.).Tr. of Mi dia. 14p. (J). bds. 7.95 (978-0-7525-7979-5(7)) Parragon, Inc.

My Family & Me. 2005. (Look, Listen, & Speak Ser.). 80p. (gr. k-3). cd-rom 29.99 (978-1-55799-924-5(4) , EMC 2737) Evan-Moor Educational Pubs.

My First 100 Words. 2003. 32p. (J). 11.95 (978-0-7525-7767-8(0)) Parragon, Inc.

My First 100 Words in Spanish/English. 2003. 32p. (J). 11.95 (978-0-7525-7769-2(7)) Parragon, Inc.

My First Library. 2000. 112p. (J). bds. 15.95 (978-0-7525-3741-2(5)) Parragon, Inc.

My First Sight Words (Gr. K-1) 2003. (J). (978-1-58232-090-8(X)) Bryan Hse. Pubs., Inc.

My First Word BK. 2007. 12p. pap. 7.99 (***978-1-4037-3060-2(1)***) Dalmatian Pr.

My First Word Book Large Bd. 2004. 12p. (J). bds. 7.99 (978-1-85854-467-0(X)) Brimax Books Ltd. GBR. *Dist:* Byeway Bks.

My Little Box of First Words. Date not set. (Illus.). (J). bds. 6.98 (978-1-4054-0811-0(1)) Parragon, Inc.

My Nest, 6 vols. 8p. (gr. k-1). 21.50 (978-0-322-02063-4(8)) Wright Group, The.

Nadler, Ellis. The Busy World Word Book. 1998. 32p. (J). pap. 12.95 (978-0-7894-3111-0(4)) Dorling Kindersley Publishing, Inc.

Narvaez, Concha Lopez & Salmeron, Carmelo. Tomas Es Distinto a los Demas.Tr. of Tomas Is Different from the Others. (SPA.). 64p. (J). (gr. 2-4). (978-84-216-3432-5(1)) Bruño, Editorial ESP. *Dist:* Lectorum Pubns., Inc.

Nathan, Ruth. Graphophonemic Knowledge - Decoding Nonsense Words: Early Literacy Diagnostic. 2002. (J). (gr. k-1). spiral bd. 1.50 (978-1-58605-534-9(8) , LeapFrog Schl. Hse.) LeapFrog Enterprises, Inc.

—Graphophonemic Knowledge - High Frequency Words: Early Literacy Diagnostic. 2002. (J). (gr. k-1). spiral bd. 1.50 (978-1-58605-535-6(6) , LeapFrog Schl. Hse.) LeapFrog Enterprises, Inc.

The Natural: Teaching Unit. 2002. 49p. (J). ring bd. (978-1-58049-421-2(8) , TU202) Prestwick Hse., Inc.

Nelson, J. Ron & Marchland-Martella, Nancy. The Multiple Meaning Vocabulary Program: Level I. 2005. (Illus.). 248p. per. (978-1-59318-405-6(0) , 267STU1) Sopris West Educational Services.

—The Multiple Meaning Vocabulary Program: Level II. 2005. (Illus.). 328p. per. (978-1-59318-406-3(9)) Sopris West Educational Services.

—The Multiple Meaning Vocabulary Program Instructor's Manual: Level I & Level II. 2005. 64p. (978-1-59318-422-3(0) , 267TE) Sopris West Educational Services.

Nickelsen, Leann. Quick Activities to Build a Very Voluminous Vocabulary. 1998. 64p. (J). pap. 9.95 (978-0-590-22179-5(5)) Scholastic, Inc.

Nilsen, Anna. I Can Spell Words with Four Letters. 1998. (I Can Spell Ser.). (Illus.). 26p. (J). (ps-k). tchr. ed. 9.95 (978-0-7534-5125-0(5) , Kingfisher) Houghton Mifflin Co. Trade & Reference Div.

Nussbaum, Ben. First Words Playtime. 2004. 36p. (J). bds. 12.99 incl. audio compact disk (978-1-59069-410-7(4) , 1A109) Studio Mouse LLC.

Onish, Liane. Word Families. 2004. (Reading Skills Card Games Ser.). 48p. pap. 10.99 (978-0-439-46595-3(8) , Teaching Resources) Scholastic, Inc.

Orero, Maria Jesus. Nico y Sus Trajes. 2005. (SPA & ESP., Illus.). 12p. (ps-ps). per. 6.99 (978-84-272-6152-5(7)) Molino, Editorial ESP. *Dist:* Santillana USA Publishing Co., Inc.

Paragon Publishing Staff, ed. Words. 2003. (J). per. (978-1-884907-41-8(5)) Paradise Pr., Inc.

Parragon Staff, ed. Words. (J). Date not set. (Illus.). bds. 5.98 (978-0-7525-8559-8(2)); 2002. 16p. pap. 2.98 (978-1-84273-837-5(2) , Exclusive Editions) Parragon, Inc.

Patterns. 2007. (J). lib. bdg. 9.95 (***978-0-9768706-3-0(0)***) Learning Props.

Perrett, Lisa, illus. Princess Opposites. 2004. 12p. (J). bds. 4.95 (978-1-4027-1489-4(0)) Sterling Publishing Co., Inc.

Phillips, Mark. Pinocchio Intermediate Vocabulary. 2004. 336p. pap. 16.95 (978-0-9727439-2-1(8)) Cornell, A.J. Pubns.

Phillips, Sarah. My First 100 Words. 2007. (Busy Baby Ser.). (Illus.). 26p. (ps-k). per., bds. 6.95 (***978-1-84610-464-0(5)***) Make Believe Ideas GBR. *Dist:* Ingram Pub. Services.

Phonemic Awareness, Level 1. 2003. (Illus.). (J). spiral bd. (978-1-58605-822-7(3) , LeapFrog Schl. Hse.) LeapFrog Enterprises, Inc.

PhotoFile Picture Cards. (gr. 1 up). 41.90 (978-0-7362-1841-2(6)); (gr. 2 up). 41.90 (978-0-7362-1890-0(4)); (gr. 3 up). 55.87 (978-0-7362-1683-8(9)); (gr. 4 up). 55.87 (978-0-7362-1719-4(3)); (gr. 5 up). 55.87 (978-0-7362-1755-2(X)) Hampton-Brown Bks.

Piazza, Linda. Building Reading Comprehension: High-Interest Selections for Critical Reading Skills. 2000. (100+ Seriestm Ser.). 128p. (YA). (gr. 7-8). pap. 12.99 (978-1-56822-915-7(1) , IF8720, Instructional Fair) Schaffer, Frank Pubns.

Picture/Word Cards. (ps-12). 75.18 (978-0-7362-0345-6(1)) Hampton-Brown Bks.

Pihl, Marshall R. Korean Word Book. 2004. (KOR., Illus.). 112p. pap. 19.95 (978-1-57306-197-1(2)) Bess Pr., Inc.

Play Bac Edu-Team, creator. Vocabulary Power Kindergarten. 2007. (Illus.). 160p. (J). 9.95 (***978-1-60214-021-9(9)***) Play Bac Publishing, USA.

Play Bac Publishing Staff, ed. Vocabulary Power Grade 1. 2007. 210p. 9.95 (***978-1-60214-015-8(4)***) Black Dog & Leventhal Pubs., Inc.

—Vocabulary Power Grade 1. 2007. 210p. (J). spiral bd. 9.95 (***978-1-60214-003-5(0)***) Play Bac Publishing, USA.

—Vocabulary Power Grade 2. 2007. 210p. 9.95 (***978-1-60214-016-5(2)***) Black Dog & Leventhal Pubs., Inc.

—Vocabulary Power Grade 2. 2007. 210p. (J). spiral bd. 9.95 (***978-1-60214-004-2(9)***) Play Bac Publishing, USA.

—Vocabulary Power Grade 3. 2007. 210p. spiral bd. 9.95 (***978-1-60214-005-9(7)***) Play Bac Publishing, USA.

POWer Words Gr. 7-8. 2005. (YA). per. (978-1-57022-521-5(4)) ECS Learning Systems, Inc.

POWer Words Gr. 9-12. 2005. (YA). per. (978-1-57022-549-9(4)) ECS Learning Systems, Inc.

Practice Pals Bilingual Practice Book: First Words. 2006. (ENG & FRE., Illus.). 16p. (J). (ps-1). spiral bd. (978-1-930355-55-2(6)) Greenbrier/Scentex.

Practice Power Flip & Learn First Words. 2000. (Illus.). 16p. (J). (ps-1). spiral bd. (978-1-930355-23-1(8)) Greenbrier/Scentex.

Prefixes, Suffixes, & Root Words (Gr. 2-3) 2003. (J). (978-1-58232-123-3(X)) Bryan Hse. Pubs., Inc.

Priddy Books Staff. First Words. rev. ed. 2004. (Bright Baby Ser.). (Illus.). 26p. (J). bds. 4.95 (978-0-312-49388-2(6) , Priddy Bks.) St. Martin's Pr.

Priddy Books Staff & Priddy, Roger. Happy Baby: Words. 2004. (Illus.). 28p. (J). bds. 8.95 (978-0-312-49193-2(X) , Priddy Bks.) St. Martin's Pr.

—My Little Word Book. rev. ed. 2004. (Illus.). 32p. (J). bds. 9.95 (978-0-312-49387-5(8) , Priddy Bks.) St. Martin's Pr.

Priddy, Roger. Bright Baby Soft-to-Touch Large: Words, Animals, Colors. 2005. (J). 22.95 (978-0-312-49555-8(2) , Priddy Bks.) St. Martin's Pr.

—Happy Baby Words. (J). 2007. bds. 3.95 (***978-0-312-49954-9(X)***); 2001. (Illus.). 28p. bds. 5.95 (978-0-312-49009-6(7)) St. Martin's Pr. (Priddy Bks.).

—Magnetic Learning Book Words. 2006. (Illus.). 16p. (J). bds. 8.95 (978-0-312-49809-2(8) , Priddy Bks.) St. Martin's Pr.

—Mi Libro Grande de Las Palabras. 2003. Tr. of My Big Word Book. (SPA., Illus.). 12p. (J). bds. 14.95 (978-0-312-49117-8(4) , Priddy Bks.) St. Martin's Pr.

—My Big Word Book: Over 1000 Essential First Words & Pictures. 2002. (Smart Kids Ser.). (Illus.). 80p. (J). 14.95 (978-0-312-49075-1(5) , Priddy Bks.) St. Martin's Pr.

—Los Pequenos: Primeras Palabras. 2002. (SPA.). 32p. (J). bds. 8.95 (978-0-312-49118-5(2) , Priddy Bks.) St. Martin's Pr.

—Soft-to-Touch Slipcase 1: Things,Words & Animals. 2004. 84p. (J). bds. 22.95 (978-0-312-49422-3(X) , Priddy Bks.) St. Martin's Pr.

—Sticker Flash Cards - Words. 2006. 30p. (J). bds. 5.95 (978-0-312-49826-9(8) , Priddy Bks.) St. Martin's Pr.

—Sticker Flash Cards Words Bi-Lingual. 2006. 30p. (J). bds. 5.95 (978-0-312-49792-7(X) , Priddy Bks.) St. Martin's Pr.

—Wipe Clean Letters. 2006. (Wipe Clean Ser.). 12p. (J). bds., act. bk. ed. 3.47 (978-0-312-49832-0(2) , Priddy Bks.) St. Martin's Pr.

Primeras Palabras. 2007. (Sesame Street Ser.).Tr. of Everyday Words. (SPA & ENG.). 50p. (J). 2.95 (***978-1-59545-060-9(2)***) Learning Horizons, Inc.

Prince Wallaker, Jillayne. Building Reading Comprehension: High-Interest Selections for Critical Reading Skills. 2000. (100+ Seriestm Ser.). 128p. (J). (gr. 3-4). pap. 12.99 (978-1-56822-913-3(5) , IF8718, Instructional Fair) Schaffer, Frank Pubns.

Pulse. Fun with Vocabulary & Spelling. 2006. cd-rom 4.99 (***978-1-60245-041-7(2)***) GDL Multimedia, LLC.

Quinley, Elliott. Everyday Living Words: Vocabulary in Context. 2002. (Illus.). 112p. per., wbk. ed. 8.95 (978-1-56254-392-1(X) , SP 392X) Saddleback Educational Publishing.

—Science & Technology Words: Vocabulary in Context. 2002. (Illus.). 112p. per., wbk. ed. 8.95 (978-1-56254-400-3(4) , SP 4004) Saddleback Educational Publishing.

—Workplace & Career Words: Vocabulary in Context. 2002. (Illus.). 112p. per., wbk. ed. 8.95 (978-1-56254-402-7(0) , SP 4020) Saddleback Educational Publishing.

Rabbit's Book of Words. 2004. 12p. (J). bds. 2.99 (978-1-85997-431-5(7)) Byeway Bks.

Rainbow Bridge Publishing Staff. Vocabulary Third Grade: Skill Builders. 2002. (Skill Builders Ser.). (Illus.). 64p. (gr. 3 up). 2.49 (978-1-887923-45-3(4)) Rainbow Bridge Publishing.

Random House Staff. Thomas' Railway Word Book. Milliron, Kerry, ed. Nichols, Paul, illus. 2000. (Pictureback Ser.). 24p. (J). (gr. k-3). pap. 3.25 (978-0-375-80281-2(9) , Random Hse. Bks. for Young Readers) Random Hse. Children's Bks.

Rasinski, Timothy. Daily Word Ladders: 100 Reproducible Word Study Lessons That Help Kids Boost Reading, Vocabulary, Spelling & Phonics Skills-Independently! 2005. (Daily Word Ladders Ser.). (Illus.). 112p. (gr. 4-6). pap. 15.99 (978-0-439-77345-4(8) , Teaching Resources) Scholastic, Inc.

—Daily Word Ladders Grades 2-3. 2005. (Daily Word Ladders Ser.). (Illus.). 112p. (gr. 2-3). pap. 15.99 (978-0-439-51383-8(9) , Teaching Resources) Scholastic, Inc.

—Making & Writing Words. 2000. (Four-Blocks Ser.). (Illus.). 160p. (gr. 3-6). pap. 14.99 (978-0-88724-560-2(9) , CD-2600) Carson-Dellosa Publishing Co., Inc.

Rau, Dana Meachen. At the Beach. 2007. (Fun Time Ser.). 24p. (J). lib. bdg. 22.79 (***978-0-7614-2609-7(4)*** , Benchmark Bks.) Cavendish, Marshall Corp.

—Baker. 2007. (Jobs in Town Ser.). 24p. (J). lib. bdg. 22.79 (***978-0-7614-2623-3(X)*** , Benchmark Bks.) Cavendish, Marshall Corp.

—Climbing. 2006. (On the Move Ser.). (Illus.). 24p. (J). lib. bdg. 22.79 (***978-0-7614-2318-8(4)*** , Benchmark Bks.) Cavendish, Marshall Corp.

Rau, Dana Meachen. Rolling. 2006. (On the Move Ser.). (Illus.). 31p. (J). (ps-1). lib. bdg. 22.79 (978-0-7614-2314-0(1) , Benchmark Bks.) Cavendish, Marshall Corp.

Rau, Dana Meachen, ed. ¡A Volar! 2006. (En Movimiento Ser.). (SPA & ENG., Illus.). 24p. (J). lib. bdg. 22.79 (978-0-7614-2425-3(3) , Benchmark Bks.) Cavendish, Marshall Corp.

—Flying. 2006. (On the Move Ser.). (Illus.). 24p. (J). (ps-1). lib. bdg. 22.79 (978-0-7614-2319-5(2) , Benchmark Bks.) Cavendish, Marshall Corp.

Reading Rods Prefixes & Suffixes: Instruction & Activity Book. 2003. (J). pap. 12.95 (978-1-56911-107-9(3)) Learning Resources, Inc.

Reading Rods Prefixes & Suffixes Activity Cards. 2003. (J). pap. 12.95 (978-1-56911-108-6(1)) Learning Resources, Inc.

Reading Rods Sentence Building Activity Cards, Set 2. 2003. (J). 19.95 (978-1-56911-116-1(2)) Learning Resources, Inc.

Reading Rods Simple Sentences Activity Cards. 2003. (J). pap. 12.95 (978-1-56911-111-6(1)) Learning Resources, Inc.

Reading Rods Simple Sentences Activity Cards, Set 2. 2003. (J). pap. 19.95 (978-1-56911-112-3(X)) Learning Resources, Inc.

Reading Rods Simple Sentences Instruction & Activity Book. 2003. (J). pap. 12.95 (978-1-56911-110-9(3)) Learning Resources, Inc.

Reading Rods Word Building Activity Book. 2003. (J). pap. 4.95 (978-1-56911-119-2(7)) Learning Resources, Inc.

Reading Rods Word Building Activity Cards, Set 2. 2003. (J). 19.95 (978-1-56911-115-4(4)) Learning Resources, Inc.

Reading Rods Word Families Double-Sided Activity Cards. 2001. (J). 12.95 (978-1-56911-071-3(9)) Learning Resources, Inc.

Realtime Associates and Mazer Corporation Staff & LeapFrog Staff, compiled by. Decode Regular & Unfamiliar Multi-Syllabic Words. 2002. (J). (gr. 3). 66.75 (978-1-58605-389-5(2)); (gr. 4). 66.75 (978-1-58605-448-9(1)); (gr. 5). 66.75 (978-1-58605-508-0(9)) LeapFrog Enterprises, Inc. (LeapFrog Schl. Hse.).

—Derive Word Meaning. 2002. (J). (gr. 2). 66.75 (978-1-58605-301-7(9)); (gr. 3). 66.75 (978-1-58605-363-5(9)) LeapFrog Enterprises, Inc. (LeapFrog Schl. Hse.).

—Identify Root Words. 2002. (J). (gr. 2). 66.75 (978-1-58605-328-4(0)); (gr. 3). 66.75 (978-1-58605-388-8(4)); (gr. 4). 66.75 (978-1-58605-447-2(3)) LeapFrog Enterprises, Inc. (LeapFrog Schl. Hse.).

—Match Oral & Printed Words. 2002. (J). (gr. 2). 66.75 (978-1-58605-324-6(8)); (gr. 3). 66.75 (978-1-58605-384-0(1)) LeapFrog Enterprises, Inc. (LeapFrog Schl. Hse.).

—Recognize Common Word Families. 2002. (J). (gr. 2). 66.75 (978-1-58605-329-1(9) , LeapFrog Schl. Hse.) LeapFrog Enterprises, Inc.

—Recognize Compound Words. 2002. (J). (gr. 2). 66.75 (978-1-58605-325-3(6)); (gr. 3). 66.75 (978-1-58605-385-7(X)); (gr. 4). 66.75 (978-1-58605-444-1(9)) LeapFrog Enterprises, Inc. (LeapFrog Schl. Hse.).

—Recognize Sensory Words & Imagery. 2002. (J). (gr. 5). 66.75 (978-1-58605-480-9(5) , LeapFrog Schl. Hse.) LeapFrog Enterprises, Inc.

—Sort Common Words. 2002. (J). (gr. 2). 66.75 (978-1-58605-309-3(4) , LeapFrog Schl. Hse.) LeapFrog Enterprises, Inc.

Understand & Explain Shades of Meaning. 2002. (J). (gr. 4). 66.75 (978-1-58605-442-7(2) , LeapFrog Schl. Hse.) LeapFrog Enterprises, Inc.

—Understand Shades of Meaning in Related Words. 2002. (J). (gr. 5). 66.75 (978-1-58605-505-9(4) , LeapFrog Schl. Hse.) LeapFrog Enterprises, Inc.

—Use Context to Derive Word Meaning. 2002. (J). (gr. 5). 66.75 (978-1-58605-500-4(3) , LeapFrog Schl. Hse.) LeapFrog Enterprises, Inc.

—Use Context to Determine Word Meaning. 2002. (J). (gr. 3). 66.75 (978-1-58605-379-6(5) , LeapFrog Schl. Hse.) LeapFrog Enterprises, Inc.

—Use Context to Drive Word Meaning. 2002. (J). (gr. 2). 66.75 (978-1-58605-311-6(6)); (gr. 4). 66.75 (978-1-58605-437-3(6)) LeapFrog Enterprises, Inc. (LeapFrog Schl. Hse.).

—Use Root Words & Affixes. 2002. (J). (gr. 5). 66.75 (978-1-58605-502-8(X) , LeapFrog Schl. Hse.) LeapFrog Enterprises, Inc.

Red Hot Root Word Book 2: Mastering Vocabulary with Prefixes, Suffixes & Root Words. 2000. (J). per. 19.95 (978-1-883055-35-6(0)) Dandy Lion Pubns.

Reeve, Christine E. Functional Vocabulary for Children Ben Likes All Kinds of Sports. 2005. (J). spiral bd. 14.95 (978-0-7606-0627-8(7)) LinguiSystems, Inc.

—Functional Vocabulary for Children Dontel Learns about Transportation. 2005. (J). spiral bd. 14.95 (978-0-7606-0625-4(0)) LinguiSystems, Inc.

—Functional Vocabulary for Children Jasmine Sets the Table. 2005. (J). spiral bd. 14.95 (978-0-7606-0623-0(4)) LinguiSystems, Inc.

—Functional Vocabulary for Children Kira Likes to Go to Schools. 2005. (J). spiral bd. 14.95 (978-0-7606-0628-5(5)) LinguiSystems, Inc.

—Functional Vocabulary for Children Michelle Goes for a Walk. 2005. (J). spiral bd. 14.95 (978-0-7606-0624-7(2)) LinguiSystems, Inc.

—Functional Vocabulary for Children Ramon Plays on the Playground. 2005. (J). spiral bd. 14.95 (978-0-7606-0626-1(9)) LinguiSystems, Inc.

—Functional Vocabulary for Children Sarah Goes to Bed. 2005. (J). spiral bd. 14.95 (978-0-7606-0620-9(X)) LinguiSystems, Inc.

—Functional Vocabulary for Children Tyler Gets Cleaned Up. 2005. (J). spiral bd. 14.95 (978-0-7606-0621-6(8)) LinguiSystems, Inc.

—Functional Vocabulary for Children Zoey Uses the Bathroom. 2005. (J). spiral bd. 14.95 (978-0-7606-0622-3(6)) LinguiSystems, Inc.

Rex, Michael. The Pie Is Cherry. 2001. (J). 15.95 (978-0-8050-6308-0(0) , Holt, Henry & Co. Bks. For Young Readers) Holt, Henry & Co.

Rey, H. A. & Rey, Margaret. Curious George's Big Book of Curiosity. Paprocki, Greg, illus. 2005. 48p. (J). (ps-k). 11.99 (978-0-618-58338-6(6)) Houghton Mifflin Co. Trade & Reference Div.

Rey, H. A. & Rey, Margret. Curious George's First Words at the Aquarium, 4 vols. 2006. (Illus.). 12p. (J). (ps-k). bds. 3.95 (978-0-618-55458-4(0)) Houghton Mifflin Co.

—Curious George's First Words at the Circus, 4 vols. 2006. (Illus.). 12p. (J). (ps-k). bds. 3.95 (978-0-618-55457-7(2)) Houghton Mifflin Co.

—Curious George's First Words at the Farm, 4 vols. 2006. (Illus.). 12p. (J). (ps-k). bds. 3.95 (978-0-618-55455-3(6)) Houghton Mifflin Co.

—Curious George's First Words at the Zoo, 4 vols. 2006. (Illus.). 12p. (J). (ps-k). bds. 3.95 (978-0-618-55456-0(4)) Houghton Mifflin Co.

Reynolds, Edith. Working with Words. 2003. 132p. (YA). pap. 16.95 (978-1-59330-093-7(X)) Aventine Pr.

Rhyming & Sight Words. 2003. (Full-Color Literacy Activities Ser.). (Illus.). 176p. (J). (ps-1). 19.99 (978-0-7439-3236-3(6)) Teacher Created Materials, Inc.

Rhyming & Word Families Big Book. 2004. (J). pap. 39.95 (978-1-56911-175-8(8)) Learning Resources, Inc.

Rhyming Words (Gr. 1-2) 2003. (J). (978-1-58232-112-7(4)); (978-1-58232-117-2(5)) Bryan Hse. Pubs., Inc.

Rhyming Words in Context (Gr. K-2) 2003. (J). (978-1-58232-098-4(5)) Bryan Hse. Pubs., Inc.

Richard, Elaine. 10 Vocabulary Card Games: Easy-to-Play, Reproducible Card & Board Games That Boost Kids' Vocabulary-and Help Them Succeed on Tests. 2005. (Illus.). 64p. (ps-k). pap. 12.99 (978-0-439-51378-4(2) , Teaching Resources) Scholastic, Inc.

Rigby Education Staff. Turkey. (Sails Literacy Ser.). (Illus.). 16p. (gr. 1-2). 27.00 (978-0-7635-9894-5(1) , 698941C99) Rigby Education.

Riley, Jeni. First Word Book. Stanley, Mandy, illus. 2000. 48p. (J). (gr. k-ps). tchr. ed. 12.95 (978-0-7534-5272-1(3) , Kingfisher) Houghton Mifflin Co. Trade & Reference Div.

—First Word Fun. Stanley, Mandy, illus. 2003. 48p. (J). (gr. k-ps). 7.95 (978-0-7534-5628-6(1) , Kingfisher) Houghton Mifflin Co. Trade & Reference Div.

Riley, Karen. The Eco Deck. 2002. (Illus.). 36p. (YA). (gr. 5-12). pap. 5.99 (978-0-9708135-1-0(1)) S.C.R.A.P. Gallery.

Robles, D. & Minquini, Lourdes. Los 100 Mejores Acertijos Matematicos (The One Hundred Best Word Problems) (SPA., Illus.). 151p. (J). (gr. k-6). pap. 7.95 (978-968-416-820-6(9) , FN8209) Fernandez USA Publishing.

Rochelle, Belinda. Words with Wings: A Treasury of African-American Poetry & Art. 2001. (Amistad Ser.). (Illus.). 48p. (J). 17.99 (978-0-688-16415-7(3)) HarperCollins Pubs.

Roets, Philip G. Greek & Latin Prefixes & Word Parts. 4th rev. expurg. ed. 2000. 64p. (YA). (gr. 5-12). pap. 16.00 (978-0-911943-68-9(4)) Leadership Pub., Inc.

Rofé, April, illus. The SENSEsational Alphabet: See-Read, Touch-Feel, Scratch & Smell, Hear-Learn, Have Fun! 2006. (J). (978-0-9779189-1-2(1)) Waldenhouse Pub., Inc.

Roffey, C. My Red Busy Book. 2003. (Illus.). 12p. (J). 6.99 (978-0-333-65970-0(8)) Macmillan Publishers Ltd. GBR. *Dist:* Trafalgar Square Publishing.

Roffey, M. First Words Indoors. 2003. (Illus.). 12p. (J). 3.99 (978-1-85292-227-6(3) , Campbell Bks.) Pan Macmillan GBR. *Dist:* Trafalgar Square Publishing.

Rogala, Jennifer. Ways to Say the Words You've Heard. 2006. 28p. (J). per. 11.95 (978-1-58939-864-1(5)) Virtualbookworm.com Publishing, Inc.

—When My Nose Runs, Where Does It Go? Nicholas, Jacob, illus. 2006. 36p. per. 11.95 (978-1-58939-866-5(1)) Virtualbookworm.com Publishing, Inc.

Rolbin, Cyrus. Kana-OK! A New Approach to Learning the ABC's of Japanese: Hiragana & Katakana. 2004. (JPN & ENG., Illus.). 128p. pap. 9.95 (978-4-7700-2988-1(8)) Kodansha International JPN. *Dist:* Kodansha America, Inc.

Rondeau, Amanda. Ed As in Bed. 2003. (Word Families Ser.). (Illus.). 23p. (J). (ps-3). lib. bdg. 19.93 (978-1-59197-228-0(0) , SandCastle) ABDO Publishing Co.

—Ob As in Knob. 2003. (Word Families Ser.). (Illus.). 23p. (J). (ps-3). lib. bdg. 19.93 (978-1-59197-249-5(3) , SandCastle) ABDO Publishing Co.

—Ock As in Block. 2003. (Word Families Ser.). (Illus.). 23p. (J). (ps-3). lib. bdg. 19.93 (978-1-59197-250-1(7) , SandCastle) ABDO Publishing Co.

—Og As in Dog. 2003. (Word Families Ser.). (Illus.). 23p. (J). (ps-3). lib. bdg. 19.93 (978-1-59197-251-8(5) , SandCastle) ABDO Publishing Co.

—Op As in Top. 2003. (Word Families Ser.). (Illus.). 23p. (J). (ps-3). lib. bdg. 19.93 (978-1-59197-252-5(3) , SandCastle) ABDO Publishing Co.

—Ore As in Core. 2003. (Word Families Ser.). (Illus.). 23p. (J). (ps-3). lib. bdg. 19.93 (978-1-59197-267-9(1) , SandCastle) ABDO Publishing Co.

—Ot As in Knot. 2003. (Word Families Ser.). (Illus.). 23p. (J). (ps-3). lib. bdg. 19.93 (978-1-59197-253-2(1) , SandCastle) ABDO Publishing Co.

—Ow As in Cow. 2003. (Word Families Ser.). (Illus.). 23p. (J). (ps-3). lib. bdg. 19.93 (978-1-59197-254-9(X) , SandCastle) ABDO Publishing Co.

Rooney, Anne. Working with Words. 2004. (QEB Learn Computing Ser.). (Illus.). 32p. (J). lib. bdg. 18.95 (978-1-59566-038-1(0)) QEB Publishing Inc.

Rosa-Mendoza, Gladys. Opposites. Cifuentes, Carolina, ed. McGeehan, Dan, illus. 2004. (English-Spanish Foundations Ser.: Vol. 5). Tr. of Opuestos. (ENG & SPA.). 20p. (J). (ps-4). bds. 6.95 (978-0-9679748-6-6(0)) Me+Mi Publishing.

Roso, Calvin. Where the Red Fern Grows. 1998. 58p. (J). (gr. 5-7). stu. ed., ring bd. 12.99 (978-1-58609-151-4(4)) Progeny Pr.

Round the World in Spanish. (SPA., Illus.). 47p. pap. 7.95 (978-0-7460-4078-2(4) , EDC847) EDC Publishing.

Running Press Staff. First Words 24-Copy Display. 2005. 239.52 (978-0-7624-2286-9(6)) Running Pr. Bk. Pubs.

Ryan, Pam Muñoz. A Pinky Is a Baby Mouse: And Other Baby Animal Names. 1999. (978-0-606-16665-2(3)) Tandem Library Bks.

Salzmann, Mary Elizabeth. -Ad As in Dad. 2003. (Word Families Ser.). (Illus.). 23p. (J). (ps-3). lib. bdg. 19.93 (978-1-59197-226-6(4) , SandCastle) ABDO Publishing Co.

—Ag As in Flag. 2003. (Word Families Ser.). (Illus.). 23p. (J). (ps-3). lib. bdg. 19.93 (978-1-59197-225-9(6) , SandCastle) ABDO Publishing Co.

—Am As in Ham. 2003. (Word Families Ser.). (Illus.). 23p. (J). (ps-3). lib. bdg. 19.93 (978-1-59197-223-5(X) , SandCastle) ABDO Publishing Co.

—Am I Happy? (Illus.). 23p. (J). (ps-3). 2006. 19.93 (978-1-59679-350-7(3) , SandCastle); 2005. pap. (978-1-59679-351-4(1)) ABDO Publishing Co.

—Ap As in Cap. 2003. (Word Families Ser.). (Illus.). 23p. (J). (ps-3). lib. bdg. 19.93 (978-1-59197-224-2(8) , SandCastle) ABDO Publishing Co.

—An As in Fan. 2003. (Word Families Ser.). (Illus.). 23p. (J). (ps-3). lib. bdg. 19.93 (978-1-59197-222-8(1) , SandCastle) ABDO Publishing Co.

—At As in Cat. 2003. (Word Families Ser.). (Illus.). 23p. (J). (ps-3). lib. bdg. 19.93 (978-1-59197-221-1(3) , SandCastle) ABDO Publishing Co.

—Ay As in Clay. 2003. (Word Families Ser.). (Illus.). 23p. (J). (ps-3). lib. bdg. 19.93 (978-1-59197-264-8(7) , SandCastle) ABDO Publishing Co.

—Come Home with Me! 2004. (Sight Words Ser.). (Illus.). 23p. (J). (ps-3). lib. bdg. 19.93 (978-1-59197-465-9(8)) ABDO Publishing Co.

—Did You See One Jump? 2004. (Sight Words Ser.). (Illus.). 23p. (J). (ps-3). lib. bdg. 19.93 (978-1-59197-466-6(6)) ABDO Publishing Co.

—Ell As in Well. 2003. (Word Families Ser.). (Illus.). 23p. (J). (ps-3). lib. bdg. 19.93 (978-1-59197-231-0(0) , SandCastle) ABDO Publishing Co.

—Here Is a Zoo. (Illus.). 23p. (J). (ps-3). 2006. 19.93 (978-1-59679-378-1(3) , SandCastle); 2005. pap. (978-1-59679-379-8(1)) ABDO Publishing Co.

—I Am a Kitten. (Illus.). 23p. (J). (ps-3). 2006. 19.93 (978-1-59679-380-4(5) , SandCastle); 2005. pap. (978-1-59679-381-1(3)) ABDO Publishing Co.

—I Had a Great Time! 2004. (Sight Words Ser.). (Illus.). 23p. (J). (ps-3). lib. bdg. 19.93 (978-1-59197-477-2(1)) ABDO Publishing Co.

—I See a Costume. (Illus.). 23p. (J). (ps-3). 2006. 19.93 (978-1-59679-384-2(8) , SandCastle); 2005. pap. (978-1-59679-385-9(6)) ABDO Publishing Co.

—It's Not Good, It's Great! 2003. (Sight Words Ser.). (Illus.). 23p. (J). (ps-3). lib. bdg. 19.93 (978-1-59197-479-6(8)) ABDO Publishing Co.

—Look at the Playground! (Illus.). 23p. (J). (ps-3). 2006. 19.93 (978-1-59679-398-9(8) , SandCastle); 2005. pap. (978-1-59679-399-6(6)) ABDO Publishing Co.

—No Pigs on the Farm! 2004. (Sight Words Ser.). (Illus.). 23p. (J). (ps-3). lib. bdg. 19.93 (978-1-59197-471-0(2)) ABDO Publishing Co.

—Out for the Summer! 2004. (Sight Words Ser.). (Illus.). 23p. (J). (ps-3). lib. bdg. 19.93 (978-1-59197-472-7(0)) ABDO Publishing Co.

—The Parade Is Here! (Illus.). 23p. (J). (ps-3). 2006. 19.93 (978-1-59679-406-1(2) , SandCastle); 2005. pap. (978-1-59679-407-8(0)) ABDO Publishing Co.

—See the Farm! (Illus.). 23p. (J). (ps-3). 2006. 19.93 (978-1-59679-414-6(3) , SandCastle); 2005. pap. (978-1-59679-415-3(1)) ABDO Publishing Co.

—Snow & More Snow! 2004. (Sight Words Ser.). (Illus.). 23p. (J). (ps-3). lib. bdg. 19.93 (978-1-59197-470-3(4)) ABDO Publishing Co.

—They Are the Best! 2004. (Sight Words Ser.). (Illus.). 23p. (J). (ps-3). lib. bdg. 19.93 (978-1-59197-474-1(7)) ABDO Publishing Co.

—Way to Go! 2004. (Sight Words Ser.). (Illus.). 23p. (J). (ps-3). lib. bdg. 19.93 (978-1-59197-468-0(2)) ABDO Publishing Co.

—We All Like It! 2004. (Sight Words Ser.). (Illus.). 23p. (J). (ps-3). lib. bdg. 19.93 (978-1-59197-467-3(4)) ABDO Publishing Co.

—We Are at the Park. 2005. (Illus.). (J). 23p. pap. (978-1-59679-425-2(9)); 24p. lib. bdg. 19.93 (978-1-59679-424-5(0) , SandCastle) ABDO Publishing Co.

—We Are Playing! 2005. (Illus.). (J). 23p. pap. (978-1-59679-427-6(5)); 24p. lib. bdg. 19.93 (978-1-59679-426-9(7) , SandCastle) ABDO Publishing Co.

—We Look at Food. (Illus.). 23p. (J). (ps-3). 2006. 19.93 (978-1-59679-436-8(4) , SandCastle); 2005. pap. (978-1-59679-437-5(2)) ABDO Publishing Co.

—We See the Beach! (Illus.). 23p. (J). (ps-3). 2006. 19.93 (978-1-59679-440-5(2) , SandCastle); 2005. pap. (978-1-59679-441-2(0)) ABDO Publishing Co.

—What a Day in the Park! 2004. (Sight Words Ser.). (Illus.). 23p. (J). (ps-3). lib. bdg. 19.93 (978-1-59197-476-5(3)) ABDO Publishing Co.

—Who Is This at the Beach? 2004. (Sight Words Ser.). (Illus.). 23p. (J). (ps-3). lib. bdg. 19.93 (978-1-59197-480-2(1)) ABDO Publishing Co.

Sanders, Nancy I. 25 Read & Write Mini-Books That Teach Word Families: Fun & Interactive Rhyming Stories That Give Kids Practice with the 25 Key Word Families - And Put Them on the Path to Reading Success! 2001. (Joyful Learning Ser.). (Illus.). 64p. pap. 10.95 (978-0-439-40810-3(5) , Teaching Resources) Scholastic, Inc.

Sanseri, Wanda. Play by the Sea. 2003. (J). 5.00 (978-1-880045-26-8(5)) Back Home Industries.

Sather, Edgar, et al. People at Work Student Text/3 CD's Package. 2005. pap. 27.00 incl. audio compact disk (978-0-86647-210-4(X)) Pro Lingua Assocs., Inc.

—People at Workt. 2005. pap., tchr. ed. 39.00 incl. audio compact disk (978-0-86647-211-1(8)) Pro Lingua Assocs., Inc.

Saunders, Catherine. Barbie Word Board Book. 2004. (SPA & ENG., Illus.). 36p. (J). bds. 6.99 (978-0-7566-0451-6(6)) Dorling Kindersley Publishing, Inc.

Scarry, Richard. Best Little Word Book Ever! 2001. (Richard Scarry's Ser.). (Illus.). 24p. (J). 2.99 (978-0-307-00136-8(9) , 98778, Golden Bks.) Random Hse. Children's Bks.

—Best Word Book Ever! Scarry, Richard, illus. 1999. (Richard Scarry's Ser.). (Illus.). 72p. (J). (ps-2). 15.99 (978-0-307-15510-8(2) , 15510, Golden Bks.) Random Hse. Children's Bks.

—Richard Scarry's Early Words. Scarry, Richard, illus. 1999. (Jellybean Bks.). (Illus.). 24p. (J). (ps-k). lib. bdg. 7.99 (978-0-375-90190-4(6) , Random Hse. Bks. for Young Readers) Random Hse. Children's Bks.

Schecter, Deborah. Sight Word Manipulatives for Reading Success: Wheels, Pull-Throughs, Puzzles, & Dozens of Other Easy-to-Make Manipulatives That Help Kids Read, Write, & Really Learn High-Frequency Words. 2005. 144p. pap. 17.99 (978-0-439-54259-3(6) , Teaching Resources) Scholastic, Inc.

Scheunemann, Pam. -Ack As in Snack. 2003. (Word Families Ser.). (Illus.). 23p. (J). (ps-3). lib. bdg. 19.93 (978-1-59197-261-7(2) , SandCastle) ABDO Publishing Co.

—Ash As in Trash. 2003. (Word Families Ser.). (Illus.). 23p. (J). (ps-3). lib. bdg. 19.93 (978-1-59197-260-0(4) , SandCastle) ABDO Publishing Co.

—Aw As in Paw. 2003. (Word Families Ser.). (Illus.). 23p. (J). (ps-3). lib. bdg. 19.93 (978-1-59197-263-1(9) , SandCastle) ABDO Publishing Co.

—Big Bug, Little Bug. (Illus.). 23p. (J). (ps-3). 2006. 19.93 (978-1-59679-356-9(2) , SandCastle); 2005. (978-1-59679-357-6(0)) ABDO Publishing Co.

—Come & See My Game! (Illus.). 23p. (J). (ps-3). 2006. 19.93 (978-1-59679-362-0(7) , SandCastle); 2005. pap. (978-1-59679-363-7(5)) ABDO Publishing Co.

—Come for a Party! (Illus.). 23p. (J). (ps-3). 2006. 19.93 (978-1-59679-364-4(3) , SandCastle); 2005. pap. (978-1-59679-365-1(1)) ABDO Publishing Co.

—The Cow Said Meow! (Illus.). 23p. (J). (ps-3). 2006. 19.93 (978-1-59679-368-2(6) , SandCastle); 2005. pap. (978-1-59679-369-9(4)) ABDO Publishing Co.

—Ent As in Cent. 2003. (Word Families Ser.). (Illus.). 23p. (J). (ps-3). lib. bdg. 19.93 (978-1-59197-233-4(7) , SandCastle) ABDO Publishing Co.

—Ick As in Kick. 2003. (Word Families Ser.). (Illus.). 23p. (J). (ps-3). lib. bdg. 19.93 (978-1-59197-258-7(2) , SandCastle) ABDO Publishing Co.

—Ing As in King. 2003. (Word Families Ser.). (Illus.). 23p. (J). (ps-3). lib. bdg. 19.93 (978-1-59197-256-3(6) , SandCastle) ABDO Publishing Co.

—Ink As in Drink. 2003. (Word Families Ser.). (Illus.). 23p. (J). (ps-3). lib. bdg. 19.93 (978-1-59197-257-0(4) , SandCastle) ABDO Publishing Co.

—Is This a Flower? (Illus.). 23p. (J). (ps-3). 2006. 19.93 (978-1-59679-390-3(2) , SandCastle); 2005. pap. (978-1-59679-391-0(0)) ABDO Publishing Co.

—Look at Me! (Illus.). 23p. (J). (ps-3). 2006. 19.93 (978-1-59679-396-5(1) , SandCastle); 2005. pap. (978-1-59679-397-2(X)) ABDO Publishing Co.

—Meg & I. (Illus.). 23p. (J). (ps-3). 2006. 19.93 (978-1-59679-400-9(3) , SandCastle); 2005. (978-1-59679-401-6(1)) ABDO Publishing Co.

—The Puppy Is for Me! (Illus.). 23p. (J). (ps-3). 2006. 19.93 (978-1-59679-408-5(9) , SandCastle); 2005. pap. (978-1-59679-409-2(7)) ABDO Publishing Co.

—Rainy Day. 2005. (Illus.). (J). 23p. pap. (978-1-59679-411-5(9)); 24p. lib. bdg. 19.93 (978-1-59679-410-8(0) , SandCastle) ABDO Publishing Co.

—This Is Not My Dog! 2005. (Illus.). (J). 23p. pap. (978-1-59679-419-1(4)); 24p. lib. bdg. 19.93 (978-1-59679-418-4(6) , SandCastle) ABDO Publishing Co.

—Unk as in Skunk. 2003. (Word Families Ser.). (Illus.). 23p. (J). (ps-3). lib. bdg. 19.93 (978-1-59197-259-4(0) , SandCastle) ABDO Publishing Co.

—We Like Music! 2005. (Illus.). (J). 23p. pap. (978-1-59679-433-7(X)); 24p. lib. bdg. 19.93 (978-1-59679-432-0(1) , SandCastle) ABDO Publishing Co.

—We Like to Play! (Illus.). 23p. (J). (ps-3). 2006. 19.93 (978-1-59679-434-4(8) , SandCastle); 2005. pap. (978-1-59679-435-1(6)) ABDO Publishing Co.

Scholastic, Inc. Staff. Scholastic 100 Words Kids Need to Read by 1st Grade Workbook. 2001. (J). pap. 3.95 (978-0-439-37064-6(7)) Scholastic, Inc.

—Scholastic 100 Words Kids Need to Read by 2nd Grade Workbook. 2001. (J). pap. 3.95 (978-0-439-37065-3(5)) Scholastic, Inc.

—Scholastic 100 Words Kids Need to Read by 3rd Grade Workbook. 2001. (J). pap. 3.95 (978-0-439-37066-0(3)) Scholastic, Inc.

Scholastic, Inc. Staff, contrib. by. 100 Words Kids Need to Read by 2nd Grade. 2002. 32p. (gr. 2). pap. 3.95 (978-0-439-39930-2(0) , Teaching Resources) Scholastic, Inc.

—100 Words Kids Need to Read by 3rd. 2002. 32p. (gr. 3). pap. 3.95 (978-0-439-39931-9(9) , Teaching Resources) Scholastic, Inc.

—100 Write-and-Learn Sight Word Practice Pages: Engaging, Reproducible Activity Pages That Help Kids Recognize, Write & Really Learn the Top 100 High-Frequency Words That Are Key to Reading Success, Grade K-2. 2002. (Illus.). 112p. pap., tchr. ed. 14.95 (978-0-439-36562-8(7)) Scholastic, Inc.

Scholastic, Inc. Staff, et al. 100 Words Kids Need to Read by 1st Grade: Sight Word Practice to Build Strong Readers. 2003. (100 Words Workbook Ser.). (Illus.). 256p. (J). wbk. ed. 12.95 (978-0-439-32024-5(0)) Scholastic, Inc.

—100 Words Kids Need to Read by 2nd Grade. 2003. (100 Words Workbook Ser.). (Illus.). 256p. (J). pap., wbk. ed. 12.95 (978-0-439-32023-8(2)) Scholastic, Inc.

School Renaissance Institute Staff, creator. Vocabulary Builders: Grades 3-5. 2000. (J). (gr. 3-5). 79.95 (978-1-893751-93-4(7)) Renaissance Learning, Inc.

—Vocabulary Builders: Grades 6-8. 2000. (YA). (gr. 6-8). 79.95 (978-1-893751-95-8(3)) Renaissance Learning, Inc.

School Specialty Publishing. Connect with Words, Grade 1. 2007. (Connect with Words Ser.). 352p. (J). pap. 16.95 (***978-0-7696-7431-5(3)*** , American Education Publishing) School Specialty Publishing.

—Connect with Words, Grade 2. 2007. (Connect with Words Ser.). 352p. (J). pap. 16.95 (***978-0-7696-7432-2(1)*** , American Education Publishing) School Specialty Publishing.

—Connect with Words, Grade 3. 2007. (Connect with Words Ser.). 352p. (J). pap. 16.95 (***978-0-7696-7433-9(X)*** , American Education Publishing) School Specialty Publishing.

—Connect with Words, Grade K. 2007. (Connect with Words Ser.). 352p. (J). pap. 16.95 (***978-0-7696-7430-8(5)*** , American Education Publishing) School Specialty Publishing.

—Easy Action Picture Words. 2001. (Phonics Flash Cards Ser.). 104p. (C). 6.99 (978-0-86734-414-1(8) , Schaffer, Frank) Schaffer, Frank Pubns.

—Easy Picture Word Opposites. 2001. (Phonics Flash Cards Ser.). 104p. (C). 6.99 (978-0-86734-419-6(9) , Schaffer, Frank) Schaffer, Frank Pubns.

—Easy Sight Words. 2001. (Phonics Flash Cards Ser.). 104p. (C). 6.99 (978-0-86734-403-5(2) , Schaffer, Frank) Schaffer, Frank Pubns.

—First Words. 2004. (On-File Ser.). 4p. (J). (gr. k-k). ring bd. 4.99 (978-0-7424-2859-1(1) , Instructional Fair) Schaffer, Frank Pubns.

—First Words. 2006. (Brighter Child Flash Cards Ser.). 54p. (J). 2.99 (978-0-7696-4719-7(7) , Brighter Child) School Specialty Publishing.

—First Words / Primeras Palabras. 2006. (Brighter Child Flash Cards Ser.). 54p. (J). 2.99 (978-0-7696-4779-1(0) , Brighter Child) School Specialty Publishing.

—Flip-Flash Math Vocabulary. 2004. 160p. (J). (gr. 4-5). pap. 7.99 (978-0-7424-2768-6(4) , ID99073); (gr. k-1). pap. 7.99 (978-0-7424-2766-2(8) , ID99074); (gr. 2-3). pap. 7.99 (978-0-7424-2767-9(6) , ID99072) School Specialty Publishing.

—Flip-Flash Phonics & Vocabulary: Prefixes. 2004. 160p. (J). (gr. 3-6). pap. 7.99 (978-0-7424-2686-3(6) , ID99060) School Specialty Publishing.

—Flip-Flash Phonics & Vocabulary: Suffixes. 2004. 160p. (J). (gr. 3-6). pap. 7.99 (978-0-7424-2687-0(4) , ID99061) School Specialty Publishing.

—Flip-Flash Phonics & Vocabulary: Vocabulary. 2004. 160p. (J). (gr. k-1). pap. 7.99 (978-0-7424-2694-8(7) , ID99064); (gr. 2-3). pap. 7.99 (978-0-7424-2695-5(5) , ID99062); (gr. 4-5). pap. 7.99 (978-0-7424-2696-2(3) , ID99063) School Specialty Publishing.

—Hablo Ingles! Level 1 - Pictures & Words. 1999. (Homework Booklets Ser.). (SPA.). 80p. (C). pap. 2.99 (978-0-88012-921-3(2) , IF0200, Instructional Fair) Schaffer, Frank Pubns.

—Hablo Ingles! Level 2 - Words & Phrases. 1999. (Homework Booklets Ser.). (SPA.). 80p. (C). pap. 2.99 (978-0-88012-922-0(0) , IF0201, Instructional Fair) Schaffer, Frank Pubns.

—Learning Basic Vocabulary. 2004. (Kindergarten Standards Ser.). 144p. (C). pap. 16.99 (978-0-7682-2810-6(7) , FS99275) Schaffer, Frank Pubns.

—Sight Word Comprehension, Grades K-2. 2006. (Frank Schaffer Classic Reproducibles Ser.). 48p. (J). (gr. k-2). pap. 6.99 (978-0-7682-3450-3(6) , Schaffer, Frank) Schaffer, Frank Pubns.

—Sight Words. 2001. (Flip-Flashtm Phonics Ser.). 160p. (J). (gr. k up). pap. 7.99 (978-1-56451-386-1(6) , ID2425) School Specialty Publishing.

—Sight Words. 2001. (Phonics Flash Cards Ser.). 104p. (C). 6.99 (978-0-86734-404-2(0) , Schaffer, Frank) Schaffer, Frank Pubns.

—Sight Words. 2006. (Brighter Child Flash Cards Ser.). 54p. (J). 2.99 (978-0-7696-6470-5(9) , Brighter Child) School Specialty Publishing.

—Theme-Based Vocabulary Builders. 2003. (100+ Seriestm Ser.). 128p. (J). (gr. 2 up). pap. 12.99 (978-0-7424-1932-2(0) , IFG99112); (gr. 3 up). pap. 12.99 (978-0-7424-1933-9(9) , IFG99113) School Specialty Publishing.

—Word Problems Gr 4. 2005. (Math 2 Master Ser.). 32p. (J). pap. 3.99 (978-0-7696-3924-6(0) , Brighter Child) School Specialty Publishing.

—Word Wall Materials. 2004. 40p. (J). (gr. k-1). pap. 8.99 (978-0-7424-2744-0(7) , ID99070); (gr. 2-3). pap. 8.99 (978-0-7424-2745-7(5) , ID99071) School Specialty Publishing.

—100 Lifelong Words: Recognizing & Using High-Frequency Words. 2006. 112p. (J). (gr. 3-6). pap. 12.99 (978-0-7682-3373-5(9) , Schaffer, Frank) Schaffer, Frank Pubns.

School Zone Publishing. Vocabulary Puzzles. 2003. (Language Arts Ser.). cd-rom 19.99 (978-1-58947-931-9(9)) School Zone Publishing Co.

School Zone Publishing Co. Make-A-Word Bingo Game. 2006. (J). 5.99 (***978-1-58947-496-3(1)***) School Zone Publishing Co.

School Zone Publishing Company Staff. Basic Sight Word Fun! deluxe ed. 2005. 64p. (J). pap., wbk. ed. 3.79 (978-1-58947-338-6(8)) School Zone Publishing Co.

—Beginning Sight Words. 2000. (Flash Cards Spanish Ser.). (SPA & ENG., Illus.). 56p. (J). 2.89 (978-0-88743-620-8(X) , 04042) School Zone Publishing Co.

—Big Activity Ages 8-Up: Word Searches, Crosswords, Puzzles, & Codes. 2004. 320p. (J). pap. 9.99 (978-1-58947-422-2(8)) School Zone Publishing Co.

—Ups & Downs: A Book of Positional Words. 2000. (Illus.). 16p. (J). bds. 4.99 (978-0-88743-605-5(6)) School Zone Publishing Co.

—Vocabulary Puzzles 2. (Illus.). (J). 19.99 incl. audio compact disk (978-0-88743-968-1(3)) School Zone Publishing Co.

—Whimsy Picture Words. 2001. (Flash Cards Whimsy Ser.). 56p. (J). 2.79 (978-0-88743-672-7(2) , 04063) School Zone Publishing Co.

—Whimsy Readiness. 2001. (Flash Cards Whimsy Ser.). 56p. (J). 2.79 (978-0-88743-671-0(4) , 04062) School Zone Publishing Co.

—Word Families. rev. ed. 1999. (Flash Cards Ser.). (Illus.). 56p. (J). 2.79 (978-0-938256-82-3(3) , 04015) School Zone Publishing Co.

School Zone Publishing Interactive Staff. Vocabulary Puzzles. 2001. (On-Track Software Ser.). 32p. (J). wbk. ed. 13.99 incl. cd-rom (978-0-88743-955-1(1) , 08831) School Zone Publishing Co.

School Zone Staff. Beginning Sight Words. 2004. 54p. (J). 2.79 (978-1-58947-982-1(3)) School Zone Publishing Co.

—Picture Words. 2005. 56p. (J). 2.79 (978-1-58947-480-2(5)) School Zone Publishing Co.

School Zone Staff, ed. My First 100 Magnetic Words. 2006. (J). (gr. k-2). bds. 15.99 (***978-1-58947-318-8(3)***) School Zone Publishing Co.

Schwartz, Avroham. Shas Milim. 2002. 82p. (gr. 3-8). wbk. ed. 10.00 (978-1-878895-37-0(0) , M509) Torah Umesorah Pubns.

Scott, James. Vocabulary for the College Bound - D. 1999. 72p. (YA). (gr. 12 up). pap. 7.95 (978-1-58049-263-8(0) , VC63A) Prestwick Hse., Inc.

—Watership Down: Reproducible Teaching Unit. 2002. 86p. (J). ring bd. (978-1-58049-413-7(7)) Prestwick Hse., Inc.

—Young Goodman Brown: Reproducible Teaching Unit. 2002. 88p. (J). ring bd. (978-1-58049-416-8(1) , TU199) Prestwick Hse., Inc.

Scrambled Word Building. 2003. (J). (gr. 1). pap., act. bk. ed. 12.95 (978-1-56911-128-4(6)); (gr. 2). pap., act. bk. ed. 12.95 (978-1-56911-129-1(4)); (gr. 3). pap., act. bk. ed. 12.95 (978-1-56911-130-7(8)) Learning Resources, Inc.

Scrambled Word Building: Cross-Curricular. 2002. (J). pap. 19.95 (978-1-56911-036-2(0)) Learning Resources, Inc.

Scrambled Word Building: Thematic. 2002. (J). pap. 19.95 (978-1-56911-035-5(2)) Learning Resources, Inc.

Scrambled Word Building Cards. 2002. (J). 9.95 (978-1-56911-034-8(4)) Learning Resources, Inc.

Seeger, Laura Vaccaro. Black? White! Day? Night! A Book of Opposites. 2006. (Illus.). 24p. (J). (ps-2). 16.95 (978-1-59643-185-0(7)) Roaring Brook Pr.

Seelig, Renate, illus. Mein Kleiner Brockhaus: Erste Woerter. 28p. (J). (ps up). (978-3-7653-2561-8(9)) Brockhaus, F. A., GmbH DEU. *Dist:* International Bk. Import Service, Inc.

Sentence Building Activity Cards (OCR) 2004. (J). 14.95 (978-1-56911-195-6(2)) Learning Resources, Inc.

Serlin, Andra & Luther, Jacqui Moody. Super Sheep Saves the Day. Nicholls, Paul & Codor, Richard, illus. 2005. 10p. (J). (ps-ps). pap. 7.95 (978-0-7624-1993-7(8) , Running Pr. Kids) Running Pr. Bk. Pubs.

Sesame Street Beginning Words. 2005. (J). 2.95 (***978-1-58610-981-3(2)***) Learning Horizons, Inc.

Shabanu. (J). pap., stu. ed. (978-0-13-620295-0(0)) Prentice Hall (Schl. Div.).

Shaw, Marie-José. Jumbo Vocabulary Development Yearbook: Grade 3. (Jumbo Vocabulary Ser.). 96p. (J). (gr. 3). 15.95 (978-0-8209-0052-0(4) , B JVDY 3) ESP, Inc.

Shiotsu, Vicky. Build-a-Skill Instant Books Beginning & Ending Consonant Sounds. Faulkner, Stacey, ed. Campbell, Jenny & Tom, Darcy, illus. 2007. (J). 4.99 (***978-1-59198-416-0(5)***) Creative Teaching Pr., Inc.

Shiotsu, Vicky. Second Grade Vocabulary. 2000. (Grade Boosters Ser.). (Illus.). 64p. (J). (gr. 2-3). pap. 4.95 (978-0-7373-0375-9(1) , 03751W) Lowell Hse.

Shireman, Myrl. Phonics & Vocabulary Skills Practice & Apply: Grade 4. 2000. (Illus.). 128p. (J). (gr. 4). pap. 10.95 (978-1-58037-131-5(0)) Twain, Mark Media, Inc. Pubs.

—Phonics & Vocabulary Skills Practice & Apply: Grade 5. 2000. (Illus.). 128p. (J). (gr. 5). pap. 10.95 (978-1-58037-132-2(9)) Twain, Mark Media, Inc. Pubs.

—Phonics & Vocabulary Skills Practice & Apply: Grade 6. 2000. (Illus.). 128p. (J). (gr. 6). pap. 10.95 (978-1-58037-133-9(7)) Twain, Mark Media, Inc. Pubs.

Short Vowels Phonics Windows with Answers. 2002. (Phonics Windows Ser.). (J). pap. 0.99 (978-0-88724-833-7(0) , CD-3032) Carson-Dellosa Publishing Co., Inc.

Shostak, Jerome. Vocabulary Workshop: Level E. 2002. (Vocabulary Workshop Ser.). 182p. (YA). (gr. 10 up). stu. ed. 8.84 (978-0-8215-7610-6(0)) Sadlier, William H. Inc.

—Vocabulary Workshop, Student Text, Level A. 2002nd ed. 2005. (Vocabulary Workshop Ser.). 192p. (YA). (gr. 6 up). stu. ed. 6.90 (978-0-8215-7606-9(2)) Sadlier, William H. Inc.

—Vocabulary Workshop, Student Text, Level B. 2002nd ed. 2005. (Vocabulary Workshop Ser.). 192p. (YA). (gr. 7 up). stu. ed. 6.90 (978-0-8215-7607-6(0)) Sadlier, William H. Inc.

—Vocabulary Workshop, Student Text, Level C. 2002nd ed. 2005. (Vocabulary Workshop Ser.). 182p. (YA). (gr. 8 up). stu. ed. 6.90 (978-0-8215-7608-3(9)) Sadlier, William H. Inc.

—Vocabulary Workshop, Student Text, Level D. 2002nd ed. 2002. (Vocabulary Workshop Ser.). 182p. (YA). (gr. 9 up). stu. ed. (978-0-8215-7609-0(7)) Sadlier, William H. Inc.

—Vocabulary Workshop, Student Text, Level F. 2002nd ed. 2002. (Vocabulary Workshop Ser.). 182p. (YA). (gr. 11 up). stu. ed. (978-0-8215-7611-3(9)) Sadlier, William H. Inc.

—Vocabulary Workshop, Student Text, Level G. 2002nd ed. 2002. (Vocabulary Workshop Ser.). 182p. (YA). (gr. 12 up). stu. ed. (978-0-8215-7612-0(7)) Sadlier, William H. Inc.

—Vocabulary Workshop, Student Text, Level H. 2002nd ed. 2002. (Vocabulary Workshop Ser.). 182p. (YA). (gr. 12 up). stu. ed. (978-0-8215-7613-7(5)) Sadlier, William H. Inc.

Siede, George & Press, Donna, photos by. Collections. 1998. (Active Minds Ser.). (Illus.). 40p. (J). bds. 12.98 (978-1-58048-032-1(2)) Sandvik Publishing.

—First Words. 1998. (Active Minds Ser.). (Illus.). 10p. (J). bds. 3.99 (978-1-58048-031-4(4)) Sandvik Publishing.

Siede Preis Photography (Firm) Staff & Brian Warling Photography (Firm) Staff, contrib. by. First Words. 2003. (Lift-A-Flap Ser.). (Illus.). 12p. (J). bds. 12.98 (978-0-7853-8624-7(6) , 7188400) Publications International, Ltd.

Sight Word Fun. (Basic Skills Ser.). 48p. (ps-2). 5.99 (978-0-513-02335-2(6) , TSD23356) Denison, T. S. & Co., Inc.

Sight Word Rhymes (Gr. K-2) 2003. (J). (978-1-58232-093-9(4)) Bryan Hse. Pubs., Inc.

Sight Word Stories (Gr. K-2) 2003. (J). (978-1-58232-092-2(6)) Bryan Hse. Pubs., Inc.

Sight Words (Gr. 1-2) 2003. (J). (978-1-58232-039-7(X)) Bryan Hse. Pubs., Inc.

Sight Words (Gr. K-1) 2003. (J). (978-1-58232-031-1(4)) Bryan Hse. Pubs., Inc.

Sight Words in Context (Gr. K-2) 2003. (J). (978-1-58232-097-7(7)) Bryan Hse. Pubs., Inc.

Sight Words Word Search (Gr. K-2) 2003. (J). (978-1-58232-094-6(2)) Bryan Hse. Pubs., Inc.

SIPPS Beginning Hand-held Sight Word Cards. 2004. (978-1-57621-457-2(5)) Developmental Studies Ctr.

SIPPS Beginning Sight Word Wall Cards. 2004. (978-1-57621-456-5(7)) Developmental Studies Ctr.

SIPPS Beginning Sound Wall Cards. 2004. (978-1-57621-454-1(0)) Developmental Studies Ctr.

Skidmore, Sharon, et al. Balanced Literacy. 2008. per. 34.00 ***(978-1-879097-34-6(6))*** Kagan Publishing.

Skultety, Nancy Laney. 101 Words Your Child Will Read by the End of Grade 1. 2006. (Illus.). viii, 151p. (J). ***(978-0-7641-3305-3(5))*** Barron's Educational Series, Inc.

Smart Kids Publishing Staff. My First Words Sticker Book - Bi-Lingual. Smart Kids Publishing Staff, illus. 2007. (Illus.). 10p. bds. 8.99 ***(978-0-8249-6696-6(1))*** Ideals Pubns.

Smith & Mare. Concepts for Today: Answer Key. 2000. (978-0-8384-1224-4(6)) Thomson Heinle.

—Issues for Today: Answer Key. 2nd ed. 2000. (978-0-8384-2138-3(5)) Thomson Heinle.

—Themes for Today: Answer Key. 2nd ed. 2000. 5.00 net. (978-0-8384-1973-1(9)) Thomson Heinle.

—Topics for Today: Answer Key. 2nd ed. 2000. (978-0-8384-1208-4(4)) Thomson Heinle.

Smith, Robert. How to Solve Word Problems: Grades 3-4. 2000. (Illus.). 48p. (J). (gr. 3-4). pap., tchr. ed. 7.99 (978-1-57690-483-1(0) , TCA2483) Teacher Created Materials, Inc.

Snap! Student Dictionary. 2002. cd-rom 4.99 (978-1-59150-161-9(X)) TOPICS Entertainment.

Sneller, Norm. Building Reading Comprehension: High-Interest Selections for Critical Reading Skills. 2000. (100+ Seriestm Ser.). 128p. (J). (gr. 5-6). pap. 12.99 (978-1-56822-914-0(3) , IF8719, Instructional Fair) Schaffer, Frank Pubns.

Solotareff, Gregoire. Nieve. 2003. (SPA.). 86p. 21.99 (978-84-8470-039-5(9)) Corimbo, Editorial S.L. ESP. *Dist:* Lectorum Pubns., Inc.

Soundprints. Pooh's First Concepts Pack. rev. ed. (First Concepts Ser.). (Illus.). 36p. (J). 12.99 incl. cd-rom (978-1-59069-363-6(9) , 1A502) Studio Mouse LLC.

Southwater Books Staff. Let's Stick & Learn. 2000. (Illus.). 64p. pap. 7.95 (978-1-84215-124-2(X) , Southwater) Anness Publishing GBR. *Dist:* National Bk. Network.

Southwater Staff. My Day: Look & Learn. 2000. (Look & Learn Ser.). (Illus.). 32p. (ps). 7.95 (978-1-84215-165-5(7) , Southwater) Anness Publishing GBR. *Dist:* National Bk. Network.

—My Home: Look & Learn. 2000. (Look & Learn Ser.). (Illus.). 32p. (ps). 7.95 (978-1-84215-169-3(X) , Southwater) Anness Publishing GBR. *Dist:* National Bk. Network.

Spanish & English Vocabulary Development. 2005. 123p. (J). spiral bd. 14.99 (978-1-59441-470-1(X) , K04021) Carson-Dellosa Publishing Co., Inc.

Spann, Mary Beth. The Scholastic Big Book of Word Walls. 2003. 112p. (J). pap. 14.95 (978-0-439-16519-8(9)) Scholastic, Inc.

—Word Family File-Folder Word Walls: 30 Reproducible Patterns for Portable Word Walls to Teach the Top Word Families & Help Kids Become Better Readers, Writers, & Spellers. 2001. 64p. pap. 10.95 (978-0-439-26170-8(8)) Scholastic, Inc.

Spelling & Vocabulary, Set. 2004. (gr. 2). 38.95 (978-0-7403-0219-0(1) , Horizons) Alpha Omega Pubns., Inc.

Stamper, Judith Bauer & Ross Keyes, Joan. Monster Parade. 2005. (Oxford Picture Dictionary for Kids Ser.). (Illus.). 16p. 4.50 (978-0-19-430929-5(0)) Oxford Univ. Pr., Inc.

—Trip to Toy Town. 2005. (Oxford Picture Dictionary for Kids Ser.). (Illus.). 16p. 4.50 (978-0-19-430930-1(4)) Oxford Univ. Pr., Inc.

Stanek, Robert. Student's Classroom Handbook for the Kingdoms & the Elves of the Reaches. 2003. 128p. pap. 15.00 (978-1-57545-033-9(X) , Ruin Mist Pubns.) Reagent Pr.

Stanley, Mandy. At the Pool. 2004. (All Aboard Ser.). Orig. Title: Vamos a la Piscina. (ENG & SPA., Illus.). 12p. (J). (ps-k). bds. 3.95 (978-0-7534-5747-4(4) , Kingfisher) Houghton Mifflin Co. Trade & Reference Div.

—In the Park. 2004. (All Aboard Ser.). Orig. Title: Vamos al Parqu. (Illus.). 12p. (J). (ps-k). bds. 3.95 (978-0-7534-5750-4(4) , Kingfisher) Houghton Mifflin Co. Trade & Reference Div.

—Mascotas Maravillosas/Perfect Pets. 2004. (Todos A Bordo Ser.). (ENG & SPA., Illus.). 12p. (J). (ps-k). bds. 4.95 (978-0-7534-5813-6(6) , Kingfisher) Houghton Mifflin Co. Trade & Reference Div.

—Vamos a la Piscina: Todos a Bordo. 2004. (ENG & SPA., Illus.). 12p. (J). (ps-k). bds. 3.95 (978-0-7534-5810-5(1) , Kingfisher) Houghton Mifflin Co. Trade & Reference Div.

—Vamos al Parque/In the Park. 2004. (Todos A Bordo Ser.). (ENG & SPA., Illus.). 12p. (J). (ps-k). bds. 3.95 (978-0-7534-5811-2(X) , Kingfisher) Houghton Mifflin Co. Trade & Reference Div.

—Vamos de Viaje/On the Move. 2004. (Todos A Bordo Ser.). (ENG & SPA., Illus.). 12p. (J). (ps-k). bds. 4.95 (978-0-7534-5812-9(8) , Kingfisher) Houghton Mifflin Co. Trade & Reference Div.

Steck-Vaughn Staff. Build-a-Word: Blends & Digraphs. 2001. (J). pap. (978-0-7398-4734-3(1)); pap., tchr. ed. (978-0-7398-4656-8(6)) Steck-Vaughn.

—Build-a-Word: Complete Class. 2001. (J). pap. (978-0-7398-4667-4(1)) Steck-Vaughn.

—Build-a-Word: Phonograms Class. 2001. (J). pap. (978-0-7398-4735-0(X)) Steck-Vaughn.

—Build-a-Word Combined, Set. 2001. (J). pap. (978-0-7398-4665-0(5)) Steck-Vaughn.

—Middle School Vocabulary. 1999. (Illus.). (J). pap. (978-0-7398-1305-8(6)) Steck-Vaughn.

—Phonograms-Build-a-Word. 2001. (J). pap., tchr.'s planning gde. ed. (978-0-7398-4657-5(4)) Steck-Vaughn.

—Phonograms Set-Build-a-Word. 2001. (J). pap. (978-0-7398-4664-3(7)) Steck-Vaughn.

—Vocabulary Connections. 2004. Level C. (Illus.). pap. 13.73 incl. cd-rom (978-0-7398-9170-4(7)); Level D. (Illus.). pap. 13.73 incl. cd-rom (978-0-7398-9171-1(5)); Level A. (Illus.). pap. 13.73 incl. cd-rom (978-0-7398-9168-1(5)); Level B. pap. 13.73 incl. cd-rom (978-0-7398-9169-8(3)); Level E. (Illus.). pap. 13.73 incl. cd-rom (978-0-7398-9172-8(3)); Level F. (Illus.). pap. 13.73 incl. cd-rom (978-0-7398-9173-5(1)); Level G. (Illus.). pap. 13.73 incl. cd-rom (978-0-7398-9174-2(X)); Level H. (Illus.). pap. 13.73 incl. cd-rom (978-0-7398-9175-9(8)) Steck-Vaughn.

—Vocabulary Connections Classroom Package. 2001. pap. 170.50 (978-0-7398-9757-7(8)) Steck-Vaughn.

—Vocabulary Skills. 2003. (J). (gr. 2). pap. (978-0-7398-6901-7(9)); (gr. 3). pap. (978-0-7398-6902-4(7)); (gr. 4). pap. (978-0-7398-6903-1(5)); (gr. 5). pap. (978-0-7398-6904-8(3)); (gr. 6). pap. (978-0-7398-6905-5(1)) Steck-Vaughn.

—Vocabulary Usage & Spelling Core Skills. 2001. pap. (978-0-7398-4902-6(6)) Steck-Vaughn.

—Vocabulary Ventures. 2004. (gr. 1-2). pap. 14.99 (978-0-7398-8561-1(8)); (gr. 3-4). pap. 14.99 (978-0-7398-8562-8(6)) Steck-Vaughn.

—What Can We Make Together. 2000. pap. (978-0-7398-4484-7(9)) Steck-Vaughn.

—Word Building for Primary Grades. 2000. (Illus.). (J). pap. (978-0-7398-2371-2(X)); (gr. 1). pap. (978-0-7398-2372-9(8)); (gr. 2). pap. (978-0-7398-2373-6(6)); (gr. 3). pap. (978-0-7398-2374-3(4)) Steck-Vaughn.

Suarez, Elizabeth. Fluency, Vocabulary, & Comprehension E-Book. 2005. 80p. (J). per. 10.99 (978-1-59441-564-7(1) , CD-104017-EB) Carson-Dellosa Publishing Co., Inc.

Sunshine TM Word Books Set: 1 Each of 4 Big Books. (gr. k-1). 125.50 (978-0-7802-6930-9(6)); Vol. 2. 125.50 (978-0-7802-6984-2(5)) Wright Group, The.

Sunshine TM Word Books Set: 1 Each of 4 Student Books. (gr. k-1). 19.50 (978-0-7802-3848-0(6)); Vol. 2. 22.95 (978-0-7802-6821-0(0)) Wright Group, The.

Sunshine TM Word Books Set: 6 Each of 4 Student Books. (gr. k-1). 116.95 (978-0-7802-6820-3(2)); Vol. 2. 150.95 (978-0-7802-6822-7(9)) Wright Group, The.

Supermarket Language. 2001. (YA). (gr. 6-12). pap. 16.95 (978-0-8359-1510-6(7)) Globe Fearon Educational Publishing.

Survival Vocabulary 1. 2000. 100p. ring bd. 29.95 (978-1-56254-218-4(4) , SP 2184) Saddleback Educational Publishing.

Survival Vocabulary 2. 2000. 100p. ring bd. 29.95 (978-1-56254-219-1(2) , SP 2192) Saddleback Educational Publishing.

Survival Words. 96p. 9.99 (978-0-7424-0198-3(7) , LL80002) School Specialty Publishing.

Suter, Joanne. History & Geography Words: Vocabulary in Context. 2002. (Illus.). 112p. per., wbk. ed. 8.95 (978-1-56254-394-5(6) , SP 3946) Saddleback Educational Publishing.

—Media & Marketplace Words: Vocabulary in Context. 2002. (Illus.). 112p. per., wbk. ed. 8.95 (978-1-56254-396-9(2) , SP 3962) Saddleback Educational Publishing.

—Music, Arts, & Literature Words: Vocabulary in Context. 2002. (Illus.). 112p. per., wbk. ed. 8.95 (978-1-56254-398-3(9) , SP 3989) Saddleback Educational Publishing.

Sutinis, Beth, ed. Touch & Feel. 2001. (My First Word Books). (Illus.). 12p. (J). (ps). bds. 9.99 (978-0-7894-7931-0(1)) Dorling Kindersley Publishing, Inc.

Tam on Sam: Consonants m, s, t; Short Vowel a; -am, -at word families: Level A, 6 vols. (Wright Skills Ser.). 12p. (gr. k-3). 17.95 (978-0-322-01445-9(X)) Wright Group, The.

Tat Is Sad: Consonant d: Level A, 6 vols. (Wright Skills Ser.). 12p. (gr. k-3). 17.95 (978-0-322-03105-0(2)) Wright Group, The.

Ten Essential Vocabulary Strat. 2004. pap. 5.95 (978-0-8388-3020-8(X)) Educators Publishing Service, Inc.

Terban, Marvin. Building Your Vocabulary. Brace, Eric, illus. (Scholastic Guides). 192p. (J). 2003. pap. 7.95 (978-0-439-28562-9(3)); 2002. (gr. 4 up). pap. 12.95 (978-0-439-28561-2(5)) Scholastic, Inc. (Scholastic Reference).

The Things They Carried: Reproducible Teaching Unit. 2002. 65p. (J). ring bd. (978-1-58049-450-2(1) , TU206) Prestwick Hse., Inc.

Thomson, Ruth. A First Word Bank. 2002. (Adventures in Literacy Ser.). (Illus.). 64p. (J). lib. bdg. 28.50 (978-1-931983-09-9(7)) Chrysalis Education.

Thorburn, P. & Cobb, S., contrib. by. Picture Words. 1999. (Illus.). 46p. (J). (ps-2). 24.00 (978-0-7217-0658-0(4)) Schofield & Sims Ltd. GBR. *Dist:* State Mutual Bk. & Periodical Service, Ltd.

Thorne, Pat. My First Word Book. (Illus.). (J). (ps up). pap. 16.95 (978-0-590-74011-1(3)) Scholastic, Inc.

El Tiempo. 2005. Tr. of Weather. 88p. (J). spiral bd. 14.99 (978-1-59441-463-3(7) , K04014) Carson-Dellosa Publishing Co., Inc.

El Tiempo. (Coleccion Planeta Vivo).Tr. of Weather. (SPA.). (J). (gr. 5-8). 12.00 (978-84-342-1945-8(X)) Parramon Ediciones S.A. ESP. *Dist:* Distribuidora Norma, Inc., Lectorum Pubns., Inc.

Tilton, Patricia. Reproducible Little Books for Sight Words. 2004. 176p. (gr. k-2). pap. 15.99 (978-0-7439-3225-7(0)) Teacher Created Materials, Inc.

Timeless Voices, Timeless Themes: Copper, Vocabulary & Spelling Practice Book. 2001. (J). (gr. 6). pap. 6.97 (978-0-13-052344-0(5)) Prentice Hall PTR.

Timeless Voices, Timeless Themes: Gold, Vocabulary & Spelling Practice Book. 2000. (YA). (gr. 9). pap. 6.97 (978-0-13-437572-4(6)) Prentice Hall PTR.

Timeless Voices, Timeless Themes: Platinum, Vocabulary & Spelling Practice Book. 2000. (YA). (gr. 10). pap. 6.97 (978-0-13-437576-2(9)) Prentice Hall PTR.

Timeless Voices, Timeless Themes: Silver, Vocabulary & Spelling Practice Book. 2001. (YA). (gr. 8). pap. 6.97 (978-0-13-052346-4(1)) Prentice Hall PTR.

Timeless Voices, Timeless Themes: The American Experience, Vocabulary & Spelling Practice Book. 2000. (YA). (gr. 11). pap. 6.97 (978-0-13-437579-3(3)) Prentice Hall PTR.

Timeless Voices, Timeless Themes: The British Tradition, Vocabulary & Spelling Practice Book. 2000. (YA). (gr. 12). pap. 6.97 (978-0-13-437582-3(3)) Prentice Hall PTR.

Top That Publishing Staff, ed. Bobby Badgers Box of Books. 2005. (Illus.). 16p. bds. (978-1-84510-542-6(7)) Top That! Publishing PLC.

—First Words. 2004. (Magnetic Play & Learn Ser.). (Illus.). 12p. (J). (978-1-84510-049-0(2)) Top That! Publishing PLC.

Trattles, Patricia. Flying Butter. Swift, Gary, illus. 2005. (Rookie Reader Skill Set Ser.). (J). (gr. k-2). 23p. pap. 4.95 (978-0-516-25280-3(1)); 24p. 19.50 (978-0-516-25150-9(3)) Scholastic Library Publishing. (Children's Pr.).

Trisler, Alana & Cardiel, Patrice Howe. Advanced Words I Use When I Write. 2000. (Illus.). 88p. (J). (gr. 5-6). pap., wbk. ed. 3.25 (978-1-56762-139-6(2)) Modern Learning Pr.

Tronick, Ed, contrib. by. Learn, Practice & Play Set: Word Sounds. (Home Learning Tools(R) Ser.). 32p. (J). pap. 3.99 (978-1-4037-0778-9(2)) Dalmatian Pr.

Tucker, Sian. My Book of First Words. Tucker, Sian, illus. 2003. (My Book of. . . Ser.). (Illus.). 48p. (YA). (978-1-85602-439-6(3)) Chrysalis Children's Bks.

Tuffin, Jenny. Vocabulary Development through Dictionary Skills, 3 vols. 2000. 48p. (J). Vol. 1. (gr. 3-4). pap. 7.95 (978-1-58324-061-8(6)); Vol. 2. (gr. 2-3). pap. 7.95 (978-1-58324-062-5(4)) Didax Educational Resources, Inc. (World Teachers Pr.).

Tulip, Jenny. My Big Book of Words. 2000. (My Big Book of Ser.). (Illus.). 48p. (gr. k-4). pap. 7.95 (978-0-7548-0229-7(9) , Lorenz Bks.) Anness Publishing, Inc.

Tullet, Herve. Blue & Square. 2002. (Illus.). 24p. (J). 7.99 (978-1-84059-343-3(1)) Milet Publishing.

—Yellow & Round. 2002. (Illus.). 24p. (J). 7.99 (978-1-84059-344-0(X)) Milet Publishing.

Tuminelly, Nancy. -Est As in Nest. 2003. (Word Families Ser.). (Illus.). 23p. (J). (ps-3). lib. bdg. 19.93 (978-1-59197-232-7(9) , SandCastle) ABDO Publishing Co.

—Ook As in Hook. 2003. (Word Families Ser.). (Illus.). 23p. (J). (ps-3). lib. bdg. 19.93 (978-1-59197-268-6(X) , SandCastle) ABDO Publishing Co.

—Ub As in Tub. 2003. (Word Families Ser.). (Illus.). 23p. (J). (ps-3). lib. bdg. 19.93 (978-1-59197-242-6(6) , SandCastle) ABDO Publishing Co.

—Uck As in Duck. 2003. (Word Families Ser.). (Illus.). 23p. (J). (ps-3). lib. bdg. 19.93 (978-1-59197-247-1(7) , SandCastle) ABDO Publishing Co.

—Uff As in Cuff. 2003. (Word Families Ser.). (Illus.). 23p. (J). (ps-3). lib. bdg. 19.93 (978-1-59197-246-4(9) , SandCastle) ABDO Publishing Co.

—Ug As in Bug. 2003. (Word Families Ser.). (Illus.). 23p. (J). (ps-3). lib. bdg. 19.93 (978-1-59197-243-3(4) , SandCastle) ABDO Publishing Co.

—Um As in Drum. Marx, Monica, ed. 2003. (Word Families Ser.). (Illus.). 23p. (J). (ps-3). lib. bdg. 19.93 (978-1-59197-244-0(2)) ABDO Publishing Co.

—Ump As in Jump. 2003. (Word Families Ser.). (Illus.). 23p. (J). (ps-3). lib. bdg. 19.93 (978-1-59197-245-7(0) , SandCastle) ABDO Publishing Co.

Tuxworth, Nicola. Hop, Skip, & Jump, 12 vols. (Illus.). 2006. 12p. bds. 6.99 (978-0-7548-1364-4(9)); 2002. 20p. 5.95 (978-0-7548-1032-2(1)) Anness Publishing GBR. (Lorenz Bks.). *Dist:* National Bk. Network.

—Messy, 12 vols. (Illus.). 2006. 12p. bds. 6.99 (978-0-7548-1369-9(X)); 2002. 20p. 5.95 (978-0-7548-1033-9(X)) Anness Publishing GBR. (Lorenz Bks.). *Dist:* National Bk. Network.

—Mix & Match, 12 vols. 2006. (Learn-A-Word Picture Bks.). (Illus.). 12p. bds. 6.99 (978-0-7548-1465-8(3) , Lorenz Bks.) Anness Publishing GBR. *Dist:* National Bk. Network.

—Nature, 12 vols. 2006. (Learn-A-Word Picture Bks.). (Illus.). 12p. (ps-k). bds. 6.99 (978-0-7548-1454-2(8) , Lorenz Bks.) Anness Publishing GBR. *Dist:* National Bk. Network.

—Peek-a-Boo. 2002. (Very First Picture Book Ser.). (Illus.). 20p. 5.95 (978-0-7548-1034-6(8) , Lorenz Bks.) Anness Publishing GBR. *Dist:* National Bk. Network.

—Peek-A-Boo. 2005. (Illus.). 12p. (ps). bds. 6.99 (978-0-7548-1337-8(1) , Lorenz Bks.) Anness Publishing GBR. *Dist:* National Bk. Network.

—Pictures & Words, 10 bks. Incl. Baby Animals : A Very First Picture Book. lib. bdg. 22.00 (978-0-8368-2379-0(6)); Farm Animals : A Very First Picture Book. lib. bdg. 22.00 (978-0-8368-2271-7(4)); Food : A Very First Picture Book. lib. bdg. 22.00 (978-0-8368-2430-8(X)); Funny Faces : A Very First Picture Book. lib. bdg. 22.00 (978-0-8368-2272-4(2)); Hop, Skip, Jump : A Very First Picture Book. lib. bdg. 22.00 (978-0-8368-2431-5(8)); Kittens : A Very First Picture Book. lib. bdg. 22.00 (978-0-8368-2273-1(0)); Machines at Work : A Very First Picture Book. lib. bdg. 22.00 (978-0-8368-2432-2(6)); Puppies : A Very First Picture Book. lib. bdg. 22.00 (978-0-8368-2380-6(X)); Splish, Splash : A Very First Picture Book. lib. bdg. 22.00 (978-0-8368-2433-9(4)); Wild Animals : A Very First Picture Book. lib. bdg. 22.00 (978-0-8368-2274-8(9)); 24p. (J). (ps up). (Illus.). 1999. Set lib. bdg. 110.00 (978-0-8368-2456-8(3)) Stevens, Gareth Inc.

—Splish Splash, 12 vols. 2006. (Illus.). 12p. bds. 6.99 (978-0-7548-1366-8(5) , Lorenz Bks.) Anness Publishing GBR. *Dist:* National Bk. Network.

—Teddies. 2002. (Very First Picture Book Ser.). (Illus.). 20p. 5.95 (978-0-7548-1035-3(6) , Lorenz Bks.) Anness Publishing GBR. *Dist:* National Bk. Network.

—Teddy Bears. 2005. (Illus.). 12p. (ps). bds. 6.99 (978-0-7548-1338-5(X) , Lorenz Bks.) Anness Publishing GBR. *Dist:* National Bk. Network.

Uncle Bill Is Feeling Iii, 6 vols. 8p. (gr. k-1). 21.50 (978-0-322-02078-8(6)) Wright Group, The.

Under the Clock, 6 vols. 8p. (gr. k-1). 21.50 (978-0-322-02064-1(6)) Wright Group, The.

University Games Staff. I Have. 2007. 32p. (J). (978-1-57528-888-8(5)) University Games.

Using the Right Words (Gr. 3+) 2003. (J). (978-1-58232-053-3(5)) Bryan Hse. Pubs., Inc.

Ustaris, Steven. Small Fox; Jazmin & the Wugling; Shane the Brave; Malik & His Pals: Lannett Runs Off; Kate & Dane, 6 vols.; set. Janos, Robert, illus. 1999. 609p. (YA). (gr. 1-12). per. 50.00 (978-0-9726099-8-2(9)) BurnsBooks.

Ustaris, Steven, illus. Middle to High School Set: Malik & His Pals; Lannett Runs Off; Kate & Dane, 3 vols.; set. 1999. 305p. (YA). (gr. 7-12). per. 26.00 (978-0-9726099-7-5(0)) BurnsBooks.

Ustaris, Steven & Janes, Robert, illus. Elementary Set: Small Fox; Jazmin & the Wugling; Shane the Brave, 3 vols.; set. 2001. 304p. (J). (gr. 1-6). per. 25.00 (978-0-9726099-6-8(2)) BurnsBooks.

Valentino, Catherine. Blue Ribbon Spelling & Vocabulary, Level 1. (J). pap. 7.95 (978-0-86651-196-4(2)) Seymour, Dale Pubns.

Varma, Michael. Mental Blocks - at the Movies - Take 2: At the Movies - Take 2, 2 vols. 2002. (Illus.). 114p. per. 6.95 (978-0-9717815-1-1(6)) Magical Concepts.

Vaughn, Jim. Jumbo Vocabulary Development Yearbook: Grade 7. (Jumbo Vocabulary Ser.). 96p. (J). (gr. 7-9). 15.95 (978-0-8209-0056-8(7) , B JVDY J) ESP, Inc.

Vinopol, Corinne. Spell Well: CD-ROM American Sign Language Spelling Game. 2003. (YA). cd-rom 19.95 (978-0-9752933-0-0(3)) Institute for Disabilities Research & Training, Inc.

VocabuLaminas: VocabuLaminas Kit. (J). (ps-2). 407.79 (978-0-7362-2605-9(2)) Hampton-Brown Bks.

Vocabulary. 2003. (Practice Makes Perfect Ser.). 48p. (J). (gr. 4). pap. 4.99 (978-0-7439-3363-6(X)); (gr. 5). pap. 4.99 (978-0-7439-3364-3(8)); (gr. 6). pap. 4.99 (978-0-7439-3365-0(6)) Teacher Created Materials, Inc.

T U V

Vocabulary: English in Context. 2000. (Illus.). 112p. per., wbk. ed. 8.95 (978-1-56254-356-3(3) , SP 3563) Saddleback Educational Publishing.

Vocabulary Builders: Level A. 2003. 128p. (C). pap. 13.99 (978-0-7424-1858-5(8) , LL90018) School Specialty Publishing.

Vocabulary Builders: Level B. 2003. 128p. (C). pap. 13.99 (978-0-7424-1859-2(6) , LL90019) School Specialty Publishing.

Vocabulary Building with Crosswords. (Homework Booklets Ser.). 96p. (gr. 2-3). 2.99 (978-0-88012-770-7(8) , IF0127); (gr. 3-4). 2.99 (978-0-88012-771-4(6) , IF0137); (gr. 5-6). 2.99 (978-0-88012-773-8(2) , IF0157); (gr. 6-8). 2.99 (978-0-88012-774-5(0) , IF0167) School Specialty Publishing.

Vocabulary Building with Wordsearches. 2003. (Homework Booklets Ser.). (Illus.). 96p. (gr. 3-4). 2.99 (978-0-88012-778-3(3) , IF0138); (gr. 4-5). 2.99 (978-0-88012-779-0(1) , IF0148) School Specialty Publishing.

Vocabulary Centers. 2006. (J). 24.99 (978-1-59673-147-9(8) , EMC 3347); 24.99 (978-1-59673-148-6(6) , EMC 3348); 24.99 (978-1-59673-149-3(4) , EMC 3349); 24.99 (978-1-59673-150-9(8) , EMC 3350); 24.99 (978-1-59673-151-6(6) , EMC 3351); 24.99 (978-1-59673-152-3(4) , EMC 3352) Evan-Moor Educational Pubs.

Vocabulary Development. 2002. (Home Workbooks Ser.). 64p. pap. 2.49 (978-0-88724-720-0(2) , CD-4522) Carson-Dellosa Publishing Co., Inc.

Vocabulary Development. (Basics First Ser.). 32p. (gr. 1 up). 4.99 (978-0-7647-0026-2(X) , FS30028); (gr. 2 up). 4.99 (978-0-7647-0027-9(8) , FS30029); (gr. 3 up). 4.99 (978-0-7647-0028-6(6) , FS30030); (gr. 4 up). 4.99 (978-0-7647-0029-3(4) , FS30031); (gr. 5 up). 4.99 (978-0-7647-0030-9(8) , FS30032); (gr. 6 up). 4.99 (978-0-7647-0031-6(6) , FS30033); (gr. 7 up). 4.99 (978-0-7647-0032-3(4) , FS30034); (gr. 8 up). 4.99 (978-0-7647-0033-0(2) , FS30035) Schaffer, Frank Pubns.

Vocabulary Flip Chart. 2004. (gr. 1 up). suppl. ed. 109.15 (978-0-673-62166-5(9)); 2004. (gr. 2 up). suppl. ed. 109.15 (978-0-673-62167-2(7)); 2000. (SPA.). (gr. 1 up). suppl. ed. 116.50 (978-0-673-63370-5(5)); 2000. (SPA.). (gr. 2 up). suppl. ed. 116.50 (978-0-673-63371-2(3)) Addison-Wesley Educational Pubs., Inc.

Vocabulary for an Educated Society. 2002. 200p. (YA). (gr. 7-12). pap. 16.95 (978-0-9709734-1-2(1)) Threshold Publishing.

Vocabulary from Classical Root. 2004. (gr. 10 up). pap. 9.95 (978-0-8388-2258-6(4)); (gr. 10 up). pap. 7.25 (978-0-8388-2259-3(2)); (gr. 11 up). pap. 9.95 (978-0-8388-2260-9(6)); (gr. 11 up). pap. 7.25 (978-0-8388-2261-6(4)); (gr. 7 up). pap. 7.25 (978-0-8388-2253-1(3)); (gr. 7 up). pap. 9.35 (978-0-8388-2252-4(5)); (gr. 8 up). pap. 9.35 (978-0-8388-2254-8(1)); (gr. 8 up). pap. 7.25 (978-0-8388-2255-5(X)); (gr. 9 up). pap. 9.35 (978-0-8388-2256-2(8)); (gr. 9 up). pap. 7.25 (978-0-8388-2257-9(6)) Educators Publishing Service, Inc.

Vocabulary in Action: Level A; Testing Program (Masters) 2004. (gr. 4 up). (978-0-8294-1333-5(2)) Loyola Pr.

Vocabulary in Action: Level B; Testing Program (Masters) 2004. (gr. 5 up). (978-0-8294-1335-9(9)) Loyola Pr.

Vocabulary in Action: Level C; Testing Program (Masters) 2004. (gr. 6 up). (978-0-8294-1337-3(5)) Loyola Pr.

Vocabulary in Action: Level D; Testing Program (Masters) 2004. (gr. 7 up). (978-0-8294-1339-7(1)) Loyola Pr.

Vocabulary in Action: Level E; Testing Program (Masters) 2004. (gr. 8 up). (978-0-8294-1341-0(3)) Loyola Pr.

Vocabulary Puzzles. 2004. (Kids Can Learn with Franklin Ser.). (Illus.). 32p. (J). (gr. k-3). (978-1-55337-596-8(3)) Kids Can Pr., Ltd.

Vocabulary Vocabulary, Level A, Grades 10-11. 2005. (Vocabulary Workshop Ser.). 182p. (YA). (gr. 6 up). tchr. ed. 13.80 (978-0-8215-7616-8(X)) Sadlier, William H. Inc.

Vocabulary Vocabulary Test Booklets, Level C, Form A. 2005. (Vocabulary Workshop Ser.). 64p. (YA). (gr. 8 up). 39.00 (978-0-8215-7628-1(3)) Sadlier, William H. Inc.

Vocabulary Vocabulary Test Booklets, Level D, Form A. 2002nd ed. 2002. (Vocabulary Workshop Ser.). 64p. (YA). (gr. 9 up). (978-0-8215-7629-8(1)) Sadlier, William H. Inc.

Vocabulary Workshop: Student Text; Level Purple. 2005. (YA). (gr. 2 up). 5.25 (978-0-8215-0302-7(2)) Sadlier, William H. Inc.

Vocabulary Workshop: Test Booklet Form A; Level Purple. 2005. (YA). (gr. 2 up). 33.00 (978-0-8215-0382-9(0)) Sadlier, William H. Inc.

Vocabulary Workshop: Test Booklet Form B; Level Purple. 2005. (YA). (gr. 2 up). 33.00 (978-0-8215-0392-8(8)) Sadlier, William H. Inc.

Vocabulary Workshop: Test Generator CD-ROM, Level A, (Mac) 2005. (YA). (gr. 6 up). cd-rom 114.00 (978-0-8215-0196-2(8)) Sadlier, William H. Inc.

Vocabulary Workshop: Test Generator CD-ROM, Level B, (Mac) 2005. (YA). (gr. 7 up). cd-rom 114.00 (978-0-8215-0197-9(6)) Sadlier, William H. Inc.

Vocabulary Workshop: Test Generator CD-ROM, Level C, (Mac) 2005. (YA). (gr. 8 up). cd-rom 114.00 (978-0-8215-0198-6(4)) Sadlier, William H. Inc.

Vocabulary Workshop: Test Generator CD-ROM, Level D, (Mac) 2002. (YA). (gr. 9 up). cd-rom (978-0-8215-0199-3(2)) Sadlier, William H. Inc.

Vocabulary Workshop: Test Generator CD-ROM, Level E, (Mac) 2002. (YA). (gr. 10 up). cd-rom (978-0-8215-0200-6(X)) Sadlier, William H. Inc.

Vocabulary Workshop: Test Generator CD-ROM, Level F, (Mac) 2002. (YA). (gr. 11 up). cd-rom (978-0-8215-0201-3(8)) Sadlier, William H. Inc.

Vocabulary Workshop: Test Generator CD-ROM, Level G, (Mac) 2002. (YA). (gr. 12 up). cd-rom (978-0-8215-0202-0(6)) Sadlier, William H. Inc.

Vocabulary Workshop: Test Generator CD-ROM, Level G, (Win) 2002. (YA). (gr. 12 up). cd-rom (978-0-8215-0192-4(5)) Sadlier, William H. Inc.

Vocabulary Workshop: Test Generator CD-ROM, Level H, (Mac) 2002. (YA). (gr. 12 up). cd-rom (978-0-8215-0203-7(4)) Sadlier, William H. Inc.

Vocabulary Workshop: Test Generator CD-ROM, Level H, (Win) 2002. (YA). (gr. 12 up). cd-rom (978-0-8215-0193-1(3)) Sadlier, William H. Inc.

Vocabulary Workshop: (with Answer Key to Tests, Forms A & B); Level Purple. annot. ed. 2005. (YA). (gr. 2 up). 12.00 (978-0-8215-0372-0(3)) Sadlier, William H. Inc.

Vocabulary Workshop, Level 12+ annot. ed. 2002. (Vocabulary Workshop Ser.). 182p. (YA). (gr. 12 up). tchr. ed. (978-0-8215-7623-6(2)) Sadlier, William H. Inc.

Vocabulary Workshop, Level B. annot. ed. 2005. (Vocabulary Workshop Ser.). 182p. (YA). (gr. 7 up). tchr. ed. 13.80 (978-0-8215-7617-5(8)) Sadlier, William H. Inc.

Vocabulary Workshop, Level C. annot. ed. 2005. (Vocabulary Workshop Ser.). 182p. (YA). (gr. 8 up). tchr. ed. 13.80 (978-0-8215-7618-2(6)) Sadlier, William H. Inc.

Vocabulary Workshop, Level D: 2002. annot. ed. 2002. (Vocabulary Workshop Ser.). 64p. (YA). (gr. 9 up). tchr. ed. (978-0-8215-7619-9(4)) Sadlier, William H. Inc.

Vocabulary Workshop, Level E. annot. ed. 2002. (Vocabulary Workshop Ser.). 182p. (YA). (gr. 10 up). tchr. ed. (978-0-8215-7620-5(8)) Sadlier, William H. Inc.

Vocabulary Workshop, Level F. annot. ed. 2002. (Vocabulary Workshop Ser.). 182p. (YA). (gr. 11 up). tchr. ed. (978-0-8215-7621-2(6)) Sadlier, William H. Inc.

Vocabulary Workshop, Level G. annot. ed. 2002. (Vocabulary Workshop Ser.). 182p. (YA). (gr. 12 up). tchr. ed. (978-0-8215-7622-9(4)) Sadlier, William H. Inc.

Vocabulary Workshop Test Booklets. (Vocabulary Workshop Ser.). 64p. (YA). 2002. (gr. 12 up). (978-0-8215-7643-4(7)); Level B, Form B. 2005. (gr. 7 up). 39.00 (978-0-8215-7637-3(2)) Sadlier, William H. Inc.

Vocabulary Workshop, Test Booklets, Cycle 1, Level Blue. 2005. (Vocabulary Workshop Ser.). (YA). (gr. 5 up). 39.00 (978-0-8215-0438-3(X)) Sadlier, William H. Inc.

Vocabulary Workshop, Test Booklets, Cycle 2, Level Blue. 2005. (Vocabulary Workshop Ser.). (YA). (gr. 5 up). 39.00 (978-0-8215-0439-0(8)) Sadlier, William H. Inc.

Vocabulary Workshop Test Booklets, Level A, Form A: 2002. 2005. (Vocabulary Workshop Ser.). 64p. (YA). (gr. 6 up). 39.00 (978-0-8215-7626-7(7)) Sadlier, William H. Inc.

Vocabulary Workshop Test Booklets, Level A, Form B: 2002. 2005. (Vocabulary Workshop Ser.). 64p. (YA). (gr. 6 up). 39.00 (978-0-8215-7636-6(4)) Sadlier, William H. Inc.

Vocabulary Workshop Test Booklets, Level B, Form A. 2005. (Vocabulary Workshop Ser.). 64p. (YA). (gr. 7 up). 39.00 (978-0-8215-7627-4(5)) Sadlier, William H. Inc.

Vocabulary Workshop Test Booklets, Level C, Form B. 2005. (Vocabulary Workshop Ser.). 64p. (YA). (gr. 8 up). 39.00 (978-0-8215-7638-0(0)) Sadlier, William H. Inc.

Vocabulary Workshop Test Booklets, Level E, Form A: 2002. 2002. (Vocabulary Workshop Ser.). 64p. (YA). (gr. 10 up). (978-0-8215-7630-4(5)) Sadlier, William H. Inc.

Vocabulary Workshop Test Booklets, Level E, Form B. 2002. (Vocabulary Workshop Ser.). 64p. (YA). (gr. 10 up). (978-0-8215-7640-3(2)) Sadlier, William H. Inc.

Vocabulary Workshop Test Booklets, Level F, Form A. 2002. (Vocabulary Workshop Ser.). 64p. (YA). (gr. 11 up). (978-0-8215-7631-1(3)) Sadlier, William H. Inc.

Vocabulary Workshop Test Booklets, Level F, Form B. 2002. (Vocabulary Workshop Ser.). 64p. (YA). (gr. 11 up). (978-0-8215-7641-0(0)) Sadlier, William H. Inc.

Vocabulary Workshop Test Booklets, Level G, Form A. 2002. (Vocabulary Workshop Ser.). 64p. (YA). (gr. 12 up). (978-0-8215-7632-8(1)) Sadlier, William H. Inc.

Vocabulary Workshop Test Booklets, Level G, Form B. 2002. (Vocabulary Workshop Ser.). 64p. (YA). (gr. 12 up). (978-0-8215-7642-7(9)) Sadlier, William H. Inc.

Vocabulary Workshop Test Booklets, Level H, Form A. 2002. (Vocabulary Workshop Ser.). 64p. (YA). (gr. 12 up). (978-0-8215-7633-5(X)) Sadlier, William H. Inc.

Vocabulary Workshop, Test Booklets Level Orange Cycle 1. 2005. (Vocabulary Workshop Ser.). (YA). (gr. 4 up). 39.00 (978-0-8215-0436-9(3)) Sadlier, William H. Inc.

Vocabulary Workshop, Test Booklets Level Orange, Cycle 2. 2005. (Vocabulary Workshop Ser.). (YA). (gr. 4 up). 39.00 (978-0-8215-0437-6(1)) Sadlier, William H. Inc.

Vocabulary Workshop Test Generator, Level A, PC Version: 2002. 2005. (Vocabulary Workshop Ser.). (YA). (gr. 6 up). cd-rom 114.00 (978-0-8215-0186-3(0)) Sadlier, William H. Inc.

Vocabulary Workshop Test Generator, Level B, PC Version: 2002. 2005. (Vocabulary Workshop Ser.). (YA). (gr. 7 up). cd-rom 114.00 (978-0-8215-0187-0(9)) Sadlier, William H. Inc.

Vocabulary Workshop Test Generator, Level C, PC Version: 2002. 2005. (Vocabulary Workshop Ser.). (YA). (gr. 8 up). cd-rom 114.00 (978-0-8215-0188-7(7)) Sadlier, William H. Inc.

Vocabulary Workshop Test Generator, Level D, PC Version: 2002. 2002. (Vocabulary Workshop Ser.). (YA). (gr. 9 up). cd-rom (978-0-8215-0189-4(5)) Sadlier, William H. Inc.

Vocabulary Workshop Test Generator, Level E, PC Version: 2002. 2002. (Vocabulary Workshop Ser.). (YA). (gr. 10 up). cd-rom (978-0-8215-0190-0(9)) Sadlier, William H. Inc.

Vocabulary Workshop Test Generator, Level F, PC Version: 2002. 2002. (Vocabulary Workshop Ser.). (YA). (gr. 11 up). cd-rom (978-0-8215-0191-7(7)) Sadlier, William H. Inc.

Vocabulary Workshop, TEST PREP Blackline Masters, Level A. 2005. (Vocabulary Workshop Ser.). (YA). (gr. 6 up). 28.50 (978-0-8215-7676-2(3)) Sadlier, William H. Inc.

Vocabulary Workshop TEST PREP Blackline Masters, Level B. 2005. (Vocabulary Workshop Ser.). 64p. (YA). (gr. 7 up). 28.50 (978-0-8215-7677-9(1)) Sadlier, William H. Inc.

Vocabulary Workshop TEST PREP Blackline Masters, Level C. 2005. (Vocabulary Workshop Ser.). 64p. (YA). (gr. 8 up). 28.50 (978-0-8215-7678-6(X)) Sadlier, William H. Inc.

Vocabulary Workshop TEST PREP Blackline Masters, Level D. 2002. (Vocabulary Workshop Ser.). 64p. (YA). (gr. 9 up). (978-0-8215-7679-3(8)) Sadlier, William H. Inc.

Vocabulary Workshop TEST PREP Blackline Masters, Level E. 2002. (Vocabulary Workshop Ser.). 64p. (YA). (gr. 10 up). (978-0-8215-7680-9(1)) Sadlier, William H. Inc.

Vocabulary Workshop TEST PREP Blackline Masters, Level F. 2002. (Vocabulary Workshop Ser.). 64p. (YA). (gr. 11 up). (978-0-8215-7681-6(X)) Sadlier, William H. Inc.

Vocabulary Workshop TEST PREP Blackline Masters, Level G. 2002. (Vocabulary Workshop Ser.). 64p. (YA). (gr. 12 up). (978-0-8215-7682-3(8)) Sadlier, William H. Inc.

Vocabulary Workswhop Test Booklets, Level D, Form B. 2002. (Vocabulary Workshop Ser.). 64p. (YA). (gr. 9 up). (978-0-8215-7639-7(9)) Sadlier, William H. Inc.

Los Volcanes. (Coleccion Planeta Vivo).Tr. of Volvanoes. (SPA.). (YA). (gr. 5-8). 10.36 (978-84-342-1943-4(3)) Parramon Ediciones S.A. ESP. *Dist:* Lectorum Pubns., Inc.

Votry, Kim & Waller, Curt. Baby's First Signs. 2001. (Illus.). 16p. (J). (ps-2). pap. 7.95 (978-1-56368-114-1(5)) Gallaudet Univ. Pr.

—More Baby's First Signs. 2001. (Illus.). 16p. (J). (ps-2). pap. 7.95 (978-1-56368-115-8(3)) Gallaudet Univ. Pr.

Wade, Angela. New York City. 2006. (Illus.). 8p. (J). pap. (**978-0-439-74035-7(5)*) Scholastic, Inc.

Wall Words Word Search (Gr. 1-2) 2003. (J). (978-1-58232-095-3(0)) Bryan Hse. Pubs., Inc.

Watson, Robert W. A Student's Companion to the Tragedy of Julius Caesar. 1999. stu. ed. 6.96 (978-1-929579-52-5(7) , SG6003) Smarr Pubs.

A Way with Words: Individual Title Six-Packs. (Rigby Infoquest Ser.). (gr. 5 up). 37.00 (978-0-7578-6485-8(6)) Rigby Education.

Weintraub, Aileen. Vocabulary Development. 2005. 48p. pap. 6.95 (978-1-4042-8556-9(3)); pap. 6.95 (978-1-4042-8568-2(7)) Rosen Publishing Group, Inc., The.

Wernham, Sara & Lloyd, Sue. Jolly Dictionary (US Ed) North American Edition. 2003. (Jolly Grammar Ser.: DICTIONARY). (Illus.). 300p. per. 9.95 (978-1-84414-001-5(6) , JL016) Jolly Learning, Ltd. GBR. *Dist:* American International Distribution Corp.

What a Spelling Test!, 6 Packs. (ps-2). 27.00 (978-0-7635-9483-1(0)) Rigby Education.

What Is That? 2002. (Interactive Book of Words). (J). 14.95 (978-1-74047-201-2(2)) Book Co. Publishing Pty, Ltd., The AUS. *Dist:* Penton Overseas, Inc.

What Is the Word? 2003. (Bear in the Big Blue House Ser.). (Illus.). 16p. (J). (ps-k). pap., act. bk. ed. 4.99 (978-1-57768-712-2(4)) School Specialty Publishing.

Where Will You Find Me? 2007. (J). lib. bdg. 9.95 (**978-0-9768706-5-4(7)*) Learning Props.

Whiting, Sue & Book Company Staff. Flippity Frogs Word Adventure. Texidor, Dee, illus. 2002. (Novelty Bks.). 14p. (J). bds. 9.95 (978-1-74047-198-5(9)) Book Co. Publishing Pty, Ltd., The AUS. *Dist:* Penton Overseas, Inc.

WHS Staff, contrib. by. Vocabulary Workshop, Level Green, Grade 3: Student Test Book. 1999. (Illus.). 144p. (YA). (gr. 3 up). stu. ed. 6.90 (978-0-8215-0403-1(7)) Sadlier, William H. Inc.

Wickings, Ruth. Letter Box. 2007. (Illus.). 14p. 19.95 (**978-1-84560-036-5(3)*) Mercury Bks. Ltd. GBR. *Dist:* International Publishers Marketing.

Wilbur, Richard. The Pig in the Spigot. Seibold, J. Otto, illus. 2004. 56p. (J). pap. 7.00 (978-0-15-205066-5(3) , Voyager Bks./Libros Viajeros) Harcourt Children's Bks.

—The Pig in the Spigot. Siebold, J. Otto, illus. 2004. (J). reprint ed. pap. 7.00 (978-0-15-525066-6(3) , Voyager Books/Libros Viajeros) Harcourt Children's Bks. CAN. *Dist:* Raincoast Bk. Distribution.

Wildsmith, Brian. Brian Wildsmith's Opuestos. Fiol, Maria A., tr. Wildsmith, Brian, illus. l.t. ed. 1998. (SPA., Illus.). 16p. (J). (ps). bds. 4.95 (978-1-887734-18-9(X)) Star Bright Bks., Inc.

Wilkes, Angela. My First Spanish Word Board Book. 2002. (SPA., Illus.). 36p. (J). (ps-1). bds. 6.99 (978-0-7894-8593-9(1)) Dorling Kindersley Publishing, Inc.

Williams, Deborah. Cats. 2004. 12p. (Orig.). (J). (gr. k-3). pap. 4.25 (978-1-57874-081-9(9)) Kaeden Corp.

Williams, Garth. Baby's First Book. Williams, Garth, illus. 2007. (Little Golden Book Ser.). (Illus.). 24p. (J). (gr. k-k). 2.99 (978-0-375-83916-0(X) , Golden Bks.) Random Hse. Children's Bks.

Williams, Rozanne Lanczak. Build-a-Skill Instant Books Sight Words, Part 1. Faulkner, Stacey, ed. Campbell, Jenny & Tom, Darcy, illus. 2007. (J). 4.99 (**978-1-59198-414-6(9)*) Creative Teaching Pr., Inc.

—Build-a-Skill Instant Books Sight Words, Part 2. Faulkner, Stacey, ed. Campbell, Jenny & Tom, Darcy, illus. 2007. (J). 4.99 (**978-1-59198-415-3(7)*) Creative Teaching Pr., Inc.

Williams, S. J. Grade Boosters First Grade Vocabulary: Boosting Your Way to Success in School. Gorman, Linda, ed. Guianan, Eve, illus. 1999. (Grade Boosters Ser.). 64p. (J). (ps-3). pap. 4.95 (978-0-7373-0058-1(2) , 00582W) McGraw-Hill/Contemporary.

Windridge, C. How to Choose Your Words Exercises. 1999. 23p. (J). (gr. 4-8). 35.00 (978-0-7217-0397-8(6)) Schofield & Sims Ltd. GBR. *Dist:* State Mutual Bk. & Periodical Service, Ltd.

Wise, Sue. How Do I Say That? Como Se Dice? Coirault, Christine, illus. 2006. (ENG & SPA.). 32p. (J). pap. 8.95 (978-0-8368-6583-7(9)); lib. bdg. 23.33 (978-0-8368-6259-1(7)) Stevens, Gareth Inc.

Wixted, Kristen, creator. Five Ways of Looking¿. 2005. (J). (978-1-58650-518-9(1)) Super Duper Pubns.

Wolf, Tony. In the City. 2005. (Illus.). 10p. (J). (ps-ps). pap. 9.98 (978-0-7624-2030-8(8) , Courage Bks.) Running Pr. Bk. Pubs.

Wong, Benedict Norbert. Lo & Behold: Words That Walk & Run. 2004. (Illus.). 40p. (J). (gr. 1-12). 16.95 (978-0-9728192-2-0(3)) Taiji Arts Publishing.

A Word a Day, Intermediate. 2002. 192p. (gr. 1-3). pap. 19.99 (978-1-55799-870-5(1) , EMC 2718) Evan-Moor Educational Pubs.

A Word a Day, Primary. 2002. 192p. (gr. 1-3). per. 19.99 (978-1-55799-869-9(8) , EMC 2717) Evan-Moor Educational Pubs.

Word Builder Tiles. 2000. (gr. 1-3). suppl. ed. 22.90 (978-0-673-28946-9(X)) Addison-Wesley Educational Pubs., Inc.

Word Building Activity Cards (OCR) 2004. (J). 14.95 (978-1-56911-194-9(4)) Learning Resources, Inc.

Word Building Board Package. 2000. (SPA.). (gr. k-5). stu. ed. 70.60 (978-0-673-60334-0(2)) Addison-Wesley Educational Pubs., Inc.

Word Building Wall. 2000. (SPA.). (gr. k-5). suppl. ed. 43.00 (978-0-673-63019-3(6)) Addison-Wesley Educational Pubs., Inc.

Word Endings in Context (Gr. K-2) 2003. (J). (978-1-58232-099-1(3)) Bryan Hse. Pubs., Inc.

Word Families Ad Libs. 2004. (J). pap. 10.95 (978-1-56911-160-4(X)) Learning Resources, Inc.

Word Family Fun. 2003. (Language Arts Card Games Ser.). (Illus.). (gr. 1 up). 9.99 (978-0-7682-2086-5(6) , J801298) School Specialty Publishing.

Word Family Tales Learning Library, 25 bks., Set. Incl. Billy the Bug's New Jug. Lewison, Wendy Cheyette. Chambliss, Maxie, illus. pap. 2.95 (978-0-439-26252-1(6)); Bop, Bop at the Bunny Hop. Fitzsimmons, Robin C. Sasaki, Ellen Joy, illus. pap. 2.95 (978-0-439-26261-3(5)); Chicken Soup with Rice & Mice. Fleming, Maria. Sasaki, Ellen Joy, illus. pap. 2.95 (978-0-439-26259-0(3)); Clock Who Would Not Tock. Chanko, Pamela. Guido, Lisa Chauncey, illus. pap. 2.95 (978-0-439-26254-5(2)); Day Duck's Truck Got Stuck. Fleming, Maria. Fletcher, Rusty, illus. pap. 2.95 (978-0-439-26264-4(X)); Day Mr. Gump Helped Katie Krump. Clifford, Gale. Billin-Frye, Paige, illus. pap. 2.95 (978-0-439-26253-8(4)); Hank's Bank. Higgins, Maxwell. Alley, R. W., illus. pap. 2.95 (978-0-439-26271-2(2)); Jan & Stan. Berger, Samantha. Brown, Rick, illus. pap. 2.95 (978-0-439-26256-9(9)); Jumping Jill Went down the Hill. Fleming, Maria. Weissman, Bart, illus. pap. 2.95 (978-0-439-26267-5(4)); Scot & Dot. Higgins, Maxwell. Fletcher, Rusty, illus. pap. 2.95 (978-0-439-26263-7(1)); Spend a Day in Backwards Bay. Berger, Samantha. Brown, Rick, illus. pap. 2.95 (978-0-439-26273-6(9)); Word Family Tales : Dine with Nine Messy Monsters. Charlesworth, Liza. Phillips, Matt, illus. pap. 2.95 (978-0-439-26250-7(X)); Word Family Tales : Lin & Min Are Twins. Chanke, Pamela & Chanko, Pamela. Pillo, Cary, illus. pap. 2.95 (978-0-439-26270-5(4)); Word Family Tales : Please Don't Tell about Mom's Bell. Berger, Samantha. Brown, Rick, illus. pap. 2.95 (978-0-439-26258-3(5)); Word Family Tales : Snail Mail. Fleming, Maria. Fletcher, Rusty, illus. pap. 2.95 (978-0-439-26262-0(3)); Word Family Tales : Take a Trip to Planet Blip. Einhorn, Kama. Phillips, Matt, illus. pap. 2.95 (978-0-439-26251-4(8)); Word Family Tales -Ack : A Snack for Mack. Hollander, Cass & Scholastic, Inc. Staff. Brown, Rick, illus. pap. 2.95 (978-0-439-26255-2(0) , Teaching Resources); Word Family Tales -Ake : Jake's Cake Mistake. Franco, Betsy. Hervey, Paul, illus. pap. 2.95 (978-0-439-26265-1(8)); Word Family Tales -Ap : A Nap for Zap. Einhorn, Kama. Jabar, Cynthia, illus. pap. 2.95 (978-0-439-26269-9(0)); Word Family Tales -At : A Bat Named Pat. Franco, Betsy. Weissman, Bart, illus. pap. 2.95 (978-0-439-26266-8(6)); Word Family Tales -Eep : To Sleep, Count Sheep. Fleming, Maria. Pillo, Cary, illus. pap. 2.95 (978-0-439-26268-2(2)); Word Family Tales -Est : The Pest in the Nest. Huberman, Lisa Eve. Phillips, Matt, illus. pap. 2.95 (978-0-439-26249-1(6)); Word Family Tales -Ide : Ride & Slide. Berger, Samantha. Alley, R. W., illus. pap. 2.95 (978-0-439-26272-9(0)); Word Family Tales -Ing : Spring in the Kingdom of Ying. Charlesworth, Liza. Sasaki, Ellen Joy, illus. pap. 2.95 (978-0-439-26260-6(7)); Word Family Tales -Ink : When Zelda Zink Spilled Purple Ink. Charlesworth, Liza. Phillips, Matt, illus. pap. 2.95 (978-0-439-26257-6(7)); (ps-2). 16p. 2002. Set pap. 77.95 (978-0-439-26246-0(1) , Teaching Resources) Scholastic, Inc.

Word Wall Cards. 2000. (SPA.). (gr. k up). suppl. ed. 42.35 (978-0-673-64407-7(3)); (gr. 1 up). suppl. ed. 235.50 (978-0-673-64408-4(1)); (gr. 2 up). suppl. ed. 235.20 (978-0-673-64409-1(X)); (gr. 3 up). suppl. ed. 235.20 (978-0-673-64410-7(3)) Addison-Wesley Educational Pubs., Inc.

Word Wall Words. 2004. (gr. k up). suppl. ed. 39.70 (978-0-673-62182-5(0)); (gr. 1 up). suppl. ed. 220.50 (978-0-673-62183-2(9)); (gr. 2 up). suppl. ed. 220.50 (978-0-673-62184-9(7)); (gr. 3 up). suppl. ed. 220.50 (978-0-673-62185-6(5)) Addison-Wesley Educational Pubs., Inc.

Wordly Wise 30. 2004. pap. 35.95 (978-0-8388-8133-0(5)) Educators Publishing Service, Inc.

T U V

Wordly Wise 3000 Bk. 1: Key. 2004. pap. 3.65 (978-0-8388-2441-2(2)) Educators Publishing Service, Inc.

Wordly Wise 3000 Bk. 3: Key. 2004. pap. 3.65 (978-0-8388-2443-6(9)) Educators Publishing Service, Inc.

Wordly Wise 3000 Bk. 4: Key. 2004. pap. 3.65 (978-0-8388-2444-3(7)) Educators Publishing Service, Inc.

Wordly Wise 3000 Bk. 8: Student. 2004. pap. 9.65 (978-0-8388-2438-2(2)) Educators Publishing Service, Inc.

Wordly Wise 3000 Bk. 9: Student. 2004. pap. 9.65 (978-0-8388-2439-9(0)) Educators Publishing Service, Inc.

Wordly Wise 3000 Bk. C: Student. 2004. pap. 6.70 (978-0-8388-2427-6(7)) Educators Publishing Service, Inc.

Wordly Wise 3000 Bk. a: Student. 2004. pap. 6.70 (978-0-8388-2425-2(0)) Educators Publishing Service, Inc.

Wordly Wise 3000 Bk. B: Student. 2004. pap. 6.70 (978-0-8388-2426-9(9)) Educators Publishing Service, Inc.

Wordly Wise 3000 in Dividual. 2004. pap. 8.70 (978-0-8388-8328-0(1)); pap. 8.70 (978-0-8388-8329-7(X)); pap. 8.70 (978-0-8388-8331-0(1)); pap. 8.70 (978-0-8388-8332-7(X)); pap. 8.70 (978-0-8388-8333-4(8)); pap. 8.70 (978-0-8388-8334-1(6)); pap. 9.65 (978-0-8388-8336-5(2)); pap. 9.65 (978-0-8388-8337-2(0)); pap. 9.65 (978-0-8388-8338-9(9)); pap. 9.65 (978-0-8388-8339-6(7)) Educators Publishing Service, Inc.

Wordly Wise Bk. 1: Student. 2004. pap. 8.70 (978-0-8388-0431-5(4)) Educators Publishing Service, Inc.

Wordly Wise Bk. 2: Quick Quiz. 2004. pap. 2.55 (978-0-8388-4432-8(4)) Educators Publishing Service, Inc.

Wordly Wise Bk. 2: Student. 2004. pap. 8.70 (978-0-8388-0432-2(2)) Educators Publishing Service, Inc.

Wordly Wise Bk. 3: Quick Quiz. 2004. pap. 2.55 (978-0-8388-4433-5(2)) Educators Publishing Service, Inc.

Wordly Wise Bk. 3: Student. 2004. pap. 8.70 (978-0-8388-0433-9(0)) Educators Publishing Service, Inc.

Wordly Wise Bk. 4: Quick Quiz. 2004. pap. 2.55 (978-0-8388-4434-2(0)) Educators Publishing Service, Inc.

Wordly Wise Bk. 4: Student. 2004. pap. 8.70 (978-0-8388-0434-6(9)) Educators Publishing Service, Inc.

Wordly Wise Bk. 5: Quick Quiz. 2004. pap. 2.55 (978-0-8388-4435-9(9)) Educators Publishing Service, Inc.

Wordly Wise Bk. 5: Student. 2004. pap. 8.70 (978-0-8388-0435-3(7)) Educators Publishing Service, Inc.

Wordly Wise Bk. 6: Quick Quiz. 2004. pap. 2.55 (978-0-8388-4436-6(7)) Educators Publishing Service, Inc.

Wordly Wise Bk. 6: Student. 2004. pap. 9.65 (978-0-8388-0436-0(5)) Educators Publishing Service, Inc.

Wordly Wise Bk. 7: Quick Quiz. 2004. pap. 2.55 (978-0-8388-4437-3(5)) Educators Publishing Service, Inc.

Wordly Wise Bk. 7: Student. 2004. pap. 9.65 (978-0-8388-0437-7(3)) Educators Publishing Service, Inc.

Wordly Wise Bk. 8: Quick Quiz. 2004. pap. 2.55 (978-0-8388-4438-0(3)) Educators Publishing Service, Inc.

Wordly Wise Bk. 8: Student. 2004. pap. 9.65 (978-0-8388-0438-4(1)) Educators Publishing Service, Inc.

Wordly Wise Bk. 9: Quick Quiz. 2004. pap. 2.55 (978-0-8388-4439-7(1)) Educators Publishing Service, Inc.

Wordly Wise Bk. 9: Student. 2004. pap. 9.65 (978-0-8388-0439-1(X)) Educators Publishing Service, Inc.

Wordly Wise Bk. C: Student. 2004. pap. 6.70 (978-0-8388-0430-8(6)) Educators Publishing Service, Inc.

Wordly Wise Bk. a: Student. 2004. pap. 6.70 (978-0-8388-0428-5(4)) Educators Publishing Service, Inc.

Wordly Wise Bk. B: Student. 2004. pap. 6.70 (978-0-8388-0429-2(2)) Educators Publishing Service, Inc.

Words are Fun. 2004. (Play & Learn Pads Ser.). 48p. (J). 3.99 (978-1-85997-722-4(7)) Byeway Bks.

Words for 3-5 Years. Date not set. (Play & Learn Ser.). (Illus.). 192p. (J). 3.98 (978-0-7525-6914-7(7)) Parragon, Inc.

Words for 5 7 Years. Date not set. (Play & Learn Ser.). (Illus.). 192p. (J). 3.98 (978-0-7525-6915-4(5)) Parragon, Inc.

Wordsearch. 2004. (Play & Learn Pads Ser.). 48p. (J). 3.99 (978-1-85997-716-3(2)) Byeway Bks.

Wordsearch Fun. 2004. (Play & Learn Pads Ser.). 48p. (J). 3.99 (978-1-85997-723-1(5)) Byeway Bks.

Wordskills. 2000. (gr. 10 up). tchr. ed. (978-0-395-97987-7(0) , 2-22341); (gr. 10 up). stu. ed. (978-0-395-97986-0(2) , 2-22334); (gr. 11 up). tchr. ed. (978-0-395-97989-1(7) , 2-22342); (gr. 11 up). stu. ed. (978-0-395-97988-4(9) , 2-22335); (gr. 12 up). tchr. ed. (978-0-395-97991-4(9) , 2-22343); (gr. 12 up). stu. ed. (978-0-395-97990-7(0) , 2-22336); (gr. 6 up). tchr. ed. (978-0-395-97978-5(1) , 2-22337); (gr. 6 up). stu. ed. (978-0-395-97977-8(3) , 2-22330); (gr. 7 up). tchr. ed. (978-0-395-97980-8(3) , 2-22338); (gr. 7 up). stu. ed. (978-0-395-97979-2(X) , 2-22331); (gr. 8 up). tchr. ed. (978-0-395-97982-2(X) , 2-22339); (gr. 8 up). stu. ed. (978-0-395-97981-5(1) , 2-22332); (gr. 9 up). tchr. ed. (978-0-395-97984-6(6) , 2-22340); (gr. 9 up). stu. ed. (978-0-395-97983-9(8) , 2-22333) McDougal Littell Inc.

Wortgeschichte. (Duden-Schuelerduden Ser.). (GER.). 491p. (YA). 27.95 (978-3-411-02212-0(4) , B2212E) Bibliographisches Institut & F. A. Brockhaus AG DEU. *Dist:* Continental Bk. Co., Inc., International Bk. Import Service, Inc.

Worth-Baker, Marcia. Greek Mythology Activities: Activities to Help Students Build Background Knowledge about Ancient Greece, Explore the Genre of Myths, & Learn Important Vocabulary. 2005. 80p. pap. 12.99 (978-0-439-51788-1(5) , Teaching Resources) Scholastic, Inc.

Wright, Reg & Hedge, Tricia. Ear-rings from Frankfurt, Level 2. 2nd ed. 2000. (Bookworms Ser.). (Illus.). 64p. 6.50 (978-0-19-422972-2(6)) Oxford Univ. Pr., Inc.

Yamamoto, Fukiko. Kika, My First Word Book. Yamamoto, Fukiko, illus. 2006. (Illus.). 120p. (J). 11.95 (978-0-8118-5298-2(9)) Chronicle Bks. LLC.

Yes I Can Staff. Words Are Everywhere. (J). 29.70 (978-0-8136-4402-8(X)) Modern Curriculum Pr.

Yoon, Salina. My Little Shimmery Neighborhood, 4 vols. Yoon, Salina, illus. 2002. (Illus.). 12p. (J). bds. 5.95 (978-1-58117-164-8(1) , Intervisual/Piggy Toes) Dalmatian Pr.

Yoon, Salina, creator. Bug Buddies: A Sparkling Little Colors Book. 2005. (Illus.). 12p. (J). 5.95 (978-1-58117-166-2(8) , Intervisual/Piggy Toes) Dalmatian Pr.

Yoon, Salina, illus. My Shimmery Fun Time Book. 2000. 10p. (J). (ps-k). bds. 8.95 (978-1-58117-082-5(3) , Intervisual/Piggy Toes) Dalmatian Pr.

Yoyo Books Staff. Words: Mini Baby's First Library. 2005. 42p. bds. 4.95 (978-90-5843-803-4(1)) YoYo Bks. BEL. *Dist:* National Bk. Network.

Zakiyyah. ChatterWorld: My Numbers in Spanish/French. 2006. 40p. 14.99 (978-0-9777085-0-5(0)) Little Linguists Press.

Zanimo. My Animal Friends. Perkes, Carolyn, tr. from FRE. 2002. (Maki's Words Ser.). (Illus.). 24p. (J). (ps up). pap. (978-1-894363-72-3(8)) Dominique & Friends.

Ziefert, Harriet. I'm Going to Read Workbook: Long Vowels. Roitman, Tanya, illus. 2007. (I'm Going to Read Ser.). 64p. (J). pap. 5.95 (***978-1-4027-5057-1(9)***) Sterling Publishing Co., Inc.

—I'm Going to Read Workbook: Rhyming Words. Kido, Yukiko, illus. 2007. (I'm Going to Read Ser.). 64p. (J). pap. 5.95 (***978-1-4027-5059-5(5)***) Sterling Publishing Co., Inc.

—I'm Going to Read Workbook: Short Vowels. Roitman, Tanya, illus. 2007. (I'm Going to Read Ser.). 64p. (J). pap. 5.95 (***978-1-4027-5056-4(0)***) Sterling Publishing Co., Inc.

—I'm Going to Read Workbook: Sight Words. Roitman, Tanya, illus. 2007. (I'm Going to Read Ser.). 64p. (J). pap. 5.95 (***978-1-4027-5058-8(7)***) Sterling Publishing Co., Inc.

—Lowercase Letters. Kido, Yukiko, illus. 2007. (I'm Going to Read Ser.). 64p. (J). pap. 5.95 (***978-1-4027-5055-7(2)***) Sterling Publishing Co., Inc.

—Simms Taback's Big Book of Words. 2004. (Illus.). 96p. 12.95 (978-1-59354-035-7(3)) Blue Apple Bks.

Ziefert, Harriet. Upper-case Letters. Kido, Yukiko, illus. 2007. (I'm Going to Write Ser.). 64p. (J). pap. 5.95 (***978-1-4027-5054-0(4)***) Sterling Publishing Co., Inc.

4th Word Problems Booster. 2005. 64p. (J). per. 1.49 (978-1-59441-350-6(9) , C04026) Carson-Dellosa Publishing Co., Inc.

100 Lifelong Words: Helping Students Become Better Spellers. 112p. (gr. 3-6). 14.99 (978-0-7682-0107-9(1) , GA13011) School Specialty Publishing.

200 High Frequency Spanish & English Sight Words. 2005. 95p. (J). spiral bd. 14.99 (978-1-59441-469-5(6) , K04020) Carson-Dellosa Publishing Co., Inc.

VOCABULARY—FICTION

Baker, Alan. Los conejitos aprenden Las Primeras Palabras. 2003. (Little Rabbit Bks.). (SPA.). 32p. (J). (gr. k-ps). pap. 4.95 (978-0-7534-5596-8(X) , Kingfisher) Houghton Mifflin Co. Trade & Reference Div.

Battle-Lavert, Gwendolyn. The Barber's Cutting Edge. Holbert, Raymond, illus. 2004. 32p. (J). pap. 7.95 (978-0-89239-196-7(0)) Children's Bk. Pr.

Beinstein, Phoebe. Dora's Book of Words (Libro de Palabras de Dora) A Bilingual Pull-Tab Adventure! Thompson Brothers Staff, illus. 2003. (Dora the Explorer Ser.). 16p. (J). 10.95 (978-0-689-85626-6(1) , Simon Spotlight/Nickelodeon) Simon & Schuster Children's Publishing.

Bell-Myers, Darcy, illus. Higgledy-Piggledy: Mabel's World. 2006. 32p. 16.95 (978-0-9716631-1-4(4)) Attitude Pr., Inc.

Beobi & the Magic Coloring Book ABC First Words. 2005. (J). cd-rom 15.99 (978-0-9743847-8-8(X)) Cohn, Tricia.

Bizcochitos de Cumpleanos Story Pack. 2003. (Coleccion Parvulitos). (SPA., Illus.). 67.50 (978-0-8136-8531-1(1)) Modern Curriculum Pr.

Black, Jessica L. Opposites Board Book & Felt Puppet Set. Cress, Michelle H., illus. 2005. (J). bds. (978-1-57332-363-5(2)) HighReach Learning, Inc.

Blackaby, Susan. The Word of the Day. Muehlenhardt, Amy Bailey, illus. 2004. (Read-It! Readers Ser.). 32p. (C). (gr. k-3). 18.60 (978-1-4048-0588-0(5)) Picture Window Bks.

Boehm, Richard G., et al. Take-Home Review Books. 2003. (Harcourt Brace Social Studies). (gr. 1 up). 6.20 (978-0-15-310293-6(4)); (gr. 2 up). 6.20 (978-0-15-310294-3(2)) Harcourt Schl. Pubs.

Bonnell, Kris. Ben's First Words. 2005. (J). 3.75 (978-1-933727-00-4(4)) Reading Reading Bks., LLC.

Claire, Elizabeth. The New Boy Is Lost! An ESL Picture Novel. 2004. Orig. Title: Where Is Taro?. (Illus.). 70p. 12.00 (978-0-937630-12-9(8)) Eardley Pubns.

Cox, Phil Roxbee. Fat Cat on A Mat. Cartwright, Stephen, illus. rev. ed. 2006. 16p. (J). pap. 6.99 (978-0-7945-1502-7(9) , Usborne) EDC Publishing.

Curry, Peter. Millie Goes Shopping. 2004. (First Words with Millie Ser.). (Illus.). 12p. (J). bds. 3.99 (978-1-85854-505-9(6)) Brimax Books Ltd. GBR. *Dist:* Byeway Bks.

Davis, Lee. P. B. Bear's Words. 2000. (Pajama Bedtime Bear Ser.). (Illus.). 14p. (J). (ps). bds. 3.99 (978-0-7894-1425-0(2) , D K Ink) Dorling Kindersley Publishing, Inc.

Disculpe Usted, Senor. 2003. (SPA., Illus.). stu. ed. 35.50 (978-0-8136-8033-0(6)) Modern Curriculum Pr.

Disney: My First 1000 Words:A Picture Wordbook. 2003. (Illus.). 144p. (gr. 1-5). 14.99 (978-0-7868-3409-9(9) , Disney Editions) Disney Pr.

A Donde Vamos? 2003. (Coleccion Parvulitos). (SPA., Illus.). (J). stu. ed. 35.50 (978-0-8136-8027-9(1)) Modern Curriculum Pr.

A Donde Vamos? Big Book. 2003. (Coleccion Parvulitos). (SPA., Illus.). 35.50 (978-0-8136-8029-3(8)) Modern Curriculum Pr.

A Donde Vamos? Story Pack. 2003. (Coleccion Parvulitos). (SPA., Illus.). 67.50 (978-0-8136-8524-3(9)) Modern Curriculum Pr.

Eduar, Gilles. Gigi & Zachary's Around-the-World Adventure: A Seek-and-Find Game. Eduar, Gilles, illus. 2003. (Illus.). 56p. (J). 16.95 (978-0-8118-3909-9(5)) Chronicle Bks. LLC.

Frasier, Debra. Miss Alaineus: A Vocabulary Disaster. 2007. (Illus.). 40p. (J). (gr. k-3). pap. 7.00 (***978-0-15-206053-4(7)***, Voyager Bks./Libros Viajeros) Harcourt Children's Bks.

Grosset and Dunlap Staff, contrib. by. The World of Dick & Jane Anderson. 2003. (Illus.). (J). 9.97 (978-0-448-43479-7(2) , Grosset & Dunlap) Penguin Group (USA) Inc.

Gutman, Anne. Gaspard & Lisa's Ready-for-School Words. Hallensleben, Georg, illus. 2004. 22p. (J). (gr. k-ps). bds. 6.99 (978-0-375-82890-4(7) , Knopf Bks. for Young Readers) Random Hse. Children's Bks.

Howard-Parham, Pam. Caillou Gets in Shape. Gillen, Lisa P., illus. l.t. ed. 2006. (Hrl Board Book Ser.). (J). (gr. k up). pap. 10.95 (978-1-57332-331-4(4)) HighReach Learning, Inc.

Jarrell, Pamela R. Time for Bed. Coillen, Lisa P., illus. l.t. ed. 2005. (Hrl Board Book Ser.). (J). (ps-k). pap. 10.95 (978-1-57332-325-3(X)) HighReach Learning, Inc.

Kelley, Maria Felicia. Buz Words: Discovering Words in Pairs. Kelley, Maria Felicia, illus. 2006. (Illus.). 32p. (J). 14.95 (978-0-9650918-1-7(3)) April Arts Press & Productions.

Lederer, Susan. I Can Say That: Two Stories to Encourage Vocabulary & Literacy Development. l.t. ed. 2006. (Illus.). 32p. (J). 19.95 incl. cd-rom (978-0-9725803-7-3(9)) Children's Publishing.

Lee, Huy Youn, ed. In the Snow. 2000. (Illus.). (J). (ps-ps). lib. bdg. 15.25 (978-0-613-30516-7(7)) Tandem Library Bks.

Lobato, Arcadio, illus. Volando por las Palabras. 2004. Tr. of Flying through Words. (SPA.). 48p. (J). 10.50 (978-84-263-5018-3(6)) Vives, Luis Editorial (Edelvives) ESP. *Dist:* Lectorum Pubns., Inc.

Luna Rising Staff, ed. Elmo's Big Word Book. 2006. (Elmo's World Ser.). (SPA & ENG., Illus.). 12p. (J). 6.95 (978-0-87358-906-2(8) , Luna Rising) Northland Publishing.

Mansfield, Katherine. The Garden Party & Other Stories, Level 5. 2nd ed. 2000. (Bookworms Ser.). (Illus.). 112p. pap. 6.50 (978-0-19-423065-0(1)) Oxford Univ. Pr., Inc.

A Mi Abuelita Le Gusta Correr. 2003. (Coleccion Parvulitos). (SPA., Illus.). stu. ed. 35.50 (978-0-8136-8141-2(3)) Modern Curriculum Pr.

A Mi Abuelita Le Gusta Correr Big Book. 2003. (Coleccion Parvulitos). (SPA., Illus.). 35.50 (978-0-8136-8535-9(4)) Modern Curriculum Pr.

Mitton, Tony. Planet Ocky: Ham & Jam. Chatterton, Ann & Chatterton, Martin, illus. 1999. (Cambridge Reading Ser.). 14p. pap. 5.00 (978-0-521-64704-5(5)); pap., pap. 16.95 (978-0-521-66701-2(1)) Cambridge Univ. Pr.

—Planet Ocky: Jump & Bump. Chatterton, Ann & Chatterton, Martin, illus. 1999. (Cambridge Reading Ser.). 14p. pap., pap. 16.95 (978-0-521-66700-5(3)) Cambridge Univ. Pr.

Moore, Karen Ann, et al. Sticks & Stones: What You Say Really Matters! 2006. (Illus.). 16p. (J). (gr. 3-8). bds. 9.95 (978-1-59125-745-5(X) , Penton Kids) Penton Overseas, Inc.

Moss, Miriam. One Day It Was Wet. 2000. (Cambridge Reading Ser.). (Illus.). 14p. pap. 5.00 (978-0-521-65950-5(7)) Cambridge Univ. Pr.

Mouse Works Staff. Butter's First Words. 1999. (P B & J Otter Noodle Stories Ser.). (Illus.). 16p. (J). (ps-k). 3.50 (978-0-7364-0184-5(9)) Mouse Works.

Muench-Williams, Heather. Adam's Grouchy Day. Meier, Kerry L., illus. l.t. ed. 2005. (Hrl Big Book Ser.). (J). (ps-k). pap. 10.95 (978-1-57332-320-8(9)); pap. 10.95 (978-1-57332-321-5(7)) HighReach Learning, Inc.

Mullican, Judy. Caillou & the Storyteller. Storch, Ellen N., illus. l.t. ed. 2006. (Hrl Board Book Ser.). (J). (gr. k up). pap. 10.95 (978-1-57332-330-7(6)) HighReach Learning, Inc.

Patrice, Christina. The Alphabet Mystery Starring Letters A-Z. Brown, Erin, illus. 2002. 26p. (J). (gr. k-1). 7.95 (978-1-889743-22-6(4)) Robbie Dean Pr.

Prater, John. Hide & Seek Big Book. 1999. (Cambridge Reading Ser.). (Illus.). 14p. pap. 16.95 (978-0-521-66702-9(X)) Cambridge Univ. Pr.

Quienes Son Tus Amigos? 2003. (Coleccion Parvulitos). (SPA., Illus.). stu. ed. 35.50 (978-0-8136-8525-0(7)) Modern Curriculum Pr.

Reed, Holcomb. Wird Bird. Reed, Holcomb, illus. 2000. (Illus.). 32p. (J). (ps-3). 16.50 (978-0-9670198-1-9(8)) Potser, T.T. , Inc.

—Wird Bird. 2000. (Illus.). 32p. (J). (ps-3). pap. 9.50 (978-0-9670198-2-6(6)); lib. bdg. 18.00 (978-0-9670198-0-2(X)) Potser, T.T. , Inc.

Ricci, Christine. Dora in the Deep Sea. Roper, Robert, illus. 2003. (Dora the Explorer Ser.: Vol. 3). 24p. (J). pap. 3.99 (978-0-689-85845-1(0) , Simon Spotlight/ Nickelodeon) Simon & Schuster Children's Publishing.

—Dora in the Deep Sea. 2003. (ps-2). lib. bdg. 11.80 (978-0-613-73392-2(4)) Tandem Library Bks.

Ruppert, Larry, illus. My First Words. 2007. (Dick & Jane Ser.). 10p. (J). (ps-k). bds. 7.99 (978-0-448-44572-4(7) , Grosset & Dunlap) Penguin Group (USA) Inc.

Schotter, Roni. The Boy Who Loved Words. Potter, Giselle, illus. 2006. 40p. (J). (ps-3). 16.95 (978-0-375-83601-5(2)); lib. bdg. 18.99 (978-0-375-93601-2(7)) Random Hse. Children's Bks. (Schwartz & Wade Bks.).

Shannon, David. Huy! David en Paneles! Shannon, David, illus. 2005. (Oops! Ser.). (SPA., Illus.). 12p. (J). 6.99 (978-0-439-70972-9(5) , Scholastic en Espanol) Scholastic, Inc.

—Oops! A Diaper David Book. Shannon, David, illus. 2005. (Oops! Ser.). (Illus.). 12p. (J). (gr. k). bds. 6.99 (978-0-439-68882-6(5) , Blue Sky Pr., The) Scholastic, Inc.

Si Yo Tuviera un Cordel... 2003. (Coleccion Parvulitos). (SPA., Illus.). stu. ed. 35.50 (978-0-8136-8530-4(3)) Modern Curriculum Pr.

Steck-Vaughn Staff. Take Home Vocabulary Stories. 2000. (Illus.). (J). pap. (978-0-7398-2948-6(3)); (gr. 1). pap. (978-0-7398-2949-3(1)); (gr. 2). pap. (978-0-7398-2950-9(5)); (gr. 3). pap. (978-0-7398-2951-6(3)) Steck-Vaughn.

Steinberg, Laya. Thesaurus Rex. Harter, Debbie, illus. 2005. 24p. (J). 15.99 (978-1-84148-042-8(8)); pap. 6.99 (978-1-84148-180-7(7)) Barefoot Bks., Inc.

Storch, Ellen N. Here We Go! Storch, Ellen N., illus. l.t. ed. 2005. (Hrl Board Book Ser.). (Illus.). (J). (ps-k). pap. 10.95 (978-1-57332-322-2(5)) HighReach Learning, Inc.

Taylor, Damon. Bible Opposites. 2002. (Child Sockology Ser.). 24p. (J). (ps-k). 6.99 (978-0-8254-3852-3(7)) Kregel Pubns.

Tu Mama es una Llama? 2004. (SPA.). pap. 14.95 incl. audio (978-1-55592-697-7(5)) Weston Woods Studios, Inc.

Ustaris, Steven, illus. Shane the Brave. 2001. (It's up to You Ser.). 132p. (J). (gr. 1-6). per. 8.95 (978-0-9726099-4-4(6)) BurnsBooks.

Vonthron, Satanta C. Caillou's Community. Storch, Ellen N., illus. l.t. ed. 2006. (Hrl Board Book Ser.). (J). (gr. k up). pap. 10.95 (978-1-57332-332-1(2)) HighReach Learning, Inc.

Ward, Deborah. Bug a Bug. 2006. (ENG.). 32p. per. 17.99 (***978-1-4259-6955-4(0)***) AuthorHouse.

Yoyo. Learning Words. 2005. 40p. bds. 6.95 (978-90-5843-887-4(2)) YoYo Bks. BEL. *Dist:* National Bk. Network.

VOCAL CULTURE

see Voice

VOCATION, CHOICE OF

see Vocational Guidance

VOCATIONAL GUIDANCE

see also Blind—Education; Counseling; Deaf—Education; Educational Counseling; Job Hunting; Occupations; Professions

also subdivision Vocational Guidance under names of occupations, fields of endeavor, military services, and types of industries

Abraham, Philip. Firefighter. 2003. (High Interest Bks.). (Illus.). 48p. (YA). (gr. 7-12). pap. 6.95 (978-0-516-27866-7(5) , Children's Pr.) Scholastic Library Publishing.

—Firefighter. 2003. (gr. 7-12). lib. bdg. 15.25 (978-0-613-67896-4(6)) Tandem Library Bks.

ACK! - American Careers for Kids. 2nd ed. 1998. (J). (gr. 4-5). pap. 178.50 (978-0-9653667-1-7(5)) Career Communications, Inc.

AG Publishers Editors. The Best That I Can Be: Inspiring Words for American Girls. 2002. (American Girls Collection Ser.). (Illus.). 80p. (J). (gr. 2). 9.95 (978-1-58485-516-3(9)) American Girl Publishing, Inc.

Anonymous. Book of Old-Time Trades & Tools. 2005. (Pictorial Archive Ser.). (Illus.). 320p. pap. 12.95 (978-0-486-44342-3(6)) Dover Pubns., Inc.

Apel, Melanie Ann. Careers in Information Science. 2000. (Careers Ser.). (Illus.). 105p. (YA). (gr. 7-12). lib. bdg. 18.95 (978-0-8239-2892-7(6) , CAINSC, PowerKids Pr.) Rosen Publishing Group, Inc., The.

Applying for a Job. 1999. (SmartReader Ser.). Level 1. (J). pap., tchr. ed. 19.95 incl. audio (978-0-7887-1155-8(5) , 79416T3); Level 2. (YA). pap., tchr. ed. 19.95 incl. audio (978-0-7887-0553-3(9) , 79335T3) Recorded Bks., LLC.

Asher, Dana. Epidemiologists: Life Tracking Deadly Diseases. 2005. (Extreme Careers Ser.). (Illus.). 64p. (YA). (gr. 5-8). 26.50 (978-0-8239-3633-5(3)) Rosen Publishing Group, Inc., The.

Austin, Sandy. Focus on Your Future: High School Planning for Career - College Choices. 2000. x, 54p. (YA). (gr. 9 up). 14.99 (978-0-9678027-0-1(9)) Focus on Your Future.

Bankston, John. Careers in Community Service. 2001. (Latinos at Work Ser.). (Illus.). 96p. (gr. 5-12). lib. bdg. 32.75 (978-1-58415-082-4(3)) Mitchell Lane Pubs., Inc.

Barrows, Laurie. Job Jungle. 1998. (Illus.). 72p. (J). (gr. k-4). pap. 6.32 (978-0-934783-48-4(9)) CFKR Career Materials, Inc.

Berman, Ron. Future Stars of America. 2005. (Illus.). 90p. (J). (***978-0-9741997-4-0(5)***) Scobre Pr. Corp.

Beyer, Mark. Demolition Experts: Life Blowing Things Up. 2005. (Extreme Careers Ser.). (Illus.). 64p. (YA). (gr. 5-8). 26.50 (978-0-8239-3365-5(2)) Rosen Publishing Group, Inc., The.

Bickerstaff, Linda. Oil Power of the Future: New Ways of Turning Petroleum into Energy. 2003. (Library of Future Energy). (Illus.). 64p. (YA). lib. bdg. 26.50 (978-0-8239-3662-5(7)) Rosen Publishing Group, Inc., The.

Bolles, Richard Nelson & Christen, Carol. What Color Is Your Parachute? For Teens. 2006. (Parachute Library Ser.). (Illus.). 176p. (YA). pap. 14.95 (978-1-58008-713-1(2)) Ten Speed Pr.

Bonnice, Sherry. Computer Programmer. 2003. (Careers with Character Ser.). (Illus.). 96p. (YA). (gr. 7 up). lib. bdg. 22.95 (978-1-59084-312-3(6)) Mason Crest Pubs.

—Financial Advisor. 2003. (Careers with Character Ser.). (Illus.). 96p. (J). (gr. 7 up). lib. bdg. 22.95 (978-1-59084-313-0(4)) Mason Crest Pubs.

Boraas, Tracey. Animal Caretaker. 2000. (Career Exploration Ser.). (Illus.). 48p. (J). (gr. 3-4). lib. bdg. 21.26 (978-0-7368-0590-2(7) , LifeMatters Bks.) Capstone Pr., Inc.

—Automotive Master Mechanic. 2000. (Career Exploration Ser.). (Illus.). 48p. (J). (gr. 3-4). lib. bdg. 21.26 (978-0-7368-0486-8(2) , LifeMatters Bks.) Capstone Pr., Inc.

TUV

—Cosmetologist. 2000. (Career Exploration Ser.). (Illus.). 48p. (J). (gr. 3-4). lib. bdg. 21.26 (978-0-7368-0592-6(3) , LifeMatters Bks.) Capstone Pr., Inc.

—Machinist. 2000. (Career Exploration Ser.). (Illus.). 48p. (J). (gr. 3-4). lib. bdg. 21.26 (978-0-7368-0491-2(9) , LifeMatters Bks.) Capstone Pr., Inc.

Bozak, Kristin & Cohen, Judith Love. You Can Be a Woman Botanist. Katz, David Arthur, illus. 1999. 40p. (J). (gr. 3-6). pap. 7.00 (978-1-880599-31-0(7)) Cascade Pass, Inc.

Brandon, Karen & Diani, Stephanie. Nurse. 2005. (How Do I Become a... Ser.). (Illus.). 32p. (J). (gr. 4-7). lib. bdg. 23.70 (978-1-56711-744-8(9) , Blackbirch Pr., Inc.) Thomson Gale.

Bright Futures Press, prod. Kids Career Collection. (YA). 179.95 (978-0-7365-4584-6(0)) Films Media Group.

Brinkerhoff, Shirley. Research Scientist. 2002. (Careers with Character Ser.). (Illus.). 96p. (YA). (gr. 7 up). lib. bdg. 22.95 (978-1-59084-323-9(1)) Mason Crest Pubs.

Brown, Marty. Webmaster. 2000. (CoolCareers.com Ser.). (Illus.). 48p. (YA). (gr. 5-8). lib. bdg. 23.95 (978-0-8239-3111-8(0) , CCWEMA, Rosen Central) Rosen Publishing Group, Inc., The.

Bryan, Betsy M. & Cohen, Judith Love. You Can Be a Woman Egyptologist. Martin, Janice, ed. Katz, David Arthur, illus. rev. ed. 1999. 40p. (J). (gr. 3-6). reprint ed. 13.95 (978-1-880599-45-7(7)) Cascade Pass, Inc.

Buell, Tonya. Careers with Successful Dot-Com Companies. 2005. (Library of E-Commerce & Internet Careers). (Illus.). 64p. (YA). (gr. 7-12). lib. bdg. 26.50 (978-0-8239-3424-9(1)) Rosen Publishing Group, Inc., The.

Bullock, Linda. Careers on the Web. 2002. (Technology & You Ser.). (Illus.). 48p. (J). lib. bdg. 27.12 (978-0-7398-4694-0(9)) Raintree.

Burby, Liza N. A Day in the Life of a Park Ranger. 1999. (Kids' Career Library). (Illus.). 24p. (J). (gr. 3). lib. bdg. 18.75 (978-0-8239-5300-4(9) , PowerKids Pr.) Rosen Publishing Group, Inc., The.

Cambridge Educational, prod. Cambridge Career Center Hybrid. (YA). cd-rom 385.95 (978-0-7365-3872-5(0)) Films Media Group.

—Career Center Mac Labpak. (YA). cd-rom 962.50 (978-0-7365-4350-7(3)) Films Media Group.

—Career Center Windows Labpack. (YA). cd-rom 962.50 (978-0-7365-4349-1(X)) Films Media Group.

—Job Search Win Labpak. (YA). cd-rom 247.50 (978-0-7365-4351-4(1)) Films Media Group.

—Multimedia Career Center. (YA). cd-rom 385.95 (978-0-7365-4374-3(0)) Films Media Group.

Camenson, Blythe. Firefighting. 1999. (VGM Career Portraits Ser.). (Illus.). 96p. (gr. 7 up). 13.95 (978-0-8442-4374-0(4) , 9780844243740) McGraw-Hill Cos., The.

Camp, William G. & Daugherty, Thomas B. Managing Our Natural Resources. 4th rev. ed. 2000. (Illus.). 416p. (C). 108.95 (978-0-7668-1554-4(4)) Thomson Delmar Learning.

Caraccilo, Dominic J. E-Tailing: Careers Selling over the Web. 2005. (Library of E-Commerce & Internet Careers). (Illus.). 64p. (YA). (gr. 7-12). lib. bdg. 26.50 (978-0-8239-3428-7(4)) Rosen Publishing Group, Inc., The.

Career Clusters (AVA) 2001. (YA). pap. 6.00 (978-1-57078-010-3(2) , CEV00010); pap. 8.00 (978-1-57078-011-0(0) , CEV00011) C E V Multimedia, Ltd.

Career Exploration. 255p. (gr. 10 up). pap. 99.00 incl. VHS (978-1-56370-043-9(3) , CXV) JIST Publishing.

Career Exploration, 24 bks. Incl. Animal Caretaker. Boraas, Tracey. (J). (gr. 3-4). 2000. lib. bdg. 21.26 (978-0-7368-0590-2(7)); Athletic Trainer. Voeller, Edward A. (J). (gr. 3-4). 1999. lib. bdg. 21.26 (978-0-7368-0326-7(2)); Automotive Master Mechanic. Boraas, Tracey. (J). (gr. 3-4). 2000. lib. bdg. 21.26 (978-0-7368-0486-8(2)); Computer Engineer. Maupin, Melissa. (J). (gr. 3-4). 2000. lib. bdg. 21.26 (978-0-7368-0591-9(5)); Computer Programmer. Wallner, Rosemary. (J). (gr. 3-4). 2000. lib. bdg. 21.26 (978-0-7368-0488-2(9)); Construction Carpenter. Wallner, Rosemary. (J). (gr. 3-4). 2000. lib. bdg. 21.26 (978-0-7368-0487-5(0)); Cosmetologist. Boraas, Tracey. (J). (gr. 3-4). 2000. lib. bdg. 21.26 (978-0-7368-0592-6(3)); Dental Assistant. Wallner, Rosemary. (J). (gr. 3-4). 2000. lib. bdg. 21.26 (978-0-7368-0593-3(1)); Director. Sotnak, Lewann. (J). (gr. 3-4). 1999. lib. bdg. 21.26 (978-0-7368-0327-4(0)); Electrician. Donnelley, Karen J. (J). (gr. 3-4). 2000. lib. bdg. 21.26 (978-0-7368-0594-0(X)); Fashion Designer. Wallner, Rosemary. (J). (gr. 3-4). 2000. lib. bdg. 21.26 (978-0-7368-0595-7(8)); Flight Attendant. Wallner, Rosemary. (J). (gr. 3-4). 2000. lib. bdg. 21.26 (978-0-7368-0489-9(7)); Graphic Designer. Sotnak, Lewann. (J). (gr. 3-4). 1999. lib. bdg. 21.26 (978-0-7368-0328-1(9)); Human Services Worker. Wallner, Rosemary. (J). (gr. 3-4). 2000. lib. bdg. 21.26 (978-0-7368-0596-4(6)); Landscape Contractor. Maupin, Melissa. (J). (gr. 3-4). 2000. lib. bdg. 21.26 (978-0-7368-0490-5(0)); Licensed Practical Nurse. Wallner, Rosemary. 1999. lib. bdg. 21.26 (978-0-7368-0329-8(7)); Machinist. Boraas, Tracey. (J). (gr. 3-4). 2000. lib. bdg. 21.26 (978-0-7368-0491-2(9)); Marine Biologist. Wendt, Jennifer. (J). (gr. 3-4). 1999. lib. bdg. 21.26 (978-0-7368-0330-4(0)); Mechanical Drafter. Wallner, Rosemary. (J). (gr. 3-4). 1999. lib. bdg. 21.26 (978-0-7368-0331-1(9)); Park Naturalist. Dawson, Jim. (J). (gr. 3-4). 1999. lib. bdg. 21.26 (978-0-7368-0332-8(7)); Pediatrician. Wallner, Rosemary. (J). (gr. 3-4). 1999. lib. bdg. 21.26 (978-0-7368-0333-5(5)); Police Detective. Boraas, Tracey. (J). (gr. 3-4). 2000. lib. bdg. 21.26 (978-0-7368-0597-1(4)); Travel Agent. Burgan, Michael. (J). (gr. 3-4). 2000. lib. bdg. 21.26 (978-0-7368-0492-9(7)); Veterinarian. Burgan, Michael. (J). (gr. 3-4). 2000. lib. bdg. 21.26 (978-0-7368-0493-6(5)); 48p. (Illus.). 2001. Set lib. bdg. 510.24 (978-0-7368-0678-7(4) , LifeMatters Bks.) Capstone Pr., Inc.

Career Guide to America's Top Industries. 2002. (gr. 7-12). lib. bdg. 22.20 (978-0-613-51108-7(5)) Tandem Library Bks.

The Career Resource Library. 2005. (Illus.). (gr. 7-12). lib. bdg. 638.40 (978-0-8239-3910-7(3)) Rosen Publishing Group, Inc., The.

The Career Resource Library Set 1. 2005. (Illus.). (gr. 7-12). lib. bdg. 79.50 (978-0-8239-8040-6(5)) Rosen Publishing Group, Inc., The.

The Career Resource Library Set 2. 2005. (Illus.). (gr. 7-12). lib. bdg. 159.00 (978-0-8239-3951-0(0)) Rosen Publishing Group, Inc., The.

The Career Resource Library Set 3. 2005. (Illus.). (gr. 7-12). lib. bdg. 159.00 (978-0-8239-4066-0(7)) Rosen Publishing Group, Inc., The.

The Career Resource Library Set 4. 2005. (Illus.). (gr. 7-12). lib. bdg. 212.00 (978-0-8239-3949-7(9)) Rosen Publishing Group, Inc., The.

The Career Resource Library Set 5. 2005. (Illus.). (gr. 7-12). lib. bdg. 238.50 (978-0-8239-4065-3(9)) Rosen Publishing Group, Inc., The.

Careers in the New Economy, 5 bk. set. 2005. (YA). (gr. 7-12). lib. bdg. 159.75 (978-1-4042-0374-7(5)) Rosen Publishing Group, Inc., The.

Careers Set: Promising Careers, 8 vols. Incl. Careers in Alternative Medicine. Steinfeld, Alan. 192p. 2000. lib. bdg. 18.95 (978-0-8239-2963-4(9) , CAALME); Careers in Coaching. Nagle, Jeanne M. 192p. 2005. lib. bdg. 26.50 (978-0-8239-2966-5(3) , CACOAC); Careers in Cosmetology. Lytle, Elizabeth Stewart. 192p. 1999. lib. bdg. 26.50 (978-0-8239-2889-7(6) , CACOSM); Careers in Graphic Arts & Computer Graphics. McGuire-Lytle, Erin. 192p. 1999. lib. bdg. 26.50 (978-0-8239-2228-4(6) , CAGRAR); Careers in Pro Sports. Nelson, Cordner. 192p. 1999. lib. bdg. 26.50 (978-0-8239-2896-5(9) , CAPRSP); Careers in Starting & Building Franchises. Frisch, Carlienne A. 192p. 1999. lib. bdg. 26.50 (978-0-8239-2781-4(4) , CAFRAN); Careers in the Fashion Industry. Giacobello, John. 122p. 1999. lib. bdg. 18.95 (978-0-8239-2890-3(X) , CAFASH); Exploring Careers in Social Work. Simpson, Carolyn & Simpson, Dwain. 192p. 1999. lib. bdg. 26.50 (978-0-8239-2879-8(9) , CASOWO); (YA). (gr. 7-12). (Illus.). Set lib. bdg. 135.60 o.p. (978-0-8239-9085-6(0)) Rosen Publishing Group, Inc., The.

Cassedy, Patrice, tr. Finance. 2003. (Illus.). 112p. (J). 29.95 (978-1-59018-520-9(X) , Lucent Bks.) Thomson Gale.

Cefrey, Holly. Bounty Hunter. 2003. (gr. 7-12). lib. bdg. 15.25 (978-0-613-67877-3(X)) Tandem Library Bks.

—Race Car Drivers: Life on the Fast Track. 2005. (Extreme Careers Ser.). (Illus.). 64p. (YA). (gr. 5-8). 26.50 (978-0-8239-3367-9(9)) Rosen Publishing Group, Inc., The.

CFKR Career Materials Staff. High School Career Course Planner. 2nd rev. ed. 2002. 6p. (YA). (gr. 6-10). pap. (978-0-934783-16-3(0)) CFKR Career Materials, Inc.

Chui, David. Choosing a Career in the Post Office. 2005. (World of Work Ser.). (Illus.). 64p. (YA). (gr. 7-12). lib. bdg. 25.25 (978-0-8239-3242-9(7)) Rosen Publishing Group, Inc., The.

Clark, Betty. Choosing a Career in Real Estate. 2005. (World of Work Ser.). (Illus.). 64p. (YA). (gr. 7-12). lib. bdg. 25.25 (978-0-8239-3246-7(X) , WWREES) Rosen Publishing Group, Inc., The.

Clinton, Susan. Correction Officer. (Careers Without College Ser.). pap. 6.95 (978-0-7368-8542-3(0) , LifeMatters Bks.) Capstone Pr., Inc.

—Correction Officer. 1998. (Careers Without College Ser.). (Illus.). 48p. (J). (gr. 3-7). pap. 19.00 (978-0-516-21279-1(6) , Children's Pr.) Scholastic Library Publishing.

—Heating & Air Conditioning Servicer. (Careers Without College Ser.). pap. 6.95 (978-0-7368-8545-4(5) , LifeMatters Bks.) Capstone Pr., Inc.

—Tractor-Trailer-Truck Driver. 1998. (Careers Without College Ser.). (Illus.). 48p. (J). (gr. 3-7). pap. 19.00 (978-0-516-21289-0(3) , Children's Pr.) Scholastic Library Publishing.

Cohen, Judith Love & Siegel, Margot. You Can Be a Woman Architect. Yañez, Juan, tr. Katz, David Arthur, illus. 1998. 40p. (J). (gr. k-6). 19.95 incl. cd-rom (978-1-880599-28-0(7)) Cascade Pass, Inc.

Conrad, David. The Work We Do. 2002. (Spyglass Books). (Illus.). 24p. (J). (gr. 1 up). lib. bdg. 18.60 (978-0-7565-0382-6(5)) Compass Point Bks.

Cool Careers Without College, 8 bks., Set. Incl. People Who Love Everything Digital. Romano, Amy. (YA). lib. bdg. 33.25 (978-1-4042-0748-6(1)); People Who Love Houses. Beco, Alice. (Illus.). (J). lib. bdg. 33.25 (978-1-4042-0753-0(8)); People Who Love Manga, Comics, & Animation. Glass, Sherri & Wentzel, Jim. (Illus.). (YA). lib. bdg. 33.25 (978-1-4042-0754-7(6)); People Who Love Sports. Hofstetter, Adam B. (Illus.). (J). lib. bdg. 33.25 (978-1-4042-0749-3(X)); People Who Love to Buy Things. Santos, Edson. (Illus.). (J). lib. bdg. 33.25 (978-1-4042-0751-6(1)); People Who Love to Organize, Manage, & Plan. Greenberger, Robert. (Illus.). (YA). lib. bdg. 33.25 (978-1-4042-0752-3(X)); People Who Love to Write. Roza, Greg. (YA). lib. bdg. 33.25 (978-1-4042-0750-9(3)); People Who Love Video Games. Croce, Nicholas. (Illus.). (J). lib. bdg. 33.25 (978-1-4042-0747-9(3)); 144p. (gr. 5-8). 2006. 2006. 266.00 (978-1-4042-1015-8(6)) Rosen Publishing Group, Inc., The.

Coolcareers.com, 8 bks. Incl. Computer Animator. O'Donnell, Annie. lib. bdg. 23.95 (978-0-8239-3101-9(3) , CCCOAN); Hardware Engineer. Donelly, Karen. lib. bdg. 23.95 (978-0-8239-3118-7(8) , CCHAEN); Multimedia & New Media Developer. Mazor, Barry. lib. bdg. 23.95 (978-0-8239-3102-6(1) , CCMEDE); Software Designer. McGinty, Alice B. lib. bdg. 23.95 (978-0-8239-3149-1(8) , CCSODE); Video Game Designer. Olesky, Walter. lib. bdg. 23.95 (978-0-8239-3117-0(X) , CCVIGA); Web Entrepreneur. Oleksy, Walter. lib. bdg. 23.95 (978-0-8239-3103-3(X) , CCWEEN); Web Page Designer. Oleksy, Walter. lib. bdg. 23.95 (978-0-8239-3112-5(9) , CCWEPA); Webmaster. Brown, Marty. lib. bdg. 23.95 (978-0-8239-3111-8(0) , CCWEMA); 48p. (YA). (gr. 5-8). 2000. (Illus.). Set lib. bdg. 191.60 o.p. (978-0-8239-9089-4(3) , CCCOCA, Rosen Central) Rosen Publishing Group, Inc., The.

Coon, Nora E. Teen Dream Jobs: How to Find the Job You Really Want! 2004. (Illus.). 132p. (YA). (gr. 6-12). pap. (978-1-58270-093-9(1)) Beyond Words Publishing, Inc.

Corwen, Leonard. Successful Job Hunting. 2005. 99p. pap. 7.95 (978-1-56450-220-9(1)) Films Media Group.

Corwin, Gene. Your Bright Future in Information Technology. 2002. (gr. 7-12). lib. bdg. 21.10 (978-0-613-56713-8(7)) Tandem Library Bks.

Cowan, Carla Romaine. E-Commerce Careers in Multimedia. 2005. (Library of E-Commerce & Internet Careers). (Illus.). 64p. (YA). (gr. 7-12). lib. bdg. 26.50 (978-0-8239-3427-0(6)) Rosen Publishing Group, Inc., The.

Craig, Tom. Internet: Technology, People, Process. 2003. (Media Wise Ser.). 64p. (J). lib. bdg. 28.50 (978-1-58340-257-3(8)) Smart Apple Media.

Croce, Nicholas. Detectives: Life of Investigating Crime. 2005. (Extreme Careers Ser.). (Illus.). 64p. (YA). (gr. 5-8). 26.50 (978-0-8239-3796-7(8)) Rosen Publishing Group, Inc., The.

Culbreath, Alice N. & Neal, Saundra K. Testing the Waters: A Teen's Guide to Career Exploration. 1999. 250p. (YA). pap. 24.95 (978-0-9672502-0-5(X)) JRC Consulting.

Cutler, Art, et al. Job-O 2000. 1999. (Illus.). 16p. (YA). (gr. 7 up). pap. 4.20 (978-1-887481-08-3(7)) CFKR Career Materials, Inc.

Cutting-Edge Careers, 6 bks., Set. Incl. Careers Creating Search Engines. Levin, Judith. (Illus.). (J). lib. bdg. 27.95 (978-1-4042-0957-2(3)); Careers in Artificial Intelligence. Greenberger, Robert. (Illus.). (YA). lib. bdg. 27.95 (978-1-4042-0953-4(0)); Careers in Biotechnology. Hall, Linley Erin. (Illus.). (J). lib. bdg. 27.95 (978-1-4042-0954-1(9) , 1267025); Careers in Computer Gaming. Robinson, Matthew. (YA). lib. bdg. 27.95 (978-1-4042-0958-9(1)); Careers in Nanotechnology. Brezina, Corona. (Illus.). (J). lib. bdg. 27.95 (978-1-4042-0955-8(7)); Careers in Robotics. Kupperberg, Paul. (Illus.). (YA). lib. bdg. 27.95 (978-1-4042-0956-5(5)); 64p. (gr. 7-12). 2006. 2007. Set lib. bdg. 167.70 (***978-1-4042-0934-3(4)***) Rosen Publishing Group, Inc., The.

Davis, Mary L. Working in Law & Justice. 1999. (Exploring Careers Ser.). (Illus.). 112p. (YA). (gr. 6-9). lib. bdg. (978-0-8225-1766-5(3) , Lerner Pubns.) Lerner Publishing Group.

Davis, Wendy & Knight, Bertram T. Working at a Marine Institute. 1998. (Working Here Ser.). (Illus.). 32p. (J). (gr. 2-4). 23.50 (978-0-516-21223-4(0) , Children's Pr.) Scholastic Library Publishing.

Devantier, Alecia T. & Turkington, Carol A. Extraordinary Jobs, 6 vols., Set. 2006. 128p. (gr. 6-12). 210.00 (978-0-8160-6835-7(6) , Ferguson Publishing Co.) Facts On File, Inc.

Donelly, Karen. Hardware Engineer. 2000. (CoolCareers.com Ser.). (Illus.). 48p. (YA). (gr. 5-8). lib. bdg. 23.95 (978-0-8239-3118-7(8) , CCHAEN, Rosen Central) Rosen Publishing Group, Inc., The.

Draper, Allison Stark. Choosing a Career in the Pulp & Paper Industry. 2005. (World of Work Ser.). (Illus.). 64p. (YA). (gr. 7-12). lib. bdg. 25.25 (978-0-8239-3333-4(4)) Rosen Publishing Group, Inc., The.

—Fighter Pilots: Life at Mach Speed. 2001. (Extreme Careers Ser.). (Illus.). 64p. (YA). (gr. 5-8). lib. bdg. 26.50 (978-0-8239-3366-2(0) , Rosen Central) Rosen Publishing Group, Inc., The.

Dubois, Muriel L. I Like Animals: What Can I Be? 2000. (What Can I Be? Ser.). (Illus.). 24p. (J). (gr. 1-2). lib. bdg. 18.60 (978-0-7368-0630-5(X) , Bridgestone Bks.) Capstone Pr., Inc.

Elliott, Jane, ed. 50 Cutting-Edge Jobs. (Illus.). 348p. (YA). pap. (978-0-89434-312-4(2) , Ferguson Publishing Co.) Facts On File, Inc.

Ellis, Amy, des. Looking at Myself I. 2nd ed. 2003. (J). pap. (978-1-887481-27-4(3) , LAM1KIT) CFKR Career Materials, Inc.

—Looking at Myself I Answer Folder. 2nd ed. 2003. (J). pap. (978-1-887481-28-1(1)) CFKR Career Materials, Inc.

Ellis, Amy, rev. Major-Minor Finder: College to Career Planner. 2nd ed. 2003. (YA). (978-1-887481-38-0(9)) CFKR Career Materials, Inc.

Englart, Mindi. Architect. 2002. (How Do I Become a... Ser.). (Illus.). 32p. (J). 23.70 (978-1-56711-686-1(8) , Blackbirch Pr., Inc.) Thomson Gale.

—Chef. 2002. (How Do I Become a... Ser.). (Illus.). 32p. (J). 22.45 (978-1-56711-418-8(0) , Blackbirch Pr., Inc.) Thomson Gale.

—Firefighter. 2002. (How Do I Become a... Ser.). (Illus.). 32p. (J). 23.70 (978-1-56711-687-8(6) , Blackbirch Pr., Inc.) Thomson Gale.

—Police Officer. 2002. (How Do I Become a... Ser.). (Illus.). 32p. (J). 22.45 (978-1-56711-417-1(2) , Blackbirch Pr., Inc.) Thomson Gale.

Ermitage, Kathleen. Veterinarian. 2000. (Workers You Know Ser.). (Illus.). 32p. (J). (ps-3). lib. bdg. 25.70 (978-0-8172-5592-3(3)) Raintree.

Exploring Careers: A Young Person's Guide to 1,000 Jobs. 2003. (gr. 7-12). lib. bdg. 41.95 (978-0-613-65224-7(X)) Tandem Library Bks.

Exploring Careers Activities. 3rd ed. 2003. 32p. (YA). 2.25 (978-1-56370-984-5(8)) JIST Publishing.

Extreme Careers: Buy Sets 1, 2, 3, And 4, 24 vols. 2005. (Illus.). 64p. (gr. 5-8). 518.70 (978-0-8239-7685-0(8)) Rosen Publishing Group, Inc., The.

Extreme Careers Set 2. 2005. (gr. 5-8). 159.00 (978-0-8239-3884-1(0)) Rosen Publishing Group, Inc., The.

Extreme Careers Set 3. 2005. (gr. 5-8). 159.00 (978-0-8239-4050-9(0)) Rosen Publishing Group, Inc., The.

Facts on File, Inc. Staff. Physicians. 2nd rev. ed. 2005. (Careers in Focus Ser.). (Illus.). 204p. (J). (gr. 6-12). 22.95 (978-0-8160-5868-6(7) , Ferguson Publishing Co.) Facts On File, Inc.

—Social Work. 2nd rev. ed. 2005. (Careers in Focus Ser.). (Illus.). 204p. (J). (gr. 6-12). 22.95 (978-0-8160-5869-3(5) , Ferguson Publishing Co.) Facts On File, Inc.

—Top Careers for Economics Graduates. 2004. (Top Careers Ser.). (Illus.). 384p. (gr. 9). pap. 14.95 (978-0-8160-5566-1(1) , Checkmark Bks.) Facts On File, Inc.

—Top Careers for History Graduates. 2004. (Top Careers Ser.). (Illus.). 384p. (gr. 9). pap. 14.95 (978-0-8160-5567-8(X) , Checkmark Bks.) Facts On File, Inc.

Facts on File, Inc. Staff, contrib. by. Top Careers for Art Graduates. 2004. (Top Careers Ser.). (Illus.). 368p. (gr. 9). pap. 14.95 (978-0-8160-5565-4(3) , Checkmark Bks.) Facts On File, Inc.

Facts on File, Inc. Staff, ed. Aviation. 2005. (Careers in Focus Ser.). (Illus.). 192p. (YA). (gr. 6-12). 22.95 (978-0-8160-5850-1(4)) Facts On File, Inc.

Fall, Mitchell. Careers in the Fire Department's Search & Rescue Unit. 2005. (Careers in Search & Rescue Operations Ser.). (Illus.). 64p. (YA). (gr. 5-8). lib. bdg. 26.50 (978-0-8239-3833-9(6)) Rosen Publishing Group, Inc., The.

Ferguson. Career Skills Library Set. 2004. (Career Skills Library). 128-144p. (gr. 6-12). 175.60 (978-0-8160-5824-2(5) , Ferguson Publishing Co.) Facts On File, Inc.

—Careers in Focus: Personal Services. 2nd rev. ed. 2007. (Careers in Focus Ser.). 192p. (YA). (gr. 6-12). 29.95 (***978-0-8160-6592-9(6)*** , Ferguson Publishing Co.) Facts On File, Inc.

—Careers in Focus: Public Relations. 2007. (Careers in Focus Ser.). 160p. (J). (gr. 6-12). 29.95 (***978-0-8160-6574-5(8)*** , Ferguson Publishing Co.) Facts On File, Inc.

—Careers in Focus: Public Safety. 3rd rev. ed. 2007. (Careers in Focus Ser.). 224p. (gr. 6-12). 29.95 (***978-0-8160-6594-3(2)*** , Ferguson Publishing Co.) Facts On File, Inc.

—Careers in Focus: Publishing. 3rd rev. ed. 2007. (Careers in Focus Ser.). 192p. (YA). (gr. 6-12). 29.95 (***978-0-8160-6572-1(1)*** , Ferguson Publishing Co.) Facts On File, Inc.

—Careers in Focus: Writing. 3rd rev. ed. 2007. (Careers in Focus Ser.). 224p. (J). (gr. 6-12). 29.95 (***978-0-8160-6596-7(9)*** , Ferguson Publishing Co.) Facts On File, Inc.

—Discovering Careers for Your Future Set. 2005. (Discovering Careers for Your Future Ser.). 96-96p. (gr. 4-9). 439.00 (978-0-8160-6331-4(1)); 482.90 (978-0-8160-6533-2(0) , Ferguson Publishing Co.) Facts On File, Inc.

—Ferguson's Careers in Focus Set. 2005. (Careers in Focus Ser.). (gr. 9-12). 176p. 1032.75 (978-0-8160-6531-8(4) , Ferguson Publishing Co.); 176-224p. 1032.75 (978-0-8160-6333-8(8)) Facts On File, Inc.

—Mastering Career Skills: Communication Skills. 2nd rev. ed. 2007. (Mastering Career Skills Ser.). (Illus.). 144p. pap. 12.95 (***978-0-8160-7115-9(2)*** , Checkmark Bks.) Facts On File, Inc.

—Mastering Career Skills: Organization Skills. 2nd rev. ed. (Mastering Career Skills Ser.). 144p. pap. 12.95 (***978-0-8160-7116-6(0)*** , Checkmark Bks.) Facts On File, Inc.

—Mastering Career Skills: Research & Information Management. 2nd rev. ed. (Mastering Career Skills Ser.). 128p. pap. 12.95 (***978-0-8160-7118-0(7)*** , Checkmark Bks.) Facts On File, Inc.

—What Can I Do Now: Nursing. 2nd rev. ed. 2007. (What Can I Do Now Ser.). 208p. (gr. 6-12). 29.95 (***978-0-8160-6028-3(2)*** , Ferguson Publishing Co.) Facts On File, Inc.

Ferguson, creator. Biology. 2nd rev. ed. 2005. (Careers in Focus Ser.). (Illus.). 204p. (J). (gr. 6-12). 22.95 (978-0-8160-5867-9(9) , Ferguson Publishing Co.) Facts On File, Inc.

Ferry, Francis R. Career Steps. 1999. (Illus.). 20p. (J). (gr. 4-7). pap. 6.36 (978-1-887481-11-3(7)) CFKR Career Materials, Inc.

—Job-O Advanced. 1998. 20p. (YA). (gr. 10-12). pap. 4.20 (978-0-934783-46-0(2)) CFKR Career Materials, Inc.

—Reflections of Your Future. Sabich, Marty, ed. 1999. (Illus.). 146p. (J). (gr. 1-9). pap. 14.95 (978-1-887481-10-6(9)) CFKR Career Materials, Inc.

Fields, Jennifer. Choosing a Career as a Nurse-Midwife. 2005. (World of Work Ser.). (Illus.). 64p. (YA). (gr. 7-12). lib. bdg. 25.25 (978-0-8239-3293-1(1)) Rosen Publishing Group, Inc., The.

Fine, Jil. Bomb Squad Specialist: Danger Is My Business. 2003. (gr. 7-12). lib. bdg. 15.25 (978-0-613-67876-6(1)) Tandem Library Bks.

—Bomb Squad Specialists. 2003. (High Interest Bks.). 48p. (J). 24.00 (978-0-516-24340-5(3) , Children's Pr.) Scholastic Library Publishing.

Flanagan, Alice K. Mayors. 2001. (Community Workers Ser.). (Illus.). 32p. (J). (gr. 1 up). lib. bdg. 21.26 (978-0-7565-0064-1(8)) Compass Point Bks.

Forbes, Dina E. Laura Bush: Teacher, Librarian, & First Lady. 2005. (Ferguson Career Biographies Ser.). (Illus.). 144p. (J). (gr. 6-12). 25.00 (978-0-8160-5886-0(5) , Ferguson Publishing Co.) Facts On File, Inc.

Franks, Katie. Dream Jobs, 6 bks., Set. Incl. I Want to Be a Baseball Star. lib. bdg. 21.25 (978-1-4042-3622-6(8) , PowerKids Pr.); I Want to Be a Basketball Player. lib. bdg. 21.25 (978-1-4042-3621-9(X)); I Want to Be a Movie Star. lib. bdg. 21.25 (978-1-4042-3623-3(6)); I Want to Be a Race Car Driver. lib. bdg. 21.25 (978-1-

4042-3623-3(6)); I Want to Be a Rock Star. lib. bdg. 21.25 (978-1-4042-3618-9(X) , PowerKids Pr.); I Want to Be a Supermodel. lib. bdg. 21.25 (978-1-4042-3620-2(1) , PowerKids Pr.); (Illus.). 24p. (J). (gr. 3-5). 2007. Set lib. bdg. 127.50 (978-1-4042-3598-4(1)) Rosen Publishing Group, Inc., The.

Frisch, Carlienne A. Everything You Need to Know about Getting a Job. 2005. (Need to Know Library). (Illus.). 64p. (YA). (gr. 7-12). lib. bdg. 25.25 (978-0-8239-2961-0(2) , NTGEJO) Rosen Publishing Group, Inc., The.

Gabler, Laura R., ed. Career Exploration on the Internet: A Student's Guide to More Than 500 Web Sites. 2nd ed. (Illus.). 752p. (YA). pap. (978-0-89434-305-6(X) , Ferguson Publishing Co.) Facts On File, Inc.

Gabriel, Diane L. & Cohen, Judith Love. You Can Be a Woman Paleontologist. Martin, Janice, ed. Katz, David Arthur, illus. rev. ed. 1999. 40p. (J). (gr. 3-6). reprint ed. 13.95 (978-1-880599-43-3(0)) Cascade Pass, Inc.

Gardner, Garth. Careers in Computer Graphics & Animation: Gardner's Guide Series. Ford, Bonney, ed. 2006. (Gardner's Guide Ser.). (Illus.). 256p. pap. 29.95 (978-0-9661075-2-4(7)) Gardner, Garth Co., Inc. (GGC).

Getting Ready for Careers, 8 bks. Incl. Getting Ready for a Career As a Computer Animator. Lund, Bill. 1997. lib. bdg. 21.26 (978-1-56065-549-7(6)); Getting Ready for a Career As a Computer Technician. Lund, Bill. 1997. lib. bdg. 21.26 (978-1-56065-550-3(X)); Getting Ready for a Career As a Video Game Designer. Lund, Bill. 1997. lib. bdg. 21.26 (978-1-56065-552-7(6)); Getting Ready for a Career As an Internet Designer. Lund, Bill. 1997. lib. bdg. 21.26 (978-1-56065-551-0(8)); Getting Ready for a Career in Computers. Lund, Bill. 1996. lib. bdg. 21.26 (978-1-56065-290-8(X)); Getting Ready for a Career in Food Service. Streissguth, Thomas. 1996. lib. bdg. 21.26 (978-1-56065-291-5(8)); Getting Ready for a Career in Health Care. Lund, Bill. 1996. lib. bdg. 21.26 (978-1-56065-292-2(6)); Getting Ready for a Career in Professional Sports. Savage, Jeff. 1996. lib. bdg. 21.26 (978-1-56065-293-9(4)); 48p. (J). (gr. 3-4). (Illus.). Set lib. bdg. 170.08 (978-1-56065-637-1(9) , LifeMatters Bks.) Capstone Pr., Inc.

Giacobello, John. Choosing a Career in the Toy Industry. 2005. (World of Work Ser.). (Illus.). 64p. (YA). (gr. 7-12). lib. bdg. 25.25 (978-0-8239-3438-6(1)) Rosen Publishing Group, Inc., The.

—Scuba Divers: Life under Water. 2005. (Extreme Careers Ser.). (Illus.). 64p. (J). (gr. 5-8). 26.50 (978-0-8239-3368-6(7)) Rosen Publishing Group, Inc., The.

Goldberg, Jan. Fire Fighter. (Careers Without College Ser.). pap. 6.95 (978-0-7368-8543-0(9)); 1998. (Illus.). 48p. (J). (gr. 3-4). lib. bdg. 21.26 (978-0-7368-0033-4(6)) Capstone Pr., Inc. (LifeMatters Bks.).

—Medical Record Technician. 1998. (Careers Without College Ser.). (Illus.). 48p. (J). (gr. 3-4). lib. bdg. 21.26 (978-0-7368-0035-8(2) , LifeMatters Bks.) Capstone Pr., Inc.

—Private Investigator. 1998. (Careers Without College Ser.). (Illus.). 48p. (J). (gr. 3-4). lib. bdg. 21.26 (978-0-7368-0038-9(7) , LifeMatters Bks.) Capstone Pr., Inc.

—Security Guard. 1998. (Careers Without College Ser.). (Illus.). 48p. (J). (gr. 3-4). lib. bdg. 21.26 (978-0-7368-0039-6(5) , LifeMatters Bks.) Capstone Pr., Inc.

Gosling, Maureen, et al. You Can Be a Woman Movie Maker. l.t. ed. 2003. (Illus.). 80p. (J). 19.95 incl. DVD (978-1-880599-64-8(3)); pap. 14.95 incl. DVD (978-1-880599-63-1(5)) Cascade Pass, Inc.

Green, Michael. Motorcycle Police. 1999. (Law Enforcement Ser.). (Illus.). 48p. (J). (gr. 3-4). lib. bdg. 21.26 (978-0-7368-0187-4(1) , Capstone High-Interest Bks.) Capstone Pr., Inc.

—Sheriffs & Deputy Sheriffs. 1999. (Law Enforcement Ser.). (Illus.). 48p. (J). (gr. 3-4). lib. bdg. 21.26 (978-0-7368-0188-1(X) , Capstone High-Interest Bks.) Capstone Pr., Inc.

—The United States Air Force. 1998. (Serving Your Country Ser.). (Illus.). 48p. (J). (gr. 4-7). lib. bdg. 19.00 (978-0-516-21310-1(5) , Children's Pr.) Scholastic Library Publishing.

—The United States Army. 1998. (Serving Your Country Ser.). (Illus.). 48p. (J). (gr. 4-7). lib. bdg. 19.00 (978-0-516-21311-8(3) , Children's Pr.) Scholastic Library Publishing.

—The United States Marine Corps. 1998. (Serving Your Country Ser.). (Illus.). 48p. (J). (gr. 3-7). lib. bdg. 19.00 (978-0-516-21312-5(1) , Children's Pr.) Scholastic Library Publishing.

—United States Marshals Service. 1999. (Law Enforcement Ser.). (Illus.). 48p. (J). (gr. 3-4). lib. bdg. 21.26 (978-0-7368-0189-8(8) , Capstone High-Interest Bks.) Capstone Pr., Inc.

—The United States Navy. 1998. (Serving Your Country Ser.). (Illus.). 48p. (J). (gr. 3-7). lib. bdg. 19.00 (978-0-516-21313-2(X) , Children's Pr.) Scholastic Library Publishing.

Greene, Meg. Careers in the National Guards' Search & Rescue Units. 2005. (Careers in Search & Rescue Operations Ser.). (Illus.). 64p. (YA). (gr. 5-8). lib. bdg. 26.50 (978-0-8239-3836-0(0)) Rosen Publishing Group, Inc., The.

Haegele, Katie. E-Advertising & E-Marketing: Online Opportunities. 2005. (Library of E-Commerce & Internet Careers). (Illus.). 64p. (YA). (gr. 7-12). lib. bdg. 26.50 (978-0-8239-3426-3(8)) Rosen Publishing Group, Inc., The.

Hambleton, Vicki & Greenwood, Cathleen, eds. So, You Wanna Be a Writer? How to Write, Get Published, & Maybe Even Make It Big! Eldridge, Laura & Mistretta, Corey, illus. 2001. (So, You Wanna Be ... Ser.). 120p. (gr. 3-11). pap. (978-1-58270-043-4(5)) Beyond Words Publishing, Inc.

Hammonds, Heather. Geologists. 2004. (J). lib. bdg. 27.10 (978-1-58340-543-7(7)) Smart Apple Media.

—Meteorologists. 2004. (J). lib. bdg. 27.10 (978-1-58340-542-0(9)) Smart Apple Media.

Harbeke, Dan. Get In! How to Market Yourself & Become Successful at a Young Age. 2003. 128p. pap. 23.95 (978-1-57886-031-9(8)) Scarecrow Pr., Inc.

Harrison, Scott & Ross, Allison J. Choosing a Career in Waste Management. 2005. (World of Work Ser.). (Illus.). 64p. (YA). (gr. 7-12). lib. bdg. 25.25 (978-0-8239-3240-5(0) , WWWAMA) Rosen Publishing Group, Inc., The.

Haydon, Julie. Astronomers. 2004. (J). lib. bdg. 27.10 (978-1-58340-541-3(0)) Smart Apple Media.

—Marine Biologists. 2004. (J). lib. bdg. 27.10 (978-1-58340-540-6(2)) Smart Apple Media.

Hayhurst, Chris. Astronauts: Life Exploring Outer Space. 2005. (Extreme Careers Ser.). (Illus.). 64p. (YA). (gr. 5-8). 26.50 (978-0-8239-3364-8(4)) Rosen Publishing Group, Inc., The.

Heath, David. Crime Lab Technician. (Careers Without College Ser.). pap. 6.95 (978-0-7368-8533-1(1) , LifeMatters Bks.) Capstone Pr., Inc.

Holderness, Ginny W. & Palmer, Forrest C. Career & Calling: A Guide for Counselors, Youth & Young Adults. 2000. (Illus.). 176p. (YA). 21.95 (978-0-664-22232-1(3)) Westminster John Knox Pr.

Hospitality & Tourism Careers (AVA) 2001. (YA). pap. 6.00 (978-1-57078-018-9(8) , CEV00018); pap. 8.00 (978-1-57078-019-6(6) , CEV00019) C E V Multimedia, Ltd.

Hovanec, Erin M. Careers as Content Provider for the Web. 2005. (Commerce & Internet Careers Ser.). (Illus.). 64p. (YA). (gr. 7-12). lib. bdg. 26.50 (978-0-8239-3418-8(7)) Rosen Publishing Group, Inc., The.

Howard, Ayanna. On the Job with an Engineer. 2003. (Adventures in Science Ser.). (J). lib. bdg. (978-1-58417-059-4(X)) Lake Street Pubs.

Howey, Paul M. Working in Construction. 1998. (Exploring Careers Ser.). (J). 17.95 (978-0-8225-1764-1(7)) Lerner Publishing Group.

Hunt, Christopher. Victory after High School: Survive or Thrive—You Choose! 2005. 144p. (YA). per. 16.95 (978-0-9765973-4-6(9)) Adjust Communications.

Inserra, Rose. Archaeologists. 2004. (J). lib. bdg. 27.10 (978-1-58340-544-4(5)) Smart Apple Media.

—Forensic Scientists. 2004. (J). lib. bdg. 27.10 (978-1-58340-545-1(3)) Smart Apple Media.

Is There Life after High School? 2004. (Faith 4 Life Ser.). 48p. 14.99 (978-0-7644-2467-0(X) , Flagship Church Resources) Group Publishing, Inc.

J. G. Ferguson Publishing Company Staff. Careers in Focus: Business Managers. 2003. (Careers in Focus Ser.). 192p. (YA). (gr. 6-12). 22.95 (978-0-89434-414-5(5) , Ferguson Publishing Co.) Facts On File, Inc.

—Careers in Focus: Design. 2002. (Careers in Focus Ser.). (Illus.). 176-192p. (YA). (gr. 7 up). lib. bdg. 22.95 (978-0-89434-410-7(2) , F725, Ferguson Publishing Co.) Facts On File, Inc.

—Careers in Focus: Mathematics. 2003. (Careers in Focus Ser.). (Illus.). 192p. (YA). (gr. 6-12). 22.95 (978-0-89434-413-8(7) , Ferguson Publishing Co.) Facts On File, Inc.

—Careers in Focus: Personal Services. 2002. (Careers in Focus Ser.). (Illus.). 192p. (YA). (gr. 6-12). 22.95 (978-0-89434-404-6(8) , F719, Ferguson Publishing Co.) Facts On File, Inc.

—Careers in Focus: Therapists. 2003. (Careers in Focus Ser.). 192p. (YA). (gr. 6-12). 22.95 (978-0-89434-412-1(9) , Ferguson Publishing Co.) Facts On File, Inc.

—Discovering Careers for Your Future/Adventure. 2001. (Discovering Careers for Your Future Ser.). (Illus.). 96p. (J). (gr. 4-9). 21.95 (978-0-89434-359-9(9) , F540, Ferguson Publishing Co.) Facts On File, Inc.

—Discovering Careers for Your Future/Animals. 2000. (Discovering Careers for Your Future Ser.) (Illus.). 94p. (J). (gr. 4-8). lib. bdg. 21.95 (978-0-89434-360-5(2) , F542, Ferguson Publishing Co.) Facts On File, Inc.

—Discovering Careers for Your Future/Computers. 2001. (Discovering Careers for Your Future Ser.). (Illus.). 96p. (J). (gr. 4-9). 21.95 (978-0-89434-389-6(0) , Ferguson Publishing Co.) Facts On File, Inc.

—Great Careers in 2 Years: The Associate Degree Option. J. G. Ferguson Publishing Company Staff, ed. 2nd ed. (Careers in Focus Ser.). 368p. (gr. 9). pap. 19.95 (978-0-89434-415-2(3) , Ferguson Publishing Co.) Facts On File, Inc.

J. G. Ferguson Publishing Company Staff, contrib. by. Career Discovery Encyclopedia. 2003. (J). (978-0-89434-475-6(7)); 5th ed. 2003. (Illus.). 1536p. (J). (gr. 4-9). 175.00 (978-0-8160-5469-5(X)); 6th rev. ed. 2006. (Illus.). 1616p. (YA). (gr. 4-9). 225.00 (978-0-8160-6696-4(5)) Facts On File, Inc. (Ferguson Publishing Co.).

—Careers in Focus: Alternative Health Care. 2nd ed. 2003. (Careers in Focus Ser.). (Illus.). 224p. (YA). (gr. 6-12). 22.95 (978-0-8160-5483-1(5) , Ferguson Publishing Co.) Facts On File, Inc.

—Careers in Focus: Child Care. 2006. (Careers in Focus Ser.). (Illus.). 176p. (J). (gr. 6-12). 29.95 (978-0-8160-6565-3(9) , Ferguson Publishing Co.) Facts On File, Inc.

—Careers in Focus: Earth Sciences. 2002. (Careers in Focus Ser.). (Illus.). 192p. (YA). (gr. 6-12). 22.95 (978-0-89434-409-1(9) , F724, Ferguson Publishing Co.) Facts On File, Inc.

—Careers in Focus: Fashion. 2nd ed. 2002. (Careers in Focus Ser.). 192p. (YA). (gr. 6-12). 22.95 (978-0-89434-434-3(X) , F707, Ferguson Publishing Co.) Facts On File, Inc.

—Careers in Focus: Internet. 2nd ed. 2002. (Careers in Focus Ser.). 192p. (YA). (gr. 6-12). 22.95 (978-0-89434-435-0(8) , F708, Ferguson Publishing Co.) Facts On File, Inc.

—Careers in Focus: Law. 2nd ed. 2003. (Careers in Focus Ser.). 192p. (YA). (gr. 6-12). 22.95 (978-0-89434-476-3(5) , Ferguson Publishing Co.) Facts On File, Inc.

—Careers in Focus: Performing Arts. 2nd ed. 2002. (Careers in Focus Ser.). (Illus.). 192p. (YA). (gr. 6-12). 22.95 (978-0-89434-431-2(5) , F615, Ferguson Publishing Co.) Facts On File, Inc.

—Careers in Focus: Transportation. 2nd ed. 2002. (Careers in Focus Ser.). 192p. (YA). (gr. 6-12). 22.95 (978-0-89434-438-1(2) , F510, Ferguson Publishing Co.) Facts On File, Inc.

—Careers in Focus: Writing. 2nd ed. 2002. (Careers in Focus Ser.). (Illus.). 192p. (YA). (gr. 6-12). 22.95 (978-0-89434-439-8(0) , F507, Ferguson Publishing Co.) Facts On File, Inc.

—Design. 2nd ed. 2005. (Careers in Focus Ser.). (Illus.). 192p. (YA). (gr. 6-12). 22.95 (978-0-8160-5865-5(2) , Ferguson Publishing Co.) Facts On File, Inc.

—Discovering Careers for Your Future/Government. 2002. (Discovering Careers for Your Future Ser.). (Illus.). 96p. (J). (gr. 4-9). 21.95 (978-0-89434-397-1(1) , Ferguson Publishing Co.) Facts On File, Inc.

—Discovering Careers in Your Future/Nature. 2002. (Discovering Careers for Your Future Ser.). (Illus.). 96p. (J). (gr. 4-9). 21.95 (978-0-89434-396-4(3) , Ferguson Publishing Co.) Facts On File, Inc.

—Discovering Careers in Your Future/Teaching. 2002. (Discovering Careers for Your Future Ser.). (Illus.). 96p. (J). (gr. 4-9). 21.95 (978-0-89434-398-8(X) , Ferguson Publishing Co.) Facts On File, Inc.

—Discovering Careers in Your Future/Transportation. 2002. (Discovering Careers for Your Future Ser.). (Illus.). 96p. (J). (gr. 4-9). 21.95 (978-0-89434-399-5(8) , Ferguson Publishing Co.) Facts On File, Inc.

—History. 2001. (Discovering Careers for Your Future Ser.). (Illus.). 96p. (J). (gr. 4-9). 21.95 (978-0-89434-391-9(2) , Ferguson Publishing Co.) Facts On File, Inc.

J. G. Ferguson Publishing Company Staff, ed. Careers in Focus: Engineering. (Careers in Focus Ser.). (YA). 1999. 488p. (gr. 7 up). pap. 22.95 (978-0-89434-282-0(7) , F702); 2nd ed. 2002. 192p. (gr. 6-12). 22.95 (978-0-89434-473-2(0)) Facts On File, Inc. (Ferguson Publishing Co.).

—Careers in Focus: Entrepreneurs. 1999. (Careers in Focus Ser.). (Illus.). 484p. (YA). (gr. 7 up). pap. 22.95 (978-0-89434-284-4(3) , F703, Ferguson Publishing Co.) Facts On File, Inc.

—Careers in Focus: Fashion. 2001. (Careers in Focus Ser.). 187p. (YA). (gr. 7 up). lib. bdg. (978-0-89434-329-2(7) , F707, Ferguson Publishing Co.) Facts On File, Inc.

—Careers in Focus: Internet. 2001. (Careers in Focus Ser.). 172p. (YA). (gr. 7 up). lib. bdg. (978-0-89434-330-8(0) , F708, Ferguson Publishing Co.) Facts On File, Inc.

—Careers in Focus: Medical Technicians. 3rd ed. 2001. (Careers in Focus Ser.). (Illus.). 176-192p. (YA). (gr. 7 up). lib. bdg. 22.95 (978-0-89434-408-4(0) , F616, Ferguson Publishing Co.) Facts On File, Inc.

—Careers in Focus: Transportation. 2000. (Careers in Focus Ser.). 176-192p. (YA). (gr. 7 up). lib. bdg. (978-0-89434-317-9(3) , F510, Ferguson Publishing Co.) Facts On File, Inc.

—Careers in Focus: Writing. 2000. (Careers in Focus Ser.). 188p. (J). (gr. 7 up). lib. bdg. (978-0-89434-318-6(1) , F507, Ferguson Publishing Co.) Facts On File, Inc.

—Exploring Health Care Careers, 2 vols., Set. 2nd ed. 2002. (Illus.). 984p. (gr. 9). 89.95 (978-0-89434-311-7(4) , Ferguson Publishing Co.) Facts On File, Inc.

J. G. Ferguson Publishing Company Staff & Pfiefer, Paul. Quick Prep Careers. 3rd ed. 304p. (gr. 9). pap. 18.95 (978-0-89434-383-4(1) , F138, Ferguson Publishing Co.) Facts On File, Inc.

Jacobs, Nancy R., et al, eds. Careers & Occupations: Looking to the Future. 1998. (Information Plus Reference Ser.). (Illus.). 172p. (YA). pap. 32.00 (978-1-57302-079-4(6)) Thomson Gale.

JIST Publishing Staff. Dream Catchers: Developing Career & Educational Awareness. 3rd ed. 2003. 80p. (YA). pap. 5.95 (978-1-59357-002-6(3)) JIST Publishing.

JIST Works, Inc. Staff. Career Explorers: A Fun & Educational Board Game, 3. 1998. (J). 19.95 (978-1-57112-092-2(0)) JIST Publishing.

—Young Person's Occupational Outlook Handbook. 5th ed. 2004. (Illus.). 336p. pap. 19.95 (978-1-59357-125-2(9) , J1259, JIST Works) JIST Publishing.

Job-O 2000+ 2000. (Job-O Ser.). 16p. (J). pap. 4.20 (978-1-887481-24-3(9)) CFKR Career Materials, Inc.

Job-O Advanced. 2nd rev. l.t. ed. 2000. (Job-O Ser.). 16p. (YA). pap. 4.20 (978-1-887481-22-9(2)) CFKR Career Materials, Inc.

Job-O Enhanced. 2nd rev. ed. 2000. (Job-O Ser.). 16p. (J). pap. 4.20 (978-1-887481-18-2(4)) CFKR Career Materials, Inc.

Job-O Enhanced Answer Folder. 2nd rev. ed. 2002. (Job-O Ser.). (YA). pap. (978-1-887481-19-9(2)) CFKR Career Materials, Inc.

Jones, Sarah. Film. 2003. (Media Wise Ser.). (Illus.). 64p. (J). lib. bdg. 28.50 (978-1-58340-256-6(X)) Smart Apple Media.

Kahn, Jetty. Women in Computer Science Careers. 1999. (Short Biographies Ser.). (Illus.). 48p. (J). (gr. 3-4). lib. bdg. 22.60 (978-0-7368-0316-8(5) , Bridgestone Bks.) Capstone Pr., Inc.

—Women in Computer Science Careers. 1999. (Illus.). 48p. (J). (gr. 3-7). pap. 19.93 (978-0-516-21883-0(2) , Children's Pr.) Scholastic Library Publishing.

Kauk, Robert. Looking at Myself, Form II. 1999. (Illus.). 16p. (YA). (gr. 7). pap. 4.20 (978-0-934783-56-9(X)) CFKR Career Materials, Inc.

Kimbrell, Grady & Vineyard, Ben S. Entering the World of Work. 3rd ed. 1999. (Illus.). (YA). (gr. 6-12). 384p. stu. ed. 30.67 (978-0-02-676730-9(9)); stu. ed., wbk. ed. 8.23 (978-0-02-676740-8(6)) Glencoe/McGraw-Hill.

—Succeeding in the World of Work. 6th ed. 1999. (Illus.). (YA). (gr. 6-12). stu. ed., wbk. ed. 7.99 (978-0-02-814222-7(5)) Glencoe/McGraw-Hill.

—Succeeding in the World of Work: School-to-Work Activity Handbook. 6th ed. 1999. (YA). (gr. 6-12). stu. ed. 6.26 (978-0-02-814225-8(X)) Glencoe/McGraw-Hill.

Knight, Bertram T. Working at a Zoo. 1998. (Working Here Ser.). (Illus.). 32p. (J). (gr. 2-4). 23.50 (978-0-516-20751-3(2) , Children's Pr.) Scholastic Library Publishing.

Lambie, Brian, ed. Creative Job Search. 2002. spiral bd. 15.95 (978-0-9670505-4-6(5)) Minnesota Dept. Employment & Economic Development.

Lansky, Bruce. When I Grow Up: Cool Jobs I Might Want to Have. Blough, Tim, illus. 2002. 12p. 9.95 (978-0-7432-2855-8(3)) Meadowbrook Pr.

Lehn, Barbara. What Is A Scientist? 1999. 3. (Illus.). 32p. (J). (gr. k-3). pap. 7.95 (978-0-7613-1298-7(6) , Millbrook Pr.) Lerner Publishing Group.

—What Is A Scientist? Krauss, Carol, photos by. 1998. (What Is...? Ser.). (Illus.). 32p. (gr. k-3). lib. bdg. 21.90 (978-0-7613-1272-7(2) , Millbrook Pr.) Lerner Publishing Group.

Libal, Joyce. Military & Elite Forces Officer. 2003. (Careers with Character Ser.). (Illus.). 96p. (YA). (gr. 7 up). lib. bdg. 22.95 (978-1-59084-318-5(5)) Mason Crest Pubs.

Liebman, Dan. Quiero ser Vaquero. 2003. (Quiero Ser.). (Illus.). 24p. (J). (ps-2). pap. 5.99 (978-1-55297-747-7(1)) Firefly Bks., Ltd.

Liebman, Daniel. Quiero Ser Guardian de Zoologico. 2003. (Quiero Ser.). (SPA.). 24p. (J). (ps-2). pap. 5.99 (978-1-55297-730-9(7)) Firefly Bks., Ltd.

Linn, Dennis, et al. What Is My Song? Miranda, Francisco, illus. 2005. 32p. 16.95 (978-0-8091-6722-7(0) , 6722-0) Paulist Pr.

Little, Robert. What Can I Be? Fitzpatrick, Audrey, illus. 2002. 32p. (J). (gr. 4-6). 15.95 (978-0-9701863-3-1(9)) Relde Publishing.

MacGregor, Lucy. Choosing a Career as an Entrepreneur. 2005. (World of Work Ser.). (Illus.). 64p. (J). (gr. 7-12). lib. bdg. 25.25 (978-0-8239-3329-7(6)) Rosen Publishing Group, Inc., The.

Mack, John P. Priests: An Inside Look. 2003. (Illus.). 72p. (J). pap. 6.95 (978-0-88489-720-0(6)) St. Mary's Pr.

MacKall, Dandi Daley. Problem Solving. 2nd ed. 2004. (Career Skills Library). (Illus.). 144p. (YA). (gr. 6-12). 21.95 (978-0-8160-5522-7(X) , Ferguson Publishing Co.) Facts On File, Inc.

Mackall, Joe. Research & Information Management. 2nd ed. 2004. (Career Skills Library). (Illus.). 128p. (YA). (gr. 6-12). 21.95 (978-0-8160-5518-0(1) , Ferguson Publishing Co.) Facts On File, Inc.

Mandel-Maczko, Linda. Hanging Out with Thermoforming: A Puffee - Stretch Adventure. 1998. (Illus.). 48p. (J). (gr. 1-6). pap. 9.95 (978-0-9639432-4-8(3)) Cardinal Enterprises of Florida.

Manley, Claudia B. Secret Agents: Life as a Professional Spy. 2005. (Extreme Careers Ser.). (Illus.). 64p. (YA). (gr. 5-8). 26.50 (978-0-8239-3369-3(5)) Rosen Publishing Group, Inc., The.

Marcom Group Ltd, prod. Moving on up Win Labpak. (YA). cd-rom 222.50 (978-0-7365-4359-0(7)) Films Media Group.

Marcovitz, Hal. Teens & Career Choices. 2005. (Gallup Youth Survey, Major Issues & Trends Ser.). (Illus.). 112p. (YA). (gr. 7-17). lib. bdg. 22.95 (978-1-59084-870-8(5)) Mason Crest Pubs.

Marsh, Carole. Heroes & Helpers Careers Book. 2003. 48p. (J). (gr. 2-8). pap. 9.95 (978-0-635-01095-7(X)) Gallopade International.

Maupin, Melissa. Computer Engineer. 2000. (Career Exploration Ser.). (Illus.). 48p. (J). (gr. 3-4). lib. bdg. 21.26 (978-0-7368-0591-9(5) , LifeMatters Bks.) Capstone Pr., Inc.

—Landscape Contractor. 2000. (Career Exploration Ser.) (Illus.). 48p. (J). (gr. 3-4). lib. bdg. 21.26 (978-0-7368-0490-5(0) , LifeMatters Bks.) Capstone Pr., Inc.

Maybury, Richard J. Uncle Eric Talks about Personal, Career, & Financial Security. Williams, Jane A. & Daniels, Kathryn, eds. 2nd ed. 2004. ("Uncle Eric" Bk.). (Illus.). 187p. (YA). pap. 14.95 (978-0-942617-38-2(X)) Bluestocking Pr.

Maynard, Thane. Working with Wildlife: A Guide to Careers in the Animal World. 2000. (Single Title Science Pb Ser.). (Illus.). 144p. (YA). (gr. 8-12). pap. 12.95 (978-0-531-16415-0(2) , Watts, Franklin) Scholastic Library Publishing.

—Working with Wildlife: A Guide to Careers in the Animal World. 2000. (J). (978-0-606-19406-8(1)) Tandem Library Bks.

Maze, Stephanie. I Want to Be a Chef. 1999. (I Want to Be Ser.). (Illus.). 48p. (YA). (gr. 2-7). pap. 10.00 (978-0-15-201936-5(7)) Harcourt Children's Bks.

—I Want to Be a Fashion Designer. Maze, Stephanie, photos by. 2000. (I Want to Be Ser.). (Illus.). 48p. (J). (gr. 3-7). pap. 10.00 (978-0-15-201938-9(3)) Harcourt Children's Bks.

—I Want to Be a Fashion Designer. 2000. (I Want to Be Ser.). (Illus.). 48p. (YA). (gr. 4-9). lib. bdg. 27.12 (978-0-7398-1970-8(4)) Raintree.

—I Want to Be a Fashion Designer. (I Want to Be Ser.). 2000. (Illus.). (J). (978-0-606-18177-8(6)); 1999. (gr. 3-6). lib. bdg. 17.65 (978-0-613-25642-1(5)) Tandem Library Bks.

—I Want to Be a Firefighter. 2000. (I Want to Be Ser.). (Illus.). 48p. (YA). (gr. 4-9). lib. bdg. 18.98 (978-0-7398-1365-2(X)) Raintree.

—I Want to Be an Environmentalist. 2000. (I Want to Be Ser.). (Illus.). 48p. (YA). (gr. 4-9). lib. bdg. 27.12 (978-0-7398-3071-0(6)) Raintree.

—I Want to Be an Environmentalist. 2000. 15.80 (978-0-606-20327-2(3)); (gr. 3-6). lib. bdg. 17.65 (978-0-613-30505-1(1)) Tandem Library Bks.

Mazor, Barry. Multimedia & New Media Developer. 2000. (CoolCareers.com Ser.). (Illus.). 48p. (YA). (gr. 5-8). lib. bdg. 23.95 (978-0-8239-3102-6(1) , CCMEDE, Rosen Central) Rosen Publishing Group, Inc., The.

McAlpine, Margaret. Working with Children. 2004. (My Future Career Ser.). (Illus.). 64p. lib. bdg. 26.00 (978-0-8368-4241-8(3)) Stevens, Gareth Inc.

McGinty, Alice B. Software Designer. (CoolCareers.com Ser.). 48p. (YA). 2004. lib. bdg. 23.95 (978-0-8239-4086-8(1)); 2000. (Illus.). (gr. 5-8). lib. bdg. 23.95 (978-0-8239-3149-1(8) , CCSODE, Rosen Central) Rosen Publishing Group, Inc., The.

McGraw-Hill Staff. Entering the World of Work. 4th ed. 2006. stu. ed. 61.28 (978-0-07-861458-3(9) , 9780078614583) Glencoe/McGraw-Hill.

Mellin, Joe. Starting Young: Getting a Jump on Getting Ahead in Business. Mellin, Bob, ed. Weston, Martha, illus. Mellin, Bob, photos by. 1999. 112p. (J). (gr. 4-12). pap. 12.00 (978-0-935902-33-4(3)) Balboa Publishing Corp.

Menard, Valerie. Careers in Sports. 2001. (Latinos at Work Ser.). (Illus.). 96p. (gr. 5-12). lib. bdg. 32.75 (978-1-58415-086-2(6)) Mitchell Lane Pubs., Inc.

Messina, Noreen E. TeenWork: Four Teens Tell All: A Guide for Finding Jobs. 2006. (Illus.). 126p. (gr. 6-12). pap. 12.75 (978-1-59070-598-8(X)) Goodheart-Willcox Pub.

Meyer, Jone, ed. Vocational Biographies, 7. 2001. (YA). lib. bdg. 265.00 (978-0-87063-807-7(6) , E-01) Vocational Biographies.

—Vocational Biographies - Series D-00: 175 Titles, 7 vols., Set. 2000. (Illus.). (YA). spiral bd. 265.00 (978-0-87063-780-3(0) , D-00) Vocational Biographies.

—Vocational Biographies Comprehensive Career Library. 2000. (YA). lib. bdg. 1255.00 (978-0-87063-822-0(X) , C.L.-2-a-b-c-d) Vocational Biographies.

—Vocational Biographies Economy Career Library. 2000. (YA). spiral bd. 995.00 (978-0-87063-824-4(6) , E.L.-a-b-c-d) Vocational Biographies.

Miller, Heather. Esto Es lo Que Quiero Ser, 10 vols., Set 1. 2003. Tr. of This Is What I Want to Be. (SPA., Illus.). (J). (ps-1). lib. bdg. 185.00 (978-1-4034-0384-1(8)) Heinemann Library.

Morem, Susan. How to Get a Job & Keep It. 2002. 292p. (gr. 9). pap. 16.95 (978-0-89434-351-3(3) , Ferguson Publishing Co.) Facts On File, Inc.

Nagle, Jeanne M. Careers in Coaching. 2005. (Careers). (Illus.). 192p. (YA). (gr. 7-12). lib. bdg. 26.50 (978-0-8239-2966-5(3) , CACOAC) Rosen Publishing Group, Inc., The.

—Careers in Television. 2005. (Careers Ser.). (Illus.). 192p. (J). (gr. 7-12). lib. bdg. 26.50 (978-0-8239-3187-3(0)) Rosen Publishing Group, Inc., The.

—Choosing a Career as a Coach. 2005. (World of Work Ser.). (Illus.). 64p. (YA). (gr. 7-12). lib. bdg. 25.25 (978-0-8239-3285-6(0)) Rosen Publishing Group, Inc., The.

Naylor, Sharon. Learning the Ropes. 2nd ed. 2004. (Career Skills Library). (Illus.). 128p. (YA). (gr. 6-12). 21.95 (978-0-8160-5520-3(3) , Ferguson Publishing Co.) Facts On File, Inc.

Neale, Vivienne. Keep Your Options Open. (Illus.). x, 134p. (J). pap. 8.99 (978-0-340-66088-1(0) , Hodder & Stoughton) Hodder General Publishing Division GBR. *Dist:* Trafalgar Square Publishing.

Nelson, Cordner. Careers in Pro Sports. rev. ed. 1999. (Careers). (Illus.). 192p. (YA). (gr. 7-12). lib. bdg. 26.50 (978-0-8239-2896-5(9) , CAPRSP) Rosen Publishing Group, Inc., The.

Occupational Outlook Handbook 2004-2005. 2003. (gr. 7-12). lib. bdg. 29.20 (978-0-613-67572-7(X)) Tandem Library Bks.

O'Donnell, Annie. Computer Animator. 2000. (CoolCareers.com Ser.). (Illus.). 48p. (YA). (gr. 5-8). lib. bdg. 23.95 (978-0-8239-3101-9(3) , CCCOAN, Rosen Central) Rosen Publishing Group, Inc., The.

O'Donnell, Kerri. Careers in Modeling. 2005. (Career Resource Library). (Illus.). 192p. (YA). (gr. 7-12). lib. bdg. 26.50 (978-0-8239-3183-5(8)) Rosen Publishing Group, Inc., The.

Olesky, Walter. Choosing a Career in Agriculture. 2005. (World of Work Ser.). (Illus.). 64p. (YA). (gr. 7-12). lib. bdg. 25.25 (978-0-8239-3332-7(6)) Rosen Publishing Group, Inc., The.

On-the-Job Skills. 1999. (Overcoming Obstacles). 34p. (YA). (gr. 9-12). pap. 9.38 (978-1-929393-25-1(3)) Community for Education Foundation.

On Your Own. 1999. (Overcoming Obstacles). 28p. (YA). (gr. 9-12). pap. 9.38 (978-1-929393-26-8(1)) Community for Education Foundation.

O'Neill, Lucy. Job Smarts. 2002. (Smarts Ser.). (Illus.). 48p. (YA). (gr. 7-12). pap. 23.00 (978-0-516-23928-6(7) , Children's Pr.) Scholastic Library Publishing.

—Job Smarts. 2002. (gr. 7-12). lib. bdg. 15.25 (978-0-613-58703-7(0)) Tandem Library Bks.

Overcamp, David. Electrician. 2004. (Great Jobs Ser.). (Illus.). 48p. (J). 24.00 (978-0-516-24086-2(2)); (gr. 7-12). pap. 6.95 (978-0-516-25924-6(5)) Scholastic Library Publishing. (Children's Pr.).

Parks, Peggy J. Computer Programming. 2003. (Exploring Careers Ser.). (Illus.). 48p. (J). (gr. 3-5). 26.20 (978-0-7377-1483-8(2) , Kidhaven) Thomson Gale.

—Music. 2002. (Careers for the Twenty-First Century Ser.). (Illus.). 112p. (J). 27.45 (978-1-59018-223-9(5) , Lucent Bks.) Thomson Gale.

—Veterinarian. 2004. (J). 26.20 (978-0-7377-2068-6(9) , Greenhaven Pr., Inc.) Thomson Gale.

—Writer. 2003. (Illus.). 48p. (J). 26.20 (978-0-7377-2069-3(7) , Greenhaven Pr., Inc.) Thomson Gale.

Pasternak, Ceel. Cool Careers for Girls in Performing Arts. 2000. (gr. 7-12). lib. bdg. 22.20 (978-0-613-79028-4(6)) Tandem Library Bks.

—Cool Careers for Girls in Sports. (Cool Careers for Girls Ser.). 1999. 135p. pap. 12.95 (978-1-57023-104-9(4)); 1998. (J). 19.95 (978-1-57023-107-0(9)) Impact Pubns.

—Cool Careers for Girls in Travel & Hospitality. 2003. (Illus.). 144p. pap. 13.95 (978-1-57023-192-6(3)) Impact Pubns.

Pasternak, Ceel & Thornburg, Linda. Cool Careers for Girls in Computers. 1999. (Cool Careers for Girls Ser.). (Illus.). (gr. 5). 125p. pap. 12.95 (978-1-57023-103-2(6)); 124p. (YA). 19.95 (978-1-57023-106-3(0)) Impact Pubns.

—Cool Careers for Girls in Construction. 2000. (Illus.). 116p. (YA). (gr. 7 up). 19.95 (978-1-57023-135-3(4)) Impact Pubns.

—Cool Careers for Girls in Engineering. 1999. (Cool Careers for Girls Ser.). (Illus.). 134p. (YA). (gr. 5-8). 19.95 (978-1-57023-126-1(5)) Impact Pubns.

—Cool Careers for Girls in Food. 1999. (Illus.). 118p. (J). (gr. 5 up). 19.95 (978-1-57023-127-8(3)) Impact Pubns.

—Cool Careers for Girls in Health. 1999. (Illus.). 148p. (YA). 19.95 (978-1-57023-125-4(7)) Impact Pubns.

—Cool Careers for Girls in Performing Arts. 2000. (Illus.). viii, 171p. (J). 19.95 (978-1-57023-136-0(2)) Impact Pubns.

—Cool Careers for Girls with Animals. 1999. (Cool Careers for Girls Ser.). 145p. pap. 12.95 (978-1-57023-105-6(2)) Impact Pubns.

—Food. 1999. (Cool Careers for Girls Ser.). (Illus.). 125p. (gr. 4-7). pap. 12.95 (978-1-57023-120-9(6)) Impact Pubns.

—Health. 1999. (Cool Careers for Girls Ser.). (Illus.). 125p. (gr. 4-7). pap. 12.95 (978-1-57023-118-6(4)) Impact Pubns.

Patrice Cassedy. Computer Technology. 2004. (Careers for the Twenty-First Century Ser.). (Illus.). 112p. (J). 29.95 (978-1-56006-896-9(5)) Thomson Gale.

Pervola, Cindy & Hobgood, Debby. How to Get a Job If You're a Teenager. 2nd rev. ed. 2000. 68p. (YA). (gr. 6-13). pap. 14.95 (978-1-57950-059-7(5) , Upstart Bks.) Highsmith Inc.

Petley, Julian. Newspapers & Magazines. 2003. (Media Wise Ser.). (Illus.). 64p. (J). lib. bdg. 28.50 (978-1-58340-258-0(6)) Smart Apple Media.

Plum, Jennifer. Careers in the Police Department's Search & Rescue Unit. 2005. (Careers in Search & Rescue Operations Ser.). (Illus.). 64p. (YA). (gr. 5-8). lib. bdg. 26.50 (978-0-8239-3834-6(4)) Rosen Publishing Group, Inc., The.

Price, Sharon M. Tuning Into My Future: A Career Exploration & Education Planning Program. 2nd rev. ed. 2002. 72p. (Orig.). (YA). (gr. 7-11). pap. 19.95 incl. audio compact disk (978-0-9660694-8-8(X)) PrepWorks Publishing.

Primm, E. Russell. Emergency Medical Technician. 1998. (Careers Without College Ser.). (Illus.). 48p. (J). (gr. 3-7). pap. 19.00 (978-0-516-21281-4(8) , Children's Pr.) Scholastic Library Publishing.

Primm, Russ, ed. Career Exploration Through Children's Literature, Grades 6-8. 1999. (Illus.). 256p. (J). pap. (978-0-89434-286-8(X) , F115, Ferguson Publishing Co.) Facts On File, Inc.

Quinlan, Kathryn A. Child Care Worker. (Careers Without College Ser.). 48p. pap. 6.95 (978-0-7368-8541-6(2)); 1998. (Illus.). (J). (gr. 3-4). lib. bdg. 21.26 (978-0-7368-0032-7(8)) Capstone Pr., Inc. (LifeMatters Bks.).

—Customer Service Representative. 1999. (Careers Without College Ser.). (Illus.). 48p. (J). (gr. 3-4). lib. bdg. 21.26 (978-0-7368-0174-4(X) , LifeMatters Bks.) Capstone Pr., Inc.

—Food Service Manager. (Careers Without College Ser.). pap. 6.95 (978-0-7368-8544-7(7) , LifeMatters Bks.) Capstone Pr., Inc.

—Nurse Assistant. 1998. (Careers Without College Ser.). (Illus.). 48p. (J). (gr. 3-4). lib. bdg. 21.26 (978-0-7368-0036-5(0) , LifeMatters Bks.) Capstone Pr., Inc.

Rae, Tara A. Universe on the Move: Be All You Can Be Without Joining the Army. Guire, Cindy, ed. 1999. (More Universe on the Move Ser.). 180p. (YA). per. 15.95 (978-0-9671872-0-4(6)) Angel Heart Publishing.

Raintree IL Staff. Raintree Professional Development Program. 2003. 999.00 (978-1-4109-0478-2(4)) Raintree.

Ramaprian, Sheela. The FBI. 2003. (High-Top Secret Ser.). (Illus.). 48p. (J). 23.00 (978-0-516-24312-2(8)); (YA). (gr. 7-12). pap. 6.95 (978-0-516-24375-7(6)) Scholastic Library Publishing. (Children's Pr.).

Ready, Dee. Bomberos y Bomberas. Schon, Isabel, ed. Ferrer, Martín Luis Guzman, tr. 1998. (Servidores Comunitarios Ser.). (SPA., Illus.). 24p. (J). (gr. 2-4). lib. bdg. 18.60 (978-1-56065-797-2(9) , Bridgestone Bks.) Capstone Pr., Inc.

Reeves, Diane Lindsey. Career Ideas for Kids Who Like Adventure & Travel. 2nd rev. ed. (Career Ideas for Kids Ser.). (gr. 4-9). 2008. 64p. pap. 9.95 ***(978-0-8160-6548-6(9));*** 2007. 208p. 32.95 ***(978-0-8160-6547-9(0))*** Facts On File, Inc. (Checkmark Bks.).

—Career Ideas for Kids Who Like Animals & Nature. 2nd rev. ed. (Career Ideas for Kids Ser.). 208p. (J). (gr. 4-9). pap. 16.95 ***(978-0-8160-6540-0(3)*** , Checkmark Bks.); 2007. 32.95 ***(978-0-8160-6539-4(X)*** , Ferguson Publishing Co.) Facts On File, Inc.

—Career Ideas for Kids Who Like Computers. 2nd rev. ed. (Career Ideas for Kids Ser.). 208p. (J). (gr. 4-9). pap. 16.95 ***(978-0-8160-6544-8(6)*** , Checkmark Bks.); 2007. 32.95 ***(978-0-8160-6543-1(8)*** , Ferguson Publishing Co.) Facts On File, Inc.

—Career Ideas for Kids Who Like Math & Money. 2nd rev. ed. (Career Ideas for Kids Ser.). 208p. (J). (gr. 4-9). pap. 16.95 ***(978-0-8160-6546-2(2)*** , Checkmark Bks.); 2007. 32.95 ***(978-0-8160-6545-5(4)*** , Ferguson Publishing Co.) Facts On File, Inc.

—Career Ideas for Kids Who Like Sports. 2nd rev. ed. (Career Ideas for Kids Ser.). (J). (gr. 4-9). 2008. 408p. pap. 18.95 ***(978-0-8160-6552-3(7));*** 2007. 208p. 32.95 ***(978-0-8160-6551-6(9))*** Facts On File, Inc. (Checkmark Bks.).

—Career Ideas for Kids Who Like Talking. (Career Ideas for Kids Ser.). 1998. (Illus.). 176p. (YA). (gr. 5-9). pap. 12.95 (978-0-8160-3689-9(6)); 2nd rev. ed. 2008. 304p. (J). (gr. 4-9). pap. 18.95 ***(978-0-8160-6554-7(3)*** , Checkmark Bks.); 2nd rev. ed. 2007. 192p. (J). (gr. 4-9). 32.95 ***(978-0-8160-6553-0(5)*** , Checkmark Bks.) Facts On File, Inc.

—Career Ideas for Kids Who Like Talking. 1998. (gr. 5-8). lib. bdg. 22.20 (978-0-613-76190-1(1)) Tandem Library Bks.

—Career Ideas for Kids Who Like Travel. 2001. (gr. 3-6). lib. bdg. 22.20 (978-0-613-76202-1(9)) Tandem Library Bks.

Reeves, Diane Lindsey. Career Ideas for Kids Who Like Writing. 2nd rev. ed. (Career Ideas for Kids Ser.). 200p. (J). (gr. 4-9). pap. 16.95 ***(978-0-8160-6556-1(X)*** , Checkmark Bks.); 2007. 32.95 ***(978-0-8160-6555-4(1)*** , Ferguson Publishing Co.) Facts On File, Inc.

Reeves, Diane Lindsey, ed. Career Ideas for Kids Who Like Writing. Bond, Nancy, illus. 1998. (Career Ideas for Kids Ser.). 166p. (J). (gr. 4-8). pap. 12.95 (978-0-8160-3691-2(8)) Facts On File, Inc.

Reeves, Diane Lindsey & Bryan, Gayle. Career Ideas for Kids Who Like Money. Bond, Nancy, illus. 2001. (Career Ideas for Kids Ser.). (J). (gr. 4-8). 144p. pap. 12.95 (978-0-8160-4320-0(5)); 192p. 23.00 (978-0-8160-4319-4(1)) Facts On File, Inc. (Checkmark Bks.).

—Career Ideas for Kids Who Like Travel. Bond, Nancy, illus. 2001. (Career Ideas for Kids Ser.). (J). 144p. pap. 12.95 (978-0-8160-4326-2(4)); 192p. (gr. 4-9). 23.00 (978-0-8160-4325-5(6)) Facts On File, Inc.

Reeves, Diane Lindsey & Heubeck, Nancy. Career Ideas for Kids Who Like Adventure. Bond, Nancy, illus. 2001. (Career Ideas for Kids Ser.). 170p. (J). (gr. 4-8). pap. 12.95 (978-0-8160-4322-4(1) , Checkmark Bks.) Facts On File, Inc.

—Career Ideas for Kids Who Like Animals & Nature. Bond, Nancy, illus. 2000. (Career Ideas for Kids Ser.). 183p. (J). (gr. 4-8). 23.00 (978-0-8160-4097-1(4) , Checkmark Bks.) Facts On File, Inc.

—Career Ideas for Kids Who Like Math. Bond, Nancy, illus. 2000. (Career Ideas for Kids Ser.). (J). (gr. 4-7). 186p. pap. 12.95 (978-0-8160-4096-4(6)); 192p. 23.00 (978-0-8160-4095-7(8)) Facts On File, Inc.

Reeves, Diane Lindsey & Kent, Peter. Career Ideas for Kids Who Like Sports. 1998. (Career Ideas for Kids Ser.). (Illus.). 176p. (J). (gr. 4-8). pap. 12.95 (978-0-8160-3690-5(X)) Facts On File, Inc.

Richer, William. What Do You Wanna-Bee? An Encyclopedia Activity Coloring Book of Professional Busy Bee's. 2nd ed. 2000. Orig. Title: To Be or not to Be, What Do You Wanna-Be?. (Illus.). 68p. (J). (gr. 1). pap. 6.95 (978-0-9703609-0-8(8)) I Wanna Bee.

Riggs, Ernestine G. & Gholar, Cheryl, contrib. by. Careers with Character, 18 vols., Set. 2002. (Careers with Character Ser.). (Illus.). 96p. (J). (gr. 7 up). (978-1-59084-327-7(4)) Mason Crest Pubs.

—Psychologist. 2003. (Careers with Character Ser.). (Illus.). 96p. (YA). (gr. 7 up). lib. bdg. 22.95 (978-1-59084-322-2(3)) Mason Crest Pubs.

Roberts, Robin. Careers for Women Who Love Sports. 2000. (Illus.). (J). (978-0-606-18281-2(0)) Tandem Library Bks.

Roff, Jason T. & Roff, Kimberly A. Careers in E-Commerce Software Development. 2005. (Library of E-Commerce & Internet Careers). (Illus.). 64p. (YA). (gr. 7-12). lib. bdg. 26.50 (978-0-8239-3421-8(7)) Rosen Publishing Group, Inc., The.

Rosinsky, Natalie M. Earning Money. 2003. (Let's See Library). (Illus.). 24p. (J). (gr. 1 up). 19.93 (978-0-7565-0483-0(X)) Compass Point Bks.

Ross, Allison J. Choosing a Career in Desktop Publishing. 2005. (World of Work Ser.). (Illus.). 64p. (J). (gr. 7-12). lib. bdg. 25.25 (978-0-8239-3295-5(8) , WWDEPU) Rosen Publishing Group, Inc., The.

Ross, Allison J. & Harrison, Scott. Choosing a Career in Carpentry. 2005. (World of Work Ser.). (Illus.). 64p. (YA). (gr. 7-12). lib. bdg. 25.25 (978-0-8239-3294-8(X)) Rosen Publishing Group, Inc., The.

Rossiter, Diane E. Leadership Skills. 2nd ed. 2004. (Career Skills Library). (Illus.). 128p. (YA). (gr. 6-12). 21.95 (978-0-8160-5519-7(X) , Ferguson Publishing Co.) Facts On File, Inc.

Roza, Greg. Careers in the Coast Guard's Search & Rescue Unit. 2005. (Careers in Search & Rescue Operations Ser.). (Illus.). 64p. (YA). (gr. 5-8). lib. bdg. 26.50 (978-0-8239-3835-3(2)) Rosen Publishing Group, Inc., The.

—Careers in the Military. 2005. (World of Work Ser.). (Illus.). 64p. (YA). (gr. 7-12). lib. bdg. 25.25 (978-0-8239-3331-0(8)) Rosen Publishing Group, Inc., The.

Ryan, Jerry & Ryan, Roberta. Preparing for Career Success ExamView' Test Generator. 3rd ed. 2005. (YA). cd-rom 119.95 (978-1-59357-211-2(5) , J2115, JIST Works) JIST Publishing.

—Preparing for Career Success Student Activity Book. 3rd ed. 2005. 208p. (YA). pap. 8.95 (978-1-59357-209-9(3) , J2093, JIST Works) JIST Publishing.

Sanna, Ellyn. Career Assessments & Their Meanings. 2002. (Careers with Character Ser.). (Illus.). 96p. (YA). (gr. 7 up). lib. bdg. 22.95 (978-1-59084-309-3(6)) Mason Crest Pubs.

—Childcare Worker. 2002. (Careers with Character Ser.). (Illus.). 96p. (YA). (gr. 7 up). lib. bdg. 22.95 (978-1-59084-310-9(X)) Mason Crest Pubs.

—Homeland Security Officer. 2002. (Careers with Character Ser.). (Illus.). 96p. (YA). (gr. 7 up). lib. bdg. 22.95 (978-1-59084-315-4(0)) Mason Crest Pubs.

—Politician. 2003. (Careers with Character Ser.). (Illus.). 96p. (YA). (gr. 7 up). lib. bdg. 22.95 (978-1-59084-320-8(7)) Mason Crest Pubs.

Schaefer, A. R. Booking a First Gig. 2003. (Rock Music Library). (Illus.). 32p. (J). lib. bdg. 22.60 (978-0-7368-2144-5(9) , Capstone High/Low Bks.) Capstone Pr., Inc.

—Forming a Band. 2003. (Rock Music Library). (Illus.). 32p. (J). lib. bdg. 22.60 (978-0-7368-2146-9(5) , Capstone High/Low Bks.) Capstone Pr., Inc.

Schauer, Donald D. Careers in Trucking. rev. ed. (Career Resource Library). (Illus.). (YA). (gr. 7-12). 2005. 192p. lib. bdg. 26.50 (978-0-8239-3755-4(0)); 2000. lib. bdg. 18.95 (978-0-8239-3189-7(7) , CATRUC) Rosen Publishing Group, Inc., The.

Schomp, Virginia. If You Were A... - Group 3, 4 bks., Set. Incl. If You Were a Farmer. lib. bdg. 22.79 (978-0-7614-1001-0(5)); If You Were a Musician. lib. bdg. 22.79 (978-0-7614-1002-7(3)); If You Were a Truck Driver. lib. bdg. 22.79 (978-0-7614-1003-4(1)); 32p. (J). (gr. 2-4). (Illus.). 2000. Set lib. bdg. 91.14 (978-0-7614-1004-1(X) , Benchmark Bks.) Cavendish, Marshall Corp.

Schwager, Tina & Schuerger, Michele. Cool Women, Hot Jobs... And How You Can Go for It, Too! 2004. (Illus.). 288p. (YA). (gr. 6 up). pap. 11.95 (978-1-57542-109-4(7)) Free Spirit Publishing, Inc.

Schwartz, Linda & Wolfgang, Toni. Children's Occupational Outlook Handbook. Barrows, Laurie, photos by. 2nd ed. 1998. (Illus.). 240p. (J). pap. 18.95 (978-1-887481-09-0(5)) CFKR Career Materials, Inc.

Schwartz, Stuart B. Finding Work. 1998. (Looking at Work Ser.). 32p. (J). lib. bdg. 19.00 (978-0-516-21300-2(8) , Children's Pr.) Scholastic Library Publishing.

—Interviewing for a Job. 1998. (Looking at Work Ser.). (Illus.). 32p. (J). (gr. 7-12). lib. bdg. 19.00 (978-0-516-21301-9(6) , Children's Pr.) Scholastic Library Publishing.

Schwartz, Stuart B. & Conley, Craig. Being a Leader. (Job Skills Ser.). pap. 6.95 (978-0-7368-8517-1(X) , LifeMatters Bks.) Capstone Pr., Inc.

—Considering a Job Offer. (Looking at Work Ser.). pap. 6.95 (978-0-7368-8521-8(8)); 1999. (Illus.). 32p. (J). (gr. 3-4). lib. bdg. 21.26 (978-0-7368-0178-2(2)) Capstone Pr., Inc. (LifeMatters Bks.).

—Exploring Job Skills. (Looking at Work Ser.). 48p. pap. 6.95 (978-0-7368-8523-2(4) , LifeMatters Bks.) Capstone Pr., Inc.

—Finding Work. (Looking at Work Ser.). pap. 6.95 (978-0-7368-8023-7(2) , LifeMatters Bks.) Capstone Pr., Inc.

—Improving Work Habits. (Life Skills-Career Bks.). pap. 6.95 (978-0-7368-8027-5(5) , LifeMatters Bks.) Capstone Pr., Inc.

—Interviewing for Information. 1999. (Looking at Work Ser.). (Illus.). 32p. (J). (gr. 3-4). lib. bdg. 21.26 (978-0-7368-0179-9(0) , LifeMatters Bks.) Capstone Pr., Inc.

Simon, Chaman. Dental Hygienist. (Careers Without College Ser.). pap. 6.95 (978-0-7368-8018-3(6) , LifeMatters Bks.) Capstone Pr., Inc.

—Home Health Aide. (Careers Without College Ser.). pap. 6.95 (978-0-7368-8546-1(3) , LifeMatters Bks.) Capstone Pr., Inc.

Simon, Charnan. Dental Hygienist. 1998. (Careers Without College Ser.). (Illus.). 48p. (J). (gr. 4-7). pap. 19.00 (978-0-516-21280-7(X) , Children's Pr.) Scholastic Library Publishing.

—Home Health Aide. 1998. (Careers Without College Ser.). (Illus.). 48p. (J). (gr. 3-7). pap. 19.00 (978-0-516-21283-8(4) , Children's Pr.) Scholastic Library Publishing.

Simons, Rae & Gommer, Viola Ruelke. Nurse. 2002. (Careers with Character Ser.). (Illus.). 96p. (YA). (gr. 7 up). (978-1-59084-319-2(3)) Mason Crest Pubs.

Simpson, Carolyn. Careers Inside the World of Offices. rev. ed. 1998. (Careers & Opportunities Ser.). (Illus.). 64p. (YA). (gr. 7-12). lib. bdg. 26.50 (978-0-8239-2737-1(7) , CIOFFI) Rosen Publishing Group, Inc., The.

Stair, Nancy. Choosing a Career in Mortuary Science & the Funeral Industry. 2005. (World of Work Ser.). (Illus.). 64p. (YA). (gr. 7-12). lib. bdg. 25.25 (978-0-8239-3568-0(X)) Rosen Publishing Group, Inc., The.

Steck-Vaughn Staff. Teen's Guide to Working. 2002. (Illus.). pap. 41.60 incl. audio compact disk (978-0-7398-6976-5(0)) Steck-Vaughn.

Strong, Sherry. Career Search. 1998. (Illus.). 80p. (YA). (gr. 5). pap. 10.95 (978-1-58037-033-2(0)) Twain, Mark Media, Inc. Pubs.

Students' Occupational Outlook Handbook: SOOH. 3rd rev. ed. 2000. (YA). pap. (978-1-887481-26-7(5) , SK00) CFKR Career Materials, Inc.

Success in the World of Work: Getting a Job. (Success in the World of Work Ser.). (YA). cd-rom 159.95 (978-1-56191-659-7(5)) Films Media Group.

Success in the World of Work: Succeeding on the Job. (Success in the World of Work Ser.). (YA). cd-rom 159.95 (978-1-56191-660-3(9)) Films Media Group.

Tate, Lori. Plan Your Future. Ogg, Jim et al, eds. Tate, Lori, illus. 2nd ed. 2000. (YA). (gr. 9-12). pap. (978-0-9678649-6-9(8)) Coole Schl.

Thompson, Valerie & Cohen, Judith Love. You Can Be a Woman Zoologist. Katz, David Arthur, illus. 2001. 40p. (J). 13.95 (978-1-880599-56-3(2)); pap. 7.00 (978-1-880599-55-6(4)) Cascade Pass, Inc.

Thornburg, Linda. Cool Careers for Girls As Crime Solvers. (Illus.). 2002. 144p. pap. 12.95 (978-1-57023-174-2(5)); 2001. 120p. (J). pap. 19.95 (978-1-57023-175-9(3)) Impact Pubns.

—Cool Careers for Girls as Crime Solvers. 2002. (gr. 5-8). lib. bdg. 22.20 (978-0-613-79031-4(6)) Tandem Library Bks.

Thornton, Craig. Career Diary of a TV Production Manager. 2005. (Gardner's Guide Ser.: No. 003). (Illus.). 178p. pap. 14.95 (978-1-58965-015-2(8)) Gardner, Garth Co., Inc. (GGC).

Tobey, Cheryl. Choosing a Career as a Model. 2005. (World of Work Ser.). (Illus.). 64p. (YA). (gr. 7-12). lib. bdg. 25.25 (978-0-8239-3243-6(5)) Rosen Publishing Group, Inc., The.

Trabajo en Grupo Series, 6 bks., Set. 2003. (Trabajo en Grupo Ser.). (SPA & ENG., Illus.). (J). lib. bdg. 103.50 (978-0-8239-6915-9(0) , Buenas Letra) Rosen Publishing Group, Inc., The.

Tuning in to My Future - Student Workbook. 1998. (Illus.). 40p. (J). (gr. 6-10). pap., stu. ed., wbk. ed. 6.95 (978-0-9660694-1-9(2)) PrepWorks Publishing.

Turner, Cherie. Stunt Performers: Life Before the Camera. 2005. (Extreme Careers Ser.). (Illus.). 64p. (YA). (gr. 5-8). 26.50 (978-0-8239-3371-6(7)) Rosen Publishing Group, Inc., The.

Underwood, Dessie & Cohen, Judith Love. You Can Be a Woman Entomologist. Katz, David Arthur, illus. 2002. 40p. (J). (gr. 4-6). lib. bdg. 13.95 (978-1-880599-60-0(0)); per. 7.00 (978-1-880599-59-4(7)) Cascade Pass, Inc.

Vernon, Naomi. A Teen's Guide to Finding a Job. Caldwell, Candice J., illus. 2000. xviii, 149p. (YA). (gr. 9 up). pap. 19.95 (978-0-9676383-9-3(9) , SAN:253-0481) New Bee-ginnings.

Vitale, Ann E. Manager. 2002. (Careers with Character Ser.). (Illus.). 96p. (J). (gr. 7 up). (978-1-59084-317-8(7)) Mason Crest Pubs.

Volz-Patton, Ruth & Kelly, Joan M. Exploring Careers. 3rd ed. 1999. (Illus.). (YA). (gr. 6-12). stu. ed., wbk. ed. (978-0-02-642589-6(0)) Glencoe/McGraw-Hill.

Volz-Patton, Ruth, et al. Exploring Careers. 3rd rev. ed. 2000. (Illus.). (C). (gr. 6-12). stu. ed. 60.64 (978-0-02-643183-5(1) , 9780026431835) Glencoe/McGraw-Hill.

Wallner, Rosemary. Computer Programmer. 2000. (Career Exploration Ser.). (Illus.). 48p. (J). (gr. 3-4). lib. bdg. 21.26 (978-0-7368-0488-2(9) , LifeMatters Bks.) Capstone Pr., Inc.

—Flight Attendant. 2000. (Career Exploration Ser.). (Illus.). 48p. (J). (gr. 3-4). lib. bdg. 21.26 (978-0-7368-0489-9(7) , LifeMatters Bks.) Capstone Pr., Inc.

—Human Services Worker. 2000. (Career Exploration Ser.). (Illus.). 48p. (J). (gr. 3-4). lib. bdg. 21.26 (978-0-7368-0596-4(6) , LifeMatters Bks.) Capstone Pr., Inc.

Webber, Diane. Shot & Framed: Photographers at the Crime Scene. 2007. (24/7 - Science Behind the Scenes Ser.). (Illus.). 64p. (J). (gr. 8-12). 25.00 (***978-0-531-12063-7(5)*** , Watts, Franklin) Scholastic Library Publishing.

Weintraub, Aileen. Choosing a Career in Child Care. 2005. (World of Work Ser.). (Illus.). 64p. (YA). (gr. 7-12). lib. bdg. 25.25 (978-0-8239-3241-2(9) , WWCHCA) Rosen Publishing Group, Inc., The.

Weiss, Ann. The Glass Ceiling: A Look at Women in the Workforce. 1999. (Single Titles Ser.: up). 128p. (gr. 7 up). lib. bdg. 23.90 (978-0-7613-1365-6(6) , Twenty-First Century Bks.) Lerner Publishing Group.

Weiss, Ellen. Odd Jobs: The Wackiest Jobs You've Never Heard Of. 2000. (978-0-606-17931-7(3)) Tandem Library Bks.

Wendt, Jennifer. Park Naturalist. 1999. (Illus.). (YA). (gr. 5-12). pap. 19.93 (978-0-516-21891-5(3) , Children's Pr.) Scholastic Library Publishing.

Wilkinson, Beth. Careers Inside the World of Health Care. rev. ed. 1999. (Careers & Opportunities Ser.). (Illus.). 64p. (YA). (gr. 7-12). lib. bdg. 26.50 (978-0-8239-2886-6(1) , CIHECA) Rosen Publishing Group, Inc., The.

Williams, Anna Graf, et al. The Family Guide to the American Workplace. Williams, Anna Graf, ed. 2003. (Illus.). 272p. per. 31.00 (978-0-9705790-4-1(7) , 866/332-5905) Learnovation, LLC.

Wilson, Wayne. Careers in Entertainment. 2001. (Latinos at Work Ser.). (Illus.). 96p. (gr. 5-12). lib. bdg. 32.75 (978-1-58415-083-1(1)) Mitchell Lane Pubs., Inc.

—Careers in Publishing & Communications. 2001. (Latinos at Work Ser.). (Illus.). 96p. (J). (gr. 5-12). lib. bdg. 22.95 (978-1-58415-088-6(2)) Mitchell Lane Pubs., Inc.

Winters, Adam. Choosing a Career in the Fishing Industry. 2005. (World of Work Ser.). (Illus.). 64p. (YA). (gr. 7-12). lib. bdg. 25.25 (978-0-8239-3330-3(X)) Rosen Publishing Group, Inc., The.

Wolff, James H. Work Exploration Checklist. rev. ed. 2000. (YA). (gr. 7 up). 24.95 (978-0-912486-86-4(4) , F-WEC) Finney Co., Inc.

Woods, Bob. Earning a Ride: How to Become a NASCAR Driver. 2003. (World of NASCAR Ser.). (Illus.). 32p. (J). (gr. 2-6). 25.64 (978-1-59187-028-9(3)) Child's World, Inc.

The World of Work. 2005. (Illus.). (gr. 7-12). lib. bdg. 682.20 (978-0-8239-3909-1(X)) Rosen Publishing Group, Inc., The.

World of Work: A Path to an Exciting Career, 8 bks. Incl. Choosing a Career as a Model. Tobey, Cheryl. (YA). lib. bdg. 25.25 (978-0-8239-3243-6(5)); Choosing a Career as a Nurse-Midwife. Fields, Jennifer. (YA). lib. bdg. 25.25 (978-0-8239-3293-1(1)); Choosing a Career as an Entrepreneur. MacGregor, Lucy. (J). lib. bdg. 25.25 (978-0-8239-3329-7(6)); Choosing a Career in Agriculture. Olesky, Walter. (YA). lib. bdg. 25.25 (978-0-8239-3332-7(6)); Choosing a Career in Real Estate. Clark, Betty. (YA). lib. bdg. 25.25 (978-0-8239-3246-7(X) , WWRESS); Choosing a Career in Teaching. Calhoun, Florence. (YA). lib. bdg. 25.25 (978-0-8239-3247-4(8)); Choosing a Career in the Fishing Industry. Winters, Adam. (YA). lib. bdg. 25.25 (978-0-8239-3330-3(X)); Choosing a Career in the Post Office. Chui, David. (YA). lib. bdg. 25.25 (978-0-8239-3242-9(7)); 64p. (gr. 7-12). 2005. (Illus.). 2001. Set lib. bdg. 191.60 (978-0-8239-9207-2(1)) Rosen Publishing Group, Inc., The.

The World of Work Set 1. 2005. (Illus.). (gr. 7-12). lib. bdg. 176.75 (978-0-8239-9727-5(8)) Rosen Publishing Group, Inc., The.

The World of Work Set 2. 2005. (Illus.). (gr. 7-12). lib. bdg. 202.00 (978-0-8239-9444-1(9)) Rosen Publishing Group, Inc., The.

The World of Work Set 3. 2005. (Illus.). (gr. 7-12). lib. bdg. 202.00 (978-0-8239-9443-4(0)) Rosen Publishing Group, Inc., The.

The World of Work Set 4. 2005. (Illus.). (gr. 7-12). lib. bdg. 202.00 (978-0-8239-9442-7(2)) Rosen Publishing Group, Inc., The.

The World of Work Set 5. 2005. (Illus.). (gr. 7-12). lib. bdg. 126.25 (978-0-8239-9716-9(2)) Rosen Publishing Group, Inc., The.

Wormser, Richard. To the Young Filmmaker: Conversations with Working Filmmakers. 2002. (To the Young Ser.). (Illus.). 128p. (YA). (gr. 8-10). pap. 24.00 (978-0-531-11727-9(8) , Watts, Franklin) Scholastic Library Publishing.

Wright, Dixie Lee. Job Smarts: 12 Steps to Job Success. 2nd ed. 2003. 80p. pap. 9.95 (978-1-59357-028-6(7) , JIST Works) JIST Publishing.

—Job Smarts Instructor's Manual: 12 Steps to Job Success for Students with Special Needs. 2nd ed. 2003. 96p. pap., tchr. ed. 24.95 (978-1-59357-029-3(5) , JIST Works) JIST Publishing.

Zeigler, Heidi. Bodyguard. 2003. (gr. 7-12). lib. bdg. 15.25 (978-0-613-67875-9(3)) Tandem Library Bks.

VOCATIONS

see Professions

VOICE

see also Phonetics; Public Speaking; Singing; Speech; Ventriloquism

Comprehending & Verbalizing Visual Clues. 2003. 100p. (J). spiral bd. 28.00 (978-1-886143-54-8(4)) Great Ideas for Teaching, Inc.

Feierabend, John M. The Book of Pitch Exploration: Can Your Voice Do This? 2004. (First Steps in Music Ser.). 33p. (J). pap. 11.95 (978-1-57999-242-2(0)); (Illus.). pap. 11.95 (978-1-57999-265-1(X) , G-5276) GIA Pubns., Inc.

VOICE CULTURE

see also Singing; Voice

Aikin, William A. The Voice: An Introduction to Practical Phonology. 2001. 159p. (YA). reprint ed. 88.00 (978-0-7222-6201-6(9)) Library Reprints, Inc.

Bates, James. Voice Culture for Children. 2001. (YA). reprint ed. 150.00 (978-0-7222-6202-3(7)) Library Reprints, Inc.

Breare, William H. Vocal Faults & Their Remedies. 2001. (YA). reprint ed. 150.00 (978-0-7222-6203-0(5)) Library Reprints, Inc.

Drewry, William S. Voice Training. 2001. (YA). reprint ed. 150.00 (978-0-7222-6078-4(4)) Library Reprints, Inc.

Evans, Edwin. The Vocal Works. 2001. 599p. (YA). reprint ed. 98.00 (978-0-7222-5364-9(8)) Library Reprints, Inc.

Garcia-Castillas, G. A Guide to Solo Singing. 2001. (YA). reprint ed. 150.00 (978-0-7222-6080-7(6)) Library Reprints, Inc.

Henderson, William J. The Art of the Singer: Practical Hints about Vocal Technics & Style. 2001. 270p. (YA). reprint ed. 98.00 (978-0-7222-6084-5(9)) Library Reprints, Inc.

Marafioti, Pasqual M. Caruso's Method of Voice Production: The Scientific Culture of the Voice. 2001. 308p. (YA). reprint ed. 98.00 (978-0-7222-6102-6(0)) Library Reprints, Inc.

McLellan, Eleanor. Voice Education. 2001. (YA). reprint ed. 150.00 (978-0-7222-6209-2(4)) Library Reprints, Inc.

Miller, Frank E. Vocal Art-Science & Its Application. 2001. 278p. (YA). reprint ed. 98.00 (978-0-7222-6091-3(1)) Library Reprints, Inc.

Mills, Wesley Joseph. Voice Production in Singing & Speaking, Based on Scientific Principles. 2001. 294p. (YA). reprint ed. 98.00 (978-0-7222-6210-8(8)) Library Reprints, Inc.

Rice, Charles M. Voice Production with the Aid of Phonetics. 2nd ed. 2001. 87p. (YA). reprint ed. 88.00 (978-0-7222-6212-2(4)) Library Reprints, Inc.

Staines, J. Choral Society Vocalization. 2001. (YA). reprint ed. 150.00 (978-0-7222-6127-9(6)) Library Reprints, Inc.

Sutro, Emil. Duality of Voice: An Outline of Original Research. 2001. 224p. (YA). reprint ed. 98.00 (978-0-7222-6214-6(0)) Library Reprints, Inc.

Wronski, Thaddeus. The Singer & His Art. 2001. 265p. (YA). reprint ed. 98.00 (978-0-7222-6100-2(4)) Library Reprints, Inc.

VOLCANOES

Adams, Simon. The Best Book of Volcanoes. (Best Book of... Ser.). (Illus.). 32p. (J). 2007. pap. 6.95 (***978-0-7534-6092-4(0));*** 2001. tchr. ed. 12.95 (978-0-7534-5351-3(7)) Houghton Mifflin Co. Trade & Reference Div. (Kingfisher).

Anonymous. Wonders of Creation. 2006. 62.99 (***978-1-4280-2461-8(1))*** IndyPublish.com.

—Wonders of Creation: Volcanoes & Their. 2004. reprint ed. pap. 15.95 (978-1-4191-9484-9(4)) Kessinger Publishing, LLC.

—Wonders of Creation: Volcanoes & Their Phenomena. 2004. reprint ed. pap. 1.99 (978-1-4192-9484-6(9)) Kessinger Publishing, LLC.

Armentrout, David & Armentrout, Patricia. Volcanoes. 2007. (Illus.). 32p. (J). (978-1-60044-235-3(8)) Rourke Publishing, LLC.

Ashworth, William B., Jr. Vulcan's Forge anda Fingal's Cave: Volcanoes, Basalt, & the Discovery of Geological Time. 2004. (Illus.). per. 20.00 (978-0-9763590-0-5(6)) Linda Hall Library.

Bankier, William. Mount St. Helens Volcano. 2000. (gr. 5-8). lib. bdg. 11.80 (978-0-613-51219-0(7)) Tandem Library Bks.

—The Mount St. Helens Volcano. Taylor, Marjorie, illus. rev. ed. 1999. (Take Ten Ser.). 45p. (YA). (gr. 4-12). pap. 3.95 (978-1-58659-023-9(5)) Artesian Pr.

Barlow, Dave. Tome of Knowledge; Volcanoes. 2005. (ENG., Illus.). 20p. (YA). per. 4.95 (978-0-9725230-9-7(X)) Wandering Sage Bookstore & More, LLC.

Barr, Linda. Volcano! When a Mountain Explodes. 2003. (High Five Reading (Red Level) Ser.). (Illus.). (J). 64p. lib. bdg. 22.60 (978-0-7368-2787-4(0)); 48p. pap. 23.93 (978-0-7368-2826-0(5)) Capstone Pr., Inc.

Berger, Melvin. Why Do Volcanoes Blow Their Tops? Questions & Answers about Volcanoes & Earthquakes. 2000. (Question & Answer Ser.). (J). (978-0-606-19623-9(4)) Tandem Library Bks.

Berger, Melvin & Berger, Gilda. Why Do Volcanoes Blow Their Tops? Questions & Answers about Volcanoes & Earthquakes. Bond, Barbara Higgins, illus. 2000. (Question & Answer Ser.). 48p. (J). (gr. 2-5). pap. 14.95 (978-0-439-09580-8(8)) Scholastic, Inc.

Berger, Melvin, et al. Why Do Volcanoes Blow Their Tops? Questions & Answers about Volcanoes & Earthquakes. 1999. (Question & Answer Ser.). (J). (978-0-439-09581-5(6)) Scholastic, Inc.

Blast Zone: The Eruption & Recovery of Mount St. Helens. 2005. (Book Treks Ser.). (J). 37.95 (978-0-7652-3245-8(6)) Celebration Pr.

Bodden, Valerie. Volcanoes. 2006. 24p. 16.95 (978-1-58341-466-8(5) , Creative Education) Creative Co., The.

Branley, Franklyn M. Volcanoes. Date not set. (J). lib. bdg. 16.89 (978-0-06-028012-3(3)) HarperCollins Pubs.

—Volcanoes. Lloyd, Megan, illus. 2008. (Let's-Read-and-Find-Out Science Ser.). 40p. (J). 16.99 (978-0-06-028011-6(5)); pap. 5.99 (978-0-06-445189-5(5) , Harper Trophy) HarperCollins Pubs.

Bredeson, Carmen. Mount St. Helens Volcano: Violent Eruption. 2001. (American Disasters Ser.). (Illus.). 48p. (YA). (gr. 4-10). lib. bdg. 23.93 (978-0-7660-1552-4(1)) Enslow Pubs., Inc.

Buckwalter, Stephanie. Volcanoes: Disaster & Survival. 2005. (Deadly Disasters Ser.). (Illus.). 48p. (J). (ps-10). lib. bdg. 23.93 (978-0-7660-2384-0(2)) Enslow Pubs., Inc.

Bulletpoints Volcanoes & Earthquakes. 2005. (Illus.). (J). per. 4.99 (978-1-933581-06-4(9)) Byeway Bks.

Bunce, Vincent J. Volcanoes. 1999. (Restless Planet Ser.). (Illus.). 48p. (J). (gr. 4-6). lib. bdg. 27.12 (978-0-7398-1327-0(7)) Raintree.

Burleigh, Robert. Volcanoes: Journey to the Crater's Edge. Giraudon, David, illus. Bourseiller, Philippe, photos by. 2003. 80p. (J). (gr. 3-7). 14.95 (978-0-8109-4590-6(8)) Abrams, Harry N. , Inc.

Caplan, Jeremy. Volcanoes! 2006. 32p. (J). lib. bdg. 13.85 (****978-1-4242-0399-4(6))*** Fitzgerald Bks.

Challen, Paul C. Volcano Alert! 2004. (Disaster Alert! Ser.). (Illus.). 32p. (J). pap. (978-0-7787-1602-0(3)); (978-0-7787-1570-2(1)) Crabtree Publishing Co.

Chambers, Catherine. Volcanoes. (Disasters in Nature Ser.). (Illus.). 48p. (J). (gr. 4-7). 2002. pap. 8.50 (978-1-58810-336-9(6) , 91082); 2000. lib. bdg. 24.22 (978-1-57572-431-7(6)) Heinemann Library.

Clarke, Penny. Volcanoes. 1998. (Worldwise Ser.: Vol. 22). (Illus.). 40p. (J). (gr. 3-5). 24.00 (978-0-531-14462-6(3) , Watts, Franklin) Scholastic Library Publishing.

Claybourne, Anna. Volcanoes. 2007. (Illus.). 64p. (J). (gr. 1-5). 16.95 (****978-0-7534-6137-2(4)*** , Kingfisher) Houghton Mifflin Co. Trade & Reference Div.

Colson, Mary. Earth Erupts: Volcanoes. 2005. (Turbulent Planet Ser.). (J). (978-1-4109-1735-5(5)); pap. (978-1-4109-1745-4(2)) Steck-Vaughn.

Cormack, Allan Drew Brook & Cormack, Deborah Drew Brook, illus. Volcanoes Inside & Out. 2006. (On My Own Science Ser.). 48p. (J). (gr. 2-4). lib. bdg. 25.26 (978-1-57505-761-3(1)) Lerner Publishing Group.

The Crying Mountain: 6 Small Books. (Greetings Ser.: Vol. 1). 32p. (gr. 3-5). 31.00 (978-0-7635-1841-7(7)) Rigby Education.

The Crying Mountain: Big Book. (Greetings Ser.: Vol. 1). 32p. (gr. 3-5). 31.00 (978-0-7635-3222-2(3)) Rigby Education.

Dalgleish, Sharon. Volcanoes. 2002. (Junior Adventure Ser.). (Illus.). 32p. (J). (gr. 3 up). lib. bdg. (978-1-59084-185-3(9)) Mason Crest Pubs.

Day, Trevor. Savage Earth. 2006. (DK Guides Ser.). 64p. (J). pap. 7.99 (978-0-7566-1791-2(X)) Dorling Kindersley Publishing, Inc.

Dayton, Connor. Volcanic Rocks. 2007. (Rocks & Minerals Ser.). (Illus.). 24p. (J). (gr. 2-5). lib. bdg. 21.25 (****978-1-4042-3688-2(0)*** , PowerKids Pr.) Rosen Publishing Group, Inc., The.

Dinaberg, Leslie. Volcanoes. 2006. (Boys Rock! Ser.). (Illus.). 32p. (J). (gr. 1-5). 24.21 (978-1-59296-739-1(6)) Child's World, Inc.

Dineen, Jacqueline. Volcanoes. 2004. (Natural Disasters Ser.). (J). lib. bdg. 27.10 (978-1-932799-04-0(4)) Stargazer Bks.

Dobeck, Maryann. Volcanes: El poder asombroso de la naturaleza & Volcanoes: Nature's Awesome Power. 2005. spiral bd. 88.00 (****978-1-4108-5737-8(9))*** Benchmark Education Co.

Dorling Kindersley Publishing Staff. Eruption! The Story of Volcanoes. 2001. (Readers Ser.). (Illus.). 32p. (J). (ps-3). 12.99 (978-0-7894-7362-2(3)) Dorling Kindersley Publishing, Inc.

—Volcano. 2003. (Eye Wonder Ser.). (Illus.). 48p. (J). (gr. k-3). lib. bdg. 17.99 (978-0-7894-9612-6(7)) Dorling Kindersley Publishing, Inc.

—The Volcano. 2003. (Eye Wonder Ser.). (Illus.). 48p. (J). 9.99 (978-0-7894-9270-8(9)) Dorling Kindersley Publishing, Inc.

Dorling Kindersley Publishing Staff, ed. Volcanoes & Earthquakes. 2004. (Dk Eyewitness Books Ser.). (Illus.). 72p. (J). 15.99 (978-0-7566-0735-7(3)) Dorling Kindersley Publishing, Inc.

Downs, Sandra. Earth's Fiery Fury. 2000. (Exploring Planet Earth Ser.). (Illus.). 64p. (gr. 5-8). lib. bdg. (978-0-7613-1413-4(X) , Twenty-First Century Bks.) Lerner Publishing Group.

Drohan, Michele Ingber. Volcanoes. 1999. (Natural Disasters Ser.). (Illus.). 24p. (J). (gr. k-4). lib. bdg. 19.95 (978-0-8239-5284-7(3) , PowerKids Pr.) Rosen Publishing Group, Inc., The.

Durban, Chris. Volcanoes. 2004. (Geography First Ser.). (J). 23.70 (978-1-4103-0321-9(7) , Blackbirch Pr., Inc.) Thomson Gale.

Exciting World: Includes: Fossil & Bones; The Hidden Past; The Search for Riches; Volcano, Earthquake & Hurricane, 4 bks., Set. (Remarkable World Ser.). (Illus.). (J). (gr. 4-7). lib. bdg. 75.92 (978-0-8172-5155-0(3)) Raintree.

Farndon, John & Riley, Peter D. Volcanoes & Earthquakes & Other Facts about Planet Earth: Bulletpoints. 2003. (Bulletpoints Ser.). (Illus.). 40p. (J). pap. 6.95 (978-1-84236-238-9(0)) Miles Kelly Publishing, Ltd. GBR. *Dist:* Independent Pubs. Group.

Firestone, Mary. Volcanologist. 2005. (Weird Careers in Science Ser.). (Illus.). 77p. (J). (gr. 4-8). lib. bdg. 25.00 (978-0-7910-8702-2(6) , Chelsea Hse.) Facts On File, Inc.

Formby, Caroline. Tristan's Bedtime Story. Formby, Caroline, illus. l.t. ed. 1998. (Children's Stories Published in Other Lands Ser.). (Illus.). 32p. (J). (gr. 2 up). lib. bdg. 12.95 (978-1-56674-269-6(2)) Forest Hse. Publishing Co., Inc.

Fradin, Dennis & Fradin, Judith. Volcanoes. 2007. (Witness to Disaster Ser.). (Illus.). 48p. (J). (gr. 3-6). 16.95 (978-0-7922-5376-1(0) , National Geographic Children's Bks.) National Geographic Society.

Frisch, Aaron. Volcanoes. 2001. (Natural Disasters Ser.). (Illus.). 24p. (J). 21.35 (978-1-58340-124-8(5)) Smart Apple Media.

Furgang, Kathy. Mount Vesuvius: Europe's Mighty Volcano of Smoke & Ash. 2001. (Volcanoes of the World Ser.). (Illus.). 24p. (J). lib. bdg. 19.95 (978-0-8239-5658-6(X) , PowerKids Pr.) Rosen Publishing Group, Inc., The.

—Mt. Kilauea: Home of the Hawaiian Goddess of Fire. 2001. (Volcanoes of the World Ser.). (Illus.). 24p. (J). lib. bdg. 19.95 (978-0-8239-5659-3(8) , PowerKids Pr.) Rosen Publishing Group, Inc., The.

—Mt. Krakatoa: History's Loudest Volcano. 2001. (Volcanoes of the World Ser.). (Illus.). 24p. (J). lib. bdg. 19.95 (978-0-8239-5662-3(8) , PowerKids Pr.) Rosen Publishing Group, Inc., The.

—Mt. Pelbee: The Biggest Volcano Eruption of the 20th Century. 2001. (Volcanoes of the World Ser.). (Illus.). 24p. (J). lib. bdg. 19.95 (978-0-8239-5663-0(6) , PowerKids Pr.) Rosen Publishing Group, Inc., The.

—Mt. St. Helens: The Smoking Mountain. 2001. (Volcanoes of the World Ser.). (Illus.). 24p. (J). lib. bdg. 19.95 (978-0-8239-5660-9(1) , PowerKids Pr.) Rosen Publishing Group, Inc., The.

—Mt. Tamabora: A Killer Volcano from Indonesia. 2001. (Volcanoes of the World Ser.). 24p. (J). lib. bdg. 19.95 (978-0-8239-5661-6(X) , PowerKids Pr.) Rosen Publishing Group, Inc., The.

Gaff, Jackie, et al. Volcanoes. Polt, Gabrielle, ed. 2003. (Extraordinary Ser.). (Illus.). 32p. (J). pap. 5.95 (978-0-439-28725-8(1) , Scholastic Paperbacks) Scholastic, Inc.

Gallant, Roy A. Plates: Restless Earth. 2002. (Earthworks Ser.). (Illus.). 80p. (J). 29.93 (978-0-7614-1370-7(7) , Benchmark Bks.) Cavendish, Marshall Corp.

Ganeri, Anita. Earth Erupts. 2004. (Turbulent Planet Ser.). (Illus.). 48p. (J). 28.56 (978-1-4109-0587-1(X)) Raintree.

—The Earth Erupts. 2004. (Turbulent Planet Ser.). (Illus.). pap. 8.50 (978-1-4109-1025-7(3)) Raintree.

—Earth Erupts 6-Pack. 2004. (Turbulent Planet Ser.). (Illus.). pap. 45.90 (978-1-4109-1030-1(X)) Raintree.

—Eruption: The Story of Volcanoes. (Eyewitness Readers Ser.). 2001. (Illus.). (J). 10.75 (978-0-606-21182-6(9)); 2000. lib. bdg. 11.80 (978-0-613-35111-9(8)) Tandem Library Bks.

—Esos Violentos Volcanes. (Coleccion Esa Horrible Geografia).Tr. of Violent Volcanoes. (SPA., Illus.). 128p. (YA). (gr. 5-8). 9.95 (978-84-272-2151-2(7) , ML1621) Molino, Editorial ESP. *Dist:* Lectorum Pubns., Inc.

—Volcano! 2007. (Illus.). 32p. (J). (978-1-84193-561-4(1)) Arcturus Pubs., Inc.

Ganeria, Anita. Eruption! The Story of Volcanoes. Martin, Linda, ed. 2001. (Readers Ser.). (Illus.). 32p. (J). (gr. 5-3). pap. 3.99 (978-0-7894-7361-5(5)) Dorling Kindersley Publishing, Inc.

Gates, Alexander E. & Ritchie, David. Encyclopedia of Earthquakes & Volcanoes. 3rd rev. ed. (Science Encyclopedia Ser.). 368p. pap. 21.95 (****978-0-8160-7120-3(9)*** , Checkmark Bks.) Facts On File, Inc.

Gentle, Victor & Perry, Janet. Volcanoes. 2001. (Natural Disasters Ser.). (Illus.). 24p. (J). (gr. 2 up). lib. bdg. 22.00 (978-0-8368-2836-8(4)) Stevens, Gareth Inc.

George, Linda. Plate Tectonics. 2002. (Kidhaven Science Library). (Illus.). 48p. (J). (gr. 3-5). 23.70 (978-0-7377-1405-0(0) , Greenhaven Pr., Inc.) Thomson Gale.

George, Michael. Volcanoes: The Fiery Mountains. 2003. (LifeViews Ser.). (Illus.). 32p. (J). lib. bdg. (978-1-58341-255-8(7) , Creative Education) Creative Co., The.

T U V

Goldie, Sonia. My Favorite Nature Book: Volcanoes of the World: Includes an Activity Kit with a Poster, Stickers & a Do-It-Yourself Flip Book. 2007. (Illus.). 24p. (J). 9.95 (978-1-57990-921-5(3)) Lark Bks.

Green, Emily K. Volcanoes. 2006. (Blastoff! Readers Ser.). (Illus.). 24p. (J). lib. bdg. 16.95 (978-1-60014-041-9(6)) Bellwether Media.

Green, Jen. Mount St. Helens. 2005. (Illus.). 32p. (J). lib. bdg. 24.67 (978-0-8368-4498-6(X)) Stevens, Gareth Inc.

Griffey, Harriet. Volcanoes & Other Natural Disasters. 1998. (Eyewitness Readers). (Illus.). 48p. (J). (gr. 2-4). pap. 3.99 (978-0-7894-2964-3(0)) Dorling Kindersley Publishing, Inc.

Griffey, Harriet & Dorling Kindersley Publishing Staff. Volcanoes & Other Natural Disasters. 1999. (Eyewitness Readers). (Illus.). 48p. (J). (gr. 2-4). 12.99 (978-0-7894-4257-4(4)) Dorling Kindersley Publishing, Inc.

Group/McGraw-Hill, Wright. Forces of Nature: Level K, 6 vols., Vol. 2. (First Explorers Ser.). 24p. (gr. 1-2). 34.95 (978-0-7699-1458-9(6)) Shortland Pubns. (U. S. A.) Inc.

—Volcanoes: The Hottest Spots on Earth, 6 vols. (Book2WebTM Ser.). (gr. 4-8). 36.50 (978-0-322-04425-8(1)) Wright Group, The.

Gutner, Howard. Boom! 2002. (Illus.). 16p. (J). (978-0-439-35086-0(7)) Scholastic, Inc.

Haduch, Bill. Volcano! An Explosive Tour of Earth's Hot Spots. 2001. (Eyewitness Readers Ser.). (Illus.). (J). (978-0-606-21505-3(0)) Tandem Library Bks.

Hall, M. C. Hawaii Volcanoes National Park. 2005. (Heinemann First Library). (Illus.). 32p. (J). (gr. k-2). pap. 7.60 (978-1-4034-6707-2(2)); lib. bdg. 25.36 (978-1-4034-6700-3(5)) Heinemann Library.

Halpern, Monica. Rivers of Fire: The Story of Volcanoes. 2006. (National Geographic Science Chapters Ser.). (Illus.). 48p. (gr. 1-4). 17.90 (978-0-7922-5946-6(7) , National Geographic Children's Bks.) National Geographic Society.

Harbo, Christopher L. The Explosive World of Volcanoes with Max Axiom, Super Scientist. Smith, Tod, illus. 2008. (J). (*978-1-4296-0144-3(2)) Capstone Pr., Inc.

Harcourt School Publishers Staff. Look Out for Lava. 3rd ed. 2002. (Horizons Ser.). (Illus.). (J). pap. 5.50 (978-0-15-333417-7(7)) Harcourt Schl. Pubs.

—Making Mountains On Level. 3rd ed. 2002. (Trophies Reading Program Ser.). (Illus.). pap. 5.10 (978-0-15-323446-0(6)) Harcourt Schl. Pubs.

—The Mighty Volcano Below Level. 3rd ed. 2002. (Trophies Reading Program Ser.). (Illus.). pap. 5.10 (978-0-15-323426-2(1)) Harcourt Schl. Pubs.

—Ring of Fire. 3rd ed. 2002. (Trophies English Language Learners Ser.). (Illus.). pap. 5.10 (978-0-15-327821-1(8)) Harcourt Schl. Pubs.

—Ring of Fire: Take-Home Book. 1999. (Collections Ser.). (Illus.). (J). pap. 1.90 (978-0-15-317318-9(1)) Harcourt Schl. Pubs.

—Ring of Fire Below Level. 3rd ed. 2002. (Trophies Reading Program Ser.). (Illus.). pap. 5.10 (978-0-15-323158-2(0)) Harcourt Schl. Pubs.

—Volcanoes: Reader's Choice Book. 2001. (Collections Ser.). (Illus.). (J). 5.90 (978-0-15-314392-2(4)) Harcourt Schl. Pubs.

—Volcanos Advanced Level: Destroyers & Craters. 3rd ed. 2002. (Trophies Reading Program Ser.). (Illus.). pap. 5.10 (978-0-15-323384-5(2)) Harcourt Schl. Pubs.

Harper, D. Volcanoes & Earthquakes. (Information Ser.). (Illus.). 32p. (J). (gr. 2-6). 3.50 (978-0-7214-1744-8(2) , Dutton Juvenile) Penguin Group (USA) Inc.

Harper, Kristine. The Mount St. Helens Volcanic Eruption. 2005. (Environmental Disasters Ser.). (Illus.). 112p. (J). (gr. 6-12). 35.00 (978-0-8160-5757-3(5)) Facts On File, Inc.

Harris, Nancy. Volcanoes. 2003. (gr. 7-12). lib. bdg. 30.35 (978-0-613-73871-2(3)) Tandem Library Bks.

Harris, Nicholas & Dennis, Peter. Volcano. 2006. (Illus.). 31p. (J). (*978-0-7607-7530-1(3)) backpackbook.

Hayhurst, Chris. Volcanologists: Life under a Volcano. 2005. (Extreme Careers Ser.). (Illus.). 64p. (YA). (gr. 5-8). 26.50 (978-0-8239-3637-3(6)) Rosen Publishing Group, Inc., The.

Hill of Fire. 1998. (J). (gr. 2). 3.95 (978-0-439-04434-9(0)) Scholastic, Inc.

Holt, Rinehart and Winston Staff. Holt Science & Technology Chapter 9: Earth Science: Volcanoes. 5th ed. 2004. (Illus.). pap. 12.86 (978-0-03-030306-7(0)) Holt, Rinehart & Winston.

—Holt Science & Technology Chptr. 13: Volcanoes: Chapter Resources - Tennessee Edition. 3rd ed. 2003. (YA). pap. 11.40 (978-0-03-069173-7(7)) Holt, Rinehart & Winston.

Hort, Leonard. Ring of Fire. 2003. (Science Links Ser.). (Illus.). 32p. (gr. 3-5). 23.00 (978-0-7910-7431-2(5) , Chelsea Hse.) Facts On File, Inc.

How a Volcano Is Formed: Level M, 6 vols. (Wonder Worldtm Ser.). 16p. 34.95 (978-0-7802-2913-6(4)) Wright Group, The.

Hunter, Rebecca M. Volcanoes & Earthquakes. 2001. (Discovering Science Ser.). (Illus.). 32p. (J). (gr. 4-7). lib. bdg. 25.69 (978-0-7398-3249-3(2)) Raintree.

Jennings, Terry. Volcanoes & Earthquakes. 2002. (Restless Earth Ser.). (Illus.). 32p. (J). lib. bdg. 24.25 (978-1-931983-21-1(6)) Chrysalis Education.

Jerome, Kate Boehm. Volcanoes & Earthquakes. 2003. (National Geographic Reading Expeditions Ser.). (Illus.). 32p. (J). (978-0-7922-8874-9(2)) National Geographic Society.

Johnson, Rebecca L. Surviving Volcanoes & Glaciers. 2003. (National Geographic Reading Expeditions Ser.). (Illus.). 32p. (J). (978-0-7922-8448-2(8)) National Geographic Society.

Kelsey, Michael R. Climber's & Hiker's Guide to the World's Mountains & Volcanos. 4th ed. 2001. (Illus.). 1248p. (YA). pap. 36.95 (978-0-944510-18-6(3)) Kelsey Publishing.

Kerrod, Robin. Shaking Earth: Volcanoes, Earthquakes, Hurricanes Etc. 2005. (Illus.). 128p. pap. 17.99 (978-1-84476-097-8(9) , Southwater) Anness Publishing GBR. *Dist:* National Bk. Network.

Lassieur, Allison. Volcanoes. 2000. (Natural Disasters Ser.). (Illus.). 48p. (J). (gr. 3-4). lib. bdg. 21.26 (978-0-7368-0589-6(3) , Capstone High-Interest Bks.) Capstone Pr., Inc.

Lauber, Patricia. Volcano: The Eruption & Healing of Mount St. Helens. 1998. (J). pap. 8.99 (978-0-87628-349-3(0)) Ctr. for Applied Research in Education, The.

Leigh, Autumn. Warning: Volcano! The Story of Mount St. Helens. 2002. (Reading Room Collection). (Illus.). 24p. (J). pap. 4.40 (978-0-8239-8157-1(6)); lib. bdg. 18.75 (978-0-8239-3720-2(8)) Rosen Publishing Group, Inc., The.

Lewis, Peter B., prod. Mount St. Helens: Into the Valley of the Volcano. Lewis, Peter B., . 2000. pap. 16.95 incl. audio (978-0-9666910-5-4(9) , Car Tours) Audisee Sound & Music.

Lindeen, Mary. Anatomy of a Volcano. 2007. (Shockwave: Earth & Physical Science Ser.). (Illus.). 36p. (J). (gr. 4-6). lib. bdg. 25.00 (*978-0-531-17791-4(2) , Children's Pr.) Scholastic Library Publishing.

Lindop, Laurie. Probing Volcanoes. 2003. (Science on the Edge Ser.). (Illus.). 80p. (gr. 5 up). lib. bdg. 26.90 (978-0-7613-2700-4(2) , Twenty-First Century Bks.) Lerner Publishing Group.

Llewellyn, Claire. Volcanoes. 2000. 32p. (J). (gr. k-2). lib. bdg. 21.36 (978-1-57572-207-8(0)) Heinemann Library.

—Volcanoes. 2000. (gr. k-3). lib. bdg. 14.75 (978-0-613-45848-1(6)) Tandem Library Bks.

Llewellyn, Claire, et al. Volcanoes. 2002. (Geography Starts Ser.). (Illus.). 32p. (J). (gr. k-2). pap. 6.95 (978-1-58810-979-8(8) , 91462) Heinemann Library.

Mallory, Kenneth. Diving to a Deep-Sea Volcano. 2006. (Scientists in the Field Ser.). (Illus.). 64p. (J). (gr. 4-6). 17.00 (978-0-618-33205-2(7)) Houghton Mifflin Co.

Manatt, Kathleen G. Volcanologist. 2008. (J). lib. bdg. 25.26 (*978-1-60279-050-6(7)) Cherry Lake Publishing.

Markle, Sandra. Can You Believe? B Volcanoes. Bosson, Jo-Ellen C., tr. Bosson, Jo-Ellen C., illus. 2002. 48p. (J). (978-0-439-35611-4(3)) Scholastic, Inc.

Mattern, Joanne. Mauna Loa: World's Largest Active Volcano. 2002. (Reading Power Ser.). (Illus.). 24p. (J). (gr. 2). lib. bdg. 17.25 (978-0-8239-6014-9(5) , PowerKids Pr.) Rosen Publishing Group, Inc., The.

Mauna Loa, 6 Pks. (On Deck Ser.). 24p. (gr. 4-5). 35.00 (978-0-7578-1076-3(4)) Rigby Education.

Mauna Loa: Individual Title Six-Packs. (On Deck en Espanol Ser.). (SPA.). 24p. (gr. 4-5). 35.00 (978-0-7578-6447-6(3)) Rigby Education.

Mayer, Cassie. Volcanes. 2006. (SPA & ENG., Illus.). 24p. (J). (*978-1-4034-8679-0(4)) Heinemann Library.

—Volcanes (Volcanoes) 2006. (SPA & ENG., Illus.). 24p. (J). pap. (*978-1-4034-8685-1(9)) Heinemann Library.

Mayer, Cassie. Volcanoes. 2006. (Illus.). 24p. (J). (978-1-4034-8438-3(4)); pap. (978-1-4034-8444-4(9)) Heinemann Library.

McGlone, Catherine. Visiting Volcanoes with a Scientist. 2004. (I Like Science! Ser.). (Illus.). 24p. (J). lib. bdg. 21.26 (978-0-7660-2269-0(2)) Enslow Pubs., Inc.

Meister, Cari. Volcanoes. 1999. (Nature's Fury Ser.). (Illus.). 32p. (J). (gr. 3-8). lib. bdg. 24.21 (978-1-57765-084-3(0) , ABDO & Daughters) ABDO Publishing Co.

Nault, Jennifer. Volcanoes. 2004. (Science Matters Ser.). (Illus.). 24p. (J). lib. bdg. 24.45 (978-1-59036-211-2(X)) Weigl Pubs., Inc.

Nelson, Sharlene P. & Nelson, Ted. Mount St. Helens National Volcanic Monument. 1998. (True Bks.). (Illus.). 48p. (J). (gr. 3-5). pap. 6.95 (978-0-516-26269-7(6) , Children's Pr.) Scholastic Library Publishing.

Nelson, Sharlene P. & Nelson, Ted W. Hawaii Volcanoes National Park. 1998. (True Bks.). (Illus.). 48p. (J). (gr. 3-5). 25.00 (978-0-516-20623-3(0) , Children's Pr.) Scholastic Library Publishing.

Nicolson, Cynthia Pratt. Volcano! 2001. (Disaster Ser.). (Illus.). 32p. (J). (gr. 4-6). (978-1-55074-908-3(0)); (978-1-55074-966-3(8)) Kids Can Pr., Ltd.

Niz, Xavier. Volcanoes. 2005. (Illus.). 24p. (J). (ps-7). lib. bdg. 21.26 (978-0-7368-4309-6(4)) Capstone Pr., Inc.

Nuttall, Gina. Volcanoes & Earthquakes. 2004. (QEB Start Writing Ser.). (Illus.). 24p. (J). lib. bdg. 15.95 (978-1-59566-018-3(6)) QEB Publishing Inc.

O'Meara, Donna. Into the Volcano: A Volcano Researcher at Work. 2005. (Illus.). 56p. (YA). (gr. 3-7). (978-1-55337-692-7(7)) Kids Can Pr., Ltd.

O'Neil, Sarah. Volcanoes. 2001. (gr. k-3). lib. bdg. 11.80 (978-0-613-33451-8(5)) Tandem Library Bks.

Oxlade, Chris. Earthquakes & Volcanoes. 2004. (Earth's Changing Landscape Ser.). (Illus.). 46p. (J). lib. bdg. 28.50 (978-1-58340-479-6(1)) Smart Apple Media.

Park, Louise. Volcanoes. 2007. (J). (*978-1-59920-110-8(0)) Smart Apple Media.

Pierce, Terry. Volcanoes A to Z Coloring Book. Villalobos, Ethel M., illus. 2003. 24p. pap. 4.95 (978-1-57306-123-0(9)) Bess Pr., Inc.

Prager, Ellen J. Volcano. Prager, Ellen J. et al, illus. 2001. (Jump into Science Ser.). 32p. (J). (ps-3). 16.95 (978-0-7922-8201-3(9) , National Geographic Children's Bks.) National Geographic Society.

—Volcano! Woodman, Nancy, illus. 2007. (Jump into Science Ser.). 32p. (J). (ps-3). 6.95 (978-1-4263-0091-2(3) , National Geographic Children's Bks.) National Geographic Society.

Putnam, James & Van Rose, Sussanna. Volcano & Earthquake. (Dk Eyewitness Books Ser.). (J). pap. 8.95 (978-0-7894-5781-3(4)) Dorling Kindersley Publishing, Inc.

QEB Start Reading & Writing National Book Stores Edition: Volcanoes & Earthquakes. 2006. (J). per. (978-1-59566-265-1(0)) QEB Publishing Inc.

Quadrillion Media Staff. Volcanoes. 1998. (Start Me Up Ser.: Vol. 9). Orig. Title: Vulkane. 48p. (J). (gr. 3-8). mass mkt. 12.95 (978-1-58185-010-9(7) , Tessloff Publishing) Quadrillion Media LLC.

Rae, Alison. Earthquakes & Volcanoes. 2005. (Looking at Landscapes Ser.). (Illus.). 47p. (J). (gr. 6-9). lib. bdg. 29.95 (978-1-58340-729-5(4)) Smart Apple Media.

Rau, Dana Meachen. Los Volcanes. 2007. (Maravillas de la Naturaleza Ser.). (SPA.). 32p. (J). lib. bdg. 22.79 (*978-0-7614-2808-4(9) , Benchmark Bks.) Cavendish, Marshall Corp.

—Volcanoes. 2007. (Wonders of Nature Ser.). 32p. (J). lib. bdg. 22.79 (*978-0-7614-2670-7(1) , Benchmark Bks.) Cavendish, Marshall Corp.

—Volcanoes/Los Volcanes. 2007. (Wonders of Nature/ Maravillas de la Naturaleza Ser.). (SPA & ENG.). 32p. (J). lib. bdg. 22.79 (*978-0-7614-2832-9(1) , Benchmark Bks.) Cavendish, Marshall Corp.

Richards, Julie. Vibrating Volcanoes. 2001. (Natural Disasters Ser.). (Illus.). 32p. (J). (gr. 5 up). 28.00 (978-0-7910-6581-5(2) , 010455, Chelsea Hse.) Facts On File, Inc.

Riley, Gail Blasser. Volcano! The 1980 Mount St. Helens Eruption. 2006. (X-Treme Disasters That Changed America Ser.). (Illus.). 32p. (J). lib. bdg. 25.27 (978-1-59716-072-8(5)) Bearport Publishing Co., Inc.

Riley, Joelle. Volcanoes. 2008. (Pull Ahead Books-Forces of Nature Ser.). (J). lib. bdg. 22.60 (*978-0-8225-7909-0(X) , Lerner Pubns.) Lerner Publishing Group.

Rogers, Daniel. Volcanoes. 1999. (Geography Starts Here Ser.). (Illus.). 32p. (J). (gr. 1-4). lib. bdg. 25.69 (978-0-8172-5547-3(8)) Raintree.

Rubin, Ken. Volcanoes & Earthquakes. 2007. (Insiders Ser.). 64p. (J). (gr. 3-7). 16.99 (*978-1-4169-3862-0(1)) Simon & Schuster Children's Publishing.

Rusch, Elizabeth. Will It Blow? Become a Volcano Detective at Mount St. Helens. Lewis, K. E., illus. 2007. 48p. (J). (gr. 4-6). 18.95 (*978-1-57061-510-8(1)); pap. 13.95 (*978-1-57061-509-2(8)) Sasquatch Bks.

Ruth, Angie. My Adventure on a Volcano. 2006. 44p. (J). 8.99 (978-1-59092-443-3(6) , Orchard Academy Pr.) Windstorm Creative.

Schuh, Mari C. What Are Volcanoes? Saunders-Smith, Gail, ed. 2002. (Earth Features Ser.). (Illus.). 24p. (J). (gr. k-1). lib. bdg. 15.93 (978-0-7368-1172-9(9) , Pebble Bks.) Capstone Pr., Inc.

Sengupta, Monalisa. Volcanoes & Earthquakes. 2008. (J). lib. bdg. (*978-1-4042-3901-2(4) , PowerKids Pr.) Rosen Publishing Group, Inc., The.

Senior, Kathryn. Volcanoes. 2005. (What on Earth? Ser.). (Illus.). 32p. (J). 25.50 (978-0-516-25324-4(7) , Children's Pr.) Scholastic Library Publishing.

Shone, Rob. Volcanoes. 2007. (Illus.). 48p. (J). (*978-1-4042-1976-2(5)); pap. (*978-1-4042-1975-5(7)); (gr. 5-8). lib. bdg. 29.25 (*978-1-4042-1988-5(9)) Rosen Publishing Group, Inc., The.

Sillet, Helen. The Awesome Power of Volcanoes & Earthquakes. 2005. (YA). pap. 12.95 (978-1-4105-0421-0(2)); cd-rom (978-1-4105-0423-4(9)) Johnston, Don Inc.

—Understanding Volcanoes & Earthquakes. 2005. (YA). pap. 12.95 (978-1-4105-0417-3(4)); cd-rom (978-1-4105-0419-7(0)) Johnston, Don Inc.

Silverstein, Alvin, et al. Plate Tectonics. 1998. (Science Concepts Ser.: 8). (Illus.). 64p. (gr. 5-8). lib. bdg. 26.90 (978-0-7613-3225-1(1) , Twenty-First Century Bks.) Lerner Publishing Group.

Simon, Seymour. Danger! Volcanoes. 2002. (SeeMore Readers Ser.). (Illus.). 32p. (J). (gr. 1-3). 13.95 (978-1-58717-181-9(3)); Vol. 2. pap. 3.95 (978-1-58717-182-6(1)) Chronicle Bks. LLC. (SeaStar Bks.).

—Danger! Volcanoes. 2002. (gr. 3-6). lib. bdg. 11.80 (978-0-613-64168-5(X)) Tandem Library Bks.

—Volcanoes. 2006. 32p. (J). 16.99 (978-0-06-087716-3(2)); pap. 6.99 (978-0-06-087717-0(0)) HarperCollins Pubs.

Sipiera, Paul P. & Sipiera, Diane M. Volcanoes. 1999. (True Bks.). (Illus.). 48p. (J). (gr. 3-5). pap. 6.95 (978-0-516-26444-8(3) , Children's Pr.) Scholastic Library Publishing.

Spilsbury, Louise & Spilsbury, Richard. Violent Volcanoes. 2004. (Heinemann Infosearch Ser.). (Illus.). 32p. (J). pap. 7.50 (978-1-4034-5448-5(5)); lib. bdg. (978-1-4034-4788-3(8)) Heinemann Library.

Stamper, Judith Bauer. Voyage to the Volcano. Speirs, John, illus. 2003. (Magic School Bus Ser.: Bk. 15). 96p. (gr. 3-7). mass mkt. 4.99 (978-0-439-42935-1(8)) Scholastic, Inc.

—Voyage to the Volcano. 2003. (gr. 3-6). lib. bdg. 11.80 (978-0-613-63363-5(6)) Tandem Library Bks.

Steele, Christy. Volcanoes. 1999. (Nature on the Rampage Ser.). (Illus.). 32p. (J). (gr. 4-7). lib. bdg. 22.83 (978-0-7398-1796-4(5)) Raintree.

Steele, Philip. Inside Volcanoes. 2006. (Inside Nature's Disasters Ser.). (Illus.). 36p. (J). (978-0-8368-7250-7(9)) Stevens, Gareth Inc.

—Volcanoes. 1999. (Natural Disasters Ser.). (Illus.). 31p. (J). (gr. 5 up). pap. 5.95 (978-0-7641-1057-3(8)) Barron's Educational Series, Inc.

Stewart, Melissa. Earthquakes & Volcanoes. 2008. 80p. (J). 16.99 (*978-0-06-089951-6(4)); pap. 7.99 (*978-0-06-089950-9(6)) HarperCollins Pubs.

Storey, Melinda. Volcanoes: A Comprehensive Hands-on Science Unit. Mitchell, Judy & Lindeen, Mary, eds. Armbrust, Janet, illus. 2007. 32p. (J). pap. 6.95 (*978-1-57310-530-9(9)) Teaching & Learning Co.

Sutherland, Lin. Terremotos y Volcanes. Lopez-Izquierdo, Nieves, tr. 2003. (Exploradores de National Geographic Ser.). (SPA., Illus.). 64p. (gr. 4-7). (978-970-651-716-6(2) , 1610) Editorial Oceano De Mexico, S.A. DE C.V.

Taylor, Barbara. Mountains & Volcanoes: Geography Facts & Experiments. 2002. (Young Discoverers Ser.). (Illus.). 32p. (J). (gr. k-3). pap. 7.95 (978-0-7534-5507-4(2) , Kingfisher) Houghton Mifflin Co. Trade & Reference Div.

—Mountains & Volcanoes: Geography Facts & Experiments. 2002. (gr. k-3). lib. bdg. 16.40 (978-0-613-90354-7(4)) Tandem Library Bks.

Thoron, Joe. Volcanoes. 2006. (Kaleidoscope Natural Disasters Ser.). (Illus.). 48p. (J). lib. bdg. 28.50 (978-0-7614-2105-4(X) , Benchmark Bks.) Cavendish, Marshall Corp.

Time for Kids Editors. Almanac 2007. 2006. (Time for Kids Ser.). 360p. 24.95 (978-1-933405-08-7(2)); (Illus.). (J). pap. 12.99 (978-1-933405-33-9(3)) Time, Inc. Home Entertainment.

—Volcanoes! 2006. (Time for Kids Ser.). (Illus.). 32p. (J). 14.99 (978-0-06-078224-5(2)); pap. 3.99 (978-0-06-078223-8(4) , Harper Trophy) HarperCollins Pubs.

Timon & the Volcano, Level 1. 1999. (SmartReader Ser.). (J). pap., tchr. ed. 19.95 incl. audio (978-0-7887-0776-6(0) , 79340T3) Recorded Bks., LLC.

Townsend, John. Earthquakes & Volcanoes: A Survival Guide. 2005. (Illus.). 32p. (J). (978-1-4109-1927-4(7)) Steck-Vaughn.

—Earthquakes & Volcanoes: A Survival Guide; Earth's Physical Processes. 2005. (Illus.). 32p. (J). (gr. 6-9). 7.85 (978-1-4109-1958-8(7)) Steck-Vaughn.

Trueit, Trudi Strain. Volcanoes. (Watts Library). (Illus.). 64p. (J). 2003. (gr. 5-7). pap. 8.95 (978-0-531-16244-6(3)); 2002. 25.50 (978-0-531-12198-6(4)) Scholastic Library Publishing. (Watts, Franklin).

Trueno de la Tierra: 6 Small Books. (Saludos Ser.: Vol. 2). (SPA.). (gr. 3-5). 31.00 (978-0-7635-2068-7(3)) Rigby Education.

Turnbull, Stephanie. Volcanoes. Tudor, Andy, illus. 2005. 32p. (J). pap. (*978-0-439-84610-3(2)) Scholastic, Inc.

Turnbull, Stephanie. Volcanoes (Level 2) - Internet Referenced. 2006. 32p. (J). 4.99 (978-0-7945-1401-3(4) , Usborne) EDC Publishing.

van Rose, Susanna. Volcano & Earthquake. 2008. (DK Eyewitness Bks.). 72p. (J). (gr. 3-8). 15.99 (*978-0-7566-3780-4(5)) Dorling Kindersley Publishing, Inc.

Van Rose, Susanna & Dorling Kindersley Publishing Staff. Volcanoes & Earthquakes. Stevenson, James, illus. 2004. (Eyewitness Books). 72p. (J). lib. bdg. 19.99 (978-0-7566-0734-0(5)) Dorling Kindersley Publishing, Inc.

El volcan de Quinto. 2000. (McGraw-Hill Ciencias Ser.). (ENG & SPA.). (gr. 5 up). (978-0-02-279684-6(3)) Macmillan/McGraw-Hill Schl. Div.

Los Volcanes, 6 vols., Vol. 2. (Explorers. Exploradores Nonfiction Sets Ser.).Tr. of Volvanoes. (SPA.). 32p. (gr. 3-6). 44.95 (978-0-7699-0645-4(1)) Shortland Pubns. (U. S. A.) Inc.

Volcano! When a Mountain Explodes, 6 vols. (gr. 4 up). 49.95 (978-0-7368-2836-9(2) , High Five) Red Brick Learning.

Volcanoes: Level O, 6 vols., Vol. 2. (Explorers Ser.). 32p. (gr. 3-6). 44.95 (978-0-7699-0609-6(5)) Shortland Pubns. (U. S. A.) Inc.

Volcanoes Learning about the Earth. 2006. (Illus.). 24p. (J). (gr. k-2). 18.50 (*978-0-531-17893-5(5)) Scholastic Library Publishing.

Waiakea High Writer's Group. Hot Lava, Cool Rain. 2001. (gr. 7-12). lib. bdg. 25.20 (978-0-613-74532-1(9)) Tandem Library Bks.

Waldron, Melanie & Lapthorn, Nicholas. Volcanoes. 2007. (J). (*978-1-4034-9606-5(4)); pap. (*978-1-4034-9616-4(1)) Heinemann.

Walker, Sally M. Volcanoes. 2007. (Early Bird Earth Science Ser.). (J). 26.60 (*978-0-8225-6733-2(4) , Lerner Pubns.) Lerner Publishing Group.

Watt, Fiona. Earthquakes & Volcanoes. rev. ed. 2007. (Geography Ser.). 32p. (J). pap. 7.99 (*978-0-7945-1531-7(2) , Usborne) EDC Publishing.

Webster, Christine. Mauna Loa. (Natural Wonders of the U. S. A. Ser.). (Illus.). 32p. (J). 2004. pap. 7.95 (978-1-59036-162-7(8)); 2003. lib. bdg. 18.20 (978-1-59036-040-8(0)) Weigl Pubs., Inc.

Weil, Ann. Volcanoes. 2003. (Illus.). 64p. (YA). per. 3.95 (978-1-56254-668-7(6) , SP6686) Saddleback Educational Publishing.

What Are Volcanoes?, 6 vols., Vol. 2. 2005. (Earth & Outer Space Ser.). (gr. k-2). 28.95 (978-0-7368-3280-9(7)) Red Brick Learning.

Whiting, Jim. The Volcanic Eruption on Santorini, 1500 BCE. 2007. (Natural Disasters Ser.). (J). lib. bdg. 25.70 (*978-1-58415-568-3(X)) Mitchell Lane Pubs., Inc.

Wood, Jennifer. Volcanoes. 2004. (Interfact Ser.). (SPA., Illus.). 48p. (J). (gr. 3-6). 14.95 incl. cd-rom (978-1-58728-468-7(5) , Two Can Publishing) T&N Children's Publishing.

Wood, Jenny. Los Volcanes. 2004. (Interfact Ser.). (SPA., Illus.). 48p. (J). (gr. 3-6). 14.95 incl. cd-rom (978-1-58728-977-4(6) , Two Can Publishing) T&N Children's Publishing.

Wood, Lily. Volcanoes. (Scholastic Science Readers Ser.). 48p. (J). 2001. (gr. 2-3). pap. 3.99 (978-0-439-29585-7(8) , Scholastic Reference); 2000. (Illus.). (978-0-439-16294-4(7)) Scholastic, Inc.

—Volcanoes. 2001. (Scholastic Science Ser.). (Illus.). (J). (978-0-606-21418-6(6)) Tandem Library Bks.

Woods, Michael & Woods, Mary B. Volcanoes. 2007. (Disasters up Close Ser.). (Illus.). 64p. (J). (gr. 4-6). 27.93 (978-0-8225-4715-0(5) , Lerner Pubns.) Lerner Publishing Group.

World Book, Inc Staff, contrib. by. Volcanoes. 2007. (J). (***978-0-7166-9815-9(3)***) World Bk., Inc.

VOLCANOES—FICTION

Abela, Deborah. Mission: the Nightmare Vortex. O'Connor, George, illus. 2007. (Spy Force Ser.). 256p. (J). pap. 5.99 (978-1-4169-3484-4(7) , Aladdin) Simon & Schuster Children's Publishing.

Avalon, Dawn. Bubbles. A Wet Dragon. 2006. 59p. pap. 8.21 (978-1-4116-1177-1(2)) Lulu.com.

Cook, Sherry & Johnson, Terri. Vinnie Volcano, 26. Kuhn, Jesse, illus. l.t. ed. 2006. (Quirkles—Exploring Phonics through Science Ser.: 22). 32p. (J). 7.99 (978-1-933815-21-3(3) , Quirkles, The) Creative 3, LLC.

Dulin, Daniel L. The Littlest Volcano. Dulin, Daniel L., illus. 2000. (Illus.). 16p. (J). (ps-2). pap. (978-0-9677274-1-7(3)) BlackKat Publishing.

Galarza, Sheri & Entz, Susan. Pele, the Volcano Goddess. Hale, Bruce, illus. 1999. (Hawaiian Values Ser.: Vol. 6). 24p. (J). (ps-2). 5.95 (978-1-57306-092-9(5)) Bess Pr., Inc.

George, Jean Craighead. Dear Katie, the Volcano Is a Girl. 32p. (J). pap. (978-0-7868-1178-6(1)) Hyperion Bks. for Children.

Geraghty, Paul. Dinosaur in Danger. 2005. (Illus.). 32p. (J). pap. (***978-0-09-943865-6(8)*** , Red Fox) Random Hse. Children's Bks.

Gleasner, Diana C. Popoki's Incredible Adventure at the Volcano. Winton, Andrea E., illus. 1999. (J). (978-0-9651185-5-2(X)) Gleasner, Bill & Diana Inc.

Godkin, Celia. When the Giant Stirred: Legend of a Volcanic Island. Godkin, Celia, illus. 2005. (Illus.). 40p. (J). pap. (978-1-55041-965-8(X)) Fitzhenry & Whiteside, Ltd.

—When the Giant Stirred: Legend of a Volcanic Island. 2002. (Illus.). 40p. (J). (978-1-55041-683-1(9)) Fitzhenry & Whiteside, Ltd.

Hathorn, Libby. Volcano Boy. 2002. 208p. (YA). pap. (978-0-7344-0249-3(X) , Lothian Bks.) Hachette Livre Australia.

Hayler, Kate. Volcano Alert! Team Mission: A Pop-up Book. Giraffe, Red & Doughty, Clare, illus. 2006. 10p. (J). (gr. k-4). reprint ed. 19.00 (978-1-4223-5075-1(4)) DIANE Publishing Co.

Jennings, Richard W. Mystery in Mt. Mole. 2003. 160p. (J). (gr. 4-6). 15.00 (978-0-618-28478-8(8)) Houghton Mifflin Co. Trade & Reference Div.

Kehret, Peg & Beckoff, Samuel. The Volcano Disaster. 1998. (FRIGHTMARES). 144p. (J). (gr. 4-7). pap. 4.99 (978-0-671-00968-7(0) , Aladdin) Simon & Schuster Children's Publishing.

Lawrence, Caroline. Secrets of Vesuvius. 2004. (Roman Mysteries Ser.: No. 2). (Illus.). 192p. (J). (gr. 3 up). pap. 5.99 (978-0-14-240118-7(8) , Puffin) Penguin Group (USA) Inc.

Lewis, Paul Owen. Frog Girl. Lewis, Paul Owen, illus. 1999. (Illus.). 32p. (J). (gr. 2 up). lib. bdg. 24.67 (978-0-8368-2228-1(5)) Stevens, Gareth Inc.

—Frog Girl. 2001. (gr. k-3). lib. bdg. 15.25 (978-0-613-37144-5(5)) Tandem Library Bks.

—Frog Girl. 2004. (Illus.). 38p. (J). tchr. ed., tchr.'s planning gde. ed. 2.95 (978-1-58246-009-3(4) , Tricycle Pr.) Ten Speed Pr.

—Frog Girl. (Illus.). 32p. (J). (ps-5). 18.95 (978-1-55110-658-8(2)) Whitecap Bks., Ltd. CAN. *Dist:* Graphic Arts Ctr. Publishing Co.

Oliver, Jack. Volcano Power. Staton, Joe et al, illus. 2005. (Teen Titans Ser.). 32p. (J). (ps-3). pap. 3.99 (978-0-439-75475-0(5) , Scholastic Paperbacks) Scholastic, Inc.

Osborne, Mary Pope. Vacation under the Volcano, Vol. 13. unabr. ed. 2004. (Magic Tree House Ser. : No. 13). 74p. (J). (gr. k-3). pap. 17.00 incl. audio (978-0-8072-0782-6(9) , LFTR 241 SP, Listening Library) Random Hse. Audio Publishing Group.

—Vacation under the Volcano. Murdocca, Sal, illus. 1998. (Magic Tree House Ser.: No. 13). (J). (gr. k-3). 96p. lib. bdg. 11.99 (978-0-679-99050-5(X)); 80p. mass mkt. 3.99 (978-0-679-89050-8(5)) Random Hse. Children's Bks. (Random Hse. Bks. for Young Readers).

—Vacation under the Volcano, nO. 13. Murdocca, Sal, illus. 1998. (Magic Tree House Ser. : No. 13). (J). (gr. k-3). (978-0-606-13972-4(9)) Tandem Library Bks.

Pugin-Rodas, M. C. The Eight Ball Club: Ocean of Fire. 2007. (Illus.). 144p. pap. 15.95 (***978-0-9793761-2-2(2)***) ESOL Publishing.

Smith, Roland. Sasquatch. 2002. (Illus.). (J). 13.19 (978-0-7587-6524-6(X)) Book Wholesalers, Inc.

—Sasquatch. 1999. 188p. (gr. 4-9). pap. 5.99 (978-0-7868-1334-6(2)) Hyperion Bks. for Children.

—Sasquatch. 1999. (gr. k-9). 188p. (J). per. 14.15 (978-0-613-22930-2(4)); (978-0-606-17386-5(2)) Tandem Library Bks.

Spirn, Michele Sobel. Race to the Sea. 2001. (gr. 3-6). lib. bdg. 11.80 (978-0-613-43952-7(X)) Tandem Library Bks.

Sweeney, Jacqueline. Lava. Hart, G. K. & Hart, Vikki, illus. Hart, G. K. & Hart, Vikki, photos by. 2002. (We Can Read! Ser.). 32p. (J). 21.36 (978-0-7614-1511-4(4) , Benchmark Bks.) Cavendish, Marshall Corp.

Teitelbaum, Michael. Volcano Rescue!, No. 2. Roper, Marty, illus. 2001. 24p. (ps-3). pap. 3.50 (978-0-439-25911-8(8)) Scholastic, Inc.

Timon & the Volcano. 1999. (SmartReader Ser.). (J). Level 1. pap., tchr. ed. 19.95 incl. audio (978-0-7887-0776-6(0) , 79340T3); Level 2. pap., tchr. ed. 19.95 incl. audio (978-0-7887-0778-0(7) , 79341T3) Recorded Bks., LLC.

Verne, Jules. Voyage au Centre de la Terre.Tr. of Voyage to the Center of the Earth. (FRE.). (J). pap. 14.95 (978-2-07-051437-3(4)) Gallimard, Editions FRA. *Dist:* Distribooks, Inc.

Wilson, Wendy. The First Book of Red. 2005. 99p. pap. 14.95 (978-1-4137-5570-1(4)) PublishAmerica, Inc.

VOLLEYBALL

Balcavage, Dynise. Gabrielle Reece. 2001. (Women Who Win Ser.). (J). pap. (978-0-7910-6532-7(4)); (Illus.). 64p. (gr. 3 up). 25.00 (978-0-7910-6531-0(6)) Facts On File, Inc. (Chelsea Hse.).

Barth, Katrin. Learning Volleyball. 2006. (Illus.). 152p. 14.95 (***978-1-84126-197-3(1)***) Meyer & Meyer Sport, Ltd. GBR. *Dist:* Perseus Distribution.

Barth, Katrin & Linkerhand, Antje. Training... Volleyball. 2007. (Illus.). 152p. (J). pap. 14.95 (978-1-84126-211-6(0)) Meyer & Meyer Sport, Ltd. GBR. *Dist:* Perseus Distribution.

Beeson, Chris. Volleyball. 2003. (Sports Injuries Ser.). (Illus.). 64p. (J). lib. bdg. (978-1-59084-640-7(0)) Mason Crest Pubs.

Blackall, Bernie. Volleyball. 1999. (Top Sport Ser.). (Illus.). 32p. (J). (gr. 4-6). lib. bdg. 21.36 (978-1-57572-706-6(4)) Heinemann Library.

Crossingham, John. Volleyball in Action. 2000. (gr. 3-6). lib. bdg. 14.10 (978-0-613-22576-2(7)); 1999. (978-0-606-22854-1(3)) Tandem Library Bks.

Crossingham, John & Dann, Sarah. Volleyball in Action. 1999. (Sports in Action Ser.). (Illus.). 32p. (J). (gr. 3-4). (978-0-7787-0164-4(6)); pap. (978-0-7787-0176-7(X)) Crabtree Publishing Co.

Ditchfield, Christin. Volleyball. 2003. (True Book Ser.). (Illus.). 48p. (J). 25.00 (978-0-516-22587-6(1) , Children's Pr.) Scholastic Library Publishing.

—Volleyball. 2003. (Illus.). 47p. (J). (ps-7). lib. bdg. 15.25 (978-0-613-67995-4(4)) Tandem Library Bks.

Evdokimoff, Natasha. For the Love of Volleyball. Craats, Rennay, ed. 2001. (For the Love of Sports Ser.). (Illus.). 24p. (J). (gr. 1-3). lib. bdg. 15.95 (978-1-930954-20-5(4)) Weigl Pubs., Inc.

Fauchald, Nick. Bump! Set! Spike! You Can Play Volleyball. Rooney, Ronnie, illus. 2005. (Game Day Ser.). 24p. (J). (ps). lib. bdg. 22.60 (978-1-4048-1153-9(2)) Picture Window Bks.

Giddens, Sandra & Giddens, Owen. Volleyball: Rules, Tips, Strategy, & Safety. 2005. (Sports from Coast to Coast Ser.). (Illus.). 48p. (J). (gr. 5-8). lib. bdg. 26.50 (978-1-4042-0185-9(8)) Rosen Publishing Group, Inc., The.

Grozdanovic, Sava, et al. Volleyball for Boys & Girls. 2004. (Illus.). 168p. pap. 17.95 (978-1-84126-126-3(2)) Meyer & Meyer Sport, Ltd. GBR. *Dist:* Lewis International, Inc., Perseus Distribution.

Huff, Richard M. The Composite Guide to Volleyball. 2000. (Composite Guides Ser.). (Illus.). 64p. (J). (gr. 8-12). 18.65 (978-0-7910-5869-5(7) , Chelsea Hse.) Facts On File, Inc.

Jensen, Julie. Play-by-Play Volleyball. King, Andy, photos by. 2005. (Play-by-Play Ser.). (Illus.). 80p. (gr. 4-8). pap., lib. bdg. 23.93 (978-0-8225-9882-4(5)) Lerner Publishing Group.

Kadupski, Charlie, ed. The Official Athletic College Guide: Volleyball. 2001. (Illus.). 864p. (YA). (gr. 9 up). pap. 34.95 (978-1-893588-04-2(1)) Sport Source, Inc., The.

Lockman, Darcy. Volleyball for Fun! 2006. (Sports for Fun! Ser.). (Illus.). 48p. (J). (gr. 3-5). 22.60 (978-0-7565-1683-3(8)) Compass Point Bks.

Manley, Claudia B. Competitive Volleyball for Girls. 2005. (SportsGirl Ser.). (Illus.). 64p. (YA). (gr. 5-8). lib. bdg. 26.50 (978-0-8239-3404-1(7)) Rosen Publishing Group, Inc., The.

Morgan, Terri. Gabrielle Reece: Volleyball's Model Athlete. 1999. (Sports Achievers Biographies Ser.). (Illus.). (YA). (gr. 4-9). 80p. lib. bdg. 22.60 (978-0-8225-3667-3(6)); 64p. pap. (978-0-8225-9828-2(0)) Lerner Publishing Group. (LernerSports).

—Gabrielle Reece: Volleyball's Model Athlete. 1999. (Illus.). (J). (978-0-606-18819-7(3)) Tandem Library Bks.

Panamericana Staff. Reglamento de Voleibol.Tr. of Volleyball. (SPA.). 160p. (J). 6.95 (978-958-30-0015-7(9)) Panamericana Editorial COL. *Dist:* AIMS International Bks., Inc.

Schwartz, Heather E. Girls' Volleyball: Setting up Success. 2007. (Illus.). 32p. (J). (978-0-7368-6826-6(7)) Capstone Pr., Inc.

Sherrow, Victoria. Volleyball. 2002. (History of Sports Ser.). (Illus.). 104p. (YA). (gr. 6-9). 28.70 (978-1-56006-961-4(9) , Lucent Bks.) Thomson Gale.

Slupskiy, Leon. Volleyball with the Family: Fife Steps to Success. Synepolsky, I. & Belomlinsky, M., illus. 2003. 105/35p. (YA). pap. (978-0-9728301-3-3(8)) Publishing Hse. Gelany.

YMCA of the USA Staff. Playing YMCA Volleyball: Bronze Edition. 2000. (Illus.). 48p. (J). pap. 6.00 (978-0-7360-3049-6(2) , YMCA of the U.S.A.) Human Kinetics Pubs.

—Playing YMCA Volleyball: Gold Edition. 2000. (Illus.). 48p. (J). pap. 6.00 (978-0-7360-3051-9(4) , YMCA of the U.S.A.) Human Kinetics Pubs.

—Playing YMCA Volleyball: Silver Edition. 2000. (Illus.). 48p. (J). pap. 6.00 (978-0-7360-3050-2(6) , YMCA of the U.S.A.) Human Kinetics Pubs.

VOLUNTARISM

Black, Michael A. Volunteering to Help Kids. 2000. (High Interest Bks.). (Illus.). 48p. (YA). (gr. 7-12). 23.00 (978-0-516-23372-7(6) , Children's Pr.) Scholastic Library Publishing.

—Volunteering to Help Kids. 2000. (gr. 3-6). lib. bdg. 15.25 (978-0-613-89019-9(1)) Tandem Library Bks.

Ditchfield, Christin. Serving Your Community. 2004. (True Bks.). (Illus.). 48p. (J). (gr. 3-5). pap. 6.95 (978-0-516-27911-4(4) , Children's Pr.) Scholastic Library Publishing.

Harcourt School Publishers Staff. Everyone Can Help Below Level. 3rd ed. 2002. (Trophies Reading Program Ser.). (Illus.). pap. 5.10 (978-0-15-323140-7(8)) Harcourt Schl. Pubs.

—Together, We Can Do It. 3rd ed. 2002. (Trophies English Language Learners Ser.). (Illus.). pap. 5.10 (978-0-15-327816-7(1)) Harcourt Schl. Pubs.

Hoose, Phillip. It's Our World, Too! 2002. (gr. 5-8). lib. bdg. 22.25 (978-0-613-57308-5(0)) Tandem Library Bks.

—It's Our World, Too! Young People Who Are Making a Difference. 2002. (Illus.). 176p. (J). pap. 13.00 (978-0-374-33622-6(9) , Sunburst) Farrar, Straus & Giroux.

Isler, Claudia. Volunteering to Help in Your Neighborhood. 2000. (High Interest Bks.). (Illus.). 48p. (YA). (gr. 7-12). 23.00 (978-0-516-23374-1(2)); pap. 6.95 (978-0-516-23574-5(5)) Scholastic Library Publishing. (Children's Pr.).

—Volunteering to Help with Animals. 2000. (High Interest Bks.). (Illus.). 48p. (gr. 7-12). (J). 23.00 (978-0-516-23397-0(1)); (YA). pap. 6.95 (978-0-516-23575-2(3)) Scholastic Library Publishing. (Children's Pr.).

—Volunteering to Help with Animals. 2000. (gr. 3-6). lib. bdg. 15.25 (978-0-613-90482-7(6)) Tandem Library Bks.

Klee, Sheila. Volunteering for a Political Campaign. 2000. (High Interest Bks.). (Illus.). 48p. (YA). (gr. 7-12). pap. 6.95 (978-0-516-23576-9(1) , Children's Pr.) Scholastic Library Publishing.

—Volunteering for a Political Campaign. 2000. (gr. 3-6). lib. bdg. 15.25 (978-0-613-89021-2(3)) Tandem Library Bks.

Lewis, Barbara A. The Kid's Guide to Service Projects: Over 500 Service Ideas for Young People Who Want to Make a Difference. 2004. (Self-Help for Kids Ser.). 184p. (YA). (gr. 5 up). pap. 12.95 (978-0-915793-82-2(2) , FS323) Free Spirit Publishing, Inc.

Louis, Nancy. United We Stand. 2002. (War on Terrorism Ser.). (Illus.). 64p. (J). (gr. 4-8). lib. bdg. 25.65 (978-1-57765-660-9(1) , ABDO & Daughters) ABDO Publishing Co.

Marcovitz, Hal. Teens & Voluntarism. 2005. (Gallup Youth Survey, Major Issues & Trends Ser.). (Illus.). 112p. (YA). (gr. 8-12). lib. bdg. 22.95 (978-1-59084-877-7(2)) Mason Crest Pubs.

Mintzer, Richard. Helping Hands: How Families Can Reach Out to Their Community. 2002. (Focus on Family Matters Ser.). (Illus.). 64p. (YA). (gr. 6-12). 25.00 (978-0-7910-6952-3(4)) Facts On File, Inc.

Murdico, Suzanne J. Volunteering to Help the Environment. 2000. (High Interest Bks.). (Illus.). 48p. (YA). (gr. 7-12). pap. 6.95 (978-0-516-23573-8(7) , Children's Pr.) Scholastic Library Publishing.

Newell, Patrick. Volunteering to Help Seniors. 2000. (High Interest Bks.). (Illus.). 48p. (gr. 7-12). (J). 23.00 (978-0-516-23399-4(8)); (YA). pap. 6.95 (978-0-516-23577-6(X)) Scholastic Library Publishing. (Children's Pr.).

Orr, Tamra. Beyond Government. 2008. (J). lib. bdg. 25.26 (***978-1-60279-060-5(4)***) Cherry Lake Publishing.

Perry, Susan K. Catch the Spirit: Teen Volunteers Tell How They Made a Difference. 2000. (gr. 7-12). lib. bdg. 24.55 (978-0-613-72664-1(2)) Tandem Library Bks.

Rondeau, Amanda. Do Something about It! 2004. (Illus.). (J). (ps-3). lib. bdg. 119.58 (978-1-59197-570-0(0) , SandCastle) ABDO Publishing Co.

—Do Something in Your City. 2004. (Do Something about It! Ser.). 23p. (J). (ps-3). lib. bdg. 19.93 (978-1-59197-571-7(9)) ABDO Publishing Co.

—Do Something in Your Community. 2004. (Do Something about It! Ser.). (Illus.). 23p. (J). (ps-3). lib. bdg. 19.93 (978-1-59197-572-4(7)) ABDO Publishing Co.

—Do Something in Your Country. 2004. (Do Something about It! Ser.). (Illus.). 23p. (J). (ps-3). lib. bdg. 19.93 (978-1-59197-573-1(5)) ABDO Publishing Co.

—Do Something in Your Family. 2004. (Do Something about It! Ser.). (Illus.). 23p. (J). (ps-3). lib. bdg. 19.93 (978-1-59197-574-8(3)) ABDO Publishing Co.

—Do Something in Your State. 2004. (Do Something about It! Ser.). (Illus.). 23p. (J). (ps-3). lib. bdg. 19.93 (978-1-59197-575-5(1)) ABDO Publishing Co.

—Do Something in Your World. 2004. (Do Something about It! Ser.). (Illus.). 23p. (J). (ps-3). lib. bdg. 19.93 (978-1-59197-576-2(X)) ABDO Publishing Co.

—Volunteering. 2003. (United We Stand Ser.). (Illus.). 24p. (J). (ps-3). lib. bdg. 19.93 (978-1-57765-882-5(5)) ABDO Publishing Co.

Siegel, Danny & Eisenberger, Naomi. Mitzvah Magic: Kids Can Do Mitzvahs. 2002. (Illus.). 64p. (J). (gr. 2 up). pap. 8.95 (978-1-58013-034-9(8)) Kar-Ben Publishing.

The Truth about Serving Others. 1998. (Core Belief Bible Study Ser.). (YA). (gr. 7-9). pap. 11.99 (978-0-7644-0871-7(2)) Group Publishing, Inc.

Volunteering: Do What You Like to Do. 2004. (YA). (978-1-929888-38-2(4)) National Crime Prevention Council.

Waldman, Jackie. Teens with the Courage to Give: Young People Who Triumphed over Tragedy & Volunteered to Make a Difference. 2000. (Call to Action Ser.). (Illus.). 192p. (gr. 9-12). pap. 15.95 (978-1-57324-504-3(6) , Red Wheel) Red Wheel/Weiser.

—Teens with the Courage to Give: Young People Who Triumphed over Tragedy & Volunteered to Make a Difference. 2000. (gr. 7-12). lib. bdg. 25.70 (978-0-613-79193-9(2)) Tandem Library Bks.

Wandberg, Robert. Volunteering: Giving Back. 2000. (Contemporary Issues Ser.). (Illus.). 64p. (YA). (gr. 4-6). lib. bdg. 23.93 (978-0-7368-1022-7(6) , LifeMatters Bks.) Capstone Pr., Inc.

Weeldreyer, Laura. Everything You Need to Know about Volunteering. 2005. (Need to Know Library). (Illus.). 64p. (J). (gr. 7-12). 25.25 (978-0-8239-3220-7(6) , NTVOLU) Rosen Publishing Group, Inc., The.

Wheeler, Jill C. Red Cross Volunteers. 2003. (Everyday Heroes (cb) Ser.). (Illus.). 32p. (J). (gr. k-6). lib. bdg. 22.78 (978-1-57765-857-3(4)) ABDO Publishing Co.

Why Serving Others Matters. 1998. (Core Belief Bible Study Ser.). (YA). (gr. 10-12). pap. 11.99 (978-0-7644-0895-3(X)) Group Publishing, Inc.

VOLUNTARISM—FICTION

Dower, Laura. From the Files of Madison Finn: Heart to Heart. 2003. (gr. 3-6). lib. bdg. 13.00 (978-0-613-75026-4(8)) Tandem Library Bks.

Fergus, Maureen. Exploits of a Reluctant (But Extremely Goodlooking) Hero. 2007. 216p. (YA). (gr. 7 up). (***978-1-55453-025-0(3)***); (***978-1-55453-024-3(5)***) Kids Can Pr., Ltd.

Grogan, Joy. Into the Fold. 2003. 156p. per. 15.00 (978-0-9740321-6-0(6)) Open Bk. Publishing.

Harcourt School Publishers Staff. Everyone Can Help: Take-Home Book. 1999. (Collections Ser.). (Illus.). (J). pap. 1.90 (978-0-15-317299-1(1)) Harcourt Schl. Pubs.

May, Eleanor. Ty's Triple Trouble. Wummer, Amy, illus. 2007. (Social Studies Connects). 32p. (J). (***978-1-4287-1957-6(1)***); (gr. 2-4). pap. 4.99 (***978-1-57565-237-5(4)***) Kane Pr., The.

Payne, James L. Princess Navina Visits Voluntaria. Schuppel, Diana, illus. 2002. (C). per. 12.95 (978-0-915728-16-9(8)) Lytton Publishing Co.

Prentiss, Timothy. Miss Keen Needs Help. 2006. (Early Explorers Ser.). (J). 34.00 (***978-1-4108-6113-9(9)***) Benchmark Education Co.

Reinhardt, Dana. How to Build a House. 2008. 240p. (YA). (gr. 7). lib. bdg. 18.99 (***978-0-375-94454-3(0)*** , Lamb, Wendy) Random Hse. Children's Bks.

Van Syckle, A. & Schwartz, Josh. The OC: 'twas the Night Before Chrismukkah. 2005. 206p. (YA). (978-1-4156-3915-3(9)) Scholastic, Inc.

VOLUNTEERS IN SERVICE TO AMERICA

Erlbach, Arlene. The Kids' Volunteering Book. 1998. (Kids' Ventures Ser.). (Illus.). 64p. (J). (gr. 3-6). pap. (978-0-8225-9820-6(5) , Lerner Pubns.) Lerner Publishing Group.

VON BRAUN, WERNHER, 1912-1977

Spangenburg, Ray & Moser, Diane Kit. Wernher Von Braun: Out of the Fire, the Stars. 2nd rev. ed. 2008. (Makers of Modern Science Ser.). 160p. (gr. 6-12). 29.95 (***978-0-8160-6179-2(3)*** , Chelsea Hse.) Facts On File, Inc.

VOTING

see Elections; Suffrage

VOYAGERS

see Explorers; Travelers

VOYAGES AND TRAVELS

Alderfer, Zoe, et al. Ann & Liv Cross Antarctica: A Dream Come True! 2003. (Illus.). 32p. (J). 15.95 (978-0-7382-0934-0(1)) Da Capo Pr., Inc.

Araujo, Orlando. Los Viajes de Miguel Vicente Pata Caliente. (SPA.). (J). pap. (978-980-01-0933-5(1) , XO8023) Monte Avila Editores Latinoamericana CA VEN. *Dist:* Lectorum Pubns., Inc.

Axworthy, Anni. Anni's Diary of France. Axworthy, Anni, illus. 2000. (Illus.). 32p. (J). (gr. 2-5). pap. 6.95 (978-1-58089-024-3(5)) Charlesbridge Publishing, Inc.

—Anni's Diary of France. 2000. (gr. 3-6). lib. bdg. 15.25 (978-0-613-35063-1(4)); (Illus.). (J). (978-0-606-18746-6(4)) Tandem Library Bks.

—Anni's India Diary. 2000. (J). (978-0-606-18747-3(2)) Tandem Library Bks.

Bandon, Alex & O'Brien, Patrick. The Travels of Marco Polo. 1999. (Explorers & Exploration Ser.). (Illus.). 48p. (J). (gr. 4-7). lib. bdg. 22.83 (978-0-7398-1485-7(0)) Raintree.

Banyard, Antonia. Dangerous Crossings! 2007. (True Stories from the Edge Ser.). (Illus.). 144p. (J). (gr. 4-12). 18.95 (***978-1-55451-086-3(4)***); pap. 8.95 (***978-1-55451-085-6(6)***) Annick Pr., Ltd. CAN. *Dist:* Firefly Bks., Ltd.

Benjamin, Rachel. Take a Trip. 2003. (Compass Point Phonics Readers Ser.). (Illus.). 16p. (J). (gr. 1 up). 13.26 (978-0-7565-0526-4(7)) Compass Point Bks.

Bligh, William. The Mutiny on Board HMS Bounty. Lynch, Brendan, illus. 2002. (Great Illustrated Classics Ser.). 240p. (J). (gr. 3-8). 21.35 (978-1-57765-696-8(2) , ABDO & Daughters) ABDO Publishing Co.

Brown, Don. Far Beyond the Garden Gate: Alexandra David-Neel's Journey to Lhasa. Brown, Don, illus. 2002. (Illus.). 32p. (J). (gr. k-3). tchr. ed. 16.00 (978-0-618-08364-0(2)) Houghton Mifflin Co. Trade & Reference Div.

Burgan, Michael. Marco Polo: Marco Polo & the Silk Road to China. 2002. (Exploring the World Ser.). (Illus.). 48p. (J). (gr. 4 up). lib. bdg. 22.60 (978-0-7565-0180-8(6)) Compass Point Bks.

Burton, Frances. That's Me, Tyler! Thompson, Karmen, illus. 2002. 32p. (J). (ps-3). lib. bdg. 15.95 (978-0-9650769-2-0(X)) Stonehill Publishing.

Canetti, Yanitzia. Our World of Wonders. 2000. (Pair-It Books). (Illus.). 40p. (J). pap. (978-0-7398-0887-0(7)) Steck-Vaughn.

Chait, Baruch. The Lost Treasure of Tikkun Hamiddos Island. Pollack, Gadi, illus. (Good Middos Ser.: Vol. 2). 62p. 25.99 (978-1-58330-478-5(9)) Feldheim Pubs.

Childress, Diana. Marco Polo's Travels in China. 2006. (Pivotal Moments in History Ser.). 160p. (YA). (gr. 9-12). lib. bdg. 38.60 (978-0-8225-5903-0(X) , Twenty-First Century Bks.) Lerner Publishing Group.

Crichton, Andrew. The History of Arabia , Ancient & Modern Volume I, Vol. 1. 2006. (Illus.). cd-rom (978-1-892824-43-1(4)) AFCHRON.

Currie, Stephen. Travels to Distant Lands: 1000-1400. 2004. (Reading Expeditions Ser.). (Illus.). 32p. (J). (978-0-7922-4542-1(3)) National Geographic Society.

Enchantment of the World, Second Series, 93 bks., Set. Incl. Argentina. 2nd ed. Hintz, Martin. (Illus.). 144p. (J). 1998. 36.00 (978-0-516-20647-9(8)); Armenia. Hintz, Martin. (Illus.). 144p. (YA). 2004. 36.00 (978-0-516-24257-6(1)); Australia. 2nd ed. Heinrichs, Ann. (Illus.). 144p. (J). 1998. 36.00 (978-0-516-20648-6(6)); Austria. Stein, R. Conrad. (Illus.). 144p. (YA). 2000. 36.00 (978-

T U V

0-516-21049-0(1)); Belgium. Burgan, Michael. (Illus.). 144p. (J). 2000. 36.00 (978-0-516-21006-3(8)); Bolivia. 2nd ed. Augustin, Byron & Morrison, Marion. (Illus.). 144p. (J). 2001. 36.00 (978-0-516-21050-6(5)); Bosnia & Herzegovina. Milivojevic, JoAnn. (Illus.). 144p. (YA). 2004. 36.00 (978-0-516-24247-7(4)); Cambodia. Kras, Sara Louise. (Illus.). 144p. (YA). 2005. 36.00 (978-0-516-23679-7(2)); Cameroon. Kummer, Patricia K. 144p. (YA). 2004. 36.00 (978-0-516-24256-9(3)); Canada. Rogers, Barbara Radcliffe & Rogers, Stillman D. (Illus.). 144p. (YA). 2000. 36.00 (978-0-516-21076-6(9)); Chile. McNair, Sylvia. (Illus.). 144p. (J). 2000. 36.00 (978-0-516-21007-0(6)); Costa Rica. 2nd ed. Morrison, Marion. (Illus.). 144p. (J). 1998. 36.00 (978-0-516-20469-7(6)); Croatia. Hintz, Martin. (Illus.). 144p. (YA). 2004. 36.00 (978-0-516-24253-8(9)); Czech Republic. Milivojevic, JoAnn. (Illus.). 144p. (YA). 2004. 36.00 (978-0-516-24255-2(5)); Democratic Republic of the Congo. Willis, Terri. (Illus.). 144p. (YA). 2004. 36.00 (978-0-516-24250-7(4)); Denmark. Stein, R. Conrad. (Illus.). 144p. (J). 2003. 36.00 (978-0-516-24213-2(X)); Ecuador. Morrison, Marion. (Illus.). 144p. (YA). 2000. 36.00 (978-0-516-21544-0(2)); Egypt. Heinrichs, Ann. (Illus.). 143p. (J). 1997. 36.00 (978-0-516-20470-3(X)); England. Black, Jean Blashfield. (Illus.). 144p. (J). 1997. 36.00 (978-0-516-20471-0(8)); Ethiopia. Heinrichs, Ann. (Illus.). 144p. (J). 2005. 36.00 (978-0-516-23680-3(6)); Germany. Blashfield, Jean F. (Illus.). 144p. (J). 2003. 36.00 (978-0-516-22376-6(3)); Greece. Heinrichs, Ann. (Illus.). 144p. (YA). 2002. pap. 36.00 (978-0-516-22271-4(6)); Greenland. Blashfield, Jean F. (Illus.). 144p. (YA). 2005. 36.00 (978-0-516-23678-0(4)); Guatemala. Morrison, Marion. (Illus.). 144p. (YA). 2005. 36.00 (978-0-516-23674-2(1)); Guyana. Morrison, Marion. (Illus.). 144p. (J). 2003. 36.00 (978-0-516-22377-3(1)); Hungary. Stalcup, Ann. (Illus.). 144p. (J). 2005. 36.00 (978-0-516-23683-4(0)); Iceland. Somervill, Barbara A. (Illus.). 144p. (J). 2003. 36.00 (978-0-516-22694-1(0)); India. Swan, Erin Pembrey. (Illus.). 144p. (J). 2002. 36.00 (978-0-516-21121-3(8)); Indonesia. Orr, Tamra & Greenblatt, Miriam. (Illus.). 144p. (J). 2005. 36.00 (978-0-516-23684-1(9)); Ireland. Blashfield, Jean F. (Illus.). 144p. (J). 2002. 36.00 (978-0-516-21127-5(7)); Kuwait. Foster, Leila Merrell. (Illus.). 143p. (YA). 1998. 36.00 (978-0-516-20604-2(4)); Lebanon. Willis, Terri. (Illus.). 144p. (J). 2005. 36.00 (978-0-516-23685-8(7)); Libya. Willis, Terri. (Illus.). 144p. (J). 1999. 36.00 (978-0-516-21008-7(4)); Luxembourg. Heinrichs, Ann. (Illus.). 144p. (YA). 2005. 36.00 (978-0-516-23681-0(4)); Madagascar. Blauer, Ettagale & Laure, Jason. (Illus.). 144p. (YA). 2000. 36.00 (978-0-516-21634-8(1)); Malaysia. McNair, Sylvia. (Illus.). 144p. (YA). 2002. pap. 36.00 (978-0-516-21009-4(2)); Monaco. Hintz, Martin. (Illus.). 144p. (YA). 2004. 36.00 (978-0-516-24251-4(2)); Morocco. Blauer, Ettagale & Laure, Jason. (Illus.). 144p. (YA). 1999. 36.00 (978-0-516-20961-6(2)); New Zealand. Shepherd, Donna Walsh. (Illus.). 144p. (J). 2002. 36.00 (978-0-516-21099-5(8)); Nicaragua. Morrison, Marion. (Illus.). 144p. (YA). 2002. 36.00 (978-0-516-20963-0(9)); Niger : Enchantment of the World. Heinrichs, Ann. (Illus.). 144p. (J). 2001. 36.00 (978-0-516-21633-1(3)); Norway. Blashfield, Jean F. (Illus.). 144p. 2000. 36.00 (978-0-516-20651-6(6)); Oman. Foster, Leila Merrell. (Illus.). 144p. (YA). 1999. 36.00 (978-0-516-20964-7(7)); Pakistan. Heinrichs, Ann. (Illus.). 144p. (YA). 2004. 36.00 (978-0-516-24248-4(2)); Panama. Augustin, Byron. (Illus.). 144p. 2005. 36.00 (978-0-516-23676-6(8)); Paraguay. Augustin, Byron. (Illus.). 144p. (YA). 2005. 36.00 (978-0-516-23675-9(X)); People's Republic of China. Dramer, Kim. (Illus.). 144p. (YA). 1999. 36.00 (978-0-516-21077-3(7)); Philippines. Oleksy, Walter G. (Illus.). 144p. (YA). 2000. 36.00 (978-0-516-21010-0(6)); Portugal. Blauer, Ettagale & Laure, Jason. (Illus.). 144p. (YA). 2002. pap. 36.00 (978-0-516-21109-1(9)); Qatar. Willis, Terri. (Illus.). 144p. (J). 2004. 36.00 (978-0-516-24254-5(7)); Romania. Willis, Terri & Carran, Betty B. (Illus.). 114p. (J). 2001. 36.00 (978-0-516-21635-5(X)); Russia. Rogers, Stillman D. (Illus.). 144p. (YA). 2002. pap. 36.00 (978-0-516-22494-7(8)); Salvador. Morrison, Marion. (Illus.). 144p. (J). 2001. 36.00 (978-0-516-21118-3(8)); Saudi Arabia. Heinrichs, Ann. (Illus.). 144p. (YA). 2002. pap. 36.00 (978-0-516-22287-5(2)); Scotland. Stein, R. Conrad. (Illus.). 144p. (J). 2001. 36.00 (978-0-516-21112-1(9)); Serbia. rev. ed. Milivojevic, JoAnn. (Illus.). 144p. (YA). 2003. 36.00 (978-0-516-22695-8(9)); Singapore. Kummer, Patricia K. (Illus.). 144p. (YA). 2003. 36.00 (978-0-516-22531-9(6)); Slovenia. Orr, Tamra. (Illus.). 144p. (YA). 2004. 36.00 (978-0-516-24249-1(0)); Spain. Rogers, Lura. (Illus.). 144p. (J). 2001. 36.00 (978-0-516-21123-7(4)); Switzerland. Rogers, Lura & Hintz, Martin. (Illus.). 144p. (J). 2001. 36.00 (978-0-516-21080-3(7)); Syria. Kummer, Patricia K. 144p. (YA). 2005. 36.00 (978-0-516-23677-3(6)); Tibet. Kummer, Patricia K. (Illus.). 144p. (YA). 2003. 36.00 (978-0-516-22693-4(2)); Turkey. Orr, Tamra. (Illus.). 144p. (J). 2003. 36.00 (978-0-516-22679-8(7)); Ukraine. Kummer, Patricia K. (Illus.). 144p. (J). 2001. 36.00 (978-0-516-21101-5(3)); Uruguay. Morrison, Marion. (Illus.). 144p. (J). 2005. 36.00 (978-0-516-23682-7(2)); Venezuela. Willis, Terri. (Illus.). 144p. (YA). 2003. 36.00 (978-0-516-24214-9(8)); Vietnam. Willis, Terri. (Illus.). 144p. (YA). 2002. pap. 36.00 (978-0-516-22150-2(7)); Wales. Heinrichs, Ann. (Illus.). 144p. (J). 2003. 36.00 (978-0-516-22288-2(0)); Zimbabwe. Rogers, Barbara Radcliffe & Rogers, Stillman D. (Illus.). 144p. (J). 2002. 36.00 (978-0-516-21113-8(7)); (gr. 5-9). (Enchantment of the World, Second Ser.). (Illus.). 144p. 2004. Set lib. bdg. 3348.00 (978-0-516-20870-1(5) , Children's Pr.) Scholastic Library Publishing.

Excitement & Adventure on the High Seas: Includes: Monsters of the Deep; Pirates & Treasure; Voyages of Exploration; The Whalers, 4 bks., Set. (Remarkable World Ser.). (Illus.). (J). (gr. 4-7). lib. bdg. 75.92 (978-0-8172-5396-7(3)) Raintree.

Feeney, Kathy. Marco Polo: Explorer of China. 2004. (Explorers! Ser.). (Illus.). 48p. (J). lib. bdg. 23.93 (978-0-7660-2145-7(9)) Enslow Pubs., Inc.

Flowers, Pam. Big-Enough Anna: The Little Sled Dog Who Braved the Arctic. 2003. (gr. k-3). lib. bdg. 17.60 (978-0-613-77220-4(2)) Tandem Library Bks.

Flowers, Pam & Dixon, Ann. Big-Enough Anna: The Little Sled Dog Who Braved the Arctic. Farnsworth, Bill, illus. 2005. (Seldovia Sam Ser.). 32p. (ps up). 15.95 (978-0-88240-577-3(2)) Graphic Arts Ctr. Publishing Co.

—Big-Enough Anna: The Little Sled Dog Who Braved the Arctic. Farnsworth, Bill, tr. Farnsworth, Bill, illus. 2005. 32p. pap. 8.95 (978-0-88240-580-3(2)) Graphic Arts Ctr. Publishing Co.

Franck, Irene M. & Brownstone, David M. Around Africa & Asia by Sea: Trade & Travel Routes. 1999. (Illus.). 114p. (gr. 5-12). reprint ed. 18.00 (978-0-7881-6255-8(1)) DIANE Publishing Co.

Gallagher, Jim. Ferdinand Magellan & the First Voyage Around the World. 1999. (Explorers of the New World Ser.). (Illus.). 63p. (YA). (gr. 4 up). 31.00 (978-0-7910-5508-3(6) , Chelsea Hse.) Facts On File, Inc.

Gefen, Keren. Marco Polo. (Great Explorers Ser.). (Illus.). 48p. (J). (gr. 5 up). 2002. pap. 14.60 (978-0-8368-5177-9(3)); 2001. lib. bdg. 30.00 (978-0-8368-5017-8(3)) Stevens, Gareth Inc. (World Almanac Library).

Great Journeys - Group 3, 4 bks., Set. 131.14 (978-0-7614-1320-2(0) , Benchmark Bks.) Cavendish, Marshall Corp.

Harcourt School Publishers Staff. East Meets West. 3rd ed. 2002. (Trophies English Language Learners Ser.). (Illus.). pap. 5.10 (978-0-15-327764-1(5)) Harcourt Schl. Pubs.

—The 3 Orbits of John Glenn: Take-Home Book. 2001. (Collections Ser.). (Illus.). (J). pap. 1.90 (978-0-15-319668-3(8)) Harcourt Schl. Pubs.

Haywood, John. How We Lived: Invasion, Conquest & War. 2006. (Illus.). 64p. pap., pap. 8.99 (978-1-84476-083-1(9) , Southwater) Anness Publishing GBR. *Dist:* National Bk. Network.

Herbert, Janis. Marco Polo for Kids: His Marvelous Journey to China, 21 Activities. 2001. (For Kids Ser.). (Illus.). 144p. (J). (gr. 4-7). pap. 16.95 (978-1-55652-377-9(7)) Chicago Review Pr., Inc.

Jess, Denise. Colonial Adventures: Charting a Course down the Coast. Lins, Cathy, ed. Behring, Allan, illus. 2nd rev. ed. 2000. (Past Ports Ser.). 270p. (YA). (gr. 5-9). ring bd. 79.95 (978-1-885360-22-9(3)) Demco, Inc.

Journey to the New World: Individual Title Six-Packs. (Action Packs Ser.). 104p. (gr. 3-5). 44.00 (978-0-7635-3301-4(7)) Rigby Education.

Lewin, Ted. Tooth & Claw: Animal Adventures in the Wild. Lewin, Ted, illus. 2003. (Illus.). 112p. (J). (gr. 3-6). 17.99 (978-0-688-14105-9(6)) HarperCollins Pubs.

Lyne, William R. Voyage to Quiburio Vol. 1: Dawn at Galistea. 1998. (Illus.). 264p. (Orig.). (YA). pap. 18.00 (978-0-9637467-4-0(X)) Creatopia Productions - Lamy, New Mexico.

Marcovitz, Hal. Marco Polo & the Wonders of the East. 1999. (Explorers of the New World Ser.). (Illus.). 63p. (J). (gr. 4 up). 31.00 (978-0-7910-5511-3(6) , Chelsea Hse.) Facts On File, Inc.

Mason, Paul. Journeys. 2003. (Rites of Passage Ser.). (Illus.). 32p. (J). pap. (978-1-4034-2513-3(2)); lib. bdg. 24.22 (978-1-4034-3988-8(5)) Heinemann Library.

—Journeys. 2003. (gr. k-3). lib. bdg. 15.90 (978-0-613-89118-9(X)) Tandem Library Bks.

McGraw-Hill Staff. Bon Voyage!, Level 2. 2005. (C). stu. ed. 106.00 incl. cd-rom (978-0-07-868658-0(X) , 9780078686580) Glencoe/McGraw-Hill.

—Bon Voyage!, Level 3. 2005. stu. ed. 107.32 incl. cd-rom (978-0-07-868659-7(8) , 9780078686597) Glencoe/McGraw-Hill.

McHaffie, Natalie. C-Growl: The Daring Little Airplane. McHaffie, Natalie, illus. 1999. (Illus.). 32p. (J). (978-1-55125-015-1(2)) Vanwell Publishing, Ltd.

Michels, Dia L. Look What I See! Where Can I Be? Visiting China. Bowles, Michael J. N., photos by. 2003. (Look What I See! Where Can I Be? Ser.: Vol. 5). (Illus.). 32p. 16.95 (978-1-930775-15-2(6)) Platypus Media, L.L.C.

Nye, Naomi Shihab. I'll Ask You Three Times, Are You OK? Tales of Driving & Being Driven. 2007. 256p. (YA). (gr. 7 up). 15.99 (***978-0-06-085392-1(1)***); lib. bdg. 16.89 (***978-0-06-085393-8(X)***) HarperCollins Pubs. (Greenwillow Bks.).

O'Donnell, Kerri. A Trip Around the World. 2004. (PowerMath Ser.). (J). lib. bdg. (978-0-8239-8871-6(6) , PowerKids Pr.) Rosen Publishing Group, Inc., The.

—A Trip Around the World: Using Expanded Notation to Represent Numbers. 2004. (PowerMath Ser.). 24p. (J). lib. bdg. 21.25 (978-0-8239-8966-9(6) , PowerKids Pr.) Rosen Publishing Group, Inc., The.

Orme, David. Great Journeys. 2008. (Trailblazers Ser.). (Illus.). 36p. pap. 7.95 (***978-1-84167-653-1(5)***) Ransom Publishing Ltd. GBR. *Dist:* International Publishers Marketing.

Otfinoski, Steven. Marco Polo: To China & Back. 2002. (Great Explorations Ser.). (Illus.). 77p. (J). 29.93 (978-0-7614-1480-3(0) , Benchmark Bks.) Cavendish, Marshall Corp.

Park, Ted. Taking Your Camera, 6 bks., Set. 2000. (J). (978-0-7398-4171-6(8)); (Illus.). (978-0-7398-4170-9(X)) Raintree.

Partridge, Elizabeth, et al. Open Your Eyes: Extraordinary Experiences in Faraway Places. Davis, Jill & Morgenstern, Susie, eds. 2003. (Illus.). 208p. (J). (gr. 7). 16.99 (978-0-670-03616-5(1) , Viking Juvenile) Penguin Group (USA) Inc.

Patterson, Kevin. Water in Between: A Journey at Sea. 2001. (gr. 7-12). lib. bdg. 22.25 (978-0-613-36892-6(4)) Tandem Library Bks.

Potter, Giselle. The Year I Didn't Go to School. Potter, Giselle, illus. 2002. (Illus.). 40p. (J). (ps-3). 16.95 (978-0-689-84730-1(0) , Atheneum/Anne Schwartz Bks.) Simon & Schuster Children's Publishing.

Raintree. Steadwell Books: Arkansas Edition, 55 bks., Set. 2003. (Illus.). (J). 1370.90 (978-1-4109-0154-5(8)) Raintree.

Raintree Steck-Vaughn Staff. Our World of Wonders. 1999. (Illus.). (J). pap. 35.60 (978-0-7398-0918-1(0)) Steck-Vaughn.

—Steadwell Books II: Arkansas Edition, 54 bks., Set. 2003. 1359.40 (978-1-4109-0161-3(0)) Raintree.

—Steadwell Books III: Arkansas Edtion, 30 bks., Set. 2003. (Illus.). 776.76 (978-1-4109-0166-8(1)) Raintree.

Raskin, Lawrie & Pearson, Debora. 52 Days by Camel: My Sahara Adventure. Raskin, Lawrie, photos by. 1998. (Adventure Travel Ser.). (Illus.). 88p. (J). (gr. 3-7). pap. 14.95 (978-1-55037-518-3(0)) Annick Pr., Ltd. CAN. *Dist:* Firefly Bks., Ltd.

River Journeys, 6 vols. 2003. (Illus.). (978-0-7398-6075-5(5)) Raintree.

Rumford, James. Traveling Man: The Journey of Ibn Battuta, 1325-1354. Rumford, James, illus. 2001. (Illus.). 40p. (J). (gr. k-3). tchr. ed. 16.00 (978-0-618-08366-4(9)) Houghton Mifflin Co. Trade & Reference Div.

Schmitt, et al. Buen Viaje! 3rd ed. (SPA.). (C). (gr. 6-12). Pt. A. 1999. stu. ed. 59.32 (978-0-02-641256-8(X) , 9780026412568); Pt. B. 2001. stu. ed. 61.32 (978-0-07-825681-3(X) , 9780078256813) Glencoe/McGraw-Hill.

Shuter. Travel Through Time, 36 bks, 6 Packs., Set. 2004. pap. 243.00 (978-1-4109-1274-9(4)) Raintree.

Smith, Barbara Sweetland. Science under Sail: Russia's Great Voyages to America, 1728-1867. 2000. (J). pap. (978-1-885267-02-3(9)) Anchorage Museum of History & Art.

Smith, Barbara Sweetland & Matthews, Donna. Science under Sail: Russia's Great Voyages to America, 1728-1867. 2000. (J). (gr. 4-8). pap. (978-1-885267-03-0(7)) Anchorage Museum of History & Art.

Stefoff, Rebecca. Exploration. 2004. (J). 27.07 (978-0-7614-1640-1(4) , Benchmark Bks.) Cavendish, Marshall Corp.

Tusiani, Joseph & Dante Alighieri. Dante's Divine Comedy. 2001. (Illus.). 170p. (J). (978-1-881901-29-7(7)) LEGAS.

Vergés, Gloria & Vergés, Oiol. La Edad Moderna: Viaje a Traves de la Historia. Rius, María, illus. 2002. (SPA.). 29p. (J). (gr. 2-6). reprint ed. pap. 15.00 (978-0-7567-6061-8(5)) DIANE Publishing Co.

Willems, Mo. You Can Never Find a Rickshaw When It Monssons: The World on One Cartoon a Day. 2006. (Illus.). 408p. (YA). (gr. 8-17). pap. 12.99 (978-0-7868-3747-2(0)) Hyperion Pr.

Windham, Ryder. What You Don't Know about Dangerous Places. 2002. (Illus.). 144p. (J). (gr. 3-7). pap. 4.50 (978-0-439-22541-0(8) , Scholastic Paperbacks) Scholastic, Inc.

Yates, Elizabeth. With Pipe, Paddle & Song: A Story of the French-Canadian Voyageurs. rev. ed. 1999. (Young Adult Historical Library). (Illus.). 276p. (J). (gr. 9-12). reprint ed. pap. 12.95 (978-1-883937-37-9(X) , 37-X) Bethlehem Bks.

Zannos, Susan. The Life & Times of Marco Polo. 2004. (Biography from Ancient Civilizations Ser.). (Illus.). 48p. (J). (gr. 4-8). lib. bdg. 29.95 (978-1-58415-264-4(8)) Mitchell Lane Pubs., Inc.

VOYAGES AND TRAVELS—FICTION

Abarca, Jesse, Jr. Las Adventuras de Dodie el Pajaro Dodo y sus amigos: En el Vidrio Magico. Abarca, Jesse, Jr., ed. Gutierrez, Ericka, tr. 2001. (Las Aventuras de Dodie el Pajaro Dodo y sus amigos). (SPA., Illus.). 48p. (Orig.). (J). (gr. 1-6). pap. 12.95 (978-0-9704850-2-1(6)) Dodo Bks.

—The Adventures of Dodi the Dodo Bird & His Friends: In the Magic Glass. Abarca, Jesse, Jr., ed. 2001. (Illus.). 48p. (J). (gr. 1-10). pap. 12.95 (978-0-9704850-1-4(8)) Dodo Bks.

Adios, Mr. Cox. 2001. (YA). (gr. 6-12). pap. incl. audio (978-0-8224-3284-5(6)) Globe Fearon Educational Publishing.

Aiken, Joan. Bridle the Wind. 2007. (Illus.). 352p. (YA). pap. 6.95 (978-0-15-206058-9(8)) Harcourt Trade Pubs.

Alger, Horatio. A Boy's Fortune: Or, The Strange Adventures of Ben Baker. unabr. ed. 2002. (Polyglot Press Alger Ser.). (Illus.). (J). pap. 17.95 (978-1-931927-79-6(0)) Polyglot Pr., Inc.

Arends, Donald L. Grandpa Grouper, the Fish with Glasses. 2006. (J). (978-0-9768880-0-0(9)) Mission Manuscripts, Inc.

Arenstam, Peter. Nicholas: A Massachusetts Tale. Holman, Karen Busch, illus. 2007. (J). 14.95 (***978-1-58726-519-8(2)*** , Mitten Pr.) Ann Arbor Media Group, LLC.

Avi. The End of the Beginning: Being the Adventures of a Small Snail (and an Even Smaller Ant) Tusa, Tricia, illus. 144p. (J). 2008. pap. 6.95 (***978-0-15-205532-5(0)*** , Harcourt Paperbacks); 2004. 14.95 (978-0-15-204968-3(1)) Harcourt Children's Bks.

Avi Staff. Crispin: At the Edge of the World. 2nd rev. ed. 2006. 240p. (gr. 5-9). 16.99 (978-0-7868-5152-2(X)) Hyperion Pr.

Bahrampour, Ali. Otto, the Story of a Mirror. 2002. (Illus.). (J). (978-0-374-35663-7(7)) Farrar, Straus & Giroux.

Banks, Lynne Reid. The Dungeon. 2002. 288p. (J). (gr. 7 up). 16.99 (978-0-06-623782-4(3)) HarperCollins Pubs.

Barnum, P. T. Dick Broadhead: A Story of Perilous Adve. 2006. pap. 30.95 (***978-1-4286-1959-3(3)***) Kessinger Publishing, LLC.

Bencastro, Mario. A Promise to Keep. Giersbach-Rascon, Susan, tr. from SPA. 2005. 134p. (J). (gr. 3-7). pap. 9.95 (978-1-55885-457-4(6) , Piñata Books) Arte Publico Pr.

Berkner, Laurie. Victor Vito & Freddie Vasco. 2007. 40p. (J). pap. 5.99 (***978-0-439-91529-8(5)*** , Cartwheel Bks.) Scholastic, Inc.

Bingham, Jane, retold by. Around the World in Eighty Days. 2004. (Young Reading Gift Books Ser.). 64p. (J). (gr. 2 up). 8.95 (978-0-7945-0826-5(X) , Usborne) EDC Publishing.

Bird, Helen. La Suelta de Globos, Level 2. Dimitri, Simona, illus. 2005. (Lightning Readers Ser.). 32p. (J). (gr. k-1). pap., pap. 3.95 (978-0-7696-4240-6(3) , Gingham Dog Pr.) School Specialty Publishing.

Bird/Dimitri, Helen/Simona. The Balloon Launch. 2005. (Illus.). 32p. (J). lib. bdg. 9.00 (***978-1-4242-0887-6(4)***) Fitzgerald Bks.

Biro, Val. Gumdrop's Magic Journey. (Illus.). 30p. (J). (978-0-340-71455-3(7)); pap. (978-0-340-71441-6(7)) Hodder General Publishing Division. (Hodder & Stoughton).

Blackstone, Stella. My Granny Went to Market: A Round-the-World Counting Rhyme. Corr, Christopher, illus. 2005. 24p. (J). 16.99 (978-1-84148-792-2(9)) Barefoot Bks., Inc.

Blundell, Judy. Star Wars: The Last of the Jedi #9. 2008. 160p. pap. 5.99 (***978-0-439-68142-1(1)***) Scholastic, Inc.

Bohner, Charles H. Bold Journey: West with Lewis & Clark. 2004. 192p. (J). (gr. 5-9). pap. 6.95 (978-0-618-43718-4(5)) Houghton Mifflin Co. Trade & Reference Div.

Bondoux, Anne-Laure. The Princetta. 2008. 448p. (YA). pap. 8.95 (***978-1-59990-098-8(X)*** , Bloomsbury Children) Bloomsbury Publishing.

—The Princetta. Bell, Anthea, tr. from FRE. 2006. 500p. (YA). 17.95 (978-1-58234-924-4(X) , Bloomsbury Children) Bloomsbury Publishing.

Bondoux, Anne-Laure. Vasco, Leader of the Tribe. Maudet, Y., tr. from FRE. 2007. (J). (gr. 3-7). 352p. 15.99 (***978-0-385-73363-2(1)***); 256p. lib. bdg. 18.99 (***978-0-385-90378-3(2)***) Random Hse. Children's Bks. (Delacorte Bks. for Young Readers).

Boren, Douglas. The Final Voyage of the Sea Explorer. 2004. 92p. pap. 14.95 (978-1-4137-3823-0(0)) PublishAmerica, Inc.

Bowman, Eddie. Gilbert the Goose. Prater, Howard, illus. 1998. (J). pap. 6.95 (978-1-56763-428-0(1)); lib. bdg. 19.95 (978-1-56763-427-3(3)) Ozark Publishing.

Buel, Hubert & Erskine, Dorothy Ward. North with de Anza. 2004. (Illus.). 234p. (J). (gr. 6-10). pap. 9.95 (978-0-8263-3631-6(0)) Univ. of New Mexico Pr.

Burnford, Sheila. The Incredible Journey. (J). (gr. 6-8). 18.95 (978-0-88411-099-6(0)) Amereon LTD.

Buss, Fran Leeper. Journey of the Sparrows. 2002. 160p. (J). pap. 6.99 (978-0-14-230209-5(0) , Puffin) Penguin Group (USA) Inc.

Carlson, Melody. Notes from a Spinning Planet—Papua, New Guinea. 2007. (Notes from a Spinning Planet Ser.). 240p. (YA). pap. 12.99 (978-1-4000-7145-6(3) , WaterBrook Pr.) WaterBrook Pr.

Carman, Patrick. The Tenth City. 2006. (Land of Elyon Ser.: Bk. 3). 208p. (J). pap. 11.99 (978-0-439-70095-5(7) , Orchard Bks.) Scholastic, Inc.

—The Tenth City. l.t. ed. 2006. (Land of Elyon Ser.: Bk. 3). 225p. (J). 23.95 (978-0-7862-7789-6(0)) Thorndike Pr.

Carmody, Isobelle. The Legend Begins. 2006. (Illus.). 208p. (J). (gr. 1-7). 12.95 (978-0-375-83854-5(6)); (gr. 3-7). lib. bdg. 14.99 (978-0-375-93854-2(0)) Random Hse. Children's Bks. (Random Hse. Bks. for Young Readers).

—Little Fur: The Legend Begins. 2006. (Illus.). 272p. (J). (978-0-375-83855-2(4)) Random Hse., Inc.

Cech, John. My Grandmother's Journey. 1998. (978-0-606-13633-4(9)) Tandem Library Bks.

Cheng, Andrea. Shanghai Messenger. Young, Ed, illus. 2005. 40p. (J). (ps-7). 17.95 (978-1-58430-238-4(0)) Lee & Low Bks., Inc.

Christie, Amanda. Drive You Crazy. 2001. (7th Heaven Ser.). 128p. (J). (gr. 5-8). mass mkt. 4.99 (978-0-375-81159-3(1) , Random Hse. Bks. for Young Readers) Random Hse. Children's Bks.

Clement-Davies, David. The Sight. 2002. (gr. 7-12). lib. bdg. 16.45 (978-0-613-68285-5(8)) Tandem Library Bks.

Clements, Bruce. A Chapel of Thieves. 2002. 224p. (J). (gr. 6-9). 16.00 (978-0-374-37701-4(4) , Farrar, Straus & Giroux (BYR)) Farrar, Straus & Giroux.

Conboy, Fiona. Mr. Mombo's Balloon Flight. Holmes, Steve, illus. 1998. (J). 15.99 (978-1-884628-62-7(1) , Flying Frog Publishing) Allied Publishing.

Cooney, Barbara. Miss Rumphius. Cooney, Barbara, illus. 2002. (Illus.). (J). 14.04 (978-0-7587-3148-7(5)) Book Wholesalers, Inc.

—Miss Rumphius. Cooney, Barbara, illus. 2004. (Illus.). 28p. (J). (gr. k-2). reprint ed. pap. 6.00 (978-0-7567-7107-2(2)) DIANE Publishing Co.

Corder, Zizou. Lionboy. (Lionboy Trilogy : Bk. 1). (Illus.). (gr. 3-6). 2003. 288p. (J). 15.99 (978-0-8037-2982-7(0) , Dial); 2004. 304p. (YA). reprint ed. pap. 7.99 (978-0-14-240226-9(5) , Puffin) Penguin Group (USA) Inc.

—Truth. 2006. (Lionboy Trilogy : Bk. 3). 240p. (J). (gr. 3). pap. 6.99 (978-0-14-240705-9(4) , Puffin) Penguin Group (USA) Inc.

Craft, Elizabeth & Fain, Sarah. Bass Ackwards & Belly Up. 2006. 240p. (J). (gr. 7-17). 16.99 (978-0-316-05793-6(2)) Little Brown & Co.

—Bass Ackwards & Belly Up. 2007. 404p. (J). (gr. 10 up). pap. 8.99 (***978-0-316-05794-3(0)*** , Poppy) Little, Brown Bks. for Young Readers.

Crawford, Neil. The Journeyers. 2006. (J). pap. (***978-0-9778205-4-2(8)***) Helm Publishing.

Creech, Sharon. Ruby Holler. (J). 2004. 336p. pap. 6.99 (978-0-06-056015-7(0) , Harper Trophy); 2002. 320p. (gr. 3-7). lib. bdg. 17.89 (978-0-06-027733-8(5) , Cotler, Joanna Books); 2002. 320p. (gr. 4-7). 16.99 (978-0-06-027732-1(7) , Cotler, Joanna Books) HarperCollins Pubs.

—Ruby Holler. 2004. (gr. 3-6). lib. bdg. 14.15 (978-0-613-86272-1(4)) Tandem Library Bks.

—Ruby Holler. l.t. ed. 2003. (Juvenile Ser.). 250p. (J). 22.95 (978-0-7862-5429-3(7)) Thorndike Pr.

Cruz, Maria Colleen. Border Crossing. 128p. (YA). pap. 9.95 (978-1-55885-405-5(3) , Piñata Books) Arte Publico Pr.

—Border Crossing. 2003. (gr. 7-12). lib. bdg. 18.75 (978-0-613-90255-7(6)) Tandem Library Bks.

Czuchna-Curl, Ardyce. Days of Gold. 2002. (Illus.). 128p. (J). pap. 12.95 (978-0-88196-012-9(8)) Oak Woods Media.

Dahlberg, Maurine F. The Story of Jonas. 2007. (Illus.). 160p. (J). (gr. 4-7). 16.00 (978-0-374-37264-4(0) , Farrar, Straus & Giroux (BYR)) Farrar, Straus & Giroux.

de Brunhoff, Jean & de Brunhoff, Laurent. Babar y Sus Amigos Van de Viaje. 2001. Tr. of Babar & Friends Go on a Trip. (978-84-7546-677-4(X)) Beascoa, Ediciones S.A.

de Brunhoff, Laurent. Babar's World Tour. 2005. (Illus.). 48p. (J). (ps-3). 16.95 (978-0-8109-5780-0(9) , Abrams Bks. for Young Readers) Abrams, Harry N. , Inc.

DeFelice, Cynthia C. Bringing Ezra Back. 2006. 160p. (J). 16.00 (978-0-374-39939-9(5)) Farrar, Straus & Giroux.

Demas, Corinne. If Ever I Return Again. (gr. 5 up). 2000. (Illus.). 208p. (J). lib. bdg. 15.89 (978-0-06-028718-4(7)); 2000. 208p. (J). 15.95 (978-0-06-028717-7(9)); 1999. (Illus.). 196p. (YA). pap. 4.95 (978-0-06-440844-8(2)) HarperCollins Pubs.

deRubertis, Barbara. Marty Aardvark. Cockrille, Eva V., illus. 1998. (Let's Read Together Ser.). 32p. (J). (ps-3). pap. 4.95 (978-1-57565-042-5(8)); pap. 8.95 (978-1-57565-047-0(9)) Kane Pr., The.

DiPucchio, Kelly S. Liberty's Journey. Egielski, Richard, illus. 2004. 32p. (ps-2). 15.99 (978-0-7868-1876-1(X)) Hyperion Bks. for Children.

Divakaruni, Chitra Banerjee. The Conch Bearer. 2005. 265p. (J). (gr. 3-7). per. 12.64 (978-0-606-33382-5(7)); per. 14.45 (978-1-4176-6930-1(6)) Tandem Library Bks.

Doyon, Stephanie. Leaving Home. 1999. (On the Road Ser.: No.1). (978-0-606-18626-1(3)) Tandem Library Bks.

Draper, Rochelle, illus. The Stone Wall Dragon. 2007. 32p. 15.95 (***978-0-89272-690-5(3)***) Down East Bks.

Dunbar, Joyce. Shoe Baby. Dunbar, Polly, illus. 2005. 40p. (J). (gr. k-k). 15.99 (978-0-7636-2779-9(8)) Candlewick Pr.

Dunrea, Olivier. Hanne's Quest. 2006. (Illus.). 96p. (J). (gr. 3). 16.99 (978-0-399-24216-8(3) , Philomel) Penguin Group (USA) Inc.

Easton, Kelly. Aftershock. 176p. (YA). 2007. pap. 6.99 (***978-1-4169-0053-5(5)*** , Simon Pulse); 2006. (gr. 7 up). 16.95 (978-1-4169-0052-8(7) , McElderry, Margaret K.) Simon & Schuster Children's Publishing.

Eduar, Gilles. Gigi & Zachary's Around-the-World Adventure: A Seek-and-Find Game. Eduar, Gilles, illus. 2003. (Illus.). 56p. (J). 16.95 (978-0-8118-3909-9(5)) Chronicle Bks. LLC.

Edwards, Julie Andrews & Cole, Henry. Little Bo: The Story of Bonnie Boadicea. 2006. (Illus.). 89p. (J). (gr. k-4). reprint ed. 17.00 (978-1-4223-5481-0(4)) DIANE Publishing Co.

Egan, Tim. Dodsworth in New York. 2007. (Illus.). 48p. (J). (gr. 3-5). 15.00 (***978-0-618-77708-2(3)***) Houghton Mifflin Co.

Evans, Douglas. MVP: Magellan Voyage Project. Shelley, John, illus. 2004. 232p. (J). 16.95 (978-1-932425-13-0(6) , Lemniscaat) Boyds Mills Pr.

Evans, Lezlie. The Bunnies' Trip. Chorao, Kay, illus. 2008. 32p. 16.99 (***978-0-7868-1898-3(0)***) Hyperion Bks. for Children.

Everett Hale, Edward. Last of the Peterkins with Others of the. 2006. pap. (***978-1-4068-1087-5(8)***) Echo Library.

Fabrick, Harriet. Furello Journeys: Furello Questions. Date not set. (Illus.). 200p. (J). (gr. 7-9). wbk. ed. 12.95 (978-0-9646698-9-5(7)) Wild Flower USA.

Feneziani, Serena. In My Basket. 1998. 10p. (J). (ps-1). pap. 15.95 (978-0-7894-2451-8(7)) Dorling Kindersley Publishing, Inc.

Finley, Martha. Elsie's Great Hope, Vol. 8. 2006. (Life of Faith': Elsie Dinsmore Ser.). 224p. (J). pap. 7.99 (978-1-928749-87-5(9)) Zonderkidz.

—Elsie's New Life, Bk. 3. Williams, Scott, illus. Grisco, Michelle, photos by. 1999. (Elsie Dinsmore: Bk. 3). 232p. (YA). (gr. 5-9). 12.99 (978-1-928749-03-5(8)) Zonderkidz.

—Elsie's New Life, Vol. 3. 2006. (Life of Faith': Elsie Dinsmore Ser.). 224p. (J). pap. 7.99 (978-1-928749-82-0(8)) Zonderkidz.

Fisher, Norma Grusy. Anna's Amazing Journey. Knudson, Rachel, tr. Perry, Judy, illus. unabr. ed. 1998. 16p. (Orig.). (J). (gr. 3-5). pap. 5.95 (978-0-9664797-9-9(3)) Roaninn Pubns.

Fleischman, Paul. Whirligig. rev. ed. 1998. 160p. (J). (gr. 7 up). 17.95 (978-0-8050-5582-5(7) , Holt, Henry & Co. Bks. For Young Readers) Holt, Henry & Co.

—Whirligig. 1999. (Laurel-Leaf Bks.). 144p. (YA). (gr. 7-12). reprint ed. pap. 5.99 (978-0-440-22835-6(2) , Laurel Leaf) Random Hse. Children's Bks.

—Whirligig. 1999. 133p. (YA). (gr. 7-12). lib. bdg. 13.55 (978-0-613-23052-0(3)); (978-0-606-17219-6(X)) Tandem Library Bks.

Ford, Sally. Bungee down Under. Dudley, Peter, illus. 2004. 40p. (J). 14.95 (978-1-931807-26-5(4)) Randall, Peter E. Pub.

Fowles, Shelley, illus. The Seven Voyages of Sinbad. 2008. 64p. (J). 18.95 (***978-1-84507-531-6(5)***) Lincoln, Frances Ltd. GBR. *Dist:* Perseus Distribution.

Fox, Christyan & Fox, Diane. Around the World Piggy-wiggy. 2002. (Illus.). 24p. (J). 14.95 (978-1-929766-58-1(0)) Handprint Bks.

Ganz, Yaffa. Savta Simcha & the Roundabout Journey to Jerusalem. Klineman, Harvey, illus. 2000. 128p. (J). 15.99 (978-1-58330-452-5(5)) Feldheim Pubs.

Garis, Howard Roger. Uncle Wiggily's Travels. Date not set. 192p. (J). 20.95 (978-0-8488-2278-1(1)) Amereon LTD.

Gavin, Jamila. The Blood Stone. 2005. (Illus.). 352p. (YA). (gr. 6-8). 18.00 (978-0-374-30846-9(2)) Farrar, Straus & Giroux.

George, Lindsay B. Around the World. George, Lindsay B., illus. 1999. (Who's Been Here? Ser.). (Illus.). 48p. (J). (gr. k-3). 17.99 (978-0-688-15268-0(6)) HarperCollins Pubs.

Gravett, Emily. Meerkat Mail. Gravett, Emily, illus. 2007. (Illus.). 24p. (J). (ps-3). 17.99 (***978-1-4169-3473-8(1)***) Simon & Schuster Children's Publishing.

Gunn, Robin Jones. Hold on Tight. 1998. (Sierra Jensen Ser.: Bk. 10). 160p. (YA). (gr. 7-11). pap. (978-1-56179-637-3(9)) Focus on the Family Publishing.

—Hold on Tight. 1998. (Sierra Jensen Ser.: Bk. 10). (gr. 7-12). lib. bdg. 15.30 (978-0-613-82316-6(8)) Tandem Library Bks.

—Open Your Heart. 1998. (Sierra Jensen Ser.: Bk. 7). 160p. (YA). (gr. 7-11). pap. (978-1-56179-562-8(3)) Focus on the Family Publishing.

Hale, Kathleen. Orlando: A Trip Abroad. 1999. (Illus.). 32p. (YA). (gr. k up). (978-0-7232-4456-1(1) , Warne, Frederick Publishers) Penguin Bks., Ltd. GBR. *Dist:* Penguin Group (USA) Inc.

Hall, Lucy. From England to Jamestowne: A Journey to Find My Father. 2007. (J). (***978-0-9763706-5-9(4)***) Tendril Pr. LLC.

Handford, Martin. Where's Waldo? Handford, Martin, illus. 2007. (Waldo Ser.). (Illus.). 32p. (J). (gr. k-7). pap. 7.99 (***978-0-7636-3498-8(0)***) Candlewick Pr.

—Where's Waldo? The Fantastic Journey. Handford, Martin, illus. 2002. (Where's Waldo? Ser.). (Illus.). 32p. (J). (gr. 1-5). 5.99 (978-0-7636-1922-0(1)) Candlewick Pr.

—Where's Waldo? Now. Handford, Martin, illus. 2007. (Waldo Ser.). (Illus.). 32p. (J). (gr. k-7). pap. 7.99 (***978-0-7636-3499-5(9)***) Candlewick Pr.

—Where's Waldo? the Fantastic Journey. Handford, Martin, illus. 2007. (Illus.). 32p. (J). (gr. k-7). pap. 7.99 (***978-0-7636-3500-8(6)***) Candlewick Pr.

—Where's Waldo? The Great Picture Hunt. Handford, Martin, illus. 2006. (Illus.). 24p. (J). (gr. 1-7). 14.99 (978-0-7636-3043-0(8)) Candlewick Pr.

Handford, Martin. Where's Waldo? the Wonder Book. Handford, Martin, illus. 2007. (Waldo Ser.). (Illus.). 32p. (J). (gr. k-7). pap. 7.99 (***978-0-7636-3502-2(2)***) Candlewick Pr.

Hesse, Karen. Stowaway. unabr. ed. 2004. 328p. (J). (gr. 5-9). pap. 48.00 incl. audio (978-0-8072-8760-6(1) , LYA 259 SP, Listening Library) Random Hse. Audio Publishing Group.

—Stowaway. Parker, Robert Andrew, illus. 2002. 320p. (J). (gr. 5-9). pap. 6.99 (978-0-689-83989-4(8) , Aladdin) Simon & Schuster Children's Publishing.

—Stowaway. Parker, Robert Andrew & Prato, Rodica, illus. 2000. 328p. (J). (gr. 5-9). 17.95 (978-0-689-83987-0(1) , McElderry, Margaret K.) Simon & Schuster Children's Publishing.

—Stowaway. 2002. (gr. 5-8). lib. bdg. 15.30 (978-0-613-45110-9(4)) Tandem Library Bks.

Hirsch, Odo. Bartlett & the Ice Voyage. 2004. (Illus.). 175p. (J). reprint ed. pap. 6.95 (978-1-58234-918-3(5) , Bloomsbury Children) Bloomsbury Publishing.

The Hitchhiker. 2001. (YA). (gr. 6-12). pap. incl. audio (978-0-8224-3280-7(3)) Globe Fearon Educational Publishing.

Hobbs, Will. Crossing the Wire. 224p. (J). 2007. pap. 5.99 (978-0-06-074140-2(6) , Harper Trophy); 2006. (Illus.). lib. bdg. 16.89 (978-0-06-074139-6(2)) HarperCollins Pubs.

—Crossing the Wire: Hobbs Mid Grade 1. 2006. (Illus.). 224p. (J). 15.99 (978-0-06-074138-9(4)) HarperCollins Pubs.

—Jason's Gold. 2000. (gr. 5-8). lib. bdg. 14.15 (978-0-613-29995-4(7)) Tandem Library Bks.

Hobbs, William. Down the Yukon. 2001. (Illus.). 208p. (J). (gr. 5 up). 17.99 (978-0-688-17472-9(8)) HarperCollins Pubs.

—Down the Yukon. 2002. (gr. 5-8). lib. bdg. 14.10 (978-0-613-60801-5(1)) Tandem Library Bks.

—Jason's Gold. (Illus.). 240p. (J). (gr. 6 up). 2000. pap. 5.99 (978-0-380-72914-2(8)); 1999. 16.99 (978-0-688-15093-8(4)) HarperCollins Pubs.

—Jason's Gold. unabr. ed. 2004. 240p. (J). (gr. 5-9). pap. 38.00 incl. audio (978-0-8072-8229-8(4) , Listening Library) Random Hse. Audio Publishing Group.

—Jason's Gold. 2000. (J). (978-0-606-19979-7(9)) Tandem Library Bks.

Hull, Maureen. Rainy Days with Bear. Franson, Leanne, illus. 2004. 32p. (J). 15.95 (978-1-894222-85-3(7)) Lobster Pr. CAN. *Dist:* Univ. of Toronto Pr.

Hunt, Angela Elwell. The Deadly Chase. 2000. (Colonial Captives Ser.: Vol. 2). 192p. (gr. 4-7). pap. 12.95 (978-0-595-08997-0(6) , Backinprint.com) iUniverse, Inc.

Hunt, L. J. The Abernathy Boys. 2004. (Abernathy Boys Ser.). 208p. (J). 15.99 (978-0-06-440953-7(8)); (Illus.). lib. bdg. 16.89 (978-0-06-029259-1(8)) HarperCollins Pubs.

Hunter, Derek. Pirate Club Vol. 2: Brainwash Escape Victims. 2006. (Illus.). 144p. (YA). pap. 12.95 (978-1-59362-051-6(9)) Slave Labor Bks.

Hutchins, Hazel. The List. Van Lieshout, Maria, illus. 2007. 32p. (J). (ps-1). pap. 7.95 (***978-1-55451-063-4(5)***); lib. bdg. 19.95 (***978-1-55451-064-1(3)***) Annick Pr., Ltd. CAN. *Dist:* Firefly Bks., Ltd.

Hyde, Catherine Ryan. Becoming Chloe. 2006. 224p. (YA). (gr. 9). 15.95 (978-0-375-83258-1(0)); lib. bdg. 17.99 (978-0-375-93258-8(5)) Random Hse. Children's Bks. (Knopf Bks. for Young Readers).

Incredible Journey. 1999. (YA). 11.95 (978-1-56137-469-4(5)) Novel Units, Inc.

Jarman, Julia. The Magic Backpack. Gon, Adriano, illus. 2004. (Flying Foxes Ser.). 48p. (J). (978-0-7787-1487-3(X)); pap. (978-0-7787-1533-7(7)) Crabtree Publishing Co.

Jeffers, Oliver. Lost & Found. Jeffers, Oliver, illus. 2005. (Illus.). 32p. (J). (ps-3). 15.99 (978-0-399-24503-9(0) , Philomel) Penguin Group (USA) Inc.

Jones, Chuck. The White Seal. Jones, Chuck, illus. 2006. (Illus.). 32p. (J). 8.95 (978-0-8249-6598-3(1) , Ideals Children's Bks.) Ideals Pubns.

Jones, Veda Boyd. Adventure in the Wilderness: The Journey to Cincinnati's Frontier, 1999. (American Adventure Ser.: No. 13). (Illus.). 143p. (J). (gr. 3-7). 11.95 (978-0-7910-5587-8(6) , Chelsea Hse.) Facts On File, Inc.

Journey. 1999. (YA). 9.95 (978-1-56137-485-4(7)) Novel Units, Inc.

Karr, Kathleen. Born for Adventure. 2007. (Illus.). 208p. (J). (gr. 7 up). 16.99 (***978-0-7614-5348-2(2)***) Cavendish, Marshall Corp.

Kay, Verla. Tattered Sails. Andreasen, Dan, illus. 2001. 32p. (J). 15.99 (978-0-399-23345-6(8) , Putnam Juvenile) Penguin Group (USA) Inc.

Keeling, Annie E. Andrew Golding A Tale of the Great Plague. 2004. reprint ed. pap. 15.95 (978-1-4191-0694-1(5)); pap. 1.99 (978-1-4192-0694-8(X)) Kessinger Publishing, LLC.

Keeling, E. Annie. Andrew Golding (a Tale of the Great Plag. 2006. 40.99 (***978-1-4280-0516-7(1)***); pap. 34.99 (***978-1-4280-0515-0(3)***) IndyPublish.com.

Kelby, Tom. Nathaniel's Journey: Journey Through the Great Woods. 2nd ed. 2000. (Illus.). 50p. (J). (978-1-930914-01-8(6)) Hands to the Plow, Inc.

—Nathaniel's Journey: The King's Armory. Yaeger, Mark, illus. 2003. (J). per. (978-1-930914-04-9(0)) Hands to the Plow, Inc.

Kerby, Mona. Owney, the Mail Pouch Pooch. Barasch, Lynne, illus. 2008. 40p. (J). 16.95 (978-0-374-35685-9(8)) Farrar, Straus & Giroux.

Khanduri, Kamini. Great World Search. Hancock, David, illus. rev. ed. 2005. 48p. (J). pap. 8.99 (978-0-7945-1030-5(2) , Usborne) EDC Publishing.

Kidd, Richard. Daisy Quiere Ser Famosa. 2002. Tr. of Almost Famous Daisy!. (Illus.). (J). (gr. k-3). (SPA.). 200p. 14.95 (978-84-8488-008-0(7)); (CAT., 32p. 14.95 (978-84-8488-012-7(5)) Serres, Ediciones, S. L. ESP. *Dist:* Lectorum Pubns., Inc.

Kierstead-Farber, Vera M. America Is My Country. 2007. 170p. pap. 11.95 (***978-0-533-15643-6(2)***) Vantage Pr., Inc.

Kirkpatrick, Katherine. Escape Across the Wide Sea. 2004. (Illus.). 224p. (J). (gr. 4-6). tchr. ed. 17.95 (978-0-8234-1854-1(5)) Holiday Hse., Inc.

Kolb, Diane. Star to Guide Me: A Journey at Sea. 2000. (gr. 7-12). lib. bdg. 32.70 (978-0-613-73924-5(8)) Tandem Library Bks.

Kompaneyets, Marc. The Squishiness of Things. 2005. (Illus.). 40p. (J). (gr. k-3). 15.95 (978-0-375-82750-1(1) , Knopf Bks. for Young Readers) Random Hse. Children's Bks.

Kowitt, Holly. Road Trip Vol. 2. 2006. (Teenick Ser.). 128p. (J). pap. 4.99 (978-0-439-89041-0(1) , Scholastic) Scholastic, Inc.

Krensky, Stephen. Dangerous Crossing: The Revolutionary Voyage of John & John Quincy Adams. Harlin, Greg, tr. Harlin, Greg, illus. 2004. 32p. (J). (gr. k). 16.99 (978-0-525-46966-7(4) , Dutton Juvenile) Penguin Group (USA) Inc.

Langen, Annette. Letters from Felix: A Little Rabbit on a World Tour. Droop, Constanza, illus. 2003. 47p. (J). 14.99 (978-1-59384-034-1(9)) Parklane Publishing.

Langley, Charles P. North, East, South, West: Catherine, Anna & Geku Take a Long Trip. Holbrook, Kathryn, illus. 2001. (J). (gr. 1-5). per. 9.95 (978-0-9674510-0-8(0)) Anacat Pubns.

Langrish, Katherine. Troll Blood. Stevens, Tim, illus. 2008. 352p. (J). 16.99 (***978-0-06-111674-2(2)***); lib. bdg. 17.89 (***978-0-06-111675-9(0)***) HarperCollins Pubs. (Eos).

Lasky, Kathryn. A Journey to the New World: The Diary of Remember Patience Whipple, Mayflower, 1620. 1999. (Dear America Ser.). (J). 9.95 (978-0-439-15601-1(7)) Scholastic, Inc.

Lawlor, Laurie. Down the Rio Grande, Eighteen Twenty-Nine. 2001. (gr. 3-6). lib. bdg. 12.40 (978-0-613-51210-7(3)) Tandem Library Bks.

—Horseback on the Boston Post Road 1704. Lyall, Dennis, illus. 2002. (American Sisters Ser.: Vol. 7). 208p. (J). pap. 4.99 (978-0-7434-3626-7(1) , Aladdin) Simon & Schuster Children's Publishing.

Layton, Neal. Bartholomew & the Bug. 2006. (Illus.). (J). (ps). 14.99 (978-0-340-87328-1(0)); pap. 9.99 (978-0-340-87329-8(9)) Hodder General Publishing Division GBR. (Hodder & Stoughton). *Dist:* Trafalgar Square Publishing.

Lazo, Caroline. Someday When My Cat Can Talk. Brooker, Kyrsten, illus. 2008. 32p. (J). (ps-3). lib. bdg. 19.99 (***978-0-375-93754-5(4)*** , Schwartz & Wade Bks.) Random Hse. Children's Bks.

Lazo, Caroline Evensen. Someday When My Cat Can Talk. Brooker, Kyrsten, illus. 2008. 32p. (J). (***978-0-375-83754-8(X)*** , Schwartz & Wade Bks.) Random Hse. Children's Bks.

Lees, Stuart. The Lucky Sovereign. Lees, Stuart, illus. 2002. (Illus.). (J). (gr. 3-5). 15.95 (978-1-57091-488-1(5)) Charlesbridge Publishing, Inc.

Lees, Stuart, illus. The Lucky Sovereign. 2002. (J). pap. (978-1-57091-489-8(3)) Charlesbridge Publishing, Inc.

Lester, Alison. Are We There Yet? A Journey Around Australia. Lester, Alison, illus. 2005. (Illus.). 32p. (J). 15.95 (978-1-929132-73-7(5)) Kane/Miller Bk. Pubs., Inc.

Lin, Grace. Olvina Flies. Lin, Grace, illus. rev. ed. 2003. (Illus.). 32p. (J). (ps-2). 15.95 (978-0-8050-6711-8(6) , Holt, Henry & Co. Bks. For Young Readers) Holt, Henry & Co.

List, Gloria A. The Journey. UCR, Center for Visual Comp. Staff, illus. unabr. ed. 1998. 32p. (J). (gr. k-4). pap. 12.95 (978-1-891168-01-7(0)) Univ. of California, Riverside.

Lofting, Hugh. The Voyages of Doctor Dolittle. 2004. (Illus.). 224p. (J). pap. 3.95 (978-0-486-43491-9(5)) Dover Pubns., Inc.

—The Voyages of Doctor Dolittle. Hague, Michael, illus. 2001. (Doctor Dolittle Ser.). 368p. (J). (gr. 4-6). 28.99 (978-0-688-14002-1(5)) HarperCollins Pubs.

—The Voyages of Doctor Dolittle. 2000. (Doctor Dolittle Ser.). (Illus.). 272p. (gr. 4-6). mass mkt. 4.95 (978-0-451-52769-1(0) , Signet Classics) Penguin Group (USA) Inc.

—The Voyages of Doctor Dolittle. Lamut, Sonja, illus. 1998. (Doctor Dolittle Ser.). 288p. (J). (gr. 1-6). 16.99 (978-0-448-41863-6(0) , Grosset & Dunlap) Penguin Group (USA) Inc.

Louis, Catherine. Liu & the Bird Journey Chinese Calligraphy. 2006. (Illus.). 40p. (J). 16.95 (978-0-7358-2050-0(3)) North-South Bks., Inc.

Ma, Jyoti. Sparkling Together: Starbright & His Earthling Friends. Devi, Chandra, illus. 2004. 96p. pap. 19.95 (978-0-932040-54-1(3)) Integral Yoga Pubns.

Maisner, Heather. Diary of a Princess: A Tale from Marco Polo's Travels. Moxley, Sheila, illus. 2004. 32p. (J). (978-0-7112-1854-3(4)); pap. 7.95 (978-1-84507-148-6(4)) Lincoln, Frances Ltd. GBR. *Dist:* Transition Vendor, Perseus Distribution.

Martin, Rafe & Bellm, Dan. Birdwing. (J). 2007. 384p. pap. 6.99 (978-0-439-21168-0(9)); 2005. 368p. pap. 16.99 (978-0-439-21167-3(0)) Scholastic, Inc. (Levine, Arthur A. Bks.).

Mateboer, Hans. Peter the Cruise Ship. 2007. (J). 16.95 (***978-0-9759487-1-2(7)***) Mateboer, Johannes Aart.

Mauner, Claudia & Smalley, Elisa. Zoe Sophia's Scrapbook: An Adventure in Venice. Mauner, Claudia, illus. 2003. (Illus.). 40p. (J). (ps-1). 14.95 (978-0-8118-3606-7(1)) Chronicle Bks. LLC.

McClintock, Barbara. Adèle & Simon in America. 2008. (J). (***978-0-374-39924-5(7)***) Farrar, Straus & Giroux.

McDonald, Megan. Julie's Journey, Bk. 5. McAliley, Susan, illus. 2007. 88p. (YA). (gr. 3 up). 12.95 (***978-1-59369-353-4(2)***) American Girl Publishing, Inc.

McDonnell, Kathleen. The Shining World. 2005. 235p. (YA). pap. 6.95 (978-1-896764-79-5(7)) Second Story Pr. CAN. *Dist:* Orca Bk. Pubs. USA, Univ. of Toronto Pr.

McFadden, Deanna & Verne, Jules. Around the World in 80 Days. Akib, Jamel, illus. 2007. (Classic Starts Ser.). 151p. (J). (***978-1-4287-4207-9(7)***) Sterling Publishing Co., Inc.

Mellentin, Kath. Wheels on the Bus. Tulip, Jenny, illus. 1998. 16p. (J). (ps). 13.99 (978-1-884628-37-5(0) , Flying Frog Publishing) Allied Publishing.

Meyer, L. A. Mississippi Jack: Being an Account of the Further Waterborne Adventures of Jacky Faber, Midshipman, Fine Lady, & Lily of the West. 2007. (Bloody Jack Adventures Ser.). (Illus.). 624p. (YA). (gr. 7 up). 17.00 (***978-0-15-206003-9(0)***) Harcourt Trade Pubs.

Minshall, Caleigh. Blue: Voyage to the Sky. 2005. 54p. (J). pap. 19.95 net. (978-1-59975-284-6(0)) Independent Pub.

Montgomery, Bobbie. Donkey Cart Kids. 2000. (Pathfinder Junior Book Club Ser.). 110p. (J). pap. 6.99 (978-0-8280-1442-7(6)) Review & Herald Publishing Assn.

Morgan, Anna. Daughters of the Ark. 2005. (Illus.). 230p. (J). (gr. 5-9). pap. 7.95 (978-1-896764-92-4(4)) Second Story Pr. CAN. *Dist:* Orca Bk. Pubs. USA, Univ. of Toronto Pr.

Morpurgo, Michael. Kenshuke's Kingdom. 2003. 176p. (J). (gr. 3-6). 16.95 (978-0-439-38202-1(5) , Scholastic Pr.) Scholastic, Inc.

—Kensuke's Kingdom. Foreman, Michael, illus. l.t. ed. 2000. 215p. (J). pap. (978-0-7540-6096-3(9) , CLP 295) BBC Audio.

—Kensuke's Kingdom. 2005. (Illus.). 176p. (J). pap. (***978-1-4052-2174-0(7)***) Egmont Bks., Ltd.

—Kensuke's Kingdom. 2004. 176p. (J). mass mkt. 4.99 (978-0-439-59181-2(3) , Scholastic Paperbacks) Scholastic, Inc.

—Twist of Gold. 2004. 304p. (J). pap. 8.99 (978-0-7497-4687-2(4)) Egmont Bks., Ltd. GBR. *Dist:* Trafalgar Square Publishing.

Moss, Marissa. Amelia's Family Ties. Moss, Marissa, illus. 2007. (Amelia's Notebooks). 40p. (J). (gr. 2-5). 9.99 (***978-1-4169-0914-9(1)*** , Simon & Schuster/Paula Wiseman Bks.) Simon & Schuster Children's Publishing.

—Amelia's Family Ties. 2000. (Amelia's Notebooks). (Illus.). (J). (gr. 3-5). 12.75 (978-0-606-18352-9(3)) Tandem Library Bks.

Mueller, Pamela Bauer. The Bumpedy Road. Weiler, Naomi M., illus. 1999. 112p. (J). (gr. 2-8). reprint ed. pap. 6.00 (978-0-9685097-0-8(3)) Pinata Publishing.

T
U
V

Neitzel, Shirley. I'm Taking a Trip on My Train. Parker, Nancy Winslow, illus. 1999. 40p. (J). (ps-3). 14.89 (978-0-688-15834-7(X)) HarperCollins Pubs.

—Our Class Took a Trip to the Zoo. Parker, Nancy Winslow, illus. 2002. 32p. (J). 15.99 (978-0-688-15543-8(X)) HarperCollins Pubs.

Newman, Patricia. Jingle the Brass. Chesworth, Michael, illus. 2004. 32p. (J). 16.50 (978-0-374-33679-0(2) , Farrar, Straus & Giroux (BYR)) Farrar, Straus & Giroux.

Oades, Joy. Willie the Whale. Vagnozzi, Barbara, illus. 2004. (Read-It! Readers Ser.). 32p. (C). (gr. k-3). 18.60 (978-1-4048-0557-6(5)) Picture Window Bks.

Pasquali, Elena. Ituku's Christmas Journey. Kolanovic, Dubravka, illus. 2005. 32p. (J). (ps-3). 16.00 (978-1-56148-495-9(4)) Good Bks.

Paulsen, Gary. Tucket's Ride, 3. 1998. (Tucket Adventures Ser.). (J). (978-0-606-13877-2(3)) Tandem Library Bks.

—Tucket's Travels Bks.1-5: Francis Tucket's Adventures in the West, 1847-1849, Bks. 1-5. 2003. 560p. (YA). (gr. 4-7). pap. 7.50 (978-0-440-41967-9(0) , Yearling) Random Hse. Children's Bks.

Paver, Michelle. Hermano Lobo: Cronicas de la Prehistoria. Anton de vez, Patricia, tr. 2005. (Illus.). 222p. 17.25 (978-84-7888-933-4(7)) Emece Editores ESP. *Dist:* Ediciones Universal.

—Soul-Eater. Taylor, Geoff, illus. 2007. (Chronicles of Ancient Darkness: No. 3). 336p. (J). lib. bdg. 17.89 (978-0-06-072832-8(9) , Tegen, Katherine Bks) HarperCollins Pubs.

—Spirit Walker. Taylor, Geoff, illus. (Chronicles of Ancient Darkness: No.2). (J). 2007. 384p. pap. 6.99 (978-0-06-072830-4(2) , Harper Trophy); 2006. 368p. 16.99 (978-0-06-072828-1(0) , Tegen, Katherine Bks); 2006. 368p. lib. bdg. 17.89 (978-0-06-072829-8(9) , Tegen, Katherine Bks) HarperCollins Pubs.

—Wolf Brother. Taylor, Geoff, illus. 2005. (Chronicles of Ancient Darkness). 304p. (J). (gr. 5 up). lib. bdg. 17.89 (978-0-06-072826-7(4)) HarperCollins Pubs.

—Wolf Brother. 2005. (Chronicles of Ancient Darkness: Bk. 1). (Illus.). 304p. (J). (gr. 5 up). 16.99 (978-0-06-072825-0(6)) HarperCollins Pubs.

—Wolf Brother. Taylor, Geoff, illus. 2006. (Chronicles of Ancient Darkness). 320p. (J). reprint ed. pap. 6.99 (978-0-06-072827-4(2) , Harper Trophy) HarperCollins Pubs.

Peck, Dale. Drift House: The First Voyage. 2005. 420p. (J). 16.95 (978-1-58234-969-5(X) , Bloomsbury Children) Bloomsbury Publishing.

Pene Du Bois, William & Pene DuBois, William. The Twenty-One Balloons. Pene Du Bois, William, illus. 2005. (Puffin Modern Classics Ser.). (Illus.). 192p. (J). (ps-7). pap. 5.99 (978-0-14-240330-3(X) , Puffin) Penguin Group (USA) Inc.

Penn, Audrey. Blackbeard & the Sandstone Pillar: When Lightning Strikes. Howard, Philip, illus. 2007. 400p. (gr. 3-7). 15.95 (***978-1-933718-08-8(0)***) Tanglewood Pr.

The Phillie Phanatic's Phantastic Journey. 2005. (J). (978-0-9705804-9-8(5)) Middle Atlantic Pr.

Pilegard, Virginia Walton. The Warlord's Fish. Debon, Nicolas, illus. 2002. 32p. (J). 15.95 (978-1-56554-964-7(3)) Pelican Publishing Co., Inc.

Ponti, James & Thorpe, Kiki. Around the World in Eighty Days: Junior Novel. 2004. (Illus.). 144p. (gr. 3-7). pap. 4.99 (978-0-7868-5475-2(8)) Hyperion Bks. for Children.

Pryor, Bonnie. Luke: 1849 - On the Golden Trail. Dodson, Bert, illus. 1999. (American Adventures Ser.). 272p. (J). (gr. 3-7). 15.00 (978-0-688-15670-1(3)) HarperCollins Pubs.

—Luke: 1849—On the Golden Trail. 2000. (American Adventures Ser.). (Illus.). 176p. (J). (gr. 3-7). pap. 4.50 (978-0-380-73102-2(9) , Harper Trophy) HarperCollins Pubs.

—Luke: 1849-On the Golden Trail. 2000. (Illus.). (J). (978-0-606-17977-5(1)) Tandem Library Bks.

Race to Moonrise Rev. 2006. 9.95 (978-1-932738-31-5(2)) Western Reflections Publishing Co.

Ray, Blaine. Patricia Va a California, Vol. 2. 2001. (TPRS First-Year Spanish Novels Ser.). (SPA.). ii, 45p. (YA). (gr. 7-12). pap. 3.95 (978-0-929724-50-8(X)) Command Performance Language Institute.

Razzell, Mary. Runaway at Sea. unabr. ed. 2005. (Illus.). 150p. (YA). (gr. 7-9). 9.95 (978-1-55017-327-7(8)) Harbour Publishing Co., Ltd. CAN. *Dist:* Graphic Arts Ctr. Publishing Co.

Reece, Colleen L. The Mayflower Adventure. 1999. (American Adventure Ser.: No. 1). 144p. (J). (gr. 3-7). lib. bdg. 15.95 (978-0-7910-5041-5(6) , Chelsea Hse.) Facts On File, Inc.

Rees, Celia. Witch Child. 272p. (YA). (gr. 7 up). 2002. pap. 8.99 (978-0-7636-1829-2(2)); 2001. (Illus.). 15.99 (978-0-7636-1421-8(1)) Candlewick Pr.

—Witch Child. unabr. ed. 2004. (Young Adult Cassette Librariestm Ser.). 304p. (J). (gr. 5-9). pap. 40.00 incl. audio (978-0-8072-1198-4(2) , S YA 343 SP, Listening Library) Random Hse. Audio Publishing Group.

—Witch Child. 2002. (gr. 7-12). lib. bdg. 16.45 (978-0-613-60740-7(6)) Tandem Library Bks.

—Witch Child. l.t. ed. 2002. 284p. (J). 22.95 (978-0-7862-3896-5(8)) Thomson Gale.

Rewa. Molly May on the High Seas. Westmoreland, Christy Hulden & Westmoreland, Lori, illus. 2000. 96p. (J). (gr. 2-7). pap. 9.95 (978-1-56474-340-4(3)) Fithian Pr.

—Molly May on the High Seas. (Illus.). 9.95 (978-0-9726375-1-0(6)) Little Red Cat Publishing.

Rey, H. A. & Rey, Margret. Whiteblack the Penguin Sees the World. 2000. (Illus.). 32p. (J). (gr. k-3). tchr. ed. 16.00 (978-0-618-07389-4(2)) Houghton Mifflin Co. Trade & Reference Div.

Riggs, Sandy. Joe Boat. 2006. (Reader's Clubhouse Set B Ser.). (Illus.). 24p. (J). pap. 3.99 (978-0-7641-3296-4(2)) Barron's Educational Series, Inc.

Rinaldi, Ann. The Journal of Jasper Jonathan Pierce: A Pilgrim Boy, Plymouth, 1620. 2000. (My Name Is America Ser.). (Illus.). 160p. (J). (gr. 4-8). pap. 10.95 (978-0-590-51078-3(9)) Scholastic, Inc.

Rockwell, Anne F., tr. & illus. At the Train Station. Rockwell, Anne F., illus. 2005. (J). 15.99 (978-0-06-056227-4(7)); 16.89 (978-0-06-056228-1(5)) HarperCollins Pubs.

Rogers, Alan. Bon Voyage! 2003. (Little Giants Ser.). (FRE., Illus.). 16p. (J). (ps-k). 5.95 (978-1-58728-176-1(7) , Two Can Publishing) T&N Children's Publishing.

Roni Bear's Journey. 1998. (PNI Healing Stories for Children Ser.: No. 1). 24p. (J). (gr. k-6). 6.95 (978-1-893351-01-1(7)) Asclepian Pr.

Rubalcaba, Jill. The Wadjet Eye. 2006. 160p. (J). (gr. 4-6). pap. 5.95 (978-0-618-68927-9(3) , Clarion Bks.) Houghton Mifflin Co. Trade & Reference Div.

Rylant, Cynthia. Tulip Sees America. Desimini, Lisa, illus. 32p. (J). (ps up). 2002. pap. 6.99 (978-0-439-39978-4(5)); 1998. pap. 15.95 (978-0-590-84744-5(9) , Blue Sky Pr., The) Scholastic, Inc.

—Tulip Sees America. 2002. (gr. k-3). lib. bdg. 14.15 (978-0-613-53874-9(9)) Tandem Library Bks.

Sampson, Jeff. Wizard's Betrayal. 2006. (New Adventures Ser.). (Illus.). 241p. (J). (***978-1-4156-4798-1(4)*** , Mirrorstone) Wizards of the Coast.

Schaaf, Ron. Tiger's Quest: Rounding Cape Horn. 2007. (J). (***978-0-9787555-0-8(2)***) Hickory Tales Publishing.

Schomer Wendel, Gretchen & Schomer, Adam Anthony. Becka & the Big Bubble: All Around Town. 2007. (Illus.). 32p. (J). 11.99 (***978-1-933754-10-9(9)***) Waterside Publishing.

Shulevitz, Uri. The Travels of Benjamin of Tudela: Through Three Continents in the Twelfth Century. 2005. (Illus.). 48p. (J). 17.00 (978-0-374-37754-0(5) , Farrar, Straus & Giroux (BYR)) Farrar, Straus & Giroux.

Sidney, Margaret. Five Little Peppers Abroad. (J). 24.95 (978-0-8488-1475-5(4)) Amereon LTD.

Sigsawa, Keiichi. Kino No Tabi, Vol. 2. 2008. (Illus.). 192p. mass mkt. 9.99 (978-1-59816-456-5(2) , Tokyopop Adult) TOKYOPOP, Inc.

Skinner, Daphne. All Aboard! Smath, Jerry, illus. 2007. 32p. (J). (gr. 1-3). pap. 4.95 (***978-1-57565-239-9(0)***) Kane Pr., The.

Smith, Maggie. Counting Our Way to Maine. 1999. (ps-2). lib. bdg. 15.30 (978-0-613-72619-1(7)); (J). (978-0-606-16918-9(0)) Tandem Library Bks.

Soto, Gary. Pacific Crossing. 2003. (Illus.). 144p. (YA). pap. 5.95 (978-0-15-204696-5(8) , Harcourt Paperbacks) Harcourt Children's Bks.

—Pacific Crossing. 1999. (YA). pap., stu. ed. 43.25 incl. audio (978-0-7887-3000-9(2) , 40882) Recorded Bks., LLC.

—Pacific Crossing. 1998. (J). (gr. 5). pap. 3.95 (978-0-439-04479-0(0)) Scholastic, Inc.

Steinkamp, Mary J. The Bear, the Rug, & the Echo Tree. 2004. (Illus.). 64p. (J). (978-1-55306-661-3(8) , Epic Pr.) Essence Publishing.

Stern, Shirley. Around the World. 2008. (Franny's Feet Ser.). 224p. (J). (ps-1). 4.99 (***978-1-4169-4919-0(4)*** , Simon Scribbles) Simon & Schuster Children's Publishing.

Stevenson, Robert Louis. Treasure Island. Todd, Justin, illus. 1999. (Abbeville Classics Ser.). 176p. (J). pap. 7.95 (978-0-7892-0551-3(3) , Abbeville Kids) Abbeville Pr., Inc.

—Treasure Island. Cruz, Nardo, illus. 2nd ed. 1998. (Illustrated Classic Book Ser.). 61p. (J). (gr. 3 up). reprint ed. pap. 4.95 (978-1-56767-239-8(6)) Educational Insights, Inc.

—Treasure Island. 2001. (YA). (gr. 5-12). pap. 8.50 (978-0-8359-0234-2(X)) Globe Fearon Educational Publishing.

—Treasure Island. unabr. ed. 1998. (Wordsworth Classics Ser.). (YA). (gr. 6-12). 5.27 (978-0-89061-103-6(3) , R1033WW) Jamestown.

—Treasure Island. (Young Collector's Illustrated Classics Ser.). (Illus.). 192p. (J). (gr. 3-7). 9.95 (978-1-56156-456-9(7)) Kidsbooks, Inc.

—Treasure Island. 1999. (Illus.). 240p. (YA). (gr. 3 up). reprint ed. 7.95 (978-1-56852-233-3(9) , Konecky & Konecky) Konecky, William S. Assocs., Inc.

—Treasure Island. 1998. (Twelve-Point Ser.). 204p. reprint ed. lib. bdg. 25.00 (978-1-58287-075-5(6)) North Bks.

—Treasure Island. Seelye, John, ed. 1999. (Classics Ser.). (Illus.). 240p. (gr. 12). pap. 7.00 (978-0-14-043768-3(1) , Penguin Classics) Penguin Group (USA) Inc.

—Treasure Island. 1998. (Signet Classic Shakespeare Ser.). 224p. mass mkt. 3.95 (978-0-451-52704-2(6) , Signet Classics) Penguin Group (USA) Inc.

—Treasure Island. Wyeth, N. C., illus. 2000. (Aladdin Classics Ser.). 368p. (gr. 3-7). mass mkt. 5.99 (978-0-689-83212-3(5) , Aladdin) Simon & Schuster Children's Publishing.

—Treasure Island. 1998. (Children's Classics). (ENG., Illus.). 224p. (J). (gr. 3-7). pap. (978-1-85326-103-9(3) , 1033WW) Wordsworth Editions, Ltd.

—Treasure Island: With Story of the Treasure of Normon Island. Date not set. (J). (gr. 5-6). reprint ed. lib. bdg. 22.95 (978-0-89190-236-2(8) , American Reprint Co.) Amereon LTD.

Stilton, Geronimo, text. A Cheese-Colored Camper. 2005. (Geronimo Stilton Ser.: No. 16). (Illus.). 111p. (J). (ps-k). lib. bdg. 12.64 (978-0-606-33281-1(2)) Tandem Library Bks.

Stockton, Frank Richard. RoundAbout Rambles in Lands of Fact and. 2006. pap. (***978-1-4068-3083-5(6)***) Echo Library.

Stohner, Anu. Santa's Littlest Helper Travels the World. Wilson, Henrike, illus. 2007. 32p. (J). (ps-3). 15.95 (***978-1-59990-187-9(0)*** , Bloomsbury Children) Bloomsbury Publishing.

Strickland, Brad & Strickland, Barbara. Gullifur's Travels. l.t. ed. 1999. (Adventures of Wishbone Ser.: No. 18). (Illus.). (J). (gr. 4 up). lib. bdg. 22.60 (978-0-8368-2596-1(9)) Stevens, Gareth Inc.

Sullivan, Arlene R. The Journey of Hanna Heart: You Never Know Where the Wind Will Blow. Sullivan, Arlene R., illus. 1998. (Illus.). 16p. (J). (gr. k-5). pap. 12.95 (978-0-9665793-0-7(5)) Changing Images Art Foundation, Inc.

Swan. The Voyages of Sindbad the Sailor, Level 2. 2001. (Illus.). v, 40p. (C). pap. 9.00 (978-0-582-42122-6(5)) Longman Publishing Group.

Swift, Jonathan. Gulliver's Travels. Marcos, Pablo, illus. 2002. (Great Illustrated Classics Ser.). 240p. (J). (gr. 3-8). 21.35 (978-1-57765-818-4(3) , ABDO & Daughters) ABDO Publishing Co.

—Gulliver's Travels. Akib, Jamel, illus. 2006. (Classic Starts Ser.). 160p. 4.95 (978-1-4027-2662-0(7)) Sterling Publishing Co., Inc.

—Gulliver's Travels. Riddell, Chris, illus. abr. ed. 2005. 144p. (J). (gr. 2 up). 19.99 (978-0-7636-2409-5(8)) Candlewick Pr.

—Viajes de Gulliver. 2003. (Advanced Reading Ser.). (SPA.). 344p. (J). 11.95 (978-84-670-0095-5(3)) Espasa Calpe, S.A. ESP. *Dist:* Planeta Publishing Corp.

Taylor, Cora. Ghost Voyages II: The Matthew. 2003. (gr. 3-6). lib. bdg. 14.10 (978-0-613-78473-3(1)) Tandem Library Bks.

Thomson, Sarah L. Dragon's Egg. 2007. 272p. (J). (gr. 3-7). 16.99 (***978-0-06-128848-7(9)***); lib. bdg. 17.89 (***978-0-06-128847-0(0)***) HarperCollins Pubs. (Greenwillow Bks.).

Thornton, Duncan. The Star-Glass: The Return of Kalifax & Captain Jenny. Noblet, Yves, illus. 2003. (Kalifax Trilogy Ser.). 432p. (J). (gr. 5-7). pap. 10.95 (978-1-55050-269-5(7)) Coteau Bks. CAN. *Dist:* Fitzhenry & Whiteside, Ltd.

Tibo, Gilles. The Grand Journey of Mr. Man. Melanson, Luc, illus. 2001. 32p. (J). (ps up). pap. (978-1-894363-64-8(7)) Dominique & Friends.

Torrey, Michele. To the Edge of the World. 2004. 240p. (YA). (gr. 7). pap. 5.99 (978-0-440-23793-8(9) , Laurel Leaf) Random Hse. Children's Bks.

—Voyage of Midnight. 2006. 240p. (gr. 5). (J). 17.99 (978-0-375-92382-1(9)); (YA). 15.95 (978-0-375-82382-4(4)) Random Hse. Children's Bks. (Knopf Bks. for Young Readers).

Trottier, Maxine. A Circle of Silver. 2000. (Circle of Silver Chronicles Ser.). 216p. (J). (gr. 7-12). pap. 7.95 (978-0-7737-6055-4(5)) Stoddart Kids CAN. *Dist:* Fitzhenry & Whiteside, Ltd.

Turner, Ann Warren. Nettie's Trip South. 1998. (J). pap. 4.95 (978-0-87628-955-6(3)) Ctr. for Applied Research in Education, The.

Twain, Mark. The Adventures of Huckleberry Finn. Andreasen, Dan, illus. 2006. (Classic Starts Ser.). 160p. 4.95 (978-1-4027-2499-2(3)) Sterling Publishing Co., Inc.

—The Adventures of Huckleberry Finn: With a Discussion of Friendship. Lauter, Richard, tr. Lauter, Richard, illus. 2003. (Values in Action Illustrated Classics Ser.). (J). (978-1-59203-042-2(4)) Learning Challenge, Inc.

—Mark Twain/the Adventures of Huckleberry Finn. Redondo, Frank, illus. 2005. 48p. (gr. 5-8). 25.50 (978-0-7910-9101-2(5)) Facts On File, Inc.

Uhlberg, Myron. Lemuel the Fool. Lamut, Sonja, illus. 2001. 32p. (J). (ps-3). 15.95 (978-1-56145-220-0(3)) Peachtree Pubs., Ltd.

Uncle Markie. Piglette Goes Hawaiian. l.t. ed. 2001. 56p. ring bd. 9.95 (978-0-9633943-3-0(9)) Studio 403.

—Piglette Goes to Argentina. l.t. ed. 2001. 66p. ring bd. (978-0-9633943-1-6(2)) Studio 403.

—Piglette Goes to Northern California. l.t. ed. 2001. 36p. (978-0-9633943-2-3(0)) Studio 403.

—Piglette Takes the Concorde! l.t. ed. 2002. 56p. ring bd. 9.95 (978-0-9633943-4-7(7)) Studio 403.

Verne, Jules. Around the World in 80 Days. l.t. ed. 1999. (Large Print Heritage Ser.). 325p. (gr. 7-12). lib. bdg. 32.95 (978-1-58118-040-4(3) , 22509) LRS.

—Around the World in Eighty Days. 2004. (Young Reading Series Two Ser.). 64p. (J). (gr. 2 up). pap. 5.95 (978-0-7945-0741-1(7) , Usborne) EDC Publishing.

—Dick Sands: The Boy Captain. ELLEN E. FREWER, tr. 2006. 298p. pap. 13.99 (978-1-4264-3403-7(0)) BiblioBazaar.

—Dick Sands: The Boy Captain. Frewer, Ellen E., tr. l.t. ed. 2006. 328p. pap. 18.99 (978-1-4264-3453-2(7)) BiblioBazaar.

—The Field of Ice: Part II of the Adventures of Captain Hatteras. 2006. 154p. pap. 11.99 (***978-1-4264-3591-1(6)***); 168p. pap. 12.99 (***978-1-4264-3642-0(4)***) BiblioBazaar.

Verne, Jules. Le Tour du Monde en 80 Jours.Tr. of Around the World in 80 Days. (FRE.). (J). pap. 19.95 (978-2-07-051436-6(6)) Gallimard, Editions FRA. *Dist:* Distribooks, Inc.

The Wanderer. 2000. (J). (978-0-06-029061-0(7)) HarperCollins Pubs.

Watson, Jude. Underworld. 2005. (Star Wars Ser.: No. 3). 137p. (J). lib. bdg. 20.00 (***978-1-4242-0776-3(2)***) Fitzgerald Bks.

Weaver, Anne H. The Voyage of the Beetle: A Journey Around the World with Charles Darwin & the Search for the Solution to the Mystery of Mysteries, as Narrated by Rosie, an Articulate Beetle. Lawrence, George, tr. Lawrence, George, illus. 2004. (Roman Mysteries Ser.). 80p. (J). (gr. 5-8). lib. bdg. 26.90 (978-0-7613-2923-7(4) , Millbrook Pr.) Lerner Publishing Group.

Weston, Carol. The Diary of Melanie Martin. 2001. (Illus.). 144p. (J). (ps-7). per. 13.00 (978-0-613-33751-9(4)) Tandem Library Bks.

—The Diary of Melanie Martin: Or How I Survived Matt the Brat, Michelangelo & the Leaning Tower of Pizza. Roth, Marci Doane, illus. 2001. 160p. (gr. 3-7). 5.50 (978-0-440-41667-8(1) , Yearling) Random Hse. Children's Bks.

Whelan, Gloria. The Impossible Journey. 2004. 256p. (J). (gr. 5 up). reprint ed. pap. 5.99 (978-0-06-441083-0(8) , Harper Trophy) HarperCollins Pubs.

—The Impossible Journey. 2004. 248p. (J). (gr. k-9). per. 14.30 (978-0-613-99970-0(3)) Tandem Library Bks.

Whelan, Gloria. Parade of Shadows. 2007. 304p. (J). (gr. 5 up). 15.99 (***978-0-06-089028-5(2)***); lib. bdg. 16.89 (***978-0-06-089029-2(0)***) HarperCollins Pubs.

Where's Waldo? anniv. ed. 2002. (Where's Waldo? Ser.). (Illus.). (J). 20.53 (978-0-7587-4384-8(X)) Book Wholesalers, Inc.

Where's Waldo: the Complete Set. 2006. (J). 82.94 (***978-0-7636-3510-7(3)***) Candlewick Pr.

White, E. B. Stuart Little. Date not set. 141p. 18.95 (978-0-8488-2602-4(7)) Amereon LTD.

—Stuart Little. Williams, Garth, illus. 2001. (SPA.). 144p. (gr. 3-5). 22.90 (978-84-204-4669-1(6)) Harcourt Schl. Pubs.

—Stuart Little. Williams, Garth & Wells, Rosemary, illus. 60th anniv. ed. 2001. (Stuart-Little Ser.). 144p. (J). (gr. 5 up). pap. 8.99 (978-0-06-441092-2(7)) HarperCollins Pubs.

—Stuart Little. Williams, Garth, illus. 60th collector's anniv. ed. 1999. (Stuart-Little Ser.). 144p. (J). (gr. 4-7). 24.95 (978-0-06-028297-4(5)) HarperCollins Pubs.

—Stuart Little. Williams, Garth, illus. l.t. ed. 2000. (LRS Large Print Cornerstone Ser.). 175p. (J). (gr. 2-8). lib. bdg. 27.95 (978-1-58118-064-0(0) , 23655) LRS.

—Stuart Little. 131p. (J). pap. 5.95 (978-0-8072-8333-2(9)); 2004. (gr. 3-7). pap. 29.00 incl. audio (978-0-8072-8332-5(0) , YA165SP) Random Hse. Audio Publishing Group. (Listening Library).

—Stuart Little: Read-Aloud Edition. Williams, Garth, illus. 1999. (Stuart-Little Ser.). 144p. (J). (gr. 7 up). 19.95 (978-0-06-028334-6(3)) HarperCollins Pubs.

Wilson, Jacqueline. The Suitcase Kid. 2001. (Yearling Book Ser.). (Illus.). 32p. 9.95 (978-0-440-86311-3(2) , Corgi) Transworld Publishers Ltd. GBR. *Dist:* Trafalgar Square Publishing.

Winick, Judd. Fantastic Voyage. Youngquist, Jeff, ed. Calafiore, Jim, illus. 2004. (Marvel Heroes Ser.). 168p. (YA). 17.99 (978-0-7851-1197-9(2)) Marvel Enterprises, Inc.

Youmans, Marly. Ingledove. 2005. (Illus.). 208p. (YA). 16.00 (978-0-374-33599-1(0) , Farrar, Straus & Giroux) Farrar, Straus & Giroux.

—Ingledove. 2006. 208p. (YA). (gr. 7). pap. 7.99 (978-0-14-240704-2(6) , Puffin) Penguin Group (USA) Inc.

Yueh, Tung. The Tower of Myriad Mirrors. Schulz, Larry J. & Lin, Shuen-Fu, trs. from CHI. 2nd ed. 2000. (Michigan Classics in Chinese Studies: No. 1). (Illus.). 150p. pap. 20.00 (978-0-89264-142-0(8)) Ctr. for Chinese Studies Pubns.

VOYAGES AROUND THE WORLD

see also Adventure and Adventurers; Aeronautics—Flights; Discoveries in Geography; Explorers; Northwest Passage; Overland Journeys to the Pacific; Scientific Expeditions; Seafaring Life; Shipwrecks; Travel; Travelers; Voyages around the World

also names of countries, continents, etc. with the subdivision Description and Travel (e.g. United States—Description and Travel); also names of regions (e.g. Antarctic Regions)

Anthony, Laurence. Ferdinand Magellan. 2001. (Great Explorers Ser.). (Illus.). 48p. (J). (gr. 5 up). lib. bdg. 30.00 (978-0-8368-5016-1(5) , World Almanac Library) Stevens, Gareth Inc.

Bailey, Katie. Ferdinand Magellan: Circumnavigating the World. 2005. (In the Footsteps of Explorers Ser.). (Illus.). 32p. (J). (gr. 3-9). (978-0-7787-2416-2(6)); pap. (978-0-7787-2452-0(2)) Crabtree Publishing Co.

Bastable, Tony. Ferdinand Magellan. 2003. (Great Explorers Ser.). (Illus.). 48p. (J). (gr. 5 up). pap. 14.60 (978-0-8368-5176-2(5) , World Almanac Library) Stevens, Gareth Inc.

Bingham, Jane. Captain Cook's Pacific Explorations. 2007. (J). (***978-1-4034-9756-7(7)***) Heinemann Library.

Blackwood, Gary L. The Great Race: Around the World by Automobile. 2008. 144p. (J). 19.95 (***978-0-8109-9489-8(5)***) Abrams, Harry N. , Inc.

Bredeson, Carmen. After the Last Dog Died: The True-Life, Hair-Raising Adventure of Douglas Mawson's 1912 Antarctic Expedition. 2003. (Illus.). 64p. (J). (gr. 5). 18.95 (978-0-7922-6140-7(2) , National Geographic Children's Bks.) National Geographic Society.

Broderick, Enid. Capt. James Cook. 2003. (Great Explorers Ser.). (Illus.). 48p. (J). (gr. 5 up). pap. 14.60 (978-0-8368-5174-8(9) , World Almanac Library) Stevens, Gareth Inc.

—Captain James Cook. 2001. (Great Explorers Ser.). (Illus.). 48p. (J). (gr. 5 up). lib. bdg. 30.00 (978-0-8368-5014-7(9) , World Almanac Library) Stevens, Gareth Inc.

Burgan, Michael. Magellan: Ferdinand Magellan & the First Trip Around the World. 2001. (Exploring the World Ser.). (Illus.). 48p. (J). (gr. 4 up). lib. bdg. 22.60 (978-0-7565-0125-9(3)) Compass Point Bks.

Butcher, Nancy. It Can't Be Done, Nellie Bly! A Reporter's Race Around the World. 2003. (Illus.). 144p. (J). (gr. 1-5). 12.95 (978-1-56145-289-7(0)) Peachtree Pubs., Ltd.

Crompton, Samuel Willard. Ferdinand Magellan: And the Quest to Circle the Globe. Goetzmann, William H., ed. 2005. (Explorers of New Lands Ser.). (Illus.). 144p. (J). (ps-8). lib. bdg. 30.00 (978-0-7910-8608-7(9) , Chelsea Hse.) Facts On File, Inc.

Davis, Kenneth C. Don't Know Much about Planet Earth. 2001. (gr. 3-6). lib. bdg. 15.25 (978-0-613-36148-4(2)) Tandem Library Bks.

Fandel, Jennifer. Ferdinand Magellan. 2003. (Explorers of the Unknown Ser.). (J). (978-1-58417-036-5(0)); pap. (978-1-58417-099-0(9)) Lake Street Pubs.

Gaines, Ann Graham. Captain Cook Explores the Pacific in World History. 2002. (In World History Ser.). (Illus.). 128p. (J). (gr. 5-12). lib. bdg. 26.60 (978-0-7660-1823-5(7)) Enslow Pubs., Inc.

Glasspoole, Louise, et al. I-Read Year 2 Anthology: Magical Journeys. 2007. (I-read Ser.). (Illus.). 40p. pap. (***978-0-521-70472-4(3)***) Cambridge Univ. Pr.

Great Journeys - Group 1, 4 bks., Set. 2000. (Illus.). (J). (gr. 5 up). 131.14 (978-0-7614-0966-3(1) , Benchmark Bks.) Cavendish, Marshall Corp.

Harcourt School Publishers Staff. Pumpkin's Trip Around the World Advanced Level. 3rd ed. 2002. (Trophies Reading Program Ser.). (Illus.). pap. 5.10 (978-0-15-323115-5(7)) Harcourt Schl. Pubs.

Hoogenboom, Lynn. Ferdinand Magellan: A Primary Source Biography. 2006. (J). lib. bdg. (978-1-4042-3039-2(4) , PowerKids Pr.) Rosen Publishing Group, Inc., The.

Kline, Trish. James Cook. (Rourke Discovery Library). 2003. (Illus.). 24p. (gr. 2-5). 14.95 (978-1-58952-292-3(3)); 2002. lib. bdg. 19.27 (978-1-58952-426-2(8)) Rourke Publishing, LLC.

Kramer, S. A. Who Was Ferdinand Magellan? Wolf, Elizabeth & Harrison, Nancy, illus. 2004. (Who Was...? Ser.). 112p. (J). (gr. 3-7). pap. 4.99 (978-0-448-43105-5(X) , Grosset & Dunlap) Penguin Group (USA) Inc.

Landau, Elaine. Ferdinand Magellan. 2006. (History Maker Bios Ser.). (Illus.). 48p. (J). (gr. 3-7). 26.60 (978-0-8225-2942-2(4) , Lerner Pubns.) Lerner Publishing Group.

Levinson, Nancy Smiler. Magellan: And the First Voyage Around the World. 2001. (Illus.). 144p. (J). (gr. 5-9). tchr. ed. 19.00 (978-0-395-98773-5(3) , Clarion Bks.) Houghton Mifflin Co. Trade & Reference Div.

Mattern, Joanne. The Travels of Ferdinand Magellan. 2000. (Explorers & Exploration Ser.). (Illus.). 48p. (J). (gr. 4-7). lib. bdg. 22.83 (978-0-7398-1484-0(2)) Raintree.

Mayhew, James. Miranda the Explorer: A Magical-Round-the-World Adventure. 2003. (Illus.). (J). pap. 9.99 (978-1-84255-280-3(5)); 32p. 20.00 (978-1-84255-000-7(4)) Dolphin Paperbacks GBR. *Dist:* Trafalgar Square Publishing.

McCarthy, Shaun & Cook, James. James Cook. 2002. (Groundbreakers Ser.). (Illus.). 48p. (J). (gr. 5-7). lib. bdg. 27.07 (978-1-58810-595-0(4)) Heinemann Library.

Meltzer, Milton, et al. Captain James Cook: Three Times Around the World. 2001. (Great Explorations Ser.). (Illus.). 80p. (J). (gr. 4 up). lib. bdg. 28.50 (978-0-7614-1240-3(9) , Benchmark Bks.) Cavendish, Marshall Corp.

—Ferdinand Magellan: First to Sail Around the World. 2001. (Great Explorations Ser.: Vol. 1). (Illus.). 80p. (J). (gr. 4 up). lib. bdg. 29.93 (978-0-7614-1238-0(7) , Benchmark Bks.) Cavendish, Marshall Corp.

Molzahn, Arlene Bourgeois. Ferdinand Magellan: First Explorer Around the World. 2003. (Illus.). 48p. (J). (gr. 1-4). lib. bdg. 23.93 (978-0-7660-2068-9(1)) Enslow Pubs., Inc.

Peck, Ira & Bly, Nellie. Nellie Bly's Book: Around the World in 72 Days. abr. ed. 1998. (Single Titles Ser.). (Illus.). 128p. (gr. 5-9). lib. bdg. 27.90 (978-0-7613-0971-0(3) , Millbrook Pr.) Lerner Publishing Group.

Penner, Lucille Recht. Ice Wreck. LaFleur, David, illus. 2004. (Stepping Stones Ser.). 48p. (J). (gr. k-3). pap. 3.99 (978-0-307-26408-4(4) , Random Hse. Bks. for Young Readers) Random Hse. Children's Bks.

Petrie, Kristin. Ferdinand Magellan. 2007. (Illus.). 32p. (J). 22.78 (978-1-59679-744-4(4)) ABDO Publishing Co.

—James Cook. 2004. (Explorers Set I Ser.). (Illus.). 32p. (J). (gr. k-6). lib. bdg. 22.78 (978-1-59197-596-0(4)) ABDO Publishing Co.

Raintree Steck-Vaughn Staff. World Tour: Arkansas Edition, 47 bks., Set. 2003. (Illus.). 1246.94 (978-1-4109-0162-0(9)) Raintree.

Reid, Struan. Ferdinand Magellan. (Groundbreakers Ser.). (Illus.). 48p. (J). (gr. 5-7). 2002. pap. 8.50 (978-1-58810-369-7(2) , 91091); 2001. lib. bdg. 25.64 (978-1-58810-045-0(6)) Heinemann Library.

Senker, Cath. Magellan's Voyage Around the World. 2007. (J). (***978-1-4034-9754-3(0)***) Heinemann Library.

Shields, Charles J. James Cook & the Exploration of the Pacific. 2001. (Explorers of New Worlds Ser.). (Illus.). (J). 63p. pap. 25.00 (978-0-7910-6423-8(9)); 64p. 25.00 (978-0-7910-6422-1(0)) Facts On File, Inc. (Chelsea Hse.).

Waldman, Stuart. Magellan's World. Manchess, Gregory, illus. 2007. (Great Explorers Ser.). 48p. (J). (gr. 4-8). 22.95 (***978-1-931414-19-7(X)***) Mikaya Pr.

White, David. The First Voyage Around the World. 2002. (Exploration & Discovery Ser.). (Illus.). 64p. (J). (gr. 5 up). lib. bdg. (978-1-59084-054-2(2)) Mason Crest Pubs.

VOYAGES, IMAGINARY

McNulty, Faith. If You Decide to Go to the Moon. Kellogg, Steven, illus. 2005. 48p. (J). (ps-3). pap. 16.99 (978-0-590-48359-9(5) , Scholastic Pr.) Scholastic, Inc.

VOYAGES, IMAGINARY—FICTION

Fearon Staff. Gulliver's Travels. (YA). (gr. 5-12). pap. 6.50 (978-0-8359-0944-0(1)) Globe Fearon Educational Publishing.

Lia, Simone. Follow the Line. 2002. (Illus.). 32p. (J). pap. 8.99 (978-0-7497-4858-6(3)) Egmont Bks., Ltd. GBR. *Dist:* Independent Pubs. Group.

Steele, Philip. Incredible Journeys: World Myths. 2003. (Myths & Legends from Around the World Ser.). (Illus.). 48p. (gr. 3-7). 10.99 (978-0-7548-1095-7(X)) Anness Publishing GBR. *Dist:* National Bk. Network.

Swift, Jonathan. Gulliver's Travels. Date not set. (J). (gr. 5-6). reprint ed. lib. bdg. 26.95 (978-0-89190-845-6(5) , American Reprint Co.) Amereon LTD.

—Gulliver's Travels. 2004. (Young Reading Ser.). (Illus.). 64p. (J). (gr. 2 up). pap. 5.95 (978-0-7945-0329-1(2) , Usborne) EDC Publishing.

—Gulliver's Travels. (Young Collector's Illustrated Classics Ser.). (Illus.). 192p. (J). (gr. 3-7). 9.95 (978-1-56156-457-6(5)) Kidsbooks, Inc.

—Gulliver's Travels. 1999. (Classics Ser.). (Illus.). 336p. mass mkt. 5.95 (978-0-451-52732-5(1) , Signet Classics) Penguin Group (USA) Inc.

—Gulliver's Travels. 2002. (Classic Tales Ser.). (Illus.). 32p. (J). incl. audio compact disk (978-1-59069-106-9(7) , T1108); (978-1-59069-039-0(7) , T1008) Studio Mouse LLC.

VOYAGES TO THE MOON

see Space Flight to the Moon

VULTURES

Harris, Tim. Vultures. 2004. (Nature's Children Ser.). (J). (978-0-7172-5977-9(3) , Grolier) Scholastic Library Publishing.

Houston, David. Condors & Vultures. rev. ed. 2001. (World-Life Library). (Illus.). 72p. (gr. 5 up). pap. 17.95 (978-0-89658-523-2(9)) Voyageur Pr., Inc.

Johnson, Jinny. Vultures. 2003. (Predators Ser.). (Illus.). 32p. (J). lib. bdg. 25.70 (978-0-7398-6603-0(6)) Raintree.

Kops, Deborah. Vultures. 2000. (Wild Birds of Prey! Ser.). (Illus.). 24p. (J). (gr. 3-6). 24.94 (978-1-56711-273-3(0) , Blackbirch Pr., Inc.) Thomson Gale.

Lynch, Wayne. Vultures. Neidigh, Sherry, illus. 2005. (Our Wild World Ser.). 48p. (J). pap. 7.95 (978-1-55971-918-6(4) , NorthWord Bks. for Young Readers) T&N Children's Publishing.

Lynch, Wayne, contrib. by. Vultures. 2005. (Our Wild World Ser.). (Illus.). 48p. 10.95 (978-1-55971-917-9(6) , NorthWord Bks. for Young Readers) T&N Children's Publishing.

Macken, JoAnn Early. Vultures. 2005. (Illus.). 24p. (J). pap. (978-0-8368-4838-0(1)); lib. bdg. 19.33 (978-0-8368-4831-1(4)) Stevens, Gareth Inc.

—Vultures: Buitres. 2005. (ENG & SPA., Illus.). 24p. (J). pap. (978-0-8368-4852-6(7)) Stevens, Gareth Inc.

—Vultures/Buitres. 2005. (ENG & SPA., Illus.). 24p. (J). (ps-17). lib. bdg. 19.33 (978-0-8368-4845-8(4)) Stevens, Gareth Inc.

Markle, Sandra. Los Buitres (Vultures) 2007. (Animales carroñeros (Animal Scavengers) Ser.). (SPA.). 40p. (J). (gr. 3-6). pap. 7.95 (***978-0-8225-7735-5(6)***); lib. bdg. 25.26 (***978-0-8225-7731-7(3)***) Lerner Publishing Group. (Ediciones Lerner).

Markle, Sandra. Vultures. 2005. (Animal Scavengers Ser.). (Illus.). 39p. (J). (ps-7). 25.26 (978-0-8225-3195-1(X) , Lerner Pubns.) Lerner Publishing Group.

O'Donnell, Kerri. Vultures. 2006. (Illus.). 24p. (J). lib. bdg. (978-1-4042-3526-7(4)) Rosen Publishing Group, Inc., The.

Redmond, Jim. King Vultures. 2003. (Animals of the Rain Forest Ser.). (Illus.). 32p. (J). lib. bdg. 24.28 (978-0-7398-6837-9(3)) Raintree.

Vultures. 2006. (J). pap. 7.95 (978-0-8225-3471-6(1) , First Avenue Editions) Lerner Publishing Group.

Wechsler, Doug. Vultures. 2001. (Really Wild Life of Birds of Prey Ser.). (Illus.). 24p. (J). lib. bdg. 18.75 (978-0-8239-5594-7(X) , PowerKids Pr.) Rosen Publishing Group, Inc., The.

VULTURES—FICTION

Grindley, Sally. The Sulky Vulture. Terry, Michael, illus. 2003. 32p. (J). (gr. k-3). 15.95 (978-1-58234-794-3(8) , Bloomsbury Children) Bloomsbury Publishing.

McAuliffe, Nichola. Attila, Loolagax & the Eagle. Collins, Ross, tr. Collins, Ross, illus. 2003. 126p. pap. 10.99 (978-0-7475-6499-7(X)) Bloomsbury Publishing Plc GBR. *Dist:* Independent Pubs. Group.

McDermott, Gerald. Jabuti the Tortoise: A Trickster Tale from the Amazon. 2005. (Illus.). 32p. (J). (ps-ps). pap., pap. 7.00 (978-0-15-205374-1(3) , Voyager Bks./Libros Viajeros) Harcourt Children's Bks.

McGregor, Don. Vultures! Lima, Sidney, illus. 3rd rev. ed. 2006. (Zorro Graphic Novel Ser.: No. 3). 96p. (J). 12.95 (978-1-59707-021-8(1)); pap. 7.95 (978-1-59707-020-1(3)) Papercutz.

Quantz, Daniel. Duel to the Death with the Vulture. 2006. (Illus.). (J). (gr. 2-6). 21.35 (978-1-59961-012-2(4)) Spotlight.

Sayre, April Pulley. Vulture View. Jenkins, Steve, illus. rev. ed. 2007. 32p. (J). (gr. k-3). 16.95 (978-0-8050-7557-1(7) , Holt, Henry & Co. Bks. For Young Readers) Holt, Henry & Co.

W

WAGNER, RICHARD, 1813-1883

Cencetti, Greta. Wagner. 2002. (World of Composers Ser.). (Illus.). 40p. (J). (gr. 1-5). 18.95 (978-1-58845-474-4(6) , Bedrick, Peter Bks.) School Specialty Publishing.

—Wagner: Getting to Know Your Classical Composers. 2002. (Classic Composers Ser.). (Illus.). 32p. (978-1-59069-031-4(1) , T2008) Studio Mouse LLC.

Ellis, W. Ashton. Wagner-Sketches, 1849: A Vindication. 2001. (YA). reprint ed. 150.00 (978-0-7222-5567-4(5)) Library Reprints, Inc.

Finck, Henry Theophilus. Wagner & His Works: The Story of His Life, 2 vols., set. 7th ed. 2001. (YA). reprint ed. 250.00 (978-0-7222-5570-4(5)) Library Reprints, Inc.

Gautier, Judith. Wagner at Home. 2001. 257p. (YA). reprint ed. 98.00 (978-0-7222-5572-8(1)) Library Reprints, Inc.

Getzinger, Donna & Felsenfeld, Daniel. Richard Wagner & German Opera. 2004. (Classical Composers Ser.). (Illus.). 144p. (YA). (gr. 6-12). 26.95 (978-1-931798-24-2(9)) Reynolds, Morgan Inc.

Glasenapp, Carl F. The Life of Richard Wagner, 6 vols., set. 2001. (YA). reprint ed. 750.00 (978-0-7222-5573-5(X)) Library Reprints, Inc.

Henderson, William J. Richard Wagner, His Life & His Dramas: A Biographical Study of the Man & an Explanation of His Work. 2nd ed. 2001. 504p. (YA). reprint ed. 98.00 (978-0-7222-5578-0(0)) Library Reprints, Inc.

Hight, George A. Richard Wagner: A Critical Biography, 2 vols., set. 2001. (YA). reprint ed. 250.00 (978-0-7222-5579-7(9)) Library Reprints, Inc.

Irvine, David. A Wagnerian Midsummer Madness. 2001. 348p. (YA). reprint ed. 98.00 (978-0-7222-5584-1(5)) Library Reprints, Inc.

Lidgey, Charles A. Wagner. 2001. 268p. (YA). reprint ed. 98.00 (978-0-7222-5589-6(6)) Library Reprints, Inc.

Nietzsche, Friedrich. The Nietzsche-Wagner Correspondence. 2001. 312p. (YA). reprint ed. 98.00 (978-0-7222-5558-2(6)) Library Reprints, Inc.

Nohl, Ludwig. The Life of Wagner. 2001. 204p. (YA). reprint ed. 98.00 (978-0-7222-5597-1(7)) Library Reprints, Inc.

Runciman, F. John. Wagner. 2006. 77.99 (***978-1-4280-2550-9(2)***) IndyPublish.com.

Wagner. 2002. (Classic Composers Ser.). (Illus.). 40p. (J). incl. audio compact disk (978-1-59069-098-7(2) , T2108) Studio Mouse LLC.

Wagner, Richard. Correspondence of Wagner & Liszt, 2 vols., set. 2001. (YA). reprint ed. 250.00 (978-0-7222-5445-5(8)) Library Reprints, Inc.

—Letters, 2 Vols., Set. 2001. (YA). reprint ed. 250.00 (978-0-7222-6303-7(1)) Library Reprints, Inc.

—Letters to August Roeckel. 2001. 178p. (YA). reprint ed. 88.00 (978-0-7222-5557-5(8)) Library Reprints, Inc.

—Letters to His Dresden Friends. 2001. 512p. (YA). reprint ed. 98.00 (978-0-7222-5556-8(X)) Library Reprints, Inc.

—My Life: Authorized Translation from the German, 2 vols., set. 2001. (YA). reprint ed. 250.00 (978-0-7222-5555-1(1)) Library Reprints, Inc.

—Richard to Minna Wagner: The Letters to His First Wife, 2 vols., set. 2001. (YA). reprint ed. 250.00 (978-0-7222-5560-5(8)) Library Reprints, Inc.

—Richard Wagner to Mathilde Wesendonck. 2001. 386p. (YA). reprint ed. 98.00 (978-0-7222-5561-2(6)) Library Reprints, Inc.

Wallace, William. Richard Wagner As He Lived. 2001. 313p. (YA). reprint ed. 98.00 (978-0-7222-5602-2(7)) Library Reprints, Inc.

Whiting, Jim. The Life & Times of Richard Wagner. 2004. (Masters of Music Ser.). (Illus.). 48p. (gr. 4-8). lib. bdg. 20.95 (978-1-58415-278-1(8)) Mitchell Lane Pubs., Inc.

WALES

Britton, Tamara L. Wales. 2003. (Countries Ser.). (Illus.). 40p. (J). (gr. k-6). lib. bdg. 22.78 (978-1-57765-759-0(4)) ABDO Publishing Co.

Evans, Robin. Cymru A'r Byd: Pecyn Lluniau a Llyfr Athrawon. 2005. (WEL., Illus.). (978-1-85644-873-4(8)) Univ. of Wales, Aberystwyth, Centre for Educational Studies.

Ganeri, Anita & Oxlade, Chris. A Visit to Wales. 2003. (Visit to Ser.). (Illus.). 32p. (J). lib. bdg. 22.79 (978-1-4034-0967-6(6)) Heinemann Library.

Heinrichs, Ann. Wales. 2003. (Enchantment of the World, Second Ser.). (Illus.). 144p. (J). (gr. 5-9). 36.00 (978-0-516-22288-2(0) , Children's Pr.) Scholastic Library Publishing.

Hestler, Anna. Wales. 2001. (Cultures of the World Ser.). (Illus.). 128p. (J). (gr. 5-12). lib. bdg. 37.07 (978-0-7614-1195-6(X) , Benchmark Bks.) Cavendish, Marshall Corp.

Meirion, Dafydd, et al. Anturio ar Ynys Mon: Sawl Taith Stori i Ti ac i'r Teulu. 2005. (WEL., Illus.). 84p. (978-0-86381-863-9(3)) Gwasg Carreg Gwalch.

Stevens, Catrin, et al. Yr Oesoedd Canol. 2005. (WEL., Illus.). 144p. 4.99 (978-1-84323-423-4(8)) Gomer Pr. GBR. *Dist:* Gomer Pr.

Wlodarski, Loran. Killer Whales: Creatures of Legend & Wonder. 2001. (Seaworld Education Ser.). (Illus.). 76p. per. 7.99 (978-1-893698-19-2(X) , B02, SeaWorld Education Dept.) SeaWorld, Inc.

WALES—FICTION

Anrias, Donnan. Targ - the King of Eagles. 2005. 138p. (YA). per. 23.00 (978-1-4116-1923-4(4)) Lulu.com.

Armour, Michael C. Orca Song. Lee, Katie, illus. 32p. (J). (ps-2). 6.95 (978-1-59249-479-8(X) , S4004) Soundprints.

Bond, Nancy. A String in the Harp. 2006. 384p. (J). pap. 6.99 (978-1-4169-2771-6(9) , Aladdin) Simon & Schuster Children's Publishing.

Boyce, Frank Cottrell. Framed. 2006. 320p. pap. 15.95 (***978-0-330-43425-6(X)***) Macmillan Publishers Ltd. GBR. *Dist:* Trans-Atlantic Pubns., Inc.

Boyce, Frank Cottrell, ed. Framed. 2006. 320p. (J). 16.99 (978-0-06-073402-2(7)); lib. bdg. 17.89 (978-0-06-073403-9(5)) HarperCollins Pubs.

Brown, Richard. A Welsh Lamb. 2005. (Cambridge Storybooks Ser.). 32p. pap. 7.00 (978-0-521-67482-9(4)) Cambridge Univ. Pr.

Carpenter, Suzanne. Barti & Bel Whizz Around Wales. 2003. (Illus.). 32p. pap. 12.95 (978-1-84323-238-4(3)) Beekman Bks., Inc.

Carradice, Phil. Nat & the Havannah. 2000. 104p. pap. 12.95 (978-1-85902-719-6(9)) Beekman Bks., Inc.

Cooper, Clare. Stonehead. 2000. 132p. (J). pap. 12.95 (978-1-85902-782-0(2)) Beekman Bks., Inc.

Cooper, Susan. The Grey King. 2002. (Dark Is Rising Sequence Ser.). (Illus.). (J). 13.40 (978-0-7587-0188-6(8)) Book Wholesalers, Inc.

—The Grey King. (Dark Is Rising Sequence Ser.). 2007. 192p. (YA). pap. 8.99 (***978-1-4169-4967-1(4)*** , Simon Pulse); 1999. 176p. (J). (gr. 4-7). pap. 5.99 (978-0-689-82984-0(1) , Aladdin) Simon & Schuster Children's Publishing.

—The Grey King. 1999. (Dark Is Rising Sequence Ser.). (gr. 5-8). lib. bdg. 13.00 (978-0-613-73286-4(3)) Tandem Library Bks.

—The Grey King. l.t. ed. 2002. (Dark Is Rising Sequence Ser.). 262p. (J). 21.95 (978-0-7862-2919-2(5)) Thomson Gale.

Cooper, Susan. Silver on the Tree. 2002. (Dark Is Rising Sequence Ser.). (Illus.). (J). 13.40 (978-0-7587-5639-8(9)) Book Wholesalers, Inc.

—Silver on the Tree. (Dark Is Rising Sequence Ser.). 288p. 2007. (YA). pap. 8.99 (***978-1-4169-4968-8(2)*** , Simon Pulse); 2000. (J). (gr. 4-7). pap. 5.99 (978-0-689-84033-3(0) , Aladdin) Simon & Schuster Children's Publishing.

—Silver on the Tree. 2000. (Dark Is Rising Sequence Ser.). (gr. 5-8). lib. bdg. 13.00 (978-0-613-30127-5(7)) Tandem Library Bks.

—Silver on the Tree. l.t. ed. 2002. (Dark Is Rising Sequence Ser.). (Illus.). 430p. (J). 23.95 (978-0-7862-2921-5(7)) Thomson Gale.

Corlett, William. The Tunnel Behind the Waterfall. 2001. (gr. 7-12). lib. bdg. 13.00 (978-0-613-74172-9(2)) Tandem Library Bks.

Cottrell Boyce, Frank. Framed. 2008. 320p. (J). pap. 6.99 (***978-0-06-073404-6(3)*** , Harper Trophy) HarperCollins Pubs.

Davies, Elgan Philip & Ceredigion, Cymdeithas Lyfrau. Olion Hen Elyn. 2005. (WEL.). 199p. (978-1-84512-004-7(3)) Cymdeithas Lyfrau Ceredigion.

Davies, Nicola. Tangled Webs. 2000. 120p. (YA). pap. 12.95 (978-1-85902-847-6(0)) Beekman Bks., Inc.

Drake, Gillian. The Girl in Green. 2000. 125p. pap. 12.95 (978-1-85902-872-8(1)) Beekman Bks., Inc.

Eames, Marion. Baner Beca. 2005. (WEL.). 80p. pap. (978-0-86243-729-9(6)) Y Lolfa.

Eynon, Bob & Wen, Dref. Crwydro'r Mor Mawr. 2005. (WEL & ENG.). 72p. (978-1-85596-656-7(5)) Dref Wen.

Fisk, Pauline. The Red Judge. 2005. 208p. (YA). 16.95 (978-1-58234-942-8(8) , Bloomsbury Children) Bloomsbury Publishing.

Henty, A. G. Both Sides the Border A Tale of Hotspur. 2007. 22.99 (***978-1-4280-5127-0(9)***); pap. 15.99 (***978-1-4280-5117-1(1)***) IndyPublish.com.

Henty, G. A. Both Sides of the Border: A Tale of Hotspur & Glendower. 2000. 252p. (J). pap. 9.95 (978-0-594-01504-8(9)) 1873 Pr.

Holliday, Susan. Riding the Storm. 2000. 128p. (J). (978-1-85902-870-4(5)) Pont Bks.

Jenkins, Mike. Child of Dust. 2005. 192p. pap. 15.95 (978-1-84323-491-3(2)) Beekman Bks., Inc.

Jones, Brenda W. Giant Tales from Wales. Saer, Ann, tr. from WEL. Brown, Peter, illus. 1998. (J). (gr. 1-5). pap. 29.95 (978-0-8464-4930-0(7)) Beekman Bks., Inc.

Jones, Jac. In Chatter Wood. 2004. (Illus.). 48p. pap. 13.95 (978-1-84323-290-2(1)) Beekman Bks., Inc.

Jones, Margaret. Nat. 2004. (Illus.). 111p. pap. 13.95 (978-1-84323 327 5(4)) Beekman Bks., Inc.

Jones, T. Llew. Storiau Cwm-Pen-Llo. 2005. (WEL., Illus.). 100p. (978-0-86381-750-2(5)) Gwasg Carreg Gwalch.

Kimmel, Elizabeth Cody. In the Stone Circle. 1998. 225p. (J). (gr. 5-9). pap. 15.95 (978-0-590-21308-0(3)) Scholastic, Inc.

Lewis, Caryl & Lolfa, Y. Iawn Boi? 2005. (WEL.). 80p. pap. (978-0-86243-699-5(0)) Y Lolfa.

Morgan, Gwyn & Owen, Dai. Babi Ben. 2005. (WEL., Illus.). 64p. (978-1-85596-611-6(5)) Dref Wen.

Morgan, Ruth. Things That Go Bump in the Night. Glyn, Chris, illus. 2001. 48p. pap. 11.95 (978-1-85902-944-2(2)) Beekman Bks., Inc.

Newbery, Linda. Lost Boy. 2008. (J). (***978-0-375-84574-1(7)***); lib. bdg. (***978-0-375-93617-3(3)***) Random Hse. Children's Bks. (Fickling, David Bks.).

Nimmo, Jenny. Branwen. Jones, Jac, illus. 1998. (Legends from Wales Ser.: Vol. 2). (J). (gr. 2-5). pap. 12.95 (978-0-8464-4602-6(2)) Beekman Bks., Inc.

—The Chestnut Soldier. 2007. (Snow Spider Trilogy: Bk. 3). 208p. (J). (gr. 4-7). 9.99 (978-0-439-84677-6(3) , Orchard Bks.) Scholastic, Inc.

—Emlyn's Moon. 2007. (Snow Spider Trilogy: Bk. 2). 176p. (J). (gr. 4-7). 9.99 (978-0-439-84676-9(5) , Orchard Bks.) Scholastic, Inc.

—Griffin's Castle. 2007. 288p. (J). 16.99 (***978-0-439-02554-6(0)*** , Orchard Bks.) Scholastic, Inc.

Nimmo, Jenny. The Snow Spider. 2006. (Snow Spider Trilogy: Bk. 1). (J). 39.95 (978-0-439-89844-7(7)); 160p. (gr. 3-7). 9.99 (978-0-439-84675-2(7) , Orchard Bks.) Scholastic, Inc.

Oldham, Mary. No Fire, No Candle. 2001. 217p. (YA). pap. 12.95 (978-1-85902-945-9(0)) Beekman Bks., Inc.

Orca Song. 1998. (J). (gr. 2). pap. 3.95 (978-0-439-04440-0(5)) Scholastic, Inc.

W X Y Z

Orca Song. (Illus.). 32p. (J). (ps-2). 6.95 incl. reel tape (978-1-59249-488-0(9) , SC4004) Soundprints.

Orme, Helen. Wet! 2008. (Siti's Sisters Ser.). 36p. pap. 7.95 (***978-1-84167-688-3(8)***) Ransom Publishing Ltd. GBR. *Dist:* International Publishers Marketing.

Pullman, Philip. The Broken Bridge. 2002. 20.50 (978-0-8446-7229-8(7)) Smith, Peter Pub., Inc.

Roberts, Esyllt Nest & Owen, Carys Eurwen. Dinas Emrys. 2005. (WEL., Illus.). 34p. (978-0-86381-439-6(5)) Gwasg Carreg Gwalch.

—Rhita Gawr. 2005. (WEL., Illus.). 35p. (978-0-86381-624-6(X)) Gwasg Carreg Gwalch.

Twigg, Aeres. The Green Hawk. 2003. (Illus.). 87p. (J). pap. 12.95 (978-1-85902-787-5(3)) Beekman Bks., Inc.

Weatherly, Lee. Breakfast at Sadie's. 208p. (gr. 7). 2008. (YA). mass mkt. 6.99 (***978-0-440-24069-3(7)*** , Laurel Leaf); 2006. (J). 15.95 (978-0-385-75094-3(3) , Fickling, David Bks.); 2006. (J). lib. bdg. 17.99 (978-0-385-75095-0(1) , Fickling, David Bks.) Random Hse. Children's Bks.

WALKING

see also Hiking

Barraclough, Sue. Road Safety. 2007. (J). (***978-1-4034-9853-3(9)***); pap. (***978-1-4034-9860-1(1)***) Heinemann Library.

Bruce, Dan Wingfoot. The Thru-Hiker's Handbook 2004: #1 Guide for Long-Distance Hikes on the Appalachian Trail. 2004. (Illus.). 184p. per. 15.95 (978-0-9707916-5-8(8)) Ctr. for Appalachian Trail Studies.

Caminando: Individual Title Six-Packs. (Literatura 2000 Ser.). (SPA.). (gr. 2-3). 33.00 (978-0-7635-1085-5(8)) Rigby Education.

Fredericks, Anthony D. Weird Walkers. 2000. (gr. 3-6). lib. bdg. 16.40 (978-0-613-27488-3(1)) Tandem Library Bks.

Mayer, Cassie. On Foot. 2006. (Illus.). 24p. (J). (978-1-4034-8393-5(0)); pap. (978-1-4034-8400-0(7)) Heinemann Library.

Oregon Center for Applied Science, creator. Walk Smart: Children's Pedestrian Safety Program. 2005. (J). cd-rom 19.95 (***978-1-933898-10-0(0)***) Oregon Ctr. for Applied Science, Inc.

Powell, Jillian. Moving. 2004. (Body in Action Ser.). (J). pap. (978-1-58340-437-9(6)) Smart Apple Media.

Roca, Nuria. How We Move Around. Curto, Rosa M., illus. 2007. (What Do You Know about? Bks.). 36p. (J). (gr. k-1). pap. 6.99 (978-0-7641-3653-5(4)) Barron's Educational Series, Inc.

Royston. Moving. 2004. (My Amazing Body Ser.). (Illus.). pap. 7.50 (978-1-4109-0951-0(4)) Raintree.

Votry, Kim & Waller, Curt. Out for a Walk. 2003. (Baby's First Signs Bks.). (Illus.). 16p. (J). bds. 6.95 (978-1-56368-146-2(3)) Gallaudet Univ. Pr.

Walking in the City. (J). 26.20 (978-0-8136-8422-2(6)); 26.20 (978-0-8136-8423-9(4)); 59.50 (978-0-8136-7966-2(4)); 1998. pap. (978-0-8136-8300-3(9)) Modern Curriculum Pr.

WALL STREET (NEW YORK, N.Y.)

Whitcraft, Melissa. Wall Street. 2003. (Cornerstones of Freedom, 2ND Ser.). (Illus.). 48p. (J). 26.00 (978-0-516-24217-0(2) , Children's Pr.) Scholastic Library Publishing.

WALL STREET (NEW YORK, N.Y.)—FICTION

Standish, Burt L. Frank Merriwell in Wall Street. Rudman, Jack, ed. 2003. (Frank Merriwell Ser.). pap. 9.95 (978-0-8373-9159-5(8)) Merriwell, Frank Inc.

WALLACE, GEORGE C. (GEORGE CORLEY), 1919-1998

Yeager, Alice. George C. Wallace: Alabama Political Power. 2003. (Alabama Roots Biography Ser.). (Illus.). 104p. (J). pap. (978-1-59421-003-7(9)) Seacoast Publishing, Inc.

WALLACE, LEW, 1827-1905

Boomhower, Ray E. The Sword & the Pen: A Life of Lew Wallace. 2005. (Illus.). x, 164p. (J). (978-0-87195-185-4(1)) Indiana Historical Society.

WALLACE, WILLIAM ALEXANDER ANDERSON, 1817-1899

Harper, Jo. Big Foot Wallace: A Hero of Early Texas. Roeder, Virginia M., illus. 1999. 48p. (gr. 1-3). 14.95 (978-1-57168-223-9(6)) Eakin Pr.

WALLACE AND GROMIT (FICTITIOUS CHARACTERS)—FICTION

Aardman & Park, Nick. Welcome to West Wallaby Street. 2005. (Wallace & Gromit Ser.). (Illus.). 24p. (J). 15.99 (978-0-7434-6783-4(3)) Simon & Schuster, Ltd. GBR. *Dist:* Independent Pubs. Group.

Aardman Animations Staff. Furry Gromit. 2006. (Wallace & Gromit Ser.). (Illus.). 10p. (J). (ps). bds. 6.99 (978-0-7434-8926-3(8)) Simon & Schuster, Ltd. GBR. *Dist:* Independent Pubs. Group, Trafalgar Square Publishing.

—Good Night Gromit! 2005. (Wallace & Gromit Ser.). (Illus.). 16p. (ps). 6.99 (978-0-7434-8929-4(2) , Simon & Schuster Children's) Simon & Schuster, Ltd. GBR. *Dist:* Independent Pubs. Group.

—Gromit's Busy Day. 2005. (Wallace & Gromit Ser.). (Illus.). 10p. (ps). 6.99 (978-0-7434-8930-0(6) , Simon & Schuster Children's) Simon & Schuster, Ltd. GBR. *Dist:* Independent Pubs. Group.

—Woolly Shaun. 2005. (Wallace & Gromit Ser.). (Illus.). 10p. (ps). 6.99 (978-0-7434-8927-0(6) , Simon & Schuster Children's) Simon & Schuster, Ltd. GBR. *Dist:* Independent Pubs. Group.

Bowler, Bill. Wrong Trousers. 2005. (Dominoes Ser.). (Illus.). 48p. 6.50 (978-0-19-424396-4(6)) Oxford Univ. Pr., Inc.

Dakin, Glenn. Wallace & Gromit Curse of the Were-Rabbit: The Essential Guide. 2005. (Illus.). 48p. (J). (ps-7). 12.99 (978-0-7566-1153-8(9)) Dorling Kindersley Publishing, Inc.

Davies, Tristan. Anoraknophobia. 1999. (Illus.). 48p. (J). pap. (978-0-340-72834-5(5) , Hodder & Stoughton) Hodder General Publishing Division.

—Wallace & Gromit: The Lost Slipper & The Curse of the Ramsbottoms. 1998. (Wallace & Gromit Comic Strip Bks.). (J). (ps-3). pap. 9.95 (978-0-8417-3035-9(0)) Adventure Medical Kits.

Davies, Tristan & Newman, Nick. Wallace & Gromit: Anoraknophobia. 1998. (Wallace & Gromit Comic Strip Bks.). (Illus.). 48p. (J). 9.95 (978-0-8417-2031-2(2)) Adler's Foreign Bks., Inc.

Davies, Tristan, et al. Crackers in Space. 2000. (Illus.). 48p. (J). pap. (978-0-340-71290-0(2) , Hodder & Stoughton) Hodder General Publishing Division.

—Crackers in Space. 2000. (Illus.). 48p. (J). 16.99 (978-0-340-71289-4(9) , Hodder & Stoughton) Hodder General Publishing Division GBR. *Dist:* Trafalgar Square Publishing.

Dorling Kindersley Publishing Staff. Wallace & Gromit: Curse of the Were-Rabbit. 2005. (Ultimate sticker Bks.). (Illus.). 16p. (J). 6.99 (978-0-7566-1154-5(7)) Dorling Kindersley Publishing, Inc.

Park, Nick, et al. Close Shave. 2006. 31.95 (978-0-19-459239-0(1)) Oxford Univ. Pr., Inc.

Rimmer, Ian. Catch of the Day. Hansen, Jimmy, illus. 2003. 48p. (gr. 2-7). 12.95 (978-1-84023-495-4(4)) Titan Bks. Ltd. GBR. *Dist:* Random Hse., Inc.

Selby, Rona & Aardman, A. Wallace & Gromit: Welcome to West Wallaby Street. Kerwin, Bill, illus. 2003. (Wallace & Gromit Ser.). 24p. (gr. 1-2). pap. 9.99 (978-1-4169-1050-3(6)) Simon & Schuster, Ltd. GBR. *Dist:* Independent Pubs. Group.

WALRUSES

Baines, Rebecca. Arctic Tale. 2007. 32p. (J). (gr. k-4). lib. bdg. 22.90 (978-1-4263-0085-1(9) , National Geographic Children's Bks.) National Geographic Society.

Baines, Rebecca & Fifield, Donnali. Arctic Tale. 2007. 32p. (J). (gr. k-4). 5.95 (978-1-4263-0084-4(0) , National Geographic Children's Bks.) National Geographic Society.

Berger, Melvin & Berger, Gilda. Sea Horses. 2003. (Scholastic Readers Ser.). (Illus.). (J). pap. (978-0-439-47392-7(6)) Scholastic, Inc.

Dingwall, Laima & Switzer, Merebeth. Walrus. 1999. (Getting to Know ... Nature's Children Ser.). (Illus.). 47p. (J). (978-0-7172-8838-0(2) , Grolier) Scholastic Library Publishing.

Fifield, Donnali. Arctic Tale: Official Companion to the Major Motion Picture. 2007. (Illus.). 160p. 30.00 (978-1-4262-0065-6(X) , National Geographic) National Geographic Society.

Group/McGraw-Hill, Wright. I am the Walrus: Level N, 6 vols. 128p. (gr. 3-6). 36.95 (978-0-322-06734-9(0)) Wright Group, The.

Hirschmann, Kris. The Walrus. 2003. (Illus.). 48p. (J). 23.70 (978-0-7377-1557-6(X) , Greenhaven Pr., Inc.) Thomson Gale.

Hodge, Judith. Seals, Sea Lions & Walruses. 2001. (Animals of the Ocean Ser.). (Illus.). (J). lib. bdg. 15.95 (978-1-56674-301-3(X)) Forest Hse. Publishing Co., Inc.

Jones, Veda Boyd. Jazz Age Poet: A Story about Langston Hughes. Kiwak, Barbara, illus. 1999. (Early Bird Nature Bks.). 64p. (J). (ps-7). pap. 6.95 (978-0-8225-3092-3(9)) Lerner Publishing Group.

Miller, Connie Colwell. Walruses. 2005. (Illus.). 24p. (J). (ps-7). lib. bdg. 21.26 (978-0-7368-4313-3(2)) Capstone Pr., Inc.

Murray, Julie. Walruses. 2002. (Buddy Book Ser.). (Illus.). 24p. (J). (gr. k-4). lib. bdg. 21.35 (978-1-57765-726-2(8)) ABDO Publishing Co.

Rake, Jody Sullivan. Walruses. 2007. (J). (978-0-7368-6726-9(0)) Capstone Pr., Inc.

Rustad, Martha E. H. Walruses. 2003. (Ocean Life Ser.). (Illus.). 24p. (J). (gr. k-1). lib. bdg. 15.93 (978-0-7368-1659-5(3) , Pebble Bks.) Capstone Pr., Inc.

Sexton, Colleen. Walruses. 2007. (Illus.). 24p. (J). lib. bdg. 19.95 (978-1-60014-110-2(2)) Bellwether Media.

Soundprints Staff, ed. Oceanic Collection III: Beluga Whale, Harp Seal, Walrus & Lobster Books, 4 micro bks. (Smithsonian Oceanic Collection). (Illus.). 128p. (J). (ps-2). 18.95 (978-1-56899-633-2(0)) Soundprints.

Staub, Frank. Walruses. 1999. (Early Bird Nature Bks.). (Illus.). 48p. (J). (gr. 2-4). lib. bdg. 25.26 (978-0-8225-3039-8(2) , Lerner Pubns.) Lerner Publishing Group.

Varela, Barry. Arctic Tale (Junior Novelization) 2007. 128p. (J). (gr. 2-5). lib. bdg. 21.90 (978-1-4263-0107-0(3)); (Illus.). pap. 4.99 (978-1-4263-0106-3(5)) National Geographic Society. (National Geographic Children's Bks.).

Walruses, Vol. 2. 2005. (Ocean Life Ser.). (YA). (gr. k-3). (978-0-7368-3416-2(8) , Pebble Bks.) Capstone Pr., Inc.

WALRUSES—FICTION

Barg, Lois. Muktuk Makes It. 2003. 33 p. pap. 17.95 (978-1-4137-0930-8(3)) PublishAmerica, Inc.

Clarke, Jane. Tooth Trouble. Johansson, Cecilia, illus. 2005. (J). (978-0-439-74496-6(2)) Scholastic, Inc.

Clarke, Jane & Johansson, Cecilia. Tusk Trouble. (Illus.). 25p. (J). (978-0-340-87725-8(1) , Hodder Children's Books) Hodder Children's Division.

—Tusk Trouble. 2004. (Illus.). 32p. (J). pap. 8.99 (978-0-340-86079-3(0) , Hodder & Stoughton) Hodder General Publishing Division GBR. *Dist:* Trafalgar Square Publishing.

Cook, Sherry & Johnson, Terri. Watery William, 26. Kuhn, Jesse, illus. l.t. ed. 2006. (Quirkles—Exploring Phonics through Science Ser.: 23). 32p. (J). 7.99 (978-1-933815-22-0(1) , Quirkles, The) Creative 3, LLC.

Derrick, Patricia. Mr Walrus & the Old School Bus. 2007. 32p. 18.95 (978-1-933818-13-9(1)) Animalations.

deRubertis, Barbara. Wally Walrus. Pyk, Jan, illus. 1998. (Let's Read Together Ser.). 32p. (J). (ps-3). pap. 4.95 (978-1-57565-046-3(0)); pap. 8.95 incl. audio (978-1-57565-051-7(7)) Kane Pr., The.

Kiana, Chris. Wally the Lost Baby Walrus. 1999. (Illus.). 32p. (gr. 3-6). 14.95 (978-1-888125-59-7(4)) Publication Consultants.

Little Walrus Saves the Day. 2002. (Oceanic Mini Bks.). (Illus.). 32p. (J). (978-1-59069-005-5(2) , H1006) Studio Mouse LLC.

Myers, Bill. My Life as a Walrus Whoopee Cushion, Vol. 16. 1999. (Incredible Worlds of Wally McDoogle Ser.: No. 16). 128p. (J). (gr. 3-7). pap. 6.99 (978-0-8499-4025-5(7)) Nelson, Thomas Inc.

Rice, R. Hugh. Flip Flop. Becker, Neesa, illus. 1998. (Books for Young Learners). 12p. (J). (gr. k-2). pap. 5.00 (978-1-57274-115-7(5) , A2455) Owen, Richard C. Pubs., Inc.

Young, Carol. Little Walrus Warning: Smithsonains Oceanic. Stuart, Walter, illus. 2005. 32p. (J). (ps-2). pap. 6.95 (978-1-56899-937-1(2) , S4009) Soundprints.

WAR

see also Aeronautics, Military; Armies; Battles; Disarmament; International Law; Military Art and Science; Naval Art and Science; Peace; Soldiers; Submarine Warfare

also names of wars, battles, etc., e.g. United States—History—Civil War; Gettysburg, Battle of, 1863

American Education Publishing Staff. War. 2003. (Brighter Child Card Games Ser.). (Illus.). 36p. (J). 2.99 (978-1-56189-457-4(5) , 31040, American Education Publishing) School Specialty Publishing.

Bennett, Paul. War. 2002. 32p. pap. 14.95 (978-0-7641-2224-8(X)) Barron's Educational Series, Inc.

—War. 1999. (World Reacts Ser.). (Illus.). 32p. (J). (gr. 2-5). lib. bdg. 16.95 (978-1-887068-90-1(2)) Smart Apple Media.

—War: The World Reacts. 2002. (J). pap. 13.95 (978-0-7641-5534-5(2)) Barron's Educational Series, Inc.

Brownlie, Ali & Mason, Chris. Why Do People Fight Wars? 2002. (Exploring Tough Issues Ser.). (Illus.). 48p. (J). lib. bdg. 25.69 (978-0-7398-4961-3(1)) Raintree.

Cobb, Allan B. Biological & Chemical Weapons: The Debate over Modern Warfare. 2000. (Focus on Science & Society Ser.). (Illus.). 64p. (YA). (gr. 4-6). lib. bdg. 26.50 (978-0-8239-3214-6(1) , FSWEAP) Rosen Publishing Group, Inc., The.

Connolly, Sean. War. 2003. (Illus.). 32p. (J). lib. bdg. 27.10 (978-1-58340-391-4(4)) Smart Apple Media.

Fox, Carol, ed. In Times of War: An Anthology of War & Peace in Children's Literature. 2000. (Illus.). 272p. (J). 27.50 (978-1-86205-446-2(0) , Pavilion Bks., Ltd.) Anova Bks. GBR. *Dist:* Independent Pubs. Group.

Gay, Kathlyn & Gay, Martin. After the Shooting Stops: The Aftermath of War. 1998. (Single Titles Ser.: up). (Illus.). 128p. (gr. 7 up). lib. bdg. 24.90 (978-0-7613-3006-6(2) , Twenty-First Century Bks.) Lerner Publishing Group.

Haulley, Fletcher. Critical Perspectives on 9/11. 2005. (Critical Anthologies of Nonfiction Writing Ser.). 176p. (J). (gr. 7-12). lib. bdg. 30.60 (978-1-4042-0060-9(6)) Rosen Publishing Group, Inc., The.

Hoffman, Mary. Lines in the Sand: New Writing on War & Peace. 2003. (gr. 3-6). lib. bdg. 17.60 (978-0-613-84768-1(7)) Tandem Library Bks.

Hoffman, Mary & Lassiter, Rhiannon, eds. Lines in the Sand: New Writing on War & Peace. 2003. (Illus.). 288p. (gr. 2 up). pap. 8.95 (978-0-9729529-1-0(8)) Disinformation Co. Ltd., The.

Kenney, Karen Latchana. The Spoils of War. (Shockwave: History & Politics Ser.). (J). 2008. 32p. pap. 6.95 (***978-0-531-18837-8(X)***); 2007. (Illus.). 36p. (gr. 4-6). lib. bdg. 25.00 (***978-0-531-17757-0(2)***) Scholastic Library Publishing. (Children's Pr.).

Keoke, Emory Dean & Porterfield, Kay Marie. American Indian Contributions to the World. 2005. (American Indian Contributions to the World Ser.). (Illus.). 160p. (gr. 4-9). (J). 35.00 (978-0-8160-5395-7(2)); (YA). 35.00 (978-0-8160-5397-1(9)) Facts On File, Inc.

Kim, Henny H. War Crimes. 2000. (Contemporary Issues Companion Ser.). 176p. (YA). (gr. 9-12). lib. bdg. 36.20 (978-0-7377-0171-5(4)); (Illus.). (gr. 10 up). pap. 24.95 (978-0-7377-0170-8(6)) Thomson Gale. (Greenhaven Pr., Inc.).

Lackey Jordan, Hellyn. Escape from the Little White Crosses: Stories from the Front Lines to the Home Front. 2000. (Illus.). xii, 93p. (YA). pap. 11.95 (978-0-9704474-0-1(X)) Jordan, Hellyn Lackey.

Landau, Elaine. Land Mines: 100 Million Hidden Killers. 2000. (Issues in Focus Ser.). (Illus.). 128p. (YA). (gr. 6-12). lib. bdg. 26.60 (978-0-7660-1240-0(9)) Enslow Pubs., Inc.

Lazar, Wendy Phillips, ed. Theaters of War: We Remember. 2002. (Illus.). 360p. (YA). (gr. 7 up). pap. 19.95 (978-0-9710246-9-4(3)) Glendale.

Letters from the Homefront, 5 bks., Set. Incl. Civil War. Schomp, Virginia. lib. bdg. 29.93 (978-0-7614-1095-9(3)); Revolutionary War. Beller, Susan Provost. lib. bdg. 29.93 (978-0-7614-1094-2(5)); Vietnam War. Schomp, Virginia. lib. bdg. 29.93 (978-0-7614-1099-7(6)); World War I. George, Linda S. lib. bdg. 29.93 (978-0-7614-1096-6(1)); World War II. Schomp, Virginia. lib. bdg. 29.93 (978-0-7614-1098-0(8)); (Illus.). 96p. (J). (gr. 6 up). 2001. Set lib. bdg. 149.64 (978-0-7614-1097-3(X) , Benchmark Bks.) Cavendish, Marshall Corp.

Lobel, Anita. No Pretty Pictures: A Child of War. 2000. (Illus.). 208p. (J). (gr. 5 up). pap. 6.99 (978-0-380-73285-2(8)) HarperCollins Pubs.

—No Pretty Pictures: A Child of War. 2000. (978-0-606-17979-9(8)); (gr. 5-8). lib. bdg. 14.15 (978-0-613-28590-2(5)) Tandem Library Bks.

Marsh, Carole. War What Kids Should Know. 2003. 32p. (gr. 2-8). pap. 7.95 (978-0-635-01715-4(6)) Gallopade International.

Murray, Stuart. Encyclopedia of War & Weaponry. 2003. (gr. 3-6). lib. bdg. 30.35 (978-0-613-72674-0(X)) Tandem Library Bks.

Nusbacher, Aryeh S. War & Conflict. 2003. (Face the Facts Ser.). (Illus.). 56p. (J). lib. bdg. 28.56 (978-0-7398-6435-7(1)) Raintree.

—War & Conflict. 2003. (gr. 5-8). lib. bdg. 17.60 (978-0-613-78128-2(7)) Tandem Library Bks.

On the Frontline, 6 bks., Set 1. 2004. 179.58 (978-1-4109-1469-9(0)); pap. 53.70 (978-1-4109-1476-7(3)) Raintree.

Phillips, Larissa. Cochise: Jefe Apache. de la Vega, Eida, tr. from ENG. 2003. (Grandes Personajes en la Historia de Los Estados Unidos Ser.). (ENG & SPA., Illus.). 32p. (J). pap. (978-0-8239-4223-7(6)) Rosen Publishing Group, Inc., The.

Pringle, Laurence P. Chemical & Biological Warfare: The Cruelest Weapons. rev. ed. 2000. (Issues in Focus Ser.). (Illus.). 112p. (YA). (gr. 6-12). lib. bdg. 26.60 (978-0-7660-1241-7(7)) Enslow Pubs., Inc.

Quinlan. The History of Weapons of War. 2004. (World History Ser.). (Illus.). 112p. (J). 32.45 (978-1-59018-183-6(2) , Lucent Bks.) Thomson Gale.

Raintree Steck-Vaughn Staff. History of Warfare, 5 vols., Set. 1998. (YA). (gr. 7 up). 149.85 (978-0-8172-5447-6(1)) Raintree.

Rivera, Sheila. Rebuilding Iraq. 2004. (War in Iraq Ser.). (Illus.). 48p. (J). (gr. 4-8). lib. bdg. 25.65 (978-1-59197-498-7(4)) ABDO Publishing Co.

Road to War: Causes of Conflict, 5 vols., Set. Incl. Causes of the American Revolution. Strum, Richard M. 64p. (J). lib. bdg. 22.95 (978-1-59556-001-8(7)); Causes of the Civil War. Epperson, James F. 64p. (J). lib. bdg. 22.95 (978-1-59556-002-5(5)); Causes of the Iraq War. Gallagher, Jim. 72p. (J). lib. bdg. 22.95 (978-1-59556-009-4(2)); Causes of World War I. Ziff, John. 72p. (J). lib. bdg. 22.95 (978-1-59556-003-2(3)); Causes of World War II. Corrigan, Jim. 64p. lib. bdg. 22.95 (978-1-59556-004-9(1)); (gr. 4 up). 2005. (Road to War Ser.). (Illus.). 64p. 2005. Set lib. bdg. 114.75 (978-1-59556-000-1(9)) OTTN Publishing.

Savage, Douglas J. Ironclads & Blockades in the Civil War. 2000. (Untold History of the Civil War Ser.). (Illus.). 64p. (J). (gr. 3 up). 25.00 (978-0-7910-5429-1(2) , Chelsea Hse.) Facts On File, Inc.

Verrept, Paul. El Pequeno Soldado. Bourgeois, Elodie, tr. Verrept, Paul, illus. 2004. (SPA., Illus.). 26p. (J). (ps-3). 17.99 (978-84-261-3306-9(1)) Juventud, Editorial ESP. *Dist:* Lectorum Pubns., Inc., Iaconi, Mariuccia Bk. Imports.

Walter, Virginia A. War & Peace: A Guide to Literature & New Media, Grades 4-8. 2006. (Children's & Young Adult Literature Reference Ser.). 288p. pap. 40.00 (978-1-59158-271-7(7) , LU2717) Libraries Unlimited, Inc.

Wassiljewa, Tatjana. Hostage to War: A True Story. Trenter, Anna, tr. 1999. 192p. (J). (gr. 3-7). pap. 5.99 (978-0-590-29886-5(0)) Scholastic, Inc.

The World Wars Series, 10 bks., Set. 2003. 285.60 (978-0-7398-5484-6(4)); (Illus.). 114.24 (978-0-7398-5483-9(6)) Raintree.

The World Wars Series, 6 bks., Set. Incl. Great Battles of World War II. Hansen, Ole Steen. lib. bdg. 27.12 (978-0-7398-2757-4(X)); Leaders of World War II. Ross, Stewart. lib. bdg. 27.12 (978-0-7398-2756-7(1)); World War I : Armistice 1918. Grant, R. G. lib. bdg. 27.12 (978-0-7398-2753-6(7)); World War I : War in the Trenches. Hansen, Ole Steen. lib. bdg. 27.12 (978-0-7398-2752-9(9)); World War II : Allied Victory. Sheehan, Sean. lib. bdg. 27.12 (978-0-7398-2755-0(3)); World War II : Germany & Japan Attack. Sheehan, Sean. Sloan, Frank, ed. lib. bdg. 27.12 (978-0-7398-2754-3(5)); 64p. (J). (gr. 5). (Illus.). 2001. Set lib. bdg. 171.36 (978-0-7398-2758-1(8)) Raintree.

Yancey, Diane. Leaders & Generals. 2003. (American War Library). (Illus.). 112p. (J). 29.95 (978-1-59018-328-1(2) , Lucent Bks.) Thomson Gale.

WAR—FICTION

Alcorn, Anita C. Caught in the Crossfire: A Boy's View of the Battle of Mill Springs, KY. 2006. 48p. pap. 8.95 (***978-0-7414-3581-1(0)***) Infinity Publishing.

Alexander, Lloyd. The Illyrian Adventure. 2000. (Vesper Holly Ser.). (YA). (gr. 5-8). lib. bdg. 14.15 (978-0-8085-9586-1(5)) Tandem Library Bks.

Alfonseca, Manuel. El Sello de Eolo (The Aeolus Seal) 2000. (SPA.). 162p. (YA). (gr. 6-8). 9.75 (978-84-236-5515-1(6)) Edebé ESP. *Dist:* Baker & Taylor Bks.

Alshalabi, Firyal M. Summer 1990. 1999. 138 p. pap. 6.99 (978-0-9669988-0-1(4)) Aunt Strawberry Bks.

Altsheler, A. Joseph. Guns of Shiloh A Story of the Great West. 2006. 26.99 (***978-1-4280-2738-1(6)***) IndyPublish.com.

Altsheler, Joseph A. The Forest Runners: A Story of the Great. 2006. pap. (***978-1-4065-0810-9(1)***) Dodo Pr.

—The Guns of Shiloh: A Story of the Great. 2006. pap. (***978-1-4065-0813-0(6)***) Dodo Pr.

—The Texan Scouts: A Story of the Alamo A. 2006. pap. (***978-1-4065-0826-0(8)***) Dodo Pr.

Anderson, Kevin J., et al. The Fall of the Sith Empire. 1998. (Star Wars Ser.). (Illus.). 136p. (YA). (gr. 7 up). pap. 14.95 (978-1-56971-320-4(0)) Dark Horse Comics.

Antle, Nancy. Lost in the War. 2000. (Illus.). 144p. (J). (gr. 3-7). pap. 5.99 (978-0-14-130836-4(2) , Puffin) Penguin Group (USA) Inc.

—Lost in the War. 2000. 137p. (J). (gr. 6-12). per. 13.00 (978-0-613-28562-9(X)); (978-0-606-17864-8(3)) Tandem Library Bks.

Armstrong, Jennifer. Shattered: Stories of Children & War. 2003. 176p. (YA). (gr. 7). pap. 5.99 (978-0-440-23765-5(3) , Laurel Leaf) Random Hse. Children's Bks.

—Shattered: Stories of Children & War. l.t. ed. 2004. 201p. (J). 22.95 (978-0-7862-6508-4(6)) Thorndike Pr.

Avery, Pat McGrath. Tommy's War: A Parent Goes to War, 1. Ray, Eric, illus. 2003. 36p. (J). per. 5.95 (978-0-9663276-8-7(3)) Red Engine Pr.

Avi. Iron Thunder: The Battle Between the Monitor & the Merrimac: A Civil War Novel. rev. ed. 2007. 224p. (J). (gr. 2-7). 15.99 (***978-1-4231-0446-9(3)***) Hyperion Pr.

Banks, Lynne Reid. Maura's Angel. 1999. (J). (978-0-606-16353-8(0)) Tandem Library Bks.

Bates, Gordon. The Khaki Boys over the Top: Doing & Daring for Uncle Sam. 2007. 140p. pap. 10.99 (***978-1-4264-6542-0(4)***) BiblioBazaar.

Beckwith, Kathy. Playing War. Lyons, Lea, illus. 2005. 32p. (J). (gr. 3-6). 16.95 (978-0-88448-267-3(7)) Tilbury Hse. Pubs.

Beddor, Frank. Seeing Redd. 2007. (Looking Glass Wars Trilogy: Bk. 2). 384p. (YA). (gr. 6 up). 17.99 (***978-0-8037-3155-4(8)*** , Dial) Penguin Group (USA) Inc.

Bennett, Holly. The Bonemender. 2005. (Illus.). 208p. (YA). (gr. 7-12). pap. 7.95 (978-1-55143-336-3(2)) Orca Bk. Pubs. USA.

Birmajer, Marcelo. Una Vida Mas: Noticias Extranas IV. 2004. (SPA.). 111p. (J). pap. 9.95 (978-958-04-7081-6(2)) Norma S.A. COL. *Dist:* Lectorum Pubns., Inc.

Black, Judith. Home Front. (YA). 12.00 (978-0-9701073-7-4(4)) Black, Judith Storyteller.

Booth, Martin. Pow. l.t. ed. 2001. 224p. (J). 16.95 (978-0-7540-6160-1(4) , Galaxy Children's Large Print) BBC Audiobooks America.

Brennan, Herbie. Ruler of the Realm. 2006. (Faerie Wars Chronicles Ser.: Bk. 3). (Illus.). 432p. (YA). 18.95 (978-1-58234-881-0(2)) Bloomsbury Publishing.

Breslin, Theresa. Remembrance. 2004. 304p. (YA). (gr. 7). mass mkt. 6.50 (978-0-440-23778-5(5) , Laurel Leaf) Random Hse. Children's Bks.

Browne, N. M. Warriors of Alavna. (J). 2004. 312p. (gr. 5-10). pap. 7.95 (978-1-58234-916-9(9)); 2002. 319p. 16.95 (978-1-58234-775-2(1)) Bloomsbury Publishing. (Bloomsbury Children).

—Warriors of Camlann. 2003. (Illus.). 275p. (J). 16.95 (978-1-58234-817-9(0) , Bloomsbury Children) Bloomsbury Publishing.

Brudlos, Christopher. Alpha Shade Chapter One. Brudlos, Joseph, illus. 2005. (YA). per. 24.95 net. (978-0-9768705-0-0(9)) Alpha Shade, Inc.

Bunting, Eve. Gleam & Glow. Sylvada, Peter, illus. 2005. 32p. (J). (ps-ps). reprint ed. pap., pap. 7.00 (978-0-15-205380-2(8) , Voyager Bks./Libros Viajeros) Harcourt Children's Bks.

—Gleam & Glow. Sylvada, Peter, illus. 2005. 32p. (J). (gr. 1-4). lib. bdg. 14.20 (978-0-606-33528-7(5)) Tandem Library Bks.

Butler, Ted D. The Pandora Project, Bk. 5. 2007. 280p. (YA). pap. 14.99 (978-1-59092-292-7(1) , Blue Works) Windstorm Creative.

Caballero, Erica. Mount Mole. 2006. pap. 10.00 (***978-1-4257-2301-9(2)***) Xlibris Corp.

Camus, William. Azules Contra Grises. (Barco de Vapor). (SPA.). 200p. (YA). (gr. 5-8). 7.95 (978-84-348-1455-4(2)) SM Ediciones ESP. *Dist:* AIMS International Bks., Inc.

Carey, Mike, et al. Mirror Mirror. 2006. (Illus.). 152p. (YA). pap. 16.99 (978-0-7851-1902-9(7)) Marvel Enterprises, Inc.

Carmi, Daniella. Samir & Yonatan. Lotan, Yael, tr. from HEB. 2002. 192p. (J). (gr. 3-7). pap. 4.99 (978-0-439-13523-8(0) , Scholastic Paperbacks) Scholastic, Inc.

—Samir & Yonatan. 2000. (gr. 3-6). lib. bdg. 13.00 (978-0-613-45824-5(9)) Tandem Library Bks.

—Samir & Yonatan. 2000. (Illus.). 192p. (J). (gr. 3-7). pap. 15.95 (978-0-439-13504-7(4) , Levine, Arthur A. Bks.) Scholastic, Inc.

Chan, Gillian. A Foreign Field. 2004. (Illus.). 192p. (YA). (gr. 13 up). (978-1-55337-350-6(2)) Kids Can Pr., Ltd.

Chandler, Norman A. & Chandler, Roy F. The One Shot Brotherhood. Chandler, Roy F., illus. l.t. ed. 2001. (Illus.). 450p. (YA). (gr. 6 up). 65.00 (978-1-885633-20-0(3)) Iron Brigade Armory, Ltd.

Chickasaw Adventures: War with the Creeks. 2005. (J). (978-1-4265-0001-5(7)) Layne Morgan Media, Inc.

Cole, Barbara. Anna & Natalie. Himler, Ronald, illus. 2007. 32p. (J). 16.95 (***978-1-59572-105-1(3)***) Star Bright Bks., Inc.

Collins, Suzanne. Gregor & the Code of Claw. 2007. (Underland Chronicles). 416p. (YA). (gr. 5-9). pap. 17.99 (***978-0-439-79143-4(X)*** , Scholastic Pr.) Scholastic, Inc.

—Gregor & the Marks of Secret. 352p. (J). 2007. pap. 6.99 (***978-0-439-79146-5(4)*** , Scholastic Paperbacks); Vol. 4. 2006. pap. 16.99 (978-0-439-79145-8(6) , Scholastic Pr.) Scholastic, Inc.

—Gregor & the Marks of Secret. rev. l.t. ed. 2007. (Underland Chronicles Ser.). 343p. (YA). 23.95 (***978-0-7862-9553-1(8)***) Thorndike Pr.

Cormier, Robert. La Guerra del Chocolate. 2004. (SPA., Illus.). 256p. (978-84-7720-864-8(6)) Obelisco, Ediciones S.A.

Crane, Stephen. Stephen Crane/the Red Badge of Courage. Carrillo, Fred, illus. 2005. 48p. (gr. 5-8). 25.50 (978-0-7910-9103-6(1)) Facts On File, Inc.

Cutler, Jane. The Cello of Mr. O. Couch, Greg, illus. 1999. 32p. (J). (gr. k-4). 15.99 (978-0-525-46119-7(1) , Dutton Juvenile) Penguin Group (USA) Inc.

Dark Horse Comics Staff & Lucas, George. The Empire Strikes Back. 1999. (Star Wars Manga Ser.: No. 3). (Illus.). 96p. (J). (gr. 3 up). pap. 9.95 (978-1-56971-392-1(8)) Dark Horse Comics.

—Episode I: The Phantom Menace. 1999. (Star Wars Manga Ser.: No. 1). (Illus.). 88p. (J). (gr. 3 up). pap. 9.95 (978-1-56971-483-6(5)) Dark Horse Comics.

—Episode I: The Phantom Menace Manga. 2000. (Star Wars Manga Ser.: No. 2). (Illus.). 88p. (J). (gr. 3 up). pap. 9.95 (978-1-56971-484-3(3)) Dark Horse Comics.

Davis, Benjamin Doron. The Balloon Project. 2004. 75p. pap. 14.95 (978-1-4137-3663-2(7)) PublishAmerica, Inc.

de Brunhoff, Laurent. Babar's Battle. 2002. (Babar Ser.). (Illus.). 38p. (J). (ps-3). 16.95 (978-0-8109-5714-5(0)) Abrams, Harry N., Inc.

Decker, Timothy. The Letter Home. 2005. (Illus.). 32p. (J). (ps). 16.95 (978-1-932425-50-5(0) , Lemniscaat) Boyds Mills Pr.

Deutsch, Stacia, et al. Washington's War. Francis, Guy & Lyon, Tammie, illus. 2007. (Blast to the Past Ser.). 128p. (J). pap. 3.99 (978-1-4169-3390-8(5) , Aladdin) Simon & Schuster Children's Publishing.

DiMarco, Carol. Rumors of War. Huft, Maggie, illus. 2005. (Delimit Nonpariel Ser.). 88p. (YA). pap. 9.99 (978-1-59092-052-7(X) , Blue Works) Windstorm Creative.

DiMarco, Carol & Bowman, Sharon. The Tale of Two Kingdoms. 2007. 88p. (J). pap. 10.99 (978-1-59092-170-8(4) , Little Blue Works) Windstorm Creative.

Dowswell, Paul. Prison Ship: Adventures of a Young Sailor. 2007. 320p. (YA). pap. 7.95 (***978-1-59990-156-5(0)*** , Bloomsbury Children) Bloomsbury Publishing.

Drake, L. Robert. The Boy Allies at Jutland or the Greates. 2006. 96.99 (***978-1-4280-0402-3(5));*** pap. 89.99 (***978-1-4280-0405-4(X)***) IndyPublish.com.

Driscoll, James R. The Brighton Boys with the Flying Corps. 2005. 152p. pap. 11.95 (978-1-59540-820-4(7) , 1st World Library - Literary Society) 1st World Publishing, Inc.

—The Brighton Boys with the Flying Corps. 2007. 128p. pap. 10.99 (***978-1-4264-6537-6(8));*** 138p. pap. 13.99 (***978-1-4264-6596-3(3)***) BiblioBazaar.

Driscoll, Laura. Beck & the Great Berry Battle. Clarke, Judith, illus. 2006. (Stepping Stone Bks.). 128p. (J). (gr. 2-4). 5.99 (978-0-7364-2373-1(7) , RH/Disney) Random Hse. Children's Bks.

Dunmore, Helen. Amina's Blanket. Dainton, Paul, illus. 2002. (Yellow Bananas Ser.). 48p. (J). (gr. 3-4). pap. (978-0-7787-0984-8(1)); lib. bdg. (978-0-7787-0938-1(8)) Crabtree Publishing Co.

—Amina's Blanket. 2002. (gr. 3-6). lib. bdg. 12.95 (978-0-613-52802-3(6)) Tandem Library Bks.

Ellis, Warren. Switchblade Honey. 2003. (Illus.). 88p. (gr. 11 up). pap. 9.95 (978-1-932051-13-1(9)) A i T/Planet Lar.

Entwistle, Charles. The Promise. 2004. 114p. (YA). per. 9.95 (978-0-9709104-2-4(8)) Hickory Tales Publishing.

Erwood, G. Stepping Stones of War. 2004. 48p. pap. 12.95 (978-1-4137-5497-1(X)) PublishAmerica, Inc.

Fan, Nancy Yi. Sword Quest. Rioux, Jo-Anne, illus. 2008. 288p. (J). 15.99 (***978-0-06-124335-6(3));*** lib. bdg. 16.89 (***978-0-06-124336-3(1)***) HarperCollins Pubs.

—Swordbird. Zug, Mark, illus. 2008. 256p. (J). pap. 6.99 (***978-0-06-113101-1(6)*** , Harper Trophy) HarperCollins Pubs.

Finley, Martha. Elsie's Troubled Times, Vol. 6. 2006. (Life of Faith': Elsie Dinsmore Ser.). 224p. (J). pap. 7.99 (978-1-928749-88-2(7)) Zonderkidz.

Fitzpatrick, Marie-Louise. I Am I. Fitzpatrick, Marie-Louise, illus. 2006. (Illus.). 32p. (J). 16.95 (978-1-59643-054-9(0)) Roaring Brook Pr.

Flanagan, John. The Burning Bridge. 2007. (Ranger's Apprentice Ser.: Bk. 2). 288p. (J). (gr. 5 up). pap. 7.99 (978-0-14-240842-1(5) , Puffin) Penguin Group (USA) Inc.

Flegg, Aubrey. The Cinnamon Tree: A Novel Set in Africa. 2003. 208p. (YA). reprint ed. pap. 7.95 (978-0-86278-657-1(6)) O'Brien Pr., Ltd., The IRL. *Dist:* Independent Pubs. Group.

Fontes, Ron, et al. The Trojan Horse: The Fall of Troy. Purcell, Gordon, illus. 2007. (Graphic Myths & Legends Ser.). 48p. (J). 26.60 (978-0-8225-3085-5(6)) Lerner Publishing Group.

Foon, Dennis. Freewalker. 2004. (Longlight Legacy Ser.). 320p. (YA). (gr. 6). 19.95 (978-1-55037-885-6(6)); pap. 9.95 (978-1-55037-884-9(8)) Annick Pr., Ltd. CAN. *Dist:* Firefly Bks., Ltd.

Foreman, Michael. War Boy: A Country Childhood. 2000. (Illus.). 92p. (J). pap. 17.99 (978-1-85145-704-5(6) , Pavilion Bks., Ltd.) Anova Bks. GBR. *Dist:* Trafalgar Square Publishing.

—War Game. 2002. (Illus.). 65p. (YA). pap. 19.99 (978-1-85793-713-8(9)) Pavillion, Ltd.

Fullerton, Charlotte. Battle at Ice Palace. 2006. (Sonic X Ser.). (Illus.). 48p. (J). (gr. 1-3). pap. 4.99 (978-0-448-44409-3(7) , Grosset & Dunlap) Penguin Group (USA) Inc.

—Dr. Eggman Goes to War. 2006. (Sonic X Ser.). (Illus.). 48p. (J). (gr. 1-3). pap. 4.99 (978-0-448-44327-0(9) , Grosset & Dunlap) Penguin Group (USA) Inc.

Geras, Adele. Ithaka. 2007. (Illus.). 368p. (YA). (gr. 9 up). pap. 6.95 (978-0-15-206104-3(5) , Harcourt Paperbacks) Harcourt Children's Bks.

—Troy. 2002. 376p. (YA). (gr. 9 up). pap. 6.95 (978-0-15-204570-8(8) , Harcourt Paperbacks) Harcourt Children's Bks.

—Troy. 2004. 368p. (J). (gr. 8 up). pap. 48.00 incl. audio (978-0-8072-2288-1(7) , Listening Library) Random Hse. Audio Publishing Group.

—Troy. 2002. (gr. 7-12). lib. bdg. 15.25 (978-0-613-55224-0(5)) Tandem Library Bks.

Gerstein, Mordicai. The Old Country. 144p. 2006. (J). pap. 7.95 (978-1-59643-192-8(X)); 2005. (YA). 14.95 (978-1-59643-047-1(8)) Roaring Brook Pr.

Glory Be! A Penny Parrish Story. 2001. (Penny Parrish Story). 207p. pap. 12.95 (978-1-930009-28-8(3)) Image Cascade Publishing.

Golden, Christopher, et al. Wurm War. 2005. (OutCast Ser.). 208p. (J). pap. 5.99 (978-0-689-86664-7(X) , Aladdin) Simon & Schuster Children's Publishing.

Gonzalez Jensen, Margarita. Botas Negras. Sanchez, Enrique O., illus. (SPA.). (J). (gr. 2-4). 3.96 net. (978-0-590-26842-4(2)) Scholastic, Inc.

Graff, Nancy Price. A Long Way Home. 2001. 208p. (J). (gr. 5-9). tchr. ed. 15.00 (978-0-618-12042-0(4) , Clarion Bks.) Houghton Mifflin Co. Trade & Reference Div.

Guest, Jacqueline. Belle of Batoche. 2004. (Orca Young Readers Ser.). (Illus.). 144p. (J). (gr. 3-6). pap. 4.99 (978-1-55143-297-7(8)) Orca Bk. Pubs. USA.

Halsey, Jacqueline. Peggy's Letter. 2005. (Orca Young Readers Ser.). (Illus.). 144p. (J). (gr. 3-6). pap. 5.95 (978-1-55143-363-9(X)) Orca Bk. Pubs. USA.

Hamley, Dennis. Without Warning: Ellen's Story, 1914-1918. 2007. (Illus.). 336p. (YA). (gr. 7). 17.99 (***978-0-7636-3338-7(0)***) Candlewick Pr.

Hand, Elizabeth. A New Threat. 2004. (Star Wars Ser.: Vol. 5). 139p. (J). lib. bdg. 20.00 (***978-1-4242-0781-7(9)***) Fitzgerald Bks.

Hardy, LeAnne. The Wooden Ox: A Novel. 2002. 192p. (gr. 4-8). pap. 6.99 (978-0-8254-2794-7(0)) Kregel Pubns.

Harpur, James. Warriors. 2007. 32p. (J). (gr. 3-9). 21.99 (***978-1-4169-3951-1(2)*** , Atheneum) Simon & Schuster Children's Publishing.

Harrell, Deborah A. Pintos Hope. 2003. 124p. (YA). pap. 10.95 (978-0-595-26514-5(6)) iUniverse, Inc.

Harris, Christine. The Silver Path. (Illus.). (J). (CHI & ENG.). 32p. (978-1-85430-323-3(6) , 93425); (ENG & VIE., 26p. (978-1-85430-327-1(9) , 93381) Magi Pubns.

Heibel, Dorothy. Message for a Spy. 2004. (Illus.). 94p. (J). pap. (978-1-932663-07-5(X)) History Compass, LLC.

Henderson, Jason & Salvaggio, Tony. Psy-Comm. 2007. (Kaplan SAT/ACT Score-Raising Manga Ser.). 192p. pap. 9.99 (***978-1-4277-5496-7(9)***) Kaplan Publishing.

Henty, G. A. By Sheer Pluck: A Tale of the Ashanti War. 2006. 246p. pap. 12.99 (978-1-4264-3065-7(5)); 272p. pap. 16.99 (978-1-4264-3130-2(9)) BiblioBazaar.

Henty, G. A. True to the Old Flag: A Tale of the American War of Independence. 2006. (ENG.). 64.99 (***978-1-4219-8196-3(3));*** pap. 58.99 (***978-1-4219-9348-5(1)***) IndyPublish.com.

—True to the Old Flag: A Tale of the American War of Independence. 2004. reprint ed. pap. 27.95 (978-1-4191-9123-7(3)); pap. 1.99 (978-1-4192-9123-4(8)) Kessinger Publishing, LLC.

Hill, Stuart. Blade of Fire: Icemark Chronicles #2. 2008. (Blade of Fire Ser.). 592p. (J). pap. 8.99 (***978-0-439-87327-7(4)*** , Scholastic Paperbacks) Scholastic, Inc.

Hill, Stuart. The Cry of the Icemark. 2005. 480p. (YA). pap. 18.95 (978-0-439-68626-6(1) , Chicken Hse., The) Scholastic, Inc.

Holub, Josef. An Innocent Soldier. Hofmann, Michael, tr. from GER. 2005. (Illus.). 240p. (J). (gr. 8 up). pap. 16.99 (978-0-439-62771-9(0) , Levine, Arthur A. Bks.) Scholastic, Inc.

Holub, Josef & Hofmann, Michael. An Innocent Soldier. 2007. (Illus.). 256p. (J). pap. 6.99 (978-0-439-62772-6(9) , Levine, Arthur A. Bks.) Scholastic, Inc.

Hughes, Dean. Search & Destroy. 2008. 224p. (YA). mass mkt. 5.99 (***978-1-4169-5371-5(X)*** , Simon Pulse) Simon & Schuster Children's Publishing.

Hunter, John P. Red Thunder: Secrets, Spies, & Scoundrels at Yorktown. 2006. (J). (***978-0-87935-231-8(0)***) Colonial Williamsburg Foundation.

Jacques, Brian. The Long Patrol. Curless, Allan, illus. 2004. (Redwall Ser.). 368p. (YA). pap. 8.99 (978-0-14-240245-0(1) , Puffin) Penguin Group (USA) Inc.

Jinks, Catherine. Pagan's Daughter. 2008. (YA). (***978-0-7636-3650-0(9)***) Candlewick Pr.

Johnstone, William W. & Kensington Publishing Corporation Staff. Flames from the Ashes, Vol. 1. 1999. 352p. mass mkt. 5.99 (978-0-7860-1038-7(X) , Pinnacle Bks.) Kensington Publishing Corp.

Kaneko, Shinya. Culdcept, Vol. 5. 5th rev. ed. 2006. (Illus.). pap. 9.99 (978-1-59816-553-1(4) , Tokyopop Adult) TOKYOPOP, Inc.

Khanduri, K. Tales of the trojan War. 2005. 144p. (J). pap. 4.95 (978-0-7945-0323-9(3) , Usborne) EDC Publishing.

Kubert, Joe. Fax from Sarajevo: A Story of Survival. Kubert, Joe, illus. 1998. (Illus.). 224p. (YA). (gr. 9 up). pap. 16.95 (978-1-56971-346-4(4)) Dark Horse Comics.

Lalonde, Carolyn. Hide Tommy Turkey. Lalonde, Johnathan, illus. 2005. 20p. (J). (978-1-4120-4893-4(1)) Trafford Publishing.

Lasky, Kathryn. The Shattering. 2004. (Guardians of Ga'Hoole Ser.: Bk. 5). (Illus.). 192p. (J). (gr. 3-7). pap. 4.99 (978-0-439-40561-4(0) , Scholastic Paperbacks) Scholastic, Inc.

—The Siege. 2004. (Guardians of Ga'Hoole Ser.: Bk. 4). (Illus.). 224p. (J). (gr. 3-7). mass mkt. 4.99 (978-0-439-40560-7(2) , Scholastic Paperbacks) Scholastic, Inc.

—To Be a King. 2006. (Guardians of Ga'Hoole Ser.: Bk. 11). 224p. (J). (gr. 4-7). pap. 4.99 (978-0-439-79570-8(2) , Scholastic Paperbacks) Scholastic, Inc.

Lawlor, Laurie. Wind on the River. 2004. 156p. (J). lib. bdg. 16.92 (***978-1-4242-0771-8(1)***) Fitzgerald Bks.

Lawlor, Laurie. Wind on the River: A Story of the Civil War. 2001. (American Portraits Ser.). (Illus.). iv, 156p. (J). (gr. 5-8). 15.32 (978-0-8092-0582-0(3) , 9780809205820) Jamestown.

—Wind on the River: A Story of the Civil War. 2000. (978-0-606-21880-1(7)); (gr. 5-8). lib. bdg. 15.70 (978-0-613-36904-6(1)) Tandem Library Bks.

Lawlor, Laurie & McGraw-Hill Staff. Wind on the River: A Story of the Civil War. 2001. (Jamestown Classics Ser.). (Illus.). iv, 156p. (J). (gr. 5-8). pap. 10.00 (978-0-8092-0624-7(2) , 9780809206247) Jamestown.

Lawrence, Iain. B for Buster. (Illus.). 336p. (YA). (gr. 7). 2004. 15.95 (978-0-385-73086-0(1) , Delacorte Bks. for Young Readers); 2006. reprint ed. 5.99 (978-0-440-23810-2(2) , Laurel Leaf) Random Hse. Children's Bks.

—Lord of the Nutcracker Men. (gr. 5). 2003. (Illus.). 240p. (J). pap. 5.99 (978-0-440-41812-2(7) , Laurel Leaf); 2001. 224p. lib. bdg. 17.99 (978-0-385-90024-9(4) , Delacorte Bks. for Young Readers) Random Hse. Children's Bks.

—Lord of the Nutcracker Men. l.t. ed. 2002. 280p. (J). 24.95 (978-0-7862-4155-2(1)) Thomson Gale.

Lethcoe, Jason. Wishing Well. Damkoehler, Katrina, illus. 2007. (Benjamin Bartholomew Piff Ser.: No. 3). 224p. (J). (gr. 3-7). 9.99 (***978-0-448-44498-7(4)*** , Grosset & Dunlap) Penguin Group (USA) Inc.

Lobel, Anita. Potatoes, Potatoes. 2004. 40p. (J). 15.99 (978-0-06-023927-5(1)); lib. bdg. 16.89 (978-0-06-023928-2(X)) HarperCollins Pubs.

—Potatoes, Potatoes. Lobel, Anita, illus. 2004. (Illus.). 40p. (J). reprint ed. 15.99 (978-0-06-051817-2(0)) HarperCollins Pubs.

Macatee, Susan. Under the Guns. 2002. (gr. 7-12). lib. bdg. 30.35 (978-0-613-85842-7(5)) Tandem Library Bks.

Maddox, Joseph & Maddox, Diana. See You in Hell. 2004. 215p. (YA). pap. 14.95 (978-0-7414-1872-2(X)) Infinity Publishing.

Marsden, John. Burning for Revenge. 2000. 272p. (YA). (gr. 7-12). 16.00 (978-0-395-96054-7(1)) Houghton Mifflin Co. Trade & Reference Div.

—Darkness Be My Friend. 1999. 288p. (YA). (gr. 7-12). 16.00 (978-0-395-92274-3(7)) Houghton Mifflin Co. Trade & Reference Div.

—The Dead of Night. 2006. (Tomorrow Ser.: No. 2). 272p. (J). pap. 8.99 (978-0-439-82911-3(9) , Scholastic Paperbacks) Scholastic, Inc.

—The Dead of Night. 1999. (J). (978-0-606-16450-4(2)) Tandem Library Bks.

—A Killing Frost. 1998. 288p. (YA). (gr. 7-12). 16.00 (978-0-395-83735-1(9)) Houghton Mifflin Co. Trade & Reference Div.

—A Killing Frost. 2006. (Tomorrow Ser.: No. 3). 288p. (J). pap. 8.99 (978-0-439-82912-0(7) , Scholastic Paperbacks) Scholastic, Inc.

—The Night Is for Hunting. 2001. (Tomorrow Ser.). (Illus.). 256p. (YA). (gr. 7 up). 16.00 (978-0-618-07026-8(5)) Houghton Mifflin Co. Trade & Reference Div.

—The Night Is for Hunting. 2007. (Tomorrow Ser.: Vol. 6). 256p. (J). pap. 8.99 (978-0-439-85804-5(6) , Scholastic Paperbacks) Scholastic, Inc.

—The Other Side of Dawn. 2002. (Tomorrow Ser.). (Illus.). 352p. (YA). (gr. 7 up). 16.00 (978-0-618-07028-2(1)) Houghton Mifflin Co. Trade & Reference Div.

—Other Side of Dawn. 2007. (Tomorrow Ser.). 336p. (J). pap. 8.99 (978-0-439-85805-2(4) , Scholastic Paperbacks) Scholastic, Inc.

—Tomorrow, When the War Began. ed. 2006. (Tomorrow Ser.: No. 1). 304p. (J). pap. 8.99 (978-0-439-82910-6(0) , Scholastic Paperbacks) Scholastic, Inc.

—While I Live. 2007. (Elli Chronicles Ser.: No. 1). 304p. (J). (gr. 7 up). pap. 16.99 (978-0-439-78318-7(6) , Scholastic Pr.) Scholastic, Inc.

Mason, Prue. Camel Rider. 2007. 204p. (J). (gr. 5-9). 15.95 (***978-1-58089-314-5(7)***) Charlesbridge Publishing, Inc.

Matas, Carol. The War Within: A Novel of the Civil War. 2002. 160p. (J). pap. 9.95 (978-0-689-84358-7(5) , Aladdin) Simon & Schuster Children's Publishing.

Matthews, L. S. Fish. 2004. 192p. (gr. 5). 14.95 (978-0-385-73180-5(9) , Delacorte Bks. for Young Readers) Random Hse. Children's Bks.

Maxwell, Ruth. Eighteen Roses Red: A Young Girl's Heroic Mission in the Revolutionary War. 2006. (YA). pap. 8.95 (978-1-57249-380-3(1) , White Mane Kids) White Mane Publishing Co., Inc.

McElroy, Lisa Tucker. Love, Lizzie: Letters to a Military Mom. Paterson, Diane, illus. 2005. 32p. (J). (gr. k-3). lib. bdg. 15.95 (978-0-8075-4777-9(8)) Whitman, Albert & Co.

McKee, David. The Conquerors. 2004. (Illus.). 25p. (J). (gr. k-3). 16.95 (978-1-59354-078-4(7)) Handprint Bks.

McKinty, Adrian. The Lighthouse War. 2007. 403p. (J). (gr. 7-17). 16.95 (***978-0-8109-9354-9(6)***) Abrams, Harry N., Inc.

Menchen, Antonio Martinez. Fosco. (SPA.). 104p. (YA). (gr. 5-8). (978-84-204-4101-6(5) , AF1750) Alfaguara, Ediciones, S.A.- Grupo Santillana ESP. *Dist:* Lectorum Pubns., Inc.

Metcalf, Rosamond. Tell Us More Grammy: Rosamond Metcalf. 2000. (Illus.). 12p. (J). pap. 1.00 (978-0-9622471-6-3(2)) Old Fort 4 Assocs.

Mikaelsen, Ben. Tree Girl. 2004. 240p. (J). 16.99 (978-0-06-009004-3(9)); lib. bdg. 17.89 (978-0-06-009005-0(7)) HarperCollins Pubs. (Rayo).

Mitchel, Pratima. Petar's Song. Binch, Caroline, illus. 2004. 32p. (J). 15.95 (978-1-84507-266-7(9)) Lincoln, Frances Ltd. GBR. *Dist:* Perseus Distribution.

Mitchell, Pratima. Petar's Song. Binch, Caroline, illus. 2004. 32p. (J). pap. 7.95 (978-1-84507-352-7(5)) Lincoln, Frances Ltd. GBR. *Dist:* Perseus Distribution.

Momaday, N. Scott. House Made of Dawn. 1999. 198p. (gr. 7-12). per. 22.25 (978-0-613-37149-0(6)) Tandem Library Bks.

Morpurgo, Michael. I Believe in Unicorns. Blythe, Gary, illus. 2006. 80p. (J). (gr. 1-4). 12.99 (978-0-7636-3050-8(0)) Candlewick Pr.

W X Y Z

Moverley, Richard. The Reluctant Rajput. Dean, David, illus. 2005. (Yellow Go Bananas Ser.). 48p. (J). lib. bdg. (978-0-7787-2723-1(8)) Crabtree Publishing Co.

Mrazek, Robert J. Stonewall's Gold: A Novel of the Civil War. 2000. (Illus.). 223p. (gr. 7-12). per. 22.20 (978-0-613-28198-0(5)) Tandem Library Bks.

Myers, Walter Dean. Patrol: An American Soldier in Vietnam. Grifalconi, Ann, illus. 2005. 40p. (J). pap. 6.99 (978-0-06-073159-5(1) , Harper Trophy) HarperCollins Pubs.

Nilsson, Troy, 2nd. Hiroshima Stones: The Shadow Stones of Hiroshima. Nilsson, Troy, 2nd, illus. 2003. (Illus.). 248p. (YA). pap. 9.95 (978-0-9724771-0-9(1) , Nilsson, Troy) Nilsson Media.

Oldham, June. In the Blood. 2003. 240p. (J). pap. (978-0-340-86653-5(5) , Hodder Children's Books) Hodder Children's Division.

Olson, Tod, et al. War of the Worlds: A Graphic Classic by Tod Olson & Terry West: Based on the Novel by H.G. Wells. 2002. (Read 180 Ser.). (Illus.). 28p. (J). (978-0-439-12340-2(2)) Scholastic, Inc.

Optic, Oliver. Stand by the Union. 2006. 96.99 (***978-1-4280-4413-5(2)***); pap. 90.99 (***978-1-4280-4406-7(X)***) IndyPublish.com.

—Within the Enemy's Line. Fitterling, Michael A., illus. 1998. (Blue & the Gray Ser.). 351p. (J). (gr. 4-7). reprint ed. per. 14.95 (978-1-890623-09-8(1)) Lost Classics Bk. Co.

Optic, Oliver. Within the Enemys Lines. 2006. 20.99 (***978-1-4280-2613-1(4)***); pap. 13.99 (***978-1-4280-2631-5(2)***) IndyPublish.com.

Orban, Marianne. To Earn a Star. 2000. 172p. (YA). pap. 14.95 (978-0-595-17080-7(3)) iUniverse, Inc.

Orlev, Ori. El Hombre del Otro Lado. (SPA., Illus.). 192p. (YA). (gr. 5-8). (978-84-348-6721-5(4) , SM30476) SM Ediciones ESP. *Dist:* Lectorum Pubns., Inc.

Oughton, Jerrie. The War in Georgia. 1999. (978-0-606-16444-3(8)) Tandem Library Bks.

Palmer, W. G. Awaiting Whisperland: The Calling of Galahad Green. 2007. 340p. 29.95 (***978-0-595-68248-5(0)***); per. 19.95 (***978-0-595-43560-9(2)***) iUniverse, Inc.

Parker, Robert Andrew. Edenville Owls. 2008. 208p. (YA). (gr. 4-6). pap. 7.99 (***978-0-14-241161-2(2)*** , Puffin) Penguin Group (USA) Inc.

Paulsen, Gary. Soldier's Heart: Being the Story of the Enlistment & Due Service of the Boy Charley Goddard in the First Minnesota Volunteers. 2000. (Illus.). 128p. (YA). (gr. 7-12). pap. 5.99 (978-0-440-22838-7(7) , Laurel Leaf) Random Hse. Children's Bks.

—The White Fox Chronicles. 2002. (gr. 5-8). lib. bdg. 13.55 (978-0-613-67131-6(7)) Tandem Library Bks.

Penning, L. & Nelson, Marietjie. The Hero of Spionkop. 2006. (Illus.). 166p. (YA). pap. (978-1-894666-92-3(5)) Inheritance Pubns.

—The Lion of Modderspruit. 2004. (Illus.). 142p. (YA). pap. (978-1-894666-91-6(7)) Inheritance Pubns.

Phan's Diary: Individual Chapter Book Title Six-Packs. Vol. 27. 32p. (gr. 4 up). 44.00 (978-0-7635-4496-6(5)) Rigby Education.

Pochenko. Conspiracy Prophecy II: WWIII & Rumors of WWIV in Revelation. 2003. 230p. (YA). pap. 14.95 (978-0-595-26419-3(0) , Writer's Showcase Pr.) iUniverse, Inc.

Pratchett, Terry. Only You Can Save Mankind. 224p. (J). 2006. pap. 5.99 (978-0-06-054187-3(3) , Harper Trophy); 2005. (gr. 3 up). 15.99 (978-0-06-054185-9(7)); 2005. (gr. 3 up). lib. bdg. 16.89 (978-0-06-054186-6(5)) HarperCollins Pubs.

Propp, Vera W. When the Soldiers Were Gone. 2001. 112p. (J). (gr. 3-7). pap. 4.99 (978-0-698-11881-2(2) , Putnam Juvenile) Penguin Group (USA) Inc.

Randall, Homer. Army Boys on German Soil Our Doughboys Q. 2006. 62.99 (***978-1-4280-2321-5(6)***) IndyPublish.com.

Ransom, Candice F. The Promise Quilt. Beier, Ellen, illus. 2002. 32p. (J). (gr. k-3). pap. 7.95 (978-0-8027-7648-8(5)) Walker & Co.

Rayo, Miguel. El Camino del Faro. 2000. Tr. of Lighthouse Road. (SPA., Illus.). 114p. (978-84-236-5532-8(6)) Edebé ESP. *Dist:* Baker & Taylor Bks.

Rennie, Gordon. Glimmer Rats. 2002. 64p. pap. 14.95 (978-1-56971-698-4(6)) Dark Horse Comics.

Robertson, William P. & Rimer, David. The Battling Bucktails at Fredericksburg. 2004. (WM Kids Ser.: Vol. 16). (Illus.). 164p. (J). 7.95 (978-1-57249-345-2(3) , White Mane Kids) White Mane Publishing Co., Inc.

—The Bucktails' Shenandoah March. 2002. (WM Kids Ser.: Vol. 12). (Illus.). 170p. (J). pap. 7.95 (978-1-57249-293-6(7) , White Mane Kids) White Mane Publishing Co., Inc.

Roop, Peter. Eye for an Eye: A Story of the Revolutionary War. 2000. (gr. 5-8). lib. bdg. 15.70 (978-0-613-36805-6(3)) Tandem Library Bks.

Roop, Peter & Roop, Connie. An Eye for an Eye: A Story of the American Revolution. 2001. (Jamestown Classics Ser.). (Illus.). 168p. (J). (gr. 5-8). 15.32 (978-0-8092-0587-5(4) , 9780809205875) Jamestown.

—An Eye for an Eye: A Story of the Revolutionary War. 2004. (Jamestown's American Portraits Ser.). (Illus.). 176p. (J). (gr. 5-7). pap. 4.95 (978-0-7696-3422-7(2) , Waterbird Bks.) School Specialty Publishing.

Roop, Peter and Connie. An Eye for an Eye. 2004. 168p. (J). lib. bdg. 16.92 (***978-1-4242-0772-5(X)***) Fitzgerald Bks.

Rosoff, Meg. How I Live Now. (YA). (gr. 7). 2004. 208p. 16.95 (978-0-385-74677-9(6)); 2006. 224p. reprint ed. pap. 7.99 (978-0-553-37605-0(5)) Random Hse. Children's Bks. (Lamb, Wendy).

—How I Live Now. 2006. 250p. (YA). 23.95 (978-0-7862-8878-6(7)) Thorndike Pr.

Schmidt, C. A. Useful Fools. 2007. 272p. (YA). (gr. 8 up). 18.99 (***978-0-525-47814-0(0)*** , Dutton Juvenile) Penguin Group (USA) Inc.

Separate Peace. 1999. (J). 11.95 (978-1-56137-400-7(8)); 22p. (gr. 9-12). 9.95 (978-1-56137-399-4(0) , BK8553) Novel Units, Inc.

Seymour, Tres. We Played Marbles. Andreasen, Dan, illus. 1998. 32p. (J). (gr. k-4). 16.99 (978-0-531-33074-6(5)); pap. 15.95 (978-0-531-30074-9(9)) Scholastic, Inc. (Orchard Bks.).

Shinn, Sharon. General WInston's Daughter. 2007. 352p. (YA). (gr. 7 up). 17.99 (***978-0-670-06248-5(0)*** , Viking Juvenile) Penguin Group (USA) Inc.

Singer, Sarah Jane. Two Bullets for Sergeant Franks. 2003. (Illus.). 112p. (YA). pap. 7.99 (978-0-9721216-9-9(2) , 0972121692) Computer Classics (R).

Smucker, Barbara. Nubes Negras. (SPA.). (YA). (gr. 5-8). pap. (978-84-279-3148-0(4) , NG3493) Noguer y Caralt Editores, S. A. ESP. *Dist:* Lectorum Pubns., Inc.

Speare, Elizabeth George. Calico Captive. 2001. (gr. 5-8). lib. bdg. 15.25 (978-0-613-44381-4(0)) Tandem Library Bks.

Spillebeen, Geert. Kipling's Choice. Edelstein, Terese, tr. 2007. 160p. (YA). (gr. 7 up). pap. 7.99 (***978-0-618-80035-3(2)*** , Graphia) Houghton Mifflin Co. Trade & Reference Div.

Staples, Suzanne Fisher. Under the Persimmon Tree. 2005. (Illus.). 288p. (YA). 17.00 (978-0-374-38025-0(2)) Farrar, Straus & Giroux.

Stead, Richard. With Marlborough to Malplaquet. 2006. pap. (***978-1-4068-3012-5(7)***) Echo Library.

Steele, William O. The Perilous Road. 2004. (Illus.). 176p. (J). 17.00 (978-0-15-205203-4(8) , Harcourt Young Classics); pap. 5.95 (978-0-15-205204-1(6) , Odyssey Classics) Harcourt Children's Bks.

—The Perilous Road. 2004. 156p. (J). (gr. 4-7). per. 13.00 (978-0-606-31268-4(4)) Tandem Library Bks.

Stevenson, Robert Louis. The Black Arrow. l.t. ed. 2005. 448p. pap. (978-1-84637-164-6(3)) Echo Library.

Stragier, Meg. Growing Free. 2005. 86p. pap. 14.95 (978-1-4137-3878-0(8)) PublishAmerica, Inc.

Strang, Herbert. With Marlborough to Malplaquet. 2006. pap. (***978-1-4068-3126-9(3)***) Echo Library.

Suter, Joanne. War of the Worlds. 2003. (gr. 7-12). lib. bdg. 15.25 (978-0-613-65749-5(7)) Tandem Library Bks.

Thomas, Roy, et al. Avengers. 2006. (Marvel Essentials Ser.: Vol. 5). (Illus.). 552p. pap. 16.99 (978-0-7851-2087-2(4)) Marvel Enterprises, Inc.

Tilly, Meg. Porcupine. 2007. 192p. (J). (gr. 5-9). 15.95 (***978-0-88776-810-1(5)***) Tundra Bks., Inc./Livres Toundra, Inc. CAN. *Dist:* Random Hse., Inc.

Tomlinson, Theresa. The Moon Riders. 2006. (Illus.). 400p. (J). lib. bdg. 18.89 (978-0-06-084737-1(9)) HarperCollins Pubs.

Trout, Robert J. Drumbeat: The Story of a Civil War Drummer Boy. 2007. (J). pap. 12.95 (***978-1-57249-390-2(9)*** , White Mane Kids) White Mane Publishing Co., Inc.

Turner, Priscilla. War Between the Vowels & the Consonants. 1999. (gr. k-3). lib. bdg. 15.25 (978-0-613-22958-6(4)) Tandem Library Bks.

—The War Between the Vowels & the Consonants. Turner, Whitney, illus. 1999. 29p. (J). (ps-7). lib. bdg. 13.40 (978-0-606-17221-9(1)) Tandem Library Bks.

Turtledove, Harry. Into the Darkness. 2000. (gr. 7-12). lib. bdg. 16.45 (978-0-613-27901-7(8)) Tandem Library Bks.

Vaugelade, Anais. The War. Rouffiac, Marie-Christine & Streissguth, Thomas, trs. from FRE. Vaugelade, Anais, illus. 2005. (Picture Bks.). (Illus.). 32p. (J). (gr. k-2). 15.25 (978-1-57505-562-6(7)) Lerner Publishing Group.

Wahl, Jan. How the Children Stopped the Wars. 2007. 112p. pap. 6.95 (***978-1-58246-200-4(3)*** , Tricycle Pr.) Ten Speed Pr.

Walker, Alice. Why War Is Never a Good Idea. Vitale, Stefano, illus. 2007. 32p. (J). (ps-3). lib. bdg. 17.89 (***978-0-06-075386-3(2)***) HarperCollins Pubs.

Weisleder, Stanley. Wings of the Panther. 2004. 224p. 15.00 (978-0-936783-38-3(9)) Merril Pr.

Williams, Mary. Brothers in Hope: The Story of the Lost Boys of Sudan. Christie, R. Gregory, illus. 2005. (J). 17.95 (978-1-58430-232-2(1)) Lee & Low Bks., Inc.

Yatate, Hajime & Tomino, Yoshiyuki, creators. Lost War Chronicles, 2 vols., Vol. 1. 2006. (Mobile Suit Gundam Ser.). (Illus.). 144p. pap. 9.99 (978-1-59816-213-4(6) , Tokyopop Kids) TOKYOPOP, Inc.

Zephaniah, Benjamin. Refugee Boy. 2004. 296p. (J). (gr. 5-12). reprint ed. pap. 7.95 (978-1-58234-908-4(8) , Bloomsbury Children) Bloomsbury Publishing.

Zerfing, Robert A. The Silencer: A U. N. Conspiracy Novel. 2nd ed. 2003. 326p. (YA). per. 14.95 (978-0-9747881-0-4(4)) Clawfoot Publishing.

WAR CORRESPONDENTS

see Reporters and Reporting

WAR CRIME TRIALS

Banfield, Susan. The Andersonville Prison Civil War Crimes Trial: A Headline Court Case. 2000. (Headline Court Cases Ser.). (Illus.). 112p. (J). (gr. 6-12). lib. bdg. 26.60 (978-0-7660-1386-5(3)) Enslow Pubs., Inc.

WAR OF 1812

see United States—History—War of 1812

WAR OF 1914

see World War, 1914-1918

WAR OF 1939-1945

see World War, 1939-1945

WAR OF SECESSION, U.S., 1861-1865

see United States—History—Civil War, 1861-1865

WAR OF THE AMERICAN REVOLUTION

see United States—History—Revolution, 1775-1783

WAR POETRY

Dieterman, Nicole. A Child's View of War: A Collection of Poems by Nicole Dieterman. 2003. mass mkt. 12.95 (978-0-9742472-0-5(0)) Pleiness Publishing.

Granfield, Linda. In Flanders Fields. Wilson, Janet, illus. 2000. 32p. (gr. 4-7). 8.95 (978-0-7737-5925-1(5)) Stoddart Kids CAN. *Dist:* Fitzhenry & Whiteside, Ltd.

Philip, Neil. War & the Pity of War. McCurdy, Michael, illus. 1998. 96p. (YA). (gr. 7-9). 20.00 (978-0-395-84982-8(9) , Clarion Bks.) Houghton Mifflin Co. Trade & Reference Div.

Wade, Stephen. The War Poets: The Secrets of Poems from the Great War. 2003. (Studymates Ser.). (Illus.). 128p. pap. 27.50 (978-1-84285-030-5(X)) Studymates Ltd. GBR. *Dist:* Trans-Atlantic Pubns., Inc.

WAR SHIPS

see Warships

WARFARE, SUBMARINE

see Submarine Warfare

WARLOCKS

see Witches; Wizards

WARREN, EARL, 1891-1974

Compston, Christine L. Earl Warren: Justice for All. 2001. (Oxford Portraits Ser.). (Illus.). 160p. (YA). (gr. 9 up). 28.00 (978-0-19-513001-0(4)) Oxford Univ. Pr., Inc.

WARS

see Military History; Naval History; War

WARSAW (POLAND)

Ayer, Eleanor H. In the Ghettos: Teens Who Survived the Ghettos of the Holocaust. 1999. (Teen Witnesses to the Holocaust Ser.). (Illus.). 64p. (YA). (gr. 7-12). lib. bdg. 26.50 (978-0-8239-2845-3(4) , TWGHET) Rosen Publishing Group, Inc., The.

Spielman, Gloria. Janusz Korczak's Children. 2007. (Kar-Ben for Older Readers Ser.). (Illus.). (J). (gr. 2-5). 17.95 (978-1-58013-255-8(3)) Kar-Ben Publishing.

—Janusz Korczak's Children. Archambault, Matthew, illus. 2007. (Kar-Ben for Older Readers Ser.). (J). (gr. 2-5). pap. 7.95 (***978-0-8225-7050-9(5)***) Kar-Ben Publishing.

Willoughby, Susan. The Holocaust. (20th Century Perspectives Ser.). (Illus.). 48p. (J). (gr. 5-7). 2001. lib. bdg. 25.64 (978-1-57572-436-2(7)); Set 1. 2002. pap. 7.95 (978-1-58810-375-8(7) , 91127) Heinemann Library.

WARSAW (POLAND)—FICTION

Orlev, Uri. Run, Boy, Run. Halkin, Hillel, tr. 10th ed. 2007. 192p. (J). (gr. 5 up). 6.95 (***978-0-618-95706-4(5)***) Houghton Mifflin Co. Trade & Reference Div.

Spinelli, Jerry. Milkweed. 2003. (Illus.). 224p. (J). (gr. 5). lib. bdg. 17.99 (978-0-375-91374-7(2) , Knopf Bks. for Young Readers) Random Hse. Children's Bks.

WARSHIPS

see also Aircraft Carriers; Submarines (Ships)

also names of countries with the subhead Navy (e.g. United States—Navy)

Baldwin, Carol & Baldwin, Ron. Navy Fighting Vessels. 2004. (Heinemann Know It Ser.). (Illus.). 48p. (J). pap. 7.95 (978-1-4034-4558-2(3)) Heinemann Library.

—U. S. Navy Fighting Vessels. 2004. (Heinemann Know It Ser.). (Illus.). 48p. (J). lib. bdg. (978-1-4034-4552-0(4)) Heinemann Library.

Barron's Educational Editorial Staff. Warships. 1998. (History Ser.). (Illus.). 32p. (J). (gr. 5). pap. 5.95 (978-0-7641-0535-7(3)) Barron's Educational Series, Inc.

Dartford, Mark. Warships. 2004. (Military Hardware in Action Ser.). (Illus.). 48p. (J). (gr. 4-9). lib. bdg. 25.26 (978-0-8225-4703-7(1)) Lerner Publishing Group.

Delgado, James P. Wrecks of American Warships. 2000. (Watts Library). (Illus.). 64p. (J). (gr. 5-7). 25.50 (978-0-531-20376-7(X) , Watts, Franklin) Scholastic Library Publishing.

—Wrecks of American Warships. 2000. (gr. 3-6). lib. bdg. 17.60 (978-0-613-54796-3(9)) Tandem Library Bks.

Doeden, Matt. Destroyers. 2008. (J). (***978-1-4296-0029-3(2)***) Capstone Pr., Inc.

Fighting Ships. 2003. (Illus.). 32p. (YA). pap. (978-1-904516-33-0(5)) Chrysalis Children's Bks.

Green, Michael. Amphibious Ships. 1998. (Land & Sea Ser.). (Illus.). 48p. (J). (gr. 3-4). lib. bdg. 21.26 (978-0-7368-0040-2(9) , Capstone High-Interest Bks.) Capstone Pr., Inc.

—Destroyers. 1998. (Land & Sea Ser.). (Illus.). 48p. (J). (gr. 3-4). lib. bdg. 21.26 (978-0-7368-0041-9(7) , Capstone High-Interest Bks.) Capstone Pr., Inc.

—Destroyers. 1998. (J). lib. bdg. 19.93 (978-0-516-21453-5(5) , Children's Pr.) Scholastic Library Publishing.

—PT Boats. 1998. (Land & Sea Ser.). (Illus.). 48p. (J). (gr. 3-4). lib. bdg. 21.26 (978-0-7368-0042-6(5) , Capstone High-Interest Bks.) Capstone Pr., Inc.

—River Patrol Boats. 1998. (Land & Sea Ser.). (Illus.). 48p. (J). (gr. 3-4). lib. bdg. 21.26 (978-0-7368-0043-3(3) , Capstone High-Interest Bks.) Capstone Pr., Inc.

Green, Michael & Green, Gladys. Aircraft Carriers: The Nimitz Class. 2004. (War Machines Ser.). (Illus.). 32p. (J). lib. bdg. 22.60 (978-0-7368-2720-1(X)) Capstone Pr., Inc.

—Destroyers: The Arleigh Burke Class. 2004. (Edge Books, War Machines). (Illus.). 32p. (J). lib. bdg. 22.60 (978-0-7368-2722-5(6)) Capstone Pr., Inc.

Mueller, Richard. Naval Warfare of the Future. 2005. (Library of Future Weaponry). (Illus.). 64p. (YA). (978-1-4042-0526-0(8)) Rosen Publishing Group, Inc., The.

Rustad, Martha E. H. U.S. Navy Cruisers. 2007. (Blazers—Military Vehicles Ser.). (Illus.). 32p. (J). 19.93 (978-0-7368-6459-6(8)) Capstone Pr., Inc.

—U.S. Navy Destroyers. 2007. (Blazers—Military Vehicles Ser.). (Illus.). 32p. (J). 19.93 (978-0-7368-6460-2(1)) Capstone Pr., Inc.

Stone, Lynn M. Battleships. 2006. (Fighting Forces Ser.). (Illus.). 32p. (gr. 4-8). 19.95 (978-1-59515-461-3(2) , 1244403) Rourke Publishing, LLC.

—Cruisers. 2006. (Fighting Forces Ser.). (Illus.). 32p. (gr. 4-8). 19.95 (978-1-59515-463-7(9) , 1244405) Rourke Publishing, LLC.

—Destroyers. 2006. (Fighting Forces Ser.). (Illus.). 32p. (gr. 4-8). 19.95 (978-1-59515-464-4(7) , 1244406) Rourke Publishing, LLC.

—Frigates. 2006. (Fighting Forces Ser.). (Illus.). 32p. (gr. 4-8). 19.95 (978-1-59515-465-1(5) , 1244407) Rourke Publishing, LLC.

War Planes: Attack Helicopters; Combat Rescue Helicopters; Jump Jets; Radar Jammers; Stealth Bombers; Strike Fighters; Supersonic Fighters, 8 bks. (Illus.). (J). (gr. 3-4). lib. bdg. 170.08 (978-0-7368-1083-8(8) , Capstone High-Interest Bks.) Capstone Pr., Inc.

White, Steve. Naval Warship: FSF-1 Sea Fighter. 2007. (High-Tech Military Weapons Ser.). (Illus.). 48p. (J). (***978-1-4287-3127-1(X)***) Children's Pr., Ltd.

Zuehlke, Jeffrey. Warships. 2006. (Pull Ahead Books). (Illus.). 32p. (J). (ps-ps). 22.60 (978-0-8225-2866-1(5) , Lerner Pubns.) Lerner Publishing Group.

WARSHIPS—FICTION

Appleton, Victor. Tom Swift & His Aerial Warship or the. 2006. pap. (***978-1-4065-0894-9(2)***) Dodo Pr.

Appleton, Victor. Tom Swift & His Aerial Warship or the Naval Terror of the Seas. 2005. reprint ed. pap. 24.95 (978-0-7661-9446-5(9)) Kessinger Publishing, LLC.

Weitzman, David L. Old Ironsides: Americans Build A Fighting Ship. 2003. (gr. 3-6). lib. bdg. 15.25 (978-0-613-60780-3(5)) Tandem Library Bks.

WASHINGTON, BOOKER T., 1856-1915

Amper, Thomas. Booker T. Washington. Reeves, Jeni, illus. (On My Own Biographies Ser.). 48p. 2003. (J). (gr. 1-3). pap. 5.95 (978-0-87614-534-0(9) , Carolrhoda Bks.); 1998. (gr. 2-5). lib. bdg. 23.93 (978-1-57505-094-2(3)) Lerner Publishing Group.

Booker T Washington. (Photo Illustrated Biographies Ser.). 24p. (J). 6.95 (978-1-56065-942-6(4)); 32p. (YA). 7.95 (978-0-7368-6190-8(4)); Vol. 2. 2005. (YA). (978-0-7368-3379-0(X) , Pebble Bks.) Capstone Pr., Inc.

Braun, Eric. Booker T. Washington: Great American Educator. Martin, Cynthia, illus. 2005. (Graphic Library). 32p. (J). (gr. 3-7). lib. bdg. 25.26 (978-0-7368-4630-1(1)) Capstone Pr., Inc.

Frost, Helen. Let's Meet Booker T. Washington. 2003. (Let's Meet Biographies Ser.). (Illus.). 32p. (gr. 2-4). 23.00 (978-0-7910-7318-6(1) , Chelsea Hse.) Facts On File, Inc.

Gosda, Randy T. Booker T. Washington. 2002. (First Biographies Ser.). (Illus.). 32p. (J). (gr. k-4). lib. bdg. 22.78 (978-1-57765-734-7(9) , Buddy Bks.) ABDO Publishing Co.

Harcourt School Publishers Staff. Booker T. Washington: Library Edition. 1999. (Collections Ser.). (Illus.). (J). 5.30 (978-0-15-314344-1(4)) Harcourt Schl. Pubs.

Marsh, Carole. Booker T. Washington. 2002. (One Thousand Readers Ser.). (Illus.). 12p. (J). (gr. k-4). 2.95 (978-0-635-01479-5(3) , 14793) Gallopade International.

—Booker T. Washington: An Ohio Experience Reader. 2001. (J). (gr. k-5). pap. 1.95 (978-0-635-00449-9(6)) Gallopade International.

—The Virginia Reader: Booker T. Washington. 2001. (Virginia Experience! Ser.). (Illus.). 12p. (J). (gr. k-5). pap. 2.95 (978-0-635-00361-4(9)) Gallopade International.

McKissack, Patricia C. & McKissack, Fredrick L. Booker T. Washington: Leader & Educator. rev. ed. 2001. (Great African Americans Ser.). (Illus.). 32p. (J). (gr. 1-4). lib. bdg. 18.60 (978-0-7660-1679-8(X)) Enslow Pubs., Inc.

Nicholson, Lois P. Booker T. Washington - Educator/Activist: A Modern Moses. 1998. (Junior Black Americans of Achievement Ser.). (Illus.). 80p. (J). (gr. 3-6). pap. 10.20 (978-0-7910-4461-2(0) , Chelsea Hse.) Facts On File, Inc.

Schaefer, Lola M. Booker T. Washington. Saunders-Smith, Gail, ed. 2003. (First Biographies Ser.). (Illus.). 24p. (J). (gr. k-1). lib. bdg. 15.93 (978-0-7368-1647-2(X) , Pebble Bks.) Capstone Pr., Inc.

Schraff, Anne E. Booker T. Washington: Character Is Power. 2006. (African-American Biography Library). (Illus.). 128p. (J). lib. bdg. 31.93 (978-0-7660-2535-6(7)) Enslow Pubs., Inc.

Schroeder, Alan. Booker T. Washington: Educator & Racial Spokesman. (Black Americans of Achievement Ser.). (Illus.). 112p. (J). (gr. 6-12). 2005. pap. 13.25 (978-0-7910-8374-1(8)); 2004. 30.00 (978-0-7910-8253-9(9)) Facts On File, Inc. (Chelsea Hse.).

Swain, Gwenyth. A Hunger for Learning: A Story about Booker T. Washington. Johnson, Larry, illus. (Creative Minds Biography Ser.). 64p. (J). 2006. (gr. 3-7). lib. bdg. 22.60 (978-1-57505-754-5(9)); 2005. (gr. 4-8). pap. 6.95 (978-0-8225-3090-9(2)) Lerner Publishing Group.

Taylor-Butler, Christine. Booker T. Washington. 2006. (Illus.). 31p. (J). (978-0-516-29842-9(9)) Children's Pr., Ltd.

Thoennes Keller, Kristin. Booker T. Washington. 2005. (Fact Finders Ser.). (Illus.). 32p. (J). (978-0-7368-4343-0(4)) Capstone Pr., Inc.

—Booker T. Washington: Innovative Educator. 2006. (J). (978-0-7565-1881-3(4)) Compass Point Bks.

WASHINGTON, GEORGE, 1732-1799

Abnett, Dan. George Washington & the American Revolution. 2007. (Jr. Graphic Biographies Ser.). (Illus.). 24p. (J). (978-1-4042-2338-7(X)); pap. (978-1-4042-2148-2(4)); (gr. 2-6). lib. bdg. 21.25 (978-1-4042-3395-9(4)) Rosen Publishing Group, Inc., The. (PowerKids Pr.).

Abraham, Philip. George Washington. 2002. (Wel-Real People Ser.). (Illus.). 24p. (J). (ps-2). 18.00 (978-0-516-23949-1(X)); pap. 4.95 (978-0-516-23603-2(2)) Scholastic Library Publishing. (Children's Pr.).

—George Washington. 2002. (gr. k-3). lib. bdg. 12.95 (978-0-613-58835-5(5)) Tandem Library Bks.

—How to Draw the Life & Times of George Washington. 2005. (Kid's Guide to Drawing the Presidents of the United States of America Ser.). (J). lib. bdg. 31.95 (978-1-4042-0364-8(8) , PowerKids Pr.) Rosen Publishing Group, Inc., The.

Adler, David A. George Washington: An Illustrated Biography. (Illus.). 288p. (J). (gr. 4-6). tchr. ed. 24.95 (978-0-8234-1838-1(3)) Holiday Hse., Inc.

—A Picture Book of George Washington. Wallner, John & Wallner, Alexandra, illus. 32p. (J). (gr. k-3). pap. 6.95 (978-0-8234-0800-9(0)) Holiday Hse., Inc.

—A Picture Book of George Washington. Wallner, John & Wallner, Alexandra, illus. 2004. (J). (ps-3). audio compact disk 18.95 (978-1-59112-765-9(3)) Live Oak Media.

—President George Washington. Wallner, John C., illus. 2005. 32p. (J). 14.95 (978-0-8234-1604-2(6)) Holiday Hse., Inc.

Allen, Thomas B. George Washington, Spymaster: How the Americans Outspied the British & Won the Revolutionary War. 2007. (Illus.). 192p. (J). (gr. 5). pap. 5.95 (978-1-4263-0041-7(7) , National Geographic Children's Bks.) National Geographic Society.

—George Washington, Spymaster: How the Americans Outspied the British & Won the Revolutionary War. Harness, Cheryl, illus. 2004. 192p. (gr. 3-7). 16.95 (978-0-7922-5126-2(1) , National Geographic Children's Bks.) National Geographic Society.

Ammon, Richard. Valley Forge. Farnsworth, Bill, illus. 2004. 32p. (J). (gr. 4-6). tchr. ed. 16.95 (978-0-8234-1746-9(8)) Holiday Hse., Inc.

Armentrout, David & Armentrout, Patricia. George Washington. 2004. (Discover the Life of an American Legend Ser.). (Illus.). 24p. (gr. 2-5). 20.64 (978-1-58952-662-4(7)) Rourke Publishing, LLC.

Ashby, Ruth. George & Martha Washington. 2005. (Illus.). 48p. (J). pap. (978-0-8368-5703-0(8)); lib. bdg. 30.00 (978-0-8368-5697-2(X)) Stevens, Gareth Inc. (World Almanac Library).

Baldwin, James. Four Great Americans. 2006. pap. (*978-1-4065-0509-2(9)) Dodo Pr.

Baldwin, James. Four Great Americans: Washington, Franklin, Webster, Lincoln: A Book for Young Americans. 2000. (Illus.). (J). (978-0-89526-203-5(7)) Regnery Publishing, Inc., An Eagle Publishing Co.

Benchmark Education Staff. George Washington & the AMER Revolution. 2005. 2.00 (*978-1-4108-4681-5(4)) Benchmark Education Co.

Benge, Janet & Benge, Geoff. George Washington: True Patriot. 2001. (Illus.). 224p. pap. 8.99 (978-1-883002-81-7(8)) Emerald Bks.

Benge, Janet & Benge, Geoffrey Francis. George Washington Unit Study Curriculum Guide. 2002. (Heroes of History Unit Study Curriculum Guides). 64p. 8.99 (978-1-883002-86-2(9)) Emerald Bks.

Benge, Janet and Geoff. George Washington Carver What Do You See? Read-along, 1bk. James, Kennon, illus. 2003. (Another Great Achiever Ser.). (J). lib. bdg. 23.95 incl. audio compact disk (978-1-57537-742-1(X)); lib. bdg. 23.95 incl. audio (978-1-57537-792-6(6)) Advance Publishing, Inc.

Bial, Raymond. Where Washington Walked. 2004. (Illus.). 48p. (J). 17.95 (978-0-8027-8899-3(8)) Walker & Co.

Botones para el General Washington (Buttons for General Washington) 2006. (J). pap. 5.95 (978-0-8225-6617-5(6) , Ediciones Lerner) Lerner Publishing Group.

Brannon, Barbara. Discover George Washington. 2005. 39.00 (*978-1-4108-5158-1(3)) Benchmark Education Co.

Brown, Don. Dolley Madison Saves George Washington. 2007. 32p. (J). (gr. k-3). 16.00 (978-0-618-41199-3(2)) Houghton Mifflin Co.

Burgan, Michael. George Washington. 2002. (Profiles of the Presidents Ser.). (Illus.). 64p. (J). (gr. 4 up). lib. bdg. 23.93 (978-0-7565-0204-1(7)) Compass Point Bks.

—Valley Forge. 2004. (We the People Ser.). (Illus.). 48p. (J). (gr. 4 up). lib. bdg. 22.60 (978-0-7565-0615-5(8)) Compass Point Bks.

Burke, Rick. George Washington. (American Lives Ser.). (ENG & SPA., Illus.). 32p. (J). 2003. (gr. 2-4). lib. bdg. (978-1-4034-0158-6(6)); 2002. pap. 6.95 (978-1-4034-0414-5(3)) Heinemann Library.

—George Washington. 2003. (gr. 3-6). lib. bdg. 15.25 (978-0-613-60876-3(3)) Tandem Library Bks.

Calkhoven, Laurie. George Washington: An American Life. 2007. (Sterling Biographies Ser.). (Illus.). 128p. (J). 12.95 (978-1-4027-4748-9(9)); pap. 5.95 (978-1-4027-3546-2(4)) Sterling Publishing Co., Inc.

Chandra, Deborah & Comora, Madeleine. George Washington's Teeth. Cole, Brock, illus. 2007. 40p. (J). pap. 6.99 (*978-0-312-37604-8(9)) Square Fish.

Cheney, Lynne V. When Washington Crossed the Delaware: A Wintertime Story for Young Patriots. Fiore, Peter M., illus. 2004. 40p. (J). 16.95 (978-0-689-87043-9(4)) Simon & Schuster Children's Publishing.

Coleman, Wim & Perrin, Pat. George Washington: Creating a Nation. 2004. (America's Founding Fathers Ser.). (Illus.). 128p. (J). lib. bdg. 26.60 (978-0-7660-2290-4(0)) Enslow Pubs., Inc.

Collier, James Lincoln. The George Washington You Never Knew. (You Never Knew Ser.). (J). 2004. (gr. 4-6). pap. 6.95 (978-0-516-25833-1(8)); 2003. (Illus.). 80p. 25.50 (978-0-516-24343-6(8)) Scholastic Library Publishing. (Children's Pr.).

Dahl, Michael. Row, Row, Row the Boats: A Fun Song about George Washington Crossing the Delaware. D'Antonio, Sandra, illus. 2004. (Fun Songs Ser.). 24p. (gr. k-3). 22.60 (978-1-4048-0128-8(6)) Picture Window Bks.

Dean, Sheri. Presidents Day/dia De Los Presidentes. 2006. (Illus.). 24p. (J). pap. (978-0-8368-6515-8(4)); (SPA., pap. 5.95 (978-0-8368-6529-5(4)); lib. bdg. 19.33 (978-0-8368-6508-0(1)); (SPA., lib. bdg. 19.33 (978-0-8368-6522-6(7)) Stevens, Gareth Inc.

Devillier, Christy. George Washington. 2001. (First Biographies Ser.). (Illus.). 32p. (J). (gr. k-4). lib. bdg. 22.78 (978-1-57765-593-0(1) , Buddy Bks.) ABDO Publishing Co.

Doeden, Matt. George Washington: Leading a New Nation. Martin, Cynthia, illus. 2005. (Graphic Library). 32p. (J). (gr. 3-7). lib. bdg. 25.26 (978-0-7368-4963-0(7)) Capstone Pr., Inc.

—Winter at Valley Forge. Barnett, Charles & Frenz, Ron, illus. 2006. (Graphic Library). 32p. (J). 25.26 (978-0-7368-4975-3(0)) Capstone Pr., Inc.

Dolan, Edward F. George Washington. 2007. (Presidents & Their Times Ser.). 96p. (J). lib. bdg. 32.79 (*978-0-7614-2427-7(X) , Benchmark Bks.) Cavendish, Marshall Corp.

Dolan, Edward F., Jr. The Winter at Valley Forge. 2001. (Kaleidoscope Ser.). (Illus.). 48p. (J). (gr. 3 up). lib. bdg. 25.64 (978-0-7614-1304-2(9) , Benchmark Bks.) Cavendish, Marshall Corp.

Donlan, Leni. George Washington: Revolution & the New Nation. 2006. (American History Through Primary Sources Ser.). (Illus.). 32p. (J). (978-1-4109-2420-9(3)); pap. (978-1-4109-2431-5(9)) Steck-Vaughn.

Draper, Allison Stark. George Washington Elected: How America's First President Was Chosen. 2001. (Headlines from History Ser.). (Illus.). 24p. (J). (gr. 3). lib. bdg. 19.95 (978-0-8239-5675-3(X) , PKFIPR, PowerKids Pr.) Rosen Publishing Group, Inc., The.

Dubois, Muriel L. The Washington Monument. 2002. (National Landmarks Ser.). (Illus.). 24p. (J). (gr. 2-3). lib. bdg. 18.60 (978-0-7368-1117-0(6) , Bridgestone Bks.) Capstone Pr., Inc.

Egan, Tracie. George Washington: The Father of the American Nation. 2003. (Primary Sources of Famous People in American History Ser.). (Illus.). 32p. (J). pap. (978-0-8239-4183-4(3)) Rosen Publishing Group, Inc., The.

Espinosa, Rod. George Washington. 2007. (Bio-Graphics Ser.). (Illus.). 32p. (J). (gr. 3-6). lib. bdg. 27.07 (*978-1-60270-067-3(2) , Graphic Planet) Magic Wagon.

Feinstein, Stephen. George Washington: A MyReportLinks.com Book. 2002. (Presidents Ser.). (Illus.). 48p. (J). (gr. 4-10). lib. bdg. 25.26 (978-0-7660-5000-6(9) , MyReportLinks.com Bks.) Enslow Pubs., Inc.

Ferrie, Richard. The World Turned Upside Down: George Washington & the Battle of Yorktown. 1999. (Illus.). 168p. (J). (gr. 7 up). tchr. ed. 18.95 (978-0-8234-1402-4(7)) Holiday Hse., Inc.

Fontes, Ron & Fontes, Justine. George Washington: Soldier, Hero, President. 2001. (Readers Ser.). (Illus.). 32p. (J). (gr. 5-3). pap. 3.99 (978-0-7894-7377-6(1)) Dorling Kindersley Publishing, Inc.

Fontes, Ron, et al. George Washington: Soldier, Hero, President. 2001. (Readers Ser.). (Illus.). 32p. (J). (ps-3). 14.99 (978-0-7894-7378-3(X)) Dorling Kindersley Publishing, Inc.

Ford, Carin T. George Washington: The First President. 2003. (Heroes of American History Ser.). (Illus.). 32p. (J). (gr. 1-4). lib. bdg. 22.60 (978-0-7660-1999-7(3)) Enslow Pubs., Inc.

Gaff, Jackie. George Washington: The Life of an American Patriot. 2005. (Graphic Nonfiction Ser.). (Illus.). 48p. (J). (gr. 4-6). lib. bdg. 26.50 (978-1-4042-0236-8(6)) Rosen Publishing Group, Inc., The.

Gedacht, Daniel C. George Washington: Leader of a New Nation. 2005. (Library of American Lives & Times). (Illus.). 112p. (J). (gr. 4-8). lib. bdg. 31.95 (978-0-8239-6622-6(4)) Rosen Publishing Group, Inc., The.

George Washington. (First Biographies Ser.). 24p. (J). 5.95 (978-0-7368-3383-7(8)); 24p. (J). 6.95 (978-0-7368-4466-6(X)); 48p. (YA). 7.95 (978-0-7368-4497-0(X)); Vol. 3. 2005. (YA). (978-0-7368-8111-1(5) , Pebble Bks.) Capstone Pr., Inc.

George Washington. (Compass Point Early Biographies Ser.). 32p. (J). 7.95 (978-0-7565-1170-8(4)) Compass Point Bks.

George Washington. (Biographies Ser.). 24p. (J). 7.95 (978-1-4048-0457-9(9)) Picture Window Bks.

George Washington, 6 vols. (gr. 2-5). 36.95 (978-0-7368-4558-8(5)); 39.95 (978-0-7368-4583-0(6)) Red Brick Learning.

George Washington: A Life of Leadership. 2006. (J). pap. 5.95 (978-0-8225-5696-1(0)) Lerner Publishing Group.

George Washington: Una vida de liderazgo (A Life of Leadership) 2007. (J). pap. 5.95 (978-0-8225-6555-0(2) , Ediciones Lerner) Lerner Publishing Group.

George Washington Carver. 2006. (J). 23.93 (978-0-8225-6258-0(8)); pap. 5.95 (978-0-8225-6625-0(7)) Lerner Publishing Group. (Ediciones Lerner).

Grabowski, John F. George Washington: Soldier, Hero, President. 2001. (Eyewitness Readers Ser.). (Illus.). (J). 10.79 (978-0-606-20670-9(1)) Tandem Library Bks.

Group/McGraw-Hill, Wright. George Washington: A Quiet Leader, 6 vols. (Book2WebTM Ser.). (gr. 4-8). 36.50 (978-0-322-04461-6(8)) Wright Group, The.

Hamilton, Lynn. Presidents Day. 2004. (American Holidays Ser.). (Illus.). 24p. (J). lib. bdg. 17.10 (978-1-59036-108-5(3)) Weigl Pubs., Inc.

—Presidents' Day. 2004. (American Holidays Ser.). (Illus.). 24p. (J). pap. 6.95 (978-1-59036-169-6(5)) Weigl Pubs., Inc.

Harness, Cheryl. George Washington. (Illus.). 48p. (J). 2006. (gr. 3). pap. 7.95 (978-0-7922-5490-4(2)); 2000. (gr. 4-9). 17.95 (978-0-7922-7096-6(7)) National Geographic Society. (National Geographic Children's Bks.).

Heilbroner, Joan. Meet George Washington. Marchesi, Stephen, illus. 2001. (Landmark Bks.). 80p. (J). (gr. 2-5). pap. 4.99 (978-0-375-80397-0(1) , Random Hse. Bks. for Young Readers) Random Hse. Children's Bks.

—Meet George Washington. 2001. (gr. 3-6). lib. bdg. 11.80 (978-0-613-82497-2(0)); (Illus.). (J). (978-0-606-20792-8(9)) Tandem Library Bks.

Hort, Lenny. George Washington: A Photographic Story of a Life. 2005. (Biography Ser.). (Illus.). 128p. (J). 14.99 (978-0-7566-0832-3(5)); (gr. 8). pap. 4.99 (978-0-7566-0835-4(X)) Dorling Kindersley Publishing, Inc.

Jackson, Garnet N. George Washington: Our First President. Van Wright, Cornelius, illus. 2002. (Hello Reader! Ser.). 32p. (J). pap. 3.99 (978-0-439-09867-0(X)) Scholastic, Inc.

—George Washington: Our First President. 2001. (J). 10.79 (978-0-606-22245-7(6)); 2000. lib. bdg. 11.80 (978-0-613-63543-1(4)) Tandem Library Bks.

January, Brendan. George Washington. 2003. (Encyclopedia of Presidents Ser.: Vol. 1). (Illus.). 110p. (J). 34.00 (978-0-516-24209-5(1) , Children's Pr.) Scholastic Library Publishing.

Jurmain, Suzanne Tripp. George Did It. Day, Larry, illus. 40p. (J). 2007. (ps). pap. 6.99 (*978-0-14-240895-7(6) , Puffin); 2005. (gr. 1-4). 16.99 (978-0-525-47560-6(5) , Dutton Juvenile) Penguin Group (USA) Inc.

Kallen, Stuart A. George Washington. 2001. (Founding Fathers Ser.). (Illus.). 64p. (J). (gr. 3-8). lib. bdg. 25.65 (978-1-57765-017-1(4) , ABDO & Daughters) ABDO Publishing Co.

Keller, Kristin Thoennes. George Washington. 2000. (Let Freedom Ring Ser.). (Illus.). 48p. (J). (gr. 3-4). lib. bdg. 22.60 (978-0-7368-1034-0(X) , Bridgestone Bks.) Capstone Pr., Inc.

Knox, Barbara. George Washington. Saunders-Smith, Gail, ed. 2003. (First Biographies Ser.). (Illus.). 24p. (J). (gr. k-1). lib. bdg. 15.93 (978-0-7368-2082-0(5) , Pebble Bks.) Capstone Pr., Inc.

Korman, Justine. George Washington: Soldier, Hero, President. 2001. (gr. k-3). lib. bdg. 11.80 (978-0-613-35125-6(8)) Tandem Library Bks.

Krensky, Stephen. George Washington: The Man Who Would Not Be King. 1999. (YA). pap. 32.75 incl. audio (978-0-7887-3186-0(6) , 40921) Recorded Bks., LLC.

—George Washington's First Victory. Dawson Hearn, Diane, illus. ed. 2005. 32p. (J). lib. bdg. 15.00 (978-1-59054-943-8(0)) Fitzgerald Bks.

—George Washington's First Victory. Hearn, Diane Dawson, illus. 2005. (Ready-to-Read Stories of Famous Americans Ser.). 32p. (J). pap. 3.99 (978-0-689-85942-7(2) , Aladdin) Simon & Schuster Children's Publishing.

Landau, Elaine. The Washington Monument. 2004. (Cornerstones of Freedom Ser.). (J). 26.00 (978-0-516-24238-5(5) , Children's Pr.) Scholastic Library Publishing.

Leighton, Marian. George Washington. Salvador, Martin, illus. 2005. (Heroes of America Ser.). 240p. (J). (gr. 3-8). lib. bdg. 21.35 (978-1-59679-262-3(0)) ABDO Publishing Co.

Loesch, Joe. George Washington: Father of a Nation. Hutchinson, Cheryl, ed. Cox, Brian T., illus. unabr. ed. 2002. (Backyard Adventure Ser.). 56p. (J). (gr. k-5). 16.95 incl. audio compact disk (978-1-932332-00-1(6)); pap. 14.95 incl. audio (978-1-887729-94-9(1)); pap. 16.95 incl. audio compact disk (978-1-887729-95-6(X)) Toy Box Productions.

Lusted, Marcia Amidon. Revolution & the New Nation. 2007. (*978-1-59036-739-1(1)); (*978-1-59036-740-7(5)) Weigl Pubs., Inc.

Manolis, Kay. George Washington: A Life of Self-discipline. 2007. (Illus.). 24p. (J). lib. bdg. 19.95 (978-1-60014-094-5(7)) Bellwether Media.

Mara, Wil. George Washington. (Rookie Biographies Ser.). (Illus.). 32p. (J). (gr. 1-2). 2003. pap. 4.95 (978-0-516-27335-8(3)); 2002. 20.50 (978-0-516-22519-7(7)) Scholastic Library Publishing. (Children's Pr.).

—George Washington. 2002. (gr. k-3). lib. bdg. 12.95 (978-0-613-59485-1(1)) Tandem Library Bks.

Marcovitz, Hal. The Washington Monument. 2002. (American Symbols & Their Meanings Ser.). (Illus.). 48p. (YA). (gr. 4 up). lib. bdg. (978-1-59084-028-3(3)) Mason Crest Pubs.

Margaret, Amy. Presidents' Day. 2002. (Library of Holidays). (Illus.). 24p. (J). lib. bdg. 18.75 (978-0-8239-5786-6(1) , PowerKids Pr.) Rosen Publishing Group, Inc., The.

Marrin, Albert. George Washington & the Founding of a Nation. Brooks, Donna, ed. 2001. (Illus.). 256p. (J). (gr. 7 up). 30.00 (978-0-525-46481-5(6) , Dutton Juvenile) Penguin Group (USA) Inc.

Marsh, Carole. George Washington. 2002. (One Thousand Readers Ser.). (Illus.). 12p. (J). (gr. k-4). 2.95 (978-0-635-01470-2(X) , 1470X) Gallopade International.

—George Washington: An Ohio Experience Reader. 2001. (J). (gr. k-5). pap. 1.95 (978-0-635-00427-7(5)) Gallopade International.

—The Virginia Reader: George Washington. 2001. (Virginia Experience! Ser.). (Illus.). 12p. (J). (gr. k-5). pap. 2.95 (978-0-635-00349-2(X)) Gallopade International.

Martin, Justin. Easy Reader Biographies: George Washington: George Washington. 2007. 16p. pap. 2.99 (*978-0-439-92331-6(X) , Teaching Resources) Scholastic, Inc.

Marx, David F. Presidents' Day. 2002. (Rookie Read-About Holidays Ser.). (Illus.). 32p. (J). (gr. 1-2). 20.50 (978-0-516-22268-4(6)); pap. 5.95 (978-0-516-27376-1(0)) Scholastic Library Publishing. (Children's Pr.).

Mayer, Cassie. George Washington. 2007. (J). (*978-1-4034-9972-1(1)); pap. (*978-1-4034-9981-3(0)) Heinemann Library.

McClung, Robert M. Young George Washington & the French & Indian War, 1753-1758. 2002. (Illus.). 128p. (YA). (gr. 6-12). 22.50 (978-0-208-02509-8(X) , Linnet Bks.) Shoe String Pr., Inc.

McNeese, Tim. George Washington: America's Leaders in War & Peace. 2005. (Leaders of the American Revolution Ser.). (Illus.). 140p. (J). (ps-8). lib. bdg. 30.00 (978-0-7910-8619-3(4) , Chelsea Hse.) Facts On File, Inc.

Mead, David. Little George Washington Learns about Responsibility: Responsibility. Sharp, Chris, illus. 2004. (American Virtues for Kids Ser.). (J). bds. 6.95 (978-0-9746440-1-1(3)) Ideals Pubns.

Mello, Tara Baukus. George Washington. 1999. (Revolutionary War Leaders Ser.). (Illus.). 80p. (YA). (gr. 3 up). pap. 27.50 (978-0-7910-5695-0(3)); (J). (gr. 4-7). 31.00 (978-0-7910-5352-2(0)) Facts On File, Inc. (Chelsea Hse.).

—George Washington: First U. S. President. 2000. (gr. 5-8). lib. bdg. 17.60 (978-0-613-43323-5(8)) Tandem Library Bks.

Meloche, Renee. George Washington: Patriot & President. 2005. (Illus.). 32p. (J). 6.99 (978-1-932096-28-6(0)) Emerald Bks.

—George Washington Carver: America's Scientist. Pollard, Bryan, illus. 2005. (Heroes for Young Readers Ser.). (J). 6.99 (978-1-932096-17-0(5)) Emerald Bks.

Micklos, John. From Thirteen Colonies to One Nation. 2008. (Revolutionary War Library). (Illus.). 48p. (J). (gr. 3-4). lib. bdg. 23.93 (*978-0-7660-3015-2(6)) Enslow Pubs., Inc.

Miller, Brandon Marie. George Washington for Kids: His Life & Times with 21 Activities. 2007. (For Kids Ser.). 144p. (J). pap. 14.95 (*978-1-55652-655-8(5)) Chicago Review Pr., Inc.

Miller, Chuck. George Washington. 2003. (America's Founders Ser.). (J). pap. (978-1-58417-080-8(8)); lib. bdg. (978-1-58417-017-4(4)) Lake Street Pubs.

Murphy, Frank. George Washington & the General's Dog. Walz, Richard, illus. 2002. (Step into Reading Ser.). 48p. (J). (gr. 1-3). pap. 3.99 (978-0-375-81015-2(3)); lib. bdg. 11.99 (978-0-375-91015-9(8)) Random Hse. Children's Bks. (Random Hse. Bks. for Young Readers).

Nelson, Robin. George Washington: A Life of Leadership. 2006. (Pull Ahead Books). (Illus.). 32p. (J). 22.60 (978-0-8225-3474-7(6) , Lerner Pubns.) Lerner Publishing Group.

—George Washington: Una Vida de Liderazgo (A Life of Leadership) 2006. (Libros para Avanzar Ser.). (ENG & SPA.). 32p. (J). lib. bdg. 22.60 (978-0-8225-6235-1(9) , Ediciones Lerner) Lerner Publishing Group.

Nettleton, Pamela Hill. George Washington. Yesh, Jeff, illus. 2004. (Biographies Ser.). 24p. (C). (gr. k-3). 22.60 (978-1-4048-0184-4(7)) Picture Window Bks.

Nobleman, Marc Tyler. The Washington Monument. 2004. (Let's See Library). (Illus.). 24p. (J). (gr. 1 up). lib. bdg. 19.93 (978-0-7565-0621-6(2)) Compass Point Bks.

North, Sterling. George Washington: Frontier Colonel. 2006. (Sterling Point Bks.). (Illus.). 176p. (J). 12.95 (978-1-4027-3187-7(6)); pap. 6.95 (978-1-4027-3611-7(8)) Sterling Publishing Co., Inc.

Ocker, Karen, illus. George W. Bush Coloring Book. 2005. 24p. pap. 8.95 (978-1-891053-94-8(9)) Garrett County Pr.

Parin D'Aulaire, Ingri & Parin D'Aulaire, Edgar. George Washington. unabr. ed. 2001. (J). (gr. 3-5). pap. 20.00 incl. audio (978-0-8045-6717-6(4) , 65125E/6) Spoken Arts, Inc.

Parker, Lewis M. George Washington. 2002. (Triangle History of the American Revolution Ser.). (Illus.). 104p. (J). 28.70 (978-1-56711-607-6(8) , Blackbirch Pr., Inc.) Thomson Gale.

Pingry, Patricia. Discover George Washington. 2005. (Discovery Readers Ser.). 32p. (J). pap. 3.95 (978-0-8249-5505-2(6)) Ideals Pubns.

Pingry, Patricia A. Meet George Washington. 2001. (Meet Ser.). (Illus.). 32p. (J). (ps-3). 9.95 (978-0-8249-4131-4(4)) Ideals Pubns.

Pollard, Josephine. Life of Washington, Vol. 3. 1998. (Illus.). 136p. (J). 15.00 (978-1-889128-44-3(9)) Mantle Ministries.

Ransom, Candice F. George Washington. 2002. (History Maker Bios Ser.). (Illus.). 47p. (J). pap. 6.95 (978-0-8225-0384-2(0)); (gr. 2-4). 26.60 (978-0-8225-0374-3(3)) Lerner Publishing Group. (Lerner Pubns.).

Roberts, Jeremy. George Washington. 2004. (Presidential Leaders Ser.). (Illus.). 112p. (J). (gr. 6-12). lib. bdg. 29.27 (978-0-8225-0818-2(4)) Lerner Publishing Group.

Rockwell, Anne F. Big George. Trueman, Matthew, illus. 2004. (J). 16.00 (978-0-15-216583-3(5) , Silver Whistle) Harcourt Trade Pubs.

Roop, Peter. Buttons for General Washington. unabr. ed. 2007. (Readalongs for Beginning Readers Ser.). (J). (gr. 2-3). pap. 18.95 incl. audio compact disk (*978-1-59519-933-1(0)) Live Oak Media.

Roop, Peter & Roop, Connie. Botones para el General Washington (Buttons for General Washington) Hanson, Peter E., illus. 2006. (Yo Solo - Historia (on My Own - History) Ser.). (SPA.). 48p. (J). (gr. 2-4). lib. bdg. 25.26 (978-0-8225-6261-0(8) , Ediciones Lerner) Lerner Publishing Group.

Roop, Peter & Roop, Connie. Buttons for General Washington. Hanson, Peter E., illus. unabr. ed. 2007. (Readalongs for Beginning Readers Ser.). (J). (gr. 2-3). pap. 16.95 incl. audio (*978-1-59519-929-4(2)) Live Oak Media.

—Buttons for General Washington, 4 bks., Set. unabr. ed. 2007. (Readalongs for Beginning Readers Ser.). (J). (gr. 2-3). pap. 37.95 incl. audio (*978-1-59519-931-7(4)) Live Oak Media.

W
X
Y
Z

—Buttons for General Washington, 4 bks., Set. Hanson, Peter E., illus. unabr. ed. 2007. (Readalongs for Beginning Readers Ser.). (J). (gr. 2-3). pap. 39.95 incl. audio compact disk (***978-1-59519-935-5(7)**) Live Oak Media.

Rosenberg, John M. First in Peace: George Washington, the Constitution & the Presidency. 1998. (Single Titles Ser.: up). (Illus.). 256p. (gr. 7-12). lib. bdg. 25.90 (978-0-7613-0422-7(3) , Millbrook Pr.) Lerner Publishing Group.

Rosinsky, Natalie M. Presidents' Day. 2004. (Let's See Ser.). (Illus.). 24p. (J). (gr. 1 up). lib. bdg. 19.93 (978-0-7565-0773-2(1)) Compass Point Bks.

Rustad, Martha E. H. George Washington Carver, 6 vols. Saunders-Smith, Gail, ed. (gr. k-2). 28.95 (978-0-7368-9445-6(4)) Red Brick Learning.

Santella, Andrew. George Washington. 2000. (Compass Point Early Biographies Ser.). (Illus.). 32p. (J). (gr. 2 up). lib. bdg. 21.26 (978-0-7565-0014-6(1)) Compass Point Bks.

—Mount Vernon. 2004. (Illus.). 48p. (J). (gr. 4 up). lib. bdg. 22.60 (978-0-7565-0682-7(4)) Compass Point Bks.

Schaefer, Lola M. George Washington. Saunders-Smith, Gail, ed. 1998. (Famous Americans Ser.). (Illus.). 24p. (J). (gr. k-1). lib. bdg. 15.93 (978-0-7368-0110-2(3) , Pebble Bks.) Capstone Pr., Inc.

—George Washington, 6 vols. Saunders-Smith, Gail, ed. (gr. k-2). 28.95 (978-0-7368-8135-7(2)) Red Brick Learning.

—George Washington. 1998. (Famous Americans Ser.). (Illus.). (J). lib. bdg. 13.25 (978-0-516-21502-0(7) , Children's Pr.) Scholastic Library Publishing.

Schanzer, Rosalyn. George vs. George: The American Revolution As Seen from Both Sides. 2007. (Illus.). 64p. (J). (gr. 4-9). pap. 6.95 (978-1-4263-0042-4(5) , National Geographic Children's Bks.) National Geographic Society.

—George vs. George: The American Revolution as Seen from Both Sides. Schanzer, Rosalyn, illus. 2007. (Illus.). 60p. (J). reprint ed. 17.00 (***978-1-4223-6812-1(2)**) DIANE Publishing Co.

Schanzer, Rosalyn. George vs. George: The Revolutionary War as Seen by Both Sides. 2004. (Illus.). 64p. (J). (gr. 4-9). 16.95 (978-0-7922-7349-3(4)); 25.90 (978-0-7922-6999-1(3)) National Geographic Society. (National Geographic Children's Bks.).

Schauffler, Robert Haven. Washington's Birthday: Its History, Observance, Spirit, & Significance as Related in Prose & Verse, with a Selection from Washington's Speeches & Writings. 2006. 34.99 (***978-1-4280-3413-6(7)**); pap. 27.99 (***978-1-4280-3412-9(9)**) IndyPublish.com.

Schlesinger, Arthur M., Sr., et al, eds. The Elections of 1789 & 1792. 2003. (Major Presidential Elections & the Administrations That Followed Ser.). (Illus.). 154p. (J). (gr. 7 up). lib. bdg. (978-1-59084-351-2(7)) Mason Crest Pubs.

Snyder, Gail. George Washington. 2003. (Childhoods of the Presidents Ser.). (Illus.). 48p. (J). (gr. 4 up). lib. bdg. (978-1-59084-270-6(7)) Mason Crest Pubs.

St. George, Judith. Take the Lead, George Washington. Powers, Daniel, illus. 2005. (Turning Point Bk.). 48p. (J). (gr. 3-5). 16.99 (978-0-399-23887-1(5) , Philomel) Penguin Group (USA) Inc.

Stevens, C. M. The Wonderful Story of Washington & Th. 2004. reprint ed. pap. 24.95 (978-1-4179-2621-3(X)) Kessinger Publishing, LLC.

Stevenson, Augusta. Abraham Lincoln & George Washington. 2003. (gr. 3-6). lib. bdg. 15.30 (978-0-613-61599-0(9)) Tandem Library Bks.

The Story of George Washington. 2000. (Illus.). 24p. (J). (ps-k). 6.95 (978-0-8249-4188-8(8)) Ideals Pubns.

Stout, Mary. George Washington. 2002. (Raintree Biographies Ser.). (Illus.). 32p. (J). lib. bdg. 25.69 (978-0-7398-5681-9(2)) Raintree.

Strum, Richard. Henry Knox: Washington's Artilleryman. 2006. (Forgotten Heroes of the American Revolution Ser.). (Illus.). 88p. (J). (gr. 5-11). lib. bdg. 23.95 (978-1-59556-013-1(0)) OTTN Publishing.

Strum, Richard M. Henry Knox: Washington's Artilleryman. 2006. (J). pap. (978-1-59556-018-6(1)) OTTN Publishing.

Thomas, Peggy. Farmer George Plants a Nation. Johnson, Layne, illus. 2008. (J). (***978-1-59078-460-0(X)** , Calkins Creek) Boyds Mills Pr.

Trumbauer, Lisa. Life in the Time of George Washington & the Revolutionary War. 2007. (J). (***978-1-4034-9667-6(6)**); pap. (***978-1-4034-9675-1(7)**) Heinemann Library.

Usel, T. M. George Washington. Schon, Isabel, ed. Ferrer, Martín Luis Guzman, tr. from ENG. 1998. (Biografías Ilustradas con Fotografías Ser.). (SPA., Illus.). 24p. (J). (gr. 2-3). lib. bdg. 18.60 (978-1-56065-805-4(3) , CAP2623, Bridgestone Bks.) Capstone Pr., Inc.

Venezia, Mike. George Washington. Venezia, Mike, illus. 2005. (Getting to Know the U. S. Presidents Ser.). (Illus.). 32p. (J). (gr. 3-4). pap. 7.95 (978-0-516-27475-1(9) , Children's Pr.) Scholastic Library Publishing.

Venezia, Mike, illus. George Washington. 2004. (Gtk Us Presidents Ser.). (J). 27.00 (978-0-516-22606-4(1) , Children's Pr.) Scholastic Library Publishing.

Wachter, Joanne. George Washington & the AMER Revolution. 2005. 42.00 (***978-1-4108-4633-4(4)**) Benchmark Education Co.

Wagner, Heather Lehr. George Washington. (Great American Presidents Ser.). (Illus.). (gr. 4-8). 2004. 112p. pap. 30.00 (978-0-7910-7784-9(5)); 2003. 100p. 30.00 (978-0-7910-7601-9(6)) Facts On File, Inc. (Chelsea Hse.).

Weinberger, Kimberly. George Washington. Doucet, Bob, illus. 2002. (Primeras Biografías de Scholastic Ser.). (SPA.). 32p. (J). (gr. 2-4). pap. 3.99 (978-0-439-37484-2(7) , SO31319, Scholastic en Espanol) Scholastic, Inc.

Weintraub, Aileen. Lee sobre George Washington/Read about George Washington. 2006. (I Like Biographies! Bilingual Ser.). (ENG & SPA., Illus.). 24p. (J). (gr. 1-3). lib. bdg. 21.26 (978-0-7660-2673-5(6) , Enslow Elementary) Enslow Pubs., Inc.

—Read about George Washington. 2004. (I Like Biographies! Ser.). (Illus.). 24p. (J). lib. bdg. 21.26 (978-0-7660-2301-7(X)) Enslow Pubs., Inc.

Welsbacher, Anne. George Washington. 1999. (United States Presidents Ser.). (Illus.). 32p. (J). (gr. k-6). lib. bdg. 22.78 (978-1-56239-737-1(0)) ABDO Publishing Co.

Williamson, Mary. The Life of George Washington. 2004. (ENG.). 128p. per. 6.95 (978-1-930367-91-3(0) , CLP29870) Christian Liberty Pr.

Yoder, Carolyn P. George Washington, the Writer: A Treasury of Letters, Diaries, & Public Documents. 2003. (Illus.). 144p. (YA). (gr. 4-6). 16.95 (978-1-56397-199-0(2)) Boyds Mills Pr.

WASHINGTON, GEORGE, 1732-1799—FICTION

Fritz, Jean. George Washington's Breakfast. 1998. 13.79 (978-0-606-13418-7(2)) Tandem Library Bks.

—George Washington's Breakfast. Galdone, Paul, illus. 1998. (J). (ps-6). lib. bdg. 15.30 (978-0-613-07849-8(7)) Tandem Library Bks.

—George Washington's Mother. DiSalvo-Ryan, DyAnne, illus. 2000. (J). (gr. k-5). pap. 12.95 incl. audio (978-1-55592-065-4(9) , QPRA433) Weston Woods Studios, Inc.

Griffin, Judith Berry. Phoebe, the Spy. Tomes, Margot, illus. 2002. 48p. (J). pap. 6.99 (978-0-698-11956-7(8) , Putnam Juvenile) Penguin Group (USA) Inc.

Hedstrom-Page, Deborah. From Colonies to Country with George Washington. Martinez, Sergio, illus. 2007. 80p. (J). (gr. 3-9). 9.99 (978-0-8054-3265-7(5)) B&H Publishing Grp.

Hemphill, Kris. Ambush in the Wilderness. 2003. (Adventures in America Ser.). (Illus.). 90p. (J). 14.95 (978-1-893110-34-2(6)) Silver Moon Pr.

Krensky, Stephen. Hanukkah at Valley Forge. Harlin, Greg, illus. 2006. 32p. (J). (gr. k). 17.99 (978-0-525-47738-9(1) , Dutton Juvenile) Penguin Group (USA) Inc.

Osborne, Mary Pope. Revolutionary War on Wednesday, Vol. 22. unabr. ed. 2004. (Magic Tree House Ser. : No. 22). 69p. (J). (gr. k-3). pap. 17.00 incl. audio (978-0-8072-0931-8(7) , S FTR 254 SP, Listening Library) Random Hse. Audio Publishing Group.

—Revolutionary War on Wednesday. Loehr, Mallory, ed. Murdocca, Sal, illus. 2000. (Magic Tree House Ser.: No. 22). 96p. (J). (gr. k-3). lib. bdg. 11.99 (978-0-679-99068-0(2)); pap. 3.99 (978-0-679-89068-3(8)) Random Hse. Children's Bks. (Random Hse. Bks. for Young Readers).

—Revolutionary War on Wednesday. Murdocca, Salvatore, illus. 2000. (Magic Tree House Ser. : No. 22). 69p. (J). (gr. k-3). lib. bdg. 11.80 (978-0-613-28355-7(4)) Tandem Library Bks.

—Revolutionary War on Wednesday. Murdocca, Sal, illus. 2000. (Magic Tree House Ser. : No. 22). (J). (gr. k-3). (978-0-606-19907-0(1)) Tandem Library Bks.

Rinaldi, Ann. Taking Liberty: The Story of Oney Judge, George Washington's Runaway Slave. Dudash, C. Michael, illus. 2004. 272p. (YA). mass mkt. 5.99 (978-0-689-85188-9(X) , Simon Pulse) Simon & Schuster Children's Publishing.

—Taking Liberty: The Story of Oney Judge, George Washington's Runaway Slave. 2002. 272p. (YA). (gr. 7 up). 16.95 (978-0-689-85187-2(1)) Simon & Schuster Children's Publishing.

—Taking Liberty: The Story of Oney Judge, George Washington's Runaway Slave. 2004. (gr. 7-12). lib. bdg. 14.15 (978-0-613-73369-4(X)) Tandem Library Bks.

Rosenburg, John M. First in War: George Washington in the American Revolution. 1998. (Single Titles Ser.: up). (Illus.). 256p. (gr. 7-12). lib. bdg. 25.90 (978-0-7613-0311-4(1) , Millbrook Pr.) Lerner Publishing Group.

Sargent, Dave & Sargent, Pat. Biscuit: (Skewbald) Follow the Rules, 25, vol. 3. Lenoir, Jane, illus. 2001. (Saddle Up Ser.: 3). 36p. (J). pap. 6.95 (978-1-56763-676-5(4)); lib. bdg. 22.60 (978-1-56763-675-8(6)) Ozark Publishing.

Scieszka, Jon. Oh Say, I Can't See. McCauley, Adam, illus. 2007. (Time Warp Trio Ser.: No. 15). 80p. (J). (gr. 2-6). pap. 4.99 (978-0-14-240808-7(5) , Puffin) Penguin Group (USA) Inc.

Stratemeyer, Edward. With Washington in the West or A Soldier Boy's Battles in the Wilderness. Shute, A. B., illus. 2004. reprint ed. pap. 30.95 (978-1-4179-2977-1(4)) Kessinger Publishing, LLC.

Tunnell, Michael. Joke's on George. 2001. (gr. 3-6). lib. bdg. 18.75 (978-0-613-49572-1(1)) Tandem Library Bks.

Tunnell, Michael O. The Joke's on George. Osborn, Kathy, illus. 2003. 32p. (J). (gr. k-2). 9.95 (978-1-56397-970-5(5)) Boyds Mills Pr.

Woodruff, Elvira. George Washington's Socks. 1999. (YA). pap. 40.75 incl. audio (978-0-7887-2995-9(0) , 40877) Recorded Bks., LLC.

WASHINGTON, MARTHA, 1731-1802

Ashby, Ruth. George & Martha Washington. 2005. (Illus.). 48p. (J). pap. (978-0-8368-5703-0(8)); lib. bdg. 30.00 (978-0-8368-5697-2(X)) Stevens, Gareth Inc. (World Almanac Library).

Haugen, Brenda. Martha Washington: First Lady of the United States. 2005. (Signature Lives Ser.). (Illus.). 112p. (J). (gr. 5-7). (978-0-7565-0983-5(1)) Compass Point Bks.

Larkin, Tanya. What Was Cooking in Martha Washington's Presidential Mansions? 2001. (Cooking Throughout American History Ser.). (Illus.). 24p. (J). (gr. 3). lib. bdg. 19.95 (978-0-8239-5606-7(7) , PowerKids Pr.) Rosen Publishing Group, Inc., The.

Manera, Alexandria. Martha Washington. 2003. (Women of the Revolution Ser.). (J). pap. (978-1-58417-087-7(5)); lib. bdg. (978-1-58417-024-2(7)) Lake Street Pubs.

Mattern, Joanne. Martha Washington. 2007. (First Ladies Ser.). (Illus.). 32p. (J). (gr. k-6). lib. bdg. 24.21 (***978-1-59928-801-7(X)** , Checkerboard Library) ABDO Publishing Co.

McPherson, Stephanie Sammartino. Martha Washington: First Lady. 1998. (Historical American Biographies Ser.). (Illus.). 128p. (YA). (gr. 6-12). lib. bdg. 26.60 (978-0-7660-1017-8(1)) Enslow Pubs., Inc.

Ransom, Candice. Martha Washington. Ritz, Karen, illus. 2003. 48p. (J). (ps-3). lib. bdg. 14.10 (978-0-613-58928-4(9)) Tandem Library Bks.

Ransom, Candice F. Martha Washington. Ritz, Karen, illus. 2003. (On My Own Biography Ser.). 48p. (J). (gr. 1-3). pap. 5.95 (978-0-87614-107-6(6)); 25.26 (978-0-87614-918-8(2)) Lerner Publishing Group. (Carolrhoda Bks.).

Slade, Suzanne. Martha Washington: First Lady of the United States. Moore, Frances, illus. 2007. (J). lib. bdg. (***978-1-4048-3727-0(2)**) Picture Window Bks.

WASHINGTON (D.C.)

Alderfer, Jonathan. National Geographic Field Guide to Birds: Maryland & D. C. 2006. (Illus.). 272p. pap. 14.95 (978-1-4262-0007-6(2) , National Geographic) National Geographic Society.

Alter, Judy. Washington, D. C. A MyReportLinks. Com Book. 2003. (States Ser.). (Illus.). 48p. (J). lib. bdg. 25.26 (978-0-7660-5137-9(4) , MyReportLinks.com Bks.) Enslow Pubs., Inc.

Arbelbide, C. L. The White House Easter Egg Roll. Gibson, Barbara Leonard, illus. 2005. 29p. (J). (gr. k-4). reprint ed. 17.00 (978-0-7567-4772-5(4)) DIANE Publishing Co.

Ashabranner, Brent. Remembering Korea: Korean War. Ashabranner, Jennifer, photos by. 2001. (Great American Memorials Ser.). (Illus.). 64p. (gr. 4-8). lib. bdg. 25.90 (978-0-7613-2156-9(X) , Twenty-First Century Bks.) Lerner Publishing Group.

—Their Names to Live: What the Vietnam Veterans Memorial Means to America. Ashabranner, Jennifer, photos by. 1998. (Great American Memorials Ser.). (Illus.). 64p. (gr. 4-8). lib. bdg. 24.90 (978-0-7613-3235-0(9) , Twenty-First Century Bks.) Lerner Publishing Group.

Ashabranner, Jennifer, illus. & photos by. On the Mall in Washington, D. C. A Visit to America's Front Yard. Ashabranner, Jennifer, photos by. Ashabranner, Brent K., photos by. 2002. (Single Titles Ser.). 64p. (gr. 5 up). lib. bdg. 23.90 (978-0-7613-2351-8(1) , Twenty-First Century Bks.) Lerner Publishing Group.

Benchmark Education Staff. The United States Government. 2005. 2.00 (***978-1-4108-4640-2(7)**) Benchmark Education Co.

Benson, Laura Lee. Washington D. C. A Scrapbook. 1999. (978-0-606-18032-0(X)) Tandem Library Bks.

—Washington, D C: A Scrapbook. 1999. (gr. k-3). lib. bdg. 15.25 (978-0-613-35258-1(0)) Tandem Library Bks.

Braithwaite, Jill. The White House. 2004. (Pull Ahead Bks.). (Illus.). 32p. (J). (gr. k-3). lib. bdg. 22.60 (978-0-8225-3800-4(8)) Lerner Publishing Group.

Britton, Tamara L. The Vietnam Veterans Memorial. 2005. (Symbols, Landmarks, & Monuments Set Ii Ser.). (Illus.). 32p. (J). (gr. k-6). lib. bdg. 22.78 (978-1-59197-523-6(9)) ABDO Publishing Co.

Brown, Vanessa. District of Columbia/Distrito de Columbia. 2005. (Bilingual Library of the United States of America: Set 1). (ENG & SPA., Illus.). 32p. (J). (ps-k). lib. bdg. 22.50 (978-1-4042-3072-9(6) , Buenas Letra) Rosen Publishing Group, Inc., The.

C. Q. Press Staff. CQ's Information Directory Set of 2: Federal Regulatory Directory & Washington Information Directory, 2 vols. 2005. (gr. 9 up). 250.00 (978-1-933116-29-7(3)) CQ Pr.

Clark, Diane C. & Chernick, Miriam. A Kid's Guide to Washington, D.C. Brown, Richard E., illus. 2008. (J). pap. (***978-0-15-206125-8(8)**) Harcourt Trade Pubs.

Cooper, Terry, ed. Washington D. C. Scholastic Technology Activity Folder. 2001. 6p. 3.95 (978-0-439-30949-3(2)) Scholastic, Inc.

CQ Press, creator. Washington Information Directory. 30th ed. 2005. (Illus.). 1012p. (gr. 9 up). per. 128.00 (978-1-56802-973-3(X)) CQ Pr.

Curlee, Lynn. Capital. Curlee, Lynn, illus. 2003. (Illus.). 48p. (J). (gr. 2-5). 17.95 (978-0-689-84947-3(8) , Atheneum) Simon & Schuster Children's Publishing.

DeGezelle, Terri. The U. S. Capitol. 2003. (First Facts Ser.). (Illus.). 24p. (J). lib. bdg. 19.93 (978-0-7368-2294-7(1)) Capstone Pr., Inc.

Dorling Kindersley Publishing Staff. Washington, D. C. 2003. (Illus.). 184p. (J). (gr. 5). bds. 7.99 (978-0-7894-9899-1(5)) Dorling Kindersley Publishing, Inc.

Douglas, Lloyd G. The White House. 2003. (Welcome Bks.). (Illus.). 24p. (J). (ps-2). pap. 4.95 (978-0-516-27878-0(9) , Children's Pr.) Scholastic Library Publishing.

Elish, Dan. Washington, D. C. (Celebrate the States Ser.). 1998. (Illus.). 144p. (gr. 4-8). lib. bdg. 37.07 (978-0-7614-0423-1(6)); 2nd ed. 2007. (J). lib. bdg. 39.93 (978-0-7614-2352-2(4)) Cavendish, Marshall Corp. (Benchmark Bks.).

Feeney, Kathy. Washington, D. C. Facts & Symbols. (States & Their Symbols Ser.). 24p. (J). 2000. (Illus.). (gr. 2-3). lib. bdg. 18.60 (978-0-7368-0527-8(3) , Bridgestone Bks.); 2003. lib. bdg. 19.93 (978-0-7368-2278-7(X)) Capstone Pr., Inc.

Figueroa, Acton. Washington, D. C. 2003. (World Almanac Library of the States). (Illus.). 48p. (J). (gr. 5 up). pap. 14.95 (978-0-8368-5333-9(4)); lib. bdg. 30.00 (978-0-8368-5162-5(5)) Stevens, Gareth Inc. (World Almanac Library).

Furman, Elina. Washington, D. C. 2002. (From Sea to Shining Sea Ser.: 2). (Illus.). 80p. (J). (gr. 3-5). 30.50 (978-0-516-22319-3(4) , Children's Pr.) Scholastic Library Publishing.

Gamble, Adam. Good Night Washington, DC. Veno, Joe, illus. 2006. (Good Night Our World Ser.). 20p. (J). bds. 9.95 (978-0-9777979-1-2(0)) Our World of Books.

Glaser, Jason. Washington, D. C. 2003. (Land of Liberty Ser.). (Illus.). 64p. (J). lib. bdg. 25.26 (978-0-7368-2204-6(6)) Capstone Pr., Inc.

Group/McGraw-Hill, Wright. Washington D. C. Heartbeat of a Nation, 6 vols. (Book2WebTM Ser.). (gr. 4-8). 36.50 (978-0-322-04457-9(X)) Wright Group, The.

Hancock, Maryann. The U. S. Capitol. 2006. (Land of the Free Ser.). (Illus.). 32p. (J). lib. bdg. 28.21 (978-1-4034-7000-3(6)) Heinemann Library.

—The U.S. Capitol. 2006. (Illus.). 32p. (J). pap. (978-1-4034-7007-2(3)) Heinemann Library.

Harcourt School Publishers Staff. A Day in the Life of Washington, D. C. 3rd ed. 2002. (Horizons Ser.). (Illus.). (J). pap. 5.50 (978-0-15-333425-2(8)) Harcourt Schl. Pubs.

—Our Nation's Capital. 3rd ed. 2002. (Trophies English Language Learners Ser.). (Illus.). pap. 5.10 (978-0-15-327754-2(8)) Harcourt Schl. Pubs.

Hargrove, Julia. Tomb of the Unknowns. 2003. (Illus.). 48p. (J). pap. 6.95 (978-1-57310-405-0(1)) Teaching & Learning Co.

Heinrichs, Ann. Washington. 2003. (This Land Is Your Land Ser.). (Illus.). 48p. (J). (gr. 3 up). lib. bdg. 22.30 (978-0-7565-0350-5(7)) Compass Point Bks.

—Washington, D. C. Kania, Matt, illus. 2005. (Welcome to the USA Ser.). 40p. (J). (gr. 1-5). 27.07 (978-1-59296-492-5(3)) Child's World, Inc.

—Washington, D. C. 2003. (This Land Is Your Land Ser.). (Illus.). 48p. (J). (gr. 3 up). lib. bdg. 22.60 (978-0-7565-0335-2(3)) Compass Point Bks.

Hicks, Terry Allan. Washington, D. C. 2006. (It's My State! Ser.). (Illus.). 80p. (J). (gr. 3-6). lib. bdg. 29.93 (978-0-7614-1929-7(2) , Benchmark Bks.) Cavendish, Marshall Corp.

Horn, Geoffrey M. Washington, D.C. 2006. (Portraits of the States Ser.). (Illus.). 32p. (J). pap. 8.95 (978-0-8368-4695-9(8)) ; lib. bdg. 23.33 (978-0-8368-4676-8(1)) Stevens, Gareth Inc.

Jakobsen, Kathy. My Washington D. C. Jakobsen, Kathy, illus. 2000. (Illus.). 32p. (J). (978-0-316-45622-7(5)) Little Brown & Co.

January, Brendan. National Mall. 2000. (gr. 3-6). lib. bdg. 14.10 (978-0-613-52154-3(4)) Tandem Library Bks.

Johnson, Etta. The United States Government. 2005. 42.00 (***978-1-4108-4592-4(3)**) Benchmark Education Co.

Johnston, Joyce. Washington D C. rev. ed. 2003. (gr. 3-6). lib. bdg. 15.25 (978-0-613-52523-7(X)) Tandem Library Bks.

—Washington D. C. 2nd exp. rev. ed. 2003. (Hello U. S. A. Ser.). (Illus.). 84p. (J). (gr. 3-6). 25.26 (978-0-8225-4091-5(6) , Lerner Pubns.) Lerner Publishing Group.

Kennedy, Edward M. My Senator & Me: A Dog¿s-Eye View of Washington, D. C. Small, David, illus. 2007. 53p. (J). reprint ed. 17.00 (***978-1-4223-6791-9(6)**) DIANE Publishing Co.

Kennedy, Edward Moore. My Senator & Me: A Dog's Eye View of Washington, D.C. Small, David, illus. 2006. (J). (***978-1-4156-7168-9(0)**); (***978-0-439-65078-6(X)**) Scholastic, Inc. (Scholastic Pr.).

Kummer, Patricia K. Washington, D. C. rev. ed. 2002. (One Nation Ser.). (Illus.). 48p. (J). (gr. 3-4). lib. bdg. 22.60 (978-0-7368-1273-3(3) , Bridgestone Bks.) Capstone Pr., Inc.

Landphair, Ted. Washington, D.C. Highsmith, Carol M., photos by. 2000. (Illus.). 160p. 19.99 (978-0-517-16235-4(0) , Crescent) Random Hse. Value Publishing.

Linde, Barbara M. Building Washington, D. C. Measuring the Area of Rectangular Spaces. 2004. (PowerMath Ser.). (Illus.). 32p. (J). lib. bdg. (978-0-8239-8867-9(8) , PowerKids Pr.) Rosen Publishing Group, Inc., The.

—Building Washington, DC: Measuring the Area of Rectangular Shapes. 2004. (PowerMath Ser.). (Illus.). 32p. (J). lib. bdg. 22.50 (978-0-8239-8980-5(1) , PowerKids Pr.) Rosen Publishing Group, Inc., The.

MacMillan, Daniel Emerson. Golfing in Washington. 17th ed. 2003. 360p. per. 14.95 (978-1-878591-58-6(4)) MAC Productions.

Marcovitz, Hal. The Lincoln Memorial. 2002. (American Symbols & Their Meanings Ser.). (Illus.). 48p. (J). (gr. 4 up). lib. bdg. (978-1-59084-029-0(1)) Mason Crest Pubs.

—The Washington Monument. 2002. (American Symbols & Their Meanings Ser.). (Illus.). 48p. (YA). (gr. 4 up). lib. bdg. (978-1-59084-028-3(3)) Mason Crest Pubs.

—The White House. 2002. (American Symbols & Their Meanings Ser.). (Illus.). 48p. (YA). (gr. 4 up). lib. bdg. (978-1-59084-024-5(0)) Mason Crest Pubs.

Marsh, Carole. The Big Washington Reproducible Activity Book. 2001. (Carole Marsh Washington Bks.). 96p. (J). (gr. 2-6). pap. 9.95 (978-0-7933-9960-4(2)) Gallopade International.

—District of Columbia 2000! Coming Soon to a Calendar Near You - The 21st Century! - Complete Set of All 2000 Items. 1998. (Two Thousand! Ser.). (Illus.). (J). (gr. 3-12). pap. 75.00 (978-0-7933-9325-1(6)); lib. bdg. 85.00 (978-0-7933-9326-8(4)) Gallopade International.

—District of Columbia 2000! Coming Soon to a Calendar Near You-The 21st Century! 1998. (Two Thousand! Ser.). (Illus.). (J). (gr. 3-12). pap. 19.95 (978-0-7933-8700-7(0)); lib. bdg. 29.95 (978-0-7933-8699-4(3)) Gallopade International.

—My First Book about Washington D. C. Line Art Staff, illus. 2001. (Washington Experience! Ser.). 32p. (J). (gr. k-4). pap. 7.95 (978-0-7933-9902-4(5)) Gallopade International.

W X Y Z

—Washington Classic Christmas Trivia. 2002. (Carole Marsh Washington Bks.). (Illus.). 32p. lib. bdg. 21.95 (978-0-635-01460-3(2) , 14602, Marsh, Carole Bks.) Gallopade International.

—Washington Jeopardy! Line Art Staff, illus. 2001. 32p. (J). (gr. 3-8). pap. 7.95 (978-0-7933-9815-7(0)) Gallopade International.

—Washington "Jography" A Fun Run Thru Our State! 2001. (Carole Marsh Washington Bks.). 32p. (J). (gr. 3-8). pap. 7.95 (978-0-7933-9844-7(4)) Gallopade International.

Mattern, Joanne. Washington, D.C. 2007. (Cities Ser.). (Illus.). 32p. (J). 22.78 (978-1-59679-725-3(8)) ABDO Publishing Co.

Melmed, Laura Krauss. Capital! Washington D. C. from A to Z. Lessac, Frane, illus. 48p. (J). (gr. 1-6). 2007. pap. 6.99 (978-0-06-113614-6(X)); 2003. 16.99 (978-0-688-17561-0(9)); 2003. lib. bdg. 16.89 (978-0-688-17562-7(7)) HarperCollins Pubs.

Nelson, Kristin L. The Washington Monument. (Pull Ahead Bks.). 32p. (J). (gr. k-3). 2004. (Illus.). lib. bdg. 22.60 (978-0-8225-0250-0(X)); 2003. pap. 5.95 (978-0-8225-3759-5(1)) Lerner Publishing Group.

Nobleman, Marc Tyler. The Lincoln Memorial. 2004. (Let's See Library). (Illus.). 24p. (J). (gr. 1 up). lib. bdg. 19.93 (978-0-7565-0618-6(2)) Compass Point Bks.

—The Washington Monument. 2004. (Let's See Library). (Illus.). 24p. (J). (gr. 1 up). lib. bdg. 19.93 (978-0-7565-0621-6(2)) Compass Point Bks.

Rappoport, Bernice. The Community of Washington, D. C. 2005. (Navigators Ser.). (J). pap. 38.00 ***(978-1-4108-5094-2(3))*** Benchmark Education Co.

Ribke, Simone T. Washington, D. C. (Rookie Español Geografía Ser.). (Illus.). (J). 2005. (ENG & SPA.). 31p. (ps-ps). 19.50 (978-0-516-25248-3(8)); 2004. 31p. (gr. 1-2). pap. 5.95 (978-0-516-27897-1(5)); 2003. 32p. 20.50 (978-0-516-22744-3(0)) Scholastic Library Publishing. (Children's Pr.).

—Washington D. C. 2006. (SPA.). 32p. (J). (gr. k-2). pap. 5.95 (978-0-516-25049-6(3) , Children's Pr.) Scholastic Library Publishing.

Sanders. Washington, D. C. 1999. (American Government Today Ser.). (Illus.). pap. 7.20 (978-0-7398-2127-5(X)) Steck-Vaughn.

Santella, Andrew. U. S. Presidential Inaugurations. 2002. (Cornerstones of Freedom). (Illus.). 48p. (J). (gr. 4-6). 26.00 (978-0-516-22533-3(2) , Children's Pr.) Scholastic Library Publishing.

Schaefer, Lola M. The U. S. Capitol. (Symbols of Freedom Ser.). (Illus.). 32p. (J). (gr. k-2). 2002. pap. 6.95 (978-1-58810-399-4(4) , 91194); 2001. lib. bdg. (978-1-58810-178-5(9)) Heinemann Library.

—The Washington Monument. (Symbols of Freedom Ser.). (Illus.). 32p. (J). (gr. k-2). 2002. pap. 6.95 (978-1-58810-400-7(1) , 91195); 2001. lib. bdg. (978-1-58810-179-2(7)) Heinemann Library.

Segal, Robin. ABC in Washington, DC. 2007. (J). 12.95 ***(978-0-9719697-7-3(9))*** Murray Hill Bks., LLC.

Silate, Jennifer. The United States Capitol. 2004. (Illus.). 24p. (J). lib. bdg. (978-1-4042-2694-4(X)) Rosen Publishing Group, Inc., The.

—The White House. 2004. (Illus.). 24p. (J). lib. bdg. (978-1-4042-2695-1(8)) Rosen Publishing Group, Inc., The.

Somervill, Barbara A. The Holocaust Museum. 2007. (J). lib. bdg. ***(978-0-7565-3357-1(0))*** Compass Point Bks.

Steadwell Books Publishing Staff, ed. Washington D. C. 1999. (American Government Today Ser.). (Illus.). 48p. (J). lib. bdg. 22.83 (978-0-7398-1789-6(2)) Raintree.

Stein, R. Conrad. Washington, D. C. 2000. (Cities of the World Ser.). (Illus.). 64p. (J). (gr. 4-9). pap. 9.95 (978-0-516-26532-2(6) , Children's Pr.) Scholastic Library Publishing.

Vincent, Mary. Follow the Leader: A Dog's-Eye View of Washington, D. C. 2nd l.t. ed. 2000. 117p. (gr. 5 up). per. 12.95 (978-0-9670911-0-5(1)); (YA). 19.95 (978-0-9670911-1-2(X)) Eastbank Publishing.

Weintraub, A. How to Draw Washingtons Sights & Symbols. 2002. (Kids Guide to Drawing America Ser.). 32p. (J). lib. bdg. 25.25 (978-0-8239-6104-7(4) , PowerKids Pr.) Rosen Publishing Group, Inc., The.

Williams, China. City Walks Deck: Washington, DC. 2006. 14.95 (978-0-8118-5128-2(1)) Chronicle Bks. LLC.

Zschock, Martha Day. Journey Around Washington D. C. from A to Z. Zschock, Martha Day, illus. 2004. (Journey Around Ser.: Bk. 5). (Illus.). 32p. (J). 17.95 (978-1-889833-62-0(2)) Commonwealth Editions.

WASHINGTON (D.C.)—CAPITOL

see United States Capitol (Washington, D.C.)

WASHINGTON (D.C.)—FICTION

Aboff, Marcie. Clifford's Puppy Days: Party Time! Goldberg, Barry, illus. 2005. (Clifford Ser.). 33p. (J). 3.99 (978-0-439-69048-5(X) , Cartwheel Bks.) Scholastic, Inc.

Ali, Khayyam Esab. The Wormhole Kids Visit President Kennedy. 2004. (ENG., Illus.). 56p. (J). per. 7.95 (978-1-59526-231-8(8)) Media Creations, Inc.

Allred, Alexandra Powe. The Code. 2002. 167p. (J). pap. 5.95 (978-0-7569-0692-4(X)); (gr. 3-6). lib. bdg. 13.95 (978-0-7569-0693-1(8)) Perfection Learning Corp.

Barnes, Peter W. Woodrow, the White House Mouse. Barnes, Cheryl Shaw, illus. 2nd rev. ed. 1998. 32p. (J). (gr. 1-3). (978-0-9637688-9-6(1)) Vacation Spot Publishing.

Barnes, Peter W. & Barnes, Cheryl Shaw. Woodrow, the White House Mouse. 2000. 32p. (J). (gr. k-3). pap. 5.99 (978-0-439-12952-7(4)) Scholastic, Inc.

Battle, Cleaton D. A Saturday Surprise. Cooper, Emmanuel B., illus. 2006. 68p. (J). pap. 11.95 (978-1-59663-504-3(5) , Castle Keep Pr.) Rock, James A. & Co. Pubs.

Blackwood, Gary. Second Sight. 2007. 288p. (J). pap. 6.99 (978-0-14-240747-9(X) , Puffin) Penguin Group (USA) Inc.

Blair, Margaret Whitman. House of Spies: Danger in the Civil War. 1999. (White Mane Kids Ser.: Vol. 7). (Illus.). 169p. (YA). (ps up). pap. 8.95 (978-1-57249-161-8(2) , White Mane Kids) White Mane Publishing Co., Inc.

Bodel, Garrett. A Trip to the City. Bodel, Garrett, photos by. 2002. (Doll's Life Story Ser.: Vol. 2). (Illus.). 32p. (J). (gr. 2-4). pap. 7.90 (978-0-9720072-4-5(5)) Doll's Life.

Bridwell, Norman. Clifford Goes to Washington. Bridwell, Norman, illus. 2005. (Clifford Ser.). (Illus.). 32p. (J). 3.50 (978-0-439-69656-2(9) , Cartwheel Bks.) Scholastic, Inc.

Cabot, Meg. All-am. 2008. 256p. (J). pap. 7.99 ***(978-0-06-147989-2(6)*** , HarperTeen) HarperCollins Pubs.

—All American Girl. 2003. 416p. (YA). (gr. 7 up). pap. 6.99 (978-0-06-447277-7(9)) HarperCollins Pubs.

—All American Girl. 2002. (gr. 7-12). lib. bdg. 15.30 (978-0-613-62192-2(1)) Tandem Library Bks.

—All American Girl. l.t. ed. 2003. 354p. (J). 25.95 (978-0-7862-6102-4(1) , Large Print Pr.) Thorndike Pr.

—Ready or No. 2008. 256p. (J). pap. 7.99 ***(978-0-06-147996-0(9)*** , HarperTeen) HarperCollins Pubs.

Cabot, Meg. Ready or Not. 2nd ed. 2005. 256p. (gr. 7 up). (J). lib. bdg. 16.89 (978-0-06-072451-1(X)); (YA). 16.99 (978-0-06-072450-4(1)) HarperCollins Pubs.

—Ready or Not. l.t. ed. 2006. 322p. (YA). 23.95 (978-0-7862-8282-1(7)) Thorndike Pr.

Chavez, Michael A., Jr. The Adventures of Tom Turkey: Thanksgiving in the White House. 2001. (J). 8.00 (978-0-8059-5079-3(6)) Dorrance Publishing Co., Inc.

Cobot, Meg. All-American Girl. 2004. 416p. (J). (gr. 7 up). pap. 44.00 incl. audio (978-0-8072-2281-2(X) , Listening Library) Random Hse. Audio Publishing Group.

Cohn, Rachel. You Know Where to Find Me. 2008. 208p. (YA). 15.99 ***(978-0-689-87859-6(1)*** , Simon & Schuster Children's Publishing) Simon & Schuster Children's Publishing.

Collins, Dennis. Spinley's Spaceship. 2007. (Illus.). (J). per. 8.99 ***(978-1-60247-100-9(2))*** Tate Publishing & Enterprises, L.L.C.

Cuyler, Margery. That's Good! That's Bad! in Washington, D. C. Garland, Michael, illus. rev. ed. 2007. 32p. (J). (ps-2). 16.95 ***(978-0-8050-7727-8(8))*** Holt, Henry & Co.

Davis, Rachel. My Life at Mapleleaf Cabin. 2nd ed. 2004. (YA). per. 10.00 (978-0-9741176-8-3(4)) Wu Li Turtle Corp.

Duey, Kathleen. Francesca Vigilucci: Washington, D. C. 1913. 2000. (American Diaries Ser.: No. 17). (J). (gr. 3-7). (978-0-606-20079-0(7)) Tandem Library Bks.

Ehrenberg, Pamela. Ethan, Suspended. 2007. 336 Pagesp. 16.00 ***(978-0-8028-5317-2(X));*** vi, 266p. (J). (gr. 6 up). 16.00 ***(978-0-8028-5324-0(2)*** , Eerdmans Bks For Young Readers) Eerdmans, William B. Publishing Co.

Emerson, Alice B. Betty Gordon in Washington. 2004. reprint ed. pap. 20.95 (978-1-4191-0977-5(4)); pap. 1.99 (978-1-4192-0977-2(9)) Kessinger Publishing, LLC.

Emmer, E. R. Me, Minerva & the Flying Car. 2000. (Going to Ser.). (Illus.). 96p. (J). pap. 5.99 (978-1-893577-03-9(1)) Four Corners Publishing Co., Inc.

—Me, Minerva & the Flying Flora. Huerta, Catherine, illus. 2nd rev. ed. 2003. (Going to Ser.). Orig. Title: Me, Minera & the Flying Car. 136p. (gr. 4-8). pap. 6.95 (978-1-893577-10-7(4)) Four Corners Publishing Co., Inc.

Ewing, Lynne. Divine One. 2nd rev. ed. 2007. (Sisters of Isis Ser.: No. 2). 272p. (gr. 7 up). 9.99 ***(978-1-4231-0343-1(2))*** Hyperion Pr.

—The Summoning. 2007. (Sisters of Isis Ser.: No. 1). 272p. (gr. 7 up). 9.99 ***(978-1-4231-0342-4(4))*** Hyperion Pr.

Fisher, Anne. Look What Brains Can Do! 2005. reprint ed. pap. 20.95 (978-1-4179-9453-3(3)) Kessinger Publishing, LLC.

Franklin, Kristine L. Cuss. 2007. (Illus.). 320p. (J). (gr. 5-8). 6.99 ***(978-0-7636-2362-3(8))*** Candlewick Pr.

Frederick, Heather Vogel. The Black Paw. Comport, Sally Wern, illus. (Spy Mice Ser.). (J). 2006. 256p. pap. 5.99 (978-1-4169-2770-9(0) , Aladdin); 2006. 256p. pap. 2.99 (978-1-4169-2502-6(3) , Aladdin); 2005. 240p. 9.95 (978-0-689-87753-7(6) , Simon & Schuster Children's Publishing) Simon & Schuster Children's Publishing.

Furtney, Charles S. Tryconnel: An Antebellum Adventure along the C & O Canal. 2004. (Illus.). iii, 156p. (J). pap. (978-0-9711835-3-7(8)) Local History Co., The.

Goldsberry, Booty. Scaredy-Cat, I'm Not. 2007. (Illus.). 40p. pap. 9.95 ***(978-0-9792875-0-3(2))*** Goldsberry, Booty.

Grisham, John. The Street Lawyer. 1999. (gr. 7-12). lib. bdg. 16.45 (978-0-613-12332-7(8)) Tandem Library Bks.

Harness, Cheryl. Ghosts of the White House. Harness, Cheryl, illus. 2002. (Illus.). 48p. (J). (gr. 2-5). pap. 7.99 (978-0-689-84892-6(7) , Aladdin) Simon & Schuster Children's Publishing.

—Ghosts of the White House. 2001. (gr. 3-6). lib. bdg. 15.30 (978-0-613-45047-8(7)) Tandem Library Bks.

Hope, Laura Lee. The Bobbsey Twins' Adventure in Washington, Vol. 12. 2004. (Bobbsey Twins Ser.: Vol. 12). (Illus.). 182p. (J). (gr. 3-8). 5.99 (978-0-448-43763-7(5) , Grosset & Dunlap) Penguin Group (USA) Inc.

Hope, Laura Lee. Bobbsey Twins in Washington. 2006. 62.99 ***(978-1-4280-2468-7(9))*** IndyPublish.com.

Jackson, Venna. The Realm of Beyond. 2002. 252p. (YA). pap. 16.50 (978-0-9722808-3-9(9)) Bighorn Publishing.

Jolin, Dominique. Merry Christmas, Washington! Perkes, Carolyn, tr. from FRE. 2000. (Illus.). 16p. (J). (ps-k). bds. (978-1-894363-61-1(9)) Dominique & Friends.

—Washington Loves Washington. Perkes, Carolyn, tr. from FRE. 2000. (Illus.). 16p. (J). (ps). bds. (978-1-894363-62-4(0)) Dominique & Friends.

Keffer, Ann. The Seventh Chair. 2007. 76p. (J). per. 8.95 ***(978-0-595-45917-9(X))*** iUniverse, Inc.

Kelly, Katy. Busy Like You Can't Believe. Rex, Adam, illus. 2006. (Lucy Rose Ser.). 176p. (J). (gr. 3-7). 12.95 (978-0-385-73319-9(4) , Delacorte Bks. for Young Readers) Random Hse. Children's Bks.

—Lucy Rose: Big on Plans. Rex, Adam, illus. 2005. 176p. (gr. 3-7). (J). 12.95 (978-0-385-73204-8(X)); lib. bdg. 14.99 (978-0-385-90235-9(2)) Random Hse. Children's Bks. (Delacorte Bks. for Young Readers).

—Lucy Rose: Here's the Thing about Me. Rex, Adam, illus. (J). (gr. 3-7). 2004. 144p. 12.95 (978-0-385-73203-1(1) , Delacorte Bks. for Young Readers); 2004. 144p. lib. bdg. 14.99 (978-0-385-90234-2(4) , Delacorte Bks. for Young Readers); 2006. 160p. reprint ed. 5.99 (978-0-440-42026-2(1) , Yearling) Random Hse. Children's Bks.

—Lucy Rose: Working Myself to Pieces & Bits. Ferguson, Peter, illus. 2007. (J). (gr. 3-7). 208p. 12.99 ***(978-0-385-73408-0(5));*** 128p. lib. bdg. 15.99 ***(978-0-385-90425-4(8))*** Random Hse. Children's Bks. (Delacorte Bks. for Young Readers).

—Lucy Rose: Big on Plans. Rex, Adam, illus. 2007. 192p. (gr. 3-5). 5.50 (978-0-440-42027-9(X) , Yearling) Random Hse. Children's Bks.

—Lucy Rose: Busy Like You Can't Believe. Rex, Adam, illus. 2006. 176p. (J). (gr. 3-7). lib. bdg. 14.99 (978-0-385-90338-7(3) , Delacorte Bks. for Young Readers) Random Hse. Children's Bks.

Labrecque, Candida. A Riverside Walk with Grandma. Labrecque, Candida, illus. l.t. ed. 2006. (Illus.). 23p. (J). per. 11.95 (978-1-59879-137-2(0)) Lifevest Publishing, Inc.

Lasky, Kathryn. A Time for Courage: The Suffragette Diary of Kathleen Bowen, Washington D. C., 1917. 2002. (Dear America Ser.). (Illus.). 176p. (J). (gr. 4-9). pap. 10.95 (978-0-590-51141-4(6)) Scholastic, Inc.

Lindbergh, Anne M. The People in Pineapple Place. 2003. (Illus.). 192p. (J). (gr. 3-7). pap. 5.99 (978-0-7636-1739-4(3)) Candlewick Pr.

—People in Pineapple Place. 2003. (gr. 3-6). lib. bdg. 14.15 (978-0-613-70998-9(5)) Tandem Library Bks.

McMullan, Kate. Fluffy Goes to Washington. Smith, Mavis, illus. 2002. (Hello Reader! Level 3 Ser.). (J). 3.99 (978-0-439-31943-0(9)) Scholastic, Inc.

McPherson, Missie & O'Neill, Elizabeth. Alfred Visits Washington D. C. 2006. 24p. (J). pap. 12.00 (978-0-9771836-1-6(0)) Funny Bone Bks.

Mills, Charles. Stranger in the Shadows. 1998. (Shadow Creek Ranch Ser.: Vol. 11). 151p. (Orig.). (J). (gr. 4-7). pap. 5.99 (978-0-8280-1316-1(0)) Review & Herald Publishing Assn.

Myers, Anna. Assassin. 2007. 224p. (YA). pap. 6.95 ***(978-0-8027-9643-1(5));*** 2005. (J). (978-978-080-278-3(9)); 2005. 192p. (YA). (gr. 7 up). 16.95 (978-0-8027-8989-1(7)) Walker & Co.

Osborne, Mary Pope. After the Rain Bk. 2: Virginia's Civil War Diary. 2002. (My America Ser.). 112p. (J). (gr. 2-5). pap. 10.95 (978-0-439-20138-4(1)); (Illus.). pap. 4.99 (978-0-439-36904-6(5)) Scholastic, Inc. (Scholastic Pr.).

Quattlebaum, Mary. Underground Train. Smith, Cat Bowman, illus. 1999. (J). (ps-ps). lib. bdg. 12.54 (978-0-606-20025-7(8)) Tandem Library Bks.

Rinaldi, Ann. An Acquaintance with Darkness. 1999. (J). 12.65 (978-0-606-16525-9(8)) Tandem Library Bks.

—Girl in Blue. 2005. 320p. (J). pap. 5.99 (978-0-439-67646-5(0) , Scholastic Paperbacks) Scholastic, Inc.

Roitman, Tanya, illus. I'm Going to Read (Level 1): I'm Going to Washington to Visit the President. 2006. (I'm Going to Read Ser.). 24p. (J). pap. 3.95 (978-1-4027-3408-3(5)) Sterling Publishing Co., Inc.

Roosevelt, Anna. Scamper: Bunny Who Went to the White House. Flack, Marjorie, illus. 2000. 72p. (J). (gr. 3-6). pap. 11.95 (978-1-888683-20-2(1)) Wooster Bk. Co., The.

Roy, Ron. Mystery at the Washington Monument. Bush, Timothy, illus. 2007. (Capital Mysteries Ser.: No. 8). 96p. (J). (gr. 2-6). 3.99 (978-0-375-83970-2(4)); lib. bdg. 11.99 (978-0-375-93970-9(9)) Random Hse. Children's Bks. (Random Hse. Bks. for Young Readers).

—The Skeleton in the Smithsonian. 2003. (Capital Mysteries Ser.: Vol. 3). (Illus.). 96p. (J). (gr. 2-5). lib. bdg. 11.99 (978-0-307-46517-7(9) , Random Hse. Bks. for Young Readers) Random Hse. Children's Bks.

—The Skeleton in the Smithsonian. Bush, Timothy, illus. 2003. (Capital Mysteries Ser.: Vol. 3). 96p. (J). (gr. 2-5). 3.99 (978-0-307-26517-3(X) , Random Hse. Bks. for Young Readers) Random Hse. Children's Bks.

—A Spy in the White House. Bush, Timothy, tr. Bush, Timothy, illus. 2004. (Capital Mysteries Ser.: Vol. 4). 96p. (J). (gr. 1-4). pap. 3.99 (978-0-375-82557-6(6)); lib. bdg. 11.99 (978-0-375-92557-3(0)) Random Hse. Children's Bks. (Random Hse. Bks. for Young Readers).

—Trouble at the Treasury. Bush, Timothy, illus. 2006. (Capital Mysteries Ser.: No. 7). 96p. (J). (gr. 2-4). pap. 3.99 (978-0-375-83969-6(0) , Random Hse. Bks. for Young Readers) Random Hse. Children's Bks.

—Who Broke Lincoln's Thumb? Bush, Timothy, illus. 2005. (Capital Mysteries Ser.: Vol. 5). 96p. (J). lib. bdg. 11.99 (978-0-375-92558-0(9) , Random Hse. Bks. for Young Readers) Random Hse. Children's Bks.

—Who Broke Lincoln's Thumb. Bush, Timothy, illus. 2005. (Capital Mysteries Ser.: Vol. 5). 96p. (J). (gr. 2-4). pap. 3.99 (978-0-375-82558-3(4) , Random Hse. Bks. for Young Readers) Random Hse. Children's Bks.

Sappey, Maureen. Letters from Vinnie. 2007. 248p. (J). (gr. 4-6). pap. 10.95 ***(978-1-59078-538-6(X))*** Boyds Mills Pr.

Sargent, Dave & Sargent, Pat. Whiskers: (Roan) Pride & Peace, 30, 59. Lenoir, Jane, illus. 2002. (Saddle Up Ser.: Vol. 59). 42p. (J). lib. bdg. 22.60 (978-1-56763-805-9(8)) Ozark Publishing.

Schneider, Howie. Wilky the White House Cockroach. Schneider, Howie, illus. 2006. (Illus.). 32p. (J). (ps-3). 16.99 (978-0-399-24388-2(7)) Penguin Group (USA) Inc.

Sisters of Isis3 & Ewing, Lynne. Enchantress. 3rd rev. ed. 2007. 256p. (gr. 7 up). 9.99 ***(978-1-4231-0684-5(9))*** Hyperion Bks. for Children.

St. George, Judith. The Ghost, the White House, & Me. 2007. 128p. (J). (gr. 3-7). 16.95 (978-0-8234-2045-2(0)) Holiday Hse., Inc.

Stine, Megan. Prom Night: Making Out. 2006. 256p. (YA). (gr. 12). pap. 9.99 (978-0-425-21179-3(7) , Berkley Trade) Penguin Group (USA) Inc.

Weitzman, Jacqueline Preiss. You Can't Take a Balloon into the National Gallery. Glasser, Robin Preiss, illus. 2002. 40p. (J). pap. 7.99 (978-0-14-230131-9(0) , Puffin) Penguin Group (USA) Inc.

—You Can't Take a Balloon into the National Gallery. 2002. (ps-2). lib. bdg. 16.45 (978-0-613-83550-3(6)) Tandem Library Bks.

WASHINGTON (D.C.)—HISTORY

Ashabranner, Brent. The Washington Monument: A Beacon for America. Ashabranner, Jennifer, photos by. 2002. (Great American Memorials Ser.). (Illus.). 64p. (gr. 4-8). lib. bdg. 25.90 (978-0-7613-1524-7(1) , Twenty-First Century Bks.) Lerner Publishing Group.

Ashabranner, Jennifer & Ashabranner, Brent. No Better Hope: What the Lincoln Memorial Means to America. 2001. (Great American Memorials Ser.). (Illus.). 64p. (J). (gr. 4-8). lib. bdg. 25.90 (978-0-7613-1523-0(3) , Twenty-First Century Bks.) Lerner Publishing Group.

Benson, Laura Lee. Washington, D. C. A Scrapbook. Van Rynbach, Iris, illus. 1999. 32p. (J). (ps-3). 15.95 (978-0-88106-064-5(X)); pap. 6.95 (978-0-88106-063-8(1)) Charlesbridge Publishing, Inc.

Binns, Tristan Boyer. El Capitolio. 2003. (Simbolos de Libertad Ser.).Tr. of Capitol. (SPA., Illus.). 32p. (J). lib. bdg. 22.79 (978-1-4034-3000-7(4)) Heinemann Library.

Britton, Tamara L. The Capitol. 2005. (Checkerboard History Library). (Illus.). 40p. (J). (gr. k-6). lib. bdg. 22.78 (978-1-57765-848-1(5)) ABDO Publishing Co.

—World War II Memorial. 2005. (Illus.). 32p. (J). (gr. k-6). lib. bdg. 22.78 (978-1-59197-837-4(8)) ABDO Publishing Co.

Brown, Don. Dolley Madison Saves George Washington. 2007. 32p. (J). (gr. k-3). 16.00 (978-0-618-41199-3(2)) Houghton Mifflin Co.

Carole Marsh. Washington Dc Coloring & Activity Book. 2004. (City Bks.). 24p. (gr. k-5). pap. 3.95 (978-0-635-02232-5(X)) Gallopade International.

—Washington Indians. 2004. (Washington Experienc Ser.). lib. bdg. 29.95 (978-0-635-02339-1(3)); 36p. (gr. 3-8). pap. 7.95 (978-0-635-02338-4(5)) Gallopade International.

Cunningham, Alvin Robert. Washington Is Burning! The War of 1812. 2003. (Reading Essentials in Social Studies). (Illus.). 48p. (J). (978-0-7891-5896-3(5)) Perfection Learning Corp.

Figley, Marty Rhodes. Washington Is Burning. Orback, Craig, illus. 2006. (On My Own History Ser.). 48p. (J). 25.26 (978-1-57505-875-7(8)) Lerner Publishing Group.

Hanstick, Kevin R., illus. My Trip to Washington DC. 2005. 81p. (J). (ps-7). spiral bd. 14.95 (978-1-58980-360-2(4)) Pelican Publishing Co., Inc.

Harper, Kristine. The Mount St. Helens Volcanic Eruption. 2005. (Environmental Disasters Ser.). (Illus.). 112p. (J). (gr. 6-12). 35.00 (978-0-8160-5757-3(5)) Facts On File, Inc.

Hopkinson, Deborah. Sweet Land of Liberty. Jenkins, Leonard, illus. 2007. 32p. (J). (gr. 1-5). 16.95 (978-1-56145-395-5(1) , Peachtree Junior) Peachtree Pubs., Ltd.

Ingram, Scott. The 1963 Civil Rights March. 2004. (Landmark Events in American History Ser.). (Illus.). 48p. (J). 11.95 (978-0-8368-5420-6(9)); lib. bdg. 30.00 (978-0-8368-5392-6(X)) Stevens, Gareth Inc. (World Almanac Library).

Mattern, Joanne. The White House. 2005. (Building World Landmarks Ser.). (Illus.). 48p. (J). (gr. 4-7). lib. bdg. 24.95 (978-1-4103-0561-9(9) , Blackbirch Pr., Inc.) Thomson Gale.

Nelson, Kristin L. Washington Monument. 2004. (gr. k-3). lib. bdg. 14.10 (978-0-613-84028-6(3)) Tandem Library Bks.

O'Connor, Jane. If the Walls Could Talk: Family Life at the White House. Hovland, Gary, illus. 2004. 48p. (J). 16.95 (978-0-689-86863-4(4) , Simon & Schuster/Paula Wiseman Bks.) Simon & Schuster Children's Publishing.

O'Shei, Tim. Volcanic Eruption! Susan Ruff & Bruce Nelson's Story of Survival. 2007. 32p. (J). (978-0-7368-6779-5(1)) Capstone Pr., Inc.

Owens, Tom. Washington, D.C. 2003. (Reading Essentials in Social Studies). (Illus.). 48p. (J). pap. (978-0-7891-5839-0(6)) Perfection Learning Corp.

Robinson, Kate. The National Mall: A MyReportLinks.com Book. 2005. (Virtual Field Trips Ser.). (Illus.). 48p. (J). (gr. 4-10). lib. bdg. 25.26 (978-0-7660-5222-2(2) , MyReportLinks.com Bks.) Enslow Pubs., Inc.

Rosinsky, Natalie M. Vietnam Veterans Memorial. 2006. (J). (978-0-7565-2032-8(0)) Compass Point Bks.

Ruffin, Frances E. The Lincoln Memorial. 2006. (Illus.). 24p. (J). pap. (978-0-8368-6418-2(2)); lib. bdg. 19.33 (978-0-8368-6411-3(5)) Stevens, Gareth Inc.

Santella, Andrew. The Library of Congress. 2006. (Illus.). 48p. (J). (gr. 4-6). 23.93 (978-0-7565-1631-4(5)) Compass Point Bks.

Schaefer, A. Ted & Schaefer, Lola M. The National World War II Memorial. 2005. (Symbols of Freedom Ser.). (Illus.). 32p. (J). pap. (978-1-4034-6667-9(X)) Heinemann Library.

W X Y Z

—The National World War II Memorial. 2005. (Symbols of Freedom Ser.). (Illus.). 32p. (J). (gr. k-2). lib. bdg. 25.36 (978-1-4034-6658-7(0)) Heinemann Library.

Schaefer, Ted & Schaefer, Lola. The Franklin Delano Roosevelt Memorial. 2005. (Symbols of Freedom Ser.). (Illus.). 32p. (J). (gr. k-2). lib. bdg. 25.36 (978-1-4034-6661-7(0)) Heinemann Library.

—The Thomas Jefferson Memorial. 2005. (Symbols of Freedom Ser.). (Illus.). 32p. (J). (gr. k-2). lib. bdg. 25.36 (978-1-4034-6660-0(2)) Heinemann Library.

—The Vietnam Veterans Memorial. 2005. (Symbols of Freedom Ser.). (Illus.). 32p. (J). (gr. 1-3). lib. bdg. 25.36 (978-1-4034-6659-4(9)) Heinemann Library.

Schaefer, Ted & Schaefer, Lola M. The Franklin Delano Roosevelt Memorial. 2005. (Symbols of Freedom Ser.). (Illus.). 32p. (J). pap. (978-1-4034-6670-9(X)) Heinemann Library.

—The Thomas Jefferson Memorial. 2005. (Symbols of Freedom Ser.). (Illus.). 32p. (J). pap. (978-1-4034-6669-3(6)) Heinemann Library.

—The Vietnam Veterans Memorial. 2005. (Symbols of Freedom Ser.). (Illus.). 31p. (J). pap. (978-1-4034-6668-6(8)) Heinemann Library.

Schultz, Randy. Washington Ablaze: The War of 1812. 2007. (Events in American History Ser.). (Illus.). 48p. (J). (gr. 4-6). lib. bdg. 29.93 (978-1-60044-137-0(8)) Rourke Publishing, LLC.

Smalley, Roger. Dolley Madison Saves History. Cool, Anna-Maria et al, illus. 2005. (Graphic Library). 32p. (J). (gr. 3-7). lib. bdg. 25.26 (978-0-7368-4972-2(6)) Capstone Pr., Inc.

Symbols of Freedom, 8 bks., Set 3. Incl. Alamo. Schaefer, Ted & Schaefer, Lola M. lib. bdg. 25.36 (978-1-4034-6662-4(9)); Arlington National Cemetery. Schaefer, Ted & Schaefer, Lola M. (gr. 1-3). lib. bdg. 25.36 (978-1-4034-6665-5(3)); Franklin Delano Roosevelt Memorial. Schaefer, Ted & Schaefer, Lola. (gr. k-2). lib. bdg. 25.36 (978-1-4034-6661-7(0)); Independence Hall. Schaefer, Ted & Schaefer, Lola M. (gr. 1-3). lib. bdg. 25.36 (978-1-4034-6664-8(5)); National World War II Memorial. Schaefer, A. Ted & Schaefer, Lola M. (gr. k-2). lib. bdg. 25.36 (978-1-4034-6658-7(0)); Pentagon. Schaefer, Ted & Schaefer, Lola. (gr. 1-3). lib. bdg. 25.36 (978-1-4034-6663-1(7)); Thomas Jefferson Memorial. Schaefer, Ted & Schaefer, Lola. (gr. k-2). lib. bdg. 25.36 (978-1-4034-6660-0(2)); Vietnam Veterans Memorial. Schaefer, Ted & Schaefer, Lola. (gr. 1-3). lib. bdg. 25.36 (978-1-4034-6659-4(9)); (Illus.). (J). 2005. (Symbols of Freedom Ser.). 32p. 2005. Set lib. bdg. 202.86 (978-1-4034-6666-2(1)) Heinemann Library.

Washington Is Burning. 2007. (J). pap. 5.95 ***978-0-8225-6050-0(X)*** , First Avenue Editions) Lerner Publishing Group.

WASHINGTON (D.C.)—WHITE HOUSE

see White House (Washington, D.C.)

WASHINGTON (STATE)

Barenblat, Rachel. Washington: The Evergreen State. 2002. (World Almanac Library of the States). (Illus.). 48p. (J). (gr. 5 up). pap. 14.95 (978-0-8368-5294-3(X)); lib. bdg. 30.00 (978-0-8368-5122-9(6)) Stevens, Gareth Inc. (World Almanac Library).

—Washington: The Evergreen State. 2002. (gr. 5-8). lib. bdg. 24.15 (978-0-613-52524-4(8)) Tandem Library Bks.

Boekhoff, P. M. & Brown, Jonatha A. Washington. 2005. (Portraits of the States Ser.). (Illus.). 32p. (J). pap. (978-0-8368-4656-0(7)); lib. bdg. 23.33 (978-0-8368-4637-9(0)) Stevens, Gareth Inc.

Capstone Press Staff, contrib. by. Washington. rev. ed. 2002. (One Nation Ser.). (Illus.). 48p. (J). (gr. 3-4). lib. bdg. 22.60 (978-0-7368-1272-6(5) , Bridgestone Bks.) Capstone Pr., Inc.

Covert, Kim. Washington. 2003. (Land of Liberty Ser.). (Illus.). 64p. (J). lib. bdg. 25.26 (978-0-7368-2203-9(8)) Capstone Pr., Inc.

Feinstein, Stephen. Washington: A MyReportLinks.com Book. 2003. (States Ser.). (Illus.). 48p. (J). (gr. 4-10). lib. bdg. 25.26 (978-0-7660-5026-6(2) , MyReportLinks.com Bks.) Enslow Pubs., Inc.

Green, Jen. Mount St. Helens. 2005. (Illus.). 32p. (J). lib. bdg. 24.67 (978-0-8368-4498-6(X)) Stevens, Gareth Inc.

Heinrichs, Ann. Washington. Kania, Matt, illus. 2005. (Welcome to the USA Ser.). 40p. (J). (gr. 1-5). 27.07 (978-1-59296-489-5(3)) Child's World, Inc.

Hood, Karen Jean Matsko. Washington State: Activity & Coloring Book. Parker, Michael, illus. l.t. ed. 2001. (Educational Activity & Coloring Book Ser.). 160p. (J). 9.95 (978-1-930948-56-3(5)) Whispering Pine Pr., Inc.

Johns, Linda. Uniquely Washington. 2003. (State Studies). (Illus.). 48p. (J). pap. 8.50 (978-1-4034-4513-1(3)); lib. bdg. 27.07 (978-1-4034-4498-1(6)) Heinemann Library.

Kortes-Erkkila, Helmi. Before Modern Conveniences: One Finnish Farm Family 1917-1927. Meier, Lynne, illus. 2004. 176p. (J). pap. 14.95 (978-1-58736-271-2(6) , Hats Off Bks.) Wheatmark.

Labella, Susan. Washington. 2006. (Rookie Read-About Geography Ser.). (Illus.). 32p. (J). (gr. 1-2). 20.50 (978-0-516-24993-3(2) , Children's Pr.) Scholastic Library Publishing.

Leigh, Autumn. Warning: Volcano! The Story of Mount St. Helens. 2002. (Reading Room Collection). (Illus.). 24p. (J). pap. 4.40 (978-0-8239-8157-1(6)); lib. bdg. 18.75 (978-0-8239-3720-2(8)) Rosen Publishing Group, Inc., The.

Marsh, Carole. The Survivor: A Class Challenge. 2001. (Washington Experience! Ser.). lib. bdg. 29.95 (978-0-635-00693-6(6)) Gallopade International.

—Washington Classic Christmas Trivia. 2002. (Carole Marsh Washington Bks.). (Illus.). 32p. pap. 6.95 (978-0-635-01459-7(9) , 14599, Marsh, Carole Bks.) Gallopade International.

—Washington Current Events Projects: 30 Cool, Activities, Crafts, Experiments & More for Kids to Do to Learn about Your State! 2003. (Washington Experience Ser.). 32p. (gr. k-8). pap. 5.95 (978-0-635-02066-6(1) , Marsh, Carole Bks.) Gallopade International.

—Washington Geography Projects: 30 Cool, Activities, Crafts, Experiments & More for Kids to Do to Learn about Your State! 2003. (Washington Experience Ser.). 32p. (gr. k-5). pap. 5.95 (978-0-635-01865-6(9) , Marsh, Carole Bks.) Gallopade International.

—Washington Government Projects: 30 Cool, Activities, Crafts, Experiments & More for Kids to Do to Learn about Your State! 2003. (Washington Experience Ser.). 32p. (gr. k-5). pap. 5.95 (978-0-635-01966-0(3) , Marsh, Carole Bks.) Gallopade International.

—Washington Millionaire. 2001. (GameBook Ser.). (Illus.). 32p. (J). (gr. 3-8). pap., act. bk. ed. 9.95 (978-0-635-00110-8(1)) Gallopade International.

—Washington People Projects: 30 Cool, Activities, Crafts, Experiments & More for Kids to Do to Learn about Your State! 2003. (Washington Experience Ser.). 32p. (gr. k-5). pap. 5.95 (978-0-635-02016-1(5) , Marsh, Carole Bks.) Gallopade International.

—Washington Symbols & Facts Projects: 30 Cool, Activities, Crafts, Experiments & More for Kids to Do to Learn about Your State! 2003. (Washington Experience Ser.). 32p. (gr. k-5). pap. 5.95 (978-0-635-01916-5(7) , Marsh, Carole Bks.) Gallopade International.

—Washington Wheel of Fortune. 2001. (GameBook Ser.). (Illus.). 32p. (J). (gr. 3-8). pap., act. bk. ed. 9.95 (978-0-635-00010-1(5)) Gallopade International.

—Who Wants to Be a Millionaire? 2001. (Carole Marsh Washington Bks.). lib. bdg. 29.95 (978-0-635-00111-5(X)) Gallopade International.

McAuliffe, Emily. Washington Facts & Symbols. (States & Their Symbols Ser.). 24p. (J). 1998. (Illus.). (gr. 2-3). lib. bdg. 18.60 (978-0-7368-0087-7(5) , Bridgestone Bks.); 2003. lib. bdg. 19.93 (978-0-7368-2277-0(1)) Capstone Pr., Inc.

Murray, Julie. Washington. 2006. (Buddy Book Ser.). (Illus.). 32p. (J). (gr. k-4). lib. bdg. 22.78 (978-1-59197-706-3(1) , Buddy Bks.) ABDO Publishing Co.

Otfinoski, Steven. Washington. 2003. (It's My State! Ser.). (Illus.). 80p. (J). 27.07 (978-0-7614-1522-0(X) , Benchmark Bks.) Cavendish, Marshall Corp.

Pascoe, Elaine, ed. World's Largest Building. 2003. (Super Structures of the World Ser.). (Illus.). 48p. (J). 24.95 (978-1-56711-871-1(2)); 11.20 (978-1-4103-0187-1(7)) Thomson Gale. (Blackbirch Pr., Inc.).

Powell, E. Sandy. Washington. 2nd exp. rev. ed. (Hello U. S. A. Ser.). (Illus.). 84p. (J). (gr. 3-6). 2003. pap. 6.95 (978-0-8225-4155-4(6)); 2002. 25.26 (978-0-8225-4053-3(3) , Lerner Pubns.) Lerner Publishing Group.

Sayres, Meghan Nuttall. The Shape of Betts Meadow: A Wetlands Story. Friar, Joanne, illus. 2002. 32p. (ps-3). lib. bdg. 22.90 (978-0-7613-2115-6(2) , Millbrook Pr.) Lerner Publishing Group.

Smith, Roland & Smith, Marie. E Is for Evergreen: A Washington State Alphabet. Holt Ayriss, Linda, illus. 2004. (State Ser.). 40p. (J). 17.95 (978-1-58536-143-4(7)) Sleeping Bear Pr.

Stefoff, Rebecca. Washington. (Celebrate the States Ser.). 1998. (Illus.). 144p. (gr. 4-8). lib. bdg. 37.07 (978-0-7614-0422-4(8)); 2nd ed. 2007. (J). lib. bdg. 39.93 ***978-0-7614-2561-8(6))*** Cavendish, Marshall Corp. (Benchmark Bks.).

Strudwick, Leslie. A Guide to Washington. 2001. (American States Ser.). 32p. (J). (Illus.). (gr. 4-7). lib. bdg. 16.95 (978-1-930954-95-3(6)); per. 7.95 (978-1-930954-62-5(X)) Weigl Pubs., Inc.

Webster, Christine. Washington. 2003. (Geography Ser.: 2). (Illus.). 80p. (J). 30.50 (978-0-516-22386-5(0) , Children's Pr.) Scholastic Library Publishing.

Weintraub, Aileen. Cape Disappointment Light: The First Lighthouse in the Pacific Northwest. 2003. (Great Lighthouses of North America Ser.). (Illus.). 24p. (J). pap. 18.75 (978-0-8239-6172-6(9) , PowerKids Pr.) Rosen Publishing Group, Inc., The.

Womack, Randy L. Washington Geography. 1998. (Illus.). 80p. (YA). (gr. 4 up). stu. ed. 8.95 (978-1-56500-036-0(6)) Golden Educational Ctr.

Wright-Frierson, Virginia. A North American Rain Forest Scrapbook. Wright-Frierson, Virginia, illus. 2003. (Illus.). 40p. (J). (gr. 1-5). pap. 8.95 (978-0-8027-7651-8(5)) Walker & Co.

WASHINGTON (STATE)—FICTION

Boutwell, Florence. Love According to Teresa. Ivie, Janet, illus. 2000. 190p. (J). (978-0-87062-298-4(6) , Clark, Arthur H. Co., The) Univ. of Oklahoma Pr.

—Teresa of Northwood Prairie: An Historical Adventure Story for Young & Old. Haff, Monica, illus. 1998. 175p. (J). 17.95 (978-0-87062-284-7(6) , Clark, Arthur H. Co., The) Univ. of Oklahoma Pr.

Caletti, Deb. The Fortunes of Indigo Skye. 2008. 304p. (YA). 15.99 ***978-1-4169-1007-7(7)*** , Simon & Schuster Children's Publishing) Simon & Schuster Children's Publishing.

—The Queen of Everything. 2002. 384p. (YA). (gr. 9 up). pap. 6.99 (978-0-7434-3684-7(9) , Simon Pulse) Simon & Schuster Children's Publishing.

—Wild Roses. (YA). (gr. 7 up). 2006. 320p. pap. 6.99 (978-0-689-86475-9(2) , Simon Pulse); 2005. 304p. 15.95 (978-0-689-86766-8(2)) Simon & Schuster Children's Publishing.

Deuker, Carl. Gym Candy. 2007. 320p. (J). (gr. 7 up). 16.00 ***978-0-618-77713-6(X))*** Houghton Mifflin Co. Trade & Reference Div.

Drake, Jane & Love, Ann. Forestry. Cupples, Pat, illus. (America at Work Ser.). (J). 2002. 32p. (gr. k-3). (978-1-55074-462-0(3)); 2000. 118p. (gr. 2-5). (978-1-55074-819-2(X)) Kids Can Pr., Ltd.

Duey, Kathleen. Josie Poe Palouse: Washington, 1943. 1999. (American Diaries Ser.: No. 13). (J). (gr. 3-7). 11.64 (978-0-606-16304-0(2)) Tandem Library Bks.

Franklin, Kristine L. Grape Thief. 2003. (Illus.). 304p. (J). (gr. 5-8). 16.99 (978-0-7636-1325-9(8)) Candlewick Pr.

Frazier, Sundee Tucker. Brendan Buckley's Universe & Everything in It. 2007. 208p. (J). (gr. 4-7). 14.99 ***978-0-385-73439-4(5));*** lib. bdg. 17.99 ***978-0-385-90445-2(2))*** Random Hse. Children's Bks. (Delacorte Bks. for Young Readers).

Goode, Suzi. The Lost Wizard Series Bk 1. 2007. pap. 11.95 ***978-1-59374-817-3(5))*** Whiskey Creek Pr., LLC.

Hamilton, Richard & McCord, Patricia. Pictures in the Dark. 2004. (Illus.). 225p. (J). (gr. 5 up). 16.95 (978-1-58234-848-3(0) , Bloomsbury Children) Bloomsbury Publishing.

Henry, Chad. Dogbreath Victorious. 1999. 192p. (J). (gr. 7 up). tchr. ed. 16.95 (978-0-8234-1458-1(2)) Holiday Hse., Inc.

Holm, Jennifer L. An Adventure. 2002. (Boston Jane Ser.). 288p. (J). (gr. k-17). pap. 6.99 (978-0-06-440849-3(3)) HarperCollins Pubs.

—Boston Jane. 2002. (gr. 3-6). lib. bdg. 15.30 (978-0-613-56251-5(8)) Tandem Library Bks.

—Our Only May Amelia. (Harper Trophy Bks.). (Illus.). (J). 2001. 272p. (gr. 4 up). pap. 5.99 (978-0-06-440856-1(6) , Harper Trophy); 1999. 253p. (gr. k-9). per. 15.89 (978-0-06-028354-4(8)); 1999. 272p. (gr. 4 up). 18.99 (978-0-06-027822-9(6)) HarperCollins Pubs.

—Our Only May Amelia. unabr. ed. 2004. 253p. (J). (gr. 5-9). pap. 36.00 incl. audio (978-0-8072-8366-0(5) , YA191SP, Listening Library) Random Hse. Audio Publishing Group.

—Our Only May Amelia. 2001. (Illus.). (J). (gr. k-9). 251p. lib. bdg. 14.15 (978-0-613-35995-5(X)); (978-0-606-21371-4(6)) Tandem Library Bks.

—Our Only May Amelia. l.t. ed. 2000. (Illus.). 261p. (J). (ps up). 21.95 (978-0-7862-2742-6(7)) Thorndike Pr.

—Wilderness Days. (Boston Jane Ser.). 256p. (J). (gr. 5 up). 2004. pap. 5.99 (978-0-06-440881-3(7) , Harper Trophy); 2002. 16.99 (978-0-06-029043-6(9)); 2002. lib. bdg. 18.89 (978-0-06-029044-3(7)) HarperCollins Pubs.

Holsather, Kent. Henry of York: The Secret of Juan de Vega. Holsather, Bill, illus. 2003. 176p. (YA). (gr. 5 up). 22.95 (978-0-9729101-0-1(7)); 2nd ed. per. 12.95 (978-0-9729101-1-8(5)) Lonejack Mountain Pr.

Jackson, Dave & Jackson, Neta. Exiled to the Red River: Chief Spokane Garry. 2003. (Trailblazer Bks.). (Illus.). 144p. (J). pap. 6.99 (978-0-7642-2235-1(X)) Bethany Hse. Pubs.

Kehret, Peg. The Ghost's Grave. 224p. 2007. pap. 5.99 ***978-0-14-280819-1(9)*** , Puffin); 2007. (YA). (gr. 5). 5.99 (978-0-14-240819-3(0) , Puffin); 2005. (J). (gr. 5). 16.99 (978-0-525-46162-3(0) , Dutton Juvenile) Penguin Group (USA) Inc.

Kehret, Peg. The Stranger Next Door. (J). 2003. (Illus.). 176p. (gr. 3-7). pap. 5.99 (978-0-14-250178-8(6) , Puffin); 2002. 160p. (gr. 4-8). 15.99 (978-0-525-46829-5(3) , Dutton Juvenile) Penguin Group (USA) Inc.

—The Stranger Next Door. 2003. (gr. 5-8). lib. bdg. 14.15 (978-0-613-82994-6(8)) Tandem Library Bks.

Meyer, Stephenie. Twilight. 2005. (Twilight Saga Ser.). 512p. (J). (gr. 9-17). 18.99 (978-0-316-16017-9(2)) Little Brown & Co.

—Twilight. 2006. (Twilight Saga Ser.). 544p. (J). (gr. 9-12). reprint ed. pap. 9.99 (978-0-316-01584-4(9) , Tingley, Megan Bks.) Little, Brown Bks. for Young Readers.

Meyer, Stephenie. The Twilight Collection. rev. ed. 2007. (YA). (gr. 7-17). 55.00 ***978-0-316-00372-8(7))*** Little, Brown Bks. for Young Readers.

Patneaude, David. Deadly Drive. 184p. (J). 2007. pap. 6.95 ***978-0-8075-0845-9(4));*** 2005. (gr. 6-8). 15.95 (978-0-8075-0844-2(6)) Whitman, Albert & Co.

Pierson, Jan. The Carson Kids & the Mystery of Five Finger Island. 2000. (Carson Kids Ser.: Vol. 1). (Illus.). 128p. (gr. 4-7). pap. 9.95 (978-0-595-09075-4(3) , Backinprint.com) iUniverse, Inc.

Rallison, Janette. Revenge of the Cheerleaders. 2007. (Illus.). 247p. (YA). (gr. 7 up). 16.95 ***978-0-8027-8999-0(4))*** Walker & Co.

Reece, Colleen L. Saturday Scare. l.t. ed. 2002. (Juli Scott, Super Sleuth Ser.). (Illus.). 211p. (J). 24.95 (978-0-7862-3195-9(5)) Thomson Gale.

—Thursday Trials. 1998. (Juli Scott, Super Sleuth Ser.: Bk. 4). 176p. (J). (gr. 4-10). pap. 2.97 (978-1-57748-180-5(1)) Barbour Publishing, Inc.

—Thursday Trials. l.t. ed. 2001. (Juli Scott, Super Sleuth Ser.). (Illus.). 204p. (J). 23.95 (978-0-7862-3201-7(3)) Thorndike Pr.

Rushford, Patricia H. Secrets of Ghost Island. 2007. (J). ***978-88-02-46255-4(0))*** Moody Pubs.

Sargent, Dave & Sargent, Pat. Whiskers: (Roan) Pride & Peace, 30, 59. Lenoir, Jane, illus. 2003. (Saddle Up Ser.: Vol. 59). 42p. (J). pap. 6.95 (978-1-56763-806-6(0)) Ozark Publishing.

The Secret of Bunratty Castle: Individual Title Six-Packs. (Action Packs Ser.). 104p. (gr. 3-5). 44.00 (978-0-7635-3302-1(5)) Rigby Education.

Sullivan, Jaqueline Levering. Annie's War. 2007. 190p. (J). (gr. 3-7). 15.00 ***978-0-8028-5325-7(0)*** , Eerdmans Bks For Young Readers) Eerdmans, William B. Publishing Co.

Trueman, Terry. No Right Turn. 2006. 176p. (J). 16.99 (978-0-06-057491-8(7)); lib. bdg. 16.89 (978-0-06-057492-5(5)) HarperCollins Pubs. (HarperTeen).

Washington State: Activity & Coloring Book. 2005. (J). spiral bd. 15.95 (978-1-59649-434-3(4)) Whispering Pine Pr., Inc.

Washington State Adventures in Learning Book. 2005. (J). 15.95 (978-1-59210-336-2(7)) Whispering Pine Pr., Inc.

Washington State Story Book. 2005. (J). 15.95 (978-1-59649-435-0(2)) Whispering Pine Pr., Inc.

Wilsdon, Christina. On the Trail of Bigfoot in Washington. McCreary, Jane, illus. 2006. 26p. (J). 7.99 (978-1-59939-012-3(4) , Reader's Digest Young Families, Inc.) Reader's Digest Children's Publishing, Inc.

WASHINGTON (STATE)—HISTORY

Labella, Susan. Washington. 2006. 32p. (YA). (gr. 1-2). pap. 5.95 (978-0-516-26455-4(9) , Children's Pr.) Scholastic Library Publishing.

Marsh, Carole. My First Pocket Guide Washington. 2000. (Washington Experience! Ser.). (Illus.). 96p. (J). (gr. 3-8). 12.95 (978-0-635-01337-8(1) , 13371) Gallopade International.

—Washington History Projects: 30 Cool, Activities, Crafts, Experiments & More for Kids to Do to Learn about Your State! 2003. (Washington Experience Ser.). 32p. (gr. k-5). pap. 5.95 (978-0-635-01816-8(0) , Marsh, Carole Bks.) Gallopade International.

Pelz, Ruth. The Washington Adventure. 2003. (Illus.). 216p. (J). (978-0-87905-986-6(9)) Gibbs Smith, Publisher.

Way, Jennifer. Washington. 2006. (Bilingual Library of the United States of America: Set 2). (ENG & SPA., Illus.). 32p. (J). (gr. 3-6). lib. bdg. 22.50 (978-1-4042-3113-9(7) , Buenas Letra) Rosen Publishing Group, Inc., The.

The Wonderful Washington Events Guide, 2006. 2005. (YA). per. 21.95 (978-1-881005-49-0(6)) Gail's Guides.

WASHINGTON MONUMENT (WASHINGTON, D.C.)

Ashabranner, Brent. The Washington Monument: A Beacon for America. Ashabranner, Jennifer, photos by. 2002. (Great American Memorials Ser.). (Illus.). 64p. (gr. 4-8). lib. bdg. 25.90 (978-0-7613-1524-7(1) , Twenty-First Century Bks.) Lerner Publishing Group.

Ashley, Susan. The Washington Monument. 2004. (Weekly Reader Early Learning Library). (Illus.). 24p. (J). (gr. 2 up). pap. 5.95 (978-0-8368-4151-0(4)); lib. bdg. 19.33 (978-0-8368-4144-2(1)) Stevens, Gareth Inc. (Weekly Reader Early Learning Library).

Hargrove, Julia. Washington Monument. Mitchell, Judy, ed. Mohrman, Gary, illus. 2001. (Historic Monuments Ser.). 48p. (J). (gr. 4-8). pap. 6.95 (978-1-57310-284-1(9)) Teaching & Learning Co.

Landau, Elaine. The Washington Monument. 2004. (Cornerstones of Freedom Ser.). (J). 26.00 (978-0-516-24238-5(5) , Children's Pr.) Scholastic Library Publishing.

Marcovitz, Hal. The Washington Monument. 2002. (American Symbols & Their Meanings Ser.). (Illus.). 48p. (YA). (gr. 4 up). lib. bdg. (978-1-59084-028-3(3)) Mason Crest Pubs.

Murray, Julie. Washington Monument. 2005. (Buddy Book Ser.). (Illus.). 24p. (J). (gr. k-4). lib. bdg. 21.35 (978-1-59197-509-0(3)) ABDO Publishing Co.

Nelson, Kristin L. The Washington Monument. (Pull Ahead Bks.). 32p. (J). (gr. k-3). 2004. (Illus.). lib. bdg. 22.60 (978-0-8225-0250-0(X)); 2003. pap. 5.95 (978-0-8225-3759-5(1)) Lerner Publishing Group.

—Washington Monument. 2004. (gr. k-3). lib. bdg. 14.10 (978-0-613-84028-6(3)) Tandem Library Bks.

Nobleman, Marc Tyler. The Washington Monument. 2004. (Let's See Library). (Illus.). 24p. (J). (gr. 1 up). lib. bdg. 19.93 (978-0-7565-0621-6(2)) Compass Point Bks.

Schaefer, Lola M. The Washington Monument. (Symbols of Freedom Ser.). (Illus.). 32p. (J). (gr. k-2). 2002. pap. 6.95 (978-1-58810-400-7(1) , 91195); 2001. lib. bdg. (978-1-58810-179-2(7)) Heinemann Library.

WASHINGTON REDSKINS (FOOTBALL TEAM)

Aryal, Aimee. Hail to the Redskins! de Angel, Miguel, illus. 2007. (J). 14.95 ***978-1-932888-91-1(8))*** Mascot Bks., Inc.

Goodman, Michael E. The History of the Washington Redskins. 2004. (NFL Today Ser.). (Illus.). 32p. 18.95 (978-1-58341-317-3(0) , Creative Education) Creative Co., The.

Washington Redskins Staff. Washington Redskins. CWC Sports Inc., ed. 1998. (NFL Team Yearbooks Ser.). (J). (gr. 1-12). pap. 9.99 (978-1-891613-04-3(9)) Everett Sports Publishing & Marketing.

WASHINGTON'S BIRTHDAY

Schauffler, Robert Haven. Washington's Birthday: Its History, Observance, Spirit, & Significance as Related in Prose & Verse, with a Selection from Washington's Speeches & Writings. 2006. 34.99 ***978-1-4280-3413-6(7));*** pap. 27.99 ***978-1-4280-3412-9(9))*** IndyPublish.com.

WASPS

Bees & Wasps, 6 Packs. (Sails Literacy Ser.). (gr. 1-2). 36.00 (978-0-7578-4019-7(1)) Rigby Education.

Claybourne, Anna. Bees & Wasps. (Illus.). 32p. (YA). (gr. 3 up). lib. bdg. 27.10 (978-1-932799-56-9(7)) Stargazer Bks.

Frost, Helen. Wasps. Saunders-Smith, Gail, ed. 2001. (Insects Ser.). (Illus.). 24p. (J). (gr. k-1). lib. bdg. 15.93 (978-0-7368-0855-2(8) , Pebble Bks.) Capstone Pr., Inc.

—Wasps, Vol. 2. 2005. (Bugs, Bugs, Bugs Ser.). 24p. (YA). (gr. k-3). pap. (978-0-7368-9090-8(4) , Pebble Bks.) Capstone Pr., Inc.

Green, Jen. Ants, Bees, Wasps & Termites. 2004. (Illus.). 64p. pap. 8.99 (978-1-84215-977-4(1) , Southwater) Anness Publishing GBR. *Dist:* National Bk. Network.

Hall, Margaret. Wasps. 2006. (Bugs, Bugs, Bugs! Ser.). (J). (978-0-7368-4254-9(3)) Capstone Pr., Inc.

Harris, Monica. Paper Wasp. 2003. (Bug Books). (Illus.). 32p. (J). lib. bdg. 22.79 (978-1-4034-0767-2(3)); pap. 6.50 (978-1-4034-0991-1(9)) Heinemann Library.

Morgan, Sally. Ants, Bees, & Wasps. 2001. (Illus.). 32p. (J). lib. bdg. 24.25 (978-1-930643-10-9(1)) Chrysalis Education.

—Bees & Wasps. 2006. (Illus.). 32p. (J). lib. bdg. 19.95 (978-1-59566-202-6(2)) QEB Publishing Inc.

Pyers, Greg. Wasps up Close. (Minibeasts up Close Ser.). (Illus.). 32p. (J). (ps-ps). 2005. lib. bdg. 26.36 (978-1-4109-1533-7(6)); 2004. pap. (978-1-4109-1540-5(9)) Harcourt Schl. Pubs.

Rustad, Martha E. H. Wasps. 2007. (Illus.). 24p. (J). lib. bdg. 19.95 (978-1-60014-076-1(9)) Bellwether Media.

WASTE (ECONOMICS)

Berry, Joy Wilt. A Book about Being Wasteful. 2005. (Illus.). (J). (978-0-7172-8587-7(1)) Scholastic, Inc.

WASTE DISPOSAL

see Refuse and Refuse Disposal; Sewage Disposal; Waste Products

WASTE PRODUCTS

see also Refuse and Refuse Disposal

Holt, Rinehart and Winston Staff. Environmental Science Chptr. 19: Waste. 4th ed. Date not set. pap. 11.20 (978-0-03-068081-6(6)) Holt, Rinehart & Winston.

Junk. (Jump Ser.). (Illus.). 36p. (J). (gr. 2-6). pap. (978-1-882210-37-4(9)) Action Publishing, Inc.

Lamerand, Violaine. Crafts from Junk. 2002. (Step by Step Ser.). (Illus.). 32p. (J). (gr. 2-3). lib. bdg. 22.60 (978-0-7368-1479-9(5) , Bridgestone Bks.) Capstone Pr., Inc.

WATCHES

see Clocks and Watches

WATER

see also Floods; Fog; Glaciers; Hydraulic Engineering; Ice; Lakes; Ocean; Rain and Rainfall; Rivers; Snow

Aigner-Clark, Julie. Water, Water Everywhere: A Splash & Giggle Bath Book. Zaidi, Nadeem, illus. 2003. (Baby Einstein Ser.: No. 3). 10p. (ps-17). 6.99 (978-0-7868-1911-9(1)) Hyperion Bks. for Children.

—What Floats? Bk. 4: A Splash & Giggle Bath. 2003. (Baby Einstein Ser.: Bk. 4). 10p. (ps-17). pap. 6.99 (978-0-7868-1912-6(X)) Hyperion Bks. for Children.

Annan, Nane. Tip & Top: The Adventures of Two Water Drops! Annan, Nane, illus. 2002. (Illus.). 63p. (J). 7.00 (978-0-944675-70-0(0)) American Forum For Global Education.

Arato, Rona. World of Water. 2004. (Rocks, Minerals, & Resources Ser.). (Illus.). 32p. (J). (978-0-7787-1416-3(0)); pap. (978-0-7787-1448-4(9)) Crabtree Publishing Co.

Arnold, Caroline. Splashtime for Zoo Animals. 1999. (Zoo Animals Ser.). (Illus.). 32p. (J). (ps-2). 9.95 (978-1-57505-394-3(2) , Carolrhoda Bks.) Lerner Publishing Group.

—Splashtime for Zoo Animals. Hewett, Richard, illus. 1998. (Zoo Animals Ser.). 32p. (J). (ps-2). lib. bdg. 21.27 (978-1-57505-288-5(1) , Carolrhoda Bks.) Lerner Publishing Group.

Asch, Frank. Water. 2000. (Illus.). 32p. (YA). (ps-2). pap. 7.00 (978-0-15-202348-5(8) , Harcourt Paperbacks) Harcourt Children's Bks.

—Water. 2000. (978-0-606-18194-5(6)); lib. bdg. 14.15 (978-0-613-28690-9(1)) Tandem Library Bks.

Bailey, Jacqui. A Drop in the Ocean: The Story of Water. Lilly, Matthew, illus. 2004. (Science Works Ser.). 32p. (J). (gr. 3-6). 23.93 (978-1-4048-0566-8(4)) Picture Window Bks.

Bailey, Jill. Life in a Garbage Dump. 2003. (Microhabitats Ser.). (Illus.). 32p. (J). pap. 7.50 (978-1-4109-0348-8(6)) Raintree.

Ballard, Carol. How We Use Water. 2004. (Using Materials Ser.). (Illus.). 32p. (J). (gr. 3-5). lib. bdg. 25.70 (978-1-4109-0607-6(8)) Harcourt Schl. Pubs.

—Water. 2004. (Using Materials Ser.). (Illus.). 32p. (J). (gr. 2-4). pap. 7.50 (978-1-4109-0898-8(4)) Harcourt Schl. Pubs.

Beers, Bonnie. Earth's Land & Water. 2000. (Yellow Umbrella Books). (Illus.). 16p. (J). (gr. 1). lib. bdg. 14.60 (978-0-7368-0737-1(3) , Pebble Bks.) Capstone Pr., Inc.

Benchmark Education Staff. Water on Earth. 2005. 2.00 (***978-1-4108-4637-2(7))** Benchmark Education Co.

Benchmark Education Staff, compiled by. Water. 2006. spiral bd. 375.00 (***978-1-4108-6792-6(7))** Benchmark Education Co.

—Water & Weather. 2006. spiral bd. 330.00 (***978-1-4108-7018-6(9));** 2006. spiral bd. 189.00 (***978-1-4108-7056-8(1));** 2006. spiral bd. 199.00 (***978-1-4108-7132-9(0));** 2005. (J). spiral bd. 265.00 (***978-1-4108-5759-0(X))** Benchmark Education Co.

Berger, Melvin & Berger, Gilda. Water, Water Everywhere: A Book about the Water Cycle. Tull, Bobbi, ed. 1999. (Discovery Readers Ser.). (Illus.). 48p. (J). (gr. 4-7). lib. bdg. 17.55 (978-0-7910-5069-9(6) , Chelsea Hse.) Facts On File, Inc.

Billings. True Tales of Raging Waters. 1999. (Illus.). (J). pap. 13.00 (978-0-7398-2391-0(4)) Steck-Vaughn.

Brannon, Barbara. Discover Water. 2005. 39.00 (***978-1-4108-5125-3(7))** Benchmark Education Co.

Bryant-Mole, Karen & Ansary, Mir Tamim. Floating & Sinking. 2002. (Illus.). 24p. (J). (gr. 1-3). pap. 6.50 (978-1-4034-0049-9(0) , 91493) Heinemann Library.

Burgan, Michael. Land & Water. 2004. (Discovery Channel School Science Ser.). (Illus.). 32p. (J). (gr. 5 up). lib. bdg. 24.67 (978-0-8368-3381-2(3)) Stevens, Gareth Inc.

Burton, Margie, et al. Water Goes Up! Water Comes Down! Adams, Alison, ed. 1999. (Early Connections Ser.). 16p. (J). (gr. k-2). pap. 4.50 (978-1-58344-085-8(2)) Benchmark Education Co.

—We Use Water. Evento, Susan, ed. 1998. (Early Connections Ser.). 16p. (gr. k-2). pap. 4.25 (978-1-892393-59-3(X)) Benchmark Education Co.

Canizares, Susan & Chanko, Pamela. Water. 1998. (Science Emergent Readers Ser.). (Illus.). (J). pap. 2.50 (978-0-590-10727-3(5)) Scholastic, Inc.

Carroll, Colleen. Elements: Earth, Air, Fire & Water. 1998. (How Artists See Ser.). (Illus.). 48p. (gr. 3 up). 12.95 (978-0-7892-0476-9(2)) Abbeville Pr., Inc.

Cobb, Vicki. I Get Wet. Gorton, Julia, illus. 2002. (Vicki Cobb Science Play Ser.). 40p. (J). (ps-k). 16.99 (978-0-688-17838-3(3)) HarperCollins Pubs.

—Squirts & Spurts: Science Fun with Water. Haefele, Steve, illus. 2000. (Science Fun with Vicki Cobb Ser.). 48p. (gr. 3-6). lib. bdg. 24.90 (978-0-7613-1572-8(1) , Millbrook Pr.) Lerner Publishing Group.

Cooper, Jason. Water. 2003. (Science Secrets Discovery Library). (Illus.). 24p. (gr. 1-4). 14.95 (978-1-58952-414-9(4)) Rourke Publishing, LLC.

Cooper, Sharon Katz. Using Water. 2007. (Illus.). 24p. (J). (***978-1-4034-9322-4(7));** lib. bdg. 21.36 (***978-1-4034-9314-9(6))** Heinemann.

Curry, Don L. The Water Cycle. 2000. (Yellow Umbrella Books). (Illus.). 16p. (J). (gr. 1). lib. bdg. 14.60 (978-0-7368-0727-2(6) , Pebble Bks.) Capstone Pr., Inc.

Dalton, Cindy Devine. Drink More Water. 2000. (Why Should I... Ser.). (Illus.). 24p. (J). (gr. 1-4). lib. bdg. 19.27 (978-1-55916-302-6(X)) Rourke Publishing, LLC.

Day, Trevor. Water. 2007. (See for Yourself Ser.). (Illus.). 64p. (YA). (gr. 5 up). 14.99 (978-0-7566-2562-7(9)) Dorling Kindersley Publishing, Inc.

del Moral, Susana. Baby Einstein: Agua por todas Partes: Baby Einstein: Water, Water Everywhere, Spanish-Language Edition. Zaidi, Nadeem, illus. 2006. 8p. (J). 6.95 (***978-970-718-452-7(3)** , Silver Dolphin en Español) Advanced Marketing, S. de R. L. de C. V. MEX. *Dist:* Perseus Distribution.

Desonie, Dana. Hydrosphere. 2007. (Our Fragile Planet Ser.). 208p. (J). (gr. 6-12). 35.00 (***978-0-8160-6215-7(3)** , Chelsea Hse.) Facts On File, Inc.

Disney Publishing Staff. The Wonders of Water, 15 vols. 2003. (It's Fun to Learn Ser.). (Illus.). 32p. (J). (ps-3). 3.99 (978-1-57973-137-3(6)) Advance Pubs. LLC.

Ditchfield, Christin. Water. (True Bks.). (Illus.). 48p. (J). (gr. 3-5). 2003. pap. 6.95 (978-0-516-29369-1(9)); 2002. pap. 25.00 (978-0-516-22345-2(3)) Scholastic Library Publishing. (Children's Pr.).

—Water. 2002. (gr. 3-6). lib. bdg. 15.25 (978-0-613-59554-4(8)) Tandem Library Bks.

DK Publishing Staff. Water Everywhere. 2007. (Dk Readers Ser.). (Illus.). 32p. (J). 14.99 (978-0-7566-2533-7(5)); pap. 3.99 (978-0-7566-2532-0(7)) Dorling Kindersley Publishing, Inc.

Dorling Kindersley Publishing Staff. Look & Explore: Splish, Splash. 2002. (Babys World Touch & Explore Ser.). (Illus.). 12p. (J). bds. 6.99 (978-0-7894-8829-9(9)) Dorling Kindersley Publishing, Inc.

—Plant. 2006. (Eye Know Ser.). (Illus.). 24p. (J). 8.99 (978-0-7566-1858-2(4)) Dorling Kindersley Publishing, Inc.

Dorros, Arthur. Follow the Water from Brook to Ocean. Dorros, Arthur, illus. 2000. (Let's-Read-and-Find-Out Science Ser.). (Illus.). 32p. (J). (gr. k-4). 15.89 (978-0-06-021599-6(2)) HarperCollins Pubs.

Douglas, Vincent & School Specialty Publishing Staff. Air & Water Science Kit. 2004. (Science Kits Ser.). (Illus.). 52p. (J). pap. 16.95 (978-1-58845-613-7(7) , Brighter Child) School Specialty Publishing.

Drinking Water, 6 vols. (gr. k-2). 28.95 (978-0-7368-8742-7(3)) Red Brick Learning.

A Drop in the Ocean. (Science Works). 32p. (YA). 8.95 (978-1-4048-1127-0(3)) Picture Window Bks.

Edom, Helen. Science with Water. rev. ed. 2007. 24p. (J). pap. 5.99 (978-0-7945-1484-6(7) , Usborne) EDC Publishing.

Everthing Changes Interactive Packages: Water Changes. (Pebble Soup Explorations Ser.). (ps up). 52.00 (978-0-7578-5239-8(4)) Rigby Education.

Farndon, John. Buoyancy. 2002. (Science Experiments Ser.). (J). 25.64 (978-0-7614-1467-4(3) , Benchmark Bks.) Cavendish, Marshall Corp.

—Water. 2001. (Science Experiments Ser.). (Illus.). 32p. (J). (gr. 3-5). lib. bdg. 25.64 (978-0-7614-1087-4(2) , Benchmark Bks.) Cavendish, Marshall Corp.

Faucets & Water Sets: 1 Each of 3 Big Books. (Sunshinetm Science Ser.). (gr. 1-2). 111.50 (978-0-7802-2814-6(6)) Wright Group, The.

Firely, G. M. The Raindrop. Holmes, Joshua D., illus. 2004. 21p. pap. 14.95 (978-1-4137-3388-4(3)) PublishAmerica, Inc.

Flanagan, Alice K. Water. 2000. (Simply Science Ser.). (Illus.). 32p. (J). (gr. 3 up). lib. bdg. 19.93 (978-0-7565-0038-2(9)) Compass Point Bks.

Flynn, James. Water. 2003. (Matter & Materials Ser.). (J). pap. (978-1-58417-167-6(7)); lib. bdg. (978-1-58417-161-4(8)) Lake Street Pubs.

Fourment, Tiffany. My Water Comes from the Mountains. Emerling, Dorothy, illus. 2004. 32p. 19.95 (978-1-57098-387-0(9)) Rinehart, Roberts Pubs.

Fowler, Allan. The Wonder of a Waterfall. 1999. (Rookie Read-About Science Ser.). (Illus.). 32p. (J). (gr. 1-2). 19.50 (978-0-516-20813-8(6) , Children's Pr.) Scholastic Library Publishing.

Frank, Marjorie Slavick, et al. Science Instant Readers Bk. 5: Water at Work. 1999. (Harcourt Science Ser.). (gr. 2 up). pap. 15.50 (978-0-15-316215-2(5)) Harcourt Schl. Pubs.

—Science Instant Readers Bk. 6: Water's Journey. 1999. (Harcourt Science Ser.). (gr. 1 up). pap. 15.50 (978-0-15-316204-6(X)) Harcourt Schl. Pubs.

—Science Instant Readers Bk. 8: The Water Cycle. 1999. (Harcourt Science Ser.). (gr. 2 up). pap. 15.50 (978-0-15-316218-3(X)) Harcourt Schl. Pubs.

Freed, Shirley Ann & Moon, Louise. Water. Morelan, Bill, ed. Harrell, Rob, illus. l.t. ed. 2002. 8p. (J). (gr. 1-2). pap. 3.99 (978-1-58938-019-6(3)) Concerned Communications.

Frisch, Aaron. Water. 2002. (Illus.). 23p. lib. bdg. 22.80 (978-1-58340-076-0(1)) Smart Apple Media.

Fromm, Jim, prod. Water Cd Mac Labpak. (YA). cd-rom 324.88 (978-0-7365-4372-9(4)) Films Media Group.

—Water Cd Win Labpak. (YA). cd-rom 324.88 (978-0-7365-4373-6(2)) Films Media Group.

Frost, Helen. El Agua Como Gas: Water As a Gas. 2003. (Water Bilingual Ser.). (SPA & ENG., Illus.). 24p. (J). lib. bdg. 15.93 (978-0-7368-2311-1(5)) Capstone Pr., Inc.

—El Agua Como Solido: Water As a Solid. 2003. (Water Bilingual Ser.). (SPA & ENG., Illus.). 24p. (J). lib. bdg. 15.93 (978-0-7368-2313-5(1)) Capstone Pr., Inc.

—El Agua Como un Liquido: Water As a Liquid. 2003. (Pebble Bilingual Books). (ENG & SPA., Illus.). 24p. (J). lib. bdg. 15.93 (978-0-7368-2312-8(3)) Capstone Pr., Inc.

—El Ciclo del Agua: The Water Cycle. 2003. (Water Bilingual Ser.). (SPA & ENG., Illus.). 24p. (J). lib. bdg. 15.93 (978-0-7368-2314-2(X)) Capstone Pr., Inc.

—Drinking Water. Saunders-Smith, Gail, ed. 2000. (Food Guide Pyramid Ser.). (Illus.). 24p. (J). (gr. k-1). lib. bdg. 15.93 (978-0-7368-0534-6(6) , Pebble Bks.) Capstone Pr., Inc.

—Water, 6 bks. Saunders-Smith, Gail, ed. Incl. Keeping Water Clean. lib. bdg. 15.93 (978-0-7368-0408-0(0)); Water As a Gas. lib. bdg. 15.93 (978-0-7368-0412-7(9)); Water As a Liquid. lib. bdg. 15.93 (978-0-7368-0410-3(2)); Water As a Solid. lib. bdg. 15.93 (978-0-7368-0411-0(0)); Water Cycle. lib. bdg. 15.93 (978-0-7368-0409-7(9)); We Need Water. lib. bdg. 15.93 (978-0-7368-0413-4(7)); 24p. (J). (gr. k-1). 1999. (Illus.). 2000. Set lib. bdg. 95.58 (978-0-7368-0454-7(4) , Pebble Bks.) Capstone Pr., Inc.

—Water as a Gas, Vol. 5. 2005. (Our Seasons & Weather Ser.). 24p. (YA). (gr. k-3). pap. (978-0-7368-8636-9(2) , Pebble Bks.) Capstone Pr., Inc.

—Water as a Liquid, Vol. 5. 2005. (Our Seasons & Weather Ser.). 24p. (YA). (gr. k-3). pap. (978-0-7368-8634-5(6) , Pebble Bks.) Capstone Pr., Inc.

—Water as a Solid, Vol. 5. 2005. (Our Seasons & Weather Ser.). 24p. (YA). (gr. k-3). pap. (978-0-7368-8635-2(4) , Pebble Bks.) Capstone Pr., Inc.

—Water As a Vapor. 1999. pap. 13.25 (978-0-516-21918-9(9) , Children's Pr.) Scholastic Library Publishing.

—We Need Water, Vol. 5. 2005. (Our Seasons & Weather Ser.). 24p. (YA). (gr. k-3). pap. (978-0-7368-8638-3(9) , Pebble Bks.) Capstone Pr., Inc.

Furgang, Kathy. Water All Around. 2003. (Early Connections Ser.). (J). pap. 33.00 (978-1-4108-1071-7(2)) Benchmark Education Co.

Gallant, Roy A. Water. 2001. (Kaleidoscope Ser.). (Illus.). 48p. (J). (gr. 3 up). lib. bdg. 25.64 (978-0-7614-1040-9(6) , Benchmark Bks.) Cavendish, Marshall Corp.

—Water: Our Precious Resource. 2002. (Earthworks Ser.). (Illus.). 79p. (J). 29.93 (978-0-7614-1365-3(0) , Benchmark Bks.) Cavendish, Marshall Corp.

Gallardo, Mary, illus. & as told by. The Tiny Little Raindrop. Gallardo, Mary, as told by. 2007. 32p. (J). 15.99 (***978-0-9779763-0-0(0))** Blue Cat Bks.

Gardner, Robert. Experimenting with Water. 2004. (Illus.). 144p. (gr. 5-8). pap. 7.95 (978-0-486-43400-1(1)) Dover Pubns., Inc.

—Super Science Projects about Earth's Soil & Water. LaBaff, Tom, illus. 2007. (Rockin' Earth Science Experiments Ser.). 48p. (J). (gr. 4-6). lib. bdg. 23.93 (978-0-7660-2735-0(X) , Enslow Elementary) Enslow Pubs., Inc.

Glover, David. Wonderful Water. 2001. (Experiments in Science Ser.). (Illus.). (J). (978-0-7894-7468-1(9)) Dorling Kindersley Publishing, Inc.

Godwin, Sam. The Drop Goes Plop: A First Look at the Water Cycle. Abel, Simone, illus. 2004. (First Look Science Ser.). 32p. (C). (gr. k-3). 22.60 (978-1-4048-0657-3(1)) Picture Window Bks.

Gold-Dworkin, Heidi, et al. Fun with Water & Bubbles. 1999. (Little Scientists Ser.). (Illus.). 58p. (gr. k-3). pap. 12.95 (978-0-07-134823-2(9) , 9780071348232) McGraw-Hill Trade.

Goodrich, Randi S. & Goodrich, Michael S. Hydro's Adventure Through the Water Cycle. Maiers, Joan, ed. Han, Michele, illus. 2004. 56p. (J). lib. bdg. 24.95 (978-0-9651101-6-7(8)); per. 17.95 (978-0-9651101-5-0(X)) GeoQuest Pubns.

Gordon, Sharon. Mojado Seco. 2006. (Bookworms Ser.). (SPA & ENG., Illus.). 24p. (J). lib. bdg. 22.79 (978-0-7614-2370-6(2)) Cavendish, Marshall Corp.

—Wet Dry (Mojado Seco) 2006. (Bookworms Ser.). (ENG & SPA., Illus.). 24p. (J). lib. bdg. 22.79 (978-0-7614-2450-5(4)) Cavendish, Marshall Corp.

Gr 4 Earth's Water, Sci Pe. 2000. (McGraw-Hill Science Ser.). (gr. 4 up). (978-0-02-278221-4(4)) Macmillan/McGraw-Hill Schl. Div.

Graham, Ian. Water: A Resource Our World Depends On. 2004. (J). (978-1-4034-5620-5(8)); pap. 7.50 (978-1-4034-5628-1(3)) Heinemann Library.

Greenaway, Theresa. The Water Cycle. 2000. (Cycles in Nature Ser.). (Illus.). 32p. (J). (gr. 2-4). lib. bdg. 25.69 (978-0-7398-2728-4(6)) Raintree.

Greenfield, Eloise. Water, Water. Gilchrist, Jan Spivey, illus. 1999. (Growing Tree Ser.). 24p. (J). (ps-k). 9.99 (978-0-694-01247-3(5) , Harper Festival) HarperCollins Pubs.

Gunzi, Christiane. Water. (Collectafact Ser.). (J). 2002. 14.95 (978-1-58728-678-0(5)); 2002. pap. 7.95 (978-1-58728-768-8(4)); 2001. (Illus.). 48p. (gr. 1-5). 4.95 (978-1-58728-761-9(7)) T&N Children's Publishing. (Two Can Publishing).

Hamilton, Kersten R. & Siomades, Lorianne. This Is the Ocean. 2003. (Illus.). 32p. (J). (gr. k-2). 14.95 (978-1-56397-890-6(3)) Boyds Mills Pr.

Hammersmith, Craig. Rising up, Falling Down. 2002. (Spyglass Books). (Illus.). 24p. (J). (gr. 1 up). lib. bdg. 18.60 (978-0-7565-0233-1(0)) Compass Point Bks.

Harcourt School Publishers Staff. Harcourt Science: Water at Work Reader. 1999. (Illus.). pap. 3.10 (978-0-15-314867-5(5)) Harcourt Schl. Pubs.

—Harcourt Science: Water's Journey Reader. 1999. (Illus.). pap. 3.10 (978-0-15-314855-2(1)) Harcourt Schl. Pubs.

—Look at the Pond. 3rd ed. 2002. (Trophies English Language Learners Ser.). (Illus.). (J). pap. 3.20 (978-0-15-327571-5(5)) Harcourt Schl. Pubs.

—Water & Weather. 3rd ed. 2002. (Trophies English Language Learners Ser.). (Illus.). pap. 5.10 (978-0-15-327648-4(7)) Harcourt Schl. Pubs.

—Water at Work: Science Reader. 1999. (SPA., Illus.). (J). pap. 3.70 (978-0-15-316120-9(5)) Harcourt Schl. Pubs.

—The Water Cycle: Science Reader. 2000. (SPA., Illus.). (J). pap. 3.70 (978-0-15-316123-0(X)) Harcourt Schl. Pubs.

—Water's Journey: Science Reader. 1999. (SPA., Illus.). (J). pap. 3.70 (978-0-15-316109-4(4)) Harcourt Schl. Pubs.

—Where Water Comes From. 3rd ed. 2002. (Horizons Ser.). (Illus.). (J). pap. 5.50 (978-0-15-333258-6(1)) Harcourt Schl. Pubs.

—The World of Water Advanced Level. 3rd ed. 2002. (Trophies Reading Program Ser.). (Illus.). pap. 5.10 (978-0-15-323037-0(1)) Harcourt Schl. Pubs.

Harman, Rebecca. The Water Cycle. 2005. (Heinemann Infosearch Ser.). (Illus.). 32p. (J). (978-1-4034-7059-1(6)) Heinemann Library.

—The Water Cycle: Evaporation, Condensation & Erosion. 2005. (Heinemann Infosearch Ser.). (Illus.). 32p. (J). (gr. 3-5). pap. 7.85 (978-1-4034-7066-9(9)) Heinemann Library.

Haswell, Arthur. Water. 2000. (Earth Strikes Back Ser.). (Illus.). 48p. (J). (gr. 4-7). lib. bdg. 16.95 (978-1-929298-60-0(9)) Chrysalis Education.

Hatchard, Louise, illus. The Water: First Wave Satellite Individual, 6 Packs. (Sails Literacy Ser.). 16p. (gr. k up). 27.00 (978-0-7578-7506-9(8)) Rigby Education.

Hewitt, Sally. Live Underwater with the Fish? 2001. (Why Can't I Ser.). (Illus.). 30p. (J). lib. bdg. 24.25 (978-1-930643-00-0(4)) Chrysalis Education.

Hodge, Judith. Las riquezas de la tierra & Riches from Earth. 2005. spiral bd. 84.00 (***978-1-4108-5716-3(6))** Benchmark Education Co.

Huggins-Cooper, Lynn. Water. McNicholas, Shelagh & Burroughs, David, trs. McNicholas, Shelagh & Burroughs, David, illus. 2004. 30p. (J). lib. bdg. (978-1-58340-449-2(X)) Smart Apple Media.

Hughes, Monica. Water Cycle (Natures Pattern) 2004. (Nature's Patterns Ser.). (Illus.). 32p. (J). lib. bdg. 24.21 (978-1-4034-5880-3(4)) Heinemann Library.

Investigating Earth Systems Water As a Resource. 2002. stu. ed., bds. (978-1-58591-111-0(9)); 2001. stu. ed. (978-1-58591-077-9(5)) It's About Time, Herff Jones Education Diiv.

Issues, Evidence & You - Water Mega Module Complete Materials Package. 2003. (Illus.). tchr. ed., ring bd. (978-1-887725-42-2(3)); (YA). tchr. ed., stu. ed., per. (978-1-887725-60-6(1)) Lab-Aids, Inc.

Jakab, Cheryl. The Water Cycle. 2007. (J). (***978-1-59920-144-3(5))** Smart Apple Media.

Johnson, Heather Domjan. The Itsy Bitsy Water Cycle. 2007. (J). lib. bdg. 19.95 (***978-1-933732-21-3(0)** , Bear Hug Bks.) MidAmerica Publishing Co.

—Itsy Bitsy Water Cycle Audiobook. 2007. (J). lib. bdg. 24.95 (***978-1-933732-22-0(9)** , Bear Hug Bks.) MidAmerica Publishing Co.

Just Add Water: Individual Title Six-Packs. (Discovery World Ser.). 12p. (gr. k-1). 28.00 (978-0-7635-8451-1(7)) Rigby Education.

Kalman, Bobbie & Sjonger, Rebecca. El Ciclo del Agua. 2006. (SPA., Illus.). 32p. (gr. 3). pap. (978-0-7787-8388-6(X)) Crabtree Publishing Co.

—Le cycle de L'eau. rev. ed. 2007. (FRE., Illus.). 32p. (J). (gr. 2-3). pap. (***978-2-89579-127-0(9))** Editions Banjo.

Kalman, Bobbie & Sjonger, Rebecca. The Water Cycle. 2006. (Nature's Changes Ser.). (Illus.). 32p. (J). (gr. k-6). pap. (978-0-7787-2310-3(0)); (978-0-7787-2276-2(7)) Crabtree Publishing Co.

Kalz, Jill. Water. 2003. 24p. (J). lib. bdg. 21.35 (978-1-58340-302-0(7)) Smart Apple Media.

Katz Cooper, Sharon. Usar el Agua. 2007. (SPA & ENG.). (J). pap. (***978-1-4329-0252-0(0));** lib. bdg. (***978-1-4329-0244-5(X))** Heinemann.

Kerley, Barbara. A Cool Drink of Water. 2002. (Illus.). 32p. (J). (ps-2). 16.95 (978-0-7922-6723-2(0) , National Geographic Children's Bks.) National Geographic Society.

Kessler, Cristina. My Great-Grandmother's Gourd. Krudop, Walter Lyon, illus. 2000. 32p. (J). (gr. k-4). 17.99 (978-0-531-33284-9(5) , Orchard Bks.) Scholastic, Inc.

KIDs: Discover Ground Water & Springs. 2000. 16p. pap. (978-1-888631-09-8(0)) Watercourse, The.

KIDs: Healthy Water, Healthy People. 2001. 16p. (J). pap. 0.60 (978-1-888631-08-1(2)) Watercourse, The.

Kids: Healthy Water Healthy People. 2005. (SPA.). (J). 1.00 (978-1-888631-40-1(6)) Watercourse, The.

Kids: The Water Story. 2004. (J). 1.00 (978-1-888631-31-9(7)) Watercourse, The.

Kids: Water, Every Drop Counts. 2004. (J). 1.00 (978-1-888631-35-7(X)) Watercourse, The.

Korb, Rena B. The Wild Water Cycle. Reibeling, Brandon, illus. 2007. (Science Rocks Ser.). 32p. (J). (ps-4). lib. bdg. 27.07 (***978-1-60270-041-3(9)** , Looking Glass Library) Magic Wagon.

Lauw, Darlene. Water. 2003. (gr. 3-6). lib. bdg. 16.40 (978-0-613-52926-6(X)) Tandem Library Bks.

Lauw, Darlene & Puay, Lim Cheng. Water. 2002. (Science Alive! Ser.). (Illus.). 32p. (J). (gr. 4-5). pap. (978-0-7787-0613-7(3)); lib. bdg. (978-0-7787-0567-3(6)) Crabtree Publishing Co.

Lerner, K. Lee, et al. UXL Encyclopedia of Water Science, 3 vols. 2004. (Illus.). xlviii, 510p. (J). (978-0-7876-7673-5(X)); (978-0-7876-7674-2(8)); (978-0-7876-7675-9(6)) Thomson Gale. (UXL).

Levine, Shar. Bathtub Science. 2003. (Illus.). 80p. pap. 10.95 (978-0-8069-7243-5(2)) Sterling Publishing Co., Inc.

Levine, Shar & Johnstone, Leslie. Bathtub Science. 2006. (Illus.). 80p. (J). pap. 9.95 (978-1-4027-4094-7(8)) Sterling Publishing Co., Inc.

Lilly, Melinda. Water & Ice. (Read & Do Science Ser.). (Illus.). (J). 20.64 (978-1-58952-639-6(2)) Rourke Publishing, LLC.

—Water & Ice. Thompson, Scott M., photos by. 2006. (Rourke Discovery Library). (Illus.). 24p. (gr. 1-4). 14.95 (978-1-59515-406-4(X) , 1244277) Rourke Publishing, LLC.

Linde, Barbara M. Water on Earth. 2005. 42.00 (***978-1-4108-4589-4(3)***) Benchmark Education Co.

Lindeen, Carol. Natural & Human-Made. 2008. (J). (***978-1-4296-0001-9(2)*** , Pebble Bks.) Capstone Pr., Inc.

—Water Basics. 2008. (J). (***978-1-4296-0005-7(5)*** , Pebble Bks.) Capstone Pr., Inc.

Madgwick, Wendy. Water Play. 1998. (Science Starters Ser.). (Illus.). 32p. (J). (gr. k-4). lib. bdg. 25.69 (978-0-8172-5326-4(2)) Raintree.

Manheim, James. Water. 2006. (Fueling the Future Ser.). (Illus.). 244p. (J). (gr. 10-12). 34.95 (978-0-7377-3593-2(7) , 1256648, Greenhaven Pr., Inc.) Thomson Gale.

Manning, Mick, et al. Splish, Splash, Splosh! A Book about Water. 1998. (Wonderwise Ser.). (Illus.). 32p. (J). (gr. k-3). pap. 6.95 (978-0-531-15326-0(6) , Watts, Franklin) Scholastic Library Publishing.

Marzollo, Jean. Soy el Agua. Moffatt, Judith, illus. 1999. (Coleccion "Hola, Lector" Ser.). (SPA.). 32p. (J). (ps-1). pap. 3.99 (978-0-439-08743-8(0) , SO2913, Scholastic en Espanol) Scholastic, Inc.

—Soy el Agua. 1999. (SPA.). (gr. k-3). lib. bdg. 11.80 (978-0-613-28314-4(7)) Tandem Library Bks.

McKinney, Barbara Shaw. Water Words Rhymed & Defined. Stich, Carolyn R., illus. 2007. 32p. (J). lib. bdg. 19.95 (***978-0-9712692-8-6(9)***) EDCO Publishing, Inc.

Meacham, Nancy. Water: Science Discovery. Zuman, John & Barra, Nancy, eds. Deming, Linda, illus. 2002. (Sunflower/Girasol Ser.). 20p. (J). 5.00 (978-1-58332-004-4(0)) Intercultural Center for Research in Education (I N C R E).

Meiani, Antonella. Water. 2003. (Experimenting with Science Ser.). (Illus.). 40p. (J). (gr. 4-8). 23.93 (978-0-8225-0083-4(3)) Lerner Publishing Group.

Mezzanotte, Jim. Como Cambia el Agua. 2006. (ENG & SPA., Illus.). 24p. (J). pap. (978-0-8368-7407-5(2)); lib. bdg. (978-0-8368-7402-0(1)) Stevens, Gareth Inc. (Weekly Reader Early Learning Library).

—How Water Changes. 2006. (States of Matter Ser.). (J). pap. (978-0-8368-6803-6(X)); lib. bdg. (978-0-8368-6798-5(X)) Stevens, Gareth Inc.

Modules: Earth Science; Earth's Waters TE. 2005. (gr. 6-12). (978-0-618-33418-6(1) , 2-01008) McDougal Littell Inc.

Moor, Jo Ellen. Water. Evans, Marilyn, ed. Robison, Don, illus. 1998. (ScienceWorks for Kids Ser.: Vol. 10). 80p. (J). (gr. 1-3). pap., tchr. ed. 9.95 (978-1-55799-691-6(1) , EMC 862) Evan-Moor Educational Pubs.

Morris, Neil. Water. 2002. (Our World Ser.). (Illus.). 32p. (J). lib. bdg. 24.25 (978-1-930643-78-9(0)) Chrysalis Education.

Morrison, Gordon. Drop of Water. 2006. (Illus.). 32p. (J). (gr. k-3). 16.00 (978-0-618-58557-1(5)) Houghton Mifflin Co.

Murphy, Brian. Experimenta Con el Agua. 2004. (Experiment with Ser.).Tr. of Experiment with Air. (SPA., Illus.). 32p. (gr. 2-5). 9.95 (978-1-58728-437-5(5)); (J). pap. 5.95 (978-1-58728-436-6(7)) Quayside. (Creative Publishing International).

—Water. 2004. (Experiment with Ser.). (SPA., Illus.). 32p. (J). (gr. 2-5). pap. 5.95 (978-1-58728-119-8(8)); 32p. (gr. 2-5). 9.95 (978-1-58728-242-3(9)); 48p. (J). (gr. 3-6). pap. 14.95 incl. cd-rom (978-1-58728-469-4(3)) T&N Children's Publishing. (Two Can Publishing).

Murray, Julie. Water. 2007. (Illus.). 24p. (J). 21.35 (978-1-59679-832-8(7) , Buddy Bks.) ABDO Publishing Co.

Nadeau, Isaac. Learning about the Water Cycle with Graphic Organizers. 2005. (Graphic Organizers in Science Ser.). (Illus.). 24p. (J). pap. (978-1-4042-5046-8(8) , PowerKids Pr.) Rosen Publishing Group, Inc., The.

—Learning about the Water Cycles with Graphic Organizers. 2005. (Graphic Organizers in Science Ser.). (Illus.). 24p. (J). 19.95 (978-1-4042-2808-5(X) , PowerKids Pr.) Rosen Publishing Group, Inc., The.

—Water in Plants & Animals. 2003. (Water Cycle Ser.). (Illus.). 24p. (J). lib. bdg. 18.75 (978-0-8239-6264-8(4) , PowerKids Pr.) Rosen Publishing Group, Inc., The.

—Water in the Atmosphere. 2003. (Water Cycle Ser.). (Illus.). 24p. (J). lib. bdg. 18.75 (978-0-8239-6262-4(8) , PowerKids Pr.) Rosen Publishing Group, Inc., The.

—Water under Ground. 2003. (Water Cycle Ser.). (Illus.). 24p. (J). lib. bdg. 18.75 (978-0-8239-6263-1(6) , PowerKids Pr.) Rosen Publishing Group, Inc., The.

Nankivell-Aston, Sally. Science Experiments with Water. 2000. (Science Experiments Ser.). (Illus.). 32p. (J). (gr. 3-6). pap. 6.95 (978-0-531-15432-8(7) , Watts, Franklin) Scholastic Library Publishing.

Nelson, Robin. El Ciclo Del Agua. 2003. (First Step Nonfiction Ser.). (SPA., Illus.). 24p. (J). (gr. k-2). lib. bdg. 18.60 (978-0-8225-4866-9(6)) Lerner Publishing Group.

—Donde Hay Agua? 2003. (First Step Nonfiction Ser.). (SPA., Illus.). 24p. (J). (gr. k-2). lib. bdg. 18.60 (978-0-8225-4868-3(2)) Lerner Publishing Group.

—Flotar y Hundirse (Float & Sink) 2007. (Mi Primer Paso al Mundo Real - Fuerzas y Movimiento (First Step Nonfiction - Forces & Motion) Ser.). (SPA.). 24p. (J). (gr. k-2). lib. bdg. 18.60 (***978-0-8225-7808-6(5)*** , Ediciones Lerner) Lerner Publishing Group.

—Freezing & Melting. 2003. (First Step Nonfiction Ser.). (Illus.). 24p. (J). (gr. k-2). lib. bdg. 18.60 (978-0-8225-4590-3(X)) Lerner Publishing Group.

—Que Es el Agua? 2003. (First Step Nonfiction Ser.). (SPA., Illus.). 24p. (J). (gr. k-2). lib. bdg. 18.60 (978-0-8225-4869-0(0)) Lerner Publishing Group.

—Se Congela y Se Derrite. 2003. (First Step Nonfiction Ser.). (SPA., Illus.). 24p. (J). (gr. k-2). lib. bdg. 18.60 (978-0-8225-4865-2(8)) Lerner Publishing Group.

—Water. 2004. (First Step Nonfiction Ser.). (J). pap. (978-0-8225-5390-8(2)) Lerner Publishing Group.

—Water: By Robin Nelson. 2005. (First Step Nonfiction Ser.). (Illus.). 23p. (J). (ps-7). 18.60 (978-0-8225-2600-1(X) , Lerner Pubns.) Lerner Publishing Group.

—What Is Water? 2003. (First Step Nonfiction Ser.). (Illus.). 24p. (J). (gr. k-2). lib. bdg. 18.60 (978-0-8225-4588-0(8)) Lerner Publishing Group.

—Where Is Water? 2003. (First Step Nonfiction Ser.). (Illus.). 24p. (J). (gr. k-2). lib. bdg. 18.60 (978-0-8225-4592-7(6)) Lerner Publishing Group.

New England Water Pollution Staff. That Magnificient Ground Water Connection Vol. TM101: A Resource Book for Grades K-6. ENOSIS - The Environmental Staff, illus. 1999. 145p. (J). (gr. k-6). 25.00 (978-1-56791-239-5(7)) Environmental Media Corp.

Newman, Marjorie. Ideas with Water. 1999. (Ideas Activity Bks.). (Illus.). 12p. (J). (ps-3). pap. 5.99 (978-0-89051-246-3(9)) Master Bks.

Neye, Emily. Water. Revell, Cynthia, illus. 2002. (All Aboard Science Reader Ser.: Vol. 1). 32p. (J). pap. 3.99 (978-0-448-42847-5(4) , Grosset & Dunlap) Penguin Group (USA) Inc.

—Water. 2002. (Illus.). 32p. (ps-3). lib. bdg. 11.80 (978-0-613-64428-0(X)) Tandem Library Bks.

Nichols, Catherine. Water All Around. 2001. (We Can Read about Nature Ser.). (Illus.). 32p. (J). (gr. 1-2). lib. bdg. 21.36 (978-0-7614-1256-4(5) , Benchmark Bks.) Cavendish, Marshall Corp.

Olien, Rebecca. Sources of Water. 2005. (Illus.). 24p. (J). 21.26 (978-0-7368-3700-2(0)) Capstone Pr., Inc.

—Water & the Weather. 2005. (Illus.). 24p. (J). 21.26 (978-0-7368-3702-6(7)) Capstone Pr., Inc.

—The Water Cycle. 2005. (Illus.). 24p. (J). 21.26 (978-0-7368-3701-9(9)) Capstone Pr., Inc.

—What Is Water? 2005. (Illus.). 24p. (J). 21.26 (978-0-7368-3704-0(3)) Capstone Pr., Inc.

Oxlade, Chris. How We Use Water, 6, Pack. 2004. (Using Materials Ser.). (Illus.). (J). pap. 40.50 (978-1-4109-0905-3(0)) Harcourt Schl. Pubs.

—Water. 2002. (Materials, Materials, Materials Ser.). (Illus.). 32p. (J). (gr. k-2). lib. bdg. 22.79 (978-1-58810-588-2(1)); pap. 6.95 (978-1-4034-0089-5(X) , 91530) Heinemann Library.

—Water. 2002. (gr. k-3). lib. bdg. 14.75 (978-0-613-45850-4(8)) Tandem Library Bks.

Parker, Janice. The Science of Water. 1999. (Living Science Ser.). (Illus.). 32p. (J). (gr. 2 up). lib. bdg. 24.67 (978-0-8368-2469-8(5)) Stevens, Gareth Inc.

Parker, Steve. The Science of Water: Projects with Experiments with Water & Power. 2005. (Tabletop Scientist Ser.). (Illus.). 32p. (J). (gr. 4-7). lib. bdg. 29.29 (978-1-4034-7282-3(3)) Heinemann Library.

—The Science of Water: Projects with Experiments with Water Science & Power. 2005. (Illus.). 32p. (J). (gr. 4-6). pap. 7.95 (978-1-4034-7289-2(0)) Heinemann Library.

—Water Power. 2004. (Science Files Ser.). (Illus.). 32p. (J). (gr. 3 up). lib. bdg. 24.67 (978-0-8368-4033-9(X)) Stevens, Gareth Inc.

Parker, Victoria. Water. 2006. (Heinemann Read & Learn Ser.). (Illus.). 24p. (J). (978-1-4034-7883-2(X)); pap. (978-1-4034-7889-4(9)) Steck-Vaughn.

Peterson, Virginia, ed. Water: The Vital Source. rev. ed. 1999. (Information Plus Compact Ser.). (Illus.). 80p. (YA). (gr. 4-7). pap. 28.00 (978-1-57302-107-4(5) , GML00502-172342) Thomson Gale.

Pipe, Jim. Water. 2004. (Earthwise Ser.). (J). lib. bdg. 27.10 (978-1-932799-45-3(1)) Stargazer Bks.

Pluckrose, Henry Arthur. Water. 2006. 32p. (J). (978-1-59771-035-0(0)) Sea-To-Sea Pubns.

Popular Science Editors. Just Add Water: Science Projects You Can Sink, Squirt, Splash, & Sail. 2007. (Experiment with Science Ser.). 32p. (J). 7.95 (***978-0-531-18762-3(4)***); (Illus.). (gr. 3-6). lib. bdg. 25.00 (***978-0-531-18545-2(1)***) Scholastic Library Publishing. (Children's Pr.).

Purslow, Frances. The Water Cycle. 2005. (Science Matters Ser.). (Illus.). 24p. (J). (ps-7). pap. 6.95 (978-1-59036-312-6(4) , 1251285); lib. bdg. 24.45 (978-1-59036-306-5(X) , 1251285) Weigl Pubs., Inc.

Richards, Jon. Water & Boats. 2008. (J). lib. bdg. (***978-1-4042-3909-8(X)*** , PowerKids Pr.) Rosen Publishing Group, Inc., The.

Roca, Nuria. Aprendamos sobre los 4 Elementos: The 4 Elements (Spanish Edition) Curto, Rosa M., illus. 2006. (Let's Learn About Ser.). (SPA.). 36p. (J). pap. 6.99 (978-0-7641-3315-2(2)) Barron's Educational Series, Inc.

—Let's Learn about the 4 Elements. Curto, Rosa M., illus. 2006. (Let's Learn About Ser.). 36p. (J). pap. 6.99 (978-0-7641-3314-5(4)) Barron's Educational Series, Inc.

Rookie Read-About Geography: Bodies of Water, 7 bks., Set. Incl. Amazon River. Schulte, Mary. 20.50 (978-0-516-25031-1(0)); Chesapeake Bay. Bennett, Kelly. 20.50 (978-0-516-25032-8(9)); Colorado River. Bryan, Dale-Marie. 20.50 (978-0-516-25033-5(7)); Great Salt Lake. Schulte, Mary Knudson. 20.50 (978-0-516-25034-2(5)); Gulf of Mexico. Zollman, Pam. 20.50 (978-0-516-25035-9(3)); Lake Tahoe. Zollman, Pam. 20.50 (978-0-516-25036-6(1)); Missouri River. Taylor-Butler, Christine. 20.50 (978-0-516-25037-3(X)); (Illus.). 32p. (J). (gr. 1-2). 2006. 2006. 136.50 (978-0-516-25414-2(6) , Children's Pr.) Scholastic Library Publishing.

Rosenberg, Pam. Yikes! Icky, Sticky, Gross Stuff Underwater. 2007. (Icky, Sticky, Gross-Out Bks.). 24p. (J). (gr. 2-6). 22.79 (***978-1-59296-901-2(1)***) Child's World, Inc.

Rosinsky, Natalie M. Water: Up, Down, & All Around. John, Matthew, illus. 2004. (Amazing Science Ser.). 24p. (C). (gr. k-4). 22.60 (978-1-4048-0017-5(4)) Picture Window Bks.

Royston, Angela. Agua: Miremos un Charco. 2006. (Illus.). 24p. (J). 21.36 (978-1-4034-7548-0(2)); pap. 6.00 (978-1-4034-7557-2(1)) Heinemann Library.

—The Life & Times of a Drop of Water: The Water Cycle. 2005. (Illus.). 32p. (J). (978-1-4109-1956-4(0)); lib. bdg. (978-1-4109-1925-0(0)) Steck-Vaughn.

—Water. (My World of Science Ser.). (Illus.). 32p. (J). (gr. k-2). 2002. pap. 6.95 (978-1-4034-0047-5(4) , 91491); 2001. lib. bdg. 21.36 (978-1-58810-247-8(5)) Heinemann Library.

—Water. 2002. (gr. k-3). lib. bdg. 15.25 (978-0-613-88702-1(6)) Tandem Library Bks.

—Water: Let's Look at a Puddle. 2005. (Illus.). 24p. (J). pap. (978-1-4034-7685-2(3)); lib. bdg. (978-1-4034-7676-0(4)) Heinemann Library.

—Water: Let's Look at a Puddle. 2005. (J). pap. (978-1-4109-1832-1(7)); lib. bdg. (978-1-4109-1823-9(8)) Steck-Vaughn.

—Water & Fiber for a Healthy Body. 2003. (Body Needs Ser.). (Illus.). 48p. pap. 7.99 (978-1-4034-3314-5(3)); (J). (gr. 4-6). lib. bdg. 27.07 (978-1-4034-0760-3(6)) Heinemann Library.

—Water & Fiber for a Healthy Body. 2003. (gr. 3-6). lib. bdg. 16.40 (978-0-613-60999-9(9)) Tandem Library Bks.

—Why Do We Need to Drink Water? 2005. (Heinemann Read & Learn Ser.). (Illus.). 24p. (J). pap. (978-1-4034-7613-5(6)); (gr. 3-7). lib. bdg. 21.36 (978-1-4034-7608-1(X)) Heinemann Library.

Schmauss, Judy Kentor. The Water Planet. 2007. (Shockwave: Earth & Physical Science Ser.). 36p. (J). (gr. 3-5). pap. 6.95 (***978-0-531-18793-7(4)***); (Illus.). (gr. 4-6). lib. bdg. 25.00 (***978-0-531-17795-2(5)***) Scholastic Library Publishing. (Children's Pr.).

—Wicked & Wonderful Water. 2007. (Shockwave: Economics & Geography Ser.). 36p. (J). pap. 6.95 (***978-0-531-18799-9(3)***); (Illus.). (gr. 4-6). lib. bdg. 25.00 (***978-0-531-17751-8(3)***) Scholastic Library Publishing. (Children's Pr.).

School Specialty Publishing. Water. 2004. (On-File Ser.). 4p. (J). (gr. 5-7). ring bd. 4.99 (978-0-7424-2924-6(5) , Instructional Fair) Schaffer, Frank Pubns.

Schuh, Mari C. Drinking Water. 2006. (Illus.). 24p. (J). 19.93 (978-0-7368-5375-0(8) , Pebble Bks.) Capstone Pr., Inc.

Sian Revision Water Cycle. 2004. (J). (978-1-59242-081-0(8)) Delta Education, LLC.

Singer, Marilyn. How to Cross a Pond: Poems about Water. So, Meilo, illus. 2003. 48p. (J). (gr. 3-7). lib. bdg. 16.99 (978-0-375-92376-0(4) , Knopf Bks. for Young Readers) Random Hse. Children's Bks.

Slade, Suzanne. The Water Cycle. 2007. (Changes Occurring in Cycles Ser.). (Illus.). 24p. (J). (978-1-4042-2391-2(6)); pap. (978-1-4042-2201-4(4)) Rosen Publishing Group, Inc., The. (PowerKids Pr.).

—Water on the Move. 2007. (Cycles in Nature Ser.). (Illus.). 24p. (J). (gr. 4-6). lib. bdg. 21.25 (978-1-4042-3492-5(6) , PowerKids Pr.) Rosen Publishing Group, Inc., The.

Sloan, Peter. Water for You. 1999. (gr. k-3). lib. bdg. 11.65 (978-0-613-30847-2(6)) Tandem Library Bks.

Smuskiewicz, Alfred J. Properties of Water. 2006. (J). pap. (***978-0-8368-7875-2(2)***); (Illus.). 48p. (YA). (gr. 6-8). lib. bdg. 26.60 (***978-0-8368-7764-9(0)***) Stevens, Gareth Inc.

Spilsbury, Louise. Running Water. 2004. (Illus.). 48p. (J). 28.56 (978-1-4109-1116-2(0)) Raintree.

Spilsbury, Louise & Spilsbury, Richard. Water. 2006. (Planet under Pressure Ser.). (Illus.). 48p. (YA). (gr. 5-8). lib. bdg. 31.43 (978-1-4034-8214-3(4)) Heinemann Library.

Spilsbury, Richard. Air & Water Pressure. 2006. (Fantastic Forces Ser.). (Illus.). 32p. (J). (978-1-4034-8170-2(9)); pap. (978-1-4034-8175-7(X)) Heinemann Library.

Squirts & Spurts: Science Fun with Water. 2007. (J). pap. 7.95 (***978-0-8225-7024-0(6)*** , First Avenue Editions) Lerner Publishing Group.

Stearns, Carolyn. Where Did All the Water Go? Aiken, David, illus. 1998. 30p. (J). (gr. 4-7). 12.95 (978-0-87033-506-8(5) , Tidewater Pubs.) Cornell Maritime Pr., Inc.

Stewart, Melissa. The Wonders of Water. 2004. (Investigate Science Ser.). 32p. (J). (gr. 1 up). lib. bdg. 21.26 (978-0-7565-0637-7(9)) Compass Point Bks.

Stone, Lynn M. Water Cycle. 2007. (Illus.). 24p. (J). (978-1-60044-182-0(3)) Rourke Publishing, LLC.

Strauss, Rochelle. One Well: The Story of Water on Earth. Woods, Rosemary, illus. 2007. 32p. (YA). (gr. 3 up). (***978-1-55337-954-6(3)***) Kids Can Pr., Ltd.

Swanson, Diane. The Wonder in Water. 2005. (Illus.). 48p. (J). (gr. 1-3). pap. 8.95 (978-1-55037-936-5(4)); lib. bdg. 19.95 (978-1-55037-937-2(2)) Annick Pr., Ltd. CAN. *Dist:* Firefly Bks., Ltd.

Taylor, Kim. Water. (Illus.). 32p. (YA). (gr. 3 up). lib. bdg. 27.10 (978-1-931983-79-2(8)) Chrysalis Education.

Tocci, Salvatore. Experiments with Water. 2002. (True Bks.). (Illus.). 48p. (J). (gr. 3-5). 25.00 (978-0-516-22508-1(1) , Children's Pr.) Scholastic Library Publishing.

—Experiments with Water. 2002. (gr. 3-6). lib. bdg. 15.25 (978-0-613-54215-9(0)) Tandem Library Bks.

Trueit, Trudi Strain. The Water Cycle. 2002. (Watts Library). (Illus.). 64p. (J). (gr. 5-7). 25.50 (978-0-531-11972-3(6) , Watts, Franklin) Scholastic Library Publishing.

—Water Cycle. 2002. (gr. 5-8). lib. bdg. 17.60 (978-0-613-53877-0(3)) Tandem Library Bks.

Trumbauer, Lisa. Agua. 2006. (SPA & ENG., Illus.). 18p. (J). (978-0-7368-5995-0(0)) Capstone Publishing.

—Water. 2006. (Yellow Umbrella Books for Early Readers). (Illus.). 16p. (J). (978-0-7368-5977-6(2)) Yellow Umbrella Pr.

—Water: Aqua. 2006. (Yellow Umbrella Books for Early Readers). (SPA & ENG., Illus.). 18p. (J). (978-0-7368-6013-0(4)) Yellow Umbrella Pr.

Two-Can Publishing Ltd. Staff. Experiment with Water. 2001. (gr. 3-6). lib. bdg. 14.10 (978-0-613-83316-5(3)) Tandem Library Bks.

United Nations Environment Programme, Division of Environmental Policy Implementation Staff, et al, contrib. by. A Trip with Drip the Water Drop: A Learning-by-Doing Workbook on Water for Children. 2005. (Illus.). 44p. (J). (gr. k-12). 10.00 (978-92-807-2581-0(5) , E.05.III.D.43) United Nations Environment Programme KEN. *Dist:* United Nations Pubns.

United Nations Environment Programme Staff. Water World: Children's Voices - An Educational Booklet on Water for Children. 2005. (Illus.). 86p. pap. 12.00 (978-92-807-2388-5(X) , E.04.III.D.5) United Nations Environment Programme KEN. *Dist:* United Nations Pubns.

Vogt, Gregory L. The Hydrosphere: Agent of Change. 2007. (Earth's Spheres Ser.). (Illus.). 80p. (J). (gr. 6-8). 29.27 (978-0-7613-2839-1(4) , Twenty-First Century Bks.) Lerner Publishing Group.

Waldman, Neil. The Snowflake: A Water Cycle Story. Waldman, Neil, illus. 2003. 32p. lib. bdg. 23.90 (978-0-7613-1762-3(7) , Millbrook Pr.) Lerner Publishing Group.

Warhol, Tom. Water. 2006. (Earth's Biomes Ser.). (Illus.). 80p. (J). lib. bdg. 32.79 (978-0-7614-2192-4(0) , Benchmark Bks.) Cavendish, Marshall Corp.

Water. (Jump Ser.). (Illus.). 32p. (J). (gr. 2-7). pap. 4.95 (978-1-882210-29-9(8)) Action Publishing, Inc.

Water, Vol. 5. 2005. (Our Seasons & Weather Ser.). (YA). (gr. k-3). 178.20 (978-0-7368-4202-0(0) , Pebble Bks.) Capstone Pr., Inc.

Water. 2004. (Illus.). lib. bdg. 7.95 (978-0-8225-4753-2(8)) Lerner Publishing Group.

Water. 2001. (Physical Science Ser.). (J). (gr. k-12). vinyl bd. 4.95 (978-1-58845-112-5(7)) School Specialty Publishing.

Water. 2000. (What About...? Ser.). (J). (gr. 1-4). pap. 5.72 (978-0-8114-4948-9(3)) Steck-Vaughn.

Water All Around. 2005. (First Facts Ser.). (Illus.). (J). (gr. 1-2). lib. bdg. 127.56 (978-0-7368-3811-5(2)) Capstone Pr., Inc.

Water as a Gas, 6 vols. (gr. k-2). 28.95 (978-0-7368-8642-0(7)) Red Brick Learning.

Water as a Liquid, 6 vols. (gr. k-2). 28.95 (978-0-7368-8640-6(0)) Red Brick Learning.

Water as a Solid, 6 vols. (gr. k-2). 28.95 (978-0-7368-8641-3(9)) Red Brick Learning.

Water Bugs, 6 vols. (gr. k-2). 28.95 (978-0-7368-9112-7(9)) Red Brick Learning.

The Water Cycle, Vol. 5. 2005. (Our Seasons & Weather Ser.). (YA). (gr. k-3). (978-0-7368-8637-6(0) , Pebble Bks.) Capstone Pr., Inc.

The Water Cycle, 6 vols. (gr. k-2). 28.95 (978-0-7368-8643-7(5)) Red Brick Learning.

Water, Ice, & Steam. (Rosen Real Readers Big Bookstm Ser.). 12p. (J). (gr. 1-2). 31.95 (978-1-4042-6215-7(6)) Rosen Publishing Group, Inc., The.

Water Set. (gr. k-2). 172.95 (978-0-7368-9049-6(1)) Red Brick Learning.

We Need Water, 6 vols. (gr. k-2). 28.95 (978-0-7368-8644-4(3)) Red Brick Learning.

Der Weg des Wassers.Tr. of Characteristics of Water. (GER., Illus.). (YA). 31.95 (978-3-411-09131-7(2)) Bibliographisches Institut & F. A. Brockhaus AG DEU. *Dist:* Continental Bk. Co., Inc.

Wells, Robert E., illus. Did a Dinosaur Drink This Water? 2006. 32p. (J). 15.95 (978-0-8075-8839-0(3)); lib. bdg. 6.95 (978-0-8075-8840-6(7)) Whitman, Albert & Co.

Who Likes Water? KinderWords Individual Title Six-Packs. (Kinderstarters Ser.). 8p. (ps-1). 21.00 (978-0-7635-8713-0(3)) Rigby Education.

Williams, Brenda. Water. 1999. (Environment Starts Here Ser.). (Illus.). 32 p. (J). (gr. 1-4). lib. bdg. 25.69 (978-0-8172-5350-9(5)) Raintree.

Williams, John. Water Projects. 1998. (Design & Create Ser.). (Illus.). 32p. (J). (gr. 2-5). lib. bdg. 17.98 (978-0-8172-4890-1(0)) Raintree.

Yates, Irene. Water. 2004. (Activities for 3-5 Year Olds Ser.). (Illus.). 32p. pap. 11.00 (978-1-897675-25-0(9)) Brilliant Pubns. GBR. *Dist:* Parkwest Pubns., Inc.

Ylvisaker, Anne. Land & Water: World Rivers. (Fact Finders Ser.). (Illus.). (J). (gr. 3-4). lib. bdg. 90.40 (978-0-7368-2559-7(2)) Capstone Pr., Inc.

WATER—CONSERVATION

see Water Conservation

WATER—POLLUTION

see also Refuse and Refuse Disposal; Sewage Disposal also Petroleum Pollution of Water and similar headings

Bang, Molly. Nobody Particular: One Woman's Fight to Save the Bays; the Diane Wilson Story. 2005. (Illus.). 48p. (J). (gr. 4-7). pap. 10.00 (978-1-931498-94-4(6)) Chelsea Green Publishing.

Benchmark Education Staff. Ocean Pollution. 2005. 2.00 (***978-1-4108-4678-5(4)***) Benchmark Education Co.

Brannon, Barbara. Discover Ocean Pollution. 2005. 39.00 (***978-1-4108-5140-6(0)***) Benchmark Education Co.

Bryan, Nichol. Danube: Cyanide Spill. 2003. (Environmental Disasters Ser.). (Illus.). 48p. (gr. 5 up). (YA). lib. bdg. 30.00 (978-0-8368-5505-0(1)); (J). pap. 11.95 (978-0-8368-5512-8(4)) Stevens, Gareth Inc. (World Almanac Library).

Capstone Press Editors. Our Planet in Peril, 4 bks. Incl. Acid Rain. lib. bdg. 22.60 (978-0-7368-1360-0(8)); Global Warming. lib. bdg. 22.60 (978-0-7368-1361-7(6)); Nuclear Waste. lib. bdg. 22.60 (978-0-7368-1362-4(4)); Oil Spills. lib. bdg. 22.60 (978-0-7368-1363-1(2)); 48p. (J). (gr. 3-4). 2002. (Illus.). 2002. Set lib. bdg. 90.40 (978-0-7368-1364-8(0) , Bridgestone Bks.) Capstone Pr., Inc.

ENOSIS - The Environmental Staff, ed. That Magnificent Ground Water Connection Vol. TM102: A Resource Book for Grades 7-12. 1999. (Illus.). 296p. (YA). (gr. 7-12). 25.00 (978-1-56791-240-1(0)) Environmental Media Corp.

Fix, Alexandra. Water. 2007. (J). (***978-1-4034-9714-7(1));*** pap. (***978-1-4034-9722-2(2))*** Heinemann Library.

Harlow, Rosie. Pollution & Waste: Environmental Facts & Experiments. 2002. (Young Discoverers Ser.). (Illus.). 32p. (J). (gr. k-3). 7.95 (978-0-7534-5505-0(6) , Kingfisher) Houghton Mifflin Co. Trade & Reference Div.

—Pollution & Waste: Environmental Facts & Experiments. 2002. (gr. k-3). lib. bdg. 16.40 (978-0-613-90577-0(6)) Tandem Library Bks.

Harper, Joel. All the Way to the Ocean. Spusta, Marq, illus. 2006. (J). (***978-0-9714254-1-5(8))*** Harper, Joel D.

Keeping Water Clean, Vol. 5. 2005. (Our Seasons & Weather Ser.). (YA). (gr. k-3). (978-0-7368-8633-8(8) , Pebble Bks.) Capstone Pr., Inc.

Markle, Sandra. After the Spill: The Exxon Valdez Disaster, Then & Now. 1999. (Illus.). 32p. (J). (gr. 3-7). lib. bdg. 17.85 (978-0-8027-8611-1(1)) Walker & Co.

—After the Spill: The Exxon Valdez Disaster Then & Now. 1999. (Illus.). 32p. (J). (gr. 3-7). 16.95 (978-0-8027-8610-4(3)) Walker & Co.

Nelson, Sara Elizabeth. Let's Save Water! 2007. (Pebble Books). (Illus.). 24p. (J). 15.93 (978-0-7368-6322-3(2)) Capstone Pr., Inc.

Ostopowich, Melanie. Water Pollution. 2005. (Science Matters Ser.). (Illus.). 24p. (J). (ps-7). pap. 6.95 (978-1-59036-313-3(2)); lib. bdg. 24.45 (978-1-59036-307-2(8)) Weigl Pubs., Inc.

Parks, Peggy J. Water Pollution. 2007. (Our Environment Ser.). (Illus.). 48p. (J). (gr. 4-8). 26.20 (***978-0-7377-3667-0(4)*** , Kidhaven) Thomson Gale.

Parsons, Michelle Hyde. Ocean Pollution. 2005. 42.00 (***978-1-4108-4630-3(X))*** Benchmark Education Co.

Roleff, Tamara L., ed. Pollution. 2000. (Opposing Viewpoints Ser.). (Illus.). 244p. (YA). (gr. 10-12). pap. 21.20 (978-0-7377-0134-0(X) , Greenhaven Pr., Inc.) Thomson Gale.

Stefanow, Jennifer. Polluted Water. 2004. (Green Alert Ser.). (Illus.). 48p. (J). lib. bdg. 28.56 (978-0-7398-7016-7(5)) Raintree.

WATER—POLLUTION—FICTION

Atwell, Debby. River. Atwell, Debby, illus. 1999. (Illus.). 32p. (J). (gr. k-3). tchr. ed. 16.00 (978-0-395-93546-0(6) , Walter Lorraine) Houghton Mifflin Co. Trade & Reference Div.

—River. 2004. (Illus.). 32p. (J). (gr. k-3). reprint ed. pap. 5.95 (978-0-618-43952-2(8) , Walter Lorraine) Houghton Mifflin Co. Trade & Reference Div.

—River. 2004. (Illus.). 31p. (J). (ps-ps). lib. bdg. 12.75 (978-0-606-30309-5(X)) Tandem Library Bks.

Base, Graeme. The Sign of the Seahorse: A Tale of Greed & High Adventure in Two Acts. 1998. (Picture Puffin Ser.). (Illus.). 48p. (J). (gr. 1-4). pap. 8.99 (978-0-14-056387-0(3) , Puffin) Penguin Group (USA) Inc.

Gratz, Alan M. Something Rotten: A Horatio Wilkes Mystery. 2007. 208p. (J). (gr. 6). 16.99 (***978-0-8037-3216-2(3)*** , Dial) Penguin Group (USA) Inc.

Helsaple, Brian J. Pixiewater: The Miracle of the Pixie Pool. 1999. (Life Lessons Ser.). (J). (gr. k-5). 20.95 incl. audio (978-1-928714-00-2(5)) 2 Brian's Pr.

Kline, Trish & Donev, Mary. Coming Home: KA Reader 8. 2007. (Illus.). 32p. (J). per. 20.00 (***978-1-934307-01-4(7))*** Ghost Hunter Productions.

Shaw, Daniel, illus. Journey to Pansophigus. ed. 2005. (J). per. 9.95 (978-0-9772168-0-2(2)) Water Lily Pr., Inc.

Taylor-Butler, Christine. Water Everywhere! Manning, Maurie J., illus. 2005. (Rookie Reader Skill Set Ser.). 31p. (J). (gr. k-2). pap. 4.95 (978-0-516-25285-8(2) , Children's Pr.) Scholastic Library Publishing.

Veit, Barbara. Atencion! Rio Contaminado, 1999. Tr. of Look! The River Is Contaminated. (978-0-606-17616-3(0)) Tandem Library Bks.

Zinsser, Anne. More Dolphin Magic: The Adventure Continues. Sohl, Lee Ellen, illus. 2001. viii, 120p. (J). per. 6.95 (978-0-933951-20-4(5)) Locust Hill Pr.

WATER—PURIFICATION

Olien, Rebecca. Making Water Clean. 2005. (Illus.). 24p. (J). (ps). lib. bdg. 21.26 (978-0-7368-3703-3(5)) Capstone Pr., Inc.

Water for the World, 6 Packs. (gr. k-1). 23.00 (978-0-7635-8852-6(0)) Rigby Education.

WATER ANIMALS

see Fresh-Water Animals; Marine Animals

WATER BIRDS

see also names of water birds, e.g. Penguins

Arnosky, Jim. Watching Water Birds. Arnosky, Jim, illus. 2002. (Illus.). 32p. (J). (gr. 4-7). pap. 7.95 (978-0-7922-6739-3(7) , National Geographic Children's Bks.) National Geographic Society.

Brown, Mary Barrett. Wings along the Waterway. Brown, Mary Barrett, illus. 1999. (Illus.). 80p. (J). (gr. 3-6). pap. 8.95 (978-0-531-07114-4(6) , Orchard Bks.) Scholastic, Inc.

—Wings along the Waterway. 1999. (978-0-606-16919-6(9)) Tandem Library Bks.

Hall, Margaret. Herons. Saunders-Smith, Gail, ed. 2004. (Wetland Animals Ser.). (Illus.). 24p. (J). (gr. k-1). lib. bdg. 15.93 (978-0-7368-2064-6(7) , Pebble Bks.) Capstone Pr., Inc.

Horak, Steven A. Swans & Other Swimming Birds, Vol. 10. World Book, Inc. Staff, ed. 2001. (World Book's Animals of the World Ser.: Set 2). (Illus.). 64p. (J). (978-0-7166-1217-9(8)) World Bk., Inc.

Miller, Sara Swan. Waterfowl: From Swans to Screamers. 1999. (Animals in Order Ser.). (Illus.). 48p. (J). (gr. 4-6). 26.50 (978-0-531-11584-8(4) , Watts, Franklin) Scholastic Library Publishing.

—Waterfowl: From Swans to Screamers. 1999. (gr. 3-6). lib. bdg. 15.25 (978-0-613-35033-4(2)) Tandem Library Bks.

Spencer, Jim. A Young Hunter's Guide to Waterfowling & Conservation. Cox, Gary, illus. 2004. 104p. pap. 12.95 (978-1-932052-18-3(6)) Ducks Unlimited, Inc.

Waterbirds: Individual Title Six-Packs. (Rigby Infoquest Ser.). 24p. (gr. 3 up). 34.00 (978-0-7578-5783-6(3)) Rigby Education.

Welsbacher, Anne. Wading Birds. Netherton, John, photos by. (Pull Ahead Bks.). (Illus.). 32p. (J). (gr. k-2). 1999. lib. bdg. 22.60 (978-0-8225-3614-7(5) , Lerner Pubns.); 1998. pap. 5.95 (978-0-8225-3620-8(X) , Carolrhoda Bks.) Lerner Publishing Group.

Wildlife Education, Ltd. Staff & Wagner, Beth. Sea Otters. Hayward, Tim, illus. 2000. (Zoobooks Ser.). 18p. (J). pap. 2.95 (978-0-937934-66-1(6)) Wildlife Education, Ltd.

—Seabirds. Hayward, Tim, illus. 2001. (Zoobooks Ser.). 24p. (J). 15.95 (978-0-937934-90-6(9)) Wildlife Education, Ltd.

WATERCOLOR PAINTING

Dutta-Yean, Tutu & Maire, Lucy Bedoya. Twelve Treasures of the East: Legends & Folk Tales from Asia. Dutta-Yean, Tutu, ed. Konatich, James, illus. ed. 2005. (J). per. (978-0-9768436-0-3(9) , 20) Maire, Lucy Bedoya.

Etape Par Etape L'aquarelle. 2002. (How to Draw & Paint Ser.). Orig. Title: Step-by-Step Watercolor. (FRE.). pap. 7.95 (978-1-56010-677-7(8)) Foster, Walter Publishing, Inc.

Les Fleurs a L'aquarelle. 2002. (How to Draw & Paint Ser.). Orig. Title: Watercolor - Flowers - Special Effects. (FRE.). pap. 7.95 (978-1-56010-673-9(5)) Foster, Walter Publishing, Inc.

Garland, Sarah. Zoom! 2006. (Illus.). 16p. (J). bds. 5.95 (978-1-84507-346-6(0)) Lincoln, Frances Ltd. GBR. *Dist:* Perseus Distribution.

Giddy Up Staff. Go Diego Go Water Wow! Book. 2006. 4p. (J). 6.99 (978-1-59524-215-0(5)) Giddy Up, LLC.

Lipsitt, Judy. Hello Kitty Painting. 2002. (Hello Kitty & Her Friends Crafts Club Ser.). (Illus.). 44p. (J). act. bk. ed. (978-0-439-32846-3(2)) Scholastic, Inc.

Seligman, Patricia. The Watercolor Artist's Flower Handbook: Leading Floral Artists Show How to Capture the Beauty of Flowers. 2005. (Illus.). 144p. 19.95 (978-0-8230-5616-3(3)) Watson-Guptill Pubns., Inc.

Top That Publishing Staff, ed. Sketching with Watercolor Pencils. 2005. (Illus.). 48p. (978-1-84510-300-2(9)) Top That! Publishing PLC.

—Watercolor Painting. 2004. (Art Tricks Ser.). (Illus.). 48p. (978-1-84510-318-7(1)) Top That! Publishing PLC.

Whitney, Edgar A. Complete Guide to Watercolor Painting. 2001. (Illus.). 176p. pap. 17.95 (978-0-486-41742-4(5)) Dover Pubns., Inc.

WATER CONSERVATION

see also Water-Supply

Dalgleish, Sharon. Saving Water. 2002. (Our World Ser.). (Illus.). 32p. (J). (gr. 4-8). 28.00 (978-0-7910-7016-1(6) , Chelsea Hse.) Facts On File, Inc.

Emoto, Masaru. The Secret of Water. 2006. (Illus.). 32p. (J). 14.95 (978-1-58270-157-8(1) , Atria) Simon & Schuster.

Finton, Nancy. Wonders of Water. 2004. (Illus.). 32p. (J). (978-0-7922-4572-8(5)) National Geographic Society.

Fix, Alexandra. Water. 2007. (J). (***978-1-4034-9714-7(1));*** pap. (***978-1-4034-9722-2(2))*** Heinemann Library.

Ganeri, Anita & Oxlade, Chris. Down the Drain: Conserving Water. 2005. (You Can Save the Planet Ser.). (J). (978-1-4034-6845-1(1)); pap. (978-1-4034-6851-2(6)) Heinemann Library.

Green, Jen. Saving Water. 2005. (Improving Our Environment Ser.). (Illus.). 32p. (J). lib. bdg. 24.67 (978-0-8368-4431-3(9)) Stevens, Gareth Inc.

—Why Should I Save Water? Gordon, Mike, illus. 2005. (Why Should I? Bks.). 32p. (J). pap. 6.99 (978-0-7641-3157-8(5)) Barron's Educational Series, Inc.

—Why Should I Save Water? Gordon, Mike, illus. 2005. 32p. (J). (ps-3). lib. bdg. 13.15 (978-0-606-33634-5(6)) Tandem Library Bks.

Inskipp, Carol. Conserving Our Fresh Water. 2006. (Sustainable Futures Ser.). (Illus.). 48p. (J). (978-1-58340-977-0(7) , 1262620) Smart Apple Media.

Llewellyn, Claire. Stop Water Waste. 2005. (Illus.). 32p. (YA). (gr. 1 up). lib. bdg. 27.10 (978-1-932333-24-4(X)) Chrysalis Education.

Nelson, Sara Elizabeth. Let's Save Water! 2007. (Pebble Books). (Illus.). 24p. (J). 15.93 (978-0-7368-6322-3(2)) Capstone Pr., Inc.

Olien, Rebecca. Saving Water. 2005. (Illus.). 24p. (J). 21.26 (978-0-7368-3699-9(3)) Capstone Pr., Inc.

WATER FOWL

see Water Birds

WATER PLANTS

see Marine Plants

WATER POLLUTION

see Water—Pollution

WATER POLO

Egan, Tracie. Water Polo. 2005. (Sports from Coast to Coast Ser.). (Illus.). 48p. (J). (gr. 5-8). lib. bdg. 26.50 (978-1-4042-0186-6(6)) Rosen Publishing Group, Inc., The.

WATER POWER

Costain, Meredith. Water Power. 2000. (gr. k-3). lib. bdg. 11.80 (978-0-613-30848-9(4)) Tandem Library Bks.

Draper, Allison Stark. Hydropower for the Future: New Ways of Turning Water into Energy. 2005. (Library of Future Energy). (Illus.). 64p. (YA). (gr. 7-12). lib. bdg. 26.50 (978-0-8239-3664-9(3)) Rosen Publishing Group, Inc., The.

Graham, Ian. Water Power. 1999. (Energy Forever? Ser.). (Illus.). 48p. (J). (gr. 3-7). lib. bdg. 27.12 (978-0-8172-5363-9(7)) Raintree.

Harcourt School Publishers Staff. Emperador y Campesino: Take-Home Book. 2001. (Vamos Ser.). (SPA., Illus.). (J). pap. 2.80 (978-0-15-319943-1(1)) Harcourt Schl. Pubs.

—Energy from Water: Take-Home Book. 2001. (Collections Ser.). (Illus.). (J). pap. 1.90 (978-0-15-319525-9(8)) Harcourt Schl. Pubs.

—Energy from Water Below Level. 3rd ed. 2002. (Trophies Reading Program Ser.). (Illus.). pap. 5.10 (978-0-15-323323-4(0)) Harcourt Schl. Pubs.

Harris, William. Water Makes Hydropower. 2003. (From Resource to Energy Source Ser.). (J). (978-1-58417-286-4(X)); pap. (978-1-58417-287-1(8)) Lake Street Pubs.

Hydroelectric Power. (Energy at Work Ser.). 32p. (J). 7.95 (978-0-7368-5192-3(5)) Capstone Pr., Inc.

Mahaney, Ian F. Water Power. 2007. (Illus.). 24p. (J). pap. (978-1-4042-2190-1(5) , PowerKids Pr.) Rosen Publishing Group, Inc., The.

Morris, Neil. Water Power. 2006. (Illus.). 32p. (J). (978-1-58340-909-1(2)) Smart Apple Media.

Orr, Tamra. Hydroelectric Energy. 2008. (J). pap. 7.95 (***978-1-60279-098-8(1));*** lib. bdg. 25.26 (***978-1-60279-049-0(3))*** Cherry Lake Publishing.

Oxlade, Chris. Energy: Water Power. 2006. (Illus.). 32p. (978-1-59604-103-5(X) , 1262726) Stargazer Bks.

Petersen, Christine. Water Power. 2004. (True Book Ser.). (Illus.). 48p. (J). 25.00 (978-0-516-22808-2(0) , Children's Pr.) Scholastic Library Publishing.

The Power of Water: Individual Title Six-Packs. (gr. k-1). 23.00 (978-0-7635-8848-9(2)) Rigby Education.

Richards, Julie. Water Power. 2003. 32p. (J). lib. bdg. 24.25 (978-1-58340-335-8(3)) Smart Apple Media.

Sheehan, Thomas F. Wind & Water at Work: A Book about Change. 2008. (J). (***978-1-60044-538-5(1))*** Rourke Publishing, LLC.

Sherman, Josepha. Hydroelectric Power. 2004. (Fact Finders Ser.). (Illus.). 32p. (J). 16.95 (978-0-7368-2472-9(3)) Capstone Pr., Inc.

Solway, Andrew. Water Power. 2007. (J). pap. (***978-0-8368-8413-5(2));*** 24p. (gr. 3-5). lib. bdg. 26.60 (***978-0-8368-8404-3(3))*** Stevens, Gareth Inc.

Spilsbury, Richard & Spilsbury, Louise. Water Power: Pros & Cons. 2007. (J). lib. bdg. (***978-1-4042-3743-8(7)*** , Rosen Central) Rosen Publishing Group, Inc., The.

Webster, Christine. Water Power. 2005. (Science Matters Ser.). (Illus.). 24p. (J). (ps-7). pap. 6.95 (978-1-59036-314-0(0)); lib. bdg. 24.45 (978-1-59036-308-9(6)) Weigl Pubs., Inc.

WATER PURIFICATION

see Water—Purification

WATER RESOURCES DEVELOPMENT

see also Inland Navigation; Water Power; Water-Supply

Harris, William. Water Makes Hydropower. 2003. (From Resource to Energy Source Ser.). (J). (978-1-58417-286-4(X)); pap. (978-1-58417-287-1(8)) Lake Street Pubs.

WATER SKIING

Firestone, Mary. Extreme Waterskiing Moves. 2003. (Behind the Moves Ser.). (Illus.). 32p. (J). lib. bdg. 22.60 (978-0-7368-2155-1(4)) Capstone Pr., Inc.

Robinson, Kimberly P. Wake up & Waterski. 2000. (Illus.). 34p. (J). (gr. k-3). spiral bd. 9.95 (978-1-892216-33-5(7)) Bristol Fashion Publishing Co.

Thompson, Luke. Essential Waterskiing for Teens. 2000. (High Interest Bks.). (Illus.). 48p. (gr. 7-12). (J). 23.00 (978-0-516-23359-8(9)); (YA). pap. 6.95 (978-0-516-23559-2(1)) Scholastic Library Publishing. (Children's Pr.).

—Essential Waterskiing for Teens. 2000. (gr. 7-12). lib. bdg. 15.25 (978-0-613-52036-2(X)) Tandem Library Bks.

WATER SPORTS

see Aquatic Sports

WATER-SUPPLY

see also Dams; Water—Pollution; Water—Purification; Water Conservation

Annan, Nane. Tip & Top: The Adventures of Two Water Drops! Annan, Nane, illus. 2002. (Illus.). 63p. (J). 7.00 (978-0-944675-70-0(0)) American Forum For Global Education.

Berger, Melvin & Berger, Gilda. Water, Water Everywhere: A Book about the Water Cycle. Tull, Bobbi, ed. 1999. (Discovery Readers Ser.). (Illus.). 48p. (J). (gr. 4-7). lib. bdg. 17.55 (978-0-7910-5069-9(6) , Chelsea Hse.) Facts On File, Inc.

Bowden, Rob. Water Supply. 2003. (21st Century Debates Ser.). (Illus.). 64p. (J). lib. bdg. 28.56 (978-0-7398-5506-5(9)) Raintree.

Bringing Water to People: 6 Small Books. (Greetings Ser.: Vol. 3). 32p. (gr. 3-5). 31.00 (978-0-7635-1821-9(2)) Rigby Education.

Bringing Water to People: Big Book. (Greetings Ser.: Vol. 3). 32p. (gr. 3-5). 31.00 (978-0-7635-3269-7(X)) Rigby Education.

Brunelle, Lynn. Turn on the Faucet. 2003. (Step Back Science Ser.). (Illus.). 48p. (J). 24.95 (978-1-56711-681-6(7) , Blackbirch Pr., Inc.) Thomson Gale.

Calhoun, Yael. Water in the News. 2007. (Science News Flash Ser.). 112p. (gr. 6-12). 31.95 (***978-0-7910-9254-5(2)*** , Chelsea Hse.) Facts On File, Inc.

Casper, Julie Kerr. Water & Atmosphere: The Lifeblood of Natural Systems. 2007. (Natural Resources Ser.). 224p. (J). (gr. 6-12). 39.50 (***978-0-8160-6359-8(1)*** , Chelsea Hse.) Facts On File, Inc.

Cole, Joanna. The Magic School Bus at the Waterworks. Degen, Bruce, illus. (Magic School Bus Ser.). (FRE.). (J). (gr. 1-4). 13.99 (978-0-590-73932-0(8)); pap. 6.99 (978-0-590-71792-2(8)); bds. 35.99 (978-0-590-73528-5(4)) Scholastic, Inc.

Dalgleish, Sharon. Saving Water. 2002. (Our World Ser.). (Illus.). 32p. (gr. 4-8). 28.00 (978-0-7910-7016-1(6) , Chelsea Hse.) Facts On File, Inc.

Finton, Nancy. Wonders of Water. 2004. (Illus.). 32p. (J). (978-0-7922-4572-8(5)) National Geographic Society.

Fix, Alexandra. Water. 2007. (J). (***978-1-4034-9714-7(1));*** pap. (***978-1-4034-9722-2(2))*** Heinemann Library.

Foran, Jill & Keen, Jared, eds. The Water Crisis: Understanding Global Issues. 2002. (Understanding Global Issues). (Illus.). 56p. (YA). (gr. 10-12). lib. bdg. 19.95 (978-1-58340-165-1(2)) Weigl Pubs., Inc.

Fourment, Tiffany. My Water Comes from the Mountains. Emerling, Dorothy, illus. 2004. 32p. pap. 9.95 (978-1-57098-388-7(7)) Rinehart, Roberts Pubs.

Green, Jen. Saving Water. 2005. (Improving Our Environment Ser.). (Illus.). 32p. (J). lib. bdg. 24.67 (978-0-8368-4431-3(9)) Stevens, Gareth Inc.

How Faucets Work. (Sunshinetm Science Ser.). 24p. (gr. 1-2). 37.50 (978-0-7802-2778-1(6)) Wright Group, The.

How Faucets Work: 6 Each of 1 Student Book, 6 vols. (Sunshinetm Science Ser.). 24p. (gr. 1-2). 41.95 (978-0-7802-2688-3(7)) Wright Group, The.

Keen, Jared, ed. The Water Crisis. 2002. (Understanding Global Issues Ser.). (Illus.). 56p. (J). (gr. 10-12). lib. bdg. 28.50 (978-1-58340-172-9(5)) Weigl Pubs., Inc.

Kegley, David E. Where Does Rain Come From? 2002. (Reading Room Collection). (Illus.). 24p. (J). pap. (978-0-8239-8166-3(5)); lib. bdg. 18.75 (978-0-8239-3729-5(1)) Rosen Publishing Group, Inc., The.

Kerley, Barbara. A Cool Drink of Water. 2006. 32p. (J). (gr. 5 up). 7.95 (978-0-7922-5489-8(9) , National Geographic Children's Bks.) National Geographic Society.

Miller, Debra. Will the World Run Out of Fresh Water? 2007. (At Issue Ser.). 128p. (J). (gr. 10-12). 29.95 (***978-0-7377-3403-4(5));*** pap. 21.20 (***978-0-7377-3404-1(3))*** Thomson Gale. (Greenhaven Pr., Inc.).

Morgan, Sally. Water for All. 2006. (Earth Watch Ser.). (Illus.). 32p. (J). (978-1-59771-066-4(0)) Sea-To-Sea Pubns.

Nelson, Robin. We Use Water. 2003. (First Step Nonfiction Ser.). (Illus.). 24p. (J). (gr. k-2). lib. bdg. 18.60 (978-0-8225-4594-1(2)) Lerner Publishing Group.

New England Water Pollution Staff. That Magnificent Ground Water Connection Vol. TM101: A Resource Book for Grades K-6. ENOSIS - The Environmental Staff, illus. 1999. 145p. (J). (gr. k-6). 25.00 (978-1-56791-239-5(7)) Environmental Media Corp.

Spilsbury, Louise & Spilsbury, Richard. Water. 2006. (Planet under Pressure Ser.). (Illus.). 48p. (YA). (gr. 5-8). lib. bdg. 31.43 (978-1-4034-8214-3(4)) Heinemann Library.

Towler, Sureva. From Snowflake to Sirloin Steak: The Story of Water in Steamboat Springs. 1999. (Illus.). 48p. (J). (978-0-9666054-2-6(X)) Legacy Bks. & Resources.

United Nations Environment Programme, Division of Environmental Policy Implementation Staff, et al, contrib. by. A Trip with Drip the Water Drop: A Learning-by-Doing Workbook on Water for Children. 2005. (Illus.). 44p. (J). (gr. k-12). 10.00 (978-92-807-2581-0(5) , E.05.III.D.43) United Nations Environment Programme KEN. *Dist:* United Nations Pubns.

Watching Every Drop, 6 Packs. (gr. k-1). 23.00 (978-0-7635-8851-9(2)) Rigby Education.

Water, Water Everywhere. (Discovery Readers Ser.). 48p. (J). pap. 3.95 (978-0-8249-5312-6(6) , Ideals Children's Bks.) Ideals Pubns.

Well... What's All That Drilling About? 2007. (Illus.). 31p. (J). 12.99 (***978-0-9641186-3-8(7))*** American Ground Water Trust.

Welton, Jude. Water Supplies. 2005. (Action for the Environment Ser.). (Illus.). 32p. (J). (gr. 4-7). lib. bdg. 27.10 (978-1-58340-601-4(8) , 1247299) Smart Apple Media.

WATER-SUPPLY ENGINEERING

Holt, Rinehart and Winston Staff. Holt Science & Technology Chptr. 14: The Flow of Water: Chapter Resources - Tennessee Edition. 3rd ed. 2003. (YA). pap. 11.40 (978-0-03-069146-1(X)) Holt, Rinehart & Winston.

WATER WORKS

see Waterworks

WATERGATE AFFAIR, 1972-1974

Anderson, Dale. Watergate: Scandal in the White House. 2006. (J). (978-0-7565-2010-6(X)) Compass Point Bks.

Cohen, Daniel. Watergate: Deception in the White House. 1998. (Spotlight on American History Ser.). (Illus.). 64p. (gr. 4-6). lib. bdg. 24.90 (978-0-7613-0271-1(9) , Millbrook Pr.) Lerner Publishing Group.

Edelman, Rob. Watergate. 2005. (People at the Center of Ser.). (Illus.). 48p. (J). (ps-7). lib. bdg. 24.95 (978-1-56711-928-2(X) , Blackbirch Pr., Inc.) Thomson Gale.

W X Y Z

Elish, Dan. The Watergate Scandal. (Cornerstones of Freedomtrade;, Second Ser.). 48p. (J). 2007. pap. 5.95 (***978-0-531-18771-5(3)***); 2004. (Illus.). 26.00 (978-0-516-24239-2(3)) Scholastic Library Publishing. (Children's Pr.).

Fremon, David K. The Watergate Scandal in American History. 1998. (In American History Ser.). (Illus.). 128p. (YA). (gr. 5-12). lib. bdg. 26.60 (978-0-89490-883-5(9)) Enslow Pubs., Inc.

Hillstrom, Kevin. Watergate. 2004. (Defining Moments Ser.). (Illus.). 217p. (YA). lib. bdg. 49.00 (978-0-7808-0769-3(3)) Omnigraphics, Inc.

Miller, Debra A. Living Through Watergate. 2006. (Living Through the Cold War Ser.). (Illus.). 192p. (gr. 10-12). 33.70 (978-0-7377-2917-7(1) , Greenhaven Pr., Inc.) Thomson Gale.

Tracy, Kathleen. The Watergate Scandal. 2006. (Monumental Milestones Ser.). (Illus.). 48p. (J). lib. bdg. 20.95 (978-1-58415-470-9(5)) Mitchell Lane Pubs., Inc.

Van Meter, Larry A. & McNeese, Tim. United States V. Nixon: The Question of Executive Privilege. 2007. (Great Supreme Court Decisions Ser.). 112p. (J). (gr. 5-8). 30.00 (978-0-7910-9381-8(6) , Chelsea Hse.) Facts On File, Inc.

WATERLOO, BATTLE OF, WATERLOO, BELGIUM, 1815

Crompton, Samuel Willard. Waterloo. 2002. (Battles That Changed the World Ser.). (Illus.). (J). 111p. pap. 13.25 (978-0-7910-7110-6(3)); 112p. (gr. 7-10). 30.00 (978-0-7910-6683-6(5)) Facts On File, Inc. (Chelsea Hse.).

WATERMELONS

Galindo, Mary Sue & Howard, Pauline Rodriguez. Icy Watermelon. 2000. Tr. of Sandia Fria. (SPA & ENG., Illus.). 32p. (J). (ps-2). 14.95 (978-1-55885-306-5(5) , Piñata Books) Arte Publico Pr.

Murray, Julie. Watermelon. 2007. (Life Cycles Ser.). 24p. (J). (gr. k-4). lib. bdg. 21.35 (***978-1-59928-712-6(9)*** , Buddy Bks.) ABDO Publishing Co.

WATERSHIP DOWN (IMAGINARY PLACE)—FICTION

Adams, Richard. Watership Down. 2001. (Perennial Classics Ser.). (Illus.). 512p. pap. 13.00 (978-0-06-093545-0(6)) HarperCollins Pubs.

WATERWAYS

see also Canals; Inland Navigation; Rivers

Beckett, Harry. Waterways to the Great Lakes. 1999. (Great Lakes of North America Ser.). (Illus.). 32p. (J). (gr. 3-6). lib. bdg. 26.60 (978-0-86593-529-7(7)) Rourke Publishing, LLC.

Malone, Bobbie & Gray, Jefferson J. Working with Water: Wisconsin Waterways. 2001. (New Badger History Ser.). (Illus.). 88p. (gr. 4-8). pap. 11.95 (978-0-87020-329-9(0)) Wisconsin Historical Society.

Malone, Bobbie, et al. Working with Water: Wisconsin Waterways. 2001. (New Badger History Ser.). (Illus.). 84p. (J). (gr. 4-8). pap., instr.'s gde. ed. 39.95 (978-0-87020-331-2(2)) Wisconsin Historical Society.

Radley, Gail. Waterways. Sherlock, Jean & Matheny, Jean, illus. 2005. (Vanishing from Ser.). 32p. (gr. 6-12). lib. bdg. 22.60 (978-1-57505-408-7(6)) Lerner Publishing Group.

WATERWORKS

see also Water-Supply

Cole, Joanna. The Magic School Bus at the Waterworks. 2001. (Early Readers Ser.: Vol. 1). (J). lib. bdg. (978-1-59054-522-5(2)) Fitzgerald Bks.

Murphy, Kevin. Water for Hartford: The Story of the Hartford Water Works & the Metropolitan District Commission. 2004. (Illus.). xxi, 318p. 29.95 (978-0-9749352-0-1(4)) Shining Tramp Pr.

WATIE, STAND, 1806-1871—FICTION

Rifles for Watie. 1999. (YA). 9.95 (978-1-56137-598-1(5)) Novel Units, Inc.

WATT, JAMES, 1736-1819

Whiting, Jim. James Watt & the Steam Engine. 2005. (Uncharted, Unexplored, & Unexplained Ser.). (Illus.). 48p. (J). (gr. 4-8). lib. bdg. 29.95 (978-1-58415-371-9(7)) Mitchell Lane Pubs., Inc.

WAVES

see also Light; Ocean Waves; Radiation

Cambridge Educational, prod. Waves & Vibrations Hyb Lb D. (YA). cd-rom 222.50 (978-0-7365-4358-3(9)) Films Media Group.

Gardner, Robert. Light, Sound, & Waves Science Fair Projects Using Sunglasses, Guitars, & Other Stuff. 2004. (Physics! Best Science Projects Ser.). (Illus.). 128p. (J). lib. bdg. 26.60 (978-0-7660-2126-6(2)) Enslow Pubs., Inc.

Holt, Rinehart and Winston Staff. Holt Science & Technology Chapter 20: Physical Science: The Energy of Waves. 5th ed. 2004. (Illus.). pap. 13.13 (978-0-03-030431-6(8)) Harcourt Trade Pubs.

—Holt Science & Technology Chptr. 15: Energy & Waves: Chapter Resources - Tennessee Edition. 3rd ed. 2003. (J). pap. 11.40 (978-0-03-069123-2(0)) Holt, Rinehart & Winston.

Jennings, Terry. Floods & Tidal Waves. 1999. (Natural Disasters Ser.). (Illus.). (J). lib. bdg. 16.95 (978-1-929298-46-4(3)) Chrysalis Education.

Rothstein, Ruth S., et al. ARIES Exploring Waves: Ripple Tanks, Vibrations & Sound: Science Journal. 2000. (Aries Ser.). (Illus.). (J). pap. 3.80 (978-1-57091-254-2(8)) Charlesbridge Publishing, Inc.

Salway, Andrew. Waves, Vibration & Radiation. 2007. (J). lib. bdg. (***978-1-4042-3746-9(1)*** , Rosen Central) Rosen Publishing Group, Inc., The.

Stille, Darlene R. Waves: Energy on the Move. 2005. (Exploring Science Ser.). (Illus.). 48p. (J). (gr. 5-7). 25.27 (978-0-7565-1259-0(X)) Compass Point Bks.

Wondering about Waves. 2000. (YA). 189.00 (978-1-886998-24-7(8)) Pasco Scientific.

Wright, Holly. Wave. 2004. (J). (978-0-9743690-7-5(1)) Britt Allcroft Productions.

Zubrowski, Bernie. Making Waves: Finding Out about Rhythmic Motion. 2001. 73p. spiral bd. 9.00 (978-1-58651-901-8(8)) Pitsco/Pitsco LEGO Dacta.

WAXES

Murray, Julie. Wax to Crayon. 2007. (Illus.). 24p. (J). 21.35 (978-1-59679-915-8(3) , Buddy Bks.) ABDO Publishing Co.

Snyder, Inez. Wax to Crayons. 2003. (Welcome Bks.). (Illus.). 24p. (J). (ps-2). 18.00 (978-0-516-24267-5(9) , Children's Pr.); pap. 4.95 (978-0-516-24359-7(4) , Watts, Franklin) Scholastic Library Publishing.

—Wax to Crayons. 2003. (gr. k-3). lib. bdg. 12.95 (978-0-613-59761-6(3)) Tandem Library Bks.

WAYNE, ANTHONY, 1745-1796

Grabowski, Patricia A. General "Mad" Anthony Wayne. 2001. (Revolutionary War Leaders Ser.). (Illus.). 80p. (J). pap. 27.50 (978-0-7910-6383-5(6)); 27.50 (978-0-7910-6382-8(8)) Facts On File, Inc. (Chelsea Hse.).

WAYNE, ANTHONY, 1745-1796—FICTION

Rinaldi, Ann. A Ride into Morning: The Story of Tempe Wick. 2003. (Great Episodes Ser.). 368p. (YA). pap. 6.95 (978-0-15-204683-5(6) , Gulliver Bks.) Harcourt Children's Bks.

—A Ride into Morning: The Story of Tempe Wick. l.t. ed. 2005. 383p. (YA). 21.95 (978-0-7862-7957-9(5) , Large Print Pr.) Thorndike Pr.

WEAPONS

see Arms and Armor; Firearms

WEASELS—FICTION

Berger, Melvin & Berger, Gilda. Can It Rain Cats & Dogs? Sullivan, Robert, illus. 1999. (Scholastic Question & Answer Ser.). 48p. (J). (gr. 2-4). pap. 5.95 (978-0-439-08573-1(X) , Scholastic Reference) Scholastic, Inc.

George, Jean Craighead. Frightful's Daughter Meets the Baron Weasel. San Souci, Daniel, illus. 2007. 48p. (J). (ps). 16.99 (***978-0-525-47202-5(9)*** , Dutton Juvenile) Penguin Group (USA) Inc.

Jackson, Bobby L. Boon the Raccoon & Easel the Weasel. Rodriguez, Christina, illus. 2004. 32p. (J). pap. 11.95 (978-1-884242-03-8(0) , BREW2NED); 19.95 (978-1-884242-02-1(2) , BREW2NED) Multicultural Pubns.

Montgomery, Rutherford G. Pekan the Shadow. Nenninger, J. D., illus. 2004. (Classic Ser.). 164p. (gr. 4-7). pap. 13.95 (978-0-87004-406-9(0)) Caxton Pr.

Sargent, Dave & Sargent, Pat. Bandit: I Help Others, 56 bks., 14. Huff, Jeane, illus. 2003. (Animal Pride Ser.: 14). 42p. (J). lib. bdg. 19.95 (978-1-56763-785-4(X)) Ozark Publishing.

Smith, Stephanie. Ermine's New Home. Hynes, Robert, illus. 2nd ed. 2005. (Soundprints' Read-And-Discover Ser.). (J). (gr. 1-3). 48p. 7.95 (978-1-931465-18-2(5) , B2001); 32p. pap. 3.95 (978-1-931465-17-5(7) , S2001) Soundprints.

The Weasel Brothers: One Too Many Weasels. 2000. 32p. (978-0-9678807-0-9(X)) Jurik, Cynthia L.

Young, Diane B. Wee Willy Weasel. Bienvenu, Lisa, illus. 2001. 23p. (Orig.). (J). (ps-k). pap. (978-0-9706269-0-5(8)) Young, Diane B.

WEATHER

see also Climate; Meteorology; Rain and Rainfall; Snow; Storms; Winds

Adams, Simon. The Best Book of Weather. Saunders, Mike & Stewart, Roger, illus. 2001. (Best Book of... Ser.). 32p. (J). (gr. k-3). tchr. ed. 12.95 (978-0-7534-5368-1(1) , Kingfisher) Houghton Mifflin Co. Trade & Reference Div.

Allaby, Michael. A Chronology of Weather. 2nd rev. ed. 2003. (Dangerous Weather Ser.). (Illus.). 208p. (YA). (gr. 6-12). 35.00 (978-0-8160-4792-5(8)) Facts On File, Inc.

—How the Weather Works: 100 Ways Parents & Kids Can Share the Secrets of the Atmosphere. 1999. (How It Works Ser.). (Illus.). 192p. (gr. 12-9). pap. 16.95 (978-0-7621-0234-1(9)) Reader's Digest Assn., Inc., The.

—Weather. 2006. 64p. (J). (gr. 8). pap. 7.99 (978-0-7566-2229-9(8)) Dorling Kindersley Publishing, Inc.

—The World's Weather. 2002. (Inside Look Ser.). (Illus.). 48p. (J). (gr. 4 up). lib. bdg. 26.00 (978-0-8368-3178-8(0)) Stevens, Gareth Inc.

Amazing Science: Weather. (Illus.). (C). (gr. k-3). 271.20 (978-1-4048-0994-9(5)) Picture Window Bks.

Arner, Elizabeth. Weather Detectives. 2004. (Illus.). (J). (gr. 4-6). 40.00 (978-1-57336-404-1(5) , I2065) Interaction Pubs., Inc.

Arnold, Caroline. El Nino: Stormy Weather for People & Wildlife. (Illus.). 48p. (J). (gr. 4-6). 2005. pap., pap. 5.95 (978-0-618-55110-1(7)); 1998. tchr. ed. 16.00 (978-0-395-77602-5(3)) Houghton Mifflin Co. Trade & Reference Div. (Clarion Bks.).

Artell, Mike. Weather Whys. 2nd ed. 2005. (Illus.). 96p. (J). pap. (978-1-59647-001-9(1)) Good Year Bks.

Baker, Sue. Child's Play Weather. 2005. (Illus.). 32p. (J). (ps-3). 12.95 (978-0-85953-929-6(6)) Child's Play International Ltd. GBR. *Dist:* Child's Play-International.

Banqueri, Eduardo. Weather. Estudio Marcel Socias Staff & Marfil, Gabi, illus. 2006. (Field Guides). 32p. (J). (gr. 4-8). 16.95 (978-1-59270-059-2(4)) Enchanted Lion Bks., LLC.

Barnett, Michelle Noble, et al. Theme Pockets - March: St. Patrick's Day; Weather; Our Community. Evans, Marilyn, ed. Larsen, Jo, illus. 1999. (Making Books with Pockets). 96p. (J). pap., tchr. ed. 12.99 (978-1-55799-700-5(4) , EMC 586) Evan-Moor Educational Pubs.

Beaton, Clare, illus. Weather (El Tiempo) 2001. (Bilingual First Bks.). (SPA & ENG.). 24p. (J). (ps up). pap. 4.99 (978-0-7641-1690-2(8)) Barron's Educational Series, Inc.

Bednarz, Robert, et al. Grade K Time for Kids Readers: What's the Weather? 3rd ed. 2002. (Harcourt Horizons Ser.). (gr. k up). pap. 19.40 (978-0-15-333113-8(5)) Harcourt Schl. Pubs.

Benchmark Education Staff. Weather & Climate. 2005. 2.00 (***978-1-4108-4635-8(0)***) Benchmark Education Co.

—Weathering & Erosion. 2005. 2.00 (***978-1-4108-4648-8(2)***) Benchmark Education Co.

Benchmark Education Staff, compiled by. Science Theme: Weather. 2005. spiral bd. 115.00 (***978-1-4108-5316-5(0)***) Benchmark Education Co.

—Water & Weather. 2006. spiral bd. 330.00 (***978-1-4108-7018-6(9)***); 2006. spiral bd. 189.00 (***978-1-4108-7056-8(1)***); 2006. spiral bd. 199.00 (***978-1-4108-7132-9(0)***); 2005. (J). spiral bd. 265.00 (***978-1-4108-5759-0(X)***) Benchmark Education Co.

—Weather & Season. 2006. spiral bd. 249.00 (***978-1-4108-7031-5(6)***) Benchmark Education Co.

Berendes, Mary. Seasons & Weather. 2007. (WordBooks/ Libros de Palabras Ser.). (SPA & ENG.). 24p. (J). 19.93 (***978-1-59296-801-5(5)***) Child's World, Inc.

Berger, Melvin. Can It Rain Cats & Dogs? 1999. (gr. 3-6). lib. bdg. 14.10 (978-0-613-16903-5(4)) Tandem Library Bks.

Berger, Melvin & Berger, Gilda. Can It Rain Cats & Dogs? Sullivan, Robert, illus. 1999. (Scholastic Question & Answer Ser.). 48p. (J). (gr. 2-4). pap. 12.95 (978-0-590-13083-7(8)); pap. 5.95 (978-0-439-08573-1(X)) Scholastic, Inc. (Scholastic Reference).

—How's the Weather? A Look at Weather & How It Changes. Cymerman, John E., illus. 1999. (Discovery Readers Ser.). 48p. (J). (gr. 1 up). lib. bdg. 15.95 (978-0-7910-5067-5(X) , Chelsea Hse.) Facts On File, Inc.

—Hurricanes Have Eyes but Can't See. 2004. (Speedy Facts Ser.). 48p. (J). pap. 7.99 (978-0-439-62534-0(3) , Scholastic Reference) Scholastic, Inc.

—Hurricanes Have Eyes but Can't See: And Other Amazing Facts about Wild Weather. 2003. (Illus.). 48p. (J). (978-0-439-54980-6(9)) Scholastic, Inc.

Bittinger, Gayle. All about Weather. MacMahon, Kelly, illus. 1999. (Rhyme & Reason Workbook Ser.). 32p. (J). (ps-k). pap. 3.95 (978-1-57029-255-2(8) , WPH 01107, Totline Pubns.) Schaffer, Frank Pubns.

Bliss, Pamela. Introduction to Weather. 2004. (National Geographic Reading Expeditions Ser.). (Illus.). 32p. (J). (978-0-7922-4800-2(7)) National Geographic Society.

Boerger, Kristin & Boyett, Suzi. Let's Read about Rain. 2006. (J). lib. bdg. (***978-0-8368-7805-9(1)***); (Illus.). 12p. pap. (***978-0-8368-7810-3(8)***) Stevens, Gareth Inc. (Weekly Reader Early Learning Library).

—Llueve. 2006. (ENG & SPA.). (J). pap. (***978-0-8368-8118-9(4)***); lib. bdg. (***978-0-8368-8113-4(3)***) Stevens, Gareth Inc. (Weekly Reader Early Learning Library).

Bortz, Fred. Dr. Fred's Weather Watch: Create & Run Your Own Weather Station. 2000. (Illus.). 98p. (C). (gr. 7 up). pap. 11.95 (978-0-07-134799-0(2) , 9780071347990) McGraw-Hill Cos., The.

Boyett, Suzi. Let's Read about Snow. 2006. (J). lib. bdg. (***978-0-8368-7806-6(X)***); (Illus.). 12p. pap. (***978-0-8368-7811-0(6)***) Stevens, Gareth Inc. (Weekly Reader Early Learning Library).

—Nieva. 2006. (J). lib. bdg. (***978-0-8368-8114-1(1)*** , Weekly Reader Early Learning Library) Stevens, Gareth Inc.

—Que Tiempo Hace? Nieva. 2006. (Que Tiempo Hace? (Let's Read about Weather) Ser.). (SPA., Illus.). 12p. (J). pap. (***978-0-8368-8119-6(2)*** , Weekly Reader Early Learning Library) Stevens, Gareth Inc.

Brannon, Barbara. Discover Weather. 2005. 39.00 (***978-1-4108-5123-9(0)***) Benchmark Education Co.

Brighter Vision Publishing Staff. Weather: A Skill-Builder Workbook. 1999. (Learning Adventures Kindergarten Ser.). (Illus.). (J). (gr. k-1). pap., wbk. ed. 2.25 (978-1-55254-058-9(8) , BV12020) Brighter Vision Pubns.

Brotak, Ed. Wild about Weather: 50 Wet, Windy & Wonderful Activities. 2005. (Illus.). 128p. (J). (ps-17). pap. 12.95 (978-1-57990-749-5(0)) Lark Bks.

Brotak, Edward. Wild about Weather: 50 Wet, Windy & Wonderful Activities. 2004. (Illus.). 128p. 19.95 (978-1-57990-468-5(8)) Lark Bks.

Bruce, Hank. Where Do Snowmen Go When They Melt? Lampert, Erv, ed. Berkowitz, Henry, illus. 1999. (Winner Coloring Bks.). (J). (gr. k-3). pap. 4.95 (978-0-932855-58-9(X)) Winner Enterprises.

Bundey, Nikki. Drought & People. 2005. (Science of Weather Ser.). (Illus.). 32p. (gr. 4-6). lib. bdg. 21.27 (978-1-57505-498-8(1)) Lerner Publishing Group.

—Drought & the Earth. 2005. (Science of Weather Ser.). (Illus.). 32p. (gr. 4-6). lib. bdg. 21.27 (978-1-57505-473-5(6)) Lerner Publishing Group.

—Ice & the Earth. 2005. (Science of Weather Ser.). (Illus.). 32p. (gr. 4-6). lib. bdg. 21.27 (978-1-57505-472-8(8)) Lerner Publishing Group.

—Storms & People. 2005. (Science of Weather Ser.). (Illus.). 32p. (gr. 4-6). lib. bdg. 21.27 (978-1-57505-499-5(X)) Lerner Publishing Group.

—Storms & the Earth. 2005. (Science of Weather Ser.). (Illus.). 32p. (gr. 4-6). lib. bdg. 21.27 (978-1-57505-474-2(4)) Lerner Publishing Group.

—Wind & the Earth. 2005. (Science of Weather Ser.). (Illus.). 32p. (gr. 4-6). lib. bdg. 21.27 (978-1-57505-470-4(1)) Lerner Publishing Group.

Burby, Liza N. Heatwaves & Droughts. 1999. (Extreme Weather Ser.). (Illus.). 24p. (J). (gr. k-4). lib. bdg. 18.75 (978-0-8239-5292-2(4) , PowerKids Pr.) Rosen Publishing Group, Inc., The.

Burke, Jennifer S. Cold Days. 2000. (gr. k-3). lib. bdg. 12.95 (978-0-613-62198-4(0)) Tandem Library Bks.

—Hot Days. 2000. (gr. k-3). lib. bdg. 12.95 (978-0-613-62206-6(5)) Tandem Library Bks.

—Rainy Days. 2000. (Illus.). 24p. (J). (gr. 4-7). lib. bdg. 12.95 (978-0-613-50492-8(5)) Tandem Library Bks.

—Weather Report, 6 bks., Set. 2004. (Illus.). 24p. (J). (ps-2). 87.00 (978-0-516-23232-4(0) , Children's Pr.) Scholastic Library Publishing.

Burton, Margie & French, Tammy, Cathy - Jones. Cambios en el clima & Changing Weather. 2005. spiral bd. 66.00 (***978-1-4108-5623-4(2)***) Benchmark Education Co.

Burton, Margie, et al. Weather. Evento, Susan, ed. 1998. (Early Connections Ser.). 16p. (J). (gr. k-2). pap. 4.25 (978-1-892393-67-8(0)) Benchmark Education Co.

Carroll, Colleen. The Weather: Sun, Rain, Wind, Snow. 1998. (How Artists See Ser.). (Illus.). 48p. (gr. 4-7). 12.95 (978-0-7892-0478-3(9)) Abbeville Pr., Inc.

Carroll, Michael W., et al. Sky & Sea, Vol. 2. 2005. (God's Creation Ser.). 40p. (J). 7.99 (978-0-310-70579-6(7)) Zonderkidz.

Carson, Mary Kay. Weather Projects for Young Scientists: Experiments & Science Fair Ideas. 2007. (Illus.). 144p. (J). pap. 14.95 (978-1-55652-629-9(6)) Chicago Review Pr., Inc.

—Wow's & Why's of Weather. 2000. (Illus.). 80p. (J). pap. 12.95 (978-0-590-36508-6(8)) Scholastic, Inc.

Casado, Dami & Casado, Alicia. El Otono. 2005. (Brujita Mo). (SPA & ESP., Illus.). 14p. (J). per. 7.99 (978-84-272-6236-2(1)) Molino, Editorial ESP. *Dist:* Santillana USA Publishing Co., Inc.

Challoner, Jack & Dorling Kindersley Publishing Staff. Hurricane & Tornado. 2004. (Eyewitness Books). (Illus.). 72p. (J). lib. bdg. 19.99 (978-0-7566-0689-3(6)) Dorling Kindersley Publishing, Inc.

Chambers, Catherine. Blizzard. 2007. (Wild Weather Ser.). (Illus.). 32p. (J). (gr. 2-4). lib. bdg. 25.36 (***978-1-4034-9575-4(0)***) Heinemann Library.

—Drought. (Wild Weather Ser.). (Illus.). (J). 2002. 32p. (gr. k-2). lib. bdg. 21.36 (978-1-58810-656-8(X)); 2000. 48p. (gr. 4-7). lib. bdg. 24.24 (978-1-57572-426-3(X)) Heinemann Library.

—Wild Weather, 8 bks., Set. 2002. (gr. k-2). lib. bdg. 170.88 (978-1-58810-463-2(X)) Heinemann Library.

Charles, Bob. What Will the Weather Be? 2003. (Early Connections Ser.). (J). pap. 33.00 (978-1-4108-1073-1(9)) Benchmark Education Co.

Childrens Press Staff. Weather & Seasons. 1998. (Rookie Read-About Science Ser.). pap. 23.22 (978-0-516-29990-7(5) , Children's Pr.) Scholastic Library Publishing.

Cipriano, Jeri. El tiempo a Prueba. ed. 2004. (SPA.). 32p. (J). pap. 6.00 (978-1-4108-2340-3(7) , A23407) Benchmark Education Co.

Clarke, Catriona. Weather (Level 2) - Interent Referenced. 2006. (Illus.). 32p. (J). 4.99 (978-0-7945-1253-8(4) , Usborne) EDC Publishing.

Coder, Kelly, ed. Investigating Science - Weather & the Seasons. 2003. 48p. 9.95 (978-1-56234-548-8(6) , Mailbox Bks., The) Education Ctr., Inc.

Conrad, David. The Weather Watcher. McEwen, Rebecca et al, eds. 2002. (Spyglass Books). (Illus.). 24p. (J). (gr. 1 up). lib. bdg. 18.60 (978-0-7565-0247-8(0)) Compass Point Bks.

Corn, John. Weather & Climates. 2005. (Earth's Changing Landscape Ser.). (Illus.). 46p. (J). lib. bdg. (978-1-58340-478-2(3) , 1236346) Smart Apple Media.

Cosgrove, Brian. Weather. 2007. (DK Eyewitness Bks.). 72p. (J). (gr. 3-8). 15.99 incl. cd-rom (978-0-7566-3006-5(1)) Dorling Kindersley Publishing, Inc.

Cosgrove, Brian & Dorling Kindersley Publishing Staff. Weather. Shone, Karl & Percival, Keith, illus. 2004. (Eyewitness Books). 72p. (J). lib. bdg. 19.99 (978-0-7566-0737-1(X)) Dorling Kindersley Publishing, Inc.

Crook, Jennifer. Mrs. Crook's Kindergarten Sings about the Weather. 2003. (Musical Colors Rhyming Story Coloring Book Ser.). (Illus.). 21p. (J). spiral bd. 14.95 (978-1-931844-05-5(4) , PP1017) Piano Pr.

Crump, Irving, ed. Investigating Science - Weather. 2000. 48p. 9.95 (978-1-56234-399-6(8) , Mailbox Bks., The) Education Ctr., Inc.

Dalgleish, Sharon. Rain or Shine. 2002. (Junior Adventure Ser.). (Illus.). 32p. (J). (gr. 3 up). lib. bdg. (978-1-59084-168-6(9)) Mason Crest Pubs.

—Rain or Shine. 1999. (Explorers Ser.). (Illus.). 32p. (J). (978-0-7699-0473-3(4)) Shortland Pubns. (U. S. A.) Inc.

—Weather Watching. 2002. (Junior Adventure Ser.). (Illus.). 32p. (J). (gr. 3 up). lib. bdg. (978-1-59084-197-6(2)) Mason Crest Pubs.

D'Aubuisson, Elisabeth. Snowy Days. 2007. (What's the Weather? Ser.). (Illus.). 24p. (J). (gr. k-3). lib. bdg. 21.25 (***978-1-4042-3684-4(8)*** , PowerKids Pr.) Rosen Publishing Group, Inc., The.

—Sunny Days. 2007. (What's the Weather? Ser.). (Illus.). 24p. (J). (gr. k-3). lib. bdg. 21.25 (***978-1-4042-3685-1(6)*** , PowerKids Pr.) Rosen Publishing Group, Inc., The.

—What's the Weather?, 4 bks., Set. Incl. Rainy Days. lib. bdg. 21.25 (978-1-4042-3682-0(1)); Snowy Days. lib. bdg. 21.25 (***978-1-4042-3684-4(8)***); Sunny Days. lib. bdg. 21.25 (***978-1-4042-3685-1(6)***); Windy Days. lib. bdg. 21.25 (***978-1-4042-3683-7(X)***); (Illus.). 24p. (J). (gr. k-3). 2007. 2007. Set lib. bdg. 85.00 (***978-1-4042-3609-7(0)*** , PowerKids Pr.) Rosen Publishing Group, Inc., The.

—Windy Days. 2007. (What's the Weather? Ser.). (Illus.). 24p. (J). (gr. k-3). lib. bdg. 21.25 (***978-1-4042-3683-7(X)*** , PowerKids Pr.) Rosen Publishing Group, Inc., The.

Davis, Barbara J. Air & Weather. 2006. (J). pap. (***978-0-8368-7871-4(X))*** Stevens, Gareth Inc.

Delano, Marfe Ferguson. Sky. 1998. (National Geographic Nature Library). (J). (978-0-7922-7047-8(9)) National Geographic Society.

Desmond, Jones. Eye of the Storm Vol. 2: Storm, E Weather, Set. abr. ed. 1999. (YA). (gr. 7-12). pap. 30.00 incl. audio (978-0-9669585-3-9(5)) Eye of the Storm.

—Eye of the Storm Vol. 2: Storm, E Weather, Set. Golden Arts Photos and Graphics Staff, tr. 2nd abr. rev. ed. 1999. 72p. (YA). (gr. 7-12). 22.00 incl. audio (978-0-9669585-4-6(3)) Eye of the Storm.

DeWitt, Lynda. What Will the Weather Be? 2002. (Let's-Read-and-Find-Out Science Ser.). 32p. (gr. k-4). lib. bdg. 15.89 (978-0-06-000173-5(9)) HarperCollins Pubs.

DiSpezio, Michael Anthony. Weather Mania: Discovering What's up & What's Coming Down. Garbot, Dave, illus. 2003. 80p. (J). pap. 6.95 (978-1-4027-0860-2(2)) Sterling Publishing Co., Inc.

DK Publishing. Weather. 2008. (EW Travel Guide Phrase Bks.). 288p. pap. 20.00 (***978-0-7566-3686-9(8));*** 48p. (J). (gr. 2-8). pap. 9.99 (***978-0-7566-3823-8(2))*** Dorling Kindersley Publishing, Inc.

DK Publishing Staff. Extreme Weather. 2007. (Experience Ser.). 64p. (J). (gr. 3-8). 15.99 (978-0-7566-2837-6(7)) Dorling Kindersley Publishing, Inc.

—Weather. 2007. (Eye Know Ser.). (Illus.). 24p. (J). 8.99 (978-0-7566-2531-3(9)) Dorling Kindersley Publishing, Inc.

DK Publishing Staff. Weather Watch: Cub Scout Activity Series. 2006. 16p. (J). pap. 2.49 (***978-0-7566-3108-6(4))*** Dorling Kindersley Publishing, Inc.

Dolphin, Colleen. Advisories to Zero Degrees: Weather from A to Z. 2007. (Let's See A to Z Ser.). (ENG., Illus.). 32p. (J). (ps-3). lib. bdg. 25.65 (***978-1-59928-879-6(6)*** , Super SandCastle) ABDO Publishing Co.

Dorion, Christiane. Earth's Garbage Crisis. 2006. (J). pap. (***978-0-8368-7760-1(8)*** , World Almanac Library) Stevens, Gareth Inc.

Dorling Kindersley Publishing Staff, ed. Hurricane & Tornado. 2004. (Dk Eyewitness Books Ser.). (Illus.). 72p. (J). 15.99 (978-0-7566-0690-9(X)) Dorling Kindersley Publishing, Inc.

Doubleday Entertainment USA - Sun: Weather Watch. 2006. (J). per. 7.95 (978-1-59566-229-3(4)) QEB Publishing Inc.

Dunn, Andrew. Fog, Mist & Smog. 1998. (Living with the Weather Ser.). (Illus.). 48p. (J). (gr. 4-7). 18.98 (978-0-8172-5053-9(0)) Raintree.

Dussling, Jennifer. Pink Snow & Other Weird Weather. Petach, Heidi, illus. 1998. (All Aboard Reading Ser.). 48p. (J). (gr. 1-3). pap. 3.99 (978-0-448-41858-2(4) , Grosset & Dunlap) Penguin Group (USA) Inc.

Eckart, Edana. Watching the Weather. 2004. (Wel-Watching Nature-Ppbk Ser.). (Illus.). 24p. (J). (ps-2). pap. 4.95 (978-0-516-25940-6(7) , Children's Pr.) Scholastic Library Publishing.

Egan, Lorraine Hopping. Today's Weather Is... A Book of Experiments. Johnson, Meredith, illus. 2000. 32p. (J). (gr. 2-4). pap. 4.95 (978-1-57255-809-0(1)) Mondo Publishing.

—Today's Weather Is... A Book of Experiments. 2000. (978-0-606-22658-5(3)) Tandem Library Bks.

Estigarribia, Diana. Learning about Weather with Graphic Organizers. 2005. (Graphic Organizers in Science Ser.). (Illus.). 24p. (J). (ps-7). lib. bdg. 19.95 (978-1-4042-2803-0(9)); pap. (978-1-4042-5036-9(0)) Rosen Publishing Group, Inc., The. (PowerKids Pr.).

Eubank, Mark. The Weather Detectives. Hicks, Mark A., illus. 2004. 80p. (YA). (gr. 1-7). pap. 9.95 (978-1-58685-412-6(7)) Gibbs Smith, Publisher.

Evans, David & Williams, Claudette. Seasons & Weather. (Let's Explore Science Ser.). (Illus.). (J). 12.95 (978-0-590-74592-5(1)) Scholastic, Inc.

Finke, Stephanie. Exploring Weather: 30 Amazing Projects That Explore the Wonders of God's Creation. 2000. (And God Created Science Ser.). (Illus.). 100p. (J). (gr. 1-6). pap. 9.99 (978-1-57748-885-9(7)) Barbour Publishing, Inc.

Flanagan, Alice K. Weather. 2000. (Simply Science Ser.). (Illus.). 32p. (J). (gr. 3 up). lib. bdg. 19.93 (978-0-7565-0039-9(7)) Compass Point Bks.

Foxxe, Ellen. The Rising Seas: Shorelines under Threat. 2006. (Extreme Environmental Threats Ser.). (Illus.). 64p. (J). lib. bdg. (978-1-4042-0742-4(2)) Rosen Publishing Group, Inc., The.

Frank, Marjorie Slavick, et al. Science Instant Readers Bk. 7: Check the Weather. 1999. (Harcourt Science Ser.). (gr. 1 up). pap. 15.50 (978-0-15-316205-3(8)) Harcourt Schl. Pubs.

Gakken Co. Ltd. Editors. Wind & Weather. Time-Life Books Editors, tr. 1999. (Illus.). 88p. (J). (gr. 1-4). 14.95 (978-0-8094-4829-6(7)) Time-Life, Inc.

Galiano, Dean. Clouds, Rain & Snow. 2003. (Weather Watchers' Library). (Illus.). 48p. (YA). (gr. 5-8). lib. bdg. 23.95 (978-0-8239-3092-0(0) , WECLRA, Rosen Central) Rosen Publishing Group, Inc., The.

—Hurricanes. rev. ed. 2005. (Weather Watchers' Library). (Illus.). 48p. (YA). (gr. 5-8). lib. bdg. 23.95 (978-0-8239-3095-1(5) , WEHURR) Rosen Publishing Group, Inc., The.

—Thunderstorms & Lightning. 2003. (Weather Watchers' Library). (Illus.). 48p. (YA). (gr. 5-8). lib. bdg. 23.95 (978-0-8239-3093-7(9) , WETHLI, Rosen Central) Rosen Publishing Group, Inc., The.

—Tornadoes. 2005. (Weather Watchers' Library). (Illus.). 48p. (YA). (gr. 5-8). lib. bdg. 23.95 (978-0-8239-3094-4(7) , WETORN) Rosen Publishing Group, Inc., The.

—The Weather Watcher's Library, 4 bks. Incl. Clouds, Rain & Snow. 2003. lib. bdg. 23.95 (978-0-8239-3092-0(0) , WECLRA, Rosen Central); Hurricanes. 2005. lib. bdg. 23.95 (978-0-8239-3095-1(5) , WEHURR); Thunderstorms & Lightning. 2003. lib. bdg. 23.95 (978-0-8239-3093-7(9) , WETHLI, Rosen Central); Tornadoes. 2005. lib. bdg. 23.95 (978-0-8239-3094-4(7) , WETORN); (YA). (gr. 5-8). (Illus.). 48p. 2005. Set lib. bdg. 95.80 (978-0-8239-9048-1(6) , WEWATC) Rosen Publishing Group, Inc., The.

Gardner, Robert. Weather Science Fair Projects Using Sunlight, Rainbows, Ice Cubes, & More. 2005. (Earth Science! Best Science Projects Ser.). (Illus.). 128p. (J). lib. bdg. 26.60 (978-0-7660-2361-1(3)) Enslow Pubs., Inc.

—Wild Science Projects about Earth's Weather. LaBaff, Tom, illus. 2007. (Rockin' Earth Science Experiments Ser.). 48p. (J). lib. bdg. 23.93 (978-0-7660-2734-3(1) , Enslow Elementary) Enslow Pubs., Inc.

Gifford, Clive. Weathering & Erosion. 2005. (Looking at Landscapes Ser.). (Illus.). 47p. (J). (gr. 6-9). lib. bdg. 29.95 (978-1-58340-731-8(6)) Smart Apple Media.

Gilbert, Miquel Angel. Weather. 2002. (Living Planet Ser.). (Illus.). 32p. (J). 23.70 (978-1-56711-683-0(3) , Blackbirch Pr., Inc.) Thomson Gale.

God's World of Weather. 2006. 16p. (J). pap. 1.99 (978-0-7847-1704-2(4) , 04165) Standard Publishing.

Gold, Susan Dudley. Blame It on El Nino. 1999. (Illus.). 96p. (YA). (gr. 5-9). lib. bdg. 28.54 (978-0-7398-1376-8(5)) Raintree.

Green, Jen. Weather. 2002. (Young Library). (Illus.). 32p. (J). lib. bdg. 25.69 (978-0-7398-6318-3(5)) Raintree.

Group/McGraw-Hill, Wright. Forces of Nature: Level K, 6 vols., Vol. 2. (First Explorers Ser.). 24p. (gr. 1-2). 34.95 (978-0-7699-1458-9(6)) Shortland Pubns. (U. S. A.) Inc.

—Winter Weather: Collection 2. (Storyteller Interactive Writing Cards Ser.). (gr. k-3). (978-0-322-09341-6(4)) Wright Group, The.

Haddon, Jean. It's a Beautiful Day! Enright, Vicky, illus. 2005. (Silly Millies Ser.). 32p. (J). (ps-ps). pap. 4.99 (978-0-7613-2397-6(X) , First Avenue Editions) Lerner Publishing Group.

—It's a Beautiful Day! Enright, Vicky, tr. Enright, Vicky, illus. 2004. (Silly Millies Ser.). 32p. (J). lib. bdg. (978-0-7613-2834-6(3) , Millbrook Pr.) Lerner Publishing Group.

Hall, Julie. Weather: Grades 2 & 3. (Illus.). (J). pap., wbk. ed. 4.99 (978-0-88743-962-9(4)) School Zone Publishing Co.

Harcourt School Publishers Staff. All Kinds of Weather. 3rd ed. 2002. (Trophies English Language Learners Ser.). (Illus.). (J). pap. 4.10 (978-0-15-327592-0(8)) Harcourt Schl. Pubs.

—All Kinds of Weather - 5 Pack - Grade 1. 3rd ed. 2002. (Trophies English Language Learners Ser.). 20.10 (978-0-15-327626-2(6)) Harcourt Schl. Pubs.

—Check the Weather: Science Reader. 2000. (SPA., Illus.). (J). pap. 3.70 (978-0-15-316110-0(8)) Harcourt Schl. Pubs.

—Water & Weather. 3rd ed. 2002. (Trophies English Language Learners Ser.). (Illus.). (J). pap. 5.10 (978-0-15-327648-4(7)) Harcourt Schl. Pubs.

—What's the Weather. 3rd ed. 2002. (Horizons Ser.). (Illus.). (J). (gr. k). pap. 3.70 (978-0-15-333112-1(7)) Harcourt Schl. Pubs.

Harman, Rebecca. The Earth's Weather. 2005. (Heinemann Infosearch Ser.). (Illus.). 32p. (J). pap. (978-1-4034-7065-2(0)); lib. bdg. (978-1-4034-7058-4(8)) Heinemann Library.

Harris, Caroline & Faidley, Warren. Wild Weather. 2005. (Kingfisher Voyages Ser.). (Illus.). 60p. (J). (gr. 4-6). 14.95 (978-0-7534-5911-9(6) , Kingfisher) Houghton Mifflin Co. Trade & Reference Div.

Haslam, Andrew. Temps et Climat. 2000. (Make It Work! Geography Ser.). (FRE.). (J). (gr. 3-6). pap. 6.95 (978-1-58728-191-4(0) , Two Can Publishing) T&N Children's Publishing.

Heat Hazard 6-Pack: Droughts. 2004. pap. 45.90 (978-1-4109-1215-2(9)) Harcourt Schl. Pubs.

Herriges, Ann. Clouds. 2006. (Blastoff! Readers Ser.). (Illus.). 24p. (J). lib. bdg. 16.95 (978-1-60014-024-2(6)) Bellwether Media.

—Lightning. 2006. (Blastoff! Readers Ser.). (Illus.). 24p. (J). lib. bdg. 16.95 (978-1-60014-025-9(4)) Bellwether Media.

—Rain. 2006. (Blastoff! Readers Ser.). (Illus.). 24p. (J). lib. bdg. 16.95 (978-1-60014-027-3(0)) Bellwether Media.

—Snow. 2006. (Blastoff! Readers Ser.). (Illus.). 24p. (J). lib. bdg. 16.95 (978-1-60014-029-7(7)) Bellwether Media.

—Sunshine. 2006. (Blastoff! Readers Ser.). (Illus.). 24p. (J). lib. bdg. 16.95 (978-1-60014-028-0(9)) Bellwether Media.

—Wind. 2006. (Blastoff! Readers Ser.). (Illus.). 24p. (J). lib. bdg. 16.95 (978-1-60014-026-6(2)) Bellwether Media.

Hewitt, Sally. Weather. 2000. (It's Science! Ser.). (Illus.). 32p. (J). (gr. k-3). 23.50 (978-0-516-21657-7(0) , Children's Pr.) Scholastic Library Publishing.

Hiscock, Bruce. The Big Storm. 2000. (Illus.). (J). (978-0-606-17912-6(7)) Tandem Library Bks.

Holt, Rinehart and Winston Staff. Holt Science & Technology Chptr. 17: Understanding the Weather: Chapter Resources - Tennessee Edition. 3rd ed. 2003. (YA). pap. 11.40 (978-0-03-069148-5(6)) Holt, Rinehart & Winston.

—Weather Science Kit: Consumable Edition, Module I. 2nd ed. 2002. (Holt Science & Technology Ser.). 142.73 (978-0-03-067641-3(X)) Holt, Rinehart & Winston.

Hosack, Karen. Weather. 2005. (Illus.). 32p. (J). (gr. 1-3). lib. bdg. 24.22 (978-1-4034-4855-2(8)) Heinemann Library.

Hot & Cold Weather, 6 vols. (Sunshinetm Science Ser.). 24p. (gr. 1-2). 37.50 (978-0-7802-1380-7(7)); 41.95 (978-0-7802-1379-1(3)) Wright Group, The.

Howell, Laura. Introduction to Weather & Climate Change. 2004. (Geography Ser.). (Illus.). 96p. (J). pap. 14.95 (978-0-7945-0629-2(1)) EDC Publishing.

—Weather & Climate Change. 2004. (Geography Ser.). 96p. (J). lib. bdg. 22.95 (978-1-58086-613-2(1) , Usborne) EDC Publishing.

—Weather & Climate Change. 2004. (Discovery Channel School Science Ser.). (Illus.). 32p. (J). (gr. 5 up). lib. bdg. 24.67 (978-0-8368-3386-7(4)) Stevens, Gareth Inc.

How's the Weather? (Discovery Readers Ser.). 48p. (J). pap. 3.95 (978-0-8249-5316-4(9) , Ideals Children's Bks.) Ideals Pubns.

Huggins-Cooper, Lynn. Weather. McNicholas, Shelagh & Burroughs, David, illus. 2004. 30p. (J). lib. bdg. (978-1-58340-445-4(7)) Smart Apple Media.

Hunter, Rebecca M. Weather. 2001. (Discovering Science Ser.). (Illus.). 32p. (J). (gr. 4-7). lib. bdg. 25.69 (978-0-7398-3245-5(X)) Raintree.

Jackson, Randy. Get Ready for Hazardous Weather: Learning Through Puzzles, Games & Exercises. 2004. 40p. (YA). 3.50 (978-0-9742794-2-8(0)) HazardousWeather Preparedness Institute.

James, Diane. Sun, Snow & Rainbow! Bulloch, Ivan, illus. rev. ed. 2004. (My Turn Ser.). 12p. (J). (ps-k). bds. 6.95 (978-1-58728-007-8(8) , Two Can Publishing) T&N Children's Publishing.

Jennings, Terry. Atmosphere & Weather. 2005. (Illus.). 48p. (J). (gr. 6-9). lib. bdg. 29.95 (978-1-58340-725-7(1)) Smart Apple Media.

—Droughts. 1999. (Natural Disasters Ser.). (Illus.). 32p. (J). lib. bdg. 16.95 (978-1-929298-45-7(5)) Chrysalis Education.

—Weather. 1998. (Find Out about Ser.). (Illus.). 24p. (J). (ps-3). (978-0-563-37382-7(2)) BBC Worldwide.

—Weather Patterns. 2005. (Illus.). 48p. (J). (gr. 6-9). lib. bdg. 29.95 (978-1-58340-726-4(X)) Smart Apple Media.

Jennings, Terry J. The Weather: Clouds. 2004. (J). lib. bdg. 27.10 (978-1-59389-147-3(4)) Chrysalis Education.

—The Weather: Rain. 2004. (J). lib. bdg. 27.10 (978-1-59389-143-5(1)) Chrysalis Education.

—The Weather: Snow. 2004. (J). lib. bdg. 27.10 (978-1-59389-145-9(8)) Chrysalis Education.

—The Weather: Sunshine. 2004. (J). lib. bdg. 27.10 (978-1-59389-144-2(X)) Chrysalis Education.

—The Weather: Wind. 2004. (J). lib. bdg. 27.10 (978-1-59389-146-6(6)) Chrysalis Education.

Johnson, Rebecca L. Weather & Climate. 2003. (National Geographic Reading Expeditions Ser.). (Illus.). 32p. (J). pap. (978-0-7922-8876-3(9)) National Geographic Society.

Jones, Lorraine. Super Science Projects about Weather & Natural Forces. 2005. (Psyched for Science Ser.). (Illus.). 48p. (YA). (gr. 5-8). lib. bdg. 23.95 (978-0-8239-3105-7(6) , SCWENA) Rosen Publishing Group, Inc., The.

Juettner, Bonnie. Weather. 2003. (Kidhaven Science Library). (Illus.). 48p. (J). 26.20 (978-0-7377-2078-5(6) , Greenhaven Pr., Inc.) Thomson Gale.

Kauffman, Dorothy. The Weather. 2005. (Content Area Readers Ser.). 4.95 (978-0-19-430957-8(6)) Oxford Univ. Pr., Inc.

Kenah, Katharine. Wild Weather. 2004. (Extreme Readers Ser.). (Illus.). 32p. (J). (ps-2). pap. 3.95 (978-0-7696-3178-3(9)) School Specialty Publishing.

Kerrod, Robin. Weather. 1999. (Learn about Ser.). (Illus.). 64p. (gr. 4-7). 12.95 (978-1-85967-189-4(6) , Lorenz Bks.) Anness Publishing, Inc.

—Weather: Fantastic Facts. 2000. (Fantastic Facts Ser.). (Illus.). 64p. (gr. 2-7). pap. 6.95 (978-1-84215-083-2(9) , Southwater) Anness Publishing GBR. *Dist:* National Bk. Network.

—Wild Weather. (All about Ser.). (Illus.). 64p. (gr. 3-7). 2004. pap. 7.99 (978-1-84215-768-8(X) , Southwater); 2000. 14.95 (978-0-7548 0151 2(8) , Lorenz Bks.) Anness Publishing GBR. *Dist:* National Bk. Network.

Kierein, Tom. Weather: A National Geographic Action Book. Buxton, John, illus. 2005. 10p. (J). (gr. 4-8). reprint ed. 16.00 (978-0-7567-9148-3(0)) DIANE Publishing Co.

Knapp, Brian J. Weather Watch Set: A Month-by-Month Guide to World Weather, 12 vols., Set. 1999. (Illus.). 576p. (J). (gr. 3-8). lib. bdg. 285.00 (978-0-7172-9458-9(7) , Grolier) Scholastic Library Publishing.

Koehler, Susan. Weather. 2008. (J). (***978-1-60044-625-2(6))*** Rourke Publishing, LLC.

Ladd, Karol. The Glad Scientist Learn about the Weather. 2004. (Glad Scientist Ser.). pap., act. bk. ed. 6.99 (978-0-8054-0830-0(4)) B&H Publishing Grp.

LaFontaine, Bruce. All about the Weather. 2004. (Illus.). 48p. (J). (gr. 3). pap. 3.95 (978-0-486-43036-2(7)) Dover Pubns., Inc.

Lambert, Jonathan. Weather. 2000. (Picture Magic Ser.). (Illus.). 12p. (J). (ps-1). pap. 6.95 (978-0-439-11207-9(9) , Cartwheel Bks.) Scholastic, Inc.

Lauw, Darlene. Weather. 2003. (gr. 3-6). lib. bdg. 16.40 (978-0-613-52927-3(8)) Tandem Library Bks.

Lauw, Darlene & Puay, Lim Cheng. Weather. 2002. (Science Alive! Ser.). (Illus.). 32p. (J). (gr. 4-5). pap. (978-0-7787-0611-3(7)); lib. bdg. (978-0-7787-0565-9(X)) Crabtree Publishing Co.

Lawson, Julia & Browne, Naima. Weather Watch! Millard, Peter, photos by. 2005. (Stepping Stones Ser.). (Illus.). 24p. (J). (ps). pap. 9.95 (978-0-237-52921-5(1) , Evans Brothers, Limited) Evans Publishing Group GBR. *Dist:* Independent Pubs. Group.

Levine, Shar & Johnstone, Leslie. Wonderful Weather. Harpster, Steve, illus. 2005. (First Science Experiments Ser.). 48p. (J). (ps). pap. 4.95 (978-1-4027-2768-9(2)) Sterling Publishing Co., Inc.

Linde, Barbara M. Weather & Climate. 2005. 39.00 (***978-1-4108-4587-0(7))*** Benchmark Education Co.

Lindsay, Elizabeth, ed. Investigating Science - Weather & Climate. 2000. 48p. 9.95 (978-1-56234-394-1(7) , Mailbox Bks., The) Education Ctr., Inc.

Llewellyn, Claire. Weather. 2006. (Illus.). 24p. (J). (978-1-59771-020-6(2)) Sea-To-Sea Pubns.

Lonsdale, Mary, illus. Whatever the Weather: When the Snow Comes. 2004. (Whatever the Weather Ser.). 10p. (J). bds. 4.99 (978-1-85854-103-7(4)) Brimax Books Ltd. GBR. *Dist:* Byeway Bks.

—Whatever the Weather: When the Sun Shines. 2004. (Whatever the Weather Ser.). 10p. (J). bds. 4.99 (978-1-85854-105-1(0)) Brimax Books Ltd. GBR. *Dist:* Byeway Bks.

—Whatever the Weather: When the Wind Blows. 2004. (Whatever the Weather Ser.). 10p. (J). bds. 4.99 (978-1-85854-102-0(6)) Brimax Books Ltd. GBR. *Dist:* Byeway Bks.

Look Out the Window: First Grade Big Books. (On Our Way to English Ser.). (gr. 1 up). 29.95 (978-0-7578-1501-0(4)) Rigby Education.

Look Out the Window: Small Versions of Big Books. (On Our Way to English Ser.). (gr. 1 up). 29.00 (978-0-7578-7228-0(X)) Rigby Education.

Low, Robert S., ed. My Guide to Our Weather. 2002. 32p. (J). (gr. 2-3). pap., wbk. ed. 2.75 (978-1-56762-173-0(2)) Modern Learning Pr.

Lowel, Margaret. Weather Tools: A Content Area Reader-science. 2005. (Sadlier Phonics Reading Program). (Illus.). 12p. (YA). (ps-2). 25.20 (978-0-8215-7814-8(6)) Sadlier, William H. Inc.

Lynn, Sara. Rain & Shine: A First Look at Seasons. James, Diane, illus. rev. ed. 2000. (Play & Discover Ser.). (J). (ps-2). 9.95 (978-1-58728-042-9(6) , Two Can Publishing) T&N Children's Publishing.

MacDonald, Fiona. Weather. 2000. (gr. 3-6). lib. bdg. 15.25 (978-0-613-56872-2(9)) Tandem Library Bks.

Mack, Lorrie & Dorling Kindersley Publishing Staff. Weather. 2004. (Eye Wonder Ser.). 48p. (J). lib. bdg. 17.99 (978-0-7566-0324-3(2)); (Illus.). 9.99 (978-0-7566-0323-6(4)) Dorling Kindersley Publishing, Inc.

Made by God: Weather. 2004. 32p. (C). pap. 5.99 (978-0-7424-2809-6(5)) School Specialty Publishing.

Mahaney, Ian F. Reading Weather Maps. 2007. (Illus.). 24p. (J). (978-1-4042-2403-2(3)); pap. (978-1-4042-2213-7(8)); lib. bdg. (978-1-4042-3057-6(2)) Rosen Publishing Group, Inc., The. (PowerKids Pr.).

Maisner, Heather. Amazing Weather. 2006. (Amazing World). 28p. (J). (gr. 3-8). 17.95 (978-0-7696-4835-4(5)) School Specialty Publishing.

Making a Weather Chart: KinderFacts Individual Title Six-Packs. (Kinderstarters Ser.). 8p. (ps-1). 21.00 (978-0-7635-8753-6(2)) Rigby Education.

Mandell, Muriel. Weather Experiments. Gallagher, Jack, illus. 2006. (No Sweat Science Ser.). 128p. pap. 5.95 (978-1-4027-2157-1(9)) Sterling Publishing Co., Inc.

Mann, Rachel. Sun & Rain. 2003. (Compass Point Phonics Readers Ser.). (Illus.). 16p. (J). (gr. 1 up). 13.26 (978-0-7565-0525-7(9)) Compass Point Bks.

Marsico, Katie. Wild Weather Days. 2006. (Scholastic News Nonfiction Readers Ser.). (Illus.). 24p. (J). (gr. k-2). 19.00 (978-0-531-16771-7(2) , Children's Pr.) Scholastic Library Publishing.

Mayer, Cassie. Clouds. 2006. (Illus.). 24p. (J). (978-1-4034-8411-6(2)); pap. 5.99 (978-1-4034-8419-2(8)) Heinemann Library.

—Nubes. 2006. (ENG & SPA., Illus.). 24p. (J). (***978-1-4034-8652-3(2))*** Heinemann Library.

—Nubes (Clouds) 2006. (ENG & SPA., Illus.). 24p. (J). pap. (***978-1-4034-8660-8(3))*** Heinemann Library.

—Viento. 2006. (ENG & SPA., Illus.). 24p. (J). (***978-1-4034-8653-0(0))*** Heinemann Library.

—Viento (Wind) 2006. (ENG & SPA., Illus.). 24p. (J). pap. (***978-1-4034-8661-5(1))*** Heinemann Library.

Mayer, Cassie. Wind. 2006. (Illus.). 24p. (J). (978-1-4034-8412-3(0)); pap. 5.99 (978-1-4034-8420-8(1)) Heinemann Library.

Maynard, Christopher & Martin, Terry. Why Does Lightning Strike? Questions Children Ask about Weather. (Why Bks.). (Illus.). 24p. (J). pap. 10.99 (978-0-590-24945-4(2)) Scholastic, Inc.

Mehling, Randi. Weather, & How It Works. 2007. (Scientific American Ser.). 72p. (J). (gr. 5-8). 30.00 (978-0-7910-9053-4(1) , Chelsea Hse.) Facts On File, Inc.

Meredith Books Staff, ed. Wicked Weather. 2007. 48p. (J). pap. 6.99 (***978-0-696-23689-1(3))*** Meredith Bks.

Merk, A. Studying Weather. 2003. (Weather Report Discovery Library). (Illus.). 24p. (gr. 1-4). 14.95 (978-1-58952-573-3(6)) Rourke Publishing, LLC.

—Weather Signs. 2003. (Weather Report Discovery Library). (Illus.). 24p. (gr. 1-4). 14.95 (978-1-58952-575-7(2)) Rourke Publishing, LLC.

Meses y Estaciones. (Coleccion Picaros Peluchines). (SPA.). (J). 5.50 (978-950-11-0401-1(X) , SGM401) Sigmar ARG. *Dist:* Continental Bk. Co., Inc.

Michaels, Pat. W Is for Wind: A Weather Alphabet. Rose, Melanie, illus. rev. ed. 2005. 40p. (J). 16.95 (978-1-58536-237-0(9)) Sleeping Bear Pr.

Michaels, Pat. A Weather Alphabet. rev. ed. 2007. 40p. pap. 7.95 (***978-1-58536-330-8(8))*** Sleeping Bear Pr.

Milbourne, Anna. Snowy Day. 2005. 24p. (J). 9.99 (978-0-7945-1147-0(3) , Usborne) EDC Publishing.

Mitchell, Nancy, et al. Raging Skies. Christensen, Edie et al, illus. 1999. (Changing Earth Trilogy Ser.: Bk. 2). 191p. (Orig.). (J). (ps-12). mass mkt. 5.95 (978-1-892713-01-8(2)) Lightstream Pubns.

Mitzo Thompson, Kim. What Is the Weather Like Today? 2006. (Dual Language Readers Ser.). 32p. (J). pap. 4.99 (978-0-7696-4617-6(4)) School Specialty Publishing.

W X Y Z

Mogil, H. Michael & Discovery Books Staff. Weather. 1999. (Explore Your World Ser.). (Illus.). 192p. (J). pap. 13.95 (978-1-56331-802-3(4)) Discovery Bks.

Moore, Jo Ellen. Learning about Weather. Smith, Phillip et al, illus. 2000. (ScienceWorks for Kids Ser.). 80p. (J). (gr. k-1). pap. 9.95 (978-1-55799-774-6(8) , EMC 870) Evan-Moor Educational Pubs.

Morris, Neil. Weather. 2003. (Knowledge Masters Ser.). (Illus.). 32p. (YA). pap. incl. cd-rom (978-1-903954-52-2(5)) Chrysalis Children's Bks.

—Weather. 2002. (Our World Ser.). (Illus.). 32p. (J). lib. bdg. 24.25 (978-1-930643-76-5(4)) Chrysalis Education.

Murphy, Brian & Whalley, Margaret. Weather. 2004. (Experiment with Ser.). (SPA., Illus.). 32p. (gr. 2-5). (J). pap. 5.95 (978-1-58728-120-4(1)); 9.95 (978-1-58728-249-2(6)) T&N Children's Publishing. (Two Can Publishing).

Nankin, Frances. Weather. 2000. (Eyes on Nature Ser.). (Illus.). 109p. (J). (978-1-56156-914-4(3)) Kidsbooks, Inc.

Nardo, Don. The Ice Ages. 2005. (KidHaven Science Library). (Illus.). 48p. (J). (gr. 4-8). 26.20 (978-0-7377-3055-5(2) , Greenhaven Pr., Inc.) Thomson Gale.

National Audubon Society Staff, et al. Weather. 1998. (Audubon Society First Field Guide Ser.). (Illus.). 160p. (J). (gr. 3-7). pap. 8.95 (978-0-590-05488-1(0) , Scholastic Reference) Scholastic, Inc.

National Geographic Society Staff, ed. Weather. 2001. (My First Pocket Guides Ser.). (Illus.). 80p. (J). (gr. 1-5). pap. 7.95 (978-0-7922-6588-7(2) , National Geographic Children's Bks.) National Geographic Society.

Nature on the Rampage, 6 bks., Set. 2000. (Illus.). (J). pap. (978-0-7398-4169-3(6)) Raintree.

Nayer, Judy. Weather. Chicko, Terri, illus. 1999. (At Your Fingertips Ser.). 5p. (J). (ps-3). mass mkt. 6.95 (978-0-7681-0102-7(6) , McClanahan Bk.) Learning Horizons, Inc.

Nelson, Robin. Rainy Day. 2001. (gr. k-3). lib. bdg. 11.80 (978-0-613-76618-0(0)) Tandem Library Bks.

—A Windy Day. 2001. (Illus.). 23p. (J). (ps-3). lib. bdg. 11.80 (978-0-613-35344-1(7)) Tandem Library Bks.

Newson, Lesley & Wadsworth, Pamela. Rhagor Am Greigiau, Pridd a Thywydd. 2005. (WEL., Illus.). 24p. pap. (978-1-85596-238-5(1)) Dref Wen.

Oard, Michael. The Weather Book -Study Guide. 2005. pap. 3.99 (978-1-893345-59-1(9)) Answers in Genesis Ministries.

Olien, Rebecca. Water & the Weather. 2005. (Illus.). 24p. (J). 21.26 (978-0-7368-3702-6(7)) Capstone Pr., Inc.

On All Kinds of Days. 2006. (Yellow Umbrella Science Ser.). 8,16p. (J). 6.50 (978-0-7368-1704-2(2)) Red Brick Learning.

Orero, Maria Jesus. Nico y Las Estaciones. 2005. (SPA & ESP., Illus.). 12p. (ps-ps). per. 6.99 (978-84-272-6154-9(3)) Molino, Editorial ESP. *Dist:* Santillana USA Publishing Co., Inc.

Orme, Helen. What Makes Weather? 2003. (What? Where? Why? Ser.). (Illus.). 24p. (J). (gr. 1 up). lib. bdg. 20.67 (978-0-8368-3788-9(6)) Stevens, Gareth Inc.

Osborne, Will & Osborne, Mary Pope. Twisters & Other Terrible Storms. Murdocca, Sal, illus. 2003. (Magic Tree House Research Guide Ser.: No. 8). 128p. (J). (gr. k-3). 4.99 (978-0-375-81358-0(6) , Random Hse. Bks. for Young Readers) Random Hse. Children's Bks.

—Twisters & Other Terrible Storms: A Nonfiction Companion to Twister on Tuesday. Murdocca, Sal, illus. 2003. (Magic Tree House Research Guide Ser.: No. 8). 128p. (J). (gr. k-3). lib. bdg. 11.99 (978-0-375-91358-7(0) , Random Hse. Bks. for Young Readers) Random Hse. Children's Bks.

—Twisters & Other Terrible Storms: A Nonfiction Companion to Twister on Tuesday. Murdocca, Sal, illus. 2003. (Magic Tree House Research Guide Ser.: No. 8). 119p. (J). (gr. k-3). per. 13.00 (978-0-613-62411-4(4)) Tandem Library Bks.

Oxlade, Chris. Weather. 2000. (Science Fact Files Ser.). (Illus.). 48p. (J). (gr. 4-7). lib. bdg. 27.12 (978-0-7398-1008-8(1)) Raintree.

Parker, Janice. The Science of Weather. 2000. (Living Science Ser.). (Illus.). 32p. (J). (gr. 2 up). lib. bdg. 24.67 (978-0-8368-2684-5(1)) Stevens, Gareth Inc.

Pebble Books: Our Seasons & Weather. 2005. (YA). (gr. k-3). 712.80 (978-0-7368-4219-8(5) , Pebble Bks.) Capstone Pr., Inc.

Petelinsek, Kathleen & Primm, E. Russell. Weather. 2006. (Talking Hands Ser.).Tr. of El Tiempo. (ENG & SPA., Illus.). 24p. (J). 21.36 (978-1-59296-684-4(5)) Child's World, Inc.

Peterson, Roger T., et al. Peterson First Guide to Clouds & Weather. 2nd ed. 1998. (First Guides). (Illus.). 128p. pap. 5.95 (978-0-395-90663-7(6)) Houghton Mifflin Co. Trade & Reference Div.

Petrie, Allyson. Where Did the Sun Go? Wise, Noreen, ed. Landrie, Don, illus. 2000. (Book-a-Day Collection). 32p. (YA). (ps up). pap. 5.95 (978-1-58584-395-4(4)) Huckleberry Pr.

Pettigrew, Mark. Weather. 2004. (J). lib. bdg. (978-1-932799-30-9(3)) Stargazer Bks.

Phelan, Glen. Extreme Weather. 2004. (National Geographic Reading Expeditions Ser.). (Illus.). 32p. (J). pap. (978-0-7922-4575-9(X)) National Geographic Society.

Pipe, Jim. Weather. (J). 2007. (***978-1-59604-130-1(7));*** 2004. lib. bdg. 27.10 (978-1-932799-47-7(8)) Stargazer Bks.

Pocket Chart Science: Weather. 2000. (J). pap. 9.95 (978-1-56911-700-2(4)) Learning Resources, Inc.

Powell, Jillian. Rain & Us. 1998. (Weather Ser.). (Illus.). 32p. (J). (gr. 1-5). lib. bdg. 16.95 (978-1-887068-38-3(4)) Smart Apple Media.

Preszler, June. Where Does Lightning Come From? A Book about Weather. 2007. 24p. (J). (978-0-7368-6754-2(6)) Capstone Pr., Inc.

Primm & Petelinsek. Seasons/Estaciones. 2004. (Talking Hands, Listening Eyes Ser.). (ENG & SPA., Illus.). 24p. (J). (ps-3). 21.36 (978-1-59296-023-1(5)) Child's World, Inc.

Pugliano-Martin, Carol. Summer to Fall. 2006. (Early Explorers Ser.). (J). 34.00 (***978-1-4108-6102-3(3)***) Benchmark Education Co.

Quin, Caroline & Pearce, Sue. Weather. 2004. (Activities for 3-5 Year Olds Ser.). (Illus.). 32p. pap. 11.00 (978-1-897675-39-7(9)) Brilliant Pubns. GBR. *Dist:* Parkwest Pubns., Inc.

Rabe, Tish. The Cat in the Hat's Learning Library: All about Weather. Ruiz, Aristides, illus. 2004. (Cat in the Hat's Learning Library). 48p. (J). (gr. k-3). 8.99 (978-0-375-82276-6(3) , Random Hse. Bks. for Young Readers) Random Hse. Children's Bks.

—Oh Say Can You Say What's the Weather Today? All about Weather. Ruiz, Aristides, illus. 2004. (Cat in the Hat's Learning Library Ser.). 48p. (J). (gr. k-3). lib. bdg. 11.99 (978-0-375-92276-3(8) , Random Hse. Bks. for Young Readers) Random Hse. Children's Bks.

Rain or Shine. 2001. (First Discovery Look-Inside Board Bks.). 10p. (J). (ps). bds. 4.95 (978-0-439-29730-1(3) , Cartwheel Bks.) Scholastic, Inc.

Rain or Shine: Level O, 6 vols. (Explorers Ser.). 32p. (gr. 3-6). 44.95 (978-0-7699-0596-9(X)) Shortland Pubns. (U. S. A.) Inc.

Raintree Steck-Vaughn Staff. Weather: Concepts & Application. 2000. pap. (978-0-7398-2710-9(3)) Steck-Vaughn.

Rau, Dana Meachen. Fluffy, Flat, & Wet: A Book about Clouds. Shea, Denise, illus. 2005. (Amazing Science Ser.). 24p. (J). (ps-k). lib. bdg. 22.60 (978-1-4048-1134-8(6)) Picture Window Bks.

Richards, Julie. It's Raining! 2004. (J). lib. bdg. 27.10 (978-1-58340-536-9(4)) Smart Apple Media.

—It's Snowing! 2004. (J). lib. bdg. 27.10 (978-1-58340-539-0(9)) Smart Apple Media.

—It's Stormy! 2004. (J). lib. bdg. 27.10 (978-1-58340-534-5(8)) Smart Apple Media.

—It's Sunny! 2004. (J). lib. bdg. 27.10 (978-1-58340-535-2(6)) Smart Apple Media.

Rigby Education Staff. Hot & Cold. (Sails Literacy Ser.). (Illus.). 16p. (gr. 1-2). 27.00 (978-0-7635-9920-1(4) , 699204C99) Rigby Education.

Ring, Susan. On All Kinds of Days. 2006. (Yellow Umbrella Books for Early Readers). (Illus.). 18p. (J). (978-0-7368-5976-9(4)); (ENG & SPA., (978-0-7368-6012-3(6)) Yellow Umbrella Pr.

Rodgers, Alan & Streluk, Angelia. Measuring the Weather. 2002. (J). (gr. 3-5). lib. bdg. 113.95 (978-1-58810-468-7(0)) Heinemann Library.

Rodgers, Alan & Streluk, Angelia. Temperature. 2002. (Measuring the Weather Ser.). (Illus.). 32p. (J). (gr. 3-5). lib. bdg. 22.79 (978-1-58810-689-6(6)) Heinemann Library.

Rogers, Alan. Sol y Lluvia. 2004. (Pequenos Gigantes Ser.).Tr. of Bright & Breezy. (SPA., Illus.). 16p. (ps-k). 5.95 (978-1-58728-298-0(4) , Two Can Publishing) T&N Children's Publishing.

Rogers, Allen & Streluk, Angella. Temperature. 2002. (Illus.). 32p. (J). (gr. 3-5). pap. (978-1-4034-0129-8(2) , 91634) Heinemann Library.

Rosa-Mendoza, Gladys. The Weather. Cifuentes, Carolina, ed. Hullinger, C. D., illus. 2004. (English-Spanish Foundations Ser.: Vol. 6). Orig. Title: El Tiempo. (ENG & SPA.). 20p. (J). (ps-4). bds. 6.95 (978-0-9679748-5-9(2)) Me+Mi Publishing.

Rosenberg, Pam. Fun Weather Days. 2006. (Scholastic News Nonfiction Readers Ser.). (Illus.). 24p. (J). 19.00 (978-0-531-16772-4(0) , Children's Pr.) Scholastic Library Publishing.

Ross, Kathy. Crafts for Kids Who Are Learning about the Weather. Barger, Jan, illus. 2006. (Crafts for Kids Who Are Learning about... Ser.). 47p. (J). 25.26 (978-0-7613-2796-7(7) , Millbrook Pr.) Lerner Publishing Group.

Royston, Angela. Looking at Weather & Seasons: How Do They Change? 2008. (Looking at Science: How Things Change Ser.). 32p. (J). (gr. 1-3). lib. bdg. 22.60 (***978-0-7660-3093-0(8)***) Enslow Pubs., Inc.

Royston, Angela. Weather Around You. 1998. (Geography Starts Here Ser.). (Illus.). 32p. (J). (gr. 1-4). lib. bdg. 25.69 (978-0-8172-5115-4(4)) Raintree.

Rubin, Joel. Weather. 2007. (J). (***978-1-4034-7912-9(7)***) Heinemann Library.

Rupp, Rebecca. Weather: A Book about Pink Snow, Fighting Kites, Lightning Rods, Rains of Frogs, Typhoons, Tornadoes, & Ice Balls from Space. Nap, Dug & Sweet, Melissa, illus. 2003. 144p. (J). (gr. 3-7). pap. 14.95 (978-1-58017-420-6(5) , 67420, Storey Kids) Storey Publishing, LLC.

Rustad, Martha E. H. Today Is Cold. 2006. (Illus.). 24p. (J). 19.93 (978-0-7368-5342-2(1)) Capstone Pr., Inc.

—Today Is Hot. 2006. (Illus.). 24p. (J). 19.93 (978-0-7368-5343-9(X)) Capstone Pr., Inc.

—Today Is Rainy. 2006. (Illus.). 24p. (J). 19.93 (978-0-7368-5344-6(8)) Capstone Pr., Inc.

—Today Is Snowy. 2006. (Illus.). 24p. (J). 19.93 (978-0-7368-5345-3(6)) Capstone Pr., Inc.

—Today Is Sunny. 2006. (Illus.). 24p. (J). (978-0-7368-5346-0(4)) Capstone Pr., Inc.

—Today Is Windy. 2006. (Illus.). 24p. (J). (978-0-7368-5347-7(2)) Capstone Pr., Inc.

Sacks, Janet. Weather & Art Activities. 2002. (Arty Facts Ser.). (Illus.). 48p. (J). (gr. 3-4). pap. (978-0-7787-1146-9(3)); lib. bdg. (978-0-7787-1118-6(8)) Crabtree Publishing Co.

—Weather & Art Activities. 2002. (gr. 3-6). lib. bdg. 17.60 (978-0-613-52928-0(6)) Tandem Library Bks.

Saunders-Smith, Gail. Lightning. 1998. (Weather Ser.). (Illus.). 24p. (J). (ps-2). pap. 13.25 (978-0-516-21332-3(6) , Children's Pr.) Scholastic Library Publishing.

—Rain. 1998. (Weather Ser.). (Illus.). 24p. (J). (ps-2). pap. 13.25 (978-0-516-21331-6(8) , Children's Pr.) Scholastic Library Publishing.

—Sunshine. 1998. (Weather Ser.). (Illus.). 24p. (J). (gr. k-2). pap. 13.25 (978-0-516-21333-0(4) , Children's Pr.) Scholastic Library Publishing.

—Weather, 4 bks. 1998. (J). (978-0-516-29741-5(4) , Children's Pr.) Scholastic Library Publishing.

—Weather & the Seasons Science. (gr. k-2). 19.95 (978-0-7368-9219-3(2)) Red Brick Learning.

Saunders-Smith, Gail & Guzman Ferrer, Martin Luis. La Luz Del Sol. 2004. (Pebble Bilingual Books). (ENG & SPA., Illus.). 24p. (J). 15.93 (978-0-7368-2310-4(7)) Capstone Pr., Inc.

Savage, Stephen & Harris, Caroline. Weather. 2006. (Kingfisher Young Knowledge Ser.). (Illus.). 48p. (J). (gr. k-3). 9.95 (978-0-7534-5983-6(3) , Kingfisher) Houghton Mifflin Co. Trade & Reference Div.

Schaefer, Lola M. A Cold Day. Saunders-Smith, Gail, ed. 1999. (What Kind of Day Is It? Ser.). (Illus.). 24p. (J). (gr. k-1). lib. bdg. 15.93 (978-0-7368-0402-8(1) , Pebble Bks.) Capstone Pr., Inc.

—A Cold Day. 1999. pap. 13.25 (978-0-516-21927-1(8) , Children's Pr.) Scholastic Library Publishing.

—What Kind of Day Is It?, 6 bks. Saunders-Smith, Gail, ed. Incl. Cold Day. 1999. lib. bdg. 15.93 (978-0-7368-0402-8(1)); Hot Day. 2000. lib. bdg. 15.93 (978-0-7368-0403-5(X)); Rainy Day. 1999. lib. bdg. 15.93 (978-0-7368-0404-2(8)); Snowy Day. 1999. lib. bdg. 15.93 (978-0-7368-0405-9(6)); Sunny Day. 1999. lib. bdg. 15.93 (978-0-7368-0406-6(4)); Windy Day. 1999. lib. bdg. 15.93 (978-0-7368-0407-3(2)); 24p. (J). (gr. k-1). (Illus.). 2000. Set lib. bdg. 95.58 (978-0-7368-0453-0(6) , Pebble Bks.) Capstone Pr., Inc.

—What Kind of Day Is It? Series, 6 bks., Set. 1999. (Illus.). (J). (ps-2). pap. 79.50 (978-0-516-29666-1(3) , Children's Pr.) Scholastic Library Publishing.

Scholastic Clubs US Weather Watch Pack (exc. Snow) Weather Watch. 2006. (J). pap. 31.80 (978-1-59566-320-7(7)) QEB Publishing Inc.

School Specialty Publishing. Phonemic Awareness & Beginning Phonics: Weather & Seasons. 2004. 96p. (J). pap. 10.99 (978-1-57029-494-5(1) , WPH99044, Totline Pubns.) Schaffer, Frank Pubns.

—Weather. 2005. (Science Search Lab Ser.). (J). (gr. 3-5). pap. 24.95 (978-0-7682-2848-9(4) , Ideal School Supply) Schaffer, Frank Pubns.

School Zone Publishing Company Staff & Hall, Julie. Weather, Seeds, Plants. deluxe ed. 2000. (Deluxe Wkbks.). (Illus.). 64p. (J). (gr. 2-4). pap., wbk. ed. 4.16 (978-0-88743-861-5(X) , 02261) School Zone Publishing Co.

The Science of Weather. 2004. (Illus.). lib. bdg. 7.95 (978-0-8225-4341-1(9)) Lerner Publishing Group.

Seasons/Weather - PowerPhonics Skill Set III, 6 bks. Incl. Clouds : Learning the CL Sound. Tanner, Susan. lib. bdg. 18.50 (978-0-8239-5942-6(2)); I Like Winter : Learning the ER Sound. Moskal, Greg. lib. bdg. 18.50 (978-0-8239-5939-6(2)); It Grows in Spring : Learning the GR Sound. Leigh, Autumn. lib. bdg. 18.50 (978-0-8239-5941-9(4)); Rain : Learning the AI Sound. Vastola, Pam. lib. bdg. 18.50 (978-0-8239-5943-3(0)); Summer at the Beach : Learning the EA Sound. Thomas, Maryann. lib. bdg. 18.50 (978-0-8239-5950-1(3)); When Leaves Turn : Learning the UR Sound. Sheffield, Sarah. lib. bdg. 18.50 (978-0-8239-5940-2(6)); 24p. (J). (gr. 1). 2002. (Illus.). 2001. Set lib. bdg. 108.00 (978-0-8239-7211-1(9) , PowerKids Pr.) Rosen Publishing Group, Inc., The.

Seibert, Patricia. Discovering El Nino: How Fable & Fact Together Help Explain the Weather. Ellis, Jan Davey, illus. 1999. (Our World Ser.). 32p. (gr. 2-5). lib. bdg. 22.90 (978-0-7613-1273-4(0) , Millbrook Pr.) Lerner Publishing Group.

Sengupta, Monalisa. Wild Weather. 2008. (J). lib. bdg. (***978-1-4042-3902-9(2)*** , PowerKids Pr.) Rosen Publishing Group, Inc., The.

Sherman, Joseph. Amazing Science - Weather, 6 bks. Incl. Flakes & Flurries : A Book about Snow. Wesley, Omarr, illus. (J). 22.60 (978-1-4048-0098-4(0)); Gusts & Gales : A Book about Wind. (C). 22.60 (978-1-4048-0094-6(8)); Nature's Fireworks : A Book about Lightning. Wesley, Omarr, illus. (C). 22.60 (978-1-4048-0093-9(X)); Shapes in the Sky : A Book about Clouds. Wesley, Omarr, illus. (C). 22.60 (978-1-4048-0097-7(2)); Splish! Splash! A Book about Rain. Wesley, Omarr, illus. (C). 22.60 (978-1-4048-0095-3(6)); Sunshine : A Book about Sunlight. Wesley, Omarr, illus. (C). 22.60 (978-1-4048-0096-0(4)); 24p. (gr. k-3). 2004. 2003. Set lib. bdg. 127.56 (978-1-4048-0092-2(1)) Picture Window Bks.

Sian Revision Weather Wise. 2004. (J). (978-1-59242-085-8(0)) Delta Education, LLC.

Silverstein, Alvin, et al. Weather & Climate. (Illus.). 2007. (Science Concepts, Second Ser.). 96p. (YA). (gr. 6-8). lib. bdg. 31.93 (***978-0-8225-6796-7(2));*** 1998. (Science Concepts Ser.: 8). 64p. (gr. 5-8). lib. bdg. 26.90 (978-0-7613-3223-7(5)) Lerner Publishing Group. (Twenty-First Century Bks.).

Simon, Seymour. Weather. (J). 2006. 40p. 16.99 (978-0-06-088440-6(1)); 2006. (Illus.). 40p. pap. 6.99 (978-0-06-088439-0(8)); 2000. (Illus.). pap. 6.99 (978-0-688-17521-4(X) , Harper Trophy) HarperCollins Pubs.

Solway, Andrew. A Pirate Adventure: Weather. 2005. (Illus.). 32p. (J). lib. bdg. 28.21 (978-1-4109-1926-7(9)) Raintree.

—A Pirate Adventure: Weather. 2005. (Illus.). 32p. (J). (978-1-4109-1957-1(9)) Steck-Vaughn.

Spilsbury, Richard & Spilsbury, Louise. Weather. 2006. (Science in Focus Ser.). (Illus.). 48p. (J). 27.00 (978-0-7910-8859-3(6) , Chelsea Hse.) Facts On File, Inc.

Steck-Vaughn Staff. Early Reader Program Level C: Weird Weather, 6 Pack. 2004. (Illus.). pap. 33.00 (978-0-7398-8319-8(4)) Steck-Vaughn.

—My Weather Journal. 2003. pap. 4.10 (978-0-7398-7654-1(6)) Steck-Vaughn.

—Stormy Weather. 2003. pap. 4.10 (978-0-7398-7637-4(6)) Steck-Vaughn.

—Weather Climate & You: 10 Lab Classroom. 1998. pap. 748.30 (978-0-8172-8534-0(2)) Steck-Vaughn.

—Weather Climate & You: 3 Lab Classroom. 1998. pap. 415.70 (978-0-8172-8532-6(6)) Steck-Vaughn.

—Weather Climate & You: 5 Lab Classroom. 1998. pap. 582.00 (978-0-8172-8533-3(4)) Steck-Vaughn.

—Weather, Climate & You: Windows & Macintosh Version. 1998. pap. 83.10 incl. cd-rom (978-0-8172-8530-2(X)) Steck-Vaughn.

—Weather, Climate & You: Windows/Macintosh Labs. 1998. pap. 249.40 incl. cd-rom (978-0-8172-8531-9(8)) Steck-Vaughn.

—Weather Sights & Sounds. 2000. (Illus.). (J). bds. (978-0-7398-4451-9(2)) Steck-Vaughn.

Steele, Philip. Snow & Ice. 1998. (Living with the Weather Ser.). (Illus.). 48p. (J). (gr. 4-7). lib. bdg. 18.98 (978-0-8172-5052-2(2)) Raintree.

Stein, Paul. Droughts of the Future. 2001. (Library of Future Weather & Climate). (Illus.). 64p. (YA). (gr. 4-6). lib. bdg. 26.50 (978-0-8239-3411-9(X)) Rosen Publishing Group, Inc., The.

Sterling, Mary E. Weather Photo Fun Activities. Rogers, Kathy, ed. Carrozza, John, illus. 1998. (Science Photo Fun Activities Ser.). 8p. (J). pap. 6.95 (978-1-56472-087-0(X)) Edupress, Inc.

Stewart, Melissa. What's the Weather? 2004. (Investigate Science Ser.). 32p. (J). (gr. 1 up). lib. bdg. 21.26 (978-0-7565-0639-1(5)) Compass Point Bks.

Stradling, Jan. Erosion & Weathering: Level K, 6 vols., Vol. 2. (First Explorers Ser.). 24p. (gr. 1-2). 34.95 (978-0-7699-1457-2(8)) Shortland Pubns. (U. S. A.) Inc.

Sunshine Weather. 2006. (Illus.). 24p. (J). (gr. k-2). 18.50 (***978-0-531-17880-5(3)***) Scholastic Library Publishing.

Superlibro de el tiempo y las Estaciones: Unit 5: el tiempo y las estaciones (Weather & Seasons) 2000. (McGraw-Hill Ciencias Ser.). (ENG & SPA.). (gr. k up). (978-0-02-277162-1(X)) Macmillan/McGraw-Hill Schl. Div.

Taylor, Barbara. Weather. 2004. (Make It Work! Geography Ser.). (Illus.). 48p. (J). (gr. 3-6). 12.95 (978-1-58728-257-7(7) , Two Can Publishing) T&N Children's Publishing.

—Weather. Haslam, Andrew, illus. 2004. (Make It Work! Geography Ser.). 48p. (J). (gr. 3-6). pap. 6.95 (978-1-58728-253-9(4) , Two Can Publishing) T&N Children's Publishing.

—Weather: The Hands-on Approach to Geography. 2001. (gr. 3-6). lib. bdg. 15.25 (978-0-613-43395-2(5)) Tandem Library Bks.

—Weather & Climate. 2002. (Young Discoverers Ser.). (Illus.). 32p. (J). (gr. k-3). 7.95 (978-0-7534-5509-8(9) , Kingfisher) Houghton Mifflin Co. Trade & Reference Div.

—Weather & Climate. 2002. (gr. k-3). lib. bdg. 16.40 (978-0-613-90903-7(8)) Tandem Library Bks.

Tiempo y clima: Recursos para el maestro con clave de Respuestas: Unit 2: Tiempo y clima (Weather & Climate) 2000. (McGraw-Hill Ciencias Ser.). (ENG & SPA.). (gr. 5 up). (978-0-02-278708-0(9)) Macmillan/McGraw-Hill Schl. Div.

El tiempo y las estaciones: Cuaderno de Actividades: Unit 5: el tiempo y las estaciones (Weather & Seasons) 2000. (McGraw-Hill Ciencias Ser.). (ENG & SPA.). (gr. k up). (978-0-02-278995-4(2)) Macmillan/McGraw-Hill Schl. Div.

Tocci, Salvatore. Experiments with Weather. (True Bks.). (J). 2004. (gr. 3-5). pap. 6.95 (978-0-516-27809-4(6)); 2003. (Illus.). 48p. 25.00 (978-0-516-22790-0(4)) Scholastic Library Publishing. (Children's Pr.).

Top That Publishing Staff, ed. Weather Watch. 2004. (Fun Kits Ser.). (Illus.). 48p. (J). (978-1-84510-131-2(6)) Top That! Publishing PLC.

Trumbauer, Lisa. Weathering & Erosion. 2005. 39.00 (***978-1-4108-4600-6(8)***) Benchmark Education Co.

Tuxworth, Nicola & Lorenz Editors. Weather. 2001. (Let's Look at... Ser.). (Illus.). 20p. 5.95 (978-0-7548-0953-1(6)) Anness Publishing GBR. *Dist:* National Bk. Network.

Varilla, Mary, ed. Scholastic Atlas of Weather. 2004. (Illus.). 80p. (J). pap. 17.95 (978-0-439-41902-4(6) , Scholastic Reference) Scholastic, Inc.

Vogel, Carole Garbuny. Nature's Fury. 2000. (Illus.). 126p. (J). pap. (978-0-590-11503-2(0)) Scholastic, Inc.

—Weather Legends: Native American Lore & the Science of Weather. 2001. (Illus.). 80p. (gr. 4-6). lib. bdg. 29.90 (978-0-7613-1900-9(X) , Millbrook Pr.) Lerner Publishing Group.

Wacky Weather, 6 vols., Vol. 4. 2005. (Book Treks Ser.). (Illus.). (J). (gr. 4-8). stu. ed. 35.95 (978-0-673-61778-1(5)) Celebration Pr.

Wadsworth, Pamela. Creigiau, Pridd a Thywydd. 2005. (WEL., Illus.). 24p. pap. (978-1-85596-237-8(3)) Dref Wen.

Wadsworth, Pamela & Tate, Sylvia. Golwg Gyntaf Ar Greigiau, Pridd a Thywydd. 2005. (WEL., Illus.). 24p. pap. (978-1-85596-253-8(5)) Dref Wen.

Walker, Nick. Sing along with the Weather Dude. Strobe, Carl, illus. 2nd ed. 2000. 20p. (J). pap. 15.98 incl. audio compact disk (978-0-9643389-1-3(2)) Small Gate Media.

Wallace, Jessica. Weather: KinderConcepts Individual Title Six-Packs. Ross, Christine, illus. (Kinderstarters Ser.). 8p. (ps-1). 21.00 (978-0-7635-8725-3(7)) Rigby Education.

W X Y Z

Wallace, Karen. Whatever the Weather. 1999. (Eyewitness Readers). (Illus.). 32p. (J). (gr. 5-3). pap. 3.99 (978-0-7894-4750-0(9)) Dorling Kindersley Publishing, Inc.

—Whatever the Weather. 1999. (Eyewitness Readers Ser.). (J). (978-0-606-19396-2(0)); lib. bdg. 11.80 (978-0-613-22611-0(9)) Tandem Library Bks.

Walsh, Kieran. Weather Math. 2003. (Math & My World Ser.). (Illus.). 48p. (J). 29.93 (978-1-58952-384-5(9)) Rourke Publishing, LLC.

Warning! Extreme Weather Set E, 6 vols. (Phonics Readers Ser.). (gr. k-2). 28.95 (978-0-7368-4074-3(5)) Red Brick Learning.

Weather, 4 bks. Incl. Clouds. Saunders-Smith, Gail. 1998. lib. bdg. 15.93 (978-1-56065-777-4(4)); Fog. Frost, Helen. Saunders-Smith, Gail, ed. 2004. lib. bdg. 15.93 (978-0-7368-2093-6(0)); Ice. Frost, Helen. Saunders-Smith, Gail, ed. 2004. lib. bdg. 15.93 (978-0-7368-2094-3(9)); Lightning. Frost, Helen. Saunders-Smith, Gail, ed. 1998. lib. bdg. 15.93 (978-1-56065-779-8(0)); Rain. Saunders-Smith, Gail. 1998. lib. bdg. 15.93 (978-1-56065-778-1(2)); Snow. Frost, Helen. Saunders-Smith, Gail, ed. 2004. lib. bdg. 15.93 (978-0-7368-2095-0(7)); Sunshine. Saunders-Smith, Gail. 1998. lib. bdg. 15.93 (978-1-56065-780-4(4)); Wind. Frost, Helen. Saunders-Smith, Gail, ed. 2004. lib. bdg. 15.93 (978-0-7368-2096-7(5)); 24p. (J). (gr. k-1). (Illus.). Set lib. bdg. 127.44 (978-0-7368-2323-4(9) , Pebble Bks.) Capstone Pr., Inc.

Weather, Set. 2002. (J). (ps-3). lib. bdg. 119.58 (978-1-57765-532-9(X)) ABDO Publishing Co.

Weather. (Jump Ser.). (Illus.). 32p. (J). (gr. 2-7). pap. (978-1-882210-25-1(5)) Action Publishing, Inc.

Weather. 2005. (Our Seasons & Weather Ser.). (YA). (gr. k-3). 118.80 (978-0-7368-4198-6(9) , Pebble Bks.) Capstone Pr., Inc.

Weather. 2002. (ScienceWorks for Kids Ser.). (Illus.). (J). (gr. 4-6). pap. 9.99 (978-1-55799-832-3(9) , EMC 876) Evan-Moor Educational Pubs.

Weather, 6 vols., Set. 2006. (Blastoff! Readers Ser.). (Illus.). (J). (gr. k-2). 111.00 (***978-0-531-16878-3(6)***) Scholastic Library Publishing.

Weather. 2002. (Super Science Activities Ser.). 48p. (J). (gr. 2-5). 7.99 (978-0-7439-3667-5(1) , 3667) Teacher Created Materials, Inc.

Weather, 6 bks., Set. Incl. Fun Weather Days. Rosenberg, Pam. (Illus.). 19.00 (978-0-531-16772-4(0) , Children's Pr.); Rainy Weather Days. Rosenberg, Pam. 19.00 (978-0-531-16769-4(0) , Children's Pr.); Snowy Weather Days. Marsico, Katie. 19.00 (978-0-531-16773-1(9)); Sunny Weather Days. Rosenberg, Pam. 19.00 (978-0-531-16770-0(4) , Children's Pr.); Wild Weather Days. Marsico, Katie. (Illus.). 19.00 (978-0-531-16771-7(2) , Children's Pr.); Windy Weather Days. Marsico, Katie. (Illus.). 19.00 (978-0-531-16774-8(7) , Children's Pr.); 24p. (J). 2006. (Scholastic News Nonfiction Readers Ser.). (Illus.). 2006. 114.00 (***978-0-531-12473-4(8)***, Children's Pr.) Scholastic Library Publishing.

Weather: Individual Title Six-Packs. (Chiquilibros Ser.). (gr. k-1). 23.00 (978-0-7635-0416-8(5)) Rigby Education.

Weather: Kindergarten Newcomer Books. (On Our Way to English Ser.). (gr. k up). 23.50 (978-0-7578-7185-6(2)) Rigby Education.

Weather & Climate Assessment Book: Unit 2: Weather & Climate. 2000. (McGraw-Hill Science Ser.). (gr. 5 up). (978-0-02-277764-7(4)) Macmillan/McGraw-Hill Schl. Div.

Weather & Climate Pupil Edition: Unit 2: Weather & Climate. 2000. (McGraw-Hill Science Ser.). (gr. 5 up). (978-0-02-278224-5(9)) Macmillan/McGraw-Hill Schl. Div.

Weather & Seasons. (Make Your Own Emergent Readers Ser.). 48p. (gr. k-2). 8.99 (978-0-7682-0018-8(0) , FS69006) Schaffer, Frank Pubns.

Weather & Seasons. 2004. lib. bdg. 152.00 (978-0-516-29321-9(4) , Children's Pr.) Scholastic Library Publishing.

Weather & Seasons Classroom Library. (gr. k-2). lib. bdg. 128.95 (978-0-7368-1828-5(6)) Red Brick Learning.

Weather & Seasons Complete Unit. (gr. k-2). 642.95 (978-0-7368-1829-2(4)) Red Brick Learning.

Weather Facts. 2004. (Pocket Guides). 160p. (J). pap. 6.95 (978-0-328-09817-0(5) , Scott Foresman) Addison Wesley Schl.

Weather Series. 2005. (J). pap. (***978-1-60015-015-9(2)***) Steps To Literacy, LLC.

Weather Set. (gr. k-2). 114.95 (978-0-7368-9047-2(5)) Red Brick Learning.

Weather Sets: 1 Each of 3 Big Books. (Sunshinetm Science Ser.). (gr. 1-2). (978-0-7802-1451-4(X)) Wright Group, The.

Weather Sets: 1 Each of 3 Student Books. (Sunshinetm Science Ser.). (gr. 1-2). 20.95 (978-0-7802-1753-9(5)) Wright Group, The.

Weather Update. 2005. (Illus.). (J). (gr. 2-3). lib. bdg. 212.60 (978-0-7368-4421-5(X)) Capstone Pr., Inc.

Weather Watching: Individual Title Six-Packs. (Rigby Focus Ser.). 24p. (gr. 2 up). 28.00 (978-0-7578-5355-5(2)); 30.00 (978-0-7578-5585-6(7)) Rigby Education.

Weather Watching: Level P, 6 vols., Vol. 3. (Explorers Ser.). 32p. (gr. 3-6). 44.95 (978-0-7699-0618-8(4)) Shortland Pubns. (U. S. A.) Inc.

West, Krista. Hands-On Projects about Weather & Climate. 2002. (Great Earth Science Projects Ser.). (Illus.). 24p. (J). lib. bdg. 19.95 (978-0-8239-5845-0(0) , PowerKids Pr.) Rosen Publishing Group, Inc., The.

What a Week!, 6 packs. (ps-2). 23.00 (978-0-7635-9010-9(X)) Rigby Education.

What Is the Weather Outside? First Grade Big Books. (On Our Way to English Ser.). (gr. 1 up). 29.95 (978-0-7578-1507-2(3)) Rigby Education.

What Is the Weather Outside? Small Versions of Big Books. (On Our Way to English Ser.). (gr. 1 up). 29.00 (978-0-7578-7232-7(8)) Rigby Education.

What Kind of Day Is It?, Vol. 2. 2005. (Our Seasons & Weather Ser.). (YA). (gr. k-3). 178.20 (978-0-7368-4199-3(7) , Pebble Bks.) Capstone Pr., Inc.

What Kind of Day Is It? Collection. 2005. (J). pap. (***978-1-60015-014-2(4)***) Steps To Literacy, LLC.

Wiebe, Ann. Weather Sense: Temperature, Air Pressure, & Wind. 2002. (Illus.). (YA). (gr. 5-8). pap. 18.95 (978-1-881431-96-1(7)) AIMS Education Foundation.

Wild Weather, 6 Packs. (Rigby Focus Ser.). 16p. (gr. 1 up). 30.00 (978-0-7578-5557-3(1)) Rigby Education.

Wild Weather: Individual Title Six-Packs. (Rigby Focus Ser.). 16p. (gr. 1 up). 28.00 (978-0-7578-5325-8(0)) Rigby Education.

Wilkes, Angela. Lluvia y Sol. 2004. (Ladders Ser.).Tr. of Rain & Sunshine. (SPA., Illus.). 32p. (ps-3). 12.95 (978-1-58728-405-2(7) , Two Can Publishing) T&N Children's Publishing.

—Rain & Shine. 2000. (ps-2). lib. bdg. 15.25 (978-0-613-43495-9(1)) Tandem Library Bks.

—Weather. 2000. (Ladders Ser.). (Illus.). 30p. (J). (gr. k-3). (978-0-7166-7719-2(9)) World Bk., Inc.

Wilkes, Angela, et al. Rain & Shine. Jordan, Fran, illus. rev. ed. 2004. (Ladders Ser.). (ps-3). 32p. (J). pap. 6.95 (978-1-58728-619-3(X)); 30p. 12.95 (978-1-58728-609-4(2)) T&N Children's Publishing. (Two Can Publishing).

Williams, Judith. How Does the Sun Make Weather? 2005. (I Like Weather! Ser.). (Illus.). 24p. (J). lib. bdg. 21.26 (978-0-7660-2317-8(6) , Enslow Elementary) Enslow Pubs., Inc.

Williams, Zella. Experiments on the Weather. 2007. (Do-It-Yourself Science Ser.). (Illus.). 24p. (J). (gr. 2-5). lib. bdg. 23.95 (978-1-4042-3663-9(5)) Rosen Publishing Group, Inc., The.

Willis, Shirley. Dime por Que Es Mojada la Lluvia. 1999. (Coleccion los Estupendos). (SPA., Illus.). 32p. (J). (gr. 2-4). 20.00 (978-0-531-11849-8(5) , OD30029, Watts, Franklin) Scholastic Library Publishing.

—Dime por Que Es Mojada la Lluvia. 2000. (Estupendos Ser.). (J). 12.75 (978-0-606-20150-6(5)) Tandem Library Bks.

—Dime Por Que Es Mojada la Lluvia. 2000. (SPA.). (gr. k-3). lib. bdg. 14.10 (978-0-613-72671-9(5)) Tandem Library Bks.

Wind & Clouds & Heat & Rain. 2002. (Illus.). 48p. (J). 2.99 (978-0-88724-806-1(3) , WG 3035) Carson-Dellosa Publishing Co., Inc.

Woodward, John. Weather. 2007. (Google E Guides). (Illus.). 96p. (J). 17.99 (978-0-7566-1953-4(X)) Dorling Kindersley Publishing, Inc.

—Weather Watcher. 2006. (Nature Activities Ser.). (Illus.). 72p. (J). pap. 9.99 (978-0-7566-2068-4(6)) Dorling Kindersley Publishing, Inc.

World Almanac Library Staff, contrib. by. Understanding the Weather. 2002. (Twenty-First Century Science Ser.). (Illus.). 64p. (J). (gr. 5 up). lib. bdg. 32.67 (978-0-8368-5009-3(2) , World Almanac Library) Stevens, Gareth Inc.

World Book, Inc Staff, contrib. by. Forces of Nature. 2007. (J). (***978-0-7166-9806-7(4)***) World Bk., Inc.

—Weather. 2007. (J). (***978-0-7166-7732-1(6)***) World Bk., Inc.

Wyatt, Valerie. FAQ Weather. Share, Brian, illus. unabr. ed. 2004. (FAQ Ser.). 40p. (J). (gr. 4-6). (978-1-55074-582-5(4)) Kids Can Pr., Ltd.

—Weather. Share, Brian, illus. 2000. 40p. (J). (ps-ps). lib. bdg. 15.25 (978-0-613-25129-7(6)) Tandem Library Bks.

—Weather. 2000. (978-0-606-18234-8(9)) Tandem Library Bks.

—Weather: Frequently Asked Questions. Share, Brian, illus. unabr. ed. 2004. (FAQ Ser.). 40p. (J). (gr. 4-6). (978-1-55074-815-4(7)) Kids Can Pr., Ltd.

Ylvisaker, Anne. Droughts. 2003. (Natural Disasters Ser.). (Illus.). 48p. (J). (gr. 3-4). lib. bdg. 21.26 (978-0-7368-1505-5(8) , Capstone High-Interest Bks.) Capstone Pr., Inc.

WEATHER—FICTION

The Adventures of Sammy the Snowflake: The Facts of Life, Flying & Friendship Weather. 2007. (J). 19.95 (***978-0-9795260-0-8(0)***) Courtyard Publishing, LLC.

Alberts, Nancy Markham & Alley, R. W. Joselina Piggy Goes Out. 2007. (I'm Going to Read Ser.). (Illus.). 32p. (J). pap. 3.95 (978-1-4027-4299-6(1)) Sterling Publishing Co., Inc.

Anaya, Rudolfo. The First Tortilla: A Bilingual Story. Lamadrid, Enrique R., tr. Cordova, Amy, illus. 2007. (SPA & ENG.). 32p. (J). (gr. 2-4). 16.95 (***978-0-8263-4214-0(0)***) Univ. of New Mexico Pr.

Barclay, Jane. How Cold Was It? ed. 2004. (Illus.). (J). (gr. k-3). spiral bd. (978-0-616-01538-4(0)) Canadian National Institute for the Blind/Institut National Canadien pour les Aveugles.

—How Cold Was It? Donato, Janice, illus. ed. 2004. (J). (gr. k-3). spiral bd. (978-0-616-11862-7(7)) Canadian National Institute for the Blind/Institut National Canadien pour les Aveugles.

—How Cold Was It? Pavanel, Jane, ed. Donato, Janice, illus. 2000. 24p. (J). (ps-4). pap. 7.95 (978-1-894222-19-8(9)) Lobster Pr. CAN. *Dist:* Univ. of Toronto Pr.

—How Cold Was It? Donato, Janice, illus. 2nd ed. 2000. 24p. (J). (ps-4). reprint ed. 14.95 (978-1-894222-03-7(2)) Lobster Pr. CAN. *Dist:* Univ. of Toronto Pr.

Barile, Colleen. Weather Watch. Yeagle, Dean, illus. 2002. (Read-To-Me Ser.). 24p. (J). (978-0-7665-1223-8(1)) Abrams, Harry N. , Inc.

Barrett, Judi. Cloudy with a Chance of Meatballs. Barrett, Ron, illus. 2002. (J). 14.47 (978-0-7587-2256-0(7)) Book Wholesalers, Inc.

—Cloudy with a Chance of Meatballs. Barrett, Ron, illus. 2005. (J). pap. 18.95 incl. audio compact disk (978-1-59112-701-7(7)) Live Oak Media.

—Pickles to Pittsburgh: The Sequel to Cloudy with A Chance of Meatballs. (Illus.). (J). 2005. pap. 16.95 incl. audio (978-0-87499-537-4(X)); 2005. pap. 18.95 incl. audio compact disk (978-1-59112-749-9(1)); 1999. (gr. 1-6). 25.95 incl. audio (978-0-87499-538-1(8)) Live Oak Media.

—Pickles to Pittsburgh: The Sequel to Cloudy with A Chance of Meatballs. Barrett, Ron, illus. 1999. 28.95 incl. audio compact disk (978-1-59112-750-5(5)); pap. 37.95 incl. audio (978-0-87499-539-8(6)); pap. 39.95 incl. audio compact disk (978-1-59112-751-2(3)) Live Oak Media.

—Pickles to Pittsburgh: The Sequel to Cloudy with A Chance of Meatballs. Barrett, Ron, illus. 2000. 32p. (J). (ps-3). pap. 6.99 (978-0-689-83929-0(4) , Aladdin) Simon & Schuster Children's Publishing.

—Pickles to Pittsburgh: The Sequel to Cloudy with A Chance of Meatballs. 2000. (J). (978-0-606-20089-9(4)); lib. bdg. 15.30 (978-0-613-30090-2(4)) Tandem Library Bks.

—Pickles to Pittsburgh & Cloudy with a Change of Meaballs. Barrett, Ron, illus. 1999. pap. 30.95 incl. audio (978-0-87499-819-1(0)); pap. 34.95 incl. audio compact disk (978-1-59112-842-7(0)) Live Oak Media.

Bauer, Marion Dane. If Frogs Made the Weather. Donohue, Dorothy, illus. 2005. 32p. (J). 16.95 (978-0-8234-1622-6(4)) Holiday Hse., Inc.

Blackstone, Stella. Oso Bajo el Sol. 2003. (SPA.). (gr. k-3). lib. bdg. 14.15 (978-0-613-65704-4(7)) Tandem Library Bks.

Blotnick, Elihu. The Fog Line. Robinson, Barbara J., illus. 2000. (Mr. Blot Ser.: No. 3). 72p. (YA). (gr. 6 up). pap. 5.95 (978-0-915090-12-9(0)) California Street.

Bonnell, Kris. Clouds Tell the Weather. 2007. (J). 3.95 (***978-1-933727-47-9(0)***) Reading Reading Bks., LLC.

Bridwell, Norman & Fry, Sonali. Clifford the Weather Dog. Edwards, Ken & Haefele, Steve, illus. 2002. (Clifford, the Big Red Dog Ser.). 5p. (J). bds. 6.99 (978-0-439-39448-2(1)) Scholastic, Inc.

Carle, Eric. Little Cloud. Carle, Eric, illus. 2002. (Illus.). (J). 23.64 (978-0-7587-2998-9(7)) Book Wholesalers, Inc.

—Little Cloud. Carle, Eric, illus. (Illus.). (J). (ps-1). 2001. 32p. pap. 5.99 (978-0-698-11830-0(8) , Putnam Juvenile); 1998. 28p. bds. 6.99 (978-0-399-23191-9(9) , Philomel) Penguin Group (USA) Inc.

—Little Cloud. Carle, Eric, illus. 2001. (Illus.). (ps-ps). lib. bdg. 14.15 (978-0-613-35972-6(0)) Tandem Library Bks.

—Little Cloud. 2001. (Illus.). (J). (978-0-606-21301-1(5)) Tandem Library Bks.

Cicciarelli, Joellyn. Weather Watching. 2000. (gr. k-3). lib. bdg. 11.80 (978-0-613-29780-6(6)) Tandem Library Bks.

A Cold & Snowy Day. l.t. ed. 1999. (Illus.). 20p. (J). pap. 19.00 (978-1-893467-02-6(3)) Spedial Editions Pr.

Cole, Joanna & White, Nancy. The Magic School Bus Kicks up a Storm: A Book about Weather. 2000. (Magic School Bus Ser.). (J). (gr. 1-4). (978-0-606-18577-6(1)) Tandem Library Bks.

Coolidge, Nellie & Manutoli, Sophie. Ellaliuryaraq. Slim, Zacharias & Horesh, David, illus. 1998. Tr. of Weather. (ESK.). 28p. (J). (gr. k-3). pap. 8.00 (978-1-58084-048-4(5)) Lower Kuskokwim Schl. District.

Cote, Nancy. It Feels Like Snow. Cote, Nancy, illus. 2003. (Illus.). 32p. (YA). (gr. k-2). 15.95 (978-1-59078-054-1(X)) Boyds Mills Pr.

Cousins, Lucy. Maisy's Wonderful Weather Book. Cousins, Lucy, illus. 2006. 14p. (J). (ps). 11.99 (978-0-7636-2987-8(1)) Candlewick Pr.

Crews, Donald. Cloudy Day Sunny Day. 2003. (Green Light Readers Level 1 Ser.). (Illus.). 24p. (J). pap. 3.95 (978-0-15-204850-1(2) , Green Light Readers) Harcourt Children's Bks.

—Cloudy Day Sunny Day. 1999. (ps-2). lib. bdg. 11.80 (978-0-613-62277-6(4)) Tandem Library Bks.

Doherty, Ellen. Mondo & Gordo Weather the Storm. ed. 2003. (Early Connections Ser.). (J). pap. 35.00 (978-1-4108-1556-9(0)) Benchmark Education Co.

Dorfman, Ariel & Dorfman, Joaquin. The Burning City. 2005. 272p. (J). (gr. 5-9). lib. bdg. 17.95 (978-0-375-93203-8(8) , Random Hse. Bks. for Young Readers) Random Hse. Children's Bks.

—Burning City. (YA). mass mkt. (978-0-375-83205-5(X)); 2006. 288p. (J). (gr. 5-9). reprint ed. pap. 7.95 (978-0-375-83204-8(1) , Random Hse. Bks. for Young Readers) Random Hse. Children's Bks.

Dougherty, Terri. Days of the Week. Greathouse, Justin, illus. 2006. (Read-It! Readers Ser.). 32p. (J). (ps-3). 18.60 (978-1-4048-1581-0(3)) Picture Window Bks.

Durant, Alan. Bird Flies South, Level 2. Lucas, Kath, illus. 2005. (Lightning Readers Ser.). 32p. (J). (gr. k-1). pap., pap. 3.95 (978-0-7696-4210-9(1) , Gingham Dog Pr.) School Specialty Publishing.

Durant/Lucas, Alan/Kath. Bird Flies South. 2005. (Illus.). 32p. (J). lib. bdg. 9.00 (***978-1-4242-0888-3(2)***) Fitzgerald Bks.

Dussling, Jennifer. Rainbow Mystery. 2002. (gr. 3-6). lib. bdg. 13.00 (978-0-613-53764-3(5)) Tandem Library Bks.

Eagle, Kin. It's Raining, It's Pouring. Eagle, Kin, illus. 1998. (Nursery Rhyme Ser.). (Illus.). 26p. (J). (ps-k). bds. 6.95 (978-1-58089-017-5(2)) Charlesbridge Publishing, Inc.

Evans, Catrin & Evans, Guto. Peiriant y Tywydd. 2005. (WEL., Illus.). 36p. (978-0-86243-412-0(2)) Y Lolfa.

Farmer Bob Weather Series. 2001. (978-1-883772-85-7(0)) Flying Rhinoceros, Inc.

Fleming, Sarah. The Weather Forecast. 2000. (Cambridge Reading Ser.). (Illus.). 10p. pap. 5.00 (978-0-521-77453-6(5)); Pack. 8p. pap. 28.00 (978-0-521-78770-3(X)) Cambridge Univ. Pr.

Franson, Scott E. Un-Brella. 2007. (Illus.). 40p. (J). (ps-3). 15.95 (978-1-59643-179-9(2)) Roaring Brook Pr.

Furgang, Kathy. Stanley no tiene suerte & Unlucky Stanley. 2005. spiral bd. 66.00 (***978-1-4108-5633-3(X)***) Benchmark Education Co.

George, Olivia. The Weather. Fletcher, Rusty, illus. 2005. (My First Reader Ser.). 31p. (J). (ps-ps). 18.50 (978-0-516-24880-6(4) , Children's Pr.) Scholastic Library Publishing.

—Weather. Fletcher, Rusty, illus. 2006. 32p. (J). (gr. k-1). pap. 3.95 (978-0-516-24968-1(1) , Children's Pr.) Scholastic Library Publishing.

Gliori, Debi. Little Bear & the Wish Fish. (Illus.). 32p. (J). (ps-2). pap. 9.99 (978-0-7112-0986-2(3)) Lincoln, Frances Ltd. GBR. *Dist:* Transition Vendor.

Graves, Kassie. Brave Little Sailboat. Graves, Kassie, illus. 2003. (Illus.). 20p. (J). 14.95 (978-0-9728019-0-4(1)) Bright Eyes Pr.

Hammond, Rebecca. Winds Cove. 2004. 248p. (YA). pap. 6.99 (978-1-932307-00-9(1) , Ambassador-Emerald, International) Emerald Hse. Group, Inc.

Hare, Sharon C. Poppy's Clouds. Landing, Alex, illus. 1998. 20p. (J). pap. 10.00 (978-1-885938-16-9(0)) Cathedral Foundation Pr.

Holmes, Melody Moore. Buenos Dias, Carlitos! Garvin, Elaine, illus. 1999. Tr. of Good Day, Carlitos. (SPA.). 32p. (J). (ps-1). pap. 6.49 (978-1-57924-230-5(8) , 115022) Jones, Bob Univ. Pr.

Howell, Will C. I Call It Sky. Ward, John, illus. 1999. 32p. (J). (ps-1). 15.95 (978-0-8027-8686-9(3)); lib. bdg. 16.85 (978-0-8027-8687-6(1)); 15.95 (978-0-8027-8677-7(4)); lib. bdg. 16.85 (978-0-8027-8678-4(2)) Walker & Co.

Hughes, Shirley. Alfie's Weather. 2007. (Illus.). 48p. (J). pap. 8.95 (***978-0-09-940425-5(7)***, Red Fox) Random Hse. Children's Bks. GBR. *Dist:* Independent Pubs. Group.

—Alfie's Weather. 2007. (Illus.). 48p. (J). 18.95 (***978-0-370-32561-3(3)***) Transworld Publishers Ltd. GBR. *Dist:* Independent Pubs. Group.

Inkpen, Mick. Splosh. 1999. (978-0-606-22347-8(9)) Tandem Library Bks.

Knowles, Kent. Lucius & the Storm. Knowles, Kent, illus. 2007. (Illus.). 32p. (J). 15.95 (978-1-60108-005-9(0)) Red Cygnet Pr.

Korba, Joanne. Wild Weather. 2005. 40.00 (***978-1-4108-4218-3(5)***) Benchmark Education Co.

Krupinski, Loretta. Pirate Treasure. Krupinski, Loretta, illus. 2006. (Illus.). 32p. (J). (gr. k). 15.99 (978-0-525-47579-8(6) , Dutton Juvenile) Penguin Group (USA) Inc.

Look Out the Window: Individual Title Six-Packs. (Story Steps Ser.). (gr. k-2). 29.00 (978-0-7635-9587-6(X)) Rigby Education.

McGuire, Leslie. I Get Dressed: A Fun Sticker Book. Espinosa, Leo, illus. 1999. 20p. (J). reprint ed. 7.95 (978-1-892374-22-6(6)) Weldon Owen, Inc.

McKee, David. Elmer's Weather. 2004. (Elmer Ser.). (Illus.). 16p. (J). (ARA & ENG.). bds. 6.95 (978-1-84059-404-1(7)); (ENG & ITA., bds. 6.95 (978-1-84059-405-8(5)); (ENG & SOM., bds. 6.95 (978-1-84059-406-5(3)); (ENG, URD, TUR, VIE & SPA., bds. 6.95 (978-1-84059-076-0(9)); (ENG, URD, TUR, VIE & SPA., bds. 6.95 (978-1-84059-080-7(7)); (ENG, TUR, URD, VIE & SPA., bds. 6.95 (978-1-84059-081-4(5)); (GUJ, ENG, URD, TUR & VIE., bds. 6.95 (978-1-84059-078-4(5)) Milet Publishing.

—Elmer's Weather. Pullin, Beatriz, tr. from ENG. 2004. (Elmers Ser.). (ENG, URD, TUR, VIE & CHI., Illus.). 16p. (J). bds. 6.95 (978-1-84059-079-1(3)) Milet Publishing.

—Elmer's Weather. Wood, Kim Marie, tr. from ENG. 2004. (Elmers Ser.). (ENG, URD, TUR, SPA & CHI., Illus.). 16p. (J). bds. 6.95 (978-1-84059-082-1(3)) Milet Publishing.

Nelson, Ray, et al. A Snack for Phillip. Siegel, Joseph & Habecker, Mary Beth, eds. Peeples, Aaron et al, illus. 32p. (J). (gr. 1-3). 2000. pap. 12.00 (978-1-883772-51-2(6)); 1999. 39.95 (978-1-883772-52-9(4)) Flying Rhinoceros, Inc.

—The Weather, 5 bks. Siegel, Joseph, ed. 2000. (Farmer Bob Weather Ser.: No. 1). (Illus.). 31p. (Orig.). (J). (gr. k-2). pap. 60.00 (978-1-883772-77-2(X)) Flying Rhinoceros, Inc.

The North Pole Is Sinking! 2005. (J). 9.99 (978-0-9773674-0-5(1)) Blue State Pr.

Osborne, Mary Pope. Twister on Tuesday, 23. Murdocca, Sal, illus. 2001. (Magic Tree House Ser.: No. 23). 96p. (J). (gr. k-3). pap. 3.99 (978-0-679-89069-0(6) , Random Hse. Bks. for Young Readers) Random Hse. Children's Bks.

Raintree Steck-Vaughn Staff, contrib. by. How's the Weather? 2000. (Read All about It Ser.). (J). (ps-3). pap. 4.95 (978-0-8114-3700-4(0)) Steck-Vaughn.

Random House Disney Staff. Weather Watcher. 2006. 96p. (J). (ps-2). pap. 2.99 (978-0-7364-2407-3(5) , Golden/Disney) Random Hse. Children's Bks.

Reber, Deborah. Blue's Best Rainy Day. Cardinali, Kevin, illus. 2000. (Blue's Clues Ser.). 24p. (J). (ps-k). pap. 3.50 (978-0-689-83279-6(6) , Simon Spotlight/Nickelodeon) Simon & Schuster Children's Publishing.

—Blue's Best Rainy Day. 2000. (gr. k-3). lib. bdg. 11.25 (978-0-613-24387-2(0)) Tandem Library Bks.

Riley, Denise. Quuneq. Riley, Denise & Brunk, Cara, illus. 1998. Tr. of Calm Weather. (ESK.). 12p. (J). (gr. k-3). pap. 6.00 (978-1-58084-029-3(9)) Lower Kuskokwim Schl. District.

Rockwell, Anne F. & Rockwell, Lizzy, illus. Apples & Pumpkins. 2nd ed. 2005. (Stories to Go! Ser.). (J). (*978-1-4156-2884-3(X)*, Aladdin) Simon & Schuster Children's Publishing.

Rogers, Alan. Bright & Breezy. 2004. (Little Giants Ser.). (Illus.). 16p. (ps-k). (J). pap. 3.95 (978-1-58728-394-9(8)); 5.95 (978-1-58728-151-8(1)) T&N Children's Publishing. (Two Can Publishing).

Ross, Tony. El Tiempo. 2006. (Little Princess Ser.).Tr. of Weather. (SPA.). (J). (ps-k). bds. 7.95 (978-968-19-1487-5(2) , AT33281) Lectorum Pubns., Inc.

Ruffenach, Jessie, ed. Baby Learns about Weather. Thomas, Peter, tr. from ENG. Blacksheep, Beverly, illus. 2005. (NAV & ENG.). 16p. (J). bds. 7.95 (978-1-893354-62-3(8)) Salina Bookshelf.

Schmidt, Karen. Carl's Nose. 2006. (Illus.). 40p. (J). 16.00 (978-0-15-205049-8(3)) Harcourt Trade Pubs.

Scholastic, Inc. Staff. What's the Weather? 2008. (Little Secrets Ser.). 28p. (J). 9.99 (*978-0-545-02599-7(0)*, Cartwheel Bks.) Scholastic, Inc.

Scott, Janine. Sunny Sunday Drive. Forss, Ian, illus. 2006. 32p. (J). (gr. k-2). 22.60 (978-1-4048-1696-1(8)) Picture Window Bks.

Shackman, Julie. What's That up There? 1999. (Illus.). 22p. (J). (ps-1). pap. (978-1-902586-61-8(1)) Mentor Bks.

Shearer, Alex. Professor Sniff & the Lost Spring Breezes. Kenyon, Tony, illus. 1998. 102p. (J). (gr. 4-7). lib. bdg. 15.99 (978-0-531-33079-1(6) , Orchard Bks.) Scholastic, Inc.

—The Summer Sisters & the Dance Disaster. Kenyon, Tony, illus. 1998. 103p. (J). (gr. 3-7). pap. 14.95 (978-0-531-30080-0(3) , Orchard Bks.) Scholastic, Inc.

Sneezles & Wheezles. 2006. (J). 15.99 (978-1-55517-912-0(6) , Cedar Fort, Inc.) Cedar Fort, Inc./CFI Distribution.

Spalding, Andrea. It's Raining, It's Pouring. Watts, Leslie Elizabeth, illus. 2001. 32p. (J). (ps-2). 15.95 (978-1-55143-186-4(6)) Orca Bk. Pubs. USA.

Stanley, Mandy. Out & About. 2003. (Illus.). 12p. (J). (ps-k). 3.95 (978-0-7534-5679-8(6) , Kingfisher) Houghton Mifflin Co. Trade & Reference Div.

Thompson, Kate. Switchers. 220p. (J). (gr. 4-7). pap. 5.99 (978-0-8072-1553-1(8)); 2004. (Switchers Ser.: Vol. 1). (gr. 5-9). pap. 38.00 incl. audio (978-0-8072-8138-3(7) , YA115SP) Random Hse. Audio Publishing Group. (Listening Library).

—Switchers. 1999. (978-0-606-17387-2(0)); (gr. 5-8). lib. bdg. 14.15 (978-0-613-20224-4(4)) Tandem Library Bks.

White, Carolyn. Snowff & the Rowdy-Cloudy Bunch. 2006. (Snowff the Snowflake Kid Adventure Ser.). (J). 24.95 (978-1-893563-05-6(7)) AARO Publishing.

—Snowff Visits Razorteeth Village. 2006. (J). 24.95 (978-1-893563-10-0(3)) AARO Publishing.

—Snowff's MIST.erious Journey (Snowff the Snowflake Kid Adventure, 1) 2006. (J). 24.95 (978-1-893563-00-1(6)) AARO Publishing.

White, Kathryn. Snowshoe the Hare. Rivers, Ruth, illus. 2005. (Red Go Bananas Ser.). 43p. (J). lib. bdg. (978-0-7787-2677-7(0) , 1253648) Crabtree Publishing Co.

White, Nancy. The Magic School Bus Kicks up a Storm: A Book about Weather. Ruiz, Art, illus. 2000. (Magic School Bus Ser.). 32p. (J). (gr. 1-4). pap. 3.50 (978-0-439-10275-9(8)) Scholastic, Inc.

Wojtowycz, David. Get Dressed Dudley! Weather. 2002. (Dudley! Ser.). (Illus.). (J). 3.95 (978-1-58925-670-5(0) , tiger tales) ME Media LLC.

Yaccarino, Dan. Where the Four Winds Blow. Yaccarino, Dan, illus. 2003. (Illus.). 104p. (J). 17.89 (978-0-06-623627-8(4) , Cotler, Joanna Books) HarperCollins Pubs.

W X Y Z

WEATHER FORECASTING

And Now for the Weather! Individual Title Six-Packs. (Bookweb Ser.). 32p. (gr. 5 up). 34.00 (978-0-7635-3799-9(3)) Rigby Education.

Breen, Mark. Kids Book of Weather Forecasting. 2000. (gr. 3-6). lib. bdg. 22.20 (978-0-613-27924-6(7)) Tandem Library Bks.

Christian, Sandra J. Meteorologists. 2002. (Community Helpers Ser.). (Illus.). 24p. (J). (gr. 1-2). lib. bdg. 18.60 (978-0-7368-1130-9(3) , Bridgestone Bks.) Capstone Pr., Inc.

Cicciarelli, Joellyn. Weather Watching. 2000. (gr. k-3). lib. bdg. 11.80 (978-0-613-29780-6(6)) Tandem Library Bks.

Gibbons, Gail. Weather Forecasting. 1998. (J). pap. 5.99 (978-0-87628-428-5(4)) Ctr. for Applied Research in Education, The.

Jackson, Randy, et al. Tropical Weather Tracking Book. 2004. (YA). 7.95 (978-0-9742794-1-1(2)) HazardousWeather Preparedness Institute.

Miles, Elizabeth. Forecasting the Weather. 2005. (Illus.). 32p. (J). pap. (978-1-4034-6558-0(4)); lib. bdg. (978-1-4034-6553-5(3)) Heinemann Library.

Phelan, Glen. Extreme Weather. 2004. (National Geographic Reading Expeditions Ser.). (Illus.). 32p. (J). pap. (978-0-7922-4575-9(X)) National Geographic Society.

Rodgers, Alan & Streluk, Angella. Forecasting the Weather. 2002. (Measuring the Weather Ser.). (Illus.). 32p. (J). (gr. 3-5). lib. bdg. 22.79 (978-1-58810-687-2(X)) Heinemann Library.

Rogers, Allen & Streluk, Angela. Forecasting the Weather. 2002. (Illus.). 32p. (J). (gr. 3-5). pap. (978-1-4034-0127-4(6) , 91632) Heinemann Library.

Sievert, Terri. Weather Forecasting. 2005. (Weather Update Ser.). (Illus.). 24p. (J). 21.26 (978-0-7368-3739-2(6)) Capstone Pr., Inc.

Stein, Paul. The Library of Future Weather & Climate, 8 bks. Incl. Biomes of the Future. lib. bdg. 26.50 (978-0-8239-3410-2(1)); Droughts of the Future. lib. bdg. 26.50 (978-0-8239-3411-9(X)); Floods of the Future. lib. bdg. 26.50 (978-0-8239-3412-6(8)); Forecasting the Climate of the Future. lib. bdg. 26.50 (978-0-8239-3413-3(6)); Global Warming : A Threat to Our Future. lib. bdg. 26.50 (978-0-8239-3414-0(4)); Ice Ages in the Future. lib. bdg. 26.50 (978-0-8239-3415-7(2)); Oceans of the Future. lib. bdg. 26.50 (978-0-8239-3416-4(0)); Storms of the Future. lib. bdg. 26.50 (978-0-8239-3417-1(9)); 64p. (YA). (gr. 4-6). 2001. (Illus.). Set lib. bdg. 212.00 (978-0-8239-9431-1(7)) Rosen Publishing Group, Inc., The.

Weber, Rebecca. Weather Wise. 2002. (Spyglass Books). (Illus.). 24p. (J). (gr. 1 up). lib. bdg. 18.60 (978-0-7565-0385-7(X)) Compass Point Bks.

Wills, Susan & Wills, Steven R. Meteorology: Predicting the Weather. 2003. (Innovators Ser.: Vol. 12). (Illus.). 144p. (gr. 5 up). lib. bdg. 21.95 (978-1-881508-61-8(7)) Oliver Pr., Inc.

WEATHER SATELLITES

see Meteorological Satellites

WEAVING

see also Basket Making; Beadwork; Textile Industry
also names of woven articles, e.g. Carpets

Ahiagble, Gilbert & Meyer, Louise. Master Weaver from Ghana. Hernandez, Nestor, photos by. 1998. (Illus.). 32p. (YA). (gr. 2-8). 18.00 (978-0-940880-61-0(X)) Open Hand Publishing, LLC.

Charlie Needs a Cloak. 2004. 24.95 incl. audio (978-1-56008-023-7(X)); pap. 18.95 incl. audio compact disk (978-1-55592-382-2(8)); pap. 18.95 incl. audio compact disk (978-1-55592-384-6(4)); pap. 38.75 incl. audio compact disk (978-1-55592-383-9(6)); pap. 38.75 incl. audio compact disk (978-1-55592-385-3(2)); pap. 32.75 incl. audio (978-1-55592-200-9(7)); pap. 32.75 incl. audio (978-1-55592-201-6(5)); pap. 14.95 incl. audio (978-1-55592-719-6(X)) Weston Woods Studios, Inc.

De Angelis, Therese. The Navajo: Weavers of the Southwest. 2003. (America's First Peoples Ser.). (Illus.). 32p. (J). (gr. 2-3). lib. bdg. 23.93 (978-0-7368-2172-8(4) , Bridgestone Bks.) Capstone Pr., Inc.

de Paola, Tomie. Charlie Needs a Cloak. 2002. (J). (ps-2). lib. bdg. 14.15 (978-0-8335-0342-8(1)) Tandem Library Bks.

Martin, Christina. Weaving: Methods, Patterns, & Traditions of the Oldest Art. 2005. (Wooden Books). (Illus.). 64p. 10.00 (978-0-8027-1457-2(9)) Walker & Co.

Rodee, Marian. Weaving of the Southwest. 2nd rev. ed. 2003. (Schiffer Book for Collectors Ser.). (Illus.). 248p. (gr. 10-13). pap. 29.95 (978-0-7643-1854-2(3)) Schiffer Publishing, Ltd.

Switzer, Chris. Projects for Alpaca & Llama. 2004. 16.00 (978-0-9642663-2-2(6)) Switzer Land Enterprises.

WEB SITES

Bingham, Jane, et al. Encyclopedia of World History: Prehistoric, Ancient, Medieval, Last 500 Years. 2004. (World History Ser.). (Illus.). 415p. (J). (gr. 3 up). 39.95 (978-0-7460-4168-0(3)) EDC Publishing.

Doherty, Gillian. Birds. 2004. (Discovery Program Ser.). (SPA., Illus.). 64p. (J). (gr. 2 up). lib. bdg. 16.95 (978-1-58086-334-6(5)) EDC Publishing.

Ekman, Joseph Anthony. Kids Ultimate Online Homework Resource Guide 2004. 2003. spiral bd. 14.95 (978-0-9745406-0-3(9)) Duke Publishing & Software Corp.

Hawthorne, Kate, et al. The Young Person's Guide to the Internet: An Essential Website Reference Book for Young People, Parents, & Teachers. 2nd ed. 2005. (Illus.). 224p. 30.95 (978-0-415-34505-7(7)) Routledge.

McMorrow, Scott. Web Start-Ups. 1999. (Illus.). 96p. (J). pap. 11.95 (978-1-57612-115-3(1)) Monday Morning Bks., Inc.

Prince, Sarah. Whales on the World Wide Web. 2001. (gr. k-3). lib. bdg. 11.65 (978-0-613-33454-9(X)) Tandem Library Bks.

Toronto Public Library Staff. The Research Virtuoso: Brilliant Methods for Normal Brains. Weissmann, Joe, illus. 2006. 88p. (gr. 12). 19.95 (978-1-55037-957-0(7)); pap. 10.95 (978-1-55037-956-3(9)) Annick Pr., Ltd. CAN. *Dist:* Firefly Bks., Ltd.

WEB SITES—DESIGN

Aho, Kirsti & Underwood, Dale, contrib. by. Town Website Project Using Macromedia Dreamweaver MX 2004: Communicating Information & Ideas on the Web. 2003. (YA). ring bd. 10.00 (978-0-9742273-3-7(1)) Macromedia, Inc.

Amihud, Zohar. Look Mom! I Built My Own Web Site. 2nd ed. 2006. (Illus.). 204p. (J). pap. 18.95 (978-0-9760111-1-8(5)) BookChamp LLC.

Brown, Marty. Webmaster. 2000. (CoolCareers.com Ser.). (Illus.). 48p. (YA). (gr. 5-8). lib. bdg. 23.95 (978-0-8239-3111-8(0) , CCWEMA, Rosen Central) Rosen Publishing Group, Inc., The.

Bullock, Linda. Careers on the Web. 2002. (Technology & You Ser.). (Illus.). 48p. (J). lib. bdg. 27.12 (978-0-7398-4694-0(9)) Raintree.

Garth Gardner Company Staff, des. Gardner's Web Design Sketchbook: A Drawing Book for Planning & Organizing the Design of Web Pages. 2003. (Gardner's Guide Ser.). 200p. spiral bd. 24.95 (978-1-58965-009-1(3) , 703 793 8604) Gardner, Garth Co., Inc. (GGC).

Hovanec, Erin M. Careers as Content Provider for the Web. 2005. (Commerce & Internet Careers Ser.). (Illus.). 64p. (YA). (gr. 7-12). lib. bdg. 26.50 (978-0-8239-3418-8(7)) Rosen Publishing Group, Inc., The.

Lindsay, Dave & Lindsay, Bruce. Dave's Quick 'n' Easy Web Pages: An Introductory Guide to Creating Web Sites. 2nd ed. 2001. (Illus.). 116p. (J). (gr. 8-12). (978-0-9690609-8-7(X)) Erin Pubns.

Mackinnon, Mairi. Introduction to Web Site Design. (Computer Guides Ser.). 64p. (YA). lib. bdg. 18.95 (978-1-58086-392-6(2)) EDC Publishing.

Oleksy, Walter. Web Page Designer. 2000. (CoolCareers.com Ser.). (Illus.). 48p. (YA). (gr. 5-8). lib. bdg. 23.95 (978-0-8239-3112-5(9) , CCWEPA, Rosen Central) Rosen Publishing Group, Inc., The.

Selfridge, Benjamin & Selfridge, Peter. A Kid's Guide to Creating Web Pages for Home & School. 2004. (Illus.). 128p. (J). (gr. 5-10). pap. 19.95 (978-1-56976-180-9(9) , Zephyr Pr.) Chicago Review Pr., Inc.

Souter, Gerry, et al. Bringing Photos, Music, & Video into Your Web Page. 2003. (Internet Library). (Illus.). 64p. (J). (gr. 4-12). lib. bdg. 22.60 (978-0-7660-2082-5(7)) Enslow Pubs., Inc.

—Creating Animation for Your Web Page. 2003. (Internet Library). (Illus.). 64p. (J). (gr. 4-12). lib. bdg. 22.60 (978-0-7660-2083-2(5)) Enslow Pubs., Inc.

—Creating e-Reports & Online Presentations. 2003. (Internet Library). (Illus.). 64p. (J). (gr. 4-12). lib. bdg. 22.60 (978-0-7660-2080-1(0)) Enslow Pubs., Inc.

Underwood, Dale & Aho, Kirsti. Town Website Project for Macromedia Dreamweaver MX 2004: Communicating Information & Ideas on the Web, 2 bks. Dharkar, Anuja & McCain, Malinda, eds. Morgan, Mark & Gallenson, Ann, illus. 2003. 39p. spiral bd. 10.00 (978-0-9742273-8-2(2) , Macromedia Education) Macromedia, Inc.

Valqui, Kelly. Web Site Creation Kit. 2001. (CyberRookies Ser.). (Illus.). 350p. pap. 34.95 incl. cd-rom (978-1-58450-043-4(2)) Charles River Media.

Wolinsky, Art. Creating & Publishing Web Pages on the Internet. (Internet Library). (Illus.). 64p. (YA). (gr. 4-12). 2000. pap. 11.93 (978-0-7660-1744-3(3)); 1999. lib. bdg. 22.60 (978-0-7660-1262-2(X)) Enslow Pubs., Inc.

WEB SITES—DIRECTORIES

Brookes, Kate. Top Websites for Homework. 2nd ed. 2003. (Illus.). 160p. pap. (978-0-7502-4468-8(2) , Hodder Wayland) Hodder Children's Division.

Cangero, Karen, et al. 101 Best Web Sites for Kids. Caldwell, Tony, illus. 2001. 106p. (J). lib. bdg. 18.95 (978-1-56674-310-5(9)) Forest Hse. Publishing Co., Inc.

Dyson, Marianne J. Homework Help on the Internet. 2000. (gr. 3-6). lib. bdg. 11.80 (978-0-613-25546-2(1)) Tandem Library Bks.

Hovanec, Erin M. An Online Visit to Antarctica. (Internet Field Trips Ser.). 24p. (J). 2002. lib. bdg. 18.75 (978-0-8239-6423-9(X)); 2001. (Illus.). (gr. 3). lib. bdg. 18.75 (978-0-8239-5656-2(3)) Rosen Publishing Group, Inc., The. (PowerKids Pr.).

—An Online Visit to Europe. (Internet Field Trips Ser.). 24p. (J). 2002. lib. bdg. 18.75 (978-0-8239-6419-2(1)); 2001. (Illus.). (gr. 3). lib. bdg. 18.75 (978-0-8239-5657-9(1)) Rosen Publishing Group, Inc., The. (PowerKids Pr.).

—An Online Visit to North America. (Internet Field Trips Ser.). 24p. (J). 2002. lib. bdg. 18.75 (978-0-8239-6424-6(8)); 2001. (Illus.). (gr. 3). lib. bdg. 18.75 (978-0-8239-5654-8(7)) Rosen Publishing Group, Inc., The. (PowerKids Pr.).

—An Online Visit to South America. (Internet Field Trips Ser.). 24p. (J). 2002. lib. bdg. 18.75 (978-0-8239-6418-5(3)); 2001. (Illus.). (gr. 3). lib. bdg. 18.75 (978-0-8239-5655-5(5)) Rosen Publishing Group, Inc., The. (PowerKids Pr.).

Polly, Jean Armour. Internet Kids & Family Yellow Pages. 3rd ed. 1999. 744p. (J). pap. 34.99 (978-0-07-212206-0(4)) McGraw-Hill School Education Group.

Pondiscio, Robert. Get on the Net: Everything You Need to Know about the Internet, Including Hundreds of Fun & Useful Sites. 1999. 240p. (J). (gr. 5-9). pap. 5.99 (978-0-380-80334-7(8)) HarperCollins Pubs.

—Get on the Net: Everything You Need to Know about the Internet, Including the World Wide Web & Addresses for Hours of Fun & Ease. 1999. (Illus.). (J). (978-0-606-17972-0(0)) Tandem Library Bks.

Trumbauer, Lisa. Homework Help for Kids on the Net. 2000. (gr. 3-6). lib. bdg. 12.95 (978-0-613-25545-5(3)); (Illus.). (J). (978-0-606-20708-9(2)) Tandem Library Bks.

Varner, Linnea Smith. Web Feet for Health: Subject Guide to the Best Web Sites. 2001. (Illus.). 140p. (YA). (gr. 6-12). pap. 95.00 (978-1-890604-05-9(4)) RockHill Communications.

WEBSTER, DANIEL, 1782-1852

Baldwin, James. Four Great Americans. 2006. pap. (*978-1-4065-0509-2(9)*) Dodo Pr.

Baldwin, James. Four Great Americans: Washington, Franklin, Webster, Lincoln: A Book for Young Americans. 2000. (Illus.). (J). (978-0-89526-203-5(7)) Regnery Publishing, Inc., An Eagle Publishing Co.

Harvey, Bonnie Carman. Daniel Webster: "Liberty & Union, Now & Forever" 2001. (Historical American Biographies Ser.). (Illus.). 112p. (J). (gr. 6-12). lib. bdg. 26.60 (978-0-7660-1392-6(8)) Enslow Pubs., Inc.

WEDDINGS

see Etiquette; Marriage; Marriage Customs and Rites

WEEDS

May, Suellen. Invasive Aquatic & Wetland Plants. 2006. (Invasive Species Ser.). (Illus.). 112p. (J). (gr. 6-12). 30.00 (978-0-7910-9130-2(9) , Chelsea Hse.) Facts On File, Inc.

—Invasive Terrestrial Plants. 2006. (Invasive Species Ser.). (Illus.). 112p. (J). (gr. 6-12). 30.00 (978-0-7910-9128-9(7) , Chelsea Hse.) Facts On File, Inc.

WEIGHT CONTROL

see also Diet; Exercise

Abramovitz, Melissa. Obesity. 2004. (Illus.). 112p. (J). 32.45 (978-1-59018-413-4(0)) Thomson Gale.

Alters, Sandra, ed. Obesity. 2006. (Introducing Issues with Opposing Viewpoints Ser.). 119p. (YA). (gr. 7 up). lib. bdg. 33.70 (978-0-7377-3545-1(7) , Greenhaven Pr., Inc.) Thomson Gale.

Amos, Janine. Jimahl Is Overweight. 2002. (Body Matters Ser.). (Illus.). 32p. (YA). 19.99 (978-1-84234-111-7(1) , Cherrytree Books) Evans Publishing Group GBR. *Dist:* Independent Pubs. Group.

Bartell, Susan S. Dr. Susan's Girls-Only Weight Loss Guide: The Easy, Fun Way to Look & Feel Good! 2006. (Illus.). 272p. (J). pap. 14.95 (978-0-9721502-0-0(X)) Parent Positive Pr.

Boutaudou, Sylvie & Daly, Melissa. Weighing In: How to Understand Your Body, Lose Weight, & Live a Healthier Lifestyle. Aynié, Laetitia, illus. 2006. (Sunscreen Ser.). 112p. (J). (gr. 5-11). pap. 9.95 (978-0-8109-9228-3(0)) Abrams, Harry N., Inc.

Clayton, Lawrence. Diet Pill Drug Dangers. 2000. (Drug Dangers Ser.). (Illus.). 64p. (YA). (gr. 4-10). pap. 13.26 (978-0-7660-1737-5(0)) Enslow Pubs., Inc.

Cordes, Helen. Girl Power in the Mirror: Your Body, Your Self. 1999. (Girl Power Ser.). (Illus.). 64p. (YA). (gr. 6-9). lib. bdg. (978-0-8225-2691-9(3) , Lerner Pubns.) Lerner Publishing Group.

Dweck, Joey. Losing for Good. 2005. (YA). per. 19.95 (978-0-9754448-6-3(7)) Weight Loss Buddy, Inc.

Ford, Jean. Diseases & Disabilities Caused by Weight Problems: The Overloaded Body. 2005. (Obesity Ser.). (Illus.). 104p. (J). (ps-7). (978-1-59084-944-6(2)) Mason Crest Pubs.

Gay, Kathlyn. Am I Fat? The Obesity Issue for Teens. 2006. (Issues in Focus Today Ser.). (Illus.). 112p. (YA). (gr. 8-12). lib. bdg. 31.93 (978-0-7660-2527-1(6)) Enslow Pubs., Inc.

Gedatus, Gus. Exercise for Weight Management. 2000. (Nutrition & Fitness Ser.). (Illus.). 64p. (J). (gr. 4-6). lib. bdg. 23.93 (978-0-7368-0706-7(3) , LifeMatters Bks.) Capstone Pr., Inc.

Glaser, Jason. Obesity. 2007. (First Facts Ser.). (Illus.). 24p. (J). 21.26 (978-0-7368-6331-5(1)) Capstone Pr., Inc.

Greene, Meg. Obesity. 2006. (Gallup Major Trends & Events Ser.). (Illus.). 112p. (J). (gr. 7 up). lib. bdg. (978-1-59084-967-5(1)) Mason Crest Pubs.

Harmon, Daniel E. Obesity. 2006. (Coping in a Changing World Ser.). 112p. (YA). (gr. 7-12). lib. bdg. 31.95 (978-1-4042-0949-7(2)) Rosen Publishing Group, Inc., The.

Hunter, William. How Genetics & Environment Shape Us: The Destined Body. 2005. (Obesity Ser.). (Illus.). 104p. (J). (ps-7). lib. bdg. 23.95 (978-1-59084-948-4(5)) Mason Crest Pubs.

Hyde, Margaret O., et al. Obesity. 2005. (J). (978-0-531-12369-0(3) , Watts, Franklin) Scholastic Library Publishing.

Jamuna Carroll. Obesity. 2006. 80-244*p. (gr. 6-10). 29.95 (978-0-7377-3463-8(9) , Greenhaven Pr., Inc.) Thomson Gale.

Jimerson, Maxine Newman. Childhood Obesity. 2007. (Diseases & Disorders Ser.). (Illus.). 128p. (gr. 7-10). 31.20 (*978-1-59018-997-9(3)*, Lucent Bks.) Thomson Gale.

Johnson, Susan & Mellin, Laurel. Just for Kids! Obesity Prevention Program Workbook. 2000. (Illus.). 154p. (J). (gr. 1-6). pap. 12.00 (978-0-935902-34-1(1)) Balboa Publishing Corp.

Libal, Autumn. Fats, Sugars, & Empty Calories: The Fast Food Habit. 2004. (Obesity Ser.). (Illus.). 104p. (J). (ps-7). lib. bdg. 23.95 (978-1-59084-943-9(4)) Mason Crest Pubs.

—The Importance of Physical Activity & Exercise: The Fitness Factor. 2005. (Obesity Ser.). (Illus.). 104p. (J). (ps-7). lib. bdg. 23.95 (978-1-59084-945-3(0)) Mason Crest Pubs.

—Social Discrimination & Body Size: Too Big to Fit? 2005. (Obesity Ser.). (Illus.). 104p. (J). (ps-7). lib. bdg. 23.95 (978-1-59084-949-1(3)) Mason Crest Pubs.

Lombardo, Michelle. The OrganWise Guys - Balancing the Energy Equation: One Step at a Time! Herron, Mark, illus. 2003. (J). lib. bdg. 14.95 (978-1-931212-51-9(1)) Wellness, Inc.

—The OrganWise Guys - Pepto's Place: Where Every Portion Size Is OrganWise! Herron, Mark, illus. 2003. 32p. (J). lib. bdg. 14.95 (978-1-931212-50-2(3)) Wellness, Inc.

Marcovitz, Hal. Diet Drugs. 2006. (Drug Education Library). 112p. (J). (gr. 7-10). 32.45 (978-1-56006-914-0(7) , Lucent Bks.) Thomson Gale.

Mattern, Joanne. Obesity: Causes & Consequences. 2005. (Behind the News Ser.). (Illus.). 112p. (J). (gr. 5 up). lib. bdg. 24.95 (978-1-881508-67-0(6)) Oliver Pr., Inc.

McGraw, Jay. Ultimate Weight Solution for Teens: The 7 Keys to Weight Freedom. 2003. (gr. 7-12). lib. bdg. 24.55 (978-0-613-90788-0(4)) Tandem Library Bks.

Monroe, Judy. Understanding Weight-Loss Programs. 1999. (Teen Eating Disorder Prevention Book Ser.). (Illus.). 192p. (YA). (gr. 7-12). lib. bdg. 25.25 (978-0-8239-2866-8(7) , E2WEPR) Rosen Publishing Group, Inc., The.

Naik, Anita. Eating. 2nd ed. 2005. (Illus.). 144p. (YA). pap. 12.00 (978-0-340-88393-8(6) , Hodder & Stoughton) Hodder General Publishing Division GBR. *Dist:* Trafalgar Square Publishing.

Obesity: Modern-Day Epidemic, 10 vols., Set. Incl. America's Unhealthy Lifestyle : Supersize It! Sanna, Ellyn. 2004. (978-1-59084-942-2(6)); Clothing, Cosmetic, & Self-Esteem Tips : Making the Most of the Body You Have. Esherick, Joan. 2005. (978-1-59084-951-4(5)); Diet & Your Emotions : The Comfort Food Falsehood. Esherick, Joan. 2004. lib. bdg. 23.95 (978-1-59084-950-7(7)); Diseases & Disabilities Caused by Weight Problems : The Overloaded Body. Ford, Jean. 2005. (978-1-59084-944-6(2)); Fats, Sugars, & Empty Calories : The Fast Food Habit. Libal, Autumn. 2004. lib. bdg. 23.95 (978-1-59084-943-9(4)); How Genetics & Environment Shape Us : The Destined Body. Hunter, William. 2005. lib. bdg. 23.95 (978-1-59084-948-4(5)); Importance of Physical Activity & Exercise : The Fitness Factor. Libal, Autumn. 2005. lib. bdg. 23.95 (978-1-59084-945-3(0)); Medications & Surgeries for Weight Loss : When Dieting Isn't Enough. Hunter, William. 2005. (978-1-59084-947-7(7)); Social Discrimination & Body Size : Too Big to Fit? Libal, Autumn. 2005. lib. bdg. 23.95 (978-1-59084-949-1(3)); Truth about Diets : The Pros & Cons. Ford, Jean & Libal, Autumn. 2005. lib. bdg. 23.95 (978-1-59084-946-0(9)); (J). (ps-7). (Illus.). 104p. 2005. Set lib. bdg. 239.50 (978-1-59084-941-5(8)) Mason Crest Pubs.

Oliver, Pamela. Weight Loss with Humor: Also Featuring over 100 Body Transformers Body Tips. Oliver, Tyler, illus. l.t. ed. 2001. 140p. per. 9.95 net. (978-0-9715488-0-0(3)) Brandworks Publishing.

Owens, Peter. Teens Health & Obesity. 2005. (Gallup Youth Survey, Major Issues & Trends Ser.). (Illus.). 112p. (J). (ps-7). lib. bdg. 22.95 (978-1-59084-872-2(1)) Mason Crest Pubs.

Parsons, William B., Jr. Tough Talk about Fat! How to Reach & Maintain Your Ideal Weight. 2003. 134p. per. 12.95 (978-0-9662568-9-5(1)) Lilac Pr.

Sanna, Ellyn. America's Unhealthy Lifestyle: Supersize It! 2004. (Obesity Ser.). (Illus.). 104p. (J). (ps-7). (978-1-59084-942-2(6)) Mason Crest Pubs.

Sartori, Rosanne Sheritz. A New Start: One Child's Struggle with Obesity. 2004. (Illus.). 88p. (J). per. 19.95 (978-1-931636-33-9(8)) National Center For Youth Issues.

Stewart, Gail. Fat in America. 2007. (Ripped from the Headlines Ser.). 64p. (J). (gr. 5). 23.95 (***978-1-60217-002-5(9)***) Erickson Pr.

Tecco, Betsy Dru. Food for Fuel: The Connection Between Food & Physical Activity. 2004. (Library of Nutrition). (Illus.). 48p. (J). lib. bdg. 25.25 (978-1-4042-0303-7(6)) Rosen Publishing Group, Inc., The.

Turck, Mary. Healthy Eating for Weight Management. 2000. (Nutrition & Fitness Ser.). (Illus.). 64p. (J). (gr. 4-6). lib. bdg. 23.95 (978-0-7368-0709-8(8) , LifeMatters Bks.) Capstone Pr., Inc.

Williams, Kara. Diet Drugs. 2006. (Danger Zone Ser.). (Illus.). 64p. (J). (gr. 7-12). lib. bdg. 27.95 (***978-1-4042-1994-6(3)***) Rosen Publishing Group, Inc., The.

Zahensky, Barbara A. Diet Fads. 2006. (Danger Zone Ser.). (Illus.). 64p. (J). (gr. 7-12). lib. bdg. 27.95 (***978-1-4042-1999-1(4)***) Rosen Publishing Group, Inc., The.

WEIGHT CONTROL—FICTION

Bennett, Cherie. Life in the Fat Lane. 1999. 272p. (YA). (gr. 7-12). pap. 5.99 (978-0-440-22029-9(7) , Laurel Leaf) Random Hse. Children's Bks.

—Life in the Fat Lane. 1999. (YA). (gr. 7 up). pap., stu. ed. 57.24 incl. audio (978-0-7887-2665-1(X) , 40825) Recorded Bks., LLC.

—Life in the Fat Lane. 1999. (YA). (978-0-606-16720-8(X)); (gr. 7-12). lib. bdg. 13.00 (978-0-613-16143-5(2)) Tandem Library Bks.

—Life in the Fat Lane. l.t. ed. 2000. 351p. (YA). (gr. 8-12). 21.95 (978-0-7862-2887-4(3)) Thorndike Pr.

Blumenthal, Deborah. Fat Camp. 2006. 240p. (gr. 12). pap. 9.99 (978-0-451-21865-0(5) , N A L) Penguin Group (USA) Inc.

Brown, Gladys. The Adventures of King Flapjack. 2005. 36p. pap. 13.95 (978-1-4116-2694-2(X)) Lulu.com.

Campbell, Bebe Moore. I Get So Hungry. Bates, Amy, illus. 2008. 32p. (J). (gr. 1-3). 16.99 (***978-0-399-24311-0(9)*** , Putnam Juvenile) Penguin Group (USA) Inc.

Caple, Kathy. Starring Hillary. Caple, Kathy, illus. 2003. (Picture Bks.). (Illus.). 28p. (J). (ps-3). 15.95 (978-1-57505-261-8(X) , Carolrhoda Bks.) Lerner Publishing Group.

Carter, Catherine. Anna's Choice. Pittman, Gail, illus. 2005. 24p. (J). (gr. 3-7). 12.95 (978-1-893062-79-5(1)) Quail Ridge Pr., Inc.

Clarke, Ray. Fat Girl Kicks Butt Sarahs Program to A. 2006. pap. 23.49 (***978-1-4259-7231-8(4)***) AuthorHouse.

Cohn, Rachel. You Know Where to Find Me. 2008. 208p. (YA). 15.99 (***978-0-689-87859-6(1)*** , Simon & Schuster Children's Publishing) Simon & Schuster Children's Publishing.

Colbert, June. The King of Large. 2005. 160p. pap. (978-0-7344-0615-6(0) , Lothian Bks.) Hachette Livre Australia.

Crew, Gary. The End of the Line. Rogers, Gregory, illus. 2008. 80p. (J). pap. (***978-1-59889-915-3(5));*** (YA). (gr. 5-9). lib. bdg. 16.95 (***978-1-59889-859-0(0))*** Stone Arch Bks.

Dessen, Sarah. Keeping the Moon. 1999. (Illus.). 288p. (J). (gr. 7-12). 16.99 (978-0-670-88549-7(5) , Viking Juvenile) Penguin Group (USA) Inc.

—Keeping the Moon. 2000. (J). (978-0-606-20047-9(9)) Tandem Library Bks.

Gershon, Dann. Extra Large. Robinson, David, illus. 1999. (Hangin' with the Hombeez Ser.: Vol. 3). 40p. (J). (gr. k-6). 14.95 (978-0-9656985-5-9(6)) Noware Bks.

Halverson, Deborah. Big Mouth. 2008. 144p. (J). (gr. 5). 15.99 (***978-0-385-73394-6(1));*** lib. bdg. 18.99 (***978-0-385-90408-7(8))*** Random Hse. Children's Bks. (Delacorte Bks. for Young Readers).

Hanson, Ann. Thin Veils. 1999. 105p. (YA). (gr. 5-9). 14.95 (978-1-881636-99-1(2)); 207p. (J). (gr. 6-10). pap. 8.95 (978-1-881636-87-8(9)) Windsor Hse. Publishing Group, The.

Hardy, Zoey. Everything Changes. 2006. 288p. (YA). per. 9.95 (978-0-9765423-0-8(7)) Eudon Publishing.

Hodgson, Mona Gansberg. Sour Snacks. Sharp, Chris, illus. 1998. (Desert Critter Friends Ser.: Vol. 3). 48p. (J). (ps-2). 4.99 (978-0-570-05070-4(7) , 56-1894) Concordia Publishing Hse.

—Sour Snacks. 1998. (ps-2). lib. bdg. 13.00 (978-0-613-72806-5(8)) Tandem Library Bks.

Hopkins, Cathy. Mates, Dates & Chocolate Cheats. 2005. (Mates, Dates Ser.). (Illus.). 224p. (YA). mass mkt. 5.99 (978-0-689-87696-7(3) , Simon Pulse) Simon & Schuster Children's Publishing.

Jackson, A. Isaiah J. Jiffy: You, You, You. Bully! 2005. 50p. pap. 12.95 (978-1-4137-8524-1(7)) PublishAmerica, Inc.

Kern, Merilee A. It's Not Your Fault That You're Overweight: A Story of Enlightenment, Empowerment, & Accomplishment for Overweight & Obese Kids; Boys' Edition. DeCrotie, Jerry, illus. 2005. 72p. (J). (gr. 3-5). pap. 11.95 (978-1-58736-566-9(9) , Starbound Bks.) Wheatmark.

—It's Not Your Fault That You're Overweight: A Story of Enlightenment, Empowerment, & Accomplishment for Overweight & Obese Kids: Girls' Edition. DeCrotie, Jerry, illus. 2005. 72p. (J). (gr. 3-5). pap. 11.95 (978-1-58736-567-6(7) , Starbound Bks.) Wheatmark.

Kerr, M. E. Dinky Hocker Shoots Smack! 2007. 224p. (J). pap. 6.99 (978-0-06-113989-5(0) , HarperTeen) HarperCollins Pubs.

Lee, Kathy. Fabulous Phoebe. 2003. 128p. 6.49 (978-1-85999-678-2(7)) Scripture Union GBR. *Dist:* Gabriel Resources.

Lewis, Beverly. Photo Perfect. 2001. (Girls Only (Go!) Ser.: Vol. 7). 128p. (J). (gr. 4-7). pap. 6.99 (978-1-55661-642-6(2)) Bethany Hse. Pubs.

Liberto, Lorenzo. Matt the Rat Fights Back / Raton Mateo se Defiende. Gomez, Rocio, tr. from ENG. Torres, Irving, illus. 2005. (Matt the Rat Ser. / La Serie de Raton Mateo). (ENG & SPA.). 32p. (J). lib. bdg. 20.00 (978-0-9743668-4-5(6)) Harvest Sun Pr., LLC.

Lipsyte, Robert. One Fat Summer. rev. ed. 2004. 240p. (J). (gr. 7 up). pap. 5.99 (978-0-06-447073-5(3) , Harper Trophy) HarperCollins Pubs.

Lowry, Brigid. Things You Either Hate or Love. 2005. 179p. (YA). 16.95 (978-0-8234-2004-9(3)) Holiday Hse., Inc.

Lynch, Chris. Extreme Elvin. 1999. 240p. (YA). (gr. 7 up). 15.95 (978-0-06-028040-6(9)) HarperCollins Pubs.

Mackler, Carolyn. The Earth, My Butt, & Other Big Round Things. 2005. 256p. (YA). (gr. 9 up). reprint ed. pap. 8.99 (978-0-7636-2091-2(2)) Candlewick Pr.

Marino, Peter. Dough Boy. 176p. (YA). (gr. 7-12). 16.95 (978-0-8234-1873-2(1)); 2007. pap. 6.95 (***978-0-8234-2096-4(5))*** Holiday Hse., Inc.

May, Eleanor. The Great Shape-Up. Gott, Barry, illus. 2007. (Science Solves It! Ser.). 32p. (J). (gr. 1-3). 4.99 (***978-1-57565-248-1(X))*** Kane Pr., The.

Morgan McKinney Was Portly, Not Skinny: A Christmas Story. 2nd ed. 2003. (Illus.). 50p. (J). per. 59.95 (978-0-9654843-3-6(5) , 1) MacGregor, Doug.

Mulert, Laurie. Am I Fat? A Story about Dieting. Fabian, Melinda, illus. 1998. 39p. (YA). (gr. 5-11). pap. 5.95 (978-1-57543-063-8(0)) MAR*CO Products, Inc.

Olsen, Judith K. I Can Hardly Wait. 2006. 100p. (J). pap. 7.95 (***978-1-59800-999-6(0))*** Outskirts Press, Inc.

Patneaude, David. Colder Than Ice. 2003. 168p. (J). (gr. 4-7). 15.95 (978-0-8075-8135-3(6)) Whitman, Albert & Co.

Peters, Julie Anne. A Snitch in the Snob Squad. 2001. 24p. (J). 5.95 (978-0-316-54561-7(9) , Tingley, Megan Bks.) Little, Brown Bks. for Young Readers.

Sachs, Marilyn. The Fat Girl. 2nd ed. 2007. 240p. (J). pap. 8.95 (978-0-7387-1000-6(8) , Flux) Llewellyn Pubns.

Seymour's Weight Loss Challenge! 2004. (J). (978-0-9777159-2-3(2)) Health New England.

Sparks, Beatrice. Kim: Empty Inside. 2002. (gr. 7-12). lib. bdg. 14.15 (978-0-613-56919-4(9)) Tandem Library Bks.

Sparks, Beatrice, ed. Kim: Empty Inside: The Diary of an Anonymous Teenager. 2002. 176p. (YA). (gr. 7 up). pap. 5.99 (978-0-380-81460-2(9)) HarperCollins Pubs.

Strasser, Todd. How I Changed My Life. 2008. 240p. (YA). mass mkt. 6.99 (***978-1-4169-5409-5(0)*** , Simon Pulse) Simon & Schuster Children's Publishing.

Vaught, Susan. Big Fat Manifesto. 2007. 320p. (YA). 16.95 (***978-1-59990-206-7(0)*** , Bloomsbury Children) Bloomsbury Publishing.

Wells, Rosemary. The Gulps. Brown, Marc, illus. 2007. 40p. (J). (gr. 1-4). 16.99 (***978-0-316-01460-1(5))*** Little, Brown Bks. for Young Readers.

Whytock, Cherry. My Cup Runneth Over: The Life of Angelica Cookson Potts. Whytock, Cherry, illus. (YA). 2003. (Illus.). 176p. 14.95 (978-0-689-86546-6(5)); 2004. 192p. reprint ed. mass mkt. 5.99 (978-0-689-86551-0(1) , Simon Pulse) Simon & Schuster Children's Publishing.

—My Scrumptious Scottish Dumplings: The Life of Angelica Cookson Potts. Whytock, Cherry, illus. 2006. 192p. (YA). mass mkt. 5.99 (978-0-689-86552-7(X) , Simon Pulse) Simon & Schuster Children's Publishing.

Whytock, Cherry, illus. My Scrumptious Scottish Dumplings: The Life of Angelica Cookson Potts. 2004. 176p. (YA). 14.95 (978-0-689-86549-7(X)) Simon & Schuster Children's Publishing.

WEIGHTS AND MEASURES

see also Measuring Instruments; Mensuration; Metric System

Aboff, Marcie. The Tallest Snowman. Gray, Sara, illus. 2007. (J). lib. bdg. (***978-1-4048-3666-2(7))*** Picture Window Bks.

Adler, David A. How Tall, How Short, How Far Away. Tobin, Nancy, illus. 1999. 32p. (J). (gr. k-3). pap. 6.95 (978-0-8234-1632-5(1)) Holiday Hse., Inc.

Benjamin, Lindsay. Measurement Action! 2005. (Yellow Umbrella Books for Early Readers). (Illus.). 17p. (J). (978-0-7368-5286-9(7)); (978-0-7368-5322-4(7)) Capstone Pr., Inc.

Bullock, Linda. You Can Use a Balance. (Rookie Read-About Science Ser.). (Illus.). (J). 2004. 31p. (gr. 1-2). pap. 4.95 (978-0-516-27899-5(1)); 2003. 32p. 20.50 (978-0-516-22869-3(2)) Scholastic Library Publishing. (Children's Pr.).

Chrismer, Melanie. Math Tools. 2006. 32p. (gr. 1-2). (YA). pap. 5.95 (978-0-516-25550-7(9)); (Illus.). (J). 20.50 (978-0-516-24961-2(4)) Scholastic Library Publishing. (Children's Pr.).

Clark, John Owens Edward. Electrical Measurement, 9 vols., Vol. 4. 2002. (Illus.). (J). (978-0-7172-5632-7(4) , Grolier) Scholastic Library Publishing.

—Force & Pressure, 9 vols., Vol. 3. 2002. (Illus.). (J). (978-0-7172-5631-0(6) , Grolier) Scholastic Library Publishing.

—Length & Distance, 9 vols., Vol. 1. 2002. (Illus.). (J). (978-0-7172-5629-7(4) , Grolier) Scholastic Library Publishing.

—Measuring Time, 9 vols., Vol. 2. 2002. (Illus.). (J). (978-0-7172-5630-3(8) , Grolier) Scholastic Library Publishing.

—Scientific Analysis, 9 vols., Vol. 8. 2002. (Illus.). (J). (978-0-7172-5636-5(7) , Grolier) Scholastic Library Publishing.

—Scientific Classification, 9 vols., Vol. 9. 2002. (Illus.). (J). (978-0-7172-5637-2(5) , Grolier) Scholastic Library Publishing.

—Under the Microscope: Science Tools, 9 vols., Set. Incl. Vol. 1. Length & Distance. (978-0-7172-5629-7(4)); Vol. 2. Measuring Time. (978-0-7172-5630-3(8)); Vol. 3. Force & Pressure. (978-0-7172-5631-0(6)); Vol. 4. Electrical Measurement. (978-0-7172-5632-7(4)); Vol. 5. Using Visible Light. (978-0-7172-5633-4(2)); Vol. 6. Using Invisible Light. (978-0-7172-5634-1(0)); Vol. 7. Using Sound. (978-0-7172-5635-8(9)); Vol. 8. Scientific Analysis. (978-0-7172-5636-5(7)); Vol. 9. Scientific Classification. (978-0-7172-5637-2(5)); (J). (Illus.). 432p. 2002. 239.00 (978-0-7172-5628-0(6) , Grolier) Scholastic Library Publishing.

—Using Invisible Light, 9 vols., Vol. 6. 2002. (Illus.). (J). (978-0-7172-5634-1(0) , Grolier) Scholastic Library Publishing.

—Using Sound, 9 vols., Vol. 7. 2002. (Illus.). (J). (978-0-7172-5635-8(9) , Grolier) Scholastic Library Publishing.

—Using Visible Light, 9 vols., Vol. 5. 2002. (Illus.). (J). (978-0-7172-5633-4(2) , Grolier) Scholastic Library Publishing.

Cleary, Brian P. How Long or How Wide? A Measuring Guide. Gable, Brian, illus. 2007. (Math Is CATegorical Ser.). 32p. (J). (gr. 1-5). 15.95 (978-0-8225-6694-6(X) , Millbrook Pr.) Lerner Publishing Group.

Cobb, Vicki. I Fall Down. Gorton, Julia, illus. 2004. (Science Play Ser.). 40p. (J). (ps-k). lib. bdg. 16.89 (978-0-688-17843-7(X)) HarperCollins Pubs.

Coulton, Mia. How Much Does This Hold? Graves, Dennis, illus. l.t. ed. 1998. 24p. (J). (gr. k-2). pap. 4.95 (978-1-57874-020-8(7)) Kaeden Corp.

Doudna, Kelly. It's My Pleasure to Measure the Treasure. 2007. (Illus.). 24p. (J). 19.93 (978-1-59928-602-0(5) , SandCastle) ABDO Publishing Co.

—It's My Pleasure to Measure the Treasure! 2006. (Illus.). 24p. (J). pap. (978-1-59928-603-7(3)) ABDO Publishing Co.

—It's Time to Dance, We can use a Balance. 2007. (Illus.). 24p. (J). 19.93 (978-1-59928-608-2(4) , SandCastle) ABDO Publishing Co.

—It's Time to Dance, We Can Use a Balance! 2006. (Illus.). 24p. (J). pap. (978-1-59928-609-9(2)) ABDO Publishing Co.

—Let's Be Kids & Measure Liquids. 2007. (Illus.). 24p. (J). 19.93 (978-1-59928-610-5(6) , SandCastle) ABDO Publishing Co.

—Let's Be Kids & Measure Liquids! 2006. (Illus.). 24p. (J). pap. (978-1-59928-611-2(4)) ABDO Publishing Co.

Freudentha. Measure for Measure. 2003. (Mathematics in Context Ser.). (SPA.). stu. ed. 7.86 (978-0-03-072336-0(1)) Holt, Rinehart & Winston.

—Measure for Measure Math/Context. 98th ed. 2002. (SPA.) 7.86 (978-0-85229-718-6(1)) Encyclopaedia Britannica, Inc.

Furgang, Kathy. Measuring Length. 2003. (Early Connections Ser.). (J). pap. 33.00 (978-1-4108-1088-5(7)) Benchmark Education Co.

Gardner, Robert. Heavy-Duty Science Projects with Weight: How Much Does It Weigh? 2003. (Sensational Science Experiments Ser.). (Illus.). 48p. (J). (gr. 1-4). lib. bdg. 23.93 (978-0-7660-2013-9(4)) Enslow Pubs., Inc.

—Super-Sized Science Projects with Volume: How Much Space Does It Take Up? 2003. (Sensational Science Experiments Ser.). (Illus.). 48p. (J). lib. bdg. 23.93 (978-0-7660-2014-6(2)) Enslow Pubs., Inc.

Gold, Kari Jenson. Units of Measure. Date not set. (Early Math Big Bks.). (Illus.). 16p. (J). (ps-2). pap. 16.95 (978-1-58273-488-0(7)) Sundance/Newbridge Educational Publishing.

Harris, Nancy. What Is Big Compared to Me? A Book about Measurements. 2008. (J). (***978-1-60044-635-1(3))*** Rourke Publishing, LLC.

Harris, Nicholas. How Tall? 2003. (How? Ser.). (Illus.). 30p. (J). 23.70 (978-1-4103-0065-2(X)); 11.20 (978-1-4103-0194-9(X)) Thomson Gale. (Blackbirch Pr., Inc.).

Hirschmann, Kris. The Dog: Is a Paw a Foot? Learn Measurement. 2007. (Illus.). 32p. (J). pap. 3.99 (***978-0-439-92213-5(5))*** Scholastic, Inc.

Holland, Gini. Light & Heavy. 2007. (J). pap. (***978-0-8368-8300-8(4));*** 24p. lib. bdg. 17.27 (***978-0-8368-8295-7(4))*** Stevens, Gareth Inc. (Weekly Reader Early Learning Library).

Holt, Rinehart and Winston Staff. Measure for Measure. 2003. (Mathematics in Context Ser.). tchr. ed. 33.53 (978-0-03-071282-1(3)) Holt, Rinehart & Winston.

—Measures & Measurement. 2002. (Math in Context Ser.). tchr. ed. 31.60 (978-0-7826-1491-6(4)) Holt, Rinehart & Winston.

Kauffman, Dorothy. Measurement All over the World. 2005. (Content Area Readers Ser.). 4.95 (978-0-19-430959-2(2)) Oxford Univ. Pr., Inc.

Mattern, Joanne. Let's Visit Canada: The Metric System. 2004. (PowerMath Ser.). (Illus.). 24p. (J). pap. (978-0-8239-8872-3(4)); lib. bdg. 21.25 (978-0-8239-8967-6(4)) Rosen Publishing Group, Inc., The. (PowerKids Pr.).

Measure Mints. 2002. (J). stu. ed. 10.95 (978-1-58123-293-6(4)) Larson Learning, Inc.

Miura, Taro. Ton. 2006. (Illus.). 40p. (J). 15.95 (978-0-8118-5246-3(6)) Chronicle Bks. LLC.

Murphy, Patricia J. Measuring Puppies & Kittens. 2007. (Puppy & Kitten Math Ser.). (Illus.). 32p. (J). lib. bdg. 22.60 (978-0-7660-2727-5(9) , Enslow Elementary) Enslow Pubs., Inc.

Murphy, Stuart J. Mighty Maddie. Lum, Bernice, illus. 2004. (MathStart Ser.). 40p. (J). 15.99 (978-0-06-053159-1(2)); pap. 5.99 (978-0-06-053161-4(4)) HarperCollins Pubs.

Nieker, Diane. Heavy & Light. 2005. (Heinemann Read & Learn Ser.). (Illus.). 24p. lib. bdg. (978-1-4034-7570-1(9)); (J). pap. 6.00 (978-1-4034-7575-6(X)) Steck-Vaughn.

—Pesado y Liviano. 2006. (ENG & SPA., Illus.). 24p. (J). (978-1-4034-7585-5(7)); pap. (978-1-4034-7590-9(3)) Heinemann Library.

Nsrc. Science & Technology for Children Books, Measuring Time. 2004. (Illus.). 64p. (J). (978-1-933008-09-7(1)) National Science Resources Ctr.

Olenych, Bob, et al. Geometry & Measurement. 2003. (Rtg Reproducibles Ser.). 48p. pap., tchr. ed. 10.95 (978-0-439-38526-8(1) , Teaching Resources) Scholastic, Inc.

Osborne, J. E. Measuring Up. Date not set. (Early Math Big Bks.). (Illus.). 16p. (J). (ps-2). pap. 16.95 (978-1-56784-428-3(6)) Sundance/Newbridge Educational Publishing.

Pallotta, Jerry. Hershey's Weights & Measures Book. Bolster, Rob, illus. 2003. (Hershey's Ser.). 32p. (J). pap. 5.99 (978-0-439-38877-1(5)); pap. 16.99 (978-0-439-38876-4(7)) Scholastic, Inc. (Cartwheel Bks.).

—Hershey's Weights & Measures Book. 2002. (gr. k-3). lib. bdg. 14.10 (978-0-613-63041-2(6)) Tandem Library Bks.

Patilla, Peter. Weight. 2001. (Illus.). 32p. (J). lib. bdg. 24.25 (978-1-930643-18-5(7)) Chrysalis Education.

—Weight. Cockcroft, David, illus. 1999. (J). (978-0-382-42234-8(1)) Silver, Burdett & Ginn, Inc.

Practice Power Practice Book - Fractions & Measures. 2000. (Illus.). 16p. (J). (gr. 3-5). spiral bd. (978-1-930355-19-4(X)) Greenbrier/Scentex.

Richardson, Adele D. Balances. 2004. (First Facts Ser.). (Illus.). 24p. (J). 15.95 (978-0-7368-2516-0(9)) Capstone Pr., Inc.

Rivera, Sheila. Balance. 2006. (First Step Nonfiction Ser.). (Illus.). 8p. (J). lib. bdg. (978-0-8225-5716-6(9) , Lerner Pubns.) Lerner Publishing Group.

—Scale. 2007. (First Step Nonfiction Ser.). (J). lib. bdg. (978-0-8225-6854-4(3)) Lerner Publishing Group.

—Tape Measure. 2007. (First Step Nonfiction Ser.). (J). lib. bdg. (978-0-8225-6855-1(1)) Lerner Publishing Group.

Royston, Angela. Heavy & Light. 2003. (Illus.). 32p. pap. 6.50 (978-1-4034-3166-0(3)); (J). lib. bdg. 22.79 (978-1-4034-0853-2(X)) Heinemann Library.

Sargent, Brian. How Heavy Is It? 2005. (Rookie Read-About Math Ser.). (Illus.). 31p. (J). (ps-ps). 20.50 (978-0-516-25267-4(4) , Children's Pr.) Scholastic Library Publishing.

—How Heavy Is It. 2006. 32p. (J). (gr. 1-2). pap. 5.95 (978-0-516-25368-8(9) , Children's Pr.) Scholastic Library Publishing.

Schwartz, David M. Millions to Measure. Kellogg, Steven, illus. 40p. (J). 2003. lib. bdg. 17.89 (978-0-06-623784-8(X)); 2003. 16.99 (978-0-688-12916-3(1)); 2006. reprint ed. pap. 6.99 (978-0-06-084806-4(5) , Harper Trophy) HarperCollins Pubs.

Science & Technology for Children Books, Measuring Time Set, 8 vols. 2004. (Illus.). 64p. (J). (978-1-933008-21-9(0)) National Science Resources Ctr.

Smith, Robert. How to Calculate Measurements: Grades 3-4. 2000. (Illus.). 48p. (J). pap., tchr. ed. 7.99 (978-1-57690-486-2(5) , TCA2486) Teacher Created Materials, Inc.

Steck-Vaughn Staff. Math: Data Analysis, Measurement, Geometry. 2002. (Illus.). pap. (978-0-7398-5429-7(1)) Steck-Vaughn.

—Measurement: Practical Applications. 1999. (Illus.). (J). (gr. 2). pap. (978-0-7398-2066-7(4)); (gr. 3). pap. (978-0-7398-2067-4(2)); (gr. 4). pap. (978-0-7398-2068-1(0)); (gr. 5). pap. (978-0-7398-2069-8(9)) Steck-Vaughn.

Sullivan, Navin. Weight. 2006. (Measure Up! Ser.). (Illus.). 48p. (J). (gr. 4-7). lib. bdg. 29.93 (978-0-7614-2324-9(9) , Benchmark Bks.) Cavendish, Marshall Corp.

Sweeney, Joan. Me & the Measure of Things. Cable, Annette, illus. 2002. 32p. (J). (ps-3). pap. 6.99 (978-0-440-41756-9(2) , Dragonfly Bks.) Random Hse. Children's Bks.

Taylor, Loretta & Taylor, Harold. Understanding Measurement, Bk. 6. 2000. (Basic Computation Ser.: Bk. 6). 123p. (YA). (gr. 6-12). pap. 18.95 (978-0-7690-0119-7(X)) Seymour, Dale Pubns.

Taylor, Terilyn & Milleret, Toni. Basic Viola Scales. 2000. (Color Connection Ser.). (Illus.). 44p. (YA). (gr. 1 up). pap. 15.95 (978-0-9671719-6-8(2)) T&T Publishing.

Trumbauer, Lisa. Animal Giants. 16p. (J). (gr. k-2). 2006. 15.93 (978-0-7368-5862-5(8) , Yellow Umbrella Bks.); 2005. (Illus.). (978-0-7368-5328-6(6)); 2005. (Illus.). (978-0-7368-5292-0(1)) Capstone Pr., Inc.

—What Is Volume? 2006. (Rookie Read-About Science Ser.). (Illus.). 32p. (J). (gr. 1-2). 20.50 (978-0-516-23621-6(0) , Children's Pr.) Scholastic Library Publishing.

—What Is Volume? 2006. 32p. (YA). (gr. 1-2). pap. 4.95 (978-0-516-24661-1(5) , Children's Pr.) Scholastic Library Publishing.

Walsh, Kieran. Kitchen Math. 2003. (Math & My World Ser.). (Illus.). 48p. (J). 29.93 (978-1-58952-382-1(2)) Rourke Publishing, LLC.

Willis, Shirley. Dime Cuanto Pesa. 1999. (Coleccion los Estupendos). (SPA., Illus.). 32p. (J). (gr. 2-4). 20.00 (978-0-531-11844-3(4) , OD30021, Watts, Franklin) Scholastic Library Publishing.

—Tell Me How Far It Is. 2000. (Whiz Kids Ser.). (Illus.). 32p. (J). (gr. 1-3). pap. 5.95 (978-0-531-15975-0(2) , Watts, Franklin) Scholastic Library Publishing.

—Tell Me How Far It Is. 1999. (gr. k-3). lib. bdg. 14.10 (978-0-613-29522-2(6)) Tandem Library Bks.

—Tell Me How Much It Weighs. 2000. (Whiz Kids Ser.). (Illus.). 32p. (J). (gr. 1-3). pap. 5.95 (978-0-531-15977-4(9) , Watts, Franklin) Scholastic Library Publishing.

Woodford, Chris. Volume. 2005. (J). 11.20 (978-1-4103-0523-7(6)); (Illus.). 32p. lib. bdg. 23.70 (978-1-4103-0367-7(5)) Thomson Gale. (Blackbirch Pr., Inc.).

WELDING

Multimedia Welding Safety. (Shop Safety Ser.). (YA). cd-rom 69.95 (978-0-7365-9986-3(X)); cd-rom 69.95 (978-0-7365-9988-7(6)) Films Media Group.

WELFARE STATE

see Economic Policy

WELFARE WORK

see Social Service

WELLINGTON, ARTHUR WELLESLEY, DUKE OF, 1769-1852

Crompton, Samuel Willard. Waterloo. 2002. (Battles That Changed the World Ser.). (Illus.). (J). 111p. pap. 13.25 (978-0-7910-7110-6(3)); 112p. (gr. 7-10). 30.00 (978-0-7910-6683-6(5)) Facts On File, Inc. (Chelsea Hse.).

WELLS, H. G. (HERBERT GEORGE), 1866-1946

Boerst, William J. Time Machine: The Story of H. G. Wells. 2004. (World Writers Ser.). (Illus.). 112p. (YA). (gr. 6-12). 23.95 (978-1-883846-40-4(4) , First Biographies) Reynolds, Morgan Inc.

H G Wells, hombre del Futuro 10: Leveled Books. 2001. (McGraw-Hill, Lectura Ser.). (ENG & SPA.). (gr. 4 up). (978-0-02-188210-6(X)) Macmillan/McGraw-Hill Schl. Div.

WELLS, JEFF (FICTITIOUS CHARACTER)—FICTION

Asimov, Isaac & Asimov, Janet. Norby & the Lost Princess. 129p. (J). lib. bdg. 20.90 (978-0-8027-6593-2(9)) Walker & Co.

Asimov, Janet & Asimov, Isaac. Norby & the Court Jester. l.t. ed. 1999. 168p. 24.95 (978-0-7838-8610-7(1)) Thorndike Pr.

WELLS-BARNETT, IDA B., 1862-1931

Dray, Philip. Daughter of Freedom: The Life & Times of Ida B. Wells. Alcorn, Stephen, illus. 2007. (J). ***(978-1-56145-417-4(6))*** Peachtree Pubs., Ltd.

Fradin, Dennis Brindell & Fradin, Judith Bloom. Ida B. Wells: Mother of the Civil Rights Movement. 2000. (Illus.). 192p. (J). (gr. 5-9). tchr. ed. 19.00 (978-0-395-89898-7(6) , Clarion Bks.) Houghton Mifflin Co. Trade & Reference Div.

McKissack, Patricia C. & McKissack, Fredrick L. Ida B. Wells-Barnett: A Voice Against Violence. rev. ed. 2001. (Great African Americans Ser.). (Illus.). 32p. (J). (gr. 1-4). lib. bdg. 18.60 (978-0-7660-1677-4(3)) Enslow Pubs., Inc.

Moore, Heidi. Ida B. Wells-Barnett. 2004. (Illus.). 32p. (J). pap. 6.95 (978-1-4034-5706-6(9)); lib. bdg. (978-1-4034-4997-9(X)) Heinemann Library.

Schraff, Anne E. Ida B. Wells-Barnett: Strike a Blow Against Glaring Evil. 2008. (African-American Biography Library). (Illus.). 128p. (J). (gr. 6 up). lib. bdg. 31.93 ***(978-0-7660-2704-6(X))*** Enslow Pubs., Inc.

Welch, Catherine A. Ida B. Wells-Barnett: Powerhouse with a Pen. 2005. (Trailblazers Biographies Ser.). (Illus.). 112p. (gr. 5-9). 27.93 (978-1-57505-352-3(7)) Lerner Publishing Group.

WELLS

see also Petroleum; Water-Supply

Shoveller, Herb. Ryan & Jimmy: And the Well in Africa That Brought Them Together. 2006. (Illus.). 56p. (J). (gr. 3-7). (978-1-55337-967-6(5)) Kids Can Pr., Ltd.

Well... What's All That Drilling About? 2007. (Illus.). 31p. (J). 12.99 ***(978-0-9641186-3-8(7))*** American Ground Water Trust.

WELLS FARGO AND COMPANY

Moody, Ralph. Wells Fargo. Mays, Victor, illus. 2005. 1p. pap. 11.95 (978-0-8032-8303-9(2) , MOOWEX, Bison Bks.) Univ. of Nebraska Pr.

WELSH LANGUAGE

Davies, Helen Emanuel & Cooper, Anne Lloyd. Torri Gair. 2005. (WEL., Illus.). 16p. (978-1-85644-545-0(3)) Univ. of Wales, Aberystwyth, Centre for Educational Studies.

Gruffydd, Stella. Haws Dweud: Gweithgareddau Llefaredd, Darllen Ac Ysgrifennu I Blant Cyfnod Allweddol 2. 2005. (WEL., Illus.). 150p. (978-1-85644-601-3(8)) Univ. of Wales, Aberystwyth, Centre for Educational Studies.

Hughes, Mair Wynn. Y Dewis. 2005. (WEL., Illus.). 16p. (978-1-85644-747-8(2)) Univ. of Wales, Aberystwyth, Centre for Educational Studies.

Jones, Marlis. Wyn Melangell. 2005. (WEL., Illus.). 12p. (978-1-85644-744-7(8)) Univ. of Wales, Aberystwyth, Centre for Educational Studies.

Jones, Marlis & Jên, Ruth. Cuddio'r Colur. 2005. (WEL., Illus.). 15p. (978-1-85644-547-4(X)) Univ. of Wales, Aberystwyth, Centre for Educational Studies.

Lasarus, Gwen. Hud Hen Hanes. 2005. (WEL., Illus.). 12p. (978-1-85644-745-4(6)) Univ. of Wales, Aberystwyth, Centre for Educational Studies.

Lewis, Sian & Thomas, Rhianedd. Cris Croes. 2005. (WEL., Illus.). 16p. (978-1-85644-544-3(5)) Univ. of Wales, Aberystwyth, Centre for Educational Studies.

Maelor, Gwawr, et al. Tan Yn y Jyngl. 2005. (WEL., Illus.). 16p. (978-1-85644-842-0(8)) Univ. of Wales, Aberystwyth, Centre for Educational Studies.

Non ap Emlyn. Hamddena - Llyfr 1 Lefel 3/4. 2005. (WEL & ENG., Illus.). 20p. (978-1-86085-600-6(4)) ICA Video.

—Hamddena - Llyfr 3 Lefel 5/6. 2005. (WEL & ENG., Illus.). 20p. (978-1-86085-602-0(0)) ICA Video.

—Hamddena - Llyfr 4 Lefel 6/7. 2005. (WEL & ENG., Illus.). 20p. (978-1-86085-603-7(9)) ICA Video.

Richards, Aled. Stori Dda. 2005. (WEL., Illus.). 16p. (978-1-85644-746-1(4)) Univ. of Wales, Aberystwyth, Centre for Educational Studies.

Richards, Aled & Pritchard, Richard Huw. Am y Copa. 2005. (WEL., Illus.). 16p. (978-1-85644-549-8(6)) Univ. of Wales, Aberystwyth, Centre for Educational Studies.

Roberts, Eirlys. Dweud ein Dweud. 2005. (WEL., Illus.). 72p. pap. (978-1-85644-906-9(8)) Univ. of Wales, Aberystwyth, Centre for Educational Studies.

Roberts, Heulwen. Anifeiliaid Anwes. 2005. (WEL., Illus.). 16p. (978-1-85644-778-2(2)) Univ. of Wales, Aberystwyth, Centre for Educational Studies.

University of Wales, Aberystwyth, Centre for Educational Studies Staff, contrib. by. Arch Noa: Casgliad o Sbardunau Ac Ymarferion Ar Thema Creaduriaid. 2005. (WEL., Illus.). 72p. (978-1-85644-959-5(9)) Univ. of Wales, Aberystwyth, Centre for Educational Studies.

Williams, Carol. What's the World for - ? Beth Yw'r Gair Am - ? 2004. (WEL & ENG., Illus.). 160p. (J). pap. (978-0-7083-1736-5(7)) Univ. of Wales Pr.

WEREWOLVES

Cohen, Daniel. Werewolves. 128p. (J). pap. 4.99 (978-0-14-038621-9(1) , Puffin) Penguin Group (USA) Inc.

Hirschmann, Kris. Werewolves. 2006. (Mysterious Encounters Ser.). 48p. (J). (gr. 4-8). 26.20 (978-0-7377-3532-1(5) , Kidhaven) Thomson Gale.

Krensky, Stephen. Werewolves. 2007. (Monster Chronicles Ser.). (Illus.). 48p. (J). (gr. 4-8). lib. bdg. 26.60 (978-0-8225-5922-1(6)) Lerner Publishing Group.

Ollhoff, Jim. Werewolves. 2007. (ENG., Illus.). 32p. (J). lib. bdg. 24.21 ***(978-1-59928-775-1(7)*** , ABDO & Daughters) ABDO Publishing Co.

Oxlade, Chris. The Mystery of Vampires & Werewolves. 2002. (Can Science Solve? Ser.). 32p. (J). (gr. 4-7). (Illus.). lib. bdg. 22.79 (978-1-58810-668-1(3)); pap. 7.50 (978-1-58810-932-3(1) , 91568) Heinemann Library.

Pipe, Jim. Werewolves. 2007. (Tales of Horror Ser.). 32p. (J). (gr. 3-6). lib. bdg. 25.27 (978-1-59716-206-7(X)) Bearport Publishing Co., Inc.

Sautter, Aaron. Werewolves. 2007. (Blazers Ser.). (Illus.). 32p. (J). 19.93 (978-0-7368-6444-2(X)) Capstone Pr., Inc.

Stefoff, Rebecca. Vampires, Zombies, & Shape-Shifters. 2007. (Secrets of the Supernatural Ser.). 96p. (J). lib. bdg. 32.79 ***(978-0-7614-2635-6(3)*** , Benchmark Bks.) Cavendish, Marshall Corp.

WEREWOLVES—FICTION

Bernstein, Nina. Magic by the Book. Kulikov, Boris, illus. 2005. 240p. (J). 17.00 (978-0-374-34718-5(2) , Farrar, Straus & Giroux (BYR)) Farrar, Straus & Giroux.

—Magic by the Book. unabr. ed. 2005. (J). 63.75 incl. audio (978-1-4193-3607-2(X) , 42048) Recorded Bks., LLC.

—Magic by the Book. l.t. ed. 2006. 248p. (J). 22.95 (978-0-7862-8382-8(3)) Thorndike Pr.

Buchanan, Paul. Dances with Werewolves, Vol. 8. 2000. (Heebie Jeebies Ser.: Vol. 6). 128p. (J). (gr. 3-7). pap. 5.99 (978-0-8054-1982-5(9)) B&H Publishing Grp.

Cole, Stephen. Prey. 2004. 256p. (YA). pap. ***(978-0-7475-6503-1(1))*** Bloomsbury Pr.

Cole, Stephen. Resurrection, No. 3. 2005. (Wereling Ser.). 272p. (YA). (gr. 7-12). mass mkt. 5.99 (978-1-59514-043-2(3) , Razorbill) Penguin Group (USA) Inc.

Dent, Sue. Never Ceese: Can Two Who Were Wronged Make It Right? 2006. 336p. (YA). lib. bdg. 17.99 (978-1-59958-017-3(9)) Journey Stone Creations, LLC.

Dunkle, Clare B. By These Ten Bones. rev. ed. 2005. 240p. (YA). (gr. 6-9). 16.95 (978-0-8050-7496-3(1) , Holt, Henry & Co. Bks. For Young Readers) Holt, Henry & Co.

Dunne, Colin. Werewolf. 128p. (J). pap. 7.95 (978-0-233-99580-9(3)) Andre Deutsch GBR. *Dist:* Trans-Atlantic Pubns., Inc.

French, Jackie. My Uncle the Werewolf. King, Stephen Michael, illus. 2007. (J). 112p. ***(978-1-59889-346-5(7));*** 107p. pap. ***(978-1-59889-439-4(0))*** Stone Arch Bks.

Garfield, Henry. My Father the Werewolf. 2005. (Illus.). 240p. (J). (gr. 8-12). 17.95 (978-0-689-85180-3(4) , Atheneum) Simon & Schuster Children's Publishing.

—Tartabull's Throw. 2001. (Illus.). 272p. (J). (gr. 7 up). 16.00 (978-0-689-83840-8(9) , Atheneum/Richard Jackson Bks.) Simon & Schuster Children's Publishing.

—Tartabull's Throw. 2003. (gr. 7-12). lib. bdg. 14.15 (978-0-613-61823-6(8)) Tandem Library Bks.

Garmon, Larry Mike. The Wolf Man: Blood Moon Rising. 2001. (Universal Monsters Ser.: No. 2). 160p. (J). (gr. 5 up). pap. 4.50 (978-0-439-20847-5(5)) Scholastic, Inc.

Greenburg, Dan. My Teacher Ate My Homework, Vol. 27. Davis, Jack E., illus. 2002. (Zack Files Ser.: 27). 64p. (J). pap. 4.99 (978-0-448-42683-9(8) , Grosset & Dunlap) Penguin Group (USA) Inc.

—My Teacher Ate My Homework. 2002. (gr. 3-6). lib. bdg. 13.00 (978-0-613-61645-4(6)) Tandem Library Bks.

Hoffman, Alice & Martin, Wolfe. Moondog. Heo, Yumi, illus. 2004. (J). pap. (978-0-439-09862-5(9)); 32p. pap. 16.95 (978-0-439-09861-8(0)) Scholastic, Inc.

Jennings, Patrick. The Wolving Time. 208p. (J). 2005. pap. 5.99 (978-0-439-39556-4(9) , Scholastic Paperbacks); 2003. pap. 15.95 (978-0-439-39555-7(0)) Scholastic, Inc.

Keene, Carolyn. Werewolf in a Winter Wonderland. 2003. (Nancy Drew Mystery Stories). 160p. (J). pap. 4.99 (978-0-689-86182-6(6) , Aladdin) Simon & Schuster Children's Publishing.

Klause, Annette Curtis. Blood & Chocolate. 2007. 288p. (J). pap. 8.99 ***(978-0-385-73421-9(2)*** , Delacorte Bks. for Young Readers); 2007. 272p. (J). lib. bdg. 11.99 ***(978-0-385-90434-6(7)*** , Delacorte Bks. for Young Readers); 1999. 288p. (YA). (gr. 9-12). mass mkt. 6.99 (978-0-440-22668-0(6) , Laurel Leaf) Random Hse. Children's Bks.

—Blood & Chocolate. 1999. (J). 12.64 (978-0-606-17216-5(5)); (gr. 7-12). lib. bdg. 13.55 (978-0-613-22836-7(7)) Tandem Library Bks.

La Fevers, Robin. Werewolf Rising. 2006. 176p. (J). (gr. 5). 16.99 (978-0-525-47665-8(2) , Dutton Juvenile) Penguin Group (USA) Inc.

McCann, James. Pyre. 2007. 180p. (J). pap. 8.95 (978-1-894965-66-8(3)) Simply Read Bks. CAN. *Dist:* Perseus Distribution.

Meyer, Stephenie. Eclipse. rev. ed. 2007. (Twilight Saga Ser.). 640p. (YA). (gr. 7 up). 18.99 ***(978-0-316-16020-9(2))*** Little, Brown Bks. for Young Readers.

Pinkwater, Daniel M. The Lunchroom of Doom. 2000. (gr. 3-6). lib. bdg. 11.80 (978-0-613-31437-4(9)) Tandem Library Bks.

—The Magic Pretzel. 2000. (gr. 3-6). lib. bdg. 11.80 (978-0-613-26097-8(X)); (Werewolf Club Ser.: No. 1). (978-0-606-17942-3(9)) Tandem Library Bks.

—The Magic Pretzel. Pinkwater, Jill, illus. 2000. (Werewolf Club Ser.). (J). (978-0-606-19734-2(6)) Tandem Library Bks.

—The Werewolf Club Meets Dorkula. Pinkwater, Jill, illus. 2001. (Werewolf Club Ready for Chapters Ser.: Vol. 3). 80p. (J). (gr. 2-5). pap. 7.95 (978-0-689-83847-7(6) , Aladdin) Simon & Schuster Children's Publishing.

—The Werewolf Club Meets Oliver Twit. 2002. (gr. 3-6). lib. bdg. 11.80 (978-0-613-45123-9(6)) Tandem Library Bks.

—The Werewolf Club Meets the Hound of the Basketballs. Pinkwater, Jill, illus. 4th ed. 2001. (Werewolf Club Ser.: Vol. 4). 64p. (J). pap. 7.95 (978-0-689-84473-7(5) , Aladdin) Simon & Schuster Children's Publishing.

—The Werewolf Club Meets the Hound of the Basketballs. 2001. (978-0-606-22089-7(5)) Tandem Library Bks.

Pinkwater, Daniel M. & Pinkwater, Jill. The Magic Pretzel. 2000. (Werewolf Club Ready for Chapters Ser.: Bk. 1). (Illus.). 80p. (J). (gr. 2-4). pap. 3.99 (978-0-689-83790-6(9) , Aladdin) Simon & Schuster Children's Publishing.

Romero Gutierrez, Astrid. Cuentos de Hombres-Lobo Para Nios. 2000. Tr. of Werewolves Stories for Children. (SPA.). lib. bdg. 20.00 (978-0-613-81986-2(1)) Tandem Library Bks.

Scholastic Editorial Staff. Super Spooky Double Storybook. 2008. (Puppy Place Ser.). 48p. (J). pap. 4.99 ***(978-0-545-03153-0(2))*** Scholastic, Inc.

Scroggs, Kirk Brandon. Super Soccer Freak Show. 4th ed. 2007. (Wiley & Grampa's Creature Features Ser.: No. 4). (Illus.). 112p. (J). (gr. 3-7). 12.99 (978-0-316-05946-6(3)); pap. 3.99 (978-0-316-05947-3(1)) Little Brown & Co.

Shusterman, Neal. Red Rider's Hood. (Dark Fusion Ser.). 192p. 2006. (YA). (gr. 7). pap. 6.99 (978-0-14-240678-6(3) , Puffin); 2005. (J). (gr. 5-7). 15.99 (978-0-525-47562-0(1) , Dutton Juvenile) Penguin Group (USA) Inc.

Smith, Cynthia Leitich. Tantalize. 2007. (Illus.). 336p. (YA). (gr. 9). 16.99 (978-0-7636-2791-1(7)) Candlewick Pr.

Sulzenko, J. C. Annabella & the Werewolves of Whale Cove. Goldney, Katherine, illus. 2001. 48p. (J). pap. (978-0-9685094-2-5(8)) Blue Poodle Bks.

Taylor, Kelly. Praise the Moon. 2005. 131p. pap. 19.95 (978-1-4137-8059-8(8)) PublishAmerica, Inc.

Van Belkom, Edo. Cry Wolf. 2007. 184p. (J). (gr. 5-9). pap. 9.95 ***(978-0-88776-818-7(0))*** Tundra Bks., Inc./Livres Toundra, Inc. CAN. *Dist:* Random Hse., Inc.

Windsor, Patricia. The Blooding. 1999. 288p. (gr. 7-12). pap. 4.50 (978-0-590-43308-2(3)) Scholastic, Inc.

Zornow, Jeff. Werewolf. Zornow, Jeff, illus. 2007. (Graphic Horror Ser.). (Illus.). 32p. (YA). (gr. 5-8). lib. bdg. 27.07 ***(978-1-60270-062-8(1)*** , Graphic Planet) Magic Wagon.

WESLEY, JOHN, 1703-1791

Benge, Janet & Benge, Geoff. John Wesley: The World, His Parish. 2007. (J). ***(978-1-57658-382-1(1))*** YWAM Publishing.

Wellman, Sam. John Wesley: Founder of the Methodist Church. 1999. (Heroes of the Faith Ser.). 208p. (YA). (gr. 4-7). lib. bdg. 17.95 (978-0-7910-5036-1(X) , Chelsea Hse.) Facts On File, Inc.

WEST, BENJAMIN, 1738-1820

Brenner, Barbara. The Boy Who Loved to Draw: Benjamin West. Dunrea, Olivier, illus. 48p. (J). (gr. k-3). 2003. pap. 5.95 (978-0-618-31089-0(4)); 1999. tchr. ed. 15.00 (978-0-395-85080-0(0)) Houghton Mifflin Co. Trade & Reference Div.

—Boy Who Loved to Draw: Benjamin West. 1999. (gr. k-3). lib. bdg. 14.10 (978-0-613-60796-4(1)) Tandem Library Bks.

WEST (U.S.)

see also Northwest, Pacific; Pacific States

Alter, Judy. Exploring & Mapping the American West. 2001. (gr. 3-6). lib. bdg. 14.10 (978-0-613-52037-9(8)) Tandem Library Bks.

The American West, 15 vols., Set. 2002. (Illus.). 64p. (YA). (gr. 5 up). lib. bdg. (978-1-59084-058-0(5)) Mason Crest Pubs.

The American West. 2004. (Historical Readers Ser.). (Illus.). 223p. (gr. 6-12). (978-0-618-08523-1(8) , 2-00188) McDougal Littell Inc.

Anastasio, Dina. Wild, Wild West. 1999. (Illus.). 176p. (gr. 3-7). pap. 4.99 (978-0-439-08653-0(1)) Scholastic, Inc.

Andrews, Barbara. Discover the West Region. 2006. pap. 39.00 ***(978-1-4108-6437-6(5))*** Benchmark Education Co.

—The West Region. 2006. pap. 42.00 ***(978-1-4108-6434-5(0))*** Benchmark Education Co.

Aston, Claire. The Wild West. Stacey, Mark, tr. Stacey, Mark, illus. 2001. (Fast Forward Bks.). 24p. (J). (gr. 2 up). 14.95 (978-0-7641-5312-9(9)) Barron's Educational Series, Inc.

Barkan, Joanne. A Libro de actividades del Oeste & Western Activity Book. 2005. spiral bd. 88.00 ***(978-1-4108-5734-7(4))*** Benchmark Education Co.

Bial, Raymond. Ghost Towns of the American West. 2001. (Illus.). 48p. (J). (gr. 4-6). tchr. ed. 16.00 (978-0-618-06557-8(1)) Houghton Mifflin Co. Trade & Reference Div.

Blue, Rose & Naden, Corinne J. Exploring the Western Mountains. 2004. (J). lib. bdg. 32.79 (978-1-4109-0674-8(4)) Raintree.

Burger, James P. The Library of the Westward Expansion, 6 bks. Incl. Lewis & Clark's Voyage of Discovery. lib. bdg. 19.95 (978-0-8239-5848-1(5)); Mountain Men of the West. lib. bdg. 19.95 (978-0-8239-5853-5(1)); Oregon Trail. lib. bdg. 19.95 (978-0-8239-5850-4(7)); Quest for California's Gold. lib. bdg. 19.95 (978-0-8239-5849-8(3)); Rocky Mountain Fur Trade. lib. bdg. 19.95 (978-0-8239-5851-1(5)); Transcontinental Railroad. lib. bdg. 19.95 (978-0-8239-5852-8(3)); 24p. (J). (gr. 3). 2002. (Illus.). 2001. Set lib. bdg. 117.00 (978-0-8239-7131-2(7) , PowerKids Pr.) Rosen Publishing Group, Inc., The.

Carlson, Laurie M. Westward Ho! An Activity Guide to the Wild West. 2003. (Kid's Guide Ser.). (Illus.). 160p. (J). (gr. k-7). pap. 14.95 (978-1-55652-271-0(1)) Chicago Review Pr., Inc.

Carlson, Laurie M. & Dorling Kindersley Publishing Staff. Boss of the Plains: The Hat That Won the West. 2000. (Illus.). 32p. (J). (ps-5). pap. 7.99 (978-0-7894-2657-4(9)) Dorling Kindersley Publishing, Inc.

Demund, Tom. From Slave to Superstar of the Wild West: The Awesome Story of Jim Beckwourth. 2007. 160p. (YA). 18.95 ***(978-0-9786904-0-3(0))*** Legends of the West Publishing Co.

Dillon, Christine J., ed. Western United States. rev. ed. 1999. (My First Report Ser.). (Illus.). 62p. (J). (gr. 1-3). ring bd. 5.95 (978-1-57896-023-1(1)) Hewitt Research Foundation, Inc.

Dolan, Edward F., Jr. Beyond the Frontier: The Story of the Trails West. 2000. (Great Journeys Ser.). (Illus.). 112p. (J). (gr. 5 up). lib. bdg. 32.79 (978-0-7614-0969-4(6) , Benchmark Bks.) Cavendish, Marshall Corp.

Drinkard, Lawson. Riding on a Range: Western Activities for Kids. Lee, Fran, illus. 2003. 64p. (YA). pap. 8.95 (978-1-58685-036-4(9)) Gibbs Smith, Publisher.

Edwards, Judith. Lewis & Clark's Journey of Discovery in American History. 1999. (In American History Ser.). (Illus.). 128p. (YA). (gr. 5-12). lib. bdg. 26.60 (978-0-7660-1127-4(5)) Enslow Pubs., Inc.

Eisenberg, Jana. Lewis & Clark: Path to the Pacific. 2005. (Trailblazers of the West Ser.). (Illus.). 48p. (J). (ps-7). 24.00 (978-0-516-25126-4(0)); (gr. 7-12). pap. 6.95 (978-0-516-25096-0(5)) Scholastic Library Publishing. (Children's Pr.).

Epstein, Dwayne. Lawmen of the Old West. 2004. (History Makers Ser.). (Illus.). 96p. (J). (gr. 7-10). 29.95 (978-1-59018-560-5(9) , Lucent Bks.) Thomson Gale.

Etulain, Richard W. With Badges & Bullets: Lawmen & Outlaws in the Old West. 1999. (gr. 7-12). lib. bdg. 28.00 (978-0-613-37077-6(5)) Tandem Library Bks.

Exploring the West Classroom Library. (gr. 2-5). lib. bdg. 49.95 (978-0-7368-4514-4(3)) Red Brick Learning.

Exploring the West Complete Unit. (gr. 2-5). 286.95 (978-0-7368-4513-7(5)) Red Brick Learning.

Frazier, Neta Lohnes. Path to the Pacific: The Story of Sacajawea. 2007. (Sterling Point Bks.). (Illus.). 192p. (J). pap. 6.95 (978-1-4027-4138-8(3)) Sterling Publishing Co., Inc.

—Sterling Point Books: Path to the Pacific: The Story of Sacajawea. 2007. (Sterling Point Bks.). (Illus.). 192p. (J). 12.95 (978-1-4027-4518-8(4)) Sterling Publishing Co., Inc.

Gilbert, Sara. Calamity Jane. 2005. (Illus.). 48p. (gr. 5-9). 21.95 (978-1-58341-337-1(5) , Creative Education) Creative Co., The.

Glasscock, Sarah. The Western States. 2006. (Navigators Ser.). (J). pap. 42.00 ***(978-1-4108-6254-9(2))*** Benchmark Education Co.

Granfield, Linda. Cowboy: An Album. (J). 9.99 (978-1-55054-230-1(3)) Douglas & McIntyre, Ltd. CAN. *Dist:* Transition Vendor.

Gregson, Susan R. James Beckwourth: Mountaineer, Scout & Pioneer. 2005. (Signature Lives Ser.). (Illus.). 112p. (J). (gr. 5-7). (978-0-7565-1000-8(7)) Compass Point Bks.

Gunderson, Jessica Sarah. The Lewis & Clark Expedition. 2007. (Graphic Library). (Illus.). 32p. (J). 25.26 (978-0-7368-6493-0(8)) Capstone Pr., Inc.

Isaacs, Sally Senzell. The West. 2006. (Regions of the USA Ser.). (Illus.). 56p. (J). (978-1-4109-2312-7(6)); pap. (978-1-4109-2320-2(7)) Steck-Vaughn.

Johmann, Carol A. The Lewis & Clark Expedition: Join the Corps of Discovery to Explore Uncharted Territory. 2004. (Kaleidoscope Kids Bks.). (Illus.). 112p. (YA). (gr. 4-6). pap. 12.95 (978-1-885593-73-3(2) , Williamson Bks.) Ideals Pubns.

Jones, Charlotte Foltz. Westward Ho! Eleven Explorers of the American West. 2005. (Illus.). 240p. (J). (gr. 4-6). tchr. ed. 22.95 (978-0-8234-1586-1(4)) Holiday Hse., Inc.

Kallen, Stuart A. Women of the American Frontier. 2004. (Illus.). 111p. (J). (gr. 7-10). 32.45 (978-1-59018-471-4(8) , Lucent Bks.) Thomson Gale.

Kalman, Bobbie. The Wagon Train. 1998. (Life in the Old West Ser.). (Illus.). 32p. (J). (gr. 3-4). pap. (978-0-7787-0102-6(6)) Crabtree Publishing Co.

King, David C. Wild West Days: Discover the Past with Fun Projects, Games, Activities, & Recipes. 1998. (American Kids in History Ser.: Vol. 5). (Illus.). 128p. (gr. 3-7). pap. 12.95 (978-0-471-23919-2(4) , Wiley-Interscience) Wiley, John & Sons, Inc.

Klingel, Cynthia Fitterer & Noyed, Robert B. Lewis & Clark: Explorers. 2002. (Spirit of America: Our People Ser.). (Illus.). 32p. (J). (gr. 2-6). 27.07 (978-1-56766-164-4(5)) Child's World, Inc.

Krensky Stephen. Calamity Jane. Carlson, Lisa, illus. 2007. (On My Own Folklore Ser.). (J). pap. 6.95 (***978-0-8225-6480-5(7)*** , First Avenue Editions) Lerner Publishing Group.

Krohn, Katherine. Women of the Wild West. 2000. (gr. 7-12). lib. bdg. 16.40 (978-0-613-68395-1(1)) Tandem Library Bks.

Krohn, Katherine E. Women of the Wild West. (Biography Ser.). (Illus.). 112p. (gr. 6 up). 2003. (YA). pap. 7.95 (978-0-8225-9690-5(3) , Carolrhoda Bks.); 2000. (J). lib. bdg. 27.93 (978-0-8225-4980-2(8) , Lerner Pubns.) Lerner Publishing Group.

Latham, Frank. Jed Smith: Trail Blazer of the West. McHugh, Michael J., ed. Murch, Frank, illus. 2003. 121p. pap. 6.95 (978-1-930367-86-9(4)) Christian Liberty Pr.

Leacock, Elspeth. The West. 2002. (Reading Expeditions Ser.). (Illus.). 32p. (J). (978-0-7922-8682-0(0)) National Geographic Society.

MacGregor, Carol Lynn. Lewis & Clark's Bittersweet Crossing. Hoopes, Gaye, tr. Hoopes, Gaye, illus. 2004. 32p. (J). 16.95 (978-0-87004-437-3(0) , 043700) Caxton Pr.

Manheimer, Ann S. James Beckwourth: Legendary Mountain Man. 2006. (Trailblazer Biography Ser.). (Illus.). 112p. (J). (ps-7). 30.60 (978-1-57505-892-4(8) , Twenty-First Century Bks.) Lerner Publishing Group.

McCormick, Lisa Wade. Lewis & Clark. 2006. (Rookie Biographies Ser.). (Illus.). 32p. (J). (gr. 1-2). 20.50 (978-0-516-25039-7(6) , Children's Pr.) Scholastic Library Publishing.

Miller, Heather. Cowboy. 2003. (This Is What I Want to Be Ser.). (Illus.). 24p. (ps-1). (J). lib. bdg. 18.50 (978-1-4034-0366-7(X)); pap. 5.25 (978-1-4034-0588-3(3)) Heinemann Library.

Miller, Robert H. Reflections of a Black Cowboy: Buffalo Soldiers. 2004. (J). pap. 9.95 (978-0-940975-69-9(6) , Sankofa Bks.) Just Us Bks., Inc.

—Reflections of a Black Cowboy: Cowboys. 2004. (J). pap. 9.95 (978-0-940975-70-5(X) , Sankofa Bks.) Just Us Bks., Inc.

Moran, Margaret. Los vaqueros y el arreo de ganado & Cowhands & Cattle Trails. 2005. spiral bd. 84.00 (***978-1-4108-5700-2(X)***) Benchmark Education Co.

Morley, Jacqueline. You Wouldn't Want to Be an American Pioneer! Antram, David, illus. 2002. (You Wouldn't Want to Ser.). 32p. (J). (gr. 2-5). pap. 9.95 (978-0-531-16369-6(5) , Watts, Franklin) Scholastic Library Publishing.

—You Wouldn't Want to Be an American Pioneer! 2002. (gr. 3-6). lib. bdg. 18.75 (978-0-613-53886-2(2)) Tandem Library Bks.

Munro, Roxie. The Wild West Trail Ride Maze. 2006. (Illus.). 40p. (J). 16.95 (978-1-931721-67-7(X)) Bright Sky Pr.

National Geographic Society Staff, contrib. by. The West Today. 2004. (Illus.). 32p. (J). pap. (978-0-7922-4536-0(9)) National Geographic Society.

Nelson, Sharlene P. & Nelson, Ted W. Jedediah Smith. 2004. (Watts Library). (Illus.). 64p. (J). 25.50 (978-0-531-12287-7(5) , Watts, Franklin) Scholastic Library Publishing.

Petrie, Kristin. Lewis & Clark. 2007. (Illus.). 32p. (J). 22.78 (978-1-59679-743-7(6)) ABDO Publishing Co.

Plain, Nancy. Frederic Remington: Artist of the American West. 2003. (Historical American Biographies Ser.). (Illus.). 160p. (J). (gr. 6-12). lib. bdg. 26.60 (978-0-7660-1975-1(6)) Enslow Pubs., Inc.

Pringle, Laurence P. American Slave, American Hero: York of the Lewis & Clark Expedition. Van Wright, Cornelius & Hu, Ying-Hwa, illus. 2006. 40p. (J). (gr. 3-5). 17.95 (978-1-59078-282-8(8)) Boyds Mills Pr.

Raum, Elizabeth. Lewis & Clark's Continental Journey. 2007. (J). (***978-1-4034-9757-4(5)***) Heinemann Library.

Renehan, Edward J. The Transcontinental Railroad: The Gateway to the West. 2007. (Milestones in American History Ser.). 128p. (J). (gr. 6-12). 35.00 (***978-0-7910-9351-1(4)*** , Chelsea Hse.) Facts On File, Inc.

Rocky Mountain States Grades 4-6. 2002. (J). (gr. 4-6). pap. 8.94 (978-1-889369-44-0(6)) Teaching Ink, Inc.

Rosa, Joseph G. Wild Bill Hickok: Sharpshooter & U.S. Marshal of the Wild West. 2005. (Library of American Lives & Times). (Illus.). 112p. (gr. 4-8). lib. bdg. 31.95 (978-0-8239-6632-5(1)) Rosen Publishing Group, Inc., The.

Ross, Michael Elsohn. Exploring the Earth with John Wesley Powell. Smith, Wendy, illus. 2005. (Naturalist's Apprentice Biographies Ser.). 48p. (gr. 3-6). lib. bdg. 19.93 (978-1-57505-254-0(7)) Lerner Publishing Group.

Santillo, LuAnn. Wild West, 6 vols. Santillo, LuAnn, ed. 2003. (Half-Pint Kids Readers Ser.). (Illus.). 42p. (J). (ps-1). pap. 6.99 (978-1-59256-077-6(6)) Half-Pint Kids, Inc.

Savage, Candace. Born to Be a Cowgirl. 2001. (gr. 3-6). lib. bdg. 18.75 (978-0-613-49287-4(0)) Tandem Library Bks.

Savage, Candace C. Born to Be a Cowgirl: A Spirited Ride Through the Old West. 2004. (Illus.). (978-1-55054-838-9(7) , Greystone Bks.) Douglas & McIntyre, Ltd. CAN. *Dist:* Transition Vendor.

—Born to Be a Cowgirl: A Spirited Ride Through the Old West. 2004. (Illus.). 64p. (J). pap. 10.95 (978-1-58246-020-8(5)); (gr. 4-8). 15.95 (978-1-58246-019-2(1)) Ten Speed Pr. (Tricycle Pr.).

Seidman, Laurence I. Once in the Saddle: The Cowboy's Frontier 1866-1896. 1999. 158p. (J). lib. bdg. 21.95 (978-0-7351-0221-7(X)) Replica Bks.

Slovey, Christine & Pendergast, Sara, contrib. by. Westward Expansion: Almanac. 2000. (Illus.). xlvi, 254p. (J). 66.00 (978-0-7876-4862-6(0) , GML00502-114906, UXL) Thomson Gale.

Souza, Dorothy M. John C. Fremont. 2004. (Watts Library). (Illus.). 64p. (J). 25.50 (978-0-531-12288-4(3) , Watts, Franklin) Scholastic Library Publishing.

—John Wesley Powell. 2004. (Watts Library). (Illus.). 64p. (J). 25.50 (978-0-531-12289-1(1) , Watts, Franklin) Scholastic Library Publishing.

Staeger, Rob. The Spanish Missions of California. 2002. (History of the Old West Ser.). (Illus.). 64p. (J). (gr. 5 up). lib. bdg. (978-1-59084-059-7(3)) Mason Crest Pubs.

Stefoff, Rebecca. The Opening of the West. 2002. (American Voices From Ser.). (Illus.). xxii, 105p. (J). 34.21 (978-0-7614-1201-4(8) , Benchmark Bks.) Cavendish, Marshall Corp.

Sundling, Charles W. Cowboys of the Frontier. 2000. (Frontier Land Ser.). (Illus.). 32p. (J). (gr. 3-8). lib. bdg. 24.21 (978-1-57765-045-4(X) , ABDO & Daughters) ABDO Publishing Co.

—Women of the Frontier. 2000. (Frontier Land Ser.). (Illus.). 32p. (J). (gr. 3-8). lib. bdg. 24.21 (978-1-57765-046-1(8) , ABDO & Daughters) ABDO Publishing Co.

Thompson, Gare. Our Journey West: The Oregon Trail Adventures of Sarah Marshall. 2003. (gr. 3-6). lib. bdg. 15.30 (978-0-613-67111-8(2)) Tandem Library Bks.

Urbigkit, Cat. The Shepherd's Trail. 2008. (J). (***978-1-59078-509-6(6)***) Boyds Mills Pr.

Waldman, Stuart. The Last River: John Wesley Powell & the Colorado River Exploring Expedition. Manchess, Gregory, illus. 2005. (Great Explorers Ser.). 48p. (J). (gr. 4-12). 19.95 (978-1-931414-09-8(2)) Mikaya Pr.

Williams, Colleen Madonna Flood. My Adventure in the Wild West. 2007. 44p. (J). 8.99 (978-1-59092-439-6(8) , Orchard Academy Pr.) Windstorm Creative.

Wilson, Mike. The Alamo. 2002. (History of the Old West Ser.). (Illus.). 64p. (J). (gr. 5 up). lib. bdg. (978-1-59084-062-7(3)) Mason Crest Pubs.

Winter, Jonah. Wild Women of the Wild West. Morgan, Mary, illus. 2002. (J). (978-0-8234-1601-1(1)) Holiday Hse., Inc.

Woog, Adam. A Cowboy in the Old West. 2002. (Daily Life Ser.). (Illus.). 48p. (J). (gr. 3-5). 23.70 (978-0-7377-0990-2(1) , LML00902-178599, Kidhaven) Thomson Gale.

WEST (U.S.)—FICTION

Adams, Jean Ekman. Clarence & the Great Surprise. Adams, Jean Ekman, illus. 2001. (Illus.). 32p. (J). (gr. k-2). 15.95 (978-0-87358-795-2(2) , Rising Moon Bks. for Young Readers) Northland Publishing.

Arrigan, Mary. PA Jinglebob: The Fastest Knitter in the West. 2005. (Red Bananas Ser.). (Illus.). 48p. (J). (ps). pap. (978-0-7787-1088-2(2)) Crabtree Publishing Co.

—Pa Jinglebob, the Fastest Knitter in the West. Paul, Korky, illus. 2005. (Red Bananas Ser.). 48p. (J). (978-0-7787-1072-1(6)) Crabtree Publishing Co.

Arrigan, Mary & Paul, Korky. Pa Jinglebob & the Grabble Gang. 2006. (Red Bananas Ser.). (Illus.). 47p. (J). (978-0-7787-1074-5(2)) Crabtree Publishing Co.

Asfar, Dan. Ghost Stories of Old West. rev. ed. 2003. (Ghost Stories Ser.: 28). (Illus.). 88p. (J). 10.95 (978-1-55105-332-5(2)) Lone Pine Publishing USA.

Barth, Jeff. The Homesteaders. Barth, Marge, ed. 2002. (Illus.). 304p. pap. (978-1-891484-04-9(4)) Barth Family Ministries.

Berenstain, Stan & Berenstain, Jan. The Berenstain Bears Out West. Berenstain, Stan & Berenstain, Jan, illus. 2006. (Berenstain Bears Ser.). (Illus.). 32p. (J). 15.99 (978-0-06-058353-8(3)); pap. 3.99 (978-0-06-058354-5(1) , Harper Trophy) HarperCollins Pubs.

Blakeslee, Ann R. A Different Kind of Hero. 2005. 144p. (YA). pap. 5.95 (978-0-7614-5147-1(1)) Cavendish, Marshall Corp.

Bloomfield, Susanne George & Reed, Melvin, eds. Adventures in the West: Stories for Young Readers. 2007. (Illus.). 302p. (gr. 3 up). pap. 19.95 (***978-0-8032-5974-4(3)*** , Bison Bks.) Univ. of Nebraska Pr.

Bly, Stephen A. The Buffalo's Last Stand. 2002. (Retta Barre's Oregon Trail Ser.: 2). 111p. pap. 5.99 (978-1-58134-392-2(2)) Crossway Bks.

—The Lost Wagon Train. 2005. (Retta Barre's Oregon Trail Ser.: Vol. 1). 110p. pap. 5.99 (978-1-58134-391-5(4) , Crossway Bibles) Crossway Bks.

Brimner, Larry Dane. Merry Christmas, Old Armadillo. Catalano, Dominic, illus. 2003. 32p. (J). (gr. k-2). pap. 7.95 (978-1-56397-678-0(1)) Boyds Mills Pr.

Brouwer, Sigmund. Phantom Outlaw at Wolf Creek. 2005. (Accidental Detectives Ser.). 144p. (J). pap. 5.99 (978-0-7642-2578-9(2)) Bethany Hse. Pubs.

Burgess, Thornton W. Old Mother West Wind's "When" Stories. (J). 21.95 (978-0-8488-0387-2(6)) Amereon LTD.

Byars, Betsy. The Golly Sisters Go West. 2002. (Illus.). (J). 12.30 (978-0-7587-6115-6(5)) Book Wholesalers, Inc.

—The Golly Sisters Go West. 2000. (YA). pap. 23.20 incl. audio (978-0-7887-4335-1(X) , 41130) Recorded Bks., LLC.

—The Golly Sisters Ride Again: An I Can Read Book. 2002. (Illus.). (J). 12.34 (978-0-7587-6116-3(3)) Book Wholesalers, Inc.

Campbell, Roy. Song of the Jackalope. Bosworth, David, illus. 2nd ed. 2006. 140p. (YA). pap. 12.95 (978-1-933538-04-4(X)) Bridgeway Bks.

Campbell, Roy B. Song of the Jackalope. Bosworth, David, illus. 2002. viii, 108p. (YA). (gr. 4-9). 20.00 (978-0-9718282-0-9(2)) Fireside Bks.

Cannon, A. E. Way Out West with Pirate Pete & Pirate Joe. Smith, Elwood H., illus. 2006. (Viking Easy-To-Read Ser.). 32p. (J). (ps). 13.99 (978-0-670-06080-1(1) , Viking Juvenile) Penguin Group (USA) Inc.

Carabine, Sue. A Cowgirl's Night Before Christmas. Kawasaki, Shauna Mooney, illus. 2001. 60p. 5.95 (978-1-58685-086-9(5)) Gibbs Smith, Publisher.

—A Cowgirl's Night Before Christmas. Kawasaki, Shauna Mooney, photos by. 2nd gif. ed. 2001. (Illus.). 60p. 5.95 (978-1-58685-121-7(7)) Gibbs Smith, Publisher.

Carson, William C. Peter Becomes a Trail Man: The Story of a Boy's Journey on the Santa Fe Trail. Oliphant, Pat, illus. 2002. 192p. (J). (gr. 6 up). 12.95 (978-0-8263-2895-3(4)) Univ. of New Mexico Pr.

Coren, Alan. Arthur the Kid. 2004. (Illus.). 64p. (978-0-903895-76-7(5) , Robson Bks. Ltd.) Anova Bks.

—Buffalo Arthur. 2004. (Illus.). 64p. (978-0-903895-75-0(7) , Robson Bks. Ltd.) Anova Bks.

—Railroad Arthur. 2004. (Illus.). 64p. (978-0-903895-92-7(7) , Robson Bks. Ltd.) Anova Bks.

Crummel, Susan Stevens. Ten-Gallon Bart & the Wild West Show. Donohue, Dorothy, illus. 2008. (J). (***978-0-7614-5391-8(1)***) Cavendish, Marshall Corp.

Crunk, Tony. Railroad John & the Red Rock Run. Austin, Michael, illus. 2006. 32p. (J). 16.95 (978-1-56145-363-4(3)) Peachtree Pubs., Ltd.

Cushman, Karen. Rodzina. 2003. Tr. of Rodzina. 224p. (J). (gr. 5-9). tchr. ed. 16.00 (978-0-618-13351-2(8) , Clarion Bks.) Houghton Mifflin Co. Trade & Reference Div.

—Rodzina. 2005. Tr. of Rodzina. 224p. (gr. 5). 6.50 (978-0-440-41993-8(X) , Yearling) Random Hse. Children's Bks.

Davies, Robert, adapted by. Lit a Shuck for Texas: Adapted Louis l'Amour Short Stories Series. 2003. (Adapted Louis L'Amour Short Stories Ser.). (Illus.). 56p. (YA). (978-1-57035-983-5(0) , 233LIT) Sopris West Educational Services.

—Merrano of the Dry Country: Adapted Louis l'Amour Short Story Series. 2003. (Adapted Louis L'Amour Short Stories Ser.). (Illus.). 60p. (J). (978-1-57035-985-9(7) , 233MERRANO) Sopris West Educational Services.

—A Trail to the West: Adapted Louis l'Amour Short Stories Series. 2003. (Adapted Louis L'Amour Short Stories Ser.). (Illus.). 56p. (J). (978-1-57035-984-2(9) , 233TRAIL) Sopris West Educational Services.

Davis, Tim. More Tales from Dust River Gulch. 2002. (Tales from Dust River Gulch Ser.). (Illus.). 108p. (J). (gr. 4-7). 7.49 (978-1-57924-855-0(1)) Jones, Bob Univ. Pr.

—Tales from Dust River Gulch. 2000. (J). (gr. 4-7). pap. 14.98 incl. audio (978-0-89084-956-9(0) , 110742) Jones, Bob Univ. Pr.

Delton, Judy. Wild, Wild West. 1999. (Pee Wee Scouts Ser.: No. 37). (J). (gr. 2-5). 10.55 (978-0-606-16585-3(1)) Tandem Library Bks.

Dundy, Melanie Richardson. Westward Ho with Ollie Ox! Date not set. (Illus.). 56p. (J). (gr. k-5). per. 12.95 (978-0-9674491-4-2(6)) MDCT Publishing.

Erickson, John R. The Case of the Black-Hooded Hangmans. Holmes, Gerald L., illus. 1998. (Hank the Cowdog Ser.: No. 24). 144p. (J). (gr. 2-5). 15.99 (978-0-670-88431-5(6) , Viking Juvenile); Vol. 24. pap. 4.99 (978-0-14-130400-7(6) , Puffin) Penguin Group (USA) Inc.

—The Case of the Black-Hooded Hangmans. 1999. (Hank the Cowdog Ser.: No. 24). (gr. 3-6). lib. bdg. 13.00 (978-0-7857-6345-1(7)) Tandem Library Bks.

—The Case of the Burrowing Robot, Vol. 42. Holmes, Gerald L., illus. 2003. (Hank the Cowdog Ser.: No. 42). 144p. (J). (gr. 3). 15.99 (978-0-670-03632-5(3) , Viking Juvenile); (gr. 4-6). pap. 4.99 (978-0-14-250063-7(1) , Puffin) Penguin Group (USA) Inc.

—The Case of the Burrowing Robot. 2003. (Hank the Cowdog Ser.: No. 42). (gr. 3-6). lib. bdg. 13.00 (978-0-613-66353-3(5)) Tandem Library Bks.

—The Case of the Car-Barkaholic Dog. Holmes, Gerald L., illus. 1998. (Hank the Cowdog Ser.: No. 17). 144p. (J). (gr. 2-5). pap. 4.99 (978-0-14-130393-2(X) , Puffin) Penguin Group (USA) Inc.

—The Case of the Deadly Ha-Ha Game. 2001. (Hank the Cowdog Ser.: No. 37). (gr. 3-6). lib. bdg. 13.00 (978-0-613-33649-9(6)) Tandem Library Bks.

—The Case of the Double Bumblebee Sting. Holmes, Gerald L., illus. 1998. (Hank the Cowdog Ser.: No. 22). 144p. (J). (gr. 2-5). 14.99 (978-0-670-88429-2(4) , Viking Juvenile); Vol. 22. pap. 4.99 (978-0-14-130398-7(0) , Puffin) Penguin Group (USA) Inc.

—The Case of the Falling Sky. Holmes, Gerald L., illus. 2005. (Hank the Cowdog Ser.: No. 45). 129p. (J). lib. bdg. 17.00 (***978-1-4242-1602-4(8)***) Fitzgerald Bks.

—The Case of the Falling Sky. Holmes, Gerald L., illus. 2005. (Hank the Cowdog Ser.: No. 45). 160p. (J). (gr. 3-7). 15.99 (978-0-670-05999-7(4) , Viking Juvenile) Penguin Group (USA) Inc.

—The Case of the Garbage Monster from Outer Space. Holmes, Gerald L., illus. 1999. (Hank the Cowdog Ser.: No. 32). 144p. (J). (gr. 2-5). 13.99 (978-0-670-88488-9(X) , Viking Juvenile) Penguin Group (USA) Inc.

—The Case of the Halloween Ghost. Holmes, Gerald L., illus. 1998. (Hank the Cowdog Ser.: No. 9). 144p. (J). (gr. 2-5). 14.99 (978-0-670-88416-2(2) , Viking Juvenile); No. 9. pap. 4.99 (978-0-14-130385-7(9) , Puffin) Penguin Group (USA) Inc.

—The Case of the Haystack Kitties. Holmes, Gerald L., illus. 1998. (Hank the Cowdog Ser.: No. 30). 144p. (J). (gr. 2-5). 14.99 (978-0-670-88437-7(5) , Viking Juvenile); Vol. 30. pap. 4.99 (978-0-14-130406-9(5) , Puffin) Penguin Group (USA) Inc.

—The Case of the Hooking Bull, Vol. 18. Holmes, Gerald L., illus. 1998. (Hank the Cowdog Ser.: No. 18). 144p. (J). (gr. 2-5). pap. 4.99 (978-0-14-130394-9(8) , Puffin) Penguin Group (USA) Inc.

—The Case of the Kidnapped Collie. Holmes, Gerald L., illus. 1998. (Hank the Cowdog Ser.: No. 26). 144p. (J). (gr. 2-5). 14.99 (978-0-670-88433-9(2) , Viking Juvenile); Vol. 26. pap. 4.99 (978-0-14-130402-1(2) , Puffin) Penguin Group (USA) Inc.

—The Case of the Kidnapped Collie. 1999. (Hank the Cowdog Ser.: No. 26). (gr. 3-6). lib. bdg. 13.00 (978-0-7857-9075-4(6)) Tandem Library Bks.

—The Case of the Kidnapped Collie. Holmes, Gerald L., illus. 1999. (Hank the Cowdog Ser.: No. 26). (J). (gr. 2-5). 11.64 (978-0-606-09375-0(3)) Tandem Library Bks.

—The Case of the Midnight Rustler. Holmes, Gerald L., illus. 1998. (Hank the Cowdog Ser.: No. 19). 144p. (J). (gr. 2-5). 14.99 (978-0-670-88426-1(X) , Viking Juvenile); pap. 4.99 (978-0-14-130395-6(6) , Puffin) Penguin Group (USA) Inc.

—The Case of the Missing Bird Dog, Vol. 40. Holmes, Gerald L., illus. 2002. (Hank the Cowdog Ser.: No. 40). 144p. (J). 15.99 (978-0-670-03558-8(0) , Viking Juvenile); pap. 4.99 (978-0-14-230141-8(8) , Puffin) Penguin Group (USA) Inc.

—The Case of the Missing Cat. Holmes, Gerald L., illus. (Hank the Cowdog Ser.: No. 15). 144p. (J). (gr. 2-5). 2000. 14.99 (978-0-670-88422-3(7) , Viking Juvenile); 1998. pap. 4.99 (978-0-14-130391-8(3) , Puffin) Penguin Group (USA) Inc.

—The Case of the Missing Cat. 1999. (Hank the Cowdog Ser.: No. 15). (gr. 3-6). lib. bdg. 13.00 (978-0-8335-6828-1(0)) Tandem Library Bks.

—The Case of the Monkey Burglar. Holmes, Gerald L., illus. 2006. (Hank the Cowdog Ser.: NMo. 48). 129p. (J). lib. bdg. 17.00 (***978-1-4242-1604-8(4)***) Fitzgerald Bks.

—The Case of the Most Ancient Bone. Holmes, Gerald L., illus. 2007. (Hank the Cowdog Ser.). 192p. (J). (gr. 3). 16.99 (978-0-670-06224-9(3) , Viking Juvenile) Penguin Group (USA) Inc.

—The Case of the Most Ancient Bone, No. 50. Holmes, Gerald L., illus. 2007. (Hank the Cowdog Ser.: No. 50). 256p. (J). (gr. 3). pap. 5.99 (978-0-14-240800-1(X) , Puffin) Penguin Group (USA) Inc.

—The Case of the Night-Stalking Bone Monster. Holmes, Gerald L., illus. 1998. (Hank the Cowdog Ser.: No. 27). 144p. (J). (gr. 2-5). 14.99 (978-0-670-88434-6(0) , Viking Juvenile); Vol. 27. pap. 4.99 (978-0-14-130403-8(0) , Puffin) Penguin Group (USA) Inc.

—The Case of the One-Eyed Killer Stud Horse, Vol. 8. Holmes, Gerald L., illus. 1998. (Hank the Cowdog Ser.: No. 8). 144p. (gr. 2-5). pap. 4.99 (978-0-14-130384-0(0) , Puffin) Penguin Group (USA) Inc.

—The Case of the Raging Rottweiler. Holmes, Gerald L., illus. 2000. (Hank the Cowdog Ser.: No. 36). (J). (gr. 2-5). 144p. 14.99 (978-0-670-89364-5(1) , Viking Juvenile); Vol. 36. 160p. pap. 4.99 (978-0-14-130668-1(8) , Puffin) Penguin Group (USA) Inc.

—The Case of the Raging Rottweiler. 2000. (Hank the Cowdog Ser.: No. 36). (gr. 3-6). lib. bdg. 13.00 (978-0-613-31048-2(9)); (Illus.). (J). 11.64 (978-0-606-20460-6(1)) Tandem Library Bks.

—The Case of the Saddle House Robbery. Holmes, Gerald L., illus. 2000. (Hank the Cowdog Ser.: No. 35). 144p. (J). (gr. 2-5). 14.99 (978-0-670-88890-0(7) , Viking Juvenile); Vol. 35. pap. 4.99 (978-0-14-130678-0(5) , Puffin) Penguin Group (USA) Inc.

—The Case of the Saddle House Robbery. unabr. ed. 2000. (Hank the Cowdog Ser.: No. 35). (J). (gr. 2-5). pap. 23.00 incl. audio (978-0-8072-8376-9(2) , YA172SP, Listening Library) Random Hse. Audio Publishing Group.

—The Case of the Saddle House Robbery. 2000. (Hank the Cowdog Ser.: No. 35). (gr. 3-6). lib. bdg. 13.00 (978-0-613-24495-4(8)); (Illus.). (J). (gr. 2-5). 11.64 (978-0-606-18409-0(0)) Tandem Library Bks.

—The Case of the Shipwrecked Tree. Holmes, Gerald L., illus. 2003. (Hank the Cowdog Ser.: No. 41). 144p. (J). (gr. 3-7). 14.99 (978-0-670-03603-5(X) , Viking Juvenile); (gr. 4-6). pap. 4.99 (978-0-14-230225-5(2) , Puffin) Penguin Group (USA) Inc.

—The Case of the Shipwrecked Tree. 2003. (Hank the Cowdog Ser.: No. 41). (gr. 3-6). lib. bdg. 13.00 (978-0-613-61613-3(8)) Tandem Library Bks.

W X Y Z

—The Case of the Swirling Killer Tornado. Holmes, Gerald L., illus. 1998. (Hank the Cowdog Ser.: No. 25). 144p. (J). (gr. 2-5). 14.99 (978-0-670-88432-2(4) , Viking Juvenile); Vol. 25. pap. 4.99 (978-0-14-130401-4(4) , Puffin) Penguin Group (USA) Inc.

—The Case of the Tender Cheeping Chickies. Holmes, Gerald L., illus. 2005. (Hank the Cowdog Ser.: No. 47). 129p. (J). lib. bdg. 17.00 (***978-1-4242-1605-5(2))** Fitzgerald Bks.

—The Case of the Tricky Trap. Holmes, Gerald L., illus. 2005. (Hank the Cowdog Ser.: No. 46). 126p. (J). lib. bdg. 17.00 (***978-1-4242-1603-1(6))** Fitzgerald Bks.

—The Case of the Twisted Kitty. Holmes, Gerald L., illus. 2004. (Hank the Cowdog Ser.: No. 43). 131p. (J). lib. bdg. 17.00 (***978-1-4242-1600-0(1))** Fitzgerald Bks.

—The Case of the Vampire Cat. Holmes, Gerald L., illus. 1998. (Hank the Cowdog Ser.: No. 21). 144p. (J). (gr. 2-5). 14.99 (978-0-670-88428-5(6) , Viking Juvenile); Vol. 21. pap. 4.99 (978-0-14-130397-0(2) , Puffin) Penguin Group (USA) Inc.

—The Case of the Vampire Vacuum Sweeper. Holmes, Gerald L., illus. 1998. (Hank the Cowdog Ser.: No. 29). 144p. (J). (gr. 2-5). 14.99 (978-0-670-88436-0(7) , Viking Juvenile); (gr. 3-7). pap. 4.99 (978-0-14-130405-2(7) , Puffin) Penguin Group (USA) Inc.

—The Case of the Vanishing Fishhook. Holmes, Gerald L., illus. 1999. (Hank the Cowdog Ser.: No. 31). 144p. (J). (gr. 2-5). 14.99 (978-0-670-88438-4(3) , Viking Juvenile); Vol. 31. pap. 4.99 (978-0-14-130356-7(5) , Puffin) Penguin Group (USA) Inc.

—The Case of the Vanishing Fishhook. 1999. (Hank the Cowdog Ser.: No. 31). (gr. 3-6). lib. bdg. 13.00 (978-0-613-11389-2(6)) Tandem Library Bks.

—The Curse of the Incredible Priceless Corncob. Holmes, Gerald L., illus. 1998. (Hank the Cowdog Ser.: No. 7). 144p. (J). (gr. 2-5). 14.99 (978-0-670-88414-8(6) , Viking Juvenile); Vol. 7. pap. 4.99 (978-0-14-130383-3(2) , Puffin) Penguin Group (USA) Inc.

—Discovery at Flint Springs. 2004. 192p. (J). (gr. 3-7). 16.99 (978-0-670-05946-1(3) , Viking Juvenile) Penguin Group (USA) Inc.

—The Dungeon of Doom. Holmes, Gerald L., illus. 2004. (Hank the Cowdog Ser.: No. 44). 122p. (J). lib. bdg. 17.00 (***978-1-4242-1601-7(X))** Fitzgerald Bks.

—Every Dog Has His Day. Holmes, Gerald L., illus. 1998. (Hank the Cowdog Ser.: No. 10). 144p. (J). (gr. 2-5). 15.99 (978-0-670-88417-9(0) , Viking Juvenile); pap. 4.99 (978-0-14-130386-4(7) , Puffin) Penguin Group (USA) Inc.

—Faded Love. Holmes, Gerald L., illus. 1998. (Hank the Cowdog Ser.: No. 5). 144p. (J). (gr. 2-5). 14.99 (978-0-670-88412-4(X) , Viking Juvenile); Vol. 5. pap. 4.99 (978-0-14-130381-9(6) , Puffin) Penguin Group (USA) Inc.

—The Fling, Vol. 38. Holmes, Gerald L., illus. 2001. (Hank the Cowdog Ser.: No. 38). 144p. (J). (gr. 2-5). pap. 4.99 (978-0-14-131174-6(6) , Puffin) Penguin Group (USA) Inc.

—The Further Adventures of Hank the Cowdog. Holmes, Gerald L., illus. (Hank the Cowdog Ser.: No. 2). 144p. (J). 1999. (gr. 2-5). pap. 4.99 (978-0-14-130378-9(6) , Puffin); 1998. (gr. 3-5). 14.99 (978-0-670-88409-4(X) , Viking Juvenile) Penguin Group (USA) Inc.

—The Further Adventures of Hank the Cowdog. Holmes, Gerald L., illus. 1999. (Hank the Cowdog Ser.: No. 2). (J). (gr. 2-5). lib. bdg. 13.00 (978-0-8335-6816-8(7)) Tandem Library Bks.

—The Garbage Monster from Outer Space, Vol. 32. Holmes, Gerald L., illus. 1999. (Hank the Cowdog Ser.: No. 32). 144p. (J). (gr. 2-5). pap. 4.99 (978-0-14-130422-9(7) , Puffin) Penguin Group (USA) Inc.

—The Garbage Monster from Outer Space. 1999. (Hank the Cowdog Ser.: No. 32). (J). (gr. 2-5). 11.64 (978-0-606-16827-4(3)); (gr. 3-6). lib. bdg. 13.00 (978-0-613-14748-4(0)) Tandem Library Bks.

—Hank the Cowdog & Monkey Business. Holmes, Gerald L., illus. 1999. (Hank the Cowdog Ser.: No. 14). (J). (gr. 3-6). lib. bdg. 13.00 (978-0-8335-6827-4(2)) Tandem Library Bks.

—It's a Dog's Life. Holmes, Gerald L., illus. (Hank the Cowdog Ser.: No. 3). 100p. (J). (gr. 2-5). 9.95 (978-0-916941-04-8(3)); pap. 5.95 (978-0-9608612-9-3(7)) Maverick Bks., Inc.

—It's a Dog's Life. Holmes, Gerald L., illus. 1998. (Hank the Cowdog Ser.: No. 3). 144p. (J). (gr. 2-5). 14.99 (978-0-670-88410-0(3) , Viking Juvenile); pap. 4.99 (978-0-14-130379-6(4) , Puffin) Penguin Group (USA) Inc.

—Let Sleeping Dogs Lie. Holmes, Gerald L., illus. 1998. (Hank the Cowdog Ser.: No. 6). 144p. (J). (gr. 2-5). pap. 4.99 (978-0-14-130382-6(4) , Puffin) Penguin Group (USA) Inc.

—Lost in the Blinded Blizzard. Holmes, Gerald L., illus. 1998. (Hank the Cowdog Ser.: No. 16). 144p. (J). (gr. 2-5). 14.99 (978-0-670-88423-0(5) , Viking Juvenile); pap. 4.99 (978-0-14-130392-5(1) , Puffin) Penguin Group (USA) Inc.

—Lost in the Dark Unchanted Forest, Vol. 11. Holmes, Gerald L., illus. 1998. (Hank the Cowdog Ser.: No. 11). 144p. (J). (gr. 2-5). pap. 4.99 (978-0-14-130387-1(5) , Puffin) Penguin Group (USA) Inc.

—Monkey Business. Holmes, Gerald L., illus. 1998. (Hank the Cowdog Ser.: No. 14). 144p. (J). (gr. 2-5). 14.99 (978-0-670-88421-6(9) , Viking Juvenile); Vol. 14. pap. 4.99 (978-0-14-130390-1(5) , Puffin) Penguin Group (USA) Inc.

—Moonlight Madness. Holmes, Gerald L., illus. 1998. (Hank the Cowdog Ser.: No. 23). 144p. (J). (gr. 2-5). 15.99 (978-0-670-88430-8(8) , Viking Juvenile); Vol. 23. pap. 4.99 (978-0-14-130399-4(9) , Puffin) Penguin Group (USA) Inc.

—The Mopwater Files. Holmes, Gerald L., illus. 1998. (Hank the Cowdog Ser.: No. 28). 144p. (J). (gr. 2-5). 14.99 (978-0-670-88435-3(9) , Viking Juvenile); pap. 4.99 (978-0-14-130404-5(9) , Puffin) Penguin Group (USA) Inc.

—Murder in the Middle Pasture. Holmes, Gerald L., illus. 1998. (Hank the Cowdog Ser.: No. 4). 144p. (J). (gr. 2-5). 14.99 (978-0-670-88411-7(1) , Viking Juvenile); Vol. 4. pap. 4.99 (978-0-14-130380-2(8) , Puffin) Penguin Group (USA) Inc.

—Murder in the Middle Pasture. Holmes, Gerald L., illus. 1999. (Hank the Cowdog Ser.: No. 4). (J). (gr. 3-6). lib. bdg. 13.00 (978-0-8335-6817-5(5)) Tandem Library Bks.

—The Original Adventures of Hank the Cowdog. Holmes, Gerald L., illus. 1998. (Hank the Cowdog Ser.: No. 1). 144p. (J). (gr. 2-5). pap. 4.99 (978-0-14-130377-2(8) , Puffin) Penguin Group (USA) Inc.

—The Original Adventures of Hank the Cowdog. Holmes, Gerald L., illus. 1999. (Hank the Cowdog Ser.: No. 1). (J). (gr. 3-6). lib. bdg. 13.00 (978-0-8335-6815-1(9)) Tandem Library Bks.

—The Phantom in the Mirror. Holmes, Gerald L., illus. (Hank the Cowdog Ser.: No. 20). 144p. (J). (gr. 2-5). 2000. 14.99 (978-0-670-88427-8(8) , Viking Juvenile); Vol. 20. 1998. pap. 4.99 (978-0-14-130396-3(4) , Puffin) Penguin Group (USA) Inc.

—The Secret Laundry Monster Files, Vol. 39. Holmes, Gerald L., illus. 2002. (Hank the Cowdog Ser.: No. 39). 144p. (J). pap. 4.99 (978-0-14-230076-3(4) , Puffin) Penguin Group (USA) Inc.

—The Secret Laundry Monster Files. 2002. (Hank the Cowdog Ser.: No. 39). (gr. 3-6). lib. bdg. 13.00 (978-0-613-43642-7(3)) Tandem Library Bks.

—Slim's Good-Bye. Holmes, Gerald L., illus. 2000. (Hank the Cowdog Ser.: No. 34). 144p. (J). (gr. 2-5). 15.99 (978-0-670-88889-4(3) , Viking Juvenile); Vol. 34. pap. 4.99 (978-0-14-130677-3(7) , Puffin) Penguin Group (USA) Inc.

—Slim's Good-Bye. 2000. (Hank the Cowdog Ser.: No. 34). (Illus.). (J). (gr. 2-5). (978-0-606-18408-3(2)) Tandem Library Bks.

Farrell, Clifford T. Patchsaddle Drive. 1998. 184p. pap. 17.50 (978-0-7540-8032-9(3)) BBC Audiobooks America.

Finlayson, Ann. Greenhorn on the Frontier. 2000. (Golden Triangle Bks.). (Illus.). 224p. (J). (gr. 4-7). pap. 9.95 (978-0-8229-5722-5(1)) Univ. of Pittsburgh Pr.

Finley, Mary Pearce. White Grizzly. 2000. (gr. 5-9). (Illus.). 215p. (J). 15.95 (978-0-86541-053-4(4)); 216p. (YA). pap. 8.95 (978-0-86541-058-9(5)) Filter Pr., LLC.

Fitzgerald, John D. Brave Buffalo Fighter. 2003. (Young Adult Historical Library). 192p. (YA). pap. 11.95 (978-1-883937-59-1(0)) Bethlehem Bks.

Fleischman, Sid. Jim Ugly. Smith, Jos. A., illus. 2003. 144p. (J). (gr. 3-6). pap. 6.99 (978-0-06-052121-9(X) , Harper Trophy) HarperCollins Pubs.

Frank, John. The Toughest Cowboy: Or How the Wild West Was Tamed. Pullen, Zachary, illus. 2004. 48p. (J). (gr. k-3). 17.95 (978-0-689-83461-5(6)) Simon & Schuster Children's Publishing.

Garland, Sherry. The Buffalo Soldier. Himler, Ronald, illus. 2006. 32p. (J). (gr. 3-6). 15.95 (978-1-58980-391-6(4)) Pelican Publishing Co., Inc.

Gerrard, Roy. Wagons West! Gerrard, Roy, illus. 2000. (Illus.). 32p. (J). (ps-3). pap. 5.95 (978-0-374-48210-7(1) , Sunburst) Farrar, Straus & Giroux.

—Wagons West! 2000. (J). (ps-ps). (Illus.). lib. bdg. 14.10 (978-0-613-30179-4(X)); (978-0-606-20138-4(6)); (Illus.). (978-0-606-20401-9(6)) Tandem Library Bks.

Getzinger, Donna. For a Speck of Gold. 2002. pap. 8.95 (978-0-87714-828-9(7)) Denlingers Pubs., Ltd.

Gifaldi, David. Gregory, Maw & the Mean One. 2000. (Illus.). 148p. (J). (gr. 4-7). pap. 10.95 (978-0-595-14504-1(3) , Backinprint.com) iUniverse, Inc.

Goscinny, René. Calamity Jane: A Lucky Luke Adventure. 1998. (Lucky Luke Ser.). (Illus.). 48p. (J). (gr. 3-9). pap. 9.95 (978-1-902172-02-6(7)) Glo'worm GBR. *Dist:* Last Gasp of San Francisco.

—Dalton City: A Lucky Luke Adventure. 1998. (Lucky Luke Ser.). (Illus.). 48p. (J). (gr. 3-9). 9.95 (978-1-902172-01-9(9)) Glo'worm GBR. *Dist:* Last Gasp of San Francisco.

—The Dashing White Cowboy: A Lucky Luke Adventure. 2000. (Lucky Luke Ser.). (Illus.). 48p. (J). (gr. 3-9). 9.95 (978-1-902172-06-4(X)) Glo'worm GBR. *Dist:* Last Gasp of San Francisco.

—Ma Dalton: A Lucky Luke Adventure. 1999. (Lucky Luke Ser.). (Illus.). 48p. (J). (gr. 3-9). 9.95 (978-1-902172-04-0(3)) Glo'worm GBR. *Dist:* Last Gasp of San Francisco.

—The Tenderfoot: A Lucky Luke Adventure. 1999. (Lucky Luke Ser.). (Illus.). 48p. (J). (gr. 3-9). 9.95 (978-1-902172-03-3(5)) Glo'worm GBR. *Dist:* Last Gasp of San Francisco.

Goscinny, René & Morris. Jesse James: A Lucky Luke Adventure. 1998. (Lucky Luke Ser.). (Illus.). 48p. (J). (gr. 3-9). pap. 9.95 (978-1-902172-00-2(0)) Glo'worm GBR. *Dist:* Last Gasp of San Francisco.

—Western Circus: A Lucky Luke Adventure. 2000. (Lucky Luke Ser.). (Illus.). 48p. (J). (gr. 3-9). pap. 9.95 (978-1-902172-05-7(1)) Glo'worm GBR. *Dist:* Last Gasp of San Francisco.

Gregory, Kristiana. The Great Railroad Race: The Diary of Libby West, Utah Territory, 1868. 1999. (Dear America Ser.). (Illus.). 208p. (J). (gr. 4-9). pap. 10.95 (978-0-590-10991-8(X)) Scholastic, Inc.

—Winter Tidings. 2004. (Prairie River Ser.: No. 3). 192p. (J). (gr. 4-7). pap. 4.99 (978-0-439-44001-1(7) , Scholastic Paperbacks) Scholastic, Inc.

Gregory, Kristinana. Hope Springs Eternal. 2005. (Prairie River Ser.: No. 4). 176p. (J). pap. 4.99 (978-0-439-44003-5(3) , Scholastic Paperbacks) Scholastic, Inc.

Griffin, Kitty, et al. Cowboy Sam & Those Confounded Secrets. Wohnoutka, Mike, illus. 2001. 32p. (J). (gr. k-3). tchr. ed. 16.00 (978-0-618-08854-6(7) , Clarion Bks.) Houghton Mifflin Co. Trade & Reference Div.

Guzman, Lila. Lorenzo's Revolutionary Quest. 2003. (gr. 7-12). lib. bdg. 18.75 (978-0-613-84279-2(0)) Tandem Library Bks.

Guzman, Lila & Guzman, Rick. Lorenzo's Revolutionary Quest. 176p. (YA). pap. 9.95 (978-1-55885-392-8(8) , Piñata Books) Arte Publico Pr.

Hahn, Mary Downing. The Gentleman Outlaw & Me: A Story of the Old West. 2007. 224p. (YA). (gr. 7-9). pap. 6.95 (978-0-618-83000-8(6) , Clarion Bks.) Houghton Mifflin Co. Trade & Reference Div.

Hamilton, K. R. Caleb, Son of None. 2007. (J). pap. (978-0-7847-1859-9(8)) Standard Publishing.

Hamilton, Kersten. The Battle of Trickum County. 2007. (Caleb Pascal & the Peculiar People Ser.). 141p. (J). per. 6.99 (***978-0-7847-1910-7(1))** Standard Publishing.

Harcourt School Publishers Staff. Wagon Wheels. 3rd ed. 2002. (Trophies English Language Learners Ser.). (Illus.). pap. 5.10 (978-0-15-327776-4(9)) Harcourt Schl. Pubs.

Harper, Jo. Ollie Jolly, Rodeo Clown. Meissner, Amy, illus. 2002. 32p. (J). (gr. k-3). 15.95 (978-1-55868-552-9(9)); pap. 8.95 (978-1-55868-553-6(7)) Graphic Arts Ctr. Publishing Co. (West Winds Pr.).

—Ollie Jolly, Rodeo Clown. 2002. (gr. k-3). lib. bdg. 17.60 (978-0-613-89457-9(X)) Tandem Library Bks.

Harris, Peter. Ordinary Audrey. Runert, David, illus. 2001. 32p. (J). tchr. ed. 14.95 (978-1-58925-014-7(1) , tiger tales) ME Media LLC.

Heaton, Layce D. The Many Tracks of Lap'n Tap, 1. Heaton, Layce D., illus. 2006. (Illus.). 32p. (J). lib. bdg. 18.95 (978-0-9761128-3-9(3)) Hafabanana Pr.

Henry, Marguerite. San Domingo: The Medicine Hat Stallion. 2001. (J). (gr. 4-8). 21.75 (978-0-8446-7178-9(9)) Smith, Peter Pub., Inc.

Henty, G. A. A Tale of the Western Plains. 2006. (Dover Value Editions Ser.). (Illus.). 352p. pap. 8.95 (978-0-486-45261-6(1)) Dover Pubns., Inc.

—A Tale of the Western Plains. 1998. (Illus.). 444p. (J). (gr. 4-7). reprint ed. per. 16.95 (978-1-890623-00-5(8)) Lost Classics Bk. Co.

Hergé. Land of Black Gold. Orig. Title: Tintin au Pays de l'Or Noir. (Illus.). 62p. (J). 19.95 (978-0-8288-5048-3(8)) French & European Pubns., Inc.

—Tintin au Pays de l'Or Noir. 1999. (Tintin Ser.).Tr. of Land of Black Gold. (FRE., Illus.). 62p. (J). (gr. 4-7). 21.95 (978-2-203-00114-5(3)) Casterman, Editions FRA. *Dist:* Distribooks, Inc.

—Tintin au Pays de l'Or Noir.Tr. of Land of Black Gold. (FRE.). (J). (gr. 7-9). 24.95 (978-0-8288-5091-9(7)) French & European Pubns., Inc.

—Tintin en el Pais del Oro Negro.Tr. of Land of Black Gold. (SPA., Illus.). 62p. (J). 24.95 (978-0-8288-4995-1(1)) French & European Pubns., Inc.

Hermes, Patricia. Westward to Home Bk. 1: Joshua's Oregon Trail Diary. 2002. (gr. 3-6). lib. bdg. 13.00 (978-0-613-60738-4(4)); 2001. (J). (gr. 4-8). per. (978-0-606-19582-9(3)) Tandem Library Bks.

Holub, Joan. Cinderdog & the Wicked Stepcat. 2001. (Illus.). 32p. (J). (ps-3). 15.95 (978-0-8075-1178-7(1)) Whitman, Albert & Co.

Howe, James. Dances with Wolves: The Movie Story. 2004. (Medallion Edition Ser.). 160p. 7.95 (978-1-55704-633-8(6)) Newmarket Pr.

Hughes, Holly. Hoofbeats of Danger. 1999. 13.60 (978-0-606-17517-3(2)) Tandem Library Bks.

Hunt, L. J. The Abernathy Boys. 2004. (Abernathy Boys Ser.). 208p. (J). 15.99 (978-0-06-440953-7(8)); (Illus.). lib. bdg. 16.89 (978-0-06-029159-1(8)) HarperCollins Pubs.

Ives, David. Scrib. 2005. 208p. (J). (gr. 5 up). 16.99 (978-0-06-059841-9(7)); lib. bdg. 17.89 (978-0-06-059842-6(5)) HarperCollins Pubs.

James, Will. Home Ranch. rev. ed. (Tumbleweed Ser.). (Illus.). 302p. (J). (gr. 4). pap. 16.00 (978-0-87842-406-1(7) , 802) Mountain Pr. Publishing Co., Inc.

—In the Saddle with Uncle Bill. rev. ed. 2001. (Illus.). 208p. (J). (gr. 3-4). 26.00 (978-0-87842-427-6(X) , 808); pap. 14.00 (978-0-87842-428-3(8) , 807) Mountain Pr. Publishing Co., Inc.

—Look-See with Uncle Bill. (Illus.). 190p. 26.00 (978-0-87842-459-7(8) , 815); (J). (gr. 4). pap. 14.00 (978-0-87842-458-0(X) , 814) Mountain Pr. Publishing Co., Inc.

—Smokey: The Cowhorse, Vol. 1. rev. ed. (Tumbleweed Ser.). (Illus.). 260p. (gr. 4-7). pap. 16.00 (978-0-87842-413-9(X) , 804) Mountain Pr. Publishing Co., Inc.

—Smokey Vol. 1: The Cowhorse. rev. ed. (Tumbleweed Ser.). (Illus.). 260p. (J). (gr. 4-7). 36.00 (978-0-87842-414-6(8) , 805) Mountain Pr. Publishing Co., Inc.

—Smoky Cowhorse. 2008. 336p. (J). pap. 6.99 (***978-1-4169-4941-1(0)** , Aladdin) Simon & Schuster Children's Publishing.

James, Will. Smoky the Cowhorse. 2005. reprint ed. pap. 30.95 (978-0-7661-9507-3(4)) Kessinger Publishing, LLC.

Johnston, Tony. The Sunsets of the West. Lewin, Ted, illus. 2002. 32p. (J). (gr. k up). 16.99 (978-0-399-22659-5(1) , Putnam Juvenile) Penguin Group (USA) Inc.

Jones, Katina, et al. Cowdog Caper: Little Lucy & Friends. Ottinger, Jon, illus. Zaidan, Rick, photos by. 2001. (Little Lucy & Friends Ser.). 24p. (J). (ps-3). 9.99 (978-1-57151-701-2(4)) Playhouse Publishing.

Karas, G. Brian, illus. Carlita Ropes the Twister. 1999. (J). 27.84 (978-0-8172-7256-2(9)) Steck-Vaughn.

Karr, Kathleen. The Great Turkey Walk. 208p. (J). 2000. (gr. 4-7). pap. 6.95 (978-0-374-42798-6(4) , Sunburst); 1998. (gr. 5-9). 17.00 (978-0-374-32773-6(4) , Farrar, Straus & Giroux (BYR)) Farrar, Straus & Giroux.

—Great Turkey Walk. 2000. 199p. (J). (gr. 4-7). lib. bdg. 12.60 (978-0-606-20395-1(8)); (gr. 3-6). lib. bdg. 12.95 (978-0-613-30449-8(7)) Tandem Library Bks.

—The Great Turkey Walk. unabr. ed. 2000. (YA). (gr. 5 up). pap. 59.00 incl. audio (978-0-7887-3631-5(0) , 41006X4) Recorded Bks., LLC.

Katz, S. Natives. 2002. (Larbu & Tia Adventures Ser.). (Illus.). 88p. (YA). (gr. 2-10). pap. 16.00 (978-0-9648834-1-3(4)) Really Alive Bks.

Kay, Verla. Gold Fever. Schindler, S. D., illus. (Picture Puffin Ser.). (J). (gr. k-3). 2003. 32p. pap. 6.99 (978-0-14-250183-2(2) , Puffin); 1999. 1p. 15.99 (978-0-399-23027-1(0) , Putnam Juvenile) Penguin Group (USA) Inc.

—Gold Fever. 2003. (gr. k-3). lib. bdg. 15.30 (978-0-613-89796-9(X)) Tandem Library Bks.

Kelton, Elmer. Cloudy in the West. 1999. (gr. 7-12). lib. bdg. 14.15 (978-0-613-28796-8(7)) Tandem Library Bks.

Kimmel, Eric A. The Great Texas Hamster Drive: An Original Tall Tale. Whatley, Bruce, illus. 2007. 40p. (J). (ps-2). 16.99 (***978-0-7614-5357-4(1))** Cavendish, Marshall Corp.

L'Amour, Louis. Hanging Woman Creek. 1999. (gr. 7-12). lib. bdg. 12.40 (978-0-8085-1672-9(8)) Tandem Library Bks.

Lampman, Evelyn Sibley. The Shy Stegosaurus of Cricket Creek. Buel, Hubert, illus. 2001. 220p. (J). 17.95 (978-1-930900-09-7(0)) Purple Hse. Pr.

Levine, Ellen. The Journal of Jedediah Barstow: An Emigrant on the Oregon Trail. 2002. (My Name Is America Ser.). (Illus.). 176p. (J). (gr. 4-9). pap. 10.95 (978-0-439-06310-4(8) , Scholastic Pr.) Scholastic, Inc.

Levitin, Sonia. Clem's Chances. 2001. (Illus.). 208p. (J). (gr. 2-7). pap. 17.95 (978-0-439-29314-3(6) , Orchard Bks.) Scholastic, Inc.

—Nine for California. Smith, Cat Bowman, illus. 2001. 40p. (J). (ps-3). pap. 6.95 (978-0-531-07176-2(6) , Orchard Bks.) Scholastic, Inc.

Lowell, Susan. Cindy Ellen: A Wild Western Cinderella. Manning, Jane, illus. 2001. 40p. (J). (ps-3). pap. 6.99 (978-0-06-443864-3(3) , Harper Trophy) HarperCollins Pubs.

—Cindy Ellen: A Wild Western Cinderella. 2000. (gr. k-3). lib. bdg. 15.30 (978-0-613-44444-6(2)) Tandem Library Bks.

McKissack, Patricia. Away West. James, Gordon, illus. 2006. (Scraps of Time Ser.). 128p. (J). (gr. 3). pap. 4.99 (978-0-14-240688-5(0) , Puffin) Penguin Group (USA) Inc.

Mercati, Cynthia. Wagons Ho! A Diary of the Oregon Trail. Kabel, Larassa, illus. 2000. (Cover-to-Cover Bks.). 56p. (J). pap. (978-0-7891-5039-4(5)); (gr. 1-4). lib. bdg. 16.95 (978-0-7807-9011-7(1)) Perfection Learning Corp.

Miller, Christopher & Miller, Allan. The Legend of Gid the Kid & the Black Bean Bandits: Doing the Right Thing Ain't Always Easy. 2007. (Illus.). 32p. (J). (gr. 1-5). 12.99 (***978-1-59317-202-2(8))** Warner Pr. Pubs.

Mitchell, Marianne. Joe Cinders. Langdo, Bryan, illus. rev. ed. 2002. 48p. (J). (ps-3). 17.95 (978-0-8050-6529-9(6) , Holt, Henry & Co. Bks. For Young Readers) Holt, Henry & Co.

Montana Showdown. 1999. (SmartReader Ser.). (J). Level 1. pap., tchr. ed. 19.95 incl. audio (978-0-7887-0768-1(X) , 79349T3); Level 2. pap., tchr. ed. 19.95 incl. audio (978-0-7887-0543-4(1) , 79330T3) Recorded Bks., LLC.

Moss, Marissa. Amelia Hits the Road. 1999. (Amelia's Notebooks). (J). (gr. 3-5). 12.75 (978-0-606-19867-7(9)) Tandem Library Bks.

—Amelia's Are-We-There-yet Longest Ever Car Trip. Moss, Marissa, illus. 2006. (Amelia's Notebooks). (Illus.). 40p. (J). 9.95 (978-1-4169-0906-4(0) , Simon & Schuster/Paula Wiseman Bks.) Simon & Schuster Children's Publishing.

Myers, Bill. My Life as a Cowboy Cowpie, Vol. 19. 2001. (Incredible Worlds of Wally McDoogle Ser.: No. 19). 128p. (J). (gr. 3-7). pap. 6.99 (978-0-8499-5990-5(X)) Nelson, Thomas Inc.

Myers, Walter Dean. The Journal of Joshua Loper: A Black Cowboy: The Chisholm Trail, 1871. 1999. (My Name Is America Ser.). (Illus.). 160p. (J). (gr. 4-8). pap. 10.95 (978-0-590-02691-8(7)) Scholastic, Inc.

—The Righteous Revenge of Artemis Bonner. 2003. (J). (gr. 5 up). 22.25 (978-0-8446-7250-2(5)) Smith, Peter Pub., Inc.

Nislick, June Levitt. Zayda Was a Cowboy. 2005. 128p. (J). pap. 9.95 (978-0-8276-0817-7(9)) Jewish Publn. Society.

Nixon, Hershell. The Long Way West. 2003. (Illus.). 176p. (J). 16.95 (978-0-89672-508-9(1)) Texas Tech Univ. Pr.

Nolen, Jerdine. Thunder Rose. Nelson, Kadir, illus. 2007. 32p. (J). pap. 7.00 (***978-0-15-206006-0(5)** , Voyager Bks./Libros Viajeros) Harcourt Children's Bks.

Novara, Joe. Road Wrangler: Cowboys on Wheels. Lawson, Robert & Spatrisano, Kimberly, illus. 2007. (J). pap. 7.95 (***978-1-58980-507-1(0))** Pelican Publishing Co., Inc.

Osborne, Mary Pope. Ghost Town at Sundown. unabr. ed. 2004. (Magic Tree House Ser.: No. 10). 73p. (J). (gr. k-3). pap. 17.00 incl. audio (978-0-8072-0535-8(4) , Listening Library) Random Hse. Audio Publishing Group.

Paulsen, Gary. Tucket's Gold. 2001. (Tucket Adventures Ser.). (Illus.). 112p. (J). (gr. 4-7). pap. 5.50 (978-0-440-41376-9(1) , Yearling) Random Hse. Children's Bks.

—Tucket's Gold. 2001. (J). (978-0-606-20958-8(1)); (gr. 5-8). lib. bdg. 12.40 (978-0-613-33781-6(6)) Tandem Library Bks.

—Tucket's Travels Bks.1-5: Francis Tucket's Adventures in the West, 1847-1849, Bks. 1-5. 2003. 560p. (YA). (gr. 4-7). pap. 7.50 (978-0-440-41967-9(0) , Yearling) Random Hse. Children's Bks.

Peck, Richard. Fair Weather. 2001. (Illus.). 160p. (J). (gr. 4-8). 16.99 (978-0-8037-2516-4(7) , Dial) Penguin Group (USA) Inc.

Piepmeier, Charlotte. Lucy's Journey to the Wild West: A True Story. Blakemore, Sally, illus. 2003. 40p. (J). (gr. k-7). 19.95 (978-1-929115-07-5(5)) Azro Pr., Inc.

Pierson, Jan. Shadow of Shaniko (Shaniko, Oregon) 2002. (Ghostowners Ser.: Vol. 3). (Illus.). 105p. (Orig.). pap. 10.00 (978-0-9721800-2-3(8)) WildWest Publishing.

Pinkwater, Daniel M. Go West. Rash, Andy, illus. 2002. (Fat Camp Commandos Ser.). 96p. (J). (gr. 3-8). pap. 14.95 (978-0-439-29772-1(9) , Scholastic Pr.) Scholastic, Inc.

—Go West. 2003. (gr. 3-6). lib. bdg. 12.40 (978-0-613-62511-1(0)) Tandem Library Bks.

Platt, Chris. Moon Shadow. 2006. 192p. (J). 14.95 (978-1-56145-382-5(X) , Peachtree Junior) Peachtree Pubs., Ltd.

Plowhead, Ruth Gipson. Lucretia Ann in the Golden West. Moore, Agnes Randall, illus. 2004. (Classic Ser.). 246p. (gr. 4-7). pap. 17.95 (978-0-87004-409-0(5)) Caxton Pr.

Postgate, Daniel. Wild West Willy. 2000. (Illus.). 32p. (J). 19.99 (978-0-00-198317-5(2)) HarperCollins Pubs. Ltd. GBR. *Dist:* Trafalgar Square Publishing.

Rankin, Laura, illus. The Cowgirl Aunt of Harriet Bean. 2007. 81p. (J). (gr. 2-4). per. 4.95 (***978-1-59990-055-1(6)*** , Bloomsbury Children) Bloomsbury Publishing.

Reid, Mayne. The Boy Hunters or Adventures in Search of a White Buffalo. 2005. reprint ed. pap. 30.95 (978-1-4179-0412-9(7)) Kessinger Publishing, LLC.

Rizzo, Kay D. Wagon Train West. 2003. 96p. (J). (978-0-8163-1986-2(3)) Pacific Pr. Publishing Assn.

Robinet, Harriette Gillem. Twelve Travelers, Twenty Horses. 208p. (J). 2005. pap. 4.99 (978-0-689-87607-3(6) , Aladdin); 2003. (Illus.). 16.95 (978-0-689-84561-1(8) , Atheneum) Simon & Schuster Children's Publishing.

Rogers, Lisa Waller. Get along Little Dogies: The Chisholm Trail Diary of Hallie Lou Wells. 2001. (Lone Star Journals: Vol. 1). (Illus.). 174p. (J). (gr. 4-7). 14.50 (978-0-89672-446-4(8)) Texas Tech Univ. Pr.

—Get along, Little Dogies: The Chisholm Trail Diary of Hallie Lou Wells, South Texas 1878. 2001. (Lone Star Journals). (Illus.). 174p. (J). (gr. 4-7). 8.95 (978-0-89672-448-8(4)) Texas Tech Univ. Pr.

Ross, Eileen. Nellie & the Bandit. Kono, Erin Eitter, illus. 2005. 32p. (J). 16.00 (978-0-374-35508-1(8) , Farrar, Straus & Giroux (BYR)) Farrar, Straus & Giroux.

Ross, Harriet, compiled by. Exciting Western Stories. 2001. (Illus.). 160p. (J). (gr. 4-7). lib. bdg. 12.95 (978-0-87460-312-5(9)) Lion Bks.

Rowe, Gordon J. Showdown at Pecos. 2004. (Illus.). 32p. (ps-3). 11.95 (978-1-57197-192-0(0)) Pentland Pr., Inc.

Rumford, James. Don't Touch My Hat. 2007. (Illus.). 40p. (J). (ps-3). lib. bdg. 18.99 (978-0-375-93782-8(X) , Knopf Bks. for Young Readers) Random Hse. Children's Bks.

—Don't Touch My Hat! 2007. (Illus.). 40p. (J). (ps-3). 16.99 (978-0-375-83782-1(5) , Knopf Bks. for Young Readers) Random Hse. Children's Bks.

Rylant, Cynthia. Henry & Mudge & the Tumbling Trip. Bracken, Carolyn, illus. 2006. (Henry & Mudge Ser.). 40p. (J). pap. 3.99 (978-0-689-83452-3(7) , Aladdin) Simon & Schuster Children's Publishing.

Rylant, Cynthia & Bracken, Carolyn. Henry & Mudge & the Tumbling Trip. Stevenson, Sucie, illus. 2005. (Henry & Mudge Ser.). 40p. (J). (gr. k-3). 14.95 (978-0-689-81180-7(2)) Simon & Schuster Children's Publishing.

Sargent, Dave & Sargent, Pat. Ginger: (Lilac Roan) Be Likeable, 30 vols., Vol. 27. Lenoir, Jane, illus. 2003. (Saddle Up Ser.: Vol. 27). 42p. (J). pap. 6.95 (978-1-56763-812-7(0)); lib. bdg. 22.60 (978-1-56763-811-0(2)) Ozark Publishing.

Schnetzler, Pattie L. Fast 'n Snappy. Manning, Jane K., tr. Manning, Jane K., illus. 2004. (Carolrhoda Picture Books Ser.). 32p. (J). (gr. k-3). 16.95 (978-1-57505-539-8(2)) Lerner Publishing Group.

—Widdermaker. Sealock, Rick, illus. 2005. 32p. (gr. k-2). 15.95 (978-0-87614-647-7(7)) Lerner Publishing Group.

Scieszka, Jon. The Good, the Bad, & the Goofy, Vol. 3. 2004. (Time Warp Trio Ser.: No. 3). (Illus.). 80p. (J). (gr. 2-6). pap. 4.99 (978-0-14-240046-3(7) , Puffin) Penguin Group (USA) Inc.

—You Can't, but Genghis Khan. 2006. (Time Warp Trio). 80p. (J). (gr. 2-5). pap. 4.99 (978-0-06-111636-0(X) , Harper Trophy) HarperCollins Pubs.

Shire, Poppy. Star the Western Pony. Berg, Ron, illus. 2007. (J). (***978-0-06-083783-9(7)***); (Magic Pony Carousel Ser.: No.3). 96p. (gr. 2-5). pap. 3.99 (***978-0-06-083785-3(3)***) HarperCollins Pubs. (Harper Trophy).

Simmons, Marc. Teddy's Cattle Drive: A Story from History. Kil, Ronald R., illus. 2005. 56p. (J). 18.95 (978-0-8263-3921-8(2)) Univ. of New Mexico Pr.

Smith, Alexander McCall. The Cowgirl Aunt of Harriet Bean. Rankin, Laura, illus. 2006. (Harriet Bean Ser.). 80p. (J). (gr. 2-4). 9.95 (978-1-58234-977-0(0) , Bloomsbury Children) Bloomsbury Publishing.

Smith, Janice Lee. Jess & the Stinky Cowboys. Thiesing, Lisa, illus. 2004. (Dial Easy-to-Read Ser.). 48p. (J). (gr. k-3). 14.99 (978-0-8037-2641-3(4) , Dial) Penguin Group (USA) Inc.

Smith, Roland. The Captain's Dog: My Journey with the Lewis & Clark Tribe. 2000. (Great Episodes Ser.). (Illus.). 304p. (YA). (gr. 4-7). pap. 6.00 (978-0-15-202696-7(7) , Harcourt Paperbacks) Harcourt Children's Bks.

—The Captain's Dog: My Journey with the Lewis & Clark Tribe. 2000. (J). 12.65 (978-0-606-19000-8(7)); (gr. 3-6). lib. bdg. 14.15 (978-0-613-29900-8(0)) Tandem Library Bks.

Sneed, Brad. Deputy Harvey & the Ant Cow Caper. 2005. (Illus.). 32p. (J). (ps). 16.99 (978-0-8037-3023-6(3) , Dial) Penguin Group (USA) Inc.

Sperry, Armstrong. Wagons Westward: The Old Trail to Santa Fe. Sperry, Armstrong, illus. 2005. (Illus.). 200p. (YA). (gr. 6-11). reprint ed. pap. 15.00 (978-0-7567-9693-8(8)) DIANE Publishing Co.

—Wagons Westward: The Old Trail to Santa Fe. 2000. (Illus.). 224p. (J). pap. 14.95 (978-1-56792-128-1(0)) Godine, David R. Pub.

Spooner, Michael. Daniel's Walk. rev. ed. 176p. 2004. (J). pap. 7.95 (978-0-8050-7543-4(7)); 2001. (Illus.). (YA). (gr. 7 up). 16.95 (978-0-8050-6750-7(7)) Holt, Henry & Co. (Holt, Henry & Co. Bks. For Young Readers).

Stamper, Judith Bauer. The Pony Express. Lewis, Anthony, illus. 2000. (Scholastic At-Home Phonics Reading Program Ser.: Vol. 54). 24p. (J). (978-0-590-68851-2(0)) Scholastic, Inc.

Stanley, Diane. Saving Sweetness. Karas, G. Brian, illus. 2002. 13.19 (978-1-4046-0940-2(7)) Book Wholesalers, Inc.

—Saving Sweetness. Karas, G. Brian, illus. 2005. (J). pap. 18.95 incl. audio compact disk (978-1-59112-330-9(5)); 2002. 28.95 incl. audio compact disk (978-1-59112-548-8(0)); 2002. pap. 39.95 incl. audio compact disk (978-1-59112-547-1(2)) Live Oak Media.

—Saving Sweetness. Karas, G. Brian, illus. 2001. 32p. (J). (ps-ps). pap. 5.99 (978-0-698-11767-9(0) , Putnam Juvenile) Penguin Group (USA) Inc.

—Saving Sweetness. Karas, G. Brian, illus. 2001. (J). (ps-ps). lib. bdg. 14.15 (978-0-613-44412-5(4)) Tandem Library Bks.

Steig, Jeanne. Tales from Gizzard's Grill. Turner, Sandy, illus. 2004. 80p. (J). 17.89 (978-0-06-000960-1(8)); 16.99 (978-0-06-000959-5(4)) HarperCollins Pubs. (Cotler, Joanna Books).

Stein, David Ezra. Cowboy Ned & Andy. Stein, David Ezra, illus. 2006. (Illus.). 32p. (J). (ps-1). 14.95 (978-1-4169-0041-2(1) , Simon & Schuster Children's Publishing) Simon & Schuster Children's Publishing.

—Ned's New Friend. Stein, David Ezra, illus. 2007. (Cowboy Ned & Andy Ser.). 32p. (J). (ps-1). 14.99 (978-1-4169-2490-6(6) , Simon & Schuster Children's Publishing) Simon & Schuster Children's Publishing.

Stilton, Geronimo. The Wild, Wild West. Stilton, Geronimo et al, illus. 2005. (Geronimo Stilton Ser.: No. 21). 121p. (J). lib. bdg. 18.46 (***978-1-4242-0290-4(6)***) Fitzgerald Bks.

Thomas, Rosie. Cowgirl Rosie & Her Five Baby Bison. 2001. (Illus.). 24p. (J). (ps-3). 12.95 (978-0-316-64712-0(8)) Little Brown & Co.

Van Dyne, Edith. Aunt Jane's Nieces Out West. 2004. reprint ed. pap. 21.95 (978-1-4191-0826-6(3)) Kessinger Publishing, LLC.

Van Leeuwen, Jean. Papa & the Pioneer Quilt. Bond, Rebecca, illus. 2007. (J). (gr. k-3). 32p. 16.99 (978-0-8037-3028-1(4)); (***978-1-4287-3972-7(6)***) Penguin Group (USA) Inc. (Dial).

Van Steenwyk, Elizabeth. My Name Is York. Farnsworth, Bill, illus. 2000. 32p. (J). (ps-3). 7.95 (978-0-87358-758-7(8) , Rising Moon Bks. for Young Readers) Northland Publishing.

Vande Velde, Vivian. Ghost of a Hanged Man. 96p. (J). 2005. pap. 5.95 (978-0-7614-5154-9(4)); 1998. (gr. 3-7). 14.95 (978-0-7614-5015-3(7) , Cavendish Children's Bks.) Cavendish, Marshall Corp.

Vens, William D. Alias Pecos Bill. 2003. per. 13.95 (978-1-891929-92-2(5)) Four Seasons Pubs.

Watson, Esther Pearl. Trouble at Sugar-Dip Well. 2002. (Illus.). 32p. (J). (gr. k-3). 15.00 (978-0-618-11863-2(2)) Houghton Mifflin Co. Trade & Reference Div.

The Wild, Wild West. 2005. (Illus.). 106p. (J). (978-1-4156-0684-1(6)) Scholastic, Inc.

Williams, Jennifer. Stringbean's Trip to the Shining Sea. Williams, Vera B., illus. 1999. 48p. (J). (ps-3). pap. 6.99 (978-0-688-16701-1(2) , Harper Trophy) HarperCollins Pubs.

Williams, Vera B. Stringbean's Trip to the Shining Sea. 1999. (978-0-606-16744-4(7)); lib. bdg. 14.10 (978-0-613-18280-5(4)) Tandem Library Bks.

Wilson, Diane Lee. Black Storm Comin' (J). 2006. 240p. pap. 5.99 (978-0-689-87138-2(4) , Aladdin); 2005. 304p. (gr. 5-9). 17.99 (978-0-689-87137-5(6) , McElderry, Margaret K.) Simon & Schuster Children's Publishing.

Wisler, G. Clifton. Mustang Flats. 1999. (J). (978-0-606-16769-7(2)) Tandem Library Bks.

Wolf, Allan. New Found Land: Lewis & Clark's Voyage of Discovery. 2007. (Illus.). 512p. (YA). (gr. 7). pap. 8.99 (***978-0-7636-3288-5(0)***) Candlewick Pr.

—New Found Land: Lewis & Clark's Voyage of Discovery. Wolf, Allan, illus. 2004. (Illus.). 512p. (J). (gr. 5 up). 18.99 (978-0-7636-2113-1(7)) Candlewick Pr.

Yep, Laurence. The Traitor: Golden Mountain Chronicles: 1885. (Golden Mountain Chronicles). 320p. (J). (gr. 5 up). 2004. pap. 6.99 (978-0-06-000831-4(8) , Harper Trophy); 2003. 17.99 (978-0-06-027522-8(7)) HarperCollins Pubs.

WEST (U.S.)—HISTORY

Alter, Judy. Great Women of the Old West. 2001. (We the People Ser.). (Illus.). 48p. (J). (gr. 4 up). lib. bdg. 22.60 (978-0-7565-0099-3(0)) Compass Point Bks.

Anderson, Dale. The Civil War in the West (1861-July 1863) 2004. (World Almanac Library of the Civil War). (Illus.). 48p. (J). (gr. 5 up). pap. 11.95 (978-0-8368-5592-0(2)); lib. bdg. 30.00 (978-0-8368-5583-8(3)) Stevens, Gareth Inc. (World Almanac Library).

—Westward Expansion. 2000. (Making of America Ser.). (Illus.). 96p. (J). (gr. 4-7). lib. bdg. 28.54 (978-0-8172-5705-7(5)) Raintree.

Bard, Jessica. Lawmen & Outlaws: The Wild, Wild West. 2005. (Trailblazers of the West Ser.). (Illus.). 48p. (J). (ps-7). 24.00 (978-0-516-25130-1(9)); (YA). (gr. 7-12). pap. 6.95 (978-0-516-25085-4(X)) Scholastic Library Publishing. (Children's Pr.).

Barnett, Tracy. The Buffalo Soldiers. 2002. (History of the Old West Ser.). (Illus.). 64p. (YA). (gr. 5 up). lib. bdg. (978-1-59084-072-6(0)) Mason Crest Pubs.

Bial, Raymond. Cow Towns. 2004. (American Community Ser.). (Illus.). 48p. (J). (gr. 2-5). 29.00 (978-0-516-23706-0(3) , Children's Pr.) Scholastic Library Publishing.

Blue, Rose. Exploring the Western Mountains. 2004. (Illus.). (J). pap. 9.50 (978-1-4109-0676-2(0)) Raintree.

Blue, Rose & Naden, Corinne J. Exploring the Western Mountains. 2004. (J). lib. bdg. 32.79 (978-1-4109-0674-8(4)) Raintree.

Boraas, Tracey. Kit Carson: Mountain Man. 2002. (Let Freedom Ring Ser.). (Illus.). 48p. (J). (gr. 3-4). lib. bdg. 22.60 (978-0-7368-1349-5(7) , Bridgestone Bks.) Capstone Pr., Inc.

Boule, Mary Null. California's Native American Tribes, 26 vols. Liddell, Daniel & Basta, Mary, illus. 2000. 52p. (J). (gr. 3-6). pap. 108.00 (978-1-877599-23-1(9)) Merryant Pubs.

Braidich, Victoria. Making History: A Covered Wagon. 2006. (Tony Stead Nonfiction Independent Reading Collection). (J). pap. (978-1-4042-5589-0(3)) Rosen Publishing Group, Inc., The.

Bryant, Jill. Wagon Train. 2003. (Real Life Stories Ser.). (Illus.). 24p. (J). lib. bdg. 15.95 (978-1-59036-082-8(6)) Weigl Pubs., Inc.

—Women in the West. 2003. (Real Life Stories Ser.). (Illus.). 24p. (J). lib. bdg. 15.95 (978-1-59036-083-5(4)) Weigl Pubs., Inc.

Buffalo Soldiers & the Western Frontier Vol. 2: Individual Title Six-Packs. (On Deck Ser.: Vol. 2). 24p. (gr. 4-5). 35.00 (978-0-7578-5805-5(8)) Rigby Education.

Burger, James P. The Rocky Mountain Fur Trade. 2002. (Library of the Westward Expansion). (Illus.). 24p. (J). (gr. 3). lib. bdg. 19.95 (978-0-8239-5851-1(5) , PowerKids Pr.) Rosen Publishing Group, Inc., The.

Burnett, Linda. Pioneers: Adventure in a New Land. 2005. (Trailblazers of the West Ser.). (Illus.). 48p. (J). (ps-7). 24.00 (978-0-516-25127-1(9)); (YA). (gr. 7-12). pap. 6.95 (978-0-516-25097-7(3)) Scholastic Library Publishing. (Children's Pr.).

Calvert, Patricia. Kit Carson: He Led the Way. 2006. (Great Explorations Ser.). (Illus.). 80p. (J). lib. bdg. 32.79 (978-0-7614-2223-5(4) , Benchmark Bks.) Cavendish, Marshall Corp.

Cheney, Martha. History Pockets: Moving West. McClain, Lynn, illus. 2003. (History Pockets Ser.). 96p. (J). (gr. 4-6). suppl. ed. 12.99 (978-1-55799-902-3(3) , EMC 3704) Evan-Moor Educational Pubs.

Clee, Paul. Photography & the Making of the American West. 2002. (Illus.). x, 124p. (J). 27.50 (978-0-208-02512-8(X)) Shoe String Pr., Inc.

Coleman, Wim & Perrin, Pat. What Made the Wild West Wild. 2006. (Wild History of the American West Ser.). (Illus.). 128p. (J). lib. bdg. 33.27 (978-1-59845-016-3(6) , MyReportLinks.com Bks.) Enslow Pubs., Inc.

Conant, Susan Sens. Lewis & Clark's Journey of Discovery: A Guide for Young Explorers. Lynn, Rick, illus. 2004. 48p. (J). pap. (***978-0-9725584-1-9(1)***) Little Blue Pr.

Corrigan, Jim. Civil War in the West. 2002. (History of the Old West Ser.). (Illus.). 64p. (J). (gr. 5 up). lib. bdg. (978-1-59084-067-2(4)) Mason Crest Pubs.

Craats, Rennay. Ranching. 2003. (Real Life Stories Ser.). (Illus.). 24p. (J). lib. bdg. 15.95 (978-1-59036-081-1(8)) Weigl Pubs., Inc.

Crewe, Sabrina & Uschan, Michael V. The Oregon Trail. 2004. (Events That Shaped America Ser.). (Illus.). 32p. (J). lib. bdg. 24.67 (978-0-8368-3405-5(4)) Stevens, Gareth Inc.

Davis, Lucile. Medicine in the American West. 2001. (gr. 3-6). lib. bdg. 14.10 (978-0-613-51662-4(1)) Tandem Library Bks.

De Capua, Sarah. Great Women of Pioneer America. 2005. (We the People Ser.). (Illus.). 48p. (J). (gr. 4-6). (978-0-7565-1269-9(7) , 1244091) Compass Point Bks.

Dean, Arlan. The Mormon Pioneer Trail: From Nauvoo, Illinois to the Great Salt Lake, Utah. 2003. (Reading Power Ser.). (Illus.). 24p. (J). lib. bdg. 17.25 (978-0-8239-6476-5(0) , PowerKids Pr.) Rosen Publishing Group, Inc., The.

—The Oregon Trail: From Independence, Missouri to Oregon City, Oregon. 2003. (Reading Power Ser.). (Illus.). 24p. (J). lib. bdg. 17.25 (978-0-8239-6478-9(7) , PowerKids Pr.) Rosen Publishing Group, Inc., The.

—The Overland Trail: From Atchison, Kansas, to Fort Bridger, Wyoming. 2003. (Reading Power Ser.). (Illus.). 24p. (J). lib. bdg. 17.25 (978-0-8239-6479-6(5) , PowerKids Pr.) Rosen Publishing Group, Inc., The.

Deangelis, Gina. The Wild West. 1998. (Costume, Tradition & Culture). (Illus.). 64p. (YA). 19.75 (978-0-7910-5169-6(2) , Chelsea Hse.) Facts On File, Inc.

Deitch, JoAnne Weisman, ed. A Century of Westward Expansion. 2000. (Researching American History Ser.). (Illus.). 56p. (J). (978-1-57960-064-8(6)) History Compass, LLC.

Ditchfield, Christin. The Lewis & Clark Expedition. 2006. 48p. (gr. 3-5). (YA). pap. 6.95 (978-0-516-25222-3(4)); (Illus.). (J). 25.00 (978-0-516-22835-8(8)) Scholastic Library Publishing. (Children's Pr.).

Doak, Robin S. Zebulon Pike: Explorer & Soldier. 2005. (Signature Lives Ser.). (Illus.). 112p. (J). (gr. 5-7). (978-0-7565-0998-9(X)) Compass Point Bks.

Doherty, Kieran. Explorers, Missionaries & Trappers: Trailblazers of the West. 2000. (Shaping America Ser.). (Illus.). 176p. (gr. 7 up). lib. bdg. 22.95 (978-1-881508-52-6(8)) Oliver Pr., Inc.

Dorling Kindersley Publishing Staff. Wild West. 2005. (Eyewitness Books). 72p. (J). 15.99 (978-0-7566-1097-5(4)); (Illus.). lib. bdg. 19.99 (978-0-7566-1098-2(2)) Dorling Kindersley Publishing, Inc.

Drake, Samuel Adams. The Making of the Great West 1512-1883. 2001. 350p. (YA). reprint ed. (978-1-58218-439-5(9)); pap. (978-1-58218-438-8(0)) Digital Scanning, Inc.

Draper, Allison Stark. What People Wore During the Westward Expansion. 2001. (Clothing, Costumes & Uniforms Thoughout American History Ser.). (Illus.). 24p. (J). (gr. 3). lib. bdg. 19.95 (978-0-8239-5667-8(9) , PK-CLPL, PowerKids Pr.) Rosen Publishing Group, Inc., The.

Edwards, Judith & Comport, Sally Wern. The Great Expedition of Lewis & Clark: By Private Reubin Field, Member of the Corps of Discovery. Comport, Sally Wern, illus. 2003. (Illus.). 40p. (J). 17.00 (978-0-374-38039-7(2) , Farrar, Straus & Giroux (BYR)) Farrar, Straus & Giroux.

Espinosa, Rod. Lewis & Clark. 2007. (Bio-Graphics Ser.). (Illus.). 32p. (J). (gr. 3-6). lib. bdg. 27.07 (***978-1-60270-069-7(9)*** , Graphic Planet) Magic Wagon.

Faber, Harold. John Charles Fremont: Pathfinder to the West. 2002. (Great Explorations Ser.). (Illus.). 79p. (J). 29.93 (978-0-7614-1481-0(9) , Benchmark Bks.) Cavendish, Marshall Corp.

Faber, Harold, et al. Lewis & Clark: From Ocean to Ocean. 2001. (Great Explorations Ser.). (Illus.). 80p. (J). (gr. 4 up). lib. bdg. 29.93 (978-0-7614-1241-0(7) , Benchmark Bks.) Cavendish, Marshall Corp.

Favor, Lesli J. A Historical Atlas of America's Manifest Destiny. 2005. (United States, Historical Atlases of the Growth of a New Nation Ser.). (Illus.). 64p. (J). (gr. 7-12). lib. bdg. 30.60 (978-1-4042-0201-6(3)) Rosen Publishing Group, Inc., The.

Flanagan, Alice K. The Buffalo Soldiers. 2004. (We the People Ser.). (Illus.). 48p. (J). 22.60 (978-0-7565-0833-3(9)) Compass Point Bks.

Foran, Jill. Homesteading. 2003. (Real Life Stories Ser.). (Illus.). 24p. (J). lib. bdg. 15.95 (978-1-59036-079-8(6)) Weigl Pubs., Inc.

Fradin, Judith Bloom & Fradin, Dennis B. The Lewis & Clark Expedition. 2007. (Turning Points in U. S. History Ser.). (J). lib. bdg. (***978-0-7614-2044-6(4)*** , Benchmark Bks.) Cavendish, Marshall Corp.

Frazier, Neta Lohnes. Path to the Pacific: The Story of Sacagawea. 2007. (Sterling Point Bks.). (Illus.). 177p. (J). (***978-1-4287-2899-8(6)***) Sterling Publishing Co., Inc.

Frisch, Aaron. Jesse James. 2005. (Illus.). 48p. (gr. 5-9). 21.95 (978-1-58341-338-8(3) , Creative Education) Creative Co., The.

Glaser, Jason. Lewis & Clark. 2004. (Fact Finders Ser.). (Illus.). 32p. (J). lib. bdg. 22.60 (978-0-7368-2665-5(3)) Capstone Pr., Inc.

Glass, Andrew. Bad Guys: True Stories of Legendary Gunslingers. 2000. (Illus.). (J). (978-0-606-18781-7(2)) Tandem Library Bks.

Graham, Ian. You Wouldn't Want to Work on the Railroad! 2001. (gr. 3-6). lib. bdg. 18.75 (978-0-613-44281-7(4)) Tandem Library Bks.

—You Wouldn't Want to Work on the Railroad! A Track You'd Rather Not Go Down. Antram, David, illus. 2001. (You Wouldn't Want to Be Ser.). 32p. (J). (gr. 2-5). 28.50 (978-0-531-14603-0(0)); pap. 9.95 (978-0-531-16208-8(7)) Scholastic Library Publishing. (Watts, Franklin).

Green, John. Horses of the Old West. 2007. 32p. (J). pap. 3.95 (***978-0-486-45675-1(7)***) Dover Pubns., Inc.

Gunderson, Mary. Cooking on the Lewis & Clark Expedition. 2000. (Blue Earth Books). (Illus.). 32p. (J). (gr. 3-4). lib. bdg. 22.60 (978-0-7368-0354-0(8) , Bridgestone Bks.) Capstone Pr., Inc.

—Cooking on the Lewis & Clark Expedition. 1999. (Exploring History Through Simple Recipes Ser.). (Illus.). 32p. (J). (gr. 2-7). pap. 14.60 (978-0-516-21865-6(4) , Children's Pr.) Scholastic Library Publishing.

Harrison, Peter. Wild West. 2000. (World Of... Ser.). (Illus.). 64p. (gr. 3-7). pap. 7.95 (978-1-84215-233-1(5) , Southwater); 12.95 (978-0-7548-0508-3(5) , Lorenz Bks.) Anness Publishing GBR. *Dist:* National Bk. Network.

Harrison, Peter & Bancroft-Hunt, Norman. Amazing World of the Wild West: Discover the Trailblazing History of Cowboys, Outlaws & Native Americans. 2004. (Illus.). 64p. 15.99 (978-0-7548-1148-0(4) , Lorenz Bks.) Anness Publishing GBR. *Dist:* National Bk. Network.

Hatch, Lynda. The Santa Fe Trail. 2003. (Crossing America Ser.). 48p. (YA). (gr. 5-8). pap. 5.99 (978-1-56822-655-2(1) , IF6023-E4, Instructional Fair) Schaffer, Frank Pubns.

Hatt, Christine. The American West. 2004. (Questioning History Ser.). (J). lib. bdg. 28.50 (978-1-58340-443-0(0)) Smart Apple Media.

Hicks, Peter. You Wouldn't Want to Live in a Wild West Town! Antram, David, illus. 2002. (You Wouldn't Want to Ser.). 32p. (J). (gr. 2-5). 28.50 (978-0-531-14606-4(5)); pap. 9.95 (978-0-531-16367-2(9)) Scholastic Library Publishing. (Watts, Franklin).

—You Wouldn't Want to Live in a Wild West Town! 2002. (gr. 3-6). lib. bdg. 18.75 (978-0-613-53888-6(9)) Tandem Library Bks.

Hirschfelder, Arlene B. Photo Odyssey: Solomon Carvalho's Remarkable Western Adventure 1853-54. 2000. (Illus.). 128p. (J). (gr. 5-9). tchr. ed. 18.00 (978-0-395-89123-0(X) , Clarion Bks.) Houghton Mifflin Co. Trade & Reference Div.

Hominick, Judy & Spreier, Jeanne. Best Cowboy in the West: The Story of Nat Love. 2001. (Heroes to Remember Ser.). (Illus.). 60p. (J). 14.95 (978-1-893110-25-0(7)) Silver Moon Pr.

W X Y Z

Isaacs, Sally Senzell. America in the Time of Sitting Bull: 1840 to 1890, 2 vols. 1999. (America in the Time of... Ser.). (Illus.). 48p. (gr. 4-7). lib. bdg. (978-1-57572-762-2(5)) Heinemann Library.

—Stagecoaches & the Pony Express. 2004. (Illus.). 32p. (J). pap. 7.50 (978-1-4034-4793-7(4)); lib. bdg. (978-1-4034-2508-9(6)) Heinemann Library.

James, Will. The Will James Cowboy Book, Vol. 1. rev. ed. (Illus.). 128p. (J). (gr. 4). 18.00 (978-0-87842-469-6(5) , 816) Mountain Pr. Publishing Co., Inc.

Johmann, Carol A. Going West! Journey on a Wagon Train to Settle a Frontier Town. 2000. (J). 17.60 (978-0-606-22459-8(9)) Tandem Library Bks.

Johmann, Carol A. & Rieth, Elizabeth J. Going West! Journey on a Wagon Train to Settle a Frontier Town. 2000. (Illus.). 96p. (J). (gr. 2-7). per. 19.90 (978-0-613-27857-7(7)) Tandem Library Bks.

Jordan, Shirley. Pioneer Days: Moments in History. 1999. (Cover-to-Cover Bks.). (Illus.). 64p. (J). pap. (978-0-7891-2912-3(4)); (gr. 4-7). lib. bdg. 17.95 (978-0-7807-8160-3(0)) Perfection Learning Corp.

Kalman, Bobbie. Bandannas, Chaps, & Ten-Gallon Hats. 1999. (gr. 3-6). lib. bdg. 16.40 (978-0-613-11305-2(5)) Tandem Library Bks.

—Life in the Old West, 11 bks. Incl. Bandanas, Chaps & Ten-Gallon Hats. 1998. lib. bdg. (978-0-7787-0073-9(9)); Boomtowns of the West. 1999. lib. bdg. (978-0-7787-0078-4(X)); Gold Rush. 1999. lib. bdg. (978-0-7787-0079-1(8)); Homes of the West. 1998. lib. bdg. (978-0-7787-0074-6(7)); Life of a Miner. Calder, Kate. 1999. lib. bdg. (978-0-7787-0077-7(1)); Life on the Ranch. 1998. lib. bdg. (978-0-7787-0071-5(2)); Life on the Trail. 1998. lib. bdg. (978-0-7787-0072-2(0)); Railroad. 1999. lib. bdg. (978-0-7787-0076-0(3)); Wagon Train. 1998. lib. bdg. (978-0-7787-0070-8(4)); Who Settled the West? 1999. lib. bdg. (978-0-7787-0075-3(5)); Women of the West. Lewis, Jane. 1999. lib. bdg. (978-0-7787-0080-7(1)); 32p. (J). (gr. 3-4). (Illus.). 1999. (978-0-7787-0066-1(6)); Set pap. (978-0-7787-0098-2(4)) Crabtree Publishing Co.

—Life on the Trail. 1998. (Life in the Old West Ser.). (Illus.). 32p. (J). (gr. 3-4). pap. (978-0-7787-0104-0(2)) Crabtree Publishing Co.

—A Visual Dictionary of the Old West. 2007. (Visual Dictionaries Ser.). (Illus.). 32p. (J). (gr. 1-7). pap. ***(978-0-7787-3523-6(0))*** Crabtree Publishing Co.

—Wagon Train. 1999. (gr. 3-6). lib. bdg. 16.40 (978-0-613-12241-2(0)) Tandem Library Bks.

—Who Settled the West. 1999. (gr. 3-6). lib. bdg. 16.40 (978-0-613-12276-4(3)) Tandem Library Bks.

Keating, Susan K. Women of the West. 2002. (History of the Old West Ser.). (Illus.). 64p. (YA). (gr. 5 up). lib. bdg. (978-1-59084-069-6(0)) Mason Crest Pubs.

Kimmel, Elizabeth Cody. As Far as the Eye Can Reach: Lewis & Clark's Westward Quest. 2005. (Illus.). 119p. (YA). (gr. 4-8). reprint ed. 5.00 (978-0-7567-9660-0(1)) DIANE Publishing Co.

King, David C. AmericanHeritage American Voices Westward Expansion. 2003. (American Heritage, American Voices Ser.). (Illus.). 144p. 22.95 (978-0-471-44394-0(8) , Wiley) Wiley, John & Sons, Inc.

Kline, Trish. Lewis & Clark. 2002. (Discover the Life of an Explorer Ser.). (Illus.). 24p. (gr. 2-5). 14.95 (978-1-58952-067-7(X)) Rourke Publishing, LLC.

Klobuchar, Lisa. The History & Activities of the Wagon Trail. 2004. (Hands-On American History Ser.). (Illus.). 32p. (J). pap. (978-1-4034-6062-2(0)) Heinemann Library.

—History & Activities of the Wagon Trail. 2004. (Hands-On American History Ser.). (Illus.). 32p. (J). 27.07 (978-1-4034-6055-4(8)) Heinemann Library.

Landau, Elaine. The Homestead Act. 2006. 48p. (gr. 3-5). (YA). pap. 6.95 (978-0-516-27902-5(7)); (Illus.). (J). 25.00 (978-0-516-25870-6(2)) Scholastic Library Publishing. (Children's Pr.).

—The Mormon Trail. 2006. 48p. (gr. 3-5). (YA). pap. 6.95 (978-0-516-27904-6(1)); (Illus.). (J). 25.00 (978-0-516-25872-0(9)) Scholastic Library Publishing. (Children's Pr.).

Langellier, J. Phillip. Sound the Charge: The U. S. Cavalry in the American West, 1861-1916. 1999. (G. I. Ser.). (Illus.). 80p. (YA). (gr. 5 up). 27.50 (978-0-7910-5376-8(6) , Chelsea Hse.) Facts On File, Inc.

Langley, Andrew. 100 Things You Should Know about the Wild West. 2003. (Illus.). 48p. (J). (gr. 3 up). lib. bdg. (978-1-59084-458-8(0)) Mason Crest Pubs.

Life on a Wagon Train. (Rosen Real Readers Big Bookstm Ser.). 16p. (J). (gr. 2-3). 38.75 (978-1-4042-6224-9(5)) Rosen Publishing Group, Inc., The.

Lightfoot, D. J. Trail Fever: The Life of a Texas Cowboy. Bobbish, John, illus. exp. ed. 2003. 88p. (J). (gr. 3 up). pap. 12.95 (978-0-9728768-0-3(4)) Seven Rivers Publishing.

Lilly, Melinda. Sacagawea, Lewis, & Clark. 2003. (Rourke Discovery Library). (Illus.). 24p. (gr. 1-4). 14.95 (978-1-58952-362-3(8)) Rourke Publishing, LLC.

Littlefield, Holly. Children of the Trail West. 1999. (Picture the American Past Ser.). (Illus.). 48p. (gr. 2-5). lib. bdg. 22.60 (978-1-57505-304-2(7)) Lerner Publishing Group.

Loeper, John J. Meet the Wards on the Oregon Trail. 1998. (Early American Family Ser.). (Illus.). 64p. (J). (gr. 2-4). lib. bdg. 25.64 (978-0-7614-0844-4(4) , Benchmark Bks.) Cavendish, Marshall Corp.

Lourie, Peter. On the Trail of Sacagawea. 2003. (Exploration Ser.). (Illus.). 48p. (J). (gr. 4-6). 18.95 (978-1-56397-840-1(7)) Boyds Mills Pr.

Marsh, Carole. Lewis & Clark Go on a Hike. 2003. 32p. (J). (gr. 3-8). pap. 5.95 (978-0-635-02122-9(6)) Gallopade International.

Maynard, Charles W. Jim Bridger: Frontiersman & Mountain Guide. 2003. (Famous Explorers of the American West Ser.). (Illus.). 24p. (J). lib. bdg. 18.75 (978-0-8239-6288-4(1) , PowerKids Pr.) Rosen Publishing Group, Inc., The.

—John Charles Fremont: The Pathfinder. 2003. (Famous Explorers of the American West Ser.). (Illus.). 24p. (J). lib. bdg. 18.75 (978-0-8239-6289-1(X) , PowerKids Pr.) Rosen Publishing Group, Inc., The.

—Zebulon Pike: Soldier Explorer of the American Southwest. 2003. (Famous Explorers of the American West Ser.). (Illus.). 24p. (J). lib. bdg. 18.75 (978-0-8239-6286-0(5) , PowerKids Pr.) Rosen Publishing Group, Inc., The.

McCall, Edith. Adventures of Cowboys on Cattle Drivers, Vol. 5. 2001. (Adventures on the American Frontiers Ser.). (Illus.). 127p. (J). (gr. 3-7). pap. 9.99 (978-0-89824-306-2(8) , 306-8) Royal Fireworks Publishing Co.

McCormick, Lisa Wade. Lewis & Clark. 2006. 32p. (YA). (gr. 1-2). pap. 4.95 (978-0-516-21443-6(8) , Children's Pr.) Scholastic Library Publishing.

McPherson, James M. Into the West: From Reconstruction to the Final Days of the American Frontier. 2006. 96p. (J). (gr. 4-9). 22.95 (978-0-689-86543-5(0) , Atheneum) Simon & Schuster Children's Publishing.

Mercati, Cynthia. The Pony Express. 2000. (Cover-to-Cover Bks.). (Illus.). 56p. (J). pap. (978-0-7891-5041-7(7)); (gr. 1-4). lib. bdg. 16.95 (978-0-7807-9012-4(X)) Perfection Learning Corp.

Merchant, Peter. Cowboys. 2002. (Illus.). 16p. (J). pap. (978-0-439-35103-4(0)) Scholastic, Inc.

Miller, Steven G. The Legend of Jessie James. 2001. (History Channel History Guides Ser.). (Illus.). 40p. (J). pap. 9.99 (978-0-86730-845-7(1)) Lebhar-Friedman Bks.

Monceaux, Morgan & Katcher, Ruth. My Heroes, My People: African Americans & Native Americans in Thewest. Monceaux, Morgan, illus. 2004. (Illus.). 63p. (J). (gr. k-4). reprint ed. 18.00 (978-0-7567-7868-2(9)) DIANE Publishing Co.

Nelson, Sharlene P. & Nelson, Ted W. Jedediah Smith. 2004. (Watts Library). (Illus.). 64p. (J). 25.50 (978-0-531-12287-7(5) , Watts, Franklin) Scholastic Library Publishing.

Nobleman, Marc Tyler. Cowboy. 2007. (J). ***(*978-1-4109-2961-7(2));*** pap. ***(*978-1-4109-2982-2(5))*** Steck-Vaughn.

The Oregon Trail, 6 Packs. (On Deck Ser.: Vol. 2). 24p. (gr. 4-5). 35.00 (978-0-7578-5813-0(9)) Rigby Education.

The Overland Trail: Individual Title Six-Packs. (On Deck Ser.: Vol. 2). 24p. (gr. 4-5). 35.00 (978-0-7578-5814-7(7)) Rigby Education.

Patent, Dorothy Hinshaw. Homesteading: Settling America's Heartland. Munoz, William, photos by. 1998. (Illus.). 32p. (J). (gr. 2-5). lib. bdg. 17.85 (978-0-8027-8665-4(0)); (gr. 3-7). 16.95 (978-0-8027-8664-7(2)) Walker & Co.

—The Lewis & Clark Trail: Then & Now. Munoz, William, photos by. 2006. (Illus.). 60p. (J). (gr. 4-8). reprint ed. 20.00 (978-1-4223-5732-3(5)) DIANE Publishing Co.

Patrick, Bethanne Kelly. Forts of the West. 2002. (History of the Old West Ser.). (Illus.). 64p. (YA). (gr. 5 up). lib. bdg. (978-1-59084-071-9(2)) Mason Crest Pubs.

Penn, Sarah. Nat Love: African American Cowboy. 2003. (Famous People in American History Ser.). (Illus.). 32p. (J). pap. (978-0-8239-4188-9(4)) Rosen Publishing Group, Inc., The.

Petrie, Kristin. John C. Fremont. 2004. (Explorers Ser.). (Illus.). 32p. (J). (gr. k-6). lib. bdg. 22.78 (978-1-59197-602-8(2) , Checkerboard Library) ABDO Publishing Co.

Porterfield, Jason. The Homestead ACT of 1862. 2005. (Illus.). 64p. (J). (gr. 5-8). lib. bdg. 29.25 (978-1-4042-0178-1(5)) Rosen Publishing Group, Inc., The.

Price Hossell, Karen. John C. Fremont. (Groundbreakers Ser.). (Illus.). 48p. (J). 2003. (gr. 5-7). lib. bdg. 27.07 (978-1-4034-0244-8(2)); 2002. pap. 8.50 (978-1-4034-0480-0(1)) Heinemann Library.

Price, Sean. Crooks, Cowboys, & Characters: The Wild West. 2007. (J). ***(*978-1-4109-2695-1(8));*** pap. ***(*978-1-4109-2706-4(7))*** Steck-Vaughn.

Price, Sean. The Dirty Thirties: Documenting the Dust Bowl. 2006. (American History Through Primary Sources Ser.). (Illus.). 32p. (J). (978-1-4109-2416-2(5)); pap. (978-1-4109-2427-8(0)) Steck-Vaughn.

Raabe, Emily. Pioneers: Life as a Homesteader. 2003. (Reading Power Ser.). (Illus.). 24p. (J). lib. bdg. 17.25 (978-0-8239-6498-7(1) , PowerKids Pr.) Rosen Publishing Group, Inc., The.

Radevsky, Anton. The Wild West Pop-Up Book. 2007. (Illus.). 8p. (gr. 3-7). 24.95 ***(*978-1-4027-4628-4(8))*** Sterling Publishing Co., Inc.

Randolph, Ryan P. Black Cowboys. 2003. (Library of the Westward Expansion). (Illus.). 24p. (J). lib. bdg. 19.95 (978-0-8239-6294-5(6)) Rosen Publishing Group, Inc., The.

—Frontier Women Who Helped Shape the American West. 2003. (Library of the Westward Expansion). (Illus.). 24p. (J). lib. bdg. 19.95 (978-0-8239-6297-6(0) , PowerKids Pr.) Rosen Publishing Group, Inc., The.

—Wild West Lawmen & Outlaws. 2003. (Library of the Westward Expansion). (Illus.). 24p. (J). lib. bdg. 19.95 (978-0-8239-6293-8(8) , PowerKids Pr.) Rosen Publishing Group, Inc., The.

Raum, Elizabeth. Wild West Legends. 2007. (J). ***(*978-1-4109-2968-6(X));*** pap. ***(*978-1-4109-2989-1(2))*** Steck-Vaughn.

Ray, Deborah Kogan. Down the Colorado: The Story of John Wesley Powell, the One-Armed Explorer. 2007. (Illus.). 48p. (J). (gr. 3 up). 17.00 (978-0-374-31838-3(7)) Farrar, Straus & Giroux.

Reece, Paula. Settling the West: Adventures in Pioneering & Westward Expansion. 2002. (Skill-Based Reading Anthology Ser.). (Illus.). 124p. (978-0-7891-5582-5(6)) Perfection Learning Corp.

Riddle, John. The Pony Express. 2002. (History of the Old West Ser.). (Illus.). 64p. (YA). (gr. 5 up). lib. bdg. (978-1-59084-061-0(5)) Mason Crest Pubs.

Robinson, J. Dennis. Jesse James: Legendary Rebel & Outlaw. 2006. (J). (978-0-7565-1871-4(7)) Compass Point Bks.

Ross, Michael Elsohn. Exploring the Earth with John Wesley Powell. Smith, Wendy, illus. 2006. 48p. (J). (gr. 4-10). reprint ed. 19.00 (978-1-4223-5581-7(0)) DIANE Publishing Co.

Saffer, Barbara. The California Gold Rush. 2002. (History of the Old West Ser.). (Illus.). 64p. (J). (gr. 5-7). lib. bdg. (978-1-59084-060-3(7)) Mason Crest Pubs.

—Life on the Reservation. 2002. (History of the Old West Ser.). (Illus.). 64p. (J). (gr. 5 up). lib. bdg. (978-1-59084-070-2(4)) Mason Crest Pubs.

Sakurai, Gail. Asian-Americans in the Old West. 2000. (Cornerstones of Freedom Ser.). (Illus.). 32p. (J). (gr. 4). pap. 5.95 (978-0-516-27035-7(4) , Children's Pr.) Scholastic Library Publishing.

Sandler, Martin W. Cowboys. 2000. (Library of Congress Classics). (Illus.). 96p. (J). (gr. 3 up). pap. 10.95 (978-0-06-446745-2(7) , Harper Trophy) HarperCollins Pubs.

—Cowboys. 1999. (Illus.). (J). (978-0-606-18685-8(9)) Tandem Library Bks.

Sanford, Carl R. & Sanford, William R. Outlaws & Lawmen of the Wild West, 10 bks., Set. (Illus.). (YA). (gr. 4-10). lib. bdg. 169.50 (978-0-89490-391-5(8)) Enslow Pubs., Inc.

Sanford, William R. The Chisholm Trail in American History. 2000. (Illus.). 112p. (YA). (gr. 5-12). lib. bdg. 26.60 (978-0-7660-1345-2(6)) Enslow Pubs., Inc.

Schaefer, Ted. Westward to the Pacific. 2006. (Making a New Nation Ser.). (Illus.). 48p. (J). (978-1-4034-7829-0(5)); pap. (978-1-4034-7836-8(8)) Heinemann Library.

Schlissel, Lillian. Black Frontiers. 2000. (Illus.). 80p. (J). (gr. 3-7). pap. 7.99 (978-0-689-83315-1(6) , Aladdin) Simon & Schuster Children's Publishing.

—Black Frontiers: A History of African American Heroes in the Old West. 2000. (gr. 3-6). lib. bdg. 16.45 (978-0-613-21229-8(0)); (Illus.). (J). 14.79 (978-0-606-17914-0(3)) Tandem Library Bks.

Sinnott, Susan. Welcome to Kirsten's World, 1854: Growing up in Pioneer America. 1999. (American Girls Collection). (Illus.). 64p. (J). (gr. 2 up). 16.95 (978-1-56247-770-7(6)) American Girl Publishing, Inc.

Sioux, Tracee. Immigrants & the Westward Expansion. 2004. (Primary Sources of Immigration & Migration in America Ser.). (Illus.). 24p. (J). lib. bdg. 19.95 (978-0-8239-6824-4(3) , PowerKids Pr.) Rosen Publishing Group, Inc., The.

Sonneborn, Liz. The Mormon Trail. 2005. (Watts Library). (Illus.). 63p. (J). (gr. 5-8). 25.50 (978-0-531-12317-1(0) , Watts, Franklin) Scholastic Library Publishing.

—Women of the American West. 2005. (Watts Library). (Illus.). 63p. (J). (gr. k-7). 25.50 (978-0-531-12318-8(9) , Watts, Franklin) Scholastic Library Publishing.

Souza, Dorothy M. John C. Fremont. 2004. (Watts Library). (Illus.). 64p. (J). (gr. 5-7). pap. 8.95 (978-0-531-16652-9(X) , Watts, Franklin) Scholastic Library Publishing.

—John Wesley Powell. 2004. (Watts Library). (Illus.). 64p. (J). (gr. 5-7). pap. 8.95 (978-0-531-16653-6(8) , Watts, Franklin) Scholastic Library Publishing.

Staeger, Rob. The Boom Towns. 2002. (History of the Old West Ser.). (Illus.). 64p. (YA). (gr. 5 up). lib. bdg. (978-1-59084-068-9(2)) Mason Crest Pubs.

Steele, Christy. Famous Wagon Trails. 2005. (Illus.). 48p. (J). pap. (978-0-8368-5795-5(X)); lib. bdg. 30.00 (978-0-8368-5788-7(7)) Stevens, Gareth Inc. (World Almanac Library).

—Pioneer Life in the American West. 2005. (Illus.). 48p. (J). pap. (978-0-8368-5797-9(6)); lib. bdg. 30.00 (978-0-8368-5790-0(9)) Stevens, Gareth Inc. (World Almanac Library).

Stefoff, Rebecca. Texas & the Far West. 2002. (North American Historical Atlases Ser.). (Illus.). 48p. (J). 27.07 (978-0-7614-1345-5(6) , Benchmark Bks.) Cavendish, Marshall Corp.

—The Wild West. 2006. (American Voices Ser.). (Illus.). 111p. (J). lib. bdg. 37.07 (978-0-7614-2170-2(X) , Benchmark Bks.) Cavendish, Marshall Corp.

Stone, Lynn M. Bison. 2003. (Animals in U.S. History Ser.). (Illus.). 24p. (J). 25.64 (978-1-58952-698-3(8)) Rourke Publishing, LLC.

—Mustang. 2003. (Animals in U.S. History Ser.). (Illus.). 24p. (J). 25.64 (978-1-58952-700-3(3)) Rourke Publishing, LLC.

Stotter, Mike. The Wild West. 1999. (Single Subject References Ser.). (Illus.). 64p. (J). (gr. 4-8). pap. 10.95 (978-0-7534-5249-3(9) , Kingfisher) Houghton Mifflin Co. Trade & Reference Div.

—Wild West. 1999. (gr. 3-6). lib. bdg. 19.90 (978-0-613-86949-2(4)) Tandem Library Bks.

Suen, Anastasia. Trappers & Mountain Men. 2007. (Events in American History Ser.). (Illus.). 48p. (J). (gr. 4-6). lib. bdg. 29.93 (978-1-60044-134-9(3)) Rourke Publishing, LLC.

Sullivan, George E. Lewis & Clark. 2000. (In Their Own Words Ser.). (Illus.). 128p. (J). (gr. 4-7). pap. 4.99 (978-0-439-09553-2(0)); pap. 12.95 (978-0-439-14749-1(2)) Scholastic, Inc.

Sundling, Charles W. Explorers of the Frontier. 2000. (Frontier Land Ser.). (Illus.). 32p. (J). (gr. 3-8). lib. bdg. 24.21 (978-1-57765-044-7(1) , ABDO & Daughters) ABDO Publishing Co.

—Mountain Men of the Frontier. 2000. (Frontier Land Ser.). (Illus.). 32p. (J). (gr. 3-8). lib. bdg. 24.21 (978-1-57765-043-0(3) , ABDO & Daughters) ABDO Publishing Co.

—Pioneers of the Frontier. 2000. (Frontier Land Ser.). (Illus.). 32p. (J). (gr. 3-8). lib. bdg. 24.21 (978-1-57765-047-8(6) , ABDO & Daughters) ABDO Publishing Co.

Thompson, Linda. The Mississippi & the West. 2004. (Expansion of America Ser.). 48p. pap. 7.95 (978-1-59515-327-2(6)) Rourke Publishing, LLC.

Torr, James D. Westward Expansion. 2002. (gr. 7-12). lib. bdg. 33.25 (978-0-613-73610-7(9)) Tandem Library Bks.

Torr, James D., ed. Westward Expansion. 2003. (Interpreting American History Through Primary Documents Ser.x). (Illus.). 208p. (J). 32.45 (978-0-7377-1134-9(5) , Greenhaven Pr., Inc.) Thomson Gale.

Two-Can Publishing Ltd. Staff & Martin, Alex. The Trail West. 2004. (Picture That! Ser.). (Illus.). 64p. (gr. 3 up). 19.95 (978-1-58728-442-7(1) , Two Can Publishing) T&N Children's Publishing.

Uschan, Michael V. A Mountain Man of the American Frontier. 2005. (Working Life Ser.). (Illus.). 111p. (J). (gr. 5-8). lib. bdg. 29.95 (978-1-59018-582-5(7) , Lucent Bks.) Thomson Gale.

Wadsworth, Ginger. Words West: The Voices of Young Pioneers. 2003. (Illus.). 208p. (J). (gr. 5-9). tchr. ed. 18.00 (978-0-618-23475-2(6) , Clarion Bks.) Houghton Mifflin Co. Trade & Reference Div.

Walker, Paul Robert. True Tales of the Wild West. 2002. (Illus.). 128p. (J). (gr. 3). 17.95 (978-0-7922-8218-1(3) , National Geographic Children's Bks.) National Geographic Society.

Warren, Andrea. The Orphan Train Rider: One Boy's True Story. 1998. (Illus.). 80p. (J). (gr. 4-6). pap. 8.95 (978-0-395-91362-8(4)) Houghton Mifflin Co. Trade & Reference Div.

Williams, Jean Kinney. The Pony Express, 2002. (We the People Ser.). (Illus.). 48p. (J). (gr. 4 up). lib. bdg. 22.60 (978-0-7565-0301-7(9)) Compass Point Bks.

Witteman, Barbara. John Charles Fremont: Western Pathfinder. 2002. (Let Freedom Ring Ser.). (Illus.). 48p. (J). (gr. 3-4). lib. bdg. 22.60 (978-0-7368-1348-8(9) , Bridgestone Bks.) Capstone Pr., Inc.

—Zebulon Pike: Soldier & Explorer. 2002. (Let Freedom Ring Ser.). (Illus.). 48p. (J). (gr. 3-4). lib. bdg. 22.60 (978-0-7368-1351-8(9) , Bridgestone Bks.) Capstone Pr., Inc.

Wittmann, Kelly. Explorers of the American West. 2002. (Exploration & Discovery Ser.). (Illus.). 64p. (YA). (gr. 5 up). lib. bdg. (978-1-59084-049-8(6)) Mason Crest Pubs.

WEST INDIES

Duhgam, P. Island Hopping with Anancy. 24p. (978-976-8184-11-5(6)) LMH Publishing, Ltd.

Hernandez, Romel. Caribbean Islands: Facts & Figures. 2003. (Discovering the Caribbean Ser.). (Illus.). 64p. (J). (gr. 5 up). lib. bdg. (978-1-59084-308-6(8)) Mason Crest Pubs.

Kozleski, Lisa. The Leeward Islands: Anguilla, St. Martin, St. Barts, St. Eustatius, St. Kitts, Nevis, Antigua, Barbuda, & Montserrat. 2003. (Discovering the Caribbean Ser.). (Illus.). 64p. (J). (gr. 5 up). lib. bdg. (978-1-59084-307-9(X)) Mason Crest Pubs.

Kras, Sara Louise. Antigua & Barbuda. 2007. (Cultures of the World Ser.). (J). lib. bdg. ***(*978-0-7614-2570-0(5) ,*** Benchmark Bks.) Cavendish, Marshall Corp.

Orr, Tamra. The Windward Islands. 2003. (Discovering the Caribbean Ser.). (Illus.). 64p. (J). (gr. 5 up). lib. bdg. (978-1-59084-305-5(3)) Mason Crest Pubs.

Spenceley, Angela. Virgin Islands Coloring Book. 2006. (Illus.). 24p. (J). 2.00 net. (978-0-9778913-9-9(9)) Coconut Pr., LLC.

WEST INDIES—FICTION

Berry, Connie Lee. The Criminal in the Caymans. 2007. (Incredible Journey Bks.). 85p. (J). pap. 3.95 ***(*978-0-9772848-0-1(8))*** Kid's Fun Pr.

Collison, Linda. Star-Crossed. 2006. (Illus.). 416p. (YA). (gr. 9). 16.95 (978-0-375-83363-2(3)); lib. bdg. 18.99 (978-0-375-93363-9(8)) Random Hse. Children's Bks. (Knopf Bks. for Young Readers).

Francis, Claudia Elizabeth Ruth. Island Issues. 2003. 196p. per. 15.00 net. (978-1-931934-18-3(5)) Back Yard Pub.

Gershator, Phillis. Tiny & Bigman. Cravath, Lynne W., illus. 1999. (Accelerated Reader Bks.). 32p. (J). (gr. k-3). 15.95 (978-0-7614-5044-3(0) , Cavendish Children's Bks.) Cavendish, Marshall Corp.

Rahaman, Vashanti. O Christmas Tree. Lessac, Frane, illus. 2003. 32p. (J). (gr. 2-4). 14.95 (978-1-56397-237-9(9)) Boyds Mills Pr.

San Souci, Robert D. Faithful Friend. 1999. (gr. 3-6). lib. bdg. 15.30 (978-0-613-11526-1(0)) Tandem Library Bks.

WEST INDIES—HISTORY

Longman Publishing Staff. The People Who Came, Bk. 1. Date not set. (Illus.). 92p. pap. 9.95 (978-0-582-76648-8(6)) Addison-Wesley Longman, Ltd. GBR. *Dist:* Trans-Atlantic Pubns., Inc.

Vamos a Series, 4 bks., Set. Incl. Vamos a Colombia. Fox, Mary Virginia. 2001. lib. bdg. 21.36 (978-1-57572-382-2(4)); Vamos a Costa Rica. Fox, Mary Virginia. 2000. lib. bdg. 21.36 (978-1-57572-383-9(2)); Vamos a Cuba. Gillis, Jennifer & Schreier, Alta. 2001. lib. bdg. 21.36 (978-1-57572-384-6(0)); Vamos a Puerto Rico. Manning, Ruth. 2000. lib. bdg. 21.36 (978-1-57572-385-3(9)); (J). (gr. k-2). (SPA., Illus.). 32p. 2000. Set lib. bdg. 85.44 (978-1-58810-145-7(2)) Heinemann Library.

WEST POINT (MILITARY ACADEMY)

see United States Military Academy

WEST VIRGINIA

Brown, Jonatha A. West Virginia. 2006. (Portraits of the States Ser.). (J). pap. (978-0-8368-4728-4(8)); lib. bdg. (978-0-8368-4711-6(3)) Stevens, Gareth Inc.

Cribben, Patrick. Uniquely West Virginia. 2004. (Heinemann State Studies). (Illus.). 48p. (J). (ps-k). lib. bdg. 31.36 (978-1-4034-4665-7(2)); pap. 9.00 (978-1-4034-4734-0(9)) Heinemann Library.

DiPiazza, Domenica. West Virginia. 2nd rev. exp. ed. (Hello U. S. A. Ser.). (Illus.). 84p. (J). (gr. 3-6). 2003. pap. 6.95 (978-0-8225-4141-7(6)); 2002. 25.26 (978-0-8225-4068-7(1) , Lerner Pubns.) Lerner Publishing Group.

Fazio, Wende. West Virginia. 2000. (America the Beautiful, Second Ser.). (J). (978-0-516-15951-5(8) , Children's Pr.) Scholastic Library Publishing.

Feeney, Kathy. West Virginia Facts & Symbols. (States & Their Symbols Ser.). 24p. (J). 2000. (Illus.). (gr. 2-3). lib. bdg. 18.60 (978-0-7368-0528-5(1) , Bridgestone Bks.); 2003. lib. bdg. 19.93 (978-0-7368-2279-4(8)) Capstone Pr., Inc.

Fein, E. How to Draw West Virginias Sights & Symbols. 2002. (Kids Guide to Drawing America Ser.). 32p. (J). lib. bdg. 25.25 (978-0-8239-6105-4(2) , PowerKids Pr.) Rosen Publishing Group, Inc., The.

Fontes, Justine & Fontes, Ron. West Virginia: The Mountain State. 2003. (World Almanac Library of the States). (Illus.). 48p. (J). (gr. 5 up). pap. 14.95 (978-0-8368-5334-6(2)); lib. bdg. 30.00 (978-0-8368-5163-2(3)) Stevens, Gareth Inc. (World Almanac Library).

Fradin, Dennis Brindell. West Virginia. 1998. (From Sea to Shining Sea Ser.). (Illus.). 64p. (J). (gr. 3-5). pap. 7.95 (978-0-516-26283-3(1) , Children's Pr.) Scholastic Library Publishing.

Heinrichs, Ann. West Virginia. Kania, Matt, illus. 2005. (Welcome to the USA Ser.). 40p. (J). (gr. 1-5). 27.07 (978-1-59296-490-1(7)) Child's World, Inc.

—West Virginia. 2003. (This Land Is Your Land Ser.). (Illus.). 48p. (J). (gr. 3 up). lib. bdg. 22.60 (978-0-7565-0351-2(5)) Compass Point Bks.

Hoffman, Nancy. West Virginia. 1998. (Celebrate the States Ser.). (Illus.). 144p. (gr. 4-8). lib. bdg. 37.07 (978-0-7614-0665-5(4) , Benchmark Bks.) Cavendish, Marshall Corp.

Hoffman, Nancy & Hart, Joyce. West Virginia. 2nd ed. 2007. (Celebrate the States Ser.). (J). lib. bdg. 39.93 (***978-0-7614-2562-5(4)*** , Benchmark Bks.) Cavendish, Marshall Corp.

Kummer, Patricia K. West Virginia. rev. ed. 2002. (One Nation Ser.). (Illus.). 48p. (J). (gr. 3-4). lib. bdg. 22.60 (978-0-7368-1274-0(1) , Bridgestone Bks.) Capstone Pr., Inc.

Labella, Susan. West Virginia. 2006. (Rookie Read-About Geography Ser.). (Illus.). 32p. (J). (gr. 1-2). 20.50 (978-0-516-24994-0(0) , Children's Pr.) Scholastic Library Publishing.

Lawton, Val. A Guide to West Virginia. 2001. (American States Ser.). (Illus.). 32p. (J). lib. bdg. 16.95 (978-1-930954-58-8(1)); per. 7.95 (978-1-930954-02-1(6)) Weigl Pubs., Inc.

Marsh, Carole. The Big West Virginia Reproducible Activity Book. 2001. (Carole Marsh West Virginia Bks.). (Illus.). 96p. (J). (gr. 2-6). per. 9.95 (978-0-7933-9961-1(0)) Gallopade International.

—My First Book about West Virginia. Line Art Staff, illus. 2001. (West Virginia Experience! Ser.). 32p. (J). (gr. k-4). pap. 7.95 (978-0-7933-9903-1(3)) Gallopade International.

—The Survivor: A Class Challenge. 2001. (West Virginia Experience! Ser.). lib. bdg. 29.95 (978-0-635-00694-3(4)) Gallopade International.

—West Virginia Classic Christmas Trivia. 2002. (Carole Marsh West Virginia Bks.). (Illus.). 32p. pap. 6.95 (978-0-635-01461-0(0) , 14610); lib. bdg. 21.95 (978-0-635-01462-7(9) , 14629) Gallopade International. (Marsh, Carole Bks.).

—West Virginia Current Events Projects: 30 Cool, Activities, Crafts, Experiments & More for Kids to Do to Learn about Your State! 2003. (West Virginia Experience Ser.). 32p. (gr. k-8). pap. 5.95 (978-0-635-02067-3(X) , Marsh, Carole Bks.) Gallopade International.

—The West Virginia Experience Pocket Guide. 2001. (Carole Marsh West Virginia Bks.). (Illus.). 96p. (J). (gr. 3-8). pap. 6.95 (978-0-7933-9932-1(7)) Gallopade International.

—West Virginia Government Projects: 30 Cool, Activities, Crafts, Experiments & More for Kids to Do to Learn about Your State! 2003. (West Virginia Experience Ser.). 32p. (gr. k-5). pap. 5.95 (978-0-635-01967-7(1) , Marsh, Carole Bks.) Gallopade International.

—West Virginia Hot Zones! Viruses, Diseases, & Epidemics in Our State's History. 1998. (Hot Zones! Ser.). (Illus.). (J). (gr. 3-12). pap. 19.95 (978-0-7933-8973-5(9)); lib. bdg. 29.95 (978-0-7933-8972-8(0)) Gallopade International.

—West Virginia Jeopardy! Answers & Questions about Our State! Line Art Staff, illus. 2001. 32p. (J). (gr. 3-8). pap. 7.95 (978-0-7933-9816-4(9)) Gallopade International.

—West Virginia Jography. 2001. (Carole Marsh West Virginia Bks.). 32p. (J). (gr. 3-8). pap. 7.95 (978-0-7933-9845-4(2)) Gallopade International.

—West Virginia Millionaire. 2001. (GameBook Ser.). (Illus.). 32p. (J). (gr. 3-8). pap., act. bk. ed. 9.95 (978-0-635-00112-2(8)) Gallopade International.

—West Virginia People Projects: 30 Cool, Activities, Crafts, Experiments & More for Kids to Do to Learn about Your State! 2003. (West Virginia Experience Ser.). 32p. (gr. k-5). pap. 5.95 (978-0-635-02017-8(3) , Marsh, Carole Bks.) Gallopade International.

—West Virginia Survivor. 2001. (GameBook Ser.). (Illus.). 32p. (J). (gr. 3-8). pap., act. bk. ed. 9.95 (978-0-635-00569-4(7)) Gallopade International.

—West Virginia Symbols & Facts Projects: 30 Cool, Activities, Crafts, Experiments & More for Kids to Do to Learn about Your State! 2003. (West Virginia Experience Ser.). 32p. (gr. k-5). pap. 5.95 (978-0-635-01917-2(5) , Marsh, Carole Bks.) Gallopade International.

—West Virginia Wheel of Fortune. 2001. (GameBook Ser.). (Illus.). 32p. (J). (gr. 3-8). pap., act. bk. ed. 9.95 (978-0-635-00012-5(1)) Gallopade International.

—Wheel of Fortune. 2001. (Carole Marsh West Virginia Bks.). lib. bdg. 29.95 (978-0-635-00013-2(X) , Marsh, Carole Bks.) Gallopade International.

Murray, Julie. West Virginia. 2006. (Buddy Book Ser.). (Illus.). 32p. (J). (gr. k-4). lib. bdg. 22.78 (978-1-59197-707-0(X) , Buddy Bks.) ABDO Publishing Co.

Petreycik, Rick. West Virginia. 2007. (J). (***978-0-7614-2216-7(1)***) Cavendish, Marshall Bks., Ltd.

Riehle, Mary Ann McCabe. M Is for Mountain State: A West Virginia Alphabet. Bryant, Laura J., illus. 2004. (State Ser.). 40p. (J). 17.95 (978-1-58536-151-9(8)) Sleeping Bear Pr.

Somervill, Barbara A. West Virginia. 2003. (From Sea to Shining Sea Ser.: 2). (Illus.). 80p. (J). 30.50 (978-0-516-22389-6(5) , Children's Pr.) Scholastic Library Publishing.

Teets, Ashley Catherine. West Virginia State Government: A Kid's View. 2000. (Illus.). 32p. (J). (gr. 2-10). pap. 4.95 (978-0-929915-27-2(5)) Headline Bks., Inc.

WEST VIRGINIA—FICTION

Baker, Julie. Up Molasses Mountain. 2002. 224p. (YA). (gr. 7). lib. bdg. 17.99 (978-0-385-90048-5(1) , Lamb, Wendy) Random Hse. Children's Bks.

Bryant, Louella. Father by Blood. 1999. (Illus.). 160p. (YA). (gr. 6-8). pap. 12.95 (978-1-881535-33-1(9)) New England Pr., Inc., The.

Cabot, Meg. Project Princess. 2003. (Princess Diaries: Vol. 4 1/2). 64p. (J). (gr. 7 up). pap. 2.99 (978-0-06-057131-3(4)) HarperCollins Pubs.

—Project Princess. 2003. (Princess Diaries: Vol. 4 1/2). (gr. 7-12). lib. bdg. 10.65 (978-0-613-67515-4(0)) Tandem Library Bks.

Dell, Pamela. Aquila's Drinking Gourd: A Story of the Underground Railroad. 2002. (Scrapbooks of America Ser.). (Illus.). 48p. (J). (gr. 2-6). 28.50 (978-1-59187-013-5(5)) Child's World, Inc.

Durrant, Lynda. Betsy Zane, the Rose of Fort Henry. 2000. 208p. (J). (gr. 5-9). tchr. ed. 15.00 (978-0-395-97899-3(8) , Clarion Bks.) Houghton Mifflin Co. Trade & Reference Div.

Faine, Edward Allan. Little Ned Stories. Waites, Joan C., illus. 1999. 128p. (J). (gr. k-3). pap. 9.99 (978-0-9654651-5-1(2)) IM Pr.

—More Little Ned Stories. 2003. 112p. (J). pap. 6.95 (978-0-9716911-2-4(6)) IM Pr.

Hahn, Mary Downing. Witch Catcher. 2006. 240p. (J). (gr. 4-6). 16.00 (978-0-618-50457-2(5) , Clarion Bks.) Houghton Mifflin Co. Trade & Reference Div.

Hedrick, Helen Groves. Baas on the Bus. 2000. (J). 12.00 (978-0-8059-5003-8(6)) Dorrance Publishing Co., Inc.

Hickam, Homer H., Jr. October Sky. 1999. Orig. Title: Rocket Boys. (gr. 7-12). lib. bdg. 15.90 (978-0-613-16784-0(8)) Tandem Library Bks.

Kay, Alan N. On the Trail of John Brown's Body. 2001. (Young Heroes of History Ser.: Vol. 2). (Illus.). 175p. (J). (gr. 4-7). pap. 5.95 (978-1-57249-239-4(2) , 1572492406, Burd Street Pr.) White Mane Publishing Co., Inc.

Laskas, Gretchen Moran. The Miner's Daughter. 2007. 256p. (YA). 15.99 (978-1-4169-1262-0(2)) Simon & Schuster Children's Publishing.

Naylor, Phyllis Reynolds. Saving Shiloh. 144p. (J). 1999. (Shiloh Ser.: No. 3). (gr. 4-7). reprint ed. pap. 5.99 (978-0-689-81461-7(5)); 2nd ed. 2006. (Illus.). (gr. 3-7). pap. 5.99 (978-1-4169-1422-8(6)) Simon & Schuster Children's Publishing. (Aladdin).

—Saving Shiloh. 1999. (978-0-606-14310-3(6)); (Shiloh Ser.: No. 3). (J). (gr. 3-6). lib. bdg. 13.55 (978-0-613-12073-9(6)) Tandem Library Bks.

—Saving Shiloh. l.t. ed. 2002. 193p. (J). 22.95 (978-0-7862-3713-5(9)) Thorndike Pr.

—Shiloh. (SPA.). 146p. (YA). (gr. 5-8). (978-968-16-5805-2(1) , FC0086) Fondo de Cultura Economica MEX. *Dist:* Lectorum Pubns., Inc.

—Shiloh. l.t. ed. 2000. (Shiloh Ser.: No. 1). 155p. (J). (gr. 4-7). lib. bdg. 27.95 (978-1-58118-058-9(6) , 23472) LRS.

—Shiloh. 144p. (J). (Shiloh Ser.: No. 1). (gr. 4-7). pap. 4.99 (978-0-8072-8330-1(4)); No. 1. 2004. (gr. 3-7). pap. 29.00 incl. audio (978-0-8072-8329-5(0) , YA164SP) Random Hse. Audio Publishing Group. (Listening Library).

—Shiloh. Moser, Barry, illus. 2000. (Shiloh Ser.: No. 1). 144p. (J). (gr. 3-7). pap. 5.99 (978-0-689-83582-7(5) , Aladdin) Simon & Schuster Children's Publishing.

—Shiloh. movie tie-in ed. 2000. (Shiloh Ser.: No. 6). (Illus.). 144p. (J). (gr. 4-7). pap. 5.99 (978-0-689-83583-4(3) , Aladdin) Simon & Schuster Children's Publishing.

—Shiloh. 2000. (gr. 3-6). lib. bdg. 14.15 (978-0-613-73274-1(X)); (J). (978-0-606-19724-3(9)); (gr. 3-6). lib. bdg. 14.15 (978-0-613-30125-1(0)) Tandem Library Bks.

—Shiloh Season. unabr. ed. 2004. (Shiloh Ser.: No. 2). 120p. (J). (gr. 3-7). pap. 29.00 incl. audio (978-0-8072-8707-1(5) , YA242SP, Listening Library) Random Hse. Audio Publishing Group.

—Shiloh Season. Moser, Barry, illus. (Shiloh Ser.: No. 2). 128p. (J). 1999. (gr. 3-7). pap. 5.99 (978-0-689-82931-4(0)); 1998. (gr. 4-7). pap. 5.99 (978-0-689-80646-9(9)) Simon & Schuster Children's Publishing. (Aladdin).

—Shiloh Season. 1999. (gr. 3-6). lib. bdg. 13.55 (978-0-613-90607-4(1)); 1998. (Shiloh Ser.: No. 2). (J). (gr. 4-7). (978-0-606-13085-1(3)) Tandem Library Bks.

—Shiloh Trilogy. (J). 2000. 432p. (gr. 3-7). pap. 16.99 (978-0-689-01525-0(9) , Aladdin); 1998. (Shiloh Ser.: Nos. 1-3). (gr. 4-7). 35.00 (978-0-689-82327-5(4) , Atheneum) Simon & Schuster Children's Publishing.

Rinaldi, Ann. The Coffin Quilt: The Feud Between the Hatfields & the McCoys. 2001. (gr. 5-8). lib. bdg. 14.15 (978-0-613-35451-6(6)) Tandem Library Bks.

—Mine Eyes Have Seen. 2002. (978-0-606-22271-6(5)) Tandem Library Bks.

Rylant, Cynthia. Missing May. unabr. ed. 2004. 89p. (J). (gr. 5-9). pap. 29.00 incl. audio (978-0-8072-8701-9(6) , YA240SP, Listening Library) Random Hse. Audio Publishing Group.

—Missing May. 2004. 112p. (J). pap. 5.99 (978-0-439-61383-5(3) , Scholastic Paperbacks) Scholastic, Inc.

Sandrof, George. Me, a Hero? 2000. (Illus.). 77p. (J). (ps up). pap. 7.99 (978-1-58930-006-4(8)) Selah Publishing Group, LLC.

Slate, Joseph. Crossing the Trestle. 1999. (Accelerated Reader Bks.). 144p. (J). (gr. 3-7). 14.95 (978-0-7614-5053-5(X) , Cavendish Children's Bks.) Cavendish, Marshall Corp.

Wach, Martin & Wach, Delia. The Great West Virginia Snow Adventure. Wach, Delia, illus. 2006. (Illus.). 32p. (J). 16.95 (978-0-929915-42-5(9)) Headline Bks., Inc.

White, Ruth. Way down Deep. 2007. (Illus.). 208p. (J). (gr. 5 up). 16.00 (978-0-374-38251-3(4) , Farrar, Straus & Giroux (BYR)) Farrar, Straus & Giroux.

Yep, Laurence. Dream Soul. 2000. (Illus.). 224p. (J). (gr. 3-7). 16.89 (978-0-06-028390-2(4)) HarperCollins Pubs.

WEST VIRGINIA—HISTORY

Carole Marsh. West Virginia Indians. 2004. (West Virginia Experi Ser.). 36p. (gr. 3-8). pap. 7.95 (978-0-635-02340-7(7)); lib. bdg. 29.95 (978-0-635-02341-4(5)) Gallopade International.

Di Piazza, Domenica. West Virginia. 2001. (gr. 3-6). lib. bdg. 15.25 (978-0-613-76616-6(4)) Tandem Library Bks.

Fluharty, Linda Cunningham. Civil War - West Virginia: Union Lives Lost. 2004. (Illus.). 175p. lib. bdg. 35.00 (978-0-9759097-1-3(1)) Fluharty, Linda Cunningham.

Hallock, Marilyn R. Central Glass Company: The First Thirty Years, 1863-1893. 2003. (Illus.). 176p. 39.95 (978-0-7643-1762-0(8)) Schiffer Publishing, Ltd.

Hodgkins, Fran. West Virginia. 2003. (Land of Liberty Ser.). (Illus.). 64p. (J). lib. bdg. 25.26 (978-0-7368-2205-3(4)) Capstone Pr., Inc.

Hoffman, Nancy. Eleanor Roosevelt & the Arthurdale Experiment. 2001. (Illus.). xii, 100p. (J). (gr. 5-9). 22.50 (978-0-208-02504-3(9) , Linnet Bks.) Shoe String Pr., Inc.

Labella, Susan. West Virginia. 2006. 32p. (YA). (gr. 1-2). pap. 5.95 (978-0-516-26456-1(7) , Children's Pr.) Scholastic Library Publishing.

Lillard, David. West Virginia: A MyReportLinks. Com Book. 2003. (States Ser.). (Illus.). 48p. (J). lib. bdg. 25.26 (978-0-7660-5143-0(9) , MyReportLinks.com Bks.) Enslow Pubs., Inc.

Marsh, Carole. My First Pocket Guide West Virginia. 2000. (West Virginia Experience! Ser.). (Illus.). 96p. (J). (gr. 3-8). 12.95 (978-0-635-01338-5(X)) Gallopade International.

—West Virginia History Projects: 30 Cool, Activities, Crafts, Experiments & More for Kids to Do to Learn about Your State! 2003. (West Virginia Experience Ser.). 32p. (gr. k-5). pap. 5.95 (978-0-635-01817-5(9) , Marsh, Carole Bks.) Gallopade International.

Phillips, Margaret Coull. West Virginia. 2003. (Seeds of a Nation Ser.). (Illus.). 48p. (J). (gr. 3-5). 23.70 (978-0-7377-1567-5(7) , Kidhaven) Thomson Gale.

Smucker, Anna. History of West Virginia. 2004. (Illus.). per. 6.95 (978-1-891852-39-8(6)) Quarrier Pr.

Taylor County Historical Society Staff. Taylor County, West Virginia. 2000. (Images of America Ser.). (Illus.). 128p. (J). (gr. 5 up). pap. 18.99 (978-0-7385-0588-6(9)) Arcadia Publishing.

Way, Jennifer. West Virginia (Virginia Occidental) 2006. (Bilingual Library of the United States of America: Set 2). (ENG & SPA., Illus.). 32p. (J). (gr. 3-6). lib. bdg. 22.50 (978-1-4042-3114-6(3) , Buenas Letra) Rosen Publishing Group, Inc., The.

Zaunders, Bo. The Great Bridge-Building Contest. Munro, Roxie, illus. 2004. 32p. (J). (gr. k-4). 16.95 (978-0-8109-4929-4(6)) Abrams, Harry N. , Inc.

—The Great Bridge-Building Contest. Munro, Roxie, illus. 2006. 30p. (J). (gr. 4-8). reprint ed. 17.00 (978-1-4223-5239-7(0)) DIANE Publishing Co.

WESTMARK (IMAGINARY PLACE)—FICTION

Alexander, Lloyd. The Beggar Queen. 2002. (Westmark Trilogy: Vol. 3). (Illus.). 256p. (J). (gr. 7). pap. 6.99 (978-0-14-131070-1(7) , Puffin) Penguin Group (USA) Inc.

WETLAND ECOLOGY

Aloian, Molly. Un Habitat de Pantano. 2007. (SPA.). 32p. (J). (gr. 1-2). (***978-0-7787-8328-2(6)***) Crabtree Publishing Co.

Aloian, Molly. A Wetland Habitat. 2006. (Illus.). 32p. (J). (gr. 2). pap. (978-0-7787-2983-9(4)) Crabtree Publishing Co.

Aloian, Molly & Kalman, Bobbie. Un Habitat de Pantano. rev. ed. 2007. (SPA.). 32p. (J). (gr. 1-2). pap. (***978-0-7787-8352-7(9)***) Crabtree Publishing Co.

Aloian, Molly & Kalman, Bobbie. A Wetland Habitat. 2006. (Illus.). 32p. (J). (978-0-7787-2955-6(9)) Crabtree Publishing Co.

Blaustein, Daniel. The Everglades & the Gulf Coast. 2000. (Ecosystems of North America Ser.). (Illus.). 64p. (YA). (gr. 6 up). lib. bdg. 28.50 (978-0-7614-0896-3(7) , Benchmark Bks.) Cavendish, Marshall Corp.

Collard, Sneed B., III. Our Wet World. Needham, James M., illus. 1998. 32p. (J). (gr. 8-12). 16.95 (978-0-88106-267-0(7)); (gr. k-5). pap. 6.95 (978-0-88106-268-7(5)) Charlesbridge Publishing, Inc.

Dover. Animals of the Forest, Wetlands & Desert. 2006. 144p. (J). pap. 8.95 (***978-0-486-45939-4(X)***) Dover Pubns., Inc.

Dunphy, Madeleine. Here Is the Wetland. McLoughlin, Wayne, illus. 2007. (Web of Life Ser.). 32p. (J). 16.95 (978-0-9773795-9-0(0)); pap. 9.95 (978-0-9773795-8-3(2)) Web of Life Children's Bks.

Frisch, Aaron. Wetlands. 2008. (J). (***978-1-58341-575-7(0)*** , Creative Education) Creative Co., The.

Galko, Francine. Wetland Animals. 2003. (Animals in Their Habitats Ser.). (Illus.). 32p. (gr. k-2). (J). lib. bdg. 21.36 (978-1-4034-0186-1(1)); pap. 6.95 (978-1-4034-0443-5(7)) Heinemann Library.

—Wetland Animals. 2003. (gr. k-3). lib. bdg. 14.75 (978-0-613-45853-5(2)) Tandem Library Bks.

Hall, Margaret. Wetlands Animals, 4 bks. Saunders-Smith, Gail, ed. Incl. Beavers. lib. bdg. 15.93 (978-0-7368-2063-9(9)); Herons. lib. bdg. 15.93 (978-0-7368-2064-6(7)); Mallards. lib. bdg. 15.93 (978-0-7368-2065-3(5)); Muskrats. lib. bdg. 15.93 (978-0-7368-2066-0(3)); 24p. (J). (gr. k-1). 2004. (Illus.). 2003. Set lib. bdg. 63.72 (978-0-7368-2317-3(4) , Pebble Bks.) Capstone Pr., Inc.

Harcourt School Publishers Staff. Wetlands Advanced Level: Hidden Treasures. 3rd ed. 2002. (Trophies Reading Program Ser.). (Illus.). pap. 5.10 (978-0-15-323479-8(2)) Harcourt Schl. Pubs.

Johansson, Philip. Marshes & Swamps: A Wetland Web of Life. 2007. (Wonderful Water Biomes Ser.). (Illus.). 48p. (J). (gr. 3-4). lib. bdg. 23.93 (***978-0-7660-2814-2(3)*** , Enslow Elementary) Enslow Pubs., Inc.

Kalman, Bobbie & Bishop, Amanda. Les Terres Humides. 2004. (FRE., Illus.). 32p. (J). pap. (978-2-89579-014-3(0)) Crabtree Publishing Co.

Kalman, Bobbie & Burns, Kylie. Wetland Food Chains. 2006. (Food Chains Ser.). (Illus.). 32p. (J). (gr. 3-5). pap. (978-0-7787-1999-1(5)) Crabtree Publishing Co.

Leeson, Cole. Wetland/Swamp. 2003. (Wild America Habitats Ser.). (Illus.). 24p. (J). 21.20 (978-1-56711-810-0(0) , Blackbirch Pr., Inc.) Thomson Gale.

Lindeen, Carol. Life in a Wetland. 2003. (Pebble Plus: Living in a Biome Ser.). (Illus.). 24p. (J). lib. bdg. 17.26 (978-0-7368-2104-9(X)) Capstone Pr., Inc.

Macken, JoAnn Early. Wetlands: Terrenos Pantanosos. 2005. (SPA., Illus.). 24p. (J). (978-0-8368-6039-9(X)) Stevens, Gareth Inc.

McKissack, Fredrick, Jr. & McKissack, Lisa Beringer. Counting in the Wetlands. 2008. (J). (***978-0-7660-2993-4(X)***) Enslow Pubs., Inc.

Moore & Peter, D. Wetlands. 2nd rev. ed. 2007. (Ecosystem Ser.). 256p. (J). (gr. 9). 70.00 (***978-0-8160-5931-7(4)***) Facts On File, Inc.

Quigley, Mary. Wetlands Explorer. 2004. (Habitat Explorer Ser.). lib. bdg. 25.70 (978-1-4109-0514-7(4)) Raintree.

Reid, Greg. Wetlands. 2004. (Ecosystems Ser.). (Illus.). 32p. (J). (gr. 3-5). 23.00 (978-0-7910-7943-0(0) , Chelsea Hse.) Facts On File, Inc.

Richardson, Adele D. Wetlands. 2001. (Bridgestone Science Library). (Illus.). 24p. (J). (gr. 2-3). lib. bdg. 18.60 (978-0-7368-0840-8(X) , Bridgestone Bks.) Capstone Pr., Inc.

Ring, Elizabeth. Wetlands. 2004. (Illus.). 48p. (J). (gr. 2-4). 24.95 (978-1-4103-0315-8(2) , Blackbirch Pr., Inc.) Thomson Gale.

Rotter, Charles. Wetlands: A Vanishing Resource. 2001. (Life on Earth Ser.). (Illus.). 32p. (J). lib. bdg. (978-1-58341-024-0(4) , Creative Education) Creative Co., The.

Stewart, Melissa. Life in a Wetland. 2003. (Ecosystems in Action Ser.). (Illus.). 72p. (J). (gr. 6-12). lib. bdg. 26.60 (978-0-8225-4687-0(6)) Lerner Publishing Group.

Stone, Lynn M. Wetlands. 2003. (Rourke Discovery Library). (Illus.). 24p. (J). 20.64 (978-1-58952-688-4(0)) Rourke Publishing, LLC.

Wallace, Marianne. America's Wetlands: Guide to Plant & Animals. (America's EcoSystem Ser.: Vol. 4). (Illus.). 48p. (J). (gr. 3-6). pap. 11.95 (978-1-55591-484-4(5)) Fulcrum Publishing.

Watson, Galadriel Findlay. Wetlands. 2005. (Illus.). 32p. (J). (gr. 4-6). lib. bdg. 24.45 (978-1-59036-349-2(3)); (ps-7). pap. 7.95 (978-1-59036-355-3(8)) Weigl Pubs., Inc.

WETLANDS

see also Marshes

Beatty, Wetlands. 2003. (Biomes Atlas Ser.). (Illus.). pap. 8.95 (978-1-4109-0023-4(1)); pap. 48.30 (978-1-4109-0258-0(7)) Raintree.

Beatty, Richard. Wetlands. 2002. (Biomes Atlases Ser.). (Illus.). 64p. (J). lib. bdg. 31.40 (978-0-7398-5251-4(5)) Raintree.

Campbell, Andrew. Protecting Wetlands. 2005. (Protecting Habitats Ser.). (Illus.). 32p. (J). lib. bdg. 24.67 (978-0-8368-4996-7(5)) Stevens, Gareth Inc.

Champion, Neil. Rivers & Wetlands. 2005. (Caring for the Planet Ser.). (Illus.). 48p. (J). (978-1-58340-510-9(0)) Smart Apple Media.

Costain, Meredith. Wetlands. 2000. (gr. k-3). lib. bdg. 11.80 (978-0-613-30851-9(4)) Tandem Library Bks.

Endres, Hollie. Wetlands. 2007. (Illus.). 24p. (J). lib. bdg. 19.95 (978-1-60014-116-4(1)) Bellwether Media.

Gray, Shirley W. Wetlands. 2000. (First Reports). (Illus.). 48p. (J). (gr. 3 up). lib. bdg. 21.26 (978-0-7565-0025-2(7)) Compass Point Bks.

Green, Jen. Saving Oceans & Wetlands. 2004. (J). lib. bdg. 27.10 (978-1-59389-139-8(3)) Chrysalis Education.

Harcourt School Publishers Staff. Signatures: Hidden Treasures. 99th ed. 1999. (gr. 6). Vol. 1. tchr. ed. 218.40 (978-0-15-310127-4(X)); Vol. 2. tchr. ed. 218.40 (978-0-15-310128-1(8)) Harcourt Schl. Pubs.

Howard, Fran. Wetlands. 2007. (Habitats Ser.). (Illus.). 32p. (J). (gr. k-4). lib. bdg. 22.78 (978-1-59679-783-5(5)) ABDO Publishing Co.

Johnson, Rebecca L. A Journey into a Wetland. Saroff, Phyllis V., illus. 2004. (Biomes of North America Ser.). (J). pap. 6.95 (978-0-8225-2047-4(8)) Lerner Publishing Group.

—A Journey into a Wetlands. Saroff, Phyllis V., illus. 2004. (Biomes of North America Ser.). 48p. (J). (gr. 3-6). lib. bdg. 23.93 (978-1-57505-593-0(7)) Lerner Publishing Group.

Kalman, Bobbie. What Are Wetlands? 2002. (Science of Living Things Ser.). (Illus.). 32p. (J). (gr. 2-3). (978-0-86505-993-1(4)); pap. (978-0-86505-970-2(5)) Crabtree Publishing Co.

—What Are Wetlands? 2003. (gr. 3-6). lib. bdg. 14.10 (978-0-613-52930-3(8)) Tandem Library Bks.

Kanfush, Philip M. Emma's Wetlands Adventure: The Story of the Monastery Run Impovement Project Wetlands at Saint Vincent. 2006. (J). (***978-0-9708216-9-0(7)***) St. Vincent Archabbey Pubns.

Kids: Celebrate Wetlands Activity Guide. 2003. (J). 1.00 (978-1-888631-25-8(2)) Watercourse, The.

Leeson, Cole. Wetland/Swamp. 2003. (Wild America Habitats Ser.). (Illus.). 24p. (J). 21.20 (978-1-56711-810-0(0) , Blackbirch Pr., Inc.) Thomson Gale.

Levy, Janey. Discovering Wetlands. 2008. (J). lib. bdg. (***978-1-4042-3784-1(4)*** , PowerKids Pr.) Rosen Publishing Group, Inc., The.

Lindeen, Carol K. Life in a Wetland, Vol. 3. 2005. (Earth & Outer Space Ser.). 24p. (YA). (gr. k-3). pap. (978-0-7368-3405-6(2) , Pebble Bks.) Capstone Pr., Inc.

Loughran, Donna. Living near the Wetland. 2004. (Rookie Read-About Geography Ser.). (Illus.). 31p. (J). (gr. 1-2). pap. 5.95 (978-0-516-27332-7(9) , Children's Pr.) Scholastic Library Publishing.

Macken, JoAnn Early. Wetlands. 2005. (Illus.). 24p. (J). (978-0-8368-4894-6(2)); lib. bdg. 19.33 (978-0-8368-4887-8(X)) Stevens, Gareth Inc.

—Wetlands: Terrenos Pantanosos. 2005. (SPA., Illus.). 24p. (J). (978-0-8368-6039-9(X)); lib. bdg. 19.33 (978-0-8368-6032-0(2)) Stevens, Gareth Inc.

McKissack, Fredrick, Jr. & McKissack, Lisa Beringer. Counting in the Wetlands. 2008. (J). (***978-0-7660-2993-4(X)***) Enslow Pubs., Inc.

Moore & Peter, D. Wetlands. 2nd rev. ed. 2007. (Ecosystem Ser.). 256p. (J). (gr. 9). 70.00 (***978-0-8160-5931-7(4)***) Facts On File, Inc.

Nichols, Catherine. Wetlands. 2002. (We Can Read about Nature! Ser.). (Illus.). 32p. (J). 21.36 (978-0-7614-1434-6(7) , Benchmark Bks.) Cavendish, Marshall Corp.

Pratt-Serafini, Kristin Joy. Salamander Rain: A Lake & Pond Journal. 2004. (Sharing Nature with Children Book Ser.). (Illus.). 32p. (YA). (gr. 4-7). 16.95 (978-1-58469-018-4(6)) Dawn Pubns.

Pratt-Serafini, Kristin Joy & Pratt, Kristin Joy. Salamander Rain: A Lake & Pond Journal. 2004. (Sharing Nature with Children Book Ser.). (Illus.). 32p. (YA). (gr. 4-7). pap. 7.95 (978-1-58469-017-7(8)) Dawn Pubns.

Pyers. Wetlands Explorer. 2004. (Habitat Explorer Ser.). (Illus.). pap. 7.50 (978-1-4109-0842-1(9)); lib. bdg. 40.50 (978-1-4109-0848-3(8)) Raintree.

Reid, Greg. Wetlands. 2004. (Ecosystems Ser.). (Illus.). 32p. (J). (gr. 3-5). 23.00 (978-0-7910-7943-0(0) , Chelsea Hse.) Facts On File, Inc.

Richardson, Adele D. Wetlands. 2001. (Bridgestone Science Library). (Illus.). 24p. (J). (gr. 2-3). lib. bdg. 18.60 (978-0-7368-0840-8(X) , Bridgestone Bks.) Capstone Pr., Inc.

Ring, Elizabeth. Wetlands. 2004. (Illus.). 48p. (J). (gr. 2-4). 24.95 (978-1-4103-0315-8(2) , Blackbirch Pr., Inc.) Thomson Gale.

Rivera, Sheila. Wetland. 2005. (First Step Nonfiction Ser.). (Illus.). 23p. (J). (ps-7). 18.60 (978-0-8225-2598-1(4) , Lerner Pubns.) Lerner Publishing Group.

Rood. Wetlands. 1999. (Nature Study Ser.). 48p. (J). (gr. 2-5). pap. 7.95 (978-0-06-446158-0(0)) HarperCollins Pubs.

Rotter, Charles. Wetlands: A Vanishing Resource. 2001. (Life on Earth Ser.). (Illus.). 32p. (J). lib. bdg. (978-1-58341-024-0(4) , Creative Education) Creative Co., The.

Salas, Laura Purdie. Wetlands. 2007. (Amazing Science Ser.). (Illus.). 24p. (J). (***978-1-4048-3474-3(5)*** , 1265697) Picture Window Bks.

Salas, Laura Purdie. Wetlands: Soggy Habitat. Yesh, Jeff, illus. 2006. (Amazing Science Ser.). 24p. (J). (978-1-4048-3100-1(2) , 1265697) Picture Window Bks.

Sasman, Irene D. H. Wetlands: Everglades Children's Library, Set. 1998. (Illus.). (J). (ps-6). pap. 99.95 (978-1-56831-950-6(9)) Learning Connection, The.

Scrace, Carolyn. Life in the Wetlands. 2005. (What on Earth? Ser.). (Illus.). 32p. (J). (gr. 2-4). 25.50 (978-0-516-25318-3(2) , Children's Pr.) Scholastic Library Publishing.

Snedden, Robert. Wetlands. 2003. (Illus.). 32p. (J). lib. bdg. 27.10 (978-1-58340-387-7(6)) Smart Apple Media.

Somervill, Barbara A. Animal Survivors of the Wetlands. 2004. (Watts Library). (Illus.). 64p. (J). 25.50 (978-0-531-12203-7(4) , Watts, Franklin) Scholastic Library Publishing.

—Our Living World: Earth's Biomes, 7 vols., Set. 2005. (Illus.). (J). (gr. 4-8). 350.00 (978-1-59187-052-4(6)) Tradition Publishing Co.

Stille, Darlene R. Wetlands. 1999. (True Bks.). (Illus.). 48p. (J). (gr. 3-5). 25.00 (978-0-516-21512-9(4) , Children's Pr.) Scholastic Library Publishing.

Stone, Lynn M. Wetlands. 2003. (Rourke Discovery Library). (Illus.). 24p. (J). 20.64 (978-1-58952-688-4(0)) Rourke Publishing, LLC.

Taylor, Barbara. Inland Water Habitats. 2006. (Exploring Habitats Ser.). 36p. (J). lib. bdg. (978-0-8368-7254-5(1)) Stevens, Gareth Inc.

Walker, Pam & Wood, Elaine. The Saltwater Wetland. 2005. (Life in the Sea Ser.). (Illus.). 152p. (J). (gr. 4-9). 35.00 (978-0-8160-5702-3(8)) Facts On File, Inc.

Wallace, Marianne. America's Wetlands: Guide to Plant & Animals. (America's EcoSystem Ser.: Vol. 4). (Illus.). 48p. (J). (gr. 3-6). pap. 11.95 (978-1-55591-484-4(5)) Fulcrum Publishing.

Weaver, Jeanne. Wetlands Journey. 2007. (Science Chapters Ser.). 48p. (J). (gr. 1-4). lib. bdg. 17.90 (***978-1-4263-0185-8(5)*** , National Geographic Children's Bks.) National Geographic Society.

Wetlands. (Ecosystems Ser.). 24p. (J). 6.95 (978-0-7368-9167-7(6)) Capstone Pr., Inc.

Wetlands, 6 vols. (gr. 2-5). 36.95 (978-0-7368-9267-4(2)) Red Brick Learning.

Wetlands, 6 Packs. (Rigby Focus Ser.). 16p. (gr. 1 up). 30.00 (978-0-7578-5551-1(2)) Rigby Education.

Wetlands: Individual Title Six-Packs. (Rigby Focus Ser.). 16p. (gr. 1 up). 28.00 (978-0-7578-5319-7(6)) Rigby Education.

WETLANDS—FICTION

Auer, Chris. The Legend of the Sand Dollar: An Inspirational Story of Hope for Easter. Johnson, Rick, illus. 2005. 32p. (J). 15.99 (978-0-310-70780-6(3)) Zonderkidz.

WHALES

Adelman, Beth. Killer Whales. 2006. (Boys Rock! Ser.). (Illus.). 32p. (J). (gr. 1-5). 24.21 (978-1-59296-732-2(9)) Child's World, Inc.

Animal Lives: Whales. 2006. pap. 4.99 (978-1-4206-8157-4(5)) Teacher Created Materials, Inc.

Arnold, Caroline. Baby Whale Rescue: The True Story of J. J. 1999. (Illus.). (J). (978-0-606-18663-6(8)) Tandem Library Bks.

Arnold, Caroline, illus. A Killer Whale's World. 2006. 24p. (J). (gr. k-2). 23.93 (978-1-4048-1321-2(7) , 1253183) Picture Window Bks.

Baird, Robin W. Killer Whales of the World: Natural History & Conservation. rev. ed. 2002. (WorldLife Discovery Guide Ser.). (Illus.). 132p. 29.95 (978-0-89658-512-6(3)) Voyageur Pr., Inc.

La ballena Azul: Individual Title Six-Packs. (On Deck en Espanol Ser.).Tr. of Blue Whale. (SPA.). 24p. (gr. 4-5). 35.00 (978-0-7578-6437-7(6)) Rigby Education.

Bancroft, Bronwyn. Whalers. 1998. (Illus.). 32p. (ps-3). pap. 6.95 (978-0-207-19177-0(8)) HarperCollins Pubs.

Barnett, Michelle Noble, et al. Theme Pockets - September: School Days; Africa; Whales. Evans, Marilyn, ed. Larsen, Jo, illus. 1999. (Making Books with Pockets). 96p. (J). (gr. 1-3). pap., tchr. ed. 12.99 (978-1-55799-706-7(3) , EMC 592) Evan-Moor Educational Pubs.

Battistoni, Ilse. What a Whale! Learning the WH Sound. (PowerPhonics Ser.). (Illus.). (J). 2002. 24p. (gr. 1). lib. bdg. 18.50 (978-0-8239-5929-7(5)); 2001. 23p. pap. 26.40 (978-0-8239-8274-5(2)) Rosen Publishing Group, Inc., The. (PowerKids Pr.).

Becker, John E. Gray Whales. 2004. (Returning Wildlife Ser.). (Illus.). 48p. (J). (gr. 4-7). 26.20 (978-0-7377-2293-2(2) , Greenhaven Pr., Inc.) Thomson Gale.

Berendes, Mary. Beluga Whales. 2007. (New Naturebooks Ser.). 32p. (J). (gr. 1-5). 27.07 (***978-1-59296-843-5(0)***) Child's World, Inc.

Berger, Melvin. Do Whales Have Belly Buttons? 1999. (gr. 3-6). lib. bdg. 14.10 (978-0-613-16922-6(0)) Tandem Library Bks.

—Do Whales Have Belly Buttons? Questions & Answers about Whales & Dolphins. 1999. (Question & Answer Ser.). (J). 12.75 (978-0-606-20055-4(X)) Tandem Library Bks.

—Splash! A Book about Whales & Dolphins. 2001. (Hello Reader! Ser.). (Illus.). (J). (978-0-606-21449-0(6)) Tandem Library Bks.

Berger, Melvin & Berger, Gilda. Do Whales Have Belly Buttons? Questions & Answers about Whales & Dolphins. Bond, Higgins, illus. 1999. (Scholastic Question & Answer Ser.). 48p. (J). (gr. 2-4). 5.95 (978-0-439-08571-7(3)); pap. 12.95 (978-0-590-13081-3(1)) Scholastic, Inc. (Scholastic Reference).

—Whales. 2003. (Scholastic Readers Ser.). (J). (978-0-439-47390-3(X)) Scholastic, Inc.

Bingham, Caroline. Whales & Dolphins. 2003. (Eye Wonder Ser.). (Illus.). 48p. (J). 9.99 (978-0-7894-9269-2(5)) Dorling Kindersley Publishing, Inc.

Bingham, Caroline & Dorling Kindersley Publishing Staff. Whales & Dolphins. 2003. (Eye Wonder Ser.). (Illus.). 48p. (J). lib. bdg. 17.99 (978-0-7894-9613-3(5)) Dorling Kindersley Publishing, Inc.

Block, Cheryl. True Blue Friend. Takeshita, Gene, illus. 2006. 32p. (J). 21.95 (***978-0-9761625-2-0(0)***) Block Publishing.

The Blue Whale: Individual Title Six-Packs. (On Deck Ser.). 24p. (gr. 4-5). 35.00 (978-0-7578-1066-4(7)) Rigby Education.

Books Are Fun 8 Title Animal Lives Set: Whales. 2006. (J). (978-1-59566-308-5(8)) QEB Publishing Inc.

Bright, Michael & Kerrod, Robin. Giants of the Ocean. 2004. (Illus.). 128p. pap. 17.99 (978-1-84215-989-7(5) , Southwater) Anness Publishing GBR. *Dist:* National Bk. Network.

Buettner, Debi. Discover Killer Whales Vol. 2: The Long Journey North. Karecki, Jason & Branson, Kim, illus. 1998. 24p. (J). (gr. k-5). (978-1-890716-05-9(7)) K&M International.

Buffington, Kath. Whales. 2003. (Learn All About Ser.). (Illus.). 64p. pap. 10.95 (978-0-439-51885-7(7)) Scholastic, Inc.

Camm, Martin, illus. Meyers Buch der Wale und Delfine. (GER.). 48p. (978-3-411-07451-8(5)) Bibliographisches Institut & F. A. Brockhaus AG DEU. *Dist:* i.b.d., Ltd.

Carwardine, Mark. Killer Whale. 1999. (Natural World Ser.). (Illus.). 48p. (J). (gr. 4-7). pap. 7.95 (978-0-7398-0949-5(0)) Steck-Vaughn.

—Killer Whale: Habitats, Life Cycles, Food Chains, Threats. 1999. (Natural World Ser.). (Illus.). 48p. (J). (gr. 3-7). lib. bdg. 27.12 (978-0-7398-1058-3(8)) Raintree.

Clapham, Phil. Right Whales: Natural History & Conservation. rev. ed. 2004. (WorldLife Library). (Illus.). 72p. pap. 17.95 (978-0-89658-657-4(X)) Voyageur Pr., Inc.

—Whales of the World. rev. ed. 2001. (WorldLife Discovery Guides Ser.). (Illus.). 132p. (gr. 8 up). reprint ed. pap. 21.95 (978-0-89658-537-9(9)) Voyageur Pr., Inc.

Cole. El Ballena. 2002. (Animales Marinos Salvajes Serie).Tr. of Wild Marine Animals: The Whale. (SPA.). 24p. (J). (gr. 3-5). 24.94 (978-1-4103-0007-2(2) , Blackbirch Pr., Inc.) Thomson Gale.

Collard, Sneed B., III. A Whale Biologist at Work. (Wildlife Conservation Society Bks.). (Illus.). 48p. (J). (gr. 4-6). 2001. pap. 6.95 (978-0-531-16526-3(4)); 2000. 24.50 (978-0-531-11786-6(3)) Scholastic Library Publishing. (Watts, Franklin).

—A Whale Biologist at Work. 2000. (Illus.). (J). (978-0-606-20984-7(0)) Tandem Library Bks.

Cooper, Jason. Great Whale. 2003. (Life Cycles II Ser.). (Illus.). 24p. (J). 25.64 (978-1-58952-709-6(7)) Rourke Publishing, LLC.

Corrigan, Patricia. Whales. McGee, John F., illus. 2004. (Our Wild World Ser.). 48p. (J). (gr. 2-5). pap. 7.95 (978-1-55971-780-9(7) , NorthWord Bks. for Young Readers) T&N Children's Publishing.

—Whales. 2001. (gr. 3-6). lib. bdg. 16.40 (978-0-613-55923-2(1)) Tandem Library Bks.

Craft, Sarah S. Mother Beluga Whales & Their Babies. 1999. (Zoo Life Book Ser.). 24p. (J). (gr. k-4). lib. bdg. 18.75 (978-0-8239-5315-8(7) , PowerKids Pr.) Rosen Publishing Group, Inc., The.

Daigle, Evelyne. As Long As There Are Whales. Wright, Genevieve, tr. from FRE. Grenier, Daniel, illus. 2004. 48p. (J). (gr. 4). 15.95 (978-0-88776-692-3(7)) Tundra Bks., Inc./Livres Toundra, Inc. CAN. *Dist:* Random Hse., Inc.

Davidson, Susannah. Whales & Dolphins. 2004. (Discovery Program Ser.). (Illus.). 48p. (J). pap. 8.95 (978-0-7945-0316-1(0) , Usborne); lib. bdg. 16.95 (978-1-58086-478-7(3)) EDC Publishing.

—Whales & Dolphins. 2002. (gr. 3-6). lib. bdg. 17.60 (978-0-613-67679-3(3)) Tandem Library Bks.

Davidson, Susannah, et al. Whales & Dolphins. Woodcock, John, illus. 2003. (Usborne Discovery Ser.). 48p. (J). pap. (978-0-439-56060-3(8)); pap. (978-0-439-57780-9(2)) Scholastic, Inc.

Davies, Nicola. Big Blue Whale. Maland, Nick, illus. (Read & Wonder Ser.). 32p. (J). 2001. (ps up). pap. 6.99 (978-0-7636-1080-7(1)); 2000. (gr. 1-4). pap. 19.99 (978-0-7636-1282-5(0)) Candlewick Pr.

—Big Blue Whale. 2001. (ps-2). lib. bdg. 14.15 (978-0-613-35907-8(0)); (Illus.). (J). 12.79 (978-0-606-21065-2(2)) Tandem Library Bks.

Do Whales Have Wings? (Animals All Around Ser.). 24p. (J). 7.95 (978-1-4048-0373-2(4)) Picture Window Bks.

Dorling Kindersley Publishing Staff, ed. Shark & Whale. 2004. (Ultimate Sticker Bks.). 16p. (J). pap. 6.99 (978-0-7566-0237-6(8)) Dorling Kindersley Publishing, Inc.

—Whale. 2004. (Dk Eyewitness Books Ser.). (Illus.). 72p. (J). 15.99 (978-0-7566-0739-5(6)) Dorling Kindersley Publishing, Inc.

Douglas, Lloyd G. Humpback Whale. 2005. (Ocean Life Ser.). (Illus.). 24p. (J). (ps-2). pap. 4.95 (978-0-516-23741-1(1) , Children's Pr.) Scholastic Library Publishing.

—Humpback Whale: Early Intervention Level 9. 2005. (Welcome Bookstm Ser.). 24p. (J). (ps-ps). 18.00 (978-0-516-25028-1(0) , Children's Pr.) Scholastic Library Publishing.

Dyer, Hadley & Kalman, Bobbie. Wonderful Whales. 2005. (Living Ocean Ser.). (Illus.). 32p. (J). (978-0-7787-1302-9(4)); pap. (978-0-7787-1324-1(5)) Crabtree Publishing Co.

Ericson, Anton. Whales & Dolphins. 2001. (Nature's Wild Ser.). (J). lib. bdg. (978-1-58952-206-0(0)) Rourke Publishing, LLC.

Faiella, Graham. Whales. MacCombie, Turi, illus. 2002. (All Aboard Reading Ser.). 48p. (J). mass mkt. 3.99 (978-0-448-42600-6(5) , Grosset & Dunlap) Penguin Group (USA) Inc.

—Whales. 2002. (gr. k-3). lib. bdg. 11.80 (978-0-613-45323-3(9)) Tandem Library Bks.

Fenton, Julie A. Killer Whales & Other Toothed Whales, Vol. 8. World Book, Inc. Staff, ed. 2001. (World Book's Animals of the World Ser.: Set 2). (Illus.). 64p. (J). (978-0-7166-1215-5(1)) World Bk., Inc.

Fromm, Peter. Whale Tales Vol. 2: Human Interactions with Whales. Seltser, Andrew, ed. 2000. (Illus.). 160p. (YA). (gr. 5 up). pap. 13.95 (978-0-9648704-1-3(X)) Whale Tales Pr.

Gallimard, Jeunesse. Whales. 2008. (Doodlebops Ser.). 24p. (J). pap. 5.99 (***978-0-545-00140-3(4)*** , Scholastic Reference) Scholastic, Inc.

Gentle, Victor & Perry, Janet. Blue Whales. 2001. (Whales & Dolphins Ser.). (Illus.). 24p. (YA). (gr. 2 up). lib. bdg. 22.00 (978-0-8368-2880-1(1)) Stevens, Gareth Inc.

—Humpback Whales. 2001. (Whales & Dolphins Ser.). (Illus.). 24p. (YA). (gr. 2 up). lib. bdg. 22.00 (978-0-8368-2882-5(8)) Stevens, Gareth Inc.

—Orcas: Killer Whales. 2001. (Whales & Dolphins Ser.). (Illus.). 24p. (YA). (gr. 2 up). lib. bdg. 22.00 (978-0-8368-2883-2(6)) Stevens, Gareth Inc.

—Right Whales. 2001. (Whales & Dolphins Ser.). (Illus.). 24p. (YA). (gr. 2 up). lib. bdg. 22.00 (978-0-8368-2884-9(4)) Stevens, Gareth Inc.

—Sperm Whales. 2001. (Whales & Dolphins Ser.). (Illus.). 24p. (YA). (gr. 2 up). lib. bdg. 22.00 (978-0-8368-2885-6(2)) Stevens, Gareth Inc.

—Whales & Dolphins, 6 bks. Incl. Blue Whales. lib. bdg. 22.00 (978-0-8368-2880-1(1)); Bottlenose Dolphins. lib. bdg. 22.00 (978-0-8368-2881-8(X)); Humpback Whales. lib. bdg. 22.00 (978-0-8368-2882-5(8)); Orcas : Killer Whales. lib. bdg. 22.00 (978-0-8368-2883-2(6)); Right Whales. lib. bdg. 22.00 (978-0-8368-2884-9(4)); Sperm Whales. lib. bdg. 22.00 (978-0-8368-2885-6(2)); 24p. (YA). (gr. 2 up). 2001. (Illus.). Set lib. bdg. 132.00 (978-0-8368-2879-5(8)) Stevens, Gareth Inc.

Gilkerson, Patricia. My Adventure with Whales. 2007. 44p. (J). 8.99 (978-1-59092-475-4(4) , Orchard Academy Pr.) Windstorm Creative.

Gowell, Elizabeth Tayntor. Whales & Dolphins: What They Have in Common. 2000. (Animals in Order Ser.). (Illus.). 48p. (J). (gr. 4-6). pap. 6.95 (978-0-531-16454-9(3)); 26.50 (978-0-531-20396-5(4)) Scholastic Library Publishing. (Watts, Franklin).

Green, John. Great Whales Stained Glass Coloring Book. 2006. 16p. (J). pap. 5.95 (978-0-486-45022-3(8)) Dover Pubns., Inc.

Greenaway, Theresa. Whales. 2001. (Secret World Of... Ser.). (Illus.). 48p. (J). (gr. 4-7). lib. bdg. 27.12 (978-0-7398-3508-1(4)) Raintree.

Greenberg, Daniel A. Whales. (Animalways Ser.). (Illus.). (J). 2002. 110p. 31.36 (978-0-7614-1389-9(8)); 2000. 48p. (gr. 3-5). lib. bdg. 25.64 (978-0-7614-1167-3(4)) Cavendish, Marshall Corp. (Benchmark Bks.).

Gunzi, Christiane. The Best Book of Whales & Dolphins. (Best Book of... Ser.). 32p. (J). (gr. k-3). 2006. pap. 6.95 (978-0-7534-5987-4(6)); 2001. (Illus.). tchr. ed. 12.95 (978-0-7534-5369-8(X)) Houghton Mifflin Co. Trade & Reference Div. (Kingfisher).

Gustafson, Sarah. Whales, Dolphins, & More Marine Mammals. 2005. (Illus.). 48p. (J). pap. (978-0-439-71189-0(4)) Scholastic, Inc.

Harcourt School Publishers Staff. Ibis: Library Edition. 1999. (Collections Ser.). (Illus.). (J). 4.70 (978-0-15-314320-5(7)) Harcourt Schl. Pubs.

—Saving Ben Advanced Level. 3rd ed. 2002. (Trophies Reading Program Ser.). (Illus.). pap. 5.10 (978-0-15-323118-6(1)) Harcourt Schl. Pubs.

Harris, Caroline. Whales & Dolphins. 2005. (Kingfisher Young Knowledge Ser.). (Illus.). 48p. (J). (gr. k-3). 9.95 (978-0-7534-5869-3(1) , Kingfisher) Houghton Mifflin Co. Trade & Reference Div.

Harris, Greg, illus. Whales & Dolphins. 1998. (At Your Fingertips Ser.). 10p. (J). (ps-3). 6.95 (978-0-7681-0031-0(3) , McClanahan Bk.) Learning Horizons, Inc.

Herriges, Ann. Whales. 2006. (Oceans Alive! Ser.). (Illus.). 24p. (J). lib. bdg. 16.95 (978-1-60014-023-5(8)) Bellwether Media.

Heymsfeld, Carla & Li, Xiaojun. The Narwhal's Tusk. 2001. 32p. (J). (gr. 2-6). 17.95 (978-1-891992-03-2(1)) Owl's Hse. Pr.

Hirschmann, Kris. The Killer Whale. 2004. (J). 26.20 (978-0-7377-2058-7(1) , Greenhaven Pr., Inc.) Thomson Gale.

Hodge, Deborah. Whales: Killer whales, blue whales & more. Stephens, Pat, illus. unabr. ed. 2004. (Kids Can Press Wildlife Ser.). 32p. (J). (gr. k-3). (978-1-55074-418-7(6)) Kids Can Pr., Ltd.

Hodge, Judith. Whales. 1999. (Animals of the Ocean Ser.: Vol. 3). (Illus.). 32p. (J). (gr. 2-6). lib. bdg. 14.95 (978-1-56674-233-7(1)) Forest Hse. Publishing Co., Inc.

Hodgkins, Fran. The Whale Scientists: Solving the Mystery of Whale Strandings. 2007. (Illus.). 64p. (J). (gr. 5). 18.00 (***978-0-618-55673-1(7)***) Houghton Mifflin Co.

Hoelzel, A. Rus & Stern, S. Jonathan. Minke Whales. rev. ed. 2000. (WorldLife Library). (Illus.). 72p. pap. 12.95 (978-0-89658-490-7(9)) Voyageur Pr., Inc.

Hopkins, Ellen H. Orcas: High Seas Supermen. 2000. (Illus.). 56p. (J). (gr. 5-6). pap. 8.96 (978-0-7891-5258-9(4)) Perfection Learning Corp.

Hoyt, Erich. Whale Rescue: Changing the Future for Endangered Wildlife. 2005. (Firefly Animal Rescue Ser.). (Illus.). 64p. (J). (gr. 5-8). pap. 9.95 (978-1-55297-600-5(9)); lib. bdg. 19.95 (978-1-55297-601-2(7)) Firefly Bks., Ltd.

—Whale Rescue: Changing the Future for Endangered Wildlife. 2004. (gr. 5-8). lib. bdg. 18.75 (978-0-613-78603-4(3)) Tandem Library Bks.

The Humpback Whale. (Wildlife of North America Ser.). 48p. (YA). 7.95 (978-0-7368-8487-7(4)) Capstone Pr., Inc.

The Humpback Whale, 6 vols. (gr. 4 up). 39.95 (978-0-7368-8499-0(8)) Red Brick Learning.

Imbriaco, Alison. The Sperm Whale: Help Save This Endangered Species! 2008. (Saving Endangered Species Ser.). 128p. (J). (gr. 6 up). lib. bdg. 33.27 (***978-1-59845-071-2(9)*** , MyReportLinks.com Bks.) Enslow Pubs., Inc.

Immel, Norma. The Story of Keiko. Burroughs, Robert, illus. 1998. 14p. (J). (ps-3). pap. 9.95 (978-0-9665148-0-3(7)) Partner Productions.

Inskipp, Carol. Killer Whale. 2004. (Animals under Threat Ser.). (Illus.). 48p. (J). 29.93 (978-1-4034-5584-0(8)) Heinemann Library.

—The Killer Whale. 2004. (Animals under Threat Ser.). (Illus.). 48p. (J). pap. 8.50 (978-1-4034-5691-5(7)) Heinemann Library.

Jenner, Caryn. Journey of a Humpback Whale, Level 2. 2002. (Readers Ser.). (Illus.). 32p. (gr. 5). pap. 3.99 (978-0-7894-8515-1(X)) Dorling Kindersley Publishing, Inc.

—Journey of a Humpback Whale. 2002. (gr. k-3). lib. bdg. 11.80 (978-0-613-55727-6(1)) Tandem Library Bks.

Jenner, Caryn & Dorling Kindersley Publishing Staff. Journey of a Humpback Whale, Level 2. 2002. (Readers Ser.). (Illus.). 32p. (J). 12.99 (978-0-7894-8514-4(1)) Dorling Kindersley Publishing, Inc.

W X Y Z

Jones, Michael P. Whales—The Gentle Giants: Calendar 1988. (Illus.). (J). 10.00 (978-0-89904-211-4(2)); 25.00 (978-0-89904-213-8(9)) Crumb Elbow Publishing.

Kalman, Bobbie. Life Cycle of a Whale. 2002. (gr. 3-6). lib. bdg. 14.10 (978-0-613-52977-8(4)) Tandem Library Bks.

—What Is a Whale? 2000. (gr. 3-6). lib. bdg. 14.10 (978-0-613-22606-6(2)) Tandem Library Bks.

Kalman, Bobbie & Levigne, Heather. Les Baleines. 2002. (FRE.). (J). pap. (978-2-920660-85-4(3)) Crabtree Publishing Co.

—What Is a Whale? 1999. (Science of Living Things Ser.). (Illus.). 32p. (J). (gr. 2-3). (978-0-86505-935-1(7)); pap. (978-0-86505-953-5(5)) Crabtree Publishing Co.

Kalman, Bobbie & Thal, Karuna. Les Baleines. 2005. (FRE., Illus.). 32p. pap. (978-2-89579-049-5(3)) Crabtree Publishing Co.

—The Life Cycle of a Whale. 2001. (Life Cycle Ser.). (Illus.). 32p. (J). (gr. 2-3). (978-0-7787-0653-3(2)); pap. (978-0-7787-0683-0(4)) Crabtree Publishing Co.

Kelsey, Elin. Finding Out about Whales. 1998. (Science Explorers Ser.). (Illus.). 40p. (J). (gr. k-7). 19.95 (978-1-895688-79-5(5)); pap. 9.95 (978-1-895688-80-1(9)) Maple Tree Pr. CAN. *Dist:* Firefly Bks., Ltd.

Kerrod, Robin. Whales & Dolphins. (Illus.). 64p. (gr. 3-7). 2001. pap. 7.95 (978-1-84215-424-3(9) , Southwater); 1998. 14.99 (978-1-85967-611-0(1) , Lorenz Bks.) Anness Publishing GBR. *Dist:* National Bk. Network.

Killer Whales, 6 bks. 2005. (Animal Predators Ser.). (Illus.). 40p. (J). (gr. 3-6). pap. 46.95 (978-0-8225-5492-9(5)) Lerner Publishing Group.

Kinder, Cando. Birth of Whale Big Book. 1999. (J). pap. 26.95 (978-0-8136-0658-3(6)) Modern Curriculum Pr.

—Birth of Whale Read-Along. (J). 7.95 incl. audio (978-0-8136-0649-1(7)) Modern Curriculum Pr.

Kops, Deborah. The Humpback Whale: Help Save This Endangered Species! 2006. (Saving Endangered Species Ser.). (Illus.). 128p. (J). lib. bdg. 33.27 (978-1-59845-036-1(0) , MyReportLinks.com Bks.) Enslow Pubs., Inc.

Kurth, Linda Moore. Keiko's Story: A Killer Whale Goes Home. 2000. (Worlds Beyond Ser.). (Illus.). 72p. (gr. 5-8). lib. bdg. 24.90 (978-0-7613-1500-1(4) , Millbrook Pr.) Lerner Publishing Group.

Laskey, Elizabeth. Whales. 2003. (Sea Creatures Ser.). 32p. (J). (gr. 3-5). lib. bdg. 22.79 (978-1-4034-0960-7(9)); (Illus.). pap. 6.95 (978-1-4034-3567-5(7)) Heinemann Library.

Le Bloas, Renee. Orca: Admiral of the Sea. 2001. (Animal Close-Ups Ser.). (Illus.). (J). (978-0-606-20834-5(8)) Tandem Library Bks.

Lee, Justin. How to Draw Whales. 2002. (Kid's Guide to Drawing Ser.). (Illus.). 24p. (J). lib. bdg. 21.25 (978-0-8239-5789-7(6) , PowerKids Pr.) Rosen Publishing Group, Inc., The.

Leon, Vicki. A Pod of Killer Whales: The Mysterious Life of the Intelligent Orca. Foott, Jeff, photos by. 2nd ed. 2006. (Jean-Michel Cousteau Presents Ser.). (Illus.). 48p. (J). pap. 8.95 (978-0-9766134-7-3(6)) London Town Pr.

Lewis, Paul Owen. Davy's Dream: A Young Boy's Adventure with Wild Orca Whales. 2004. (Illus.). 64p. (J). (ps-3). 8.95 (978-1-58246-001-7(9) , Tricycle Pr.) Ten Speed Pr.

The Life Cycle of a Whale, Vol. 2. 2005. (Animals, Animals, Animals Ser.). (YA). (gr. k-3). (978-0-7368-3398-1(6) , Pebble Bks.) Capstone Pr., Inc.

Lindeen, Carol K. Whales. 2004. (Under the Sea Ser.). (Illus.). 24p. (J). lib. bdg. 19.93 (978-0-7368-2603-7(3) , Pebble Bks.) Capstone Pr., Inc.

Lockwood, Sophie. Whales. 2008. (World of Mammals Ser.). 40p. (J). (gr. 2-6). 29.93 (***978-1-59296-930-2(5)***) Child's World, Inc.

Malam, John. Killer Whale. (Scary Creatures Ser.). 32p. (J). 2008. pap. 8.95 (***978-0-531-21006-2(5)*** , Watts, Franklin); 2007. spiral bd. 26.00 (***978-0-531-20447-4(2)*** , Children's Pr.) Scholastic Library Publishing.

Markle, Sandra. Killer Whales. (Animal Predators Ser.). 40p. (J). 2005. (gr. 4-6). pap. 7.95 (978-1-57505-743-9(3)); 2004. (Illus.). (gr. 3 6). lib. bdg. 25.26 (978-1-57505-728-6(X)) Lerner Publishing Group.

Martin, Louise. Whales. 2001. (Wildlife in Danger Ser.). (Illus.). 24p. (J). (gr. 1-4). 14.95 (978-1-58952-024-0(6)) Rourke Publishing, LLC.

McMillan, Diane. Humpback Whales. 2004. (Nature Watch Ser.). (Illus.). 48p. (J). 25.26 (978-1-57505-347-9(0)) Lerner Publishing Group.

McMorrow, Annalisa. Whales. Chalk, Philip, illus. 1999. 48p. (J). (gr. 3-6). pap. 7.95 (978-1-57612-077-4(5) , No. MM2091) Monday Morning Bks., Inc.

McNulty, Faith. How Whales Walked into the Sea. Lewin, Ted, illus. 1999. (J). pap. (978-0-590-89831-7(0)) Scholastic, Inc.

Moore, Eva. The Wild Whale Watch. Spiers, John, illus. 3rd ed. 2000. (Magic School Bus Chapter Bks.: No. 3). 80p. (J). (gr. 1-4). pap. 4.99 (978-0-439-10990-1(6)) Scholastic, Inc.

—The Wild Whale Watch. 2000. (Magic School Bus Chapter Bks.: No. 3). (J). (gr. 1-4). (978-0-606-18576-9(3)) Tandem Library Bks.

Morgan, Sally. Whales, 12 vols. 2005. (QEB Animal Lives Ser.). (Illus.). 32p. (J). (gr. 4-7). lib. bdg. 18.95 (978-1-59566-122-7(0)) QEB Publishing Inc.

Murray, Julie. Beluga Whales. 2002. (Buddy Book Ser.). (Illus.). 24p. (J). (gr. k-4). lib. bdg. 21.35 (978-1-57765-709-5(8)) ABDO Publishing Co.

—Blue Whales. 2005. (Animal Kingdom Set Ii Ser.). (Illus.). 24p. (J). (gr. k-4). lib. bdg. 21.35 (978-1-59197-303-4(1)) ABDO Publishing Co.

—Gray Whales. 2005. (Animal Kingdom Set Ii Ser.). (Illus.). 24p. (J). (gr. k-4). lib. bdg. 21.35 (978-1-59197-318-8(X)) ABDO Publishing Co.

—Humpback Whales. 2002. (Buddy Book Ser.). (Illus.). 24p. (J). (gr. k-4). lib. bdg. 21.35 (978-1-57765-708-8(X)) ABDO Publishing Co.

Nuzzolo, Deborah & Parham, Donna. Whales K-3, 1. 2003. (Illus.). 28p. (J). (gr. k-3). tchr.'s training gde. ed. 5.99 (978-1-893698-33-8(5) , T15) SeaWorld, Inc.

O'Loughlin, Chloe & Borrowman, Mary. The Rescue of Nanoose. Wang, Jacqueline, illus. 2004. 32p. pap. 12.95 (978-1-894898-20-1(6)) Heritage Hse. Publishing Co., Ltd. CAN. *Dist:* Midpoint Trade Bks., Inc.

Paige, Joy. La Ballena Azul: El Mamifero Mas Grande Del Mundo. 2004. (Campeones Del Mundo Animal Ser.). (SPA & ENG., Illus.). 24p. (J). (gr. 3-6). lib. bdg. 17.25 (978-0-8239-6896-1(0) , Buenas Letra) Rosen Publishing Group, Inc., The.

—The Blue Whale: World's Largest Mammal. 2002. (Reading Power Ser.). (Illus.). 24p. (J). (gr. 1). lib. bdg. 17.25 (978-0-8239-5962-4(7) , PowerKids Pr.) Rosen Publishing Group, Inc., The.

Papastavrou, Vassili & Dorling Kindersley Publishing Staff. Whale. Greenaway, Frank, photos by. 2004. (Eyewitness Books). (Illus.). 72p. (J). lib. bdg. 19.99 (978-0-7566-0738-8(8)) Dorling Kindersley Publishing, Inc.

Parker, Steve & Dewan, Ted. Inside the Whale & Other Animals. (Illus.). (J). 18.95 (978-0-590-73869-9(0)) Scholastic, Inc.

Petrie, Kristin. Baird's Beaked Whales. 2006. (Checkerboard Animal Library). (Illus.). 24p. (J). (gr. k-6). 21.35 (978-1-59679-306-4(6) , Checkerboard Library) ABDO Publishing Co.

—Bowhead Whales. 2006. (Checkerboard Animal Library). (Illus.). 24p. (J). (gr. k-6). 21.35 (978-1-59679-307-1(4) , Checkerboard Library) ABDO Publishing Co.

—Dwarf Sperm Whales. 2006. (Checkerboard Animal Library). (Illus.). 24p. (J). (gr. k-6). 21.35 (978-1-59679-308-8(2) , Checkerboard Library) ABDO Publishing Co.

—Fin Whales. 2006. (Checkerboard Animal Library). (Illus.). 24p. (J). (gr. k-6). 21.35 (978-1-59679-309-5(0) , Checkerboard Library) ABDO Publishing Co.

—Minke Whales. 2006. (Illus.). 24p. (J). (gr. k-6). 21.35 (978-1-59679-310-1(4) , Checkerboard Library) ABDO Publishing Co.

—Pilot Whales. 2006. (Checkerboard Animal Library). (Illus.). 24p. (J). (gr. k-6). 21.35 (978-1-59679-311-8(2) , Checkerboard Library) ABDO Publishing Co.

Prince, Sarah. Whales on the World Wide Web. 2001. (gr. k-3). lib. bdg. 11.65 (978-0-613-33454-9(X)) Tandem Library Bks.

Pringle, Laurence P. Whales! Strange & Wonderful. Henderson, Meryl, illus. 2003. 32p. (J). (gr. 2-4). 15.95 (978-1-56397-439-7(8)) Boyds Mills Pr.

Quadrillion Media Staff. Whales & Dolphins. 1998. (Start Me Up Ser.: Vol. 5). Orig. Title: Wale und Delphine. 48p. (J). (gr. 3-8). mass mkt. 12.95 (978-1-58185-005-5(0) , Tessloff Publishing) Quadrillion Media LLC.

Raff, Courtney Granet. Giant of the Sea: The Story of a Spermaceti Whale. Gould, Shawn, illus. 2005. (Smithsonian Oceanic Collection). 32p. (J). (ps-2). 4.95 (978-1-931465-72-4(X) , B4073); 15.95 (978-1-931465-71-7(1) , B4023); 19.95 incl. audio (978-1-931465-73-1(8) , BC4023); pap. 6.95 (978-1-931465-80-9(0) , S4023) Soundprints.

—Giant of the Sea: The Story of a Spermaceti Whale, Including 12" Toy. Thomas, Doug, illus. 2002. (Smithsonian Oceanic Collection). 32p. (J). (ps-2). 29.95 (978-1-931465-75-5(4) , PB4023) Soundprints.

—Giant of the Sea: The Story of a Spermaceti Whale, Including 6" Toy. Gould, Shawn, illus. 2005. (Smithsonian Oceanic Collection). 32p. (J). (ps-2). 9.95 (978-1-931465-76-2(2) , PB4073) Soundprints.

Rau, Dana Meachen. Guess Who Hunts. 2008. (J). (***978-0-7614-2907-4(7)***) Cavendish, Marshall Bks., Ltd.

Rau, Dana Meachen. The Whale in the Water. 2005. (Nature Ser.). (Illus.). 24p. (J). lib. bdg. 22.79 (978-0-7614-2307-2(9) , Benchmark Bks.) Cavendish, Marshall Corp.

Reiter, Chris. The Blue Whale: A MyReportLinks.com Book. 2003. (Endangered & Threatened Animals Ser.). (Illus.). 48p. (J). (gr. 4-10). lib. bdg. 25.26 (978-0-7660-5055-6(6) , MyReportLinks.com Bks.) Enslow Pubs., Inc.

Rennert, Violette. Little Whales. 2005. (Born to Be Wild Ser.). (Illus.). 23p. (J). lib. bdg. 22.00 (978-0-8368-4740-6(7)) Stevens, Gareth Inc.

Richardson, Adele D. Whales: Giants of the Deep. 2002. (Wild World of Animals Ser.). (Illus.). 24p. (J). (gr. 1-2). lib. bdg. 18.60 (978-0-7368-1141-5(9) , Bridgestone Bks.) Capstone Pr., Inc.

Ripley's Whales & Dolphins, 6 vols., Vol. 2. 2nd ed. 2000. 64p. (YA). 14.95 (978-1-893951-01-3(4)) Ripley Entertainment, Inc.

Ripple, William J. Keiko the Whale, the Star of Free Willy. VanDeVelder, Paul & Jewett, Tim, photos by. 1998. (Illus.). iv, 40p. (J). (ps-4). pap. 9.95 (978-0-9665844-0-0(6)) Nu, Inc.

Robinson, Claire. Whale. 1999. (In the Wild Ser.). 24p. (J). (gr. k-2). lib. bdg. 21.36 (978-1-57572-865-0(6)) Heinemann Library.

—Whales. 2002. (In the Wild Ser.). (Illus.). 24p. (J). (gr. k-2). pap. 6.95 (978-1-58810-325-3(0) , 91050) Heinemann Library.

—Whales. 1999. (gr. k-3). lib. bdg. 14.75 (978-0-613-36137-8(7)); (Illus.). (J). (978-0-606-22025-5(9)) Tandem Library Bks.

Roop, Peter. Whales & Dolphins. 2000. (gr. k-3). lib. bdg. 11.80 (978-0-613-63573-8(6)) Tandem Library Bks.

Roop, Peter & Roop, Connie. Whales & Dolphins. Schwartz, Carol, illus. 2002. (Hello Reader! Science Ser.). 32p. (J). (ps-1). pap. 3.99 (978-0-439-09912-7(9) , Cartwheel Bks.) Scholastic, Inc.

Rosenthal, Sue. Whales. McGinty, Mick, illus. 2003. (Magic School Bus Fact Finder Ser.). 96p. (J). pap. 4.99 (978-0-439-38174-1(6)) Scholastic, Inc.

Rountree, Monica, tr. Ballenas. 2003. (Zoobooks). Orig. Title: Whales. (SPA., Illus.). 24p. (J). (gr. 1-7). lib. bdg. 15.95 (978-1-888153-84-2(9)) Wildlife Education, Ltd.

Royston, Angela. Blue Whales. 2003. (Amazing Animals Ser.). (Illus.). 24p. (J). lib. bdg. 21.35 (978-1-58340-226-9(8)) Weigl Pubs., Inc.

Rustad, Martha E. Whales, Vol. 2. 2005. (Ocean Life Ser.). 24p. (YA). (gr. k-3). pap. (978-0-7368-9085-4(8) , Pebble Bks.) Capstone Pr., Inc.

Rustad, Martha E. H. Whales. Saunders-Smith, Gail, ed. 2001. (Ocean Life Ser.). (Illus.). 24p. (J). (gr. k-1). lib. bdg. 15.93 (978-0-7368-0862-0(0) , Pebble Bks.) Capstone Pr., Inc.

Rylant, Cynthia. The Whales. 2000. (978-0-606-18613-1(1)) Tandem Library Bks.

Salariya, David. The Journey of a Whale. Sorace, Carolyn, photos by. 2000. (Lifecycles Ser.). (Illus.). 32p. (J). (gr. k-2). 25.50 (978-0-531-14521-0(2) , Watts, Franklin) Scholastic Library Publishing.

Seaworld Photographers, photos by. Baby Beluga. 2006. (SeaWorld Library: Vol. 6). (Illus.). 26p. (J). bds. 6.95 (978-0-8249-6643-0(0) , Candy Cane Pr.) Ideals Pubns.

Simon, Seymour. Killer Whales. 2002. (See More Readers Ser.). (Illus.). 32p. (J). (gr. k-4). pap. 3.95 (978-1-58717-142-0(2) , SeaStar Bks.) Chronicle Bks. LLC.

—Killer Whales. 2007. 32p. (J). (ps-3). 16.99 (***978-0-06-028395-7(5)***); lib. bdg. 17.89 (***978-0-06-028396-4(3)***) HarperCollins Pubs.

—Killer Whales. 2002. (gr. 3-6). lib. bdg. 11.80 (978-0-613-58418-0(X)) Tandem Library Bks.

—Seemore Killer Whales. 2006. (J). (SPA.). 14.50 (978-0-8118-5473-3(6)); 32p. pap. 3.95 (978-0-8118-5474-0(4)) Chronicle Bks. LLC.

Skerry, Brian. A Whale on Her Own: The True Story of Wilma the Beluga Whale. Skerry, Brian, photos by. 2000. (Illus.). 32p. (J). (gr. 3-6). 26.19 (978-1-56711-431-7(8) , Blackbirch Pr., Inc.) Thomson Gale.

Smith, Molly. Blue Whale: The World's Biggest Mammal. 2007. (SuperSized! Ser.). (Illus.). 24p. (J). lib. bdg. 21.28 (978-1-59716-385-9(6) , 1265930) Bearport Publishing Co., Inc.

So-Big Whale. 2004. (Plush Pals Board Bks.). (Illus.). (J). (gr. k-1). bds. (978-0-7666-0558-9(2) , 39395) Modern Publishing.

Sobol, Richard. Adelina's Whales. 2003. (Illus.). 32p. (J). (gr. 1-3). 17.99 (978-0-525-47110-3(3) , Dutton Juvenile) Penguin Group (USA) Inc.

Sorace, Carolyn & Salariya, David. The Journey of a Whale. 2000. (Lifecycles Ser.). (Illus.). 32p. (J). (gr. k-2). pap. 6.95 (978-0-531-15420-5(3) , Watts, Franklin) Scholastic Library Publishing.

Spilsbury, Louise & Spilsbury, Richard. A Pod of Whales. 2003. (Animal Groups Ser.). (Illus.). 32p. pap. 6.95 (978-1-4034-3286-5(4)); (J). lib. bdg. 24.22 (978-1-4034-0743-6(6)) Heinemann Library.

—Save the Blue Whale. 2006. (Illus.). 32p. (J). 25.36 (978-1-4034-7805-4(8)); pap. (978-1-4034-7813-9(9)) Heinemann Library.

Squire, Ann. Beluga Whales. 2006. (True Book Ser.). (Illus.). 47p. (J). (978-0-516-25469-2(3)) Children's Pr., Ltd.

—Beluga Whales. 2006. (True Book Ser.). (J). (978-0-516-22822-8(6) , Children's Pr.) Scholastic Library Publishing.

Steck-Vaughn Staff. Amazing Whales Level B: Early Reader. 2003. (Illus.). bds. (978-0-7398-8223-8(6)) Steck-Vaughn.

—Early Reader Program Level B: Amazing Whales, 6 Pack. 2004. (Illus.). pap. 33.00 (978-0-7398-8256-6(2)) Steck-Vaughn.

Stille, Darlene. I Am a Whale: The Life of a Humpback Whale. Ouren, Todd, illus. 2004. (I Live in the Ocean Ser.). 24p. (J). (gr. k-2). lib. bdg. 22.60 (978-1-4048-0600-9(8)) Picture Window Bks.

Stonehouse, Bernard. Sharks. Camm, Martin, illus. (Animal Watch Ser.). 48p. (YA). (gr. 4-9). 16.95 (978-0-8160-3924-1(0)) Facts On File, Inc.

Swanson, Diane. Whales. 1998. (Welcome to the World of Animals Ser.). (Illus.). 32p. (J). (gr. 3 up). lib. bdg. 23.33 (978-0-8368-2216-8(1)) Stevens, Gareth Inc.

The Tale of a White Whale: Digraph wh: Level B, 6 vols. (Wright Skills Ser.). 16p. (gr. k-3). 17.95 (978-0-322-01474-9(3)) Wright Group, The.

Theodorou, Rod. Blue Whale. (Animals in Danger Ser.). (Illus.). 32p. (J). (gr. k-2). 2002. pap. 6.95 (978-1-58810-443-4(5) , 91151); 2000. lib. bdg. 21.36 (978-1-57572-263-4(1)) Heinemann Library.

Thomas, Isabel. Shark vs. Killer Whale. 2006. (Illus.). 32p. (J). (978-1-4109-2392-9(4)); pap. (978-1-4109-2399-8(1)) Steck-Vaughn.

Thomson, Sarah L. Amazing Whales! (I Can Read Bks.). (Illus.). 32p. (J). 2006. pap. 3.99 (978-0-06-054467-6(8) , Harper Trophy); 2005. 15.99 (978-0-06-054465-2(1)); 2005. lib. bdg. 17.89 (978-0-06-054466-9(X)) HarperCollins Pubs.

Tracqui, Valerie. The Whale. 2004. (Animal Close-Ups Ser.). (Illus.). 28p. (J). pap. 6.95 (978-1-57091-625-0(X)) Charlesbridge Publishing, Inc.

Trumbauer, Lisa. The Life Cycle of a Whale. 2002. (Life Cycles Ser.). (Illus.). 24p. (J). (gr. k-1). lib. bdg. 15.93 (978-0-7368-1186-6(9) , Pebble Bks.) Capstone Pr., Inc.

Welsbacher, Anne. Killer Whales. 2002. (Predators in the Wild Ser.). (Illus.). 32p. (J). (gr. 2-3). lib. bdg. 21.26 (978-0-7368-1065-4(X) , Capstone High-Interest Bks.) Capstone Pr., Inc.

Welvaert, Scott R. Whales. 2005. (World of Mammals Ser.). (Illus.). 24p. (J). 21.26 (978-0-7368-3721-7(3)) Capstone Pr., Inc.

Wexo, John Bonnett. Whales. (Zoobooks). (Illus.). 24p. (J). (gr. 1-7). 2001. 15.95 (978-1-888153-34-7(2) , 272-6); 2003. 10.95 (978-1-888153-97-2(0) , Zoo Bks.) Wildlife Education, Ltd.

The Whale: Review & Practice Book for Level B, 6 vols. (Wright Skills Ser.). 16p. (gr. k-3). 26.50 (978-0-322-03100-5(1)) Wright Group, The.

Whale Museum Staff. Gentle Giants of the Sea. 2nd ed. 214p. (J). (gr. k-6). pap. 15.95 (978-0-933331-25-9(8)) Whale Museum/Moclips Cetological Society, The.

The Whale Watchers, 6, Pack. (gr. 1-2). 22.00 (978-0-7635-9181-6(5)) Rigby Education.

Whales. (Under the Sea Ser.). (J). 24p. 6.95 (978-0-7368-5115-2(1)); 32p. 6.95 (978-0-7368-8073-2(9)) Capstone Pr., Inc.

Whales, 6 vols. (gr. k-2). 28.95 (978-0-7368-9106-6(4)); (gr. 2-5). 36.95 (978-0-7368-8183-8(2)) Red Brick Learning.

Whales: Individual Title Six-Packs. 16p. (gr. 3 up). 36.00 (978-0-7635-9684-2(1)) Rigby Education.

Whales: Level N, 6 vols. (Wonder Worldtm Ser.). 48p. 34.95 (978-0-7802-2915-0(0)) Wright Group, The.

Whales & Dolphins. (Eyes on Nature Ser.). 32p. (J). (gr. 1). pap. (978-1-882210-56-5(5)) Action Publishing, Inc.

Whales & Dolphins. (Eyes on Nature Ser.). (Illus.). 32p. (J). (gr. 1 up). 7.95 (978-1-56156-423-1(0)) Kidsbooks, Inc.

Whales & Other Sea Mammals. 2002. (Wild, Wild World Ser.). 32p. (J). 9.95 (978-0-7525-4683-4(X)) Parragon, Inc.

Whales Oceans Alive. 2006. (Illus.). 24p. (J). (gr. k-2). 18.50 (***978-0-531-17875-1(7)***) Scholastic Library Publishing.

Whales Set II. 2006. (J). (gr. k-6). 128.10 (978-1-59679-305-7(8) , Checkerboard Library) ABDO Publishing Co.

Whitecap Books Staff. Whales. 2000. (Investigate Ser.). (Illus.). 64p. (J). (gr. 1-7). pap. 3.95 (978-1-55285-066-4(8)) Whitecap Bks., Ltd. CAN. *Dist:* Firefly Bks., Ltd.

Wildlife Education, Ltd Staff, contrib. by. Whales. 2006. (Critters Up Close Ser.). (Illus.). (J). bds. 5.95 (***978-1-932396-17-1(9)***) Wildlife Education, Ltd.

Williams, Alwena & Drake, Gwasg Addysgol. Morfilod. 2005. (WEL., Illus.). 33p. (978-0-86174-101-4(3)) Drake Educational Assocs. Ltd.

Wolpert, Tom. Whales for Kids. McGee, John F., illus. 2nd ed. 2000. (Wildlife for Kids Ser.). 45p. (J). (gr. 3-7). pap. 6.95 (978-1-55971-727-4(0) , NorthWord Bks. for Young Readers) T&N Children's Publishing.

World Book, Inc. Staff, contrib. by. Blue Whales & Other Baleen Whales. 2005. (World Book's Animals of the World Ser.). (Illus.). 64p. (J). (978-0-7166-1264-3(X)) World Bk., Inc.

A World of Whales, 6 vols. (Book2WebTM Ser.). (gr. 4-8). 36.50 (978-0-322-02969-9(4)) Wright Group, The.

Worth, Bonnie. A Whale of a Tale! All about Porpoises, Dolphins, & Whales. Ruiz, Aristides & Mathieu, Joseph, illus. 2006. (Cat in the Hat's Learning Library). 48p. (J). (gr. k-3). 8.99 (978-0-375-82279-7(8)); lib. bdg. 12.99 (978-0-375-92279-4(2)) Random Hse. Children's Bks. (Random Hse. Bks. for Young Readers).

WHALES—FICTION

Anderson, M. T. & Moore, Stephen. Whales on Stilts: M. T. Anderson's Thrilling Tales. Cyrus, Kurt, illus. 2006. (M. T. Anderson's Thrilling Tales Ser.). 224p. (J). reprint ed. pap. 5.95 (978-0-15-205394-9(8) , Harcourt Paperbacks) Harcourt Children's Bks.

—Whales on Stilts! Thrilling Tales. Cyrus, Kurt, illus. 2005. (M. T. Anderson's Thrilling Tales Ser.). 208p. (J). 15.00 (978-0-15-205340-6(9)) Harcourt Children's Bks.

Bailer, Darice. Humpback Goes North. Marchesi, Stephen, illus. 1998. (Smithsonian Oceanic Collection). 32p. (J). (ps-3). 15.95 (978-1-56899-525-0(3)) Soundprints.

—Humpback Goes North: (Includes Large Plush Toy) Marchesi, Stephen, illus. 1998. (Smithsonian Oceanic Collection). 32p. (J). (ps-2). 29.95 (978-1-56899-529-8(6)) Soundprints.

—Humpback Goes North. (Includes Micro Book) Marchesi, Stephen, illus. 1998. (Smithsonian Oceanic Collection). 32p. (J). (ps-2). 4.95 (978-1-56899-526-7(1) , B4065) Soundprints.

—Humpback Goes North: (Includes Small & Large Plush Toy) Marchesi, Stephen, illus. 1998. (Smithsonian Oceanic Collection). 32p. (J). (ps-2). 38.95 incl. audio (978-1-56899-631-8(4)) Soundprints.

Baird, Alison. White as the Waves: A Novel of Moby Dick. 1999. 288p. (J). pap. (978-1-894294-03-4(3)) Creative Bk. Publishing.

Baruffi, Andrea, illus. Henry's Wrong Turn. 2006. (I'm Going to Read Ser.). 32p. (J). pap. 3.95 (978-1-4027-2107-6(2)) Sterling Publishing Co., Inc.

Because of Walter, 6 Packs. (Action Packs Ser.). 104p. (gr. 3-5). 44.00 (978-0-7635-8402-3(9)) Rigby Education.

Beluga Goes South. 2002. (Oceanic Mini Bks.). (Illus.). 32p. (J). (978-1-59069-004-8(4) , H1005) Studio Mouse LLC.

Blanchet, M. Wylie. A Whale Named Henry. Matthews, Miriam, illus. unabr. ed. 78p. (Orig.). (J). (978-0-920080-33-7(2)) Harbour Publishing Co., Ltd.

Blume, Rebecca. Baby Whales. Blume, Rebecca, illus. 2007. (Illus.). 8p. (J). 5.00 (***978-0-9785427-2-6(X)***) Liberty Artists Management.

Bonnell, Kris. The Little Boat. 2006. (J). 3.95 (***978-1-933727-34-9(9)***) Reading Reading Bks., LLC.

Borchard, Therese Johnson. Whitney Rides the Whale with Jonah: And Learns She Can't Run Away. 1999. (Emerald Bible Collection). (Illus.). 80p. (gr. 3-7). 5.95 (978-0-8091-6663-3(1) , 6663-1) Paulist Pr.

Broger, Achim. Adios, Querida Ballena. (SPA.). (J). (gr. k-2). 12.95 (978-84-261-2268-1(X) , JV0009) Juventud, Editorial ESP. *Dist:* AIMS International Bks., Inc., Lectorum Pubns., Inc.

—Buenos Dias... Ballena. 9th ed. (SPA., Illus.). 32p. (J). (gr. k-2). 12.95 (978-84-261-1548-5(9) , JV0116) Juventud, Editorial ESP. *Dist:* AIMS International Bks., Inc., Lectorum Pubns., Inc.

Brook, Henry, retold by. Moby Dick. 2005. (Paperback Classics Ser.). 144p. (J). pap. 4.95 (978-0-7945-0899-9(5) , Usborne) EDC Publishing.

Brown, Janet Allison, et al. Jonah & the Whale. Durantz, Summer, illus. 2003. (Inspirational Collection). 24p. (J). pap. 3.99 (978-0-7696-3126-4(6) , Brighter Child) School Specialty Publishing.

Bunting, Eve. Whales Passing. Davis, Lambert, illus. 2003. 32p. (J). pap. 15.95 (978-0-590-60358-4(2) , Blue Sky Pr., The) Scholastic, Inc.

Burton, Martin Nelson. The Whale Comedian. Jordan, Charles, illus. 1999. 32p. (ps-3). 15.95 (978-0-9666490-8-6(7)) London Town Pr.

Capdevila, Roser. Moby Dick. 2002. (Cuentos Fantasticos de las Tres Mellizas Coleccion: Vol. 1). (SPA.). (J). (gr. k-2). pap. 5.95 (978-1-930332-38-6(6) , LC6629) Lectorum Pubns., Inc.

Carey, Kathleen. Anna & the Whale. Wells, Matt, illus. 2005. 42p. (J). (978-0-9769500-0-4(6)) Carey, Kathleen.

Collier, Kevin Scott. Journeys of Hope, Pearl of Wisdom. Collier, Kevin Scott, illus. 2006. (Illus.). 28p. (J). E-Book 9.95 incl. cd-rom (978-1-933090-31-3(6)) Guardian Angel Publishing, Inc.

Curran, Steven Earl. Whales used to Fly in the Sky. 2005. 9.00 (978-0-8059-8086-8(5)) Dorrance Publishing Co., Inc.

Dahlin, Bill. The Pig & the Whale. Hohnstadt, Cedric, illus. 1999. 15p. (J). pap. 8.97 (978-0-9678028-0-0(6)) Dahlin, Bill.

Dalmatian Press Staff, adapted by. Moby Dick. 2002. (Spot the Classics Ser.). (Illus.). 180p. (J). (gr. k-5). 4.99 (978-1-57759-547-2(5)) Dalmatian Pr.

—Moby Dick. (J). 9.95 (978-1-56156-308-1(0)) Kidsbooks, Inc.

Davis, Buddy. Whale of a Story: Adventures on the High Seas. 2003. 40p. (J). 14.99 (978-0-89051-390-3(2)) Master Bks.

Davis, Maggie Steincrohn. Garden of Whales. 2000. (gr. k-3). lib. bdg. 15.25 (978-0-613-77755-1(7)) Tandem Library Bks.

—A Garden of Whales. O'Connell, Jennifer Barrett, illus. 2000. 32p. (J). (ps-2). reprint ed. pap. 6.95 (978-0-944475-35-5(3)) Camden Hse. Publishing CAN. *Dist:* Firefly Bks., Ltd.

Disney Staff & Trimble, Irene. A Whale of a Time. Goudreau, Daryl, illus. 2002. 24p. (J). (gr. k-k). pap. 3.25 (978-0-7364-1307-7(3) , RH/Disney) Random Hse. Children's Bks.

D'Lacey, Chris. Dexter's Journey. Roberts, David, illus. 2001. (Blue Bananas Ser.). 48p. (J). (gr. 1-2). (978-0-7787-0846-9(2)); pap. (978-0-7787-0892-6(6)) Crabtree Publishing Co.

—Dexter's Journey. 2002. (gr. k-3). lib. bdg. 12.95 (978-0-613-52829-0(8)) Tandem Library Bks.

Donahue, Shari Faden. The Zebra-Striped Whale with the Polka-Dot Tail. Donahue, Shari Faden, illus. 2001. (Illus.). 48p. (ps up). 16.95 (978-0-9634287-3-8(X)) Arimax, Inc.

Donaldson, Julia. The Snail & the Whale. Scheffler, Axel, tr. Scheffler, Axel, illus. 2004. 32p. (J). (gr. k-3). 16.99 (978-0-8037-2922-3(7) , Dial) Penguin Group (USA) Inc.

—The Snail & the Whale. Scheffler, Axel, illus. 2006. 32p. (J). reprint ed. pap. 6.99 (978-0-14-240580-2(9) , Puffin) Penguin Group (USA) Inc.

Douglas, Babette. Kiss a Me: A Little Whale Watching. 2004. (J). 9.99 (978-1-890343-08-8(0)) Kiss A Me Productions, Inc.

—Kiss A Me: Goes to School. 2004. (J). 9.99 (978-1-890343-09-5(9)) Kiss A Me Productions, Inc.

—Kiss a Me: To the Rescue. 2004. (J). 9.99 (978-1-890343-11-8(0)) Kiss A Me Productions, Inc.

Dresden, Sean. Killer Tales of the Great White. 2001. (Illus.). 96p. (J). (gr. 3-7). pap. 5.95 (978-0-7373-0589-0(4)) Lowell Hse. Juvenile.

Duane, Diane. Deep Wizardry. (Young Wizards Ser.: Bk. 2). 384p. (YA). 2003. (Illus.). pap. 6.95 (978-0-15-204942-3(8)); 2001. (gr. 5 up). pap. 6.95 (978-0-15-216257-3(7)) Harcourt Children's Bks. (Magic Carpet Bks.).

—Deep Wizardry. 2003. (gr. 3-6). lib. bdg. 15.25 (978-0-613-71628-4(0)); 2001. (gr. 5-8). lib. bdg. 15.25 (978-0-613-36059-3(1)) Tandem Library Bks.

Dunn, Richard & Sprick, Jessica. Whales: Read Well Level K Unit 18 Storybook. Koontz, Robin Michal, illus. 2003. (Read Well Level K Ser.). 20p. (J). (978-1-57035-689-6(0) , 55589) Sopris West Educational Services.

Durkee, Noura. Yunus & the Whale. Durkee, Noura, illus. 1999. (Illus.). 25p. (J). (gr. 1-5). 10.00 (978-1-879402-59-1(9)) Tahrike Tarsile Quran, Inc.

Edwardson, Debby Dahl. Whale Snow. Patterson, Annie, illus. 2004. 32p. (J). (ENG.). pap. 7.95 (978-1-57091-496-6(6)); pap. (978-1-57091-394-5(3)); 15.95 (978-1-57091-393-8(5)) Charlesbridge Publishing, Inc.

Evans, Sally. Sea Treasure. Richardson, Linda, illus. 2004. (J). 16.95 (978-1-59094-073-0(3) , 1590940733, Jawbreakers for Kids) Jawbone Publishing Corp.

Farrelly, Peter. Abigale the Happy Whale. Rama, Jamie, illus. 2006. 32p. (J). (ps-1). 15.99 (978-0-316-01190-7(8) , Tingley, Megan Bks.) Little, Brown Bks. for Young Readers.

Franklin, Kristine L. The Gift. Lavallee, Barbara, illus. 1999. 40p. (J). (ps-3). 14.95 (978-0-8118-0447-9(X)) Chronicle Bks. LLC.

French, Vivian. Whale Journey. 1998. (Illus.). 32p. (J). (gr. k-4). (978-1-84089-022-8(3) , Zero to Ten, Limited) Evans Publishing Group.

Garner, Alan. The Owl Service. 2006. (Illus.). 240p. (J). pap. 6.95 (978-0-15-205618-6(1) , Magic Carpet Bks.) Harcourt Children's Bks.

Gill, Shelley. Big Blue. Barrow, Ann, illus. 32p. (J). (ps-6). 2005. pap. 6.95 (978-1-57091-667-0(5)); 2004. 15.95 (978-1-57091-352-5(8)) Charlesbridge Publishing, Inc.

Greenburg, J. C. In the Whale. Reed, Mike, illus. 2003. (Andrew Lost Ser.: Bk. 6). 96p. (J). (gr. 2-5). pap. 3.99 (978-0-375-82524-8(X) , Random Hse. Bks. for Young Readers) Random Hse. Children's Bks.

Grigg, Carol. The Singing Snowbear. Grigg, Carol, illus. 1999. (Illus.). 32p. (J). (gr. k-3). tchr. ed. 15.00 (978-0-395-94223-9(3)) Houghton Mifflin Co. Trade & Reference Div.

Grokett, Jan. Songs of the Orcas. l.t. ed. 2002. 48p. (J). per. 9.99 (978-1-893108-72-1(4)) Neighborhood Pr. Publishing.

Hagerty, Carol, ed. Moby Dick. 1998. (Classics Ser.: Set II). 77p. (YA). (gr. 5-12). pap. 7.95 (978-1-56254-258-0(3) , SP2583) Saddleback Educational Publishing.

Hanson, Anders. Whale Tale. Nobens, C. A., illus. 2007. (Fact & Fiction Ser.). 24p. (J). pap. (978-1-59928-477-4(4)); 21.35 (978-1-59928-476-7(6)) ABDO Publishing Co.

Heaney, Jocelyn. Tales of the Great White. 1999. (Roxbury Park Bks.). (Illus.). 96p. (J). (gr. 3-7). pap. 5.95 (978-0-7373-0183-0(X) , 0183XW) McGraw-Hill/ Contemporary.

Hernandez, Ruben. Elisa Escuchaba el Canto de Las Ballenas. Corichi, Yadhira, illus. rev. ed. 2003. (Castillo de la Lectura Blanca Ser.). (SPA.). 48p. (J). (gr. 1-3). pap. 6.95 (978-970-20-0141-6(2)) Castillo, Ediciones, S. A. de C. V. MEX. *Dist:* Macmillan.

Hicks, Bob. Narvick the Whark (or a Shwale) 2003. (Illus.). cd-rom 9.95 (978-0-9729703-0-3(4)) Kidderature Publishing.

Hiebert, Elfrieda H. Humpback Whales. (Little Book Practice Reader Ser.). (J). (978-0-8136-0809-9(0)) Modern Curriculum Pr.

Hill, Ros. Shamooo: A Whale of a Cow. Hill, Ros, illus. 2005. (Illus.). 32p. (J). 15.95 (978-0-689-04634-6(0) , Milk & Cookies) ibooks, Inc.

Himmelman, John. Pipaluk & the Whales. 2002. (Illus.). 32p. (J). (gr. 3-7). 16.95 (978-0-7922-8217-4(5) , National Geographic Children's Bks.) National Geographic Society.

Holler, Paul. Nicholas & the Whales. 2001. 180p. (J). pap. 13.00 (978-1-58338-400-8(6) , CrossroadsPub.Org) CrossroadsPub.com.

Humpback's Springtime Journey. 2002. (Oceanic Mini Bks.). (Illus.). 32p. (J). (978-1-59069-007-9(9) , H1008) Studio Mouse LLC.

Ihimaera, Witi. The Whale Rider. 2003. Orig. Title: Te Kaieke Tohora. (YA). (gr. 3-6). 152p. 17.00 (978-0-15-205017-7(5)); 168p. pap. 8.00 (978-0-15-205016-0(7) , Harcourt Paperbacks) Harcourt Children's Bks.

—Whale Rider. 2003. (gr. 5-8). lib. bdg. 16.45 (978-0-613-70660-5(9)) Tandem Library Bks.

Ita, Sam. Moby-Dick: A Pop-up Book. 2007. (Illus.). 8p. (J). 24.95 ***(978-1-4027-4528-7(1))*** Sterling Publishing Co., Inc.

Jake's Tale. 2004. (Illus.). (J). (978-1-59577-006-6(2)) Starfall Education.

James, Simon. Querido Salvatierra. de la Vega, Eida, tr. from ENG. 2003. Tr. of Dear Mr. Blueberry. (SPA.). (J). (gr. k-2). pap. 6.95 (978-1-930332-45-4(9)) Lectorum Pubns., Inc.

—Querido Salvatierra. 2003. Tr. of Dear Mr. Blueberry. (SPA.). (gr. k-3). lib. bdg. 15.25 (978-0-613-64586-7(3)) Tandem Library Bks.

Jennings, Richard W. The Great Whale of Kansas. 2001. (Illus.). 160p. (J). (gr. 5-9). tchr. ed. 15.00 (978-0-618-10228-0(0) , Walter Lorraine) Houghton Mifflin Co. Trade & Reference Div.

Katz, Welwyn W. Whalesinger. 2002. 212p. (YA). pap. 5.95 (978-0-88899-191-1(6)) Groundwood Bks. CAN. *Dist:* Perseus Distribution.

Kessler, Deirdre. Lena & the Whale. Burden, P. John, illus. 2002. 36p. (J). pap. 7.95 (978-1-55109-425-0(8)) Nimbus Publishing, Ltd. CAN. *Dist:* National Bk. Network.

Kita, Suzanne. Three Whales Who Won the Heart of the World. Sundram, Steve, illus. 2000. (ENG & JPN.). (J). 12.99 (978-0-89610-336-8(6)) Island Heritage Publishing.

Lewis, Paul Owen. Storm Boy. Lewis, Paul Owen, illus. 1999. (Illus.). 32p. (J). (gr. 2 up). lib. bdg. 22.60 (978-0-8368-2229-8(3)) Stevens, Gareth Inc.

—Storm Boy. 2004. (Illus.). 32p. (J). (gr. k-5). 6.95 (978-1-58246-057-4(4) , Tricycle Pr.) Ten Speed Pr.

London, Jonathan. Baby Whale's Journey. Van Zyle, Jon, illus. 40p. (J). 2007. pap. 6.95 (978-0-8118-5761-1(1)); 1999. 15.95 (978-0-8118-2496-5(9)) Chronicle Bks. LLC.

Lower, Joseph N. Cry from the Blue. 2005. pap. 9.00 (978-0-8059-6971-9(3)) Dorrance Publishing Co., Inc.

Lucas, David. Whale. 2007. 32p. (J). (gr. k-3). 16.99 (978-0-375-84338-9(8)); lib. bdg. 19.99 (978-0-375-94338-6(2)) Random Hse. Children's Bks. (Knopf Bks. for Young Readers).

Lum, Leimomi o. Kamahae Kuamoo Mookini. The Legend of Kuamo'o Mo'okini & Hamumu the Great Whale. Kam, Kathleen, illus. 2004. 24p. (J). 12.95 (978-1-58178-036-9(2)) Bishop Museum Pr.

McCloskey, Robert. Burt Dow: Deep-Water Man. 2001. (J). (gr. 1-4). 12.00 (978-0-7887-5510-1(2)) Recorded Bks., LLC.

McFarlane, Sheryl. Waiting for the Whales. 1998. (gr. k-3). lib. bdg. 16.40 (978-0-613-86453-4(0)) Tandem Library Bks.

McNulty, Faith & Shiffman, Lena. Le Chant des Baleines. (Hello Reader! Ser.). (FRE., Illus.). 40p. (J). pap. 5.99 (978-0-590-16027-8(3)) Scholastic, Inc.

MCP Staff. Humpback Whales, 6 bks., set, Level 10, Bk. 36. 2003. (J). (ps-3). 33.50 (978-0-8136-0808-2(2)) Modern Curriculum Pr.

McVeity, Jen. On Different Shores. 1998. (Illus.). 167p. (YA). (gr. 5-9). 17.99 (978-0-531-33115-6(6)); pap. 16.95 (978-0-531-30115-9(X)) Scholastic, Inc. (Orchard Bks.).

Melville, Herman. Cities of the Fantastic: Brusel. Eisner, Will, illus. 2003. (Cities of the Fantastic Ser.). 120p. 19.95 (978-1-56163-291-6(0)) NBM Publishing Co.

—Herman Melville/Moby Dick. Niño, Alex, illus. 2005. 48p. (gr. 5-8). 25.50 (978-0-7910-9106-7(6)) Facts On File, Inc.

—Moby Dick. 2002. (Great Illustrated Classics Ser.). (Illus.). 240p. (J). (gr. 3-8). 21.35 (978-1-57765-695-1(4) , ABDO & Daughters) ABDO Publishing Co.

—Moby Dick. Giordano, Dick, illus. 2002. 48p. (J). (gr. 5). tchr. ed. 16.00 (978-0-618-26571-8(6)) Houghton Mifflin Co. Trade & Reference Div.

—Moby Dick. 2000. (Coleccion "Clasicos Juveniles" Ser.). (SPA.). 228p. (YA). pap. 12.95 (978-0-595-13218-8(9)) iUniverse, Inc.

—Moby Dick. 2003. (Illus.). 32p. 7.95 (978-1-56163-294-7(5)) NBM Publishing Co.

—Moby Dick. Eisner, Will, illus. 2003. 32p. (gr. 4-7). 15.95 (978-1-56163-293-0(7)) NBM Publishing Co.

—Moby Dick. Nino, Alex, illus. 2nd ed. 1998. (Illustrated Classic Book Ser.). 61p. (J). (gr. 3 up). reprint ed. pap. 4.95 (978-1-56767-235-0(3)) Educational Insights, Inc.

—Moby Dick. adapted ed. (YA). (gr. 5-12). pap. 8.50 (978-0-8359-0225-0(0)) Globe Fearon Educational Publishing.

—Moby Dick. 2nd ed. 2003. (Historias de Siempre Ser.). (SPA., Illus.). 92p. (J). (gr. 5-8). pap. 9.95 (978-84-204-5732-1(9)) Santillana USA Publishing Co., Inc.

—Moby Dick: With a Discussion of Determination. 2003. (Values in Action Illustrated Classics Ser.). (Illus.). 190p. (J). (978-1-59203-033-0(5)) Learning Challenge, Inc.

—Moby Dick, Grades 5-12. adapted ed. pap., tchr. ed. 4.95 (978-0-8359-0123-9(8)) Globe Fearon Educational Publishing.

—Moby Dick, or the Whale. 2005. (J). Pt. 1. pap. 9.95 (978-1-4105-0263-6(5)); Pt. 1. cd-rom (978-1-4105-0265-0(1)); Pt. 2. pap. 9.95 (978-1-4105-0267-4(8)); Pt. 2. cd-rom (978-1-4105-0269-8(4)) Johnston, Don Inc.

Melville, Herman & Huth, Michael. Moby Dick. 2004. (GER., Illus.). 92p. (978-3-921743-52-2(4)) Maximilian-Gesellschaft e. V.

Melville, Herman & Schwartz, Lew Sayre. Moby Dick. Giordano, Dick, illus. 2002. 48p. (J). pap. 6.95 (978-0-618-26572-5(4)) Houghton Mifflin Co. Trade & Reference Div.

Melville, Herman, et al. Moby Dick. (Classics Illustrated Ser.). (Illus.). 52p. (YA). pap. 4.95 (978-1-57209-003-3(0)) Classics International Entertainment, Inc.

Metaxas, Eric & Kenney, Cindy. Jonah & the Pirates Who Don't Do Anything. Eddy, Ron & Vann, Robert, illus. 2002. 32p. (J). 12.99 (978-0-310-70460-7(X)) Zonderkidz.

Moore, Eva. Wild Whale Watch. 2000. (gr. 3-6). lib. bdg. 11.80 (978-0-613-27585-9(3)) Tandem Library Bks.

Nobisso, Josephine. Shh! The Whale Is Smiling. Hyde, Maureen, illus. 2nd rev. ed. 2000. 40p. (J). (ps-2). reprint ed. 16.95 (978-0-940112-03-2(5)); pap. 8.95 (978-0-940112-06-3(X)) Gingerbread Hse.

—Shh! The Whale Is Smiling. 2000. (gr. k-3). lib. bdg. 17.60 (978-0-613-70818-0(0)) Tandem Library Bks.

Oades, Joy. Willie the Whale. Vagnozzi, Barbara, illus. 2004. (Read-It! Readers Ser.). 32p. (C). (gr. k-3). 18.60 (978-1-4048-0557-6(5)) Picture Window Bks.

Oppel, Kenneth. Peg & the Whale. ed. 2004. (Illus.). (J). (gr. k-3). spiral bd. (978-0-616-07245-5(7)) Canadian National Institute for the Blind/Institut National Canadien pour les Aveugles.

Orca's Escape. 2002. (Oceanic Mini Bks.). (Illus.). 32p. (J). (978-1-59069-010-9(9) , H1011) Studio Mouse LLC.

Pearl, Barbara. Whale of a Tale. 2005. (Illus.). 32p. (J). 14.95 (978-0-9647924-7-0(8)) Crane Bks.

Pfister, Marcus. Pez Arco Iris y la Balena Azul, el Big Book: Rainbow Fish. Pfister, Marcus, illus. 1999. (Rainbow Fish Ser.). Orig. Title: Regenbogenfisch und Grosser Blauer Wal. (SPA., Illus.). 32p. (J). (ps-3). pap. 25.00 (978-0-7358-1215-4(2)) North-South Bks., Inc.

—Pez Arco Iris y la Ballena Azul. Pfister, Marcus, illus. 1998. (Rainbow Fish Ser.). Orig. Title: Regenbogenfisch und Grosser Blauer Wal. (SPA., Illus.). 32p. (J). (ps-3). 18.95 (978-0-7358-1002-0(8) , NSB028) North-South Bks., Inc.

—Rainbow Fish & the Big, Blue Whale. James, J. Alison, tr. from GER. Pfister, Marcus, illus. 1998. (Rainbow Fish Ser.). Orig. Title: Regenbogenfisch und Grosser Blauer Wal. (Illus.). 32p. (J). (ps-3). 18.88 (978-0-7358-1010-5(9)) North-South Bks., Inc.

—Rainbow Fish & the Big Blue Whale. 2001. (Rainbow Fish Ser.). Orig. Title: Regenbogenfisch und Grosser Blauer Wal. (Illus.). 14p. (J). (ps-3). bds. 9.95 (978-0-7358-1430-1(9)) North-South Bks., Inc.

—Rainbow Fish & the Big Blue Whale. James, J. Alison, tr. from GER. Pfister, Marcus, illus. 1998. (Rainbow Fish Ser.). Orig. Title: Regenbogenfisch und Grosser Blauer Wal. (Illus.). 32p. (J). (ps-3). 18.95 (978-0-7358-1009-9(5)) North-South Bks., Inc.

—Rainbow Fish & the Big Blue Whale. Pfister, Marcus, illus. 1999. (Rainbow Fish Ser.). Orig. Title: Regenbogenfisch und Grosser Blauer Wal. (Illus.). 32p. (J). (ps-3). reprint ed. pap. 25.00 (978-0-7358-1214-7(4)) North-South Bks., Inc.

Pinkney, Andrea Davis. Peggony-Po: A Whale of a Tale. Pinkney, Brian, illus. 2006. 32p. (ps-2). 16.99 (978-0-7868-1958-4(8) , Jump at the Sun) Hyperion Bks. for Children.

Pitcher, Caroline & Morris, Jackie. The Snow Whale. 1999. (Illus.). 32p. (J). (ps-2). pap. 7.99 (978-0-7112-1093-6(4)) Lincoln, Frances Ltd. GBR. *Dist:* Transition Vendor.

Polak, Monique. No More Pranks. 2006. (Orca Soundings Ser.). 112p. (YA). lib. bdg. 14.95 (978-1-55143-584-8(5)) Orca Bk. Pubs. USA.

Raff, Courtney Granet. Giant of the Sea: A Story of a Sperm Whale. 2002. (gr. k-3). lib. bdg. 15.25 (978-0-613-70909-5(8)) Tandem Library Bks.

Randall, Ronne. Get off My Tail, Little Whale! Church, Caroline Jayne, illus. 2002. (Little Friends Ser.). 14p. (J). (ps-1). 12.95 (978-1-57145-772-1(0) , Silver Dolphin Bks.) Advantage Pubs. Group.

Rea, Ba & Rea, C. J. A Whale's Tale from the Supper Sea. Rea, Ba, illus. 1999. (Illus.). 32p. (J). (gr. k-6). pap. 10.95 (978-0-9657472-1-9(2)) Bas Relief Publishing.

Reader's Digest Editors. The Whale's Tale. Moroney, Tracey, illus. 1998. (Little Bible Playbooks Ser.: Vol. 2). 18p. (J). (ps-3). bds. 4.99 (978-1-57584-261-5(0) , Reader's Digest Children's Bks.) Reader's Digest Children's Publishing, Inc.

Riner, Sherry. Wally the Whale Learns How to Be a Winner. Morris, Lillie, illus. 2004. 43p. pap. 19.95 (978-1-4137-3129-3(5)) PublishAmerica, Inc.

Rockhill, Dennis. Ocean Whisper/Susurro del Océano. de la Vega, Eida, tr. Rockhill, Dennis, illus. 2005. Tr. of Susurro del Océano. (SPA & ENG., Illus.). 32p. (J). 16.95 (978-0-9741992-4-5(9) , 626999) Raven Tree Pr.

Rylant, Cynthia. The Whale. McDaniels, Preston, illus. 2004. (Lighthouse Family Ser.). 61p. (J). (ps-k). lib. bdg. 10.79 (978-0-606-33956-8(6)) Tandem Library Bks.

—The Whales. 2000. (Illus.). 40p. (J). (ps-3). pap. 5.99 (978-0-590-61560-0(2)) Scholastic, Inc.

Rylant, Cynthia & McDaniels, Preston. The Whale. 2004. (Lighthouse Family Ser.). (Illus.). 96p. (J). pap. 3.99 (978-0-689-84883-4(8) , Aladdin) Simon & Schuster Children's Publishing.

Scholes, Katherine. El Nino y la Ballena. (SPA.). (J). 7.95 (978-958-04-6020-6(5)) Norma S.A. COL. *Dist:* Distribuidora Norma, Inc.

Schuch, Steve. A Symphony of Whales. Sylvada, Peter, illus. 2002. 32p. (J). (gr. 1-4). pap. 7.00 (978-0-15-216548-2(7) , Voyager Bks./Libros Viajeros) Harcourt Children's Bks.

—Symphony of Whales. 2002. (gr. k-3). lib. bdg. 14.15 (978-0-613-56636-0(X)) Tandem Library Bks.

Schuch, Steve & Sylvada, Peter. A Symphony of Whales. 1998. (J). 16.00 (978-0-15-100289-4(4)) Harcourt Trade Pubs.

Schwartz, Lew Sayre. Moby Dick: Based on the Novel by Herman Melville. 2002. (gr. 5-8). lib. bdg. 15.25 (978-0-613-70733-6(8)) Tandem Library Bks.

Scott, James, adapted by. Moby Dick: Reproducible Teaching Unit. 2001. 110p. (YA). (gr. 7-12). tchr. ed., ring bd. 29.50 (978-1-58049-283-6(5) , TU169) Prestwick Hse., Inc.

Segal, John. Alistair & Kip's Great Adventure. Segal, John, illus. 2008. 32p. (J). 15.99 (978-1-4169-0280-5(5) , McElderry, Margaret K.) Simon & Schuster Children's Publishing.

Shaw, Nancy. Bello Says Goodbye. Chapin, Patrick, illus. 2002. (Two Can Read Ser.). 16p. (J). 2.99 (978-1-56472-654-4(1)) Edupress, Inc.

Sis, Peter. An Ocean World. Sis, Peter, illus. 2002. (Illus.). (YA). 14.43 (978-1-4046-0278-6(X)) Book Wholesalers, Inc.

Skurzynski, Gloria. Out of the Deep. 2002. (gr. 3-6). lib. bdg. 14.10 (978-0-613-62818-1(7)) Tandem Library Bks.

Skurzynski, Gloria & Ferguson, Alane. Out of the Deep. 2002. (Mysteries in Our National Parks Ser.: Vol. 10). 160p. (J). (gr. 3-7). 15.95 (978-0-7922-8230-3(2)); pap. 5.95 (978-0-7922-8231-0(0)) National Geographic Society. (National Geographic Children's Bks.).

Smedley, Gord. Orca's Calling. Hammond, Gaye, illus. unabr. ed. 58p. (J). (978-0-920576-46-5(X)) Caitlin Pr., Inc.

Steele, Alexander. Moby Dog. l.t. ed. 1999. (Adventures of Wishbone Ser.: No. 10). (Illus.). 144p. (J). (gr. 4 up). lib. bdg. 22.60 (978-0-8368-2306-6(0)) Stevens, Gareth Inc.

Steig, William. Amos & Boris. 1999. (J). 13.75 (978-0-606-16476-4(6)) Tandem Library Bks.

—Amos Y Boris. 1999. (SPA.). (gr. k-3). lib. bdg. 15.25 (978-0-613-17762-7(2)) Tandem Library Bks.

Sweeney, Joyce. Waiting for June. 2006. 160p. 5.99 (978-0-7614-5329-1(6)) Cavendish, Marshall Corp.

Tate, Suzanne. Katie K. Whale: A Whale of a Tale. Melvin, James, illus. 2004. (Suzanne Tate's Nature Ser.). 32p. (J). per. 10.95 (978-1-878405-47-0(0)) Nags Head Art, Inc.

Tobin, Deborah. Tangled in the Bay: The Story of a Baby Right Whale. Domm, Jeff, illus. 2003. 33p. (J). pap. (978-1-55109-441-0(X)) Nimbus Publishing, Ltd.

Van Dusen, Chris. Down to the Sea with Mr. Magee. (Illus.). 36p. (J). 2006. pap. 6.95 (978-0-8118-5225-8(3)); 2000. 14.95 (978-0-8118-2499-6(3)) Chronicle Bks. LLC.

Van Scoyoc, Pam. I Could Catch a Whale/ Yo Podria Pescar una Ballena. Santillan-Cruz, Sylvia R., tr. Lewis, R. J., illus. l.t. ed. 2005. (ENG & SPA.). 32p. (J). (gr. k-2). lib. bdg. 16.98 (978-0-9663629-5-4(0)) By Grace Enterprises.

Velmans, Hester. Isabel of the Whales. 192p. 2006. (gr. 4-7). 5.99 (978-0-440-42025-5(3) , Yearling); 2005. (J). (gr. 3-7). 15.95 (978-0-385-73202-4(3) , Delacorte Bks. for

Young Readers); 2005. (J). (gr. 3-7). lib. bdg. 17.99 (978-0-385-90233-5(6) , Delacorte Bks. for Young Readers) Random Hse. Children's Bks.

Verne, Jules. Dick Sands: The Boy Captain. ELLEN E. FREWER, tr. 2006. 298p. pap. 13.99 (978-1-4264-3403-7(0)) BiblioBazaar.

—Dick Sands: The Boy Captain. Frewer, Ellen E., tr. l.t. ed. 2006. 328p. pap. 18.99 (978-1-4264-3453-2(7)) BiblioBazaar.

Volke, Gordon. The Little Lost Whale. Bowler, Colin, illus. 2004. 24p. pap. 7.00 (978-1-84161-118-1(2)) Ravette Publishing, Ltd. GBR. *Dist:* Parkwest Pubns., Inc.

Whale Mail. 2003. (J). spiral bd. 9.99 (978-0-89610-126-5(6)) Island Heritage Publishing.

Wilson, Bob. Stanley Bagshaw & Twenty Two Foot Whale. 2006. (Stanley Bagshaw Ser.). (Illus.). 32p. (J). pap. 6.95 (978-1-903015-50-6(2)) Barn Owl Bks, London GBR. *Dist:* Independent Pubs. Group.

Wiskur, Darrell. Timothy Whale's Rainbow. Wiskur, Darrell, illus. 2000. (Illus.). 40p. (J). (gr. 1-3). 11.99 (978-0-89051-289-0(2)) Master Bks.

Young, Selina. Big Dog & Little Dog Go Sailing. Young, Selina, illus. 2001. (Blue Bananas Ser.). (Illus.). 48p. (J). (gr. 1-2). (978-0-7787-0845-2(4)); pap. (978-0-7787-0891-9(8)) Crabtree Publishing Co.

—Big Dog & Little Dog Go Sailing. 2002. (gr. k-3). lib. bdg. 12.95 (978-0-613-52810-8(7)) Tandem Library Bks.

Zalme, Ron, illus. A Humpback Whale Tale. 2006. (Go, Diego, Go! Ser.: Vol. 2). 24p. (J). pap. 3.99 (978-1-4169-1511-9(7) , Simon Spotlight/Nickelodeon) Simon & Schuster Children's Publishing.

WHALING

Branse, J. L. A Day in the Life of a Colonial Sea Captain. 2002. (Library of Living & Working in Colonial Times). (Illus.). 24p. (J). (gr. 3). lib. bdg. 18.75 (978-0-8239-5821-4(3) , PowerKids Pr.) Rosen Publishing Group, Inc., The.

Cook, Peter. You Wouldn't Want to Sail on 19th Century Whaling Ship. Antram, David, illus. 2004. (You Wouldn't Want to Ser.). 32p. (J). (gr. 2-5). pap. 9.95 (978-0-531-16399-3(7) , Watts, Franklin) Scholastic Library Publishing.

Cook, Peter & Salariya, David. You Wouldn't Want to Sail on a 19th-Century Whaling Ship! Grisly Tasks You'd Rather Not Do. Antram, David, illus. 2004. (You Wouldn't Want To Ser.). (J). 28.50 (978-0-531-12356-0(1) , Watts, Franklin) Scholastic Library Publishing.

Cosson, M. J. Yankee Whalers. 2007. (Events in American History Ser.). (Illus.). 48p. (J). (gr. 4-6). lib. bdg. 29.93 (978-1-60044-140-0(8)) Rourke Publishing, LLC.

Currie, Stephen. Thar She Blows: American Whaling in the Nineteenth Century. 2005. (People's History Ser.). (Illus.). 96p. (gr. 6 up). lib. bdg. 26.60 (978-0-8225-0646-1(7)) Lerner Publishing Group.

Foster, Mark. Whale Port: A History of Tuckanucket. Foster, Gerald L., illus. 2007. 64p. (J). (gr. 5-9). 18.00 (978-0-618-54722-7(3)) Houghton Mifflin Co.

Herold, Vickey. A Whaling Community: Nantucket. 2006. pap. 39.00 (***978-1-4108-6426-0(X)***) Benchmark Education Co.

Hodgkins, Fran. The Whale Scientists: Solving the Mystery of Whale Strandings. 2007. (Illus.). 64p. (J). (gr. 5). 18.00 (***978-0-618-55673-1(7)***) Houghton Mifflin Co.

Isaacs, Sally Senzell. Life in a Whaling Town. (Picture the Past Ser.). (Illus.). 32p. (J). 2002. (gr. k-3). pap. 7.50 (978-1-58810-416-8(8) , 91189); 2001. (gr. 2-4). lib. bdg. 21.36 (978-1-58810-251-5(3)) Heinemann Library.

Jernegan, Laura. A Whaling Captain's Daughter: The Diary of Laura Jernegan, 1868-1871. O'Hara, Megan, ed. 2000. (Blue Earth Books). (Illus.). 32p. (J). (gr. 3-4). lib. bdg. 22.60 (978-0-7368-0346-5(7) , Bridgestone Bks.) Capstone Pr., Inc.

McKissack, Patricia C. & McKissack, Fredrick L. Black Hands, White Sails: The Story of African-American Whalers. 1999. (Illus.). 192p. (J). (gr. 3-8). pap. 17.95 (978-0-590-48313-1(7)) Scholastic, Inc.

Murphy, Jim. Gone A-Whaling: The Lure of the Sea & the Hunt for the Great Whale. 1998. (Illus.). 208p. (YA). (gr. 7-7). tchr. ed. 18.00 (978-0-395-69847-1(2) , Clarion Bks.) Houghton Mifflin Co. Trade & Reference Div.

O'Hara, Megan, ed. A Whaling Captain's Daughter: The Diary of Laura Jernegan, 1868-1871. 1999. (Diaries, Letters & Memoirs Ser.). (Illus.). 32p. (J). (gr. 2-7). pap. 21.00 (978-0-516-21851-9(4) , Children's Pr.) Scholastic Library Publishing.

Philbrick, Nathaniel. Revenge of the Whale: The True Story of the Whaleship Essex. 176p. 2002. (Illus.). (YA). (gr. 4 up). 16.99 (978-0-399-23795-9(X) , Putnam Juvenile); 2004. (J). (gr. 5-9). reprint ed. pap. 7.99 (978-0-14-240068-5(8) , Puffin) Penguin Group (USA) Inc.

—Revenge of the Whale: The True Story of the Whaleship Essex. 2004. (Illus.). 164p. (J). (gr. k-9). per. 16.65 (978-0-613-97779-1(3)) Tandem Library Bks.

Prohibited! Individual Title Six-Packs. (Bookweb Ser.). 32p. (gr. 6 up). 34.00 (978-0-7578-0908-8(1)) Rigby Education.

WHALING—FICTION

Beaudouin, Frank, et al, illus. Cleared for Action: Four Tales of the Sea. 2002. (Bethlehem Budget Books). 600p. (J). 19.95 (978-1-883937-55-3(8)) Bethlehem Bks.

Browne, Susan Chalker. The Land of a Thousand Whales. 2006. (Illus.). 32p. pap. (***978-1-897174-08-1(X)***) Creative Bk. Publishing.

Capdevila, Roser. Moby Dick. 2002. (Cuentos Fantasticos de las Tres Mellizas Coleccion: Vol. 1). (SPA.). (J). (gr. k-2). pap. 5.95 (978-1-930332-38-6(6) , LC6629) Lectorum Pubns., Inc.

Dalmatian Press Staff, adapted by. Moby Dick. 2002. (Spot the Classics Ser.). (Illus.). 180p. (J). (gr. k-5). 4.99 (978-1-57759-547-2(5)) Dalmatian Pr.

—Moby Dick. (J). 9.95 (978-1-56156-308-1(0)) Kidsbooks, Inc.

Demas, Corinne. If Ever I Return Again. (gr. 5 up). 2000. (Illus.). 208p. (J). lib. bdg. 15.89 (978-0-06-028718-4(7)); 2000. 208p. (J). 15.95 (978-0-06-028717-7(9)); 1999. (Illus.). 196p. (YA). pap. 4.95 (978-0-06-440844-8(2)) HarperCollins Pubs.

Edwardson, Debby Dahl. Whale Snow. Patterson, Annie, illus. 2004. 32p. (J). (ENG.). pap. 7.95 (978-1-57091-496-6(6)); pap. (978-1-57091-394-5(3)); 15.95 (978-1-57091-393-8(5)) Charlesbridge Publishing, Inc.

Frederick, Heather Vogel. The Voyage of Patience Goodspeed. 2004. (Illus.). 224p. (J). pap. 5.99 (978-0-689-84869-8(2) , Aladdin) Simon & Schuster Children's Publishing.

Hagerty, Carol, ed. Moby Dick. 1998. (Classics Ser.: Set II). 77p. (YA). (gr. 5-12). pap. 7.95 (978-1-56254-258-0(3) , SP2583) Saddleback Educational Publishing.

Ita, Sam. Moby-Dick: A Pop-up Book. 2007. (Illus.). 8p. (J). 24.95 (***978-1-4027-4528-7(1)***) Sterling Publishing Co., Inc.

Kassirer, Sue. Thar She Blows! Whaling in The 1860s. Fridell, Pat, illus. 2007. 32p. (J). 15.00 (***978-1-4223-6721-6(5)***) DIANE Publishing Co.

Melville, Herman. Cities of the Fantastic: Brusel. Eisner, Will, illus. 2003. (Cities of the Fantastic Ser.). 120p. 19.95 (978-1-56163-291-6(0)) NBM Publishing Co.

—Herman Melville/Moby Dick. Niño, Alex, illus. 2005. 48p. (gr. 5-8). 25.50 (978-0-7910-9106-7(6)) Facts On File, Inc.

—Moby Dick. 2002. (Great Illustrated Classics Ser.). (Illus.). 240p. (J). (gr. 3-8). 21.35 (978-1-57765-695-1(4) , ABDO & Daughters) ABDO Publishing Co.

—Moby Dick. Giordano, Dick, illus. 2002. 48p. (J). (gr. 5). tchr. ed. 16.00 (978-0-618-26571-8(6)) Houghton Mifflin Co. Trade & Reference Div.

—Moby Dick. 2000. (Coleccion "Clasicos Juveniles" Ser.). (SPA.). 228p. (YA). pap. 12.95 (978-0-595-13218-8(9)) iUniverse, Inc.

—Moby Dick. 2003. (Illus.). 32p. 7.95 (978-1-56163-294-7(5)) NBM Publishing Co.

—Moby Dick. Eisner, Will, illus. 2003. 32p. (gr. 4-7). 15.95 (978-1-56163-293-0(7)) NBM Publishing Co.

—Moby Dick. Nino, Alex, illus. 2nd ed. 1998. (Illustrated Classic Book Ser.). 61p. (J). (gr. 3 up). reprint ed. pap. 4.95 (978-1-56767-235-0(3)) Educational Insights, Inc.

—Moby Dick. adapted ed. (YA). (gr. 5-12). pap. 8.50 (978-0-8359-0225-0(0)) Globe Fearon Educational Publishing.

—Moby Dick. 2nd ed. 2003. (Historias de Siempre Ser.). (SPA., Illus.). 92p. (J). (gr. 5-8). pap. 9.95 (978-84-204-5732-1(9)) Santillana USA Publishing Co., Inc.

—Moby Dick: With a Discussion of Determination. 2003. (Values in Action Illustrated Classics Ser.). (Illus.). 190p. (J). (978-1-59203-033-0(5)) Learning Challenge, Inc.

—Moby Dick, Grades 5-12. adapted ed. pap., tchr. ed. 4.95 (978-0-8359-0123-9(8)) Globe Fearon Educational Publishing.

—Moby Dick, or the Whale. 2005. (J). Pt. 1. pap. 9.95 (978-1-4105-0263-6(5)); Pt. 1. cd-rom (978-1-4105-0265-0(1)); Pt. 2. pap. 9.95 (978-1-4105-0267-4(8)); Pt. 2. cd-rom (978-1-4105-0269-8(4)) Johnston, Don Inc.

Melville, Herman & Huth, Michael. Moby Dick. 2004. (GER., Illus.). 92p. (978-3-921743-52-2(4)) Maximilian-Gesellschaft e. V.

Melville, Herman & Schwartz, Lew Sayre. Moby Dick. Giordano, Dick, illus. 2002. 48p. (J). pap. 6.95 (978-0-618-26572-5(4)) Houghton Mifflin Co. Trade & Reference Div.

Melville, Herman, et al. Moby Dick. (Classics Illustrated Ser.). (Illus.). 52p. (YA). pap. 4.95 (978-1-57209-003-3(0)) Classics International Entertainment, Inc.

Murphy, Jim. Gone A-Whaling: The Lure of the Sea & the Hunt for the Great Whale. 2004. (Illus.). 208p. (J). (gr. 7 up). pap. 8.95 (978-0-618-43243-1(4) , Clarion Bks.) Houghton Mifflin Co. Trade & Reference Div.

Pinkney, Andrea Davis. Peggony-Po: A Whale of a Tale. Pinkney, Brian, illus. 2006. 32p. (ps-2). 16.99 (978-0-7868-1958-4(8) , Jump at the Sun) Hyperion Bks. for Children.

Prins, Piet. Stefan Derksen's Polar Adventure. 2004. (Illus.). 237p. (J). pap. (978-1-894666-67-1(4)) Inheritance Pubns.

Scott, James, adapted by. Moby Dick: Reproducible Teaching Unit. 2001. 110p. (YA). (gr. 7-12). tchr. ed., ring bd. 29.50 (978-1-58049-283-6(5) , TU169) Prestwick Hse., Inc.

Thompson, Gare. A Whaling Community: New Bedford, Mass. 2006. (Navigators Ser.). (J). pap. 38.00 (***978-1-4108-6248-8(8)***) Benchmark Education Co.

Torrey, Michele. Voyage of Ice. 2004. 208p. (J). (gr. 5). 15.95 (978-0-375-82381-7(6)); lib. bdg. 17.99 (978-0-375-92381-4(0)) Random Hse. Children's Bks. (Knopf Bks. for Young Readers).

WHARTON, EDITH, 1862-1937

Bloom, Harold, ed. & intro. Edith Wharton's The Age of Innocence. Bloom, Harold, intro. 1999. (Bloom's Notes Ser.). (Illus.). 90p. (YA). (gr. 8-12). 32.00 (978-0-7910-4515-2(3) , Chelsea Hse.) Facts On File, Inc.

WHEAT

Anderson, Catherine. Bread Bakery. 2004. (Field Trip! Ser.). (Illus.). 24p. (J). pap. 5.75 (978-1-4034-6167-4(8)); lib. bdg. 20.64 (978-1-4034-6161-2(9)) Heinemann Library.

Canizares, Susan & Chanko, Pamela. Wheat. 1999. (J). 2.50 (978-0-439-04563-6(0)) Scholastic, Inc.

—Wheat. 1999. (ps-2). lib. bdg. 10.10 (978-0-613-22615-8(1)) Tandem Library Bks.

Fowler, Allan. The Wheat We Eat. 1999. (Rookie Read-About Science Ser.). (Illus.). 32p. (J). (gr. 1-2). 19.50 (978-0-516-21212-8(5) , Children's Pr.) Scholastic Library Publishing.

—The Wheat We Eat. 1999. (gr. k-3). lib. bdg. 12.95 (978-0-613-54775-8(6)) Tandem Library Bks.

Franck, Irene M. & Brownstone, David M. Wheat. 2003. (Illus.). 32p. (J). (978-0-7172-5727-0(4) , Grolier) Scholastic Library Publishing.

Harcourt School Publishers Staff. The Story of Wheat Advanced Level. 3rd ed. 2002. (Trophies Reading Program Ser.). (Illus.). pap. 5.10 (978-0-15-323286-2(2)) Harcourt Schl. Pubs.

Lackey, Jennifer. The Biography of Wheat. 2007. (How Did That Get Here? Ser.). (Illus.). 32p. (J). (gr. 2-9). (***978-0-7787-2495-7(6)***); pap. (***978-0-7787-2531-2(6)***) Crabtree Publishing Co.

Landau, Elaine. Wheat. 1999. (True Bks.). (Illus.). 48p. (J). (gr. 3-5). 25.00 (978-0-516-21029-2(7) , Children's Pr.) Scholastic Library Publishing.

—Wheat. 1999. (gr. 3-6). lib. bdg. 15.25 (978-0-613-37584-9(X)) Tandem Library Bks.

Levenson, George. Bread Comes to Life: A Garden of Wheat & a Loaf to Eat. Thaler, Shmuel, photos by. 2004. (Illus.). 32p. (J). 15.95 (978-1-58246-114-4(7) , Tricycle Pr.) Ten Speed Pr.

Snyder, Inez. Wheat. 2004. (Harvesttime Ser.). (Illus.). 24p. (J). 18.00 (978-0-516-27596-3(8)); pap. 4.95 (978-0-516-25915-4(6)) Scholastic Library Publishing. (Children's Pr.).

Welvaert, Scott R. Follow That Crop: From the Farmer's Field to Our Grocery Store. 2003. (From Here to There Ser.). (J). (978-1-58417-194-2(4)); pap. (978-1-58417-195-9(2)) Lake Street Pubs.

WHEATLEY, PHILLIS, 1753-1784

Borland, Kathryn Kilby & Speicher, Helen Ross. Phillis Wheatley: Young Revolutionary Poet, 10 vols. Morrison, Cathy, illus. 2nd rev. ed. 2005. (Young Patriots Ser.: 10). 120p. (J). (ps-7). pap. 9.95 (978-1-882859-48-1(0) , Young Patriots Series) Patria Pr., Inc.

Burke, Rick. Phillis Wheatley. 2003. (American Lives Ser.). (Illus.). 32p. (J). lib. bdg. 24.22 (978-1-4034-0730-6(4)); pap. 6.50 (978-1-4034-3105-9(1)) Heinemann Library.

Carretta, Vincent. Phillis Wheatley: Complete Writings. 2001. (gr. 7-12). lib. bdg. 21.10 (978-0-613-64311-5(9)) Tandem Library Bks.

Clinton, Catherine, illus. Phillis's Big Test. 2008. 32p. (J). (gr. k-3). 16.00 (***978-0-618-73739-0(1)***) Houghton Mifflin Co.

Doak, Robin S. Phillis Wheatley: Slave & Poet. 2005. (Signature Lives Ser.). (Illus.). 112p. (J). 30.60 (978-0-7565-0984-2(X)) Compass Point Bks.

Gregson, Susan R. Phillis Wheatley. 2000. (Let Freedom Ring Ser.). (Illus.). 48p. (J). (gr. 3-4). lib. bdg. 22.60 (978-0-7368-1033-3(1) , Bridgestone Bks.) Capstone Pr., Inc.

Jarnow, Jesse. Phillis Wheatley. 2003. (Primary Sources of Famous People in American History Ser.). (Illus.). 32p. (J). pap. 6.50 (978-0-8239-4191-9(4)) Rosen Publishing Group, Inc., The.

Kent, Deborah. Phillis Wheatley: First Published African-American Poet. 2003. (Spirit of America). (Illus.). 32p. (J). (gr. 2-6). 27.07 (978-1-59296-009-5(X)) Child's World, Inc.

Kent, Jacqueline C. Phillis Wheatley. 2003. (Women of the Revolution Ser.). (J). pap. (978-1-58417-089-1(1)); lib. bdg. (978-1-58417-026-6(3)) Lake Street Pubs.

Lasky, Kathryn. A Voice of Her Own: The Story of Phillis Wheatley, Slave Poet. Lee, Paul, illus. 2003. 40p. (J). (gr. 3-7). 17.99 (978-0-7636-0252-9(3)) Candlewick Pr.

McLeese, Don. Phillis Wheatley. (Heroes of the American Revolution Ser.). (Illus.). 32p. 2005. (gr. 2-5). 19.95 (978-1-59515-220-6(2)); 2004. (J). (ps-ps). pap. 5.95 (978-1-59515-320-3(9)) Rourke Publishing, LLC.

Mclendon, Jacquelyn. Phillis Wheatley. A Revolutionary Poet. (Library of American Lives & Timestm Ser.). 112p. (J). (gr. 4-8). lib. bdg. (978-1-4042-5750-4(0)) Rosen Publishing Group, Inc., The.

McLendon, Jacquelyn Y. Phillis Wheatley: A Revolutionary Poet. 2005. (Library of American Lives & Times). (Illus.). 112p. (YA). (gr. 4-8). lib. bdg. 31.95 (978-0-8239-5750-7(0)) Rosen Publishing Group, Inc., The.

Phillis Wheatley. (American Revolution Biographies Ser.). 48p. (YA). 7.95 (978-0-7368-4498-7(8)) Capstone Pr., Inc.

Pickford, Susan B. Expectations: The Life of Phillis Wheatley. 18p. (J). (gr. 5-9). pap., wbk. ed. 10.00 (978-1-878668-67-7(6)) History Compass, LLC.

Salas, Laura Purdie. Phillis Wheatley: Colonial American Poet. 2006. (Fact Finders Ser.). (Illus.). 32p. (J). (978-0-7368-5435-1(5)) Capstone Pr., Inc.

Salisbury, Cynthia. Phillis Wheatley: Legendary African-American Poet. 2001. (Historical American Biographies Ser.). (Illus.). 112p. (J). (gr. 6-12). lib. bdg. 26.60 (978-0-7660-1394-0(4)) Enslow Pubs., Inc.

Speicher, Helen Ross & Borland, Kathryn Kilby. Phillis Wheatley: Young Revolutionary Poet. Morrison, Cathy, illus. 2nd rev. ed. 2005. (Young Patriots Ser.: No. 10). 120p. (J). (ps-7). 15.95 (978-1-882859-47-4(2) , Young Patriots Series) Patria Pr., Inc.

WHEELS

Armentrout, David & Armentrout, Patricia. Una Rueda. 2002. (Como Podemos Utilizar Maquinas Simples? Ser.). (SPA.). (J). 26.60 (978-1-58952-439-2(X)) Rourke Publishing, LLC.

—A Wheel. 2003. (How Can I Experiment with Simple Machines? Ser.). (Illus.). 32p. (gr. 1-4). 19.95 (978-1-58952-338-8(5)) Rourke Publishing, LLC.

Canizares, Susan. Wheels. 1999. (J). pap. 2.50 (978-0-439-08123-8(8)) Scholastic, Inc.

Cobb, Annie. Wheels! Jones, Davy, illus. 2002. (J). 11.91 (978-0-7587-6318-1(2)) Book Wholesalers, Inc.

Cobb, Annie & Jones, Davy. Ruedas! Jones, Davy, illus. 2003. (Road to Reading Ser.). (J). lib. bdg. 11.99 (978-0-375-91500-0(1) , Golden Bks.) Random Hse. Children's Bks.

Dahl, Michael. Tires, Spokes, & Sprockets: A Book about Wheels. Shea, Denise, illus. 2006. (Amazing Science Ser.). 24p. (J). (gr. k-4). 22.60 (978-1-4048-1308-3(X)) Picture Window Bks.

Dahl, Michael & Shea, Denise. Ruedas y Rayos: Un Libro Sobre Ruedas y Ejes. Shea, Denise, illus. 2007. (ENG & SPA.). (J). lib. bdg. (***978-1-4048-3235-0(1)***) Picture Window Bks.

Douglas, Lloyd G. What Is a Wheel & Axle? 2002. (Welcome Simple MacHines Ser.). (Illus.). 24p. (J). (ps-2). 18.00 (978-0-516-23962-0(7)); pap. 4.95 (978-0-516-24027-5(7)) Scholastic Library Publishing. (Children's Pr.).

—What Is a Wheel & Axle? 2002. (gr. k-3). lib. bdg. 12.95 (978-0-613-58886-7(X)) Tandem Library Bks.

Frost, Helen. What Are Wheels & Axles? Saunders-Smith, Gail, ed. 2001. (Looking at Simple Machines Ser.). (Illus.). 24p. (J). (gr. k-1). lib. bdg. 15.93 (978-0-7368-0850-7(7) , Pebble Bks.) Capstone Pr., Inc.

Glover, David. Wheels & Cranks. 2002. (Simple Machines Ser.). (Illus.). 24p. (J). (gr. 2-4). pap. 6.50 (978-1-4034-0061-1(X) , 91505) Heinemann Library.

Hoenecke, Karen. What Has Wheels? 2005. 8p. (J). pap. 4.25 (978-1-57874-085-7(1)) Kaeden Corp.

How Things Work Interactive Packages: Wheels on the Bus. (Pebble Soup Explorations Ser.). (ps up). 52.00 (978-0-7578-5244-2(0)) Rigby Education.

Mezzanotte, Jim. How Wheels & Axles Work. 2006. (Illus.). 24p. (J). pap. (978-0-8368-7355-9(6)); lib. bdg. (978-0-8368-7350-4(5)) Stevens, Gareth Inc.

Oxlade, Chris. Wheels. 2003. (Useful Machines Ser.). (Illus.). 32p. (J). pap. (978-1-4034-3680-1(0)); lib. bdg. 22.79 (978-1-4034-3665-8(7)) Heinemann Library.

—Wheels. 2007. (***978-1-59920-087-3(2)***) Smart Apple Media.

Prince, April Jones. What Do Wheels Do All Day? Laroche, Giles, illus. 2006. 32p. (J). (gr. k-3). 16.00 (978-0-618-56307-4(5)) Houghton Mifflin Co.

Randolph, Joanne. Wheels & Axles in My World. 2006. (My World of Science Ser.). (Illus.). 24p. (J). 16.00 (978-1-4042-3313-3(X) , PowerKids Pr.) Rosen Publishing Group, Inc., The.

—Wheels & Axles in My World: Ejes y Ruedas en Mi Mundo. 2006. (My World of Science/ Mi mundo y la Ciencia Ser.). (ENG & SPA.). (J). 16.00 (978-1-4042-3325-6(3) , Buenas Letra) Rosen Publishing Group, Inc., The.

Rockwell, Anne. Big Wheels. 2006. (Illus.). 24p. (J). bds. 6.95 (978-0-8027-8903-7(X)) Walker & Co.

Rosa y el Escarabajo: Individual Title Six-Packs. (Literatura 2000 Ser.). (SPA.). (gr. 2-3). 33.00 (978-0-7635-1250-7(8)) Rigby Education.

Round & Round, 6 Packs. (gr. k-1). 23.00 (978-0-7635-9057-4(6)) Rigby Education.

Royston, Angela. Wheels & Cranks. (Machines in Action Ser.). 32p. pap. 7.50 (978-1-4034-4089-1(1)); 2000. (Illus.). (J). (gr. 3-5). lib. bdg. 22.79 (978-1-57572-324-2(7)) Heinemann Library.

Sian Revision Wheels at Work. 2004. (Science in A Nutshell(R) Ser.). (J). (978-1-59242-087-2(7)) Delta Education, LLC.

Sloan, Peter. Wheels at Work. 1999. (gr. k-3). lib. bdg. 11.80 (978-0-613-30871-7(9)) Tandem Library Bks.

Thales, Sharon. Wheels & Axles to the Rescue. 2007. (First Facts Ser.). (Illus.). 24p. (J). (978-0-7368-6751-1(1) , 1264902) Capstone Pr., Inc.

Tieck, Sarah. Wheels & Axles. 2007. (Simple Machines Ser.). (Illus.). 24p. (J). (gr. k-4). lib. bdg. 21.35 (978-1-59679-819-9(X)) ABDO Publishing Co.

Tiner, John Hudson. Wheels & Axles. 2002. (Illus.). 25p. (J). lib. bdg. 21.35 (978-1-58340-137-8(7)) Smart Apple Media.

Tunis, Edwin. Wheels: A Pictorial History. 2002. (Illus.). 96p. pap. 25.00 (978-0-8018-6929-7(3)) Johns Hopkins Univ. Pr.

Walker, Sally M. & Feldmann, Roseann. Ruedas y Ejes. 2005. (Libros de Fisica para Madrugadores (Early Bird Physics) Ser.). (SPA & ENG., Illus.). 48p. (J). (gr. 3-7). lib. bdg. 25.26 (978-0-8225-2982-8(3) , Ediciones Lerner) Lerner Publishing Group.

—Wheels & Axles. 2005. (Early Bird Physics Ser.). (Illus.). 48p. (J). (gr. 3-6). lib. bdg. 25.26 (978-0-8225-2219-5(5)) Lerner Publishing Group.

—Wheels & Axles. King, Andy, photos by. 2002. (Illus.). 48p. (YA). (978-0-8225-2213-3(6) , Lerner Pubns.) Lerner Publishing Group.

Welsbacher, Anne. Wheels & Axles. 2000. (Bridgestone Science Library). (Illus.). 24p. (J). (gr. 1-2). lib. bdg. 18.60 (978-0-7368-0615-2(6) , Bridgestone Bks.) Capstone Pr., Inc.

What Are Wheels & Axles?, 6 vols. (gr. k-2). 28.95 (978-0-7368-9225-4(7)) Red Brick Learning.

Wheels, 8 bks. Incl. Experimental & Concept Cars. Coughlan, John. 1994. lib. bdg. 21.26 (978-1-56065-210-6(1)); Green Cars : Earth-Friendly Electric Vehicles. Coughlan, John. 1994. lib. bdg. 21.26 (978-1-56065-211-3(X)); Humvees & Other Military Vehicles. Smith, Jay H. 1995. lib. bdg. 21.26 (978-1-56065-219-9(5)); Lowriders & Other Customized Cars. Lake, E. D. 1995. lib. bdg. 21.26 (978-1-56065-217-5(9)); Most Rugged All-Terrain Vehicles. Smith, Jay H. 1995. lib. bdg. 21.26 (978-1-56065-218-2(7)); Super Sport Trucks. Smith, Jay H. 1995. lib. bdg. 21.26 (978-1-56065-216-8(0)); World's Fastest Motorcycles. Martin, John. 1994. lib. bdg. 21.26 (978-1-56065-208-3(X));

W X Y Z

World's Most Exotic Cars. Martin, John. 1994. lib. bdg. 21.26 (978-1-56065-209-0(8)); 48p. (J). (gr. 3-4). (Illus.). Set lib. bdg. 170.08 (978-1-56065-667-8(0) , Capstone High-Interest Bks.) Capstone Pr., Inc.

Wheels: Individual Title Six-Packs. (Literatura 2000 Ser.). (gr. k-1). 28.00 (978-0-7635-0077-1(1)); 16p. 27.00 (978-0-7635-4446-1(9)) Rigby Education.

WHISKEY REBELLION, PA., 1794

Schiel, Katy. The Whiskey Rebellion: An Early Challenge to America's New Government. 2004. (Life in the New American Nation Ser.). (Illus.). 32p. (YA). lib. bdg. (978-0-8239-4262-6(7)) Rosen Publishing Group, Inc., The.

WHITE HOUSE (WASHINGTON, D.C.)

Aaseng, Nathan. The White House. 2001. (Building History Ser.). (Illus.). 96p. (J). (gr. 6-9). 32.45 (978-1-56006-708-5(X) , Lucent Bks.) Thomson Gale.

Arbelbide, C. L. The White House Easter Egg Roll. Gibson, Barbara Leonard, illus. 2005. 29p. (J). (gr. k-4). reprint ed. 17.00 (978-0-7567-4772-5(4)) DIANE Publishing Co.

Ashley, Susan. The White House. 2004. (Weekly Reader Early Learning Library). (Illus.). 24p. (J). (gr. 2 up). pap. 5.95 (978-0-8368-4152-7(2)); lib. bdg. 19.33 (978-0-8368-4145-9(X)) Stevens, Gareth Inc. (Weekly Reader Early Learning Library).

Binns, Tristan Boyer. The White House. (Symbols of Freedom Ser.). (Illus.). 32p. (J). (gr. k-2). 2002. pap. 6.95 (978-1-58810-406-9(0) , 91148); 2001. lib. bdg. 21.36 (978-1-58810-122-8(3)) Heinemann Library.

—The White House. 2001. (J). (978-0-606-22928-9(0)) Tandem Library Bks.

Braithwaite, Jill. White House. 2004. (gr. k-3). lib. bdg. 14.10 (978-0-613-76615-9(6)) Tandem Library Bks.

Campodonica, Carol A. How to Build the White House, Vol. 3. Scouten, Rex et al, eds. Anderson, Bill, illus. White House Historical Society Staff, photos by. 1998. 40p. (J). (gr. 4-5). pap. 19.95 (978-0-9648488-6-3(4)) Buzzard Pr. International.

Davis, Gibbs. First Kids. Comport, Sally Wern, illus. 2004. (Step into Reading Ser.). 48p. (J). (gr. 2-4). pap. 3.99 (978-0-375-82218-6(6) , Random Hse. Bks. for Young Readers) Random Hse. Children's Bks.

Douglas, Lloyd G. The White House. 2003. (Welcome Book Ser.). (Illus.). 24p. (J). 18.00 (978-0-516-25855-3(9)); pap. 4.95 (978-0-516-27878-0(9)) Scholastic Library Publishing. (Children's Pr.).

—White House. 2003. (gr. k-3). lib. bdg. 12.95 (978-0-613-67781-3(1)) Tandem Library Bks.

Feinberg, Barbara Silberdick. The Changing White House. 2001. (Cornerstones of Freedom Ser.). (Illus.). 32p. (J). (gr. 4-6). pap. 5.95 (978-0-516-27164-4(4) , Children's Pr.) Scholastic Library Publishing.

Firestone, Mary. The White House. Skeens, Matthew, illus. 2006. 24p. (J). (ps-2). lib. bdg. 23.93 (978-1-4048-2217-7(8)) Picture Window Bks.

Gray, Susan Heinrichs. The White House. 2001. (Let's See Library). 24p. (J). lib. bdg. 18.60 (978-0-7565-0161-7(X)); (Illus.). (gr. 1 up). lib. bdg. 19.93 (978-0-7565-0145-7(8)) Compass Point Bks.

Hancock, Maryann. The White House. 2006. 32p. (J). pap. (978-1-4034-7006-5(5)); (Illus.). lib. bdg. 28.21 (978-1-4034-6999-1(7)) Heinemann Library.

Harcourt School Publishers Staff. A Home for the President On Level. 3rd ed. 2002. (Trophies Reading Program Ser.). (Illus.). pap. 5.10 (978-0-15-323367-8(2)) Harcourt Schl. Pubs.

Harris, Nancy. The White House. 2007. (J). (***978-1-4034-9383-5(9)***); pap. (***978-1-4034-9390-3(1)***) Heinemann Library.

Healy, Nick. The White House. 2003. (J). pap. (978-1-58417-120-1(0)); lib. bdg. (978-1-58417-056-3(5)) Lake Street Pubs.

Hicks, Terry Allan. Symbols of America Group 2, 6 bks., Set. Incl. Bald Eagle. lib. bdg. 28.50 (978-0-7614-2133-7(5)); Capitol. lib. bdg. 28.50 (978-0-7614-2132-0(7)); Declaration of Independence. lib. bdg. 28.50 (978-0-7614-2135-1(1)); Ellis Island. lib. bdg. 28.50 (978-0-7614-2134-4(3)); Pledge of Allegiance. lib. bdg. 28.50 (978-0-7614-2136-8(X)); Uncle Sam. lib. bdg. 28.50 (978-0-7614-2137-5(8)); (Illus.). 40p. (J). 2006. 2007. Set lib. bdg. 171.00 (***978-0-7614-2130-6(0)*** , Benchmark Bks.) Cavendish, Marshall Corp.

Hines, Gary. Thanksgiving in the White House. Wallner, Alexandra, illus. rev. ed. 2003. 32p. (J). 15.95 (978-0-8050-6530-5(X) , Holt, Henry & Co. Bks. For Young Readers) Holt, Henry & Co.

Karr, Kathleen. It Happened Inside the White House: Extraordinary Tales from America's Most Famous Home. Meisel, Paul, illus. 2000. 112p. (gr. 2-5). 16.99 (978-0-7868-0369-9(X)) Hyperion Bks. for Children.

—It Happened Inside the White House: Extraordinary Tales from America's Most Famous Home. 2000. (Illus.). 112p. pap. 5.99 (978-0-7868-1560-9(4)) Hyperion Paperbacks for Children.

Katzin, Nathan. White House. 2002. (Instant Social Studies Activities Folders Ser.). (Illus.). 6p. (gr. 4-8). 3.95 (978-0-439-37086-8(8)) Scholastic, Inc.

Marcovitz, Hal. The White House. 2002. (American Symbols & Their Meanings Ser.). (Illus.). 48p. (YA). (gr. 4 up). lib. bdg. (978-1-59084-024-5(0)) Mason Crest Pubs.

Mattern, Joanne. The White House. 2005. (Building World Landmarks Ser.). (Illus.). 48p. (J). (gr. 4-7). lib. bdg. 24.95 (978-1-4103-0561-9(9) , Blackbirch Pr., Inc.) Thomson Gale.

Murray, Julie. Statue of Liberty. 2005. (Buddy Book Ser.). (Illus.). 24p. (J). (gr. k-4). lib. bdg. 21.35 (978-1-57765-668-5(7)) ABDO Publishing Co.

—White House. 2005. (Buddy Book Ser.). (Illus.). 24p. (J). (gr. k-4). lib. bdg. 21.35 (978-1-57765-669-2(5)) ABDO Publishing Co.

O'Connor, Jane. If the Walls Could Talk: Family Life at the White House. Hovland, Gary, illus. 2004. 48p. (J). 16.95 (978-0-689-86863-4(4) , Simon & Schuster/Paula Wiseman Bks.) Simon & Schuster Children's Publishing.

Price Hossell, Karen. The White House. 2005. (Places in History Ser.). (Illus.). 48p. (J). pap. (978-0-8368-5821-1(2)); lib. bdg. 30.00 (978-0-8368-5814-3(X)) Stevens, Gareth Inc. (World Almanac Library).

Rinaldo, Denise. White House Q & A. 2008. 48p. (J). (gr. k-4). 16.99 (***978-0-06-089966-0(2)***); pap. 7.99 (***978-0-06-089965-3(4)***) HarperCollins Pubs. (Collins).

Sandak, Cass R. The White House. 1999. (American Government Today Ser.). (Illus.). 48p. (J). (gr. 4-7). lib. bdg. 22.83 (978-0-7398-1791-9(4)) Raintree.

Sanders. The White House. 1999. (American Government Today Ser.). (Illus.). pap. 7.20 (978-0-7398-2130-5(X)) Steck-Vaughn.

Seeley, Mary Evans. Grandmother Remembers Christmas at the White House. Hunt, Virginia Koenke, ed. Rae, Terri Sopp, illus. 48p. (J). (gr. k-7). 2000. lib. bdg. 16.95 (978-0-9657684-2-9(2)); 2nd rev. l.t. ed. 2002. lib. bdg. 16.95 (978-0-9657684-4-3(9)) Presidential Christmas, A.

Silate, Jennifer. The White House. 2004. (Illus.). 24p. (J). lib. bdg. (978-1-4042-2695-1(8)) Rosen Publishing Group, Inc., The.

Sorensen, Lynda. La Casa Blanca. Palacios, Argentina, tr. 2002. (Simbolos Americanos Ser.). (SPA., Illus.). 24p. (J). mass mkt. 5.95 (978-1-58952-270-1(2) , RK31483) Rourke Publishing, LLC.

TNT Stone and Associates Staff & Petertil Design Partners Staff, illus. Our Presidents & the White House. 1998. (Powertools for Kids Ser.: No. 14). 4p. (J). (gr. 2-5). pap., wbk. ed. 4.95 (978-1-58220-013-2(0) , 32504, PowerTools for Kids) Navigator Systems, Inc.

Tribble, Mimi. The American Presidents: Everything You Wanted to Know about the 43 Leaders of Our Country. 2004. (Illus.). 48p. (J). (978-1-4027-1794-9(6) , Sterling/Main St.) Sterling Publishing Co., Inc.

Wirth, Crystal. At 1600 Pennsylvania Avenue. Lee, Jared D., illus. 2002. 16p. (J). (978-0-439-35108-9(1)) Scholastic, Inc.

Yanuck, Debbie L. The White House. 2003. (American Symbols Ser.). (Illus.). 24p. (J). (gr. 1-2). lib. bdg. 18.60 (978-0-7368-1633-5(X) , Bridgestone Bks.) Capstone Pr., Inc.

WHITMAN, NARCISSA (PRENTISS), 1808-1847

Harness, Cheryl. The Tragic Tale of Narcissa Whitman & a Faithful History of the Oregon Trail. Harness, Cheryl, illus. 2006. (Illus.). 144p. (J). (gr. 5-9). 16.95 (978-0-7922-5920-6(3)); lib. bdg. 25.90 (978-0-7922-5921-3(1)) National Geographic Society. (National Geographic Children's Bks.).

WHITMAN, WALT, 1819-1892

Kerley, Barbara. Walt Whitman: Words for America. Selznick, Brian, illus. 2004. 56p. (J). (gr. 2-5). pap. 16.95 (978-0-439-35791-3(8) , Scholastic Pr.) Scholastic, Inc.

Meltzer, Milton. Walt Whitman: A Biography. 2002. (Single Titles Ser.). (Illus.). 160p. (gr. 7 up). lib. bdg. 31.90 (978-0-7613-2272-6(8) , Twenty-First Century Bks.) Lerner Publishing Group.

Reef, Catherine. Walt Whitman. 2002. (Illus.). 160p. (J). (gr. 4-6). pap. 7.95 (978-0-618-24616-8(9) , Clarion Bks.) Houghton Mifflin Co. Trade & Reference Div.

—Walt Whitman. 2002. (gr. 5-8). lib. bdg. 16.40 (978-0-613-70734-3(6)) Tandem Library Bks.

WHITNEY, ELI, 1765-1825

Cefrey, Holly. The Inventions of Eli Whitney: The Cotton Gin. 2003. (19th Century American Inventors Ser.). (Illus.). 24p. (J). lib. bdg. 17.25 (978-0-8239-6443-7(4) , PowerKids Pr.) Rosen Publishing Group, Inc., The.

Davis, Marc & Santella, Andrew. The Wright Brothers: Inventors & Aviators. 2003. (Spirit of America: Our People Ser.). (Illus.). 32p. (J). (gr. 2-6). 27.07 (978-1-56766-369-3(9)) Child's World, Inc.

Gaines, Ann Graham. Eli Whitney. Sarfatti, Esther & de la Vega, Eida, trs. from ENG. 2001. (Inventores Famosos Ser.). (SPA., Illus.). 24p. (J). (gr. 1-4). lib. bdg. 19.27 (978-1-58952-177-3(3) , RK7727) Rourke Publishing, LLC.

—Eli Whitney. 2002. (SPA.). (gr. k-3). lib. bdg. 14.10 (978-0-613-79830-3(9)) Tandem Library Bks.

Gaines, Ann Graham & Whitney, Eli. Eli Whitney. 2001. (Illus.). 24p. (J). (gr. 1-4). lib. bdg. 20.64 (978-1-58952-118-6(8)) Rourke Publishing, LLC.

Gibson, Karen Bush. Eli Whitney. 2006. (Profiles in American History Ser.). (Illus.). 48p. (J). (gr. 4-8). lib. bdg. 20.95 (978-1-58415-434-1(9)) Mitchell Lane Pubs., Inc.

Gunderson, Jessica. Eli Whitney & the Cotton Gin. 2007. (Illus.). 32p. (J). (978-0-7368-6843-3(7)) Capstone Publishing.

Hall, Margaret. Eli Whitney. 2004. (Illus.). 32p. (J). pap. 6.50 (978-1-4034-5333-4(0)); lib. bdg. 22.79 (978-1-4034-5325-9(X)) Heinemann Library.

Mitchell, Barbara. Maker of Machines: A Story about Eli Whitney. Jones, Jan Naimo, tr. Jones, Jan Naimo, illus. 2004. (Creative Minds Biography Ser.). 64p. (J). 22.60 (978-1-57505-603-6(8) , Carolrhoda Bks.) Lerner Publishing Group.

Robinson Masters, Nancy. The Cotton Gin. 2006. (Inventions That Shaped the World Ser.). (Illus.). 80p. (J). (gr. 5-8). 30.50 (978-0-531-12406-2(1) , Watts, Franklin) Scholastic Library Publishing.

WHITTINGTON, RICHARD, 1358-1423

Potter, Mélisande, illus. Dick Whittington & His Cat. 2006. 32p. (J). (ps-3). 16.95 (978-0-8234-1987-6(8)) Holiday Hse., Inc.

WHITTLING

see Wood-Carving

WIESEL, ELIE, 1928-

Bayer, Linda N. Elie Wiesel: Spokesman for Remembrance. 2005. (Holocaust Biographies Ser.). (Illus.). 112p. (J). (gr. 7-12). lib. bdg. 26.50 (978-0-8239-3306-8(7) , HB-WIES) Rosen Publishing Group, Inc., The.

—Elie Wiesel: Spokesman for Remembrance. 1999. (Illus.). 112p. (YA). per. 10.95 (978-1-56254-456-0(X) , SP456X) Saddleback Educational Publishing.

Houghton, Sarah. Elie Wiesel: A Holocaust Survivor Cries Out for Peace. 2003. (High Five Reading Ser.). (Illus.). (J). 64p. lib. bdg. 22.60 (978-0-7368-2792-8(7)); 48p. pap. 8.75 (978-0-7368-2833-8(8)) Capstone Pr., Inc.

—Elie Wiesel: A Holocaust Survivor Cries Out for Peace, 6 vols. (gr. 4 up). 49.95 (978-0-7368-2843-7(5) , High Five) Red Brick Learning.

Moore, Lisa. Elie Wiesel: Surviving the Holocaust, Speaking Out Against Genocide. 2005. (Holocaust Heroes & Nazi Criminals Ser.). (Illus.). 160p. (YA). (gr. 7-13). lib. bdg. 27.93 (978-0-7660-2576-9(4)) Enslow Pubs., Inc.

Wagner, Heather Lehr. Elie Wiesel: Messenger for Peace. 2007. (Modern Peacemakers Ser.). (Illus.). 120p. (YA). (gr. 9 up). 30.00 (978-0-7910-9220-0(8) , Chelsea Hse.) Facts On File, Inc.

WILD ANIMALS

see Animals

WILD BOAR—FICTION

Rosoff, Meg. Meet Wild Boars. Blackall, Sophie, illus. rev. ed. 2005. 40p. (J). 15.95 (978-0-8050-7488-8(0) , Holt, Henry & Co. Bks. For Young Readers) Holt, Henry & Co.

WILD FLOWERS

Bauld, Jane Scoggins. Texas in Bloom: A Wildflower Guide for Children. Waldrip, Gayle, illus. Waldrip, Gayle, photos by. 2002. 45p. (J). (978-1-57168-568-1(5) , Eakin Pr.) Eakin Pr.

Burns, Diane L. Wildflowers, Blooms & Blossoms. Garrow, Linda, illus. 2004. (Take-Along Guide Ser.). 48p. (J). (gr. 2-5). pap. 7.95 (978-1-55971-642-0(8) , NorthWord Bks. for Young Readers) T&N Children's Publishing.

Clausen, Ruth Rogers. Wildflowers. 1999. (Fandex Family Field Guides Ser.). (Illus.). 97p. (J). (gr. 5-9). 9.95 (978-0-7611-1464-2(5) , 11464) Workman Publishing Co., Inc.

Cooke, Arthur O. Flowers of the Farm. 2007. (ENG., Illus.). 80p. per. (***978-1-4065-1515-2(9)***) Dodo Pr.

Crowe, Andrew. The Life-Size Guide to New Zealand Wildflowers. 2003. (Illus.). 32p. (J). pap. (978-0-14-301847-6(7)) Penguin Group (USA) Inc.

Fell, Derek. Wildflowers. 1999. (Let's Investigate Ser.). (Illus.). 32p. (J). (gr. 1-4). pap. (978-1-58341-001-1(5) , Creative Education) Creative Co., The.

Forey, Pamela. Wild Flowers of the United States & Canada. 2004. (World Book's Science & Nature Guides Ser.). (Illus.). 80p. (J). (978-0-7166-4220-6(4)) World Bk., Inc.

Hood, Susan & National Audubon Society Staff. Wildflowers. 1998. (Audubon Society First Field Guide Ser.). (Illus.). 17.95p. (YA). (gr. 3-7). pap. 17.95 (978-0-590-05464-5(3)) Scholastic, Inc.

Kavanagh, James. British Columbia Trees & Wildflowers. Leung, Raymond, illus. 1999. (Pocket Naturalist Ser.). (J). 5.95 (978-1-58355-045-8(3)) Waterford Pr., Ltd.

Kershaw, Linda. Alberta Wayside Wildflowers. Kershaw, Linda, illus. rev. ed. 2003. (Illus.). 160p. (J). (gr. 4). pap. 12.95 (978-1-55105-350-9(0)) Lone Pine Publishing USA.

—Saskatchewan Wayside Wildflowers. Kershaw, Linda, illus. rev. ed. 2003. (Illus.). 160p. (gr. 4). pap. 12.95 (978-1-55105-354-7(3)) Lone Pine Publishing USA.

Kershaw, Linda J. Manitoba Wayside Wildflowers. rev. ed. 2003. (Illus.). 160p. (J). (gr. 4). pap. 12.95 (978-1-55105-352-3(7)) Lone Pine Publishing USA.

Kukolax, Andy. Ultralight Wildflower Guide to the Central Montana Rocky Mountains: Wildflower Montana. 2003. (Illus.). 64p. pap. 19.95 (978-0-9729940-0-2(9)) Diamond Springs Pr.

Latimer, Jonathan P. & Nolting, Karen Stray. Wildflowers. Peterson, Roger Tory, illus. 2000. (Peterson Field Guides for Young Naturalists). 48p. (J). (gr. 3-7). tchr. ed. 15.00 (978-0-395-97940-2(4)); (gr. 4-6). pap. 5.95 (978-0-395-97947-1(1)) Houghton Mifflin Co.

Mariner Books Staff & Peterson, Roger Tory. Wildflowers: The Concise Field Guide to 188 Common Flowers of North Eastern & North-Central North America. 2nd ed. 1998. (First Guides). (Illus.). 128p. pap. 5.95 (978-0-395-90667-5(9)) Houghton Mifflin Co. Trade & Reference Div.

National Geographic Society Staff. Wildflowers. 2002. (My First Pocket Guides Ser.). (Illus.). 80p. (J). (gr. 1-5). pap. 5.95 (978-0-7922-6612-9(9) , National Geographic Children's Bks.) National Geographic Society.

—Wildflowers. 2002. (gr. 3-6). lib. bdg. 14.10 (978-0-613-89190-5(2)) Tandem Library Bks.

Pomeroy, Diana. Wildflower ABC. 2001. (gr. k-3). lib. bdg. 14.15 (978-0-613-35479-0(6)) Tandem Library Bks.

—Wildflower ABC: An Alphabet of Potato Prints. Pomeroy, Diana, illus. 2001. (Illus.). 32p. (J). (ps). pap. 6.00 (978-0-15-202455-0(7) , Harcourt Paperbacks) Harcourt Children's Bks.

—Wildflower ABC: An Alphabet of Potato Prints. 2001. (Illus.). (J). (978-0-606-20992-2(1)) Tandem Library Bks.

Ruggiero, M. Wild Flowers of North America. rev. ed. 2004. (Spotter's Guides). 64p. (J). pap. 5.95 (978-0-7945-0256-0(3)) EDC Publishing.

Scogginsbauld, Jane. Texas in Bloom: A Wildflower Guide for Children. Waldrup, Gayle, photos by. l.t. ed. 1999. (Illus.). 24p. (J). (ps-3). pap. 14.95 (978-1-929701-00-1(4)) Under the Green Umbrella.

Voake, Charlotte. A Little Guide to Wild Flowers. 2007. (Illus.). 80p. (J). pap. 12.95 (***978-1-903919-11-8(8)***) Transworld Publishers Ltd. GBR. *Dist:* Independent Pubs. Group.

Wildflowers. (Color & Learn Ser.). 36p. (J). (gr. 1-5). pap. (978-1-882210-02-2(6)) Action Publishing, Inc.

WILD FOWL

see Water Birds

WILD LIFE CONSERVATION

see Wildlife Conservation

WILDER, LAURA INGALLS, 1867-1957

Alter, Judy. Laura Ingalls Wilder: Pioneer & Author. 2003. (Spirit of America). (Illus.). 32p. (J). (gr. 2-6). 27.07 (978-1-59296-007-1(3)) Child's World, Inc.

Anderson, William. Laura Ingalls Wilder: A Biography. 2007. (Little House Ser.). 256p. (J). pap. 6.99 (978-0-06-088552-6(1) , Harper Trophy) HarperCollins Pubs.

—Laura's Album: A Remembrance Scrapbook of Laura Ingalls Wilder. 1998. (Little House Ser.). (Illus.). 80p. (J). (gr. 3 up). 21.99 (978-0-06-027842-7(0)) HarperCollins Pubs.

—Pioneer Girl: The Story of Laura Ingalls Wilder. 2000. (gr. k-3). lib. bdg. 15.30 (978-0-613-28607-7(3)) Tandem Library Bks.

Anderson, William T. Pioneer Girl: The Story of Laura Ingalls Wilder. Andreasen, Dan, illus. (Little House Ser.). 32p. (J). (gr. 2 up). 2000. pap. 6.99 (978-0-06-446234-1(X) , Harper Trophy); 1998. 15.89 (978-0-06-027244-9(9)) HarperCollins Pubs.

—Pioneer Girl: The Story of Laura Ingalls Wilder. 2000. (978-0-606-18712-1(X)) Tandem Library Bks.

Armentrout, David & Armentrout, Patricia. Laura Ingalls Wilder. 2004. (Discover the Life of an American Legend Ser.). (Illus.). 24p. (gr. 2-5). 14.95 (978-1-58952-663-1(5)) Rourke Publishing, LLC.

Benge, Janet & Benge, Geoff. Laura Ingalls Wilder: A Storybook Life. 2005. (Illus.). 196p. (YA). (gr. 4-7). pap. 6.99 (978-1-932096-32-3(9)) Emerald Bks.

Berne, Emma Carlson. Laura Ingalls Wilder. 2007. (Essential Lives Ser.). (ENG., Illus.). 112p. (J). (gr. 6-8). lib. bdg. 32.79 (***978-1-59928-843-7(5)*** , Essential Library) ABDO Publishing Co.

Ford, Carin T. Laura Ingalls Wilder: Real-Life Pioneer of the Little House Books. 2003. (People to Know Ser.). (Illus.). 112p. (J). lib. bdg. 26.60 (978-0-7660-2105-1(X)) Enslow Pubs., Inc.

Glassock, Sarah J. Laura Ingalls Wilder: An Author's Story. 1998. (Illus.). 24p. (ps-3). pap. 4.95 (978-0-8172-7976-9(8)) Steck-Vaughn.

Gormley, Beatrice. Laura Ingalls Wilder: Young Pioneer. Henderson, Meryl, illus. 2001. (Childhood of Famous Americans Ser.). 224p. (J). (gr. 3-7). pap. 5.99 (978-0-689-83924-5(3) , Aladdin) Simon & Schuster Children's Publishing.

—Laura Ingalls Wilder: Young Pioneer. 2001. (Childhood of Famous Americans Ser.). (Illus.). (J). (978-0-606-21290-8(6)) Tandem Library Bks.

Hanson-Harding, Alexandra. Laura Ingalls Wilder: Instant Social Studies Activities. 2002. (Instant Social Studies Activities Folders Ser.). (Illus.). 6p. (gr. 4-8). pap. 3.95 (978-0-439-37088-2(4)) Scholastic, Inc.

Mara, Wil. Laura Ingalls Wilder. 2003. (Rookie Biographies Ser.). (gr. 1-2). pap. 4.95 (978-0-516-27840-7(1)); (Illus.). 32p. (J). 20.50 (978-0-516-22855-6(2)) Scholastic Library Publishing. (Children's Pr.).

—Laura Ingalls Wilder. 2003. (YA). lib. bdg. 12.95 (978-0-613-67639-7(4)) Tandem Library Bks.

Marsh, Carole. Laura Ingalls Wilder. 2002. (One Thousand Readers Ser.). (Illus.). 12p. (J). (gr. k-4). 2.95 (978-0-635-01485-6(8) , 14858) Gallopade International.

Martinucci-Marsh, Licia. Laura: A Story about Laura Ingalls Wilder. 2002. (Illus.). 16p. (J). (978-0-439-35118-8(9)) Scholastic, Inc.

Patchett, Kaye. Laura Ingalls Wilder. 2005. (Inventors & Creators Ser.). (Illus.). 48p. (J). (gr. 4-8). 26.20 (978-0-7377-3159-0(1) , Greenhaven Pr., Inc.) Thomson Gale.

Raatma, Lucia. Laura Ingalls Wilder: Teacher & Author. 2001. (Career Biographies Ser.). (Illus.). 128p. (J). (gr. 6-12). 25.00 (978-0-89434-375-9(0) , F418, Ferguson Publishing Co.) Facts On File, Inc.

Scraper, Katherine. Laura Ingalls Wilder (Spanish) & Laura Ingalls Wilder. 2005. spiral bd. 66.00 (***978-1-4108-5620-3(8)***) Benchmark Education Co.

Sickels, Amy. Laura Ingalls Wilder. 2007. (Who Wrote That? Ser.). 144p. (J). (gr. 6-12). 30.00 (***978-0-7910-9525-6(8)*** , Chelsea Hse.) Facts On File, Inc.

Strudwick, Leslie. Laura Ingalls Wilder. 2002. (My Favorite Writer Ser.). (Illus.). 32p. (J). lib. bdg. 18.20 (978-1-59036-027-9(3)) Weigl Pubs., Inc.

Vavra, Stephanie A. Who Really Saved Laura Ingalls: Soldat du Chene or a soldat du chien? 2001. 9p. (YA). (gr. 5 up). pap. 3.00 (978-0-9712785-0-9(4)) Quill Works.

Wadsworth, Ginger. Laura Ingalls Wilder. Haas, Shelly O., illus. (On My Own Biographies Ser.). 48p. (J). (gr. 1-3). 2003. pap. 5.95 (978-1-57505-423-0(X)); 1999. lib. bdg. 23.93 (978-1-57505-266-3(0) , Carolrhoda Bks.) Lerner Publishing Group.

—Laura Ingalls Wilder. 2000. (gr. 3-6). lib. bdg. 14.10 (978-0-613-68249-7(1)); (Illus.). (J). (978-0-606-21947-1(1)) Tandem Library Bks.

Walker, Pamela. Laura Ingalls Wilder. 2001. (Real People Ser.). (Illus.). 24p. (J). (ps-2). 17.00 (978-0-516-23435-9(8)); pap. 4.95 (978-0-516-23589-9(3)) Scholastic Library Publishing. (Children's Pr.).

—Laura Ingalls Wilder. 2001. (gr. k-3). lib. bdg. 12.95 (978-0-613-58846-1(0)) Tandem Library Bks.

Ward, S. Meet Laura Ingalls Wilder. 2001. (About the Author Ser.). (Illus.). 24p. (J). (gr. 3). lib. bdg. 18.75 (978-0-8239-5712-5(8) , PowerKids Pr.) Rosen Publishing Group, Inc., The.

Wilder, Laura Ingalls. A Little House Reader: A Collection of Writings by Laura Ingalls Wilder. Anderson, William, ed. Andreasen, Dan, illus. 2005. (Little House Ser.). 208p. (J). (gr. 3 up). pap. 9.99 (978-0-06-058695-9(8) , Harper Trophy) HarperCollins Pubs.

Woods, Mae. Laura Ingalls Wilder. 2000. (Children's Authors Ser.). (Illus.). 24p. (J). (gr. k-6). lib. bdg. 21.35 (978-1-57765-113-0(8) , Checkerboard Library) ABDO Publishing Co.

WILDERNESS SURVIVAL

Dewey, Jennifer Owings. Finding Your Way: The Art of Natural Navigation. Trimble, Stephen, photos by. 2001. (Illus.). 64p. (gr. 4-6). lib. bdg. 23.90 (978-0-7613-0956-7(X) , Millbrook Pr.) Lerner Publishing Group.

Lewis, Brenda Ralph. Wilderness Rescue with the U. S. Search & Rescue Task Force. 2003. (Rescue & Prevention Ser.). (Illus.). 96p. (J). (gr. 7 up). lib. bdg. (978-1-59084-404-5(1)) Mason Crest Pubs.

Llewellyn, Claire. The Kid's Survival Guide. 2002. (Illus.). 96p. (J). pap. 9.95 (978-0-439-35325-0(4)) Scholastic, Inc.

O'Connor, Brion. Handwarmer & Survival Manual Kit. 2004. (Illus.). 32p. pap. 8.95 (978-0-7624-2140-4(1) , Running Pr. Minature Editions) Running Pr. Bk. Pubs.

O'Shei, Tim. Alone in the Wilderness! Brennan Hawkins' Story of Survival. 2008. ***(*978-1-4296-0087-3(X))*** Capstone Pr., Inc.

—Disaster in the Mountains! Colby Coombs' Story of Survival. 2007. (Illus.). 32p. (J). ***(*978-0-7368-6778-8(3))*** Capstone Pr., Inc.

—Stranded! Amy Racina's Story of Survival. 2008. (J). ***(*978-1-4296-0088-0(8))*** Capstone Pr., Inc.

—Stranded in the Snow! Eric LeMarque's Story of Survival. 2007. (Illus.). 32p. (J). ***(*978-0-7368-6777-1(5))*** Capstone Pr., Inc.

O'Shei, Tim. Volcanic Eruption! Susan Ruff & Bruce Nelson's Story of Survival. 2007. 32p. (J). (978-0-7368-6779-5(1)) Capstone Pr., Inc.

Riley, Peter D. The Forest. 2004. (Survivor's Science Ser.). 28.56 (978-1-4109-0225-2(0)) Harcourt Schl. Pubs.

—The Polar Regions. 2004. (Survivor's Science Ser.). 28.56 (978-1-4109-0228-3(5)) Harcourt Schl. Pubs.

—Rain Forest. 2004. (Survivor's Science Ser.). (J). 28.56 (978-1-4109-0227-6(7)) Harcourt Schl. Pubs.

—Survivor's Science on an Island. 2004. (Survivor's Science Ser.). (Illus.). 48p. (J). (gr. 6-8). lib. bdg. 28.56 (978-1-4109-0226-9(9)) Harcourt Schl. Pubs.

WILDERNESS SURVIVAL—FICTION

Ahlman, Larry. Missing in the Boundary Waters. Larsen, Chuck, ed. Hanson, Dana, illus. rev. ed. 2001. 200p. (YA). (gr. 9-12). pap. 9.95 (978-0-9712906-3-1(6)) Ahlman Publishing.

Curtiss, A. B. Time of the Wild. Nathan, Jules, illus. 1998. 40p. (gr. 4-8). 18.95 (978-0-932529-55-8(0)) Oldcastle Publishing.

Eustache, Harold. Shuswap Journey. 2004. 176p. pap. 15.95 (978-1-894778-15-2(4)) Theytus Bks., Ltd. CAN. *Dist:* Orca Bk. Pubs. USA.

George, Jean Craighead. My Side of the Mountain. 2002. (J). 13.28 (978-0-7587-8771-2(5)) Book Wholesalers, Inc.

—My Side of the Mountain. l.t. ed. 2003. (LRS Large Print Cornerstone Ser.). 205p. (J). lib. bdg. 32.95 (978-1-58118-114-2(0)) LRS.

—My Side of the Mountain. (Illus.). (J). (gr. 3). 2004. 192p. pap. 6.99 (978-0-14-240111-8(0) , Puffin); 1999. 176p. 15.99 (978-0-525-46346-7(1) , Dutton Juvenile) Penguin Group (USA) Inc.

—My Side of the Mountain. 2001. (J). (978-0-606-21342-4(2)); (gr. 3-6). lib. bdg. 15.30 (978-0-613-35990-0(9)) Tandem Library Bks.

—On the Far Side of the Mountain. 1999. (Illus.). 144p. (J). (gr 4-7). 16.99 (978 0-525-46348-1(8) , Dutton Juvenile) Penguin Group (USA) Inc.

Gilliland, Hap. Alone in the Wilderness. 2003. (Illus.). 160p. (YA). (gr. 6-10). pap. 14.95 (978-0-87961-257-3(6)) Naturegraph Pubs., Inc.

Goodspeed, Betsy. The Reluctant Mountaineer. 2004. 230p. (YA). per. (978-1-59196-617-3(5)) Instantpublisher.com.

Gutman, Dan. Getting Air. 2007. 240p. (J). (gr. 3-7). 15.99 (978-0-689-87680-6(7)) Simon & Schuster Children's Publishing.

Hobbs, William. River Thunder. 1999. (978-0-606-15817-6(0)) Tandem Library Bks.

—Wild Man Island. 192p. (J). (gr. 5 up). 2003. pap. 5.99 (978-0-380-73310-1(2) , Harper Trophy); 2002. (Illus.). 19.99 (978-0-688-17473-6(6)); 2002. (Illus.). lib. bdg. 16.89 (978-0-06-029810-4(3)) HarperCollins Pubs.

—Wild Man Island. 2003. (gr. 5-8). lib. bdg. 14.15 (978-0-613-61741-3(X)) Tandem Library Bks.

Hokenson, Terry. The Winter Road. 2006. 176p. (J). 16.95 (978-1-932425-45-1(4) , Front Street) Boyds Mills Pr.

Key, Watt. Alabama Moon. 2006. 304p. (J). 16.00 (978-0-374-30184-2(0)) Farrar, Straus & Giroux.

Korman, Gordon. Escape. 2001. (Island Ser.). (Illus.). (J). 11.64 (978-0-606-21253-3(1)) Tandem Library Bks.

—Survival. 2001. (Island Ser.). (Illus.). (J). (978-0-606-21252-6(3)) Tandem Library Bks.

London, Jack. The Call of the Wild. 1999. 65p. (J). reprint ed. pap. 8.95 (978-1-57002-094-0(9)) University Publishing Hse., Inc.

Marsden, John. A Killing Frost. 1998. 288p. (YA). (gr. 7-12). 16.00 (978-0-395-83735-1(9)) Houghton Mifflin Co. Trade & Reference Div.

Mccabe, Jr. Planting the Wilderness or, the Pioneer Boys: a Story of Frontier Life. 2007. pap. 27.95 ***(*978-1-4304-8187-4(0))*** Kessinger Publishing, LLC.

Mills, Charles. Storm on Shadow Mountain. 2003. 127p. (J). (978-0-8163-1993-0(6)) Pacific Pr. Publishing Assn.

Osborne, Mary Pope. Adaline Falling Star. unabr. ed. 2004. (Middle Grade Cassette Librariestm Ser.). 176p. (J). (gr. 3-7). pap. 29.00 incl. audio (978-0-8072-1195-3(8) , S YA 319 SP, Listening Library) Random Hse. Audio Publishing Group.

Ostrow, Kim & Burnett, Mark. Marquesas. 2005. (Survivor—Outwit, Outplay, Outlast Ser.: Vol. 2). 143p. (J). (978-1-4155-7990-9(3) , Simon Spotlight) Simon & Schuster Children's Publishing.

Paulsen, Gary. Brian's Return. unabr. ed. 2004. (Middle Grade Cassette Librariestm Ser.). 115p. (J). (gr. 5-9). pap. 29.00 incl. audio (978-0-8072-0658-4(X) , S YA 292 SP, Listening Library) Random Hse. Audio Publishing Group.

—Brian's Return. (GLB Reprints Ser.). (gr. 5). 2004. 128p. (YA). lib. bdg. 17.99 (978-0-385-90223-6(9) , Delacorte Bks. for Young Readers); 1999. 128p. (J). 15.95 (978-0-385-32500-4(2) , Delacorte Bks. for Young Readers); 2001. 144p. (J). reprint ed. pap. 5.99 (978-0-440-41379-0(6) , Laurel Leaf) Random Hse. Children's Bks.

—Brian's Return. 2001. (J). 12.15 (978-0-606-21086-7(5)); (gr. 7-12). lib. bdg. 13.55 (978-0-613-33796-0(4)) Tandem Library Bks.

—Brian's Winter. 2004. (GLB Reprints Ser.). 144p. (YA). (gr. 5). lib. bdg. 17.99 (978-0-385-90222-9(0) , Delacorte Bks. for Young Readers) Random Hse. Children's Bks.

—Hatchet. 2006. 192p. (J). pap. 6.99 (978-1-4169-3647-3(5) , Aladdin); 208p. (YA). (gr. 5-9). mass mkt. 6.99 (978-1-4169-3646-6(7) , Simon Pulse) Simon & Schuster Children's Publishing.

—Hatchet. Willis, Drew, illus. 20th ed. 2007. 188p. (J). (gr. 5-9). 19.99 ***(*978-1-4169-2508-8(2))*** Simon & Schuster Children's Publishing.

—The River. unabr. ed. 2004. (Middle Grade Cassette Librariestm Ser.). 132p. (J). (gr. 5-9). pap. 29.00 incl. audio (978-0-8072-8704-0(0) , S YA 241 SP, Listening Library) Random Hse. Audio Publishing Group.

—The River. 2004. (GLB Reprints Ser.). 144p. (YA). (gr. 5). lib. bdg. 17.99 (978-0-385-90221-2(2) , Delacorte Bks. for Young Readers) Random Hse. Children's Bks.

—The Transall Saga. 1998. (J). (978-0-385-43196-5(1)) Dell Distributing.

—The Transall Saga. 1999. 256p. (J). (gr. 5-7). mass mkt. 6.99 (978-0-440-21976-7(0) , Laurel Leaf) Random Hse. Children's Bks.

—The Transall Saga. l.t. ed. 1999. 312p. (YA). (gr. 7-12). 21.95 (978-0-7862-2187-5(9)) Thorndike Pr.

Robeson, K. S. A Home for Chloe. 2002. (Tales from Wind Creek Ser.: Bk. 1). 114p. (J). (gr. 3-6). per. 8.95 (978-0-9723530-0-7(3)) Falcor Bks.

Siegal, Aranka. Grace in the Wilderness: After the Liberation 1945-1948. 2003. 240p. (J). pap. 5.95 (978-0-374-42794-8(1) , Sunburst) Farrar, Straus & Giroux.

Swiss Family Robinson. 2002. (Illus.). 80p. (YA). per. 6.95 (978-1-56254-531-4(0) , SP5310) Saddleback Educational Publishing.

Turnbull, Ann. Maroo of the Winter Caves. 20th anniv. ed. 2004. (Illus.). 144p. (J). (gr. 4-6). 15.00 (978-0-618-43408-4(9)); (YA). (gr. 3-5). pap. 6.95 (978-0-618-44299-7(5)) Houghton Mifflin Co. Trade & Reference Div. (Clarion Bks.).

Wheeler, Jordan & Jackson, Dennis. Christmas at Wapos Bay. 2006. 176p. (J). pap. ***(*978-1-55050-324-1(3))*** Coteau Bks.

Withers, Pam. Camp Wild. 2006. (Orca Currents Ser.). 112p. (J). lib. bdg. 14.95 (978-1-55143-557-2(8)) Orca Bk. Pubs. USA.

WILDLIFE CONSERVATION

see also Birds—Protection; Endangered Species; Forests and Forestry; Game Protection; National Parks and Reserves

Arnold, Caroline. El Nino: Stormy Weather for People & Wildlife. 2005. (Illus.). 48p. (J). (gr. 4-6). pap., pap. 5.95 (978-0-618-55110-1(7) , Clarion Bks.) Houghton Mifflin Co. Trade & Reference Div.

Beattie, Laura C. Discover African Wildlife: Activity Book. Plazek, Caroline, illus. 2008. 24p. pap., stu. ed. 2.95 ***(*978-0-911239-38-6(3))*** Rinehart, Roberts Pubs.

Becker, John. Manatees. 2002. (Returning Wildlife Ser.). (Illus.). 48p. (J). (gr. 3-5). 23.70 (978-0-7377-1010-6(1) , Kidhaven) Thomson Gale.

Become a Junior Ranger. 2001. (Illus.). 12p. (J). (gr. 1-7). pap. 2.50 (978-1-888213-55-3(8)) Eastern National.

Bellamy, David. Our Changing World: The Roadside. Dow, Jill, illus. 2004. (Our Changing World Ser.). 32p. (J). pap. 7.95 (978-1-84507-219-3(7)) Lincoln, Frances Ltd. GBR. *Dist:* Perseus Distribution.

Bellamy, Rufus. Saving Wildlife. 2005. (Action for the Environment Ser.). (Illus.). 32p. (J). (gr. 4-7). lib. bdg. 27.10 (978-1-58340-596-3(8)) Smart Apple Media.

Berkowitz, Henry. Vanishing Wildlife: An Educational Coloring Book. 2002. 32p. (J). (gr. k-3). pap. 4.95 (978-0-932855-72-5(5)) Winner Enterprises.

Brown, Vinson. The Californian Wildlife Region. 3rd rev. ed. 2003. (Illus.). 302p. (J). pap. 14.95 (978-0-87961-201-6(0)) Naturegraph Pubs., Inc.

Bruchac, Joseph. Buffalo Song. Farnsworth, Bill, illus. 2008. (J). Lee & Low Bks., Inc.

Burns, Diane L. Berries, Nuts & Seeds. McGee, John F., illus. 2004. (Take-Along Guide Ser.). 48p. (J). (gr. 2-5). pap. 7.95 (978-1-55971-573-7(1) , NorthWord Bks. for Young Readers) T&N Children's Publishing.

Burroughs, Caleb. Animal Rescue Adventure. 2006. (Illus.). (J). ***(*978-1-4127-6491-9(2))*** Publications International, Ltd.

Burton, Lawrence D. Fish & Wildlife: Principles of Zoology & Ecology. 2nd rev. ed. 2001. (Illus.). 480p. (C). 100.95 (978-0-7668-3260-2(0)) Thomson Delmar Learning.

Calhoun, Yael. Wildlife Protection. 2004. (Environmental Issues Ser.). (Illus.). 150p. (gr. 9-13). 31.95 (978-0-7910-8204-1(0) , Chelsea Hse.) Facts On File, Inc.

Casterline, Linda. Rare Animals: A Chapter Book. 2003. (True Tales Ser.). (Illus.). 48p. (J). 22.50 (978-0-516-22914-0(1) , Children's Pr.) Scholastic Library Publishing.

Costain, Meredith. Animals at Risk. 2000. (gr. k-3). lib. bdg. 11.80 (978-0-613-30229-6(X)) Tandem Library Bks.

Crum, Anna-Maria. Conductistas de animales & Animal Behaviorists. 2005. spiral bd. 77.00 ***(*978-1-4108-5679-1(8))*** Benchmark Education Co.

Dalgleish, Sharon. Protecting Wildlife. 2002. (Our World - Our Future Ser.). (Illus.). 32p. (gr. 4-8). 28.00 (978-0-7910-7021-5(2) , Chelsea Hse.) Facts On File, Inc.

Dewey, Jennifer Owings. Wildlife Rescue: The Work of Dr. Kathleen Ramsay. MacCarter, Don, photos by. 2003. (Illus.). 64p. (YA). (gr. 4-6). pap. 9.95 (978-1-56397-762-6(1)) Boyds Mills Pr.

Discover Series: Science, Nature, Wildlife, 11 bks. (Illus.). (J). (gr. 3-6). lib. bdg. 175.45 (978-1-56674-935-0(2)) Forest Hse. Publishing Co., Inc.

Ebersole, Rene. Gorilla Mountain: The Story of Wildlife Biologist Amy Vedder. 2005. (Women's Adventures in Science Ser.). (Illus.). 118p. (YA). (gr. 5-8). 31.00 (978-0-531-16779-3(8) , Watts, Franklin) Scholastic Library Publishing.

Fleming, Denise. Where Once There Was a Wood. Fleming, Denise, illus. 2002. (Illus.). (J). 15.49 (978-0-7587-3992-6(3)) Book Wholesalers, Inc.

—Where Once There Was a Wood. Fleming, Denise, illus. rev. ed. 2000. (Illus.). 32p. (J). (ps-5). pap. 7.95 (978-0-8050-6482-7(6) , Holt, Henry & Co. Bks. For Young Readers) Holt, Henry & Co.

—Where Once There Was a Wood. 2000. (ps-2). lib. bdg. 15.25 (978-0-613-28698-5(7)) Tandem Library Bks.

Goodall, Jane. With Love: Ten Heartwarming Stories of Chimpanzees in the Wild. Marks, Alan, illus. 1998. 44p. (J). (gr. 1-5). 15.95 (978-1-55858-911-7(2)) North-South Bks., Inc.

Hamilton, Garry. Rhino Rescue: Changing the Future for Endangered Wildlife. 2006. (Firefly Animal Rescue Ser.). (Illus.). 64p. (J). (gr. 5-12). pap. 9.95 (978-1-55297-910-5(5)); lib. bdg. 19.95 (978-1-55297-912-9(1)) Firefly Bks., Ltd.

Harcourt School Publishers Staff. Croc! Below Level. 3rd ed. 2002. (Trofeos Ser.). (SPA., Illus.). pap. 6.80 (978-0-15-324110-9(1)) Harcourt Schl. Pubs.

Harlow, Rosie. Nature in Danger. 2002. (Young Discoverers Ser.). (Illus.). 32p. (J). (gr. k-3). pap. 7.95 (978-0-7534-5504-3(8) , Kingfisher) Houghton Mifflin Co. Trade & Reference Div.

Haswell, Arthur. Wildlife. 2000. (Earth Strikes Back Ser.). (Illus.). 48p. (J). (gr. 2-6). lib. bdg. 16.95 (978-1-929298-61-7(7)) Chrysalis Education.

Hickman, Pamela. Birds of Prey Rescue: Changing the Future for Endangered Wildlife. 2006. (Firefly Animal Rescue Ser.). (Illus.). 64p. (J). (gr. 5-12). pap. 9.95 (978-1-55407-144-9(5)); lib. bdg. 19.95 (978-1-55407-145-6(3)) Firefly Bks., Ltd.

Hirschi, Ron. Lions, Tigers, & Bears: Why Are Big Predators So Rare? Mangelsen, Thomas D., photos by. 2007. (Illus.). 32p. (J). (gr. 2-5). 16.95 ***(*978-1-59078-435-8(9))*** Boyds Mills Pr.

Humane Society of the U. S. Staff & Sirch, Willow Ann. Careers with Animals. 2004. (Illus.). 128p. (gr. 4-6). 16.95 (978-1-55591-408-0(X)) Fulcrum Publishing.

Jackson, Donna. Wildlife Detectives. 2000. (gr. 3-6). lib. bdg. 12.95 (978-0-613-60739-1(2)) Tandem Library Bks.

Jackson, Donna M. The Wildlife Detectives: How Forensic Scientists Fight Crimes Against Nature. Shattil, Wendy & Rozinski, Bob, photos by. 2002. (Scientists in the Field Ser.). (Illus.). 48p. (J). (gr. 4-6). pap. 6.95 (978-0-618-19683-8(8)) Houghton Mifflin Co. Trade & Reference Div.

Kavanagh, James. Rocky Mountain Wildlife Nature. 2004. (Pocket Naturalist Ser.). (Illus.). 32p. pap., act. bk. ed. 6.95 (978-1-58355-264-3(2)) Waterford Pr., Ltd.

—Southwestern Desert Wildlife Nature. 2004. (Pocket Naturalist Ser.). (Illus.). 32p. pap., act. bk. ed. 6.95 (978-1-58355-262-9(6)) Waterford Pr., Ltd.

Kendell, Patricia. Wwf (World Watch (Chicago, Ill.) 2004. (World Watch Ser.). 48p. (YA). (gr. 6-8). lib. bdg. 27.14 (978-0-7398-6615-3(X)) Raintree.

Kenyon, Linda J. Rainforest Bird Rescue: Changing the Future for Endangered Wildlife. 2006. (Firefly Animal Rescue Ser.). (Illus.). 64p. (J). (gr. 5-12). pap. 9.95 (978-1-55407-152-4(6)); lib. bdg. 19.95 (978-1-55407-153-1(4)) Firefly Bks., Ltd.

Kinsner, Kathy. ¿Condenadas a desaparecer? Especies en peligro de extincion & Doomed to Disappear? Endangered Species. 2005. spiral bd. 84.00 ***(*978-1-4108-5698-2(4))*** Benchmark Education Co.

Lasky, Kathryn. Interrupted Journey: Saving Endangered Sea Turtles. Knight, Christopher G., photos by. 48p. (J). (gr. 1-5). 2006. pap. 6.99 (978-0-7636-2883-3(2)); 2001. (Illus.). 16.99 (978-0-7636-0635-0(9)) Candlewick Pr.

Mattern, Joanne. Going, Going, Gone? Saving Animals in Danger. 2001. (Animal Adventures Ser.). (Illus.). 56p. (J). pap. (978-0-7891-5398-2(X)); (gr. 1-4). lib. bdg. 16.95 (978-0-7807-9850-2(3)) Perfection Learning Corp.

Meissner, David. Rescate del habitat & Habitat Rescue. 2005. spiral bd. 77.00 ***(*978-1-4108-5676-0(3))*** Benchmark Education Co.

Nagel, Rob. Endangered Species. 1998. 84.00 (978-0-7876-1876-6(4)); 84.00 (978-0-7876-1878-0(0)); pap. 84.00 (978-0-7876-1877-3(2)) Thomson Gale. (UXL).

Parish, Steve. Australian Wildlife. 2002. (Nature Kids Ser.). (Illus.). 52p. (J). (gr. 3 up). lib. bdg. (978-1-59084-210-2(3)) Mason Crest Pubs.

Patent, Dorothy Hinshaw. The Bald Eagle Returns. Munoz, William, illus. 2000. 80p. (J). (gr. 4-6). tchr. ed. 16.00 (978-0-395-91416-8(7) , Clarion Bks.) Houghton Mifflin Co. Trade & Reference Div.

Penny, Malcolm. Endangered Species: Our Impact on the Planet. 2002. (Twenty-First Century Debates Ser.). (Illus.). 64p. (YA). (gr. 6-8). lib. bdg. 27.12 (978-0-7398-4873-9(9)) Raintree.

Pinderhughes, John, photos by. Hurt No Living Thing. 1999. (Illus.). 18p. (J). (ps-k). mass mkt. 4.99 (978-0-7681-0104-1(2) , McClanahan Bk.) Learning Horizons, Inc.

Pipe, Jim. Conservation. 2007. (J). ***(*978-1-59604-136-3(6))*** Stargazer Bks.

Posewitz, James. Rifle in Hand: How Wild America Was Saved. 2004. (Illus.). 128p. per. 9.95 (978-1-931832-41-0(2) , 8667872363) Riverbend Publishing.

Powell, Jillian. World Wildlife Fund. 2001. (World Organizations Ser.). (Illus.). 32p. (J). (gr. 6-8). 24.00 (978-0-531-14626-2(X) , Watts, Franklin) Scholastic Library Publishing.

—World Wildlife Fund. 2001. (gr. 5-8). lib. bdg. 15.25 (978-0-613-54795-6(0)) Tandem Library Bks.

Priebe, Mac. The Peregrine Falcon: Endangered No More. Priebe, Jennifer, illus. 1999. (Wildlife Winners). 30p. (J). (gr. 2-5). 15.95 (978-0-9669551-9-4(6)) Mindfull Publishing.

Ryan, Marla Felkins & Corwin, Jeff. Into Wild India 2. 2004. (Jeff Corwin Experience Ser.). (Illus.). 48p. (J). 11.20 (978-1-4103-0234-2(2)); (gr. 4-7). 24.95 (978-1-4103-0233-5(4)) Thomson Gale. (Blackbirch Pr., Inc.).

—Into Wild Thailand. 2004. (Jeff Corwin Experience Ser.). (Illus.). 48p. (J). 11.20 (978-1-4103-0254-0(7)); (gr. 4-7). 24.95 (978-1-4103-0253-3(9)) Thomson Gale. (Blackbirch Pr., Inc.).

Salmansohn, Pete & Kress, Stephen. Saving Birds: Heroes Around the World. 2005. (Illus.). 40p. (gr. 3-6). 16.95 (978-0-88448-237-6(5)) Tilbury Hse. Pubs.

Smith, Randy & Smith, Madelyn. Wildlife Wise. 2000. (Illus.). 30p. (J). (ps-3). pap. 9.95 (978-0-9677781-0-5(7)) Randell Productions, Inc.

Smith van Frankenhuyzen, Robbyn. Saving Samantha: A True Story. van Frankenhuyzen, Gijsbert, illus. 2004. 48p. (J). 17.95 (978-1-58536-220-2(4)) Sleeping Bear Pr.

Snyder, Trish. Alligator & Crocodile Rescue: Changing the Future for Endangered Wildlife. 2006. (Firefly Animal Rescue Ser.). (Illus.). 64p. (J). (gr. 5-12). pap. 9.95 (978-1-55297-919-8(9)); lib. bdg. 19.95 (978-1-55297-920-4(2)) Firefly Bks., Ltd.

Somervill, Barbara A. Animal Survivors of the Arctic. 2004. (Watts Library). (Illus.). 64p. (J). 25.50 (978-0-531-12204-4(2) , Watts, Franklin) Scholastic Library Publishing.

—Animal Survivors of the Wetlands. 2004. (Watts Library). (Illus.). 64p. (J). 25.50 (978-0-531-12203-7(4) , Watts, Franklin) Scholastic Library Publishing.

Spilsbury, Louise & Spilsbury, Richard. Animals under Threat. 2006. (Planet under Pressure Ser.). (Illus.). 48p. (J). lib. bdg. (978-1-4034-8217-4(9)) Heinemann Library.

—Save the Asian Elephant. 2006. (Illus.). 32p. (J). (978-1-4034-7802-3(3)); pap. (978-1-4034-7810-8(4)) Heinemann Library.

—Save the Bengal Tiger. 2006. (Illus.). 32p. (J). 25.36 (978-1-4034-7803-0(1)) Heinemann Library.

—Save the Giant Panda. 2006. (Illus.). 32p. (J). pap. (978-1-4034-7815-3(5)) Heinemann Library.

Stetson, Emily. Create a Wildlife Habitat for Urban & Suburban Small Spaces. 2004. (Quick Starts for Kids! Ser.). (Illus.). 128p. (J). pap. 12.95 (978-0-8249-8665-0(2)) Ideals Pubns.

Stone, Lynn M. American Wildlife, 4 vols., Set. 2001. (Illus.). (J). (gr. 2-7). lib. bdg. 90.40 (978-1-58340-014-2(1)) Smart Apple Media.

—Saving Wolves. 2000. (Wolves Discovery Library). (Illus.). 24p. (J). (gr. 1-4). lib. bdg. 19.27 (978-1-55916-240-1(6)) Rourke Publishing, LLC.

Swanson, Diane. Why Seals Blow Their Noses: Canadian Wildlife in Fact & Fiction. Penhale, Douglas, illus. 80p. (J). (gr. 3-2). pap. 12.95 (978-1-55110-038-8(X)) Whitecap Bks., Ltd. CAN. *Dist:* Graphic Arts Ctr. Publishing Co.

Swinburne, Stephen R. Bobcat: North America's Cat. 2003. (Illus.). 32p. (YA). (gr. 4-6). 15.95 (978-1-56397-843-2(1)) Boyds Mills Pr.

—Once A Wolf: How Wildlife Biologists Fought to Bring Back the Gray Wolf. Brandenburg, Jim, photos by. (Scientists in the Field Ser.). (Illus.). 48p. (gr. 5-9). 2001. (YA). pap. 6.95 (978-0-618-11120-6(4)); 1999. (J). reprint ed. tchr. ed. 16.00 (978-0-395-89827-7(7)) Houghton Mifflin Co. Trade & Reference Div.

—The Woods Scientist. Morse, Susan C., photos by. 2003. (Scientists in the Field Ser.). (Illus.). 48p. (J). (gr. 4-6). tchr. ed. 16.00 (978-0-618-04602-7(X)) Houghton Mifflin Co. Trade & Reference Div.

Thomas, Keltie. Bear Rescue: Changing the Future for Endangered Wildlife. 2006. (Firefly Animal Rescue Ser.). (Illus.). 64p. (J). (gr. 5-12). pap. 9.95 (978-1-55297-921-1(0)); lib. bdg. 19.95 (978-1-55297-922-8(9)) Firefly Bks., Ltd.

Thomas, Peggy. Bird Alert. 2000. (Science of Saving Animals Ser.: 8). (Illus.). 64p. (gr. 5-8). lib. bdg. (978-0-7613-1457-8(1) , Twenty-First Century Bks.) Lerner Publishing Group.

Toon, Ann & Toon, Steve. Rhinos: Natural History & Conservation. 2002. (WorldLife Library Ser.). (Illus.). 72p. pap. 17.95 (978-0-89658-586-7(7)) Voyageur Pr., Inc.

Tracqui, Valérie. Panda: Wild about Bamboo. 1999. (Animal Close-Ups Ser.). (978-0-606-18028-3(1)) Tandem Library Bks.

VanBlaricom, Glenn, text. Sea Otters. 2001. (WorldLife Library Ser.). (Illus.). 72p. (gr. 5 up). pap. 17.95 (978-0-89658-562-1(X)) Voyageur Pr., Inc.

Vergoth, Karin & Lampton, Christopher. Endangered Species. rev. ed. 1999. (Impact Bks.). (Illus.). 112p. (YA). (gr. 8-12). 26.00 (978-0-531-11480-3(5) , Watts, Franklin) Scholastic Library Publishing.

Vergoth, Karin & Vergoth, Christopher. Endangered Species. rev. ed. 2000. (Impact Bks.). (Illus.). 112p. (J). (gr. 8-12). pap. 12.95 (978-0-531-16438-9(1) , Watts, Franklin) Scholastic Library Publishing.

Wilkes, Angela. My World: Weird & Wonderful Wildlife. 2001. (Illus.). 96p. (J). (ps-k). pap. 10.95 (978-0-7534-5424-4(6) , Kingfisher) Houghton Mifflin Co. Trade & Reference Div.

Wilkinson, Rick. Endangered! Working to Save Animals at Risk. 2002. (Illus.). 32p. (J). (978-1-86508-664-4(9)) Allen & Unwin.

Williams, Judith. Saving Endangered Animals with a Scientist. 2004. (I Like Science! Ser.). (Illus.). 24p. (J). (gr. 2-4). lib. bdg. 21.26 (978-0-7660-2276-8(5)) Enslow Pubs., Inc.

Williams, Kimberly Joan & Stoops, Erik Daniel. Bat Conservation, 6 vols., Set. 2001. (Young Explorer Ser.). (Illus.). 32p. (J). (gr. 3-7). lib. bdg. 4.85 net. (978-1-890475-13-0(0)) Faulkner's Publishing Group.

Winn, Carol A. Buffalo Jones: The Man Who Saved America's Bison. Geer, William J., illus. 2000. 59p. (J). (gr. 5-7). 12.95 (978-1-877810-30-5(4)) Rayve Productions, Inc.

WILDLIFE CONSERVATION—FICTION

Blake, Quentin. Loveykins. Blake, Quentin, illus. 2003. (Illus.). 32p. (J). 15.95 (978-1-56145-282-8(3)) Peachtree Pubs., Ltd.

Bledsoe, Lucy Jane. Cougar Canyon. 2001. 136p. (J). (gr. 4-6). tchr. ed. 16.95 (978-0-8234-1599-1(6)) Holiday Hse., Inc.

Bow, Patricia. Chimpanzee Rescue: Changing the Future for Endangered Wildlife. 2004. (Illus.). 64p. (J). (gr. k-9). lib. bdg. 16.60 (978-0-606-33844-8(6)) Tandem Library Bks.

Brooks, John. Balloons, Sea Creatures, & Me. 2006. 34p. (J). 14.58 (978-0-9661789-3-7(9)) Lulu.com.

Collard, Sneed B., III. Butterfly Count. Kratter, Paul, illus. 2002. 32p. (J). (gr. k-3). tchr. ed. 16.95 (978-0-8234-1607-3(0)) Holiday Hse., Inc.

Cowcher, Helen. Tigress. 2001. (Illus.). 40p. (YA). (BEN, ENG, URD, TUR & VIE.). 16.95 (978-1-84059-024-1(6)); (GRE, ENG, URD, TUR & VIE., 16.95 (978-1-84059-026-5(2)); (GUJ, ENG, URD, TUR & VIE., 16.95 (978-1-84059-027-2(0)); (TUR, ENG, URD, VIE & CHI., 16.95 (978-1-84059-028-9(9)); (URD, ENG, TUR, VIE & CHI., 16.95 (978-1-84059-029-6(7)) Milet Publishing.

Crowe, Carole. Turtle Girl. Postier, Jim, illus. 2007. (J). (***978-1-59078-262-0(3)***) Boyds Mills Pr.

Cry of the Falcon. 2006. 208p. (J). pap. 9.95 (978-0-9788541-0-2(1)) m.d. hughes.

Doerr, Bonnie J. Kenzie's Key. Aberle, Xylena Apotheloz, illus. 2003. 211p. (J). 16.95 (978-0-9619155-6-8(0)) Laurel & Herbert, Inc.

George, Jean Craighead. Frightful's Daughter. San Souci, Daniel, illus. 2002. 32p. (J). (ps-3). 16.99 (978-0-525-46907-0(9) , Dutton Juvenile) Penguin Group (USA) Inc.

—Frightful's Mountain. 1999. (Illus.). 272p. (J). (gr. 4-7). 15.99 (978-0-525-46166-1(3) , Dutton Juvenile) Penguin Group (USA) Inc.

Gilmore, Kate. The Exchange Student. 2006. 222p. (J). (gr. 7). pap. 6.95 (978-0-618-68948-4(6)) Houghton Mifflin Co.

—The Exchange Student. 1999. 224p. (J). (gr. 5-9). tchr. ed. 15.00 (978-0-395-57511-6(7)) Houghton Mifflin Co. Trade & Reference Div.

Grote, Rich. Megan & the Borealis Butterfly. 1999. (Magic Attic Club Ser.). (J). lib. bdg. (978-0-606-16953-0(9)) Tandem Library Bks.

Harlow, Patty F. Rock with Rodney & Party with Perky to Preserve Wildlife. 2006. (Illus.). 108p. (J). per. 16.95 (978-1-60002-002-5(X) , 3583, Airleaf Publishing) Airleaf Publishing & Bookselling.

Harms, John. Saving of Valiant Blue Heron. 2001. (gr. 3-6). lib. bdg. 15.25 (978-0-613-77815-2(4)) Tandem Library Bks.

Hay, Jerry M. & Pollema-Cahill, Phyllis. A Goose Named Gilligan. 2004. (Illus.). 32p. 15.95 (978-1-932073-09-6(4)) Kramer, H.J. Inc.

Henry, Marguerite. Mustang: Wild Spirit of the West. 2002. (Illus.). 13.40 (978-1-4046-1358-4(7)) Book Wholesalers, Inc.

Himmelman, John. The Animal Rescue Club. Himmelman, John, illus. 1999. (Illus.). 46p. (J). (ps-ps). lib. bdg. 11.80 (978-0-613-18234-8(0)) Tandem Library Bks.

Hobbs, Will. The Maze. 1999. 248p. (J). (gr. k-9). lib. bdg. 14.15 (978-0-613-19524-9(8)) Tandem Library Bks.

Hobbs, William. The Maze. (J). (gr. 5 up). 1999. (Illus.). 256p. pap. 5.99 (978-0-380-72913-5(X) , Harper Trophy); 1998. 208p. 17.99 (978-0-688-15092-1(6)) HarperCollins Pubs.

—The Maze. unabr. ed. 1999. (YA). pap., stu. ed. 59.00 incl. audio (978-0-7887-3990-3(5) , 41062X4) Recorded Bks., LLC.

—The Maze. 1999. (J). (978-0-606-16369-9(7)) Tandem Library Bks.

Kerr, Rita. Dearie Deer: Wild & Free. Kerr, Rita, illus. 1998. (Illus.). 40p. (gr. 1-4). 13.95 (978-1-57168-273-4(2)) Eakin Pr.

Lasky, Kathryn. She's Wearing a Dead Bird on Her Head! Catrow, David, illus. 1999. 40p. pap. 6.99 (978-0-7868-1164-9(1)) Disney Pr.

Lears, Laurie. Nathan's Wish: A Story about Cerebral Palsy. Schuett, Stacey, illus. 2005. 32p. (J). (gr. 1-4). 15.95 (978-0-8075-7101-9(6)) Whitman, Albert & Co.

Levin, Betty. Creature Crossing. Smith, Joseph A., illus. 1999. 96p. (J). (gr. 3 up). 15.00 (978-0-688-16220-7(7)) HarperCollins Pubs.

Lumry, Amanda & Hurwitz, Laura. Tigers in Terai. McIntyre, Sarah, illus. 2nd rev. ed. 2007. 36p. 15.95 (***978-1-60040-003-2(5)***) Centro Bks., LLC.

—Tigers in Terai. McIntyre, Sarah, illus. 2nd ed. 2007. 36p. (***978-0-9748411-6-8(1)***) Eaglemont Pr.

Malone, Geoffrey. Tiger. 2007. 304p. pap. 10.95 (***978-0-340-89358-6(3)***) Hodder Children's Division GBR. *Dist:* Independent Pubs. Group.

McDonald, Megan. Julie & the Eagles, Bk. 4. McAliley, Susan, illus. 2007. 88p. (YA). (gr. 3 up). 12.95 (***978-1-59369-351-0(6)***) American Girl Publishing, Inc.

—Julie & the Eagles, Bk. 4. McAliley, Susan & Hunt, Robert, illus. 2007. 88p. (YA). (gr. 3 up). pap. 6.95 (***978-1-59369-350-3(8)***) American Girl Publishing, Inc.

Messer, Celeste M. Forever & Always. Hoeffner, Deb, illus. 2004. 82-92p. 4.95 (978-0-9710145-0-3(7)) AshleyAlan Enterprises.

Montgomery, Rutherford G. Pekan the Shadow. Nenninger, J. D., illus. 2004. (Classic Ser.). 164p. (gr. 4-7). pap. 13.95 (978-0-87004-406-9(0)) Caxton Pr.

Myers, Anna. Flying Blind. 2003. 192p. (YA). 16.95 (978-0-8027-8879-5(3)) Walker & Co.

Peterson, Cris. Wild Horses: Black Hills Sanctuary. Upitis, Alvis, illus. 2003. 32p. (YA). (gr. 4-6). 16.95 (978-1-56397-745-9(1)) Boyds Mills Pr.

Plowden, Sally H. Turtle Tracks. Plowden, Tee, illus. 2002. 32p. (J). (gr. 4-6). 14.95 (978-0-9679016-6-4(9)) Palmetto Conservation Foundation.

Riederer, Joe. Trouble in the Barrens. Riederer, Joe, photos by. 2002. 160p. (YA). (gr. 6-9). per. 14.95 (978-0-9671386-1-9(2)) Big Bluestem Pr.

Schuch, Steve. Symphony of Whales. 2002. (gr. k-3). lib. bdg. 14.15 (978-0-613-56636-0(X)) Tandem Library Bks.

Seidler, Tor. The Silent Spillbills. 1998. 224p. (J). (gr. 3-7). 14.95 (978-0-06-205180-6(6)); 14.89 (978-0-06-205181-3(4)) HarperCollins Pubs.

Skurzynski, Gloria. Wolf Stalker. 2001. (gr. 3-6). lib. bdg. 14.10 (978-0-613-84040-8(2)) Tandem Library Bks.

Skurzynski, Gloria & Ferguson. Wolf Stalker. 2001. (National Parks Mystery Ser.). (Illus.). (J). (978-0-606-21533-6(6)) Tandem Library Bks.

Skurzynski, Gloria & Ferguson, Alane. Wolf Stalker. 1998. (National Parks Mysteries Ser.: Vol. 1). (Illus.). 160p. (J). (gr. 3-7). 15.95 (978-0-7922-7034-8(7) , National Geographic Children's Bks.) National Geographic Society.

Smith, Lauren. Ashley Enright & the Mystery at Miller's Pond. 2006. (ENG.). 60p. per. 12.95 (***978-1-4241-5268-1(2)***) PublishAmerica, Inc.

Spirin, Gennady. Martha. Spirin, Gennady, illus. 2005. (Illus.). 32p. (J). (ps-3). 14.99 (978-0-399-23980-9(4) , Philomel) Penguin Group (USA) Inc.

Taylor, Theodore. The Weirdo. 2006. (Illus.). 304p. (J). pap. 6.95 (978-0-15-205666-7(1) , Harcourt Paperbacks) Harcourt Children's Bks.

Van Frankenhuyzen, Robbyn Smith. Kelly of Hazel Ridge. van Frankenhuyzen, Gijsbert, illus. 3rd rev. ed. 2006. 48p. (J). (gr. k-5). 17.95 (978-1-58536-268-4(9)) Sleeping Bear Pr.

Weirdo. 2002. stu. ed. (978-1-56137-815-9(1)) Novel Units, Inc.

Woods, Shirley. Black Nell: The Adventures of a Coyote. 2000. (Illus.). (J). 13.75 (978-0-606-21882-5(3)) Tandem Library Bks.

Wyss, Tyan. African Dream. Immelman, Sarita, illus. 2006. 48p. (J). pap. 15.95 (***978-1-58939-915-0(3)***) Virtualbookworm.com Publishing, Inc.

WILKES, CHARLES, 1798-1877

Philbrick, Nathaniel. Sea of Glory: America's Voyage of Discovery, the U. S. Exploring Expedition, 1838-1842. 2004. (Illus.). 452p. per. 22.65 (978-0-606-33469-3(6)) Tandem Library Bks.

WILLIAM I, KING OF ENGLAND, 1027 OR 8-1087

Abbott, Jacob. History of William the Conqueror. 2003. 291p. 89.00 (978-0-7950-4508-0(5)) New Library Press-.Net.

Green, Robert. William the Conqueror. 1998. (First Bks.). 64p. (J). 23.00 (978-0-531-20353-8(0) , Watts, Franklin) Scholastic Library Publishing.

Hamilton, Janice. The Norman Conquest of England. 2007. (Pivotal Moments in History Ser.). 160p. (YA). (gr. 9-12). lib. bdg. 38.60 (***978-0-8225-5902-3(1)*** , Twenty-First Century Bks.) Lerner Publishing Group.

Hilliam, Paul. William the Conqueror: First Norman King of England. 2004. (Leaders of the Middle Ages Ser.). (Illus.). 112p. (J). lib. bdg. 31.95 (978-1-4042-0166-8(1)) Rosen Publishing Group, Inc., The.

McGowen, Tom. William the Conqueror: Last Invader of England. 2007. (Rulers of the Middle Ages Ser.). (Illus.). 160p. (YA). (gr. 7-9). lib. bdg. 34.60 (978-0-7660-2713-8(9)) Enslow Pubs., Inc.

Ross, Stewart. Will's Dream. Shields, Susan, illus. 28p. pap. 9.99 (978-0-7502-2965-4(9) , Hodder & Stoughton) Hodder General Publishing Division GBR. *Dist:* Trafalgar Square Publishing.

WILLIAMS, ROGER, 1604?-1683

Allison, Amy. Roger Williams. 2001. (gr. 3-6). lib. bdg. 17.60 (978-0-613-37646-4(3)) Tandem Library Bks.

—Roger Williams: Founder of Rhode Island. 2000. (Colonial Leaders Ser.). (Illus.). 80p. (J). (gr. 8-12). 27.50 (978-0-7910-5964-7(2) , Chelsea Hse.) Facts On File, Inc.

Burgan, Michael. Roger Williams: Founder of Rhode Island. 2006. (Signature Lives Ser.). (Illus.). 112p. (J). (gr. 5-7). 30.60 (978-0-7565-1596-6(3)) Compass Point Bks.

Gaustad, Edwin S. Roger Williams: Prophet of Liberty. 2001. (Oxford Portraits Ser.). (Illus.). 144p. (YA). (gr. 9 up). 28.00 (978-0-19-513000-3(6)) Oxford Univ. Pr., Inc.

Harcourt School Publishers Staff. The Exile of Roger Williams. 3rd ed. 2002. (Horizons Ser.). (Illus.). (J). pap. 7.30 (978-0-15-333565-5(3)) Harcourt Schl. Pubs.

The Puritans, Algonkians & Roger Williams (NCHS) (J). (gr. 5-8). spiral bd., tchr.'s planning gde. ed. 13.50 (978-0-382-44447-0(7)) Cobblestone Publishing Co.

The Puritans, Algonkians & Roger Williams (NCHS) Grades 5-8. (J). tchr. ed. 18.00 (978-0-382-44537-8(6)) Cobblestone Publishing Co.

Raum, Elizabeth. Roger Williams. 2004. (Illus.). 32p. (J). pap. 7.50 (978-1-4034-5969-5(X)); lib. bdg. 25.64 (978-1-4034-5961-9(4)) Heinemann Library.

Walsh, Kieran. Roger Williams. 2005. (Discover the Life of a Colonial American Ser.). (Illus.). 24p. (J). (gr. 2-5). 14.95 (978-1-59515-140-7(0)) Rourke Publishing, LLC.

WILLIAMS, SERENA, 1981-

Armentrout, David & Armentrout, Patricia, trs. Venus & Serena Williams. 2003. (Discover the Life of a Sports Star Ser.). (Illus.). 24p. (J). 20.64 (978-1-58952-655-6(4)) Rourke Publishing, LLC.

Aronson, Virginia. Venus & Serena Williams. 2000. (Women Who Win Ser.). (Illus.). 64p. (J). (gr. 4-7). pap. 25.00 (978-0-7910-6158-9(2)); 25.00 (978-0-7910-5799-5(2)) Facts On File, Inc. (Chelsea Hse.).

—Venus & Serena Williams. 2000. (Illus.). 64p. (J). (gr. 4-7). lib. bdg. 17.60 (978-0-613-33180-7(X)) Tandem Library Bks.

Brown, Jonatha A. Venus & Serena Williams. 2005. (People to Know Ser.). (Illus.). 24p. (J). pap. (978-0-8368-4477-1(7)); (YA). lib. bdg. 19.33 (978-0-8368-4470-2(X)) Stevens, Gareth Inc.

—Venus y Serena Williams.Tr. of Venus & Serena Williams. 19.33 (978-0-8368-4586-0(2)) Stevens, Gareth Inc.

Buckley, James, Jr. Venus & Serena Williams. 2003. (Trailblazers of the Modern World Ser.). (Illus.). 48p. (J). (gr. 5 up). pap. 14.95 (978-0-8368-5246-2(X)); lib. bdg. 30.00 (978-0-8368-5086-4(6)) Stevens, Gareth Inc. (World Almanac Library).

Christopher, Matt. On the Court with... Venus & Serena Williams. 2002. (Matt Christopher Sports Biographies Ser.). (Illus.). 112p. (J). (gr. 4-7). pap. 4.99 (978-0-316-13814-7(2)) Little, Brown Bks. for Young Readers.

—On the Court with... Venus & Serena Williams. 2002. (gr. 3-6). lib. bdg. 12.95 (978-0-613-70947-7(0)) Tandem Library Bks.

Donaldson, Madeline. Venus & Serena Williams. 2005. (Amazing Athletes Ser.). (Illus.). 32p. (gr. 3-4). lib. bdg. 22.60 (978-0-8225-3316-0(2)) Lerner Publishing Group.

—Venus & Serena Williams. 2004. (Illus.). 32p. (J). (ps-6). lib. bdg. 12.75 (978-0-606-30527-3(0)) Tandem Library Bks.

Donaldson Madeline. Venus & Serena Willliams (Revised Edition) 2007. (Amazing Athletes Ser.). (J). 23.93 (***978-0-8225-7595-5(7)*** , Lerner Pubns.); pap. 6.95 (***978-0-8225-8857-3(9)*** , First Avenue Editions) Lerner Publishing Group.

Dorrie, Roxanne. Venus & Serena Williams: The Smashing Sisters. 2003. (High Five Reading (Red Level) Ser.). (Illus.). (J). 64p. lib. bdg. 22.60 (978-0-7368-2784-3(6)); 48p. pap. 23.93 (978-0-7368-2827-7(3)) Capstone Pr., Inc.

—Venus & Serena Williams: The Smashing Sisters, 6 vols. (gr. 4 up). 49.95 (978-0-7368-2837-6(0) , High Five) Red Brick Learning.

Fillon, Mike. Young Superstars of Tennis: The Venus & Serena Williams Story. 1999. (Illus.). 144p. (YA). (gr. 6-12). lib. bdg. 19.95 (978-1-888105-43-8(7)) Avisson Pr., Inc.

Fuller, Barbara. Great Britain. 2004. (Illus.). (J). 48p. 27.07 (978-0-7614-1760-6(5)); 2nd ed. 144p. 37.07 (978-0-7614-1845-0(8)) Cavendish, Marshall Corp. (Benchmark Bks.).

Gutman, Bill. Venus & Serena: The Grand Slam Williams Sisters. 2001. (Scholastic Biography Ser.). (Illus.). 144p. (J). (gr. 3-7). pap. 4.50 (978-0-439-27152-3(5)) Scholastic, Inc.

—Venus & Serena: The Grand Slam Williams Sisters. 2001. (Illus.). (978-0-606-21502-2(6)) Tandem Library Bks.

Hill, Mary. Serena & Venus Williams. 2003. (Welcome Bks.). (Illus.). 24p. (J). (ps-2). pap. 4.95 (978-0-516-27889-6(4) , Children's Pr.) Scholastic Library Publishing.

—Serena & Venus Williams. 2003. (gr. k-3). lib. bdg. 12.95 (978-0-613-67764-6(1)) Tandem Library Bks.

Morgan, Terri. Venus & Serena Williams. 2003. (gr. 3-6). lib. bdg. 14.10 (978-0-613-76644-9(X)) Tandem Library Bks.

—Venus & Serena Williams: Grand Slam Sisters. (Sports Achievers Biographies Ser.). (Illus.). 2005. 80p. (gr. 7-12). lib. bdg. 22.60 (978-0-8225-3684-0(6)); 2003. 64p. (J). (gr. 4-9). pap. 5.95 (978-0-8225-9866-4(3) , Carolrhoda Bks.) Lerner Publishing Group.

Pyle, Lydia. Venus & Serena Williams. 2004. (Awesome Athletes Ser.). (Illus.). 32p. (J). (gr. k-6). lib. bdg. 22.78 (978-1-59197-486-4(0)) ABDO Publishing Co.

Roza, Greg. Venus & Serena Williams: The Sisters of Tennis. 2006. (Tony Stead Nonfiction Independent Reading Collection). (J). pap. (978-1-4042-5537-1(0)) Rosen Publishing Group, Inc., The.

Schaefer, A. R. Serena & Venus Williams. 2002. (Sports Heroes Ser.). (Illus.). 48p. (J). (gr. 3-4). lib. bdg. 21.26 (978-0-7368-1054-8(4) , Capstone High-Interest Bks.) Capstone Pr., Inc.

Stewart, Mark. Venus & Serena Williams: Sisters in Arms. 2000. (New Wave Ser.). (Illus.). 48p. (gr. 4 up). lib. bdg. 22.90 (978-0-7613-1803-3(8) , Millbrook Pr.) Lerner Publishing Group.

Swanson, June. Venus & Serena Williams. Burke, Susan S., illus. 2003. (You Must Be Joking! Riddle Bks.). 32p. (J). (gr. 2-5). pap. 5.95 (978-0-8225-9842-8(6)) Lerner Publishing Group.

Trailblazers of the Modern World: Winston Churchill; Alexander Fleming; Pablo Picasso; Elvis Presley; Venus & Serena Williams; Oprah Winfrey, 6 bks. 2002. (Illus.). (J). (gr. 5 up). pap. 89.70 (978-0-8368-5241-7(9) , World Almanac Library) Stevens, Gareth Inc.

Venus y Serena Williams. 2006. (People We Should Know Ser.).Tr. of Venus & Serena Williams. (SPA.). (J). (gr. 3-4). 4.76 (978-0-8368-4593-8(5) , GHS33829) Stevens, Gareth Inc.

Watson, Galadriel Findlay. Venus & Serena Williams. 2005. (Great African American Women for Kids Ser.). (Illus.). 24p. (J). (978-1-59036-338-6(8)); lib. bdg. 26.00 (978-1-59036-332-4(9)) Weigl Pubs., Inc.

Williams, Venus, et al. Venus & Serena: 10 Rules for Living, Loving, & Winning. 2005. (Illus.). 144p. (YA). (gr. 7). pap. 14.00 (978-0-618-57653-1(3)) Houghton Mifflin Co. Trade & Reference Div.

WILLIAMS, TENNESSEE, 1914-1983

Hermann, Spring. A Student's Guide to Tennessee Williams. 2007. (Understanding Literature Ser.). (Illus.). 160p. (YA). (gr. 6). lib. bdg. 27.93 (***978-0-7660-2706-0(6)***) Enslow Pubs., Inc.

Smith-Howard, Alycia & Heintzelman, Greta. Critical Companion to Tennessee Williams: A Literary Reference to His Life & Work. (Critical Companion To Ser.). (Illus.). 448p. (gr. 9). pap. 19.95 (978-0-8160-6429-8(6) , Checkmark Bks.) Facts On File, Inc.

Tracy, Kathleen. Tennessee Williams. 2006. (Poets & Playwrights Ser.). (Illus.). 112p. (YA). (gr. 6-12). lib. bdg. 37.10 (978-1-58415-427-3(6)) Mitchell Lane Pubs., Inc.

WILLIAMS, TED, 1918-2002

Kemmerer, Russ. Ted Williams: 'Hey Kid, Just Get It over the Plate!' 2002. (Illus.). 260p. (YA). mass mkt. 19.95 (978-0-9645819-7-0(0)) Madden Publishing Co., Inc.

Nolan, Bill, et al. Ted Williams: A Splendid Life. collector's ed. 2004. (Illus.). 51p. (YA). reprint ed. 13.00 (978-0-7567-8094-4(2)) DIANE Publishing Co.

WILLIAMS, VENUS, 1980-

Armentrout, David & Armentrout, Patricia, trs. Venus & Serena Williams. 2003. (Discover the Life of a Sports Star Ser.). (Illus.). 24p. (J). 20.64 (978-1-58952-655-6(4)) Rourke Publishing, LLC.

Aronson, Virginia. Venus & Serena Williams. 2000. (Women Who Win Ser.). (Illus.). 64p. (J). (gr. 4-7). pap. 25.00 (978-0-7910-6158-9(2)); 25.00 (978-0-7910-5799-5(2)) Facts On File, Inc. (Chelsea Hse.).

—Venus & Serena Williams. 2000. (Illus.). 64p. (J). (gr. 4-7). lib. bdg. 17.60 (978-0-613-33180-7(X)) Tandem Library Bks.

—Venus Williams. 1999. (Galaxy of Superstars Ser.). (Illus.). 64p. (J). pap. 25.00 (978-0-7910-5329-4(6)); (YA). (gr. 4-7). 25.00 (978-0-7910-5153-5(6)) Facts On File, Inc. (Chelsea Hse.).

—Venus Williams. 1999. (Galaxy of Superstars Ser.). (978-0-606-16419-1(7)); (gr. 5-8). lib. bdg. 17.60 (978-0-613-17759-7(2)) Tandem Library Bks.

Asirvatham, Sandy. Venus Williams. 2001. (Black Americans of Achievement Ser.). (Illus.). (J). 104p. pap. 30.00 (978-0-7910-6290-6(2)); 112p. 30.00 (978-0-7910-6289-0(9)) Facts On File, Inc. (Chelsea Hse.).

Bankston, John. Venus Williams. l.t. ed. 2002. (Real Life Reader Biography Ser.). (Illus.). 32p. (gr. 3-8). lib. bdg. 15.95 (978-1-58415-129-6(3)) Mitchell Lane Pubs., Inc.

Boekhoff, P. M. & Kallen, Stuart A. Venus Williams. 2002. (Stars of Sports Ser.). (Illus.). 48p. (J). 26.20 (978-0-7377-1395-4(X) , Greenhaven Pr., Inc.) Thomson Gale.

Brown, Jonatha A. Venus & Serena Williams. 2005. (People to Know Ser.). (Illus.). 24p. (J). pap. (978-0-8368-4477-1(7)); (YA). lib. bdg. 19.33 (978-0-8368-4470-2(X)) Stevens, Gareth Inc.

—Venus y Serena Williams.Tr. of Venus & Serena Williams. 19.33 (978-0-8368-4586-0(2)) Stevens, Gareth Inc.

Buckley, James, Jr. Venus & Serena Williams. 2003. (Trailblazers of the Modern World Ser.). (Illus.). 48p. (J). (gr. 5 up). pap. 14.95 (978-0-8368-5246-2(X)); lib. bdg. 30.00 (978-0-8368-5086-4(6)) Stevens, Gareth Inc. (World Almanac Library).

Christopher, Matt. On the Court with... Venus & Serena Williams. 2002. (Matt Christopher Sports Biographies Ser.). (Illus.). 112p. (J). (gr. 4-7). pap. 4.99 (978-0-316-13814-7(2)) Little, Brown Bks. for Young Readers.

—On the Court with... Venus & Serena Williams. 2002. (gr. 3-6). lib. bdg. 12.95 (978-0-613-70947-7(0)) Tandem Library Bks.

Donaldson, Madeline. Venus & Serena Williams. 2005. (Amazing Athletes Ser.). (Illus.). 32p. (gr. 3-4). lib. bdg. 22.60 (978-0-8225-3316-0(2)) Lerner Publishing Group.

—Venus & Serena Williams. 2004. (Illus.). 32p. (J). (ps-6). lib. bdg. 12.75 (978-0-606-30527-3(0)) Tandem Library Bks.

W X Y Z

Donaldson Madeline. Venus & Serena Williams (Revised Edition) 2007. (Amazing Athletes Ser.). (J). 23.93 (***978-0-8225-7595-5(7)*** , Lerner Pubns.); pap. 6.95 (***978-0-8225-8857-3(9)*** , First Avenue Editions) Lerner Publishing Group.

Dorrie, Roxanne. Venus & Serena Williams: The Smashing Sisters. 2003. (High Five Reading (Red Level) Ser.). (Illus.). (J). 64p. lib. bdg. 22.60 (978-0-7368-2784-3(6)); 48p. pap. 23.93 (978-0-7368-2827-7(3)) Capstone Pr., Inc.

—Venus & Serena Williams: The Smashing Sisters, 6 vols. (gr. 4 up). 49.95 (978-0-7368-2837-6(0) , High Five) Red Brick Learning.

Feldman, Heather. Venus Williams, 6 Packs. (On Deck Ser.). 24p. (gr. 4-5). 35.00 (978-0-7578-1000-8(4)) Rigby Education.

—Venus Williams: Campeona del Tenis. 2002. (Superestrellas del Deporte Ser.).Tr. of Venus Williams: Tennis Champion. (SPA.). 24p. (J). lib. bdg. 17.25 (978-0-8239-6120-7(6) , Buenas Letra) Rosen Publishing Group, Inc., The.

—Venus Williams: Campeona del Tenis. de Leon, Mauricio V., tr. 2001. Tr. of Venus Williams: Tennis Champion. (SPA.). 24p. 11.95 Rosen Publishing Group, Inc., The.

—Venus Williams: Tennis Champion. 2001. (Reading Power Ser.). (Illus.). 24p. (J). (gr. 1). lib. bdg. 17.25 (978-0-8239-5717-0(9) , PKSUST, PowerKids Pr.) Rosen Publishing Group, Inc., The.

—Venus Williams, Campeona del Tenis. 2002. (Coleccion Power Kids). (SPA & ENG., Illus.). 24p. (J). (gr. k-2). lib. bdg. 17.25 (978-0-8239-6138-2(9) , RN31300, Buenas Letra) Rosen Publishing Group, Inc., The.

Fillon, Mike. Young Superstars of Tennis: The Venus & Serena Williams Story. 1999. (Illus.). 144p. (YA). (gr. 6-12). lib. bdg. 19.95 (978-1-888105-43-8(7)) Avisson Pr., Inc.

Franzen, Lenore. Venus Williams. 2003. (Ovations Ser.). (Illus.). 32p. (J). (978-1-58341-249-7(2) , Creative Education) Creative Co., The.

Gutman, Bill. Venus & Serena: The Grand Slam Williams Sisters. 2001. (Scholastic Biography Ser.). (Illus.). 144p. (J). (gr. 3-7). pap. 4.50 (978-0-439-27152-3(5)) Scholastic, Inc.

—Venus & Serena: The Grand Slam Williams Sisters. 2001. (Illus.). (978-0-606-21502-2(6)) Tandem Library Bks.

Hill, Mary. Serena & Venus Williams. 2003. (Welcome Bks.). (Illus.). 24p. (J). (ps-2). pap. 4.95 (978-0-516-27889-6(4) , Children's Pr.) Scholastic Library Publishing.

—Serena & Venus Williams. 2003. (gr. k-3). lib. bdg. 12.95 (978-0-613-67764-6(1)) Tandem Library Bks.

Morgan, Terri. Venus & Serena Williams. 2003. (gr. 3-6). lib. bdg. 14.10 (978-0-613-76644-9(X)) Tandem Library Bks.

—Venus & Serena Williams: Grand Slam Sisters. (Sports Achievers Biographies Ser.). (Illus.). 2005. 80p. (gr. 7-12). lib. bdg. 22.60 (978-0-8225-3684-0(6)); 2003. 64p. (J). (gr. 4-9). pap. 5.95 (978-0-8225-9866-4(3) , Carolrhoda Bks.) Lerner Publishing Group.

Pyle, Lydia. Venus & Serena Williams. 2004. (Awesome Athletes Ser.). (Illus.). 32p. (J). (gr. k-6). lib. bdg. 22.78 (978-1-59197-486-4(0)) ABDO Publishing Co.

Roza, Greg. Venus & Serena Williams: The Sisters of Tennis. 2006. (Tony Stead Nonfiction Independent Reading Collection). (J). pap. (978-1-4042-5537-1(0)) Rosen Publishing Group, Inc., The.

Sandler, Michael. Tennis: Victory for Venus Williams. 2006. (Upsets & Comebacks Ser.). (Illus.). 32p. (J). lib. bdg. 25.27 (978-1-59716-170-1(5)) Bearport Publishing Co., Inc.

Schaefer, A. R. Serena & Venus Williams. 2002. (Sports Heroes Ser.). (Illus.). 48p. (J). (gr. 3-4). lib. bdg. 21.26 (978-0-7368-1054-8(4) , Capstone High-Interest Bks.) Capstone Pr., Inc.

Sherman, Josepha. Venus Williams. 2001. (Sports Files Ser.). (Illus.). 32p. (J). (gr. 1-3). lib. bdg. (978-1-58810-116-7(9)) Heinemann Library.

Stewart, Mark. Venus & Serena Williams: Sisters in Arms. 2000. (New Wave Ser.). (Illus.). 48p. (gr. 4 up). lib. bdg. 22.90 (978-0-7613-1803-3(8) , Millbrook Pr.) Lerner Publishing Group.

Swanson, June. Venus & Serena Williams. Burke, Susan S., illus. 2003. (You Must Be Joking! Riddle Bks.). 32p. (J). (gr. 2-5). pap. 5.95 (978-0-8225-9842-8(6)) Lerner Publishing Group.

Trailblazers of the Modern World: Winston Churchill; Alexander Fleming; Pablo Picasso; Elvis Presley; Venus & Serena Williams; Oprah Winfrey, 6 bks. 2002. (Illus.). (J). (gr. 5 up). pap. 89.70 (978-0-8368-5241-7(9) , World Almanac Library) Stevens, Gareth Inc.

Venus Williams, 6 Packs. (On Deck en Espanol Ser.). (SPA.). 24p. (gr. 4-5). 35.00 (978-0-7578-6383-7(3)) Rigby Education.

Venus y Serena Williams. 2006. (People We Should Know Ser.).Tr. of Venus & Serena Williams. (SPA.). (J). (gr. 3-4). 4.76 (978-0-8368-4593-8(5) , GHS33829) Stevens, Gareth Inc.

Watson, Galadriel Findlay. Venus & Serena Williams. 2005. (Great African American Women for Kids Ser.). (Illus.). 24p. (J). (978-1-59036-338-6(8)); lib. bdg. 26.00 (978-1-59036-332-4(9)) Weigl Pubs., Inc.

Williams, Venus, et al. Venus & Serena: 10 Rules for Living, Loving, & Winning. 2005. (Illus.). 144p. (YA). (gr. 7). pap. 14.00 (978-0-618-57653-1(3)) Houghton Mifflin Co. Trade & Reference Div.

Wilson, Mike. The Williams Sisters: Venus & Serena. 2005. (Illus.). 32p. pap. 8.50 (978-0-340-84876-0(6)) Cambridge Univ. Pr.

WILLIAMSBURG (VA.)

Brenner, Barbara. If You Lived in Williamsburg in Colonial Days. Williams, Jennie, illus. 2000. (If You Lived Ser.). 80p. (J). (gr. 4-7). pap. 5.99 (978-0-590-92922-6(4)) Scholastic, Inc.

Chorao, Kay. D Is for Drums: A Colonial Williamsburg ABC. 2004. (Illus.). 32p. (J). (ps-1). 16.95 (978-0-8109-4927-0(X)) Abrams, Harry N. , Inc.

McNeese, Tim. Williamsburg. 2007. (Colonial Settlements in America Ser.). (Illus.). 112p. (YA). (gr. 5-8). 30.00 (***978-0-7910-9333-7(6)*** , Chelsea Hse.) Facts On File, Inc.

WILLIAMSBURG (VA.)—FICTION

Elliott, L. M. Give Me Liberty. 2008. 384p. (J). pap. 6.99 (***978-0-06-074423-6(5)*** , Harper Trophy) HarperCollins Pubs.

Moore, Eva. Good Children Get Rewards: A Story of Colonial Times. 2001. (Hello Reader! Ser.). (J). 10.79 (978-0-606-19563-8(7)) Tandem Library Bks.

Nixon, Joan Lowery. Ann's Story, 1747. 2004. (J). (978-0-87935-198-4(5)) Colonial Williamsburg Foundation.

—Caesar's Story, 1759. 2004. (J). (978-0-87935-199-1(3)) Colonial Williamsburg Foundation.

—John's Story, 1775. 2004. (J). (978-0-87935-228-8(0)) Colonial Williamsburg Foundation.

—Maria's Story, 1773. 2004. (J). (978-0-87935-227-1(2)) Colonial Williamsburg Foundation.

—Nancy's Story, 1765. 2004. (J). (978-0-87935-225-7(6)) Colonial Williamsburg Foundation.

—Will's Story, 1771. 2004. (J). (978-0-87935-226-4(4)) Colonial Williamsburg Foundation.

Rue, Nancy N. The Invasion. 1998. (Christian Heritage Ser.). 192p. (J). (gr. 3-7). pap. (978-1-56179-541-3(0)) Focus on the Family Publishing.

—Invasion. 1998. (gr. 3-6). lib. bdg. 14.15 (978-0-613-85284-5(2)) Tandem Library Bks.

Waters, Kate. Mary Geddy's Day: A Colonial Girl in Williamsburg. 2002. (gr. k-3). lib. bdg. 14.15 (978-0-613-57317-7(X)) Tandem Library Bks.

WILLIAMSBURG (VA.)—HISTORY

Alter, Judy. Williamsburg. 2002. (We the People Ser.). (Illus.). 48p. (J). (gr. 4 up). lib. bdg. 22.60 (978-0-7565-0300-0(0)) Compass Point Bks.

Chorao, Kay. D Is for Drums: A Colonial Williamsburg A. B. C. 2004. (J). 16.95 (978-0-87935-197-7(7)) Colonial Williamsburg Foundation.

—D Is for Drums: A Colonial Williamsburg ABC. 2004. (Illus.). 32p. (J). (ps-1). 16.95 (978-0-8109-4927-0(X)) Abrams, Harry N. , Inc.

—D Is for Drums: A Colonial Williamsburg ABC. Chorao, Kay, illus. 2006. (Illus.). 30p. (J). (gr. k-4). reprint ed. 17.00 (978-1-4223-5240-3(4)) DIANE Publishing Co.

Coleman, Wim & Perrin, Pat. Colonial Williamsburg: A MyReportLinks.com Book. 2005. (Virtual Field Trips Ser.). (Illus.). 48p. (J). (gr. 4-10). lib. bdg. 25.26 (978-0-7660-5220-8(6) , MyReportLinks.com Bks.) Enslow Pubs., Inc.

WILLOW—FICTION

Grahame, Kenneth. The Wind in the Willows: Juvenile Classic. 2005. (Illus.). 192p. (J). 5.99 (978-1-4037-1386-5(3)) Dalmatian Pr.

Harcourt School Publishers Staff. Willow Way Advanced Level. 3rd ed. 2002. (Trophies Reading Program Ser.). (Illus.). pap. 5.10 (978-0-15-323304-3(4)) Harcourt Schl. Pubs.

Trottier, Maxine. Prairie Willow. 1999. (gr. k-3). lib. bdg. 15.25 (978-0-613-28614-5(6)) Tandem Library Bks.

The Willow Pattern: Individual Title Six-Packs. (Action Packs Ser.). 104p. (gr. 3-5). 44.00 (978-0-7635-2996-3(6)) Rigby Education.

WILLS—FICTION

Alger, Horatio. Luck & Pluck; Or, John Oakley's Inheritance. unabr. ed. 2002. (Polyglot Press Alger Ser.). (Illus.). (J). pap. 17.95 (978-1-4115-0019-8(9)) Polyglot Pr., Inc.

Bill Waite's Will. 2001. 32p. (YA). (gr. 6-12). pap. (978-0-8224-3466-5(0)) Globe Fearon Educational Publishing.

Grisham, John. The Testament. 2000. (gr. 7-12). lib. bdg. 16.45 (978-0-613-23044-5(2)) Tandem Library Bks.

Wilson, Nancy Hope. Mountain Pose. 2001. 240p. (J). (gr. 5 up). 17.00 (978-0-374-35078-9(7) , Farrar, Straus & Giroux (BYR)) Farrar, Straus & Giroux.

WILSON, SAMUEL, 1766-1854

Hicks, Terry Allan. Uncle Sam. 2006. (Symbols of America Ser.). (Illus.). 40p. (J). lib. bdg. 28.50 (978-0-7614-2137-5(8) , Benchmark Bks.) Cavendish, Marshall Corp.

Yanuck, Debbie L. Uncle Sam. 2003. (First Facts Ser.). (Illus.). 24p. (J). lib. bdg. 19.93 (978-0-7368-2295-4(X)) Capstone Pr., Inc.

WILSON, WOODROW, 1856-1924

Ashby, Ruth. Woodrow & Edith Wilson. 2005. (Illus.). 48p. (J). pap. (978-0-8368-5765-8(8)); lib. bdg. 30.00 (978-0-8368-5759-7(3)) Stevens, Gareth Inc. (World Almanac Library).

Brunelli, Carol & Gaines, Ann Graham. Woodrow Wilson: Our Twenty-Eighth President. 2001. (Spirit of America: Our Presidents Ser.). (Illus.). 48p. (J). (gr. 2-6). 28.50 (978-1-56766-863-6(1)) Child's World, Inc.

Dommermuth-Costa, Carol. Woodrow Wilson. 2003. (Presidential Leaders Ser.). (Illus.). 112p. (J). 29.27 (978-0-8225-0094-0(9) , Lerner Pubns.) Lerner Publishing Group.

Feinberg, Barbara Silberdick. Woodrow Wilson. 2004. (Encyclopedia of Presidents Ser.). (Illus.). 110p. (J). 34.00 (978-0-516-22968-3(0) , Children's Pr.) Scholastic Library Publishing.

Gaines, Ann Graham. Woodrow Wilson. 2003. (Great American Presidents Ser.). (Illus.). 100p. (J). pap. (978-0-7910-7783-2(7)); (gr. 4-8). 30.00 (978-0-7910-7597-5(4)) Facts On File, Inc. (Chelsea Hse.).

Green, Robert. Woodrow Wilson. 2003. (Profiles of the Presidents Ser.). (Illus.). 64p. (J). (gr. 4 up). lib. bdg. 23.93 (978-0-7565-0274-4(8)) Compass Point Bks.

Harmon, Daniel E. Woodrow Wilson. 2003. (Childhoods of the Presidents Ser.). (Illus.). 48p. (J). (gr. 4 up). lib. bdg. (978-1-59084-277-5(4)) Mason Crest Pubs.

Holden, Henry M. Woodrow Wilson: A MyReportLinks.com Book. 2003. (Presidents Ser.). (Illus.). 48p. (J). (gr. 4-10). lib. bdg. 25.26 (978-0-7660-5123-2(4) , MyReportLinks.com Bks.) Enslow Pubs., Inc.

Joseph, Paul. Woodrow Wilson. 2001. (United States Presidents Ser.). (Illus.). 32p. (J). (gr. k-6). lib. bdg. 22.78 (978-1-56239-812-5(1) , Checkerboard Library) ABDO Publishing Co.

Lukes, Bonnie L. Woodrow Wilson & the Progressive Era. 2006. (World Leaders Ser.). (Illus.). 192p. (J). (gr. 6-10). lib. bdg. 26.95 (978-1-931798-79-2(6)) Reynolds, Morgan Inc.

Marsh, Carole. Woodrow Wilson. 2002. (One Thousand Readers Ser.). (Illus.). 12p. (J). (gr. k-4). 2.95 (978-0-635-01534-1(X) , 1534X) Gallopade International.

Mis, Melody S. How to Draw the Life & Times of Woodrow Wilson. 2007. (Kid's Guide to Drawing the Presidents of the United States of America Ser.). (Illus.). 32p. (J). 25.25 (978-1-4042-3004-0(1) , PowerKids Pr.) Rosen Publishing Group, Inc., The.

Schlesinger, Arthur M., Sr., et al, eds. The Election of 1912 & the Administration of Woodrow Wilson. 2002. (Major Presidential Elections & the Administrations That Followed Ser.). (Illus.). 154p. (YA). (gr. 7 up). lib. bdg. (978-1-59084-358-1(4)) Mason Crest Pubs.

Schraff, Anne, ed. Woodrow Wilson. 1998. (United States Presidents Ser.). (Illus.). 112p. (YA). (gr. 5-12). lib. bdg. 26.60 (978-0-89490-936-8(3)) Enslow Pubs., Inc.

Schwartz, Eric. A World Contender. 2005. (How America Became America Ser.). (Illus.). 96p. (J). lib. bdg. (978-1-59084-911-8(6)) Mason Crest Pubs.

Venezia, Mike, illus. Woodrow Wilson. 2006. 32p. (J). (978-0-516-22632-3(0)) Children's Pr., Ltd.

Waxman, Laura Hamilton. Woodrow Wilson. 2006. (History Maker Bios Ser.). (Illus.). 48p. (J). 26.60 (978-0-8225-6053-1(4) , Lerner Pubns.) Lerner Publishing Group.

WIND

see Winds

WIND INSTRUMENTS

see also Bands (Music)

Archibald, Paul. Playing the Trumpet & Brass. 2004. (Young Musician Ser.). (J). lib. bdg. 27.10 (978-1-932799-60-6(5)) Stargazer Bks.

Aylmore, Angela. Blowing. 2005. (Raintree Sprouts Ser.). (Illus.). 24p. pap. (978-1-4109-1610-5(3)); (J). 20.64 (978-1-4109-1605-1(7)) Steck-Vaughn.

Daubeny, Ulric. Orchestral Wind Instruments, Ancient & Modern. 2001. 147p. (YA). reprint ed. 88.00 (978-0-7222-5868-2(2)) Library Reprints, Inc.

Dearling, Robert. Woodwind & Brass Instruments. 2000. (Encyclopedia of Musical Instruments Ser.). (Illus.). 48p. (J). (gr. 4-7). 22.95 (978-0-7910-6091-9(8) , Chelsea Hse.) Facts On File, Inc.

Klingel, Cynthia Fitterer & Noyed, Robert B. Trumpets. 2002. (Wonder Books Level 1: Musical Instuments Ser.). (Illus.). 24p. (J). (ps-3). 22.79 (978-1-56766-949-7(2)) Child's World, Inc.

Knight, M. J. Brass & Woodwinds. 2005. (Musical Instruments of the World Ser.). (Illus.). 32p. (J). (gr. 3-7). lib. bdg. 27.10 (978-1-58340-415-7(5)) Smart Apple Media.

Lynch, Wendy. Brass. 2001. (Musical Instruments Ser.). (Illus.). 32p. (J). (gr. k-2). lib. bdg. 21.36 (978-1-58810-233-1(5)) Heinemann Library.

—Woodwind. 2001. (Musical Instruments Ser.). (Illus.). 32p. (J). (gr. k-2). lib. bdg. 21.36 (978-1-58810-237-9(8)) Heinemann Library.

Reid, Elizabeth. Woodwind Instruments. 2002. (Music Makers Ser.). (Illus.). 24p. (J). (gr. 1-5). 22.79 (978-1-56766-988-6(3)) Child's World, Inc.

Sharth, Sharon. Saxophones. 2002. (Music Makers Ser.). (Illus.). 24p. (J). (gr. 1-5). 22.79 (978-1-56766-044-9(4)) Child's World, Inc.

Temple, Bob. Trombones. 2002. (Music Makers Ser.). (Illus.). 24p. (J). (gr. 1-5). 22.79 (978-1-56766-045-6(2)) Child's World, Inc.

—Tubas. 2002. (Music Makers Ser.). (Illus.). 24p. (J). (gr. 1-5). 22.79 (978-1-56766-046-3(0)) Child's World, Inc.

Thomas, Roger. Brass. 2001. (Soundbites Ser.). (Illus.). 32p. (YA). (gr. 6-8). lib. bdg. 22.79 (978-1-58810-262-1(9)) Heinemann Library.

—Woodwinds. 2001. (Soundbites Ser.). (Illus.). 32p. (YA). (gr. 6-8). lib. bdg. 22.79 (978-1-58810-267-6(X)) Heinemann Library.

Turner, Barrie Carson. Woodwinds & Brass. 1998. (Musical Instruments of the World Ser.). (Illus.). 32p. (J). (gr. 1-5). lib. bdg. 16.95 (978-1-887068-48-2(1)) Smart Apple Media.

WIND POWER

Bowden, Rob. Energy: Wind Energy. 2006. (Illus.). 32p. (J). (978-1-59604-107-3(2)) Stargazer Bks.

Gibson, Diane. Wind Power. 2001. (Sources of Energy Ser.). (Illus.). 24p. (J). (gr. 2-7). lib. bdg. 21.30 (978-1-887068-79-6(1)) Smart Apple Media.

Graham, Ian. Wind Power. 1999. (Energy Forever? Ser.). (Illus.). 48p. (J). (gr. 4-7). lib. bdg. 27.12 (978-0-8172-5364-6(5)) Raintree.

Iwinski, Melissa. The Wind at Work. 2007. (Shockwave: Technology & Manufacturing Ser.). (Illus.). 36p. (J). (gr. 4-6). lib. bdg. 25.00 (***978-0-531-17586-6(3)*** , Children's Pr.) Scholastic Library Publishing.

Morris, Neil. Wind Power. 2006. 32p. (J). (978-1-58340-910-7(6)) Smart Apple Media.

Muschal, Frank. Energy from Wind, Sun, & Tides. 2008. (J). pap. 7.95 (***978-1-60279-096-4(5)***) Cherry Lake Publishing.

—Energy fromWind, Sun, & Tides. 2008. (J). lib. bdg. 25.26 (***978-1-60279-046-9(9)***) Cherry Lake Publishing.

Nazzaro, Robin M. Wind Power: Impacts on Wildlife & Government Responsibilities for Regulating Development & Protecting Wildlife. 2006. (Illus.). 59p. (C). pap. 20.00 (978-1-4223-0354-2(3)) DIANE Publishing Co.

Parker, Steve. Wind Power. 2004. (Science Files Ser.). (Illus.). 32p. (J). (gr. 3 up). lib. bdg. 24.67 (978-0-8368-4034-6(8)) Stevens, Gareth Inc.

Petersen, Christine. Wind Power. 2004. (True Book Ser.). (Illus.). 48p. (J). 25.00 (978-0-516-22809-9(9) , Children's Pr.) Scholastic Library Publishing.

Pluckrose, Henry Arthur. Air. 2006. (Illus.). 32p. (J). (978-1-59771-033-6(4)) Sea-To-Sea Pubns.

Richards, Julie. Wind Power. 2003. 32p. (J). lib. bdg. 24.25 (978-1-58340-333-4(7)) Smart Apple Media.

Saunders, N. Wind Power. 2007. (J). pap. (***978-0-8368-8414-2(0)***) Stevens, Gareth Inc.

Saunders, Nigel. Wind Power. 2007. 24p. (J). (gr. 3-5). lib. bdg. 26.60 (***978-0-8368-8405-0(1)***) Stevens, Gareth Inc.

Sheehan, Thomas F. Wind & Water at Work: A Book about Change. 2008. (J). (***978-1-60044-538-5(1)***) Rourke Publishing, LLC.

Sherman, Josepha. Wind Energy. 2004. (Fact Finders Ser.). (Illus.). 32p. (J). 16.95 (978-0-7368-2475-0(8)) Capstone Pr., Inc.

Spilsbury, Richard & Spilsbury, Louise. Wind Power: The Pros & Cons. 2007. (J). lib. bdg. (***978-1-4042-3745-2(3)*** , Rosen Central) Rosen Publishing Group, Inc., The.

Tecco, Betsy Dru. Wind Power of the Future: New Ways of Turning Wind into Energy. 2003. (Library of Future Energy). (Illus.). 64p. (YA). lib. bdg. 26.50 (978-0-8239-3665-6(1)) Rosen Publishing Group, Inc., The.

Walker, Niki. Generating Wind Power. (Energy Revolution Ser.). (Illus.). 32p. (J). 2007. (***978-1-4287-1024-5(8)); *** 2006. (gr. 3-9). pap. (978-0-7787-2927-3(3)); 2006. (gr. 3-9). lib. bdg. (978-0-7787-2913-6(3)) Crabtree Publishing Co.

Wind Power. (Energy at Work Ser.). 32p. (J). 7.95 (978-0-7368-5195-4(X)) Capstone Pr., Inc.

WINDING CIRCLE TEMPLE (IMAGINARY PLACE)—FICTION

Pierce, Tamora. Briar's Book. (Circle of Magic Ser.: No. 4). (Illus.). 272p. (J). 2000. 5.99 (978-0-590-55411-4(5) , Scholastic Paperbacks); 1999. (gr. 6-12). pap. 15.95 (978-0-590-55359-9(3)) Scholastic, Inc.

—Briar's Book. 1999. (Circle of Magic Ser.: No. 4). (J). 11.64 (978-0-606-19550-8(5)) Tandem Library Bks.

—Daja's Book. (Circle of Magic Ser.: No. 3). (Illus.). 240p. (J). 2000. 5.99 (978-0-590-55410-7(7) , Scholastic Paperbacks); 1998. (gr. 6-12). pap. 15.95 (978-0-590-55358-2(5)) Scholastic, Inc.

—Daja's Book. 2000. (Circle of Magic Ser.: No. 3). (gr. 5-8). lib. bdg. 13.00 (978-0-613-28460-8(7)) Tandem Library Bks.

—Magic Steps. 2000. (Circle Opens Ser.: No. 1). (Illus.). 272p. (J). (gr. 4-7). pap. 16.95 (978-0-590-39588-5(2) , Scholastic Pr.) Scholastic, Inc.

—Sandry's Book. 1999. (Circle of Magic Ser.: No. 1). 272p. (YA). (gr. 6-12). mass mkt. 6.99 (978-0-590-55408-4(5)) Scholastic, Inc.

WINDMILLS

Bial, Raymond. The Mills: Building America. 2001. (Building America Ser.). (Illus.). 56p. (J). (gr. 4-7). lib. bdg. 27.07 (978-0-7614-1333-2(2) , Benchmark Bks.) Cavendish, Marshall Corp.

Woelfle, Gretchen. The Wind at Work: An Activity Guide to Windmills. 2003. (Illus.). 156p. (J). (gr. 3-8). pap. 14.95 (978-1-55652-308-3(4)) Chicago Review Pr., Inc.

WINDOWS, STAINED GLASS

see Glass Painting and Staining

WINDS

see also Hurricanes; Storms; Tornadoes

Bauer, Marion Dane. Wind. Wallace, John, illus. ed. 2005. 32p. (J). lib. bdg. 15.00 (978-1-59054-938-4(4)) Fitzgerald Bks.

Bauer, Marion Dane & Wallace, John. Wind. 2003. (Ready-to-Read Ser.). (Illus.). 32p. (J). pap. 3.99 (978-0-689-85443-9(9) , Aladdin) Simon & Schuster Children's Publishing.

Billings. True Tales of Howling Winds. 1999. (J). pap. 13.00 (978-0-7398-2394-1(9)) Steck-Vaughn.

Boerger, Kristin. Hace Viento. 2006. (ENG & SPA.). (J). pap. (***978-0-8368-8117-2(6)***); lib. bdg. (***978-0-8368-8112-7(5)***) Stevens, Gareth Inc. (Weekly Reader Early Learning Library).

—Let's Read about Wind. 2006. (J). pap. (***978-0-8368-7813-4(2)***); lib. bdg. (***978-0-8368-7808-0(6)***) Stevens, Gareth Inc. (Weekly Reader Early Learning Library).

Bundey, Nikki. Wind & People. 2005. (Science of Weather Ser.). (Illus.). 32p. (gr. 4-6). lib. bdg. 21.27 (978-1-57505-495-7(7)) Lerner Publishing Group.

Burke, Jennifer S. Windy Days. 2000. (gr. k-3). lib. bdg. 12.95 (978-0-613-62229-5(4)) Tandem Library Bks.

Cobb, Vicki. I Face the Wind. Gorton, Julia, illus. 2003. (Science Play Ser.). 40p. (J). (ps-k). 15.99 (978-0-688-17840-6(5)); lib. bdg. 16.89 (978-0-688-17841-3(3)) HarperCollins Pubs.

W X Y Z

D'Aubuisson, Elisabeth. Windy Days. 2007. (What's the Weather? Ser.). (Illus.). 24p. (J). (gr. k-3). lib. bdg. 21.25 (*978-1-4042-3683-7(X)*, PowerKids Pr.) Rosen Publishing Group, Inc., The.

Un Día con Viento (A Windy Day) (J). 2007. pap. 4.25 (978-0-8225-6549-9(8)); 2006. 18.60 (978-0-8225-6214-6(6)) Lerner Publishing Group. (Ediciones Lerner).

Dorros, Arthur. Feel the Wind. Dorros, Arthur, illus. 2000. (Let's-Read-and-Find-Out Science Ser.). (Illus.). 32p. (J). (gr. k-4). 15.89 (978-0-690-04741-7(X)) HarperCollins Pubs.

Doudna, Kelly. It Is Windy. 2003. (Weather Ser.). (Illus.). 23p. (J). (ps-3). lib. bdg. 19.93 (978-1-57765-778-1(0)) ABDO Publishing Co.

Eagen, Rachael. Flood & Monsoon Alert! 2004. (Disaster Alert! Ser.). (Illus.). 32p. (J). (978-0-7787-1577-1(9)) Crabtree Publishing Co.

Eagen, Rachel. Flood & Monsoon Alert! 2004. (Disaster Alert! Ser.). (Illus.). 32p. (J). pap. (978-0-7787-1609-9(0)) Crabtree Publishing Co.

Eckart, Edana. Watching the Wind. 2004. (Welcome Bks.). (Illus.). 24p. (J). (ps-2). pap. 4.95 (978-0-516-25941-3(5), Children's Pr.) Scholastic Library Publishing.

Fandel, Jennifer. Wind. 2002. (Illus.). 23p. (J). lib. bdg. 21.35 (978-1-58340-153-8(9)) Smart Apple Media.

Flanagan, Alice K. Wind. 2003. (Wonder Books Level 1: Weather Ser.). (Illus.). 24p. (J). (ps-2). 22.79 (978-1-56766-455-3(5)) Child's World, Inc.

Fowler, Allan. Can You See the Wind? 1999. (Rookie Read-About Science Ser.). (Illus.). 32p. (gr. 1-2). pap. 4.95 (978-0-516-26479-0(6), Children's Pr.) Scholastic Library Publishing.

—Can You See the Wind? (ps-ps). 2004. (Illus.). 32p. (J). lib. bdg. 11.75 (978-0-606-29964-0(5)); 1999. lib. bdg. 12.95 (978-0-613-53980-7(X)) Tandem Library Bks.

Friend, Sandra. Earth's Wild Winds. 2002. (Exploring Planet Earth Ser.). (Illus.). 64p. (gr. 5-8). lib. bdg. 24.90 (978-0-7613-2673-1(1), Twenty-First Century Bks.) Lerner Publishing Group.

Frost, Helen. Wind. Saunders-Smith, Gail, ed. 2004. (Weather Ser.). (Illus.). 24p. (J). (gr. k-1). lib. bdg. 15.93 (978-0-7368-2096-7(5), Pebble Bks.) Capstone Pr., Inc.

Ganeri, Anita. Wind. 2004. (Illus.). 24p. (J). pap. (978-0-8368-4307-1(X)); lib. bdg. 19.33 (978-0-8368-4302-6(9)) Stevens, Gareth Inc.

Grossnickle, Anna H. What Can You Do in the Wind? Kliros, Thea, illus. 1999. 10p. (J). (ps-k). pap. 5.95 (978-0-688-16079-1(4)) HarperCollins Pubs.

Hammersmith, Craig. The Wind. 2003. (Spyglass Books). (Illus.). 24p. (J). (gr. 1 up). lib. bdg. 18.60 (978-0-7565-0456-4(2)) Compass Point Bks.

Herriges, Ann. Wind. 2006. (Blastoff! Readers Ser.). (Illus.). 24p. (J). lib. bdg. 16.95 (978-1-60014-026-6(2)) Bellwether Media.

Jennings, Terry J. The Weather: Wind. 2004. (J). lib. bdg. 27.10 (978-1-59389-146-6(6)) Chrysalis Education.

Kaner, Etta. Who Likes the Wind? Lafrance, Marie, illus. 2006. 32p. 14.95 (978-1-55337-839-6(3)) Kids Can Pr., Ltd. CAN. *Dist:* Wybel Marketing Group.

Lonsdale, Mary, illus. Whatever the Weather: When the Wind Blows. 2004. (Whatever the Weather Ser.). 10p. (J). bds. 4.99 (978-1-85854-102-0(6)) Brimax Books Ltd. GBR. *Dist:* Byeway Bks.

Marsico, Katie. Windy Weather Days. 2006. (Scholastic News Nonfiction Readers Ser.). (Illus.). 24p. (J). 19.00 (978-0-531-16774-8(7), Children's Pr.) Scholastic Library Publishing.

Mayer, Cassie. Viento. 2006. (ENG & SPA., Illus.). 24p. (J). (*978-1-4034-8653-0(0)*) Heinemann Library.

—Viento (Wind) 2006. (ENG & SPA., Illus.). 24p. (J). pap. (*978-1-4034-8661-5(1)*) Heinemann Library.

Mayer, Cassie. Wind. 2006. (Illus.). 24p. (J). (978-1-4034-8412-3(0)); pap. 5.99 (978-1-4034-8420-8(1)) Heinemann Library.

Miles, Elizabeth. Wind. 2005. (Illus.). 32p. (J). pap. (978-1-4034-6555-9(X)); lib. bdg. (978-1-4034-6550-4(9)) Heinemann Library.

Murphy, Patricia J. How Does the Wind Blow? 2006. (Tell Me Why, Tell Me How Ser.). (Illus.). 32p. (J). lib. bdg. 28.50 (978-0-7614-2107-8(6), Benchmark Bks.) Cavendish, Marshall Corp.

Naff, Clay Farris. Wind. 2006. (Fueling the Future Ser.). (Illus.). 244p. (J). (gr. 10-12). 34.95 (978-0-7377-3580-2(5), Greenhaven Pr., Inc.) Thomson Gale.

Nelson, Robin. Windy. 2004. (First Step Nonfiction Ser.). (Illus.). 8p. (J). pap. (978-0-8225-5364-9(3), Lerner Pubns.) Lerner Publishing Group.

—A Windy Day. (First Step Nonfiction Ser.). (Illus.). 24p. (J). (gr. k-2). 2005. lib. bdg. 17.27 (978-0-8225-0174-9(0)); 2003. pap. 4.25 (978-0-8225-1963-8(1)) Lerner Publishing Group.

—A Windy Day. 2001. (Illus.). 23p. (J). (ps-3). lib. bdg. 11.80 (978-0-613-35344-1(7)) Tandem Library Bks.

Nichols, Catherine. It's the Wind! 2001. (We Can Read about Nature Ser.). (Illus.). 32p. (J). (gr. 1-2). lib. bdg. 21.36 (978-0-7614-1254-0(9), Benchmark Bks.) Cavendish, Marshall Corp.

Parker, Steve. Wind Power. 2004. (Science Files Ser.). (Illus.). 32p. (J). (gr. 3 up). lib. bdg. 24.67 (978-0-8368-4034-6(8)) Stevens, Gareth Inc.

Picture Window Books, contrib. by. Gusts & Gales. (Amazing Science Ser.). 24p. (J). pap. 7.95 (978-1-4048-0338-1(6)) Picture Window Bks.

Richards, Julie. It's Windy! 2004. (J). lib. bdg. 27.10 (978-1-58340-538-3(0)) Smart Apple Media.

Rodgers, Alan & Streluk, Angella. Wind & Air Pressure. 2002. (Illus.). 32p. (J). (gr. 3-5). pap. (978-1-4034-0130-4(6), 91635); lib. bdg. 22.79 (978-1-58810-690-2(X)) Heinemann Library.

Rosinsky, Natalie M. Wind. 2004. (Illus.). 32p. (J). (gr. 3 up). 21.26 (978-0-7565-0599-8(2)) Compass Point Bks.

Rustad, Martha E. H. Today Is Windy. 2006. (Illus.). 24p. (J). (978-0-7368-5347-7(2)) Capstone Pr., Inc.

Scholastic, Inc. Staff & Capeci, Anne. Wind. 2007. (Msb Science Reader Ser.). 32p. (J). pap. 3.99 (*978-0-439-80108-9(7)*, Cartwheel Bks.) Scholastic, Inc.

Sherman, Joseph. Gusts & Gales: A Book about Wind. 2004. (Amazing Science Ser.). (Illus.). 24p. (C). (gr. k-3). 22.60 (978-1-4048-0094-6(8)) Picture Window Bks.

Sievert, Terri. Wind. 2005. (Weather Update Ser.). (Illus.). 24p. (J). 21.26 (978-0-7368-3740-8(X)) Capstone Pr., Inc.

When the Wind Blows: Individual Title Six-Packs. (Rigby Focus Ser.). 16p. (gr. 1 up). 28.00 (978-0-7578-5305-0(6)); 30.00 (978-0-7578-5537-5(7)) Rigby Education.

Williams, Judith. Why Is It Windy? 2005. (I Like Weather! Ser.). (Illus.). 24p. (J). (ps-ps). lib. bdg. 21.26 (978-0-7660-2320-8(6), Enslow Elementary) Enslow Pubs., Inc.

The Wind: Level D, 6 vols. (Wonder Worldtm Ser.). 16p. 24.95 (978-0-7802-1057-8(3)) Wright Group, The.

Wind & Storms: 6 Each of 1 Student Book, 6 vols. (Sunshinetm Science Ser.). 24p. (gr. 1-2). 41.95 (978-0-7802-1376-0(9)) Wright Group, The.

Wind & Storms: Big Book. (Sunshinetm Science Ser.). 24p. (gr. 1-2). 37.50 (978-0-7802-1377-7(7)) Wright Group, The.

Wind Weather. 2006. (Illus.). 24p. (J). (gr. k-2). 18.50 (*978-0-531-17878-2(1)*) Scholastic Library Publishing.

A Windy Day, Vol. 2. 2005. (Our Seasons & Weather Ser.). (YA). (gr. k-3). (978-0-7368-8625-3(7), Pebble Bks.) Capstone Pr., Inc.

A Windy Day, 6 vols. (gr. k-2). 28.95 (978-0-7368-8631-4(1)) Red Brick Learning.

WINDS—FICTION

Asch, Frank & Asch, Devin. Like a Windy Day. Asch, Frank & Asch, Devin, illus. 2002. (Illus.). 32p. (J). (gr. k-2). 16.00 (978-0-15-216376-1(X), Gulliver Bks.) Harcourt Children's Bks.

Asch, Frank & Asch, Devin. Like a Windy Day. 2008. (Illus.). 32p. (J). pap. 7.00 (*978-0-15-206403-7(6)*, Voyager Bks./Libros Viajeros) Harcourt Children's Bks.

Bloom, Stephanie. A Place to Grow. Murphy, Kelly, illus. 2002. 32p. (J). lib. bdg. 16.95 (978-1-931969-07-9(8)) Bloom & Grow Bks.

Busy Little Breezie. 2006. (J). per. 7.95 (978-0-9742714-2-2(X)) I C Creative, Inc.

Derby, Sally. Whoosh Went the Wind! Nguyen, Vincent, illus. 2006. 32p. (J). 16.99 (978-0-7614-5309-3(1)) Cavendish, Marshall Corp.

Dipucchio, Kelly. What's the Magic Word? Winborn, Marsha, illus. 2005. 32p. (J). (ps-1). 15.99 (978-0-06-000578-8(5)) HarperCollins Pubs.

Disney Publishing Staff. Blow, Wind, Blow, 15 vols. 2003. (It's Fun to Learn Ser.). (Illus.). 32p. (J). (ps-3). 3.99 (978-1-57973-134-2(1)) Advance Pubs. LLC.

Dwyer, Mindy. Just Close Your Eyes. 2005. (J). (978-0-88240-592-6(6)); pap. (978-0-88240-593-3(4)) Graphic Arts Ctr. Publishing Co. (Alaska Northwest Bks.).

Ehlert, Lois. Leaf Man. 2005. (Illus.). 40p. (J). (ps-ps). 16.00 (978-0-15-205304-8(2), Harcourt Children's Bks) Harcourt Children's Bks.

Ets, Marie Hall. Gilberto & the Wind. 2004. (Live Oak Readalong Ser.). (Illus.). (J). pap. 18.95 incl. audio compact disk (978-1-59112-837-3(4)) Live Oak Media.

—Gilberto & the Wind, 2 vols. Ets, Marie Hall, illus. unabr. ed. 1999. (ENG & SPA., Illus.). (J). (gr. k-3). pap. 33.95 incl. audio (978-0-87499-568-8(X)) Live Oak Media.

—Gilberto y el Viento. Ets, Marie Hall et al, illus. unabr. ed. 2005. (SPA., Illus.). (J). (gr. k-3). pap. 16.95 incl. audio (978-0-87499-362-2(8), LK1058) Live Oak Media.

Forest, Heather & Aesop. The Contest Between the Sun & the Wind: An Aesop's Fable. Gaber, Susan, illus. 2008. 32p. (*978-0-87483-832-9(0)*, August Hse. Little Folk) August Hse. Pubs., Inc.

Gilberto & the Wind. 2004. (J). 24.95 incl. audio (978-1-56008-203-3(8)) Weston Woods Studios, Inc.

Grahame, Kenneth. The Wind in the Willows. McKowen, Scott, illus. 2005. (Unabridged Classics Ser.). 208p. (J). (gr. 5-9). 9.95 (978-1-4027-2505-0(1)) Sterling Publishing Co., Inc.

Grambling, Lois G. Abigail Muchmore & Mr. West Wind. Havice, Susan, illus. 2003. 32p. (J). 16.95 (978-0-7614-5116-7(1)) Cavendish, Marshall Corp.

Gray, Rita. The Wild Little Horse. Wolff, Ashley, illus. 2005. 32p. (J). (ps-ps). 15.99 (978-0-525-47455-5(2), Dutton Juvenile) Penguin Group (USA) Inc.

Grossnickle, Anna H. What Can You Do in the Wind? Kliros, Thea, illus. 1999. 10p. (J). (ps-k). pap. 5.95 (978-0-688-16079-1(4)) HarperCollins Pubs.

Hancock, Susan G. The Wind & Little Cloud. Simmons, Robert, illus. 2006. (J). per. 10.95 (978-0-9741743-0-3(0)) Perlycross Pubs.

Hutchins, Pat. The Wind Blew. Hutchins, Pat, illus. 2002. (Illus.). 14.47 (978-0-7587-4036-6(0)) Book Wholesalers, Inc.

Lipson, Michael. How the Wind Plays. Kirk, Daniel, illus. 1999. 28p. (J). (ps-1). reprint ed. 15.00 (978-0-7881-6652-5(2)) DIANE Publishing Co.

Loehr, Mallory. Wind Spell. 2000. (Magic Elements Quartet Ser.: No. 3). (Illus.). 128p. (J). (gr. 3-5). pap. 3.99 (978-0-679-89217-5(6), Random Hse. Bks. for Young Readers) Random Hse. Children's Bks.

—Wind Spell. 2000. (gr. 3-6). lib. bdg. 11.80 (978-0-613-27595-8(0)); (Illus.). (J). (978-0-606-20993-9(X)) Tandem Library Bks.

MacDonald, George. The Wind & the Moon. rev. ed. 2002. 32p. (J). 15.95 (978-0-8050-4127-9(3), Holt, Henry & Co. Bks. For Young Readers) Holt, Henry & Co.

Mackinnon, Mairi. Sun & the Wind. 2007. (First Reading Level 1 Ser.). 32p. (J). 8.99 (*978-0-7945-1811-0(7)*, Usborne) EDC Publishing.

McKee, David. Elmer Takes Off. McKee, David, illus. 2004. (Elmer Bks.). 32p. (J). 9.99 (978-0-06-075241-5(6)) HarperCollins Pubs.

McKissack, Patricia C. Mirandy & Brother Wind. 2002. (Illus.). (J). 14.79 (978-0-7587-3143-2(4)) Book Wholesalers, Inc.

McMillan, Bruce. How the Ladies Stopped the Wind. Gunnella, illus. 2007. 32p. (J). (gr. k-3). 16.00 (*978-0-618-77330-5(4)*) Houghton Mifflin Co.

Milbourne, Anna. The Windy Day. Temporin, Elena, illus. 2007. (Picture Bks). 24p. (J). 9.99 (*978-0-7945-1616-1(5)*, Usborne) EDC Publishing.

Mitra, Annie. Chloe's Windy Day. 1998. (Chloe Weather Board Bks.). (Illus.). 14p. (J). bds. 5.95 (978-1-86233-036-8(0)) Sterling Publishing Co., Inc.

Mollel, Tololwa M. Kitoto the Mighty. Frost, Kristi, illus. 1998. 28p. (J). (gr. k-3). 14.95 (978-0-7737-3019-9(2)) Stoddart Kids CAN. *Dist:* Fitzhenry & Whiteside, Ltd.

Montgomery, L. M. Ana la de Alamos Ventosos. (SPA.). 288p. (YA). (gr. 5-8). (978-84-7888-636-4(2), SAL3944) Emece Editores ESP. *Dist:* Lectorum Pubns., Inc.

Morack, Kathy. Anuqlirtuq. Afcan, Paschal, tr. Keim, Geri & Horesh, David, illus. 1998. Tr. of Its Windy. (ESK.). 40p. (J). (gr. k-3). pap. 10.00 (978-1-58084-046-0(9)) Lower Kuskokwim Schl. District.

Morrison, P. R. The Wind Tamer. 2006. 336p. (YA). 16.95 (978-1-58234-781-3(6)) Bloomsbury Publishing.

Morrison, P. R. Wind Tamer. 2007. 336p. (YA). pap. 7.95 (*978-1-59990-147-3(1)*, Bloomsbury Children) Bloomsbury Publishing.

Murphy, Shirley Rousseau. Wind Child. Dillon, Leo & Dillon, Diane, illus. 1999. 40p. (J). (gr. k-4). 15.95 (978-0-06-024903-8(X)); 15.89 (978-0-06-024904-5(8)) HarperCollins Pubs.

Nash, Margaret. Hetty's New Hat. Impey, Martin, illus. 2005. (Reading Corner Ser.). 24p. (J). (gr. k-3). lib. bdg. 22.80 (978-1-59771-007-7(5)) Sea-To-Sea Pubns.

Newman, Dolores A. Papa, How Do You Know? 2000. (Illus.). 32p. (J). pap. 9.95 (978-0-9676438-0-9(5)) Sanctuary Pr.

Noble, Trinka Hakes. The Legend of Michigan. Frankenhuyzen, Gijsbert van, illus. 2006. 48p. (J). 17.95 (978-1-58536-278-3(6)) Sleeping Bear Pr.

O'Day, Joseph E. I Like Wind! Foster, Ron, illus. 2007. (J). (*978-1-929039-42-5(5)*) Ambassador Bks., Inc.

Oldfield, Jenny. Dreamseeker Trilogy. 2005. (J). pap. 13.00 (978-0-340-89322-7(2), Hodder & Stoughton) Hodder General Publishing Division GBR. *Dist:* Trafalgar Square Publishing.

Rhema, Dan. Bluegrass Breeze. Leonard, Michael, illus. 2004. (J). per. 19.95 (978-0-9729835-1-8(1)) Mesquite Tress Pr., LLC.

Rink, Cindy. Where Does the Wind Blow? 2002. (gr. k-3). lib. bdg. 16.40 (978-0-613-52797-2(6)) Tandem Library Bks.

Rink, Cynthia A. Where Does the Wind Blow? Rink, Cynthia A., illus. 2004. (Sharing Nature with Children Book Ser.). (Illus.). 32p. (J). (gr. k-5). 16.95 (978-1-58469-041-2(0)) Dawn Pubns.

Rink, Cynthia A., illus. Where Does the Wind Blow? 2004. (Sharing Nature with Children Book Ser.). 32p. (J). pap. 7.95 (978-1-58469-040-5(2)) Dawn Pubns.

Roche, Hannah. Corey's Kite. 1998. (My First Weather Bks.). (Illus.). 24p. (J). (ps-3). (978-1-84089-033-4(9), Zero to Ten, Limited) Evans Publishing Group.

Rymond, Lynda Gene. The Village of Basketeers. Ceccoli, Nicoletta, illus. 2005. 40p. (J). (gr. k-3). 16.00 (978-0-618-39671-9(3)) Houghton Mifflin Co. Trade & Reference Div.

Samuelson, Christian. Anuqa. Samuelson, Christian & Brunk, Cara, illus. 1998. Tr. of Wind. (ESK.). 16p. (J). (gr. k-3). pap. 6.00 (978-1-58084-030-9(2)) Lower Kuskokwim Schl. District.

Shearer, Alex. Professor Sniff & the Lost Spring Breezes. Kenyon, Tony, illus. 1998. 102p. (J). (gr. 3-7). pap. 14.95 (978-0-531-30079-4(X), Orchard Bks.) Scholastic, Inc.

Solomon, Heather, illus. Willa & the Wind. 2005. 40p. (J). (gr. 1-4). 16.95 (978-0-7614-5232-4(X)) Cavendish, Marshall Corp.

Spalding, Andrea. Sarah May & the New Red Dress. ed. 2004. (Illus.). (J). (gr. k-3). spiral bd. (978-0-616-01782-1(0)) Canadian National Institute for the Blind/Institut National Canadien pour les Aveugles.

—Sarah May & the New Red Dress. 2000. (ps-2). lib. bdg. 15.25 (978-0-613-83716-3(9)); (978-0-606-18329-1(9)) Tandem Library Bks.

Thompson, Lauren. Mouse's First Spring. Erdogan, Buket, illus. 2005. 32p. (J). 12.95 (978-0-689-85838-3(8), Simon & Schuster Children's Publishing) Simon & Schuster Children's Publishing.

Thompson, Lauren & Erdogan, Buket. Mouse's First Fall. 2006. 32p. (J). (ps-1). 12.95 (978-0-689-85837-6(X), Simon & Schuster Children's Publishing) Simon & Schuster Children's Publishing.

Tibo, Gilles. Simon et le Vent d'Automne. Tibo, Gilles, illus. 1999. (Simon Ser.).Tr. of Simon & the Wind. (FRE & SPA., Illus.). 24p. (J). (ps-1). pap. 4.95 (978-0-88776-277-2(8), Livres Toundra) Tundra Bks., Inc./Livres Toundra, Inc. CAN. *Dist:* Random Hse., Inc.

Tiernan, Cate. A Chalice of Wind, No. 1. 2005. (Balefire Ser.: Vol. 1). 256p. (YA). (gr. 7-12). mass mkt. 6.99 (978-1-59514-045-6(X), Razorbill) Penguin Group (USA) Inc.

El Viento Sopla. (Enciclopedia Me Pregunto Por Que). (SPA., Illus.). 32p. (J). (gr. 3-5). 12.99 (978-84-241-2174-7(0), EV2036) Everest de Ediciones y Distribucion, S.L. ESP. *Dist:* Lectorum Pubns., Inc.

Westall, Robert. Voces en el Viento. (SPA.). 9.95 (978-958-04-4700-9(4)) Norma S.A. COL. *Dist:* Distribuidora Norma, Inc.

Wilhelm, Hans. It's Too Windy! 2004. 32p. (J). lib. bdg. 15.00 (978-1-59054-367-2(X)) Fitzgerald Bks.

—It's Too Windy! 2000. (Hello Reader! Ser.). (Illus.). 32p. (J). (gr. 1-3). pap. 3.99 (978-0-439-10849-2(7)) Scholastic, Inc.

—It's Too Windy! 2000. (gr. k-3). lib. bdg. 11.80 (978-0-613-25758-9(8)); (Illus.). (J). 10.79 (978-0-606-18571-4(2)) Tandem Library Bks.

Wind. 2000. (What About...? Ser.). (J). (gr. 1-4). pap. 5.72 (978-0-8114-9662-9(7)) Steck-Vaughn.

The Wind & Little Cloud. 2006. (J). 17.95 (978-0-9741743-3-4(5)) Perlycross Pubs.

Wolff, Ferida. It Is the Wind. Ransome, James E., illus. Date not set. 32p. (J). (ps-1). 5.99 (978-0-06-443530-7(X)) HarperCollins Pubs.

—It Is the Wind. Ransome, James, illus. 2005. 32p. (J). (ps-1). lib. bdg. 17.89 (978-0-06-028192-2(8)); 14.99 (978-0-06-028191-5(X)) HarperCollins Pubs.

Zolotow, Charlotte. When the Wind Stops. ed. 2004. (Illus.). (J). (gr. 2-4). spiral bd. (978-0-616-01822-4(3)); spiral bd. (978-0-616-01823-1(1)) Canadian National Institute for the Blind/Institut National Canadien pour les Aveugles.

WINDSOR, HOUSE OF

Billinghurst, Jane. Growing up Royal: Life in the Shadow of the British Throne. 2001. (Illus.). 176p. (J). (gr. 3-7). 22.95 (978-1-55037-623-4(3)); pap. 12.95 (978-1-55037-622-7(5)) Annick Pr., Ltd. CAN. *Dist:* Firefly Bks., Ltd.

WINE AND WINE MAKING

Johnston, Jack. The Vineyard Book. Manion, Moira, illus. 2005. 48p. (J). 25.00 (978-0-9629880-0-4(6)) ACME Pr.

WINFREY, OPRAH, 1954-

Alter, Judith. Oprah Winfrey. 2008. (J). lib. bdg. 26.00 (*978-1-60279-069-8(8)*) Cherry Lake Publishing.

Blashfield, Jean F. Oprah Winfrey. 2003. (Trailblazers of the Modern World Ser.). (ENG & SPA., Illus.). 48p. (J). (gr. 5 up). pap. 14.95 (978-0-8368-5247-9(8)); lib. bdg. 30.00 (978-0-8368-5087-1(4)) Stevens, Gareth Inc. (World Almanac Library).

Brooks, Philip. Oprah Winfrey: A Voice for the People. 2000. (Book Report Bios Ppbk Ser.). (Illus.). (YA). pap. 6.95 (978-0-531-16406-8(3), Watts, Franklin) Scholastic Library Publishing.

—Oprah Winfrey: A Voice for the People. 1999. (978-0-606-18159-4(8)) Tandem Library Bks.

Brown, Jonatha A. Oprah Winfrey. 2004. (Gente Que Hay Que Conocer Ser.). (ENG & SPA.). pap. 5.95 (978-0-8368-4361-3(4)) Stevens, Gareth Inc.

—Oprah Winfrey. Acosta, Tatiana & Gutierrez, Guillermo, trs. 2004. (Gente Que Hay Que Conocer Ser.). (ENG & SPA.). 24p. (J). lib. bdg. 19.33 (978-0-8368-4354-5(1)) Stevens, Gareth Inc.

—Oprah Winfrey. 2004. (Illus.). 24p. pap. (978-0-8368-4319-4(3)); (YA). lib. bdg. 19.33 (978-0-8368-4312-5(6)) Stevens, Gareth Inc.

Cooper, Ilene. Up Close: Oprah Winfrey: Oprah Winfrey. 2008. (Up Close Ser.). 208p. (J). (gr. 6). pap. 6.99 (*978-0-14-241045-5(4)*, Puffin) Penguin Group (USA) Inc.

Feinstein, Stephen. Oprah Winfrey. 2007. (African-American Heroes Ser.). (Illus.). 24p. (J). (gr. 1-3). lib. bdg. 21.26 (978-0-7660-2764-0(3), Enslow Elementary) Enslow Pubs., Inc.

Friedrich, Belinda. Oprah Winfrey. 2001. (Women of Achievement Ser.). (Illus.). 112p. (J). pap. (978-0-7910-5892-3(1)); (gr. 4-7). 30.00 (978-0-7910-5891-6(3)) Facts On File, Inc. (Chelsea Hse.).

Guilfoyle, Peg. Oprah Winfrey. 1999. (Ovations Ser.). (Illus.). 32p. (YA). (gr. 4-7). pap. (978-0-88682-941-4(0), Creative Education) Creative Co., The.

Jeffrey, Gary. Oprah Winfrey: The Life of a Media Superstar. 2006. 48p. (J). (978-1-4042-0924-4(7)); pap. (978-1-4042-0925-1(5)) Rosen Publishing Group, Inc., The.

Krohn, Katherine. Oprah Winfrey. 2005. (Lighting Bolt Bios Ser.). (Illus.). 112p. (J). (gr. 6-12). 27.93 (978-0-8225-2472-4(4)) Lerner Publishing Group.

Krohn, Katherine E. Oprah Winfrey. (Biography Ser.). (Illus.). 112p. (J). (gr. 6 up). 2003. pap. 7.95 (978-0-8225-5000-6(8)); 2001. 27.93 (978-0-8225-4999-4(9), Lerner Pubns.) Lerner Publishing Group.

—Oprah Winfrey. 2002. (gr. 7-12). lib. bdg. 16.40 (978-0-613-84025-5(9)) Tandem Library Bks.

McIntosh-Wooten, Sara. Oprah Winfrey: Talk Show Legend. 1999. (African-American Biographies Ser.). (Illus.). 128p. (YA). (gr. 6-12). lib. bdg. 26.60 (978-0-7660-1207-3(7)) Enslow Pubs., Inc.

McLeese, Don. Oprah Winfrey. 2002. (Discover the Life of an American Legend Ser.). (Illus.). 24p. (J). lib. bdg. 20.64 (978-1-58952-306-7(7)) Rourke Publishing, LLC.

Presnall, Judith Janda. Oprah Winfrey. 1998. (People in the News Ser.). (Illus.). 112p. (YA). (gr. 6-9). 27.45 (978-1-56006-360-5(2), Lucent Bks.) Thomson Gale.

Stone, Tanya Lee. Oprah Winfrey: Success with an Open Heart. 2001. (Gateway Biography Ser.). (Illus.). 48p. (gr. 2-4). (J). lib. bdg. 23.90 (978-0-7613-1814-9(3)); pap. (978-0-7613-1389-2(3)) Lerner Publishing Group. (Millbrook Pr.).

Ward, Kristin. Learning about Assertiveness from the Life of Oprah Winfrey. 1999. (Character Building Book Ser.). (Illus.). 24p. (J). (gr. 3). lib. bdg. 18.75 (978-0-8239-5348-6(3), PowerKids Pr.) Rosen Publishing Group, Inc., The.

Wheeler, Jill C. Oprah Winfrey. 2002. (Breaking Barriers Ser.). (Illus.). 64p. (J). (gr. 3-8). lib. bdg. 25.65 (978-1-57765-319-6(X), ABDO & Daughters) ABDO Publishing Co.

Woronoff, Kristen. Oprah Winfrey: Media Superstar. 2002. (Famous Women Juniors Ser.). (Illus.). 32p. (J). (gr. 3-5). 24.94 (978-1-56711-588-8(8) , Blackbirch Pr., Inc.) Thomson Gale.

WINNIE-THE-POOH (FICTITIOUS CHARACTER)—FICTION

American Education Publishing Staff. Pooh's Day to Play with Sticker & Other. 2000. (I Can Learn with Pooh Ser.). 32p. (J). (ps-3). pap., wbk. ed. 2.99 (978-1-56189-528-1(8) , 31221, American Education Publishing) School Specialty Publishing.

—Pooh's Go-Together Game. 2000. (I Can Learn with Pooh Ser.). (Illus.). 36p. (J). (ps-3). ring bd. 2.99 (978-1-56189-538-0(5) , 31231, American Education Publishing) School Specialty Publishing.

—Pooh's Learning Library. 2000. (Illus.). 192p. (J). (ps-3). pap. 10.95 (978-1-56189-534-2(2) , 31227, American Education Publishing) School Specialty Publishing.

—Pooh's Number Game. 2001. (Illus.). 36p. (J). suppl. ed. 2.99 (978-1-56189-537-3(7) , 31230, American Education Publishing) School Specialty Publishing.

Bendon Publishing Intl. Staff. Pooh Workbook Bindup #1040. 2004. pap. 9.99 (978-1-59394-323-3(7)) Bendon Publishing International.

Berrios, Frank. Christmas with Pooh. Disney Storybook Artists Staff, illus. 2005. (Disney Winnie the Pooh Ser.). 18p. (J). (gr. k-ps). bds. 3.99 (978-0-7364-2337-3(0) , RH/Disney) Random Hse. Children's Bks.

Berry, Bob, illus. Pooh 'Where Are You Roo?' 14p. (J). bds. 15.98 (978-0-7853-8449-6(9) , 7186100) Publications International, Ltd.

Braybrooks, Ann. Pooh's Happy Halloween. 2003. (Illus.). 24p. (J). (gr. k-3). 3.99 (978-0-7364-1329-9(4) , RH/Disney) Random Hse. Children's Bks.

—Tiggers Hate to Lose. 1999. (Winnie the Pooh First Readers Ser.: No. 8). (Illus.). 40p. (J). (gr. k-3). pap. 3.99 (978-0-7868-4266-7(0)) Disney Pr.

Classic Sticker Stories: Winnie-the-Pooh. (Illus.). 80p. (J). pap. 14.95 (978-0-525-46782-3(3)) Penguin Group (USA) Inc.

de Alba, Arlette, tr. Musica en Casa: Libro de Cuentos. 2005. (SPA., Illus.). 40p. (J). (ps-7). 24.95 (978-970-718-290-5(3) , Silver Dolphin en Español) Advanced Marketing, S. de R. L. de C. V. MEX. *Dist:* Perseus Distribution.

Disney Press Staff. Book of Pooh Tabbed Board Book, Bk. 1. 2002. 14p. (J). bds. (978-0-7868-3357-3(2)) Hachette Bk. Group.

—Piglet Feels Small. 2002. (gr. k-3). lib. bdg. 11.80 (978-0-613-73604-6(4)) Tandem Library Bks.

—Pooh's Easter Egg Hunt. 2002. (ps-2). lib. bdg. 11.80 (978-0-613-73601-5(X)) Tandem Library Bks.

—The Trouble with Honey. Ulkutay Design Group Staff, illus. 2006. 10p. (ps-2). 15.99 (978-0-7868-4941-3(X)) Disney Pr.

Disney Press Staff & Board Books Staff. Book of Pooh Bk. 2: Hide & Seek. 2002. (Illus.). 10p. (ps-k). 5.99 (978-0-7868-3356-6(4)) Disney Pr.

Disney Staff. Big Things, Little Things. Disney Staff, illus. 1999. (Pooh's Learn & Grow Ser.: Vol. 9). (Illus.). 12p. (J). 3.49 (978-1-57973-043-7(4)) Advance Pubs. LLC.

—Fruity-Tooty Picnic. Disney Staff, illus. 1999. (Pooh's Learn & Grow Ser.: Vol. 5). (Illus.). 12p. (J). 3.49 (978-1-57973-039-0(6)) Advance Pubs. LLC.

—Give It Your All. 2000. (Lessons from the Hundred-Acre Woods: Vol. 10). (Illus.). 32p. (J). (ps-3). 3.49 (978-1-57973-096-3(5)) Advance Pubs. LLC.

—Hooray for Teamwork. 2000. (Lessons from the Hundred-Acre Woods: Vol. 12). (Illus.). 32p. (J). (ps-3). 3.49 (978-1-57973-098-7(1)) Advance Pubs. LLC.

—I'm Really Sorry. 2000. (Lessons from the Hundred-Acre Woods: Vol. 6). (Illus.). 32p. (J). (ps-4). 3.49 (978-1-57973-092-5(2)) Advance Pubs. LLC.

—Listen Up, Tigger. 2000. (Lessons from the Hundred-Acre Woods: Vol. 9). (Illus.). 32p. (J). (ps-4). 3.49 (978-1-57973-095-6(7)) Advance Pubs. LLC.

—Pooh's Garden. 1999. (Pooh's Learn & Grow Ser.: Vol. 11). (Illus.). 12p. (J). 3.49 (978-1-57973-045-1(0)) Advance Pubs. LLC.

—Pooh's Hero Party, No. 12. 1999. (Winnie the Pooh First Readers Ser.: No. 12). (Illus.). 37p. (J). (gr. k-3). pap. 3.99 (978-0-7868-4270-4(9)) Disney Pr.

—Pooh's Rainy Day. Disney Staff, illus. 1999. (Pooh's Learn & Grow Ser.: Vol. 10). (Illus.). 12p. (J). 3.49 (978-1-57973-044-4(2)) Advance Pubs. LLC.

—A Pumpkin for Pooh. 2002. (Illus.). 12p. (J). (gr. k-ps). bds. 3.99 (978-0-7364-1359-6(6) , RH/Disney) Random Hse. Children's Bks.

—Ready, Set, Go! Disney Staff, illus. 1999. (Pooh's Learn & Grow Ser.: Vol. 8). (Illus.). 12p. (J). 3.49 (978-1-57973-042-0(6)) Advance Pubs. LLC.

—Sweet Dreams. Disney Staff, illus. 1999. (Pooh's Learn & Grow Ser.: Vol. 12). (Illus.). 12p. (J). 3.49 (978-1-57973-046-8(9)) Advance Pubs. LLC.

—Use Your Words! 2000. (Lessons from the Hundred-Acre Woods: Vol. 18). (Illus.). 32p. (J). (ps-3). 3.49 (978-1-57973-104-5(X)) Advance Pubs. LLC.

—What to Do wth Winnie the Pooh. 2002. (J). pap. 2.99 (978-0-7364-2115-7(7) , RH/Disney) Random Hse. Children's Bks.

—Winnie the Pooh. (FRE.). 96p. (J). (gr. k-5). pap. 9.95 (978-0-7859-8848-9(3)) French & European Pubns., Inc.

—Winnie the Pooh CD Storybook. rev. ed. 2005. (Illus.). 128p. (J). (gr. 4-12). 14.95 incl. audio compact disk (978-1-74121-969-2(8)) Hinkler Bks. Pty, Ltd. AUS. *Dist:* Penton Overseas, Inc.

—Winnie the Pooh CD Storybook: Winnie the Pooh & the Blustery Day, Winnie the Pooh & the Honey Tree, Winnie the Pooh & a Day for Eeyore, Winnie the Pooh & Tigger Too. Milne, A. A. & Shepard, Ernest H., eds. rev. ed. 2004. (Disney CD Storybooks Ser.). (Illus.). 128p. (J). (gr. 4-12). 14.95 incl. cd-rom (978-1-86515-303-2(6)) Hinkler Bks. Pty, Ltd. AUS. *Dist:* Penton Overseas, Inc.

Disney Staff & LeapFrog Staff, compiled by. Disney's Bounce, Tigger, Bounce. (J). (ps-2). 2002. 14.95 (978-1-58605-909-5(2) , LeapFrog Schl. Hse.); 2001. spiral bd. 14.99 (978-1-58605-000-9(1)) LeapFrog Enterprises, Inc.

—Disney's Pooh Gets Stuck. 2002. (J). (ps-2). 14.95 (978-1-58605-910-1(6) , LeapFrog Schl. Hse.) LeapFrog Enterprises, Inc.

Dorling Kindersley Publishing Staff. Winnie the Pooh. 2004. (Ultimate Sticker Bks.). 16p. (J). pap. 6.99 (978-0-7894-9996-7(7)) Dorling Kindersley Publishing, Inc.

Douglas, Vincent. The Blustery Day. 2001. (Disney Parent & Child Read Together Ser.). (Illus.). 40p. (ps-k). 4.99 (978-1-57768-730-6(2)) School Specialty Publishing.

—Pooh Helps Out. 2001. (Disney Parent & Child Read Together Ser.). (Illus.). 40p. (ps-k). 4.99 (978-1-57768-731-3(0)) School Specialty Publishing.

Edgar, Amy. Winnie the Pooh's Bedtime Hummables. 2000. (Winnie the Pooh Ser.). (Illus.). 16p. (J). (ps-k). bds. 7.99 (978-0-7364-1020-5(1) , RH/Disney) Random Hse. Children's Bks.

Equipo Staff. Aprende las Horas con Winnie Pooh. 2000. (Adventures of Winnie the Pooh! Ser.). (SPA., Illus.). 124p. (J). 16.95 (978-84-488-0671-2(9)) Beascoa, Ediciones S.A. ESP. *Dist:* Distribooks, Inc.

Ferguson, Don. Winnie the Pooh's A to ZZZZ. Wakeman, Bill & Langley, Diana, illus. 2020. 32p. (J). (ps-2). pap. 4.99 (978-0-7868-4094-6(3)) Disney Pr.

Gaines, Isabel. Be Quiet, Pooh! 1999. 40p. (J). pap. 3.99 (978-0-7868-4385-5(3)) Disney Pr.

—Giving Bear. 2001. (Winnie the Pooh First Readers Ser.). (Illus.). (J). (978-0-606-21649-4(9)) Tandem Library Bks.

—Happy Birthday, Eeyore! 2001. (Winnie the Pooh First Readers Ser.). (Illus.). (J). (978-0-606-21650-0(2)) Tandem Library Bks.

—Happy Valentine's Day, Pooh. 2000. (Winnie the Pooh Ser.: Vol. 25). (Illus.). 37p. (J). pap. 3.99 (978-0-7868-4372-5(1)) Disney Pr.

—Pooh & the Storm That Sparkled. 2001. (Winnie the Pooh First Readers Ser.). (Illus.). (J). (978-0-606-21651-7(0)) Tandem Library Bks.

—Pooh Gets Stuck, No. 1. 1998. (Winnie the Pooh First Readers Ser.). (Illus.). 48p. (J). (ps-3). pap. 3.95 (978-0-7868-4184-4(2)) Disney Pr.

—Pooh's Christmas Gift. 1999. 40p. (J). pap. 3.99 (978-0-7868-4402-9(7)) Disney Pr.

—Pooh's Christmas Gifts. 2001. (Winnie the Pooh First Readers Ser.). (Illus.). (J). (978-0-606-21653-1(7)) Tandem Library Bks.

—Pooh's Christmas Sled Ride. Studio Orlando Staff, illus. 2003. 32p. (J). (ps-1). pap. 3.99 (978-0-7364-2165-2(3) , RH/Disney) Random Hse. Children's Bks.

—Pooh's Easter Egg Hunt. 1999. (Winnie the Pooh First Readers Ser.: No. 10). (Illus.). 40p. (J). (gr. k-3). pap. 3.99 (978-0-7868-4268-1(7)) Disney Pr.

—Pooh's Fall Harvest. 2000. (Winnie the Pooh First Readers Ser.: No. 23). (Illus.). 35p. (J). (ps-3). pap. 3.99 (978-0-7868-4370-1(5)) Disney Pr.

—Pooh's Graduation. 2001. (Winnie the Pooh First Readers Ser.). (Illus.). (J). (978-0-606-21655-5(3)) Tandem Library Bks.

—Pooh's Halloween Parade. 2001. (Winnie the Pooh First Readers Ser.). (Illus.). (J). (978-0-606-21656-2(1)) Tandem Library Bks.

—Pooh's Leaf Pile. 2001. (Winnie the Pooh First Readers Ser.). (Illus.). (J). (978-0-606-21659-3(6)) Tandem Library Bks.

—Pooh's Pumpkin. 2001. (Winnie the Pooh First Readers Ser.). (Illus.). (J). (978-0-606-21660-9(X)) Tandem Library Bks.

—Pooh's Scavenger Hunt. 2001. (Winnie the Pooh First Readers Ser.). (Illus.). (J). (978-0-606-21661-6(8)) Tandem Library Bks.

—Pooh's Scavenger Hunt: Special Sales Edition. 1999. 40p. (J). pap. 3.99 (978-0-7868-4386-2(1)) Disney Pr.

—Pooh's Sled Ride. 2000. (Winnie the Pooh First Readers Ser.: No. 24). (Illus.). 34p. (J). (ps-3). pap. 3.99 (978-0-7868-4371-8(3)) Disney Pr.

—Pooh's Surprise Basket. 2001. (Winnie the Pooh First Readers Ser.). (Illus.). (J). (978-0-606-21662-3(6)) Tandem Library Bks.

—Rabbit Gets Lost. 2001. (Winnie the Pooh First Readers Ser.). (Illus.). (J). (978-0-606-21663-0(4)) Tandem Library Bks.

—Tiggers Hate to Lose. 1999. 40p. (J). pap. 3.99 (978-0-7868-4389-3(6)) Disney Pr.

—Tiggers Hate to Lose. 2001. (Winnie the Pooh First Readers Ser.). (Illus.). (J). (978-0-606-21664-7(2)) Tandem Library Bks.

—Winnie the Pooh: Pooh's Best Friend Club Edition. 1999. 40p. (J). pap. 3.99 (978-0-7868-4406-7(X)) Disney Pr.

Gaines, Isabel & Disney Press Staff. Easy-to-Read Stories. 2000. (Winnie the Pooh Ser.). (Illus.). 192p. (ps-3). 9.99 (978-0-7868-3317-7(3)) Disney Pr.

Gaines, Isabel & Random House Disney Staff. Pooh's Halloween Pumpkin. Yee, Josie, illus. 2003. (Disney Winnie the Pooh Ser.). 32p. (J). (ps-1). pap. 3.99 (978-0-7364-2160-7(2) , RH/Disney) Random Hse. Children's Bks.

Gaines, Isabel, et al. The Giving Bear. Yee, Josie, illus. 1999. (Winnie the Pooh First Readers Ser.: No. 9). 37p. (J). (gr. k-3). pap. 3.99 (978-0-7868-4267-4(9)) Disney Pr.

Galvin, Laura Gates. Best Book of Pooh, Ever: Reading to Grow. rev. ed. 2005. (Reading to Grow Ser.). (Illus.). 40p. (J). (ps-3). 12.99 (978-1-59069-450-3(3) , 1A701) Studio Mouse LLC.

Golden Books Staff. Fun with Letters. 2000. (Disney Ser.). (Illus.). 48p. (J). (ps-k). pap. 2.99 (978-0-307-20130-0(9) , 20130, Golden Bks.) Random Hse. Children's Bks.

—Pooh: Coloring, Paint with Water, Activities. 2000. (Disney Ser.). (Illus.). 96p. (J). (ps-3). pap. 3.99 (978-0-307-25401-6(1) , Golden Bks.) Random Hse. Children's Bks.

—Winnie The Boo! Paint Box. 2000. (Illus.). 32p. (ps-3). pap. 3.99 (978-0-307-09237-3(2) , Golden Bks.) Random Hse. Children's Bks.

—Winnie the Pooh. 2000. (J). (ps-3). pap. 2.99 (978-0-307-05545-3(0) , 05545, Golden Bks.) Random Hse. Children's Bks.

Goodnight Pooh. 2001. (Illus.). (J). 7.98 (978-0-7853-4788-0(7)) Publications International, Ltd.

Hal Leonard Corporation Staff. Winnie the Pooh. 1998. (Style Collections). 40p. (ps-3). pap. 10.95 (978-0-7935-8754-4(9) , 0793587549) Leonard, Hal Corp.

Here Comes Winter! 2003. (J). per. (978-1-57657-967-1(0)) Paradise Pr., Inc.

Hogan, Mary. Winnie the Pooh Shapes. 2002. (Illus.). 10p. (J). (978-0-7868-3395-5(5)); (978-0-7868-3396-2(3)); (978-0-7868-3397-9(1)); (978-0-7868-3398-6(X)); (978-0-7868-3399-3(8)) Disney Pr.

I Can Learn with Pooh. 2002. 32p. pap. 83.76 (978-1-56189-818-3(X) , American Education Publishing) School Specialty Publishing.

Ice Water Press Package, ed. My Very First Winnie the Pooh Scrapbook. 2007. 14p. (J). (ps-3). 12.99 (***978-1-4231-0274-8(6)***) Disney Pr.

Kennedy, Marge. The Book of Boo! 2002. (Illus.). 32p. (ps-1). 5.99 (978-0-7868-3364-1(5)) Disney Pr.

Krensky, Stephen. Winnie the Pooh & Some Bees. 2001. (978-0-606-22513-7(7)) Tandem Library Bks.

Krulik, Nancy E. Puzzlers. 1999. (My Very First Winnie the Pooh Ser.). (Illus.). 64p. (J). (ps-1). pap. 4.99 (978-0-7868-4344-2(6)) Disney Pr.

LeapFrog Staff. Lots & Lots of Honeypots. 2003. (Illus.). (J). spiral bd. 14.99 (978-1-59319-002-6(6)) LeapFrog Enterprises, Inc.

LeapFrog Staff, compiled by. Pooh Gets Stuck. 2001. (SPA.). (J). (ps-2). spiral bd. 14.99 (978-1-58605-133-4(4)) LeapFrog Enterprises, Inc.

—Pooh's Honey Tree: MFLP. 2001. (J). (ps-2). spiral bd. 12.99 (978-1-58605-111-2(3)) LeapFrog Enterprises, Inc.

Lift-A-Flap. Book of Pooh: Beginning Sounds: Match the Flap. 2001. (Learn to Read Ser.). (Illus.). 10p. (ps-1). 7.99 (978-0-7868-3344-3(0)) Disney Pr.

Little Red Riding Pooh: A Fairy Tale Friend a Board Book & Plush Figure. 2004. (Pooh's Fairy Tale Theater Ser.). 12p. (J). 6.99 (978-0-7364-2239-0(0) , RH/Disney) Random Hse. Children's Bks.

Lou Weber Staff, ed. Winnie the Pooh (Clock) 2004. 10p. (J). bds. 16.98 (978-1-4127-3243-7(3) , 7236300) Publications International, Ltd.

Marshall, Hallie. Disney's Winnie the Pooh's Telling Time: Book & Watch Set. 2000. (Illus.). 24p. (J). (ps-3). 9.99 (978-0-7364-1028-1(7)) Mouse Works.

Milne, A. A. Bedtime with Winnie-the-Pooh. Shepard, Ernest H., illus. 2003. 22p. (J). (ps). 9.99 (978-0-525-47148-6(0) , Dutton Juvenile) Penguin Group (USA) Inc.

—The Complete Tales of Winnie the Pooh. 70th ed. 1999. (Illus.). 368p. (J). (gr. 4-7). 40.00 (978-0-525-45060-3(2) , Dutton Juvenile) Penguin Group (USA) Inc.

—The Honey Tree. 2006. (Illus.). 24p. (J). (gr. k-k). 2.99 (978-0-7364-2392-2(3) , Golden/Disney) Random Hse. Children's Bks.

—In Which a House Is Built at Pooh Corner for Eeyore. Shepard, Ernest H., illus. unabr. ed. (Classic Pooh Treasury Ser.). (J). incl. audio (978-1-57375-527-6(3) , 71394) Audioscope.

—In Which Christopher Robin Gives Pooh a Party. Shepard, Ernest H., illus. unabr. ed. (Winnie-the-Pooh Ser.). (J). incl. audio (978-1-57375-046-2(8) , 70554) Audioscope.

—In Which Pooh Goes Visiting & Gets into a Tight Place & in Which Pooh & Piglet Go Hunting & Nearly Catch a Woozle. Shepard, Ernest H., illus. unabr. ed. (Winnie-the-Pooh Ser.). (J). incl. audio (978-1-57375-001-1(8) , 70014) Audioscope.

—In Which Tigger Is Unbounced. Shepard, Ernest H., illus. unabr. ed. (Classic Pooh Treasury Ser.). (J). incl. audio (978-1-57375-528-3(1) , 71404) Audioscope.

—In Which We Are Introduced to Winnie the Pooh & Some Bees, & the Stories Begin. Shepard, Ernest H., illus. unabr. ed. (Winnie-the-Pooh Ser.). (J). incl. audio (978-1-57375-000-4(X) , 70004) Audioscope.

—The Magical Pop-Up World of Winnie-the-Pooh. Shepard, Ernest H., illus. deluxe ed. 2003. 5p. (J). (ps). 24.99 (978-0-525-47141-7(3) , Dutton Juvenile) Penguin Group (USA) Inc.

—My Very First Winnie-the-Pooh. Shepard, Ernest H., illus. 2002. 22p. (J). bds. 9.99 (978-0-525-46838-7(2) , Dutton Juvenile) Penguin Group (USA) Inc.

—Pooh & Friends. Shepard, Ernest H., illus. 2004. 16p. (J). (gr. 1). bds. 7.99 (978-0-525-47253-7(3) , Dutton Juvenile) Penguin Group (USA) Inc.

—Pooh Goes Visiting. 2002. (gr. k-3). lib. bdg. 11.80 (978-0-613-62567-8(6)) Tandem Library Bks.

—Pooh Touch & Feel: A Pooh Texture Book. abr. ed. 1998. (Illus.). 12p. (J). (ps). 9.99 (978-0-525-45830-2(1) , Dutton Juvenile) Penguin Group (USA) Inc.

—Pooh's First Clock. Shepard, Ernest H., illus. 1998. 12p. (J). (ps-3). bds. 12.99 (978-0-525-45983-5(9) , Dutton Juvenile) Penguin Group (USA) Inc.

—Pu Baut ein Haus.Tr. of Pooh Builds a House. (GER.). (J). pap. 12.95 (978-3-423-07395-0(0)) Deutscher Taschenbuch Verlag GmbH & Co KG DEU. *Dist:* Distribooks, Inc.

—Slide & Seek Alphabet: A Sliding Window Book. 1999. (Illus.). 8p. (J). bds. 10.99 (978-0-7868-3240-8(1)) Disney Pr.

—Slide & Seek Numbers: A Sliding Window Book. 1999. (Illus.). 8p. (J). 10.99 (978-0-7868-3241-5(X)) Disney Pr.

—A Smackerel of Pooh: Ten Favorite Stories & Poems. Shepard, Ernest H., illus. 2006. 79p. (J). (gr. k-4). 16.00 (978-1-4223-5283-0(8)) DIANE Publishing Co.

—Tigger Comes to the Forest. 2002. (gr. k-3). lib. bdg. 11.80 (978-0-613-62575-3(7)) Tandem Library Bks.

—Winnie Puh. (ITA., Illus.). pap. 29.95 (978-88-7782-278-9(3)) Salani ITA. *Dist:* Distribooks, Inc.

—Winnie-the-Pooh. Shepard, Ernest H., illus. 2005. 176p. (J). pap. 5.99 (978-0-14-240467-6(5) , Puffin) Penguin Group (USA) Inc.

—Winnie the Pooh: Touch & Feel. Shepard, Ernest H., illus. 2002. 10p. (J). 12.99 (978-0-525-47007-6(7) , Dutton Juvenile) Penguin Group (USA) Inc.

—Winnie the Pooh 80th Anniversary Edition. Shepard, Ernest H., illus. 2006. 160p. (YA). (ps). 19.99 (978-0-525-47768-6(3) , Dutton Juvenile) Penguin Group (USA) Inc.

—Winnie the Pooh & When We Were Young. Shepard, Ernest H., illus. 32p. (J). Boxed set. pap. incl. audio compact disk (978-1-57375-583-2(4) , 71512); Set. pap. incl. audio (978-1-57375-652-5(0) , 71514) Audioscope.

—Winnie the Pooh at Pooh Corner & Now We Are Six, Set. 1998. (J). 29.98 incl. audio Audioscope.

—Winnie the Pooh's Storys. Shepard, Ernest H., illus. 2002. 16.95 (978-0-525-47065-6(4) , Dutton Juvenile) Penguin Group (USA) Inc.

—Winny de Puh. Shepard, Ernest H., illus. 2000. (SPA.). 176p. (J). (gr. 3 up). 15.99 (978-0-525-44986-7(8) , DT1541, Dutton Juvenile) Penguin Group (USA) Inc.

Milne, A. A. & Krensky, Stephen. Pooh Goes Visiting, Vol. 2. Shepard, Ernest H., illus. 2002. (Puffin-Easy-to-Read Ser.). 48p. (J). pap. 3.99 (978-0-14-230184-5(1) , Puffin) Penguin Group (USA) Inc.

Milne, A. A. & Shepard, Ernest H. Where Is Poohs Honey: Slide & Find Books. 2001. (Illus.). 8p. (J). (ps-k). 6.99 (978-0-525-46539-3(1) , Dutton Juvenile) Penguin Group (USA) Inc.

Milnes, Ellen. Trick or Treat, Pooh! 2000. (Learn & Grow Ser.). (Illus.). 14p. (J). (ps up). 5.99 (978-0-7364-0104-3(0)) Mouse Works.

Mouse Works Staff. Pooh. 1999. (My Very First Cloth Book Ser.). (J). 6.99 (978-0-7364-0177-7(6)) Disney Pr.

—Pooh. 1998. 10p. (J). 6.99 (978-0-7364-0019-0(2)) Mouse Works.

—Pooh Cuddler. 2001. 6p. (J). 2.10 (978-0-7364-0234-7(9)) Mouse Works.

—Pooh Seek & See. 1998. (J). 3.98 (978-0-7364-0008-4(7)) Disney Pr.

—Tigger Cuddler. 2001. 6p. (J). 2.10 (978-0-7364-0235-4(7)) Mouse Works.

—Winnie the Pooh Spanish Read. 1999. 48p. (J). pap. 4.99 (978-0-7364-0108-1(3)) Mouse Works.

—Winnie the Pooh's Friendly Adventures. 1999. (Disney's Read-Aloud Storybooks Ser.). (Illus.). 72p. (J). (ps-2). 8.99 (978-0-7364-0107-4(5) , RH/Disney) Random Hse. Children's Bks.

—Winnie the Pooh's Touch & Feel Book. 2nd ed. 2005. 10p. (J). 6.99 (978-0-7364-1021-2(X)) Hyperion Pr.

Nursery Rhymes of Winnie the Pooh. 2000. (Books Are Fun Ser.). 96p. (J). 14.95 (978-0-7868-3263-7(0)) Disney Pr.

Parent, Nancy. Pooh Says Boo. 1998. (Pooh Ser.). (Illus.). 10p. (J). (ps). 4.99 (978-1-57082-752-5(4)) Mouse Works.

Playhouse Disney: My Friends Tigger & Pooh. 2007. 22p. (J). mass mkt. 4.99 (***978-1-4037-3941-4(2)***) Dalmatian Pr.

Pooh Paint with Water. 1999. (J). pap. 1.79 (978-0-307-08263-3(6) , 08263, Golden Bks.) Random Hse. Children's Bks.

Pooh Hello Friend Book & Box. 2002. (Illus.). (J). pap. 9.98 (978-0-7853-5251-8(1)) Publications International, Ltd.

Pooh Hundred Acre Music Maker. pap. 16.98 (978-0-7853-6068-1(9)) Publications International, Ltd.

Pooh Play a Song Dulces Suenos. 2001. (SPA., Illus.). 8p. (J). 9.98 (978-0-7853-5227-3(9)) Publications International, Ltd.

Pooh Play a Song Juegos y Fiestas. 2001. (SPA., Illus.). 8p. (J). 7.98 (978-0-7853-5228-0(7)) Publications International, Ltd.

Pooh Please & Thank You. 2002. (Illus.). (J). 7.98 (978-0-7853-6038-4(7)) Publications International, Ltd.

Pooh's Perfect Day. 2000. (Giant Pooh Book Ends Ser.). (Illus.). 10p. (J). (ps). (978-1-57584-807-5(4)) Reader's Digest Children's Publishing, Inc.

Posner-Sanchez, Andrea. Stickety - Stick. Brown, Adrienne, illus. 2005. (Pooh Ser.). 16p. (J). (gr. k-ps). bds. 6.99 (978-0-7364-2281-9(1) , RH/Disney) Random Hse. Children's Bks.

Publications International Staff. A Good Day for Spring. 2002. (Illus.). (J). 15.98 (978-0-7853-6042-1(5)) Publications International, Ltd.

Random House Disney Staff. Pooh Blocks. 2005. (Pooh Adorables Ser.). (Illus.). 12p. (J). (gr. k-k). bds. 8.99 (978-0-7364-2306-9(0) , RH/Disney) Random Hse. Children's Bks.

—Pooh Builds. Hahn, Rebecca, illus. 2007. (Pooh Adorables Ser.). 12p. (J). (ps-k). 7.99 (978-0-7364-2443-1(1) , RH/Disney) Random Hse. Children's Bks.

—Pooh Counts. 2005. (Illus.). 12p. (J). (gr. k-k). bds. 8.99 (978-0-7364-2307-6(9) , RH/Disney) Random Hse. Children's Bks.

W X Y Z

—Pooh Draws. Hahn, Rebecca, illus. 2007. (Pooh Adorables Ser.). 12p. (J). (ps-k). 7.99 (978-0-7364-2444-8(X) , RH/Disney) Random Hse. Children's Bks.

—Pooh Opposites. 2006. (Disney Winnie the Pooh Ser.). (Illus.). 12p. (J). (gr. k-k). bds. 8.99 (978-0-7364-2413-4(X) , RH/Disney) Random Hse. Children's Bks.

Random House Disney Staff & Barad, Alexis. No Honey! 2006. (Illus.). 16p. (J). (gr. k-ps). bds. 6.99 (978-0-7364-2284-0(6) , RH/Disney) Random Hse. Children's Bks.

Random House Disney Staff & Berrios, Frank. Playfully Pooh. Alavezos, Costa, illus. 2003. 32p. (J). (ps-3). pap. 3.99 (978-0-7364-2124-9(6) , Golden/Disney) Random Hse. Children's Bks.

Random House Disney Staff & Disney Storybook Artists Staff. Picnic with Pooh. 2006. (Illus.). 32p. (J). (ps-2). pap. 4.99 (978-0-375-87513-7(1) , Golden/Disney) Random Hse. Children's Bks.

Random House Disney Staff & Liberts, Jennifer. Pooh: Tricks & Treats. Alvin & Associates, Inc., illus. 2001. 16p. (J). (ps-3). pap. 2.99 (978-0-7364-1191-2(7) , Golden/Disney) Random Hse. Children's Bks.

Random House Disney Staff & Posner, Fran. Pooh Loves You. Alavezos, Costa, illus. 2002. (Disney Winnie the Pooh Ser.). 24p. (J). (gr. k-k). pap. 3.25 (978-0-7364-1305-3(7) , RH/Disney) Random Hse. Children's Bks.

Random House Disney Staff & Worth, Bonnie. Pom-Pom, Tiddly-Pom. 2005. (Pooh Hummables Ser.). (Illus.). 16p. (J). (gr. k-ps). bds. 6.99 (978-0-7364-2282-6(X) , RH/Disney) Random Hse. Children's Bks.

Reader's Digest Editors, ed. Winnie the Pooh's: Movie Theater: Storybook & Movie Projector. 2005. (Diseny Winnie the Pooh Ser.). (Illus.). 48p. (J). bds. 24.99 (978-0-7944-0522-9(3) , Reader's Digest Children's Bks.) Reader's Digest Children's Publishing, Inc.

Rhyme Time. 2002. (978-0-9720825-1-8(4)) Toy Box Pr., The.

Rhyme Time. 2000. (Wipe-Off Activity Bks.). (Illus.). 16p. (J). (ps-1). wbk. ed. 3.79 (978-1-889319-82-7(1)) Trend Enterprises, Inc.

Richards, Helene. Disney Winnie the Pooh Music Play Storybook. 2005. (RD Innovative Book & Player Format Ser.). (Illus.). 40p. (J). 24.99 (978-0-7944-0768-1(4)) Reader's Digest Assn., Inc., The.

Salas, Macarena, ed. Pooh's Best Day/El Mejor Dia de Pooh: A Book about Weather/Un Libro sobre el Tiempo. 2005. (Disney Bil Ser.). (SPA & ENG., Illus.). 10p. (J). bds. 3.99 (978-0-439-66364-9(4) , Scholastic en Espanol) Scholastic, Inc.

Shue, Ken, intro. The Art of Winnie the Pooh: Disney Artist Celebrate the Silly Old Bear. 2006. (Illus.). 176p. (ps-17). 35.00 (978-1-4231-0252-6(5) , Disney Editions) Disney Pr.

Silver Dolphin en Español Editors. Caritas felices: Winnie the Pooh: Happy Faces: Winnie the Pooh, Spanish-Language Edition. 2007. (Illus.). 8p. (J). bds. 7.95 ***978-970-718-393-3(4)** , Silver Dolphin en Español) Advanced Marketing, S. de R. L. de C. V. MEX. *Dist:* Perseus Distribution.

Silver Dolphin en Español Editors, ed. Tesoros Para Llevar: Winnie the Pooh. 2006. (Illus.). 24p. (J). bds. 12.95 (978-970-718-358-2(6) , Silver Dolphin en Español) Advanced Marketing, S. de R. L. de C. V. MEX. *Dist:* Perseus Distribution.

Talkington, Bruce. Disney's: Winnie the Pooh's - Easter. 1998. 32p. (J). 5.95 (978-0-7868-3202-6(9)) Hyperion Bks. for Children.

—Winnie the Pooh & the Bumble Bee Chase. rev. ed. 1998. 14p. (J). 11.95 (978-0-7868-3228-6(2)) Disney Pr.

—Winnie the Pooh's Valentine Mini. 1998. (Illus.). 32p. (J). 11.95 (978-0-7868-3201-9(0)) Disney Pr.

Templar Publishing Staff. Winnie the Pooh: Winnie's Hologram Book. 2005. (Illus.). 32p. (J). pap. 11.99 (978-0-7868-4162-2(1)) Disney Pr.

Things to Do. 2001. (Illus.). 10p. (ps-ps). 15.99 (978-0-7868-3302-3(5)) Disney Pr.

Thomas, Valerie. Winnie at the Seaside. (Illus.). 32p. (978-0-19-279199-3(0)) Oxford Univ. Pr., Inc.

Tigger & Pooh 100 Acre Woods Friends. 2007. 48p. pap. 3.99 (***978-1-4037-3227-9(2)**) Dalmatian Pr.

Tigger Early Learning: My First Library. 2004. (J). bds. (978-1-4127-0317-8(4) , 7217900) Publications International, Ltd.

Time for School. 2001. (Disney's Winnie the Pooh Ser.). (Illus.). 10p. (J). bds. 7.95 (978-0-7853-4790-3(9)) Publications International, Ltd.

Walt Disney Records Staff. Winnie the Pooh: Winnie the Pooh Springtime with Roo/Pooh's Huffalump Movie/ Piglet's Big Movie. unabr. ed. 2005. (Disney's Read along Collection Ser.). (J). audio compact disk 14.99 (978-0-7634-1147-3(7)) Walt Disney Records.

Weber, Lou, ed. Magic Screen Pooh. 2005. 14p. (J). bds. 15.98 (978-1-4127-3548-3(3) , 7263600) Publications International, Ltd.

—Pooh ABC Adventure: Sound Activity Pad. 2004. 48p. (J). 12.98 (978-1-4127-0171-6(6) , 7218300) Publications International, Ltd.

—Pooh Color & Play Stories. 2005. 32p. 7.98 (978-1-4127-3393-9(6)) Publications International, Ltd.

—Pooh Friendly Stories Musical Treasury. 2005. 40p. (J). bds. 12.98 (978-1-4127-3480-6(0) , 7259600) Publications International, Ltd.

—Pooh Look & Find Wipe Off, 3, Pack. 2004. 72p. (J). spiral bd. 15.98 (978-1-4127-3313-7(8) , 7244800) Publications International, Ltd.

—Pooh Numbers: Sound Activity Pad. 2004. 48p. (J). 12.98 (978-1-4127-0172-3(4) , 7218400) Publications International, Ltd.

—Pooh's Heffalump Movie. 2004. (Illus.). 24p. (J). 15.98 (978-1-4127-3555-1(6) , 7259300) Publications International, Ltd.

—Poohs Sunny Day Songs. 2005. 14p. (J). bds. 15.98 (978-1-4127-3401-1(0) , 7254700) Publications International, Ltd.

Winnie the Pooh. (Sing-Along Ser.). (J). 11.99 incl. audio (978-1-55723-933-4(9)) Walt Disney Records.

Winnie the Pooh: Catch a Heffalump. 2005. (Illus.). 120p. (J). mass mkt. 1.89 (978-1-4037-1248-6(4)) Dalmatian Pr.

Winnie the Pooh: Heffelump Hollow. 2005. (Illus.). 64p. (J). mass mkt. 1.89 (978-1-4037-1247-9(6)) Dalmatian Pr.

Winnie the Pooh & a Day for Eeyore, (Read-Along Ser.). (J). 7.99 incl. audio (978-1-55723-176-5(1)) Walt Disney Records.

Winnie the Pooh & the Blustery Day. 1999. (Disney Ser.). (Illus.). 56p. (J). (ps-3). pap. 2.99 (978-0-307-28029-9(2) , Golden Bks.) Random Hse. Children's Bks.

Winnie the Pooh & the Hanukkah Dreidel. 1998. (Winnie the Pooh Ser.). (Illus.). 8p. (J). (ps-1). pap. 2.99 (978-1-57082-994-9(2)) Mouse Works.

Winnie the Pooh Helping Songs. 2003. (Illus.). 10p. (J). bds. 9.98 (978-0-7853-8284-3(4) , 7182200) Publications International, Ltd.

Winnie the Pooh Shapes. 2002. (Illus.). 10p. (J). (978-0-7868-3401-3(3)) Disney Pr.

Winnie the Pooh Sweet Dreams. 2003. (Musical Nightlight Bks.). 14p. (J). bds. 15.98 (978-0-7853-7982-9(7) , 7177700) Publications International, Ltd.

Worth, Bonnie. Who Cares? Pooh Cares! Hollister, Samantha, illus. 2007. 16p. (J). (gr. k-ps). bds. 6.99 (978-0-7364-2283-3(8) , RH/Disney) Random Hse. Children's Bks.

Zoehfeld, Kathleen Weidner. Be Patient, Pooh. 2000. (Illus.). 32p. (J). (ps-k). 12.99 (978-0-7868-3250-7(9)) Disney Pr.

—Don't Talk to Strangers, Pooh! 2000. (My Very First Winnie the Pooh Ser.). (Illus.). 32p. (J). (ps-k). pap. 4.99 (978-0-7868-4378-7(0)) Disney Pr.

—Happy New Year, Pooh! 2000. (My Very First Winnie the Pooh Ser.). (Illus.). 32p. (J). (ps-k). pap. 4.99 (978-0-7868-4418-0(3)) Disney Pr.

—Pooh's Bad Dream. 2000. (My Very First Winnie the Pooh Ser.). (Illus.). 32p. (J). (ps-k). pap. 4.99 (978-0-7868-4377-0(2)) Disney Pr.

—Pooh's Bad Dream. Cuddy, Robbin, illus. 1998. (My Very First Winnie the Pooh Ser.). 32p. (J). (ps-k). 11.95 (978-0-7868-3137-1(5)) Disney Pr.

—Pooh's Jingle Bells. (Illus.). 32p. (J). (ps-k). 2000. pap. 4.99 (978-0-7868-4419-7(1)); 1998. 11.95 (978-0-7868-3204-0(5)) Disney Pr.

—Pooh's Scrapbook. 1999. (My Very First Winnie the Pooh Ser.: No. 11). (Illus.). 32p. (J). 11.99 (978-0-7868-3226-2(6)) Disney Pr.

—Roo's New Babysitter. 1999. (My Very First Winnie the Pooh Ser.). (Illus.). 32p. (J). (ps-k). 11.99 (978-0-7868-3215-6(0)) Disney Pr.

—Where Are You Pooh? Pooh's First Discovery. 1999. (Disney's Winnie the Pooh Ser.). (Illus.). 12p. (J). (ps-1). 5.99 (978-0-7364-0051-0(6)) Mouse Works.

—Winnie the Pooh Storybook Collection. Cuddy, Robbin, illus. 2003. 336p. (J). (ps-k). 15.99 (978-0-7868-3444-0(7) , Disney Editions) Disney Pr.

—Winnie the Pooh's Honey Adventures. 1999. 64p. (J). 6.99 (978-0-7364-0139-5(3)) Mouse Works.

Zoehfeld, Kathleen Weidner & Milne, A. A. Don't Talk to Strangers, Pooh! Cuddy, Robbin, illus. 1998. (My Very First Winnie the Pooh Ser.). 32p. (J). (ps). pap. 11.95 (978-0-7868-3145-6(6)) Disney Pr.

Zoehfeld, Kathleen Weidner & Random House Disney Staff. Hello, Spring! Cuddy, Robbin & Marrucchi, Elisa, illus. 2001. (Disney's Winnie the Pooh Ser.). 24p. (J). (gr. k-k). pap. 3.99 (978-0-7364-1109-7(7) , RH/Disney) Random Hse. Children's Bks.

Zolotow, Charlotte. Growing up Stories for 5-6 Year Olds. 2020. 114p. (J). (ps-17). 19.99 (978-0-7868-0519-8(6)) Disney Pr.

WINNING AND LOSING—FICTION

Adler, C. S. Winning. 1999. (Illus.). 160p. (J). (gr. 5-9). tchr. ed. 15.00 (978-0-395-65017-2(8) , Clarion Bks.) Houghton Mifflin Co. Trade & Reference Div.

Anderson, Joseph P. The Kickball Game. 2007. (Illus.). 24p. (J). (***978-1-4048-2443-0(X)**) Picture Window Bks.

—The Kickball Game. Greathouse, Justin, illus. 2006. 24p. (J). (***978-1-4048-2413-3(8)**) Picture Window Bks.

Black, Denise & Schwartz, Janet. Around Atlanta with Children: A Guide to Family Activities. 7th ed. 2004. 334p. pap. 15.95 (978-1-56145-202-6(5)) Peachtree Pubs., Ltd.

Brimner, Larry Dane. The Big Tee Ball Game. Tripp, Christine, illus. 2001. (Rookie Choices Ser.). 32p. (J). (gr. 1-2). 20.50 (978-0-516-22158-8(2) , Children's Pr.) Scholastic Library Publishing.

Catalanotto, Peter. Emily's Art. Catalanotto, Peter, illus. (Illus.). 32p. (J). 2006. pap. 6.99 (978-1-4169-2688-7(7) , Aladdin); 2001. 17.99 (978-0-689-83831-6(X) , Atheneum/Richard Jackson Bks.) Simon & Schuster Children's Publishing.

Chaconas, Dori. Cork & Fuzz: Good Sports. McCue, Lisa, illus. 2007. (Viking Easy-To-Read Ser.). 32p. (J). (gr. k-2). 13.99 (978-0-670-06145-7(X) , Viking Adult) Penguin Group (USA) Inc.

Chardiet, Jon. Parker Penguin & the Winter Games. Micucci, Charles, illus. 1999. (Read with Me Ser.). 32p. (J). (gr. k-2). pap. 3.25 (978-0-590-14925-9(3)) Scholastic, Inc.

Christopher, Matt. Body Check. 2003. (gr. 3-6). lib. bdg. 12.40 (978-0-613-70808-1(3)) Tandem Library Bks.

—Body Check. 2003. (Matt Christopher Sports Ser.). 144p. (J). (gr. 3-7). pap. 4.99 (978-0-316-13405-7(8)) Little Brown & Co.

Cooper, Ann Goode. Zebordee Goes to the Races. Jessee, Diana, illus. 2005. 30p. (J). (978-1-933251-01-1(8)) Parkway Pubs., Inc.

Gaines, Isabel. Tiggers Hate to Lose. 1999. 40p. (J). pap. 3.99 (978-0-7868-4389-3(6)) Disney Pr.

Krosoczka, Jarrett J. Max for President. 2004. (Illus.). 40p. (J). (ps-3). 15.95 (978-0-375-82428-9(6)); lib. bdg. 17.99 (978-0-375-92428-6(0)) Random Hse. Children's Bks. (Knopf Bks. for Young Readers).

Myers, Bill. Sky Surfing Skateboarder, Vol. 21. 2002. (Incredible Worlds of Wally McDoogle Ser.). (Illus.). 128p. (J). (gr. 3-7). pap. 6.99 (978-0-8499-5992-9(6)) Nelson, Thomas Inc.

Neugebauer, Charise. Real Winner. Nascimbeni, Barbara, illus. 2000. 32p. (J). (gr. k-3). 16.50 (978-0-7358-1253-6(5) , Michael Neugebauer Bks.) North-South Bks., Inc.

Park, Barbara. Junie B. Jones Is Captain Field Day. Brunkus, Denise, illus. 2001. (Junie B. Jones Ser.: No. 16). 80p. (J). (gr. k-3). lib. bdg. 11.99 (978-0-375-90291-8(0) , Random Hse. Bks. for Young Readers) Random Hse. Children's Bks.

Purciello, Gerard. The Year They Won: A Tale of the Boston Red Sox. 2005. 112p. (YA). pap. (978-0-9746481-5-6(9)) Brown Barn Bks.

Rayner, Robert. Miss Little's Losers. 2003. (Sports Stories Ser.). 128p. (J). (gr. 4-8). 7.95 (978-1-55028-810-0(5)); (***978-1-55028-811-7(3)**) Lorimer, James & Co., Ltd., Pubs. CAN. *Dist:* Casemate Pubs. & Bk. Distributors, LLC.

Reiss-Weimann, Elayne & Friedman, Rita. Real Friends. Yeagle, Barbara, illus. 2002. (Read-To-Me Ser.). 24p. (J). (978-0-7665-1218-4(5)) Abrams, Harry N., Inc.

Robberecht, Thierry. Sam Is Not a Loser. Goossens, Philippe, illus. 2008. (J). (ps-1). 12.00 (***978-0-618-99210-2(3)** , Clarion Bks.) Houghton Mifflin Co. Trade & Reference Div.

Simon, Charnan. I Like to Win! Handelman, Dorothy, photos by. 1999. (Real Kids Readers Ser.). (Illus.). 32p. (J). (gr. k-1). pap. 4.99 (978-0-7613-2087-6(3) , Millbrook Pr.) Lerner Publishing Group.

—I Like to Win! 1999. (ps-2). lib. bdg. 13.00 (978-0-613-18157-0(3)) Tandem Library Bks.

Sion Charnan. ¡Me gusta ganar! (I Like to Win!) 2007. (Lecturas para niños de verdad - Nivel 1 (Real Kids Readers - Level 1) Ser.). (J). pap. 5.95 (***978-0-8225-7801-7(8)** , Ediciones Lerner) Lerner Publishing Group.

Townson, Hazel. The Adventures of a Lottery Winner. 2004. (Illus.). 96p. (J). pap. 9.99 (978-1-84270-332-8(3)) Andersen GBR. *Dist:* Independent Pubs. Group.

Wong, Janet S. Alex & the Wednesday Chess Club. Schuett, Stacey, illus. 2004. 40p. (J). 16.95 (978-0-689-85890-1(6) , McElderry, Margaret K.) Simon & Schuster Children's Publishing.

WINTER

Abeel, Samantha. My Thirteenth Winter: A Memoir. 2005. 208p. (J). pap. 5.99 (978-0-439-33905-6(7) , Scholastic Paperbacks) Scholastic, Inc.

Adams, Colleen. On My Sled: Learning the SL Sound. (PowerPhonics Ser.). (Illus.). (J). 2002. 24p. (gr. 1). lib. bdg. 18.50 (978-0-8239-5952-5(X)); 2001. 23p. pap. (978-0-8239-8297-4(1)) Rosen Publishing Group, Inc., The. (PowerKids Pr.).

Albert, Toni. A Kid's Winter EcoJournal: With Nature Activities for Exploring the Season. Brandt, Margaret, illus. 1998. 56p. (J). (gr. 3 up). pap. 9.95 (978-0-9640742-6-2(5)) Trickle Creek Bks.

Anderson, Maxine. Explore Winter! 25 Great Ways to Learn about Winter. 2007. (Explore the Seasons Ser.). (Illus.). 96p. (J). (gr. 1-4). pap. 12.95 (***978-0-9785037-5-8(9)**) Nomad Pr.

Barklem, Jill. Cuento de Invierno.Tr. of Winter Story. (SPA.). 32p. (J). 8.95 (978-84-233-2617-4(9)) Ediciones Destino ESP. *Dist:* Planeta Publishing Corp.

Berger, Melvin, et al. What Do Animals Do in Winter? How Animals Survive the Cold. Harrison, Susan J., illus. 1999. (Discovery Readers Ser.). 48p. (J). (ps-3). lib. bdg. 17.55 (978-0-7910-5070-5(X) , Chelsea Hse.) Facts On File, Inc.

Brode, Robyn. December. 2003. (Illus.). 24p. (J). pap. (978-0-8368-3623-3(5)); lib. bdg. 19.33 (978-0-8368-3587-8(5) , Weekly Reader Early Learning Library) Stevens, Gareth Inc.

Bryant, Margaret A., et al. Learning about Winter with Children's Literature. 2006. 160p. (J). pap. 14.95 (978-1-56976-205-9(8) , Zephyr Pr.) Chicago Review Pr., Inc.

Burke, Jennifer S. Cold Days. 2000. (gr. k-3). lib. bdg. 12.95 (978-0-613-62198-4(0)) Tandem Library Bks.

Burton, Jane & Taylor, Kim. The Nature & Science of Winter. 1999. (Exploring the Science of Nature Ser.). (Illus.). 32p. (J). (gr. 3 up). lib. bdg. 24.67 (978-0-8368-2191-8(2)) Stevens, Gareth Inc.

Butterworth Moira. Winter. James, Helen, illus. 2005. 32p. (J). (gr. 2-5). lib. bdg. 27.10 (978-1-58340-617-5(4)) Smart Apple Media.

Casado, Dami & Casado, Alicia. El Invierno. 2005. (ESP., Illus.). 14p. (J). per. 7.99 (978-84-272-6237-9(X)) Molino, Editorial ESP. *Dist:* Santillana USA Publishing Co., Inc.

Castaldo, Nancy F. Winter Day Play! Activities, Crafts, & Games for Indoors & Out. 2001. (Illus.). 176p. (J). pap. 13.95 (978-1-55652-381-6(5)) Chicago Review Pr., Inc.

Claybourne, Anna. Winter. 2001. (Seasons Ser.). (Illus.). 32p. (J). lib. bdg. 24.25 (978-1-930643-08-6(X)) Chrysalis Education.

A Cold Day, Vol. 2. 2005. (Our Seasons & Weather Ser.). (YA). (gr. k-3). (978-0-7368-8620-8(6) , Pebble Bks.) Capstone Pr., Inc.

Conrad, Heather. Lights of Winter: Winter Celebrations Around the World. 2001. (Illus.). 26p. (J). 11.95 (978-0-9712425-1-7(8)) Lightport Bks.

Davis, Rebecca Fjelland. Snowflakes & Ice Skates: A Winter Counting Book. 2006. (A+ Books). (Illus.). 32p. (J). (978-0-7368-5379-8(0)) Capstone Pr., Inc.

DeGezelle, Terri. Winter. 2002. (Bridgestone Science Library). (Illus.). 24p. (J). (gr. 1-2). lib. bdg. 18.60 (978-0-7368-1412-6(4) , Bridgestone Bks.) Capstone Pr., Inc.

Finnegan, Mary Pat. Winter: Signs of the Season Around North America. Thomas, Eric, illus. 2004. (Through the Seasons Ser.). 24p. (C). (gr. k-1). 22.60 (978-1-4048-0001-4(8)) Picture Window Bks.

George, Jean Craighead. Winter Moon. 2001. (gr. 3-6). lib. bdg. 14.10 (978-0-613-50525-3(5)) Tandem Library Bks.

Green, Rod. Bing & Bong's Winter Adventures. 2003. (Tiny Planets Ser.). (Illus.). 24p. (J). pap. 7.99 (978-1-84222-877-7(3)) Carlton Bks., Ltd. GBR. *Dist:* Independent Pubs. Group.

Group/McGraw-Hill, Wright. Winter Weather: Collection 2. (Storyteller Interactive Writing Cards Ser.). (gr. k-3). (978-0-322-09341-6(4)) Wright Group, The.

Harcourt School Publishers Staff. Groundhog Day. 3rd ed. 2002. (Horizons Ser.). (Illus.). (J). pap. 3.70 (978-0-15-333114-5(3)) Harcourt Schl. Pubs.

—Winter Celebrations. 3rd ed. 2002. (Horizons Ser.). (Illus.). (J). pap. 3.70 (978-0-15-333168-8(2)) Harcourt Schl. Pubs.

Herriges, Ann. Winter. 2006. (Blastoff! Readers Ser.). (Illus.). 24p. (J). lib. bdg. 16.95 (978-1-60014-030-3(0)) Bellwether Media.

Kalz, Jill. Winter. 2005. (Illus.). 24p. (gr. k-3). 15.95 (978-1-58341-365-4(0) , Creative Education) Creative Co., The.

Latta, Sara L. What Happens in Winter? 2006. (I Like the Seasons! Ser.). (Illus.). 24p. (J). lib. bdg. 21.26 (978-0-7660-2418-2(0) , Enslow Elementary) Enslow Pubs., Inc.

Lawlor, Elizabeth P., et al. Discover Nature in Winter. 1998. (Discover Nature Ser.). (Illus.). 198p. pap. 14.95 (978-0-8117-2719-8(X)) Stackpole Bks.

Macken, JoAnn Early. Winter. 2006. (Illus.). 16p. (J). pap. 4.50 (978-0-8368-6361-1(5)); lib. bdg. 16.67 (978-0-8368-6356-7(9)) Stevens, Gareth Inc.

—Winter: Invierno. 2006. (ENG & SPA.). 16p. (J). pap. (978-0-8368-6540-0(5)); lib. bdg. 16.67 (978-0-8368-6535-6(9)) Stevens, Gareth Inc.

Marsh, Carole. Winter, the Wow! Season. 2002. (Carole Marsh Bks.). (Illus.). 32p. (J). (gr. 1-8). pap. 7.95 (978-0-635-01367-5(3) , 13673); (gr. 3-9). lib. bdg. 21.95 (978-0-635-01368-2(1) , 13681, Marsh, Carole Bks.) Gallopade International.

Maurer, Tracy. Winter. 2006. (to Z Ser.). (Illus.). 32p. (gr. k-2). 20.95 (978-1-58952-199-5(4)) Rourke Publishing, LLC.

McCarroll, Tolbert. A Winter Walk: Glimpses of the Sacred in Ordinary Life. 2006. (Illus.). 160p. 14.95 (978-0-8245-2416-6(0)) Crossroad Publishing Co.

Meyer, Mary L. Winter. 2002. (Illus.). 23p. (J). 21.35 (978-1-58340-142-2(3)) Smart Apple Media.

Moskal, Greg. I Like Winter: Learning the ER Sound. (PowerPhonics Ser.). (Illus.). (J). 2002. 24p. (gr. 1). lib. bdg. 18.50 (978-0-8239-5939-6(2)); 2001. 23p. pap. 26.40 (978-0-8239-8284-4(X)) Rosen Publishing Group, Inc., The. (PowerKids Pr.).

Muller, Gerda, illus. Winter. 2004. 10p. (J). 10.00 (978-0-86315-192-7(2)) Floris Bks. GBR. *Dist:* SteinerBooks, Inc.

O'Hare, Jeffrey A., ed. The Big Book of Winter Fun: Puzzles, Mazes, Jokes, & Games to Last the Entire Season. 2002. (Illus.). 64p. (YA). (gr. 2-5). pap. 7.95 (978-1-59078-001-5(9)) Boyds Mills Pr.

Parker, Victoria. Days In... Winter. 2004. (Raintree Sprouts Ser.). (Illus.). 24p. (J). pap. 5.50 (978-1-4109-0744-8(9)) Raintree.

—Winter. 2004. (Raintree Sprouts Ser.). (Illus.). 24p. (J). lib. bdg. 18.56 (978-1-4109-0739-4(2)) Raintree.

Pascoe, Elaine. Animals Prepare for Winter. Kuhn, Dwight, photos by. 2002. (Springboards into Science Ser.). (Illus.). 24p. (J). (gr. 1 up). lib. bdg. 20.67 (978-0-8368-3006-4(7)) Stevens, Gareth Inc.

Pfeffer, Wendy. The Shortest Day: Celebrating the Winter Solstice. Reisch, Jesse, illus. 2003. 40p. (J). (gr. 1-4). 16.99 (978-0-525-46968-1(0) , Dutton Juvenile) Penguin Group (USA) Inc.

Posner, Renee & Quinton, Sasha. Suzy Season Loves Winter. D'Argo, Laura, illus. 2003. (Be Mine Bears Ser.). (J). bds. 4.99 (978-1-58209-353-6(9)) Books Are Fun, Ltd.

Powell, Consie. The First Day of Winter. Powell, Consie, illus. 2005. (Illus.). 32p. (J). (gr. k-4). lib. bdg. 15.95 (978-0-8075-2450-3(6)) Whitman, Albert & Co.

Preparing for Winter, Vol. 3. 2005. (Our Seasons & Weather Ser.). (YA). (gr. k-3). 118.80 (978-0-7368-4200-6(4) , Pebble Bks.) Capstone Pr., Inc.

Preparing for Winter Set. (gr. k-2). 114.95 (978-0-7368-9045-8(9)) Red Brick Learning.

Richmond, Marianne R. Holiday Wishes. 2005. (Illus.). 40p. (YA). 7.95 (978-0-9770000-5-0(2)) Marianne Richmond Studios, Inc.

Roca, Nuria. El Invierno. 2004. (Cuatro Estaciones Ser.).Tr. of Winter. (SPA., Illus.). 36p. (J). pap. 6.95 (978-0-7641-2732-8(2)) Barron's Educational Series, Inc.

—Winter. 2004. (Four Seasons Ser.). (Illus.). 36p. (J). pap. 6.95 (978-0-7641-2731-1(4)) Barron's Educational Series, Inc.

Sabuda, Robert. Winter's Tale: An Original Pop-Up Journey. 2005. (Illus.). 12p. (J). 26.95 (978-0-689-85363-0(7) , Little Simon) Simon & Schuster Children's Publishing.

Saunders, Gail. Winter. 1998. (Seasons Ser.). (Illus.). 24p. (J). (ps-2). pap. 13.25 (978-0-516-21329-3(6) , Children's Pr.) Scholastic Library Publishing.

Saunders-Smith, Gail. Preparing for Winter, 3 bks. 1998. (J). pap. 53.00 (978-0-516-29780-4(5) , Children's Pr.) Scholastic Library Publishing.

Schaefer, Lola M. A Cold Day. Saunders-Smith, Gail, ed. 1999. (What Kind of Day is It? Ser.). (Illus.). 24p. (J). (gr. k-1). lib. bdg. 15.93 (978-0-7368-0402-8(1) , Pebble Bks.) Capstone Pr., Inc.

—A Cold Day. 1999. pap. 13.25 (978-0-516-21927-1(8) , Children's Pr.) Scholastic Library Publishing.

Schnur, Steven. Winter: An Alphabet Acrostic. Evans, Leslie, illus. 2002. 32p. (J). (ps-k). tchr. ed. 15.00 (978-0-618-02374-5(7) , Clarion Bks.) Houghton Mifflin Co. Trade & Reference Div.

Schuette, Sarah L. Let's Look at Winter. 2007. (Pebble Plus Ser.). (Illus.). 24p. (J). (978-0-7368-6706-1(6) , 1264874) Capstone Pr., Inc.

Stille, Darlene R. Winter. 2001. (Simply Science Ser.). (Illus.). 32p. (J). (gr. 3 up). lib. bdg. 19.93 (978-0-7565-0096-2(6)) Compass Point Bks.

Thayer, Tanya. Winter. (First Step Nonfiction Ser.). (Illus.). 24p. (gr. k-2). 2005. lib. bdg. 17.27 (978-0-8225-1985-0(2)); 2003. (J). pap. 4.25 (978-0-8225-1989-8(5)) Lerner Publishing Group.

—Winter. 2001. (gr. k-3). lib. bdg. 11.80 (978-0-613-76621-0(0)) Tandem Library Bks.

What Do Animals Do in Winter? (Discovery Readers Ser.). 48p. (J). pap. 3.95 (978-0-8249-5314-0(2) , Ideals Children's Bks.) Ideals Pubns.

Whitehouse, Patricia. Invierno. 2003. (Las Estaciones (Seasons) Ser.). (SPA.). 24p. (J). (ps-1). lib. bdg. 17.08 (978-1-4034-0336-0(8)) Heinemann Library.

—Winter. 2003. (Seasons Ser.). (Illus.). 24p. (J). (ps-1). lib. bdg. 17.08 (978-1-58810-893-7(7)); pap. 5.25 (978-1-4034-0544-9(1)) Heinemann Library.

Winter, Vol. 4. 2005. (Our Seasons & Weather Ser.). (YA). (gr. k-3). (978-1-56065-847-4(9) , Pebble Bks.) Capstone Pr., Inc.

Winter in the Woods. 2003. (YA). (978-0-8374-0007-5(4)); lib. bdg. (978-0-8374-0006-8(6)) Weekly Reader Corp.

Winter Seasons. 2006. (Illus.). 24p. (J). (gr. k-2). 18.50 (***978-0-531-17882-9(X)***) Scholastic Library Publishing.

Winter Sunshine: Level P, 6 vols. (Wonder Worldtm Ser.). 48p. 39.95 (978-0-7802-7080-0(0)) Wright Group, The.

Winter Survival: Individual Title Six-Packs. (Action Packs Ser.). 104p. (gr. 3-5). 44.00 (978-0-7635-8400-9(2)) Rigby Education.

World Book, Inc. Staff, contrib. by. Winter Celebrations. 2003. (World Book's Celebrations & Rituals Around the World Ser.). (Illus.). 46p. (J). (978-0-7166-5013-3(4)) World Bk., Inc.

WINTER—FICTION

Abbott, Jacob. Jonas on a Farm in Winter (Illustrated E. 2006. pap. (***978-1-4065-0358-6(4)***) Dodo Pr.

Alcott, Louisa May. Jack & Jill. Date not set. 352p. (YA). 25.95 (978-0-8488-2671-0(X)) Amereon LTD.

Allison, Samuel Buel. An American Robinson Crusoe. 2006. pap. (***978-1-4065-0803-1(9)***) Dodo Pr.

Andersen, Hans Christian. The Little Match Girl. Bell, Anthea, tr. from DAN. Pacovska, Kveta, illus. 2005. 40p. (J). (ps-3). 18.99 (978-0-698-40027-6(5) , Minedition) Penguin Group (USA) Inc.

Atkinson, Elizabeth. Lisa's Totally Unforgettable Winter. 2006. (ENG.). 56p. per. 12.95 (***978-1-4241-6249-9(1)***) PublishAmerica, Inc.

Bachand, Stephen. Where's Floater? Bachand, Stephen, illus. 2000. (Booktime Buddies Ser.). (Illus.). (J). (ps-2). pap. 5.00 (978-1-928972-05-1(5)) Critter Pubns.

Barrett George, Lindsay. In the Snow, Who's Been Here? 1999. (J). (978-0-606-17395-7(1)) Tandem Library Bks.

Bengs, Sandra. "Noel Winter" Flanagan, Patricia A., ed. 2001. (Illus.). 14p. (YA). 2.50 (978-1-930695-72-6(1)) Sparrowgrass Chapbooks.

Blackaby, Susan. Winter Fun for Kat. Collier-Morales, Roberta, illus. 2005. (Read-It! Readers Ser.). 32p. (J). (gr. k-3). 18.60 (978-1-4048-1007-5(2)) Picture Window Bks.

Bratun, Katy. Gingerbread Mouse. Bratun, Katy, illus. 2007. 32p. (J). pap. 6.99 (***978-0-06-009082-1(0)*** , Harper Trophy) HarperCollins Pubs.

Brennan, Linda Crotta. Flannel Kisses. Takabayashi, Mari, illus. 2006. 32p. (J). (gr. k-3). 6.95 (978-0-618-73752-9(9)) Houghton Mifflin Co. Trade & Reference Div.

Brett, Jan. Jan Brett's Christmas Treasury. Brett, Jan, illus. 2001. (Illus.). 254p. (J). (ps-3). 39.95 (978-0-399-23741-6(0) , Putnam Juvenile) Penguin Group (USA) Inc.

Brown. Little Bear Friendship Box: Love Song of Winter. 2002. (J). bds. (978-0-7868-0899-1(3)) Hyperion Bks. for Children.

Brown, Richard. Snow in the Kitchen. 2005. (Cambridge Storybooks Ser.). 32p. pap. 7.00 (978-0-521-67480-5(8)) Cambridge Univ. Pr.

Bunting, Eve. December. 2002. (Illus.). (J). 13.19 (978-0-7587-4119-6(7)) Book Wholesalers, Inc.

—December. Diaz, David, illus. 2000. 36p. (J). (ps-3). pap. 7.00 (978-0-15-202422-2(0) , Voyager Bks./Libros Viajeros) Harcourt Children's Bks.

—December. 2000. (gr. 3-6). lib. bdg. 15.30 (978-0-613-29923-7(X)) Tandem Library Bks.

Burt, Steven E. Snowstorm Christmas. Lindsey, Terry, illus. 2002. (J). pap. 9.95 (978-0-9649283-5-0(3)) Burt Creations.

Butler, M. Christina. One Winter's Day. Macnaughton, Tina, illus. 2006. 28p. (J). 16.00 (978-1-56148-532-1(2)) Good Bks.

Caple, Kathy. Hillary to the Rescue. Caple, Kathy, illus. 2003. (Picture Bks.). (Illus.). 32p. (J). (ps-3). 15.95 (978-1-57505-420-9(5) , Carolrhoda Bks.) Lerner Publishing Group.

Carmody, Isobelle. Winter Door. (Gateway Trilogy Ser.). 336p. (J). (gr. 3-5). 2007. 5.99 (978-0-375-83019-8(7) , Yearling); 2006. 16.95 (978-0-375-83018-1(9) , Random Hse. Bks. for Young Readers); 2006. lib. bdg. 18.99 (978-0-375-93018-8(3) , Random Hse. Bks. for Young Readers) Random Hse. Children's Bks.

Carr, Annie Roe. Nan Sherwoods Winter Holidays or Rescuing. 2007. pap. (***978-1-4065-1296-0(6)***) Dodo Pr.

Carr, Roe Annie. Nan Sherwood's Winter Holidays or Rescui. 2006. 78.99 (***978-1-4219-9942-5(0)***); pap. 72.99 (***978-1-4219-9946-3(3)***) IndyPublish.com.

Chronicle Books LLC Staff. Winter Dreams. 2008. (J). 12.95 (978-0-8118-4672-1(5)) Chronicle Bks. LLC.

Clark, Catherine. Icing on the Lake. 2005. 368p. (YA). (gr. 8 up). pap. 5.99 (978-0-06-081534-9(5)) HarperCollins Pubs.

Contijoch, Josefa. Mariquilla en la Nieve. Filella, Lluis, illus. 2003. (Caballo Alado Ser.). (SPA & ENG.). 24p. 6.95 (978-84-7864-647-0(7)) Combel Editorial, S.A. ESP. *Dist:* Independent Pubs. Group.

Cooper, Mimi. Me Versus Snow. 2006. 17p. 9.99 (978-1-4116-8257-3(2)) Lulu.com.

Crandall, Janet. Winter on the Farm. 2006. (J). per. 9.95 (978-1-59872-612-1(9)) Instantpublisher.com.

Crane Johnson, Amy. Lewis Cardinal's First Winter/el primer invierno de Luis, el Cardenal: A Solomon Raven Story/un cuento del cuervo Salomon, 4 vols. de la Vega, Eida, tr. Mommaerts, Robb, illus. rev. ed. 2002. (Solomon Raven Ser. : 2). Tr. of primer invierno de Luis, el cardenal: un cuento del cuervo Salomon. (SPA & ENG.). 32p. (J). 16.95 (978-0-9724973-5-0(8) , 626999) Raven Tree Pr.

Cumming, Peter. Out on the Ice in the Middle of the Bay. Priestley, Alice, illus. 10th rev. anniv. ed. 2004. 32p. (J). (gr. k-3). lib. bdg. 19.95 (978-1-55037-871-9(6)); pap. 7.95 (978-1-55037-870-2(8)) Annick Pr., Ltd. CAN. *Dist:* Firefly Bks., Ltd.

Debowski, Sharon. The Snowman, the Owl, & the Groundhog. 2007. (J). lib. bdg. 15.95 (***978-1-60227-468-6(1)***); (Illus.). 32p. 14.95 (***978-1-60227-470-9(3)***) Above the Clouds Publishing.

DePrisco, Dorothea. Mini Snowbears Winter Day. 2006. 10p. (J). 4.95 (978-1-58117-506-6(X) , Intervisual/Piggy Toes) Dalmatian Pr.

Dixon, Ann. Winter Is. Dwyer, Mindy, illus. 2005. 32p. (ps-1). 15.95 (978-0-88240-543-8(8)); pap. 8.95 (978-0-88240-544-5(6)) Graphic Arts Ctr. Publishing Co.

—Winter Is. 2002. (ps-2). lib. bdg. 17.60 (978-0-613-61929-5(3)) Tandem Library Bks.

Dower, Laura. Give Me a Break. 18th rev. ed. 2005. (From the Files of Madison Finn Ser.: Bk. 18). 176p. (gr. 3-7). pap. 4.99 (978-0-7868-0988-2(4) , Volo) Hyperion Bks. for Children.

Doyle, Brian. Spud in Winter. 2006. 140p. (J). pap. 5.95 (978-0-88899-755-5(8)) Groundwood Bks. CAN. *Dist:* Perseus Distribution.

Dunn, Hunter S. A Winter's Dream. Ellis, Joey, illus. 2004. 65p. (J). 19.95 (978-0-9761732-0-5(4)) Dunn, Hunter.

Edwards, Frank B. Snug As a Big Red Bug. Bianchi, John, illus. 1999. (New Reader Ser.). 24p. (J). (ps-1). lib. bdg. 14.95 (978-1-894323-01-7(7)) Pokeweed Pr. CAN. *Dist:* Fitzhenry & Whiteside, Ltd.

—Snug As a Big Red Bug. 1999. (gr. k-3). lib. bdg. 12.95 (978-0-613-37045-5(7)) Tandem Library Bks.

Edwards, Frank B. & Bianchi, John. Snug As a Big Red Bug. 1999. (New Reader Ser.). (Illus.). 24p. (J). (ps-1). pap. 4.95 (978-1-894323-00-0(9)) Pokeweed Pr. CAN. *Dist:* Fitzhenry & Whiteside, Ltd.

Edwards, Richard. Where Are You Hiding Copycub? Winter, Susan, illus. 2005. 32p. (J). pap. 7.95 (978-1-84507-362-6(2)) Lincoln, Frances Ltd. GBR. *Dist:* Perseus Distribution.

Egner, Susan. Has Anyone Seen Woodfin? Dewey, A. J., illus. 2002. 32p. (J). lib. bdg. 16.95 (978-0-9711711-1-4(4)) Egner, Inc.

Emerson, Carl. Old Oak & the Cold Winter Day. Doerrfeld, Cori, illus. 2007. (J). (978-1-4048-2627-4(0)) Picture Window Bks.

Evans, Clay Bonnyman. The Winter Witch. Bender, Robert, illus. 2005. 32p. (J). (ps-ps). 16.95 (978-0-8234-1615-8(1)) Holiday Hse., Inc.

Fakkema, Julie Ann. Water Is A Wonderful Thing. 2007. (J). per. 10.99 (***978-1-59886-927-9(2)***) Tate Publishing & Enterprises, L.L.C.

Fleming, Denise. The First Day of Winter. rev. ed. 2005. (Illus.). 32p. (J). (ps-1). 16.95 (978-0-8050-7384-3(1) , Holt, Henry & Co. Bks. For Young Readers) Holt, Henry & Co.

Frampton, Caytie. Bernard's Winter Nap. 2004. 21p. pap. 14.95 (978-1-4137-3083-8(3)) PublishAmerica, Inc.

Fraser, C. Rhanna. (Illus.). 535p. (J). (gr. k-6). pap. 11.95 (978-0-340-76565-4(8) , Hodder & Stoughton) Hodder General Publishing Division GBR. *Dist:* Trafalgar Square Publishing.

Frazer, Rebecca. Winter Wonderland. Wolcott, Karen, illus. 2007. (Pictureback(R) Ser.). 24p. (J). (ps-2). 3.99 (***978-0-375-84222-1(5)*** , Golden Bks.) Random Hse. Children's Bks.

Freedman, Claire & Cabban, Vanessa. Gooseberry Goose. 2003. (Illus.). 32p. (J). (ps-2). tchr. ed. 15.95 (978-1-58925-030-7(3) , tiger tales) ME Media LLC.

Gammell, Stephen. Is That You, Winter? 2000. 13.80 (978-0-606-20328-9(1)); (J). (978-0-606-20165-0(3)) Tandem Library Bks.

Garis, Howard Roger. Buddy & His Winter Fun or a Boy in a Snow Camp. 2005. reprint ed. pap. 24.95 (978-1-4179-0679-6(0)) Kessinger Publishing, LLC.

Glaser, Linda. It's Winter! Swan, Susan, illus. 2002. (Celebrate the Seasons! Ser.). 32p. (J). (gr. 1-3). pap. 7.95 (978-0-7613-1680-0(9) , First Avenue Editions) Lerner Publishing Group.

—It's Winter! Swan, Susan, illus. 2002. (J). (ps-ps). lib. bdg. 16.40 (978-0-613-50626-7(X)) Tandem Library Bks.

Golden Books Staff & Scott, Evelyn. The Fourteen Bears in Summer & Winter. 2005. (Illus.). 64p. (J). (gr. k-k). lib. bdg. 16.99 (978-0-375-93279-3(8) , Golden Bks.) Random Hse. Children's Bks.

Grosset and Dunlap Staff & Lamb, Stacey. Winter Wonderland. 2000. (Sticker Stories Ser.). (Illus.). 1p. (J). (ps-3). mass mkt. 4.99 (978-0-448-42408-8(8) , Grosset & Dunlap) Penguin Group (USA) Inc.

Gutman, Anne. Penelope in the Winter. Hallensleben, Georg, illus. 2005. 12p. (J). (ps-k). pap. 9.99 (978-0-439-67360-0(7) , Cartwheel Bks.) Scholastic, Inc.

Hallwood, Cheri L. Winter's First Snowflake. Rose, Patricia M., illus. l.t. ed. 2006. 32p. (J). per. 15.99 (978-0-9774422-0-1(9)) Forever Young Pubs.

Harcourt School Publishers Staff. G. Hopper's Summer Fun Advanced Level. 3rd ed. 2002. (Trophies Reading Program Ser.). (Illus.). pap. 5.10 (978-0-15-323109-4(2)) Harcourt Schl. Pubs.

—Winter in the Prairie: Take-Home Book. 2001. (Collections Ser.). (Illus.). (J). pap. 1.90 (978-0-15-319487-0(1)) Harcourt Schl. Pubs.

Harper, Piers. Snow Bear. Black, Sonia, ed. Harper, Piers, illus. 2003. (Illus.). 32p. (J). lthr. 15.95 (978-0-439-54426-9(2) , Cartwheel Bks.) Scholastic, Inc.

Hawley, C. Mabel. Four Little Blossoms & Their Winter Fu. 2006. 77.99 (***978-1-4280-4760-0(3)***); pap. 70.99 (***978-1-4280-4769-3(7)***) IndyPublish.com.

Hayes, Karel. The Winter Visitors. 2007. 32p. (ps-3). 16.95 (***978-0-89272-750-6(0)***) Down East Bks.

Hedrick, Helen Groves. Baas on the Bus. 2000. (J). 12.00 (978-0-8059-5003-8(6)) Dorrance Publishing Co., Inc.

Here Comes Winter! 2003. (J). per. (978-1-57657-967-1(0)) Paradise Pr., Inc.

Hest, Amy. You Can Do It, Sam. Jeram, Anita, illus. 2007. (Sam Bks.). 32p. (J). (ps). pap. 4.99 (***978-0-7636-3688-3(6)***) Candlewick Pr.

Hillert, Margaret. Merry Christmas, Dear Dragon. Kock, Carl, illus. rev. exp. ed. 2007. (Beginning to Read Ser.). 32p. (J). lib. bdg. 19.93 (978-1-59953-042-0(2)) Norwood Hse. Pr.

Hope, Laura Lee. Six Little Bunkers at Mammy Junes. 2006. 41.99 (***978-1-4280-3233-0(9)***); pap. 35.99 (***978-1-4280-3212-5(6)***) IndyPublish.com.

Hubbard, Coleen. Westie Winter: A Story of a West Highland Terrier. 1999. (Dog Tales Ser.: 2). (Illus.). 163p. (J). pap. 4.50 (978-0-590-18976-7(X)) Scholastic, Inc.

Johnson, Andi. Hailey Snowstorm. 2004. (Illus.). 16p. 9.00 (978-1-84161-113-6(1)) Ravette Publishing, Ltd. GBR. *Dist:* Parkwest Pubns., Inc.

Johnson, Tiffany Kira. Why Snow Falls in Winter. 2006. pap. 8.95 (978-0-533-15149-3(X)) Vantage Pr., Inc.

Jones, Christianne C. Busy Bear. 2007. (Illus.). 24p. (J). (***978-1-4048-2426-3(X)***) Picture Window Bks.

—Busy Bear. Jensen, Brian, illus. 2006. 24p. (J). lib. bdg. (***978-1-4048-2396-9(4)***) Picture Window Bks.

Jordan, Apple. Winter Wishes. Marrucchi, Elisa, illus. 2006. (Step into Reading Ser.). 32p. (J). (ps-2). pap. 3.99 (978-0-7364-2409-7(1)); lib. bdg. 11.99 (978-0-7364-8049-9(8)) Random Hse. Children's Bks. (RH/Disney).

Kelley, Marty, illus. Winter Woes. 2003. 32p. (J). 12.95 (978-1-55933-306-1(5)) Zino Pr. Children's Bks.

Kirk, Daniel. Snow Dude. 2004. (Illus.). 32p. (ps-3). 16.99 (978-0-7868-1942-3(1)) Hyperion Bks. for Children.

Krensky, Stephen. Lionel in the Winter. unabr. ed. 1999. (Puffin Ser.). (J). pap., stu. ed. 21.75 incl. audio (978-0-7887-3956-9(5) , 41060X4) Recorded Bks., LLC.

Kroll, Linda. Winter, Awake! Lieberherr, Ruth, illus. rev. ed. 2003. 32p. (J). pap. 11.95 (978-0-88010-528-6(3)) SteinerBooks, Inc.

Larsen, Sandy. Ice Festival. Taylor, Wanda, illus. 1999. (Jackpine Point Adventure Ser.: Vol. 2). 126p. (J). (gr. 4-6). pap. 5.99 (978-0-9666677-1-4(9)) Merritt Park Pr.

Lasky, Kathryn. River of Wind. 2007. (Guardians of Ga'Hoole Ser.: No. 13). 224p. (J). pap. 5.99 (***978-0-439-88807-3(7)***) Scholastic, Inc.

El Libro de Homero en el Invierno. 2001. (SPA.). per. (978-1-883772-34-5(6)) Flying Rhinoceros, Inc.

El Libro de Homero en el Invierno Paquete de Aventuras. 2001. (SPA.). (978-1-883772-57-4(5)) Flying Rhinoceros, Inc.

Little, Jean. Emma's Magic Winter. Plecas, Jennifer, illus. 2000. (I Can Read Bks.). 64p. (J). (ps-3). pap. 3.99 (978-0-06-443706-6(X) , Harper Trophy) HarperCollins Pubs.

Lloyd, Jennifer. One Winter Night. Ray, Lynn, illus. 2006. 32p. 16.95 (978-1-894965-48-4(5)) Simply Read Bks. CAN. *Dist:* Perseus Distribution.

Lujan, Jorge. Winter Afternoon: Tarde de Invierno. Sadat, Mandana, illus. 2006. (ENG & SPA.). 32p. (J). 16.95 (978-0-88899-718-0(3)) Groundwood Bks. CAN. *Dist:* Perseus Distribution.

MacLean, Kerry Lee, creator. Pigs Ski over Colorado: The Top Ten Reasons Winter Is the Piggies Favorite Season. 2005. (J). per. 15.95 (978-0-9652998-7-9(2)) On the Spot! Bks.

Manutoli, Sophie. Uksuq Wallu-qaa Kiak? Andrew, John et al, illus. 1998. Tr. of Winter or Summer?. (ESK.). 20p. (J). (gr. k-3). pap. 8.00 (978-1-58084-042-2(6)) Lower Kuskokwim Schl. District.

Matthews, Caitlin & Negrin, Fabian. Fireside Stories: Tales for a Winter's Eve. Cann, Helen, illus. 2007. 96p. (J). (ps-5). 19.99 (***978-1-84686-065-2(2)***) Barefoot Bks., Inc.

McAllister, Angela. Brave Bitsy & the Bear. Beeke, Tiphanie, illus. 2006. 32p. (J). (ps-k). 16.00 (978-0-618-63994-6(2) , Clarion Bks.) Houghton Mifflin Co. Trade & Reference Div.

Millard, Glenda. Kaito's Cloth. Chapman, Gaye, illus. 2008. 32p. (J). (gr. k). 15.99 (***978-0-399-24797-2(1)*** , Philomel) Penguin Group (USA) Inc.

Milligan, Bryce. Comanche Captive. 2005. (Illus.). 168p. (YA). (gr. 7). pap. (978-1-57168-849-1(8)) Eakin Pr.

Miranda, Hialeah. One Fun Winter's Day. 2004. 49p. pap. 12.95 (978-1-4137-4816-1(3)) PublishAmerica, Inc.

Moulton, Mark Kimballl. The Annual Snowman's Ball. Hillaard, Karen, illus. 2007. 32p. (J). (ps-3). 14.99 (***978-0-8249-5564-9(1)*** , Ideals Children's Bks.) Ideals Pubns.

Muench-Williams, Heather. A Cold Winter Day. Crowell, Knox, illus. l.t. ed. 2006. (Hrl Board Book Ser.). (J). (ps-k). pap. 10.95 (978-1-57332-326-0(8)) HighReach Learning, Inc.

Myers, Anna. Hoggee. 2007. 192p. (J). pap. 6.95 (***978-0-8027-9683-7(4)***) Walker & Co.

Natti, Susanna, illus. Lionel in the Winter. 2002. (Lionel Ser.). (J). 11.49 (978-0-7587-1393-3(2)) Book Wholesalers, Inc.

Nelson, Ray, et al. Sam's Winter Book. Siegel, Joseph & Habecker, Mary Beth, eds. Peeples, Aaron et al, illus. 2000. (Farmer Bob Weather Ser.: No. 1). 32p. (J). (gr. 1-3). pap. 12.00 (978-1-883772-22-2(2)) Flying Rhinoceros, Inc.

Obed, Ellen B. A Letter from the Snow. Hammond, Gordon, illus. 1999. 36p. (J). (gr. 1-4). pap. 10.00 (978-0-9618592-8-2(8)) Maine Writers & Pubs. Alliance.

Off to School: Individual Title Six-Packs. (Story Steps Ser.). (gr. k-2). 29.00 (978-0-7635-9577-7(2)) Rigby Education.

On a Cold, Cold Day: 6 Small Books. (gr. k-3). 24.00 (978-0-7635-6231-1(9)) Rigby Education.

Osborne, M. D. The Rescue of Mr. Goldsmith. l.t. ed. 2005. (Illus.). 40p. (J). 12.95 (978-0-9762852-1-2(5)) Wooden Shoe Pr.

Page, Nick & Claire. The Winter Prince. 2006. (Read with Me (Make Believe Ideas) Ser.). (Illus.). 31p. (J). (gr. k-2). 3.95 (978-1-84610-172-4(7)) Make Believe Ideas GBR. *Dist:* Ingram Pub. Services.

Paulsen, Gary. Brian's Winter. 2004. (GLB Reprints Ser.). 144p. (YA). (gr. 5). lib. bdg. 17.99 (978-0-385-90222-9(0) , Delacorte Bks. for Young Readers) Random Hse. Children's Bks.

Peters, Lisa Westberg. Cold Little Duck, Duck, Duck. Williams, Sam, illus. 2000. 32p. (J). (ps-3). 16.99 (978-0-688-16178-1(2)) HarperCollins Pubs.

Pickering, Jimmy. It's Winter. 2003. (Illus.). 32p. (J). (ps-3). 16.95 (978-1-931290-16-6(4)) Tallfellow Pr.

Pinkwater, Daniel M. Big Bob & the Winter Holiday Potato. Pinkwater, Jill, illus. 2001. (Hello Reader! Ser.). 32p. (J). (gr. 1-3). pap. 3.99 (978-0-439-04243-7(7) , Cartwheel Bks.) Scholastic, Inc.

Pitcher, Caroline. The Winter Dragon. Williams, Sophy, illus. 2005. 36p. (J). (ps-7). pap. 7.95 (978-1-84507-445-6(9)) Lincoln, Frances Ltd. GBR. *Dist:* Perseus Distribution.

Pratchett, Terry. Wintersmith. (J). 2007. 464p. pap. 7.99 (***978-0-06-089033-9(9)***); 2006. 336p. (gr. 6-8). 16.99 (978-0-06-089031-5(2)); 2006. 336p. (gr. 6-8). lib. bdg. 17.89 (978-0-06-089032-2(0)) HarperCollins Pubs. (HarperTeen).

Preller, James. The Case of the Great Sled Race. 1999. (Jigsaw Jones Mystery Ser.: No. 8). (Illus.). (J). (gr. 1-4). 10.79 (978-0-606-18527-1(5)) Tandem Library Bks.

Preller, James & Preller, Jimmy. The Great Sled Race. Alley, R. W., illus. 2001. (Jigsaw Jones Mystery Ser.: No. 8). 80p. (J). (gr. 1-4). pap. 3.99 (978-0-439-11427-1(6) , Scholastic Paperbacks) Scholastic, Inc.

Princess Rosa's Winter: Level M, 6 vols. 128p. (gr. 2-3). 49.95 (978-0-7699-0986-8(8)) Shortland Pubns. (U. S. A.) Inc.

Reiss, Kathryn. Blackthorn Winter: A Murder Mystery. 2006. 352p. (YA). 17.00 (978-0-15-205479-3(0)) Harcourt Children's Bks.

Renaud, Philip Francis. The Adventures of Sonny the Snow Snake. Wohlers, Lori, illus. l.t. ed. 2002. 22p. (J). bds. 10.95 (978-0-9711805-0-5(4)) Renaud & Co.

Rey, Margret & Rey, H. A. Curious George in the Snow. 1998. (Curious George Ser.). (Illus.). 24p. (J). (gr. k-3). tchr. ed. 12.00 (978-0-395-91902-6(9)) Houghton Mifflin Co. Trade & Reference Div.

Rius, Maria. Winter. 1998. (Four Seasons Ser.). (Illus.). 32p. (J). (ps-k). pap. 6.95 (978-0-7641-0553-1(1)) Barron's Educational Series, Inc.

Roberts, Laura Peyton. New Beginnings. 1999. (Clearwater Crossing Ser.: No. 7). (J). (978-0-606-16380-4(8)) Tandem Library Bks.

Roche, Hannah. Su's Snowgirl. 1998. (My First Weather Bks.). (Illus.). 24p. (J). (ps-3). (978-1-84089-034-1(7) , Zero to Ten, Limited) Evans Publishing Group.

Root, Phyllis. Grandmother Winter. Krommes, Beth, illus. 32p. (J). (gr. k-3). 1999. tchr. ed. 16.00 (978-0-395-88399-0(7)); 2004. reprint ed. pap. 5.95 (978-0-618-49485-9(5)) Houghton Mifflin Co. Trade & Reference Div.

—Lucia & the Light. GrandPré, Mary, illus. 2006. 40p. (J). (gr. k-3). 16.99 (978-0-7636-2296-1(6)) Candlewick Pr.

Rose, Deborah Lee. The Twelve Days of Winter: A School Counting Book. Armstrong-Ellis, Carey, illus. 2006. 32p. (J). (ps-3). 14.95 (978-0-8109-5472-4(9) , Abrams Bks. for Young Readers) Abrams, Harry N. , Inc.

Rylant, Cynthia. Henry & Mudge in the Sparkle Days. Stevenson, Sucie, illus. 2002. (Henry & Mudge Ser.). (J). 11.91 (978-0-7587-1270-7(7)) Book Wholesalers, Inc.

—Henry & Mudge in the Sparkle Days. Stevenson, Sucie, illus. 1999. (Henry & Mudge Ser.). 28.95 incl. audio compact disk (978-1-59112-583-9(9)); pap. 31.95 incl. audio compact disk (978-1-59112-582-2(0)) Live Oak Media.

—Henry & Mudge in the Sparkle Days. 2006. (Henry & Mudge Ser.). (J). (gr. 1-6). 24.21 (978-1-59961-086-3(8)) Spotlight.

W X Y Z

—Poppleton in Winter. Teague, Mark, illus. 2002. (Poppleton Ser.). (J). 11.91 (978-0-7587-6873-5(7)) Book Wholesalers, Inc.

—Poppleton in Winter. Teague, Mark, illus. 2001. (Poppleton Ser.). 58p. (J). (ps-2). pap. 15.95 (978-0-590-84837-4(2) , Blue Sky Pr., The) Scholastic, Inc.

—Poppleton in Winter. 2001. (Poppleton Ser.). (978-0-606-22154-2(9)) Tandem Library Bks.

—Special Gifts. Halperin, Wendy Anderson, illus. 2000. (Cobble Street Cousins Ser.: No. 4). 64p. (J). pap. 3.99 (978-0-689-81715-1(0) , Aladdin) Simon & Schuster Children's Publishing.

—Special Gifts. 2000. (Cobble Street Cousins Ser.: No. 4). (gr. 3-6). lib. bdg. 11.80 (978-0-613-30140-4(4)) Tandem Library Bks.

—Special Gifts. Halperin, Wendy Anderson, illus. 2000. (Cobble Street Cousins Ser.: No. 4). (J). (978-0-606-20026-4(6)) Tandem Library Bks.

Sabuda, Robert. Winter in White: A Mini Pop-up Treat. Sabuda, Robert, illus. 2007. 18p. (J). 12.99 ***(978-0-689-85365-4(3)*** , Little Simon) Simon & Schuster Children's Publishing.

Sam's Winter Book Adventure Pack. 2001. (978-1-883772-33-8(8)) Flying Rhinoceros, Inc.

Sando, Lois L. Erick's Hungry Winter. Lane, Tammie, illus. 1999. 32p. (J). (ps-4). 18.95 (978-0-9660774-0-7(7)) Coventry Pr., LLC.

Santomero, Angela C. A Blue's Clues Holiday. 2004. (Blue's Clues Ser.). 24p. (J). pap. 3.99 (978-0-689-86797-2(2) , Simon Spotlight/Nickelodeon) Simon & Schuster Children's Publishing.

Sargent, Dave. Sammy's First Winter #10, 10 vols. 2007. (Little Stinker Ser.: 10). (J). lib. bdg. 22.60 ***(978-1-59381-300-0(7))*** Ozark Publishing.

—Sammy's First Winter #10 (PB), 10 vols. 2007. (Little Stinker Ser.: 10). (J). pap. 9.95 ***(978-1-59381-301-7(5))*** Ozark Publishing.

Scott, Evelyn & Golden Books Staff. The Fourteen Bears in Summer & Winter. Parsons, Virginia, illus. 2005. 64p. (J). (gr. k-k). reprint ed. 14.95 (978-0-375-83279-6(3) , Golden Bks.) Random Hse. Children's Bks.

Sher, Abby. Kissing Snowflakes. 2007. 256p. (YA). (gr. 7 up). pap. 8.99 ***(978-0-545-00010-9(6))*** Scholastic, Inc.

Sinclair, Michelle Colman. Winter Babies Wear Layers. Dion, Nathalie, illus. 2007. 20p. (J). bds. 6.95 ***(978-1-58246-209-7(7)*** , Tricycle Pr.) Ten Speed Pr.

Skudera, George. The Adventures of Freddie the Little Fir. 2006. pap. 10.49 ***(978-1-4259-5950-0(4))*** AuthorHouse.

Spinelli, Eileen. Now It Is Winter. DePalma, Mary Newell, illus. 2004. 32p. (J). 16.00 (978-0-8028-5244-1(0)) Eerdmans, William B. Publishing Co.

—Three Pebbles & a Song. Schindler, S. D., illus. 2003. 32p. (J). (gr. k). 16.99 (978-0-8037-2528-7(0) , 53666302, Dial) Penguin Group (USA) Inc.

Stevens, Carla. Anna, Grandpa, & the Big Storm. Tomes, Margot, illus. 1998. (Puffin Chapters for Readers on the Move Ser.). 64p. (J). (gr. 2-5). pap. 5.99 (978-0-14-130083-2(3) , Puffin) Penguin Group (USA) Inc.

Stewart, Paul. A Little Bit of Winter. Riddell, Chris, illus. 32p. (J). (ps-2). 2000. pap. 5.95 (978-0-06-443749-3(3) , Harper Trophy); 1999. 14.95 (978-0-06-028278-3(9)) HarperCollins Pubs.

—A Little Bit of Winter. 2000. (J). (978-0-606-20287-9(0)) Tandem Library Bks.

—Little Bit of Winter. 2000. (978-0-606-20340-1(0)) Tandem Library Bks.

Stringer, Lauren. Winter Is the Warmest Season. 2006. (Illus.). 40p. (J). 16.00 (978-0-15-204967-6(3)) Harcourt Trade Pubs.

Tetro, Marc. New Boots for Hudson. 2006. (Illus.). 32p. 14.95 (978-1-55278-397-9(9)) McArthur & Co. CAN. *Dist:* National Bk. Network.

Tregebov, Rhea & Desputeaux, Helene. Tempete et Chocolat Chaud. (FRE., Illus.). 24p. (J). pap. 6.99 (978-0-590-16018-6(4)) Scholastic, Inc.

Trisler, Alana & Cardiel, Patrice Howe. My Winter Journal. 1999. 72p. (J). (gr. 2-3). pap., wbk. ed. 2.10 (978-1-56762-105-1(8)) Modern Learning Pr.

Van Laan, Nancy. When Winter Comes: A Lullaby. Gaber, Susan, illus. 2000. 40p. (J). (ps-2). 16.95 (978-0-689-81778-6(9) , Atheneum/Anne Schwartz Bks.) Simon & Schuster Children's Publishing.

Van Steenwyk, Elizabeth. Three Dog Winter. 1999. (978-0-606-16440-5(5)) Tandem Library Bks.

van Stockum, Hilda. A Day on Skates: 2007 Commemorative Edition. van Stockum, Hilda, illus. 2007. (Illus.). 44p. (J). 19.95 ***(978-1-932350-18-0(7))*** Bethlehem Bks.

Waddell, Martin. Can't You Sleep, Little Bear? Firth, Barbara, illus. 10th anniv. ed. 2002. 32p. (J). (ps-2). 15.99 (978-0-7636-1929-9(9)) Candlewick Pr.

Waldron, Kathleen Cook. Five Stars for Emily. 2004. (Orca Young Readers Ser.). (Illus.). 144p. (J). (gr. 3-6). pap., tchr. ed. 4.99 (978-1-55143-296-0(X) , 1234541) Orca Bk. Pubs. USA.

Wallace, Carol & Wallace, Bob. Bub, Snow, & the Burly Bear Scare. 2003. (gr. 3-6). lib. bdg. 13.00 (978-0-613-70870-8(9)) Tandem Library Bks.

Wallace, Karen. A Bed for the Winter. 2000. (Readers Ser.). (Illus.). 32p. (J). (ps-3). pap. 3.99 (978-0-7894-5707-3(5)) Dorling Kindersley Publishing, Inc.

—Bed for the Winter. 2000. (gr. k-3). lib. bdg. 11.80 (978-0-613-32318-5(1)) Tandem Library Bks.

Wallace, Karen & Dorling Kindersley Publishing Staff. A Bed for the Winter. 2000. (Readers Ser.). (Illus.). 32p. (J). (ps-3). 12.99 (978-0-7894-5706-6(7)) Dorling Kindersley Publishing, Inc.

Warner, Gertrude Chandler. Boxcar Children Winter Special. 2007. 376p. (J). pap. 7.95 ***(978-0-8075-0886-2(1))*** Whitman, Albert & Co.

Wells, Rosemary. Max & Ruby's Winter Adventure. 2007. (Max & Ruby Ser.). 16p. (J). (ps-k). pap. 5.99 ***(978-0-448-44684-4(7)*** , Grosset & Dunlap) Penguin Group (USA) Inc.

Whybrow, Ian. Harry & the Snow King Book & Plush Set. Reynolds, Adrian, illus. 1999. 32p. (J). (ps-2). pap. 19.95 (978-1-86233-132-7(4)) Sterling Publishing Co., Inc.

Williamson, Greg. How Do I Cure This Cold? Popko, Wendy, illus. 2005. (J). 7.99 (978-0-9666076-4-2(3)) Peerless Publishing, L.L.C.

Winter Beauty. 2005. (J). 8.00 (978-0-9769843-0-6(X)) Simmons, Kristina.

Winter Recess. 2003. (J). (978-1-58453-113-5(4)) Pioneer Valley Educational Pr., Inc.

YKids Staff. Little Women. 2007. (Manga Literary Classics Ser.). 148p. (J). (gr. 4-7). pap. 14.95 ***(978-981-05-4943-5(1))*** Youngjin (Singapore) Pte Ltd. SGP. *Dist:* Independent Pubs. Group.

Yolen, Jane & Stemple, Heidi E. Y. Sleep, Black Bear, Sleep. Dyer, Brooke, illus. 2007. 32p. (J). (ps-1). 15.99 (978-0-06-081560-8(4) , HarperCollins); lib. bdg. 16.89 (978-0-06-081561-5(2)) HarperCollins Pubs.

Young, Wenda. Angels in the Snow. 1999. 298p. (J). (gr. 6-9). pap. 6.95 (978-1-55050-131-5(3)) Coteau Bks. CAN. *Dist:* Fitzhenry & Whiteside, Ltd.

WINTER—POETRY

Florian, Douglas. Winter Eyes. Florian, Douglas, illus. 1999. (Illus.). 48p. (J). (gr. k-3). 15.99 (978-0-688-16458-4(7)) HarperCollins Pubs.

Hines, Anna Grossnickle. Winter Lights: A Season in Poems & Quilts. Hines, Anna Grossnickle, illus. 2005. (Illus.). 32p. (J). 16.99 (978-0-06-000817-8(2)); lib. bdg. 17.89 (978-0-06-000818-5(0)) HarperCollins Pubs.

Lenski, Lois. I Like Winter. Kilgras, Heidi, ed. Lenski, Lois, illus. 2000. (Lois Lenski Bks.). (Illus.). 56p. (J). (gr. k-3). lib. bdg. 11.99 (978-0-375-91068-5(9) , Random Hse. Bks. for Young Readers) Random Hse. Children's Bks.

Rogasky, Barbara. Winter Poems, Vol. 1. Hyman, Trina Schart & Cooper, Martha, illus. 1999. 40p. (J). (gr. 2-6). pap. 5.99 (978-0-590-42873-6(X)) Scholastic, Inc.

Whipple, Laura. A Snowflake Fell: Poems about Winter. Hori, Hatsuki, illus. 2003. 40p. (J). 16.99 (978-1-84148-033-6(9)) Barefoot Bks., Inc.

Yolen, Jane. Snow, Snow: Winter Poems for Children. Stemple, Jason, illus. 2003. 32p. (J). (gr. 4-6). 16.95 (978-1-56397-721-3(4)) Boyds Mills Pr.

WINTER SPORTS

see also Hockey; Skating; Skis and Skiing

Askew, Kim. Surfers of Snow. 1999. 160p. (YA). (gr. 7-12). pap. (978-1-55041-379-3(1)) Fitzhenry & Whiteside, Ltd.

—Surfers of Snow. 1999. (gr. 7-12). lib. bdg. 12.95 (978-0-613-84762-9(8)) Tandem Library Bks.

Bourassa, Barbara. Winter Sports. 2007. (J). lib. bdg. 18.95 ***(978-1-59566-348-1(7))*** QEB Publishing Inc.

Boy Scouts of America Staff. Snow Sports. 1999. (Merit Badge Ser.). (Illus.). 93p. (YA). (gr. 6-12). pap. 2.90 (978-0-8395-3365-8(9)) Boy Scouts of America.

Brimner, Larry Dane. Snowboarding. 1998. (First Bks.). (Illus.). 64p. (J). (gr. 5-7). pap. 6.95 (978-0-531-15890-6(X) , Watts, Franklin) Scholastic Library Publishing.

—Snowboarding. 1998. (Illus.). 63p. (J). (ps-7). lib. bdg. 15.25 (978-0-613-15167-2(4)) Tandem Library Bks.

Budd, E. S. Snowmobiles. 2004. (Machines at Work Ser.). (Illus.). 24p. (J). (ps-3). 21.36 (978-1-59296-165-8(7)) Child's World, Inc.

Dahl, Michael. Downhill Fun: A Counting Book about Winter. Ouren, Todd, illus. 2004. (Know Your Numbers Ser.). 24p. (C). (gr. k-3). 22.60 (978-1-4048-0579-8(6)) Picture Window Bks.

Dorling Kindersley Publishing Staff & Saunders, Catherine. Ultimate Barbie Winter Fun Sticker Book. 2003. (Ultimate Sticker Bks.). (Illus.). 1p. (J). pap. 6.99 (978-0-7894-9880-9(4)) Dorling Kindersley Publishing, Inc.

Fraser, Andy. Snowboarding. 2002. (Radical Sports Ser.). 32p. (J). (gr. 5-7). pap. 7.50 (978-1-4034-0108-3(X) , 91656) Heinemann Library.

Fraser, Andy, contrib. by. Snowboarding. 1999. (Radical Sports Ser.). (Illus.). 32p. (J). (gr. 5-7). lib. bdg. 24.22 (978-1-57572-946-6(6)) Heinemann Library.

George, Charles & George, Linda. Ice Climbing. 1998. (Sports Alive! Ser.). (Illus.). 48p. (J). (gr. 3-4). lib. bdg. 21.26 (978-0-7368-0052-5(2) , Capstone High-Interest Bks.) Capstone Pr., Inc.

Golden Books Staff. Snowed Under: The Bobblesberg Winter Games. Baker, Darrell, illus. 2004. 64p. (J). (ps-2). pap. 3.99 (978-0-375-83007-5(3) , Golden Bks.) Random Hse. Children's Bks.

Griffin, Steven A. Snowshoeing. 1998. (Illus.). 152p. pap. 14.95 (978-0-8117-2928-4(1)) Stackpole Bks.

Hedlund, Stephanie F. Snowboarding. 2003. (X-Treme Sports Ser.). (Illus.). 32p. (J). (gr. k-6). lib. bdg. 22.78 (978-1-57765-929-7(5)) ABDO Publishing Co.

Hubbell, Gary. Catching Air! The Wild World of Snowboarding. Holder, Sherie, ed. 1998. 32p. (J). (gr. 3-6). pap. 3.99 (978-1-886749-47-4(7)) Sports Illustrated For Kids.

Jefferis, David. Snow Sports. 2001. (Young Library - Super Sports). (Illus.). 32p. (J). lib. bdg. 25.69 (978-0-7398-4342-0(7)) Raintree.

Malthouse, Becci, et al. Snowboarding. 1998. (Extreme Sports Ser.). (Illus.). 32p. (J). (gr. 5-9). pap. 6.95 (978-0-7641-0794-8(1)) Barron's Educational Series, Inc.

McClellan, Ray. Snocross. 2008. (Illus.). 24p. (J). lib. bdg. 19.95 ***(978-1-60014-143-0(9))*** Bellwether Media.

McKenna, Anne T. Big-Air Snowboarding. 1999. (Extreme Sports Ser.). (Illus.). 48p. (J). (gr. 3-4). lib. bdg. 21.26 (978-0-7368-0166-9(9) , Capstone High-Interest Bks.) Capstone Pr., Inc.

McNeil, Niki, et al. HOCPP 1143 Winter Sports. 2007. spiral bd. 14.00 ***(978-1-60308-143-6(7))*** In the Hands of a Child.

Rigby Education Staff. Gliders & Sliders. (Sails Literacy Ser.). (Illus.). 16p. (gr. 1-2). 27.00 (978-0-7635-9922-5(0) , 699220C99) Rigby Education.

Salas, Laura Purdie. Snowmobiling. 2002. (Great Outdoors Ser.). (Illus.). 48p. (J). (gr. 3-4). lib. bdg. 21.26 (978-0-7368-1058-6(7) , Capstone High-Interest Bks.) Capstone Pr., Inc.

Sommers, Michael A. Snowmobiling: Have Fun, Be Smart. (Explore the Outdoors Ser.). (Illus.). 64p. 2005. (YA). (gr. 7-12). lib. bdg. 26.50 (978-0-8239-3761-5(5)); 2000. (J). (gr. 4-6). lib. bdg. 26.50 (978-0-8239-3171-2(4) , EOSNOW) Rosen Publishing Group, Inc., The.

Sullivan, Sean. Lines: The Snowboard Photography of Sean Sullivan. 2003. (Illus.). 176p. (YA). pap. 19.95 (978-0-7603-1678-8(3)) MBI Publishing Co. LLC.

Waters, Jennifer. Slip & Slide. 2002. (Spyglass Books). (Illus.). 24p. (J). (gr. 1 up). 18.60 (978-0-7565-0241-6(1)) Compass Point Bks.

Young, Ian. The Iditarod: The Last Great Race. 2002. (High Five Reading Ser.). (Illus.). 48p. (J). (gr. 3-4). lib. bdg. 22.60 (978-0-7368-9545-3(0) , Capstone High-Interest Bks.); pap. (978-0-7368-9523-1(X)) Capstone Pr., Inc.

WINTER SPORTS—FICTION

Blake, Robert J. Akiak: A Tale from the Iditarod. Blake, Robert J., illus. 2004. (Illus.). 32p. (J). (gr. k-3). reprint ed. pap. 6.99 (978-0-14-240185-9(4) , Puffin) Penguin Group (USA) Inc.

Bunting, Eve. Snowboarding on Monster Mountain. 2003. (Illus.). 64p. (J). 15.95 (978-0-8126-2704-6(0)) Cricket Bks.

Christopher, Matt. Snowboard Champ. 2004. (Matt Christopher Sports Classics Ser.). 160p. (J). (gr. 3-7). pap. 4.99 (978-0-316-79643-9(3) , Tingley, Megan Bks.) Little, Brown Bks. for Young Readers.

Costello, Emily. Trouble in Pembrook. 2005. (Ski Share Ser.). 288p. (YA). pap. 8.99 (978-1-4169-1466-2(8) , Simon Pulse) Simon & Schuster Children's Publishing.

Farnes, Catherine. Snowblind. 2004. 108p. (J). (978-1-59166-329-4(6)) Jones, Bob Univ. Pr.

Ferguson, Donald. The Chums of Scranton High at Ice Hockey. 2006. 77.99 ***(978-1-4142-5876-8(3));*** pap. 70.99 ***(978-1-4142-5881-2(X))*** IndyPublish.com.

Lantz, Francess L. Hawaii Five-Go! 2003. (gr. 3-6). lib. bdg. 13.00 (978-0-613-81422-5(3)) Tandem Library Bks.

Lester, Helen. Tacky & the Winter Games. Munsinger, Lynn, illus. 2007. 32p. (J). (ps-3). 6.95 ***(978-0-618-95674-6(3))*** Houghton Mifflin Co. Trade & Reference Div.

—Tacky & the Winter Games. Munsinger, Lynn M., illus. 2005. 32p. (J). (gr. k-3). 16.00 (978-0-618-55659-5(1) , Walter Lorraine) Houghton Mifflin Co. Trade & Reference Div.

WISCONSIN

Apps, Jerry. Tents, Tigers, & the Ringling Brothers. 2006. (Badger Biography Ser.). (Illus.). 128p. (J). pap. 12.95 (978-0-87020-374-9(6)) Wisconsin Historical Society.

Barenblat, Rachel. Wisconsin: The Badger State. 2002. (World Almanac Library of the States). (Illus.). 48p. (J). (gr. 5 up). pap. 14.95 (978-0-8368-5295-0(8)); lib. bdg. 30.00 (978-0-8368-5126-7(9)) Stevens, Gareth Inc. (World Almanac Library).

—Wisconsin: The Badger State. 2002. (gr. 5-8). lib. bdg. 19.90 (978-0-613-52527-5(2)) Tandem Library Bks.

Blashfield, Jean F. Wisconsin. 2007. (America the Beautiful, Third Ser.). (Illus.). 144p. (YA). (gr. 5-8). lib. bdg. 38.00 ***(978-0-531-18568-1(0)*** , Children's Pr.) Scholastic Library Publishing.

Bratvold, Gretchen. Wisconsin. 2nd exp. rev. ed. (Hello U. S. A. Ser.). (Illus.). 84p. (J). (gr. 3-6). 2003. pap. 6.95 (978-0-8225-4156-1(4)); 2002. 25.26 (978-0-8225-4052-6(5) , Lerner Pubns.) Lerner Publishing Group.

—Wisconsin. 2001. (gr. 3-6). lib. bdg. 15.25 (978-0-613-84030-9(5)) Tandem Library Bks.

Butler, Dori Hillestad. ABC's of Wisconsin. Stoga, Stan, ed. Relyea, Alison, illus. 2000. 32p. (J). (ps-1). 14.95 (978-0-915024-79-7(9)) Big Earth Publishing.

Capstone Press Staff, contrib. by. Wisconsin. rev. ed. 2002. (One Nation Ser.). (Illus.). 48p. (J). (gr. 3-4). lib. bdg. 22.60 (978-0-7368-1275-7(X) , Bridgestone Bks.) Capstone Pr., Inc.

Chamberlain, Delores. River Stories: Growing up on the Wisconsin. Chamberlain, Joe et al, illus. 2000. xiv, 131p. (J). pap. 14.95 (978-1-879483-70-5(X) , Prairie Oak Pr.) Big Earth Publishing.

Cohen, Sheila. Mai Ya's Long Journey. 2005. (Badger Biographies Ser.). (Illus.). 80p. (J). (gr. 3-8). pap. 12.95 (978-0-87020-365-7(7)) Wisconsin Historical Society.

Covert, Kim. Wisconsin. 2003. (Land of Liberty Ser.). (Illus.). 64p. (J). lib. bdg. 25.26 (978-0-7368-2206-0(2)) Capstone Pr., Inc.

Dornfeld, Margaret. Wisconsin. 2003. (It's My State! Ser.). (Illus.). 78p. (J). 27.07 (978-0-7614-1524-4(6) , Benchmark Bks.) Cavendish, Marshall Corp.

Hart, Joyce & Zeinert, Karen. Wisconsin. 2nd ed. 2006. (Celebrate the States Ser.). (J). lib. bdg. 39.93 (978-0-7614-2157-3(2) , Benchmark Bks.) Cavendish, Marshall Corp.

Heinrichs, Ann. Wisconsin. 2005. (Welcome to the USA Ser.). 40p. (J). (gr. 1-5). 27.07 (978-1-59296-288-4(2)) Child's World, Inc.

—Wisconsin. 2003. (This Land Is Your Land Ser.). (Illus.). 48p. (J). (gr. 3 up). lib. bdg. 22.60 (978-0-7565-0328-4(0)) Compass Point Bks.

Holden, Henry M. Wisconsin: A MyReportLinks. Com Book. 2003. (States Ser.). (Illus.). 48p. (J). lib. bdg. 25.26 (978-0-7660-5125-6(0) , MyReportLinks.com Bks.) Enslow Pubs., Inc.

Kono, Erin Eitter, illus. The Twelve Days of Christmas in Wisconsin. 2007. 32p. (J). (gr. k up). 9.95 ***(978-1-4027-3815-9(3))*** Sterling Publishing Co., Inc.

Lantier, Patricia. Wisconsin. 2005. (Portraits of the States Ser.). (Illus.). 32p. (J). pap. (978-0-8368-4657-7(5)); lib. bdg. 23.33 (978-0-8368-4638-6(9)) Stevens, Gareth Inc.

Learning about Wisconsin: Activities, Historical Documents & Resources Linked to Wisconsin's Model Academic Standards for Social Studies in Grades 4-12. 1999. (Illus.). 250p. (J). (gr. 4-12). 30.00 (978-1-57337-075-2(4)) Wisconsin Dept. of Public Instruction.

Ling, Bettina. Wisconsin. 80p. (J). 2008. (From Sea to Shining Sea, Second Ser.). pap. 7.95 ***(978-0-531-18810-1(8));*** 2002. (From Sea to Shining Sea Ser.: 2). (Illus.). (gr. 3-5). 30.50 (978-0-516-22380-3(1)) Scholastic Library Publishing. (Children's Pr.).

Marsh, Carole. My First Book about Wisconsin. 2004. (Wisconsin Experience! Ser.). (Illus.). 32p. (J). (gr. k-4). pap. 7.95 (978-0-7933-9539-2(9)) Gallopade International.

—Rene Menard: A Wisconsin Experience Reader. 2002. (One Thousand Readers Ser.). (Illus.). 12p. (J). (gr. k-4). 2.95 (978-0-635-01550-1(1) , 15501) Gallopade International.

—The Survivor: A Class Challenge. 2001. (Wisconsin Experience! Ser.). lib. bdg. 29.95 (978-0-635-00695-0(2)) Gallopade International.

—Wisconsin Current Events Projects: 30 Cool, Activities, Crafts, Experiments & More for Kids to Do to Learn about Your State! 2003. (Wisconsin Experience Ser.). 32p. (gr. k-8). pap. 5.95 (978-0-635-02068-0(8) , Marsh, Carole Bks.) Gallopade International.

—The Wisconsin Experience Pocket Guide. 2004. (Wisconsin Experience! Ser.). (Illus.). 96p. (J). (gr. 3-8). pap. 6.95 (978-0-7933-9538-5(0)) Gallopade International.

—The Wisconsin Experience Sol Biographies. 2001. (Illus.). (J). (gr. 2-9). pap. 12.95 (978-0-635-00392-8(9)) Gallopade International.

—Wisconsin Geography Projects: 30 Cool, Activities, Crafts, Experiments & More for Kids to Do to Learn about Your State! 2003. (Wisconsin Experience Ser.). 32p. (gr. k-5). pap. 5.95 (978-0-635-01867-0(5) , Marsh, Carole Bks.) Gallopade International.

—Wisconsin Government Projects: 30 Cool, Activities, Crafts, Experiments & More for Kids to Do to Learn about Your State! 2003. (Wisconsin Experience Ser.). 32p. (gr. k-5). pap. 5.95 (978-0-635-01968-4(X) , Marsh, Carole Bks.) Gallopade International.

—Wisconsin Jeopardy! Answers & Questions about Our State! 2004. (Wisconsin Experience! Ser.). (Illus.). 32p. (J). (gr. 3-8). pap. 7.95 (978-0-7933-9540-8(2)) Gallopade International.

—Wisconsin "Jography" A Fun Run Thru Our State! 2004. (Wisconsin Experience! Ser.). (Illus.). 32p. (J). (gr. 3-8). pap. 7.95 (978-0-7933-9541-5(0)) Gallopade International.

—Wisconsin People Projects: 30 Cool, Activities, Crafts, Experiments & More for Kids to Do to Learn about Your State! 2003. (Wisconsin Experience Ser.). 32p. (gr. k-5). pap. 5.95 (978-0-635-02018-5(1) , Marsh, Carole Bks.) Gallopade International.

—Wisconsin Survivor. 2001. (GameBook Ser.). (Illus.). 32p. (J). (gr. 3-8). pap., act. bk. ed. 9.95 (978-0-635-00570-0(0)) Gallopade International.

—Wisconsin Symbols & Facts Projects: 30 Cool, Activities, Crafts, Experiments & More for Kids to Do to Learn about Your State! 2003. (Wisconsin Experience Ser.). 32p. (gr. k-5). pap. 5.95 (978-0-635-01918-9(3) , Marsh, Carole Bks.) Gallopade International.

—Wisconsin Wheel of Fortune. 2001. (GameBook Ser.). (Illus.). 32p. (J). (gr. 3-8). pap., act. bk. ed. 9.95 (978-0-635-00014-9(8)) Gallopade International.

—Wisconsin's Big Activity Book. 2004. (Wisconsin Experience! Ser.). (Illus.). 96p. (J). (gr. 2-6). pap. 9.95 (978-0-7933-9542-2(9)) Gallopade International.

—The Wonderful Wisconsin Coloring Book. 2004. (Wisconsin Experience! Ser.). (Illus.). 32p. (J). (gr. k-2). pap. 3.95 (978-0-7933-9543-9(7)) Gallopade International.

McAuliffe, Emily. Wisconsin Facts & Symbols. (States & Their Symbols Ser.). 24p. (J). 1999. (Illus.). (gr. 2-3). lib. bdg. 18.60 (978-0-7368-0217-8(7) , Bridgestone Bks.); 2003. lib. bdg. 19.93 (978-0-7368-2280-0(1)) Capstone Pr., Inc.

McNamara, Connie. My First Wisconsin Words Go Badgers. 2004. (J). bds. 11.95 (978-0-9743244-2-5(6)) Shamrock Publishing, Inc.

Murray, Julie. Wisconsin. 2006. (Buddy Book Ser.). (Illus.). 32p. (J). (gr. k-4). lib. bdg. 22.78 (978-1-59197-708-7(8) , Buddy Bks.) ABDO Publishing Co.

Parker, Janice. A Guide to Wisconsin. 2001. (American States Ser.). 32p. (J). (Illus.). (gr. 4-7). lib. bdg. 16.95 (978-1-930954-80-9(8)); per. 7.95 (978-1-930954-57-1(3)) Weigl Pubs., Inc.

Peters, S. True. How to Draw Wisconsins Sights & Symbols. 2002. (Kids Guide to Drawing America Ser.). 32p. (J). lib. bdg. 25.25 (978-0-8239-6106-1(0) , PowerKids Pr.) Rosen Publishing Group, Inc., The.

Peterson, Cris. Century Farm: One Hundred Years on a Family Farm. Upitis, Alvis, photos by. 2003. (Illus.). 32p. (YA). (gr. k-2). 17.95 (978-1-56397-710-7(9)) Boyds Mills Pr.

Rosebrough, Amy & Malone, Bobbie. Water Panthers, Bears, & Thunderbirds: Exploring the Effigy Mounds of Wisconsin. 2003. (New Badger History Ser.). (Illus.). 32p. (J). pap. 9.95 (978-0-87020-357-2(6)) Wisconsin Historical Society.

Steele, Christy. Uniquely Wisconsin. 2003. (State Studies). (Illus.). 48p. (J). pap. 8.50 (978-1-4034-4514-8(1)); lib. bdg. 27.07 (978-1-4034-4499-8(4)) Heinemann Library.

Trumbauer, Lisa. Wisconsin. (Rookie Read-About Geography Ser.). (Illus.). (J). 2004. 31p. (gr. 1-2). pap. 5.95 (978-0-516-23607-0(5)); 2003. 32p. 20.50 (978-0-516-22745-0(9)) Scholastic Library Publishing. (Children's Pr.).

Wargin, Kathy-Jo. B Is for Badger: A Wisconsin Alphabet. Graef, Renee, illus. 2004. 40p. (J). 17.95 (978-1-58536-135-9(6)) Sleeping Bear Pr.

WISCONSIN—FICTION

Addy, Sharon. In Grandpa's Woods. Akins, Tamlyn, illus. 2004. (J). (*978-1-931599-42-9(4) , Trails Bks.) Big Earth Publishing.

Aryal, Aimee. Go, Pack, Go! de Angel, Miguel, illus. 2007. (J). 14.95 (*978-1-932888-94-2(2)) Mascot Bks., Inc.

Bauer, Joan. Hope Was Here. 2000. (Illus.). 192p. (J). (gr. 7-12). 16.99 (978-0-399-23142-1(0) , Putnam Juvenile) Penguin Group (USA) Inc.

Bjornson, Nancy. Sleds, Skins & Snow. 2007. (J). (*978-1-930596-83-2(9)) Amherst Pr.

Brink, Carol Ryrie. Caddie Woodlawn. Hyman, Trina Schart, illus. 2002. (J). 13.94 (978-0-7587-0174-9(8)) Book Wholesalers, Inc.

—Caddie Woodlawn. 288p. (J). 2007. pap. 2.99 (*978-1-4169-4818-6(X)); 2006. pap. 6.99 (978-1-4169-4028-9(6)) Simon & Schuster Children's Publishing. (Aladdin).

—Caddie Woodlawn. l.t. ed. 2003. 260p. pap. 10.95 (978-0-7862-6182-6(X)) Thorndike Pr.

Brookins, Cara. Doris Free. Barrow, Ann, illus. 2006. 127p. (J). pap. (978-1-59336-333-8(8)) Mondo Publishing.

Brown, Marc. Buster & the Dance Contest. 2005. (Postcards from Buster Ser.). (Illus.). 32p. (J). (gr. 1-4). 14.99 (978-0-316-15889-3(5)); pap., pap. 3.99 (978-0-316-00118-2(X)) Little, Brown Bks. for Young Readers.

Cameron, Ann. The Secret Life of Amanda K. Woods. 1999. (978-0-606-17429-9(X)) Tandem Library Bks.

—Secret Life of Amanda K Woods. 1999. (gr. 3-6). lib. bdg. 14.15 (978-0-613-23031-5(0)) Tandem Library Bks.

Carter, Alden R. Crescent Moon. 1999. 160p. (YA). (gr. 7 up). tchr. ed. 16.95 (978-0-8234-1521-2(X)) Holiday Hse., Inc.

—Crescent Moon. 1999. (J). 15.95 (978-0-590-29882-7(8)) Scholastic, Inc.

—Up Country. 2004. 256p. (J). (gr. 5). pap. 6.99 (978-0-14-240243-6(5) , Puffin) Penguin Group (USA) Inc.

Clarissa - Evaluation Guide: Evaluation Guide. 2006. (J). (978-1-55942-402-8(8)) Marsh Media.

Clark, Catherine. Wurst Case Scenario. 2001. 320p. (J). (gr. 8 up). 16.89 (978-0-06-029525-7(2)) HarperCollins Pubs.

Cumbie, Patricia. Where People Like Us Live. 2008. 224p. (J). 16.99 (*978-0-06-137597-2(7)); lib. bdg. 17.89 (*978-0-06-137598-9(5)) HarperCollins Pubs. (Geringer, Laura Book).

Daly, Maureen. Seventeenth Summer. 2002. 320p. (YA). 17.95 (978-0-689-85383-8(1)) Simon & Schuster Children's Publishing.

Enright, Elizabeth. Thimble Summer. 2006. 21.75 (978-0-8446-7281-6(5)) Smith, Peter Pub., Inc.

—Thimble Summer. 2008. (Illus.). 124p. (J). pap. 6.99 (*978-0-312-38002-1(X)) Square Fish.

Erickson, John R. The Case of the Fiddle-Playing Fox, Vol. 12. Holmes, Gerald L., illus. 1998. (Hank the Cowdog Ser.: No. 12). 144p. (J). (gr. 2-5). pap. 4.99 (978-0-14-130388-6(3) , Puffin) Penguin Group (USA) Inc.

Geisert, Arthur. The Giant Ball of String. 2007. (Illus.). 32p. (J). (gr. k-3). 6.95 (*978-0-618-84067-0(2) , Walter Lorraine) Houghton Mifflin Co. Trade & Reference Div.

Hannigan, Katherine. Ida B: ... And Her Plans to Maximize Fun, Avoid Disaster, & (Possibly) Save the World. 256p. 2004. (J). (gr. 4 up). 16.99 (978-0-06-073024-6(2)); 2004. (gr. 4 up). lib. bdg. 16.89 (978-0-06-073025-3(0)); 2007. reprint ed. pap. 5.99 (978-0-06-073026-0(9) , Harper Trophy) HarperCollins Pubs.

Henson, Heather & Wilkins, Celia. A Little House of Their Own. Andreasen, Dan, illus. 2005. (Little House Ser.). 320p. (J). 16.99 (978-0-06-027009-4(8)) HarperCollins Pubs.

Horner, William. Gene Shepard's Wisconsin Hodag. Mommaerts, Robb, illus. 2001. 32p. (J). (gr. 2-5). lib. bdg. 24.95 (978-1-931765-03-9(0) , BHC501) Badger Hse., LLC.

Hysen, Sylvia. A Very Dairy Christmas. 2005. 312p. (YA). 24.95 (978-0-9763365-6-3(1)) 1st Impression Publishing.

Kopetz, Mark. Red Herrings at Rock Island: A Door County Mystery. 2005. 15.00 (978-0-940473-42-3(9)) Caxton, Wm Ltd.

Lafaye, Alexandria. Edith Shay. 2001. (J). 11.64 (978-0-606-21170-3(5)) Tandem Library Bks.

Lansing, Richard D., Jr. The Blue Moose. Lansing, Randy, illus. 1999. 48p. (J). (ps-4). mass mkt. 6.00 (978-0-9661844-5-7(9)) Purple Gorilla, LLC, The.

Liebig, Nelda J. Carrie & the Apple Pie. 1999. 122p. (J). (gr. 3-7). pap. (978-1-883953-30-0(8)) Midwest Traditions, Inc.

Liebig, Nelda Johnson. Carrie & the Boarding House. 2005. 128p. (J). pap. 10.95 (978-1-883953-35-5(9)) Midwest Traditions, Inc.

Mechelke, Violet. The Woodshed. Miller, Arlene, illus. 2002. 165p. (YA). (gr. 4-9). pap. 12.00 (978-0-9719623-0-9(8)) Whispering Hope Publishing.

Merkel, Ruth. Hannah's Girls: Ann. 2006. 112p. (J). pap. 9.99 (*978-0-8280-1951-4(7)) Review & Herald Publishing Assn.

—Hannah's Girls: Grace, 6. 2006. (Illus.). 128p. (J). pap. 9.99 (*978-0-8280-1953-8(3)) Review & Herald Publishing Assn.

—Hannah's Girls: Marilla, 6 bks. 2006. (Illus.). 144p. (J). pap. 9.99 (*978-0-8280-1952-1(5)) Review & Herald Publishing Assn.

—Hannah's Girls: Ruthie. 2007. 144p. (J). pap. 9.99 (*978-0-8280-1954-5(1)) Review & Herald Publishing Assn.

Nation, Kay. Jamie Learns to Love. 2006. pap. 10.00 (*978-1-4257-0534-3(0)) Xlibris Corp.

Nelson, Bruce. Captain Black Licorice. 2004. (Illus.). 60p. (J). per. 7.95 (978-1-59466-026-9(3)) Port Town Publishing.

Olin, Sean. Killing Britney. 2005. 240p. (YA). (gr. 9 up). pap. 8.99 (978-0-689-87778-0(1) , Simon Pulse) Simon & Schuster Children's Publishing.

Oliver, Andrew. Haunted Hill. 2006. (Sam & Stephanie Mystery Ser.). 268p. (J). (gr. 5-9). per. 12.95 (978-0-9661009-7-6(2)) Adams-Pomeroy Pr.

—If Photos Could Talk. 2005. (Sam & Stephanie Mystery Ser.). 264p. (J). per. 12.95 (978-0-9661009-6-9(4)) Adams-Pomeroy Pr.

Oliver, Andrew. Scrambled. 2007. 288p. (J). per. 12.95 (*978-0-9661009-8-3(0)) Adams-Pomeroy Pr.

Paulsen, Gary. The Island. 2006. 208p. (J). pap. 5.99 (978-0-439-78662-1(2) , Scholastic Paperbacks) Scholastic, Inc.

Pferdehirt, Julia. Wisconsin Forest Tales. 2004. (Illus.). vii, 152p. (J). (978-1-931599-47-4(5) , Trails Bks.) Big Earth Publishing.

Qualey, Marsha. Thin Ice. 2007. (YA). (*978-0-9793444-0-4(9)) Quercus Pr.

—Thin Ice. 1999. (978-0-606-17348-3(X)) Tandem Library Bks.

Riordan, Robert. Medicine for Wildcat: A Story of the Friendship between a Menominee Indian & Frontier Priest Samuel Mazzuchelli. 2006. (Illus.). 132p. (YA). per. 14.95 (978-0-9774934-0-1(7)) Sinsinawa Dominicans, Inc.

Soileau, Hodges, illus. The Mystery of the Runaway Ghost, Vol. 98. 2004. (Boxcar Children Mysteries Ser.: 98). 128p. (J). (gr. 2-7). pap. 4.50 (978-0-8075-5551-4(7)) Whitman, Albert & Co.

Tews, Susan. The Gingerbread Doll. 2001. (gr. k-3). lib. bdg. 14.10 (978-0-613-35518-6(0)) Tandem Library Bks.

Wargin, Kathy-Jo. The Legend of Old Abe: A Civil War Eagle. Caple, Laurie, illus. 2006. 40p. (J). (gr. k-5). 17.95 (978-1-58536-232-5(8)) Sleeping Bear Pr.

Wilder, Laura Ingalls. The Deer in the Wood. Graef, Renee, illus. 1999. (My First Little House Bks.). 32p. (J). (ps-3). pap. 6.99 (978-0-06-443498-0(2) , Harper Trophy) HarperCollins Pubs.

—The Deer in the Wood. 1999. (My First Little House Bks.). (J). 12.79 (978-0-606-15841-1(3)) Tandem Library Bks.

—Little House in the Big Woods. 2007. (Little House Ser.). 224p. (J). pap. 6.99 (978-0-06-088537-3(8) , Harper Trophy) HarperCollins Pubs.

—Little House in the Big Woods. Williams, Garth, illus. (Little House Ser.). 256p. (J). (gr. k-4). 2001. 19.95 (978-0-06-029647-6(X)); 2007. 19.99 (*978-0-06-128980-4(9)) HarperCollins Pubs.

—Little House in the Big Woods. Williams, Garth, illus. l.t. ed. 2000. (Little House Ser.). 244p. (J). (gr. 3-6). lib. bdg. 28.95 (978-1-58118-078-7(0) , 24070) LRS.

—Little House in the Big Woods A Special Read Aloud Edition. Williams, Garth, illus. 2001. (Little House Ser.). 256p. (J). (gr. 3-5). 19.89 (978-0-06-029648-3(8)) HarperCollins Pubs.

—Summertime in the Big Woods. Graef, Renee, illus. 2000. (My First Little House Bks.). 40p. (J). (ps-3). pap. 6.99 (978-0-06-443497-3(4) , Harper Trophy) HarperCollins Pubs.

Wilkes, Maria D. Brookfield Days. Ettlinger, Doris, illus. 1999. (Little House Chapter Bks.: No. 1). 80p. (J). (gr. 3-6). 14.89 (978-0-06-027952-3(4)) HarperCollins Pubs.

—Brookfield Days. 1999. (Little House Chapter Bks.: No.1). (Illus.). (J). (gr. 3-6). 11.05 (978-0-606-18680-3(8)) Tandem Library Bks.

—Brookfield Friends. Andreasen, Dan, illus. 2000. (Little House Chapter Bks.: No. 4). 80p. (J). (gr. 3-6). 14.89 (978-0-06-028552-4(4)) HarperCollins Pubs.

—Little Clearing in the Woods. Andreasen, Dan, illus. 1998. (Little House Ser.). 336p. (J). (gr. 3-7). 15.95 (978-0-06-026997-5(9)); 15.89 (978-0-06-026998-2(7)) HarperCollins Pubs.

—Little House in Brookfield. 2007. (Little House Ser.). 144p. (J). pap. 5.99 (*978-0-06-114821-7(0) , Harper Trophy) HarperCollins Pubs.

—Little Town at the Crossroads Bk. 2: The Caroline Years. 2007. (Little House Ser.). 176p. (J). pap. 5.99 (*978-0-06-114822-4(9) , Harper Trophy) HarperCollins Pubs.

—A New Little Cabin. Ettlinger, Doris, illus. 2001. (Little House Chapter Bks.: Vol. 5). 80p. (J). (gr. 2-5). 14.89 (978-0-06-028554-8(0)) HarperCollins Pubs.

—On Top of Concord Hill. Andreasen, Dan, illus. 2000. (Little House Ser.). 288p. (J). (gr. 3-7). 15.89 (978-0-06-027003-2(9)) HarperCollins Pubs.

Wilkins, Celia. Across the Rolling River. Andreasen, Dan, illus. 2001. (Little House Ser.). 272p. (J). 16.95 (978-0-06-027004-9(7)); 16.89 (978-0-06-027005-6(5)); (gr. 5 up). pap. 6.99 (978-0-06-440734-2(9) , Harper Trophy) HarperCollins Pubs.

—Across the Rolling River. Andreasen, Dan, illus. 2001. (gr. 3-6). lib. bdg. 14.15 (978-0-613-51524-5(2)) Tandem Library Bks.

—A Little House of Their Own. Andreasen, Dan, illus. 2005. (Little House Ser.). 320p. (J). pap. 6.99 (978-0-06-440736-6(5)) HarperCollins Pubs.

Wright, Betty Ren. Crandall's Castle. 2005. 184p. (YA). (gr. 4-6). tchr. ed. 16.95 (978-0-8234-1726-1(3)) Holiday Hse., Inc.

WISCONSIN—HISTORY

Ball, Jacqueline A. Wildfire! The 1871 Peshtigo Firestorm. 2005. (X-Treme Disasters That Changed America Ser.). 32p. (J). lib. bdg. 25.27 (978-1-59716-011-7(3)) Bearport Publishing Co., Inc.

Blessing, Matt. Wisconsin History on Stage: Scripts for Grades 4 Through 8. 1999. (New Badger History Ser.). (Illus.). 80p. (J). (gr. 4-8). pap. 14.95 (978-0-87020-312-1(6)) Wisconsin Historical Society.

Carole Marsh. Wisconsin Indians. 2004. (Wisconsin Experience Ser.). 36p. (gr. 3-8). 29.95 (978-0-635-02343-8(1)); pap. 7.95 (978-0-635-02342-1(3)) Gallopade International.

Davis, Susan Burdick. Old Forts & Real Folks. 2006. pap. 31.95 (*978-1-4286-5582-9(4)) Kessinger Publishing, LLC.

Galiano, Dean. Wisconsin. 2006. (Bilingual Library of the United States of America: Set 2). (ENG & SPA., Illus.). 32p. (J). (gr. 3-6). lib. bdg. 22.50 (978-1-4042-3115-3(3) , Buenas Letra) Rosen Publishing Group, Inc., The.

Hintz, Martin. Wisconsin Portraits: 55 People Who Made a Difference. Stoga, Stan, ed. 2000. (Illus.). 122p. (J). (gr. 4-7). pap. 14.95 (978-0-915024-80-3(2)) Big Earth Publishing.

Holliday, Diane Young & Malone, Bobbie. Digging & Discovery: Wisconsin Archaeology. 2nd ed. 2006. (New Badger History Ser.). (Illus.). 120p. pap. 15.95 (978-0-87020-376-3(2)) Wisconsin Historical Society.

Malone, Bobbie & Gray, Jefferson J. Working with Water: Wisconsin Waterways. 2001. (New Badger History Ser.). (Illus.). 88p. (gr. 4-8). pap. 11.95 (978-0-87020-329-9(0)) Wisconsin Historical Society.

Malone, Bobbie, et al. Working with Water: Wisconsin Waterways. 2001. (New Badger History Ser.). (Illus.). 84p. (J). (gr. 4-8). pap., instr.'s gde. ed. 39.95 (978-0-87020-331-2(2)) Wisconsin Historical Society.

Marsh, Carole. My First Pocket Guide Wisconsin. 2000. (Wisconsin Experience! Ser.). (Illus.). 96p. (J). (gr. 3-8). 12.95 (978-0-635-01339-2(8) , 13398) Gallopade International.

—Wisconsin History Projects: 30 Cool, Activities, Crafts, Experiments & More for Kids to Do to Learn about Your State! 2003. (Wisconsin Experience Ser.). 32p. (gr. k-5). pap. 5.95 (978-0-635-01818-2(7) , Marsh, Carole Bks.) Gallopade International.

Pferdehirt, Julia. Freedom Train North: Stories of the Underground Railroad in Wisconsin. Butler, Jerry, illus. Date not set. (J). (gr. 3-8). pap. 10.00 (978-0-9664925-0-7(1)) Living History Pr.

—They Came to Wisconsin. 2002. (New Badger History Ser.). (Illus.). 144p. (J). pap. 15.95 (978-0-87020-328-2(2)) Wisconsin Historical Society.

Reaves, Shiela. Wisconsin: An Illustrated History. 2004. (Illus.). 352p. 34.95 (978-1-892724-42-7(1)) American Historical Pr.

Uschan, Michael V. Wisconsin. 2003. (Seeds of a Nation Ser.). (Illus.). 48p. (J). (gr. 3-5). 23.70 (978-0-7377-1481-4(6) , Kidhaven) Thomson Gale.

WISHBONE (FICTITIOUS CHARACTER)—FICTION

Adventures of Wishbone, 14 bks. l.t. ed. Incl. Digging to the Center of the Earth. Steele, Michael Anthony. Punchatz, Don, illus. (gr. 4 up). lib. bdg. 22.60 (978-0-8368-2595-4(0)); Digging up the Past. Sathre, Vivian. 144p. (gr. 4 up). lib. bdg. 22.60 (978-0-8368-2302-8(8)); Dog Overboard! Sathre, Vivian. (gr. 4 up). lib. bdg. 22.60 (978-0-8368-2590-9(X)); Dr. Jekyll & Mr. Dog. Butcher, Nancy. (gr. 4 up). lib. bdg. 22.60 (978-0-8368-2592-3(6)); Gullifur's Travels. Strickland, Brad & Strickland, Barbara. (gr. 4 up). lib. bdg. 22.60 (978-0-8368-2596-1(9)); Homer Sweet Homer. Jablonski, Carla. Punchatz, Don, illus. (gr. 4 up). lib. bdg. 22.60 (978-0-8368-2591-6(8)); Hunchdog of Notre Dame. Friedman, Michael Jan. 139p. (gr. 4 up). lib. bdg. 22.60 (978-0-8368-2301-1(X)); Last of the Breed. Steele, Alexander. Punchatz, Don, illus. 163p. (gr. 4 up). lib. bdg. 22.60 (978-0-8368-2594-7(2)); Mutt in the Iron Muzzle. Friedman, Michael Jan. 144p. (gr. 4 up). lib. bdg. 22.60 (978-0-8368-2303-5(6)); Pawloined Paper. Litowinsky, Olga. (gr. 4 up). lib. bdg. 22.60 (978-0-8368-2589-3(6)); Prince & the Pooch. Leavitt, Caroline. 144p. (gr. 4 up). lib. bdg. 22.60 (978-0-8368-2299-1(4)); Pup in King Arthur's Court. Barkan, Joanne. 164p. (gr. 2-5). lib. bdg. 22.60 (978-0-8368-2593-0(4)); Robinhound Crusoe. Leavitt, Caroline. 144p. (gr. 4 up). lib. bdg. 22.60 (978-0-8368-2300-4(1)); Tale of Two Sitters. Barkan, Joanne. 144p. (gr. 4 up). lib. bdg. 22.60 (978-0-8368-2305-9(2)); (J). 1999. (Illus.). 1999. Set lib. bdg. 316.40 (978-0-8368-2654-8(X)) Stevens, Gareth Inc.

Barkan, Joanne. A Pup in King Arthur's Court. l.t. ed. 1999. (Adventures of Wishbone Ser.: No. 15). (Illus.). 164p. (J). (gr. 2-5). lib. bdg. 22.60 (978-0-8368-2593-0(4)) Stevens, Gareth Inc.

—A Pup in King Arthur's Court. 1999. (Adventures of Wishbone Ser.: No. 15). (J). (gr. 2-5). (978-0-606-17609-5(8)) Tandem Library Bks.

—A Tale of Two Sitters. l.t. ed. 1999. (Adventures of Wishbone Ser.: No. 9). (Illus.). 144p. (J). (gr. 4 up). lib. bdg. 22.60 (978-0-8368-2305-9(2)) Stevens, Gareth Inc.

Butcher, Nancy. Dr. Jekyll & Mr. Dog. l.t. ed. 1999. (Adventures of Wishbone Ser.: No. 14). (Illus.). (J). (gr. 4 up). lib. bdg. 22.60 (978-0-8368-2592-3(6)) Stevens, Gareth Inc.

—Lights! Camera! Action Dog! l.t. ed. 2000. (Wishbone Mysteries Ser.: No. 11). (Illus.). 139p. (J). (gr. 4 up). lib. bdg. 23.33 (978-0-8368-2694-4(9)) Stevens, Gareth Inc.

Capeci, Anne. Case of the Cyber-Hacker. l.t. ed. 2000. (Wishbone Mysteries Ser.: No. 19). (Illus.). 141p. (J). (gr. 4 up). lib. bdg. 23.33 (978-0-8368-2702-6(3)) Stevens, Gareth Inc.

—Case of the Cyber-Hacker. 2000. (gr. 3-6). lib. bdg. 11.80 (978-0-613-27764-8(3)) Tandem Library Bks.

—Key to the Golden Dog. l.t. ed. 1999. (Wishbone Mysteries Ser.: No. 8). 144p. (J). (gr. 4 up). lib. bdg. 23.33 (978-0-8368-2389-9(3)) Stevens, Gareth Inc.

—The Maltese Dog. l.t. ed. 1999. (Wishbone Mysteries Ser.: No. 6). 144p. (J). (gr. 4 up). lib. bdg. 23.33 (978-0-8368-2387-5(7)) Stevens, Gareth Inc.

Crider, Bill. Muttketeer! l.t. ed. 1999. (Adventures of Wishbone Ser.: No. 8). (Illus.). 144p. (J). (gr. 4 up). lib. bdg. 22.60 (978-0-8368-2304-2(4)) Stevens, Gareth Inc.

Friedman, Michael Jan. Hunchdog of Notre Dame. l.t. ed. 1999. (Adventures of Wishbone Ser.: No. 5). (Illus.). 139p. (J). (gr. 4 up). lib. bdg. 22.60 (978-0-8368-2301-1(X)) Stevens, Gareth Inc.

—The Sirian Conspiracy. 1999. (Wishbone Mysteries Ser.: No. 16). (J). (gr. 2-5). (978-0-606-17768-9(X)) Tandem Library Bks.

—The Stolen Trophy. l.t. ed. 1999. (Wishbone Mysteries Ser.: No. 5). 144p. (J). (gr. 4 up). lib. bdg. 23.33 (978-0-8368-2386-8(9)) Stevens, Gareth Inc.

—The Stolen Trophy. 1998. (Wishbone Mysteries Ser.: No. 5). (J). (gr. 2-5). (978-0-606-12859-9(X)) Tandem Library Bks.

Friedman, Michael Jan, et al. The Sirian Conspiracy. l.t. ed. 2000. (Wishbone Mysteries Ser.: No. 16). (Illus.). 141p. (J). (gr. 4 up). lib. bdg. 23.33 (978-0-8368-2699-9(X)) Stevens, Gareth Inc.

Gantt, Leticia. Phantom of the Video Store. l.t. ed. 2000. (Wishbone Mysteries Ser.: No. 18). (Illus.). 141p. (J). (gr. 4 up). lib. bdg. 23.33 (978-0-8368-2701-9(5)) Stevens, Gareth Inc.

Jablonski, Carla. Homer Sweet Homer. Punchatz, Don, illus. l.t. ed. 1999. (Adventures of Wishbone Ser.: No. 13). (J). (gr. 4 up). lib. bdg. 22.60 (978-0-8368-2591-6(8)) Stevens, Gareth Inc.

Leavitt, Caroline. The Haunted Clubhouse. l.t. ed. 1999. (Wishbone Mysteries Ser.: No. 2). 144p. (J). (gr. 4 up). lib. bdg. 22.60 (978-0-8368-2383-7(4)) Stevens, Gareth Inc.

—The Prince & the Pooch. l.t. ed. 1999. (Adventures of Wishbone Ser.: No. 3). (Illus.). 144p. (J). (gr. 4 up). lib. bdg. 22.60 (978-0-8368-2299-1(4)) Stevens, Gareth Inc.

—Robinhound Crusoe. l.t. ed. 1999. (Adventures of Wishbone Ser.: No. 4). (Illus.). 144p. (J). (gr. 4 up). lib. bdg. 22.60 (978-0-8368-2300-4(1)) Stevens, Gareth Inc.

Litowinsky, Olga. The Pawloined Paper. l.t. ed. 1999. (Adventures of Wishbone Ser.: No. 11). (Illus.). (J). (gr. 4 up). lib. bdg. 22.60 (978-0-8368-2589-3(6)) Stevens, Gareth Inc.

Orr, Wendy. Ark in the Park. Millard, Kerry, illus. rev. ed. 2000. (Redfeather Book Ser.). 80p. (J). (gr. k-5). 15.95 (978-0-8050-6221-2(1) , Holt, Henry & Co. Bks. For Young Readers) Holt, Henry & Co.

Sathre, Vivian. Digging up the Past. l.t. ed. 1999. (Adventures of Wishbone Ser.: No. 6). (Illus.). 144p. (J). (gr. 4 up). lib. bdg. 22.60 (978-0-8368-2302-8(8)) Stevens, Gareth Inc.

—Dog Overboard! l.t. ed. 1999. (Adventures of Wishbone Ser.: No. 12). (Illus.). (J). (gr. 4 up). lib. bdg. 22.60 (978-0-8368-2590-9(X)) Stevens, Gareth Inc.

—Stage Invader. l.t. ed. 2000. (Wishbone Mysteries Ser.: No. 15). (Illus.). 140p. (J). (gr. 4 up). lib. bdg. 23.33 (978-0-8368-2698-2(1)) Stevens, Gareth Inc.

—Stage Invader. 1999. (Wishbone Mysteries Ser.: No. 15). (J). (gr. 2-5). (978-0-606-15826-8(X)) Tandem Library Bks.

Steele, Alexander. Case of the Breaking Story. l.t. ed. 2000. (Wishbone Mysteries Ser.: No. 20). (Illus.). 144p. (J). (gr. 4 up). lib. bdg. 23.33 (978-0-8368-2703-3(1)) Stevens, Gareth Inc.

—Case of the On-Line Alien. l.t. ed. 1999. (Wishbone Mysteries Ser.: No. 9). 144p. (J). (gr. 4 up). lib. bdg. 23.33 (978-0-8368-2449-0(0)) Stevens, Gareth Inc.

—Case of the Unsolved Case. l.t. ed. 2000. (Wishbone Mysteries Ser.: No. 13). (Illus.). 139p. (J). (gr. 4 up). lib. bdg. 23.33 (978-0-8368-2696-8(5)) Stevens, Gareth Inc.

—The Last of the Breed. Punchatz, Don, illus. l.t. ed. 1999. (Adventures of Wishbone Ser.: No. 16). 163p. (J). (gr. 4 up). lib. bdg. 22.60 (978-0-8368-2594-7(2)) Stevens, Gareth Inc.

—The Last of the Breed. 1999. (Adventures of Wishbone Ser.: No. 16). (J). (gr. 2-5). (978-0-606-17610-1(1)) Tandem Library Bks.

—Moby Dog. l.t. ed. 1999. (Adventures of Wishbone Ser.: No. 10). (Illus.). 144p. (J). (gr. 4 up). lib. bdg. 22.60 (978-0-8368-2306-6(0)) Stevens, Gareth Inc.

—Tale of the Missing Mascot. l.t. ed. 1999. (Wishbone Mysteries Ser.: No. 4). 144p. (J). (gr. 4 up). lib. bdg. 23.33 (978-0-8368-2385-1(0)) Stevens, Gareth Inc.

Steele, Michael Anthony. Case of the Impounded Hounds. l.t. ed. 2000. (Wishbone Mysteries Ser.: No. 17). 138p. (J). (gr. 4 up). lib. bdg. 23.33 (978-0-8368-2700-2(7)) Stevens, Gareth Inc.

—Case of the Impounded Hounds. 1999. (Wishbone Mysteries Ser.: No. 17). (978-0-606-17769-6(8)) Tandem Library Bks.

—Digging to the Center of the Earth. Punchatz, Don, illus. l.t. ed. 1999. (Adventures of Wishbone Ser.: No. 17). (J). (gr. 4 up). lib. bdg. 22.60 (978-0-8368-2595-4(0)) Stevens, Gareth Inc.

—Digging to the Center of the Earth. 1999. (Adventures of Wishbone Ser.: No. 17). (J). (gr. 2-5). (978-0-606-17611-8(X)) Tandem Library Bks.

—Forgotten Heroes. l.t. ed. 2000. (Wishbone Mysteries Ser.: No. 12). (Illus.). 139p. (J). (gr. 4 up). lib. bdg. 23.33 (978-0-8368-2695-1(7)) Stevens, Gareth Inc.

—The Ghost of Camp Ka Nowato. 1999. (Wishbone Super Mysteries Ser.: No. 2). (J). (gr. 2-5). (978-0-606-19033-6(3)) Tandem Library Bks.

Strickland, Brad. Be a Wolf! l.t. ed. 1999. (Adventures of Wishbone Ser.: No. 1). (Illus.). 144p. (J). (gr. 4 up). lib. bdg. 22.60 (978-0-8368-2297-7(8)) Stevens, Gareth Inc.

—Gullifur's Travels. 1999. (Adventures of Wishbone Ser.: No. 18). (J). (gr. 2-5). (978-0-606-19456-3(8)) Tandem Library Bks.

—Salty Dog. l.t. ed. 1999. (Adventures of Wishbone Ser.: No. 2). (Illus.). 140p. (J). (gr. 4 up). lib. bdg. 22.60 (978-0-8368-2298-4(6)) Stevens, Gareth Inc.

—Terrier of the Lost Mines. 1999. (Adventures of Wishbone Ser.: No. 19). (J). (gr. 2-5). (978-0-606-19457-0(6)) Tandem Library Bks.

Strickland, Brad & Fuller, Thomas E. The Disappearing Dinosaurs. l.t. ed. 1999. (Wishbone Mysteries Ser.: No. 10). 144p. (J). (gr. 4 up). lib. bdg. 23.33 (978-0-8368-2450-6(4)) Stevens, Gareth Inc.

—The Riddle of the Wayward Books. l.t. ed. 1999. (Wishbone Mysteries Ser.: No. 3). 144p. (J). (gr. 4 up). lib. bdg. 23.33 (978-0-8368-2384-4(2)) Stevens, Gareth Inc.

Strickland, Brad & Strickland, Barbara. Gullifur's Travels. l.t. ed. 1999. (Adventures of Wishbone Ser.: No. 18). (Illus.). (J). (gr. 4 up). lib. bdg. 22.60 (978-0-8368-2596-1(9)) Stevens, Gareth Inc.

Strickland, Brad, et al. Disoriented Express. l.t. ed. 2000. (Wishbone Mysteries Ser.: No. 14). 167p. (J). (gr. 4 up). lib. bdg. 23.33 (978-0-8368-2697-5(3)) Stevens, Gareth Inc.

Twain, Mark. Personal Recollections of Joan of Arc. 1999. reprint ed. pap. 28.00 (978-1-4047-1122-8(8)); pap. 28.00 (978-1-4047-1123-5(6)) Classic Textbooks.

Williamson, Barbara. Wishbone. 2007. (Illus.). 24p. (J). per. 12.95 (***978-1-60002-197-8(2)** , 4216, Airleaf Publishing) Airleaf Publishing & Bookselling.

The Wishbone Mysteries, 20 bks. l.t. ed. Incl. Case of the Breaking Story. Steele, Alexander. (Illus.). 144p. 2000. lib. bdg. 23.33 (978-0-8368-2703-3(1)); Case of the Cyber-Hacker. Capeci, Anne. (Illus.). 141p. 2000. lib. bdg. 23.33 (978-0-8368-2702-6(3)); Case of the Impounded Hounds. Steele, Michael Anthony. 138p. 2000. lib. bdg. 23.33 (978-0-8368-2700-2(7)); Case of the On-Line Alien. Steele, Alexander. 144p. 1999. lib. bdg. 23.33 (978-0-8368-2449-0(0)); Case of the Unsolved Case. Steele, Alexander. (Illus.). 139p. 2000. lib. bdg. 23.33 (978-0-8368-2696-8(5)); Disappearing Dinosaurs. Strickland, Brad & Fuller, Thomas E. 144p. 1999. lib. bdg. 23.33 (978-0-8368-2450-6(4)); Disoriented Express. Strickland, Brad. 167p. 2000. lib. bdg. 23.33 (978-0-8368-2697-5(3)); Drive-In of Doom. Strickland, Brad & Fuller, Thomas E. 144p. 1999. lib. bdg. 23.33 (978-0-8368-2388-2(5)); Forgotten Heroes. Steele, Michael Anthony. (Illus.). 139p. 2000. lib. bdg. 23.33 (978-0-8368-2695-1(7)); Haunted Clubhouse. Leavitt, Caroline. 144p. 1999. lib. bdg. 22.60 (978-0-8368-2383-7(4)); Key to the Golden Dog. Capeci, Anne. 144p. 1999. lib. bdg. 23.33 (978-0-8368-2389-9(3)); Lights! Camera! Action Dog! Butcher, Nancy. (Illus.). 139p. 2000. lib. bdg. 23.33 (978-0-8368-2694-4(9)); Maltese Dog. Capeci, Anne. 144p. 1999. lib. bdg. 23.33 (978-0-8368-2387-5(7)); Phantom of the Video Store. Gantt, Leticia. (Illus.). 141p. 2000. lib. bdg. 23.33 (978-0-8368-2701-9(5)); Riddle of the Wayward Books. Strickland, Brad & Fuller, Thomas E. 144p. 1999. lib. bdg. 23.33 (978-0-8368-2384-4(2)); Sirian Conspiracy. Friedman, Michael Jan. (Illus.). 141p. 2000. lib. bdg. 23.33 (978-0-8368-2699-9(X)); Stage Invader. Sathre, Vivian. (Illus.). 140p. 2000. lib. bdg. 23.33 (978-0-8368-2698-2(1)); Stolen Trophy. Friedman, Michael Jan. 144p. 1999. lib. bdg. 23.33 (978-0-8368-2386-8(9)); Tale of the Missing Mascot. Steele, Alexander. 144p. 1999. lib. bdg. 23.33 (978-0-8368-2385-1(0)); Treasure of Skeleton Reef. Strickland, Brad & Fuller, Thomas E. 144p. 1999. lib. bdg. 23.33 (978-0-8368-2382-0(6)); (J). (gr. 4 up). Set lib. bdg. 443.27 (978-0-8368-2752-1(X)) Stevens, Gareth Inc.

Worley, Roger. The Wishbone Journal. 2003. 173p. pap. 16.95 (978-1-4137-0101-2(9)) PublishAmerica, Inc.

WIT AND HUMOR

see also Anecdotes; Comedy; Humorists; Nonsense Verses also American Wit and Humor; English Wit and Humor

Aalgaard, Wendy. Venezuela in Pictures. 2nd ed. 2005. (Visual Geography Ser.). (Illus.). 80p. (J). (gr. 5-12). lib. bdg. 27.93 (978-0-8225-1172-4(X)) Lerner Publishing Group.

Abrams, Pete. Yippy Skippy, the Evil! Sluggy Freelance #5. 2000. (Sluggy Freelance Ser.). 152p. (C). pap. 12.95 (978-1-929462-23-0(9)) Plan Nine Publishing, Inc.

Agee, Jon. Who Ordered the Jumbo Shrimp? And Other Oxymorons. Agee, Jon, illus. 2002. (Illus.). 80p. (J). pap. 8.95 (978-0-374-48372-2(8) , Sunburst) Farrar, Straus & Giroux.

Arnold, Eric. Jokes You Shouldn't Tell a Dog. 1999. (Illus.). (J). (978-0-606-17926-3(7)) Tandem Library Bks.

—Jokes You Shouldn't Tell a Ghost. 1999. (Illus.). (J). (978-0-606-17927-0(5)) Tandem Library Bks.

—Jokes You Shouldn't Tell Your Teacher. 1999. (J). (978-0-606-16331-6(X)) Tandem Library Bks.

Artell, Mike. Ten-Second Tongue Twisters. Jones, Buck, illus. 2006. 96p. (J). 14.95 (978-1-4027-2258-5(3)) Sterling Publishing Co., Inc.

Artell, Mike & Rosenbloom, Joseph. Zany Tongue-Twisters. Harpster, Steve, illus. 2005. (Giggle Fit Ser.). 48p. (J). (ps). pap. 4.95 (978-1-4027-2774-0(7)) Sterling Publishing Co., Inc.

Austin, Alyssa. It Was an Accident. 2003. 80p. pap. 11.95 (978-1-4137-0102-9(7)) PublishAmerica, Inc.

Barrett, Judi. Animals Should Definitely Not Wear Clothing. Barrett, Ron, illus. 2006. (Stories to Go! Ser.). 32p. (J). pap. 4.99 (978-1-4169-1232-3(0) , Aladdin) Simon & Schuster Children's Publishing.

Barrett, Ron. The Nutty News. 2005. (Illus.). 80p. (J). (gr. 5 up). lib. bdg. 13.99 (978-0-375-92751-5(4) , Knopf Bks. for Young Readers) Random Hse. Children's Bks.

Barwin, Gary. The Magic Mustache. Jorisch, Stephane, illus. 1999. 32p. (J). (ps-2). lib. bdg. 17.95 (978-1-55037-607-4(1)) Annick Pr., Ltd. CAN. *Dist:* Firefly Bks., Ltd.

Bathroom Readers' Institute Staff. Uncle John's Ahh-Inspiring Bathroom Reader. ltd. ed. 2002. (Bathroom Readers Institute Ser.). 522p. pap. 24.95 (978-1-57145-891-9(3) , Portable Pr.) Advantage Pubs. Group.

—Uncle John's Book of Do You Know: Bathroom Reader for Kids Only. 2006. (Illus.). 224p. pap. 12.95 (978-1-59223-682-4(0) , Portable Pr.) Advantage Pubs. Group.

—Uncle John's Curiously Compelling Bathroom Reader. 19th ed. 2006. (Bathroom Reader Ser.). 522p. pap. 17.95 (978-1-59223-679-4(0) , Portable Pr.) Advantage Pubs. Group.

—Uncle John's Electrifying Bathroom Reader for Kids Only! 2003. (gr. 5-8). lib. bdg. 22.20 (978-0-613-67438-6(3)) Tandem Library Bks.

Bathroom Readers' Institute Staff, contrib. by. Uncle John's Electrifying Bathroom Reader for Kids Only! 2003. (Bathroom Readers Institute Ser.: 2). (Illus.). 324p. (J). pap. 12.95 (978-1-59223-021-1(0)) Advantage Pubs. Group.

Becker, Helaine. Funny Business: Clowning Around, Practical Jokes, Cool Comedy, Cartooning, & More... Davila, Claudia, illus. 2005. 160p. (J). (gr. 4-7). 21.95 (978-1-897066-40-9(6)); pap. 9.95 (978-1-897066-41-6(4)) Maple Tree Pr. CAN. *Dist:* Perseus Distribution.

Behnke, Alison. South Korea in Pictures. 2nd ed. 2005. (Visual Geography Ser.). (Illus.). 80p. (J). (gr. 5-12). 27.93 (978-0-8225-1174-8(6)) Lerner Publishing Group.

Benny, Mike. Kids' Nuttiest Jokes. Hoffman, Sanford, illus. 2003. 96p. (J). pap. 4.95 (978-1-4027-0624-0(3)) Sterling Publishing Co., Inc.

Benson, Edmund F. Life Isn't Fair. 2001. 80p. (J). per. 9.95 (978-1-58614-296-4(8)) Arise Foundation.

Best Ever Jokes. 2002. 256p. (J). 19.95 (978-0-7525-8928-2(8)) Parragon, Inc.

The Biggest Ever Knock Knock Joke Book. 2002. 256p. (J). 19.95 (978-0-7525-8929-9(6)) Parragon, Inc.

Binder, Helga, illus. Wild Wicked Winifred & Horrible Hank. 1999. (J). (978-0-7608-3206-6(4)) Sundance/Newbridge Educational Publishing.

Birtles. Dumb Jokes For Smart Kids. (Illus.). 96p. (J). pap. 5.95 (978-1-85479-649-3(6)) O'Mara, Michael Bks., Ltd. GBR. *Dist:* Trans-Atlantic Pubns., Inc.

Blair, Beth L. Jumbo Jokes & Riddles Book: Hours of Gut-Busting Fun! 2006. 384p. pap. 8.95 (978-1-59869-049-1(3)) Adams Media Corp.

Bloomsbury Staff. Mr. Bean's Holiday. 2007. (Illus.). 40p. (J). pap., act. bk. ed. 7.95 (978-1-59990-101-5(3)) Bloomsbury Publishing.

Boczkowski, Tricia. SpongeBob WetPants. Style Guide Staff, illus. 2003. (SpongeBob SquarePants Ser.). 8p. (J). 7.99 (978-0-689-85894-9(9) , Simon Spotlight/Nickelodeon) Simon & Schuster Children's Publishing.

Boyds Mills Press. Laugh Out Loud: Jokes & Riddles from Highlights for Children. 2004. (Illus.). 256p. (J). 10.95 (978-1-59078-347-4(6)); Vol. 2. 10.95 (978-1-59078-348-1(4)) Boyds Mills Pr.

Brandreth, Gyles. Biggest Kids Joke Book Ever. 2002. (Illus.). 576p. pap. 12.00 (978-0-233-05062-1(0)) Andre Deutsch GBR. *Dist:* Trafalgar Square Publishing.

—Jokes Jokes Jokes. 1999. (Illus.). 288p. (J). pap. 6.99 (978-0-233-99583-0(8)) Andre Deutsch GBR. *Dist:* Independent Pubs. Group.

Brewer, Paul. You Must Be Joking! Lots of Cool Jokes, Plus 17 1/2 Tips for Remembering, Telling, & Making up Your Own Jokes. 2003. (Illus.). 128p. (J). 16.95 (978-0-8126-2661-2(3)) Cricket Bks.

Brewer, Paul. You Must Be Joking, Two! Brewer, Paul, illus. 2007. (Illus.). 128p. (J). (gr. 2 up). 16.95 (***978-0-8126-2752-7(0))** Cricket Bks.

Browning. Mega Joke Book For Kids. (Illus.). 162p. (J). pap. 9.95 (978-1-85479-249-5(0)) O'Mara, Michael Bks., Ltd. GBR. *Dist:* Trans-Atlantic Pubns., Inc.

The Bunty Annual 2005. 2004. (Illus.). 128p. (J). 9.95 (978-0-85116-849-4(3)) Thomson, D.C. & Co., Ltd. GBR. *Dist:* APG Sales and Fulfillment.

Burns, Diane L. Horsing Around: Jokes to Make Ewe Smile. Gable, Brian, illus. 2005. (Make Me Laugh! Ser.). 32p. (J). (gr. k-3). lib. bdg. 19.93 (978-1-57505-662-3(3)) Lerner Publishing Group.

Burns, Diane L., et al. Backyard Beasties: Jokes to Snake You Smile. Gable, Brian, illus. (Make Me Laugh! Ser.). (J). 2004. 32p. (gr. k-3). lib. bdg. 19.93 (978-1-57505-646-3(1)); 2nd ed. 2005. 80p. (gr. 5-12). 27.93 (978-0-8225-1173-1(8)) Lerner Publishing Group.

Caseley, Judith & Wisniewski, David. The Secret Knowledge of Grown-ups: The Second File. Wisniewski, David, illus. 2001. (Secret Knowledge of Grown-Ups Ser.). (Illus.). 48p. (J). (gr. 2 up). 18.99 (978-0-688-17854-3(5)) HarperCollins Pubs.

Charney, Steve. Hocus-Jokus: 50 Funny Magic Tricks Complete with Jokes. 2003. (Illus.). ix, 132p. (J). (978-0-88166-376-1(X)) Meadowbrook Pr.

Chatterton, Martin, illus. Yuck! The Grossest Joke Book Ever. 2004. (Sidesplitters Ser.). 64p. (J). (gr. 3-5). pap. 3.95 (978-0-7534-5709-2(1) , Kingfisher) Houghton Mifflin Co. Trade & Reference Div.

Chmielewski, Gary. The Animal Zone. Caputo, Jim, illus. 2008. (J). (***978-1-59953-139-7(9))** Norwood Hse. Pr.

—The History Zone. Caputo, Jim, illus. 2007. (***978-1-59953-141-0(0))** Norwood Hse. Pr.

—The Sports Zone. 2007. (J). (***978-1-59953-144-1(5))** Norwood Hse. Pr.

Churchill, E. Richard. The Little Giant Book of Tricks & Pranks. 2005. (Illus.). 352p. pap. 6.95 (978-1-4027-2168-7(4)) Sterling Publishing Co., Inc.

Churchill, E. Richard. Tricks & Pranks. 2007. (Illus.). 360p. (J). pap. 6.95 (***978-1-4027-4977-3(5))** Sterling Publishing Co., Inc.

Cibula, Matt S. What's up with You, Taquandra Fu? Strassburg, Brian J., illus. 1998. 40p. (J). (ps-3). 16.95 (978-1-55933-212-5(3)) Zino Pr. Children's Bks.

Clinch, Lori. Are We There Yet? From Diapers to Puberty. 2004. (Illus.). 308p. (YA). per. 15.95 (978-0-9721613-9-8(2)) Old Hundred & One Pr. Publishing Co., The.

Cole, Eric. The Writings on the Stall Walls, 10. 2002. (Illus.). 120p. (YA). per. 14.95 (978-0-9725784-0-0(4)) Heritage Information Systems.

Crane, Walter Sanger, IV. Sheba: The Falcon & The Flame. 2001. 176p. (YA). pap. 15.95 (978-0-9701814-1-1(8)) Sick Mind Pr.

Crosbie, Duncan, compiled by. 500 Irish Jokes Book. 2003. (Illus.). 64p. 11.95 (978-0-7171-3532-5(2)) Gill & MacMillan, Ltd. IRL. *Dist:* Irish Bks. & Media, Inc.

Crowest, Frederick J. Musicians' Wit, Humour & Anecdote. 2001. 423p. (YA). reprint ed. 98.00 (978-0-7222-5296-3(X)) Library Reprints, Inc.

Dahl, Michael. Alphabet Soup: A Book of Riddles about Letters. Reibeling, Brandon, illus. 2004. (Read-It! Joke Books). 24p. (C). (gr. k-3). 18.60 (978-1-4048-0228-5(2)) Picture Window Bks.

—Animal Quack-Ups: Foolish & Funny Jokes about Animals. Yesh, Jeff, illus. 2004. (Read-It! Joke Books Ser.). 24p. (C). (gr. k-3). 18.60 (978-1-4048-0125-7(1)) Picture Window Bks.

—Bell Buzzers: A Book of Knock-Knock Jokes. Landmark, Ken, illus. 2004. (Read-It! Joke Books). 24p. (C). (gr. k-3). 18.60 (978-1-4048-0236-0(3)) Picture Window Bks.

—Chewy Chuckles: Deliciously Funny Jokes about Food. Yesh, Jeff, illus. 2004. (Read-It! Joke Books Ser.). 24p. (C). (gr. k-3). 18.60 (978-1-4048-0124-0(3)) Picture Window Bks.

—Ding Dong: A Book of Knock-Knock Jokes. Landmark, Ken, illus. 2004. (Read-It! Joke Books). 24p. (C). (gr. k-3). 18.60 (978-1-4048-0235-3(5)) Picture Window Bks.

—Dino Rib Ticklers: Hugely Funny Jokes about Dinosaurs. Reibeling, Brandon, illus. 2004. (Read-It! Joke Books). 24p. (C). (gr. k-3). 18.60 (978-1-4048-0122-6(7)) Picture Window Bks.

—Doctor, Doctor: A Book of Doctor Jokes. Jensen, Brian, illus. 2004. (Read-It! Joke Books). 24p. (C). (gr. k-3). 18.60 (978-1-4048-0305-3(X)) Picture Window Bks.

—Door Knockers: A Book of Knock-Knock Jokes. Landmark, Ken, illus. 2004. (Read-It! Joke Books Ser.). 24p. (C). (gr. k-3). 18.60 (978-1-4048-0238-4(X)) Picture Window Bks.

—The Everything Kids' Joke Book: Side-Splitting, Rib-Tickling Fun. 2001. (Everything Kids Ser.). (Illus.). 144p. (J). (gr. 4-7). 6.95 (978-1-58062-686-6(6)) Adams Media Corp.

—Everything Kids' Joke Book: Side-Splitting, Rib-Tickling Fun. 2002. (gr. 3-6). lib. bdg. 15.25 (978-0-613-79322-3(6)) Tandem Library Bks.

—Family Funnies: A Book of Family Jokes. Haugen, Ryan, illus. 2004. (Read-It! Joke Books). 24p. (C). (gr. k-3). 18.60 (978-1-4048-0304-6(1)) Picture Window Bks.

—Kids' Joke Book. 2001. (J). (978-0-606-22486-4(6)) Tandem Library Bks.

—Laughs on a Leash: A Book of Pet Jokes. Haugen, Ryan, illus. 2004. (Read-It! Joke Books). 24p. (C). (gr. k-3). 18.60 (978-1-4048-0303-9(3)) Picture Window Bks.

—Monster Laughs: Frightfully Funny Jokes about Monsters. Reibeling, Brandon, illus. 2004. (Read-It! Joke Books). 24p. (C). (gr. k-3). 18.60 (978-1-4048-0123-3(5)) Picture Window Bks.

—Nutty Neighbors: A Book of Knock-Knock Jokes. Landmark, Ken, illus. 2004. (Read-It! Joke Books). 24p. (C). (gr. k-3). 18.60 (978-1-4048-0234-6(7)) Picture Window Bks.

—Open Up & Laugh: A Book of Knock-Knock Jokes. Landmark, Ken, illus. 2004. (Read-It! Joke Books). 24p. (C). (gr. k-3). 18.60 (978-1-4048-0237-7(1)) Picture Window Bks.

—Read-It! Joke Books, 24 bks. Incl. Alphabet Soup : A Book of Riddles about Letters. Reibeling, Brandon, illus. 18.60 (978-1-4048-0228-5(2)); Animal Quack-Ups : Foolish & Funny Jokes about Animals. Yesh, Jeff, illus. 18.60 (978-1-4048-0125-7(1)); Bell Buzzers : A Book of Knock-Knock Jokes. Landmark, Ken, illus. 18.60 (978-1-4048-0236-0(3)); Chewy Chuckles : Deliciously Funny Jokes about Food. Yesh, Jeff, illus. 18.60 (978-1-4048-0124-0(3)); Crazy Criss-Cross : A Book of Mixed-Up Riddles. Reibeling, Brandon, illus. 18.60 (978-1-4048-0232-2(0)); Ding Dong : A Book of Knock-Knock Jokes. Landmark, Ken, illus. 18.60 (978-1-4048-0235-3(5)); Dino Rib Ticklers : Hugely Funny Jokes about Dinosaurs. Reibeling, Brandon, illus. 18.60 (978-1-4048-0122-6(7)); Doctor, Doctor : A Book of Doctor Jokes. Jensen, Brian, illus. 18.60 (978-1-4048-0305-3(X)); Door Knockers : A Book of Knock-Knock Jokes. Landmark, Ken, illus. 18.60 (978-1-4048-0238-4(X)); Family Funnies : A Book of Family Jokes. Haugen, Ryan, illus. 18.60 (978-1-4048-0304-6(1)); Funny Talk : A Book of Chitchat Riddles. Reibeling, Brandon, illus. 18.60 (978-1-4048-0229-2(0)); Galactic Giggles : Far-Out & Funny Jokes about Outer Space. Reibeling, Brandon, illus. 18.60 (978-1-4048-0126-4(X)); Laughs on a Leash : A Book of Pet Jokes. Haugen, Ryan, illus. 18.60 (978-1-4048-0303-9(3)); Monster Laughs : Frightfully Funny Jokes about Monsters. Reibeling, Brandon, illus. 18.60 (978-1-4048-0123-3(5)); Nutty Neighbors : A Book of Knock-Knock Jokes. Landmark, Ken, illus. 18.60 (978-1-4048-0234-6(7)); Open Up & Laugh : A Book of Knock-Knock Jokes. Landmark, Ken, illus. 18.60 (978-1-4048-0237-7(1)); Rhyme Time : A Book of Rhyming Riddles. Reibeling, Brandon, illus. 18.60 (978-1-4048-0227-8(4)); School Buzz : Classy & Funny Jokes about School. Yesh, Jeff, illus. 18.60 (978-1-4048-0121-9(9)); School Daze : A Book of Riddles about School. Reibeling, Brandon, illus. 18.60 (978-1-4048-0231-5(2)); Teacher Says : A Book of Teacher Jokes. Haugen, Ryan, illus. 18.60 (978-1-4048-0301-5(7)); Three-Alarm Jokes : A Book of Firefighter Jokes. Jensen, Brian, illus. 18.60 (978-1-4048-0302-2(5)); Under Arrest : A Book of Police Jokes. Jensen, Brian, illus. 18.60 (978-1-4048-0306-0(8)); Who's There? A Book of Knock-Knock Jokes. Landmark, Ken, illus. 18.60 (978-1-4048-0233-9(9)); Zoodles : A Book of Riddles about Animals. Reibeling, Brandon, illus. 18.60 (978-1-4048-0230-8(4)); 24p. (C). (gr. k-3). 2004. 2003. 446.40 (978-1-4048-0300-8(9)) Picture Window Bks.

—Roaring with Laughter: A Book of Animal Jokes. Haberstroh, Anne, illus. 2004. (Read-It! Joke Books Ser.). 24p. (C). (gr. 1-3). 18.60 (978-1-4048-0628-3(8)) Picture Window Bks.

—School Buzz: Classy & Funny Jokes about School. Yesh, Jeff, illus. 2004. (Read-It! Joke Books). 24p. (C). (gr. k-3). 18.60 (978-1-4048-0121-9(9)) Picture Window Bks.

—School Daze: A Book of Riddles about School. Reibeling, Brandon, illus. 2004. (Read-It! Joke Books). 24p. (C). (gr. k-3). 18.60 (978-1-4048-0231-5(2)) Picture Window Bks.

—Teacher Says: A Book of Teacher Jokes. Haugen, Ryan, illus. 2004. (Read-It! Joke Books). 24p. (C). (gr. k-3). 18.60 (978-1-4048-0301-5(7)) Picture Window Bks.

—Three-Alarm Jokes: A Book of Firefighter Jokes. Jensen, Brian, illus. 2004. (Read-It! Joke Books). 24p. (C). (gr. k-3). 18.60 (978-1-4048-0302-2(5)) Picture Window Bks.

—Under Arrest: A Book of Police Jokes. Jensen, Brian, illus. 2004. (Read-It! Joke Books). 24p. (C). (gr. k-3). 18.60 (978-1-4048-0306-0(8)) Picture Window Bks.

—Who's There? A Book of Knock-Knock Jokes. Landmark, Ken, illus. 2004. (Read-It! Joke Books Ser.). 24p. (C). (gr. k-3). 18.60 (978-1-4048-0233-9(9)) Picture Window Bks.

Davis, James (Jim) W. Out-takes of 55 Years of Camping. 2004. (Illus.). 168p. (YA). per. 5.95 (978-0-9760960-0-9(5)) Davis, James (Jim).

Davis, Jim. Menace of the Nutanator. 1998. (Garfield's Pet Force Ser.: No. 4). (Illus.). (J). (gr. 3-7). pap. 4.50 (978-0-590-05945-9(9)) Scholastic, Inc.

De La Hoz, Cindy. Shrek 3 Practical Joke Kit. 2007. 24p. (J). pap. 9.95 (***978-0-7624-3045-1(1)** , Running Pr. Kids) Running Pr. Bk. Pubs.

DeTellis, Luc. Who's There: 101 Knock Knock Jokes for Kids. 2003. pap. 5.95 (978-0-9722774-1-9(2)) Muscatello Publishing.

—Who's There Again? 101 More Knock Knock Jokes for Kids. 2004. 108p. (J). per. 6.99 (978-0-9722774-3-3(9)) Muscatello Publishing.

Dewhurst. Why Am I Laughing? (J). (978-0-02-531345-3(2) , Scribner) Simon & Schuster.

Dewin, Howie. Dexter's Joke Book for Geniuses. 2004. (Dexter's Laboratory Ser.). (Illus.). 64p. (J). pap. 4.50 (978-0-439-54582-2(X) , Scholastic Paperbacks) Scholastic, Inc.

—Monsters Unleashed: Joke Book. 2004. (Scooby-Doo Ser.). 64p. (J). pap. 4.99 (978-0-439-56880-7(3) , Scholastic Paperbacks) Scholastic, Inc.

Dinneen, John. The Practical Joker's Handbook. (Illus.). 71p. (J). pap. 4.95 (978-0-330-34634-4(2) , Pan) Pan Macmillan GBR. *Dist:* Trafalgar Square Publishing.

—The Practical Joker's Handbook 2. Maddison, Lucy, illus. 70p. (J). pap. 4.95 (978-0-330-35524-7(4) , Pan) Pan Macmillan GBR. *Dist:* Trafalgar Square Publishing.

Dipiazza, Francesca. Turkey in Pictures. 2nd ed. 2005. (Visual Geography Ser.). (Illus.). 80p. (J). (gr. 5-12). 27.93 (978-0-8225-1169-4(X)) Lerner Publishing Group.

Doering, Jennie Spray. Beach Riddles. Pica, Steve, illus. 2006. (Silly Millies Ser.). 32p. (J). 21.27 (978-0-7613-2885-8(8) , Millbrook Pr.) Lerner Publishing Group.

Donahue, Jill L. Artful Antics: A Book of Art, Music, & Theater Jokes. Muehlenhardt, Amy Bailey, illus. 2006. (Read-It! Joke Books—Supercharged!). (J). 19.93 (978-1-4048-2363-1(8)) Picture Window Bks.

—How Do You Get There? A Book of Transportation Jokes. Muehlenhardt, Amy Bailey, illus. 2006. (Read-It! Joke Books—Supercharged!). (J). 19.93 (978-1-4048-2367-9(0)) Picture Window Bks.

—Laughing Letters & Nutty Numerals: A Book of Jokes about ABCs & 123s. Trover, Zachary, illus. 2006. (Read-It! Joke Books—Supercharged!). (J). 19.93 (978-1-4048-2365-5(4)) Picture Window Bks.

—Silly Sports: A Book of Sport Jokes. Muehlenhardt, Amy Bailey, illus. 2006. (Read-It! Joke Books—Supercharged!). (J). 19.93 (978-1-4048-2366-2(2)) Picture Window Bks.

—What's in a Name? A Book of Name Jokes. Trover, Zachary, illus. 2006. (Read-It! Joke Books—Supercharged!). (J). 19.93 (978-1-4048-2364-8(6)) Picture Window Bks.

Dow, T. E. J. Scooby-Doo! Movie Ultimate Joke Book. 2002. (gr. k-3). lib. bdg. 12.40 (978-0-613-50740-0(1)) Tandem Library Bks.

Dow, T. E. J. & Dewin, Howie. Scooby-Doo! Movie Ultimate Joke Book. movie tie-in ed. 2002. (Scooby-Doo Ser.). (Illus.). 64p. (J). pap. 4.99 (978-0-439-46820-6(5)) Scholastic, Inc.

Downs, Michael. Pig Giggles & Rabbit Rhymes: A Book of Animal Riddles. Sheldon, David, illus. 2002. 32p. (J). (ps-3). 13.95 (978-0-8118-3114-7(0)) Chronicle Bks. LLC.

Dreams that Lye Within. 2005. (YA). (978-1-59872-101-0(1)) Instantpublisher.com.

Eisenberg, Lisa. Silly School Riddles. Smith, Elwood H., illus. 2008. 40p. (J). (gr. 1-3). 14.99 (***978-0-8037-3165-3(5)** , Dial) Penguin Group (USA) Inc.

Eliot, Jan. Road Kill in the Closet: The Fourth Collection of the Syndicated Cartoon Stone Soup, No. 4. 2004. (Illus.). 192p. pap. 13.95 (978-0-9674102-3-4(1)) Four Panel Pr.

Exley, Helen. Chuckle of Kids Jokes. 1998. (Joke Bks.). (Illus.). 64p. (J). 8.50 (978-1-85015-999-5(8)) Exley, Helen Giftbooks GBR. *Dist:* Exley Giftbooks.

Exley, Helen, ed. Crazy Kids' Jokes. 2000. (Joke Bks.). (Illus.). 64p. (978-1-86187-126-8(0)) Exley, Helen Giftbooks GBR. *Dist:* Exley Giftbooks.

Filling, Gregory, illus. The Valley Forgers: History Jokes. 2001. 40p. (J). (gr. 3-7). lib. bdg. 13.95 (978-0-945912-50-7(1)) Pippin Pr.

Fisch, Sarah & Dewin, Howie. The Gag Book (Joke Book) 2004. (Shrek 2 Ser.). (Illus.). 48p. (J). pap. 3.99 (978-0-439-53848-0(3)) Scholastic, Inc.

Fitch, Sheree. There Were Monkeys in My Kitchen! braille ed. 2004. (Illus.). (J). (gr. k-3). spiral bd. (978-0-616-01639-8(5)) Canadian National Institute for the Blind/Institut National Canadien pour les Aveugles.

Fleischman, Sid. Jim Ugly. Smith, Jos. A., illus. 2003. 144p. (J). (gr. 3-6). pap. 6.99 (978-0-06-052121-9(X) , Harper Trophy) HarperCollins Pubs.

—McBroom's Ghost. Wummer, Amy, illus. 1998. 62p. lib. bdg. 11.79 (978-0-606-15963-0(0)) Tandem Library Bks.

Fox, Lori Miller. The Craziest Riddle Book in the World. 2004. 96p. (J). pap. 4.95 (978-1-4027-0898-5(X)) Sterling Publishing Co., Inc.

—2,001 Jokes & Riddles. 2004. (Illus.). 479p. (978-1-4027-1533-4(1) , Sterling/Main St.) Sterling Publishing Co., Inc.

Franklin, Janet. My Skin Has Fallen & It Won't Get Up. Wellborn, Patty Rae, illus. 2002. 42p. per. 13.95 (978-0-9718002-0-5(0)) Wrinkle Pr.

Frazer, J. D. User Friendly 1. 0. 2002. 112p. (C). pap. 14.95 (978-1-929462-39-1(5) , UF-4) Plan Nine Publishing, Inc.

Fremont, Victoria. Knock Knock Jokes. Daste, Larry, illus. 1998. 64p. pap. 1.50 (978-0-486-40402-8(1)) Dover Pubns., Inc.

Friedman, Sharon. Grin & Bear It: Zoo Jokes to Make You Roar. Gable, Brian, illus. 2005. (Make Me Laugh! Ser.). 32p. (J). (gr. k-3). lib. bdg. 19.93 (978-1-57505-660-9(7)) Lerner Publishing Group.

Fuhrer, David & Silbermintz, Marvin. Backwords. 2007. 96p. (J). pap. 12.95 ***(*978-0-9788178-7-9(7))*** Falls Media.

Gaber, Susan. Little Bill's Big Book of Jokes. 1999. (J). pap. 2.99 (978-0-689-83998-6(7) , Simon Spotlight) Simon & Schuster Children's Publishing.

Gatacre, Sophie. Please Don't Call Me Mad! 2005. Orig. Title: Don't Call Me Mad. (YA). pap. 9.99 (978-0-9746697-1-7(7)) Three Cents Publishing.

Geoghegan, Adrienne. Dogs Don't Wear Glasses. 2000. (Illus.). 32p. (J). (ps-3). pap. 7.95 (978-1-56656-274-4(0) , Crocodile Bks.) Interlink Publishing Group, Inc.

Gilchrist, Guy. When Cats Fly. 2001. (Mudpies Ser.: Vol. 2). 128p. pap. 9.95 (978-1-929462-24-7(7)) Plan Nine Publishing, Inc.

Gomez, Rebecca. The Emperor's New Groove: Joke Book. 2000. (Illus.). 64p. (J). (gr. 3-7). pap. 2.99 (978-0-7868-4428-9(0)) Disney Pr.

—Toy Story II Joke Book. 1999. 64p. (J). pap. 2.99 (978-0-7868-4393-0(4)) Disney Pr.

Gomez, Rebecca, et al. Toy Story II Joke Book. McCormack, Erin, ed. 1999. (Toy Story 2 Ser.). (Illus.). 63p. (J). (gr. 2-5). pap. 2.99 (978-0-7868-4357-2(8)) Disney Pr.

Goode, Ben. The Fine Art of Worrying: The Official Guide Book for Worry Warts. 2003. (YA). per. 9.95 (978-1-885027-21-4(4)) Apricot Pr.

—How to Humor the Ornery People in Your Life. Mecham, David, illus. 2002. 93p. (YA). per. 6.95 (978-1-885027-12-2(5)) Apricot Pr.

—How to Make People Think You're Normal. Mecham, David, illus. 2002. 93p. (YA). per. 6.95 (978-1-885027-14-6(1)) Apricot Pr.

—Understanding Women: A Guidebook for Guys Who Are Often Confused. Mecham, David, illus. 2001. 91p. (YA). per. 6.95 (978-1-885027-13-9(3)) Apricot Pr.

Grambs, Alison. Crazy Christmas Jokes. Harpster, Steve, illus. 2004. (Giggle Fit Ser.). 48p. (J). 12.95 (978-1-4027-1244-9(8)) Sterling Publishing Co., Inc.

—Crazy Christmas Jokes. Harpster, Steve, illus. 2005. 48p. (J). (ps-ps). pap. 4.95 (978-1-4027-2769-6(0)) Sterling Publishing Co., Inc.

—Hilarious Halloween Jokes. Harpster, Steve, illus. 2005. (Giggle Fit Ser.). 48p. (J). (ps). pap. 4.95 (978-1-4027-2771-9(2)) Sterling Publishing Co., Inc.

—Totally Silly Jokes. 2004. (Illus.). 96p. (J). pap. 4.95 (978-1-4027-1726-0(1)) Sterling Publishing Co., Inc.

Green, Rod. The Mr. Bean Joke Book. 2002. (Illus.). 144p. (J). mass mkt. 8.99 (978-1-84222-655-1(X)) Carlton Bks., Ltd. GBR. *Dist:* Independent Pubs. Group.

Grossman, Bill. Cowboy Ed. Wint, Florence, illus. 2004. 28p. (J). (ps-3). reprint ed. (978-0-7567-7851-4(4)) DIANE Publishing Co.

Gumm, Merry L. Help! I'm in Middle School... How Will I Survive? 2005. (Illus.). 80p. (J). per. 9.95 (978-0-9761724-5-1(3) , B-HMS) NSR Pubns.

Haberstroh, Anne, illus. Read-It! Joke Books: Supercharged, 6 bks. Incl. Beastly Laughs : A Book of Monster Jokes. Moore, Mark. 18.60 (978-1-4048-0625-2(3)); Chalkboard Chuckles : A Book of Classroom Jokes. Moore, Mark. 18.60 (978-1-4048-0626-9(1)); Creepy Crawlers : A Book of Bug Jokes. Moore, Mark. 18.60 (978-1-4048-0627-6(X)); Roaring with Laughter : A Book of Animal Jokes. Dahl, Michael. 18.60 (978-1-4048-0628-3(8)); Sit! Stay! Laugh! A Book of Pet Jokes. Moore, Mark. 18.60 (978-1-4048-0629-0(6)); Spooky Sillies : A Book of Ghost Jokes. Moore, Mark. 18.60 (978-1-4048-0630-6(X)); 24p. (C). (gr. 1-3). 2004. (Illus.). 2004. Set lib. bdg. 111.60 (978-1-4048-0638-2(5)) Picture Window Bks.

Hall, Katy, pseud. Creepy Riddles. 2000. (Easy-to-Read Ser.). (J). 10.79 (978-0-606-20230-5(7)) Tandem Library Bks.

—Dino Riddles. 2003. (gr. k-3). lib. bdg. 11.80 (978-0-613-70800-5(8)) Tandem Library Bks.

—Really, Really, Really Bad Jokes. 1999. (978-0-606-16401-6(4)) Tandem Library Bks.

Hall, Katy, pseud & Eisenberg, Lisa. Boo Who? And Other Wicked Halloween Knock-Knock Jokes. Carpenter, Stephen, illus. 2000. (Lift-the-Flap Knock-Knock Bk.). 16p. (J). (gr. k-3). pap. 6.99 (978-0-694-01359-3(5) , Harper Festival) HarperCollins Pubs.

—Dino Riddles. Rubel, Nicole, illus. (J). (gr. k-3). 2003. 48p. pap. 3.99 (978-0-14-250179-5(4) , Puffin); 2002. 40p. 13.99 (978-0-8037-2239-2(7) , Dial) Penguin Group (USA) Inc.

—Easter Crack-Ups: Knock-Knock Jokes Funny-Side Up. Carpenter, Stephen, illus. 2000. (Lift-the-Flap Knock-Knock Bk.). 16p. (J). (gr. k-3). pap. 6.99 (978-0-694-01356-2(0) , Harper Festival) HarperCollins Pubs.

—Olive You! And Other Valentine Knock-Knock Jokes You'll A-Door. Carpenter, Stephen, illus. 2000. (Lift-the-Flap Knock-Knock Bk.). 16p. (J). (gr. k-3). pap. 6.99 (978-0-694-01355-5(2) , Harper Festival) HarperCollins Pubs.

—Stinky Riddles. Andriani, Renee, illus. 2005. (Easy-to-Read, Dial Ser.). 40p. (J). (ps-4). 14.99 (978-0-8037-2928-5(6) , Dial) Penguin Group (USA) Inc.

Hample, Stuart E. Silly Book. 2004. (Illus.). 32p. (J). 15.99 (978-0-7636-2256-5(7)) Candlewick Pr.

Hapka, Catherine. Joke Book. 2002. (ps-2). lib. bdg. 11.80 (978-0-613-50540-6(9)) Tandem Library Bks.

Harpster, Steve. Silly Knock-Knocks. Rosenbloom, Joseph, illus. 2001. (Giggle Fit Ser.). 48p. (J). 12.95 (978-0-8069-8015-7(X)) Sterling Publishing Co., Inc.

Havel, Geoff. Punzie, ICQ! Bell, Owen, illus. 1999. 32p. (J). 12.95 (978-1-86368-198-8(1)) Fremantle Pr. AUS. *Dist:* International Specialized Bk. Services.

Hayes, Daniel. Eye of the Beholder. 1998. 192p. (YA). (gr. 7-12). pap. 6.99 (978-0-449-00235-3(7) , Fawcett) Random House Publishing Group.

Hills, Tad. Knock, Knock! Who's There? My First Book of Knock-Knock Jokes. 2000. (Illus.). 22p. (J). (gr. k-3). per. (978-0-689-82711-2(3) , Simon & Schuster Children's Publishing) Simon & Schuster Children's Publishing.

Hirschman, Jessica Elin & Cole, Jennifer Elin. I'm in the Bathroom! Bright, Bonnie, illus. 2002. 24p. (J). per. 6.95 (978-0-9701155-2-2(0) , 0970115520) Cookie Bear Pr., Inc.

Hogan, Mary & Fontes, Justine. Dinosaur Joke Book. 2000. (Illus.). 64p. (J). (gr. 4-7). pap. 2.99 (978-0-7868-4417-3(5)) Disney Pr.

Horsfall, Jacqueline. Bug Jokes. Harpster, Steve, illus. 2006. (Giggle Fit Ser.). 48p. (J). 12.95 (978-1-4027-2882-2(4)) Sterling Publishing Co., Inc.

—Dinosaur Jokes. Harpster, Steve, illus. 2004. (Giggle Fit Ser.). 48p. pap. 4.95 (978-1-4027-1761-1(X)) Sterling Publishing Co., Inc.

—Joke & Riddle Ballyhoo. Snider, Jackie, illus. 96p. (J). 2007. pap. 4.95 (978-1-4027-2547-0(7)); 2005. (gr. 4-7). 14.95 (978-1-4027-1953-0(1)) Sterling Publishing Co., Inc.

—Kids' Silliest Jokes. Jones, Buck, illus. 2003. 96p. (J). pap. 4.95 (978-1-4027-0598-4(0)) Sterling Publishing Co., Inc.

—Kids' Silliest Jokes. 2003. (gr. k-3). lib. bdg. 12.95 (978-0-613-77992-0(4)) Tandem Library Bks.

—Kids' Silliest Knock-Knocks. Jones, Buck, illus. 96p. (J). 2005. pap. 4.95 (978-1-4027-2221-9(4)); 2004. 14.95 (978-1-4027-1135-0(2)) Sterling Publishing Co., Inc.

—Super Goofy Jokes. Collinet, Rob, illus. 96p. (J). (ps-ps). 2005. pap. 4.95 (978-1-4027-2788-7(7)); 2004. 14.95 (978-1-4027-0927-2(7)) Sterling Publishing Co., Inc.

Horsfall, Jacqueline & Pierce, Terry. A Little Giant Book: Laughin' Jammin' Slammin' Jokefest. 2007. (Illus.). 360p. (J). pap. 6.95 ***(*978-1-4027-4991-9(0))*** Sterling Publishing Co., Inc.

Howell, Laura, ed. Animal Jokes. Rolland, Leonard Le, illus. 2004. (Jokes Ser.). 96p. (J). pap. 6.95 (978-0-7945-0655-1(0) , Usborne) EDC Publishing.

—School Jokes. Rolland, Leonard Le, illus. 2004. (Jokes Ser.). 96p. (J). pap. 6.95 (978-0-7945-0394-9(2) , Usborne) EDC Publishing.

—Silly Jokes. Rolland, Leonard Le, illus. 2004. (Jokes Ser.). 96p. (J). pap. 6.95 (978-0-7945-0395-6(0) , Usborne) EDC Publishing.

Hunt, Sara, ed. Coconut's Joke Book. 2007. 48p. (J). pap. 5.95 ***(*978-1-59369-171-4(8)*** , Pleasant Co.) American Girl Publishing, Inc.

Hurt-Newton, Tania. Unforgettable Elephant Jokes. 2004. (Sidesplitters Ser.). 64p. (J). (gr. 3-5). pap. 3.95 (978-0-7534-5706-1(7) , Kingfisher) Houghton Mifflin Co. Trade & Reference Div.

Johnson, Erik O. Insult Stickies: 100 Funny Insults to Write & Leave Behind. 2007. (Illus.). 208p. (J). pap. 4.95 (978-1-60059-076-4(4)) Lark Bks.

Joke Fun. 2002. 192p. (J). pap. 3.98 (978-0-7525-7916-0(9)) Parragon, Inc.

Jokes, 6 vols. 2005. (Illus.). (J). (gr. k-4). lib. bdg. 170.80 (978-1-59197-619-6(7) , Buddy Bks.) ABDO Publishing Co.

Jokes & More Jokes! 2005. (Illus.). (J). (gr. k-4). lib. bdg. 170.80 (978-1-59197-869-5(6)) ABDO Publishing Co.

Jumbo Shrimp, the Ultimate Oxymoron Book. 2003. per. 19.95 (978-0-9745049-0-2(4)) Fein, Bruce.

Juster, Norton. As Silly as Knees, as Busy as Bees: An Astounding Assortment of Similes. Small, David, illus. 1998. 80p. (J). (gr. 3 up). pap. 4.95 (978-0-688-16360-0(2)) HarperCollins Pubs.

Keller, Charles. Animal Jokes. Harpster, Steve, illus. 2004. (Giggle Fit Ser.). 48p. pap. 4.95 (978-1-4027-1760-4(1)) Sterling Publishing Co., Inc.

—Best Joke Book Ever. Sinclair, Jeff, illus. 2006. 96p. (J). pap. 4.95 (978-1-4027-2373-5(3)) Sterling Publishing Co., Inc.

—Best Joke Book Ever. 1998. (Illus.). 96p. (J). 14.95 (978-0-8069-9865-7(2)) Sterling Publishing Co., Inc.

—Best Knock-Knock Book Ever. Sinclair, Jeff, illus. 2001. 96p. (J). (gr. 1-4). pap. 4.95 (978-0-8069-6529-1(0)) Sterling Publishing Co., Inc.

—Best Knock-Knock Book Ever. 2001. (ps-2). lib. bdg. 12.95 (978-0-613-45387-5(5)); (Illus.). (J). (978-0-606-21062-1(8)) Tandem Library Bks.

—Giggle Fit: Super Knock-Knocks. Harpster, Steve, illus. 2006. 48p. (J). pap. 4.95 (978-1-4027-2772-6(0)) Sterling Publishing Co., Inc.

—Giggles. 2007. (Illus.). 360p. (J). pap. 6.95 ***(*978-1-4027-4984-1(8))*** Sterling Publishing Co., Inc.

—Goofy Jokes & Giggles. Garbot, Dave, illus. 2002. 96p. (J). (gr. 1-4). pap. 4.95 (978-0-8069-7627-3(6)) Sterling Publishing Co., Inc.

—Kids' Funniest Knock-Knocks. Sinclair, Jeff, illus. 2001. (Rattle Bear Bks.). 96p. (J). (gr. 1-4). pap. 4.95 (978-0-8069-5882-8(0)) Sterling Publishing Co., Inc.

—Kids' Funniest Knock-Knocks. 2001. (gr. k-3). lib. bdg. 12.95 (978-0-613-75552-8(9)) Tandem Library Bks.

—Knock-Knocks. Hoffman, Sanford, illus. 2007. 360p. (J). pap. 6.95 ***(*978-1-4027-4970-4(8))*** Sterling Publishing Co., Inc.

Keller, Charles. The Little Giant Book of Knock-Knocks. Hoffman, Sanford, illus. 2003. 360p. (J). (gr. 4-7). pap. 6.95 (978-0-8069-8108-6(3)) Sterling Publishing Co., Inc.

Keller, Charles & Rosenbloom, Joseph. The Gigantic Book of Giggles. 2004. (Illus.). 255p. (J). pap. 4.98 (978-1-4027-1535-8(8) , Sterling/Main St.) Sterling Publishing Co., Inc.

King-Smith, Dick. Robin Hood & His Miserable Men & Other Topsy-Turvy Stories. abr. ed. (Illus.). 32p. (J). pap. 7.95 (978-0-14-130035-1(3)) Penguin Bks., Ltd. GBR. *Dist:* Trafalgar Square Publishing.

Kingfisher, ed. A Joke a Day: 365 Guarenteed Giggles. Chatterton, M. & Trimmer, Tony, illus. 2007. (Sidesplitters Ser.). 160p. (J). (gr. 1-5). pap. 5.95 ***(*978-0-7534-6128-0(5)*** , Kingfisher) Houghton Mifflin Co. Trade & Reference Div.

Kingfisher Editors, ed. Ho! Ho! Ho! 150 Hysterical Christmas Jokes. 2005. (Sidesplitters Ser.). (Illus.). 64p. (J). (gr. 3-5). pap. 3.95 (978-0-7534-5849-5(7) , Kingfisher) Houghton Mifflin Co. Trade & Reference Div.

Kirby, Robert. Kirby Soup for the Soul. Bagley, Pat, illus. 2003. 128p. (YA). per. 9.95 (978-0-9744860-2-4(7)) White Horse Bks.

Klutz Press Staff. Caribiners: Random Riddles; Really Dumb Jokes; Weird Facts. 2004. 40p. (J). (gr. 1 up). 3.95 (978-1-57054-871-0(4)) Klutz.

—Scratch Off Carabiners: Punch Lines; Truth or Dare; Your Future. 2005. 40p. (J). (gr. 1 up). 3.95 (978-1-57054-878-9(1)) Klutz.

Kowitt, Holly. Funny Bones: Jokes, Riddles, Knock-Knocks, & Loads of Laughs Starring the Fabulous Crazy Bones! 2000. 64p. (J). pap. (978-0-439-18019-1(8)) Scholastic, Inc.

—Jokes from the Sewer. Talbot, Eric, illus. 2004. (Teenage Mutant Ninja Turtles Ser.). 48p. (J). pap. 2.99 (978-0-689-86966-2(5) , Simon Spotlight) Simon & Schuster Children's Publishing.

—Jokes from the Sewer. 2004. (gr. k-3). lib. bdg. 10.65 (978-0-613-88303-0(9)) Tandem Library Bks.

—This Book Is a Joke. 2004. (Illus.). 128p. (J). (gr. 4-7). pap. 5.99 (978-0-439-67171-2(X) , Scholastic Paperbacks) Scholastic, Inc.

Kushner, Maureen. Funniest Excuse Book Ever. 1998. (gr. 3-6). lib. bdg. 12.95 (978-0-613-75559-7(6)) Tandem Library Bks.

Laden, Nina. When Pigasso Met Mootisse. 1998. (Illus.). 40p. (J). (ps-5). 16.95 (978-0-8118-1121-7(2)) Chronicle Bks. LLC.

Ladybird Books Staff. Mad Millennium Joke Book. 1999. (978-0-7214-9743-3(8) , Ladybird Books) Penguin Bks., Ltd.

Laffin, Ima. Knock-Knock Jokes. 2005. (Jokes Ser.). (Illus.). 24p. (J). (gr. k-4). lib. bdg. 21.35 (978-1-59197-622-6(7) , Buddy Bks.) ABDO Publishing Co.

—Monster Jokes. 2005. (Jokes Ser.). (Illus.). 24p. (J). (gr. k-4). lib. bdg. 21.35 (978-1-59197-623-3(5) , Buddy Bks.) ABDO Publishing Co.

—More Monster Jokes. 2005. (More Jokes! Ser.). (Illus.). 24p. (gr. k-4). lib. bdg. 21.35 (978-1-59197-874-9(2)) ABDO Publishing Co.

Laughter. 2004. per. 9.95 (978-0-9760484-0-4(X)) Dennison, Donna.

Laughter Is the Best Medicine: Individual Title Six-Packs. (Action Packs Ser.). 120p. (gr. 3-5). 44.00 (978-0-7635-8433-7(9)) Rigby Education.

Lavado, Joaquin Salvador Quino. Esto No es Todo (This Isn't All) 2001. (SPA., Illus.). 528p. 49.95 (978-950-515-750-1(9)) De La Flor ARG. *Dist:* Editorial Cultural, Inc.

Lawrence, Jan. The Revenge of the Substitute Teacher. 1998. (J). (gr. 3-7). pap. 4.50 (978-0-590-05902-2(5) , Scholastic Paperbacks) Scholastic, Inc.

Le Rolland, L. Classroom Jokes. 2004. (What's Happening Ser.). 96p. (J). pap. 6.95 (978-0-7945-0391-8(8)) EDC Publishing.

Leblanc, Louise. Leo & Julio. Cummins, Sarah, tr. Brochard, Phillippe, illus. 1999. (First Novels Ser.). 64p. (gr. 1-5). 4.95 (978-0-88780-478-6(0)) Formac Publishing Co., Ltd. CAN. *Dist:* Casemate Pubs. & Bk. Distributors, LLC.

Lederer, Richard. Pun & Games: Jokes, Riddles, Daffynitions, Tairy Fales, Rhymes, & More Word Play for Kids. Morice, Dave, illus. 2003. 112p. (J). (gr. 5 up). pap. 9.95 (978-1-55652-264-2(9)) Chicago Review Pr., Inc.

Lee, Cyl. Really Silly Jokes. 2005. (Jokes Ser.). (Illus.). 24p. (J). (gr. k-4). lib. bdg. 21.35 (978-1-59197-624-0(3) , Buddy Bks.) ABDO Publishing Co.

—Ridiculous Riddles. 2005. (Jokes Ser.). (Illus.). 24p. (J). (gr. k-4). lib. bdg. 21.35 (978-1-59197-625-7(1) , Buddy Bks.) ABDO Publishing Co.

Leighton, Audrey O. Alaska Knock-Knock Jokes. 1999. (Illus.). 32p. 4.95 (978-0-9666647-2-0(8)) Flying Frog Publishing.

Lewman, David. Adventures of Rocky & Bullwinkle Movie Joke Book. 2000. (gr. 3-6). lib. bdg. 10.65 (978-0-613-24091-8(X)) Tandem Library Bks.

—Hands Off! Greenblatt, C. H. & Reiss, William, illus. 2003. (SpongeBob SquarePants Ser.). 24p. (J). pap. 3.50 (978-0-689-85603-7(2) , Simon Spotlight/Nickelodeon) Simon & Schuster Children's Publishing.

—Joke Book. 2000. (SpongeBob SquarePants Ser.). (Illus.). 48p. (J). (gr. 1-4). pap. 3.99 (978-0-689-84017-3(9) , Simon Spotlight) Simon & Schuster Children's Publishing.

—My Book of Stupid Jokes. 2001. (Angela Anaconda Ser.). (Illus.). 48p. (Orig.). (J). (ps-3). pap. 2.99 (978-0-689-83994-8(4) , Simon Spotlight) Simon & Schuster Children's Publishing.

—Rugrats in Paris: Joke Book. 2000. (gr. k-3). lib. bdg. 10.65 (978-0-613-31652-1(5)) Tandem Library Bks.

—Scared Silly! SpongeBob's Book of Spooky Jokes. 2007. (SpongeBob SquarePants Ser.). 48p. (J). pap. 3.99 ***(*978-1-4169-4735-6(3)*** , Simon Spotlight) Simon & Schuster Children's Publishing.

—Spongebob Squarepants Joke Book. 2000. (gr. 3-6). lib. bdg. 10.65 (978-0-613-31744-3(0)) Tandem Library Bks.

—SpongeBob SquarePants Survival Guide. 2002. (Illus.). 144p. pap. 10.95 (978-0-7434-6987-6(9) , Pocket) Simon & Schuster.

Lewman, David & Fain, David. Ready for Laughs! A Treasury of Undersea Humor. Style Guide Staff, illus. 2004. (SpongeBob SquarePants Ser.). 144p. (J). pap. 5.99 (978-0-689-86782-8(4) , Simon Spotlight) Simon & Schuster Children's Publishing.

Lisboa, David M. The World Best Jokes. 2004. 160p. 12.00 (978-0-9752740-0-2(7)) Lisboa, David.

Lundeen, Connie R. Alpha-Pets: A to Z. Lundeen, Bob, illus. 1998. 32p. (J). (gr. k-1). pap. 12.95 (978-1-880090-72-5(4) , Weasel Bks.) Galde Pr., Inc.

Lynch, Chris. Wolf Gang. 1998. (He-Man Women Haters Club Ser.). 128p. (YA). (gr. 3-7). pap. 4.50 (978-0-06-440659-8(8)) HarperCollins Pubs.

Macfarlane, David. The Little Giant Encyclopedia of Outrageous Excuses. 2006. 512p. pap. 9.95 (978-1-4027-1926-4(4) , Chapelle) Sterling Publishing Co., Inc.

A Mal Tiempo, Buena Cara: El Humor en el Periodismo Puertorriqueno. 1.t. ed. 2003. (SPA., Illus.). 48p. pap. (978-0-9743102-0-6(4)) Casa de Periodistas Editorial.

Martin, Joe. The 200 Best Jokes Ever Written by Joe Martin Out of 26,000. 2003. per. 15.95 (978-0-9745967-0-9(1)) Neatly Chiseled Features.

Martin, Justin. Vocabulary Boosting Jokes & Riddles: Fast & Fun Rib-Ticklers That Teach Kids More Than 100 Great New Words. 2004. 64p. pap. 11.99 (978-0-439-54256-2(1) , Teaching Resources) Scholastic, Inc.

McCann, Jesse Leon. Looney Tunes Back in Action Joke Book. 2003. (gr. 3-6). lib. bdg. 12.40 (978-0-613-72240-7(X)) Tandem Library Bks.

McCann, Jesse Leon & Mc Cann, Jesse Leon. Looney Tunes Back in Action Joke Book. 2003. (Looney Tunes Ser.). (Illus.). 64p. (J). pap. 4.50 (978-0-439-52138-3(6) , Scholastic Paperbacks) Scholastic, Inc.

McKay, Helen & Dudley, Berice. Riotous Riddles. Mannix, Max, illus. 1999. 172p. (J). pap. 8.00 (978-0-86806-664-6(8)) Hale & Iremonger Pty., Ltd. AUS. *Dist:* Empire Publishing Service.

Mcky, Katie. It All Began with a Bean. 2004. (Illus.). 32p. 14.95 (978-0-9749303-0-5(X)) American Media Intl.

Mead, Richard. The England Team Quiz & Joke Book. 2006. (Illus.). 144p. pap. 6.99 (978-0-00-721697-0(1)) HarperCollins Pubs. Ltd. GBR. *Dist:* Independent Pubs. Group.

Medearis, Angela Shelf. We Eat Dinner in the Bathtub. Rogers, Jacqueline, illus. 2004. 32p. (J). lib. bdg. 15.00 (978-1-59054-395-5(5)) Fitzgerald Bks.

Miglis, Jenny. Lights! Camera! Action! A Funny Fill-ins Book. Style Guide Staff, illus. 2004. (SpongeBob SquarePants Ser.). 48p. (J). pap. 2.99 (978-0-689-86598-5(8) , Simon Spotlight) Simon & Schuster Children's Publishing.

Moore, Hugh. Bug Jokes. 2005. (More Jokes! Ser.). (Illus.). 24p. (gr. k-4). lib. bdg. 21.35 (978-1-59197-870-1(X)) ABDO Publishing Co.

—School Jokes. 2005. (Jokes Ser.). (Illus.). 24p. (J). (gr. k-4). lib. bdg. 21.35 (978-1-59197-626-4(X)) ABDO Publishing Co.

—Sports Jokes. 2005. (Jokes Ser.). (Illus.). 24p. (J). (gr. k-4). lib. bdg. 21.35 (978-1-59197-627-1(8)) ABDO Publishing Co.

Moore, Mark. Beastly Laughs: A Book of Monster Jokes. Haberstroh, Anne, illus. 2004. (Read-It! Joke Books Ser.). 24p. (C). (gr. 1-3). 18.60 (978-1-4048-0625-2(3)) Picture Window Bks.

—Chalkboard Chuckles: A Book of Classroom Jokes. Haberstroh, Anne, illus. 2004. (Read-It! Joke Books Ser.). 24p. (C). (gr. 1-3). 18.60 (978-1-4048-0626-9(1)) Picture Window Bks.

W X Y Z

—Creepy Crawlers: A Book of Bug Jokes. Haberstroh, Anne, illus. 2004. (Read-It! Joke Books Ser.). 24p. (C). (gr. 1-3). 18.60 (978-1-4048-0627-6(X)) Picture Window Bks.

—Sit! Stay! Laugh! A Book of Pet Jokes. Haberstroh, Anne, illus. 2004. (Read-It! Joke Books Ser.). 24p. (C). (gr. 1-3). 18.60 (978-1-4048-0629-0(6)) Picture Window Bks.

—Spooky Sillies: A Book of Ghost Jokes. Haberstroh, Anne, illus. 2004. (Read-It! Joke Books Ser.). 24p. (C). (gr. 1-3). 18.60 (978-1-4048-0630-6(X)) Picture Window Bks.

Morse, Donald. Animal Talk: An Illustrated Workbook of Animal Sayings. Morse, Donald & Herring, Marvin, illus. 2001. 134p. spiral bd. 14.95 (978-1-928681-06-9(9)) Gladstone Publishing.

—It's a Zoo Out There. Morse, Donald & Herring, Marvin, illus. 2002. pap. (978-1-928681-08-3(5)) Gladstone Publishing.

Mouse Works Staff. The Emperor's New Groove Joke Book. 2001. 64p. (J). pap. 2.99 (978-0-7364-1272-8(7)) Mouse Works.

Mutchnick, Brenda & Casden, Ron. A Noteworthy Tale. Penney, Ian, illus. 2004. 30p. (J). (gr. k-4). reprint ed. 19.00 (978-0-7567-7654-1(6)) DIANE Publishing Co.

Myers, Bill. My Life as a Screaming Skydiver, Vol. 14. 1998. (Incredible Worlds of Wally McDoogle Ser.: No. 14). (Illus.). 128p. (J). (gr. 3-7). pap. 6.99 (978-0-8499-4023-1(0)) Nelson, Thomas Inc.

—My Life as a Torpedo Test Target. Mangiat, Jeff, illus. 2005. (Incredible Worlds of Wally McDoogle Ser.: Vol. 6). 128p. (J). (ps-7). 9.99 (978-1-4003-0638-1(8)) Nelson, Thomas Inc.

—My Life as Alien Monster Bait. Mangiat, Jeff, illus. 2005. (Incredible Worlds of Wally McDoogle Ser.: Vol. 2). 128p. (J). (ps-7). 9.99 (978-1-4003-0572-8(1)) Nelson, Thomas Inc.

—My Life as Dinosaur Dental Floss. Mangiat, Jeff, illus. 2005. (Incredible Worlds of Wally McDoogle Ser.). 128p. (J). 9.99 (978-1-4003-0614-5(0)) Nelson, Thomas Inc.

Namm, Diane. Gags & Giggles from A to Z. Becker, Wayne, illus. 2008. (Laugh-A-Long Readers Ser.). 32p. (J). pap. 3.95 (*978-1-4027-5000-7(5)) Sterling Publishing Co., Inc.

—Laugh Out Loud Jokes. Becker, Wayne, illus. 2004. (Laugh-A-Long Readers Ser.). (J). (978-0-7607-5281-4(8)) Barnes & Noble, Inc.

—Laugh Out Loud Jokes. Becker, Wayne, illus. 2008. (Laugh-A-Long Readers Ser.). 32p. (J). pap. 3.95 (*978-1-4027-5002-1(1)) Sterling Publishing Co., Inc.

—School Jokes. Becker, Wayne, illus. 2008. (Laugh-A-Long Readers Ser.). 32p. (J). pap. 3.95 (*978-1-4027-5001-4(3)) Sterling Publishing Co., Inc.

—Slithery Squirmy Jokes. Becker, Wayne, illus. 2004. (Laugh-A-Long Readers Ser.). (J). (978-0-7607-5282-1(6)) Barnes & Noble, Inc.

Namm, Diane. Slithery, Squirmy Jokes. Becker, Wayne, illus. 2008. (Laugh-A-Long Readers Ser.). 32p. (J). pap. 3.95 (*978-1-4027-5003-8(X)) Sterling Publishing Co., Inc.

Nappa, Tony & Nappa, Mike. Lunch Box Laughs: Over 75 Tear-Out Jokes to Make Your Child Giggle. Caldwell, Lise, ed. 2000. (Illus.). 60p. (J). (gr. 1-6). pap. 7.99 (978-0-7847-1064-7(3), 04323) Standard Publishing.

Nuevas Adivinanzas. 2003. (SPA.). (J). pap. (978-956-13-1304-0(9), AB8001) Bello, Andres CHL. *Dist:* Lectorum Pubns., Inc.

O'Hare, Jeff. Big Book of Fun: An Amazing Collection of Jokes, Riddles, Puzzles, & More. 2002. (gr. k-3). lib. bdg. 18.75 (978-0-613-79873-0(2)) Tandem Library Bks.

Olsson, Soren, et al. In Ned's Head. Read, Kevin, tr. from SWE. Clarke, Greg, illus. 2001. 144p. (J). (gr. 4-6). 16.00 (978-0-689-83870-5(0), Atheneum) Simon & Schuster Children's Publishing.

Orme, David. Nothing Tastes Quite Like a Gerbil: And Other Vile Verses. 2000. (Illus.). 64p. (J). (gr. 3). pap. (978-0-330-34632-0(6), Macmillan Children's Bks.) Pan Macmillan.

Oscar's New Home. 12p. (J). bds. (978-2-7643-0050-3(6)) Phidal Publishing, Inc./Editions Phidal, Inc.

Paillot, Jim. Life's Least Important Questions. 2002. (gr. 5-8). lib. bdg. 15.25 (978-0-613-75697-6(5)) Tandem Library Bks.

Pellowski, Michael. Knock-Knocks. Sterling Publishing Company Staff, ed. 2004. (Kids' Bathroom Bks.). (Illus.). 96p. (J). pap. 4.95 (978-1-4027-1711-6(3)) Sterling Publishing Co., Inc.

—Lunchroom Laughs: Joke Book. 2005. 128p. (J). (gr. 2-6). pap. 3.99 (978-1-58196-032-7(8)) Darby Creek Publishing.

Pellowski, Michael J. Joke & Riddle Jackpot. Reed, Chris, illus. 96p. 2007. (J). pap. 4.95 (*978-1-4027-4056-5(5)); 2005. 14.95 (978-1-4027-1696-6(6)) Sterling Publishing Co., Inc.

Perret, Gene, et al. Super Silly School Jokes. Hoffman, Sanford, illus. 2001. (Rattle Bear Bks.). 96p. (J). (gr. 1-4). pap. 4.95 (978-0-8069-9738-4(9)) Sterling Publishing Co., Inc.

Peterson, Ruth. Dinner at Five. Jarvis, Nathan Y., illus. rev. ed. 1998. 32p. (J). (gr. k-3). 1.95 (978-1-891992-00-1(2)) Owl's Hse. Pr.

Peterson, Scott K. Let the Fun Begin: Nifty Knock-Knocks, Playful Puns, & More. Gable, Brian, illus. 2005. (Make Me Laugh! Ser.). 32p. (J). (gr. k-3). lib. bdg. 19.93 (978-1-57505-661-6(5)) Lerner Publishing Group.

Pfeiffer, Florise C. The Price of Love: In Praise of Canine Companions. 2002. (Illus.). 88p. per. 12.50 (978-0-9721752-0-3(2)) Pfeiffer, Florise C. & Henry B.

Phillips, Bob. All-Time Awesome Collection of Good Clean Jokes for Kids. 2006. (Illus.). 368p. (J). pap. 10.99 (978-0-7369-1777-3(2)) Harvest Hse. Pubs.

—Awesome Knock-Knock Jokes for Kids. 2006. 112p. (J). pap. 4.99 (978-0-7369-1714-8(4)) Harvest Hse. Pubs.

—Dude, Got Another Joke? 2002. (gr. 3-6). lib. bdg. 13.00 (978-0-613-73729-6(6)) Tandem Library Bks.

—Dude, Gotta Another Joke? Clean Jokes for Kids. 2002. 176p. pap. 4.99 (978-0-7369-0455-1(7)) Harvest Hse. Pubs.

—Extremely Good Clean Jokes for Kids. 2001. 176p. (gr. 4-7). pap. 4.99 (978-0-7369-0309-7(7)) Harvest Hse. Pubs.

—Extremely Good Clean Jokes for Kids. 2001. (gr. 3-6). lib. bdg. 13.00 (978-0-613-73812-5(8)) Tandem Library Bks.

—Good Clean Knock-Knock Jokes for Kids. 2007. 112p. (YA). pap. 4.99 (978-0-7369-1778-0(0)) Harvest Hse. Pubs.

—Slam Dunk Jokes for Kids. 2004. 160p. pap. 4.99 (978-0-7369-1346-1(7)) Harvest Hse. Pubs.

—The World's Greatest Knock-Knock Jokes for Kids. 2000. 192p. (J). (gr. 4-7). pap. 4.99 (978-0-7369-0273-1(2)) Harvest Hse. Pubs.

—World's Greatest Knock-Knock Jokes for Kids. 2000. (gr. 3-6). lib. bdg. 13.00 (978-0-613-73750-0(4)) Tandem Library Bks.

—World's Most Crazy, Wacky & Goofy Good Clean Jokes for Kids. 1999. 288p. (gr. 4-7). 7.99 (978-1-57866-046-9(7), Galahad Bks.) BBS Publishing Corp.

Phillips, Bob & Russo, Steve. Fabulous & Funny Clean Jokes for Kids. 2nd ed. 2004. 176p. (YA). reprint ed. pap. 4.99 (978-0-7369-1365-2(3)) Harvest Hse. Pubs.

Phillips, Louis. Haunted House Jokes. Marshall, James, illus. 1999. (Chapters Ser.). 64p. (J). pap. 3.99 (978-0-14-130650-6(5), Puffin) Penguin Group (USA) Inc.

—Monster Riddles. Dubanevich, Arlene, illus. 1998. (Puffin Easy-to-Read Program Ser.). 32p. (J). (gr. 1-4). pap. 3.99 (978-0-14-038790-2(0), Puffin) Penguin Group (USA) Inc.

—Monster Riddles. Dubanevich, Arlene, illus. 1998. (J). (ps-ps). lib. bdg. 11.80 (978-0-613-08373-7(3)) Tandem Library Bks.

Phunny, U. R. Animal Jokes. 2005. (Jokes Ser.). (Illus.). 24p. (J). (gr. k-4). lib. bdg. 21.35 (978-1-59197-620-2(0), Buddy Bks.) ABDO Publishing Co.

—Dinosaur Jokes. 2005. (Jokes Ser.). (Illus.). 24p. (J). (gr. k-4). lib. bdg. 21.35 (978-1-59197-621-9(9), Buddy Bks.) ABDO Publishing Co.

—More Animal Jokes. 2005. (More Jokes! Ser.). (Illus.). 24p. (gr. k-4). lib. bdg. 21.35 (978-1-59197-872-5(6)) ABDO Publishing Co.

Pierce, Terry. Goofy Knock-Knocks. 2004. (Illus.). 96p. (J). 14.95 (978-1-4027-1403-0(3)) Sterling Publishing Co., Inc.

—Greatest Goofiest Jokes. Jones, Buck, illus. 2005. 96p. pap. 4.95 (978-1-4027-2287-5(7)) Sterling Publishing Co., Inc.

—Greatest Goofiest Jokes. 2004. (Illus.). 96p. (J). 14.95 (978-1-4027-0769-8(X)) Sterling Publishing Co., Inc.

Pierce, Terry & Musgrave, Ruth. Pet Jokes That Will Make You Howl! Coyle, Laura, illus. 96p. (J). 2007. pap. 4.95 (*978-1-4027-4839-4(6)); 2005. (gr. 4-7). 14.95 (978-1-4027-1904-2(3), 1249653) Sterling Publishing Co., Inc.

Pilkey, Dav. The All New Captain Underpants Extra-Crunchy Book O' Fun 2. 2002. (Captain Underpants Ser.). (gr. 3-6). lib. bdg. 11.80 (978-0-613-49472-4(5)) Tandem Library Bks.

Pinkwater, Daniel M. Ice Cream Larry. Pinkwater, Jill, illus. 1999. (Accelerated Reader Bks.). 32p. (J). (ps up). 15.95 (978-0-7614-5043-6(2), Cavendish Children's Bks.) Cavendish, Marshall Corp.

Plume, Naomi. Joke Book. 2003. (gr. k-3). lib. bdg. 11.80 (978-0-613-71413-6(X)) Tandem Library Bks.

Practical Pranks. 2004. (Formula Fun Ser.). (Illus.). 48p. (J). (978-1-84229-579-3(9)) Top That! Publishing PLC.

Price, Roger. Camp Daze/Mad Mad Mad Libs, 2 bks., Pack. 2003. (Illus.). (J). pap. 3.99 (978-0-8431-0357-1(4), Price Stern Sloan) Penguin Group (USA) Inc.

—Kid Libs/Goofy Mad Libs, 2 bks., Pack. 2003. (Illus.). (J). pap. 3.99 (978-0-8431-0354-0(X), Price Stern Sloan) Penguin Group (USA) Inc.

—On the Road/Kid Libs Mad Libs, 2 bks., Pack. 2003. (Illus.). (J). pap. 3.99 (978-0-8431-0352-6(3), Price Stern Sloan) Penguin Group (USA) Inc.

—Original #1/Monster Mad Libs, 2 bks., Pack. 2003. (Illus.). (J). pap. 3.99 (978-0-8431-0351-9(5), Price Stern Sloan) Penguin Group (USA) Inc.

—Upside down Mad Libs & Sooper Dooper Mad Libs, 2 bks., Pack. 2003. (Illus.). (J). pap. 3.99 (978-0-8431-0348-9(5), Price Stern Sloan) Penguin Group (USA) Inc.

—Vacation Fun/Mad Libs from Outer Space Mad Libs, 2 bks. 2003. (Illus.). (J). pap. 3.99 (978-0-8431-0343-4(4), Price Stern Sloan) Penguin Group (USA) Inc.

Price, Roger & Stern, Leonard. Cool Mad Libs. 2001. (Mad Libs Ser.). (Illus.). 48p. (J). mass mkt. 3.99 (978-0-8431-7660-5(1), Price Stern Sloan) Penguin Group (USA) Inc.

—The Haunted. 2002. (Mad Libs Ser.). (Illus.). 48p. (J). pap. 3.99 (978-0-8431-4906-7(X), Price Stern Sloan) Penguin Group (USA) Inc.

Pruett, Scott & Pruett, Judy. Twelve Little Race Cars. Eytchison, Glen, ed. Dietz, Mike & Toft, Kevin, illus. 1999. 32p. (J). (ps-3). 12.95 (978-0-9670600-0-2(1)) Word Weaver Bks., Inc.

Quackenbush, Robert. Henry's Awful Mistake. Quackenbush, Robert, illus. rev. deluxe ed. 2005. (Illus.). 40p. (J). (gr. k-2). reprint ed. 12.95 (978-0-9712757-0-6(X)) Quackenbush, Robert Studios.

Queenan, Joseph. Confessions of a Cineplex Heckler: Celluloid Tirades & Escapades. 1999. viii, 264p. (J). 22.45 (978-0-7868-6508-6(3)) Hyperion Pr.

Ransford, Sandy. Joke Ziga Zaga Organiser. 2003. (Ziga Zaga Ser.). 192p. (YA). (978-1-84347-052-6(7)) Chrysalis Children's Bks.

—Jokes & Pranks. 2003. (Wicked Wallets Ser.). (Illus.). 96p. (YA). pap. (978-1-84347-040-3(3)) Chrysalis Children's Bks.

—Oink! The Pig Joke Book. 1999. (Illus.). 6.95p. (J). (gr. k-5). pap. 7.99 (978-0-233-99570-0(6)) Andre Deutsch GBR. *Dist:* Independent Pubs. Group.

—2001 A Joke Odyssey: The Millennium Joke Book. 2003. (Illus.). 281p. (J). pap. 8.99 (978-0-330-34988-8(0), Pan) Pan Macmillan GBR. *Dist:* Trafalgar Square Publishing.

Read-it! Joke Books-Supercharged! (Illus.). (C). (gr. 1-3). (978-1-4048-0997-0(X)) Picture Window Bks.

Rissinger, Matt. Greatest Giggles Ever. 2003. (gr. k-3). lib. bdg. 12.95 (978-0-613-78017-9(5)) Tandem Library Bks.

—It's Not My Fault Because: The Kids' Book of Excuses. 2002. (gr. 3-6). lib. bdg. 12.95 (978-0-613-75514-6(6)) Tandem Library Bks.

—Totally Terrific Jokes. 2001. (J). (978-0-606-21494-0(1)) Tandem Library Bks.

Rissinger, Matt & Yates, Philip. Cleverest Comebacks Ever. Collinet, Rob, illus. 2005. 96p. (J). (gr. 4-7). pap. 4.95 (978-1-4027-1076-6(3), 1249651) Sterling Publishing Co., Inc.

—Greatest Giggles Ever. Sinclair, Jeff, illus. 2003. 96p. (J). pap. 4.95 (978-1-4027-0806-0(8)) Sterling Publishing Co., Inc.

—Greatest Kids' Comebacks Ever. Sinclair, Jeff, illus. 2003. 96p. (J). pap. 4.95 (978-1-4027-0560-1(3)) Sterling Publishing Co., Inc.

—The Little Giant Book of Laughs. 2005. (Illus.). 352p. (J). pap. 6.95 (978-1-4027-1716-1(4)) Sterling Publishing Co., Inc.

—Nutty Jokes. Harpster, Steve, illus. 2002. (Giggle Fit Ser.). 48p. (J). (gr. k-2). pap. 4.95 (978-1-4027-0120-7(9)) Sterling Publishing Co., Inc.

—Silly Jokes & Giggles. Shems, Ed, illus. 2005. 96p. (J). 14.95 (978-1-4027-1075-9(5)) Sterling Publishing Co., Inc.

—Wacky Jokes. Harpster, Steve, illus. 2005. 48p. (J). (ps-ps). pap. 4.95 (978-1-4027-2773-3(9)) Sterling Publishing Co., Inc.

Ristas. Chistes para Ninos, Vol. II.Tr. of Jokes for Children. (SPA.). (J). 6.98 (978-970-643-265-0(5)) Selector, S.A. de C.V. MEX. *Dist:* AIMS International Bks., Inc., Giron Bks.

Roark, Walter. Keeping Your Toddler on Track till Mommy Gets Back: The Toddler Survival Guide for 21st-Century Dads. 2003. (Illus.). 224p. (J). pap. 15.95 (978-0-9707937-1-3(5)) Clearing Skies Pr.

Rogers, Fred. You Are Special: Neighborly Wit & Wisdom from Mister Rogers. 2002. (Irresistible Miniature Editionstm Ser.). (Illus.). 128p. 4.95 (978-0-7624-1247-1(X), Running Pr. Minature Editions) Running Pr. Bk. Pubs.

Roop, Peter. Holiday Howlers: Jokes for Punny Parties. 2004. (gr. k-3). lib. bdg. 12.95 (978-0-613-79288-2(2)) Tandem Library Bks.

Roop, Peter & Roop, Connie. Holiday Howlers: Jokes for Punny Parties. Gable, Brian, illus. 2004. (Make Me Laugh! Ser.). 32p. (J). (gr. k-3). lib. bdg. 19.93 (978-1-57505-645-6(3)) Lerner Publishing Group.

Rosenberg, Pam. Animal Jokes. 2005. (Laughing Matters Ser.). (Illus.). 24p. (J). (gr. k-4). 22.79 (978-1-59296-277-8(7)) Child's World, Inc.

—Baseball Jokes. 2007. (Laughing Matters Ser.). 24p. (J). (gr. k-4). 22.79 (978-1-59296-705-6(1)) Child's World, Inc.

—Dinosaur Jokes. 2004. (Laughing Matters Ser.). 24p. (J). (gr. k-4). 22.79 (978-1-59296-073-6(1)) Child's World, Inc.

—Doctor Jokes. 2005. (Laughing Matters Ser.). (Illus.). 24p. (J). (gr. k-4). 22.79 (978-1-59296-278-5(5)) Child's World, Inc.

—Eek! Icky, Sticky, Gross Stuff in Your Food. 2007. (Icky, Sticky, Gross-Out Bks.). 24p. (J). (gr. 2-6). 22.79 (*978-1-59296-895-4(3)) Child's World, Inc.

—Food Jokes. 2005. (Laughing Matters Ser.). (Illus.). 24p. (J). (gr. k-4). 22.79 (978-1-59296-279-2(3)) Child's World, Inc.

—Gross-Out Jokes. 2005. (Laughing Matters Ser.). (Illus.). 24p. (J). (gr. k-4). 22.79 (978-1-59296-280-8(7)) Child's World, Inc.

—Historical Jokes. 2005. (Laughing Matters Ser.). (Illus.). 24p. (J). (gr. k-4). 22.79 (978-1-59296-281-5(5)) Child's World, Inc.

—Knock-Knock Jokes. 2004. (Laughing Matters Ser.). 24p. (J). (gr. k-4). 22.79 (978-1-59296-075-0(8)) Child's World, Inc.

—Monster Jokes. 2007. (Laughing Matters Ser.). 24p. (J). (gr. k-4). 22.79 (978-1-59296-707-0(8)) Child's World, Inc.

—Outdoor Jokes. 2007. (Laughing Matters Ser.). 24p. (J). (gr. k-4). 22.79 (978-1-59296-709-4(4)) Child's World, Inc.

—Safari Jokes. 2007. (Laughing Matters Ser.). 24p. (J). (gr. k-4). 22.79 (978-1-59296-708-7(6)) Child's World, Inc.

—School Jokes. 2005. (Laughing Matters Ser.). (Illus.). 24p. (J). (gr. k-4). 22.79 (978-1-59296-282-2(3)) Child's World, Inc.

—Space Jokes. 2007. (Laughing Matters Ser.). 24p. (J). (gr. k-4). 22.79 (978-1-59296-710-0(8)) Child's World, Inc.

—Sports Jokes. 2004. (Laughing Matters Ser.). 24p. (J). (gr. k-4). 22.79 (978-1-59296-077-4(4)) Child's World, Inc.

—Tongue Twisters. 2004. (Laughing Matters Ser.). 24p. (J). (gr. k-4). 22.79 (978-1-59296-078-1(2)) Child's World, Inc.

Rosenbloom, Joseph. Giggle Fit: Silly Knock-Knocks. 2002. (ps-2). lib. bdg. 12.95 (978-0-613-90084-3(7)) Tandem Library Bks.

—Jokes. Hoffman, Sanford, illus. 2007. 360p. (J). pap. 6.95 (*978-1-4027-4973-5(2)) Sterling Publishing Co., Inc.

—Laughs, Hoots & Giggles. Behr, Joyce & Hoffman, Sanford, illus. 2007. 416p. (J). 9.95 (*978-1-4027-5063-2(3)) Sterling Publishing Co., Inc.

—School Jokes. Harpster, Steve, illus. 2004. (Giggle Fit Ser.). 48p. pap. 4.95 (978-1-4027-1762-8(8)) Sterling Publishing Co., Inc.

—Side-Splitters. 2007. (Illus.). 360p. (J). pap. 6.95 (*978-1-4027-4975-9(9)) Sterling Publishing Co., Inc.

—Silly Knock-Knocks. Harpster, Steve, illus. 2002. (Giggle Fit Ser.). 48p. (J). (ps-2). pap. 4.95 (978-1-4027-0121-4(7)) Sterling Publishing Co., Inc.

—Spooky Jokes. Harpster, Steve, illus. 2004. (Giggle Fit Ser.). 48p. pap. 4.95 (978-1-4027-1763-5(6)) Sterling Publishing Co., Inc.

—696 Silly School Jokes & Riddles. 2003. (gr. 3-6). lib. bdg. 12.95 (978-0-613-78033-9(7)) Tandem Library Bks.

—696 Silly School Jokes & Riddles. Kendrick, Dennis, illus. 2004. 128p. (J). pap. 4.95 (978-1-4027-1095-7(X)) Sterling Publishing Co., Inc.

Rosenbloom, Joseph & Artel, Mike. Tongue Twisters. 2007. (Illus.). 360p. (J). pap. 6.95 (*978-1-4027-4974-2(0)) Sterling Publishing Co., Inc.

Rosenbloom, Joseph & Harpster, Steve. Goofy Riddles. 2002. (Giggle Fit Ser.). (Illus.). 48p. (J). (ps-2). pap. 4.95 (978-1-4027-0119-1(5)) Sterling Publishing Co., Inc.

Ross, Tony. Silly, Silly. 1999. (Illus.). 29p. (J). (ps-k). 19.95 (978-0-86264-740-7(1)) Andersen GBR. *Dist:* Trafalgar Square Publishing.

Ross, Tony, illus. Funny Stories for 7 Year Olds. 2003. 237p. (J). pap. 9.99 (978-0-330-34945-1(7), Pan) Pan Macmillan GBR. *Dist:* Trafalgar Square Publishing.

—Funny Stories for 8 Year Olds. 2003. 235p. (J). 9.99 (978-0-330-34946-8(5), Pan) Pan Macmillan GBR. *Dist:* Trafalgar Square Publishing.

Rothman, Joel. Shut up & Straighten the Bolt in Your Neck. 2007. (Illus.). 80p. (J). pap. 6.95 (*978-1-930596-71-9(5)) Amherst Pr.

Sachar, Louis. Kidnapped at Birth? Hughes, Neal, illus. 2004. (Marvin Redpost Ser.: Vol. 1). 80p. (J). (gr. k-3). 11.99 (978-0-679-91946-9(5), Random Hse. Bks. for Young Readers) Random Hse. Children's Bks.

Sandburg, Carl. The Huckabuck Family: And How They Raised Popcorn in Nebraska & Quit & Came Back. Small, David, illus. 1999. 40p. (J). (ps-3). 16.00 (978-0-374-33511-3(7), Farrar, Straus & Giroux (BYR)) Farrar, Straus & Giroux.

Santini, Nicky. Christes y Sorpresas prar Ninos.Tr. of Jokes & Surprises for Kids. (SPA.). (J). 6.98 (978-968-403-937-7(9)) Selector, S.A. de C.V. MEX. *Dist:* AIMS International Bks., Inc.

Saunders, Zina, contrib. by. Buried Treasure! Tales from Bikini Bottom. 2004. (Spongebob Squarepants Ser.). 160p. (J). 10.95 (978-0-689-87467-3(7), Simon Spotlight/Nickelodeon) Simon & Schuster Children's Publishing.

Schachner, Judith Byron. Knock, Knock! Schachner, Judith Byron et al, illus. 2007. 40p. (J). (ps). 16.99 (*978-0-8037-3152-3(3), Dial) Penguin Group (USA) Inc.

Scheunemann, Pam. Ape Cape. 2004. (Rhyming Riddles Ser.). (Illus.). 23p. (J). (ps-3). lib. bdg. 19.93 (978-1-59197-457-4(7)) ABDO Publishing Co.

—Chipper Flipper. 2004. (Rhyming Riddles Ser.). (Illus.). 23p. (J). (ps-3). lib. bdg. 19.93 (978-1-59197-458-1(5)) ABDO Publishing Co.

—Cooler Ruler. 2004. (Rhyming Riddles Ser.). (Illus.). 23p. (J). (ps-3). lib. bdg. 19.93 (978-1-59197-459-8(3)) ABDO Publishing Co.

—Loud Crowd. 2004. (Rhyming Riddles Ser.). (Illus.). 23p. (J). (ps-3). lib. bdg. 19.93 (978-1-59197-461-1(5)) ABDO Publishing Co.

—Overdue Kangaroo. 2004. (Rhyming Riddles Ser.). (Illus.). 23p. (J). (ps-3). lib. bdg. 19.93 (978-1-59197-462-8(3)) ABDO Publishing Co.

Schiller, David & Rosenthal, Marc. The Runaway Beard: A Hairy Tale. 1998. (Illus.). 32p. (J). (ps-1). 12.95 (978-0-7611-1359-1(2), 11359) Workman Publishing Co., Inc.

Scholastic, Inc. Staff. Su Doku: Jokes! Jokes! Jokes! 2007. (Su Doku Ser.). 144p. (J). pap. 4.99 (*978-0-439-02279-8(7)) Scholastic, Inc.

Schreiber, Brad. Weird Wonders & Bizarre Blunders: The Official Book of Ridiculous Records. 1998. (Illus.). 88p. (YA). pap. 5.00 (978-0-7881-5220-7(3)) DIANE Publishing Co.

Schultz, Sam. Don't Kid Yourself: Relatively Great. 2004. (gr. k-3). lib. bdg. 12.95 (978-0-613-79284-4(X)) Tandem Library Bks.

—Don't Kid Yourself: Relatively Great (Family) Jokes. Gable, Brian, illus. 2004. (Make Me Laugh! Ser.). 32p. (J). (gr. k-3). lib. bdg. 19.93 (978-1-57505-641-8(0)) Lerner Publishing Group.

—Game-Day Gigglers: Winning Jokes to Score Some Laughs. 2004. (gr. k-3). lib. bdg. 12.95 (978-0-613-79210-3(6)) Tandem Library Bks.

—Ivan to Make You Laugh: Jokes about Novel, Nifty, & Notorious Names. Gable, Brian, illus. 2005. (Make Me Laugh! Ser.). 32p. (J). (gr. k-3). lib. bdg. 19.93 (978-1-57505-659-3(3)) Lerner Publishing Group.

—Monster Mayhem: Jokes to Scare You Silly. Gable, Brian, illus. 2004. (Make Me Laugh! Ser.). 32p. (J). (gr. k-3). lib. bdg. 19.93 (978-1-57505-642-5(9)) Lerner Publishing Group.

—Monster Mayhem: Jokes to Scare You Silly! 2004. (gr. k-3). lib. bdg. 12.95 (978-0-613-79213-4(0)) Tandem Library Bks.

—Schoolyard Snickers: Classy Jokes That Make the Grade. Gable, Brian, illus. 2004. (Make Me Laugh! Ser.). 32p. (J). (gr. k-3). lib. bdg. 19.93 (978-1-57505-643-2(7)) Lerner Publishing Group.

—Schoolyard Snickers: Classy Jokes That Make the Grade. 2004. (gr. k-3). lib. bdg. 12.95 (978-0-613-79211-0(4)) Tandem Library Bks.

Schulz, Charles M. Peanuts 2000. 2000. (gr. 3-6). lib. bdg. 21.05 (978-0-613-32933-0(3)) Tandem Library Bks.

Schwartz, Joel. Noses are Red. 2006. pap. (978-0-9785885-0-2(9)) Schwartz, Joel.

Scott, Jerry. Don't Roll Your Eyes at Me, Young Man!, Vol. 3. 2000. (Illus.). (J). pap. 59.70 (978-0-7407-1288-3(8)) Andrews McMeel Publishing.

Sea Star Editors. Silly Stories to Tickle Your Funny Bone. 2000. (Reading Rainbow Readers Ser.). (YA). (978-0-606-19631-4(5)) Tandem Library Bks.

Seaburn, Paul. Jestercises & Gamestorms. 2004. (J). pap. 5.50 (978-1-931334-39-6(0)) Pieces of Learning.

Singleton, Glen. Crazy Book of Gross Jokes. 2004. (Illus.). 192p. pap. (978-1-74121-544-1(7)) Hinkler Bks. Pty, Ltd.

—1001 Even More Cool Jokes. (Illus.). 208p. pap. (978-1-86515-868-6(2)) Hinkler Bks. Pty, Ltd.

Sklansky, Amy E. Zoom Fun Outside. 2000. (Zoom Ser.). (Illus.). 62p. (J). (gr. 1-7). pap. 7.95 (978-0-316-95278-1(8)) Little Brown & Co.

Souza, Iza R. The Tree That Ran Away...! Lima, Gabriel S., tr. from POR. Lima, M., illus. 1999. 32p. (J). (gr. 2-7). pap. 3.25 (978-0-9662298-2-0(7)) Alba Bk. Co.

Spoon, Ben D. Burp! Gross Jokes & Awesome Body Tricks. 2000. (Illus.). 96p. (YA). (gr. 3 up). pap. 3.95 (978-1-902618-34-0(3)) Element Children's Bks.

Sports Illustrated for Kids Editors, ed. Laugh Locker Joke & Puzzle Book. 2000. (Illus.). (J). (gr. 2-8). pap. (978-1-930623-10-1(0)) Sports Illustrated For Kids.

Stamper, Judith Bauer. 101 Wacky Computer Jokes. 1998. (YA). (978-0-606-13105-6(1)) Tandem Library Bks.

Stamper, Judith Bauer & Stamper, Genevieve. 101 Wacky Computer Jokes. 1998. 96p. (J). (gr. 2-5). pap. 2.99 (978-0-590-13004-2(8)) Scholastic, Inc.

Steck-Vaughn Staff. Riddles & Jokes: Pet Riddles/You'll Roar. 1998. (Illus.). (J). pap. (978-0-8172-8650-7(0)) Steck-Vaughn.

—You'll Roar. 1999. (Illus.). pap. 1.20 (978-0-8172-8725-2(6)) Steck-Vaughn.

Sterling Publishing Company Staff. Jokes. 2003. (Kids' Bathroom Bks.). (Illus.). 96p. (J). (gr. 2-7). pap. 4.95 (978-1-4027-0717-9(7)) Sterling Publishing Co., Inc.

—Optical Illusions. 2003. (Kids' Bathroom Bks.). (Illus.). 96p. (J). (gr. 2-7). pap. 4.95 (978-1-4027-0718-6(5)) Sterling Publishing Co., Inc.

Sterling Publishing Company Staff, et al. Optical Illusions. 2000. (Pocket Puzzlers Ser.). (Illus.). 96p. (gr. 5-9). pap. 2.95 (978-0-8069-4993-2(7)) Sterling Publishing Co., Inc.

Strasser, Todd. Y2K-9: The Dog Who Saved the World. 1999. (YA). pap. 4.50 (978-0-439-14247-2(4)) Scholastic, Inc.

—Y2K-9: The Dog Who Saved the World. 1999. (978-0-606-18619-3(0)) Tandem Library Bks.

Streissguth, Tom. Costa Rica in Pictures. 2nd ed. 2005. (Visual Geography Ser.). (Illus.). 80p. (J). (gr. 5-12). 27.93 (978-0-8225-1168-7(1)) Lerner Publishing Group.

Swanson, June. Punny Places: Jokes That Go the Extra Mile. Gable, Brian, illus. 2004. (Make Me Laugh! Ser.). 32p. (J). (gr. k-3). lib. bdg. 19.93 (978-1-57505-647-0(X)) Lerner Publishing Group.

Szpirglas, Jeff. They Did What?! Your Guide to Weird & Wacky Things People Do. Whamond, Dave, illus. 2005. 64p. (J). 16.95 (978-1-897066-22-5(8)); pap. 9.95 (978-1-897066-23-2(6)) Maple Tree Pr. CAN. *Dist:* Perseus Distribution.

Tait, Chris. How to Be a Kid. Paillot, Jim, illus. 2003. 96p. (J). pap. 6.95 (978-0-8069-8503-9(8)) Sterling Publishing Co., Inc.

Tait, Chris & Horsfall, Jacqueline. A Little Giant Book: Super Colossal Knock-Knocks. 2007. (Illus.). 360p. (J). pap. 6.95 (***978-1-4027-4993-3(7)***) Sterling Publishing Co., Inc.

Taylor, Brad. The Family Joke Book: Jokes & Stories for Everyone. Blaustein, Hank, illus. 2000. 64p. (YA). pap. 8.95 (978-0-86534-294-1(6)) Sunstone Pr.

Temko, Florence. Funny Money: Jokes, Coin Tricks, Trivia, Money-Folding Fun & More. 2005. (Illus.). 48p. (J). (gr. 2-6). 4.99 (978-1-58196-037-2(9)) Darby Creek Publishing.

Thomas, Lyn. Ha! Ha! Ha! 1,000+ Jokes, Riddles, Facts, & More. Eastman, Dianne, illus. 2004. 128p. (J). pap. 9.95 (978-1-897066-12-6(0)) Maple Tree Pr. CAN. *Dist:* Perseus Distribution.

Top That Publishing Staff, ed. Practical Jokes. 2004. (I-Quest Ser.). (Illus.). 48p. (J). per. (978-1-84510-194-7(4)) Top That! Publishing PLC.

Tremaine, Jon. Practical Jokes. 2002. (Illus.). 64p. (J). pap. 9.98 (978-0-7525-3960-7(4)) Parragon, Inc.

Trimble, Marshall. Never Give a Heifer a Bum Steer. 1999. (Illus.). 144p. 6.95 (978-0-916179-98-4(2)) Arizona Highways.

Trimmer, Tony, illus. Seriously Silly School Jokes. 2005. (Sidesplitters Ser.). 64p. (J). (gr. 3-5). pap. 3.95 (978-0-7534-5725-2(3) , Kingfisher) Houghton Mifflin Co. Trade & Reference Div.

Ullman, Tracey. Tracey Takes On. 1999. (Illus.). 304p. (J). 14.95 (978-0-7868-8361-5(8)) Hyperion Pr.

Vahn. Street Jokes. 2005. (YA). per. 14.95 (978-0-9766770-2-4(4)) BAU PUBLISHING GROUP.

Vaughan, Christina. The Crooked Mustache of Emperor Gustav Gooftoff. 2000. (Illus.). 32p. (J). (gr. 1-5). spiral bd. 18.95 (978-0-9641697-1-5(1) , You-Draw-It Bks.) Castlebrook Pubns.

Verno, Michael F., ed. Camp Good Days Joke Book A-Z. Camp, Jared J., illus. 1998. 72p. (J). (ps-6). pap. 5.95 (978-0-9668130-0-5(6)) Children's Oncology Pubns.

Vilsaint, Fequiere. Jokes, Riddles & Proverbs: In Haitian Creole. Date not set. 28p. (J). (gr. 3-6). wbk. ed. 2.50 (978-1-881839-54-5(0)) Educa Vision.

Walter, Gramela Pamela. Yeben! Definitions for Groans (Grown-Ups) Walter, Gramela Pamela, illus. ltd. ed. 1999. (Illus.). 19p. (J). pap. 5.95 (978-1-929110-25-4(1)) Colter Enterprises, Inc.

Walton, Rick. The Sky's the Limit: Naturally Funny Jokes. Gable, Brian, illus. 2005. (Make Me Laugh! Ser.). 32p. (J). (gr. k-3). lib. bdg. 19.93 (978-1-57505-663-0(1)) Lerner Publishing Group.

Walton, Rick & Walton, Ann. Foul Play: Sports Jokes That Won't Strike Out. Gable, Brian, illus. 2005. (Make Me Laugh! Ser.). 32p. (J). (gr. k-3). lib. bdg. 19.93 (978-1-57505-666-1(6)) Lerner Publishing Group.

—Magical Mischief: Jokes That Shock & Amaze. Gable, Brian, illus. 2005. (Make Me Laugh! Ser.). 32p. (J). (gr. k-3). lib. bdg. 19.93 (978-1-57505-664-7(X)) Lerner Publishing Group.

Walton, Rick, et al. Real Classy: Silly School Jokes. Gable, Brian, illus. 2005. (Make Me Laugh! Ser.). 32p. (J). (gr. k-3). lib. bdg. 19.93 (978-1-57505-665-4(8)) Lerner Publishing Group.

Weeks, Sarah. Mrs. McNosh Hangs up Her Wash. Westcott, Nadine Bernard, illus. 1998. (Growing Tree Ser.). 24p. (J). (ps up). 12.99 (978-0-694-01076-9(6) , Harper Festival) HarperCollins Pubs.

Weintraub, Aileen. The Everything Kids' Gross Jokes Book: Side-Splitting Jokes That Make Your Skin Crawl! 2005. (Illus.). 144p. (J). (ps). pap. 6.95 (978-1-59337-448-8(8)) Adams Media Corp.

—The Everything Kids' Knock Knock Book. 2004. (Illus.). 144p. (J). 6.95 (978-1-59337-127-2(6)) Adams Media Corp.

Weitzman, Ilana, et al. Jokelopedia: The Biggest, Best, Silliest, Dumbest Joke Book Ever. 2nd rev. ed. 2006. (Illus.). 278p. (J). pap. 11.95 (978-0-7611-4208-9(8)) Workman Publishing Co., Inc.

Wendt, Irmela. Jewish Humor Stories for Kids: An Anthology of Short Stories. 208p. (J). (gr. 4 up). 1999. 16.95 (978-0-943706-77-1(7)); 1998. pap. 12.95 (978-0-943706-78-8(5)) Pitspopany Pr. (Devora Publishing).

Whiter, Barb, ed. 1001 More Cool Jokes. Singleton, Glen, illus. 2002. 208p. pap. (978-1-86515-441-1(5)) Hinkler Bks. Pty, Ltd.

WIlcox, Jean K. & Cameron, E. Jane. AbuLLard's ABC's of Branding: 26 Concepts That Capture the Essence of Good Brand Management. Kopervas, Gary & Hanes, Don, illus. unabr. ed. 2003. 64p. 19.95 (978-0-9745612-0-2(7) , CPN-BMS-001) CattLeLogos Brand Management Systems.

Wilder, Laura Ingalls. Santa Comes to Little House. Graef, Renee, illus. 2004. (Little House Ser.). 32p. (J). (ps-3). pap. 5.99 (978-0-06-058694-2(X) , Harper Trophy) HarperCollins Pubs.

Willans, Tom. Wait! I Want to Tell You a Story. Willans, Tom, illus. 2005. 32p. (J). 15.95 (978-0-689-87166-5(X)) Simon & Schuster Children's Publishing.

Wisniewski, David. The Secret Knowledge of Grown-Ups. Wisniewski, David, illus. 1998. (Illus.). 48p. (J). (gr. 2 up). 16.99 (978-0-688-15339-7(9)) HarperCollins Pubs.

—Secret Knowledge of Grown-Ups. 2001. (gr. 3-6). lib. bdg. 15.25 (978-0-613-44254-1(7)) Tandem Library Bks.

—The Secret Knowledge of Grown-ups. Wisniewski, David, illus. 2001. (Secret Knowledge Ser.). (Illus.). 48p. (J). (gr. 2 up). pap. 6.99 (978-0-06-443753-0(1) , Harper Trophy) HarperCollins Pubs.

—The Secret Knowledge of Grown-ups. 2001. (YA). (978-0-606-22279-2(0)) Tandem Library Bks.

Wodehouse, P. G. Mike at Wrykyn. reprint ed. (J). lib. bdg. 98.00 (978-0-7426-3265-3(2)); 2001. pap. 28.00 (978-0-7426-8265-8(X)) Classic Bks.

Wyllie, Stephen. A Flea in the Ear. 1999. (J). pap. 5.99 (978-0-14-056189-0(7) , Puffin) Penguin Group (USA) Inc.

Wynne-Jones, Tim. Mischief City. (J). 16.95 (978-0-88899-049-5(9) , Libros Tigrillo) Groundwood Bks. CAN. *Dist:* Transition Vendor.

Yates, Philip & Rissinger, Matt. Laughs. 2007. (Illus.). 360p. (J). pap. 6.95 (***978-1-4027-4979-7(1)***) Sterling Publishing Co., Inc.

—Silly Jokes & Giggles. Shems, Ed, illus. 2007. 96p. (J). pap. 4.95 (***978-1-4027-4071-8(9)***) Sterling Publishing Co., Inc.

Yoe, Craig. Knock Knock Jokes. Yoe, Craig, illus. 2002. (Mighty Big Bks.). (Illus.). 288p. mass mkt. 6.99 (978-0-8431-7735-0(7) , Price Stern Sloan) Penguin Group (USA) Inc.

—Mighty Big Book of Jokes. 2001. (gr. 3-6). lib. bdg. 14.15 (978-0-613-76929-7(5)); 2000. (978-0-606-18471-7(6)) Tandem Library Bks.

—The Mighty Big Book of Jokes. Yoe, Craig, illus. 2001. (Library O'Laughs). (Illus.). 288p. (J). (gr. 4 up). pap. 6.99 (978-0-8431-7582-0(6) , Price Stern Sloan) Penguin Group (USA) Inc.

—The Mighty Big Book of School Jokes. 2003. (Mighty Big Bks.). (Illus.). 288p. (gr. 2-6). mass mkt. 6.99 (978-0-8431-7790-9(X) , Price Stern Sloan) Penguin Group (USA) Inc.

—Mighty Big Book of School Jokes. 2003. (gr. 3-6). lib. bdg. 15.30 (978-0-613-68920-5(8)) Tandem Library Bks.

Ziegler, Mark. Chitchat Chuckles: A Book of Funny Talk. Haugen, Ryan, illus. 2005. (Read-It! Readers Ser.). 24p. (J). (ps). lib. bdg. 18.60 (978-1-4048-1160-7(5)) Picture Window Bks.

—Giggle Bubbles: A Book of Underwater Jokes. Haberstroh, Anne, illus. 2005. (Read-It! Readers Ser.). 24p. (C). (gr. 1-3). 18.60 (978-1-4048-0968-0(6)) Picture Window Bks.

—Wacky Workers: A Book of Job Jokes. Haugen, Ryan, illus. 2005. (Read-It! Readers Ser.). 24p. (J). (ps). lib. bdg. 18.60 (978-1-4048-1164-5(8)) Picture Window Bks.

—Whats up, Doc? A Book of Doctor Jokes. Haugen, Ryan, illus. 2005. (Read-It! Readers Ser.). 24p. (J). (ps). lib. bdg. 18.60 (978-1-4048-1165-2(6)) Picture Window Bks.

Zuehlke, Jeffrey. Ethiopia in Pictures. 2nd ed. 2005. (Visual Geography Ser.). (Illus.). 80p. (J). (gr. 5-12). 27.93 (978-0-8225-1170-0(3)) Lerner Publishing Group.

WIT AND HUMOR, PICTORIAL

Benton, Jim. It's All About Me, Deal With It. 2006. (It's Happy Bunny Ser.: Bk. 1). 32p. (J). bds. 7.99 (978-0-439-84774-2(5) , Scholastic) Scholastic, Inc.

Esos Prodigiosos Actores. 2003. (Coleccion Esa Gran Cultura).Tr. of Dreadful Drama. (SPA., Illus.). (YA). pap. 7.96 (978-84-272-2138-3(X)) Molino, Editorial ESP. *Dist:* Lectorum Pubns., Inc.

Feiffer, Jules. A Barrel of Laughs, a Vale of Tears. 1998. (978-0-606-13181-0(7)) Tandem Library Bks.

Fieffe, Kathleen, ed. Laugh Out Loud: Funny Photos, Comic Cards & Other Sports Funnies. rev. ed. 2000. (J). (gr. 3-9). pap. (978-1-930623-14-9(3)) Sports Illustrated For Kids.

Frazee, Marla. Why Did the Chicken Cross the Road? 2006. (Illus.). 32p. (J). lib. bdg. (***978-0-8037-3203-2(1)*** , Dial) Penguin Group (USA) Inc.

Grishaver, Joel Lurie & Glass, C. J. Torah Toons I. 1998. (Illus.). 199p. (J). (gr. 4-8). pap. 10.95 (978-0-933873-95-7(6)) Torah Aura Productions.

Macmillan Children's Books Staff. The Little Guide to Dads. 2000. (Little Guides Ser.). (Illus.). 18p. (J). (ps-3). (978-0-333-73420-9(3) , Macmillan Children's Bks.) Pan Macmillan.

—The Little Guide to Mums. 2000. (Little Guides Ser.). (Illus.). 24p. (J). (ps-3). (978-0-333-73419-3(X) , Macmillan Children's Bks.) Pan Macmillan.

—The Little Guide to Pets. 2000. (Little Guides Ser.). (Illus.). 24p. (J). (ps-3). (978-0-333-73421-6(1) , Macmillan Children's Bks.) Pan Macmillan.

Macmillan Children's Books Staff & Pilbrow, Giles. The Little Guide to Babies. 2000. (Little Guides Ser.). (Illus.). 20p. (J). (ps-3). (978-0-333-73422-3(X) , Macmillan Children's Bks.) Pan Macmillan.

O'Hare, Jeffrey A., ed. The Highlights Big Book of Fun: An Amazing Collection of Jokes, Riddles, Puzzles, & More! 2003. (Illus.). 96p. (YA). (gr. k-7). pap., act. bk. ed. 9.95 (978-1-59078-006-0(X)) Boyds Mills Pr.

Thebo, Patricia J. Uncle Looker & the Hurricane. 2003. (Illus.). 50p. (J). (gr. k-9). 16.50 (978-0-9725706-0-2(8)) Seaforth Publishing.

WITCHCRAFT

see also Charms; Occultism

Aronson, Marc. Witch-Hunt: Mysteries of the Salem Witch Trials. l.t. ed. 2004. (Thorndike Press Large Print the Literacy Bridge Ser.). 368p. (J). 21.95 (978-0-7862-6442-1(X)) Thorndike Pr.

Baker, Marina. Spells for Teenage Witches: Get Your Way with Magical Power. 2000. (Illus.). 96p. (YA). pap. 9.95 (978-1-56975-244-9(3)) Ulysses Pr.

Boraas, Tracey. The Salem Witch Trials. 2004. (Let Freedom Ring Ser.). (Illus.). 48p. (J). lib. bdg. 23.93 (978-0-7368-2464-4(2) , Bridgestone Bks.) Capstone Pr., Inc.

Burgan, Michael. The Salem Witch Trials. 2004. (We the People Ser.). (Illus.). 48p. (J). 22.60 (978-0-7565-0845-6(2)) Compass Point Bks.

Colbert, David. Magical Worlds of Harry Potter: A Treasury of Myths, Legends, & Fascinating Facts. 2001. (Illus.). 223p. (YA). (gr. 5 up). 14.95 (978-0-9708442-0-0(4)) Lumina Pr. LLC.

Crewe, Sabrina & Uschan, Michael V. The Salem Witch Trials. 2004. (Events That Shaped America Ser.). (Illus.). 32p. (J). lib. bdg. 24.67 (978-0-8368-3406-2(2)) Stevens, Gareth Inc.

Dolan, Edward F., Jr. The Salem Witch Trials. 2001. (Kaleidoscope Ser.). (Illus.). 48p. (J). (gr. 3 up). lib. bdg. 25.64 (978-0-7614-1302-8(2) , Benchmark Bks.) Cavendish, Marshall Corp.

Dowswell, Paul. The Amazing World of Witches: Discover the Spellbinding History of Witches, Wizardry , Magic & Mystery. 2003. (Illus.). 64p. (gr. 3-7). 14.99 (978-0-7548-1205-0(7)) Anness Publishing GBR. *Dist:* National Bk. Network.

—Witches & Wizards. 2001. (Discovery Ser.). (Illus.). 64p. (gr. 4-7). 14.95 (978-0-7548-0587-8(5)) Anness Publishing GBR. *Dist:* National Bk. Network.

Ellis, Stacy. A Wiccan ABC Book for Babies. 2005. (J). pap. 13.00 (978-0-9773731-2-3(6)) MaestroMedia Pr.

Giordano, Geraldine. Everything You Need to Know about Wicca: Ancient Beliefs for a Modern World. 2001. (Need to Know Library). (Illus.). 64p. (YA). (gr. 4-6). lib. bdg. 25.25 (978-0-8239-3401-0(2)) Rosen Publishing Group, Inc., The.

Greenhaven Staff. Black Magic & Witches. 2002. (gr. 7-12). lib. bdg. 30.35 (978-0-613-73885-9(3)) Tandem Library Bks.

Greenwood, S. World of Witches & Wizards. 2002. (Illus.). 64p. pap. 7.95 (978-1-84215-626-1(8) , Southwater) Anness Publishing GBR. *Dist:* National Bk. Network.

Horne, Fiona. Witchin' A Handbook for Teen Witches. 2003. (Illus.). 224p. pap. (978-0-00-713695-7(1) , Harper-Thorsons) HarperCollins Pubs. Ltd.

Kallen, Stuart A. Figures of the Salem Witch Trials. 2004. (History Makers Ser.). (Illus.). 112p. (J). (gr. 7-10). 29.95 (978-1-59018-559-9(5) , Lucent Bks.) Thomson Gale.

—Possessions & Exorcisms. 2004. (Illus.). 112p. (J). (gr. 7-10). 29.95 (978-1-59018-130-0(1) , Lucent Bks.) Thomson Gale.

—Witches. 2000. (Mystery Library). (Illus.). 112p. (J). (gr. 4-12). 29.95 (978-1-56006-688-0(1) , Lucent Bks.) Thomson Gale.

Landau, Elaine. Witness the Salem Witchcraft Trials with Elaine Landau. 2006. (Explore Colonial America with Elaine Landau Ser.). (Illus.). 48p. (J). lib. bdg. 23.93 (978-0-7660-2558-5(6) , Enslow Elementary) Enslow Pubs., Inc.

Manoy, Laureen. Where to Park Your Broomstick: A Teen's Guide to Witchcraft. 2004. (Illus.). 311p. (YA). (gr. 7-11). reprint ed. pap. 13.00 (978-0-7567-7048-8(3)) DIANE Publishing Co.

Manoy, Lauren. Where to Park Your Broomstick. 2002. (gr. 7-12). lib. bdg. 22.25 (978-0-613-56954-5(7)) Tandem Library Bks.

—Where to Park Your Broomstick: A Teen's Guide to Witchcraft. 2002. (Illus.). 320p. pap. 13.00 (978-0-684-85500-4(3) , Fireside) Simon & Schuster.

Martin, Michael. The Salem Witch Trials. (Graphic History Ser.). 32p. (YA). pap. 7.95 (978-0-7368-5246-3(8)) Capstone Pr., Inc.

—The Salem Witch Trials. Kamerer, Justin, illus. 2005. (Graphic Library). 32p. (J). 22.60 (978-0-7368-3847-4(3)) Capstone Pr., Inc.

Marvel, Laura, ed. The Salem Witch Trials. 2002. (At Issue in History Ser.). (Illus.). 144p. (J). (gr. 7-10). lib. bdg. 33.70 (978-0-7377-0823-3(9) , Greenhaven Pr., Inc.) Thomson Gale.

Meltzer, Milton. Witches & Witch-Hunts: A History of Persecution. Moser, Barry, illus. 2001. 128p. (J). pap. 4.99 (978-0-590-48630-9(6)) Scholastic, Inc.

—Witches & Witch-Hunts: A History of Persecution. 2001. (YA). (978-0-606-22161-0(1)) Tandem Library Bks.

Moorey, Teresa. Spell Bound: The Teenage Witch's Wiccan Handbook. 2002. (Illus.). 256p. pap. 12.95 (978-1-56975-312-5(1)) Ulysses Pr.

Nardo, Don. The Salem Witch Trials. 2007. (American History Ser.). 128p. (J). (gr. 7-10). 32.45 (***978-1-59018-950-4(7)*** , Lucent Bks.) Thomson Gale.

Olivares, Katie Lydon. ABC Book of Shadows. l.t. ed. 2005. (Illus.). 30p. (J). bds. 9.99 (978-0-9768573-0-3(8)) Itty Bitty Witch Works.

Orr, Tamra. The Salem Witch Trials. 2003. (People at the Center of Ser.). (Illus.). 48p. (J). 24.95 (978-1-56711-770-7(8) , Blackbirch Pr., Inc.) Thomson Gale.

Parks, Peggy J. Witches. 2007. (J). lib. bdg. (***978-1-60152-031-9(X)***) ReferencePoint Pr., Inc.

Priestley, Chris. Witch Hunt. 160p. (J). pap. 9.99 (978-0-340-86056-4(1)) Hodder General Publishing Division GBR. *Dist:* Independent Pubs. Group.

RavenWolf, Silver. Teen Witch: Wicca for a New Generation. 1998. (Illus.). 288p. (gr. 7-12). pap. 14.95 (978-1-56718-725-0(0) , K725) Llewellyn Pubns.

Rieth, Velvet. My First Little Workbook of Wicca: A Child's Guide to Wicca Through Interactive Play. 2007. (J). per. 16.95 (***978-0-9794533-0-4(5)*** , Full Circle Pr.) WillowTree Pr., L.L.C.

Roach, Marilynne K. In the Days of the Salem Witchcraft Trials. 2003. 96p. (J). (gr. 5 up). pap. 5.95 (978-0-618-39196-7(7)) Houghton Mifflin Co. Trade & Reference Div.

—In the Days of the Salem Witchcraft Trials. 2003. (gr. 3-6). lib. bdg. 14.10 (978-0-613-86973-7(7)) Tandem Library Bks.

Roleff, Tamara L., ed. Black Magic & Witches. 2003. (Illus.). 127p. (J). pap. 18.70 (978-0-7377-1319-0(4)); lib. bdg. 32.45 (978-0-7377-1318-3(6)) Thomson Gale. (Greenhaven Pr., Inc.).

Running Press Staff & Ruditis, Paul. The Charmed Book of Love Spells. ed. 2004. (Illus.). 128p. 4.95 (978-0-7624-2065-0(0) , Running Pr. Miniature Editions) Running Pr. Bk. Pubs.

The Salem Witch Trials, 6 vols. (gr. 2-5). 39.95 (978-0-7368-4570-0(4)) Red Brick Learning.

Salem Witch Trials. (Colonial America Ser.). 48p. (YA). 7.95 (978-0-7368-4481-9(3)) Capstone Pr., Inc.

Scamander, Newt, pseud & Rowling, J. K. Fantastic Beasts & Where to Find Them. 2001. (Harry Potter Ser.). (Illus.). 64p. (J). (gr. 3 up). mass mkt. 3.99 (978-0-439-29501-7(7)) Scholastic, Inc.

Stefoff, Rebecca. Witches & Witchcraft. 2007. (Secrets of the Supernatural Ser.). 96p. (J). lib. bdg. 32.79 (***978-0-7614-2637-0(X)*** , Benchmark Bks.) Cavendish, Marshall Corp.

Telesco, Patricia. The Teen Book of Shadows: Star Signs, Spells, Potions, & Powers. 2004. (Illus.). 224p. pap. 12.95 (978-0-8065-2410-8(3)) Kensington Publishing Corp.

UXL Staff. Witchcraft in America. 2001. (Illus.). xxxvii, 235p. (J). 68.00 (978-0-7876-4835-0(3) , GML00502-114879, UXL) Thomson Gale.

Wallis, Jeffrey. Trials in Salem. 2005. (Houghton Mifflin Social Studies Leveled Readers). (Illus.). 16p. (J). pap. (***978-0-618-56037-0(8)***) Houghton Mifflin Co.

Wood, Jamie. The Enchanted Diary: A Teen's Guide to Magick & Life. 2005. (Illus.). 193p. pap. 12.95 (978-1-58761-245-9(3) , Celestial Arts Publishing Company) Ten Speed Pr.

—The Teen Spell Book: Magick for Young Witches. 2004. (Illus.). 304p. 12.95 (978-1-58761-115-5(5) , Celestial Arts Publishing Company) Ten Speed Pr.

Woods, Geraldine. The Salem Witchcraft Trials: A Headline Court Case. 2000. (Headline Court Cases Ser.). (Illus.). 104p. (YA). (gr. 6-12). lib. bdg. 26.60 (978-0-7660-1383-4(9)) Enslow Pubs., Inc.

W X Y Z

WITCHCRAFT—FICTION

Adams, Georgie. The Three Little Witches Storybook. Bolam, Emily, illus. 2002. 96p. (ps-3). 15.99 (978-0-7868-0824-3(1)) Hyperion Bks. for Children.

Archway Paperbacks Staff. Salem Goes to Rome. 1998. lib. bdg. 11.80 (978-0-613-73074-7(7)) Tandem Library Bks.

Atwater-Rhodes, Amelia. In the Forests of the Night. 2000. (Illus.). 176p. (YA). (gr. 7-12). mass mkt. 5.99 (978-0-440-22816-5(6) , Laurel Leaf) Random Hse. Children's Bks.

—In the Forests of the Night. 2000. (gr. 7-12). lib. bdg. 13.55 (978-0-613-28537-7(9)); (Illus.). (J). 12.15 (978-0-606-17999-7(2)) Tandem Library Bks.

Baird, Alison. The Warding of Willowmere. 2005. 224p. (YA). pap. 15.00 (978-0-14-301529-1(X) , Penguin Global) Penguin Group (USA) Inc.

Balian, Lorna. Humbug Witch. 2004. (Illus.). 32p. (J). pap. 4.95 (978-1-59572-009-2(X)) Star Bright Bks., Inc.

—Humbug Witch. Balian, Lorna, illus. 2003. (Illus.). 32p. (J). 12.95 (978-1-932065-32-9(6) , 1-718-784-9112) Star Bright Bks., Inc.

Barry, Margaret S. The Witch & the Holiday Club. Birch, Linda, illus. l.t. ed. 1998. 126p. (J). pap. 16.95 (978-0-7540-6035-2(7) , Galaxy Children's Large Print) BBC Audiobooks America.

Batrae, Margot. While the Cat's Away. 1999. (gr. 7-12). lib. bdg. 13.00 (978-0-613-73060-0(7)) Tandem Library Bks.

Bellairs, John. The Letter, the Witch & the Ring. Egielski, Richard, illus. 2004. (Lewis Barnavelt Ser.). 208p. (J). pap. 5.99 (978-0-14-240261-0(3) , Puffin) Penguin Group (USA) Inc.

Benson, Amber, et al. Willow & Tara. Watson, Andi, illus. 2003. 80p. (gr. 12 up). pap. 9.95 (978-1-56971-905-3(5)) Dark Horse Comics.

Bird, Isobel. Circle of Three: Merry Meat. 2001. (gr. 7-12). lib. bdg. 13.00 (978-0-613-49297-3(8)) Tandem Library Bks.

—Circle of Three: So Mote It Be. 2001. (gr. 7-12). lib. bdg. 13.00 (978-0-613-49300-0(1)) Tandem Library Bks.

—Circle of Three No.15: Initiation. 2002. (gr. 7-12). lib. bdg. 13.00 (978-0-613-71371-9(0)) Tandem Library Bks.

—Second Sight. 2001. (gr. 7-12). lib. bdg. 13.00 (978-0-613-49299-7(4)) Tandem Library Bks.

Boston, Lucy M. Enemy at Green Knowe. 2002. (gr. 3-6). lib. bdg. 14.15 (978-0-613-54436-8(6)) Tandem Library Bks.

—An Enemy at Green Knowe. Boston, Peter, illus. 2002. (Green Knowe Ser.). 192p. (YA). (gr. 4-7). reprint ed. pap. 6.00 (978-0-15-202481-9(6) , Odyssey Classics) Harcourt Children's Bks.

Bova, Louise. Harry Potter & the Sorcerer's Stone: Stationery Kit. 2000. (Illus.). (J). (gr. 1-5). 10.95 (978-0-439-23658-4(4)) Scholastic, Inc.

Brin, Susannah. The Water Witch. rev. ed. 1999. (Take Ten Ser.). 64p. (YA). (gr. 4-12). pap. 3.95 (978-1-58659-055-0(3)) Artesian Pr.

Burge, Constance M. Seasons of the Witch, Vol. 1. Simon and Schuster Children's Staff, ed. 2003. (Charmed Ser.). 192p. (YA). pap. 7.99 (978-0-689-86545-9(7) , Simon Pulse) Simon & Schuster Children's Publishing.

Cabot, Meg. Jinx. 2007. 272p. (gr. 7 up). (J). 16.99 (***978-0-06-083764-8(0));*** (YA). lib. bdg. 17.89 (***978-0-06-083765-5(9)***) HarperCollins Pubs. (HarperTeen).

Carrol, Jacqueline. Strongest Evil. 2003. (gr. 3-6). lib. bdg. 13.00 (978-0-613-72477-7(1)) Tandem Library Bks.

Chew, Ruth. The Wednesday Witch. 2001. 128p. (J). 13.49 (978-0-7868-2598-1(7)) Hyperion Pr.

Codell, Esmé Raji. Diary of a Fairy Godmother. Lillis, Rachael & Kozjan, Drazen, illus. 2006. 176p. (gr. 2-5). pap. 5.99 (978-0-7868-0966-0(3)) Hyperion Pr.

Cooper, Clare. Stonehead. 2000. 132p. (J). pap. 12.95 (978-1-85902-782-0(2)) Beekman Bks., Inc.

Dahl, Roald. Las Brujas. Date not set. (SPA.). 208p. 15.95 (978-84-204-3655-5(0)) Alfaguara, Ediciones, S.A.-Grupo Santillana ESP. *Dist:* Santillana USA Publishing Co., Inc.

—Las Brujas. Blake, Quentin, illus. 2003. (SPA.). 200p. (YA). (gr. 5-8). pap. 12.95 (978-958-24-0100-9(1)) Santillana USA Publishing Co., Inc.

Dalmatian Press Staff. Winifred Witch & Her Very Own Cat. 2002. (Illus.). 24p. (J). (gr. k-5). pap. 2.99 (978-1-57759-363-8(4)) Dalmatian Pr.

Denney, Jim. Invasion of the Time Troopers, Vol. 3. 2002. (Time Benders Ser.). 144p. (J). (gr. 3-7). pap. 5.99 (978-1-4003-0041-9(X)) Nelson, Thomas Inc.

Desplechin, Marie. Poor Little Witch Girl. Rosner, Gillian, tr. 2007. 144p. (J). pap. 6.95 (***978-1-59990-128-2(5)*** , Bloomsbury Children) Bloomsbury Publishing.

Diamond, Bobby. What's Waiting at Wellington Mansion. 2002. 244p. (J). per. 18.00 (978-1-58982-026-5(6) , Bedside Bks.) American Bk. Publishing Group.

Dokey, Cameron. Haunted by Desire. 2000. (Charmed Ser.: Vol. 6). 192p. (YA). (gr. 7 up). mass mkt. 6.99 (978-0-671-04167-0(3) , Simon Pulse) Simon & Schuster Children's Publishing.

—Haunted by Desire. 2000. (gr. 7-12). lib. bdg. 14.15 (978-0-613-73079-2(8)) Tandem Library Bks.

Druce, Arden. The Wheels on the Bus. 2001. (Illus.). 16p. (J). 15.95 (978-0-85953-887-9(7)) Child's Play-International.

Duble, Kathleen Benner. The Sacrifice. 2007. 224p. (J). pap. 5.99 (***978-0-689-87651-6(3)*** , Aladdin) Simon & Schuster Children's Publishing.

Duble, Kathleen Benner & Vojnar, Kamil. The Sacrifice. 2005. 224p. (J). (gr. 4-8). 16.99 (978-0-689-87650-9(5) , McElderry, Margaret K.) Simon & Schuster Children's Publishing.

Dubowski, Cathy East. Fortune Cookie Fox. 1999. (gr. 3-6). lib. bdg. 12.40 (978-0-613-21556-5(7)) Tandem Library Bks.

Duce, Gillian. Magic & Mayhem. 2006. 208p. per. (***978-1-894936-64-4(7)***) Saga Bks.

Easton, Kelly. White Magic: Spells to Hold You, A Novel. 2007. 208p. (YA). (gr. 7-11). 15.99 (***978-0-375-83769-2(8));*** lib. bdg. 18.99 (***978-0-375-93769-9(2)***) Random Hse. Children's Bks. (Lamb, Wendy).

Forde, Catherine. The Drowning Pond. 2006. 256p. (J). pap. 8.99 (***978-1-4052-2176-4(3)***) Egmont Bks., Ltd. GBR. *Dist:* Independent Pubs. Group.

Forrester, Sandra. Witches of Friar's Lantern. 2003. (gr. 3-6). lib. bdg. 12.95 (978-0-613-84057-6(7)) Tandem Library Bks.

Freer, Jeannette. When Harry Met the Potter. 2007. 76p. (J). per. 9.99 (***978-1-933899-72-5(7)***) Holy Fire Publishing.

Furlong, Monica. Colman. 2005. 288p. (J). (gr. 5). reprint ed. pap. 5.99 (978-0-375-81515-7(5) , Laurel Leaf) Random Hse. Children's Bks.

—Wise Child. 2004. (Monica Furlong Ser.). 240p. (J). (gr. 5 up). 15.95 (978-0-394-89105-7(8) , Random Hse. Bks. for Young Readers) Random Hse. Children's Bks.

—Wise Child. 2001. (gr. 7-12). lib. bdg. 13.00 (978-0-613-29386-0(X)) Tandem Library Bks.

Gallagher, Diana G. & Burge, Constance M. Trickery Treat. 2008. (Charmed Ser.). 208p. (YA). mass mkt. 6.99 (***978-1-4169-3670-1(X)*** , Simon Spotlight Entertainment) Simon & Schuster.

Garton, Ray. All That Glitters. 1998. (Sabrina, the Teenage Witch Ser.: No. 12). (Illus.). 176p. (YA). (gr. 5 up). mass mkt. 4.99 (978-0-671-02116-0(8) , Simon Pulse) Simon & Schuster Children's Publishing.

Gelsey, James. Sinister Sorcerer. del Sur, Duendes, illus. 2003. (Scooby Doo Mystery Ser.). 64p. (J). 3.99 (978-0-439-42074-7(1) , Scholastic Paperbacks) Scholastic, Inc.

—Sinister Sorcerer. 2003. (gr. 3-6). lib. bdg. 11.80 (978-0-613-66383-0(7)) Tandem Library Bks.

Gilmour, H. B. Witch Hunters. 2003. (gr. 5-8). lib. bdg. 12.40 (978-0-613-72011-3(3)) Tandem Library Bks.

Greenburg, Dan. It's Itchcraft! Davis, Jack E., illus. 2003. (Zack Files Ser.). 128p. (J). (gr. 1-4). pap. 4.99 (978-0-448-42888-8(1) , Grosset & Dunlap) Penguin Group (USA) Inc.

—It's Itchcraft! 2003. (gr. 3-6). lib. bdg. 13.00 (978-0-613-72486-9(0)) Tandem Library Bks.

Haddad, Charles. Meet Calliope Day. 1999. (J). (978-0-606-16452-8(9)) Tandem Library Bks.

Hansen, Lynne. A Time for Witches. 2007. (YA). (***978-1-4114-9671-2(X)***) Spark Publishing Group.

Hautzig, Deborah. Little Witch Goes to School. Wickstrom, Sylvie K., illus. 1998. (Little Witch Ser.: Vol. 3). 48p. (J). (gr. k-3). pap. 3.99 (978-0-679-88738-6(5) , Random Hse. Bks. for Young Readers) Random Hse. Children's Bks.

—Little Witch's Bad Dream. 2000. (Illus.). (J). (978-0-606-18855-5(X)) Tandem Library Bks.

Hearn, Diane Dawson. Bad Luck Boswell. 1999. (J). (978-0-606-17312-4(9)) Tandem Library Bks.

Hearn, Julie. Merrybegot. 2005. 288p. (YA). (***978-0-19-279157-3(5)***) Oxford Univ. Pr., Inc.

Hearn, Julie. The Minister's Daughter. 2006. 272p. (YA). pap. 7.99 (978-0-689-87691-2(2) , Simon Pulse) Simon & Schuster Children's Publishing.

Hearn, Julie & Frost, Michael. The Minister's Daughter. 2005. 272p. (YA). (gr. 7 up). 17.99 (978-0-689-87690-5(4) , Atheneum) Simon & Schuster Children's Publishing.

Hébert, Marie-Francine & Germain, Philippe. Une Sorciere dans la Soupe. 2001. (FRE., Illus.). 64p. (J). pap. (978-2-89021-478-1(8)) Diffusion du livre Mirabel.

Hermes, Patricia. Salem Witch. 2006. (My Side of the Story Ser.). 192p. (J). (gr. 5-9). pap. 7.95 (978-0-7534-5991-1(4) , Kingfisher) Houghton Mifflin Co. Trade & Reference Div.

Hickey, Tony. Granny & the American Witch. 1998. (Illus.). 112p. (YA). (gr. 1 up). pap. 7.95 (978-1-901737-13-4(6)) Anvil Bks., Ltd. IRL. *Dist:* Dufour Editions, Inc.

Holder, Nancy. Feline Felon. 1999. (gr. 3-6). lib. bdg. 11.80 (978-0-613-21530-5(3)) Tandem Library Bks.

—Scarabian Nights. 1999. (gr. 7-12). lib. bdg. 12.40 (978-0-613-73075-4(5)) Tandem Library Bks.

Howe, James. Pinky & Rex & the Mean Old Witch. 1999. (Pinky & Rex Ser.). (J). (gr. 1-4). (978-0-606-17510-4(5)) Tandem Library Bks.

Hyung, Min-Woo. Priest. Forbes, Jake, ed. Kim, Jessica, tr. from KOR. 2002. (Illus.). 208p. pap. 9.99 (978-1-59182-008-6(1) , Tokyopop Adult) TOKYOPOP, Inc.

—Priest. rev. ed. 2002. (Illus.). 208p. Vol. 2. pap. 9.99 (978-1-59182-009-3(X)); Vol. 3. pap. 9.99 (978-1-59182-010-9(3)) TOKYOPOP, Inc. (Tokyopop Adult).

John Brown Publishing Ltd. & Murphy, Harriet. Dora's Enchanted Adventure: Follow the Reader Level II. 2007. (Dora the Explorer Ser.). 24p. (J). 24.99 (***978-1-4169-4992-3(5)*** , Simon Scribbles) Simon & Schuster Children's Publishing.

Johnson, Lissa Halls & Vogel, Jane. Grasping at Moonbeams, Vol. 6. 2005. (Brio Girls Ser.). 192p. (YA). pap. 7.99 (978-1-58997-052-6(7)) Focus on the Family Publishing.

Jones, Diana Wynne. The Chronicles of Chrestomanci, 2 vols. 2001. (Chronicles of Chrestomanci Ser.: Vol. I). (J). (gr. 7-12). Vol. I. 608p. pap. 7.99 (978-0-06-447268-5(X) , Harper Trophy); Vol. II. 560p. pap. 7.99 (978-0-06-447269-2(8)) HarperCollins Pubs.

—Chronicles of Chrestomanci: Lives of Christopher Chant & Charmed Life. 2001. (gr. 5-8). lib. bdg. 15.30 (978-0-613-31070-3(5)) Tandem Library Bks.

—Chronicles of Chrestomanci: Magicians of Caprona & Witch Week. 2001. (gr. 5-8). lib. bdg. 15.30 (978-0-613-31071-0(3)) Tandem Library Bks.

—Conrad's Fate. (J). 2006. 400p. pap. 6.99 (978-0-06-074745-9(5)); 2005. 384p. (gr. k-17). lib. bdg. 17.89 (978-0-06-074744-2(7)); 2005. 384p. (gr. 5 up). 16.99 (978-0-06-074743-5(9)) HarperCollins Pubs.

—Conrad's Fate: Read-Along/Homework Pack. 2005. (Chrestomanci Ser.). (YA). (gr. 5-8). 102.74 incl. audio (978-1-4193-3551-8(0) , 42039) Recorded Bks., LLC.

—The Pinhoe Egg: A Chrestomanci Book. (J). 2007. 480p. pap. 7.99 (***978-0-06-113126-4(1)*** , Eos); 2006. 528p. 17.99 (978-0-06-113124-0(5) , Greenwillow Bks.); 2006. 528p. lib. bdg. 18.89 (978-0-06-113125-7(3)) HarperCollins Pubs.

Jones, Diana Wynne. Witch Week. l.t. ed. 2005. (Illus.). 300p. (J). pap. (978-0-7540-6177-9(9) , CLP 371) BBC Audio.

Karas, Phyllis. Spellbound. 1999. (Enchanted Hearts Ser.). (Illus.). (J). (978-0-606-17967-6(4)) Tandem Library Bks.

Kellogg, Steven. The Christmas Witch. Kellogg, Steven, illus. 2002. (Illus.). (J). 25.45 (978-0-7587-2238-6(9)) Book Wholesalers, Inc.

Konigsburg, E. L. Jennifer, Hecate, Macbeth, William McKinley, & Me, Elizabeth. (J). 177p. (gr. 3-6). pap. 4.99 (978-0-8072-1524-1(4)); 117p. (gr. 3-6). pap. 4.99 (978-0-8072-1417-6(5)); 1998. 177p. (gr. 4-7). pap. 29.00 incl. audio (978-0-8072-8001-0(1) , YA963SP) Random Hse. Audio Publishing Group. (Listening Library).

—Jennifer, Hecate, Macbeth, William McKinley, & Me, Elizabeth. 128p. (J). 2007. pap. 2.99 (***978-1-4169-4829-2(5));*** 2007. pap. 5.99 (978-1-4169-3396-0(4)); 2001. (Illus.). pap. 5.99 (978-0-689-84625-0(8)) Simon & Schuster Children's Publishing. (Aladdin).

Krulik, Nancy E. Rulin' the School. 2000. (Sabrina, the Teenage Witch: No. 12). (Illus.). 85p. (J). (gr. 2-5). per. (978-0-671-77335-9(6) , Simon & Schuster Children's Publishing) Simon & Schuster Children's Publishing.

—Rulin' the School. 2000. (gr. 3-6). lib. bdg. 11.80 (978-0-613-28047-1(4)) Tandem Library Bks.

Lachtman, Ofelia Dumas. The Trouble with Tessa. 122p. (J). (ps-7). pap. 9.95 (978-1-55885-448-2(7) , Piñata Books) Arte Publico Pr.

Lenhard, Elizabeth. Charmed Again. 2001. (Charmed Ser.: Vol. 11). 192p. (YA). pap. 6.99 (978-0-7434-4264-0(4) , Simon Pulse) Simon & Schuster Children's Publishing.

—Charmed Again. 2002. (gr. 7-12). lib. bdg. 14.15 (978-0-613-74238-2(9)) Tandem Library Bks.

Low, Alice. The Witch Who Was Afraid of Witches. Manning, Jane, illus. 2000. (I Can Read Chapter Bks.). 48p. (J). (gr. 3 up). pap. 3.99 (978-0-06-444255-8(1) , Harper Trophy) HarperCollins Pubs.

McAllister, Margaret. High Cragg Linn. 2008. 224p. (YA). pap. 9.95 (***978-0-7459-6062-3(6)***) Lion Hudson plc GBR. *Dist:* Independent Pubs. Group.

Moon, Angelina. The Christmas of the Witch. Biltis, Gary, illus. 1999. (Tales from NoWay Ser.: Vol. I). (J). (gr. 2-6). pap. 10.95 (978-1-892247-00-1(3)) Family Time Tales.

—Havoc at Holiday House. Biltis, Gary, illus. 1999. (Tales from NoWay Ser.: Vol. III). (J). (gr. 2-6). pap. (978-1-892247-02-5(X)) Family Time Tales.

—The Witchmaker: The Birth of Carmella. Biltis, Gary, illus. 1999. (Tales from NoWay Ser.: Vol. II). (J). (gr. 2-6). pap. (978-1-892247-01-8(1)) Family Time Tales.

Moon, Russell. Witch Boy. 2002. (gr. 7-12). lib. bdg. 15.25 (978-0-613-71472-3(5)) Tandem Library Bks.

Muntean, Michaela. Which Witch Is Which? Brannon, Tom, illus. 2004. 24p. (J). (gr. k-ps). bds. 4.99 (978-0-375-82782-2(X) , Random Hse. Bks. for Young Readers) Random Hse. Children's Bks.

Myers, Anna. Wart. 2007. 224p. (J). (gr. 5-9). 16.95 (***978-0-8027-8977-8(3)***) Walker & Co.

Myers, Bill & Riordan, James. The Wiccan. 2003. (Forbidden Doors Ser.: Vol. 11). 160p. (J). mass mkt. 5.99 (978-0-8423-7203-9(2) , 75 7203-2) Tyndale Hse. Pubs.

Myracle, Lauren. Rhymes with Witches. (YA). (gr. 8-17). 2006. 272p. pap. 6.95 (978-0-8109-9215-3(9)); 2005. 224p. 16.95 (978-0-8109-5859-3(7) , Amulet Bks.) Abrams, Harry N., Inc.

Naylor, Phyllis Reynolds. The Witch Herself. 2002. (gr. 3-6). lib. bdg. 13.00 (978-0-613-88157-9(5)) Tandem Library Bks.

—Witch Water. 2002. 192p. (J). pap. 4.99 (978-0-689-85316-6(5) , Aladdin) Simon & Schuster Children's Publishing.

—Witch Water. 2002. (gr. 3-6). lib. bdg. 13.00 (978-0-613-90185-7(1)) Tandem Library Bks.

—Witch Weed. 2004. 192p. (J). pap. 4.99 (978-0-689-85381-4(5) , Aladdin) Simon & Schuster Children's Publishing.

Nelson, Warren. A Ditch of Witches. Holman, Karlyn, illus. 1999. 32p. (J). (ps-3). 16.95 (978-0-9670683-0-5(4)) Bayfield Street Publishing, Inc.

Nix, Garth. The Ragwitch. 2004. (Illus.). 400p. (gr. 7 up). pap. 6.99 (978-0-06-050807-4(8)) HarperCollins Pubs.

Norton, Mary. Bedknob & Broomstick. Blegvad, Erik, illus. 2000. 240p. (J). (gr. 3 up). pap. 6.00 (978-0-15-202456-7(5) , Odyssey Classics) Harcourt Children's Bks.

Ocelot, Michel. Kirikou et la Sorciere. pap. 14.95 (978-2-01-321877-1(X)) Hachette Groupe Livre FRA. *Dist:* Distribooks, Inc.

O'Connell, Jennifer. Ten Timid Ghosts. O'Connell, Jennifer, illus. 2000. (Read with Me Paperbacks Ser.). (Illus.). 32p. (J). (ps-3). 3.99 (978-0-439-15804-6(4)) Scholastic, Inc.

Odom, Mel. Mummy Dearest. 2000. (Sabrina, the Teenage Witch Ser.: No. 31). 161p. (YA). (gr. 5 up). (978-0-671-77324-3(0) , Simon & Schuster Children's Publishing) Simon & Schuster Children's Publishing.

—Mummy Dearest. 2000. (gr. 3-6). lib. bdg. 12.40 (978-0-613-27985-7(9)) Tandem Library Bks.

Palatini, Margie. Zoom Broom. Fine, Howard, illus. 2000. 32p. (ps-4). pap. 5.99 (978-0-7868-1467-1(5)) Disney Pr.

Papineau, Lucie. Baby Witch, Yuck! ed. 2004. (Illus.). (J). (ps up). spiral bd. (978-0-616-03052-3(5)); spiral bd. (978-0-616-04560-2(3)) Canadian National Institute for the Blind/Institut National Canadien pour les Aveugles.

Papineau, Lucie, et al. Baby Witch, Yuck! Beshwaty, Steve, illus. 1999. (Monster Country Ser.). 32p. (J). pap. (978-1-894363-22-8(1)) Dominique & Friends.

Peters, Nancy L. Wishmagic. 1998. 24p. (J). (gr. k-4). pap. 6.00 (978-0-8059-4304-7(8)) Dorrance Publishing Co., Inc.

Pitcher. Pitcher - Cloud Cat Quartet Bind-up. 2008. 320p. (YA). pap. 9.95 (***978-1-4052-0851-2(1)***) Egmont Bks., Ltd. GBR. *Dist:* Independent Pubs. Group.

Poole, Josephine. Moon Eyes. 2002. 160p. pap. 9.99 (978-0-340-84374-1(8) , Hodder & Stoughton) Hodder General Publishing Division GBR. *Dist:* Trafalgar Square Publishing.

RavenWolf, Silver. Witches' Key to Terror. Zins, Rebecca, ed. 2001. (Witches Chillers Ser.: Vol. 3). (Illus.). 288p. (gr. 8-12). pap. 5.99 (978-0-7387-0049-6(5)) Llewellyn Pubns.

—Witches' Key to Terror. 2001. (gr. 7-12). lib. bdg. 14.15 (978-0-613-87046-7(8)) Tandem Library Bks.

—Witches' Night of Fear. Zins, Rebecca, ed. 2001. (Witches Chillers Ser.). 368p. (gr. 7-12). pap. 5.99 (978-1-56718-718-2(8)) Llewellyn Pubns.

Rees, Celia. Sorceress. (Illus.). 352p. (YA). (gr. 9). 2003. pap. 8.99 (978-0-7636-2183-4(8)); 2002. 15.99 (978-0-7636-1847-6(0)) Candlewick Pr.

Reinhardt, Laurel Ann. Seasons of Magic. Hill, Connie, ed. 2001. (Illus.). 168p. (gr. 6-12). pap. 9.95 (978-1-56718-564-5(9)) Llewellyn Pubns.

Reisfeld, Randi. All You Need Is a Love Spell. 1998. (gr. 7-12). lib. bdg. 13.00 (978-0-613-73088-4(7)) Tandem Library Bks.

Rinaldi, Ann. A Break with Charity: A Story about the Salem Witch Trials. 2003. (Great Episodes Ser.). 320p. (YA). pap. 6.95 (978-0-15-204682-8(8) , Gulliver Bks.) Harcourt Children's Bks.

Ross, Eileen. The Halloween Showdown. Reed, Lynn R., illus. 1999. 32p. (J). (gr. k-3). tchr. ed. 15.95 (978-0-8234-1395-9(0)) Holiday Hse., Inc.

Rowling, J. K. Harry Potter & the Order of the Phoenix. GrandPré, Mary, illus. 2004. (Harry Potter Ser.: Year 5). 896p. (J). (gr. 4-7). mass mkt. 9.99 (978-0-439-35807-1(8) , Scholastic Paperbacks) Scholastic, Inc.

Rowling, J. K. Harry Potter et l'Ecole des Sorciers.Tr. of Harry Potter & the Sorcerer's Stone. 2007. 311p. pap. 14.95 (***978-2-07-061236-9(8));*** 2000. (FRE.). (J). pap. 14.95 (978-2-07-051426-7(9)) Gallimard, Editions FRA. *Dist:* Distribooks, Inc.

Schietinger-Cachina, Daryl A. The Witch Who Couldn't Spell. Schietinger-Cachina, Daryl A., illus. 1999. (Illus.). 8p. (J). (ps-5). pap. 5.00 (978-1-928641-03-2(2)) Daryl Ann Pubns.

Schisgall, Jim. The Sand Witch Saves Christmas. Timmins, John, illus. 1998. 32p. (J). (ps-3). mass mkt. 6.95 (978-1-890997-01-4(3)) Hardy Hill Enterprises, Inc.

Simmons, Steven J. Alice & Greta: A Tale of Two Witches. Moore, Cyd, illus. 1999. 32p. (J). (ps-3). pap. 6.95 (978-0-88106-976-1(0)) Charlesbridge Publishing, Inc.

Snyder, Zilpha Keatley. The Witches of Worm. 2006. 22.00 (978-0-8446-7290-8(4)) Smith, Peter Pub., Inc.

Speare, Elizabeth George. The Witch of Blackbird Pond. 2002. (Illus.). (J). 14.47 (978-0-7587-0227-2(2)) Book Wholesalers, Inc.

—The Witch of Blackbird Pond. Dell Publishing.

—The Witch of Blackbird Pond. Moser, Barry, illus. 2001. (Illustrated American Classics Ser.). 224p. (YA). (gr. 7-9). tchr. ed. 22.00 (978-0-395-91367-3(5)) Houghton Mifflin Co. Trade & Reference Div.

—The Witch of Blackbird Pond. 2004. 223p. (J). (gr. 4-7). pap., tchr.'s planning gde. ed. 38.00 incl. audio (978-0-8072-0862-5(0) , Listening Library) Random Hse. Audio Publishing Group.

—The Witch of Blackbird Pond. l.t. ed. 2005. 328p. pap. 10.95 (978-0-7862-7250-1(3) , Large Print Pr.) Thorndike Pr.

Spence, Craig. Josh & the Magic Vial. 2007. 396p. pap. 16.95 (***978-1-897235-10-2(0)***) Thistledown Pr., Ltd. CAN. *Dist:* Fitzhenry & Whiteside, Ltd.

Staub, Wendy Corsi. Voodoo Moon. 2000. (gr. 7-12). lib. bdg. 14.15 (978-0-613-73080-8(1)) Tandem Library Bks.

Stolarz, Laurie Faria. The Blue Is for Nightmares Collection. 2006. 1224p. pap., pap. 29.95 (978-0-7387-0988-8(3) , Flux) Llewellyn Pubns.

—Red Is for Remembrance. 2005. (Blue Is for Nightmares Ser.: Vol. 4). 336p. pap. 8.95 (978-0-7387-0760-0(0)) Llewellyn Pubns.

—Silver Is for Secrets. 2005. (Blue Is for Nightmares Ser.: Vol. 3). 288p. pap. 8.95 (978-0-7387-0631-3(0)) Llewellyn Pubns.

—White Is for Magic. Karre, Andrew, ed. 2004. (Blue Is for Nightmares Ser.: Vol. 2). 312p. pap. 8.95 (978-0-7387-0443-2(1)) Llewellyn Pubns.

Stone, Kelsey. The Predahil Chronicles. 2005. (YA). per. 6.49 (978-1-59196-995-2(6)) Instantpublisher.com.

Talbott, Hudson. O'sullivan Stew. 2001. (gr. k-3). lib. bdg. 15.30 (978-0-613-33718-2(2)) Tandem Library Bks.

Thesman, Jean. The Other Ones. 2001. (Illus.). 192p. (J). (gr. 5-7). pap. 5.99 (978-0-14-131246-0(7) , Puffin) Penguin Group (USA) Inc.

—The Other Ones. 2001. (978-0-606-21368-4(6)) Tandem Library Bks.

—Other Ones. 2001. (gr. 5-8). lib. bdg. 14.15 (978-0-613-43861-2(2)) Tandem Library Bks.

Thomas, Valerie, et al. Winnie the Witch. 2002. (Illus.). 64p. pap. 16.95 (978-1-84002-255-1(8) , Oberon Bks.) Theatre Communications Group, Inc.

Tiernan, Cate. Awakening, Bk. 5. 2007. (Sweep Ser.). 192p. (YA). pap. 6.99 (*978-0-14-241020-2(9) , Puffin) Penguin Group (USA) Inc.

—Blood Witch. 2001. (gr. 7-12). lib. bdg. 13.00 (978-0-613-64024-4(1)) Tandem Library Bks.

—The Blood Witch, Vol. 3. 2001. (Sweep Ser.: Bk. 3). (Illus.). 192p. (YA). (gr. 7 up). pap. 5.99 (978-0-14-131111-1(8) , Puffin) Penguin Group (USA) Inc.

—Book of Shadows, Bk. 1. 2007. (Sweep Ser.). 192p. (YA). pap. 6.99 (*978-0-14-240986-2(3) , Puffin) Penguin Group (USA) Inc.

—Calling, Bk. 7. 2008. (Sweep Ser.: Bk. 7). 192p. (YA). (gr. 7). 6.99 (*978-0-14-241022-6(5) , Puffin) Penguin Group (USA) Inc.

—Changeling: Book Eight. 2008. (Sweep Ser.). 192p. (YA). (gr. 7). 6.99 (*978-0-14-241023-3(3) , Puffin) Penguin Group (USA) Inc.

—The Coven. 2001. (Sweep Ser.: Bk. 2). (Illus.). 192p. (YA). (gr. 7-12). pap. 5.99 (978-0-14-131047-3(2) , Puffin) Penguin Group (USA) Inc.

—Coven. 2001. (gr. 7-12). lib. bdg. 13.00 (978-0-613-31093-2(4)) Tandem Library Bks.

—The Coven, Bk. 2. 2007. (Sweep Ser.). 192p. (YA). pap. 6.99 (*978-0-14-240987-9(1) , Puffin) Penguin Group (USA) Inc.

—Dark Magick, Bk. 4. 2007. (Sweep Ser.). 192p. (YA). pap. 6.99 (*978-0-14-240989-3(8) , Puffin) Penguin Group (USA) Inc.

—Eclipse. 2002. (gr. 7-12). lib. bdg. 13.00 (978-0-613-64038-1(1)) Tandem Library Bks.

—A Necklace of Water, Vol. 4. 2006. (Balefire Ser.). 240p. (YA). (gr. 7-12). mass mkt. 5.99 (978-1-59514-048-7(4) , Razorbill) Penguin Group (USA) Inc.

—Origins. 2002. (gr. 7-12). lib. bdg. 13.00 (978-0-613-64091-6(8)) Tandem Library Bks.

—Reckoning. 2002. (gr. 7-12). lib. bdg. 14.15 (978-0-613-64099-2(3)) Tandem Library Bks.

Tiernan, Cate. Spellbound. 2007. (Sweep Ser.: Bk. 6). 192p. (YA). pap. 6.99 (*978-0-14-241021-9(7) , Puffin) Penguin Group (USA) Inc.

Townsend, Tom. Nadia of the Night Witches. Kemnitz, Myrna, ed. 1998. 158p. (YA). (gr. 8 up). 9.99 (978-0-88092-273-9(7) , 2737) Royal Fireworks Publishing Co.

Utton, Peter. The Witch's Hand. 2001. (Illus.). 32p. (J). (ps-2). 14.95 (978-1-86233-410-6(2)) Levinson Bks. Ltd. GBR. *Dist:* Sterling Publishing Co., Inc.

Vande Velde, Vivian. Dragon's Bait. 2003. (Illus.). 208p. (YA). pap. 5.95 (978-0-15-216663-2(7) , Magic Carpet Bks.) Harcourt Children's Bks.

—Magic Can Be Murder. 2000. (Illus.). 208p. (YA). (gr. 7-12). 17.00 (978-0-15-202665-3(7)) Harcourt Children's Bks.

Varela, Gabrielle Charbonnet & Tiernan, Cate. Origins. 2002. (Sweep Ser.: Vol. 11). 192p. (YA). 5.99 (978-0-14-230109-8(4) , Puffin) Penguin Group (USA) Inc.

—Seeker. 2002. (Sweep Ser.: Vol. 10). 192p. (YA). pap. 6.99 (978-0-14-230108-1(6) , Puffin) Penguin Group (USA) Inc.

Velde, Vivian V. Magic Can Be Murder. 2002. 208p. (J). pap. 6.99 (978-0-14-230210-1(4) , Puffin) Penguin Group (USA) Inc.

Vornholt, John. Witchopoly. 1999. (gr. 7-12). lib. bdg. 13.00 (978-0-613-73076-1(3)) Tandem Library Bks.

Walton, Rick. Pig, Pigger, Piggest. Holder, Jimmy, illus. 2003. 32p. (J). reprint ed. pap. 6.95 (978-1-58685-318-1(X)) Gibbs Smith, Publisher.

—Pig, Pigger, Piggest. 2003. (gr. k-3). lib. bdg. 15.25 (978-0-613-79635-4(7)) Tandem Library Bks.

Weiss, Bobbi J. G. Prom Time. 1999. (gr. 7-12). lib. bdg. 13.00 (978-0-613-73077-8(1)) Tandem Library Bks.

Weiss, David Cody. Kitty Cornered. 2000. (Sabrina, the Teenage Witch: No. 13). (Illus.). 64p. (J). (gr. 2-5). per. (978-0-671-77336-6(4) , Simon & Schuster Children's Publishing) Simon & Schuster Children's Publishing.

Wigington, Patti. Summer's Ashes. 2007. 208p. (YA). pap. 15.00 (*978-0-9766805-9-8(9) Keene Publishing.

Witch of Blackbird Pond. 1999. (J). 11.95 (978-1-56137-534-9(9)) Novel Units, Inc.

Wood, Audrey. Heckedy Peg. Wood, Audrey, illus. 2002. (Illus.). (J). 14.04 (978-0-7587-2710-7(0)) Book Wholesalers, Inc.

—Heckedy Peg. Wood, Don, illus. 2001. 36p. (J). (ps-5). pap. 6.95 (978-0-9629298-6-1(7) , MHC-6-7) Minnesota Humanities Commission.

Wood, Frances M. Becoming Rosemary. 1998. (J). (978-0-606-13186-5(8)) Tandem Library Bks.

Youngberg, Norma R. Miracle of the Song. 2000. (Illus.). 188p. (J). (gr. 3-6). reprint ed. per. 11.95 (978-1-57258-187-6(5) , 945-6049) TEACH Services, Inc.

Ziefert, Harriet. Two Little Witches: A Counting Story. Taback, Simms, illus. 2002. 20p. (J). (gr. k-k). bds. 6.99 (978-0-7636-1894-0(2)) Candlewick Pr.

WITCHES

Besel, Jennifer M. Witches. 2007. (Blazers Ser.). 32p. (J). 19.93 (978-0-7368-6445-9(8)) Capstone Pr., Inc.

Busquets, Jordi. Leo y Veo, las Brujas.Tr. of I Read & See, the Witches. (SPA.). (J). 3.48 (978-84-305-9406-1(X)) Susaeta Ediciones, S.A. ESP. *Dist:* AIMS International Bks., Inc., Giron Bks.

Christensen, Jo-Anne. Ghosts, Werewolves, Witches & Vampires, Vol. 1. rev. ed. 2001. (Ghost Stories Ser.). (Illus.). 224p. (J). (gr. 4). pap. 11.95 (978-1-55105-333-2(0)) Lone Pine Publishing USA.

Dolan, Edward F., Jr. The Salem Witch Trials. 2001. (Kaleidoscope Ser.). (Illus.). 48p. (J). (gr. 3 up). lib. bdg. 25.64 (978-0-7614-1302-8(2) , Benchmark Bks.) Cavendish, Marshall Corp.

Dorling Kindersley Publishing Staff. Witch & Wizard. 2005. 16p. (J). pap. 6.99 (978-0-7566-1269-6(1)) Dorling Kindersley Publishing, Inc.

Fremont, Victoria & Stewart, Pat. Invisible Witches Magic Picture Book. 1998. (Illus.). 16p. (J). pap. 1.00 (978-0-486-40529-2(X)) Dover Pubns., Inc.

Greenhaven Staff. Black Magic & Witches. 2002. (gr. 7-12). lib. bdg. 30.35 (978-0-613-73885-9(3)) Tandem Library Bks.

Greenwood, S. World of Witches & Wizards. 2002. (Illus.). 64p. pap. 7.95 (978-1-84215-626-1(8) , Southwater) Anness Publishing GBR. *Dist:* National Bk. Network.

Hamilton, John. Witches. 2007. (ENG., Illus.). 32p. (J). lib. bdg. 24.21 (*978-1-59928-776-8(5) , ABDO & Daughters) ABDO Publishing Co.

Hamilton, John. Wizards & Witches. 2005. (Fantasy & Folklore Ser.). (Illus.). 32p. (J). (gr. 4-8). lib. bdg. 24.21 (978-1-59197-716-2(9)) ABDO Publishing Co.

Lynette, Rachel. Witches. 2007. (Mysterious Encounters Ser.). 48p. (J). (gr. 4-8). 26.20 (*978-0-7377-3643-4(7) , Kidhaven) Thomson Gale.

Narayan, Natasha. Witches, Wizards & Warlocks of London. 2004. (... of London Ser.). (Illus.). 96p. 8.99 (978-1-904153-12-2(7)) Watling St., Ltd. GBR. *Dist:* Trafalgar Square Publishing.

Parks, Peggy J. Witches. 2007. (J). lib. bdg. (*978-1-60152-031-9(X)) ReferencePoint Pr., Inc.

Rawson, C. Witches. 2004. (Young Reading Ser.: Vol. 1). 48p. (J). (gr. 2 up). lib. bdg. 13.95 (978-1-58086-630-9(1) , Usborne) EDC Publishing.

Stefoff, Rebecca. Witches & Witchcraft. 2007. (Secrets of the Supernatural Ser.). 96p. (J). lib. bdg. 32.79 (*978-0-7614-2637-0(X) , Benchmark Bks.) Cavendish, Marshall Corp.

Witch Sticker Book. 2003. (Illus.). 16p. (J). 2.98 (978-1-84273-117-8(3) , Exclusive Editions) Parragon, Inc.

WITCHES—FICTION

Abbott, Candy. Gavin Goodfellow: The Lure of Burnt Swamp. 2007. 368p. pap. 14.95 (*978-1-886068-03-2(8)) Fruitbearer Publishing.

Abouzeid, Chris. Anatopsis. 2006. 336p. (J). (gr. 5). 16.99 (978-0-525-47583-5(4) , Dutton Juvenile) Penguin Group (USA) Inc.

Adams, Denise H. Itchy the Witch. 2007. (J). per. 13.99 (*978-1-59879-385-7(3)) Lifevest Publishing, Inc.

Aiken, Joan. The Witch of Clatteringshaws. 2005. 144p. (J). (gr. 5). lib. bdg. 17.99 (978-0-385-90252-6(2) , Delacorte Bks. for Young Readers) Random Hse. Children's Bks.

—The Witch of Clatteringshaws. 2006. 160p. (gr. 4-7). 5.99 (978-0-440-42037-8(7) , Yearling) Random Hse. Children's Bks.

Akinyemi, Rowena. The Witches of Pendle, Level 1. 2nd ed. 2000. (Bookworms Ser.). (Illus.). 64p. 6.50 (978-0-19-422957-9(2)) Oxford Univ. Pr., Inc.

Alcantara, Ricardo. Bruja Que Quiso Matar el Sol. 2001. Tr. of Witch That Wanted to Kill the Sun. (SPA.). (YA). 12.50 (978-84-7183-183-5(X)) El Hogar y La Moda, S.A. ESP. *Dist:* AIMS International Bks., Inc.

—Huy, Que Miedo! 13th ed. 2003. (SPA., Illus.). 44p. (978-84-236-2559-8(1) , ED6263) Edebé ESP. *Dist:* Lectorum Pubns., Inc.

Alexander, Brandon. Kiss of Darkness. 2000. (gr. 7-12). lib. bdg. 14.15 (978-0-613-73078-5(X)) Tandem Library Bks.

Alfonsi, Alice. Trust Your Heart. novel rev. ed. 2007. (W. I. T. C. H. Ser.: Bk. 24). 144p. (gr. 3-7). pap. 4.99 (*978-1-4231-0288-5(6)) Hyperion Pr.

Alfonsi, Alice. A Weakened Heart. rev. ed. 2006. (W. I. T. C. H. Ser.: Bk. 21). 144p. (gr. 3-7). pap. 4.99 (978-0-7868-5595-7(9)) Hyperion Pr.

Allen, Kathleen. Witch Hunter. 2005. 131p. pap. 19.95 (978-1-4137-7839-7(9)) PublishAmerica, Inc.

Alton, Steve. The Firehills. 2005. 192p. (J). (gr. 7-13). 15.95 (978-1-57505-798-9(0) , Carolrhoda Bks.) Lerner Publishing Group.

—The Malifex. 2003. (Middle Readers Ser.). (Illus.). 182p. (J). (gr. 3-7). 14.95 (978-0-8225-0959-2(8)) Lerner Publishing Group.

Anderson, Al. Pegasus: Adventures with Bingo Borden. Kurzyca, Krystyna Emilia, illus. 2006. 77p. (J). per. 19.50 (*978-1-887250-46-7(8)) Agora Pubns., Inc.

Andrews, Natalie. Clara's Witch. 2004. 272p. (YA). pap. 22.50 (978-1-920731-62-5(8)) Fremantle Pr. AUS. *Dist:* International Specialized Bk. Services.

Atwater-Rhodes, Amelia. Demon in My View. 2001. 192p. (YA). (gr. 7). mass mkt. 5.99 (978-0-440-22884-4(0) , Laurel Leaf) Random Hse. Children's Bks.

—Demon in My View. 2000. (gr. 7-12). lib. bdg. 13.00 (978-0-613-69052-2(4)) Tandem Library Bks.

—Shattered Mirror. 240p. (YA). (gr. 7). 2003. mass mkt. 5.99 (978-0-440-22940-7(5) , Laurel Leaf); 2001. 9.95 (978-0-385-32793-0(5) , Delacorte Bks. for Young Readers) Random Hse. Children's Bks.

—Shattered Mirror. 2003. (gr. 7-12). lib. bdg. 13.55 (978-0-613-72330-5(9)) Tandem Library Bks.

Atwell, Debby. The Warthog's Tail. 2005. (Illus.). 32p. (J). (gr. k-3). 16.00 (978-0-618-50781-8(7) , Walter Lorraine) Houghton Mifflin Co. Trade & Reference Div.

Baker, E. D. Dragon's Breath. 2003. 250p. (J). 15.95 (978-1-58234-858-2(8) , Bloomsbury Children) Bloomsbury Publishing.

—Dragon's Breath: Read-Along/Homework Pack. unabr. ed. 2005. (YA). (gr. 5-8). 92.70 incl. audio (978-1-4193-3563-1(4) , 42041) Recorded Bks., LLC.

—The Frog Princess. 2002. 200p. (J). (gr. 3-9). 15.95 (978-1-58234-799-8(9) , Bloomsbury Children) Bloomsbury Publishing.

—Once upon a Curse: The Sequel to the Frog Princess & Dragon's Breath. 2006. (Tales of the Frog Princess Ser.). (Illus.). 256p. (J). pap. 6.95 (978-1-58234-911-4(8) , Bloomsbury Children) Bloomsbury Publishing.

Baker, E. D. The Salamander Spell. 2007. (Tales of the Frog Princess Ser.). 250p. (J). (gr. 3-7). 16.95 (*978-1-59990-018-6(1) , Bloomsbury Children) Bloomsbury Publishing.

Bateson-Hill, Margaret. Masha & the Firebird. Wilson, Anne, illus. 2005. (Folk Tales Ser.). (RUS & ENG.). 32p. (J). pap. 7.99 (978-1-84089-201-7(3) , Zero to Ten, Limited) Evans Publishing Group GBR. *Dist:* Independent Pubs. Group.

Bell, Hilari. The Goblin Wood. (Illus.). (J). 2003. 304p. (gr. 5 up). 17.99 (978-0-06-051371-9(3)); 2004. 384p. (gr. 7 up). reprint ed. pap. 6.99 (978-0-06-051373-3(X)) HarperCollins Pubs.

Bennett, David. Witch & Wizard Stories. Thomas, Jacqui, illus. 2004. 158p. (J). (ps-ps). per. 12.60 (978-0-606-33268-2(5)) Tandem Library Bks.

BeSwitched. 2004. (YA). mass mkt. 7.99 (978-0-9759784-0-5(3)) Joseph's Coat Publishing.

Bird, Isobel. Circle of Three: Merry Meat. 2001. (gr. 7-12). lib. bdg. 13.00 (978-0-613-49297-3(8)) Tandem Library Bks.

—Circle of Three No.13: And It Harm None. 2002. (gr. 7-12). lib. bdg. 13.00 (978-0-613-71369-6(9)) Tandem Library Bks.

—Circle of Three No.15: Initiation. 2002. (gr. 7-12). lib. bdg. 13.00 (978-0-613-71371-9(0)) Tandem Library Bks.

Bird, Sheila & Bird, Sheila M. Dr. Witch's Animal Hospital. Parrish, Emma, illus. 2007. (I Am Reading Ser.). 48p. (J). (ps-3). pap. 3.95 (*978-0-7534-5977-5(9) , Kingfisher) Houghton Mifflin Co. Trade & Reference Div.

Blacker, Terence & Ross, Tony. En la Carcel. 2003. (Serafina the Little Witch Ser.). (SPA., Illus.). 72p. (J). 7.95 (978-84-8453-011-4(6)) Ediciones del Bronce ESP. *Dist:* Planeta Publishing Corp.

—Estrella de la Tele. 2003. (Serafina the Little Witch Ser.). (SPA.). 80p. (J). 7.95 (978-84-8453-066-4(3)) Ediciones del Bronce ESP. *Dist:* Planeta Publishing Corp.

—Fuera de Control. 2003. (Serafina the Little Witch Ser.). (SPA., Illus.). 72p. (J). 7.95 (978-84-8453-049-7(3)) Ediciones del Bronce ESP. *Dist:* Planeta Publishing Corp.

—Una Intrusa en el Hospital. 2003. (Serafina the Little Witch Ser.). (SPA., Illus.). 72p. (J). 7.95 (978-84-8453-010-7(8)) Ediciones del Bronce ESP. *Dist:* Planeta Publishing Corp.

—Un Mundo de Problemas. 2003. (Serafina the Little Witch Ser.). (SPA.). 80p. (J). 7.95 (978-84-8453-009-1(4)) Ediciones del Bronce ESP. *Dist:* Planeta Publishing Corp.

Brinkerhoff, Phillip. To the Magical Pond. 2004. 116p. (YA). pap. 11.95 (978-0-7414-1982-8(3)) Infinity Publishing.

Broadribb, Donald. Marcia. 2006. 211p. (J). pap. 16.00 (978-1-4116-7222-2(4)) Lulu.com.

Brothers Grimm Staff. Hansel & Gretel. Price, Margaret Evans, illus. 2005. 16p. (J). (ps-3). 9.95 (978-1-59583-012-8(X) , Green Tiger Pr.) Laughing Elephant.

Brown, Anne. The Dumari Chronicles: Year One: Year One. 2007. 376p. (YA). per. 20.95 (*978-0-595-45725-0(8)) iUniverse, Inc.

Buehner, Caralyn & Buehner, Mark. A Job for Wittilda. Buehner, Caralyn & Buehner, Mark, illus. 2004. (Illus.). 32p. (J). (gr. k-3). pap. 5.99 (978-0-14-240137-8(4) , Puffin) Penguin Group (USA) Inc.

Burge, Constance M. Seasons of the Witch, Vol. 1. Simon and Schuster Children's Staff, ed. 2003. (Charmed Ser.). 192p. (YA). pap. 7.99 (978-0-689-86545-9(7) , Simon Pulse) Simon & Schuster Children's Publishing.

Burge, Constance M., creator. The Warren Witches. 2005. (Charmed Ser.). 320p. (YA). pap. 9.99 (978-0-689-87876-3(1) , Simon Spotlight Entertainment) Simon & Schuster.

Burns, Laura J. Inherit the Witch. 2004. (Charmed Ser.). 224p. (YA). mass mkt. 6.99 (978-0-689-86708-8(5) , Simon Spotlight Entertainment) Simon & Schuster.

Canfield, Andrea. Sassy the Seahag. Hallinan, Susan, illus. 2003. Orig. Title: Sassy the Seahag. (J). per. (978-0-9721327-3-2(2)) Eight Dog Publishing.

Cardwell, Helen. Amber Janusson: Protector of the Magic Lands. 2003. 136p. pap. 11.95 (978-0-595-29436-7(7)) iUniverse, Inc.

Chase, Mary. The Wicked, Wicked Ladies in the Haunted House. Sis, Peter, illus. 2005. 144p. (J). (gr. 3-7). 5.99 (978-0-440-41956-3(5) , Yearling) Random Hse. Children's Bks.

Chesterfield, Sadie. Lion, the Witch, & the Wardrobe. Marderosian, Mark, illus. movie tie-in ed. 2005. (Narnia Ser.). 32p. (J). pap., act. bk. ed. 4.99 (978-0-06-076557-6(7)) Zonderkidz.

Coll, Ivar Da. Medias Dulces. (SPA.). (J). (gr. 3-5). 7.95 (978-958-04-3398-9(4) , NR7686) Norma S.A. COL. *Dist:* Distribuidora Norma, Inc., Lectorum Pubns., Inc.

Colon, Suzan. Runaway. 2003. (gr. 7-12). lib. bdg. 14.15 (978-0-613-71775-5(9)) Tandem Library Bks.

Comella, Maria Angeles. Donde Esta la Reina? Comella, Maria Angeles, illus. 2001. (CAT., Illus.). 32p. (J). (gr. k-4). 14.95 (978-84-8488-001-1(X)) Serres, Ediciones, S. L. ESP. *Dist:* Lectorum Pubns., Inc.

—Donde Esta la Reina? Comella, Maria Angeles, illus. Dominguez, Juan Manuel, photos by. 2001. (SPA., Illus.). 126p. (J). (gr. k-4). 14.95 (978-84-95040-98-5(0)) Serres, Ediciones, S. L. ESP. *Dist:* Lectorum Pubns., Inc.

Conroy, Don. Witches, 4 vols., Set. 2000. (J). (gr. 1-4). per. (978-1-84210-015-8(7)) Mentor Bks.

—The Witches A-Haunting. 1999. (Illus.). 80p. (J). (gr. 1-4). per. (978-1-902586-03-8(4)) Mentor Bks.

—The Witches on Vacation. 1999. (Illus.). 78p. (J). (gr. 1-4). per. (978-0-947548-89-6(0)) Mentor Bks.

—The Witches W-Files. 1999. (Illus.). 80p. (J). (gr. 1-4). per. (978-1-902586-52-6(2)) Mentor Bks.

Cooney, Caroline B. & Shakespeare, William. Enter Three Witches: A Story of Macbeth. 2007. 281p. (*978-1-4287-3716-7(2) , Scholastic Pr.) Scholastic, Inc.

Cooper, Clare. One Day on Morfa. 2001. 112p. pap. 12.95 (978-1-85902-946-6(9)) Beekman Bks., Inc.

Cort, Ben. Little Witch. 2007. (Illus.). 12p. (J). 8.99 (*978-1-4052-0745-4(0)) Egmont Bks., Ltd. GBR. *Dist:* Independent Pubs. Group.

Curran, Casner. The Witch Across the Street. 2002. 113p. pap. 9.95 (978-0-595-21593-5(9) , Writers Club Pr.) iUniverse, Inc.

Dagg, Stephanie. De-Witched. 1999. (Illus.). 48p. (J). (gr. 1-4). per. (978-1-902586-46-5(8)) Mentor Bks.

—Witching Again! 2000. (Illus.). 48p. (J). (gr. 1-4). per. (978-1-84210-016-5(5)) Mentor Bks.

—The Witch's Dog. 1999. (Illus.). 39p. (J). (gr. 1-4). per. (978-1-902586-00-7(X)) Mentor Bks.

Dahl, Michael. The Princess & the Tower. Zhurkina, Svetlana A., illus. 2005. (Read-It! Readers Ser.). 32p. (J). (ps). lib. bdg. 18.60 (978-1-4048-1184-3(2)) Picture Window Bks.

Dahl, Roald. The Witches. 2002. (J). pap. 29.95 incl. audio (978-0-7540-6247-9(3)) BBC Audiobooks America.

—The Witches. Blake, Quentin, illus. 208p. (J). 2007. (gr. 2). 6.99 (*978-0-14-241011-0(X) , Puffin); 1999. (gr. 3-7). pap. 3.95 (978-0-14-031730-5(9) , Viking Juvenile) Penguin Group (USA) Inc.

—The Witches. 1999. (J). (gr. 3-6). lib. bdg. 14.15 (978-0-8085-7491-0(4)) Tandem Library Bks.

Dale, Anna. Whispering to Witches. 304p. (J). 2004. 16.95 (978-1-58234-890-2(1) , Bloomsbury Children); 2005. reprint ed. pap. 7.95 (978-1-58234-699-1(2)) Bloomsbury Publishing.

Dalmatian Press Staff. Winifried Witch & Her Very Own Cat. 2005. (Illus.). 12p. (J). bds. 4.99 (978-1-4037-1494-7(0)) Dalmatian Pr.

De Lint, Charles. The Harp of the Grey Rose: The Legend of Cerin Songweaver. 2004. (gr. 7-12). lib. bdg. 15.30 (978-0-613-71570-6(5)) Tandem Library Bks.

de Paola, Tomie. Strega Nona Takes a Vacation. (Illus.). 32p. (J). (gr. k-3). 2003. pap. 5.99 (978-0-14-250076-7(3) , Puffin); 2000. 16.99 (978-0-399-23562-7(0) , Putnam Juvenile) Penguin Group (USA) Inc.

—Strega Nona Takes a Vacation. 2003. (gr. k-3). lib. bdg. 14.15 (978-0-613-89803-4(6)) Tandem Library Bks.

De Witt, Peter. Isabella & the Room of Lost Brooms. 2007. 210p. (J). pap. 12.95 (*978-1-933255-35-4(8)) DNA Pr.

Deary, Terry. Witch in Time. Williams, Matthew, illus. l.t. ed. 2005. (J). pap. (978-0-7540-7895-1(7) , CLP 464) BBC Audio.

Delaney, Joseph. Curse of the Bane. Arrasmith, Patrick, illus. 2006. (Last Apprentice Ser.). 480p. (J). 16.99 (978-0-06-076621-4(2) , Greenwillow Bks.); lib. bdg. 17.89 (978-0-06-076622-1(0)) HarperCollins Pubs.

—The Last Apprentice: Attack of the Fiend. Arrasmith, Patrick, illus. 2008. (Last Apprentice Ser.). 560p. (J). 16.99 (*978-0-06-089127-5(0)); lib. bdg. 17.89 (*978-0-06-089128-2(9)) HarperCollins Pubs. (Greenwillow Bks.).

—Last Apprentice Curse of Bane. 2007. (Last Apprentice Ser.). 480p. (J). pap. 7.99 (*978-0-06-076623-8(9) , Harper Trophy) HarperCollins Pubs.

Night of the Soul Stealer, No. 3. 2007. (Last Apprentice Ser.). 512p. (J). (gr. 5 up). lib. bdg. 17.89 (*978-0-06-076625-2(5) , Greenwillow Bks.) HarperCollins Pubs.

—Night of the Soul Stealer, No. 3. Arrasmith, Patrick, illus. 2007. (Last Apprentice Ser.). 512p. (J). (gr. 5 up). 16.99 (*978-0-06-076624-5(7) , Greenwillow Bks.) HarperCollins Pubs.

Delaney, Joseph. Revenge of the Witch. Arrasmith, Patrick, illus. (Last Apprentice Ser.). (J). 2005. 368p. 16.99 (978-0-06-076618-4(2)); 2005. 368p. lib. bdg. 17.89 (978-0-06-076619-1(0)); 2006. 384p. reprint ed. pap. 7.99 (978-0-06-076620-7(4) , Harper Trophy) HarperCollins Pubs.

Desimini, Lisa. Trick-or-Treat, Smell My Feet! Desimini, Lisa, illus. 2005. (Illus.). 40p. (J). pap. 16.95 (978-0-439-23323-1(2) , Blue Sky Pr., The) Scholastic, Inc.

Desplechin, Marie. Poor Little Witch Girl. Rosner, Gillian, tr. from FRE. 2006. 128p. (J). 15.95 (978-1-58234-898-8(7) , Bloomsbury Children) Bloomsbury Publishing.

Dokey, Cameron. The Crimson Spell. 2000. (gr. 7-12). lib. bdg. 14.15 (978-0-613-27780-8(5)) Tandem Library Bks.

—Truth & Consequences. 2003. (gr. 7-12). lib. bdg. 14.15 (978-0-613-73389-2(4)) Tandem Library Bks.

Dokey, Cameron & Burge, Constance M. Truth & Consequences. 2003. (Charmed Ser.). (Illus.). 208p. (YA). pap. 6.99 (978-0-689-85791-1(8) , Simon Pulse) Simon & Schuster Children's Publishing.

Domoslai, Autumn. Grandmother Witch: Samhain at Grandmother's, 10 bks., Vol. 2. Price, Starr, ed. Domoslai, Autumn, illus. l.t. ed. 2005. (Illus.). 44p. (J). pap. 6.49 (978-0-9755403-7-4(8)) Spiral Publishing, Inc.

—Grandmother Witch Vol. I: Springtime. Domoslai, Autumn, illus. l.t. ed. 2004. (Illus.). 44p. (J). pap. 6.49 (978-0-9755403-5-0(1)) Spiral Publishing, Inc.

W X Y Z

Donaldson, Julia. Room on the Broom. Scheffler, Axel, illus. 32p. (J). (gr. k-3). 2003. pap. 6.99 (978-0-14-250112-2(3) , Puffin); 2001. 16.99 (978-0-8037-2657-4(0) , Dial) Penguin Group (USA) Inc.

—Room on the Broom. 2003. (gr. k-3). lib. bdg. 15.30 (978-0-613-83001-0(6)) Tandem Library Bks.

Dubowski, Cathy East. Strangeling. Richardson, Julia, ed. 2000. (So Weird Ser.: 4). (Illus.). 128p. (gr. 3-7). pap. 4.99 (978-0-7868-1431-2(4)) Disney Pr.

Dyer, Jill. The Plant of the Zorks. 2005. 11p. 6.65 (978-1-4116-6641-2(0)) Lulu.com.

Edgson, Alison, et al. Hansel & Gretel. 2006. (Illus.). 24p. pap. 5.99 (978-1-904550-73-0(8)); pap. 9.99 (978-1-904550-45-7(2)) Child's Play-International.

Egan, Kate, adapted by. World's Apart. 2005. (W. I. T. C. H. Ser.: Bk. 14). 134p. (J). lib. bdg. 16.92 ***978-1-4242-0788-6(6))** Fitzgerald Bks.

Elizondo, Gabriela Riveros. El Encargo de Fernanda. Castillo, Jesus, illus. rev. ed. 2006. (Castillo de la Lectura Blanca Ser.). (SPA.). 64p. (J). (gr. 1-3). pap. 6.95 (978-970-20-0126-3(9)) Castillo, Ediciones, S. A. de C. V. MEX. *Dist:* Macmillan.

Enric, Larreula I. Vidal. Bruja Aburrida Viaja Pro el Mundo. 1998. (SPA.). 124p. (J). (gr. 2-4). (978-84-08-02574-0(0)) GeoPlaneta, Editorial, S. A.

Estes, Eleanor. The Witch Family. 2000. (978-0-606-20338-8(9)); (J). (978-0-606-20176-6(9)); (gr. 3-6). lib. bdg. 14.15 (978-0-613-30884-7(0)) Tandem Library Bks.

Evans, Catrin & Evans, Guto. Peiriant y Tywydd. 2005. (WEL, Illus.). 36p. (978-0-86243-412-0(2)) Y Lolfa.

Evans, Robert J. Dorothy's Mystical Adventures in Oz. 2004. reprint ed. pap. 1.99 (978-1-4192-1658-9(9)) Kessinger Publishing, LLC.

Fienberg, Anna. The Witch in the Lake: A Novel. 2002. 220p. (J). (gr. 5-9). pap. 7.95 (978-1-55037-722-4(1)); lib. bdg. 18.95 (978-1-55037-723-1(X)) Annick Pr., Ltd. CAN. *Dist:* Firefly Bks., Ltd.

Fisher, Catherine. Snow-Walker. 2004. 512p. (J). (gr. 5 up). 17.99 (978-0-06-072474-0(9)) HarperCollins Pubs.

Fodi, Edward Lee. Corranda's Crown. 2002. 218p. (YA). (gr. 4-6). 9.99 (978-0-88092-573-0(6) , 5736) Royal Fireworks Publishing Co.

Fontes, Justine. Hocus-Pocus Halloween. Regan, Dana, illus. 2003. (Magical Color Bks.). 10p. (J). 5.95 (978-1-4027-0992-0(7) , Sterling/Pinwheel) Sterling Publishing Co., Inc.

Forrester, Sandra. Everyday Witch. 2002. (gr. 5-8). lib. bdg. 12.95 (978-0-613-70938-5(1)) Tandem Library Bks.

—The Everyday Witch: A Tale of Magic & High Adventure. 2002. (Illus.). 186p. (J). (gr. 5-9). pap. 4.95 (978-0-7641-2220-0(7)) Barron's Educational Series, Inc.

—The Witches of Bailiwick. 2005. (Adventures of Beatrice Bailey Ser.). (Illus.). 240p. (J). pap. 4.95 (978-0-7641-3025-0(0)) Barron's Educational Series, Inc.

—The Witches of Friar's Lantern. 2003. (Illus.). 240p. (J). (gr. 5-9). pap. 4.95 (978-0-7641-2436-5(6)) Barron's Educational Series, Inc.

—The Witches of Sea-Dragon Bay: The Adventures of Beatrice Bailey. 2003. (Illus.). 224p. (J). pap. 4.95 (978-0-7641-2633-8(4)) Barron's Educational Series, Inc.

—The Witches of Widdershins Academy. 2007. (Beatrice Bailey's Adventures Ser.). (Illus.). 256p. (J). (gr. 5-9). pap. 4.99 (978-0-7641-3578-1(3)) Barron's Educational Series, Inc.

—The Witches of Winged-Horse Mountain: The Adventures of Beatrice Bailey. 2004. (Adventures of Beatrice Bailey Ser.). 256p. (J). pap. 4.95 (978-0-7641-2784-7(5)) Barron's Educational Series, Inc.

Friel, Maeve. Charming or What? (Witch-in-Training Ser.). (Illus.). 96p. Vol. 1. 2002. (J). pap. 7.50 (978-0-00-713341-3(3) , Collins); Vol. 2. 2003. pap. 7.50 (978-0-00-713342-0(1)); Vol. 3. 2003. pap. 7.50 (978-0-00-713343-7(X)); Vol. 4. 2003. pap. 7.50 (978-0-00-713344-4(8)) HarperCollins Pubs. Ltd. GBR. *Dist:* Independent Pubs. Group.

—Moonlight Mischief. Reed, Nathan, illus. 2006. (Witch-in-Training Ser.). 96p. (J). pap. 7.50 (978-0-00-718527-6(8) , HarperCollins Children's Bks.) HarperCollins Pubs. Ltd. GBR. *Dist:* Independent Pubs. Group.

—Moonlight Mischief. (Witch-in-Training Ser.). (Illus.). 96p. 2005. pap. 7.50 ***978-0-00-718526-9(X));** 2005. pap. 7.50 (978-0-00-718525-2(1)); 2004. pap. 7.50 (978-0-00-718524-5(3)) HarperCollins Pubs. Ltd. GBR. *Dist:* Independent Pubs. Group.

Gaiman, Neil. Stardust. movie tie-in ed. 2007. 368p. (J). (gr. 7 up). pap. 6.99 (978-0-06-124048-5(6) , Harper Entertainment) HarperCollins Pubs.

Gallagher, Diana G. Mist & Stone. 2003. (Charmed Ser.). 208p. (YA). pap. 5.99 (978-0-689-85789-8(6) , Simon Pulse) Simon & Schuster Children's Publishing.

—Mist & Stone. 2003. (gr. 7-12). lib. bdg. 14.15 (978-0-613-66520-9(1)) Tandem Library Bks.

—Spirit of the Wolf. 2001. (Charmed Ser.: bk. 12). 224p. (YA). (gr. 7 up). pap. 5.99 (978-0-7434-4255-8(5) , Simon Pulse) Simon & Schuster Children's Publishing.

—Spirit of the Wolf. 2002. (gr. 7-12). lib. bdg. 14.15 (978-0-613-74235-1(4)) Tandem Library Bks.

—Worth a Shot. 2000. (gr. 3-6). lib. bdg. 11.80 (978-0-613-28143-0(8)) Tandem Library Bks.

Gallagher, Diana G. & Burge, Constance M. Mystic Knoll. 2005. (Charmed Ser.). 224p. (YA). pap. 6.99 (978-0-689-86854-2(5) , Simon Spotlight Entertainment) Simon & Schuster.

—Mystic Knoll. 2005. 217p. (J). (978-1-4155-8004-2(9) , Simon Spotlight) Simon & Schuster Children's Publishing.

Gilleland, Rebecca. The Witch of Blackbird Pond: Study Guide. 2000. 72p. (J). (gr. 5-7). stu. ed., ring bd. 12.99 (978-1-58609-171-2(9)) Progeny Pr.

Gilmour, H. B. Building a Mystery. 2001. (gr. 5-8). lib. bdg. 12.40 (978-0-613-43800-1(0)); No. 2. (Illus.). (J). (978-0-606-21477-3(1)) Tandem Library Bks.

—The Power of Two, No. 1. 2001. (T*Witches Ser.). (Illus.). (J). (978-0-606-21476-6(3)) Tandem Library Bks.

Gilmour, H. B. & Reisfeld, Randi. Double Jeopardy. 2002. (T*Witches Ser.: No. 6). 192p. (J). 4.50 (978-0-439-24075-8(1)) Scholastic, Inc.

Gilson. Melusine: Hocus Pocus. Jeffrey, Erica, tr. from FRE. Clarke, illus. 2007. 48p. pap. 9.99 ***978-1-905460-20-5(1))** CineBook GBR. *Dist:* Biblio Distribution.

Glassman, Peter. My Working Mom. Arnold, Tedd, illus. 2001. 32p. (J). (ps-3). pap. 5.95 (978-0-06-441033-5(1) , Harper Trophy) HarperCollins Pubs.

Gliori, Debi. Pure Dead Batty. (Illus.). (J). 2007. 320p. (gr. 4-7). 6.50 ***978-0-440-42074-3(1)** , Yearling); 2006. 304p. (gr. 5). 15.95 (978-0-375-83316-8(1) , Knopf Bks. for Young Readers); 2006. 304p. (gr. 5). lib. bdg. 17.99 (978-0-375-93316-5(6) , Knopf Bks. for Young Readers) Random Hse. Children's Bks.

—Pure Dead Brilliant. 2005. 288p. (J). (gr. 5). 6.50 (978-0-440-42006-4(7) , Yearling) Random Hse. Children's Bks.

—Pure Dead Brilliant. l.t. ed. 2004. (Pure Dead Ser.: Vol. 5). (Illus.). 378p. (J). 21.95 (978-0-7862-6148-2(X)) Thorndike Pr.

—Pure Dead Frozen. 2007. (J). (gr. 5). 320p. 15.99 ***978-0-375-83317-5(X));** 304p. lib. bdg. 18.99 ***978-0-375-93317-2(4))** Random Hse. Children's Bks. (Knopf Bks. for Young Readers).

—Pure Dead Magic. 2002. (Illus.). 208p. (gr. 5). mass mkt. 6.50 (978-0-440-41849-8(6) , Yearling) Random Hse. Children's Bks.

—Pure Dead Trouble. 2006. 304p. (J). (gr. 4-7). 6.50 (978-0-440-42070-5(9) , Yearling) Random Hse. Children's Bks.

—Pure Dead Wicked. 2003. 240p. (gr. 5 up). 6.50 (978-0-440-41936-5(0) , Yearling) Random Hse. Children's Bks.

—Pure Dead Wicked. 2003. (gr. 3-6). lib. bdg. 13.00 (978-0-613-72261-2(2)) Tandem Library Bks.

Glow in the Dark. 2002. 64p. (J). pap. 9.98 (978-0-7525-6289-6(4)) Parragon, Inc.

Golden Books Staff. Journey to Fairytale Land. 2007. (Book & CD Ser.). (Illus.). 24p. (J). (ps-2). 9.99 (978-0-375-84025-8(7) , Golden Bks.) Random Hse. Children's Bks.

Goldstein, Gary. The Mythfits. 2005. 280p. (YA). (ps-7). pap. 14.99 (978-1-59092-125-8(9) , Blue Works) Windstorm Creative.

Gore, Jim. Witch Snatchit & Mr Grabbit. 2005. (Illus.). 80p. pap. ***978-1-84401-486-6(X))** Athena Pr.

Grambling, Lois G. The Witch Who Wanted to Be a Princess. Love, Judy, illus. 32p. (J). (ps-2). 2007. pap. 6.95 ***978-1-58089-063-2(6));** 2002. 15.95 (978-1-58089-062-5(8)) Charlesbridge Publishing, Inc.

Gray, Luli. Falcon & the Carousel of Time. 2005. 128p. (J). (gr. 5-9). 15.00 (978-0-618-44895-1(0)) Houghton Mifflin Co. Trade & Reference Div.

—Falcon & the Charles Street Witch. 2002. 144p. (J). (gr. 5-9). 16.00 (978-0-618-16410-3(3)) Houghton Mifflin Co. Trade & Reference Div.

Grban, Tanguy. Sarah So Small. 2004. 32p. (978-1-59687-179-3(2) , Milk & Cookies) ibooks, Inc.

Greban, Tanguy. Sarah So Small. Greban, Quentin, illus. 2004. 32p. (J). 16.95 (978-0-689-03594-4(2) , Milk & Cookies) ibooks, Inc.

Griffin, Adele. Witch Twins & Melody Malady. Rogers, Jacqueline, illus. 2004. 144p. (gr. 2-6). pap. 5.99 (978-0-7868-0964-6(7)) Hyperion Pr.

—Witch Twins & the Ghost of Glenn Bly. Rogers, Jacqueline, illus. 2005. 128p. (gr. 2-6). pap. 5.99 (978-0-7868-5496-7(0)) Hyperion Bks. for Children.

—Witch Twins at Camp Bliss. Rogers, Jacqueline, illus. 2003. 144p. (gr. 2-6). pap. 5.99 (978-0-7868-1583-8(3)) Hyperion Bks. for Children.

—Witch Twins at Camp Bliss. 2003. (gr. 3-6). lib. bdg. 14.15 (978-0-613-63671-1(6)) Tandem Library Bks.

Gritton, Steve. The Kandy Witch. 2007. (J). 18.95 ***978-0-9795361-0-6(3))** Bad Frog Art/SMG Bks.

Gruber, Michael. The Witch's Boy. (gr. 6-9). 2006. 400p. (J). pap. 7.99 (978-0-06-076167-7(9)); 2005. 384p. (YA). 16.99 (978-0-06-076164-6(4)) HarperCollins Pubs. (HarperTeen).

—The Witch's Boy. l.t. ed. 2006. 448p. (YA). 22.95 (978-0-7862-8580-8(X)) Thorndike Pr.

Guinane, Carole. The Wolves of Witchmaker. 2002. 258p. pap. 14.95 (978-0-595-21360-3(X) , Writers Club Pr.) iUniverse, Inc.

Gummelt, Donna & Melchiorre, Dondino. Michelina the Magical Musical Good Witch of the Forest. Wall, Randy Hugh, ed. Varela, Juan D., tr. Varela, Juan D., illus. 2006. (SPA.). 34p. (J). 14.95 (978-0-9764798-6-4(9)) Story Stone Collection Publishing.

Hahn, Mary Downing. Witch Catcher. 2006. 240p. (J). (gr. 4-6). 16.00 (978-0-618-50457-2(5) , Clarion Bks.) Houghton Mifflin Co. Trade & Reference Div.

Halfmann, Janet. Bewitching the Chickadees. 2007. 88p. (J). pap. 14.99 (978-1-59092-573-7(4) , Orchard Academy Pr.) Windstorm Creative.

Hamilton, Virginia. Wee Winnie Witch's Skinny: An Original African American Scare Tale. Moser, Barry, illus. 2004. 32p. (J). pap. 16.95 (978-0-590-28880-4(6) , Blue Sky Pr., The) Scholastic, Inc.

Hardie, Samantha. Samantha's Oracle: A Fortune Teller for Teenage Witches. (Illus.). 80p. 12.95 (978-1-55285-282-8(2)) Whitecap Bks., Ltd. CAN. *Dist:* Graphic Arts Ctr. Publishing Co.

Hardinge, Frances. Well Witched. 2008. 400p. (J). 16.99 ***978-0-06-088038-5(4));** lib. bdg. 17.89 ***978-0-06-088039-2(2))** HarperCollins Pubs.

Hargreaves, Roger. Little Miss Sunshine & the Wicked Witch. 2007. (Mr. Men & Little Miss Ser.). 32p. (J). (ps). pap. 3.99 (978-0-8431-2490-3(3) , Price Stern Sloan) Penguin Group (USA) Inc.

Harris, Joe. Halloween Ball. 2008. (J). ***978-0-375-84975-6(0)); (*978-0-375-84373-0(6));** lib. bdg. ***978-0-375-94975-3(5))** Random Hse., Inc.

Harrison, Emma. Garden of Evil. 2002. (Charmed Ser.: Bk. 13). 208p. (YA). (gr. 7 up). pap. 6.99 (978-0-689-85077-6(8) , Simon Pulse) Simon & Schuster Children's Publishing.

—Garden of Evil. 2002. (gr. 7-12). lib. bdg. 14.15 (978-0-613-73370-0(3)) Tandem Library Bks.

—Something Wiccan This Way Comes. 2003. (gr. 7-12). lib. bdg. 14.15 (978-0-613-61818-2(1)) Tandem Library Bks.

Harrison, Mette. Mira, Mirror. 2006. 320p. (YA). (gr. 7). pap. 6.99 (978-0-14-240643-4(0) , Puffin) Penguin Group (USA) Inc.

Hautzig, Deborah. Little Witch Goes to Camp. 2002. (gr. k-3). lib. bdg. 10.95 (978-0-613-82447-7(4)) Tandem Library Bks.

—Little Witch Learns to Read. Wickstrom, Sylvie K., illus. 2003. (Step into Reading Ser.). 48p. (J). (gr. 1-3). pap. 3.99 (978-0-375-82179-0(1) , Random Hse. Bks. for Young Readers) Random Hse. Children's Bks.

—Little Witch Learns to Read. 2003. (gr. k-3). lib. bdg. 11.80 (978-0-613-89789-1(7)) Tandem Library Bks.

—Little Witch Loves to Write. Wickstrom, Sylvie, illus. 2004. (Stepping into Reading Ser.: Vol. 3). 48p. (J). (gr. 1-3). pap. 3.99 (978-0-375-82893-5(1) , Random Hse. Bks. for Young Readers) Random Hse. Children's Bks.

Hawkins, Colin & Hawkins, Jacqui. Witch Pigs. 2006. (Illus.). 32p. (J). (gr. 1-2). pap. 9.99 (978-0-09-943429-0(6)) Transworld Publishers Ltd. GBR. *Dist:* Independent Pubs. Group.

Hawthorne, Nathaniel & San Souci, Robert D. Feathertop: Based on the Tale by Nathaniel Hawthorne. San Souci, Robert D. & San Souci, Daniel, illus. 2006. (J). reprint ed. pap. 10.95 (978-1-59078-382-5(4)) Boyds Mills Pr.

Haynes, Lori. The Wallenda Witches Flying School. 2005. (Illus.). 24p. (J). pap. 13.13 (978-0-9746959-4-5(7) , 2000) Falcon Publishing LTD.

Heller, Nicholas. Elwood & the Witch. Smith, Jos. A., illus. 2000. 32p. (J). (gr. k-3). 15.89 (978-0-688-16946-6(5)) HarperCollins Pubs.

—Elwood & the Witch. Smith, Jos. A., illus. 2000. 32p. (J). (gr. k-3). 15.95 (978-0-688-16945-9(7)) HarperCollins Pubs.

Herman, Gail. When Wishes Come True. 2000. (Fairy School Ser.). (Illus.). (J). (978-0-606-21637-1(5)) Tandem Library Bks.

Higgenson, Hadley. Keeker & the Sugar Shack. Andersen, Maja, illus. 2006. (Sneaky Pony Ser.: Bk. 3). 48p. (J). pap. 3.95 (978-0-8118-5456-6(6)) Chronicle Bks. LLC.

Higginson, Hadley. Keeker & the Sugar Shack, Bk. 3. Andersen, Maja, illus. 2006. 48p. (J). 15.50 (978-0-8118-5455-9(8)) Chronicle Bks. LLC.

Hill, Stuart. Cry of the Icemark (library Edition) 2006. (J). 99.95 (978-0-439-87914-9(0)) Scholastic, Inc.

Holder, Nancy. Witch. 2002. lib. bdg. 14.15 (978-0-613-74180-4(3)) Tandem Library Bks.

Holder, Nancy & Viguié, Debbie. Witch. 2002. (Wicked Ser.). 368p. (YA). (gr. 7 up). pap. 5.99 (978-0-7434-2696-1(7) , Simon Pulse) Simon & Schuster Children's Publishing.

Horn, Emily. Excuse Me... Are You a Witch? Pawlak, Pawel, illus. 32p. (J). 2005. pap. 6.95 (978-1-58089-103-5(9)); 2004. 15.95 (978-1-58089-093-9(8)) Charlesbridge Publishing, Inc.

Horowitz, Anthony. Ravens Gate. (Power of Five Ser.: Vol. 1). 2006. 272p. (J). pap. 6.99 (978-0-439-68009-7(3) , Scholastic Paperbacks); 2005. 256p. (YA). pap. 17.95 (978-0-439-67995-4(8)) Scholastic, Inc.

—Ravens Gate. l.t. ed. 2006. (Power of Five Ser.: Vol. 1). (YA). 23.95 (978-0-7862-8584-6(2)) Thorndike Pr.

Howard, Arthur. Hoodwinked. Howard, Arthur, illus. 2005. (Illus.). 32p. (J). (ps-ps). pap., pap. 6.00 (978-0-15-205386-4(7) , Voyager Bks./Libros Viajeros) Harcourt Children's Bks.

Howell, Robert. Third Times the Charm. 2007. 224p. (J). (gr. 1-7). pap. 10.95 ***978-1-897235-20-1(8))** Thistledown Pr., Ltd. CAN. *Dist:* Fitzhenry & Whiteside, Ltd.

Hunter, Mollie. The Thirteenth Member. 2002. (Kelpies Ser.). (Illus.). 160p. (J). pap. (978-0-86315-405-8(0)) Floris Bks. GBR. *Dist:* SteinerBooks, Inc.

Hurston, Zora Neale. The Three Witches. Tankersley, Ann & Ringgold, Faith, illus. 2006. 32p. (J). (gr. 1-5). 15.99 (978-0-06-000649-5(8)) HarperCollins Pubs.

Hyperion Staff. Legends Revealed. rev. ed. 2006. (W. I. T. C. H. Graphic Novels Ser.: Bk. 6). (Illus.). 128p. (gr. 3-7). pap. 4.99 (978-0-7868-4876-8(6)) Hyperion Pr.

—The Other Truth. 19th rev. ed. 2006. (W. I. T. C. H. Ser.: Bk. 19). 144p. (gr. 3-7). pap. 4.99 (978-0-7868-5280-2(1)) Hyperion Pr.

Ibbotson, Eva. Not Just a Witch. Hawkes, Kevin, illus. 2004. 192p. (gr. 3). pap. 5.99 (978-0-14-240232-0(X) , Puffin) Penguin Group (USA) Inc.

—Which Witch? 2002. (Illus.). 13.19 (978-1-4046-1490-1(7)) Book Wholesalers, Inc.

—Which Witch? Large, Annabel, illus. 2000. 256p. (YA). (gr. 3-7). pap. 5.99 (978-0-14-130427-4(8) , Puffin); 1999. 224p. (J). (gr. 4-7). 15.99 (978-0-525-46164-7(7) , Dutton Juvenile) Penguin Group (USA) Inc.

—Which Witch? 2000. (J). (978-0-606-19882-0(2)); (gr. 3-6). lib. bdg. 14.15 (978-0-613-31926-3(5)) Tandem Library Bks.

Impey, Rose. Wanda Witch & the Bullies. Mcewen, Katherine, illus. 2005. (Scholastic Reader Level 3 Ser.). 32p. (J). pap. 3.99 (978-0-439-73000-6(7) , Cartwheel Bks.) Scholastic, Inc.

—Wanda Witch & the Stray Dragon. 2006. (Scholastic Reader Ser.). (Illus.). 32p. (J). pap. 3.99 (978-0-439-78452-8(2) , Cartwheel Bks.) Scholastic, Inc.

—Wanda Witch & the Wobbly Fang. Mcewen, Katharine, illus. 2006. (Scholastic Reader Level 3 Ser.). 32p. (J). pap. 3.99 (978-0-439-78450-4(6) , Cartwheel Bks.) Scholastic, Inc.

—Wanda Witch & Too Many Frogs. McEwen, Katharine, illus. 2006. (Scholastic Reader Ser.). 32p. (J). pap. 3.99 (978-0-439-78451-1(4) , Cartwheel Bks.) Scholastic, Inc.

Jarvis, Robin. The Whitby Witches. Petersen, Jeff, illus. 2006. 296p. (J). 17.95 (978-0-8118-5413-9(2)) Chronicle Bks. LLC.

John Brown Publishing Ltd. & Murphy, Harriet. Dora's Enchanted Adventure: Follow the Reader Level II. 2007. (Dora the Explorer Ser.). 24p. (J). 24.99 ***978-1-4169-4992-3(5)** , Simon Scribbles) Simon & Schuster Children's Publishing.

Johnston, Tony. Alice Nizzy Nazzy, the Witch of Santa Fe. de Paola, Tomie, illus. 1998. 32p. (J). (ps-3). pap. 6.99 (978-0-698-11650-4(X) , Putnam Juvenile) Penguin Group (USA) Inc.

Jones, Diana Wynne. Witch's Business. 2002. 208p. (J). (gr. 3 up). 15.99 (978-0-06-008782-1(X)); lib. bdg. 17.89 (978-0-06-008783-8(8)) HarperCollins Pubs.

Jones, Ursula. The Witch's Children. Ayto, Russell, illus. 2003. 32p. (J). (ps-2). 16.95 (978-0-8050-7205-1(5) , Holt, Henry & Co. Bks. For Young Readers) Holt, Henry & Co.

Jordan, Annie Laurie. Bogwaddle Pond. La Grange, Myrtle, illus. 2004. 25p. pap. 14.95 (978-1-4137-2013-6(7)) PublishAmerica, Inc.

Jordan, Jennifer. Silly Tilly Witch: And Other Stories. Guile, Gill, illus. 2004. (Early Learning Ser.). 18p. (J). bds. 2.99 (978-1-85854-825-8(X)) Brimax Books Ltd. GBR. *Dist:* Byeway Bks.

Joseph Delaney. Revenge of the Witch. l.t. ed. 2006. 375p. 21.95 (978-0-7862-8641-6(5)) Thorndike Pr.

Joyce, Rita. Wandawillie. 2005. (J). lib. bdg. 17.95 (978-1-59094-095-2(4)) Jawbone Publishing Corp.

Kaaberbol, Lene. Heartbreak Island. 2005. (W. I. T. C. H. Adventures Ser. : Bk. 3). (Illus.). 105p. (J). lib. bdg. 11.00 ***978-1-4242-0786-2(X))** Fitzgerald Bks.

Kaaberbol, Lene. Stolen Spring. rev. ed. 2005. (W. I. T. C. H. Adventures Ser. : Bk. 3). (Illus.). 112p. (gr. 3-7). pap. 4.99 (978-0-7868-0980-6(9) , Volo) Hyperion Bks. for Children.

Kadono, Eiko. Kiki's Delivery Service. Riggs, Lynne E., tr. from JPN. Hayashi, Akiko, illus. 2003. 176p. (J). (gr. 4 up). 18.95 (978-1-55037-789-7(2)); pap. 6.95 (978-1-55037-788-0(4)) Annick Pr., Ltd. CAN. *Dist:* Firefly Bks., Ltd.

—Kiki's Delivery Service. 2003. (gr. 3-6). lib. bdg. 15.25 (978-0-613-67558-1(4)) Tandem Library Bks.

Kakinouchi, Narumi. My Codename Is Charmer, Vol. 3. 208p. pap. 12.95 (978-1-932575-08-8(1)) International Comics & Entertainment L.L.C.

Katz, Welwyn W. Come Like Shadows. 2001. (J). (978-0-606-21823-8(8)); 2000. (gr. 7-12). lib. bdg. 16.40 (978-0-613-35089-1(8)) Tandem Library Bks.

Kayser, Megan. Finishing What I Didn't Start. 2006. 108p. pap. 16.95 (978-1-4241-1271-5(0)) PublishAmerica, Inc.

Kellerhals-Stewart, Heather. Witch's Fang. 2002. (Illus.). 192p. (J). (gr. 8 up). pap. 6.95 (978-1-55192-368-0(8)) Raincoast Bk. Distribution CAN. *Dist:* Transition Vendor.

—Witch's Fang. 2001. (gr. 7-12). lib. bdg. 15.25 (978-0-613-78642-3(4)) Tandem Library Bks.

King-Smith, Dick. The Nine Lives of Aristotle. Graham, Bob, illus. 2003. 80p. (J). (gr. 1-4). 14.99 (978-0-7636-2260-2(5)) Candlewick Pr.

—The Witch of Blackberry Bottom. unabr. l.t. ed. 2001. (Read-Along Ser.). 144p. (J). 29.95 incl. audio (978-0-7540-6238-7(4) , RAO39, Chivers Children's Audio Bks.) BBC Audiobooks America.

Kipfer, Roger. TimePortal. 2002. 157p. (J). (gr. 4-7). pap. 9.99 (978-0-88092-568-6(X) , 568X) Royal Fireworks Publishing Co.

Kitamura, Satoshi. Me & My Cat? Kitamura, Satoshi, illus. 2000. (Illus.). 40p. (J). (ps-3). 16.00 (978-0-374-34906-6(1) , Farrar, Straus & Giroux (BYR)) Farrar, Straus & Giroux.

—Me & My Cat? 2005. (Illus.). 40p. (J). reprint ed. pap. 6.95 (978-0-374-44796-0(9) , Sunburst) Farrar, Straus & Giroux.

Konigsburg, E. L. Jennifer, Hecate, Macbeth, William McKinley, & Me, Elizabeth. 2001. (gr. 3-6). lib. bdg. 13.00 (978-0-613-73310-6(X)) Tandem Library Bks.

Korba, Joanna. Sleepless Beauty. 2006. spiral bd. 42.00 ***978-1-4108-7171-8(1))** Benchmark Education Co.

Kreib. We're off to Find the Witch's House. Alley, Robert W., illus. 2005. 32p. (J). (ps-ps). 14.99 (978-0-525-47003-8(4) , Dutton Juvenile) Penguin Group (USA) Inc.

Krulik, Nancy E. Witch Switch. John and Wendy Staff, illus. 2006. (Katie Kazoo, Switcheroo Ser.). 160p. (J). (gr. 2-5). mass mkt. 4.99 (978-0-448-44330-0(9) , Grosset & Dunlap) Penguin Group (USA) Inc.

—The Witch That Launched a Thousand Ships. 2002. (gr. 3-6). lib. bdg. 13.00 (978-0-613-74230-6(3)) Tandem Library Bks.

Lacy, Kendra. Drachen. 2007. 188p. per. 13.95 ***978-0-595-43809-9(1))** iUniverse, Inc.

Lagoon Books Staff, ed. Wanda the Witch & the Magical Maze. Rule, Anthony, illus. 2000. 20p. (J). (gr. 2-7). 9.95 (978-1-902813-11-0(1)) Lagoon Bks. GBR. *Dist:* Midpoint Trade Bks., Inc.

Lemire, Lillie. A Young Witch's Magical Adventure. 2006. (ENG.). 48p. per. 12.95 ***978-1-4241-5413-5(8))** PublishAmerica, Inc.

Lenagh, Cecilia. La Brujita Fregona. (Raton de Biblioteca Coleccion). (SPA., Illus.). 64p. (J). (gr. 3-5). 7.95 (978-84-88061-83-6(8)) Serres, Ediciones, S. L. ESP. *Dist:* Lectorum Pubns., Inc.

Lenhard, Elizabeth. Date with Death. 2002. (Charmed Ser.). 192p. (YA). pap. 5.99 (978-0-689-85078-3(6) , Simon Pulse) Simon & Schuster Children's Publishing.

—Date with Death. 2002. 186p. (YA). (gr. 7-12). lib. bdg. 14.15 (978-0-613-73365-6(7)) Tandem Library Bks.

—Different Path. 2004. (W. I. T. C. H. Ser.: Bk. 13). 158p. (J). lib. bdg. 16.92 ***978-1-4242-0791-6(6))** Fitzgerald Bks.

Lenhard, Elizabeth. The Return of a Queen. rev. ed. 2005. (W. I. T. C. H. Ser.: Bk. 12). (Illus.). 144p. (gr. 3-7). pap. 4.99 (978-0-7868-5140-9(6) , Volo) Hyperion Bks. for Children.

Lenhard, Elizabeth & Kaaberbol, Lene. When Lightning Strikes. 2004. (W. I. T. C. H. Adventures Ser. : Bk. 1). (Illus.). 112p. (J). (gr. 3-7). pap. 4.99 (978-0-7868-0977-6(9) , Volo) Hyperion Bks. for Children.

Leuck, Laura. One Witch. Schindler, S. D., illus. 32p. (J). 2005. pap. 6.95 (978-0-8027-7729-4(5)); 2004. 15.95 (978-0-8027-8860-3(2)) Walker & Co.

Lewis, C. S. Chronicles of Narnia: The Lion, the Witch & the Wardrobe Chapter Book. 2006. (Narnia Ser.). 384p. (J). pap. 14.99 (978-0-06-117453-7(X)) HarperCollins Pubs.

—El Leon, la Bruja y el Ropera. 2002. (SPA.). (gr. 5-8). lib. bdg. 16.45 (978-0-613-62176-2(X)) Tandem Library Bks.

—The Magician's Nephew. Baynes, Pauline, illus. 2006. (Narnia Ser.). 208p. (J). 11.99 (978-0-06-112526-3(1)) HarperCollins Pubs.

—The Magician's Nephew Read-Aloud Edition. Baynes, Pauline, illus. 2006. (Narnia Ser.). 208p. (J). 15.99 (978-0-06-087588-6(7)) HarperCollins Pubs.

—La Silla de Plata. 2003. (SPA.). pap. (978-956-13-1672-0(2) , AB3881) Bello, Andres CHL. *Dist:* Lectorum Pubns., Inc.

Lewis, Kevin & Reeves, Howard. There Was an Old Witch Paperback. Catrow, David, illus. abr. ed. 2000. 32p. (ps-3). pap. 5.99 (978-0-7868-1492-3(6)) Disney Pr.

Linklater, Eric. The Wind on the Moon. Bentley, Nicolas, illus. 2004. (New York Review Children's Collection). 376p. (J). 18.95 (978-1-59017-100-4(4) , NYR Children's Collection) New York Review of Bks., Inc., The.

Low, Alice. Witch Who Was Afraid of Witches. 2000. (978-0-606-20312-8(5)); (gr. 3-6). lib. bdg. 11.80 (978-0-613-29149-1(2)) Tandem Library Bks.

Lowe, Wesley. The Griffin's Gauntlet. 2003. (YA). per. 14.95 (978-1-59453-013-5(0) , 1171) Airleaf Publishing & Bookselling.

Luberto, Bradley. Clide & Druce: A Repulsive Tale of Trolls & Tax Money. 2006. (ENG.). 48p. per. 12.95 ***978-1-4241-5012-0(4))** PublishAmerica, Inc.

Lurie, Alison. Baba Yaga & the Stolen Baby. Souhami, Jessica, illus. ed. 2008. 32p. (J). pap. 7.95 ***978-1-84507-753-2(9))** Lincoln, Frances Ltd. GBR. *Dist:* Perseus Distribution.

MacDonald, Alan. The Sand Witch. Mould, Chris, illus. 2006. 32p. (J). lib. bdg. ***978-1-4048-3128-5(2))** Picture Window Bks.

Maguire, Gregory. The Dream Stealer. Bryan, Diana, illus. 2002. 144p. (J). (gr. 3-5). tchr. ed. 15.00 (978-0-618-18188-9(1) , Clarion Bks.) Houghton Mifflin Co. Trade & Reference Div.

Man-Kong, Mary. The Magic of the Rainbow. 2008. 24p. (J). (gr. k-k). bds. 4.99 ***978-0-375-84796-7(0)** , Golden Bks.) Random Hse., Inc.

Mariotte, Jeff. Fall. 2004. (Witch Season Ser.). 320p. (YA). mass mkt. 5.99 (978-0-689-86724-8(7) , Simon Pulse) Simon & Schuster Children's Publishing.

Markowicz, Elaine C. Bride of the Blood Moon. 2004. 190p. pap. 19.95 (978-1-4137-3927-5(X)) PublishAmerica, Inc.

Marlow, Layn. The Witch with a Twitch. Dreidemy, Joelle, illus. 2005. 32p. (J). (ps-ps). 15.95 (978-1-58925-052-9(4) , tiger tales) ME Media LLC.

—Witch with a Twitch. Dreidemy, Joelle, illus. 2006. 32p. (J). pap. 6.95 (978-1-58925-400-8(7) , tiger tales) ME Media LLC.

Martin, W. Lyon. Aidan's First Full Moon Circle. Martin, W. Lyon, illus. 2008. (Illus.). 32p. (J). lib. bdg. 16.95 ***978-0-9796834-4-2(0))** Shades of White.

Mass, Wendy. Rapunzel: The One with All the Hair. 2006. (Twice upon a Time Ser.: No. 1). 208p. (J). pap. 5.99 (978-0-439-79656-9(3) , Scholastic Paperbacks) Scholastic, Inc.

Mateos, Pilar. La Bruja Mon. 24th ed. 2000. (Barco de Vapor). (SPA., Illus.). 64p. (J). (gr. 2-3). (978-84-348-1461-5(7)) SM Ediciones.

McClear, Preston. The Salior & the Sea Witch. Dollak, Micholas, illus. 2002. 32p. (J). (gr. 3-5). 16.95 (978-1-929084-11-1(0)) Malibu Bks. for Children.

McClymer, Kelly. Competition's a Witch. 2007. 256p. (YA). (gr. 6 up). pap. 8.99 (978-1-4169-1645-1(8) , Simon Pulse) Simon & Schuster Children's Publishing.

—The Salem Witch Tryouts. 2006. 272p. (YA). pap. 8.99 (978-1-4169-1644-4(X) , Simon Pulse) Simon & Schuster Children's Publishing.

McGhee, Alison. A Very Brave Witch. Bliss, Harry, illus. 2006. 32p. (J). (ps-3). 12.95 (978-0-689-86730-9(1) , Simon & Schuster Children's Publishing) Simon & Schuster Children's Publishing.

McGrath, Barbara Barbieri. The Little Green Witch. Alexander, Martha, illus. 32p. (J). 2006. pap. 6.95 (978-1-58089-150-3(0)); 2005. per. 14.95 (978-1-58089-042-7(3)) Charlesbridge Publishing, Inc.

McGraw-Hill Staff. Rapunzel. 2001. (gr. k-3). lib. bdg. 11.80 (978-0-613-87941-5(4)) Tandem Library Bks.

McMullan, Kate. Sir Lancelot, Where Are You? Basso, Bill, illus. 2003. (Dragon Slayers' Academy Ser.: No. 6). 112p. (gr. 3-7). pap. 4.99 (978-0-448-43278-6(1) , Grosset & Dunlap) Penguin Group (USA) Inc.

—Sir Lancelot, Where Are You? 2003. (Dragon Slayers' Academy Ser.: No. 6). (gr. 3-6). lib. bdg. 13.00 (978-0-613-72537-8(9)) Tandem Library Bks.

Meddaugh, Susan. The Witch's Walking Stick. 2005. (Illus.). 32p. (J). (gr. k-3). 16.00 (978-0-618-52948-3(9) , Walter Lorraine) Houghton Mifflin Co. Trade & Reference Div.

Melling, O. R. The Hunter's Moon. 2005. (Chronicles of Faerie Ser.: No. 1). (Illus.). 296p. (J). (gr. 5-10). 16.95 (978-0-8109-5857-9(0)) Abrams, Harry N. , Inc.

—Hunter's Moon. 2006. (Chronicles of Faerie Ser.: No. 1). 304p. (J). (gr. 5-10). pap. 7.95 (978-0-8109-9214-6(0)) Abrams, Harry N. , Inc.

Melmed, Laura Krauss. Fright Night Flight. Cole, Henry, illus. 2002. 32p. (J). (ps-3). 15.99 (978-0-06-029701-5(8)) HarperCollins Pubs.

Minor, Wendell. Pumpkin Heads! 2007. 32p. (J). (ps-3). pap. 6.99 ***978-0-590-52138-3(1))** Scholastic, Inc.

Miyazaki, Hayao. Kiki's Delivery Service Film Comic. 2006. (Kiki's Delivery Service Film Comics Ser.). 208p. (YA). Vol. 3. pap. 9.99 (978-1-59116-784-6(1)); Vol. 4. pap. 9.99 (978-1-4215-0595-4(9)) Viz Media.

—Kiki's Delivery Service Picture Book, Vol. 1. 2006. (Kiki's Delivery Service Film Comics Ser.). 208p. (YA). pap. 14.99 (978-1-4215-0596-1(7)) Viz Media.

Mlynowski, Sarah. Bras & Broomsticks. 2005. 320p. (YA). (gr. 7). 15.95 (978-0-385-73181-2(7) , Delacorte Bks. for Young Readers) Random Hse. Children's Bks.

—Frogs & French Kisses. (gr. 7). 2007. 304p. (YA). pap. 8.99 ***978-0-385-73185-0(X));** 2006. (Illus.). 288p. (J). 15.95 (978-0-385-73182-9(5)); 2006. (Illus.). 288p. (YA). lib. bdg. 17.99 (978-0-385-90219-9(0)) Random Hse. Children's Bks. (Delacorte Bks. for Young Readers).

Moerbeek, Kees. The Diary of Hansel & Gretel. Moerbeek, Kees, illus. 2002. (Illus.). 12p. (J). (gr. k-3). 12.95 (978-0-689-84602-1(9) , Little Simon) Simon & Schuster Children's Publishing.

Molloy, Michael. The Time Witches. 2002. (Illus.). 272p. (J). (gr. 5-8). 4.99 (978-0-439-42090-7(3) , Chicken Hse., The) Scholastic, Inc.

—Wild West Witches. 2003. 288p. (J). (gr. 3-6). pap. 4.99 (978-0-439-54510-5(2) , Chicken Hse., The) Scholastic, Inc.

Mooney, Jane-Marie. Wings in Dragon Dance. 2007. (ENG.). 168p. per. ***978-1-84685-551-1(9)** , Exposure Publishing) Meadow Bks.

Moray-Williams, Ursula & Williams, Ursula Moray. The Further Adventures of Gobbolino & the Little Wooden Horse. Howard, Paul, illus. 2002. (Kingfisher Modern Classics Ser.). 240p. (J). (gr. k-3). tchr. ed. 15.95 (978-0-7534-5495-4(5) , Kingfisher) Houghton Mifflin Co. Trade & Reference Div.

Murphy, Jill. A Bad Spell for the Worst Witch. 2000. (Worst Witch Ser.). (J). (978-0-606-19310-8(3)) Tandem Library Bks.

—The Worst Witch at School. Murphy, Jill, illus. 2007. (Worst Witch Ser.). (Illus.). 192p. (J). (gr. 3). 6.99 ***978-0-7636-3435-3(2))** Candlewick Pr.

—The Worst Witch in Trouble. Murphy, Jill, illus. 2007. (Worst Witch Ser.). (Illus.). 352p. (J). (gr. 3). 6.99 ***978-0-7636-3436-0(0))** Candlewick Pr.

—The Worst Witch Saves the Day. Murphy, Jill, illus. 2007. (Worst Witch Ser.). (Illus.). 160p. (J). (gr. 3). 13.99 ***978-0-7636-3319-6(4))** Candlewick Pr.

Naifeh, Ted. Courtney Crumrin & the Coven of Mystics, 2 vols., Vol. 2. Naifeh, Ted, illus. 2003. (Illus.). 128p. (YA). pap. 11.95 (978-1-929998-59-3(7)) Oni Pr., Inc.

Naylor, Phyllis Reynolds. The Witch Herself. 2002. 176p. (J). pap. 4.99 (978-0-689-85317-3(3) , Aladdin) Simon & Schuster Children's Publishing.

—Witch's Sister. 2002. 160p. (J). pap. 4.99 (978-0-689-85315-9(7) , Aladdin) Simon & Schuster Children's Publishing.

—Witch's Sister. 2002. (gr. 3-6). lib. bdg. 13.00 (978-0-613-90184-0(3)) Tandem Library Bks.

Naylor, Phyllis Reynolds & McMillan, Ken. The Witch Returns. 2005. (Illus.). 192p. (J). pap. 4.99 (978-0-689-85382-1(3) , Aladdin) Simon & Schuster Children's Publishing.

Negrin, Fabian, illus. Wizard Tales. 2003. 96p. 19.95 (978-1-55285-558-4(9)) Whitecap Bks., Ltd. CAN. *Dist:* Graphic Arts Ctr. Publishing Co.

Nicoll, Helen, et al. Meg y Mog Juegan Al Escondite. Pienkowski, Jan, illus. 2005. (SPA.). 12p. (ps-k). bds. 14.95 (978-84-666-1819-9(8)) Ediciones B ESP. *Dist:* Independent Pubs. Group.

Night of the Witches: The Beginnings, 8. 2002. 113p. (YA). mass mkt. 4.99 (978-0-9667232-1-2(X) , 152091) Rhapsody Branding, Inc.

Nimmo, Jenny. The Witch's Tears. 2002. (Roaring Good Reads Ser.). (Illus.). 96p. (J). pap. 7.50 (978-0-00-714162-3(9)) HarperCollins Pubs. Ltd. GBR. *Dist:* Independent Pubs. Group.

Norton, Mary. Bedknob & Broomstick. 2000. 12.65 (978-0-606-20322-7(2)); (J). (978-0-606-20159-9(9)); (gr. 3-6). lib. bdg. 14.15 (978-0-613-29886-5(1)) Tandem Library Bks.

O'Connell, Jennifer. Ten Timid Ghosts. 2000. (ps-2). lib. bdg. 10.95 (978-0-613-27197-4(1)) Tandem Library Bks.

Ostow, Micol & Burge, Constance M. Changeling Places: An Original Novel. 2005. 152p. (J). (978-1-4155-8183-4(5) , Simon Spotlight) Simon & Schuster Children's Publishing.

Papademetriou, Lisa. The Wizard, the Witch, & Two Girls from Jersey. 2006. 240p. (J). (gr. 7-12). pap. 8.99 (978-1-59514-074-6(3) , Razorbill) Penguin Group (USA) Inc.

Pardoe, David. Jasper Tippett's Amazing Journey to Page 42. 2006. (Illus.). 132p. pap. ***978-1-84401-785-0(0))** Athena Pr.

Pascual, P. V. The Beautiful Witch. 2004. (J). per. 28.95 (978-1-58939-603-6(0)) Virtualbookworm.com Publishing, Inc.

Paterson, Judy. Tamlane. Collins, Sally J., illus. 1999. 32p. (J). (gr. k-4). pap. (978-1-871512-62-5(X)) Glowworm Bks., Ltd.

—The Witch of Fife. Collins, Sally J., illus. 1998. 32p. (J). (gr. k-4). pap. (978-1-871512-58-8(1)) Glowworm Bks., Ltd.

PC Treasures, prod. Hansel & Gretel. 2007. (J). ***978-1-60072-030-7(7))** PC Treasures, Inc.

Peralta, Maria Antonia. Brujitas. Fuenmayor, Morella, illus. 2005. Tr. of Little Witches. (SPA.). (J). (gr. k-2). 15.95 (978-980-6437-11-1(X)) Playco Editores, C.A.

Peters, Andrew & Player, Stephen. Ed & the Witchblood. 2005. (Illus.). (J). 18.00 (978-0-340-86551-4(2) , Hodder & Stoughton) Hodder General Publishing Division GBR. *Dist:* Trafalgar Square Publishing.

Peters, Andrew Fusek & Player, Stephen. Ed & the Witchblood. 2005. (Illus.). (J). pap. 9.99 (978-0-340-86557-6(1) , Hodder & Stoughton) Hodder General Publishing Division GBR. *Dist:* Trafalgar Square Publishing.

Philpot, Graham, illus. Hansel & Gretel. 2007. (First Fairy Tales Ser.). 31p. (J). ***978-1-59771-075-6(X))** Sea-To-Sea Pubns.

Pierce, Meredith Ann. The Pearl of the Soul of the World. 2008. (Darkangel Trilogy Ser.). 256p. (YA). (gr. 7-17). pap. 7.99 ***978-0-316-06724-9(5))** Little, Brown Bks. for Young Readers.

Pike, Christopher, pseud. Witch. 2001. 240p. (YA). reprint ed. mass mkt. 5.99 (978-0-7434-2799-9(8) , Simon Pulse) Simon & Schuster Children's Publishing.

—Witch. 2001. (J). (978-0-606-21531-2(X)); (gr. 7-12). lib. bdg. 14.15 (978-0-613-61002-5(4)) Tandem Library Bks.

—The Witch's Gift. 1999. (Spooksville Ser.). (gr. 3-6). lib. bdg. 11.80 (978-0-613-85085-8(8)) Tandem Library Bks.

Plourde, Paulette. Smitty Moose, Petey & Me - Episode One, the Witch. Golen, Jessica, illus. l.t. ed. 2005. 32p. (J). per. 9.95 (978-1-59879-038-2(2)) Lifevest Publishing, Inc.

Popper, Garry. Worm's Eye View: A Witch's Tale. Forshaw, John, illus. 2004. 48p. 7.00 (978-1-84161-025-2(9)) Ravette Publishing, Ltd. GBR. *Dist:* Parkwest Pubns., Inc.

Pratchett, Terry. A Hat Full of Sky. 2004. (Discworld Ser.). 288p. (J). (gr. 7 up). 16.99 (978-0-06-058660-7(5)) HarperCollins Pubs.

—The Wee Free Men. Player, Stephen, illus. 2007. 256p. (J). 24.99 ***978-0-06-134080-2(4))** HarperCollins Pubs.

—The Wee Free Men. (gr. 7 up). 2003. 272p. (J). 16.99 (978-0-06-001236-6(6)); 2004. 400p. (YA). reprint ed. pap. 6.99 (978-0-06-001238-0(2) , Harper Trophy) HarperCollins Pubs.

—Wintersmith. (J). 2007. 464p. pap. 7.99 ***978-0-06-089033-9(9));** 2006. 336p. (gr. 6-8). 16.99 (978-0-06-089031-5(2)); 2006. 336p. (gr. 6-8). lib. bdg. 17.89 (978-0-06-089032-2(0)) HarperCollins Pubs. (HarperTeen).

Pullman, Philip. Lyra's Oxford. Lawrence, John, illus. 2007. 64p. (YA). (gr. 7-12). per. 6.99 ***978-0-375-84369-3(8)** , Knopf Bks. for Young Readers) Random Hse. Children's Bks.

RavenWolf, Silver. Jovenes y Brujas. 2004. (SPA.). 352p. pap. (978-84-7720-753-5(4)) Obelisco, Ediciones S.A.

Rawson, C. Stories of Witches. 2004. (Young Reading Ser.: Vol. 1). 48p. (J). (gr. 2 up). pap. 5.95 (978-0-7945-0647-6(X)) EDC Publishing.

Rees, Celia. Witch Child. 272p. (YA). (gr. 7 up). 2002. pap. 8.99 (978-0-7636-1829-2(2)); 2001. (Illus.). 15.99 (978-0-7636-1421-8(1)) Candlewick Pr.

—Witch Child. unabr. ed. 2004. (Young Adult Cassette Librariestm Ser.). 304p. (J). (gr. 5-9). pap. 40.00 incl. audio (978-0-8072-1198-4(2) , S YA 343 SP, Listening Library) Random Hse. Audio Publishing Group.

—Witch Child. 2002. (gr. 7-12). lib. bdg. 16.45 (978-0-613-60740-7(6)) Tandem Library Bks.

—Witch Child. l.t. ed. 2002. 284p. (J). 22.95 (978-0-7862-3896-5(8)) Thomson Gale.

Reeves, Howard. There Was an Old Witch. 2000. (gr. k-3). lib. bdg. 14.15 (978-0-613-31797-9(1)) Tandem Library Bks.

Rex, Michael. Brooms Are for Flying. Rex, Michael, illus. rev. ed. 2000. (Illus.). 32p. (J). (ps-2). 16.00 (978-0-8050-6410-0(9) , Holt, Henry & Co. Bks. For Young Readers) Holt, Henry & Co.

Robertson, M. P. The Great Dragon Rescue. 2004. (Illus.). 32p. (J). (ps-2). 16.99 (978-0-8037-2973-5(1) , Dial) Penguin Group (USA) Inc.

Robey, M. Ye Olde Witch Club in the Order of the C. 2005. 226p. pap. 19.95 (978-1-4137-6627-1(7)) PublishAmerica, Inc.

Rodda, Emily. The Key to Rondo. 2008. (J). ***978-0-545-03536-1(8));** 224p. pap. 16.99 ***978-0-545-03535-4(X))** Scholastic, Inc. (Scholastic Pr.).

Rose, Alice. Maria Dracula: A Fantasy Novel for Children. 2007. (Illus.). 191p. pap. 13.50 ***978-0-615-15099-4(3))** DUENDE Bks.

Rowling, J. K. Harry Potter et la Chambre des Secrets. 1999. (Harry Potter Ser.: Year 2). Tr. of Harry Potter & the Chamber of Secrets. (FRE., Illus.). 358p. (YA). (gr. 3 up). pap. 16.95 (978-2-07-052455-6(8)) Gallimard, Editions FRA. *Dist:* Distribooks, Inc.

—Harry Potter et le Prisonnier d'Azkaban. 1999. (Harry Potter Ser.: Year 3). Tr. of Harry Potter & the Prisoner of Azkaban. (FRE.). 465p. (YA). (gr. 3 up). pap. 16.95 (978-2-07-052818-9(9)) Gallimard, Editions FRA. *Dist:* Distribooks, Inc.

—Harry Potter et l'Ecole des Sorciers. 3rd ed. 1998. (Harry Potter Ser.: Year 1). Tr. of Harry Potter & the Sorcerer's Stone. (FRE., Illus.). (YA). (gr. 3 up). pap. 14.95 (978-2-07-050142-7(6)) Distribooks, Inc.

—Harry Potter y el Caliz de Fuego. 2001. (SPA.). (gr. 3-6). lib. bdg. 26.35 (978-0-613-35957-3(7)) Tandem Library Bks.

Ruditis, Paul & Burge, Constance M. As Puck Would Have It. 2006. (Charmed Ser.). 240p. (YA). pap. 6.99 (978-1-4169-1468-6(4) , Simon Spotlight Entertainment) Simon & Schuster.

Ruggles, Lucy. The Witch's Amulet. rev. ed. 2007. 128p. (gr. 3-7). pap. 4.99 ***978-1-4231-0881-8(7))** Disney Pr.

Sampson, Fay. Shape-Shifter: The Naming of Pangur Ban. 2002. (Illus.). 160p. (J). (gr. 5-8). pap. 7.99 (978-0-7459-4762-4(X) , Lion) Lion Hudson plc GBR. *Dist:* Independent Pubs. Group.

Samwell, Cynthia A. Witches Anonymous. 2006. (Illus.). 84p. pap. ***978-1-84401-660-0(9))** Athena Pr.

Saunders, Kate. The Belfry Witches: Witch You Were Here. l.t. ed. 2005. (Illus.). 128p. (J). pap. (978-0-7540-6161-8(2) , CLP 355) BBC Audio.

—Spell of Witches. l.t. ed. 2005. (Illus.). 144p. (J). pap. (978-0-7540-6146-5(9) , CLP 339) BBC Audio.

Scharf, J. L. Grace & the Ice Prince. 2007. 262p. pap. 15.95 ***978-1-897235-09-6(7))** Thistledown Pr., Ltd. CAN. *Dist:* Fitzhenry & Whiteside, Ltd.

Scooby-Doo & the Hex Files. 1999. (gr. k-3). lib. bdg. 11.25 (978-0-613-22339-3(X)) Tandem Library Bks.

Scooby-Doo & the Witch's Ghost. 1999. (gr. k-3). lib. bdg. 11.25 (978-0-613-22340-9(3)) Tandem Library Bks.

Seibold, J. Otto. The Fuchsia Is Now. 2006. (Illus.). 40p. (J). (ps-k). pap. 16.99 (978-0-439-63559-2(4) , Orchard Bks.) Scholastic, Inc.

Serafin, Jordan. Bella: The Crooked Hat Witch. Rubino, Alisa A., illus. 2004. (J). (978-0-932991-57-7(2)) Place In The Woods, The.

Serrano, Tomas. Salfon el Limpiador de Tejados. (SPA.). 48p. (J). (gr. 1-3). pap. (978-84-264-3746-4(X)) Editorial Lumen ESP. *Dist:* Lectorum Pubns., Inc.

Sharratt, Nick. Muddlewitch on the Farm. 2007. (Illus.). 18p. (J). (ps-k). bds. 14.95 ***978-1-4052-2651-6(X))** Egmont Bks., Ltd. GBR. *Dist:* Independent Pubs. Group.

Simmons, H. Two Tales from Our Corner Lot. 2004. 68p. pap. 14.95 (978-1-4137-5251-9(9)) PublishAmerica, Inc.

Simmons, Steven J. Alicia y Greta: Un Cuento de Dos Brujas. Mlawer, Teresa, tr. Moore, Cyd, illus. 2004. Tr. of Alice & Greta. (SPA.). 32p. (J). (gr. k-2). pap. 7.95 (978-0-88106-133-8(6) , CH5119) Charlesbridge Publishing, Inc.

Simon & Schuster, eds. Millennium Madness. 2000. (gr. 3-6). lib. bdg. 14.15 (978-0-613-22002-6(1)) Tandem Library Bks.

Simon-Kerr, Julia. The Lion, the Witch, & the Wardrobe: Coloring & Activity Book & Magnets. Redondo, Jesus, illus. movie tie-in ed. 2005. (Narnia Ser.). 32p. (J). pap., act. bk. ed. 4.99 (978-0-06-076558-3(5)) Zonderkidz.

Skinner, Daphne. My Side of the Story Bk. 3: The Little Mermaid & Ursula. Daly, Catherine, ed. 3rd rev. ed. 2004. (Disney Princess Ser.). (Illus.). 72p. (ps-17). 12.99 (978-0-7868-3503-4(6)) Disney Pr.

The Sleeping Beauty: Individual Title Six-Packs. 32p. (gr. 3 up). 37.00 (978-0-7635-9680-4(9)) Rigby Education.

Smith, Audrey. The Halloween Misfits. 2004. 23p. (J). pap. 14.95 incl. audio compact disk (978-0-9722673-4-2(4)) Audrey Productions.

Smith, Gordon. The Forest in the Hallway. 2006. 160p. (J). (gr. 5-9). 16.00 (978-0-618-68847-0(1) , Clarion Bks.) Houghton Mifflin Co. Trade & Reference Div.

Smith, L. J. Initiation. 1999. (gr. 7-12). lib. bdg. 13.00 (978-0-613-22679-0(8)) Tandem Library Bks.

Spurr, Elizabeth. Halloween Sky Ride. Long, Ethan, illus. 32p. (J). (ps). 16.95 (978-0-8234-1870-1(7)) Holiday Hse., Inc.

Stanley, John. Little Lulu Volume 13: Too Much Fun: Too Much Fun. 2006. (Illus.). 208p. pap. 9.95 (978-1-59307-621-4(5)) Dark Horse Comics.

Stead, Rebecca. First Light. 2007. 336p. (J). (gr. 4-7). 15.99 ***978-0-375-84017-3(6));** lib. bdg. 18.99 ***978-0-375-94017-0(0))** Random Hse. Children's Bks. (Lamb, Wendy).

Steig, William. Wizzil. Blake, Quentin, illus. 2000. 32p. (J). (ps-3). 16.00 (978-0-374-38466-1(5) , Farrar, Straus & Giroux (BYR)) Farrar, Straus & Giroux.

Steinberg, David. The Witches' Ball. Conrad, Liz, illus. 2007. 10p. (J). (ps-1). bds. 6.99 (978-0-8431-2494-1(6) , Price Stern Sloan) Penguin Group (USA) Inc.

Stern, Steven L. Witches among Us. 2001. (YA). pap. (978-1-56765-067-9(8) , R696P) AMSCO Schl. Pubns., Inc.

Stewart, Mary. The Little Broomstick. pap. (978-0-440-44897-6(2)) Random Hse. Children's Bks.

Strega Nona. 2005. (J). (978-1-59564-834-1(8)) Steps To Literacy, LLC.

Tagg, Christine. Who Will You Meet on Scary Street? Nine Pop-up Nightmares! Fuge, Charles, illus. 2004. 20p. (J). reprint ed. 15.00 (978-0-7567-8003-6(9)) DIANE Publishing Co.

Tatcheva, Eva. Witch Zelda's Birthday Cake: A Wild & Wicked Pop-up, Pull-the-Tab Book. Tatcheva, Eva, illus. 2004. (Illus.). 12p. (J). (gr. k-3). reprint ed. 18.00 (978-0-7567-7225-3(7)) DIANE Publishing Co.

Thomas, Becky. Hansel & Gretel. Zwerger, Lisbeth, illus. 2008. 32p. (J). (ps-3). 16.99 ***978-0-698-40078-8(X)** , Minedition) Penguin Group (USA) Inc.

Thomas, Jacqui, illus. The Kingfisher Treasury of Witch & Wizard Stories. 2004. (Kingfisher Treasury of Stories Ser.: Vol. 23). 160p. (J). (gr. k-3). pap. 5.95 (978-0-7534-5729-0(6) , Kingfisher) Houghton Mifflin Co. Trade & Reference Div.

Thomas, Valerie. Winnie Flies Again. 2000. (978-0-606-19823-3(7)) Tandem Library Bks.

Thomas, Valerie. Winnie the Witch. Paul, Korky, illus. 2007. 32p. (J). (ps-3). 14.99 (***978-0-06-117312-7(6))*** HarperCollins Pubs.

Thompson. The Follower. 2003. 32p. (J). pap. (978-1-55041-880-4(7)) Fitzhenry & Whiteside, Ltd.

Thompson, Colin. The Floods #1: Good Neighbors. Scrambly, Crab, illus. 2008. (Floods Ser.). 224p. (J). 15.99 (***978-0-06-113196-7(2));*** lib. bdg. 16.89 (***978-0-06-113199-8(7))*** HarperCollins Pubs.

Thompson, Jill, illus. Magic Trixie. 2008. 96p. (J). pap. 7.99 (***978-0-06-117045-4(3)*** , Harper Trophy) HarperCollins Pubs.

Thompson, Richard. The Follower. Springett, Martin, illus. 2000. 28p. (J). (gr. k-4). (978-1-55041-532-2(8)) Fitzhenry & Whiteside, Ltd.

Three Witches & Other Stories. 2002. per. (978-1-931456-05-0(4)) Athena Pr.

Tiernan, Cate. Awakening, Bk. 5. 2007. (Sweep Ser.). 192p. (YA). pap. 6.99 (***978-0-14-241020-2(9)*** , Puffin) Penguin Group (USA) Inc.

—The Blood Witch, Vol. 3. 2001. (Sweep Ser.: Bk. 3). (Illus.). 192p. (YA). (gr. 7 up). pap. 5.99 (978-0-14-131111-1(8) , Puffin) Penguin Group (USA) Inc.

—Book of Shadows. 2001. (gr. 7-12). lib. bdg. 13.00 (978-0-613-31016-1(0)) Tandem Library Bks.

—Moira's Story. 2003. (gr. 7-12). lib. bdg. 15.30 (978-0-613-66595-7(3)) Tandem Library Bks.

—Night's Child Vol. 15: Moira's Story. 2003. (Sweep Ser.). 320p. pap. 6.99 (978-0-14-250119-1(0) , Puffin) Penguin Group (USA) Inc.

—Origins. 2002. (gr. 7-12). lib. bdg. 13.00 (978-0-613-64091-6(8)) Tandem Library Bks.

—The Reckoning. 2002. (Sweep Ser.). 192p. (YA). pap. 6.99 (978-0-14-230086-2(1) , Puffin) Penguin Group (USA) Inc.

—Reckoning. 2002. (gr. 7-12). lib. bdg. 14.15 (978-0-613-64099-2(3)) Tandem Library Bks.

Tomos, Angharad. Ceridwen. 2005. (WEL., Illus.). 48p. pap. (978-0-86243-066-5(6)) Y Lolfa.

—Cosyn. 2005. (WEL., Illus.). 24p. pap. (978-0-86243-566-0(8)) Y Lolfa.

—Rala Rwdins. 2005. (WEL., Illus.). 48p. pap. (978-0-86243-065-8(8)) Y Lolfa.

Torkelson, Debie. New Witches Club (Book No. 1) Bk. 1: The Sleepover Curse. ed. 2005. (Illus.). 80p. (J). per. 6.99 (978-1-59772-010-6(0) , Your Own World Bks.) Your Own World, Inc.

—New Witches Club (Book No. 2) Bk. 2: Witch Hanne Returns. 2005. (Illus.). 88p. (J). per. 6.99 (978-1-59772-015-1(1) , Your Own World Bks.) Your Own World, Inc.

Tremblay, Carole. Emily Lee. Jorisch, Stephane, illus. 2005. (Read-It! Readers Ser.). 32p. (J). (gr. k-3). 18.60 (978-1-4048-1077-8(3)) Picture Window Bks.

Troulis, Jennifer. Penelope & Priscilla & the City of the Banished. 2007. (J). per. 14.95 (***978-0-9768602-1-1(X))*** Twin Monkeys Pr.

Tyrrell, Melissa. Hansel & Gretel. McMullen, Nigel, illus. 2005. (Fairytale Friends Ser.). 12p. (J). bds. 5.95 (978-1-58117-152-5(8) , Intervisual/Piggy Toes) Dalmatian Pr.

Vande Velde, Vivian. Magic Can Be Murder. 2002. 197p. (J). (gr. 4-7). per. 14.15 (978-0-613-53832-9(3)) Tandem Library Bks.

—Three Good Deeds. (Illus.). 160p. 2007. (YA). pap. 5.95 (***978-0-15-205455-7(3)*** , Magic Carpet Bks.); 2005. (J). (gr. 3-7). 16.00 (978-0-15-205382-6(4)) Harcourt Children's Bks.

Vande Velde, Vivian. Witch Dreams. 2005. 128p. (J). (gr. 5-9). 15.95 (978-0-7614-5235-5(4)) Cavendish, Marshall Corp.

Vaught, Susan. Stormwitch. 2005. 200p. (J). 16.95 (978-1-58234-952-7(5) , Bloomsbury Children) Bloomsbury Publishing.

Velde, Vivan V. Never Trust a Dead Man. 2001. (YA). (978-0-606-21346-2(5)) Tandem Library Bks.

Villarreal Elizondo, Cesar. La Tierra de las Adivinanzas. Garcia, Nasario, tr. from SPA. Accardo, Anthony, illus. 2002. Tr. of Land of the Riddles. (ENG & SPA.). 32p. (J). (gr. 2-3). 14.95 (978-1-55885-352-2(9) , Piñata Books) Arte Publico Pr.

Walker, Chris, creator. Collision Course Goad by Zombienose. 2005. (Illus.). 60p. (YA). 13.95 (978-0-9768670-0-5(1)) Icecat Bks.

Wallace, Barbara Brooks. Miss Switch Online. 2002. 192p. (J). (gr. 4-6). 16.00 (978-0-689-84376-1(3) , Atheneum) Simon & Schuster Children's Publishing.

—Miss Switch Online. 2003. (gr. 3-6). lib. bdg. 13.00 (978-0-613-91040-8(0)) Tandem Library Bks.

—Trouble with Miss Switch. 2002. 140p. (gr. 3-6). lib. bdg. 13.00 (978-0-613-57930-8(5)) Tandem Library Bks.

—The Trouble with Miss Switch. 2002. 144p. (J). (gr. 5 up). reprint ed. pap. 4.99 (978-0-689-85177-3(4) , Aladdin) Simon & Schuster Children's Publishing.

Wallace, Jessica. The Present 6 Packs. KinderConcepts. Gardner, Marjory, illus. (Kinderstarters Ser.). 8p. (ps-1). 21.00 (978-0-7635-8720-8(6)) Rigby Education.

Washington, Linda & Pyykkonen, Carrie. Secrets of the Wee Free Men & Discworld: The Myths & Legends of Terry Pratchett's Multiverse. 2008. (Illus.). 192p. (J). pap. 9.95 (***978-0-312-37243-9(4)*** , St. Martin's Griffin) St. Martin's Pr.

Watson, Sally. Witch of the Glens. 2004. (YA). pap. 12.95 (978-1-59511-001-5(1) , 800-691-7779) Image Cascade Publishing.

Weiss, Bobbi J. G. Age of Aquariums. 1999. (gr. 3-6). lib. bdg. 13.00 (978-0-613-17071-0(7)) Tandem Library Bks.

Weiss, David Cody. Now & Again. 2003. (gr. 5-8). lib. bdg. 13.00 (978-0-613-73348-9(7)) Tandem Library Bks.

Whalen, Erin T. Charlie Gets Spooked, 3 vols. 2004. (Illus.). 32p. (J). (gr. k-3). 16.95 (978-1-929265-04-6(2)); pap. 8.95 (978-1-929265-05-3(0)) Lily & Co. Publishing.

Willard, Eliza. Power of Three. 1999. (gr. 5-8). lib. bdg. 14.15 (978-0-613-22213-6(X)) Tandem Library Bks.

Williams, Guana Dunbar. The Wacky Winter Witch. William, Iceberg Dunbar, illus. 2003. (J). per. (978-0-9740673-1-5(8)) Graphix Network.

Wrede, Patricia C. Searching for Dragons. 2002. (Enchanted Forest Chronicles: Bk. 2). (Illus.). 272p. (YA). (gr. 5 up). pap. 5.95 (978-0-15-204565-4(1) , Magic Carpet Bks.) Harcourt Children's Bks.

—Searching for Dragons. unabr. ed. 2004. (Enchanted Forest Chronicles Ser.). 242p. (J). (gr. 5 up). pap. 38.00 incl. audio (978-0-8072-0670-6(9) , Listening Library) Random Hse. Audio Publishing Group.

—Searching for Dragons. 2002. 242p. (J). (ps-ps). per. 14.10 (978-0-613-55189-2(3)) Tandem Library Bks.

Yolen, Jane. Baba Yaga. Date not set. 32p. (J). (ps-1). pap. 5.99 (978-0-06-443599-4(7)) HarperCollins Pubs.

—The Flying Witch. Vagin, Vladimir, illus. 2003. 40p. (J). (ps-1). 15.99 (978-0-06-028536-4(2)) HarperCollins Pubs.

—The Wizard of Washington Square. 2005. 96p. (J). 5.99 (978-0-7653-5016-9(5) , Starscape) Doherty, Tom Assocs., LLC.

Yolen, Jane & Stemple, Heidi Elisabet Yolen. The Salem Witch Trials: An Unsolved Mystery from History. Roth, Roger, illus. 2004. 32p. (J). 16.95 (978-0-689-84620-5(7)) Simon & Schuster Children's Publishing.

Yorinks, Arthur. The Witch's Child. Smith, Joseph A., illus. 2007. 34p. (J). (gr. k-4). 16.95 (***978-0-8109-9349-5(X)*** , Abrams Bks. for Young Readers) Abrams, Harry N. , Inc.

Ziefert, Harriet. Two Little Witches 8x8 Stkr Bk. Taback, Simms, illus. 2007. 20p. (J). (gr. k-k). pap. 3.99 (***978-0-7636-3309-7(7))*** Candlewick Pr.

WIZARDS

Beahm, George & Goldin, Stan, eds. The Whimsic Alley Book of Spells: Mythical Incantations for Magicians of All Ages. 2007. (Illus.). 192p. (J). pap. 14.95 (***978-1-57174-535-4(1))*** Hampton Roads Publishing Co., Inc.

Clibbon, Lucy, illus. Imagine You're a Wizard! 2003. (Imagine This! Ser.). 32p. (J). (gr. 1-4). 19.95 (978-1-55037-793-4(0)) Annick Pr., Ltd. CAN. *Dist:* Firefly Bks., Ltd.

Clibbon, Meg. Imagine You're a Wizard! Clibbon, Lucy, illus. 2003. (Imagine This! Ser.). 32p. (J). (gr. 1-4). pap. 7.95 (978-1-55037-792-7(2)) Annick Pr., Ltd. CAN. *Dist:* Firefly Bks., Ltd.

Dorling Kindersley Publishing Staff. Witch & Wizard. 2005. 16p. (J). pap. 6.99 (978-0-7566-1269-6(1)) Dorling Kindersley Publishing, Inc.

Fremont, Victoria & Stewart, Pat. Invisible Oz Magic Picture Book. 1998. 16p. (J). (ps-2). pap. 1.50 (978-0-486-40528-5(1)) Dover Pubns., Inc.

Hamilton, John. Wizards & Witches. 2005. (Fantasy & Folklore Ser.). (Illus.). 32p. (J). (gr. 4-8). lib. bdg. 24.21 (978-1-59197-716-2(9)) ABDO Publishing Co.

Kilby, Janice Eaton & Taylor, Terry. The Book of Wizard Parties: In Which the Wizard Shares the Secrets of Creating Enchanted Gatherings. Baggetta, Marla, illus. 2002. 144p. 19.95 (978-1-57990-292-6(8)) Lark Bks.

Kilby, Janice Eaton, et al. The Book of Wizard Craft: In Which the Apprentice Finds Spells, Potions, Fantastic Tales & 50 Enchanting Things to Make. Burnett, Lindy, illus. deluxe ed. 2001. 144p. (J). (gr. 4-6). 7.95 (978-1-57990-206-3(5)) Lark Bks.

Kimble, Evan & Kimble, Lael. Wizard's World Dot-to-Dot. 2004. (Illus.). 80p. pap. 5.95 (978-1-4027-0995-1(1)) Sterling Publishing Co., Inc.

Kronzek, Allan Zola & Kronzek, Elizabeth. The Sorcerer's Companion: A Guide to the Magical World of Harry Potter. 2nd ed. 2004. (Illus.). 352p. 15.95 (978-0-7679-1944-9(0) , Broadway) Broadway Bks.

Master Merlin & Steer, Dugald. Wizardology Handbook: A Course for Apprentices. Gilbert, Anne Young et al, illus. 2007. (Ologies Ser.). 80p. (J). (gr. 3 up). 12.99 (***978-0-7636-3401-8(8))*** Candlewick Pr.

Merlin, Master. Wizardology: A Guide to the Wizards of the World. Steer, Dugald A., ed. 2007. (Ologies Ser.). (Illus.). 40p. (J). (gr. 3-7). 14.99 (***978-0-7636-3710-1(6))*** Candlewick Pr.

Moreau, Roger. Wizard Magic Mazes: An A-maze-ing Colorful Quest! 2003. (Illus.). 80p. (J). pap. 7.95 (978-1-4027-0198-6(5)) Sterling Publishing Co., Inc.

Narayan, Natasha. Witches, Wizards & Warlocks of London. 2004. (... . of London Ser.). (Illus.). 96p. 8.99 (978-1-904153-12-2(7)) Watling St., Ltd. GBR. *Dist:* Trafalgar Square Publishing.

Rumstuckle, Cornelius. The Book of Wizardry: The Apprentice's Guide to the Secrets of the Wizards' Guild. 2003. (Illus.). 336p. pap. 12.95 (978-0-7387-0165-3(3)) Llewellyn Pubns.

Savage, Candace. Wizards: An Amazing Journey Through the Last Great Age of Magic. (Illus.). 80p. 2004. pap. 12.00 (978-1-55365-039-3(5)); 2003. (J). (gr. 4-7). 17.95 (978-1-55054-943-0(X)) Douglas & McIntyre, Ltd. CAN. *Dist:* Transition Vendor.

Wickings, Ruth. Wizards. 2007. (Enchanted World Ser.). (Illus.). 12p. (J). (ps-3). 9.95 (***978-1-84560-033-4(9))*** Mercury Bks. Ltd. GBR. *Dist:* International Publishers Marketing.

Wizard Sticker Book. 2003. (Illus.). 16p. (J). 2.98 (978-1-84273-118-5(1) , Exclusive Editions) Parragon, Inc.

Wizards are Magic. 2002. (Little Friends Ser.). (J). 2.98 (978-1-84273-425-4(3) , Exclusive Editions) Parragon, Inc.

WIZARDS—FICTION

Abbott, Tony. Chariot of Queen Zara. Merrell, David, illus. 2006. 124p. (J). lib. bdg. 15.38 (***978-1-4242-0308-6(2))*** Fitzgerald Bks.

—Flight of the Genie. Merrell, David, illus. 2004. (Secrets of Droon Ser.). 128p. (J). 3.99 (978-0-439-56043-6(8) , Scholastic Paperbacks) Scholastic, Inc.

—Flight of the Genie. 2003. (gr. 3-6). lib. bdg. 11.80 (978-0-613-87594-3(X)) Tandem Library Bks.

—Keeah's Test. 2004. (gr. 3-6). lib. bdg. 14.15 (978-0-613-87595-0(8)) Tandem Library Bks.

Alton, Steve. The Firehills. 2005. 192p. (J). (gr. 7-13). 15.95 (978-1-57505-798-9(0) , Carolrhoda Bks.) Lerner Publishing Group.

—The Malifex. 2003. (Middle Readers Ser.). (Illus.). 182p. (J). (gr. 3-7). 14.95 (978-0-8225-0959-2(8)) Lerner Publishing Group.

Banerjee, Anjali. The Silver Spell. Fiegenshuh, Emily, illus. 2005. (Knights of the Silver Dragon Ser.: Bk. 8). 174p. (J). (***978-1-4156-1645-1(0)*** , Mirrorstone) Wizards of the Coast.

Barlow, Steve & Skidmore, Steve. Whizzard. 2002. (Tales of the Dark Forest Ser.). (Illus.). 256p. pap. 11.00 (978-0-00-710864-0(8)) HarperCollins Pubs. Ltd. GBR. *Dist:* Independent Pubs. Group.

Barrera, F. M. Tales of the Blue Wizard: The Children of Jamomere. Barrera, F. M., illus. 2005. (Illus.). 180p. (YA). (gr. 4-9). per. 12.95 (978-0-9670848-1-7(4)) Talisman Pr.

Barron, T. A. The Eternal Flame. 2006. (Great Tree of Avalon Trilogy: Bk. 3). (Illus.). 400p. (YA). (gr. 5). 19.99 (978-0-399-24213-7(9) , Philomel) Penguin Group (USA) Inc.

—The Fires of Merlin. 2007. (Lost Years of Merlin (Hardcover) Ser.). 261p. (J). (gr. 5-7). 10.99 (***978-0-399-25022-4(0)*** , Philomel) Penguin Group (USA) Inc.

—Fires of Merlin. (gr. 3-6). 2002. lib. bdg. 14.15 (978-0-613-89067-0(1)); 2000. lib. bdg. 15.30 (978-0-613-81176-7(3)) Tandem Library Bks.

—Lost Years of Merlin. (gr. 3-6). 2002. lib. bdg. 14.15 (978-0-613-83896-2(3)); 1999. lib. bdg. 15.30 (978-0-613-23013-1(2)) Tandem Library Bks.

—The Lost Years of Merlin. unabr. ed. 2004. (Lost Years of Merlin Ser.). 284p. (J). (gr. 5-9). pap. 46.00 incl. audio (978-0-8072-8766-8(0) , YA261SP, Listening Library) Random Hse. Audio Publishing Group.

—Seven Songs of Merlin. 2002. (gr. 7-12). lib. bdg. 14.15 (978-0-613-81177-4(1)); 2000. (978-0-606-17833-4(3)); 2000. (gr. 5-8). lib. bdg. 15.30 (978-0-613-28637-4(5)) Tandem Library Bks.

—Shadows on the Stars. (Great Tree of Avalon Trilogy: Bk. 2). 2006. 384p. (gr. 12). mass mkt. 7.99 (978-0-441-01447-7(X) , Ace Bks.); 2005. (Illus.). 432p. (YA). (gr. 5 up). 19.99 (978-0-399-23764-5(X) , Philomel) Penguin Group (USA) Inc.

Baum, L. Frank. Dorothy & the Wizard in Oz. 2006. pap. 26.99 (***978-1-4219-7695-2(1))*** IndyPublish.com.

—Dorothy & the Wizard of Oz. 2004. (Twelve-Point Ser.). lib. bdg. 24.00 (978-1-58287-273-5(2)); lib. bdg. 25.00 (978-1-58287-769-3(6)) North Bks.

—The Wizard of Oz. 2004. reprint ed. pap. 19.95 (978-1-4191-8832-9(1)) Kessinger Publishing, LLC.

—The Wonderful Wizard of Oz. Hildebrandt, Greg, illus. 2003. 64p. (J). 9.98 (978-0-7624-1628-8(9) , Courage Bks.) Running Pr. Bk. Pubs.

—The Wonderful Wizard of Oz. Sabuda, Robert, illus. 2000. (Classic Collectible Pop-Up Ser.). 16p. (J). (ps-3). pap. 26.99 (978-0-689-81751-9(7) , Little Simon) Simon & Schuster Children's Publishing.

—The Wonderful Wizard of Oz. Foreman, Michael, illus. 2005. 176p. (J). (gr. 2-7). 12.95 (978-1-4027-2535-7(3)) Sterling Publishing Co., Inc.

—Wonderful Wizard of Oz: A Classic Story about Cooperation. 2003. (Illus.). 32p. per. 3.95 (978-0-9747133-5-9(X) , Values to Live By Classic Stories) Thomas, Frederic Inc.

Baum, L. Frank & Dickins, Rosie. Wizard of Oz. 2007. 64p. (J). 8.99 (978-0-7945-1457-0(X) , Usborne) EDC Publishing.

Bell, Hilari. The Wizard Test. 176p. (J). 2006. pap. 5.99 (978-0-06-059942-3(1)); 2005. (gr. 5 up). 15.99 (978-0-06-059940-9(5)); 2005. (gr. 5 up). lib. bdg. 16.89 (978-0-06-059941-6(3)) HarperCollins Pubs.

Benjamin, A. H. Shamwood. 2006. 140p. pap. 19.95 (978-1-4137-9193-8(X)) PublishAmerica, Inc.

Bennett, David. Witch & Wizard Stories. Thomas, Jacqui, illus. 2004. 158p. (J). (ps-ps). per. 12.60 (978-0-606-33268-2(5)) Tandem Library Bks.

Bergsma, Jody Lynn. The Little Wizard. Bergsma, Jody Lynn, illus. l.t. ed. 2000. (Illus.). 32p. (J). (ps-7). 15.95 (978-0-935699-19-7(8)) Illumination Arts Publishing Co., Inc.

Bernasconi, Pablo. The Wizard, the Ugly, & the Book of Shame. Bernasconi, Pablo, illus. 2005. (Illus.). 32p. (J). (ps-3). 16.95 (978-1-58234-673-1(9)) Bloomsbury Publishing.

Birney, Betty G. The Princess & the Peabodys. 2007. 256p. (J). lib. bdg. 16.89 (***978-0-06-084721-0(2));*** (gr. 5 up). 15.99 (***978-0-06-084720-3(4))*** HarperCollins Pubs.

Bova, Louise. School Crests. 2000. 144p. (J). pap. 8.99 (978-0-439-20128-5(4)) Scholastic, Inc.

Brittain. The Wizards & the Monster. Date not set. 96p. (J). (gr. 2-5). pap. 4.25 (978-0-06-442003-7(5)) HarperCollins Pubs.

Carmody, Isobelle. Night Gate. 2006. 272p. (gr. 4-7). 6.50 (978-0-375-83017-4(0) , Yearling) Random Hse. Children's Bks.

Chambless, M. The Ring of Starling. 2005. 276p. pap. 21.95 (978-1-4137-7821-2(6)) PublishAmerica, Inc.

Charles, Veronika Martenova. Stretch, Swallow & Stare. Charles, Veronika Martenova, illus. l.t. ed. 1999. (Illus.). 31p. (J). (ps-3). 16.95 (978-0-7737-3098-4(2)) Stoddart Kids CAN. *Dist:* Fitzhenry & Whiteside, Ltd.

Chima, Cinda Williams. The Warrior Heir. 2006. 432p. (gr. 7-17). 16.99 (978-0-7868-3916-2(3)) Hyperion Bks. for Children.

—The Warrior Heir. 2007. 448p. (gr. 7-17). pap. 8.99 (***978-0-7868-3917-9(1))*** Hyperion Pr.

Clish, Marian L. You Choose the Way: A Book That Reads Like a Game - Mazash the Wizard. Anderson, Jan, illus. unabr. ed. 1999. (J). (gr. k-5). pap. 14.95 incl. audio compact disk (978-1-928632-09-2(2)) Writers Marketplace:Consulting, Critiquing & Publishing.

—You Choose the Way: A Book That Reads Like a Game: Mazash the Wizard. 1999. (J). (gr. 2-7). 22.95 incl. cd-rom (978-1-928632-25-2(4)) Writers Marketplace:Consulting, Critiquing & Publishing.

—You Choose the Way: A Book That Reads Like a Game: Mazash the Wizard. Anderson, Jan, illus. unabr. ed. 1999. (J). (gr. 2-7). 18.95 incl. audio (978-1-928632-24-5(6)); (gr. 3-5). 15.95 (978-1-928632-23-8(8)) Writers Marketplace:Consulting, Critiquing & Publishing.

Cole, Bob. Power Reading: Chapter Books/Wizard of OZ. Sirrell, Terri, illus. 2004. 94p. (J). (gr. 3-4). vinyl bd. 39.95 (978-1-883186-64-7(1) , PPCL1) National Reading Styles Institute, Inc.

—Power Reading: Comic Book/Wizard of OZ. Sirrell, Terri, illus. 2005. 60p. (J). (gr. 3-4). vinyl bd. 39.95 (978-1-883186-80-7(3) , PPCLC1) National Reading Styles Institute, Inc.

Cormier, Shawn P. Nomadin. 2003. 296p. (YA). per. 12.95 (978-0-9740151-0-1(5)) Pine View Pr.

Cort, Ben. Little Wizard. 2007. (Illus.). 12p. (J). 8.99 (***978-1-4052-0746-1(9))*** Egmont Bks., Ltd. GBR. *Dist:* Independent Pubs. Group.

Curtis, Jillian M. The Little Prince & His Magic Wand. 2005. (Illus.). 28p. (J). 24.95 (978-1-59858-015-0(9)); pap. 16.95 (978-1-59858-010-5(8)) Dog Ear Publishing, LLC.

de Brunhoff, Laurent. Babar & the Succotash Bird. 2000. (Babar Ser.). (Illus.). 38p. (J). (ps-3). 16.95 (978-0-8109-5700-8(0)) Abrams, Harry N. , Inc.

Dokey, Cameron. Golden: A Retelling of Rapunzel. 2007. (Once upon a Time Ser.). 192p. (YA). pap. 5.99 (***978-1-4169-3926-9(1)*** , Simon Pulse) Simon & Schuster Children's Publishing.

Downer, Ann. The Dragon of Never-Was. Rayyan, Omar, illus. 2006. 320p. (J). (gr. 3-6). 16.95 (978-0-689-85571-9(0) , Atheneum) Simon & Schuster Children's Publishing.

—Hatching Magic. 256p. (J). 2005. pap. 2.99 (978-1-4169-0535-6(9) , Aladdin); 2003. (Illus.). (gr. 3-7). 17.95 (978-0-689-83400-4(4) , Atheneum) Simon & Schuster Children's Publishing.

Dozier, Kim. The Backwards Wizard. Dozier, Ashlyn McCauley & Dozier, Makenna Joy, illus. l.t. ed. 2005. (ENG.). 28p. (J). 10.00 (978-0-9745839-4-5(4) , Fun to Read Bks. with Royally Good Morals) MKADesigns.

Duane, Diane. Deep Wizardry. (Young Wizards Ser.: Bk. 2). 384p. (YA). 2003. (Illus.). pap. 6.95 (978-0-15-204942-3(8)); 2001. (gr. 5 up). pap. 6.95 (978-0-15-216257-3(7)) Harcourt Children's Bks. (Magic Carpet Bks.).

—Deep Wizardry. 2003. (gr. 3-6). lib. bdg. 15.25 (978-0-613-71628-4(0)); 2001. (gr. 5-8). lib. bdg. 15.25 (978-0-613-36059-3(1)) Tandem Library Bks.

—High Wizardry. (Young Wizards Ser.: Bk. 3). (YA). 2003. 372p. (ps-7). pap. 6.95 (978-0-15-204941-6(X)); 2001. 368p. (gr. 5 up). pap. 6.95 (978-0-15-216244-3(5)) Harcourt Children's Bks. (Magic Carpet Bks.).

—High Wizardry. 2000. (YA). (gr. 5 up). pap. 58.25 incl. audio (978-0-7887-3799-2(6) , 41043) Recorded Bks., LLC.

—High Wizardry. 2003. (gr. 3-6). lib. bdg. 15.25 (978-0-613-71634-5(5)); 2001. (gr. 5-8). lib. bdg. 15.25 (978-0-613-36065-4(6)) Tandem Library Bks.

—So You Want to Be a Wizard. (Young Wizards Ser.). (YA). 2003. 408p. pap. 6.95 (978-0-15-204940-9(1) , Magic Carpet Bks.); 2001. 400p. (gr. 5 up). pap. 6.95 (978-0-15-216250-4(X) , Magic Carpet Bks.); 20th anniv. ed. 2003. (Illus.). 336p. 16.95 (978-0-15-204738-2(7)) Harcourt Children's Bks.

—So You Want to Be a Wizard. 2003. (gr. 3-6). lib. bdg. 15.25 (978-0-613-71630-7(2)); 2001. (gr. 5-8). lib. bdg. 15.25 (978-0-613-36077-7(X)) Tandem Library Bks.

—A Wizard Abroad. (Young Wizards Ser.: Bk. 4). 2005. (Illus.). 372p. (ps-17). pap. 6.95 (978-0-15-205503-5(7)); 2001. 368p. (YA). (gr. 5 up). pap. 6.95 (978-0-15-216238-2(0)) Harcourt Children's Bks. (Magic Carpet Bks.).

—A Wizard Abroad. 2001. (gr. 5-8). lib. bdg. 14.75 (978-0-613-36083-8(4)) Tandem Library Bks.

—A Wizard Alone. (Young Wizards Ser.: Bk. 6). 2005. (Illus.). 348p. (ps-17). pap. 6.95 (978-0-15-205509-7(6) , Magic Carpet Bks.); 2003. 352p. (YA). pap. 6.95 (978-0-15-204911-9(8) , Magic Carpet Bks.); 2002. (Illus.). 336p. (YA). (gr. 7 up). 17.00 (978-0-15-204562-3(7)) Harcourt Children's Bks.

—Wizards at War. 2005. (Young Wizards Ser.: Bk. 8). (Illus.). 560p. (YA). (gr. 7-12). 17.00 (978-0-15-204772-6(7)) Harcourt Children's Bks.

—Wizards at War: The Eighth Book in the Young Wizards Series. 2007. (Young Wizards Ser.). (Illus.). 560p. (YA). pap. 6.95 (978-0-15-205223-2(2) , Magic Carpet Bks.) Harcourt Children's Bks.

—The Wizard's Dilemma. (Young Wizards Ser.: Bk. 5). 432p. 2005. (Illus.). (J). (ps-17). pap. 6.95 (978-0-15-205491-5(X)); 2002. (YA). (gr. 7 up). pap. 6.95 (978-0-15-202460-4(3)) Harcourt Children's Bks. (Magic Carpet Bks.).

—The Wizard's Dilemma. 2002. (gr. 5-8). lib. bdg. 15.25 (978-0-613-55225-7(3)) Tandem Library Bks.

—Wizard's Holiday. (Young Wizards Ser.: Bk. 7). (YA). 2005. 448p. (gr. 8-12). pap. 6.95 (978-0-15-205207-2(0), Magic Carpet Bks.); 2003. 432p. 17.00 (978-0-15-204771-9(9)) Harcourt Children's Bks.

Eubank, Patti Reeder, illus. The Princess & the Snarls. 2006. 32p. (J). (ps). 16.95 (978-0-8249-5536-6(6), Ideals Children's Bks.) Ideals Pubns.

Fienberg, Anna. The Witch in the Lake: A Novel. 2002. 220p. (J). (gr. 5-9). pap. 7.95 (978-1-55037-722-4(1)); lib. bdg. 18.95 (978-1-55037-723-1(X)) Annick Pr., Ltd. CAN. *Dist:* Firefly Bks., Ltd.

Fox, Mem. The Magic Hat. Tusa, Tricia, illus. 2002. 32p. (J). (ps-3). 16.00 (978-0-15-201025-6(4)) Harcourt Children's Bks.

Gallego García, Laura & Peden, Margaret Sayers. The Valley of the Wolves. 2006. 247p. (J). pap. (978-0-439-58554-5(6), Levine, Arthur A. Bks.) Scholastic, Inc.

Garcia, Laura Gallego. The Valley of the Wolves. 2006. 336p. (J). (gr. 4-7). pap. 16.99 (978-0-439-58553-8(8), Levine, Arthur A. Bks.) Scholastic, Inc.

Garner, Alan. The Moon of Gomrath: A Tale of Alderley. Call, Greg, illus. 2006. 216p. (J). pap. 6.95 (978-0-15-205630-8(0), Odyssey Classics) Harcourt Children's Bks.

Gerfin, Ann & Farmer, Katy Jo. Wizard's Warning/Power of the Shaman: Twin Spins #4. 2004. (Twin Spins Ser.: 4). 104p. (YA). pap. 9.95 (978-0-7599-1003-4(0)) Hard Shell Word Factory.

Goodyear-Brown, Paris. Gabby the Gecko. 2003. per. (978-1-932203-54-7(0)) Sundog, Ltd.

Hague, Michael, illus. The Book of Wizards. 2008. 144p. (J). 19.99 (*978-0-688-14005-2(X)) HarperCollins Pubs.

Haining, Peter, ed. Magician's Circle: More Spellbinding Stories of Wizards & Wizardry. 2004. (Illus.). 256p. (J). 19.95 (978-0-285-63681-1(2)) Souvenir Pr. Ltd. GBR. *Dist:* Independent Pubs. Group.

Haining, Peter & Strings Magazine Staff. The Wizard's Den: Spellbinding Stories of Magic & Magicians. 2003. (Illus.). 320p. (J). 22.95 (978-0-285-63628-6(6)) Souvenir Pr. Ltd. GBR. *Dist:* Independent Pubs. Group.

Harry Potter & the Chamber of Secrets. 2002. (Harry Potter Ser.). (Illus.). (J). 15.23 (978-0-7587-4426-5(9)) Book Wholesalers, Inc.

Harry Potter & the Sorcerer's Stone. 2002. (Harry Potter Ser.). (Illus.). (J). 15.23 (978-0-7587-0016-2(4)) Book Wholesalers, Inc.

Ibbotson, Eva. El Secreto Del Andén 13. 3rd ed. 2003. (SPA., Illus.). 190p. (978-84-7888-764-4(4), 1952) Emece Editores.

—Which Witch? 2002. (Illus.). 13.19 (978-1-4046-1490-1(7)) Book Wholesalers, Inc.

—Which Witch? Large, Annabel, illus. 2000. 256p. (YA). (gr. 3-7). pap. 5.99 (978-0-14-130427-4(8), Puffin); 1999. 224p. (J). (gr. 4-7). 15.99 (978-0-525-46164-7(7), Dutton Juvenile) Penguin Group (USA) Inc.

—Which Witch? 2000. (J). (978-0-606-19882-0(2)); (gr. 3-6). lib. bdg. 14.15 (978-0-613-31926-3(5)) Tandem Library Bks.

iBooks Staff. The Wonderful Wizard of Oz: Centennial Edition. 100th ed. 2001. (Illus.). 320p. pap. 14.95 (978-0-7434-1298-8(2)) ibooks, Inc.

Jones, Frewin. The Sorcerer King. 2008. (Faerie Path Ser.: Bk. 3). 336p. (J). 16.99 (*978-0-06-087108-6(3)); lib. bdg. 17.89 (*978-0-06-087109-3(1)) HarperCollins Pubs. (Eos).

Jones, Marcia Thornton & Dadey, Debbie. Spooky Spells. 1999. (Bailey City Monsters Ser.: No. 6). (Illus.). 80p. (J). (gr. 2-4). pap. 3.99 (978-0-439-05871-1(6)) Scholastic, Inc.

—Spooky Spells. 1999. (Bailey City Monsters Ser.: No. 6). (J). (gr. 2-4). (978-0-606-16656-0(4)) Tandem Library Bks.

King, J. R. Arianna Kelt & the Wizards of Skyhall. 2006. (Illus.). (J). 200p. pap. 11.95 (978-1-57545-115-2(8)); 148p. per. 18.95 (978-1-57545-106-0(9), Reagent Pr. Echo) Reagent Pr.

Klett, David E. Rachel & the Wizard of Lake Lure: The Lake Lure Chronicles - Book 2. 2006. (J). lib. bdg. 17.95 (*978-0-9779325-1-1(6)) Five Oaks Pr.

Koller, Jackie French. A Wizard Named Nell. Guay, Rebecca, illus. 2003. (Keepers Ser.: Bk. 1). 208p. pap. 11.95 (978-0-689-85591-7(5), Aladdin) Simon & Schuster Children's Publishing.

—The Wizard's Apprentice. Guay, Rebecca, illus. 2003. 192p. (J). pap. 4.99 (978-0-689-85592-4(3), Aladdin) Simon & Schuster Children's Publishing.

—The Wizard's Scepter. 2004. (Keepers Ser.: No. 3). (Illus.). 176p. (J). pap. 4.99 (978-0-689-85593-1(1), Aladdin) Simon & Schuster Children's Publishing.

Lee, Brian. Bouncey the Elf & Friends - Bedtime St. 2005. (ENG., Illus.). 53p. pap. (*978-0-7552-1023-7(9)) Authors OnLine, Ltd.

Levine, Gail Carson. The Two Princesses of Bamarre. (J). 2003. 256p. (gr. 5 up). pap. 6.99 (978-0-06-440966-7(X)); 2001. 256p. (gr. 5 up). 17.99 (978-0-06-029315-4(2)); 2001. 256p. (gr. 5 up). lib. bdg. 17.89 (978-0-06-029316-1(0)); 2004. (Illus.). 304p. (gr. 7 up). reprint ed. pap. 6.99 (978-0-06-057580-9(8)) HarperCollins Pubs.

—The Two Princesses of Bamarre. 2003. (Illus.). (gr. 7-12). lib. bdg. 14.15 (978-0-613-67233-7(X)) Tandem Library Bks.

Levinson, Marilyn. Rufus & Magic Run Amok. 112p. 2005. (YA). pap. 5.95 (978-0-7614-5176-1(5)); 2001. (Illus.). (J). (gr. 2-6). 14.25 (978-0-7614-5102-0(1), Cavendish Children's Bks.) Cavendish, Marshall Corp.

Lubar, David. Wizards of the Game. 2004. 176p. (J). (gr. 5). pap. 5.99 (978-0-14-240215-3(X), Puffin) Penguin Group (USA) Inc.

Luberto, Bradley. Clide & Druce: A Repulsive Tale of Trolls & Tax Money. 2006. (ENG.). 48p. per. 12.95 (*978-1-4241-5012-0(4)) PublishAmerica, Inc.

Martin, Dick. The Ozmapolitan of Oz. 2006. (J). 24.95 (978-1-930764-11-8(1)) International Wizard of Oz Club, The.

Mayer, Mercer. Wizard Comes to Town. 2002. (gr. k-3). lib. bdg. 14.10 (978-0-613-86842-6(0)) Tandem Library Bks.

McAllister, Angela. Digory & the Lost King. Beck, Ian, illus. 2007. 128p. (J). (gr. 3-5). 14.95 (*978-1-59990-088-9(2)); pap. 5.95 (*978-1-59990-089-6(0)) Bloomsbury Publishing.

McCullough, Karen. Wizard's Bridge. 2004. pap. (978-0-9759653-0-6(1)) ImaJinn Bks.

McGraw, Eloise Jarvis & McGraw, Lauren Lynn. The Forbidden Fountain of Oz. 2006. (J). 24.95 (978-1-930764-12-5(X)) International Wizard of Oz Club, The.

McKillip, Patricia A. The Forgotten Beasts of Eld. 2006. 352p. (YA). pap. 6.95 (978-0-15-205536-3(3), Magic Carpet Bks.) Harcourt Children's Bks.

McMullan, Kate. Danger! Wizard at Work. Basso, Bill, illus. 2004. (Dragon Slayers' Academy Ser.: No. 11). 112p. (J). (gr. 2-5). pap. 4.99 (978-0-448-43529-9(2), Grosset & Dunlap) Penguin Group (USA) Inc.

—Pig Latin—Not Just for Pigs! 2006. (Dragon Slayers' Academy Ser.: No. 14). (J). (gr. 1-6). 24.21 (978-1-59961-127-3(9)) Spotlight.

McMylor, Phil. Trouble Brewing. Ward, Matt, illus. 2002. (Wizard! Bks.). 16p. (J). (ps-2). bds. 4.95 (978-0-7641-5566-6(0)) Barron's Educational Series, Inc.

—Twinkle's Treat. Ward, Matt, illus. 2002. (Wizard! Bks.). 16p. (J). (ps-2). bds. 4.95 (978-0-7641-5567-3(9)) Barron's Educational Series, Inc.

Mitchell, N. J. W. Saraly & the Dragons. 2003. 124p. pap. 10.95 (978-0-595-30264-2(5)) iUniverse, Inc.

Molina, Alicia. No Me lo Vas a Creer. Castillon, Jose Luis, illus. 2002. (SPA.). 42p. (J). pap. 3.99 (978-968-16-6671-2(2)) Fondo de Cultura Economica USA.

Nagy, Gloria & Chwast, Seymour. The Wizard Who Wanted to Be Santa. 2000. (Illus.). (J). (ps-3). 16.95 (978-0-9679436-0-2(4)) Sheer Bliss Communications, LLC.

Nimmo, Jenny. Charlie Bone & the Hidden King. 2006. (Children of the Red King Ser.: Bk. 5). xx, 441p. (J). (*978-1-4156-7832-9(4), Orchard Bks.) Scholastic, Inc.

O'Brien, John. Poof! 2005. (Illus.). 32p. (J). (ps-ps). reprint ed. pap. 8.95 (978-1-59078-374-0(3)) Boyds Mills Pr.

Ogilvy, Ian. Measle & the Dragodon. 2006. 352p. (J). pap. 6.99 (978-0-06-058690-4(7), Harper Trophy) HarperCollins Pubs.

—Measle & the Mallockee. 2006. 384p. (J). 15.99 (978-0-06-058691-1(5)) HarperCollins Pubs.

—Measle & the Wrathmonk. 2004. 224p. (J). (gr. 4-6). 15.99 (978-0-06-058685-0(0)); lib. bdg. 16.89 (978-0-06-058686-7(9)) HarperCollins Pubs.

Orme, David. Boffin Boy & the Rock Men. 2007. (Boffin Boy Ser.). (Illus.). 36p. pap. 7.95 (*978-1-84167-624-1(1)) Ransom Publishing Ltd. GBR. *Dist:* International Publishers Marketing.

Papademetriou, Lisa. The Wizard, the Witch, & Two Girls from Jersey. 2006. 240p. (J). (gr. 7-12). pap. 8.99 (978-1-59514-074-6(3), Razorbill) Penguin Group (USA) Inc.

Parsons, Colin. Wizards' Kingdom. 2005. (ENG., Illus.). 117p. pap. (*978-1-84401-522-1(X)) Athena Pr.

Plummer, Rachel. Mystery of the Wizard's Tomb. 2006. (Knights of the Silver Dragon Ser.: Bk. 11). (Illus.). 192p. (J). pap. 5.99 (978-0-7869-3990-9(7), Mirrorstone) Wizards of the Coast.

Posner-Sanchez, Andrea & Man-Kong, Mary. Barbie & the Magic of Pegasus: A Storybook. 2005. (Random House Pictureback Book Ser.). (Illus.). (J). (*978-1-4156-2366-4(X)) Random Hse. Children's Bks.

Pratchett, Terry. Equal Rites. 2000. (gr. 7-12). lib. bdg. 15.30 (978-0-613-27808-9(9)) Tandem Library Bks.

—Hogfather. 2000. (gr. 5-8). lib. bdg. 15.30 (978-0-613-57222-4(X)) Tandem Library Bks.

Prineas, Sarah. Stolen. 2008. (Magic Thief Ser.). 416p. (J). 16.99 (*978-0-06-137587-3(X)) HarperCollins Pubs.

Pritchard, G. Rosemary Sage & the Man in Black. 2005. 78p. pap. 14.95 (978-1-4137-9809-8(8)) PublishAmerica, Inc.

Pullen, G. L. Under Viking Hollows: And the Twelve Passages to Valhalla. 2004. 74p. pap. 14.95 (978-1-4137-1569-9(9)) PublishAmerica, Inc.

Rawson, C. Wizards. 2004. (Young Reading Ser.). (Illus.). 48p. (J). (gr. 2 up). pap. 5.95 (978-0-7945-0328-4(4), Usborne) EDC Publishing.

Rawson, C. & Harvey, G. Wizards. (Young Reading Ser.: Vol. 1). 48p. (J). (gr. 2 up). lib. bdg. 13.95 (978-1-58086-789-4(8), Usborne) EDC Publishing.

Rawson, Christopher. Wizards. 2002. (gr. k-3). lib. bdg. 14.10 (978-0-613-65138-7(3)) Tandem Library Bks.

Robertson, M. P. The Dragon Snatcher. 2005. (Illus.). 32p. (J). (ps-3). 16.99 (978-0-8037-3103-5(5), Dial) Penguin Group (USA) Inc.

Robertson, Mark. Dragon Snatcher. 2005. (Illus.). 32p. (J). (*978-1-84507-398-5(3)) Lincoln, Frances Ltd.

Rodgers, Frank. Little T & Lizard the Wizard. 2007. (Read-It! Chapter Books). (J). 21.26 (978-1-4048-2725-7(0)) Picture Window Bks.

Rodriguez, AJ. Theodore Da Baer. 2004. 113p. pap. 16.95 (978-1-4137-5247-2(0)) PublishAmerica, Inc.

—Theodore Da Baer Ii: A New Beginning. 2006. 207p. pap. 19.95 (978-1-4241-1125-1(0)) PublishAmerica, Inc.

Rowling, J. K. Harri Potter Maen yr Athronydd. 2003. (WEL.). 300p. (J). 21.95 (978-1-58234-827-8(8), Bloomsbury Children) Bloomsbury Publishing.

—Harrius Potter et Camera Secretorum. Needham, Peter, tr. from ENG. 2006. Orig. Title: Harry Potter & the Chamber of Secrets. (LAT., Illus.). 300p. (J). 23.95 (978-1-59990-067-4(X), Bloomsbury Children) Bloomsbury Publishing.

—Harrius Potter et Philosophi Lapis. Needham, Peter, tr. from ENG. 2003. (Harry Potter Ser.: Year 1). Orig. Title: Harry Potter & the Philosopher's Stone. (LAT., Illus.). 300p. (J). 23.95 (978-1-58234-825-4(1), Bloomsbury Children) Bloomsbury Publishing.

—Harry Potter & the Chamber of Secrets. braille ed. 1999. (Harry Potter Ser.: Year 2). 520p. (YA). (gr. 3 up). pap. 17.99 (978-0-939173-35-8(2)) National Braille Pr.

—Harry Potter & the Chamber of Secrets. 2003. 203p. 23.95 (978-7-02-003344-7(X), HAP02) People's Literature Publishing Hse. CHN. *Dist:* China Bks. & Periodicals, Inc.

—Harry Potter & the Chamber of Secrets. unabr. ed. 2004. (Harry Potter Ser.: Year 2). 352p. (J). (gr. 3 up). pap. 46.00 incl. audio (978-0-8072-8207-6(3), S YA 137 SP, Listening Library) Random Hse. Audio Publishing Group.

—Harry Potter & the Chamber of Secrets. (RUS., Illus.). 28.95 (978-5-8451-0947-7(7)) Rosmen-Izdat RUS. *Dist:* Distribooks, Inc.

—Harry Potter & the Chamber of Secrets. 2003. (Harry Potter Ser.: Year 2). 352p. (J). 24.95 (978-0-439-55489-3(6), Levine, Arthur A. Bks.) Scholastic, Inc.

—Harry Potter & the Chamber of Secrets. GrandPré, Mary, illus. (Harry Potter Ser.: Year 2). (J). 2002. 448p. mass mkt. 6.99 (978-0-439-42010-5(5), Levine, Arthur A. Bks.); 2000. 352p. (gr. 3 up). mass mkt. 8.99 (978-0-439-06487-3(2)); 1999. 352p. (gr. 3 up). 22.99 (978-0-439-06486-6(4), Levine, Arthur A. Bks.) Scholastic, Inc.

—Harry Potter & the Chamber of Secrets. l.t. ed. 2003. 464p. 13.95 (978-1-59413-001-4(9)) Thorndike Pr.

—Harry Potter & the Chamber of Secrets. GrandPré, Mary, illus. l.t. ed. 2000. (Harry Potter Ser.: Year 2). 464p. (gr. 3 up). 24.95 (978-0-7862-2273-5(5), Large Print Pr.) Thorndike Pr.

—Harry Potter & the Deathly Hallows. braille ed. 2007. (Harry Potter Ser.: Year 7). 34.99 (*978-0-939173-57-0(3)) National Braille Pr.

—Harry Potter & the Deathly Hallows. GrandPré, Mary, illus. 2007. (Harry Potter Ser.: Year 7). 784p. (J). (gr. 4-7). 34.99 (*978-0-545-01022-1(5)); 784p. (YA). (gr. 6 up). 39.99 (*978-0-545-02936-0(8)); 816p. (J). 65.00 (*978-0-545-02937-7(6)) Scholastic, Inc. (Levine, Arthur A. Bks.).

—Harry Potter & the Deathly Hallows. l.t. ed. 2007. (Harry Potter Ser.: Year 7). (YA). 34.95 (*978-0-7862-9665-1(8)) Thorndike Pr.

—Harry Potter & the Goblet of Fire. braille ed. 2000. (Harry Potter Ser.: Year 4). 650p. (YA). (gr. 3 up). pap. 25.95 (978-0-939173-37-2(9)) National Braille Pr.

—Harry Potter & the Goblet of Fire. 2003. (Harry Potter Ser.: Year 4). 752p. (J). 30.95 (978-0-439-55490-9(X), Levine, Arthur A. Bks.) Scholastic, Inc.

—Harry Potter & the Goblet of Fire. GrandPré, Mary, illus. (Harry Potter Ser.: Year 4). 752p. (J). (gr. 3 up). 2002. mass mkt. 9.99 (978-0-439-13960-1(0)); 2000. 29.99 (978-0-439-13959-5(7)) Scholastic, Inc. (Levine, Arthur A. Bks.).

—Harry Potter & the Goblet of Fire. 2002. (gr. 3-6). lib. bdg. 17.60 (978-0-613-49674-2(4)) Tandem Library Bks.

—Harry Potter & the Goblet of Fire. l.t. ed. 2003. 936p. 14.95 (978-1-59413-003-8(5)) Thorndike Pr.

—Harry Potter & the Goblet of Fire. GrandPré, Mary, illus. l.t. ed. 2000. (Harry Potter Ser.: Year 4). 936p. (gr. 3 up). 25.95 (978-0-7862-2927-7(6), Large Print Pr.) Thorndike Pr.

—Harry Potter & the Half-Blood Prince, 9 vols. braille ed. 2005. (Harry Potter Ser.: 6). (YA). 29.99 (978-0-939173-39-6(5), HALF) National Braille Pr.

—Harry Potter & the Half-Blood Prince. 2003. (Harry Potter Ser.). 496p. 24.95 (*978-7-02-005323-0(8), HAP06) People's Literature Publishing Hse. CHN. *Dist:* China Bks. & Periodicals, Inc.

—Harry Potter & the Half-Blood Prince. GrandPré, Mary, illus. (J). 2005. (Harry Potter Ser.: Year 6). 672p. 34.99 (978-0-439-78677-5(0)); 2005. (Harry Potter Ser.: Year 6). 672p. 29.99 (978-0-439-78454-2(9)); 2005. (Harry Potter Ser.: Year 6). 704p. 60.00 (978-0-439-79132-8(4)); 2006. 672p. reprint ed. pap. 9.99 (978-0-439-78596-9(0)) Scholastic, Inc. (Levine, Arthur A. Bks.).

—Harry Potter & the Half-Blood Prince. 832p. 2007. pap. 14.95 (*978-1-59413-221-6(6)); 2005. (Harry Potter Ser.: Year 6). 29.95 (978-0-7862-7745-2(9)) Thorndike Pr. (Large Print Pr.).

—Harry Potter & the Order of the Phoenix, 13 vols. braille ed. 2003. (Harry Potter Ser.: Year 5). (YA). 29.99 (978-0-939173-38-9(7)) National Braille Pr.

—Harry Potter & the Order of the Phoenix. 2003. (Harry Potter Ser.). 575p. 25.95 (978-7-02-004327-9(5), HAP05) People's Literature Publishing Hse. CHN. *Dist:* China Bks. & Periodicals, Inc.

—Harry Potter & the Order of the Phoenix. GrandPré, Mary, illus. 2003. (Harry Potter Ser.: Year 5). (J). (gr. 3-6). 870p. 29.99 (978-0-439-35806-4(X)); 896p. 34.99 (978-0-439-56761-9(0)); 896p. 60.00 (978-0-439-56762-6(9)) Scholastic, Inc.

—Harry Potter & the Order of the Phoenix. l.t. ed. 2003. (Harry Potter Ser.: Year 5). 1093p. 29.95 (978-0-7862-5778-2(4), Large Print Pr.) Thorndike Pr.

—Harry Potter & the Order of the Phoenix. GrandPré, Mary, illus. l.t. ed. 2003. 1232p. (J). (gr. 4-7). pap. 14.95 (978-1-59413-112-7(0), Large Print Pr.) Thorndike Pr.

—Harry Potter & the Prisoner of Azkaban. 2002. (Harry Potter Ser.). (Illus.). (YA). 16.26 (978-0-7587-5662-6(3)) Book Wholesalers, Inc.

—Harry Potter & the Prisoner of Azkaban. braille ed. 1999. (Harry Potter Ser.: Year 3). (YA). (gr. 3 up). pap. 19.95 (978-0-939173-36-5(0)) National Braille Pr.

—Harry Potter & the Prisoner of Azkaban. 2000. (J). tchr. ed. 9.95 (978-1-58130-656-9(3)); stu. ed. 11.95 (978-1-58130-657-6(1)) Novel Units, Inc.

—Harry Potter & the Prisoner of Azkaban. 2004. (Harry Potter Ser.: Year 3). 560p. mass mkt. 7.99 (978-0-439-65548-4(X), Scholastic Paperbacks) Scholastic, Inc.

—Harry Potter & the Prisoner of Azkaban. GrandPré, Mary, illus. (Harry Potter Ser.: Year 3). 448p. (gr. 3 up). 2001. (YA). mass mkt. 8.99 (978-0-439-13636-5(9), Levine, Arthur A. Bks.); 1999. (J). 22.99 (978-0-439-13635-8(0)) Scholastic, Inc.

—Harry Potter & the Prisoner of Azkaban. 2001. (gr. 3-6). lib. bdg. 16.45 (978-0-613-37106-3(2)) Tandem Library Bks.

—Harry Potter & the Prisoner of Azkaban. l.t. ed. 2003. 592p. 13.95 (978-1-59413-002-1(7)) Thorndike Pr.

—Harry Potter & the Prisoner of Azkaban. GrandPré, Mary, illus. l.t. ed. 2000. (Harry Potter Ser.: Year 3). 592p. (gr. 3 up). 24.95 (978-0-7862-2274-2(3), Large Print Pr.) Thorndike Pr.

—Harry Potter & the Sorcerer's Stone. unabr. ed. (Harry Potter Ser.: Year 1). 320p. (gr. 3 up). (YA). pap. 62.00 incl. audio (978-0-8072-1547-0(3)); 2004. (J). pap. 46.00 incl. audio (978-0-8072-8119-2(0), S YA 108 SP) Random Hse. Audio Publishing Group. (Listening Library).

—Harry Potter & the Sorcerer's Stone. GrandPré, Mary, illus. (Harry Potter Ser.: Year 1). (gr. 3 up). 2001. 400p. (J). mass mkt. 6.99 (978-0-439-36213-9(X)); 1999. 320p. (YA). mass mkt. 8.99 (978-0-590-35342-7(X)); 1998. 320p. (J). pap. 22.99 (978-0-590-35340-3(3), Levine, Arthur A. Bks.) Scholastic, Inc.

—Harry Potter & the Sorcerer's Stone. collector's ed. 2000. (Harry Potter Ser.: Year 1). 320p. (YA). (gr. 3 up). 75.00 (978-0-439-20352-4(X)) Scholastic, Inc.

—Harry Potter & the Sorcerer's Stone. l.t. ed. 2003. 423p. 13.95 (978-1-59413-000-7(0)) Thorndike Pr.

—Harry Potter & the Sorcerer's Stone. GrandPré, Mary, illus. l.t. ed. 1999. (Harry Potter Ser.: Year 1). 422p. (gr. 3 up). 24.95 (978-0-7862-2272-8(7), Large Print Pr.) Thorndike Pr.

—Harry Potter Boxed Set, Bks. 1-7. 2007. (Harry Potter Ser.: Years 1-7). (J). 195.00 (*978-0-545-04425-7(1), Levine, Arthur A. Bks.) Scholastic, Inc.

—Harry Potter Boxed Set: Harry Potter & the Sorcerer's Stone; Harry Potter & the Chamber of Secrets; Harry Potter & the Prisoner of Azkaban, 3 vols. GrandPré, Mary, illus. (Harry Potter Ser.: Years 1-3). (YA). 2002. pap. 21.97 (978-0-439-32466-3(1)); 1999. (J). pap. 55.85 (978-0-439-13316-6(5)) Scholastic, Inc. (Levine, Arthur A. Bks.).

—Harry Potter Boxed Set: Harry Potter & the Sorcerer's Stone; Harry Potter & the Chamber of Secrets; Harry Potter & the Prisoner of Azkaban; Harry Potter & the Goblet of Fire, 4 vols. GrandPré, Mary, illus. 2000. (Harry Potter Ser.: Years 1-4). (YA). (gr. 3 up). 85.80 (978-0-641-06631-3(7), Levine, Arthur A. Bks.) Scholastic, Inc.

—Harry Potter Coffret: Harry Potter a l'Ecole des Sorciers; Harry Potter et la Chambre des Secrets; Harry Potter et le Prisonnier d'Azkaban. 1999. (Harry Potter Ser.: Years 1-3). Tr. of Harry Potter Boxed Set: Harry Potter & the Chamber of Secrets; Harry Potter & the Sorcerer's Stone; Harry Potter & the Prisoner of Azkaban. (FRE.). (YA). (gr. 3 up). pap. 43.95 (978-2-07-052929-2(0)) Gallimard, Editions FRA. *Dist:* Distribooks, Inc.

—Harry Potter Coffret: Harry Potter a l'Ecole des Sorciers; Harry Potter et la Chambre des Secrets; Harry Potter et le Prisonnier d'Azkaban; Harry Potter et la Coupe de Feu. 1999. (Harry Potter Ser.: Years 1-3). Tr. of Harry Potter Boxed Set: Harry Potter & the Chamber of Secrets; Harry Potter & the Sorcerer's Stone; Harry Potter & the Prisoner of Azkaban; Harry Potter et la COupe de Feu. (FRE.). 1400p. (YA). (gr. 3 up). pap. 34.95 (978-0-320-03843-3(2)) French & European Pubns., Inc.

—Harry Potter e a Camara Secreta. (POR.). pap. 28.95 (978-85-325-1166-9(X)) Rocco, Editora, Ltda BRA. *Dist:* Distribooks, Inc.

—Harry Potter e a Pedra Filosofal. (POR.). pap. 28.95 (978-85-325-1101-0(5)) Rocco, Editora, Ltda BRA. *Dist:* Distribooks, Inc.

—Harry Potter e a Prisioneiro de Azkaban. (POR.). pap. 29.95 (978-85-325-1206-2(2)) Rocco, Editora, Ltda BRA. *Dist:* Distribooks, Inc.

—Harry Potter e o Calice de Fogo. (POR.). pap. 38.95 (978-85-325-1252-9(6)) Rocco, Editora, Ltda BRA. *Dist:* Distribooks, Inc.

—Harry Potter et la Chambre des Secrets. 1999. (Harry Potter Ser.: Year 2). Tr. of Harry Potter & the Chamber of Secrets. (FRE.). (YA). (gr. 3 up). pap. 13.95 (978-0-320-03778-8(9)) French & European Pubns., Inc.

—Harry Potter et la Chambre des Secrets. 1999. (Harry Potter Ser.: Year 2). Tr. of Harry Potter & the Chamber of Secrets. (FRE., Illus.). 358p. (YA). (gr. 3 up). pap. 16.95 (978-2-07-052455-6(8)) Gallimard, Editions FRA. *Dist:* Distribooks, Inc.

—Harry Potter et la Coupe de Feu. 2001. (Harry Potter Ser.: Year 4). Tr. of Harry Potter & the Goblet of Fire. (FRE.). (YA). (gr. 3 up). pap. 34.95 (978-0-320-03932-4(3)) French & European Pubns., Inc.

—Harry Potter et la Coupe de Feu.Tr. of Harry Potter & the Goblet of Fire. (FRE., Illus.). 766p. pap. 19.95 (978-2-07-054351-9(X)) Gallimard, Editions FRA. *Dist:* Distribooks, Inc.

—Harry Potter et le Prisonnier d'Azkaban. 1999. (Harry Potter Ser.: Year 3). Tr. of Harry Potter & the Prisoner of Azkaban. (FRE.). 465p. (YA). (gr. 3 up). pap. 16.95 (978-2-07-052818-9(9)) Gallimard, Editions FRA. *Dist:* Distribooks, Inc.

W X Y Z

—Harry Potter et l'Ecole des Sorciers. 3rd ed. 1998. (Harry Potter Ser.: Year 1). Tr. of Harry Potter & the Sorcerer's Stone. (FRE., Illus.). (YA). (gr. 3 up). pap. 14.95 (978-2-07-050142-7(6)) Distribooks, Inc.

—Harry Potter et l'Ecole des Sorciers. 1999. (Harry Potter Ser.: Year 1). Tr. of Harry Potter & the Sorcerer's Stone. (FRE.). (YA). (gr. 3 up). pap. 16.95 (978-0-320-03780-1(0)) French & European Pubns., Inc.

—Harry Potter et l'Ecole des Sorciers.Tr. of Harry Potter & the Sorcerer's Stone. 2007. 311p. pap. 14.95 (***978-2-07-061236-9(8)***); 2000. (FRE.). (J). pap. 14.95 (978-2-07-051426-7(9)) Gallimard, Editions FRA. *Dist:* Distribooks, Inc.

—Harry Potter und der Gefangene von Azkaban. 1999. (Harry Potter Ser.: Year 3). Tr. of Harry Potter & the Prisoner of Azkaban. (GER.). (YA). (gr. 3 up). pap. 34.95 (978-3-551-55169-6(3)) Carlsen Verlag DEU. *Dist:* Distribooks, Inc.

—Harry Potter und der Stein der Weisen. 1999. (Harry Potter Ser.: Year 1). (GER.). 335p. (YA). (gr. 3 up). pap. 34.95 (978-3-551-55167-2(7)) Carlsen Verlag DEU. *Dist:* Distribooks, Inc.

—Harry Potter und die Kammer des Schreckens. 1999. (Harry Potter Ser.: Year 2). Tr. of Harry Potter & Chamber of Secrets. (GER.). (YA). (gr. 3 up). pap. 36.95 (978-3-551-55168-9(5)) Carlsen Verlag DEU. *Dist:* Distribooks, Inc.

—Harry Potter y el Caliz de Fuego. 2001. (SPA.). (gr. 3-6). lib. bdg. 26.35 (978-0-613-35957-3(7)) Tandem Library Bks.

—Harry Potter y el Prisionero de Azkaban. 2004. (Harry Potter Ser.: Year 3). (SPA., Illus.). 360p. (gr. 3 up). 17.95 (978-84-7888-519-0(6), SAL1889) Emece Editores ESP. *Dist:* Lectorum Pubns., Inc.

—Harry Potter y el Prisionero de Azkaban. 2000. (Harry Potter Ser.: Year 3). (SPA.). (YA). (gr. 3 up). 16.95 (978-0-320-03783-2(5)) French & European Pubns., Inc.

—Harry Potter y el Prisionero de Azkaban. 2001. (SPA.). (gr. 3-6). lib. bdg. 21.10 (978-0-613-35958-0(5)) Tandem Library Bks.

—Harry Potter y la Camara Secreta. 2004. (Harry Potter Ser.: Year 2). (SPA., Illus.). 288p. (YA). (gr. 3 up). 15.95 (978-84-7888-495-7(5), SAL4595) Emece Editores ESP. *Dist:* Lectorum Pubns., Inc.

—Harry Potter y la Camara Secreta. 1999. (Harry Potter Ser.: Year 2). (SPA.). (YA). (gr. 3 up). 14.95 (978-0-320-03781-8(9)) French & European Pubns., Inc.

—Harry Potter y la Camara Secreta. 2001. (SPA.). (gr. 3-6). lib. bdg. 18.80 (978-0-613-35959-7(3)) Tandem Library Bks.

—Harry Potter y la Piedra Filosofal. 2004. (Harry Potter Ser.: Bk. 1). (SPA., Illus.). 256p. (YA). (gr. 7 up). 15.95 (978-84-7888-445-2(9), SAL2819) Emece Editores ESP. *Dist:* Lectorum Pubns., Inc.

—Harry Potter y la Piedra Filosofal. 1999. (Harry Potter Ser.: Year 1). (SPA.). (YA). (gr. 3 up). 14.95 (978-0-320-03782-5(7)) French & European Pubns., Inc.

—Harry Potter y la Piedra Filosofal. 2001. (SPA.). (gr. 3-6). lib. bdg. 18.80 (978-0-613-35960-3(7)) Tandem Library Bks.

Rowling, J. K. & Dale, Jim. Harry Potter & the Goblet of Fire. unabr. ed. 2004. (Harry Potter Ser.). 752p. (J). pap. 65.00 incl. audio (978-0-8072-1196-0(6), S YA 270 SP, Listening Library) Random Hse. Audio Publishing Group.

Ruth, Nick. The Dark Dreamweaver. Concannon, Sue, illus. 2007. (Remin Chronicles: 1). 256p. (J). per. 11.95 (***978-0-9745603-5-9(9)***) Imaginator Pr.

Ryan, Brittney. Holly Claus: The Christmas Princess. Long, Laurel & Bedrick, Jeffrey K., illus. 2007. 48p. (J). lib. bdg. 19.89 (***978-0-06-144023-6(X)***); 18.99 (***978-0-06-144022-9(1)***) HarperCollins Pubs. (Julie Andrews Collection).

—The Legend of Holly Claus. Long, Laurel, illus. 2004. 544p. (J). (gr. 4 up). 16.99 (978-0-06-058511-2(0)); lib. bdg. 17.89 (978-0-06-058514-3(5)) HarperCollins Pubs. (Julie Andrews Collection).

—Legend of Holly Claus. Long, Laurel, illus. 2006. 544p. (J). pap. 7.99 (978-0-06-058515-0(3), Julie Andrews Collection) HarperCollins Pubs.

Sage, Angie. Flyte. Zug, Mark, illus. (Septimus Heap Ser.: Bk. 2). 544p. (J). (gr. 4 up). 2007. pap. 7.99 (978-0-06-057736-0(3), Harper Trophy); 2006. lib. bdg. 18.89 (978-0-06-057735-3(5)); 2006. 17.99 (978-0-06-057734-6(7), Tegen, Katherine Bks) HarperCollins Pubs.

—Magyk. Zug, Mark, illus. (Septimus Heap Ser.: Bk. 1). (J). (gr. 4 up). 2005. 576p. 17.99 (978-0-06-057731-5(2), Tegen, Katherine Bks); 2005. 576p. lib. bdg. 18.89 (978-0-06-057732-2(0)); 2006. 608p. reprint ed. pap. 7.99 (978-0-06-057733-9(9), Harper Trophy) HarperCollins Pubs.

—Physik. Zug, Mark, illus. (Septimus Heap Ser.: Bk. 3). 560p. (J). (gr. 4-6). 2008. pap. 7.99 (***978-0-06-057739-1(8)***, Harper Trophy); 2007. 17.99 (978-0-06-057737-7(1), Tegen, Katherine Bks); 2007. lib. bdg. 18.89 (978-0-06-057738-4(X), Tegen, Katherine Bks) HarperCollins Pubs.

—Septimus Heap Box Set: Books 1 And 2. Zug, Mark, illus. 2007. (Septimus Heap Ser.). (J). pap. 15.99 (***978-0-06-136195-1(X)***, Harper Trophy) HarperCollins Pubs.

Sampson, Jeff. Wizard's Betrayal. 2006. (New Adventures Ser.). (Illus.). 241p. (J). (***978-1-4156-4798-1(4)***, Mirrorstone) Wizards of the Coast.

Santillo, LuAnn. Look at Me. Santillo, LuAnn, ed. 2003. (Half-Pint Kids Readers Ser.). (Illus.). 7p. (J). (ps-1). pap. (978-1-59256-052-3(0)) Half-Pint Kids, Inc.

Satoru, Akahori. Sorcerer Hunter, Vol. 3. 3rd rev. ed. 2001. (MIXX Manga Ser.). (Illus.). 200p. (gr. 8-12). pap. 12.99 (978-1-892213-55-6(9)) TOKYOPOP, Inc.

—Sorcerer Hunter, Vol. 13. Satoru, Akahori, illus. 13th rev. ed. 2003. (Illus.). 192p. (gr. 11 up). pap. 12.99 (978-1-59182-066-6(9)) TOKYOPOP, Inc.

Schend, Steven E. Blackstaff. 2006. (Wizards Ser.). 320p. pap. 6.99 (978-0-7869-4016-5(6)) Wizards of the Coast.

Scieszka, Jon. Knights of the Kitchen Table. unabr. ed. 1998. (Time Warp Trio Ser.: No. 1). 55p. (J). (gr. 2-5). pap. 17.00 incl. audio (978-0-8072-0391-0(2), FTR193SP, Listening Library) Random Hse. Audio Publishing Group.

Service, Pamela F. Tomorrow's Magic. 2007. 448p. (J). (gr. 3-7). 15.99 (978-0-375-84087-6(7)); (gr. 4-9). lib. bdg. 18.99 (978-0-375-94087-3(1)) Random Hse. Children's Bks. (Random Hse. Bks. for Young Readers).

—Tomorrow's Magic. 2007. (J). pap. (978-0-375-84088-3(5)) Random Hse., Inc.

Service, Pamela F. Yesterday's Magic. 2008. (J). (gr. 3-7). 224p. 16.99 (***978-0-375-85577-1(7)***); 320p. lib. bdg. 19.99 (***978-0-375-95577-8(1)***) Random Hse. Children's Bks. (Random Hse. Bks. for Young Readers).

Shaskan, Trisha Speed. Marconi the Wizard. 2007. (Illus.). 24p. (J). (***978-1-4048-1234-5(2)***) Picture Window Bks.

—Marconi the Wizard. Muehlenhardt, Amy Bailey, illus. 2006. 24p. (J). lib. bdg. (***978-1-4048-3167-4(3)***) Picture Window Bks.

Simon, Morris. Wizards Keep. 2007. 124p. pap. 4.99 (***978-1-931567-67-1(0)***) Sovereign Pr.

Smith, Janice Lee. Wizard & Wart in Trouble. Meisel, Paul, illus. (I Can Read Bks.). 48p. (J). (ps-3). 2000. pap. 3.99 (978-0-06-444274-9(8)); 1998. 15.89 (978-0-06-027762-8(9)) HarperCollins Pubs.

—Wizard & Wart in Trouble. 2000. (I Can Read Bks.). (978-0-606-18731-2(6)) Tandem Library Bks.

Soesbee, Ree. Queen of the Sea. 2007. (Elements Ser.: Vol. 2). 256p. (J). (gr. 5 up). 5.99 (***978-0-7869-4281-7(9)***, Mirrorstone) Wizards of the Coast.

Spence, Stephen Mark. Merlin's Curse. 2000. (Round Table Cycle: 3). 226p. (YA). (gr. 4-12). pap. 11.99 (978-0-9705324-2-8(3)) Spence, Stephen Mark.

Stasheff, Christopher. The Oathbound Wizard. 2004. (Wizard in Rhyme Ser.: Bk. 2). 408p. lib. bdg. 14.04 (978-0-606-30694-2(3)) Tandem Library Bks.

Stewart, Mary. The Last Enchantment. 2003. (gr. 7-12). lib. bdg. 24.55 (978-0-613-66978-8(9)) Tandem Library Bks.

Stewart, Pat. Invisible Wizards Magic Picture Book. 2003. (Dover Little Activity Bks.). (Illus.). 16p. (J). pap. 1.50 (978-0-486-42636-5(X)) Dover Pubns., Inc.

Stewart, Paul. Muddle Earth. Riddell, Chris, illus. 2007. 464p. (gr. 5). (J). lib. bdg. 19.99 (***978-0-385-90335-6(9)***); (YA). 16.99 (***978-0-385-73316-8(X)***) Random Hse. Children's Bks. (Delacorte Bks. for Young Readers).

Strickland, Brad. The House Where Nobody Lived. 2006. 176p. (J). (gr. 4-7). 16.99 (978-0-8037-3148-6(5), Dial) Penguin Group (USA) Inc.

—The Tower at the End of the World. Schindler, S. D., illus. 2001. (Lewis Barnavelt Ser.). 160p. (J). 16.99 (978-0-8037-2620-8(1), Dial) Penguin Group (USA) Inc.

Stroud, Jonathan. The Amulet of Samarkand. 2003. (Bartimaeus Trilogy Ser.: Bk. 1). (Illus.). 464p. (gr. 5-17). 17.95 (978-0-7868-1859-4(X)) Hyperion Bks. for Children.

Sullivan, Jenny. Magic Maldwyn. 2002. (WEL.). 72p. pap. 11.95 (978-1-84323-074-8(7)) Beekman Bks., Inc.

Terry Lowey's Children's Stories Staff. The Secret of the Wizard's Wand. 2007. (Illus.). 24p. (J). 18.95 (***978-0-9792695-0-9(4)***) Terry Lowey's Children's Stories, LLC.

Thomas, Jacqui, illus. The Kingfisher Treasury of Witch & Wizard Stories. 2004. (Kingfisher Treasury of Stories Ser.: Vol. 23). 160p. (J). (gr. k-3). pap. 5.95 (978-0-7534-5729-0(6), Kingfisher) Houghton Mifflin Co. Trade & Reference Div.

Thompson, Colin. The Floods #1: Good Neighbors. Scrambly, Crab, illus. 2008. (Floods Ser.). 224p. (J). 15.99 (***978-0-06-113196-7(2)***); lib. bdg. 16.89 (***978-0-06-113199-8(7)***) HarperCollins Pubs.

Thompson, Ruth Plumly. The Enchanted Island of Oz. 2006. (J). 24.95 (978-1-930764-10-1(3)) International Wizard of Oz Club, The.

—The Wonder Book. 2006. (J). 24.95 (978-1-930764-15-6(4)) International Wizard of Oz Club, The.

—Yankee in Oz. 2006. (J). 24.95 (978-1-930764-13-2(8)) International Wizard of Oz Club, The.

Tolkien, J. R. R. Roverandom. Scull, Christina & Hammond, Wayne G., eds. (Illus.). 1999. 106p. pap. 12.00 (978-0-395-95799-8(0)); 1998. 128p. (gr. 3-5). 17.00 (978-0-395-89871-0(4)) Houghton Mifflin Co. Trade & Reference Div.

Tolkien, J. R. R., et al. Roverandom. Scull, Christina & Hammond, Wayne G., eds. 783rd l.t. ed. 1998. (Illus.). 191p. (J). 25.95 (978-0-7838-0299-2(4)) Thorndike Pr.

Townsend, Tom. Never Trust a One-Eyed Wizard: The Fairie Ring, Vol. 2. 2000. (Fairie Ring Ser.: Vol. 2). 171p. (YA). (gr. 8 up). 9.99 (978-0-88092-526-6(4)) Royal Fireworks Publishing Co.

Vande Velde, Vivian. The Book of Mordred. 2005. (Illus.). 352p. (YA). (gr. 7-7). 18.00 (978-0-618-50754-2(X)) Houghton Mifflin Co. Trade & Reference Div.

—Wizard at Work. 2003. (Illus.). 144p. (YA). 16.00 (978-0-15-204559-3(7)) Harcourt Children's Bks.

—Wizard at Work: A Novel in Stories. 2004. (Illus.). 144p. (J). pap. 5.95 (978-0-15-205309-3(3), Magic Carpet Bks.) Harcourt Children's Bks.

Velde, Vivian Vande. The Book of Mordred. 2007. 352p. (YA). (gr. 7). pap. 8.99 (***978-0-618-80916-5(3)***, Graphia) Houghton Mifflin Co. Trade & Reference Div.

Wasson, Christopher. Quest for Adlaremzee Molair Nopeeoh. 2003. 120p. pap. 14.95 (978-1-4137-0117-3(5)) PublishAmerica, Inc.

Werner, Niels. The Wiley Wizard of Hveen. Cornelinson, Anne, illus. 1999. 64p. (Orig.). (J). (gr. k-8). pap. 9.95 (978-0-9663019-7-7(8)) Pocket of Sanity.

Willis, Dan. Wizard's Return. 2006. (Dragonlance Ser.: Vol. 3). (Illus.). 256p. (J). pap. 5.99 (978-0-7869-4025-7(5), Mirrorstone) Wizards of the Coast.

Wilson, Karma. Baby Cakes. Williams, Sam, illus. 2006. 32p. (J). 7.99 (978-1-4169-0289-8(9), Little Simon) Simon & Schuster Children's Publishing.

Wilson, Wendy. The First Book of Red. 2005. 99p. pap. 14.95 (978-1-4137-5570-1(4)) PublishAmerica, Inc.

Wizard Academies I: The Heart of Darkness. 2006. 658p. pap. 23.72 (978-1-4116-7787-6(0)) Lulu.com.

Wrede, Patricia C. Talking to Dragons. 2003. (Enchanted Forest Chronicles: Bk. 4). (Illus.). 272p. (YA). pap. 5.95 (978-0-15-204691-0(7), Magic Carpet Bks.) Harcourt Children's Bks.

—Talking to Dragons. unabr. ed. 2004. (Enchanted Forest Chronicles Ser.). 255p. (J). (gr. 6 up). pap. 38.00 incl. audio (978-0-8072-0983-7(X), S YA 385 SP, Listening Library) Random Hse. Audio Publishing Group.

—Talking to Dragons. 2003. (gr. 7-12). lib. bdg. 14.10 (978-0-613-59931-3(4)) Tandem Library Bks.

Wrede, Patricia C. & Stevermer, Caroline. Sorcery & Cecelia or the Enchanted Chocolate Pot: Being the Correspondence of Two Young Ladies of Quality Regarding Various Magical Scandals in London & the Country. 2003. (Illus.). 336p. (YA). 17.00 (978-0-15-204615-6(1)) Harcourt Children's Bks.

Yolen, Jane. Wizard's Hall. 1999. 144p. (YA). pap. 6.95 (978-0-15-202085-9(3), Magic Carpet Bks.) Harcourt Children's Bks.

—Wizard's Hall. 144p. (J). (gr. 3-5). pap. 6.00 (978-0-8072-1544-9(9), Listening Library) Random Hse. Audio Publishing Group.

—Wizard's Hall. 1999. (978-0-606-16528-0(2)); (gr. 3-6). lib. bdg. 14.15 (978-0-7857-1069-1(8)) Tandem Library Bks.

—Wizard's Map. 2002. (gr. 3-6). lib. bdg. 14.10 (978-0-613-53882-4(X)) Tandem Library Bks.

Youmans, Marly. The Curse of the Raven Mocker. 2003. 288p. (J). 18.00 (978-0-374-31667-9(8), Farrar, Straus & Giroux (BYR)) Farrar, Straus & Giroux.

—The Curse of the Raven Mocker. 2006. 288p. (YA). (gr. 7). pap. 7.99 (978-0-14-240696-0(1), Puffin) Penguin Group (USA) Inc.

WOLFE, JAMES, 1727-1759—FICTION

Henty, G. A. With Wolfe in Canada: The Winning of a Continent. 2001. (Illus.). 353p. (J). (978-0-921100-86-7(8)); pap. (978-0-921100-87-4(6)) Inheritance Pubns.

—With Wolfe in Canada: The Winning of a Continent. (Illus.). 353p. (J). 2000. (gr. 8-12). pap. 14.99 (978-1-887159-30-2(4)); 1998. lib. bdg. 20.99 (978-1-887159-18-0(5)) Preston-Speed Pubns.

WOLVERINE

Markle, Sandra. Los Glotones (Wolverines) 2007. (Animales carroñeros (Animal Scavengers) Ser.). (SPA.). (J). (gr. 3-6). 40p. pap. 7.95 (***978-0-8225-7736-2(4)***); 40p. lib. bdg. 25.26 (***978-0-8225-7732-4(1)***) Lerner Publishing Group. (Ediciones Lerner).

Markle, Sandra. Wolverines. 2005. (Animal Scavengers Ser.). (Illus.). 39p. (J). (ps-7). 25.26 (978-0-8225-3198-2(4), Lerner Pubns.) Lerner Publishing Group.

Stevens, Kathryn & Somervill, Barbara A. The New York Colony. 2003. (Spirit of America: Our Colonies Ser.). (Illus.). 40p. (J). (gr. 2-6). 28.50 (978-1-56766-654-0(X)) Child's World, Inc.

Stevenson, Kathy & Somervill, Barbara A. The Massachusetts Colony. 2003. (Spirit of America: Our Colonies Ser.). (Illus.). 40p. (J). (gr. 2-6). 28.50 (978-1-56766-616-8(7)) Child's World, Inc.

Swanson, Diane. Welcome to the World of Wolverines. 2007. (Welcome to the World Ser.). (Illus.). 32p. (J). (ps-2). pap. 5.95 (***978-1-55285-840-0(5)***, Walrus Bks.) Whitecap Bks., Ltd. CAN. *Dist:* Firefly Bks., Ltd.

WOLVERINE—FICTION

Caballero, Erica. Mount Mole. 2006. pap. 10.00 (***978-1-4257-2301-9(2)***) Xlibris Corp.

Jacques, Brian. Rakkety Tam. David, Elliot, illus. 2006. (Redwall Ser.). 384p. (J). (gr. 5). pap. 8.99 (978-0-14-240683-0(X), Puffin) Penguin Group (USA) Inc.

—Rakkety Tam. Elliot, David, illus. 2004. (Redwall Ser.). 432p. (YA). (gr. 4-6). 23.99 (978-0-399-23725-6(9), Philomel) Penguin Group (USA) Inc.

Montgomery, Rutherford G. Carcajou. Cram, L. D., illus. 2004. 300p. (gr. 4-7). pap. 17.95 (978-0-87004-403-8(6)) Caxton Pr.

Sargent, Dave & Sargent, Pat. Wally Wolverine: Eager, 56 vols., 59. Lenoir, Jane, illus. 2001. (Animal Pride Ser.: Vol. 59). 36p. (J). lib. bdg. 19.95 (978-1-56763-559-1(8)) Ozark Publishing.

Sargent, Dave, et al. Wally Wolverine: Eager, 56, 59. 2000. (Animal Pride Ser.: 59). (Illus.). 36p. (J). pap. 6.95 (978-1-56763-560-7(1)) Ozark Publishing.

Skurzynski, Gloria. Buried Alive. 2003. (gr. 3-6). lib. bdg. 14.10 (978-0-613-70935-4(7)) Tandem Library Bks.

Skurzynski, Gloria & Ferguson, Alane. Buried Alive. 2003. (Mysteries in Our National Parks Ser.: No. 12). 160p. (J). (gr. 3-7). 15.95 (978-0-7922-6966-3(7)); pap. 5.95 (978-0-7922-6968-7(3)) National Geographic Society. (National Geographic Children's Bks.).

Way, Daniel. Sabretooth: Open Season. Sears, Bart, illus. 2005. (Wolverine Ser.). 96p. pap. 9.99 (978-0-7851-1507-6(2)) Marvel Enterprises, Inc.

WOLVES

Animal Watch: Wolves. (J). (gr. 1-3). 75.00 (978-0-669-15881-6(X)) Houghton Mifflin Co. (Schl. Div.).

Bailey, Jill. Gray Wolf. 2004. (Animals under Threat Ser.). (Illus.). 48p. (J). pap. 8.50 (978-1-4034-5690-8(9)) Heinemann Library.

—Grey Wolf. 2004. (Animals under Threat Ser.). (J). pap. 91.80 (978-1-4034-5695-3(X)); (Illus.). 48p. 29.93 (978-1-4034-5583-3(X)) Heinemann Library.

Banner, Melanie Jane. Smoke: A Wolf's Story. Kveta, tr. Kveta, illus. 2003. 160p. pap. (978-1-55041-322-9(8)) Fitzhenry & Whiteside, Ltd.

—Smoke: A Wolf's Story. 2003. (gr. 7-12). lib. bdg. 17.60 (978-0-613-87479-3(X)) Tandem Library Bks.

Barnes, Julia. The Secret Lives of Wolves. 2006. (Illus.). 32p. (J). lib. bdg. (***978-0-8368-7660-4(1)***) Stevens, Gareth Inc.

Barret & Allen. El Lobo. 2002. (Perros Salvajes Serie).Tr. of Wild Dogs: The Wolf. (SPA.). 24p. (J). (gr. 3-5). 22.45 (978-1-4103-0014-0(5), Blackbirch Pr., Inc.) Thomson Gale.

Barrett, Jalma. Wolf. Allan, Larry, photos by. 2000. (Wild Canines of North America). (Illus.). 24p. (J). (gr. 3-6). 24.94 (978-1-56711-262-7(5), Blackbirch Pr., Inc.) Thomson Gale.

Batten, Mary. Baby Wolf. Stammen, JoEllen McAllister, illus. 1998. (All Aboard Reading Ser.). 48p. (J). (gr. 1-3). pap. 3.99 (978-0-448-41645-8(X), Grosset & Dunlap) Penguin Group (USA) Inc.

Berger, Gilda & Berger, Melvin. Por Que Aullan Los Lobos. 2007. 48p. (J). pap. 5.99 (***978-0-439-85315-6(X)***, Scholastic en Espanol) Scholastic, Inc.

Berger, Melvin. Call of the Wolves: Theme Pack. Reed, Janet, ed. Date not set. (Ranger Rick Science Spectacular Ser.). (Illus.). (J). (gr. 2-4). pap. 36.90 (978-1-56784-271-5(2)) Sundance/Newbridge Educational Publishing.

Berger, Melvin & Berger, Gilda. Howl! A Book about Wolves. 2002. (Hello Reader! Ser.). (Illus.). 40p. (J). (gr. 1-3). pap. 3.99 (978-0-439-20167-4(5), Cartwheel Bks.) Scholastic, Inc.

—Why Do Wolves Howl? Questions & Answers about Wolves. Osti, Roberto, illus. 2001. (Question & Answer Ser.). 48p. (J). (gr. 2-4). 12.95 (978-0-439-19378-8(8), Scholastic Reference) Scholastic, Inc.

Berger, Melvin, et al. Why Do Wolves Howl? Questions & Answers about Wolves. Osti, Roberto, illus. 2002. (Question & Answer Ser.). 48p. (J). (gr. 2-4). pap. 5.95 (978-0-439-19379-5(6), Scholastic Reference) Scholastic, Inc.

Bowman, Susan. The Adventures of Dakota: A Friendly Wolf Who Teaches Children (Grades K-4) Lessons about Life. 2004. (Illus.). 56p. (J). (978-1-889636-60-3(6)) Youthlight, Inc.

Brandenburg, Jim. Scruffy: A Wolf Finds His Place in the Pack. 2000. (J). (978-0-606-20295-4(1)); (Illus.). (978-0-606-20410-1(5)) Tandem Library Bks.

Butz, Christopher. Red Wolves. 2003. (Endangered Plants & Animals of North America Ser.). (J). pap. (978-1-58417-213-0(4)); lib. bdg. (978-1-58417-212-3(6)) Lake Street Pubs.

Clarke, Penny. Wolves. Hersey, Bob, illus. 2004. (Scary Creatures Ser.). (J). 22.50 (978-0-531-12378-2(2)); 32p. (gr. 2-4). pap. 6.95 (978-0-531-16749-6(6)) Scholastic Library Publishing. (Watts, Franklin).

Clever Coyote & other Wild Dogs: Level L, 6 vols. 128p. (gr. 2-3). 40.50 (978-0-7699-1033-8(5)) Shortland Pubns. (U. S. A.) Inc.

Creative Publishing international Editors. Forest Animals. 2004. (Our Wild World Ser.). (Illus.). 192p. (J). (gr. 2-5). ring bd. 16.95 (978-1-55971-708-3(4), NorthWord Bks. for Young Readers) T&N Children's Publishing.

Dornhoffer, Mary K. & Scherrer, Robert F. Wolves. 2004. (First Reports). (Illus.). 48p. (J). (gr. 3 up). lib. bdg. 22.60 (978-0-7565-0579-0(8)) Compass Point Bks.

Eckart, Edana. Gray Wolf. 2003. (Animals of the World Ser.). (Illus.). 24p. (J). 17.00 (978-0-516-24303-0(9)); pap. 4.95 (978-0-516-27891-9(6)) Scholastic Library Publishing. (Children's Pr.).

—Gray Wolf. 2003. (gr. k-3). lib. bdg. 12.95 (978-0-613-67719-6(6)) Tandem Library Bks.

Economos, Christine. Wolves. 2003. (Science Links Ser.). (Illus.). 32p. (gr. 3-5). 23.00 (978-0-7910-7433-6(1), Chelsea Hse.) Facts On File, Inc.

Egielski, Richard. Saint Francis & the Wolf. Egielski, Richard, illus. 2005. (Illus.). 40p. (J). (gr. 1-3). 15.99 (978-0-06-623870-8(6), Geringer, Laura Book) HarperCollins Pubs.

—Saint Francis & the Wolf of Gubbio. Egielski, Richard, illus. 2005. (Illus.). 40p. (J). (gr. 1-3). lib. bdg. 16.89 (978-0-06-623871-5(4), Geringer, Laura Book) HarperCollins Pubs.

Evert, Laura. Wolves. McGee, John F., illus. 2004. (Our Wild World Ser.). 48p. (J). (gr. 2-5). pap. 7.95 (978-1-55971-748-9(3), NorthWord Bks. for Young Readers) T&N Children's Publishing.

—Wolves. 2000. (gr. 3-6). lib. bdg. 16.40 (978-0-613-27613-9(2)) Tandem Library Bks.

Gareth Stevens Publishing Staff, contrib. by. Wolves. 2004. (All about Wild Animals Ser.). (Illus.). 32p. (J). (gr. 2 up). lib. bdg. 23.33 (978-0-8368-4124-4(7)) Stevens, Gareth Inc.

Gentle, Victor & Perry, Janet. Wolves. 2002. (Imagination Library). (Illus.). 24p. (J). (gr. 2 up). lib. bdg. 22.00 (978-0-8368-3099-6(7)) Stevens, Gareth Inc.

George, Jean Craighead. And the Wolves Came Back. Minor, Wendell, illus. 2008. 32p. (J). (gr. k). 16.99 (***978-0-525-47947-5(3)***, Dutton Juvenile) Penguin Group (USA) Inc.

—Autumn Moon. 2003. (J). (gr. 3-7). 20.75 (978-0-8446-7241-0(6)) Smith, Peter Pub., Inc.

—Autumn Moon. 2001. (gr. 3-6). lib. bdg. 14.10 (978-0-613-50407-2(0)) Tandem Library Bks.

—Look to the North: A Wolf Pup Diary. Washburn, Lucia, illus. 1998. 32p. (J). (gr. k-4). pap. 6.99 (978-0-06-443510-9(5), Harper Trophy) HarperCollins Pubs.

Gibbons, Gail. Wolves. Gibbons, Gail, illus. 1999. (Illus.). 28.95 incl. audio compact disk (978-1-59519-115-1(1)); pap. 39.95 incl. audio compact disk (978-1-59519-114-4(3)); (J). pap. 18.95 incl. audio compact disk (978-1-59519-113-7(5)) Live Oak Media.

Gilkerson, Patricia. My Adventure with Wolves. 2006. 44p. (J). 8.99 (978-1-59092-476-1(2) , Orchard Academy Pr.) Windstorm Creative.

Gish, Melissa. Wolves. 2000. (Northern Trek Ser.). (Illus.). 24p. (J). lib. bdg. 15.95 (978-1-58340-037-1(0)) Smart Apple Media.

Goecke, Michael P. Dire Wolf. 2003. (Prehistoric Animals Ser.). (Illus.). 24p. (J). (gr. k-4). lib. bdg. 21.35 (978-1-57765-966-2(X)) ABDO Publishing Co.

Green, Jen. Wolves. (Nature Fact File Ser.). (Illus.). 64p. 2003. pap. 7.99 (978-1-84215-667-4(5) , Southwater); 2001. (gr. 3-7). 14.95 (978-0-7548-0654-7(5)) Anness Publishing GBR. *Dist:* National Bk. Network.

—Wolves. 2003. (gr. 3-6). lib. bdg. 16.45 (978-0-613-85237-1(0)) Tandem Library Bks.

Greenaway, Theresa. Wolves, Wild Dogs & Foxes. 2001. (Secret World Of... Ser.). (Illus.). 48p. (J). (gr. 4-7). lib. bdg. 27.12 (978-0-7398-3507-4(6)) Raintree.

Greenberg, Daniel A. Wolves. 2002. (Animals, Animals Ser.). (Illus.). 48p. (J). 25.64 (978-0-7614-1447-6(9) , Benchmark Bks.) Cavendish, Marshall Corp.

Grolier Educational Staff. Animal Families, 16 vols., Set. 2001. (Illus.). 32p. (J). (978-0-7172-5500-9(X) , Grolier) Scholastic Library Publishing.

Gunzi, Christiane. The Best Book of Wolves & Wild Dogs. Rowe, Mike, illus. 2003. (Best Book of... Ser.). 32p. (J). (gr. k-3). tchr. ed. 12.95 (978-0-7534-5574-6(9) , Kingfisher) Houghton Mifflin Co. Trade & Reference Div.

Halfpenny, James C. Yellowstone Wolves in the Wild. 2003. (Illus.). 104p. per. 19.95 (978-1-931832-26-7(9) , 8667872363) Riverbend Publishing.

Harcourt School Publishers Staff. All about Wolves Advanced Level. 3rd ed. 2002. (Trophies Reading Program Ser.). (Illus.). pap. 5.10 (978-0-15-323209-1(9)) Harcourt Schl. Pubs.

—The Return of the Wolf: Take-Home Book. 2001. (Collections Ser.). (Illus.). (J). (gr. 4). pap. 1.90 (978-0-15-319496-2(0)) Harcourt Schl. Pubs.

—The Return of the Wolf Below Level. 3rd ed. 2002. (Trophies Reading Program Ser.). (Illus.). pap. 5.10 (978-0-15-323235-0(8)) Harcourt Schl. Pubs.

—Trofeos Advanced Level: Todo Sobre... 3rd ed. 2002. (SPA., Illus.). pap. 6.80 (978-0-15-324120-8(9)) Harcourt Schl. Pubs.

Harrington, Fred H. The Arctic Wolf. 2002. (Library of Wolves & Wild Dogs). (Illus.). 24p. (J). lib. bdg. 18.75 (978-0-8239-5766-8(7)) Rosen Publishing Group, Inc., The.

—The Ethiopian Wolf. 2002. (Library of Wolves & Wild Dogs). (Illus.). 24p. (J). (gr. 2-4). lib. bdg. 18.75 (978-0-8239-5767-5(5)) Rosen Publishing Group, Inc., The.

—The Gray Wolf. 2002. (Library of Wolves & Wild Dogs). (Illus.). 24p. (J). lib. bdg. 18.75 (978-0-8239-5764-4(0) , PowerKids Pr.) Rosen Publishing Group, Inc., The.

—The Red Wolf. 2002. (Library of Wolves & Wild Dogs). (Illus.). 24p. (J). lib. bdg. 18.75 (978-0-8239-5765-1(9) , PowerKids Pr.) Rosen Publishing Group, Inc., The.

Havard, Christian. The Wolf: Night Howler. 2006. (Animal Close-Ups Ser.). (Illus.). 27p. (Orig.). (J). pap. 6.95 (978-1-57091-630-4(6)) Charlesbridge Publishing, Inc.

Heinz, Brian. The Wolves. Fuchs, Bernie, illus. 2005. 32p. (J). lib. bdg. 15.99 (978-0-936335-11-7(4)) Ballyhoo BookWorks, Inc.

Hillert, Margaret. Wolves: For the Earliest Reader. 2005. (Illus.). 32p. (J). (978-1-59577-038-7(0)); (978-1-59577-037-0(2)) Starfall Education.

Hodge, Deborah. Wild dogs: Wolves, coyotes & foxes. Stephens, Pat, illus. unabr. ed. 2004. (Kids Can Press Wildlife Ser.). 32p. (J). (gr. k-3). (978-1-55074-420-0(8)) Kids Can Pr., Ltd.

Imbriaco, Alison. The Red Wolf: Help Save This Endangered Species! 2007. (Saving Endangered Species Ser.). (Illus.). 128p. (J). lib. bdg. 33.27 (978-1-59845-038-5(7) , MyReportLinks.com Bks.) Enslow Pubs., Inc.

El invierno de los Lobos. 2000. (McGraw-Hill Ciencias Ser.). (ENG & SPA.). (gr. 3 up). (978-0-02-279639-6(8)) Macmillan/McGraw-Hill Schl. Div.

Jaffe, Elizabeth Dana. Wolves Have Pups. 2002. (Animals & Their Young Ser.). (Illus.). 24p. (J). (gr. 1 up). lib. bdg. 18.60 (978-0-7565-0171-6(7)) Compass Point Bks.

Kalman, Bobbie. Endangered Wolves. 2004. (Earth's Endangered Animals Ser.). (Illus.). 32p. (J). (978-0-7787-1854-3(9)); pap. (978-0-7787-1900-7(6)) Crabtree Publishing Co.

—Life Cycle of a Wolf. 2002. (gr. 3-6). lib. bdg. 14.10 (978-0-613-52978-5(2)) Tandem Library Bks.

Kalman, Bobbie & Bishop, Amanda. The Life Cycle of a Wolf. Reiach, Margaret Amy, illus. 2002. (Life Cycle Ser.). 32p. (J). (gr. 2-3). (978-0-7787-0657-1(5)); pap. (978-0-7787-0687-8(7)) Crabtree Publishing Co.

Kalman, Bobbie, et al. Les Loups. 2005. (FRE., Illus.). 32p. (J). pap. (978-2-89579-030-3(2)) Crabtree Publishing Co.

Leon, Vicki, contrib. by. A Pack of Wolves. 1999. (J). (978-0-382-39722-6(3)) Cobblestone Publishing Co.

Los Lobos (Wolves) 2006. (J). pap. 7.95 (978-0-8225-6626-7(5)); (SPA.). 40p. lib. bdg. 25.26 (978-0-8225-6489-8(0)) Lerner Publishing Group. (Ediciones Lerner).

Los Lobos: Individual Title Six-Packs. (Literatura 2000 Ser.). (SPA.). (gr. 2-3). 33.00 (978-0-7635-1262-0(1)) Rigby Education.

Markle, Sandra. Wolves. (Animal Predators Ser.). (J). 2005. 40p. (gr. 4-6). pap. 7.95 (978-1-57505-748-4(4)); 2004. (Illus.). 40p. (gr. 3-6). lib. bdg. 25.26 (978-1-57505-732-3(8)); 2003. lib. bdg. (978-0-8225-5107-2(1) , Lerner Pubns.) Lerner Publishing Group.

—Wolves. 2001. (Growing up Wild Ser.). (Illus.). 32p. (J). (ps-3). 16.00 (978-0-689-81886-8(6) , Atheneum) Simon & Schuster Children's Publishing.

Martin, Patricia. Gray Wolves. 2002. (gr. 3-6). lib. bdg. 15.25 (978-0-613-59494-3(0)) Tandem Library Bks.

Martin, Patricia A. Fink. Gray Wolves. 2003. (True Bks.). (Illus.). 48p. (J). (gr. 3-5). pap. 6.95 (978-0-516-27472-0(4) , Children's Pr.) Scholastic Library Publishing.

McNulty, Faith. Red Wolves. Courtney, Richard, illus. 2000. (Hello Reader! Science Ser.). 48p. (J). pap. (978-0-439-08751-3(1)) Scholastic, Inc.

Miller, Sara Swan. Wolves. 2008. (J). lib. bdg. (****978-1-4042-4161-9(2)*** , PowerKids Pr.) Rosen Publishing Group, Inc., The.

Montardre, Helene. Little Wolves. Castile, Muriel, tr. from FRE. 2005. (Born to Be Wild Ser.). (Illus.). 24p. (J). (gr. 1-3). lib. bdg. 22.00 (978-0-8368-4440-5(8)) Stevens, Gareth Inc.

Mowat, Farley. Never Cry Wolf: Amazing True Story of Life among Arctic Wolves. 2001. (gr. 7-12). lib. bdg. 21.95 (978-0-613-62532-6(3)) Tandem Library Bks.

Otto, Carolyn B. Wolves. (Scholastic Science Readers Ser.). (Illus.). 48p. (J). 2001. (gr. 2-3). pap. 3.99 (978-0-439-29584-0(X) , Scholastic Reference); 2000. (978-0-439-16295-1(5)) Scholastic, Inc.

—Wolves. 2001. (gr. 3-6). lib. bdg. 11.80 (978-0-613-36755-4(3)); (Illus.). (J). (978-0-606-21419-3(4)) Tandem Library Bks.

Perry, Phyllis J. Crafty Canines: Coyotes, Foxes & Wolves. 1999. (Watts Library). (Illus.). 64p. (J). (gr. 5-7). 25.50 (978-0-531-11680-7(8) , Watts, Franklin) Scholastic Library Publishing.

—Crafty Canines: Coyotes, Foxes, & Wolves. 1999. (gr. 3-6). lib. bdg. 17.60 (978-0-613-29416-4(5)) Tandem Library Bks.

Preszler, June. Wolves. 2006. (Illus.). 24p. (J). (978-0-7368-5418-4(5)) Capstone Pr., Inc.

Quadrillion Media Staff. Wolves. 2000. (Start Me Up Ser.: Vol. 11). (Illus.). 48p. (J). (ps-3). 12.95 (978-1-58185-013-0(1)) Quadrillion Media LLC.

Raintree Steck-Vaughn Staff. Los Lobos. 1999. (SPA.). (J). pap., stu. ed. 31.05 (978-0-7398-0770-5(6)) Steck-Vaughn.

—Wolves. 2000. (Illus.). (J). (gr. 1-2). pap. 29.12 (978-0-8172-6459-8(0)) Steck-Vaughn.

Reid, Mary Ebeltoft. Wolves & Other Wild Dogs, Vol. 10. World Book, Inc. Staff, ed. 2002. (World Book's Animals of the World Ser.: Set 1). 64p. (J). (978-0-7166-1247-6(X)) World Bk., Inc.

Reiter, Chris. The Gray Wolf: A MyReportLinks.com Book. 2003. (Endangered & Threatened Animals Ser.). (Illus.). 48p. (J). (gr. 4-10). lib. bdg. 25.26 (978-0-7660-5056-3(4) , MyReportLinks.com Bks.) Enslow Pubs., Inc.

Richardson, Adele D. Wolves: Life in the Pack. 2001. (Wild World of Animals Ser.). (Illus.). 24p. (J). (gr. 1-2). lib. bdg. 18.60 (978-0-7368-0830-9(2) , Bridgestone Bks.) Capstone Pr., Inc.

Ripple, William John. Wolves. 2005. (Woodland Animals Ser.). (Illus.). 24p. (J). (978-0-7368-4247-1(0)) Capstone Pr., Inc.

Romeu, Emma. Ahi Viene el Lobo Gris. Sanchez Vigil, Luis Gerardo & Vanden Broeck, Fabricio, illus. 2004. (Coleccion Animales de America). (SPA.). 32p. (J). (gr. 3-5). pap. 7.95 (978-970-29-0512-7(5)) Santillana USA Publishing Co., Inc.

Royston, Angela. Wolves. 2003. (Amazing Animals Ser.). (Illus.). 24p. (J). lib. bdg. 21.35 (978-1-58340-228-3(4)) Weigl Pubs., Inc.

Scholastic, Inc. Staff. Wolves. Wasserman, Robin, ed. 2002. (Face-to-Face Ser.). (Illus.). 24p. (J). (gr. 1-3). pap. 3.50 (978-0-439-31712-2(6) , Scholastic Paperbacks) Scholastic, Inc.

Scholl, Elizabeth J. Wolves. 2003. (Animal Attacks Ser.). (Illus.). 48p. (J). 26.20 (978-0-7377-1527-9(8) , Greenhaven Pr., Inc.) Thomson Gale.

Searl, Duncan. Wolves. 2007. (Smart Animals! Ser.). (Illus.). 32p. (J). lib. bdg. 25.27 (978-1-59716-370-5(8) , 1265961) Bearport Publishing Co., Inc.

Silver & Prince: Individual Title Six-Packs. (gr. 3 up). 35.00 (978-0-7635-9671-2(X)) Rigby Education.

Solway, Andrew. Wolves & Other Dogs. 2004. (J). 27.07 (978-1-4034-5769-1(7)); pap. 8.50 (978-1-4034-5775-2(1)) Heinemann Library.

Spilsbury, Richard & Spilsbury, Louise. A Pack of Wolves. 2003. (Heinemann Infosearch Ser.). (Illus.). 32p. (J). pap. (978-1-4034-3285-8(6)) Heinemann Library.

Stewart, Josie & Salem, Lynn. Wolves. Smith, Shane, illus. 2000. 8p. (J). (gr. k-2). pap. 3.75 (978-1-58323-034-3(3) , Seedling Pubns.) Continental Pr., Inc.

Stone, Lynn M. Gray Wolves. 2004. (Early Bird Nature Bks.). (Illus.). 47p. (J). 25.26 (978-0-8225-3050-3(3) , Lerner Pubns.) Lerner Publishing Group.

—The Lives of Wolves. 2000. (Wolves Discovery Library). (Illus.). 24p. (J). (gr. 1). lib. bdg. 19.27 (978-1-55916-239-5(2)) Rourke Publishing, LLC.

—Saving Wolves. 2000. (Wolves Discovery Library). (Illus.). 24p. (J). (gr. 1-4). lib. bdg. 19.27 (978-1-55916-240-1(6)) Rourke Publishing, LLC.

—Wolves: Family & Pack. 2000. (Wolves Discovery Library). (Illus.). 24p. (J). (gr. 1-4). lib. bdg. 19.27 (978-1-55916-241-8(4)) Rourke Publishing, LLC.

—Wolves: The Hunters. 2000. (Wolves Discovery Library). (Illus.). 24p. (J). (gr. 1-4). lib. bdg. 19.27 (978-1-55916-243-2(0)) Rourke Publishing, LLC.

—Wolves & People. 2001. (Wolves Discovery Library). (Illus.). 24p. (J). (gr. 1-4). lib. bdg. 19.27 (978-1-55916-242-5(2)) Rourke Publishing, LLC.

—Wolves of the World. 2000. (Wolves Discovery Library). (Illus.). 24p. (J). (gr. 1-4). lib. bdg. 19.27 (978-1-55916-244-9(9)) Rourke Publishing, LLC.

Swanson, Diane. Wolves. 1998. (Welcome to the World of Animals Ser.). (Illus.). 32p. (J). (gr. 3 up). lib. bdg. 23.33 (978-0-8368-2218-2(8)) Stevens, Gareth Inc.

Swinburne, Stephen R. Once a Wolf: How Wildlife Biologists Brought Back the Gray Wolf. 1999. (gr. 3-6). lib. bdg. 14.10 (978-0-613-35546-9(6)) Tandem Library Bks.

—Once A Wolf: How Wildlife Biologists Fought to Bring Back the Gray Wolf. Brandenburg, Jim, photos by. 1999. (Scientists in the Field Ser.). (Illus.). 48p. (J). (gr. 5-9). reprint ed. tchr. ed. 16.00 (978-0-395-89827-7(7)) Houghton Mifflin Co. Trade & Reference Div.

Tanner, Susan. The Wild Wolf: Learning the W Sound. (PowerPhonics Ser.). (Illus.). (J). 2002. 24p. (gr. 1). lib. bdg. 18.50 (978-0-8239-5927-3(9)); 2001. 23p. pap. 26.40 (978-0-8239-8272-1(6)) Rosen Publishing Group, Inc., The. (PowerKids Pr.).

Weide, Bruce & Tucker, Pat. Tales of Two Canines - Koani & Indy: The Adventures of a Wolf & a Dog. Sidhu, Amber, illus. 1998. 168p. (J). pap. 10.00 (978-0-87842-392-7(3)) Mountain Pr. Publishing Co., Inc.

Welsbacher, Anne. Wolves. 2001. (Predators in the Wild Ser.). (Illus.). 48p. (J). (gr. 3-4). lib. bdg. 21.26 (978-0-7368-0788-3(8) , Capstone High-Interest Bks.) Capstone Pr., Inc.

Wexo, John Bonnett. Wolves. (Zoobooks). (Illus.). 24p. (J). (gr. 1-7). 2001. 15.95 (978-1-888153-33-0(4) , 267-X); 2003. 10.95 (978-1-932396-01-0(2) , Zoo Bks.) Wildlife Education, Ltd.

Wilsdon, Christina. Wolves. 2006. (J). 7.99 (978-1-59939-031-4(0)) Reader's Digest Young Families, Inc.

The Wolf. (Wildlife of North America Ser.). 48p. (YA). 7.95 (978-0-7368-8491-4(2)) Capstone Pr., Inc.

Wolves, 6 bks. 2005. (Animal Predators Ser.). (Illus.). 40p. (J). (gr. 3-6). pap. 46.95 (978-0-8225-5494-3(1)) Lerner Publishing Group.

Wolves, 6 Packs. (Literatura 2000 Ser.). (gr. 2-3). 33.00 (978-0-7635-0271-3(5)); 16p. (gr. 3 up). 36.00 (978-0-7635-9689-7(2)) Rigby Education.

Wolves. 2001. (gr. 3-6). lib. bdg. 11.25 (978-0-613-58142-4(3)) Tandem Library Bks.

Wolves & Coyotes. (Eyes on Nature Ser.). 32p. (J). (gr. 1). pap. (978-1-882210-57-2(3)) Action Publishing, Inc.

Wolves & Coyotes. (Eyes on Nature Ser.). (Illus.). 32p. (J). (gr. 1 up). 7.95 (978-1-56156-424-8(9)) Kidsbooks, Inc.

Wolves Have Pups. (Animals & Their Young Ser.). 24p. (J). 7.95 (978-0-7565-1248-4(4)) Compass Point Bks.

WOLVES—FICTION

Aesop. The Wolf in Sheep's Clothing: A Tale about Appearances. 2006. (J). (978-1-59939-086-4(8) , Reader's Digest Young Families, Inc.) Reader's Digest Children's Publishing, Inc.

Alexis, André. Ingrid & the Wolf. 2005. 168p. (J). (gr. 3-7). pap. 8.95 (978-0-88776-691-6(9)) Tundra Bks., Inc./ Livres Toundra, Inc. CAN. *Dist:* Random Hse., Inc.

Alily, Joseph. The Boy & the Wolf. 2007. 9.00 (****978-0-8059-9053-9(4)***) Dorrance Publishing Co., Inc.

Alily, Joseph. Untold- the Never Ending Tales: The Boy & the Wolf - Children's Story. 2006. 10.00 (978-0-8059-8133-9(0)) Dorrance Publishing Co., Inc.

Anderson, Max Elliot. Legend of the White Wolf. 2005. (Illus.). 125p. (J). (ps-7). pap. 10.95 (978-0-9752880-3-0(2)) Baker Trittin Pr.

Anholt, Laurence. Little Red Riding Wolf. 2004. (Illus.). 64p. (J). (gr. 3 up). 13.26 (978-0-7565-0632-2(8)) Compass Point Bks.

Ansley, Frank & Wheeler, Lisa. Invasion of the Pig Sisters. Ansley, Frank, illus. 2006. (Fitch & Chip Ser.). (Illus.). 48p. (J). 14.95 (978-0-689-84953-4(2) , Atheneum) Simon & Schuster Children's Publishing.

—Who's Afraid of Granny Wolf? Ansley, Frank, tr. 2004. (Fitch & Chip Ser.). (Illus.). 48p. (J). 14.95 (978-0-689-84952-7(4) , Atheneum/Richard Jackson Bks.) Simon & Schuster Children's Publishing.

Asch, Frank. Ziggy Piggy & the Three Little Pigs. Asch, Frank, illus. (Illus.). 32p. (J). (gr. k-3). 2001. (978-1-55074-913-7(7)); 1998. (978-1-55074-515-3(8)) Kids Can Pr., Ltd.

Asher, Sandra Fenichel. The Wolf & Its Shadows. 2000. (J). pap. 7.00 (978-0-87602-379-2(0)) Anchorage Pr.

Atwater-Rhodes, Amelia. Wolfcry. 2008. 208p. (YA). (gr. 9). pap. 7.99 (****978-0-440-23886-7(2)*** , Delacorte Bks. for Young Readers) Random Hse. Children's Bks.

Atwater-Rhodes, Amelia. Wolfcry Vol. 4: The Kiesha'ra. 2006. (Illus.). 208p. (YA). (gr. 7). 14.95 (978-0-385-73195-9(7)); lib. bdg. 16.99 (978-0-385-90354-7(5)) Random Hse. Children's Bks. (Delacorte Bks. for Young Readers).

Avi. The Good Dog. 2001. (Illus.). 256p. (J). (gr. 3-6). 17.99 (978-0-689-83824-8(7) , Atheneum/Richard Jackson Bks.) Simon & Schuster Children's Publishing.

Baglio, Ben M. Wolf at the Window. Baum, Ann, illus. 2003. (Animal Ark Hauntings Ser.: Vol. 7). 144p. (J). pap. 3.99 (978-0-439-44896-3(4) , Scholastic Paperbacks) Scholastic, Inc.

Bailey, Norman. Fight for Freedom. 2006. pap. (****978-1-84375-267-7(0)***) Universal Publishing Solutions Online, Limited (UPSO).

Bauer, Marion Dane. Runt. 2002. (Illus.). 144p. (J). (gr. 3-5). tchr. ed. 14.00 (978-0-618-21261-3(2) , Clarion Bks.) Houghton Mifflin Co. Trade & Reference Div.

—Runt. 2004. 144p. (gr. 4-7). reprint ed. 5.50 (978-0-440-41978-5(6) , Yearling) Random Hse. Children's Bks.

Bedard, Michael. The Wolf of Gubbio. ed. 2004. (Illus.). (J). (gr. k-3). spiral bd. (978-0-616-07213-4(9)) Canadian National Institute for the Blind/Institut National Canadien pour les Aveugles.

—The Wolf of Gubbio. Kimber, Murray, illus. 2001. 23p. (J). (gr. k-5). 15.95 (978-0-7737-3250-6(0)) Stoddart Kids CAN. *Dist:* Fitzhenry & Whiteside, Ltd.

Bergen, Lara. Diego & Click Take a Pic! Hom, John, illus. 2006. (Go, Diego, Go! Ser.). 10p. (J). bds. 7.99 (978-1-4169-1753-3(5) , Simon Spotlight/Nickelodeon) Simon & Schuster Children's Publishing.

Bergen, Lara Rice. Stanley: Crying Wolf. 2003. (ps-2). lib. bdg. 11.25 (978-0-613-75009-7(8)) Tandem Library Bks.

Bergna, Monica, illus. Juguemos en el Bosque. 2004. (SPA.). 28p. (J). (gr. k up). pap. 6.50 (978-980-257-282-3(9)) Ekare, Ediciones VEN. *Dist:* Lectorum Pubns., Inc., Iaconi, Mariuccia Bk. Imports.

Bernard, Greg. Alpha Summer. 2005. (YA). per. 12.95 (978-0-926147-21-8(8)) Loonfeather Pr.

Blair, Eric. El Lobo y el Perro: Version de la Fabula de Esopo. Silverman, Dianne, illus. 2006. (Read-It! Readers en Espanol Ser.).Tr. of Dog & the Wolf: A Retelling of Aesop's Fable. (SPA.). 32p. (J). (ps-3). 19.95 (978-1-4048-1619-0(4)) Picture Window Bks.

—El Lobo y los Siete Cabritos: Version del Cuento de los Hermanos Grimm. Petrusek, Brett, illus. 2006. (Read-It! Readers en Espanol Ser.).Tr. of Wolf & the Seven Little Kids: A Retelling of the Grimm's Fairy Tale. (SPA.). 32p. (J). (ps-3). 19.95 (978-1-4048-1645-9(3)) Picture Window Bks.

Bloom, Becky. Wolf. Biet, Pascal, illus. 1999. 32p. (J). (ps-3). pap. 16.95 (978-0-531-30155-5(9) , Orchard Bks.) Scholastic, Inc.

—Wolf. Biet, Pascal, illus. 2001. (J). 26.90 incl. audio (978-0-8045-6864-7(2)) Spoken Arts, Inc.

Bowen, Asta. Wolf: The Journey Home. 2005. 288p. (J). 16.95 (978-1-58234-689-2(5) , Bloomsbury Children) Bloomsbury Publishing.

Bradford, Karleen. Ghost Wolf. Cormack, Allan & Drew-Brook, Deborah, illus. 2005. 59p. (J). lib. bdg. 20.00 (****978-1-4242-1254-5(5)***) Fitzgerald Bks.

—Ghost Wolf. Cormack, Allan & Drew-Brook, Deborah, illus. 2005. (Orca Echoes Ser.). 64p. (J). (gr. 2-3). pap. 4.99 (978-1-55143-341-7(9)) Orca Bk. Pubs. USA.

Bradman, Tony. Look Out, He's Behind You! Chamberlain, Margaret, illus. 2007. 28p. (J). 7.95 (****978-1-84507-734-1(2)***) Lincoln, Frances Ltd. GBR. *Dist:* Perseus Distribution.

Branford, Henrietta. White Wolf. 2007. 96p. (J). (gr. 4-7). pap. 5.99 (****978-0-7636-3289-2(9)***) Candlewick Pr.

Brave M.A., Kathryn A. & Lavin, Paul J. A Fit ting Fairy Tale. 2006. 60p. pap. 12.95 (978-1-4241-2992-8(3)) PublishAmerica, Inc.

Brightwood, Laura, illus. Wolf under the Bed. Brightwood, Laura, . 2007. (J). DVD (****978-1-934409-04-6(9)***) 3-C Institute for Social Development.

Broadley, Leo. Pedro the Brave. Swain, Holly, illus. 2002. (J). 5.95 (978-1-58925-375-9(2)); 32p. tchr. ed. 14.95 (978-1-58925-024-6(9)) ME Media LLC. (tiger tales).

—Pedro the Brave. 2002. (gr. k-3). lib. bdg. 14.10 (978-0-613-56567-7(3)) Tandem Library Bks.

Brown, Ken, illus. What's the Time, Grandma Wolf? 2001. 32p. (J). (ps-1). 15.95 (978-1-56145-250-7(5) , Q33285) Peachtree Pubs., Ltd.

Burns, Laura J. & Metz, Melinda. Apocalypse Memories. 2004. (Buffy the Vampire Slayer Ser.). 256p. (YA). pap. 6.99 (978-0-689-86700-2(X) , Simon Spotlight Entertainment) Simon & Schuster.

Butler, Dori. A Sheep in Wolf's Clothing. 2006. 23.00 (****978-1-4108-6185-6(6)***) Benchmark Education Co.

Caballero, Erica. Mount Mole. 2006. pap. 10.00 (****978-1-4257-2301-9(2)***) Xlibris Corp.

Campos, Jacqueline. The Adventures of Lil' Wolf, Twinkie, to. 2005. 63p. pap. 12.95 (978-1-4137-8494-7(1)) PublishAmerica, Inc.

Capdevila, Roser. El Lobo y los Siete Cabritos. 2002. (Cuentos Fantasticos de las Tres Mellizas Coleccion: Vol. 2). (SPA.). (J). (gr. k-2). pap. 5.95 (978-1-930332-36-2(X)) Lectorum Pubns., Inc.

—El Loby Y Los Siete Cabritos. 2002. (SPA.). (gr. k-3). lib. bdg. 14.10 (978-0-613-64537-9(5)) Tandem Library Bks.

Cappucceto Rosso. 1999. Tr. of Little Red Riding Hood. (ITA., Illus.). 24p. (J). (ps-5). pap. 7.95 (978-88-8148-254-2(1)) European Language Institute ITA. *Dist:* Distribooks, Inc., Midwest European Pubns.

Capriola, Arlene & Swenson, Rigmor. The Boy Who Cried Wolf. Mastry, Cherisse, ed. Burns, Kathy, illus. 1998. (Once upon a Time Ser.). (J). (gr. k-2). pap., wbk. ed. incl. audio (978-1-57022-170-5(7)) ECS Learning Systems, Inc.

Carbone, Elisa. The Pack. 2006. 160p. (YA). (gr. 7). pap. 5.99 (978-0-14-240535-2(3) , Puffin) Penguin Group (USA) Inc.

Casanova, Mary. Wolf Shadows. 1999. (978-0-606-16667-6(X)) Tandem Library Bks.

Catchpool, Michael. Where There's a Bear, There's Trouble! Cabban, Vanessa, illus. 2002. 28p. (J). (ps-k). tchr. ed. 14.95 (978-1-58925-022-2(2) , tiger tales) ME Media LLC.

Chichester-Clark, Emma. Wicked Wolf Tales. 2004. (Illus.). 80p. pap. 12.50 (978-1-84365-018-8(5) , Pavilion Bks., Ltd.) Anova Bks. GBR. *Dist:* Trafalgar Square Publishing.

Child, Lauren. Cuidado con los Cuentos de Lobos. (Illus.). 36p. (J). (ps-3). 2004. (SPA.). 17.99 (978-84-95040-80-0(8)); 2000. (CAT., 17.95 (978-84-95040-81-7(6)) Serres, Ediciones, S. L. ESP. *Dist:* Lectorum Pubns., Inc.

Christelow, Eileen. Where's the Big Bad Wolf? Christelow, Eileen, illus. 2002. (Illus.). 40p. (J). (gr. k-3). tchr. ed. 16.00 (978-0-618-18194-0(6) , Clarion Bks.) Houghton Mifflin Co. Trade & Reference Div.

Clark, Emma Chichester, illus. Wicked Wolf Stories. 2003. 80p. (J). 19.95 (978-1-86205-460-8(6) , Pavilion Bks., Ltd.) Anova Bks. GBR. *Dist:* Trafalgar Square Publishing.

Clement-Davies, David. Fell. 2007. 542p. (YA). (gr. 7-17). 19.95 (****978-0-8109-1185-7(X)***) Abrams, Harry N. , Inc.

—Fell. 2007. 432p. (YA). pap. 19.95 (****978-0-8109-9470-6(4)***) Abrams, Harry N. , Inc.

Clement-Davies, David. The Sight. 2002. (gr. 7-12). lib. bdg. 16.45 (978-0-613-68285-5(8)) Tandem Library Bks.

Clish, Marian L. A Wolf's Tale. 1999. (J). (gr. 5-10). 22.95 incl. audio compact disk (978-1-928632-22-1(X)) Writers Marketplace:Consulting, Critiquing & Publishing.

—A Wolf's Tale. Anderson, Jan, illus. unabr. ed. (J). (gr. k-5). 1999. 18.95 incl. audio (978-1-928632-21-4(1)); 1999. 15.95 (978-1-928632-20-7(3)); pap. 14.95 incl. audio compact disk (978-1-928632-01-6(7)); 1999. pap. 10.95 incl. audio (978-1-928632-00-9(9)) Writers Marketplace:Consulting, Critiquing & Publishing.

Condon, Bill. Miss Wolf & the Porkers: These Little Porkers Are in for a Shock! Magerl, Caroline, illus. 2006. (Bites Ser.). 96p. (J). pap. 3.95 (978-0-7624-2649-2(7) , Running Pr. Kids) Running Pr. Bk. Pubs.

Connolly, Brian A. Hawk. 2007. 156p. 20.95 (***978-1-60264-030-6(0)***); 160p. per. 13.95 (***978-1-60264-029-0(7)***) Virtualbookworm.com Publishing, Inc.

Connolly, Brian A. Wolf Journal: A Novel. 2005. 164p. 20.95 (978-1-58939-795-8(9)); 168p. per. 13.95 (978-1-58939-794-1(0)) Virtualbookworm.com Publishing, Inc.

Corentin, Philippe. Chaf! 2005. (SPA.). (J). 9.95 (978-84-8470-131-6(X)) Corimbo, Editorial S.L. ESP. *Dist:* Iaconi, Mariuccia Bk. Imports.

Corentin, Philippe. El Ogro, el Lobo, la Niña y el Pastel. 2004. (SPA.). 202p. (J). 17.99 (978-84-8470-157-6(3)) Corimbo, Editorial S.L. ESP. *Dist:* Lectorum Pubns., Inc.

Costello, Emily. Runaway Wolf Pups, No. 4. 1999. (Animal Emergency Ser.: No. 4). (Illus.). 128p. (J). (gr. 3-7). pap. 3.99 (978-0-380-79757-8(7)) HarperCollins Pubs.

Crabtree, Zona Mae. White Dove. 2005. (Corn Cave Ser.: 3). (Illus.). (YA). per. 8.00 (978-0-9726826-2-6(7)) Owl Hollow Publishing.

Creedon, Catherine. Blue Wolf. Bentley, James, illus. 192p. (J). 2005. pap. 5.99 (978-0-06-050870-8(1)); 2003. lib. bdg. 16.89 (978-0-06-050869-2(8)) HarperCollins Pubs. (Julie Andrews Collection).

Cresswell, Helen. Sophie & the Sea Wolf. (Illus.). 32p. (J). (978-0-340-65608-2(5) , Hodder & Stoughton) Hodder General Publishing Division.

Cummins, Amanda Lynn. The Wolf: The Untold Story. 2005. (Illus.). 32p. (J). (gr. 5-6). 10.00 (978-0-9670947-7-9(1)) Green Sheet Inc., The.

Curwood, James Oliver. Baree: The Story of a Wolf-Dog. 2005. (Medallion Edition Ser.). 256p. (YA). (gr. 4-7). pap. 5.95 (978-1-55704-132-6(6)) Newmarket Pr.

—Kazan: Father of Baree. 2005. 240p. (YA). (gr. 4-7). pap. 5.95 (978-1-55704-225-5(X)) Newmarket Pr.

De Velasco, Miguel Martin Fernandez. Pabluras. (SPA.). 120p. (YA). (gr. 5-8). (978-84-279-3146-6(8) , NG3678) Noguer y Caralt Editores, S. A. ESP. *Dist:* Lectorum Pubns., Inc.

—Pabluras y Gris. (SPA.). 112p. (YA). (gr. 5-8). (978-84-279-3178-7(6) , NG3679) Noguer y Caralt Editores, S. A. ESP. *Dist:* Lectorum Pubns., Inc.

Delessert, Etienne. Big & Bad. 2008. 32p. (J). (gr. 3-5). 17.00 (***978-0-618-88934-1(5)***) Houghton Mifflin Co.

DeLisa, Patricia, illus. Little Red Riding Hood: A Book for the Thoughtful Parent. 2006. 32p. (J). 14.95 (978-0-88010-571-2(2) , Bell Pond Bks.) SteinerBooks, Inc.

Denslow, Sharon Phillips. Big Wolf & Little Wolf. 2000. (Illus.). 32p. (J). (ps up). 15.89 (978-0-688-16175-0(8)) HarperCollins Pubs.

—Big Wolf & Little Wolf. Felstead, Cathie, illus. 2000. 32p. (J). (ps up). 16.99 (978-0-688-16174-3(X)) HarperCollins Pubs.

Disney Book Club Staff. Henny Penny & Big Bad Wolf. 1999. (J). lib. bdg. (978-0-394-94008-3(3) , Random Hse. Bks. for Young Readers) Random Hse. Children's Bks.

The Dog & the Wolf, Set 1. l.t. ed. 1999. (Illus.). 25p. (J). (gr. k-6). reprint ed. pap. 2.50 (978-1-893688-04-9(6)) Carroll Schl., The.

Donovan, Kevin. Billy & His Friends Tame a Wild Wolf. 2003. (Illus.). 32p. 10.95 (978-0-9641338-1-5(4)) Billy the Bear & His Friends, Inc.

Douzou, Olivier. Lobo. Sanchez, Diana Luz, tr. Douzou, Olivier, illus. 1999. (Los Especiales de A la Orilla Del Viento Ser.). (SPA., Illus.). 30p. (J). (ps-1). 13.99 (978-968-16-6079-6(X)) Fondo de Cultura Economica USA.

Dudley, Maywill. The Story of Little Red Riding Hood. 2005. reprint ed. pap. 15.95 (978-1-4191-5430-0(3)) Kessinger Publishing, LLC.

Dunker, Bon. An Almost True Tale of Three Pigs & a Wolf. 2000. (Illus.). vi, 132p. (J). (gr. 2-6). pap. 5.99 (978-0-9701371-0-4(9)) Z 3 Universe.

Edwards, Julie Andrews & Hamilton, Emma Walton. Dragon: Hound of Honor. (J). (gr. 4 up). 2005. 208p. pap. 5.99 (978-0-06-057121-4(7)); 2004. 192p. 16.99 (978-0-06-057119-1(5)); 2004. 192p. lib. bdg. 17.89 (978-0-06-057120-7(9)) HarperCollins Pubs. (Julie Andrews Collection).

Egan, Tim. The Experiments of Doctor Vermin. Egan, Tim, illus. 2002. (Illus.). 32p. (J). (gr. k-3). tchr. ed. 15.00 (978-0-618-13224-9(4)) Houghton Mifflin Co. Trade & Reference Div.

Evans, Nicholas. The Loop. 1999. (gr. 7-12). lib. bdg. 16.45 (978-0-613-21928-0(7)) Tandem Library Bks.

Farrell, Liam. The Return of the Big Bad Wolf. Myler, Terry, illus. 2004. 64p. pap. 8.95 (978-1-901737-48-6(9)) Anvil Bks., Ltd. IRL. *Dist:* Dufour Editions, Inc.

—The Trial of the Big Bad Wolf. Myler, Terry, illus. 2003. (Elephant Ser.). 64p. (YA). (gr. 1 up). pap. 8.95 (978-1-901737-40-0(3)) Anvil Bks., Ltd. IRL. *Dist:* Dufour Editions, Inc.

—The True Story of the Three Little Pigs & the Big Bad Wolf. 2002. (Illus.). 64p. (YA). (gr. 1 up). pap. 8.95 (978-1-901737-35-6(7)) Anvil Bks., Ltd. IRL. *Dist:* Dufour Editions, Inc.

Farrow, Stephanie, ed. Blue Wolf & Friends Storybook, 1 Vol., Units 1-4. l.t. ed. 2004. (Illus.). 93p. (978-0-9758759-2-6(2)) Progressive Language, Inc.

Fearnley, Jan. Mr. Wolf & the Enormous Turnip. 2005. (Illus.). 40p. (Orig.). (J). (ps-ps). pap. 9.99 (978-1-4052-1580-0(1)) Egmont Bks., Ltd. GBR. *Dist:* Trafalgar Square Publishing.

—Mr. Wolf & the Three Bears. 2002. (Illus.). 32p. (J). (ps-2). 16.00 (978-0-15-216423-2(5)) Harcourt Children's Bks.

—Mr. Wolf's Pancakes. 2001. (Illus.). 32p. (J). (ps-k). 6.95 (978-1-58925-354-4(X)); 15.95 (978-1-58925-004-8(4)) ME Media LLC. (tiger tales).

—Mr. Wolf's Pancakes. 2001. (Illus.). (J). (978-0-606-20483-5(0)) Tandem Library Bks.

—Mr Wolf's Pancakes. 2001. (gr. k-3). lib. bdg. 14.10 (978-0-613-53842-8(0)) Tandem Library Bks.

Fetzner, Mary. Simple Story of the 3 Pigs & the Scientific Wolf. 2000. (Illus.). 64p. (J). (gr. k-3). pap. 11.95 (978-1-880505-78-6(9) , CLC0238) Pieces of Learning.

Forward, Toby. The Wolf's Story: What Really Happened to Little Red Riding Hood. Cohen, Izhar, illus. 2005. 32p. (J). (ps-3). 15.99 (978-0-7636-2785-0(2)) Candlewick Pr.

Fraser, W. A. The Gold Wolf. 2004. reprint ed. pap. 15.95 (978-1-4191-6404-0(X)); pap. 1.99 (978-1-4192-6404-7(4)) Kessinger Publishing, LLC.

Freedman, Claire. New Kid in Town. Stephenson, Kristina, illus. 2006. 28p. (J). 16.00 (978-1-56148-547-5(0)) Good Bks.

Frontiera, Deborah K. Eric & the Enchanted Leaf / Eric y la Hoja Encantada: A Visit with Canis Lupis / una Visita con Canis Lupis. Santillan-Cruz, Silvia R., tr. Scott, Korey, illus. 2nd l.t. ed. 2005. (SPA & ENG.). 32p. (J). lib. bdg. 16.95 (978-0-9663629-8-5(5)) By Grace Enterprises.

Gaiman, Neil. Los lobos de la Pared: Wolves in the Walls. 2006. (SPA.). 64p. 22.95 (978-1-59497-222-5(2)) Public Square Bks.

—The Wolves in the Walls. McKean, Dave, illus. 2003. 56p. (J). 16.99 (978-0-380-97827-4(X)) HarperCollins Pubs.

Gallaz, Christophe. The Wolf Who Loved Music. Logue, Mary, tr. from FRE. 2003. (Illus.). 32p. 17.95 (978-1-56846-178-6(X) , Creative Editions) Creative Co., The.

George, Jean Craighead. Julie of the Wolves. Schoenherr, John, illus. 2003. (Julie of the Wolves Ser.). 208p. (YA). (gr. 7 up). pap. 5.99 (978-0-06-054095-1(8) , Harper Trophy) HarperCollins Pubs.

—Julie of the Wolves. l.t. ed. 2004. (Beeler Mystery Ser.). 32.95 (978-1-58118-121-0(3)) LRS.

—Julie of the Wolves. l.t. ed. 2005. 180p. (YA). pap. 10.95 (978-0-7862-7955-5(9)) Thorndike Pr.

—Julie y los Lobos. 26th ed. 2003. (SPA., Illus.). 184p. (J). (gr. 5-8). pap. 12.95 (978-84-204-4887-9(7) , AF0842) Santillana USA Publishing Co., Inc.

—Julie's Wolf Pack. Minor, Wendell, illus. 1999. (Julie of the Wolves Ser.). 208p. (J). (gr. 5 up). pap. 5.99 (978-0-06-440721-2(7) , Harper Trophy) HarperCollins Pubs.

—Julie's Wolf Pack. unabr. ed. 2000. (YA). pap., stu. ed. 53.20 incl. audio (978-0-7887-3849-4(6) , 41047X4) Recorded Bks., LLC.

—Julie's Wolf Pack. Minor, Wendell, illus. 1999. 192p. (J). (gr. k-9). per. 14.15 (978-0-613-17815-0(7)) Tandem Library Bks.

—Julie's Wolf Pack. 1999. (Illus.). (J). 12.64 (978-0-606-18700-8(6)) Tandem Library Bks.

—Nutik & Amaroq Play Ball. 2000. 32p. (J). (gr. k-3). pap. 5.95 (978-0-06-443523-9(7)) HarperCollins Pubs.

—Nutik, the Wolf Pup. Rand, Ted, illus. 2001. 40p. (J). (gr. k-3). 15.99 (978-0-06-028164-9(2)); lib. bdg. 17.89 (978-0-06-028165-6(0)) HarperCollins Pubs.

—Nutik, the Wolf Pup. 2000. 32p. (J). (gr. k-3). pap. 5.95 (978-0-06-443522-2(9)) HarperCollins Pubs.

Godkin, Celia. Wolf Island. Godkin, Celia, illus. 2006. (Illus.). (J). (gr. 1-4). 40p. (***978-1-55455-007-4(6)***); 32p. pap. (***978-1-55455-008-1(4)***) Fitzhenry & Whiteside, Ltd.

Golden Books Staff. Little Lost Wolf Pup. Fruchter, Jason, illus. 2006. 64p. (J). (ps-2). pap. 3.99 (978-0-375-83590-2(3) , Golden Bks.) Random Hse. Children's Bks.

Grambo, Rebecca L. Lupe: A Wolf Cub's First Year. Cox, Daniel J., illus. 2004. (Wild Beginnings Ser.). 48p. (J). (ps-3). pap. 9.95 (978-1-55285-611-6(9)) Whitecap Bks., Ltd. CAN. *Dist:* Firefly Bks., Ltd.

Gravett, Emily. Wolves. Gravett, Emily, illus. 2006. (Illus.). 40p. (J). (gr. k-3). 16.99 (978-1-4169-1491-4(9) , Simon & Schuster Children's Publishing) Simon & Schuster Children's Publishing.

Greene, Janice. White Fang. 2003. (gr. 7-12). lib. bdg. 15.25 (978-0-613-65750-1(0)) Tandem Library Bks.

Grimm, Jacob W. Little Red Riding Hood. 1999. (gr. k-3). lib. bdg. 15.25 (978-0-613-89995-6(4)) Tandem Library Bks.

Grimm, Jacob W. & Grimm, Wilhelm K. Little Red Riding Hood: Caperucita Roja. Surges, James, tr. Estrada, Pau, illus. 2006. 22p. (J). (gr. k-4). reprint ed. 15.00 (978-0-7567-9994-6(5)) DIANE Publishing Co.

—The Wolf & the Seven Little Kids. Routiaux, Claudine, illus. 2001. (Little Pebbles Ser.).Tr. of Wolf und die Sieben Jungen Geisslein. 32p. 6.95 (978-0-7892-0735-7(4)) Abbeville Pr., Inc.

Grimm, Jacob W., et al. Little Red Riding Hood/Caperucita Roja: A Bilingual Book. Surges, James, tr. from CAT. Estrada, Pau, illus. 1999. (ENG & SPA.). 32p. (J). (ps-3). 12.95 (978-0-8118-2561-0(2)) Chronicle Bks. LLC.

Grimm, Wilhelm K. & Grimm, Jacob W. Little Red Cap. Zwerger, Lisbeth, illus. 37p. (J). (gr. k-2). pap. 5.95 (978-0-8072-1285-1(7) , Listening Library) Random Hse. Audio Publishing Group.

Grimm. Caperucita Roja. 2001. Tr. of Little Red Ridinghood. (SPA.). (978-968-6347-35-7(6)) Larousse, Ediciones, S. A. de C. V.

Grooms, Molly. We Are Wolves. 2002. (Illus.). 32p. (J). (ps-2). pap. 7.95 (978-1-55971-835-6(8) , NorthWord Bks. for Young Readers) T&N Children's Publishing.

Gruffudd, Elena. Gelert. 2005. (WEL., Illus.). 34p. (978-0-86381-291-0(0)) Gwasg Carreg Gwalch.

Guinane, Carole. The Wolves of Witchmaker. 2002. 258p. pap. 14.95 (978-0-595-21360-3(X) , Writers Club Pr.) iUniverse, Inc.

Haesche, Richard P., Sr. Cry of the Werewolf. Spatola, Paul, illus. aut. ed. 2000. 226p. (J). pap. 11.99 (978-1-929381-61-6(1) , Third Millennium Publishing) Sci Fi-Arizona, Inc.

—Spirit of the Great White Wolf. Spatola, Paul, illus. aut. ed. 2000. 190p. (J). pap. 11.99 (978-1-929381-64-7(6) , Third Millennium Publishing) Sci Fi-Arizona, Inc.

Harcourt School Publishers Staff. Wolf Tales. 3rd ed. 2002. (Trophies Reading Program Ser.). (Illus.). pap. 5.10 (978-0-15-323179-7(3)) Harcourt Schl. Pubs.

Harland, Richard. Walter Wants to Be a Werewolf: Will Walter Grimm Ever Fit In? 2006. (Chomps Ser.). 96p. (J). pap. 3.95 (978-0-7624-2651-5(9) , Running Pr. Kids) Running Pr. Bk. Pubs.

Harrison, Cora. Nuala & Her Secret Wolf. 1998. (Drumshee Timeline Ser.: Bk. 1). (Illus.). 128p. (J). (gr. 4-8). pap. 6.95 (978-0-86327-585-2(0)) Wolfhound Pr. IRL. *Dist:* Irish American Bk. Co.

Harrison, Troon. Eye of the Wolf. 212p. 2004. pap. (978-1-55005-073-8(7)); 2003. (Illus.). (YA). (978-1-55005-072-1(9)) Fitzhenry & Whiteside, Ltd.

Hartman, Bob. The Wolf Who Cried Boy. Raglin, Tim, illus. 2002. 32p. (J). (gr. 1-3). 16.99 (978-0-399-23578-8(7) , Putnam Juvenile) Penguin Group (USA) Inc.

—The Wolf Who Cried Boy. Raglin, Tim, illus. 2004. 32p. (J). (gr. k up). pap. 6.99 (978-0-14-240159-0(5) , Puffin) Penguin Group (USA) Inc.

—The Wolf Who Cried Boy. Rayla, Tim, illus. ed. 2004. (J). (gr. 1-3). spiral bd. (978-0-616-14574-6(8)) Canadian National Institute for the Blind/Institut National Canadien pour les Aveugles.

Hartnett, Sonya. Stripes of Sidestep Wolf. 2007. (Illus.). 208p. (YA). (gr. 7). pap. 7.99 (***978-0-7636-3416-2(6)***) Candlewick Pr.

Hartnett, Sonya. Stripes of the Sidestep Wolf. 2005. 208p. (J). (gr. 7 up). 16.99 (978-0-7636-2644-0(9)) Candlewick Pr.

Helakoski, Leslie. Big Chickens. Cole, Henry, illus. 2008. 32p. (J). (ps). pap. 6.99 (***978-0-14-241057-8(8)***, Puffin) Penguin Group (USA) Inc.

Hennessy, B. G. The Boy Who Cried Wolf. Kulikov, Boris, illus. 2006. 40p. (J). (ps-2). 15.95 (978-0-689-87433-8(2)) Simon & Schuster Children's Publishing.

Hillert, Margaret. Little Red Riding Hood. (Illus.). (J). 6.00 (978-0-87895-680-7(8)) Modern Curriculum Pr.

Holdren, Mark W. Spirit Wolf. 2004. (Illus.). 158p. reprint ed. pap. 13.95 (978-0-9760648-0-0(4)) Powell Hill Pr.

Hoover, Helen. Great Wolf & the Good Woodsman. Bowen, Betsy, illus. 2005. (Fesler-Lampert Minnesota Heritage Book Ser.). 40p. (J). 14.95 (978-0-8166-4445-2(4)) Univ. of Minnesota Pr.

Hopkins, Suzette. Little Wolf's Christmas. Taylor, Jill, illus. 2004. 19p. (J). 12.95 (978-1-932133-72-1(0)) Writers' Collective, The.

Howker, Janni. Walk with a Wolf. 2002. (gr. k-3). lib. bdg. 14.15 (978-0-613-74757-8(7)) Tandem Library Bks.

—Walk with a Wolf: Read & Wonder. Fox-Davies, Sarah, illus. 2002. (Read & Wonder Bks.). 32p. (J). (ps-3). pap. 6.99 (978-0-7636-1872-8(1)) Candlewick Pr.

Hubbell, Patricia & Westcott, Nadine Bernard. Pig Picnic. 1999. (Road to Reading Ser.). (Illus.). 32p. (J). (ps-1). 11.99 (978-0-307-46108-7(4) , Random Hse. Bks. for Young Readers) Random Hse. Children's Bks.

Hutchinson, Hanna. Caperucita Roja. Nofziger, Edward, illus. 1998. (Interlingo Ser.). (SPA.). 20p. (J). (ps-2). pap. 2.95 (978-0-922852-54-3(5)) Another Language Pr.

Irvin-Marston, Hope. My Little Book of Timber Wolves. Magdalena-Brown, Maria, illus. 2nd ed. 2004. 32p. (J). pap. 7.95 (978-0-89317-052-3(6) , WW-0526, Windward Publishing) Finney Co., Inc.

Janovitz, Marilyn. Can I Help? 1998. (Illus.). 32p. (J). (ps-3). pap. 5.95 (978-1-55858-904-9(X)) North-South Bks., Inc.

Jennings, Patrick. The Wolving Time. 2003. 208p. (J). pap. 15.95 (978-0-439-39555-7(0)) Scholastic, Inc.

Johnson, Sandi. White Wolf at Dawn. Johnson, Britt, ed. Sturgen, Bobbi, illus. 2002. 25p. (J). (gr. k-5). spiral bd. 5.99 (978-1-929063-72-7(5) , 171) Moons & Stars Publishing For Children.

Julie of the Wolves. 1999. (J). (gr. 4-7). 11.95 (978-1-56137-821-0(6)) Novel Units, Inc.

Julietta, Melinda. We Are Wolves. Guamotta, Lucia, illus. 1999. 32p. (ps-3). 12.95 (978-1-55971-713-7(0) , NorthWord Bks. for Young Readers) T&N Children's Publishing.

Jungman, Ann. Lucy & the Big Bad Wolf. Littlewood, Karin, illus. 2005. 120p. (J). (ps-6). pap. 4.95 (978-1-903015-39-1(1)) Barn Owl Bks, London GBR. *Dist:* Independent Pubs. Group.

Karu, Tim, et al. Henry & the White Wolf. Karu, Tyler, illus. 2000. (Illus.). 32p. (J). (ps-3). 12.95 (978-0-7611-2135-0(8) , 12135) Workman Publishing Co., Inc.

Karu, Tyler & Karu, Tim. Henry & the White Wolf. 2001. (YA). (ps up). 12.95 (978-0-7611-2356-9(3)) Workman Publishing Co., Inc.

Kasza, Keiko. The Dog Who Cried Wolf. Kasza, Keiko, illus. 2005. (Illus.). 32p. (J). (ps-3). 15.99 (978-0-399-24247-2(3) , Putnam Juvenile) Penguin Group (USA) Inc.

Keene, Carolyn. Mystery of the Mother Wolf. 2002. (gr. 5-8). lib. bdg. 13.00 (978-0-613-45084-3(1)) Tandem Library Bks.

Kelly, John & Tincknell, Cathy. The Mystery of Eatum Hall. Kelly, John & Tincknell, Cathy, illus. 2004. (Illus.). 32p. (J). (gr. k-3). 15.99 (978-0-7636-2594-8(9)) Candlewick Pr.

Kempter, C. & Weldin, F. Dear Little Lamb. 2006. (Illus.). 32p. (J). 16.95 (978-0-7358-2086-9(4)) North-South Bks., Inc.

Kimura & North, Lucy. One Stormy Night. Abe, Hiroshi, illus. 2005. 48p. (J). (gr. 1-3). 16.00 (978-4-7700-2970-6(5)) Kodansha International JPN. *Dist:* Cheng & Tsui Co.

—One Sunny Day, 2 vols., Vol. 2. Abe, Hiroshi, illus. 2005. 48p. (J). 16.00 (978-4-7700-2971-3(3)) Kodansha International JPN. *Dist:* Cheng & Tsui Co.

Kitamura, Satoshi. Por el Hilo se Saca el Ovillo. Kitamura, Satoshi, illus. 2003. (Picture Books Collection). (SPA., Illus.). 32p. (J). (gr. k-3). 14.95 (978-84-372-2357-5(1)) Altea, Ediciones, S.A. - Grupo Santillana ESP. *Dist:* Santillana USA Publishing Co., Inc.

Knopp, Sue, creator. Study Guide for Wolf Journal: A Novel. 2005. 60p. per. 7.95 (978-1-58939-827-6(0)) Virtualbookworm.com Publishing, Inc.

Krensky, Stephen. Big Bad Wolves at School. Sneed, Brad, illus. 2001. 32p. (J). (ps-3). 15.99 (978-0-689-83799-9(2) , Simon & Schuster Children's Publishing) Simon & Schuster Children's Publishing.

Kubler, Annie. What's the Time Mr Wolf? 2003. (Illus.). 24p. (J). 9.99 (978-0-85953-944-9(X)) Child's Play-International.

La Fevers, Robin. Werewolf Rising. 2006. 176p. (J). (gr. 5). 16.99 (978-0-525-47665-8(2) , Dutton Juvenile) Penguin Group (USA) Inc.

Langton, Jane. Saint Francis & the Wolf. Plume, Ilse, illus. 2007. 32p. (J). 16.95 (***978-1-56792-320-9(8)***) Godine, David R. Pub.

Law, Felicia. Rumble Meets Wilson Wolf. Pak, Yoon Mi, illus. 2006. (Read-It! Readers: Rumble's Cave Hotel Ser.). 32p. (J). (gr. k-3). (978-1-4048-1288-8(1)) Picture Window Bks.

Lefèvre, A. M. Hugan Fach Goch. 2005. (WEL., Illus.). 10p. (978-0-86381-645-1(2)) Gwasg Carreg Gwalch.

Lemieux, Margo. Wolf Song. Taylor, Stephen, illus. 2000. (Books for Young Learners). 16p. (J). pap. 5.00 (978-1-57274-147-8(3)) Owen, Richard C. Pubs., Inc.

Lester, Helen. The Sheep in Wolf's Clothing. Munsinger, Lynn, illus. 2007. 32p. (J). (gr. k-3). 16.00 (***978-0-618-86844-5(5)***) Houghton Mifflin Co. Trade & Reference Div.

Levine, Gail Carson. Betsy Who Cried Wolf. Nash, Scott, illus. 40p. (J). (ps-3). 2002. 15.95 (978-0-06-028763-4(2)); 2002. lib. bdg. 16.89 (978-0-06-028764-1(0)); 2005. reprint ed. pap. 6.99 (978-0-06-443640-3(3)) HarperCollins Pubs.

Lindskold, Jane. Through Wolf's Eyes. 2002. (gr. 5-8). lib. bdg. 16.45 (978-0-613-64450-1(6)) Tandem Library Bks.

Little Red Riding Hood: 6 Small Books. (gr. k-2). 23.00 (978-0-7635-8510-5(6)) Rigby Education.

Little Red Riding Hood: Individual Title Six-Packs. (Story Steps Ser.). (gr. k-2). 32.00 (978-0-7635-9841-9(0)) Rigby Education.

Lo Que el Lobo le Conto a la Luna. 2004. Tr. of What the Wolf Told the Moon. (SPA., Illus.). (J). 20.99 (978-84-261-3275-8(8)) Juventud, Editorial ESP. *Dist:* Lectorum Pubns., Inc.

Lomba, Ana. Easy French Storybook: Little Red Riding Hood. 2005. (ENG & FRE., Illus.). 41p. 14.95 incl. cd-rom (978-0-07-146167-2(1) , 9780071461672) McGraw-Hill Cos., The.

—Easy Spanish Storybook: Little Red Riding Hood. 2005. (ENG & SPA., Illus.). 41p. 14.95 incl. cd-rom (978-0-07-146164-1(7) , 9780071461641) McGraw-Hill Cos., The.

London, Jack. The Call of the Wild. Pablo Marcos Studio Staff, illus. 2002. (Great Illustrated Classics Ser.). 240p. (J). (gr. 3-8). 21.35 (978-1-57765-682-1(2) , ABDO & Daughters) ABDO Publishing Co.

—The Call of the Wild. 2001. (Fast Track Classics Ser.). (Illus.). 48p. pap. 9.95 (978-0-237-52285-8(3) , Evans Brothers, Limited) Evans Publishing Group GBR. *Dist:* Independent Pubs. Group.

—The Call of the Wild. Davidson, Andrew, illus. 2002. (Kingfisher Classics Ser.). 208p. (J). (gr. k-3). tchr. ed. 15.95 (978-0-7534-5493-0(9) , Kingfisher) Houghton Mifflin Co. Trade & Reference Div.

—The Call of the Wild. 2003. (Aladdin Classics Ser.). 160p. mass mkt. 4.99 (978-0-689-85674-7(1) , Aladdin) Simon & Schuster Children's Publishing.

—The Call of the Wild. Clift, Eva, tr. Clift, Eva, illus. 2003. (Values in Action Illustrated Classics Ser.). (J). (978-1-59203-047-7(5)) Learning Challenge, Inc.

—The Call of the Wild. Corvino, Lucy, illus. 2005. (Classic Starts Ser.). 160p. 4.95 (978-1-4027-1274-6(X)) Sterling Publishing Co., Inc.

—The Call of the Wild. unabr. ed. 2002. (YA). pap. incl. audio compact disk (978-1-58472-221-2(5) , In Audio) Sound Room Pubs., Inc.

—The Call of the Wild & Selected Short Stories. 2006. (Scholastic Classics Ser.). (Illus.). iv, 260p. (J). (gr. 9-12). 25.00 (978-0-531-16982-7(0) , Watts, Franklin) Scholastic Library Publishing.

—Colmillo Blanco. 2003. (Advanced Reading Ser.: Vol. 56). (SPA., Illus.). 268p. (J). (gr. 4-7). 11.95 (978-84-239-9030-6(3)) Espasa Calpe, S.A. ESP. *Dist:* Planeta Publishing Corp., i.b.d., Ltd.

—Colmillo Blanco. 2000. (SPA., Illus.). 280p. (YA). (gr. 7 up). 9.95 (978-84-207-1229-1(9)) Grupo Anaya, S.A. ESP. *Dist:* Libros Sin Fronteras.

—Colmillo Blanco. (SPA.). (J). 8.00 (978-958-04-7143-1(6)) Norma S.A. COL. *Dist:* Distribuidora Norma, Inc.

—Colmillo Blanco, la Llama de la Selva. 2002. (Classics for Young Readers Ser.). (SPA.). (YA). 14.95 (978-84-392-0902-7(9) , EV30600) Gaviota Ediciones ESP. *Dist:* Lectorum Pubns., Inc.

—Encender un Fuego. Gonzalez Batlle, Jorge, tr. Vogel, Nathaele, illus. 2004. (SPA.). 79p. pap. 12.95 (978-84-95939-52-4(5)) Blume ESP. *Dist:* Independent Pubs. Group.

—Jack London/the Call of the Wild. Carrillo, Fred, illus. 2005. 48p. (gr. 5-8). 25.50 (978-0-7910-9104-3(X)) Facts On File, Inc.

—White Fang. 2005. 28.95 (978-1-4218-1472-8(2)); 276p. pap. 13.95 (978-1-4218-1572-5(9)) 1st World Publishing, Inc. (1st World Library - Literary Society).

—White Fang. Vera, Ross, illus. 2002. (Great Illustrated Classics Ser.). 240p. (J). (gr. 3-8). 21.35 (978-1-57765-810-8(8) , ABDO & Daughters) ABDO Publishing Co.

—White Fang. 2005. (ENG.). 176p. (gr. 3-7). per. 14.95 (***978-1-59818-531-7(4)***) Aegypan.

—White Fang. 2003. 192p. (J). 4.99 (978-1-57759-566-3(1)) Dalmatian Pr.

—White Fang. 2005. 120p. per. 5.95 (978-1-4209-2246-2(7)) Digireads.com.

—White Fang. 2006. (Scholastic Classics Ser.). v, 206p. (J). (gr. 9-12). 25.00 (978-0-531-16964-3(2) , Watts, Franklin) Scholastic Library Publishing.

—White Fang. 2001. (Classics Ser.). (Illus.). 272p. (J). (gr. 10). pap. 3.99 (978-0-439-23619-5(3)) Scholastic, Inc.

—White Fang. 2006. (Aladdin Classics Ser.). (Illus.). 368p. (J). pap. 5.99 (978-1-4169-1414-3(5) , Aladdin) Simon & Schuster Children's Publishing.

—White Fang. Andreasen, Dan, illus. 2006. (Classic Starts Ser.). 160p. 4.95 (978-1-4027-2500-5(0)) Sterling Publishing Co., Inc.

—White Fang. 2004. reprint ed. pap. 22.95 (978-1-4191-9386-6(4)); pap. 1.99 (978-1-4192-9386-3(9)) Kessinger Publishing, LLC.

—White Fang. 1999. 200p. (YA). reprint ed. pap. 9.95 (978-1-57002-095-7(7)) University Publishing Hse., Inc.

—White Fang: The Whole Story. 1999. (Whole Story Ser.). (Illus.). 248p. (J). (gr. 7-12). pap. 18.99 (978-0-670-88480-3(4) , Viking Juvenile) Penguin Group (USA) Inc.

—White Fang: With a Discussion of Resilience. Walker, Karen, illus. 2003. (Values in Action Illustrated Classics Ser.). 191p. (J). (978-1-59203-038-5(6)) Learning Challenge, Inc.

London, Jack & Olmos. Colmillo Blanco. 2004. (SPA.). 280p. pap. 13.95 (***978-84-263-5246-0(4)***) Vives, Luis Editorial (Edelvives) ESP. *Dist:* Lectorum Pubns., Inc.

London, Jonathan. Eyes of Gray Wolf. Van Zyle, Jon, illus. 2004. 32p. (J). pap. 6.95 (978-0-8118-4141-2(3)) Chronicle Bks. LLC.

Maguire, Gregory. The Dream Stealer. Bryan, Diana, illus. 2002. 144p. (J). (gr. 3-5). tchr. ed. 15.00 (978-0-618-18188-9(1) , Clarion Bks.) Houghton Mifflin Co. Trade & Reference Div.

Malone, Geoffrey. Wolf! 2002. 304p. (J). pap. 11.00 (978-0-340-85065-7(5) , Hodder & Stoughton) Hodder General Publishing Division GBR. *Dist:* Trafalgar Square Publishing.

Martin, Nicole. The Werewolf. 2006. 146p. pap. (***978-1-4120-8802-2(X)***) Trafford Publishing.

Masurel, Claire. Big Bad Wolf. Iwai, Melissa, illus. 2002. 32p. (J). pap. 12.95 (978-0-439-28243-7(8) , Cartwheel Bks.) Scholastic, Inc.

Mawhinney, Art, illus. Diego rescata al lobito (Diego's Wolf Pup Rescue) 2006. (Go, Diego, Go! Ser.). (SPA.). 24p. (J). pap. 3.99 (978-1-4169-1566-9(4) , Libros Para Niños) Simon & Schuster Children's Publishing.

—Diego's Wolf Pup Rescue. 2006. (Go, Diego, Go! Ser.). 24p. (J). pap. 3.99 (978-1-4169-1559-1(1) , Simon Spotlight/Nickelodeon) Simon & Schuster Children's Publishing.

McClintock, Barbara, illus. Goldilocks & the Three Bears. 2003. 32p. (J). (ps-2). pap. 15.95 (978-0-439-39545-8(3) , Scholastic Pr.) Scholastic, Inc.

McGee, Marni. Winston the Book Wolf. Beck, Ian, illus. 2006. 32p. (J). 16.95 (978-0-8027-9569-4(2)) Walker & Co.

McGraw-Hill Staff. Little Red Riding Hood. 2001. (gr. k-3). lib. bdg. 11.80 (978-0-613-89912-3(1)) Tandem Library Bks.

McMullan, Kate. Knight for a Day. 2007. (Dragon Slayers' Academy Ser.: No. 5). 112p. (J). (gr. 1-6). 24.21 (***978-1-59961-377-2(8)***) Spotlight.

McNaughton, Colin. De Repente! (Buenas Noches Coleccion). (SPA.). (J). (gr. 1-3). 8.95 (978-958-04-5627-8(5)) Norma S.A. COL. *Dist:* Distribuidora Norma, Inc., Lectorum Pubns., Inc.

—Oops! 2000. (978-0-606-20332-6(X)); (J). (978-0-606-20169-8(6)) Tandem Library Bks.

—Preston's Goal! 2001. (978-0-606-22599-1(4)) Tandem Library Bks.

—S. W. A. L. K. A Preston Pig Story. 2002. (Illus.). 27p. 17.99 (978-1-84270-098-3(7)) Random Hse. GBR. *Dist:* Trafalgar Square Publishing.

—Suddenly! McNaughton, Colin, illus. 2002. (Illus.). (J). 13.19 (978-0-7587-3725-0(4)) Book Wholesalers, Inc.

—Suddenly! 1998. (Preston Pig Ser.). (Illus.). 32p. (J). (ps-3). pap. 7.00 (978-0-15-201699-9(6) , Harcourt Paperbacks) Harcourt Children's Bks.

McNaughton, Colin, et al. Gol! 2005. (WEL., Illus.). 24p. (978-0-948930-79-9(9)) Cymdeithas Lyfrau Ceredigion.

—Mwsg. 2005. (WEL., Illus.). 28p. (978-1-902416-62-5(7)) Cymdeithas Lyfrau Ceredigion.

—Wps! 2005. (WEL., Illus.). 27p. (978-1-902416-29-8(5)) Cymdeithas Lyfrau Ceredigion.

Meddaugh, Susan. The Best Place. Meddaugh, Susan, illus. 1999. (Illus.). 32p. (J). (gr. k-3). tchr. ed. 15.00 (978-0-395-97994-5(3) , Walter Lorraine) Houghton Mifflin Co. Trade & Reference Div.

—The Best Place. 2004. (Illus.). 32p. (J). (gr. k-3). reprint ed. pap. 5.95 (978-0-618-44882-1(9) , Walter Lorraine) Houghton Mifflin Co. Trade & Reference Div.

—Hog-Eye. 1998. (Illus.). 32p. (J). (gr. k-3). 6.95 (978-0-395-93746-4(9) , Walter Lorraine) Houghton Mifflin Co. Trade & Reference Div.

—Hog-Eye. Meddaugh, Susan, illus. 1998. (Illus.). 32p. (J). (ps-ps). lib. bdg. 14.10 (978-0-613-10513-2(3)) Tandem Library Bks.

Melling, David. The Scallywags. 2006. 32p. (J). (ps-2). 14.99 (978-0-7641-5991-6(7)) Barron's Educational Series, Inc.

Milani, Mino. El Ultimo Lobo. (Barco de Vapor).Tr. of Last Wolf. (SPA.). 144p. (YA). (gr. 5-8). (978-84-348-4520-6(2)) SM Ediciones.

Murphy, Yannick. Ahwoooooooo! Muñoz, Claudio, illus. 2006. (J). (gr. k-3). 32p. 16.00 (978-0-618-11762-8(8)); 31p. (978-1-4156-8100-8(7)) Houghton Mifflin Co. Trade & Reference Div. (Clarion Bks.).

Murray, Donna. Mottsie, Wolf of Great Price. 2003. 80p. pap. 11.95 (978-1-4137-0080-0(2)) PublishAmerica, Inc.

Murray, Marjorie D. Little Wolf & the Moon. Schuett, Stacey, illus. 2002. 32p. (J). (ps-2). 16.95 (978-0-7614-5100-6(5)) Cavendish, Marshall Corp.

Novak, Matt. Little Wolf, Big Wolf. Novak, Matt, illus. 2000. (I Can Read Bks.: 2). (Illus.). 48p. (J). (gr. k-3). 14.95 (978-0-06-027486-3(7)) HarperCollins Pubs.

—Little Wolf, Big Wolf. 2001. (I Can Read Bks.). (Illus.). (J). (978-0-606-20769-0(4)) Tandem Library Bks.

Numeroff, Laura Joffe. The Chicken Sisters. Collicott, Sharleen, illus. 2002. 28.95 incl. audio compact disk (978-1-59112-533-4(2)); pap. 39.95 incl. audio compact disk (978-1-59112-532-7(4)); (J). pap. 18.95 incl. audio compact disk (978-1-59112-310-1(0)) Live Oak Media.

—The Chicken Sisters. abr. ed. 2002. (Live Oak Readalong Ser.). (Illus.). (J). pap. 16.95 incl. audio (978-0-87499-890-0(5)) Live Oak Media.

—The Chicken Sisters. Collicott, Sharleen, illus. abr. ed. 2002. (J). pap., tchr.'s planning gde. ed. 37.95 incl. audio (978-0-87499-892-4(1)); 25.95 incl. audio (978-0-87499-891-7(3)) Live Oak Media.

—The Chicken Sisters. Collicott, Sharleen, illus. 1999. (J). (ps-ps). lib. bdg. 15.30 (978-0-613-11404-2(3)) Tandem Library Bks.

Once upon a Time Spanish Version-Little Red Riding Hood. 2005. (J). (978-1-57022-562-8(1)) ECS Learning Systems, Inc.

Once upon a Time Spanish Version-the Boy Who Cried Wolf. 2005. (J). (978-1-57022-557-4(5)) ECS Learning Systems, Inc.

Owings, Rae. Wolf Music. Owings, Rae, illus. 2001. (Illus.). 118p. (J). (gr. 4-6). 9.99 (978-0-88092-565-5(5) , 5655) Royal Fireworks Publishing Co.

Ozeta, Valerie. Legend of the Red Wolf. 2nd ed. 1999. (Illus.). 34p. (J). (gr. 3-7). pap. 5.95 (978-0-9661687-1-6(2)) Red Wolf Publishing.

Palatini, Margie. Bad Boys. Cole, Henry, illus. 40p. (J). (ps-2). 2003. 15.99 (978-0-06-000102-5(X)); 2003. lib. bdg. 16.89 (978-0-06-000103-2(8)); 2006. reprint ed. pap. 6.99 (978-0-06-000104-9(6) , Tegen, Katherine Bks) HarperCollins Pubs.

—Bad Boys Get Cookie. Cole, Henry, illus. 2006. 32p. (J). lib. bdg. 17.89 (978-0-06-074437-3(5)) HarperCollins Pubs.

—Bad Boys Get Cookie! Cole, Henry, illus. 2006. 32p. (J). 16.99 (978-0-06-074436-6(7)) HarperCollins Pubs.

Papineau, Lucie. Bamboo at Jungle School. Jolin, Dominique, illus. 2005. (Read-It! Readers Ser.). 32p. (J). (gr. k-3). 18.60 (978-1-4048-1036-5(6)) Picture Window Bks.

Paver, Michelle. Chronicles of Ancient Darkness #3: Soul Eater. Taylor, Geoff, illus. 2008. (Chronicles of Ancient Darkness). 352p. (J). pap. 6.99 (***978-0-06-077833-5(7)*** , Harper Trophy) HarperCollins Pubs.

—Hermano Lobo: Cronicas de la Prehistoria. Anton de vez, Patricia, tr. 2005. (Illus.). 222p. 17.25 (978-84-7888-933-4(7)) Emece Editores ESP. *Dist:* Ediciones Universal.

—Soul-Eater. Taylor, Geoff, illus. 2007. (Chronicles of Ancient Darkness: No. 3). 336p. (J). lib. bdg. 17.89 (978-0-06-072832-8(9) , Tegen, Katherine Bks) HarperCollins Pubs.

—Spirit Walker. Taylor, Geoff, illus. (Chronicles of Ancient Darkness: No.2). (J). 2007. 384p. pap. 6.99 (978-0-06-072830-4(2) , Harper Trophy); 2006. 368p. 16.99 (978-0-06-072828-1(0) , Tegen, Katherine Bks); 2006. 368p. lib. bdg. 17.89 (978-0-06-072829-8(9) , Tegen, Katherine Bks) HarperCollins Pubs.

—Wolf Brother. Taylor, Geoff, illus. 2005. (Chronicles of Ancient Darkness). 304p. (J). (gr. 5 up). lib. bdg. 17.89 (978-0-06-072826-7(4)) HarperCollins Pubs.

—Wolf Brother. 2005. (Chronicles of Ancient Darkness: Bk. 1). (Illus.). 304p. (J). (gr. 5 up). 16.99 (978-0-06-072825-0(6)) HarperCollins Pubs.

—Wolf Brother. Taylor, Geoff, illus. 2006. (Chronicles of Ancient Darkness). 320p. (J). reprint ed. pap. 6.99 (978-0-06-072827-4(2) , Harper Trophy) HarperCollins Pubs.

Pean, Stanley. L' Appel des Loups, Vol. 45. 2002. (Roman + Ser.). (FRE.). 160p. (YA). (gr. 8 up). pap. (978-2-89021-290-9(4)) Diffusion du livre Mirabel.

Pennac, Daniel. Eye of the Wolf. Adams, Sarah, tr. from FRE. Grafe, Max, illus. 2003. 112p. (J). (gr. 5 up). 15.99 (978-0-7636-1896-4(9)) Candlewick Pr.

Pennart, Geoggroy. El Lobo Sentimental. 2004. (SPA.). 88p. (J). 18.99 (978-84-8470-120-0(4)) Corimbo, Editorial S.L. ESP. *Dist:* Lectorum Pubns., Inc.

Perret, Delphine. The Big Bad Wolf & Me. 2006. (Illus.). 64p. (J). 9.95 (978-1-4027-3725-1(4)) Sterling Publishing Co., Inc.

Pinkwater, Daniel M. Wolf Christmas. Pinkwater, Jill, illus. 1998. (Accelerated Reader Bks.). 32p. (J). (ps-3). 15.95 (978-0-7614-5030-6(0) , Cavendish Children's Bks.) Cavendish, Marshall Corp.

Plante, Raymond. Marilou Polaire Crie au Loup. 2000. (Premier Roman Ser.). (FRE.). 64p. (J). (gr. 2-5). pap. (978-2-89021-396-8(X)) Diffusion du livre Mirabel.

Pledger, Maurice. Lalo Lobo. 2001. (Peek & Find Ser.).Tr. of Wally Wolf. (SPA., Illus.). 18p. (J). (ps-3). (978-968-5308-42-7(X) , Silver Dolphin en Español) Advanced Marketing, S. de R. L. de C. V.

Price, Susan. The Wolf's Footprint. 2003. (Illus.). 96p. pap. (978-0-340-85589-8(4) , Hodder Children's Books) Hodder Children's Division.

Prince, Sarah. Mr Wolf Tries Again. 1999. (gr. k-3). lib. bdg. 11.80 (978-0-613-19404-4(7)) Tandem Library Bks.

Puttock, Simon. Big Bad Wolf Is Good. Chapman, Lynne, illus. 2002. 32p. (J). (ps-2). 12.95 (978-0-8069-0027-8(X)) Sterling Publishing Co., Inc.

Raines, Kristy. Grizzer the Goofy Wolf. Raines, Morgan, illus. 2007. 80p. per. 11.95 (***978-1-59594-132-9(0)*** , Wingspan Pr.) WingSpan Publishing.

Raintree Steck-Vaughn Staff. Caperucita Roja y Lobo Feroz. (SPA.). (J). 2000. (gr. 1-2). pap. 29.12 (978-0-7398-0740-8(4)); 1999. pap., stu. ed. 31.05 (978-0-7398-0769-9(2)) Steck-Vaughn.

—Little Red & the Wolf. 2000. (Illus.). (J). pap. 29.12 (978-0-8172-6458-1(2)) Steck-Vaughn.

Rameaka, T. Mystery of Wolf Den Cave. 2005. 74p. pap. 14.95 (978-1-4137-5551-0(8)) PublishAmerica, Inc.

Ransom, Candice F. Little Red Riding Hood. Lyon, Tammie Speer, illus. 2002. (Brighter Child Keepsake Stories Ser.). 32p. (J). (ps-3). pap. 3.99 (978-1-57768-198-4(3) , Brighter Child) School Specialty Publishing.

El Regreso de los Lobos 17: Leveled Books. 2001. (McGraw-Hill. Lectura Ser.). (ENG & SPA.). (gr. 3 up). (978-0-02-188114-7(6)) Macmillan/McGraw-Hill Schl. Div.

Richards, Pat. Bardolph Bedivere Wolf Returns. Richards, Charles, illus. 2007. 42p. (J). (***978-0-9790796-4-1(0)***) PJR Assocs., Ltd.

Rigby Education Staff. Red Riding Hood: Jumbled Tumble. (gr. k-2). 26.00 (978-0-7635-2416-6(6)) Rigby Education.

Roberts, Lynn. Little Red: A Fizzingly Good Yarn. Roberts, David, illus. 2005. 32p. (J). (ps-3). 16.95 (978-0-8109-5783-1(3) , Abrams Bks. for Young Readers) Abrams, Harry N. , Inc.

Rocco, John. Wolf! Wolf! 2007. 32p. (ps-2). 15.99 (978-1-4231-0012-6(3)) Hyperion Pr.

Roddie, Shen. Not Now, Mrs. Wolf. 2000. (J). (978-0-606-19386-3(3)) Tandem Library Bks.

Roll, Renee. The Wolf Pups. 2006. (YA). pap. (***978-0-9727995-2-2(4)***) Roll, Renee.

Romeu, Emma. Here Comes the Grey Wolf. Vigil, Luis Gerardo Sanchez & Broeck, Fabricio Vanden, illus. (SPA.). 32p. (J). (gr. 3-5). pap. 7.95 (978-1-59437-843-0(6)) Santillana USA Publishing Co., Inc.

Rosa, Nina M. & Nardini, Amy G., eds. The Warm Springs Wolf Words of Wisdom a Book of Daily Affirmations: Wolf Words of Wisdom. 2000. (J). pap. 16.99 (978-0-9740267-1-8(9)) Mz. Rosa Notions.

Ross, Jackie Leigh. The Wherewolf? Guevara, Linda L., ed. Ko, Steve, illus. 2002. 32p. (J). (ps-5). 16.95 (978-0-615-11427-9(X)) All About Kids Publishing.

Rovira, Francesca, illus. Caperucita Roja / Little Red Riding Hood. 2006. (Bilingual Tales Ser.). 24p. (J). pap. 3.50 (978-0-439-77375-1(X) , Scholastic en Espanol) Scholastic, Inc.

Roy, Ron. The White Wolf. Gurney, John Steven, tr. Gurney, John Steven, illus. 2004. (A to Z Mysteries Ser.: No. 23). 96p. (J). (gr. 1-4). pap. 3.99 (978-0-375-82480-7(4)); lib. bdg. 11.99 (978-0-375-92480-4(9)) Random Hse. Children's Bks. (Random Hse. Bks. for Young Readers).

Rozanski, Bonnie. Borderline. 2007. 224p. (YA). pap. 22.95 (***978-0-88984-293-9(0)***) Porcupine's Quill, Inc. CAN. *Dist:* Univ. of Toronto Pr.

Rueda, Claudia. Let's Play in the Forest While the Wolf Is Not Around. 2006. (Illus.). 32p. (J). pap. 16.99 (978-0-439-82323-4(4) , Scholastic Pr.) Scholastic, Inc.

Sanders, Alex. Un Lobo! (SPA.). 36p. (978-84-95150-34-9(4)) Corimbo, Editorial S.L.

—Un Lobo! (SPA.). 36p. 16.95 (978-84-95150-24-0(7)) Corimbo, Editorial S.L. ESP. *Dist:* Distribooks, Inc.

Santore, Charles. Three Hungry Pigs & the Wolf Who Came to Dinner. 2005. (Illus.). 32p. (J). (ps-3). 16.95 (978-0-375-82946-8(6)); lib. bdg. 18.99 (978-0-375-92946-5(0)) Random Hse. Children's Bks. (Random Hse. Bks. for Young Readers).

Sargent, Dave & Sargent, Pat. Annie Antelope: Don't Worry, 56 vols. Huff, Jeane, illus. 2001. (Animal Pride Ser.: 21). 36p. (J). lib. bdg. 19.95 (978-1-56763-358-0(7)) Ozark Publishing.

—Bo Bo's Big Imagination, 10, 13. Robinson, Laura, illus. 2004. (Learn to Read Ser.: 10). Tr. of La Gran Imaginacion de Bo Bo. 18p. (J). pap. 9.95 (978-1-56763-822-6(8)); lib. bdg. 19.95 (978-1-56763-821-9(X)) Ozark Publishing.

—Katy Koala: Affectionate, 56 vols., 48. Lenoir, Jane, illus. 2001. (Animal Pride Ser.: Vol. 48). 36p. (J). lib. bdg. 19.95 (978-1-56763-537-9(7)) Ozark Publishing.

Sargent, Dave, et al. Katy Koala: Affectionate, 17, 48. 2000. (Animal Pride Ser.: 48). (Illus.). 42p. (J). pap. 6.95 (978-1-56763-538-6(5)) Ozark Publishing.

Sargent, Pat L. Topper: Son of Barney, 8. Lenoir, Jane, illus. 2007. (Barney the Bear Killer Ser.: 7). 147p. (YA). lib. bdg. 25.25 (***978-1-56763-425-9(7)***) Ozark Publishing.

—Topper, Son of Barney #7, 6 vols. 2007. (Barney the Bear Killer Ser.: 7). (YA). pap. 9.95 (***978-1-56763-426-6(5)***); lib. bdg. 25.25 (***978-1-59381-609-4(X)***) Ozark Publishing.

Scieszka, Jon. The True Story of the 3 Little Pigs. 2002. (Illus.). (J). 14.04 (978-0-7587-5387-8(X)) Book Wholesalers, Inc.

Scraper, Katherine. The Boy Who Cried Wolf: An Aesop's Fable. 2006. 42.00 (***978-1-4108-6166-5(X)***) Benchmark Education Co.

Skurzynski, Gloria. Wolf Stalker. 2001. (gr. 3-6). lib. bdg. 14.10 (978-0-613-84040-8(2)) Tandem Library Bks.

Skurzynski, Gloria & Ferguson. Wolf Stalker. 2001. (National Parks Mystery Ser.). (Illus.). (J). (978-0-606-21533-6(6)) Tandem Library Bks.

Skurzynski, Gloria & Ferguson, Alane. Wolf Stalker. 1998. (National Parks Mysteries Ser.: Vol. 1). (Illus.). 160p. (J). (gr. 3-7). 15.95 (978-0-7922-7034-8(7) , National Geographic Children's Bks.) National Geographic Society.

Smallman, Steve. The Lamb Who Came for Dinner. Dreidemy, Joelle, illus. 2007. 32p. (J). (ps-2). 15.95 (***978-1-58925-067-3(2)*** , tiger tales) ME Media LLC.

Smith, Roland. The Last Lobo. 2001. (gr. 3-6). lib. bdg. 14.15 (978-0-613-74960-2(X)) Tandem Library Bks.

Smith, Stephanie. Gray Wolf Pup's Adventure. Hynes, Robert, illus. 2nd ed. 2005. (Soundprints' Read-And-Discover Ser.). (J). (gr. 1-3). 48p. 7.95 (978-1-931465-14-4(2) , B2027); 32p. pap. 3.95 (978-1-931465-13-7(4) , S2027) Soundprints.

—Gray Wolf Pup's Adventure. 2002. (gr. k-3). lib. bdg. 11.80 (978-0-613-61912-7(9)) Tandem Library Bks.

—Grey Wolf. Hynes, Robert, illus. 2002. (J). bds. (978-1-59069-257-8(8) , HS3003) Studio Mouse LLC.

Sommer, Carl. No One Will Ever Know. 2003. (Another Sommer-Time Story Ser.). (Illus.). 48p. (J). (gr. 1-4). 16.95 incl. audio compact disk (978-1-57537-506-9(0)); 16.95 incl. audio (978-1-57537-555-7(9)) Advance Publishing, Inc.

Steck-Vaughn Staff. Animals: Wolf Talking/Hiding in Place. 1998. (Illus.). (J). pap. (978-0-8172-8633-0(0)) Steck-Vaughn.

Stockham, Jessica, illus. Little Red Riding Hood. 2005. 24p. pap. (978-1-904550-22-8(3)) Child's Play-International.

Sweet, Melissa. Carmine: A Little More Red. 2005. (Illus.). 40p. (J). (gr. k-3). 16.00 (978-0-618-38794-6(3)) Houghton Mifflin Co. Trade & Reference Div.

Tremblay, Marc. Le Petit Frere du Chaperon Rouge. Fil et al, illus. 2004. (était une Fois Ser.). (FRE.). 24p. (J). (ps). pap. (978-2-89021-698-3(5)) Diffusion du livre Mirabel.

Trivizas, Eugene. The Three Little Wolves & the Big Bad Pig: A Pop-up Storybook. Oxenbury, Helen, illus. 2006. 16p. (J). (gr. k-4). reprint ed. 27.00 (978-0-7567-9913-7(9)) DIANE Publishing Co.

—The Three Little Wolves & the Big Bad Pig: A Pop-Up Storybook with a Twist in the Tale! Oxenbury, Helen, illus. 2004. 16p. (J). 24.95 (978-1-4052-0669-3(1)) Egmont Bks., Ltd. GBR. *Dist:* Trafalgar Square Publishing.

—Los Tres Lobitos y el Cochino Feroz. Oxenbury, Helen, illus. 2003. (SPA.). 32p. (J). (gr. k-3). pap. 12.99 (978-980-257-246-5(2) , EK1366) Ekare, Ediciones VEN. *Dist:* Kane/Miller Bk. Pubs., Inc., Lectorum Pubns., Inc.

Tsaliovich, Anatoly. Of Wolves & Lambs & Others. Burke, Daniel, illus. 2005. 73p. (YA). pap. 12.99 (978-0-9773816-0-9(9)) ATInternational Pubs.

Velez, Walter, illus. Little Red Riding Hood: A Tale about Staying Safe. 2006. (J). 6.99 (978-1-59939-021-5(3) , Reader's Digest Young Families, Inc.) Reader's Digest Children's Publishing, Inc.

Verne, Jules. White Fang. 1999. (J). 11.95 (978-1-56137-527-1(6)) Novel Units, Inc.

Wehrle, Rene. Charlie, Wolf & the Crystal Pyramids. 2004. pap. 8.95 (978-0-533-14803-5(0)) Vantage Pr., Inc.

Whatley, Bruce. Wait! No Paint! Whatley, Bruce, illus. 32p. (J). 2005. pap. 6.99 (978-0-06-443546-8(6) , Harper Trophy); 2001. (Illus.). 15.99 (978-0-06-028270-7(3)); 2001. (Illus.). lib. bdg. 16.89 (978-0-06-028271-4(1)) HarperCollins Pubs.

Wheeler, Lisa. Invasion of the Pig Sisters. Ansley, Frank, illus. 2006. (Fitch & Chip Ser.). 48p. (J). pap. 3.99 (978-0-689-84958-9(3)) Simon & Schuster Children's Publishing.

Wheeler, Lisa & Ansley, Frank. New Pig in Town. 2003. (Ready-to-Read Ser.). (Illus.). 48p. (J). 14.95 (978-0-689-84950-3(8) , Atheneum/Richard Jackson Bks.) Simon & Schuster Children's Publishing.

White Fang Study Guide. 2002. (Illus.). 48p. (YA). per. 17.95 (978-1-56254-536-9(1) , SP5361) Saddleback Educational Publishing.

White, Kathy. Little Green Riding Hood. 2006. 42.00 (***978-1-4108-6182-5(1)***) Benchmark Education Co.

White, Mark. El Lobo con Piel de Oveja: Version de la Fabula de Esopo. Rojo, Sara, illus. 2006. (Read-It! Readers en Espanol Ser.).Tr. of Wolf in Sheep's Clothing: A Retelling of Aesop's Fable. (SPA.). 32p. (J). (ps-3). 19.95 (978-1-4048-1625-1(9)) Picture Window Bks.

Whybrow, Ian. Badness for Beginners: A Little Wolf & Smellybreff Adventure. 2005. (Illus.). 32p. (J). (ps-ps). 16.95 (978-1-57505-861-0(8) , Carolrhoda Bks.) Lerner Publishing Group.

—Dear Little Wolf. Ross, Tony, illus. 2005. (Little Wolf Adventures Ser.). 64p. (gr. 3-6). pap., lib. bdg. 14.95 (978-0-87614-902-7(6)) Lerner Publishing Group.

—Little Wolf, Forest Detective. Ross, Tony, illus. 2005. (Middle Grade Fiction Ser.). 112p. (J). (gr. 3-6). 14.95 (978-1-57505-413-1(2)); pap. 6.95 (978-1-57505-829-0(4)) Lerner Publishing Group.

W X Y Z

—Little Wolf, Pack Leader. Ross, Tony, illus. 2005. (Little Wolf Adventures Ser.). 126p. (gr. 3-6). 14.95 (978-1-57505-400-1(0)) Lerner Publishing Group.

—Little Wolf, Terror of the Shivery Sea. Ross, Tony, illus. 2005. (Middle Grade Fiction Ser.). 144p. (J). (gr. 3-6). 14.95 (978-1-57505-629-6(1)) Lerner Publishing Group.

—Little Wolf's Book of Badness. Ross, Tony, illus. 2005. (Middle Grade Fiction Ser.). 132p. (gr. 3-6). 14.95 (978-1-57505-410-0(8)) Lerner Publishing Group.

—Little Wolf's Diary of Daring Deeds. Ross, Tony, illus. (Middle Grade Fiction Ser.). 132p. (gr. 3-6). 2005. 14.95 (978-1-57505-411-7(6)); 2003. (J). pap. 6.95 (978-0-87614-536-4(5), Carolrhoda Bks.) Lerner Publishing Group.

—Little Wolf's Diary of Daring Deeds. 2000. (gr. 3-6). lib. bdg. 15.25 (978-0-613-68105-6(3)) Tandem Library Bks.

—Little Wolf's Handy Book of Poems. Ross, Tony, illus. 2005. (Little Wolf Adventures Ser.). 80p. (gr. 3-6). pap., lib. bdg. 14.95 (978-0-87614-927-0(1)) Lerner Publishing Group.

—Little Wolf's Handy Book of Poems. 2002. (gr. 3-6). lib. bdg. 12.95 (978-0-613-52430-8(6)) Tandem Library Bks.

—Little Wolf's Haunted Hall for Small Horrors. Ross, Tony, illus. (Middle Grade Fiction Ser.). 132p. (J). 2005. (gr. 3-6). 14.95 (978-1-57505-412-4(4)); 2004. (gr. 2-6). pap. 6.95 (978-1-57505-794-1(8)) Lerner Publishing Group.

—Lobito Aprende a Ser Malo (Little Wolf's Book of Badness) Azaola, Miguel, tr. Ross, Tony, illus. 2007. (Ediciones Lerner Single Titles Ser.). (SPA.). (J). (gr. 3-7). pap. 6.95 (***978-0-8225-8644-9(4)**, Ediciones Lerner) Lerner Publishing Group.

—Malicia para Principiantes: Una Aventura de Lobito y Apestosito. 2005. (Libros Ilustrados (Picture Bks.)). (SPA., Illus.). 32p. (gr. k-2). 16.95 (978-0-8225-3211-8(5), Ediciones Lerner) Lerner Publishing Group.

—What's the Time, Little Wolf? Another Little Wolf & Smellybreff Adventure. Ross, Tony, illus. 2006. 32p. (J). 15.95 (978-1-57505-939-6(8), Carolrhoda Bks.) Lerner Publishing Group.

Willson, Sarah. What's with Dad? Marantz, Larissa & Di-Paolo, Katharine, illus. 2006. (All Grown Up! Ser.). 32p. (J). pap. 3.99 (978-1-4169-0669-8(X), Simon Spotlight/Nickelodeon) Simon & Schuster Children's Publishing.

Wisnewski, Andrea, illus. & retold by. Little Red Riding Hood. Wisnewski, Andrea, retold by. 2007. 32p. (J). (ps-3). 18.95 (978-1-56792-303-2(8)) Godine, David R. Pub.

Wolf Pup's Lesson. 2002. (Wild Heritage Collection Mini Bks.). (Illus.). 32p. (J). (978-1-59069-157-1(1), H3001) Studio Mouse LLC.

Young, Ed. Lon Po Po. unabr. ed. 2006. (J). (gr. k-4). pap. 18.95 incl. audio compact disk (978-0-439-87366-6(5), WPCD690); (Illus.). 29.95 incl. audio compact disk (978-0-439-87367-3(3), WHCD690); (Illus.). 24.95 incl. audio (978-0-439-87365-9(7), WHRA690); (Illus.). pap. 14.95 incl. audio (978-0-439-87364-2(9), WPRA690) Weston Woods Studios, Inc.

—Lon Po Po: A Red Riding Hood Story from China. Young, Ed, illus. 2002. (Illus.). (J). 14.04 (978-0-7587-0055-1(5)) Book Wholesalers, Inc.

WOMBATS—FICTION

Fox, Mem. Wombat Divine. 2002. (Illus.). (J). 13.19 (978-0-7587-4046-5(8)) Book Wholesalers, Inc.

—Wombat Divine. Argent, Kerry, illus. 1999. 32p. (J). (ps-3). pap. 6.00 (978-0-15-202096-5(9), Harcourt Paperbacks) Harcourt Children's Bks.

—Wombat Divine. 1999. (gr. k-3). lib. bdg. 14.15 (978-0-613-22962-3(2)) Tandem Library Bks.

Fuge, Charles. Swim, Little Wombat, Swim! (Illus.). (J). 2006. 32p. bds. 5.95 (978-1-4027-3632-2(0)); 2005. 24p. 12.95 (978-1-4027-2375-9(X)) Sterling Publishing Co., Inc.

—Where to, Little Wombat? 2007. (Illus.). 22p. (J). bds. 5.95 (978-1-4027-4764-9(0)) Sterling Publishing Co., Inc.

Fuge, Charles & Gullane Children's Books Staff. Where to, Little Wombat? 2006. (Illus.). 24p. (J). (ps-k). 12.95 (978-1-4027-3698-8(3)) Sterling Publishing Co., Inc.

Lester, Helen. Batter up Wombat. Munsinger, Lynn, illus. 2006. 32p. (J). (***978-1-4287-0160-1(5)**) Houghton Mifflin Co.

—Batter up Wombat. Munsinger, Lynn M., illus. 2006. 32p. (J). (gr. k-3). 16.00 (978-0-618-73784-0(7), Walter Lorraine) Houghton Mifflin Co. Trade & Reference Div.

McAllister, Angela. Found You, Little Wombat! Fuge, Charles, illus. 2004. 22p. (J). bds. 5.95 (978-1-4027-1599-0(4)) Sterling Publishing Co., Inc.

McAllister, Angela & Fuge, Charles. Found You, Little Wombat! 2003. (Illus.). 24p. (J). 12.95 (978-1-4027-0708-7(8)) Sterling Publishing Co., Inc.

McAllister, Angela, et al. Dyna Lle'r Wyt Ti! 2005. (WEL., Illus.). 20p. (978-1-902416-90-8(2)) Cymdeithas Lyfrau Ceredigion.

WOMEN

see also Girls; Mothers

Angelou, Maya. My Painted House, My Friendly Chicken & Me. Courtney-Clarke, Margaret, illus. 2003. 48p. (J). (gr. 1-4). pap. 7.99 (978-0-375-82567-5(3)); lib. bdg. 17.99 (978-0-375-92567-2(8)) Random Hse. Children's Bks. (Crown Books For Young Readers).

—My Painted House, My Friendly Chicken & Me. 2003. (gr. k-3). lib. bdg. 16.45 (978-0-613-71911-7(5)) Tandem Library Bks.

Chaterjee. With Our Own Minds: Women Organizing & Developing on Indian Plantation. 2010. (Gender, Culture, & Global Politics Ser.: 10). (gr. 13). 85.00 (978-0-8153-3701-0(9)) Routledge.

Dinaberg, Leslie. Women in Charge. 2007. (Girls Rock! Ser.). 32p. (J). (gr. 1-5). 24.21 (***978-1-59296-870-1(8)**) Child's World, Inc.

Esherick, Joan. Women in the Arab World. 2005. (Women's Issues, Global Trends Ser.). (Illus.). 112p. (J). lib. bdg. (978-1-59084-861-6(0)) Mason Crest Pubs.

—Women in the World of Africa. 2005. (Women's Issues Ser.). (Illus.). 112p. (J). lib. bdg. (978-1-59084-857-9(8)) Mason Crest Pubs.

Fortin, Noonie. Women at Risk: We Also Served. 2001. xxiii, 595p. (J). (gr. 12 up). pap. 20.95 (978-0-9700176-4-2(2)) Tales & Whales Publishing.

Goldenstern, Joyce. American Women Against Violence. 1998. (Collective Biographies Ser.). (Illus.). 128p. (YA). (gr. 6-12). lib. bdg. 26.60 (978-0-7660-1025-3(2)) Enslow Pubs., Inc.

Hamilton, John. Princesses & Heroines. 2006. (Illus.). 32p. (J). (gr. 4-8). 24.21 (978-1-59679-339-2(2), ABDO & Daughters) ABDO Publishing Co.

Hantman, Clea. Goddesses, No. 2. 2001. (YA). (gr. 5-9). pap. 4.99 (978-0-06-440876-9(0), Harper Trophy) HarperCollins Pubs.

Harik, Ramsay M. & Marston, Elsa. Women in the Middle East: Tradition & Change. rev. ed. 2003. (Women Then - Women Now Ser.). (Illus.). 192p. (YA). 30.50 (978-0-531-12222-8(0), Watts, Franklin) Scholastic Library Publishing.

Hughes, Morgan. Women's Hall of Fame. 2000. (Halls of Fame Ser.). (Illus.). 24p. (J). (gr. 2-6). lib. bdg. 23.93 (978-1-55916-272-2(4)) Rourke Publishing, LLC.

Hunter, Shaun. Visual & Performing Artists. 1998. (Women in Profile Ser.). (Illus.). 48p. (J). (gr. 4). lib. bdg. (978-0-7787-0013-5(5)) Crabtree Publishing Co.

Kalman, Bobbie. Women of the West. 2000. (gr. 3-6). lib. bdg. 16.40 (978-0-613-22653-0(4)) Tandem Library Bks.

Kalman, Bobbie & Lewis, Jane. Women of the West. 1999. (Life in the Old West Ser.). (Illus.). 32p. (J). (gr. 3-4). pap. (978-0-7787-0112-5(3)); lib. bdg. (978-0-7787-0080-7(1)) Crabtree Publishing Co.

Krisher, Trudy B. Her Story. 1998. (J). (978-0-385-32270-6(4), Dell Books for Young Readers) Random Hse. Children's Bks.

Libal, Autumn. Women in the Hispanic World. 2005. (Women's Issues, Global Trends Ser.). (Illus.). 112p. (J). lib. bdg. (978-1-59084-858-6(6)) Mason Crest Pubs.

—Women in the World of Southeast Asia. 2005. (Women's Issues, Global Trends Ser.). (Illus.). 112p. (J). lib. bdg. (978-1-59084-867-8(5)) Mason Crest Pubs.

MacDonald, Fiona. Women in 19th Century Europe. 2001. (Other Half of History Ser.). (Illus.). 48p. (J). (gr. 3 up). 17.95 (978-0-87226-565-3(X), 6565XB, Bedrick, Peter Bks.) School Specialty Publishing.

—Women in Peace & War, 1900-1945. (Other Half of History Ser.). (gr. 3 up). 2001. (Illus.). 48p. (J). 17.95 (978-0-87226-571-4(4)); 2000. (YA). 17.95 (978-0-87226-666-7(4)) School Specialty Publishing. (Bedrick, Peter Bks.).

Malam, John. Ancient Egyptian Women. 2002. (People in the Past Ser.). (Illus.). 48p. (J). pap. 8.50 (978-1-4034-0517-3(4)) Heinemann Library.

Martz, Sandra, ed. When I Am an Old Woman I Shall Wear Purple: Petite Version. 2nd gif. rev. ed. 2006. (Illus.). 64p. (C). pap. 47.70 (978-1-57601-093-8(7), Papier-Mache Pr.) Moyer Bell.

Phelps, Ethel J., ed. Tatterhood & Other Tales. Baldwin-Ford, Pamela, illus. 2004. 192p. (gr. 4-7). pap. 10.95 (978-0-912670-50-8(9)) Feminist Pr. at The City Univ. of New York.

Prestwidge, K. J. Bibliography of Women in Engineering, Science & the Health Professions. 5th rev. ed. 2002. 9p. (YA). pap. (978-0-9701755-2-6(3)) Huespin Productions.

Rivera, Sheila. Women of the Middle East. 2004. (World in Conflict-the Middle East Ser.). (Illus.). 48p. (J). (gr. 4-8). lib. bdg. 25.65 (978-1-59197-415-4(1)) ABDO Publishing Co.

Rutledge, Rachel. The Best of the Best in Track & Field. 1999. (Women of Sports Ser.). (Illus.). 64p. (gr. 5 up). lib. bdg. 24.90 (978-0-7613-1300-7(1), Twenty-First Century Bks.) Lerner Publishing Group.

San Souci, Robert D. Cut from the Same Cloth: American Women of Myth, Legend & Tall Tales. Pinkney, Brian, illus. 2000. 160p. (J). (gr. 3-7). pap. 6.99 (978-0-698-11811-9(1), Putnam Juvenile) Penguin Group (USA) Inc.

—Cut from the Same Cloth: American Women of Myth, Legend & Tall Tales. 2000. (Illus.). (J). 13.64 (978-0-606-18398-7(1)) Tandem Library Bks.

Should Women Be Allowed to Serve in Combat in the U. S. Armed Forces? [New Title]. 2007. (At Issue Ser.). (Illus.). 128p. (gr. 10-12). 29.95 (***978-0-7377-3938-1(X)**); pap. 21.20 (***978-0-7377-3939-8(8)**) Thomson Gale. (Greenhaven Pr., Inc.).

Sideman, Jill, intro. Women in Science. 2005. (Illus.). 112p. (gr. 6-12). pap. 180.00 (978-0-7910-7250-9(9), Chelsea Hse.) Facts On File, Inc.

Thimmesh, Catherine. Girls Think of Everything: Stories of Ingenious Inventions by Women. Sweet, Melissa, illus. 2002. 64p. (YA). (gr. 4-6). reprint ed. pap. 6.95 (978-0-618-19563-3(7)) Houghton Mifflin Co. Trade & Reference Div.

—Girls Think of Everything: Stories of Ingenious Inventions by Women. 2000. (gr. 3-6). lib. bdg. 15.25 (978-0-613-60676-9(0)) Tandem Library Bks.

Vennema, Peter & Stanley, Diane. Good Queen Bess: The Story of Elizabeth I of England. Stanley, Diane, illus. 2001. (Illus.). 40p. (J). (gr. 2 up). 16.99 (978-0-688-17961-8(4)) HarperCollins Pubs.

Waters, Sophie. Seeing the Gynecologist. 2007. (J). (***978-1-4042-1948-9(X)**) Rosen Publishing Group, Inc., The.

Williams, Brian. Ancient Roman Women. (People in the Past Ser.). (Illus.). 48p. (J). 2003. (gr. 4-6). lib. bdg. 27.07 (978-1-58810-632-2(2)); 2002. pap. 8.50 (978-1-4034-0522-7(0)) Heinemann Library.

Women Warriors Through the Ages. 2000. (Illus.). 48p. (J). (gr. 3-7). pap. 16.00 (978-0-9675409-0-0(9)) Taylor, Lu Warrior Girls Pr.

Zeinert, Karen. Those Courageous Women of the Civil War. 1998. (Women at War Ser.). (Illus.). 96p. (gr. 5 up). lib. bdg. 29.90 (978-0-7613-0212-4(3), Twenty-First Century Bks.) Lerner Publishing Group.

WOMEN—BIOGRAPHY

Abbott, J. S. C. History of Madame Roland. 2003. 304p. 99.00 (978-0-7950-3642-2(6)) New Library Press.Net.

Abbott, L. A. House by the Side of the Road: Stories of 20th Century Farm Life beside Illinois' Lincoln Highway. Abbott Gidel, Susan & Abbott Landow, Jan, eds. 2005. (Illus.). 120p. (YA). per. 14.95 (978-0-9766820-0-4(1)) Pines Publishing.

Acker, Kerry. Nina Simone. (Women in the Arts Ser.). (Illus.). 112p. 2004. pap. 30.00 (978-0-7910-7952-2(X)); 2003. (gr. 6-12). 30.00 (978-0-7910-7456-5(0)) Facts On File, Inc. (Chelsea Hse.).

Ada, Alma Flor. Under the Royal Palms: A Childhood in Cuba. 1998. (Illus.). 96p. (J). (gr. 3-7). 17.99 (978-0-689-80631-5(0), Atheneum) Simon & Schuster Children's Publishing.

Adler, David A. Helen Keller. Wallner, John, illus. 32p. (J). 4.95 (978-0-8234-2042-1(6)) Holiday Hse., Inc.

—A Picture Book of Anne Frank. Ritz, Karen, illus. 2004. (J). (ps-3). audio compact disk 18.95 (978-1-59112-781-9(5)) Live Oak Media.

—A Picture Book of Sacagawea. Brown, Dan, illus. 2000. (Picture Book Biography Ser.). 32p. (J). (gr. k-3). tchr. ed. 16.95 (978-0-8234-1485-7(X)) Holiday Hse., Inc.

Agins, Donna Brown. Jacqueline Kennedy Onassis: Legendary First Lady. 2004. (People to Know Ser.). (Illus.). 128p. (J). lib. bdg. 26.60 (978-0-7660-2186-0(6)) Enslow Pubs., Inc.

Alderfer, Zoe, et al. Ann & Liv Cross Antarctica: A Dream Come True! 2003. (Illus.). 32p. (J). 15.95 (978-0-7382-0934-0(1)) Da Capo Pr., Inc.

Allman, Barbara. Her Piano Sang: A Story about Clara Schumann. 2003. (Creative Minds Biographies Ser.). (Illus.). 64p. (J). (gr. 3-6). pap. 22.60 (978-1-57505-151-2(6)) Lerner Publishing Group.

Alter, Judy. Cissie Palmer: Putting Wealth to Work. 1999. (Community Builders Ser.). (Illus.). 48p. (J). (gr. 3-5). pap. 6.95 (978-0-516-26345-8(5), Children's Pr.) Scholastic Library Publishing.

—Sacagawea: Native American Interpreter. 2002. (Spirit of America: Our People Ser.). (Illus.). 32p. (J). (gr. 2-6). 27.07 (978-1-56766-166-8(1)) Child's World, Inc.

Alter, Judy & Rosenberg, Pam. Pocahontas: Native American Peacemaker. 2003. (Spirit of America). (Illus.). 32p. (J). (gr. 2-6). 27.07 (978-1-59296-010-1(3)) Child's World, Inc.

Altgeld, John P. & Jones, Mother. Autobiography of Mother Jones. 2003. (Labor Classics Ser.). (Illus.). 304p. (Orig.). reprint ed. 25.00 (978-0-88286-167-8(0)) Kerr, Charles H. Publishing Co.

Anderson, Dale. Elizabeth Dole. 2004. (Women in Politics Ser.). (Illus.). 120p. 30.00 (978-0-7910-7733-7(0)); 104p. pap. 30.00 (978-0-7910-7997-3(X)) Facts On File, Inc. (Chelsea Hse.).

Anderson, Joan. Rookie: A First Year with the WNBA. 2000. (YA). (978-0-606-19506-5(8)) Tandem Library Bks.

Anderson, Mercedes Padrino. Benazir Bhutto. 2004. (Women in Politics Ser.). (Illus.). 120p. 30.00 (978-0-7910-7732-0(2)); 110p. pap. 30.00 (978-0-7910-8000-9(5)) Facts On File, Inc. (Chelsea Hse.).

Anderson, Wendy & Anderson, W. M. Livewire Real Lives Cate Blanchett. 2003. (Livewires Ser.). 32p. pap. 4.50 (978-0-521-53838-1(6)) Cambridge Univ. Pr.

Anholt, Laurence. Stone Girl, Bone Girl: The Story of Mary Anning. Moxley, Sheila, illus. 1999. 32p. (J). (gr. k-4). pap. 15.95 (978-0-531-30148-7(6), Orchard Bks.) Scholastic, Inc.

Ardagh, Philip. Marie Curie. 2003. (Illus.). 64p. (J). pap. 6.99 (978-0-330-37571-9(7), Pan) Pan Macmillan GBR. *Dist:* Trafalgar Square Publishing.

Armentrout, David & Armentrout, Patricia. Florence Nightingale. Sarfatti, Esther & de la Vega, Eida, trs. 2002. (Personas que Cambiaron la Historia (People Who Made a Difference) Ser.). (SPA., Illus.). 24p. mass mkt. 5.95 (978-1-58952-250-3(8), RK31466) Rourke Publishing, LLC.

—Florence Nightingale. 2001. (Illus.). 24p. (J). (gr. 1-4). lib. bdg. 20.64 (978-1-58952-053-0(X)) Rourke Publishing, LLC.

—Florence Nightingale. Sarfatti, Esther & de la Vega, Eida, trs. 2001. (Personas que Cambiaron la Historia Ser.). (SPA., Illus.). 24p. (J). (gr. 1-3). lib. bdg. 19.27 (978-1-58952-169-8(2), RK5887) Rourke Publishing, LLC.

Aronson, Virginia. Abigail Van Buren/Ann Landers: Advice Columnists. 1999. (Women of Achievement Ser.). (Illus.). 112p. (YA). (gr. 6 up). 32.00 (978-0-7910-5297-6(4), Chelsea Hse.) Facts On File, Inc.

Atkins, Jeannine. How High Can We Climb? The Story of Women Explorers. Petricic, Dusan, illus. 2005. 224p. (J). 17.00 (978-0-374-33503-8(6), Farrar, Straus & Giroux (BYR)) Farrar, Straus & Giroux.

—Mary Anning & the Sea Dragon. Dooling, Michael, illus. 1999. 32p. (J). (gr. k-3). 16.00 (978-0-374-34840-3(5), Farrar, Straus & Giroux (BYR)) Farrar, Straus & Giroux.

Avakian, Monique. The Reformers: Activists, Educators, Religious Leaders. 2000. (Remarkable Women). (Illus.). 80p. (YA). (gr. 6-9). lib. bdg. 32.85 (978-0-8172-5733-0(0)) Raintree.

Aykroyd, Clarissa. Julia Alvarez. 2007. (Twentieth Century Most Influential Hispanics Ser.). (Illus.). 128p. (gr. 7-10). 31.20 (***978-1-4205-0022-6(8)**, Lucent Bks.) Thomson Gale.

Bailer, Darice. Great Women Athletes. 2001. (Step into Reading Ser.). (Illus.). (J). 10.79 (978-0-606-21219-9(1)) Tandem Library Bks.

Ball, Heather. Astonishing Women Artists. 2007. (Women's Hall of Fame Ser.). (Illus.). 120p. (J). (gr. 4-8). pap. 10.95 (***978-1-897187-23-4(8)**) Second Story Pr. CAN. *Dist:* Orca Bk. Pubs. USA.

—Great Women Leaders. 2005. (Women's Hall of Fame Ser.). (Illus.). 100p. (YA). pap. 7.95 (978-1-896764-81-8(9)) Second Story Pr. CAN. *Dist:* Orca Bk. Pubs. USA, Univ. of Toronto Pr.

—Remarkable Women Writers. 2006. (Illus.). 100p. (J). pap. 7.95 (978-1-897187-08-1(4)) Second Story Pr. CAN. *Dist:* Orca Bk. Pubs. USA.

Bank Street Staff & Glimm, Adele. Elizabeth Blackwell: First Woman Doctor to Modern Times. 2000. (Ideas on Trial Ser.). (Illus.). 124p. (C). (gr. 5-10). pap. 8.95 (978-0-07-134335-0(0)) McGraw-Hill Cos., The.

Bankston, John. Alicia Keys. l.t. ed. 2002. (Real Life Reader Biography Ser.). (Illus.). 32p. (J). (gr. 3-8). lib. bdg. 15.95 (978-1-58415-133-3(1)) Mitchell Lane Pubs., Inc.

—Julia Stiles. l.t. ed. 2002. (Real-Life Reader Biography Ser.). (Illus.). 32p. (gr. 3-8). lib. bdg. 24.95 (978-1-58415-130-2(7)) Mitchell Lane Pubs., Inc.

—Missy Elliott: Hip-Hop Superstar. l.t. ed. 2004. (Blue Banner Biography Ser.). (Illus.). 32p. (J). (gr. 3-8). lib. bdg. 25.70 (978-1-58415-219-4(2)) Mitchell Lane Pubs., Inc.

Barnham, Kay. Florence Nightingale: The Lady of the Lamp. 2002. (Famous Lives Ser.). 48p. (J). lib. bdg. 27.12 (978-0-7398-5523-2(9)) Raintree.

Barron's Educational Editorial Staff. Winning Women in Baseball & Softball. 2000. (Sport Success Ser.). 112p. (J). (gr. 5-9). pap. 6.95 (978-0-7641-1231-7(7)) Barron's Educational Series, Inc.

Bauer, Christina. The ABCs of Hidden Heroines. 2007. 280p. (J). 16.99 (978-1-59092-367-2(7), Orchard Academy Pr.) Windstorm Creative.

Bayer, Linda N. Ruth Bader Ginsburg: Supreme Court Justice. 1999. (Illus.). 112p. (gr. 5-9). pap. 9.95 (978-0-7910-5288-4(5), Chelsea Hse.) Facts On File, Inc.

Becker, Leah B. & Beck, Carol. My Grandma's Angels. 2000. 48p. (J). (ps-3). 12.00 (978-1-57921-308-4(1)) WinePress Publishing.

Beller, Susan Provost. The Confederate Ladies of Richmond. 1999. (Single Titles Ser.). (Illus.). 96p. (gr. 4-7). lib. bdg. 26.90 (978-0-7613-1470-7(9), Millbrook Pr.) Lerner Publishing Group.

Benavidez, Barbara. My School Years: Kindergarten Through Graduation. (Illus.). (J). (gr. 5-12). 24.95 (978-0-9619463-0-2(X)) Barmarle Pubns.

Benge, Janet & Benge, Geoff. Lillian Trasher: The Greatest Wonder in Egypt. 2003. (Christian Heroes, Then & Now Ser.). 190p. (J). pap. 8.99 (978-1-57658-305-0(8)) YWAM Publishing.

Benge, Janet Hazel & Benge, Geoffrey Francis. Gladys Aylward: The Adventure of a Lifetime. 1998. (Christian Heroes Ser.). (Illus.). 208p. (gr. 5-9). pap. 8.99 (978-1-57658-019-6(9)) YWAM Publishing.

Benson, Michael. Gloria Estefan. 2005. (Biography Ser.). (Illus.). 112p. (gr. 6-12). lib. bdg. 27.93 (978-0-8225-4982-6(4)) Lerner Publishing Group.

Birch, Beverley. Marie Curie: Courageous Pioneer in the Study of Radioactivity. 2000. (Giants of Science Ser.). (Illus.). 64p. (J). (gr. 5-8). 24.95 (978-1-56711-333-4(8), Blackbirch Pr., Inc.) Thomson Gale.

Birchfield, D. L. Sacagawea. 2002. (Raintree Biographies Ser.). (Illus.). 32p. (J). lib. bdg. 25.69 (978-0-7398-5680-2(4)) Raintree.

Bitton-Jackson, Livia. I Have Lived a Thousand Years: Growing up in the Holocaust. 1999. 224p. (YA). (gr. 7-12). pap. 5.99 (978-0-689-82395-4(9), Simon Pulse) Simon & Schuster Children's Publishing.

—My Bridges of Hope. 2002. (gr. 7-12). lib. bdg. 13.00 (978-0-613-73376-2(2)) Tandem Library Bks.

—My Bridges of Hope: Searching for Life & Love after Auschwitz. 2001. (YA). (978-0-606-20815-4(1)) Tandem Library Bks.

Black, Mary H. Mary Herd Black, Her Story: Autobiography: Letterography: Pictography. 1998. (Illus.). 600p. (Orig.). (YA). (gr. 6-12). pap. 35.00 (978-0-9657775-1-3(0)) E-Z Printing Pr.

Black, Sonia W. Mae Jemison. 2000. (Illus.). 64p. (J). (gr. 3-7). pap. 3.95 (978-1-57255-801-4(6)) Mondo Publishing.

—Mae Jemison. 2000. (gr. 3-6). lib. bdg. 11.80 (978-0-613-35854-5(6)) Tandem Library Bks.

Blashfield, Jean F. Shirley Temple Black: Actor & Diplomat. 2000. (Career Biographies Ser.). (Illus.). 128p. (J). (gr. 6-12). 25.00 (978-0-89434-338-4(6), F408, Ferguson Publishing Co.) Facts On File, Inc.

Bloom Fradin, Judith & Brindell Fradin, Dennis. Who Was Sacagawea? Taylor, Van Paul & Harrison, Nancy, illus. 2002. (Who Was...? Ser.). 112p. (J). pap. 4.99 (978-0-448-42485-9(1), Grosset & Dunlap) Penguin Group (USA) Inc.

Bloom, Harold. Sylvia Plath. 2000. (Major Poets Ser.). 120p. (YA). (gr. 10 up). 31.95 (978-0-7910-5935-7(9), Chelsea Hse.) Facts On File, Inc.

Blue, Rose, et al. Madeleine Albright: U. S. Secretary of State. 1998. (Library of Famous Women). (Illus.). 64p. (J). 26.20 (978-1-56711-253-5(6), Blackbirch Pr., Inc.) Thomson Gale.

Bodie, Idella. The Secret Message. 1998. (Heroes & Heroines of the American Revolution Ser.: Vol. 2). (Illus.). 45p. (J). (ps-3). pap. 5.95 (978-0-87844-145-7(X)) Sandlapper Publishing Co., Inc.

—Spunky Revolutionary War Heroine. 2000. (Heroes & Heroines of the American Revolution Ser.). (Illus.). 38p. (J). 5.95 (978-0-87844-154-9(9)) Sandlapper Publishing Co., Inc.

Bohannon, Lisa Frederiksen. Failure Is Impossible: The Story of Susan B. Anthony. 2004. (Feminist Voices Ser.). (Illus.). 112p. (YA). (gr. 6-12). 23.95 (978-1-883846-77-0(3) , First Biographies) Reynolds, Morgan Inc.

Bolden, Sherita M. Been There Once Ain't Going There Twice: A Southern Girl's View on Life Love & Relationships. 2002. 192p. (YA). per. (978-0-9715842-0-4(6)) Wild Dreams.

Bolden, Tonya. And Not Afraid to Dare: The Stories of Ten African-American Women. (J). (gr. 4-8). 2003. (Illus.). 224p. pap. 4.99 (978-0-439-47139-8(7) , Scholastic Paperbacks); 1998. 244p. pap. 16.95 (978-0-590-48080-2(4)) Scholastic, Inc.

Borden, Louise & Kroeger, Mary Kay. Fly High! The Story of Bessie Coleman. Flavin, Teresa, illus. 2001. 40p. (J). (gr. 4 up). 16.99 (978-0-689-82457-9(2) , McElderry, Margaret K.) Simon & Schuster Children's Publishing.

—Fly High Story of Bessie Coleman. Flavin, Teresa, illus. 2004. 40p. (J). pap. 6.99 (978-0-689-86462-9(0) , Aladdin) Simon & Schuster Children's Publishing.

Boulais, Sue. Vanessa Williams. 1998. (Real-Life Reader Biographies Ser.). (Illus.). 32p. (gr. 3-8). lib. bdg. 15.95 (978-1-883845-75-9(0)) Mitchell Lane Pubs., Inc.

Brackett, Virginia. A Home in the Heart: The Story of Sandra Cisneros. 2004. (World Writers Ser.). (Illus.). 112p. (J). (gr. 6-12). 23.95 (978-1-931798-42-6(7)) Reynolds, Morgan Inc.

—Restless Genius: The Story of Virginia Woolf. 2004. (World Writers Ser.). (Illus.). 144p. (YA). (gr. 6-12). 23.95 (978-1-931798-37-2(0)) Reynolds, Morgan Inc.

Braun, Eric. Wilma Rudolph. 2005. (Pebble Books). (Illus.). 24p. (J). 15.93 (978-0-7368-4234-1(9) , Pebble Bks.) Capstone Pr., Inc.

Briggs, Carole S. Women in Space. rev. ed. 1998. (Biography Ser.). (Illus.). 128p. (YA). (gr. 6-12). lib. bdg. 27.93 (978-0-8225-4937-6(9) , Lerner Pubns.) Lerner Publishing Group.

Brighton, Catherine. The Fossil Girl: Mary Anning's Dinosaur Discovery. 1999. (Illus.). 32p. (gr. k-3). lib. bdg. 22.90 (978-0-7613-1468-4(7) , Millbrook Pr.) Lerner Publishing Group.

Britton, Tamara L., contrib. by. Mary-Kate & Ashley Olsen. 1999. (Young Profiles Ser.). (Illus.). 32p. (J). (gr. 3). lib. bdg. 21.35 (978-1-57765-351-6(3) , Checkerboard Library) ABDO Publishing Co.

Broadwater, Andrea. Marian Anderson: Singer & Humanitarian. 2000. (African-American Biographies Ser.). (Illus.). 128p. (YA). (gr. 6-12). lib. bdg. 26.60 (978-0-7660-1211-0(5)) Enslow Pubs., Inc.

Brown, Don. Uncommon Traveler: Mary Kingsley in Africa. 2003. (Illus.). 32p. (J). (gr. k-3). 5.95 (978-0-618-36916-4(3)) Houghton Mifflin Co. Trade & Reference Div.

—A Voice from the Wilderness: The Story of Anna Howard Shaw. 32p. (J). (gr. k-3). 2010. pap. 5.95 (978-0-618-58544-1(3)); 2001. (Illus.). tchr. ed. 16.00 (978-0-618-08362-6(6)) Houghton Mifflin Co. Trade & Reference Div.

Brown, Jonatha A. Eleanor Roosevelt. (Illus.). 2005. 24p. (J). pap. (978-0-8368-4475-7(0)); 2005. 24p. (YA). lib. bdg. 19.33 (978-0-8368-4468-9(8) , Weekly Reader Early Learning Library); 2002. 48p. (J). (gr. 5 up). pap. 14.95 (978-0-8368-5239-4(7) , World Almanac Library); 2002. 48p. (J). (gr. 5 up). lib. bdg. 30.00 (978-0-8368-5079-6(3) , World Almanac Library) Stevens, Gareth Inc.

Brown, Lauren. Lindsay Lohan: The It Girl Next Door. 2004. (Illus.). 112p. (J). pap. 4.99 (978-0-689-87888-6(5) , Simon Spotlight) Simon & Schuster Children's Publishing.

Bruchac, Joseph. Rachel Carson: Preserving a Sense of Wonder. Locker, Thomas, illus. 2004. (Thomas Locker Images of Conservation Ser.). 32p. (J). 17.95 (978-1-55591-482-0(9)) Fulcrum Publishing.

Buckley, Carol. Travels with Tarra. 2005. (Illus.). 40p. (J). (gr. 3-7). 16.95 (978-0-88448-241-3(3)) Tilbury Hse. Pubs.

Buckley, James. Soccer Superwomen. 2006. (Girls Rock! Ser.). 32p. (J). (gr. 1-5). 24.21 (978-1-59296-750-6(7)) Child's World, Inc.

Bush, Karen Elizabeth. First Lady of Detroit: The Story of Marie-Therese Guyon, MME Cadillac. 2001. (Detroit Biography Series for Young Readers). (Illus.). 191p. (J). (gr. 5 up). pap. 16.00 (978-0-8143-2984-9(5)) Wayne State Univ. Pr.

Butts, Ed. She Dared: True Stories of Heroines, Scoundrels, & Renegades. Collins, Heather, illus. 2005. 121p. (J). (gr. 6-9). lib. bdg. 16.00 (978-0-606-33860-8(8)) Tandem Library Bks.

Butts, Edward. She Dared: True Stories of Heroines, Scoundrels, & Renegades. Collins, Heather, illus. 2005. 128p. (J). (gr. 6-9). pap. 8.95 (978-0-88776-718-0(4)) Tundra Bks., Inc./Livres Toundra, Inc. CAN. *Dist:* Random Hse., Inc.

Butts, Ellen R. & Schwartz, Joyce R. Eugenie Clark: Adventures of a Shark Scientist. 1999. (Illus.). 100p. (YA). (gr. 4-7). 19.50 (978-0-208-02440-4(9) , Linnet Bks.) Shoe String Pr., Inc.

B*Witched: Backstage Pass. 1999. (gr. 3-6). lib. bdg. 14.15 (978-0-613-21275-5(4)) Tandem Library Bks.

Camp, Carole Ann. American Women of Science. 2001. (Collective Biographies Ser.). (Illus.). 112p. (J). (gr. 6-12). lib. bdg. 26.60 (978-0-7660-1538-8(6)) Enslow Pubs., Inc.

Caper, William. Whoopi Goldberg: Comedian & Movie Star. 1999. (African-American Biographies Ser.). (Illus.). 128p. (YA). (gr. 6-12). lib. bdg. 26.60 (978-0-7660-1205-9(0)) Enslow Pubs., Inc.

Caravantes, Peggy. Petticoat Spies: Six Women Spies of the US Civil War. 2004. (Notable Americans Ser.). (Illus.). 112p. (YA). (gr. 6-12). 23.95 (978-1-883846-88-6(9) , First Biographies) Reynolds, Morgan Inc.

Carriere, Fanie Ann. The Legend of Rim Rock Annie: Autobiography of Fanie Ann Carriere. 2000. (Illus.). 91p. per. 7.00 (978-0-937242-22-3(5)) Scandia Pubs.

Chelsea House Publishing Staff. Female Firsts in Their Fields, 8 vols., Set. 1999. 135.60 (978-0-7910-5138-2(2) , Chelsea Hse.) Facts On File, Inc.

Cheney, Lynne. A Is for Abigail: An Almanac of Amazing American Women. Glasser, Robin Preiss, illus. 2003. 48p. (J). 16.95 (978-0-689-85819-2(1)) Simon & Schuster Children's Publishing.

Cherry, Lynne. Making a Difference in the World. Fine, John Christopher, photos by. 2000. (Meet the Author Ser.). (Illus.). 32p. (J). (gr. 2-5). 14.95 (978-1-57274-373-1(5)) Owen, Richard C. Pubs., Inc.

Chin-Lee, Cynthia. Amelia to Zora: Twenty-Six Women Who Changed the World. Halsey, Megan & Addy, Sean, illus. 2005. 32p. (J). 15.95 (978-1-57091-522-2(9)) Charlesbridge Publishing, Inc.

Chipman, Dawn, et al. Cool Women: The Thinking Girls Guide to the Hippest Women in History. Nelson, Pamela, ed. Inouye, Amy, illus. 1998. 128p. (J). (gr. 8-12). pap. 19.95 (978-0-9659754-0-7(1)) Girl Pr., Inc.

Christensen, Bonnie. The Daring Nellie Bly: America's Star Reporter. Christensen, Bonnie, illus. 2003. (Illus.). 32p. (J). (gr. 1-7). 16.95 (978-0-375-81568-3(6) , Knopf Bks. for Young Readers) Random Hse. Children's Bks.

—The Daring Nellie Bly: America's Star Reporter. 2003. (Illus.). 32p. (J). (gr. 1-7). lib. bdg. 18.99 (978-0-375-91568-0(0) , Knopf Bks. for Young Readers) Random Hse. Children's Bks.

Christopher, Matt. In the Goal with... Brianna Scurry. 2000. (YA). 11.60 (978-0-606-19839-4(3)) Tandem Library Bks.

—On the Court with... Lisa Leslie. 1998. (Matt Christopher Sports Biographies Ser.). 128p. (J). (gr. 3-7). pap. 4.99 (978-0-316-14216-8(6)) Little, Brown Bks. for Young Readers.

—On the Ice with... Tara Lipinski. 1999. (978-0-606-16725-3(0)) Tandem Library Bks.

Clara Barton. 2005. (First Biographies Ser.). (YA). (gr. k-3). (978-0-7368-9410-4(1) , Pebble Bks.) Capstone Pr., Inc.

Claybourne, Anna. Golda Meir. 2003. (Leading Lives Ser.). (Illus.). 64p. (J). lib. bdg. 28.50 (978-1-4034-0835-8(1)) Heinemann Library.

Cole, Melanie. Mary Joe Fernandez. 1998. (Real-Life Reader Biographies Ser.). (Illus.). 32p. (J). (gr. 3-8). lib. bdg. 15.95 (978-1-883845-63-6(7)) Mitchell Lane Pubs., Inc.

Coles, Robert. The Story of Ruby Bridges. Ford, George, illus. 2004. (Scholastic Bookshelf Ser.). 32p. (J). pap. 5.99 (978-0-439-59844-6(3) , Scholastic Paperbacks) Scholastic, Inc.

Collier, James Lincoln. The Eleanor Roosevelt You Never Knew. Copeland, Greg, illus. 2004. (You Never Knew Ser.). 80p. (J). 25.50 (978-0-516-24425-9(6) , Children's Pr.) Scholastic Library Publishing.

Collins, David R. Clara Barton. Landgraf, Ken, illus. 1999. (Young Reader's Christian Library). 224p. (J). (gr. 4-7). pap. 1.39 (978-1-57748-601-5(3)) Barbour Publishing, Inc.

Collins, Ellen. A Biography: My Life As a Basset Hound (2005. 51p. pap. 12.95 (978-1-4137-8776-4(2)) PublishAmerica, Inc.

Colman, Penny. Adventurous Women: Eight True Stories about Women Who Made a Difference. rev. ed. 2006. (Illus.). 192p. (J). 18.95 (978-0-8050-7744-5(8)) Holt, Henry & Co.

Conlan, Kathy. Under the Ice. 2004. (Illus.). 56p. (J). (gr. 4-6). (978-1-55337-060-4(0)) Kids Can Pr., Ltd.

Connolly, Sean. Margaret Thatcher. 2000. (Profiles Ser.). (Illus.). 56p. (J). (gr. 4-6). lib. bdg. 24.22 (978-1-57572-224-5(0)) Heinemann Library.

Constanza, Orozco Vargas. Coco Chanel. 2005. 156p. pap. (978-958-30-1765-0(5)) Panamericana Editorial.

Cook, Judy, et al. Natural Writer: A Story about Marjorie Kinnan Rawlings. Harden, Laurie, illus. 2001. (Creative Minds Biographies Ser.). 64p. (J). (gr. 3-6). lib. bdg. 22.60 (978-1-57505-468-1(X) , Carolrhoda Bks.) Lerner Publishing Group.

Covington, Karen. The Creators: Artists, Designers, Craftswomen. 2000. (Remarkable Women). (Illus.). 80p. (YA). (gr. 6-9). lib. bdg. 32.85 (978-0-8172-5725-5(X)) Raintree.

—The Performing Artists: Actors, Directors, Dancers, Entertainers, Musicians. 2002. (Remarkable Women). (Illus.). 80p. (YA). (gr. 6-9). lib. bdg. 32.85 (978-0-8172-5727-9(6)) Raintree.

Cullen, J. Heather. Barbara McClintock. 2003. (Women in the Science Ser.). (Illus.). 122p. pap. 30.00 (978-0-7910-7522-7(2)); 112p. (gr. 6-12). 30.00 (978-0-7910-7248-6(7)) Facts On File, Inc. (Chelsea Hse.).

Cummins, Julie. Tomboy of the Air: Daredevil Pilot Blanche Stuart Scott. 2001. (Illus.). 80p. (J). (gr. 3-6). lib. bdg. 17.89 (978-0-06-029243-0(1)) HarperCollins Pubs.

Cummins, Julie. Women Daredevils. Harness, Cheryl, illus. 2008. 48p. (J). (gr. 3). 17.99 ***(978-0-525-47948-2(1)*** , Dutton Juvenile) Penguin Group (USA) Inc.

Currie, Stephen. Women Inventors. 2001. (History Makers Ser.). (Illus.). 96p. (YA). (gr. 7-10). 27.45 (978-1-56006-865-5(5) , Lucent Bks.) Thomson Gale.

Danneberg, Julie. Amidst the Gold Dust: Women Who Forged the West. 2004. (Illus.). 96p. (gr. 5 up). pap. 12.95 (978-1-55591-997-9(9)) Fulcrum Publishing.

Darraj, Susan Muaddi. Mairead Corrigan & Betty Williams: Partners for Peace in Northern Ireland. 2006. (Modern Peacemakers Ser.). (Illus.). 112p. (J). (gr. 9 up). 30.00 (978-0-7910-9001-5(9) , Chelsea Hse.) Facts On File, Inc.

—Queen Noor. 2004. (Women in Politics Ser.). (Illus.). 120p. 30.00 (978-0-7910-7736-8(5)); 116p. pap. 30.00 (978-0-7910-8002-3(1)) Facts On File, Inc. (Chelsea Hse.).

Darrow, Sharon. Through the Tempests Dark & Wild: A Story of Mary Shelley, Creator of "Frankenstein" Barrett, Angela, illus. 2003. 40p. (J). (gr. 3-7). 18.99 (978-0-7636-0835-4(1)) Candlewick Pr.

Davis, Rebecca Henry. Fanny Crosby: Queen of Gospel Songs. 2003. (Illus.). 107p. (J). 6.49 (978-1-57924-970-0(1)) Jones, Bob Univ. Pr.

De Angelis, Gina. Lucretia Mott: Woman Suffragist. 2000. (Women of Achievement Ser.). (Illus.). 112p. (J). (gr. 4-7). 30.00 (978-0-7910-5295-2(8) , Chelsea Hse.) Facts On File, Inc.

De Angelis, Therese. Jodie Foster. 2000. (Illus.). 112p. (J). (ps-7). lib. bdg. 18.75 (978-0-613-21812-2(4)) Tandem Library Bks.

Deady, Kathleen W. Clara Barton. 2003. (Photo-Illustrated Biographies Ser.). (Illus.). 24p. (J). (gr. 2-3). lib. bdg. 18.60 (978-0-7368-1604-5(6) , Bridgestone Bks.) Capstone Pr., Inc.

DeBoer, Andy. Whoopi Goldberg. 1998. (Ovations Ser.: Vol. 8). (Illus.). 32p. (YA). (gr. 4-7). 21.30 (978-0-88682-696-3(9) , Creative Education) Creative Co., The.

DeKeyser, Stacy. Sacagawea. 2004. (Watts Library). (Illus.). 64p. (J). 25.50 (978-0-531-12290-7(5) , Watts, Franklin) Scholastic Library Publishing.

Demi. Mother Teresa. 2005. (Illus.). 40p. (J). (gr. 1-4). 19.95 (978-0-689-86407-0(8) , McElderry, Margaret K.) Simon & Schuster Children's Publishing.

Devillier, Christy. Clara Barton. 2004. (First Biographies Set Iv Ser.). (Illus.). 32p. (J). (gr. k-4). lib. bdg. 22.78 (978-1-59197-511-3(5)) ABDO Publishing Co.

—Helen Keller. 2004. (First Biographies Set Iv Ser.). (Illus.). 32p. (J). (gr. k-4). lib. bdg. 22.78 (978-1-59197-514-4(X)) ABDO Publishing Co.

Di Domenico, Kelly. Super Women in Science. 2005. (Women's Hall of Fame Ser.). (Illus.). 102p. (YA). pap. 7.95 (978-1-896764-66-5(5)) Second Story Pr. CAN. *Dist:* Orca Bk. Pubs. USA, Univ. of Toronto Pr.

—Super Women in Science. 2003. (gr. 3-6). lib. bdg. 16.40 (978-0-613-80433-2(3)) Tandem Library Bks.

Dils, Tracy. Mother Theresa. 2001. (Women of Achievement Ser.). (Illus.). 112p. (J). pap. 9.95 (978-0-7910-5888-6(3)); (gr. 4-7). 30.00 (978-0-7910-5887-9(5)) Facts On File, Inc. (Chelsea Hse.).

Ditchfield, Christin. Clara Barton: Founder of the American Red Cross. 2004. (Great Life Stories Ser.). (Illus.). 111p. (J). 30.50 (978-0-531-12276-1(X) , Watts, Franklin) Scholastic Library Publishing.

—Top 10 American Women's Olympic Gold Medalists. 2000. (Sports Top 10 Ser.). (Illus.). 48p. (YA). (gr. 4-10). lib. bdg. 23.93 (978-0-7660-1277-6(8)) Enslow Pubs., Inc.

DiVito, Anna. Annie Oakley Saves the Day! DiVito, Anna, illus. 2004. (Ready-to-Read Cofa Ser.). 32p. (J). pap. 3.99 (978-0-689-86520-6(1) , Aladdin) Simon & Schuster Children's Publishing.

Donovan, Sandy. Mary McLeod Bethune. 2003. (African-American Biographies Ser.). 64p. (YA). pap. 8.95 (978-1-4109-0039-5(8)); (Illus.). (J). lib. bdg. 28.56 (978-0-7398-6868-3(3)) Raintree.

Dougherty, Terri. Mia Hamm. 2000. (Jam Session Ser.). (Illus.). 32p. (J). (gr. 3-8). lib. bdg. 24.21 (978-1-57765-364-6(5) , ABDO & Daughters) ABDO Publishing Co.

—Tara Lipinski. 1999. (Jam Session Ser.). (Illus.). 32p. (J). (gr. 3-8). lib. bdg. 24.21 (978-1-57765-312-7(2) , ABDO & Daughters) ABDO Publishing Co.

Douty, Sheila Cornell & Cohen, Judith Love. You Can Be a Woman Softball Player. 2000. (Illus.). 40p. (YA). (gr. 4-9). 13.95 (978-1-880599-47-1(3)); 7.00 (978-1-880599-46-4(5)) Cascade Pass, Inc.

Dubois, Muriel L. Helen Keller. 2003. (Photo-Illustrated Biographies Ser.). (Illus.). 24p. (J). (gr. 2-3). lib. bdg. 18.60 (978-0-7368-1605-2(4) , Bridgestone Bks.) Capstone Pr., Inc.

Duden, Jane. Betsy Ross. 2000. (Let Freedom Ring Ser.). (Illus.). 48p. (J). (gr. 3-4). lib. bdg. 22.60 (978-0-7368-1036-4(6) , Bridgestone Bks.) Capstone Pr., Inc.

Dyson, Cindy. Laila Ali. 2001. (Women Who Win Ser.). (J). pap. (978-0-7910-6538-9(3)); (Illus.). 64p. (gr. 3 up). 25.00 (978-0-7910-6537-2(5)) Facts On File, Inc. (Chelsea Hse.).

Eddy, Susan. Mother Teresa. (Rookie Biographies Ser.). (Illus.). (J). 2004. 31p. (gr. 1-2). pap. 4.95 (978-0-516-27922-0(X)); 2003. 32p. 20.50 (978-0-516-25881-2(8)) Scholastic Library Publishing. (Children's Pr.).

Edgar, Susan E. & Edgar, Kathleen J. Life Stories of 100 Famous Women. 2001. (Values in Action Ser.). (Illus.). 573p. (J). (978-1-56156-979-3(8)) Kidsbooks, Inc.

Egan, Tracie. Cynthia Ann Parker: Cautiva de los Comanches. Gonzalez, Tomas, tr. 2003. (Grandes Personajes en la Historia de Los Estados Unidos Ser.). (ENG & SPA.). (J). pap. (978-0-8239-4225-1(2)) Rosen Publishing Group, Inc., The.

—Francisca Alavez, the Angel of Goliad. 2003. (Famous People in American History Ser.). (Illus.). 32p. (J). pap. (978-0-8239-4181-0(7)) Rosen Publishing Group, Inc., The.

Elleman, Barbara. Virginia Lee Burton: A Life in Art. 2002. (Illus.). 144p. (J). (gr. 7 up). tchr. ed. 20.00 (978-0-618-00342-6(8)) Houghton Mifflin Co. Trade & Reference Div.

Ellsworth, Mary Ellen. Gertrude Chandler Warner & the Boxcar Children. 2002. (gr. 3-6). lib. bdg. 15.25 (978-0-613-75732-4(7)) Tandem Library Bks.

—Gertrude Chandler Warner & the Boxcar Children. DeJohn, Marie, illus. 2004. (Boxcar Children Ser.). 64p. (J). (gr. 2-7). pap. 6.95 (978-0-8075-2838-9(2)) Whitman, Albert & Co.

Emery, Joanna. Caring for a Colony: The Story of Jeanne Mance. 2005. (Stories of Canada Ser.). (Illus.). 66p. (J). 16.95 (978-1-894917-07-0(3)) Napoleon Publishing/ Rendezvous Pr. CAN. *Dist:* AtlasBooks Distribution.

Englar, Mary. Benazir Bhutto: Pakistani Prime Minister & Activist. 2006. (Signature Lives Ser.). (Illus.). 112p. (J). (gr. 5-7). 30.60 (978-0-7565-1578-2(5)) Compass Point Bks.

Epstein, Rachel. Estee Lauder: Beauty-Business Success. 2000. (Book Report Biographies Ser.). (Illus.). 112p. (YA). (gr. 6-8). pap. 6.95 (978-0-531-16492-1(6) , Watts, Franklin) Scholastic Library Publishing.

—Estee Lauder: Beauty-Business Success. 2000. (YA). (978-0-606-19783-0(4)) Tandem Library Bks.

Erdrich, Lise. Sacagawea. Buffalohead, Julie, illus. 2003. 40p. (J). (gr. 3-6). 16.95 (978-0-87614-646-0(9) , Carolrhoda Bks.) Lerner Publishing Group.

Evento, Susan. Mary McLeod Bethune. 2004. (Rookie Biographies Ser.). (Illus.). 31p. (J). 20.50 (978-0-516-21720-8(8) , Children's Pr.) Scholastic Library Publishing.

Extraordinary Women. (Illus.). (gr. 6-12). pap. (978-0-7910-8050-4(1)); lib. bdg. 688.50 (978-0-7910-8416-8(7)) Facts On File, Inc. (Chelsea Hse.).

Extraordinary Women Explorers. 2005. (Women's Hall of Fame Ser.). (Illus.). 118p. (YA). (gr. 4-7). pap. 7.95 (978-1-896764-98-6(3)) Second Story Pr. CAN. *Dist:* Orca Bk. Pubs. USA, Univ. of Toronto Pr.

Feinberg, Barbara Silberdick. Eleanor Roosevelt: Everything She Could Be. 2003. (Gateway Biography Ser.: 4). (Illus.). 48p. lib. bdg. 23.90 (978-0-7613-2623-6(5) , Millbrook Pr.) Lerner Publishing Group.

Feinstein, Stephen. Read about Sacagawea. 2004. (I Like Biographies Ser.!). (Illus.). 24p. (J). lib. bdg. 21.26 (978-0-7660-2297-3(8)) Enslow Pubs., Inc.

Feldman, Heather. Marion Jones, Atleta de Categoria Internacional. 2002. (Coleccion Power Kids). (SPA & ENG., Illus.). 24p. (J). (gr. k-2). lib. bdg. 17.25 (978-0-8239-6141-2(9) , RN31310, Buenas Letra) Rosen Publishing Group, Inc., The.

—Valentina Tereshkova: The First Woman in Space. 2003. (Space Firsts Ser.). (Illus.). 24p. (J). lib. bdg. 19.95 (978-0-8239-6246-4(6) , PowerKids Pr.) Rosen Publishing Group, Inc., The.

Ferris, Jeri Chase. Demanding Justice: A Story about Mary Ann Shadd Cary. Smith, Kimanne, illus. 2003. 64p. (J). 6.95 (978-0-87614-928-7(X) , Carolrhoda Bks.); (gr. 4-8). 22.60 (978-1-57505-177-2(X)) Lerner Publishing Group.

—Demanding Justice: A Story about Mary Ann Shadd Cary. 2003. (gr. 3-6). lib. bdg. 14.10 (978-0-613-58898-0(3)) Tandem Library Bks.

—With Open Hands: A Story about Biddy Mason. 2003. (Creative Minds Biographies Ser.). (Illus.). 64p. (J). (gr. 3-6). pap. 6.95 (978-0-87614-845-7(3) , Carolrhoda Bks.) Lerner Publishing Group.

—With Open Hands: A Story about Biddy Mason. Ramstad, Ralph L., illus. 1999. (Creative Minds Biographies Ser.). 64p. (J). (gr. 3-6). lib. bdg. 22.60 (978-1-57505-330-1(6) , Carolrhoda Bks.) Lerner Publishing Group.

—With Open Hands: A Story about Biddy Mason. 1999. (gr. 3-6). lib. bdg. 15.25 (978-0-613-68482-8(6)) Tandem Library Bks.

Ferry, Joseph. Maria Goeppert Mayer. 2003. (Women in Science Ser.). (Illus.). 112p. (J). (gr. 6-12). 30.00 (978-0-7910-7247-9(9) , Chelsea Hse.) Facts On File, Inc.

Findley, Violet. Easy Reader Biographies: Harriet Tubman: Follow the North Star. 2007. 16p. pap. 2.99 ***(978-0-439-92330-9(1)*** , Teaching Resources) Scholastic, Inc.

Fisher, Mary McMillan. Rosita's Bridge. Whitehead, Barbara Mathews, illus. 2001. 32p. (J). (gr. 2-4). 16.95 (978-1-893271-18-0(8)) Maverick Publishing Co.

Fitzpatrick, Anne. Mother Teresa. 2005. (Genius Ser.). (Illus.). 48p. (gr. 5-9). 21.95 (978-1-58341-330-2(8) , Creative Education) Creative Co., The.

Fleming, Denise. Maker of Things. Bowers, Karen & Bowers, Karen, photos by. 2002. (Meet the Author Ser.). (Illus.). 32p. (J). (gr. 2-5). 14.95 (978-1-57274-596-4(7) , 729) Owen, Richard C. Pubs., Inc.

Flynn, Jean. Texas Women Who Dared to Be First. 2004. (Illus.). 144p. (gr. 4-7). 18.95 (978-1-57168-232-1(5)) Eakin Pr.

Ford, Carin T. Pocahontas: American Indian Princess. 2006. (Heroes of American History Ser.). (Illus.). 32p. (J). lib. bdg. 22.60 (978-0-7660-2604-9(3) , Enslow Elementary) Enslow Pubs., Inc.

—Sacagawea: Meet an American Legend. 2003. (Meeting Famous People Ser.). (Illus.). 32p. (J). lib. bdg. 22.60 (978-0-7660-2004-7(5)) Enslow Pubs., Inc.

Forten, Charlotte L., et al. A Free Black Girl Before the Civil War: The Diary of Charlotte Forten, 1854. Steele, Christy & Graves, Kerry, eds. 2000. (Blue Earth Books). (Illus.). 32p. (J). (gr. 3-4). lib. bdg. 22.60 (978-0-7368-0345-8(9) , Bridgestone Bks.) Capstone Pr., Inc.

Fradin, Dennis Brindell. Who Was Sacagawea? 2002. (gr. 3-6). lib. bdg. 13.00 (978-0-613-43655-7(5)) Tandem Library Bks.

Francis, Dorothy Brenner. Clara Barton: Founder of the American Red Cross. 2002. (Gateway Biography Ser.). (Illus.). 48p. (gr. 2-4). lib. bdg. 23.90 (978-0-7613-2621-2(9) , Millbrook Pr.) Lerner Publishing Group.

Franklin, Virgil. The Story of Sacagawea. 2002. (Reading Room Collection). (Illus.). 24p. (J). pap. (978-0-8239-8162-5(2)); lib. bdg. 18.75 (978-0-8239-3725-7(9)) Rosen Publishing Group, Inc., The.

WXYZ

Freedman, Russell. The Voice That Challenged a Nation: Marian Anderson & the Struggle for Equal Rights. 2004. (Illus.). 128p. (J). (gr. 4-6). tchr. ed. 18.00 (978-0-618-15976-5(2) , Clarion Bks.) Houghton Mifflin Co. Trade & Reference Div.

Frith, Margaret. Frida Kahlo: The Artist Who Painted Herself. 2003. (gr. k-3). lib. bdg. 14.15 (978-0-613-68237-4(8)) Tandem Library Bks.

Fritz, Jean. The Double Life of Pocahontas. 2004. 24.95 incl. audio (978-1-56008-189-0(9)) Weston Woods Studios, Inc.

Fuller, Barbara. Great Britain. 2004. (Illus.). (J). 48p. 27.07 (978-0-7614-1760-6(5)); 2nd ed. 144p. 37.07 (978-0-7614-1845-0(8)) Cavendish, Marshall Corp. (Benchmark Bks.).

Fullick, Ann. Marie Curie. (Groundbreakers Ser.). 48p. (J). (gr. 5-7). 2002. (Illus.). pap. 8.50 (978-1-58810-994-1(1) , 91469); 2000. lib. bdg. 25.64 (978-1-57572-374-7(3)) Heinemann Library.

Gaines, Ann Graham. Coco Chanel. (Women in the Arts Ser.). 2004. 116p. pap. 30.00 (978-0-7910-7950-8(3)); 2003. (Illus.). 112p. (gr. 6-12). 30.00 (978-0-7910-7455-8(2)) Facts On File, Inc. (Chelsea Hse.).

—Faith Hill. 2001. (Real-Life Reader Biography Ser.). (Illus.). 32p. (gr. 3-8). lib. bdg. 15.95 (978-1-58415-091-6(2)) Mitchell Lane Pubs., Inc.

—J. K. Rowling. 2001. (Real-Life Reader Biography Ser.). (Illus.). 32p. (J). (gr. 3-8). lib. bdg. 15.95 (978-1-58415-078-7(5)) Mitchell Lane Pubs., Inc.

Gale Research Staff. Contemporary Heroes & Heroines, Bk. III. 1998. (Illus.). 699p. (J). 110.00 (978-0-7876-2215-2(X) , GML14099-111730) Thomson Gale.

Gallagher, Jim. Shania Twain: Grammy Award-Winning Singer. 1999. (Real-Life Reader Biography Ser.). (Illus.). 32p. (gr. 3-8). lib. bdg. 15.95 (978-1-58415-000-8(9)) Mitchell Lane Pubs., Inc.

Gallop-Goodman, Gerda. Diane Sawyer. 2001. (Women of Achievement Ser.). (Illus.). (J). 108p. pap. 30.00 (978-0-7910-6317-0(8)); 112p. 30.00 (978-0-7910-6316-3(X)) Facts On File, Inc. (Chelsea Hse.).

—Diane Sawyer. 2002. (gr. 5-8). lib. bdg. 18.75 (978-0-613-50889-6(0)) Tandem Library Bks.

Gatto, Kimberly. Michelle Kwan: Champion on Ice. 1998. (Sports Achievers Biographies Ser.). (Illus.). 64p. (J). (gr. 4-9). lib. bdg. (978-0-8225-3669-7(2)); pap. 5.95 (978-0-8225-9830-5(2)) Lerner Publishing Group. (LernerSports).

Geoghegan, Bronwyn. Livewire Real Lives Kylie Minogue. 2000. (Livewires Ser.). (Illus.). 32p. pap. 7.00 (978-0-521-77617-2(1)) Cambridge Univ. Pr.

Georgiady, Nicholas P., et al. Michigan Women, Vol. 1. Nixon, Buford, illus. 2nd rev. ed. 1998. 32p. (J). (gr. 4-8). pap. 4.50 (978-0-917961-08-3(0)) Argee Pubs.

Gertner, Sheina Sachar. The Tree Stood Still. 2006. 96p. per. 9.95 (***978-1-58939-886-3(6)**) Virtualbookworm.com Publishing, Inc.

Gilbert, Sara. Calamity Jane. 2005. (Illus.). 48p. (gr. 5-9). 21.95 (978-1-58341-337-1(5) , Creative Education) Creative Co., The.

Glavich, Mary Kathleen. Blessed Teresa of Calcutta: Missionary of Charity. Kiwak, Barbara, tr. Kiwak, Barbara, illus. 2003. (Encounter the Saints Ser.: Vol. 17). 136p. (J). pap. 7.95 (978-0-8198-1160-8(2) , 332-024) Pauline Bks. & Media.

—Saint Julie Billiart: The Smiling Saint. Bentley, James, illus. 2001. (Encounter the Saints Ser.: Vol. 11). 120p. (J). pap. 5.95 (978-0-8198-7050-6(1) , 332-352) Pauline Bks. & Media.

—Saint Therese of Lisieux: The Way of Love. Esquinaldo, Virginia, tr. Esquinaldo, Virginia, illus. 2003. (Encounter the Saints Ser.). 132p. (J). pap. 5.95 (978-0-8198-7074-2(9) , 332-370) Pauline Bks. & Media.

Gloria Estefan. 1999. (SmartReader Ser.). (J). Level 1. pap., tchr. ed. 19.95 incl. audio (978-0-7887-1032-2(X) , 79338T3); Level 2. pap., tchr. ed. 19.95 incl. audio (978-0-7887-1036-0(2) , 79339T3) Recorded Bks., LLC.

Gogerly, Liz. Dian Fossey. 2002. (Scientists Who Made History Ser.). (Illus.). 48p. (J). lib. bdg. 27.12 (978-0-7398-5225-5(6)) Raintree.

Gogol, Sara. Katy Steding: Pro Basketball Pioneer. 1998. (Sports Achievers Biographies Ser.). (Illus.). 64p. (J). (gr. 4-9). lib. bdg. (978-0-8225-3668-0(4) , LernerSports) Lerner Publishing Group.

Gomez, Rebecca. Sally Ride. 2003. (First Biographies Ser.). (Illus.). 32p. (J). (gr. k-4). lib. bdg. 22.78 (978-1-57765-948-8(1)) ABDO Publishing Co.

Goodman, Michael E. Monica Seles. 1998. (Ovations Ser.). (Illus.). 32p. (YA). (gr. 4-7). lib. bdg. 21.30 (978-0-88682-699-4(3) , Creative Education) Creative Co., The.

Gordon, Janet & Merkur, Janet. Livewire Real Lives Caroline Chisholm. 2000. (Livewires Ser.). 32p. pap. 6.00 (978-0-521-77638-7(4)) Cambridge Univ. Pr.

Gorman, Jacqueline Laks. Queen Latifah. 2006. (Today's Superstars). (Illus.). 32p. (J). (gr. 5 up). lib. bdg. 23.93 (***978-0-8368-7652-9(0)**) Stevens, Gareth Inc.

Gosling, Maureen, et al. You Can Be a Woman Movie Maker. l.t. ed. 2003. (Illus.). 80p. (J). 19.95 incl. DVD (978-1-880599-64-8(3)); pap. 14.95 incl. DVD (978-1-880599-63-1(5)) Cascade Pass, Inc.

Gottlieb, Lori. Stick Figure: A Diary of My Former Self. 2000. (gr. 7-12). lib. bdg. 21.10 (978-0-613-69088-1(5)) Tandem Library Bks.

Granados, Christine. Sheila E. 1999. (Real-Life Reader Biography Ser.). (Illus.). 32p. (J). (gr. 3-8). lib. bdg. 15.95 (978-1-58415-019-0(X)) Mitchell Lane Pubs., Inc.

Graves, Kerry, ed. Nineteenth-Century Schoolgirl: The Diary of Caroline Cowles Richards, 1852-1854. 1999. (Diaries, Letters & Memoirs Ser.). 32p. (J). (gr. 2-7). pap. 21.00 (978-0-516-21853-3(0) , Children's Pr.) Scholastic Library Publishing.

Grealy, Lucy. Autobiography of a Face. 2003. (gr. 7-12). lib. bdg. 22.20 (978-0-613-64839-4(0)) Tandem Library Bks.

Green, Robert. Queen Victoria. 1998. (First Bks.). 64p. (J). (gr. 4-7). 23.00 (978-0-531-20330-9(1) , Watts, Franklin) Scholastic Library Publishing.

Grunwell, Jeanne Marie & Goering, Mari, illus. Saint Elizabeth Ann Seton: Daughter of America. 1999. (Encounter the Saints Ser.: No. 3). 132p. (YA). (gr. 5-9). pap. 7.95 (978-0-8198-7022-3(6) , 332-340) Pauline Bks. & Media.

Gulotta, Charles. Extraordinary Women in Politics. 1998. (Extraordinary People Ser.). (Illus.). 288p. (YA). (gr. 6 up). 37.50 (978-0-516-20610-3(9) , Children's Pr.) Scholastic Library Publishing.

Hacker, Carlotta. Explorers. 1998. (Women in Profile Ser.). (Illus.). 48p. (J). (gr. 4). pap. (978-0-7787-0026-5(7)); lib. bdg. (978-0-7787-0004-3(6)) Crabtree Publishing Co.

—Humanitarians. 1998. (Women in Profile Ser.). (Illus.). 48p. (J). (gr. 4). pap. (978-0-7787-0033-3(X)) Crabtree Publishing Co.

—Nobel Prize Winners. 1998. (Women in Profile Ser.). (Illus.). 48p. (J). (gr. 4). pap. (978-0-7787-0029-6(1)); lib. bdg. (978-0-7787-0007-4(0)) Crabtree Publishing Co.

—Rebels. 1998. (Women in Profile Ser.). (Illus.). 48p. (J). (gr. 4). pap. (978-0-7787-0036-4(4)) Crabtree Publishing Co.

—Scientists. 1998. (Women in Profile Ser.). (Illus.). 48p. (J). (gr. 4). pap. (978-0-7787-0028-9(3)); lib. bdg. (978-0-7787-0006-7(2)) Crabtree Publishing Co.

Hall, Margaret. Madam C. J. Walker. 2003. (Lives & Times Ser.). (Illus.). 24p. (J). pap. (978-1-4034-4257-4(6)) Heinemann Library.

Hanson, Jillian. Fearless Women: Explorers, Athletes, Other Competitors. 2000. (Remarkable Women). (Illus.). 80p. (YA). (gr. 6-9). lib. bdg. 32.85 (978-0-8172-5729-3(2)) Raintree.

—The Professionals: Magnates, Entrepreneurs, Career Women. 2002. (Remarkable Women). (Illus.). 80p. (YA). (gr. 6-9). lib. bdg. 32.85 (978-0-8172-5726-2(8)) Raintree.

Harcourt School Publishers Staff. In Two Worlds Advanced Level. 3rd ed. 2002. (Trophies Reading Program Ser.). (Illus.). pap. 5.10 (978-0-15-323192-6(0)) Harcourt Schl. Pubs.

Harness, Cheryl. Remember the Ladies: 100 Great American Women. Harness, Cheryl, illus. (Illus.). 64p. (J). (gr. 3 up). 2003. pap. 8.99 (978-0-06-443869-8(4)); 2001. 16.99 (978-0-688-17017-2(X)) HarperCollins Pubs.

Harrigan, Margaret Sheridan. Maggie: Millhand & Farmer. Gill, Kathleen M., ed. 2002. (Illus.). 184p. (YA). pap. 19.95 (978-0-9714620-1-4(1)) Peckhaven Publishing.

Hart, Phillip S. Bessie Coleman. 2005. (Just the Facts Biographies Ser.). (Illus.). 112p. (J). (gr. 6-12). 27.93 (978-0-8225-2469-4(4)) Lerner Publishing Group.

Hartzog, Brooke. Ichthyosaurus & Little Mary Anning. 1999. (Dinosaurs & Their Discoverers Ser.). 24p. (J). (gr. k-4). lib. bdg. 18.75 (978-0-8239-5326-4(2) , PowerKids Pr.) Rosen Publishing Group, Inc., The.

Hasday, Judy L. Extraordinary Women Athletes. 2000. (gr. 7-12). lib. bdg. 26.85 (978-0-613-54473-3(0)) Tandem Library Bks.

—Marie Curie: Pioneer on the Frontier of Radioactivity. 2004. (Nobel Prize-Winning Scientists Ser.). (Illus.). 112p. (YA). lib. bdg. 26.60 (978-0-7660-2440-3(7)) Enslow Pubs., Inc.

Head, Judith. America's Daughters: 400 Years of American Women. 1999. 130p. (J). (gr. 4 up). pap. 16.95 (978-0-9622036-8-8(8)) Perspective Publishing, Inc.

—America's Daughters: 400 Years of American Women. 1999. (Illus.). 130p. (J). (ps-7). per. 26.85 (978-0-613-90517-6(2)) Tandem Library Bks.

Hearne, Betsy. Seven Brave Women. Andersen, Bethanne, illus. 2006. 24p. (J). reprint ed. pap. 6.99 (978-0-06-079921-2(8) , Harper Trophy) HarperCollins Pubs.

Heffernan, Anne Eileen, et al. Saint Bernadette Soubirous: Light in the Grotto. 1999. (Encounter the Saints Ser.: No. 2). Orig. Title: Light in the Grotto. (Illus.). 120p. (YA). (gr. 5-9). pap. 5.95 (978-0-8198-7020-9(X) , 332-338) Pauline Bks. & Media.

Heinemann, Sue & New York Public Library Staff. Amazing Women in American History: A Book of Answers for Kids. 1998. (New York Public Library Books for Kids Ser.: Vol. 6). (Illus.). 192p. (gr. 5-9). pap. 12.95 (978-0-471-19216-9(3) , Wiley-Interscience) Wiley, John & Sons, Inc.

Hendrickson, Sue & Weinberger, Kimberly. Hunt for the Past: My Life as an Explorer. 2001. (Illus.). 48p. (J). (gr. 1-4). pap. 3.99 (978-0-439-27191-2(6)) Scholastic, Inc.

Herstek, Amy Paulson. Dorothea Dix: Crusader for the Mentally Ill. 2001. (Historical American Biographies Ser.). (Illus.). 128p. (YA). (gr. 6-12). lib. bdg. 26.60 (978-0-7660-1258-5(1)) Enslow Pubs., Inc.

Hill, Anne E. Broadcasting & Journalism. 1999. (Female Firsts in Their Fields Ser.). (Illus.). 64p. (YA). (gr. 4-7). 28.00 (978-0-7910-5139-9(0) , Chelsea Hse.) Facts On File, Inc.

—Celine Dion. 2004. (World Musicmakers Ser.). (Illus.). 64p. (J). 26.20 (978-1-56711-971-8(9) , Blackbirch Pr., Inc.) Thomson Gale.

—Ekaterina Gordeeva. 1999. (Overcoming Adversity Ser.). (J). (978-0-606-19345-0(6)) Tandem Library Bks.

—Gwyneth Paltrow. 2001. (Galaxy of Superstars Ser.). 64p. (J). 25.00 (978-0-7910-6463-4(8) , Chelsea Hse.) Facts On File, Inc.

—Michelle Kwan. 2004. (Sports Heroes & Legends Ser.). (Illus.). 112p. (J). (gr. 6-12). lib. bdg. 27.93 (978-0-8225-1795-5(7)) Lerner Publishing Group.

Hill, Mary. J K Rowling. 2003. (gr. k-3). lib. bdg. 12.95 (978-0-613-67727-1(7)) Tandem Library Bks.

—Sandra Day O'Connor. 2003. (Welcome Book Ser.). (Illus.). 24p. (J). 17.00 (978-0-516-25868-3(0) , Children's Pr.) Scholastic Library Publishing.

—Sandra Day O'Connor. 2003. (gr. k-3). lib. bdg. 12.95 (978-0-613-67763-9(3)) Tandem Library Bks.

Hill, Mary Lea. Saint Edith Stein: Blessed by the Cross. Goering, Mari, illus. 2000. (Encounter the Saints Ser.: Vol. 5). 130p. (J). (gr. 5-9). pap. 5.95 (978-0-8198-7036-0(6) , 332-345) Pauline Bks. & Media.

Hilliam, David. Joan of Arc: Heroine of France. 2004. (Medieval Leaders in Ancient History Ser.). (Illus.). 112p. (J). lib. bdg. 31.95 (978-1-4042-0164-4(5)) Rosen Publishing Group, Inc., The.

Hitchcock, Susan Tyler. Sylvia A. Earle: Deep Sea Explorer. 2004. (Women Explorers Ser.). (Illus.). 120p. 30.00 (978-0-7910-7712-2(8) , Chelsea Hse.) Facts On File, Inc.

Hodges, Margaret. Joan of Arc: The Lily Maid. Rayevsky, Robert, illus. 1999. 32p. (J). (gr. 4-6). tchr. ed. 16.95 (978-0-8234-1424-6(8)) Holiday Hse., Inc.

Holden, Henry M. American Women of Flight: Pilots & Pioneers. 2003. (Collective Biographies Ser.). (Illus.). 112p. (J). (gr. 6-12). lib. bdg. 26.60 (978-0-7660-2005-4(3)) Enslow Pubs., Inc.

Homan, Lynn M. & Reilly, Thomas. Women Who Fly. Shepherd, Rosalie M., illus. 2004. 104p. (J). pap. 14.95 (978-1-58980-160-8(1)) Pelican Publishing Co., Inc.

Horn, Geoffrey M. Margaret Mead. 2004. (Trailblazers of the Modern World Ser.). (Illus.). 48p. (J). (gr. 5 up). lib. bdg. 30.00 (978-0-8368-5099-4(8) , World Almanac Library) Stevens, Gareth Inc.

Howard, Megan. Madeleine Albright. 1998. (Biography Ser.). (Illus.). 128p. (YA). (gr. 6-12). lib. bdg. 25.26 (978-0-8225-4935-2(2) , Lerner Pubns.) Lerner Publishing Group.

Howat, Irene. Ten Girls Who Changed the World. 160p. (J). pap. 5.99 (978-1-85792-649-1(8) , Christian Focus) Christian Focus Pubns. GBR. *Dist:* Riverside.

—Ten Girls Who Made a Difference. 160p. (J). pap. 5.99 (978-1-85792-776-4(1) , Christian Focus) Christian Focus Pubns. GBR. *Dist:* Riverside.

Hudson, Margaret. Pocahontas. 2002. (Lives & Times Ser.). (Illus.). 24p. (J). (gr. k-3). pap. 6.50 (978-1-4034-0031-4(8) , 91475) Heinemann Library.

Hunsaker, Joyce Badgley. They Call Me Sacagawea. 2003. (Illus.). n/ap. pap. 9.95 (978-0-7627-2580-9(X) , Falcon) Globe Pequot Pr., The.

Hunter, Ryan Ann. In Disguise: Stories of Real Women Spies. 2004. (Illus.). 133p. (YA). (gr. 4-12). pap. (978-1-58270-095-3(8)) Beyond Words Publishing, Inc.

Hunter, Shaun. Leaders in Medicine. 1998. (Women in Profile Ser.). (Illus.). 48p. (J). (gr. 4). pap. (978-0-7787-0032-6(1)) Crabtree Publishing Co.

—Visual & Performing Artists. 1998. (Women in Profile Ser.). (Illus.). 48p. (J). (gr. 4). pap. (978-0-7787-0035-7(6)) Crabtree Publishing Co.

—Writers. 1998. (Women in Profile Ser.). (Illus.). 48p. (J). (gr. 4). pap. (978-0-7787-0027-2(5)); lib. bdg. (978-0-7787-0005-0(4)) Crabtree Publishing Co.

—Writers. 1998. (Illus.). 48p. (J). (ps-11). lib. bdg. 17.60 (978-0-613-09123-7(X)) Tandem Library Bks.

Hurst, Heidi. Britney Spears. 2003. (Illus.). 112p. (J). 32.45 (978-1-59018-224-6(3) , Lucent Bks.) Thomson Gale.

Hurwitz, Johanna. A Dream Come True. Craine, Michael, photos by. 1998. (Meet the Author Ser.). (Illus.). 32p. (J). (gr. 2-5). 14.95 (978-1-57274-193-5(7) , 719) Owen, Richard C. Pubs., Inc.

Iverson, Teresa. Ellen Ochoa. (Hispanic-American Biographies Ser.). (Illus.). 64p. (J). 2005. pap. 9.50 (978-1-4109-1307-4(4)); 2004. (gr. 4-6). 32.86 (978-1-4109-1299-2(X)) Raintree.

Jackson, Ian. Livewire Real Lives Dawn Fraser. 2000. (Livewire Real Lives Ser.). 32p. pap. 6.00 (978-0-521-77631-8(7)) Cambridge Univ. Pr.

James, Lesley. Women Who Made a Scene: Heroines, Villainesses, Eccentrics. 2002. (Remarkable Women). (Illus.). 80p. (YA). (gr. 6-9). lib. bdg. 32.85 (978-0-8172-5735-4(7)) Raintree.

January, Brendan. Jane Goodall: Animal Behaviorist & Writer. 2001. (Career Biographies Ser.). (Illus.). 128p. (YA). (gr. 6-12). 25.00 (978-0-89434-370-4(X) , F413, Ferguson Publishing Co.) Facts On File, Inc.

Jean, Norma. Britney Spears. 1999. (Galaxy of Superstars Ser.). (Illus.). 64p. (YA). pap. 25.00 (978-0-7910-5500-7(0) , Chelsea Hse.) Facts On File, Inc.

Jeffrey, Laura S. Christa McAuliffe: A Space Biography. 1998. (Countdown to Space Ser.). (Illus.). 48p. (YA). (gr. 4-10). lib. bdg. 23.93 (978-0-89490-976-4(2)) Enslow Pubs., Inc.

Jemison, Mae. Find Where the Wind Goes: Moments from My Life. (Find Where the Wind Goes Ser.). (Illus.). 208p. (J). 2003. pap. 4.99 (978-0-439-13196-4(0) , Scholastic Paperbacks); 2001. (gr. 5-9). pap. 16.95 (978-0-439-13195-7(2)) Scholastic, Inc.

—Find Where the Wind Goes: Moments from My Life. 2003. (gr. 5-8). lib. bdg. 13.00 (978-0-613-72017-5(2)) Tandem Library Bks.

Jenner, Caryn. The Story of Pocahontas, Vol. 2. Martin, Linda, ed. 2000. (Readers Ser.). (Illus.). 32p. (J). (gr. 1-3). pap. 3.99 (978-0-7894-6636-5(8)) Dorling Kindersley Publishing, Inc.

—The Story of Pocahontas. 2000. (Illus.). 32p. (J). (ps-ps). lib. bdg. 11.80 (978-0-613-33108-1(7)) Tandem Library Bks.

Jenner, Caryn & Dorling Kindersley Publishing Staff. The Story of Pocahontas. 2000. (Readers Ser.). (Illus.). 32p. (J). (gr. 1-3). 14.99 (978-0-7894-6637-2(6)) Dorling Kindersley Publishing, Inc.

Jernegan, Laura. A Whaling Captain's Daughter: The Diary of Laura Jernegan, 1868-1871. O'Hara, Megan, ed. 2000. (Blue Earth Books). (Illus.). 32p. (J). (gr. 3-4). lib. bdg. 22.60 (978-0-7368-0346-5(7) , Bridgestone Bks.) Capstone Pr., Inc.

Jerome, Kate Boehm. Who Was Amelia Earhart? Cain, David & Harrison, Nancy, illus. 2002. (Who Was...? Ser.). 112p. (J). mass mkt. 4.99 (978-0-448-42856-7(3) , Grosset & Dunlap) Penguin Group (USA) Inc.

—Who Was Amelia Earhart? 2002. (gr. 3-6). lib. bdg. 13.00 (978-0-613-61667-6(7)) Tandem Library Bks.

Jiang, Cheng A. Empress of China Zhongguo De Nu Huangdi: Wu Ze Tian. Xu, De Y., illus. 1998. 32p. (J). (gr. 3-6). 14.95 (978-1-878217-32-5(1)); pap. 7.95 (978-1-878217-31-8(3)) Victory Pr.

Johnson, Emma. Anne Frank. 2003. (Twentieth Century History Makers Ser.). (Illus.). 112p. (J). lib. bdg. 32.85 (978-0-7398-5261-3(2)) Raintree.

—Mother Teresa. 2003. (20th Century History Makers Ser.). (Illus.). 112p. (J). lib. bdg. 32.85 (978-0-7398-6143-1(3)) Raintree.

Jones, Gerald Colman. Mary Robinson: Citizen of the World. 2000. (Contemporary Profiles & Policy Series for the Younger Reader). (Illus.). 72p. (J). (gr. 8 up). 24.00 (978-0-934272-63-6(8)); pap. 15.00 (978-0-934272-64-3(6)) Burke, John Gordon Pub., Inc.

Jones, Mary H. & Kerr, Charles H. Autobiography of Mother Jones. 10th annot. ed. 2006. (Labor Classics Ser.). (Illus.). 160p. (Orig.). pap. 15.00 (978-0-88286-311-5(8)) Kerr, Charles H. Publishing Co.

Jones, Veda Boyd. Nicole Bobek. 1999. (Female Figure Skating Legends Ser.). (Illus.). 64p. (YA). (ps up). lib. bdg. 18.65 (978-0-7910-5029-3(7) , Chelsea Hse.) Facts On File, Inc.

—Tara Lipinski. 1999. (Female Figure Skating Legends Ser.). (Illus.). 64p. (YA). (gr. 4-7). lib. bdg. 18.65 (978-0-7910-4876-4(4) , Chelsea Hse.) Facts On File, Inc.

Kahn, Jetty. Women in Chemistry Careers. 1999. (Short Biographies Ser.). (Illus.). 48p. (J). (gr. 3-4). lib. bdg. 22.60 (978-0-7368-0315-1(7) , Bridgestone Bks.) Capstone Pr., Inc.

—Women in Chemistry Careers. 1999. (Illus.). 48p. (J). (gr. 3-7). pap. 19.93 (978-0-516-21882-3(4) , Children's Pr.) Scholastic Library Publishing.

—Women in Computer Science Careers. 1999. (Short Biographies Ser.). (Illus.). 48p. (J). (gr. 3-4). lib. bdg. 22.60 (978-0-7368-0316-8(5) , Bridgestone Bks.) Capstone Pr., Inc.

—Women in Computer Science Careers. 1999. (Illus.). 48p. (J). (gr. 3-7). pap. 19.93 (978-0-516-21883-0(2) , Children's Pr.) Scholastic Library Publishing.

—Women in Earth Science Careers. 1998. (Short Biographies Ser.). (Illus.). 48p. (J). (gr. 3-4). lib. bdg. 22.60 (978-0-7368-0012-9(3) , Bridgestone Bks.) Capstone Pr., Inc.

—Women in Engineering Careers. 1998. (Short Biographies Ser.). (Illus.). 48p. (J). (gr. 3-4). lib. bdg. 22.60 (978-0-7368-0013-6(1) , Bridgestone Bks.) Capstone Pr., Inc.

—Women in Life Science Careers. 1998. (Short Biographies Ser.). (Illus.). 48p. (J). (gr. 3-4). lib. bdg. 22.60 (978-0-7368-0014-3(X) , Bridgestone Bks.) Capstone Pr., Inc.

—Women in Physical Science Careers. 1998. (Short Biographies Ser.). (Illus.). 48p. (J). (gr. 3-4). lib. bdg. 22.60 (978-0-7368-0015-0(8) , Bridgestone Bks.) Capstone Pr., Inc.

Kalman, Bobbie. Famous Native North Americans. 2003. (gr. 3-6). lib. bdg. 17.60 (978-0-613-85049-0(1)) Tandem Library Bks.

Kalman, Bobbie & Aloian, Molly. Famous Native North Americans. 2003. (Native Nations of North America Ser.). (Illus.). 32p. (J). (gr. 5). (978-0-7787-0379-2(7)); pap. (978-0-7787-0471-3(8)) Crabtree Publishing Co.

Karnes, Frances A. & Bean, Suzanne M. Adventures & Challenges: Real Life Stories by Girls & Young Women. 2000. (Illus.). 208p. (YA). 12.95 (978-0-910707-35-0(9)) Great Potential Pr., Inc.

Kathleen, Kudlinski. Dk Biography Joan of Arc Hc. 2008. 128p. 14.99 (***978-0-7566-3527-5(6)**) Dorling Kindersley Publishing, Inc.

Keating, Susan K. Isadora Duncan: American Dancer. 2002. (Great Names Ser.). (Illus.). 32p. (J). (gr. 3 up). lib. bdg. (978-1-59084-144-0(1)) Mason Crest Pubs.

Keefe, Maryellen. Saint Angela Merici: Leading People to God. Curreli, Augusta, illus. 2000. (Along the Paths of the Gospel Ser.). 74p. (J). (gr. 2-5). 6.95 (978-0-8198-7031-5(5) , 332-343) Pauline Bks. & Media.

Kelley, Brent. Lisa Leslie. 2000. (Illus.). 64p. (J). (gr. 4-7). lib. bdg. 17.60 (978-0-613-32788-6(8)) Tandem Library Bks.

Kemeny, Esther. On the Shores of Darkness: The Memoir of Esther Kemeny. Haller, Heather, ed. 2003. (Illus.). 144p. per. (978-0-9743961-7-0(6)) Haller Company, The.

Kenschaft, Lori J. Lydia Maria Child: The Quest for Racial Justice. 2002. (Oxford Portraits Ser.). (Illus.). 128p. (YA). 28.00 (978-0-19-513257-1(2)) Oxford Univ. Pr., Inc.

Kent, Deborah. Frida Kahlo: An Artist Celebrates Life. 2004. (Proud Heritage: the Hispanic Library Ser.). 40p. (J). (gr. 3-7). 28.50 (978-1-59296-167-2(3)) Child's World, Inc.

Kepnes, Caroline. Stephen Crane. 2004. (Classic Storytellers Ser.). (Illus.). 48p. (J). (gr. 4-8). lib. bdg. 20.95 (978-1-58415-272-9(9)) Mitchell Lane Pubs., Inc.

Kimmel, Elizabeth Cody. Ladies First: 40 Daring Women Who Were Second to None. 2006. 192p. (gr. 5). 27.90 (978-0-7922-5394-5(9)); (Illus.). (J). 18.95 (978-0-7922-5393-8(0)) National Geographic Society. (National Geographic Children's Bks.).

Kinstad-Pupeza, Lori. Brandy. 1999. (Young Profiles Ser.). (Illus.). 32p. (J). (gr. k-6). lib. bdg. 22.78 (978-1-57765-323-3(8) , Checkerboard Library) ABDO Publishing Co.

Kirsh, Sharon. Fabulous Female Physicians. 2002. (gr. 5-8). lib. bdg. 16.40 (978-0-613-88449-5(3)) Tandem Library Bks.

Kirsh, Sharon & Kirsh, Florence. Fabulous Female Physicians. 2005. (Illus.). 100p. (YA). (gr. 4-8). pap. 7.95 (978-1-896764-43-6(6)) Second Story Pr. CAN. *Dist:* Orca Bk. Pubs. USA, Univ. of Toronto Pr., Univ. of Toronto Pr.

Kite, L. Patricia. Maya Angelou. (Just the Facts Biographies Ser.). (Illus.). 112p. 2006. (J). 27.93 (978-0-8225-3426-6(6)); 2006. (J). pap. (***978-0-8225-5997-9(8)***); 1999. (YA). (gr. 6-12). lib. bdg. 27.93 (978-0-8225-4944-4(1)) Lerner Publishing Group. (Lerner Pubns.).

Kjelle, Marylou. Katherine Paterson. 2004. (Classic Storytellers Ser.). (Illus.). 48p. (J). (gr. 4-8). lib. bdg. 20.95 (978-1-58415-268-2(0)) Mitchell Lane Pubs., Inc.

Klingel, Cynthia Fitterer & Court, Rob. Art of Early Africa. 2003. (Scribbles Institute : Art in Ancient Civilizations Ser.). (Illus.). 32p. (J). (gr. 1-5). 21.36 (978-1-56766-551-2(9) , 65519) Child's World, Inc.

Klingel, Cynthia Fitterer & Noyed, Robert B. Clara Barton: Founder of the American Red Cross. 2002. (Spirit of America: Our People Ser.). (Illus.). 32p. (J). (gr. 2-6). 27.07 (978-1-56766-172-9(6)) Child's World, Inc.

—Dolley Madison: First Lady. 2002. (Spirit of America: Our People Ser.). (Illus.). 32p. (J). (gr. 2-6). 27.07 (978-1-56766-170-5(X)) Child's World, Inc.

Kloepfer, Deanne & Abarca, Patricia. Francisco Dallmeier. 2004. (Hispanic-American Biographies Ser.). (Illus.). 64p. (J). (gr. 4-6). 32.86 (978-1-4109-1300-5(7)) Raintree.

Koeppel, Ruth. Emma Watson. 2005. 128p. (J). pap. 4.99 (978-1-4169-1395-5(5) , Simon Spotlight) Simon & Schuster Children's Publishing.

Koestler-Grack, Rachel A. Mary Baker Eddy. 2004. (Spiritual Leaders & Thinkers Ser.). (Illus.). 120p. (gr. 9-13). 30.00 (978-0-7910-7866-2(3) , Chelsea Hse.) Facts On File, Inc.

—Sacagawea. 2004. (Illus.). 32p. (J). pap. 7.50 (978-1-4034-5011-1(0)); lib. bdg. 24.22 (978-1-4034-5004-3(8)) Heinemann Library.

Koopmans, Andy. Madonna. 2002. (People in the News Ser.). (Illus.). 112p. (YA). (gr. 6-9). 32.45 (978-1-59018-138-6(7) , Lucent Bks.) Thomson Gale.

Kops, Deborah. The Women Suffrage Movement. 2003. (People at the Center of Ser.). (Illus.). 48p. (J). 24.95 (978-1-56711-772-1(4) , Blackbirch Pr., Inc.) Thomson Gale.

Kovatch, Sarah & Crumpler, Rebecca Lee. Rebecca Lee Crumpler. 2005. (Illus.). 16p. (J). (***978-0-7367-2891-1(0)***) Zaner-Bloser, Inc.

Kozleski, Lisa. Jane Goodall. 2003. (Women in Science Ser.). pap. 30.00 (978-0-7910-7519-7(2)); (Illus.). 112p. (gr. 6-12). 30.00 (978-0-7910-6905-9(2)) Facts On File, Inc. (Chelsea Hse.).

Kramer, Barbara. Mahalia Jackson: The Voice of Gospel & Civil Rights. 2003. (African-American Biographies Ser.). (Illus.). 128p. (J). lib. bdg. 26.60 (978-0-7660-2115-0(7)) Enslow Pubs., Inc.

—Tipper Gore: Activist, Author, Photographer. 1999. (People to Know Ser.). (Illus.). 112p. (YA). (gr. 6-12). lib. bdg. 26.60 (978-0-7660-1142-7(9)) Enslow Pubs., Inc.

Kramer, Sydelle A. The Look-It-Up Book of First Ladies. 2000. (J). (978-0-606-19901-8(2)) Tandem Library Bks.

Krensky Stephen. Calamity Jane. Carlson, Lisa, illus. 2007. (On My Own Folklore Ser.). (J). pap. 6.95 (***978-0-8225-6480-5(7)*** , First Avenue Editions) Lerner Publishing Group.

Krensky, Stephen, adapted by. Calamity Jane. 2007. (On My Own Folklore Ser.). 48p. (J). (gr. 2-5). lib. bdg. 25.26 (978-1-57505-886-3(3) , Millbrook Pr.) Lerner Publishing Group.

Krohn, Katherine. Women of the Wild West. 2000. (gr. 7-12). lib. bdg. 16.40 (978-0-613-68395-1(1)) Tandem Library Bks.

Krohn, Katherine E. Ella Fitzgerald: First Lady of Song. 2005. (Lerner Biographies Ser.). (Illus.). 128p. (gr. 6-12). lib. bdg. 27.93 (978-0-8225-4933-8(6)) Lerner Publishing Group.

—Madam C.J. Walker. 2005. (Fact Finders Ser.). (Illus.). 32p. (J). (978-0-7368-4346-1(9)) Capstone Pr., Inc.

—Rosie O'Donnell. 1998. (Biography Ser.). (Illus.). 112p. (YA). (gr. 6-12). lib. bdg. 27.93 (978-0-8225-4939-0(5) , Lerner Pubns.) Lerner Publishing Group.

—Sojourner Truth. 2005. (Fact Finders Ser.). (Illus.). 32p. (J). (978-0-7368-4348-5(5)) Capstone Pr., Inc.

Krudwig, Vickie Leigh. Searching for Chipeta: The Story of a Ute & Her People. 2004. (Illus.). 128p. (J). (gr. 4). pap. 12.95 (978-1-55591-466-0(7)) Fulcrum Publishing.

Krull, Kathleen. Wilma Sin Limites. 2000. Tr. of Wilma Unlimited. (978-0-606-18197-6(0)); (SPA.). (gr. 3-6). lib. bdg. 14.15 (978-0-613-27592-7(6)) Tandem Library Bks.

—Wilma Unlimited. 2000. (978-0-606-18198-3(9)) Tandem Library Bks.

Kudlinski, Kathleen. Dk Biography Joan of Arc Pb. 2008. 128p. pap. 4.99 (***978-0-7566-3526-8(8)***) Dorling Kindersley Publishing, Inc.

Kulling, Monica. Escape North! the Story of Harriet Tubman. 2000. (gr. k-3). lib. bdg. 11.80 (978-0-613-32507-3(9)) Tandem Library Bks.

Laidlaw, Jill A. Frida Kahlo. 2003. (Artists in Their Time Ser.). (Illus.). 48p. (J). 23.50 (978-0-531-12236-5(0)); (gr. 5-7). pap. 6.95 (978-0-531-16642-0(2)) Scholastic Library Publishing. (Watts, Franklin).

—Frida Kahlo. 2003. (gr. 5-8). lib. bdg. 15.25 (978-0-613-59483-7(5)) Tandem Library Bks.

Lakin, Patricia, et al. Amelia Earhart: More Than a Flier. 2003. (Ready-to-Read Stories of Famous Americans Ser.). (Illus.). 48p. (J). pap. 3.99 (978-0-689-85575-7(3) , Aladdin) Simon & Schuster Children's Publishing.

Lannin, Joanne. Billie Jean King: Tennis Trailblazer. 1999. (Lerner Biographies Ser.). (Illus.). 128p. (gr. 6-12). lib. bdg. 27.93 (978-0-8225-4959-8(X)) Lerner Publishing Group.

Larkin, Tanya. What Was Cooking in Abigail Adam's White House? 2001. (Cooking Throughout American History Ser.). (Illus.). 24p. (J). (gr. 3). lib. bdg. 19.95 (978-0-8239-5607-4(5) , PowerKids Pr.) Rosen Publishing Group, Inc., The.

—What Was Cooking in Dolly Madison's White House? 2001. (Cooking Throughout American History Ser.). (Illus.). 24p. (J). (gr. 3). lib. bdg. 19.95 (978-0-8239-5608-1(3) , PowerKids Pr.) Rosen Publishing Group, Inc., The.

Lasky, Kathryn. Searching for Laura Ingalls: A Reader's Journey. 1998. (978-0-606-13766-9(1)) Tandem Library Bks.

—Vision of Beauty: The Story of Sarah Breedlove Walker. Bennett, Nneka, illus. 48p. (J). (gr. 3-7). 2003. pap. 6.99 (978-0-7636-1834-6(9)); 2000. 17.99 (978-0-7636-0253-6(1)) Candlewick Pr.

—Vision of Beauty: The Story of Sarah Breedlove Walker. 2003. (gr. 3-6). lib. bdg. 15.30 (978-0-613-74818-6(2)) Tandem Library Bks.

Laslo, Cynthia. Sarah Michelle Gellar. 2000. (gr. 7-12). lib. bdg. 15.25 (978-0-613-58730-3(8)) Tandem Library Bks.

Laslo, Cynthia, contrib. by. Lauryn Hill. 2000. (J). (978-0-531-12110-8(0) , Orchard Bks.) Scholastic, Inc.

—Sarah Michelle Gellar. 2000. (Celebrity Bios Ser.). (Illus.). 48p. (J). (978-0-531-12114-6(3) , Watts, Franklin) Scholastic Library Publishing.

Lassieur, Allison. Marie Curie: A Scientific Pioneer. 2003. (Great Life Stories Ser.). (Illus.). 112p. (J). 30.50 (978-0-531-12270-9(0) , Watts, Franklin) Scholastic Library Publishing.

Leininger, Tracy. Nothing Can Separate Us: The Story of Nan Harper. 2nd ed. 2000. (Illus.). 64p. (J). mass mkt. 15.99 (978-0-9724287-1-2(2)) His Seasons.

Leon, Vicki. Outrageous Women of the Middle Ages. 1998. (Outrageous Women Ser.: Vol. 2). (Illus.). 128p. (gr. 4-7). pap. 12.95 (978-0-471-17004-4(6) , Wiley) Wiley, John & Sons, Inc.

—Outrageous Women of the Renaissance. 1999. (Outrageous Women Ser.: Vol. 4). (Illus.). 128p. (gr. 5-12). pap. 12.95 (978-0-471-29684-3(8) , Wiley-Interscience) Wiley, John & Sons, Inc.

Leslie, Roger. Isak Dinesen: Gothic Storyteller. 2004. (World Writers Ser.). (Illus.). 128p. (YA). (gr. 6-12). 23.95 (978-1-931798-17-4(6)) Reynolds, Morgan Inc.

Lester, Helen. Author: A True Story. Lester, Helen, illus. 2002. (Illus.). 32p. (J). (gr. k-3). pap. 5.95 (978-0-618-26010-2(2) , Walter Lorraine) Houghton Mifflin Co. Trade & Reference Div.

Literature Connections English: So Far from the Bamboo Grove. 2004. (gr. 6-12). (978-0-395-77138-9(2) , 2-70216) McDougal Littell Inc.

Lloyd, Tanya. Canadian Girls Who Rocked the World. 2001. (Illus.). 128p. (J). (gr. 3-2). pap. 8.95 (978-1-55285-203-3(2)) Whitecap Bks., Ltd. CAN. *Dist:* Firefly Bks., Ltd.

Lord, Christel. Child of the Enemy. 2003. 142p. (YA). pap. 13.95 (978-0-9715554-3-3(5)) WLA Publishing (Writers Literary Agency).

Loughrey, Eithne. Annie Moore: New York City Girl. 2001. 128p. (YA). pap. 7.95 (978-1-85635-348-9(6)) Mercier Pr., Ltd., The IRL. *Dist:* Irish Bks. & Media, Inc.

Love, D. Anne. Of Numbers & Stars: The Story of Hypatia. Papparone, Pam, illus. 2005. 32p. (J). (ps-3). 16.95 (978-0-8234-1621-9(6)) Holiday Hse., Inc.

Lowery, Linda. Aunt Clara Brown: Official Pioneer. Porter, Janice Lee, illus. 1999. (On My Own Biographies Ser.). 48p. (J). (gr. 2-5). lib. bdg. 23.93 (978-1-57505-045-4(5)) Lerner Publishing Group.

Lucas, Eileen. Elizabeth Dole: A Leader in Washington. 1999. (Illus.). (J). (978-0-606-18288-1(8)) Tandem Library Bks.

Lyon, George Ella. Mother to Tigers. Catalanotto, Peter, illus. 2003. 32p. (J). (gr. k-5). 17.95 (978-0-689-84221-4(X) , Atheneum/Richard Jackson Bks.) Simon & Schuster Children's Publishing.

Lyon, George Ella & Soentpiet, Chris K. A Sign. 1998. (Illus.). 32p. (J). (gr. k-4). 16.99 (978-0-531-33073-9(7)); pap. 15.95 (978-0-531-30073-2(0)) Scholastic, Inc. (Orchard Bks.).

MacDonald, Fiona. Cleopatra. 2006. (DK Discoveries Ser.). 48p. (J). pap. 6.99 (978-0-7566-1964-0(5)) Dorling Kindersley Publishing, Inc.

Mace, Nancy. In the Company of Men: A Woman at the Citadel. 2002. (gr. 7-12). lib. bdg. 16.45 (978-0-613-51841-3(1)) Tandem Library Bks.

Macy, Sue. Bull's Eye: A Photobiography of Annie Oakley. 2006. 64p. (gr. 5). pap. 7.95 (978-0-7922-5933-6(5) , National Geographic Children's Bks.) National Geographic Society.

Malam, John. Florence Nightingale. 2001. (Groundbreakers Ser.). (Illus.). 48p. (J). (gr. 5-7). lib. bdg. 25.64 (978-1-58810-051-1(0)) Heinemann Library.

Mara, Wil. Dian Fossey: Among the Gorillas. 2004. (Great Life Stories Ser.). (Illus.). 127p. (J). 30.50 (978-0-531-12059-0(7) , Watts, Franklin) Scholastic Library Publishing.

—Laura Ingalls Wilder. 2003. (YA). lib. bdg. 12.95 (978-0-613-67639-7(4)) Tandem Library Bks.

Marcovitz, Hal. Nancy Pelosi. 2004. (Women in Politics Ser.). (Illus.). 120p. 30.00 (978-0-7910-7737-5(3)); 112p. pap. 30.00 (978-0-7910-8001-6(3)) Facts On File, Inc. (Chelsea Hse.).

—Sacagawea: Guide for the Lewis & Clark Expedition. 2000. (Explorers of the New World Ser.). (Illus.). (J). 63p. (gr. 4-7). pap. 25.00 (978-0-7910-6169-5(8)); 64p. (gr. 8-12). 25.00 (978-0-7910-5959-3(6)) Facts On File, Inc. (Chelsea Hse.).

—Sacagawea: Guide for the Lewis & Clark Expedition. 2001. (gr. 3-6). lib. bdg. 17.60 (978-0-613-33014-5(5)) Tandem Library Bks.

Marinelli, Deborah A. Virginia Hamilton. 2003. (Library of Author Biographies). (Illus.). 112p. (YA). (gr. 5-8). lib. bdg. 26.50 (978-0-8239-3777-6(1) , Rosen Central) Rosen Publishing Group, Inc., The.

Marsh, Carole. Calamity Jane: An Ohio Experience Reader. 2001. (J). (gr. k-5). pap. 1.95 (978-0-635-00425-3(9)) Gallopade International.

—Carrie Chapman Catt. 2002. (One Thousand Readers Ser.). (Illus.). 12p. (J). (gr. k-4). 2.95 (978-0-635-01541-9(2) , 15412) Gallopade International.

—Georgia O'Keeffe. 2002. (One Thousand Readers Ser.). (Illus.). 12p. (J). (gr. k-4). 2.95 (978-0-635-01507-5(2) , 15072) Gallopade International.

—Golda Meir. 2002. (One Thousand Readers Ser.). (Illus.). 12p. (J). (gr. k-4). 2.95 (978-0-635-01513-6(7) , 15137) Gallopade International.

—Harriet Tubman. 2002. (One Thousand Readers Ser.). (Illus.). 12p. (J). (gr. k-4). 2.95 (978-0-635-01480-1(7) , 14807) Gallopade International.

—Helen Keller. 2002. (One Thousand Readers Ser.). (Illus.). 12p. (J). (gr. k-4). 2.95 (978-0-635-01478-8(5) , 14785) Gallopade International.

—Jane Addams. 2002. (One Thousand Readers Ser.). (Illus.). 12p. (J). (gr. k-4). 2.95 (978-0-635-01472-6(6) , 14726) Gallopade International.

Martin, Carol. Catharine Parr Traill: Backwoods Pioneer. 2004. (Illus.). (YA). pap. (978-0-88899-495-0(8) , Libros Tigrillo) Groundwood Bks. CAN. *Dist:* Transition Vendor.

Martins-Miller, Susan. Betsy Ross. 1999. (Revolutionary War Leaders Ser.). (Illus.). 80p. (J). (gr. 3 up). 31.00 (978-0-7910-5360-7(1) , Chelsea Hse.) Facts On File, Inc.

Mary Anning: Fossil Hunter. 2007. (J). pap. 5.95 (***978-1-57505-457-5(4)*** , First Avenue Editions) Lerner Publishing Group.

Masso, Phyllis H. Never the Same Again . . . A Young Woman's Story of Life in the Blackstone Valley in the 1820s. 1998. 150p. (YA). (gr. 5-12). pap. 14.95 (978-1-57960-046-4(8)) History Compass, LLC.

Mathews, Tom L. Light Shining Through the Mist: A Photobiography of Dian Fossey. 1998. (Illus.). 64p. (J). (gr. 4-7). 17.95 (978-0-7922-7300-4(1) , T07300C, National Geographic Children's Bks.) National Geographic Society.

Mattern, Joanne. Celine Dion. 2002. (Illus.). 104p. (J). (gr. 4-12). 32.45 (978-1-59018-137-9(9) , Lucent Bks.) Thomson Gale.

—Katharine Graham & 20th Century American Journalism. 2003. (Reading Power Ser.). (Illus.). 24p. (J). lib. bdg. 17.25 (978-0-8239-6500-7(7) , PowerKids Pr.) Rosen Publishing Group, Inc., The.

McCarthy, Shaun. All about J. K. Rowling. 2003. (All About Ser.). (Illus.). 32p. (J). pap. 7.50 (978-1-4109-0719-6(8)); lib. bdg. 24.28 (978-1-4109-0718-9(X)) Raintree.

—All about J. K. Rowling. 2003. (gr. 3-6). lib. bdg. 15.90 (978-0-613-78210-4(0)) Tandem Library Bks.

McCauley-Bell, Pamela. Winners Don't Quit. . . Today They Call Me Doctor! 2003. (YA). per. 16.95 (978-0-9729912-6-1(3)) Infinite Possibilities Publishing Group, Inc.

McClure, Judy. Theoreticians & Builders: Mathematicians, Physical Scientists, Inventors. 2002. (Remarkable Women). (Illus.). 80p. (YA). (gr. 6-9). lib. bdg. 32.85 (978-0-8172-5728-6(4)) Raintree.

McCracken, Kristin. LeAnn Rimes. 2001. (gr. 7-12). lib. bdg. 15.25 (978-0-613-52111-6(0)) Tandem Library Bks.

McDonnell, Peter. The Last Princess. 2005. (Illus.). 16p. (***978-0-7367-2910-9(0)***) Zaner-Bloser, Inc.

McElroy, Lisa Tucker & Mead, Russell T. Meet My Grandmother: She's a Deep Sea Explorer. Benjamin, Joel & Gardner, Mark, illus. 2000. (Grandmothers at Work Ser.). 32p. (gr. 2-4). lib. bdg. 22.90 (978-0-7613-1720-3(1) , Millbrook Pr.) Lerner Publishing Group.

McGinty, Alice B. Meet Gail Carson Levine. 2003. (About the Author Ser.). (Illus.). 24p. (J). lib. bdg. 18.75 (978-0-8239-6409-3(4) , PowerKids Pr.) Rosen Publishing Group, Inc., The.

—Meet Jane Yolen. 2003. (About the Author Ser.). (Illus.). 24p. (J). lib. bdg. 18.75 (978-0-8239-6407-9(8) , PowerKids Pr.) Rosen Publishing Group, Inc., The.

McLean, Jacqueline. Victoria Woodhull: First Woman Presidential Candidate. 2004. (Feminist Voices Ser.). (Illus.). 112p. (YA). (gr. 6-12). 23.95 (978-1-883846-47-3(1) , First Biographies) Reynolds, Morgan Inc.

—Women of Adventure. 2003. (Profiles Ser.). (Illus.). 160p. (gr. 5 up). lib. bdg. 19.95 (978-1-881508-73-1(0)) Oliver Pr., Inc.

—Women with Wings. Anderson, Jenna, ed. 2001. (Profiles Ser.: Vol. 30). (Illus.). 160p. (gr. 5 up). lib. bdg. 19.95 (978-1-881508-70-0(6)) Oliver Pr., Inc.

McLeese, Don. Eleanor Roosevelt. 2003. (Discover the Life of an Equal Rights Leader Discovery Library Ser.). (Illus.). 24p. (gr. 2-5). 14.95 (978-1-58952-289-3(3)) Rourke Publishing, LLC.

—Oprah Winfrey. 2002. (Discover the Life of an American Legend Ser.). (Illus.). 24p. (J). lib. bdg. 20.64 (978-1-58952-306-7(7)) Rourke Publishing, LLC.

—Sacagawea. 2003. (Native American Legends Ser.). (Illus.). 32p. (J). 28.50 (978-1-58952-729-4(1)) Rourke Publishing, LLC.

—Susan B. Anthony. 2002. (Illus.). 24p. (J). lib. bdg. 20.64 (978-1-58952-284-8(2)) Rourke Publishing, LLC.

McLuskey, Krista. Entrepreneurs. 1998. (Women in Profile Ser.). (Illus.). 48p. (J). (gr. 4). pap. (978-0-7787-0034-0(8)) Crabtree Publishing Co.

Meachum, Virginia. Martha Stewart: Successful Businesswoman. 1998. (People to Know Ser.). (Illus.). 112p. (YA). (gr. 6-12). lib. bdg. 26.60 (978-0-89490-984-9(3)) Enslow Pubs., Inc.

—Rosie O'Donnell: Talk Show Host & Comedian. 2000. (People to Know Ser.). (Illus.). 112p. (YA). (gr. 6-12). lib. bdg. 26.60 (978-0-7660-1148-9(8)) Enslow Pubs., Inc.

Meister, Cari. Beverly Cleary. 2001. (Children's Authors Ser.). (Illus.). 24p. (J). (gr. k-6). lib. bdg. 21.35 (978-1-57765-480-3(3) , Checkerboard Library) ABDO Publishing Co.

—J. K. Rowling. 2001. (Children's Authors Ser.). (Illus.). 24p. (J). (gr. k-6). lib. bdg. 21.35 (978-1-57765-482-7(X) , Checkerboard Library) ABDO Publishing Co.

Meloche, Renee. Gladys Aylward: The Adventure of a Lifetime. Pollard, Bryan, illus. 2002. (Heroes for Young Readers Ser.). 32p. 8.99 (978-1-57658-228-2(0)) YWAM Publishing.

Meltzer, Milton. Emily Dickinson: A Biography. 2006. (American Literary Greats Ser.). 128p. (YA). (gr. 7 up). lib. bdg. 31.93 (978-0-7613-2949-7(8) , Millbrook Pr.) Lerner Publishing Group.

—Ten Queens: Portraits of Women of Power. Andersen, Bethanne, illus. 2003. 144p. (J). (gr. 7-12). reprint ed. pap. 14.99 (978-0-525-47158-5(8) , Dutton Juvenile) Penguin Group (USA) Inc.

—Ten Queens: Portraits of Women of Power. 2004. (gr. 7-12). lib. bdg. 24.60 (978-0-613-72581-1(6)) Tandem Library Bks.

Menard, Valerie. Salma Hayek. 1999. (Real-Life Reader Biography Ser.). (Illus.). 32p. (gr. 3-8). lib. bdg. 15.95 (978-1-58415-018-3(1)) Mitchell Lane Pubs., Inc.

Merritt, Susan E. Her Story II: Women from Canada's Past. 1998. (Illus.). vii, 184p. (YA). pap. (978-1-55125-022-9(5)) Vanwell Publishing, Ltd.

Meynell, Esther. The Little Chronicle of Magdalena Bach. 2001. 183p. (YA). reprint ed. 88.00 (978-0-7222-5320-5(6)) Library Reprints, Inc.

Middleton, Haydn. Mother Teresa. 2000. (Profiles Ser.). (Illus.). 56p. (J). (gr. 4-6). lib. bdg. 24.22 (978-1-57572-227-6(5)) Heinemann Library.

Miles, Ellen. Superstars of Womens Tennis. 2000. (YA). (978-0-606-19251-4(4)) Tandem Library Bks.

Miller, Calvin Craig. Spirit Like a Storm: The Story of Mary Shelley. 2nd rev. ed. 2004. (World Writers Ser.). (Illus.). 144p. (YA). (gr. 6-12). 23.95 (978-1-931798-08-2(7)) Reynolds, Morgan Inc.

Miller, Susan Martins. Betsy Ross: American Patriot. 2000. (Revolutionary War Leaders Ser.). (J). 15.75 (978-0-606-19340-5(5)) Tandem Library Bks.

Miller, William. Zora Hurston Y el Arbol Sonador. 2001. (SPA.). (gr. k-3). lib. bdg. 15.25 (978-0-613-36034-0(6)) Tandem Library Bks.

Mills, Cliff. Virginia Woolf. 2003. (Women in the Arts Ser.). (Illus.). 112p. (gr. 6-12). 30.00 (978-0-7910-7459-6(5) , Chelsea Hse.) Facts On File, Inc.

Mohan, Claire J. The Way of the Cross: A Story of Padre Pio. Gallagher, Patricia, ed. Robbins, Jane, illus. 2002. (Christian Hero Ser.). 64p. (YA). (gr. 5 up). pap. 8.95 (978-0-9621500-9-8(6)) Young Sparrow Pr., The.

—The Young Life of St. Maria Faustina. Robbins, Jane, illus. 2000. (Young Life Ser.). 114p. (gr. 5-8). pap. 10.95 (978-0-944203-36-1(1)) Marian Pr.

Molzahn, Arlene Bourgeois. Top 10 American Women Sprinters. 1998. (Sports Top 10 Ser.). (Illus.). 48p. (YA). (gr. 4-10). lib. bdg. 23.93 (978-0-7660-1011-6(2)) Enslow Pubs., Inc.

Morgan, Nina. Mother Teresa: Saint of the Poor. 1998. (Illus.). 48p. (gr. 4-7). pap. 7.95 (978-0-8172-7848-9(6)) Steck-Vaughn.

Morgan, Terri. Gabrielle Reece: Volleyball's Model Athlete. 1999. (Sports Achievers Biographies Ser.). (Illus.). (YA). (gr. 4-9). 80p. lib. bdg. 22.60 (978-0-8225-3667-3(6)); 64p. pap. (978-0-8225-9828-2(0)) Lerner Publishing Group. (LernerSports).

—Gabrielle Reece: Volleyball's Model Athlete. 1999. (Illus.). (J). (978-0-606-18819-7(3)) Tandem Library Bks.

—Venus & Serena Williams. 2003. (gr. 3-6). lib. bdg. 14.10 (978-0-613-76644-9(X)) Tandem Library Bks.

Morrison, John. Mathilde Krim. 2004. (Women in Medicine Ser.). (Illus.). 112p. (gr. 6-12). 30.00 (978-0-7910-8026-9(9) , Chelsea Hse.) Facts On File, Inc.

Morrison, John F. Frida Kahlo. 2003. (Great Hispanic Heritage Ser.). (Illus.). 112p. (J). (gr. 6-12). 30.00 (978-0-7910-7254-7(1)); pap. 30.00 (978-0-7910-7517-3(6)) Facts On File, Inc. (Chelsea Hse.).

Moss, Marissa. Brave Harriet: The First Woman to Fly the English Channel. Payne, C. F., illus. 2001. 32p. (J). (gr. 1-4). 17.00 (978-0-15-202380-5(1) , Silver Whistle) Harcourt Trade Pubs.

Muckenhoupt, Margaret. Dorothea Dix: Advocate for Mental Health Care. 2004. (Oxford Portraits Ser.). (Illus.). 128p. (YA). 28.00 (978-0-19-512921-2(0)) Oxford Univ. Pr., Inc.

Murdico, Suzanne J. Monica Seles. 1998. (Overcoming the Odds Ser.). (Illus.). 48p. (J). (gr. 4-7). pap. 7.95 (978-0-8172-8001-7(4)) Steck-Vaughn.

Murphy, Claire Rudolf. I Am Sacagawea, I Am York: Our Journey West with Lewis & Clark. Bond, Higgins, illus. 2005. 32p. (J). (gr. 3-5). 17.85 (978-0-8027-8921-1(8)); 16.95 (978-0-8027-8919-8(6)) Walker & Co.

Murphy, Patricia J. Grace Hopper: Computer Pioneer. 2004. (Famous Inventors Ser.). (Illus.). 32p. (J). lib. bdg. 22.60 (978-0-7660-2273-7(0)) Enslow Pubs., Inc.

Musgrave, Susan, ed. Perfectly Secret: The Hidden Lives of Seven Teen Girls. 2004. 128p. (YA). (gr. 8). 18.95 (978-1-55037-865-8(1)); pap. 8.95 (978-1-55037-864-1(3)) Annick Pr., Ltd. CAN. *Dist:* Firefly Bks., Ltd.

W
X
Y
Z

Myers, Nancy C. Nancy Landon Kassebaum: A Senate Profile. 1998. (Contemporary Profiles & Policy Series for the Younger Reader). 70p. (YA). (gr. 8 up). 20.00 (978-0-934272-47-6(6)); pap. 12.95 (978-0-934272-46-9(8)) Burke, John Gordon Pub., Inc.

Myers, Walter Dean. African Princess: At Her Majesty's Request. 1999. (Illus.). 160p. (J). (gr. 4-7). pap. 17.95 (978-0-590-48669-9(1)) Scholastic, Inc.

—At Her Majesty's Request: An African Princess in Victorian England. (Illus.). (J). (978-0-439-07762-0(1)) Scholastic, Inc.

Naden, Corinne J. Halle Berry. 2001. (gr. 3-6). lib. bdg. 18.75 (978-0-613-86157-1(4)) Tandem Library Bks.

Naden, Corinne J. & Blue, Rose. Dian Fossey: At Home with the Giant Gorillas. 2002. (Gateway Greens Ser.). (Illus.). 48p. (gr. 2-4). lib. bdg. 23.90 (978-0-7613-2569-7(7) , Millbrook Pr.) Lerner Publishing Group.

—Mae Jeminson: Out of This World. 2003. (Gateway Biography Ser.: 4). (Illus.). 48p. lib. bdg. 23.90 (978-0-7613-2570-3(0) , Millbrook Pr.) Lerner Publishing Group.

Nardo, Don. Women Leaders of Nations. 1998. (History Makers Ser.). (Illus.). 112p. (YA). (gr. 7-10). 27.45 (978-1-56006-397-1(1) , Lucent Bks.) Thomson Gale.

Nault, Jennifer. Judy Blume. 2002. (My Favorite Writer Ser.). (Illus.). 32p. (J). lib. bdg. 18.20 (978-1-59036-025-5(7)) Weigl Pubs., Inc.

Neering, Rosemary. Emily Carr. 2nd ed. 1999. (Canadians Ser.). (Illus.). 64p. (YA). (gr. 4-7). pap. (978-1-55041-483-7(6)) Fitzhenry & Whiteside, Ltd.

Nelson, Kristi. WNBA: The Chamique Holdsclaw Story. 2000. 11.79 (978-0-606-18616-2(6)) Tandem Library Bks.

Nichols, Catherine. Madam C.J. Walker. 2005. (Scholastic News Nonfiction Readers Ser.). (Illus.). 24p. (J). pap. (978-0-516-24784-7(0)) Children's Pr., Ltd.

Nicholson, Lois. Dian Fossey. 2003. (Women in Science Ser.). (Illus.). 112p. (gr. 6-12). 30.00 (978-0-7910-6907-3(9) , Chelsea Hse.) Facts On File, Inc.

Nicholson, Lois P. Dian Fossey. 2003. (Women in Science Ser.). pap. 30.00 (978-0-7910-7521-0(4) , Chelsea Hse.) Facts On File, Inc.

Nivola, Claire A. Planting the Trees of Kenya: The Story of Wangari Maathai. 2008. 32p. (J). 16.95 (***978-0-374-39918-4(2)*** , Farrar, Straus & Giroux) Farrar, Straus & Giroux.

Nixon, Joan Lowery. The Making of a Writer. 2003. (gr. 5-8). lib. bdg. 13.00 (978-0-613-70572-1(6)) Tandem Library Bks.

Noland, Thelma. Annie Sweet Annie. 2004. 174p. (J). pap. 13.95 (978-0-595-31138-5(5)) iUniverse, Inc.

Noyed, Robert B. Susan B. Anthony: Reformer. 2002. (Spirit of America: Our People Ser.). (Illus.). 32p. (J). (gr. 2-6). 27.07 (978-1-56766-171-2(8)) Child's World, Inc.

O'Connell, Diane. People Person: The Story of Sociologist Marta Tienda. 2005. (Women's Adventures in Science Ser.). (Illus.). 108p. (YA). (gr. 5-8). 31.00 (978-0-531-16781-6(X) , Watts, Franklin) Scholastic Library Publishing.

O'Hara, Megan, ed. The Girlhood Diary of Wanda Gag, 1908-1909: Portrait of a Young Artist. 2000. (Blue Earth Books). (Illus.). 32p. (J). (gr. 3-4). lib. bdg. 22.60 (978-0-7368-0598-8(2) , Bridgestone Bks.) Capstone Pr., Inc.

—A Whaling Captain's Daughter: The Diary of Laura Jernegan, 1868-1871. 1999. (Diaries, Letters & Memoirs Ser.). (Illus.). 32p. (J). (gr. 2-7). pap. 21.00 (978-0-516-21851-9(4) , Children's Pr.) Scholastic Library Publishing.

Olmstead, Mary. Judy Baca. 2004. (Hispanic-American Biographies Ser.). (Illus.). 64p. (J). pap. 9.50 (978-1-4109-0915-2(8)) Harcourt Schl. Pubs.

—Judy Baca. 2004. (Hispanic-American Biographies Ser.). (Illus.). 64p. (J). (gr. 4-6). 32.86 (978-1-4109-0709-7(0)) Raintree.

Orgill, Roxane. Mahalia: A Life in Gospel Music. 2004. (Illus.). 132p. (gr. 4-8). reprint ed. 20.00 (978-0-7567-7945-0(6)) DIANE Publishing Co.

—Shout Sister, Shout! Ten Girl Singers who Shaped a Century. 2001. (Illus.). 160p. (YA). (gr. 7 up). 19.95 (978-0-689-81991-9(9) , McElderry, Margaret K.) Simon & Schuster Children's Publishing.

Orr, Tamra. Marie Curie. 2003. (World Was Never the Same Ser.). (J). pap. (978-1-58417-263-5(0)); lib. bdg. (978-1-58417-262-8(2)) Lake Street Pubs.

Ouriou, Katie. Love Ya Like a Sister: A Story of Friendship. Johnston, Julie, ed. 1999. (Illus.). 208p. (J). (gr. 5-9). pap. 7.95 (978-0-88776-454-7(1)) Tundra Bks., Inc./ Livres Toundra, Inc. CAN. *Dist:* Random Hse., Inc.

The Padded Girdle: The Unbelievable True Story of Overcoming Adversity Again, & Again, & Again. . . 2003. (Illus.). 198p. pap. 19.95 (978-0-9745860-0-7(5)) Eaglesquest Publishing.

Paprocki, Sherry. Katie Couric. 2001. (gr. 5-8). lib. bdg. 18.75 (978-0-613-32737-4(3)) Tandem Library Bks.

—Michelle Kwan. 2000. (Women Who Win Ser.). (Illus.). 64p. (J). (gr. 4-7). 25.00 (978-0-7910-5792-6(5) , Chelsea Hse.) Facts On File, Inc.

Parish, James Robert. Gloria Estefan: Singer. 2006. (Illus.). 128p. (gr. 6-12). 25.00 (978-0-8160-5833-4(4) , Ferguson Publishing Co.) Facts On File, Inc.

Parker, Janice. Political Leaders. 1998. (Women in Profile Ser.). (Illus.). 48p. (J). (gr. 4). lib. bdg. (978-0-7787-0008-1(9)) Crabtree Publishing Co.

Parsons, Cynthia. The Discoverer, Mary Baker Eddy. Longyear Museum Staff, photos by. 2000. (Illus.). 132p. (J). (gr. 4-8). 20.00 (978-1-892286-00-0(9)) Vermont Schoolhouse Pr., The.

Partridge, Elizabeth. Restless Spirit: The Life & Work of Dorothea Lange. 1998. (Illus.). 128p. (J). (gr. 4-7). 22.99 (978-0-670-87888-8(X) , Viking Juvenile) Penguin Group (USA) Inc.

Patrick, Jean L. S. The Girl Who Struck Out Babe Ruth. 2000. (gr. 3-6). lib. bdg. 14.10 (978-0-613-53509-0(X)) Tandem Library Bks.

Patrick Jean L. S. La niña que poncho a Babe Ruth (the Girl Who Struck Out Babe Ruth) Reeves, Jeni, illus. 2007. (Yo solo Historia (on My Own History) Ser.). (J). pap. 6.95 (***978-0-8225-7788-1(7)*** , Ediciones Lerner) Lerner Publishing Group.

Patrick, Jean L. S. La Niña Que Poncho a Babe Ruth (The Girl Who Struck Out Babe Ruth) Reeves, Jeni, illus. 2007. (Yo Solo - Historia (on My Own - History) Ser.). (SPA.). 48p. (J). (gr. 2-4). 25.26 (***978-0-8225-7785-0(2)*** , Ediciones Lerner) Lerner Publishing Group.

Patteson, Nelda. Adina de Zavala: "Angel of the Alamo" Her Life Story Presented Through the Clothes She Wore. Patteson, Nelda, illus. 2003. (Women of Texas Ser.: Vol. 3). Orig. Title: Angel of the Alamo. (Illus.). 32p. (J). (gr. 4-8). pap. 14.95 (978-0-9629001-2-9(5)) Smiley Co.

Perlyn, Marilyn B. The Biggest & Brightest Light: A True Story of the Heart. Perlyn, Amanda, illus. 2004. 48p. (J). 16.95 (978-1-931741-30-9(1)) Reed, Robert D. Pubs.

Petrick, Neila A. Woman of Texas: The Story of Jane Wilkinson Long. Petrick, Thomas W., ed. 1998. 52p. (YA). (gr. 7-12). stu. ed. 11.95 (978-1-880384-13-8(2)) Coldwater Pr.

Petrick, Neila Skinner. Katherine Stinson Otero, High Flyer. Wallace, Daggi, illus. 2006. 32p. (J). 15.95 (978-1-58980-368-8(X)) Pelican Publishing Co., Inc.

Pflueger, Lynda. Dolley Madison: Courageous First Lady. 1999. (Historical American Biographies Ser.). (Illus.). 128p. (YA). (gr. 6-12). lib. bdg. 26.60 (978-0-7660-1092-5(9)) Enslow Pubs., Inc.

Pickels, Dwayne E. Shania Twain. 2001. (Overcoming Adversity Ser.). (Illus.). 112p. (J). 30.00 (978-0-7910-5901-2(4) , Chelsea Hse.) Facts On File, Inc.

Plantz, Connie. Bessie Coleman: First Black Woman Pilot. 2001. (African-American Biographies Ser.). (Illus.). 128p. (J). (gr. 6-12). lib. bdg. 26.60 (978-0-7660-1545-6(9)) Enslow Pubs., Inc.

Platt, Janet. Livewire Real Lives Susie O'Neill. 2000. (Livewires Ser.). (Illus.). 32p. pap. 6.00 (978-0-521-77611-0(2)) Cambridge Univ. Pr.

Polacco, Patricia. Betty Doll. Polacco, Patricia, illus. (Illus.). (J). (ps-3). 2001. 1p. 16.99 (978-0-399-23638-9(4) , Philomel); 2004. 40p. reprint ed. pap. 6.99 (978-0-14-240196-5(X) , Puffin) Penguin Group (USA) Inc.

Polcovar, Jane. Rosalind Franklin & the Structure of Life. 2006. (Profiles in Science Ser.). 144p. (J). (gr. 6-12). lib. bdg. 27.95 (978-1-59935-022-6(X)) Reynolds, Morgan Inc.

Polette, Nancy. Mae Jemison. 2003. (Rookie Biographies Ser.). (gr. 1-2). pap. 4.95 (978-0-516-27783-7(9)); (Illus.). 32p. (J). 20.50 (978-0-516-22856-3(0)) Scholastic Library Publishing. (Children's Pr.).

—Mae Jemison. 2003. (gr. k-3). lib. bdg. 12.95 (978-0-613-67641-0(6)) Tandem Library Bks.

Power-Waters, Alma. St. Catherine Labore & the Miraculous Medal. 2000. (Illus.). 138p. (J). pap. 9.95 (978-0-89870-765-6(X)) Ignatius Pr.

Poynter, Margaret. Top 10 American Women's Figure Skaters. 1998. (Sports Top 10 Ser.). (Illus.). 48p. (YA). (gr. 4-10). lib. bdg. 23.93 (978-0-7660-1075-8(9)) Enslow Pubs., Inc.

Price-Groff, Claire. Twentieth-Century Women Political Leaders. 1998. (Global Profiles Ser.). (Illus.). 160p. (YA). (gr. 5-12). lib. bdg. 25.00 (978-0-8160-3672-1(1)) Facts On File, Inc.

Prince, Mary. The History of Mary Prince, a West Indian Slave, Related by Herself. 2001. (Penguin Classics Ser.). (Illus.). (J). (978-0-606-20705-8(8)) Tandem Library Bks.

Raatma, Lucia. Alice Walker: African-American Author & Activist. 2003. (Journey to Freedom Ser.). (Illus.). 40p. (J). (gr. 3-7). 28.50 (978-1-56766-512-3(8)) Child's World, Inc.

—Amelia Earhart. 2001. (Trailblazers of the Modern World Ser.). (Illus.). 48p. (J). (gr. 5 up). pap. 14.95 (978-0-8368-5223-3(0)); lib. bdg. 30.00 (978-0-8368-5063-5(7)) Stevens, Gareth Inc. (World Almanac Library).

—Oprah Winfrey: Entertainer, Producer & Businesswoman. 2001. (Career Biographies Ser.). (Illus.). 128p. (J). (gr. 6-12). 25.00 (978-0-89434-376-6(9) , F419, Ferguson Publishing Co.) Facts On File, Inc.

Raintree Steck-Vaughn Staff. Remarkable Women: Past & Present. (J). 2000. 196.92 (978-0-8172-5731-6(4)); 1999. (Illus.). 171.30 (978-0-7398-2791-8(X)) Raintree.

Raintree Steck-Vaughn Staff, ed. Remarkable Women: Past & Present Series Index. 1999. (Remarkable Women). (Illus.). 48p. (J). (gr. 5-9). 18.54 (978-0-7398-2789-5(8)) Raintree.

Rambeck, Richard & Klingel, Cynthia Fitterer. Gymnastics. 2003. (Wonder Books Level 2: Sports Ser.). (Illus.). 24p. (J). (ps-2). 22.79 (978-1-56766-459-1(8)) Child's World, Inc.

—Ice Skating. 2003. (Nonfiction Readers: Level 2 Ser.). (Illus.). 24p. (J). (ps-2). 22.79 (978-1-56766-461-4(X)) Child's World, Inc.

Ransom, Candice F. Mother Teresa. Verstraete, Elaine, illus. 2000. (On My Own Biographies Ser.). 48p. (J). (gr. 1-3). 23.93 (978-1-57505-441-4(8) , Carolrhoda Bks.) Lerner Publishing Group.

Rappaport, Doreen. The Flight of Red Bird: The Life of Zitkala-sa. 1999. (J). (978-0-606-16777-2(3)) Tandem Library Bks.

Rappoport, Ken. Ladies First: Women Athletes Who Made a Difference. 2005. (Illus.). 192p. (J). 14.95 (978-1-56145-338-2(2)) Peachtree Pubs., Ltd.

Rau, Dana Meachen. Elizabeth Dole: Public Servant & Senator. 2005. (J). (978-0-7565-1583-6(1)) Compass Point Bks.

Raum, Elizabeth. Anne Hutchinson. 2004. (Illus.). 32p. (J). pap. 7.50 (978-1-4034-5966-4(5)); lib. bdg. (978-1-4034-5958-9(4)) Heinemann Library.

—Jane Addams. 2004. (American Lives (Heinemann Library (Firm))). (Illus.). 32p. (J). pap. 7.50 (978-1-4034-5707-3(7)); lib. bdg. (978-1-4034-4992-4(9)) Heinemann Library.

—Julia Ward Howe. 2004. (Illus.). 32p. (J). pap. 6.95 (978-1-4034-5708-0(5)); lib. bdg. (978-1-4034-4995-5(3)) Heinemann Library.

Rausch, Monica. Harriet Tubman. 2006. 24p. (J). pap. (***978-0-8368-7693-2(8)***); lib. bdg. (***978-0-8368-7686-4(5)***) Stevens, Gareth Inc. (Weekly Reader Early Learning Library).

Reich, Susanna. Clara Schumann: Piano Virtuoso. 1999. (Illus.). 128p. (J). (gr. 4-6). tchr. ed. 18.00 (978-0-395-89119-3(1) , Clarion Bks.) Houghton Mifflin Co. Trade & Reference Div.

Reid, Jamie. Diana Krall. 2004. 224p. pap. 17.95 (978-1-894997-07-2(7)) Kingston Pr. CAN. *Dist:* SCB Distributors.

Remarkable Women: Past & Present, 11 bks., Set. Incl. Creators : Artists, Designers, Craftswomen. Covington, Karen. 2000. lib. bdg. 32.85 (978-0-8172-5725-5(X)); Fearless Women : Explorers, Athletes, Other Competitors. Hanson, Jillian. 2000. lib. bdg. 32.85 (978-0-8172-5729-3(2)); Healers & Researchers : Physicians, Biologists, Social Scientists. McClure, Judy. 2000. lib. bdg. 32.85 (978-0-8172-5734-7(9)); Literary Crowd : Writers, Critics, Scholars, Wits. Benedict, Kitty & Covington, Karen. 2000. lib. bdg. 32.82 (978-0-8172-5732-3(2)); Performing Artists : Actors, Directors, Dancers, Entertainers, Musicians. Covington, Karen. 2002. lib. bdg. 32.85 (978-0-8172-5727-9(6)); Professionals : Magnates, Entrepreneurs, Career Women. Hanson, Jillian. 2002. lib. bdg. 32.85 (978-0-8172-5726-2(8)); Reformers : Activists, Educators, Religious Leaders. Avakian, Monique. 2000. lib. bdg. 32.85 (978-0-8172-5733-0(0)); Theoreticians & Builders : Mathematicians, Physical Scientists, Inventors. McClure, Judy. 2002. lib. bdg. 32.85 (978-0-8172-5728-6(4)); Women in Government : Politicians, Lawmakers, Law Enforcers. James, Lesley. 2000. lib. bdg. 32.85 (978-0-8172-5730-9(6)); Women Who Made a Scene : Heroines, Villainesses, Eccentrics. James, Lesley. 2002. lib. bdg. 32.85 (978-0-8172-5735-4(7)); 80p. (YA). (gr. 6-9). (Illus.). 1999. Set lib. bdg. 328.28 (978-0-7398-2792-5(8)) Raintree.

Remarkable Women: Plus Index, 4 vols. 1999. (Illus.). (J). 149.82 (978-0-7398-2790-1(1)) Raintree.

Rhodes, Lisa Renee. Toni Morrison: Great American Writer. 2001. (Book Report Biographies Ser.). (Illus.). 100p. (YA). (gr. 6-8). pap. 6.95 (978-0-531-15555-4(2) , Watts, Franklin) Scholastic Library Publishing.

Rice, Tanya. Mother Teresa. 1999. (Life & Times of Ser.). (Illus.). 48p. (YA). (gr. 5 up). 12.95 (978-0-7910-4637-1(0) , Chelsea Hse.) Facts On File, Inc.

Richter, Glenda. The Stories of Juana Briones: Alta California Pioneer. Heywood, Della, illus. 2002. 64p. (J). (gr. 3-6). 14.95 (978-0-9700379-0-9(2)); pap. 7.95 (978-0-9700379-1-6(0)) Bookhandler Pr.

Riley, John B. Jane Addams: A Photo Biography. l.t. ed. 2004. (First Biographies Ser.). (Illus.). 24p. (YA). (gr. 5 up). 16.95 (978-1-883846-61-9(7) , First Biographies) Reynolds, Morgan Inc.

Rinaldo, Denise. Eleanor Roosevelt: With a Discussion of Respect. 2003. (Values in Action Ser.). (J). (978-1-59203-063-7(7)) Learning Challenge, Inc.

—Jane Goodall: With a Discussion of Responsibility. 2003. (Values in Action Ser.). (J). (978-1-59203-062-0(9)) Learning Challenge, Inc.

Riner, Dax. Annika Sorenstam. 2007. (J). lib. bdg. (***978-0-8225-7160-5(9)***) Twenty First Century Bks.

Ring, Susan. Beverly Cleary. 2002. (My Favorite Writer Ser.). (Illus.). 32p. (J). lib. bdg. 16.95 (978-1-59036-030-9(3)) Weigl Pubs., Inc.

Rivera, Elizabeth. The Power of the Word: The Story of Dorcas Camacho Byrd. 1998. (Illus.). 118p. (YA). (gr. 7-12). pap. 7.95 (978-1-56309-235-0(2) , W986104) Woman's Missionary Union.

Rivera, Ursula. Aretha Franklin. 2006. (Rock & Roll Hall of Famers Ser.). (Illus.). 112p. (YA). (gr. 5-8). lib. bdg. 29.25 (978-0-8239-3639-7(2)) Rosen Publishing Group, Inc., The.

—The Supremes. 2006. (Rock & Roll Hall of Famers Ser.). (Illus.). 112p. (YA). (gr. 5-8). lib. bdg. 29.25 (978-0-8239-3527-7(2)) Rosen Publishing Group, Inc., The.

Robb, Jacqueline. Go, Girl! Young Women Superstars of Pop Music. 2000. (Illus.). 144p. (J). (gr. 6-12). lib. bdg. 19.95 (978-1-888105-45-2(3)) Avisson Pr., Inc.

Roberts, Candace. The Diary of Candace Roberts, 1801-1806. Leach, Gail, ed. 2001. (Illus.). 63p. (YA). (gr. 9-12). pap. 14.00 (978-0-9715501-0-0(7)) Bristol Historical Society.

Roberts, Marjorie H., told to. Wingtip to Wingtip: 8 WASPS, Women's Airforce Service Pilots of World War II. 2000. (Illus.). ix, 128p. (J). pap. 15.95 (978-1-928760-01-6(5)) Aviatrix Publishing, Inc.

Robinson, Ella M. Stars in her Heart. 2005. 127p. per. 10.95 (978-1-57258-318-4(5)) TEACH Services, Inc.

Roehm, Michelle. Girls Who Rocked the World, Vol. 2. 2000. (YA). (978-0-606-19486-0(X)) Tandem Library Bks.

Roehm, Michelle, compiled by. Girls Who Rocked the World Vol. 2: Heroines from Harriet Tubman to Mia Hamm. 2000. (Girls Know Best Ser.). (Illus.). 152p. (J). (gr. 3 up). lib. bdg. 23.33 (978-0-8368-2673-9(6)) Stevens, Gareth Inc.

Roop, Peter & Roop, Connie. Give Me a Sign, Helen Keller! 2004. (Scholastic Chapter Book Biography Ser.). (Illus.). 55p. (J). (978-0-439-55444-2(6)) Scholastic, Inc.

Rosen, Roslyn, intro. Entertainment & Performing Arts. 1999. (Female Firsts in Their Fields Ser.). (Illus.). 64p. (YA). (gr. 4-7). 18.95 (978-0-7910-5145-0(5) , Chelsea Hse.) Facts On File, Inc.

—Science & Medicine. 1999. (Female Firsts in Their Fields Ser.). (Illus.). 64p. (YA). 28.00 (978-0-7910-5143-6(9) , Chelsea Hse.) Facts On File, Inc.

—Sports & Athletics. 1999. (Female Firsts in Their Fields Ser.). (Illus.). 64p. (YA). (gr. 4-7). 12.95 (978-0-7910-5144-3(7) , Chelsea Hse.) Facts On File, Inc.

Rosenthal, Marilyn S. & Freeman, Daniel. Amelia Earhart. 1999. (Photo-Illustrated Biographies Ser.). (Illus.). 24p. (J). (gr. 2-3). lib. bdg. 18.60 (978-0-7368-0203-1(7) , Bridgestone Bks.) Capstone Pr., Inc.

Ross, Michael Elsohn. Fish Watching with Eugenie Clark. Smith, Wendy, illus. 2005. (Naturalist's Apprentice Biographies Ser.). 48p. (gr. 3-6). lib. bdg. 19.93 (978-1-57505-384-4(5)) Lerner Publishing Group.

Ross, Nancy Wilson. Joan of Arc. 2003. vii, 182p. pap. 29.00 (978-0-7581-5017-2(2)) Textbook Pubs.

Ross, Stewart. The Story of Mother Teresa. 2001. (Illus.). 48p. (J). lib. bdg. 24.25 (978-1-930643-21-5(7)) Chrysalis Education.

Roux, Marie-Genevieve & Charpy, Elisabeth. Saint Catherine Laboure: Mary's Messenger. Curreli, Augusta, illus. 2000. (Along the Paths of the Gospel Ser.). 74p. (J). (gr. 5-9). 6.95 (978-0-8198-7037-7(4) , 332-346) Pauline Bks. & Media.

Ruffin, Frances E. Sally Hemings. 2002. (American Legends Ser.). (Illus.). 24p. (J). (gr. 3). lib. bdg. 18.75 (978-0-8239-5828-3(0) , PowerKids Pr.) Rosen Publishing Group, Inc., The.

—"Unsinkable" Molly Brown. 2002. (American Legends Ser.). (Illus.). 24p. (J). (gr. 3). lib. bdg. 18.75 (978-0-8239-5827-6(2) , PowerKids Pr.) Rosen Publishing Group, Inc., The.

Ruth, Amy. Mother Teresa. 1999. (Biography Ser.). (Illus.). 112p. (YA). (gr. 6-12). lib. bdg. 27.93 (978-0-8225-4943-7(3) , Lerner Pubns.) Lerner Publishing Group.

—Queen Latifah. 2000. (Biography Ser.). (Illus.). 112p. (YA). (gr. 6-12). lib. bdg. 27.93 (978-0-8225-4988-8(3) , Lerner Pubns.) Lerner Publishing Group.

Rutledge, Rachel. The Best of the Best in Basketball. 1998. (Women of Sports Ser.). (Illus.). 64p. (gr. 5 up). lib. bdg. 24.90 (978-0-7613-1301-4(X) , Twenty-First Century Bks.) Lerner Publishing Group.

—The Best of the Best in Figure Skating. 1998. (Women of Sports Ser.). (Illus.). 64p. (gr. 5 up). lib. bdg. 24.90 (978-0-7613-1302-1(8) , Twenty-First Century Bks.) Lerner Publishing Group.

—The Best of the Best in Gymnastics. 1999. (Women of Sports Ser.). (Illus.). 64p. (gr. 5 up). lib. bdg. 24.90 (978-0-7613-1321-2(4)); pap. 7.95 (978-0-7613-0784-6(2)) Lerner Publishing Group. (Twenty-First Century Bks.).

—The Best of the Best in Gymnastics. 1999. (Women of Sports Ser.). (978-0-606-17031-4(6)) Tandem Library Bks.

—The Best of the Best in Soccer. 1999. (J). (978-0-606-19848-6(2)) Tandem Library Bks.

—The Best of the Best in Track & Field. 1999. (Women of Sports Ser.). (Illus.). 64p. (gr. 5 up). lib. bdg. 24.90 (978-0-7613-1300-7(1)); pap. 7.95 (978-0-7613-0446-3(0)) Lerner Publishing Group. (Twenty-First Century Bks.).

—The Best of the Best in Track & Field. 1999. (Women of Sports Ser.). (978-0-606-17030-7(8)) Tandem Library Bks.

Ryan, Pam Muñoz. When Marian Sang: The True Recital of Marian Anderson. Selznick, Brian, illus. pap. 16.95 incl. audio (978-1-59112-943-1(5)); pap. incl. audio (978-1-59112-945-5(1)); pap. 18.95 incl. audio compact disk (978-1-59112-947-9(8)); pap. incl. audio compact disk (978-1-59112-949-3(4)) Live Oak Media.

—When Marian Sang: The True Recital of Marian Anderson. Selznick, Brian, illus. 2002. 40p. (J). (gr. 1-5). pap. 16.95 (978-0-439-26967-4(9) , Scholastic Pr.) Scholastic, Inc.

Sally Ride Science Editors, Sally Ride Science. What Do You Want to Be? Explore Earth Sciences. 2004. (J). 6.00 (978-0-9753920-2-7(6)) Sally Ride Science.

—What Do You Want to Be? Explore Health Sciences. 2004. (J). 6.00 (978-0-9753920-3-4(4)) Sally Ride Science.

Santella, Andrew. Marie Curie. 2001. (Trailblazers of the Modern World Ser.). (Illus.). 48p. (J). (gr. 5 up). pap. 14.95 (978-0-8368-5221-9(4)); lib. bdg. 30.00 (978-0-8368-5061-1(0)) Stevens, Gareth Inc. (World Almanac Library).

Savage, Candace C. Born to Be a Cowgirl: A Spirited Ride Through the Old West. 2004. (Illus.). (978-1-55054-838-9(7) , Greystone Bks.) Douglas & McIntyre, Ltd. CAN. *Dist:* Transition Vendor.

—Born to Be a Cowgirl: A Spirited Ride Through the Old West. 2004. (Illus.). 64p. (J). pap. 10.95 (978-1-58246-020-8(5)); (gr. 4-8). 15.95 (978-1-58246-019-2(1)) Ten Speed Pr. (Tricycle Pr.).

Savage, Jeff. Sports Great Rebecca Lobo. 2001. (Sports Great Bks.). (Illus.). 64p. (J). (gr. 4-10). lib. bdg. 22.60 (978-0-7660-1466-4(5)) Enslow Pubs., Inc.

—Top 10 Women's Sports Legends. 2001. (Sports Top 10 Ser.). (Illus.). 48p. (J). (gr. 4-10). lib. bdg. 23.93 (978-0-7660-1495-4(9)) Enslow Pubs., Inc.

Schaefer, Lola M. Amelia Earhart. Saunders-Smith, Gail, ed. 2002. (First Biographies Ser.). (Illus.). 24p. (J). (gr. k-1). lib. bdg. 15.93 (978-0-7368-1433-1(7) , Pebble Bks.) Capstone Pr., Inc.

—Clara Barton. Saunders-Smith, Gail, ed. 2002. (First Biographies Ser.). (Illus.). 24p. (J). (gr. k-1). lib. bdg. 15.93 (978-0-7368-1434-8(5) , Pebble Bks.) Capstone Pr., Inc.

—Jane Goodall. (First Biographies Ser.). 24p. (J). pap. 5.95 (978-0-7368-5085-8(6)) Capstone Pr., Inc.

—Mother Teresa. Saunders-Smith, Gail, ed. 2003. (First Biographies Ser.). (Illus.). 24p. (J). (gr. k-1). lib. bdg. 15.93 (978-0-7368-1646-5(1) , Pebble Bks.) Capstone Pr., Inc.

—Mother Teresa, Vol. 2. 2005. (First Biographies Ser.). 24p. (YA). (gr. k-3). pap. (978-0-7368-3381-3(1) , Pebble Bks.) Capstone Pr., Inc.

Schaefer, Lola M. & Schaefer, Wyatt S. Jane Goodall. 2004. (First Biographies Ser.). 24p. (J). lib. bdg. 15.93 (978-0-7368-2083-7(3) , Pebble Bks.) Capstone Pr., Inc.

—Marie Curie. 2004. (First Biographies Ser.). 24p. (J). lib. bdg. 15.93 (978-0-7368-2084-4(1) , Pebble Bks.) Capstone Pr., Inc.

Scheader, Catherine. Lorraine Hansberry: Playwright & Voice of Justice. 1998. (African-American Biographies Ser.). (Illus.). 128p. (YA). (gr. 6-12). lib. bdg. 26.60 (978-0-89490-945-0(2)) Enslow Pubs., Inc.

Schnakenberg, Robert E. Mia Hamm. 2001. (Women Who Win Ser.). (Illus.). (J). (978-0-606-20798-0(8)) Tandem Library Bks.

Schott, Jane A. Dian Fossey & the Mountain Gorillas. Ramstad, Ralph L., illus. 2005. (On My Own Biographies Ser.). 48p. (gr. 2-5). lib. bdg. 23.93 (978-1-57505-082-9(X)) Lerner Publishing Group.

—Dian Fossey & the Mountain Gorillas. Shine, Andrea, illus. 2000. (On My Own Biographies Ser.). 56p. (J). (gr. 1-3). pap. 5.95 (978-1-57505-477-3(9) , First Avenue Editions) Lerner Publishing Group.

Schoyer-Brooks, Polly. Beyond the Myth: The Story of Joan of Arc. 1999. (J). 15.60 (978-0-606-17364-3(1)) Tandem Library Bks.

Schraff, Anne. Wilma Rudolph: The Greatest Woman Sprinter in History. 2004. (African-American Biographies Ser.). (Illus.). 112p. (J). lib. bdg. 26.60 (978-0-7660-2291-1(9)) Enslow Pubs., Inc.

Schroeder, Alan. Minty: A Story of Young Harriet Tubman. Pinkney, Jerry, illus. 2000. (J). (ps-ps). lib. bdg. 15.30 (978-0-613-33712-0(3)) Tandem Library Bks.

Schur, Maxine Rose. Hannah Szenes: A Song of Light. rev. ed. 1998. 106p. pap. 9.95 (978-0-8276-0628-9(1)) Jewish Pubn. Society.

Schwager, Tina & Schuerger, Michele. Gutsy Girls: Young Women Who Dare. 1999. (Illus.). 272p. (YA). (gr. 6 up). pap. 15.95 (978-1-57542-059-2(7)) Free Spirit Publishing, Inc.

—Gutsy Girls; Young Women Who Dare. 1999. (Illus.). 261p. (J). (gr. 6-12). per. 25.70 (978-0-613-23721-5(8)) Tandem Library Bks.

Scott, Kieran. Cameron Diaz. (Latinos in the Limelight Ser.). (Illus.). 64p. (J). 2002. pap. 27.50 (978-0-7910-6109-1(4)); 2001. (gr. 3 up). 19.75 (978-0-7910-6108-4(6) , Chelsea Hse.) Facts On File, Inc.

Seminara-Kennedy, Concetta. The Dixie Chicks. 2002. (Galaxy of Superstars Ser.). (Illus.). 64p. (J). 25.00 (978-0-7910-6768-0(8) , Chelsea Hse.) Facts On File, Inc.

Senker, Cath. Rosalind Franklin. 2002. (Scientists Who Made History Ser.). (Illus.). 48p. (J). 27.12 (978-0-7398-5226-2(4)) Raintree.

Shapiro, Marc. J. K. Rowling: The Wizard Behind Harry Potter. 2007. 288p. pap. 6.99 ***978-0-312-37697-0(9)*** , St. Martin's Griffin) St. Martin's Pr.

—J. K. Rowling: The Wizard Behind Harry Potter. 2000. (J). (978-0-606-19640-6(4)) Tandem Library Bks.

—J. K. Rowling: The Wizard Behind Harry Potter. l.t. ed. 2001. (J). (gr. 8-12). 23.95 (978-0-7862-3225-3(0)) Thorndike Pr.

—Mariah Carey. 2001. (Illus.). 220p. pap. 16.95 (978-1-55022-444-3(1)) ECW Pr. CAN. *Dist:* Independent Pubs. Group.

Shaw, Maura D. Dorothy Day: A Catholic Life of Action. Marchesi, Stephen, illus. 2004. (Spiritual Biographies for Young Readers Ser.). 32p. (J). 12.99 (978-1-59473-011-5(3)) SkyLight Paths Publishing.

Shea, Pegi Deitz. Ekatarina Gordeeva. 1999. (Female Figure Skating Legends Ser.). (Illus.). 64p. (YA). (gr. 2-7). 12.95 (978-0-7910-5027-9(0) , Chelsea Hse.) Facts On File, Inc.

Sheafer, Silvia Anne. Aimee Semple McPherson. 2004. (Spiritual Leaders & Thinkers Ser.). (Illus.). 120p. (gr. 9-13). 30.00 (978-0-7910-7867-9(1) , Chelsea Hse.) Facts On File, Inc.

Shields, Charles J. Martha Stewart. 2001. (Women of Achievement Ser.). (Illus.). 112p. (J). pap. 30.00 (978-0-7910-6319-4(4)); 30.00 (978-0-7910-6318-7(6)) Facts On File, Inc. (Chelsea Hse.).

Shull, Jodie A. Georgia O'Keeffe: Legendary American Painter. 2003. (People to Know Ser.). (Illus.). 128p. (J). lib. bdg. 26.60 (978-0-7660-2104-4(1)) Enslow Pubs., Inc.

Sills, Leslie. In Real Life: Stories about Women Photographers. 1998. (J). (978-0-7868-0092-6(5)) Hyperion Pr.

Silverstone, Michael. Winona Laduke: Restoring Land & Culture in Native America. 2001. (Women Changing the World Ser.). (Illus.). 112p. (gr. 4-7). 19.95 (978-1-55861-260-0(2)) Feminist Pr. at The City Univ. of New York.

Silverthorne, Elizabeth. Louisa May Alcott. 2002. (Who Wrote That? Ser.). (Illus.). 112p. (gr. 6-12). 30.00 (978-0-7910-6721-5(1) , Chelsea Hse.) Facts On File, Inc.

Singer, Linda-Marie. Elizabeth Taylor: Actress/Activist. 1999. (Women of Achievement Ser.). (Illus.). 112p. (J). (gr. 4-7). pap. 30.00 (978-0-7910-4790-3(3) , Chelsea Hse.) Facts On File, Inc.

Sinnott, Susan. Lorraine Hansberry: Award-Winning Playwright & Civil Rights Activist. 1999. (J). (978-0-606-19366-5(9)) Tandem Library Bks.

Skelton, Renee. Forecast Earth: The Story of Climate Scientist Inez Fung. 2005. (Women's Adventures in Science Ser.). (Illus.). 116p. (YA). (gr. 7-9). 31.00 (978-0-531-16777-9(1) , Watts, Franklin) Scholastic Library Publishing.

—Harriet Tubman: A Woman of Courage. 2005. (Time for Kids Ser.). (Illus.). 48p. (J). pap. 3.99 (978-0-06-057607-3(3)) HarperCollins Pubs.

Skelton, Renee & Time for Kids Editors. Harriet Tubman: A Woman of Courage. 2005. (Time for Kids Ser.). (Illus.). 48p. (J). 15.99 (978-0-06-057608-0(1)) HarperCollins Pubs.

Somervill, Barbara A. Mary McLeod Bethune: African-American Educator. 2003. (Spirit of America). (Illus.). 32p. (J). (gr. 2-6). 27.07 (978-1-59296-008-8(1)) Child's World, Inc.

Sonneborn, Liz. Pocahontas 1595-1617. 2002. (American Indian Biographies Ser.). (Illus.). 32p. (J). (gr. 3-4). lib. bdg. 23.93 (978-0-7368-1214-6(8) , Blue Earth Bks.) Capstone Pr., Inc.

Soto, Gary. Jessie de la Cruz: A Profile of a United Farm Worker. 2002. (Illus.). 128p. (gr. 7-12). pap. 9.95 (978-0-89255-285-6(9)) Persea Bks., Inc.

Spain, Valerie. Meet Maya Angelou. 2003. (gr. 3-6). lib. bdg. 13.00 (978-0-613-83536-7(0)) Tandem Library Bks.

Spangenburg, Ray & Moser, Kit. Georgia O'Keeffe: The Life of an Artist. 2002. (Artist Biographies Ser.). (Illus.). 48p. (J). (gr. 1-4). lib. bdg. 23.93 (978-0-7660-1882-2(2)) Enslow Pubs., Inc.

Spinner, Stephanie. Who Was Annie Oakley? Day, Larry & Harrison, Nancy, illus. 2002. (Who Was...? Ser.). 112p. (J). (gr. 3-5). pap. 4.99 (978-0-448-42497-2(5) , Grosset & Dunlap) Penguin Group (USA) Inc.

—Who Was Annie Oakley? 2002. (gr. 3-6). lib. bdg. 13.00 (978-0-613-43653-3(9)) Tandem Library Bks.

Splear, Elsie L. & Pratt, Carolyn. Growing Seasons. Stark, Ken, illus. 2000. 1p. (J). (ps-3). 16.99 (978-0-399-23460-6(8) , Putnam Juvenile) Penguin Group (USA) Inc.

Stanley, Diane. Joan of Arc. Stanley, Diane, illus. 1998. (Illus.). 48p. (J). (gr. 3 up). 16.89 (978-0-688-14330-5(X)) HarperCollins Pubs.

—Joan of Arc. 2002. (gr. 3-6). lib. bdg. 15.25 (978-0-613-44855-0(3)) Tandem Library Bks.

Stanley, Phyllis M. Elizabeth Terwilliger - Someone Special: A Biography of the Celebrated Naturalist. 2003. (Illus.). 110p. (J). (gr. 4-10). pap. 17.95 (978-1-878044-54-9(0)) Mayhaven Publishing.

Stanton, Sue. Great Women of Faith: Inspiration for Action. 2003. (Illus.). 128p. (J). 12.95 (978-0-8091-4123-4(X) , 4123-x) Paulist Pr.

Steele, Christy & Graves, Kerry, eds. A Free Black Girl Before the Civil War: The Diary of Charlotte Forten, 1854. 1999. (Diaries, Letters & Memoirs Ser.). 32p. (J). (gr. 2-7). pap. 21.00 (978-0-516-21339-2(3) , Children's Pr.) Scholastic Library Publishing.

Steele, Christy & Todd, Anne M. A Confederate Girl: The Diary of Carrie Berry, 1864. 1999. (Diaries, Letters & Memoirs Ser.). (Illus.). 32p. (J). (gr. 2-7). pap. 21.00 (978-0-516-21338-5(5) , Children's Pr.) Scholastic Library Publishing.

Steinbauer, Janine. Carson McCullers. 2002. (Profiles Ser.). (Illus.). 56p. (YA). (gr. 6 up). lib. bdg. 17.95 (978-0-88682-652-9(7) , Creative Education) Creative Co., The.

Sterling, Kristin. Jane Goodall: A Life of Loyalty. 2008. (Pull Ahead Books-Biographies Ser.). (J). lib. bdg. 22.60 ***(978-0-8225-8727-9(0)*** , Lerner Pubns.) Lerner Publishing Group.

Stewart, Mark. Jackie Stiles: Gym Dandy. 2002. (New Wave Ser.). (Illus.). 48p. (gr. 4 up). lib. bdg. 22.90 (978-0-7613-2614-4(6) , Millbrook Pr.) Lerner Publishing Group.

—Lisa Leslie. 1998. (gr. 3-6). lib. bdg. 14.10 (978-0-613-90733-0(7)) Tandem Library Bks.

—Mia Hamm: Good As Gold. 1999. (gr. 3-6). lib. bdg. 14.10 (978-0-613-62302-5(9)) Tandem Library Bks.

Stewart, Melissa. Rachel Carson: Biologist & Writer. 2001. (Career Biographies Ser.). (Illus.). 128p. (YA). (gr. 6-12). 25.00 (978-0-89434-368-1(8) , F411, Ferguson Publishing Co.) Facts On File, Inc.

Stille, Darlene R. Eva Peron, First Lady of Argentina. 2006. (Signature Lives Ser.). (Illus.). 112p. (J). (gr. 5-7). 30.60 (978-0-7565-1585-0(8)) Compass Point Bks.

Stone, Amy. Dorothea Lange. 2003. (Raintree Biographies Ser.). (J). 25.70 (978-0-7398-6862-1(4)) Raintree.

—Dorothea Lange. 2003. (gr. 3-6). lib. bdg. 15.90 (978-0-613-78225-8(9)) Tandem Library Bks.

Stone, Tanya Lee. Rosie O' Donnell: America's Favorite Grown-Up Kid. 2000. (Gateway Biography Ser.). (Illus.). 48p. (gr. 2-4). lib. bdg. 23.90 (978-0-7613-1724-1(4) , Millbrook Pr.) Lerner Publishing Group.

Streissguth, Thomas. Christa McAuliffe. 2003. (Explore Space! Ser.). (Illus.). 24p. (J). (gr. 1-2). lib. bdg. 18.60 (978-0-7368-1624-3(0) , Bridgestone Bks.) Capstone Pr., Inc.

—Mae Jemison. 2003. (Explore Space! Ser.). (Illus.). 24p. (J). (gr. 1-2). lib. bdg. 18.60 (978-0-7368-1626-7(7) , Bridgestone Bks.) Capstone Pr., Inc.

Strudwick, Leslie. Athletes. 1998. (Women in Profile Ser.). (Illus.). 48p. (J). (gr. 4). pap. (978-0-7787-0037-1(2)) Crabtree Publishing Co.

—Musicians. 1998. (Women in Profile Ser.). (Illus.). 48p. (J). (gr. 4). pap. (978-0-7787-0031-9(3)); lib. bdg. (978-0-7787-0009-8(7)) Crabtree Publishing Co.

Sullivan, Anne Marie. Mother Theresa: Religious Humanitarian. 2002. (Great Names Ser.). (Illus.). 32p. (J). (gr. 3 up). lib. bdg. (978-1-59084-142-6(5)) Mason Crest Pubs.

Sutcliffe, Jane. Amelia Earhart. 2003. (History Maker Bios Ser.). (Illus.). 48p. (J). (gr. 3-5). lib. bdg. 26.60 (978-0-8225-0396-5(4)) Lerner Publishing Group.

—Babe Didrikson Zaharias: All-Around Athlete. Reeves, Jeni, illus. (On My Own Biographies Ser.). 48p. 2005. (gr. 2-5). lib. bdg. 23.93 (978-1-57505-421-6(3)); 2000. (J). (gr. 1-3). pap. 5.95 (978-1-57505-447-6(7)) Lerner Publishing Group.

Tallchief, Maria. Tallchief: America's Prima Ballerina. 2001. (J). (978-0-606-22511-3(0)) Tandem Library Bks.

Thatcher, Rebecca. Dolores Huerta. 2002. (Latinos in American History). (Illus.). 56p. (gr. 4-8). lib. bdg. 29.95 (978-1-58415-155-5(2)) Mitchell Lane Pubs., Inc.

Theisen, Gordon. The Mystery of Anastasia Romanov. 2001. (History Channel History Guides Ser.). (Illus.). 40p. (J). pap. 9.99 (978-0-86730-846-4(X)) Lebhar-Friedman Bks.

Thro, Ellen. Twentieth-Century Women Politicians. 1998. (American Profiles Ser.). (Illus.). 144p. (YA). (gr. 5-12). 25.00 (978-0-8160-3758-2(2)) Facts On File, Inc.

Tilton, Rafael. Mother Teresa. 1999. (Importance of Ser.). (Illus.). 120p. (YA). (gr. 7-10). 27.45 (978-1-56006-565-4(6) , Lucent Bks.) Thomson Gale.

Torres, John Albert. Mia Hamm. 1999. (Real-Life Reader Biography Ser.). (Illus.). 32p. (J). (gr. 3-8). lib. bdg. 15.95 (978-1-883845-94-0(7)) Mitchell Lane Pubs., Inc.

Townsley, Janet Howe. Dakota Dreams: Fannie Sabra Howe's Own Story, 1881-1884. 2003. (Illus.). 77p. (J). 19.95 (978-0-9715171-4-1(2)) South Dakota State Historical Society.

Trachtenberg, Martha P. Anne McCaffrey: Science Fiction Storyteller. 2001. (People to Know Ser.). (Illus.). 112p. (YA). (gr. 6-12). lib. bdg. 26.60 (978-0-7660-1151-9(8)) Enslow Pubs., Inc.

Tracy, Kathleen. Mary Kate & Ashley Olsen. l.t. ed. 2002. (Real-Life Reader Biography Ser.). (Illus.). 32p. (J). (gr. 3-8). lib. bdg. 15.95 (978-1-58415-124-1(2)) Mitchell Lane Pubs., Inc.

Tryszynska-Frederick, Luba. Luba: The Angel of Bergen-Belsen. Marshall, Ann, illus. 2004. 48p. (J). 16.95 (978-1-58246-098-7(1) , Tricycle Pr.) Ten Speed Pr.

Valentine, Emily. Mother Teresa: With a Discussion of Compassion. 2004. (Values in Action Ser.). (J). (978-1-59203-070-5(X)) Learning Challenge, Inc.

Venable, Alan. The Story of Anne Frank. Ham, Jeff, illus. 2001. (J). (gr. 5-6). 65.00 incl. audio, cd-rom (978-1-58702-398-9(9)) Johnston, Don Inc.

Venezia, Mike. Dorothea Lange. 2000. (Getting to Know the World's Greatest Artists Ser.). (Illus.). 32p. (J). (gr. 3-4). 27.00 (978-0-516-22026-0(8) , Children's Pr.) Scholastic Library Publishing.

—Frida Kahlo. 1999. (Getting to Know the World's Greatest Artists Ser.). (Illus.). 32p. (gr. 3-4). pap. 6.95 (978-0-516-26466-0(4)); (J). 27.00 (978-0-516-20975-3(2)) Scholastic Library Publishing. (Children's Pr.).

—Frida Kahlo. 1999. (gr. 3-6). lib. bdg. 15.25 (978-0-613-37352-4(9)) Tandem Library Bks.

Vickers, Rebecca. Florence Nightingale. (Groundbreakers Ser.). 48p. pap. 8.50 (978-1-4034-4063-1(8)); 2002. (Illus.). 24p. (J). pap. 6.50 (978-1-4034-0028-4(8) , 91472); 2000. (Illus.). 24p. (J). lib. bdg. 19.92 (978-1-57572-402-7(2)) Heinemann Library.

—Florence Nightingale. 2002. (gr. k-3). lib. bdg. 12.95 (978-0-613-86990-4(7)) Tandem Library Bks.

Volovar, Vivian. Lobster Lady. 2007. (Illus.). 32p. (J). pap. 14.95 ***(978-0-9773725-8-4(8))*** Flat Hammock Pr.

Wade, Linda R. Sally Ride: First American Female in Space. l.t. ed. 2002. (Unlocking the Secrets of Science Ser.). (Illus.). 56p. (gr. 4-10). lib. bdg. 25.70 (978-1-58415-139-5(0)) Mitchell Lane Pubs., Inc.

Wade, Mary Dodson. Jane Long's Journey. Roeder, Virginia M., illus. 1998. 32p. (J). (gr. 1-4). 16.95 (978-1-882539-23-9(0)); pap. 7.95 (978-1-882539-24-6(9)) Colophon Hse.

—Joan Lowery Nixon: Masterful Mystery Writer. 2004. (Authors Teens Love Ser.). (Illus.). 128p. (J). lib. bdg. 26.60 (978-0-7660-2194-5(7)) Enslow Pubs., Inc.

Wagner, Heather Lehr. Amelia Earhart. 2003. (Famous Flyers Ser.). (Illus.). 112p. (gr. 6-12). 30.00 (978-0-7910-7213-4(4)); pap. 30.00 (978-0-7910-7498-5(6)) Facts On File, Inc. (Chelsea Hse.).

—Amelia Earhart. 2003. (gr. 5-8). lib. bdg. 18.75 (978-0-613-65152-3(9)) Tandem Library Bks.

—Gertrude Bell: Explorer of the Middle East. 2004. (Women Explorers Ser.). (Illus.). 120p. 30.00 (978-0-7910-7711-5(X) , Chelsea Hse.) Facts On File, Inc.

—Mary Kingsley: Explorer of the Congo. 2004. (Women Explorers Ser.). 120p. 30.00 (978-0-7910-7714-6(4) , Chelsea Hse.) Facts On File, Inc.

Waldman, Deborah J. Wow! The World's Outstanding Women Athletes. Sieck, Margaret, ed. 1998. 32p. (J). (gr. 5-7). pap. 3.99 (978-1-886749-46-7(9)) Sports Illustrated For Kids.

Walker, Pamela. Ellen Ochoa. 2001. (Welcome Bks.). (Illus.). 24p. (J). (ps-2). pap. 4.95 (978-0-516-23587-5(7) , Children's Pr.) Scholastic Library Publishing.

—Ellen Ochoa. 2001. (gr. k-3). lib. bdg. 12.95 (978-0-613-53832-4(0)) Tandem Library Bks.

Wallis, Jeremy. Coco Chanel. 2001. (Creative Lives Ser.). (Illus.). 64p. (J). (gr. 6-8). lib. bdg. 27.07 (978-1-58810-202-7(5)) Heinemann Library.

Wallner, Rosemary. Sacagawea 1788-1812. 2002. (American Indian Biographies Ser.). (Illus.). 32p. (J). (gr. 3-4). lib. bdg. 23.93 (978-0-7368-1213-9(X) , Blue Earth Bks.) Capstone Pr., Inc.

Ward, S. Meet J. K. Rowling. (About the Author Ser.). 24p. (J). 2003. lib. bdg. 18.75 (978-0-8239-6808-4(1)); 2000. (Illus.). (gr. 3). lib. bdg. 18.75 (978-0-8239-5711-8(X)) Rosen Publishing Group, Inc., The. (PowerKids Pr.).

Waxman, Laura Hamilton. Marie Curie. 2004. (History Maker Bios Ser.). (Illus.). 48p. (J). 26.60 (978-0-8225-0300-2(X) , Lerner Pubns.) Lerner Publishing Group.

Weatherly, Myra. Women Pirates: Eight Stories of Adventure. 1998. (Women Adventurers Ser.). (Illus.). 112p. (YA). (gr. 6-12). 21.95 (978-1-883846-24-4(2) , First Biographies) Reynolds, Morgan Inc.

Webb, Ruth. Virginia Woolf. 2000. (British Library Writers' Lives). (Illus.). 128p. (978-0-7123-4616-0(3)) British Library Document Supply Ctr.

Weber, Valerie & Lewis, Geneva. Home Life in Grandma's Day. 1999. (In Grandma's Day Ser.). (Illus.). 32p. (J). (gr. 2-4). lib. bdg. 21.27 (978-1-57505-329-5(2) , Carolrhoda Bks.) Lerner Publishing Group.

Weinberger, Kimberly. Journey to a New Land: An Oral History. Meers, Tony, illus. 2000. 32p. (J). (978-1-57255-813-7(X)); pap. (978-1-57255-812-0(1)) Mondo Publishing.

—Let's Read About— Pocahontas. Marchesi, Stephen, illus. 2003. (Scholastic First Biographies Ser.). (J). pap. (978-0-439-56148-8(5)) Scholastic, Inc.

Welch, Michael F. Maureen M. Welch: A Biography of a Teacher, Wife & Mother. 2000. (Illus.). 48p. (J). (gr. k-7). (978-0-9705969-0-1(1)) Welch, Michael F.

Welden, Amelie. Girls Who Rocked the World: Heroines from Sacagawea to Sheryl Swoopes. McCann, Jerry, illus. l.t. ed. 1999. (Girls Know Best Ser.). 117p. (J). (gr. 3 up). lib. bdg. 23.33 (978-0-8368-2454-4(7)) Stevens, Gareth Inc.

Wellman, Sam. Kristi Yamaguchi. 1999. (Female Figure Skating Legends Ser.). (Illus.). 64p. (YA). (gr. 2-5). 12.95 (978-0-7910-5025-5(4) , Chelsea Hse.) Facts On File, Inc.

—Mariah Carey. 1999. (Galaxy of Superstars Ser.). (Illus.). 64p. (J). pap. 25.00 (978-0-7910-5333-1(4) , Chelsea Hse.) Facts On File, Inc.

—Michelle Kwan. 1999. (Female Figure Skating Legends Ser.). (Illus.). 64p. (YA). (gr. 4-7). 12.95 (978-0-7910-4875-7(6) , Chelsea Hse.) Facts On File, Inc.

—Mother Teresa: Missionary of Charity. 1999. (Heroes of the Faith Ser.). 208p. (YA). (gr. 4-7). 14.95 (978-0-7910-5033-0(5) , Chelsea Hse.) Facts On File, Inc.

—Mother Teresa: Missionary of Charity. l.t. ed. 2001. (Thorndike Christian Fiction Ser.). 274p. (J). 24.95 (978-0-7862-3250-5(1)) Thorndike Pr.

Wells, Rosemary. Mary on Horseback: Three Mountain Stories. McCarty, Peter, illus. (J). 2000. 64p. (gr. 3-7). pap. 4.99 (978-0-14-130815-9(X) , Puffin); 1999. 56p. (gr. 4-7). 16.99 (978-0-670-88923-5(7) , Viking Juvenile) Penguin Group (USA) Inc.

—Mary on Horseback: Three Mountain Stories. 2000. (J). (978-0-606-20243-5(9)); (gr. 3-6). lib. bdg. 13.00 (978-0-613-33711-3(5)) Tandem Library Bks.

Wells, Rosemary, et al. Streets of Gold. Fogelman, Phyllis J., ed. Andreasen, Dan, illus. 1999. 40p. (J). (gr. k-3). 16.99 (978-0-8037-2149-4(8) , Dial) Penguin Group (USA) Inc.

Werther, Scott P. Dr. Jerri Nielsen: Cheating Death in Antarctica. 2003. (Illus.). 48p. (J). (gr. 4-7). lib. bdg. 15.25 (978-0-613-67881-0(8)) Tandem Library Bks.

Westervelt, Virginia. Here Comes Eleanor: A New Life of Eleanor Roosevelt for Young People. 1998. (Illus.). 142 p. (J). (gr. 6-12). pap. 16.00 (978-1-888105-33-9(X)) Avisson Pr., Inc.

Wheeler, Jill C. Amelia Earhart. 2002. (Breaking Barriers Ser.). (Illus.). 64p. (J). (gr. 3-8). lib. bdg. 25.65 (978-1-57765-318-9(1) , ABDO & Daughters) ABDO Publishing Co.

—Benazir Bhutto. 2004. (Women of the World Ser.). (J). (978-1-59197-612-7(X)) ABDO Publishing Co.

—Clara Barton. 2002. (Breaking Barriers Ser.). (Illus.). 64p. (J). (gr. 3-8). lib. bdg. 25.65 (978-1-57765-317-2(3) , ABDO & Daughters) ABDO Publishing Co.

—Gertrude Chandler Warner. 2005. (Children's Authors Ser.). (Illus.). 24p. (J). (gr. k-6). lib. bdg. 21.35 (978-1-59197-609-7(X)) ABDO Publishing Co.

—Golda Meir. 2004. (Women of the World Ser.). (J). (978-1-59197-615-8(4)) ABDO Publishing Co.

—Indira Gandhi. 2004. (Women of the World Ser.). (J). (978-1-59197-614-1(6)) ABDO Publishing Co.

—Margaret Thatcher. 2004. (Women of the World Ser.). (J). (978-1-59197-618-9(9)) ABDO Publishing Co.

—Mary Robinson. 2004. (Women of the World Ser.). (J). (978-1-59197-617-2(0)) ABDO Publishing Co.

—Mother Teresa. 2002. (Breaking Barriers Ser.). (Illus.). 64p. (J). (gr. 3-8). lib. bdg. 25.65 (978-1-57765-315-8(7) , ABDO & Daughters) ABDO Publishing Co.

Wilkinson, Philip. Joan of Arc: The Teenager Who Saved Her Nation. 2007. (World History Biographies Ser.). (Illus.). 64p. (J). (gr. 3-7). 17.95 (978-1-4263-0116-2(2)); lib. bdg. 27.90 (978-1-4263-0117-9(0)) National Geographic Society. (National Geographic Children's Bks.).

Williams, Jean Kinney. Sandra Day O'Connor: Lawyer & Supreme Court Justice. 2000. (Career Biographies Ser.). (Illus.). 128p. (J). (gr. 6-12). 25.00 (978-0-89434-355-1(6) , F407, Ferguson Publishing Co.) Facts On File, Inc.

Wilner, Barry. Girls Rule! The Glory & Spirit of Women in Sports. 2000. (Illus.). 160p. (J). pap. 22.95 (978-0-7407-1171-8(7)) Andrews McMeel Publishing.

—Tara Lipinski: Star Figure Skater. 2001. (Sports Reports). (Illus.). 104p. (J). (gr. 4-10). lib. bdg. 26.60 (978-0-7660-1505-0(X)) Enslow Pubs., Inc.

Wilson, Antoine. S. E. Hinton. 2003. (Library of Author Biographies). (Illus.). 112p. (YA). (gr. 5-8). lib. bdg. 26.50 (978-0-8239-3778-3(X) , Rosen Central) Rosen Publishing Group, Inc., The.

Wilson, Mike. Destiny's Child. 2005. (Illus.). 32p. pap. (978-0-340-87647-3(6)) Cambridge Univ. Pr.

Wilson, Wayne. Shakira. 2001. (Real-Life Reader Biography Ser.). (Illus.). 32p. (J). (gr. 3-8). lib. bdg. 15.95 (978-1-58415-071-8(8)) Mitchell Lane Pubs., Inc.

Winegarten, Debra L. Katherine Stinson: The Flying Schoolgirl. 2004. (Illus.). 133p. (gr. 4-7). 26.95 (978-1-57168-459-2(X)) Eakin Pr.

Winter, Jeanette. My Name Is Georgia. 2003. (gr. k-3). lib. bdg. 14.15 (978-0-613-59912-2(8)) Tandem Library Bks.

—My Name Is Georgia: A Portrait by Jeanette Winter. 2003. (Illus.). 48p. (J). pap. 7.00 (978-0-15-204597-5(X) , Voyager Bks./Libros Viajeros) Harcourt Children's Bks.

W X Y Z

—My Name Is Georgia: A Portrait by Jeanette Winter. 1998. (Illus.). 48p. (J). (gr. 1-5). 16.00 (978-0-15-201649-4(X), Silver Whistle) Harcourt Trade Pubs.

Winter, Jonah. Wild Women of the Wild West. Morgan, Mary, illus. 2002. (J). (978-0-8234-1601-1(1)) Holiday Hse., Inc.

Witteman, Barbara. Dolley Madison: First Lady. 2003. (Let Freedom Ring Ser.). (Illus.). 48p. (J). (gr. 3-4). lib. bdg. 22.60 (978-0-7368-1551-2(1), Bridgestone Bks.) Capstone Pr., Inc.

—Dorothea Dix: Social Reformer. 2003. (Let Freedom Ring Ser.). (Illus.). 48p. (J). (gr. 3-4). lib. bdg. 22.60 (978-0-7368-1552-9(X), Bridgestone Bks.) Capstone Pr., Inc.

—Sacagawea. 2002. (Photo-Illustrated Biographies Ser.). (Illus.). 24p. (J). (gr. 2-3). lib. bdg. 18.60 (978-0-7368-1112-5(5), Bridgestone Bks.) Capstone Pr., Inc.

Women Explorers. (J). pap. 4.95 (978-0-88388-203-0(5)) Bellerophon Bks.

Women in Profile, 12 bks. Incl. Athletes. Strudwick, Leslie. lib. bdg. (978-0-7787-0015-9(1)); Entrepreneurs. McLuskey, Krista. lib. bdg. (978-0-7787-0012-8(7)); Explorers. Hacker, Carlotta. lib. bdg. (978-0-7787-0004-3(6)); Humanitarians. Hacker, Carlotta. lib. bdg. (978-0-7787-0011-1(9)); Leaders in Medicine. Hunter, Shaun. lib. bdg. (978-0-7787-0010-4(0)); Musicians. Strudwick, Leslie. lib. bdg. (978-0-7787-0009-8(7)); Nobel Prize Winners. Hacker, Carlotta. lib. bdg. (978-0-7787-0007-4(0)); Political Leaders. Parker, Janice. lib. bdg. (978-0-7787-0008-1(9)); Rebels. Hacker, Carlotta. lib. bdg. (978-0-7787-0014-2(3)); Scientists. Hacker, Carlotta. lib. bdg. (978-0-7787-0006-7(2)); Visual & Performing Artists. Hunter, Shaun. lib. bdg. (978-0-7787-0013-5(5)); Writers. Hunter, Shaun. lib. bdg. (978-0-7787-0005-0(4)); 48p. (J). (gr. 4). 1998. (Illus.). 1999. (978-0-7787-0001-2(1)) Crabtree Publishing Co.

Women of Achievement. 2005. pap. 840.00 (978-0-7910-9160-9(0), Chelsea Hse.) Facts On File, Inc.

Wood, Richard & Barton-Wood, Sara. The Queen Mother: Grandmother of a Nation. 2000. (Famous Lives Ser.). (Illus.). 48p. (J). (gr. 3-7). lib. bdg. 27.12 (978-0-8172-5715-6(2)) Raintree.

Woodhouse, Jayne. Helen Keller. 2002. (Lives & Times Ser.). (Illus.). 24p. (J). (gr. k-3). pap. 6.50 (978-1-4034-0030-7(X), 91474) Heinemann Library.

—Helen Keller. 2002. (gr. k-3). lib. bdg. 12.95 (978-0-613-88095-4(1)) Tandem Library Bks.

Woog, Adam. Anne Frank. 2004. (Heroes & Villains Ser.). (Illus.). 112p. (J). 29.95 (978-1-59018-349-6(5), Lucent Bks.) Thomson Gale.

Wooldridge, Connie N. When Esther Morris Headed West: Women, Wyoming, & the Right to Vote. Rogers, Jacqueline, illus. 2001. 32p. (J). (gr. k-3). tchr. ed. 16.95 (978-0-8234-1597-7(X)) Holiday Hse., Inc.

Wooten, Sara McIntosh. Willa Cather: Writer of the Prairie. 1998. (People to Know Ser.). (Illus.). 128p. (YA). (gr. 6-12). lib. bdg. 20.95 (978-0-89490-980-1(0)) Enslow Pubs., Inc.

Wooten, Sarah M. Martha Stewart: America's Lifestyle Expert. 1998. (Library of Famous Women). (Illus.). 64p. (J). (gr. 4-8). 24.95 (978-1-56711-254-2(4), Blackbirch Pr., Inc.) Thomson Gale.

Woronoff, Kristen. Frida Kahlo: Mexican Painter. 2002. (Famous Women Juniors Ser.). (Illus.). 32p. (J). (gr. 3-5). 23.70 (978-1-56711-594-9(2), Blackbirch Pr., Inc.) Thomson Gale.

—Jane Goodall: Animal Scientist. 2002. (Famous Women Juniors Ser.). (Illus.). 32p. (J). (gr. 3-5). 23.70 (978-1-56711-585-7(3), Blackbirch Pr., Inc.) Thomson Gale.

—Leontyne Price: Singing Star. 2002. (Famous Women Juniors Ser.). (Illus.). 32p. (J). (gr. 3-5). 23.70 (978-1-56711-589-5(6), Blackbirch Pr., Inc.) Thomson Gale.

—Mother Teresa: Helper of the Poor. 2002. (Famous Women Juniors Ser.). (Illus.). 32p. (J). (gr. 3-5). 23.70 (978-1-56711-591-8(8), Blackbirch Pr., Inc.) Thomson Gale.

Yamaguchi, Kristi. Always Dream. 1998. 40p. 14.95 (978-0-87833-996-9(5)) Taylor Trade Publishing.

Yannuzzi, Della A. Mae Jemison: A Space Biography. 1998. (Countdown to Space Ser.). (Illus.). 48p. (YA). (gr. 4-10). lib. bdg. 23.93 (978-0-89490-813-2(8)) Enslow Pubs., Inc.

Yen Mah, Adeline. Chinese Cinderella: The True Story of an Unwanted Daughter. 2001. (gr. 7-12). lib. bdg. 14.15 (978-0-613-34012-0(4)) Tandem Library Bks.

Yolen, Jane. Tea with an Old Dragon: A Story of Sophia Smith, Founder of Smith College. Vachula, Monica, illus. 2003. 32p. (J). (gr. 4-6). 15.95 (978-1-56397-657-5(9)) Boyds Mills Pr.

Zach, Kim K. Hidden from History: The Lives of Eight American Women Scientists. 2002. (Avisson Young Adult Ser.). (Illus.). 144p. (Orig.). (J). (gr. 6-12). pap. 19.95 (978-1-888105-54-4(2)) Avisson Pr., Inc.

Zachry, Juanita Daniel. Katy O'Neil: She Found a Way or Made One. 2004. 224p. per. 14.95 (978-0-9749725-1-0(7)); bds. 24.95 (978-0-9749725-0-3(9)) LoneStar Abilene Publishing, LLC.

Zannos, Susan. Female Stars of Nutrition & Weight Control. 2000. (Legends of Health & Fitness Ser.). (Illus.). 96p. (gr. 6-10). lib. bdg. 25.70 (978-1-58415-015-2(7)) Mitchell Lane Pubs., Inc.

—Paula Abdul. 1998. (Real-Life Reader Biographies Ser.). (Illus.). 32p. (J). (gr. 4-7). lib. bdg. 15.95 (978-1-883845-74-2(2)) Mitchell Lane Pubs., Inc.

Zymet, Cathy Alder. Leann Rimes. 2000. (Illus.). 64p. (J). (ps-7). lib. bdg. 17.60 (978-0-613-17693-4(6)) Tandem Library Bks.

WOMEN—CLOTHING

see Clothing and Dress

WOMEN—DRESS

see Clothing and Dress; Costume

WOMEN—EDUCATION

Peterson, Virginia, et al, eds. Women: New Roles in Society. 3rd rev. ed. 1998. (Information Plus Compact Ser.). (Illus.). 84p. (YA). (gr. 6-9). pap. 22.00 (978-1-57302-083-1(4)) Thomson Gale.

Williams, Julie. A Smart Girl's Guide to Starting Middle School: Everything You Need to Know about Making the Grade, Staying Cool at a New School, & Juggling More Homework, More Teachers, & More Friends! Martini, Angela, illus. 2004. (Americangirl Library(R) Ser.). 96p. (J). 9.95 (978-1-58485-877-5(X)) American Girl Publishing, Inc.

WOMEN—EDUCATION—FICTION

Brazil, Angela. The Luckiest Girl in the School. 2006. pap. 13.99 (***978-1-4280-2027-6(6)***) IndyPublish.com.

—Luckiest Girl in the School. 2006. 20.99 (***978-1-4280-2006-1(3)***) IndyPublish.com.

WOMEN—EMPLOYMENT

Bozak, Kristin & Cohen, Judith Love. You Can Be a Woman Botanist. Katz, David Arthur, illus. 1999. 40p. (J). (gr. 3-6). pap. 7.00 (978-1-880599-31-0(7)) Cascade Pass, Inc.

Cohen, Judith Love & Ghez, Andrea M. You Can Be a Woman Astronomer. Katz, David Arthur, illus. 1998. 40p. (J). (gr. 1-6). 19.95 incl. cd-rom (978-1-880599-27-3(9)) Cascade Pass, Inc.

Cohen, Judith Love & Siegel, Margot. You Can Be a Woman Architect. Yañez, Juan, tr. Katz, David Arthur, illus. 1998. 40p. (J). (gr. k-6). 19.95 incl. cd-rom (978-1-880599-28-0(7)) Cascade Pass, Inc.

—You Can Be a Woman Architect. Katz, David Arthur, illus. rev. ed. 1999. 40p. (J). pap. 7.00 (978-1-880599-04-4(X)) Cascade Pass, Inc.

Colman, Penny. Rosie the Riveter: Women Working on the Home Front in World War II. 1998. (978-0-606-13026-4(8)) Tandem Library Bks.

—Rosie the Riveter: Women Working on the Homefront in World War II. 1998. (Illus.). 128p. (J). (gr. 5-9). pap. 10.99 (978-0-517-88567-3(0), Crown Books For Young Readers) Random Hse. Children's Bks.

Flanagan, Alice K. The Lowell Mill Girls. 2005. (We the People Ser.). (Illus.). 48p. (J). (gr. 4-6). (978-0-7565-1262-0(X), 1244102) Compass Point Bks.

Gourley, Catherine. Good Girl Work. 1999. (Single Titles Ser.: up). (Illus.). 96p. (gr. 7 up). lib. bdg. 26.90 (978-0-7613-0951-2(9), Millbrook Pr.) Lerner Publishing Group.

MacDonald, Fiona. Equal Opportunities. (World Issues Ser.). (Illus.). 57p. (J). lib. bdg. 28.50 (978-1-931983-30-3(5)) Chrysalis Education.

—Equal Opportunities. 2006. (Global Issues Ser.). 64p. (J). (gr. 4-12). pap. 12.95 (978-1-55285-744-1(1), Walrus Bks.) Whitecap Bks., Ltd. CAN. *Dist:* Firefly Bks., Ltd.

Petersen, Christine. Rosie the Riveter. 2005. (Cornerstones of Freedom Ser.). (Illus.). 48p. (J). 26.00 (978-0-516-23634-6(2), Children's Pr.) Scholastic Library Publishing.

Peterson, Virginia, et al, eds. Women: New Roles in Society. 3rd rev. ed. 1998. (Information Plus Compact Ser.). (Illus.). 84p. (YA). (gr. 6-9). pap. 22.00 (978-1-57302-083-1(4)) Thomson Gale.

Riley, Jocelyn. Work Talk. 2000. (Women in Nontraditional Careers Ser.: No. 10). 114p. (J). 45.00 (978-1-877933-95-0(3), 28002) Her Own Words.

Roberts, Robin. Careers for Women Who Love Sports. 2000. (Illus.). (J). (978-0-606-18281-2(0)) Tandem Library Bks.

Schwager, Tina & Schuerger, Michele. Cool Women, Hot Jobs... And How You Can Go for It, Too! 2004. (Illus.). 288p. (YA). (gr. 6 up). pap. 11.95 (978-1-57542-109-4(7)) Free Spirit Publishing, Inc.

WOMEN—EMPLOYMENT—FICTION

Bell, Lili. The Sea Maidens of Japan. Brammer, Erin McGonigle, illus. 2004. 28p. (J). (gr. k-4). reprint ed. (978-0-7567-7881-1(6)) DIANE Publishing Co.

—The Sea Maidens of Japan. Brammer, Erin McGonigle, illus. 2001. 32p. (J). (ps-3). 14.95 (978-0-8249-5426-0(2), Ideals Children's Bks.) Ideals Pubns.

Gray, Kes & Milgrim, David. My Mum Goes to Work. 2006. (Illus.). 32p. (J). (ps). 15.99 (978-0-340-88368-6(5), Hodder & Stoughton) Hodder General Publishing Division GBR. *Dist:* Trafalgar Square Publishing.

Howard, Ginger. A Basket of Bangles: How a Business Begins. Noll, Cheryl Kirk, illus. 2002. (Around the World Ser.). 32p. (gr. k-3). lib. bdg. 21.90 (978-0-7613-1902-3(6), Millbrook Pr.) Lerner Publishing Group.

Maury, Inez. My Mother the Mail Carrier - Mi Mama la Cartera. Alemany, Norah, tr. from SPA. McCrady, Lady, illus. 2004. (ENG & SPA.). 32p. (ps-4). pap. 7.95 (978-0-935312-23-2(4)) Feminist Pr. at The City Univ. of New York.

WOMEN—ENFRANCHISEMENT

see Women—Suffrage

WOMEN—FICTION

Alcott, Louisa May. Louisa May Alcott's Little Women at Christmas. Flint, Russ, illus. 1999. 48p. (J). (gr. 4-7). 14.95 (978-0-8249-4161-1(6), Candy Cane Pr.) Ideals Pubns.

Anderson, William. Little Woman. 32p. (J). (gr. 2-5). Date not set. pap. 5.99 (978-0-06-443574-1(1)); 2001. 15.95 (978-0-06-028402-2(1)); 2001. lib. bdg. 15.89 (978-0-06-028403-9(X)) HarperCollins Pubs.

Anonymous. Notable Women of Olden Time. 2006. 40.99 (***978-1-4280-2687-2(8)***); pap. 34.99 (***978-1-4280-2681-0(9)***) IndyPublish.com.

Arroyo, Madeline. Calie's Gift. Vavak, S. Dean, illus. 2003. 32p. (gr. 2-5). 16.95 (978-0-9740061-0-9(6)) Stairway Pubns.

Asai, Carrie. Book of the Wind. 2003. lib. bdg. 15.30 (978-0-613-73443-1(2)) Tandem Library Bks.

Austen, Jane. Pride & Prejudice. 1999. (YA). 11.95 (978-1-56137-767-1(8)) Novel Units, Inc.

—Pride & Prejudice. 2002. (gr. 7-12). lib. bdg. 16.45 (978-0-613-64095-4(0)) Tandem Library Bks.

—Pride & Prejudice: Penguin Readers Level 5. 1998. (Illus.). 80p. pap. 7.00 (978-0-14-081507-8(4)) Penguin Group (USA) Inc.

Aylesworth, Jim. Aunt Pitty Patty's Piggy. McClintock, Barbara, illus. 1999. 32p. (J). (ps-2). pap. 15.95 (978-0-590-89987-1(2)) Scholastic, Inc.

Bang, Betsy. Old Woman & the Red Pumpkin: Level 4, Green, 7 vols. Merriman, Rachel, illus. 2nd ed. 1999. (Reading Together Ser.). 32p. (J). pap. (978-0-7636-0857-6(2)) Candlewick Pr.

Bardham, Sudipta. Vinnie & Abe Lincoln. 2008. (J). 16.95 (978-0-8118-5133-6(8)) Chronicle Bks. LLC.

Bertola, Ann Marie, et al, contrib. by. Four in the Afternoon. 2003. 118p. pap. 11.99 (978-0-9743661-0-4(2)) Circle Pr.

Bibee, John. The Mystery of the Widow's Watch. 1998. (Home School Detectives Ser.: Vol. 8). 123p. (J). (gr. 3-7). mass mkt. 5.00 (978-0-8308-1918-8(5), 1918) InterVarsity Pr.

Boland, Janice. Los Cuervos de la Senora Murphy. Romo, Alberto, tr. Hartung, Susan Kathleen, illus. 1999. (Books for Young Learners).Tr. of Mrs. Murphy's Crows. (SPA.). 12p. (J). (gr. k-2). pap. 5.00 (978-1-57274-339-7(5), A2844) Owen, Richard C. Pubs., Inc.

Browning, Teresa Mason. Why I Kept My Past a Secret. 2003. (gr. 7-12). lib. bdg. 23.40 (978-0-613-78154-1(6)) Tandem Library Bks.

Chetin, Helen. Angel Island Prisoner 1922. Harvey, Catherine, tr. Lee, Jan, illus. 2002. (CHI.). 64p. (J). 8.95 (978-0-9667352-3-9(4)) Angel Island Assoc.

Ciencin, Scott, et al. Masters of Mayhem. 2005. (Illus.). 79p. (J). (***978-1-4156-3054-9(2)***) Disney Pr.

Cookson. Mrs. Flanagan's Trumpet. 2000. 189p. (J). 17.95 (978-0-385-40134-0(5)) Transworld Publishers Ltd. GBR. *Dist:* Trafalgar Square Publishing.

Cookson, Catherine. The Cultured Handmaiden. 2000. 319p. (J). mass mkt. 10.95 (978-0-552-12476-8(1), Corgi) Transworld Publishers Ltd. GBR. *Dist:* Trafalgar Square Publishing.

Corey, Shana. You Forgot Your Skirt, Amelia Bloomer! McLaren, Chesley, illus. unabr. ed. 2001. (J). (gr. k-3). 27.95 incl. audio (978-0-8045-6876-0(6), 6876) Spoken Arts, Inc.

Cowcher, Helen. Tigress. 2001. (Illus.). 40p. (YA). (BEN, ENG, URD, TUR & VIE.). 16.95 (978-1-84059-024-1(6)); (GRE, ENG, URD, TUR & VIE., 16.95 (978-1-84059-026-5(2)); (GUJ, ENG, URD, TUR & VIE., 16.95 (978-1-84059-027-2(0)); (TUR, ENG, URD, VIE & CHI., 16.95 (978-1-84059-028-9(9)); (URD, ENG, TUR, VIE & CHI., 16.95 (978-1-84059-029-6(7)) Milet Publishing.

Crook, Connie Brummel. Nellie's Victory. 2000. (gr. 7-12). lib. bdg. 14.10 (978-0-613-28980-1(3)) Tandem Library Bks.

Dadey, Debbie & Jones, Marcia Thornton. Mrs. Jeepers' Secret Cave. Gurney, John Steven, illus. 1998. (Adventures of the Bailey School Kids Super Special Ser.: No. 3). 128p. (J). (gr. 2-4). pap. 4.99 (978-0-590-11712-8(2), Scholastic Paperbacks) Scholastic, Inc.

Dolbeck, Andrew. Fever Jenny, Bk. 1. 2006. 120p. pap. 10.99 (978-1-59092-324-5(3)) Windstorm Creative.

Durkee, Noura. Yunus & the Whale. Durkee, Noura, illus. 1999. (Illus.). 28p. (J). (gr. 1-5). 16.00 (978-1-879402-60-7(2)) Tahrike Tarsile Quran, Inc.

Edwards, Jo. Go Figure. 2007. 288p. (YA). (gr. 9 up). pap. 8.99 (***978-1-4169-2492-0(2)***, Simon Pulse) Simon & Schuster Children's Publishing.

Ellen Tebbits. 2000. (J). 9.95 (978-1-56137-387-1(7)) Novel Units, Inc.

Finley, Martha. Elsie Dinsmore, Vol. 1. (Elsie Bks.: Bk. 1). 320p. (gr. 7-12). pap. 5.95 (978-1-58182-064-5(X)) Cumberland Hse. Publishing.

—Elsie's Girlhood, Vol. 3. (Elsie Bks.: Bk. 3). 320p. (gr. 7-12). pap. 5.95 (978-1-58182-066-9(6)) Cumberland Hse. Publishing.

—Elsie's Holidays at Roselands, Vol. 2. (Elsie Bks.: Bk. 2). 320p. (gr. 7-12). pap. 5.95 (978-1-58182-065-2(8)) Cumberland Hse. Publishing.

—Elsie's Widowhood, Vol. 1. (Elsie Bks.: Bk. 7). 320p. (gr. 7-12). pap. 5.95 (978-1-58182-070-6(4)) Cumberland Hse. Publishing.

—Elsie's Widowhood. 1998. (Elsie Bks.: Vol. 7). 229p. (J). (gr. 7-12). reprint ed. pap. 6.99 (978-1-888306-40-8(8), Full Quart Pr.) Holly Hall Pubns., Inc.

—Elsie's Womanhood, Vol. 4. (Elsie Bks.: Bk. 4). 320p. (gr. 7-12). pap. 5.95 (978-1-58182-067-6(4)) Cumberland Hse. Publishing.

—Grandmother Elsie, Vol. 8. (Elsie Bks.: Bk. 8). 320p. (gr. 7-12). pap. 5.95 (978-1-58182-071-3(2)) Cumberland Hse. Publishing.

Fire & Wind: Individual Title Six-Packs. (gr. 3 up). 35.00 (978-0-7635-9665-1(5)) Rigby Education.

Fowler, Earlene. Mariner's Compass. 2000. (gr. 7-12). lib. bdg. 15.30 (978-0-613-42752-4(1)) Tandem Library Bks.

Fraustino, Lisa Rowe, ed. Don't Cramp My Style. 2004. (Illus.). 304p. (J). 15.95 (978-0-689-85882-6(5)) Simon & Schuster Children's Publishing.

Froese, Deborah. Out of the Fire. 2001. (gr. 7-12). lib. bdg. 16.40 (978-0-613-60644-8(2)) Tandem Library Bks.

Fukushima, Haruka. Instant Teen: Just Add Nuts, 4 vols., Vol. 1. Yang, Yoohae, tr. 2004. (Illus.). 208p. (YA). pap. 9.99 (978-1-59532-146-6(2), Tokyopop Kids) TOKYOPOP, Inc.

Garden, Nancy. Nora & Liz. 2002. (gr. 7-12). lib. bdg. 22.20 (978-0-613-60499-4(7)) Tandem Library Bks.

Gisbert, Joan M. La Mansion de los Ablsmos. 1999. Tr. of Mansion of the Abyss. (SPA.). (978-0-606-17685-9(3)) Tandem Library Bks.

Golden, Arthur. Memoirs of a Geisha. 1999. (gr. 7-12). lib. bdg. 24.55 (978-0-613-35817-0(1)) Tandem Library Bks.

Greene, Janice. No Way to Run: Set 1. 2002. 32p. (YA). 2.95 (978-1-56254-411-9(X), SP 411X) Saddleback Educational Publishing.

Guttentag, Devora. Saving Soraya. 236p. (YA). 18.99 (978-1-56871-256-7(1)) Targum Pr., Inc.

Haddix, Margaret Peterson. Turnabout. 2007. 240p. (YA). mass mkt. 5.99 (978-1-4169-3653-4(X), Simon Pulse) Simon & Schuster Children's Publishing.

Hale, Stephanie. Revenge of the Homecoming Queen. 2007. 272p. (YA). (gr. 6 up). pap. 9.99 (***978-0-425-21615-6(2)***, Berkley Trade) Penguin Group (USA) Inc.

Hawthorne, Nathaniel. The Scarlet Letter. 1999. reprint ed. pap. 28.00 (978-1-4047-1352-9(2)) Classic Textbooks.

—The Scarlet Letter. 1999. (Saddleback Classics). (Illus.). (J). (978-0-606-21568-8(9)); (gr. 7-12). lib. bdg. 15.25 (978-0-613-33024-4(2)) Tandem Library Bks.

Hedderwick, Mairi. Katie Morag & the Wedding. 2005. (Illus.). 32p. (J). pap. 9.99 (978-0-09-946341-2(5), Red Fox) Random Hse. Children's Bks. GBR. *Dist:* Trafalgar Square Publishing.

Heitzmann, Kristen. Sweet Boundless. 2001. (gr. 5-8). lib. bdg. 22.25 (978-0-613-55670-5(4)) Tandem Library Bks.

Helen Keller 2: Leveled Books. 2001. (McGraw-Hill. Lectura Ser.). (ENG & SPA.). (gr. 5 up). (978-0-02-188274-8(6)) Macmillan/McGraw-Hill Schl. Div.

Hemon, Louis. Maria Chapdelaine. Kupesic, Rajka, illus. 2004. 40p. (J). (gr. 3-7). 15.95 (978-0-88776-697-8(8)) Tundra Bks., Inc./Livres Toundra, Inc. CAN. *Dist:* Random Hse., Inc.

Hoobler, Dorothy & Hoobler, Thomas. The Second Decade: Voyages. Hoffman, Robin, illus. 2000. (Century Kids Ser.). 160p. (gr. 5-8). lib. bdg. 22.90 (978-0-7613-1601-5(9), Twenty-First Century Bks.) Lerner Publishing Group.

Huff, Tanya. Valor's Choice. 2000. (SPA.). (gr. 7-12). lib. bdg. 15.30 (978-0-613-28123-2(3)) Tandem Library Bks.

Irwin, Hadley. The Lilith Summer. 2004. 128p. (gr. 4-7). pap. 8.95 (978-0-912670-52-2(5)) Feminist Pr. at The City Univ. of New York.

James, Henry. The Ambassadors. 312p. reprint ed. pap. 99.00 (978-1-4047-3431-9(7)) Classic Textbooks.

Jorda, Jordi Suris. La Chica de los Zapatos Verdes. 1998. (SPA.). (gr. 7-12). lib. bdg. 14.10 (978-0-613-80705-0(7)) Tandem Library Bks.

Keene, Carolyn. Dangerous Plays. 2006. (Nancy Drew Ser.: No. 16). 160p. (J). pap. 4.99 (978-1-4169-0605-6(3), Aladdin) Simon & Schuster Children's Publishing.

King-Smith, Dick. The Stray. unabr. ed. 2002. (J). pap. 24.95 incl. audio (978-0-7540-6201-1(5)) BBC Audiobooks America.

Komada, Yoshihiro, et al. Flesh for the Beast. Pannone, Frank, ed. Ohtsuka, Tommy et al, illus. 2004. 272p. (YA). pap. 9.99 (978-1-58655-556-6(1), SSNOV-0419, Shriek Show) Media Blasters, Inc.

Koontz, Dean. False Memory. 2000. (gr. 7-12). lib. bdg. 16.45 (978-0-613-33586-7(4)) Tandem Library Bks.

—Intensity. 2000. (gr. 7-12). lib. bdg. 16.45 (978-0-613-39476-5(3)) Tandem Library Bks.

Lasky, Kathryn. A Time for Courage: The Suffragette Diary of Kathleen Bowen, Washington D. C., 1917. 2002. (Dear America Ser.). (Illus.). 176p. (J). (gr. 4-9). pap. 10.95 (978-0-590-51141-4(6)) Scholastic, Inc.

Leather, Sue. Dead Cold Book/Audio CD Pack: Level 2 Elementary/Lower Intermediate. 2007. (Cambridge English Readers Ser.). (Illus.). 48p. pap. 11.00 incl. audio compact disk (978-0-521-69392-9(6)) Cambridge Univ. Pr.

Lindgren, Astrid. Pippi Longstocking. Nunally, Tina, tr. from SWE. 2007. 208p. (J). (gr. k). 25.00 (***978-0-670-06276-8(6)***, Viking Juvenile) Penguin Group (USA) Inc.

Literature Connections English: Picture Bride. 2004. (gr. 6-12). (978-0-395-77540-0(X), 2-80109) McDougal Littell Inc.

MacDonald, Margaret Read. The Old Woman & Her Pig: An Appalachian Folktale. Kanzler, John, illus. 2001. 32p. (J). (ps-1). lib. bdg. 17.89 (978-0-06-028090-1(5)) HarperCollins Pubs.

Maltby Jr., Richard. Miss Potter. 2006. 196p. (J). pap. 7.99 (978-0-7232-5899-5(6), Warne) Penguin Group (USA) Inc.

Man-Kong, Mary. Fairytopia: A Storybook. 2005. (Illus.). 16p. (J). (ps-2). pap. 3.99 (978-0-375-83318-2(8), Golden Bks.) Random Hse. Children's Bks.

—High Fashion: Cool & Casual, No. 2. 2007. (Illus.). 32p. (J). (ps-2). 4.99 (978-0-375-83548-3(2), Golden Bks.) Random Hse. Children's Bks.

—High Fashion Glam & Glitz, No. 1. 2007. (Illus.). 32p. (J). (ps-2). 4.99 (978-0-375-83547-6(4), Golden Bks.) Random Hse. Children's Bks.

Manning, Sarra. French Kiss. 2006. 224p. (YA). (gr. 9). pap. 6.99 (978-0-14-240632-8(5), Puffin) Penguin Group (USA) Inc.

Marillier, Juliet. Cybele's Secret. 2008. 432p. (YA). (gr. 7). lib. bdg. 20.99 (***978-0-375-93365-3(4)***, Knopf Bks. for Young Readers) Random Hse. Children's Bks.

Marlo's Rainbow Pony. 2004. Tr. of Marlo'w Rainbow Pony. (Illus.). 12p. (J). 5.95 net. (978-0-9728871-0-6(5)) Rainbow Pony Publishing.

Martin, C. L. G. Tres Mujeres Valientes. Elwell, Peter, illus. 2001. (SPA.). 32p. (J). (gr. k-2). 12.95 (978-84-241-3340-5(4) , EV4939) Everest de Ediciones y Distribucion, S.L. ESP. *Dist:* Lectorum Pubns., Inc.

Martinez, Alejandro Cruz. La Mujer que Brillaba Aun Mas Que el Sol. ed. 2004. (SPA.). (J). (gr. k-3). spiral bd. (978-0-616-07278-3(3)) Canadian National Institute for the Blind/Institut National Canadien pour les Aveugles.

Mayer, Mercer. The Wizard Comes to Town. 2003. (Mercer Mayer Picture Bks.). (Illus.). 48p. (J). pap. 5.95 (978-1-57768-387-2(0)) School Specialty Publishing.

McDonald, Brix. Riding on the Wind. 1998. 243p. (YA). (gr. 5-10). pap. 5.95 (978-0-9661306-0-7(X)) Avenue Publishing.

McDonald, Janet. Harlem Hustle. 2006. 192p. (YA). 16.00 (978-0-374-37184-5(9) , Farrar, Straus & Giroux (BYR)) Farrar, Straus & Giroux.

McKenzie, Nancy. Guinevere's Gift. 2008. 336p. (J). (gr. 5-9). 15.99 (***978-0-375-84345-7(0)*** , Knopf Bks. for Young Readers) Random Hse. Children's Bks.

McOmber, Rachel B., ed. McOmber Phonics Storybooks: Miss Vie. rev. ed. (Illus.). (J). (978-0-944991-48-0(3)) Swift Learning Resources.

Merriam, Eve. The Wise Woman & Her Secret. 1999. (978-0-606-16243-2(7)) Tandem Library Bks.

Moore, Lonnie W. The Beautiful Lady: Without a Name. Moore, Iola, illus. 1999. (J). pap. 14.95 (978-1-930002-12-8(2)) I & L Publishing.

Mora, Pat. Dona Flor: A Tall Tale about a Giant Lady with a Great Big Heart. Colon, Raul, illus. 2005. 40p. (J). (ps-3). lib. bdg. 17.99 (978-0-375-92337-1(3) , Knopf Bks. for Young Readers) Random Hse. Children's Bks.

—Dona Flor: A Tall Tale about a Giant Woman with a Great Big Heart. Colon, Raul, illus. 2005. 40p. (J). (ps-3). 15.95 (978-0-375-82337-4(9) , Knopf Bks. for Young Readers) Random Hse. Children's Bks.

Nanami, Shingo & Tezuka, Kaname. Kamui, Vol. 7. Seto, Dietrich & Yamashita, Shizuki, eds. Yamashita, Satsuki, tr. O'Leary, Keiran & McDougall, Chris, illus. 2007. (Kamui Ser.). 224p. pap. 9.99 (***978-1-59741-054-0(3)***) Broccoli International USA, Inc.

Nimh, Sonia & Shaw, Hannah. Ghaddar the ghould & other palestinian Tales. 2008. (Illus.). 96p. (J). 14.95 (***978-1-84507-771-6(7)***) Lincoln, Frances Ltd. GBR. *Dist:* Perseus Distribution.

O'Brien, Robert C. La Senora Frisby y las Ratas de NIMH. 2001. (SPA.). (YA). (gr. 5-8). pap., wbk. ed. 7.96 net. (978-1-56137-551-6(9) , NU6108) Novel Units, Inc.

—La Senora Frisby y las Ratas de NIMH. (Barco de Vapor). (SPA., Illus.). 200p. (J). (gr. 4-7). 6.36 (978-84-348-1601-5(6) , SM2855) SM Ediciones ESP. *Dist:* Lectorum Pubns., Inc.

Palmer, Adam. Mooch. 2006. 272p. pap. 12.99 (978-1-60006-047-2(1) , Th1nk Bks.) NavPress Publishing Group.

Parker, Gary. Highland Hopes. 2001. (gr. 5-8). lib. bdg. 22.25 (978-0-613-55605-7(4)) Tandem Library Bks.

Pielle, Sue. T'aal: The One Who Takes Bad Children. Guzek, Greta, illus. unabr. ed. 1998. 28p. (J). (978-1-55017-180-8(1)) Harbour Publishing Co., Ltd.

Polacco, Patricia. Mrs. Katz & Tush. Polacco, Patricia, illus. 2002. (Illus.). (J). 14.79 (978-0-7587-3191-3(4)) Book Wholesalers, Inc.

Pride & Prejudice. 2002. (Illus.). (YA). 48p. stu. ed., per. 17.95 (978-1-56254-530-7(2) , SP5302); 80p. per. 6.95 (978-1-56254-529-1(9) , SP5299) Saddleback Educational Publishing.

Rigby Education Staff. Birdwoman Interview. (Sails Literacy Ser.). (Illus.). 16p. (gr. 2-3). 27.00 (978-0-7635-9953-9(0) , 699530C99) Rigby Education.

Robichaud, Janeen. They Killed Me. 2002. 108p. (YA). pap. 9.95 (978-0-595-26143-7(4) , Writers Club Pr.) iUniverse, Inc.

Rueda, Claudia, illus. I Know an Old Lady Who Swallowed a Fly. 2005. 14p. (J). 12.95 (978-1-58117-267-6(2) , Intervisual/Piggy Toes) Dalmatian Pr.

Rylant, Cynthia. The Old Woman Who Named Things. 2002. (Illus.). (J). 14.21 (978-0-7587-3314-6(3)) Book Wholesalers, Inc.

—The Old Woman Who Named Things. Brown, Kathryn, illus. 2000. 32p. (J). (ps-3). pap. 7.00 (978-0-15-202102-3(7) , Harcourt Paperbacks) Harcourt Children's Bks.

—The Old Woman Who Named Things. 2000. (978-0-606-20331-9(1)); (J). (978-0-606-20168-1(8)); lib. bdg. 14.15 (978-0-613-30073-5(4)) Tandem Library Bks.

Sage, Elizabeth. Finding Home. 2002. (Five Star First Edition Women's Fiction Ser.). 225p. (J). 26.95 (978-0-7862-4111-8(X) , Five Star) Thomson Gale.

Saltzberg, Barney. Mrs. Morgan's Lawn. 1998. 32p. 4.95 (978-0-7868-1365-0(2)) Hyperion Paperbacks for Children.

Sanroman, Susana. Senora Reganona: A Mexican Bedtime Story. Domi, illus. 1998. (SPA.). 24p. (J). (ps-k). 14.95 (978-0-88899-320-5(X)) Groundwood Bks. CAN. *Dist:* Perseus Distribution.

Santolaya Ruiz-Clavijo, Adoracion. Las Damas de la Luz. 2000. Tr. of Ladies of the Light. (SPA., Illus.). (J). (ps-2). 14.95 (978-84-233-3208-3(X)) Ediciones Destino ESP. *Dist:* Baker & Taylor Bks.

Schwabach, Karen. The Hope Chest. 2008. 288p. (J). (gr. 4-7). 16.99 (***978-0-375-84095-1(8)***); lib. bdg. 19.99 (***978-0-375-94095-8(2)***) Random Hse., Inc.

Sharp, N. L. Effie's Image. Rohner, Dorothia, illus. 2006. 32p. (J). 17.95 (978-0-9759829-5-2(8)) Prairieland Pr.

Siegel, R. V. The Son of Olympia. 2005. 20p. 7.43 (978-1-4116-2888-5(8)) Lulu.com.

Simpson, Catherine. Red Earth Woman. 2002. 128p. (YA). (gr. 7 up). pap. (978-1-894294-44-7(0)) Creative Bk. Publishing.

Smith, Alexander McCall. Tears of the Giraffe. 2002. (No. 1 Ladies' Detective Agency Ser.: Bk. 2). (gr. 7-12). lib. bdg. 21.05 (978-0-613-64790-8(4)) Tandem Library Bks.

Steptoe, John L. Las Bellas Hijas de Mufaro. Kohen, Clarita, tr. Steptoe, John L., illus. unabr. ed. 1998. Tr. of Mufaro's Beautiful Daughters: An African Tale. (SPA., Illus.). (J). (gr. k-3). pap. 16.95 incl. audio (978-0-87499-461-2(6)) BBC Audiobooks America.

—Las Bellas Hijas de Mufaro. Kohen, Clarita, tr. Steptoe, John L., illus. 1998. Tr. of Mufaro's Beautiful Daughters: An African Tale. (SPA., Illus.). pap., tchr. ed. 41.95 incl. audio (978-0-87499-463-6(2)); (J). 24.95 incl. audio (978-0-87499-462-9(4)) Live Oak Media.

Thaler, Mike. The Cafeteria Lady from the Black Lagoon. Lee, Jared D., illus. 1998. (Black Lagoon Ser.). (J). (ps-3). 10.30 (978-0-606-13234-3(1)) Tandem Library Bks.

Town, Florida Ann. With a Silent Companion. 1999. (gr. 7-12). lib. bdg. 16.40 (978-0-613-89150-9(3)) Tandem Library Bks.

Traditional FolkSongs Staff. I Know an Old Lady Who Swallowed a Fly. Gulbis, Stephen, illus. 2001. 20p. (J). (ps-1). pap. 14.95 (978-0-439-24328-5(9) , Cartwheel Bks.) Scholastic, Inc.

Turner, Morrie. Super Sistahs: Featuring the Accomplishments of African-American Women. 2005. (Illus.). 112p. pap. 14.95 (978-0-9656739-5-2(2)) BYE Publishing Services.

Tytler, Sarah. Girlhood & Womanhood the Story of Some. 2007. 43.99 (***978-1-4280-5160-7(0)***); pap. 36.99 (***978-1-4280-5161-4(9)***) IndyPublish.com.

Vanderhoop, Jannette, illus. The Legend of Katama: The Creation Story of Dolphins, A Wampanoag Legend of Martha's Vineyard. 2004. 80p. (J). lib. bdg. 18.95 (978-0-9755605-0-1(6)) Island Moon Pr.

Voigt, Cynthia. Elske: A Novel of the Kingdom. Vermeer, Jan, illus. 2003. (Kingdom Ser.). 320p. (YA). mass mkt. 5.99 (978-0-689-86438-4(8) , Simon Pulse) Simon & Schuster Children's Publishing.

—Elske: A Novel of the Kingdom. 2001. (Kingdom Ser.). (gr. 7-12). lib. bdg. 18.80 (978-0-613-73327-4(4)) Tandem Library Bks.

Westcott, Nadine Bernard & Hoberman, Mary Ann. The Lady with the Alligator Purse, 1. 1998. (Illus.). 24p. (J). (ps-17). bds. 6.99 (978-0-316-93074-1(1)) Little Brown & Co.

Wilder, Alice. Mrs. Pepper's Special Day. 2001. (Illus.). 8p. (J). mass mkt. (978-0-689-85015-8(8) , Simon Spotlight/Nickelodeon) Simon & Schuster Children's Publishing.

Woolf, Paula. Old Ladies with Brooms Aren't Always Witches. 1998. 154p. (YA). (gr. 4-6). 9.99 (978-0-88092-395-8(4) , 3954) Royal Fireworks Publishing Co.

Woolf, Virginia. The Voyage Out. 2001. (gr. 7-12). lib. bdg. 21.05 (978-0-613-50140-8(3)) Tandem Library Bks.

Zeinert, Karen. To Touch the Stars: A Story of World War II. 2004. (Jamestown's American Portraits Ser.). (Illus.). 136p. (J). (gr. 5-7). pap. 4.95 (978-0-7696-3442-5(7) , Waterbird Bks.) School Specialty Publishing.

WOMEN—HISTORY

Alter, Judy. Great Women of the Old West. 2001. (We the People Ser.). (Illus.). 48p. (J). (gr. 4 up). lib. bdg. 22.60 (978-0-7565-0099-3(0)) Compass Point Bks.

Bolden, Tonya, ed. 33 Things Every Girl Should Know about Women's History: From Suffragettes to Skirt Lengths to the E.R.A. 2002. (Illus.). 240p. (YA). (gr. 7 up). pap. 12.95 (978-0-375-81122-7(2) , Crown Books For Young Readers) Random Hse. Children's Bks.

Carlson, Dale B. & Carlson, Hannah. Girls Are Equal Too: The Teenage Girls How-to-Survive Book. Nicklaus, Carol, illus. 2nd rev. ed. 2000. (Psychology for Teenagers Ser.: Vol. 1). 231p. (gr. 5-12). pap. 14.95 (978-1-884158-18-6(8)) Bick Publishing Hse.

Currie, Stephen. Women of the Civil War. 2002. (Women in History Ser.). (Illus.). 112p. (J). 32.45 (978-1-59018-170-6(0) , Lucent Bks.) Thomson Gale.

Eastwood, Kay Women & Girls in the Middle Ages. 2003. (Medieval World Ser.). (Illus.). 32p. (J). (gr. 5). (978-0-7787-1346-3(6)); pap. (978-0-7787-1378-4(4)) Crabtree Publishing Co.

Furbee, Mary Rodd. Outrageous Women of Civil War Times. 2003. (gr. 5-8). lib. bdg. 22.20 (978-0-613-81400-3(2)) Tandem Library Bks.

—Outrageous Women of Civil War Times. 2003. (Outrageous Women Ser.). (Illus.). 124p. pap. 12.95 (978-0-471-22926-1(1) , Jossey-Bass) Wiley, John & Sons, Inc.

Grolier Educational Staff, ed. , 10 vols. 1998. (Illus.). (J). lib. bdg. (978-0-7172-9255-4(X)); lib. bdg. (978-0-7172-9256-1(8)); lib. bdg. (978-0-7172-9257-8(6)); lib. bdg. (978-0-7172-9258-5(4)); lib. bdg. (978-0-7172-9259-2(2)); lib. bdg. (978-0-7172-9260-8(6)); lib. bdg. (978-0-7172-9261-5(4)); lib. bdg. (978-0-7172-9262-2(2)); lib. bdg. (978-0-7172-9263-9(0)); lib. bdg. (978-0-7172-9264-6(9)) Scholastic Library Publishing. (Grolier).

—Illustrated History of Women, 10 vols. Incl. lib. bdg. (978-0-7172-9255-4(X)); lib. bdg. (978-0-7172-9256-1(8)); lib. bdg. (978-0-7172-9257-8(6)); lib. bdg. (978-0-7172-9258-5(4)); lib. bdg. (978-0-7172-9259-2(2)); lib. bdg. (978-0-7172-9260-8(6)); lib. bdg. (978-0-7172-9261-5(4)); lib. bdg. (978-0-7172-9262-2(2)); lib. bdg. (978-0-7172-9263-9(0)); lib. bdg. (978-0-7172-9264-6(9)); (J). 1998. (Illus.). 1200p. 1999. Set lib. bdg. 305.00 (978-0-7172-7497-0(7) , Grolier) Scholastic Library Publishing.

Harness, Cheryl. Remember the Ladies: 100 Great American Women. Harness, Cheryl, illus. 2001. (Illus.). 64p. (J). (gr. 3 up). 16.99 (978-0-688-17017-2(X)) HarperCollins Pubs.

Head, Judith. America's Daughters: 400 Years of American Women. 1999. 130p. (J). (gr. 4 up). pap. 16.95 (978-0-9622036-8-8(8)) Perspective Publishing, Inc.

—America's Daughters: 400 Years of American Women. 1999. (Illus.). 130p. (J). (ps-7). per. 26.85 (978-0-613-90517-6(2)) Tandem Library Bks.

Kalman, Bobbie. Colonial Women. (Colonial People Ser.). (Illus.). 32p. (J). (gr. 3). 2003. (978-0-7787-0749-3(0)); 2002. pap. (978-0-7787-0795-0(4)) Crabtree Publishing Co.

—Colonial Women. 2003. (ps-2). lib. bdg. 16.40 (978-0-613-52823-8(9)) Tandem Library Bks.

Keating, Susan K. Women of the West. 2002. (History of the Old West Ser.). (Illus.). 64p. (YA). (gr. 5 up). lib. bdg. (978-1-59084-069-6(0)) Mason Crest Pubs.

Leon, Vicki. Outrageous Women of the Middle Ages. 1998. (Outrageous Women Ser.: Vol. 2). (Illus.). 128p. (gr. 4-7). pap. 12.95 (978-0-471-17004-4(6) , Wiley) Wiley, John & Sons, Inc.

Libal, Autumn. Women in the World of Russia. 2005. (Women's Issues, Global Trends Ser.). (Illus.). 112p. (J). lib. bdg. (978-1-59084-866-1(7)) Mason Crest Pubs.

Lilly, Melinda. Princess. 2002. (Illus.). 32p. (J). lib. bdg. 26.60 (978-1-58952-231-2(1)) Rourke Publishing, LLC.

Middleton, Haydn. Ancient Greek Women. 2002. (People in the Past Ser.). (Illus.). 48p. (J). (gr. 4-6). lib. bdg. 27.07 (978-1-58810-637-7(3)) Heinemann Library.

Middleton, Haydn & Tames, Richard. Ancient Greek Women. 2002. (People in the Past Ser.). 64p. (J). (gr. 4-7). pap. 8.50 (978-1-4034-0135-9(7) , 91640) Heinemann Library.

Nardo, Don. Women of Ancient Rome. 2002. (Women in History Ser.). (Illus.). 112p. (J). 27.45 (978-1-59018-169-0(7) , Lucent Bks.) Thomson Gale.

Plowden, Martha Ward. Famous Firsts of Black Women. Jones, Ronald, illus. 2nd ed. 2002. 176p. (J). (gr. 5-9). pap. 18.95 (978-1-56554-197-9(9)) Pelican Publishing Co., Inc.

Ross, Mandy. The Changing Role of Women. 2002. (20th-Century Perspectives Ser.). (Illus.). 48p. (J). (gr. 5-7). lib. bdg. 27.07 (978-1-58810-660-5(8)) Heinemann Library.

—Changing Role of Women. 2002. (gr. 5-8). lib. bdg. 16.40 (978-0-613-58200-1(4)) Tandem Library Bks.

—The Changing Role of Women, Set 2. 2002. (20th Century Perspectives Ser.). (Illus.). 48p. (J). (gr. 5-7). pap. 7.95 (978-1-58810-920-0(8) , 91511) Heinemann Library.

Sharp, Anne Wallace. Women of Ancient Egypt. 2005. (Women in History Ser.). (Illus.). 112p. (YA). (gr. 7-10). lib. bdg. 32.45 (978-1-59018-361-8(4) , Lucent Bks.) Thomson Gale.

Sigerman, Harriet. Laborers for Liberty Vol. 6: American Women 1865-1890. 1998. (Young Oxford History of Women in the United States Ser.). (Illus.). 144p. (YA). reprint ed. pap. 12.95 (978-0-19-512404-0(9)) Oxford Univ. Pr., Inc.

Simpson, Kathleen. Women in the Renaissance. 2006. (Navigators Ser.). (J). pap. 44.00 (***978-1-4108-6266-2(6)***) Benchmark Education Co.

Swisher, Clarice. Women of Victorian England. 2004. (Illus.). 112p. (YA). (gr. 7-12). lib. bdg. 32.45 (978-1-59018-571-1(4) , Lucent Bks.) Thomson Gale.

Thomson, Melissa & Dean, Ruth. Women of the Renaissance. 2004. (Illus.). 128p. (YA). (gr. 7-10). lib. bdg. 32.45 (978-1-59018-473-8(4) , Lucent Bks.) Thomson Gale.

The Trail West. 2004. (Illus.). lib. bdg. 7.95 (978-0-8225-4283-4(8)) Lerner Publishing Group.

Women in the Ancient Near East: Stories & Primary Sources from the Sumerians through the Early Israelites. l.t. ed. 1999. 94p. (YA). spiral bd. 16.95 net. (978-1-890380-07-6(5)) Women in World History Curriculum.

WOMEN—OCCUPATIONS

see Women—Employment

WOMEN—SUFFRAGE

see also Suffragists

Bausum, Ann. With Courage & Cloth: Winning the Fight for a Woman's Right to Vote. 2004. (Illus.). 112p. (J). (gr. 5). 21.95 (978-0-7922-7647-0(7) , National Geographic Children's Bks.) National Geographic Society.

Bjornlund, Lydia D. Women of the Suffrage Movement. 2003. (Women in History Ser.). (Illus.). 112p. (J). 32.45 (978-1-59018-173-7(5) , Lucent Bks.) Thomson Gale.

Bozonelis, Helen Koutras. A Look at the Nineteenth Amendment: Women Win the Right to Vote. 2008. (J). (***978-1-59845-067-5(0)***) Enslow Pubs., Inc.

Burgan, Michael. The 19th Amendment. 2005. (We the People Ser.). (Illus.). 48p. (J). (gr. 4-6). 23.93 (978-0-7565-1260-6(3) , 1244104) Compass Point Bks.

Donlan, Leni. Working for Change: The Struggle for Women's Rights. 2007. (J). (***978-1-4109-2700-2(8)***); pap. (***978-1-4109-2711-8(3)***) Steck-Vaughn.

Fritz, Jean. You Want Women to Vote, Lizzie Stanton? DiSalvo-Ryan, DyAnne, illus. 1999. 96p. (J). (gr. 3-7). pap. 6.99 (978-0-698-11764-8(6) , Putnam Juvenile) Penguin Group (USA) Inc.

—You Want Women to Vote, Lizzie Stanton? 1999. (978-0-606-16848-9(6)); (gr. 3-6). lib. bdg. 15.30 (978-0-613-17893-8(9)) Tandem Library Bks.

Harvey, Miles. Women's Voting Rights. 1998. (Cornerstones of Freedom Ser.). (Illus.). 32p. (J). (gr. 4-6). pap. 5.95 (978-0-516-26288-8(2) , Children's Pr.) Scholastic Library Publishing.

Hossell, Karen Price. The Nineteenth Amendment: Women Get the Vote. 2003. (Point of Impact Ser.). (Illus.). 32p. (J). (gr. 5-7). pap. 7.50 (978-1-4034-0535-7(2)) Heinemann Library.

Keller, Kristin Thoennes. The Women Suffrage Movement, 1848-1920. 2003. (Let Freedom Ring Ser.). (Illus.). 48p. (J). (gr. 3-4). lib. bdg. 22.60 (978-0-7368-1562-8(7) , Bridgestone Bks.) Capstone Pr., Inc.

Kops, Deborah. The Women Suffrage Movement. 2003. (People at the Center of Ser.). (Illus.). 48p. (J). 24.95 (978-1-56711-772-1(4) , Blackbirch Pr., Inc.) Thomson Gale.

Landau, Elaine. Women's Right to Vote. (Cornerstones of Freedomtrade;, Second Ser.). 48p. (J). 2007. (gr. 4-6). pap. 5.95 (***978-0-531-18833-0(7)***); 2005. (Illus.). 26.00 (978-0-516-23639-1(3)) Scholastic Library Publishing. (Children's Pr.).

Lasky, Kathryn. A Time for Courage: The Suffragette Diary of Kathleen Bowen, Washington D. C., 1917. 2002. (Dear America Ser.). (Illus.). 176p. (J). (gr. 4-9). pap. 10.95 (978-0-590-51141-4(6)) Scholastic, Inc.

Loos, Pamela. Elizabeth Cady Stanton: Woman Suffragist. 2000. (Women of Achievement Ser.). (Illus.). 112p. (J). (gr. 4-7). 30.00 (978-0-7910-5293-8(1) , Chelsea Hse.) Facts On File, Inc.

MacBain-Stephens, Jennifer. Women's Suffrage: Giving the Right to Vote to All Americans. 2004. (Progressive Movement, 1900-1920 Ser.). (Illus.). 32p. (J). lib. bdg. (978-1-4042-0199-6(8)) Rosen Publishing Group, Inc., The.

McCully, Emily Arnold. The Ballot Box Battle. 1998. (Dragonfly Books Ser.). (Illus.). 32p. (J). (gr. k-3). pap. 6.99 (978-0-679-89312-7(1) , Dragonfly Bks.) Random Hse. Children's Bks.

Mosley, Shelley & Charles, John. The Suffragists in Literature for Youth: The Fight for the Vote. 2006. (Literature for Youth Ser.: Vol. 10). 336p. (J). pap. 45.00 (978-0-8108-5372-0(8)) Scarecrow Pr., Inc.

Nash, Carol Rust. The Fight for Women's Right to Vote in American History. 1998. (In American History Ser.). (Illus.). 128p. (YA). (gr. 5-12). lib. bdg. 26.60 (978-0-89490-986-3(X)) Enslow Pubs., Inc.

Rau, Dana Meachen. Great Women of the Suffrage Movement. 2005. (We the People Ser.). (Illus.). 48p. (J). (gr. 4-6). (978-0-7565-1270-5(0)) Compass Point Bks.

Raum, Elizabeth. Alice Paul. 2004. (American Lives (Heinemann Library (Firm))). (Illus.). 32p. (J). pap. 7.50 (978-1-4034-5703-5(4)); lib. bdg. (978-1-4034-4996-2(1)) Heinemann Library.

Salisbury, Cynthia. Elizabeth Cady Stanton: Leader of the Fight for Women's Rights. 2002. (Historical American Biographies Ser.). (Illus.). 128p. (YA). (gr. 6-9). lib. bdg. 26.60 (978-0-7660-1616-3(1)) Enslow Pubs., Inc.

Sigerman, Harriet. Elizabeth Cady Stanton: The Right Is Ours. 2001. (Oxford Portraits Ser.). (Illus.). 144p. (YA). (gr. 8 up). suppl. ed. 28.00 (978-0-19-511969-5(X)) Oxford Univ. Pr., Inc.

Stalcup, Brenda. Women's Suffrage. 2000. (Turning Points in World History Ser.). (Illus.). 256p. (YA). (gr. 9-12). pap. 21.20 (978-0-7377-0325-2(3)); lib. bdg. 32.45 (978-0-7377-0326-9(1)) Thomson Gale. (Greenhaven Pr., Inc.).

Weidt, Maryann N. Fighting for Equal Rights: A Story about Susan B. Anthony. Sartor, Amanda, tr. Sartor, Amanda, illus. 2004. (Creative Minds Biography Ser.). 64p. (J). 22.60 (978-1-57505-181-9(8) , Carolrhoda Bks.) Lerner Publishing Group.

White, Linda Arms. I Could Do That! Esther Morris Gets Women the Vote. Carpenter, Nancy, illus. 2005. 40p. (J). (ps-7). 16.00 (978-0-374-33527-4(3) , Farrar, Straus & Giroux (BYR)) Farrar, Straus & Giroux.

—I Could Do That! Esther Morris Gets Women the Vote. unabr. ed. 2006. (J). (gr. 2-4). 24.95 incl. audio (***978-0-439-90576-3(1)*** , WHRA692); 29.95 incl. audio compact disk (***978-0-439-90582-4(6)*** , WHCD692) Weston Woods Studios, Inc.

Winter, Barbara. Fight for Rights. Kostic, Dimitri, illus. 2007. 48p. (J). lib. bdg. 23.08 (***978-1-4242-1636-9(2)***) Fitzgerald Bks.

Women's Suffrage. 2003. (Eye on History Ser.). 32p. (gr. 5-12). 5.99 (978-1-56822-629-3(2) , IF2669) School Specialty Publishing.

WOMEN—UNITED STATES

see also Presidents—United States—Spouses

Altgeld, John P. & Jones, Mother. Autobiography of Mother Jones. 2003. (Labor Classics Ser.). (Illus.). 304p. (Orig.). reprint ed. 25.00 (978-0-88286-167-8(0)) Kerr, Charles H. Publishing Co.

Barbour, Scott, et al, eds. Violence Against Women. 1998. (Current Controversies Ser.). (Illus.). 224p. (YA). (gr. 7-12). pap. 21.20 (978-0-7377-0014-5(9)); (gr. 9-12). lib. bdg. 32.45 (978-0-7377-0015-2(7)) Thomson Gale. (Greenhaven Pr., Inc.).

Bausum, Ann. With Courage & Cloth: Winning the Fight for a Woman's Right to Vote. 2004. (Illus.). 112p. (J). (gr. 5). 21.95 (978-0-7922-7647-0(7) , National Geographic Children's Bks.) National Geographic Society.

Bjornlund, Lydia D. Women in Colonial America. 2003. (Illus.). 112p. (J). 32.45 (978-1-59018-470-7(X) , Lucent Bks.) Thomson Gale.

Clifford, Mary Louise & Clifford, J. Candace. Mind the Light, Katie: The History of Thirty-Three Female Lighthouse Keepers. 2006. (YA). per. 12.95 (978-0-9636412-7-4(1)) Cypress Communications.

Donlan, Leni. Working for Change: The Struggle for Women's Rights. 2007. (J). (***978-1-4109-2700-2(8)***); pap. (***978-1-4109-2711-8(3)***) Steck-Vaughn.

Felder, Deborah G. 100 American Women Who Shaped American History. 2005. (Illus.). 112p. (J). (gr. 4-7). per. 15.90 (978-0-606-33775-5(X)) Tandem Library Bks.

Florida's Women's Heritage Trail. (Heritage Trail Ser.). (J). (ps-7). pap. 2.40 (978-1-889030-19-7(8)) Florida Div. of Historical Resources.

Friedman, Michael & Friedman, Brett. Settlement Houses: Improving the Social Welfare of America's Immigrants. 2006. (Progressive Movement, 1900-1920—Efforts to Reform America's New Industrial Society Ser.). (Illus.). 32p. (J). (978-1-4042-0859-9(3)) Rosen Publishing Group, Inc., The.

Gourley, Catherine. Welcome to Samantha's World, 1904: Growing up in America's New Century. 1999. (American Girls Collection). (Illus.). 64p. (J). (gr. 2 up). 14.95 (978-1-56247-772-1(2)) American Girl Publishing, Inc.

Jackson, Waukesha. Where Would the World Be Without Women: Stories from the 9th Ward. 2005. (Neighborhood Story Project Ser.). (Illus.). 88p. (J). pap. (978-1-933368-32-0(2)) Counterpoint.

Jerome, Janice. A Dust of Flour. . . Beyond the Family Tree. 2003. spiral bd. 20.00 (978-0-9729741-0-3(5)) Jan & San.

Jones, Mary H. & Kerr, Charles H. Autobiography of Mother Jones. 10th annot. ed. 2006. (Labor Classics Ser.). (Illus.). 160p. (Orig.). pap. 15.00 (978-0-88286-311-5(8)) Kerr, Charles H. Publishing Co.

Kallen, Stuart A. Women of the 1960s. 2003. (Women in History Ser.). (Illus.). 128p. (J). 32.45 (978-1-59018-251-2(0) , Lucent Bks.) Thomson Gale.

Kamma, Anne. If You Lived When Women Won Their Rights. 2008. 64p. pap. 5.99 ***(978-0-439-74869-8(0)** , Scholastic Reference) Scholastic, Inc.

Miller, Brandon Marie. Good Women of a Well-Blessed Land: Women's Lives in Colonial America. 2003. (People's History Ser.). (Illus.). 96p. (J). 29.27 (978-0-8225-0032-2(9)) Lerner Publishing Group.

Moore, Heidi. Ida B. Wells-Barnett. 2004. (Illus.). 32p. (J). lib. bdg. (978-1-4034-4997-9(X)) Heinemann Library.

Page, Mary S. & Metzger, Larry. Voices & Masks: The Experience of Nineteenth Century Mill Girls & Enslaved Women from Primary Sources. 2000. 223p. (YA). (gr. 10-12). 12.67 (978-1-877653-67-4(5)) Wayside Publishing.

Rossi, Ann. Created Equal: Women Campaign for the Right to Vote, 1840-1920. 2005. (Crossroads America Ser.). (Illus.). 40p. (J). (978-0-7922-8626-4(X)) National Geographic Society.

San Souci, Robert D. Cut from the Same Cloth: American Women of Myth, Legend & Tall Tale. 2000. (gr. 3-6). lib. bdg. 15.30 (978-0-613-28458-5(5)) Tandem Library Bks.

Somervill, Barbara A. Great Women of the Confederacy. 2006. 48p. (J). (gr. 4-6). lib. bdg. (978-0-7565-2033-5(9)) Compass Point Bks.

Stevens, Doris. Jailed for Freedom. 2006. (Illus.). cd-rom (978-1-892824-59-2(0)) AFCHRON.

Sundling, Charles W. Women of the Frontier. 2000. (Frontier Land Ser.). (Illus.). 32p. (J). (gr. 3-8). lib. bdg. 24.21 (978-1-57765-046-1(8) , ABDO & Daughters) ABDO Publishing Co.

Swisher, Clarice. Women of the Roaring Twenties. 2005. (Women in History Ser.). (Illus.). 112p. (J). (gr. 8-12). lib. bdg. 32.45 (978-1-59018-363-2(0) , Lucent Bks.) Thomson Gale.

WOMEN—UNITED STATES—BIOGRAPHY

Acker, Kerry. Dorothea Lange. 2003. (Women in the Arts Ser.). (Illus.). 112p. (gr. 6-12). 30.00 (978-0-7910-7460-2(9) , Chelsea Hse.) Facts On File, Inc.

—Madeleine Albright. 2004. (Women in Politics Ser.). (Illus.). 120p. 30.00 (978-0-7910-7734-4(9)); 116p. pap. 30.00 (978-0-7910-7998-0(8)) Facts On File, Inc. (Chelsea Hse.).

Adler, David A. Picture Book Biography Series: Remarkable Women, 3 bks., Set. Casilla, Robert, illus. unabr. ed. 1999. (J). (gr. 1-6). pap. 45.95 incl. audio (978-0-87499-574-9(4)) Live Oak Media.

—A Picture Book of Rosa Parks. Casilla, Robert, illus. 2004. 28.95 incl. audio compact disk (978-1-59112-762-8(9)) Live Oak Media.

Aller, Susan Bivin. Juliette Low. 2007. (History Maker Biographies Ser.). (J). 26.60 (978-0-8225-6580-2(3) , Lerner Pubns.) Lerner Publishing Group.

—Madam C. J. Walker. 2007. (History Maker Biographies Ser.). (J). 26.60 (978-0-8225-6582-6(X) , Lerner Pubns.) Lerner Publishing Group.

Alter, Judy. Extraordinary Women of the American West. 1999. (gr. 7-12). lib. bdg. 26.85 (978-0-613-54476-4(5)) Tandem Library Bks.

—Henrietta King: Rancher & Philanthropist. Messersmith, Patrick, illus. 2005. (Stars of Texas Ser.). 72p. 17.95 (978-1-880510-98-8(7)) State Hse. Pr.

—Laura Ingalls Wilder: Pioneer & Author. 2003. (Spirit of America). (Illus.). 32p. (J). (gr. 2-6). 27.07 (978-1-59296-007-1(3)) Child's World, Inc.

Anderson, Jane. My Name Is Deborah Samson. 2005. 40.00 ***(978-1-4108-4225-1(8))*** Benchmark Education Co.

Anema, Durlynn. Ynes Mexia: Botanist & Adventurer. 2005. (Women Adventurers Ser.). (Illus.). 144p. (J). (gr. 3-7). lib. bdg. 26.95 (978-1-931798-67-9(2)) Reynolds, Morgan Inc.

Armentrout, David & Armentrout, Patricia. Coretta Scott King. 2004. (Discover the Life of an American Legend Ser.). (Illus.). 24p. (gr. 2-5). 20.64 (978-1-58952-659-4(7)) Rourke Publishing, LLC.

—Laura Ingalls Wilder. 2004. (Discover the Life of an American Legend Ser.). (Illus.). 24p. (gr. 2-5). 14.95 (978-1-58952-663-1(5)) Rourke Publishing, LLC.

Armentrout, David & Armentrout, Patricia, trs. Venus & Serena Williams. 2003. (Discover the Life of a Sports Star Ser.). (Illus.). 24p. (J). 20.64 (978-1-58952-655-6(4)) Rourke Publishing, LLC.

Aronson, Virginia. Drew Barrymore. (Overcoming Adversity Ser.). (Illus.). (YA). 2000. 112p. 30.00 (978-0-7910-5306-5(7)); 1999. 128p. pap. 30.00 (978-0-7910-5307-2(5)) Facts On File, Inc. (Chelsea Hse.).

—Drew Barrymore. 2000. (gr. 5-8). lib. bdg. 18.75 (978-0-613-21469-8(2)) Tandem Library Bks.

—Venus & Serena Williams. 2000. (Women Who Win Ser.). (Illus.). 64p. (J). (gr. 4-7). pap. 25.00 (978-0-7910-6158-9(2)); 25.00 (978-0-7910-5799-5(2)) Facts On File, Inc. (Chelsea Hse.).

—Venus & Serena Williams. 2000. (Illus.). 64p. (J). (gr. 4-7). lib. bdg. 17.60 (978-0-613-33180-7(X)) Tandem Library Bks.

—Venus Williams. 1999. (Galaxy of Superstars Ser.). (Illus.). 64p. (J). pap. 25.00 (978-0-7910-5329-4(6)); (YA). (gr. 4-7). 25.00 (978-0-7910-5153-5(6)) Facts On File, Inc. (Chelsea Hse.).

—Venus Williams. 1999. (Galaxy of Superstars Ser.). (978-0-606-16419-1(7)); (gr. 5-8). lib. bdg. 17.60 (978-0-613-17759-7(2)) Tandem Library Bks.

Asirvatham, Sandy. Venus Williams. 2001. (Black Americans of Achievement Ser.). (Illus.). (J). 104p. pap. 30.00 (978-0-7910-6290-6(2)); 112p. 30.00 (978-0-7910-6289-0(9)) Facts On File, Inc. (Chelsea Hse.).

Auch, Allison. Mujeres que se atrevieron & Women Who Dared. 2005. spiral bd. 84.00 ***(978-1-4108-5692-0(5))*** Benchmark Education Co.

Bankston, John. Venus Williams. l.t. ed. 2002. (Real Life Reader Biography Ser.). (Illus.). 32p. (gr. 3-8). lib. bdg. 15.95 (978-1-58415-129-6(3)) Mitchell Lane Pubs., Inc.

Banting, Erinn. Rosa Parks. 2005. (Great African American Women for Kids Ser.). (Illus.). 24p. (J). (ps-7). pap. 6.95 (978-1-59036-342-3(6)); lib. bdg. 26.00 (978-1-59036-336-2(1)) Weigl Pubs., Inc.

Barasch, Lynne. Hiromi's Hands. Barasch, Lynne, illus. 2007. (Illus.). 40p. (J). (gr. k-6). 17.95 (978-1-58430-275-9(5)) Lee & Low Bks., Inc.

Bausum, Ann. With Courage & Cloth: Winning the Fight for a Woman's Right to Vote. 2004. (Illus.). 112p. (J). (gr. 5-17). 32.90 (978-0-7922-6996-0(9) , National Geographic Children's Bks.) National Geographic Society.

Bayer-Berenbaum, Linda. Ruth Bader Ginsburg: Supreme Court Justice. 2000. (Women of Achievement Ser.). (Illus.). 112p. (J). (gr. 4-7). 30.00 (978-0-7910-5287-7(7) , Chelsea Hse.) Facts On File, Inc.

Bednarz, Robert, et al. TIME for Kids Readers: Carrie Chapman Catt. 3rd ed. 2002. (Harcourt Horizons Ser.). (gr. k-7). pap. 38.10 (978-0-15-335264-5(7)) Harcourt Schl. Pubs.

Benson, Michael. Gloria Estefan. 2003. (Biography Ser.). (Illus.). 112p. (YA). (gr. 6 up). pap. 7.95 (978-0-8225-9692-9(X) , Carolrhoda Bks.) Lerner Publishing Group.

Bernard, Catherine J. Sojourner Truth: Abolitionist & Women's Rights Activist. 2001. (Historical American Biographies Ser.). (Illus.). 112p. (YA). (gr. 6-12). lib. bdg. 26.60 (978-0-7660-1257-8(3)) Enslow Pubs., Inc.

Bert, Ruth J. Everyone Called Her Sister Sarah. 2004. (ENG., Illus.). 32p. (J). pap. 4.99 (978-1-928915-62-1(0)) Evangel Publishing Hse.

Bertanzetti, Eileen Dunn. Molly Pitcher. 2001. (Revolutionary War Leaders Ser.). (Illus.). 80p. (J). 31.00 (978-0-7910-6400-9(X)); pap. 27.50 (978-0-7910-6401-6(8)) Facts On File, Inc. (Chelsea Hse.).

Blakely, Gloria. Condoleezza Rice. 2003. (African American Leaders Ser.). (Illus.). 112p. (gr. 6-12). 30.00 (978-0-7910-7683-5(0) , Chelsea Hse.) Facts On File, Inc.

Blashfield, Jean F. Oprah Winfrey. 2003. (Trailblazers of the Modern World Ser.). (ENG & SPA., Illus.). 48p. (J). (gr. 5 up). pap. 14.95 (978-0-8368-5247-9(8)); lib. bdg. 30.00 (978-0-8368-5087-1(4)) Stevens, Gareth Inc. (World Almanac Library).

Blevins, Wiley. Eleanor Roosevelt. 2002. (Illus.). 16p. (J). pap. (978-0-439-35193-5(6)) Scholastic, Inc.

Bloom, Harold. Gwendolyn Brooks. 2004. (Bloom's BioCritiques Ser.). (Illus.). 112p. (YA). (gr. 9-13). 35.00 (978-0-7910-8114-3(1) , Chelsea Hse.) Facts On File, Inc.

Bloom, Harold, ed. & intro. Hilda Doolittle (H. D.) Bloom, Harold, intro. 2002. (Bloom's Major Poets Ser.). 120p. (YA). 31.95 (978-0-7910-6817-5(X) , Chelsea Hse.) Facts On File, Inc.

Bodie, Idella. The Courageous Widow. 2001. 55p. (J). 5.95 (978-0-87844-157-0(3)) Sandlapper Publishing Co., Inc.

—Heroines of the American Revolution. 2003. (Illus.). 99p. (J). pap. 6.95 (978-0-87844-170-9(0)) Sandlapper Publishing Co., Inc.

Boekhoff, P. M. & Kallen, Stuart A. Venus Williams. 2002. (Stars of Sports Ser.). (Illus.). 48p. (J). 26.20 (978-0-7377-1395-4(X) , Greenhaven Pr., Inc.) Thomson Gale.

Bohannon, Lisa Frederiksen. Woman's Work: The Story of Betty Friedan. 2004. (Illus.). 144p. (YA). (gr. 6-12). 23.95 (978-1-931798-41-9(9)) Reynolds, Morgan Inc.

Bortz, Fred. Beyond Jupiter: The Story of Planetary Astronomer Heidi Hammel. 2005. (Women's Adventures in Science Ser.). (Illus.). 110p. (YA). (gr. 7-9). 31.00 (978-0-531-16775-5(5) , Watts, Franklin) Scholastic Library Publishing.

Boulais, Sue. Gloria Estefan. 1999. (Real-Life Reader Biographies Ser.). (Illus.). 32p. (gr. 3-8). lib. bdg. 15.95 (978-1-883845-62-9(9)) Mitchell Lane Pubs., Inc.

Bowdish, Lynea. With Courage: Seven Women Who Changed America. 2004. (Illus.). 48p. (J). 6.95 (978-1-59336-280-5(3)) Mondo Publishing.

Bozzuti-Jones, Mark Francisco. The Miter Fits Just Fine: A Story about the Rt. Rev. Barbara Clementine Harris, Suffragan Bishop, Diocese of Massachusetts. 2003. 86p. pap. 10.95 (978-1-56101-220-6(3)) Cowley Pubns.

Brainard, Cecilia Manguerra. Cecilia's Diary 1962-1969. 2003. (YA). per. 15.95 (978-0-9719458-1-4(0)) PALH.

Brandon, DeeAnn. The Bird with a Broken Wing. 2002. 236p. pap. 15.00 (978-0-9720123-0-0(3)) WORDS ON WINGS, Ltd.

Brean, Alta. Dear Grandchildren: Growing up on the Frontier. 2003. (Illus.). 144p. 18.95 (978-0-9726360-0-1(5) , (408) 718-5654) Alta Omnimedia.

Brooks, Philip. Oprah Winfrey: A Voice for the People. 2000. (Book Report Bios Ppbk Ser.). (Illus.). (YA). pap. 6.95 (978-0-531-16406-8(3) , Watts, Franklin) Scholastic Library Publishing.

—Oprah Winfrey: A Voice for the People. 1999. (978-0-606-18159-4(8)) Tandem Library Bks.

Brown, Don. Alice Ramsey's Grand Adventure. 2000. (YA). 12.75 (978-0-606-19423-5(1)) Tandem Library Bks.

Brown, Fern. Daisy & the Girl Scouts: The Story of Juliette Gordon Low. Dejohn, Marie, illus. 2005. 111p. (J). (gr. 3-6). lib. bdg. 15.90 (978-0-606-33708-3(3)) Tandem Library Bks.

Brown, Jonatha A. Rosa Parks. 2005. (Illus.). 24p. (J). (ENG & SPA.). pap. (978-0-8368-4769-7(5)); (ENG & SPA., lib. bdg. 19.33 (978-0-8368-4762-8(8)); pap. (978-0-8368-4755-0(5)); lib. bdg. 19.33 (978-0-8368-4748-2(2)) Stevens, Gareth Inc.

Buckley, Annie. Ellen Ochoa. 2008. (J). lib. bdg. 26.00 ***(978-1-60279-075-9(2))*** Cherry Lake Publishing.

Buckley, James, Jr. Venus & Serena Williams. 2003. (Trailblazers of the Modern World Ser.). (Illus.). 48p. (J). (gr. 5 up). pap. 14.95 (978-0-8368-5246-2(X)); lib. bdg. 30.00 (978-0-8368-5086-4(6)) Stevens, Gareth Inc. (World Almanac Library).

Burgan, Michael. Great Women of the American Revolution. 2004. (We the People Ser.). (Illus.). 48p. (J). 22.60 (978-0-7565-0838-8(X)) Compass Point Bks.

—Madeleine Albright. 1998. (Single Titles Ser.: up). (Illus.). 144p. (gr. 7-12). lib. bdg. 24.90 (978-0-7613-0367-1(7) , Millbrook Pr.) Lerner Publishing Group.

Burke, John. Sterling Point Books: Amelia Earhart: Flying Solo. 2007. (Sterling Point Bks.). (Illus.). 208p. (J). 12.95 (978-1-4027-4520-1(6)); pap. 6.95 (978-1-4027-4140-1(5)) Sterling Publishing Co., Inc.

Burke, Rick. Molly Pitcher. 2003. (American Lives Ser.). (Illus.). 32p. (J). lib. bdg. 24.22 (978-1-4034-0727-6(4)); pap. 6.50 (978-1-4034-3102-8(7)) Heinemann Library.

Butler, Mary G. Sojourner Truth: From Slave to Activist for Freedom. 2005. (Library of American Lives & Times). (Illus.). 112p. (YA). (gr. 4-8). lib. bdg. 31.95 (978-0-8239-5736-1(5)) Rosen Publishing Group, Inc., The.

Byman, Jeremy. Madam Secretary: The Story of Madeleine Albright. (Notable Americans Ser.). (Illus.). 1998. 96p. (gr. 5 up). 21.95 (978-1-883846-23-7(4)); 2004. 128p. (YA). (gr. 6-12). 23.95 (978-1-931798-34-1(6)) Reynolds, Morgan Inc.

Canizares, Susan & Chanko, Pamela. Up, up, & Away: The Story of Amelia Earhart. 1999. (ps-2). lib. bdg. 10.10 (978-0-613-22557-1(0)) Tandem Library Bks.

Cantwell, Lois & Smith, Pohla. Women Winners: Then & Now. 2005. (Sports Illustrated for Kids Bks.). (Illus.). 176p. (YA). (gr. 7-12). lib. bdg. 25.25 (978-0-8239-3695-3(3)) Rosen Publishing Group, Inc., The.

—Women Winners: Then & Now. (J). (gr. 3-9). pap. 3.99 (978-1-930623-09-5(7)) Sports Illustrated For Kids.

Caravantes, Peggy. Waging Peace: The Story of Jane Addams. 2004. (Illus.). 144p. (YA). (gr. 6-12). 23.95 (978-1-931798-40-2(0)) Reynolds, Morgan Inc.

Cayleff, Susan E. Babe Didrikson. 2000. (gr. 7-12). lib. bdg. 17.45 (978-0-613-27718-1(X)) Tandem Library Bks.

Cheney, Lynne. A Is for Abigail: An Almanac of Amazing American Women. Glasser, Robin Preiss, illus. 2003. 48p. (J). 16.95 (978-0-689-85819-2(1)) Simon & Schuster Children's Publishing.

Christopher, Matt. On the Court with... Venus & Serena Williams. 2002. (Matt Christopher Sports Biographies Ser.). (Illus.). 112p. (J). (gr. 4-7). pap. 4.99 (978-0-316-13814-7(2)) Little, Brown Bks. for Young Readers.

Cohen, Sheila. Mai Ya's Long Journey. 2005. (Badger Biographies Ser.). (Illus.). 80p. (J). (gr. 3-8). pap. 12.95 (978-0-87020-365-7(7)) Wisconsin Historical Society.

Collins, David R. Servant to the Slaves: The Story of Henriette Delille. 2000. (Weaver Bks.). 68p. (J). (gr. 7-9). pap. 3.95 (978-0-8198-7039-1(0)) Pauline Bks. & Media.

Collins, Kathleen. Sojourner Truth: Equal Rights Advocate. 2003. (Famous People in American History Ser.). (Illus.). 32p. (J). pap. 6.50 (978-0-8239-4193-3(0)) Rosen Publishing Group, Inc., The.

Crawford, Ann Fears. Rosa: A German Woman on the Texas Frontier. Fain, Cheryl, illus. l.t. ed. 2003. 60p. (J). (gr. 3-8). 16.95 (978-1-931823-09-8(X)) Halcyon Pr.

Delmege, Sarah & Andrews McMeel Publishing Staff. Britney Spears. 2000. (Illus.). 47p. (YA). (gr. 8-12). pap., pap. 5.95 (978-1-84222-173-0(6)) Carlton Bks., Ltd. GBR. *Dist:* Ingram Pub. Services.

Devillier, Christy. Helen Keller. 2004. (First Biographies Set Iv Ser.). (Illus.). 32p. (J). (gr. k-4). lib. bdg. 22.78 (978-1-59197-514-4(X)) ABDO Publishing Co.

—Molly Pitcher. 2004. (First Biographies Set Iv Ser.). (Illus.). 32p. (J). (gr. k-4). lib. bdg. 22.78 (978-1-59197-515-1(8)) ABDO Publishing Co.

Ditchfield, Christin. Condoleezza Rice: America's Leading Stateswoman. 2006. (Great Life Stories Ser.). (Illus.). 111p. (J). (gr. 5-8). 30.50 (978-0-531-13874-8(7) , Watts, Franklin) Scholastic Library Publishing.

—Condoleezza Rice: National Security Advisor. 2003. (Great Life Stories: Political Figures Ser.). (Illus.). 112p. (J). 30.50 (978-0-531-12307-2(3) , Watts, Franklin) Scholastic Library Publishing.

DiVito, Anna. Annie Oakley Saves the Day. DiVito, Anna, illus. 2004. (Illus.). 29p. (J). (ps-7). lib. bdg. 10.79 (978-0-606-32656-8(1)) Tandem Library Bks.

Dolan, Sean J. Helen Keller. 2005. (Rookie Biographies(R) Ser.). (Illus.). 31p. (J). (ps-2). 20.50 (978-0-516-25269-8(0) , Children's Pr.) Scholastic Library Publishing.

Donaldson, Madeline. Venus & Serena Williams. 2005. (Amazing Athletes Ser.). (Illus.). 32p. (gr. 3-4). lib. bdg. 22.60 (978-0-8225-3316-0(2)) Lerner Publishing Group.

Donovan, Sandy. Rosa Parks. 2003. (Illus.). 64p. (J). (gr. 4-7). pap. 9.50 (978-1-4109-0320-4(6)); lib. bdg. 28.56 (978-0-7398-7032-7(7)) Raintree.

Dorrie, Roxanne. Venus & Serena Williams: The Smashing Sisters. 2003. (High Five Reading (Red Level) Ser.). (Illus.). (J). 64p. lib. bdg. 22.60 (978-0-7368-2784-3(6)); 48p. pap. 23.93 (978-0-7368-2827-7(3)) Capstone Pr., Inc.

Dubois, Muriel L. Rosa Parks. 2003. (Photo-Illustrated Biographies Ser.). (Illus.). 24p. (J). (gr. 2-3). lib. bdg. 18.60 (978-0-7368-1607-6(0) , Bridgestone Bks.) Capstone Pr., Inc.

Dubowski, Cathy East. Rosa Parks: Don't Give In! 2005. (Defining Moments Ser.). (Illus.). 32p. (J). lib. bdg. 25.27 (978-1-59716-078-0(4)) Bearport Publishing Co., Inc.

Edge, Laura Bufano. Laura Bush: Portrait of a First Lady. 2006. (People to Know Today Ser.). (Illus.). 128p. (J). lib. bdg. 31.93 (978-0-7660-2629-2(9)) Enslow Pubs., Inc.

Edwards, Pamela Duncan. The Bus Ride That Changed History: The Story of Rosa Parks. Shanahan, Danny, illus. 2005. 32p. (J). (gr. k-3). 16.00 (978-0-618-44911-8(6)) Houghton Mifflin Co. Trade & Reference Div.

Ehrlich, Amy. Rachel: The Story of Rachel Carson. Minor, Wendell, illus. 2008. 32p. (J). pap. 6.00 ***(978-0-15-206324-5(2)** , Voyager Bks./Libros Viajeros) Harcourt Children's Bks.

—Rachel: The Story of Rachel Carson. Minor, Wendell, illus. 2003. 32p. (J). (gr. k-3). 16.00 (978-0-15-216227-6(5) , Silver Whistle) Harcourt Trade Pubs.

Ellen Ochoa: Reaching for the Stars. 2005. (Book Treks Ser.). (J). (gr. 3 up). stu. ed. 34.95 (978-0-673-62081-1(6)) Celebration Pr.

Enander, Glen. Elisabeth Schussler Fiorenza. 2005. (Spiritual Leaders & Thinkers Ser.). (Illus.). 120p. (J). (gr. 9-13). 30.00 (978-0-7910-8105-1(2) , Chelsea Hse.) Facts On File, Inc.

Feldman, Heather. Mia Hamm, Super-Estrella del Futbol Soccer. 2002. (Coleccion Power Kids). (SPA., Illus.). 24p. (J). (gr. k-2). lib. bdg. 17.25 (978-0-8239-6136-8(2) , RN31306, Buenas Letra) Rosen Publishing Group, Inc., The.

—Mia Hamm, Superestrella del Futbol Soccer. 2002. (Superestrellas del Deporte Ser.). (SPA & ENG., Illus.). 24p. (J). lib. bdg. 17.25 (978-0-8239-6118-4(4) , Buenas Letra) Rosen Publishing Group, Inc., The.

—Venus Williams: Campeona del Tenis. 2002. (Superestrellas del Deporte Ser.).Tr. of Venus Williams: Tennis Champion. (SPA.). 24p. (J). lib. bdg. 17.25 (978-0-8239-6120-7(6) , Buenas Letra) Rosen Publishing Group, Inc., The.

—Venus Williams: Campeona del Tenis. de Leon, Mauricio V., tr. 2001. Tr. of Venus Williams: Tennis Champion. (SPA.). 24p. 11.95 Rosen Publishing Group, Inc., The.

—Venus Williams: Tennis Champion. 2001. (Reading Power Ser.). (Illus.). 24p. (J). (gr. 1). lib. bdg. 17.25 (978-0-8239-5717-0(9) , PKSUST, PowerKids Pr.) Rosen Publishing Group, Inc., The.

—Venus Williams, Campeona del Tenis. 2002. (Coleccion Power Kids). (SPA & ENG., Illus.). 24p. (J). (gr. k-2). lib. bdg. 17.25 (978-0-8239-6138-2(9) , RN31300, Buenas Letra) Rosen Publishing Group, Inc., The.

Fillon, Mike. Young Superstars of Tennis: The Venus & Serena Williams Story. 1999. (Illus.). 144p. (YA). (gr. 6-12). lib. bdg. 19.95 (978-1-888105-43-8(7)) Avisson Pr., Inc.

Fine, Edith Hope. Rosa Parks: Meet a Civil Rights Hero. 2004. (Meeting Famous People Ser.). (Illus.). 32p. (J). lib. bdg. 22.60 (978-0-7660-2099-3(1)) Enslow Pubs., Inc.

Fiorelli, June Estep. Fannie Lou Hamer: A Voice for Freedom. 2004. (Avisson Young Adult Ser.). (Illus.). 117p. (J). pap. 19.95 (978-1-888105-62-9(3)) Avisson Pr., Inc.

Flanagan, Alice K. Great Women of the Union. 2006. 48p. (J). (gr. 4-6). lib. bdg. (978-0-7565-2035-9(5)) Compass Point Bks.

Ford, Carin T. Clara Barton: Brave Nurse. 2006. (Heroes of American History Ser.). (Illus.). 32p. (J). lib. bdg. 22.60 (978-0-7660-2602-5(7) , Enslow Elementary) Enslow Pubs., Inc.

—Laura Ingalls Wilder: Real-Life Pioneer of the Little House Books. 2003. (People to Know Ser.). (Illus.). 112p. (J). lib. bdg. 26.60 (978-0-7660-2105-1(X)) Enslow Pubs., Inc.

Fradin, Dennis Brindell & Fradin, Judith Bloom. Jane Addams: Champion of Democracy. 2006. (Illus.). 192p. (J). (gr. 5-9). 21.00 (978-0-618-50436-7(2) , Clarion Bks.) Houghton Mifflin Co. Trade & Reference Div.

Fradin, Judith Bloom & Fradin, Dennis Brindell. The Power of One: Daisy Bates & the Little Rock Nine. 2004. (Illus.). 192p. (YA). (gr. 5-9). tchr. ed. 19.00 (978-0-618-31556-7(X) , Clarion Bks.) Houghton Mifflin Co. Trade & Reference Div.

Franzen, Lenore. Venus Williams. 2003. (Ovations Ser.). (Illus.). 32p. (J). (978-1-58341-249-7(2) , Creative Education) Creative Co., The.

Frazier, Neta Lohnes. Path to the Pacific: The Story of Sacajawea. 2007. (Sterling Point Bks.). (Illus.). 192p. (J). pap. 6.95 (978-1-4027-4138-8(3)) Sterling Publishing Co., Inc.

—Sterling Point Books: Path to the Pacific: The Story of Sacajawea. 2007. (Sterling Point Bks.). (Illus.). 192p. (J). 12.95 (978-1-4027-4518-8(4)) Sterling Publishing Co., Inc.

Freedman, Jeri. Hillary Rodham Clinton: Profile of a Leading Democrat. 2007. (J). ***(978-1-4042-1910-6(2))*** Rosen Publishing Group, Inc., The.

Friedrich, Belinda. Oprah Winfrey. 2001. (Women of Achievement Ser.). (Illus.). 112p. (J). pap. (978-0-7910-5892-3(1)); (gr. 4-7). 30.00 (978-0-7910-5891-6(3)) Facts On File, Inc. (Chelsea Hse.).

Friend, Robyn C. The Women of Apollo. Katz, David Arthur, illus. l.t. ed. 2006. 80p. (J). 17.95 (978-1-880599-80-8(5)); pap. 12.95 (978-1-880599-79-2(1)) Cascade Pass, Inc.

Fritz, Jean. You Want Women to Vote, Lizzie Stanton? DiSalvo-Ryan, DyAnne, illus. 1999. 96p. (J). (gr. 3-7). pap. 6.99 (978-0-698-11764-8(6) , Putnam Juvenile) Penguin Group (USA) Inc.

—You Want Women to Vote, Lizzie Stanton? 1999. (978-0-606-16848-9(6)); (gr. 3-6). lib. bdg. 15.30 (978-0-613-17893-8(9)) Tandem Library Bks.

Frost, Helen. Sojourner Truth. Saunders-Smith, Gail, ed. 2003. (Famous Americans Ser.). (Illus.). 24p. (J). (gr. k-1). lib. bdg. 15.93 (978-0-7368-1640-3(2) , Pebble Bks.) Capstone Pr., Inc.

Fry, Erin. The Power of Friendship. 2005. (Illus.). 16p. (J). pap. (978-0-7367-2920-8(8)) Zaner-Bloser, Inc.

Furbee, Mary Rodd. Outrageous Women of Civil War Times. 2003. (gr. 5-8). lib. bdg. 22.20 (978-0-613-81400-3(2)) Tandem Library Bks.

—Outrageous Women of Civil War Times. 2003. (Outrageous Women Ser.). (Illus.). 124p. pap. 12.95 (978-0-471-22926-1(1) , Jossey-Bass) Wiley, John & Sons, Inc.

—Outrageous Women of Colonial America. 2001. (Outrageous Women Ser.: Vol. 5). (Illus.). 128p. (gr. 5-9). pap. 12.95 (978-0-471-38299-7(X) , Wiley) Wiley, John & Sons, Inc.

Gaines, Ann Graham. Whoopi Goldberg. 2000. (Illus.). 112p. (J). (ps-7). per. 18.75 (978-0-613-12278-8(X)) Tandem Library Bks.

Garza, Carmen Lomas. Family Pictures/Cuadros de Familia. 15th ed. 2005. (ENG & SPA., Illus.). 32p. (J). pap. 7.95 (978-0-89239-207-0(X)) Children's Bk. Pr.

Gay, Kathlyn. Mother Jones. 2006. (American Workers Ser.). (Illus.). 144p. (J). lib. bdg. 26.95 (978-1-59935-016-5(5)) Reynolds, Morgan Inc.

Gayle, Sharon. Harriet Tubman & the Freedom Train. Marshall, Felicia, illus. 2003. (Ready-to-Read Ser.). 32p. (J). pap. 3.99 (978-0-689-85480-4(3) , Aladdin) Simon & Schuster Children's Publishing.

Giesecke, Ernestine. Mary Cassatt. 2006. (Heinemann First Library). (Illus.). 32p. (J). lib. bdg. ***978-1-4034-8493-2(7))** Heinemann Library.

Gillis, Jennifer Blizin. Dolores Huerta. 2005. (Illus.). 32p. (J). (978-1-4034-6980-9(6)); pap. (978-1-4034-6987-8(3)) Heinemann Library.

—Sojourner Truth. 2005. (Illus.). 32p. (J). (978-1-4034-6981-6(4)); pap. (978-1-4034-6988-5(1)) Heinemann Library.

Glaser, Jason. Molly Pitcher: Young American Patriot. Smith, Tod et al, illus. 2006. (Graphic Library). 32p. (J). 25.26 (978-0-7368-5486-3(X)) Capstone Pr., Inc.

Goodridge, Catherine. Michelle Kwan. ed. 2004. (SPA.). (J). pap. 5.00 (978-1-4108-2428-8(4) , A24284) Benchmark Education Co.

Goodridge, Catherine. Michelle Kwan (Spanish) & Michelle Kwan. 2005. spiral bd. 70.00 **(*978-1-4108-5659-3(3))** Benchmark Education Co.

Gorman, Jacqueline Laks. Gloria Steinem. 2003. (Trailblazers of the Modern World Ser.). (Illus.). 48p. (J). (gr. 5 up). pap. 14.60 (978-0-8368-5253-0(2) , World Almanac Library) Stevens, Gareth Inc.

Gormley, Beatrice. Laura Ingalls Wilder: Young Pioneer. Henderson, Meryl, illus. 2001. (Childhood of Famous Americans Ser.). 224p. (J). (gr. 3-7). pap. 5.99 (978-0-689-83924-5(3) , Aladdin) Simon & Schuster Children's Publishing.

—Laura Ingalls Wilder: Young Pioneer. 2001. (Childhood of Famous Americans Ser.). (Illus.). (J). (978-0-606-21290-8(6)) Tandem Library Bks.

Graves, Jeseca, illus. Bessie Coleman: The Story of an Aviation Pioneer. 2007. 24p. (J). **(*978-0-9745294-1-7(9))** San Diego County Regional Airport Authority.

Green, Michelle Y. A Strong Right Arm: The Story of Mamie "Peanut" Johnson. 2004. (gr. 5-8). lib. bdg. 14.15 (978-0-613-83004-1(0)) Tandem Library Bks.

Greenberg, Jan & Jordan, Sandra. Runaway Girl: The Artist Louise Bourgeois. 2003. (Illus.). 80p. (J). (gr. 7-17). 19.95 (978-0-8109-4237-0(2)) Abrams, Harry N. , Inc.

Greenfield, Eloise. Rosa Parks. Ashby, Gil, illus. 2002. 12.62 (978-0-7587-0755-0(X)) Book Wholesalers, Inc.

Guilfoyle, Peg. Oprah Winfrey. 1999. (Ovations Ser.). (Illus.). 32p. (YA). (gr. 4-7). pap. (978-0-88682-941-4(0) , Creative Education) Creative Co., The.

Gullo, James. Hillary Rodham Clinton. 2003. (Importance of Ser.). (Illus.). 112p. (J). 32.45 (978-1-59018-310 6(X) , Lucent Bks.) Thomson Gale.

Gutman, Bill. Marion Jones: The Fastest Woman in the World. 2000. (YA). (978-0-606-19499-0(1)) Tandem Library Bks.

—Venus & Serena: The Grand Slam Williams Sisters. 2001. (Scholastic Biography Ser.). (Illus.). 144p. (J). (gr. 3-7). pap. 4.50 (978-0-439-27152-3(5)) Scholastic, Inc.

—Venus & Serena: The Grand Slam Williams Sisters. 2001. (Illus.). (978-0-606-21502-2(6)) Tandem Library Bks.

Guzman, Lila & Guzman, Rick. Ellen Ochoa: First Latina Astronaut. 2006. (Famous Latinos Ser.). (Illus.). 32p. (J). lib. bdg. 22.60 (978-0-7660-2642-1(6) , Enslow Elementary) Enslow Pubs., Inc.

Hansen, Joyce. African Americans Who Made a Difference. 2007. (Women of Hope Ser.). 32p. (J). pap. 6.99 **(*978-0-590-93974-4(2))** Scholastic, Inc.

Hansen, Joyce & Bread and Roses Staff. African Americans Who Made a Difference. 1998. (Illus.). 32p. (J). (gr. 3-7). pap. 16.95 (978-0-590-93973-7(4)) Scholastic, Inc.

Harcourt School Publishers Staff. Marjory Stineman Douglas Advanced Level. 3rd ed. 2002. (Trophies Reading Program Ser.). (Illus.). pap. 5.10 (978-0-15-323381-4(8)) Harcourt Schl. Pubs.

Harkins, Susan. Betsy Ross. 2006. (Profiles in American History Ser.). (Illus.). 48p. (J). (gr. 4-8). lib. bdg. 20.95 (978-1-58415-446-4(2)) Mitchell Lane Pubs., Inc.

Harness, Cheryl. Rabble Rousers: 20 Women Who Made a Difference. Harness, Cheryl, illus. 2003. (Illus.). 64p. (J). (gr. 2-6). 17.99 (978-0-525-47035-9(2) , Dutton Juvenile) Penguin Group (USA) Inc.

—Remember the Ladies: 100 Great American Women. 2003. (gr. 3-6). lib. bdg. 15.30 (978-0-613-61843-4(2)) Tandem Library Bks.

Hart, Elva Trevino. Barefoot Heart: Stories of A Migrant Child. 1999. (gr. 7-12). lib. bdg. 26.90 (978-0-613-24295-0(5)) Tandem Library Bks.

Hartman, Holly. Girlwonder: Every Girl's Guide to the Fantastic Feats, Cool Qualities, & Remar. 2003. (gr. 3-6). lib. bdg. 18.75 (978-0-613-88663-5(1)) Tandem Library Bks.

Harvey, Bonnie Carman. Carry A. Nation: Saloon Smasher & Prohibitionist. 2002. (Historical American Biographies Ser.). (Illus.). 128p. (YA). (gr. 6-12). lib. bdg. 26.60 (978-0-7660-1907-2(1)) Enslow Pubs., Inc.

Hasday, Judy L. Agnes de Mille. 2003. (Women in the Arts Ser.). (Illus.). 112p. (gr. 6-12). 30.00 (978-0-7910-7457-2(9) , Chelsea Hse.) Facts On File, Inc.

—Madeleine Albright: Stateswoman. 1999. (Women of Achievement Ser.). (Illus.). (J). (978-0-606-18035-1(4)) Tandem Library Bks.

Haugen, Brenda. Amelia Earhart: Legendary Aviator. 2006. (J). (978-0-7565-1880-6(6)) Compass Point Bks.

Haugen, Brenda. Annie Oakley: American Sharpshooter. (Illus.). 112p. (J). 2007. pap. **(*978-0-7565-1974-2(8));** 2006. lib. bdg. **(*978-0-7565-1869-1(5))** Compass Point Bks.

Hawthrone, Nora B. Love Knows No Distance. Nell Nix House of Photography, photos by. 1998. 143p. (YA). (gr. 3 up). pap. 9.95 (978-0-9721787-0-9(8)) Veach, Betty H. Veach & Lester H.

Hill, Christine M. Gwendolyn Brooks: Poetry Is Life Distilled. 2005. (African-American Biography Library). (Illus.). 128p. (J). (gr. 6-12). lib. bdg. 31.93 (978-0-7660-2292-8(7)) Enslow Pubs., Inc.

Hill, Mary. Serena & Venus Williams. 2003. (Welcome Bks.). (Illus.). 24p. (J). (ps-2). pap. 4.95 (978-0-516-27889-6(4) , Children's Pr.) Scholastic Library Publishing.

—Serena & Venus Williams. 2003. (gr. k-3). lib. bdg. 12.95 (978-0-613-67764-6(1)) Tandem Library Bks.

Hitchcock, Susan Tyler. Karen Horney: Pioneer of Feminine Psychology. 2004. (Women in Medicine Ser.). (Illus.). 112p. (gr. 6-12). 30.00 (978-0-7910-8025-2(0) , Chelsea Hse.) Facts On File, Inc.

Holden, Henry M. Pioneering Astronaut Sally Ride: A MyReportLinks. com Book. 2004. (Space Flight Adventures & Disasters Ser.). (Illus.). 48p. (J). lib. bdg. 25.26 (978-0-7660-5169-0(2) , MyReportLinks.com Bks.) Enslow Pubs., Inc.

Hopping, Lorraine Jean. Bone Detective: The Story of Forensic Anthropologist Diane France. 2005. (Women's Adventures in Science Ser.). (Illus.). 118p. (J). (gr. 7-9). 31.00 (978-0-531-16776-2(3) , Watts, Franklin) Scholastic Library Publishing.

Horn, Geoffrey M. Laila Ali. 2006. (Today's Superstars). (Illus.). 32p. (YA). (gr. 5 up). lib. bdg. 23.93 (978-0-8368-6181-5(7)) Stevens, Gareth Inc.

—Margaret Mead. 2004. (Trailblazers of the Modern World Ser.). (Illus.). 48p. (J). (gr. 5 up). pap. 11.95 (978-0-8368-5259-2(1) , World Almanac Library) Stevens, Gareth Inc.

Horner, Matina S., intro. Hillary Rodham Clinton: First Lady/Attorney. 1999. (Women of Achievement Ser.). (Illus.). 112p. (YA). (gr. 4-7). 32.00 (978-0-7910-4712-5(1)); pap. 30.00 (978-0-7910-4713-2(X)) Facts On File, Inc. (Chelsea Hse.).

Hull, Mary E. Rosa Parks: Civil Rights Leader. (Black Americans of Achievement Ser.). (Illus.). 112p. (J). (gr. 6-12). 2005. pap. 13.25 (978-0-7910-8338-3(1)); 2004. 30.00 (978-0-7910-8164-8(8)) Facts On File, Inc. (Chelsea Hse.).

Jablonski, Carla. Esther Dyson: Web Guru. 2002. (Techies Ser.). (Illus.). 80p. (gr. 5 up). lib. bdg. 23.90 (978-0-7613-2657-1(X) , Twenty-First Century Bks.) Lerner Publishing Group.

Jaffe, Elizabeth Dana. Sojourner Truth. 2001. (Compass Point Early Biographies Ser.). (Illus.). 32p. (J). (gr. 2 up). lib. bdg. 21.26 (978-0-7565-0068-9(0)) Compass Point Bks.

Johnston, Johanna. They Led the Way: 14 American Women. 2004. (Illus.). 128p. (J). pap. 5.99 (978-0-14-240057-9(2) , Puffin) Penguin Group (USA) Inc.

Jones, Joyce Adams. Remembering the Marches in Selma, Alabama. 2006. 8.00 **(*978-0-8059-7237-5(4))** Dorrance Publishing Co., Inc.

Kann, Bob. A Recipe for Success: Lizzie Kander & Her Cookbook. 2006. (Badger Biographies Ser.). (Illus.). 144p. (J). pap. 12.95 (978-0-87020-373-2(8)) Wisconsin Historical Society.

Kernan, Elizabeth. Harriet Tubman: A Lesson in Bravery. 2002. (Reading Room Collection). (Illus.). 24p. (J). pap. (978-0-8239-8229-5(7)); lib. bdg. 18.75 (978-0-8239-3750-9(X)) Rosen Publishing Group, Inc., The.

Kishel, Ann-Marie. Elizabeth Blackwell: A Life of Diligence. 2007. (Pull Ahead Books-Biographies Ser.). (J). 22.60 (978-0-8225-6459-1(9) , Lerner Pubns.) Lerner Publishing Group.

—Jane Addams: A Life of Cooperation. 2007. (Pull Ahead Books). (Illus.). 32p. (J). 22.60 (978-0-8225-6382-2(7) , Lerner Pubns.) Lerner Publishing Group.

—Rosa Parks: A Life of Courage. 2006. (Pull Ahead Books). (Illus.). 32p. (J). 22.60 (978-0-8225-3478-5(9) , Lerner Pubns.) Lerner Publishing Group.

Koestler-Grack, Rachel A. Molly Pitcher: Heroine of the War for Independence. 2005. (Leaders of the American Revolution Ser.). (Illus.). 120p. (J). (gr. 4-8). lib. bdg. 30.00 (978-0-7910-8622-3(4) , Chelsea Hse.) Facts On File, Inc.

Kovatch, Sarah. Record Breaking Woman. 2005. (Voices Reading Ser.). (Illus.). 16p. (J). (978-0-7367-2914-7(3)) Zaner-Bloser, Inc.

Kozar, Richard. Elizabeth Dole. (Women of Achievement Ser.). (Illus.). 112p. (J). 2000. 30.00 (978-0-7910-5289-1(3)); 1999. (gr. 5-9). pap. 30.00 (978-0-7910-5290-7(7)) Facts On File, Inc. (Chelsea Hse.).

—Elizabeth Dole. 2000. (gr. 5-8). lib. bdg. 18.75 (978-0-613-21488-9(9)) Tandem Library Bks.

Kraft, Betsy Harvey. Mother Jones: One Woman's Fight for Labor. 2006. (Illus.). 116p. (YA). (gr. 6-10). reprint ed. 17.00 (978-1-4223-5443-8(1)) DIANE Publishing Co.

Kramer, Barbara. Madeleine Albright: First Woman Secretary of State. 2000. (People to Know Ser.). (Illus.). 112p. (J). (gr. 6-12). lib. bdg. 26.60 (978-0-7660-1143-4(7)) Enslow Pubs., Inc.

—Trailblazing American Women: First in Their Fields. 2000. (Collective Biographies Ser.). (Illus.). 112p. (YA). (gr. 6-12). lib. bdg. 26.60 (978-0-7660-1377-3(4)) Enslow Pubs., Inc.

Kramer, Sydelle A. U. S. Soccer Superstars. 2000. (All Aboard Reading Ser.). (978-0-606-18474-8(0)) Tandem Library Bks.

Krass, Peter. Sojourner Truth. 2004. (Black Americans of Achievement Ser.). (Illus.). 112p. (J). (gr. 6-12). 30.00 (978-0-7910-8165-5(6) , Chelsea Hse.) Facts On File, Inc.

—Sojourner Truth: Antislavery Activist. 2005. (Black Americans of Achievement Ser.). (Illus.). 112p. (J). (gr. 6-12). pap. 13.25 (978-0-7910-8339-0(X) , Chelsea Hse.) Facts On File, Inc.

Krawiec, Richard. Sudden Champion: The Sarah Hughes Story. 2002. (Illus.). 100p. (Orig.). (J). (gr. 6-12). pap. 19.95 (978-1-888105-53-7(4)) Avisson Pr., Inc.

Krohn, Katherine E. Madam C.J. Walker & New Cosmetics. Dominguez, Richard, illus. 2007. (Graphic Library). 32p. **(*978-0-7368-9647-4(3))** Capstone Pr., Inc.

—Oprah Winfrey. (Biography Ser.). (Illus.). 112p. (J). (gr. 6 up). 2003. pap. 7.95 (978-0-8225-5000-6(8)); 2001. 27.93 (978-0-8225-4999-4(9) , Lerner Pubns.) Lerner Publishing Group.

—Oprah Winfrey. 2002. (gr. 7-12). lib. bdg. 16.40 (978-0-613-84025-5(9)) Tandem Library Bks.

—Vera Wang. 2007. (Biography Ser.). 112p. (J). (gr. 6-12). 29.27 **(*978-0-8225-6612-0(5)** , Twenty-First Century Bks.) Lerner Publishing Group.

Krohn, Katherine E. Women of the Wild West. (Biography Ser.). (Illus.). 112p. (gr. 6 up). 2003. (YA). pap. 7.95 (978-0-8225-9690-5(3) , Carolrhoda Bks.); 2000. (J). lib. bdg. 27.93 (978-0-8225-4980-2(8) , Lerner Pubns.) Lerner Publishing Group.

Krulik, Nancy E. Angels! The Inside Scoop on the Stars of Charlie's Angels. 2000. (gr. 5-8). lib. bdg. 13.00 (978-0-613-30949-3(9)) Tandem Library Bks.

Kucharczyk, Emily Rose. Georgia O'Keeffe: Desert Painter. 2002. (Famous Women Juniors Ser.). (Illus.). 32p. (J). 23.70 (978-1-56711-592-5(6) , Blackbirch Pr., Inc.) Thomson Gale.

Kudlinski, Kathleen. Sojourner Truth. 2003. (gr. 3-6). lib. bdg. 13.00 (978-0-613-61658-4(8)) Tandem Library Bks.

—Sojourner Truth: Voice for Freedom. Wooden, Lenny, illus. 2003. (Childhood of Famous Americans Ser.). 160p. (Orig.). mass mkt. 5.99 (978-0-689-85274-9(6) , Aladdin) Simon & Schuster Children's Publishing.

Kudlinski, Kathleen V. Rosa Parks. Henderson, Meryl, illus. 2001. (Childhood of Famous Americans Ser.). 224p. (gr. 3-7). mass mkt. 5.99 (978-0-689-83925-2(1) , Aladdin) Simon & Schuster Children's Publishing.

Kulling, Monica. Escape North! The Story of Harriet Tubman. Corey, Shana, ed. Flavin, Teresa, illus. 2000. (Step into Reading Step 3 Bks.). 48p. (J). (gr. 2-4). pap. 3.99 (978-0-375-80154-9(5) , Random Hse. Bks. for Young Readers) Random Hse. Children's Bks.

—Escape North! The Story of Harriet Tubman. Flavin, Teresa, illus. 2000. (Step into Reading Ser.). (J). 10.79 (978-0-606-19895-0(4)) Tandem Library Bks.

Kunstler, James Howard. Annie Oakley. Warter, Fred, illus. 2005. (Rabbit Ears-A Classic Tale Ser.). 40p. (J). (gr. k-5). 25.65 (978-1-59197-759-9(2)) Spotlight.

Lakin, Patricia. Abigail Adams: First Lady of the American Revolution. Bandelin, Debra & Dacey, Bob, illus. 2006. 48p. (J). lib. bdg. 15.00 **(*978-1-4242-1560-7(9))** Fitzgerald Bks.

Landau, Elaine. Heroine of the Titanic: The Real Unsinkable Molly Brown. 2001. (Illus.). 144p. (J). (gr. 5-9). tchr. ed. 19.00 (978-0-395-93912-3(7) , Clarion Bks.) Houghton Mifflin Co. Trade & Reference Div.

Larkin, Tanya. What Was Cooking in Julia Grant's White House? 2001. (Cooking Throughout American History Ser.). (Illus.). 24p. (J). (gr. 3). lib. bdg. 19.95 (978-0-8239-5611-1(3) , PowerKids Pr.) Rosen Publishing Group, Inc., The.

—What Was Cooking in Martha Washington's Presidential Mansions? 2001. (Cooking Throughout American History Ser.). (Illus.). 24p. (J). (gr. 3). lib. bdg. 19.95 (978-0-8239-5606-7(7) , PowerKids Pr.) Rosen Publishing Group, Inc., The.

Lauber, Leah F. Soccer Dreams: My True Adventure Following the U. S. Women's National Soccer Team, As a Fan & 12-Year Old Junior Reporter for the St. Petersburg Times During the History-Making 1999 FIFA Women's World Cup! 2003. (Illus.). 96p. (YA). per. 19.99 (978-0-9745480-0-5(6)) WCI Pr.

Leavitt, Amie. Nancy Pelosi. 2007. (Blue Banner Biography Ser.). (Illus.). 32p. (J). (gr. 4-8). lib. bdg. 25.70 **(*978-1-58415-613-0(9))** Mitchell Lane Pubs., Inc.

Leebrick, Kristal. Sojourner Truth. 2002. (Let Freedom Ring Ser.). (Illus.). 48p. (J). (gr. 3-4). lib. bdg. 22.60 (978-0-7368-1090-6(0) , Bridgestone Bks.) Capstone Pr., Inc.

Letters of a Woman Homesteader. 2003. (Our American Heritage Ser.). (J). pap. 62.00 incl. audio compact disk (978-1-58472-527-5(3) , In Audio) Sound Room Pubs., Inc.

LeVert, Suzanne. Hillary Rodham Clinton: First Lady. 1998. (Gateway Biography Ser.: 4). (Illus.). 48p. (gr. 2-4). pap. (978-1-56294-726-2(5) , Millbrook Pr.) Lerner Publishing Group.

Lewis, Meharry H. Mary Lena Lewis Tate - Vision! The Woman Who Compassed a Man, 2005. (Illus.). 484p. 75.00 (978-0-910003-08-7(4)) New & Living Way Publishing Co.

Livorse, Kay. Let Freedom Sing. Copeland, Greg, illus. 2002. 16p. (J). (978-0-439-35159-1(6)) Scholastic, Inc.

Loewen, Nancy. Hillary Rodham Clinton. 1998. (Ovations Ser.: Vol. 8). (Illus.). 32p. (YA). (gr. 4-7). lib. bdg. (978-0-88682-636-9(5) , Creative Education) Creative Co., The.

Lohse, Joyce B. Unsinkable: The Molly Brown Story. 2006. (Now You Know Bio Ser.). (J). pap. 8.95 **(*978-0-86541-081-7(X))** Filter Pr., LLC.

Lowery, Linda. Tia Clara Brown: Pionera Oficial. Porter, Janice Lee, illus. 2005. (SPA.). 48p. (J). (gr. 2-4). pap. 5.95 (978-0-8225-3129-6(1)) Lerner Publishing Group.

Lowry, Lois. Looking Back: A Book of Memories. 1998. (Illus.). 192p. (J). (gr. 4-6). tchr. ed. 17.00 (978-0-395-89543-6(X) , Walter Lorraine) Houghton Mifflin Co. Trade & Reference Div.

—Looking Back: A Book of Memories. 2000. (Illus.). 192p. (J). (gr. 4-7). pap. 14.95 (978-0-385-32699-5(8) , Delacorte Bks. for Young Readers) Random Hse. Children's Bks.

—Looking Back: A Book of Memories. 2000. (Illus.). (J). (978-0-606-18106-8(7)) Tandem Library Bks.

Ludwig, Elisa. Judy Blume. 2003. (Who Wrote That? Ser.). (Illus.). 112p. (gr. 6-12). 30.00 (978-0-7910-7619-4(9) , Chelsea Hse.) Facts On File, Inc.

Lutz, Norma Jean. Sojourner Truth. 2001. (gr. 5-8). lib. bdg. 17.60 (978-0-613-33074-9(9)) Tandem Library Bks.

—Sojourner Truth: Abolitionist, Suffragist, & Preacher. (Famous Figures of the Civil War Era Ser.). (Illus.). 80p. (J). (gr. 4-7). 2001. 25.00 (978-0-7910-6007-0(1)); 2000. pap. 25.00 (978-0-7910-6145-9(0)) Facts On File, Inc. (Chelsea Hse.).

Lynetter, Rachel. Julia Butterfly Hill. 2007. (Young Heros Ser.). 64p. (J). (gr. 4-8). 27.45 **(*978-0-7377-3628-1(3)** , Kidhaven) Thomson Gale.

MacLeod, Elizabeth. Helen Keller: A Determined Life. 2004. (Snapshots Ser.). (Illus.). 32p. (J). (gr. 4-6). (978-1-55337-509-8(2)); (978-1-55337-508-1(4)) Kids Can Pr., Ltd.

Mader, Jan. Elizabeth Blackwell. 2007. (J). (978-0-7368-6704-7(X) , Pebble Bks.) Capstone Pr., Inc.

Malam, John. Sojourner Truth. 2000. (Tell Me about Ser.). (Illus.). 22p. (J). 16.95 (978-0-237-51972-8(0) , Evans Brothers, Limited) Evans Publishing Group GBR. *Dist:* Independent Pubs. Group.

Mara, Wil. Laura Bush. 2003. (Rookie Biographies Ser.). (gr. 1-2). pap. 4.95 (978-0-516-27839-1(8)); (Illus.). 32p. (J). 20.50 (978-0-516-22854-9(4)) Scholastic Library Publishing. (Children's Pr.).

—Laura Bush. 2003. (gr. k-3). lib. bdg. 12.95 (978-0-613-67638-0(6)) Tandem Library Bks.

—Laura Ingalls Wilder. 2003. (Rookie Biographies Ser.). (gr. 1-2). pap. 4.95 (978-0-516-27840-7(1)); (Illus.). 32p. (J). 20.50 (978-0-516-22855-6(2)) Scholastic Library Publishing. (Children's Pr.).

—Rosa Parks. (Rookie Biographies Ser.). (Illus.). (J). 2004. 31p. (gr. 1-2). pap. 4.95 (978-0-516-27916-9(5)); 2003. 32p. 19.50 (978-0-516-25876-8(1)) Scholastic Library Publishing. (Children's Pr.).

Marcovitz, Hal. Eleanor Holmes Norton. 2003. (African American Leaders Ser.). (Illus.). 112p. (gr. 6-12). 30.00 (978-0-7910-7682-8(2) , Chelsea Hse.) Facts On File, Inc.

Marsh, Carole. Ada Deer. 2002. (One Thousand Readers Ser.). (Illus.). 12p. (J). (gr. k-4). 2.95 (978-0-635-01542-6(0) , 15420) Gallopade International.

—Condoleezza Rice. 2003. 12p. (gr. k-4). 2.95 **(*978-0-635-02385-8(7))** Gallopade International.

Marsh, Carole. Maggie Lena Walker. 2002. (One Thousand Readers Ser.). (Illus.). 12p. (J). (gr. k-4). 2.95 (978-0-635-01531-0(5) , 15315) Gallopade International.

Martinucci-Marsh, Licia. Laura: A Story about Laura Ingalls Wilder. 2002. (Illus.). 16p. (J). (978-0-439-35118-8(9)) Scholastic, Inc.

Mattern, Joanne. Coretta Scott King: Civil Rights Activist. 2003. (Reading Power Ser.). (Illus.). 24p. (J). lib. bdg. 17.25 (978-0-8239-6504-5(X) , PowerKids Pr.) Rosen Publishing Group, Inc., The.

—Elizabeth Cady Stanton & Susan B. Anthony: Fighting Together for Women's Rights. 2003. (Reading Power Ser.). (Illus.). 24p. (J). lib. bdg. 17.25 (978-0-8239-6503-8(1) , PowerKids Pr.) Rosen Publishing Group, Inc., The.

—Sojourner Truth: Early Abolitionist. 2003. (Reading Power Ser.). (Illus.). 24p. (J). lib. bdg. 17.25 (978-0-8239-6502-1(3) , PowerKids Pr.) Rosen Publishing Group, Inc., The.

Mayo, Edith P., ed. The Smithsonian Book of the First Ladies. 2004. (J). 29.95 (978-0-8050-7272-3(1) , Holt, Henry & Co. Bks. For Young Readers) Holt, Henry & Co.

McChesney, Sandra. Emily Dickinson. 2003. (gr. 7-12). lib. bdg. 21.05 (978-0-613-57178-4(9)) Tandem Library Bks.

McElroy, Lisa Tucker. Meet My Grandmother: She's a Supreme Court Justice. Benjamin, Joel, photos by. 1999. (Grandmothers at Work Ser.). (Illus.). 32p. (gr. 2-4). lib. bdg. 22.90 (978-0-7613-1566-7(7) , Millbrook Pr.) Lerner Publishing Group.

—Meet My Grandmother: She's a Supreme Court Justice. 1999. (978-0-606-18294-2(2)) Tandem Library Bks.

McElroy, Lisa Tucker & Feinstein Mariano, Eileen. Meet My Grandmother: She's a United States Senator. Benjamin, Joel, photos by. 2000. (Grandmothers at Work Ser.). (Illus.). 32p. (gr. 2-4). lib. bdg. 22.90 (978-0-7613-1721-0(X) , Millbrook Pr.) Lerner Publishing Group.

McIntosh-Wooten, Sara. Oprah Winfrey: Talk Show Legend. 1999. (African-American Biographies Ser.). (Illus.). 128p. (YA). (gr. 6-12). lib. bdg. 26.60 (978-0-7660-1207-3(7)) Enslow Pubs., Inc.

McKissack, Patricia C. & McKissack, Fredrick L. Sojourner Truth: A Voice for Freedom. rev. ed. 2002. (Great African Americans Ser.). (Illus.). 32p. (J). (gr. 1-4). lib. bdg. 18.60 (978-0-7660-1693-4(5)) Enslow Pubs., Inc.

McLeese, Don. Rosa Parks. 2002. (Rourke Discovery Library). (Illus.). 24p. (J). lib. bdg. 20.64 (978-1-58952-287-9(7)) Rourke Publishing, LLC.

McPherson, Stephanie Sammartino. Sisters Against Slavery: A Story about Sarah & Angelina Grimke. Ritz, Karen, illus. 64p. (J). pap. 22.60 (978-1-57505-815-3(4)); 1999. (gr. 3-6). lib. bdg. 21.27 (978-1-57505-361-5(6) , Carolrhoda Bks.) Lerner Publishing Group.

Medearis, Angela Shelf. Dare to Dream: Coretta Scott King & the Civil Rights Movement. Rich, Anna, illus. 1999. (Rainbow Biography Ser.). 64p. (J). (gr. 3-7). pap. 4.99 (978-0-14-130202-7(X) , Puffin) Penguin Group (USA) Inc.

—Dare to Dream: Coretta Scott King & the Civil Rights Movement. 1999. (gr. 3-6). lib. bdg. 13.00 (978-0-613-14663-0(8)) Tandem Library Bks.

Mello, Tara Baukus. Danica Patrick. 2007. (Race Car Legends: Ser.). 72p. (J). (gr. 5-8). 25.00 (*978-0-7910-9126-5(0) , Chelsea Hse.) Facts On File, Inc.

Mendelsohn, James. Barbara Jordan: Getting Things Done. 2000. (Single Titles Ser.: up). (Illus.). 192p. (J). (gr. 7 up). lib. bdg. (978-0-7613-1467-7(9) , Twenty-First Century Bks.) Lerner Publishing Group.

Miller, Connie Colwell. Mother Jones: Labor Leader. Erwin, Steve & Barnett, Charles, illus. 2007. (Graphic Library). 32p. (J). (*978-0-7368-9662-7(7)) Capstone Pr., Inc.

Miller, Debra A. Dolores Huerta: Labor Leader. 2006. (Twentieth Century's Most Influential Hispanics Ser.). 112p. (J). (gr. 7-10). lib. bdg. 32.45 (978-1-59018-971-9(X) , Lucent Bks.) Thomson Gale.

Miller, Norma. Stompin' at the Savoy: The Story of Norma Miller. French, Martin, illus. 2006. 64p. (J). (gr. 4-8). 15.99 (978-0-7636-2244-2(3)) Candlewick Pr.

Milton, Joyce. Sacajawea: Her True Story. 2001. (gr. k-3). lib. bdg. 11.80 (978-0-613-64103-6(5)) Tandem Library Bks.

Moore, Heidi. Elizabeth Cady Stanton. 2004. (American Lives (Heinemann Library (Firm))). (Illus.). 32p. (J). pap. 6.95 (978-1-4034-5705-9(0)); lib. bdg. (978-1-4034-4994-8(5)) Heinemann Library.

—Ida B. Wells-Barnett. 2004. (Illus.). 32p. (J). pap. 6.95 (978-1-4034-5706-6(9)) Heinemann Library.

—Luisa Moreno. 2005. 32p. (J). (978-1-4034-6978-6(4)); pap. (978-1-4034-6985-4(7)) Heinemann Library.

Morales, Leslie. Esther Dyson: Internet Visionary. 2003. (Internet Biographies Ser.). (Illus.). 48p. (J). (gr. 4-10). lib. bdg. 23.93 (978-0-7660-1973-7(X)) Enslow Pubs., Inc.

Morgan, Terri. Venus & Serena Williams: Grand Slam Sisters. (Sports Achievers Biographies Ser.). (Illus.). 2005. 80p. (gr. 7-12). lib. bdg. 22.60 (978-0-8225-3684-0(6)); 2003. 64p. (J). (gr. 4-9). pap. 5.95 (978-0-8225-9866-4(3) , Carolrhoda Bks.) Lerner Publishing Group.

Morris, Roz. Rosa Parks: Mother of the Civil Rights Movement. 2003. (Alabama Roots Biography Ser.). (Illus.). 109p. (J). (978-1-878561-57-2(X)) Seacoast Publishing, Inc.

Mortensen, Lori. Amelia Earhart: Female Pioneer in Flight. McGuire, Robert, illus. 2007. (J). lib. bdg. (*978-1-4048-3728-7(0)) Picture Window Bks.

—Harriet Tubman: Hero of the Underground Railroad. Moore, Frances, illus. 2006. (Biographies Ser.). 24p. (J). (gr. k-3). lib. bdg. 23.93 (*978-1-4048-3103-2(7)) Picture Window Bks.

Moss, Marissa. Mighty Jackie: The Strike-Out Queen. Payne, C. F., tr. Payne, C. F., illus. 2004. 32p. (J). 16.95 (978-0-689-86329-5(2) , Simon & Schuster/Paula Wiseman Bks.) Simon & Schuster Children's Publishing.

Naden, Corinne J. & Blue, Rose. Condoleeza Rice. 2004. (African-American Biographies Ser.). (Illus.). 64p. (J). 28.56 (978-1-4109-1039-4(3)) Raintree.

Nichols, Joan Kane. Civil War Heroines. 2005. (Illus.). 16p. (J). (*978-0-328-14901-8(2) , Scott Foresman) Addison-Wesley Educational Pubs., Inc.

—The Civil War Sisterhood: Women Who Made a Difference. 2005. (Illus.). 16p. (J). (*978-0-328-14902-5(0) , Scott Foresman) Addison-Wesley Educational Pubs., Inc.

—Women of the Civil War. 2005. (Illus.). 16p. (J). (*978-0-328-14900-1(4) , Scott Foresman) Addison-Wesley Educational Pubs., Inc.

Nobleman, Marc Tyler. Rosa Parks. 2002. (Trailblazers of the Modern World Ser.). (Illus.). 48p. (J). (gr. 5 up). pap. 14.95 (978-0-8368-5231-8(1)); lib. bdg. 30.00 (978-0-8368-5071-0(8)) Stevens, Gareth Inc. (World Almanac Library).

—Rosa Parks. 2002. (gr. 3-6). lib. bdg. 19.90 (978-0-613-76804-7(3)) Tandem Library Bks.

Norgren, Jill. Belva Lockwood: The Woman Who Would Be President. 2007. (Illus.). 344p. 35.00 (*978-0-8147-5834-2(7)) New York Univ. Pr.

Nothing Stood in Her Way, Captain Julie Clark. 2004. 232p. 24.95 (978-0-9749190-0-3(4)) Women in Aviation, International.

O'Connell, Diane. Strong Force: The Story of Physicist Shirley Ann Jackson. 2005. (Women's Adventures in Science Ser.). (Illus.). 110p. (YA). (gr. 5-8). 31.00 (978-0-531-16784-7(4) , Watts, Franklin) Scholastic Library Publishing.

Olmstead, Mary. Antonia Novella. 2004. (J). pap. 9.50 (978-1-4109-0918-3(2)); (Illus.). lib. bdg. 28.56 (978-1-4109-0712-7(0)) Raintree.

Pappas, Rita. Barbra Streisand: Entertainer. 2000. (Women of Achievement Ser.). (Illus.). 112p. (J). (gr. 4-7). 30.00 (978-0-7910-5285-3(0) , Chelsea Hse.) Facts On File, Inc.

Parks, Deborah. Nature's Machines: The Story of Biomechanist Mimi Koehl. 2006. (Women's Adventures in Science Ser.). (Illus.). 128p. pap. 9.95 (978-0-309-09559-4(X) , Joseph Henry Pr.) National Academies Pr.

Parks, Deborah A. Nature's Machines: The Story of Biomechanist Mimi Koehl. 2005. (Women's Adventures in Science Ser.). (Illus.). ix, 118p. (J). (978-0-531-16955-1(3) , Watts, Franklin) Scholastic Library Publishing.

Parks, Rosa. I Am Rosa Parks. 2000. (gr. k-3). lib. bdg. 11.80 (978-0-613-22996-8(7)); (Illus.). (J). 10.79 (978-0-606-18410-6(4)) Tandem Library Bks.

—Rosa Parks: My Story. 1999. (Illus.). 200p. (YA). (gr. 5-9). pap. 6.99 (978-0-14-130120-4(1) , Puffin) Penguin Group (USA) Inc.

—Rosa Parks: My Story. 1999. (978-0-606-15995-1(9)); (gr. 5-8). lib. bdg. 15.30 (978-0-613-15120-7(8)) Tandem Library Bks.

Parks, Rosa & Haskins, Jim. I Am Rosa Parks. Clay, Wil, illus. 1999. (Easy-to-Read Ser.). 48p. (J). (gr. 1-3). pap. 3.99 (978-0-14-130710-7(2) , Puffin) Penguin Group (USA) Inc.

Patrick, Jean L. S. The Girl Who Struck Out Babe Ruth. 2000. (J). (978-0-606-19443-3(6)) Tandem Library Bks.

Petrick, Neila Skinner. Jane Wilkinson Long: Texas Pioneer. Haynes, Joyce, illus. 2004. 32p. (J). pap. 15.95 (978-1-58980-147-9(4)) Pelican Publishing Co., Inc.

Philips, Jane H. Gloria Estefan. 2001. (Women of Achievement Ser.). (Illus.). (J). 111p. pap. 9.95 (978-0-7910-5884-8(0)); 112p. (gr. 4-7). 30.00 (978-0-7910-5883-1(2)) Facts On File, Inc. (Chelsea Hse.).

Pingry, Patricia A. The Story of Coretta Scott King. Walker, Steven, illus. 2007. 26p. (J). (ps-k). bds. 6.99 (*978-0-8249-6717-8(8) , Candy Cane Pr.) Ideals Pubns.

Plourde, Lynn. What a President She Would Have Been: Margaret Chase Smith. 2008. (J). (*978-1-58089-234-6(5)) Charlesbridge Publishing, Inc.

Polette, Nancy. Biography, by Golly! 2004. (J). pap. 7.50 (978-1-931334-49-5(8)) Pieces of Learning.

Ponti, James. WNBA: Stars of Women's Basketball. 1999. (J). (978-0-606-19505-8(X)) Tandem Library Bks.

Presnall, Judith Janda. Oprah Winfrey. 1998. (People in the News Ser.). (Illus.). 112p. (YA). (gr. 6-9). 27.45 (978-1-56006-360-5(2) , Lucent Bks.) Thomson Gale.

Press, Petra. Coretta Scott King: An Unauthorized Biography. 1999. (Profiles Ser.). (Illus.). 56p. (J). (gr. 4-6). lib. bdg. 24.22 (978-1-57572-496-6(0)) Heinemann Library.

Pyle, Lydia. Venus & Serena Williams. 2004. (Awesome Athletes Ser.). (Illus.). 32p. (J). (gr. k-6). lib. bdg. 22.78 (978-1-59197-486-4(0)) ABDO Publishing Co.

Raatma, Lucia. Great Women of the Civil War. 2004. (We the People Ser.). (Illus.). 48p. (J). 22.60 (978-0-7565-0839-5(8)) Compass Point Bks.

—Jane Addams. 2004. (Compass Point Early Biographies Ser.). (Illus.). 32p. (J). (gr. 2 up). lib. bdg. 21.26 (978-0-7565-0566-0(6)) Compass Point Bks.

—Laura Ingalls Wilder: Teacher & Author. 2001. (Career Biographies Ser.). (Illus.). 128p. (J). (gr. 6-12). 25.00 (978-0-89434-375-9(0) , F418, Ferguson Publishing Co.) Facts On File, Inc.

Rand, Carol. Lydia Darragh: Quaker Patriot. Marshall, Dan, illus. (J). 15.95 (978-0-945912-33-0(1)) Pippin Pr.

Randolph, Ryan P. Frontier Women Who Helped Shape the American West. 2003. (Library of the Westward Expansion). (Illus.). 24p. (J). lib. bdg. 19.95 (978-0-8239-6297-6(0) , PowerKids Pr.) Rosen Publishing Group, Inc., The.

—Harriet Beecher Stowe: Author & Abolitionist. 2005. (Library of American Lives & Times). (Illus.). 112p. (J). (gr. 4-8). lib. bdg. 31.95 (978-0-8239-6623-3(2)) Rosen Publishing Group, Inc., The.

Raum, Elizabeth. Alice Paul. 2004. (American Lives (Heinemann Library (Firm))). (Illus.). 32p. (J). pap. 7.50 (978-1-4034-5703-5(4)); lib. bdg. (978-1-4034-4996-2(1)) Heinemann Library.

—Clara Barton. 2004. (Illus.). 32p. (J). pap. 6.95 (978-1-4034-5704-2(2)); lib. bdg. (978-1-4034-4993-1(7)) Heinemann Library.

—Mae Jemison. 2005. (American Lives Ser.). (Illus.). 32p. (J). (978-1-4034-6942-7(3)); pap. (978-1-4034-6949-6(0)) Heinemann Library.

Redmond, Shirley-Raye. Patriots in Petticoats. 2005. (Illus.). 128p. (J). (gr. 3-7). lib. bdg. 13.04 (978-0-606-32535-6(2)) Tandem Library Bks.

—Patriots in Petticoats: Heroines of the American Revolution. 2004. (Landmark Bks.). (Illus.). 144p. (J). (gr. 3). lib. bdg. 16.99 (978-0-375-92357-9(8) , Random Hse. Bks. for Young Readers) Random Hse. Children's Bks.

Reed, Jennifer. Elizabeth Bloomer, Child Labor Activist. 2006. (Illus.). 64p. (J). (gr. 4-8). 27.45 (978-0-7377-3615-1(1) , Kidhaven) Thomson Gale.

Renehan, Edward. The Clintons. 2005. (J). (978-0-7910-8526-4(0) , Chelsea Hse.) Facts On File, Inc.

Rhodes, Lisa Renee. Coretta Scott King: Humanitarian. 1999. (Black Americans of Achievement Ser.). (Illus.). 144p. (YA). (gr. 4-7). 30.00 (978-0-7910-4690-6(7)); (gr. 5 up). pap. 6.65 (978-0-7910-4691-3(5)) Facts On File, Inc. (Chelsea Hse.).

Rhynes, Martha E. Gwendolyn Brooks: Poet from Chicago. 2004. (World Writers Ser.). (Illus.). 112p. (YA). (gr. 6-12). 23.95 (978-1-931798-05-1(2)) Reynolds, Morgan Inc.

Rieken, Ethel Plaep. Growing Pains: A Childhood on Bear Creek. Zander, Julie McDonald, ed. Slavens, Rick, photos by. 2004. (Illus.). 140p. (YA). per. 23.00 (978-0-9740348-2-9(7) , Special Editions — Customized Biographies) Slavens Enterprises, LLC.

Rinaldo, Denise. Amelia Earhart: With a Discussion of Courage. 2004. (Values in Action Ser.). (J). (978-1-59203-068-2(8)) Learning Challenge, Inc.

—Rosa Parks: With a Discussion of Courage. 2003. (Values in Action Ser.). (J). (978-1-59203-061-3(0)) Learning Challenge, Inc.

Robbins, Trina. Hedy Lamarr & a Secret Communication System. 2007. (Illus.). 32p. (J). (*978-0-7368-9641-2(4)) Capstone Pr., Inc.

Rockwell, Anne F. Only Passing Through. 2002. (gr. 3-6). lib. bdg. 15.30 (978-0-613-86684-2(3)) Tandem Library Bks.

—Only Passing Through: The Story of Sojourner Truth. Siscoe, Nancy, ed. Christie, R. Gregory, illus. 2000. 40p. (J). (gr. 2-5). 16.95 (978-0-679-89186-4(2)); lib. bdg. 18.99 (978-0-679-99186-1(7)) Random Hse. Children's Bks. (Knopf Bks. for Young Readers).

—They Called Her Molly Pitcher. von Buhler, Cynthia, illus. 2002. 40p. (J). (gr. 2-5). 16.95 (978-0-679-89187-1(0) , Knopf Bks. for Young Readers) Random Hse. Children's Bks.

Roop, Connie & Roop, Peter. Sojourner Truth. 2003. (In Their Own Words Ser.). (Illus.). 128p. (J). (gr. 2-5). 4.99 (978-0-439-26323-8(9) , Scholastic Nonfiction) Scholastic, Inc.

Roop, Peter. Sojourner Truth. 2002. (gr. 3-6). lib. bdg. 12.40 (978-0-613-66669-5(0)) Tandem Library Bks.

Rose, Drew, illus. Molly Pitcher. 2004. (Imagination Ser.). 32p. (J). (gr. 3 up). 22.60 (978-0-7565-0604-9(2)) Compass Point Bks.

Rosen, Roslyn, intro. Business & Industry. 1999. (Female Firsts in Their Fields Ser.). (Illus.). 64p. (J). (gr. 4-7). 12.95 (978-0-7910-5142-9(0)) Facts On File, Inc.

Ross, Michael Elsohn. Pond Watching with Ann Morgan. Smith, Wendy, illus. 2005. (Naturalist's Apprentice Biographies Ser.). 48p. (J). (gr. 3-6). lib. bdg. 19.93 (978-1-57505-385-1(3)) Lerner Publishing Group.

Roycroft, Mitch. Jennifer Harman. 2008. (J). (*978-1-4222-0227-2(5)) Mason Crest Pubs.

Ruffin, Frances E. Her Story, Her Words: The Narrative of Sojourner Truth. 2004. (Great Moments in American History Ser.). (Illus.). 32p. (J). (gr. 4-8). lib. bdg. 21.25 (978-0-8239-4387-6(9) , Rosen Central) Rosen Publishing Group, Inc., The.

—Molly Pitcher. 2002. (American Legends Ser.). (Illus.). 24p. (J). (gr. 3). lib. bdg. 18.75 (978-0-8239-5829-0(9) , PowerKids Pr.) Rosen Publishing Group, Inc., The.

—Sojourner Truth. 2002. (American Legends Ser.). (Illus.). 24p. (J). (gr. 3). lib. bdg. 18.75 (978-0-8239-5826-9(4) , PowerKids Pr.) Rosen Publishing Group, Inc., The.

Rutledge, Rachel. Mia Hamm: Striking Superstar. 2000. (YA). (978-0-606-20196-4(3)) Tandem Library Bks.

Ryan, Bernard. Condoleeza Rice: National Security Advisor & Musician. 2003. (Ferguson Career Biographies Ser.). (Illus.). 160p. (J). (gr. 6-12). 25.00 (978-0-8160-5480-0(0) , Ferguson Publishing Co.) Facts On File, Inc.

—Hillary Rodham Clinton: First Lady & Senator. 2004. (Ferguson Career Biographies Ser.). (Illus.). 160p. (J). (gr. 6-12). 25.00 (978-0-8160-5544-9(0) , Ferguson Publishing Co.) Facts On File, Inc.

Sabin, Francene. Helen Keller: Una Chica Valiente. abr. ed. 2007. 64p. (J). pap. 3.99 (*978-0-439-87999-6(X) , Scholastic en Espanol) Scholastic, Inc.

Sabin, Francene & Mattern, Joanne. Helen Keller, Girl of Courage. Meyer, Jean, illus. 2006. 56p. (J). (*978-0-439-66043-3(2)) Scholastic, Inc.

Salisbury, Cynthia. Elizabeth Cady Stanton: Leader of the Fight for Women's Rights. 2002. (Historical American Biographies Ser.). (Illus.). 128p. (YA). (gr. 6-9). lib. bdg. 26.60 (978-0-7660-1616-3(1)) Enslow Pubs., Inc.

Savage, Jeff. Danica Patrick. 2007. (Amazing Athletes Ser.). (Illus.). 32p. (J). 23.93 (978-0-8225-5954-2(4) , Lerner Pubns.) Lerner Publishing Group.

—Marion Jones. 2005. (J). pap. 5.95 (978-0-8225-2040-5(0) , First Avenue Editions); (Illus.). (gr. 3-4). lib. bdg. 22.60 (978-0-8225-3657-4(9)) Lerner Publishing Group.

Schaefer, A. R. Serena & Venus Williams. 2002. (Sports Heroes Ser.). (Illus.). 48p. (J). (gr. 3-4). lib. bdg. 21.26 (978-0-7368-1054-8(4) , Capstone High-Interest Bks.) Capstone Pr., Inc.

Schaefer, Lola M. Rosa Parks. Saunders-Smith, Gail, ed. 2002. (First Biographies Ser.). (Illus.). 24p. (J). (gr. k-1). lib. bdg. 15.93 (978-0-7368-1176-7(1) , Pebble Bks.) Capstone Pr., Inc.

Schlank, Carol Hilgartner & Metzger, Barbara. A Clean Sea: The Rachel Carson Story. Cohen, Judith Love, ed. Katz, David Arthur, illus. l.t. ed. 2002. 40p. (J). 13.95 (978-1-880599-61-7(9)) Cascade Pass, Inc.

Schraff, Anne. Harriet Tubman: Moses of the Underground Railroad. 2001. (African-American Biographies Ser.). (Illus.). 128p. (J). (gr. 6-12). lib. bdg. 26.60 (978-0-7660-1548-7(3)) Enslow Pubs., Inc.

Schraff, Anne E. Rosa Parks: Tired of Giving In. 2005. (African-American Biography Library). (Illus.). 128p. (J). (gr. 6-12). lib. bdg. 31.93 (978-0-7660-2463-2(6)) Enslow Pubs., Inc.

Schroeder, Alan. Minty: A Story of Young Harriet Tubman. 2000. (YA). (978-0-606-20246-6(3)) Tandem Library Bks.

Schuman, Michael. Halle Berry: Beauty Is Not Just Physical. 2006. (African-American Biography Library). (Illus.). 112p. (YA). lib. bdg. 31.93 (978-0-7660-2467-0(9)) Enslow Pubs., Inc.

Segovia, Patty. Skate Girls. 2006. (Girls Rock! Ser.). (Illus.). 32p. (J). (gr. 1-5). 24.21 (978-1-59296-748-3(5)) Child's World, Inc.

Sharp, Anne Wallace. Condoleezza Rice. 2007. (People in the News Ser.). (Illus.). 128p. (gr. 7-10). 31.20 (*978-1-59018-521-6(8) , Lucent Bks.) Thomson Gale.

Sherman, Josepha. Venus Williams. 2001. (Sports Files Ser.). (Illus.). 32p. (J). (gr. 1-3). lib. bdg. (978-1-58810-116-7(9)) Heinemann Library.

Shichtman, Sandra H. Nancy Peolosi. 2007. (Political Profiles Ser.). (Illus.). 112p. (YA). (gr. 5 up). lib. bdg. 27.95 (*978-1-59935-049-3(1)) Reynolds, Morgan Inc.

Shields, Charles J. Martha Stewart. 2002. (gr. 5-8). lib. bdg. 18.75 (978-0-613-50964-0(1)) Tandem Library Bks.

Shores, Erika L. Rosa Parks: Civil Rights Poineer. 2005. (Fact Finders Ser.). (Illus.). 32p. (J). (ps-7). lib. bdg. 22.60 (978-0-7368-3746-0(9)) Capstone Pr., Inc.

Sigerman, Harriet. Elizabeth Cady Stanton: The Right Is Ours. 2001. (Oxford Portraits Ser.). (Illus.). 144p. (YA). (gr. 8 up). suppl. ed. 28.00 (978-0-19-511969-5(X)) Oxford Univ. Pr., Inc.

Simms, Patsy Ford. Harriet's Freedom Train. 2000. (J). stu. ed. 12.50 (978-0-7692-9377-6(8)); tchr. ed. 24.95 (978-0-7692-9376-9(X)) Alfred Publishing Co., Inc. (Warner Bros. Pubns.).

Simon, Charnan. Rachel Carson: Author & Environmentalist. 2003. (Spirit of America). (Illus.). 32p. (J). (gr. 2-6). 27.07 (978-1-59296-011-8(1)) Child's World, Inc.

Slade, Suzanne. Sojourner Truth: Preacher for Freedom & Equality. Blanks, Natascha Alex, illus. 2007. (J). lib. bdg. (*978-1-4048-3726-3(4)) Picture Window Bks.

Slavicek, Louise Chipley. Women of the American Revolution. 2002. (Women in History Ser.). (Illus.). 112p. (J). 27.45 (978-1-59018-172-0(7) , Lucent Bks.) Thomson Gale.

Slaymaker, Melissa Eskridge. Bottle Houses: The Creative World of Grandma Prisbrey. Paschkis, Julie, tr. Paschkis, Julie, illus. rev. ed. 2004. 32p. (J). 17.95 (978-0-8050-7131-3(8) , Holt, Henry & Co. Bks. For Young Readers) Holt, Henry & Co.

Somervill, Barbara A. Votes for Women! The Story of Carrie Chapman Catt. 2004. (Feminist Voices Ser.). (Illus.). 128p. (YA). (gr. 6-12). 23.95 (978-1-883846-96-1(X) , First Biographies) Reynolds, Morgan Inc.

Soto, Gary. Jessie de la Cruz: A Profile of A United Farm Worker. 2000. (gr. 7-12). lib. bdg. 18.75 (978-0-613-59154-6(2)) Tandem Library Bks.

Spangenburg, Ray & Moser, Diane Kit. Chien-Shiung Wu: The Elegance of Experiment. 2008. (Makers of Modern Science Ser.). 160p. (gr. 6-12). 29.95 (*978-0-8160-6177-8(7) , Chelsea Hse.) Facts On File, Inc.

Spirn, Michele. Against the Odds: The Jackie Joyner-Kersee Story. 2001. (YA). pap. (978-1-56765-063-1(5) , R692P) AMSCO Schl. Pubns., Inc.

Steele, Phillip. Rosa Parks & Her Protest for Civil Rights. 2002. (Dates with History Ser.). (Illus.). 31p. (J). lib. bdg. 24.25 (978-1-58340-215-3(2)) Smart Apple Media.

Stewart, Mark. Venus & Serena Williams: Sisters in Arms. 2000. (New Wave Ser.). (Illus.). 48p. (gr. 4 up). lib. bdg. 22.90 (978-0-7613-1803-3(8) , Millbrook Pr.) Lerner Publishing Group.

Stille, Darlene R. Madam C.J. Walker: Entrepreneur & Millionaire. (Signature Lives Ser.). (Illus.). 112p. (J). 2007. pap. (*978-0-7565-2203-2(X) , 1265883); 2006. (*978-0-7565-1883-7(0) , 1265883) Compass Point Bks.

Stone, Amy. Maya Lin. 2003. (Raintree Biographies Ser.). (Illus.). 32p. (J). lib. bdg. 25.70 (978-0-7398-6863-8(2)) Raintree.

—Maya Lin. 2003. (gr. 3-6). lib. bdg. 15.90 (978-0-613-78165-7(1)) Tandem Library Bks.

Stone, Tanya. Amelia Earhart. 2007. (Biography Ser.). 128p. (J). (gr. 3-8). pap. 4.99 (978-0-7566-2552-8(1)); (Illus.). 14.99 (978-0-7566-2553-5(X)) Dorling Kindersley Publishing, Inc.

Stone, Tanya Lee. Laura Welch Bush: First Lady. 2001. (gr. 3-6). lib. bdg. 18.75 (978-0-613-44592-4(9)) Tandem Library Bks.

—Oprah Winfrey: Success with an Open Heart. 2001. (Gateway Biography Ser.). (Illus.). 48p. (gr. 2-4). pap. (978-0-7613-1389-2(3) , Millbrook Pr.) Lerner Publishing Group.

Streissguth, Thomas. Wilma Rudolph. 2007. (Sports Heroes & Legends Ser.). (J). 27.93 (978-0-8225-5958-0(7) , Twenty-First Century Bks.) Lerner Publishing Group.

Strudwick, Leslie. Laura Ingalls Wilder. 2002. (My Favorite Writer Ser.). (Illus.). 32p. (J). lib. bdg. 18.20 (978-1-59036-027-9(3)) Weigl Pubs., Inc.

Sullivan, George. Berenice Abbott, Photographer: An Independent Vision. 2006. (Illus.). 176p. (J). (gr. 5-9). 20.00 (978-0-618-44026-9(7) , Clarion Bks.) Houghton Mifflin Co. Trade & Reference Div.

Sutcliffe, Jane. Helen Keller. Verstraete, Elaine, illus. 2002. (On My Own Biographies Ser.). 48p. (J). lib. bdg. 23.93 (978-0-87614-600-2(0) , Carolrhoda Bks.) Lerner Publishing Group.

—Helen Keller. 2002. (gr. 3-6). lib. bdg. 14.10 (978-0-613-52398-1(9)) Tandem Library Bks.

Swain, Gwenyth. Civil Rights Pioneer: A Story about Mary Church Terrell. Beier, Ellen, illus. 64p. (J). pap. 6.95 (978-0-8225-4170-7(X)); 1999. (gr. 4-8). lib. bdg. 22.60 (978-1-57505-355-4(1)) Lerner Publishing Group.

—Civil Rights Pioneer: A Story about Mary Church Terrell. 1999. (gr. 3-6). lib. bdg. 15.25 (978-0-613-68325-8(0)) Tandem Library Bks.

—Sojourner Truth. Archambault, Matthew, illus. 2005. (On My Own Biography Ser.). 48p. (J). (ps-ps). pap. 5.95 (978-1-57505-827-6(8)) Lerner Publishing Group.

—Sojourner Truth. 2005. (On My Own Biography Ser.). (Illus.). 48p. (J). 25.26 (978-1-57505-651-7(8) , Carolrhoda Bks.) Lerner Publishing Group.

Swanson, June. Venus & Serena Williams. Burke, Susan S., illus. 2003. (You Must Be Joking! Riddle Bks.). 32p. (J). (gr. 2-5). pap. 5.95 (978-0-8225-9842-8(6)) Lerner Publishing Group.

Sword of a Champion: The Sharon Monplaisir Story. 2003. (Anything You Can Do. . .Ser.: Vol. 2). (Illus.). 96p. (J). (gr. 2-5). pap. 9.95 (978-1-930546-39-4(4)) Wish Publishing.

Szabo, Corinne. Sky Pioneer: A Photobiography of Amelia Earhart. 2007. (Illus.). 64p. (J). (gr. 5). 7.95 (978-1-4263-0044-8(1) , National Geographic Children's Bks.) National Geographic Society.

Tamra, Orr. Abby Wambach. 2007. (No Hands Allowed Ser.). (Illus.). 32p. (J). lib. bdg. 25.70 (***978-1-58415-601-7(5)***) Mitchell Lane Pubs., Inc.

Taylor, Bonnie Highsmith. Women with Grit. 1999. (Cover-to-Cover Informational Bks.). 64p. (J). (gr. 4-7). lib. bdg. 17.95 (978-0-7807-9019-3(7) , Covercraft); (Illus.). (gr. 5-7). 8.95 (978-0-7891-5045-5(X)) Perfection Learning Corp.

Thornburg, BillieSnyder. Bertie & Me & Miles Too: Growing up on a Nebraska Sandhill Ranch in the Early 1900s. 2003. (Illus.). 144p. per. 16.95 (978-0-9721613-3-6(3)) Old Hundred & One Pr. Publishing Co., The.

Thornton, Jeremy. Famous Women of the American Revolution. 2003. (Building Americas Democracy Ser.). 24p. (J). lib. bdg. 19.95 (978-0-8239-6276-1(8) , PowerKids Pr.) Rosen Publishing Group, Inc., The.

Thorp, Annie E. J. So Very Rosemary. 2000. (Illus.). 32p. (ps-3). pap. 7.99 (978-0-8254-3846-2(2)) Kregel Pubns.

Tokunaga, Wendy. Christina Aguilera. 2002. (Famous People Ser.). (Illus.). 48p. (J). (gr. 3-5). 26.20 (978-0-7377-1385-5(2) , Kidhaven) Thomson Gale.

Tremblay, E. A. Rachel Carson. 2003. (Women in the Science Ser.). (Illus.). 118p. pap. 30.00 (978-0-7910-7520-3(6)); 112p. (gr. 6-12). 30.00 (978-0-7910-7244-8(4)) Facts On File, Inc. (Chelsea Hse.).

Troy, Don. Harriet Ross Tubman. 1999. (Journey to Freedom Ser.). (Illus.). 40p. (J). (gr. 3-7). 28.50 (978-1-56766-568-0(3)) Child's World, Inc.

Trumbauer, Lisa. Eleanor Roosevelt. 2004. (First Biographies Ser.). (Illus.). 24p. (J). lib. bdg. 15.93 (978-0-7368-2080-6(9) , Pebble Bks.) Capstone Pr., Inc.

—Let's Meet Sojourner Truth. 2003. (Let's Meet Biographies Ser.). (Illus.). 32p. (gr. 2-4). 23.00 (978-0-7910-7323-0(8) , Chelsea Hse.) Facts On File, Inc.

Venezia, Mike. Grandma Moses. 2003. (Getting to Know World Artists Ser.). (Illus.). 32p. (J). 27.00 (978-0-516-22027-7(6) , Children's Pr.) Scholastic Library Publishing.

Wade, Linda R. Condoleeza Rice. l.t. ed. 2002. (Real-Life Reader Biography Ser.). (Illus.). 32p. (gr. 3-8). lib. bdg. 15.95 (978-1-58415-145-6(5)) Mitchell Lane Pubs., Inc.

—Condoleezza Rice. 2004. (Illus.). 32p. (J). lib. bdg. (978-1-58415-332-0(6)) Mitchell Lane Pubs., Inc.

Wade, Mary. Condoleeza Rice: Being the Best. 2003. (gr. 3-6). lib. bdg. 17.60 (978-0-613-58959-8(9)) Tandem Library Bks.

Wade, Mary Dodson. Condoleezza Rice. rev. ed. 2005. (Illus.). 48p. (J). (ps-7). pap. 6.95 (978-0-7613-9549-2(0) , First Avenue Editions) Lerner Publishing Group.

—Condoleezza Rice: Being the Best. 2003. (Gateway Biography Ser.: 4). 48p. lib. bdg. 23.90 (978-0-7613-2619-9(7)); (Illus.). (gr. 2-4). pap. (978-0-7613-1927-6(1)) Lerner Publishing Group. (Millbrook Pr.).

Wagner, Heather Lehr. Hillary Rodham Clinton. 2004. (Women in Politics Ser.). (Illus.). 120p. 30.00 (978-0-7910-7735-1(7)); 110p. pap. 30.00 (978-0-7910-7999-7(6)) Facts On File, Inc. (Chelsea Hse.).

Walker, Niki. Milliner. 2002. (gr. k-3). lib. bdg. 16.40 (978-0-613-82418-7(0)) Tandem Library Bks.

Walker, Pamela. Laura Ingalls Wilder. 2001. (Real People Ser.). (Illus.). 24p. (J). (ps-2). 17.00 (978-0-516-23435-9(8)); pap. 4.95 (978-0-516-23589-9(3)) Scholastic Library Publishing. (Children's Pr.).

—Laura Ingalls Wilder. 2001. (gr. k-3). lib. bdg. 12.95 (978-0-613-58846-1(0)) Tandem Library Bks.

Walker, Sally M. Bessie Coleman: Daring to Fly. 2003. (gr. 3-6). lib. bdg. 14.10 (978-0-613-58890-4(8)) Tandem Library Bks.

Wallner, Alexandra. Abigail Adams. 2005. (Illus.). 32p. (J). pap. 6.95 (978-0-8234-1942-5(8)) Holiday Hse., Inc.

Ward, S. Meet Laura Ingalls Wilder. 2001. (About the Author Ser.). (Illus.). 24p. (J). (gr. 3). lib. bdg. 18.75 (978-0-8239-5712-5(8) , PowerKids Pr.) Rosen Publishing Group, Inc., The.

Washington, Shirley. A Gift for Girls: Words of Wisdom from Successful Women. 2005. 152p. (YA). per. 12.95 (978-1-933285-06-1(0)) Brown Bks. Publishing Group.

Watson, Marilyn Myrick. Rose Mofford. 2007. (J). per. 6.95 (***978-0-9790826-1-0(7)***) Acacia Publishing, Inc.

—Rose Perica Mofford. 2006. (J). (***978-0-9788283-5-6(6)***) Acacia Publishing, Inc.

Waxman, Laura Hamilton. Sojourner Truth. 2008. (History Maker Biographies Ser.). (J). lib. bdg. 26.60 (***978-0-8225-7172-8(2)*** , Lerner Pubns.) Lerner Publishing Group.

Weber, Terri Smith. Jennifer Lopez: Realizando Los Suenos. 2003. (SPA.). (J). pap. (978-0-9740180-4-1(X)); lib. bdg. (978-0-9740180-3-4(1)) Panda Publishing, L.L.C. (Bios for Kids).

Weidt, Maryann N. Harriet Tubman. (History Maker Bios Ser.). (Illus.). (J). 2003. 47p. 26.60 (978-0-8225-4676-4(0)); 2002. 48p. pap. 6.95 (978-0-8225-4803-4(8)) Lerner Publishing Group. (Lerner Pubns.).

—Rosa Parks. 2003. (History Maker Bios Ser.). (Illus.). 47p. (J). 26.60 (978-0-8225-4673-3(6) , Lerner Pubns.) Lerner Publishing Group.

Wells, Peggysue. Fergie. 2007. (Blue Banner Biography Ser.). (Illus.). 32p. (J). (gr. 4-8). lib. bdg. 25.70 (978-1-58415-521-8(3)) Mitchell Lane Pubs., Inc.

Westen, Robin. Oprah Winfrey: I Dont Believe in Failure. 2005. (African-American Biography Library). (Illus.). 128p. (J). (gr. 6-12). lib. bdg. 31.93 (978-0-7660-2462-5(8)) Enslow Pubs., Inc.

Whalin, W. Terry. Sojourner Truth: American Abolitionist. Landgraf, Ken, illus. 1999. (Young Reader's Christian Library). 222p. (J). (gr. 8-12). pap. 1.39 (978-1-57748-515-5(7)) Barbour Publishing, Inc.

—Sojourner Truth: American Abolitionist. 1999. (Heroes of the Faith Ser.). 208p. (YA). (gr. 4-7). 14.95 (978-0-7910-5034-7(3) , Chelsea Hse.) Facts On File, Inc.

Wheeler, Irvin, illus. Justina's Dream. 2005. 30p. (J). (***978-1-887302-12-8(3)***) Western Images Pubns., Inc.

Wheeler, Jill C. Condoleezza Rice. 2004. (Women of the World Ser.). (J). (978-1-59197-616-5(2)) ABDO Publishing Co.

—Harriet Tubman. 2003. (Breaking Barriers Ser.). (Illus.). 64p. (J). (gr. 3-8). lib. bdg. 25.65 (978-1-57765-908-2(2)) ABDO Publishing Co.

—Hillary Rodham Clinton. 2003. (Breaking Barriers Ser.). (Illus.). 64p. (J). (gr. 3-8). lib. bdg. 25.65 (978-1-57765-741-5(1)) ABDO Publishing Co.

—Judy Blume. 2005. (Children's Authors Ser.). (Illus.). 24p. (J). (gr. k-6). lib. bdg. 21.35 (978-1-59197-604-2(9)) ABDO Publishing Co.

—Madeleine Albright. 2002. (Women of the World Ser.). (J). lib. bdg. 21.35 (978-1-57765-316-5(5)) ABDO Publishing Co.

—Marjorie Weinman Sharmat. 2005. (Children's Authors Ser.). (Illus.). 24p. (J). (gr. k-6). lib. bdg. 21.35 (978-1-59197-608-0(1)) ABDO Publishing Co.

—Oprah Winfrey. 2002. (Breaking Barriers Ser.). (Illus.). 64p. (J). (gr. 3-8). lib. bdg. 25.65 (978-1-57765-319-6(X) , ABDO & Daughters) ABDO Publishing Co.

—Rosa Parks, Set II. 2003. (Breaking Barriers Ser.). (Illus.). 64p. (J). (gr. 3-8). lib. bdg. 25.65 (978-1-57765-640-1(7)) ABDO Publishing Co.

Whiting, Jim. Annie Oakley. 2006. (What's So Great About... ? Ser.). (Illus.). 32p. (J). (gr. 1-4). lib. bdg. (978-1-58415-477-8(2)) Mitchell Lane Pubs., Inc.

Whittaker, Helen DeWitt. Sisters in the Air: Louise McPhetridge Thaden & Phoebe Fairgrave Omlie. 2002. 64p. (J). pap. 9.95 (978-1-57072-229-5(3)) Overmountain Pr.

Wilkerson, J. L. Scribe of the Great Plains: Mari Sandoz. 1999. (Great Heartlanders Ser.). (Illus.). 131p. (YA). (gr. 4-12). pap. 8.95 (978-0-9664470-0-2(X)) Acorn Bks.

Wilson, Cammie. Rosa Parks: From the Back of the Bus to the Front of a Movement. 2001. (Scholastic Biography Ser.). (Illus.). 88p. (J). (gr. 3-7). pap. 4.50 (978-0-439-16330-9(7)) Scholastic, Inc.

Winget, Mary. Eleanor Roosevelt. (Biography Ser.). (Illus.). 2005. 112p. (gr. 6-12). lib. bdg. 27.93 (978-0-8225-4985-7(9)); 2003. 48p. (J). pap. 6.95 (978-0-8225-4801-0(1) , Lerner Pubns.); 2003. 48p. (J). (gr. 3-5). lib. bdg. 26.60 (978-0-8225-4675-7(2)) Lerner Publishing Group.

—Eleanor Roosevelt. 2003. (gr. 3-6). lib. bdg. 15.25 (978-0-613-84031-6(3)) Tandem Library Bks.

Wolff, Marion. Shedding Skins. 2004. pap. 12.00 (978-1-930401-27-3(2)) Central Coast Pr.

Women of the American Revolution (NCHS) Grades 5-8. 58p. (J). tchr. ed. 29.45 (978-0-382-40934-9(5)) Cobblestone Publishing Co.

Wood, Ramona. The Goat Woman of Smackover: An Arkansas Legend. Wood, Ramona, . 2006. (Illus.). 32p. (J). 11.00 (978-0-9758622-1-6(9)) ABC Pr.

Woods, Mae. Laura Ingalls Wilder. 2000. (Children's Authors Ser.). (Illus.). 24p. (J). (gr. k-6). lib. bdg. 21.35 (978-1-57765-113-0(8) , Checkerboard Library) ABDO Publishing Co.

Woronoff, Kristen. Oprah Winfrey: Media Superstar. 2002. (Famous Women Juniors Ser.). (Illus.). 32p. (J). (gr. 3-5). 24.94 (978-1-56711-588-8(8) , Blackbirch Pr., Inc.) Thomson Gale.

Wukovitz, John F. Ellen Ochoa, First Female Hispanic Astronaut. 2006. (Twentieth Century's Most Influential Hispanics Ser.). (Illus.). 112p. (J). (gr. 7-10). lib. bdg. 32.45 (978-1-59018-976-4(0) , 1256844, Lucent Bks.) Thomson Gale.

Yannuzzi, Della A. Madam C. J. Walker: Self-Made Businesswoman. 2000. (African-American Biographies Ser.). (Illus.). 112p. (J). (gr. 6-12). lib. bdg. 26.60 (978-0-7660-1204-2(2)) Enslow Pubs., Inc.

Younger, Barbara. Purple Mountain Majesties: The Story of Katharine Lee Bates & America the Beautiful. Schuett, Stacey, illus. 2005. 29p. (J). reprint ed. 16.00 (978-0-7567 8984-8(2)) DIANE Publishing Co.

WOMEN ARTISTS

Ball, Heather. Astonishing Women Artists. 2007. (Women's Hall of Fame Ser.). (Illus.). 120p. (J). (gr. 4-8). pap. 10.95 (***978-1-897187-23-4(8)***) Second Story Pr. CAN. *Dist:* Orca Bk. Pubs. USA.

Matthews, Elizabeth. Different Like Coco. 2007. (Illus.). (J). (***978-1-4287-3582-8(8)***) Candlewick Pr.

McKissack, Lisa Beringer. Women of the Harlem Renaissance. 2006. 48p. (J). (978-0-7565-2034-2(7)) Compass Point Bks.

O'Connor, Jane. Mary Cassatt: Family Pictures. Kalis, Jennifer, illus. 2003. (Smart about Art Ser.). 32p. (J). (gr. k-3). 14.89 (978-0-448-43153-6(X)); pap. 5.99 (978-0-448-43152-9(1)) Penguin Group (USA) Inc. (Grosset & Dunlap).

—Mary Cassatt: Family Pictures. 2003. (gr. k-3). lib. bdg. 14.15 (978-0-613-61641-6(3)) Tandem Library Bks.

Rembert, Winfred. Don't Hold Me Back: My Life & Art. Rembert, Winfred, illus. 2003. (Illus.). 48p. 19.95 (978-0-8126-2703-9(2)) Cricket Bks.

Wilkerson, J. L. American Illustrator: Rose O'Neill. 2001. (Great Heartlanders Ser.). (Illus.). iii, 114p. (J). (gr. 4-6). pap. 9.95 (978-0-9664470-6-4(9)) Acorn Bks.

WOMEN ATHLETES

Adler, David A. America's Champion Swimmer: Gertrude Ederle. Widener, Terry, illus. 32p. (J). (gr. k-4). 2000. 16.00 (978-0-15-201969-3(3) , Gulliver Bks.); 2005. reprint ed. pap. 6.00 (978-0-15-205251-5(8) , Voyager Bks./Libros Viajeros) Harcourt Children's Bks.

—America's Champion Swimmer: Gertrude Ederle. 2000. (Illus.). 32p. (J). (gr. 1-4). 18.98 (978-0-7398-2197-8(0)) Raintree.

Alexander, Kyle. Women of Pro Wrestling. 2000. (Pro Wrestling Legends Ser.). (Illus.). 64p. (J). (gr. 8-12). pap. 25.00 (978-0-7910-5840-4(9)); (gr. 4-7). 25.00 (978-0-7910-5839-8(5)) Facts On File, Inc. (Chelsea Hse.).

—The Women of Pro Wrestling. 2000. (Illus.). 64p. (YA). (gr. 8-12). lib. bdg. 17.60 (978-0-613-33258-3(X)) Tandem Library Bks.

Bailer, Darice. Great Women Athletes. 2001. (Step into Reading Bks.). (Illus.). 48p. (J). (gr. 2-5). pap. 3.99 (978-0-375-81186-9(9) , Random Hse. Bks. for Young Readers) Random Hse. Children's Bks.

Balcavage, Dynise. Gabrielle Reece. 2001. (Women Who Win Ser.). (J). pap. (978-0-7910-6532-7(4)); (Illus.). 64p. (gr. 3 up). 25.00 (978-0-7910-6531-0(6)) Facts On File, Inc. (Chelsea Hse.).

Barron's Educational Editorial Staff. Winning Women in Baseball & Softball. 2000. (Sport Success Ser.). 112p. (J). (gr. 5-9). pap. 6.95 (978-0-7641-1231-7(7)) Barron's Educational Series, Inc.

Berman, Connie. Anna Kournikova. 2001. (Women Who Win Ser.). (Illus.). 64p. (J). pap. (978-0-7910-6530-3(8)); (gr. 3 up). 25.00 (978-0-7910-6529-7(4)) Facts On File, Inc. (Chelsea Hse.).

Billus, Kathleen. Judy Johnson. 2002. (Baseball Hall of Famers of the Negro League Ser.). (Illus.). 112p. (YA). (gr. 5-8). lib. bdg. 29.25 (978-0-8239-3476-8(4) , Rosen Central) Rosen Publishing Group, Inc., The.

Blumenthal, Karen. Let Me Play: The Story of Title IX: the Law That Changed the Future of Girls in America. 2005. (Illus.). 160p. (J). (gr. 3-7). 17.95 (978-0-689-85957-1(0) , Atheneum) Simon & Schuster Children's Publishing.

Brill, Marlene Targ. Winning Women in Ice Hockey. 1999. (Sport Success Ser.). 90p. (YA). (gr. 5 up). pap. 6.95 (978-0-7641-1115-0(9)) Barron's Educational Series, Inc.

—Winning Women in Soccer. 1999. (Sport Success Ser.). 90p. (YA). (gr. 5 up). pap. 6.95 (978-0-7641-1116-7(7)) Barron's Educational Series, Inc.

—Winning Women in Soccer. 1999. (978-0-606-18006-1(0)) Tandem Library Bks.

Brindisi, Johanna. The Story of the Wrestler They Call "Chyna" 2001. (Pro Wrestling Legends Ser.). (Illus.). 64p. pap. 25.00 (978-0-7910-6443-6(3) , Chelsea Hse.) Facts On File, Inc.

Bryant, Jill. Amazing Women Athletes. 2005. (Women's Hall of Fame Ser.). (Illus.). 75p. (YA). (gr. 4-8). pap. 7.95 (978-1-896764-44-3(4)) Second Story Pr. CAN. *Dist:* Orca Bk. Pubs. USA, Univ. of Toronto Pr., Univ. of Toronto Pr.

—Amazing Women Athletes. 2002. (gr. 5-8). lib. bdg. 16.40 (978-0-613-85825-0(5)) Tandem Library Bks.

Burgan, Michael. Sheryl Swoopes. 2000. (Women Who Win Ser.). (Illus.). 64p. (J). (gr. 4-7). pap. 25.00 (978-0-7910-6155-8(8)); 25.00 (978-0-7910-5795-7(X)) Facts On File, Inc. (Chelsea Hse.).

—Sheryl Swoopes. 2001. (gr. 3-6). lib. bdg. 17.60 (978-0-613-33051-0(X)) Tandem Library Bks.

Burke, Rick. Mia Hamm. 2001. (Sports Files Ser.). (Illus.). 32p. (J). lib. bdg. (978-1-58810-112-9(6)) Heinemann Library.

Cain, Janet. Women in Olympic Sports. 2004. (Illus.). 80p. (J). pap. 10.99 (978-1-58000-119-9(X)) Griffin Publishing Group.

Cayleff, Susan E. Babe Didrikson: The Greatest All-Sport Athlete of All Time. 2000. (Illus.). (J). (978-0-606-18829-6(0)) Tandem Library Bks.

Christopher, Matt. Mia Hamm. 1998. (Illus.). 131p. (J). (ps-7). per. 13.00 (978-0-613-11941-2(X)) Tandem Library Bks.

—On the Field with... Mia Hamm. 1998. (Matt Christopher Sports Biographies Ser.). (978-0-606-13678-5(9)) Tandem Library Bks.

Coffey, Wayne. Meet the Women of American Soccer: An Inside Look at America's Team. 1999. (Illus.). 48p. (J). (gr. 2-7). pap. 5.99 (978-0-439-08654-7(X)) Scholastic, Inc.

Cornelius, Kay. Chamique Holdsclaw. 2000. (Women Who Win Ser.). (Illus.). 64p. (J). (gr. 4-7). pap. 25.00 (978-0-7910-6153-4(1)); (gr. 3 up). 25.00 (978-0-7910-5793-3(3)) Facts On File, Inc. (Chelsea Hse.).

—Chamique Holdsclaw. 2001. (gr. 3-6). lib. bdg. 17.60 (978-0-613-32387-1(4)) Tandem Library Bks.

Cox, Vicki. Marion Jones. 2001. (Women Who Win Ser.). (J). pap. (978-0-7910-6534-1(0)); (Illus.). 64p. (gr. 3 up). 25.00 (978-0-7910-6533-4(2)) Facts On File, Inc. (Chelsea Hse.).

Ditchfield, Christin. Martina Hingis. 2000. (Women Who Win Ser.). (Illus.). 64p. (J). (gr. 4-7). pap. 25.00 (978-0-7910-6157-2(4)); (YA). (gr. 8 up). 25.00 (978-0-7910-5797-1(6)) Facts On File, Inc. (Chelsea Hse.).

—Martina Hingis. 2001. (gr. 3-6). lib. bdg. 17.60 (978-0-613-32821-0(3)) Tandem Library Bks.

Dougherty, Terri. Lisa Leslie. 1999. (Jam Session Ser.). (Illus.). 32p. (J). (gr. 3-8). lib. bdg. 24.21 (978-1-57765-313-4(0) , ABDO & Daughters) ABDO Publishing Co.

—Mia Hamm. 2000. (Jam Session Ser.). (Illus.). 32p. (J). (gr. 3-8). lib. bdg. 24.21 (978-1-57765-364-6(5) , ABDO & Daughters) ABDO Publishing Co.

Feldman, Heather. Marion Jones: World-Class Runner. 2001. (Reading Power Ser.). (Illus.). 24p. (J). (gr. 1). lib. bdg. 17.25 (978-0-8239-5718-7(7) , PKMAJO, PowerKids Pr.) Rosen Publishing Group, Inc., The.

—Mia Hamm: Soccer Superstar. 2001. (Reading Power Ser.). (Illus.). 24p. (J). (gr. 1). lib. bdg. 17.25 (978-0-8239-5716-3(0) , PKHAMM, PowerKids Pr.) Rosen Publishing Group, Inc., The.

Forkos, Heather. Dorothy "Dot" Richardson. 2001. (J). pap. (978-0-7910-6536-5(7)); (Illus.). 64p. (gr. 3 up). 25.00 (978-0-7910-6535-8(9)) Facts On File, Inc. (Chelsea Hse.).

Frost, Shelley & Troussieux, Ann. Throw Like a Girl: Discovering the Body, Mind & Spirit of the Athlete in You! l.t. ed. 2000. (Girls Know Best Ser.). (Illus.). 128p. (J). (gr. 3 up). lib. bdg. 23.33 (978-0-8368-2674-6(4)) Stevens, Gareth Inc.

Gatto, Kimberly. Michelle Kwan: Champion on Ice. 1998. (Sports Achievers Biographies Ser.). (Illus.). 64p. (J). (gr. 4-9). lib. bdg. (978-0-8225-3669-7(2)); pap. 5.95 (978-0-8225-9830-5(2)) Lerner Publishing Group. (LernerSports).

Gogol, Sara. Katy Steding: Pro Basketball Pioneer. 1998. (Sports Achievers Biographies Ser.). (Illus.). 64p. (J). (gr. 4-9). lib. bdg. (978-0-8225-3668-0(4) , Lerner-Sports) Lerner Publishing Group.

Green, Michelle Y. A Strong Right Arm: The Story of Mamie "Peanut" Johnson. Nelson, Kadir, illus. 128p. (J). 2004. (gr. 3-6). pap. 5.99 (978-0-14-240072-2(6) , Puffin); 2002. (gr. 4-7). 15.99 (978-0-8037-2661-1(9) , Dial) Penguin Group (USA) Inc.

Greenberg, Doreen L., et al. Fast Lane to Victory: The Story of Jenny Thompson, Vol. 3. Velikan, Phil, illus. 2003. (Anything You Can Do. . .Ser.: 3). 141p. (J). (gr. 4 up). pap. 12.95 (978-1-930546-38-7(6)) Wish Publishing.

Guillermo-Newton, Judith. Competitive Tennis for Girls. 2005. (SportsGirl Ser.). (Illus.). 64p. (YA). (gr. 5-8). lib. bdg. 26.50 (978-0-8239-3407-2(1)) Rosen Publishing Group, Inc., The.

Housewright, Ed. Winning Track & Field for Girls. 2003. (Winning Sports for Girls Ser.). (Illus.). 208p. (YA). (gr. 9-12). pap. 16.95 (978-0-8160-5232-5(8) , Checkmark Bks.); (gr. 6-12). 35.00 (978-0-8160-5231-8(X)) Facts On File, Inc.

Jackel, Molly. WNBA Superstars: Leslie, Lobo & Swoopes. 1998. (Fast Breaks Ser.: Vol. 4). (Illus.). 88p. (J). (gr. 2-4). pap. 3.99 (978-0-590-12081-4(6)) Scholastic, Inc.

—WNBA Superstars: Leslie, Lobo & Swoopes, 4. 1998. (Fast Breaks Ser.). (J). (978-0-606-13378-4(X)) Tandem Library Bks.

Kelley, Brent P. Lisa Leslie. 2000. (Women Who Win Ser.). (Illus.). 64p. (gr. 4-7). (J). pap. 25.00 (978-0-7910-6154-1(X)); (YA). 25.00 (978-0-7910-5794-0(1)) Facts On File, Inc. (Chelsea Hse.).

Kennedy, Mike & Stewart, Mark. Michelle Kwan: Quest for Gold. 2002. (Inspiring People Ser.). (Illus.). 64p. (gr. 4 up). lib. bdg. 24.90 (978-0-7613-2622-9(7) , Millbrook Pr.) Lerner Publishing Group.

Kirkpatrick, Rob, et al, contrib. by. Mia Hamm, Soccer Star. 2001. (Great Record Breakers in Sports Ser.). (Illus.). 24p. (J). lib. bdg. 18.75 (978-0-8239-5635-7(0) , PowerKids Pr.) Rosen Publishing Group, Inc., The.

Kwan, Michelle. Michelle Kwan: My Book of Memories. 1998. (Illus.). (J). (gr. 4-7). pap. 5.99 (978-0-590-45890-0(6)) Scholastic, Inc.

—Michelle Kwan Chapterbook. 2000. 64p. (J). pap. 4.99 (978-0-7868-1383-4(0)) Disney Pr.

—Michelle Kwan, Heart of a Champion: An Autobiography. 1998. (978-0-606-13607-5(X)) Tandem Library Bks.

Latimer, Clay. Mia Hamm. 2000. (Sports Heroes Ser.). (Illus.). 48p. (J). (gr. 3-4). lib. bdg. 21.26 (978-0-7368-0579-7(6) , Capstone High-Interest Bks.) Capstone Pr., Inc.

Layden, Joe. Inside the WNBA: A Behind-the-Scenes Photo Scrapbook. 1999. (WNBA Ser.). (Illus.). 48p. (J). (gr. 2-7). 5.99 (978-0-439-07803-0(2)) Scholastic, Inc.

Manley, Claudia B. Competitive Track & Field for Girls. 2005. (SportsGirl Ser.). (Illus.). 64p. (YA). (gr. 5-8). lib. bdg. 26.50 (978-0-8239-3408-9(X)) Rosen Publishing Group, Inc., The.

—Competitive Volleyball for Girls. 2005. (SportsGirl Ser.). (Illus.). 64p. (YA). (gr. 5-8). lib. bdg. 26.50 (978-0-8239-3404-1(7)) Rosen Publishing Group, Inc., The.

Martin, Clare. An Insider's Guide to the WNBA. 2002. (Wnba Sticker Book Ser.). 24p. (J). pap. 7.99 (978-0-439-38013-3(8)) Scholastic, Inc.

Moss, Marissa. Mighty Jackie: The Strike-Out Queen. Payne, C. F., tr. Payne, C. F., illus. 2004. 32p. (J). 16.95 (978-0-689-86329-5(2) , Simon & Schuster/Paula Wiseman Bks.) Simon & Schuster Children's Publishing.

Murdico, Suzanne J. Monica Seles. 1998. (Overcoming the Odds Ser.). (Illus.). 48p. (J). (gr. 3-8). (978-0-8172-4128-5(0)) Raintree.

Naden, Corinne J. & Blue, Rose. Monica Seles. 2001. (Overcoming Adversity Ser.). (Illus.). 112p. (J). 30.00 (978-0-7910-5899-2(9) , Chelsea Hse.) Facts On File, Inc.

Nicholson, Lorna Schultz. Pink Power: The First Women's Hockey World Champions. 2007. (Recordbooks Ser.). (Illus.). 128p. (YA). (gr. 7-12). 8.95 (***978-1-55028-987-9(X)***) Lorimer, James & Co., Ltd., Pubs. CAN. *Dist:* Casemate Pubs. & Bk. Distributors, LLC.

Owens, Tom & Helmer, Diana Star. The Charlotte Sting: Teamwork. 1999. (Women's Professional Basketball Ser.). 24p. (J). lib. bdg. 18.75 (978-0-8239-5242-7(8) , PowerKids Pr.) Rosen Publishing Group, Inc., The.

—The Cleveland Rockers: Teamwork. 1999. (Women's Professional Basketball Ser.). 24p. (J). lib. bdg. 18.75 (978-0-8239-5241-0(X) , PowerKids Pr.) Rosen Publishing Group, Inc., The.

—The Los Angeles Sparks: Teamwork. 1999. (Women's Professional Basketball Ser.). 24p. (J). lib. bdg. 18.75 (978-0-8239-5240-3(1) , PowerKids Pr.) Rosen Publishing Group, Inc., The.

—The New York Liberty: Teamwork. 1999. (Women's Professional Basketball Ser.). 24p. (J). lib. bdg. 18.75 (978-0-8239-5239-7(8) , PowerKids Pr.) Rosen Publishing Group, Inc., The.

—Teamwork, the Houston Comets in Action. 1999. (Women's Professional Basketball Ser.). 24p. (J). lib. bdg. 18.75 (978-0-8239-5246-5(0) , PowerKids Pr.) Rosen Publishing Group, Inc., The.

W X Y Z

—Teamwork, the Phoenix Mercury in Action. 1999. (Women's Professional Basketball Ser.). 24p. (J). lib. bdg. 18.75 (978-0-8239-5243-4(6) , PowerKids Pr.) Rosen Publishing Group, Inc., The.

—Teamwork, the Sacramento Monarchs in Action. 1999. (Women's Professional Basketball Ser.). 24p. (J). lib. bdg. 18.75 (978-0-8239-5245-8(2) , PowerKids Pr.) Rosen Publishing Group, Inc., The.

—The Utah Starzz: Teamwork. 1999. (Women's Professional Basketball Ser.). 24p. (J). lib. bdg. 18.75 (978-0-8239-5244-1(4) , PowerKids Pr.) Rosen Publishing Group, Inc., The.

Paprocki, Sherry. Michelle Kwan. 2000. (Women Who Win Ser.). (Illus.). 64p. (J). (gr. 4-7). pap. 25.00 (978-0-7910-6152-7(3)); 25.00 (978-0-7910-5792-6(5)) Facts On File, Inc. (Chelsea Hse.).

—Michelle Kwan. 2001. (gr. 3-6). lib. bdg. 17.60 (978-0-613-32832-6(9)) Tandem Library Bks.

Powe-Allred, Alexandra, et al. 'Atta Girl! a Celebration of Women in Sports. 2nd ed. 2003. Orig. Title: The Quiet Storm: a Celebration of Women in Sports. (Illus.). 227p. (YA). pap. 16.95 (978-1-930546-61-5(0)) Wish Publishing.

Rambeck, Richard & Klingel, Cynthia Fitterer. Ice Skating. 2003. (Nonfiction Readers: Level 2 Ser.). (Illus.). 24p. (J). (ps-2). 22.79 (978-1-56766-461-4(X)) Child's World, Inc.

Rappoport, Ken. Ladies First: Women Athletes Who Made a Difference. 2005. (Illus.). 192p. (J). 14.95 (978-1-56145-338-2(2)) Peachtree Pubs., Ltd.

Riddles, Libby. Storm Run: The Story of the First Woman to Win the Iditarod Sled Dog Race. Cartwright, Shannon, illus. (PAWS IV Ser.). 48p. (J). 2003. 16.95 (978-1-57061-298-5(6)); 2002. pap. 9.95 (978-1-57061-293-0(5)) Sasquatch Bks.

Roberts, Robin. Which Sport Is Right for You? 2001. (Illus.). 48p. (gr. 4-8). lib. bdg. 23.90 (978-0-7613-2117-0(9) , Millbrook Pr.) Lerner Publishing Group.

Rutledge, Rachel. The Best of the Best in Basketball. 1998. (Women of Sports Ser.). (Illus.). 64p. (gr. 5 up). lib. bdg. 24.90 (978-0-7613-1301-4(X) , Twenty-First Century Bks.) Lerner Publishing Group.

—The Best of the Best in Gymnastics. 1999. (Women of Sports Ser.). (Illus.). 64p. (gr. 5 up). lib. bdg. 24.90 (978-0-7613-1321-2(4) , Twenty-First Century Bks.) Lerner Publishing Group.

—The Best of the Best in Soccer. (Women of Sports Ser.: up). (Illus.). 64p. (gr. 5 up). 1998. lib. bdg. 24.90 (978-0-7613-1315-1(X)); 2000. pap. (978-0-7613-1392-2(3)) Lerner Publishing Group. (Twenty-First Century Bks.).

—The Best of the Best in Tennis. 1998. (Women of Sports Ser.). (Illus.). 64p. (gr. 5 up). lib. bdg. 24.90 (978-0-7613-1303-8(6) , Twenty-First Century Bks.) Lerner Publishing Group.

—Mia Hamm: Striking Superstar. 2000. (Soccer's New Wave Ser.: up). (Illus.). 48p. (gr. 4-8). pap. (978-0-7613-1381-6(8) , Millbrook Pr.) Lerner Publishing Group.

—Mia Hamm: Striking Superstar. 2000. (gr. 3-6). lib. bdg. 15.25 (978-0-613-26200-2(X)) Tandem Library Bks.

Savage, Jeff. Top 10 Women's Sports Legends. 2001. (Sports Top 10 Ser.). (Illus.). 48p. (J). (gr. 4-10). lib. bdg. 23.93 (978-0-7660-1495-4(9)) Enslow Pubs., Inc.

Schnakenberg, Robert. Cynthia Cooper. 2000. (Illus.). 64p. (J). (gr. 4-7). lib. bdg. 17.60 (978-0-613-32432-8(3)) Tandem Library Bks.

—Mia Hamm. 2001. (gr. 3-6). lib. bdg. 17.60 (978-0-613-32830-2(2)) Tandem Library Bks.

Schnakenberg, Robert E. Cynthia Cooper. 2000. (Women Who Win Ser.). (Illus.). 64p. (gr. 4-7). (YA). pap. 25.00 (978-0-7910-6156-5(6)); (J). 25.00 (978-0-7910-5796-4(8)) Facts On File, Inc. (Chelsea Hse.).

—Mia Hamm. 2000. (Women Who Win Ser.). (Illus.). 64p. (J). (gr. 4-7). pap. 25.00 (978-0-7910-6151-0(5)); (YA). (gr. 8 up). 25.00 (978-0-7910-5791-9(7)) Facts On File, Inc. (Chelsea Hse.).

Sherman, Josepha. Competitive Soccer for Girls. 2005. (SportsGirl Ser.). (Illus.). 64p. (YA). (gr. 5-8). lib. bdg. 26.50 (978-0-8239-3405-8(5)) Rosen Publishing Group, Inc., The.

Smith, Michelle. Megastars. 2003. (WNBA Ser.). (Illus.). 48p. (J). pap. 3.99 (978-0-439-45602-9(9)) Scholastic, Inc.

—She's Got Game: Stars of the WNBA. 1999. (WNBA Ser.). (Illus.). 93p. (J). (gr. 3-7). pap. 4.99 (978-0-439-07804-7(0)) Scholastic, Inc.

—Stars of the WNBA. 2002. (gr. 3-6). lib. bdg. 11.80 (978-0-613-55905-8(3)) Tandem Library Bks.

Steen, Sandra. Take It to the Hoop: 100 Years of Women's Basketball. 2003. (Single Titles Ser.). (Illus.). 144p. (gr. 6 up). lib. bdg. 25.90 (978-0-7613-2470-6(4) , Twenty-First Century Bks.) Lerner Publishing Group.

Steiner, Andy. Girl Power on the Playing Field. 1999. (Girl Power Ser.). (Illus.). 96p. (YA). (gr. 6-9). lib. bdg. (978-0-8225-2690-2(5) , Lerner Pubns.) Lerner Publishing Group.

Stewart, Mark. Chamique Holdsclaw: Driving Force. 2000. (New Wave Ser.). (Illus.). 48p. (gr. 4 up). lib. bdg. 22.90 (978-0-7613-1801-9(1) , Millbrook Pr.) Lerner Publishing Group.

—Marion Jones: Fast & Fearless. 2000. (New Wave Ser.). (Illus.). 48p. (gr. 4 up). lib. bdg. 22.90 (978-0-7613-1870-5(4) , Millbrook Pr.) Lerner Publishing Group.

—Mia Hamm: Striking Superstar. 2000. (New Wave Ser.). (Illus.). 48p. (gr. 4 up). lib. bdg. 22.90 (978-0-7613-1802-6(X) , Millbrook Pr.) Lerner Publishing Group.

Stewart, Mark Alan. Lisa Leslie: Queen of the Court. 1998. (Sports Stars Ser.). (Illus.). 48p. (J). (gr. 3-4). 19.50 (978-0-516-20585-4(4) , Children's Pr.) Scholastic Library Publishing.

—Marion Jones: Sprinting Sensation. 2000. (Sports Stars Ser.). (Illus.). 48p. (J). (gr. 3-4). pap. 5.95 (978-0-516-27004-3(4) , Children's Pr.) Scholastic Library Publishing.

Stout, Glenn & Christopher, Matt. Mia Hamm: On the Field With... 1998. (Matt Christopher Sports Biographies Ser.). (Illus.). 128p. (J). (gr. 3-7). pap. 4.99 (978-0-316-14217-5(4)) Little, Brown Bks. for Young Readers.

Sutcliffe, Jane. Babe Didrikson Zaharias: All-Around Athlete. Reeves, Jeni, illus. (On My Own Biographies Ser.). 48p. 2005. (gr. 2-5). lib. bdg. 23.93 (978-1-57505-421-6(3)); 2000. (J). (gr. 1-3). pap. 5.95 (978-1-57505-447-6(7)) Lerner Publishing Group.

Wallner, Rosemary. Michelle Kwan. 2001. (Sports Heroes Ser.). (Illus.). 48p. (J). (gr. 3-4). lib. bdg. 21.26 (978-0-7368-0779-1(9) , Capstone High-Interest Bks.) Capstone Pr., Inc.

—Sheryl Swoopes. 2001. (Sports Heroes Ser.). (Illus.). 48p. (J). (gr. 3-4). lib. bdg. 21.26 (978-0-7368-0780-7(2) , Capstone High-Interest Bks.) Capstone Pr., Inc.

Wellman, Sam. Michelle Kwan. 1999. (Female Figure Skating Legends Ser.). (Illus.). 64p. (YA). (gr. 4-7). 12.95 (978-0-7910-4875-7(6) , Chelsea Hse.) Facts On File, Inc.

Wills, Charles M. Annie Oakley. 2007. (DK Biography Ser.). 128p. (J). (gr. 3-8). 14.99 (978-0-7566-2986-1(1)); pap. 4.99 (978-0-7566-2997-7(7)) Dorling Kindersley Publishing, Inc.

Wilner, Barry. Girls Rule! The Glory & Spirit of Women in Sports. 2000. (Illus.). 160p. (J). pap. 22.95 (978-0-7407-1171-8(7)) Andrews McMeel Publishing.

—Michelle Kwan: Star Figure Skater. 2001. (Sports Reports). (Illus.). 104p. (YA). (gr. 4-10). lib. bdg. 26.60 (978-0-7660-1504-3(1)) Enslow Pubs., Inc.

Wolff, Virginia Euwer & Woodson, Jacqueline. Girls Got Game: Sports Stories & Poems. Macy, Sue, ed. rev. ed. 2001. (Illus.). 160p. (YA). (gr. 6-9). 17.95 (978-0-8050-6568-8(7) , Holt, Henry & Co. Bks. For Young Readers) Holt, Henry & Co.

Women Who Win Set. 2000. (Illus.). 64p. (YA). (gr. 3 up). 143.60 (978-0-7910-5798-8(4) , Chelsea Hse.) Facts On File, Inc.

WOMEN AUTHORS

Berne, Emma Carlson. Laura Ingalls Wilder. 2007. (Essential Lives Ser.). (ENG., Illus.). 112p. (J). (gr. 6-8). lib. bdg. 32.79 (***978-1-59928-843-7(5)*** , Essential Library) ABDO Publishing Co.

Bloom, Harold, ed. American Women Fiction Writers, 1900-1960. 1999. (Women Writers of English & Their Works Ser.: Vol. 3). 200p. (YA). (gr. 4-7). 34.95 (978-0-7910-4652-4(4)); (gr. 9 up). pap. 16.95 (978-0-7910-4653-1(2)) Facts On File, Inc. (Chelsea Hse.).

—Women Memoirists. 1999. (Women Writers of English & Their Works Ser.: Vol. 2). 200p. (YA). (gr. 8-12). pap. 18.65 (978-0-7910-4655-5(9)); pap. 34.95 (978-0-7910-4654-8(0)); Vol. 1. (Illus.). 29.95 (978-0-7910-4485-8(8)) Facts On File, Inc. (Chelsea Hse.).

Breslin, Theresa. Kezzie. 2002. 256p. (J). pap. 8.99 (978-1-4052-0110-0(X)) Egmont Bks., Ltd. GBR. *Dist:* Independent Pubs. Group.

Burton, Zisca. Bloom's How to Write about Toni Morrison. 2007. (Bloom's How to Write about Literature Ser.). 256p. (YA). (gr. 9 up). 45.00 (***978-0-7910-9548-5(7)*** , Chelsea Hse.) Facts On File, Inc.

Dubois, Muriel L. To My Countrywomen: The Life of Sarah Josepha Hale. 2006. (***978-0-9723410-1-1(3)***) Apprentice Shop Bks., LLC.

Fish, Bruce. Terry McMillan. 2001. (Black Americans of Achievement Ser.). (Illus.). 112p. (J). (gr. 4-7). 30.00 (978-0-7910-5804-6(2) , Chelsea Hse.) Facts On File, Inc.

Fish, Bruce & Fish, Becky Durost. Terry McMillan. 2001. (Black Americans of Achievement Ser.). (Illus.). (YA). (gr. 8-12). pap. 30.00 (978-0-7910-5805-3(0) , Chelsea Hse.) Facts On File, Inc.

Gavin, Jamila. Interview with Jamila Gavin. 2002. (Illus.). 96p. (J). pap. 5.50 (978-1-4052-0088-2(X)) Egmont Bks., Ltd. GBR. *Dist:* Independent Pubs. Group.

Harcourt School Publishers Staff. Visiting Anne's House: Take-Home Book. 2001. (Collections Ser.). (Illus.). (J). (gr. 5). pap. 1.90 (978-0-15-319665-2(3)) Harcourt Schl. Pubs.

—Visiting Anne's House Below Level. 3rd ed. 2002. (Trophies Reading Program Ser.). (Illus.). pap. 5.10 (978-0-15-323424-8(5)) Harcourt Schl. Pubs.

Hazell, Rebecca. Women Writers. 2002. (Women in the Arts Ser.). (Illus.). 128p. 19.95 (978-0-7892-0697-8(8)) Abbeville Pr., Inc.

Kite, L. Patricia. Maya Angelou. 2006. (Just the Facts Biographies Ser.). (Illus.). 112p. (J). pap. (***978-0-8225-5997-9(8)*** , Lerner Pubns.) Lerner Publishing Group.

Lyon, George Ella & Soentpiet, Chris K. A Sign. 1998. (Illus.). 32p. (J). (gr. k-4). 16.99 (978-0-531-33073-9(7) , Orchard Bks.) Scholastic, Inc.

Marcovitz, Hal. Pat Mora. 2007. (Who Wrote That? Ser.). 136p. (J). (gr. 6-12). 30.00 (***978-0-7910-9528-7(2)*** , Chelsea Hse.) Facts On File, Inc.

McKissack, Lisa Beringer. Women of the Harlem Renaissance. 2006. 48p. (J). (978-0-7565-2034-2(7)) Compass Point Bks.

Nimmo, Jenny. Interview with Jenny Nimmo. Cooling, Wendy, ed. 2003. (Illus.). 112p. (J). pap. 5.50 (978-1-4052-0411-8(7)) Egmont Bks., Ltd. GBR. *Dist:* Independent Pubs. Group.

Potter, Beatrix. Beatrix Potter's Journal. 2006. (Illus.). 32p. (J). 19.99 (978-0-7232-5805-6(8) , Warne) Penguin Group (USA) Inc.

Raum, Elizabeth. The Story Behind Willa Cather's My Antonia. 2006. (History in Literature Ser.). (Illus.). 56p. (YA). (gr. 7 up). lib. bdg. 32.86 (978-1-4034-8211-2(X)) Heinemann Library.

Sexton, Colleen A. & Cosgrove, Martha. J.K. Rowling. 2006. (Just the Facts Biographies Ser.). (Illus.). 112p. (J). pap. (***978-0-8225-5995-5(1)*** , Lerner Pubns.) Lerner Publishing Group.

Watson, Michele Griskey. Beverly Cleary. 2006. (Classic Storytellers Ser.). (Sterling Point Bks.). (Illus.). 48p. (J). lib. bdg. 20.95 (978-1-58415-457-0(8) , 1259543) Mitchell Lane Pubs., Inc.

Wilson, Jacqueline & Carey, Joanna. Interview with Jacqueline Wilson. (Illus.). 96p. pap. 5.50 (978-1-4052-0055-4(3)) Egmont Bks., Ltd. GBR. *Dist:* Trafalgar Square Publishing.

WOMEN IN AERONAUTICS

Anderson, Jameson. Amelia Earhart: Legendary Aviator. Whigham, Rod & Barnett, Charles, illus. 2007. (Graphic Library). 32p. (J). 25.26 (978-0-7368-6496-1(2)) Capstone Pr., Inc.

Buchanan, Doug. Air & Space. 1999. (Female Firsts in Their Fields Ser.). (Illus.). 64p. (YA). (gr. 4-7). 18.65 (978-0-7910-5141-2(2) , Chelsea Hse.) Facts On File, Inc.

Burke, John. Sterling Point Books: Amelia Earhart: Flying Solo. 2007. (Sterling Point Bks.). (Illus.). 208p. (J). 12.95 (978-1-4027-4520-1(6)); pap. 6.95 (978-1-4027-4140-1(5)) Sterling Publishing Co., Inc.

Burleigh, Robert. Amelia Earhart: Free in the Skies. Wylie, Bill, illus. 2003. (American Heroes Ser.). 48p. (J). 16.00 (978-0-15-202498-7(0) , Silver Whistle) Harcourt Trade Pubs.

—Amelia Earhart: Free in the Skies. 2003. (gr. 3-6). lib. bdg. 14.10 (978-0-613-70522-6(X)) Tandem Library Bks.

Cummins, Julie. Tom Boy of the Air: Daredevil Pilot Blanche Stuart Scott. 2006. (Illus.). 80p. (J). (gr. 4-8). reprint ed. 17.00 (978-1-4223-5510-7(1)) DIANE Publishing Co.

—Tomboy of the Air: Daredevil Pilot Blanche Stuart Scott. 2001. (Illus.). 80p. (J). (gr. 3-6). lib. bdg. 17.89 (978-0-06-029243-0(1)) HarperCollins Pubs.

Davis, Anita P. & Hall, Ed Y. Harriet Quimby - America's First Lady of the Air: A Biography for Intermediate Readers. 1998. (Aviation History Ser.: Vol. 5). (Illus.). 96p. (YA). (gr. 5-12). lib. bdg. 10.95 (978-1-885354-06-8(1)) Honoribus Pr., The.

Friend, Robyn C. The Women of Apollo. Katz, David Arthur, illus. l.t. ed. 2006. 80p. (J). 17.95 (978-1-880599-80-8(5)); pap. 12.95 (978-1-880599-79-2(1)) Cascade Pass, Inc.

Grimes, Nikki. Talkin' 'Bout Bess: The Story of Aviator Bessie Coleman. Lewis, Ted G., illus. (J). 2002. (978-0-531-30069-5(2)); 1998. lib. bdg. (978-0-531-33069-2(9)) Scholastic, Inc. (Orchard Bks.).

Harcourt School Publishers Staff. Amelia Earhart. 3rd ed. 2002. (Horizons Ser.). (Illus.). (J). (gr. 2). pap. 3.70 (978-0-15-333194-7(1)) Harcourt Schl. Pubs.

—Amelia Earhart Below Level. 3rd ed. 2002. (Trophies Reading Program Ser.). (Illus.). pap. 5.10 (978-0-15-323225-1(0)); (SPA., pap. 6.80 (978-0-15-324136-9(5)) Harcourt Schl. Pubs.

Haugen, Brenda. Amelia Earhart: Legendary Aviator. 2006. (J). (978-0-7565-1880-6(6)) Compass Point Bks.

Homan, Lynn M. & Reilly, Thomas. Women Who Fly. Shepherd, Rosalie M., illus. 2004. 104p. (J). pap. 14.95 (978-1-58980-160-8(1)) Pelican Publishing Co., Inc.

Klingel, Cynthia Fitterer. Amelia Earhart: Aviation Pioneer. 2003. (Spirit of America: Our People Ser.). (Illus.). 32p. (J). (gr. 2-6). 27.07 (978-1-59296-000-2(6)) Child's World, Inc.

Lakin, Patricia, et al. Amelia Earhart: More Than a Flier. 2003. (Ready-to-Read Stories of Famous Americans Ser.). (Illus.). 48p. (J). pap. 3.99 (978-0-689-85575-7(3) , Aladdin) Simon & Schuster Children's Publishing.

Langley, Wanda. Women of the Wind: Early Women Aviators. 2006. (Women Adventurers Ser.). (Illus.). 160p. (J). lib. bdg. 26.95 (978-1-931798-81-5(8)) Reynolds, Morgan Inc.

Micklos, John. Unsolved: What Really Happened to Amelia Earhart? 2006. (Prime Ser.). (Illus.). 128p. (J). (gr. 5 up). lib. bdg. 33.27 (978-0-7660-2365-9(6)) Enslow Pubs., Inc.

Pflueger, Lynda. Amelia Earhart: Legend of Flight. 2003. (Historical American Biographies Ser.). (Illus.). 128p. (J). lib. bdg. 26.60 (978-0-7660-1976-8(4)) Enslow Pubs., Inc.

Raum, Elizabeth. Eileen Collins. 2005. (American Lives Ser.). (Illus.). 32p. (J). (978-1-4034-6943-4(1)); pap. (978-1-4034-6950-2(4)) Heinemann Library.

Reyburn, Susan. Women Who Dare: Amelia Earhart. 2006. (Illus.). 64p. 12.95 (978-0-7649-3545-9(3) , A111) Pomegranate Communications, Inc.

Rinaldo, Denise. Amelia Earhart: With a Discussion of Courage. 2004. (Values in Action Ser.). (J). (978-1-59203-068-2(8)) Learning Challenge, Inc.

Roberts, Marjorie H., told to. Wingtip to Wingtip: 8 WASPS, Women's Airforce Service Pilots of World War II. 2000. (Illus.). ix, 128p. (J). pap. 15.95 (978-1-928760-01-6(5)) Aviatrix Publishing, Inc.

Schaefer, Lola M. Amelia Earhart. 2005. (First Biographies Ser.). 24p. (YA). (gr. k-3). pap. (978-0-7368-9408-1(X) , Pebble Bks.) Capstone Pr., Inc.

Weitzman, David L. Jenny: The Airplane That Taught America to Fly. Weitzman, David L., illus. rev. ed. 2002. (Illus.). 40p. (J). (gr. 1-4). 17.95 (978-0-7613-1547-6(0)) Roaring Brook Pr.

Wheeler, Jill C. Amelia Earhart. 2002. (Breaking Barriers Ser.). (Illus.). 64p. (J). (gr. 3-8). lib. bdg. 25.65 (978-1-57765-318-9(1) , ABDO & Daughters) ABDO Publishing Co.

WOMEN IN INDUSTRY

see Women—Employment

WOMEN IN POLITICS

D'Orio, Wayne. Carol Moseley-Braun. 2003. (African American Leaders Ser.). (Illus.). 112p. (gr. 6-12). 30.00 (978-0-7910-7684-2(9) , Chelsea Hse.) Facts On File, Inc.

Evento, Susan. Mary McLeod Bethune. 2004. (Rookie Biographies Ser.). (Illus.). 31p. (J). 20.50 (978-0-516-21720-8(8) , Children's Pr.) Scholastic Library Publishing.

Felder, Deborah G. 100 American Women Who Shaped American History. 2005. (Illus.). 112p. (J). (gr. 4-7). per. 15.90 (978-0-606-33775-5(X)) Tandem Library Bks.

Friedman, Lita. Mary Robinson: Fighter for Human Rights. 2004. (Avisson Young Adult Ser.). (Illus.). 142p. (YA). pap. 19.95 (978-1-888105-65-0(8)) Avisson Pr., Inc.

Gulotta, Charles. Extraordinary Women in Politics. (Extraordinary People Ser.). (Illus.). 288p. (YA). (gr. 6 up). 1999. pap. 16.95 (978-0-516-26399-1(4)); 1998. 37.50 (978-0-516-20610-3(9)) Scholastic Library Publishing. (Children's Pr.).

Horner, Matina S., intro. Madeleine Albright: Stateswoman. 1999. (Women of Achievement Ser.). (Illus.). 134p. (YA). (gr. 4-7). pap. 30.00 (978-0-7910-4709-5(1) , Chelsea Hse.) Facts On File, Inc.

Jones, Veda Boyd. Government & Politics. 1999. (Female Firsts in Their Fields Ser.). (Illus.). 64p. (YA). (gr. 4-7). 12.95 (978-0-7910-5140-5(4) , Chelsea Hse.) Facts On File, Inc.

Krull, Kathleen. A Woman for President: The Story of Victoria Woodhull. Dyer, Jane, illus. 32p. (J). 2004. 16.95 (978-0-8027-8908-2(0)); 2006. reprint ed. pap. 6.95 (978-0-8027-9615-8(X)) Walker & Co.

Lucas, Eileen. Elizabeth Dole: A Leader in Washington. 1998. (Gateway Biography Ser.). (Illus.). 48p. (gr. 2-4). lib. bdg. 23.90 (978-0-7613-0203-2(4) , Millbrook Pr.) Lerner Publishing Group.

Marcovitz, Hal. Eleanor Holmes Norton. 2003. (African American Leaders Ser.). (Illus.). 112p. (gr. 6-12). 30.00 (978-0-7910-7682-8(2) , Chelsea Hse.) Facts On File, Inc.

Marsh, Carole. The First Woman President of the U. S. 2007. 48p. pap. 7.95 (***978-0-635-06404-2(9)***) Gallopade International.

Myers, Nancy C. Nancy Landon Kassebaum: A Senate Profile. 1998. (Contemporary Profiles & Policy Series for the Younger Reader). 70p. (YA). (gr. 8 up). 20.00 (978-0-934272-47-6(6)) Burke, John Gordon Pub., Inc.

Nivola, Claire A. Planting the Trees of Kenya: The Story of Wangari Maathai. 2008. 32p. (J). 16.95 (***978-0-374-39918-4(2)*** , Farrar, Straus & Giroux) Farrar, Straus & Giroux.

Parker, Janice. Political Leaders. 1998. (Women in Profile Ser.). (Illus.). 48p. (J). (gr. 4). lib. bdg. (978-0-7787-0008-1(9)) Crabtree Publishing Co.

Peterson, Virginia, et al, eds. Women: New Roles in Society. 3rd rev. ed. 1998. (Information Plus Compact Ser.). (Illus.). 84p. (YA). (gr. 6-9). pap. 22.00 (978-1-57302-083-1(4)) Thomson Gale.

Price-Groff, Claire. Twentieth-Century Women Political Leaders. 1998. (Global Profiles Ser.). (Illus.). 160p. (YA). (gr. 5-12). lib. bdg. 25.00 (978-0-8160-3672-1(1)) Facts On File, Inc.

Somervill, Barbara A. Votes for Women! The Story of Carrie Chapman Catt. 2004. (Feminist Voices Ser.). (Illus.). 128p. (YA). (gr. 6-12). 23.95 (978-1-883846-96-1(X) , First Biographies) Reynolds, Morgan Inc.

Thimmesh, Catherine. Madam President: The Extraordinary, True (and Evolving) Story of Women in Politics. Jones, Douglas, illus. 2008. (J). (gr. 1-5). pap. 8.95 (***978-0-618-97143-5(2)***) Houghton Mifflin Co. Trade & Reference Div.

—Madam President: The Extraordinary, True (and Evolving) Story of Women in Politics. Jones, Douglas B., illus. 2004. 80p. (J). (gr. 5-6). tchr. ed. 17.00 (978-0-618-39666-5(7)) Houghton Mifflin Co. Trade & Reference Div.

Thro, Ellen. Twentieth-Century Women Politicians. 1998. (American Profiles Ser.). (Illus.). 144p. (YA). (gr. 5-12). 25.00 (978-0-8160-3758-2(2)) Facts On File, Inc.

Wheeler, Jill C. Margaret Thatcher. 2004. (Women of the World Ser.). (J). (978-1-59197-618-9(9)) ABDO Publishing Co.

Women in Politics. 2005. 112p. pap. 180.00 (978-0-7910-7730-6(6) , Chelsea Hse.) Facts On File, Inc.

Zeinert, Karen. Women in Politics: In the Running. 2002. (Women at War Ser.). (Illus.). 112p. (gr. 7 up). lib. bdg. 29.90 (978-0-7613-2253-5(1) , Twenty-First Century Bks.) Lerner Publishing Group.

WOMEN IN THE BIBLE

Chariot Victor Publishing Staff. Four in One Toddler Book. 2000. 12.99 (978-0-7814-3423-2(8)) Cook, David C. Publishing Co.

Claussen, Janet. Biblical Women: Exploring Their Stories with Girls. 2003. 120p. (YA). pap. 24.95 (978-0-88489-699-9(4)) St. Mary's Pr.

Green, John. Women of the Bible. 2006. 32p. (J). pap. 3.95 (978-0-486-45193-0(3)) Dover Pubns., Inc.

Hodgson, Mona. Real Girls of the Bible. 2008. 192p. (J). pap. 9.99 (***978-0-310-71338-8(2)***) Zondervan.

Inspirational Press Staff, ed. Great Women of the Bible. 2000. (Arch Bks.). (Illus.). 104p. (J). (gr. 4-7). pap. 7.99 (978-0-88486-267-3(4) , Arrowood Pr.) BBS Publishing Corp.

Lo, Monica. Old Testament Heroines of the Faith. Diehl, Nichole, illus. 2007. 86p. (J). per. 17.99 (***978-1-59879-224-9(5)*** , Lifevest) Lifevest Publishing, Inc.

Nederveld, Patricia L. A Girl Named Rebekah: The Story of God's Answer to Abraham. 1998. (God Loves Me Ser.). (Illus.). 24p. (J). (ps-3). pap. 2.95 (978-1-56212-277-5(0) , 001208, Faith Alive Christian Resources) CRC Pubns.

Sanderson, Ruth. Tapestries: Stories of Women in the Bible. Sanderson, Ruth, illus. 1998. (Illus.). 32p. (J). (gr. 3-7). 15.95 (978-0-316-77093-4(0)) Little Brown & Co.

Scanlon, Gisele. The Goddess Guide. 2007. 288p. 19.95 (*978-0-06-143495-2(7), Harper Entertainment) HarperCollins Pubs.

Ward, Elaine M. Old Testament Women. 2003. (Art Revelations Ser.). (Illus.). 32p. (J). (gr. 6-9). 18.95 (978-1-59270-011-0(X)) Enchanted Lion Bks., LLC.

WOMEN JOURNALISTS

Butcher, Nancy. It Can't Be Done, Nellie Bly! A Reporter's Race Around the World. 2003. (Illus.). 144p. (J). (gr. 1-5). 12.95 (978-1-56145-289-7(0)) Peachtree Pubs., Ltd.

Colman, Penny. Where the Action Was: Women War Correspondents in World War II. 2002. (Illus.). 128p. (J). (gr. 5 up). lib. bdg. 19.99 (978-0-517-80076-8(4), Crown Books For Young Readers) Random Hse. Children's Bks.

WOMEN PHYSICIANS

Bank Street Staff & Glimm, Adele. Elizabeth Blackwell: First Woman Doctor to Modern Times. 2000. (Ideas on Trial Ser.). (Illus.). 124p. (C). (gr. 5-10). pap. 8.95 (978-0-07-134335-0(0)) McGraw-Hill Cos., The.

Kent, Jacqueline C. Women in Medicine. 1998. (Profiles Ser.). (Illus.). 160p. (YA). (gr. 5-12). lib. bdg. 19.95 (978-1-881508-46-5(3)) Oliver Pr., Inc.

Kishel, Ann-Marie. Elizabeth Blackwell: A Life of Diligence. 2007. (Pull Ahead Books-Biographies Ser.). (J). 22.60 (978-0-8225-6459-1(9), Lerner Pubns.) Lerner Publishing Group.

Klobuchar, Lisa. Elizabeth Blackwell: With Profiles of Elizabeth Garrett Anderson & Susan la Flesche Picotte. 2006. (Biographical Connections Ser.). (Illus.). 112p. (978-0-7166-1826-3(5)) World Bk., Inc.

Kovatch, Sarah & Crumpler, Rebecca Lee. Rebecca Lee Crumpler. 2005. (Illus.). 16p. (J). (*978-0-7367-2891-1(0)) Zaner-Bloser, Inc.

Leavitt, Amie. Elizabeth Blackwell. 2007. (What's So Great About...? Ser.). (J). lib. bdg. 25.70 (*978-1-58415-579-9(5)) Mitchell Lane Pubs., Inc.

Mader, Jan. Elizabeth Blackwell. 2007. (J). (978-0-7368-6704-7(X), Pebble Bks.) Capstone Pr., Inc.

Robbins, Trina. Elizabeth Blackwell: America's First Woman Doctor. Martin, Cynthia & Timmons, Anne, illus. 2007. (Graphic Library). 32p. (J). 25.26 (978-0-7368-6497-8(0)); (*978-0-7368-9660-3(0)) Capstone Pr., Inc.

Roberts, Russell. American Women of Medicine. 2002. (Collective Biographies Ser.). (Illus.). 104p. (YA). (gr. 6-12). lib. bdg. 26.60 (978-0-7660-1835-8(0)) Enslow Pubs., Inc.

Rue, Nancy N. Lily Robbins, M. D. Medical Dabbler. 2000. (Young Women of Faith Library Ser.). (Illus.). 128p. (J). pap. 5.99 (978-0-310-23249-0(X)) Zonderkidz.

Werther, Scott P. Dr. Jerri Nielsen: Cheating Death in Antarctica. 2003. (High Interest Books Ser.). (Illus.). 48p. (J). 23.00 (978-0-516-24331-3(4), Children's Pr.) Scholastic Library Publishing.

Women in Medicine. 2005. (Extraordinary Women Ser.). (Illus.). 112p. (gr. 6-12). pap. 180.00 (978-0-7910-8418-2(3), Chelsea Hse.) Facts On File, Inc.

WOMEN PIRATES

Sharp, Anne Wallace. Daring Pirate Women. 2005. (Biography Ser.). (Illus.). 112p. (gr. 6-12). 27.93 (978-0-8225-0031-5(0)) Lerner Publishing Group.

Weatherly, Myra. Women Pirates: Eight Stories of Adventure. 1998. (Women Adventurers Ser.). (Illus.). 112p. (YA). (gr. 6-12). 21.95 (978-1-883846-24-4(2), First Biographies) Reynolds, Morgan Inc.

WOMEN SCIENTISTS

Ardagh, Philip. Marie Curie. 2003. (Illus.). 64p. (J). pap. 6.99 (978-0-330-37571-9(7), Pan) Pan Macmillan GBR. *Dist:* Trafalgar Square Publishing.

Camp, Carole Ann. American Women of Science. 2001. (Collective Biographies Ser.). (Illus.). 112p. (J). (gr. 6-12). lib. bdg. 26.60 (978-0-7660-1538-8(6)) Enslow Pubs., Inc.

Casey, Susan. Women Invent: Two Centuries of Discoveries That Have Shaped Our World. 2003. (Illus.). 144p. (J). (gr. 4-8). pap. 14.95 (978-1-55652-317-5(3)) Chicago Review Pr., Inc.

Fine, Edith Hope. Barbara McClintock: Nobel Prize Geneticist. 1998. (People to Know Ser.). (Illus.). 128p. (YA). (gr. 6-12). lib. bdg. 26.60 (978-0-89490-983-2(5)) Enslow Pubs., Inc.

Haskins, Jim. Black Stars. 2001. (Black Stars Ser.: Vol. 1). 272p. 59.95 (978-0-471-21145-7(1), Wiley) Wiley, John & Sons, Inc.

Kahn, Jetty. Women in Life Science Careers. 1998. (Short Biographies Ser.). (Illus.). 48p. (J). (gr. 3-4). lib. bdg. 22.60 (978-0-7368-0014-3(X), Bridgestone Bks.) Capstone Pr., Inc.

Kozleski, Lisa. Jane Goodall. 2003. (Women in Science Ser.). pap. 30.00 (978-0-7910-7519-7(2)); (Illus.). 112p. (gr. 6-12). 30.00 (978-0-7910-6905-9(2)) Facts On File, Inc. (Chelsea Hse.).

McClure, Judy. Theoreticians & Builders: Mathematicians, Physical Scientists, Inventors. 2002. (Remarkable Women). (Illus.). 80p. (YA). (gr. 6-9). lib. bdg. 32.85 (978-0-8172-5728-6(4)) Raintree.

Nicholson, Lois. Dian Fossey. 2003. (Women in Science Ser.). (Illus.). 112p. (gr. 6-12). 30.00 (978-0-7910-6907-3(9), Chelsea Hse.) Facts On File, Inc.

Sally Ride Science Editors, Sally Ride Science. What Do You Want to Be? Explore Earth Sciences. 2004. (J). 6.00 (978-0-9753920-2-7(6)) Sally Ride Science.

Skelton, Renee. Forecast Earth: The Story of Climate Scientist Inez Fung. 2005. (Women's Adventures in Science Ser.). (Illus.). 116p. (YA). (gr. 7-9). 31.00 (978-0-531-16777-9(1), Watts, Franklin) Scholastic Library Publishing.

Stux, Erica. The Achievers: Great Women in the Biological Sciences. 2005. (Avisson Young Adult Ser.). (Illus.). 148p. (J). (978-1-888105-70-4(4)) Avisson Pr., Inc.

Thimmesh, Catherine. Girls Think of Everything: Stories of Ingenious Inventions by Women. Sweet, Melissa, illus. 2000. 64p. (J). (gr. 4-6). tchr. ed. 16.00 (978-0-395-93744-0(2)) Houghton Mifflin Co. Trade & Reference Div.

—The Sky's the Limit: Stories of Discovery by Women & Girls. Sweet, Melissa, illus. 2005. 73p. (J). (gr. 4-8). reprint ed. 16.00 (978-0-7567-9631-0(8)) DIANE Publishing Co.

—The Sky's the Limit: Stories of Discovery by Women & Girls. Sweet, Melissa, illus. 2002. 80p. (J). (gr. 5-8). 16.00 (978-0-618-07698-7(0)) Houghton Mifflin Co. Trade & Reference Div.

Wishinsky, Frieda. Manya's Dream: A Story of Marie Curie. Lamontagne, Jacques, illus. 2003. 32p. (J). (gr. 3-6). 19.95 (978-1-894379-53-3(5)); pap. 6.95 (978-1-894379-54-0(3)) Maple Tree Pr. CAN. *Dist:* Firefly Bks., Ltd.

Women's Adventures in Science, 10 bks., Set. 2005. (Illus.). (YA). (gr. 9). lib. bdg. 310.00 (978-0-531-16824-0(7), Watts, Franklin) Scholastic Library Publishing.

Zach, Kim K. Hidden from History: The Lives of Eight American Women Scientists. 2002. (Avisson Young Adult Ser.). (Illus.). 144p. (Orig.). (J). (gr. 6-12). pap. 19.95 (978-1-888105-54-4(2)) Avisson Pr., Inc.

WOMEN'S CLOTHING

see Clothing and Dress

WOMEN'S RIGHTS

Anderson, Dale. The Seneca Falls Women's Rights Convention. 2004. (Landmark Events in American History Ser.). (Illus.). 48p. (J). (gr. 5 up). pap. 11.95 (978-0-8368-5417-6(9)); lib. bdg. 30.00 (978-0-8368-5389-6(X)) Stevens, Gareth Inc. (World Almanac Library).

The Antebellum Women's Movement, 1820-1860. (YA). (gr. 6-9). spiral bd., tchr.'s planning gde. ed. 12.00 (978-0-382-44465-4(5)) Cobblestone Publishing Co.

Archer, Jules. Breaking Barriers: The Feminist Revolution from Susan B. Anthony to Margaret Sanger to Betty Friedan. 2001. (Illus.). 207p. (YA). (gr. 7-9). 20.00 (978-0-7567-5224-8(8)) DIANE Publishing Co.

Bausum, Ann. With Courage & Cloth: Winning the Fight for a Woman's Right to Vote. 2004. (Illus.). 112p. (J). (gr. 5-17). 32.90 (978-0-7922-6996-0(9), National Geographic Children's Bks.) National Geographic Society.

Bjornlund, Lydia D. Women of the Suffrage Movement. 2003. (Women in History Ser.). (Illus.). 112p. (J). 32.45 (978-1-59018-173-7(5), Lucent Bks.) Thomson Gale.

Bohannon, Lisa Frederiksen. Women's Rights & Nothing Less: The Story of Elizabeth Cady Stanton. 2004. (Feminist Voices Ser.). (Illus.). 112p. (YA). (gr. 6-12). 23.95 (978-1-883846-66-4(8), First Biographies) Reynolds, Morgan Inc.

Bohannon, Lisa Frederiksen. Failure Is Impossible: The Story of Susan B. Anthony. 2004. (Feminist Voices Ser.). (Illus.). 112p. (YA). (gr. 6-12). 23.95 (978-1-883846-77-0(3), First Biographies) Reynolds, Morgan Inc.

Bolden, Tonya, ed. 33 Things Every Girl Should Know about Women's History: From Suffragettes to Skirt Lengths to the E.R.A. 2002. (Illus.). 240p. (YA). (gr. 7 up). pap. 12.95 (978-0-375-81122-7(2), Crown Books For Young Readers) Random Hse. Children's Bks.

Boothroyd, Jennifer. Susan B. Anthony: A Life of Fairness. 2006. (Pull Ahead Books). (J). lib. bdg. (978-978-082-253-8(4)); (Illus.). 32p. 22.60 (978-0-8225-3479-2(7)) Lerner Publishing Group. (Lerner Pubns.).

—Susan B. Anthony: Una Vida de Igualdad. 2006. (Libros para Avanzar Ser.). (ENG & SPA., Illus.). 32p. (J). lib. bdg. 22.60 (978-0-8225-6234-4(0)) Lerner Publishing Group.

Carlson, Dale B. & Carlson, Hannah. Girls Are Equal Too: The Teenage Girls How-to-Survive Book. Nicklaus, Carol, illus. 2nd rev. ed. 2000. (Psychology for Teenagers Ser.: Vol. 1). 231p. (gr. 5-12). pap. 14.95 (978-1-884158-18-6(8)) Bick Publishing Hse.

Ching, Jacqueline & Ching, Juliet. Women's Rights. 2001. (Individual Rights & Civic Responsibility Ser.). (Illus.). 64p. (YA). (gr. 7-12). lib. bdg. 26.50 (978-0-8239-3233-7(8)) Rosen Publishing Group, Inc., The.

Connell, Kate. They Shall Be Heard: Susan B. Anthony & Elizabeth Cady Stanton. 2001. (Nonfiction Bookbag Ser.). (YA). (gr. 7-8). per. 8.45 (978-1-58830-207-6(5)) Metropolitan Teaching & Learning Co.

Connolly, Sean. Gender Equality. 2005. (Campaigns for Change Ser.). (Illus.). 48p. (J). (gr. 6-9). lib. bdg. 29.95 (978-1-58340-515-4(1)) Smart Apple Media.

Corey, Shana. You Forgot Your Skirt, Amelia Bloomer! McLaren, Chesley, illus. 2000. 40p. (J). (gr. k-3). pap. 16.95 (978-0-439-07819-1(9), Scholastic Reference) Scholastic, Inc.

Crewe, Sabrina & Anderson, Dale. The Seneca Falls Women's Rights Convention. 2004. (Events That Shaped America Ser.). (J). lib. bdg. 24.67 (978-0-8368-3408-6(9)) Stevens, Gareth Inc.

Elizabeth Cady Stanton. (Photo Illustrated Biographies Ser.). 24p. (J). 6.95 (978-0-7368-8428-0(9)) Capstone Pr., Inc.

Fritz, Jean. You Want Women to Vote, Lizzie Stanton? DiSalvo-Ryan, DyAnne, illus. 1999. 96p. (J). (gr. 3-7). pap. 6.99 (978-0-698-11764-8(6), Putnam Juvenile) Penguin Group (USA) Inc.

—You Want Women to Vote, Lizzie Stanton? 1999. (978-0-606-16848-9(6)); (gr. 3-6). lib. bdg. 15.30 (978-0-613-17893-8(9)) Tandem Library Bks.

Fry, Erin. The Power of Friendship. 2005. (Illus.). 16p. (J). pap. (978-0-7367-2920-8(8)) Zaner-Bloser, Inc.

Harcourt School Publishers Staff. It Happened at Seneca Falls. 3rd ed. 2002. (Horizons Ser.). (Illus.). (J). pap. 5.50 (978-0-15-333399-6(5)) Harcourt Schl. Pubs.

Harvey, Miles. Women's Voting Rights. 1998. (Cornerstones of Freedom Ser.). (Illus.). 32p. (J). (gr. 4-6). pap. 5.95 (978-0-516-26288-8(2), Children's Pr.) Scholastic Library Publishing.

Haughton, Emma. Equality of the Sexes? 2005. (Illus.). 32p. (J). (gr. 5-9). lib. bdg. 27.10 (978-1-932889-58-1(2)) Sea-To-Sea Pubns.

Hermann, Spring. The Struggle for Equality: Women & Minorities in America. 2006. (American Saga Ser.). (Illus.). 128p. (J). lib. bdg. 31.93 (978-0-7660-2573-8(X)) Enslow Pubs., Inc.

Hopkinson, Deborah. Susan B. Anthony: Fighter for Women's Rights. Bates, Amy, illus. 2005. 32p. (J). lib. bdg. 15.00 (*978-1-4242-1563-8(3)) Fitzgerald Bks.

—Susan B. Anthony: Fighter for Women's Rights. Bates, Amy June, illus. 2005. (Ready-To-Read Stories of Famous Americans Ser.). 32p. (J). (gr. 1-3). pap. 3.99 (978-0-689-86909-9(6)); lib. bdg. 11.89 (978-0-689-86910-5(X)) Simon & Schuster Children's Publishing. (Aladdin).

Howard, Melanie A. Civil Rights Marches. 2005. (American Moments Ser.). (Illus.). (J). (gr. 4-8). lib. bdg. 25.65 (978-1-59197-282-2(5), ABDO & Daughters) ABDO Publishing Co.

Kallen, Stuart A. Women of the 1960s. 2003. (Women in History Ser.). (Illus.). 128p. (J). 32.45 (978-1-59018-251-2(0), Lucent Bks.) Thomson Gale.

Kamma, Anne. If You Lived When Women Won Their Rights. 2008. 64p. pap. 5.99 (*978-0-439-74869-8(0), Scholastic Reference) Scholastic, Inc.

Kendall, Martha E. Failure Is Impossible! The History of American Women's Rights. 3rd ed. 2005. (People's History Ser.). (Illus.). 96p. (gr. 6-12). lib. bdg. 26.60 (978-0-8225-1744-3(2)) Lerner Publishing Group.

Kops, Deborah. The Women Suffrage Movement. 2003. (People at the Center of Ser.). (Illus.). 48p. (J). 24.95 (978-1-56711-772-1(4), Blackbirch Pr., Inc.) Thomson Gale.

Loos, Pamela. Elizabeth Cady Stanton: Woman Suffragist. 2000. (Women of Achievement Ser.). (Illus.). 112p. (J). (gr. 4-7). 30.00 (978-0-7910-5293-8(1), Chelsea Hse.) Facts On File, Inc.

Mattern, Joanne. Elizabeth Cady Stanton & Susan B. Anthony: Fighting Together for Women's Rights. 2003. (Reading Power Ser.). (Illus.). 24p. (J). lib. bdg. 17.25 (978-0-8239-6503-8(1), PowerKids Pr.) Rosen Publishing Group, Inc., The.

—Elizabeth Cady Stanton & Susan B Anthony Fighting Together for Women's Rights: Individual Title Six-Packs. (On Deck Ser.: Vol. 2). 24p. (gr. 4-5). 35.00 (978-0-7578-5843-7(0)) Rigby Education.

McGowan, Keith. Sexual Harassment. 1998. (Overview Ser.). (Illus.). 112p. (YA). (gr. 6-9). lib. bdg. 29.95 (978-1-56006-507-4(9), LML00902-177867, Lucent Bks.) Thomson Gale.

McGraw-Hill - Jamestown Education. American History Ink: Book 3, the Women's Rights Movement. 2007. (C). pap. 9.28 (*978-0-07-878025-7(X), 9780078780257) Glencoe/McGraw-Hill.

McPherson, Stephanie Sammartino. Susan B. Anthony. 2006. (History Maker Bios Ser.). (Illus.). 48p. (J). 26.60 (978-0-8225-5938-2(2), Lerner Pubns.) Lerner Publishing Group.

Miller, Connie Colwell. Elizabeth Cady Stanton: Women's Rights Pioneer. Webb, James, illus. 2006. (Graphic Library). 32p. (J). 25.26 (978-0-7368-4971-5(8)) Capstone Pr., Inc.

Moore, Heidi. Elizabeth Cady Stanton. 2004. (American Lives (Heinemann Library (Firm))). (Illus.). 32p. (J). pap. 6.95 (978-1-4034-5705-9(0)); lib. bdg. (978-1-4034-4994-8(5)) Heinemann Library.

Mountjoy, Shane. The Women's Rights Movement: Moving Toward Equality. 2007. (Reform Movements in American History Ser.). 152p. (gr. 6-12). 30.00 (*978-0-7910-9505-8(3), Chelsea Hse.) Facts On File, Inc.

Nash, Carol Rust. The Fight for Women's Right to Vote in American History. 1998. (In American History Ser.). (Illus.). 128p. (YA). (gr. 5-12). lib. bdg. 26.60 (978-0-89490-986-3(X)) Enslow Pubs., Inc.

Noyed, Robert B. Susan B. Anthony: Reformer. 2002. (Spirit of America: Our People Ser.). (Illus.). 32p. (J). (gr. 2-6). 27.07 (978-1-56766-171-2(8)) Child's World, Inc.

Price Hossell, Karen. The Nineteenth Amendment: Women Get the Vote. 2003. (Point of Impact Ser.). (Illus.). 32p. (J). (gr. 5-7). lib. bdg. 25.64 (978-1-58810-908-8(9)) Heinemann Library.

Raum, Elizabeth. Alice Paul. 2004. (American Lives (Heinemann Library (Firm))). (Illus.). 32p. (J). pap. 7.50 (978-1-4034-5703-5(4)); lib. bdg. (978-1-4034-4996-2(1)) Heinemann Library.

Rife, Douglas M. Seneca Falls Declaration of Sentiments & Resolutions. Mitchell, Judy, ed. Smith, Bron, illus. 2002. 48p. (J). (gr. 4-8). pap. 6.95 (978-1-57310-350-3(0)) Teaching & Learning Co.

Rossi, Ann. Created Equal: Women Campaign for the Right to Vote 1840 - 1920. 2005. (Crossroads America Ser.). (Illus.). 40p. (gr. 5-9). 12.95 (978-0-7922-8275-4(2)); 21.90 (978-0-7922-8285-3(X)) National Geographic Society. (National Geographic Children's Bks.).

—Created Equal: Women Campaign for the Right to Vote, 1840-1920. 2005. (Crossroads America Ser.). (Illus.). 40p. (J). (978-0-7922-8626-4(X)) National Geographic Society.

Salisbury, Cynthia. Elizabeth Cady Stanton: Leader of the Fight for Women's Rights. 2002. (Historical American Biographies Ser.). (Illus.). 128p. (YA). (gr. 6-9). lib. bdg. 26.60 (978-0-7660-1616-3(1)) Enslow Pubs., Inc.

Schomp, Virginia. American Voices from the Women's Movement. 2006. (American Voices Ser.). (Illus.). xix, 138p. (J). lib. bdg. 37.07 (978-0-7614-2171-9(8), Benchmark Bks.) Cavendish, Marshall Corp.

Sigerman, Harriet. Elizabeth Cady Stanton: The Right Is Ours. 2001. (Oxford Portraits Ser.). (Illus.). 144p. (YA). (gr. 8 up). suppl. ed. 28.00 (978-0-19-511969-5(X)) Oxford Univ. Pr., Inc.

—Laborers for Liberty Vol. 6: American Women 1865-1890. 1998. (Young Oxford History of Women in the United States Ser.). (Illus.). 144p. (YA). reprint ed. pap. 12.95 (978-0-19-512404-0(9)) Oxford Univ. Pr., Inc.

Slade, Suzanne. Susan B. Anthony: Fighter for Freedom & Equality. Orback, Craig, illus. 2006. (Biographies Ser.). 24p. (J). (gr. k-3). lib. bdg. 23.93 (*978-1-4048-3104-9(5)) Picture Window Bks.

Stearman, Kaye. Women's Rights: Changing Attitudes, 1900-2000. 1999. (Twentieth Century Issues Ser.). (Illus.). 64p. (J). (gr. 4-6). lib. bdg. 28.54 (978-0-8172-5892-4(2)) Raintree.

Weidt, Maryann N. Fighting for Equal Rights: A Story about Susan B. Anthony. Sartor, Amanda, tr. Sartor, Amanda, illus. 2004. (Creative Minds Biography Ser.). 64p. (J). 22.60 (978-1-57505-181-9(8), Carolrhoda Bks.) Lerner Publishing Group.

WOMEN'S RIGHTS—FICTION

Cooney, Caroline B. Prisoner of Time. 1999. (978-0-606-16455-9(3)) Tandem Library Bks.

Duey, Kathleen. Francesca Vigilucci: Washington, D. C. 1913. 2000. (American Diaries Ser.: No. 17). (J). (gr. 3-7). (978-0-606-20079-0(7)) Tandem Library Bks.

Ellis, Deborah. The Breadwinner. 2002. (gr. 3-6). lib. bdg. 14.10 (978-0-613-44488-0(4)) Tandem Library Bks.

Jocelyn, Marthe. Mable Riley: A Reliable Record of Humdrum, Peril, & Romance. 2007. 288p. (J). (gr. 5). 6.99 (978-0-7636-3287-8(2)) Candlewick Pr.

Karr, Kathleen. Mama Went to Jail for the Vote. Laugesen, Malene, illus. 2005. 32p. (gr. k-4). 15.99 (978-0-7868-0593-8(5)) Hyperion Bks. for Children.

McDonald, Megan. Meet Julie. McAliley, Susan & Hunt, Robert, illus. 2007. 104p. (YA). (gr. 3 up). pap. 6.95 (*978-1-59369-257-5(9)) American Girl Publishing, Inc.

—Meet Julie. McAliley, Susan, illus. 2007. 104p. (YA). (gr. 3 up). 12.95 (*978-1-59369-287-2(0)) American Girl Publishing, Inc.

Penson, Mary. Martha Mary Overstreet, M. D. 2007. (Chaparral Book for Young Readers Ser.). 142p. (J). pap. 11.95 (*978-0-87565-345-7(6)) Texas Christian Univ. Pr.

Schwabach, Karen. The Hope Chest. 2008. 288p. (J). (gr. 4-7). 16.99 (*978-0-375-84095-1(8)); lib. bdg. 19.99 (*978-0-375-94095-8(2)) Random Hse., Inc.

WONDER WOMAN (FICTITIOUS CHARACTER)—FICTION

Jaffe, Nina. The Journey Begins. Caldwell, Ben, illus. 2004. (Wonder Woman Ser.). 64p. (J). pap. 4.99 (978-0-06-056521-3(7), Harper Festival) HarperCollins Pubs.

—The Rain Forest. Caldwell, Ben, illus. 2004. (Festival Reader Ser.). 32p. (J). (ps-2). pap. 3.99 (978-0-06-056520-6(9), Harper Festival) HarperCollins Pubs.

—Wonder Woman: Amazon Princess. 2004. (gr. 3-6). lib. bdg. 13.00 (978-0-613-71471-6(7)) Tandem Library Bks.

—Wonder Woman: The Contest. 2004. (ps-2). lib. bdg. 11.80 (978-0-613-71841-7(0)) Tandem Library Bks.

—Wonder Woman: The Journey Begins. 2004. (gr. 3-6). lib. bdg. 13.00 (978-0-613-71470-9(9)) Tandem Library Bks.

WOOD

see also Forests and Forestry; Lumber and Lumbering; Woodwork

also kinds of wood, e.g. Oak

Bedford, Kate. Wood. 2005. (Illus.). 32p. (J). (gr. 3-7). lib. bdg. 27.10 (978-1-59604-041-0(6)) Stargazer Bks.

Jennings, Terry. Wood. 2006. (Illus.). 32p. (YA). (gr. 1 up). lib. bdg. 27.10 (978-1-932333-00-8(2)) Chrysalis Education.

Kras, Sara Louise. Wood. 2004. (First Facts Ser.). (Illus.). 24p. (J). 15.95 (978-0-7368-2515-3(0)) Capstone Pr., Inc.

Llewellyn, Claire. Wood. 2002. (Material World Ser.). (J). (gr. 2-4). pap. 6.95 (978-0-531-14835-8(1)); (Illus.). 32p. pap. 24.00 (978-0-531-14633-0(2)) Scholastic Library Publishing. (Watts, Franklin).

—Wood. 2005. (Illus.). 24p. (J). (gr. 1-4). lib. bdg. 22.80 (978-1-932889-51-2(5)) Sea-To-Sea Pubns.

Mitchell, Melanie S. Wood. 2003. (First Step Nonfiction Ser.). (Illus.). 24p. (J). (gr. k-2). lib. bdg. 18.60 (978-0-8225-4618-4(3)) Lerner Publishing Group.

Oxlade, Chris. How We Use Wood. 2004. (Illus.). 32p. (J). (gr. 3-5). pap. 7.50 (978-1-4109-0997-8(2)); 25.70 (978-1-4109-0598-7(5)) Raintree.

—Wood. (Materials, Materials Ser.). 32p. pap. 6.95 (978-1-4034-4101-0(4)); 2001. (Illus.). (J). lib. bdg. 21.36 (978-1-58810-158-7(4)) Heinemann Library.

Parker, Steve. Wood. 2002. (Science Files Ser.). (Illus.). 32p. (J). (gr. 3 up). lib. bdg. 24.67 (978-0-8368-3087-3(3)) Stevens, Gareth Inc.

Ridley, Sarah. A Wooden Chair. 2006. (Illus.). 32p. (J). lib. bdg. 23.33 (978-0-8368-6296-6(1)) Stevens, Gareth Inc.

Royston, Angela. Madera: Miremos un Bate Deportivo. 2006. (Heinemann Lee y Aprende Ser.). (Illus.). 24p. (J). (SPA & ENG.). (978-1-4034-7549-7(0)); (ENG & SPA., pap. (978-1-4034-7558-9(X)) Heinemann Library.

—Wood: Let's Look at a Baseball Bat. 2005. (Illus.). 24p. (J). (978-1-4034-7672-2(1)); pap. (978-1-4034-7681-4(0)) Heinemann Library.

—Wood: Let's Look at a Sports Bat. 2005. (J). (978-1-4109-1819-2(X)); pap. (978-1-4109-1828-4(9)) Steck-Vaughn.

W X Y Z

Tiner, John Hudson. Wood. 2003. (Matter & Materials Ser.). (J). (978-1-58417-160-7(X)); pap. (978-1-58417-166-9(9)) Lake Street Pubs.

Wallace, Holly. Wood. 2007. (J). (***978-1-59920-007-1(4)***) Smart Apple Media.

Whyman, Kathryn. Wood & the Environment. 2004. (J). lib. bdg. (978-1-932799-34-7(6)) Stargazer Bks.

WOOD-CARVING

Bates, Michelle. Midnight Horse Kid Kit. 2005. 112p. (J). 11.99 (978-1-58086-799-3(5)); 11.99 (978-1-58086-759-7(6)) EDC Publishing. (Usborne).

DK Publishing. Woodcarving. 2008. 72p. (J). 12.99 (***978-0-7566-3507-7(1)***) Dorling Kindersley Publishing, Inc.

Stampf, Bob & Stampf, Jonathan. Woodcarving Fundamentals with Bob Stampf: For PC, Vol. 1. Stampf, Jonathan, illus. 2001. (gr. 9 up). cd-rom 24.95 (978-0-9711471-0-2(8)) Jonathan Stampf Design Services.

Tiede, Karen. Carve Smart. 2004. 189p. (YA). pap. 19.95 (978-0-7414-2093-0(7)) Infinity Publishing.

Trudel, Robin. Carving for Kids: An Introduction to Woodcarving. 2006. (Illus.). 104p. pap. 16.95 (978-1-933502-02-1(9)) Linden Publishing Co., Inc.

Wainwright, Richard M. A New Life for Sir Christopher. Drorsack, Carolyn S., illus. 2nd ed. 1998. 48p. (J). reprint ed. 17.00 (978-0-9619566-4-6(X)) Family Life Publishing/Richard Wainright Bks.

WOOD WIND INSTRUMENTS

see Wind Instruments

WOODCHUCK

Dingwall, Laima, et al. Woodchucks. 1999. (Getting to Know ... Nature's Children Ser.). (Illus.). 47p. (J). (978-0-7172-8844-1(7) , Grolier) Scholastic Library Publishing.

Gibbons, Gail. Groundhog Day. Gibbons, Gail, illus. 2007. (Illus.). 32p. (J). (ps-3). pap. 6.95 (***978-0-8234-2116-9(3)***) Holiday Hse., Inc.

Gibbons, Gail. Groundhog Day! Gibbons, Gail, illus. (Illus.). 32p. (J). 16.95 (978-0-8234-2003-2(5)) Holiday Hse., Inc.

McNeil, Niki, et al. HOCPP 1146 Mr. Groundhog. 2007. spiral bd. 15.50 (***978-1-60308-146-7(1)***) In the Hands of a Child.

Nobleman, Marc Tyler. Groundhog Day. 2004. (Let's See Ser.). (Illus.). 24p. (J). (gr. 1 up). lib. bdg. 19.93 (978-0-7565-0648-3(4)) Compass Point Bks.

Old, Wendie. The Groundhog Day Book of Facts & Fun. Billin-Frye, Paige, illus. 2004. 40p. (J). (gr. 3-6). 15.95 (978-0-8075-3066-5(2)) Whitman, Albert & Co.

Richardson, Adele D. Groundhogs: Woodchucks, Marmots, & Whistle Pigs. 2002. (Wild World of Animals Ser.). (Illus.). 24p. (J). (gr. 1). lib. bdg. 18.60 (978-0-7368-1397-6(7) , Bridgestone Bks.) Capstone Pr., Inc.

WOODCHUCK—FICTION

Arno, Iris Hiskey. The Secret of the First One Up. Graef, Renee, illus. 2003. 32p. (gr. k-3). 15.95 (978-1-55971-867-7(6) , NorthWord Bks. for Young Readers) T&N Children's Publishing.

Balian, Lorna. A Garden for Groundhog. 2004. (Illus.). 40p. (J). 15.95 (978-1-932065-38-1(5)) Star Bright Bks., Inc.

Bang, Molly Garrett. Goose. Bang, Molly Garrett, illus. 2002. (Illus.). (J). 19.72 (978-0-7587-2626-1(0)) Book Wholesalers, Inc.

Birenbaum, Barbara. The Groundhog Message. 2000. (Historical Adventure Ser.: Vol. 9). (Illus.). (J). pap. 19.95 (978-0-935343-48-9(2)) Peartree.

Cherry, Lynne. How Groundhog's Garden Grew. Cherry, Lynne, illus. 2003. (Illus.). 40p. (J). (ps up). pap. 15.95 (978-0-439-32371-0(1) , Blue Sky Pr., The) Scholastic, Inc.

Cox, Judy. Go to Sleep, Groundhog. Meisel, Paul, illus. 32p. (gr. k-3). tchr. ed. 17.95 (978-0-8234-1645-5(3)) Holiday Hse., Inc.

—Go to Sleep, Groundhog! Meisel, Paul, illus. 32p. (gr. k-3). reprint ed. pap. 6.95 (978-0-8234-1874-9(X)) Holiday Hse., Inc.

Cuyler, Margery. Groundhog Stays up Late. Cassels, Jean, illus. 2005. 32p. (J). (ps-2). 16.95 (978-0-8027-8939-6(0)) Walker & Co.

Debowski, Sharon. The Snowman, the Owl, & the Groundhog. 2007. (J). lib. bdg. 15.95 (***978-1-60227-468-6(1)***); (Illus.). 32p. 14.95 (***978-1-60227-470-9(3)***) Above the Clouds Publishing.

Elish, Dan. Attack of the Frozen Woodchucks. 2008. 256p. (J). 17.89 (***978-0-06-113871-3(1)*** , Geringer, Laura Book) HarperCollins Pubs.

—Attack of the Frozen Woodchucks. Call, Greg, illus. 2008. 256p. (J). 16.99 (***978-0-06-113870-6(3)*** , Geringer, Laura Book) HarperCollins Pubs.

Freeman, Don. Gregory's Shadow. Freeman, Don, illus. (Illus.). 2005. (J). pap. 18.95 incl. audio compact disk (978-1-59112-488-7(3)); 2003. 28.95 incl. audio compact disk (978-1-59112-537-2(5)); 2003. pap. 39.95 incl. audio compact disk (978-1-59112-536-5(7)) Live Oak Media.

—Gregory's Shadow. Freeman, Don, illus. (Illus.). 32p. (J). (gr. k-2). 2002. pap. 6.99 (978-0-14-230196-8(5) , Puffin); 2000. 15.99 (978-0-670-89328-7(5) , Viking Juvenile) Penguin Group (USA) Inc.

Gregorich, Barbara. Waltur Buys a Pig in a Poke & Other Stories. Sorra, Kristin, illus. 2006. 64p. (J). (gr. 3-5). 15.00 (978-0-618-47306-9(8)) Houghton Mifflin Co.

Higginson, Hadley. Keeker & Springtime Surprise. Parrett, Lisa, illus. 2007. (Sneaky Pony Ser.: No. 4). 56p. (J). 15.50 (978-0-8118-5598-3(8)) Chronicle Bks. LLC.

—Keeker & Springtime Surprise. Perrett, Lisa, illus. 2007. (Sneaky Pony Ser.: No. 4). 56p. (J). pap. 3.95 (978-0-8118-5599-0(6)) Chronicle Bks. LLC.

Hill, Susanna Leonard. Punxsutawney Phyllis. Ebbeler, Jeffrey, illus. 32p. (J). pap. 6.95 (978-0-8234-2040-7(X)); 17.95 (978-0-8234-1872-5(3)) Holiday Hse., Inc.

Korman, Susan. Groundhog at Evergreen Road. 2005. (Smithsonian's Backyard Ser.). (Illus.). 32p. (J). (ps-2). 9.95 (978-1-59249-028-8(X) , PB5074); 8.95 incl. audio (978-1-59249-061-5(1) , SC5024) Soundprints.

—Groundhog at Evergreen Road. Bond, Higgins, illus. 2005. (Smithsonian's Backyard Ser.). 32p. (J). (ps-2). 4.95 (978-1-59249-023-3(9) , B5074); 15.95 (978-1-59249-022-6(0) , B5024); pap. 6.95 (978-1-59249-024-0(7) , S5024) Soundprints.

Koscielniak, Bruce. Geoffrey Groundhog Predicts the Weather. Koscielniak, Bruce, illus. 1998. (Illus.). 32p. (J). (gr. k-3). 6.95 (978-0-395-88398-3(9)) Houghton Mifflin Co. Trade & Reference Div.

Leigh, Tina. Groundhog Day for Essex Ed. Leigh, Tina, illus. 2001. (Illus.). 32p. (J). pap. 14.95 (978-0-9715673-0-6(1)) Leigh, Tina Illustrator.

Levine, Abby. Gretchen Groundhog, It's Your Day! Cote, Nancy, illus. 2004. 32p. (J). (gr. k-3). pap. 6.95 (978-0-8075-3059-7(X)) Whitman, Albert & Co.

Lewin, Betsy. Groundhog Day. 2000. (Hello Reader! Ser.). (Illus.). (J). pap. 10.01 (978-0-439-10802-7(0)) Scholastic, Inc.

Lewis, Beverly. Piggy Party. 1999. (Cul-de-Sac Kids Ser.: Vol. 19). (Illus.). 80p. (J). (gr. 2-5). pap. 3.99 (978-0-7642-2124-8(8)) Bethany Hse. Pubs.

McArthur, Cathy E. The Adventures of Elvis the Groundhog: The Golden Glow. 2005. 9.00 (978-0-8059-8154-4(3)) Dorrance Publishing Co., Inc.

McMullan, Kate. Fluffy Meets the Groundhog. 2001. 10.79 (978-0-606-22246-4(4)) Tandem Library Bks.

McNamara, Margaret. Groundhog Day. Gordon, Mike, illus. 2006. 32p. (J). lib. bdg. 15.00 (***978-1-4242-0954-5(4)***) Fitzgerald Bks.

Miller, Pat. Substitute Groundhog. Ember, Kathi, illus. 2006. 32p. (J). 15.95 (978-0-8075-7643-4(3)) Whitman, Albert & Co.

Reynolds, Bill. Willy Woodchuck. 2002. 52p. pap. 9.95 (978-0-7414-1012-2(5)) Infinity Publishing.

Ruelle, Karen Gray. Great Groundhogs! (Illus.). 32p. (J). pap. 4.95 (978-0-8234-1964-7(9)) Holiday Hse., Inc.

—Great Groundhogs! A Harry & Emily Adventure. Ruelle, Karen Gray, illus. (Illus.). 32p. (J). (ps). 14.95 (978-0-8234-1930-2(4)) Holiday Hse., Inc.

Sargent, Dave & Sargent, Pat. Chet Cheetah: Speed, 56 bks, Vol. 43. Lenoir, Jane, illus. 2000. (Animal Pride Ser.: Vol. 43). 36p. (J). lib. bdg. (978-1-56763-527-0(X)) Ozark Publishing.

—Greta Groundhog: I'm Special!, 20 vols., Vol. 20. Huff, Jeane, illus. 2nd rev. ed. 2003. (Animal Pride Ser.: 20). 42p. (J). pap. 6.95 (978-1-56763-798-4(1)); lib. bdg. 19.95 (978-1-56763-797-7(3)) Ozark Publishing.

Swallow, Pamela C. Groundhog Gets a Say. Bunkus, Denise, illus. 2007. 40p. (J). (ps). pap. 6.99 (***978-0-14-240896-4(4)*** , Puffin) Penguin Group (USA) Inc.

—Groundhog Gets a Say. Brunkus, Denise, illus. 2005. 40p. (J). (ps). 15.99 (978-0-399-23876-5(X) , Putnam Juvenile) Penguin Group (USA) Inc.

Vogel, Rob & Azarov, Max. Garry the Groundhog, l.t. ed. 2005. (Illus.). 10p. (J). spiral bd. 19.95 incl. DVD (978-0-9768455-0-8(4) , N/A) Vogel, Robert.

Welling, Peter J. Andrew McGroundhog & His Shady Shadow. 2001. (Illus.). 32p. (J). (gr. k-3). 15.95 (978-1-56554-711-7(X)) Pelican Publishing Co., Inc.

WOODPECKERS

Caez, Joshua, illus. To Find an Ivory-billed Woodpecker. l.t. ed. 2005. 21p. (YA). 9.95 net. (978-0-9771752-0-8(0)) Harrison, Bobby.

Dahl, Michael. Tail Feather Fun: Counting by 10s. Trover, Zachary, illus. 2006. 24p. (J). (ps-2). 22.60 (978-1-4048-1319-9(5)) Picture Window Bks.

Grolier Educational Staff. Woodpeckers. 2001. (Nature's Children Ser.). (Illus.). 47p. (J). (978-0-7172-5552-8(2) , Grolier) Scholastic Library Publishing.

Hoose, Phillip M. The Race to Save the Lord God Bird. 2004. (Illus.). 208p. (YA). 20.00 (978-0-374-36173-0(8) , Nelanie Kroupa Bks.) Farrar, Straus & Giroux.

Kalz, Jill. Woodpeckers. 2003. (Birds Ser.). (Illus.). 24p. (J). lib. bdg. 21.35 (978-1-58340-132-3(6)) Smart Apple Media.

Mania, Cathy. Woodpecker in the Backyard. 2000. (gr. 3-6). lib. bdg. 15.25 (978-0-613-34555-2(X)) Tandem Library Bks.

Mania, Cathy & Mania, Robert. Woodpecker in the Backyard. 2000. (Wildlife Conservation Society Bks.). (Illus.). 48p. (J). (gr. 4-6). 24.50 (978-0-531-11799-6(5) , Watts, Franklin) Scholastic Library Publishing.

Miller, Sara Swan. Woodpeckers, Toucans, & Their Kin. 2003. (Animals in Order Ser.). (Illus.). 48p. (J). 26.50 (978-0-531-12243-3(3) , Watts, Franklin) Scholastic Library Publishing.

Murray, Julie. Woodpeckers. 2005. (Animal Kingdom Set Ii Ser.). (Illus.). 24p. (J). (gr. k-4). lib. bdg. 21.35 (978-1-59197-340-9(6)) ABDO Publishing Co.

Soffer, Ruth. Woodpeckers Stickers. 2006. (Dover Little Activity Bks.). 4p. (J). pap. 1.50 (978-0-486-44841-1(X)) Dover Pubns., Inc.

Townsend, Emily Rose. Woodpeckers. Saunders-Smith, Gail, ed. 2004. (Woodland Animals Ser.). (Illus.). 24p. (J). (gr. k-1). lib. bdg. 15.93 (978-0-7368-2070-7(1) , Pebble Bks.) Capstone Pr., Inc.

Winner, Cherie. Woodpeckers. 2000. (Nature Watch Ser.). (Illus.). 48p. (J). (gr. 3-6). lib. bdg. 25.26 (978-1-57505-445-2(0) , Carolrhoda Bks.) Lerner Publishing Group.

WOODS, TIGER, 1975-

Acosta, Tatiana & Gutierrez, Guillermo, trs. Tiger Woods. 2004. (Gente Que Hay Que Conocer Ser.). (SPA.). 24p. (J). lib. bdg. 19.33 (978-0-8368-4355-2(X)) Stevens, Gareth Inc.

Armentrout, David & Armentrout, Patricia, trs. Tiger Woods. 2003. (Discover the Life of a Sports Star Ser.). (Illus.). 24p. (J). 20.64 (978-1-58952-656-3(2)) Rourke Publishing, LLC.

Brown, Jonatha A. & Raatma, Lucia. Tiger Woods. 2004. (Illus.). 24p. (J). pap. (978-0-8368-4320-0(7)); (YA). lib. bdg. 19.33 (978-0-8368-4313-2(4)) Stevens, Gareth Inc.

Christopher, Matt. On the Course with... Tiger Woods. rev. ed. 1998. (Matt Christopher Sports Biographies Ser.). (Illus.). 144p. (J). (gr. 3-7). pap. 4.99 (978-0-316-13445-3(7)) Little, Brown Bks. for Young Readers.

—On the Course with... Tiger Woods. 1998. (978-0-606-13676-1(2)) Tandem Library Bks.

Collins, David R. Tiger Woods: Golf Superstar. Nolte, Larry, illus. 1998. 32p. (J). (gr. k-3). pap. 15.95 (978-1-56554-321-8(1)) Pelican Publishing Co., Inc.

—Tiger Woods: Golfing Champion. Nolte, Larry, illus. 1999. 104p. (J). (gr. 3-7). 14.95 (978-1-56554-322-5(X)) Pelican Publishing Co., Inc.

Doeden, Matt. Tiger Woods. 2005. (Sports Heroes & Legends Ser.). (Illus.). 106p. (J). (gr. 3-7). 27.93 (978-0-8225-3082-4(1) , Lerner Pubns.) Lerner Publishing Group.

Dougherty, Terri. Tiger Woods. 1999. (Jam Session Ser.). (Illus.). 32p. (J). (gr. 3-8). lib. bdg. 24.21 (978-1-57765-041-6(7) , ABDO & Daughters) ABDO Publishing Co.

Durbin, William. Tiger Woods: Golf Star. 1999. (Golf Legends Ser.). (Illus.). (YA). 64p. (gr. 4-7). 18.65 (978-0-7910-4563-3(3)); 144p. (gr. 5 up). pap. 30.00 (978-0-7910-4687-6(7)) Facts On File, Inc. (Chelsea Hse.).

Edwards, Nicholas. Tiger Woods: An American Master. rev. ed. 2001. (J). (978-0-606-22872-5(1)) Tandem Library Bks.

Feinstein, Stephen. Lee sobre Tiger Woods/Read about Tiger Woods. 2006. (I Like Biographies! Bilingual Ser.). (ENG & SPA., Illus.). 24p. (J). (gr. 1-3). lib. bdg. 21.26 (978-0-7660-2743-5(0) , Enslow Elementary) Enslow Pubs., Inc.

Gallagher, Jim. Tiger Woods. 2007. (J). (***978-1-4222-0211-1(9)***) Mason Crest Pubs.

Glaser, Jason. Tiger Woods. 2008. (J). lib. bdg. (***978-1-4042-4179-4(5)*** , PowerKids Pr.) Rosen Publishing Group, Inc., The.

Goodman, Michael E. Tiger Woods. 2003. (Ovations Ser.). (Illus.). 32p. (J). (978-1-58341-246-6(8) , Creative Education) Creative Co., The.

Goodridge, Catherine. Tiger Woods. ed. 2004. (SPA.). (J). pap. 5.00 (978-1-4108-2427-1(6) , A24276) Benchmark Education Co.

Goodridge, Catherine. Tiger Woods (Spanish) & Tiger Woods. 2005. spiral bd. 70.00 (***978-1-4108-5660-9(7)***) Benchmark Education Co.

Gutelle, Andrew. Tiger Woods. Gutelle, Andrew, illus. 2002. (All Aboard Reading Ser.). (Illus.). 48p. (J). pap. 3.99 (978-0-448-42663-1(3) , Grosset & Dunlap) Penguin Group (USA) Inc.

—Tiger Woods. 2002. (gr. k-3). lib. bdg. 11.80 (978-0-613-43647-2(4)) Tandem Library Bks.

Hughes, Libby. Tiger Woods: A Biography for Kids. 2000. (Illus.). 70p. (J). pap. 5.95 (978-1-58571-003-4(2)) Kensington Publishing Corp.

—Tiger Woods: A Biography for Kids. 2000. (gr. 3-6). lib. bdg. 14.10 (978-0-613-88468-6(X)) Tandem Library Bks.

Kramer, Sydelle A. Tiger Woods: Golf's Young Master. 1998. (Step into Reading Step 4 Bks.). (J). (gr. 2-4). (978-0-606-13970-0(2)) Tandem Library Bks.

Labrecque, Ellen. Roger Federer. 2008. (World's Greatest Athletes Ser.). 32p. (J). (gr. 1-5). 27.07 (***978-1-59296-882-4(1)***) Child's World, Inc.

Lace, William W. Tiger Woods: Star Golfer. 1999. (Sports Reports). (Illus.). 104p. (YA). (gr. 4-10). lib. bdg. 20.95 (978-0-7660-1081-9(3)) Enslow Pubs., Inc.

Macnow, Glen. Sports Great Tiger Woods. 2001. (Sports Great Bks.). (Illus.). 64p. (YA). (gr. 4-10). lib. bdg. 22.60 (978-0-7660-1468-8(1)) Enslow Pubs., Inc.

Raatma, Lucia. Tiger Woods. 2008. (J). lib. bdg. 26.00 (***978-1-60279-076-6(0)***) Cherry Lake Publishing.

—Tiger Woods. 2001. (Trailblazers of the Modern World Ser.). (Illus.). 48p. (J). (gr. 5 up). pap. 14.95 (978-0-8368-5226-4(5)); lib. bdg. 30.00 (978-0-8368-5066-6(1)) Stevens, Gareth Inc. (World Almanac Library).

Roberts, Jeremy. Tiger Woods. 2007. (J). pap. 8.95 (***978-0-8225-8563-3(4)*** , First Avenue Editions) Lerner Publishing Group.

—Tiger Woods. 2002. (Illus.). 112p. (J). (gr. 6-12). lib. bdg. 16.40 (978-0-613-46178-8(9)) Tandem Library Bks.

—Tiger Woods: Biography A&E Series. 2001. (Biography Ser.). (Illus.). 112p. (YA). (gr. 6-12). 27.93 (978-0-8225-0030-8(2) , Lerner Pubns.) Lerner Publishing Group.

Savage, Jeff. Tiger Woods. 2005. (Amazing Athletes Ser.). (Illus.). 32p. (gr. 3-4). lib. bdg. 22.60 (978-0-8225-1337-7(4)) Lerner Publishing Group.

Sirimarco, Elizabeth. Tiger Woods. 2000. (Sports Heroes Ser.). (Illus.). 48p. (J). (gr. 3-4). lib. bdg. 21.26 (978-0-7368-0581-0(8) , Capstone High-Interest Bks.) Capstone Pr., Inc.

Stewart, Mark. Tiger Woods: Drive to Greatness. 2001. (Inspiring People Ser.). (Illus.). 64p. (gr. 4 up). lib. bdg. 24.90 (978-0-7613-1966-5(2) , Millbrook Pr.) Lerner Publishing Group.

Stewart, Mark Alan. Tiger Woods: Drive to Greatness. 2001. (Illus.). 64p. (gr. 4-12). pap. 7.95 (978-0-7613-1477-6(6) , Millbrook Pr.) Lerner Publishing Group.

Tiger Woods. 2006. (People We Should Know Ser.). (SPA.). (J). (gr. 3-4). 4.76 (978-0-8368-4362-0(2) , GHS33881) Stevens, Gareth Inc.

Tiger Woods (Revised Edition) 2007. (J). pap. 5.95 (***978-0-8225-6890-2(X)*** , First Avenue Editions) Lerner Publishing Group.

Torres, John Albert. Tiger Woods. 2001. (Real-Life Reader Biography Ser.). (Illus.). 32p. (J). (gr. 3-8). lib. bdg. 15.95 (978-1-58415-067-1(X)) Mitchell Lane Pubs., Inc.

Uschan, Michael V. Tiger Woods. 2002. (Stars of Sports Ser.). (Illus.). 48p. (J). 26.20 (978-0-7377-1397-8(6) , Greenhaven Pr., Inc.) Thomson Gale.

Woods, Earl & Tiger Woods Foundation Staff. Start Something: You Can Make a Difference. 2006. 144p. pap. 14.00 (978-1-4165-3704-5(X)) Simon & Schuster.

WOODS

see Forests and Forestry

WOODSON, CARTER GODWIN, 1875-1950

Durden, Robert F. Carter G. Woodson: Father of African-American History. 1998. (African-American Biographies Ser.). (Illus.). 128p. (YA). (gr. 6-12). lib. bdg. 26.60 (978-0-89490-946-7(0)) Enslow Pubs., Inc.

McKissack, Patricia C. & McKissack, Fredrick L. Carter G. Woodson: The Father of Black History. rev. ed. 2002. (Great African Americans Ser.). (Illus.). 32p. (J). (gr. 1-4). lib. bdg. 18.60 (978-0-7660-1698-9(6)) Enslow Pubs., Inc.

WOODWORK

see also Cabinet Work; Carpentry; Furniture; Wood-Carving

DK Publishing. Woodworking. 2008. 72p. (J). 12.99 (***978-0-7566-3506-0(3)***) Dorling Kindersley Publishing, Inc.

Feirer, John L. Beginning Woodwork. 7th ed. 1999. (Illus.). (YA). (gr. 6-12). 384p. stu. ed. 27.16 (978-0-02-677600-4(6)); 48p. stu. ed., wbk. ed. 7.30 (978-0-02-677602-8(2)) Glencoe/McGraw-Hill.

—Cabinetmaking & Millwork. 5th ed. 1999. (Illus.). (YA). (gr. 6-12). stu. ed., wbk. ed. 8.68 (978-0-02-675960-1(8)) Glencoe/McGraw-Hill.

Feirer, John L., et al. Carpentry & Building Construction. 5th ed. 1999. (Illus.). 161p. (YA). (gr. 6-12). pap., stu. ed., wbk. ed. 7.99 (978-0-02-838701-7(5)) Glencoe/McGraw-Hill.

Harcourt School Publishers Staff. Made from a Tree. 3rd ed. 2002. (Trophies English Language Learners Ser.). (Illus.). pap. 5.10 (978-0-15-327642-2(8)) Harcourt Schl. Pubs.

Jakab, Cheryl. Wood. 2006. (Illus.). 32p. (J). (978-1-58340-776-9(6)) Smart Apple Media.

Kalman, Bobbie. Woodworkers. 2002. (gr. k-3). lib. bdg. 16.40 (978-0-613-82417-0(2)) Tandem Library Bks.

Kalman, Bobbie & Brady, Deanna. The Woodworkers. Rouse, Bonna, illus. (Colonial People Ser.). 32p. (J). (gr. 3). 2002. (978-0-7787-0744-8(X)); 2001. pap. (978-0-7787-0790-5(3)) Crabtree Publishing Co.

Llimos Plomer, Anna. Madera y Corcho. Casanova, Jose Maria, illus. 2003. (Coleccion Ivamos a Crear!). (SPA.). 32p. (J). (gr. k-2). 12.00 (978-84-342-2344-8(9)) Parramon Ediciones S.A. ESP. *Dist:* Lectorum Pubns., Inc.

—Wood & Cork. 2003. (Let's Create! Ser.). (Illus.). 32p. (J). (gr. 2 up). lib. bdg. 23.33 (978-0-8368-3749-0(5)) Stevens, Gareth Inc.

Mason, Bernard Sterling. Boy's Book of Camping & Wood Crafts. 2001. 250p. pap. 19.95 (978-1-58667-072-6(7)) Derrydale Pr., The.

McGuire, Kevin. The All-New Woodworking for Kids. 2008. (Illus.). 160p. (J). pap. 14.95 (978-1-60059-035-1(7)) Lark Bks.

Robertson, Craig & Robertson, Barbara. The Kids' Building Workshop: 15 Woodworking Projects for Kids & Parents to Build Together. 2004. (Illus.). 144p. (J). pap. 12.95 (978-1-58017-488-6(4) , 67488, Storey Kids) Storey Publishing, LLC.

Talpai, Ayala. The Key to Dream House. Talpai, Ayala, illus. 2001. (Illus.). 32p. (YA). (ps up). pap. 9.95 (978-0-9706453-1-9(7)) Diligence Woodwork & Design.

Weinberger, Kimberly. Home Depot. Miller, Edward, illus. 2002. (J). pap. 3.50 (978-0-439-33295-8(8)); pap. 3.50 (978-0-439-33296-5(6)) Scholastic, Inc.

Willacy, David M. Craft & Design in Wood. 1998. (Illus.). 224p. pap. 36.00 (978-0-7487-1066-9(3)) State Mutual Bk. & Periodical Service, Ltd.

WOOL

see also Dyes and Dyeing

Charlie Needs a Cloak. 2004. 24.95 incl. audio (978-1-56008-023-7(X)); pap. 18.95 incl. audio compact disk (978-1-55592-382-2(8)); pap. 18.95 incl. audio compact disk (978-1-55592-384-6(4)); pap. 38.75 incl. audio compact disk (978-1-55592-383-9(6)); pap. 38.75 incl. audio compact disk (978-1-55592-385-3(2)); pap. 32.75 incl. audio (978-1-55592-200-9(7)); pap. 32.75 incl. audio (978-1-55592-201-6(5)); pap. 14.95 incl. audio (978-1-55592-719-6(X)) Weston Woods Studios, Inc.

Cox, Rhonda. La Lana de Andi. Romo, Alberto, tr. Cox, Rhonda, photos by. 1999. (Books for Young Learners).Tr. of Andi's Wool. (SPA., Illus.). 12p. (J). (gr. k-2). pap. 5.00 (978-1-57274-296-3(8)) Owen, Richard C. Pubs., Inc.

de Paola, Tomie. Charlie Needs a Cloak. 2002. (J). (ps-2). lib. bdg. 14.15 (978-0-8335-0342-8(1)) Tandem Library Bks.

Franck, Irene M. & Brownstone, David M. Wool. 2003. (Illus.). 32p. (J). (978-0-7172-5728-7(2) , Grolier) Scholastic Library Publishing.

Gibbons, Gail. From Sheep to Sweater. 2005. (J). (978-0-8234-1885-5(5)) Holiday Hse., Inc.

Gleason, Carrie. The Biography of Wool. 2007. (How Did That Get Here? Ser.). (Illus.). 32p. (J). (gr. 2-9). (***978-0-7787-2496-4(4)***); pap. (***978-0-7787-2532-9(4)***) Crabtree Publishing Co.

W X Y Z

Johnson, Guinevere. Wool. 1999. (Let's Investigate Ser.). (Illus.). 32p. (J). (gr. 1-4). lib. bdg. 18.95 (978-0-88682-965-0(8) , Creative Education) Creative Co., The.

Kras, Sara Louise. Wool. 2006. (J). (978-0-7368-4300-3(0)) Capstone Pr., Inc.

Levete, Sarah. Wool. 2006. (Material Matters Ser.). (J). (978-1-59389-274-6(8)) Chrysalis Education.

Murray, Julie. Sheep to Sweater. 2007. (Illus.). 24p. (J). 21.35 (978-1-59679-914-1(5) , Buddy Bks.) ABDO Publishing Co.

Nelson, Robin. From Sheep to Sweater. 2003. (Start to Finish Ser.). (Illus.). 24p. (J). 18.60 (978-0-8225-0716-1(1) , Lerner Pubns.) Lerner Publishing Group.

Oxlade, Chris. How We Use Wool. 2004. (Using Materials Ser.). (Illus.). 32p. (J). lib. bdg. 25.70 (978-1-4109-0599-4(3)) Raintree.

—Wool. (Materials, Materials, Materials Ser.). 32p. pap. 6.95 (978-1-4034-4102-7(2)); 2001. (Illus.). (J). lib. bdg. 21.36 (978-1-58810-159-4(2)) Heinemann Library.

Stone, Lynn M. Wool. 2002. (Harvest to Home Ser.). (Illus.). 24p. (gr. 2-5). 14.95 (978-1-58952-131-5(5)) Rourke Publishing, LLC.

WORD GAMES

Agee, Jon. Sit on a Potato Pan, Otis! More Palindromes. Agee, Jon, illus. 1999. (Illus.). 80p. (J). (gr. 4-7). 14.41 (978-0-374-31808-6(5) , Farrar, Straus & Giroux (BYR)) Farrar, Straus & Giroux.

Allen, Robert. Word Puzzles for Kids. 2000. (Mensa Ser.). (Illus.). 224p. (J). (gr. 4). pap. 4.50 (978-0-439-10840-9(3)) Scholastic, Inc.

Allen, Robert & Carlton Books Staff. Mensa Word Puzzles. 2002. (Mensa Word Games for Kids Ser.). (Illus.). 224p. pap. 7.95 (978-1-85868-308-9(4)) Carlton Bks., Ltd. GBR. *Dist:* Simon & Schuster, Inc.

Amery, Heather & Cartwright, Stephen. First One Hundred Words Sticker Book. 2004. (First Hundred Words Ser.). (Illus.). 40p. (J). pap. 8.95 (978-0-7945-0190-7(7) , Usborne) EDC Publishing.

Analogies 1 Worktext. 2003. (Illus.). 64p. (YA). per. 8.95 (978-1-56254-729-5(1) , SP7291) Saddleback Educational Publishing.

Analogies 2 Worktext. 2003. (Illus.). 64p. (YA). per. 8.95 (978-1-56254-731-8(3) , SP7313) Saddleback Educational Publishing.

Balloon Books Staff, ed. Wild Word Search. 2003. (Balloon Ser.). (Illus.). 72p. (J). (gr. 2-4). pap. 3.95 (978-0-8069-2274-4(5) , Balloon Bks.) Sterling Publishing Co., Inc.

Berthel, Alice H. Power Puzzles: John. 2007. (J). per. 12.95 (978-1-59352-193-6(6)) Christian Services Publishing.

—Power Puzzles: Luke. 2007. (J). per. 12.95 (978-1-59352-192-9(8)) Christian Services Publishing.

—Power Puzzles: Mark. 2007. (J). per. 12.95 (978-1-59352-191-2(X)) Christian Services Publishing.

—Power Puzzles: Matthew. 2006. (J). per. 12.95 (978-1-59352-174-5(X)) Christian Services Publishing.

Black, Howard & Parks, Sandra. Dr. Funster's Word Benders Level A Book 1: Thinking & Vocabulary Fun. 2003. (J). pap. 7.99 (978-0-89455-812-2(9)) Critical Thinking Bks. & Software.

—Dr. Funster's Word Benders Level B Book 1: Thinking & Vocabulary Fun. 2003. (J). pap. 7.99 (978-0-89455-813-9(7)) Critical Thinking Bks. & Software.

—Dr. Funster's Word Benders Level C Book 1: Thinking & Vocabulary Fun. 2003. (YA). pap. 7.99 (978-0-89455-814-6(5)) Critical Thinking Bks. & Software.

Blanchard, Cherie. Word Roots Level A Book 1: Learning the Building Blocks of Better Spelling & Vocabulary. 2003. (YA). (gr. 4-6). pap. 16.99 (978-0-89455-804-7(8)) Critical Thinking Bks. & Software.

—Word Roots Level B Bk. 1: Learning the Building Blocks of Better Spelling & Vocabulary. 2004. (YA). (gr. 7-12). pap. 18.99 (978-0-89455-805-4(6)) Critical Thinking Bks. & Software.

Booth, Karon. Aslan Is on the Move: Romp in Narnia with Study Helps, Art & Play. 2003. (Illus.). 196p. (J). per. (978-0-941367-13-4(4)) Peach Blossom Pubns.

Brighter Vision Publishing Staff. Crossword Puzzles. 2000. (Illus.). 32p. (J). (gr. 2). pap., act. bk. ed. 1.39 (978-1-55254-153-1(3)) Brighter Vision Pubns.

—Word Games & Puzzles. 2000. (Illus.). 32p. (J). (gr. 1). pap. 1.39 (978-1-55254-152-4(5)) Brighter Vision Pubns.

Brumbaugh, Doug, et al. Scratch Your Brain Book B1: Clever Math Ticklers. 2001. (J). (gr. 4-5). pap. 16.99 (978-0-89455-789-7(0)) Critical Thinking Bks. & Software.

—Scratch Your Brain Book C1: Clever Math Ticklers. 2002. (J). (gr. 6-8). pap. 16.99 (978-0-89455-790-3(4)) Critical Thinking Bks. & Software.

Casey, Kathy & Bunnell, Deb T. Spanish Search-a-Word Picture Puzzles. 2001. (SPA., Illus.). 32p. (J). pap. 3.95 (978-0-486-41552-9(X)) Dover Pubns., Inc.

Chaneski, John. Dinosaur Word Search. 2004. (Illus.). 80p. pap. 5.95 (978-1-4027-1558-7(7)) Sterling Publishing Co., Inc.

—Presidential Word Search Puzzles. 2004. (Illus.). 112p. pap., pap., spiral bd. 6.95 (978-1-4027-1314-9(2)) Sterling Publishing Co., Inc.

—Super Word Search Puzzles for Kids. 2001. (Official Mensa Puzzle Book Ser.). (Illus.). 96p. (J). (gr. 2-7). pap. 5.95 (978-0-8069-4417-3(X)) Sterling Publishing Co., Inc.

Chronicle Books Staff, creator. Genius Decks: Super Word Puzzles. 2005. (gr. 2-6). 9.95 (978-0-8118-5191-6(5)) Chronicle Bks. LLC.

—75 Word Puzzles. 2005. 13.95 (978-0-8118-5196-1(6)) Chronicle Bks. LLC.

—75 Word Puzzles for Kids. 2005. (gr. 2-6). 9.95 (978-0-8118-5193-0(1)) Chronicle Bks. LLC.

Chronicle Books Staff, ed. Let's Go! A Nick Jr. Travel Deck. 2004. (Illus.). 30p. (J). 8.95 (978-0-8118-4153-5(7)) Chronicle Bks. LLC.

Cloutier, Toni Lynn. Word Search USA. 2001. (Illus.). 112p. (J). (gr. 2-7). pap., pap., spiral bd. 6.95 (978-0-8069-7983-0(6)) Sterling Publishing Co., Inc.

Cranium Inc. Staff. Cranium: the Data Head Book of Outrageous Fun! Search it, Find it, Solve It! Baseman, illus. 2006. 38p. (J). (gr. 2-17). 14.99 (978-0-316-05761-5(4)) Little, Brown Bks. for Young Readers.

—Cranium: the Word Worm Book of Outrageous Fun! Write it, Read it, Say It! Baseman, illus. 2006. 38p. (J). (gr. 2-17). 14.99 (978-0-316-05762-2(2)) Little, Brown Bks. for Young Readers.

Cranium Inc. Staff. The Cranium Ultimate Book of Fantastic Fun & Games. 2007. 54p. (J). (ps-3). 19.99 (***978-0-316-01208-9(4)***) Little, Brown Bks. for Young Readers.

Danna, Mark. Amazing Word Search Puzzles for Kids. 2008. (Mensa Ser.). 96p. (J). pap. 5.95 (***978-1-4027-4676-5(8)***) Sterling Publishing Co., Inc.

—Clever Word Search Puzzles for Kids. 2004. (Mensa Ser.). (Illus.). 96p. (J). pap. 5.95 (978-1-4027-0437-6(2)) Sterling Publishing Co., Inc.

—Wacky-Shaped Word Search Puzzles to Keep You Sharp. 2004. (Illus.). 96p. pap. 7.95 (978-1-4027-0658-5(8)) Sterling Publishing Co., Inc.

Detective Shadow. Lateral Mindtrap Puzzles: Challenge the Way You Think & See. 2000. (gr. 5-8). lib. bdg. 15.25 (978-0-613-75534-4(0)) Tandem Library Bks.

DiSpezio, Michael Anthony. Challenging Critical Thinking Puzzles. Date not set. (J). (978-0-8069-3848-6(X)) Sterling Publishing Co., Inc.

Douglas, Vincent & School Specialty Publishing Staff. Word Search. l.t. ed. 2004. (Large Print Word Searches Ser.). (Illus.). 120p. (J). Vol. 33. pap. 2.99 (978-0-7696-3197-4(5)); Vol. 35. pap. 2.99 (978-0-7696-3199-8(1)) School Specialty Publishing. (Brighter Child).

—Word Searches. 2003. (Homework Helpers Ser.). (Illus.). 32p. (J). (gr. 3-3). pap. 2.99 (978-0-7696-2928-5(8) , American Education Publishing) School Specialty Publishing.

DynaNotes Lab Measurement & Equipment Workbook. 2007. (J). pap. (***978-1-933854-72-4(3)***) DynaStudy, Inc.

Fun with Antonyms - Crossword Puzlles & Word Searches. 2004. pap. 7.99 (978-1-4206-3146-3(2)) Teacher Created Materials, Inc.

Fun with Homonyms - Crossword Puzzles & Word Searches. 2004. pap. 7.99 (978-1-4206-3143-2(8)) Teacher Created Materials, Inc.

Fun with Idioms - Crossword Puzzles & Word Searches. 2004. pap. 7.99 (978-1-4206-3144-9(6)) Teacher Created Materials, Inc.

Fun with Synonyms - Crossword Puzzles & Word Searches. 2004. pap. 7.99 (978-1-4206-3145-6(4)) Teacher Created Materials, Inc.

Gobo Books Staff. My Magnetic Word Puzzle Book. 2006. 20p. 9.95 (978-1-932915-19-8(2)) National Bk. Network.

Goss, Lynn & Donaldson, Helen. New Spellaway. 1999. (Illus.). 31p. (J). (gr. 2-6). Bk. 1. pap. 20.00 (978-0-7217-0768-6(8)); Bk. 2. pap. 20.00 (978-0-7217-0769-3(6)); Bk. 3. pap. 20.00 (978-0-7217-0770-9(X)); Bk. 4. pap. 20.00 (978-0-7217-0771-6(8)) Schofield & Sims Ltd. GBR. *Dist:* State Mutual Bk. & Periodical Service, Ltd.

Grundon, Holly & Novelli, Joan. Smartpads Fun with Words: 40 Fun Games to Help Kids Master Language Skills. 2005. 48p. pap. 7.99 (978-0-439-72084-7(2) , Teaching Resources) Scholastic, Inc.

Hall, Dorothy. Guess the Covered Word for Character Development. 2005. (Four-Blocks Ser.). 48p. (J). per. 25.99 (978-1-59441-153-3(0) , CD-104071) Carson-Dellosa Publishing Co., Inc.

Hands on Crafts for Kids Staff. Find the Words on the Farm. 2002. (Balloon Ser.). (Illus.). 10p. (J). bds. 4.95 (978-1-4027-0175-7(6) , Balloon Bks.) Sterling Publishing Co., Inc.

HarperCollins Children's Books. The Happy Holiday! 2007. (Word Play Ser.). 208p. (J). pap. 5.95 (***978-0-00-725577-1(2)***) HarperCollins Pubs. Ltd. GBR. *Dist:* Independent Pubs. Group.

Harpster, Steve, illus. Fun First Phonics. 2004. (First Word Search Ser.). 64p. (J). pap. 3.95 (978-1-4027-1321-7(5)) Sterling Publishing Co., Inc.

—Fun First Words. 2004. (First Word Search Ser.). 64p. (J). pap. 3.95 (978-1-4027-1320-0(7)) Sterling Publishing Co., Inc.

Haugen, Janie & Britt, Melissa. Name It Game. 1999. 16p. (J). pap., tchr. ed. 39.95 (978-1-884074-83-7(9)) PCI Educational Publishing.

—Shortcuts Game. 1999. 16p. (J). pap., tchr. ed. (978-1-884074-85-1(5)) PCI Educational Publishing.

Hop, L. L. C. Hooked on First-Grade Super Workbook. 2006. 320p. 12.99 (978-1-931020-74-9(4)) HOP, LLC.

HOP, LLC. Hooked on Phonics Word Games. 2006. 64p. 3.79 (978-1-933863-93-1(5)) HOP, LLC.

Hovanec, Helene. The Incredible Science Puzzle Challenge. Ueland, John, illus. 2003. 96p. (J). pap. 6.95 (978-1-4027-0716-2(9)) Sterling Publishing Co., Inc.

—My First Puzzles: Word Games. Shems, Ed, illus. 2006. (My First Puzzles Ser.). 64p. (J). pap. 3.95 (978-1-4027-3641-4(X)) Sterling Publishing Co., Inc.

—My First Puzzles: Letter Games. Conger, Holli, illus. 2007. (My First Puzzles Ser.). 64p. (J). pap. 3.95 (978-1-4027-4263-7(0)) Sterling Publishing Co., Inc.

Hummon, David M. Animal Acrostics. 1999. (Sharing Nature with Children Book Ser.). (Illus.). (J). (gr. 3-7). 44p. 16.95 (978-1-883220-92-1(0)); 40p. pap. 7.95 (978-1-883220-91-4(2)) Dawn Pubns.

Joachim, Jean. Cars & Trucks Word Search. 2004. (Illus.). 80p. (J). pap. 5.95 (978-1-4027-1549-5(8)) Sterling Publishing Co., Inc.

Joachim, Jean C. Wildlife Word Search. 2005. (Illus.). 80p. (ps-6). pap. 5.95 (978-1-4027-1664-5(8)) Sterling Publishing Co., Inc.

Jones, Victoria. Under the Sea Word Search. 2005. (Illus.). 80p. (J). (ps-6). pap. 5.95 (978-1-4027-1665-2(6)) Sterling Publishing Co., Inc.

Kellaher, Karen. Grammar Games & Activities Kids Can't Resist! 40 Super-Cool Crosswords, Codes, Mazes & More. 2003. (Illus.). 64p. (J). pap. 10.95 (978-0-439-07756-9(7)) Scholastic, Inc.

Kiel, Doris. Jumble Word Games. 2002. 112p. pap. 10.00 (978-0-8059-5627-6(1)) Dorrance Publishing Co., Inc.

Kline, Michael. Wordplay Cafe: Cool Codes, Priceless Punzles & Phantastic Phonetic Phun. Kline, Michael, illus. 2005. (Kids Can Ser.). (Illus.). 128p. (J). (ps-7). pap. 12.95 (978-0-8249-6753-6(4) , Williamson Bks.) Ideals Pubns.

Kurchan, Rodolfo, et al. Giant Book of Hard-to-Solve Word Puzzles/Giant Book of Hard-to-Solve Mind Puzzles: Flip Book. Sterling Publishing Company Staff, ed. (Illus.). 512p. pap. 9.98 (978-1-4027-0285-3(X)) Sterling Publishing Co., Inc.

Leaney, Cindy. An Amazing Machine. Whitehouse, Patty, ed. King, Sue & Wilks, Peter, illus. 2004. (Friendly Phonics Ser.). 24p. (J). lib. bdg. 14.95 (978-1-59054-194-4(4)) Fitzgerald Bks.

—Desert Dream. Whitehouse, Patty, ed. King, Sue & Wilks, Peter, illus. 2004. (Friendly Phonics Ser.). 24p. (J). lib. bdg. 14.95 (978-1-59054-117-3(0)) Fitzgerald Bks.

—Fish Can Fly. Whitehouse, Patty, ed. King, Sue & Wilks, Peter, illus. 2004. (Friendly Phonics Ser.). 24p. (J). lib. bdg. 14.95 (978-1-59054-106-7(5)) Fitzgerald Bks.

—Fun at the Fair. Whitehouse, Patty, ed. King, Sue & Wilks, Peter, illus. 2004. (Friendly Phonics Ser.). 24p. (J). lib. bdg. 14.95 (978-1-59054-153-1(7)) Fitzgerald Bks.

—Harry Has Hiccups. Whitehouse, Patty, ed. King, Sue & Wilks, Peter, illus. 2004. (Friendly Phonics Ser.). 24p. (J). lib. bdg. 14.95 (978-1-59054-182-1(0)) Fitzgerald Bks.

—Jungle Journey. Whitehouse, Patty, ed. King, Sue & Wilks, Peter, illus. 2004. (Friendly Phonics Ser.). 24p. (J). lib. bdg. 14.95 (978-1-59054-183-8(9)) Fitzgerald Bks.

—Just Lazy Luke. Whitehouse, Patty, ed. King, Sue & Wilks, Peter, illus. 2004. (Friendly Phonics Ser.). 24p. (J). lib. bdg. 14.95 (978-1-59054-105-0(7)) Fitzgerald Bks.

—A Long List. Whitehouse, Peter, ed. King, Sue & Wilks, Peter, illus. 2004. (Friendly Phonics Ser.). 24p. (J). lib. bdg. 14.95 (978-1-59054-190-6(1)) Fitzgerald Bks.

—Mr. Know-it-all Crow. Whitehouse, Patty, ed. King, Sue & Wilks, Peter, illus. 2004. (Friendly Phonics Ser.). 24p. (J). lib. bdg. 14.95 (978-1-59054-086-2(7)) Fitzgerald Bks.

—A Talking Telescope. Whitehouse, Patty, ed. King, Sue & Wilks, Peter, illus. 2004. (Friendly Phonics Ser.). 24p. (J). lib. bdg. 14.95 (978-1-59054-247-7(9)) Fitzgerald Bks.

Lederer, Richard. The Circus of Words: Acrobatic Anagrams, Parading Palindromes, Wonderful Words on a Wire & More Lively Letter Play. Morice, Dave, illus. 2001. 144p. (J). (gr. 4 up). pap. 12.95 (978-1-55652-380-9(7)) Chicago Review Pr., Inc.

Lee, Betsy B. A Funny Dolch Word Book # 1: Un Libro Comico # 1 de la Palabra de Dolch. Davis, Pollyanna S., tr. 2006. (ENG & SPA.). pap. 5.95 (978-0-9720267-5-8(4)) Learning Abilities Bks.

Mad Libs Activity Kit. 2004. (978-0-8431-0752-4(9) , Price Stern Sloan) Penguin Group (USA) Inc.

Martorana, Cherie. Made You Laugh for Kids: Wacky Word Searches. 2005. (Illus.). 96p. pap. (978-1-57528-926-7(1)) University Games.

McGraw-Hill Staff. Vocabulary Building with Word Puzzles. 2003. (Homework Booklets Ser.). 96p. (gr. 1-2). 2.99 (978-0-88012-783-7(X) , IF0119); (gr. 2-3). 2.99 (978-0-88012-784-4(8) , IF0129); (Illus.). (gr. 3-4). 2.99 (978-0-88012-785-1(6) , IF0139); (Illus.). (gr. 4-5). 2.99 (978-0-88012-786-8(4) , IF0149); (Illus.). (gr. 5-6). 2.99 (978-0-88012-787-5(2) , IF0159); (Illus.). (gr. 6-8). 2.99 (978-0-88012-788-2(0) , IF0169) School Specialty Publishing.

McGraw-Hill Staff & Schaffer, Frank. Word Puzzles. 2001. (Homework Helpers Activity Bks.). (Illus.). 56p. (J). (gr. k-1). pap., act. bk. ed. 2.99 (978-0-7682-0695-1(2) , FS109024, Schaffer, Frank) Schaffer, Frank Pubns.

—Word Searches. 2001. (Homework Helpers Activity Bks.). (Illus.). 56p. (J). (gr. k-1). pap., act. bk. ed. 2.99 (978-0-7682-0692-0(8) , FS109021); (gr. 2-2). pap., act. bk. ed. 2.99 (978-0-7682-0712-5(6) , FS109041) Schaffer, Frank Pubns. (Schaffer, Frank).

McMahon, Molly. Goofy Grammar & Other Word Games: Grades 3-4. Sorensen, Amanda, illus. 2005. 80p. per. 2.95 (978-1-59441-275-2(8) , RB-904008) Carson-Dellosa Publishing Co., Inc.

Meyer, Jan, et al. Wonderful Word Puzzle. ed. 2003. (Illus.). 56p. pap. 10.95 (978-0-439-37666-2(1) , Teaching Resources) Scholastic, Inc.

Nicholas, Mother Andrea, compiled by. My Little Orthodox Christian Feast Days Activity Book. 2005. (J). spiral bd. 6.95 (978-0-9773579-0-1(2)) St. Nicholas Monastery.

Nye, Mark Aaron. Scriptureabble Game Book - Bible King James Version. 2003. 88p. (YA). spiral bd. 13.95 (978-0-9746665-1-8(3)) Nye Products.

—Scriptureabble Game Book - LDS Version. 2003. 194p. (YA). spiral bd. 17.95 (978-0-9746665-0-1(5)) Nye Products.

Parker, Sherri. God's Word Ages 4-10, Bk. 2. 2004. (J). spiral bd. 5.18 net. (978-1-56870-554-5(9)) RonJon Publishing, Inc.

Peden, Greg. Tabletop Hockey: Tips for Kids. Peden, Greg, photos by. 2000. (Illus.). 80p. (J). (gr. 2-5). (978-1-55074-864-2(5)) Kids Can Pr., Ltd.

—Tabletop Hockey: Tips for Kids. 1999. (gr. 3-6). lib. bdg. 12.95 (978-0-613-30769-7(0)) Tandem Library Bks.

Phonics Puzzles & Games. 2001. (Illus.). 32p. (J). (gr. 1). pap. 1.59 (978-1-55254-232-3(7)); (gr. 2). pap. 1.59 (978-1-55254-234-7(3)); (gr. 3). pap. 1.59 (978-1-55254-236-1(X)) Brighter Vision Pubns.

Picture Word Lotto. 2006. 4p. (J). 12.99 (978-0-7945-0308-6(X) , Usborne) EDC Publishing.

Price, Roger. Mad Libs for President. 2000. (Mad Libs Ser.). (Illus.). 48p. (J). (gr. 3-7). mass mkt. 3.99 (978-0-8431-7623-0(7) , Price Stern Sloan) Penguin Group (USA) Inc.

Price, Roger & Stein, Leonard. Mad Libs on the Road: World's Greatest Word Game. 1999. (Mad Libs Ser.). (Illus.). 48p. (gr. 4-7). pap. 3.99 (978-0-8431-7498-4(6) , Price Stern Sloan) Penguin Group (USA) Inc.

Price, Roger & Stern, Leonard. America Dad Mad Libs. 2007. (Mad Libs Ser.). 48p. (J). pap. 3.99 (978-0-8431-2493-4(8) , Price Stern Sloan) Penguin Group (USA) Inc.

—Diva Girl Mad Libs. 2004. (Mad Libs Ser.). 48p. (J). (gr. 3). mass mkt. 3.99 (978-0-8431-0837-8(1) , Price Stern Sloan) Penguin Group (USA) Inc.

—Dora the Explorer Mad Libs Junior. 2006. (Mad Libs Junior Ser.). 48p. (J). (gr. k-3). pap. 3.99 (978-0-8431-2128-5(9) , Price Stern Sloan) Penguin Group (USA) Inc.

—Family Tree Mad Libs. 2007. (Mad Libs Ser.). 48p. (J). pap. 3.99 (978-0-8431-1643-4(9) , Price Stern Sloan) Penguin Group (USA) Inc.

—Flushed Away Mad Libs. 2006. (Mad Libs Ser.). 48p. (J). (gr. 3). pap. 3.99 (978-0-8431-2089-9(4) , Price Stern Sloan) Penguin Group (USA) Inc.

—Goofy & Kid Libs, 2 bks. gif. ed. 2005. (Mad Libs Ser.). (J). pap. 3.99 (978-0-8431-1471-3(1) , Price Stern Sloan) Penguin Group (USA) Inc.

—Halloween Mad Libs Two-pack. 2003. (J). 3.99 (978-0-8431-0381-6(7) , Price Stern Sloan) Penguin Group (USA) Inc.

—Letters from Camp Mad Libs. 2006. (Mad Libs Ser.). 48p. (J). (gr. 3). pap. 4.99 (978-0-8431-1827-8(X) , Price Stern Sloan) Penguin Group (USA) Inc.

—Operation Mad Libs. 2006. (Mad Libs Ser.). 48p. (J). (gr. 3). pap. 3.99 (978-0-8431-2090-5(8) , Price Stern Sloan) Penguin Group (USA) Inc.

—SpongeBob SquarePants Mad Libs. 2006. (Mad Libs Ser.). 48p. (J). (gr. 3). pap. 3.99 (978-0-8431-2127-8(0) , Price Stern Sloan) Penguin Group (USA) Inc.

—Zoey 101 Mad Libs. 2007. (Mad Libs Ser.). 48p. (J). (gr. 3). pap. 3.99 (978-0-8431-2305-0(2) , Price Stern Sloan) Penguin Group (USA) Inc.

Puzzler's Giant Book of Word Games. 2003. (YA). Vol. 10. per. 9.45 (978-1-55956-870-8(4)); Vol. 11. per. 9.45 (978-1-55956-873-9(9)) Penny Pubns., LLC. (Penny Pr.).

Puzzler's Giant Book of Word Seeks. 2003. (YA). 10. per. 9.45 (978-1-55956-871-5(2)); 11. per. 9.45 (978-1-55956-874-6(7)) Penny Pubns., LLC. (Penny Pr.).

Quinlan, Heather. Sports & Hobbies Word Search. 2005. (Illus.). 80p. (J). (gr. 1-4). pap. 5.95 (978-1-4027-2751-1(8)) Sterling Publishing Co., Inc.

Rabe, Tish. Milly's Silly Suitcase. Janovitz, Marilyn, illus. 2006. (innovativeKids readers ser.: level 1). 24p. (J). (ps-1). pap. 6.99 (978-1-58476-476-2(7) , IKIDS) Innovative Kids.

Rosenberg, Mary. The Word Family Activity Book: Fun & Easy Reproducible Activities That Help Every Child Learn Key Word Patterns to Become Successful Readers & Writers. 2001. 104p. pap. 12.95 (978-0-439-19936-0(0)) Scholastic, Inc.

Rubins, Diane Teitel. Nature Search-a-Words. Daste, Larry, illus. 2005. 48p. (J). (ps-3). pap. 3.95 (978-0-486-44291-4(8)) Dover Pubns., Inc.

Sastrias, Martha. Lecto-Juego-Acertijos: Para Motivar a los Ninos a Leer el Mundo Natural. 2005. (SPA., Illus.). 200p. (gr. 4-7). pap. 16.95 (978-968-860-725-1(8)) Editorial Pax MEX. *Dist:* Independent Pubs. Group.

Schnur, Steven. Spring: An Alphabet Acrostic. Evans, Leslie, illus. 1999. 32p. (J). (gr. k-3). tchr. ed. 15.00 (978-0-395-82269-2(6) , Clarion Bks.) Houghton Mifflin Co. Trade & Reference Div.

—Summer: An Alphabet Acrostic. Evans, Leslie, illus. 2001. 32p. (J). (gr. k-3). tchr. ed. 15.00 (978-0-618-02372-1(0) , Clarion Bks.) Houghton Mifflin Co. Trade & Reference Div.

Scholastic, Inc. Staff. 100 Palabras En Ingles Que Los Ninos Deben Leer En: 2nd Grado. Salas, Macarena, ed. 2004. (101 Words Kids Need to Read Ser.). (SPA.). 32p. (J). (gr. 2-5). pap. 2.99 (978-0-439-56024-5(1) , Scholastic en Espanol) Scholastic, Inc.

—100 Words Kids Need to Read 1st Grade: Spanish. Salas, Macarena, ed. 2004. (100 Words Kids Need to Read Ser.). (SPA.). 32p. (J). (ps-3). pap. 2.99 (978-0-439-54845-8(4) , Scholastic en Espanol) Scholastic, Inc.

—100 Words Kids Need to Read 3rd Grade: Spanish. Salas, Macarena, ed. 2004. (102 Words Kids Need to Read Ser.). (SPA.). 32p. (J). (gr. 2-5). pap. 2.99 (978-0-439-66356-4(3) , Scholastic en Espanol) Scholastic, Inc.

School Zone Publishing. AZ Word Search/Challenges. 2004. (Activity Zone Workbook Ser.). 32p. (J). pap. 2.49 (978-1-58947-392-8(2) , 02194) School Zone Publishing Co.

—Spelling Puzzles. 2003. (Language Arts Ser.). cd-rom 19.99 (978-1-58947-914-2(9)) School Zone Publishing Co.

—Vocabulary Puzzles. 2003. (Language Arts Ser.). cd-rom 19.99 (978-1-58947-931-9(9)) School Zone Publishing Co.

Schujer, Silvia. Palabras para Jugar (Word Play) (SPA.). (J). pap. (978-950-07-0664-3(4)) Editorial Sudamericana S.A.

Schulz, Charles M. The Peanuts Guide to the Seasons: A Jumbo Activity Book. Bennett, Elizabeth, illus. 2003. (Peanuts Club with Charlie Brown & Friends Ser.). 144p. (J). (978-0-439-46826-8(4)) Scholastic, Inc.

Schulz, Charles M. & Bennett, Elizabeth. The Peanuts Guide to Sports: A Jumbo Activity Book. 2003. (Peanuts Club with Charlie Brown & Friends Ser.). (Illus.). 144p. (J). (978-0-439-46824-4(8)) Scholastic, Inc.

Seidletz, Marcia. Easy Spanish Word Power Games: Early Intermediate to Advanced. 2003. (Easy... Word Puzzles Ser.). (SPA & ENG., Illus.). 80p. pap. 5.95 (978-0-8442-7246-7(9) , 9780844272467, Contemporary Bks.) McGraw-Hill Trade.

Shaloum, Alli. Boggle Jr. Word Search Puzzles. 2007. (Illus.). 64p. (J). pap. 4.95 (*978-1-4027-5150-9(8)) Sterling Publishing Co., Inc.

Skeete, D. C., creator. Hip Hop Wordsearch. 2005. (YA). pap. 3.99 (978-0-9769012-0-4(X) , 0-9769012) Skeete, D.

Steig, William. C D B! Steig, William, illus. 2000. (Illus.). 48p. (J). 16.95 (978-0-689-83160-7(9)) Simon & Schuster Children's Publishing.

—C D B! 2003. (gr. k-3). lib. bdg. 15.30 (978-0-613-66399-1(3)) Tandem Library Bks.

—C d C ? Steig, William, illus. 2003. (Illus.). 64p. (J). 16.00 (978-0-374-31233-6(8) , Farrar, Straus & Giroux (BYR)) Farrar, Straus & Giroux.

—C d C ? 2008. (Illus.). 64p. (J). pap. 7.99 (*978-0-312-38012-0(7)) Square Fish.

Steig, William, illus. C D B! 2003. 48p. (J). pap. 6.99 (978-0-689-85706-5(3) , Aladdin) Simon & Schuster Children's Publishing.

Steinwachs, Robert. Brain Bafflers. Miller, Myron, illus. 2003. 96p. (gr. 10-12). pap. 6.95 (978-0-8069-8787-3(1)) Sterling Publishing Co., Inc.

Sterling Publishing Company Staff. Word Searches. 2003. (Kids' Bathroom Bks.). (Illus.). 96p. (J). pap. 4.95 (978-1-4027-0720-9(7)) Sterling Publishing Co., Inc.

Stern, Leonard. Around Town Mad Libs Junior. 2004. (Mad Libs Junior Ser.). (Illus.). 48p. (J). (gr. k-3). pap. 3.99 (978-0-8431-0854-5(1) , Price Stern Sloan) Penguin Group (USA) Inc.

—School Rules! Mad Libs Junior. 2004. (Mad Libs Junior Ser.). (Illus.). 48p. (J). (gr. k-3). pap. 3.99 (978-0-8431-0853-8(3) , Price Stern Sloan) Penguin Group (USA) Inc.

—You've Got Mad Libs. 2004. (Mad Libs Ser.). (Illus.). 48p. (J). (gr. 3). pap. 3.99 (978-0-8431-0855-2(X) , Price Stern Sloan) Penguin Group (USA) Inc.

Stern, Leonard & Frantz, Jennifer. Snack Attack! Mad Libs Junior. 2004. 48p. (J). (gr. k-3). pap. 3.99 (978-0-8431-1156-9(9) , Price Stern Sloan) Penguin Group (USA) Inc.

Stern, Leonard & Price, Richard. Bee Movie Mad Libs. 2007. (Mad Libs Ser.). 48p. (J). (gr. 3). pap. 3.99 (*978-0-8431-2675-4(2) , Price Stern Sloan) Penguin Group (USA) Inc.

Stern, Leonard & Price, Roger. Fear Factor Mad Libs: Ultimate Gross Out! 2004. 48p. (J). (gr. 3). mass mkt. 3.99 (978-0-8431-1157-6(7) , Price Stern Sloan) Penguin Group (USA) Inc.

—Mad Libs in Love. 2001. (Mad Libs Ser.). (Illus.). 48p. (J). (gr. 4-7). mass mkt. 3.99 (978-0-8431-7628-5(8) , Price Stern Sloan) Penguin Group (USA) Inc.

—Survivor Mad Libs. 2004. (Mad Libs Ser.). 48p. (J). (gr. 3). mass mkt. 3.99 (978-0-8431-1174-3(7) , Price Stern Sloan) Penguin Group (USA) Inc.

Stern, Leonard, et al. Animals, Animals, Animals! Mad Libs Junior. 2004. 48p. (J). (gr. k-3). pap. 3.99 (978-0-8431-0951-1(3) , Price Stern Sloan) Penguin Group (USA) Inc.

Stickels, Terry. Magic Word-Doku. 2007. 240p. (J). pap. 4.99 (978-0-06-125711-7(7)) HarperCollins Pubs.

Stillson, Alan. One-Minute Brainteasers: Official American Mensa Puzzle Book. 2001. (Official Mensa Puzzle Book Ser.). (Illus.). 96p. (gr. 4-7). pap. 6.95 (978-0-8069-0187-9(X)) Sterling Publishing Co., Inc.

Taylor-Miller, Sandra. Are We There Yet? The Wright Brothers' National Memorial Park, Kill Devil Hills, North Carolina, Site of the First Heavier-Than-Air Machine-Powered Flight. 2004. (Illus.). 56p. (J). 9.95 (978-1-887905-87-9(1)) Parkway Pubs., Inc.

Varma, Michael. Mental Blocks - at the Movies: At the Movies. 2002. (Illus.). 114p. per. 6.95 (978-0-9717815-0-4(8)) Magical Concepts.

—Mental Blocks - Return to the Movies: Return to the Movies, 3 vols. 2002. (Illus.). 114p. per. 6.95 (978-0-9717815-2-8(4)) Magical Concepts.

—Mental Blocks - TV Time: TV Time, 4. 2002. (Illus.). 114p. per. 6.95 (978-0-9717815-3-5(2)) Magical Concepts.

Vocabulary Building with Wordsearches. 2003. (Homework Booklets Ser.). (Illus.). 96p. (gr. 2-3). 2.99 (978-0-88012-777-6(5) , IF0128) School Specialty Publishing.

Ward, Gail. Animals along the Lewis & Clark Trail. 2002. 32p. (978-1-886609-32-7(2)) Tamarack Bks., Inc.

Ward, Mike. Scratch & Solve Hangman #3, Vol. 3. 2006. (Sit & Solve Ser.). 96p. pap. 5.95 (978-1-4027-2582-1(5)) Sterling Publishing Co., Inc.

—Scratch & Solve Tough Hangman #3. 2006. (Sit & Solve Ser.). 96p. pap. 5.95 (978-1-4027-2581-4(7)) Sterling Publishing Co., Inc.

Word Detective - Puzzle Jungle - What's Inside You?, 3 bks., 3 discs. Set. 2004. (Make Reading Fun! Ser.: Module 4). (SPA., Illus.). (J). (gr. k-3). 49.95 (978-1-58086-181-6(4)) EDC Publishing.

Word Games. 2004. (Play & Learn Pads Ser.). 48p. (J). 3.99 (978-1-85997-719-4(7)) Byeway Bks.

Word Play 1-2. 2004. 128p. (J). per. 11.99 (978-0-88724-208-3(1) , CD-104002) Carson-Dellosa Publishing Co., Inc.

Word Play 3-4. 2004. (J). per. 11.99 (978-0-88724-209-0(X) , CD-104003) Carson-Dellosa Publishing Co., Inc.

Word Play 5-6. 2004. (J). per. 11.99 (978-0-88724-210-6(3) , CD-104004) Carson-Dellosa Publishing Co., Inc.

Word Puzzles. (J). Date not set. (Illus.). 96p. 2.98 (978-0-7525-7520-9(1)); 2002. 24p. spiral bd. 4.98 (978-0-7525-8357-0(3)) Parragon, Inc.

Word Puzzles. 2003. (Basic Skill Ser.). (Illus.). 48p. (gr. 1 up). 5.99 (978-1-56822-040-6(5) , IF5051); (gr. 2 up). 5.99 (978-1-56822-041-3(3) , IF5052); (gr. 3 up). 5.99 (978-1-56822-042-0(1) , IF5053); (gr. 4 up). 5.99 (978-1-56822-043-7(X) , IF5054); (gr. 5 up). 5.99 (978-1-56822-044-4(8) , IF5055); (gr. 6 up). 5.99 (978-1-56822-045-1(6) , IF5056); (gr. 7-8). 5.99 (978-1-56822-046-8(4) , IF5057) School Specialty Publishing.

Word Puzzles. 2001. (Wipe-Off Activity Bks.). 16p. (J). (gr. 1). 3.79 (978-1-58792-016-5(6)) Trend Enterprises, Inc.

Word Search Activity Zone. 2004. (Activity Zone Workbook Ser.). 32p. (J). pap. 2.49 (978-1-58947-388-1(4) , 02193) School Zone Publishing Co.

Word Wizards. 2003. 64p. (YA). (gr. 5-8). pap. 3.99 (978-1-56822-633-0(0) , IF2734-E4) School Specialty Publishing.

Words are Fun. 2004. (Play & Learn Pads Ser.). 48p. (J). 3.99 (978-1-85997-722-4(7)) Byeway Bks.

Wordsearch. 2004. (Play & Learn Pads Ser.). 48p. (J). 3.99 (978-1-85997-716-3(2)) Byeway Bks.

Wordsearch Fun. 2004. (Play & Learn Pads Ser.). 48p. (J). 3.99 (978-1-85997-723-1(5)) Byeway Bks.

139. 1998. (Puzzlers Detect-a-Word Ser.). (J). (978-1-56144-795-4(1) , 50081, Honey Bear Bks.) Modern Publishing.

140. 1998. (Puzzlers Detect-a-Word Ser.). (J). (978-1-56144-796-1(X) , 50081, Honey Bear Bks.) Modern Publishing.

141. 1998. (Puzzlers Detect-a-Word Ser.). (J). (978-1-56144-797-8(8) , 50081, Honey Bear Bks.) Modern Publishing.

142. 1998. (Puzzlers Detect-a-Word Ser.). (J). (978-1-56144-798-5(6) , 50081, Honey Bear Bks.) Modern Publishing.

WORD GAMES—FICTION

Banks, Kate. Max's Words. Kulikov, Boris, illus. 2006. 32p. (J). 16.00 (978-0-374-39949-8(2) , Farrar, Straus & Giroux (BYR)) Farrar, Straus & Giroux.

Davis, Guy. Witzy's Opposites. Spafford, Suzy, illus. 2001. 12p. (J). (ps). 4.99 (978-1-58668-056-5(0)) Lyrick Studios.

Furlong Reynolds, Cynthia. S Is for Star: A Christmas Alphabet. Carroll, Pam, illus. rev. ed. 2001. 40p. (J). 18.95 (978-1-58536-064-2(3)) Sleeping Bear Pr.

Lubar, David. Punished! 2006. 96p. (J). (gr. 2-5). 15.95 (978-1-58196-042-6(5)) Darby Creek Publishing.

Parish, Peggy. Good Work, Amelia Bedelia. Sweat, Lynn, illus. 2003. (I Can Read Bks.). 64p. (J). (gr. k-3). pap. 3.99 (978-0-06-051115-9(X)) HarperCollins Pubs.

—Good Work, Amelia Bedelia. 2003. (gr. k-3). lib. bdg. 11.80 (978-0-613-68343-2(9)) Tandem Library Bks.

Perlman, Rhea. Canyon Catastrophe. Santat, Dan, illus. 2006. (Otto Undercover Ser.). 128p. (J). 14.99 (978-0-06-075498-3(2)); pap. 3.99 (978-0-06-075497-6(4)) HarperCollins Pubs.

Schreiber, Anne. Word Play. Ong, Cristina, illus. 2000. (Scholastic At-Home Phonics Reading Program Ser.: Vol. 60). 24p. (J). (978-0-590-68864-2(2)) Scholastic, Inc.

Tashjain, Janet. Multiple Choice. rev. ed. 1999. (Illus.). 192p. (YA). (gr. 5-10). 16.95 (978-0-8050-6086-7(3) , Holt, Henry & Co. Bks. For Young Readers) Holt, Henry & Co.

WORD PROCESSING

Baron, Alvin & Baron, Alvin. Bud's Easy Research Paper Computer Manual. 5th ed. 2003. (Illus.). 250p. per. 12.00 (978-1-891707-07-0(8) , 200) Lawrence Hse. Pubs.

Dalton, James. The Computer Classroom: Word Processing. (Illus.). (J). (gr. 5-6). pap. (978-1-876973-01-8(3)) Wizard Bks.

DDC Publishing Staff. Learning Word-Processing & Typing with Word 97 for Kids. 1998. (Learning Ser.). (Illus.). xvii, 488p. (J). pap. 27.00 (978-1-56243-623-0(6)) DDC Publishing, Inc.

Gilpin, Rebecca. An Introduction to Word Processing: Using Microsoft Word 2000 or Microsoft Office 2000. 2004. (Computer Guides Ser.). (SPA., Illus.). 64p. (J). (gr. 5 up). pap. 10.95 (978-0-7460-4135-2(7)); lib. bdg. 18.95 (978-1-58086-310-0(8)) EDC Publishing.

—Introduction to Word Processing Word 2000. 2001. (Computer Guide Ser.). 64p. (J). lib. bdg. 12.99 (978-1-58086-516-6(X)) EDC Publishing.

Katsaropoulos, Chris, et al. Learning Keyboarding & Word Processing for Kids. Sather, Ryan, illus. 1998. (Learning Ser.). xvii, 488p. (J). 29.00 incl. cd-rom (978-1-56243-626-1(0)) DDC Publishing, Inc.

McGraw-Hill Staff. Micro Mastery: KeyQuest. 1999. (C). stu. ed. 54.26 (978-0-02-644456-9(9) , 9780026444569) Glencoe/McGraw-Hill.

Steinhauser, Peggy L. Mousetracks: A Kid's Computer Idea Book. Steinhauser, Peggy L., illus. 2004. (Illus.). 104p. (gr. k-5). pap. 12.95 (978-1-883672-48-5(1) , Tricycle Pr.) Ten Speed Pr.

Zocchi, Judy. Dear Principal Petunia: Word Processing. Bird, Nikolai, illus. 2005. (Click & Squeak Ser.). 32p. (J). pap. 9.95 (978-1-59646-111-6(X)) Dingles & Co.

WORDS

see Vocabulary

WORDS, NEW

Dorling Kindersley Publishing Staff. My First Word Bath Book. 1999. (My First Series Ser.). (Illus.). 10p. (J). (ps-k). 6.99 (978-0-7894-4297-0(3)) Dorling Kindersley Publishing, Inc.

First Sight Words. 1998. (High Q Books Ser.). (J). (ps-6). bds. 2.99 (978-1-56293-599-3(2) , McClanahan Bk.) Learning Horizons, Inc.

Wildsmith, Brian. Brian Wildsmith's Opuestos. Fiol, Maria A., tr. Wildsmith, Brian, illus. l.t. ed. 1998. (SPA., Illus.). 16p. (J). (ps). bds. 4.95 (978-1-887734-18-9(X)) Star Bright Bks., Inc.

WORK

see also Labor and Laboring Classes

Alpern, Michele. The Effects of Job Loss on the Family. 2002. (Focus on Family Matters Ser.). (Illus.). 64p. (YA). (gr. 10 up). 25.00 (978-0-7910-6690-4(8) , Chelsea Hse.) Facts On File, Inc.

Ancona, George. Mis Quehaceres. 32p. (J). 2006. (SPA.). (gr. 1-3). pap. 8.95 (978-0-516-25499-9(5)); 2005. (ENG & SPA., Illus.). 21.00 (978-0-516-25291-9(7)) Scholastic Library Publishing. (Children's Pr.).

Brent, Lynnette R. At Work: Long Ago & Today. 2003. (Times Change Ser.). (Illus.). 32p. (J). lib. bdg. 24.22 (978-1-4034-4536-0(2)) Heinemann Library.

Carroll, Colleen. How Artists See Work: Farm, Factory, Home, Office. 2000. (How Artists See Ser.). (Illus.). 48p. 10.95 (978-0-7892-0672-5(2)) Abbeville Pr., Inc.

Chaktoura, Julia. El Baul de los Oficios: Un Libro Sobre las Vocales. Ink, Lancman, illus. (Coleccion el Baul Ser.). (SPA.). 10p. (J). (gr. k-1). (978-950-46-1158-5(3)) Santillana USA Publishing Co., Inc.

Ecker, Debbie. People Work. 2000. (Yellow Umbrella Books). (Illus.). 16p. (J). (gr. 1). lib. bdg. 14.60 (978-0-7368-0740-1(3) , Pebble Bks.) Capstone Pr., Inc.

Firestone, Mary. Earning Money. 2004. (Learning about Money Ser.). (Illus.). 24p. (J). lib. bdg. 21.26 (978-0-7368-2639-6(4)) Capstone Pr., Inc.

Freeman, Marcia S. The Work Book. 2005. (Everything Science Ser.). (Illus.). 24p. (gr. 1-4). 14.95 (978-1-59515-125-4(7)) Rourke Publishing, LLC.

Harcourt School Publishers Staff. My Place. 3rd ed. 2002. (Trophies English Language Learners Ser.). (Illus.). pap. 5.10 (978-0-15-327655-2(X)) Harcourt Schl. Pubs.

—People & Work Big Book No. 6. 2nd ed. 2003. (Illus.). pap. 139.70 (978-0-15-337571-2(X)) Harcourt Schl. Pubs.

—People Working: Little Book. 2000. (Collections Ser.). (Illus.). (J). pap. 10.20 (978-0-15-314503-2(X)) Harcourt Schl. Pubs.

Jo the Model Maker: Individual Title Six-Pack Pouch - Level J. (Lighthouse Ser.). 16p. (gr. 2 up). 28.00 (978-0-7578-0863-0(8)) Rigby Education.

Kids Publishing Science Staff. Transforming Energy: All about Heat, Work & Energy. 1999. (J). pap. 6.95 (978-1-891418-17-4(3)) Science Kids.

La Plante, Clare. A Teen's Guide to Working. 2003. (Illus.). 60p. (J). (978-0-7398-5171-5(3)) Steck-Vaughn.

Luder, George. Trabajando Con Mi Papito. Maval Publishing Inc. Staff, illus. 2001. Tr. of Working with Dad. (SPA.). 32p. (J). (gr. k-3). pap. 7.50 (978-1-59134-007-2(1)) Maval Publishing, Inc.

Maurer, Tracy. A to Z of Helping Hands. 2002. (A to Z Ser.). (Illus.). 48p. (gr. k-2). 20.95 (978-1-58952-061-5(0)) Rourke Publishing, LLC.

McGowan, Keith. Sexual Harassment. 1998. (Overview Ser.). (Illus.). 112p. (YA). (gr. 6-9). lib. bdg. 29.95 (978-1-56006-507-4(9) , LML00902-177867, Lucent Bks.) Thomson Gale.

Middleton, Haydn. Ancient Greek Jobs. 2002. (People in the Past Ser.). (Illus.). 48p. (J). (gr. 4-6). lib. bdg. 27.07 (978-1-58810-638-4(1)) Heinemann Library.

Murphy, Patricia J. Earning Money. 2006. (How Economics Works). (Illus.). 48p. (J). (ps-7). 25.26 (978-0-8225-2149-5(0) , Lerner Pubns.) Lerner Publishing Group.

Naylor, Sharon. Learning the Ropes. 2nd ed. 2004. (Career Skills Library). (Illus.). 128p. (YA). (gr. 6-12). 21.95 (978-0-8160-5520-3(3) , Ferguson Publishing Co.) Facts On File, Inc.

Nelson, Robin. Jobs. 2003. (First Step Nonfiction Ser.). (Illus.). 8p. (J). pap. 3.95 (978-0-8225-3929-2(2) , Lerner Pubns.) Lerner Publishing Group.

Nelson, Robin. Working Then & Now. 2008. (First Step Nonfiction - Then & Now Ser.). (J). lib. bdg. 18.60 (*978-0-8225-8604-3(5)) Lerner Publishing Group.

Schwartz, Stuart B. Looking at Work, 4 vols. 1998. (J). (gr. 5-12). (978-0-516-29736-1(8) , Children's Pr.) Scholastic Library Publishing.

Schwartz, Stuart B. & Conley, Craig. Looking at Work, 8 bks. Incl. Considering a Job Offer. (gr. 3-4). 1999. lib. bdg. 21.26 (978-0-7368-0178-2(2)); Earning Money. (gr. 3-4). 1998. lib. bdg. 21.26 (978-1-56065-711-8(1)); Exploring Job Skills. (gr. 3-4). 1998. lib. bdg. 21.26 (978-1-56065-712-5(X)); Finding Work. (gr. 3-4). 1998. lib. bdg. 21.26 (978-1-56065-713-2(8)); Interviewing for a Job. (gr. 3-4). 1998. lib. bdg. 21.26 (978-1-56065-714-9(6)); Interviewing for Information. (gr. 3-4). 1999. lib. bdg. 21.26 (978-0-7368-0179-9(0)); Networking to Find a Job. (gr. 2-3). 1999. lib. bdg. 21.26 (978-0-7368-0180-5(4)); Writing a Resume. (gr. 3-4). 1999. lib. bdg. 21.26 (978-0-7368-0181-2(2)); 32p. (J). (Illus.). Set lib. bdg. 170.08 (978-0-7368-0305-2(X) , LifeMatters Bks.) Capstone Pr., Inc.

Shepard, Daniel. Trabajando. 2005. Tr. of Working. (SPA., Illus.). 16p. (J). (gr. 1 up). lib. bdg. 15.93 (978-0-7368-4181-8(4)) Capstone Pr., Inc.

Stickland, Paul. Places. Stickland, Paul, illus. 1998. (Working Ser.). (Illus.). 16p. (J). (ps up). lib. bdg. 19.93 (978-0-8368-2158-1(0)) Stevens, Gareth Inc.

VanVoorst, Jennifer. Working. 2003. (Yellow Umbrella Books for Early Readers). (Illus.). 17p. (J). 15.93 (978-0-7368-2910-6(5)); pap. (978-0-7368-2869-7(9)) Yellow Umbrella Pr.

Walker, Sally M. & Feldmann, Roseann. Trabajo. 2005. (Libros de Fisica para Madrugadores (Early Bird Physics) Ser.). (SPA & ENG., Illus.). 48p. (J). (gr. 3-7). lib. bdg. 25.26 (978-0-8225-2984-2(X) , Ediciones Lerner) Lerner Publishing Group.

Yates, Vicki. Life at Work. 2007. (J). (*978-1-4034-9834-2(2)); pap. (*978-1-4034-9842-7(3)) Heinemann Library.

WORK—FICTION

Asai, Carrie. Book of the Shadow. 2003. (gr. 7-12). lib. bdg. 15.30 (978-0-613-65534-7(6)) Tandem Library Bks.

Ballard, Robin. My Day, Your Day. Ballard, Robin, illus. 2001. (Illus.). 24p. (J). (ps-3). 14.95 (978-0-688-17796-6(4)) HarperCollins Pubs.

Banks, Kate. The Night Worker. Hallensleben, Georg, illus. 40p. (J). 2007. pap. 6.95 (978-0-374-40000-2(8)); 2000. 16.00 (978-0-374-35520-3(7)) Farrar, Straus & Giroux. (Farrar, Straus & Giroux (BYR)).

Brooks, Regina. Never Finished, Never Done! Borgella, Marjorie, illus. 2004. 32p. (J). lib. bdg. 15.00 (*978-1-4242-0229-4(9)) Fitzgerald Bks.

Buehner, Caralyn & Buehner, Mark. A Job for Wittilda. Buehner, Caralyn & Buehner, Mark, illus. 2004. (Illus.). 32p. (J). (gr. k-3). pap. 5.99 (978-0-14-240137-8(4) , Puffin) Penguin Group (USA) Inc.

Bunting, Eve. A Day's Work. 2002. (Illus.). (J). 13.79 (978-0-7587-2361-1(X)) Book Wholesalers, Inc.

Carlson, Nancy L. Loudmouth George Earns His Allowance. 2007. (Illus.). 32p. (J). (gr. k-3). spiral bd. 15.95 (978-0-8225-6560-4(9) , Carolrhoda Bks.) Lerner Publishing Group.

Chouette. Caillou Goes to Work. rev. ed. 2005. (Abracadabra Ser.).Tr. of Caillou va Travailler. (Illus.). 24p. (J). (ps-1). pap. 4.95 (978-2-89450-548-9(5)) Chouette Publishing CAN. *Dist:* Independent Pubs. Group.

Clark, Eleanor. Eleanor Jo: The Farmer's Daughter. 2007. (Eleanor Jo Ser.). (J). pap. 14.99 (978-0-9788726-1-8(4)) HonorNet.

Come Back, Amelia Bedelia. 2002. (Amelia Bedelia Ser.). (Illus.). (J). 12.34 (978-0-7587-6057-9(4)) Book Wholesalers, Inc.

Dalrymple, Marilyn. Bartholomew's Buttons. 2006. 18p. (J). 9.73 (978-1-4116-9200-8(4)) Lulu.com.

de Paola, Tomie. Boss for a Day. de Paola, Tomie, illus. 2001. (All Aboard Reading Ser.). (Illus.). 32p. (J). (ps-2). pap. 3.99 (978-0-448-42544-3(0) , Grosset & Dunlap) Penguin Group (USA) Inc.

—Boss for a Day. 2001. 10.79 (978-0-606-22476-5(9)); lib. bdg. 11.80 (978-0-613-50529-1(8)) Tandem Library Bks.

deRubertis, Barbara. Perky Otter. Cockrille, Eva V., illus. 1998. (Let's Read Together Ser.). 32p. (J). (ps-3). pap. 4.95 (978-1-57565-045-6(2)) Kane Pr., The.

DeSpain, Christine. And Please Take the Banana off Your Head. 2003. (Illus.). 34p. (J). (gr. 1-3). pap. 6.95 (978-0-9678030-1-2(2)) Caribbean Scene.

Disney Staff. Hooray for Teamwork. 2000. (Lessons from the Hundred-Acre Woods: Vol. 12). (Illus.). 32p. (J). (ps-3). 3.49 (978-1-57973-098-7(1)) Advance Pubs. LLC.

Egan, Tim. The Pink Refrigerator. 2007. (Illus.). 32p. (J). (gr. 3-5). 16.00 (978-0-618-63154-4(2)) Houghton Mifflin Co.

Encinas, Carlos. The New Engine: La Maquina Nueva. 2001. (Illus.). (J). 15.95 (978-1-885772-24-4(6)) Kiva Publishing, Inc.

Gardner, Lindsey, et al. Pan Fydd Popi a Macs yn Fawr. 2005. (WEL., Illus.). 17p. (978-1-902416-45-8(7)) Cymdeithas Lyfrau Ceredigion.

Gershator, Phillis. Sky Sweeper. Meade, Holly, illus. 2007. 40p. (J). (gr. k). 16.00 (978-0-374-37007-7(9)) Farrar, Straus & Giroux.

Goldman, Leslie. On the Job. 2004. 138p. (J). lib. bdg. 16.92 (*978-1-4242-0674-2(X)) Fitzgerald Bks.

Good Job, Rob! 2006. 16p. (J). pap. 1.99 (978-0-7847-1693-9(5) , 02995) Standard Publishing.

Harcourt School Publishers Staff. Trofeos On Level: Probando. 3rd ed. 2002. (SPA., Illus.). pap. 6.80 (978-0-15-324091-1(1)) Harcourt Schl. Pubs.

Healy, Nick. Louie the Layabout. Erkocak, Sahin, illus. 2007. (Pfeffernut County Ser.). 32p. (J). (gr. k-2). lib. bdg. 23.93 (*978-1-4048-3697-6(7)) Picture Window Bks.

Hecker, Robert. The Greatest Summer Job in the Whole Wide World. 2001. 253p. pap. 14.99 (978-1-928767-11-4(7)) Royal Fireworks Publishing Co.

Herman, Gail. Dulcie's Taste of Magic. Clarke, Judith et al, illus. 2008. 128p. (J). (gr. 1-5). 5.99 (*978-0-7364-2454-7(7)) Random Hse., Inc.

Jennings, Patrick. The Weeping Willow. Alter, Anna, illus. 2002. (Ike & Mem Story Ser.: No. 3). 56p. (J). (gr. k-3). tchr. ed. 15.95 (978-0-8234-1671-4(2)) Holiday Hse., Inc.

Keilbart, L. S. One. Benson, Barbara, illus. 2007. 76p. (J). pap. 10.95 (*978-1-85756-610-9(6)) Janus Publishing Co. GBR. *Dist:* Independent Pubs. Group.

King, Stephen. Roadwork. 1999. (gr. 7-12). lib. bdg. 16.45 (978-0-613-17481-7(X)) Tandem Library Bks.

Koller, Jackie French. Mole & Shrew Have Jobs to Do. 2001. (Stepping Stone Bks.). (Illus.). (J). (978-0-606-21335-6(X)) Tandem Library Bks.

Little People at Work. 1998. (Fisher-Price Little People Toddler Skills Workbooks Ser.: Vol. 3). (Illus.). (J). pap. (978-0-7666-0184-0(6) , Honey Bear Bks.) Modern Publishing.

Look, Lenore. Love As Strong As Ginger. Johnson, Stephen T., illus. 1999. 32p. (J). (gr. 1-4). 16.99 (978-0-689-81248-4(5) , Atheneum/Anne Schwartz Bks.) Simon & Schuster Children's Publishing.

Lovett, Darrell F. Darrell's Lake Franklin. 2007. 13.00 (***978-0-8059-8807-9(6)***) Dorrance Publishing Co., Inc.

Lowry, Brigid. Things You Either Hate or Love. 2007. 192p. (YA). (gr. 4-7). pap. 8.95 (978-0-312-36308-6(7) , St. Martin's Griffin) St. Martin's Pr.

Luder, George. Trabajando con Papa. Maval Publishing Inc. Staff, illus. 2001. Tr. of Working with Dad. (SPA.). 32p. (J). (ps-3). pap. 7.50 (978-1-884083-17-4(X)) Maval Publishing, Inc.

—Working with Dad. Maval Publishing Inc. Staff, illus. 2001. 32p. (J). (ps-3). pap. 7.50 (978-1-884083-31-0(5)) Maval Publishing, Inc.

Marsden, Carolyn. Mama Had to Work on Christmas. Casilla, Robert, illus. 2003. 80p. (J). (gr. 2-5). 14.99 (978-0-670-03635-6(8) , Viking Juvenile) Penguin Group (USA) Inc.

Montes, Marisa. Juan Bob Goes to Work. Cepeda, Joe, illus. 2006. 32p. (J). pap. 6.99 (978-0-06-088227-3(1) , Rayo) HarperCollins Pubs.

—Juan Bobo Busca Trabajo. Cepeda, Joe, illus. 2006. (SPA.). 32p. (J). pap. 6.99 (978-0-06-113681-8(6) , Rayo) HarperCollins Pubs.

—Juan Bobo Goes to Work: A Puerto Rican Folk Tale. Cepeda, Joe, illus. 2000. 32p. (J). (ps-4). 16.99 (978-0-688-16233-7(9)) HarperCollins Pubs.

—Juan Bobo Goes to Work: A Puerto Rican Folktale. Cepeda, Joe, illus. 2000. 32p. (J). (ps-4). lib. bdg. 17.89 (978-0-688-16234-4(7)) HarperCollins Pubs.

North, Merry. Let's Get to Work. Adams, Lynn, illus. 1999. (Giant Flap Bks.). 10p. (J). (ps-k). bds. (978-1-57584-345-2(5) , Reader's Digest Children's Bks.) Reader's Digest Children's Publishing, Inc.

Paterson, Katherine. Lyddie. 2005. 192p. (J). (ps-7). pap. 3.99 (978-0-14-240438-6(1) , Puffin) Penguin Group (USA) Inc.

Patrick, B. Blob's Odd Jobs. Torre, Attilio, illus. 2006. 48p. (J). 16.95 (978-0-9741319-3-1(8)) 4N Publishing LLC.

Paulsen, Gary. Worksong. Paulsen, Ruth Wright, illus. 2000. 32p. (J). (ps-3). pap. 7.00 (978-0-15-202371-3(2) , Harcourt Paperbacks) Harcourt Children's Bks.

—Worksong. 2000. (978-0-606-18199-0(7)); lib. bdg. 15.30 (978-0-613-28707-4(X)) Tandem Library Bks.

Petty, Colin, illus. The Three Little Pigs: A Tale about Working Hard. 2006. (J). 6.99 (978-1-59939-016-1(7)) Reader's Digest Young Families, Inc.

Pittar, Gill. Milly, Molly & Aunt Maude. 2004. 28p. (978-1-86972-014-8(8)) Milly Molly Bks.

Polacco, Patricia & Polacco, Patricia. The Bee Tree. 1998. (Illus.). (J). (ps-ps). lib. bdg. 15.30 (978-0-613-07325-7(8)) Tandem Library Bks.

Reynolds, Peter H. So Few of Me. 2006. (Illus.). 32p. (J). (gr. k-12). 14.00 (978-0-7636-2623-5(6)) Candlewick Pr.

Roth, Carol. Here Comes the Choo Choo! Cushman, Doug, illus. 2007. (J). (***978-0-15-205582-0(7)***) Harcourt Trade Pubs.

Santillo, LuAnn. Rags. Santillo, LuAnn, ed. 2003. (Half-Pint Kids Readers Ser.). (Illus.). 7p. (J). (ps-1). pap. (978-1-59256-073-8(3)) Half-Pint Kids, Inc.

—Ted's Job. Santillo, LuAnn, ed. 2003. (Half-Pint Kids Readers Ser.). (Illus.). 7p. (J). (ps-1). pap. (978-1-59256-060-8(1)) Half-Pint Kids, Inc.

Schwartz, Amy. Bea & Mr. Jones: Story & Pictures. 2006. (Illus.). 32p. (J). 13.95 (978-0-15-205811-1(7)) Harcourt Trade Pubs.

Sommer, Carl. No Longer a Dilly Dally, 1 bk. 2003. (Another Sommer-Time Story Ser.). (Illus.). 48p. (J). 16.95 incl. audio (978-1-57537-550-2(8)); (gr. 1-4). 16.95 incl. audio compact disk (978-1-57537-501-4(X)) Advance Publishing, Inc.

—Your Job Is Easy. 2003. (Another Sommer-Time Story Ser.). (Illus.). 48p. (J). (gr. 1-4). 16.95 incl. audio compact disk (978-1-57537-517-5(6)); 16.95 incl. audio (978-1-57537-566-3(4)) Advance Publishing, Inc.

—Your Job Is Easy. James, Kennon, illus. 2000. (Another Sommer-Time Story Ser.). 48p. (J). (gr. 2-4). lib. bdg. 16.95 (978-1-57537-067-5(0)); (ps-4). 9.95 (978-1-57537-018-7(2)) Advance Publishing, Inc.

Sorenson, Margo. Clubhouse Threat. 2001. 112p. (J). pap. 5.95 (978-0-7891-5457-6(9)); (gr. 2-5). lib. bdg. 13.95 (978-0-7569-0120-2(0)) Perfection Learning Corp.

Staunton, Ted. Morgan Makes a Deal. Slavin, Bill, illus. 2005. 60p. (J). lib. bdg. 12.00 (***978-1-4242-1205-7(7)***) Fitzgerald Bks.

Stewart, Dianne. El Regalo del Sol. Daly, Jude, illus. 2000. (SPA.). 28p. (J). (ps-3). pap. 6.99 (978-980-257-258-8(6) , EK(1977)) Ekare, Ediciones VEN. *Dist:* Kane/Miller Bk. Pubs., Inc., Lectorum Pubns., Inc.

Swerling, Lisa & Lazar, Ralph. Flying Memos & Other Office Antics. 2004. (Illus.). 64p. 9.95 (978-1-84072-605-3(9)) M Q Pubns. GBR. *Dist:* Weatherhill, Inc., Wybel Marketing Group.

Trembath, Don. The Popsicle Journal. 2002. 144p. (J). (gr. 7-12). pap. 6.95 (978-1-55143-185-7(8)) Orca Bk. Pubs. USA.

Waber, Bernard. Lyle at the Office. Waber, Bernard, illus. 2002. (Lyle the Crocodile Ser.). (Illus.). (J). 13.79 (978-0-7587-3059-6(4)) Book Wholesalers, Inc.

Waddell, Martin. Charlie's Tasks. Postgate, Daniel, illus. 2006. 32p. (J). lib. bdg. (***978-1-4048-3137-7(1)***) Picture Window Bks.

Weston, Martha. Owen Foote, Money Man. 2003. (gr. k-3). lib. bdg. 12.95 (978-0-613-73020-4(8)) Tandem Library Bks.

Whitlock, Jennifer. The Principle Woods Book of Work. 2000. 60p. (J). mass mkt. 14.95 (978-0-9700601-1-2(4)) Principle Woods, Inc.

Willis, Tammy A. I Can Work With My Friends. 2006. (J). pap. (978-1-57332-441-0(8)) HighReach Learning, Inc.

—I Can Work with My Friends. ed. 2006. (J). pap. (978-1-57332-442-7(6)) HighReach Learning, Inc.

WORKING-CLASSES

see Labor and Laboring Classes

WORKING GIRLS

see Children—Employment

WORKING WOMEN

see Women—Employment

WORKINGMEN'S DWELLINGS

see Housing

WORKSHOP COUNCILS

see Management—Employee Participation

WORLD

see Earth

WORLD ECONOMICS

see Economic Geography; Economic History; Economic Policy

WORLD, END OF THE

see end of the World

WORLD GOVERNMENT

see International Organization

WORLD HEALTH ORGANIZATION

Foley, Ronan. World Health. 2003. (21st Century Debates Ser.). (Illus.). 64p. (J). lib. bdg. 28.56 (978-0-7398-5507-2(7)) Raintree.

Grahame, Deborah A. World Health Organization. 2003. (International Organizations Ser.). (Illus.). 48p. (J). (gr. 5 up). lib. bdg. 30.00 (978-0-8368-5524-1(8)); pap. 11.95 (978-0-8368-5533-3(7)) Stevens, Gareth Inc. (World Almanac Library).

Powell, Jillian. The World Health Organization. 2001. (World Organizations Ser.). (Illus.). 32p. (YA). (gr. 6-8). 24.00 (978-0-531-14621-7(9) , Watts, Franklin) Scholastic Library Publishing.

—World Health Organization. 2001. (gr. 5-8). lib. bdg. 15.25 (978-0-613-54791-8(8)) Tandem Library Bks.

Senker, Cath. World Health Organization. 2004. (World Watch Ser.). (Illus.). 48p. (YA). lib. bdg. 18.99 (978-0-7398-6614-6(1)) Raintree.

WORLD HISTORY

see also Geography; History, Ancient; History, Modern

Abraham, Henry & Pfeffer, Irwin. Enjoying Global History. rev. ed. 2005. 600p. (gr. 10-12). pap. (978-0-87720-890-7(5) , R625P) AMSCO Schl. Pubns., Inc.

Adams. Religion, Science, Medicine & Warfare. 2000. (Illus.). 256p. (J). (978-1-84215-351-2(X) , Southwater) Anness Publishing GBR. *Dist:* National Bk. Network.

Adams, Simon. Atlas of Exploration & Empires. 2007. (Kingfisher Atlas Ser.). 48p. (J). (gr. 3-5). 15.95 (978-0-7534-6033-7(5) , Kingfisher) Houghton Mifflin Co. Trade & Reference Div.

Adcock, Michael. Cambridge Checkpoints VCE History - Revolutions 2005. 2004. (Cambridge Checkpoints Ser.). 144p. pap., stu. ed. 12.00 (978-0-521-61225-8(X)) Cambridge Univ. Pr.

Allen, Mark, ed. New Tales of Euterpe: The Star of India as a British Emigrant Ship. unabr. ed. 2003. (Mains'L Haul Special Publications). (Illus.). 68p. (J). pap. (978-0-944580-13-4(0)) Maritime Museum Assn. of San Diego.

American Education Publishing Staff, et al. The Complete Book of World History. 2001. (Complete Book Ser.). (Illus.). 288p. (J). (gr. 4-8). pap. 14.95 (978-1-56189-089-7(8) , American Education Publishing) School Specialty Publishing.

Ancient World History: Patterns of Interaction. 2003. (gr. 6-12). stu. ed. (978-0-618-18393-7(0) , 2-01388) McDougal Littell Inc.

Ancient World History: Patterns of Interaction. 2005. (gr. 6-12). tchr. ed. (978-0-618-37681-0(X) , 2-00462) McDougal Littell Inc.

Ancient World History: Patterns of Interaction: EEdition. (gr. 6-12). 2005. cd-rom (978-0-618-43267-7(1) , 2-00805); 2003. cd-rom (978-0-618-28480-1(X) , 2-90159) McDougal Littell Inc.

Ancient World History: Patterns of Interaction: EEdition Plus Online. (gr. 6-12). 2005. (978-0-618-42268-5(4) , 2-00681); 2003. (978-0-618-19413-1(4) , 2-70055) McDougal Littell Inc.

Ancient World History: Patterns of Interaction: EEdition Plus Online with purchase of print Pupil's Edition-1 Year. 2005. (gr. 6-12). (978-0-618-42278-4(1) , 2-00683) McDougal Littell Inc.

Ancient World History: Patterns of Interaction: EEdition Plus Online with purchase of print Pupil's Edition-2 Year. 2005. (gr. 6-12). (978-0-618-42279-1(X) , 2-00684) McDougal Littell Inc.

Ancient World History: Patterns of Interaction: EEdition Plus Online with purchase of print Pupil's Edition-3 Year. 2005. (gr. 6-12). (978-0-618-42280-7(3) , 2-00685) McDougal Littell Inc.

Ancient World History: Patterns of Interaction: EEdition Plus Online with purchase of print Pupil's Edition-4 Year. 2005. (gr. 6-12). (978-0-618-42281-4(1) , 2-00686) McDougal Littell Inc.

Ancient World History: Patterns of Interaction: EEdition Plus Online with purchase of print Pupil's Edition-5 Year. 2005. (gr. 6-12). (978-0-618-42282-1(X) , 2-00687) McDougal Littell Inc.

Ancient World History: Patterns of Interaction: EEdition Plus Online with purchase of print Pupil's Edition-6 Year. 2005. (gr. 6-12). (978-0-618-42283-8(8) , 2-00688) McDougal Littell Inc.

Around the World Series, 5 bks., Set. 149.64 (978-0-7614-1083-6(X) , Benchmark Bks.) Cavendish, Marshall Corp.

Ash, Russell. Fantastic Millennium Facts. 1999. (Illus.). 128p. (J). (gr. 3-8). lib. bdg. (978-1-55209-441-9(3)) Firefly Bks., Ltd.

Atlas de los Animales. (Coleccion Atlas del Saber). (SPA., Illus.). (YA). (gr. 4 up). 20.95 (978-950-11-0886-6(4) , SGM64) Sigmar ARG. *Dist:* Continental Bk. Co., Inc.

Battles, Wars & Revolutions. 2001. 63p. (YA). 8.65 (978-0-7525-4880-7(8)) Parragon, Inc.

Bauer, Susan Wise. Ancient Times Vol. 1: From the Earliest Nomads to the Last Roman Emperor. 2003. (Story of the World: Vol. 1). (Illus.). 336p. (J). 21.95 (978-0-9714129-6-5(0)) Peace Hill Pr.

—Early Modern Times. Martirosian, Patty Ann et al, illus. 2004. (Story of the World: Vol. 3). 275p. (J). pap., act. bk. ed. 32.95 (978-0-9728603-2-1(0) , AB3) Peace Hill Pr.

—Early Modern Times: From Elizabeth the First to the Forty-Niners. 2004. (Story of the World: Vol. 3). (Illus.). 400p. (J). pap. 21.95 (978-0-9714129-9-6(5) , SOTW3) Peace Hill Pr.

—Early Modern Times: From Elizabeth the First to the Forty-Niners. Martirosian, Patty Ann et al, illus. 2003. (Story of the World: Vol. 3). 400p. (J). 21.95 (978-0-9728603-0-7(4)) Peace Hill Pr.

—Story of the World, Vol. 1. l.t. ed. 2002. (Story of the World: Vol. 1). (Illus.). 334p. (J). (gr. 1-7). pap. 21.95 (978-0-9714129-0-3(1) , SOTW1) Peace Hill Pr.

—The Story of the World - History for the Classical Child - the Modern Age - from the Victorian Empire to the End of the USSR, Bk. 4. 2005. (Illus.). 275p. pap., act. bk. ed. 32.95 (978-0-9728603-5-2(5)) Peace Hill Pr.

—The Story of the World: History for the Classical Child Vol. 4: The Modern Age from Victoria's Empire to the End of the USSR. Park, Sarah, illus. 2005. 400p. pap. 21.95 (978-0-9728603-3-8(9) , SOTW4) Peace Hill Pr.

Beautiful Feet U. S. & World History. 1999. 10p. (YA). ring bd. 1.00 (978-1-57896-068-2(1) , 2567, Hewitt Homeschooling Resources) Hewitt Research Foundation, Inc.

Beck, Roger B. Modern World History: Patterns of Interaction: Pupil's Edition. l.t. ed. 2005. (YA). (gr. 9-12). 83.76 (978-0-618-37711-4(5) , 2-00492) McDougal Littell Inc.

Benchmark Education Staff, compiled by. Eve Bunting's World of Stories & Citizenship. 2005. spiral bd. 225.00 (***978-1-4108-5807-8(3)***) Benchmark Education Co.

—20th Century HIST. 2006. spiral bd. 169.00 (***978-1-4108-7144-2(4)***) Benchmark Education Co.

Bennett, Paul. Time. 1999. (History Ser.). (Illus.). 32p. (J). (gr. 5-9). pap. 5.95 (978-0-7641-0643-9(0)) Barron's Educational Series, Inc.

Biesty, Stephen & Platt, Richard. The Coolest Cross-Sections Ever. 2001. (Illus.). 128p. (J). 24.99 (978-0-7894-7964-8(8)) Dorling Kindersley Publishing, Inc.

Billings. History of Our World. 2003. (Illus.). (J). 41.95 (978-0-7398-6087-8(9)) Steck-Vaughn.

Bingham, Jane. Encyclopedia of World History: Prehistoric, Ancient, Medieval, Last 500 Years. 2004. (World History Ser.). (Illus.). 415p. (J). pap. 19.99 (978-0-7945-0332-1(2) , Usborne) EDC Publishing.

Bingham, Jane, et al. Encyclopedia of World History: Prehistoric, Ancient, Medieval, Last 500 Years. 2004. (World History Ser.). (Illus.). 415p. (J). (gr. 3 up). 39.95 (978-0-7460-4168-0(3)); lib. bdg. 47.95 (978-1-58086-336-0(1)) EDC Publishing.

Biography from Ancient Civilizations: Legends, Folklore, & Stories of Ancient Worlds, 20 vols., Set. Incl. Life & Times of Alexander the Great. Bankston, John. (gr. 4-8). 2005. lib. bdg. 29.95 (978-1-58415-283-5(4)); Life & Times of Archimedes. Zannos, Susan. (gr. 4-8). 2004. lib. bdg. 29.95 (978-1-58415-242-2(7)); Life & Times of Augustus Caesar. Whiting, Jim. (ps-7). 2005. lib. bdg. 29.95 (978-1-58415-336-8(9)); Life & Times of Buddha. Gedney, Mona K. (ps-7). 2005. lib. bdg. 29.95 (978-1-58415-342-9(3)); Life & Times of Catherine the Great. Gibson, Karen Bush. (gr. 4-7). 2005. lib. bdg. 29.95 (978-1-58415-347-4(4)); Life & Times of Charlemagne. Whiting, Jim. (gr. 4-8). 2005. lib. bdg. 29.95 (978-1-58415-346-7(6)); Life & Times of Cleopatra. Adams, Michelle Medlock. (gr. 4-8). 2005. lib. bdg. 29.95 (978-1-58415-335-1(0)); Life & Times of Confucius. Tracy, Kathleen. (gr. 4-8). 2004. lib. bdg. 29.95 (978-1-58415-246-0(X)); Life & Times of Constantine. Tracy, Kathleen. (gr. 4-8). 2005. lib. bdg. 29.95 (978-1-58415-343-6(1)); Life & Times of Genghis Khan. Whiting, Jim. (gr. 4-8). 2005. lib. bdg. 29.95 (978-1-58415-348-1(2)); Life & Times of Hammurabi. Bryant, Tamera. (ps-7). 2005. lib. bdg. 29.95 (978-1-58415-338-2(5) , 1244807); Life & Times of Homer. Tracy, Kathleen. (gr. 4-8). 2004. lib. bdg. 29.95 (978-1-58415-260-6(5)); Life & Times of Joan of Arc. Whiting, Jim. (gr. 4-8). 2005. lib. bdg. 29.95 (978-1-58415-345-0(8)); Life & Times of Julius Caesar. Whiting, Jim. (ps-7). 2005. lib. bdg. 29.95 (978-1-58415-337-5(7)); Life & Times of Marco Polo. Zannos, Susan. (gr. 4-8). 2004. lib. bdg. 29.95 (978-1-58415-264-4(8)); Life & Times of Moses. Whiting, Jim. (ps-7). 2005. lib. bdg. 29.95 (978-1-58415-340-5(7)); Life & Times of Nero. Whiting, Jim. (gr. 5-8). 2005. lib. bdg. 29.95 (978-1-58415-349-8(0)); Life & Times of Pericles. Whiting, Jim. (ps-7). 2005. lib. bdg. 29.95 (978-1-58415-339-9(3)); Life & Times of Rameses the Great. Whiting, Jim. (gr. 5-8). 2005. lib. bdg. 29.95 (978-1-58415-341-2(5)); Life & Times of Socrates. Zannos, Susan. (gr. 4-8). 2004. lib. bdg. 29.95 (978-1-58415-282-8(6)); (Illus.). 48p. (J). 2005. lib. bdg. (978-1-58415-407-5(1)) Mitchell Lane Pubs., Inc.

Body, Robert J. Bob. I Survived the Bataan Death March. 2003. 2003p. per. 14.95 net. (978-1-931934-21-3(5)) Back Yard Pub.

Boehm, Richard G., et al. People & Civilizations in World History. 1999. (Harcourt Brace Social Studies). (gr. k-7). pap. 8.60 (978-0-15-314199-7(9)) Harcourt Schl. Pubs.

Brasier, Michael. The World Through A Child's Eyes: A View of Various Countries & Global Cultures from a Child's Perspective. 2005. 110p. (J). per. 29.95 (978-0-9772591-0-6(2)) Around The World Pubns., LLC.

Brenner, Barbara. If You Were There In 1492: Everyday Life in the Time of Columbus. 1998. (gr. 3-6). 17.60 (978-0-613-09952-3(4)) Tandem Library Bks.

Brief History Set. 2005. (Brief History Ser.). 304-432p. (gr. 9). 495.00 (978-0-8160-6519-6(5)) Facts On File, Inc.

Brookes, Philip. Great Civilizations: Discover the People & Places of Long Ago. 2003. (History Detectives Ser.). (Illus.). 64p. pap. 7.99 (978-1-84215-695-7(0) , Southwater) Anness Publishing GBR. *Dist:* National Bk. Network.

Brun, Henry. Reviewing Global History & Geography. 2003. pap. (978-1-56765-614-5(5) , R674W) AMSCO Schl. Pubns., Inc.

Bulliet. Study Guide: Used with ... Bulliet-The Earth & Its Peoples: A Global History. 2nd ed. 2000. (YA). (gr. 6-12). stu. ed. 37.56 (978-0-618-00081-4(X) , 307838) Houghton Mifflin College Div.

—Study Guide Vol. 1: Used with ... Bulliet-The Earth & Its Peoples: A Global History. 2nd ed. 2000. (YA). (gr. 6-12). stu. ed. 37.56 (978-0-618-00086-9(0) , 307844) Houghton Mifflin College Div.

Carnibucci, Patricia. Ancient & World History: Over 15 Complete Printable Unit Studies with Interactive Links. 2002. 160p. (gr. k-12). cd-rom 15.95 (978-1-891400-91-9(6)) Champion Pr., Ltd.

Casef, et al. Countries of the World Set, 6 vols. 2003. (Countries of the World Ser.). (Illus.). 64-64p. (gr. 9-12). 180.00 (978-0-8160-5379-7(0)) Facts On File, Inc.

Celeste, Mary. The Old World's Gifts to the New. 1999. (Illus.). 497p. (YA). (gr. 5 up). 24.00 (978-0-911845-90-7(9)) Neumann Pr., The.

Chandler, Fiona. Ancient world - internet Linked. McCaffrey, Susie, illus. rev. ed. 2004. 96p. (J). pap. 14.95 (978-0-7945-0816-6(2) , Usborne) EDC Publishing.

Chinese Kites: Level A, 6 vols. 8p. 20.95 (978-0-322-00627-0(9)) Wright Group, The.

Chisholm, Jane. Timelines of World History. 2004. (World History Ser.). (Illus.). 128p. (J). 7.95 (978-0-7945-0358-1(6) , Usborne); (gr. 3 up). 19.95 (978-0-7460-4103-1(9)); (gr. 3 up). lib. bdg. 27.95 (978-1-58086-329-2(9)) EDC Publishing.

—World History Dates. 2nd rev. ed. 1998. (Illustrated World History Ser.). (Illus.). 194p. (J). (gr. 4-7). lib. bdg. 30.95 (978-1-58086-114-4(8)); (gr. 6 up). pap. 22.95 (978-0-7460-2318-1(9)) EDC Publishing.

Churchill, E. Richard & Churchill, Linda R. Short Lessons in World History. 1999. 208p. (gr. 7-12). stu. ed. 24.99 (978-0-8251-3941-3(4) , 0-39414) Walch Publishing.

Clarke, Penny. Brain Power: World History Time Lines. 2006. (Brain Power Ser.). (Illus.). 64p. (J). 14.99 (978-0-7641-5974-9(7)) Barron's Educational Series, Inc.

Class, Michael S. Anthony & the Magic Picture Frame: The Story of the Boy Who Traveled into the Past by Stepping into the Picture Frame on His Bedroom Wall & Returned to See His Own Time in A New Light. 2005. (Illus.). 225p. (YA). (gr. 6-12). 35.00 (978-0-9749269-0-2(6)) Magic Picture Frame Studio, LLC.

Connolly, Sean. Witness to History, 4 bks., Set. 2003. (Illus.). (YA). (gr. 6-8). lib. bdg. 108.28 (978-1-4034-0975-1(7)) Heinemann Library.

The Continents. 2001. (Our World Ser.). (J). (gr. k-12). vinyl bd. 4.95 (978-1-58845-076-0(7)) School Specialty Publishing.

Cooke, Timothy, ed. History of the Modern World Vol. 1: Origins of the Modern World. 1999. (J). (978-0-7614-7148-6(0)) Cavendish, Marshall Corp.

—History of the Modern World Vol. 2: Religion & Change in Europe. 1999. (J). (978-0-7614-7149-3(9)) Cavendish, Marshall Corp.

—History of the Modern World Vol. 3: Old & New Worlds. 1999. (J). (978-0-7614-7150-9(2)) Cavendish, Marshall Corp.

—History of the Modern World Vol. 4: The Age of Enlightenment. 1999. (J). (978-0-7614-7151-6(0)) Cavendish, Marshall Corp.

—History of the Modern World Vol. 5: Revolution & Change. 1999. (J). (978-0-7614-7152-3(9)) Cavendish, Marshall Corp.

—History of the Modern World Vol. 6: The Changing Balance of Power. 1999. (J). (978-0-7614-7153-0(7)) Cavendish, Marshall Corp.

—History of the Modern World Vol. 7: World War I & Its Consequences. 1999. (J). (978-0-7614-7154-7(5)) Cavendish, Marshall Corp.

—History of the Modern World Vol. 8: World War II & the Cold War. 1999. (J). (978-0-7614-7155-4(3)) Cavendish, Marshall Corp.

—History of the Modern World Vol. 9: The World Today. 1999. (J). (978-0-7614-7156-1(1)) Cavendish, Marshall Corp.

Countries - Set III, Set. Incl. Afghanistan. Italia, Bob. lib. bdg. 22.78 (978-1-57765-653-1(9)); Canada. Fournier, Christine. lib. bdg. 22.78 (978-1-57765-751-4(9)); Cuba. Britton, Tamara L. lib. bdg. 22.78 (978-1-57765-760-6(8)); Ethiopia. Britton, Tamara L. lib. bdg. 22.78 (978-1-57765-757-6(8)); Germany. Italia, Bob. lib. bdg. 22.78 (978-1-57765-753-8(5)); India. Italia, Bob. lib. bdg. 22.78 (978-1-57765-752-1(7)); Italy. Italia, Bob. lib. bdg. 22.78 (978-1-57765-754-5(3)); Pakistan. Britton, Tamara L. lib. bdg. 22.78 (978-1-57765-654-8(7)); Peru. Italia, Bob. lib. bdg. 22.78 (978-1-57765-756-9(X)

); Portugal. Italia, Bob. lib. bdg. 22.78 (978-1-57765-758-3(6)); 40p. (J). (gr. k-6). (Illus.). 2002. Set lib. bdg. 227.80 (978-1-57765-519-0(2) , Checkerboard Library) ABDO Publishing Co.

Countries of the World Set. 2004. (Countries of the World Ser.). (gr. 9-12). 360.00 (978-0-8160-6118-1(1)) Facts On File, Inc.

Countries of the World Set 2. 2004. (Countries of the World Ser.). 61-64p. (gr. 9-12). 180.00 (978-0-8160-5500-5(9)) Facts On File, Inc.

Cox, Reg. The Seven Wonders of the Modern World. 2000. (Wonders of the World Ser.). (Illus.). 32p. (J). (gr. 4-7). 21.95 (978-0-7910-6048-3(9) , Chelsea Hse.) Facts On File, Inc.

Cribb, John, et al. The Human Odyssey, 2 vols. 2004. (Illus.). (978-1-931728-53-9(4)); (978-1-931728-56-0(9)) K12.

Cultures of the World - Group 18, 6 vols. Incl. Angola. Sheehan, Sean. (J). (gr. k-17). lib. bdg. 37.07 (978-0-7614-0953-3(X)); Estonia. Spilling, Michael. (gr. 5-12). lib. bdg. 37.07 (978-0-7614-0951-9(3)); Ghana. Levy, P. (gr. 5-12). lib. bdg. 37.07 (978-0-7614-0952-6(1)); Honduras. McGaffey, L. (gr. 5-12). lib. bdg. 37.07 (978-0-7614-0955-7(6)); Mongolia. Cheng-Pang, G. (gr. 5-12). lib. bdg. 37.07 (978-0-7614-0954-0(8)); Yemen. Hestler, Anna. (gr. 5-12). lib. bdg. 37.07 (978-0-7614-0956-4(4)); 128p. (Illus.). 1999. 222.43 (978-0-7614-0950-2(5) , Benchmark Bks.) Cavendish, Marshall Corp.

Cultures of the World Group 11, 6 bks., Set. 2nd ed. Incl. Afghanistan. Ali, Sharifah Enayat. (YA). (gr. 5-9). lib. bdg. 39.93 (978-0-7614-2064-4(9)); Belgium. Pateman, Robert & Elliot, Mark. (J). lib. bdg. 39.93 (978-0-7614-2059-0(2)); Bolivia. Pateman, Robert & Cramer, Marcus. (J). lib. bdg. 39.93 (978-0-7614-2066-8(5)); Norway. Kagda, Sakina & Alexander, Anne. (J). lib. bdg. 39.93 (978-0-7614-2067-5(3)); Peru. Falconer, Kieran & Quek, Lynette. (J). lib. bdg. 39.93 (978-0-7614-2068-2(1)); Taiwan. Moiz, Azra & Wu, Janice. (J). lib. bdg. 39.93 (978-0-7614-2069-9(X)); 144p. 2006. 2007. Set lib. bdg. 239.57 (*978-0-7614-2057-6(6) , Benchmark Bks.) Cavendish, Marshall Corp.

Cultures of the World Group 12, 6 bks., Set. 2nd ed. Incl. Cambodia. Sheehan, Sean & Cooke, Barbara. 2007. lib. bdg. 39.93 (978-0-7614-2071-2(1)); Ethiopia. Gish, Steven. (Illus.). 2006. lib. bdg. 39.93 (978-0-7614-2025-5(8)); Finland. Tan, Chung Lee. 2007. lib. bdg. 39.93 (978-0-7614-2073-6(8)); Iceland. Wilcox, Jonathan & Latif, Zawiah Abdul. 2007. lib. bdg. 39.93 (978-0-7614-2074-3(6)); Panama. Hassig, Susan M. (Illus.). 2006. lib. bdg. 39.93 (978-0-7614-2028-6(2)); Tibet. Levy, Patricia & Bosco, Don. 2007. lib. bdg. 39.93 (978-0-7614-2076-7(2)); 144p. (J). 2007. Set lib. bdg. 239.57 (*978-0-7614-2070-5(3) , Benchmark Bks.) Cavendish, Marshall Corp.

Cultures of the World Group 25, 6 bks., Set. Incl. Benin. Kneib, Martha. lib. bdg. 39.93 (978-0-7614-2328-7(1)); Botswana. LeVert, Suzanne. lib. bdg. 39.93 (978-0-7614-2330-0(3)); Chad. Kneib, Martha. lib. bdg. 39.93 (978-0-7614-2327-0(3)); Mozambique. King, David C. lib. bdg. 39.93 (978-0-7614-2331-7(1)); Rwanda. King, David C. lib. bdg. 39.93 (978-0-7614-2333-1(8)); Sierra Leone. LeVert, Suzanne. lib. bdg. 39.93 (978-0-7614-2334-8(6)); (Illus.). 128p. (J). 2007. 2007. Set lib. bdg. 239.57 (*978-0-7614-2326-3(5) , Benchmark Bks.) Cavendish, Marshall Corp.

Dalby, Liz. World Hist Sticker Atlas. 2006. (Illus.). 24p. (J). pap. 8.99 (978-0-7945-1244-6(5) , Usborne) EDC Publishing.

Dawson, Ian, et al. SHP History Elearning Activities. 2006. cd-rom (*978-0-340-90735-1(5)) Hodder General Publishing Division.

Days That Shook the World, 4 vols. 2003. 114.24 (978-0-7398-6052-6(6)); 2003. (Illus.). 285.60 (978-0-7398-6053-3(4)); 4th ed. 2004. (Illus.). 114.24 (978-0-7398-6650-4(8)) Raintree.

Days That Shook the World Series, 6 bks., Set. 2002. (Illus.). lib. bdg. 162.84 (978-0-7398-5238-5(8)) Raintree.

DBQ Practice: World History. 2003. spiral bd. 19.95 (978-1-56004-145-0(5)) Social Studies Schl. Service.

Deary, Terry. The Horrible History of the World. 2006. 96p. (J). pap. 10.99 (978-0-439-87786-2(5) , Scholastic Reference) Scholastic, Inc.

Delillio, G. S. W. Arnhem: Defeat & Glory, a Miniaturist Perspective. 2002. (Illus.). 160p. (gr. 10-13). 35.00 (978-0-7643-1443-8(2)) Schiffer Publishing, Ltd.

Discovering Cultures - Group 5, 6 Bks, Set. 2004. (J). 107.70 (978-0-7614-1790-3(7)) Cavendish, Marshall Corp.

Discovering Cultures Group 6, 6 bks., Set. Incl. Austria. Grahame, Deborah A. (Illus.). lib. bdg. 28.50 (978-0-7614-1984-6(5)); Chile. Rau, Dana Meachen. lib. bdg. 28.50 (978-0-7614-1988-4(8)); Haiti. Mara, Wil. lib. bdg. 28.50 (978-0-7614-1987-7(X)); Iran. Mara, Wil. (Illus.). lib. bdg. 28.50 (978-0-7614-1986-0(1)); Sweden. Grahame, Deborah A. (Illus.). lib. bdg. 28.50 (978-0-7614-1985-3(3)); Thailand. Rau, Dana Meachen. (Illus.). lib. bdg. 28.50 (978-0-7614-1989-1(6)); 48p. (J). 2006. 2007. Set lib. bdg. 171.00 (*978-0-7614-1983-9(7) , Benchmark Bks.) Cavendish, Marshall Corp.

Diwrnod i'r Brenin: Chwaraeon, Hamdden a Thwristiaeth Er 1900. 2005. (978-1-902346-01-4(7)) Addysg Y Cyfryngau Cymru.

Doherty, Gillian. Usborne Book of Peoples of the World. 2001. (gr. 5-8). lib. bdg. 24.55 (978-0-613-58270-4(5)) Tandem Library Bks.

—1001 Things to Spot Long Ago. 1999. (gr. k-3). lib. bdg. 15.25 (978-0-613-74410-2(1)) Tandem Library Bks.

Dorling Kindersley Publishing Staff. World History Atlas. Black, Jeremy, ed. 2005. 320p. 50.00 (978-0-7566-0967-2(4)) Dorling Kindersley Publishing, Inc.

Douglas, Vincent & School Specialty Publishing Staff. The First Civilizations. 2001. (History of the World Ser.). (Illus.). 48p. (J). (gr. 3 up). 18.95 (978-1-57768-950-8(X) , Bedrick, Peter Bks.) School Specialty Publishing.

—Revolution & Conflict. 2001. (History of the World Ser.). (Illus.). 48p. (J). (gr. 3 up). 18.95 (978-1-57768-954-6(2) , Bedrick, Peter Bks.) School Specialty Publishing.

—Tell Me about History. 2004. (Tell Me Ser.). (Illus.). 224p. (J). pap. 14.95 (978-0-7696-3381-7(1) , Waterbird Bks.) School Specialty Publishing.

Downing. Troubled World, 4 vols., Set 2. 2004. 114.24 (978-1-4109-0185-9(8)) Raintree.

Draper, Allison Stark. Headlines from History, 6 bks. Incl. America's First Traitor : Benedict Arnold Betrays the Colonies. lib. bdg. 19.95 (978-0-8239-5673-9(3) , PKTRAI); Boston Massacre : Five Colonists Killed by British Soldiers. lib. bdg. 19.95 (978-0-8239-5670-8(9) , PKBOMA); Boston Tea Party : Angry Colonists Dump British Tea. lib. bdg. 19.95 (978-0-8239-5671-5(7) , PKBOTE); End of the American Revolutionary War : The Colonists Defeat the British at Yorktown. lib. bdg. 19.95 (978-0-8239-5674-6(1) , PKENRE); George Washington Elected : How America's First President Was Chosen. lib. bdg. 19.95 (978-0-8239-5675-3(X) , PKFIPR); Start of the American Revolutionary War : Paul Revere Rides at Midnight. lib. bdg. 19.95 (978-0-8239-5672-2(5) , PKREWA); 24p. (J). (gr. 3). 2001. (Illus.). Set lib. bdg. 117.00 (978-0-8239-7068-1(X) , PKHEHI, PowerKids Pr.) Rosen Publishing Group, Inc., The.

Dupré, Judith. De las piramides a los Rascacielos. ed. 2004. (SPA.). 32p. (J). pap. 6.00 (978-1-4108-2338-0(5) , A23385) Benchmark Education Co.

Ellis, Elisabeth Gaynor, et al. World History Set: Connections to Today, 12 vols. 2003. 3951p. (YA). (gr. 9-12). stu. ed. 1978.00 (978-0-13-062790-2(9) , A-L00013-00) Prentice Hall Pr.

Embacher, Eric. Stowed Away. 2004. 64p. (YA). per. 3.95 (978-1-56254-828-5(X) , SP828X) Saddleback Educational Publishing.

Enchantment of the World, Second Series, 6 bks. 2004. (J). 207.00 (978-0-516-23715-2(2) , Children's Pr.) Scholastic Library Publishing.

Enchantment of the World, Second Series, 6 bks., Set. Incl. Argentina. Blashfield, Jean F. (YA). 36.00 (978-0-516-24872-1(3)); Australia. Heinrichs, Ann. (Illus.). (J). 36.00 (978-0-516-24873-8(1)); Bangladesh. Orr, Tamra. (Illus.). (J). 36.00 (978-0-516-25012-0(4)); Costa Rica. Morrison, Marion. (Illus.). (J). 36.00 (978-0-516-24884-4(7)); Kuwait. Willis, Terri. (Illus.). (J). 36.00 (978-0-516-24902-5(9)); Mongolia. Lassieur, Allison. (Illus.). (J). 36.00 (978-0-516-24903-2(7)); 144p. (gr. 5-9). 2007. 2007. 216.00 (*978-0-531-17732-7(7)); 216.00 (978-0-516-25407-4(3)) Scholastic Library Publishing. (Children's Pr.).

Enchantment of the World, Second Series: An Excellent Resource for World History, Geography, & Independent Study, 6 Bks., Set. 2005. (YA). 210.00 (978-0-516-25202-5(X)) Scholastic Library Publishing.

The Encyclopedia of World History. 2002. 320p. (YA). 29.95 (978-0-7525-8446-1(4)) Parragon, Inc.

Encyclopedia of World History. 2003. (Illus.). 256p. (J). 12.98 (978-1-4054-1702-0(1)) Parragon, Inc.

Enlightenment DBA. 2001. spiral bd. 16.95 (978-1-56004-109-2(9)) Social Studies Schl. Service.

Evangelista, Gloria. Ignacio's Chair. Morrison, Cathy, illus. 2002. 32p. (gr. 3-4). 17.95 (978-1-55591-966-5(9)) Fulcrum Publishing.

Evans, Charlotte. Historia (Enciclopedias Everst Internacional) (SPA.). 804p. (YA). (gr. 5-8). 39.99 (978-84-241-9403-1(9)) Everest de Ediciones y Distribucion, S.L. ESP. *Dist:* Lectorum Pubns., Inc.

Exploration Into.. 2005. 48p. pap. 200.00 (978-0-7910-6027-8(6) , Chelsea Hse.) Facts On File, Inc.

Facts on File, Inc. Staff, et al. World History on File, 4 vols. 2006. (World History on File Ser.). (Illus.). (gr. 6-12). 2nd rev. ed. 210p. (J). 140.00 (978-0-8160-6374-1(5)); 2nd rev. ed. 182p. (J). 140.00 (978-0-8160-6375-8(3)); 2nd rev. ed. 220p. 140.00 (978-0-8160-6373-4(7)); 3rd rev. ed. 210p. (J). 140.00 (978-0-8160-6376-5(1)) Facts On File, Inc.

—World History on File, 4 vols., Set. Chapman, Victoria L. & Lindroth, David, eds. 2nd rev. ed. 2006. (World History on File Ser.). (YA). (gr. 6-12). ring bd. 560.00 (978-0-8160-6372-7(9)) Facts On File, Inc.

Farman, John. Shockingly Short History Of Absolutely Everything. (Illus.). 87p. (J). pap. 8.99 (978-0-330-34904-8(X)) Pan Macmillan GBR. *Dist:* Trafalgar Square Publishing.

Farndon, John. A History of Civilization Illustrated History Encyclopedia: The Great Landmarks in the Development of Mankind. 2006. (Illus.). 256p. (gr. 7-10). reprint ed. pap. 22.00 (978-1-4223-5514-5(4)) DIANE Publishing Co.

Farndon, John, et al. A History of Civilization: The Great Landmarks in the Development of Mankind. 2003. (Illustrated History Encyclopedia Ser.). (Illus.). 264p. pap. 19.99 (978-0-7548-1227-2(8)) Anness Publishing GBR. *Dist:* National Bk. Network.

Field, Robert J. World History. 2000. 196p. (YA). (gr. 4-12). pap., wbk. ed. 10.95 (978-0-87594-352-7(7)) Book-Lab.

A First Look at History, 6 Vols. 132.00 (978-0-8368-4524-2(2)) Stevens, Gareth Inc.

First Reports - Countries, 24 bks. Incl. Australia. Gray, Shirley W. (Illus.). 2000. lib. bdg. 22.60 (978-0-7565-0026-9(5)); Bolivia. Klingel, Cynthia Fitterer & Noyed, Robert B. (Illus.). 2002. lib. bdg. 22.60 (978-0-7565-0182-2(2)); Brazil. Gray, Shirley W. (Illus.). 2000. lib. bdg. 22.60 (978-0-7565-0027-6(3)); Canada. Gray, Shirley W. (Illus.). 2000. lib. bdg. 22.60 (978-0-7565-0028-3(1)); Chile. Klingel, Cynthia Fitterer & Noyed, Robert B. (Illus.). 2002. lib. bdg. 22.60 (978-0-7565-0183-9(0)); China. Sinnott, Susan. (Illus.). 2000. lib. bdg. 22.60 (978-0-7565-0029-0(X)); Cuba. Doak, Robin S. (Illus.). 2004. lib. bdg. 22.60 (978-0-7565-0580-6(1)); Egypt. Gray, Susan Heinrichs. (Illus.). 2001. lib. bdg. 22.60 (978-0-7565-0126-6(1)); England. Gray, Susan Heinrichs. (Illus.). 2001. lib. bdg. 22.60 (978-0-7565-0127-3(X)); France. Klingel, Cynthia Fitterer & Noyed, Robert B. (Illus.). 2002. lib. bdg. 22.60 (978-0-7565-0184-6(9)); Germany. Gray, Shirley W. (Illus.). 2001. 22.60 (978-0-7565-0128-0(8)); India. De Capua, Sarah. (Illus.). 2003. lib. bdg. 22.60 (978-0-7565-0424-3(4)); Indonesia. Doak, Robin S. (Illus.). 2004. lib. bdg. 22.60 (978-0-7565-0582-0(8)); Iran. Doak, Robin S. (Illus.). 2004. lib. bdg. 22.60 (978-0-7565-0581-3(X)); Israel. Gray, Susan Heinrichs. (Illus.). 2001. lib. bdg. 22.60 (978-0-7565-0129-7(6)); Italy. De Capua, Sarah. 2003. lib. bdg. 22.60 (978-0-7565-0425-0(2)); Japan. Sinnott, Susan. (Illus.). 2000. lib. bdg. 22.60 (978-0-7565-0030-6(3)); Kenya. Raatma, Lucia. (Illus.). 2002. lib. bdg. 22.60 (978-0-7565-0185-3(7)); Mexico. Gray, Shirley W. (Illus.). 2000. lib. bdg. 22.60 (978-0-7565-0031-3(1)); Netherlands. De Capua, Sarah. (Illus.). 2003. lib. bdg. 22.60 (978-0-7565-0426-7(0)); Russia. Gray, Susan Heinrichs. (Illus.). 2001. lib. bdg. 22.60 (978-0-7565-0130-3(X)); South Africa. Raatma, Lucia. (Illus.). 2001. lib. bdg. 21.26 (978-0-7565-0131-0(8)); United States. Doak, Robin S. (Illus.). 2004. 22.60 (978-0-7565-0583-7(6)); Vietnam. De Capua, Sarah. (Illus.). 2003. lib. bdg. 22.60 (978-0-7565-0427-4(9)); 48p. (J). (gr. 3 up). (Illus.). Set lib. bdg. 542.40 (978-0-7565-0706-0(5)) Compass Point Bks.

Fleming, F. & Dowswell, P. Shock Horror History! 2004. (Illus.). 128p. (YA). (gr. 5 up). 22.95 (978-0-7460-3369-2(9)) EDC Publishing.

Fof. Nations in Transition, 7 vols., Set. 2002. (YA). (gr. 7-12). 150.00 (978-0-8160-4758-1(8)) Facts On File, Inc.

Forte, Imogene & Frank, Marjorie. Global Studies. 2002. (Basic Not Boring Ser.). tchr. ed., per. 7.95 (978-0-86530-551-9(X)) Incentive Pubns., Inc.

Fritz, Jean, et al. The World in 1492. 1998. (Illus.). 168p. (YA). (gr. 8-12). 20.00 (978-0-7881-5508-6(3)) DIANE Publishing Co.

Fry, Plantagenet Somerset & Adams, Simon. History of the World. 400p. (J). 2007. (gr. 5-8). 39.99 (*978-0-7566-3144-4(0)); 2005. (Illus.). 39.99 (978-0-7566-1244-3(6)) Dorling Kindersley Publishing, Inc.

Garcia-Alvarado, Belén & Venable, Alan. Border Crossing. Stotts, Bob, illus. (J). (gr. 5-6). 2000. 65.00 incl. audio, cd-rom (978-1-58702-310-1(5)); 2002. 150.00 (978-1-58702-032-2(7)); 2000. 50.00 (978-1-58702-478-8(0)) Johnston, Don Inc.

Gerdes, Louise, ed. Rogue Nations. 2006. (Opposing Viewpoints Ser.). (Illus.). 244p. (YA). (gr. 6 up). lib. bdg. 36.20 (978-0-7377-3421-8(3) , Greenhaven Pr., Inc.) Thomson Gale.

Gibbons, David, ed. Timechart History of the World: 6000 Years of World History Unfolded. 2004. (Illus.). 34p. 14.98 (978-0-7607-6534-0(0)) Barnes & Noble, Inc.

Gleaton, Terry. Book of the Centuries Supplemental Pages. 2002. 158p. ring bd. 9.95 (978-1-930165-03-8(X)) Small Ventures.

Global Profiles, 10 vols., Set. 2002. (YA). (gr. 5-12). 175.00 (978-0-8160-4835-9(5)) Facts On File, Inc.

Goldman, Phyllis, ed. Monkeyshines on Mysteries in History. 2003. (Illus.). 92p. per. 32.95 (978-1-888325-20-1(8)) Allosaurus Pubs.

Gombrich, E. H. A Little History of the World. Mustill, Caroline, tr. from GER. Harper, Clifford, illus. 2005. 304p. 25.00 (978-0-300-10883-5(4)) Yale Univ. Pr.

Good Apple. Gold Rush! 2001. (History in the Headlines Ser.). 32p. (J). (gr. 6-8). pap. 6.99 (978-0-7682-0223-6(X) , GA13023) School Specialty Publishing.

Gorman, Joe & Trammell, Jack. Conversations in History: 9 Important Historical Events & the People Who Starred in Them. 2004. (Illus.). 80p. (J). pap. 6.50 (978-1-931334-30-3(7)) Pieces of Learning.

Granada Learning Ltd, prod. Renaissance Explorers Hyb Lb. (YA). cd-rom 172.50 (978-0-7365-4356-9(2)) Films Media Group.

Granada Learning Ltd., prod. The Troubled Century, 2 vols. (YA). cd-rom 149.95 (978-0-7365-0361-7(7)) Films Media Group.

Gray, Dee. Po Cats (9 Lives) Cultural Adventure Series: 2 Low-Income Felines Share Their Musings on Travel, Colonialism, & Geopolitics, 4 bks., Set. 2003. (Illus.). per. 200.00 (978-0-9742007-0-5(0)) Poor Magazine.

Great Battles Through the Ages. (Illus.). (gr. 6-12). pap. (978-0-7910-8043-6(9) , Chelsea Hse.) Facts On File, Inc.

Gritzner, Charles F., ed. Modern World Nations. (Illus.). (J). 848.30 (978-0-7910-7272-1(X)); 2003. 573.85 (978-0-7910-6927-1(3)) Facts On File, Inc. (Chelsea Hse.).

Hafouta, Hofy. Ish Kash. 2000. 28p. (J). 12.95 (978-965-229-102-8(1) , 31041) Gefen Publishing Hse., Ltd ISR. *Dist:* Gefen Bks.

Hall, Margaret C. Around the World, 8 bks. (J). (gr. k-2). Set. 2003. lib. bdg. 182.32 (978-1-58810-640-7(3)); Set 1. 2001. (Illus.). lib. bdg. 85.44 (978-1-58810-019-1(7)); Set 2. 2002. lib. bdg. 91.16 (978-1-58810-428-1(1)) Heinemann Library.

Handbook to Life Set. 2005. (Handbook to Life Ser.). 400p. (gr. 9). 560.00 (978-0-8160-6520-2(9)); 420.00 (978-0-8160-6319-2(2)) Facts On File, Inc.

Hands-On History, 5 bks., Group 2. Incl. Projects about American Immigrants from China. Broida, Marian. 48p. (978-0-7614-1978-5(0)); Projects about Nineteenth-Century European Immigrants. Broida, Marian. 47p. (978-0-7614-1980-8(2)); Projects about the American Revolution. Broida, Marian. 48p. (978-0-7614-1981-5(0)); Projects about the Eastern Woodland Indians. King, David C. 44p. (978-0-7614-1979-2(9)); Projects about the Spanish West. King, David C. 47p. (978-0-7614-1982-2(9)); (Illus.). (J). 2005. 2005. (978-0-7614-1977-8(2) , Benchmark Bks.) Cavendish, Marshall Corp.

Hands-On History Group 3, 5 bks., Set. Incl. Projects about Ancient China. Bjorklund, Ruth. (gr. 4-6). lib. bdg. 29.93 (978-0-7614-2257-0(9)); Projects about Ancient Egypt. King, David C. lib. bdg. 29.93 (978-0-7614-2258-7(7)); Projects about Ancient Greece. Broida, Marian. (gr. 4-6). lib. bdg. 29.93 (978-0-7614-2259-4(5)); Projects about Ancient Rome. Frankel, Karen. lib. bdg. 29.93 (978-0-7614-2260-0(9)); Projects about the Ancient Aztecs. King, David C. lib. bdg. 29.93 (978-0-7614-2256-3(0)); (Illus.). 48p. (J). 2006. 2007. Set lib. bdg. 149.64 (*978-0-7614-2255-6(2) , Benchmark Bks.) Cavendish, Marshall Corp.

Hanes, Sharon M., et al. Cold War Reference Library: Includes Cumulative Index, 4 vols. Incl. Cold War : Almanac. 200p. 55.00 (978-0-7876-7662-9(4)); Cold War : Biographies. 400p. 120.00 (978-0-7876-7663-6(2)); Cold War : Primary Sources. 200p. 67.00 (978-0-7876-7666-7(7)); (J). (Illus.). 800p. 2003. Set lib. bdg. 290.00 (978-0-7876-7609-4(8) , UXL) Thomson Gale.

Harcourt School Publishers Staff. Beginnings, 1877. 3rd ed. 2003. (Horizons Ser.). (gr. 4-7). pupil's gde. ed. 70.10 (978-0-15-321349-6(3)) Harcourt Schl. Pubs.

—Our World's Story. 97th ed. 1999. (Stories in Time Ser.). (gr. 6-7). tchr. ed. 137.30 (978-0-15-302050-6(4)) Harcourt Schl. Pubs.

—Social Studies, Grade 4: People, Civilizations & World History: Activity Book. 1999. (Harcourt Brace Social Studies). (gr. k-7). pap., tchr. ed. 11.00 (978-0-15-316043-1(8)) Harcourt Schl. Pubs.

—World History, 5 Packs. 3rd ed. (Horizons Ser.). 2004. pap. 7.30 (978-0-15-338611-4(8)); 2003. pap. 38.10 (978-0-15-338635-0(5)); Bk. 2. 2004. pap. 7.30 (978-0-15-338612-1(6)); Bk. 2. 2003. pap. 38.10 (978-0-15-338636-7(3)); Bk. 3. 2004. pap. 7.30 (978-0-15-338613-8(4)); Bk. 3. 2003. pap. 38.10 (978-0-15-338637-4(1)); Bk. 4. 2004. pap. 7.30 (978-0-15-338614-5(2)); Bk. 5. 2004. pap. 7.30 (978-0-15-338615-2(0)); Bk. 5. 2003. pap. 38.10 (978-0-15-338639-8(8)); Bk. 6. 2004. pap. 7.30 (978-0-15-338616-9(9)); Bk. 6. 2003. pap. 38.10 (978-0-15-338640-4(1)); Bk. 7. 2004. pap. 7.30 (978-0-15-338617-6(7)); Bk. 7. 2003. pap. 38.10 (978-0-15-338641-1(X)); Bk. 8. 2004. pap. 7.30 (978-0-15-338618-3(5)); Bk. 8. 2003. pap. 38.10 (978-0-15-338642-8(8)); Bk. 9. 2004. pap. 7.30 (978-0-15-338619-0(3)); Bk. 9. 2003. pap. 38.10 (978-0-15-338643-5(6)); Bk. 10. 2004. pap. 7.30 (978-0-15-338620-6(7)); Bk. 10. 2003. pap. 38.10 (978-0-15-338644-2(4)); Bk. 11. 2004. pap. 7.30 (978-0-15-338621-3(5)); Bk. 11. 2003. pap. 38.10 (978-0-15-338645-9(2)); Bk. 12. 2004. pap. 7.30 (978-0-15-338622-0(3)); Bk. 12. 2003. pap. 38.10 (978-0-15-338646-6(0)); Bk. 13. 2004. pap. 7.30 (978-0-15-338623-7(1)); Bk. 13. 2003. pap. 38.10 (978-0-15-338647-3(9)); Bk. 14. 2004. pap. 7.30 (978-0-15-338624-4(X)); Bk. 14. 2003. pap. 38.10 (978-0-15-338648-0(7)); Bk. 15. 2004. pap. 7.30 (978-0-15-338625-1(8)); Bk. 15. 2003. pap. 38.10 (978-0-15-338649-7(5)); Bk. 16. 2004. pap. 7.30 (978-0-15-338626-8(6)); Bk. 16. 2003. pap. 38.10 (978-0-15-338650-3(9)); Bk. 17. 2004. pap. 7.30 (978-0-15-338627-5(4)); Bk. 17. 2003. pap. 38.10 (978-0-15-338651-0(7)); Bk. 18. 2004. pap. 7.30 (978-0-15-338628-2(2)); Bk. 18. 2003. pap. 38.10 (978-0-15-338652-7(5)); Bk. 19. 2004. pap. 7.30 (978-0-15-338629-9(0)); Bk. 19. 2003. pap. 38.10 (978-0-15-338653-4(3)); Bk. 20. 2004. pap. 7.30 (978-0-15-338630-5(4)); Bk. 20. 2003. pap. 38.10 (978-0-15-338654-1(1)); Bk. 21. 2004. pap. 7.30 (978-0-15-338631-2(2)); Bk. 21. 2003. pap. 38.10 (978-0-15-338655-8(X)); Bk. 22. 2004. pap. 7.30 (978-0-15-338632-9(0)); Bk. 22. 2003. pap. 38.10 (978-0-15-338656-5(8)); Bk. 23. 2004. pap. 7.30 (978-0-15-338633-6(9)); Bk. 23. 2003. pap. 38.10 (978-0-15-338657-2(6)); Bk. 24. 2004. pap. 7.30 (978-0-15-338634-3(7)); Bk. 24. 2003. pap. 38.10 (978-0-15-338658-9(4)) Harcourt Schl. Pubs.

—World History: The Civil War to the Present. 3rd ed. 2003. (Horizons Ser.). (Illus.). 68.70 (978-0-15-339621-2(0)) Harcourt Schl. Pubs.

—World History: Time for Kids Reader 5-Pack, Bk. 4. 3rd ed. 2003. (Horizons Ser.). pap. 38.10 (978-0-15-338638-1(X)) Harcourt Schl. Pubs.

—World History 2005. 2nd ed. 2002. (Horizons Ser.). stu. ed. 73.40 (978-0-15-336821-9(7)) Harcourt Schl. Pubs.

Harris, Nicholas. The Story of Civilization. Palin, Nicki, illus. 1999. (Time Trekkers Ser.). 32p. (gr. 2-4). lib. bdg. 22.90 (978-0-7613-1257-4(9) , Millbrook Pr.) Lerner Publishing Group.

Haywood, John. How We Lived: Invasion, Conquest & War. 2006. (Illus.). 64p. pap., pap. 8.99 (978-1-84476-083-1(9) , Southwater) Anness Publishing GBR. *Dist:* National Bk. Network.

—Modern Times Vol. 4: 1815 to the Present. 2000. (World Atlas of the Past Ser.). (Illus.). 64p. (YA). 25.00 (978-0-19-521692-9(X)) Oxford Univ. Pr., Inc.

Healey, Tim. The 1960s. 2005. (Picture History of the 20th Century Ser.). (Illus.). 48p. (J). (gr. 6-9). lib. bdg. 29.95 (978-1-932889-74-1(4)) Sea-To-Sea Pubns.

—The 1970s. 2005. (Picture History of the 20th Century Ser.). (Illus.). 48p. (J). (gr. 6-9). lib. bdg. 29.95 (978-1-932889-75-8(2)) Sea-To-Sea Pubns.

Heinemann Educational Ltd. Publishing Staff. You Are There Package, 6 Packs. 2004. pap. 162.00 (978-1-4109-1388-3(0)) Harcourt Schl. Pubs.

Hillyer, V. M. A Child's History of the World. 2005. pap. 40.95 (978-1-4179-2455-4(1)) Kessinger Publishing, LLC.

Hinds, Kathryn. Life in the Middle Ages, 4 bks., Set. Incl. Castle. lib. bdg. 29.93 (978-0-7614-1007-2(4)); Church. lib. bdg. 29.93 (978-0-7614-1008-9(2)); City. lib. bdg. 29.93 (978-0-7614-1005-8(8)); Countryside. lib. bdg. 29.93 (978-0-7614-1006-5(6)); 80p. (J). (gr. 5 up). (Illus.). 2000. Set lib. bdg. 119.71 (978-0-7614-1009-6(0) , Benchmark Bks.) Cavendish, Marshall Corp.

Historia del Mundo Moderno, 3 vols., Set. 2000. Tr. of History of the Modern World. (ENG & SPA.). (gr. 9 up). 250.00 (978-84-494-1797-9(X) , GML07104-176435) Oceano Grupo Editoria, S.A. ESP. *Dist:* Thomson Gale.

Historia y Geografia del Mundo: Del Renacimiento al Siglo XX. (SPA., Illus.). (J). 40.00 (978-958-04-3807-6(2)) Norma S.A. COL. *Dist:* Distribuidora Norma, Inc.

History & Geography. (Switched on Schoolhouse Ser.). 2004. (YA). (gr. 7). cd-rom 69.95 (978-0-7403-0587-0(5)); 2000. (Illus.). (J). (gr. 3-7). pap., stu. ed. 66.95 incl. cd-rom (978-0-7403-0223-7(X) , SOS300H); Set. 2004. (Illus.). (gr. 5). tchr. ed., stu. ed. 47.95 (978-1-58095-651-2(3) , HIS05015, Lifepac) Alpha Omega Pubns., Inc.

History & Geography: Government & Economics. 2004. (Illus.). (gr. 12). tchr. ed., stu. ed. 47.95 (978-1-58095-672-7(6) , HIS1215, Lifepac) Alpha Omega Pubns., Inc.

History & Geography: U. S. History, 12 vols., Set. 2004. (Illus.). (gr. 11-12). tchr. ed., stu. ed. 47.95 (978-1-58095-669-7(6) , HIS1115, Lifepac) Alpha Omega Pubns., Inc.

History Hunters, 6 bks. Incl. Dinosaur Dig. Dixon, Dougal. lib. bdg. 24.67 (978-0-8368-3739-1(8)); Frozen Mammoth. Dixon, Dougal. lib. bdg. 24.67 (978-0-8368-3740-7(1)); Gladiator's Secret. Malam, John. lib. bdg. 24.67 (978-0-8368-3741-4(X)); Mysterious Mummies. MacDonald, Fiona. lib. bdg. 24.67 (978-0-8368-3742-1(8)); Sunken Treasure. Phillips, Dee. lib. bdg. 24.67 (978-0-8368-3743-8(6)); Temple of the Sun. Thomas, Emma. lib. bdg. 24.67 (978-0-8368-3744-5(4)); 32p. (J). (gr. 3 up). (Illus.). 2003. Set lib. bdg. 148.02 (978-0-8368-3738-4(X)) Stevens, Gareth Inc.

History Starts Here, 4 bks., Set. 2000. (Illus.). (J). pap. (978-0-7398-4211-9(0)) Raintree.

Holt, Rinehart and Winston Staff. History: Practice Test: Oklahoma Version. 2001. (YA). (gr. 8). pap. 4.00 (978-0-03-066919-4(7)) Holt, Rinehart & Winston.

—Holt World History: The Human Journey. 3rd ed. 2002. 76.26 (978-0-03-064683-6(9)) Holt, Rinehart & Winston.

—The Human Journey: Online Edition. 3rd ed. 2003. 77.13 (978-0-03-072542-5(9)) Holt, Rinehart & Winston.

—The Human Journey: The Modern World: Online Edition. 3rd ed. 2003. 75.93 (978-0-03-072541-8(0)) Holt, Rinehart & Winston.

—Taks Every Day! Activities for World History - The Human Journey. 3rd ed. 2002. (Illus.). pap. 45.60 (978-0-03-065761-0(X)) Holt, Rinehart & Winston.

—Troy. 2nd ed. 2002. (Illus.). (J). pap. 5.56 (978-0-03-073836-4(9)) Holt, Rinehart & Winston of Canada, Ltd. CAN. *Dist:* Harcourt Canada, Ltd.

—World History: Standard Test Preparation: Arkansas Edition. 2001. pap. 10.60 (978-0-03-066328-4(8)) Holt, Rinehart & Winston.

—World History: The Human Journey - Ancient: Standard Test Preparation - Virginia Edition. 3rd ed. 2003. (YA). pap., wbk. ed. 10.60 (978-0-03-070168-9(6)) Holt, Rinehart & Winston.

—World History: The Human Journey - Modern Era: Standard Test Preparation - Virginia Edition. 3rd ed. 2003. (YA). pap., wbk. ed. 10.60 (978-0-03-070169-6(4)) Holt, Rinehart & Winston.

—World History: The Human Journey - Preparation Workbook. 3rd ed. 2002. (J). pap. 14.00 (978-0-03-069068-6(4)) Holt, Rinehart & Winston.

—World History: The Human Journey: Online Edition. 5th ed. 2004. (gr. 1). 17.26 (978-0-03-038134-8(7)); (gr. 6). 78.60 (978-0-03-038136-2(3)) Holt, Rinehart & Winston.

—World History: The Human Journey: Online Edition Plus. 3rd ed. 2003. 17.26 (978-0-03-037423-4(5)); 17.26 (978-0-03-037424-1(3)); 17.26 (978-0-03-037426-5(X)) Holt, Rinehart & Winston.

—World History: The Human Journey: Standard Test Preparation Booklet -Tennessee Edition. 3rd ed. 2003. (J). 12.80 (978-0-03-073842-5(3)) Holt, Rinehart & Winston.

—World History - The Human Journey: North Carolina Edition - Standard Test Preparation Workbook. 3rd ed. 2002. pap. 11.10 (978-0-03-069908-5(8)) Holt, Rinehart & Winston.

—World History & Doc-B's Questions: New York Edition. 3rd ed. 2003. (J). pap. 8.40 (978-0-03-070236-5(4)) Holt, Rinehart & Winston of Canada, Ltd. CAN. *Dist:* Harcourt Canada, Ltd.

—World History Today: The Human Journey: Virginia Edition. 3rd annot. ed. 2003. (YA). tchr. ed. 109.20 (978-0-03-070144-3(9)) Holt, Rinehart & Winston.

Hossell, Karen Price. 20th Century Perspectives Series, 2 bks., Set 4. 2003. (Illus.). (J). (gr. 5-7). lib. bdg. 54.14 (978-1-4034-0984-3(6)) Heinemann Library.

Hossell, Karen Price, et al. 20th Century Perspectives Series, 16 bks., Set 1-4. 2003. (Illus.). (J). lib. bdg. 433.12 (978-1-4034-0985-0(4)) Heinemann Library.

Images of War. (Illus.). 192p. (J). (978-0-7835-0153-6(6)) Time-Life Education, Inc.

In World History, 26 bks., Set. Incl. Cinque of the Amistad & the Slave Trade in World History. Worth, Richard. 112p. (J). 2001. lib. bdg. 26.60 (978-0-7660-1460-2(6)); Commodore Perry Opens Japan to Trade in World History. Gaines, Ann Graham. 128p. (YA). 2000. lib. bdg. 26.60 (978-0-7660-1462-6(2)); Cortes & the Conquest of the Aztec Empire in World History. Flowers, Charles. 128p. (J). 2001. lib. bdg. 26.60 (978-0-7660-1395-7(2)); Julius Caesar & Ancient Rome in World History. Barter, James. 128p. (J). 2001. lib. bdg. 26.60 (978-0-7660-1461-9(4)); King Henry VIII & the Reformation in World History. Worth, Richard. 112p. (J). 2001. lib. bdg. 26.60 (978-0-7660-1615-6(3)); Lenin & the Russian Revolution in World History. Edwards, Judith. 128p. (J). 2001. lib. bdg. 26.60 (978-0-7660-1464-0(9)); Leonardo da Vinci & the Renaissance in World History. Lassieur, Allison. 128p. (YA). 2000. lib. bdg. 26.60 (978-0-7660-1401-5(0)); Mahatma Gandhi & India's Independence in World History. Malaspina, Ann. 128p. (YA). 2000. lib. bdg. 26.60 (978-0-7660-1398-8(7)); Nelson Mandela & Apartheid in World History. Gaines, Ann Graham. 128p. (J). 2001. lib. bdg. 26.60 (978-0-7660-1463-3(0)); Philip II & Alexander the Great Unify Greece in World History. Nardo, Don. 112p. (J). 2000. lib. bdg. 26.60 (978-0-7660-1399-5(5)); Pizarro & the Conquest of the Incan Empire in World History. Worth, Richard. 128p. (YA). 2000. lib. bdg. 26.60 (978-0-7660-1396-4(0)); Robespierre & the French Revolution in World History. McGowen, Tom. 128p. (YA). 2000. lib. bdg. 26.60 (978-0-7660-1397-1(9)); Stanley & Livingstone & the Exploration of Africa in World History. Worth, Richard. 128p. (YA). 2000. lib. bdg. 26.60 (978-0-7660-1400-8(2)); (gr. 5-12). (Illus.). Set lib. bdg. 544.70 (978-0-7660-1604-0(8)) Enslow Pubs., Inc.

Incas Mayas Aztecs: Mr Donn & Maxie's World History Series. 2006. spiral bd. 29.95 net. (978-1-56004-244-0(3)) Social Studies Schl. Service.

Johnson, Terri, creator. Blackline Maps of World History: The Ancients 5000BC - 400AD, 5 vols., Vol. 1. 2001. (Illus.). (J). pap. 10.95 (978-1-932786-01-9(5)) Knowledge Quest.

—Blackline Maps of World History: The Complete Set - Revised, 4 sets. 2nd rev. ed. 2004. (Illus.). 250p. (J). ring bd. 39.95 (978-1-932786-16-3(3)) Knowledge Quest.

—Blackline Maps of World History: The Complete Set 5000BC - the Present, 5 vol. 1-5. 2001. (Illus.). (J). ring bd. 34.95 (978-1-932786-06-4(6)) Knowledge Quest.

—Blackline Maps of World History: The Modern World 1850-the Present, 5 vols., Vol. 4. 2001. (Illus.). (J). pap. 10.95 (978-1-932786-04-0(X)) Knowledge Quest.

—Blackline Maps of World History: The New World 1600-1850, 5 vols., Vol. 3. 2001. (Illus.). (J). pap. 10.95 (978-1-932786-03-3(1)) Knowledge Quest.

—Blackline Maps of World History: Unlabeled Maps of the World, US, & Selected Regions, 5 vols., Vol. 5. 2001. (Illus.). (J). pap. 5.95 (978-1-932786-05-7(8)) Knowledge Quest.

—Blackline Maps of World History Set: 5000BC - the Present, Vols. 1-5. 2002. (Illus.). (J). cd-rom 29.95 (978-1-932786-07-1(4)) Knowledge Quest.

Kelleher, Pat & Twist, Clint. Puzzle Quest Through History. Dennis, Peter, illus. 2006. (Puzzle Quest Ser.). 22p. (J). bds., bds. 22.95 (978-0-7696-4876-7(2) , Brighter Child) School Specialty Publishing.

Khanduri, Kamini. Great History Search. Hancock, David, illus. rev. ed. 2005. 48p. (J). pap. 8.95 (978-0-7945-1029-9(9) , Usborne) EDC Publishing.

Kingfisher Editors, ed. The Kingfisher History Encyclopedia. rev. ed. 2004. (Illus.). 480p. (J). (gr. 4-6). 24.95 (978-0-7534-5784-9(9) , Kingfisher) Houghton Mifflin Co. Trade & Reference Div.

Knapp-Fisher, H. C. Outline of World History: For Boys & Girls. (J). 25.00 (978-0-8196-2798-8(4)) Biblo & Tannen Booksellers & Pubs., Inc.

Kohl, David. Ancient History Facts. 2000. 10p. (J). spiral bd. 10.00 (978-1-930443-25-9(0)) Logos Schl.

Kort, Michael G. The Handbook Of, 4 vols. 2004. (Illus.). (YA). (gr. 7 up). (978-0-7613-2480-5(1) , Twenty-First Century Bks.) Lerner Publishing Group.

Larousse Mexico Staff, ed. Caballeros y Castillos. 2005. (Mi Pequena Enciclopedia Ser.). (SPA.). 38p. (ps-k). pap. 3.95 (978-970-22-0857-0(2)) Larousse, Ediciones, S. A. de C. V. MEX. *Dist:* Houghton Mifflin Co. Trade & Reference Div.

Larousse Staff. History of the World. 2000. (Peter Bedrick Young People's Encyclopedia Ser.). (Illus.). 127p. (J). (gr. 5-9). 24.95 (978-0-87226-626-1(5) , Bedrick, Peter Bks.) School Specialty Publishing.

Letters from the Homefront, 5 bks., Set. Incl. Civil War. Schomp, Virginia. lib. bdg. 29.93 (978-0-7614-1095-9(3)); Revolutionary War. Beller, Susan Provost. lib. bdg. 29.93 (978-0-7614-1094-2(5)); Vietnam War. Schomp, Virginia. lib. bdg. 29.93 (978-0-7614-1099-7(6)); World War I. George, Linda S. lib. bdg. 29.93 (978-0-7614-1096-6(1)); World War II. Schomp, Virginia. lib. bdg. 29.93 (978-0-7614-1098-0(8)); (Illus.). 96p. (J). (gr. 6 up). 2001. Set lib. bdg. 149.64 (978-0-7614-1097-3(X) , Benchmark Bks.) Cavendish, Marshall Corp.

El Libro de los Acertijos Historicos. (Coleccion Acertijos). (SPA.). (YA). (gr. 5-8). pap. (978-950-724-249-6(X) , LMA8235) Lumen ARG. *Dist:* Lectorum Pubns., Inc.

Linnihan, Ellen. Stranded at Sea. 2004. 64p. (YA). per. 3.95 (978-1-56254-830-8(1) , SP8301) Saddleback Educational Publishing.

Long Ago. 2002. (First Book of History Questions & Answers Ser.). 32p. (J). 9.95 (978-0-7525-7579-7(1)) Parragon, Inc.

Lubawy, Susan. World View: A Global Study of Geography, History & Culture, Bk. 1. (J). stu. ed. 8.95 (978-0-916591-30-4(1)) Linmore Publishing, Inc.

Maddocks, Steven. Refugees. 2003. (Face the Facts Ser.). (Illus.). 56p. (J). lib. bdg. 28.56 (978-0-7398-6850-8(0)) Raintree.

Major World Nations, 63 bks. 1998. (Illus.). 94-144p. (J). (gr. 5). 1256.85 (978-0-7910-4788-0(1) , Chelsea Hse.) Facts On File, Inc.

McGraw-Hill Staff. Exploring Our World. 2nd ed. 2007. stu. ed. 84.64 (***978-0-07-874576-8(4)*** , 9780078745768) Glencoe/McGraw-Hill.

—Exploring Our World, Reading Essentials & Note-Taking Guide Workbook. 2007. (C). pap. 18.00 (***978-0-07-877602-1(3)*** , 9780077776021) Glencoe/McGraw-Hill.

—Exploring Our World, Starndardized Test Practice Workbook. 2007. (C). pap. 10.64 (***978-0-07-877605-2(8)*** , 9780078776052) Glencoe/McGraw-Hill.

—Glencoe World History. 2007. stu. ed. 94.64 (***978-0-07-874525-6(X)*** , 9780078745256); 2002. stu. ed. 92.83 incl. cd-rom (978-0-07-829288-0(3) , 9780078292880); 2nd ed. 2005. stu. ed. 118.64 (978-0-07-865380-3(0) , 9780078653803); 2nd ed. 2004. stu. ed. 94.64 (978-0-07-860702-8(7) , 9780078607028) Glencoe/McGraw-Hill.

—Glencoe World History: Active Reading, Note-Taking Guide. 2nd ed. 2004. (C). pap., stu. ed. 18.00 (978-0-07-867553-9(7) , 9780078675539) Glencoe/McGraw-Hill.

—Glencoe World History: Modern Times. 2002. stu. ed. 90.61 incl. cd-rom (978-0-07-830058-5(4) , 9780078300585); 2nd ed. 2005. stu. ed. 117.32 (978-0-07-865302-5(9) , 9780078653025) Glencoe/McGraw-Hill.

—Glencoe World History: Modern Times, Spanish Reading Essentials & Note-Taking Guide. 2007. (C). pap. 9.00 (***978-0-07-878270-1(8)*** , 9780078782701) Glencoe/McGraw-Hill.

—Glencoe World History: Modern Times, Standardized Test Practice Workbook, Student Edition. 2007. (C). pap. 11.96 (***978-0-07-878261-9(9)*** , 9780078782619) Glencoe/McGraw-Hill.

—Glencoe World History: Spanish Reading Essentials. 2nd ed. 2004. (SPA.). pap., stu. ed., wbk. ed. 18.00 (978-0-07-865367-4(3) , 9780078653674) Glencoe/McGraw-Hill.

—Glencoe World History, Interactive Tutor: Self-Assessment CD-ROM. 2007. (C). cd-rom 93.32 (***978-0-07-878250-3(3)*** , 9780078782503) Glencoe/McGraw-Hill.

—Glencoe World History Modern Times. 2002. stu. ed. 90.61 (978-0-07-829944-5(6) , 9780078299445) Glencoe/McGraw-Hill.

—Glencoe World History, Modern Times. 2007. (C). stu. ed. 93.32 (***978-0-07-874527-0(6)*** , 9780078745270) Glencoe/McGraw-Hill.

—Glencoe World History; Modern Times. 2nd ed. 2004. (C). stu. ed. 93.32 (978-0-07-860705-9(1) , 9780078607059) Glencoe/McGraw-Hill.

—Glencoe World History, Modern Times: Spanish Reading Essentials & Study Guide. 2nd ed. 2004. (SPA.). pap., stu. ed. 18.00 (978-0-07-865295-0(2) , 9780078652950) Glencoe/McGraw-Hill.

—Glencoe World History, Modern Times, Active Reading Note-Taking Guide. 2nd ed. 2004. (C). pap., stu. ed. 18.00 (978-0-07-867561-4(8) , 9780078675614) Glencoe/McGraw-Hill.

—Glencoe World History, Reading Essentials. 2nd ed. 2004. (C). pap., stu. ed., wbk. ed. 18.00 (978-0-07-865365-0(7) , 9780078653650) Glencoe/McGraw-Hill.

—Glencoe World History, Spanish Reading Essentials & Note-Taking Guide. 2007. (C). pap. 9.00 (***978-0-07-878240-4(6)*** , 9780078782404) Glencoe/McGraw-Hill.

—Glencoe World History, Standardized Test Practice Workbook, Student Edition. 2007. (C). pap. 11.96 (***978-0-07-878230-5(9)*** , 9780078782305) Glencoe/McGraw-Hill.

—Human Heritage. 2nd ed. 2003. (gr. 6-12). stu. ed. 77.36 (978-0-07-846240-5(1) , 9780078462405) Glencoe/McGraw-Hill.

—Human Heritage, Activity Workbook, Student Edition. 3rd ed. 2005. pap. 10.00 (978-0-07-869796-8(4) , 9780078697968) Glencoe/McGraw-Hill.

—Human Heritage, Reading Essentials. 3rd ed. 2005. (C). pap., stu. ed., wbk. ed. 18.00 (978-0-07-869793-7(X) , 9780078697937) Glencoe/McGraw-Hill.

—Human Heritage, Spanish Reading Essentials & Study Guide, Student Edition. 2005. pap. 18.00 (978-0-07-869627-5(5)) Glencoe/McGraw-Hill.

—Human Heritage, StudentWorks Plus. 3rd ed. 2005. cd-rom 88.64 (978-0-07-873136-5(4) , 9780078731365) Glencoe/McGraw-Hill.

—Journey Across Time. 2nd ed. 2006. stu. ed. 83.96 (***978-0-07-875050-2(4)*** , 9780078750502) Glencoe/McGraw-Hill.

—Journey Across Time: Early Ages, Course 2. 2004. (C). stu. ed. 71.96 (978-0-07-860310-5(2) , 9780078603105) Glencoe/McGraw-Hill.

—Journey Across Time, Active Reading & Note-Taking Guide. 2nd ed. 2007. pap. 18.00 (***978-0-07-878949-6(4)*** , 9780078789496) Glencoe/McGraw-Hill.

—Journey Across Time, Activity Workbook, Student Edition. 2nd ed. 2007. pap. 10.00 (***978-0-07-878954-0(0)*** , 9780078789540) Glencoe/McGraw-Hill.

—Journey Across Time, Early Ages. 2005. stu. ed. 102.00 (978-0-07-867415-0(8) , 9780078674150); 2nd ed. 2007. stu. ed. 78.00 (***978-0-07-875047-2(4)*** , 9780078750472) Glencoe/McGraw-Hill.

—Journey Across Time, Early Ages: Reading Essentials. 2004. pap., stu. ed., wbk. ed. 18.00 (978-0-07-860318-1(8) , 9780078603181) Glencoe/McGraw-Hill.

—Journey Across Time, Early Ages, Active Reading & Note-Taking Guide. 2nd ed. 2007. (C). pap. 18.00 (***978-0-07-878926-7(5)*** , 9780078789267) Glencoe/McGraw-Hill.

—Journey Across Time, Early Ages, Active Reading Note-Taking Strategies. 2004. (C). pap., stu. ed. 18.00 (978-0-07-868132-5(4) , 9780078681325) Glencoe/McGraw-Hill.

—Journey Across Time, Early Ages, Activity Workbook, Student Edition. 2nd ed. 2007. pap. 10.00 (***978-0-07-878931-1(1)*** , 9780078789311) Glencoe/McGraw-Hill.

—Journey Across Time, Early Ages, Interactive Tutor: Self-Assessment CD. 2nd ed. 2007. (C). cd-rom 93.32 (***978-0-07-878941-0(9)*** , 9780078789410) Glencoe/McGraw-Hill.

—Journey Across Time, Early Ages, Reading Essentials & Study Guide, Workbook. 2nd ed. 2007. pap. 18.00 (***978-0-07-878923-6(0)*** , 9780078789236) Glencoe/McGraw-Hill.

—Journey Across Time, Early Ages, Spanish Reading Essentials. 2004. (SPA.). (C). pap., stu. ed., wbk. ed. 18.00 (978-0-07-868194-3(4) , 9780078681943) Glencoe/McGraw-Hill.

—Journey Across Time, Early Ages, Standardized Test Practice. 2004. (C). pap., stu. ed. 10.00 (978-0-07-868191-2(X) , 9780078681912) Glencoe/McGraw-Hill.

—Journey Across Time, Early Ages, StudentWorks. 2007. (C). cd-rom 102.00 (***978-0-07-878150-6(7)*** , 9780078781506) Glencoe/McGraw-Hill.

—Journey Across Time, Interactive Tutor Self Assessment CD-ROM. 2nd ed. 2007. (C). cd-rom 93.32 (***978-0-07-878939-7(7)*** , 9780078789397) Glencoe/McGraw-Hill.

—Journey Across Time, Reading Essentials & Study Guide. 2nd ed. 2007. (C). pap. 18.00 (***978-0-07-878946-5(X)*** , 9780078789465) Glencoe/McGraw-Hill.

—Journey Across Time, Spanish. 2005. (SPA.). (C). stu. ed. 83.96 (978-0-07-873930-9(6) , 9780078739309) Glencoe/McGraw-Hill.

—Journey Across Time, Spanish Reading Essentials & Study Guide. 2nd ed. 2007. (C). pap. 18.00 (***978-0-07-878958-8(3)*** , 9780078789588) Glencoe/McGraw-Hill.

—Journey Across Time, StudentWorks Plus. 2nd ed. 2007. (C). cd-rom 107.96 (***978-0-07-878158-2(2)*** , 9780078781582) Glencoe/McGraw-Hill.

—World & Its People. 2004. (C). pap., stu. ed., wbk. ed. 10.00 (978-0-07-865502-9(1) , 9780078655029) Glencoe/McGraw-Hill.

—World & It's People. 2nd ed. 2004. (C). stu. ed. 84.64 (978-0-07-860976-3(3) , 9780078609763) Glencoe/McGraw-Hill.

—World & Its People: Eastern Hemisphere. 2004. stu. ed. 69.32 (978-0-07-865472-5(6) , 9780078654725) Glencoe/McGraw-Hill.

—The World & Its People: Standardized Test Practice. 2004. pap., stu. ed., wbk. ed. 10.00 (978-0-07-865523-4(4) , 9780078655234) Glencoe/McGraw-Hill.

—World History: Human Experience, the Early Ages. 2nd ed. 2002. stu. ed. 89.32 incl. cd-rom (978-0-07-829328-3(6) , 9780078293283) Glencoe/McGraw-Hill.

—World History: The Human Experience the Early Ages. 2002. stu. ed. 89.32 (978-0-07-828719-0(7) , 9780078287190) Glencoe/McGraw-Hill.

McGraw-Hill Staff & Spielvogel, Jackson J. Glencoe World History, 12 vols., Set. 2002. 3899p. (gr. 9-12). stu. ed. 93.72 (978-0-07-823993-9(1) , 9780078239939) Glencoe/McGraw-Hill.

McNeese, Tim, ed. Rivers in World History. 2005. (Illus.). 120p. (gr. 9-13). pap. 180.00 (978-0-7910-8473-1(6) , Chelsea Hse.) Facts On File, Inc.

McNeill, William H., et al, eds. Berkshire Encyclopedia of World History, 5 vols. 2005. (Illus.). 2500p. lib. bdg. 575.00 (978-0-9743091-0-1(9)) Berkshire Publishing Group.

Miller, Millie. Our World: A Country-by-Country Guide. 2006. (Our World Ser.). (Illus.). 112p. (J). (gr. 3-6). pap. 16.99 (978-0-439-55004-8(1) , Scholastic Reference) Scholastic, Inc.

Modern World History. 2003. (SPA.). (gr. 6-12). (978-0-618-18478-1(3) , 2-10117) McDougal Littell Inc.

Modern World History: Patterns of Interaction. 2003. (gr. 6-12). (978-0-618-18477-4(5) , 2-10116); stu. ed. (978-0-618-18465-1(1) , 2-10104); stu. ed. (978-0-618-13177-8(9) , 2-81222); wbk. ed. (978-0-618-18483-5(X) , 2-10122); tchr. ed. (978-0-618-13178-5(7) , 2-81223) McDougal Littell Inc.

Modern World History: Patterns of Interaction: Case Studies. 2001. (gr. 6-12). stu. ed. (978-0-395-93832-4(5) , 2-81047) McDougal Littell Inc.

Modern World History: Patterns of Interaction: EEdition. (gr. 6-12). 2005. cd-rom (978-0-618-43238-7(8) , 2-00804); 2003. cd-rom (978-0-618-28481-8(8) , 2-90160) McDougal Littell Inc.

Modern World History: Patterns of Interaction: EEdition Plus Online. (gr. 6-12). 2005. (978-0-618-41039-2(2) , 2-00657); 2003. (978-0-618-19414-8(2) , 2-70056) McDougal Littell Inc.

Modern World History: Patterns of Interaction: EEdition Plus Online Parent Purchase. 2003. (gr. 6-12). (978-0-618-25844-4(2) , 2-10036) McDougal Littell Inc.

Modern World History: Patterns of Interaction: EEdition Plus Online Parent Purchase-1 Year. 2005. (gr. 6-12). (978-0-618-41040-8(6) , 2-00658) McDougal Littell Inc.

Modern World History: Patterns of Interaction: EEdition Plus Online with purchase of print Pupil's Edition-1 Year. (gr. 6-12). 2005. (978-0-618-41042-2(2) , 2-00660); 2003. (978-0-618-25845-1(0) , 2-10037) McDougal Littell Inc.

Modern World History: Patterns of Interaction: EEdition Plus Online with purchase of print Pupil's Edition-2 Year. (gr. 6-12). 2005. (978-0-618-41043-9(0) , 2-00661); 2003. (978-0-618-25846-8(9) , 2-10038) McDougal Littell Inc.

Modern World History: Patterns of Interaction: EEdition Plus Online with purchase of print Pupil's Edition-3 Year. (gr. 6-12). 2005. (978-0-618-41044-6(9) , 2-00662); 2003. (978-0-618-25847-5(7) , 2-10039) McDougal Littell Inc.

Modern World History: Patterns of Interaction: EEdition Plus Online with purchase of print Pupil's Edition-4 Year. (gr. 6-12). 2005. (978-0-618-41045-3(7) , 2-00663); 2003. (978-0-618-25848-2(5) , 2-10040) McDougal Littell Inc.

Modern World History: Patterns of Interaction: EEdition Plus Online with purchase of print Pupil's Edition-5 Year. (gr. 6-12). 2005. (978-0-618-41046-0(5) , 2-00664); 2003. (978-0-618-25849-9(3) , 2-10041) McDougal Littell Inc.

Modern World History: Patterns of Interaction: EEdition Plus Online with purchase of print Pupil's Edition-6 Year. 2005. (gr. 6-12). (978-0-618-41047-7(3) , 2-00665) McDougal Littell Inc.

Modern World History: Patterns of Interaction: Modern World History: Patterns of Interaction Workbook. 2001. (gr. 6-12). (978-0-618-15640-5(2) , 2-01348) McDougal Littell Inc.

Modern World History: Patterns of Interaction: Pupil's Edition (c)1999. 2001. (gr. 6-12). (978-0-395-93829-4(5) , 2-81044) McDougal Littell Inc.

Modern World History: Patterns of Interaction: Pupil's Edition (c)2001. 2001. (gr. 6-12). (978-0-618-10820-6(3) , 2-81212) McDougal Littell Inc.

Modern World History: Patterns of Interaction: Reading Study Guide. (gr. 6-12). 2005. (978-0-618-40991-4(2) , 2-00647); 2005. (SPA.). (978-0-618-40992-1(0) , 2-00648); 2001. (978-0-395-94206-2(3) , 2-81075); 2001. (SPA.). (978-0-395-94207-9(1) , 2-81076) McDougal Littell Inc.

Modern World History: Patterns of Interaction: Reading Study Guide Answer Key. (gr. 6-12). 2005. (978-0-618-40994-5(7) , 2-00649); 2001. (978-0-395-94208-6(X) , 2-81077) McDougal Littell Inc.

Modern World Nations. 2005. 1650.00 (978-0-7910-8320-8(9) , Chelsea Hse.) Facts On File, Inc.

Modern World Nations Set, 55-Volumes. 2006. 1555.50 (978-0-7910-9330-6(1) , Chelsea Hse.) Facts On File, Inc.

Morris, Neil, et al, contrib. by. The Illustrated History of the World: From the Big Bang to the Third Millennium. 2003. (Illus.). 288p. (J). 29.95 (978-1-59270-019-6(5)) Enchanted Lion Bks., LLC.

Morter, Peter. Atlas Visual de los Descubrimientos. (SPA., Illus.). 412p. (YA). (gr. 5-8). (978-84-216-1814-1(8) , BU4892) Bruño, Editorial ESP. *Dist:* Lectorum Pubns., Inc.

Nardo, Don. The Inquisition. 2007. (World History Ser.). 128p. (gr. 7-10). 28.70 (*978-1-59018-653-4(2)) , Lucent Bks.) Thomson Gale.

Navarro, Joaquín. Gran Cronica Oceano del Siglo XX. 2000. Tr. of Oceano's Great Chronicle of the Twentieth Century. (ENG & SPA., Illus.). 716p. (gr. 9 up). cd-rom 56.00 (978-84-494-1247-9(1) , GML07104-176314) Oceano Grupo Editoria, S.A. ESP. *Dist:* Thomson Gale.

Nineteen Sixty-Eight (World History) (Illus.). 192p. (J). (978-0-7835-0152-9(8)) Time-Life Education, Inc.

Pak, Amy. History Through the Ages - Napoleon to Now: Historical Timeline Figures (1750 AD - Present) Pak, Amy, illus. 2003. (Illus.). (J). pap. 19.95 (978-0-9720265-3-6(3)) Home Schl. in the Woods.

Palos, Lilia. Acercate a la Historia 2 de la Mentalidad Imperialista Europea al Tiempo Presente: Sociedad, Vida y Cultura. 2002. (SPA.). 312p. (YA). (978-968-7903-34-7(1)) Edere, S. A. de C. V.

Patent, Dorothy Hinshaw. Frozen in Time - Group 1, 3 bks., Set. Incl. In Search of the Maiasaurs. 1998. lib. bdg. 28.50 (978-0-7614-0787-4(1) , Benchmark Bks.); Mystery of the Lascaux Cave. 64p. 1998. lib. bdg. 28.50 (978-0-7614-0784-3(7)); Secrets of the Ice Man. 72p. 1999. lib. bdg. 28.50 (978-0-7614-0782-9(0) , Benchmark Bks.); (J). (gr. 5-9). (Illus.). 1999. Set lib. bdg. 81.21 (978-0-7614-0781-2(2) , Benchmark Bks.) Cavendish, Marshall Corp.

People of the Ancient World, 6 Bks., Set. 2005. (YA). (gr. 6-8). 177.00 (978-0-531-18754-8(3) , Watts, Franklin) Scholastic Library Publishing.

People of the Ice Age: Individual Title Six-Packs. (Rigby Focus Ser.). 24p. (gr. 2 up). 28.00 (978-0-7578-5336-4(6)); 30.00 (978-0-7578-5566-5(0)) Rigby Education.

People of the Pacific Rim, 6 Packs. (Rigby Infoquest Ser.). (gr. 5 up). 37.00 (978-0-7578-6488-9(0)) Rigby Education.

People of the Past: Individual Title Six-Packs. (Rigby Infoquest Ser.). (gr. 6 up). 37.00 (978-0-7578-7989-0(6)) Rigby Education.

People Who Changed the World, 4 bks. Incl. 100 Artists Who Changed the World. Krystal, Barbara. lib. bdg. 30.00 (978-0-8368-5469-5(1)); 100 Leaders Who Changed the World. Paparchontis, Kathleen. lib. bdg. 30.00 (978-0-8368-5472-5(1)); 100 Military Leaders Who Changed the World. Crompton, Samuel Willard. lib. bdg. 30.00 (978-0-8368-5470-1(5)); 100 Scientists Who Changed the World. Tiner, John Hudson. lib. bdg. 30.00 (978-0-8368-5471-8(3)); 112p. (J). (gr. 5 up). 2003. (Illus.). 2002. Set lib. bdg. 120.00 (978-0-8368-5468-8(3) , World Almanac Library) Stevens, Gareth Inc.

Point of Impact Series, 27 bks. (J). (gr. 5-7). Set 1-4. 2003. lib. bdg. 512.80 (978-1-58810-712-1(4)); Set 3. 2002. lib. bdg. 102.56 (978-1-58810-464-9(8)); Set 4. 2003. lib. bdg. 102.56 (978-1-4034-0327-8(9)) Heinemann Library.

Porell, John. When Things Go Wrong. 2005. (Real Deal-Red Plus Ser.). (Illus.). 32p. (gr. 4-8). 19.00 (978-0-7910-8898-2(7)) Facts On File, Inc.

Primary Sources of Countries of the World: Set 1, 6 bks, Set. 2003. (Illus.). (J). 117.00 (978-0-8239-8487-9(7) , PowerKids Pr.) Rosen Publishing Group, Inc., The.

Primary Sources of Countries of the World: Set 2, 6 bks., Set. 2003. (Illus.). (J). 117.00 (978-0-8239-7277-7(1) , PowerKids Pr.) Rosen Publishing Group, Inc., The.

Quick Revision KS3 History. Quick Revision KS3 History. 2007. 46p. pap. 9.95 (*978-0-340-94309-0(2)) , Hodder Murray) Hodder Education GBR. *Dist:* Trans-Atlantic Pubns., Inc.

Quintero, Ednodio. El Sur. (SPA.). (J). pap. (978-980-01-1011-9(9)) Monte Avila Editores Latinoamericana CA VEN. *Dist:* Lectorum Pubns., Inc.

Raintree Steck-Vaughn Staff. Nations of the World. 2000. (YA). 137.00 (978-0-8172-5787-3(X)) Raintree.

Raintree Steck-Vaughn Staff, ed. We Come From... 1999. (Illus.). (J). 154.14 (978-0-8172-5222-9(3)) Raintree.

Ramifications. 2005. pap. 720.00 (978-0-7910-9183-8(X) , Chelsea Hse.) Facts On File, Inc.

Reformation: PowerPoint Presentation in World History. 2005. cd-rom 49.95 net. (978-1-56004-216-7(8)) Social Studies Schl. Service.

Renaissance Politics/Economics DBA. 2002. spiral bd. 16.95 (978-1-56004-140-5(4)) Social Studies Schl. Service.

Rice, Chris & Rice, Melanie. How Children Lived. 2005. (Illus.). 48p. (J). pap. 7.99 (978-0-7566-1806-3(1)) Dorling Kindersley Publishing, Inc.

Rigby Education Staff. Discovery World. (Illus.). 68.00 (978-0-7635-8444-3(4)) Rigby Education.

—Discovery World Orange Encyclopedia: Tiny Big Book. (Discovery World Ser.). 12p. (gr. 1-2). 27.00 (978-0-7635-2702-0(5)) Rigby Education.

Rirdan, Daniel. Tucky Tum World Set: Essential Edition. Trail, Nubia & McDonough, Tom, eds. 1999. (Illus.). 150p. (J). (gr. 3-6). 29.95 (978-0-9670889-0-7(9)) Tucky Tum.

Road to War: Causes of Conflict, 5 vols., Set. Incl. Causes of the American Revolution. Strum, Richard M. 64p. (J). lib. bdg. 22.95 (978-1-59556-001-8(7)); Causes of the Civil War. Epperson, James F. 64p. (J). lib. bdg. 22.95 (978-1-59556-002-5(5)); Causes of the Iraq War. Gallagher, Jim. 72p. (J). lib. bdg. 22.95 (978-1-59556-009-4(2)); Causes of World War I. Ziff, John. 72p. (J). lib. bdg. 22.95 (978-1-59556-003-2(3)); Causes of World War II. Corrigan, Jim. 64p. lib. bdg. 22.95 (978-1-59556-004-9(1)); (gr. 4 up). 2005. (Road to War Ser.). (Illus.). 64p. 2005. Set lib. bdg. 114.75 (978-1-59556-000-1(9)) OTTN Publishing.

Roberts, J. M. The Illustrated History of the World, 11 vols., Set. 2000. (Illus.). 1968p. (YA). 375.00 (978-0-19-521698-1(9)) Oxford Univ. Pr., Inc.

Rountree, Elizabeth. Story of the World, Vol. 4 tests. 2007. 176p. pap. 12.95 (978-1-933339-02-3(0)) Peace Hill Pr.

Saari, Peggy, ed. U X L History Fact Finder, 3 vols. 2001. (Illus.). xxxi, 620p. (J). (978-0-7876-4844-2(2) , UXL) Thomson Gale.

—U-X-L History Fact Finder, 3 vols., Set. 2001. (Illus.). xxxi, 620p. (J). lib. bdg. 181.00 (978-0-7876-4843-5(4) , GML00602-114887, UXL) Thomson Gale.

Scientific Revolution: PowerPoints in World History. 2005. cd-rom 49.95 net. (978-1-56004-215-0(X)) Social Studies Schl. Service.

Shoreline Publishing Group Staff. Great Empires of the Past Set 2. 2005. (Great Empires of the Past Ser.). 128-128p. (gr. 9-12). 140.00 (978-0-8160-5576-0(9)) Facts On File, Inc.

SHP History: A Schools History Project Course for Year 7. 2006. (Illus.). 240p. pap. (*978-0-340-90733-7(9)) Hodder General Publishing Division.

Shukin, Barbara. Modern History Portfolio: A History of America & the World from the 17th to the 21st Centuries. 2004. (J). spiral bd. 24.95 (978-0-9762918-3-1(5)) Homeschool Journey.

Snapshots in History. 2006. (Illus.). (J). (gr. 5-7). 183.60 (978-0-7565-1706-9(0)) Compass Point Bks.

Sonneborn, Liz. The Ancient Kushites. 2005. (People of the Ancient World Ser.). (Illus.). (J). (gr. 6-8). 112p. pap. 9.95 (978-0-531-16847-9(6)); 111p. 30.50 (978-0-531-12380-5(4)) Scholastic Library Publishing. (Watts, Franklin).

Steck-Vaughn Staff. History of Our World. 2003. (J). pap., tchr. ed. 68.00 (978-0-7398-6088-5(7)) Steck-Vaughn.

—History of Our World: Chapter Resource Book. 2002. (J). pap. (978-0-7398-5742-7(8)) Steck-Vaughn.

—Social Studies: US & World History, Geography. 2002. (Illus.). pap. (978-0-7398-5426-6(7)) Steck-Vaughn.

—Step into History: Book Pack. 2001. (J). (gr. 4). pap. 30.00 (978-1-58702-689-8(9)) Johnston, Don Inc.

—Step into History: Reading Group Pack. 2001. (J). (gr. 4). pap. 399.00 (978-1-58702-688-1(0)) Johnston, Don Inc.

—Step into History: Single User Packs. 2001. (J). (gr. 4). pap. 174.00 (978-1-58702-687-4(2)) Johnston, Don Inc.

—World History & You. 2001. (J). pap., tchr. ed. (978-0-7398-3622-4(6)) Steck-Vaughn.

Steele, Philip, et al. Great Civilizations of the East. 2001. (Illustrated History Encyclopedia Ser.). (Illus.). 256p. pap. 19.95 (978-1-84215-364-2(1) , Southwater) Anness Publishing GBR. *Dist:* National Bk. Network.

Stich, Paul, et al. Global History: Geopolitical Patterns & Cultural Diffusion. Garnsey, Wayne, ed. 1998. (ENG., Illus.). 352p. (YA). (gr. 8-12). per. 19.95 (978-0-935487-66-4(2)) N&N Publishing Co., Inc.

Story of the Middle Ages, Answer Key. 2002. (J). 4.00 (978-1-930367-78-4(3) , CLP79961) Christian Liberty Pr.

Story of the Middle Ages, Tests. 2002. (J). 3.00 (978-1-930367-79-1(1) , CLP79962) Christian Liberty Pr.

Strange Histories Series, 5 vols., Set. 2003. 128.50 (978-0-7398-6444-9(0)) Raintree.

Student History Notebook Of. 2004. 12.95 (978-0-9663722-3-6(9)) Coffee Hse. Ink.

Synge, M. B. The Discovery of New Worlds (Yesterday's Classics) Synge, E. M., illus. l.t. ed. 2006. 252p. (J). per. (978-1-59915-014-7(X)) Yesterday's Classics.

—The Struggle for Sea Power (Yesterday's Classics) Synge, E. M., illus. l.t. ed. 2006. 276p. (J). per. 11.95 (978-1-59915-016-1(6)) Yesterday's Classics.

Tames, Richard. Tell Me Why Didn't Mummies Have Brains? And More about History. 2004. (Illus.). 32p. (J). pap. (978-1-84458-059-0(8)) Chrysalis Children's Bks.

—The 1930s. 2005. (Picture History of the 20th Century Ser.). (Illus.). 48p. (J). (gr. 6-9). lib. bdg. 29.95 (978-1-932889-71-0(X)) Sea-To-Sea Pubns.

—The 1950s. 2005. (Picture History of the 20th Century Ser.). (Illus.). 48p. (J). (gr. 6-9). lib. bdg. 29.95 (978-1-932889-73-4(6)) Sea-To-Sea Pubns.

—The 1980s. 2005. (Picture History of the 20th Century Ser.). (Illus.). 48p. (J). (gr. 6-9). lib. bdg. 29.95 (978-1-932889-76-5(0)) Sea-To-Sea Pubns.

Thornton, Brian. Everything Kids' States Book: Wind your way across our great Nation. 2007. 144p. pap. 7.95 (978-1-59869-263-1(1)) Adams Media Corp.

Thunder from Above. (Illus.). 192p. (J). (978-0-7835-0155-0(2)) Time-Life Education, Inc.

Trembinski, Donna. Medieval Myths, Legends & Songs. 2005. (Medieval World Ser.). (Illus.). 32p. (J). (gr. 4-9). pap. (978-0-7787-1391-3(1)) Crabtree Publishing Co.

Troubled World, 9 vols., Sets 1&2. 2004. 257.04 (978-1-4109-0186-6(6)) Raintree.

Troubled World Package, 6 vols. 2003. (Illus.). (J). 41.98 (978-1-4109-0082-1(7)) Raintree.

Turner, Tracey. Foul Facts from the Perilous Past. 2007. (Illus.). 147p. pap. 14.95 (*978-1-85074-992-9(2)) English Heritage GBR. *Dist:* Brown, David Bk. Co., The.

Twentieth Century Perspectives, 10 bks. 2002. 48p. (J). (gr. 5-7). Set. 71.55 ; Set 2. 25.62 Heinemann Library.

Understanding History: Concepts & Skills. 2006. 19.50 net. (978-1-56004-263-1(X)) Social Studies Schl. Service.

Understanding People in the Past, 5 bks. (J). (gr. 4-6). Set 1. lib. bdg. 135.35 (978-1-57572-891-9(5)); Set 1-3. 2003. lib. bdg. 370.50 (978-1-4034-0390-2(2)); Set 3. 2003. lib. bdg. 114.00 (978-1-4034-0391-9(0)) Heinemann Library.

van Loon, Hendrik. The Story of Mankind. 2006. 31.95 (*978-1-59605-956-6(7)) , Cosimo Classics) Cosimo, Inc.

Van Loon, Hendrik Willem. The Story of Mankind. 1999. (gr. 7-12). lib. bdg. 24.55 (978-0-613-88011-4(0)) Tandem Library Bks.

—The Story of Mankind. 2003. xxiv, 548p. pap. 29.00 (978-0-7581-9568-5(0)) Textbook Pubs.

Van Loon, Hendrik Willem & Merriman, John M. The Story of Mankind. 4th rev. ed. 1998. (Illus.). 704p. (J). (gr. 8-12). 32.95 (978-0-87140-171-7(1)) Liveright Publishing Corp.

Visions of History SPICE. 115p. (YA). (gr. 5-9). spiral bd., tchr.'s planning gde. ed. 39.95 (978-0-382-40952-3(3)) Cobblestone Publishing Co.

Visions of History SPICE: Grades 5-9. 115p. (YA). (gr. 5-9). tchr. ed. 48.95 (978-0-382-40953-0(1)) Cobblestone Publishing Co.

Visiting the Past Series, 14 bks. 2003. (gr. 5-7). Set 1-3. lib. bdg. 358.96 (978-1-58810-710-7(8)); Set 3. lib. bdg. 102.56 (978-1-58810-709-1(4)) Heinemann Library.

Wagner, Katherine. Life on an Indian Reservation. 2004. (Way People Live Ser.). (Illus.). 112p. (YA). (gr. 7-10). lib. bdg. 29.95 (978-1-59018-155-3(7) , 1234038) Thomson Gale.

Waring, Diana. Romans, Reformers, Revolutionaries Bk. B: A Digging Deeper Study Guide. 1998. 189p. (J). pap., stu. ed. 22.95 (978-1-930514-06-5(9)) Diana Waring Presents.

—Romans, Reformers, Revolutionaries Elementary Activity Book. Waring, Isaac, illus. 2nd l.t. ed. 2001. 96p. (J). per. 11.95 (978-1-930514-14-0(X) , RRA) Diana Waring Presents.

—World Empires, World Missions, World Wars Bk. C: A Digging Deeper Study Guide. 1999. 186p. (J). pap., stu. ed. 22.95 (978-1-930514-12-6(3)) Diana Waring Presents.

Waugh, Steven. Essential Modern World History. 2001. (Illus.). 640p. (YA). (gr. 9-11). pap. 47.50 (978-0-7487-6006-0(7)) Nelson Thornes Ltd. GBR. *Dist:* Trans-Atlantic Pubns., Inc.

We the People Series, 75 bks., Set. 2005. (J). (gr. 4-8). 1794.75 (978-0-7565-1395-5(2)) Compass Point Bks.

Why We Left, 6 bks. 1999. (Illus.). (gr. 1-9). 95.88 (978-0-8114-5611-1(0)) Raintree.

Wilkinson, Philip. Civilizations, Exploration & Conquest: The Illustrated History Encyclopedia. 2001. (gr. 3-6). lib. bdg. 30.35 (978-0-613-82097-4(5)) Tandem Library Bks.

Williams, Brenda. El Libro de los Records Atraves de la Historia. 2001. Tr. of Book of Records Through History. (SPA.). 64p. (978-84-305-7136-9(1)) Lectorum Pubns., Inc.

Williams, Brian. History: Biggest & Best. 2004. (Biggest & Best Ser.). (Illus.). 40p. (J). pap. 7.95 (978-1-84236-065-1(5)) Miles Kelly Publishing, Ltd. GBR. *Dist:* Independent Pubs. Group.

—Natural World: Biggest & Best. 2004. (Biggest & Best Ser.). (Illus.). 40p. (J). pap. 7.95 (978-1-84236-061-3(2)) Miles Kelly Publishing, Ltd. GBR. *Dist:* Independent Pubs. Group.

Willner, Mark. World History. 1999. 752p. 32.95 (978-0-7641-5191-0(6)); 2 vols. 848p. pap. 26.95 (978-0-7641-1054-2(3)) Barron's Educational Series, Inc.

The World. 2001. (Our World Ser.). (J). (gr. k-12). vinyl bd. 4.95 (978-1-58845-071-5(6)) School Specialty Publishing.

World Book, Inc. Staff. Connections, 6 vols., Set. 2001. 32p. (J). (gr. 3-8). 40.50 (978-0-7166-1323-7(9) , 30024) World Bk., Inc.

World Empires, World Missions, World Wars Elementary Activity Book. 2001. (J). per. 11.95 (978-1-930514-15-7(8) , WWA) Diana Waring Presents.

World History: Patterns of Interaction. 2003. (gr. 6-12). stu. ed. (978-0-618-13179-2(5) ; 2-81224) McDougal Littell Inc.

World History: Patterns of Interaction. 2005. (gr. 6-12). tchr. ed. (978-0-618-37774-9(3) , 2-00552) McDougal Littell Inc.

World History: Patterns of Interaction: EEdition. 2005. (gr. 6-12). cd-rom (978-0-618-42870-0(4) , 2-00769) McDougal Littell Inc.

World History: Patterns of Interaction: EEdition Plus Online. (gr. 6-12). 2005. (978-0-618-40923-5(8) , 2-00604); 2003. (978-0-618-19415-5(0) , 2-70057) McDougal Littell Inc.

World History: Patterns of Interaction: EEdition Plus Online Parent Purchase-1 Year. 2005. (gr. 6-12). (978-0-618-40924-2(6) , 2-00605) McDougal Littell Inc.

World History: Patterns of Interaction: EEdition Plus Online with purchase of print Pupil's Edition-1 Year. 2005. (gr. 6-12). (978-0-618-40925-9(4) , 2-00606) McDougal Littell Inc.

World History: Patterns of Interaction: EEdition Plus Online with Purchase of Print Pupil's Edition-1 Year. 2003. (gr. 6-12). (978-0-618-25863-5(9) , 2-01416) McDougal Littell Inc.

World History: Patterns of Interaction: EEdition Plus Online with purchase of print Pupil's Edition-2 Year. 2005. (gr. 6-12). (978-0-618-40926-6(2) , 2-00607) McDougal Littell Inc.

World History: Patterns of Interaction: EEdition Plus Online with Purchase of Print Pupil's Edition-2 Year. 2003. (gr. 6-12). (978-0-618-25864-2(7) , 2-01417) McDougal Littell Inc.

World History: Patterns of Interaction: EEdition Plus Online with purchase of print Pupil's Edition-3 Year. 2005. (gr. 6-12). (978-0-618-40927-3(0) , 2-00608) McDougal Littell Inc.

World History: Patterns of Interaction: EEdition Plus Online with Purchase of Print Pupil's Edition-3 Year. 2003. (gr. 6-12). (978-0-618-25865-9(5) , 2-01418) McDougal Littell Inc.

World History: Patterns of Interaction: EEdition Plus Online with purchase of print Pupil's Edition-4 Year. 2005. (gr. 6-12). (978-0-618-40960-0(2) , 2-00622) McDougal Littell Inc.

World History: Patterns of Interaction: EEdition Plus Online with Purchase of Print Pupil's Edition-4 Year. 2003. (gr. 6-12). (978-0-618-25866-6(3) , 2-01419) McDougal Littell Inc.

World History: Patterns of Interaction: EEdition Plus Online with purchase of print Pupil's Edition-5 Year. 2005. (gr. 6-12). (978-0-618-40961-7(0) , 2-00623) McDougal Littell Inc.

World History: Patterns of Interaction: EEdition Plus Online with Purchase of Print Pupil's Edition-5 Year. 2003. (gr. 6-12). (978-0-618-25867-3(1) , 2-01420) McDougal Littell Inc.

World History: Patterns of Interaction: EEdition Plus Online with purchase of print Pupil's Edition-6 Year. 2005. (gr. 6-12). (978-0-618-40962-4(9) , 2-00624) McDougal Littell Inc.

World History: Patterns of Interaction: Electronic Library of Primary Sources. (gr. 6-12). 2005. cd-rom (978-0-618-42871-7(2) , 2-00770); 2003. cd-rom (978-0-618-18619-8(0) , 2-01392) McDougal Littell Inc.

World History: Patterns of Interaction: Net Activities. 2001. (gr. 6-12). cd-rom (978-0-395-95567-3(X) , 2-81098) McDougal Littell Inc.

World History: Patterns of Interaction: Pupil's Edition (c)1999. 2001. (gr. 6-12). (978-0-395-87274-1(X) , 2-80400) McDougal Littell Inc.

World History: Patterns of Interaction: Pupil's Edition (c)2001. 2001. (gr. 6-12). (978-0-618-10823-7(8) , 2-81215) McDougal Littell Inc.

World History: Patterns of Interaction: Reading Study Guide. (gr. 6-12). 2005. (978-0-618-40933-4(5) , 2-00614); 2005. (SPA.). (978-0-618-40934-1(3) , 2-00615); 2003. (978-0-618-18289-3(6) , 2-01371); 2003. (SPA.). (978-0-618-18291-6(8) , 2-01372); 2001. (978-0-395-95204-7(2) , 2-81090); 2001. (SPA.). (978-0-395-95205-4(0) , 2-81091) McDougal Littell Inc.

World History: Patterns of Interaction: Reading Study Guide Answer Key. (gr. 6-12). 2005. (978-0-618-40932-7(7) , 2-00613); 2003. (978-0-618-18288-6(8) , 2-01370); 2001. (978-0-395-95206-1(9) , 2-81092) McDougal Littell Inc.

World History: Patterns of Interaction: World History: Electronic Library of Primary Sources. 2001. (gr. 6-12). cd-rom (978-0-395-89894-9(3) , 2-80422) McDougal Littell Inc.

World History: Patterns of Interaction: World History: Patterns of Interaction Workbook. (gr. 6-12). 2005. (978-0-618-40938-9(6) , 2-00619); 2001. (978-0-618-15639-9(9) , 2-01347) McDougal Littell Inc.

World History: Patterns of Interaction: World History: Patterns of Interaction Workbook Answer Key. (gr. 6-12). 2005. (978-0-618-40939-6(4) , 2-00620); 2001. (978-0-618-15638-2(0) , 2-01346) McDougal Littell Inc.

World History: Patterns of Interaction: World History Workbook. 2003. (gr. 6-12). (978-0-395-95209-2(3) , 2-81095) McDougal Littell Inc.

World History: Patterns of Interaction: World History Workbook Answer Key. 2003. (gr. 6-12). (978-0-395-95208-5(5) , 2-81094) McDougal Littell Inc.

World History Syllabus. 1999. 14p. (YA). ring bd. 2.95 (978-1-57896-052-1(5) , 1892, Hewitt Homeschooling Resources) Hewitt Research Foundation, Inc.

The World in the Time Of ... 2005. 48p. pap. 160.65 (978-0-7910-8407-6(8) , Chelsea Hse.) Facts On File, Inc.

World in the Time of... Set. 2000. (J). 143.60 (978-0-7910-6036-0(5) , Chelsea Hse.) Facts On File, Inc.

World Tour, 6 bks. 2002. (YA). 145.56 (978-0-7398-5770-0(3)) Raintree.

World View: A Global Study of Geography, History & Culture, Bk. 2. stu. ed. 21.95 (978-0-916591-45-8(X)) Linmore Publishing, Inc.

The World Wars Series, 10 bks., Set. 2003. 285.60 (978-0-7398-5484-6(4)); (Illus.). 114.24 (978-0-7398-5483-9(6)) Raintree.

The World Wars Series, 6 bks., Set. Incl. Great Battles of World War II. Hansen, Ole Steen. lib. bdg. 27.12 (978-0-7398-2757-4(X)); Leaders of World War II. Ross, Stewart. lib. bdg. 27.12 (978-0-7398-2756-7(1)); World War I : Armistice 1918. Grant, R. G. lib. bdg. 27.12 (978-0-7398-2753-6(7)); World War I : War in the Trenches. Hansen, Ole Steen. lib. bdg. 27.12 (978-0-7398-2752-9(9)); World War II : Allied Victory. Sheehan, Sean. lib. bdg. 27.12 (978-0-7398-2755-0(3)); World War II : Germany & Japan Attack. Sheehan, Sean. Sloan, Frank, ed. lib. bdg. 27.12 (978-0-7398-2754-3(5)); 64p. (J). (gr. 5). (Illus.). 2001. Set lib. bdg. 171.36 (978-0-7398-2758-1(8)) Raintree.

You Are There, Set 1. 2004. pap. 27.00 (978-1-4109-1399-9(6)) Raintree.

Zacharias, Gary. Events That Changed the World - 1900-1920. 2003. (Illus.). 224p. pap. 22.45 (978-0-7377-1753-2(X)) Thomson Gale.

19th Century Nationalism. 2003. spiral bd. 16.95 (978-1-56004-171-9(4)) Social Studies Schl. Service.

20th Century History Makers Series, 12 vols., Set. 2003. (Illus.). 394.20 (978-0-7398-6145-5(X)) Raintree.

21st Century Issues, 6 Vols. 180.00 (978-0-8368-5640-8(6)) Stevens, Gareth Inc.

WORLD ORGANIZATION

see International Organization

WORLD POLITICS

see also International Organization; International Relations; World War, 1939-1945

also names of countries with the subdivisions Foreign Relations and Politics and Government, e.g. United States—Foreign Relations; United States—Politics and Government

Arbitrary Borders: Political Boundaries in World History. 2005. 112p. 420.00 (978-0-7910-8746-6(8) , Chelsea Hse.) Facts On File, Inc.

Aronson, Marc. The Real Revolution: The Global Story of American Independence. 2005. (Illus.). 256p. (J). (gr. 7-12). 21.00 (978-0-618-18179-7(2) , Clarion Bks.) Houghton Mifflin Co. Trade & Reference Div.

Baker, Lawrence W. Cold War Reference Library Cumulative Index. 2003. (U-X-L Cold War Reference Library). 85p. (J). 5.00 (978-0-7876-7667-4(5) , UXL) Thomson Gale.

—Immigration & Migration Reference. 2003. (U-X-L Cold War Reference Library). (J). 5.00 (978-0-7876-7734-3(5)) Zagat Survey.

Bjornlund, Britta. The Cold War. 2002. (World History Ser.). (Illus.). 112p. (J). (gr. 8-11). 27.45 (978-1-59018-003-7(8) , LML00902-178725, Lucent Bks.) Thomson Gale.

Bussey, Jennifer A. 1960-1980 The Twentieth Century. 2003. (Illus.). 176p. lib. bdg. 36.20 (978-0-7377-1758-7(0)) Thomson Gale.

Chrisp, Peter. The Cuban Missile Crisis. 2002. (Cold War Ser.). (Illus.). 64p. (YA). (gr. 7 up). lib. bdg. 32.67 (978-0-8368-5273-8(7) , World Almanac Library) Stevens, Gareth Inc.

—Cuban Missile Crisis. 2002. (gr. 7-12). lib. bdg. 24.15 (978-0-613-52355-4(5)) Tandem Library Bks.

Downing, David. The Great Depression. (20th Century Perspectives Ser.). (Illus.). 48p. (J). 2001. (gr. 4-7). lib. bdg. 25.64 (978-1-57572-435-5(9)); Set 1. 2002. (gr. 5-7). pap. 7.95 (978-1-58810-374-1(9) , 91126) Heinemann Library.

—The Great Depression. 2001. (YA). 15.30 (978-0-606-22492-5(0)) Tandem Library Bks.

Durrell, Ann & Sachs, Marilyn, eds. The Big Book for Peace. 2002. (Illus.). 120p. (J). (gr. 4-7). reprint ed. 27.00 (978-0-7567-5337-5(6)) DIANE Publishing Co.

Egan, Tracie. Weapons of Mass Destruction & North Korea. 2004. (Library of Weapons of Mass Destruction). (Illus.). 64p. (J). lib. bdg. 26.50 (978-1-4042-0296-2(X)) Rosen Publishing Group, Inc., The.

Fleischman, Paul. Dateline: Troy. Frankfeldt, Gwen & Morrow, Glenn, illus. ed. 2006. 80p. (J). (gr. 7-11). 18.99 (978-0-7636-3083-6(7)) Candlewick Pr.

—Dateline: Troy. Frankfeldt, Gwen & Morrow, Glenn, illus. ed. 2006. 80p. (YA). (gr. 7-11). pap. 7.99 (978-0-7636-3084-3(5)) Candlewick Pr.

Frank, Mitch. Understanding September 11th: Answering Questions about the Attacks on America. 2002. (Illus.). 176p. (gr. 6 up). (J). pap. 8.99 (978-0-670-03587-8(4)); (YA). 16.99 (978-0-670-03582-3(3)) Penguin Group (USA) Inc. (Viking Juvenile).

—Understanding September 11th: Answering Questions about the Attacks on America. 2002. (gr. 5-8). lib. bdg. 17.60 (978-0-613-50113-2(6)) Tandem Library Bks.

Gottfried, Ted. The Cold War. 2003. (Rise & Fall of the Soviet Union Ser.). (Illus.). 160p. (gr. 7 up). lib. bdg. 28.90 (978-0-7613-2560-4(3) , Twenty-First Century Bks.) Lerner Publishing Group.

Grant, R. G. The Great Depression. 2005. (How Did It Happen? Ser.). (Illus.). 48p. (YA). (gr. 7-10). lib. bdg. 29.95 (978-1-59018-606-0(0) , Lucent Bks.) Thomson Gale.

Grapes, Bryan J. Events That Changed the World - 1980-2000. 2003. (Illus.). 187p. lib. bdg. 36.20 (978-0-7377-1760-0(2)) Thomson Gale.

Gunderson, Cory Gideon. The Need for Oil. 2004. (World in Conflict-the Middle East Ser.). (Illus.). 48p. (J). (gr. 4-8). lib. bdg. 25.65 (978-1-59197-417-8(8)) ABDO Publishing Co.

Hanes, Sharon M., et al. Cold War: Almanac, 2 vols. 2003. (Cold War Reference Library). (Illus.). (J). 200p. 55.00 (978-0-7876-7662-9(4)); (978-0-7876-9087-8(2)); lib. bdg. 120.00 (978-0-7876-9089-2(9)) Thomson Gale. (UXL).

Harrison, Paul. The Cold War. 2005. (How Did It Happen? Ser.). (Illus.). 48p. (J). (gr. 7-10). 29.95 (978-1-59018-603-9(6) , Lucent Bks.) Thomson Gale.

Hasan, Tahara. Anthrax Attacks Around the World. 2005. (Terrorist Attacks Ser.). (Illus.). 64p. (YA). (gr. 7-12). lib. bdg. 26.50 (978-0-8239-3859-9(X)) Rosen Publishing Group, Inc., The.

Hatt, Christine. The End of the Cold War. 2002. (Cold War Ser.). (Illus.). 64p. (YA). (gr. 7 up). pap. 14.60 (978-0-8368-5280-6(X)); lib. bdg. 32.67 (978-0-8368-5275-2(3)) Stevens, Gareth Inc. (World Almanac Library).

Landau, Elaine. The New Nuclear Reality. 2000. (Single Titles Ser.: up). (Illus.). 128p. (gr. 7 up). lib. bdg. (978-0-7613-1555-1(1) , Millbrook Pr.) Lerner Publishing Group.

Lawler, Rick. How to Contact World Leaders: 2003 Edition. 2003. 218p. pap. 18.95 (978-1-930322-06-6(2)) MinRef Pr.

—How to Contact World Leaders 2002 Edition: Write * Phone * Fax * E-mail. annual 2002. (C). pap. 18.95 (978-1-930322-04-2(6) , 1930322046) MinRef Pr.

Maybury, Richard J. World War II: The Rest of the Story & How It Affects You Today, 1930 to September 11 2001. Williams, Jane A., ed. rev. ed. 2003. ("Uncle Eric" Bk.). 349p. (YA). pap. 19.95 (978-0-942617-43-6(6)) Bluestocking Pr.

Nations of the World, 18 bks., Set. Incl. Argentina. Dalai, Anita. (YA). 2000. lib. bdg. 34.26 (978-0-7398-1279-2(3)); Australia. Darlington, Robert A. (J). 2000. lib. bdg. 34.26 (978-0-7398-1280-8(7)); Brazil. Dalal, Anita. Kossmann, Walter, ed. (YA). 2001. lib. bdg. 34.26 (978-0-7398-1284-6(X)); Canada. Nickles, Greg & Walker, Niki. (YA). 2000. lib. bdg. 34.26 (978-0-8172-5780-4(2)); China. Fields, Catherine. (YA). 2000. lib. bdg. 34.26 (978-0-8172-5781-1(0)); Egypt. Wilson, Neil. (J). 2001. lib. bdg. 34.26 (978-0-7398-1283-9(1)); France. Ingham, Richard. (YA). 2000. lib. bdg. 34.26 (978-0-8172-5782-8(9)); Germany. Nickles, Greg & Walker, Niki. (J). 2001. lib. bdg. 34.26 (978-0-7398-1285-3(8)); India. Dalal, Anita. (YA). 2001. lib. bdg. 34.26 (978-0-7398-1289-1(0)); Israel. Green, Jen. (YA). 2001. lib. bdg. 34.26 (978-0-7398-1286-0(6)); Italy. Cassidy, Picot. (YA). 2001. lib. bdg. 34.26 (978-0-7398-1287-7(4)); Japan. Green, Jen. (YA). 2000. lib. bdg. 34.26 (978-0-8172-5783-5(7)); Kenya. Giles, Bridget. (YA). 2001. lib. bdg. 34.26 (978-0-7398-1290-7(4)); Mexico. Green, Jen. (YA). 2000. lib. bdg. 34.26 (978-0-8172-5779-8(9)); Russia. Wilson, Neil. (J). 2000. lib. bdg. 34.26 (978-0-7398-1281-5(5)); South Africa. Green, Jen. (J). 2000. lib. bdg. 34.26 (978-0-7398-1282-2(3)); Sweden. Butler, Roberta. (J). 2000. lib. bdg. 34.26 (978-0-8172-5784-2(5)); United Kingdom. Innes, Brian. (YA). 2001. lib. bdg. 34.26 (978-0-7398-1288-4(2)); 128p. (gr. 6-8). (Illus.). 2001. Set lib. bdg. 616.68 (978-0-7398-4327-7(3)) Raintree.

Nelson, Sheila. Decolonization: Dismantling Empires & Building Independence. 2007. (United Nations Ser.). (Illus.). 88p. (YA). (gr. 5 up). lib. bdg. 21.95 (978-1-4222-0066-7(3)) Mason Crest Pubs.

Olson, Steven P. The International Atomic Energy Agency. 2004. (Library of Weapons of Mass Destruction). (Illus.). 64p. (J). lib. bdg. 26.50 (978-1-4042-0294-8(3)) Rosen Publishing Group, Inc., The.

Phillips, Tracy A. Weapons of Mass Destruction: The Threat of Chemical, Biological, & Nuclear Weapons. 2007. (Issues in Focus Today Ser.). (Illus.). 104p. (J). (gr. 6). lib. bdg. 31.93 (***978-0-7660-2685-8(X)***) Enslow Pubs., Inc.

Porterfield, Jason. Communism: A Primary Source Analysis. 2003. (Primary Sources of Political Systems Ser.). (Illus.). 64p. (J). 29.25 (978-0-8239-4517-7(0)) Rosen Publishing Group, Inc., The.

Ross, Stewart. The Causes of the Cold War. 2002. (Cold War Ser.). (Illus.). 64p. (YA). (gr. 7 up). pap. 14.60 (978-0-8368-5277-6(X)); lib. bdg. 32.67 (978-0-8368-5272-1(9)) Stevens, Gareth Inc. (World Almanac Library).

—The Cuban Missile Crisis: To the Brink of World War III. 2001. (Point of Impact Ser.). (Illus.). 32p. (J). (gr. 5-7). lib. bdg. 24.22 (978-1-58810-075-7(8)) Heinemann Library.

Sherman, Josepha. The Cold War. 2004. (Chronicle of America's Wars Ser.). (Illus.). 96p. (J). (gr. 5-12). 27.93 (978-0-8225-0150-3(3)) Lerner Publishing Group.

Smith, Jeremy. The Fall of the Berlin Wall. 2004. (Days That Changed the World Ser.). (Illus.). 48p. (J). (gr. 5 up). pap. 11.95 (978-0-8368-5576-0(0)); lib. bdg. 30.00 (978-0-8368-5569-2(8)) Stevens, Gareth Inc. (World Almanac Library).

Stanley, George Edward. An Emerging World Power (1900-1929) 2005. (Illus.). 48p. (J). pap. (978-0-8368-5837-2(9)); lib. bdg. 30.00 (978-0-8368-5828-0(X)) Stevens, Gareth Inc. (World Almanac Library).

Stein, R. Conrad. The Cold War: A MyReportLinks.com Book. 2002. (U. S. Wars Ser.). (Illus.). 48p. (J). (gr. 4-10). lib. bdg. 25.26 (978-0-7660-5095-2(5) , MyReportLinks.com Bks.) Enslow Pubs., Inc.

Stites, Bill. Democracy: A Primary Source Analysis. 2003. (Primary Sources of Political Systems Ser.). (Illus.). 64p. (J). lib. bdg. 29.25 (978-0-8239-4518-4(9)) Rosen Publishing Group, Inc., The.

Strum, Richard M. Causes of the American Revolution. 2005. (Road to War Ser.). (Illus.). 64p. (J). pap. 12.95 (978-1-59556-005-6(X)); (gr. 4 up). lib. bdg. 22.95 (978-1-59556-001-8(7)) OTTN Publishing.

Taylor, David. The Cold War. 2001. (20th Century Perspectives Ser.). (Illus.). 48p. (J). (gr. 5-7). lib. bdg. 25.64 (978-1-57572-434-8(0)) Heinemann Library.

—The Cold War. 2001. (YA). 14.75 (978-0-606-22491-8(2)) Tandem Library Bks.

—Cold War. 2001. (gr. 5-8). lib. bdg. 16.40 (978-0-613-58210-0(1)) Tandem Library Bks.

—The Cold War, Set 1. 2002. (20th Century Perspectives Ser.). (Illus.). 48p. (J). (gr. 5-7). pap. 7.95 (978-1-58810-373-4(0) , 91125) Heinemann Library.

Tripp, Penny. Human Rights. (Illus.). 64p. (YA). (gr. 5 up). lib. bdg. 29.95 (978-1-931983-82-2(8)) Chrysalis Education.

Uschan, Michael V. Political Leaders. 2002. (American War Library). (Illus.). 112p. (J). 29.95 (978-1-59018-211-6(1) , Lucent Bks.) Thomson Gale.

Walker, Tim. International Relations: Understanding the Behavior of Nations. 4th ed. 2001. (Illus.). 95p. (J). 13.95 (978-0-932765-97-0(1)) Close Up Foundation.

Wolny, Philip. Colonialism: A Primary Source Analysis. 2003. (Primary Sources of Political Systems Ser.). (Illus.). 64p. (J). lib. bdg. 29.25 (978-0-8239-4516-0(2)) Rosen Publishing Group, Inc., The.

Young, Mitch. Turning Points in World History Anthology. 2003. (Turning Points in World History Ser.). (Illus.). 224p. (YA). (gr. 9-12). pap. 24.95 (978-0-7377-1471-5(9) , Greenhaven Pr., Inc.) Thomson Gale.

—War on Terrorism. 2003. (Turning Points in World History Ser.). (Illus.). 224p. (YA). (gr. 9-12). lib. bdg. 37.45 (978-0-7377-1470-8(0) , Greenhaven Pr., Inc.) Thomson Gale.

WORLD RECORDS

Calkhoven, Laurie & Herndon, Ryan. Incredible Collection (Reader Bind-Up) 2006. 136p. (J). pap. 7.99 (978-0-439-81057-9(4)) Scholastic, Inc.

Guinness World Records: Activity Book. 2002. (Illus.). 96p. (J). (gr. k-7). pap. 3.99 (978-1-57759-464-2(9)) Dalmatian Pr.

Guinness World Records: Sticker Fun. 2002. (Illus.). 32p. (J). pap. 3.99 (978-1-57759-459-8(2)) Dalmatian Pr.

Guinness World Records Editors. Guinness World Records: Brain Stretching Quiz Pad. 2005. 48p. (J). (gr. 3). spiral bd. 5.99 (978-0-8431-1385-3(5) , Price Stern Sloan) Penguin Group (USA) Inc.

—Guinness World Records: Mind Boggling Quiz Pad. 2005. 48p. (J). (gr. 3). spiral bd. 5.99 (978-0-8431-1389-1(8) , Price Stern Sloan) Penguin Group (USA) Inc.

Manzanero, Paula, ed. Guinness World Records to the Extreme. 2007. (Illus.). 144p. (J). (gr. 2-5). pap. 14.99 (978-0-439-86562-3(X) , Scholastic Reference) Scholastic, Inc.

Mattern, Joanne & Herndon, Ryan, compiled by. Guinness World Records: Extraordinary Records of Unusual Facts & Feats. 2005. (Illus.). 90p. (J). pap. (978-0-439-79192-2(8)) Scholastic, Inc.

Mitchell, Susan K. The Longest Bridges. 2007. (Megastructures Ser.). 32p. (J). (gr. 2-4). lib. bdg. 23.93 (***978-0-8368-8364-0(0)***) Stevens, Gareth Inc.

Morse, Jenifer. Scholastic Book of World Records 2007. 2006. 320p. (J). pap. 9.99 (978-0-439-82766-9(3) , Scholastic Reference) Scholastic, Inc.

Morse, Jenifer. Scholastic Book of World Records Ultimate Quiz Challenge. 2007. 176p. (J). (gr. 3-7). pap. 7.99 (***978-0-439-88971-1(5)*** , Scholastic Reference) Scholastic, Inc.

Morse, Jenifer Corr. Scholastic Book of World Records, No. 14. 2001. (Illus.). 320p. (J). (gr. 8). mass mkt. 9.95 (978-0-439-21962-4(0)) Scholastic, Inc.

—Scholastic Book of World Records. 2000. (J). (978-0-606-20066-0(5)) Tandem Library Bks.

—Scholastic Book of World Records 2002. 2001. 320p. (YA). (gr. 3 up). pap. 9.95 (978-0-439-31398-8(8) , Scholastic Reference) Scholastic, Inc.

—Scholastic Book of World Records 2002. 2001. (YA). (978-0-606-22176-4(X)) Tandem Library Bks.

—Scholastic Book of World Records 2003. 2002. (Illus.). 320p. (J). pap. 9.95 (978-0-439-42097-6(0) , Scholastic Reference) Scholastic, Inc.

Morse, Jennifer. School Book of World Records 08. 2007. 320p. (J). pap. 9.99 (***978-0-439-91658-5(5)*** , Scholastic Reference) Scholastic, Inc.

Richie, Jason. Spectacular Space Travelers. Sterling, Denise, ed. 2001. (Profiles Ser.: Vol. No. 31). (Illus.). 160p. (gr. 5 up). lib. bdg. 19.95 (978-1-881508-71-7(4)) Oliver Pr., Inc.

Schreiber, Brad. Weird Wonders & Bizarre Blunders: The Official Book of Ridiculous Records. 1998. (Illus.). 88p. (YA). pap. 5.00 (978-0-7881-5220-7(3)) DIANE Publishing Co.

WORLD SERIES (BASEBALL)

Buckley, James. World Series Heroes. 2003. (gr. k-3). lib. bdg. 11.80 (978-0-613-62439-8(4)) Tandem Library Bks.

Buckley, James, Jr. World Series Heroes. 2003. (Major League Baseball Ser.). (Illus.). 48p. pap. 3.99 (978-0-7894-9252-4(0)) Dorling Kindersley Publishing, Inc.

Buckley, James, Jr. & Dorling Kindersley Publishing Staff. World Series. 2004. (Eyewitness Bks.). (Illus.). 72p. (J). 15.99 (978-0-7566-0256-7(4)) Dorling Kindersley Publishing, Inc.

Buckley, James & Dorling Kindersley Publishing Staff. World Series Heroes. 2003. (Major League Baseball Ser.). (Illus.). 48p. (J). 12.99 (978-0-7894-9546-4(5)) Dorling Kindersley Publishing, Inc.

Campbell, Peter A. Old Time Baseball & the First. 2002. (Illus.). 48p. (gr. 3-6). lib. bdg. 24.90 (978-0-7613-2466-9(6) , Millbrook Pr.) Lerner Publishing Group.

Cho, Alan. World Series. 2007. (J). (***978-1-59036-699-8(9)***); (***978-1-59036-700-1(6)***) Weigl Pubs., Inc.

Daddy's Heroes. Daddy's Heroes: Gibby's Homer. 2007. (1988 World Ser.). (Illus.). 32p. (J). 8.95 (***978-0-9792111-0-2(7)***) Daddy's Heroes, Inc.

Dorling Kindersley Publishing Staff, ed. World Series. 2004. (Dk Eyewitness Books Ser.). (Illus.). 64p. (J). lib. bdg. 19.99 (978-0-7566-0255-0(6)) Dorling Kindersley Publishing, Inc.

Gutman, Dan. World Series Classics (1912-1991) 2001. (Illus.). 240p. (J). (gr. 5-7). reprint ed. 15.00 (978-0-7881-9988-2(9)) DIANE Publishing Co.

Ruzich, Christian. World Series Stars & Stats. McClusky, Mark, ed. 1999. 32p. (Orig.). (J). pap. 3.99 (978-1-886749-66-5(3)) Sports Illustrated For Kids.

WORLD WAR, 1914-1918

Adams, Simon. World War I. 2007. (DK Eyewitness Bks.). 72p. (J). (gr. 3-8). 15.99 incl. cd-rom (978-0-7566-3007-2(X)) Dorling Kindersley Publishing, Inc.

Adams, Simon & Dorling Kindersley Publishing Staff. World War I. 2004. (Eyewitness Books). (Illus.). 72p. (J). lib. bdg. 19.99 (978-0-7566-0741-8(8)) Dorling Kindersley Publishing, Inc.

Avp, prod. The First World War & Its Consequences. (YA). cd-rom 89.95 (978-0-7365-0115-6(0)) Films Media Group.

Banham, Dale & Culpin, Christopher. The Trenches. 2002. (Illus.). 72p. pap. 26.00 (***978-0-7195-8565-4(1)*** , Hodder Murray) Hodder Education GBR. *Dist:* Trans-Atlantic Pubns., Inc.

Beller, Susan Provost. The Doughboys over There: Soldiering in World War I. 2007. (Soldiers on the Battlefront Ser.). (Illus.). 112p. (YA). (gr. 6-8). lib. bdg. 33.26 (978-0-8225-6295-5(2)) Lerner Publishing Group.

Blanchard, Lucy M. Chico - the story of a Homing Pigeon in the Great War. 2006. 104p. (YA). per. (978-1-84685-039-4(8) , Diggory Pr. Ltd.) Meadow Bks.

Blanchard, M. Lucy. Chico the Story of A Homing Pigeon. 2006. 62.99 (***978-1-4280-3492-1(7)***); pap. 55.99 (***978-1-4280-3493-8(5)***) IndyPublish.com.

Blohm, Craig E. Leaders & Generals. 2001. (American War Library). (Illus.). 112p. (J). (gr. 4-12). lib. bdg. 29.95 (978-1-56006-839-6(6) , LML00902-178171, Lucent Bks.) Thomson Gale.

Brocklehurst, Ruth & Brook, Henry. First World War - Internet Linked. 2007. (World Wars Ser.). 128p. (J). 19.99 (***978-0-7945-1455-6(3)*** , Usborne) EDC Publishing.

Connolly, Sean. World War I. 2003. (Illus.). 56p. (J). pap. 8.95 (978-1-4034-3640-5(1)); (gr. 6-8). lib. bdg. 27.07 (978-1-4034-0971-3(4)) Heinemann Library.

—World War I. 2003. (gr. 5-8). lib. bdg. 17.60 (978-0-613-61003-2(2)) Tandem Library Bks.

Conway, John R. World War I: A MyReportLinks. Com Book. 2003. (U.S. Wars Ser.). (Illus.). 48p. (J). lib. bdg. 25.26 (978-0-7660-5142-3(0) , MyReportLinks.com Bks.) Enslow Pubs., Inc.

Deary, Terry. ESA Espantosa Primera Guerra Mundial. 2001. Tr. of Frightful First World War. (SPA.). (gr. 3-6). lib. bdg. 18.75 (978-0-613-79906-5(2)) Tandem Library Bks.

Dowswell, Paul. True Stories of the First World War. 2004. (True Adventure Stories Ser.). (Illus.). 144p. (J). pap. 4.95 (978-0-7945-0721-3(2) , Usborne) EDC Publishing.

—War Stories. Mcnee, Ian, illus. 2006. 432p. (J). pap. 12.99 (978-0-7945-1499-0(5) , Usborne) EDC Publishing.

Feldman, Ruth Tenzer. World War I. 2004. (Chronicle of America's Wars Ser.). (Illus.). 96p. (J). (gr. 5-12). 27.93 (978-0-8225-0148-0(1)) Lerner Publishing Group.

Gail, Margaret. Moggie Grows up. 2006. (ENG.). 74p. pap. (***978-0-7552-0227-0(9)***) Authors OnLine, Ltd.

George, Linda S. World War I. 2001. (Letters from the Home Front Ser.). (Illus.). 96p. (J). (gr. 6 up). lib. bdg. 29.93 (978-0-7614-1096-6(1) , Benchmark Bks.) Cavendish, Marshall Corp.

Gilbert, Adrian. Going to War in World War One. Bergin, Mark, illus. 2001. (Armies of the Past Ser.). 32p. (J). (gr. 3-6). 25.50 (978-0-531-14595-1(6) , Watts, Franklin) Scholastic Library Publishing.

Granfield, Linda. Where Poppies Grow: A World War I Companion. 2002. (Illus.). 48p. (gr. 3 up). 16.95 (978-0-7737-3319-0(1)) Stoddart Kids CAN. *Dist:* Fitzhenry & Whiteside, Ltd.

Grant, R. G. World War I. 2005. (How Did It Happen? Ser.). (Illus.). 48p. (J). (gr. 7-10). lib. bdg. 29.95 (978-1-59018-605-3(2) , Lucent Bks.) Thomson Gale.

—World War I: Armistice 1918. 2001. (World Wars Ser.). (Illus.). 64p. (J). (gr. 5). lib. bdg. 27.12 (978-0-7398-2753-6(7)) Raintree.

Green, Robert. World War I. 2007. (World History Ser.). (Illus.). 128p. (gr. 7-10). 28.70 (***978-1-4205-0025-7(2)*** , Lucent Bks.) Thomson Gale.

Gutierrez, Peter. The Story Behind Erich Maria Remarque's All Quiet on the Western Front. 2006. (History in Literature Ser.). 56p. (J). (978-1-4034-8210-5(1)) Heinemann Library.

Hamilton, John. Aircraft of World War I. 2004. (World War I Ser.). (Illus.). 32p. (J). (gr. 4-8). lib. bdg. 24.21 (978-1-57765-912-9(0)) ABDO Publishing Co.

—Battles of World War I. 2004. (World War I Ser.). (Illus.). 32p. (J). lib. bdg. 24.21 (978-1-57765-913-6(9)) ABDO Publishing Co.

—Weapons of World War I. 2004. (World War I Ser.). (Illus.). 32p. (J). (gr. 4-8). lib. bdg. 24.21 (978-1-57765-917-4(1)) ABDO Publishing Co.

—World War I. 2004. (J). (gr. 4-8). lib. bdg. 145.26 (978-1-57765-911-2(2) , ABDO & Daughters) ABDO Publishing Co.

Hansen, Ole Steen. World War I: War in the Trenches. 2001. (World Wars Ser.). (Illus.). 64p. (J). (gr. 5). lib. bdg. 27.12 (978-0-7398-2752-9(9)) Raintree.

Hatt, Christine. World War I, 1914-18. 2001. (Documenting History Ser.). (Illus.). 64p. (J). (gr. 8-12). 24.50 (978-0-531-14611-8(1) , Watts, Franklin) Scholastic Library Publishing.

Hibbert, Adam. In the Trenches in World War I. 2006. (Illus.). 48p. (J). lib. bdg. 31.43 (***978-1-4109-2194-9(8)***) Raintree.

Hills, Ken. World War I. Phillipps, Francis, illus. 2001. (Wars That Changed the World Ser.). 31p. pap. 9.99 (978-1-84234-084-4(0) , Cherrytree Books) Evans Publishing Group GBR. *Dist:* Independent Pubs. Group.

Holmes, Richard & Dorling Kindersley Publishing Staff. Battle. 2000. (Eyewitness Bks.). (Illus.). 64p. (J). (gr. 4-7). lib. bdg. 19.99 (978-0-7894-6612-9(0)) Dorling Kindersley Publishing, Inc.

Jantzen, Steven L. & Scott, John Anthony. Hooray for Peace - Hurrah for War: The United States During World War I. 1999. (Illus.). 194p. (J). lib. bdg. 24.95 (978-0-7351-0218-7(X)) Replica Bks.

Keene, Jennifer D. World War I Almanac. Facts on File, Inc. Staff, ed. 2007. 512p. (gr. 9). 85.00 (978-0-8160-6191-4(2)) Facts On File, Inc.

Kent, Zachary. World War I: "The War to End Wars" 2000. (American War Ser.). (Illus.). 128p. (YA). (gr. 5-12). pap. 13.26 (978-0-7660-1732-0(X)) Enslow Pubs., Inc.

Langellier, John P. American Indians in the U. S. Armed Forces, 1866-1945, Vol. 20. 2006. (G. I. Ser.: Vol. 20). (Illus.). 72p. pap. 14.95 (978-1-85367-408-2(7)) Greenhill Bks./Lionel Leventhal, Ltd. GBR. *Dist:* MBI Distribution Services.

Malam, John. World War I: Armistice Day. 2003. 45p. (J). lib. bdg. 28.50 (978-1-58340-410-2(4)) Smart Apple Media.

Marquette, Scott. World War I. 2003. (America at War Ser.). (Illus.). 48p. (gr. 4-8). 20.95 (978-1-58952-392-0(X)) Rourke Publishing, LLC.

Maybury, Richard J. World War I: The Rest of the Story & How It Affects You Today, 1870 To 1935. Williams, Jane A., ed. rev. ed. 2003. ("Uncle Eric" Bk.). 253p. (YA). pap. 17.95 (978-0-942617-42-9(8)) Bluestocking Pr.

McDougal, Littell Staff & Nextext Staff, contrib. by. World War, Boom & Bust. 2004. (Stories in History Ser.). (Illus.). 224p. (J). (gr. 6-12). (978-0-618-22202-5(2) , 2-00308) McDougal Littell Inc.

McNeil, Niki, et al. HOCPP 1086 World War I. 2006. spiral bd. 19.50 ***(978-1-60308-086-6(4))*** In the Hands of a Child.

Myers, Walter Dean & Miles, Bill. The Harlem Hellfighters: When Pride Met Courage. 2006. (Illus.). 160p. (J). lib. bdg. 18.89 (978-0-06-001137-6(8) , Amistad) HarperCollins Pubs.

Nelson, Sheila. A Nation Is Born: World War I & Independence, 1910-1929. 2005. (Illus.). 87p. (J). (gr. 3-7). lib. bdg. 21.95 (978-1-4222-0006-3(X) , 1247972) Mason Crest Pubs.

Rice, Earle. The First Battle of the Marne. 2002. (Battles That Changed the World Ser.). (Illus.). 112p. (J). 30.00 (978-0-7910-6685-0(1) , Chelsea Hse.) Facts On File, Inc.

Robson, Pam. The First World War. 2003. (All about Ser.). (Illus.). 48p. pap. (978-0-7500-1936-1(0) , Hodder Wayland) Hodder Children's Division.

Ross, Stewart. The Technology of World War I. 2003. (World Wars Ser.). (Illus.). 64p. (J). lib. bdg. 28.56 (978-0-7398-5482-2(8)) Raintree.

Ross, Stewart. World War I. 2007. (J). ***(978-1-84193-729-8(0))*** Smart Apple Media.

—World War I. 2004. (Atlas of Conflicts Ser.). (Illus.). 64p. (J). pap. 11.95 (978-0-8368-5675-0(9)); lib. bdg. 32.67 (978-0-8368-5668-2(6)) Stevens, Gareth Inc. (World Almanac Library).

Ruggiero, Adriane. World War I. 2002. (American Voices From Ser.). (Illus.). xxv, 117p. (J). 34.21 (978-0-7614-1203-8(4) , Benchmark Bks.) Cavendish, Marshall Corp.

Saunders, Nicholas. World War I: A Primary Source History. 2005. (Illus.). 48p. lib. bdg. 26.00 (978-0-8368-5982-9(0)) Stevens, Gareth Inc.

Scherer, Glenn & Fletcher, Marty. Primary Source Accounts of World War I. 2006. (America's Wars Through Primary Sources Ser.). (Illus.). 128p. (J). lib. bdg. 33.27 (978-1-59845-008-8(5) , MyReportLinks.com Bks.) Enslow Pubs., Inc.

Scott, Janine. The Two Great Wars. 2007. (Shockwave: History & Politics Ser.). (Illus.). 36p. (J). (gr. 4-6). lib. bdg. 25.00 ***(978-0-531-17756-3(4)*** , Children's Pr.) Scholastic Library Publishing.

SHARMAN, et al. Headlines of World War I. 2005. (Illus.). 46p. (J). 24.95 (978-0-237-52996-3(3) , Evans Brothers, Limited) Evans Publishing Group GBR. *Dist:* Independent Pubs. Group.

Sharman, Margaret, et al. Headlines of World War I. 2005. (Illus.). 46p. (J). pap. 13.95 (978-0-237-52907-9(6) , Evans Brothers, Limited) Evans Publishing Group GBR. *Dist:* Independent Pubs. Group.

Sommerville, Donald. World War I. 1999. (History of Warfare Ser.). (Illus.). 80p. (YA). (gr. 7-12). 29.97 (978-0-8172-5450-6(1)) Raintree.

Stewart, Gail B. World War I: Weapons of War. 2001. (American War Library). (Illus.). 112p. (YA). (gr. 4-12). lib. bdg. 27.45 (978-1-56006-837-2(X) , LML00902-178169, Lucent Bks.) Thomson Gale.

Stone, Tanya Lee. The Progressive Era & World War I. 2001. (Making of America Ser.). (Illus.). 96p. (YA). (gr. 5-10). lib. bdg. 28.54 (978-0-8172-5709-5(8)) Raintree.

Torr, James D. Primary Sources. 2002. (American War Library). (Illus.). 104p. (YA). (gr. 4-12). 29.95 (978-1-59018-008-2(9) , LML00902-179656, Lucent Bks.) Thomson Gale.

Torres, Jennifer. Alan Jackson. 2006. (Blue Banner Biography Ser.). (Illus.). 32p. (J). (gr. 4-8). lib. bdg. 25.70 (978-1-58415-504-1(3) , 1259609) Mitchell Lane Pubs., Inc.

Wagner, Heather Lehr. The Division of the Middle East: The Treaty of Sevres. 2004. (Arbitrary Borders Ser.). (Illus.). 120p. (gr. 9-13). 35.00 (978-0-7910-7831-0(0) , Chelsea Hse.) Facts On File, Inc.

Walker, Kate & Argaet, Elaine. Super Spies of World War I. 2003. (Spies & Spying Ser.). 32p. (J). lib. bdg. 24.25 (978-1-58340-339-6(5)) Smart Apple Media.

Whiting, Jim. An Overview of World War I. 2006. (Monumental Milestones Ser.). (Illus.). 48p. (J). (gr. 6-9). lib. bdg. 29.95 (978-1-58415-471-6(3)) Mitchell Lane Pubs., Inc.

World War I: PowerPoint Presentations in World History. 2005. cd-rom 49.95 net. (978-1-56004-208-2(7)) Social Studies Schl. Service.

The World Wars, 4 vols. 2003. (Illus.). (J). 114.24 (978-0-7398-6066-3(6)); 399.84 (978-0-7398-6067-0(4)) Raintree.

WORLD WAR, 1914-1918—AERIAL OPERATIONS

Hansen, Ole Steen. Military Aircraft of World War One. 2003. (gr. 3-6). lib. bdg. 17.60 (978-0-613-59087-7(2)) Tandem Library Bks.

—Military Aircraft of WWI. 2003. (Story of Flight Ser.). (Illus.). 32p. (J). (gr. 4). pap. (978-0-7787-1217-6(6)); lib. bdg. (978-0-7787-1201-5(X)) Crabtree Publishing Co.

Koestler-Grack, Rachel A. Eddie Rickenbacker. 2003. (Famous Flyers Ser.). (Illus.). 112p. (gr. 6-12). 30.00 (978-0-7910-7215-8(0) , Chelsea Hse.) Facts On File, Inc.

Myhra, David. Gotha P 60. 2001. (Schiffer Military History Book Ser.). (Illus.). 120p. (gr. 10-13). pap. 19.95 (978-0-7643-1399-8(1)) Schiffer Publishing, Ltd.

—The Horten HO 9/HO 229: Retrospective. 2002. (Illus.). 224p. (gr. 10-13). 49.95 (978-0-7643-1666-1(4)) Schiffer Publishing, Ltd.

Purcell, Martha Sias. Pioneer Pilots & Flying Aces of World War I. 2003. (Reading Essentials in Social Studies). (Illus.). 48p. (J). (978-0-7891-5881-9(7)) Perfection Learning Corp.

Watson, Marilyn Myrick. Frank Luke, the Arizona Balloon Buster. 2007. ***(978-0-9790826-3-4(3)); (978-0-9790826-4-1(1))*** Acacia Publishing, Inc.

Wukovits, John F. Flying Aces. 2002. (American War Library). (Illus.). 112p. (YA). (gr. 4-12). lib. bdg. 29.95 (978-1-56006-810-5(8) , LML00902-178142, Lucent Bks.) Thomson Gale.

WORLD WAR, 1914-1918—BIOGRAPHY

Batten, Jack. Silent in an Evil Time: The Brave War of Edith Cavell. 2007. 144p. (YA). (gr. 5 up). pap. 16.95 ***(978-0-88776-737-1(0))*** Tundra Bks., Inc./Livres Toundra, Inc. CAN. *Dist:* Random Hse., Inc.

Fischer, Sue. The Mother of Eagles: The War Diary of Baroness Von Richthofen. 2001. (Schiffer Military History Ser.). (Illus.). 208p. (gr. 10-13). 29.95 (978-0-7643-1307-3(X)) Schiffer Publishing, Ltd.

Fowke, Bob. World War I. (Illus.). 128p. (J). pap. 9.99 (978-0-340-85186-9(4) , Hodder & Stoughton) Hodder General Publishing Division GBR. *Dist:* Independent Pubs. Group.

Gifford, Clive. World War One: True Stories. 2003. (Illus.). 128p. pap. (978-0-340-80496-4(3) , Hodder Children's Books) Hodder Children's Division.

Granfield, Linda. In Flanders Fields. Wilson, Janet, illus. 2000. 32p. (gr. 4-7). 8.95 (978-0-7737-5925-1(5)) Stoddart Kids CAN. *Dist:* Fitzhenry & Whiteside, Ltd.

Purcell, Martha Sias. Pioneer Pilots & Flying Aces of World War I. 2003. (Reading Essentials in Social Studies). (Illus.). 48p. (J). (978-0-7891-5881-9(7)) Perfection Learning Corp.

Ross, Stewart. Leaders of World War I. 2003. (World Wars Ser.). (Illus.). 64p. (J). lib. bdg. 28.56 (978-0-7398-5481-5(X)) Raintree.

Wukovits, John F. Flying Aces. 2002. (American War Library). (Illus.). 112p. (YA). (gr. 4-12). lib. bdg. 29.95 (978-1-56006-810-5(8) , LML00902-178142, Lucent Bks.) Thomson Gale.

Zeinert, Karen. Those Extraordinary Women of World War I. 2001. (Women at War Ser.). (Illus.). 96p. (J). (gr. 5 up). lib. bdg. 29.90 (978-0-7613-1913-9(1) , Twenty-First Century Bks.) Lerner Publishing Group.

WORLD WAR, 1914-1918—CAMPAIGNS

see also Somme, Battles of the, 1916, 1918

Carlyon, Patrick. The Gallipoli Story. 2004. (Illus.). 192p. pap. 9.99 (978-0-14-300143-0(4) , Penguin Global) Penguin Group (USA) Inc.

Dowswell, Paul. Weapons & Technology of World War I. 2002. (20th-Century Perspectives Ser.). (Illus.). 48p. (J). (gr. 5-7). lib. bdg. 27.07 (978-1-58810-662-9(4)); Set 2. pap. 7.95 (978-1-58810-922-4(4) , 91513) Heinemann Library.

—Weapons & Technology of World War I. 2002. (gr. 5-8). lib. bdg. 16.40 (978-0-613-58274-2(8)) Tandem Library Bks.

Feldman, Ruth Tenzer. World War I. 2004. (Chronicle of America's Wars Ser.). (Illus.). 96p. (J). (gr. 5-12). 27.93 (978-0-8225-0148-0(1)) Lerner Publishing Group.

Hamilton, John. Final Years of World War I. 2004. (World War I Ser.). (Illus.). 32p. (J). (gr. 4-8). lib. bdg. 24.21 (978-1-57765-915-0(5)) ABDO Publishing Co.

—Trench Fighting of World War I. 2004. (World War I Ser.). (Illus.). 32p. (J). (gr. 4-8). lib. bdg. 24.21 (978-1-57765-916-7(3)) ABDO Publishing Co.

MacLean, Alistair. Lawrence of Arabia. 2006. (Sterling Point Bks.). (Illus.). 176p. (J). pap. 6.95 (978-1-4027-3613-1(4)) Sterling Publishing Co., Inc.

Ross, Stewart. The Battle of the Somme. 2003. (World Wars Ser.). (Illus.). 64p. (J). lib. bdg. 28.56 (978-0-7398-5479-2(8)) Raintree.

Taylor, David. Key Battles of World War I. (20th Century Perspectives Ser.). (Illus.). 48p. (J). (gr. 5-7). 2001. lib. bdg. 25.64 (978-1-57572-437-9(5)); Set 1. 2002. pap. 7.95 (978-1-58810-376-5(5) , 91128) Heinemann Library.

Wukovits, John F. Strategic Battles. 2001. (American War Library). (Illus.). 112p. (YA). (gr. 4-12). lib. bdg. 29.95 (978-1-56006-836-5(1) , LML00902-178168, Lucent Bks.) Thomson Gale.

WORLD WAR, 1914-1918—CAUSES

Allan, Tony. The Causes of World War I. 2003. (20th Century Perspectives Ser.). 48p. (YA). pap. 7.95 (978-1-4034-4620-6(2)); (Illus.). (J). (gr. 5-7). lib. bdg. 27.07 (978-1-4034-0148-9(0)) Heinemann Library.

Feldman, Ruth Tenzer. World War I. 2004. (Chronicle of America's Wars Ser.). (Illus.). 96p. (J). (gr. 5-12). 27.93 (978-0-8225-0148-0(1)) Lerner Publishing Group.

Hamilton, John. Events Leading to World War I. 2004. (World War I Ser.). (Illus.). 32p. (J). (gr. 4-8). lib. bdg. 24.21 (978-1-57765-914-3(7)) ABDO Publishing Co.

Maybury, Richard J. World War I: The Rest of the Story & How It Affects You Today, 1870 To 1935. Williams, Jane A., ed. rev. ed. 2003. ("Uncle Eric" Bk.). 253p. (YA). pap. 17.95 (978-0-942617-42-9(8)) Bluestocking Pr.

Ross, Stewart. Assassination in Sarajevo: The Trigger for World War I. (Point of Impact Ser.). 32p. pap. 7.50 (978-1-4034-4111-9(1)); 2006. (Illus.). (J). ***(978-1-4034-9138-1(0));*** 2001. (Illus.). (J). (gr. 5-7). lib. bdg. 24.22 (978-1-58810-074-0(X)) Heinemann Library.

—The Causes of World War I. 2003. (World Wars Ser.). (Illus.). 64p. (J). lib. bdg. 28.56 (978-0-7398-5480-8(1)) Raintree.

Stewart Ross. Assassination in Sarajevo. 2nd ed. 2006. (Point of Impact Ser.). (Illus.). 32p. (J). pap. ***(978-1-4034-9147-3(X))*** Heinemann Library.

Woolf, Alex. Assassination in Sarajevo. 2003. (Days That Shook the World Ser.). (Illus.). 47p. (J). lib. bdg. 28.56 (978-0-7398-6048-9(8)) Raintree.

WORLD WAR, 1914-1918—FICTION

Altsheler, Joseph A. The Forest of Swords: A Story of Paris A. 2006. pap. ***(978-1-4065-0809-3(8))*** Dodo Pr.

—The Hosts of the Air (Illustrated Editio. 2006. (Illus.). pap. ***(978-1-4065-0814-7(4))*** Dodo Pr.

Bates, Gordon. The Khaki Boys over the Top or Doing and. 2006. 77.99 ***(978-1-4280-0116-9(6));*** pap. 71.99 ***(978-1-4280-0106-0(9))*** IndyPublish.com.

Black, Robert. Liberty Girl. (YA). pap. 9.99 (978-0-88092-488-7(8)) Royal Fireworks Publishing Co.

Breslin, Theresa. Remembrance. 2004. 304p. (YA). (gr. 7). mass mkt. 6.50 (978-0-440-23778-5(5) , Laurel Leaf) Random Hse. Children's Bks.

Cary, Kate. Bloodline. 2006. 352p. (YA). (gr. 7-12). pap. 8.99 (978-1-59514-078-4(6) , Razorbill) Penguin Group (USA) Inc.

—Reckoning. 2007. (Bloodline Ser.: Bk. 2). 320p. (YA). (gr. 9 up). 16.99 (978-1-59514-013-5(1) , Razorbill) Penguin Group (USA) Inc.

Crew, Gary. Memorial. Tan, Shaun, illus. 32p. (978-0-85091-983-7(5) , Lothian Bks.) Hachette Livre Australia.

—Memorial. Tan, Shaun, illus. 2004. 32p. 16.95 (978-1-894965-08-8(6)) Simply Read Bks. CAN. *Dist:* Perseus Distribution.

Debon, Nicolas. A Brave Soldier. 2002. (Illus.). (J). (gr. 1 up). 15.95 (978-0-88899-481-3(8)) Groundwood Bks. CAN. *Dist:* Transition Vendor.

Drake, Ensign Robert L. The Boy Allies with Uncle Sams Cruisers. 2004. reprint ed. pap. 21.95 (978-1-4191-5495-9(8)) Kessinger Publishing, LLC.

Drake, L. Robert. The Boy Allies under the Sea or the Vani. 2006. 78.99 ***(978-1-4280-3138-8(3))*** IndyPublish.com.

—The Boy Allies with the Victorious Fleet. 2006. 33.99 ***(978-1-4280-2825-8(0))*** IndyPublish.com.

Drake, Robert L. The Boy Allies at Jutland. 2005. 264p. pap. 13.95 (978-1-4218-0484-2(0) , 1st World Library - Literary Society) 1st World Publishing, Inc.

—The Boy Allies at Jutland. 2004. reprint ed. pap. 22.95 (978-1-4191-5492-8(3)); pap. 1.99 (978-1-4192-5492-5(8)) Kessinger Publishing, LLC.

—The Boy Allies at Jutland: Or, the Greatest Naval Battle of History. l.t. ed. 2006. 166p. pap. 11.99 ***(978-1-4264-3926-1(1));*** 188p. pap. 14.99 ***(978-1-4264-3984-1(9))*** BiblioBazaar.

—The Boy Allies under Two Flags. 2005. 256p. pap. 13.95 (978-1-4218-0483-5(2) , 1st World Library - Literary Society) 1st World Publishing, Inc.

—The Boy Allies under Two Flags. 2006. 162p. pap. 11.99 ***(978-1-4264-4925-3(9));*** 184p. pap. 14.99 ***(978-1-4264-5226-0(8))*** BiblioBazaar.

—The Boy Allies under Two Flags. 2004. reprint ed. pap. 1.99 (978-1-4192-5493-2(6)) Kessinger Publishing, LLC.

—The Boy Allies with Uncle Sams Cruisers. 2005. 27.95 (978-1-4218-1081-2(6)); 212p. pap. 12.95 (978-1-4218-1181-9(2)) 1st World Publishing, Inc. (1st World Library - Literary Society).

—The Boy Allies with Uncle Sams Cruisers. 2004. reprint ed. pap. 1.99 (978-1-4192-5495-6(2)) Kessinger Publishing, LLC.

Drake, Robert L. Ens. The Boy Allies under Two Flags. 2006. 26.99 ***(978-1-4280-0722-2(9));*** pap. 19.99 ***(978-1-4280-0717-8(2))*** IndyPublish.com.

—The Boy Allies with Uncle Sams Cruisers. 2006. 25.99 ***(978-1-4280-0719-2(9));*** pap. 19.99 ***(978-1-4280-0694-2(X))*** IndyPublish.com.

Driscoll, R. James. The Brighton Boys with the Flying Corps. 2006. 77.99 ***(978-1-4280-0121-3(2));*** pap. 70.99 ***(978-1-4280-0118-3(2))*** IndyPublish.com.

—The Brighton Boys with the Submarine Fle. 2006. 32.99 ***(978-1-4219-7846-8(6));*** pap. 26.99 ***(978-1-4219-7867-3(9))*** IndyPublish.com.

Elliott, Dorothy. Little Angel Third Class - below Stairs. 2007. 92p. per. ***(978-1-84685-562-7(4)*** , Exposure Publishing) Meadow Bks.

Farenhorst, Christine. A Cup of Cold Water: The Compassion of Nurse Edith Cavell. 2007. (J). pap. ***(978-1-59638-026-4(8))*** P & R Publishing.

Fitzhugh, Percy K. Tom Slade: Motorcycle Dispatch Bearer. 2005. pap. 26.95 (978-1-4191-6253-4(5)) Kessinger Publishing, LLC.

Hancock, Irving H. Uncle Sam's Boys with Pershing's Troops. 2006. pap. 71.99 ***(978-1-4219-9902-9(1))*** IndyPublish.com.

—Uncle Sams Boys with Pershings Troops or. 2006. 78.99 ***(978-1-4219-9892-3(0))*** IndyPublish.com.

Harris, Ruth Elwin. Julia's Story. 2002. (gr. 7-12). lib. bdg. 14.15 (978-0-613-74777-6(1)) Tandem Library Bks.

Harrison, Charles. Generals Die in Bed: A Story from the Trenches. 2002. (Illus.). 180p. (YA). (gr. 9). 18.95 (978-1-55037-731-6(0)); pap. 7.95 (978-1-55037-730-9(2)) Annick Pr., Ltd. CAN. *Dist:* Firefly Bks., Ltd.

—Generals Die in Bed: A Story from the Trenches. 2002. (gr. 7-12). lib. bdg. 16.40 (978-0-613-59810-1(5)) Tandem Library Bks.

Hartnett, Sonya. The Silver Donkey. Powers, Don, illus. 272p. (J). (gr. 5). 2007. pap. 7.99 ***(978-0-7636-3681-4(9));*** 2006. 15.99 (978-0-7636-2937-3(5)) Candlewick Pr.

—The Silver Donkey. Spudvilas, Anne, illus. 2004. viii, 193p. (J). (978-0-670-04240-1(4) , Viking Adult) Penguin Group (USA) Inc.

Hayes, Clair W. The Boy Allies at Verdun. 2005. 28.95 (978-1-4218-0324-1(0)); 264p. pap. 13.95 (978-1-4218-0424-8(7)) 1st World Publishing, Inc. (1st World Library - Literary Society).

—The Boy Allies with Haig in Flanders. 2004. reprint ed. pap. 21.95 (978-1-4191-5494-2(X)); pap. 1.99 (978-1-4192-5494-9(4)) Kessinger Publishing, LLC.

Hayes, W. Clair. The Boy Allies at Verdun or Saving Franc. 2006. 78.99 ***(978-1-4280-0009-4(7));*** pap. 72.99 ***(978-1-4280-0002-5(X))*** IndyPublish.com.

—The Boy Allies in the Balkan Campaign or. 2006. 78.99 ***(978-1-4219-9904-3(8));*** pap. 72.99 ***(978-1-4219-9919-7(6))*** IndyPublish.com.

Hayes, Wallace Clair. The Boy Allies on the Firing Line or Twe. 2006. 78.99 ***(978-1-4219-9952-4(8));*** pap. 72.99 ***(978-1-4219-9949-4(8))*** IndyPublish.com.

Jones, Elizabeth McDavid. The Night Flyers. 1999. (978-0-606-17518-0(0)) Tandem Library Bks.

Kacer, Kathy. The Night Spies. 2005. (Illus.). 148p. (YA). pap. 5.95 (978-1-896764-70-2(3)) Second Story Pr. CAN. *Dist:* Orca Bk. Pubs. USA, Univ. of Toronto Pr.

Kinsey-Warnock, Natalie. The Night the Bells Rang. 2001. (gr. 1-5). 20.50 (978-0-8446-7180-2(0)) Smith, Peter Pub., Inc.

—The Night the Bells Rang. 2000. (978-0-606-20367-8(2)) Tandem Library Bks.

—Night the Bells Rang. 2000. (gr. 3-6). lib. bdg. 13.00 (978-0-613-30071-1(8)) Tandem Library Bks.

Lalana, Fernando & Almarcegui, Jose Maria. La Bomba. 2003. (SPA.). 144p. (978-84-216-1540-9(8) , BU5058) Bruño, Editorial ESP. *Dist:* Lectorum Pubns., Inc.

Larson, Kirby. Hattie Big Sky. 2006. 304p. (J). (gr. 7). 15.95 (978-0-385-73313-7(5)); lib. bdg. 17.99 (978-0-385-90332-5(4)) Random Hse. Children's Bks. (Delacorte Bks. for Young Readers).

—Hattie Big Sky. l.t. ed. 2007. 400p. (YA). 23.95 ***(978-0-7862-9697-2(6))*** Thorndike Pr.

Lasky, Kathryn. A Time for Courage: The Suffragette Diary of Kathleen Bowen, Washington D. C., 1917. 2002. (Dear America Ser.). (Illus.). 176p. (J). (gr. 4-9). pap. 10.95 (978-0-590-51141-4(6)) Scholastic, Inc.

Lawrence, Iain. Lord of the Nutcracker Men. (gr. 5). 2003. (Illus.). 240p. (J). pap. 5.99 (978-0-440-41812-2(7) , Laurel Leaf); 2001. 224p. lib. bdg. 17.99 (978-0-385-90024-9(4) , Delacorte Bks. for Young Readers) Random Hse. Children's Bks.

—Lord of the Nutcracker Men. l.t. ed. 2002. 280p. (J). 24.95 (978-0-7862-4155-2(1)) Thomson Gale.

Levine, Beth Seidel. When Christmas Comes Again: The World War I Diary of Simone Spencer. 2002. (Dear America Ser.). (Illus.). 176p. (J). (gr. 4-9). pap. 10.95 (978-0-439-43982-4(5)) Scholastic, Inc.

Lindquist, Susan Hart. Summer Soldiers. 2000. (J). (978-0-606-19132-6(1)) Tandem Library Bks.

McCutcheon, John. Christmas in the Trenches. Sorensen, Henri, illus. 2006. 32p. (J). 18.95 incl. audio compact disk (978-1-56145-374-0(9) , Peachtree Junior) Peachtree Pubs., Ltd.

Montgomery, L. M. Rilla of Ingleside. 2002. (ENG.). 272p. 19.99 ***(978-1-4043-2710-8(X));*** pap. 14.99 ***(978-1-4043-2711-5(8))*** IndyPublish.com.

—Rilla of Ingleside. 2004. 224p. (YA). pap. 10.95 (978-1-57646-891-3(7)) Quiet Vision Publishing.

Morpurgo, Michael. The Best Christmas Present in the World. Foreman, Michael, illus. 2004. 36p. (J). (ps-7). 8.99 (978-1-4052-1518-3(6)) Egmont Bks., Ltd. GBR. *Dist:* Independent Pubs. Group.

—Farm Boy. Foreman, Michael, illus. 1999. 74p. (YA). pap. 16.99 (978-1-86205-192-8(5) , Pavilion Bks., Ltd.) Anova Bks. GBR. *Dist:* Trafalgar Square Publishing.

—Private Peaceful. (J). 2006. 176p. pap. 5.99 (978-0-439-63653-7(1) , Scholastic Paperbacks); 2004. 208p. (gr. 7 up). 16.95 (978-0-439-63648-3(5) , Scholastic Pr.) Scholastic, Inc.

—Private Peaceful. l.t. ed. 2006. 225p. (J). 21.95 (978-0-7862-8946-2(5)) Thorndike Pr.

—War Horse. 2007. 176p. (J). (gr. 4-7). 16.99 (978-0-439-79663-7(6) , Scholastic Pr.) Scholastic, Inc.

Morris, Gilbert. Amazon Quest. 2001. (gr. 5-8). lib. bdg. 21.10 (978-0-613-55559-3(7)) Tandem Library Bks.

Newbery, Linda. The Shell House. 2004. 352p. (YA). (gr. 7-11). reprint ed. mass mkt. 6.50 (978-0-440-23786-0(6) , Laurel Leaf) Random Hse. Children's Bks.

Peake, Joan. Great-Gran's Diary. 2000. 142p. pap. 12.95 (978-1-85902-884-1(5)) Beekman Bks., Inc.

Perkins, Lucy Fitch. The French Twins. 2006. 18.99 (***978-1-4280-1689-7(9)***); pap. 11.99 (***978-1-4280-1681-1(3)***) IndyPublish.com.

Randall, Homer. Army Boys in the French Trenches: Or, Hand to Hand Fighting with the Enemy. 2006. 140p. pap. 10.99 (***978-1-4264-3679-6(3)***); 156p. pap. 14.99 (***978-1-4264-3736-6(6)***) BiblioBazaar.

Remarque, Erich Maria. All Quiet on the Western Front: With Related Readings. Wheen, A. W., tr. from GER. 2002. (EMC Masterpiece Series Access Editions). (Illus.). xxv, 249p. (YA). 14.60 (978-0-8219-2420-4(6)) EMC/Paradigm Publishing.

Sedgwick, Marcus. The Foreshadowing. 2008. 304p. (J). (gr. 9). mass mkt. 6.50 (***978-0-553-48785-5(X)***, Laurel Leaf) Random Hse. Children's Bks.

Skrypuch, Marsha Forchuk. Silver Threads. Martchenko, Michael, illus. 2004. 32p. (J). (gr. 2-5). (978-1-55041-901-6(3)) Fitzhenry & Whiteside, Ltd.

Slade, Arthur. Megiddo's Shadow. 2008. 304p. (YA). (gr. 7). mass mkt. 6.50 (***978-0-553-49507-2(0)***, Laurel Leaf) Random Hse. Children's Bks.

Spillebeen, Geert. Kipling's Choice. Edelstein, Terese, tr. 160p. (YA). (gr. 7 up). 2007. pap. 7.99 (***978-0-618-80035-3(2)***, Graphia); 2005. 16.00 (978-0-618-43124-3(1)) Houghton Mifflin Co. Trade & Reference Div.

Van Dyne, Edith. Aunt Jane's Nieces in the Red Cross. rev. ed. 2006. 180p. 26.95 (978-1-4218-1724-8(1)); pap. 11.95 (978-1-4218-1824-5(8)) 1st World Publishing, Inc. (1st World Library - Literary Society).

Walters, Jennie. Standing in the Shadows 2. 2007. (Swallowcliffe Hall Trilogy: Book 2 Ser.). (Illus.). 256p. (J). pap. 9.99 (***978-0-689-87527-4(4)***, Pocket Bks.) Simon & Schuster, Ltd. GBR. *Dist:* Independent Pubs. Group.

WORLD WAR, 1914-1918—NAVAL OPERATIONS

McGowen, Tom. The Battle of Midway. 2002. (Cornerstones of Freedom Ser.). (Illus.). 32p. (J). (gr. 4-6). pap. 5.95 (978-0-516-25956-7(3), Children's Pr.) Scholastic Library Publishing.

Preston, Diana. Remember the Lusitania! (Illus.). (J). (gr. 3-7). 2004. 112p. 21.85 (978-0-8027-8847-4(5)); 2003. 102p. 20.95 (978-0-8027-8846-7(7)) Walker & Co.

WORLD WAR, 1914-1918—REGIMENTAL HISTORIES

McGowen, Tom. The Battle of Cantigny. 2002. (Cornerstones of Freedom Ser.). (Illus.). 48p. (J). (gr. 4-6). 26.00 (978-0-516-22264-6(3), Children's Pr.) Scholastic Library Publishing.

WORLD WAR, 1914-1918—UNITED STATES

Bosco, Peter & Bosco, Antoinette, revs. World War I. 2nd rev. ed. 2003. (America at War Ser.). (Illus.). 176p. (J). (gr. 6-12). 35.00 (978-0-8160-4940-0(8)) Facts On File, Inc.

Feldman, Ruth Tenzer. World War I. 2004. (Chronicle of America's Wars Ser.). (Illus.). 96p. (J). (gr. 5-12). 27.93 (978-0-8225-0148-0(1)) Lerner Publishing Group.

Hakim, Joy. War, Peace, & All That Jazz. 3rd ed. 2002. (Illus.). 218p. (J). (gr. 3-7). lib. bdg. 23.40 (978-0-613-55201-1(6)) Tandem Library Bks.

Hamilton, John. Final Years of World War I. 2004. (World War I Ser.). (Illus.). 32p. (J). (gr. 4-8). lib. bdg. 24.21 (978-1-57765-915-0(5)) ABDO Publishing Co.

Langellier, John P. American Indians in the U. S. Military: 1866-1945. 2001. (G. I. Ser.). (Illus.). 77p. (J). 32.00 (978-0-7910-6667-6(3), Chelsea Hse.) Facts On File, Inc.

McGraw-Hill Staff. The American Journey to World War 1, Active Reading Note-Taking Guide, Student Workbook. 2005. pap. 18.00 (978-0-07-870384-3(0), 9780078703843) Glencoe/McGraw-Hill.

—The American Journey to World War 1, Reading Essentials. 2005. pap., stu. ed., wbk. ed. 18.00 (978-0-07-873198-3(4), 9780078731983) Glencoe/McGraw-Hill.

—The American Journey to World War 1, Spanish Reading Essentials. 2005. pap., stu. ed., wbk. ed. 18.00 (978-0-07-873204-1(2), 9780078732041) Glencoe/McGraw-Hill.

—The American Journey to World War 1, Standardized Test Skills Practice Workbook, Student Edition. 2005. pap. 7.96 (978-0-07-873202-7(6), 9780078732027) Glencoe/McGraw-Hill.

—The American Journey to World War 1, StudentWorks Plus! 2005. (C). cd-rom 114.00 (978-0-07-873445-8(2), 9780078734458) Glencoe/McGraw-Hill.

Myers, Walter Dean. The Harlem Hellfighters: When Pride Met Courage. 2006. (Illus.). 160p. (J). 17.99 (978-0-06-001136-9(X), Amistad) HarperCollins Pubs.

Perrin, Pat, ed. World War I. 2001. (Researching American History Ser.). (Illus.). 56p. (J). pap. 7.95 (978-1-57960-075-4(1)) History Compass, LLC.

Worth, Richard. America in World War I. 2006. (Wars That Changed American History Ser.). (978-0-8368-7292-7(4)); pap. (978-0-8368-7301-6(7)) Stevens, Gareth Inc. (World Almanac Library).

WORLD WAR, 1939-1945

Adams, Simon. World War II. 2007. (DK Eyewitness Bks.). 72p. (J). (gr. 3-8). 15.99 incl. cd-rom (978-0-7566-3008-9(8)) Dorling Kindersley Publishing, Inc.

Adams, Simon & Dorling Kindersley Publishing Staff. World War II. Crawford, Andy, photos by. 2004. (Eyewitness Books). (Illus.). 72p. (J). (ps-7). lib. bdg. 19.99 (978-0-7566-0742-5(6)) Dorling Kindersley Publishing, Inc.

Aleckson, Paul & Kegel, James. World War II: Stories from Our Veterans: Wisconsin Veterans & Beyond. 2001. 300p. pap. 22.95 (978-0-9708063-0-7(2)) D.C. Everest Schl. District.

Ambrose, Stephen E. The Good Fight: How World War II Was Won. 2001. (Illus.). 96p. (J). (gr. 4-12). 19.95 (978-0-689-84361-7(5), Atheneum) Simon & Schuster Children's Publishing.

America's Secret Weapon: The Navajo Code Talkers of World War II. 2005. (Book Treks Ser.). (J). 37.95 (978-0-7652-3246-5(4)) Celebration Pr.

Beaver, Michael D. Uniforms of the Waffen SS. 2002. (Illus.). (gr. 10-13). Vol. 1. 352p. 79.95 (978-0-7643-1550-3(1)); Vol. 2. 368p. 79.95 (978-0-7643-1551-0(X)); Vol. 3. 272p. 79.95 (978-0-7643-1552-7(8)) Schiffer Publishing, Ltd.

Bell-Rehwoldt, Sheri. Great World War II Projects You Can Build Yourself. 2006. (Build It Yourself Ser.). (Illus.). 128p. (J). pap. 14.95 (978-0-9771294-1-6(1)) Nomad Pr.

Benge, Janet Hazel & Benge, Geoffrey Francis. Betty Greene. 2000. (Christian Heroes Ser.). 200p. (gr. 5-9). pap. 8.99 (978-1-57658-152-0(7)) YWAM Publishing.

Bible, Don. Third Reich Warrant Discs: 1934-1945. 2001. (Illus.). 48p. pap. 19.95 (978-0-7643-1429-2(7)) Schiffer Publishing, Ltd.

Britton, Tamara L. World War II Memorial. 2005. (Illus.). 32p. (J). (gr. k-6). lib. bdg. 22.78 (978-1-59197-837-4(8)) ABDO Publishing Co.

Burgan, Michael. The Japanese American Internment: Civil Liberties Denied. 2006. (Snapshots in History Ser.). (Illus.). 96p. lib. bdg. (***978-0-7565-2453-1(9)***) Compass Point Bks.

Butterfield, Moira. Going to War in World War Two. Bergin, Mark, illus. 2001. (Armies of the Past Ser.). 32p. (J). (gr. 3-6). 25.50 (978-0-531-14596-8(4), Watts, Franklin) Scholastic Library Publishing.

Colp, Jean C. The Walk Through Hell. 2002. (gr. 7-12). lib. bdg. 26.90 (978-0-613-79788-7(4)) Tandem Library Bks.

Connolly, Sean. World War I. 2003. (Witness to History Ser.). (Illus.). 56p. (J). (gr. 6-8). lib. bdg. 27.07 (978-1-4034-0972-0(2)) Heinemann Library.

—World War II. 2003. (Illus.). 56p. (J). pap. 8.95 (978-1-4034-3641-2(X)) Heinemann Library.

—World War II. 2003. (gr. 5-8). lib. bdg. 17.60 (978-0-613-61004-9(0)) Tandem Library Bks.

Conway, John Richard. Primary Source Accounts of World War II. 2006. (America's Wars Through Primary Sources Ser.). (Illus.). 128p. (J). lib. bdg. 33.27 (978-1-59845-002-6(6), MyReportLinks.com Bks.) Enslow Pubs., Inc.

Cooper, Michael L. Fighting for Honor: Japanese Americans & World War II. 2000. (Illus.). 128p. (J). (gr. 5-9). tchr. ed. 18.00 (978-0-395-91375-8(6), Clarion Bks.) Houghton Mifflin Co. Trade & Reference Div.

Copeland, Peter F. Story of World War II. 2004. (Illus.). 48p. (J). pap. 3.95 (978-0-486-43695-1(0)) Dover Pubns., Inc.

D Clare, John. Hodder 20th Century History: Vietnam 1939-75 2nd Edition - Foundation Edition. 2nd rev. ed. 2004. (Illus.). 48p. pap. 26.50 (***978-0-340-81476-5(4)***, Hodder Murray) Hodder Education GBR. *Dist:* Trans-Atlantic Pubns., Inc.

Deary, Terry. The Blitzed Brits. 1998. (Horrible Histories Ser.). 128p. (J). (gr. 2-5). pap. 6.99 (978-0-590-55825-9(0)) Scholastic, Inc.

—ESA Deplorable Segunda Guerra Mundial. 2001. Tr. of Woeful Second World War. (SPA.). (gr. 7-12). lib. bdg. 18.75 (978-0-613-79907-2(0)) Tandem Library Bks.

Dickson, Keith. World War II Almanac, 2 vols., Set. Facts on File, Inc. Staff, ed. 2008. (Almanacs of American Wars Ser.). 1088p. (gr. 9). 125.00 (978-0-8160-6297-3(8)) Facts On File, Inc.

Downing, David. Fighting Back. 2005. (World Almanac Library of the Holocaust). (Illus.). 48p. pap. (978-0-8368-5953-9(7), World Almanac Library) Stevens, Gareth Inc.

Dowswell, Paul. Second world war - internet Linked. Le, Leonard Rolland, illus. 2005. 128p. (J). 19.99 (978-0-7945-1044-2(2), Usborne) EDC Publishing.

—True Stories of the Second World War. 2004. (True Adventure Stories Ser.). 144p. (J). pap. 4.95 (978-0-7945-0599-8(6)); lib. bdg. 12.95 (978-1-58086-615-6(8), Usborne) EDC Publishing.

—True Stories of the Second World War. 2003. (Illus.). 169p. (J). pap. (978-0-439-79127-4(8)) Scholastic, Inc.

—War Stories. Mcnee, Ian, illus. 2006. 432p. (J). pap. 12.99 (978-0-7945-1499-0(5), Usborne) EDC Publishing.

Duey, Kathleen. Janey G. Blue: Pearl Harbor, 1941. 2001. (American Diaries Ser.). (Illus.). (J). 11.64 (978-0-606-20545-0(4)) Tandem Library Bks.

Feinstein, Stephen. The 1940s from World War II to Jackie Robinson. (Decades of the 20th Century Ser.). (Illus.). 64p. 2000. (YA). (gr. 5-12). lib. bdg. 22.60 (978-0-7660-1428-2(2)); 2006. (J). lib. bdg. 27.93 (978-0-7660-2634-6(5)) Enslow Pubs., Inc.

Feldman, George B. World War II: Almanac, 2 vols. Slovey, Christine, ed. 1999. (Illus.). (J). (978-0-7876-3831-3(5)) Thomson Gale.

Feldman, George B., ed. World War II: Almanac, 2 vols., Set. 1999. (Illus.). 416p. (YA). (gr. 6 up). lib. bdg. 120.00 (978-0-7876-3830-6(7), GML00502-113597) Thomson Gale.

Fitzgerald, Brian. Under Fire in World War II. 2004. (On the Front Line Ser.). (Illus.). 48p. (J). pap. 8.95 (978-1-4109-1475-0(5)); (gr. 4-6). 29.93 (978-1-4109-1468-2(2)) Raintree.

—Under Fire in World War II. 2006. (On the Front Line Ser.). (Illus.). 48p. (978-1-4109-2198-7(0)); pap. (978-1-4109-2205-2(7)) Steck-Vaughn.

Fletcher, Robert A. Jeeps at War. Naples, Thomas R. et al, eds. Fletcher, Robert A., illus. 2007. (Illus.). 36p. (J). 19.95 (***978-0-9722961-1-3(5)***) Iron Mountain Pr.

Foreman, Michael. Memories of Childhood. ltd. ed. 2000. (Illus.). 192p. (J). (gr. 5 up). 35.00 (978-1-86205-408-0(8), Pavilion Bks., Ltd.) Anova Bks. GBR. *Dist:* Independent Pubs. Group.

Fowke, Bob. World War II. 2003. (Who? What? When? Ser.). (Illus.). 128p. pap. 9.99 (978-0-340-85187-6(2), Hodder & Stoughton) Hodder General Publishing Division GBR. *Dist:* Trafalgar Square Publishing.

Frank, Anne. Anne Frank: The Diary of a Young Girl. unabr. ed. 2001. (J). (gr. 3-8). pap. 26.90 incl. audio Spoken Arts, Inc.

Gerdes, Louise I. World War II. 2004. (gr. 10-12). 17.45 (978-0-7377-2536-0(2), Greenhaven Pr., Inc.) Thomson Gale.

Goldstein, Margaret J. World War II: Europe. 2004. (Chronicle of America's Wars Ser.). (Illus.). 96p. (J). (gr. 5-12). 27.93 (978-0-8225-0139-8(2)) Lerner Publishing Group.

Gourley, Catherine. War, Women, & the News: How Female Journalists Won the Battle to Cover World War II. 2007. (Illus.). 208p. (J). 21.99 (978-0-689-87752-0(8), Atheneum) Simon & Schuster Children's Publishing.

—Welcome to Molly's World, 1944: Growing up in World War Two America. 1999. (American Girls Collection). (Illus.). 64p. (J). (gr. 2 up). 14.95 (978-1-56247-773-8(0)) American Girl Publishing, Inc.

Grabowski, John F. Josef Mengele. 2003. (Heroes & Villains Ser.). (Illus.). 112p. (YA). 29.95 (978-1-59018-425-7(4), Lucent Bks.) Thomson Gale.

Grant, Reg. World War II. 2008. (Dk Readers Ser.). 192p. (J). (gr. 5-12). 24.99 (***978-0-7566-3830-6(5)***) Dorling Kindersley Publishing, Inc.

Graphic Battles of World War II, 6 bks., Set. Incl. Battle of Guadalcanal : Land & Sea Warfare in the South Pacific. Hama, Larry. (J). lib. bdg. 29.25 (***978-1-4042-0784-4(8)***); Battle of Iwo Jima : Guerilla Warfare in the Pacific. Hama, Larry. Williams, Anthony, illus. (YA). lib. bdg. 29.25 (978-1-4042-0781-3(3)); Battle of Midway : The Destruction of the Japanese Fleet. White, Steve. Elson, Richard, illus. (YA). lib. bdg. 29.25 (978-1-4042-0783-7(X)); Battle of the Bulge. Cain, Bill. (YA). lib. bdg. 29.25 (***978-1-4042-0782-0(1)***); D-Day. Murray, Doug. (YA). lib. bdg. 29.25 (***978-1-4042-0786-8(4)***); Pearl Harbor : A Day of Infamy. White Steve D. (YA). lib. bdg. 29.25 (978-1-4042-0785-1(6)); (Illus.). 48p. (gr. 5-8). 2007. 2007. Set lib. bdg. 175.50 (***978-1-4042-1052-3(0)***) Rosen Publishing Group, Inc., The.

Group/McGraw-Hill, Wright. History: World War II, 6 vols. (Book2WebTM Ser.). (gr. 4-8). 36.50 (978-0-322-04455-5(3)) Wright Group, The.

Harris, Nathaniel. The Rise of Hitler. 2004. (Illus.). 56p. (J). pap. 8.95 (978-1-4034-5526-0(0)); lib. bdg. 27.07 (978-1-4034-4866-8(3)) Heinemann Library.

Harris, Nathaniel. World War II. 2007. (J). (***978-1-84193-730-4(4)***) Smart Apple Media.

Hatt, Christine. World War II, 1939-45. 2001. (Documenting History Ser.). (Illus.). 64p. (J). (gr. 8-12). 24.50 (978-0-531-14612-5(X), Watts, Franklin) Scholastic Library Publishing.

Haugen, Brenda. Adolf Hitler: Dictator of Nazi Germany. 2006. (Signature Lives Ser.). (Illus.). 112p. (J). (gr. 5-7). 30.60 (978-0-7565-1589-8(0)) Compass Point Bks.

Haugen, David M., ed. World War II: Primary Sources. 2002. (American War Library). (Illus.). 112p. (J). 29.95 (978-1-59018-204-8(9), Lucent Bks.) Thomson Gale.

Hibbert, Adam. In the Trenches During World War II. 2004. (On the Front Line Ser.). (Illus.). 48p. (J). 29.93 (978-1-4109-1466-8(6)); pap. 8.95 (978-1-4109-1473-6(9)) Raintree.

Hills, Ken & Barber, Nicola. Headlines of World War II. 2005. (Illus.). 46p. (J). pap. 13.95 (978-0-237-52908-6(4), Evans Brothers, Limited) Evans Publishing Group GBR. *Dist:* Independent Pubs. Group.

Holder, Nancy. Pearl Harbor, 1941. 2001. (Illus.). (J). (978-0-606-21379-0(1)) Tandem Library Bks.

Hynson, Colin. World War II: A Primary Source History. 2005. (Illus.). 48p. 26.00 (978-0-8368-5983-6(9)) Stevens, Gareth Inc.

In the Trenches During World War II 6-Pack. 2004. (Illus.). pap. 48.35 (978-1-4109-1480-4(1)) Raintree.

Jentz, Thomas L. & Doyle, Hilary L. Germany's Panzer in World War Two: From Pz. Kpfw. I to Tiger II. 2001. (Schiffer Military History Ser.). (Illus.). 216p. (gr. 10-13). 29.95 (978-0-7643-1425-4(4)) Schiffer Publishing, Ltd.

Jordan, Shirley. World War II: Moments in History. 1999. (Cover-to-Cover Bks.). (Illus.). 64p. (J). pap. 8.95 (978-0-7891-2907-9(8)); (gr. 4-7). lib. bdg. 17.95 (978-0-7807-8166-5(X)) Perfection Learning Corp.

Kelly, Nigel. The Fall of the Berlin Wall: The Cold War Ends. 2001. (Point of Impact Ser.). (Illus.). 32p. (J). (gr. 5-7). lib. bdg. 24.22 (978-1-57572-413-3(8)) Heinemann Library.

—The Fall of the Berlin Wall: The Cold War Ends. 2001. (Point of Impact Ser.). (Illus.). (J). 14.30 (978-0-606-21993-8(5)) Tandem Library Bks.

Keyes, Anna. Los numeros de la Segunda Guerra Mundial & World War II: By the Numbers. 2005. spiral bd. 88.00 (***978-1-4108-5736-1(0)***) Benchmark Education Co.

King, David C. World War II Days: Discover the Past with Exciting Projects, Games, Activities A. 2000. (gr. 3-6). lib. bdg. 22.20 (978-0-613-84559-5(5)) Tandem Library Bks.

Krull, Kathleen. V Is for Victory: America Remembers World War II. 2000. (Illus.). 115p. (YA). (gr. 7-9). reprint ed. 24.00 (978-0-7881-6883-3(5)) DIANE Publishing Co.

Kuhn, Betsy. Angels of Mercy: The Army Nurses of World War II. Kuhn, Betsy, photos by. 1999. (Illus.). 128p. (J). (gr. 5-9). 26.00 (978-0-689-82044-1(5), Atheneum) Simon & Schuster Children's Publishing.

Langellier, John P. American Indians in the U. S. Armed Forces, 1866-1945. Vol. 20. 2006. (G. I. Ser.: Vol. 20). (Illus.). 72p. pap. 14.95 (978-1-85367-408-2(7)) Greenhill Bks./Lionel Leventhal, Ltd. GBR. *Dist:* MBI Distribution Services.

Marchione, Margherita. Pope Pius XII: Bilingual Coloring Book. Elliott, John, illus. 2004. (SPA & ENG.). 32p. 1.00 (978-0-8091-6721-0(2), 6721-2) Paulist Pr.

Marquette, Scott. World War II. 2003. (America at War Ser.). (Illus.). 48p. (gr. 4-8). 20.95 (978-1-58952-393-7(8)) Rourke Publishing, LLC.

Marsh, Carole. World War II Reproducible Activity Book (PB) 2004. 28p. (gr. 4-12). pap. 5.95 (***978-0-635-02678-1(3)***) Gallopade International.

Maybury, Richard J. World War II: The Rest of the Story & How It Affects You Today, 1930 to September 11 2001. Williams, Jane A., ed. rev. ed. 2003. ("Uncle Eric" Bk.). 349p. (YA). pap. 19.95 (978-0-942617-43-6(6)) Bluestocking Pr.

McNeil, Niki, et al. HOCPP 1089 World War II. 2006. spiral bd. 24.50 (***978-1-60308-089-7(9)***) In the Hands of a Child.

Moore, Willamarie. StarFestival Grades 3-6 World War II Team: Exploring Cultural Heritage. Miyagawa, Shigeru, ed. 2000. (Illus.). 50p. (J). (gr. 3-6). pap., stu. ed., wbk. ed. 10.00 (978-1-929724-07-9(1)) StarFestival, Inc.

Myers, Walter Dean. The Journal of Scott Pendelton Collins: A World War II Soldier. 2003. (My Name Is America Ser.). 144p. (J). 12.95 (978-0-439-55503-6(5)) Scholastic, Inc.

Nelson, Peter. Left for Dead. 2003. 224p. (YA). (gr. 7). pap. 8.95 (978-0-385-73091-4(8), Delacorte Bks. for Young Readers) Random Hse. Children's Bks.

—Left for Dead: A Young Man's Search for Justice for the USS Indianapolis. 2003. (gr. 5-8). lib. bdg. 17.60 (978-0-613-70819-7(9)) Tandem Library Bks.

O'Neill, William L. World War II: A Student Companion. 1999. (Student Companions to American History Ser.). (Illus.). 384p. (YA). (gr. 7 up). 60.00 (978-0-19-510800-2(0)) Oxford Univ. Pr., Inc.

Opdyke, Irene Gut & Armstrong, Jennifer. In My Hands: Memories of a Holocaust Rescuer. 2001. (YA). 18.65 (978-0-606-20721-8(X)) Tandem Library Bks.

Oppenheim, Joanne. Dear Miss Breed: True Stories of the Japanese American Incarceration During World War II & a Librarian Who Made a Difference. 2006. (Illus.). 288p. (J). (gr. 7 up). pap. 22.99 (978-0-439-56992-7(3)) Scholastic, Inc.

Panchyk, Richard. World War II for Kids: A History with 21 Activities. 2002. (For Kids Ser.). (Illus.). 176p. (J). (gr. 4 up). pap. 14.95 (978-1-55652-455-4(2)) Chicago Review Pr., Inc.

—World War II for Kids: A History with 21 Activities. 2002. (Illus.). 164p. (J). (ps-7). lib. bdg. 24.55 (978-0-613-61136-7(5)) Tandem Library Bks.

Parsons, Martin. Evacuation. (Illus.). 32p. (J). pap. (978-0-7502-2844-2(X), Hodder Wayland) Hodder Children's Division.

—Rationing. (Illus.). 32p. pap. (978-0-7502-2846-6(6), Hodder Wayland) Hodder Children's Division.

—Women's War. (Illus.). 31p. (YA). pap. (978-0-7502-2845-9(8), Hodder Wayland) Hodder Children's Division.

Ramen, Fred. Hermann Goering: Hitler's Second in Command. 2005. (Holocaust Biographies Ser.). (Illus.). 112p. (YA). (gr. 7-12). lib. bdg. 26.50 (978-0-8239-3307-5(5), HBGORI) Rosen Publishing Group, Inc., The.

Reynoldson, Fiona. The Home Front. (Illus.). 48p. (J). pap. (978-0-7502-2696-7(X), Hodder Wayland) Hodder Children's Division.

Roberts, Jeremy. Joseph Goebbels: Nazi Propaganda Minister. 2005. (Holocaust Biographies Ser.). (Illus.). 112p. (J). (gr. 7-12). lib. bdg. 26.50 (978-0-8239-3309-9(1), HBGOEB) Rosen Publishing Group, Inc., The.

Robson, Pam. The Second World War, 1939-1945. 2nd ed. 2003. (Illus.). 48p. pap. (978-0-7500-2147-0(0), Hodder Wayland) Hodder Children's Division.

Ross, Stewart. The Home Front in World War II. (Illus.). 32p. 22.99 (978-0-7502-4184-7(5), Hodder & Stoughton) Hodder General Publishing Division GBR. *Dist:* Trafalgar Square Publishing.

Rubin, Susan Goldman. The Flag with Fifty-Six Stars: A Gift from the Survivors of Mauthausen. Farnsworth, Bill, illus. 2005. 40p. (J). (gr. 1-5). 16.95 (978-0-8234-1653-0(4)) Holiday Hse., Inc.

Ruggiero, Adriane. World War II. 2002. (American Voices From Ser.). (Illus.). xxi, 117p. (J). 34.21 (978-0-7614-1206-9(9), Benchmark Bks.) Cavendish, Marshall Corp.

Santella, Andrew. Navajo Code Talkers. 2004. (We the People Ser.). (Illus.). 48p. (J). (gr. 4 up). lib. bdg. 22.60 (978-0-7565-0611-7(5)) Compass Point Bks.

Schomp, Virginia. World War II. 2001. (Letters from the Home Front Ser.). (Illus.). 96p. (J). (gr. 6 up). lib. bdg. 29.93 (978-0-7614-1098-0(8), Benchmark Bks.) Cavendish, Marshall Corp.

Schur, Maxine Rose. Hannah Szenes: A Song of Light. rev. ed. 1998. 106p. pap. 9.95 (978-0-8276-0628-9(1)) Jewish Pubn. Society.

Scott, Janine. The Two Great Wars. 2007. (Shockwave: History & Politics Ser.). (Illus.). 36p. (J). (gr. 4-6). lib. bdg. 25.00 (***978-0-531-17756-3(4)***, Children's Pr.) Scholastic Library Publishing.

Senker, Cath. World War II. 2005. (How Did It Happen? Ser.). (Illus.). 48p. (YA). (gr. 7-10). lib. bdg. 29.95 (978-1-59018-604-6(4), Lucent Bks.) Thomson Gale.

Shapiro, Stephen & Forrester, Tina. Ultra Hush-Hush: Espionage & Special Missions. Craig, David, illus. 2003. (Outwitting the Enemy Ser.). 96p. (J). (gr. 5-12). lib. bdg. 29.95 (978-1-55037-779-8(5)) Annick Pr., Ltd. CAN. *Dist:* Firefly Bks., Ltd.

—Ultra Hush-hush: Espionage & Special Missions. Craig, David, illus. 2003. (Stories from the Second World War Ser.). 96p. (J). (gr. 5-12). pap. 14.95 (978-1-55037-778-1(7)) Annick Pr., Ltd. CAN. *Dist:* Firefly Bks., Ltd.

SHARMAN, et al. Headlines of World War II. 2005. (Illus.). 46p. (J). 24.95 (978-0-237-52997-0(1) , Evans Brothers, Limited) Evans Publishing Group GBR. *Dist:* Independent Pubs. Group.

Sharpe, Mike. World War II. 1999. (History of Warfare Ser.). (Illus.). 80p. (YA). (gr. 7-12). 29.97 (978-0-8172-5451-3(X)) Raintree.

Sheehan, Sean. The Death Camps. 2001. (Holocaust Ser.). (Illus.). 64p. (J). (gr. 5-8). lib. bdg. 28.54 (978-0-7398-3258-5(1)) Raintree.

—From Jessie Owens to Hiroshima: The Mid 1930s to 1945. 2005. (Modern Eras Uncovered Ser.). (Illus.). 56p. (J). (978-1-4109-1786-7(X)); pap. (978-1-4109-1795-9(9)) Steck-Vaughn.

—Germany & Japan. 2001. (World Wars Ser.). (Illus.). 64p. (J). (978-0-7502-2635-6(8)) Steck-Vaughn.

—Modern Eras Uncovered: From Jesse Owens to Hiroshima. 2005. (Modern Eras Uncovered Ser.). (Illus.). 56p. (J). (978-1-84443-962-1(3)); (978-1-84443-952-2(6)) Steck-Vaughn.

—The Technology of World War II. 2003. (World Wars Ser.). (Illus.). 64p. (J). lib. bdg. 28.56 (978-0-7398-6064-9(X)) Raintree.

—World War II: Allied Victory. 2001. (World Wars Ser.). (Illus.). 64p. (J). (gr. 5). lib. bdg. 27.12 (978-0-7398-2755-0(3)) Raintree.

—World War II: Germany & Japan Attack. Sloan, Frank, ed. 2001. (World Wars Ser.). (Illus.). 64p. (J). (gr. 5). lib. bdg. 27.12 (978-0-7398-2754-3(5)) Raintree.

Shuter, Jane. Life & Death in the Camps. 2003. (Holocaust Ser.). (Illus.). 56p. (J). lib. bdg. 28.50 (978-1-4034-0812-9(2)); pap. 8.95 (978-1-4034-3204-9(X)) Heinemann Library.

Slovey, Christine, ed. World War II: Primary Sources. 2000. (World War II Reference Library). (Illus.). xxxix, 222p. (J). (gr. 6 up). 66.00 (978-0-7876-3896-2(X) , GML00502-113697, UXL) Thomson Gale.

Slovey, Christine, et al. World War II: Cumulative Index. 2000. 34p. (J). 5.00 (978-0-7876-3902-0(8)) Thomson Gale.

Smith, Frank Dabba. Elsie's War: A Story of Courage in Nazi Germany. (Illus.). 32p. (978-0-7112-1861-1(7)) Lincoln, Frances Ltd. GBR. *Dist:* Transition Vendor.

Stein, R. Conrad. World War II in Europe: "America Goes to War" 2000. (American War Ser.). (Illus.). 128p. (YA). (gr. 5-12). pap. 13.26 (978-0-7660-1733-7(8)) Enslow Pubs., Inc.

Stephens, Chris S. A Wartime Scrapbook. 2004. (Illus.). 32p. pap. 14.95 (978-1-84323-285-8(5)) Beekman Bks., Inc.

Streissguth, Thomas & Streissguth, Tom. Adolf Eichmann: Executing the Final Solution. 2005. (Holocaust Heroes & Nazi Criminals Ser.). (Illus.). 160p. (YA). (gr. 7-13). lib. bdg. 27.93 (978-0-7660-2575-2(6)) Enslow Pubs., Inc.

Tucker, Spencer C. & Roberts, Priscilla Mary, eds. World War II: A Student Encyclopedia, 5 Vols, Set. 2005. (Illus.). 2100p. lib. bdg. 485.00 (978-1-85109-857-6(7)) ABC-CLIO, Inc.

Under Fire in World War II, 6 Packs. 2004. (Illus.). pap. 48.35 (978-1-4109-1482-8(8)) Raintree.

Walker, Kate & Argaet, Elaine. Super Spies of World War II. 2003. (Spies & Spying Ser.). 32p. (J). lib. bdg. 24.25 (978-1-58340-340-2(X)) Smart Apple Media.

Wehrertuchtigungslager der Hitler-Jugend, 1942-1945. (GER.). (978-3-928379-00-7(3)) Verein zur Fordenrung der Umweltforschung.

Williams, Brian. World at War: World War II: Women at War. 2005. (World at War— World War II Ser.). (Illus.). 32p. tchr. ed. (978-0-431-10375-4(5)) Heinemann Library.

Wood, Tim & Unsted, R. J. The 1940s. 2005. (Picture History of the 20th Century Ser.). (Illus.). 48p. (J). (gr. 6-9). lib. bdg. 29.95 (978-1-932889-72-7(8)) Sea-To-Sea Pubns.

World War II. (My Folks Ser.). 224p. pap. 6.95 (978-0-941678-43-8(1)) Capper's Bks.

World War II. 2004. (Historical Reader Ser.). (Illus.). 224p. (gr. 6-12). 13.32 (978-0-395-98666-0(4) , 2-99910) McDougal Littell Inc.

World War II: PowerPoint Presentations in World History. 2005. cd-rom 49.95 net. (978-1-56004-209-9(5)) Social Studies Schl. Service.

World War II: The European Theater. 2nd ed. 2005. (Perspectives on History Ser.). (YA). pap. (978-1-932663-12-9(6)) History Compass, LLC.

World War Two. 2000. (Dk Eyewitness Books Ser.). 64p. (J). pap. 8.95 (978-0-7894-6299-2(0)) Dorling Kindersley Publishing, Inc.

The World Wars, 4 vols. 2003. (Illus.). (J). 114.24 (978-0-7398-6066-3(6)); 399.84 (978-0-7398-6067-0(4)) Raintree.

Worth, Richard. Heinrich Himmler: Murderous Architect of the Holocaust. 2005. (Holocaust Heroes & Nazi Criminals Ser.). (Illus.). 160p. (YA). (gr. 7-13). lib. bdg. 27.93 (978-0-7660-2532-5(2)) Enslow Pubs., Inc.

Wukovits, John F. World War II in Europe. 2004. (World History Ser.). (Illus.). 112p. (gr. 7-10). 32.45 (978-1-59018-185-0(9) , Lucent Bks.) Thomson Gale.

WWII Airplanes. (Color & Learn Ser.). 36p. (J). (gr. 1-5). pap. (978-1-882210-01-5(8)) Action Publishing, Inc.

Zeinert, Karen. To Touch the Stars: A Story of World War II. 2001. (Jamestown Classics Ser.). (Illus.). 126p. (C). (gr. 5-8). pap. 10.00 (978-0-8092-0630-8(7) , 9780809206308) Jamestown.

WORLD WAR, 1939-1945—AERIAL OPERATIONS

Aldrich, Dale & Hipperson, Carol Edgemon. The Belly Gunner. 2001. (Single Titles Ser.). (Illus.). 160p. (gr. 6 up). lib. bdg. 27.90 (978-0-7613-1873-6(9) , Twenty-First Century Bks.) Lerner Publishing Group.

Brook, Henry. True Stories of the Blitz - Internet Referenced. Mcnee, Ian, illus. 2006. 160p. (J). pap. 4.99 (978-0-7945-1245-3(3) , Usborne) EDC Publishing.

Brooks, Philip. The Tuskegee Airmen. 2004. (Illus.). 48p. (J). (gr. 4 up). lib. bdg. 22.60 (978-0-7565-0683-4(2)) Compass Point Bks.

Carey, Alan C. Leatherneck Bombers: Marine Corps B-25/PBJ Mitchell Squadrons in WWII. 2002. (Illus.). 112p. (gr. 10-13). pap. 24.95 (978-0-7643-1501-5(3)) Schiffer Publishing, Ltd.

George, Linda & George, Charles. The Tuskegee Airmen. 2001. (Cornerstones of Freedom Ser.). (Illus.). 32p. (J). (gr. 4-6). pap. 5.95 (978-0-516-27280-1(2) , Children's Pr.) Scholastic Library Publishing.

Group/McGraw-Hill, Wright. Al Ataque!, 6 vols. (First Explorers. Primeros Exploradores Nonfiction Sets Ser.). (SPA.). (gr. 1-2). 29.95 (978-0-7699-1477-0(2)) Shortland Pubns. (U. S. A.) Inc.

Haberlen, Klaus. A Luftwaffe Bomber Pilot Remembers: World War Two from the Cockpit. 2001. (Schiffer Military History Ser.). (Illus.). 208p. (gr. 10-13). 29.95 (978-0-7643-1393-6(2)) Schiffer Publishing, Ltd.

Hansen, Ole Steen. Military Aircraft of World War Two. 2003. (gr. 3-6). lib. bdg. 17.60 (978-0-613-59088-4(0)) Tandem Library Bks.

—Military Aircraft of WWII. 2003. (Story of Flight Ser.). (Illus.). 32p. (J). (gr. 4). pap. (978-0-7787-1219-0(2)); lib. bdg. (978-0-7787-1203-9(6)) Crabtree Publishing Co.

Harris, Nathaniel. Hiroshima. 2004. (Illus.). 56p. (J). 27.07 (978-1-4034-4872-9(8)); pap. (978-1-4034-6259-6(3)) Heinemann Library.

Hasday, Judy L. The Tuskegee Airmen. 2003. (American Mosaic Ser.). (Illus.). 112p. (gr. 6-12). 30.00 (978-0-7910-7267-7(3) , Chelsea Hse.) Facts On File, Inc.

Homan, Lynn M. & Reilly, Thomas. Tuskegee Airmen: American Heroes. Shepherd, Rosalie M., illus. 2002. 96p. (J). 14.95 (978-1-56554-994-4(5)) Pelican Publishing Co., Inc.

—The Tuskegee Airmen Story. Shepherd, Rosalie M., illus. 2002. 32p. (J). 15.95 (978-1-58980-005-2(2)) Pelican Publishing Co., Inc.

Klam, Julie. Air War! 2002. (Illus.). 48p. (J). lib. bdg. 28.50 (978-1-58340-189-7(X)) Smart Apple Media.

Koestler-Grack, Rachel A. Eddie Rickenbacker. 2003. (Famous Flyers Ser.). (Illus.). 112p. (gr. 6-12). 30.00 (978-0-7910-7215-8(0) , Chelsea Hse.) Facts On File, Inc.

McGowen, Tom. Air Raid! The Bombing Campaigns of World War II. 2001. (Military Might Ser.: 8). (Illus.). 64p. (J). (gr. 5-8). lib. bdg. 26.90 (978-0-7613-1810-1(0) , Twenty-First Century Bks.) Lerner Publishing Group.

—Assault from the Sky: Airborne Infantry of World War II. 2002. (Military Might Ser.). (Illus.). 64p. (J). (gr. 5-8). lib. bdg. 26.90 (978-0-7613-1809-5(7) , Twenty-First Century Bks.) Lerner Publishing Group.

Mullaney, Patricia E. Documentary of an Airman' Tour with the Eighth 1944-1945. 2003. (Illus.). 355p. cd-rom 34.99 (978-1-893767-02-7(7)) E-Booksgen.

Nathan, Amy. Yankee Doodle Gals: Women Pilots of World War II. 2001. (Illus.). 96p. (J). (gr. 3-7). 21.00 (978-0-7922-8216-7(7) , National Geographic Children's Bks.) National Geographic Society.

Parsons, Martin. Air Raids. (Illus.). 32p. pap. 12.99 (978-0-7502-2843-5(1) , Hodder & Stoughton) Hodder General Publishing Division GBR. *Dist:* Trafalgar Square Publishing.

Perkins, Brent William. Memphis Belle: Biography of a B-17 Flying Fortress. 2002. (Illus.). 224p. (gr. 10-13). 45.00 (978-0-7643-1499-5(8)) Schiffer Publishing, Ltd.

Prien, Jochen & Stemmer, Gerhard. Jagdgeswader 3 Udet in WWII: II. /Jg 3 in Action with the Messerschmitt Bf 109. 2003. (Illus.). 408p. (gr. 10-13). 69.95 (978-0-7643-1774-3(1)) Schiffer Publishing, Ltd.

Rice, Earle, Jr. Claire Chennault. 2003. (Famous Flyers Ser.). (Illus.). 112p. (gr. 6-12). 30.00 (978-0-7910-7217-2(7)); pap. 30.00 (978-0-7910-7499-2(4)) Facts On File, Inc. (Chelsea Hse.).

Rice, Earle. Claire Chennault: Flying Tigers. 2003. (gr. 5-8). lib. bdg. 18.75 (978-0-613-65196-7(0)) Tandem Library Bks.

Rice, Earle, Jr. Kamikazes. 1999. (American War Library). (Illus.). 128p. (YA). (gr. 4-12). 27.45 (978-1-56006-373-5(4) , LML00902-177758, Lucent Bks.) Thomson Gale.

Rice, Earle. Manfred Von Richthofen. 2003. (Famous Flyers Ser.). (Illus.). 112p. (gr. 6-12). 30.00 (978-0-7910-7214-1(2) , Chelsea Hse.) Facts On File, Inc.

Roberts, Marjorie H., told to. Wingtip to Wingtip: 8 WASPS, Women's Airforce Service Pilots of World War II. 2000. (Illus.). ix, 128p. (J). pap. 15.95 (978-1-928760-01-6(5)) Aviatrix Publishing, Inc.

Sears, Stephen. Air War Against Hitler's Germany. 2005. 176p. pap. 9.95 (978-1-59687-004-8(4)) ibooks, Inc.

Williams, Brian. World at War: World War II: Life As a Fighter Pilot. 2005. (World at War— World War II Ser.). (Illus.). 32p. tchr. ed. (978-0-431-10379-2(8)) Heinemann Library.

WORLD WAR, 1939-1945—AFRICAN AMERICANS

Brooks, Philip. The Tuskegee Airmen. 2004. (Illus.). 48p. (J). (gr. 4 up). lib. bdg. 22.60 (978-0-7565-0683-4(2)) Compass Point Bks.

Bruning, John Robert, Jr. Elusive Glory: African-American Heroes of World War II. 2001. (Illus.). 144p. (J). (gr. 6-12). pap. 19.95 (978-1-888105-48-3(8)) Avisson Pr., Inc.

Coggins, Patrick C. The Tuskegee Airmen: Flying from the Ground Up. 2001. (Illus.). 165p. (YA). pap. (978-1-892558-03-9(3)) Kreyol Connection Pubns.

Fleischman, John. Black & White Airmen: Their True History. 2007. (Illus.). 160p. (J). (gr. 5 up). 20.00 (978-0-618-56297-8(4)) Houghton Mifflin Co.

George, Linda & George, Charles. The Tuskegee Airmen. 2001. (Cornerstones of Freedom Ser.). (Illus.). 32p. (J). (gr. 4-6). pap. 5.95 (978-0-516-27280-1(2) , Children's Pr.) Scholastic Library Publishing.

Hasday, Judy L. The Tuskegee Airmen. 2003. (American Mosaic Ser.). (Illus.). 112p. (gr. 6-12). 30.00 (978-0-7910-7267-7(3) , Chelsea Hse.) Facts On File, Inc.

Homan, Lynn M. & Reilly, Thomas. Tuskegee Airmen: American Heroes. Shepherd, Rosalie M., illus. 2002. 96p. (J). 14.95 (978-1-56554-994-4(5)) Pelican Publishing Co., Inc.

—The Tuskegee Airmen Story. Shepherd, Rosalie M., illus. 2002. 32p. (J). 15.95 (978-1-58980-005-2(2)) Pelican Publishing Co., Inc.

Ruggiero, Adriane. World War II. 2002. (American Voices From Ser.). (Illus.). xxi, 117p. (J). 34.21 (978-0-7614-1206-9(9) , Benchmark Bks.) Cavendish, Marshall Corp.

WORLD WAR, 1939-1945—BATTLES

see World War, 1939-1945—Campaigns

WORLD WAR, 1939-1945—BIOGRAPHY

Boomhower, Ray E. The Soldier's Friend: A Life of Ernie Pyle. 2006. (Illus.). 134p. 17.95 (978-0-87195-200-4(9)) Indiana Historical Society.

Bozuwa, Titia. In the Shadow of the Cathedral: Growing up in Holland During WW II. 2004. (ENG & DUT., Illus.). 199p. 22.95 (978-0-9754825-0-6(5)); 212p. per. 15.95 (978-0-9754825-1-3(3)) Triple Tulip Pr.

Bryant, Jen. Music for the End of Time. Peck, Beth, illus. 2005. 32p. (J). (gr. 3-5). 17.00 (978-0-8028-5229-8(7)) Eerdmans, William B. Publishing Co.

Cappadocio-Hashagen, Maria. I Remember: My Memories of World War II. 2002. 60p. per. 9.95 (978-1-931934-02-2(9)) Back Yard Pub.

Cefrey, Holly. Dr. Josef Mengele: The Angel of Death. 2005. (Holocaust Biographies Ser.). (Illus.). 112p. (YA). (gr. 7-12). lib. bdg. 26.50 (978-0-8239-3374-7(1)) Rosen Publishing Group, Inc., The.

Colman, Penny. Where the Action Was: Women War Correspondents in World War II. 2002. (Illus.). 128p. (J). (gr. 5 up). lib. bdg. 19.99 (978-0-517-80076-8(4) , Crown Books For Young Readers) Random Hse. Children's Bks.

DeMallie, H. R. Behind Enemy Lines: A Young Pilot's Story. 2007. (Sterling Point Bks.). (Illus.). 192p. (J). (gr. 6-9). 12.95 (978-1-4027-4517-1(6)) Sterling Publishing Co., Inc.

Dolan, Sean. Adolf Eichmann: Engineer of Death. 2005. (Holocaust Biographies Ser.). (Illus.). 112p. (J). (gr. 7-12). lib. bdg. 26.50 (978-0-8239-3308-2(3) , HBE-ICH) Rosen Publishing Group, Inc., The.

Gifford, Clive. World War II: True Stories. (Illus.). 128p. (J). pap. (978-0-340-80497-1(1) , Hodder Children's Books) Hodder Children's Division.

Hardin, Travis. The Young Writers Series: Called to Serve. 2007. (YA). pap. 5.99 (***978-1-58158-108-9(4)***) McDougal Publishing Co.

Hurwitz, Johanna. Anne Frank: Life in Hiding. 1999. (Illus.). 64p. (J). (gr. 4-7). pap. 4.99 (978-0-380-73254-8(8) , Harper Trophy) HarperCollins Pubs.

—Anne Frank: Life in Hiding. 1999. (gr. 3-6). lib. bdg. 12.95 (978-0-7857-1451-4(0)) Tandem Library Bks.

Knapp, Ron, et al. American Generals of World War II. 1998. (Collective Biographies Ser.). (Illus.). 128p. (YA). (gr. 6-12). lib. bdg. 26.60 (978-0-7660-1024-6(4)) Enslow Pubs., Inc.

Lace, William W. Leaders & Generals. 1999. (American War Library). (Illus.). 112p. (YA). (gr. 4-12). 28.70 (978-1-56006-664-4(4) , LML00902-178016, Lucent Bks.) Thomson Gale.

Rice, Earle. Erwin J. E. Rommel. 2003. (Great Military Leaders of the Twentieth Century Ser.). (Illus.). 112p. (gr. 6-12). 30.00 (978-0-7910-7405-3(6) , Chelsea Hse.) Facts On File, Inc.

—George S. Patton. 2003. (Great Military Leaders of the Twentieth Century Ser.). (Illus.). 112p. (gr. 6-12). 30.00 (978-0-7910-7403-9(X) , Chelsea Hse.) Facts On File, Inc.

Ross, Stewart. Leaders of World War II. 2001. (World Wars Ser.). (Illus.). 64p. (J). (gr. 5). lib. bdg. 27.12 (978-0-7398-2756-7(1)) Raintree.

Ruelle, Karen Gray & DeSaix, Deborah Durland. Hidden on the Mountain: Stories of Children Sheltered from the Nazis in Le Chambon. 2006. (Illus.). 272p. (J). (gr. 5 up). 24.95 (978-0-8234-1928-9(2)) Holiday Hse., Inc.

Sohma, Tanemichi. Michi, Hedda Hopper's Houseboy. 2002. 224p. per. 14.95 (978-0-9724172-0-4(6)) Southern Washington Pr.

Wee, Patricia Hachten & Wee, Robert James. World War II in Literature for Youth: A Guide & Resource Book. 2004. 404p. pap. 53.00 (978-0-8108-5301-0(9)) Scarecrow Pr., Inc.

Welter, Anni. Child of War: How We Lived & Survived under the Third Reich. 2nd ed. 2003. Orig. Title: Child of the Third Reich: How We Lived & Survived. 160p. (YA). per. 14.95 (978-0-9741434-0-8(5)) A H W Publishing.

Wills, Charles & Dorling Kindersley Publishing Staff. World War II Battles & Leaders. 2004. (Battles & Leaders Ser.). (Illus.). 96p. (J). pap. 9.99 (978-0-7566-0260-4(2)); (gr. 8). 16.99 (978-0-7566-0259-8(9)) Dorling Kindersley Publishing, Inc.

WORLD WAR, 1939-1945—CAMPAIGNS

see also Ardennes, Battle Of The, 1944-1945; Britain, Battle of, 1940; Guadalcanal, Battle of, Solomon Islands, 1942-1943; Iwo Jima, Battle of, Japan, 1945; Midway, Battle Of, 1942; Stalingrad, Battle of, Volgograd, Russia, 1942-1943

Abnett, Dan & Murray, Doug. The Tide Turns: D-Day Invasion. Elson, Richard & Williams, Anthony, illus. 2007. (Graphic History Ser.). 48p. (J). (gr. 3-7). pap. 9.95 (978-1-84603-056-7(0)) Osprey Publishing, Ltd. GBR. *Dist:* Random Hse., Inc.

Aldrich, Dale & Hipperson, Carol Edgemon. The Belly Gunner. 2001. (Single Titles Ser.). (Illus.). 160p. (gr. 6 up). lib. bdg. 27.90 (978-0-7613-1873-6(9) , Twenty-First Century Bks.) Lerner Publishing Group.

Anderson, Christopher A. The Fall of Fortress Europe. 2001. (G. I. Ser.). (Illus.). 80p. (J). 27.50 (978-0-7910-6669-0(X) , Chelsea Hse.) Facts On File, Inc.

—The Marines in World War II. 2001. (G. I. Ser.). (Illus.). 80p. (J). 27.50 (978-0-7910-6671-3(1) , Chelsea Hse.) Facts On File, Inc.

Anderson, Christopher J. Patton's Third Army. 1999. (G. I. Ser.). (Illus.). 80p. (gr. 5 up). 27.50 (978-0-7910-5374-4(1) , Chelsea Hse.) Facts On File, Inc.

Barber, Nicola. The Western Front. 2003. (Questioning History Ser.). (J). lib. bdg. 28.50 (978-1-58340-268-9(3)) Smart Apple Media.

Bednarz, Robert, et al. TIME for Kids Readers: Omaha Beach, Normandy. 3rd ed. 2002. (Harcourt Horizons Ser.). (gr. k-7). pap. 38.10 (978-0-15-335303-1(1)) Harcourt Schl. Pubs.

Bliven, Bruce, Jr. Invasion: The Story of D-Day. 2007. (Sterling Point Bks.). (Illus.). 176p. (J). 12.95 (978-1-4027-4521-8(4)); pap. 6.95 (978-1-4027-4141-8(3)) Sterling Publishing Co., Inc.

Boroughs, Ralph Z. The Devil's Tale: Stories of the Red Devils of the 508 Parachute Infantry Regiment 82nd Airborne Division in World War Two. Gintjee, Thomas J., illus. 2002. xii, 341p. (YA). mass mkt. 15.00 (978-0-9720657-0-2(9) , 2515) Zig Boroughs.

Brook, Henry. True Stories of D-Day. McNee, Ian, illus. 2006. 160p. (J). pap. (***978-0-439-89833-1(1)***) Scholastic, Inc.

Chorlton, Windsor. Weapons & Technology of World War II. 2002. (20th-Century Perspectives Ser.). (Illus.). 48p. (J). (gr. 5-7). lib. bdg. 27.07 (978-1-58810-663-6(2)); Set 2. pap. 7.95 (978-1-58810-923-1(2) , 91514) Heinemann Library.

Connolly, Sean. D-Day Landings. 2003. (Illus.). 56p. (J). pap. 8.50 (978-1-4034-4575-9(3)); lib. bdg. 27.07 (978-1-4034-4567-4(2)) Heinemann Library.

Donlan, Leni. How Did This Happen Here? Japanese Internment Camps. 2007. (***978-1-4109-2701-9(6)***); pap. (***978-1-4109-2712-5(1)***) Steck-Vaughn.

Dowswell, Paul. The Western Front in World War One. (Illus.). 32p. (978-0-7502-4183-0(7) , Hodder Wayland) Hodder Children's Division.

Drez, Ronald J. Remember D-Day: Both Sides Tell Their Stories. 2004. (Remember Ser.). (Illus.). 64p. (J). (gr. 5). 17.95 (978-0-7922-6666-2(8)); 27.90 (978-0-7922-6965-6(9)) National Geographic Society. (National Geographic Children's Bks.).

Ending the War Against Japan: Science, Morality, & the Atomic Bomb, 2 bks. 4th ed. 2005. (Illus.). 100p. (YA). pap. (978-1-891306-83-9(9)) Choices Education Program, Watson Institute, Brown Univ.

Grant, Reg. World War II: Europe. 2004. (Atlas of Conflicts Ser.). (Illus.). 64p. pap. 11.95 (978-0-8368-5676-7(7)); lib. bdg. 32.67 (978-0-8368-5669-9(4)) Stevens, Gareth Inc. (World Almanac Library).

Hansen, Ole Steen. Great Battles of World War II. 2001. (World Wars Ser.). (Illus.). 64p. (J). (gr. 5). lib. bdg. 27.12 (978-0-7398-2757-4(X)) Raintree.

Harris, Nathaniel. Hiroshima. 2004. (Illus.). 56p. (J). 27.07 (978-1-4034-4872-9(8)); pap. (978-1-4034-6259-6(3)) Heinemann Library.

Hatch, Alden. General George Patton: Old Blood & Guts. 2006. (Sterling Point Bks.). (Illus.). 208p. (J). 12.95 (978-1-4027-3186-0(8)); pap. 6.95 (978-1-4027-3614-8(2)) Sterling Publishing Co., Inc.

Heaton, Colin D. German Anti-Partisan Warfare in Europe: 1939-1945. 2001. (Schiffer Military History Ser.). (Illus.). 480p. (gr. 10-13). 29.95 (978-0-7643-1395-0(9)) Schiffer Publishing, Ltd.

Hynson, Colin. D-Day. 2004. (Days That Changed the World Ser.). (Illus.). 48p. (J). (gr. 5 up). pap. 11.95 (978-0-8368-5575-3(2)); lib. bdg. 30.00 (978-0-8368-5568-5(X)) Stevens, Gareth Inc. (World Almanac Library).

Klam, Julie. From D-Day to V-E Day. 2002. (Illus.). 48p. (J). lib. bdg. 28.50 (978-1-58340-191-0(1)) Smart Apple Media.

—Victory in the Pacific. 2002. (Illus.). 48p. (J). lib. bdg. 28.50 (978-1-58340-192-7(X)) Smart Apple Media.

Krensky, Stephen. Pearl Harbor. 2001. (gr. 3-6). lib. bdg. 11.80 (978-0-613-35550-6(4)); (Illus.). (J). (978-0-606-21378-3(3)) Tandem Library Bks.

McGowen, Tom. D-Day. 2004. (Cornerstones of Freedom Ser.). (J). 26.00 (978-0-516-24245-3(8) , Children's Pr.) Scholastic Library Publishing.

McNeese, Tim. Battle of the Bulge. (Great Battles Through the Ages Ser.). (Illus.). 112p. (gr. 6-12). 2004. pap. 13.25 (978-0-7910-7794-8(2)); 2003. 30.00 (978-0-7910-7435-0(8)) Facts On File, Inc. (Chelsea Hse.).

—Stalingrad. 2003. (Sieges That Changed the World Ser.). (Illus.). 112p. (gr. 6-12). 30.00 (978-0-7910-7230-1(4)); pap. 13.25 (978-0-7910-7528-9(1)) Facts On File, Inc. (Chelsea Hse.).

Olson, Tod. In the Line of Fire: A Story about D-Day. 2002. (Read 180 Ser.). (Illus.). 56p. (J). (978-0-439-12352-5(6)) Scholastic, Inc.

Platt, Richard. D-Day Landings: The Story of the Allied Invasion. 2004. (Dk Readers Ser.). (Illus.). 32p. (J). 12.99 (978-0-7566-0276-5(9)) Dorling Kindersley Publishing, Inc.

Rees, Bob. The D-Day Landing Sites. 2002. (Visiting the Past Ser.). (Illus.). 32p. (J). pap. 6.95 (978-1-4034-0621-7(9)) Heinemann.

—The D-Day Landing Sites. 2003. (Visiting the Past Ser.). (Illus.). 32p. (J). (gr. 5-7). lib. bdg. 25.64 (978-1-58810-705-3(1)) Heinemann Library.

Reynoldson, Fiona. Key Battles of World War II. (Twentieth Century Perspectives Ser.). (Illus.). 48p. (J). (gr. 5-7). 2001. lib. bdg. 25.64 (978-1-57572-438-6(3)); Set 1. 2002. pap. 7.95 (978-1-58810-377-2(3) , 91129) Heinemann Library.

Rice, Earle, Jr. Blitzkrieg! Hitler's Lightning War. 2007. (Monumental Milestones Ser.).Tr. of 48. (Illus.). (YA). lib. bdg. 29.95 ***(978-1-58415-542-3(6))*** Mitchell Lane Pubs., Inc.

Rice, Earle. George S. Patton. 2003. (Great Military Leaders of the Twentieth Century Ser.). (Illus.). 112p. (gr. 6-12). 30.00 (978-0-7910-7403-9(X) , Chelsea Hse.) Facts On File, Inc.

Rice, Earle, Jr. Kamikazes. 1999. (American War Library). (Illus.). 128p. (YA). (gr. 4-12). 27.45 (978-1-56006-373-5(4) , LML00902-177758, Lucent Bks.) Thomson Gale.

Sheehan, Sean. D-Day, June 6, 1944. 2002. (Days That Shook the World Ser.). (Illus.). 47p. (J). lib. bdg. 27.12 (978-0-7398-5232-3(9)) Raintree.

—World War II: The Pacific. 2004. (Atlas of Conflicts Ser.). (Illus.). 64p. pap. 11.95 (978-0-8368-5677-4(5)); lib. bdg. 32.67 (978-0-8368-5670-5(8)) Stevens, Gareth Inc. (World Almanac Library).

Stanley, George E. George S. Patton: War Hero. Henderson, Meryl, illus. 2007. (Childhood of Famous Americans Ser.). 192p. (J). pap. 5.99 ***(978-1-4169-1547-8(8)*** , Aladdin) Simon & Schuster Children's Publishing.

Stein, R. Conrad. World War II in the Pacific: A MyReportLinks.com Book. 2002. (U. S. Wars Ser.). (Illus.). 48p. (J). (gr. 4-10). lib. bdg. 25.26 (978-0-7660-5093-8(9) , MyReportLinks.com Bks.) Enslow Pubs., Inc.

—World War II in the Pacific: "Remember Pearl Harbor" 2000. (American War Ser.). (Illus.). 128p. (YA). (gr. 5-12). pap. 13.26 (978-0-7660-1734-4(6)) Enslow Pubs., Inc.

Tames, Richard. Pearl Harbor: The U. S. Enters World War II. 2001. (Point of Impact Ser.). (Illus.). (J). (978-0-606-22013-2(5)) Tandem Library Bks.

Wallace, Karen & Platt, Richard. D-Day Landings Vol. 4: The Story of the Allied Invasion. 2004. (Dk Readers Ser.). (Illus.). 32p. (J). (gr. 5). pap. 3.99 (978-0-7566-0275-8(0)) Dorling Kindersley Publishing, Inc.

Wills, Charles & Dorling Kindersley Publishing Staff. World War II Battles & Leaders. 2004. (Battles & Leaders Ser.). (Illus.). 96p. (J). pap. 9.99 (978-0-7566-0260-4(2)); (gr. 8). 16.99 (978-0-7566-0259-8(9)) Dorling Kindersley Publishing, Inc.

Wukovits, John F. Life of an American Soldier in Europe. 1999. (American War Library). (Illus.). 112p. (YA). (gr. 4-12). 27.45 (978-1-56006-666-8(0) , LML00902-178018, Lucent Bks.) Thomson Gale.

WORLD WAR, 1939-1945—CAUSES

Anthony, Nathan & Gardner, Robert. The Bombing of Pearl Harbor in American History. 2001. (In American History Ser.). (Illus.). 104p. (J). (gr. 5-12). lib. bdg. 26.60 (978-0-7660-1126-7(7)) Enslow Pubs., Inc.

Barr, Gary. Pearl Harbor. 2004. (Illus.). 56p. (J). pap. 8.95 (978-1-4034-4577-3(X)); lib. bdg. (978-1-4034-4569-8(9)) Heinemann Library.

Corrigan, Jim. Causes of World War II. 2005. (Road to War Ser.). (Illus.). 64p. (gr. 4 up). lib. bdg. 22.95 (978-1-59556-004-9(1)) OTTN Publishing.

Crewe, Sabrina & Uschan, Michael V. The Bombing of Pearl Harbor. 2003. (Events That Shaped America Ser.). (Illus.). 32p. (J). (gr. 3 up). lib. bdg. 24.67 (978-0-8368-3392-8(9)) Stevens, Gareth Inc.

Dowswell, Paul. The Causes of World War II. 2003. (20th Century Perspectives Ser.). 48p. pap. 7.95 (978-1-4034-4621-3(0)); (Illus.). (J). (gr. 5-7). lib. bdg. 27.07 (978-1-4034-0149-6(7)) Heinemann Library.

Hasday, Judy L. Pearl Harbor. 2000. (Great Disasters, Reforms & Ramifications Ser.). (Illus.). 112p. (J). (gr. 4-7). 30.00 (978-0-7910-5271-6(0) , Chelsea Hse.) Facts On File, Inc.

Klam, Julie. Pearl Harbor & the Rise of Japan. 2002. (Illus.). 48p. (J). lib. bdg. 28.50 (978-1-58340-188-0(1)) Smart Apple Media.

McGowen, Tom. The Attack on Pearl Harbor. 2007. (Cornerstones of Freedomtrade;, Second Ser.). 48p. (J). pap. 5.95 ***(978-0-531-18685-5(7)*** , Children's Pr.) Scholastic Library Publishing.

Pierce, Alan. Bombing of Pearl Harbor. 2005. (American Moments Set Ii Ser.). (Illus.). 48p. (J). (gr. 4-8). lib. bdg. 25.65 (978-1-59197-729-2(0) , ABDO & Daughters) ABDO Publishing Co.

Richard Tames. Pearl Harbor. 2nd ed. 2006. (Point of Impact Ser.). (Illus.). 32p. (J). pap. ***(978-1-4034-9151-0(8))*** Heinemann Library.

Santella, Andrew. Pearl Harbor. 2004. 48p. (J). (gr. 4 up). lib. bdg. 22.60 (978-0-7565-0680-3(8)) Compass Point Bks.

Tames, Richard. Pearl Harbor: The U. S. Enters World War II. 2001. (Point of Impact Ser.). (Illus.). 32p. (J). (gr. 5-7). lib. bdg. 24.22 (978-1-57572-416-4(2)) Heinemann Library.

—Pearl Harbor: The U. S. Enters World War II. 2001. (gr. 5-8). lib. bdg. 15.90 (978-0-613-36122-4(9)) Tandem Library Bks.

Tames, Richard. Pearl Harbor: The U.S. Enters World War II. 2006. (Point of Impact Ser.). (Illus.). 32p. (YA). (gr. 5-8). lib. bdg. 29.29 ***(978-1-4034-9142-8(9))*** Heinemann Library.

Taylor, Theodore. Air Raid—Pearl Harbor! The Story of December 7, 1941. 2001. (Great Episodes Ser.). (Illus.). 208p. (YA). (gr. 5-9). pap. 6.00 (978-0-15-216421-8(9) , Gulliver Bks.) Harcourt Children's Bks.

Uschan, Michael V. The Bombing of Pearl Harbor. 2003. (Landmark Events in American History Ser.). (Illus.). 48p. (J). (gr. 5 up). pap. 14.95 (978-0-8368-5401-5(2)); lib. bdg. 30.00 (978-0-8368-5373-5(3)) Stevens, Gareth Inc. (World Almanac Library).

WORLD WAR, 1939-1945—CHILDREN

Chase, Odette. This Child's War: A World War II Memoir. unabr. ed. 2004. (ENG., Illus.). 122p. per. 15.00 (978-0-9759421-0-9(7)) Red Bud Publishing.

Foreman, Michael. War Boy. 2006. (Illus.). 96p. (J). pap. 16.99 ***(978-1-84365-087-4(8))*** Anova Bks. GBR. *Dist:* Independent Pubs. Group.

Garner, Eleanor Ramrath. Eleanor's Story: An American Girl in Hitler's Germany. 288p. (YA). 2003. (gr. 6-10). pap. 8.95 (978-1-56145-296-5(3) , Q19196); 1999. (Illus.). (gr. 7-11). 15.95 (978-1-56145-193-7(2) , Q19196) Peachtree Pubs., Ltd.

—Eleanor's Story: An American Girl in Hitler's Germany. 2003. (gr. 7-12). lib. bdg. 16.40 (978-0-613-78736-9(6)) Tandem Library Bks.

Josephson, Judith Pinkerton. Growing up in World War II, 1941-1945. 2003. (Our America Ser.). (Illus.). 64p. (J). (gr. 4-7). lib. bdg. 26.60 (978-0-8225-0660-7(2)) Lerner Publishing Group.

Nicholson, Dorinda Makanaonalani Stagner. Remember World War II: Kids Who Survived Tell Their Stories. 2005. (Remember Ser.). (Illus.). 64p. (J). (gr. 5). 27.90 (978-0-7922-7191-8(2) , National Geographic Children's Bks.) National Geographic Society.

Oppenheim, Joanne. Dear Miss Breed: True Stories of the Japanese American Incarceration During World War II & a Librarian Who Made a Difference. 2006. (Illus.). 288p. (J). (gr. 7 up). pap. 22.99 (978-0-439-56992-7(3)) Scholastic, Inc.

Tammen, Gertrud Schakat. Diary of a War Child: The Memoir of Gertrud Schakat Tammen. 2001. (Cover-to-Cover Bks.). (Illus.). 72p. (J). pap. 8.95 (978-0-7891-5436-1(6)); (gr. 4-7). lib. bdg. 17.95 (978-0-7569-0082-3(4)) Perfection Learning Corp.

Vander Zee, Ruth. Erika's Story. Innocenti, Roberto, illus. 2003. 32p. (YA). (gr. 3 up). 15.95 (978-1-56846-176-2(3)) Creative Co., The.

Welch, Catherine A. Children of the Relocation Camps. 2005. (Picture the American Past Ser.). (Illus.). 48p. (gr. 2-5). lib. bdg. 22.60 (978-1-57505-350-9(0)) Lerner Publishing Group.

Whitman, Sylvia. Children of the World War II Home Front. 2005. (Picture the American Past Ser.). (Illus.). 48p. (J). (gr. 2-5). lib. bdg. 22.60 (978-1-57505-484-1(1)) Lerner Publishing Group.

Williams, Brian. World at War: World War II: the Evacuation of Children. 2005. (World at War— World War II Ser.). (Illus.). 32p. tchr. ed. (978-0-431-10380-8(1)) Heinemann Library.

Ziemian, Joseph. The Cigarette Sellers of Three Crosses Square. 2005. (Library of Holocaust Testimonies). (Illus.). 168p. pap. 17.50 (978-0-85303-686-9(1)) Vallentine Mitchell Pubs. GBR. *Dist:* International Specialized Bk. Services.

WORLD WAR, 1939-1945—CHINA

Events That Changed the World - 1940-1960. 2003. (Illus.). lib. bdg. 36.20 (978-0-7377-1756-3(4)) Thomson Gale.

WORLD WAR, 1939-1945—EUROPE

Altman, Linda Jacobs. The Forgotten Victims of the Holocaust. 2003. (Holocaust in History Ser.). (Illus.). 128p. (YA). (gr. 5-12). lib. bdg. 26.60 (978-0-7660-1993-5(4)) Enslow Pubs., Inc.

Heaton, Colin D. German Anti-Partisan Warfare in Europe: 1939-1945. 2001. (Schiffer Military History Ser.). (Illus.). 480p. (gr. 10-13). 29.95 (978-0-7643-1395-0(9)) Schiffer Publishing, Ltd.

Klam, Julie. Europe in Flames. 2002. (Illus.). 48p. (J). lib. bdg. 28.50 (978-1-58340-187-3(3)) Smart Apple Media.

Rice, Earle, Jr. Blitzkrieg! Hitler's Lightning War. 2007. (Monumental Milestones Ser.) Tr. of 48. (Illus.). (YA). lib. bdg. 29.95 ***(978-1-58415-542-3(6))*** Mitchell Lane Pubs., Inc.

Stein, R. Conrad. World War II in Europe: A MyReportLinks.com Book. 2002. (U. S. Wars Ser.). (Illus.). 48p. (J). (gr. 4-10). lib. bdg. 25.26 (978-0-7660-5094-5(7) , MyReportLinks.com Bks.) Enslow Pubs., Inc.

Toll, Nelly. Behind the Secret Window: A Memoir of a Hidden Childhood During World War II. 2003. 176p. (J). (gr. 3-6). pap. 5.99 (978-0-14-230241-5(4) , Puffin) Penguin Group (USA) Inc.

WORLD WAR, 1939-1945—FICTION

Adams, Gayle. Safe Harbor. 2002. (gr. 7-12). lib. bdg. 22.85 (978-0-613-74657-1(0)) Tandem Library Bks.

Adler, David A. Don't Talk to Me about the War. 2008. (YA). (gr. 5). 15.99 ***(978-0-670-06307-9(X)*** , Viking Adult) Penguin Group (USA) Inc.

Ahearn, Daniel. In the Time of War. 2002. (Illus.). 16p. (J). (978-0-439-35153-9(7)) Scholastic, Inc.

Attema, Martha. Daughter of Light. McCallum, Stephen, illus. 2001. (Young Reader Ser.). 112p. (J). (gr. 3-6). pap. 4.99 (978-1-55143-179-6(3)) Orca Bk. Pubs. USA.

—Daughter of Light. 2001. (J). 11.64 (978-0-606-22770-4(9)) Tandem Library Bks.

—Hero. 2003. (Orca Young Readers Ser.). (Illus.). 144p. (J). (gr. 3-6). pap. 5.95 (978-1-55143-251-9(X)) Orca Bk. Pubs. USA.

Avi. Don't You Know There's a War On? 208p. (J). 2003. pap. 5.99 (978-0-380-81544-9(3) , Harper Trophy); 2001. (gr. 4-6). 15.95 (978-0-380-97863-2(6)) HarperCollins Pubs.

—Don't You Know There's a War On? 2003. 200p. (J). (ps-7). lib. bdg. 14.15 (978-0-613-60338-6(9)) Tandem Library Bks.

Ayres, Katherine. Voices at Whisper Bend. 1999. (American Girl Collection Ser.). (978-0-606-17521-0(0)) Tandem Library Bks.

Barry, Rick. Gunner's Run. 2007. (YA). ***(978-1-59166-761-2(5))*** Jones, Bob Univ. Pr.

Bat-Ami, Miriam. Two Suns in the Sky. 1999. 208p. (YA). (gr. 7-12). 17.95 (978-0-8126-2900-2(0)) Cricket Bks.

—Two Suns in the Sky. 2001. 208p. (J). pap. 6.99 (978-0-14-230036-7(5) , Puffin) Penguin Group (USA) Inc.

—Two Suns in the Sky. 2001. (gr. 7-12). lib. bdg. 15.30 (978-0-613-44425-5(6)) Tandem Library Bks.

Baxter, Linda & Cornelison, Sue F. River of Freedom. 2002. (Cover-To-Cover Novel Ser.). (Illus.). 96p. pap. (978-0-7891-5537-5(0)); (gr. 2-5). lib. bdg. 13.95 (978-0-7569-0312-1(2)) Perfection Learning Corp.

Bishop, Claire Huchet. Twenty & Ten. 76p. (J). (gr. 3-5). pap. 4.99 (978-0-8072-1418-3(3) , Listening Library) Random Hse. Audio Publishing Group.

Bloor, Edward. London Calling. 304p. (gr. 5). 2008. (YA). pap. 8.99 ***(978-0-375-84363-1(9));*** 2006. (J). lib. bdg. 18.99 (978-0-375-93635-7(1)); 2006. (YA). 16.95 (978-0-375-83635-0(7)) Random Hse. Children's Bks. (Knopf Bks. for Young Readers).

Borden, Louise. Across the Blue Pacific: A World War II Story. Parker, Robert Andrew, illus. 2006. 48p. (J). (gr. k-3). 17.00 (978-0-618-33922-8(1)) Houghton Mifflin Co.

—Little Ships: The Heroic Rescue at Dunkirk in World War II. 2003. (gr. 3-6). lib. bdg. 15.30 (978-0-613-61639-3(1)) Tandem Library Bks.

Borden, Louise & Daly, Niki. The Greatest Skating Race: A World War II Story from the Netherlands. 2004. (Illus.). 48p. (J). 18.95 (978-0-689-84502-4(2) , McElderry, Margaret K.) Simon & Schuster Children's Publishing.

Borden, Louise & Foreman, Michael. The Little Ships. 2003. (Illus.). 32p. (J). (gr. 4 up). pap. 6.99 (978-0-689-85396-8(3) , Aladdin) Simon & Schuster Children's Publishing.

Bradley, Kimberly Brubaker. For Freedom: The Story of a French Spy. 2005. 192p. (J). (gr. 5-9). pap. 5.50 (978-0-440-41831-3(3) , Laurel Leaf) Random Hse. Children's Bks.

Bruchac, Joseph. Code Talker: A Novel about the Navajo Marines of World War Two. 2006. 240p. (YA). (gr. 5). pap. 7.99 (978-0-14-240596-3(5) , Puffin) Penguin Group (USA) Inc.

Buckey, Sarah Masters. The Light in the Cellar: A Molly Mystery. 2007. 176p. (J). 10.95 ***(978-1-59369-159-2(9)*** ***);*** pap. 6.95 ***(978-1-59369-158-5(0))*** American Girl Publishing, Inc.

Buckvar, Felice. Dangerous Dream. Kemnitz, Myrna, ed. 1998. 123p. (YA). (gr. 5 up). 9.99 (978-0-88092-277-7(X) , 277X) Royal Fireworks Publishing Co.

Burg, Ann E. Rebekkah's Journey: A World War II Refugee Story. Iskowitz, Joel, illus. 2006. 48p. (J). (gr. 3-5). 17.95 (978-1-58536-275-2(1)) Sleeping Bear Pr.

Burnford, Sheila. Bel Ria: Dog of War. 2006. 256p. (J). (gr. 5). 17.95 (978-1-59017-211-7(6) , NYR Children's Collection) New York Review of Bks., Inc., The.

Carradice, Phil & Thomas, Frances. Hannah Goes to War. 2005. 144p. pap. 12.95 (978-1-84323-461-6(0)) Beekman Bks., Inc.

Casanova, Mary. Klipfish Code. 2007. 240p. (J). (gr. 5-7). 16.00 ***(978-0-618-88393-6(2))*** Houghton Mifflin Co. Trade & Reference Div.

Center for Learning Network Staff. Slaughterhouse-Five: Curriculum Unit. 2005. (Novel Ser.). 76p. (YA). tchr. ed., spiral bd. 19.95 (978-1-56077-789-2(3)) Ctr. for Learning, The.

Chaconas, Dori. Pennies in a Jar. Lewin, Ted, illus. 2007. 32p. (J). (ps-3). 16.95 ***(978-1-56145-422-8(2)*** , Peachtree Junior) Peachtree Pubs., Ltd.

Chaikin, Miriam. Friends Forever. Egielski, Richard, illus. 2001. 132p. (YA). pap. 11.95 (978-0-595-19879-5(1) , Backinprint.com) iUniverse, Inc.

Chambers, Aidan. Postcards from No Man's Land. (gr. 9). 2007. 336p. (YA). pap. 10.00 (978-0-14-240788-2(7) , Puffin); 2002. 320p. (J). 19.99 (978-0-525-46863-9(3) , Dutton Juvenile); 2004. 320p. (J). reprint ed. pap. 7.99 (978-0-14-240145-3(5) , Puffin) Penguin Group (USA) Inc.

Chan, Gillian. A Foreign Field. 2002. (Illus.). 192p. (YA). (gr. 13 up). (978-1-55337-349-0(9)) Kids Can Pr., Ltd.

Cheaney, J. B. My Friend the Enemy. 2007. 272p. (J). (gr. 5-9). 6.50 ***(978-0-440-42102-3(0)*** , Yearling) Random Hse. Children's Bks.

Cheng, Andrea. Marika. 1998. 148p. (YA). (gr. 5 up). 16.95 (978-1-886910-78-2(2) , Lemniscaat) Boyds Mills Pr.

Chetkowski, Emily. Gooseman. 2001. (J). 11.95 (978-1-880158-32-6(9)) Townsend, J.N. Publishing.

Cooper, Susan. Dawn of Fear. Gill, Margery, illus. 2007. 176p. (J). pap. 5.95 ***(978-0-15-206106-7(1)*** , Harcourt Paperbacks) Harcourt Children's Bks.

Copeland, Cynthia L. Elin's Island. 2003. (Single Titles Ser.: up). 144p. (gr. 6 up). lib. bdg. 22.90 (978-0-7613-2522-2(0) , Millbrook Pr.) Lerner Publishing Group.

Cormier, Robert. Heroes. 2006. (York Notes Ser.). 112p. pap. (978-1-4058-3559-6(1)) Pearson Education, Ltd.

—Heroes. 2000. 144p. (YA). (gr. 7-12). pap. 5.99 (978-0-440-22769-4(0) , Laurel Leaf) Random Hse. Children's Bks.

—Heroes. 2000. 135p. (YA). (gr. 7-12). lib. bdg. 13.55 (978-0-613-23622-5(X)); per. 12.15 (978-0-606-17836-5(8)) Tandem Library Bks.

—Heroes. l.t. ed. 2000. 147p. (YA). (gr. 8-12). 21.95 (978-0-7862-2909-3(8)) Thorndike Pr.

—Other Bells for Us to Ring. 2000. (J). (978-0-606-19745-8(1)) Tandem Library Bks.

Courtenay, Bryce. The Power of One. 2005. 304p. (J). (gr. 5-12). lib. bdg. 17.99 (978-0-385-90274-8(3) , Delacorte Bks. for Young Readers) Random Hse. Children's Bks.

Cummings, Mary. And the Baker's Boy Went to Sea. 2006. (Illus.). 195p. (YA). 16.95 (978-0-9774855-0-5(1)) Sparkling Pr.

Daly, Maureen. The Small War of Sergeant Donkey. Dennis, Wesley, illus. 2000. (Living History Library). 104p. (J). (gr. 5-9). reprint ed. pap. 11.95 (978-1-883937-47-8(7)) Bethlehem Bks.

David, James F. Ship of the Damned. 2001. (gr. 7-12). lib. bdg. 15.30 (978-0-613-42792-0(0)) Tandem Library Bks.

Davies, Jacqueline. Where the Ground Meets the Sky. 2002. 224p. (YA). (gr. 5-9). 14.95 (978-0-7614-5105-1(6) , Cavendish Children's Bks.) Cavendish, Marshall Corp.

Deedy, Carmen Agra. The Yellow Star: The Legend of King Christian X of Denmark. Sorensen, Henri, illus. 2000. 32p. (J). (gr. 3-7). 16.95 (978-1-56145-208-8(4) , Q24691) Peachtree Pubs., Ltd.

Disher, Garry. The Divine Wind: A Love Story. 2004. 160p. (J). pap. 5.99 (978-0-439-36916-9(9)); 2002. 176p. (YA). (gr. 9 up). pap. 15.95 (978-0-439-36915-2(0)) Scholastic, Inc. (Levine, Arthur A. Bks.).

Doyle, Brian. Boy O'Boy. 2005. 162p. (YA). pap. 6.95 (978-0-88899-654-1(3)) Groundwood Bks. CAN. *Dist:* Perseus Distribution.

Duey, Kathleen. Josie Poe Palouse: Washington, 1943. 1999. (American Diaries Ser.: No. 13). (J). (gr. 3-7). 11.64 (978-0-606-16304-0(2)) Tandem Library Bks.

Dunlop, Ed. The Incredible Rescues. Halverson, Tom, illus. 2003. 166p. (J). (gr. 4-7). 7.49 (978-1-59166-012-5(2)) Jones, Bob Univ. Pr.

—The Search for the Silver Eagle. Halverson, Tom, illus. 2003. 159p. (J). (gr. 4-7). 7.49 (978-1-59166-014-9(9)) Jones, Bob Univ. Pr.

Elliott, Laura Malone. Under a War-Torn Sky. 288p. (gr. 5-17). 2003. (J). pap. 5.99 (978-0-7868-1753-5(4)); 2001. 16.49 (978-0-7868-2485-4(9)) Hyperion Bks. for Children.

—Under a War-Torn Sky. 2001. (gr. 7-12). lib. bdg. 14.15 (978-0-613-69092-8(3)) Tandem Library Bks.

Farewell to Manzanar. 2004. (Literature Connections Ser.). (gr. 6-12). (978-0-395-88455-3(1) , 2-70861) McDougal Littell Inc.

Fisher, Rick. Unknown Heroes. 2007. (ENG., Illus.). 32p. (J). per. 14.95 ***(978-1-59800-899-9(4))*** Outskirts Press, Inc.

Fleming, Candace. Boxes for Katje. Dressen-McQueen, Stacey, illus. 2003. 40p. (J). (gr. k-3). 16.00 (978-0-374-30922-0(1) , Farrar, Straus & Giroux (BYR)) Farrar, Straus & Giroux.

—Boxes for Katje. Dressen-McQueen, Stacey, illus. 2004. (J). 29.95 incl. audio compact disk (978-0-8045-4125-1(6) , SACD4125); (YA). 27.95 incl. audio (978-0-8045-6930-9(4) , SAC6930) Spoken Arts, Inc.

French, Jackie. Hitler's Daughter. 2003. 128p. (J). 15.99 (978-0-06-008652-7(1)) HarperCollins Pubs.

Friedman, D. Dina. Escaping into the Night. 2006. (Illus.). 208p. (J). 16.99 (978-1-4169-0258-4(9) , Simon & Schuster Children's Publishing) Simon & Schuster Children's Publishing.

Garrigue, Sheila. The Eternal Spring of Mr. Ito. 1998. (J). pap. 3.95 (978-0-87628-340-0(7)) Ctr. for Applied Research in Education, The.

Giff, Patricia Reilly. Lily's Crossing. 2002. (Illus.). (J). 13.94 (978-0-7587-0287-6(6)) Book Wholesalers, Inc.

—Lily's Crossing. 1999. (Yearling Newbery Ser.). 208p. (J). (gr. 5-7). reprint ed. pap. 6.50 (978-0-440-41453-7(9) , Yearling) Random Hse. Children's Bks.

—Lily's Crossing. 1999. (gr. 5-8). lib. bdg. 13.55 (978-0-613-10350-3(5)); (Illus.). (J). (978-0-606-14423-0(4)) Tandem Library Bks.

—Lily's Crossing. l.t. ed. 200p. 2003. pap. 10.95 (978-0-7862-6189-5(7)); 2000. (Illus.). (J). 22.95 (978-0-7862-2771-6(0)) Thorndike Pr.

—Willow Run. 160p. (J). (gr. 4-7). 2007. pap. 5.99 (978-0-440-23801-0(3) , Yearling); 2005. 15.95 (978-0-385-73067-9(5) , Lamb, Wendy); 2005. lib. bdg. 17.99 (978-0-385-90096-6(1) , Lamb, Wendy) Random Hse. Children's Bks.

Glatshteyn, Yankev. Emil & Karl. Shandler, Jeffrey, tr. from YID. 2006. 208p. (J). 17.95 (978-1-59643-119-5(9)) Roaring Brook Pr.

—Emil & Karl. Shandler, Jeffrey, tr. 2008. 208p. (YA). pap. 6.99 ***(978-0-312-37387-0(2))*** Square Fish.

Gleitzman, Morris. Once. 2005. 160p. (J). pap. ***(978-0-14-330195-0(0)*** , Puffin) Penguin Group (USA) Inc.

Graber, Janet. Resistance. 2005. 144p. (YA). 15.95 (978-0-7614-5214-0(1)) Cavendish, Marshall Corp.

Graff, Nancy Price. Taking Wing. Minor, Wendell, illus. 2005. 224p. (YA). (gr. 5-9). 15.00 (978-0-618-53591-0(8) , Clarion Bks.) Houghton Mifflin Co. Trade & Reference Div.

Granfield, Linda. High Flight: A Story of World War II. Martchenko, Michael, illus. 1999. 32p. (J). (gr. k-12). 15.95 (978-0-88776-469-1(X)) Tundra Bks., Inc./Livres Toundra, Inc. CAN. *Dist:* Random Hse., Inc.

Green, Connie Jordan. The War at Home. 2nd ed. 2003. 144p. (J). pap. (978-0-916078-75-1(2)) Iris Publishing Group, Inc., The.

Greene, Bette. Summer of My German Soldier. 1999. (Illus.). 208p. (J). (gr. 5-9). pap. 6.99 (978-0-14-130636-0(X) , Puffin) Penguin Group (USA) Inc.

—Summer of My German Soldier. 2000. (J). (gr. 6 up). 20.50 (978-0-8446-7144-4(4)) Smith, Peter Pub., Inc.

—Summer of My German Soldier. 1999. (978-0-606-17432-9(X)) Tandem Library Bks.

—Summer of My German Soldier. 2006. (Puffin Modern Classics Ser.). 240p. (J). (gr. 5). pap. 6.99 (978-0-14-240651-9(1) , Puffin) Penguin Group (USA) Inc.

—Summer of My German Soldier. l.t. ed. 2000. (LRS Large Print Cornerstone Ser.). 305p. (YA). (gr. 6-12). lib. bdg. 29.95 (978-1-58118-059-6(4) , 23473) LRS.

W X Y Z

Greene, Bette & Hunt, Robert, illus. Summer of My German Soldier. 2003. 256p. (J). (gr. 5). 18.99 (978-0-8037-2869-1(7) , Dial) Penguin Group (USA) Inc.

Griffis, Molly Levite. The Feester Filibuster. 2002. (Illus.). vi, 236p. (J). pap. 8.95 (978-1-57168-694-7(0) , Eakin Pr.); 224p. 18.95 (978-1-57168-693-0(2)) Eakin Pr.

—The Feester Filibuster. 2002. (gr. 3-6). lib. bdg. 17.60 (978-0-613-79188-5(6)) Tandem Library Bks.

—The Rachel Resistance. 224p. 8.95 (978-1-57168-553-7(7)); 2001. 17.95 (978-1-57168-541-4(3)) Eakin Pr.

—Simon Says. 2004. vi, 263p. (J). 22.95 (978-1-57168-836-1(6)); pap. (978-1-57168-847-7(1)) Eakin Pr. (Eakin Pr.).

Grindley, Sally. Feather Wars. 2003. 224p. pap. 12.99 (978-0-7475-6338-9(1)) Bloomsbury Publishing Plc GBR. *Dist:* Independent Pubs. Group.

Harlow, Joan Hiatt. Shadows on the Sea. (Illus.). 256p. (J). 2005. pap. 4.99 (978-0-689-84927-5(3) , Aladdin); 2003. (gr. 3-6). 17.99 (978-0-689-84926-8(5) , McElderry, Margaret K.) Simon & Schuster Children's Publishing.

—Shadows on the Sea. l.t. ed. 2003. 214p. 20.95 (978-0-7862-6145-1(5) , Large Print Pr.) Thorndike Pr.

Harris, Joanne. Five Quarters of the Orange. 2002. (gr. 7-12). lib. bdg. 23.40 (978-0-613-62140-3(9)) Tandem Library Bks.

Harrison, Cora. World War II: Rescue at Drumshee. 2001. (Drumshee Timeline Ser.). 144p. pap. 6.95 (978-0-86327-849-5(3)) Interlink Publishing Group, Inc.

—World War II: Rescue at Drumshee. 2002. (gr. 3-6). lib. bdg. 15.25 (978-0-613-86921-8(4)) Tandem Library Bks.

Hart, Derek. Secret of the Dragon's Eye. 2007. 264p. per. 16.95 (***978-0-595-42967-7(X)***) iUniverse, Inc.

Haywood, Carolyn. Primrose Day. 2005. (Illus.). 176p. (J). 16.00 (978-0-15-205228-7(3)); pap. 5.95 (978-0-15-205229-4(1)) Harcourt Children's Bks.

Hermes, Patricia. Summer Secrets. 2004. (Illus.). 144p. (YA). 15.95 (978-0-7614-5074-0(2)) Cavendish, Marshall Corp.

—Sweet by & By. 2002. 208p. (J). (gr. 3-6). 15.99 (978-0-380-97452-8(5)) HarperCollins Pubs.

Hertenstein, Jane. Beyond Paradise. 1999. (Illus.). 168p. (YA). (gr. 7 up). 16.00 (978-0-688-16381-5(5)) HarperCollins Pubs.

Hesse, Karen. Aleutian Sparrow. Zerbetz, Evon, illus. 2003. 160p. (J). (gr. 5-9). 16.95 (978-0-689-86189-5(3) , McElderry, Margaret K.) Simon & Schuster Children's Publishing.

—Aleutian Sparrow. McGillivray, Kim & Zerbetz, Evon, illus. 2005. 160p. (J). reprint ed. pap. 5.99 (978-1-4169-0327-7(5) , Aladdin) Simon & Schuster Children's Publishing.

—The Cats in Krasinski Square. Watson, Wendy, illus. 2004. 32p. (J). (gr. 2-5). pap. 16.95 (978-0-439-43540-6(4) , Scholastic Pr.) Scholastic, Inc.

Hest, Amy. Love You, Soldier. Lamut, Sonja, illus. 2000. 80p. (J). (gr. 3-7). 16.99 (978-0-7636-0943-6(9)) Candlewick Pr.

Hoffman, Emily Allen. A Friend of the Enemy. 2003. 108p. (J). pap. 7.95 (978-1-57249-312-4(7) , White Mane Kids) White Mane Publishing Co., Inc.

Hoobler, Dorothy & Hoobler, Thomas. The 1940s: Secrets. Hoffman, Robin, illus. 2001. (Century Kids Ser.). 160p. (J). (gr. 5-8). lib. bdg. 22.90 (978-0-7613-1604-6(3) , Twenty-First Century Bks.) Lerner Publishing Group.

Hughes, Dean. Soldier Boys. (YA). 2003. 240p. (gr. 7-12). mass mkt. 5.99 (978-0-689-86021-8(8) , Simon Pulse); 2001. 176p. (gr. 4-6). 16.95 (978-0-689-81748-9(7) , Atheneum) Simon & Schuster Children's Publishing.

—Soldier Boys. 2003. (gr. 3-6). lib. bdg. 13.00 (978-0-613-66437-0(X)) Tandem Library Bks.

Icenogglе, Jodi. America's Betrayal. 2001. (gr. 7-12). lib. bdg. 16.40 (978-0-613-83690-6(1)) Tandem Library Bks.

—America's Betrayal. 2001. 208p. (J). (gr. 7 up). 7.95 (978-1-57249-252-3(X) , White Mane Kids) White Mane Publishing Co., Inc.

Innocenti, Roberto. Rosa Blanca. 2nd ed. 2003. (Rosa y Manzana Ser.). (SPA., Illus.). 32p. (978-84-85334-52-0(3) , LG2811) Loguez Ediciones ESP. *Dist:* Lectorum Pubns., Inc.

—Rose Blanche. Innocenti, Roberto, illus. 2003. (Illus.). 32p. (YA). (gr. 4 up). 17.95 (978-1-56846-189-2(5)) Creative Co., The.

Johnston, Tony. The Harmonica. Mazellan, Ron, illus. 2004. 32p. (J). 15.95 (978-1-57091-547-5(4)) Charlesbridge Publishing, Inc.

Judge, Lita. One Thousand Tracings: Healing the Wounds of World War II. Judge, Lita, illus. 2007. 40p. (gr. k-4). 15.99 (***978-1-4231-0008-9(5)***) Hyperion Pr.

Jungman, Ann. Resistance. Marks, Alan, illus. 2006. 83p. (J). (gr. 2-3). lib. bdg. (978-1-59889-001-3(8)) Stone Arch Bks.

Kacer, Kathy. Secret of Gabi's Dresser. 1999. (gr. 3-6). lib. bdg. 12.95 (978-0-613-29338-9(X)) Tandem Library Bks.

Kadohata, Cynthia. Weedflower. 2006. (J). (978-0-689-04937-8(4)); (Illus.). 272p. (gr. 5 up). 16.95 (978-0-689-86574-9(0)) Simon & Schuster Children's Publishing. (Atheneum).

Katz, Jennifer A. The Era of Courting. 2006. 119p. pap. 16.95 (978-1-4241-3321-5(1)) PublishAmerica, Inc.

Kerr, Judith. En la Batalla de Inglaterra. (SPA.). 304p. (YA). (gr. 5-8). (978-84-204-3221-2(0) , AF0691) Alfaguara, Ediciones, S.A.- Grupo Santillana ESP. *Dist:* Lectorum Pubns., Inc.

—En la Batalla de Inglaterra. (SPA.). (YA). (gr. 5-8). pap. (978-84-345-8580-5(4) , AF0691) Salvat Editores, S.A. ESP. *Dist:* Lectorum Pubns., Inc.

Kerr, M. E. Slap Your Sides. 2003. 208p. (J). (gr. 7 up). pap. 5.99 (978-0-06-447274-6(4)) HarperCollins Pubs.

—Slap Your Sides. 2003. 198p. (J). (ps-7). lib. bdg. 14.15 (978-0-613-60110-8(5)) Tandem Library Bks.

Kerr, M. E. Your Eyes in Stars. 2007. 240p. (J). (gr. 7 up). pap. 6.99 (***978-0-06-075684-0(5)*** , HarperTeen) HarperCollins Pubs.

Kindt, Matt. Super Spy. 2007. 304p. (YA). pap. 19.95 (***978-1-891830-96-9(1)***) Top Shelf Productions.

King-Smith, Dick. The Crowstarver. l.t. ed. 2000. (J). (Illus.). 243p. pap. (978-0-7540-6095-6(0) , Galaxy Children's Large Print); 216p. pap. incl. audio (978-0-7540-6228-8(7) , RA029, Chivers Children's Audio Bks.) BBC Audiobooks America.

—Spider Sparrow. unabr. ed. 2004. 176p. (J). (gr. 5-9). pap. 36.00 incl. audio (978-0-8072-8407-0(6) , Listening Library) Random Hse. Audio Publishing Group.

—Spider Sparrow. 2002. (J). (gr. 5-9). 20.50 (978-0-8446-7221-2(1)) Smith, Peter Pub., Inc.

—Spider Sparrow. 2001. (Illus.). (J). (978-0-606-21445-2(3)) Tandem Library Bks.

Klar, Elizabeth. Lily's Crossing. Robbins, Dawn Michelle, ed. 2000. (J). 9.95 (978-1-58130-644-6(X)); 11.95 (978-1-58130-645-3(8)) Novel Units, Inc.

Kochenderfer, Lee. The Victory Garden. 2003. 176p. (J). (gr. 3-7). pap. 5.99 (978-0-440-41703-3(1) , Yearling) Random Hse. Children's Bks.

—The Victory Garden. 2003. (gr. 3-6). lib. bdg. 13.00 (978-0-613-85701-7(1)) Tandem Library Bks.

Kositsky, Lynne. The Thought of High Windows. 176p. (J). 2005. (gr. 7-12). (978-1-55337-622-4(6)); 2004. (gr. 13 up). (978-1-55337-621-7(8)) Kids Can Pr., Ltd.

Lawrence, Iain. B for Buster. 2006. (Illus.). 336p. (YA). (gr. 7). reprint ed. 5.99 (978-0-440-23810-2(2) , Laurel Leaf) Random Hse. Children's Bks.

Lee, Milly. Nim & the War Effort. Choi, Yangsook, illus. 2002. 40p. (J). pap. 6.95 (978-0-374-45506-4(6) , Sunburst) Farrar, Straus & Giroux.

—Nim & the War Effort. 2002. (gr. 3-6). lib. bdg. 14.10 (978-0-613-53846-6(3)) Tandem Library Bks.

LeFaucheur, Sandi. The Secret Shelter. 2005. (Illus.). 144p. (J). pap. 12.95 (978-0-9746481-4-9(0)) Brown Barn Bks.

LeSourd, Nancy. The Personal Correspondence of Catherine Clark & Meredith Lyons: Pearl Harbor, 1941. 2004. (Liberty Letters Ser.). (Illus.). 240p. (J). (gr. 5 up). 9.99 (978-0-310-70353-2(0)) Zonderkidz.

Lewis, Floyd. The Foundered Mule. 2006. (YA). (***978-0-9788283-2-5(1)***) Acacia Publishing, Inc.

Lisle, Janet Taylor. The Art of Keeping Cool. 2002. 256p. (J). (gr. 5-9). pap. 5.99 (978-0-689-83788-3(7) , Aladdin) Simon & Schuster Children's Publishing.

—The Art of Keeping Cool. Goldstrom, Robert, illus. 2000. 216p. (J). (gr. 5-7). 17.00 (978-0-689-83787-6(9) , Atheneum/Richard Jackson Bks.) Simon & Schuster Children's Publishing.

—The Art of Keeping Cool. 2002. (gr. 5-8). lib. bdg. 13.00 (978-0-613-54109-1(X)) Tandem Library Bks.

—Sirens & Spies. O'Rourke, Ericka, illus. 2002. 176p. (J). (gr. 5 up). pap. 4.99 (978-0-689-84457-7(3) , Aladdin) Simon & Schuster Children's Publishing.

—Sirens & Spies. 2002. (gr. 3-6). lib. bdg. 13.00 (978-0-613-45104-8(X)) Tandem Library Bks.

—Sirens & Spies. l.t. ed. 2003. 22.95 (978-0-7862-5378-4(9)) Thorndike Pr.

Lowry, Lois. Compte les Etoiles. pap. 16.95 (978-2-211-03436-4(5)) Archimede Editions FRA. *Dist:* Distribooks, Inc.

—Number the Stars. 2004. 144p. (J). (gr. 5-9). pap. 29.00 incl. audio (978-1-4000-8637-5(X) , Listening Library) Random Hse. Audio Publishing Group.

—Number the Stars. 1998. 144p. (YA). (gr. 5-7). reprint ed. mass mkt. 6.50 (978-0-440-22753-3(4) , Laurel Leaf) Random Hse. Children's Bks.

—Number the Stars. 1998. (J). (978-0-606-13670-9(3)); (gr. 5-8). lib. bdg. 14.15 (978-0-613-72319-0(8)) Tandem Library Bks.

—Number the Stars - Musical. 1998. 33p. (J). pap. 6.95 (978-0-87129-834-8(1) , N03) Dramatic Publishing Co.

—Quien Cuenta las Estrellas. 5th ed. 1998. (SPA., Illus.). 152p. (J). 8.95 (978-84-239-8867-9(8)) Espasa Calpe, S.A. ESP. *Dist:* Continental Bk. Co., Inc.

Lurie, April. Dancing in the Streets of Brooklyn. 208p. (gr. 3-7). 2004. pap. 5.99 (978-0-440-41825-2(9) , Yearling); 2002. lib. bdg. 17.99 (978-0-385-90066-9(X) , Delacorte Bks. for Young Readers) Random Hse. Children's Bks.

Maguire, Gregory. The Good Liar. 1999. 144p. (J). (gr. 5-9). tchr. ed. 15.00 (978-0-395-90697-2(0) , Clarion Bks.) Houghton Mifflin Co. Trade & Reference Div.

—Good Liar. 2002. (gr. 3-6). lib. bdg. 14.10 (978-0-613-46219-8(X)) Tandem Library Bks.

Mah, Adeline Yen. Chinese Cinderella & the Secret Dragon Society. (Illus.). 256p. (J). 2006. pap. 5.99 (978-0-06-056736-1(8) , Harper Trophy); 2005. (gr. 5 up). 15.99 (978-0-06-056734-7(1)) HarperCollins Pubs.

Matas, Carol. Turned Away: The World War II Diary of Devorah Bernstein. 2005. (Dear Canada Ser.). (Illus.). 199p. (J). pap. (***978-0-439-96946-8(8)***) Scholastic Canada, Ltd.

Matas, Carol & Matas, Carol. Greater Than Angels. 1999. 177p. lib. bdg. 11.64 (978-0-606-17196-0(7)) Tandem Library Bks.

Mazer, Harry. A Boy at War: A Novel of Pearl Harbor. 2002. (gr. 3-6). lib. bdg. 13.00 (978-0-613-65106-6(5)) Tandem Library Bks.

—A Boy No More. 2004. (Illus.). 144p. (J). 16.95 (978-0-689-85533-7(8)) Simon & Schuster Children's Publishing.

—Heroes Don't Run: A Novel of the Pacific War. 2005. (Illus.). 128p. (J). (gr. k-9). 15.95 (978-0-689-85534-4(6) , Simon & Schuster Children's Publishing) Simon & Schuster Children's Publishing.

—The Last Mission. 192p. (YA). (gr. 7 up). pap. 4.99 (978-0-8072-1366-7(7) , Listening Library) Random Hse. Audio Publishing Group.

McNaughton, Janet. Make or Break Spring. 1999. 192p. (YA). (gr. 7 up). pap. (978-1-895387-93-3(0)) Creative Bk. Publishing.

McSwigan, Marie. Snow Treas. 1999. (J). (gr. 3-6). lib. bdg. 12.40 (978-0-8085-6433-1(1)) Tandem Library Bks.

—Snow Treasure. Mary, Reardon, illus. 2006. 208p. (J). (gr. 3). pap. 5.99 (978-0-14-240224-5(9) , Puffin) Penguin Group (USA) Inc.

Mercer, Christa Blum. German War Child: Growing Up in World War II. 2004. (Illus.). 176p. pap. 14.95 (978-1-893597-07-5(5)) A. Borough Bks.

Merkel, Ruth. Hannah's Girls: Ann. 2006. 112p. (J). pap. 9.99 (***978-0-8280-1951-4(7)***) Review & Herald Publishing Assn.

—Hannah's Girls: Grace, 6. 2006. (Illus.). 128p. (J). pap. 9.99 (***978-0-8280-1953-8(3)***) Review & Herald Publishing Assn.

—Hannah's Girls: Marilla, 6 bks. 2006. (Illus.). 144p. (J). pap. 9.99 (***978-0-8280-1952-1(5)***) Review & Herald Publishing Assn.

—Hannah's Girls: Ruthie. 2007. 144p. (J). pap. 9.99 (***978-0-8280-1954-5(1)***) Review & Herald Publishing Assn.

Mochizuki, Ken. Baseball Saved Us. Lee, Dom, illus. (Picture Book Readalong Ser.). 28.95 incl. audio compact disk (978-1-59112-916-5(8)); pap. 39.95 incl. audio compact disk (978-1-59112-917-2(6)) Live Oak Media.

—Baseball Saved Us. 2005. (Picture Book Readalong Ser.). (Illus.). (J). pap. 18.95 incl. audio compact disk (978-1-59112-915-8(X)); pap. 16.95 incl. audio (978-1-59112-455-9(7)) Live Oak Media.

—Baseball Saved Us. Lee, Dom, illus. 2004. (Picture Book Readalong Ser.). (J). (ps-ps). audio 25.95 (978-1-59112-456-6(5)) Live Oak Media.

Morpurgo, Michael. The Amazing Story of Adolphus Tips. 2006. 208p. (J). (gr. 2-5). 16.99 (978-0-439-79661-3(X) , Scholastic Pr.) Scholastic, Inc.

—Billy the Kid. Foreman, Michael, illus. 2000. 80p. (J). 22.99 (978-1-86205-361-8(8) , Pavilion Bks., Ltd.) Anova Bks. GBR. *Dist:* Trafalgar Square Publishing.

Myers, Anna. Captain's Command. 2001. 11.15 (978-0-606-22411-6(4)) Tandem Library Bks.

Myers, Walter Dean. The Journal of Scott Pendelton Collins: A World War II Soldier. 1999. (My Name Is America Ser.). (Illus.). 144p. (J). (gr. 4-8). 10.95 (978-0-439-05013-5(8)) Scholastic, Inc.

Napoli, Donna Jo. Fire in the Hills. 2006. 256p. (YA). (gr. 7). 16.99 (978-0-525-47751-8(9) , Dutton Juvenile) Penguin Group (USA) Inc.

—Stones in Water. 1999. 224p. (J). (gr. 5-9). reprint ed. pap. 5.99 (978-0-14-130600-1(9) , Puffin) Penguin Group (USA) Inc.

—Stones in Water. 1999. (978-0-606-17262-2(9)); (gr. 5-8). lib. bdg. 14.15 (978-0-613-23039-1(6)) Tandem Library Bks.

Newbery, Linda. At the Firefly Gate. 2007. 160p. (J). (gr. 5). 15.99 (978-0-385-75113-1(3)); lib. bdg. 18.99 (978-0-385-75114-8(1)) Random Hse. Children's Bks. (Fickling, David Bks.).

Nolan, Peggy. The Spy Who Came in from the Sea. 144p. (J). 2001. pap. 8.95 (978-1-56164-245-8(2)); 2000. (gr. 5-9). 14.95 (978-1-56164-186-4(3)) Pineapple Pr., Inc.

—Spy Who Came in from the Sea. 1999. (gr. 5-8). lib. bdg. 17.60 (978-0-613-37048-6(1)) Tandem Library Bks.

Odziemek, John. Catching Wayward Sheep. 2006. 128p. 21.99 (978-1-4141-0563-5(0)) Pleasant Word.

Oldham, June. In the Blood. 2003. 240p. (J). pap. (978-0-340-86653-5(5) , Hodder Children's Books) Hodder Children's Division.

O'Neill, Joan. Daisy Chain Dream. 2003. mass mkt. (978-0-340-85468-6(5) , Hodder Children's Books) Hodder Children's Division.

Oriev, Uri. Lidia, Reina de Palestina. (SPA.). 158p. (YA). (gr. 5-8). (978-84-279-3237-1(5) , NG8035) Noguer y Caralt Editores, S. A. ESP. *Dist:* Lectorum Pubns., Inc.

O'Toole, Katherine. A Time for Heroes. Wise, Noreen, ed. Favazza, Keith, illus. 2001. (Lemonade Collection). 208p. (YA). (gr. 5 up). pap. 15.50 (978-1-58584-275-9(3)) Huckleberry Pr.

Oughton, Jerrie. The War in Georgia. 1999. (978-0-606-16444-3(8)) Tandem Library Bks.

Park, Linda Sue. When My Name Was Keoko. 2002. 208p. (YA). (gr. 5-9). 16.00 (978-0-618-13335-2(6) , Clarion Bks.) Houghton Mifflin Co. Trade & Reference Div.

—When My Name Was Keoko. 2004. (Illus.). 208p. (J). (gr. 5). pap. 6.50 (978-0-440-41944-0(1) , Yearling) Random Hse. Children's Bks.

Parkhurst, Liz S. Under One Flag: A Year at Rohwer. Clifton, Tom, illus. 2005. 32p. (J). 16.95 (978-0-87483-759-9(6) , 1241971) August Hse. Pubs., Inc.

Parkinson, Curtis. Domenic's War: A Story of the Battle of Monte Cassino. 2006. 200p. (J). (gr. 5-9). pap. 9.95 (978-0-88776-751-7(6)) Tundra Bks., Inc./Livres Toundra, Inc. CAN. *Dist:* Random Hse., Inc.

Paterson, John & Paterson, Katherine. Blueberries for the Queen. Jeffers, Susan, illus. 2004. 32p. (J). (ps-3). lib. bdg. 18.89 (978-0-06-623943-9(5)) HarperCollins Pubs.

—Blueberries for the Queen. Jeffers, Susan, tr. Jeffers, Susan, illus. 2004. 32p. (J). (ps-3). 17.99 (978-0-06-623942-2(7)) HarperCollins Pubs.

Patneaude, David. Thin Wood Walls. 2004. (Illus.). 240p. (YA). (gr. 5-9). tchr. ed. 16.00 (978-0-618-34290-7(7)) Houghton Mifflin Co. Trade & Reference Div.

Patterson, Don. Fighter Escort. Parenteau, Mary, ed. Schug, Sonny, illus. 1999. (Tales of the R. A. F. Ser.). 92p. (J). (gr. 3-8). per. 7.95 (978-1-929031-09-2(2)) Hindsight, Ltd.

Paulsen, Gary. The Cookcamp. 2003. 128p. (J). pap. 4.99 (978-0-439-52357-8(5) , Scholastic Paperbacks) Scholastic, Inc.

—The Quilt. 96p. (gr. 3-7). 2005. (Illus.). (J). 5.50 (978-0-440-22936-0(7) , Yearling); 2004. (YA). 15.95 (978-0-385-72950-5(2) , Lamb, Wendy); 2004. (YA). lib. bdg. 17.99 (978-0-385-90886-3(5) , Lamb, Wendy) Random Hse. Children's Bks.

Pausewang, Gudrun. Dark Hours. Brownjohn, John, tr. from GER. 2006. (Illus.). 212p. (YA). (gr. 7-12). 21.95 (978-1-55451-042-9(2)) Annick Pr., Ltd. CAN. *Dist:* Firefly Bks., Ltd.

—Final Journey. Crampton, Patricia, tr. 1998. 160p. (J). (gr. 7-12). pap. 6.99 (978-0-14-130104-4(X) , Puffin) Penguin Group (USA) Inc.

Pausewang, Gudrun & Ward, Rachel. Traitor. 2006. 224p. (YA). 16.95 (978-0-8225-6195-8(6) , Carolrhoda Bks.) Lerner Publishing Group.

Peck, Richard. On the Wings of Heroes. 2007. 160p. (J). (gr. 4-8). 16.99 (978-0-8037-3081-6(0) , Dial) Penguin Group (USA) Inc.

Peet, Mal. Tamar: A Novel of Espionage, Passion, & Betrayal. 2007. (Illus.). 432p. (YA). (gr. 8 up). 17.99 (***978-0-7636-3488-9(3)***) Candlewick Pr.

Piotrowski, Robert. D-Day. Ng, Drew, illus. 2007. 48p. (J). lib. bdg. 23.08 (***978-1-4242-1634-5(6)***) Fitzgerald Bks.

Platt, Randall Beth. Honor Bright. 1998. (978-0-606-13486-6(7)) Tandem Library Bks.

Polacco, Patricia. The Butterfly. Polacco, Patricia, illus. 2000. (Illus.). 48p. (J). (ps-3). 16.99 (978-0-399-23170-4(6) , Philomel) Penguin Group (USA) Inc.

Pratchett, Terry. Johnny & the Bomb. 2007. 256p. (J). lib. bdg. 17.89 (978-0-06-054192-7(X)); (gr. 5-8). 16.99 (978-0-06-054191-0(1)) HarperCollins Pubs.

Price, Dianne D. Enemy in the House: The Story of a Young Friendship Born of War in America. 2003. 123p. pap. 14.95 (978-1-59286-483-6(X)) PublishAmerica, Inc.

Prins, Piet. Hideout in the Swamp. 2006. (Illus.). 136p. (J). pap. (978-1-894666-73-2(9)) Inheritance Pubns.

—The Lonely Sentinel. 2006. (Illus.). 140p. (J). pap. (978-1-894666-72-5(0)) Inheritance Pubns.

Radin, Ruth Y. Escape to the Forest: Based on a True Story of the Holocaust. Hamlin, Janet, illus. 96p. (J). (gr. 4 up). 2001. pap. 4.25 (978-0-06-440822-6(1)); 2000. 13.89 (978-0-06-028521-0(4)) HarperCollins Pubs.

Rappaport, Doreen. The Secret Seder. McCully, Emily Arnold, illus. 2005. 40p. (gr. k-4). 16.99 (978-0-7868-0777-2(6)) Hyperion Bks. for Children.

Razzell, Mary. White Wave. (J). pap. 7.95 (978-0-88899-161-4(4)) Groundwood Bks. CAN. *Dist:* Transition Vendor.

Redmond, Shirley-Raye & Ettlinger, Doris. Pigeon Hero! 2003. (Ready-to-Reads Ser.). (Illus.). 32p. (J). pap. 3.99 (978-0-689-85486-6(2) , Aladdin) Simon & Schuster Children's Publishing.

Reeder, Carolyn. Foster's War. 2000. 272p. (J). (gr. 4-7). pap. 4.99 (978-0-590-09856-4(X)) Scholastic, Inc.

—Foster's War. 2000. (J). 11.15 (978-0-606-19697-0(8)); (gr. 5-8). lib. bdg. 12.40 (978-0-613-29960-2(4)) Tandem Library Bks.

Reid, Charles. Hurricanes over London. 2005. (Illus.). 152p. (J). (gr. 3-9). pap., tchr. ed. 8.95 (978-0-921870-82-1(5)) Ronsdale Pr. CAN. *Dist:* Literary Pr. Group of Canada.

Rice, Mel. Secrets in the Sky. 2001. (gr. 3-6). lib. bdg. 17.60 (978-0-613-86877-8(3)) Tandem Library Bks.

—Secrets in the Sky. 2001. (Lone Star Heroine Ser.). (Illus.). 116p. (gr. 4-7). pap. 8.95 (978-1-55622-787-5(6) , Republic of Texas Pr.) Wordware Publishing, Inc.

Rinaldi, Ann. Keep Smiling Through. 2005. 208p. (J). pap. 6.95 (978-0-15-205399-4(9) , Gulliver Bks.) Harcourt Children's Bks.

Rodman, Mary Ann. Jimmy's Stars. 2008. 272p. (J). 16.95 (***978-0-374-33703-2(9)***) Farrar, Straus & Giroux.

Rogers, Kirby. Operation Dewey. 2002. (Illus.). ix, 100p. (J). pap. (978-1-877633-65-2(8)) Luthers.

Roseman, Kenneth D. Escape from the Holocaust. 1998. (gr. 3-6). lib. bdg. 17.60 (978-0-613-88955-1(X)) Tandem Library Bks.

Ross, Stewart. Dear Mum, I Miss You! Clark, Linda, illus. 54p. (J). (978-0-237-52318-3(3) , Evans Brothers, Limited) Evans Publishing Group.

—Dear Mum, I Miss You! 2007. (Flashbacks Ser.). (Illus.). 64p. (J). (gr. 4-7). pap. 8.95 (***978-0-237-53149-2(6)*** , Evans Brothers, Limited) Evans Publishing Group GBR. *Dist:* Independent Pubs. Group.

Ross, Stewart. What If the Bomb Goes Off? Clark, Linda, illus. 2001. (Coming Alive Ser.). 54p. 15.99 (978-0-237-52320-6(5) , Evans Brothers, Limited) Evans Publishing Group GBR. *Dist:* Independent Pubs. Group.

Roy, James. Billy Mack's War. 2004. 245p. (J). pap. (***978-0-7022-3479-8(6)***) Univ. of Queensland Pr.

Ruby, Lois. Shanghai Shadows. 2006. 256p. (J). (gr. 7 up). 16.95 (978-0-8234-1960-9(6)) Holiday Hse., Inc.

Rue, Nancy N. The Discovery. 2001. (Christian Heritage Ser.). (Illus.). 192p. (J). (gr. 3-7). pap. (978-1-56179-862-9(2)) Focus on the Family Publishing.

—The Mission. 2001. (Christian Heritage Ser.). 192p. (J). (gr. 3-8). pap. (978-1-56179-894-0(0)) Focus on the Family Publishing.

—The Struggle. 2002. (Christian Heritage Ser.). 192p. (J). pap. 5.99 (978-1-56179-895-7(9)) Bethany Hse. Pubs.

Rylant, Cynthia. I Had Seen Castles. 2004. 128p. (YA). reprint ed. pap. 5.95 (978-0-15-205312-3(3) , Harcourt Paperbacks) Harcourt Children's Bks.

Salisbury, Graham. Eyes of the Emperor. (YA). (gr. 7-11). 2007. 256p. mass mkt. 6.50 (978-0-440-22956-8(1), Laurel Leaf); 2005. 240p. 15.95 (978-0-385-72971-0(5), Lamb, Wendy); 2005. 240p. lib. bdg. 17.99 (978-0-385-90874-0(1), Lamb, Wendy) Random Hse. Children's Bks.

—House of the Red Fish. 2008. 304p. (YA). (gr. 7). mass mkt. 6.50 (***978-0-440-23838-6(2)***, Laurel Leaf) Random Hse. Children's Bks.

Salisbury, Graham. Under the Blood-Red Sun. 2005. 272p. (YA). (gr. 7-10). pap. 6.50 (978-0-553-49487-7(2), Laurel Leaf) Random Hse. Children's Bks.

Savery, Constance. Enemy Brothers. 2001. (Living History Library). (Illus.). 304p. (J). (gr. 5-12). reprint ed. pap. 13.95 (978-1-883937-50-8(7), 50-7) Bethlehem Bks.

Say, Allen. Home of the Brave. 2002. (Illus.). 32p. (J). (gr. k-3). 17.00 (978-0-618-21223-1(X), Walter Lorraine) Houghton Mifflin Co. Trade & Reference Div.

Schott, Elizabeth, illus. Jake & Sam at the Empty Abbey. 2006. 96p. (J). per. 9.95 (978-0-9724421-1-4(1)) Fountain Square Publishing.

Schroder, Jack. Dugout. 2004. 190p. (YA). per. 12.95 (978-0-9745665-6-6(X)) Catalpa Pr.

Scrase, Leslie. An Evacuee. 2000. 206p. (J). (978-1-85200-087-5(2)) United Writers Pubns., Ltd.

Sedgwick, Marcus. The Foreshadowing. 2006. 304p. (YA). (gr. 7 up). 16.95 (978-0-385-74646-5(6), Lamb, Wendy) Random Hse. Children's Bks.

Skrypuch, Marsha Forchuk. Hope's War. 2004. 200p. pap. 8.99 (978-1-895681-19-2(7), Boardwalk Bks.) Dundurn Group, The CAN. *Dist:* Univ. of Toronto Pr.

Slate, Joseph. Crossing the Trestle. 1999. (Accelerated Reader Bks.). 144p. (J). (gr. 3-7). 14.95 (978-0-7614-5053-5(X), Cavendish Children's Bks.) Cavendish, Marshall Corp.

Smith, Annie Laura. The Legacy of Bletchley Park. 2004. (YA). mass mkt. 6.99 (***978-0-9753367-1-7(1)***) Onstage Publishing, LLC.

Smith, Roland. Elephant Run. rev. ed. 2007. 336p. (gr. 3-7). 15.99 (***978-1-4231-0402-5(1)***) Hyperion Pr.

Spinelli, Jerry. Milkweed. 2003. (Illus.). 224p. (J). (gr. 5). 15.95 (978-0-375-81374-0(8)); lib. bdg. 17.99 (978-0-375-91374-7(2)) Random Hse. Children's Bks. (Knopf Bks. for Young Readers).

—Milkweed. l.t. ed. 2003. 279p. (YA). 23.95 (978-0-7862-6146-8(3), Large Print Pr.) Thorndike Pr.

Spring, Debbie. The Righteous Smuggler: A Holocaust Remembrance Book for Young Readers. 2005. (Illus.). 160p. (YA). pap. 6.95 (978-1-896764-97-9(5)) Second Story Pr. CAN. *Dist:* Univ. of Toronto Pr.

Sullivan, Jaqueline Levering. Annie's War. 2007. 190p. (J). (gr. 3-7). 15.00 (***978-0-8028-5325-7(0)***, Eerdmans Bks For Young Readers) Eerdmans, William B. Publishing Co.

Summer of My German Soldier. 1999. (YA). 9.95 (978-1-56137-113-6(0)) Novel Units, Inc.

Suzuki, Etsuo. Anne Frank. 2006. (Illus.). 160p. pap. 9.95 (978-1-56970-974-0(2)) Digital Manga Publishing.

Swindells, Robert. Blitzed. 2003. 176p. (J). pap. 9.99 (978-0-440-86397-7(X), Corgi) Transworld Publishers Ltd. GBR. *Dist:* Trafalgar Square Publishing.

—Doodlebug Alley. (Illus.). 56p. (J). pap. 6.99 (978-0-7497-3860-0(X)) Egmont Bks., Ltd. GBR. *Dist:* Trafalgar Square Publishing.

Taylor, Mary Ann. Traitors: A Gander's Cove Mystery. Casteel, Kay, illus. 2006. (J). mass mkt. 5.99 (***978-0-9753367-9-3(7)***) Onstage Publishing, LLC.

Taylor, Theodore & Gonzalez, Tomas. El Cavo. 2000. (SPA., Illus.). 106p. (J). (gr. k-2). 9.50 (978-84-279-3250-0(2), NG0873) Lectorum Pubns., Inc.

Ter Haar, Jaap. The Ice Road. Mearns, Martha, tr. from DUT. 2005. 157p. (J). (gr. k-9). pap. 5.95 (978-1-903015-38-4(3)) Barn Owl Bks, London GBR. *Dist:* Independent Pubs. Group.

Toksvig, Sandi. Hitler's Canary. 2007. 192p. (J). (gr. 6 up). 16.95 (978-1-59643-247-5(0)) Roaring Brook Pr.

Townsend, Tom. Nadia of the Night Witches. Kemnitz, Myrna, ed. 1998. 158p. (YA). (gr. 8 up). 9.99 (978-0-88092-273-9(7), 2737) Royal Fireworks Publishing Co.

Townson, Hazel. The Secret Room. Salisbury, Martin, illus. 2006. (Pathway Books). 75p. (J). 21.26 (978-1-59889-003-7(4)) Stone Arch Bks.

Tripp, Valerie. Brave Emily. 2006. (Illus.). 85p. (J). 12.95 (***978-1-59369-211-7(0)***, American Girl) American Girl Publishing, Inc.

—Brave Emily. Backes, Nick, illus. 2006. (American Girl Ser.). 85p. (J). (gr. 2-4). pap. 6.95 (978-1-59369-210-0(2), American Girl) American Girl Publishing, Inc.

Tripp, Valerie. Molly's Short Story Collection. Bakces, Nick & Hood, Philip, illus. 2006. 232p. (J). 12.95 (***978-1-59369-123-3(8)***) American Girl Publishing, Inc.

Turtledove, Harry. Into the Darkness. 2000. (gr. 7-12). lib. bdg. 16.45 (978-0-613-27901-7(8)) Tandem Library Bks.

Ungerer, Tomi. Otto: Autobiographie Eines Teddybaeren. Von Cramer-Klett, Anna, tr. 1999. (GER., Illus.). 36p. (J). pap. (978-3-257-00857-9(0)) Diogenes Verlag AG CHE. *Dist:* International Bk. Import Service, Inc.

Van Steenwyk, Elizabeth. A Traitor among Us. 143p. (J). (gr. 4-7). 2004. (Illus.). pap. 6.00 (978-0-8028-5157-4(6)); 1998. 15.00 (978-0-8028-5150-5(9)) Eerdmans, William B. Publishing Co.

—A Traitor among Us. 1999. (978-0-606-17601-9(2)) Tandem Library Bks.

—Traitor among Us. 1999. (gr. 5-8). lib. bdg. 14.15 (978-0-613-59388-5(X)) Tandem Library Bks.

Walters, Eric. Caged Eagles. 2001. 256p. (J). (gr. 7-12). pap. 7.95 (978-1-55143-139-0(4)) Orca Bk. Pubs. USA.

—Caged Eagles. 2001. (gr. 7-12). lib. bdg. 16.40 (978-0-613-86415-2(8)) Tandem Library Bks.

—Camp 30. 2007. 224p. (J). mass mkt. 6.99 (978-0-14-301678-6(4), Penguin Global) Penguin Group (USA) Inc.

—War of the Eagles. 1998. 160p. (YA). (gr. 7-12). 14.00 (978-1-55143-118-5(1)) Orca Bk. Pubs. USA.

Waters, Zack C. Blood Moon Rider. 2006. 126p. (J). 13.95 (978-1-56164-350-9(5)) Pineapple Pr., Inc.

Watts, Irene. Remember Me: A Search for Refuge in Wartime Britain. 2000. (gr. 5-8). lib. bdg. 16.40 (978-0-613-45685-2(8)) Tandem Library Bks.

Watts, Irene N. Finding Sophie. 2002. (gr. 5-8). lib. bdg. 15.25 (978-0-613-62903-4(5)) Tandem Library Bks.

—Finding Sophie. 2002. 144p. (J). (gr. 5). pap. 6.95 (978-0-88776-613-8(7)) Tundra Bks., Inc./Livres Toundra, Inc. CAN. *Dist:* Random Hse., Inc.

—Good-Bye Marianne: A Story of Growing up in Nazi Germany. 1998. 112p. (J). (gr. 3-7). pap. 7.95 (978-0-88776-445-5(2)) Tundra Bks., Inc./Livres Toundra, Inc. CAN. *Dist:* Random Hse., Inc.

—Remember Me: A Search for Refuge in Wartime Britain. 2000. 192p. (J). (gr. 5 up). pap. 7.95 (978-0-88776-519-3(X)) Tundra Bks., Inc./Livres Toundra, Inc. CAN. *Dist:* Random Hse., Inc.

Weber, Judith Eichler. Seeking Safety. Martin, John F., illus. 2006. (Adventures in America Ser.). (J). (978-1-893110-46-5(X)) Silver Moon Pr.

Wells, Helen. Cherry Ames, Army Nurse. 2005. (YA). pap. (978-0-9771597-2-7(8)) Springer.

—Cherry Ames, Chief Nurse. 2005. (YA). pap. (978-0-9771597-3-4(6)) Springer.

—Cherry Ames, Flight Nurse. 2006. ix, 211p. (J). (978-0-8261-0397-0(9)) Springer.

—Cherry Ames, Senior Nurse. 2005. (YA). pap. (978-0-9771597-1-0(X)) Springer.

West, Nancy. Chips - the War Dog: Based on the True-Life Adventures of the World War II K-9 Hero. 2nd ed. 2004. 183p. (J). per. 8.95 (978-0-9743659-1-6(2)) Hero Dog Pubns.

Whelan, Gloria. Burying the Sun. 224p. (J). 2007. pap. 6.99 (***978-0-06-054114-9(8)***, Harper Trophy); 2004. (gr. 5 up). 15.99 (978-0-06-054112-5(1)); 2004. (gr. 5 up). lib. bdg. 16.89 (978-0-06-054113-2(X)) HarperCollins Pubs.

—Summer of the War. 2006. (J). 176p. 15.99 (978-0-06-008072-3(8)); 176p. lib. bdg. 16.89 (978-0-06-008073-0(6)); 163p. (***978-1-4287-0030-7(7)***) HarperCollins Pubs.

Wilson, John. Flames of the Tiger. 2004. 176p. (YA). (gr. 13 up). (978-1-55337-618-7(8)); (Illus.). (978-1-55337-619-4(6)) Kids Can Pr., Ltd.

Winter, Kathryn. Katarina. 1999. (J). (978-0-606-17441-1(9)) Tandem Library Bks.

Wolff, Virginia Euwer. Bat 6. 256p. (J). (gr. 4-6). pap. 4.99 (978-0-8072-8223-6(5)); 2004. (gr. 5-9). pap. 36.00 incl. audio (978-0-8072-8222-9(7), YYA144SP) Random Hse. Audio Publishing Group. (Listening Library).

—Bat 6. 240p. (gr. 5-9). 2000. (Illus.). (J). pap. 4.99 (978-0-590-89800-3(0), Scholastic Reference); 1998. (YA). pap. 16.95 (978-0-590-89799-0(3)) Scholastic, Inc.

—Bat 6. 2000. (Illus.). (J). 11.64 (978-0-606-18516-5(X)); 1999. (gr. 5-8). lib. bdg. 13.00 (978-0-613-28413-4(5)) Tandem Library Bks.

Woodbury, Mary. Flight of the Tiger Moth. 2007. 224p. (YA). (gr. 7 up). 9.95 (***978-1-55050-364-7(2)***) Coteau Bks. CAN. *Dist:* Fitzhenry & Whiteside, Ltd.

Woodson, Jacqueline. Coming on Home Soon. Lewis, Earl, illus. 2004. 32p. (J). (ps). 16.99 (978-0-399-23748-5(8), Putnam Juvenile) Penguin Group (USA) Inc.

Wouk, Herman. War & Remembrance. 2002. (gr. 7-12). lib. bdg. 25.40 (978-0-613-46182-5(7)) Tandem Library Bks.

—The Winds of War. 2002. (gr. 7-12). lib. bdg. 25.40 (978-0-613-50107-3(5)) Tandem Library Bks.

Wulffson, Don L. Soldier X. 2003. 240p. (YA). pap. 6.99 (978-0-14-250073-6(9), Puffin); 2001. 244p. (J). (gr. 5-9). 16.99 (978-0-670-88863-4(X), Viking Juvenile) Penguin Group (USA) Inc.

—Soldier X. 2003. (gr. 7-12). lib. bdg. 15.30 (978-0-613-67163-7(5)) Tandem Library Bks.

Yates, Elizabeth. American Haven. 2002. (Illus.). 112p. (J). (gr. 4-7). 7.49 (978-1-57924-896-3(9)) Jones, Bob Univ. Pr.

Ylvisaker, Anne. Dear Papa. (Illus.). 192p. (J). (gr. 4). 2007. pap. 5.99 (***978-0-7636-3402-5(6)***); 2002. 15.99 (978-0-7636-1618-2(4)) Candlewick Pr.

Zeinert, Karen. To Touch the Stars: A Story of World War II. 2004. (Jamestown's American Portraits Ser.). (Illus.). 136p. (J). (gr. 5-7). pap. 4.95 (978-0-7696-3442-5(7), Waterbird Bks.) School Specialty Publishing.

—To Touch the Stars: A Story of World War II. 2000. (978-0-606-21878-8(5)) Tandem Library Bks.

Zindel, Paul. The Gadget. 2003. (Illus.). 192p. (YA). (gr. 7). pap. 6.50 (978-0-440-22951-3(0), Laurel Leaf) Random Hse. Children's Bks.

—The Gadget. 2003. (gr. 5-8). lib. bdg. 13.55 (978-0-613-62203-5(0)) Tandem Library Bks.

Zucker, Jonny. The Bombed House. Savage, Paul, illus. 2007. (Keystone Books). 33p. (J). (gr. 5-8). lib. bdg. 19.93 (978-1-59889-092-1(1)) Stone Arch Bks.

Zusak, Markus. The Book Thief. (YA). (gr. 7 up). 2007. 576p. pap. 11.99 (***978-0-375-84220-7(9)***); 2006. 560p. 16.95 (978-0-375-83100-3(2)); 2006. 560p. lib. bdg. 18.99 (978-0-375-93100-0(7)) Random Hse. Children's Bks. (Knopf Bks. for Young Readers).

WORLD WAR, 1939-1945—FRANCE

Abnett, Dan & Murray, Doug. The Tide Turns: D-Day Invasion. Elson, Richard & Williams, Anthony, illus. 2007. (Graphic History Ser.). 48p. (J). (gr. 3-7). pap. 9.95 (978-1-84603-056-7(0)) Osprey Publishing, Ltd. GBR. *Dist:* Random Hse., Inc.

Bliven, Bruce, Jr. Invasion: The Story of D-Day. 2007. (Sterling Point Bks.). (Illus.). 176p. (J). 12.95 (978-1-4027-4521-8(4)); pap. 6.95 (978-1-4027-4141-8(3)) Sterling Publishing Co., Inc.

Brook, Henry. True Stories of D-Day. McNee, Ian, illus. 2006. 160p. (J). pap. (***978-0-439-89833-1(1)***) Scholastic, Inc.

Drez, Ronald J. Remember D-Day: Both Sides Tell Their Stories. 2004. (Remember Ser.). (Illus.). 64p. (J). (gr. 5). 17.95 (978-0-7922-6666-2(8), National Geographic Children's Bks.) National Geographic Society.

Hynson, Colin. D-Day. 2004. (Days That Changed the World Ser.). (Illus.). 48p. (J). (gr. 5 up). pap. 11.95 (978-0-8368-5575-3(2)); lib. bdg. 30.00 (978-0-8368-5568-5(X)) Stevens, Gareth Inc. (World Almanac Library).

Murray, Doug. D-Day. 2007. (Graphic Battles of World War II Ser.). (Illus.). 48p. (YA). (gr. 5-8). lib. bdg. 29.25 (***978-1-4042-0786-8(4)***) Rosen Publishing Group, Inc., The.

Price, Sean. Varian Fry: A Hero of the Holocaust. 2007. (J). (***978-1-4109-2696-8(6)***); pap. (***978-1-4109-2707-1(5)***) Steck-Vaughn.

Rice, Earle. Normandy. 2002. (Battles That Changed the World Ser.). (Illus.). (J). 122p. pap. 13.25 (978-0-7910-7109-0(X)); 112p. 30.00 (978-0-7910-6687-4(8)) Facts On File, Inc. (Chelsea Hse.).

Wallace, Karen & Platt, Richard. D-Day Landings Vol. 4: The Story of the Allied Invasion. 2004. (Dk Readers Ser.). (Illus.). 32p. (J). (gr. 5). pap. 3.99 (978-0-7566-0275-8(0)) Dorling Kindersley Publishing, Inc.

WORLD WAR, 1939-1945—GERMANY

Cain, Bill. Battle of the Bulge. 2007. (Graphic Battles of World War II Ser.). (Illus.). 48p. (YA). (gr. 5-8). lib. bdg. 29.25 (***978-1-4042-0782-0(1)***) Rosen Publishing Group, Inc., The.

Davenport, John. The Nuremberg Trials. 2006. (World History Ser.). 112p. (J). (gr. 7-10). 32.45 (978-1-59018-634-3(6), Lucent Bks.) Thomson Gale.

Drez, Ronald J. Remember D-Day: Both Sides Tell Their Stories. 2004. (Remember Ser.). (Illus.). 64p. (J). (gr. 5). 17.95 (978-0-7922-6666-2(8)); 27.90 (978-0-7922-6965-6(9)) National Geographic Society. (National Geographic Children's Bks.).

Harcourt School Publishers Staff. The Berlin Airlift. 3rd ed. 2002. (Horizons Ser.). (Illus.). (J). pap. 7.30 (978-0-15-333587-7(4)) Harcourt Schl. Pubs.

McGowen, Tom. Germany's Lightning War: Panzer Divisions of World War II. 1999. (Military Might Ser.: 8). (Illus.). 64p. (gr. 5-8). lib. bdg. 26.90 (978-0-7613-1511-7(X), Twenty-First Century Bks.) Lerner Publishing Group.

Raven, Margot Theis. Mercedes & the Chocolate Pilot: A True Story of the Berlin Airlift & the Candy That Dropped from the Sky. van Frankenhuyzen, Gijsbert, illus. 2002. 48p. (J). (gr. k-5). 17.95 (978-1-58536-069-7(4)) Sleeping Bear Pr.

Rice, Earle, Jr. Blitzkrieg! Hitler's Lightning War. 2007. (Monumental Milestones Ser.).Tr. of 48. (Illus.). (YA). lib. bdg. 29.95 (***978-1-58415-542-3(6)***) Mitchell Lane Pubs., Inc.

Rice, Earle. Manfred Von Richthofen. 2003. (Famous Flyers Ser.). (Illus.). 112p. (gr. 6-12). 30.00 (978-0-7910-7214-1(2), Chelsea Hse.) Facts On File, Inc.

Saltzwedel, Hans H. Hans' Journal: A Young German's Memories of His Family's Survival During Germany's Darkest Days. 2003. (Illus.). 234p. per. 19.95 net. (978-1-931934-17-6(7)) Back Yard Pub.

Sears, Stephen. Air War Against Hitler's Germany. 2005. 176p. pap. 9.95 (978-1-59687-004-8(4)) ibooks, Inc.

Welter, Anni. Child of War: How We Lived & Survived under the Third Reich. 2nd ed. 2003. Orig. Title: Child of the Third Reich: How We Lived & Survived. 160p. (YA). per. 14.95 (978-0-9741434-0-8(5)) A H W Publishing.

Zaugg, Sandra L. Escape. 2007. (Illus.). 95p. (J). (***978-0-8163-2140-7(X)***) Pacific Pr. Pubns.

WORLD WAR, 1939-1945—GREAT BRITAIN

Adams, Simon. Winston Churchill. 2003. (20th Century History Makers Ser.). (Illus.). 112p. (J). lib. bdg. 32.85 (978-0-7398-5254-5(X)) Raintree.

Binns, Tristan Boyer. Winston Churchill: Soldier & Politician. 2004. (Great Life Stories Ser.). (Illus.). 127p. (J). 30.50 (978-0-531-12361-4(8), Watts, Franklin) Scholastic Library Publishing.

Haugen, Brenda. Winston Churchill: British Soldier, Writer, Statesman. 2006. (Signature Lives Ser.). (Illus.). 112p. (J). (gr. 5-7). 30.60 (978-0-7565-1582-9(3)) Compass Point Bks.

Stalcup, Ann. On the Home Front: Growing up in Wartime England. 1998. (Illus.). xiv, 91p. (J). (gr. 3-6). lib. bdg. 19.50 (978-0-208-02482-4(4), Linnet Bks.) Shoe String Pr., Inc.

Stephens, Chris S. A Wartime Scrapbook: The Teachers' Pack. 2004. (Illus.). 32p. pap. 42.95 (978-1-84323-329-9(0)) Beekman Bks., Inc.

Williams, Brian. World at War: World War II: the Evacuation of Children. 2005. (World at War— World War II Ser.). (Illus.). 32p. tchr. ed. (978-0-431-10380-8(1)) Heinemann Library.

WORLD WAR, 1939-1945—GUERRILLAS

see World War, 1939-1945—Underground Movements

WORLD WAR, 1939-1945—HOSPITALS

see World War, 1939-1945—Medical Care

WORLD WAR, 1939-1945—JAPAN

Donlan, Leni. How Did This Happen Here? Japanese Internment Camps. 2007. (***978-1-4109-2701-9(6)***); pap. (***978-1-4109-2712-5(1)***) Steck-Vaughn.

Hook, Jason. Hiroshima. 2002. (Days That Shook the World Ser.). 48p. (J). lib. bdg. 27.12 (978-0-7398-5234-7(5)) Raintree.

Klam, Julie. Victory in the Pacific. 2002. (Illus.). 48p. (J). lib. bdg. 28.50 (978-1-58340-192-7(X)) Smart Apple Media.

Literature Connections English: So Far from the Bamboo Grove. 2004. (gr. 6-12). (978-0-395-77138-9(2), 2-70216) McDougal Littell Inc.

Malam, John. The Bombing of Hiroshima. 2002. (Dates with History Ser.). (Illus.). 31p. (J). lib. bdg. 24.25 (978-1-58340-213-9(6)) Smart Apple Media.

Ohlenroth, Patricia. Up from the Ashes: Rebuilding after World War II. 2007. (Lucent Library of Historical Eras:Twentieth-Century Japan Ser.). (Illus.). 128p. (gr. 7-10). 31.20 (***978-1-4205-0028-8(7)***, Lucent Bks.) Thomson Gale.

Richard Tames. Hiroshima. 2nd ed. 2006. (Illus.). 32p. (J). pap. (***978-1-4034-9149-7(6)***) Heinemann Library.

Sherman, Josepha. The Story of the Attack on Pearl Harbor. 2005. (Monumental Milestones Ser.). (Illus.). 48p. (YA). lib. bdg. (978-1-58415-397-9(0)) Mitchell Lane Pubs., Inc.

Tames, Richard. Hiroshima: The Shadow of the Bomb. 2006. (Point of Impact Ser.). (Illus.). 32p. (YA). (gr. 5-8). lib. bdg. 29.29 (***978-1-4034-9140-4(2)***) Heinemann Library.

—Hiroshima: The Shadow of the Bomb. 2001. (Illus.). 32p. (J). (gr. 4-7). lib. bdg. 15.25 (978-0-613-36102-6(4)) Tandem Library Bks.

WORLD WAR, 1939-1945—JEWS

Byers, Ann. Oskar Schindler: Saving Jews from the Holocaust. 2005. (Holocaust Heroes & Nazi Criminals Ser.). (Illus.). 160p. (J). (gr. 6-12). lib. bdg. 27.93 (978-0-7660-2534-9(9)) Enslow Pubs., Inc.

Downing, David. Fighting Back. 2005. (World Almanac Library of the Holocaust). (Illus.). 48p. (YA). (gr. 10-12). lib. bdg. 30.00 (978-0-8368-5946-1(4), World Almanac Library) Stevens, Gareth Inc.

—Nazi Death Camps. 2005. (World Almanac Library of the Holocaust). (Illus.). 48p. pap. (978-0-8368-5954-6(5)); (YA). (gr. 5 up). lib. bdg. 30.00 (978-0-8368-5947-8(2)) Stevens, Gareth Inc. (World Almanac Library).

Draper, Allison Stark. Pastor Andre Trocme: Spiritual Leader of the French Village, Le Chambon. 2005. (Holocaust Biographies Ser.). (Illus.). 112p. (YA). (gr. 7-12). lib. bdg. 26.50 (978-0-8239-3378-5(4)) Rosen Publishing Group, Inc., The.

Finkelstein, Norman H. Remember Not to Forget: A Memory of the Holocaust. Hokanson, Lois & Hokanson, Lars, illus. 2004. 32p. pap. 9.95 (978-0-8276-0770-5(9)) Jewish Pubn. Society.

Giddens, Sandra. Escape: Teens Who Escaped the Holocaust to Freedom. 1999. (Teen Witnesses to the Holocaust Ser.). (Illus.). 64p. (YA). (gr. 7-12). lib. bdg. 26.50 (978-0-8239-2843-9(8), TWESCA) Rosen Publishing Group, Inc., The.

Gottfried, Ted. Heroes of the Holocaust. Alcorn, Stephen, illus. (Holocaust History Ser.). 112p. (YA). (gr. 7-12). 22.95 (978-1-58013-222-0(7)) Kar-Ben Publishing.

—Heroes of the Holocaust. Alcorn, Stephen, illus. 2001. (Holocaust Ser.: up). 112p. (J). (gr. 7 up). lib. bdg. 29.90 (978-0-7613-1717-3(1), Twenty-First Century Bks.) Lerner Publishing Group.

—Martyrs to Madness: The Victims of the Nazis. Alcorn, Stephen, illus. 2000. (Holocaust Ser.: up). 128p. (gr. 7). lib. bdg. (978-0-7613-1715-9(5), Twenty-First Century Bks.) Lerner Publishing Group.

Lyman, Darryl. Holocaust Rescuers: Ten Stories of Courage. 1999. (Collective Biographies Ser.). (Illus.). 128p. (YA). (gr. 6-12). lib. bdg. 26.60 (978-0-7660-1114-4(3)) Enslow Pubs., Inc.

McArthur, Debra. Raoul Wallenberg: Rescuing Thousands from the Nazis' Grasp. 2005. (Holocaust Heroes & Nazi Criminals Ser.). (Illus.). 160p. (J). (gr. 6-12). lib. bdg. 27.93 (978-0-7660-2530-1(6)) Enslow Pubs., Inc.

Mochizuki, Ken. Pasajea la Libertad. ed. 2004. (SPA., Illus.). (J). (gr. k-4). spiral bd. (978-0-616-03091-2(6)) Canadian National Institute for the Blind/Institut National Canadien pour les Aveugles.

—Passage to Freedom: The Sugihara Story. Lee, Dom, illus. 1999. 32p. (J). (gr. 1 up). 15.95 (978-1-880000-49-6(0)) Lee & Low Bks., Inc.

—Passage to Freedom: The Sugihara Story. Lee, Dom, illus. 2000. pap. 35.95 incl. audio compact disk (978-1-59112-544-0(8)) Live Oak Media.

Opdyke, Irene Gut. In My Hands: Memories of a Holocaust Rescuer. (Illus.). (YA). (gr. 9-8). 2004. 304p. mass mkt. 6.99 (978-0-553-49411-2(2), Laurel Leaf); 1999. 288p. pap. 18.00 (978-0-679-89181-9(1), Knopf Bks. for Young Readers) Random Hse. Children's Bks.

—In My Hands: Memories of A Holocaust Rescuer. 2001. (gr. 7-12). lib. bdg. 21.10 (978-0-613-49500-4(4)) Tandem Library Bks.

Opdyke, Irene Gut & Armstrong, Jennifer. In My Hands: Memories of a Holocaust Rescuer. unabr. ed. 2004. 248p. (J). (gr. 5 up). pap. 42.00 incl. audio (978-0-8072-0867-0(1), LYA 150 SP, Listening Library) Random Hse. Audio Publishing Group.

Price, Sean. Varian Fry: A Hero of the Holocaust. 2007. (J). (***978-1-4109-2696-8(6)***); pap. (***978-1-4109-2707-1(5)***) Steck-Vaughn.

Roberts, Jeremy. Oskar Schindler: Righteous Gentile. 2005. (Holocaust Biographies Ser.). (Illus.). 112p. (J). (gr. 7-12). lib. bdg. 26.50 (978-0-8239-3310-5(5), HBS-CHI) Rosen Publishing Group, Inc., The.

Ruelle, Karen Gray & DeSaix, Deborah Durland. Hidden on the Mountain: Stories of Children Sheltered from the Nazis in Le Chambon. 2006. (Illus.). 272p. (J). (gr. 5 up). 24.95 (978-0-8234-1928-9(2)) Holiday Hse., Inc.

W X Y Z

Shuter, Jane. Resistance to the Nazis. 2003. (Holocaust Ser.). (Illus.). 56p. (J). lib. bdg. 28.50 (978-1-4034-0814-3(9)); pap. 8.95 (978-1-4034-3206-3(6)) Heinemann Library.

Streissguth, Thomas. Raoul Wallenberg: Swedish Diplomat & Humanitarian. 2005. (Holocaust Biographies Ser.). (Illus.). 112p. (J). (gr. 7-12). lib. bdg. 26.50 (978-0-8239-3318-1(0), HBRAWA) Rosen Publishing Group, Inc., The.

Talbott, Hudson. Forging Freedom: A True Story of Heroism During the Holocaust. Talbott, Hudson, illus. 2000. (Illus.). 1p. (J). (gr. 2 up). 15.99 (978-0-399-23434-7(9), Putnam Juvenile) Penguin Group (USA) Inc.

Tito, E. Tina. Liberation: Teens in the Concentration Camps & the Teen Soldiers Who Liberated Them. 1999. (Teen Witnesses to the Holocaust Ser.). (Illus.). 64p. (YA). (gr. 7-12). lib. bdg. 26.50 (978-0-8239-2846-0(2), TWLIBE) Rosen Publishing Group, Inc., The.

Uschan, Michael V. Women of the Holocaust. 2006. (J). (978-1-59018-570-4(6), Lucent Bks.) Thomson Gale.

Ziemian, Joseph. The Cigarette Sellers of Three Crosses Square. 2005. (Library of Holocaust Testimonies). (Illus.). 168p. pap. 17.50 (978-0-85303-686-9(1)) Vallentine Mitchell Pubs. GBR. *Dist:* International Specialized Bk. Services.

WORLD WAR, 1939-1945—MEDICAL CARE

Norman, Elizabeth. We Band of Angels: The Untold Story of American Nurses Trapped on Bataan by The. 2000. (gr. 7-12). lib. bdg. 24.55 (978-0-613-29136-1(0)) Tandem Library Bks.

WORLD WAR, 1939-1945—NAVAL OPERATIONS

Abraham, Philip. John F. Kennedy & PT109. 2002. (Survivors Ser.). (Illus.). 48p. (YA). (gr. 7-12). 24.00 (978-0-516-23905-7(8), Children's Pr.) Scholastic Library Publishing.

Grenga, Helen E., ed. Movies on the Fantail: A Sailor's Diary & Memories from Other Men of the USS Barr DE576/APD39 (World War II) 2001. (Illus.). xvi, 336p. (J). 27.95 (978-0-9709110-0-1(9)) Yeoman Pr.

McGowan, Tom. Battle of Midway. 2001. (gr. 3-6). lib. bdg. 14.10 (978-0-613-51621-1(4)) Tandem Library Bks.

Nobleman, Marc Tyler. The Sinking of the USS Indianapolis. 2006. 48p. (J). (gr. 4-7). lib. bdg. (978-0-7565-2031-1(2)) Compass Point Bks.

WORLD WAR, 1939-1945—PACIFIC OCEAN

Abraham, Philip. John F. Kennedy & PT109. 2002. (Survivors Ser.). (Illus.). 48p. (YA). (gr. 7-12). 24.00 (978-0-516-23905-7(8), Children's Pr.) Scholastic Library Publishing.

Beller, Susan Provost. Battling in the Pacific: Soldiering in World War II. 2007. (Soldiers on the Battlefront Ser.). (Illus.). 112p. (YA). (gr. 6-8). lib. bdg. 33.26 (***978-0-8225-6381-5(9)***, Twenty-First Century Bks.) Lerner Publishing Group.

Chrisp, Peter. The War in the Pacific. 2003. (World Wars Ser.). (Illus.). 64p. (J). 28.56 (978-0-7398-6063-2(1)) Raintree.

Klam, Julie. Pearl Harbor & the Rise of Japan. 2002. (Illus.). 48p. (J). lib. bdg. 28.50 (978-1-58340-188-0(1)) Smart Apple Media.

WORLD WAR, 1939-1945—PERSONAL NARRATIVES

Aldrich, Dale & Hipperson, Carol Edgemon. The Belly Gunner. 2001. (Single Titles Ser.). (Illus.). 160p. (gr. 6 up). lib. bdg. 27.90 (978-0-7613-1873-6(9), Twenty-First Century Bks.) Lerner Publishing Group.

Allen, Thomas B. Remember Pearl Harbor: American & Japanese Survivors Tell Their Stories. 2007. (Remember Ser.). (Illus.). 64p. (J). (gr. 5). 27.90 (***978-0-7922-3635-1(1)***, National Geographic Children's Bks.) National Geographic Society.

Axelrod, Toby. Rescuers Defying the Nazis: Non-Jewish Teens Who Rescued Jews. 1999. (Teen Witnesses to the Holocaust Ser.). (Illus.). 64p. (YA). (gr. 7-12). lib. bdg. 26.50 (978-0-8239-2848-4(9), TWRESC) Rosen Publishing Group, Inc., The.

Brokaw, Tom. Greatest Generation. 2001. (gr. 7-12). lib. bdg. 23.40 (978-0-613-37178-0(X)) Tandem Library Bks.

—Greatest Generation Speaks: Letters & Reflections. 2001. (gr. 7-12). lib. bdg. 22.20 (978-0-613-37179-7(8)) Tandem Library Bks.

Dahl, Roald. Going Solo. 1999. (Illus.). 224p. (gr. 7-12). pap. 6.99 (978-0-14-130310-9(7), Puffin) Penguin Group (USA) Inc.

—Going Solo. 1998. (Illus.). 209p. (YA). (gr. 7-12). per. 15.30 (978-0-613-10109-7(X)) Tandem Library Bks.

DeMallie, H. R. Behind Enemy Lines: A Young Pilot's Story. 2007. (Sterling Point Bks.). (Illus.). 192p. (J). (gr. 6-9). 12.95 (978-1-4027-4517-1(6)) Sterling Publishing Co., Inc.

Komatsu, Kimberly & Komatsu, Kaleigh. In America's Shadow. 2003. (Illus.). 96p. (gr. 3 up). 35.00 (978-0-9709829-0-2(9)) George, Thomas Bks.

Nir, Yehuda. The Lost Childhood: A World War II Memoir. 2000. (Illus.). 304p. (J). (gr. 7 up). pap. 4.99 (978-0-439-16390-3(0), Scholastic Pr.) Scholastic, Inc.

Opdyke, Irene Gut. In My Hands: Memories of a Holocaust Rescuer. (Illus.). (YA). (gr. 9-8). 2004. 304p. mass mkt. 6.99 (978-0-553-49411-2(2), Laurel Leaf); 1999. 288p. pap. 18.00 (978-0-679-89181-9(1), Knopf Bks. for Young Readers) Random Hse. Children's Bks.

Opdyke, Irene Gut & Armstrong, Jennifer. In My Hands: Memories of a Holocaust Rescuer. unabr. ed. 2004. 248p. (J). (gr. 5 up). pap. 42.00 incl. audio (978-0-8072-0867-0(1), LYA 150 SP, Listening Library) Random Hse. Audio Publishing Group.

Oppenheim, Joanne. Dear Miss Breed: True Stories of the Japanese American Incarceration During World War II & a Librarian Who Made a Difference. 2006. (Illus.). 288p. (J). (gr. 7 up). pap. 22.99 (978-0-439-56992-7(3)) Scholastic, Inc.

Roberts, Marjorie H., told to. Wingtip to Wingtip: 8 WASPS, Women's Airforce Service Pilots of World War II. 2000. (Illus.). ix, 128p. (J). pap. 15.95 (978-1-928760-01-6(5)) Aviatrix Publishing, Inc.

Schomp, Virginia. World War II. 2001. (Letters from the Home Front Ser.). (Illus.). 96p. (J). (gr. 6 up). lib. bdg. 29.93 (978-0-7614-1098-0(8), Benchmark Bks.) Cavendish, Marshall Corp.

Stalcup, Ann. On the Home Front: Growing up in Wartime England. 1998. (Illus.). xiv, 91p. (J). (gr. 3-6). lib. bdg. 19.50 (978-0-208-02482-4(4), Linnet Bks.) Shoe String Pr., Inc.

Tammen, Gertrud Schakat. Diary of a War Child: The Memoir of Gertrud Schakat Tammen. 2001. (Cover-to-Cover Bks.). (Illus.). 72p. (J). pap. 8.95 (978-0-7891-5436-1(6)); (gr. 4-7). lib. bdg. 17.95 (978-0-7569-0082-3(4)) Perfection Learning Corp.

WORLD WAR, 1939-1945—PICTORIAL WORKS

Bradley, James & Powers, Ron. Flags of Our Fathers: A Young People's Edition. 2005. (Illus.). 224p. (YA). (gr. 7). mass mkt. 5.99 (978-0-440-22920-9(0), Laurel Leaf) Random Hse. Children's Bks.

—Flags of Our Fathers: Heroes of Iwo Jima. abr. ed. (Illus.). 224p. (YA). (gr. 7). 2001. lib. bdg. 17.99 (978-0-385-90009-6(0)); 2003. reprint ed. pap. 8.95 (978-0-385-73064-8(0)) Random Hse. Children's Bks. (Delacorte Bks. for Young Readers).

Ross, Robert Todd. U. S. Army Rangers & Special Forces of WWII: Their War in Photographs. 2002. (Schiffer Military History Book Ser.). (Illus.). 216p. (gr. 10-13). 59.95 (978-0-7643-1682-1(6)) Schiffer Publishing, Ltd.

WORLD WAR, 1939-1945—POLAND

Malam, John. Hitler Invades Poland: 1 September 1939. 2002. (Dates with History Ser.). (Illus.). 31p. (J). lib. bdg. 24.25 (978-1-58340-212-2(8)) Smart Apple Media.

Mochizuki, Ken. Passage to Freedom: The Sugihara Story. Lee, Dom, illus. 2003. 32p. (J). 6.95 (978-1-58430-157-8(0)) Lee & Low Bks., Inc.

Nir, Yehuda. The Lost Childhood: A World War II Memoir. 2000. (Illus.). 304p. (J). (gr. 7 up). pap. 4.99 (978-0-439-16390-3(0), Scholastic Pr.) Scholastic, Inc.

Ziemian, Joseph. The Cigarette Sellers of Three Crosses Square. 2005. (Library of Holocaust Testimonies). (Illus.). 168p. pap. 17.50 (978-0-85303-686-9(1)) Vallentine Mitchell Pubs. GBR. *Dist:* International Specialized Bk. Services.

WORLD WAR, 1939-1945—PRISONERS AND PRISONS

Aldrich, Dale & Hipperson, Carol Edgemon. The Belly Gunner. 2001. (Single Titles Ser.). (Illus.). 160p. (gr. 6 up). lib. bdg. 27.90 (978-0-7613-1873-6(9), Twenty-First Century Bks.) Lerner Publishing Group.

Bryant, Jen. Music for the End of Time. Peck, Beth, illus. 2005. 32p. (J). (gr. 3-5). 17.00 (978-0-8028-5229-8(7)) Eerdmans, William B. Publishing Co.

DeMallie, H. R. Behind Enemy Lines: A Young Pilot's Story. 2007. (Sterling Point Bks.). (Illus.). 192p. (J). (gr. 6-9). 12.95 (978-1-4027-4517-1(6)) Sterling Publishing Co., Inc.

Grapes, Bryan J. Japanese-American Internment Camps. 2000. (History Firsthand Ser.). (Illus.). 202p. (YA). (gr. 7-10). lib. bdg. 32.45 (978-0-7377-0413-6(6), Greenhaven Pr., Inc.) Thomson Gale.

Perl, Lila. Barbed Wire & Guard Towers: The Internment of Japanese Americans During World War II. 2002. (Great Journeys Ser.). (Illus.). 112p. (J). 32.79 (978-0-7614-1321-9(9), Benchmark Bks.) Cavendish, Marshall Corp.

Yancey, Diane. The Internment of the Japanese. 2002. (World History Ser.). (Illus.). 112p. (YA). (gr. 8-11). 32.45 (978-1-59018-013-6(5), LML00902-180218, Lucent Bks.) Thomson Gale.

WORLD WAR, 1939-1945—REFUGEES

Gottfried, Ted. Displaced Persons: Growing up American after the Holocaust. 2001. (Holocaust Ser.). (Illus.). 112p. (gr. 7 up). lib. bdg. 29.90 (978-0-7613-1924-5(7), Twenty-First Century Bks.) Lerner Publishing Group.

Price, Sean. Varian Fry: A Hero of the Holocaust. 2007. (J). (***978-1-4109-2696-8(6)***); pap. (***978-1-4109-2707-1(5)***) Steck-Vaughn.

Zaugg, Sandra L. Escape. 2007. (Illus.). 95p. (J). (***978-0-8163-2140-7(X)***) Pacific Pr. Pubns.

WORLD WAR, 1939-1945—SANITARY AFFAIRS

see World War, 1939-1945—Medical Care

WORLD WAR, 1939-1945—SOVIET UNION

Gottfried, Ted. The Great Fatherland War: The Soviet Union in World War II. Reim, Melanie K., illus. 2003. (Rise & Fall of the Soviet Union Ser.). 160p. (gr. 7 up). lib. bdg. 28.90 (978-0-7613-2559-8(X), Twenty-First Century Bks.) Lerner Publishing Group.

WORLD WAR, 1939-1945—UNDERGROUND MOVEMENTS

Axelrod, Toby. Hans & Sophie Scholl: German Resisters of the White Rose. 2005. (Holocaust Biographies Ser.). (Illus.). 112p. (YA). (gr. 7-12). lib. bdg. 26.50 (978-0-8239-3316-7(4), HBHOBI) Rosen Publishing Group, Inc., The.

DeMallie, H. R. Behind Enemy Lines: A Young Pilot's Story. 2007. (Sterling Point Bks.). (Illus.). 192p. (J). (gr. 6-9). 12.95 (978-1-4027-4517-1(6)) Sterling Publishing Co., Inc.

Forrester, Tina, et al. Hoodwinked: Deception & Resistance. Craig, David, illus. 2004. (Outwitting the Enemy Ser.). 96p. (J). (gr. 5). pap. 14.95 (978-1-55037-832-0(5)) Annick Pr., Ltd. CAN. *Dist:* Firefly Bks., Ltd.

Levine, Ellen. Darkness over Denmark: The Danish Resistance & the Rescue of the Jews. 2005. (Illus.). 178p. (YA). (gr. 7 up). pap. 14.95 (978-0-8234-1755-1(7)) Holiday Hse., Inc.

Shapiro, Sheryl. Hoodwinked: Deception & Resistance. 2004. (gr. 5-8). lib. bdg. 24.55 (978-0-613-78450-4(2)) Tandem Library Bks.

Shapiro, Stephen, et al. Hoodwinked: Deception & Resistance. Craig, David, illus. 2004. (Outwitting the Enemy Ser.). 96p. (J). (gr. 5). lib. bdg. 29.95 (978-1-55037-833-7(3)) Annick Pr., Ltd. CAN. *Dist:* Firefly Bks., Ltd.

Wise, William. Secret Mission to the Philippines: The Story of "Spyron" & the American-Filipino Guerrillas of World War II. 2001. 164p. pap. 13.95 (978-0-595-19809-2(0), Backinprint.com) iUniverse, Inc.

WORLD WAR, 1939-1945—UNITED STATES

Barr, Gary. World War II Home Front. 2004. (Illus.). 56p. (J). pap. 8.95 (978-1-4034-4579-7(6)); lib. bdg. (978-1-4034-4571-1(0)) Heinemann Library.

Boroughs, Ralph Z. The Devil's Tale: Stories of the Red Devils of the 508 Parachute Infantry Regiment 82nd Airborne Division in World War Two. Gintjee, Thomas J., illus. 2002. xii, 341p. (YA). mass mkt. 15.00 (978-0-9720657-0-2(9), 2515) Zig Boroughs.

Britton, Tamara L. Pearl Harbor. 2005. (Checkerboard History Library). (Illus.). 40p. (J). (gr. k-6). lib. bdg. 22.78 (978-1-57765-851-1(5)) ABDO Publishing Co.

Burgan, Michael. America in World War II. 2006. (Wars That Changed American History Ser.). 48p. (978-0-8368-7293-4(2)); pap. (978-0-8368-7302-3(5)) Stevens, Gareth Inc. (World Almanac Library).

Center for Learning Staff. World War II: 1935-1945 — Elementary U. S. History Series, 10 bks. 2003. (Social Studies Ser.). (Illus.). vi, 147p. (J). tchr. ed., spiral bd. 29.95 (978-1-56077-737-3(0)) Ctr. for Learning, The.

Chin, Steven A. When Justice Failed: The Fred Korematsu Story. 2001. (Nonfiction Bookbag Ser.). (YA). (gr. 7-8). per. 8.45 (978-1-58830-211-3(3)) Metropolitan Teaching & Learning Co.

Collier, Christopher & Collier, James Lincoln. The United States in World War II. 2001. (Drama of American History Ser.). (Illus.). 96p. (J). (gr. 5-9). lib. bdg. 31.36 (978-0-7614-1316-5(2), Benchmark Bks.) Cavendish, Marshall Corp.

Colman, Penny. Rosie the Riveter: Women Working on the Home Front in World War II. 1998. (978-0-606-13026-4(8)) Tandem Library Bks.

—Rosie the Riveter: Women Working on the Homefront in World War II. 1998. (Illus.). 128p. (J). (gr. 5-9). pap. 10.99 (978-0-517-88567-3(0), Crown Books For Young Readers) Random Hse. Children's Bks.

Cooper, Michael L. Remembering Manzanar: Life in a Japanese Relocation Camp. 2002. (Illus.). 80p. (J). (gr. 4-6). tchr. ed. 15.00 (978-0-618-06778-7(7), Clarion Bks.) Houghton Mifflin Co. Trade & Reference Div.

Cora, Paul B. Yellowjackets! The 361st Fighter Group in WWII. 2002. (Schiffer Military History Ser.). (Illus.). 152p. (gr. 10-13). 39.95 (978-0-7643-1466-7(1)) Schiffer Publishing, Ltd.

de Paola, Tomie. I'm Still Scared: A 26 Fairmount Avenue Book. 2006. (Illus.). 96p. (J). (gr. 1-4). 13.99 (978-0-399-24502-2(2), Putnam Juvenile) Penguin Group (USA) Inc.

DePaola, Tomie. I'm Still Scared: A 26 Fairmount Avenue Book. 2007. 96p. (J). (gr. 2-6). pap. 5.99 (978-0-14-240826-1(3), Puffin) Penguin Group (USA) Inc.

Donlan, Leni. How Did This Happen Here? Japanese Internment Camps. 2007. (***978-1-4109-2701-9(6)***); pap. (***978-1-4109-2712-5(1)***) Steck-Vaughn.

Folly, Martin. The United States & World War II: The Awakening Giant. 2002. (BAAS Paperbacks Ser.). (Illus.). 160p. pap. 22.00 (978-0-7486-1526-1(1)) Edinburgh Univ. Pr. GBR. *Dist:* Columbia Univ. Pr.

Gitlin, Marty. The Great Depression & World War II. 2007. (J). (***978-1-59036-749-0(9)***); (***978-1-59036-750-6(2)***) Weigl Pubs., Inc.

Halpern, Monica. The Home Front During World War II. 2004. (Reading Expeditions Ser.). (Illus.). 40p. (978-0-7922-4558-2(X)) National Geographic Society.

Harcourt School Publishers Staff. The Berlin Airlift. 3rd ed. 2002. (Horizons Ser.). (Illus.). (J). pap. 7.30 (978-0-15-333587-7(4)) Harcourt Schl. Pubs.

Kallen, Stuart A. The War at Home. 1999. (American War Library). (Illus.). 112p. (YA). (gr. 4-12). 27.45 (978-1-56006-531-9(1), LML00902-177888, Lucent Bks.) Thomson Gale.

King, David C. World War II Days: Discover the Past with Exciting Projects, Games, Activities, & Recipes. Kirk Noll, Cheryl, illus. 2000. (American Kids in History Ser.: Vol. 7). 112p. (gr. 4-6). pap. 12.95 (978-0-471-37101-4(7), Wiley-Interscience) Wiley, John & Sons, Inc.

Klam, Julie. The War at Home. 2002. (Illus.). 48p. (J). lib. bdg. 28.50 (978-1-58340-190-3(3)) Smart Apple Media.

Langellier, John P. American Indians in the U. S. Military: 1866-1945. 2001. (G. I. Ser.). (Illus.). 77p. (J). 32.00 (978-0-7910-6667-6(3), Chelsea Hse.) Facts On File, Inc.

Levy, Pat. The Home Front in World War II. 2003. (World Wars Ser.). (Illus.). 64p. (J). 28.56 (978-0-7398-6065-6(8)) Raintree.

McNeill, Allison & Hanes, Richard Clay. American Home Front in World War II Reference Library Cumulative Index. 2004. (American Home Front in World War II Reference Library). 32p. 5.00 (978-0-7876-9125-7(9), UXL) Thomson Gale.

Nobleman, Marc Tyler. The Sinking of the USS Indianapolis. 2006. 48p. (J). (gr. 4-7). lib. bdg. (978-0-7565-2031-1(2)) Compass Point Bks.

Oppenheim, Joanne. Dear Miss Breed: True Stories of the Japanese American Incarceration During World War II & a Librarian Who Made a Difference. 2006. (Illus.). 288p. (J). (gr. 7 up). pap. 22.99 (978-0-439-56992-7(3)) Scholastic, Inc.

Petersen, Christine. Rosie the Riveter. 2005. (Cornerstones of Freedom Ser.). (Illus.). 48p. (J). 26.00 (978-0-516-23634-6(2), Children's Pr.) Scholastic Library Publishing.

Rubin, Susan Goldman. The Flag with Fifty-Six Stars: A Gift from the Survivors of Mauthausen. Farnsworth, Bill, illus. 2006. 40p. (J). (gr. 1-5). reprint ed. 6.95 (978-0-8234-2019-3(1)) Holiday Hse., Inc.

Rue, Nancy N. The Mirage. 2001. (Christian Heritage Ser.). (Illus.). 192p. (J). (gr. 3-7). pap. 5.99 (978-1-56179-863-6(0)) Bethany Hse. Pubs.

—The Stand. 2001. (Christian Heritage Ser.). 192p. (J). (gr. 3-8). pap. (978-1-56179-893-3(2)) Focus on the Family Publishing.

Sakurai, Gail. Japanese American Internment Camps. 2007. (Cornerstones of Freedomtrade;, Second Ser.). 48p. (J). pap. 5.95 (***978-0-531-18690-9(3)***, Children's Pr.) Scholastic Library Publishing.

Sherman, Josepha. The Story of the Attack on Pearl Harbor. 2005. (Monumental Milestones Ser.). (Illus.). 48p. (YA). lib. bdg. (978-1-58415-397-9(0)) Mitchell Lane Pubs., Inc.

Stein, R. Conrad. The Home Front During World War II in American History. 2003. (In American History Ser.). (Illus.). 112p. (J). (gr. 5-12). lib. bdg. 26.60 (978-0-7660-1984-3(5)) Enslow Pubs., Inc.

—World War II in the Pacific: A MyReportLinks.com Book. 2002. (U. S. Wars Ser.). (Illus.). 48p. (J). (gr. 4-10). lib. bdg. 25.26 (978-0-7660-5093-8(9), MyReportLinks.com Bks.) Enslow Pubs., Inc.

—World War II in the Pacific: "Remember Pearl Harbor" 2000. (American War Ser.). (Illus.). 128p. (YA). (gr. 5-12). pap. 13.26 (978-0-7660-1734-4(6)) Enslow Pubs., Inc.

Tames, Richard. Pearl Harbor Set 1: The US Enters World War II. 2002. (Point of Impact Ser.). (Illus.). 32p. (J). (gr. 5-7). pap. 7.50 (978-1-58810-354-3(4), 91197) Heinemann Library.

War Comes to Florida's Northern Gulf Coast. 2002. (Illus.). 208p. lib. bdg. 40.00 (978-0-9724101-0-6(4)) New Hope Pr.

Yancey, Diane. The Internment of the Japanese. 2002. (World History Ser.). (Illus.). 112p. (YA). (gr. 8-11). 32.45 (978-1-59018-013-6(5), LML00902-180218, Lucent Bks.) Thomson Gale.

WORLD WIDE WEB

see also Internet

Brimner, Larry Dane. The World Wide Web. rev. ed. 2000. (True Bks.). (Illus.). 48p. (J). (gr. 3-5). 25.00 (978-0-516-21935-6(9), Children's Pr.) Scholastic Library Publishing.

Brown, Marty. Webmaster. 2000. (CoolCareers.com Ser.). (Illus.). 48p. (YA). (gr. 5-8). lib. bdg. 23.95 (978-0-8239-3111-8(0), CCWEMA, Rosen Central) Rosen Publishing Group, Inc., The.

Bullock, Linda. The World Wide Web. 2002. (Technology & You Ser.). (Illus.). 48p. (J). lib. bdg. 27.12 (978-0-7398-4698-8(1)) Raintree.

Gaines, Ann Graham. Tim Berners-Lee & the Development of the World Wide Web. 2002. (Unlocking the Secrets of Science Ser.). (Illus.). 56p. (gr. 4-10). lib. bdg. 25.70 (978-1-58415-096-1(3)) Mitchell Lane Pubs., Inc.

Hamilton, John. Internet. 2005. (Straight to the Source Ser.). (Illus.). 32p. (J). (gr. k-6). lib. bdg. 22.78 (978-1-59197-544-1(1)) ABDO Publishing Co.

Hixson, Bryce. The Original World Wide Web. Hixson, Bryce, illus. 2003. (Illus.). (J). per. 12.95 (978-1-931801-07-2(X)) Loose In The Lab.

Hovanec, Erin M. An Online Visit to Africa. (Internet Field Trips Ser.). 24p. (J). 2002. lib. bdg. 18.75 (978-0-8239-6420-8(5)); 2001. (Illus.). (gr. 3). lib. bdg. 18.75 (978-0-8239-5651-7(2)) Rosen Publishing Group, Inc., The. (PowerKids Pr.).

—An Online Visit to Asia. (Internet Field Trips Ser.). 24p. (J). 2002. lib. bdg. 18.75 (978-0-8239-6422-2(1)); 2001. (Illus.). (gr. 3). lib. bdg. 18.75 (978-0-8239-5652-4(0)) Rosen Publishing Group, Inc., The. (PowerKids Pr.).

—An Online Visit to Australia. (Internet Field Trips Ser.). 24p. (J). 2002. lib. bdg. 18.75 (978-0-8239-6421-5(3)); 2001. (Illus.). (gr. 3). lib. bdg. 18.75 (978-0-8239-5653-1(9)) Rosen Publishing Group, Inc., The. (PowerKids Pr.).

Jefferis, David. Cyberspace: Virtual Reality & the World Wide Web. 1999. (Megatech Ser.). (Illus.). 32p. (J). (gr. 4-5). pap. (978-0-7787-0057-9(7)); lib. bdg. (978-0-7787-0047-0(X)) Crabtree Publishing Co.

—Internet: Electronic Global Village. 2002. (Megatech Ser.). (Illus.). 32p. (J). (gr. 4-5). pap. (978-0-7787-0062-3(3)); lib. bdg. (978-0-7787-0052-4(6)) Crabtree Publishing Co.

—Internet: Electronic Global Village. 2002. (gr. 3-6). lib. bdg. 17.60 (978-0-613-52962-4(0)) Tandem Library Bks.

Kalbag, Asha. World Wide Web for Beginners. 1998. (gr. 5-8). lib. bdg. 18.75 (978-0-613-74474-4(8)) Tandem Library Bks.

McGraw-Hill Staff. Connect Online! Classroom. 2002. 130.00 (978-0-07-830907-6(7)) Glencoe/McGraw-Hill.

—Connect Online! Take-Home Activities. 2002. (C). pap. 18.64 (978-0-07-825154-2(0), 9780078251542) Glencoe/McGraw-Hill.

Morgan, Sally. Internet. 2001. (Behind Media Ser.). (Illus.). 48p. (J). (gr. 6-8). lib. bdg. 24.22 (978-1-58810-032-0(4)) Heinemann Library.

Solomon, Gwen, et al. Connect Online! 2002. stu. ed. 41.32 (978-0-07-824520-6(6), 9780078245206) Glencoe/McGraw-Hill.

Spangenburg, Ray & Moser, Diane. Savvy Surfing on the Internet: Searching & Evaluating Web Sites. 2001. (Issues in Focus Ser.). (Illus.). 112p. (YA). (gr. 6-12). lib. bdg. 26.60 (978-0-7660-1590-6(4)) Enslow Pubs., Inc.

Stephens, Michael. The Library Internet Trainer's Toolkit. 2001. (Netguide Ser.). (Illus.). 223p. cd-rom 149.95 (978-1-55570-415-5(8)) Neal-Schuman Pubs., Inc.

Stewart, Melissa. Tim Berners-Lee: Inventor of the World Wide Web. 2001. (Career Biographies Ser.). (Illus.). 128p. (J). (gr. 6-12). 25.00 (978-0-89434-367-4(X), F410, Ferguson Publishing Co.) Facts On File, Inc.

Tracy, Kathleen. Marc Andreessen & the Development of the Web Browser. 2002. (Unlocking the Secrets of Science Ser.). (Illus.). 56p. (gr. 4-10). lib. bdg. 25.70 (978-1-58415-092-3(0)) Mitchell Lane Pubs., Inc.

Ward-Johnson, Chris. World Wide Web: A Magic Mouse Guide. Laughing Gravy Design Staff, illus. 2003. (Magic Mouse Guides). 32p. (J). lib. bdg. 22.60 (978-0-7660-2262-1(5)) Enslow Pubs., Inc.

Wolinsky, Art. The History of the Internet & the World Wide Web. (Internet Library). (Illus.). 64p. (YA). (gr. 4-12). 2000. pap. 11.93 (978-0-7660-1746-7(X)); 1999. lib. bdg. 22.60 (978-0-7660-1261-5(1)) Enslow Pubs., Inc.

WORLD'S FAIRS

see Exhibitions; Fairs

WORMS

Allman, Toney. Guinea Worms (Parasites) 2004. (Parasites Ser.). (Illus.). 32p. (J). (gr. 4-7). 24.95 (978-0-7377-2634-3(2)) Thomson Gale.

—Tapeworms. 2003. (Parasites Ser.). (Illus.). 32p. (J). 24.95 (978-0-7377-1783-9(1), Greenhaven Pr., Inc.) Thomson Gale.

Bailey, Jill. Worm. (Illus.). 32p. (J). 2006. (*978-1-4034-8303-4(5)); 2002. pap. 6.95 (978-1-57572-461-4(8)); 1998. lib. bdg. 21.36 (978-1-57572-665-6(3)); 2nd ed. 2006. pap. (*978-1-4034-8316-4(7)) Heinemann Library.

Chanell, Jim & Greenaway, Theresa. Worms. 1999. (Minipets Ser.). (Illus.). 32p. (J). (gr. 1-5). lib. bdg. 25.69 (978-0-8172-5588-6(5)) Raintree.

Childrens Press Staff, ed. Insects, Spiders & Worms. 1998. (Rookie Read-About Science Ser.). pap. 19.90 (978-0-516-29985-3(9), Children's Pr.) Scholastic Library Publishing.

Evans, Arthur V. Grzimek's Student Animal Life Resource: Crustaceans, Mollusks & Segmented Worms. Harris, Madeline S., ed. 2005. (Grzimek's Student Animal Life Resource Ser.). (Illus.). 322p. (J). (gr. 3-7). 67.00 (978-0-7876-9411-1(8), UXL) Thomson Gale.

Greenaway, Theresa. Worms. 1999. (Minipets Ser.). (Illus.). 32p. (gr. 1-5). pap. 7.95 (978-0-8172-4208-4(2)) Steck-Vaughn.

Harcourt School Publishers Staff. Wonderful Worms: Library Book. 1999. (Collections Ser.). (Illus.). pap. 14.90 (978-0-15-313413-5(5)) Harcourt Schl. Pubs.

Heinrichs, Ann. Worms. 2004. (Illus.). 32p. (J). (gr. 2 up). lib. bdg. 21.26 (978-0-7565-0589-9(5)) Compass Point Bks.

Himmelman, John. A Mealworm's Life. Himmelman, John, illus. 2001. (Nature Upclose Ser.). (Illus.). 32p. (J). (gr. k-2). pap. 6.95 (978-0-516-27286-3(1), Children's Pr.) Scholastic Library Publishing.

Kalman, Bobbie. The Lifecycle of an Earthworm. 2003. (Life Cycle Ser.). (Illus.). 32p. (J). (978-0-7787-0666-3(4)); pap. (978-0-7787-0696-0(6)) Crabtree Publishing Co.

Kite, L. Patricia. Leeches. 2005. (Early Bird Nature Bks.). (Illus.). 47p. (J). 25.26 (978-0-8225-3054-1(6), Lerner Pubns.) Lerner Publishing Group.

Mason, Adrienne. Mealworms: Raise Them, Watch Them, See Them Change. Vaculik, Angela, illus. 24p. (J). (gr. k-3). 2001. (978-1-55074-506-1(9)); 1998. (978-1-55074-448-4(8)) Kids Can Pr., Ltd.

Morgan, Sally. Sponges & Other Minor Phyla. 2004. (Illus.). 64p. (J). 32.79 (978-1-4109-1053-0(9)); pap. 9.50 (978-1-4109-1349-4(X)) Harcourt Schl. Pubs.

—Worms. 2001. (Illus.). 32p. (J). lib. bdg. 24.25 (978-1-930643-13-0(6)) Chrysalis Education.

Murray, Peter. Worms. 2004. (Science Around Us Ser.). 32p. (J). (gr. 2-6). 27.07 (978-1-59296-276-1(9)) Child's World, Inc.

Parker, Steve. Nematodes, Leeches & Other Worms. 2006. (Animal Kingdom Classification Ser.). (Illus.). 48p. (J). (gr. 4-6). 26.60 (978-0-7565-1615-4(3)) Compass Point Bks.

Schaefer, Lola M. La Sanguijuela. 2002. (Animales Resbalosos (Ooey-Gooey Animals) Ser.). (SPA.). 24p. (J). (ps-1). lib. bdg. 18.50 (978-1-58810-766-4(3)); (Illus.). pap. 5.25 (978-1-58810-810-4(4), 91515) Heinemann Library.

Sroda, George. Facts about Nightcrawlers: Redworms & Garden Worms. (Illus.). 157p. (J). reprint ed. 10.95 (978-0-9604486-0-9(8)) Sroda, George.

Swindells, Robert. Inside the Worm. 2000. (Illus.). 189p. (J). 15.95 (978-0-385-40307-8(0)) Transworld Publishers Ltd. GBR. *Dist:* Trafalgar Square Publishing.

Weber, Rebecca. Tricky Insects: And Other Fun Creatures. 2002. (Spyglass Books). (Illus.). 24p. (J). (gr. 1 up). lib. bdg. 18.60 (978-0-7565-0388-8(4)) Compass Point Bks.

Worms. (Nature's Friends Ser.). 32p. (J). 7.95 (978-0-7565-1234-7(4)) Compass Point Bks.

Wyborny, Sheila. Leeches. 2005. (Parasites Ser.). (Illus.). 32p. (J). (gr. 4-8). 24.95 (978-0-7377-3050-0(1), Greenhaven Pr., Inc.) Thomson Gale.

WORMS—FICTION

A. A Friend with No Name. 2006. (ENG., Illus.). 28p. per. 11.95 (978-1-59800-476-2(X)) Outskirts Press, Inc.

Amato, Mary. The Word Eater. 2005. (Illus.). 151p. (YA). (gr. 4-6). tchr. ed. 15.95 (978-0-8234-1468-0(X)) Holiday Hse., Inc.

—The Word Eater. Ryniak, Christopher, illus. 2005. 151p. (J). reprint ed. pap. 6.95 (978-0-8234-1940-1(1)) Holiday Hse., Inc.

Anderson, Derek. Blue Burt & Wiggles. Anderson, Derek, illus. 2006. (Illus.). 32p. (J). (ps-3). 14.95 (978-1-4169-0593-6(6), Simon & Schuster Children's Publishing) Simon & Schuster Children's Publishing.

Arnold, Caroline. Wiggle & Waggle. Peterson, Mary, illus. 2007. 48p. (J). (gr. k-3). 12.95 (*978-1-58089-306-0(6)) Charlesbridge Publishing, Inc.

Barwin, Gary. The Racing Worm Brothers. Macaulay, Kitty, illus. 1998. 32p. (J). (ps-1). lib. bdg. 15.95 (978-1-55037-541-1(5)) Annick Pr., Ltd. CAN. *Dist:* Firefly Bks., Ltd.

Becton, Sarah Walker, et al. Wormy Worm. Becton, Daniel Walker, illus. 2007. 88p. (J). 19.95 (*978-1-878398-59-8(8), Blue Note Bks.) Blue Note Pubns.

Bedford, William. The Glow-Worm Who Lost Her Glow. Joyce, Sophie, illus. 2005. (Blue Go Bananas Ser.). 48p. (J). pap. (978-0-7787-2652-4(5)) Crabtree Publishing Co.

Bonnell, Kris. The Worm Book. 2006. (J). 3.75 (*978-1-933727-25-7(X)) Reading Reading Bks., LLC.

Brody, Lazer. The Worry Worm. Shapiro, Rebecca, illus. 2007. 26p. (J). 26.95 (*978-0-9797530-1-5(5)) Kalcom Publishing.

Bruel, Robert O. Bob & Otto. Bruel, Nick, illus. 2007. 32p. (J). (ps-1). 15.95 (978-1-59643-203-1(9)) Roaring Brook Pr.

Caple, Kathy. Worm Drip. 2000. (Brand New Readers Ser.). (Illus.). (J). (978-0-7636-1149-1(2)) Candlewick Pr.

—Worm Gets a Job. Caple, Kathy, illus. 2004. (Illus.). 40p. (J). (gr. k-3). 15.99 (978-0-7636-1694-6(X)) Candlewick Pr.

—Worm Is Stuck. 2000. (Brand New Readers Ser.). (Illus.). (J). (978-0-7636-1148-4(4)) Candlewick Pr.

—Worm Paints. 2000. (Brand New Readers Ser.). (Illus.). (J). (978-0-7636-1151-4(4)) Candlewick Pr.

—Worm Smells. 2000. (Brand New Readers Ser.). (Illus.). (J). (978-0-7636-1150-7(6)) Candlewick Pr.

—Wow, It's Worm! Caple, Kathy, illus. 2001. (Brand New Readers Ser.). (Illus.). 32p. (J). (ps-2). pap. 5.99 (978-0-7636-1153-8(0)) Candlewick Pr.

Carr, Heather. The Jiggleworm. Carr, Greg, illus. ed. 2005. 18p. (J). 21.95 incl. audio compact disk (978-0-9768450-0-3(8), Giggletins) Le Bk. Moderne, LLC.

Cook, Sherry & Johnson, Terri. Watery William, 26. Kuhn, Jesse, illus. l.t. ed. 2006. (Quirkles—Exploring Phonics through Science Ser.: 23). 32p. (J). 7.99 (978-1-933815-22-0(1), Quirkles, The) Creative 3, LLC.

Coulton, Mia. Danny & the Little Worm. Coulton, Mia, photos by. 2004. (J). 4.95 (978-0-9746475-6-2(X)) Maryruth Bks., Inc.

Cronin, Doreen. Diary of a Worm. 2003. (Illus.). (J). (978-0-06-056884-9(4)); (J). 127.92 (978-0-06-056900-6(X)); 127.92 (978-0-06-056901-3(8)) HarperCollins Pubs.

—Diary of a Worm. Bliss, Harry, illus. 2003. 40p. (J). (ps-3). 15.99 (978-0-06-000150-6(X)); lib. bdg. 16.89 (978-0-06-000151-3(8)) HarperCollins Pubs. (Cotler, Joanna Books).

—Diary of a Worm. Bliss, Harry, illus. pap. 16.95 incl. audio (978-1-59112-867-0(6)); pap. incl. audio (978-1-59112-869-4(2)); pap. 18.95 incl. audio compact disk (978-1-59112-871-7(4)); pap. incl. audio compact disk (978-1-59112-873-1(0)) Live Oak Media.

—Diary of a Worm. 2004. (Illus.). (J). 25.95 incl. audio (978-1-59112-868-7(4)); 28.95 incl. audio compact disk (978-1-59112-872-4(2)) Live Oak Media.

Delittle, Cathy. I'd Like to Have a Worm. Delittle, Cathy, illus. 1998. (Illus.). 10p. (J). (ps-1). spiral bd. 7.95 (978-1-892633-08-8(6), OOCD206) Delittle Storyteller Co.

Diary of a Worm. 2004. (J). 24.95 incl. audio (978-0-7882-0536-1(6)) Weston Woods Studios, Inc.

Duval, Kristy. Pete & Re Pete the Computer Worms: A Story about Two Worms Surfing the Net. Gillen, Michael, illus. 2005. (ENG.). 32p. (J). (ps-7). per. 18.00 (978-1-4208-1959-5(3)) AuthorHouse.

Filippi, Sandra. Belisario y el Violin. Wernicke, Maria, illus. 2001. (SPA.). 40p. (J). 15.95 (978-950-511-518-1(0)) Alfaguara S.A. de Ediciones ARG. *Dist:* Santillana USA Publishing Co., Inc.

Freeman, Tammy A. The Earthworm Jamboree. Zangrillo, Robert P., illus. 1999. (J). (978-0-9670675-1-3(0)) Largesse Publishing, Inc.

Gott, Barry. Class Worms. 2007. (I'm Going to Read Ser.). (Illus.). 48p. (J). (gr. 3 up). pap. 3.95 (*978-1-4027-4300-9(9)) Sterling Publishing Co., Inc.

Grealish, Maureen M. Just Plain Worm. 25p. (J). (gr. k-2). (978-0-9667780-0-7(6)) Ballenwyck Publishing Corp.

Hennessy, B. G. & Caple, Kathy. Well Done, Worm! Caple, Kathy, illus. 2000. (Brand New Readers Ser.). (Illus.). 32p. (J). (ps-2). pap. 5.99 (978-0-7636-1147-7(6)) Candlewick Pr.

How to Eat Fried Worms. 116p. (J). (gr. 3-5). pap. 5.50 (978-0-8072-1382-7(9), Listening Library) Random Hse. Audio Publishing Group.

How to Eat Fried Worms. 2005. (J). (978-1-59564-950-8(6)) Steps To Literacy, LLC.

Hunter, Lee Hargus. Welby the Worm Who Lost His Wiggle. Thompson, Lydia, illus. 2004. 32p. (J). (ps-1). 14.95 (978-1-930093-04-1(7)) Brookfield Reader, Inc., The.

Huston, Donna. Inch by Inch. 2006. (J). spiral bd. 19.95 (978-0-9771192-3-3(8)) Shayne Publishing.

Johnston, Tony. The Worm Family. Innerst, Stacy, tr. Innerst, Stacy, illus. 2004. 40p. (J). 16.00 (978-0-15-205011-5(6), Harcourt Children's Bks) Harcourt Children's Bks.

Jones, Christianne C. Willy the Worm. Trover, Zachary, illus. 2006. (Read-It! Readers Ser.). 32p. (J). (ps-3). 18.60 (978-1-4048-1593-3(7)) Picture Window Bks.

Kaczman, James. A Bird & His Worm. Kaczman, James, illus. 2002. (Illus.). 32p. (J). (gr. k-3). tchr. ed. 15.00 (978-0-618-09460-8(1)) Houghton Mifflin Co. Trade & Reference Div.

Keffer, Lois. Wiggledy Worm Learns Not to Squirm. 1999. (J). 9.99 (978-1-57673-439-1(0)) Zondervan.

Knudsen, Michelle. A Slimy Story. Billin-Frye, Paige, illus. 2004. 32p. (J). lib. bdg. 20.00 (*978-1-4242-1150-0(6)) Fitzgerald Bks.

—A Slimy Story. Billin-Frye, Paige, illus. 2004. (Science Solves It! Ser.). 32p. (J). (ps-3). pap. 4.99 (978-1-57565-144-6(0)) Kane Pr., The.

Kreloff, Elliot. Found an Apple. 2007. (I'm Going to Read Ser.). (Illus.). 28p. (J). (ps-1). pap. 3.95 (*978-1-4027-4295-8(9)) Sterling Publishing Co., Inc.

Larson, Gary. There's a Hair in My Dirt! 1999. (gr. 7-12). lib. bdg. 20.05 (978-0-613-22945-6(2)) Tandem Library Bks.

Laurila, P. K. Gus & Annie: Glacier Ice Worms. Miller, Dan, illus. 2001. 12p. (J). bds. 6.95 (978-0-930931-34-6(3)) Alaska Natural History Assn.

Lionni, Leo. Inch by Inch. Lionni, Leo, illus. 2002. (Illus.). (J). 14.47 (978-0-7587-0120-6(9)) Book Wholesalers, Inc.

—Inch by Inch. Lionni, Leo, illus. unabr. ed. 2006. (J). (ps-1). pap. 14.95 incl. audio (*978-0-439-90584-8(2), WPRA699); pap. 18.95 incl. audio compact disk (*978-0-439-90585-5(0), WPCD699) Weston Woods Studios, Inc.

Lucado, Max. Hermie & Wormie in the Flood of Lies. 2004. (Max Lucado's Hermie & Friends Ser.). 24p. (J). bds. 6.99 (978-1-4003-0287-1(0)) Nelson, Thomas Inc.

Mills, Claudia. Standing up to Mr. O. 2000. (978-0-606-18215-7(2)) Tandem Library Bks.

Neumeyer, Peter F. & Gorey, Edward. Donald & The... 2004. (Illus.). 40p. (J). (ps-3). reprint ed. 12.95 (978-0-8109-4836-5(2)) Abrams, Harry N., Inc.

Noyes, Deborah. Red Butterfly: How a Princess Smuggled the Secret of Silk Out of China. Blackall, Sophie, illus. 2007. 32p. (J). (gr. 1-5). 16.99 (*978-0-7636-2400-2(4)) Candlewick Pr.

Noyes, Deborah & Haarsma, P. J. Red Butterfly: How a Princess Smuggled the Secret of Silk Out of China. Blackall, Sophie, illus. 2008. (Softwire Ser.). 272p. (J). (gr. 7). 16.99 (*978-0-7636-2710-2(0)) Candlewick Pr.

O'Callahan, Jay. Herman & Marguerite: An Earth Story. O'Callahan, Laura, illus. 2003. 36p. (J). pap. 7.95 (978-1-56145-283-5(1)) Peachtree Pubs., Ltd.

—Herman & Marguerite: An Earth Story. 2003. (gr. k-3). lib. bdg. 16.40 (978-0-613-60387-4(7)) Tandem Library Bks.

O'Loughlin, Alison & O'Loughlin, Larry. Worms Can't Fly. Caffrey, Aileen, illus. 2001. 96p. pap. 5.95 (978-0-86327-786-3(1)) Interlink Publishing Group, Inc.

Pauli, Gunter. Shiitake Love Caffeine. Salazar, Pamela, illus. 2007. 33p. pap. 9.95 (*978-958-692-833-5(0)) Marion Institute.

Pinczes, Elinor J. Inchworm & a Half. Enos, Randall, illus. 2003. 32p. (J). pap. 5.95 (978-0-618-31101-9(7)) Houghton Mifflin Co. Trade & Reference Div.

—Inchworm & a Half. Mackain, Bonnie & Enos, Randall, illus. 2001. 32p. (J). (gr. k-3). tchr. ed. 15.00 (978-0-395-82849-6(X)) Houghton Mifflin Co. Trade & Reference Div.

—Inchworm & a Half. 2001. (gr. k-3). lib. bdg. 14.10 (978-0-613-60769-8(4)) Tandem Library Bks.

Rigby Education Staff. Barnaby. (Sails Literacy Ser.). (Illus.). 16p. (gr. 1-2). 27.00 (978-0-7635-9889-1(5), 698895C99) Rigby Education.

Rivers, Freya A. Idle Inchworm. Brooks, Julian A. & Rivers, Shariba W., eds. Moore, La Mailede, illus. 2001. 32p. (J). (ps-2). pap. 20.00 (978-0-9667215-6-0(X)) Sankofa Publishing Co.

Rivers, Katie. Blown Away. 2002. 101p. (J). (gr. 3-7). per. 6.95 (978-0-9721640-4-9(9)) Whispering Wind Publishing Inc.

Rockwell, Thomas. How to Eat Fried Worms. (J). (gr. 3-5). 179p. pap. 4.99 (978-0-8072-1395-7(0)); 2004. 116p. pap. 29.00 incl. audio (978-0-8072-8797-2(0)) Random Hse. Audio Publishing Group. (Listening Library).

—How to Eat Fried Worms. 2006. 128p. (J). (gr. 2-5). 5.99 (978-0-440-42185-6(3), Yearling) Random Hse. Children's Bks.

Sheppard, Hazel A. The Inchy Books: Inch Worm Goes a Mile; Inchy Goes the Extra Mile; Inchy Goes the Distance, 3bks. 2005. (Illus.). (J). 28.85 (978-0-9725286-3-4(6)) Sheppard Publishing.

—Inchy Goes the Distance. 2005. (Illus.). (J). 9.95 (978-0-9725286-2-7(8)) Sheppard Publishing.

Sroda, George. The Life Story of TV Star Herman the Worm. Hughes, Janet, illus. 199p. (Orig.). (J). (gr. 3 up). 10.95 (978-0-9604486-2-3(4)) Sroda, George.

Tomos, Angharad. Jam Poeth. 2005. (WEL., Illus.). 48p. pap. (978-0-86243-145-7(X)) Y Lolfa.

Worm's Wagon. 2001. (ps-2). lib. bdg. 9.80 (978-0-613-33267-5(9)) Tandem Library Bks.

WORSHIP

see also Prayer

Beeke, Joel R. & Boorsma, Heidi. God's Alphabet for Life. Tenelshof, Tim, illus. 2000. 65p. (J). (ps-4). pap. 3.00 (978-1-892777-19-5(3)) Reformation Heritage Bks.

Beers, V. Gilbert. God's Little Devotional Book for Kids. 2001. (God's Little Devotional Bks.). 208p. (J). 14.99 (978-1-56292-478-2(8), 1562924788) Cook, David C. Publishing Co.

Bernard, M. My First Mass Book. Date not set. (J). (ps-3). pap. 1.95 (978-0-88271-165-2(2)) Regina Pr., Malhame & Co.

Boling, Ruth L. Come Worship with Me: A Journey Through the Church Year. Carrier, Tracey Dahle, illus. 2004. (Mouse Bks.: Vol. 2). 43p. (ps-3). 19.95 (978-0-664-50045-0(5)) Westminster John Knox Pr.

Branon, David. Heads Up! Sports Devotions for All Star Kids. 2000. (Illus.). 320p. (J). pap. 9.99 (978-0-310-70013-5(2)) Zonderkidz.

Brouwer, Sigmund. Great Adventures: Golden Tonsils & Other Great Stories. 2003. (gr. 7-12). lib. bdg. 19.95 (978-0-613-76826-9(4)) Tandem Library Bks.

—Great Adventures: Wild Ride, Buffalo Soldier, & Other Great Stories. 2003. (Illus.). 320p. (J). pap. 10.99 (978-0-8423-5239-0(2)) Tyndale Hse. Pubs.

Brown, Carolyn A. My Worship Book Student Book. 2nd ed. 2004. (J). spiral bd. 14.99 (978-0-9752605-3-1(7)) LOGOS System Assocs.

Bruce & Stan. God Is in the Small Stuff for Kids. Smouse, Phil, illus. 2004. 256p. (J). pap. 5.97 (978-1-59310-335-4(2)) Barbour Publishing, Inc.

Card, Michael. Sleep Sound in Jesus: Gentle Lullabies for Little Ones & Inspirational Devotions for Parents. 2nd ed. 2003. (Illus.). 36p. wbk. ed. 15.99 (978-0-7369-1219-8(3)) Harvest Hse. Pubs.

Carmack, Bob. Box of Letters: 93 Days of Devotions for Teens. 2000. 192p. (YA). (gr. 8-12). pap. 9.95 (978-1-57921-307-7(3)) WinePress Publishing.

Clark, Sybil A. God & Me: A Journey of Divine Encounters. 2004. 142p. per. 15.95 (978-0-9747516-4-1(2), 1005) Heart Communications.

Collins, John. Worship. Furst, Alan, illus. 2000. (Teen Pressure Points Ser.). 44p. (YA). (gr. 8-12). pap. 8.95 (978-1-931235-33-4(3)) Word of Life Fellowship, Inc.

Community of Christ Staff. Power & Light for Kids - Kidsbook. 2005. (YA). 5.95 (978-0-8309-1147-9(2)); 5.95 (978-0-8309-1141-7(3), 0830911413) Herald Publishing Hse.

David C. Cook. Quiet Moment with God Devotional Journal for Teens. 2004. (Quiet Moments with God Ser.). 384p. 17.99 (978-1-56292-983-1(6), 1562929836) Cook, David C. Publishing Co.

Draper, Edythe. Wake up Call: 365 Bible Readings to Start Your Day. 2003. (gr. 7-12). lib. bdg. 18.80 (978-0-613-76741-5(1)) Tandem Library Bks.

Exploring Worship. 2004. (Exploring Luther's Small Catechism Ser.). (gr. 5-6). 2.99 (978-0-8066-6754-6(0)) Augsburg Fortress, Pubs.

Fears, Melissa. Thank God It's Sunday. 2004. (J). per. 6.95 (978-0-89315-413-4(X)) Lambert Bk. Hse., Inc.

Fields, Doug & Eastman, Brett. Surrendering Your Life to Honor God: 6 Small Group Sessions on Worship. 2003. (Life Together Ser.). 144p. pap., stu. ed. 7.99 (978-0-310-25338-9(1)) Zondervan.

Ganeri, Martin & Ganeri, Anita. Christian Prayer & Worship. 2007. (J). (*978-1-59771-091-6(1)) Sea-To-Sea Pubns.

Gift Book Staff. Teen Devotional Journal. 2001. (Illus.). 128p. (YA). spiral bd. 9.99 (978-0-310-98429-0(7)) Zondervan.

God & Me! Devotions for Girls. 2004. (Illus.). 248p. (J). (gr. 5-7). spiral bd. 12.99 (978-1-885358-85-1(7), Legacy Pr.) Rainbow Pubs. & Legacy Pr.

God Is a Promise Keeper. 2.99 (978-0-7847-0857-6(6)) Standard Publishing.

Hanna, Robert C. The Dickens Family Gospel: A Family Devotional Guide Based on the Christian Teachings of Charles Dickens. 1998. (Illus.). 152p. (J). pap. 14.99 (978-1-885358-36-3(9), DB46721, Legacy Pr.) Rainbow Pubs. & Legacy Pr.

Harpine, Elaine Clanton. Come, Follow Me! Vol. 1: Sessions 1-26, 2 vols. 2004. (Illus.). 256p. spiral bd. 35.00 (978-0-687-09207-9(8)) Abingdon Pr.

—Come, Follow Me! Vol. 2: Sessions 27-59, Vol. 2. 2004. (Illus.). 256p. (ps-7). spiral bd. 35.00 (978-0-687-09212-3(4)) Abingdon Pr.

Henley, Karyn. Worship: The Foundation for Loving God. Eichenberger, Jim, ed. Koehler, Ed, illus. 2000. (Foundations Curriculum). 96p. (YA). (gr. 3-6). 12.99 (978-0-7847-1217-7(4), 42066) Standard Publishing.

Hudson, Geneva Johnston. Whatsoever Things: Think on These Things. 2003. (YA). per. 14.50 (978-1-59453-041-8(6), 1685) Airleaf Publishing & Bookselling.

Jeanne Grieser & Mary Rose Pearson. Worship Bulletins for Kids: Fall & Winter. 2004. (Illus.). 128p. (J). (ps-7). pap. 13.95 (978-1-58411-014-9(7)) Rainbow Pubs. & Legacy Pr.

—Worship Bulletins for Kids: Spring & Summer. 2004. 128p. (J). (ps-7). pap. 13.95 (978-1-58411-015-6(5)) Rainbow Pubs. & Legacy Pr.

Jesus Company: Worship. 32p. (J). (gr. 4). 10.99 (978-0-570-00674-9(0), 22-2777); (gr. 5). 10.99 (978-0-570-00680-0(5), 22-2783); (gr. 6). 10.99 (978-0-570-00686-2(4), 22-2789) Concordia Publishing Hse.

Kessen, Virginia. Children's Worship Activities, Year 2. 2004. pap. 20.00 (978-0-687-02828-3(0)) Abingdon Pr.

—Children's Worship Activities, Year 3. 2003. 96p. pap. 20.00 (978-0-687-02818-4(3)) Abingdon Pr.

Kielbasa, Marilyn & Claussen, Janet, eds. Listen for a Whisper: Prayers, Poems, & Reflections by Girls. 2003. (Listen for a Whisper). 204p. (J). per. 9.95 (978-0-88489-685-2(4)) St. Mary's Pr.

Kinnaman, Scot A. Worshiping with Angels & Archangels: An Introduction to the Divine Service. Kirchhoff, Art, illus. 2006. 48p. (J). (*978-0-7586-1206-9(0)) Concordia Publishing Hse.

Kitch, Anne E. What We Do in Church: An Anglican Child's Activity Book. Perez, Dorothy, illus. 2004. 48p. pap. 7.00 (978-0-8192-2105-6(8)) Morehouse Publishing.

Lawrence, Linda & Hubbard, Donna. Jesse Tree. 3rd ed. 2002. 32p. (J). 7.95 (978-1-930165-02-1(1)) Small Ventures.

Lee, Witness. The Holy Word for Morning Revival: Ephesians 4:1-6:24, Vol. 2. (J). (gr. 6). (978-0-7363-1593-7(4)) Living Stream Ministry.

Legacy Press Staff. God & Me! Devotions for Girls. 1998. (God & Me! Ser.). (Illus.). 238p. (J). (ps-k). spiral bd. 12.99 (978-1-885358-61-5(X) , LP46821); spiral bd. 12.99 (978-1-885358-60-8(1) , LP46822) Rainbow Pubs. & Legacy Pr. (Legacy Pr.).

Let's Go to Mass. 2003. (Illus.). (978-2-89507-087-0(3)) Novalis Publishing.

Lutz, A. Fowler. Stories of the Child Jesus from Many Lands. 2003. (Illus.). viii, 175p. (J). pap. 10.95 (978-1-928832-96-6(2)) Sophia Institute Pr.

Martin, Michael Heidi. TruthQuest Weekly Worship Launcher Package. 2002. cd-rom 50.00 (978-0-9709763-3-8(X)) Return To The Word.

The Mass: Catholics Worship & Celebrate. 1998. (Illus.). (YA). (gr. 7-10). pap., stu. ed. 7.45 (978-0-89837-211-3(9)) Pflaum Publishing Group.

Morina, Barbara. Daily Devotions My Gratitude Journal. Morina, Barbara, ed. 2001. (Write It down Ser.). (Illus.). 202p. 19.95 (978-1-892033-36-9(4)) Journals Unlimited, Inc.

Mortimer, F. L. Lines Left Out. 176p. (J). pap. 7.99 (978-1-85792-593-7(9)) Christian Focus Pubns. GBR. *Dist:* Riverside.

My Precious Moments with God: Quiet Time Devotionals for Girls & Boys, White. (Precious Moments Ser.). (J). 19.95 (978-1-55976-449-0(X)) CEF Pr.

Panesar, Rajinder Singh & Ganeri, Anita. Sikh Prayer & Worship. 2007. (J). (***978-1-59771-094-7(6)***) Sea-To-Sea Pubns.

Perkins, Nicole. I Believe God Will: Book of Devotion & Prayer for Children. Perkins, Nicole & Frisk, Maria, illus. 2008. 32p. (J). 7.00 (***978-0-9755566-1-0(4)***) Azreal Publishing Co.

Praise & Worship. 1998. (Cross Training Ser.: Vol. 1). 64p. (YA). (gr. 10-12). pap., tchr. ed. 15.00 incl. VHS (978-1-57405-009-7(5) , Cross Training) CharismaLife Pubs.

Preschool Children. (Illus.). 8.00 (978-0-687-04974-5(1)) Abingdon Pr.

Rasamandala Das & Ganeri, Anita. Hindu Prayer & Worship. 2007. (***978-1-59771-093-0(8)***) Sea-To-Sea Pubns.

Ricketts, Siv M. & Leuthauser, Karl, eds. Why Worship Matters. Demartino, Craig, photos by. 1998. (Core Belief Bible Study Ser.). (Illus.). 62p. (YA). (gr. 10-12). pap. 11.99 (978-0-7644-0891-5(7)) Group Publishing, Inc.

Rizzo, Kay D. Popsicles, Black Holes, & Burnt Toast. 2002. 375p. (J). 13.99 (978-0-8280-1574-5(0) , 163-720) Review & Herald Publishing Assn.

Rylant, Cynthia. Bless Us All: A Child's Yearbook of Blessings. Rylant, Cynthia, illus. 2001. (Illus.). 32p. (J). pap. 6.99 (978-0-689-84637-3(1) , Aladdin) Simon & Schuster Children's Publishing.

—Bless Us All: A Child's Yearbook of Blessings. 2001. (gr. k-3). lib. bdg. 15.30 (978-0-613-73311-3(8)) Tandem Library Bks.

Savary, Louis M. Rosary for Children. Date not set. (J). (ps-3). pap. 1.25 (978-0-88271-158-4(X)) Regina Pr., Malhame & Co.

—Way of the Cross. Date not set. (J). (ps-3). pap. 1.95 (978-0-88271-160-7(1)) Regina Pr., Malhame & Co.

Shellenberger, Susie. Dear Diary: A Girl's Book of Devotions. 2000. (Young Women of Faith Library Ser.). (Illus.). 192p. (J). pap. 9.99 (978-0-310-70016-6(7)) Zonderkidz.

SPCK. I Can Join in Common Worship: A Children's Communion Book. 2003. (Illus.). 24p. 5.00 (978-0-281-05568-5(8)) SPCK Publishing GBR. *Dist:* Pilgrim Pr., The/United Church Pr.

St. James, Rebecca. 40 Days with God: A Devotional Journey. rev. ed. 2006. 112p. pap. 12.99 (978-0-7847-1274-0(3) , 23338) Standard Publishing.

Stiegemeyer, Julie. Things I Hear in Church. Mitter, Kathy, illus. 2003. (ENG.). 20p. (J). bds. 4.99 (978-0-7586-0125-4(5)) Concordia Publishing Hse.

Tamberino, Tony. Pray Your Heart Resource Manual: Music-Based Sessions & Prayer Experiences for Teens. 2003. 32p. (YA). pap. 12.95 (978-0-88489-562-6(9)) St. Mary's Pr.

This Is My Lutheran Church. 2004. (Exploring Luther's Small Catechism Ser.). (ps-k). 2.99 (978-0-8066-6790-4(7)) Augsburg Fortress, Pubs.

Toler, Violet M. Puppet Scripts for Preschool Worship: Ages 3-6. 2005. (Illus.). 140p. (J). per. 15.99 (978-0-7847-1782-0(6) , 42301) Standard Publishing.

We Worship. 2004. (Exploring Luther's Small Catechism Ser.). (gr. 1-2). 2.99 (978-0-8066-6792-8(3)) Augsburg Fortress, Pubs.

Zondervan, et al. Our Daily Blog: Devotions by Pastor Jim Laffoon. 2005. 752p. pap. 16.99 (978-0-310-81169-5(4)) Inspirio.

5 Minute Interactive Worship Devotions for Kids Vol. 1: Names & Games. 2003. (J). per. 12.95 (978-0-9746161-0-0(9)) Vision Pubns.

WOUNDED, FIRST AID TO

see First Aid

WRECKS

see Shipwrecks

WRESTLING

see also Judo

Alexander, Kyle. Bill Goldberg. 1999. (Pro Wrestling Legends Ser.). (Illus.). 64p. (YA). (gr. 3 up). pap. 25.00 (978-0-7910-5550-2(7)); 25.00 (978-0-7910-5404-8(7)) Facts On File, Inc. (Chelsea Hse.).

—Bill Goldberg. 2000. (gr. 5-8). lib. bdg. 17.60 (978-0-613-21044-7(1)) Tandem Library Bks.

—Mankind. 2001. (Pro Wrestling Legends Ser.). (Illus.). 64p. (J). pap. 25.00 (978-0-7910-6447-4(6)) Facts On File, Inc.

—Mick Foley: The Story of the Wrestler They Cal Mankind. 2001. lib. bdg. 17.60 (978-0-613-58601-6(8)) Tandem Library Bks.

—Mick Foley: The Story of the Wrestler They Call "Mankind" 2001. (Pro Wrestling Legends Ser.). (Illus.). 64p. (J). 25.00 (978-0-7910-6446-7(8) , 005969, Chelsea Hse.) Facts On File, Inc.

—Pro Wrestling's Most Punishing Moves. 2001. (Illus.). (J). (978-0-606-20866-6(6)) Tandem Library Bks.

—The Story of the Wrestler They Call Sting. 1999. (Pro Wrestling Legends Ser.). (Illus.). 64p. (YA). (gr. 3 up). pap. 25.00 (978-0-7910-5551-9(5)); 25.00 (978-0-7910-5405-5(5)) Facts On File, Inc. (Chelsea Hse.).

—Story of the Wrestler They Call Sting. 1999. lib. bdg. 17.60 (978-0-613-21055-3(7)) Tandem Library Bks.

—Vince McMahon. 2001. (Pro Wrestling Legends Ser.). 64p. (J). (Illus.). pap. 25.00 (978-0-7910-6445-0(X)); 25.00 (978-0-7910-6444-3(1) , Chelsea Hse.) Facts On File, Inc.

—Vince McMahon, Jr. 2001. (YA). (gr. 5-8). lib. bdg. 18.75 (978-0-613-58675-7(1)) Tandem Library Bks.

—Women of Pro Wrestling. 2000. (Pro Wrestling Legends Ser.). (Illus.). 64p. (J). (gr. 8-12). pap. 25.00 (978-0-7910-5840-4(9)); (gr. 4-7). 25.00 (978-0-7910-5839-8(5)) Facts On File, Inc. (Chelsea Hse.).

—The Women of Pro Wrestling. 2000. (Illus.). 64p. (YA). (gr. 8-12). lib. bdg. 17.60 (978-0-613-33258-3(X)) Tandem Library Bks.

—Wrestling's Most Punishing Moves. 2000. (Pro Wrestling Legends Ser.). (Illus.). 64p. (J). (gr. 8-12). pap. 25.00 (978-0-7910-5834-3(4)); (gr. 4-7). 25.00 (978-0-7910-5833-6(6)) Facts On File, Inc. (Chelsea Hse.).

BradyGames Staff & Deats, Adam. Backyard Wrestling 2: There Goes the Neighborhood Official Strategy Guide. 2004. (Illus.). 128p. pap. 14.99 (978-0-7440-0498-4(5)) Brady GAMES.

Brindisi, Johanna. The Story of the Wrestler They Call "Chyna" 2001. (Pro Wrestling Legends Ser.). (Illus.). 64p. pap. 25.00 (978-0-7910-6443-6(3)); (J). 25.00 (978-0-7910-6442-9(5)) Facts On File, Inc. (Chelsea Hse.).

Burgan, Michael. Goldberg: Pro Wrestler Bill Goldberg. 2001. (Pro Wrestlers Ser.). (Illus.). 48p. (J). (gr. 3-4). lib. bdg. 21.26 (978-0-7368-0917-7(1) , Capstone High-Interest Bks.) Capstone Pr., Inc.

—The Rock: Pro Wrestler Rocky Maivia. 2001. (Pro Wrestlers Ser.). (Illus.). 48p. (J). (gr. 3-4). lib. bdg. 21.26 (978-0-7368-0918-4(X) , Capstone High-Interest Bks.) Capstone Pr., Inc.

—Stone Cold: Pro Wrestler Steve Austin. 2001. (Pro Wrestlers Ser.). (Illus.). 48p. (J). (gr. 3-4). lib. bdg. 21.26 (978-0-7368-0920-7(1) , Capstone High-Interest Bks.) Capstone Pr., Inc.

Carty, Michelle. Believe & Achieve Vol. 4553: The Olympic Sport of Wrestling, Samoiloff, Sheri, ed. Allsport Staff, photos by. 2002. (Illus.). 16p. (J). (gr. 3-6). pap. 3.49 (978-1-57471-924-6(6)) Creative Teaching Pr., Inc.

Chapman, Mike. The Sport of Lincoln. 2003. (Illus.). 48p. (YA). pap. 5.95 (978-0-9676080-6-8(6)) Culture Hse.

Chiu, David. Wrestling: Rules, Tips, Strategy, & Safety. 2005. (Sports from Coast to Coast Ser.). (Illus.). 48p. (J). (gr. 5-8). lib. bdg. 26.50 (978-1-4042-0187-3(4)) Rosen Publishing Group, Inc., The.

Cicciarelli, Stephen. Shawn Michaels: The Story of the Wrestler They Call "The Heartbreak Kid" 2001. (Pro Wrestling Legends Ser.). (Illus.). pap. 25.00 (978-0-7910-6454-2(9)); (J). 25.00 (978-0-7910-6453-5(0)) Facts On File, Inc. (Chelsea Hse.).

Cohen, Daniel. Wrestling Renegades: An in Depth Look at Today's Superstars of Pro Wrestling. 1999. (J). (978-0-606-18955-2(6)) Tandem Library Bks.

Cohen, Daniel & Graham, Kevin. Jesse Ventura: The Body, the Mouth, & the Mind. 2001. (Single Titles Ser.: up). (Illus.). 112p. (gr. 7 up). lib. bdg. 25.90 (978-0-7613-1905-4(0) , Twenty-First Century Bks.) Lerner Publishing Group.

Creative Teaching Press Staff, Press Teaching. Believe & Achieve: The Olympic Sport of Wrestling. 2002. (gr. k-3). lib. bdg. 11.25 (978-0-613-82642-6(6)) Tandem Library Bks.

Crossingham, John. Wrestling in Action. 2003. (gr. 3-6). lib. bdg. 15.25 (978-0-613-59119-5(4)) Tandem Library Bks.

Crossingham, John & Rouse, Bonna. Wrestling in Action. 2003. (Sports in Action Ser.). (Illus.). 32p. (J). (gr. 1-4). (978-0-7787-0336-5(3)); pap. (978-0-7787-0356-3(8)) Crabtree Publishing Co.

Davies, Ross. Bill Goldberg. 2005. (Wrestling Greats Ser.). (Illus.). 112p. (YA). (gr. 7-12). lib. bdg. 25.25 (978-0-8239-3495-9(0)) Rosen Publishing Group, Inc., The.

—Bobo Brazil. 2005. (Wrestling Greats Ser.). (Illus.). 112p. (YA). (gr. 7-12). lib. bdg. 25.25 (978-0-8239-3431-7(4)) Rosen Publishing Group, Inc., The.

—Bret Hart. 2005. (Wrestling Greats Ser.). (Illus.). 112p. (YA). (gr. 7-12). lib. bdg. 25.25 (978-0-8239-3494-2(2)) Rosen Publishing Group, Inc., The.

—Bruno Sammartino. 2005. (Wrestling Greats Ser.). (Illus.). 112p. (YA). (gr. 7-12). lib. bdg. 25.25 (978-0-8239-3432-4(2)) Rosen Publishing Group, Inc., The.

—Buddy Rogers. 2005. (Wrestling Greats Ser.). (Illus.). 112p. (YA). (gr. 7-12). lib. bdg. 25.25 (978-0-8239-3433-1(0)) Rosen Publishing Group, Inc., The.

—Diamond Dallas Page. 2005. (Wrestling Greats Ser.). (Illus.). 112p. (YA). (gr. 7-12). lib. bdg. 25.25 (978-0-8239-3493-5(4)) Rosen Publishing Group, Inc., The.

—The Funk Family. 2005. (Wrestling Greats Ser.). (Illus.). 112p. (YA). (gr. 7-12). lib. bdg. 25.25 (978-0-8239-3437-9(3)) Rosen Publishing Group, Inc., The.

—Gorilla Monsoon. 2005. (Wrestling Greats Ser.). (Illus.). 112p. (YA). (gr. 7-12). lib. bdg. 25.25 (978-0-8239-3434-8(9)) Rosen Publishing Group, Inc., The.

—Haystacks Calhoun. 2005. (Wrestling Greats Ser.). (Illus.). 112p. (YA). (gr. 7-12). lib. bdg. 25.25 (978-0-8239-3435-5(7)) Rosen Publishing Group, Inc., The.

—Kevin Nash. 2005. (Wrestling Greats Ser.). (Illus.). 112p. (YA). (gr. 7-12). lib. bdg. 25.25 (978-0-8239-3492-8(6)) Rosen Publishing Group, Inc., The.

—Ric Flair. 2005. (Wrestling Greats Ser.). (Illus.). 112p. (YA). (gr. 7-12). lib. bdg. 25.25 (978-0-8239-3436-2(5)) Rosen Publishing Group, Inc., The.

—Scott Steiner. 2005. (Wrestling Greats Ser.). (Illus.). 112p. (YA). (gr. 7-12). lib. bdg. 25.25 (978-0-8239-3491-1(8)) Rosen Publishing Group, Inc., The.

—Sting. 2005. (Wrestling Greats Ser.). (Illus.). 112p. (YA). (gr. 7-12). lib. bdg. 25.25 (978-0-8239-3490-4(X)) Rosen Publishing Group, Inc., The.

—Wrestling Greats, 8 bks. Incl. Andre the Giant. lib. bdg. 25.25 (978-0-8239-3430-0(6)); Bobo Brazil. lib. bdg. 25.25 (978-0-8239-3431-7(4)); Bruno Sammartino. lib. bdg. 25.25 (978-0-8239-3432-4(2)); Buddy Rogers. lib. bdg. 25.25 (978-0-8239-3433-1(0)); Funk Family. lib. bdg. 25.25 (978-0-8239-3437-9(3)); Gorilla Monsoon. lib. bdg. 25.25 (978-0-8239-3434-8(9)); Haystacks Calhoun. lib. bdg. 25.25 (978-0-8239-3435-5(7)); Ric Flair. lib. bdg. 25.25 (978-0-8239-3436-2(5)); 112p. (YA). (gr. 7-12). (Illus.). 2005. Set lib. bdg. 202.00 (978-0-8239-9446-5(5)) Rosen Publishing Group, Inc., The.

Ditchfield, Christin. Wrestling. 2000. (True Bks.). (Illus.). 48p. (J). (gr. 3-5). 25.00 (978-0-516-21611-9(2) , Children's Pr.) Scholastic Library Publishing.

—Wrestling. 2000. (gr. 3-6). lib. bdg. 15.25 (978-0-613-54797-0(7)) Tandem Library Bks.

Dorling Kindersley Publishing Staff, et al. The Ultimate WCW: World championship Wrestling. O'Neill, Cynthia, ed. 2000. (Illus.). 48p. (J). (gr. 4-7). 19.95 (978-0-7894-6673-0(2)) Dorling Kindersley Publishing, Inc.

Feldman, Heather. Hulk Hogan: Wrestling Pro. 2001. (Reading Power Ser.). (Illus.). 24p. (J). (gr. 1). lib. bdg. 17.25 (978-0-8239-5720-0(9) , PKHUHO, PowerKids Pr.) Rosen Publishing Group, Inc., The.

—Hulk Hogan, Campeon de Lucha Libre. 2002. (Coleccion Power Kids). (SPA & ENG., Illus.). 24p. (J). (gr. k-2). lib. bdg. 17.25 (978-0-8239-6140-5(0) , RN31309, Buenas Letra) Rosen Publishing Group, Inc., The.

Foley, Mick. Have a Nice Day! A Tale of Blood & Sweatsocks. 2000. (gr. 7-12). lib. bdg. 16.45 (978-0-613-33590-4(2)) Tandem Library Bks.

Gallagher, Jim. Wrestling. 1999. (Composite Guide Ser.). (Illus.). 64p. (YA). (gr. 4-7). lib. bdg. 18.65 (978-0-7910-4721-7(0) , Chelsea Hse.) Facts On File, Inc.

Grappling Greats. 1999. (World Championship Wrestling - New World Order Ser.). (Illus.). 24p. (J). pap. (978-0-7666-0443-8(8) , Honey Bear Bks.) Modern Publishing.

Greenberg, Keith Elliot. Pro Wrestling: From Carnivals to Cable TV. (Sports Legacy Ser.). (Illus.). (gr. 7-12). 2005. 144p. 26.63 (978-0-8225-3332-0(4)); 2003. 128p. (J). pap. 9.95 (978-0-8225-9864-0(7)) Lerner Publishing Group.

Hunter, Matt. Jesse Ventura: Story of the Wrestler They Call The Body. 1999. (Pro Wrestling Legends Ser.). (Illus.). 64p. (YA). (gr. 3-7). 25.00 (978-0-7910-5410-9(1) , Chelsea Hse.) Facts On File, Inc.

—Jesse Ventura: The Story of the Wrestler They Call "The Body" 1999. (Pro Wrestling Legends Ser.). (Illus.). 64p. (YA). (gr. 3 up). pap. 25.00 (978-0-7910-5556-4(6) , Chelsea Hse.) Facts On File, Inc.

—Jesse Ventura: The Story of the Wrestler They Call the Body. 2000. (gr. 5-8). lib. bdg. 17.60 (978-0-613-21049-2(2)) Tandem Library Bks.

—Pro Wrestling: The Early Years. 2001. (gr. 5-8). lib. bdg. 17.60 (978-0-613-58619-1(0)) Tandem Library Bks.

—Pro Wrestling's Greatest Matches. 2001. (Pro Wrestling Legends Ser.). (Illus.). 64p. (J). 25.00 (978-0-7910-6459-7(X)); pap. 25.00 (978-0-7910-6460-3(3)) Facts On File, Inc. (Chelsea Hse.).

—Pro Wrestling's Greatest Matches. 2001. (gr. 5-8). lib. bdg. 17.60 (978-0-613-58620-7(4)) Tandem Library Bks.

—Pro Wrestling's Greatest Tag Teams. 2000. (Pro Wrestling Legends Ser.). (Illus.). 64p. (J). pap. 25.00 (978-0-7910-5836-7(0)); (gr. 4-7). 25.00 (978-0-7910-5835-0(2) , 005964) Facts On File, Inc. (Chelsea Hse.).

—Pro Wrestling's Greatest Tag Teams. 2001. (gr. 5-8). lib. bdg. 17.60 (978-0-613-33118-0(4)); (Illus.). (J). (978-0-606-20864-2(X)) Tandem Library Bks.

—Ric Flair: The Story of the Wrestler They Call "The Nature Boy" 2000. (Pro Wrestling Legends Ser.). (Illus.). 64p. (J). (gr. 8-12). pap. 25.00 (978-0-7910-5826-8(3) , Chelsea Hse.) Facts On File, Inc.

—Story of the Wrestler They Call "Hollywood" Hulk Hogan. 1999. (Pro Wrestling Legends Ser.). (Illus.). 64p. (YA). (gr. 3 up). pap. 25.00 (978-0-7910-5552-6(3) , Chelsea Hse.) Facts On File, Inc.

—Wrestling's Early Years. 2001. (Pro Wrestling Legends Ser.). (Illus.). 64p. (J). pap. 25.00 (978-0-7910-6456-6(5)); 25.00 (978-0-7910-6455-9(7) , Chelsea Hse.) Facts On File, Inc.

Kaelberer, Angie Peterson. The Hardy Boyz: Pro Wrestlers Matt & Jeff Hardy. 2003. (Pro Wrestlers Ser.). (Illus.). 48p. (J). lib. bdg. 22.60 (978-0-7368-2142-1(2) , Capstone High/Low Bks.) Capstone Pr., Inc.

—Hulk Hogan: Pro Wrestler Terry Bollea. 2003. (Pro Wrestlers Ser.). (Illus.). 48p. (J). lib. bdg. 22.60 (978-0-7368-2140-7(6) , Capstone High/Low Bks.) Capstone Pr., Inc.

—The McMahons: Vince McMahon & Family. 2003. (Pro Wrestlers Ser.). (Illus.). 48p. (J). lib. bdg. 22.60 (978-0-7368-2143-8(0) , Capstone High/Low Bks.) Capstone Pr., Inc.

—The Nature Boy: Pro Wrestler Ric Flair. 2003. (Pro Wrestlers Ser.). (Illus.). 48p. (J). lib. bdg. 22.60 (978-0-7368-2141-4(4) , Capstone High/Low Bks.) Capstone Pr., Inc.

—Triple H: Pro Wrestler Hunter Hearst Helmsley. 2002. (Pro Wrestlers Ser.). (Illus.). 48p. (J). (gr. 3-4). lib. bdg. 21.26 (978-0-7368-1311-2(X) , Capstone High-Interest Bks.) Capstone Pr., Inc.

Kolmos, Keith. Galactic Wrestling(TM) Featuring Ultimate Muscle(TM) Official Strategy Guide. 2004. 128p. pap. 14.99 (978-0-7440-0409-0(8)) Brady GAMES.

Lebell, Gene. The Toughest Man Alive. 2003. (Illus.). 256p. 24.95 (978-0-9531766-7-0(3)) Health 'n' Life Publishing GBR. *Dist:* Midpoint Trade Bks., Inc.

Linde, Barbara M. Olympic Wrestling. 2007. (Great Moments in Olympic History Ser.). (Illus.). 48p. (J). (gr. 5-8). lib. bdg. 26.50 (***978-1-4042-0972-5(7)***) Rosen Publishing Group, Inc., The.

Main Event. 1999. (World Championship Wrestling - New World Order Colossal Sticker Activity Book Ser.). (Illus.). 240p. (J). pap. (978-0-7666-0449-0(7) , Honey Bear Bks.) Modern Publishing.

Martelli, Charles A. How to Become a State Wrestling Champion. 2002. 106p. (YA). per. 15.95 (978-0-9726395-0-7(0)) State Champion Wrestling Co.

McNab, Chris. Wrestling. 2003. (Sports Injuries Ser.). (Illus.). 64p. (J). lib. bdg. (978-1-59084-642-1(7)) Mason Crest Pubs.

Mighty Match-Ups. 1999. (World Championship Wrestling - New World Order Ser.). (Illus.). 24p. (J). pap. (978-0-7666-0444-5(6) , Honey Bear Bks.) Modern Publishing.

Molzahn, Arlene Bourgeois. Mankind: Pro Wrestler Mick Foley. 2001. (Pro Wrestlers Ser.). (Illus.). 48p. (J). (gr. 3-4). lib. bdg. 21.26 (978-0-7368-0919-1(8) , Capstone High-Interest Bks.) Capstone Pr., Inc.

Mudge, Jacqueline. Billy Kidman. 2001. (Pro Wrestling Legends Ser.). 64p. (J). (Illus.). pap. 25.00 (978-0-7910-6458-0(1)); 25.00 (978-0-7910-6457-3(3)) Facts On File, Inc. (Chelsea Hse.).

—Billy Kidman. 2001. (Illus.). 64p. (J). (gr. 1-4). lib. bdg. 17.60 (978-0-613-58542-2(9)) Tandem Library Bks.

—Bret Hart: The Story of the Wrestler They Call "The Hitman" 1999. (Pro Wrestling Legends Ser.). (Illus.). 64p. (YA). (gr. 3 up). 25.00 (978-0-7910-5408-6(X) , Chelsea Hse.) Facts On File, Inc.

—Bret Hart: The Story of the Wrestler They Call the Hitman. 2000. (gr. 5-8). lib. bdg. 17.60 (978-0-613-21045-4(X)) Tandem Library Bks.

—Diamond Dallas Page: The Story of the Wrestler They Call "Diamond Dallas Page" 2000. (Pro Wrestling Legends Ser.). (Illus.). 64p. (J). (gr. 8-12). pap. 25.00 (978-0-7910-5830-5(1) , Chelsea Hse.) Facts On File, Inc.

—Kevin Nash. 2000. (Pro Wrestling Legends Ser.). (Illus.). 64p. (J). (gr. 8-12). pap. 25.00 (978-0-7910-5828-2(X)); (gr. 4-7). 25.00 (978-0-7910-5827-5(1)) Facts On File, Inc. (Chelsea Hse.).

—Kevin Nash. 2001. (gr. 5-8). lib. bdg. 17.60 (978-0-613-32741-1(1)) Tandem Library Bks.

—Lex Luger. 2001. (Pro Wrestling Legends Ser.). (Illus.). 64p. (J). pap. 25.00 (978-0-7910-6449-8(2)); 25.00 (978-0-7910-6448-1(4) , Chelsea Hse.) Facts On File, Inc.

—Randy Savage: The Story of the Wrestler They Call "Macho Man" 1999. (Pro Wrestling Legends Ser.). (Illus.). 64p. (YA). (gr. 3 up). pap. 25.00 (978-0-7910-5555-7(8)); 25.00 (978-0-7910-5409-3(8)) Facts On File, Inc. (Chelsea Hse.).

—Randy Savage: The Story of the Wrestler They Call Macho Man. 2000. (gr. 5-8). lib. bdg. 17.60 (978-0-613-21051-5(4)) Tandem Library Bks.

Murray, Eric. Wrestling for Fun! 2006. (For Fun! Ser.). (Illus.). 48p. (J). (gr. 3-5). 22.60 (978-0-7565-1687-1(0)) Compass Point Bks.

Nardo, Don. Wrestling. 2001. (History of Sports Ser.). (Illus.). 104p. (YA). (gr. 6-9). 28.70 (978-1-56006-893-8(0) , Lucent Bks.) Thomson Gale.

Nitro Mania. 1999. (World Championship Wrestling - New World Order Coloring & Activity Bks.). (Illus.). 32p. (J). pap. (978-0-7666-0424-7(1) , Honey Bear Bks.) Modern Publishing.

Page, Jason. Combat: Fencing, Judo, Wrestling, Boxing, Taekwondo & Lots, Lots More. 2000. (Zeke's Olympic Pocket Guide Ser.). (Illus.). 32p. (J). pap. 3.95 (978-0-8225-5055-6(5) , LernerSports) Lerner Publishing Group.

Pandemonium. 1999. (World Championship Wrestling - New World Order Coloring & Activity Bks.). (Illus.). 32p. (J). pap. (978-0-7666-0422-3(5) , Honey Bear Bks.) Modern Publishing.

Payan, Michael. In the Ring with Bret Hart. 2002. (Reading Power Ser.). (Illus.). 24p. (J). (gr. 1). lib. bdg. 17.25 (978-0-8239-6047-7(1) , PowerKids Pr.) Rosen Publishing Group, Inc., The.

—In the Ring with Diamond Dallas Page. 2002. (Reading Power Ser.). (Illus.). 24p. (J). (gr. 1). lib. bdg. 17.25 (978-0-8239-6048-4(X) , PowerKids Pr.) Rosen Publishing Group, Inc., The.

—In the Ring with Goldberg. 2002. (Reading Power Ser.). (Illus.). 24p. (J). (gr. 1). lib. bdg. 17.25 (978-0-8239-6046-0(3) , PowerKids Pr.) Rosen Publishing Group, Inc., The.

—In the Ring with Kevin Nash. 2002. (Reading Power Ser.). (Illus.). 24p. (J). (gr. 1). lib. bdg. 17.25 (978-0-8239-6045-3(5) , PowerKids Pr.) Rosen Publishing Group, Inc., The.

—In the Ring with Scott Steiner. 2002. (Reading Power Ser.). (Illus.). 24p. (J). (gr. 1). lib. bdg. 17.25 (978-0-8239-6043-9(9) , PowerKids Pr.) Rosen Publishing Group, Inc., The.

—In the Ring with Sting. 2002. (Reading Power Ser.). (Illus.). 24p. (J). (gr. 1). lib. bdg. 17.25 (978-0-8239-6044-6(7) , PowerKids Pr.) Rosen Publishing Group, Inc., The.

—The World of Wrestling, 6 bks. Incl. In the Ring with Bret Hart. lib. bdg. 17.25 (978-0-8239-6047-7(1)); In the Ring with Diamond Dallas Page. lib. bdg. 17.25 (978-0-8239-6048-4(X)); In the Ring with Goldberg. lib. bdg. 17.25 (978-0-8239-6046-0(3)); In the Ring with Kevin Nash. lib. bdg. 17.25 (978-0-8239-6045-3(5)); In the Ring with Scott Steiner. lib. bdg. 17.25 (978-0-8239-6043-9(9)); In the Ring with Sting. lib. bdg. 17.25 (978-0-8239-6044-6(7)); 24p. (J). (gr. 1). (Illus.). 2002. Set lib. bdg. 96.00 (978-0-8239-7116-9(3) , PowerKids Pr.) Rosen Publishing Group, Inc., The.

Preller, James. Meet the Stars of Professional Wrestling. 2000. (J). (978-0-606-19578-2(5)) Tandem Library Bks.

—Rock Solid! 2000. (Illus.). 86p. (J). pap. 4.99 (978-0-439-23525-9(1)) Scholastic, Inc.

—Rock Solid: The Slammin' Unauthorized Biography of Professional Wrestler the Rock. 2000. (Superstars Ser.). (Illus.). 96p. (J). (gr. 1-7). pap. 4.50 (978-0-439-22221-1(4)) Scholastic, Inc.

—Smackdown! Meet the Stars of Professional Wrestling. 2000. (Illus.). (J). pap. 5.99 (978-0-439-21629-6(X)) Scholastic, Inc.

Pro Wrestlers. Incl. Goldberg : Pro Wrestler Bill Goldberg. Burgan, Michael. 2001. lib. bdg. 21.26 (978-0-7368-0917-7(1)); Mankind : Pro Wrestler Mick Foley. Molzahn, Arlene Bourgeois. 2001. lib. bdg. 21.26 (978-0-7368-0919-1(8)); Olympic Hero : Pro Wrestler Kurt Angle. Schaefer, A. R. 2002. lib. bdg. 21.26 (978-0-7368-1310-5(1)); Rock : Pro Wrestler Rocky Maivia. Burgan, Michael. 2001. lib. bdg. 21.26 (978-0-7368-0918-4(X)); Stone Cold : Pro Wrestler Steve Austin. Burgan, Michael. 2001. lib. bdg. 21.26 (978-0-7368-0920-7(1)); Triple H : Pro Wrestler Hunter Hearst Helmsley. Kaelberer, Angie Peterson. 2002. lib. bdg. 21.26 (978-0-7368-1311-2(X)); Undertaker : Pro Wrestler Mark Callaway. Schaefer, A. R. 2002. lib. bdg. 21.26 (978-0-7368-1312-9(8)); Y2J : Pro Wrestler Chris Jericho. Schaefer, A. R. 2002. lib. bdg. 21.26 (978-0-7368-1313-6(6)); 48p. (J). (gr. 3-4). (Illus.). Set lib. bdg. 170.08 (978-0-7368-1314-3(4) , Capstone High-Interest Bks.) Capstone Pr., Inc.

Pro Wrestling Legends. 2005. 64p. pap. 600.00 (978-0-7910-6797-0(1) , Chelsea Hse.) Facts On File, Inc.

Ring Masters. 1999. (World Championship Wrestling - New World Order Giant Coloring & Activity Bks.). (Illus.). 96p. (J). pap. (978-0-7666-0428-5(4) , Honey Bear Bks.) Modern Publishing.

Ring Warriors. 1999. (World Championship Wrestling - New World Order Ser.). (Illus.). 24p. (J). pap. (978-0-7666-0418-6(7) , Honey Bear Bks.) Modern Publishing.

Ross, Dan. Pro Wrestling's Greatest Wars. 2000. (Pro Wrestling Legends Ser.). (Illus.). 64p. (J). (gr. 8-12). pap. 25.00 (978-0-7910-5838-1(7)); (gr. 4-7). 25.00 (978-0-7910-5837-4(9)) Facts On File, Inc. (Chelsea Hse.).

—Pro Wrestling's Greatest Wars. 2001. (J). (978-0-606-20865-9(8)); (gr. 5-8). lib. bdg. 17.60 (978-0-613-32969-9(4)) Tandem Library Bks.

—Steve Austin: The Story of the Wrestler They Call "Stone Cold" 1999. (Pro Wrestling Legends Ser.). (Illus.). 64p. (YA). (gr. 3 up). pap. 25.00 (978-0-7910-5549-6(3) , Chelsea Hse.) Facts On File, Inc.

—Steve Austin: The Story of the Wrestler They Call Stone Cold. 2000. (gr. 5-8). lib. bdg. 17.60 (978-0-613-21052-2(2)) Tandem Library Bks.

—Story of the Wrestler They Call "the Rock" 2001. (Illus.). (J). (978-0-606-20929-8(8)) Tandem Library Bks.

—Story of the Wrestler They Call the Undertaker. 1999. (Pro Wrestling Legends Ser.). (Illus.). 64p. (J). (gr. 3 up). pap. 8.95 (978-0-7910-5553-3(1)); 25.00 (978-0-7910-5407-9(1)) Facts On File, Inc. (Chelsea Hse.).

Sampson, Julie & Ryan, Thomas. Beginning Wrestling. Curtis, Bruce, photos by. 2002. (Illus.). 96p. pap. 9.95 (978-1-4027-0107-8(1)) Sterling Publishing Co., Inc.

Schaefer, A. R. Olympic Hero: Pro Wrestler Kurt Angle. 2002. (Pro Wrestlers Ser.). (Illus.). 48p. (J). (gr. 3-4). lib. bdg. 21.26 (978-0-7368-1310-5(1) , Capstone High-Interest Bks.) Capstone Pr., Inc.

—The Undertaker: Pro Wrestler Mark Callaway. 2002. (Pro Wrestlers Ser.). (Illus.). 48p. (J). (gr. 3-4). lib. bdg. 21.26 (978-0-7368-1312-9(8) , Capstone High-Interest Bks.) Capstone Pr., Inc.

—Y2J: Pro Wrestler Chris Jericho. 2002. (Pro Wrestlers Ser.). (Illus.). 48p. (J). (gr. 3-4). lib. bdg. 21.26 (978-0-7368-1313-6(6) , Capstone High-Interest Bks.) Capstone Pr., Inc.

Sherman, Josepha. Stone Cold Steve Austin. 2001. (Sports Files Ser.). (Illus.). 32p. (J). (gr. 1-3). lib. bdg. 22.79 (978-1-58810-114-3(2)) Heinemann Library.

Slamboree. 1999. (World Championship Wrestling - New World Order Coloring Sticker Bks.). (Illus.). 24p. (J). pap. (978-0-7666-0420-9(9) , Honey Bear Bks.) Modern Publishing.

Slamfest. 1999. (World Championship Wrestling - New World Order Coloring & Activity Bks.). (Illus.). 32p. (J). pap. (978-0-7666-0425-4(X) , Honey Bear Bks.) Modern Publishing.

Squared Circle. 1999. (World Championship Wrestling - New World Order Giant Coloring & Activity Bks.). (Illus.). 96p. (J). pap. (978-0-7666-0427-8(6) , Honey Bear Bks.) Modern Publishing.

Tag Team. 1999. (World Championship Wrestling - New World Order Coloring Sticker Bks.). (Illus.). 24p. (J). pap. (978-0-7666-0421-6(7) , Honey Bear Bks.) Modern Publishing.

Teitelbaum. Feel the Sting. 2000. (Eyewitness Readers Ser.). (J). 10.75 (978-0-606-20120-9(3)) Tandem Library Bks.

U. S. Olympic Committee. A Basic Guide to Wrestling. 2001. (Olympic Guides). (Illus.). 160p. (J). (gr. 6 up). lib. bdg. 23.33 (978-0-8368-2799-6(6)) Stevens, Gareth Inc.

Uschan, Michael V. Jesse Ventura. 2000. (People in the News Ser.). (Illus.). 112p. (J). (gr. 6-9). (978-1-56006-777-1(2) , Lucent Bks.) Thomson Gale.

Velazquez, Mauricio, tr. Hulk Hogan, Campeon de Lucha Libre. 2002. (Power Kids Coleccion). (SPA.). 24p. (J). (gr. 2-3). lib. bdg. 17.25 (978-0-8239-6122-1(2) , RN30771, Buenas Letra) Rosen Publishing Group, Inc., The.

West, Terry M. Mick Foley: Behind the Mankind Mask. 2000. (Illus.). (J). (gr. 3-7). 73p. pap. 4.99 (978-0-439-24383-4(1)); 80p. mass mkt. 4.99 (978-0-439-24384-1(X)) Scholastic, Inc.

—Steve Austin: The Stone Cold Story. 2000. (Illus.). 80p. (J). (gr. 3-9). mass mkt. 4.99 (978-0-439-24386-5(6)) Scholastic, Inc.

Wrestling Greats. 2005. (Illus.). 112p. (gr. 7-12). lib. bdg. 265.30 (978-0-8239-3911-4(1)) Rosen Publishing Group, Inc., The.

Wrestling Greats Set 2. 2005. (Illus.). (gr. 7-12). lib. bdg. 151.50 (978-0-8239-9717-6(0)) Rosen Publishing Group, Inc., The.

Zannos, Susan. Hollywood Hulk Hogan: The Story of Terry Bollea. 1999. (Real Life Reader Biographies Ser.). (Illus.). 32p. (J). (gr. 3-7). lib. bdg. 15.95 (978-1-58415-021-3(1)) Mitchell Lane Pubs., Inc.

WRESTLING—FICTION

Anderson, Glenn. A Brown Bag Life. 2003. 343p. (YA). pap. 17.95 (978-0-7414-1384-0(1)) Infinity Publishing.

Benjamin, E. M. Takedown. 1999. 205p. (J). (gr. 7-12). pap. 9.95 (978-1-889199-04-7(4)) Banks Channel Bks.

Garza, Xavier. Lucha Libre: The Man in the Silver Mask. Garza, Xavier, illus. 2007. (SPA.). 40p. (J). pap. 8.95 ***(978-1-933693-10-1(X))*** Cinco Puntos Pr.

—Lucha Libre: The Man in the Silver Mask. Crosthwaite, Luis Humberto, tr. 2005. (ENG & SPA., Illus.). 40p. (gr. 2-5). 17.95 (978-0-938317-92-0(X)) Cinco Puntos Pr.

Hapka, Catherine. Fortune Donut. 2003. (gr. k-3). lib. bdg. 11.25 (978-0-613-71414-3(8)) Tandem Library Bks.

Harrigan, Matt. MTV's Celebrity Deathmatch Companion. 2000. (gr. 7-12). lib. bdg. 33.30 (978-0-613-33936-0(3)) Tandem Library Bks.

Harrison, Kenneth. How I Became Champion of the Universe. 2004. (Illus.). 30p. (J). 14.95 (978-1-58246-077-2(9) , Tricycle Pr.) Ten Speed Pr.

Martino, Alfred C. Pinned. (YA). 2005. 320p. 17.00 (978-0-15-205355-0(7)); 2006. (Illus.). 324p. reprint ed. pap. 6.95 (978-0-15-205631-5(9) , Harcourt Paperbacks) Harcourt Children's Bks.

Morgan, Allen. Matthew & the Midnight Wrestlers. 2000. (gr. k-3). lib. bdg. 15.30 (978-0-613-84051-4(8)) Tandem Library Bks.

Morgan, Allen & Martchenko, Michael. Matthew & the Midnight Wrestlers. 2000. (Matthew's Midnight Adventures Ser.). (Illus.). 32p. (J). (ps-3). 6.99 (978-0-7737-6053-0(9)) Stoddart Kids CAN. *Dist:* Fitzhenry & Whiteside, Ltd.

Nakagawa, Hirotaka. Sumo Boy. Hasegawa, Yoshifumi, illus. 2006. 40p. (J). (ps-k). 15.99 (978-0-7868-3635-2(0)) Hyperion Pr.

Poth, Karen. Tale of Two Sumos. 2004. (Big Idea Books). (Illus.). 32p. 9.99 (978-0-310-70933-6(4)) Zonderkidz.

Scieszka, Jon. Nos Vemos, Gladiador.Tr. of See you later, gladiator. (SPA.). (J). 7.95 (978-958-04-6484-6(7)) Norma S.A. COL. *Dist:* Distribuidora Norma, Inc.

—See You Later, Gladiator. McCauley, Adam, illus. (Time Warp Trio Ser.: No. 9). 96p. (J). (gr. 2-5). 2000. 14.99 (978-0-670-89340-9(4) , Viking Juvenile); Vol. 9. 2004. pap. 4.99 (978-0-14-240117-0(X) , Puffin) Penguin Group (USA) Inc.

Spinelli, Jerry. There's a Girl in My Hammerlock. 2007. 208p. (J). pap. 5.99 ***(978-1-4169-3937-5(7))*** Kaplan Bks.

Sterner, Nathan. Onami: The Great Wave. Dutchak, Shelly, illus. 2007. (J). per. ***(978-0-9795529-0-8(7))*** 716 Productions.

Strasser, Todd. Help! I'm Trapped in a Professional Wrestler's Body. 2000. (Help! I'm Trapped Ser.). (Illus.). 128p. (J). (gr. 4-7). pap. 4.50 (978-0-439-14773-6(5) , Scholastic Paperbacks) Scholastic, Inc.

—Help! I'm Trapped in a Professional Wrestler's Body. 2000. (gr. 3-6). lib. bdg. 12.40 (978-0-613-21693-7(8)) Tandem Library Bks.

Sweeney, Joyce. Headlock. 2006. 224p. (YA). 16.95 (978-0-8050-8018-6(X) , Holt, Henry & Co. Bks. For Young Readers) Holt, Henry & Co.

Wallace, Rich. Takedown, No. 8. 2007. (Winning Season Ser.: No. 8). 128p. (YA). (gr. 2). pap. 4.99 ***(978-0-14-240919-0(7)*** , Puffin) Penguin Group (USA) Inc.

Wallace, Rich. Takedown: Winning Season 8. 2006. (Winning Season Ser.). 128p. (J). (gr. 3). 14.99 (978-0-670-06096-2(8) , Viking Juvenile) Penguin Group (USA) Inc.

Weis, Lyle Percy. Let's Wrestle. (J). 5.95 (978-0-9686899-4-3(9)) Hodgepog Bks. CAN. *Dist:* Coteau Bks.

WRIGHT, FRANK LLOYD, 1869-1959

Adkins, Jan. Up Close: Frank Lloyd Wright: Frank Lloyd Wright. 2007. 208p. (YA). (gr. 6). 16.99 ***(978-0-670-06138-9(7)*** , Viking Juvenile) Penguin Group (USA) Inc.

Fandel, Jennifer. Frank Lloyd Wright. 2005. (Extraordinary Artists Ser.). (Illus.). 48p. (gr. 7 up). 21.95 (978-1-58341-378-4(2) , Creative Education) Creative Co., The.

Ingram, Scott. Frank Lloyd Wright. 2003. (Raintree Biographies Ser.). (J). lib. bdg. 25.70 (978-0-7398-6866-9(7)) Raintree.

—Frank Lloyd Wright. 2003. (gr. 3-6). lib. bdg. 15.90 (978-0-613-78232-6(1)) Tandem Library Bks.

Levy, Janey. The Architecture of Frank Lloyd Wright: Understanding the Concepts of Parallel & Perpendicular. 2005. (PowerMath Ser.). (Illus.). 32p. (J). 22.50 (978-1-4042-2940-2(X)); (978-1-4042-5145-8(6)); pap. 22.50 (978-1-4042-5144-1(8)) Rosen Publishing Group, Inc., The. (PowerKids Pr.).

Mayo, Gretchen Will. Frank Lloyd Wright. 2004. (Trailblazers of the Modern World Ser.). (Illus.). 48p. (J). (gr. 5 up). pap. 11.95 (978-0-8368-5261-5(3)); lib. bdg. 30.00 (978-0-8368-5101-4(3)) Stevens, Gareth Inc. (World Almanac Library).

Middleton, Haydn. Frank Lloyd Wright. 2001. (Creative Lives Ser.). (Illus.). 64p. (YA). (gr. 6-8). lib. bdg. 27.07 (978-1-58810-203-4(3)) Heinemann Library.

Simply Wright: A Journey into the Ideas of Frank Lloyd Wright's Architecture. 2004. (J). spiral bd. 17.95 (978-0-9677348-3-5(5)) Castleconal Pr.

Thorne-Thomsen, Kathleen. Frank Lloyd Wright for Kids: His Life & Ideas, 21 Activities. 2003. (For Kids Ser.). (Illus.). 144p. (J). (gr. 3 up). pap. 16.95 (978-1-55652-207-9(X)) Chicago Review Pr., Inc.

Wright, David K. Frank Lloyd Wright: Visionary Architect. 1999. (People to Know Ser.). (Illus.). 128p. (YA). (gr. 6-12). lib. bdg. 26.60 (978-0-7660-1032-1(5)) Enslow Pubs., Inc.

WRIGHT, ORVILLE, 1871-1948

Acosta, Tatiana & Gutierrez, Guillermo, trs. Los Hermanos Wright. 2004. (Gente Que Hay Que Conocer Ser.). (SPA., Illus.). 24p. (J). lib. bdg. 19.33 (978-0-8368-4356-9(8)) Stevens, Gareth Inc.

Arrathoon, Leigh A. Men Who Changed the World Vol. II: The First Birdmen: Wilbur & Orville Wright. Davio, John, ed. Hajdyla, Ken, illus. 56p. (J). (gr. 5-6). pap. 5.95 (978-0-9648564-6-2(8)) Paint Creek Pr., Ltd.

Berger, Melvin & Berger, Gilda. Can You Fly High, Wright Brothers? 2007. (Scholastic Science Super Giants Ser.: Vol. 1). 48p. (J). pap. 4.99 (978-0-439-83378-3(7)) Scholastic, Inc.

Borden, Louise, et al. Touching the Sky. 2003. (Illus.). 64p. (J). (gr. k-3). 18.95 (978-0-689-84876-6(5) , McElderry, Margaret K.) Simon & Schuster Children's Publishing.

Brown, Jonatha A. The Wright Brothers. 2004. (Illus.). 24p. (J). pap. (978-0-8368-4321-7(5)); (YA). lib. bdg. 19.33 (978-0-8368-4314-9(2)) Stevens, Gareth Inc.

Burleigh, Robert. Into the Air: The Story of the Wright Brothers' First Flight. Wylie, Bill, illus. 2002. (American Heroes Ser.). 48p. (J). (gr. 3-7). pap. 6.00 (978-0-15-216803-2(6) , 53227831, Silver Whistle) Harcourt Trade Pubs.

Carson, Mary Kay. The Wright Brothers for Kids: How They Invented the Airplane: 21 Activities Exploring the Science & History of Flight. 2003. (Illus.). 146p. (J). (gr. 4-7). lib. bdg. 24.55 (978-0-613-63373-4(3)) Tandem Library Bks.

—The Wright Brothers for Kids: How They Invented the Airplane with 21 Activities Exploring the Science & History of Flight. D'Argo, Laura, illus. 2003. (For Kids Ser.). 160p. (J). pap. 14.95 (978-1-55652-477-6(3)) Chicago Review Pr., Inc.

Collins, Mary. Airborne: A Photobiography of Wilbur & Orville Wright. 2003. (Illus.). 64p. (J). (gr. 5). 18.95 (978-0-7922-6957-1(8) , 53238483, National Geographic Children's Bks.) National Geographic Society.

Crompton, Samuel Willard. The Wright Brothers: First in Flight. 2007. (Milestones in American History Ser.). 120p. (gr. 6-12). 35.00 ***(978-0-7910-9356-6(5)*** , Chelsea Hse.) Facts On File, Inc.

Deines, Ann, ed. Wilbur & Orville Wright: A Handbook of Facts. 2007. (Illus.). 64p. per. 5.95 (978-1-888213-75-1(2)) Eastern National.

Dixon-Engel, Tara & Jackson, Mike. Sterling Biographies: the Wright Brothers: First in Flight. 2007. (Sterling Biographies Ser.). (Illus.). 128p. (J). 12.95 ***(978-1-4027-4954-4(6));*** pap. 5.95 ***(978-1-4027-3231-7(7))*** Sterling Publishing Co., Inc.

Dunn, Joeming W. The Wright Brothers. Dunn, Joeming W. & Dunn, Ben, illus. 2007. (Bio-Graphics Ser.). 32p. (J). (gr. 3-6). lib. bdg. 27.07 ***(978-1-60270-071-0(0)*** , Graphic Planet) Magic Wagon.

Edwards, Pamela Duncan. The Wright Brothers. Cole, Henry, illus. 2003. 40p. (gr. k-4). 16.49 (978-0-7868-2682-7(7)) Hyperion Bks. for Children.

Ford, Carin T. The Wright Brothers: Heroes of Flight. 2003. (Famous Inventors Ser.). (Illus.). 32p. (J). (gr. 1-4). lib. bdg. 22.60 (978-0-7660-2002-3(9)) Enslow Pubs., Inc.

Gaines, Ann Graham. Orville & Wilbur Wright. 2001. (Illus.). 24p. (J). (gr. 1-4). lib. bdg. 20.64 (978-1-58952-121-6(8)) Rourke Publishing, LLC.

—Orville y Wilbur Wright. Sarfatti, Esther & de la Vega, Eida, trs. 2002. (Inventores Famosos Ser.). (SPA., Illus.). 24p. mass mkt. 5.95 (978-1-58952-238-1(9) , RK31455) Rourke Publishing, LLC.

—Orville y Wilbur Wright. 2001. (Inventores Famosos Ser.). (SPA & ENG., Illus.). 24p. (J). (gr. 1-4). lib. bdg. 19.27 (978-1-58952-178-0(1) , RK5957) Rourke Publishing, LLC.

—Orville y Wilbur Wright. 2002. (SPA.). (gr. k-3). lib. bdg. 14.10 (978-0-613-79816-7(3)) Tandem Library Bks.

Graham, Ian. Wright Brothers: Pioneers of Flight. 2003. (gr. 3-6). lib. bdg. 15.25 (978-0-613-84054-5(2)) Tandem Library Bks.

Hamen, Susan E. The Wright Brothers. 2007. (Essential Lives Ser.). (ENG., Illus.). 112p. (YA). (gr. 8-12). lib. bdg. 32.79 ***(978-1-59928-846-8(X)*** , Essential Library) ABDO Publishing Co.

Harcourt School Publishers Staff. Trofeos Advanced Level: El Hermanos Wright. 3rd ed. 2002. (SPA., Illus.). pap. 6.80 (978-0-15-323944-1(1)) Harcourt Schl. Pubs.

—The Wright Brothers Advanced Level. 3rd ed. 2002. (Trophies Reading Program Ser.). (Illus.). pap. 5.10 (978-0-15-323033-2(9)) Harcourt Schl. Pubs.

—The Wright Brothers & the 1st Airplane. 3rd ed. 2002. (Horizons Ser.). (Illus.). (J). pap. 3.70 (978-0-15-333174-9(7)) Harcourt Schl. Pubs.

Los Hermanos Wright. 2006. (People We Should Know Ser.).Tr. of Wright Brothers. (SPA.). (J). (gr. 3-4). 4.76 (978-0-8368-4363-7(0) , GHS33824) Stevens, Gareth Inc.

Hill, Lee Sullivan. The Flyer Flew! The Invention of the Airplane. Naprstek, Joel, illus. (On My Own Science Ser.). 48p. (J). 2007. pap. 5.95 (978-1-57505-855-9(3) , First Avenue Editions); 2006. (gr. 2-4). lib. bdg. 25.26 (978-1-57505-758-3(1) , Millbrook Pr.) Lerner Publishing Group.

Hudson, Margaret. The Wright Brothers, Set 1. 2002. (Lives & Times Ser.). (Illus.). 24p. (J). (gr. k-3). pap. 6.50 (978-1-58810-348-2(X) , 91108) Heinemann Library.

Jenner, Caryn. First Flight: The Wright Brothers. 2003. (gr. k-3). lib. bdg. 11.80 (978-0-613-67328-0(X)) Tandem Library Bks.

—First Flight Vol. 4: The Story of the Wright Brothers. 2003. (DK Readers Ser.). (Illus.). 48p. (J). (gr. 5). pap. 3.99 (978-0-7894-9291-3(1)) Dorling Kindersley Publishing, Inc.

Jenner, Caryn & Dorling Kindersley Publishing Staff. First Flight: The Wright Brothers. 2003. (Readers Ser.). (Illus.). 48p. (J). 14.99 (978-0-7894-9541-9(4)) Dorling Kindersley Publishing, Inc.

Lynch, Emma. The Wright Brothers. 2005. (Illus.). 32p. (J). (978-1-4034-6354-8(9)); pap. (978-1-4034-6368-5(9)) Heinemann Library.

MacLeod, Elizabeth. The Wright Brothers. Krystoforski, Andrej, illus. 2008. 32p. pap. ***(978-1-55453-054-0(7))*** Kids Can Pr., Ltd.

MacLeod, Elizabeth. The Wright Brothers: A Flying Start. Spurll, Barbara, illus. 2004. (Snapshots Ser.). 32p. (J). (gr. 4-6). (978-1-55074-935-9(8)); (978-1-55074-933-5(1)) Kids Can Pr., Ltd.

Marsh, Carole. Wright Brothers. 2002. (One Thousand Readers Ser.). (Illus.). 12p. (J). (gr. k-4). 2.95 (978-0-635-01560-0(9)) Gallopade International.

—The Wright Brothers: An Ohio Experience Reader. 2001. (J). pap. 1.95 (978-0-635-00433-8(X)) Gallopade International.

—Wright Brothers: Orville & Wilbur. 2002. (Carole Marsh Bks.). (Illus.). 32p. (J). (gr. 3-8). 29.95 (978-0-635-01351-4(7) , 13517, Marsh, Carole Bks.); pap. 5.95 (978-0-635-01350-7(9) , 13509) Gallopade International.

Martin, Michael J. The Wright Brothers. 2002. (Importance of Ser.). (Illus.). 112p. (J). (gr. 7-10). 32.45 (978-1-56006-847-1(7) , Lucent Bks.) Thomson Gale.

Maurer, Richard. The Wright Sister: Katharine Wright & Her Famous Brothers. rev. ed. 2003. (Illus.). 128p. (J). (gr. 5-9). 19.95 (978-0-7613-1546-9(2)) Roaring Brook Pr.

Mayo, Gretchen Will. The Wright Brothers. 2003. (Trailblazers of the Modern World Ser.). (Illus.). 48p. (J). (gr. 5 up). lib. bdg. 30.00 (978-0-8368-5094-9(7) , World Almanac Library) Stevens, Gareth Inc.

McCormick, Lisa Wade. Wright Brothers. 2005. (Scholastic News Nonfiction Readers Ser.). (Illus.). 24p. (J). pap. (978-0-516-24786-1(7)) Children's Pr., Ltd.

—Wright Brothers. 2005. (Scholastic News Nonfiction Readers Ser.). (Illus.). 24p. (J). (gr. 1-2). 19.00 (978-0-516-24937-7(1) , Children's Pr.) Scholastic Library Publishing.

McLaughlin, Kari Massie. My Adventure with the Wright Brothers. 2007. 44p. (J). 8.99 (978-1-59092-471-6(1) , Orchard Academy Pr.) Windstorm Creative.

McPherson, Stephanie Sammartino & Gardner, Joseph Sammartino. Wilbur & Orville Wright: Taking Flight. 2004. (Trailblazer Biography Ser.). (Illus.). 120p. (J). 30.60 (978-1-57505-443-8(4) , Carolrhoda Bks.) Lerner Publishing Group.

Niz, Xavier. The Wright Brothers & the Airplane. Erwin, Steve & Barnett, Charles, illus. 2007. 32p. (J). (978-0-7368-6845-7(3)) Capstone Publishing.

O'Hern, Kerri & Mayo, Gretchen. The Wright Brothers. 2006. (Illus.). (J). pap. (978-0-8368-6251-5(1)); 32p. lib. bdg. 26.00 (978-0-8368-6199-0(X)) Stevens, Gareth Inc. (World Almanac Library).

Old, Wendie C. To Fly: The Story of the Wright Brothers. Parker, Robert Andrew, illus. 2002. 48p. (J). (gr. 3-5). tchr. ed. 16.00 (978-0-618-13347-5(X) , Clarion Bks.) Houghton Mifflin Co. Trade & Reference Div.

—The Wright Brothers: Inventors of the Airplane. 2000. (Historical American Biographies Ser.). (Illus.). 128p. (J). (gr. 6-12). lib. bdg. 26.60 (978-0-7660-1095-6(3)) Enslow Pubs., Inc.

Orr, Tamra B. The Dawn of Aviation: The Story of the Wright Brothers. 2005. (Illus.). 48p. (YA). (ps-7). lib. bdg. 29.95 (978-1-58415-396-2(2) , 1244922) Mitchell Lane Pubs., Inc.

O'Sullivan, Robyn. The Wright Brothers Fly. 2007. (History Chapters Ser.). 48p. (J). (gr. 1-4). lib. bdg. 17.90 ***(978-1-4263-0188-9(X)*** , National Geographic Children's Bks.) National Geographic Society.

Parramore, Thomas C. Triumph at Kitty Hawk: The Wright Brothers & Powered Flight. 2003. (Coastal North Carolina Ser.). (ENG., Illus.). 123p. (gr. 8-12). reprint ed. pap. 5.00 (978-0-86526-259-1(4)) North Carolina Office of Archives & History.

Price Hossell, Karen. Kitty Hawk: The Flight of the Wright Brothers. 2003. (Point of Impact Ser.). (Illus.). 32p. (J). (gr. 5-7). lib. bdg. 25.64 (978-1-58810-907-1(0)) Heinemann Library.

Rausch, Monica. The Wright Brothers & the Airplane. 2006. (Illus.). 24p. (J). pap. ***(978-0-8368-7733-5(0));*** lib. bdg. ***(978-0-8368-7502-7(8))*** Stevens, Gareth Inc. (Weekly Reader Early Learning Library).

W
X
Y
Z

Reed, Jennifer. Wilbur & Orville Wright: Trailblazers of the Sky. 2007. (Inventors Who Changed the World Ser.). (Illus.). 128p. (J). (gr. 5). lib. bdg. 33.27 (***978-1-59845-054-5(9)***, MyReportLinks.com Bks.) Enslow Pubs., Inc.

Ryan, Bernard. The Wright Brothers: Inventors of the Airplane. 2003. (Great Life Stories Ser.). (Illus.). 128p. (J). 30.50 (978-0-531-12254-9(9), Watts, Franklin) Scholastic Library Publishing.

Schaefer, Lola M. The Wright Brothers. 2000. (Famous People in Transportation Ser.). (Illus.). 24p. (J). (gr. k-1). lib. bdg. 15.93 (978-0-7368-0549-0(4), Pebble Bks.) Capstone Pr., Inc.

—The Wright Brothers. 2005. (Transportation Ser.). 24p. (YA). (gr. k-3). pap. (978-0-7368-8733-5(4), Pebble Bks.) Capstone Pr., Inc.

Schulz, Walter A. Will y Orv (Will & Orv) Schulz, Janet A., illus. 2006. (Yo Solo - Historia (on My Own - History) Ser.). (SPA.). 48p. (J). (gr. 2-4). lib. bdg. 25.26 (978-0-8225-6263-4(4), Ediciones Lerner) Lerner Publishing Group.

Shea, Kitty. The Wright Brothers. 2004. (Compass Point Early Biographies Ser.). (Illus.). 32p. (J). (gr. 1-3). lib. bdg. 21.26 (978-0-7565-0791-6(X)) Compass Point Bks.

Smith, Robert W. The Wright Brothers. 2003. (Spotlight on America Ser.). (Illus.). 48p. pap. 8.99 (978-0-7439-3210-3(2)) Teacher Created Materials, Inc.

Sproule, Anna. The Wright Brothers. 2005. (Giants of Science Bilingual Ser.). (J). 9.95 (978-1-4103-0507-7(4)); (ENG & SPA., Illus.). 64p. (gr. 5-7). 28.70 (978-1-4103-0501-5(5)) Thomson Gale. (Blackbirch Pr., Inc.).

—The Wright Brothers: The Birth of Modern Aviation. 1999. (Giants of Science Ser.). (Illus.). 64p. (YA). (gr. 5-8). 24.95 (978-1-56711-328-0(1), Blackbirch Pr., Inc.) Thomson Gale.

Tate, Suzanne. Flyer: A Tale of the Wright Dog. Melvin, James, illus. 2003. (Suzanne Tate's History Ser.). (J). pap. 4.95 (978-1-878405-42-5(X)) Nags Head Art, Inc.

—Helping the Wright Brothers: A Tale of First Flight Helpers. Melvin, James, illus. 1999. (Suzanne Tate's History Ser.: Vol. 2). 32p. (J). pap. 4.95 (978-1-878405-25-8(X)) Nags Head Art, Inc.

Taylor-Miller, Sandra. Are We There Yet? The Wright Brothers' National Memorial Park, Kill Devil Hills, North Carolina, Site of the First Heavier-Than-Air Machine-Powered Flight. 2004. (Illus.). 56p. (J). 9.95 (978-1-887905-87-9(1)) Parkway Pubs., Inc.

Tieck, Sarah. The Wright Brothers. 2007. (First Biographies Ser.). (Illus.). 32p. (J). (gr. k-3). lib. bdg. 22.78 (978-1-59679-790-1(8)) ABDO Publishing Co.

Trailblazers of the Modern World: Louis Armstrong; Anne Frank; Martin Luther King, Jr.; Theodore Roosevelt; Gloria Steinem; The Wright Brothers, 6 bks. 2003. (Illus.). (J). (gr. 5 up). lib. bdg. 175.60 (978-0-8368-5088-8(2), World Almanac Library) Stevens, Gareth Inc.

Tucker, Mary. Wright Brothers. Mitchell, Judy, ed. Hierstein, Judith, illus. 2002. (History - Hands On! Ser.). 32p. (J). (gr. 1-4). pap. 6.95 (978-1-57310-353-4(5)) Teaching & Learning Co.

Van Steenwyk, Elizabeth. One Fine Day: A Radio Play. Farnsworth, Bill, illus. 2004. 32p. (gr. 3-5). 16.00 (978-0-8028-5234-2(3)) Eerdmans, William B. Publishing Co.

Wadsworth, Ginger. The Wright Brothers. 2004. (History Maker Bios Ser.). (Illus.). 47p. (J). 26.60 (978-0-8225-0199-2(6), Lerner Pubns.) Lerner Publishing Group.

Will y Orv (Will & Orv) 2006. (J). pap. 5.95 (978-0-8225-6615-1(X), Ediciones Lerner) Lerner Publishing Group.

Wyborny, Sheila. The Wright Brothers. 2002. (Inventors & Creators Ser.). (Illus.). 48p. (J). (gr. 3-5). 18.96 (978-0-7377-1369-5(0), Kidhaven) Thomson Gale.

Yolen, Jane. My Brothers' Flying Machine: Wilbur, Orville, & Me. Burke, Jim, illus. 2003. 32p. (J). (gr. 1-4). 17.99 (978-0-316-97159-1(6)) Little, Brown Bks. for Young Readers.

WRIGHT, RICHARD, 1908-1960

Jones, Lynda & Garnett, Ron. Five Famous Writers. 2001. (Great Black Heroes Ser.). (Illus.). 48p. (J). (978-0-590-48035-2(9)) Scholastic, Inc.

Levine, Gloria. Native Son. 1999. 44p. (YA). 11.95 (978-1-56137-624-7(8)) Novel Units, Inc.

Levy, Debbie. Richard Wright. 2007. (Literary Greats Ser.). 160p. (YA). (gr. 7-12). lib. bdg. 33.26 (***978-0-8225-6793-6(8)***, Twenty-First Century Bks.) Lerner Publishing Group.

Native Son. 1999. (YA). 9.95 (978-1-56137-623-0(X)) Novel Units, Inc.

Westen, Robin. Richard Wright: Author of Native Son & Black Boy. 2002. (African-American Biographies Ser.). (Illus.). 128p. (J). (gr. 6-12). lib. bdg. 26.60 (978-0-7660-1769-6(9)) Enslow Pubs., Inc.

Wright, Richard. Black Boy. 2006. (Bloom's Modern Critical Interpretations Ser.). 150p. 45.00 (978-0-7910-8585-1(6), Chelsea Hse.) Facts On File, Inc.

WRIGHT, WILBUR, 1867-1912

Acosta, Tatiana & Gutierrez, Guillermo, trs. Los Hermanos Wright. 2004. (Gente Que Hay Que Conocer Ser.). (SPA., Illus.). 24p. (J). lib. bdg. 19.33 (978-0-8368-4356-9(8)) Stevens, Gareth Inc.

Arrathoon, Leigh A. Men Who Changed the World Vol. II: The First Birdmen: Wilbur & Orville Wright. Davio, John, ed. Hajdyla, Ken, illus. 56p. (J). (gr. 5-6). pap. 5.95 (978-0-9648564-6-2(8)) Paint Creek Pr., Ltd.

Berger, Melvin & Berger, Gilda. Can You Fly High, Wright Brothers? 2007. (Scholastic Science Super Giants Ser.: Vol. 1). 48p. (J). pap. 4.99 (978-0-439-83378-3(7)) Scholastic, Inc.

Borden, Louise, et al. Touching the Sky. 2003. (Illus.). 64p. (J). (gr. k-3). 18.95 (978-0-689-84876-6(5), McElderry, Margaret K.) Simon & Schuster Children's Publishing.

Brown, Jonatha A. The Wright Brothers. 2004. (Illus.). 24p. (J). pap. (978-0-8368-4321-7(5)); (YA). lib. bdg. 19.33 (978-0-8368-4314-9(2)) Stevens, Gareth Inc.

Burleigh, Robert. Into the Air: The Story of the Wright Brothers' First Flight. Wylie, Bill, illus. 2002. (American Heroes Ser.). 48p. (J). (gr. 3-7). pap. 6.00 (978-0-15-216803-2(6), 53227831, Silver Whistle) Harcourt Trade Pubs.

Carson, Mary Kay. The Wright Brothers for Kids: How They Invented the Airplane: 21 Activities Exploring the Science & History of Flight. 2003. (Illus.). 146p. (J). (gr. 4-7). lib. bdg. 24.55 (978-0-613-63373-4(3)) Tandem Library Bks.

—The Wright Brothers for Kids: How They Invented the Airplane with 21 Activities Exploring the Science & History of Flight. D'Argo, Laura, illus. 2003. (For Kids Ser.). 160p. (J). pap. 14.95 (978-1-55652-477-6(3)) Chicago Review Pr., Inc.

Collins, Mary. Airborne: A Photobiography of Wilbur & Orville Wright. 2003. (Illus.). 64p. (J). (gr. 5). 18.95 (978-0-7922-6957-1(8), 53238483, National Geographic Children's Bks.) National Geographic Society.

Crompton, Samuel Willard. The Wright Brothers: First in Flight. 2007. (Milestones in American History Ser.). 120p. (gr. 6-12). 35.00 (***978-0-7910-9356-6(5)***, Chelsea Hse.) Facts On File, Inc.

Deines, Ann, ed. Wilbur & Orville Wright: A Handbook of Facts. 2007. (Illus.). 64p. per. 5.95 (978-1-888213-75-1(2)) Eastern National.

Dixon-Engel, Tara & Jackson, Mike. Sterling Biographies: the Wright Brothers: First in Flight. 2007. (Sterling Biographies Ser.). (Illus.). 128p. (J). 12.95 (***978-1-4027-4954-4(6)***); pap. 5.95 (***978-1-4027-3231-7(7)***) Sterling Publishing Co., Inc.

Dunn, Joeming W. The Wright Brothers. Dunn, Joeming W. & Dunn, Ben, illus. 2007. (Bio-Graphics Ser.). 32p. (J). (gr. 3-6). lib. bdg. 27.07 (***978-1-60270-071-0(0)***, Graphic Planet) Magic Wagon.

Edwards, Pamela Duncan. The Wright Brothers. Cole, Henry, illus. 2003. 40p. (gr. k-4). 16.49 (978-0-7868-2682-7(7)) Hyperion Bks. for Children.

Ford, Carin T. The Wright Brothers: Heroes of Flight. 2003. (Famous Inventors Ser.). (Illus.). 32p. (J). (gr. 1-4). lib. bdg. 22.60 (978-0-7660-2002-3(9)) Enslow Pubs., Inc.

Gaines, Ann Graham. Orville & Wilbur Wright. 2001. (Illus.). 24p. (J). (gr. 1-4). lib. bdg. 20.64 (978-1-58952-121-6(8)) Rourke Publishing, LLC.

—Orville y Wilbur Wright. Sarfatti, Esther & de la Vega, Eida, trs. 2002. (Inventores Famosos Ser.). (SPA., Illus.). 24p. mass mkt. 5.95 (978-1-58952-238-1(9), RK31455) Rourke Publishing, LLC.

—Orville y Wilbur Wright. 2001. (Inventores Famosos Ser.). (SPA & ENG., Illus.). 24p. (J). (gr. 1-4). lib. bdg. 19.27 (978-1-58952-178-0(1), RK5957) Rourke Publishing, LLC.

—Orville y Wilbur Wright. 2002. (SPA.). (gr. k-3). lib. bdg. 14.10 (978-0-613-79816-7(3)) Tandem Library Bks.

Graham, Ian. Wright Brothers: Pioneers of Flight. 2003. (gr. 3-6). lib. bdg. 15.25 (978-0-613-84054-5(2)) Tandem Library Bks.

Hamen, Susan E. The Wright Brothers. 2007. (Essential Lives Ser.). (ENG., Illus.). 112p. (YA). (gr. 8-12). lib. bdg. 32.79 (***978-1-59928-846-8(X)***, Essential Library) ABDO Publishing Co.

Harcourt School Publishers Staff. Trofeos Advanced Level: El Hermanos Wright. 3rd ed. 2002. (SPA., Illus.). pap. 6.80 (978-0-15-323944-1(1)) Harcourt Schl. Pubs.

—The Wright Brothers Advanced Level. 3rd ed. 2002. (Trophies Reading Program Ser.). (Illus.). pap. 5.10 (978-0-15-323033-2(9)) Harcourt Schl. Pubs.

—The Wright Brothers & the 1st Airplane. 3rd ed. 2002. (Horizons Ser.). (Illus.). (J). pap. 3.70 (978-0-15-333174-9(7)) Harcourt Schl. Pubs.

Los Hermanos Wright. 2006. (People We Should Know Ser.).Tr. of Wright Brothers. (SPA.). (J). (gr. 3-4). 4.76 (978-0-8368-4363-7(0), GHS33824) Stevens, Gareth Inc.

Hill, Lee Sullivan. The Flyer Flew! The Invention of the Airplane. Naprstek, Joel, illus. (On My Own Science Ser.). 48p. (J). 2007. pap. 5.95 (978-1-57505-855-9(3), First Avenue Editions); 2006. (gr. 2-4). lib. bdg. 25.26 (978-1-57505-758-3(1), Millbrook Pr.) Lerner Publishing Group.

Hudson, Margaret. The Wright Brothers, Set 1. 2002. (Lives & Times Ser.). (Illus.). 24p. (J). (gr. k-3). pap. 6.50 (978-1-58810-348-2(X), 91108) Heinemann Library.

Jenner, Caryn. First Flight: The Wright Brothers. 2003. (gr. k-3). lib. bdg. 11.80 (978-0-613-67328-0(X)) Tandem Library Bks.

—First Flight Vol. 4: The Story of the Wright Brothers. 2003. (DK Readers Ser.). (Illus.). 48p. (J). (gr. 5). pap. 3.99 (978-0-7894-9291-3(1)) Dorling Kindersley Publishing, Inc.

Jenner, Caryn & Dorling Kindersley Publishing Staff. First Flight: The Wright Brothers. 2003. (Readers Ser.). (Illus.). 48p. (J). 14.99 (978-0-7894-9541-9(4)) Dorling Kindersley Publishing, Inc.

Krensky, Larry. Taking Flight. 2001. (Ready-to-Read Ser.). (Illus.). (J). (978-0-606-21478-0(X)) Tandem Library Bks.

Lynch, Emma. The Wright Brothers. 2005. (Illus.). 32p. (J). (978-1-4034-6354-8(9)); pap. (978-1-4034-6368-5(9)) Heinemann Library.

MacLeod, Elizabeth. The Wright Brothers. Krystoforski, Andrej, illus. 2008. 32p. pap. (***978-1-55453-054-0(7)***) Kids Can Pr., Ltd.

MacLeod, Elizabeth. The Wright Brothers: A Flying Start. Spurll, Barbara, illus. 2004. (Snapshots Ser.). 32p. (J). (gr. 4-6). (978-1-55074-935-9(8)); (978-1-55074-933-5(1)) Kids Can Pr., Ltd.

Marsh, Carole. Wright Brothers. 2002. (One Thousand Readers Ser.). (Illus.). 12p. (J). (gr. k-4). 2.95 (978-0-635-01560-0(9)) Gallopade International.

—The Wright Brothers: An Ohio Experience Reader. 2001. (J). pap. 1.95 (978-0-635-00433-8(X)) Gallopade International.

—Wright Brothers: Orville & Wilbur. 2002. (Carole Marsh Bks.). (Illus.). 32p. (J). (gr. 3-8). 29.95 (978-0-635-01351-4(7), 13517, Marsh, Carole Bks.); pap. 5.95 (978-0-635-01350-7(9), 13509) Gallopade International.

Martin, Michael J. The Wright Brothers. 2002. (Importance of Ser.). (Illus.). 112p. (J). (gr. 7-10). 32.45 (978-1-56006-847-1(7), Lucent Bks.) Thomson Gale.

Maurer, Richard. The Wright Sister: Katharine Wright & Her Famous Brothers. rev. ed. 2003. (Illus.). 128p. (J). (gr. 5-9). 19.95 (978-0-7613-1546-9(2)) Roaring Brook Pr.

Mayo, Gretchen Will. The Wright Brothers. 2003. (Trailblazers of the Modern World Ser.). (Illus.). 48p. (J). (gr. 5 up). lib. bdg. 30.00 (978-0-8368-5094-9(7)); pap. 11.95 (978-0-8368-5254-7(0)) Stevens, Gareth Inc. (World Almanac Library).

McCormick, Lisa Wade. Wright Brothers. 2005. (Scholastic News Nonfiction Readers Ser.). (Illus.). 24p. (J). pap. (978-0-516-24786-1(7)) Children's Pr., Ltd.

—Wright Brothers. 2005. (Scholastic News Nonfiction Readers Ser.). (Illus.). 24p. (J). (gr. 1-2). 19.00 (978-0-516-24937-7(1), Children's Pr.) Scholastic Library Publishing.

McLaughlin, Kari Massie. My Adventure with the Wright Brothers. 2007. 44p. (J). 8.99 (978-1-59092-471-6(1), Orchard Academy Pr.) Windstorm Creative.

McPherson, Stephanie Sammartino & Gardner, Joseph Sammartino. Wilbur & Orville Wright: Taking Flight. 2004. (Trailblazer Biography Ser.). (Illus.). 120p. (J). 30.60 (978-1-57505-443-8(4), Carolrhoda Bks.) Lerner Publishing Group.

Niz, Xavier. The Wright Brothers & the Airplane. Erwin, Steve & Barnett, Charles, illus. 2007. 32p. (J). (978-0-7368-6845-7(3)) Capstone Publishing.

O'Hern, Kerri & Mayo, Gretchen. The Wright Brothers. 2006. (Illus.). (J). pap. (978-0-8368-6251-5(1)); 32p. lib. bdg. 26.00 (978-0-8368-6199-0(X)) Stevens, Gareth Inc. (World Almanac Library).

Old, Wendie C. To Fly: The Story of the Wright Brothers. Parker, Robert Andrew, illus. 2002. 48p. (J). (gr. 3-5). tchr. ed. 16.00 (978-0-618-13347-5(X), Clarion Bks.) Houghton Mifflin Co. Trade & Reference Div.

—The Wright Brothers: Inventors of the Airplane. 2000. (Historical American Biographies Ser.). (Illus.). 128p. (J). (gr. 6-12). lib. bdg. 26.60 (978-0-7660-1095-6(3)) Enslow Pubs., Inc.

Orr, Tamra B. The Dawn of Aviation: The Story of the Wright Brothers. 2005. (Illus.). 48p. (YA). (ps-7). lib. bdg. 29.95 (978-1-58415-396-2(2), 1244922) Mitchell Lane Pubs., Inc.

O'Sullivan, Robyn. The Wright Brothers Fly. 2007. (History Chapters Ser.). 48p. (J). (gr. 1-4). lib. bdg. 17.90 (***978-1-4263-0188-9(X)***, National Geographic Children's Bks.) National Geographic Society.

Parramore, Thomas C. Triumph at Kitty Hawk: The Wright Brothers & Powered Flight. 2003. (Coastal North Carolina Ser.). (ENG., Illus.). 123p. (gr. 8-12). reprint ed. pap. 5.00 (978-0-86526-259-1(4)) North Carolina Office of Archives & History.

Price Hossell, Karen. Kitty Hawk: The Flight of the Wright Brothers. 2003. (Point of Impact Ser.). (Illus.). 32p. (J). (gr. 5-7). lib. bdg. 25.64 (978-1-58810-907-1(0)) Heinemann Library.

Rausch, Monica. The Wright Brothers & the Airplane. 2006. (Illus.). 24p. (J). pap. (***978-0-8368-7733-5(0)***); lib. bdg. (***978-0-8368-7502-7(8)***) Stevens, Gareth Inc. (Weekly Reader Early Learning Library).

Reed, Jennifer. Wilbur & Orville Wright: Trailblazers of the Sky. 2007. (Inventors Who Changed the World Ser.). (Illus.). 128p. (J). (gr. 5). lib. bdg. 33.27 (***978-1-59845-054-5(9)***, MyReportLinks.com Bks.) Enslow Pubs., Inc.

Ryan, Bernard. The Wright Brothers: Inventors of the Airplane. 2003. (Great Life Stories Ser.). (Illus.). 128p. (J). 30.50 (978-0-531-12254-9(9), Watts, Franklin) Scholastic Library Publishing.

Schaefer, Lola M. The Wright Brothers. 2000. (Famous People in Transportation Ser.). (Illus.). 24p. (J). (gr. k-1). lib. bdg. 15.93 (978-0-7368-0549-0(4), Pebble Bks.) Capstone Pr., Inc.

—The Wright Brothers. 2005. (Transportation Ser.). 24p. (YA). (gr. k-3). pap. (978-0-7368-8733-5(4), Pebble Bks.) Capstone Pr., Inc.

Schulz, Walter A. Will y Orv (Will & Orv) Schulz, Janet A., illus. 2006. (Yo Solo - Historia (on My Own - History) Ser.). (SPA.). 48p. (J). (gr. 2-4). lib. bdg. 25.26 (978-0-8225-6263-4(4), Ediciones Lerner) Lerner Publishing Group.

Shea, Kitty. The Wright Brothers. 2004. (Compass Point Early Biographies Ser.). (Illus.). 32p. (J). (gr. 1-3). lib. bdg. 21.26 (978-0-7565-0791-6(X)) Compass Point Bks.

Smith, Robert W. The Wright Brothers. 2003. (Spotlight on America Ser.). (Illus.). 48p. pap. 8.99 (978-0-7439-3210-3(2)) Teacher Created Materials, Inc.

Sproule, Anna. The Wright Brothers. 2005. (Giants of Science Bilingual Ser.). (J). 9.95 (978-1-4103-0507-7(4)); (ENG & SPA., Illus.). 64p. (gr. 5-7). 28.70 (978-1-4103-0501-5(5)) Thomson Gale. (Blackbirch Pr., Inc.).

—The Wright Brothers: The Birth of Modern Aviation. 1999. (Giants of Science Ser.). (Illus.). 64p. (YA). (gr. 5-8). 24.95 (978-1-56711-328-0(1), Blackbirch Pr., Inc.) Thomson Gale.

Tate, Suzanne. Flyer: A Tale of the Wright Dog. Melvin, James, illus. 2003. (Suzanne Tate's History Ser.). (J). pap. 4.95 (978-1-878405-42-5(X)) Nags Head Art, Inc.

—Helping the Wright Brothers: A Tale of First Flight Helpers. Melvin, James, illus. 1999. (Suzanne Tate's History Ser.: Vol. 2). 32p. (J). pap. 4.95 (978-1-878405-25-8(X)) Nags Head Art, Inc.

Taylor-Miller, Sandra. Are We There Yet? The Wright Brothers' National Memorial Park, Kill Devil Hills, North Carolina, Site of the First Heavier-Than-Air Machine-Powered Flight. 2004. (Illus.). 56p. (J). 9.95 (978-1-887905-87-9(1)) Parkway Pubs., Inc.

Tieck, Sarah. The Wright Brothers. 2007. (First Biographies Ser.). (Illus.). 32p. (J). (gr. k-3). lib. bdg. 22.78 (978-1-59679-790-1(8)) ABDO Publishing Co.

Trailblazers of the Modern World: Louis Armstrong; Anne Frank; Martin Luther King, Jr.; Theodore Roosevelt; Gloria Steinem; The Wright Brothers, 6 bks. 2003. (Illus.). (J). (gr. 5 up). lib. bdg. 175.60 (978-0-8368-5088-8(2), World Almanac Library) Stevens, Gareth Inc.

Tucker, Mary. Wright Brothers. Mitchell, Judy, ed. Hierstein, Judith, illus. 2002. (History - Hands On! Ser.). 32p. (J). (gr. 1-4). pap. 6.95 (978-1-57310-353-4(5)) Teaching & Learning Co.

Van Steenwyk, Elizabeth. One Fine Day: A Radio Play. Farnsworth, Bill, illus. 2004. 32p. (gr. 3-5). 16.00 (978-0-8028-5234-2(3)) Eerdmans, William B. Publishing Co.

Will y Orv (Will & Orv) 2006. (J). pap. 5.95 (978-0-8225-6615-1(X), Ediciones Lerner) Lerner Publishing Group.

Wyborny, Sheila. The Wright Brothers. 2002. (Inventors & Creators Ser.). (Illus.). 48p. (J). (gr. 3-5). 18.96 (978-0-7377-1369-5(0), Kidhaven) Thomson Gale.

Yolen, Jane. My Brothers' Flying Machine: Wilbur, Orville, & Me. Burke, Jim, illus. 2003. 32p. (J). (gr. 1-4). 17.99 (978-0-316-97159-1(6)) Little, Brown Bks. for Young Readers.

WRIGHT, WILBUR, 1867-1912—FICTION

Glass, Andrew. The Wondrous Whirligig: The Wright Brothers' First Flying Machine. Glass, Andrew, illus. 2007. (Illus.). 30p. (J). reprint ed. 17.00 (***978-1-4223-6765-0(7)***) DIANE Publishing Co.

Gutman, Dan. Race for the Sky. 2003. (Illus.). 192p. (J). (gr. 3-6). 16.99 (978-0-689-84554-3(5)) Simon & Schuster Children's Publishing.

—Race for the Sky: The Kitty Hawk Diaries of Johnny Moore. l.t. ed. 2004. 299p. 22.95 (978-0-7862-6466-7(7)) Thorndike Pr.

Pease, Pamela. Ingenious: How the Curiosity of the Wright Brothers Changed the World. 2003. (Illus.). 24.00 (978-0-9669433-4-4(1)) Paintbox Pr.

Rigsby, Annelle & Raffa, Edwina. Race to Kitty Hawk. 2003. (Adventures in America Ser.). (Illus.). 84p. (J). 14.95 (978-1-893110-33-5(8)) Silver Moon Pr.

WRITERS

see Authors

WRITING

see also Alphabet; Calligraphy; Ciphers; Cryptography; Hieroglyphics; Typewriting

Activity Worksheets. 2004. (J). spiral bd. 29.95 (978-1-886441-64-4(2)) Zoo-phonics, Inc.

After School Writing Activities. (100+ Seriestm Ser.). 128p. (gr. 5 up). 12.99 (978-0-7424-1785-4(9), IFG99032) School Specialty Publishing.

Allen, Margaret. Responding to Literature: Activities That Build Confident Readers & Writers. Samoiloff, Sheri, ed. Campbell, Jenny, illus. 2002. 64p. (J). (gr. 1-3). pap. 9.99 (978-1-57471-809-6(6), CTP 3367) Creative Teaching Pr., Inc.

Amaze Us!, 6 vols. (Wildcats Ser.). 2003. (gr. 2-8). (978-0-322-02442-7(0)) Wright Group, The.

Amazing Maps: Level Q, 6 vols. (Wonder Worldtm Ser.). 48p. 39.95 (978-0-7802-2945-7(2)) Wright Group, The.

American Education Publishing Staff. I Can Write Cursive. 2001. (Illus.). 64p. (J). pap. 2.99 (978-1-56189-616-5(0), 31255, American Education Publishing) School Specialty Publishing.

Analogies 1 Grd 7-8. 2004. pap. 7.25 (978-0-8388-2225-8(8)) Educators Publishing Service, Inc.

Analogies 2 Grd 9-10. 2004. pap. 7.25 (978-0-8388-2227-2(4)) Educators Publishing Service, Inc.

Analogies 3 Grd 11-12. 2004. pap. 7.25 (978-0-8388-2229-6(0)) Educators Publishing Service, Inc.

Analogies 3 Grd 11-12 Quiz Boo. 2004. pap. 8.20 (978-0-8388-2230-2(4)) Educators Publishing Service, Inc.

Apgar, Cheryl. Layer It! Each Month: Interactive Layer Books That Promote Reading, Writing, & Listening. Samoiloff, Sheri, ed. Tom, Darcy, illus. 2002. 80p. (J). (gr. k-1). pap. 10.99 (978-1-57471-818-8(5), CTP 3372) Creative Teaching Pr., Inc.

—Layer It! With Science: Interactive Layer Books that Promote Reading, Writing, & Listening. Samoiloff, Sheri, ed. Tom, Darcy, illus. 2002. 80p. (J). (gr. k-1). pap. 10.99 (978-1-57471-817-1(7), CTP 3373) Creative Teaching Pr., Inc.

Aprende a Escribir. 2003. (SPA.). 22p. (J). (ps-1). (978-968-5308-89-2(6), Silver Dolphin en Español) Advanced Marketing, S. de R. L. de C. V.

Arnold, Clareen. Handwriting - Contemporary Cursive. 2003. (Skill Builders Ser.). 80p. 2.95 (978-1-887923-07-1(1)) Rainbow Bridge Publishing.

—Handwriting - Modern Manuscript. 2003. (Skill Builders Ser.). 80p. 2.95 (978-1-932210-26-2(1)) Rainbow Bridge Publishing.

—Handwriting - Traditional Manuscript. 2003. (Skill Builders Ser.). 80p. 2.95 (978-1-887923-01-9(2)) Rainbow Bridge Publishing.

The Art of Calligraphy. 2004. (Classic Craft Cases Ser.). (Illus.). 64p. (978-1-84229-800-8(3)) Top That! Publishing PLC.

Ashton, Christine. The Genie of the Bike Lamp: Level P, 6 vols. 128p. (gr. 6 up). 36.95 (978-0-322-05892-7(9)) Wright Group, The.

Asp, et al. Spectrum Writing, Grade 6. 2002. (Starburst Spectrum Ser.). (Illus.). 128p. (J). (gr. 6 up). pap. 8.95 (978-1-56189-936-4(4) , American Education Publishing) School Specialty Publishing.

Auman, Maureen E. Step up to Writing. 2nd ed. 2002. 448p. ring bd. (978-1-57035-457-1(X) , 126STEP2) Sopris West Educational Services.

Barbie Kindergarten Learning Pads: Basic Reading & Writing. 2004. (Illus.). 48p. (J). (978-0-7666-0612-8(0) , 49870) Modern Publishing.

Barchowsky, Nan Jay. Beginners' Handwriting. Barchowsky, Paul, illus. 2002. 60p. (J). (ps-1). 27.95 (978-0-9656745-6-0(8)) Swansbury, Inc.

Barroux & Encarnacion, Elizabeth. I Spy an Eye: Mr. Potato Head Body Book. 2005. (My Little Chalkboard Ser.: No. 5). (Illus.). 20p. (J). pap. 12.95 (978-0-7624-1982-1(2) , Running Pr. Kids) Running Pr. Bk. Pubs.

Begin to Write. 2002. (First Steps Reading Ser.). 24p. (J). pap. 3.95 (978-0-7894-8488-8(9)) Dorling Kindersley Publishing, Inc.

Bell & Wheeler. Learning Grammar Through Writi. 2004. pap. 10.35 (978-0-8388-1493-2(X)) Educators Publishing Service, Inc.

Beyond the Beyond, 6 vols. (Wildcats Ser.). 32p. (gr. 2-8). (978-0-322-02444-1(7)) Wright Group, The.

Bible-Themed Cursive Writing Practice. 2003. (Illus.). 48p. 7.99 (978-0-7439-7030-3(6)) Teacher Created Materials, Inc.

BJU Staff. Handwriting Worktext Grd 2. 2004. pap. 11.50 (978-1-57924-103-2(4)) Jones, Bob Univ. Pr.

—Handwriting Worktext Grd 3. 2004. pap. 11.50 (978-1-57924-215-2(4)) Jones, Bob Univ. Pr.

—Handwriting Worktext Grd 4. 2004. pap. 11.50 (978-1-57924-263-3(4)) Jones, Bob Univ. Pr.

—Handwriting Worktext Grd 5. 2004. pap. 11.50 (978-1-57924-298-5(7)) Jones, Bob Univ. Pr.

—Handwriting Worktext Grd 6. 2004. pap. 11.50 (978-1-57924-352-4(5)) Jones, Bob Univ. Pr.

Blaxland, Wendy. My Sandwich: Emergent. Jurevicius, Luke, illus. 2002. (Bright Sparks Ser.). 16p. pap. 2.30 (978-0-521-75118-6(7)) Cambridge Univ. Pr.

—Near the Coral Reef: Emergent. Tilders, Loma, illus. 2002. (Bright Sparks Ser.). 16p. pap. 2.30 (978-0-521-75116-2(0)) Cambridge Univ. Pr.

—New School. 2002. (Bright Sparks Ser.). (Illus.). 16p. pap. 2.30 (978-0-521-75400-2(3)) Cambridge Univ. Pr.

Bradshaw, Georgine & Wrighton, Charlene. Basic Kit - Kindergarten. Clark, Irene, illus. 2005. Orig. Title: Basic Kit II. (J). 249.95 (978-1-886441-31-6(6)) Zoo-phonics, Inc.

—Kindergarten Zoo-per Kit. Clark, Irene, illus. 2005. (J). 499.95 (978-1-886441-34-7(0) , ZOP4219) Zoo-phonics, Inc.

—Preschool Zoo-per Kit. Clark, Irene, illus. 2005. (J). 449.95 (978-1-886441-32-3(4) , ZOP4218) Zoo-phonics, Inc.

Bright & Beyond - Writing. 2004. (J). (978-0-9726170-9-3(4)) Pal Toys, LLC.

Brown Conroy, Erin. Writing Skillbuilders Bk. 1: A Fun-Filled Book of Prewriting Skills for Beginning Writers. 2004. (J). spiral bd. 14.95 (978-0-9740981-6-6(7)) Celtic Cross Communications.

—Writing Skillbuilders Bk. 2: A Fun-Filled Activity Book to Build Strong Handwriting Skills. 2004. (J). spiral bd. 14.95 (978-0-9740981-7-3(5)) Celtic Cross Communications.

—Writing Skillbuilders Bk. 3: A Fun-Filled Activity Book for Beautiful Cursive Handwriting. 2004. (J). spiral bd. 14.95 (978-0-9740981-8-0(3)) Celtic Cross Communications.

Budgell, Gill & Ruttle, Kate. Penpals for Handwriting Years 5/6. 2005. (Illus.). 16p. cd-rom 155.00 (978-1-84565-106-0(5)) Cambridge Univ. Pr.

Bukiet, Suzanne. Scripts of the World. 2nd ed. (Illus.). 91p. (YA). reprint ed. 19.95 (978-0-9656274-1-2(1)) Another Language Pr.

Burke, Mary F. Four Square: The Personal Writing Coach, Grades 1-3. Radtke, Becky, illus. 2005. 112p. (J). pap. 12.95 (978-1-57310-446-3(9)) Teaching & Learning Co.

Callella, Trisha. Daily Writing Warm-ups: A Systematic Approach to Writing Practice. Faulkner, Stacey, ed. Tom, Darcy, illus. 2006. (J). pap. 13.99 (***978-1-59198-306-4(1)***) Creative Teaching Pr., Inc.

—Daily Writing Warm-ups: A Systematic Approach to Writingt Practice. Dobelmann, Colleen & Hamaguchi, Colleen, eds. 2006. (SAM.). (J). pap. 13.99 (***978-1-59198-307-1(X)***) Creative Teaching Pr., Inc.

Center for Learning Network Staff. Advanced Placement Writing 1: Strategies for Honors, Gifted, & AP Students. 1999. (English Ser.). 286p. (YA). (gr. 11-12). spiral bd. 39.95 (978-1-56077-602-4(1)) Ctr. for Learning, The.

Charlesworth, Liza. 100 Awesome Writing Prompts to Use with Any Book! Fun, Thought-provoking Questions That Inspire Kids to Write Meaningfully about Character, Plot, Setting, Theme & More. 2001. 56p. (gr. 3). pap. 9.95 (978-0-439-22723-0(2)) Scholastic, Inc.

Cheaney, Janie B. Wordsmith Craftsman Grd 10 + 2004. pap. 16.00 (978-1-929683-20-8(0)) Colbert Hse., The.

—Wordsmith Grd 7-9. 2004. pap. 16.00 (978-1-929683-18-5(9)) Colbert Hse., The.

Claire, Elizabeth. Hi! (Illus.). (J). wbk. ed. (978-0-8056-0122-0(8)) Minerva Bks., Ltd.

Clarke, Jacqueline. Teaching Reading & Writing with Song: Irresistible Pocket Chart Activities, Picture Cards & Props, Read & Write Mini-Books, & More. 2003. 64p. (gr. k-2). pap. 11.99 (978-0-439-39512-0(7) , Teaching Resources) Scholastic, Inc.

Conflict Resolution: High-Interest Stories That Encourage Critical Thinking, Creative Writing, & Dialogue. 80p. (gr. 5-8). 9.99 (978-0-7424-0180-8(4) , IF19212) School Specialty Publishing.

Conlin, Mary. Patterns Plus: A Short Prose Reader with Argumentation. 8th ed. 2004. (Illus.). 337p. (YA). 47.96 (978-0-618-42119-0(X) , 310984) Houghton Mifflin College Div.

Coon, Nora E. Teen Dream Jobs: How to Find the Job You Really Want! 2004. (Illus.). 132p. (YA). (gr. 6-12). pap. (978-1-58270-093-9(1)) Beyond Words Publishing, Inc.

Cooper, Terry, ed. Pre-Writing Practice Pages: 40 Irresistible Picture Pages That Help Children Develop the Fine Motor Skills They Need for Handwriting Success. 2004. 48p. pap. 10.99 (978-0-439-57622-2(9)) Scholastic, Inc.

Crusius, Timothy & Channell, Carolyn. Aims of Argument: Text & Reader with Student Access to Catalyst. 5th rev. ed. 2005. (C). pap. 63.44 (978-0-07-320196-2(0) , 9780073201962, McGraw-Hill Humanities, Social Sciences & World Languages) McGraw-Hill Higher Education.

Culham, Ruth & Wheeler, Amanda. 40 Reproducible Forms for the Writing Traits Classroom: Checklists, Rubrics & Scoring Sheets, Graphic Organizers, & More to Boost Students' Writing Skills in All Seven Traits. 2003. 64p. pap. 13.99 (978-0-439-55684-2(8) , Teaching Resources) Scholastic, Inc.

Cummings, Renee. Handwriting Workout: Cursive. 2000. (100+ Seriestm Ser.). 128p. (J). (gr. k-6). pap. 12.99 (978-1-56822-907-2(0) , IF8734) School Specialty Publishing.

—Handwriting Workout: Manuscript. 2000. (100+ Seriestm Ser.). 128p. (J). (gr. k-6). pap. 12.99 (978-1-56822-906-5(2) , IF8733) School Specialty Publishing.

Cummings, Renee & Lowe Wilke, Suzanne. Hand Writing - Modern Manuscript. 1999. (100+ Seriestm Ser.). 128p. (J). (gr. k-6). pap. 12.99 (978-0-88012-850-6(X) , IF8737) School Specialty Publishing.

—Hand Writing - Traditional Manuscript. 1999. (100+ Seriestm Ser.). 128p. (J). (gr. k-6). pap. 12.99 (978-0-88012-825-4(9) , IF8735) School Specialty Publishing.

Cursive D Staff. Reason for Handwriting Gr 4. 2004. pap. 11.99 (978-0-936785-42-4(X)) Concerned Communications.

Cursive F Staff. Reason for Handwriting Gr 6. 2004. pap. 11.99 (978-0-936785-44-8(6)) Concerned Communications.

Cursive Handwriting - Modern. 2005. (Kelley Wingate Ser.). 80p. (J). per. 2.99 (978-1-59441-156-4(5) , CD-104074) Carson-Dellosa Publishing Co., Inc.

Cursive Handwriting - Traditional. 2005. (Kelley Wingate Ser.). 80p. (J). per. 2.99 (978-1-59441-157-1(3) , CD-104075) Carson-Dellosa Publishing Co., Inc.

Cyberspace, 6 vols. (Wildcats Ser.). 32p. (gr. 2-8). (978-0-322-00600-3(7)) Wright Group, The.

Daily Writing Activities. 24p. (gr. 1 up). 5.99 (978-0-7682-0565-7(4) , FS8480); (gr. 1 up). 3.99 (978-0-7682-0819-1(X) , FS194118); (gr. 2 up). 5.99 (978-0-7682-0566-4(2) , FS8481); (gr. 3 up). 5.99 (978-0-7682-0567-1(0) , FS8482) Schaffer, Frank Pubns.

Dalmatian Press Staff. Cursive Writing. 2003. (Tools Ser.). 32p. (J). (gr. 3-4). pap. 2.29 (978-1-57759-198-6(4)) Dalmatian Pr.

—Cursive Writing: Practice Tablet. 2003. (Home Learning Tools Ser.). 32p. (J). (gr. 3-4). pap. 2.99 (978-1-57759-233-4(6)) Dalmatian Pr.

—Easy Wipe-Off Cursive Writing. 2003. (Easy Wipe-Off Ser.). 16p. (J). (gr. 3-4). pap., wbk. ed. 2.99 (978-1-57759-295-2(6)) Dalmatian Pr.

—Easy Wipe-Off Cursive Writing. 2002. (Illus.). 16p. (J). (gr. 3-4). pap. 2.99 (978-1-57759-130-6(5)) Dalmatian Pr.

Davidson, Kay. Writing the Simple 6(TM) A Writing Rubic for Kids. 2004. pap. 28.95 (978-1-931334-38-9(2)) Pieces of Learning.

de Diaz, Rosario Ahumada. Juguemos con Letras: Ejercicios de Iniciacion a la Escritura. (SPA.). (J). pap. 9.95 (978-968-24-0919-6(5) , TRM40) Trillas Editorial, S. A. MEX. *Dist:* Continental Bk. Co., Inc.

De Viaje! 2000. (Spanish Writing Handbooks Ser.). (SPA.). (gr. 1-6). 27.21 (978-0-7362-0713-3(9)); tchr. ed., tchr.'s training gde. ed. 26.50 (978-0-7362-0716-4(3)) Hampton-Brown Bks.

Desk Tapes: Cursive. 1999. (gr. 2-4). 9.95 (978-0-673-36028-1(8) , Scott Foresman) Addison-Wesley Educational Pubs., Inc.

Desk Tapes: Manuscript. 1999. (gr. k-3). 9.95 (978-0-673-36029-8(6) , Scott Foresman) Addison-Wesley Educational Pubs., Inc.

Dinosaur Detective: 6 Each of 1 Anthology, 6 vols. (Wildcats Ser.). 32p. (gr. 2-8). (978-0-322-00586-0(8)) Wright Group, The.

D'Nealian Handwriting: Practice Paper. 1999. (gr. 1-3). suppl. ed. 6.75 (978-0-673-59154-8(9) , Scott Foresman) Addison-Wesley Educational Pubs., Inc.

D'Nealian Handwriting Re-Write Cards: Cursive. 1999. 18.95 (978-0-673-36364-0(3)) Addison-Wesley Educational Pubs., Inc.

D'Nealian Handwriting Re-Write Cards: Ruled. 1999. (Illus.). suppl. ed. 18.95 (978-0-673-36365-7(1) , Scott Foresman) Addison-Wesley Educational Pubs., Inc.

Donoughue, Carol. The Story of Writing. 2007. (Illus.). 48p. (J). (gr. 4-12). 19.95 (***978-1-55407-306-1(5)***) Firefly Bks., Ltd.

Dot-to-Dot Stories: Creative Activities for Beginning Writers. 64p. (gr. k-3). 9.99 (978-0-7682-0311-0(2) , FE11022, Totline Pubns.) Schaffer, Frank Pubns.

Douglas, Vincent. The Complete Book of Handwriting. 2002. (Complete Book Ser.). (Illus.). 352p. (J). (gr. k-6). pap., wbk. ed. 14.95 (978-1-56189-382-9(X) , American Education Publishing) School Specialty Publishing.

Douglas, Vincent & School Specialty Publishing Staff. Every Child Can Write Cursive. 2002. (Every Child Can Write Ser.). (Illus.). 128p. (J). (gr. 2-4). pap. 8.99 (978-1-57768-477-0(X) , Instructional Fair) Schaffer, Frank Pubns.

—I Can Practice Printing. 2002. (I Can... Ser.). (Illus.). 128p. (J). pap. 3.95 (978-0-7696-2856-1(7) , American Education Publishing) School Specialty Publishing.

—I Can Practice Writing Cursive. 2002. (I Can... Ser.). (Illus.). 128p. (J). pap. 3.95 (978-0-7696-2858-5(3) , American Education Publishing) School Specialty Publishing.

—I Can Print. 2002. (I Can... Ser.). (Illus.). 128p. (J). pap. 3.95 (978-0-7696-2855-4(9) , American Education Publishing) School Specialty Publishing.

—I Can Write Cursive. 2002. (I Can... Ser.). (Illus.). 128p. (J). pap. 3.95 (978-0-7696-2857-8(5) , American Education Publishing) School Specialty Publishing.

—Practice Cursive Writing. 2002. (Edu-Slates Ser.). (Illus.). 1p. (J). 2.99 (978-1-57768-996-6(8) , Brighter Child) School Specialty Publishing.

—Spectrum Writing, Grade 1. 2002. (Starburst Spectrum Workbook Ser.). (Illus.). 128p. (J). (gr. 1 up). pap. 8.95 (978-1-56189-931-9(3) , American Education Publishing) School Specialty Publishing.

—Spectrum Writing, Grade 2. 2002. (Starburst Spectrum Ser.). (Illus.). 128p. (J). (gr. 2 up). pap. 8.95 (978-1-56189-932-6(1) , American Education Publishing) School Specialty Publishing.

—Spectrum Writing, Grade 3. 2002. (Starburst Spectrum Workbook Ser.). (Illus.). 128p. (J). (gr. 3 up). pap. 8.95 (978-1-56189-933-3(X) , American Education Publishing) School Specialty Publishing.

—Spectrum Writing, Grade 4. 2002. (Starburst Spectrum Ser.). (Illus.). 128p. (J). (gr. 4 up). pap. 8.95 (978-1-56189-934-0(8) , American Education Publishing) School Specialty Publishing.

—Spectrum Writing, Grade 5. 2002. (Starburst Spectrum Workbook Ser.). (Illus.). 128p. (J). (gr. 5 up). pap. 8.95 (978-1-56189-935-7(6) , American Education Publishing) School Specialty Publishing.

—Spectrum Writing, Grade 7. 2002. (Starburst Spectrum Ser.). (Illus.). 128p. (YA). (gr. 7 up). pap. 8.95 (978-1-56189-937-1(2) , American Education Publishing) School Specialty Publishing.

—Spectrum Writing, Grade 8. 2002. (Starburst Spectrum Ser.). (Illus.). 128p. (YA). (gr. 8 up). pap. 8.95 (978-1-56189-938-8(0) , American Education Publishing) School Specialty Publishing.

Dwyer, Carol. Cursive Writing. 2004. 64p. (Orig.). (J). (gr. 3-4). pap. 3.79 (978-1-58947-398-0(1)) School Zone Publishing Co.

Dwyer, Carolyn. Cursive Writing 3-4. 2001. (Teacher Edition Wkbks.). (Illus.). 32p. (J). (gr. 3-4). pap., tchr. ed. 3.99 (978-0-88743-399-3(5) , 02868) School Zone Publishing Co.

E. Mason Design Inc. Staff, illus. Meet Jazzy & Kitty: Color Me Cards, , No. 5. 2001. Orig. Title: Color Me Cards. (J). pap. 5.95 (978-1-933075-02-0(3)) Mason, E. Design, Inc.

Early Stage 2 Models for Writing. 2003. 135.95 (978-0-673-77820-8(7)) Celebration Pr.

Early Stage 2 Shared Writing Templates. 2003. 135.95 (978-0-673-77821-5(5)) Celebration Pr.

Einhorn, Kama. Cursive Writing Made Easy & Fun! 2000. (Illus.). 112p. pap. 12.95 (978-0-439-11369-4(5)) Scholastic, Inc.

Einhorn, Kama & Einhorn, Karma. Cursive Writing Practice Pages with a Twist! Dozens of Super Reproducible Activities That Help Kids Polish Their Handwriting - While Having Fun! 2002. (Illus.). 64p. pap. 11.95 (978-0-439-31663-7(4) , Teaching Resources) Scholastic, Inc.

Emergent Stage 1 Models for Writing. 2003. 135.95 (978-0-673-77818-5(5)) Celebration Pr.

Emergent Stage 1 Shared Writing Templates. 2003. 135.95 (978-0-673-77819-2(3)) Celebration Pr.

English I: Language Skills, Chapter 3 Activities. 2005. (Illus.). 54p. (YA). pap. 5.00 (978-1-59476-139-3(6)) Paradigm Accelerated Curriculum.

Every Child Can Write Manuscript. 2002. (Every Child Can Write Ser.). (Illus.). 128p. (J). (gr. k-2). pap. 8.99 (978-1-57768-478-7(8)) School Specialty Publishing.

Fearless Creative Writing Workbook. 2002. 7.00 (978-0-9710121-2-7(1)) Olowotot Productions.

Feldgus, Eileen G. & Cardonick, Isabell. Kid Writing: A Systematic Approach to Phonics, Journals, & Writing Workshop. 2nd rev. ed. 192p. (gr. k-2). pap. 26.50 (978-0-322-06435-5(X)) Wright Group, The.

Festival Fun: 6 Each of 1 Anthology, 6 vols. (Wildcatstm Ser.). 32p. (gr. 2-8). (978-0-322-02424-3(2)) Wright Group, The.

Fifty Ideas to Boost Writing in your Classroom 3-5. 2004. (J). per. 8.99 (978-0-88724-276-2(6) , CD-104012) Carson-Dellosa Publishing Co., Inc.

Fifty Ideas to Boost Writing in Your Classroom K-2. 2004. (J). per. 8.99 (978-0-88724-275-5(8) , CD-104011) Carson-Dellosa Publishing Co., Inc.

Fine, Jil. Writing in Ancient India. 2003. (Writing in the Ancient World Ser.). (Illus.). 24p. (J). lib. bdg. 17.25 (978-0-8239-6508-3(2) , PowerKids Pr.) Rosen Publishing Group, Inc., The.

Finn, Perdita. Julie of the Wolves: Everything You Need for Sucessful Literature Circles That Get Kids Thinking, Talking, Writing-and Loving Literature. 2001. (Literature Circle Guides Ser.). (Illus.). 32p. (gr. 4-8). pap. 5.95 (978-0-439-04390-8(5)) Scholastic, Inc.

—Teaching Memoir Writing: 20 Easy Mini-lessons & Thought-Provoking Activities That Inspire Kids. 1999. (Illus.). 48p. pap. 10.95 (978-0-439-04390-8(5)) Scholastic, Inc.

Fire! Fire! 6 Each of 1 Anthology, 6 vols. (Wildcats Ser.). 32p. (gr. 2-8). (978-0-322-00581-5(7)) Wright Group, The.

FitzGerald, Elizabeth. Cursive First: An Introduction to Cursive Penmanship. 2nd ed. 2003. (Illus.). pap. 14.95 (978-0-9744920-1-8(9)) LITHBTH Educational Services.

Fletcher, Ralph J. Live Writing: Breathing Life into Your Words. 1999. (gr. 3-6). lib. bdg. 14.15 (978-0-613-81411-9(8)) Tandem Library Bks.

Fluency Stage 3 Shared Writing Templates. 2003. 125.50 (978-0-673-77822-2(3)) Celebration Pr.

Franco, Betsy. 15 Wonderful Writing Prompt Mini-Books: Reproducible Mini-Books with Instant Prompts & Story Frames That Invite Kids to Write about Themselves & Create Fun Stories. 2001. 64p. (gr. 1). pap. 10.95 (978-0-439-26277-4(1)) Scholastic, Inc.

Fredericks, Anthony D. & Lynott, Vicky. Write to Comprehend: Using Writing as a Tool to Build Reading Comprehension. 2007. 144p. pap. 19.95 (***978-1-59647-120-7(4)***) Good Year Bks.

Fredrich, Volker, illus. Rechtschreibtraining fuer die 1. Klasse. (Duden-Lernminuten Ser.). (GER.). 32p. (J). wbk. ed. (978-3-411-70831-4(X)) Bibliographisches Institut & F. A. Brockhaus AG DEU. *Dist:* International Bk. Import Service, Inc.

—Rechtschreibtraining fuer die 1. und 2. Klasse. (Duden-Lernminuten Ser.). (GER.). 32p. (J). wbk. ed. (978-3-411-70841-3(7)) Bibliographisches Institut & F. A. Brockhaus AG DEU. *Dist:* International Bk. Import Service, Inc.

French, Vivian. Write Around the World. Collins, Ross, illus. 1998. (J). (gr. k-4). (978-1-84089-025-9(8) , Zero to Ten, Limited) Evans Publishing Group.

Fun-to-Learn: Ready for Writing. (Homework Booklets Ser.). 80p. (gr. k-1). 2.99 (978-0-7424-0261-4(4) , IF0417) School Specialty Publishing.

Get Smart Skills Staff. PSSA Writing: Pennsylvania System of School Assessment. 2004. 192p. (gr. 11 up). pap. 14.95 (978-1-932635-29-4(7)) Webster House Publishing LLC.

Gibbons, Casey Hartley. A Girl's Life with God. 2006. 160p. pap. 8.99 (978-1-56309-757-7(5) , N034115) New Hope Pubs.

Globe-Fearon Staff. Writing for Proficiency, Level C. 1998. (Writing Proficiency Ser.). (J). (gr. 10-12). (978-0-8359-2148-0(4)) Globe Fearon Educational Publishing.

—Writing for Proficiency LB Class, Level B. 1998. (J). (gr. 5-6). (978-0-8359-2147-3(6)) Globe Fearon Educational Publishing.

Golden Books Staff. I Can Print. 1999. (Step Ahead Workbooks Ser.). (Illus.). 32p. (J). (gr. k-1). pap. 2.99 (978-0-307-03554-7(9) , 03554, Golden Bks.) Random Hse. Children's Bks.

Good Apple. Writing & Thinking Skills: Paragraphs & Composition. 2001. 120p. (J). (gr. 5-8). pap. 14.99 (978-0-7682-0327-1(9) , GA13058) School Specialty Publishing.

—Writing & Thinking Skills: Sentence Writing. 2001. 160p. (J). (gr. 5-8). pap. 16.99 (978-0-7682-0326-4(0) , GA13057) School Specialty Publishing.

Good Year Books Staff. D'Nealian Handwriting Re-Write Cards: Manuscript. 1999. (gr. k-2). 18.95 (978-0-673-36363-3(5) , Scott Foresman) Addison-Wesley Educational Pubs., Inc.

Gould, Judith S. & Burke, Mary F. Four Square: The Personal Writing Coach, Grades 4-6. Ginger Illustration, illus. 2005. 112p. (J). pap. 12.95 (978-1-57310-447-0(7)) Teaching & Learning Co.

—Four Square: The Personal Writing Coach, Grades 7-9. Wheeler, Ron, illus. 2005. 112p. (J). pap. 12.95 (978-1-57310-448-7(5)) Teaching & Learning Co.

Gould, Judith S. & Gould, Evan Jay. Four Square: A Companion to the Four Square Writing Method: Writing in the Content Areas for Grades 1-4. Mitchell, Judy, ed. Radtke, Becky J., illus. 2004. 112p. (J). pap. 11.95 (978-1-57310-421-0(3)) Teaching & Learning Co.

—Four Square: A Companion to the Four Square Writing Method: Writing in the Content Areas for Grades 5-9. Mitchell, Judy, ed. Wheeler, Ron, illus. 2004. 112p. (J). pap. 11.95 (978-1-57310-422-7(1)) Teaching & Learning Co.

Group/McGraw-Hill, Wright. Babies: Collection 1. (Storyteller Interactive Writing Cards Ser.). (gr. k-3). (978-0-322-09361-4(9)) Wright Group, The.

—Bad News Good News: Level N, 6 vols. 128p. (gr. 3-6). 36.95 (978-0-322-06733-2(2)) Wright Group, The.

—The Butterfly: Collection 2. (Storyteller Interactive Writing Cards Ser.). (gr. k-3). (978-0-322-09335-5(X)) Wright Group, The.

—Cats: Collection 4. (Storyteller Interactive Writing Cards Ser.). (gr. k-3). (978-0-322-09323-2(6)) Wright Group, The.

—Early Fluency-Fluency Writing Kit. 2004. (Wright Group Literacy Ser.). (gr. k-3). 132.50 (978-0-322-07021-9(X)) Wright Group, The.

—Emergent Writing Kit. 2004. (Wright Group Literacy Ser.). (gr. k-3). 79.50 (978-0-322-06615-1(8)) Wright Group, The.

—Five Little Frogs: Collection 1. (Storyteller Interactive Writing Cards Ser.). (gr. k-3). (978-0-322-09363-8(5)) Wright Group, The.

—Fun with Fizz & Frost: Level O, 6 vols. 128p. (gr. 3-6). 36.95 (978-0-322-06725-7(1)) Wright Group, The.

—In the Rain Forest, 6 vols. (Wildcats Ser.). 32p. (gr. 2-8). (978-0-322-00599-0(X)) Wright Group, The.

—Mischief & Mayhem: Level O, 6 vols. 128p. (gr. 3-6). 36.95 (978-0-322-06727-1(8)) Wright Group, The.

—Move it & Shake It! 6 Each of 1 Anthology, 6 vols. (Wildcats Ser.). 32p. (gr. 2-8). (978-0-322-05621-3(7)) Wright Group, The.

W X Y Z

—Movie Magic, 6 vols. (Wildcats Ser.). 32p. (gr. 2-8). (978-0-322-05630-5(6)) Wright Group, The.

—The Music Scene, 6 vols. (Wildcats Ser.). 32p. (gr. 2-8). (978-0-322-05631-2(4)) Wright Group, The.

—On the Prowl: 6 Each of 1 Anthology, 6 vols. (Wildcatstm Ser.). 32p. (gr. 2-8). (978-0-322-05852-1(X)) Wright Group, The.

—The Party: Collection 1. (Storyteller Interactive Writing Cards Ser.). (gr. k-3). (978-0-322-09364-5(3)) Wright Group, The.

—Pigeon Princess: Level O, 6 vols. 128p. (gr. 3-6). 36.95 (978-0-322-06729-5(4)) Wright Group, The.

—Pixels & Paint, 6 vols. (Wildcats Ser.). 32p. (gr. 2-8). (978-0-322-05625-1(X)) Wright Group, The.

—Ready, Set, Pop! Collection 3. (Storyteller Interactive Writing Cards Ser.). (gr. k-3). (978-0-322-09348-5(1)) Wright Group, The.

—The Riddle of the Seaplanes: Level S, 6 vols. 128p. (gr. 6 up). 36.95 (978-0-322-06739-4(1)) Wright Group, The.

—River Wild: 6 Each of 1 Anthology, 6 vols. (Wildcats Ser.). 32p. (gr. 2-8). (978-0-322-05857-6(0)) Wright Group, The.

—The Salad: Collection 1. (Storyteller Interactive Writing Cards Ser.). (gr. k-3). (978-0-322-09366-9(X)) Wright Group, The.

—Sand: Collection 3. (Storyteller Interactive Writing Cards Ser.). (gr. k-3). (978-0-322-09349-2(X)) Wright Group, The.

—Slimed! 6 Each of 1 Anthology, 6 vols. (Wildcats Ser.). 32p. (gr. 2-8). (978-0-322-05853-8(8)) Wright Group, The.

—Tiger Level: Adventure Journal Set. (Wildcats Ser.). (gr. 2-8). 31.95 (978-0-322-05790-6(6)) Wright Group, The.

—Tiger Level: Lesson Plan Set. (Wildcats Ser.). (gr. 2-8). 96.50 (978-0-322-06677-9(8)) Wright Group, The.

—Tiger Level: Wildcats Tiger Complete Kit. (Wildcats Ser.). (gr. 2-8). 599.95 (978-0-322-06483-6(X)) Wright Group, The.

—What Sport Is It? Collection 3. (Storyteller Interactive Writing Cards Ser.). (gr. k-3). (978-0-322-09352-2(X)) Wright Group, The.

—Working Like a Dog: 6 Each of 1 Anthology, 6 vols. (Wildcats Ser.). 32p. (gr. 2-8). (978-0-322-05854-5(6)) Wright Group, The.

—Young & Wild: 6 Each of 1 Anthology, 6 vols. (Wildcatstm Ser.). 32p. (gr. 2-8). (978-0-322-05851-4(1)) Wright Group, The.

—Zoo Tales: 6 Each of 1 Anthology, 6 vols. (Wildcats Ser.). 32p. (gr. 2-8). (978-0-322-05856-9(2)) Wright Group, The.

—The 13th Floor: Level O, 6 vols. 128p. (gr. 3-6). 36.95 (978-0-322-06731-8(6)) Wright Group, The.

Grundon, Holly & Novelli, Joan. Smartpads Handwriting: 40 Fun Games to Help Kids Master Handwriting. 2005. 48p. pap. 7.99 (978-0-439-72078-6(8) , Teaching Resources) Scholastic, Inc.

Hablitzel, Marie & Stitzer, Kim H. Draw Write Now Bk. 6: Animal Habitats - On Land, Ponds & Rivers, Oceans. Hablitzel, Marie & Stitzer, Kim H., illus. 1999. (Draw Write Now Ser.). (Illus.). 64p. (J). (gr. k-5). pap. 10.95 (978-0-9639307-6-7(1)) Barker Creek Publishing, Inc.

—Draw Write Now Bk. 8: Animals of the World: Grassland & Desert Animals. Hablitzel, Marie & Stitzer, Kim H., illus. 2001. (Draw Write Now Ser.). (Illus.). 64p. (J). (gr. k-5). pap. 10.95 (978-0-9639307-8-1(8)) Barker Creek Publishing, Inc.

Hall, Dorothy & Cunningham, Patricia. Writing Mini-Lessons for 3rd Grade: The Four-Blocks Model. 2002. (Four-Blocks Ser.). 112p. per. 17.99 (978-0-88724-815-3(2) , CD-2419) Carson-Dellosa Publishing Co., Inc.

Hall, Dorothy, et al. Writing Mini-Lessons for First Grade: The Four-Blocks Model. 2002. (Four-Blocks Ser.). (Illus.). 80p. (J). per. 17.99 (978-0-88724-813-9(6) , CD-2417) Carson-Dellosa Publishing Co., Inc.

Hall, Dorothy P. & Williams, Elaine. Predictable Charts: Shared Writing for Kindergarten & First Grade. 2001. (Four-Blocks Ser.). 80p. (gr. k-1). pap. 14.99 (978-0-88724-627-2(3) , CD-2410) Carson-Dellosa Publishing Co., Inc.

Handwriting Program for Cursiv. 2004. pap. 8.25 (978-0-8388-1706-3(8)) Educators Publishing Service, Inc.

Harcourt School Publishers Staff. All Smiles, Grade 1 Level 5. 99th ed. 1999. (Signatures Ser.). tchr. ed. 156.40 (978-0-15-310118-2(0)) Harcourt Schl. Pubs.

—Bug Surprises: Practice Book: California Edition. 3rd ed. 2002. (Trophies Reading Program Ser.). (Illus.). (J). pap. 2.00 (978-0-15-326629-4(5)) Harcourt Schl. Pubs.

—Cave Painting to E-Mail Advanced Level: The Evolution of Wriring. 3rd ed. 2002. (Trophies Reading Program Ser.). (Illus.). pap. 5.10 (978-0-15-323489-7(X)) Harcourt Schl. Pubs.

—Collections: TAAS Preparation Book for Reading & Writing. 2000. (Illus.). (J). (gr. 1). pap. 5.90 (978-0-15-320193-6(2)); (J). (gr. 2). pap. 6.70 (978-0-15-320194-3(0)); (J). (gr. 3). pap. 6.70 (978-0-15-320195-0(9)); (gr. 4). pap. 8.30 (978-0-15-320196-7(7)); (gr. 5). pap. 8.30 (978-0-15-320197-4(5)) Harcourt Schl. Pubs.

—Collections, Grade 6: Reading & Writing Skills: Standardized Test Preparation. 2001. (Trophies Ser.). (gr. 6 up). pap., tchr. ed. 22.50 (978-0-15-321233-8(0)) Harcourt Schl. Pubs.

—Full Sails, Grade 1 Level 4. 99th ed. 1999. (Signatures Ser.). tchr. ed. 156.40 (978-0-15-310117-5(2)) Harcourt Schl. Pubs.

—Harcourt Handwriting, Grade 2: Docutech Teachers Edition & Resource Book. 88th ed. 1999. pap. 112.20 (978-0-15-319178-7(3)) Harcourt Schl. Pubs.

—Harcourt Handwriting, Grade 5: Docutech Teacher's Edition & Resourcebook. 88th ed. 1999. pap. 112.20 (978-0-15-319179-4(1)) Harcourt Schl. Pubs.

—Rhythm & Rhyme, Grade K Level 1. 99th ed. 1998. (Signatures Ser.). tchr. ed. 140.90 (978-0-15-310113-7(X)) Harcourt Schl. Pubs.

—Signatures: Practice Book. 99th ed. 1999. (Illus.). pap. 9.50 (978-0-15-310899-0(1)); (gr. k-1). pap., tchr. ed. 24.00 (978-0-15-310900-3(9)); Bk. 1. (gr. 3). pap., tchr. ed. 24.00 (978-0-15-310823-5(1)); Bk. 1-3. (gr. 1). pap., tchr. ed. 26.70 (978-0-15-310822-8(3)) Harcourt Schl. Pubs.

—Signatures: Take-Home Book. 1998. (Illus.). (gr. 4). pap. 10.50 (978-0-15-307476-9(0)); 99th ed. pap. 10.50 (978-0-15-310838-9(X)) Harcourt Schl. Pubs.

—Signatures Bk. 1: Practice Book. 1999. (Illus.). (J). (gr. 3). pap. 7.20 (978-0-15-310821-1(5)) Harcourt Schl. Pubs.

—Signatures Bk. 1-3: Practice Book. 99th ed. 1999. (Illus.). (gr. 1). pap. 11.30 (978-0-15-310820-4(7)) Harcourt Schl. Pubs.

Hazan, Maurice, creator. Escribamos: The Spanish Writing Game. 2000. (SPA.). (J). 175.00 (978-1-932770-50-6(X) , SG11) Symtalk, Inc.

—Escrivons: Introduction to Writing in French. 2000. (FRE.). (J). 175.00 (978-1-932770-66-7(6) , FG11) Symtalk, Inc.

Headley, Shannon. Writing Organizers. 2004. 120p. (J). per. 14.95 (978-0-9760534-1-5(1)) MK Publishing.

Heller, Lora. I Want ... Teaching Your Baby to Sign. 2006. (Baby Fingers Ser.). (Illus.). 24p. (J). bds. 4.95 (978-1-4027-3168-6(X)) Sterling Publishing Co., Inc.

—I'm Feeling . . . Teaching Your Baby to Sign. 2006. (Baby Fingers Ser.). (Illus.). 24p. (J). bds. 4.95 (978-1-4027-3246-1(5)) Sterling Publishing Co., Inc.

Hetzel, June. Developing Writing Fluency: Hundreds of Motivational Prompts, Vol. 2319. Hults, Alaska B., ed. Hillam, Corbin, illus. Jarrett, Michael, photos by. 2000. 64p. (J). (gr. 4-8). pap., tchr. ed. 9.99 (978-1-57471-688-7(3) , 2319) Creative Teaching Pr., Inc.

—Responding to Literature: Activities That Build Confident Readers & Writers. Samoiloff, Sheri, ed. Campbell, Jenny, illus. rev. ed. 2002. 64p. (J). (gr. 3-6). pap. 9.99 (978-1-57471-810-2(X) , CTP 3368) Creative Teaching Pr., Inc.

Hetzel, June & McIntire, Deborah. Steps to Writing Success: 28 Step-by-Step Writing Project Lesson Plans, Level 1. Fisch, Teri, ed. Flanagan, Kate, illus. 2002. 184p. (J). (gr. 1-2). pap. 17.99 (978-1-57471-821-8(5) , CTP 2267) Creative Teaching Pr., Inc.

—Steps to Writing Success: 28 Step-by-Step Writing Project Lesson Plans, Level 3. Fisch, Teri, ed. Iosa, Ann W., illus. 2002. 184p. (J). (gr. 3-4). pap. 17.99 (978-1-57471-823-2(1) , CTP 2269) Creative Teaching Pr., Inc.

Hetzel, June & Taylor, Debroah. Steps to Writing Success: 28 Step-by-Step Writing Project Lesson Plans, Level 2. Fisch, Teri, ed. Iosa, Ann W., illus. 2002. 184p. (J). (gr. 2-3). pap. 17.99 (978-1-57471-822-5(3) , CTP 2268) Creative Teaching Pr., Inc.

Hillebrandt, Ina S. The Student Prints: Educators' Guide to Pawprints Literacy Plus - the Innovative Standards-Based Literacy & Environmental Program. 2001. (Literacy Plus Program Ser.: No. 1). 88p. (gr. 1-12). spiral bd. 29.95 (978-1-880882-03-0(5)) Pawpress.

Hohenthal, K. D., creator. The Reading & Writing Connection Journal with Herman the Crab No. 1: What Is the Story About? 2003. 70p. (J). spiral bd. 15.95 (978-0-9716907-5-2(8) , Ridgewood Publishing) Ridgewood Group, The.

Holt, Rinehart and Winston Staff. Elements of Language: Active Reader's Practice Book - Grade 10. 2000. pap. 13.86 (978-0-03-064578-5(6)) Holt, Rinehart & Winston.

—Elements of Language: Active Reader's Practice Book - Grade 11. 2000. pap. 13.86 (978-0-03-064579-2(4)) Holt, Rinehart & Winston.

—Elements of Language: Active Reader's Practice Book - Grade 12. 2000. pap. 13.86 (978-0-03-064581-5(6)) Holt, Rinehart & Winston.

—Elements of Language: Active Reader's Practice Book - Grade 6. 2000. pap. 13.86 (978-0-03-064574-7(3)) Holt, Rinehart & Winston.

—Elements of Language: Active Reader's Practice Book - Grade 7. 2000. pap. 13.86 (978-0-03-064576-1(X)) Holt, Rinehart & Winston.

—Elements of Language: Active Reader's Practice Book - Grade 8. 2000. pap. 13.86 (978-0-03-064577-8(8)) Holt, Rinehart & Winston.

—Elements of Language: How-to Handbook for High School. 2000. pap. 28.40 (978-0-03-056324-9(0)) Holt, Rinehart & Winston.

—Elements of Language: How-to Handbook for Middle School. 2000. pap. 28.40 (978-0-03-056323-2(2)) Holt, Rinehart & Winston.

—Elements of Language: Language Handbook Worksheets. 1999. pap. 33.00 (978-0-03-052404-2(0)); pap. 33.00 (978-0-03-052407-3(5)) Holt, Rinehart & Winston.

—Elements of Language: Language Handbook Worksheets Answer Key. 1999. pap. 13.86 (978-0-03-052413-4(X)); pap. 13.86 (978-0-03-052412-7(1)); pap. 13.86 (978-0-03-052409-7(1)); pap. 13.86 (978-0-03-052414-1(8)); pap. 13.86 (978-0-03-052419-6(9)) Holt, Rinehart & Winston.

—Elements of Language: Literature & Communication Skills: Media - Grade 6. 2003. (Elements of Language Ser.). 148.73 (978-0-03-057398-9(X)) Holt, Rinehart & Winston.

—Elements of Language: Support & Practice - Grade 10. 2000. pap. 37.80 (978-0-03-056399-7(2)) Holt, Rinehart & Winston.

—Elements of Language: Support & Practice - Grade 12. 2000. pap. 37.80 (978-0-03-056402-4(6)) Holt, Rinehart & Winston.

—Elements of Language: Support & Practice - Grade 8. 2000. pap. 37.80 (978-0-03-056397-3(6)) Holt, Rinehart & Winston.

—Elements of Language: Support & Practice - Grade 9. 2000. pap. 37.80 (978-0-03-056398-0(4)) Holt, Rinehart & Winston.

—Elements of Language Course 3: Language & Writing Skills Worksheets. 1998. (YA). (gr. 9). pap. 10.00 (978-0-03-095730-7(3)) Holt, Rinehart & Winston.

HOP, LLC. Hooked on Handwriting Learn to Print. 2006. 24.99 (978-1-933863-15-3(3)) HOP, LLC.

—Hooked on Learning Handwriting. 2006. 64p. 3.79 (978-1-933863-91-7(9)) HOP, LLC.

I Can Write Streetland. 2003. (J). Bk. 1. mass mkt., wbk. ed. 6.95 (978-0-9743971-0-8(5)); Bk. 2. mass mkt., wbk. ed. 9.95 (978-0-9743971-1-5(3)); Bk. 3. mass mkt., wbk. ed. 9.95 (978-0-9743971-2-2(1)) Deziner Media International.

I Can Write Waterworld, Bk. 1. 2003. (J). mass mkt., wbk. ed. 6.95 (978-0-9743971-4-6(8)) Deziner Media International.

Imagine & Write, 5 Bks. (J). (gr. 2-6). (978-0-8374-0229-1(8) , 427); (978-0-8374-0239-0(5) , 428); (978-0-8374-0249-9(2) , 429); (978-0-8374-0259-8(X) , 430); (978-0-8374-0269-7(7) , 431) Weekly Reader Corp.

Improving Student Writing: Paragraphs. 2004. (J). per. 12.95 (978-1-56911-528-2(1)) Learning Resources, Inc.

Improving Student Writing: Sentences. 2004. (J). per. 12.95 (978-1-56911-526-8(5)) Learning Resources, Inc.

In the News, 6 vols. (Wildcats Ser.). 32p. (gr. 2-8). (978-0-322-02437-3(4)) Wright Group, The.

Incredible Places: 6 Each of 1 Anthology, 6 vols. (Wildcats Ser.). 32p. (gr. 2-8). (978-0-322-00587-7(6)) Wright Group, The.

Infantil. Aprendo a Escribir 2. 2004. (SPA.). 24p. (J). pap. 2.95 (978-1-4000-9306-9(6)) Random Hse., Inc.

Instructional Fair. Building Writing Skills: Laying the Foundation for Written Expression. 2002. (100+ Seriestm Ser.). 128p. (J). (gr. 2-3). pap. 12.99 (978-0-7424-0222-5(3) , IF87134); (gr. 4-5). pap. 12.99 (978-0-7424-0223-2(1) , IF87135) School Specialty Publishing.

—Guided Writing: Encourages Writing Skills & Creative Thinking. 2002. (Basic Skills Ser.). 48p. (J). (gr. 2-2). pap. 6.99 (978-0-7424-0228-7(2) , IF5026); (gr. 4-4). pap. 6.99 (978-0-7424-0230-0(4) , IF5028); (gr. 5-5). pap. 6.99 (978-0-7424-0231-7(2) , IF5029) School Specialty Publishing.

—Guided Writing: Encourages Writing Skills & Creative Thinking. 2002. (Basic Skills Ser.). 48p. (J). (gr. 3 up). pap. 6.99 (978-0-7424-0229-4(0) , IF5027) School Specialty Publishing.

Jensen, Frode. Jensen's Format Writing. 2002. 160p. (YA). per. 22.00 (978-1-886061-29-3(7)) Wordsmiths.

Kalaidjian, Walter B. Understanding & Writing about Literature: Used with ... Kalaidjian-Understanding Literature: an Introduction to Reading & Writing, MLA Update. 2003. (YA). 2.76 (978-0-618-45394-8(6) , 328829) Houghton Mifflin College Div.

Kellaher, Karen. Comic-Strip Writing Prompts: 50 Favorite Comic Strips with Terrific Writing Prompts That Get Kids Revved up for Writing. 2001. 64p. (gr. 3). pap. 10.95 (978-0-439-15977-7(6)) Scholastic, Inc.

—Writing Skills Made Fun: Capitalization, Punctuation & Spelling. 2001. (Illus.). 64p. pap. 11.95 (978-0-439-22267-9(2)) Scholastic, Inc.

Kelly, Curtis & Gargagliano, Arlen. Writing from Within Intro. 2004. (Illus.). 128p. pap., stu. ed. 24.00 (978-0-521-60626-4(8)) Cambridge Univ. Pr.

Ketch, Susan & Scraper, Katherine. Early Readers & Writers. Futrell, Ashley, ed. 2005. 128p. (J). per. 11.99 (978-1-59441-042-0(9) , CD-104042) Carson-Dellosa Publishing Co., Inc.

Kids Can Learn Franklin Staff, ed. Printing. 2005. (Kids Can Learn with Franklin! Ser.). (Illus.). 32p. (J). (gr. k up). (978-1-55337-602-6(1)) Kids Can Pr., Ltd.

—Ready to Print. 2005. (Kids Can Learn with Franklin! Ser.). (Illus.). 32p. (J). (ps-k). (978-1-55337-603-3(X)) Kids Can Pr., Ltd.

Kids Can Press Staff, Press Can. Printing Practice. 2004. (Kids Can Learn with Franklin Ser.). (Illus.). 32p. (J). (gr. k-3). (978-1-55337-590-6(4)) Kids Can Pr., Ltd.

Kieczykowski, Carol. Expanding the Primary Writer's Workshop: 50 Mini-Lessons to Improve Writing. 2001. 144p. (J). (gr. k-2). pap. 15.99 (978-0-7682-0307-3(4) , FE11021, Totline Pubns.) Schaffer, Frank Pubns.

Kirk, Daniel & Kirk, Christine. Writing from the Heart: Creative Writing from a Godward Life. 1999. (Illus.). 152p. (YA). (gr. 5-12). pap. 13.99 (978-0-9677745-0-3(0)) Godward Life Ministries.

Krulik, Nancy E. Playing with Numbers: A Learning-to-Write Book. Baroux, illus. 2004. (My Little Chalkboard Ser.). 16p. (J). pap. 12.95 (978-0-7624-1436-9(7) , Running Pr. Kids) Running Pr. Bk. Pubs.

LaCaria, Rena. Numbers. 2004. (Illus.). 24p. (J). spiral bd. 15.95 (978-1-932373-53-0(5) , Cedar Hill Pr.) Cedar Hill Publishing.

Lane, Barbara Donnelly. The Book Garden. Horton, Joy, illus. 2002. (J). pap. 6.95 (978-0-9702985-2-2(8)) Shamrock Hse., The.

Larousse Mexico Staff, ed. Escribir Preescolar Nivel A. 2005. (Yo quiero Saber Ser.). (SPA.). 32p. (ps-k). pap. 3.95 (978-970-22-0912-6(9)) Larousse, Ediciones, S. A. de C. V. MEX. *Dist:* Houghton Mifflin Co. Trade & Reference Div.

—Escribir Preescolar Nivel B. 2005. (Yo quiero Saber Ser.). (SPA.). 32p. (ps-k). pap. 3.95 (978-970-22-0915-7(3)) Larousse, Ediciones, S. A. de C. V. MEX. *Dist:* Houghton Mifflin Co. Trade & Reference Div.

—Escribir Preescolar Nivel C. 2005. (Yo quiero Saber Ser.). (SPA.). 32p. (ps-k). pap. 3.95 (978-970-22-0918-8(8)) Larousse, Ediciones, S. A. de C. V. MEX. *Dist:* Houghton Mifflin Co. Trade & Reference Div.

The Last Draw. 1998. (Comic Book Ser.). (Illus.). (J). (978-0-7652-0300-7(6)) Modern Curriculum Pr.

Laufer, Liora. Callirobics: Advanced Handwriting Exercises with Music from Around the World. (J). (gr. 2-9). pap. 19.95 incl. audio (978-0-9630478-3-0(3) , CL550) Callirobics.

Lda. Write from the Start: Developing Fine-Motor & Perceptual Skills for Effective Handwriting, 2 vols. 2001. (J). (gr. k-3). pap. 23.98 (978-0-7424-1619-2(4) , LL80162) School Specialty Publishing.

Learning Company Books Staff, ed. Reader Rabbit: Writing Mechanics. 2003. (Illus.). 32p. (J). pap., wbk. ed. 3.99 (978-0-7630-7642-9(2)) Learning Co. Bks.

Learning to Write: 1-Year Personal Use Version. 2003. E-Book incl. cd-rom (978-0-9726808-5-1(3)) MEIER Enterprises Inc.

Learning to Write: 12-Month Academic Access Version. 2003. (C). E-Book incl. cd-rom (978-0-9726808-0-6(2)) MEIER Enterprises Inc.

Learning to Write (Gr. K-1) 2003. (J). (978-1-58232-034-2(9)) Bryan Hse. Pubns., Inc.

Levithan, David, ed. You Are Here, This Is Now: The Best Young Writers & Artists in America. 2002. (Illus.). 272p. (J). pap. 6.99 (978-0-439-37618-1(1) , PUSH) Scholastic, Inc.

Libby, Kathryn. Cursive Connections: A Traditional Style. (J). 2002. 88p. 10.99 (978-0-9666572-3-4(3)); 1998. 84p. (gr. 2-6). wbk. ed. 10.99 (978-0-9666572-0-3(9)) Acacia Publishing, Inc.

—Cursive Connections: Modern Style. (J). (gr. 2-6). 2003. 84p. 10.99 (978-0-9666572-2-7(5)); 1999. 82p. wbk. ed. 10.99 (978-0-9666572-1-0(7)) Acacia Publishing, Inc.

Licker, Lori. Writing-Right with Professor Pendleton Pencil. 2006. spiral bd. 21.95 (978-0-9772196-0-5(7)) Writing-Right.

Longman Publishing Staff. My First Handwriting. Date not set. (Illus.). 32p. (J). per. 61.25 (978-0-582-51112-5(7)) Addison-Wesley Longman, Ltd. GBR. *Dist:* Trans-Atlantic Pubns., Inc.

—My Second Handwriting. Date not set. (Illus.). 32p. (J). pap. 61.25 (978-0-582-51113-2(5)) Addison-Wesley Longman, Ltd. GBR. *Dist:* Trans-Atlantic Pubns., Inc.

Lou Weber Staff, ed. Cursive & Lettering Wipe off Learning Board. 2004. 6p. (J). spiral bd., bds. 7.98 (978-1-4127-0563-9(0) , 7222400) Publications International, Ltd.

Lowe Wilke, Suzanne. Hand Writing - Contemporary Cursive. 1999. (100+ Seriestm Ser.). 128p. (J). (gr. k-6). pap. 12.99 (978-0-88012-851-3(8) , IF8738) School Specialty Publishing.

—Hand Writing - Traditional Cursive. 1999. (100+ Seriestm Ser.). 128p. (J). (gr. k-6). pap. 12.99 (978-0-88012-826-1(7) , IF8736) School Specialty Publishing.

Maps & Codes: 6 Each of 1 Anthology, 6 vols. (Wildcats Ser.). 32p. (gr. 2-8). (978-0-322-00588-4(4)) Wright Group, The.

Marks, Dave. Writing Strands 5. 1999. (Writing Strands Ser.). (J). (gr. 4-11). pap. 20.00 (978-1-888344-08-0(3)) National Writing Institute.

Martin, Michael. Handwriting Evidence. 2007. (Edge Books, Forensic Crime Solvers). (Illus.). 32p. (J). ***978-0-7368-6788-7(0)** , 1265014); ***978-0-7368-7872-2(6)** , 1265014) Capstone Pr., Inc.

Martivo, Kyalo. Herufi Zetu: African Traditional Writing Systems: Traditional Graphic Arts As Writing Systems. Leoni, Diana, illus. l.t. ed. 1999. 100p. (J). (gr. 5-8). pap. 8.95 (978-0-9642831-2-1(3)) Amenta Bks.

Mayer, Mercer. Writing: Grade 1. Cooper, Terry, ed. 2003. (Success with Workbooks Ser.). 48p. pap., wbk. ed. 4.95 (978-0-439-44494-1(2)) Scholastic, Inc.

—Writing Workbook. 2003. (Success with Workbooks Ser.). 48p. (J). 5.95 (978-0-439-44495-8(0)); 5.95 (978-0-439-44496-5(9)); 5.95 (978-0-439-44497-2(7)); 5.95 (978-0-439-44498-9(5)) Scholastic, Inc.

McDonald, Marcy. Writing: A Step-by-Step Guide to Writing Well: the Bridge Between Us. 2002. 312p. (YA). per. (978-0-9715781-0-4(9)) Popular Weasel Pr.

McGraw-Hill Staff. Bon Voyage! Level 1A Writing. 3rd ed. 2001. (FRE.). pap., wbk. ed., act. bk. ed. 10.64 (978-0-07-824271-7(1) , 9780078242717) Glencoe/McGraw-Hill.

—Bon Voyage! Level 1B Writing Activities. 3rd ed. 2001. (FRE.). (C). pap., wbk. ed. 10.64 (978-0-07-824272-4(X) , 9780078242724) Glencoe/McGraw-Hill.

—Bon Voyage! Writing Activities. 3rd ed. 2001. (FRE.). Level 1. (C). pap., wbk. ed. 14.64 (978-0-07-824269-4(X) , 9780078242694); Level. 2. pap., wbk. ed. 14.64 (978-0-07-824344-8(0) , 9780078243448) Glencoe/McGraw-Hill.

—Buen Viaje! Writing Activities. 3rd ed. 1999. (SPA & ENG.). (gr. 6-12). pap., wbk. ed. 14.64 (978-0-02-641261-2(6) , 9780026412612); pap., wbk. ed. 15.96 (978-0-02-641834-8(7) , 9780026418348); Level 2. (C). pap., wbk. ed. 14.64 (978-0-02-641546-0(1) , 9780026415460) Glencoe/McGraw-Hill.

—Writer's Choice: Florida Edition 2001, Grade 6. 2001. stu. ed. 58.64 incl. cd-rom (978-0-07-827058-1(8) , 9780078270581) Glencoe/McGraw-Hill.

—Writer's Choice: Grade 11 Texas Edition 2001. 2001. (C). stu. ed. 66.64 incl. cd-rom (978-0-07-827083-3(9) , 9780078270833) Glencoe/McGraw-Hill.

—Writer's Choice: Grade 12 Florida Edition 2001. 2001. (C). stu. ed. 66.64 incl. cd-rom (978-0-07-827064-2(2) , 9780078270642) Glencoe/McGraw-Hill.

—Writer's Choice: Grade 6 Texas Edition 2001. 2001. stu. ed. 58.64 incl. cd-rom (978-0-07-827078-9(2) , 9780078270789) Glencoe/McGraw-Hill.

—Writer's Choice: Grade 7 Florida Edition 2001. 2001. stu. ed. 61.32 incl. cd-rom (978-0-07-827059-8(6) , 9780078270598) Glencoe/McGraw-Hill.

—Writer's Choice: Grade 8 Florida Edition 2001. 2001. stu. ed. 61.32 incl. cd-rom (978-0-07-827060-4(X) , 9780078270604) Glencoe/McGraw-Hill.

—Writer's Choice: Grade 9 Texas Edition 2001. 2001. stu. ed. 65.32 incl. cd-rom (978-0-07-827081-9(2), 9780078270819) Glencoe/McGraw-Hill.
—Writer's Choice: Texas Edition 2001, Grade 10. 2001. (C). stu. ed. 65.32 incl. cd-rom (978-0-07-827082-6(0), 9780078270826) Glencoe/McGraw-Hill.
—Writer's Choice Florida Edition 2001, Grade 11. 2001. (C). stu. ed. 66.64 incl. cd-rom (978-0-07-827063-5(4), 9780078270635) Glencoe/McGraw-Hill.
—Writer's Choice Grammar Practice, Grade 9. 2000. pap., wbk. ed. 17.32 (978-0-07-823355-5(0), 9780078233555) Glencoe/McGraw-Hill.
—Writer's Choice Grammar Practice Grade 11. 2000. (C). pap., wbk. ed. 17.32 (978-0-07-823357-9(7), 9780078233579) Glencoe/McGraw-Hill.
—Writer's Choice Interactive: Grade 7 Texas Edition 2001. 2001. (C). stu. ed. 61.32 incl. cd-rom (978-0-07-827079-6(0), 9780078270796) Glencoe/McGraw-Hill.
—Writer's Choice Interactive: Grade 9 Florida Edition 2001. 2001. (C). stu. ed. 65.32 incl. cd-rom (978-0-07-827061-1(8), 9780078270611) Glencoe/McGraw-Hill.
—Writer's Choice Interactive Grade 12 Texas Edition 2001. 2001. (C). stu. ed. 66.64 incl. cd-rom (978-0-07-827084-0(7), 9780078270840) Glencoe/McGraw-Hill.
—Writer's Choice Interactive Grade 8 Texas Edition 2001. 2001. (C). stu. ed. 61.32 incl. cd-rom (978-0-07-827080-2(4), 9780078270802) Glencoe/McGraw-Hill.
—Writer's Choice Interactive Student Edition Grade 10 Florida Edition 2001. 2001. (C). stu. ed. 65.32 incl. cd-rom (978-0-07-827062-8(6), 9780078270628) Glencoe/McGraw-Hill.
McGraw-Hill Staff & School Specialty Publishing Staff. Beginning Cursive Handwriting. 2001. (Homework Helpers Activity Bks.). (Illus.). 56p. (J). (gr. 3-3). pap., act. bk. ed. 2.99 (978-0-7682-0715-6(0), FS109044, Schaffer, Frank) Schaffer, Frank Pubns.
McKinney, Maria & Gamble, Amy, eds. Beginning Manuscript: Modern Handwriting. 1999. (Illus.). 32p. (J). (gr. 1-3). pap. 4.99 (978-0-88724-502-2(1), CD-0876) Carson-Dellosa Publishing Co., Inc.
—Beginning Manuscript: Traditional Handwriting. 1999. (Illus.). 32p. (J). (gr. 1-3). pap. 4.99 (978-0-88724-503-9(X), CD-0877) Carson-Dellosa Publishing Co., Inc.
—Manuscript Practice: Modern Handwriting. Ling, George, illus. 1999. 32p. (J). (gr. 1-3). pap. 4.99 (978-0-88724-504-6(8), CD-0878) Carson-Dellosa Publishing Co., Inc.
—Manuscript Practice: Traditional Handwriting. Ling, George, illus. 1999. 32p. (J). (gr. 1-3). pap. 4.99 (978-0-88724-505-3(6), CD-0879) Carson-Dellosa Publishing Co., Inc.
McOmber, Rachel B., ed. McOmber Phonics Storybooks Vol. 1: Writing Book. rev. ed. (Illus.). (J). (978-0-944991-93-0(9)) Swift Learning Resources.
—McOmber Phonics Storybooks Vol. 2: Writing Book. rev. ed. (Illus.). (J). (978-0-944991-94-7(7)) Swift Learning Resources.
Mermelstein, Leah. Reading/Writing Connections in the K-2 Classroom: Find the Clarity & Then Blur the Lines. 2005. (Illus.). 240p. (C). pap. 26.99 (978-0-205-41277-8(7)) Allyn & Bacon, Inc.
Meyer-Hullmann, Ruth. Rechtschreibtraining fuer die 3. Klasse. (Duden-Lernminuten Ser.). (GER.). 44p. (J). wbk. ed. (978-3-411-70801-7(8)) Bibliographisches Institut & F. A. Brockhaus AG DEU. *Dist:* International Bk. Import Service, Inc.
—Rechtschreibtraining fuer die 3. und 4. Klasse. (Duden-Lernminuten Ser.). (GER.). 44p. (J). wbk. ed. (978-3-411-70811-6(5)) Bibliographisches Institut & F. A. Brockhaus AG DEU. *Dist:* International Bk. Import Service, Inc.
Meyer, Stephanie H., et al. What Matters. 2003. (Teen Ink Ser.). (Illus.). 400p. (YA). pap. 12.95 (978-0-7573-0063-9(4)) Health Communications, Inc.
Miles, Lisa, ed. Starting to Write. 1998. (Sticker Learning Bks.). (SPA., Illus.). 18p. (J). (ps-3). pap. 6.95 (978-0-7460-3108-7(4)) EDC Publishing.
Milliken, Linda. My Journal: Primary. Rogers, Kathy, ed. Fuller, Janelle, illus. 1998. 32p. (J). pap., stu. ed., wbk. ed. 1.99 (978-1-56472-143-3(4), EP143) Edupress, Inc.
Moreton, Daniel & Berger, Samantha. Why Write? 1999. (Learning Center Emergent Readers Ser.). (J). 3.25 (978-0-439-04606-0(8)) Scholastic, Inc.
Moshel, Eluzer. Learn to Write. 2004. pap. 12.00 (978-0-9728849-2-1(0)); Vol. 1. pap. 8.50 (978-0-9728849-0-7(4)); Vol. 2. pap. 8.50 (978-0-9728849-4-5(7)); Vol. 3. pap. 8.50 (978-0-9728849-7-6(1)) Cong Bais Tziporah.
A Navegar! 2000. (Spanish Writing Handbooks Ser.). (SPA.). (gr. 1-6). tchr. ed., tchr.'s training gde. ed. 26.50 (978-0-7362-0717-1(1)); stu. ed., instr.'s hndbk. ed. 29.68 (978-0-7362-0714-0(7)) Hampton-Brown Bks.
Nell, K. Duke & Bennett-Armistead, V. Susan. Reading & Writing Informational Text in the Primary Grades: Research-Based Practices. 2003. (Illus.). 272p. (gr. k-3). pap. 22.99 (978-0-439-53123-8(3)) Scholastic, Inc.
Neville, Bill, illus. Beginning Cursive: Modern Handwriting. 1999. 32p. (J). pap. 4.99 (978-0-88724-506-0(4), CD-0885) Carson-Dellosa Publishing Co., Inc.
—Beginning Cursive: Traditional Handwriting. 1999. 32p. (J). pap. 4.99 (978-0-88724-507-7(2), CD-0886) Carson-Dellosa Publishing Co., Inc.
—Cursive Practice: Modern Handwriting. 1999. 32p. (J). pap. 4.99 (978-0-88724-525-1(0), CD-0887) Carson-Dellosa Publishing Co., Inc.
—Cursive Practice: Traditional Handwriting. 1999. 32p. (J). pap. 4.99 (978-0-88724-526-8(9), CD-0888) Carson-Dellosa Publishing Co., Inc.
Norris, Jill. Traditional Cursive. Evans, Marilyn, ed. Larsen, Jo, illus. 2000. (Daily Handwriting Practice Ser.). 112p. (J). (gr. 1). pap., tchr. ed. 14.95 (978-1-55799-754-8(3), EMC 791) Evan-Moor Educational Pubs.
Olien, Rebecca. Kids Write: Fantasy & Sci Fi, Mystery, Autobiography, Adventure & More! Kline, Michael, illus. 2005. (Kids Can! Ser.). 128p. (YA). (gr. 7-14). 14.95 (978-0-8249-6775-8(5), Williamson Bks.) Ideals Pubns.
Olsen, Jan Z. Cursive Handwriting. Olsen, Jan Z., illus. 5th ed. 2003. (ENG, SPA & FRE., Illus.). 88p. (J). 5.95 (978-1-891627-04-0(X)) Handwriting Without Tears, Inc.
—Cursive Success. Olsen, Jan Z., illus. 4th ed. 2003. (ENG, SPA & FRE., Illus.). 88p. (YA). (gr. 4 up). wbk. ed. 5.95 (978-1-891627-11-8(2)) Handwriting Without Tears, Inc.
—Draw & Write Notebook: With wide double Lines. 2nd ed. 2004. (ENG.). 48p. (J). (gr. 1-2). stu. ed., wbk. ed. 2.75 (978-1-891627-09-5(0)) Handwriting Without Tears, Inc.
—Letters & Numbers for Me. Olsen, Jan Z., illus. 3rd ed. 2003. (ENG, SPA & FRE., Illus.). 88p. (J). (gr. k-1). wbk. ed. 5.95 (978-1-891627-10-1(4)) Handwriting Without Tears, Inc.
—My Printing Book. Olsen, Jan Z., illus. 7th ed. 2003. (ENG, SPA & FRE., Illus.). 84p. (J). stu. ed. 5.95 (978-1-891627-01-9(5)) Handwriting Without Tears, Inc.
—Printing Power. Olsen, Jan Z., illus. 5th ed. 2003. (ENG, SPA & FRE., Illus.). 80p. (J). stu. ed. 5.95 (978-1-891627-02-6(3)) Handwriting Without Tears, Inc.
Olson, Michael Keith. How I Feel: A Book about Diabetes. 2002. (Illus.). 48p. 15.00 (978-1-59056-037-2(X)) Lantern Bks.
On & off the Road: 6 Each of 1 Anthology, 6 vols. (Wildcatstm Ser.). 32p. (gr. 2-8). (978-0-322-02421-2(8)) Wright Group, The.
Ottaway, Jacqueline. Riddle of the Seaplanes (Level S), 6 vols. 128p. (gr. 6 up). 36.95 (978-0-322-05891-0(0)) Wright Group, The.
Pasda, Patricia J. & DiEdwardo, Mary Ann P. Writing. Pasda, Patricia J., illus. 1999. (Illus.). 145p. (J). (gr. k-12). pap. 49.95 (978-0-9641468-4-6(3)) DiEdwardo, Mary Ann P. Publishing.
Pegoraro, Laura. We'll Practice Cursive. Petertil Design Partners Staff, illus. 1998. (Powertools for Kids Ser.: No. 9). 4p. (J). (gr. 1-3). pap., wbk. ed. 4.95 (978-1-58220-008-8(4), 32109, PowerTools for Kids) Navigator Systems, Inc.
—We'll Practice Printing. Petertil Design Partners Staff, illus. 1998. (Powertools for Kids Ser.: No. 10). 4p. (J). (ps-3). pap., wbk. ed. 4.95 (978-1-58220-009-5(2), 32110, PowerTools for Kids) Navigator Systems, Inc.
Penmanship 1, 2 vols., Set. 2004. (gr. 1). 25.50 (978-0-7403-0207-7(8), JSP115); (Illus.). tchr. ed., stu. ed. 34.95 (978-0-7403-0215-2(9), JSC100) Alpha Omega Pubns., Inc. (Horizons).
Penmanship 2, 2 vols., Set. 2004. (Illus.). (J). (gr. 2-3). tchr. ed., stu. ed. 25.50 (978-0-7403-0211-4(6), JSP215) Alpha Omega Pubns., Inc.
Pomaska, Anna. I Can Write. 2001. (Illus.). 32p. (J). (ps-2). pap. 2.95 (978-0-486-41662-5(3)) Dover Pubns., Inc.
Powe, Dionne, des. I Can Write Streetland. 2005. (J). per. 9.99 (978-0-9743971-3-9(X)) Deziner Media International.
Practice Power Flip & Learn Addition. 2000. (Illus.). 16p. (J). (gr. k-2). spiral bd. (978-1-930355-20-0(3)) Greenbrier/Scentex.
Practice Power Practice Book Cursive Letters. (Illus.). (J). (gr. k-2). 2001. 18p. spiral bd., wbk. ed. (978-1-930355-28-6(9)); 2000. 16p. spiral bd., wbk. ed. (978-1-930355-00-2(9)) Greenbrier/Scentex.
Practice Power Practice Book Manuscript Letters. 2001. (Illus.). 18p. (J). (ps-1). spiral bd., wbk. ed. (978-1-930355-29-3(7)) Greenbrier/Scentex.
Practice Power Workbook Cursive Letters. 1999. (Illus.). 16p. (J). (gr. k-4). wbk. ed. (978-1-930355-15-6(7)) Greenbrier/Scentex.
Primer Paso. 2000. (Spanish Writing Handbooks Ser.). (SPA.). (gr. 1-6). tchr. ed., tchr.'s training gde. ed. 26.50 (978-0-7362-0715-7(5)); (Illus.). 18.97 (978-0-7362-0712-6(0)) Hampton-Brown Bks.
Princeton Review Staff. Roadmap to the AIMS: High School Reading. 2005. (State Test Prep Guides Ser.). 256p. pap. 16.00 (978-0-375-76503-2(4), Princeton Review) Random Hse. Information Group.
Printing Practice. 2002. (Home Workbooks Ser.). 64p. pap. 2002.00 (978-0-88724-726-2(1), CD-4528) Carson-Dellosa Publishing Co., Inc.
Pulse- Fun with Reading & Writing. 2006. cd-rom 4.99 (***978-1-60245-040-0(4)***) GDL Multimedia, LLC.
Rawlings Miller, Carol. Overhead Reading Lessons: Powerful Paragraphs. 2005. (Overhead Writing Lessons Ser.). (Illus.). 48p. (gr. 5 up). pap. 12.99 (978-0-439-23193-0(0), Teaching Resources) Scholastic, Inc.
Reading & Writing. 2004. (Help with Homework Ser.). 32p. (J). (gr. k-2). wbk. ed. 3.99 (978-1-904586-24-1(4)); (gr. 1-4). wbk. ed. 3.99 (978-1-904586-20-3(1)) Byeway Bks.
Reading & Writing. 2003. (Full-Color Literacy Activities Ser.). (Illus.). 176p. (J). (ps-1). 19.99 (978-0-7439-3237-0(4)) Teacher Created Materials, Inc.
Reason for Handwriting Gr 5. 2004. pap., tchr. ed. 11.99 (978-0-936785-48-6(9)) Concerned Communications.
Rechtschreibung 1. (Duden-Schuelerhilfen Ser.). (GER.). 80p. (J). (gr. 2-3). (978-3-411-06312-3(2)) Bibliographisches Institut & F. A. Brockhaus AG DEU. *Dist:* International Bk. Import Service, Inc.
Rechtschreibung 2. (Duden-Schuelerhilfen Ser.). (GER.). 96p. (J). (gr. 3-4). (978-3-411-06322-2(X)) Bibliographisches Institut & F. A. Brockhaus AG DEU. *Dist:* International Bk. Import Service, Inc.
Rechtschreibung 3. (Duden-Schuelerhilfen Ser.). (GER.). 96p. (J). (gr. 4-5). (978-3-411-06332-1(7)) Bibliographisches Institut & F. A. Brockhaus AG DEU. *Dist:* International Bk. Import Service, Inc.
Rechtschreibung 4. (Duden-Schuelerhilfen Ser.). (GER.). 112p. (J). (gr. 5-6). (978-3-411-05681-1(9)) Bibliographisches Institut & F. A. Brockhaus AG DEU. *Dist:* International Bk. Import Service, Inc.
Rechtschreibung 5. (Duden-Schuelerhilfen Ser.). (GER.). 112p. (YA). (gr. 7-8). (978-3-411-05691-0(6)) Bibliographisches Institut & F. A. Brockhaus AG DEU. *Dist:* International Bk. Import Service, Inc.
Rechtschreibung und Wortkunde. (Duden-Schuelerduden Ser.). (GER.). 384p. (YA). (gr. 4 up). (978-3-411-04215-9(X)) Bibliographisches Institut & F. A. Brockhaus AG DEU. *Dist:* International Bk. Import Service, Inc.
Ridgewood Analogies Grade 4, Bk. 1. 2004. pap. 6.65 (978-0-8388-2289-0(4)) Educators Publishing Service, Inc.
Ridgewood Analogies Grade 5, Bk. 2 2004. pap. 6.65 (978-0-8388-2290-6(8)) Educators Publishing Service, Inc.
Ridgewood Analogies Grade 6, Bk. 3. 2004. 6.65 (978-0-8388-2291-3(6)) Educators Publishing Service, Inc.
Ridgewood Analogies Key. 2004. Bk. 1 pap. 2.65 (978-0-8388-2292-0(4)); Bk. 3. pap. 2.65 (978-0-8388-2294-4(0)) Educators Publishing Service, Inc.
Rigby. Above Chalkboard Alpha: Cursive. 2003. (Illus.). pap. (978-0-7635-7748-3(0)) Steck-Vaughn.
—Write on Wipe off Handwriting: Cursive. 2001. (Illus.). pap. (978-0-7635-7749-0(9)) Steck-Vaughn.
—Write on Wipe off Handwriting: Manuscript. 2001. (Illus.). pap. (978-0-7635-7344-7(2)) Steck-Vaughn.
Right or Wrong? 6 Each of 1 Anthology, 6 vols. (Wildcats Ser.). 32p. (gr. 2-8). (978-0-322-00598-3(1)) Wright Group, The.
Rol 'N' Write Handwriting Activity Worksheets. 48p. spiral bd. 19.99 (978-0-7424-1583-6(X), LL00977) School Specialty Publishing.
Rudisill, J. J., et al, illus. Welcome to Wimzie's House. 1999. (Wimzie's House Bks.). 24p. (J). pap. 3.99 (978-0-88724-461-2(0)) Carson-Dellosa Publishing Co., Inc.
Ruff, Karen S. Cooney. The Sensory Pen: Unique Writing Prompts for Journalism Students & Other Writers. 2004. (Illus.). 94p. (J). spiral bd. (978-0-9761186-0-2(2)) Scribbler's Sword.
Ruffenach, Jessie E., et al. Learn along with Ashkii: First Grade Level 2. Whitethorne, Bahe, Jr., illus. 2003. (NAV & ENG.). 32p. (J). pap. 7.95 (978-1-893354-42-5(3)) Salina Bookshelf.
—Learn along with Ashkii: Second Grade Level 1. Whitethorne, Bahe, Jr., illus. 2003. (ENG & NAV.). 32p. (J). pap. 7.95 (978-1-893354-43-2(1)) Salina Bookshelf.
—Learn along with Ashkii: Second Grade Level 2. Whitethorne, Bahe, Jr., illus. 2003. (NAV & ENG.). 32p. (J). pap. 7.95 (978-1-893354-44-9(X)) Salina Bookshelf.
—Learn along with Ashkii: Third Grade Level 1. Whitethorne, Bahe, Jr., illus. 2003. (NAV & ENG.). 32p. (J). pap. 7.95 (978-1-893354-45-6(8)) Salina Bookshelf.
Sabio, et al. Libro de Califgrafia, Vol. 3. 2000. (Sabio Y Prudente Ser.). (SPA.). 64p. (J). (ps-3). 4.99 (978-0-8254-0994-3(2), Editorial Portavoz) Kregel Pubns.
Sanseri, Wanda. SWR Chart Pack. 2003. (J). pap. 9.95 (978-1-880045-30-5(3)) Back Home Industries.
Schecter, Deborah. 30 Instant Collaborative Classroom Banners: Easy Patterns for Write-and-Read Banners That Build Literacy & Brighten Your Classroom. 1999. 64p. pap. 10.95 (978-0-439-11103-4(X)) Scholastic, Inc.
Scholastic, Inc. Staff. Big Book of Classroom Stationery, the (Grades 2-3) Dozens of Motivating Writing Sheets with Illustrated Borders Kids Will Love! 2002. (Big Book of Classroom Stationery Ser.). (Illus.). 96p. pap. 13.95 (978-0-439-42065-5(2), Teaching Resources) Scholastic, Inc.
School Specialty Publishing. After School Writing Activities. 2003. (100+ Seriestm Ser.). 128p. (J). (gr. 1 up). pap. 12.99 (978-0-7424-1781-6(6), IFG99028); (gr. 2 up). pap. 12.99 (978-0-7424-1782-3(4), IFG99029); (gr. 3 up). pap. 12.99 (978-0-7424-1783-0(2), IFG99030); (gr. 4 up). pap. 12.99 (978-0-7424-1784-7(0), IFG99031) School Specialty Publishing.
—Building Writing Skills: Laying the Foundation for Written Expression. 2002. (100+ Seriestm Ser.). 128p. (J). (gr. 6-8). pap. 12.99 (978-0-7424-0224-9(X), IF87136) School Specialty Publishing.
—Graphic Planners for Writing. 2004. 48p. (J). (gr. 1-2). pap. 6.99 (978-0-7424-2717-4(X), IFG99179); (gr. 3-5). pap. 6.99 (978-0-7424-2718-1(8), IFG99180); (gr. 6-8). pap. 6.99 (978-0-7696-3326-8(9), MH1030) School Specialty Publishing.
—Handwriting, Cursive. 2006. (Skills for Scholars Ser.). 80p. (C). pap. 4.99 (***978-0-7696-4926-9(2)***, Schaffer, Frank) Schaffer, Frank Pubns.
—Handwriting, Printing. 2006. (Skills for Scholars Ser.). 80p. (C). pap. 4.99 (***978-0-7696-4925-2(4)***, Schaffer, Frank) Schaffer, Frank Pubns.
School Zone Publishing Company Staff. Cursive Writing 3-4 Bilingual Work Book: I Know It! 2004. 64p. (J). pap. 3.79 (978-1-58947-962-3(9)) School Zone Publishing Co.
—Manuscript Writing K-2 Bilingual: I Know It! 2004. 64p. (J). (gr. k-1). pap. 3.79 (978-1-58947-961-6(0)) School Zone Publishing Co.
Shirley, Molly Elizabeth. The Writing House: For Kindergarten, 1st & 2nd Grades. Wilson, Julia Hager, ed. Otto, Matthew Lloyd, illus. 2000. 150p. (Orig.). (J). (gr. k-3). pap. 36.95 (978-0-9661968-2-5(1)) Schoolhouse Secrets Unlimited.
Show What You Know on the OAT for Grade 7, Reading/Writing Student Workbook. 2006. (J). per. 16.95 (978-1-59230-172-0(X)) Englefield & Assocs., Inc.
Shulte, Sharon. Sandy's Aunt. Shulte, Sara, illus. 2004. (J). per. 12.00 (978-0-9747147-5-2(5)) MK Publishing.
Sicinski-Skeans, Sharon & Baron, Lindamichelle. Skills for Super Writers Softcover. 2003. (J). (gr. 3). stu. ed. 9.50 (978-0-7652-0756-2(7)) Modern Curriculum Pr.
—Skills for Super Writers Softcover: Grade 3. 2003. (Writing Program Ser.). (J). tchr.'s training gde. ed. 19.95 (978-0-7652-0759-3(1)) Modern Curriculum Pr.
—Skills for Super Writers Softcover Student Book. 2003. (Illus.). (J). (gr. 4). stu. ed. 9.50 (978-0-7652-0757-9(5)); (gr. 5). stu. ed. 9.50 (978-0-7652-0758-6(3)) Modern Curriculum Pr.
—Transparencies. 2003. (J). (gr. 3). 23.50 (978-0-7652-1045-6(2)); (gr. 5). 23.50 (978-0-7652-1047-0(9)) Modern Curriculum Pr.
—The Write Direction: Hardcover Student Book. 2003. (Illus.). (J). (gr. 4). stu. ed. 18.95 (978-0-7652-0751-7(6)); (gr. 5). stu. ed. 18.95 (978-0-7652-0752-4(4)) Modern Curriculum Pr.
Skills for Young Writers: Helping Students Make Good Stories Great. 48p. (gr. 2 up). 5.99 (978-1-56822-583-8(0), IF5141); (gr. 3 up). 5.99 (978-1-56822-584-5(9), IF5142); (gr. 4 up). 5.99 (978-1-56822-585-2(7), IF5143); (gr. 5 up). 5.99 (978-1-56822-586-9(5), IF5144); (gr. 6 up). 5.99 (978-1-56822-587-6(3), IF5145) School Specialty Publishing.
Smith, Jodene. How to Capitalize: Grades 1-3. 1999. (How to Ser.). (Illus.). 48p. (gr. k-3). pap., act. bk. ed. 7.99 (978-1-57690-496-1(2), TCA2496) Teacher Created Materials, Inc.
Soper, Sandra. Reading & Writing, Bk. 3. rev. ed. (Illus.). 32p. (J). pap. 5.99 (978-0-330-32075-7(0), Pan) Pan Macmillan GBR. *Dist:* Trafalgar Square Publishing.
Spelling & Writing. 2000. (gr. 1 up). 52.95 (978-0-673-28977-3(X)); (gr. 2 up). 52.95 (978-0-673-61803-0(X)); (gr. 3 up). 52.95 (978-0-673-28979-7(6)); (gr. 4 up). 52.95 (978-0-673-28980-3(X)); (gr. 5 up). 52.95 (978-0-673-28981-0(8)); (gr. 6 up). 52.95 (978-0-673-28982-7(6)); (gr. 7 up). 52.95 (978-0-673-28983-4(4)); (gr. 8 up). 52.95 (978-0-673-28984-1(2)) Addison-Wesley Educational Pubs., Inc.
Squiggles & Strokes, 6 vols., Pack. (Bookweb Ser.). 32p. (gr. 5 up). 34.00 (978-0-7635-3795-1(0)) Rigby Education.
The Standard Pocket Chart. (Professional Resources Ser.). 29.95 (978-0-7802-4243-2(2)) Wright Group, The.
Steck-Vaughn Staff. English ASAP Level 1. 1998. pap., tchr. ed. 17.60 (978-0-8172-7954-7(7)) Steck-Vaughn.
—Expository Writing. 1999. pap. (978-0-7398-2928-8(9)) Steck-Vaughn.
—HCPS: Answer Key - Reading & Writing - Level C. 2002. (Soaring Scores Ser.). pap. (978-0-7398-6097-7(6)) Steck-Vaughn.
—HCPS: Answer Key - Reading & Writing - Level E. 2002. (Soaring Scores Ser.). pap. (978-0-7398-6101-1(8)) Steck-Vaughn.
—HCPS: Answer Key - Reading & Writing - Level H. 2002. (Soaring Scores Ser.). pap. (978-0-7398-6107-3(7)) Steck-Vaughn.
—Head for Home: Handwriting - Cursive. 2004. (Illus.). pap. 5.99 (978-0-7398-8556-7(1)) Steck-Vaughn.
—Head for Home: Handwriting - Manuscript. 2004. (Illus.). pap. (978-0-7398-8555-0(3)) Steck-Vaughn.
—McDonalds Writing Dictionary. 1998. (J). pap. (978-0-7398-0857-3(5)) Steck-Vaughn.
—Writing Strategies-Start Smart. 2002. (J). pap. (978-0-7398-6018-2(6)) Steck-Vaughn.
Stephens & Harper. Writing with a Point Grd 9-12. 2004. pap. 12.95 (978-0-8388-2054-4(9)) Educators Publishing Service, Inc.
Sterling Publishing Company Staff. Learning to Write with Benjamin the Bear: Wipe & Clean Book. 1998. (Balloon Ser.). (Illus.). 14p. (J). (ps-1). pap. 5.95 (978-0-8069-3824-0(2)) Sterling Publishing Co., Inc.
Sterling Publishing Company Staff, ed. First Writing Games. 2000. (Billy the Bear Activity Bks.). (Illus.). 16p. (J). (ps-k). pap. 3.95 (978-0-8069-5593-3(7)) Sterling Publishing Co., Inc.
Sterling/Balloon. Writing Words with Benjamin the Bear. 2000. (Balloon Ser.). (Illus.). 16p. (J). (gr. 1-2). pap. 5.95 (978-0-8069-2673-5(2)) Sterling Publishing Co., Inc.
Stevenson, Dan & Gandy, Scott, eds. Dr. Bethune Children Authors, 1999. Caflin College Art Department Staff, illus. 2nd enl. ed. 1999. 128p. (J). (ps-8). 29.95 (978-0-9643500-1-4(7)) Jereleen Publishing, Inc.
Stott, Jon C. Gerald Mcdermott & YOU. McDermott, Gerald, illus. 2004. (Author & YOU Ser.). 128p. (C). pap. 35.00 (978-1-59158-175-8(3), LU1753, Greenwood Pr.) Greenwood Publishing Group, Inc.
The Student Writer's Workshop. 48p. (gr. 3-4). 8.99 (978-0-7682-0095-9(4), GA1681) School Specialty Publishing.
Sunflower, Cherlyn. Real-Life Writing Activities for Grades 4 - 9. 2002. 496p. (gr. 4-9). pap. 29.95 (978-0-13-044979-5(2), Jossey-Bass) Wiley, John & Sons, Inc.
Suter, Joanne. Beginning Writing 1. 2001. 100p. ring bd. 29.95 (978-1-56254-147-7(1), SP 1471) Saddleback Educational Publishing.
—Beginning Writing 2. 2001. 100p. ring bd. 29.95 (978-1-56254-148-4(X), SP 148X) Saddleback Educational Publishing.
Tell Me No Lies, 6 vols. (Ragged Island Mysteriestm Ser.). 161p. (gr. 5-7). 42.50 (978-0-322-01654-5(1)) Wright Group, The.
Teodorescu, Ion & Addy, Lois M. Write from the Start 1: Developing Fine-Motor & Perceptual Skills for Effective Handwriting. 2001. 128p. (J). (gr. k-3). pap. 13.99 (978-0-7424-0160-0(X), LL80160) School Specialty Publishing.
—Write from the Start 2: Developing Fine-Motor & Perceptual Skills for Effective Handwriting. 2001. 128p. (J). (gr. k-3). pap. 13.99 (978-0-7424-0161-7(8), LL80161) School Specialty Publishing.
Thurber, Donald N. Cursive Capitals Practice. 1999. (D'Nealian Handwriting from A to Z Ser.). (Illus.). 64p. (J). pap. 9.95 (978-0-673-59235-4(9), Good Year Bks.) Celebration Pr.

W X Y Z

—Lowercase Cursive Practice. 1999. (D'Nealian Handwriting from A to Z Ser.). (Illus.). 64p. (J). pap. 9.95 (978-0-673-59236-1(7) , Good Year Bks.) Celebration Pr.

—Lowercase Manuscript Readiness. 2001. (D'Nealian Handwriting from A to Z Ser.). (Illus.). 64p. (J). (ps-k). pap. 8.95 (978-0-673-59958-2(2) , Good Year Bks.) Celebration Pr.

—Uppercase Manuscript Readiness. 2001. (D'Nealian Handwriting from A to Z Ser.). (Illus.). 64p. (J). (ps-k). pap. 9.95 (978-0-673-59957-5(4) , Good Year Bks.) Celebration Pr.

Traditional Beginning Cursive. 2002. (Home Workbooks Ser.). 64p. pap. 2.49 (978-0-88724-745-3(8) , CD-4547) Carson-Dellosa Publishing Co., Inc.

Trimmer. Writing Without a Purpose: AP Version. 14th ed. 2003. (YA). (gr. 6-12). 75.96 (978-0-618-31848-3(8) , 356312) Houghton Mifflin College Div.

Trisler, Alana & Cardiel, Patrice Howe. Advanced Journal Writing. 2002. 72p. (J). (gr. 4-6). pap., wbk. ed. 2.95 (978-1-56762-172-3(4)) Modern Learning Pr.

—My August Journal. 1999. 48p. (J). (gr. 1-2). pap., wbk. ed. 1.85 (978-1-56762-114-3(7)) Modern Learning Pr.

—My July Journal. 1999. 48p. (J). (gr. 1-2). pap., wbk. ed. 1.85 (978-1-56762-113-6(9)) Modern Learning Pr.

—My June Journal. 1999. 48p. (J). (gr. 1-2). pap., wbk. ed. 1.85 (978-1-56762-112-9(0)) Modern Learning Pr.

Tuszynski, Kathy Cromwell & Yarber, Angels. The Write Answer. 2003. (Illus.). 96p. (J). pap. 11.95 (978-1-57310-407-4(8)) Teaching & Learning Co.

Tyler, Jenny. First Learning Time. 2000. (gr. k-3). lib. bdg. 12.95 (978-0-613-90025-6(1)) Tandem Library Bks.

Type it Grades K-12. 2004. pap. 14.85 (978-0-8388-1345-4(3)) Educators Publishing Service, Inc.

Vanderveen, Pam. Acing the State Writing Assessment: Grade 8. 2003. 120p. pap. 9.95 (978-1-58049-327-7(0) , PWH3270A) Prestwick Hse., Inc.

Vaughan, Marcia. Story Teller Quilts: Level S, 6 vols. 128p. (gr. 3-6). 36.95 (978-0-322-05899-6(6)) Wright Group, The.

Veinje, Marie. Manuscript Writing. 2004. 64p. (J). (gr. k-2). pap. 3.79 (978-1-58947-397-3(3)) School Zone Publishing Co.

Via Libre! 2000. (Spanish Writing Handbooks Ser.). (SPA.). (gr. 1-6). tchr. ed., tchr.'s training gde. ed. 26.50 (978-0-7362-0045-5(2)); stu. ed., instr.'s hndbk. ed. 27.78 (978-0-7362-0044-8(4)) Hampton-Brown Bks.

Voth, Danna. The First-Timer's Guide to Book Reports: And Other Writing Projects. Gates, Janise, illus. 2000. (First-Timers Guides). 80p. (J). (gr. 2-4). pap. 8.95 (978-0-7373-0475-6(8) , 04758W, Roxbury Park Juvenile) Lowell Hse. Juvenile.

Voyages in English: Writing & Grammar. 2004. (gr. 4 up). (978-0-8294-1305-2(7)); (gr. 5 up). (978-0-8294-1307-6(3)); (gr. 5 up). tchr. ed. (978-0-8294-0989-5(0)); (gr. 5 up). tchr. ed., wbk. ed. (978-0-8294-1323-6(5)); (gr. 5 up). stu. ed. (978-0-8294-0990-1(4)); (gr. 5 up). stu. ed., wbk. ed. (978-0-8294-1322-9(7)); (gr. 6 up). (978-0-8294-1310-6(3)); (gr. 6 up). tchr. ed. (978-0-8294-0991-8(2)); (gr. 6 up). tchr. ed., wbk. ed. (978-0-8294-1325-0(1)); (gr. 6 up). stu. ed. (978-0-8294-0992-5(0)); (gr. 6 up). stu. ed., wbk. ed. (978-0-8294-1324-3(3)); (gr. 7 up). (978-0-8294-1313-7(8)); (gr. 7 up). tchr. ed. (978-0-8294-0993-2(9)); (gr. 7 up). tchr. ed., wbk. ed. (978-0-8294-1328-1(6)); (gr. 7 up). stu. ed. (978-0-8294-0994-9(7)); (gr. 7 up). stu. ed., wbk. ed. (978-0-8294-1327-4(8)); (gr. 8 up). (978-0-8294-1315-1(4)); (gr. 8 up). tchr. ed. (978-0-8294-0995-6(5)); (gr. 8 up). tchr. ed., wbk. ed. (978-0-8294-1330-4(8)); (gr. 8 up). stu. ed. (978-0-8294-0996-3(3)); (gr. 8 up). stu. ed., wbk. ed. (978-0-8294-1329-8(4)) Loyola Pr.

Vu, Talia N. The Children's Handwriting Practice Book. 1998. 28p. (J). (ps-8). pap. 2.50 (978-0-9655943-1-8(9)) Nguyen, Talia.

Wasylyk, Thomas. Beginning Cursive Handwriting. 1998. (Illus.). 64p. (J). (gr. 1-3). pap., wbk. ed. 4.95 (978-1-56762-082-5(5)) Modern Learning Pr.

—Manuscript Review & Introduction to Cursive, Bk. M/C. 1999. (Illus.). 64p. (J). (gr. 2). pap. 4.95 (978-1-56762-111-2(2)) Modern Learning Pr.

—Manuscript Writing, Bk. M. 1999. (Illus.). 64p. (J). (gr. 2). pap. 4.95 (978-1-56762-110-5(4)) Modern Learning Pr.

—Writing for Learning, Bk. F. 1999. (Illus.). 48p. (J). (gr. 5). pap. 4.95 (978-1-56762-108-2(2)) Modern Learning Pr.

—Writing in Cursive. 1998. (Illus.). 48p. (J). (gr. 3-4). pap., wbk. ed. 4.95 (978-1-56762-083-2(3)) Modern Learning Pr.

Watson, Joy. The Birthday Flood: Level O, 6 vols. 128p. (gr. 3-6). 36.95 (978-0-322-05896-5(1)) Wright Group, The.

Webber, Diane. Do You Read Me? Famous Cases Solved by Handwriting Analysis! 2007. (24/7, Science Behind the Scenes Ser.). (Illus.). 64p. (J). ***(978-1-4287-2801-1(5)*** , Franklin Watts) Hodder Children's Division.

—Do You Read Me? Famous Cases Solved by Handwriting Analysis! (24/7 - Science Behind the Scenes Ser.). (Illus.). 64p. (gr. 8-12). 2007. (YA). pap. 7.95 ***(978-0-531-15456-4(4))***; 2006. (J). 25.00 (978-0-531-12066-8(X)) Scholastic Library Publishing. (Watts, Franklin).

What Is That Smell? S-Family Blends: Level B, 6 vols. (Wright Skills Ser.). 16p. (gr. k-3). 17.95 (978-0-322-01461-9(1)) Wright Group, The.

What's in the Woods? Consonant digraph review: Level C, 6 vols. (Wright Skills Ser.). 16p. (gr. k-3). 26.50 (978-0-322-01497-8(2)) Wright Group, The.

Willever, Lisa. Exciting Writing: A Handbook for Kids. 2004. 64p. 5.95 (978-0-9760469-1-2(1) , 329-003) Franklin Mason Pr.

Williams, James D., et al. Writing & Language Arts: Writer's Workbook. (gr. k up). pap. 12.60 (978-0-07-579635-0(X)); (gr. 2 up). pap. 12.60 (978-0-07-579637-4(6)) SRA/McGraw-Hill.

Williams, Rozanne Lanczak & Faulkner, Stacey. Learn to Write Resource Guide: Activities to Turn Readers into Writers. Dobelmann, Colleen, ed. Tom, Darcy, illus. 2006. (J). per. 12.99 ***(978-1-59198-314-9(2))*** Creative Teaching Pr., Inc.

Wipe-Away Books: Cursive Alphabet. 2003. (Illus.). 16p. (YA). (gr. 3 up). pap. 3.99 (978-0-7682-0066-9(0)) School Specialty Publishing.

Wong, Janet S. You Have to Write. Flavin, Teresa, illus. 2002. 40p. (J). (gr. 4 up). 17.00 (978-0-689-83409-7(8) , McElderry, Margaret K.) Simon & Schuster Children's Publishing.

Woods, Irons, & Greens: 6 Each of 1 Anthology, 6 vols. (Wildcats Ser.). 32p. (gr. 2-8). (978-0-322-00589-1(2)) Wright Group, The.

Woods, Mary Lynn. 16 Writing Lessons for State Assessments: Engaging Lessons with Planning Sheets & Evaluation Checklists, Extension Ideas, & Much, Much, More! 2002. (Illus.). 144p. pap. 17.95 (978-0-439-36548-2(1) , Teaching Resources) Scholastic, Inc.

Wrighton, Charlene & Bradshaw, Georgine. Basic Kit - Preschool. Clark, Irene, illus. 2005. Orig. Title: Basis Kit I. (J). 249.95 (978-1-886441-30-9(8)) Zoo-phonics, Inc.

Writer's Solution. Bronze Level. (YA). (gr. 7). stu. ed. 23.47 (978-0-13-828781-8(3)); Copper Level. (J). (gr. 6). stu. ed. 23.47 (978-0-13-828773-3(2)); Copper Level. (J). (gr. 6). pap. 1.97 (978-0-13-434758-5(7)); Diamond Level. (YA). (gr. 12). stu. ed. 25.47 (978-0-13-828831-0(3)); Gold Level. (YA). (gr. 9). stu. ed. 25.47 (978-0-13-828807-5(0)); Platinum Level. (YA). (gr. 10). stu. ed. 25.47 (978-0-13-828815-0(1)); Ruby Level. (YA). (gr. 11). stu. ed. 25.47 (978-0-13-828823-5(2)); Silver Level. (YA). (gr. 8). stu. ed. 23.47 (978-0-13-828799-3(6)) Prentice Hall PTR.

Writers' Workshop. 80p. (gr. 5-6). 9.99 (978-1-56822-407-7(9) , IF19202) School Specialty Publishing.

Writing. 1999. (Illus.). 16p. (YA). 2.95 (978-1-56254-359-4(8) , SP3598) Saddleback Educational Publishing.

Writing, 3 bks., Set. 2003. (J). (gr. 3-6). pap. 29.97 (978-0-7424-1697-0(6) , IFG99087) School Specialty Publishing.

Writing: English in Context. 2000. (Illus.). 112p. per., wbk. ed. 8.95 (978-1-56254-358-7(X) , SP 358X) Saddleback Educational Publishing.

Writing 1. 2000. 100p. ring bd. 29.95 (978-1-56254-220-7(6) , SP 2206) Saddleback Educational Publishing.

Writing 2. 2000. 100p. ring bd. 29.95 (978-1-56254-221-4(4) , SP 2214) Saddleback Educational Publishing.

Writing & Thinking Skills: Fun with Writing. 120p. (gr. 5-8). 14.99 (978-0-7682-0624-1(3) , GA13081) School Specialty Publishing.

Writing for Standardized Tests: A Student Guide to Writing for Standardized Tests. (YA). (gr. 9-12). stu. ed. (978-0-8215-0763-6(X)) Sadlier, William H. Inc.

Writing Grade 1. 2000. (Practice Makes Perfect Ser.). 80p. (J). (gr. 1). pap., wbk. ed. 2.99 (978-0-88724-620-3(6) , CD-3630) Carson-Dellosa Publishing Co., Inc.

Writing Grade 3. 2000. (Practice Makes Perfect Ser.). 80p. (J). (gr. 3). pap., wbk. ed. 2.99 (978-0-88724-622-7(2) , CD-3632) Carson-Dellosa Publishing Co., Inc.

Writing Grade 5. 2000. (Practice Makes Perfect Ser.). 80p. (J). (gr. 5). pap., wbk. ed. 2.99 (978-0-88724-624-1(9) , CD-3634) Carson-Dellosa Publishing Co., Inc.

The Writing Lesson: Learn Handwriting. 2nd ed. 2000. (J). cd-rom 39.95 (978-0-913063-06-4(1)) Mountcastle Co.

Writing Skills 3. 2004. pap. 12.00 (978-0-8388-2052-0(2)) Educators Publishing Service, Inc.

Writing with Grace. 2nd ed. 2003. (Academy Handwriting Program Ser.: Vol. 4). (J). pap. 5.50 (978-1-930367-88-3(0)) Christian Liberty Pr.

Writing with the Five-Paragraph Model. 2004. 64p. (J). (gr. 6-8). pap. 8.99 (978-0-7696-3402-9(8) , MH1035); (gr. 3-4). pap. 8.99 (978-0-7424-2773-0(0) , IFG99211); (gr. 4-4). pap. 8.99 (978-0-7424-2774-7(9) , IFG99212); (gr. 5-5). pap. 8.99 (978-0-7424-2775-4(7) , IFG99213) School Specialty Publishing.

Young, Sue K. Writing with Style. 1999. (Scholastic Guides Ser.). 144p. (J). (gr. 3-7). pap. 8.95 (978-0-590-25424-3(3)) Scholastic, Inc.

Zeros & Ones, 6 vols. (Wildcats Ser.). 32p. (gr. 2-8). (978-0-322-02438-0(2)) Wright Group, The.

Zoo-phonics Quick Tests for the Classroom. 2004. cd-rom (978-1-886441-41-5(3)) Zoo-phonics, Inc.

Zumbrock, Kristin. MEville to WEville: Unit 1 ME, 2 books, manual and children's book. 2004. 292p. spiral bd. 75.00 (978-0-9666667-5-5(5)) AbleNet, Inc.

WRITING—MATERIALS AND INSTRUMENTS

Hayward, Linda. I Am a Pencil. Nicklaus, Carol, illus. 2003. (Silly Millies Ser.). 32p. lib. bdg. 17.90 (978-0-7613-2904-6(8) , Millbrook Pr.) Lerner Publishing Group.

WRITING (AUTHORSHIP)

see Authorship; Journalism

WYOMING

Baldwin, Guy. Wyoming. 1998. (Celebrate the States Ser.). (Illus.). 144p. (gr. 4-8). lib. bdg. 37.07 (978-0-7614-0662-4(X) , Benchmark Bks.) Cavendish, Marshall Corp.

Baldwin, Guy & Hart, Joyce. Wyoming. 2nd ed. 2008. (Celebrate the States Ser.). (J). lib. bdg. 39.93 ***(978-0-7614-2563-2(2)*** , Benchmark Bks.) Cavendish, Marshall Corp.

Bograd, Larry. Uniquely Wyoming. 2004. (Heinemann State Studies). (J). pap. 9.00 (978-1-4034-4755-7(5)); lib. bdg. 31.36 (978-1-4034-4666-4(0)) Heinemann Library.

Britton, Tamara L. Devil's Tower. 2005. (Illus.). 32p. (J). (gr. k-6). lib. bdg. 22.78 (978-1-59197-833-6(5)) ABDO Publishing Co.

Covert, Kim. Wyoming. 2003. (Land of Liberty Ser.). (Illus.). 64p. (J). lib. bdg. 25.26 (978-0-7368-2207-7(0)) Capstone Pr., Inc.

Dubois, Muriel L. Wyoming Facts & Symbols. (States & Their Symbols Ser.). 24p. (J). 2000. (Illus.). (gr. 2-3). lib. bdg. 18.60 (978-0-7368-0529-2(X) , Bridgestone Bks.); 2003. lib. bdg. 19.93 (978-0-7368-2281-7(X)) Capstone Pr., Inc.

Feinstein, Stephen. Wyoming: A MyReportLinks.com Book. 2003. (States Ser.). (Illus.). 48p. (J). (gr. 4-10). lib. bdg. 25.26 (978-0-7660-5030-3(0) , MyReportLinks.com Bks.) Enslow Pubs., Inc.

Fontes, Justine & Fontes, Ron. Wyoming: The Equality State. 2003. (World Almanac Library of the States). (Illus.). 48p. (J). (gr. 5 up). pap. 14.95 (978-0-8368-5335-3(0)); lib. bdg. 30.00 (978-0-8368-5164-9(1)) Stevens, Gareth Inc. (World Almanac Library).

Frisch, Carlienne A. Wyoming. rev. ed. 2003. (gr. 3-6). lib. bdg. 15.25 (978-0-613-52529-9(9)) Tandem Library Bks.

Gagliano, Eugene. C Is for Cowboy: A Wyoming Alphabet. Guy, Susan, illus. 2003. 40p. (J). 17.95 (978-1-58536-097-0(X)) Sleeping Bear Pr.

Galiano, Dean. Wyoming. 2006. (Bilingual Library of the United States of America: Set 2). (ENG & SPA., Illus.). 32p. (J). (gr. 3-6). lib. bdg. 22.50 (978-1-4042-3116-0(1) , Buenas Letra) Rosen Publishing Group, Inc., The.

Hanson-Harding, Alexandra L. Wyoming. 2003. (From Sea to Shining Sea Ser.: 2). (Illus.). 80p. (J). 30.50 (978-0-516-22490-9(5) , Children's Pr.) Scholastic Library Publishing.

Heinrichs, Ann. Wyoming. Kania, Matt, illus. 2005. (Welcome to the USA Ser.). 40p. (J). (gr. 1-5). 27.07 (978-1-59296-491-8(5)) Child's World, Inc.

—Wyoming. 2003. (This Land Is Your Land Ser.). (Illus.). 48p. (J). (gr. 3 up). lib. bdg. 22.60 (978-0-7565-0359-8(0)) Compass Point Bks.

Kummer, Patricia K. Wyoming. rev. ed. 2002. (One Nation Ser.). (Illus.). 48p. (J). (gr. 3-4). lib. bdg. 22.60 (978-0-7368-1276-4(8) , Bridgestone Bks.) Capstone Pr., Inc.

Marsh, Carole. The Big Wyoming Reproducible Activity Book. 2001. (Carole Marsh Wyoming Bks.). 96p. (J). (gr. 2-6). pap. 9.95 (978-0-7933-9962-8(9)) Gallopade International.

—My First Book about Wyoming. Line Art Staff, illus. 2001. 32p. (J). (gr. k-4). pap. 7.95 (978-0-7933-9904-8(1)) Gallopade International.

—The Survivor: A Class Challenge. 2001. (Wyoming Experience! Ser.). lib. bdg. 29.95 (978-0-635-00696-7(0)) Gallopade International.

—Who Wants to Be a Millionaire? 2001. (Carole Marsh Wyoming Bks.). lib. bdg. 29.95 (978-0-635-00117-7(9)) Gallopade International.

—Wyoming Classic Christmas Trivia. 2002. (Carole Marsh Wyoming Bks.). (Illus.). 32p. pap. 6.95 (978-0-635-01465-8(3) , 14653); lib. bdg. 21.95 (978-0-635-01466-5(1) , 14661) Gallopade International. (Marsh, Carole Bks.).

—Wyoming Current Events Projects: 30 Cool, Activities, Crafts, Experiments & More for Kids to Do to Learn about Your State! 2003. (Wyoming Experience Ser.). 32p. (gr. k-5). pap. 5.95 (978-0-635-02069-7(6) , Marsh, Carole Bks.) Gallopade International.

—The Wyoming Experience Pocket Guide. 2001. (Carole Marsh Wyoming Bks.). (Illus.). 96p. (J). (gr. 3-8). pap. 6.95 (978-0-7933-9933-8(5)) Gallopade International.

—Wyoming Geography Projects: 30 Cool, Activities, Crafts, Experiments & More for Kids to Do to Learn about Your State! 2003. (Wyoming Experience Ser.). 32p. (gr. k-5). pap. 5.95 (978-0-635-01868-7(3) , Marsh, Carole Bks.) Gallopade International.

—Wyoming Government Projects: 30 Cool, Activities, Crafts, Experiments & More for Kids to Do to Learn about Your State! 2003. (Wyoming Experience Ser.). 32p. (gr. k-5). pap. 5.95 (978-0-635-01969-1(8) , Marsh, Carole Bks.) Gallopade International.

—Wyoming Hot Zones! Viruses, Diseases, & Epidemics in Our State's History. 1998. (Hot Zones! Ser.). (Illus.). (J). (gr. 3-12). pap. 19.95 (978-0-7933-8979-7(8)); lib. bdg. 29.95 (978-0-7933-8978-0(X)) Gallopade International.

—Wyoming Jeopardy! Answers & Questions about Our State! Line Art Staff, illus. 2001. 32p. (J). (gr. 3-8). pap. 7.95 (978-0-7933-9817-1(7)) Gallopade International.

—Wyoming "Jography" A Fun Run Thru Our State! 2001. (Carole Marsh Wyoming Bks.). 32p. (J). (gr. 3-8). pap. 7.95 (978-0-7933-9846-1(0)) Gallopade International.

—Wyoming Millionaire. 2001. (GameBook Ser.). (Illus.). 32p. (J). (gr. 3-8). pap., act. bk. ed. 9.95 (978-0-635-00116-0(0)) Gallopade International.

—Wyoming People Projects: 30 Cool, Activities, Crafts, Experiments & More for Kids to Do to Learn about Your State! 2003. (Wyoming Experience Ser.). 32p. (gr. k-5). pap. 5.95 (978-0-635-02019-2(X) , Marsh, Carole Bks.) Gallopade International.

—Wyoming Survivor. 2001. (GameBook Ser.). (Illus.). 32p. (J). (gr. 3-8). pap., act. bk. ed. 9.95 (978-0-635-00571-7(9)) Gallopade International.

—Wyoming Symbols & Facts Projects: 30 Cool, Activities, Crafts, Experiments & More for Kids to Do to Learn about Your State! 2003. (Wyoming Experience Ser.). 32p. (gr. k-5). pap. 5.95 (978-0-635-01919-6(1) , Marsh, Carole Bks.) Gallopade International.

—Wyoming Wheel of Fortune. 2001. (Carole Marsh Wyoming Bks.). lib. bdg. 29.95 (978-0-635-00017-0(2)); (Illus.). 32p. (J). (gr. 3-8). pap., act. bk. ed. 9.95 (978-0-635-00016-3(4)) Gallopade International.

Mis, Melody S. How to Draw Wyoming's Sights & Symbols. 2002. (Kids Guide to Drawing America Ser.). 32p. (J). lib. bdg. 25.25 (978-0-8239-6107-8(9) , PowerKids Pr.) Rosen Publishing Group, Inc., The.

Murray, Julie. Wyoming. 2006. (Buddy Book Ser.). (Illus.). 32p. (J). (gr. k-4). lib. bdg. 22.78 (978-1-59197-709-4(6) , Buddy Bks.) ABDO Publishing Co.

Parker, Janice. A Guide to Wyoming. 2001. (American States Ser.). (Illus.). 32p. (J). lib. bdg. 16.95 (978-1-930954-63-2(8)) Weigl Pubs., Inc.

Petreycik, Rick. Wyoming. 2007. (It's My State! Ser.). (Illus.). 80p. (J). lib. bdg. 29.93 ***(978-0-7614-1930-3(6)*** , Benchmark Bks.) Cavendish, Marshall Corp.

Thomas, William. Wyoming. 2006. (Portraits of the States Ser.). (J). pap. (978-0-8368-4729-1(6)); lib. bdg. (978-0-8368-4712-3(1)) Stevens, Gareth Inc.

Wyoming. 2000. (Switched on Schoolhouse Ser.). (Illus.). (YA). (gr. 7-12). pap. 24.95 incl. cd-rom (978-0-7403-0302-9(3) , SOSWY) Alpha Omega Pubns., Inc.

Zollman, Pam. Wyoming. 2006. (Rookie Read-About Geography Ser.). (Illus.). 32p. (J). (gr. 1-2). 20.50 ***(978-0-516-25389-3(1))*** Scholastic Library Publishing.

2006-2007 Tongue River Elementary 3rd Graders, text. Sheridan County History ABC Coloring & Activity Book - 2007. 2006-2007 Tongue River Elementary 3rd Graders, . 2007. (Illus.). 32p. (J). 3.95 ***(978-0-9792871-1-4(1))*** Sherian County Historical Society Pr.

WYOMING—FICTION

Ahlman, Larry. Terror in the Tetons. Larsen, Chuck, ed. Hanson, Dana, illus. 2005. (YA). (gr. 9-12). pap. 9.95 (978-0-9712906-2-4(8)) Ahlman Publishing.

Bell, Mary Reeves. Sagebrush Rebellion. 1999. (Passport to Danger Ser.: Vol. 2). 208p. (YA). (gr. 7-12). pap. 5.99 (978-1-55661-550-4(7)) Bethany Hse. Pubs.

—Sagebrush Rebellion. 1999. (J). (978-0-606-18973-6(4)) Tandem Library Bks.

Bjornson, Nancy. Llamas, Ponies & Pyrite. 2007. (J). ***(978-1-930596-82-5(0))*** Amherst Pr.

Black HIlls Summer. 2003. (YA). per. (978-0-9740718-0-0(3)) Strathmoor Pr.

Braden, Richard. South Pass. 2002. 146p. pap. 11.95 (978-0-595-21800-4(8) , Writer's Showcase Pr.) iUniverse, Inc.

Clark, Joan. Ann Drew Jackson. 2007. (J). pap. 17.95 ***(978-1-931282-45-1(5))*** Autism Asperger Publishing Co.

Clark, Joan. Jackson Whole Wyoming. 2005. 16.00 (978-1-931282-72-7(2) , 9945) Autism Asperger Publishing Co.

Ehrlich, Gretel. A Blizzard Year. Kiesler, Kate A., illus. 2001. 128p. (gr. 4-8). pap. 5.99 (978-0-7868-1245-5(1)) Hyperion Bks. for Children.

—A Blizzard Year. 2001. (J). (gr. 4-8). 12.64 (978-0-606-22572-4(2)) Tandem Library Bks.

Farnsworth, Frances Joyce. Tike & Tiny in the Tetons. 2007. (Illus.). 172p. (J). pap. 14.95 ***(978-0-943972-79-4(5))*** Homestead Publishing.

Gagliano, Eugene. The Secret of the Black Widow. 2002. 67p. (J). pap. 5.95 (978-1-57249-286-8(4) , White Mane Kids) White Mane Publishing Co., Inc.

George, Jean Craighead. Snowboard Twist. Minor, Wendell, illus. 2004. (Outdoor Adventures Ser.). 32p. (J). 15.99 (978-0-06-050595-0(8)) HarperCollins Pubs.

Gregory, Kristiana. Legend of Jimmy Spoon. 2002. (gr. 3-6). lib. bdg. 14.15 (978-0-613-58069-4(9)) Tandem Library Bks.

Harcourt School Publishers Staff. Cyber-Stuffing. 3rd ed. 2002. (Trophies English Language Learners Ser.). (Illus.). pap. 51.00 (978-0-15-327898-3(6)) Harcourt Schl. Pubs.

Keene, Carolyn. Mystery of the Mother Wolf. 2002. (gr. 5-8). lib. bdg. 13.00 (978-0-613-45084-3(1)) Tandem Library Bks.

Malcolm, Jahnna N. The Stallion of Box Canyon. Rabinowitz, Sandy & Keiffer, Christa, illus. l.t. ed. 1999. (Treasured Horses Collection). 122p. (J). (gr. 4 up). lib. bdg. 23.33 (978-0-8368-2283-0(8)) Stevens, Gareth Inc.

Marsh, Carole. The Case of the Crybaby Cowboy. 2006. 64p. (gr. 1-3). 14.95 ***(978-0-635-06199-7(6))*** Gallopade International.

—The Riddle of the Oogli Boogli. 2006. 64p. (gr. 1-3). 14.95 ***(978-0-635-06200-0(3))*** Gallopade International.

McDonald, Brix. Riding on the Wind. 1998. 243p. (YA). (gr. 5-10). pap. 9.95 (978-0-9661306-0-7(X)) Avenue Publishing.

Minich, Eric. Digger & the Search for Home. 2006. 48p. pap. 12.95 (978-1-4241-0321-8(5)) PublishAmerica, Inc.

Naylor, Phyllis Reynolds. Walker's Crossing. 2001. 240p. (J). (gr. 5-9). pap. 4.99 (978-0-689-84261-0(9) , Aladdin) Simon & Schuster Children's Publishing.

O'Hara, Mary. My Friend Flicka. 1999. (Illus.). 320p. (YA). (gr. 4-7). reprint ed. 37.95 (978-1-56849-725-9(3)) Buccaneer Bks., Inc.

—My Friend Flicka. 2003. (Charming Classics). (Illus.). 352p. (J). 6.99 (978-0-06-052429-6(4)) HarperCollins Pubs.

Ryan, Pam Muñoz. Paint the Wind. 2007. 336p. (J). (gr. 4-7). pap. 16.99 ***(978-0-439-87362-8(2)*** , Scholastic Pr.) Scholastic, Inc.

Sargent, Dave & Sargent, Pat. Hondo: (Silver Dun) Look for Good in Others, 30, 34. Lenoir, Jane, illus. 2003. (Saddle Up Ser.: Vol. 34). 42p. (J). pap. 6.95 (978-1-56763-802-8(3)); lib. bdg. 22.60 (978-1-56763-801-1(5)) Ozark Publishing.

Thomasma, Kenneth. Doe Sia: Bannock Girl & the Handcart Pioneer. 1999. (Amazing Indian Children: 8). (J). (gr. 3-8). pap. 7.99 (978-1-880114-20-9(8)); 12.99 (978-1-880114-21-6(6)) Grandview Publishing Co.

—Doe Sia: Bannock Girl & the Handcart Pioneers. 1999. (Illus.). (J). 14.64 (978-0-606-21884-9(X)) Tandem Library Bks.

Tidball, Lee. Windfork Secrets. Calderon, Dimitri, illus. unabr. ed. 1998. 280p. (J). pap. 16.95 (978-1-892896-06-3(0)) Infinity Publishing.

Wallace, Bill. Red Dog. 2002. 192p. (J). pap. 5.99 (978-0-689-85394-4(7) , Aladdin) Simon & Schuster Children's Publishing.

—Red Dog. 2002. (gr. 3-6). lib. bdg. 13.00 (978-0-613-64447-1(6)) Tandem Library Bks.

Yep, Laurence. The Traitor: Golden Mountain Chronicles: 1885. 2004. (Golden Mountain Chronicles). 320p. (J). (gr. 5 up). pap. 6.99 (978-0-06-000831-4(8) , Harper Trophy) HarperCollins Pubs.

WYOMING—HISTORY

Binns, Tristan Boyer. Fort Laramie. 2001. (Visiting the Past Ser.). 32p. (J). (gr. 5-7). lib. bdg. 24.22 (978-1-58810-271-3(8)) Heinemann Library.

Carole Marsh. Wyoming Indians. 2004. (Wyoming Experience Ser.). 36p. (gr. 3-8). 29.95 (978-0-635-02345-2(8)); pap. 7.95 (978-0-635-02344-5(X)) Gallopade International.

Gagliano, Eugene. Four Wheels West: A Wyoming Numbers Book. Guy, Susan, illus. 2006. 40p. (J). (gr. k-5). 17.95 (978-1-58536-210-3(7)) Sleeping Bear Pr.

A Guide to Wyoming. 2001. (American States Ser.). 32p. (J). per. (978-1-930954-07-6(7)) Weigl Pubs., Inc.

Lawrence, Jennie. Fort Laramie. 2004. (American Forts & Their Strategic Importance Ser.). (J). (978-1-59084-713-8(X)) Mason Crest Pubs.

Marsh, Carole. My First Pocket Guide Wyoming. 2000. (Wyoming Experience! Ser.). (Illus.). 96p. (J). (gr. 3-8). 12.95 (978-0-635-01340-8(1) , 13401) Gallopade International.

—Wyoming History Projects: 30 Cool, Activities, Crafts, Experiments & More for Kids to Do to Learn about Your State! 2003. (Wyoming Experience Ser.). 32p. (gr. k-5). pap. 5.95 (978-0-635-01819-9(5) , Marsh, Carole Bks.) Gallopade International.

Maynard, Charles W. Fort Laramie. 2002. (Famous Forts Throughout American History Ser.). (Illus.). 24p. (J). (gr. 3). lib. bdg. 18.75 (978-0-8239-5839-9(6) , PowerKids Pr.) Rosen Publishing Group, Inc., The.

Sniffin, Bill. High Altitudes, Low Multitudes: More Stories about Wyoming, the Best Part of America, 1. 2003. (Illus.). 252p. per. 14.95 (978-0-9639350-2-1(X) , 2000) WCS Corp.

Sodaro, Craig & Adams, Randy L. Wyoming: Courage in a Lonesome Land. Lynch, Don, ed. Fay, Keith, illus. 2nd rev. ed. 1998. 313p. (J). (gr. 4-6). 21.50 (978-0-913205-12-9(5)) Sage Hill Pubs., LLC.

X

X, MALCOLM, 1925-1965

Adoff, Arnold. Malcolm X. Gutierrez, Rudy, illus. 2000. (Trophy Chapter Bks.). 64p. (J). (gr. 2-5). pap. 4.99 (978-0-06-442118-8(X) , Harper Trophy) HarperCollins Pubs.

—Malcolm X. 2000. (978-0-606-18704-6(9)); (gr. 3-6). lib. bdg. 12.10 (978-0-8085-7577-1(5)) Tandem Library Bks.

Bednarz, Robert, et al. TIME for Kids Readers: Malcolm X. 3rd ed. 2002. (Harcourt Horizons Ser.). (gr. k-7). pap. 38.10 (978-0-15-335307-9(4)) Harcourt Schl. Pubs.

Benson, Michael. Malcolm X. (Just the Facts Biographies Ser.). (Illus.). 112p. (gr. 6-12). 2005. (J). 27.93 (978-0-8225-2444-1(9)); 2001. (YA). 27.93 (978-0-8225-5025-9(3) , Lerner Pubns.) Lerner Publishing Group.

Downing, David. Malcolm X. 2003. (Leading Lives Ser.). (Illus.). 64p. (J). lib. bdg. 28.50 (978-1-58810-579-0(2)) Heinemann Library.

—Malcolm X. 2003. (gr. 5-8). lib. bdg. 17.60 (978-0-613-60899-2(2)) Tandem Library Bks.

Gormley, Beatrice. Malcolm X: A Revolutionary Voice. 2008. (Sterling Biographies Ser.). (Illus.). 128p. (J). pap. 5.95 (***978-1-4027-4589-8(3)***) Sterling Publishing Co., Inc.

Graves, Renee. Malcolm X. (Cornerstones of Freedomtrade;, Second Ser.). 48p. (J). 2007. 5.95 (***978-0-531-18691-6(1)***); 2003. (Illus.). 26.00 (978-0-516-24224-8(5)) Scholastic Library Publishing. (Children's Pr.).

Jeffrey, Laura S. Betty Shabazz: Sharing the Vision of Malcolm X. 2000. (African-American Biographies Ser.). (Illus.). 128p. (YA). (gr. 6-12). lib. bdg. 26.60 (978-0-7660-1210-3(7)) Enslow Pubs., Inc.

Myers, Walter Dean. Malcolm X: A Fire Burning Brightly. Jenkins, Leonard, illus. 40p. (J). (gr. k-3). 2004. pap. 6.99 (978-0-06-056201-4(3) , Amistad); 2000. 16.99 (978-0-06-027707-9(6)); 2000. lib. bdg. 17.89 (978-0-06-027708-6(4)) HarperCollins Pubs.

—Malcolm X: A Fire Burning Brightly. 2004. (gr. k-3). lib. bdg. 14.15 (978-0-613-71960-5(3)) Tandem Library Bks.

—Malcolm X: By Any Means Necessary. 1999. pap. 5.99 (978-0-590-98759-2(3)); (YA). (gr. 5-8). pap. 4.99 (978-0-590-66221-5(X)) Scholastic, Inc.

—Malcolm X: By Any Means Necessary. 1999. (gr. 7-12). lib. bdg. 12.40 (978-0-7857-2448-3(6)) Tandem Library Bks.

Rummel, Jack & Wagner, Heather Lehr, texts. Malcolm X: Militant Black Leader. (Black Americans of Achievement Ser.). (Illus.). 112p. (J). (gr. 6-12). 2005. pap. 13.25 (978-0-7910-8336-9(5)); 2004. 30.00 (978-0-7910-8162-4(1)) Facts On File, Inc. (Chelsea Hse.).

X-MEN (FICTITIOUS CHARACTERS)—FICTION

Bedard, Tony, et al. Exiles Vol. 8: Earn Your Wings TPB. 2004. (X-Men Ser.). (Illus.). 144p. 14.99 (978-0-7851-1459-8(9)) Marvel Enterprises, Inc.

Bendis, Brian Michael. Blockbuster. Finch, David, illus. 2004. 160p. lib. bdg. 24.35 (978-1-4176-6045-2(7)) Tandem Library Bks.

—New Mutants. Finch, David, illus. 2004. lib. bdg. 24.35 (978-1-4176-6046-9(5)) Tandem Library Bks.

Bendis, Brian Michael & Finch, David. Ultimate X-Men, Vol. 4. 2005. (X-Men Ser.). (Illus.). 304p. 29.99 (978-0-7851-1251-8(0)) Marvel Enterprises, Inc.

Carey, Mike. Ultimate X-Men/Fantastic Four TPB. 2006. (Illus.). 152p. pap. 12.99 (978-0-7851-2292-0(3)) Marvel Enterprises, Inc.

Claremont, Chris. Days of Future Past. 2004. (X-Men Ser.). (Illus.). 144p. (YA). 19.99 (978-0-7851-1560-1(9)) Marvel Enterprises, Inc.

—X-Men. 2005. (Essential Ser.: Vol. 2). (Illus.). 584p. pap. 16.99 (978-0-7851-2007-0(6)) Marvel Enterprises, Inc.

—X-Men: the Dark Phoenix Saga (New Printing) TPB: The Dark Phoenix Saga (New Printing) TPB. 2006. (Illus.). 200p. pap. 24.99 (978-0-7851-2213-5(3)) Marvel Enterprises, Inc.

Claremont, Chris & Lee. X-Men: Mutant Genesis TPB: Mutant Genesis TPB. 2nd ed. 2006. (Illus.). 184p. pap. 19.99 (978-0-7851-2212-8(5)) Marvel Enterprises, Inc.

Claremont, Chris & Milligan, Peter. Decimation: X-Men - the Day after TPB: X-Men - the Day after TPB. 2006. (Illus.). 160p. pap. 15.99 (978-0-7851-1984-5(1)) Marvel Enterprises, Inc.

DeFalco, Tom. X-Men: Firestar Digest: Firestar Digest. 2006. (Illus.). 104p. pap. 7.99 (978-0-7851-2200-5(1)) Marvel Enterprises, Inc.

Dorling Kindersley Publishing Staff. Glow-in-the-Dark X-Men. 2006. (Ultimate Sticker Bks.). 16p. (J). pap. 6.99 (978-0-7566-1998-5(X)) Dorling Kindersley Publishing, Inc.

—X-Men. 2006. (Ultimate Sticker Bks.). 16p. (J). pap. 6.99 (978-0-7566-1997-8(1)) Dorling Kindersley Publishing, Inc.

Ellis, Warren & Hairsine, Trevor. Ultimate Galactus: Nightmare. 2005. (Ultimate Galactus: Vol. 1). (Illus.). 120p. pap. 12.99 (978-0-7851-1497-0(1)) Marvel Enterprises, Inc.

Fingeroth, Danny. The Last Stand: The Junior Novel. 2006. (X Men Ser.). 144p. (J). pap. 4.99 (978-0-06-082208-8(2)) HarperCollins Pubs.

Gallagher, Michael. X-Men, Magneto's Master Plan. Severin, Marie, illus. 24p. (YA). (gr. k up). 12.95 (978-0-9627001-6-3(9)) Futech Educational Products, Inc.

—X-Men, Scourge of the Savage Land. Severin, Marie, illus. 24p. (YA). (gr. k up). 12.95 (978-0-9627001-7-0(7)) Futech Educational Products, Inc.

Grayson, Devin. Am I Blue. 2006. (X-Men, Evolution Ser.). (Illus.). (J). (gr. 2-6). 21.35 (978-1-59961-052-8(3)) Spotlight.

—Hearing Things. 2006. (X-Men Evolution Ser.). (Illus.). 21.35 (978-1-59961-053-5(1)) Spotlight.

—Lines in the Sand. 2006. (X-Men, Evolution Ser.). (Illus.). (J). (gr. 2-6). 21.35 (978-1-59961-054-2(X)) Spotlight.

—Seeing Clearly. 2006. (X-Men, Evolution Ser.). (Illus.). (J). (gr. 2-6). 21.35 (978-1-59961-055-9(8)) Spotlight.

Hapka, Catherine. The Last Stand: Beast Chooses Sides. Gordon, Steven E., illus. 2006. (X Men Ser.). 24p. (J). pap. 3.99 (978-0-06-082202-6(3)) HarperCollins Pubs.

—The Last Stand: Teaming Up. Kirkland, Boyd, illus. 2006. (X Men Ser.). 24p. (J). pap. 3.99 (978-0-06-082201-9(5)) HarperCollins Pubs.

Hibbert, Clare. Meet the X-Men. 2006. (Dk Readers Ser.). (Illus.). 32p. (J). 14.99 (978-0-7566-1927-5(0)); pap. 3.99 (978-0-7566-1928-2(9)) Dorling Kindersley Publishing, Inc.

Hine, David. Mr. M. 2005. (X-Men Ser.: Vol. 1). (Illus.). 144p. (YA). pap. 14.99 (978-0-7851-1444-4(0)) Marvel Enterprises, Inc.

Jacobs, Lana. The Last Stand: Coloring & Activity Book & Crayons. Gordon, Steven E., illus. 2006. (X Men Ser.). 32p. (J). pap., act. bk. ed. 4.99 (978-0-06-082210-1(4)) HarperCollins Pubs.

Jenkins, Paul. Decimation: Generation M TPB: Generation M TPB. 2006. (Illus.). 120p. pap. 13.99 (978-0-7851-1958-6(2)) Marvel Enterprises, Inc.

Jenson, Jeff. X Factor. Ranson, Arthur, illus. 2003. (X-Men Ser.: Vol. 1). 96p. (YA). pap. 9.99 (978-0-7851-1016-3(X)) Marvel Enterprises, Inc.

Kyle, Craig & Yost, Christopher. Childhood's End, Vol. 1. 2006. (Illus.). 104p. (YA). pap. 10.99 (978-0-7851-1831-2(4)) Marvel Enterprises, Inc.

Lime, Harry. The Last Stand: Meet the X-Men. Gordon, Steven E., illus. 2006. (I Can Read Bks.). 32p. (J). pap. 3.99 (978-0-06-082204-0(X) , Harper Trophy) HarperCollins Pubs.

—The Last Stand: Rogue Finds a Home. Kirkland, Boyd, illus. 2006. (I Can Read Bks.). 32p. (J). pap. 3.99 (978-0-06-082205-7(8) , Harper Trophy) HarperCollins Pubs.

Lobdell, Scott & Robinson, James. X-Men: Zero Tolerance. Madureira, Joe & Yu, Leinil Francis, illus. 2000. (Marvels Finest Ser.). 336p. (J). pap. 24.95 (978-0-7851-0738-5(X) , Marvel's Finest) Marvel Enterprises, Inc.

Lobdell, Scott, et al. X-Men: Dreams End. 2004. (X-Men Ser.). (Illus.). 192p. pap. 17.99 (978-0-7851-1551-9(X)) Marvel Enterprises, Inc.

Marvel Characters, Inc Staff. X-Men Pop-Up: Marvel True Believers Retro Collection. Repchuck, Caroline, ed. 2007. (Marvel True Believers Ser.). (Illus.). 16p. (J). (gr. k). 24.99 (***978-0-7636-3462-9(X)***) Candlewick Pr.

McDonnell, David, ed. Spiderman & Other Amazing Heroes. 2004. (Starlog Movie Magic Ser.). (YA). pap. (978-0-88013-065-3(2)) Profile Entertainment, Inc.

Meredith Books Staff & Marvel Books Staff. The Brotherhood of Monsters. Curry, Don, ed. 2006. (X-Men Ser.). 24p. (J). pap. 3.99 (978-0-696-22984-8(6)) Meredith Bks.

Millar, Mark. Hellfire & Brimstone, 4 vols., Vol. 4. Kubert, Adam et al, illus. 2003. (Ultimate X-Men Ser.: Vol. 4). 144p. (YA). pap. 12.99 (978-0-7851-1089-7(5)) Marvel Enterprises, Inc.

—Return of the King, 7 vols., Vol. 6. Kubert, Adam & Finch, David, illus. 2003. (Ultimate X-men Ser.). 192p. pap. 16.99 (978-0-7851-1091-0(7)) Marvel Enterprises, Inc.

—Ultimate War, 6 vols., Vol. 5. Bachalo, Chris, illus. 2003. (Ultimate X-Men Ser.: Vol. 5). 112p. (J). pap. 10.99 (978-0-7851-1129-0(8)) Marvel Enterprises, Inc.

—Ultimate X-Men, 3 vols., Vol. 3. 2003. (Ultimate X-men Ser.). (Illus.). 312p. 29.99 (978-0-7851-1131-3(X)) Marvel Enterprises, Inc.

—Ultimate X-Men: The Tomorrow People. 2002. (gr. 5-8). lib. bdg. 24.55 (978-0-613-53690-5(8)) Tandem Library Bks.

Millar, Mark & Austen, Chuck. Ultimate X-Men, 2 vols., Vol. 2. Kubert, Adam et al, illus. 2003. (Ultimate X-men Ser.). 336p. (YA). 29.99 (978-0-7851-1130-6(1)) Marvel Enterprises, Inc.

Millar, Mark & Johns, Geoff. The Ultimate Collection, Vol. 1. 2006. (Illus.). 336p. pap. 24.99 (978-0-7851-2187-9(0)) Marvel Enterprises, Inc.

Milligan, Peter. Good Omens. Allred, Mike, illus. 2003. (X-Statix Ser.). 128p. (YA). 11.99 (978-0-7851-1059-0(3)) Marvel Enterprises, Inc.

—X-Force: Famous, Mutant & Mortal. Allred, Mike, illus. 2003. (X-Statix Ser.). 352p. (YA). 29.99 (978-0-7851-1023-1(2)) Marvel Enterprises, Inc.

Morrison, Grant. New Worlds, Vol. 3. Kordey, Igor & Quitely, Frank, illus. 2002. 168p. (YA). (gr. 8 up). 14.99 (978-0-7851-0976-1(5)) Marvel Enterprises, Inc.

Nicieza, Fabian. X-Force: Big Guns. Liefeld, Rob, illus. 2004. (X-Force Ser.). 136p. pap. 15.99 (978-0-7851-1483-3(1)) Marvel Enterprises, Inc.

Parker, Jeff. The Bird, the Beast & the Lizard. 2007. (X-Men: First Class Ser.). 24p. (J). (gr. 2-6). 21.35 (***978-1-59961-398-7(0)***) Spotlight.

—A Life of the Mind. 2007. (X-Men: First Class Ser.). (ENG.). 24p. (J). (gr. 2-6). lib. bdg. 21.35 (***978-1-59961-399-4(9)***) Spotlight.

—Seeing Red. 2007. (X-Men: First Class Ser.). 24p. (J). (gr. 2-6). 21.35 (***978-1-59961-400-7(6)***) Spotlight.

—X-Men 101. 2007. (X-Men: First Class Ser.). 24p. (J). (gr. 2-6). 21.35 (***978-1-59961-401-4(4)***) Spotlight.

Rodi, Robert & Richards, Cliff. Rogue: Going Rogue. 2005. (X-Men Ser.). (Illus.). 144p. pap. 14.99 (978-0-7851-1336-2(3)) Marvel Enterprises, Inc.

Roman, Steven A. & Timmons, Stan. Doctor Doom, 3 vols., Bk. 1. 2000. (Chaos Engine Trilogy Ser.: Vol. 1). (Illus.). 384p. (gr. 4-7). pap. (978-0-7434-0019-0(4)) ibooks, Inc.

—X-Men: Magneto, 3 vols. 2002. (Chaos Engine Ser.: Bk. 2). (Illus.). 320p. (gr. 4-7). pap. (978-0-7434-0023-7(2)) ibooks, Inc.

Sanderson, Peter. X-Men: The Ultimate Guide. 2006. (Illus.). 192p. (J). 24.99 (978-0-7566-2005-9(8)) Dorling Kindersley Publishing, Inc.

Simone, Gail. Gus Beezer with the X-Men: X Marks the Mutant. 2006. (Marvelous Adventures of Gus Beezer Ser.). (Illus.). (J). (gr. 2-6). 21.35 (978-1-59961-050-4(7)) Spotlight.

Simonson, Louise, et al. X-Factor. 2007. (Essential Ser.: Vol. 2). (Illus.). 544p. pap. 16.99 (978-0-7851-2099-5(8)) Marvel Enterprises, Inc.

The Story of the X-Men. 2003. (Dk Readers Ser.). (J). pap. 3.99 (978-0-7894-4299-4(X)) Dorling Kindersley Publishing, Inc.

Sumerak, Marc. Big Trouble at the Big Top. 2007. 21.35 (978-1-59961-219-5(4)) Spotlight.

—Costumes On. 2007. 21.35 (978-1-59961-220-1(8)) Spotlight.

—Mind over Matter. 2007. 21.35 (978-1-59961-222-5(4)) Spotlight.

Teitelbaum, Michael. The Story of the X-Men: How It All Began. O'Neill, Cynthia, ed. 2000. (Dorling Kindersley Readers Ser.). (Illus.). 32p. (J). (gr. 4-7). pap. 3.99 (978-0-7894-6697-6(X)) Dorling Kindersley Publishing, Inc.

—The Story of the X-Men: How It All Began. 2000. (978-0-606-22326-3(6)) Tandem Library Bks.

Teitelbaum, Michael & Dorling Kindersley Publishing Staff. The Story of the X-Men: How It All Began. 2000. (Dorling Kindersley Readers Ser.). (Illus.). 32p. (J). (gr. 4-7). 12.99 (978-0-7894-6696-9(1)) Dorling Kindersley Publishing, Inc.

Teitelbaum, Michael. X-Men School. 2006. (Dk Readers Ser.). (Illus.). 48p. (J). 14.99 (978-0-7566-1929-9(7)); pap. 3.99 (978-0-7566-1930-5(0)) Dorling Kindersley Publishing, Inc.

Thomas, Roy, et al. Essential Classic X-Men, Vol. 2. 2006. (Illus.). 640p. pap. 16.99 (978-0-7851-2116-9(1)) Marvel Enterprises, Inc.

Vaughan, Brian K. Cry Wolf. Kubert, Andy, illus. 2005. 96p. lib. bdg. 19.75 (978-1-4176-6048-3(1)) Tandem Library Bks.

—Magnetic North. 2006. (Illus.). 128p. (YA). pap. 12.99 (978-0-7851-1906-7(X)) Marvel Enterprises, Inc.

—The Tempest. 2004. (X-Men Ser.: Vol. 9). (Illus.). 112p. (YA). 10.99 (978-0-7851-1404-8(1)) Marvel Enterprises, Inc.

—Ultimate X Men, Vol. 5. 2006. (Illus.). 296p. (YA). 29.99 (978-0-7851-2103-9(X)) Marvel Enterprises, Inc.

Vaughan, Brian K. & Kubert, Andy. Cry Wolf, Vol. 10. 2005. (X-Men Ser.). (Illus.). 96p. pap. 8.99 (978-0-7851-1405-5(X)) Marvel Enterprises, Inc.

Whedon, Joss. Astonishing X-Men, Vol.1. gif. ed. (Illus.). 152p. (YA). pap. 14.99 (978-0-7851-1531-1(5)) Marvel Enterprises, Inc.

—Astonishing X-Men HC Variant, Vol. 1. (Illus.). 320p. 29.99 (978-0-7851-2301-9(6)) Marvel Enterprises, Inc.

Windsor-Smith, Barry. Wolverine Weapon X Premiere. 2007. (Illus.). 152p. 19.99 (***978-0-7851-2327-9(X)***) Marvel Enterprises, Inc.

X-Men. 2003. (J). (978-1-57657-859-9(3)) Paradise Pr., Inc.

X-Men Power Pack. 2007. 85.40 (978-1-59961-218-8(6)) Spotlight.

X-RAYS

Garcia, Kimberly. Wilhelm Roentgen & the Discovery of X-Rays. 2001. (Unlocking the Secrets of Science Ser.). (Illus.). 56p. (gr. 4-10). lib. bdg. 17.95 (978-1-58415-114-2(5)) Mitchell Lane Pubs., Inc.

McClafferty, Carla Killough. The Head Bone's Connected to the Neck Bone: The Weird, Wacky, & Wonderful X-Ray. 2001. (Illus.). 160p. (J). 17.00 (978-0-374-32908-2(7) , Farrar, Straus & Giroux (BYR)) Farrar, Straus & Giroux.

Olson, Karen. Cooper Gets a Cast. Pritchett and Hull Associates, Inc., illus. 2003. (J). 4.50 (978-0-939838-86-8(9)) Pritchett & Hull Assocs., Inc.

—Cooper Gets & Xray. 2002. (J). 4.50 (978-0-939838-85-1(0)) Pritchett & Hull Assocs., Inc.

Sarver, Amy. Science at the Airport. 2004. (Illus.). 24p. (J). pap. (978-0-7922-4568-1(7)) National Geographic Society.

Scott, Richard A. 13 Weeks - Radiographers Who Dare: The Travels & Travails of an X-Ray Tech. 2001. (Illus.). 300p. (YA). (gr. 5 up). pap. (978-1-58470-073-9(4) , Riccardini 9949) Cornerstone Productions, Inc.

Simon, Seymour. Out of Sight: Pictures of Hidden World. 2000. (gr. 3-6). lib. bdg. 15.25 (978-0-613-44470-5(1)) Tandem Library Bks.

—Out of Sight: Pictures of Hidden Worlds. 2002. (Illus.). 48p. (J). (gr. k up). 6.95 (978-1-58717-149-9(X) , SeaStar Bks.) Chronicle Bks. LLC.

Zonta, Pat. Jessica's X-Ray. Dobson, Clive, illus. 2006. 24p. (J). (gr. 1-3). 19.95 (978-1-55297-578-7(9)); pap. 8.95 (978-1-55297-577-0(0)) Firefly Bks., Ltd.

—Jessica's X-Ray. 2002. (gr. 3-6). lib. bdg. 17.60 (978-0-613-56461-8(8)) Tandem Library Bks.

Y

YANGTZE RIVER AND VALLEY

Bowden, Rob. The Yangtze. 2003. (River Journey Ser.). (Illus.). 48p. (J). lib. bdg. 28.56 (978-0-7398-6074-8(7)) Raintree.

Meister, Cari. Yangtze River. 2002. (Rivers & Lakes Ser.). (Illus.). 24p. (J). (gr. k-6). lib. bdg. 21.35 (978-1-57765-103-1(0) , Checkerboard Library) ABDO Publishing Co.

Olson, Nathan. The Yangtze River. 2004. (Fact Finders Ser.). (J). 22.60 (978-0-7368-2485-9(5)) Capstone Pr., Inc.

Simon, Charnan. The Noble Yangtze. 2004. (Geography of the World Ser.). (Illus.). 32p. (J). (gr. 2-6). 27.07 (978-1-59296-341-6(2)) Child's World, Inc.

Waterlow, Julia. The Yangtze. 2003. (Great Rivers of the World Ser.). (Illus.). 48p. (gr. 5 up). (J). pap. 14.95 (978-0-8368-5454-1(3)); (YA). lib. bdg. 30.00 (978-0-8368-5447-3(0)) Stevens, Gareth Inc. (World Almanac Library).

YANGTZE RIVER AND VALLEY—FICTION

Flack, Marjorie. The Story about Ping. Flack, Marjorie, illus. 2002. (Illus.). (J). 11.06 (978-0-7587-3710-6(6)) Book Wholesalers, Inc.

A Story about Ping. 2004. (J). pap. 14.95 incl. audio (978-1-55592-857-5(9)) Weston Woods Studios, Inc.

YEARBOOKS

see also Almanacs; Calendars

Klawitter, Pamela Amick & Schwartz, Linda. A Do-It-Yourself Yearbook. Parks, Kathy, ed. Armstrong, Beverly, illus. 1999. 64p. (J). (gr. 3-6). pap. 11.99 (978-0-88160 239-5(6) , LW-334, Learning Works, The) Creative Teaching Pr., Inc.

YELLOW FEVER

Cefrey, Holly. Yellow Fever. 2002. (Epidemics Ser.). (Illus.). 64p. (YA). (gr. 7-12). lib. bdg. 26.50 (978-0-8239-3489-8(6)) Rosen Publishing Group, Inc., The.

Murphy, Jim. An American Plague: The True & Terrifying Story of the Yellow Fever Epidemic of 1793. 2003. (Illus.). 176p. (J). (gr. 5-9). tchr. ed. 17.00 (978-0-395-77608-7(2) , Clarion Bks.) Houghton Mifflin Co. Trade & Reference Div.

Slade, Suzanne. The Four Seasons. 2007. (Cycles in Nature Ser.). (Illus.). 24p. (J). (gr. 4-6). lib. bdg. 21.25 (978-1-4042-3489-5(6)) Rosen Publishing Group, Inc., The.

YELLOW RIVER

Dramer, Kim. The Yellow River. 2001. (World of Water Ser.). (Illus.). 64p. (J). (gr. 5-7). 25.50 (978-0-531-11855-9(X) , Watts, Franklin) Scholastic Library Publishing.

—Yellow River. 2001. (gr. 3-6). lib. bdg. 17.60 (978-0-613-37600-6(5)) Tandem Library Bks.

YELLOWSTONE NATIONAL PARK

Aretha, David. Yellowstone National Park. 2008. (J). (***978-1-59845-083-5(2)*** , MyReportLinks.com Bks.) Enslow Pubs., Inc.

Bauer, Marion Dane. Yellowstone. Wallace, John, illus. 2008. (Wonders of America Ser.). 32p. (J). pap. 3.99 (***978-1-4169-5404-0(X)***); lib. bdg. 13.89 (***978-1-4169-5405-7(8)***) Simon & Schuster Children's Publishing. (Aladdin).

Craighead, Shirley A. Bugling Elk & Sleeping Grizzlies: The Who, What, & When of Yellowstone & Grand Teton National Parks. 2004. (Illus.). 48p. pap. 9.95 (978-0-7627-2864-0(7) , Falcon) Globe Pequot Pr., The.

W X Y Z

Francis, Michael H. Yellowstone Memories: 30 Years of Photographs & Stories. 2005. (Illus.). 95p. 22.95 (978-1-931832-59-5(5) , 8667872363) Riverbend Publishing.

George, Jean Craighead. And the Wolves Came Back. Minor, Wendell, illus. 2008. 32p. (J). (gr. k). 16.99 (***978-0-525-47947-5(3)*** , Dutton Juvenile) Penguin Group (USA) Inc.

Graf, Mike. Yellowstone National Park. 2002. (National Parks Ser.). (Illus.). 24p. (J). (gr. 2-3). lib. bdg. 18.60 (978-0-7368-1379-2(9) , Bridgestone Bks.) Capstone Pr., Inc.

Halfpenny, James C. Yellowstone Wolves in the Wild. 2003. (Illus.). 104p. per. 19.95 (978-1-931832-26-7(9) , 8667872363) Riverbend Publishing.

Hall, Margaret. Yellowstone National Park. 2005. (Heinemann First Library). (Illus.). 32p. (J). pap. (978-1-4034-6709-6(9)); lib. bdg. 25.36 (978-1-4034-6702-7(1)) Heinemann Library.

Harcourt School Publishers Staff. Yellowstone Advanced Level: Geology at Work. 3rd ed. 2002. (Trophies Reading Program Ser.). (Illus.). pap. 5.10 (978-0-15-323382-1(6)) Harcourt Schl. Pubs.

Hughes, Sandy & Hill, Anita. Yellowstone & Teton Kids' Field Book. Hughes, Seth, illus. 1998. 24p. (Orig.). (J). (gr. 4-10). pap. 3.50 (978-0-9665833-0-4(2)) One Feather Publishing.

Jackson, Donna. Wildlife Detectives. 2000. (gr. 3-6). lib. bdg. 12.95 (978-0-613-60739-1(2)) Tandem Library Bks.

Justesen, Kim Williams. Hey Ranger! Kids Ask Questions about Yellowstone National Park. Newhouse, Judy, illus. 2005. 48p. (J). pap. 9.95 (978-0-7627-3846-5(4) , Falcon) Globe Pequot Pr., The.

Klingel, Cynthia Fitterer & Noyed, Robert B. Yellowstone National Park. 2000. (Wonder Books Level 3: Landmarks Ser.). (Illus.). 32p. (J). (ps-3). 22.79 (978-1-56766-828-5(3)) Child's World, Inc.

Martin, Cyd. A Yellowstone ABC. 2000. (Illus.). 20p. (ps-3). pap. 5.95 (978-1-879373-12-9(2)) Rinehart, Roberts Pubs.

Meister, Cari. Yellowstone National Park. 2000. (Going Places Ser.). (Illus.). 24p. (J). (gr. k-6). lib. bdg. 21.35 (978-1-57765-026-3(3) , Checkerboard Library) ABDO Publishing Co.

Pecorella, Jane. Yellowstone, Our First National Park. 2003. (Reading Room Collection). (Illus.). 24p. (J). lib. bdg. 18.75 (978-0-8239-3712-7(7)) Rosen Publishing Group, Inc., The.

Petersen, David. Yellowstone National Park. 2001. (True Bks.). (Illus.). 48p. (J). (gr. 3-5). pap. 6.95 (978-0-516-27326-6(4) , Children's Pr.) Scholastic Library Publishing.

—Yellowstone National Park. 2001. (gr. 3-6). lib. bdg. 15.25 (978-0-613-54799-4(3)) Tandem Library Bks.

Peterson, David. Yellowstone National Park. 2001. (National Parks Ser.). (Illus.). 48p. (J). (gr. 3-5). 25.00 (978-0-516-21668-3(6) , Children's Pr.) Scholastic Library Publishing.

Robson, Gary D. Who Pooped in the Park: Yellowstone. 2004. (Illus.). 48p. (J). pap. 9.95 (978-1-56037-273-8(7)) Farcountry Pr.

Temple, Teri & Temple, Bob. Welcome to Yellowstone National Park. 2006. (Visitor Guides Ser.). (Illus.). 32p. (J). (gr. 1-5). 27.07 (978-1-59296-703-2(5)) Child's World, Inc.

Wade, Linda R. Yellowstone National Park. 2005. (National Parks Ser.). (Illus.). 32p. (J). (gr. 3-8). lib. bdg. 24.21 (978-1-59197-427-7(5)) ABDO Publishing Co.

YETI

Gilman, Laura Anne. Yeti, the Abominable Snowman. 2005. (Unsolved Mysteries Ser.). (Illus.). 48p. (YA). (gr. 5-8). lib. bdg. 25.25 (978-0-8239-3565-9(5)) Rosen Publishing Group, Inc., The.

Innes, Brian. Giant Humanlike Beasts. 1999. (Unsolved Mysteries Ser.). 48p. (YA). (gr. 3 up). lib. bdg. (978-0-8172-5484-1(6)) Raintree.

—Giant Humanlike Beasts. 1999. (Unsolved Mysteries Ser.). (Illus.). 48p. (J). (gr. 3-7). pap. 8.05 (978-0-8172-5846-7(9)) Steck-Vaughn.

Shone, Rob. Bigfoot & Other Strange Beasts. Spender, Nik, illus. 2005. (Graphic Mysteries Ser.). (J). (978-1-4042-0816-2(X)); 48p. pap. (978-1-4042-0804-9(6)) Rosen Publishing Group, Inc., The.

—Bigfoot & Other Strange Beasts. Spender, Nick, illus. 2005. (Graphic Mysteries Ser.). 48p. (J). (gr. 5-8). lib. bdg. 29.95 (978-1-4042-0793-6(7)) Rosen Publishing Group, Inc., The.

Teitelbaum, Michael. Bigfoot Caught on Film. 2007. (24/7 - Science Behind the Scenes Ser.). 64p. (J). (gr. 8-12). 26.00 (978-0-531-12078-1(3) , Watts, Franklin) Scholastic Library Publishing.

Teitelbaum, Michael. Bigfoot Caught on Film: And Other Monster Sightings! 2008. (24/7: Science Behind the Scenes: Mystery Files Ser.). 64p. (J). pap. 7.95 (***978-0-531-17531-6(6)*** , Watts, Franklin) Scholastic Library Publishing.

Wallace, Holly. The Mystery of the Abominable Snowman. 2006. (Can Science Solve? Ser.). (Illus.). 32p. (978-1-4034-8335-5(3)); 2nd ed. pap. (978-1-4034-8344-7(2)) Heinemann Library.

Yorke, Malcolm & Davis, Lee. Beastly Tales: Big Foot, Yeti & the Loch Ness Monster. 1998. (Eyewitness Readers). (Illus.). 48p. (J). (gr. 2-3). pap. 3.99 (978-0-7894-2962-9(4) , 0-7894-4754-1) Dorling Kindersley Publishing, Inc.

YOGA

Baptiste, Baron. My Daddy Is a Pretzel: Yoga for Parents & Kids. Fatus, Sophie, illus. 2004. 48p. (J). (ps-2). 16.99 (978-1-84148-151-7(3)) Barefoot Bks., Inc.

Bassett, Carol. Walk Like a Bear, Stand Like a Tree, Run Like the Wind. 2004. 40p. (978-0-9740485-0-5(X)) Nubod Concept, Inc.

Birkemoe, Karen. Strike a Pose: The Planet Girl Guide to Yoga. Collett, Heather, illus. 2007. (Planet Girl Ser.). 96p. (YA). (gr. 5-10). (***978-1-55337-004-8(X)***) Kids Can Pr., Ltd.

Buckley, Annie. The Kids' Yoga Deck: 50 Poses & Games. Buckley, Annie, illus. 2003. (Illus.). (YA). 14.95 (978-0-8118-3698-2(3)) Chronicle Bks. LLC.

Caldwell, Micheala. The Girls' Yoga Book: Stretch Your Body, Open Your Mind, & Have Fun! D#0225;vila, Claudia, illus. 2005. (Girl Zone Ser.). 64p. 16.95 (978-1-897066-24-9(4)) Maple Tree Pr. CAN. *Dist:* Perseus Distribution.

—The Girls' Yoga Book: Stretch Your Body, Open Your Mind, & Have Fun! Davila, Claudia, illus. 2005. (Girl Zone Ser.). 64p. pap. 9.95 (978-1-897066-25-6(2)) Maple Tree Pr. CAN. *Dist:* Perseus Distribution.

Chryssicas, Mary Kaye. Breathe: Yoga for Teens. 2007. (Illus.). 160p. (J). pap. 14.99 (978-0-7566-2661-7(7)) Dorling Kindersley Publishing, Inc.

—I Love Yoga: Yoga for Kids. Coppola, Angela, photos by. 2005. (Illus.). 48p. (J). (gr. 4-7). 12.99 (978-0-7566-1400-3(7)) Dorling Kindersley Publishing, Inc.

Cooper, Evan. Um, Like... OM: A Girl Goddess's Guide to Yoga. 2005. (Illus.). 192p. (J). (gr. 7-17). pap. 9.99 (978-0-316-98001-2(3)) Little Brown & Co.

de Brunhoff, Laurent. Babar's Yoga for Elephants. (Illus.). 48p. (J). (ps-3). 2006. 9.95 (978-0-8109-3076-6(5)); 2002. 16.95 (978-0-8109-1021-8(7)) Abrams, Harry N. , Inc.

Dyer, Ann. Zyoga, the Yoga Sleep Ritual, 1 vol. 2005. (Illus.). 32p. DVD, audio compact disk (978-0-9752988-1-7(X)) Sleep Garden, Inc.

Finestone, J. A Girl's Guide to Yoga. 2004. (Ener-Chi Bks.). (Illus.). 80p. (J). pap. 8.95 (978-0-7641-2839-4(6)) Barron's Educational Series, Inc.

Guber, Tara & Kalish, Leah. Yoga Pretzels: 50 Fun Yoga Activities for Kids & Grownups. Fatus, Sophie, illus. 2005. 50p. 14.99 (978-1-905236-04-6(2)) Barefoot Bks., Inc.

I Am the Sky: Yoga for Children. 2001. 60p. pap. 12.00 (978-1-885289-06-3(5)) Art of Living Books & Tapes.

Koch, Isabelle. Like a Fish in Water: Yoga for Children. 1999. (Illus.). 56p. 12.95 (978-0-89281-773-3(9) , Healing Arts Pr.) Inner Traditions International, Ltd.

Lark, Liz. Yoga for Kids. Park, Clare, photos by. 2005. (Illus.). 127p. (J). reprint ed. pap. 20.00 (978-0-7567-9410-1(2)) DIANE Publishing Co.

—Yoga for Young People: Essential Yoga Poses to Help Young People Get Fit, Flexib. 2003. (gr. 5-8). lib. bdg. 18.75 (978-0-613-78007-0(8)) Tandem Library Bks.

Lloyd, Elly. Discover Yoga. 2005. (Illus.). 96p. pap. incl. DVD (978-1-84510-566-2(4)) Top That! Publishing PLC.

MacAulay, Kelley & Kalman, Bobbie. Yoga in Action. 2005. (Illus.). 32p. (J). (978-0-7787-0344-0(4)); pap. (978-0-7787-0364-8(9)) Crabtree Publishing Co.

Miller, Cecilia. Walking the Path with Neela: An Alphabet of Siddha Yoga Meditation. Heavner, Obadinah, illus. 1998. 48p. (J). pap. 10.95 (978-0-911307-66-5(4)) SYDA Foundation.

Pierce, Karen F. Yoga Bear: Yoga for Youngsters. Brinkman, Paula, illus. 2004. 48p. (ps-1). 15.95 (978-1-55971-897-4(8) , NorthWord Bks. for Young Readers) T&N Children's Publishing.

Prakash, Shamsher. Introduction to Prevention & Yoga. (Illus.). (Orig.). (YA). (gr. 9-12). pap. (978-0-9641737-0-5(0)) Prakash, Shamsher Foundation.

Purperhart, Helen. The Yoga Adventure for Children: Playing, Dancing, Moving, Breathing, Relaxing. Von Amelsfort, Barbra, illus. 2007. 144p. pap. 14.95 (978-0-89793-470-1(9)); spiral bd. 19.95 (978-0-89793-471-8(7)) Hunter Hse., Inc.

Randall, Kat. Yoga for Youngsters: Playful Poses for Little People. 2004. (Illus.). 24p. pap. 8.95 (978-0-9749516-0-7(9)) Kat's Kids Kreation, A.

Ripslinger, Jon. I Love Yoga: A Guide for Kids & Teens. 2003. (gr. 5-8). lib. bdg. 18.75 (978-0-613-71005-3(3)) Tandem Library Bks.

Rossetta, Lani A. Freddie Froga Loves to Yoga, II. 2002. 30p. (J). 5.95 (978-0-9709866-3-4(7)) Leihuna Enterprises.

—Frieda Froga Loves to Yoga. 2001. 22p. 5.95 (978-0-9709866-2-7(9)) Leihuna Enterprises.

—Nikki & Little Lily Froga Love to Yoga, III. 2002. 23p. (J). 5.95 (978-0-9709866-4-1(5)) Leihuna Enterprises.

Ryzewski, Deborah. The Yoga ABC's with Alvin, Beatrice & Conner. ed. 2005. (Illus.). (J). ring bd. 12.95 net. (978-0-9765302-0-6(1)) Ryzewski, Deborah.

Schwartz, Ellen. I Love Yoga: A Source Book for Teens. Hodson, Ben, illus. 2003. 128p. (J). (gr. 5 up). pap. 9.95 (978-0-88776-598-8(X)) Tundra Bks., Inc./Livres Toundra, Inc. CAN. *Dist:* Random Hse., Inc.

Silas, Elizabeth & Goodney, Diane. Yoga. 2003. (Life Balance Ser.). (Illus.). 80p. (J). 20.50 (978-0-531-12258-7(1) , Watts, Franklin) Scholastic Library Publishing.

Silas, Elizabeth And Diane Goo. Yoga. 2004. (Life Balance Ser.). (YA). (gr. 5-8). pap. 6.95 (978-0-531-15577-6(3) , Watts, Franklin) Scholastic Library Publishing.

Studelska, Jana Voelke. Yoga for Fun! 2007. (J). lib. bdg. (***978-0-7565-3282-6(5)***) Compass Point Bks.

Wahi, Ashok, et al. Yoga for Kids: The Missing Peace. 2002. (Illus.). 36p. (J). (gr. 1-6). 9.95 (978-0-9708284-3-9(8)) Princeton Design Group.

Weiss, Stefanie Iris. Everything You Need to Know about Yoga: An Introduction for Teens. 1999. (Need to Know Library). (Illus.). 64p. (YA). (gr. 7-12). lib. bdg. 25.25 (978-0-8239-2959-7(0) , NTYOGA) Rosen Publishing Group, Inc., The.

Whitford, Rebecca. Little Yoga: A Toddler's First Book of Yoga. Selway, Martina, illus. 2005. 28p. (J). (ps-7). 9.95 (978-0-8050-7879-4(7)) Holt, Henry & Co.

—Sleepy Little Yoga: A Toddler's Sleepy Book of Yoga. Selway, Martina, illus. 2007. 28p. (J). 9.95 (978-0-8050-8153-4(3)) Holt, Henry & Co.

YOM KIPPUR

Fishman, Cathy Goldberg. On Rosh Hashanah & Yom Kippur. Hall, Melanie W., illus. 2000. 40p. (J). (ps-3). 6.99 (978-0-689-83892-7(1) , Aladdin) Simon & Schuster Children's Publishing.

—On Rosh Hashanah & Yom Kippur. 2000. (J). (978-0-606-19250-7(6)); (gr. 3-6). lib. bdg. 14.15 (978-0-613-31547-0(2)) Tandem Library Bks.

Hashanah, Rosh & Kippur, Yom. Rosh Hashanah & Yom Kippur Coloring Book. 2.99 (978-1-58330-168-5(2)) Feldheim Pubs.

Marx, David F. Rosh Hashanah & Yom Kippur. 2001. (Rookie Read-About Holidays Ser.). (Illus.). 32p. (J). (gr. 1-2). pap. 5.95 (978-0-516-26313-7(7) , Children's Pr.) Scholastic Library Publishing.

—Rosh Hashanah & Yom Kippur. 2001. (gr. k-3). lib. bdg. 14.10 (978-0-613-54641-6(5)) Tandem Library Bks.

Rau, Dana Meachen. Rosh Hashanah & Yom Kippur. 2001. (True Holiday Bks.). (Illus.). 48p. (J). (gr. 3-5). 25.00 (978-0-516-22243-1(0) , Children's Pr.) Scholastic Library Publishing.

Siegel, Bruce H. The Magic of Kol Nidre: A Yom Kippur Story. Haas, Shelly, illus. 1998. 32p. (J). (gr. k-4). 16.95 (978-1-58013-003-5(8)); pap. 6.95 (978-1-58013-002-8(X)) Kar-Ben Publishing.

Zimmerman, Noam. Yom Kippur Children's Machzor. 2006. 64p. 15.95 (978-965-229-362-6(8)) Gefen Publishing Hse., Ltd ISR. *Dist:* Gefen Bks.

YORKTOWN (VA.)—HISTORY—SIEGE, 1781

Anderson, Dale. The Battle of Yorktown. 2004. (Landmark Events in American History Ser.). (Illus.). 48p. (J). pap. 11.95 (978-0-8368-5421-3(7)); lib. bdg. 30.00 (978-0-8368-5393-3(8)) Stevens, Gareth Inc. (World Almanac Library).

Crewe, Sabrina & Anderson, Dale. The Battle of Yorktown. 2005. (Events That Shaped America Ser.). 32p. (J). lib. bdg. 24.67 (978-0-8368-3412-3(7)) Stevens, Gareth Inc.

Ferrie, Richard. The World Turned Upside Down: George Washington & the Battle of Yorktown. 1999. (Illus.). 168p. (J). (gr. 7 up). tchr. ed. 18.95 (978-0-8234-1402-4(7)) Holiday Hse., Inc.

Heinrichs, Ann. The Surrender of Cornwallis. 2006. (J). lib. bdg. (***978-0-7565-2462-3(8)***) Compass Point Bks.

Ready, Dee. The Battle of Yorktown. 2002. (Let Freedom Ring Ser.). (Illus.). 48p. (J). (gr. 3-4). lib. bdg. 22.60 (978-0-7368-1097-5(8) , Bridgestone Bks.) Capstone Pr., Inc.

Waldman, Scott P. The Battle of Yorktown. 2003. (Atlas of Famous Battles of the American Revolution Ser.). (Illus.). 24p. (J). lib. bdg. 21.25 (978-0-8239-6331-7(4)) Rosen Publishing Group, Inc., The.

Whitcraft, Melissa. The Surrender at Yorktown. 2004. (Cornerstones of Freedom Ser.). (Illus.). 47p. (J). 26.00 (978-0-516-24234-7(2) , Children's Pr.) Scholastic Library Publishing.

YOSEMITE NATIONAL PARK (CALIF.)

Dell, Pamela. Welcome to Yosemite National Park. 2006. (Visitor Guides Ser.). (Illus.). 32p. (J). (gr. 1-5). 27.07 (978-1-59296-704-9(3)) Child's World, Inc.

Graf, Mike. Yosemite National Park. 2002. (National Parks Ser.). (Illus.). 24p. (J). (gr. 2-3). lib. bdg. 18.60 (978-0-7368-1380-8(2) , Bridgestone Bks.) Capstone Pr., Inc.

Hall, Margaret. Yosemite National Park. 2006. (Symbols of Freedom Ser.). (Illus.). 32p. (J). (978-1-4034-7799-6(X)) Heinemann Library.

Wade, Linda R. Yosemite National Park. 2005. (National Park Ser.). (Illus.). 32p. (J). (gr. 3-8). lib. bdg. 24.21 (978-1-59197-428-4(3)) ABDO Publishing Co.

YOSEMITE VALLEY (CALIF.)—FICTION

McCully, Emily Arnold. Squirrel & John Muir. 2004. (Illus.). 40p. (J). 16.00 (978-0-374-33697-4(0) , Farrar, Straus & Giroux (BYR)) Farrar, Straus & Giroux.

YOUNG, BRIGHAM, 1801-1877

Gunderson, Cory Gideon. Brigham Young: Pioneer & Prophet. 2002. (Let Freedom Ring Ser.). (Illus.). 48p. (J). (gr. 3-4). lib. bdg. 22.60 (978-0-7368-1346-4(2) , Bridgestone Bks.) Capstone Pr., Inc.

Simon, Charnan. Brigham Young. 1999. (Community Builders Ser.). (Illus.). 48p. (J). (gr. 3-5). pap. 6.95 (978-0-516-26344-1(7) , Children's Pr.) Scholastic Library Publishing.

—Brigham Young: Mormon & Pioneer. 1998. (Community Builders Ser.). (Illus.). 48p. (J). (gr. 3-5). 25.00 (978-0-516-20392-8(4) , Children's Pr.) Scholastic Library Publishing.

YOUNG ADULTS

Here are entered works on people in the general age range of eighteen through twenty-five years.

see also Youth

Baker, Tim. Live It Loud: Devotions for Teens. 2003. (Live It Ser.). 208p. (YA). pap. 10.99 (978-0-8007-5880-6(3)) Baker Publishing Group.

—Live It Strong: Devotions for Teens. 2003. (Live It Ser.: Vol. 2). 208p. (YA). pap. 10.99 (978-0-8007-5881-3(1)) Baker Publishing Group.

Dunagan, Cindy. Journaling Toward Moral Excellence Volume Four for Young Adults: A Character Building Workbook of 100 Thought-Provoking Questions to Help the Young Discover the Value of Moral Strength. 2004. (Journaling Toward Moral Excellence Ser.: Vol. 4). 107p. (YA). (gr. 11 up). 11.95 (978-0-9759871-3-1(5)) Straight Paths Pr.

Fuyo Gaskins, Pearl, ed. What Are You? Voices of Mixed-Race Young People. rev. ed. 1999. (Illus.). 288p. (YA). (gr. 7-12). 18.95 (978-0-8050-5968-7(7) , Holt, Henry & Co. Bks. For Young Readers) Holt, Henry & Co.

Greenberg, Judith E. A Girl's Guide to Growing Up: Making the Right Choices. 2001. (Single Titles Social Studies Ser.). (Illus.). 144p. (YA). (gr. 9-12). pap. 9.95 (978-0-531-16542-3(6) , Watts, Franklin) Scholastic Library Publishing.

Pascoe, Elaine, ed. Teen Dreams: The Journey Through Puberty. 2003. (Body Story Ser.). (Illus.). 48p. (J). 24.95 (978-1-4103-0061-4(7) , Blackbirch Pr., Inc.) Thomson Gale.

Primm, E. Russell. Favorite Children's Authors & Illustrators. 2nd ed. 2006. (J). (978-1-59187-057-9(7)); (978-1-59187-058-6(5)); (978-1-59187-059-3(3)); (978-1-59187-060-9(7)); (978-1-59187-061-6(5)); (978-1-59187-062-3(3)); (978-1-59187-063-0(1)); (978-1-59187-064-7(X)) Tradition Publishing Co.

Real Teens Vol. 5: Diary of A Junior Year. 2000. (gr. 7-12). lib. bdg. 13.00 (978-0-613-26722-9(2)) Tandem Library Bks.

Rockers, Colleen. Making a Difference: Listening, Loving & Serving. Coffey, Kathy, ed. 1998. (Crossings: A Series for Young Adults Ser.: Vol. 2). 80p. (YA). pap. 2.95 (978-1-889108-28-5(6)) Living the Good News.

Schwartz, Stuart B. Finding an Apartment. 1998. (Life Skills Ser.). (J). lib. bdg. (978-0-516-21462-7(4) , Children's Pr.) Scholastic Library Publishing.

Schwartz, Stuart B. & Conley, Craig. Finding an Apartment. (Life Skills-Career Bks.). 48p. pap. 6.95 (978-0-7368-8508-9(0)); 1998. (Illus.). 32p. (J). (gr. 3-4). lib. bdg. 21.26 (978-0-7368-0046-4(8)) Capstone Pr., Inc. (Life-Matters Bks.).

YOUTH

Here are entered works on the time of life between thirteen and twenty-five years, as well as on people in this general age range, including teenagers and young adults.

see also Adolescence; Boys; Girls

Allison, Anthony. Hear These Voices: Youth at the Edge of the Millennium. 2001. (J). pap. 15.99 (978-0-7636-1395-2(9)) Candlewick Pr.

Alpern, Michele. Teen Pregnancy. 2002. (Focus on Family Matters Ser.). (Illus.). 64p. (YA). (gr. 5 up). 31.00 (978-0-7910-6695-9(9) , Chelsea Hse.) Facts On File, Inc.

Anderson, Judith. Me & My Body. 2007. (J). (***978-1-59771-086-2(5)***) Sea-To-Sea Pubns.

—Me & My Friends. 2007. (J). (***978-1-59771-089-3(X)***) Sea-To-Sea Pubns.

Aretha, David. On the Rocks: Teens & Alcohol. 2006. (Illus.). 144p. (J). (gr. 9-12). 30.50 (978-0-531-16792-2(5) , Watts, Franklin) Scholastic Library Publishing.

Ashabranner, Brent. Gavriel & Jemal: Two Boys of Jerusalem. Conklin, Paul, photos by. 2005. (Illus.). 94p. (J). (gr. 4-10). reprint ed. 12.00 (978-0-7567-9758-4(6)) DIANE Publishing Co.

Bailey, Lorilyn. The Original Dating Questionnaire for Teens: A Great Way to Get to Know Each Other. (Illus.). 128p. (Orig.). (YA). (gr. 7-12). pap. (978-0-9641239-7-7(5)) Lormax Communications.

Bamford, Janet. Street Wise: A Guide for Teen Investors. 2000. (Bloomberg Personal Bookshelf). (Illus.). 240p. (YA). (gr. 7-12). pap. 16.95 (978-1-57660-039-9(4)) Bloomberg Pr.

Bankston, John. Inhalants = Busted! 2006. (Busted! Ser.). (Illus.). 104p. (J). lib. bdg. 31.93 (978-0-7660-2472-4(5) , 1250497) Enslow Pubs., Inc.

Bauchner, Elizabeth. Teen Minorities in Rural North America: Growing up Different. 2008. (Youth in Rural North America Ser.). (J). (978-1-4222-0014-8(0)) Mason Crest Pubs.

Baumgart, Brian. Teens in Mexico. 2006. (Global Connections Ser.). (Illus.). 96p. (J). (gr. 5-7). 31.93 (978-0-7565-2064-9(9)) Compass Point Bks.

Bode, Janet. Heartbreak & Roses: Real Life Stories of Troubled Love. 2000. (YA). (978-0-606-19403-7(7)) Tandem Library Bks.

—Kids Still Having Kids: People Talk about Teen Pregnancy. rev. ed. 1999. (Single Titles-Teen Issues Ser.). (Illus.). 160p. (YA). (gr. 8-12). pap. 9.95 (978-0-531-15973-6(6) , Watts, Franklin) Scholastic Library Publishing.

Bradley, Michael J. Yes, Your Parents Are Crazy! A Teen Survival Handbook. Glasbergen, Randy, illus. 2004. 432p. pap. 14.95 (978-0-936197-48-7(X)) Harbor Pr., Inc.

Bryce, Sarah. Do Butterflies Carry Spare Parts? 2002. 295p. per. 19.50 (978-0-9713832-1-0(9)); 2001. 284p. (YA). 29.50 (978-0-9713832-0-3(0)) WordWright.biz, Inc.

Buchan, Molly. Take It from Me: Straight Talk about Life from a Teen Who's Been There. 2002. (gr. 3-6). lib. bdg. 16.45 (978-0-613-71678-9(7)) Tandem Library Bks.

Budhos, Marina. Remix: Conversations with Immigrant Teenagers. rev. ed. 1999. (Illus.). 160p. (gr. 9-12). 16.95 (978-0-8050-5113-1(9) , Holt, Henry & Co. Bks. For Young Readers) Holt, Henry & Co.

Canfield, Jack L. & Hansen, Mark Victor, creators. Chicken Soup for the Teen Soul: Life Stripped to the Core. 2007. 288p. (YA). pap. 14.95 (***978-0-7573-0682-2(9)***) Health Communications, Inc.

Canfield, Jack L., et al. Chicken Soup for the Teenage Soul: The Real Deal School. 2005. (Illus.). 300p. (YA). pap. 12.95 (978-0-7573-0255-8(6)) Health Communications, Inc.

—Chicken Soup for the Teenage Soul IV: More Stories of Life, Love & Learning, Vol. IV. Claspy, Mitch, ed. 2004. 400p. pap. 14.95 (978-0-7573-0233-6(5)) Health Communications, Inc.

Cantwell, Rebecca. Teens in Kenya. 2007. (Illus.). 96p. (J). pap. (***978-0-7565-3195-9(0)***) Compass Point Bks.

Cantwell, Rebecca & Compass Point Books Staff. Teens in Kenya. 2006. (Global Connections Ser.). (Illus.). 96p. (J). (gr. 5-7). 31.93 (***978-0-7565-2445-6(8)***) Compass Point Bks.

Carson-DeWitt, Rosalyn, ed. Drugs, Alcohol, & Tobacco: Learning about Addictive Behavior, 3 vols. 2002. (Illus.). (J). Vol. 1. (978-0-02-865757-8(8)); Vol. 2. (978-0-02-865758-5(6)); Vol. 3. (978-0-02-865759-2(4)) Thomson Gale. (Macmillan Reference USA).

Chicken Soup for the Teenage Soul Personal Organizer. 2001. (YA). (gr. 7-12). spiral bd. 12.95 (978-1-58794-020-0(5)) Day-Timers, Inc.

Chopra, Deepak. Fire in the Heart: A Spiritual Guide for Teens. 2006. 208p. (YA). pap. 9.95 (978-0-689-86217-5(2) , Simon Pulse) Simon & Schuster Children's Publishing.

Coca-Cola Valued Youth Programme: Tutor Workbook. 1998. (Illus.). 87p. (J). (gr. k-12). wbk. ed. (978-1-878550-65-1(9)) Intercultural Development Research Assn.

Constant. Teen Issues Series, 6 bks., Set 1. 2004. (Illus.). (YA). pap. 48.30 (978-1-4109-0886-5(0)) Harcourt Schl. Pubs.

Conyers, Karen Elizabeth. Teens in China. 2007. (Global Connections Ser.). (Illus.). 96p. pap. (***978-0-7565-2068-7(1)*** , 1265891) Compass Point Bks.

Coombs, Samm. Teenage Survival Manual: How to Reach '20' in One Piece. 6th ed. 2001. (Illus.). 260p. (YA). pap. 15.95 (978-1-879904-19-4(5)) Halo Bks.

CosmoGIRL! Editors. Total Body Workout: Fun Moves to Look & Feel Your Best. 2008. (CosmoGirl! Ser.). (Illus.). 128p. (J). pap. 9.95 (***978-1-58816-663-0(5)***) Hearst Bks.

Crump, Marguerite. No B. O. ! The Head-to-Toe Book of Hygiene for Preteens. Verdick, Elizabeth, ed. 2005. (Illus.). 128p. (J). (gr. 4-8). pap. 12.95 (978-1-57542-175-9(5)) Free Spirit Publishing, Inc.

Daldry, Jeremy. The Teenage Guy's Survival Guide: The Real Deal on Girls, Growing up, & Other Guy Stuff. 1999. (978-0-606-17234-9(3)) Tandem Library Bks.

Dell, Pamela. Teens in Nigeria. 2007. (J). lib. bdg. (***978-0-7565-3306-9(6)***) Compass Point Bks.

Desetta, Al & Wolin, Sybil, eds. The Struggle to Be Strong: True Stories by Teens about Overcoming Tough Times. 2004. (Illus.). 192p. (YA). (gr. 8 up). pap. 14.95 (978-1-57542-079-0(1)) Free Spirit Publishing, Inc.

Donovan, Sandra. Teens in Japan. (Illus.). 96p. (J). 2007. (***978-0-7565-3193-5(4)***); 2006. (gr. 5-7). 31.93 (***978-0-7565-2444-9(X)***) Compass Point Bks.

—Teens in South Korea. 2007. (J). lib. bdg. (***978-0-7565-3297-0(3)***) Compass Point Bks.

Dunagan, Cindy. Journaling Toward Moral Excellence Volume Three for Teenagers: A Character Building Workbook of 100 Thought-Provoking Questions to Help the Young Discover the Value of Moral Strength. 2004. (Journaling Toward Moral Excellence Ser.: Vol. 3). 107p. (YA). (gr. 8-10). 11.95 (978-0-9759871-2-4(7)) Straight Paths Pr.

Esherick, Joan. Dying for Acceptance: A Teen's Guide to Drug- & Alcohol-Related Health Issues. 2005. (Science of Health Ser.). (Illus.). 128p. (J). lib. bdg. 24.95 (978-1-59084-847-0(0)) Mason Crest Pubs.

Espejo, Roman. Suicide. 2003. (Opposing Viewpoints Ser.). (Illus.). 207p. (J). lib. bdg. 36.20 (978-0-7377-1242-1(2) , Greenhaven Pr., Inc.) Thomson Gale.

Espeland, Pamela. Life Lists for Teens: Tips, Steps, Hints, & How-tos for Growing up, Getting Al. 2003. (gr. 7-12). lib. bdg. 21.05 (978-0-613-63048-1(3)) Tandem Library Bks.

Fairview Press Staff, ed. How We Made Our World a Better Place: Kids & Teens Write on How They Changed Their Corner of the World. 1998. 256p. (ps up). pap. 9.95 (978-1-57749-079-1(7)) Fairview Pr.

—Teens Write Through It: Essays from Teens Who've Triumphed over Trouble. annual 1998. 256p. (ps up). pap. 9.95 (978-1-57749-083-8(5)) Fairview Pr.

Fighting the Monster. 2004. (YA). ring bd. 59.95 (***978-0-9661256-2-7(2)***) Youth Communication - New York Center.

Flegal, Gary L. In Wisdom & Stature: Young Men Growing in God. 2004. 64p. (gr. 4-6). pap. 15.00 (978-0-687-09354-0(6)) Abingdon Pr.

Fletcher, Anne M. Weight Loss Confidential Journal: Week-By-Week Success Strategies for Teens from Teens. 2008. 240p. spiral bd. 15.00 (***978-0-618-43372-8(4)***) Houghton Mifflin Co.

Ford, Jean. Rural Crime & Poverty: Violence, Drugs, & Other Issues. 2008. (Youth in Rural North America Ser.). (J). (978-1-4222-0016-2(7)) Mason Crest Pubs.

Franco, Betsy, ed. Things I Have to Tell You: Poems & Writing by Teenage Girls. Nickles, Nina, photos by. 2001. (Illus.). 80p. (J). (gr. 7 up). pap. 8.99 (978-0-7636-1035-7(6)) Candlewick Pr.

Gaskins, Pearl Fuyo. I Believe In. . . Christian, Jewish, & Muslim Young People Speak about Their Faiths. 2004. (Illus.). 160p. (J). 18.95 (978-0-8126-2713-8(X)) Cricket Bks.

Gibb, Fiona & Shaw, Tucker. Any Advice? Schwartz, Sara, illus. 2000. 176p. (J). pap. 5.99 (978-0-14-130921-7(0) , Puffin) Penguin Group (USA) Inc.

Gouss, Deva Joy. A Tool Box for You: Activities for Helping Kids Cope with Serious Illness. Fairview Press Staff, ed. 1998. 32p. (gr. 2-6). pap. 6.95 (978-1-57749-086-9(X)) Fairview Pr.

Haugen, Brenda & Compass Point Books Staff. Teens in Australia. 2006. (Global Connections Ser.). (Illus.). 96p. (J). (gr. 5-7). 31.93 (***978-0-7565-2441-8(5)***) Compass Point Bks.

Hersch, Patricia. A Tribe Apart: A Journey into the Heart of American Adolescence. 1999. 391p. (gr. 7-12). lib. bdg. 23.45 (978-0-613-17755-9(X)) Tandem Library Bks.

Hipp, Earl. Understanding the Human Volcano: What Teens Can Do about Violence. Hanson, L. K., illus. 2000. 190p. (gr. 8-12). pap. 16.00 (978-1-56838-359-0(2) , Z1613) Hazelden Publishing & Educational Services.

—Understanding the Human Volcano: What Teens Can Do about Violence. 2000. (gr. 7-12). lib. bdg. 25.75 (978-0-613-79022-2(7)) Tandem Library Bks.

Hot Pro/Con Issues, 12 bks., Set. Incl. Abortion Conflict : A Pro/Con Issue. Durrett, Deanne. (J). 2000. lib. bdg. 27.93 (978-0-7660-1193-9(3)); Animal Experimentation & Testing : A Pro/Con Issue. Woods, Geraldine. (YA). 1999. lib. bdg. 27.93 (978-0-7660-1191-5(7)); Death Penalty for Teens : A Pro/Con Issue. Day, Nancy. (YA). 2000. lib. bdg. 27.93 (978-0-7660-1370-4(7)); Drug Legalization. Lawler, Jennifer. (YA). 1999. lib. bdg. 27.93 (978-0-7660-1197-7(6)); Drug Testing in Schools : A Pro/Con Issue. Lawler, Jennifer. (YA). 2000. lib. bdg. 27.93 (978-0-7660-1367-4(7)); Rain Forests : A Pro/Con Issue. Johnson, Linda Carlson. (YA). 1999. lib. bdg. 21.95 (978-0-7660-1202-8(6)); School Dress Codes : A Pro/Con Issue. Cruz, Barbara C. (J). 2001. lib. bdg. 27.93 (978-0-7660-1465-7(7)); Separate Sexes, Separate Schools : A Pro/Con Issue. Cruz, Barbara C. (YA). 2000. lib. bdg. 27.93 (978-0-7660-1366-7(9)); Space Exploration : A Pro/Con Issue. Flowers, Sarah. (YA). 2000. lib. bdg. 27.93 (978-0-7660-1199-1(2)); 64p. (gr. 6-12). (Illus.). 1999. Set lib. bdg. 239.40 (978-0-7660-1404-6(5)) Enslow Pubs., Inc.

Hovius, Christopher. The Best You Can Be: A Teen's Guide to Fitness & Nutrition. 2004. (Science of Health Ser.). (Illus.). 128p. (J). (978-1-59084-848-7(9)) Mason Crest Pubs.

Hunnicutt, Nathan W. & Farris, James W. Responsible Teenz. 2002. 65p. (YA). per. (978-0-9740232-0-5(5)) Hunnicutt Farris Publishing.

Hunter, David. Teen Life among the Amish & Other Alternative Communities: Choosing a Lifestyle. 2008. (Youth in Rural North America Ser.). (J). (978-1-4222-0017-9(5)) Mason Crest Pubs.

In Our Own Words Vol. 3: A Generation Defining Itself. 2001. 160p. (YA). (gr. 11 up). per. 12.95 (978-0-9654136-4-0(0)) MW Enterprises.

Jackson, J. S. Bye-Bye, Bully: A Kid's Guide for Dealing with Bullies. Alley, R. W., tr. Alley, R. W., illus. 2003. (J). per. 6.95 (978-0-87029-369-6(9)) Abbey Pr.

—Bye-Bye, Bully: A Kid's Guide for Dealing with Bullies. 2003. (gr. k-3). lib. bdg. 15.25 (978-0-613-81284-9(0)) Tandem Library Bks.

Johnson, Julie T. Teen Psychic: Exploring Your Intuitive Spiritual Powers. 2003. (gr. 7-12). lib. bdg. 24.55 (978-0-613-90834-4(1)) Tandem Library Bks.

Jones, Caryn Gracey. Teens in Venezuela. 2006. (Global Connections Ser.). (Illus.). 96p. (J). (gr. 5-7). 31.93 (978-0-7565-2447-0(4)) Compass Point Bks.

Jones, Caryn Gracey & Compass Point Books Staff. Teens in Brazil. 2006. (Global Connections Ser.). (Illus.). 96p. (J). (gr. 5-7). 31.93 (978-0-7565-2442-5(3)) Compass Point Bks.

Joy, Donald M. Becoming a Man: A Celebration of Sexuality, Responsibility & the Christian Young Man. 2nd ed. 2001. (ENG.). 125p. pap. 12.99 (978-1-928915-18-8(3)) Evangel Publishing Hse.

Keen, Lisa. Out Law: What LGBT Youth Should Know about Their Legal Rights. 2007. (Lesbian & Gay Studies Ser.). 176p. pap. 13.00 (978-0-8070-7966-9(9)) Beacon Pr.

Keyishian, Elizabeth. Smoking. rev. ed. 2005. (Need to Know Library). (Illus.). 64p. (J). (gr. 7-12). lib. bdg. 25.25 (978-0-8239-4092-9(6)) Rosen Publishing Group, Inc., The.

Kirberger, Kimberly. No Body's Perfect: Stories by Teens about Body Image, Self-Acceptance, & the S. 2003. (gr. 5-8). lib. bdg. 22.20 (978-0-613-61510-5(5)) Tandem Library Bks.

Klee, Sheila. Volunteering for a Political Campaign. 2000. (High Interest Bks.). (Illus.). 48p. (YA). (gr. 7-12). 23.00 (978-0-516-23398-7(X) , Children's Pr.) Scholastic Library Publishing.

Kranz, Nickie & Compass Point Books Staff. Teens in France. 2006. (Global Connections Ser.). (Illus.). 96p. (J). (gr. 5-7). 31.93 (978-0-7565-2062-5(2)) Compass Point Bks.

Kuehn, Eileen. Death: Coping with the Pain. 2001. (Grief & Loss Ser.). (Illus.). 64p. (J). (gr. 4-6). lib. bdg. 23.93 (978-0-7368-0745-6(4) , LifeMatters Bks.) Capstone Pr., Inc.

Kuyper, Vicki J. Jesus Speaks to Teens: Not Your Ordinary Meditations on the Word of Jesus. 2004. (Jesus Speaks Ser.). (Illus.). 192p. (J). 14.99 (978-0-7642-2866-7(8)) Bethany Hse. Pubs.

Kyi, Tanya Lloyd. Canadian Boys Who Rocked the World. Bagley, Tom, illus. 2007. 126p. (J). (gr. 3-2). pap. 9.95 (978-1-55285-799-1(9) , Walrus Bks.) Whitecap Bks., Ltd. CAN. *Dist:* Firefly Bks., Ltd.

Lambillion, Paul. Staying Cool. 2004. (Illus.). 196p. pap. 13.95 (978-0-7171-3598-1(5)) Gill & MacMillan, Ltd. IRL. *Dist:* Hushion Hse. Publishing, Ltd.

Larson, Karl & McCay, William. The Truth about Violence. 2005. (Truth About Ser.). (Illus.). 166p. (gr. 9). 35.00 (978-0-8160-5302-5(2)) Facts On File, Inc.

Lesko, Wendy Schaetzel. Youth: The 26% Solution, 1. 1998. (YA). pap. 14.95 (978-1-878346-47-6(4)) Information U.S.A., Inc.

Libal, Autumn. Fats, Sugars, & Empty Calories: The Fast Food Habit. 2004. (Obesity Ser.). (Illus.). 104p. (J). (ps-7). lib. bdg. 23.95 (978-1-59084-943-9(4)) Mason Crest Pubs.

Lishak, Antony. Drugs. 2007. (J). (***978-1-59920-035-4(X)***) Smart Apple Media.

Lookadoo, Justin. 97: Random Thoughts about Life, Love & Relationships. 2007. (Illus.). 224p. (YA). pap. 14.99 (978-0-8007-3163-2(8)) Revell.

Marcovitz, Hal. Teens & the Supernatural & Paranormal. 2005. (Gallup Youth Survey, Major Issues & Trends Ser.). (Illus.). 112,128p. (YA). (gr. 7-9). lib. bdg. 22.95 (978-1-59084-876-0(4)) Mason Crest Pubs.

Mastromarino, Diane. Being a Teen: Words of Advice from Someone Who's Been There. (Illus.). 80p. pap. 9.95 (978-0-88396-626-6(3) , Blue Mountain Pr.) Blue Mountain Arts Inc.

—Being a Teen: Words of Advice from Someone Who's Been There. 2002. (gr. 7-12). lib. bdg. 17.60 (978-0-613-77221-1(0)) Tandem Library Bks.

McClellan, Marilyn. The Big Deal about Alcohol: What Teens Need to Know about Drinking. 2004. (Issues in Focus Ser.). (Illus.). 128p. (J). lib. bdg. 26.60 (978-0-7660-2163-1(7)) Enslow Pubs., Inc.

McGraw-Hill Staff. Teen Health Course 1, Adolescence: Growing & Changing. 5th ed. 2002. (Three-Level Middle School Health Ser.). (gr. 6 up). 15.32 (978-0-07-826143-5(0) , 9780078261435) Glencoe/McGraw-Hill.

McIntosh, Kenneth & Livingston, Phyllis. Youth with Alcohol & Drug Addiction: Escape from Bondage. 2008. (J). (978-1-4222-0143-5(0)) Mason Crest Pubs.

McIntosh, Kenneth & Livingston, Phyllis. Youth with Conduct Disorder: In Trouble with the World. 2008. (J). (***978-1-4222-0140-4(6)***) Mason Crest Pubs.

McIntosh, Kenneth & Walker, Ida. Youth with Cultural/Language Differences: Interpreting an Alien World. 2008. (J). (***978-1-4222-0141-1(4)***) Mason Crest Pubs.

McNally, Robert Aquinas, ed. Skin Health Information for Teens: Health Tips about Dermatological Concerns & Skin Cancer Risks. 2003. (Teen Health Ser.). (Illus.). 429p. (gr. 7 up). (978-0-7808-0446-3(5)) Omnigraphics, Inc.

Meier, Katie. A Girl's Guide to Life: The Real Dish on Growing up, Being True, & Making Your Teen Years Fabulous! 2004. (Illus.). 208p. (YA). pap. 13.99 (978-0-8499-4443-7(0)) Nelson, Thomas Inc.

Mercadante, Frank. Positively Dangerous: Live Loud, Be Real, Change the World. 2003. 117p. (YA). 9.95 (978-0-88489-790-3(7)) St. Mary's Pr.

Meyers Jugendlexikon. (GER., Illus.). 672p. (978-3-411-07804-2(9)) Bibliographisches Institut & F. A. Brockhaus AG DEU. *Dist:* i.b.d., Ltd.

Mintzer, Richard. Steroids=Busted! 2006. (Busted! Ser.). (Illus.). 112p. (J). lib. bdg. 31.93 (978-0-7660-2471-7(7)) Enslow Pubs., Inc.

Mosatche, Harriet S. & Lawner, Elizabeth K. Getting to Know the Real You: 50 Fun Quizzes Just for Girls. 2002. (Illus.). 240p. pap. 12.95 (978-0-7615-2954-5(3) , Three Rivers Pr.) Crown Publishing Group.

Musgrave, Susan, ed. You Be Me: Friendship in the Lives of Teen Girls. 2002. 128p. (YA). (gr. 10 up). pap. 7.95 (978-1-55037-738-5(8)) Annick Pr., Ltd. CAN. *Dist:* Firefly Bks., Ltd.

The Need to Know Library: Important Information to Solve Teen Problems, 5 bks. Incl. Everything You Need to Know about Creating Your Own Support System. Kreiner, Anna. (gr. 7-12). 1996. lib. bdg. 25.25 (978-0-8239-2215-4(4) , NTSUSY); Everything You Need to Know about Discrimination. Palmer, Ezra. (gr. 4-6). 1995. lib. bdg. 25.25 (978-0-8239-2115-7(8) , NTDISC); Everything You Need to Know about Living in a Shelter. Parker, Julie F. (gr. 7-12). 1995. lib. bdg. 25.25 (978-0-8239-1874-4(2) , NTLISH); Everything You Need to Know about Moving In with a Grandparent or Other Relative. Simpson, Carolyn. (gr. 7-12). 1995. lib. bdg. 25.25 (978-0-8239-1872-0(6) , NTLIGR); Everything You Need to Know When a Parent Has AIDS. Draimin, Barbara Hermie. (gr. 7-12). 1994. lib. bdg. 25.25 (978-0-8239-1690-0(1) , NTPAAI); 64p. (YA). (Illus.). 2005. Set lib. bdg. 101.00 (978-0-8239-8038-3(3)) Rosen Publishing Group, Inc., The.

The Need to Know Library: Important Issues Affecting Every Teen, 8 bks. Incl. Everything You Need to Know about Peer Mediation. Rue, Nancy N. (gr. 4-6). lib. bdg. 25.25 (978-0-8239-3464-5(0)); Everything You Need to Know about Peer Pressure. Feller, Robyn M. (gr. 4-6). lib. bdg. 25.25 (978-0-8239-3440-9(3)); Everything You Need to Know about Placing Your Baby for Adoption. Sherman, Aliza. (gr. 9 up). lib. bdg. 25.25 (978-0-8239-3465-2(9)); Everything You Need to Know about Relationship Violence. White, Katherine. (gr. 4-6). lib. bdg. 25.25 (978-0-8239-3398-3(9)); Everything You Need to Know about Romance & the Internet : How to Stay Safe. Brooks, Sheldon. (gr. 4-6). lib. bdg. 25.25 (978-0-8239-3399-0(7)); Everything You Need to Know about Sexual Harassment. Bouchard, Elizabeth. (gr. 4-6). lib. bdg. 25.25 (978-0-8239-3466-9(7)); Everything You Need to Know about Stress. Ayer, Eleanor H. (gr. 4-6). lib. bdg. 25.25 (978-0-8239-3467-6(5)); Everything You Need to Know about Teen Motherhood. Hammerslough, Jane. (gr. 4-6). lib. bdg. 25.25 (978-0-8239-3441-6(1)); 64p. (YA). 2001. (Illus.). Set lib. bdg. 202.00 (978-0-8239-9433-5(3)) Rosen Publishing Group, Inc., The.

Nicolai, Gregory. Teens in Vietnam. 2006. (Global Connections Ser.). 96p. (J). (gr. 5-7). 31.93 (978-0-7565-2067-0(3)) Compass Point Bks.

Njuguna, Isaac. Teenage Life Strategies - the Joy of Building on a Firm Foundation. 2007. 96p. per. (***978-1-84685-526-9(8)*** , Exposure Publishing) Meadow Bks.

Oaks, Robert C. Believe! Helping Youth Learn to Trust in the Lord. 2003. (Illus.). xiii, 126p. (J). pap. 14.95 (978-1-59038-203-5(X)) Deseret Bk. Co.

Obesity: Modern-Day Epidemic, 10 vols., Set. Incl. America's Unhealthy Lifestyle : Supersize It! Sanna, Ellyn. 2004. (978-1-59084-942-2(6)); Clothing, Cosmetic, & Self-Esteem Tips : Making the Most of the Body You Have. Esherick, Joan. 2005. (978-1-59084-951-4(5)); Diet & Your Emotions : The Comfort Food Falsehood. Esherick, Joan. 2004. lib. bdg. 23.95 (978-1-59084-950-7(7)); Diseases & Disabilities Caused by Weight Problems : The Overloaded Body. Ford, Jean. 2005. (978-1-59084-944-6(2)); Fats, Sugars, & Empty Calories : The Fast Food Habit. Libal, Autumn. 2004. lib. bdg. 23.95 (978-1-59084-943-9(4)); How Genetics & Environment Shape Us : The Destined Body. Hunter, William. 2005. lib. bdg. 23.95 (978-1-59084-948-4(5)); Importance of Physical Activity & Exercise : The Fitness Factor. Libal, Autumn. 2005. lib. bdg. 23.95 (978-1-59084-945-3(0)); Medications & Surgeries for Weight Loss : When Dieting Isn't Enough. Hunter, William. 2005. (978-1-59084-947-7(7)); Social Discrimination & Body Size : Too Big to Fit? Libal, Autumn. 2005. lib. bdg. 23.95 (978-1-59084-949-1(3)); Truth about Diets : The Pros & Cons. Ford, Jean & Libal, Autumn. 2005. lib. bdg. 23.95 (978-1-59084-946-0(9)); (J). (ps-7). (Illus.). 104p. 2005. Set lib. bdg. 239.50 (978-1-59084-941-5(8)) Mason Crest Pubs.

Paonessa, Mary. Growth & Development: Understanding Yourself, 8 vols. 3rd ed. 2003. (Human Growth & Development Ser.). (Illus.). 82p. (J). (gr. 8 up). pap. 11.00 (978-0-9711721-6-6(1) , 394) Paon Pubns.

Patnaik, Gayatri. Secret Life of Teens: Young People Speak Out about Their Lives. 2000. (gr. 7-12). lib. bdg. 22.20 (978-0-613-33961-2(4)) Tandem Library Bks.

Paulsen, Gary. The Beet Fields: Memories of a Sixteenth Summer. 2002. 176p. (YA). (gr. 9 up). mass mkt. 5.99 (978-0-440-41557-2(8) , Laurel Leaf) Random Hse. Children's Bks.

Paymar, Michelle. Teens in South Korea. 2004. (Teens Around the World Ser.). (J). (978-1-59018-034-1(8) , Lucent Bks.) Thomson Gale.

Peter, Val J. & Dowd, Tom. Boundaries: A Guide for Teens. 2004. 113p. (gr. 8-12). pap. 8.95 (978-1-889322-37-7(7) , 25-014) Boys Town Pr.

Phillips, Sherre Florence. The Teen Brain. 2007. (Gray Matter Ser.). 136p. (J). (gr. 9). 32.95 (***978-0-7910-9415-0(4)*** , Chelsea Hse.) Facts On File, Inc.

Pledge, Deanna S. When Something Feels Wrong: A Survival Guide about Abuse, for Young People. 2004. (Illus.). 224p. (YA). (gr. 8 up). pap. 14.95 (978-1-57542-115-5(1)) Free Spirit Publishing, Inc.

Rooney, Anne. Drugs on the Street. 2007. (Illus.). 48p. (J). (***978-1-58340-986-2(6)***) Smart Apple Media.

Rosenberg, Carol & Rosenberg, Gary. Jon & Jayne's Guide to Throwing, Going to, & surviving Parties. 2008. 128p. (YA). pap. 9.95 (***978-0-7573-0726-3(4)***) Health Communications, Inc.

Seidman, David. Teens in Iran. 2007. lib. bdg. (***978-0-7565-3300-7(7)***) Compass Point Bks.

Seventeen Magazine. True Love. 2007. 128p. (J). pap. 4.95 (978-1-58816-629-6(5)) Hearst Communications, Inc.

Shannon, Joyce Brennfleck, ed. Alcohol Information for Teens: Health Tips about Alcohol & Alcoholism. 2004. (Teen Health Ser.). 370p. (J). (978-0-7808-0741-9(3)) Omnigraphics, Inc.

Shea, Kitty. Teens in Canada. 2007. (J). lib. bdg. (***978-0-7565-3303-8(1)***) Compass Point Bks.

Shores, Lori. Teens in India. (Global Connections Ser.). (Illus.). 96p. (J). 2007. pap. (***978-0-7565-2071-7(1)***); 2006. (gr. 5-7). (978-0-7565-2063-2(0)) Compass Point Bks.

Singer-Towns, Brian & Calderone-Stewart, Lisa-Marie. Bringing Catholic Youth & the Bible Together: Strategies & Activities for Parishes & Schools. 2003. (Illus.). 96p. (YA). (gr. 8-12). pap. 14.95 (978-0-88489-692-0(7)) St. Mary's Pr.

Skog, Jason & Compass Point Books Staff. Teens in Spain. 2006. (Global Connections Ser.). (Illus.). 96p. (J). (gr. 5-7). 31.93 (978-0-7565-2446-3(6)) Compass Point Bks.

Smith, Jessica & Compass Point Books Staff. Teens in Russia. 2006. (Global Connections Ser.). (Illus.). 96p. (J). (gr. 5-7). 31.93 (978-0-7565-2065-6(7)) Compass Point Bks.

Smith, Roger. Teens & Rural Sports: Rodeos, Horses, Hunting, & Fishing. 2008. (J). (***978-1-4222-0022-3(1)***) Mason Crest Pubs.

Somervill, Barbara A. Teens in Egypt. 2007. (J). lib. bdg. (***978-0-7565-3294-9(9)***) Compass Point Bks.

Spangenburg, Ray & Moser, Kit. Teen Fads: Fun, Foolish, or Fatal? 2003. (Teen Issues Ser.). (Illus.). 64p. (J). (gr. 6-12). lib. bdg. 22.60 (978-0-7660-1665-1(X)) Enslow Pubs., Inc.

Stanley, Debbie. Everything You Need to Know about Student-on-Student Sexual Harassment. 2005. (Need to Know Library). (Illus.). 64p. (YA). (gr. 7-12). lib. bdg. 25.25 (978-0-8239-3281-8(8) , NTSTHA) Rosen Publishing Group, Inc., The.

Stewart, Faith. Teens & Rural Education: Opportunities & Challenges. 2008. (Youth in Rural North America Ser.). (Illus.). (J). (978-1-4222-0015-5(9)) Mason Crest Pubs.

Sullivan, Michelle. Check Him Out! Your Ultimate Guide to Guys. 2001. (Among Teens Ser.). (Illus.). 111p. (J). (978-0-439-27216-2(5)) Scholastic, Inc.

Swain. Calling You. 2005. (Illus.). 96p. (J). (978-0-8192-8142-5(5)) Morehouse Publishing.

Teal, Joyce Willard. Don't Sweat It, Kid. 2002. 152p. (J). 7.95 (978-1-56315-292-4(4)) SterlingHouse Pubs., Inc.

Tecco, Betsy Dru. Food for Fuel: The Connection Between Food & Physical Activity. 2004. (Library of Nutrition). (Illus.). 48p. (J). lib. bdg. 25.25 (978-1-4042-0303-7(6)) Rosen Publishing Group, Inc., The.

Teen Issues, 26 bks., Set. (Illus.). (YA). (gr. 6-12). lib. bdg. 344.10 (978-0-89490-887-3(1)) Enslow Pubs., Inc.

Teenage Refugees Speak Out. 2005. (Illus.). (gr. 7-12). lib. bdg. 344.50 (978-0-8239-9331-4(0)) Rosen Publishing Group, Inc., The.

Trapani, Margi. Reality Check: Teenage Fathers Speak Out. rev. ed. 1999. (Teen Pregnancy Prevention Library). (Illus.). 64p. (YA). (gr. 7-12). lib. bdg. 23.95 (978-0-8239-2995-5(7) , TPRECH) Rosen Publishing Group, Inc., The.

Ude, Ure. The Teenager. Mansi, Brij, ed. Taylor, Edward, illus. 2002. 36p. pap. 8.95 (978-0-9711564-9-4(2)) Pendleton Publishing, Inc.

Vizzini, Ned. Teen Angst? Naaah. 2000. (gr. 7-12). lib. bdg. 22.20 (978-0-613-35333-5(1)) Tandem Library Bks.

—Teen Angst? Naaah... 2000. (Illus.). 232p. (YA). (gr. 7-12). lib. bdg. 20.90 (978-0-606-21684-5(7)) Tandem Library Bks.

—Teen Angst? Naaah: A Quasi-Autobiography. 2002. (gr. 7-12). lib. bdg. 13.55 (978-0-613-72265-0(5)) Tandem Library Bks.

Waldman, Jackie. Teens with the Courage to Give: Young People Who Triumphed over Tragedy & Volunteered to Make a Difference. 2000. (Call to Action Ser.). (Illus.). 192p. (gr. 9-12). pap. 15.95 (978-1-57324-504-3(6), Red Wheel) Red Wheel/Weiser.

—Teens with the Courage to Give: Young People Who Triumphed over Tragedy & Volunteered to Make a Difference. 2000. (gr. 7-12). lib. bdg. 25.70 (978-0-613-79193-9(2)) Tandem Library Bks.

Wallerstein, Claire. Teen Suicide. 2003. (Just the Facts Ser.). (Illus.). 56p. (J). lib. bdg. 25.64 (978-1-4034-0820-4(3)) Heinemann Library.

Walsch, Neale Donald. Conversations with God for Teens. unabr. ed. 2004. 244p. (J). (gr. 7 up). pap. 38.00 incl. audio (978-0-8072-0856-4(6), LYA 368 SP, Listening Library) Random Hse. Audio Publishing Group.

Wandberg, Robert, et al. Self-Acceptance: Building Confidence. 2000. (Contemporary Issues Ser.). (Illus.). 64p. (YA). (gr. 4-6). lib. bdg. 23.93 (978-0-7368-1024-1(2), LifeMatters Bks.) Capstone Pr., Inc.

Ware, Jim. No Apologies: The Truth about Life, Love & Sex. 1999. (Life on the Edge Ser.). 240p. (YA). (gr. 9-12). pap. 5.99 (978-1-56179-654-0(9)) Focus on the Family Publishing.

Weierbach, Jane & Phillips-Hershey, Elizabeth. Mind over Basketball: Coach Yourself to Handle Stress. Beyl, Charles, illus. 2007. 48p. (J). (gr. 3-7). 14.95 (*978-1-4338-0135-8(3), 4418006); pap. 8.95 (*978-1-4338-0136-5(1), 4418007) American Psychological Assn. (Magination Pr.).

Weill, Sabrina Solin. We're Not Monsters: Teens Speak Out about Teens in Trouble. 2002. (gr. 7-12). lib. bdg. 15.25 (978-0-613-71899-8(2)) Tandem Library Bks.

Whyman, Matthew. Family Breakup. 2nd ed. 2005. (Illus.). (YA). pap. 12.00 (978-0-340-88394-5(4), Hodder & Stoughton) Hodder General Publishing Division GBR. *Dist:* Trafalgar Square Publishing.

Wilson, C. J. Limited Vision: Reflections of a Teenager. 1999. (Illus.). (YA). pap. 8.95 (978-0-9621408-1-5(3)) New Dawn Publishing Co.

The Winners. 2005. (YA). 14.95 (*978-0-9661256-4-1(9)) Youth Communication - New York Center.

Wolny, Philip. Abusing Prescription Drugs. 2007. (J). (*978-1-4042-1955-7(2)) Rosen Publishing Group, Inc., The.

Yackley-Franken, Nicki. Teens in Saudi Arabia. 2007. (Global Connections Ser.). (Illus.). 96p. (J). pap. (*978-0-7565-2074-8(6), 1265899) Compass Point Bks.

Yackley-Franken, Nicki & Compass Point Books Staff. Teens in Saudi Arabia. 2006. (Global Connections Ser.). (Illus.). 96p. (J). (gr. 5-7). 31.93 (*978-0-7565-2066-3(5), 1265899) Compass Point Bks.

Youngs, Bettie B., et al. Taste BerriesTM for Teens: Inspirational Short Stories & Encouragement on Life, Love, Friendship & Tough Issues. 1999. (Illus.). 400p. (YA). (gr. 7-12). pap. 12.95 (978-1-55874-669-5(2)) Health Communications, Inc.

Zarate, Gustavo Azgad. Youth Law: A Practical Guide to Legal Issues That Affect Young Adults. 2nd ed. 2005. (YA). per. 25.00 (978-0-9763167-9-4(X)) Living Ministry, Inc.

Zielin, Lara. Make Things Happen: The Key to Networking for Teens. 2004. (Illus.). 108p. (J). pap. 9.95 (978-1-894222-43-3(1)) Lobster Pr. CAN. *Dist:* Univ. of Toronto Pr.

YOUTH—FICTION

Abrahams, Peter, et al. Up All Night: A Short Story Collection. 2008. 240p. (J). 16.99 (*978-0-06-137076-2(2)); lib. bdg. 17.89 (*978-0-06-137077-9(0)) HarperCollins Pubs. (Geringer, Laura Book).

Adkins, Jan. A Storm Without Rain: A Novel in Time. 2004. 179p. 14.95 (978-0-937822-80-7(9)) WoodenBoat Pubns.

Alfonsi, Alice. Over the Top: Junior Novel. 14th rev. ed. 2006. (That's So Raven Ser.: Bk. 14). (Illus.). 128p. (gr. 3-7). pap. 4.99 (978-0-7868-3600-0(8)) Disney Pr.

—Rebel Raven: Junior Novel. 15th rev. ed. 2006. (That's So Raven Ser.: Bk. 15). (Illus.). 144p. (gr. 3-7). pap. 4.99 (978-0-7868-3601-7(6)) Disney Pr.

Allosso, Dan. Outside the Box. 2007. 148p. 21.95 (*978-0-595-68621-6(4)); per. 11.95 (*978-0-595-44295-9(1)) iUniverse, Inc.

Applegate, Katherine. Falling for Claire. 2000. (Making Out Ser.: No. 27). 176p. (YA). (gr. 7-12). pap. 3.99 (978-0-380-81531-9(1)) HarperCollins Pubs.

—Zoey Comes Home. 2000. (Making Out Ser.: No. 28). 176p. (YA). (gr. 7-12). pap. 3.99 (978-0-380-81532-6(X)) HarperCollins Pubs.

Asai, Carrie. Book of the Pearl. 2003. lib. bdg. 15.30 (978-0-613-73440-0(8)) Tandem Library Bks.

Aspin, Diana. Ordinary Miracles. 2004. 192p. (YA). pap. 9.95 (978-0-88995-277-5(9)) Red Deer Pr. CAN. *Dist:* Fitzhenry & Whiteside, Ltd.

Attema, Martha. A Time to Choose. braille ed. 2003. (J). (gr. 2). spiral bd. (978-0-616-15262-1(0)) Canadian National Institute for the Blind/Institut National Canadien pour les Aveugles.

—A Time to Choose. 2004. 176p. (J). (gr. 7-12). pap. 7.95 (978-1-55143-045-4(2)) Orca Bk. Pubs. USA.

Babbitt, Natalie. Tuck Everlasting. 1998. (J). pap. 3.95 (978-0-439-04472-1(3)) Scholastic, Inc.

—Tuck Everlasting. 2002. (gr. 3-6). lib. bdg. 14.10 (978-0-613-71886-8(0)) Tandem Library Bks.

Banting, Celia. I only said I couldn't Cope. 2006. 240p. (YA). per. 14.99 (*978-0-9786648-2-4(5)) Wighita Pr.

—I Only Said I Didn't Want You Because I Was Terrified. 2006. (I Only Said Ser.: 4). 240p. (YA). pap. 14.99 (*978-0-9786648-3-1(3)) Wighita Pr.

—I only said I was telling the Truth. 2006. 240p. (YA). per. 14.99 (*978-0-9786648-4-8(1)) Wighita Pr.

—I Only Said Yes So That They'd Like Me. 2006. 224p. (YA). per. 14.99 (*978-0-9786648-1-7(7)) Wighita Pr.

Baratz-Logsted, Lauren. Secrets of My Suburban Life. 2008. 240p. (YA). pap. 7.99 (*978-1-4169-2525-5(2), Simon Pulse) Simon & Schuster Children's Publishing.

Barham, Lisa. Accidentally Fabulous. 2008. (Fashion-Forward Adventures of Imogene Ser.). 256p. (YA). pap. 9.99 (*978-1-4169-1445-7(5), Simon Pulse) Simon & Schuster Children's Publishing.

Barnum, P. T. Dick Broadhead: A Story of Perilous Adve. 2006. pap. 30.95 (*978-1-4286-1959-3(3)) Kessinger Publishing, LLC.

Barrie, J. M. Peter Pan. Hague, Michael, illus. 100th annot. rev. ed. 2003. 176p. (J). 22.50 (978-0-8050-7245-7(4), Holt, Henry & Co. Bks. For Young Readers) Holt, Henry & Co.

Batista, Joaquin. Westward Eden. 2003. 196p. (YA). 28.95 (978-1-59113-371-1(8)); pap. 15.95 (978-1-59113-316-2(5)) Booklocker.com, Inc.

Beede, John R. Climb On! Dynamic Strategies for Teen Success. 2005. (YA). per. 12.95 (978-0-9765697-0-1(1)) Sierra Nevada Publishing Hse.

Blank, Jessica. Almost Home. rev. ed. 2007. 256p. (YA). (gr. 7 up). 15.99 (*978-1-4231-0642-5(3)) Hyperion Pr.

Blume, Judy. Are You There God? It's Me, Margaret. 149p. (J). (gr. 4-6). pap. 3.50 (978-0-8072-1421-3(3)); (YA). (gr. 5 up). pap. 4.99 (978-0-8072-1508-1(2)) Random Hse. Audio Publishing Group. (Listening Library).

—Are You There God Its Me Margaret. 2001. 160p. (J). (gr. 4-6). 17.95 (978-0-689-84158-3(2), Atheneum/Richard Jackson Bks.) Simon & Schuster Children's Publishing.

Boggess, Eileen. Mia the Meek. 2006. (Mia Fullerton Ser.: Bk. 1). 155p. (YA). (gr. 6-9). 16.95 (*978-1-890862-46-6(0)) Bancroft Pr.

Bolden-Thompson, Angela. When Company Comes. 2007. 224p. pap. 19.95 (*978-0-615-14774-1(7)) Thompson, Angela.

Bremer, Terry. Dandylion: The Most Misunderstood Flower. Pierce, M. Deborah, illus. 2003. 32p. (J). lib. bdg. 15.00 (978-1-931646-90-1(2)) Beaver's Pond Pr., Inc.

Buehner, Caralyn. Would I Ever Lie to You? Davis, Jack E., illus. 2007. 32p. (J). (ps up). 16.99 (978-0-8037-2793-9(3), Dial) Penguin Group (USA) Inc.

Burns, John. Runnerland. 2007. 218p. pap. 9.95 (*978-1-55192-957-6(0)) Raincoast Bk. Distribution CAN. *Dist:* Perseus Distribution.

Burns, Laura J. & Burge, Constance M. Sweet Talkin' Demon. 2006. (Charmed Ser.). 192p. (YA). pap. 6.99 (978-1-4169-1469-3(2), Simon Spotlight Entertainment) Simon & Schuster.

Burton, Rick. Running on Empty. 2005. 72p. pap. 14.95 (978-1-4137-6600-4(5)) PublishAmerica, Inc.

Cabot, Meg, et al. Shining On: 11 Star Author's Illuminating Stories. 2007. 176p. (YA). (gr. 7 up). 8.99 (978-0-385-73472-1(7), Delacorte Bks. for Young Readers) Random Hse. Children's Bks.

Carlson, Melody. Bad Connection. 2006. 256p. pap. 11.99 (978-1-59052-692-7(9), Multnomah) WaterBrook Pr.

—Meant to Be. 2005. (Diary of a Teenage Girl Ser.). 288p. (YA). pap. 12.99 (978-1-59052-322-3(9), Multnomah) WaterBrook Pr.

Carroll, Jenny, pseud. Code Name Cassandra. 2007. (1-800-Where-R-You Ser.: No. 2). 272p. (YA). mass mkt. 6.99 (978-1-4169-2704-4(2), Simon Pulse) Simon & Schuster Children's Publishing.

Choyce, Lesley. Falling Through the Cracks. 1998. (gr. 7-12). lib. bdg. 17.60 (978-0-613-88937-7(1)) Tandem Library Bks.

Ciencin, Scott & Burge, Constance M. Light of the World. 2006. (Charmed Ser.). 256p. (YA). pap. 6.99 (978-1-4169-1470-9(6), Simon Spotlight Entertainment) Simon & Schuster.

Cleary, Beverly. Fifteen. 2000. (J). (978-0-606-19735-9(4)) Tandem Library Bks.

Coming of Age Vol. 1: Fiction about Youth & Adolescence. 2nd ed. Incl. 2nd ed. Emra, Bruce & McGraw-Hill Staff. 311p. (C). pap., stu. ed. 41.32 (978-0-8442-0361-4(0), 9780844203614); Vol. 1. Coming of Age. Emra, Bruce, contrib. by. (J). (978-0-8442-0362-1(9), C03629); 1999. Set stu. ed. 46.00 (978-0-8442-0360-7(2), 9780844203607) Glencoe/McGraw-Hill.

Condon, Bill. No Worries. 2005. 216p. (YA). pap. 18.95 (978-0-7022-3491-0(5)) Univ. of Queensland Pr. AUS. *Dist:* International Specialized Bk. Services.

Cormier, Robert. The Chocolate War. 2002. (Illus.). (J). 13.94 (978-0-7587-4778-5(0)) Book Wholesalers, Inc.

—The Chocolate War. 191p. (YA). (gr. 7 up). pap. 4.99 (978-0-8072-1428-2(0), Listening Library) Random Hse. Audio Publishing Group.

—The Chocolate War. 30th ed. 2004. 272p. (YA). (gr. 7-12). pap. 8.95 (978-0-375-82987-1(3), Knopf Bks. for Young Readers) Random Hse. Children's Bks.

—The Chocolate War. 2000. 12.64 (978-0-606-20038-7(X)) Tandem Library Bks.

Cote, Denis & Poulin, Stephane. La Machine a Rajeunir. 2000. (Roman Jeunesse Ser.). 96p. (J). (gr. 4-7). pap. (978-2-89021-379-1(X)) Diffusion du livre Mirabel.

Crew, Gary. Cruel Nest. 2002. (Illus.). 160p. (YA). pap. (978-0-7344-0248-6(1), Lothian Bks.) Hachette Livre Australia.

Croteau, Marie-Danielle. Mr. Gauguin's Heart. Ouriou, Susan, tr. from FRE. Arsenault, Isabelle, illus. 2007. 24p. (J). (gr. 1-4). 18.95 (*978-0-88776-824-8(5)) Tundra Bks., Inc./Livres Toundra, Inc. CAN. *Dist:* Random Hse., Inc.

Cusick, Richie Tankersley. The Unseen III. 2005. 272p. (YA). pap. (*978-0-439-96344-2(3), Scholastic) Scholastic, Inc.

Denis, Erik & LeBlanc, Natalie. The Bubble. 2005. 16p. 10.10 (978-1-4116-6424-1(8)) Lulu.com.

DeVita, James. The Silenced. 2007. 512p. (YA). (gr. 7 up). 17.99 (978-0-06-078462-1(8)); lib. bdg. 18.89 (978-0-06-078464-5(4)) HarperCollins Pubs.

Dower, Laura. All Shook Up. 22nd rev. ed. 2006. 176p. (gr. 3-7). pap. 4.99 (978-0-7868-3779-3(9)) Hyperion Pr.

—All That Glitters. 20th rev. ed. 2005. (From the Files of Madison Finn Ser.: Bk. 20). (Illus.). 176p. (gr. 3-7). pap. 4.99 (978-0-7868-5688-6(2), Volo) Hyperion Bks. for Children.

—Off the Wall. 2004. 170p. (J). (gr. 3-7). per. 12.04 (978-0-606-33024-4(0)) Tandem Library Bks.

Dower, Laura. On the Case. 2004. 170p. (J). lib. bdg. 16.92 (*978-1-4242-0648-3(0)) Fitzgerald Bks.

Doyle, Brian. Angel Square. 2004. 144p. (J). pap. 6.95 (978-0-88899-609-1(8)) Groundwood Bks. CAN. *Dist:* Perseus Distribution.

—Covered Bridge. Date not set. (J). (gr. 4-6). pap. (978-0-88899-190-4(8)); 2004. (Illus.). 120p. (YA). pap. 6.95 (978-0-88899-603-9(9)) Groundwood Bks. CAN. *Dist:* Transition Vendor, Perseus Distribution.

—Up to Low. (J). 2004. 115p. pap. 6.95 (978-0-88899-622-0(5)); 2002. (gr. 5-7). pap. 5.95 (978-0-88899-264-2(5), Libros Tigrillo) Groundwood Bks. CAN. *Dist:* Perseus Distribution, Transition Vendor.

—You Can Pick Me up at Peggy's Cove. Date not set. (J). (gr. 4-6). reprint ed. pap. 5.95 (978-0-88899-231-4(9)) Groundwood Bks. CAN. *Dist:* Transition Vendor.

Drechsler, Debbie. The Summer of Love. 2003. (Illus.). 144p. pap. 16.95 (978-1-896597-65-2(3)) Drawn & Quarterly Pubns. CAN. *Dist:* Macmillan.

Dunnion, Kristyn. Mosh Pit. 2004. 272p. (YA). (gr. 9-12). pap. 7.95 (978-0-88995-292-8(2)) Red Deer Pr. CAN. *Dist:* Fitzhenry & Whiteside, Ltd.

Durham, David. Gabriel's Story. 2002. (gr. 7-12). lib. bdg. 22.25 (978-0-613-49406-9(7)) Tandem Library Bks.

Eaton, Anthony. Fireshadow. 2004. 352p. (YA). pap. 18.95 (978-0-7022-3381-4(1)) Univ. of Queensland Pr. AUS. *Dist:* International Specialized Bk. Services.

Echo of Hooves. 2005. (J). (978-1-933343-10-5(9), PONY) Stabenfeldt Inc.

Edwards, Hazel. Stalker. 2003. 176p. pap. (978-0-7344-0103-8(5), Lothian Bks.) Hachette Livre Australia.

Edwards, Mark. The Gang Book 1 the Saint's Bones. 2004. (YA). per. 10.95 (978-0-9755704-0-1(4)) New Classics Pr.

Ellsworth, Mark R. The Quiniela of Angels. 2006. 19p. (YA). per. 8.95 (*978-1-59453-841-4(7), 3319, Airleaf Publishing) Airleaf Publishing & Bookselling.

Emesse, Tea. Nova & the Charmed Three. 2006. (Star Sisterz Ser.: Bk. 5). 144p. (J). pap. 5.99 (978-0-7869-3991-6(5), Mirrorstone) Wizards of the Coast.

Emra, Bruce, contrib. by. Coming of Age, Vol. 1. 1999. (J). (978-0-8442-0362-1(9), C03629) McGraw-Hill/Contemporary.

Euwer Wolff, Virginia Euwer. This Full House. 2007. (J). (gr. 6-9). 17.99 (*978-0-7868-3728-1(4)) Hyperion Pr.

Evans, Mari. I'm Late: The Story of LeNeese & Moonlight & Alisha Who Didn't Have Anyone of Her Own. Honeywood, Varnette P., illus. 2006. 86p. (YA). (gr. 7 up). 14.95 (978-1-933491-00-4(0)) Just Us Bks., Inc.

Fabra, Jordi Sierra. Seis Historias en Torno a Mario. 1999. (978-0-606-17744-3(2)) Tandem Library Bks.

Forde, Catherine. Firestarter. 2006. 160p. (J). pap. 8.99 (*978-1-4052-1056-0(7)) Egmont Bks., Ltd. GBR. *Dist:* Independent Pubs. Group.

—Skarrs. 2004. 352p. (J). pap. 8.99 (*978-1-4052-0947-2(X)) Egmont Bks., Ltd. GBR. *Dist:* Independent Pubs. Group.

Francis, Panama, et al. David Gets His Drum. Velasquez, Eric, illus. 2002. 32p. (J). (gr. k-3). 16.95 (978-0-7614-5088-7(2)) Cavendish, Marshall Corp.

Frost, Helen. Keesha's House. 2003. (Illus.). 128p. (YA). 16.00 (978-0-374-34064-3(1), Farrar, Straus & Giroux (BYR)) Farrar, Straus & Giroux.

Frye, Tom. Scratchin' on the Eight Ball. 2000. 240p. (YA). pap. 12.95 (978-0-595-12971-3(4), Writer's Showcase Pr.) iUniverse, Inc.

Gallo, Donald R., compiled by. What Are You Afraid Of? Stories about Phobias. 2006. 208p. (J). (gr. 7). 16.99 (978-0-7636-2654-9(6)) Candlewick Pr.

Garisch, Dawn. Babyshoes. 2004. 288p. pap. 9.99 (978-0-689-83778-4(X)) Simon & Schuster, Ltd. GBR. *Dist:* Independent Pubs. Group.

Geary, Robert, illus. Top Teen Stories. 2004. (Red Hot Reads Ser.). 256p. (J). (gr. 4-8). pap. 6.95 (978-0-7534-5721-4(0), Kingfisher) Houghton Mifflin Co. Trade & Reference Div.

Goobie, Beth. Something Girl. 2006. 112p. (YA). lib. bdg. 14.95 (978-1-55143-560-2(8)) Orca Bk. Pubs. USA.

Gregory, Nan. Pink. Melanson, Luc, illus. 2007. 32p. (J). (ps-2). 17.95 (*978-0-88899-781-4(7)) Groundwood Bks. CAN. *Dist:* Perseus Distribution.

Griffiths, Sara. Thrown a Curve: A Novel. l.t. ed. 2007. 151p. (YA). (gr. 6-10). 16.95 (*978-1-890862-48-0(7)) Bancroft Pr.

Hadley. Tough Choices: Young Women Talk. 1999. 98p. (J). pap. 11.99 (978-0-7043-4953-7(1)) Women's Pr., Ltd., The GBR. *Dist:* Independent Pubs. Group.

Hall, S.C. Turns of Fortune & Other Tales. 2007. (ENG.). 116p. per. (*978-1-4065-1586-2(8)) Dodo Pr.

Hapka, Cathy. Over the Top. 2005. 140p. (J). (978-1-4155-7730-1(7), Aladdin) Simon & Schuster Children's Publishing.

—Star Bright. 2005. 146p. (J). (978-1-4155-7740-0(4), Aladdin) Simon & Schuster Children's Publishing.

Harley, Rex. Baby, Now That I've Found You. 2003. 220p. pap. 12.95 (978-1-84323-107-3(7)) Beekman Bks., Inc.

Hawke, Rosanne. A Kiss in Every Wave. 2002. 160p. (YA). pap. (978-0-7344-0267-7(8), Lothian Bks.) Hachette Livre Australia.

Hawley, Richard. Paul & Juliana: A Novel. 2003. 188p. (YA). 19.95 (978-1-890862-33-6(9)) Bancroft Pr.

Heldreth, L. E. Bad Trail Mix: Teenage Fugitives in the Wilderness. 2002. (gr. 7-12). lib. bdg. 18.75 (978-0-613-74650-2(3)) Tandem Library Bks.

Hill, David. Coming Back. 2007. 189p. pap. 18.95 (*978-0-9542330-2-0(6)) Aurora Metro Pubns. Ltd. GBR. *Dist:* Consortium Bk. Sales & Distribution.

Hinton, S. E. La Ley de la Calle. Lacruz, Javier, tr. 2nd ed. 2003. (SPA., Illus.). 128p. (J). (gr. 8-12). pap. 9.95 (978-84-204-4858-9(3)) Santillana USA Publishing Co., Inc.

—Rebeldes. (SPA., Illus.). 192p. (J). (gr. 5-8). pap. 9.95 (978-1-59437-807-2(X)) Santillana USA Publishing Co., Inc.

Hodgson, Miriam. Love from Dad: Stories about Fathers & Daughters. 160p. (J). pap. 8.99 (978-0-7497-4330-7(1)) Egmont Bks., Ltd. GBR. *Dist:* Trafalgar Square Publishing.

Hook. Wrinkled Crinkled Grapes: A Purple Monster. 2007. 52p. per. 8.95 (*978-0-595-42310-1(8)) iUniverse, Inc.

Hope, Laura Lee. Outdoor Girls in Florida or Wintering in. 2007. 95.99 (*978-1-4280-5353-3(0)); pap. 88.99 (*978-1-4280-5357-1(3)) IndyPublish.com.

—Outdoor Girls in the Saddle or the Girl. 2007. 95.99 (*978-1-4280-5359-5(X)); pap. 88.99 (*978-1-4280-5368-7(9)) IndyPublish.com.

—Outdoor Girls on Pine Island or A Cave A. 2007. 95.99 (*978-1-4280-5320-5(4)); pap. 89.99 (*978-1-4280-5317-5(4)) IndyPublish.com.

Hopkins, Cathy. Mates, Dates & Sizzling Summers. 2006. (Mates, Dates Ser.). 224p. (YA). mass mkt. 5.99 (978-0-689-87698-1(X), Simon Pulse) Simon & Schuster Children's Publishing.

Howe, James, ed. 13: Thirteen Stories That Capture the Agony & Ecstasy of Being Thirteen. 2003. 288p. (YA). 16.95 (978-0-689-82863-8(2), Atheneum) Simon & Schuster Children's Publishing.

Howe, Tina Field. Alysa of the Fields: Book One in the Tellings of Xunar-kun. 2006. (Illus.). 320p. (YA). pap. 16.95 (978-0-9768585-1-5(7), 002) Howe, Tina Field.

Jacobs, Deborah Lynn. Powers. 2008. 208p. (YA). pap. 6.99 (*978-0-312-37756-4(8)) Square Fish.

Jenkins, A. M. Breaking Boxes. 2000. (978-0-606-17834-1(1)) Tandem Library Bks.

Jenny, Markas. The Beginning. novel ed. 2005. (One Tree Hill Ser.: No. 1). (Illus.). 264p. (J). pap. 6.99 (978-0-439-71560-7(1)) Scholastic, Inc.

Johnston, Jeffry. Fragments. 2007. 208p. (YA). pap. 6.99 (978-1-4169-2486-9(8), Simon Pulse) Simon & Schuster Children's Publishing.

Jughead with Archie, 6 bks., Set. 2007. (J). 145.26 (*978-1-59961-271-3(2)) Spotlight.

Keaney, Brian. The Hollow People. Ceccoli, Nicoletta, illus. 2007. (Promises of Dr. Sigmundus: Bk. 1). 240p. (YA). (gr. 7-12). lib. bdg. 19.99 (*978-0-375-94332-4(3), Knopf Bks. for Young Readers) Random Hse. Children's Bks.

—The Hollow People. 2007. (Promises of Dr. Sigmundus: Bk. 1). (Illus.). 224p. (YA). (gr. 7-12). 16.99 (*978-0-375-84332-7(9), Knopf Bks. for Young Readers) Random Hse. Children's Bks.

Kearns, Ann. Dell's Discovery. 2006. 108p. (YA). per. 9.95 (978-0-9710696-6-4(2)) Jorlan Publishing, Inc.

Kennen, Ally. Beast. 2007. 224p. (J). pap. 7.99 (*978-0-439-86550-0(6)) Scholastic, Inc.

Kerr, M. E. Dinky Hocker Shoots Smack! 2007. 224p. (J). pap. 6.99 (978-0-06-113989-5(0), HarperTeen) HarperCollins Pubs.

Kijinski, Paul. Camp Limestone. 2006. (Illus.). 104p. (YA). per. 7.99 (978-1-59958-016-6(0)) Journey Stone Creations, LLC.

King, Katina. Ride Wit' Me. 2006. 144p. (J). pap. 12.00 (*978-0-9724003-8-1(9)) Power Play Media.

Koch, Edward T. & Koch Thaler, Pat. Eddie: Harold's Little Brother. Warhola, James, illus. 2004. 32p. (J). (ps). 16.99 (978-0-399-24210-6(4), Putnam Juvenile) Penguin Group (USA) Inc.

Komorn, Julie, adapted by. Out of the Dark. 2004. (W. I. T. C. H. Ser.: Bk. 8). (Illus.). 128p. (J). lib. bdg. 16.92 (*978-1-4242-0789-3(4)) Fitzgerald Bks.

Komorn, Julie & Lenhard, Elizabeth, adapted by. The Light of Meridian. 2004. (W. I. T. C. H. Ser.: Bk. 7). (Illus.). 144p. (J). lib. bdg. 16.92 (*978-1-4242-0794-7(0)) Fitzgerald Bks.

Krulik, Nancy E. From the Mouths of Babes. 2000. (Popular Ser.: Bk. 3). (Illus.). 176p. (J). (gr. 5-9). pap. 4.99 (978-0-7868-1513-5(2)) Disney Pr.

—From the Mouths of Babes. 2000. (gr. 5-8). lib. bdg. 13.00 (978-0-613-31226-4(0)) Tandem Library Bks.

—Round One. 2000. (gr. 5-8). lib. bdg. 13.00 (978-0-613-31649-1(5)) Tandem Library Bks.

Lackey, Mercedes. Take a Thief. 2002. (Heralds of Valdemar Ser.). (gr. 7-12). lib. bdg. 15.30 (978-0-613-63081-8(5)) Tandem Library Bks.

Lasky, Kathryn. Jahanara: Princess of Princesses, India, 1627. 2002. (Royal Diaries Ser.). 192p. (J). (gr. 4-8). pap. 10.95 (978-0-439-22350-8(4), Scholastic Pr.) Scholastic, Inc.

W X Y Z

Lekich, John. King of the Lost & Found. 2007. 304p. (J). (gr. 7 up). pap. 9.95 (***978-1-55192-802-9(7)***) Raincoast Bk. Distribution CAN. *Dist:* Perseus Distribution.

Lenhard, Elizabeth. A Bridge Between Worlds. 2004. (W. I. T. C. H. Ser.: Bk. 10). 158p. (J). lib. bdg. 16.92 (***978-1-4242-0796-1(7)***) Fitzgerald Bks.

—The Disappearance. 2004. (W. I. T. C. H. Ser.: Bk. 2). 158p. (J). lib. bdg. 16.92 (***978-1-4242-0799-2(1)***) Fitzgerald Bks.

—Finding Meridian. 2004. (W. I. T. C. H. Ser.: Bk. 3). 158p. (J). lib. bdg. 16.92 (***978-1-4242-0801-2(7)***) Fitzgerald Bks.

—Power of Five. 2004. 158p. (J). lib. bdg. 16.92 (***978-1-4242-0795-4(9)***) Fitzgerald Bks.

Lenhard, Elizabeth, adapted by. The Return of a Queen. 2004. (W. I. T. C. H. Ser.: Bk. 12). 152p. (J). lib. bdg. 16.92 (***978-1-4242-0797-8(5)***) Fitzgerald Bks.

Levithan, David. Boy Meets Boy. 2005. 192p. (YA). (gr. 7-12). reprint ed. pap. 8.95 (978-0-375-83299-4(8) , Knopf Bks. for Young Readers) Random Hse. Children's Bks.

Lohans, Alison. Laws of Emotion. 2004. 207p. mass mkt. (978-1-895449-07-5(3)) Thistledown Pr., Ltd.

Loughrey, Eithne. Annie Moore: First in Line for America. 1999. (Illus.). 143p. (YA). (gr. 5-10). pap. 7.95 (978-1-85635-245-1(5)) Mercier Pr., Ltd., The IRL. *Dist:* Irish Bks. & Media, Inc.

Lowry, Lois, frwd. Shining On: 11 Star Authors' Illuminating Stories. 2007. 176p. (YA). (gr. 7). lib. bdg. 11.99 (978-0-385-90470-4(3) , Delacorte Bks. for Young Readers) Random Hse. Children's Bks.

Lucashenko, Melissa. Killing D'arcy. 1998. 240p. (YA). (gr. 8-12). pap. 16.95 (978-0-7022-3041-7(3)) Univ. of Queensland Pr. AUS. *Dist:* International Specialized Bk. Services.

Manns, Nick. Dead Negative. 2003. mass mkt. (978-0-340-85566-9(5) , Hodder Children's Books) Hodder Children's Division.

McCorkle, Mark & Schooley, Bob. Grudge Match. 2005. (Illus.). 80p. (J). (978-1-4155-9100-0(8)) Disney Pr.

McPhee, Peter. Every Move. 2004. (SideStreets Ser.). 184p. (YA). (gr. 7-12). 7.95 (978-1-55028-850-6(4)); (***978-1-55028-851-3(2)***) Lorimer, James & Co., Ltd., Pubs. CAN. *Dist:* Casemate Pubs. & Bk. Distributors, LLC.

Mechling, Lauren & Moser, Laura. Foreign Exposure: The Social Climber Abroad. 2007. 320p. (YA). (gr. 7 up). pap. 8.99 (***978-0-618-66379-8(7)*** , Graphia) Houghton Mifflin Co. Trade & Reference Div.

Meyer, Carolyn. Beware, Princess Elizabeth. 2001. (Young Royals Ser.: Bk. 2). (J). 17.00 (978-0-15-202639-4(8) , Gulliver Bks.) Harcourt Children's Bks.

Meyer, Stephanie H. & Meyer, John. Written in the Dirt: A Collection of Short Stories, Poetry, Art & Photography. 2004. (Illus.). 360p. (YA). pap. 12.95 (978-0-7573-0050-9(2)) Health Communications, Inc.

Minter, J. Pass It On. 2004. (Insiders Ser.). 200p. (YA). pap. 8.95 (978-1-58234-954-1(1) , Bloomsbury Children) Bloomsbury Publishing.

Moorhead, Joshua Matthew. Baker's Dozen: In 13 Days, Justin Baker & the World Will Change. 2005. (Fresh Voices Ser.). 218p. (J). (gr. 8-17). pap. 9.95 (978-1-932802-96-2(7) , Holy Macro! Bks.) MrExcel.com Publishing.

Morgan, Marlo. Making the Message Mine. Grimme, Jeannette, ed. Garrison, Carri, illus. Date not set. 115p. (Orig.). (YA). pap. (978-1-883473-01-3(2)) MM Co.

Morris, Kimberly. The Real Deal: Junior Novel. 13th rev. ed. 2006. (That's So Raven Ser.: No. 13). (Illus.). 128p. (gr. 3-7). pap. 4.99 (978-0-7868-3599-7(0)) Disney Pr.

Murphy, Ryan. Round One. 2000. (Popular Ser.: Bk. 1). (Illus.). 144p. (J). (gr. 5-9). pap. 4.99 (978-0-7868-1486-2(1)) Disney Pr.

Myers, Walter Dean. Every Man for Himself: 10 Short Stories about Being a Guy. Mercado, Nancy, ed. 2005. (Illus.). 176p. (YA). (gr. 9). 16.99 (978-0-8037-2896-7(4) , Dial) Penguin Group (USA) Inc.

Nanami, Shingo & Tezuka, Kaname. Kamui, Vol. 7. Seto, Dietrich & Yamashita, Shizuki, eds. Yamashita, Satsuki, tr. O'Leary, Keiran & McDougall, Chris, illus. 2007. (Kamui Ser.). 224p. pap. 9.99 (***978-1-59741-054-0(3)***) Broccoli International USA, Inc.

Nelson, Blake. Girl. Smith, Ali, photos by. 2007. 256p. (YA). pap. 9.99 (***978-1-4169-4803-2(1)*** , Simon Pulse) Simon & Schuster Children's Publishing.

Night. 1998. 36p. (YA). 11.95 (978-1-56137-805-0(4) , NU8054SP) Novel Units, Inc.

Oates, Joyce Carol. Small Avalanches & Other Stories. 2004. lib. bdg. 16.45 (978-0-613-71362-7(1)) Tandem Library Bks.

Oldham, June. In the Blood. 2003. 240p. (J). pap. (978-0-340-86653-5(5) , Hodder Children's Books) Hodder Children's Division.

Oldham, Mary. No Fire, No Candle. 2001. 217p. (YA). pap. 12.95 (978-1-85902-945-9(0)) Beekman Bks., Inc.

On Thin Ice. 2005. per. (978-0-9772505-2-3(0)) Adibooks.com.

O'Neill, Joan. Daisy Chain Dream. 2003. mass mkt. (978-0-340-85468-6(5) , Hodder Children's Books) Hodder Children's Division.

Optic, Oliver. Forgive & Forget: The Young Captain. unabr. ed. 1998. (Lakeshore Ser.: Vol. 3). (Illus.). 288p. (J). reprint ed. 15.00 (978-1-889128-52-8(X)) Mantle Ministries.

—Heaping Coals: The War of the Students. unabr. ed. 1998. (Lakeshore Ser.: Vol. 4). (Illus.). 288p. reprint ed. 15.00 (978-1-889128-53-5(8)) Mantle Ministries.

—Tried & True: The Young Peacemakers. unabr. ed. 1998. (Lakeshore Ser.: Vol. 5). (Illus.). 304p. reprint ed. 15.00 (978-1-889128-54-2(6)) Mantle Ministries.

Parker, Robert B. Edenville Owls. 2007. 208p. (YA). (gr. 4 up). 17.99 (978-0-399-24656-2(8) , Philomel) Penguin Group (USA) Inc.

Parry, Glyn. Spooking the Cows. 2002. 80p. (YA). pap. 12.95 (978-1-86368-389-0(5)) Fremantle Pr. AUS. *Dist:* International Specialized Bk. Services.

Poole-Carter, Rosemary. Juliette Ascending. 2007. (YA). pap. 14.00 (***978-1-929976-41-6(0)*** , TOP) Top Pubns., Ltd.

Rallison, Janette. Life, Love, & the Pursuit of Free Throws. 2006. 192p. (J). pap. 6.95 (978-0-8027-8898-6(X)) Walker & Co.

Ravel, Edeet. The Thrilling Life of Pauline de Lammermoor. 2007. 168p. pap. 9.95 (***978-1-55192-988-0(0)***) Raincoast Bk. Distribution CAN. *Dist:* Perseus Distribution.

Reynolds, Marilyn. Baby Help. 2003. (True-To-Life Ser.: Vol. 6). 192p. (J). (gr. 7-12). 15.95 (978-1-885356-26-0(9)); pap. 8.95 (978-1-885356-27-7(7)) Morning Glory Pr., Inc.

—If You Loved Me. 1999. (True-to-Life Series from Hamilton High: Vol. 7). 32p. (J). pap., tchr. ed. 2.50 (978-1-885356-59-8(5)) Morning Glory Pr., Inc.

Roman, Annette. 1 World Manga, Vol. 5. Ng, Leandro, illus. 2007. (1 World Manga Ser.). 240p. (YA). pap. 3.99 (978-1-4215-1169-6(X)) Viz Media.

Ruditis, Paul & Burge, Constance M. As Puck Would Have It. 2006. (Charmed Ser.). 240p. (YA). pap. 6.99 (978-1-4169-1468-6(4) , Simon Spotlight Entertainment) Simon & Schuster.

Ryan, Ann. The Little Wannabee. Ryan, Ann, illus. 2006. (Illus.). 20p. (J). 16.95 (***978-1-933660-31-8(7)*** , Tadpole Pr. 4 Kids) Smooth Sailing Pr.

Samarasinghe, Sara. Dalaina. 2006. 24.99 (***978-1-4259-6502-0(4)***); pap. 17.99 (***978-1-4259-6501-3(6)***) AuthorHouse.

Shaw, Deirdre & Prince, Jonathan. Fair Play. 2005. (American Dreams Ser.). 168p. (YA). (978-1-4155-7940-4(7) , Simon Spotlight) Simon & Schuster Children's Publishing.

Shaw, Esther. The Winter Mare. 2005. (ENG., Illus.). 198p. pap. (***978-1-84401-447-7(9)***) Athena Pr.

Sherrard, Valerie. Sam's Light. 2004. 216p. pap. 8.99 (978-1-55002-535-4(X)) Dundurn Group, The CAN. *Dist:* Univ. of Toronto Pr.

Starr, Sandra. Leigh's Triumph. 2006. 295p. pap. 24.95 (978-1-4137-4660-0(8)) PublishAmerica, Inc.

Staub, Wendy Corsi. This Boy Is Mind. 2001. (Turning Seventeen Ser.: No. 6). 208p. (YA). (gr. 7 up). pap. 4.95 (978-0-06-447242-5(6) , Harper Trophy) HarperCollins Pubs.

Stevenson, Robert Louis, intro. Kidnapped: Catriona. 2007. 480p. pap. 15.00 (***978-1-84697-033-7(4)***) BirlinnPolygon GBR. *Dist:* Interlink Publishing Group, Inc.

Stinson, Kathy. 101 Ways to Dance. 2006. 150p. pap. 7.95 (978-1-897187-10-4(6)) Second Story Pr. CAN. *Dist:* Orca Bk. Pubs. USA.

Stone, Vicki L. Why Should I Stay A Virgin? 2004. 74p. (YA). per. (978-1-59196-850-4(X)) Instantpublisher.com.

Sullivan, Jenny. Nowhere Again. 2004. 228p. pap. 13.95 (978-1-84323-297-1(9)) Beekman Bks., Inc.

Summers, K. Secrets Only Teenagers Know. 2000. (gr. 7-12). lib. bdg. 27.05 (978-0-613-79744-3(2)) Tandem Library Bks.

Susi, Geraldine Lee. My Father, My Companion: Life at the Hollow, Chief Justice John Marshall's Boyhood Home in Virginia. 2001. (Illus.). 96p. (J). (gr. 4-9). pap. 10.95 (978-1-889324-22-7(1)) EPM Pubns., Inc.

Taylor, Drew Hayden. The Night Wanderer: A Native Gothic Novel. 2007. 224p. (YA). (gr. 7-12). 21.95 (***978-1-55451-100-6(3)***); pap. 10.95 (***978-1-55451-099-3(6)***) Annick Pr., Ltd. CAN. *Dist:* Firefly Bks., Ltd.

Taylor, William. Jerome: A Novel. 1999. 96p. (gr. 9 up). pap. 9.95 (978-1-55583-512-5(0)) Alyson Pubns.

Thiele, Colin. Swan Song. 2002. (Illus.). 196p. (YA). (gr. 10). pap. (978-0-7344-0325-4(9) , Lothian Bks.) Hachette Livre Australia.

Thomley, Rebecca Gundersen. I Know He Is There: A Lift-A-Flap Book about Faith. Dorman, Brandon, illus. 2006. (J). (***978-1-59038-550-0(0)***) Deseret Bk. Co.

Tiernan, Cate. Awakening, Bk. 5. 2007. (Sweep Ser.). 192p. (YA). pap. 6.99 (***978-0-14-241020-2(9)*** , Puffin) Penguin Group (USA) Inc.

Tiernan, Cate. Reckoning. 2002. (gr. 7-12). lib. bdg. 14.15 (978-0-613-64099-2(3)) Tandem Library Bks.

Tracey, Rhian. Isla & Luke: Make or Break? 2004. 208p. pap. 12.95 (978-0-7475-6649-6(6)) Bloomsbury Publishing Plc GBR. *Dist:* Independent Pubs. Group.

Tullson, Diane. Edge. 2002. (Illus.). 212p. (YA). pap. 6.95 (978-0-7737-6230-5(2)) Stoddart Kids CAN. *Dist:* Fitzhenry & Whiteside, Ltd.

—Edge. 2003. (gr. 7-12). lib. bdg. 15.25 (978-0-613-81887-2(3)) Tandem Library Bks.

Ure, Jean. Boys on the Brain. l.t. ed. 2005. (Illus.). 184p. (J). pap. incl. audio (978-0-7540-7859-3(0) , CLP 450) BBC Audio.

—Boys on the Brain. 2002. (Diary Ser.). (Illus.). 208p. (J). pap. 9.99 (978-0-00-711373-6(0)) HarperCollins Pubs. Ltd. GBR. *Dist:* Independent Pubs. Group.

Ure, Jean. Gone Missing. 2007. (Illus.). 192p. (J). pap. 8.99 (***978-0-00-722459-3(1)***) HarperCollins Pubs. Ltd. GBR. *Dist:* Independent Pubs. Group.

Valgardson, W. D. Divorced Kids Club: And Other Stories. 2000. (gr. 5-8). lib. bdg. 15.25 (978-0-613-33888-2(X)) Tandem Library Bks.

Van Dyne, Edith. Mary Louise. 2006. 148p. pap. 10.99 (978-1-4264-1952-2(X)); 144p. pap. 13.99 (978-1-4264-2063-4(3)) BiblioBazaar.

Van Syckle, A. & Schwartz, Josh. The OC: 'twas the Night Before Chrismukkah. 2005. 206p. (YA). (978-1-4156-3915-3(9)) Scholastic, Inc.

Waite, Judy. Game Girls. 2008. 352p. (YA). pap. 11.95 (***978-1-84270-618-3(7)***) Andersen GBR. *Dist:* Independent Pubs. Group.

Wallington, Aury, adapted by. The O. C. Novelization: The Misfit, No. 2. novel ed. 2004. (O. C. Novelization Ser.). (Illus.). 256p. (J). (gr. 7 up). 6.99 (978-0-439-67700-4(9)) Scholastic, Inc.

Wallington, Aury & Schwartz, Josh. The OC: Bait & Switch. 2005. 163p. (YA). (978-1-4156-2363-3(5)) Scholastic, Inc.

Walmsley, Tom. Kid Stuff: A Novel. 2003. 288p. pap. 17.95 (978-1-55152-153-4(9)) Arsenal Pulp Pr. CAN. *Dist:* Consortium Bk. Sales & Distribution.

Warren, Bertie. Sammie's Journey to Freedom. 2006. (ENG.). 52p. per. 12.95 (***978-1-4241-5142-4(2)*** PublishAmerica, Inc.

Weisberg, Joseph. 10th Grade: A Novel. 2003. (gr. 7-12). lib. bdg. 21.05 (978-0-613-62920-1(5)) Tandem Library Bks.

Welford, Sue. Secret Love Large Print. 2006. pap. (***978-1-905665-10-5(5)***) Pollinger In Print.

Weyn, Suzanne & Gonzalez, Diana. South Beach Sizzle. 2005. 249p. (YA). (gr. 9-12). per. 14.45 (978-1-4176-6059-9(7)) Tandem Library Bks.

Wheels of Danger. 64p. (YA). (gr. 9-12). pap. 9.50 (978-0-8359-1086-6(5)) Globe Fearon Educational Publishing.

Williams, Tia. The It Chicks. 2007. 304p. (gr. 7 up). pap. 8.99 (***978-1-4231-0406-3(4)*** , Jump at the Sun) Hyperion Bks. for Children.

Wilson, Jacqueline. The Diamond Girls. 2004. (Illus.). 229p. (J). (978-0-385-60607-3(9) , Doubleday) Transworld Publishers Ltd.

Yee, Paul. What Happened This Summer. 2006. 128p. (YA). 15.95 (978-1-896580-88-3(2)) Tradewind Bks. CAN. *Dist:* Orca Bk. Pubs. USA.

Zeitoun, Mary-Lou. 13. 2002. 144p. (YA). 14.95 (978-0-88984-232-8(9)) Porcupine's Quill, Inc. CAN. *Dist:* Univ. of Toronto Pr.

Zindel, Paul. My Darling, My Hamburger. 1999. mass mkt. (978-0-553-24396-3(9)); (YA). mass mkt. (978-0-553-20759-0(8)) Random Hse., Inc.

—The Pigman's Legacy. 2005. 168p. (YA). (gr. 7-12). lib. bdg. 13.04 (978-0-606-33946-9(9)) Tandem Library Bks.

Zitelman, Jem. Ventures Tested: One Teenager's Story . . . to Happiness. 2000. viii, 206p. (J). 24.95 (978-1-891612-00-8(X) , 9701); pap. 15.95 (978-1-891612-01-5(8) , 9701); lib. bdg. 24.95 (978-1-891612-02-2(6) , 9701) Celjon Bks.

YOUTH MOVEMENT

Lesko, Wendy Schaetzel. Youth: The 26% Solution, 1. 1998. (YA). pap. 14.95 (978-1-878346-47-6(4)) Information U.S.A., Inc.

YUGOSLAVIA

Hughes, Christopher. Yugoslavia. 2003. (Nations in Conflict Ser.). 48p. (YA). 26.19 (978-1-56711-549-9(7) , Blackbirch Pr., Inc.) Thomson Gale.

Milivojevic, JoAnn. Serbia. rev. ed. 2003. (Enchantment of the World, Second Ser.). (Illus.). 144p. (YA). (gr. 5-9). 36.00 (978-0-516-22695-8(9) , Children's Pr.) Scholastic Library Publishing.

YUGOSLAVIA—FICTION

Dorros, Arthur. Under the Sun. 2006. 240p. (YA). (gr. 5-11). pap. 5.95 (978-0-8109-9250-4(7)) Abrams, Harry N., Inc.

Mead, Alice. Adem's Cross. 1998. (978-0-606-13110-0(8)) Tandem Library Bks.

—Girl of Kosovo. 2001. 128p. (J). (gr. 4-7). 16.00 (978-0-374-32620-3(7) , Farrar, Straus & Giroux (BYR)) Farrar, Straus & Giroux.

—Girl of Kosovo. 2003. (Illus.). 128p. (J). (gr. 5). pap. 5.50 (978-0-440-41853-5(4) , Yearling) Random Hse. Children's Bks.

—Girl of Kosovo. 2003. (gr. 3-6). lib. bdg. 13.00 (978-0-613-62205-9(7)) Tandem Library Bks.

YUGOSLAVIA—HISTORY

Andryszewski, Tricia. Kosovo: The Splintering of Yugoslavia. 2000. (Headliners Ser.). (Illus.). 64p. (gr. 5-8). lib. bdg. 25.90 (978-0-7613-1750-0(3) , Millbrook Pr.) Lerner Publishing Group.

Behnke, Alison. Serbia & Montenegro in Pictures. 2007. (Visual Geography Ser.). (Illus.). 80p. (J). 27.93 (978-0-8225-2679-7(4) , Twenty-First Century Bks.) Lerner Publishing Group.

Flotz, Katherine Haeger. A Pebble in My Shoe: A Memoir. 2004. (Illus.). 185p. lib. bdg. 29.95 (978-0-9657793-2-6(7)) Pannonia Pr.

Honovich, Nancy. Immigration from the Former Yugoslavia. 2003. (Changing Face of North America Ser.). (Illus.). 112p. (YA). lib. bdg. (978-1-59084-690-2(7)) Mason Crest Pubs.

Taylor, David. The Wars in Former Yugoslavia. 2002. (Troubled World Ser.). (Illus.). 64p. (J). (gr. 6 up). lib. bdg. 28.54 (978-0-7398-6343-5(6)) Raintree.

Transchel, Kate. The Breakup of Yugoslavia. 2006. (Arbitrary Borders Ser.). (Illus.). 152p. (gr. 9). 35.00 (978-0-7910-8651-3(8) , Chelsea Hse.) Facts On File, Inc.

YUKON RIVER AND VALLEY

Lourie, Peter. Yukon River: An Adventure to the Gold Fields of the Klondike. 2003. (Illus.). 48p. (YA). (gr. 4-6). pap. 9.95 (978-1-56397-878-4(4)) Boyds Mills Pr.

—Yukon River: An Adventure to the Gold Fields of the Klondike. 2000. (gr. 3-6). lib. bdg. 18.75 (978-0-613-49402-1(4)) Tandem Library Bks.

Nobleman, Marc Tyler. The Klondike Gold Rush. 2006. (We the People Ser.). (Illus.). 48p. (J). (gr. 4-6). 23.93 (978-0-7565-1630-7(7)) Compass Point Bks.

Shepherd, Donna Walsh. The Klondike Gold Rush. 1998. (Illus.). 64p. (J). (ps-6). lib. bdg. 15.25 (978-0-613-18841-8(1)) Tandem Library Bks.

YUKON TERRITORY

Ferry, Steven. Yukon Territory. 2002. (Exploring Canada Ser.). (Illus.). 104p. (J). 29.95 (978-1-59018-053-2(4) , Lucent Bks.) Thomson Gale.

Hancock, Lyn. Yukon. 2nd rev. ed. (Hello Canada Ser.). (Illus.). 72p. pap. (978-1-55041-768-5(1)) Fitzhenry & Whiteside, Ltd.

—Yukon. 1998. (Hello Canada Ser.). (Illus.). (gr. 3-6). pap. 6.95 (978-0-8225-9819-0(1)) Lerner Publishing Group.

LeVert, Suzanne. Yukon. 2000. (Canada in the Twenty First Century Ser.). (Illus.). 64p. (J). 18.95 (978-0-7910-6072-8(1) , Chelsea Hse.) Facts On File, Inc.

YUKON TERRITORY—FICTION

Hill, Kirkpatrick. Toughboy & Sister. 2000. 128p. (J). (gr. 3-7). pap. 9.95 (978-0-689-83978-8(2) , Aladdin) Simon & Schuster Children's Publishing.

Hobbs, William. Down the Yukon. 2002. 208p. (J). (gr. 5 up). pap. 5.99 (978-0-380-73309-5(9)) HarperCollins Pubs.

—Jason's Gold. unabr. ed. 2004. 240p. (J). (gr. 5-9). pap. 38.00 incl. audio (978-0-8072-8229-8(4) , Listening Library) Random Hse. Audio Publishing Group.

—Jason's Gold. 2000. (J). (978-0-606-19979-7(9)) Tandem Library Bks.

London, Jack. The Call of the Wild. Pablo Marcos Studio Staff, illus. 2002. (Great Illustrated Classics Ser.). 240p. (J). (gr. 3-8). 21.35 (978-1-57765-682-1(2) , ABDO & Daughters) ABDO Publishing Co.

—The Call of the Wild. 2001. (Fast Track Classics Ser.). (Illus.). 48p. pap. 9.99 (978-0-237-52285-8(3) , Evans Brothers, Limited) Evans Publishing Group GBR. *Dist:* Independent Pubs. Group.

—The Call of the Wild. Davidson, Andrew, illus. 2002. (Kingfisher Classics Ser.). 208p. (J). (gr. k-3). tchr. ed. 15.95 (978-0-7534-5493-0(9) , Kingfisher) Houghton Mifflin Co. Trade & Reference Div.

—The Call of the Wild. 2003. (Aladdin Classics Ser.). 160p. mass mkt. 4.99 (978-0-689-85674-7(1) , Aladdin) Simon & Schuster Children's Publishing.

—The Call of the Wild. Clift, Eva, tr. Clift, Eva, illus. 2003. (Values in Action Illustrated Classics Ser.). (J). (978-1-59203-047-7(5)) Learning Challenge, Inc.

—The Call of the Wild. Corvino, Lucy, illus. 2005. (Classic Starts Ser.). 160p. 4.95 (978-1-4027-1274-6(X)) Sterling Publishing Co., Inc.

—The Call of the Wild. unabr. ed. 2002. (YA). pap. incl. audio compact disk (978-1-58472-221-2(5) , In Audio) Sound Room Pubs., Inc.

—The Call of the Wild & Selected Short Stories. 2006. (Scholastic Classics Ser.). (Illus.). iv, 260p. (J). (gr. 9-12). 25.00 (978-0-531-16982-7(0) , Watts, Franklin) Scholastic Library Publishing.

—Jack London/the Call of the Wild. Carrillo, Fred, illus. 2005. 48p. (gr. 5-8). 25.50 (978-0-7910-9104-3(X)) Facts On File, Inc.

—To Build a Fire. abr. ed. 1999. mass mkt. 3.99 (978-0-8125-6993-3(8) , Tor Bks.) Doherty, Tom Assocs., LLC.

—White Fang. Vera, Ross, illus. 2002. (Great Illustrated Classics Ser.). 240p. (J). (gr. 3-8). 21.35 (978-1-57765-810-8(8) , ABDO & Daughters) ABDO Publishing Co.

—White Fang. 2003. 192p. (J). 4.99 (978-1-57759-566-3(1)) Dalmatian Pr.

McMullan, Kate. Knight for a Day. 2007. (Dragon Slayers' Academy Ser.: No. 5). 112p. (J). (gr. 1-6). 24.21 (***978-1-59961-377-2(8)***) Spotlight.

Provensen, Alice. Klondike Gold. Provensen, Alice, illus. 2005. (Illus.). 40p. (J). (gr. 3-6). 17.95 (978-0-689-84885-8(4) , Simon & Schuster Children's Publishing) Simon & Schuster Children's Publishing.

Wallace, Ian. Trapper Jack's Missing Toe. 2001. (Illus.). (J). (978-0-7894-7666-1(5)) Dorling Kindersley Publishing, Inc.

—The True Story of Trapper Jack's Left Big Toe. (Illus.). 32p. (J). 18.95 (978-0-88899-415-8(X)) Groundwood Bks. CAN. *Dist:* Transition Vendor.

Whitehead, Catherine. Skookumchuck. 2002. (Illus.). 156p. (J). (gr. 5-12). pap. 11.95 (978-1-58151-064-5(0)) BookPartners, Inc.

Wishinsky, Frieda. Crazy for Gold! Griffiths, Dean, illus. 2007. (Canadian Flyer Adventures Ser.: No. 3). 96p. (J). (gr. 1-4). 16.95 (***978-1-897066-92-8(9)***); pap. 6.95 (***978-1-897066-93-5(7)***) Maple Tree Pr. CAN. *Dist:* Perseus Distribution.

Wyss, Thelma Hatch. A Tale of Gold. 2007. 160p. (J). (gr. 3-7). 16.99 (***978-1-4169-4212-2(2)*** , McElderry, Margaret K.) Simon & Schuster Children's Publishing.

Z

ZACCHAEUS (BIBLICAL CHARACTER)

Davidson, Alice Joyce. Zacchaeus & the Tall Tree. Lyon, Tammie Speer, illus. 1998. (Bible Friends Ser.). 12p. (J). (ps). 3.99 (978-0-310-97578-6(6)) Zondervan.

Gemmen, Heather & McNeil, Mary. Little Things, Pre-Level 1. Stormer, Karen, illus. 2003. (Rocket Readers Ser.). 40p. (J). (ps-1). pap. 8.99 (978-0-7814-3981-7(7) , 0781439817) Cook, David C. Publishing Co.

Green, Rhonda Gowler. Zacchaeus. 2007. 32p. (J). 9.99 (***978-0-310-71100-1(2)***) Zonderkidz.

Nederveld, Patricia L. Have a Great Day! The Story of Jesus & Zacchaeus. 1998. (God Loves Me Ser.). (Illus.). 24p. (J). (ps-3). pap. 2.95 (978-1-56212-310-9(6) , 001241, Faith Alive Christian Resources) CRC Pubns.

Pingry, Patricia A. The Story of Zacchaeus. Britt, Stephanie M., illus. 2001. 26p. (J). bds. 6.95 (978-0-8249-4130-7(6)) Ideals Pubns.

Taylor, Damon J. Lunchtime Life Change: The Story of Zacchaeus. 2003. (Child Sockology Ser.). (Illus.). 36p. (J). 10.99 (978-0-8254-3862-2(4)) Kregel Pubns.

Zacchaeus: Physically Small but Spiritually Tall! (Illus.). 16p. (J). pap. 1.50 (978-0-87162-871-8(6) , E6038) Warner Pr. Pubs.

Zacchaeus Meets Jesus. 2006. 16p. (J). pap. 1.99 (978-0-7847-1719-6(2) , 04180) Standard Publishing.

ZAHARIAS, BABE DIDRIKSON, 1911-1956

Brocker, Susan. Leyendas del deporte & Sports Legends. 2005. spiral bd. 77.00 (***978-1-4108-5678-4(X)***) Benchmark Education Co.

Cayleff, Susan E. Babe Didrikson. 2000. (gr. 7-12). lib. bdg. 17.45 (978-0-613-27718-1(X)) Tandem Library Bks.

—Babe Didrikson: The Greatest All-Sport Athlete of All Time. 2000. (Barnard Biography Ser.: Vol. 4). (Illus.). 168p. (YA). (gr. 7-12). pap. 8.95 (978-1-57324-194-6(6) , Red Wheel) Red Wheel/Weiser.

—Babe Didrikson: The Greatest All-Sport Athlete of All Time. 2000. (Illus.). (J). (978-0-606-18829-6(0)) Tandem Library Bks.

Ferrara, Cos. Babe Didrikson Zaharias: Outcast & Hero. 2004. (Girls Explore, Reach for the Stars Ser.). (Illus.). 109p. (J). 20.00 (978-0-9749456-2-0(5) , Girls Explore) Girls Explore LLC.

Freedman, Russell. Babe Didrikson Zaharias: The Making of a Champion. 1999. (Illus.). 192p. (J). (gr. 5-9). tchr. ed. 19.00 (978-0-395-63367-0(2) , Clarion Bks.) Houghton Mifflin Co. Trade & Reference Div.

Wakeman, Nancy. Babe Didrikson Zaharias: Driven to Win. 1999. (Lerner Biographies Ser.). (Illus.). 128p. (gr. 6-12). lib. bdg. 27.93 (978-0-8225-4917-8(4)) Lerner Publishing Group.

ZAIRE

see Congo (Democratic Republic)

ZAMBIA

Kalz, Jill. Victoria Falls. 2004. (Natural Wonders of the World Ser.). (Illus.). 32p. (J). lib. bdg. 18.95 (978-1-58341-327-2(8) , Creative Education) Creative Co., The.

ZANE, ELIZABETH, 1759?-1847?—FICTION

Durrant, Lynda. Betsy Zane, the Rose of Fort Henry. 2000. 208p. (J). (gr. 5-9). tchr. ed. 15.00 (978-0-395-97899-3(8) , Clarion Bks.) Houghton Mifflin Co. Trade & Reference Div.

ZEBRAS

Anderson, Jill. Zebras. 2005. (Wild Ones Ser.). (Illus.). 24p. (ps-1). 12.95 (978-1-55971-926-1(5)); (J). pap. 6.95 (978-1-55971-927-8(3)) T&N Children's Publishing. (NorthWord Bks. for Young Readers).

Arnold, Caroline, illus. A Zebra's World. 2006. 24p. (J). (gr. k-2). 23.93 (978-1-4048-1324-3(1) , 1253186) Picture Window Bks.

Fredericks, Anthony D. Zebras. Ellis, Gerry, photos by. 2000. (Early Bird Nature Bks.). (Illus.). 48p. (J). (gr. 2-4). lib. bdg. 25.26 (978-0-8225-3043-5(0) , Lerner Pubns.) Lerner Publishing Group.

Gareth Stevens Publishing Staff, contrib. by. Zebras. 2004. (All about Wild Animals Ser.). (Illus.). 32p. (J). lib. bdg. 23.33 (978-0-8368-4190-9(5)) Stevens, Gareth Inc.

Grimbly, Shona. Zebras. 1999. (Endangered! Ser.). (Illus.). 32p. (J). (gr. 3-5). lib. bdg. 25.64 (978-0-7614-0320-3(5) , Benchmark Bks.) Cavendish, Marshall Corp.

Guidoux, Valerie. Little Zebras. 2005. (Born to Be Wild Ser.). (Illus.). 23p. (J). (ps-17). 22.00 (978-0-8368-4741-3(5)) Stevens, Gareth Inc.

Holmes, Kevin J. Zebras. 2000. (Animals Ser.). (Illus.). 24p. (J). (gr. 2-3). lib. bdg. 18.60 (978-0-7368-0497-4(8) , Bridgestone Bks.) Capstone Pr., Inc.

Lockwood, Sophie. Zebras. 2008. (World of Mammals Ser.). 40p. (J). (gr. 2-6). 29.93 (***978-1-59296-931-9(3)***) Child's World, Inc.

MacAulay, Kelley & Kalman, Bobbie. Endangered Zebras. 2007. (Earth's Endangered Animals Ser.). (Illus.). 32p. (J). (gr. 1-7). (***978-0-7787-1864-2(6)***); pap. (***978-0-7787-1910-6(3)***) Crabtree Publishing Co.

Macken, JoAnn Early. Zebras. 2002. (Weekly Reader Early Learning Library). (Illus.). 24p. (J). (ps up). pap. 5.95 (978-0-8368-3290-7(6)); lib. bdg. 19.33 (978-0-8368-3277-8(9)) Stevens, Gareth Inc. (Weekly Reader Early Learning Library).

Malcolm, Penny. Zebra: Habitats, Life Cycles, Food Chains, Threats. 2002. (Natural World Ser.). (Illus.). 48p. (J). lib. bdg. 27.12 (978-0-7398-5229-3(9)) Raintree.

Markert, Jenny. Zebras. 2007. (New Naturebooks Ser.). 32p. (J). (gr. 1-5). 27.07 (***978-1-59296-854-1(6)***) Child's World, Inc.

Markle, Sandra. Zebras. 2007. (Animal Prey Ser.). 40p. (J). (gr. 4-6). 25.26 (978-0-8225-6062-3(3) , Lerner Pubns.) Lerner Publishing Group.

Molter, Carey. Zebras. l.t. ed. 2001. (Zoo Animals Ser.). (Illus.). 24p. (J). (ps-3). lib. bdg. 19.93 (978-1-57765-563-3(X) , SandCastle) ABDO Publishing Co.

Murray, Julie. Zebras. 2002. (Animal Kingdom Ser.). (Illus.). 24p. (J). (gr. k-4). lib. bdg. 21.35 (978-1-57765-702-6(0)) ABDO Publishing Co.

Noble-Goodman, Katherine. Zebras. 2005. (Animals Animals Ser.). (Illus.). 48p. (J). (gr. 3-7). lib. bdg. (978-0-7614-1871-9(7) , Benchmark Bks.) Cavendish, Marshall Corp.

Perkins, Wendy. Zebras. 2005. (World of Mammals Ser.). (Illus.). 24p. (J). 21.26 (978-0-7368-3722-4(1)) Capstone Pr., Inc.

Pingry, Patricia A. Baby Zebra. Sharp, Chris, illus. 2004. (San Diego Zoo Animal Library: Vol. 6). 26p. (J). bds. 6.95 (978-0-8249-6556-3(6)) Ideals Pubns.

Prudom, Sharla. Jambo! Zebra. Prudom, Sharla, photos by. 2002. (Jambo! Ser.). (SWA & ENG., Illus.). 11p. (J). cd-rom 12.50 (978-1-931792-26-4(7)) E-Digital Bks., LLC.

Schaefer, Lola M. Zebras: Striped Grass-Grazers. 2001. (Wild World of Animals Ser.). (Illus.). 24p. (J). (gr. 1-2). lib. bdg. 18.60 (978-0-7368-0968-9(6) , Bridgestone Bks.) Capstone Pr., Inc.

Stewart, Melissa. Zebras. 2002. (True Bks.). (Illus.). 48p. (J). (gr. 3-5). pap. 6.95 (978-0-516-26993-1(3)); 25.00 (978-0-516-22203-5(1)) Scholastic Library Publishing. (Children's Pr.).

Stone, Lynn M. Zebras. 2008. (Nature Watch Ser.). (J). lib. bdg. 26.60 (***978-0-8225-7511-5(6)*** , Lerner Pubns.) Lerner Publishing Group.

Whitehouse, Patricia. La Cebra. 2003. (Animales del Zoologico (Zoo Animals) Ser.). (SPA., Illus.). 24p. (ps-1). (J). lib. bdg. 17.08 (978-1-4034-0409-1(7)); pap. 5.25 (978-1-4034-0657-6(X)) Heinemann Library.

—Zebra. 2003. (Zoo Animals Ser.). (Illus.). 24p. (ps-1). (J). lib. bdg. 17.08 (978-1-58810-900-2(3)); pap. 5.25 (978-1-4034-0649-1(9)) Heinemann Library.

Wildlife Education, Ltd. Staff & Wood, Linda C. Zebras. Orr, Richard, illus. (Zoobooks Ser.). (J). 2001. 24p. 15.95 (978-0-937934-91-3(7)); 1999. 18p. pap. 2.95 (978-0-937934-57-9(7)) Wildlife Education, Ltd.

Wilsdon, Christina. Zebras. 2006. (J). 7.99 (978-1-59939-033-8(7)) Reader's Digest Young Families, Inc.

Zebra. 2004. (J). 5.99 (978-0-7566-0252-9(1)) Dorling Kindersley Publishing, Inc.

Zebras. 2006. (Zootles Ser.). (J). 4.95 (***978-1-932396-23-2(3)***) Wildlife Education, Ltd.

Zebra's Stripes. Date not set. (Touch & Feel Ser.). (Illus.). (J). 4.98 (978-0-7525-9571-9(7)) Parragon, Inc.

Zumbusch, Amelie von. Zebras. 2007. (Safari Animals Ser.). (Illus.). 24p. (J). (gr. k-3). lib. bdg. 21.25 (978-1-4042-3613-4(9) , 1266071, PowerKids Pr.) Rosen Publishing Group, Inc., The.

ZEBRAS—FICTION

Beaton, Clare. Zoe & Her Zebra. Beaton, Clare, illus. 2000. (Illus.). 32p. (J). (ps-2). reprint ed. bds. 6.99 (978-1-84148-393-1(1)) Barefoot Bks., Inc.

Beaton, Clare, illus. Zoe & Her Zebra. 1999. (Barefoot Beginner Ser.). 32p. (J). (ps-1). 14.95 (978-1-902283-75-3(9)) Barefoot Bks., Inc.

Birrer, Cynthia & Birrer, Bill, illus. The Confused Zebra. 1999. (J). 16.95 (978-0-86543-795-1(5)) Africa World Pr.

Bolam, Emily, illus. Chunky Safari Zebra. 2001. (Chunky Farm Ser.). 14p. (J). (ps). bds. 5.99 (978-0-7641-5328-0(5)) Barron's Educational Series, Inc.

Brooksbank, Angela. I've Lost My Yellow Zebra. 1999. (Illus.). 32p. (J). (ps-k). pap. 6.95 (978-0-7641-0875-4(1)) Barron's Educational Series, Inc.

Cook, Sherry & Johnson, Terri. Zany Science Zeke, 26. Kuhn, Jesse, illus. l.t. ed. 2006. (Quirkles—Exploring Phonics through Science Ser.: 26). 32p. (J). 7.99 (978-1-933815-25-1(6) , Quirkles, The) Creative 3, LLC.

Cousins, Lucy. Za-Za's Baby Brother. Cousins, Lucy, illus. 2002. (Illus.). (J). 15.74 (978-0-7587-4072-4(7)) Book Wholesalers, Inc.

Eduar, Gilles. Gigi & Zachary's Around-the-World Adventure: A Seek-and-Find Game. Eduar, Gilles, illus. 2003. (Illus.). 56p. (J). 16.95 (978-0-8118-3909-9(5)) Chronicle Bks. LLC.

Ellis, Libby. Ziggy the Zebra. Yoon, Salina, illus. 2005. 14p. (J). (gr. k-3). 9.95 (978-1-58117-104-4(8) , Intervisual/Piggy Toes) Dalmatian Pr.

Gay, Michel. Zee. Gay, Michel, illus. 2003. (Illus.). 32p. (J). (gr. k-ps). 15.00 (978-0-618-38148-7(1) , Clarion Bks.) Houghton Mifflin Co. Trade & Reference Div.

—Zee Is Not Scared. Mianowski, Marie, tr. from FRE. 2004. (Illus.). 32p. (J). (gr. k-ps). tchr. ed. 15.00 (978-0-618-43931-7(5) , Clarion Bks.) Houghton Mifflin Co. Trade & Reference Div.

Golden Books Staff. How the Zebra Got Its Stripes. 2002. (Little Golden Book Ser.). (Illus.). 24p. (J). (gr. k-k). 2.99 (978-0-307-98870-6(8) , Golden Bks.) Random Hse. Children's Bks.

Grey, Chelsea Gillian. Leperit the Zebra. Denman, Michael L. & Huiett, William J., illus. 2005. (Meet Africa's Animals Ser.). (J). (ps-2). 32p. 14.95 (978-1-59249-438-5(2) , H6505); 36p. pap. 6.95 (978-1-59249-439-2(0) , S6505) Soundprints.

—Leperit the Zebra: African Wildlife Foundation. Denman, Michael L. & Huiett, William J., illus. 2005. (Meet Africa's Animals Ser.). 36p. (J). (ps-2). 2.95 (978-1-59249-441-5(2) , S6555) Soundprints.

Haas, Jessie. Appaloosa Zebra: A Horse Lover's Alphabet. Apple, Margot, illus. 2002. (J). (gr. 2-4). 40p. 16.99 (978-0-688-17880-2(4)); 32p. 15.89 (978-0-688-17881-9(2)) HarperCollins Pubs.

Harry, Rebecca, illus. Little Zebra. 2007. (Noisy Jungle Babies Ser.). 8p. (J). bds. 5.99 (978-0-7641-6037-0(0)) Barron's Educational Series, Inc.

Henkes, Kevin. The Zebra Wall. 2005. (Illus.). 160p. (J). pap. 5.99 (978-0-06-073303-2(9) , Harper Trophy) HarperCollins Pubs.

Hood, Dianne J. The Confused Zebra. Birrer, Bill & Birrer, Cynthia, illus. 1999. (J). 8.95 (978-0-86543-796-8(3)) Africa World Pr.

Jacobs, Nadine. Zefir, la Cebrita en Peligro. Vicens, Paula, tr. Jacobs, Nadine, illus. 2004. (SPA.). 32p. (J). 15.99 (978-84-8470-108-8(5)) Corimbo, Editorial S.L. ESP. *Dist:* Lectorum Pubns., Inc.

Kompelien, Tracy. Zebra Stripes. Nobens, C. A., illus. 2006. (Fact & Fiction Ser.). 24p. (J). 21.35 (978-1-59679-971-4(4) , SandCastle); pap. (978-1-59679-972-1(2)) ABDO Publishing Co.

Law, Felicia. The Bookseller Bird. Evans, Nicola, illus. 2005. (Bamboo & Friends Ser.). 24p. (J). (ps-7). lib. bdg. 22.60 (978-1-4048-1283-3(0)) Picture Window Bks.

—The Creeping Vine. Evans, Nicola, illus. 2005. (Bamboo & Friends Ser.). 24p. (J). (ps-3). lib. bdg. 22.60 (978-1-4048-1284-0(9)) Picture Window Bks.

—The Dragonfly. Philpott, Claire, illus. 2005. (Bamboo & Friends Ser.). 24p. (J). (ps-3). lib. bdg. 22.60 (978-1-4048-1302-1(0)) Picture Window Bks.

—The Flower's Busy Day. Evans, Nicola, illus. 2005. (Bamboo & Friends Ser.). 24p. (J). (ps-3). lib. bdg. 22.60 (978-1-4048-1281-9(4)) Picture Window Bks.

—Marvelous Meals. Evans, Nicola, illus. 2005. (Bamboo & Friends Ser.). 24p. (J). (ps-3). lib. bdg. 22.60 (978-1-4048-1285-7(7)) Picture Window Bks.

—The Snowflakes. Philpott, Claire & Radford, Karen, illus. 2007. (J). (978-1-4048-2597-0(5)) Picture Window Bks.

—The Tree. Philpott, Claire, illus. 2005. (Bamboo & Friends Ser.). 24p. (J). (ps-3). lib. bdg. 22.60 (978-1-4048-1301-4(2)) Picture Window Bks.

Miranda, Anne. Alphabet Fiesta. 2001. (ENG & SPA., Illus.). 56p. (J). (ps-3). 12.95 (978-1-890515-30-0(2)) Turtle Bks.

—Alphabet Fiesta: An English/Spanish Alphabet Story. 2001. (ENG & SPA., Illus.). 56p. (J). (ps-3). 18.95 (978-1-890515-29-4(9)) Turtle Bks.

Mitchell, Melanie. Mommy & Baby: Safari. 2006. (Illus.). 10p. (J). bds., bds. 6.95 (978-0-8027-8064-5(4)) Walker & Co.

Nunez, Marisa. Camilla the Zebra. Villan, Oscar, illus. 2003. 32p. (J). 14.95 (978-84-95730-39-8(1)) Kalandraka Catalunya, Edicions, S.L. ESP. *Dist:* Independent Pubs. Group.

—La Cebra Camila. Villan, Oscar, illus. 2005. (SPA.). 216p. (J). (gr. k-2). 16.95 (978-84-95123-60-2(6) , KA8243) Kalandraka Editora, S.L. ESP. *Dist:* Lectorum Pubns., Inc., Iaconi, Mariuccia Bk. Imports.

Paterson, Brian. Dives In. (Illus.). (J). (ps). 2004. 14p. 6.99 (978-0-00-717420-1(9)); 2004. 32p. 17.99 (978-0-00-713167-9(4) , HarperCollins Children's Bks.); 2003. 32p. pap. 8.99 (978-0-00-713183-9(6) , HarperCollins Children's Bks.) HarperCollins Pubs. Ltd. GBR. *Dist:* Independent Pubs. Group.

—The Picnic: Board Book. 2006. (Illus.). 16p. (J). (ps). bds. 6.99 (978-0-00-717421-8(7)) HarperCollins Pubs. Ltd. GBR. *Dist:* Trafalgar Square Publishing.

—The Toy Box: Board Book. 2004. (Illus.). 14p. (J). 6.99 (978-0-00-717424-9(1) , HarperCollins Children's Bks.) HarperCollins Pubs. Ltd. GBR. *Dist:* Independent Pubs. Group.

—Zigby & the Ant Invaders. (Illus.). 32p. (J). (ps). 2004. 17.99 (978-0-00-713166-2(6)); 2003. pap. 8.99 (978-0-00-713182-2(8)) HarperCollins Pubs. Ltd. GBR. (HarperCollins Children's Bks.). *Dist:* Independent Pubs. Group.

—Zigby & the Ants. 2004. (J). (978-0-06-053796-8(5)) HarperCollins Pubs.

—Zigby Camps Out. 2003. (Illus.). 32p. (J). (ps). pap. 8.99 (978-0-00-713180-8(1) , HarperCollins Children's Bks.) HarperCollins Pubs. Ltd. GBR. *Dist:* Independent Pubs. Group.

Paterson, Brian, illus. Zigby & the Monster. 2005. 32p. (J). (ps). pap. 8.99 (978-0-00-717423-2(3) , HarperCollins Children's Bks.) HarperCollins Pubs. Ltd. GBR. *Dist:* Independent Pubs. Group.

Patterson, Christina. Jazz, a Horse of a Different Color. Nguyaen, Huy, illus. 2001. 31p. (J). (978-0-89802-759-4(4)) Beautiful America Publishing Co.

Potter, Tony. Over Here Zebra. 1998. (J). 7.95 (978-1-902553-05-4(5)) Grimond FRA. *Dist:* Continental Enterprises Group, Inc. (CEG).

—You Need a Bath Zebra. 1998. (J). (ps). 9.95 (978-1-902553-01-6(2)) Grimond FRA. *Dist:* Continental Enterprises Group, Inc. (CEG).

Reitano, John. What If the Zebra Lost Their Stripes? Haines, William, illus. 1998. 32p. (ps-3). 16.95 (978-0-8091-6649-7(6) , 6649-6) Paulist Pr.

School Specialty Publishing. My Very Best Coloring & Activity Book: Zebra Birthday. 2002. 120p. (J). (gr. k-3). pap. 1.99 (978-0-7696-2787-8(0) , American Education Publishing) School Specialty Publishing.

Stailey, Jay & Payne, Ruby K. Think Rather of Zebra: Dealing with Aspects of Poverty Through Story. 1998. (Illus.). 337p. (J). (gr. k-8). pap. 18.00 (978-0-9647437-5-5(2)) aha! Process, Inc.

Volker, Kerstin. Emma Goes Shopping. 2003. (Funny Friends Lift-and-Learn Bks.). 14p. (J). 5.99 (978-1-59384-021-1(7)) Parklane Publishing.

—Suzie Goes to Sleep. 2003. (Funny Friends Lift-and-Learn Bks.). (Illus.). 14p. (J). 5.99 (978-1-59384-024-2(1)) Parklane Publishing.

Wax, Wendy. Hippo Rules: A Tale of Good Manners. Terry, Michael, illus. 2007. 12p. (J). 12.99 (***978-0-7944-1289-0(0)***) Reader's Digest Assn., Inc., The.

Wax, Wendy. What Zebra Likes. Terry, Michael, illus. 2006. (Puppet & Story Book Ser.). 12p. (J). 12.99 (978-0-7944-1043-8(X)) Reader's Digest Assn., Inc., The.

Zack the Lazy Zebra. 2001. (ps-2). lib. bdg. 9.80 (978-0-613-33280-4(6)) Tandem Library Bks.

ZENDA (IMAGINARY PLACE)—FICTION

Hope-Hawkins, Anthony & Hope, Anthony. The Prisoner of Zenda, Level 3. 2nd abr. ed. 2000. (Bookworms Ser.). (Illus.). 80p. 6.50 (978-0-19-423012-4(0)) Oxford Univ. Pr., Inc.

ZENGER, JOHN PETER, 1697-1746

Gibson, Karen Bush. The Life & Times of John Peter Zenger. 2006. (Profiles in American History Ser.). (Illus.). 48p. (J). (gr. 4-8). lib. bdg. 29.95 (978-1-58415-437-2(3)) Mitchell Lane Pubs., Inc.

Westermann, Karen T. John Peter Zenger. 2000. (Colonial Leaders Ser.). (Illus.). (J). (gr. 4-7). pap. 27.50 (978-0-7910-6123-7(X) , Chelsea Hse.) Facts On File, Inc.

—John Peter Zenger: Free Press Advocate. 2000. (Colonial Leaders Ser.). (Illus.). 80p. (J). (gr. 8-12). 27.50 (978-0-7910-5966-1(9) , Chelsea Hse.) Facts On File, Inc.

—John Peter Zenger: Free Press Advocate. 2000. (Illus.). 80p. (J). (gr. 4-7). lib. bdg. 17.60 (978-0-613-32727-5(5)) Tandem Library Bks.

ZEPPELINS

see Airships

ZIMBABWE

Barnes-Svarney, Patricia L. Zimbabwe. 1999. (Major World Nations Ser.). (Illus.). 144p. (YA). (gr. 4-7). 29.95 (978-0-7910-4753-8(9) , Chelsea Hse.) Facts On File, Inc.

Baughan, Michael Gray. Zimbabwe. 2004. (Africa Ser.). (Illus.). 79p. (J). lib. bdg. (978-1-59084-810-4(1)) Mason Crest Pubs.

Brimson, Samuel. United Kingdom-Zimbabwe, 8 vols. 2003. (Nations of the World Ser.: Vol. 8). (Illus.). 64p. (J). (gr. 5 up). lib. bdg. 30.00 (978-0-8368-5492-3(6) , World Almanac Library) Stevens, Gareth Inc.

Di Piazza, Francesca. Zimbabwe in Pictures. 2005. (Visual Geography Ser.). (Illus.). 80p. (J). (gr. 5-12). 27.93 (978-0-8225-2399-4(X)) Lerner Publishing Group.

Hall, Martin & Stefoff, Rebecca. Great Zimbabwe: Digging for the Past. 2005. (Digging for the Past Ser.). (Illus.). 48p. (YA). 23.00 (978-0-19-515773-4(7)) Oxford Univ. Pr., Inc.

Haskins, James & Benson, Kathleen. Count Your Way Through Zimbabwe. Park, Janie Jaehyun, illus. 2007. (Count Your Way Ser.). 24p. (J). 19.93 (978-1-57505-885-6(5) , Millbrook Pr.) Lerner Publishing Group.

Kalz, Jill. Victoria Falls. 2004. (Natural Wonders of the World Ser.). (Illus.). 32p. (J). lib. bdg. 18.95 (978-1-58341-327-2(8) , Creative Education) Creative Co., The.

Korky Paul: Biography of an Illustrator: Individual Title Six-Packs. (Discovery World Ser.). 24p. (gr. 1-2). 33.00 (978-0-7635-8471-9(1)) Rigby Education.

Rogers, Barbara Radcliffe & Rogers, Stillman D. Zimbabwe. 2002. (Enchantment of the World, Second Ser.). (Illus.). 144p. (J). (gr. 5-9). 36.00 (978-0-516-21113-8(7) , Children's Pr.) Scholastic Library Publishing.

Tredgold, M.H. The First Ones. 2000. pap. (978-0-86922-768-8(8)) Mambo Pr.

ZIMBABWE—FICTION

Chinodya, Shimmer. Tale of Tamari. 2003. (Illus.). 56p. pap. 12.95 (978-1-77922-026-4(X)) Weaver Pr. ZWE. *Dist:* Michigan State Univ. Pr.

Deogratias Simba. The Mystery Door. 2005. (Illus.). 22p. pap. 9.95 (978-9987-417-21-6(3)) Mkuki na Nyoka Pubs. TZA. *Dist:* Michigan State Univ. Pr.

Farmer, Nancy. Ear, the Eye & the Arm. 2002. (gr. 7-12). lib. bdg. 15.30 (978-0-613-45032-4(9)) Tandem Library Bks.

—A Girl Named Disaster. 1998. 320p. (YA). (gr. 5-9). pap. 6.99 (978-0-14-038635-6(1) , Puffin) Penguin Group (USA) Inc.

—A Girl Named Disaster. 1998. (J). 12.64 (978-0-606-13430-9(1)) Tandem Library Bks.

—A Girl Named Disaster. l.t. ed. 2005. 533p. (J). (gr. 5-9). pap. 10.95 (978-0-7862-8037-7(9)) Thorndike Pr.

Lide, Emily. Zimbabwe. 2006. per. 11.95 (978-1-59094-120-1(9)) Jawbone Publishing Corp.

Literature Connections English: Nervous Conditions. 2004. (gr. 6-12). (978-0-395-77560-8(4) , 2-80129) McDougal Littell Inc.

Nyoka, Gail. Mella & the N'anga: An African Tale. 2006. 160p. (J). (gr. 4-8). pap. 9.95 (978-1-894549-49-3(X)) Sumach Pr. CAN. *Dist:* Orca Bk. Pubs. USA.

Stock, Catherine. Gugu's House. 2001. (Illus.). 32p. (J). (gr. k-3). tchr. ed. 16.00 (978-0-618-00389-1(4) , Clarion Bks.) Houghton Mifflin Co. Trade & Reference Div.

ZIONISM

Whiting, Jim. The Creation of Israel. 2007. (Monumental Milestones Ser.). (Illus.). 48p. (YA). lib. bdg. 29.95 (***978-1-58415-538-6(8)***) Mitchell Lane Pubs., Inc.

ZIONISM—FICTION

Shapiro, David L. Sara's Journey. 2005. 293p. (YA). (gr. 7-12). pap. 12.95 (978-0-8276-0776-7(8)) Jewish Pubn. Society.

ZODIAC

Mitton, Jacqueline. Zodiac: Celestial Circle of the Sun. 2005. (Illus.). 40p. (J). 16.95 (978-1-84507-074-8(7)) Lincoln, Frances Ltd. GBR. *Dist:* Perseus Distribution.

Peters, Stephanie True. Gemini. 2003. (Library of Constellations Ser.). (Illus.). 24p. (J). lib. bdg. 21.25 (978-0-8239-6167-2(2) , PowerKids Pr.) Rosen Publishing Group, Inc., The.

—Pisces. 2003. (Library of Constellations Ser.). (Illus.). 24p. (J). lib. bdg. 21.25 (978-0-8239-6166-5(4) , PowerKids Pr.) Rosen Publishing Group, Inc., The.

Starr, Amanda. My Sign Is Cancer. 2000. (gr. 7-12). lib. bdg. 12.95 (978-0-613-83026-3(1)) Tandem Library Bks.

Stewart, Pat. Learning about the Zodiac. 2003. (Learning about Ser.). (Illus.). 16p. (J). pap. 1.50 (978-0-486-43024-9(3)) Dover Pubns., Inc.

Whitfield, Susan. Animals of the Chinese Zodiac. 1999. (J). (978-0-606-17229-5(7)) Tandem Library Bks.

ZOMO, THE RABBIT (FICTITIOUS CHARACTER)—FICTION

Ralles, H. J. Keeper of the Empire, Vol. 3. 2004. (Illus.). 235p. (J). pap. 9.95 (978-1-929976-25-6(9)) Top Pubns., Ltd.

ZOO ANIMALS

Aliki. My Visit to the Zoo. Aliki, illus. 1999. (Trophy Picture Bk.). (Illus.). 40p. (J). (ps up). pap. 6.99 (978-0-06-446217-4(X) , Harper Trophy) HarperCollins Pubs.

Arnold, Caroline. Mealtime for Zoo Animals. Hewett, Richard, illus. 1999. (Zoo Animals Ser.). 32p. (J). (ps-2). lib. bdg. 21.27 (978-1-57505-286-1(5) , Carolrhoda Bks.) Lerner Publishing Group.

—Mother & Baby Zoo Animals. 1999. (Zoo Animals Ser.). (Illus.). 32p. (J). (ps-2). 9.95 (978-1-57505-390-5(X) , Carolrhoda Bks.) Lerner Publishing Group.

—Mother & Baby Zoo Animals. Hewett, Richard, illus. 1999. (Zoo Animals Ser.). 32p. (J). (ps-2). lib. bdg. 21.27 (978-1-57505-285-4(7) , Carolrhoda Bks.) Lerner Publishing Group.

—Noisytime for Zoo Animals. 1999. (Zoo Animals Ser.). (Illus.). 32p. (J). (ps-2). 9.95 (978-1-57505-392-9(6) , Carolrhoda Bks.) Lerner Publishing Group.

—Noisytime for Zoo Animals. Hewett, Richard, illus. 1999. (Zoo Animals Ser.). 32p. (J). (ps-2). lib. bdg. 21.27 (978-1-57505-289-2(X) , Carolrhoda Bks.) Lerner Publishing Group.

—Playtime for Zoo Animals. 1999. (Zoo Animals Ser.). (Illus.). 32p. (J). (ps-2). pap. 9.95 (978-1-57505-391-2(8) , Carolrhoda Bks.) Lerner Publishing Group.

—Playtime for Zoo Animals. Hewett, Richard, illus. 1999. (Zoo Animals Ser.). 32p. (J). (ps-2). lib. bdg. 21.27 (978-1-57505-287-8(3) , Carolrhoda Bks.) Lerner Publishing Group.

—Playtime for Zoo Animals. 1999. (J). (978-0-606-22862-6(4)) Tandem Library Bks.

—Sleepytime for Zoo Animals. 1999. (Zoo Animals Ser.). (Illus.). 32p. (J). (ps-2). 9.95 (978-1-57505-393-6(4) , Carolrhoda Bks.) Lerner Publishing Group.

—Sleepytime for Zoo Animals. Hewett, Richard, illus. 1999. (Zoo Animals Ser.). 32p. (J). (ps-2). lib. bdg. 21.27 (978-1-57505-290-8(3) , Carolrhoda Bks.) Lerner Publishing Group.

—Splashtime for Zoo Animals. 1999. (Zoo Animals Ser.). (Illus.). 32p. (J). (ps-2). 9.95 (978-1-57505-394-3(2) , Carolrhoda Bks.) Lerner Publishing Group.

—Splashtime for Zoo Animals. Hewett, Richard, illus. 1998. (Zoo Animals Ser.). 32p. (J). (ps-2). lib. bdg. 21.27 (978-1-57505-288-5(1) , Carolrhoda Bks.) Lerner Publishing Group.

Brown, Connie. My Visit to the Zoo. 2000. (Illus.). (J). pap. 9.00 (978-0-8059-5066-3(4)) Dorrance Publishing Co., Inc.

Canizares, Susan & Weber, Arianne. At the Zoo. 2000. (Scholastic Placebook Ser.). (Illus.). (J). pap. (978-0-439-15377-5(8)) Scholastic, Inc.

Cimarusti, Marie Torres. Peek-a-Zoo! Peterson, Stephanie, illus. 2003. 8p. (J). (ps). 10.99 (978-0-525-46971-1(0) , Dutton Juvenile) Penguin Group (USA) Inc.

Clemson, Wendy & Clemson, David. Zookeeper for a Day. 2006. (Illus.). 32p. (J). pap. ***(978-0-8368-8142-4(7));*** (gr. 2-4). lib. bdg. 25.27 ***(978-0-8368-7843-1(4))*** Stevens, Gareth Inc.

Craft, Sarah S. Mother Beluga Whales & Their Babies. 1999. (Zoo Life Book Ser.). 24p. (J). (gr. k-4). lib. bdg. 18.75 (978-0-8239-5315-8(7) , PowerKids Pr.) Rosen Publishing Group, Inc., The.

—Mother Giraffes & Their Babies. 1999. (Zoo Life Book Ser.). 24p. (J). (gr. k-4). lib. bdg. 18.75 (978-0-8239-5316-5(5) , PowerKids Pr.) Rosen Publishing Group, Inc., The.

—Mother Gorillas & Their Babies. 1999. (Zoo Life Book Ser.). 24p. (J). (gr. k-4). lib. bdg. 18.75 (978-0-8239-5313-4(0) , PowerKids Pr.) Rosen Publishing Group, Inc., The.

—Mother Indian Rhinos & Their Babies. 1999. (Zoo Life Book Ser.). (Illus.). 24p. (J). (gr. k-4). lib. bdg. 18.75 (978-0-8239-5318-9(1) , PowerKids Pr.) Rosen Publishing Group, Inc., The.

—Mother Snow Leopards & Their Babies. 1999. (Zoo Life Book Ser.). 24p. (J). (gr. k-4). lib. bdg. 18.75 (978-0-8239-5317-2(3) , PowerKids Pr.) Rosen Publishing Group, Inc., The.

—Mother Wallabies & Their Babies. 1999. (Zoo Life Book Ser.). 24p. (J). (gr. k-4). lib. bdg. 18.75 (978-0-8239-5314-1(9) , PowerKids Pr.) Rosen Publishing Group, Inc., The.

Davis, Rebecca Fjelland. Zoo Animals 1, 2, 3. 2007. (Illus.). 32p. (J). 23.93 (978-0-7368-6377-3(X)) Capstone Pr., Inc.

Deady, Kathleen W. Out & About at the Zoo. McMullen, Anne, illus. 2004. (Field Trips Ser.). 24p. (C). (gr. k-3). 23.93 (978-1-4048-0041-0(7)) Picture Window Bks.

Dena, Anael. The Zoo. Eho, Jerome, illus. 2002. (Rattle Bks.). 12p. (J). 3.95 (978-0-7641-5500-0(8)) Barron's Educational Series, Inc.

Feeding time at the Zoo: Individual Title Six-Packs. (gr. 1-2). 22.00 (978-0-7635-9178-6(5)) Rigby Education.

Fowler, Allan. Animals in the Zoo. 2001. (Rookie Read-About Science Ser.). (Illus.). 32p. (J). (gr. 1-2). pap. 4.95 (978-0-516-27087-6(7) , Children's Pr.) Scholastic Library Publishing.

Gilders, Michelle A. The Kids' Guide to Zoo Animals. 2004. (Illus.). 264p. (J). (gr. 1-5). pap. 12.95 (978-0-88995-301-7(5)) Red Deer Pr. CAN. *Dist:* Fitzhenry & Whiteside, Ltd.

Granowsky, Alvin. Hot & Cold. 2001. 11.79 (978-0-606-22435-2(1)) Tandem Library Bks.

Hanna, Jack. Jungle Jack Hanna's What Zookeepers Do. Prebeg, Rick A., illus. 1998. (Hello Reader! Ser.). 48p. (J). (gr. 2-4). pap. 3.99 (978-0-590-67324-2(6)) Scholastic, Inc.

—Jungle Jack Hanna's What Zookeepers Do. 1998. (Hello Reader! Ser.). (J). 10.79 (978-0-606-13548-1(0)) Tandem Library Bks.

Harcourt School Publishers Staff. Let's Visit the Zoo. 3rd ed. 2002. (Trophies English Language Learners Ser.). (Illus.). (J). pap. 4.10 (978-0-15-327595-1(2)) Harcourt Schl. Pubs.

Hatkoff, Isabella. Knut: How One Little Polar Bear Captivated the World. 2007. (J). pap. 16.99 ***(978-0-545-04717-3(X)*** , Scholastic Pr.) Scholastic, Inc.

Hewett, Richard, illus. & photos by. A Monkey Baby Grows Up. Hewett, Richard, photos by. Hewett, Joan, photos by. 2004. (Baby Animals Ser.). 32p. (J). (gr. k-3). lib. bdg. 21.27 (978-1-57505-199-4(0)) Lerner Publishing Group.

Hoena, B. A. A Visit to the Zoo. 2004. (Pebble Plus, Let's Visit Ser.). (Illus.). 24p. (J). 13.95 (978-0-7368-2395-1(6) , Pebble Bks.) Capstone Pr., Inc.

Hullabaloo at the Zoo. (Sails Literacy Ser.). 24p. (gr. 1 up). 27.00 (978-0-7635-5929-8(6)) ; Pack. 57.00 (978-0-7578-3208-6(3)) Rigby Education.

Hullabaloo at the Zoo: 6 Small Books. (Sails Literacy Ser.). 24p. (gr. 1 up). 25.00 (978-0-7578-3184-3(2)) Rigby Education.

Lauber, Patricia. Tiger Has a Toothache: Helping Animals at the Zoo. 2002. (gr. k-3). lib. bdg. 16.40 (978-0-613-62654-5(0)) Tandem Library Bks.

Levy, Barbara Soloff. Little Zoo Animal Mazes. 2006. 64p. (J). (ps-3). pap. 1.50 (978-0-486-44440-6(6)) Dover Pubns., Inc.

—Zoo Animals Dot to Dot. 2002. (Dover Little Activity Bks.). (Illus.). 64p. (J). (ps-3). pap. 1.50 (978-0-486-42090-5(6)) Dover Pubns., Inc.

Lock, Deborah. Petting Zoo. 2005. (Dk Readers Ser.). (Illus.). 32p. (J). (ps-7). 12.99 (978-0-7566-1463-8(5)) Dorling Kindersley Publishing, Inc.

—Petting Zoo. 2005. (Dk Readers Ser.). (Illus.). 32p. (J). (ps-7). pap. 3.99 (978-0-7566-1464-5(3)) Dorling Kindersley Publishing, Inc.

Macken, JoAnn Early. Bears. 2002. (Animals I See at the Zoo Ser.). (Illus.). 24p. (J). (ps up). lib. bdg. 19.33 (978-0-8368-3266-2(3)); pap. 5.95 (978-0-8368-3279-2(5)) Stevens, Gareth Inc. (Weekly Reader Early Learning Library).

—Bears/Los Osos. Coffey, Colleen & Carrillo, Consuelo, trs. from ENG. 2003. (Weekly Reader Early Learning Library). (ENG & SPA., Illus.). 24p. (J). (ps up). lib. bdg. 19.33 (978-0-8368-3998-2(6) , Weekly Reader Early Learning Library) Stevens, Gareth Inc.

—Bears/Los Osos. 2003. (Weekly Reader Early Learning Library). (ENG & SPA., Illus.). 24p. (J). (ps up). pap. 5.95 (978-0-8368-4003-2(8) , Weekly Reader Early Learning Library) Stevens, Gareth Inc.

—Camels. 2002. (Weekly Reader Early Learning Library). (Illus.). 24p. (J). (ps up). pap. 7.93 (978-0-8368-3280-8(9)); lib. bdg. 19.33 (978-0-8368-3267-9(1)) Stevens, Gareth Inc. (Weekly Reader Early Learning Library).

—Elephants. 2002. (Animals I See at the Zoo Ser.). (Illus.). (J). (ps up). 24p. lib. bdg. 19.33 (978-0-8368-3268-6(X)); 48p. pap. 5.95 (978-0-8368-3281-5(7)) Stevens, Gareth Inc. (Weekly Reader Early Learning Library).

—Giraffes. 2002. (Weekly Reader Early Learning Library). (Illus.). 24p. (J). (ps up). pap. 5.95 (978-0-8368-3282-2(5)); lib. bdg. 19.33 (978-0-8368-3269-3(8)) Stevens, Gareth Inc. (Weekly Reader Early Learning Library).

—Giraffes/Las Jirafas. Coffey, Colleen & Carrillo, Consuelo, trs. from SPA. 2003. (Weekly Reader Early Learning Library). (ENG & SPA., Illus.). 24p. (J). (ps up). lib. bdg. 19.33 (978-0-8368-4000-1(3) , Weekly Reader Early Learning Library) Stevens, Gareth Inc.

—Giraffes/Las Jirafas. 2003. (Weekly Reader Early Learning Library). (ENG & SPA., Illus.). 24p. (J). (ps up). pap. (978-0-8368-4005-6(4) , Weekly Reader Early Learning Library) Stevens, Gareth Inc.

—Hippos. 2002. (Weekly Reader Early Learning Library). (Illus.). 24p. (J). (ps up). pap. 5.95 (978-0-8368-3283-9(3)); lib. bdg. 19.33 (978-0-8368-3270-9(1)) Stevens, Gareth Inc. (Weekly Reader Early Learning Library).

—Lions. 2002. (Weekly Reader Early Learning Library). (Illus.). 24p. (J). (ps up). pap. (978-0-8368-3284-6(1)); lib. bdg. 19.33 (978-0-8368-3271-6(X)) Stevens, Gareth Inc. (Weekly Reader Early Learning Library).

—Monkeys. 2002. (Weekly Reader Early Learning Library). (Illus.). 24p. (J). (ps up). pap. 5.95 (978-0-8368-3285-3(X)); lib. bdg. 19.33 (978-0-8368-3272-3(8)) Stevens, Gareth Inc. (Weekly Reader Early Learning Library).

—Monkeys: Los Monos. 2004. (ENG & SPA., Illus.). 24p. (J). pap. (978-0-8368-4388-0(6)); lib. bdg. 19.33 (978-0-8368-4383-5(5)) Stevens, Gareth Inc.

—Penguins. 2002. (Animals I See at the Zoo Ser.). (Illus.). 24p. (J). (ps up). lib. bdg. 19.33 (978-0-8368-3273-0(6) , Weekly Reader Early Learning Library) Stevens, Gareth Inc.

—Penguins/Los Pinguinos. 2003. (Weekly Reader Early Learning Library). (ENG & SPA., Illus.). 24p. (J). (ps up). pap. 5.95 (978-0-8368-4006-3(2) , Weekly Reader Early Learning Library) Stevens, Gareth Inc.

—Penguins/Los Pinguinos. Coffey, Colleen & Carrillo, Consuelo, trs. from SPA. 2003. (Weekly Reader Early Learning Library). (ENG & SPA., Illus.). 24p. (J). (ps up). lib. bdg. 19.33 (978-0-8368-4001-8(1) , Weekly Reader Early Learning Library) Stevens, Gareth Inc.

—Sea Lions. 2002. (Weekly Reader Early Learning Library). (Illus.). 24p. (J). (ps up). pap. 5.95 (978-0-8368-3287-7(6)); lib. bdg. 19.33 (978-0-8368-3274-7(4)) Stevens, Gareth Inc. (Weekly Reader Early Learning Library).

—Snakes. 2002. (Weekly Reader Early Learning Library). (Illus.). 24p. (J). (ps up). pap. 5.95 (978-0-8368-3288-4(4)); lib. bdg. 19.33 (978-0-8368-3275-4(2)) Stevens, Gareth Inc. (Weekly Reader Early Learning Library).

—Tigers. 2002. (Weekly Reader Early Learning Library). (Illus.). 24p. (J). (ps up). pap. 5.95 (978-0-8368-3289-1(2)); lib. bdg. 19.33 (978-0-8368-3276-1(0)) Stevens, Gareth Inc. (Weekly Reader Early Learning Library).

—Zebras. 2002. (Weekly Reader Early Learning Library). (Illus.). 24p. (J). (ps up). pap. 5.95 (978-0-8368-3290-7(6)); lib. bdg. 19.33 (978-0-8368-3277-8(9)) Stevens, Gareth Inc. (Weekly Reader Early Learning Library).

Marx, David F. Doc Block. 2006. (Reader's Clubhouse Set A Ser.). (Illus.). 24p. (J). pap. 3.99 (978-0-7641-3288-9(1)) Barron's Educational Series, Inc.

Meeker, Clare Hodgson. Hansa, the True Story of an Asian Elephant Baby. Feltner, Linda M., illus. 2002. 48p. (J). pap. 12.95 (978-1-57061-370-8(2)); (gr. 1-5). 16.95 (978-1-57061-344-9(3)) Sasquatch Bks.

Morecroft, Richard, et al. Zoo Album. 2004. (Illus.). 48p. (J). 17.95 (978-1-59270-032-5(2)) Enchanted Lion Bks., LLC.

Nault, Jennifer. Project Polar Bear. 2003. (gr. 3-6). lib. bdg. 15.25 (978-0-613-79814-3(7)) Tandem Library Bks.

—Project Polar Bear. Kissock, Heather & Marshall, Diana, eds. 2003. (Zoo Life Ser.). (Illus.). 24p. (J). pap. 6.95 (978-1-59036-060-6(5)) Weigl Pubs., Inc.

—Project Polar Bear. 2002. (Zoo Babies Ser.). (Illus.). 24p. (J). lib. bdg. 15.15 (978-1-59036-014-9(1)) Weigl Pubs., Inc.

Nayer, Judy. Adding It up at the Zoo. 2002. (Yellow Umbrella Books). (Illus.). 16p. (J). (gr. 1). lib. bdg. 14.60 (978-0-7368-1278-8(4) , Pebble Bks.) Capstone Pr., Inc.

Oehler, David A. The Cincinnati Zoo & Botanical Garden. 2003. (Great Zoos of the United States Ser.). (Illus.). 24p. (J). lib. bdg. 18.75 (978-0-8239-6320-1(9) , PowerKids Pr.) Rosen Publishing Group, Inc., The.

Out & about at the Zoo. (Field Trips Ser.). 24p. (J). 8.95 (978-1-4048-0169-1(3)) Picture Window Bks.

Peterson, Gerry, illus. Junior-Photo-Naturalist: My Trip to the Zoo. l.t. ed. 2001. 24p. (YA). (gr. 5 up). 6.97 (978-0-9702807-0-1(X)) Build-a-Bk.

Powell, Janet. Saint Louis Zoo. 2003. (Great Zoos of the United States Ser.). (Illus.). 24p. (J). lib. bdg. 18.75 (978-0-8239-6318-8(7) , PowerKids Pr.) Rosen Publishing Group, Inc., The.

Ricciuti, Edward R. A Pelican Swallowed My Head. 2002. (Illus.). 224p. (J). (gr. 3-7). 17.00 (978-0-689-82532-3(3)) Simon & Schuster Children's Publishing.

Ring, Susan. Project Elephant. 2003. (gr. 3-6). lib. bdg. 15.25 (978-0-613-79813-6(9)) Tandem Library Bks.

—Project Elephant. Kissock, Heather & Marshall, Diana, eds. 2003. (Zoo Life Ser.). 24p. (J). pap. 6.95 (978-1-59036-056-9(7)) Weigl Pubs., Inc.

—Project Elephant. 2002. (Zoo Babies Ser.). (Illus.). 24p. (J). lib. bdg. 15.15 (978-1-59036-016-3(8)) Weigl Pubs., Inc.

—Project Hippopotomus. 2002. (Zoo Babies Ser.). (Illus.). 24p. (J). lib. bdg. 15.15 (978-1-59036-013-2(3)) Weigl Pubs., Inc.

—Project Orangutan. 2003. (gr. 3-6). lib. bdg. 15.25 (978-0-613-79812-9(0)) Tandem Library Bks.

—Project Orangutan. Marshall, Diana & Nault, Jennifer, eds. 2003. (Zoo Life Ser.). (Illus.). 24p. (J). pap. 6.95 (978-1-59036-058-3(3)) Weigl Pubs., Inc.

—Project Orangutan. 2002. (Zoo Babies Ser.). (Illus.). 24p. (J). lib. bdg. 15.15 (978-1-59036-017-0(6)) Weigl Pubs., Inc.

—Project Otter. 2003. (gr. 3-6). lib. bdg. 15.25 (978-0-613-79818-1(X)) Tandem Library Bks.

—Project Otter. Kissock, Heather & Marshall, Diana, eds. 2003. (Zoo Life Ser.). (Illus.). 24p. (J). pap. 6.95 (978-1-59036-059-0(1)) Weigl Pubs., Inc.

—Project Otter. 2002. (Zoo Life Ser.). (Illus.). 24p. (J). lib. bdg. 22.80 (978-1-59036-018-7(4)) Weigl Pubs., Inc.

—Project Tiger. Marshall, Diana & Nault, Jennifer, eds. 2003. (Zoo Life Ser.). (Illus.). 24p. (J). pap. 6.95 (978-1-59036-061-3(3)) Weigl Pubs., Inc.

—Project Tiger. 2002. (Zoo Babies Ser.). (Illus.). 24p. (J). lib. bdg. 15.15 (978-1-59036-015-6(X)) Weigl Pubs., Inc.

San Diego Zoo Staff. Count to 10 & Back Again: San Diego Zoo. 2004. (Illus.). 24p. (J). 7.95 (978-0-8249-6552-5(3)) Ideals Pubns.

Schwartz, David M. At the Zoo. Kuhn, Dwight, photos by. 1998. (Springboards into Science Ser.). (Illus.). 24p. (J). (gr. 1 up). lib. bdg. 19.93 (978-0-8368-2225-0(0)) Stevens, Gareth Inc.

Shahan, Sherry. Feeding Time at the Zoo. 2000. (Random House Pictureback Ser.). (Illus.). (J). (978-0-606-18495-3(3)) Tandem Library Bks.

Stewart, Pat L. Zoo Animals Coloring Fun. 2005. 32p. (J). pap. 2.95 (978-0-486-44698-1(0)) Dover Pubns., Inc.

Stillerman, Robbie. Color Your Own Zoo Animals Stickers. 2006. 2p. (J). pap. 2.95 (978-0-486-44887-9(8)) Dover Pubns., Inc.

Trago Publishing Staff. The Zoo Animal Travel Kit. 1999. (My Art Ser.). 35p. (J). (ps-3). pap. (978-0-9683883-8-9(8)) Sterling Publishing Co., Inc.

Wallace, Karen. A Trip to the Zoo. 2003. (Readers Ser.). (Illus.). 32p. (J). pap. 3.99 (978-0-7894-9219-7(9)) Dorling Kindersley Publishing, Inc.

—A Trip to the Zoo. 2003. (Illus.). 32p. (J). (ps-3). lib. bdg. 11.80 (978-0-613-62438-1(6)) Tandem Library Bks.

Wallace, Karen & Dorling Kindersley Publishing Staff. A Trip to the Zoo. 2003. (Readers Ser.). (Illus.). 32p. (J). 12.99 (978-0-7894-9307-1(1)) Dorling Kindersley Publishing, Inc.

Wexo, John Bonnett. Focas y Leones Marinos. Rountree, Monica, tr. 2003. (Zoobooks). Orig. Title: Seals & Sea Lions. (SPA., Illus.). 24p. (J). (gr. k-6). lib. bdg. 15.95 (978-1-888153-79-8(2)) Wildlife Education, Ltd.

Whitehouse, Patricia. Alligator. 2003. (Zoo Animals Ser.). (Illus.). 24p. (J). (ps-1). lib. bdg. 17.08 (978-1-58810-903-3(8)) ; pap. 5.25 (978-1-4034-0642-2(1)) Heinemann Library.

—Animales del Zoologico, 12 vols., Set. Cano, Patricia, tr. 2003. (SPA., Illus.). (J). (ps-1). lib. bdg. 222.00 (978-1-4034-0410-7(0)) ; pap. 56.70 (978-1-4034-2910-0(3)) Heinemann Library.

—Elephant. 2003. (Zoo Animals Ser.). (Illus.). 24p. (ps-1). (J). lib. bdg. 17.08 (978-1-58810-897-5(X)); pap. 5.25 (978-1-4034-0643-9(X)) Heinemann Library.

—Flamingo. 2003. (Zoo Animals Ser.). (Illus.). 24p. (ps-1). (J). lib. bdg. 17.08 (978-1-58810-901-9(1)); pap. 5.25 (978-1-4034-0646-0(4)) Heinemann Library.

—Giraffe. 2003. (Zoo Animals Ser.). (Illus.). 24p. (ps-1). (J). lib. bdg. 17.08 (978-1-58810-898-2(8)); pap. 5.25 (978-1-4034-0644-6(8)) Heinemann Library.

—Hippopotamus. 2003. (Zoo Animals Ser.). (Illus.). 24p. (ps-1). (J). lib. bdg. 17.08 (978-1-58810-899-9(6)); pap. 5.25 (978-1-4034-0645-3(6)) Heinemann Library.

—La Hora en el Zoologico. 2002. (Matematicas del Zoologico (Zoo Math) Ser.). 24p. (J). (ps-1). pap. 5.25 (978-1-58810-865-4(1) , 91626); (SPA.). lib. bdg. 18.50 (978-1-58810-806-7(6)) Heinemann Library.

—The Math Zoo. 2002. 24p. (J). (ps-1). pap. (978-1-58810-756-5(6) , 91409); (Illus.). lib. bdg. 17.08 (978-1-58810-548-6(2)) Heinemann Library.

—Mountain Goat. 2003. (Zoo Animals Ser.). (Illus.). 24p. (J). (ps-1). lib. bdg. 17.08 (978-1-58810-890-6(2)); pap. 5.75 (978-1-4034-0541-8(7)) Heinemann Library.

—Mountain Goat. 2002. (ps-2). lib. bdg. 13.30 (978-0-613-88918-6(5)) Tandem Library Bks.

—Ostrich. 2003. (Zoo Animals Ser.). (Illus.). 24p. (ps-1). (J). lib. bdg. 17.08 (978-1-58810-887-6(2)); pap. 5.25 (978-1-4034-0543-2(3)) Heinemann Library.

—Ostrich. 2002. (ps-2). lib. bdg. 13.30 (978-0-613-81251-1(4)) Tandem Library Bks.

—Partes Iguales en el Zoologico. 2002. (Matematicas del Zoologico (Zoo Math) Ser.). (SPA.). 24p. (J). (ps-1). 18.50 (978-1-58810-801-2(5)); pap. 5.25 (978-1-58810-860-9(0) , 91628) Heinemann Library.

—Patrones en el Zoologico. 2002. (Matematicas del Zoologico (Zoo Math) Ser.).Tr. of Zoo Patterns. 24p. (J). (ps-1). pap. 5.25 (978-1-58810-863-0(5) , 91629); (SPA.). lib. bdg. 18.50 (978-1-58810-804-3(X)) Heinemann Library.

—Sea Lion. 2003. (Zoo Animals Ser.). (Illus.). 24p. (ps-1). (J). lib. bdg. 17.08 (978-1-58810-902-6(X)); pap. 5.25 (978-1-4034-0647-7(2)) Heinemann Library.

—Tamanos en el Zoologico. 2002. (Matematicas del Zoologico (Zoo Math) Ser.). (SPA.). 24p. (J). (ps-1). pap. 5.25 (978-1-58810-864-7(3) , 91630); lib. bdg. 18.50 (978-1-58810-805-0(8)) Heinemann Library.

—Tiger. 2003. (Zoo Animals Ser.). (Illus.). 24p. (ps-1). (J). lib. bdg. 17.08 (978-1-58810-904-0(6)); pap. 5.25 (978-1-4034-0648-4(0)) Heinemann Library.

—Zebra. 2003. (Zoo Animals Ser.). (Illus.). 24p. (ps-1). (J). lib. bdg. 17.08 (978-1-58810-900-2(3)); pap. 5.25 (978-1-4034-0649-1(9)) Heinemann Library.

—Zoo Animals, 12 vols., Set. 2003. (Illus.). (ps-1). lib. bdg. 222.00 (978-1-58810-876-0(7)) Heinemann Library.

—Zoo Fair Shares. 2002. 24p. (J). (ps-1). pap. (978-1-58810-755-8(8) , 91410); (Illus.). lib. bdg. 18.50 (978-1-58810-547-9(4)) Heinemann Library.

—Zoo Fair Shares. 2002. (ps-2). lib. bdg. 13.30 (978-0-613-82273-2(0)) Tandem Library Bks.

—Zoo Pairs. 2002. 24p. (J). (ps-1). pap. (978-1-58810-757-2(4) , 91411); (Illus.). lib. bdg. 18.50 (978-1-58810-549-3(0)) Heinemann Library.

—Zoo Patterns. 2002. (Zoo Math Ser.). (Illus.). 24p. (J). (ps-1). lib. bdg. 18.50 (978-1-58810-550-9(4)) Heinemann Library.

—Zoo Sizes. 2002. 24p. (J). (ps-1). pap. (978-1-58810-759-6(0) , 91413); (Illus.). lib. bdg. 18.50 (978-1-58810-551-6(2)) Heinemann Library.

—Zoo Time. 2002. (Zoo Math Ser.). 24p. (J). (ps-1). (Illus.). lib. bdg. 18.50 (978-1-58810-552-3(0)); pap. (978-1-58810-760-2(4) , 91414) Heinemann Library.

—El Zoologico Matematico. 2002. (Matematicas del Zoologico (Zoo Math) Ser.). 24p. (J). (ps-1). (SPA.). 18.50 (978-1-58810-802-9(3)); pap. 5.25 (978-1-58810-861-6(9) , 91625) Heinemann Library.

Wildlife Education, Ltd. Staff. Zoobooks, 58 Vols. 2002. (Zoobooks Ser.). (Illus.). (J). (gr. 3-8). 1160p. 795.00 (978-1-888153-62-0(8) , 6058); (SPA., 880p. pap. 96.80 (978-1-888153-61-3(X) , 5244) Wildlife Education, Ltd.

—Zoobooks: The Teachers Set. 2002. (Zoobooks Ser.). (Illus.). 312p. (J). (gr. 3-8). pap. 38.75 (978-1-888153-60-6(1) , 5262) Wildlife Education, Ltd.

Working with Animals: Individual Title Six-Packs. (gr. k-1). 23.00 (978-0-7635-9035-2(5)) Rigby Education.

Yanofsky, Tsivia. Take Me to the Zoo: Lions, elephants & snakes in the Midrash & Nature. 2003. 19.99 (978-1-57819-099-7(1) , ZOOH) Mesorah Pubns., Ltd.

A Zoo, 6 Packs. (Literatura 2000 Ser.). (ps-1). 28.00 (978-0-7635-0044-3(5)) Rigby Education.

Zoo Animals. 2002. (Tab Board Books Ser.). 12p. (J). bds. 4.95 (978-0-7894-8477-2(3)) Dorling Kindersley Publishing, Inc.

ZOO ANIMALS—FICTION

Barretta, Gene. Dear Deer: A Book of Homophones. 2007. (Illus.). 40p. (J). (ps-2). 16.95 ***(978-0-8050-8104-6(6))*** Holt, Henry & Co.

Bernthal, Mark S. & Lyrick Publishing Staff. Barney & BJ Go to the Zoo. Full, Dennis, photos by. 1999. (Barney's Go to Ser.). (Illus.). 24p. (J). (ps-k). pap. 3.50 (978-1-57064-446-7(2)) Scholastic, Inc.

W
X
Y
Z

Browne, Anthony. Zoo. Browne, Anthony, illus. 2002. (Illus.). 32p. (J). pap. 6.95 (978-0-374-49923-5(3) , Sunburst) Farrar, Straus & Giroux.

—Zoo. 2002. (ps-2). lib. bdg. 15.25 (978-0-613-71935-3(2)) Tandem Library Bks.

Bryant, Jen. Call Me Marianne. Johnson, David A., illus. 2006. 32p. (J). 16.00 (978-0-8028-5242-7(4) , Eerdmans Bks For Young Readers) Eerdmans, William B. Publishing Co.

Campbell, Rod. Dear Zoo: A Lift-the-Flap Book. Campbell, Rod, illus. 2007. 18p. (J). 6.99 (*978-1-4169-4737-0(X) , Little Simon) Simon & Schuster Children's Publishing.

Capucilli, Alyssa Satin. Inside a Zoo in the City: A Rebus Read along Story. Arnold, Tedd, illus. 2000. (J). (ps-2). pap. 11.95 (978-0-590-99715-7(7)) Scholastic, Inc.

Carle, Eric. 1, 2, 3 to the Zoo: A Counting Book. Carle, Eric, illus. 1998. (Illus.). 32p. (J). (ps-k). pap. 6.99 (978-0-698-11645-0(3) , Putnam Juvenile) Penguin Group (USA) Inc.

—1,2,3 to the Zoo. 2007. (World of Eric Carle Ser.). 24p. (J). (ps-1). pap. 4.99 (978-0-448-44493-2(3) , Grosset & Dunlap) Penguin Group (USA) Inc.

A Change for Zoe: Individual Title Six-Packs. (gr. k-1). 23.00 (978-0-7635-8840-3(7)) Rigby Education.

Chick, Bryan. The Secret Zoo. 2007. 252p. pap. 5.99 (*978-0-9791887-3-2(3)) Second Wish Pr.

Chouette Publishing. Caillou: Zoo Animals. Brignaud, Pierre, illus. rev. ed. 2007. (Caillou Board Bks.). 24p. (J). bds. 7.95 (*978-2-89450-609-7(0)) Chouette Publishing CAN. *Dist:* Independent Pubs. Group.

Christian, Focus. God's Zoo TNT Ministries. Charnick, Tim, illus. 2005. 96p. pap. (978-1-84550-069-6(5) , Christian Focus) Christian Focus Pubns.

Cimarusti, Marie. Peek-a-Boooo! Peterson, Stephanie, illus. 2005. 12p. (J). (ps). 9.99 (978-0-525-47435-7(8) , Dutton Juvenile) Penguin Group (USA) Inc.

Cole, Babette. Tarzana. 2nd ed. 2003. (Babette Cole Ser.). (SPA., Illus.). 34p. (J). 12.95 (978-84-233-2274-9(2)) Ediciones Destino ESP. *Dist:* Planeta Publishing Corp.

Corbett, W. J. Last Chance Zoo. 2003. (Illus.). mass mkt. (978-0-340-86568-2(7) , Hodder Children's Books) Hodder Children's Division.

—Return to the Last Chance Zoo. 2003. (Illus.). 192p. pap. (978-0-340-86569-9(5) , Hodder Children's Books) Hodder Children's Division.

Crispin, Barbara. City Zoo Blizzard Revue. Houghton, Roswitha, illus. 2003. 40p. 14.95 (978-0-9716346-1-9(0)) Dancing Words Pr., Inc.

David, Erica. Quiero Ser Libre. 2005. (Madagascar Ser.).Tr. of Born to Be Wild. (SPA., Illus.). 32p. (J). 3.99 (978-0-439-71575-1(X) , Scholastic en Espanol) Scholastic, Inc.

DeAngelo, Jeremy. The Out Crowd. 2006. (J). pap. (978-0-88092-613-3(9)); lib. bdg. (978-0-88092-612-6(0)) Royal Fireworks Publishing Co.

Deich, Cheri Bivin. The Messy Monkey Tea Party. Genth, Christina, illus. 2007. 32p. (J). 15.95 (978-1-60108-006-6(9)) Red Cygnet Pr.

Donahue, Jill L. The Zoo Band. 2007. (Illus.). 24p. (J). (*978-1-4048-2381-5(6)) Picture Window Bks.

—The Zoo Band. Eroglu, Aysin D., illus. 2006. 24p. (J). (*978-1-4048-3165-0(7)) Picture Window Bks.

Dyer, Heather. Tina & the Penguin. Levert, Mireille, illus. 2004. 32p. (J). (gr. k-3). (978-1-55337-767-2(2)) Kids Can Pr., Ltd.

Ebie, Mora. Going to the Zoo in Hawaii. 2006. (Illus.). 28p. (J). 10.95 (978-1-56647-790-1(5)) Mutual Publishing LLC.

Ford, Miela. Watch Us Play. 1998. (Illus.). 24p. (J). (ps-3). 15.00 (978-0-688-15606-0(1)) HarperCollins Pubs.

Fox, Mem. Zoo-Looking. Love, Judith DuFour & Whitman, Candace, illus. 2001. (J). (ps-2). pap. 6.00 (978-1-57255-011-7(2)) Mondo Publishing.

—Zoo-Looking. 2001. (ps-2). lib. bdg. 14.15 (978-0-613-86395-7(X)) Tandem Library Bks.

Garren, Devorah-Leah. Shabbos Is Coming! We're Lost in the Zoo! Katz, Maya S., illus. 1999. 32p. (J). (ps-3). 12.95 (978-1-880582-32-9(5)) Judaica Pr., Inc., The.

Gates, Susan. Eric's Talking Ears. Remphrey, Martin, illus. 2006. 48p. (J). (*978-1-4048-3120-9(7)) Picture Window Bks.

Glassman, Bruce. Zoolidays. Kiaulevicius, Rolandas, illus. 2006. 32p. (J). 15.95 (978-1-60108-011-0(5)) Red Cygnet Pr.

Goldman, Todd Harris. The Zoo I Drew. 2008. (J). (*978-0-375-85201-5(8)); (*978-0-375-95201-2(2)) Random Hse., Inc.

Good Night Gorilla. 2004. (J). pap. 18.95 incl. audio compact disk (978-1-55592-419-5(0)); pap. 18.95 incl. audio compact disk (978-1-55592-422-5(0)); pap. 38.75 incl. audio compact disk (978-1-55592-421-8(2)); pap. 38.75 incl. audio compact disk (978-1-55592-423-2(9)); pap. 32.75 incl. audio (978-1-55592-426-3(3)); pap. 32.75 incl. audio (978-0-7882-0247-6(2)); pap. 14.95 incl. audio (978-1-55592-425-6(5)) Weston Woods Studios, Inc.

Goodman, Susan E. What Do You Do.... at the Zoo? Pica, Steve, illus. 2002. (Silly Millies Ser.). 32p. (gr. k-2). lib. bdg. 17.90 (978-0-7613-2755-4(X) , Millbrook Pr.) Lerner Publishing Group.

—What Do You Do at the Zoo? 2002. (gr. k-3). lib. bdg. 13.00 (978-0-613-55924-9(X)) Tandem Library Bks.

Hogg, Gary. Beautiful Buehla & the Zany Zoo Makeover. Chess, Victoria, illus. 2006. 32p. (J). 15.99 (978-0-06-009420-1(6)); lib. bdg. 16.89 (978-0-06-009421-8(4)) HarperCollins Pubs. (Tegen, Katherine Bks).

Hubbell, Patricia. Bouncing Time. Sweet, Melissa, illus. 2000. 32p. (YA). (ps up). 15.95 (978-0-688-17376-0(4)) HarperCollins Pubs.

Ide, Laurie Shimizu. Okazu at the Zoo. Kanekuni, Daniel, illus. 2006. (J). (978-1-56647-776-5(X)) Mutual Publishing LLC.

Jones, Julie. The Problem at Pepperpine Zoo. Jones, Julie, illus. l.t. ed. 2004. (Illus.). 24p. (J). pap. 7.95 (978-0-9745553-0-0(4)) Greenwood Street Publishing. GSP.

Jones, Lara. Me divierto en el Zoo. 2003. (Lola y Bony Ser.). (SPA., Illus.). 8p. 8.95 (978-84-7864-627-2(2)) Combel Editorial, S.A. ESP. *Dist:* Independent Pubs. Group.

Jordan, Apple. Fearless Foursome. Dever, Bob & Morris, Michael, illus. 2005. (Madagascar Ser.). (SPA.). 64p. (J). (ps-ps). 2.99 (978-0-439-71307-8(2) , Scholastic en Espanol) Scholastic, Inc.

Klein, Adria F. Max Goes to the Zoo. Gallagher-Cole, Mernie, illus. 2007. (J). lib. bdg. (*978-1-4048-3677-8(2)) Picture Window Bks.

Kline, Trish & Donev, Mary. A Day at the Zoo: KA Reader 3. 2007. (Illus.). 32p. (J). per. 20.00 (*978-0-9717234-5-0(1)) Ghost Hunter Productions.

Knowles, Sheena. Edward the Emu. Clement, Rod, illus. 1998. 32p. (J). (ps-1). pap. 6.99 (978-0-06-443499-7(0)) HarperCollins Pubs.

—Edward the Emu. Clement, Rod, illus. 1998. 13.75 (978-0-606-11288-8(X)) Tandem Library Bks.

Leaney, Cindy. Station K. I. D. S. Whitehouse, Patty, ed. King, Sue & Wilks, Peter, illus. 2004. (Friendly Phonics Ser.). 24p. (J). lib. bdg. 14.95 (978-1-59054-186-9(3)) Fitzgerald Bks.

Lombardi, Kristine. A Day at the Zoo: Learning Numbers. 2006. (Show & Tell Ser.). 12p. (J). pap. 12.99 (978-0-7944-0906-7(7)) Reader's Digest Assn., Inc., The.

Lunablau, Jani. Little Snowflake. 2006. (Illus.). 32p. (J). 14.95 (978-1-59692-139-9(0)) MacAdam/Cage Publishing, Inc.

Maccarone, Grace. The Class Trip. Lewin, Betsy, illus. 2004. 32p. (J). lib. bdg. 15.00 (978-1-59054-663-5(6)) Fitzgerald Bks.

—The Class Trip. Lewin, Betsy, illus. 1999. (Hello Reader! Science Ser.: Level 1). 32p. (J). (ps-3). pap. 3.99 (978-0-439-06755-3(3) , Cartwheel Bks.) Scholastic, Inc.

—Class Trip. 1999. (gr. k-3). lib. bdg. 11.80 (978-0-613-21357-8(2)) Tandem Library Bks.

Markowitz-Meredith, Susan. The Royal Zoo Keeper. ed. 2003. (Early Connections Ser.). (J). pap. 35.00 (978-1-4108-1551-4(X)) Benchmark Education Co.

Marsh, Carole. The Zany Zoo MYST. 2007. 128p. pap. 5.99 (*978-0-635-06332-8(8)) Gallopade International.

Martel, Yann. Life of Pi: A Novel. 2003. (gr. 7-12). lib. bdg. 23.45 (978-0-613-59907-8(1)) Tandem Library Bks.

Martin, Bill, Jr. Oso Polar, Oso Polar, Que Es Ese Ruido? Carle, Eric, illus. rev. ed. 2000. (SPA.). 32p. (J). (ps-k). 15.95 (978-0-8050-6427-8(3) , Holt, Henry & Co. Bks. For Young Readers) Holt, Henry & Co.

Martin, Bill. Oso Polar, Oso Polar, Que es Ese Ruido? Mlawer, Teresa, tr. Carle, Eric, illus. rev. ed. 2002. (SPA.). 28p. (J). (ps-k). bds. 7.95 (978-0-8050-6902-0(X) , Holt, Henry & Co. Bks. For Young Readers) Holt, Henry & Co.

Martin, Bill, Jr. Polar Bear, Polar Bear, What Do You Hear? 2002. (Illus.). (J). 26.47 (978-0-7587-3432-7(8)) Book Wholesalers, Inc.

Massie, Diane Redfield. The Baby Beebee Bird. Kellogg, Steven, illus. 32p. (J). (ps-1). 2003. pap. 6.99 (978-0-06-051784-7(0)); 2000. 16.99 (978-0-06-028083-3(2)) HarperCollins Pubs.

—The Baby Beebee Bird. 2003. (gr. k-3). lib. bdg. 14.15 (978-0-613-65762-4(4)) Tandem Library Bks.

Mayer, Mercer. My Trip to the Zoo. 2002. (Little Critter First Readers Ser.). (Illus.). 24p. (J). (ps-k). pap. 3.95 (978-1-57768-826-6(0)) School Specialty Publishing.

—My Trip to the Zoo. 2001. (gr. k-3). lib. bdg. 11.80 (978-0-613-67648-9(3)) Tandem Library Bks.

McKee, Darren. Barney Visits the Zoo. Brower, Howard, illus. 2003. (Barney Ser.). 64p. (J). (ps). 2.99 (978-1-58668-313-9(6) , Levine, Arthur A. Bks.) Scholastic, Inc.

McMillon, LaToya. Bad News! 2006. (ENG.). 28p. per. 14.99 (*978-1-4259-3563-4(X)) AuthorHouse.

Mora, Pat. ¡Marimba! Animales from A to Z. Cushman, Doug, illus. 2006. 32p. (J). (gr. k-3). 16.00 (978-0-618-19453-7(3) , Clarion Bks.) Houghton Mifflin Co. Trade & Reference Div.

Munari, Bruno. Bruno Munari's Zoo. 2005. (Illus.). 48p. (J). reprint ed. 17.95 (978-0-8118-4830-5(2)) Chronicle Bks. LLC.

Munsch, Robert. Alligator Baby. 1998. (Illus.). (J). pap. 3.99 (978-0-590-34195-0(2) , Cartwheel Bks.) Scholastic, Inc.

—Alligator Baby. Martchenko, Michael, illus. 1998. 32p. (J). (ps-3). pap. 4.99 (978-0-590-88594-2(4) , Cartwheel Bks.) Scholastic, Inc.

—Alligator Baby. 1998. 10.79 (978-0-606-13117-9(5)) Tandem Library Bks.

Nappa, Mike & Amy. Zachary's Zoo. Boyer, Lyn, illus. 2004. 24p. (J). pap. 4.99 (978-0-310-70823-0(0)) Zonderkidz.

Oke, Janette. Who's New at the Zoo? Munger, Nancy, illus. rev. ed. 2001. (Animal Friends Ser.). 80p. (J). (gr. 1-5). reprint ed. pap. 6.99 (978-0-7642-2460-7(3)) Bethany Hse. Pubs.

—Who's New at the Zoo? 2001. (gr. k-3). lib. bdg. 14.15 (978-0-613-82432-3(6)) Tandem Library Bks.

Pfister, Marcus. Charlie at the Zoo. James, J. Alison, tr. from GER. Pfister, Marcus, illus. 2007. (Illus.). 32p. (J). (ps). 17.95 (*978-0-7358-2144-6(5)) North-South Bks., Inc.

Prose, Francine. Leopold: The Liar of Leipzig. Aviram, Einav, illus. 2005. 32p. (J). 15.99 (978-0-06-008075-4(2) , Cotler, Joanna Books) HarperCollins Pubs.

Purton, Marie. Josh's Day at the Zoo. 2006. (Illus.). 48p. pap. (*978-1-84401-606-8(4)) Athena Pr.

Rathmann, Peggy. Good Night, Gorilla. Rathmann, Peggy, illus. 2002. (Illus.). (J). 13.19 (978-0-7587-2619-3(8)) Book Wholesalers, Inc.

—Good Night, Gorilla. Rathmann, Peggy, illus. (Illus.). (J). (ps-1). 2004. 34p. bds. 12.99 (978-0-399-24260-1(0) , Putnam Juvenile); 2002. bds. 9.99 (978-0-399-23994-6(4)); 2003. 32p. 16.99 (978-0-399-24195-6(7) , Putnam Juvenile); 2000. (SPA., 40p. reprint ed. pap. 5.99 (978-0-698-11649-8(6) , Putnam Juvenile) Penguin Group (USA) Inc.

—Good Night, Gorilla. 2000. (gr. k-3). lib. bdg. 14.15 (978-0-613-28500-1(X)); (Illus.). (J). 12.79 (978-0-606-18837-1(1)) Tandem Library Bks.

Rau, Dana Meachen. At the Zoo. 2007. (Fun Time Ser.). 24p. (J). lib. bdg. 22.79 (*978-0-7614-2610-3(8) , Benchmark Bks.) Cavendish, Marshall Corp.

Reader's Digest Editors. Let's Go to the Zoo! 2006. (FP A-Lift-the-Flap Play Book Ser.). (Illus.). 10p. (J). pap. 8.99 (978-0-7944-1112-1(6)) Reader's Digest Assn., Inc., The.

Rey, H. A. Curious George at the Zoo. Rey, Margret, illus. 2007. 12p. (J). (gr. k-ps). bds. 6.99 (*978-0-618-80042-1(5)) Houghton Mifflin Co. Trade & Reference Div.

Rice, Eve. Sam Who Never Forgets. Rice, Eve, illus. 2002. (Illus.). (J). 14.43 (978-0-7587-3551-5(0)) Book Wholesalers, Inc.

Richards, Chuck. Jungle Gym Jitters. Richards, Chuck, illus. 2004. (Illus.). 32p. (J). 17.85 (978-0-8027-8932-7(3)); 16.95 (978-0-8027-8931-0(5)) Walker & Co.

Richardson, Justin & Parnell, Peter. And Tango Makes Three. Cole, Henry, illus. 2005. 32p. (J). 15.99 (978-0-689-87845-9(1)) Simon & Schuster Children's Publishing.

Rose, Deborah Lee. Birthday Zoo. Munsinger, Lynne, illus. 2006. 24p. (J). pap. 6.95 (978-0-8075-0777-3(6)) Whitman, Albert & Co.

—Birthday Zoo. Munsinger, Lynn, illus. 2002. 24p. (J). (ps-1). 15.95 (978-0-8075-0776-6(8)) Whitman, Albert & Co.

Ruiz-Flores, Lupe. The Woodcutter's Gift/El Regalo del Leñador. Jerome, Elaine, illus. 2007. (SPA & ENG.). 32p. (J). (ps-2). 15.95 (*978-1-55885-489-5(4) , Piñata Books) Arte Publico Pr.

Sage, Angie. No Banana. 2002. (Illus.). (J). mass mkt. 7.50 (978-0-340-77343-7(X) , Hodder & Stoughton) Hodder General Publishing Division GBR. *Dist:* Trafalgar Square Publishing.

Schofield, Louise. The Zoo Room. Geste, Malcolm, illus. 2005. 32p. (J). (ps-7). 16.95 (978-1-894965-19-4(1)) Simply Read Bks. CAN. *Dist:* Perseus Distribution.

Schultz, Lucy & Shultz, Lucy. Zoo Faces. Larranaga, Ana, illus. 2007. 12p. (J). (ps-ps). bds. 5.99 (978-1-58476-556-1(9) , IKIDS) Innovative Kids.

Shaskan, Trisha Speed. Another Pet. Vincent, Kenneth, illus. 2006. (Read-It! Readers Ser.). (J). 19.93 (978-1-4048-2404-1(9)) Picture Window Bks.

Sierra, Judy. Wild about Books. Brown, Marc, tr. Brown, Marc, illus. 2004. 40p. (J). (ps-3). 16.95 (978-0-375-82538-5(X)); lib. bdg. 18.99 (978-0-375-92538-2(4)) Random Hse. Children's Bks. (Knopf Bks. for Young Readers).

Simpson, Fiona, ed. Madagascar: Play-Along. 2005. (Madagascar Ser.). 16p. (J). pap. 4.99 (978-0-439-69994-5(0)) Scholastic, Inc.

Steele, Michael Anthony. Esto es un Zoologico! 2005. (Madagascar Ser.).Tr. of Zoosters on the Loose. (SPA., Illus.). 24p. (J). 3.99 (978-0-439-71308-5(0)) Scholastic, Inc.

—MadagascarTM: It's a Zoo in Here! 2005. (Madagascar Ser.). (Illus.). 24p. (J). pap. 3.99 (978-0-439-69626-5(7)) Scholastic, Inc.

Swain, Cynthia. Wishing with Pennies. 2006. (Early Explorers Ser.). (J). 30.00 (*978-1-4108-6041-5(8)) Benchmark Education Co.

Waber, Bernard. A Lion Named Shirley Williamson. 2000. (Illus.). 40p. (J). (gr. k-3). pap. 6.95 (978-0-618-05580-7(0) , Walter Lorraine) Houghton Mifflin Co. Trade & Reference Div.

—A Lion Named Shirley Williamson. 2000. (Illus.). (J). (978-0-606-18212-6(8)) Tandem Library Bks.

Wilson, Karma. Animal Strike at the Zoo: It's True! Spengler, Margaret, illus. 2006. 32p. (J). 15.99 (978-0-06-057502-1(6)); lib. bdg. 17.89 (978-0-06-057503-8(4)) HarperCollins Pubs.

—Never, Ever Shout in a Zoo. Cushman, Douglas, illus. 2004. 32p. (J). (ps-3). 16.99 (978-0-316-98564-2(3)) Little Brown & Co.

Winthrop, Elizabeth. Dancing Granny. Murdocca, Sal, illus. 2003. 32p. (J). 16.95 (978-0-7614-5141-9(2)) Cavendish, Marshall Corp.

Wise, William. Zany Zoo. Munsinger, Lynn, illus. 32p. (J). (gr. k-3). 2006. 16.00 (978-0-618-18891-8(6) , Walter Lorraine); 11th ed. 2007. 6.95 (*978-0-618-95686-9(7)) Houghton Mifflin Co. Trade & Reference Div.

The Zany Zanimal Zoo. 2005. (Illus.). 40p. (J). 14.95 (978-0-9769738-0-5(4)) Redel, Nicole.

Ziefert, Harriet. Zoo Parade! Taback, Simms, illus. 2003. 14p. 8.95 (978-1-59354-014-2(0)) Blue Apple Bks.

ZOOLOGICAL GARDENS

see Zoos

ZOOLOGY

see also Anatomy, Comparative; Animals; Embryology; Evolution; Fossils; Natural History; Physiology, Comparative; Psychology, Comparative

also names of divisions, classes, etc. of the animal kingdom (e.g. Invertebrates; Vertebrates; birds; Mammals; etc.)

Andromeda. Extreme Animals. 2005. (- Z Ser.). (Illus.). 64p. (J). (gr. 5-7). 26.20 (978-1-4103-0538-1(4) , Blackbirch Pr., Inc.) Thomson Gale.

Animals of the World, 4 bks. Incl. Giant Pandas of China. Duden, Jane. 18.60 (978-1-56065-577-0(1)); Koalas of Australia. George, Linda. lib. bdg. 18.60 (978-1-56065-576-3(3)); Manatees of Florida. Lund, Bill. lib. bdg. 18.60 (978-1-56065-579-4(8)); Sea Otters of California. Duden, Jane. lib. bdg. 18.60 (978-1-56065-578-7(X)); 24p. (J). (gr. 2-3). 1997. (Illus.). Set lib. bdg. 74.40 (978-0-7368-0455-4(2) , Bridgestone Bks.) Capstone Pr., Inc.

Arnold, Caroline. Australian Animals. 2000. (Illus.). 48p. (gr. k-3). (J). 17.99 (978-0-688-16766-0(7)); (YA). 15.89 (978-0-688-16767-7(5)) HarperCollins Pubs.

Arnosky, Jim. Following the Coast. Arnosky, Jim, illus. 2004. (Illus.). 32p. (J). (gr. 3 up). 15.99 (978-0-688-17117-9(6)) HarperCollins Pubs.

Artell, Mike. Pee Yew! 2006. (Illus.). 96p. pap. (978-1-59647-054-5(2)) Good Year Bks.

Au Zoo. 2000. (Collection des Mots pour Lire). (FRE., Illus.). 28p. (J). 15.95 (978-2-03-653003-4(6)) Librairie Larousse FRA. *Dist:* Distribooks, Inc.

Baddiel, Ivor. Fantastic Creatures. 1999. (Mysterious World Ser.). (Illus.). 30p. (J). (gr. 5-9). pap. 6.95 (978-0-7641-1153-2(1)) Barron's Educational Series, Inc.

Bauer, David. Adding Arctic Animals. 2003. (Yellow Umbrella Books for Early Readers). (Illus.). 17p. (J). 15.93 (978-0-7368-2913-7(X)); pap. (978-0-7368-2872-7(9)) Yellow Umbrella Pr.

—Sumando Animales del Artico. 2005. Tr. of Adding Arctic Animals. (SPA., Illus.). 16p. (J). (gr. k-1). lib. bdg. 15.93 (978-0-7368-4147-4(4)) Capstone Pr., Inc.

Berger, Melvin. Do Penguins Get Frostbite? 2001. 12.75 (978-0-606-22177-1(8)) Tandem Library Bks.

Berkowitz, Henry. Animal Oddities: An Educational Coloring Book. Berkowitz, Henry, illus. 2002. 32p. (J). (gr. k-3). pap. 4.95 (978-0-932855-71-8(7)) Winner Enterprises.

Boreman, Thomas, ed. A Description of Three Hundred Animals. (Illus.). (J). reprint ed. 18.00 (978-0-384-05125-6(1)) Johnson Reprint Corp.

Broderip, W. J. Zoological Recreations. 2006. pap. 36.95 (*978-1-4286-3565-4(3)) Kessinger Publishing, LLC.

Burgess, Thornton W. The Burgess Animal Book for Children. 2004. reprint ed. pap. 1.99 (978-1-4192-5555-7(X)) Kessinger Publishing, LLC.

—The Burgess Animal Book for Children. Fuertes, Louis Agassiz, illus. 2004. reprint ed. pap. 37.95 (978-1-4179-2978-8(2)) Kessinger Publishing, LLC.

Burgess, W. Thornton. Burgess Animal Book for Children. 2006. pap. 57.99 (*978-1-4280-3431-0(5)) IndyPublish.com.

Casper, Julie Kerr. Animals: Creatures That Roam the Planet. 2007. (Natural Resources Ser.). 192p. (J). (gr. 6-12). 39.50 (*978-0-8160-6353-6(2) , Chelsea Hse.) Facts On File, Inc.

Chinery, Michael. Plants & Planteaters. 2000. (Secrets of the Rainforest Ser.). (Illus.). 32p. (J). (gr. 3-4). pap. (978-0-7787-0228-3(6)) Crabtree Publishing Co.

Corwin, Jeff. Into Wild Alaska. Pascoe, Elaine, ed. 2003. (Jeff Corwin Experience Ser.). (Illus.). 48p. (J). 24.95 (978-1-4103-0059-1(5)); 11.20 (978-1-4103-0180-2(X)) Thomson Gale. (Blackbirch Pr., Inc.).

—Into Wild Australia. 2004. (Animal Planet Ser.). (Illus.). 48p. (J). 24.95 (978-1-4103-0239-7(3)); 11.20 (978-1-4103-0240-3(7)) Thomson Gale. (Blackbirch Pr., Inc.).

—Into Wild Brazil. Pascoe, Elaine, ed. 2003. (Jeff Corwin Experience Ser.). (Illus.). 48p. (J). 24.95 (978-1-56711-853-7(4)); 11.20 (978-1-4103-0175-8(3)) Thomson Gale. (Blackbirch Pr., Inc.).

—Into Wild Costa Rica. 2004. (Animal Planet Ser.). (Illus.). 48p. (J). 24.95 (978-1-4103-0226-7(1)); 11.20 (978-1-4103-0227-4(X)) Thomson Gale. (Blackbirch Pr., Inc.).

—Into Wild Florida. Pascoe, Elaine, ed. 2003. (Jeff Corwin Experience Ser.). (Illus.). 48p. (J). 24.95 (978-1-56711-950-3(6)); 11.20 (978-1-4103-0177-2(X)) Thomson Gale. (Blackbirch Pr., Inc.).

—Into Wild Galapagos. Pascoe, Elaine, ed. 2003. (Jeff Corwin Experience Ser.). (Illus.). 48p. (J). 24.95 (978-1-56711-857-5(7)); 11.20 (978-1-4103-0173-4(7)) Thomson Gale. (Blackbirch Pr., Inc.).

—Into Wild India. Pascoe, Elaine, ed. 2003. (Jeff Corwin Experience Ser.). (Illus.). 48p. (J). 24.95 (978-1-56711-854-4(2)); 11.20 (978-1-4103-0171-0(0)) Thomson Gale. (Blackbirch Pr., Inc.).

—Into Wild Louisiana. Pascoe, Elaine, ed. 2003. (Jeff Corwin Experience Ser.). (Illus.). 48p. (J). 24.95 (978-1-4103-0060-7(9)); 11.20 (978-1-4103-0181-9(8)) Thomson Gale. (Blackbirch Pr., Inc.).

—Into Wild Madagascar. Pascoe, Elaine, ed. 2003. (Jeff Corwin Experience Ser.). (Illus.). 48p. (J). 24.95 (978-1-56711-855-1(0)); 11.20 (978-1-4103-0174-1(5)) Thomson Gale. (Blackbirch Pr., Inc.).

—Into Wild Namibia. Pascoe, Elaine, ed. 2003. (Jeff Corwin Experience Ser.). (Illus.). 48p. (J). 24.95 (978-1-56711-851-3(8)); 11.20 (978-1-4103-0172-7(9)) Thomson Gale. (Blackbirch Pr., Inc.).

—Into Wild Panama. Pascoe, Elaine, ed. 2003. (Jeff Corwin Experience Ser.). (Illus.). 48p. (J). 24.95 (978-1-56711-856-8(9)); 11.20 (978-1-4103-0176-5(1)) Thomson Gale. (Blackbirch Pr., Inc.).

—Into Wild Zanzibar. 2004. (Jeff Corwin Experience Ser.). (Illus.). 48p. (J). 11.20 (978-1-4103-0256-4(3)); (gr. 4-7). 24.95 (978-1-4103-0255-7(5)) Thomson Gale. (Blackbirch Pr., Inc.).

Dale, Kim. What Am I? (Illus.). 32p. pap. (978-0-7344-0125-0(6)); 2002. (YA). (978-0-7344-0044-4(6)) Hachette Livre Australia. (Lothian Bks.).

Dentro de Tanzania Salvaje. 2005. (Jeff Corwin Experience Ser.). (ENG & SPA., Illus.). 48p. (J). (ps-7). lib. bdg. 24.95 (978-1-4103-0686-9(0) , Blackbirch Pr., Inc.) Thomson Gale.

W X Y Z

Dietz, James M. African Animal Giants. Cremins, Robert & Morrison, Robert, illus. 2004. 12p. (J). (gr. k-4). reprint ed. 16.00 (978-0-7567-7641-1(4)) DIANE Publishing Co.

Discovery Channel & Staff. Thinkers. 2004. (Planet's Most Extreme Ser.). (Illus.). 48p. (J). (gr. 4-7). 24.95 (978-1-4103-0386-8(1) , Blackbirch Pr., Inc.) Thomson Gale.

Equipo Staff. Zoologia: Invertebrados. 1999. (SPA.). 96p. (978-84-494-1288-2(9) , 1380) Oceano Grupo Editoria, S.A.

—Zoologia: Vertebrados. 1999. (SPA.). 88p. (978-84-494-1278-3(1) , 1380) Oceano Grupo Editoria, S.A.

Exploring the Animal Kingdom. (First Facts Ser.). (Illus.). (J). (gr. 1-2). lib. bdg. 127.56 (978-0-7368-2751-5(X)) Capstone Pr., Inc.

Fecher, Sarah, et al. Wild Animals, 4 vols., Set. 1999. (Ladders Ser.). (Illus.). 32p. (J). (gr. k-3). (978-0-7166-7707-9(5)) World Bk., Inc.

Feinstein, Stephen. California Plants & Animals. (Heinemann State Studies). (Illus.). 48p. (J). 2003. (gr. 3-5). lib. bdg. (978-1-4034-0343-8(0)); 2002. pap. 8.50 (978-1-4034-0560-9(3)) Heinemann Library.

—California Plants & Animals. 2003. (gr. 3-6). lib. bdg. 17.05 (978-0-613-60856-5(9)) Tandem Library Bks.

Foley, Cate. Find the Polar Animal. 2000. (Welcome Bks.). (Illus.). 24p. (J). (ps-2). 17.00 (978-0-516-23093-1(X) , Children's Pr.) Scholastic Library Publishing.

Fulbright, Jeannie. Exploring Creation with Zoology 1: The Flying Creatures of Day Five. Wile, Jay L., ed. 2005. (Illus.). xvi, 240p. (J). 35.00 (978-1-932012-61-3(3)) Apologia Educational Ministries, Inc.

Glassman, Jackie. Amazing Arctic Animals, Vol. 2. Bonforte, Lisa, illus. 2002. (All Aboard Science Reader Ser.). 48p. (J). mass mkt. 3.99 (978-0-448-42844-4(X) , Grosset & Dunlap) Penguin Group (USA) Inc.

—Amazing Arctic Animals. 2002. (gr. k-3). lib. bdg. 11.80 (978-0-613-64393-1(3)) Tandem Library Bks.

Glover, David. Living & Growing. 2001. (Experiments in Science Ser.). (Illus.). (J). (978-0-7894-7470-4(0)) Dorling Kindersley Publishing, Inc.

Grupper, Jonathan. Destination Australia. 2000. (Destination Ser.). (Illus.). 31p. (J). (ps-3). 16.95 (978-0-7922-7165-9(3) , National Geographic Children's Bks.) National Geographic Society.

Gunzi, Christiane. The Best Book of Polar Animals. 2002. (Best Book of... Ser.). (Illus.). 32p. (J). (gr. k-3). tchr. ed. 12.95 (978-0-7534-5435-0(1) , Kingfisher) Houghton Mifflin Co. Trade & Reference Div.

Harcourt School Publishers Staff. Harcourt Ciencias. 1999. (Harcourt Ciencias Ser.). (SPA., Illus.). (gr. 1 up). pap., pupil's gde. ed. 62.00 (978-0-15-314803-3(9)); (gr. 2 up). pap., pupil's gde. ed. 64.00 (978-0-15-314804-0(7)) Harcourt Schl. Pubs.

Heller, Ruth. Galapagos Means Tortoises. Heller, Ruth, illus. 2000. (Books for Children). (Illus.). 40p. (J). (gr. k-4). 14.95 (978-0-87156-917-2(5)) Sierra Club Bks. for Children.

—Galapagos Means Tortoises! 2003. (gr. k-3). lib. bdg. 15.25 (978-0-613-79301-8(3)) Tandem Library Bks.

Helman, Andrea. C Is for Coyote. Wolfe, Art & Jecan, Gavriel, illus. Wolfe, Art & Jecan, Gavriel, photos by. 2002. 32p. (ps-3). 15.95 (978-0-87358-798-3(7) , Rising Moon Bks. for Young Readers) Northland Publishing.

Hess, Paul, illus. Safari Animals. 1998. (Animal Worlds Ser.). (J). (ps). (978-1-84089-007-5(X) , 868232, Zero to Ten, Limited) Evans Publishing Group.

Hirschmann, Kris. Sponges. 2005. (Creatures of the Sea Ser.). (Illus.). 48p. (J). (gr. 4-8). 26.20 (978-0-7377-3013-5(7) , Greenhaven Pr., Inc.) Thomson Gale.

Hogenkamp, Susan. They Crawl! Learning the CR Sound. 2002. (PowerPhonics Ser.). (Illus.). 24p. (J). (gr. 1). lib. bdg. 18.50 (978-0-8239-5947-1(3) , PowerKids Pr.) Rosen Publishing Group, Inc., The.

Hooper, Meredith. Antarctic Journal: Hidden Worlds of Antarctica's Animals. DeLeiris, Lucia, illus. 2001. 40p. (J). (gr. 2-5). 16.95 (978-0-7922-7188-8(2) , National Geographic Children's Bks.) National Geographic Society.

Hughes, Monica. Pill Bugs. 2003. (Raintree Sprouts Ser.). (Illus.). 24p. (J). lib. bdg. 18.56 (978-1-4109-0624-3(8)) Raintree.

—Pill Bugs. 2003. (ps-2). lib. bdg. 13.55 (978-0-613-78259-3(3)) Tandem Library Bks.

J. G. Ferguson Publishing Company Staff. Discovering Careers for Your Future/Animals. 2000. (Discovering Careers for Your Future Ser.). (Illus.). 94p. (J). (gr. 4-8). lib. bdg. 21.95 (978-0-89434-360-5(2) , F542, Ferguson Publishing Co.) Facts On File, Inc.

Jolivet, Joellc. Zoo-Ology. Jolivet, Joelle, illus. rev. ed. 2003. (Illus.). 40p. (J). (ps-3). 17.95 (978-0-7613-1894-1(1)) Roaring Brook Pr.

Kalman, Bobbie. How Do Animals Move? 2000. (gr. 3-6). lib. bdg. 14.10 (978-0-613-27883-6(6)) Tandem Library Bks.

—Qué Es el Reino Animal? 2005. (Ciencia de los Seres Vivos Ser.). (SPA., Illus.). 32p. (J). (978-0-7787-8757-0(5)) Crabtree Publishing Co.

—Le Regne des Animaux. 2005. (FRE., Illus.). 32p. (J). pap. (978-2-89579-025-9(6)) Crabtree Publishing Co.

Kalman, Bobbie & Walker, Niki. How Do Animals Move? 2000. (Science of Living Things Ser.). (Illus.). 32p. (J). (gr. 2-3). (978-0-86505-981-8(0)); pap. (978-0-86505-958-0(6)) Crabtree Publishing Co.

Kavanagh, James. African Wildlife Nature Activity Book. 2004. (Pocket Naturalist Ser.). (Illus.). 32p. pap. 6.95 (978-1-58355-259-9(6)) Waterford Pr., Ltd.

—Arctic Wildlife Nature. 2004. (Pocket Naturalist Ser.). (Illus.). 32p. pap. 6.95 (978-1-58355-261-2(8)) Waterford Pr., Ltd.

Kessel, Quinta Cattell. Mama Is A Mammal. Kessel, Margaret May, illus. 2005. 80p. (J). 16.95 (978-0-9725027-3-3(4)) Vernissage Pr., LLC.

Knight, Bertram T. Working at a Zoo. 1998. (Working Here Ser.). (Illus.). 32p. (J). (gr. 2-4). 23.50 (978-0-516-20751-3(2) , Children's Pr.) Scholastic Library Publishing.

Knight, Tim O. Amazing Nature, 8 bks., Set. 2003. (Illus.). (J). (gr. 2-4). lib. bdg. 193.76 (978-1-4034-0724-5(X)) Heinemann Library.

Knotts, Bob. Florida Plants & Animals. 2002. (State Studies). (Illus.). 48p. (J). pap. 8.50 (978-1-4034-0566-1(2)); lib. bdg. (978-1-4034-0350-6(3)) Heinemann Library.

Kovacs. Noises in the Night. 1999. (Illus.). (J). pap. (978-0-7398-2472-6(4)) Steck-Vaughn.

Kravetz, Jonathan. Locusts. 2006. (Gross Bugs Ser.). (Illus.). 24p. (J). lib. bdg. (978-1-4042-3042-2(4) , PowerKids Pr.) Rosen Publishing Group, Inc., The.

Kroll, Virginia L. & Jones, Dawn L. Kingston's Flowering Forest. Maydak, Michael S., illus. 2001. (J). (978-0-9712840-5-0(9)) Boyds Collection Ltd., The.

Leedy, Loreen & Street, Pat. There's a Frog in My Throat: 440 Animal Sayings a Little Bird Told Me. Leedy, Loreen, illus. 2003. (Ala Notable Book Ser.). (Illus.). 48p. (J). (gr. k-3). reprint ed. pap. 6.95 (978-0-8234-1819-0(7)) Holiday Hse., Inc.

El Libro de los Acertijos Zoologicos. (Coleccion Acertijos). (SPA.). (YA). (gr. 5-8). pap. (978-950-724-261-8(9) , LMA8236) Lumen ARG. *Dist:* Lectorum Pubns., Inc.

Longnecker, Theresa. Who Grows Up in the Snow? A Book about Snow Animals & Their Offspring. Carpenter, Melissa, illus. 2004. (Who Grows Up Here? Ser.). 24p. (C). (gr. k-4). 21.26 (978-1-4048-0028-1(X)) Picture Window Bks.

Macken, JoAnn Early. African Animals. Hess, Paul, illus. 2002. (Animal Worlds Ser.). 24p. (J). (ps up). lib. bdg. 20.67 (978-0-8368-3038-5(5)) Stevens, Gareth Inc.

—Polar Animals. Hess, Paul, illus. 2002. (Animal Worlds Ser.). 24p. (J). (ps up). lib. bdg. 20.67 (978-0-8368-3040-8(7)) Stevens, Gareth Inc.

Mamiferos Science, 6 vols.Tr. of Mammals Science. (SPA.). (gr. k-2). 28.95 (978-0-7368-3032-4(4) , Yellow Umbrella Bks.) Capstone Pr., Inc.

Mammals Science, 6 vols. (gr. k-2). 28.95 (978-0-7368-2996-0(2) , Yellow Umbrella Bks.) Capstone Pr., Inc.

Mara, Wil. Dian Fossey: Among the Gorillas. 2004. (Great Life Stories Ser.). (Illus.). 127p. (J). 30.50 (978-0-531-12059-0(7) , Watts, Franklin) Scholastic Library Publishing.

Martin, Patricia. Experiencing the Zoo. 2003. (J). per. 13.99 (978-1-4010-7436-4(7)) Xlibris Corp.

Mattern, Joanne. Animal Geography. 2001. (Cover-to-Cover Bks.). (Illus.). 56p. (J). pap. (978-0-7891-5355-5(6)); pap. (978-0-7891-5378-4(5)); (gr. 4-7). lib. bdg. 17.95 (978-0-7807-9733-8(7)); (gr. 4-7). lib. bdg. 17.95 (978-0-7807-9741-3(8)); (gr. 4-7). lib. bdg. 17.95 (978-0-7807-9916-5(X)) Perfection Learning Corp.

—Animal Geography: Africa. 2000. 56p. (YA). (gr. 5-12). pap. 8.95 (978-0-7891-5331-9(9)); (Illus.). (J). (gr. 4-7). lib. bdg. 17.95 (978-0-7807-9713-0(2)) Perfection Learning Corp.

—Crazy Creatures of Australia & New Zealand. 2001. (Cover-to-Cover Bks.). (Illus.). 56p. (J). (gr. 1-4). lib. bdg. 16.95 (978-0-7569-0106-6(5)) Perfection Learning Corp.

—Crazy Creatures of the World. 2001. (Cover-to-Cover Bks.). (Illus.). (J). 55p. pap. (978-0-7891-5446-0(3)); 56p. (gr. 1-4). lib. bdg. 16.95 (978-0-7569-0105-9(7)) Perfection Learning Corp.

Miles, Elizabeth. Noses. (Animal Parts Ser.). (Illus.). 32p. (J). (gr. k-2). 2003. pap. 6.95 (978-1-4034-0428-2(3)); 2002. lib. bdg. 21.36 (978-1-4034-0019-2(9)) Heinemann Library.

—Noses. 2003. (gr. k-3). lib. bdg. 14.75 (978-0-613-45808-5(7)) Tandem Library Bks.

Miller, Debbie. Arctic Lights, Arctic Nights. Van Zyle, Jon, illus. 2007. 32p. (J). pap. 7.95 (978-0-8027-9636-3(2)) Walker & Co.

Miller, Debbie S. Arctic Lights, Arctic Nights. Van Zyle, Jon, illus. 2003. 32p. (J). (gr. 1-4). 16.95 (978-0-8027-8856-6(4)) Walker & Co.

—River of Life. Van Zyle, Jon, illus. 2000. 32p. (J). (gr. k-3). tchr. ed. 16.00 (978-0-395-96790-4(2) , Clarion Bks.) Houghton Mifflin Co. Trade & Reference Div.

Miller, Janet. Cut, Color & Paste: God's Creatures. 2004. (Illus.). 96p. (J). (ps-2). 11.95 (978-1-885358-81-3(4)) Rainbow Pubs. & Legacy Pr.

Montgomery, Rutherford G. The Living Wilderness. Grant, Campbell, illus. 2004. (Classic Ser.). 202p. (gr. 4-7). pap. 18.95 (978-0-87004-418-2(4)) Caxton Pr.

Morgan, Sally. Insect Eaters. 2004. (J). lib. bdg. 27.10 (978-1-59389-174-9(1)) Chrysalis Education.

—Sponges & Other Minor Phyla. 2004. (Illus.). 64p. (J). 32.79 (978-1-4109-1053-0(9)); pap. 9.50 (978-1-4109-1349-4(X)) Harcourt Schl. Pubs.

Moss, Miriam. This Is the Tree. Kennaway, Adrienne, illus. 2005. 32p. (J). pap. 7.95 (978-1-929132-77-5(8)) Kane/Miller Bk. Pubs., Inc.

Myers, Jack. The Puzzle of the Platypus: And Other Explorations of Science in Action. Rice, John, illus. 2008. (J). ***978-1-59078-556-0(8)*** Boyds Mills Pr.

Nichols, Catherine. An Arctic Year. 2002. (We Can Read about Nature Ser.). (Illus.). 32p. (J). 21.36 (978-0-7614-1430-8(4) , Benchmark Bks.) Cavendish, Marshall Corp.

NSRC. Science & Technology for Children BOOKS: Plant Growth & Development. 2004. (Illus.). 64p. (J). (978-1-933008-39-4(3)) National Science Resources Ctr.

Oceanor Staff. Zoologia - Atlas Visual. 1999. (SPA.). (gr. 3-6). lib. bdg. 20.00 (978-0-613-80877-4(0)) Tandem Library Bks.

Of the World, 9 vols., Set. Incl. Rodents of the World. Alderton, David. Tanner, Bruce, photos by. 192p. 1996. 32.95 (978-0-8160-3229-7(7)); Seals & Sea Lions of the World. Bonner, Nigel. 224p. (J). 1994. 32.95 (978-0-8160-2955-6(5)); Spiders of the World. Preston-Mafham, Rod & Preston-Mafham, Ken. 191p. (J). 1984. 32.95 (978-0-87196-996-5(3)); Wild Bears of the World. Ward, Paul & Kynaston, Suzanne. 192p. 1995. 32.95 (978-0-8160-3245-7(9)); (Illus.). 1998. 210.90 o.p. (978-0-8160-3837-4(6)) Facts On File, Inc.

Oliver, Narelle. Baby Bilby, Where Do You Sleep? Oliver, Narelle, illus. 2002. (Illus.). 32p. (J). (978-0-7344-0230-1(9) , Lothian Bks.) Hachette Livre Australia.

Orenstein, Ronald. New Animal Discoveries. 2000. (Illus.). 64p. (J). (gr. 3-7). 16.95 (978-1-55263-152-2(4)) Key Porter Bks. CAN. *Dist:* Firefly Bks., Ltd.

—New Animal Discoveries. 2001. (Worlds Beyond Ser.). (Illus.). 64p. (gr. 4-8). lib. bdg. 24.90 (978-0-7613-2274-0(4) , Millbrook Pr.) Lerner Publishing Group.

Orr, Tamra. Camouflage & Mimicry in the Wild. 2003. (Extreme Animals Ser.). (J). pap. (978-1-58417-257-4(6)) Lake Street Pubs.

Parker, Steve. Microlife That Rots Things. 2005. (J). (978-1-4109-1848-2(3)); (Illus.). 32p. pap. 7.85 (978-1-4109-1853-6(X)) Steck-Vaughn.

Pascoe, Elaine, ed. Dentro de Alaska Salvaje. 2005. (Jeff Corwin Experience Ser.). (Illus.). 48p. (J). (ps-7). lib. bdg. 24.95 (978-1-4103-0669-2(0) , Blackbirch Pr., Inc.) Thomson Gale.

—Dentro de Arizona Salvaje. 2005. (Jeff Corwin Experience Ser.). (Illus.). 48p. (J). (ps-7). lib. bdg. 24.95 (978-1-4103-0670-8(4) , Blackbirch Pr., Inc.) Thomson Gale.

—Dentro de Australia Salvaje. 2005. (Jeff Corwin Experience Ser.). (Illus.). 48p. (J). (ps-7). lib. bdg. 24.95 (978-1-4103-0677-7(1) , Blackbirch Pr., Inc.) Thomson Gale.

—Dentro de Borneo Salvaje. 2005. (Jeff Corwin Experience Ser.). (Illus.). 48p. (J). (ps-7). lib. bdg. 24.95 (978-1-4103-0679-1(8) , Blackbirch Pr., Inc.) Thomson Gale.

—Dentro de Brasil Salvaje. 2005. (Jeff Corwin Experience Ser.). (Illus.). 48p. (J). (ps-7). lib. bdg. 24.95 (978-1-4103-0680-7(1) , Blackbirch Pr., Inc.) Thomson Gale.

—Dentro de Florida Salvaje. 2005. (Jeff Corwin Experience Ser.). (Illus.). 48p. (J). (ps-7). lib. bdg. 24.95 (978-1-4103-0672-2(0) , Blackbirch Pr., Inc.) Thomson Gale.

—Dentro de Galapagos Salvaje. 2005. (Jeff Corwin Experience Ser.). (Illus.). 48p. (J). (ps-7). lib. bdg. 24.95 (978-1-4103-0681-4(X) , Blackbirch Pr., Inc.) Thomson Gale.

—Dentro de la Amazonia Salvaje. 2005. (Jeff Corwin Experience Ser.). (Illus.). 48p. (J). (ps-7). lib. bdg. 24.95 (978-1-4103-0678-4(X) , Blackbirch Pr., Inc.) Thomson Gale.

—Dentro de la India Salvaje. 2005. (Jeff Corwin Experience Ser.). (Illus.). 48p. (J). (ps-7). lib. bdg. 24.95 (978-1-4103-0682-1(8) , Blackbirch Pr., Inc.) Thomson Gale.

—Dentro de Luisiana Salvaje. 2005. (Jeff Corwin Experience Ser.). (Illus.). 48p. (J). (ps-7). lib. bdg. 24.95 (978-1-4103-0673-9(9) , Blackbirch Pr., Inc.) Thomson Gale.

—Dentro de Nepal Salvaje. 2005. (Jeff Corwin Experience Ser.). (Illus.). 48p. (J). (ps-7). lib. bdg. 24.95 (978-1-4103-0684-5(4) , Blackbirch Pr., Inc.) Thomson Gale.

—Dentro de Panama Salvaje. 2005. (Jeff Corwin Experience Ser.). (Illus.). 48p. (J). (ps-7). lib. bdg. 24.95 (978-1-4103-0685-2(2) , Blackbirch Pr., Inc.) Thomson Gale.

—Dentro de Tailandia Salvaje. 2005. (Jeff Corwin Experience Ser.). (Illus.). 48p. (J). (gr. 3-7). lib. bdg. 24.95 (978-1-4103-0687-6(9) , Blackbirch Pr., Inc.) Thomson Gale.

—Dentro de Zanzibar Salvaje. 2005. (Jeff Corwin Experience Ser.). (Illus.). 48p. (J). (ps-7). lib. bdg. 24.95 (978-1-4103-0688-3(7) , Blackbirch Pr., Inc.) Thomson Gale.

—Encuentros Extremos. 2005. (Jeff Corwin Experience Ser.). (Illus.). 48p. (J). (ps-7). lib. bdg. 24.95 (978-1-4103-0674-6(7) , Blackbirch Pr., Inc.) Thomson Gale.

Pascoe, Elaine & Corwin, Jeff. Into Wild Borneo. 2003. (Jeff Corwin Experience Ser.). (Illus.). 48p. (J). 11.20 (978-1-4103-0170-3(2) , Blackbirch Pr., Inc.) Thomson Gale.

—Into Wild California. 2003. (Animal Planet Ser.). (Illus.). 48p. (J). 11.20 (978-1-4103-0178-9(8) , Blackbirch Pr., Inc.) Thomson Gale.

Pfeffer, Wendy. Antarctic Icy Waters. 2002. (Living on the Edge Ser.). (Illus.). 39p. (J). 25.64 (978-0-7614-1438-4(X) , Benchmark Bks.) Cavendish, Marshall Corp.

—Arctic Frozen Reaches. 2002. (Living on the Edge Ser.). (Illus.). 36p. (J). 25.64 (978-0-7614-1437-7(1) , Benchmark Bks.) Cavendish, Marshall Corp.

Pierson, Clara Dillingham. Among the Forest People (Yesterday's Classics) 2005. (Illus.). 148p. (J). per. 8.95 (978-1-59915-018-5(2)) Yesterday's Classics.

—Among the Pond People (Yesterday's Classics) 2005. (Illus.). 160p. (J). per. 8.95 (978-1-59915-021-5(2)) Yesterday's Classics.

Reeves, Diane Lindsey. Career Ideas for Kids Who Like Animals & Nature. 2nd rev. ed. (Career Ideas for Kids Ser.). 208p. (J). (gr. 4-9). pap. 16.95 ***978-0-8160-6540-0(3)*** , Checkmark Bks.); 2007. 32.95 ***978-0-8160-6539-4(X)*** , Ferguson Publishing Co.) Facts On File, Inc.

Ring, Susan. Animal Watch. 2003. (On the Job Ser.). (Illus.). 32p. (gr. 3-5). 23.00 (978-0-7910-7409-1(9) , Chelsea Hse.) Facts On File, Inc.

Rushworth, Gary. What Makes an Animal an Animal. 2006. (Navigators Ser.). (J). pap. 42.00 ***978-1-4108-6230-3(5)*** Benchmark Education Co.

Ryan, Marla Felkins. Into Wild Moracco. 2004. (Jeff Corwin Experience Ser.). (Illus.). 48p. (J). 11.20 (978-1-4103-0236-6(9)); (gr. 4-7). 24.95 (978-1-4103-0235-9(0)) Thomson Gale. (Blackbirch Pr., Inc.).

Ryan, Marla Felkins & Corwin, Jeff. Into Wild India 2. 2004. (Jeff Corwin Experience Ser.). (Illus.). 48p. (J). 11.20 (978-1-4103-0234-2(2)); (gr. 4-7). 24.95 (978-1-4103-0233-5(4)) Thomson Gale. (Blackbirch Pr., Inc.).

—Into Wild Tasmania. 2004. (Jeff Corwin Experience Ser.). (Illus.). 48p. (J). 11.20 (978-1-4103-0248-9(2)); (gr. 4-7). 24.95 (978-1-4103-0247-2(4)) Thomson Gale. (Blackbirch Pr., Inc.).

Ryan, Pam Muñoz. A Pinky Is a Baby Mouse: And Other Baby Animal Names. 1999. (978-0-606-16665-2(3)) Tandem Library Bks.

Santella, Andrew. Illinois Plants & Animals. 2002. (Heinemann State Studies). (Illus.). 48p. (J). (gr. 3-5). lib. bdg. 27.07 (978-1-4034-0011-6(3)) Heinemann Library.

Savage, Stephen. What's the Difference?, 6 bks., Set. Incl. Amphibians. lib. bdg. 25.69 (978-0-7398-1359-1(5)); Birds. lib. bdg. 25.69 (978-0-7398-1356-0(0)); Fish. lib. bdg. 25.69 (978-0-7398-1357-7(9)); Insects. lib. bdg. 25.69 (978-0-7398-1355-3(2)); Mammals. lib. bdg. 25.69 (978-0-7398-1354-6(4)); Reptiles. lib. bdg. 25.69 (978-0-7398-1358-4(7)); 32p. (J). (gr. 2-4). (Illus.). 1999. Set lib. bdg. 154.14 (978-0-7398-1360-7(9)) Raintree.

Sayre, April Pulley. If You Should Hear a Honey Guide. 2000. (J). (978-0-606-19425-9(8)) Tandem Library Bks.

Schaefer, Lola M. Tiny-Spiny Animals 123. 2003. (Heinemann Read & Learn Ser.). (Illus.). 24p. (J). pap. 5.25 (978-1-4034-3514-9(6)); lib. bdg. 18.50 (978-1-4034-3322-0(4)) Heinemann Library.

Schaefer, Lola M. & Schaefer, Wyatt S. Jane Goodall. 2004. (First Biographies Ser.). 24p. (J). lib. bdg. 15.93 (978-0-7368-2083-7(3) , Pebble Bks.) Capstone Pr., Inc.

Schonberg, Marcia. Ohio Plants & Animals. 2003. (Heinemann State Studies). (Illus.). 48p. (J). pap. 8.50 (978-1-4034-2691-8(0)); lib. bdg. 27.07 (978-1-4034-0669-9(3)) Heinemann Library.

Schwartz, David M. If You Hopped Like a Frog. Warhola, James, illus. 1999. (If You Ser.). 32p. (J). (gr. k-4). pap. 16.95 (978-0-590-09857-1(8)) Scholastic, Inc.

Silverstein, Alvin & Silverstein, Virginia B. Nature's Champions: The Biggest, the Fastest, the Best. Zallinger, Jean, tr. Zallinger, Jean, illus. 2003. 64p. (J). (gr. 5-8). pap. 5.95 (978-0-486-42888-8(5)) Dover Pubns., Inc.

Smith, Karla. Virginia Plants & Animals. 2003. (Heinemann State Studies). (Illus.). 48p. (J). pap. 8.50 (978-1-4034-0582-1(4)); (gr. 3-5). lib. bdg. (978-1-4034-0360-5(0)) Heinemann Library.

—Virginia Plants & Animals. 2003. (gr. 3-6). lib. bdg. 17.05 (978-0-613-60996-8(4)) Tandem Library Bks.

Snakes & Lizards Science, 6 vols. (gr. k-2). 28.95 (978-0-7368-3017-1(0) , Yellow Umbrella Bks.) Capstone Pr., Inc.

Somervill, Barbara A. Animal Survivors of the Arctic. 2004. (Watts Library). (Illus.). 64p. (J). 25.50 (978-0-531-12204-4(2) , Watts, Franklin) Scholastic Library Publishing.

Spilsbury, Louise & Spilsbury, Richard. Super-Flea & Other Animal Champions: Structure of Living Things. 2005. (Illus.). 32p. (J). (978-1-4109-1968-7(4)); lib. bdg. (978-1-4109-1937-3(4)) Steck-Vaughn.

Squire, Ann O. African Animals. 2001. (True Animal Bks.). (Illus.). 48p. (J). (gr. 3-5). 25.00 (978-0-516-22187-8(6) , Children's Pr.) Scholastic Library Publishing.

Steck-Vaughn Staff. Jane Goodall: A Good & True Heart. 2002. pap. (978-0-7398-6152-3(2)) Steck-Vaughn.

—Noises in the Night: Teacher's Resource Binder. 1999. (J). pap., tchr. ed. (978-0-7398-2475-7(9)) Steck-Vaughn.

Stephens, Edna Cucksey & Farstvedt, Diane Norberg. Looking at Animals with Mr. Etch a Sketch. George, Tim, illus. 2002. 32p. (J). pap. 9.95 (978-0-9712692-1-7(1)) EDCO Publishing, Inc.

Stewart, Mark. New Jersey Plants & Animals. 2003. (State Studies). (Illus.). 48p. (J). pap. 8.50 (978-1-4034-2685-7(6)); lib. bdg. 27.07 (978-1-4034-0676-7(6)) Heinemann Library.

Stone, Lynn M. Animal Cycle. 2007. (Illus.). 24p. (J). (978-1-60044-175-2(0)) Rourke Publishing, LLC.

—Wildlife of China. 2000. (China Ser.). (Illus.). 24p. (J). (gr. 1-4). lib. bdg. 19.27 (978-1-55916-321-7(6)) Rourke Publishing, LLC.

Stonehouse, Bernard. Nature Unfolds the Poles. 2001. (Nature Unfolds Ser.). (Illus.). 40p. (J). (gr. 4). pap. (978-0-7787-0321-1(5)) Crabtree Publishing Co.

—Poles. 2001. (gr. 5-8). lib. bdg. 18.75 (978-0-613-89192-9(9)) Tandem Library Bks.

Tagliaferro, Linda. Galapagos Islands: Nature's Delicate Balance at Risk. 2005. (Discovery! Ser.). (Illus.). 120p. (gr. 5-12). lib. bdg. 27.93 (978-0-8225-0648-5(3)) Lerner Publishing Group.

Thompson, Valerie & Cohen, Judith Love. You Can Be a Woman Zoologist. Katz, David Arthur, illus. 2001. 40p. (J). 13.95 (978-1-880599-56-3(2)); pap. 7.00 (978-1-880599-55-6(4)) Cascade Pass, Inc.

Uncover a T. Rex. 2004. (J). bds. 22.95 (978-1-932855-10-4(6)) becker&mayer! books.

Vaughn, Marcia. I Howl, I Growl: Southwest Animal Antics. Powell, Polly, illus. 2003. 26p. (J). (ps-k). bds. 6.95 (978-0-87358-835-5(5) , Rising Moon Bks. for Young Readers) Northland Publishing.

Vogel, Julia. Polar Animals. McGee, John F., illus. 2004. (Our Wild World Ser.). 192p. (J). (gr. 2-5). ring bd. 16.95 (978-1-55971-832-5(3) , NorthWord Bks. for Young Readers) T&N Children's Publishing.

Wadsworth, Pamela. Golwg Gyntaf Ar Bethau Byw. 2005. (WEL., Illus.). 24p. pap. (978-1-85596-250-7(0)) Dref Wen.

What Can Jump. 2002. (Illus.). (J). pap. 3.74 (978-0-7398-5835-6(1)) Steck-Vaughn.

Whitehouse, Patricia. Qué Puede Construir? 2003. (SPA., Illus.). 24p. pap. 5.25 (978-1-4034-4397-7(1)) Heinemann Library.

—Qué Puede Correr? 2003. (SPA., Illus.). 24p. pap. 5.25 (978-1-4034-4394-6(7)) Heinemann Library.

—Qué Puede Enterrarse? 2003. (SPA., Illus.). 24p. pap. 5.25 (978-1-4034-4396-0(3)) Heinemann Library.

—Qué Puede Nadar? 2003. (SPA., Illus.). 24p. pap. 5.25 (978-1-4034-4395-3(5)) Heinemann Library.

—Qué Puede Saltar? 2003. (SPA., Illus.). 24p. pap. 5.25 (978-1-4034-4393-9(9)) Heinemann Library.

WXYZ

Whittaker, Nicola. Creature Features, 4 bks. Incl. Feet. lib. bdg. 23.33 (978-0-8368-3163-4(2)); Hair. lib. bdg. 23.33 (978-0-8368-3164-1(0)); Noses. lib. bdg. 23.33 (978-0-8368-3165-8(9)); Tails. lib. bdg. 23.33 (978-0-8368-3166-5(7)); 32p. (J). (ps up). 2002. (Illus.). 2002. Set lib. bdg. 93.32 (978-0-8368-3162-7(4)) Stevens, Gareth Inc.

Wildlife Education, Ltd. Staff, contrib. by. Amazing Animals, Set. 2002. (All about Animals Ser.). (Illus.). (J). (gr. k-6). 16.95 incl. VHS (978-1-888153-89-7(X)) Wildlife Education, Ltd.

Windsor, Jo. Fangs: Early Level Satellite Individual Title Six-Packs. (Sails Literacy Ser.). 16p. (gr. 1-2). 27.00 (978-0-7578-2928-4(7)) Rigby Education.

Wolfe, Art, photos by. Northwest Animal Babies. 2006. (Illus.). 32p. (J). pap. 10.95 (978-1-57061-462-0(8)) Sasquatch Bks.

Wood, J. G. Illustrated Natural History: Arranged Fo. 2006. pap. 27.95 (***978-1-4286-0489-6(8)***) Kessinger Publishing, LLC.

Wood, Richard & Barton-Wood, Sara. Dian Fossey. (Groundbreakers Ser.). 48p. pap. 8.50 (978-1-4034-4061-7(1)); 2001. (Illus.). (J). (gr. 5-7). lib. bdg. 25.64 (978-1-58810-049-8(9)) Heinemann Library.

Woodward, John. What Lives in the Garden? 2002. (What Lives...? Ser.). (Illus.). 48p. (J). (gr. 3 up). pap. 7.95 (978-0-7641-2108-1(1)) Barron's Educational Series, Inc.

Woodward, John & Corwin, Jeff. Into Wild Tanzania. 2004. (Jeff Corwin Experience Ser.). (Illus.). 48p. (J). (gr. 4-7). 24.95 (978-1-4103-0249-6(0)); pap. 11.20 (978-1-4103-0250-2(4)) Thomson Gale. (Blackbirch Pr., Inc.).

World Book, Inc. Staff. World Book's Animals of the World. 2002. (J). 238.00 (978-0-7166-1248-3(8)) World Bk., Inc.

Yolen, Jane. Welcome to the Icehouse. Regan, Laura, illus. 1998. 1p. (J). (ps-3). 16.99 (978-0-399-23011-0(4) , Putnam Juvenile) Penguin Group (USA) Inc.

El Zoologico, 2 Packs. (SPA.). (ps-1). (Chiquilibros Ser.). 12.00 (978-0-7635-8556-3(4)); (Coleccion Pm Ser.: Vol. 1). 16p. 26.00 (978-0-7578-0669-8(4)) Rigby Education.

El zoologico de Caricias. 2000. (McGraw-Hill Ciencias Ser.). (ENG & SPA.). (gr. k up). (978-0-02-279691-4(6)) Macmillan/McGraw-Hill Schl. Div.

El zoologico de Papel 11: Leveled Books. 2001. (McGraw-Hill. Lectura Ser.). (ENG & SPA.). (gr. 5 up). (978-0-02-188259-5(2)) Macmillan/McGraw-Hill Schl. Div.

ZOOLOGY—ANATOMY

see Anatomy, Comparative

ZOOLOGY, ECONOMIC

see also Domestic Animals; Fur-Bearing Animals; Insects, Injurious and Beneficial

Dahl, Michael. Do Dogs Make Dessert? A Book about How Animals Help Humans. Yesh, Jeff, illus. 2004. (Animals All Around Ser.). 24p. (J). (gr. k-2). 22.60 (978-1-4048-0289-6(4)) Picture Window Bks.

Fredericks, Anthony D. Fearsome Fangs. 2002. (Watts Library Ser.). (Illus.). 64p. (J). (gr. 5-7). pap. 25.50 (978-0-531-11966-2(1) , Watts, Franklin) Scholastic Library Publishing.

—Fearsome Fangs. 2002. (gr. 3-6). lib. bdg. 17.60 (978-0-613-59478-3(9)) Tandem Library Bks.

Maynard, Thane. Working with Wildlife: A Guide to Careers in the Animal World. 2000. (J). (978-0-606-19406-8(1)) Tandem Library Bks.

ZOOLOGY—GEOGRAPHICAL DISTRIBUTION

see Geographical Distribution of Animals and Plants

ZOOLOGY OF THE BIBLE

see Bible—Natural History

ZOOS

Aliki. My Visit to the Zoo. Aliki, illus. 1999. (Trophy Picture Bk.). (Illus.). 40p. (J). (ps up). pap. 6.99 (978-0-06-446217-4(X) , Harper Trophy) HarperCollins Pubs.

Allin, Michael. Zarafa: A Giraffe's True Story, from Deep in Africa to the Heart of Paris. 1998. (Illus.). 224p. 22.00 (978-0-8027-1339-1(4)) Walker & Co.

Arnold, Caroline. Mealtime for Zoo Animals. 1999. (Zoo Animals Ser.). (Illus.). 32p. (J). (ps-2). 9.95 (978-1-57505-389-9(6) , Carolrhoda Bks.) Lerner Publishing Group.

Avery, Sherrie. Miami Metrozoo. 2003. (Great Zoos of the United States Ser.). (Illus.). 24p. (J). lib. bdg. 18.75 (978-0-8239-6316-4(0) , PowerKids Pr.) Rosen Publishing Group, Inc., The.

Battistoni, Ilse. At the Zoo: Learning the Z Sound. (Power-Phonics Ser.). (Illus.). (J). 2002. 24p. (gr. 1). lib. bdg. 18.50 (978-0-8239-5926-6(0)); 2001. 23p. pap. 26.40 (978-0-8239-8271-4(8)) Rosen Publishing Group, Inc., The. (PowerKids Pr.).

Beylon, Cathy. At the Zoo. 2002. (Dover Coloring Bks.). (Illus.). 32p. (J). (ps-2). pap. 2.95 (978-0-486-42372-2(7)) Dover Pubns., Inc.

Bittinger, Gayle. At the Zoo. Barr, Marilynn G., illus. 1999. (Rhyme & Reason Workbook Ser.). 32p. (J). (ps-k). pap. 3.95 (978-1-57029-256-9(6) , WPH 01108, Totline Pubns.) Schaffer, Frank Pubns.

Brighter Vision Publishing Staff. About the Zoo. (My Discovery Bks.). (ps). 2000. (Illus.). 20p. (J). pap. 2.95 (978-1-55254-204-0(1)); 1998. 32p. (J). pap. 3.99 (978-1-55254-003-9(0)); 1998. (YA). pap. 7.95 (978-1-55254-035-0(9)) Brighter Vision Pubns.

—Zoo. 2000. (Learning Adventures Grade 1 Ser.). (Illus.). (J). (gr. 1-2). pap. 2.25 (978-1-55254-063-3(4)) Brighter Vision Pubns.

Canizares, Susan & Weber, Arianne. At the Zoo. 2000. (Scholastic Placebook Ser.). (Illus.). (J). pap. (978-0-439-15377-5(8)) Scholastic, Inc.

Color All About: The Zoo: A Coloring Book about Going to the Zoo. 2004. (Illus.). (J). (978-0-9763307-2-1(5)) Food Marketing Consultants, Inc.

Costain, Meredith. Zookeepers. 2000. (gr. k-3). lib. bdg. 11.55 (978-0-613-30901-1(4)) Tandem Library Bks.

Deady, Kathleen W. Out & About at the Zoo. McMullen, Anne, illus. 2004. (Field Trips Ser.). 24p. (C). (gr. k-3). 23.93 (978-1-4048-0041-0(7)) Picture Window Bks.

Deedrick, Tami. Zoo Keepers. l.t. ed. 1998. (Community Helpers Ser.). (Illus.). 24p. (J). (gr. k-3). lib. bdg. 14.00 Scholastic Library Publishing.

DK Publishing Staff. Zoo Adventure. 2007. 1p. (J). 19.99 (978-0-7566-2542-9(4)) Dorling Kindersley Publishing, Inc.

Dorling Kindersley Publishing Staff. At the Zoo. 2003. (Little Windows Ser.). (Illus.). 12p. (J). bds. 6.99 (978-0-7894-9048-3(X)) Dorling Kindersley Publishing, Inc.

—Zoo Animals. 2004. (Baby Genius Ser.). (Illus.). 16p. (J). bds. 6.99 (978-0-7566-0271-0(8)) Dorling Kindersley Publishing, Inc.

Estigarribia, Diana. Smithsonian National Zoological Park. 2003. (Great Zoos of the United States Ser.). (Illus.). 24p. (J). lib. bdg. 18.75 (978-0-8239-6317-1(9)) Rosen Publishing Group, Inc., The.

Foley, Cate. Let's Go to the Zoo. 2001. (Weekend Fun Ser.). (Illus.). 24p. (J). (ps-2). 17.00 (978-0-516-23194-5(4)); pap. 4.95 (978-0-516-29584-8(5)) Scholastic Library Publishing. (Children's Pr.).

—Let's Go to the Zoo. 2001. (gr. k-3). lib. bdg. 12.95 (978-0-613-58989-5(0)) Tandem Library Bks.

Friedman, Sharon. Grin & Bear It: Zoo Jokes to Make You Roar. Gable, Brian, illus. 2005. (Make Me Laugh! Ser.). 32p. (J). (gr. k-3). lib. bdg. 19.93 (978-1-57505-660-9(7)) Lerner Publishing Group.

Galvin, Laura Gates. Tamarin's Mealtime. Cohen, Jessie, photos by. 2000. (Let's Go to the Zoo! Ser.). (Illus.). 16p. (J). (ps-k). bds. 5.95 (978-1-56899-858-9(9)) Soundprints.

Gangelhoff, Jeanne M. & Belk, Bradford. A Walk Through the Minnesota Zoo. Gangelhoff, Gene, illus. 32p. (J). 9.95 (978-0-9635006-1-8(9)) GJ & B Publishing.

Gorman, Jacqueline Laks. The Zoo. 2005. (I Like to Visit Ser.). (Illus.). 24p. (J). pap. (978-0-8368-4463-4(7)); (YA). lib. bdg. 19.33 (978-0-8368-4456-6(4)) Stevens, Gareth Inc.

—The Zoo: El Zoologico. 2005. (ENG & SPA., Illus.). 24p. (J). pap. (978-0-8368-4607-2(9)) Stevens, Gareth Inc.

—The Zoo/El Zoologico. Acosta, Tatiana & Gutiérrez, Guillermo, trs. from ENG. 2005. (I Like to Visit/Me Gusta Visitar Ser.). (ENG & SPA., Illus.). 24p. (J). lib. bdg. 19.33 (978-0-8368-4600-3(1)) Stevens, Gareth Inc.

Hanna, Jack. Jungle Jack Hanna's What Zookeepers Do. Prebeg, Rick A., illus. 1998. (Hello Reader! Ser.). 48p. (J). (gr. 2-4). pap. 3.99 (978-0-590-67324-2(6)) Scholastic, Inc.

—Jungle Jack Hanna's What Zookeepers Do. 1998. (Hello Reader! Ser.). (J). 10.79 (978-0-606-13548-1(0)) Tandem Library Bks.

Harcourt School Publishers Staff. Let's Visit the Zoo - Grade 1, 6 Packs. 3rd ed. 2002. (Trophies English Language Learners Ser.). 20.10 (978-0-15-327629-3(0)) Harcourt Schl. Pubs.

—Zoo-ology. 3rd ed. 2002. (Trophies English Language Learners Ser.). (Illus.). pap. 5.10 (978-0-15-327779-5(3)) Harcourt Schl. Pubs.

Hoena, B. A. A Visit to the Zoo. 2004. (Pebble Plus, Let's Visit Ser.). (Illus.). 24p. (J). 13.95 (978-0-7368-2395-1(6) , Pebble Bks.) Capstone Pr., Inc.

Hyland, Tony. Zookeepers. 2006. (J). (978-1-58340-740-0(5)) Smart Apple Media.

Johnson, Marion. Caillou - At the Zoo. Johnson, Marion et al, illus. rev. ed. 2005. (Playtime Ser.). 24p. (J). (ps-1). pap. 4.95 (978-2-89450-384-3(9)) Chouette Publishing CAN. *Dist:* Independent Pubs. Group.

Kent, Lorna, illus. At the Zoo. 2004. 8p. (J). bds. 3.99 (978-1-85854-084-9(4)) Brimax Books Ltd. GBR. *Dist:* Byeway Bks.

Kirsten, A. We Bring the Zoo to You. 2005. 32p. pap. 9.95 (978-0-9704876-5-0(7)) First Mom's Club, The.

Knight, Bertram T. Working at a Zoo. (Working Here Ser.). (Illus.). 32p. (J). (gr. 2-4). 1999. pap. 6.95 (978-0-516-20377-5(0)); 1998. 23.50 (978-0-516-20751-3(2)) Scholastic Library Publishing. (Children's Pr.).

Kumon Publishing Staff, ed. My Book of Coloring at Zoo. 2007. 80p. pap. 6.95 (***978-1-933241-39-5(X)***) Kumon Publishing North America, Inc.

Larousse Mexico Staff, ed. Mi Pequena Encicopedia Larousse el Zoologico. 2006. (Mi Pequena Enciclopedia Ser.). 38p. (ps-k). pap. 3.95 (978-970-22-1193-8(X)) Larousse, Ediciones, S. A. de C. V. MEX. *Dist:* Houghton Mifflin Co. Trade & Reference Div.

LeBoutillier, Nate. A Day in the Life of a Zookeeper. 2004. (First Facts Ser.). (Illus.). 24p. (J). (gr. k-3). lib. bdg. 21.26 (978-0-7368-2632-7(7) , First Facts) Capstone Pr., Inc.

Liebman, Daniel. I Want to Be a Zookeeper. 2003. (I Want to Be Ser.). (Illus.). 24p. (J). (ps-2). pap. 3.99 (978-1-55297-697-5(1)); lib. bdg. 14.95 (978-1-55297-699-9(8)) Firefly Bks., Ltd.

—Quiero Ser Guardian de Zoologico. 2003. (Quiero Ser.). (SPA.). 24p. (J). (ps-2). pap. 5.99 (978-1-55297-730-9(7)) Firefly Bks., Ltd.

Lyon, George Ella. Mother to Tigers. Catalanotto, Peter, illus. 2003. 32p. (J). (gr. k-5). 17.95 (978-0-689-84221-4(X) , Atheneum/Richard Jackson Bks.) Simon & Schuster Children's Publishing.

Macken, JoAnn Early. Animals I See at the Zoo/Animales Que Veo en el Zoologico, 4 bks. Coffey, Colleen & Carrillo, Consuelo, trs. Incl. Bears/Los Osos. lib. bdg. 19.33 (978-0-8368-3998-2(6)); Elephants/Los Elefantes. 19.33 (978-0-8368-3999-9(4)); Giraffes/Las Jirafas. lib. bdg. 19.33 (978-0-8368-4000-1(3)); Penguins/Los Pinguinos. lib. bdg. 19.33 (978-0-8368-4001-8(1)); 24p. (J). (ps up). (SPA & ENG., Illus.). 2003. Set lib. bdg. 74.40 (978-0-8368-3997-5(8) , Weekly Reader Early Learning Library) Stevens, Gareth Inc.

—Animals I See at the Zoo/Animales Que Veo en el Zoologico, 4 bks. Incl. Bears/Los Osos. pap. 5.95 (978-0-8368-4003-2(8)); Elephants/Los Elefantes. pap. 5.95 (978-0-8368-4004-9(6)); Giraffes/Las Jirafas. pap. (978-0-8368-4005-6(4)); Penguins/Los Pinguinos. pap. 5.95 (978-0-8368-4006-3(2)); 24p. (J). (ps up). 2003. (SPA & ENG., Illus.). 2003. pap. (978-0-8368-4002-5(X) , Weekly Reader Early Learning Library) Stevens, Gareth Inc.

McReynolds, Stacy. San Antonio Zoo. 2003. (Great Zoos of the United States Ser.). (Illus.). 24p. (J). lib. bdg. 18.75 (978-0-8239-6319-5(5) , PowerKids Pr.) Rosen Publishing Group, Inc., The.

Miller, Heather. Zookeeper. 2003. (This Is What I Want to Be Ser.). (Illus.). 24p. (ps-1). (J). lib. bdg. 18.50 (978-1-4034-0373-5(2)); pap. 5.25 (978-1-4034-0595-1(6)) Heinemann Library.

Nayer, Judy. Zoo Animals. Brown, Robert & Harris, Greg, illus. 1998. (At Your Fingertips Ser.). 5p. (J). (ps-3). 6.95 (978-0-7681-0066-2(6) , McClanahan Bk.) Learning Horizons, Inc.

Oehler, David A. The Cincinnati Zoo & Botanical Garden. 2003. (Great Zoos of the United States Ser.). (Illus.). 24p. (J). lib. bdg. 18.75 (978-0-8239-6320-1(9) , PowerKids Pr.) Rosen Publishing Group, Inc., The.

Pearce, Claudia & Worley, Karen E. San Diego Zoo. Bohn, Ken & Garrison, Ron, illus. Bohn, Ken & Garrison, Ron, photos by. 2003. (Great Zoos of the United States Ser.). 24p. (J). lib. bdg. 18.75 (978-0-8239-6321-8(7) , PowerKids Pr.) Rosen Publishing Group, Inc., The.

Powell, Janet. Saint Louis Zoo. 2003. (Great Zoos of the United States Ser.). (Illus.). 24p. (J). lib. bdg. 18.75 (978-0-8239-6318-8(7) , PowerKids Pr.) Rosen Publishing Group, Inc., The.

Priddy, Roger. Bright Baby Touch & Feel at the Zoo. 2006. (Bright Baby Ser.). (Illus.). 10p. (J). bds. 4.95 (978-0-312-49857-3(8) , Priddy Bks.) St. Martin's Pr.

Procter, Alice. At the Zoo: Telling Time by the Quarter Hour. 2007. (I Can Tell Time Ser.). 24p. (J). (gr. k-2). lib. bdg. 19.93 (***978-0-8368-8391-6(8)***) Stevens, Gareth Inc.

Proctor, Alice. At the Zoo: Telling Time by the Quarter Hour. 2007. (J). pap. (***978-0-8368-8396-1(9)***) Stevens, Gareth Inc.

Rabinovitch, Leon & Carson, Steven, illus. Alaska Zoo Activity & Guide Book. 1999. 68p. (J). pap. 6.00 (978-1-57833-120-8(X)) Todd Communications.

Rauen, Amy. Counting at the Zoo. 2007. (J). pap. (***978-0-8368-8478-4(7)***); 24p. (gr. 1-3). lib. bdg. 19.93 (***978-0-8368-8469-2(8)***) Stevens, Gareth Inc. (Weekly Reader Early Learning Library).

Ricciuti, Edward R. A Pelican Swallowed My Head. 2002. (Illus.). 224p. (J). (gr. 3-7). 17.00 (978-0-689-82532-3(3)) Simon & Schuster Children's Publishing.

Ring, Susan. Project Otter. 2003. (gr. 3-6). lib. bdg. 15.25 (978-0-613-79818-1(X)) Tandem Library Bks.

—Project Otter. Kissock, Heather & Marshall, Diana, eds. 2003. (Zoo Life Ser.). (Illus.). 24p. (J). pap. 6.95 (978-1-59036-059-0(1)) Weigl Pubs., Inc.

—Project Otter. 2002. (Zoo Life Ser.). (Illus.). 24p. (J). lib. bdg. 22.80 (978-1-59036-018-7(4)) Weigl Pubs., Inc.

Salisbury, Kent. Alpha Zoo: Have Fun with Your Animal Friends from A to Z. 1998. (Illus.). 13p. (J). (ps-k). 6.99 (978-0-7681-0082-2(8) , McClanahan Bk.) Learning Horizons, Inc.

Schaefer, Lola M. Zoo. 2001. (Who Works Here? Ser.). (Illus.). 32p. (J). (gr. 1-2). lib. bdg. 21.36 (978-1-58810-128-0(2)) Heinemann Library.

Scholastic, Inc. Staff. Peek-a-Zoo. 2007. (Little Scholastic Ser.). (J). (ps). bds. 10.99 (***978-0-439-02154-8(5)***) Scholastic, Inc.

Schomp, Virginia. If You Were a Zookeeper. 1999. (If You Were A... Ser.). (Illus.). 32p. (J). (gr. 2-4). lib. bdg. 22.79 (978-0-7614-0918-2(1) , Benchmark Bks.) Cavendish, Marshall Corp.

School Specialty Publishing. Learn about the Zoo. 2005. (Learn about Coloring Bks.). 32p. (J). (ps-3). pap. 1.99 (978-0-7696-4163-8(6) , Brighter Child) School Specialty Publishing.

—The Zoo. 2003. (Brighter Child Activity Bks.). 32p. (J). (ps-1). pap. 2.99 (978-0-7696-3215-5(7) , Brighter Child) School Specialty Publishing.

Schwartz, David M. At the Zoo. Kuhn, Dwight, photos by. 1998. (Springboards into Science Ser.). (Illus.). 24p. (J). (gr. 1 up). lib. bdg. 19.93 (978-0-8368-2225-0(0)) Stevens, Gareth Inc.

Shi, Sharon. Animals at the Zoo. Neilson, Shannon, illus. rev. ed. 2000. 23p. (J). (ps-2). pap. 4.99 (978-0-9678636-4-1(3) , B005, Tattootles Bks.) Tattoo Manufacturing.

Smith, Roland. Z Is for Zookeeper: A Zoo Alphabet. Cole, Henry, illus. 2005. 40p. (J). 16.95 (978-1-58536-158-8(5)) Sleeping Bear Pr.

Smith, Roland. A Zoo Alphabet. rev. ed. 2007. 40p. pap. 7.95 (***978-1-58536-329-2(4)***) Sleeping Bear Pr.

Stanley, Mandy. At the Zoo. Morris, Jennis, ed. 2002. (All Aboard Ser.). (Illus.). 12p. (J). (gr. k-ps). bds. 4.95 (978-0-7534-5446-6(7) , Kingfisher) Houghton Mifflin Co. Trade & Reference Div.

—Vamos al Zoo. 2003. (SPA.). 12p. (J). (ps-k). 3.95 (978-0-7534-5690-3(7) , Kingfisher) Houghton Mifflin Co. Trade & Reference Div.

Trumbauer, Lisa. We Need Zoo Keepers. Saunders-Smith, Gail, ed. 2003. (Helpers in Our Community Ser.). (Illus.). 24p. (J). (gr. k-1). lib. bdg. 15.93 (978-0-7368-1651-9(8) , Pebble Bks.) Capstone Pr., Inc.

Wagner, Jeff. My Day... at the Zoo. Alvarado, Paulo, illus. 2004. 20p. (J). bds. (978-0-9754515-0-2(2)) Wagner Entertainment.

Wallace, Karen. A Trip to the Zoo. 2003. (Illus.). 32p. (J). (ps-3). lib. bdg. 11.80 (978-0-613-62438-1(6)) Tandem Library Bks.

Wallace, Karen & Dorling Kindersley Publishing Staff. A Trip to the Zoo. 2003. (Readers Ser.). (Illus.). 32p. (J). 12.99 (978-0-7894-9307-1(1)) Dorling Kindersley Publishing, Inc.

Wallace, Karen & Lock, Deborah. A Trip to the Zoo/A Trip to the Library. 2006. (Read & Listen Bks.). 64p. (J). 9.99 (978-0-7566-1830-8(4)) Dorling Kindersley Publishing, Inc.

Who Lives at the Zoo? 2004. (Who Lives... Ser.). 12p. (J). bds. 4.99 (978-1-85854-645-2(1)) Brimax Books Ltd. GBR. *Dist:* Byeway Bks.

Wildsmith, Brian. Zoo Animals. Wildsmith, Brian, illus. 2002. (Illus.). 32p. (J). bds. 6.95 (978-1-887734-92-9(9)) Star Bright Bks., Inc.

Wilkinson, Rick. Endangered! Working to Save Animals at Risk. 2002. (Illus.). 32p. (J). (978-1-86508-664-4(9)) Allen & Unwin.

Winterberg, Jenna. Zoo: A Step-by-Step Drawing & Story Book for Kids as Young as Four Years Old. Fisher, Diana, illus. 2006. (Watch Me Draw Ser.). 24p. (J). pap. 4.95 (978-1-56010-798-9(7)) Foster, Walter Publishing, Inc.

The Zoo, 2 Packs. (Chiquilibros Ser.). (ps-1). 12.00 (978-0-7635-8536-5(X)) Rigby Education.

Zoo Animals. (Little Tot Dot-to-Dots Ser.). 32p. (gr. k-2). 4.29 (978-0-7647-0383-6(8) , FS30303) Schaffer, Frank Pubns.

Zoo (Gr. PreK-5) 2003. (J). (978-1-58232-027-4(6)) Bryan Hse. Pubs., Inc.

ZOOS—FICTION

Aboff, Marcie. Alex & Marty Run Wild. 2005. (Madagascar Ser.). 32p. (J). pap. 3.99 (978-0-439-69631-9(3)) Scholastic, Inc.

Adams, William J. Goin' to the Zoo / Vamos Al Zoologico. Stiglich, Tom, illus. 2007. (ENG & SPA.). 58p. (J). pap. (***978-0-9772757-2-4(8)***) Mandy & Andy Bks., Inc.

—Goin' to the Zoo Coloring Book: Vamos Al Zoologico. Stiglich, Tom, illus. 2007. (ENG & SPA.). (J). pap. 3.95 (***978-0-9772757-3-1(6)***) Mandy & Andy Bks., Inc.

Adler, David A. Young Cam Jansen & the Lions' Lunch Mystery. Natti, Susanna, illus. 2007. 32p. (J). 13.99 (978-0-670-06171-6(9) , Viking Juvenile) Penguin Group (USA) Inc.

Alexander, Carmen. Zoo 1000 Miles. Henderson, Cecil, illus. 2005. 42p. (J). (ps-5). pap. 9.99 (978-1-886383-57-9(X) , Little Blue Works) Windstorm Creative.

Alien at the Zoo, 6 vols. (Sunshinetm Ser.). 16p. (gr. k up). 29.50 (978-0-7802-5429-9(5)) Wright Group, The.

Anderson, Dawn. Chimpance, Como Yo ! 2006. (Illus.). (J). 15.95 (978-0-9786570-1-7(2)) Opposable Thumb Pr.

—Chimpanzee, Like Me! 2006. (Illus.). (J). 15.95 (978-0-9786570-0-0(4)) Opposable Thumb Pr.

Bamboo Zoo Set: Meet Lester Panda & his Friends. 2006. (J). 17.95 (978-0-9774493-1-6(9)) Bamboo Zoo, LLC.

Barney Let's Go to the Zoo. 2001. (Barney Ser.). (Illus.). 60p. (J). (ps-k). 1.99 (978-1-57064-940-0(5)) Scholastic, Inc.

Barra, Nancy. Monica Va Al Zoologico. Zuman, John, ed. Deming, Linda, illus. 2002. (Sunflower/Girasol Ser.). (SPA.). 20p. tchr. ed., spiral bd. 5.95 (978-1-58332-051-8(2)) Intercultural Center for Research in Education (I N C R E).

—Monica Va Al Zoologico. Deming, Linda, illus. 2002. (Sunflower/Girasol Ser.). (SPA.). 30p. (J). 5.95 (978-1-58332-050-1(4)) Intercultural Center for Research in Education (I N C R E).

Battle, Cleaton D. A Saturday Surprise. Cooper, Emmanuel B., illus. 2006. 68p. (J). pap. 11.95 (978-1-59663-504-3(5) , Castle Keep Pr.) Rock, James A. & Co. Pubs.

Bauer, Marion Dane. A Bear Named Trouble. 2005. 128p. (J). (gr. 3-5). 14.00 (978-0-618-51738-1(3) , Clarion Bks.) Houghton Mifflin Co. Trade & Reference Div.

—A Bear Named Trouble. 2006. 128p. (J). (gr. 4-7). pap. 5.99 (978-0-440-42132-0(2) , Yearling) Random Hse. Children's Bks.

Bercowetz, Cynthia. Grandpa Herman¿s Petting Zoo. 2007. (Illus.). 48p. (J). per. 14.95 (***978-0-9708430-9-8(7)***) Uitti, Daniel.

Bernthal, Mark S. & Lyrick Publishing Staff. Barney & BJ Go to the Zoo. Full, Dennis, photos by. 1999. (Barney's Go to Ser.). (Illus.). 24p. (J). (ps-k). pap. 3.50 (978-1-57064-446-7(2)) Scholastic, Inc.

Blackaby, Susan. A Trip to the Zoo. Muehlenhardt, Amy Bailey, illus. 2006. (Read-It! Readers Ser.). 24p. (J). (ps-3). 18.60 (978-1-4048-1590-2(2)) Picture Window Bks.

Blance, Ellen & Cook. Monster Goes to the Zoo. Date not set. (Illus.). 24p. pap. 129.15 (978-0-582-18599-9(8)) Addison-Wesley Longman, Ltd. GBR. *Dist:* Trans-Atlantic Pubns., Inc.

Bonnell, Kris. Look Who's at the Zoo. 2005. (J). 3.75 (978-1-933727-07-3(1)) Reading Reading Bks., LLC.

Britner, Scott & Britner, Melissa. Tyler & Destiny Tales: Lunch at the Zoo. 2004. 17p. (J). pap. 8.33 (978-1-4116-0919-8(0)) Lulu.com.

Brown, Peter. Chowder. 2006. (Illus.). 32p. (J). (ps-1). 15.99 (978-0-316-01180-8(0)) Little Brown & Co.

Browne, Anthony. Zoo. Browne, Anthony, illus. 2002. (Illus.). 32p. (J). pap. 6.95 (978-0-374-49923-5(3) , Sunburst) Farrar, Straus & Giroux.

—Zoo. 2002. (ps-2). lib. bdg. 15.25 (978-0-613-71935-3(2)) Tandem Library Bks.

Bruna, Dick. Miffy Tours the Zoo. 1998. (Miffy Ser.). (Illus.). 12p. (J). (ps-k). 4.95 (978-1-56836-266-3(8)) Kodansha America, Inc.

Pennac, Daniel. Eye of the Wolf. Adams, Sarah, tr. from FRE. Grafe, Max, illus. 2003. 112p. (J). (gr. 5 up). 15.99 (978-0-7636-1896-4(9)) Candlewick Pr.

Pfloog, Jan. The Zoo Book. Pfloog, Jan, illus. 1999. (Super Shape Bks.). (Illus.). 24p. (J). (gr. k-ps). bds. 3.99 (978-0-307-58118-1(7) , 10060, Golden Bks.) Random Hse. Children's Bks.

Phillips, Betty Lou. Emily Goes Wild. Watts, Sharon, illus. 2nd ed. 2003. 32p. (J). (ps-3). reprint ed. 16.95 (978-1-58685-268-9(X)) Gibbs Smith, Publisher.

Piano, Maureen & Sykes, Christine. When Flamingos Fly. 2006. 44p. (J). 12.99 (978-1-59092-362-7(6) , Orchard Academy Pr.) Windstorm Creative.

Piggy Toes Press Staff. Zoo Faces. 1998. (Cuddly Cloth Book Ser.). (Illus.). 6p. (J). (ps-k). 14.95 (978-1-888443-52-3(9) , Intervisual/Piggy Toes) Dalmatian Pr.

Pilkey, Dav. Dumb Bunnies Go to the Zoo, The. 2007. 32p. pap. 5.99 (*978-0-439-93049-9(9)*) Scholastic, Inc.

Pilkey, Dav, illus. The Dumb Bunnies Go to the Zoo. 2002. (Dumb Bunnies Ser.). (J). 22.91 (978-0-7587-2424-3(1)) Book Wholesalers, Inc.

Pinkwater, Daniel M. Bad Bears Go Visiting. Pinkwater, Jill, illus. 2007. 32p. (J). (gr. k-3). 16.00 (978-0-618-43126-7(8)) Houghton Mifflin Co.

Pinkwater, Daniel M. & Pinkwater, Jill, illus. Bad Bears Go Visiting: An Irving & Muktuk Story. 2007. (J). (*978-1-4287-3949-9(1)*) Houghton Mifflin Co.

Pinkwater, Daniel M. & Pinkwater, Jill, illus. Bad Bears in the Big City: An Irving & Muktuk Story. 2004. 32p. (J). (gr. k-3). tchr. ed. 16.00 (978-0-618-25208-4(8)) Houghton Mifflin Co. Trade & Reference Div.

Piper, Watty. The Little Engine That Could Goes on a Class Trip. Cardona, Jose Maria & Cardona, Joseph, illus. 2003. (Reading Railroad Bks.). 32p. (J). (ps-4). pap. 3.49 (978-0-448-43180-2(7) , Grosset & Dunlap) Penguin Group (USA) Inc.

Polisar, Barry Louis. Peculiar Zoo. Clark, David, illus. 2003. (Rainbow Morning Music Picture Bks.). 32p. (J). 14.95 (978-0-938663-14-0(3)) Rainbow Morning Music Alternatives.

Prose, Francine. Leopold: The Liar of Leipzig. Aviram, Einav, illus. 2005. 32p. (J). 15.99 (978-0-06-008075-4(2) , Cotler, Joanna Books) HarperCollins Pubs.

Rathmann, Peggy. Good Night, Gorilla. Rathmann, Peggy, illus. gif. ed. (Illus.). (J). (ps). 2003. 32p. 16.99 (978-0-399-24195-6(7)); 2000. (SPA., 40p. reprint ed. pap. 5.99 (978-0-698-11649-8(6)) Penguin Group (USA) Inc. (Putnam Juvenile).

—Good Night, Gorilla. 2000. (Illus.). (J). 12.79 (978-0-606-18837-1(1)) Tandem Library Bks.

Ready Reader Staff. Good-Bye Zoo: Consonant Z, Level K. 2003. (J). (ps-3). 24.50 (978-0-8136-1451-9(1)) Modern Curriculum Pr.

Reiss-Weimann, Elayne. Who's New at the Zoo? Wetzel, Rick, illus. 2002. (Read-To-Me Ser.). 25p. (J). (978-0-7665-1226-9(6)) Abrams, Harry N. , Inc.

Rex, Adam. Pssst! 2007. (Illus.). 40p. (J). (gr. k-3). 16.00 (978-0-15-205817-3(6)) Harcourt Trade Pubs.

Rey, H. A. Curious George Feeds the Animals. 1998. (Illus.). 24p. (J). (gr. k-3). tchr. ed. 12.95 (978-0-395-91904-0(5)) Houghton Mifflin Co. Trade & Reference Div.

Rey, Margret. Curious George Visits the Zoo. Rey, Margret, illus. 2002. (Curious George TV Bks.). (Illus.). (J). 11.87 (978-0-7587-2323-9(7)) Book Wholesalers, Inc.

Rey, Margret & Rey, H. A. Curious George Feeds the Animals. 1998. (Curious George Ser.). (Illus.). 24p. (J). (gr. k-3). pap. 3.95 (978-0-395-91910-1(X)) Houghton Mifflin Co. Trade & Reference Div.

Robbins, Sandra. No Balloons Today: A Day at the Zoo. Garzon, Alfredo, illus. 2001. (See-More's Stories Ser.). 32p. (J). pap. 16.95 incl. audio compact disk (978-1-882601-36-3(X)) See-More's Workshop.

—No Balloons Today: A Zoo Story. Garzon, Alfredo, illus. 2001. 32p. (J). (ps-3). pap. 11.95 incl. audio (978-1-882601-29-5(7)); pap. 6.95 (978-1-882601-30-1(0)) See-More's Workshop.

Rosen, Michael. The Zoo at Night. Willey, Bee, illus. 2000. 12p. (J). (ps-k). (978-1-896580-00-5(9)) Tradewind Bks.

Rosenthal, Pamela. My Trip to the Zoo. 2005. (Illus.). 48p. (J). lib. bdg. 24.95 (978-1-932762-28-0(0)) Elderberry Press, Inc.

Roy, Ron. The Panda Puzzle. Gurney, John Steven, illus. 2002. (A to Z Mysteries Ser.: No. 16). 96p. (J). (gr. k-3). lib. bdg. 11.99 (978-0-375-90271-0(6)); (gr. 2-5). mass mkt. 3.99 (978-0-375-80271-3(1)) Random Hse. Children's Bks. (Random Hse. Bks. for Young Readers).

—The Panda Puzzle. Gurney, John Steven, illus. 2002. (A to Z Mysteries Ser.: No. 16). 84p. (J). (ps-k). lib. bdg. 11.80 (978-0-613-50485-0(2)) Tandem Library Bks.

Roy, Ron. A Thief at the National Zoo. 2007. 96p. (J). lib. bdg. (*978-0-375-94804-6(X)*); pap. 3.99 (*978-0-375-84804-9(5)*) Random Hse., Inc.

Schaff, Faith R. The Wild & Crazy, Upsy-Daisy, Totally Wonderful Zoo! Simonson, Sheila, photos by. 2000. (Children's Self Esteem Ser.). (Illus.). 20p. (J). pap. 7.95 (978-1-931006-09-5(1)) SteppingStones BookCard Pubns., LLC.

Scholastic, Inc. Staff. Let's Go to the Farm & the Zoo. 2007. (Barney Ser.). 48p. (J). pap. 4.99 (*978-0-439-92724-6(2)*) Scholastic, Inc.

Sibley, Irena. Zara's Zoo. 2002. (Illus.). 32p. (978-0-7344-0173-1(6) , Lothian Bks.) Hachette Livre Australia.

Sorrentino, Dawn. Rusty Visits the Zoo. 2006. (J). spiral bd. 15.00 (978-0-8059-7007-4(X)) Dorrance Publishing Co., Inc.

Spooner, Joe. The Elephant Walk. Spooner, Joe, illus. 2004. (Illus.). (J). pap. 14.95 (978-0-9745686-3-8(5)) Arnica Publishing, Inc.

Staud, Suzanne, illus. Benjamin Bailey Goes to the Zoo! 2005. 20p. (J). bds. 10.99 (978-1-889191-19-5(1)) Clove Pubns.

Steele, Michael Anthony. It's a Zoo in Here! 2005. (Illus.). (J). (*978-0-439-78585-3(5)*) Scholastic, Inc.

Taylor, Theodore. Lord of the Kill. 2004. 256p. (J). pap. 5.99 (978-0-439-55956-0(1) , Scholastic Paperbacks) Scholastic, Inc.

Todd, John. The Zoo Savers. 2007. 140p. (J). per. (*978-0-9779680-8-4(1)*) Global Authors Pubns.

Waber, Bernard. A Lion Named Shirley Williamson. 2000. (Illus.). 40p. (J). (gr. k-3). pap. 6.95 (978-0-618-05580-7(0) , Walter Lorraine) Houghton Mifflin Co. Trade & Reference Div.

—A Lion Named Shirley Williamson. 2000. (Illus.). (J). (978-0-606-18212-6(8)) Tandem Library Bks.

—Lion Named Shirley Williamson. 2000. (gr. k-3). lib. bdg. 15.25 (978-0-613-28554-4(9)) Tandem Library Bks.

Walsh, Maria Elena. Zoo Loco. Jacoboni, Silvia, illus. 2001. (SPA.). 76p. (J). (gr. k-6). pap. 12.95 (978-950-511-617-1(9)) Santillana USA Publishing Co., Inc.

Warner, Gertrude Chandler. The Poison Frog Mystery. 2000. (Boxcar Children Ser.: No. 74). (J). (gr. 2-5). (978-0-606-18767-1(7)) Tandem Library Bks.

—Poison Frog Mystery. 2000. (gr. 3-6). lib. bdg. 11.80 (978-0-613-22192-4(3)) Tandem Library Bks.

Warner, Gertrude Chandler, creator. The Poison Frog Mystery, Vol. 74. 2004. (Boxcar Children Ser.: No. 74). (Illus.). 128p. (J). (gr. 2-5). pap. 3.95 (978-0-8075-6587-2(3)) Whitman, Albert & Co.

Westcott, Nadine Bernard. Valentine's Day at the Zoo. Westcott, Nadine Bernard, illus. 2002. (Illus.). 16p. (J). pap. 5.99 (978-0-689-84567-3(7) , Little Simon) Simon & Schuster Children's Publishing.

What Would I Do If I Lived at the Zoo? 2004. (Illus.). 12p. (J). 5.95 (978-0-9759321-2-4(8)) Rascal Treehouse Publishing.

Willson, Sarah. Have No Fear, Chuckie's Here! 2001. (gr. k-3). lib. bdg. 11.25 (978-0-613-43969-5(4)) Tandem Library Bks.

Wilson, Karma. Never, Ever Shout in a Zoo. Cushman, Douglas, illus. 2004. 32p. (J). (ps-3). 16.99 (978-0-316-98564-2(3)) Little Brown & Co.

Winnard, Rebecca Victoria & Winnard, Linda. Giraffe Liberation: An Act of Freedom. 2006. 53p. pap. 12.95 (978-1-4241-0552-6(8)) PublishAmerica, Inc.

Winthrop, Elizabeth. Dancing Granny. Murdocca, Sal, illus. 2003. 32p. (J). 16.95 (978-0-7614-5141-9(2)) Cavendish, Marshall Corp.

Wolff, Ashley. Me Baby, You Baby. Wolff, Ashley, illus. 2004. (Illus.). 32p. (J). (ps). 14.99 (978-0-525-46952-0(4) , Dutton Juvenile) Penguin Group (USA) Inc.

Ziefert, Harriet. Zoo Parade! Taback, Simms, illus. 2003. 14p. 8.95 (978-1-59354-014-2(0)) Blue Apple Bks.

ZULU (AFRICAN PEOPLE)

Gleimius, Nita, et al. The Zulu of Africa. 2005. (First Peoples Ser.). (Illus.). 48p. (gr. 4-8). 23.95 (978-0-8225-0661-4(0)) Lerner Publishing Group.

University of Cambridge Local Examinations Syndication Staff. HIGCSE First Language Zulu. 2005. (Cambridge Open Learning Project in South Africa Ser.). (ZUL.). (gr. 9). Module 1. pap. (978-0-521-78439-9(5)); Module 2. pap. (978-0-521-78440-5(9)); Module 3. pap. (978-0-521-78441-2(7)); Module 4. pap. (978-0-521-78442-9(5)) Cambridge Univ. Pr.

ZULU (AFRICAN PEOPLE)—FICTION

Erskine, Kathryn. Ibhubesi: The Lion. 2004. (Illus.). 194p. pap. 19.95 (978-1-4137-0364-1(X)) PublishAmerica, Inc.

Ferreira, Anton. Zulu Dog. 2002. (Illus.). 208p. (J). (gr. 5 up). 16.00 (978-0-374-39223-9(4) , Farrar, Straus & Giroux (BYR)) Farrar, Straus & Giroux.

ZULUS

see Zulu (African People)

W X Y Z

PUBLISHER NAME INDEX

101 Bk. *Imprint of* **Michaelson Entertainment**

114th Aviation Co. Assn., *(0-9742465)* 15151 Berry Trail, Suite 403, Dallas, TX 75248-6319 USA Tel 972-404-9922 (phone/fax)
E-mail: steve@stibbens.com.

11th Hour Productions *See* **Twilight Tales, Inc.**

1212 Pr., *(0-9764985)* 1212 Beverley Rd., Brooklyn, NY 11218 USA Tel 718-462-4004
E-mail: rgistudio@earthlink.net.

123 Bk. *Imprint of* **Michaelson Entertainment**

153 Fish Publishing, *(0-9747918)* 230 SW Railroad St., Sheridan, OR 97378-1745 USA.

16th Avenue Pr., *(0-9742854)* P.O. Box 166, Portage, MI 49081 USA Fax: 269-372-6970
E-mail: theawrites@sbcglobal.net
Web site: http://www.fearnoflame.com.

16th Place Publishing, *(0-9745152)* 171 S. 16th Pl., Pocatello, ID 83201 USA
E-mail: brobergbook@yahoo.com
Web site: http://www.stoleninnocencebook.com.

17th Street Productions, An Alloy Online Inc. Co., *(1-931497)* 151 W. 26th St., 11th Flr., New York, NY 10001 USA Tel 212-244-4307; Fax: 212-244-4311
E-mail: peterlopez@alloy.com
Web site: http://www.alloy.com.

1-800 ProColor, Incorporated *See* **Robertson Publishing**

1st Impression Publishing, *(0-9763365)* P.O. Box 10339, Burbank, CA 91510-0339 USA Tel 818-843-1300; Fax: 818-846-5657
E-mail: sahysen@earthlink.net
Web site: http://www.1stimpressionpublishing.com.

1st Place Publishing, LLC, *(0-9745457)* 5694 NW 179th Ave., Portland, OR 97229-1774 USA Tel 503-313-5395
E-mail: cs@1stplacephonics.com
Web site: http://www.1stplacephonics.com.

1st World Library *See* **Groundbreaking Pr.**

1st World Library - Literary Society *Imprint of* **1st World Publishing, Inc.**

1st World Publishing *Imprint of* **1st World Publishing, Inc.**

1st World Publishing, Inc., *(0-9638502; 1-887472; 1-59540; 1-4218)* Orders Addr.: 1100 N. 4th St. Ste. 9, Fairfield, IA 52556-2169 USA Toll Free: 877-209-5004 ; *Imprints:* 1st World Publishing (Frst Wrld Pub); 1st World Library - Literary Society (1st Wrld); Sunstar Publishing (SunstarPub)
E-mail: ed@1stworldpublishing.com; order@1stworldpublishing.com; info@1stworldpublishing.com; tim@1stworldpublishing.com
Web site: http://www.1stworldpublishing.com
Dist(s): **1st World Publishing**
AtlasBooks Distribution
Baker & Taylor Bks.
Lightning Source, Inc.
New Leaf Distributing Co., Inc.

1stBooks Library *See* **AuthorHouse**

1stCoBooks, *(0-9705237)* 8867 Highland Rd., No. 7A, Baton Rouge, LA 70808-6856 USA Toll Free: 888-805-8845 (phone/fax)
E-mail: Book@1stco.com.

1stSight Pr., *(0-9729265)* 844 Central Ave., Ocean City, NJ 08226 USA.

1stWorld Library, Limited *See* **1st World Publishing, Inc.**

2 Brian's Pr., *(1-928714)* Orders Addr.: P.O. Box 521, Seiad Valley, CA 96099 USA Toll Free: 877-606-0694; Edit Addr.: 45013 Hwy. 96, Seiad Valley, CA 96086-0521 USA Tel 530-496-3325
E-mail: Brian@sisqtel.net
Web site: http://www.sisqtel.net/~brian.

2 Donn Bks., *(0-9770893)* 11354 Links Dr., Reston, VA 20190-4807 USA (SAN 256-7407)
Web site: http://www.2donnbooks.com.

2 Imagine, *(0-9740684; 0-9759749)* 10135 E. Via Linda, D126, Scottsdale, AZ 85258 USA Tel 480-657-8506 (phone/fax); Toll Free: 866-246-2446
E-mail: info@2imaginethis.com
Web site: http://www.2imaginethis.com
Dist(s): **Biblio Distribution.**

2020 Vision Pr., *(0-9710675)* 2744 Crown Point, Las Cruces, NM 88011 USA Tel 505-532-9693; Fax: 505-532-9694
E-mail: josh@joshhunt.com
Web site: http://www.joshhunt.com.

20th Maine, Inc., *(0-9704408)* 859 Lawrence Rd., Pownal, ME 04069-6118 USA
E-mail: pat@20thmaine.com
Web site: http://www.20thmaine.com.

21st Century Pr., *(0-9717009; 0-9725719; 0-9728899; 0-9749811; 0-9766243; 0-9771964; 0-9779535)* 3308 S. Meadowlark Ave., Springfield, MO 65807 USA Tel 417-889-4803; Fax: 417-889-2210; Toll Free: 800-658-0284 ; *Imprints:* Sonship Press (Sonship Pr) Do not confuse with 21st Century Press in Portage, IN
E-mail: lee@21stcenturypress.com
Web site: http://www.21stcenturypress.com
Dist(s): **Anchor Distributors.**

21st Century Pubs., *(0-9607298)* 1320 Curt Gowdy Dr., Cheyenne, WY 82009 USA (SAN 239-1740) Tel 307-638-2254
E-mail: chismaturi@prodigy.net
Web site: http://www.triplecrownwinnerearlsande.com
Dist(s): **Baker & Taylor Bks.**
Emery-Pratt Co.
Blackwell North America.

2B Pr., *(0-9765430)* 206 Clear Springs, Peachtree City, GA 30269 USA Tel 770-487-1348
E-mail: tami@2bpress.com
Web site: http://www.2bpress.com.

2Lakes Publishing, *(0-9722400)* Orders Addr.: 205 Upper Ranchitos Rd. Unit 4, Taos, NM 87571-4353 USA
E-mail: heidi2lakes@2lakespublishing.com
Web site: http://www.2lakespublishing.com
Dist(s): **Independent Pubs. Group.**

2MPower, *(0-9767046)* 25231 Grissom Rd., Laguna Hills, CA 92653-5237 USA Tel 949-837-1268; Fax: 949-470-0659
E-mail: arnovigen@yahoo.com
Web site: http://www.2mpwr.com.

3 Millennium Publishing, *(0-9708638)* 13944 Whispering Meadows Ln., Jamul, CA 91935 USA Tel 619-669-0385; Fax: 619-669-0386
E-mail: 3millpub@msn.com; rick@3millpub.com
Web site: http://www.3millpub.com.

3 Pals Media, LLC, *(0-9770960)* 424 Greenleaf Ave., Burlington, WA 98233 USA Tel 360-755-2299; Fax: 360-755-8010
Web site: http://www.pumpkinpatchpals.com.

3 Pounds Pr., *(0-9675299)* Orders Addr.: PMB 329 25125 Santa Clara St., Hayward, CA 94544 USA Fax: 520-244-2599
E-mail: eddie@3pounds.com
Web site: http://www.3pounds.com.

300Incredible.com LLC, *(0-9658668; 1-930435)* 660 Village Trace, Bldg. 23, Marietta, GA 30067 USA Tel 770-916-0300; Fax: 770-955-0997; Toll Free: 800-909-6505
E-mail: leebow@300incredible.com
Web site: http://www.300incredible.com/
Dist(s): **M. K. Distributors, Inc.**

302 Publishing, *(0-9790165)* 9139 SW Excalibur Pl., Portland, OR 97219-9721 USA Tel 503-246-2499 (phone/fax).

316 East Publishing *See* **Tavine'ra Publishing, LLC**

3-C Institute for Social Development, *(0-9779290; 0-9789871; 1-934409)* 1903 N. Harrison Ave., Suite 101, Cary, NC 27513 USA Tel 919-677-0101; Fax: 919-677-0112
E-mail: info@3cisd.com
Web site: httpa://brightwood@3ciso.com.

3cs Publishing, The, *(0-9773341)* P.O. Box 8096, Silver Spring, MD 20907 USA
Web site: http://www.the3cs.com.

3D Pr., Inc., *(0-9634607; 0-9653751; 1-889593)* 2969 Baseline Rd., Boulder, CO 80303 USA Tel 303-623-4484; Fax: 303-623-4494; Toll Free: 888-456-3607 (orders only)
E-mail: drich@3dpress.net
Web site: http://www.3dpress.net
Dist(s): **Alpenbooks Pr. LLC**
Baker & Taylor Bks.
Bibliotech, Inc.
Books West
Koen-Levy Bk. Wholesalers LLC
Partners Bk. Distributing, Inc.
Partners/West
Southwest Cookbook Distributors
Treasure Chest Bks.

3H Dowsing International LLC, *(0-9656653; 1-932229)* W10160 Cty. Rd. C, Wautoma, WI 54982 USA Tel 920-787-4747; Fax: 920-787-2006
E-mail: ilovedowsing@hotmail.com
Web site: http://store.yahoo.com/dowsing.

3N Media Group, *(0-9741686)* P.O. Box 705, Morris Plains, NJ 07950 USA Fax: 240-220-0500
E-mail: 3nmediagrp@optonline.net.

3perfections, *(0-9759909)* 833 Great Oaks Trail, Eagan, MN 55123 USA Tel 651-905-1098
E-mail: perfections3@aol.com
Web site: http://www.3perfections.com.

4 Childrens Sake Pubns., *(0-9752982)* Orders Addr.: P.O. Box 594, Moosup, CT 06354 USA; Edit Addr.: 357 N. Main St., Moosup, CT 06354 USA.

4 Sonkist Angels *See* **Four Sonkist Angels**

4000 Years of Writing History, *(0-9748786)* P.O. Box 484, Redondo Beach, CA 90277-0484 USA
Web site: http://www.lmlk.com.

43 Degrees North LLC, *(0-9744444)* P.O. Box 781, Wilson, NY 14172 USA Tel 716-751-3604; Fax: 716-751-0105
E-mail: jeff@tailgatetrivia.com
Web site: http://www.tailgatetrivia.com.

45th Parallel Concepts Ltd., *(0-9747615)* Orders Addr.: 106 Main St. PMB 152, Houlton, ME 04730 USA
E-mail: postmaster@americanschoolhousereader.com
Web site: http://www.americanschoolhousereader.com
Dist(s): **Biblio Distribution**
Unique Bks., Inc.

4All Ages LLC, *(0-9787986)* 5 Murdock Rd., Suite 100, East Rockaway, NY 11518 USA (SAN 851-643X) Tel 516-561-3146
E-mail: laws123@aol.com
Web site: http://www.colorpets.com.

4N Publishing LLC, *(0-9741319; 0-9798841)* Orders Addr.: 44-73 21st St., D-6, Long Island City, NY 11101 USA Tel 718-482-1135
E-mail: brendan@4npublishing.com; lj@4npublishing.com; erin@4npublishing.com
Web site: http://www.4npublishing.com
Dist(s): **Consortium Bk. Sales & Distribution.**

5 Continents Editions (ITA) *(88-7439) Dist. by* **Antique Collect.**

5 Muses Publishing, *(0-9786180)* 100 Andover Pk. Ste 150-108, TUKWILA, WA 98188 USA
E-mail: rlpolhill@5musespublishing.com
Web site: http://www.5MusesPublishing.com.

5 Star Stories, Inc., *(0-9659470)* 14625 Greenville St., Houston, TX 77015-4711 USA Tel 713-455-1073; Fax: 713-583-7017
E-mail: isellfantasy@hotmail.com
Web site: http://www.TexasSecedes.com.

50/50 Publishing, *(0-9778209)* 2617 E. Hennepin Ave., Minneapolis, MN 55413 USA Tel 612-788-4341; Fax: 612-788-4347
Web site: http://www.50-50publishing.com.

5,6 Pickup Sticks Publishing, *(0-9762145)* 2493 Sunridge Ave., SE, Atlanta, GA 30315 USA Tel 404-627-9132
E-mail: tcmac1@bellsouth.net.

7 Heads Publishing, *(0-9716596)* 3972 Barranca Pkwy., Suite J, No. 225, Irvine, CA 92606 USA
E-mail: theceo@mindspring.com.

716 Productions, *(0-9795529)* 3200 Airport Ave., Suite 16, Santa Monica, CA 90405 USA
Web site: http://learningwhoweare.com.

7th Generation, *(0-9779183)* Orders Addr.: P.O. Box 99, Summertown, TN 38483 USA Tel 931-964-3571 Toll Free: 888-260-8458; Edit Addr.: 415 Farm Rd., Summertown, TN 38483 USA
E-mail: info@bookpubco.com
Web site: http://www.bookpubco.com.

80 West Publishing, Inc., *(0-9763417)* 2222 Ponce de Leon Blvd., 6th Flr., Coral Gables, FL 33134 USA Tel 305-448-8117; Fax: 305-448-8453
E-mail: joellen@adkinsadv.com.

826 Valencia, *(0-9768467; 0-9770844; 0-9779289; 0-9790073; 1-934750)* 826 Valencia St., San Francisco, CA 94110 USA
E-mail: alvaro@826valencia.com
Web site: http://www.826valencia.org
Dist(s): **Perseus Distribution.**

8-Ball Express, Inc., *(0-9747273)* 316 California, Suite 529, Reno, NV 89509-1650 USA Tel 415-776-1596 (for wholesale orders); Toll Free: 877-368-2255 (for retail sales only)
E-mail: rgivens@toast.net
Web site: http://www.8-ballbible.com.

AABC Angels, Inc., *(1-892801)* Virginia Sq. Plaza, Unit 618 801 N. Monroe St., Arlington, VA 22201-2373 USA Tel 703-527-3239
E-mail: vivianscott93@msn.com.

A & B Books *See* **A & B Distributors & Pubs. Group**

A & B Distributors & Pubs. Group, *(1-881316; 1-886433)* Div. of A&B Distributors, 1000 Atlantic Ave., Brooklyn, NY 11238 USA (SAN 630-9216) Tel 718-783-7808; Fax: 718-783-7267; Toll Free: 877-542-6657; 146 Lawrence St., Brooklyn, NY 11201 (SAN 631-385X)
E-mail: maxtay@webspan.net
Dist(s): **D&J Bk. Distributors**
Red Sea Pr.

A & C Black (GBR) *(0-245; 0-333; 0-510; 0-7136; 0-85177; 0-85314; 0-212; 0-85146; 0-85147; 0-85317; 0-86019; 0-946716; 0-9507160; 1-85691) Dist. by* **MBI Dist Svcs.**

A & C Black (GBR) *(0-245; 0-333; 0-510; 0-7136; 0-85177; 0-85314; 0-212; 0-85146; 0-85147; 0-85317; 0-86019; 0-946716; 0-9507160; 1-85691) Dist. by* **Players Pr.**

A & C Black (GBR) *(0-245; 0-333; 0-510; 0-7136; 0-85177; 0-85314; 0-212; 0-85146; 0-85147; 0-85317; 0-86019; 0-946716; 0-9507160; 1-85691) Dist. by* **Consort Bk Sales.**

A & C Black (GBR) *(0-245; 0-333; 0-510; 0-7136; 0-85177; 0-85314; 0-212; 0-85146; 0-85147; 0-85317; 0-86019; 0-946716; 0-9507160; 1-85691) Dist. by* **Empire Pub Srvs.**

A & D Bks., *(0-9743294)* 3708 E. 45th St., Tulsa, OK 74135 USA Tel 918-748-4348 (phone/fax)
E-mail: casjns@cox.net
Dist(s): **Independent Pubs. Group.**

A & E Children's Pr., *(0-9728134)* 6107 S. Jericho Way, Centennial, CO 80016 USA
E-mail: maked4@aol.com.

A & E Sivells Pubns. *Imprint of* **Word For Word Publishing Co.**

A&W Enterprises, *(0-9617896)* P.O. Box 8133, Roanoke, VA 24014 USA (SAN 665-603X) Tel 540-427-1154; Toll Free: 800-484-1492 (ext. 4267)
E-mail: gwalker@interlink.com.

ABCD Bks., *(0-9678072)* 13142 Lake St., Los Angeles, CA 90066-2205 USA Tel 310-397-0070; Fax: 310-391-6297
E-mail: abcdbooks@aol.com.

A B C International Group, Inc. *Imprint of* **Kazi Pubns., Inc.**

A B C-123 Publishing, *(0-9711474)* Orders Addr.: P.O. Box 100145, Staten Island, NY 10310 USA Fax: 718-980-4416; 718-351-4863; Toll Free: 866-339-3936; Edit Addr.: 159 New Dorp Plaza, 2nd Flr., Staten Island, NY 10306 USA
E-mail: thomas@deweydoes.com
Web site: http://www.deweydoes.com.

A B C-Clio Information Services *See* **ABC-CLIO, Inc.**

ABCs, (Applied Behaviorology Consultants), *(1-882508)* 9 Farmer St., Canton, NY 13617-1120 USA Tel 315-386-2684
E-mail: sledoux@twcny.rr.com.

A B Publishing, *(1-881545; 1-59765)* P.O. Box 83, North Star, MI 48862-0083 USA Toll Free: 800-882-6443
E-mail: abpub@abpub.com
Web site: http://www.abpub.com
Dist(s): **Spring Arbor Distributors, Inc.**

ABWE Publishing, *(1-888796)* Orders Addr.: P.O. Box 8585, Harrisburg, PA 17105-8585 USA Tel 717-774-7000; Fax: 717-774-1919; Toll Free: 877-959-2293; Edit Addr.: 522 Lewisberry Rd., New Cumberland, PA 17070 USA
E-mail: publish@abwe.org; abwe@abwe.org; info@abwe.org
Web site: http://www.abwe.org.

A Better Be Write Pub., *(0-9767732; 0-9771971; 0-9788985)* P.O. Box 639, Vineland, NJ 08360-0639 USA
E-mail: mm.stapp@comcast.net
Web site: http://www.abetterbewrite.com.

A Better Way of Learning, *(0-9665443; 1-928574)* 1936 E. Deere Ave. Ste. 120, Santa Ana, CA 92705-5732 USA Toll Free: 800-500-4263
Web site: http://www.phonicsgames.com.

A Bison Original *Imprint of* **Univ. of Nebraska Pr.**

A Blessed Heritage Educational Resources, *(0-9759320; 0-9767866)* 10602 Redwood Dr., Baytown, TX 77520 USA
E-mail: belinda.bullard@blessedheritage.com
Web site: http://www.blessedheritage.com.

A+ Bk. Publishing, *(1-929819)* Orders Addr.: P.O. Box 250165, Franklin, MI 48025-0165 USA Tel 248-223-9322; Fax: 248-223-9161; Edit Addr.: 29233 Wellington Ct., No. 61, Southfield, MI 48034 USA
E-mail: kpcartwright@ameritech.net
Dist(s): **BookMasters, Inc.**

A. Borough Bks., *(0-9640606; 1-893597)* Orders Addr.: 3901 Silver Bell Dr., Charlotte, NC 28211 USA Tel 704-364-1788; Fax: 704-366-9079; Toll Free: 800-843-8490
E-mail: HUMORBOOKS@aol.com
Dist(s): **Baker & Taylor Bks.**
Parnassus Bk. Distributors.

A C L Publishing, *(0-9708043)* 12735 W. Crescent Ave., Waukegan, IL 60085 USA Tel 847-625-9321 Do not confuse with A C L Publishing in Long Beach, CA
E-mail: vickilavi@aol.com.

A Cappela Publishing, *(0-9656309; 0-9724979; 0-9779139)* P.O. Box 3691, Sarasota, FL 34230-3691 USA (SAN 253-567X) Tel 941-351-2050; Fax: 941-351-4735 ; *Imprints:* Advocate House (Advoca Hse) Do not confuse with A Cappella Publishing, Los Angeles, CA
E-mail: acappub@aol.com
Web site: http://www.acappela.com
Dist(s): **Baker & Taylor Bks.**

A Child's Voice, *(0-9711931; 0-9798283)* P.O. Box 550, Arlington Hts, IL 60006-0550 USA
E-mail: customer_delight@childs-voice-poetry.com
Web site: http://achildvoice.com; http://www.childs-voice-poetry.com.

A. D. Vision, Inc., *(1-57813; 1-4139)* 5750 Bintliff Dr. Ste. 210, Houston, TX 77036-2123 USA Toll Free: 800-282-7202
Web site: http://www.advfilms.com
Dist(s): **Diamond Bk. Distributors**
Midwest Tape.

AEVAC, Inc., *(0-913356)* 7 Silver Lake Dr., Summit, NJ 07901-3233 USA (SAN 204-5567).

A.F.R. Software, *(0-9642829)* 1605 Pennsylvania Ave., No. 204, Miami Beach, FL 33139 USA Tel 305-531-6464.

AGA Publishing, *(1-892671)* P.O. Box 513, Apex, NC 27502 USA Tel 919-387-4568; Fax: 919-303-7111; Toll Free: 800-804-7759
E-mail: aga@pagesz.net
Dist(s): **Quality Bks., Inc.**

A H W Publishing, *(0-9741434)* 1124 W. 19th Ave., Spokane, WA 99203 USA (SAN 255-4070)
E-mail: annifrommainz@dc4pc.net.

A I G A / Art With Heart *See* **Art With Heart Press**

AIMS International Bks., Inc., *(0-922852)* 7709 Hamilton Ave., Cincinnati, OH 45231-3103 USA (SAN 630-270X) Tel 513-521-5590; Fax: 513-521-5592; Toll Free: 800-733-2067
E-mail: aimsbooks@fuse.net
Web site: http://www.aimsbooks.com
Dist(s): **Shen's Bks.**

A i T/Planet Lar, *(0-9676847; 0-9709360; 1-932051)* 2034 47th Ave., San Francisco, CA 94116 USA Tel 415-504-7516 (phone/fax)
E-mail: larry@ait-planetlar.com
Web site: http://www.ait-planetlar.com
Dist(s): **Diamond Bk. Distributors**
LPC Group.

A J B Productions, *(1-930020)* P.O. Box 221423, Anchorage, AK 99522-1423 USA Tel 907-345-5449 (phone/fax)
E-mail: N17DL@aol.com.

A JuneOne Production *Imprint of* **JuneOne Publishing Hub**

AK Peters, Ltd., *(1-56881)* 888 Worcester St., Suite 230, Wellesley, MA 02482 USA (SAN 299-1810) Tel 781-416-2888 All inquiries; Fax: 781-416-2889
E-mail: service@akpeters.com
Web site: http://www.akpeters.com.

A Kidz World *Imprint of* **ABUAA, Inc.**

ALPI International, Ltd., *(1-886647)* 1685 34th St., Oakland, CA 94608 USA Tel 510-655-6456; Fax: 510-655-2093; Toll Free: 800-678-2574
E-mail: becky@alpi.net.

AMG Pubs., *(0-89957)* Subs. of CLW Communications Group, Inc., Orders Addr.: P.O. Box 22000, Chattanooga, TN 37422 USA Tel 423-894-6060; Fax: 423-894-9511; Toll Free Fax: 800-265-6690; Toll Free: 800-266-4977; Edit Addr.: 6815 Shallowford Rd., Chattanooga, TN 37421 USA (SAN 211-3074) Toll Free Fax: 800-395-2682
E-mail: info@amgpublishers.com; sales@AMGpublishers.com
Web site: http://www.amgpublishers.com; http://www.followinggod.com
Dist(s): **Anchor Distributors**
Appalachian Bk. Distributors
Christian Bk. Distributors
Spring Arbor Distributors, Inc.
Twentieth Century Christian Bks.

AMICA Publishing Hse., *(1-884187)* Div. of AMICA International, 844 Industry Dr., No. 20, Seattle, WA 98188-3410 USA Tel 206-467-1035; Fax: 206-467-1522
E-mail: amica@ix.netcom.com
Web site: http://www.amicaint.com.

AMSC, Adventures in Math & Social Studies for Children, *(1-889639)* Orders Addr.: 818 W. Grover St., Lynden, WA 98264 USA Tel 360-354-4412; Toll Free: 800-306-1772
E-mail: math1@earthlink.net.

AMSER, *(1-893178)* 5336 N. Colonial, No. 101, Fresno, CA 93704 USA Tel 559-436-8139
E-mail: violinhorn@sbcglobal.net
Web site: http://soundsonstrings.com.

†AMS Pr., Inc., *(0-404)* Brooklyn Navy Yard Bldg. 292, Suite 417, 63 Flushing Ave., New York, NY 11205 USA (SAN 106-6706) Tel 718-875-8100; Fax: 212-995-5413 Do not confuse with companies with the same or similar name in Los Angeles, CA, Pittsburgh, PA
E-mail: amserve@earthlink.net; *CIP.*

A Miracle Cub, *(0-9679091)* Orders Addr.: P.O. Box 731088, Ormond Beach, FL 32173-1088 USA Fax: 904-676-7325; Edit Addr.: 724 Center St., Ormond Beach, FL 32174 USA
E-mail: gailmaree@juno.com.

A N A D E M, Incorporated *See* **Anadem Publishing, Inc.**

A New Day..A New Way!, *(0-9749177)* 5525-b Via La Mesa, Laguna Woods, CA 92637 USA Tel 949-458-1966 (phone/fax)
E-mail: kathleenscott@anewday-anewway.com
Web site: http://www.anewday-anewway.com
Dist(s): **New Leaf Distributing Co., Inc.**

APTE, Inc., *(1-889651; 1-931872; 1-932736; 1-933229)* 820 Davis St., Suite 224, Evanston, IL 60201 USA Toll Free: 800-494-1112
E-mail: pierred@apte.com; sally@apte.com
Web site: http://www.apte.com
Dist(s): **Brodart Co.**
Educational Resources
Follett Library Resources
Learning Services.

A Place to Remember *Imprint of* **deRuyter-Nelson Pubns., Inc.**

A Poet Born Pr., *(1-893231)* Div. of CyberNuts, Inc., Orders Addr.: P.O. Box 24238, Knoxville, TN 37933 USA Tel 423-777-1585; Edit Addr.: 212 Peters Rd., S., Knoxville, TN 37923 USA
E-mail: wm.tell.us@apoetborn.com
Web site: http://www.apoetborn.com.

+A Positive Action Pr., *(0-9670063)* 2114 Red Arrow, No. 15, Madison, WI 53711 USA.

A Press, *(1-884416)* Orders Addr.: P.O. Box 8796, Greenville, SC 29604 USA Tel 864-233-8355; Fax: 864-271-1008; Edit Addr.: 304 Ridgeland Dr., Greenville, SC 29601 USA
E-mail: apresssc@aol.com.

A. R. D. Service, Incorporated *See* **Gaines, R. L. & Assoc.**

†A.R.E. Pr., *(0-87604)* Orders Addr.: 215 67th St., Virginia Beach, VA 23451-2061 USA Tel 757-428-3588 ext 7355; Fax: 757-491-0689; Toll Free: 888-273-3400
E-mail: kkelly@edgarcayce.org
Web site: http://www.edgarcayce.org
Dist(s): **Baker & Taylor Bks.**
Brodart Co.
DeVorss & Co.
Midwest Library Service
New Concepts Bks. & Tapes Distributors
New Leaf Distributing Co., Inc.
Red Wheel/Weiser; *CIP.*

ARO Publishing Co., *(0-89868)* Box 193, 398 S. 1100 W., Provo, UT 84601 USA (SAN 212-6370) Tel 801-377-8218; Fax: 801-818-0616
E-mail: arobook@yahoo.com
Dist(s): **Forest Hse. Publishing Co., Inc.**

A R T L U Publishing, *(0-615)* 5043 SE Dupont Rd., Berryton, KS 66409 USA Tel 785-379-9533; 785-368-3700; Fax: 785-368-3743
E-mail: alancarolhayes@excite.com.

A Road to Discovery Series Guide *Imprint of* **Perry Heights Pr.**

ASDA Publishing, Inc., *(0-9632319)* 904 Forest Lake Dr., Lakeland, FL 33809 USA Tel 841-859-2194.

A. S. N. Publishing, *(0-88195; 1-59012)* 2420 Grand Ave. Ste. H, Vista, CA 92081-7827 USA (SAN 264-6005) Fax: 760-471-2645
Web site: http://www.asnpub.com
Dist(s): **National Bk. Network.**

A S Q C Quality Press *See* **ASQ Quality Pr.**

A Time To Testify/JNJT Pubns., *(0-9710705)* Orders Addr.: P.O. Box 1883, Hinesville, GA 31310 USA
E-mail: jnjt1999@yahoo.com
Web site: http://www.jnjtpublications.com.

A to Z Kinder Pr., *(0-9663228)* Orders Addr.: P.O. Box 26236, Collegeville, PA 19426-0236 USA Tel 610-287-8056; Edit Addr.: 418 Dartmoor Rd., Schwenksville, PA 19473 USA.

A Visible Diference International *See* **Scratch & Scribble Pr., Inc.**

AAA, *(0-916748; 1-56251; 1-59508)* 1000 AAA Dr., Heathrow, FL 32746-5063 USA (SAN 208-5194)
E-mail: lbonerb@national.aaa.com
Web site: http://www.aaa.com
Dist(s): **National Bk. Network**
Simon & Schuster, Inc.
Simon & Schuster Children's Publishing
Beeler, Thomas T. Pub.

AAA POP, *(0-9762282)* 4147 S. Tenmile Lake, Lakeside, OR 97449 USA
Web site: http://www.aaapop.com.

AabaGlo Media, *(0-9669818)* 632 Palmer Rd., No. 8L, Yonkers, NY 10701 USA Tel 914-793-5049 (phone/fax)
E-mail: gbuono@worldnet.att.net.

AACC Pr. *Imprint of* **American Assn. for Clinical Chemistry, Inc.**

AAcorn Bks., *(0-9663666)* P.O. Box 647, Micaville, NC 28755-0647 USA Fax: 828-675-0026
E-mail: aacorn2@excite.com
Dist(s): **Parnassus Bk. Distributors.**

Aardvark Global Publishing, *(0-9770328; 1-933570; 1-59971; 1-4276)* 9587 S. Grandview Dr., Sandy, UT 84092 USA
Web site: http://www.isbn4authors.com/
Dist(s): **AK Pr. Distribution.**

Aardvark's Weedpatch Pr., *(0-9755567)* P.O. Box 1841, Rogue River, OR 97537-1841 USA
Web site: http://www.aardvarksweedpatch.com.

AARO Publishing, *(1-893563)* Orders Addr.: P.O. Box 1281, Palisade, CO 81526 USA; Edit Addr.: 3588 E. 1/4 Rd., Palisade, CO 81526 USA (SAN 255-7185) Tel 970-464-7056 (phone/fax)970 464 4873
E-mail: carwe@earthlink.net
Web site: http://www.snowff.com.

Aaron C Ministries, *(1-933519)* 1005 Pine Oak Dr., Edmond, OK 73034-5139 USA Tel 405-348-3410
E-mail: bible@jpdawson.com
Web site: http://www.jpdawson.com.

Aaron Press *See* **Publishing Assocs., Inc.**

For full information on wholesalers and distributors, refer to the Wholesaler and Distributor Symbol Index

Aaron-Barrada, Inc., *(0-615; 0-9768671)* 79 Valley High, Ruffs Dale, PA 15679 USA Tel 724-696-4332; Fax: 612-545-3210
E-mail: aaronbarradainc@aol.com
Web site: http://www.pottiestickers.com.

Aarow Pr., *(0-9749046)* 3215 Buckingham Ave., Lakeland, FL 33803 USA (SAN 255-8653) Tel 863-709-8882 (phone/fax)
E-mail: aarowpress@yahoo.com.

A-BA-BA-HA-LA-MA-HA Pubs. *Imprint of* **Anderson House Foundation**

Abadaba Reading LLC, *(0-9789473)* P.O. Box 80, Charlottesville, VA 22902-5335 USA (SAN 852-0240).

†ABBE Pubs. Assn. of Washington, D.C., *(0-7883; 0-88164; 0-941864; 1-55914)* Orders Addr.: 4111 Gallows Rd., Virginia Div., Annandale, VA 22003 USA (SAN 239-1430) Tel 703-642-5966 (phone/fax)
E-mail: abbe.publishers@verizon.net; vze3hcqz@verizon.net
Dist(s): **Baker & Taylor Bks.**; *CIP.*

Abbeville Kids *Imprint of* **Abbeville Pr., Inc.**

†Abbeville Pr., Inc., *(0-7892; 0-89659; 1-55859)* 137 Varick St., 5th Flr., New York, NY 10013 USA (SAN 211-4755) Tel 212-366-5585; Fax: 212-366-6966; Toll Free Fax: 800-351-5073; Toll Free: 877-364-2938 ; *Imprints:* Abbeville Kids (Abbeville Kids)
E-mail: abbeville@abbeville.com
Web site: http://www.abbeville.com
Dist(s): **Perseus Distribution**; *CIP.*

Abbey Pr., *(0-87029)* 1 Hill Dr., Saint Meinrad, IN 47577-0128 USA (SAN 201-2057) Tel 812-357-8215; Fax: 812-357-8388; Toll Free: 800-325-2511
E-mail: customerservice@abbeypress.com
Web site: http://www.abbeypress.com/.

Abbot Publishing Hse., Inc., *(0-9712290)* 1431 Warner Ave. Ste. E, Tustin, CA 92780-6444 USA (SAN 253-9381).

Abbott Avenue Pr., *(0-9767514)* 859 Hollywood Way, Suite 258, Burbank, CA 91505 USA
E-mail: info@abbottavenuepress.com
Web site: http://www.abbottavenuepress.com.

Abby Publishing, *(0-9661771)* Orders Addr.: 2100 Kings Hwy. #879, Port Charlotte, FL 33980 USA Tel 941-627-4421
E-mail: anneyoungs@netscape.net.

ABC *Imprint of* **DC Comics**

ABC Bks., *(0-9785108)* P.O. Box 2246, Sunnyvale, CA 94087-2246 USA Do not confuse with ABC Books in Plano, TX.

ABC Development, Inc., *(0-9767179)* 6869 Stapoint Ct., Suite 107, Winter Park, FL 32792 USA Tel 407-671-6000; Fax: 407-671-6602; Toll Free: 800-222-3053
E-mail: sales@abc-development.com
Web site: http://www.abc-development.com.

ABC Pr., *(0-9719188)* Orders Addr.: P.O. Box 2571, Walnut Creek, CA 94595 USA (SAN 254-5535) Tel 925-946-1768; Fax: 925-935-2140; Edit Addr.: 1250 Edgewater Ct., Walnut Creek, CA 94595 USA Do not confuse with ABC Press, Inc., Ann Arbor, MI
E-mail: marjack1@aol.com.

ABC Pr., *(0-9758622)* 550 Iron Mountain Rd., El Dorado, AR 71730 USA Tel 870-863-5779
E-mail: rwood@seark.net
Web site: http:www.saac-arts.org/rwood
Dist(s): **Baker & Taylor Bks.**

ABC Pubs., *(0-9772685)* 32 Meadowlark Ln., Willingboro, NJ 08046-2108 USA Tel 609-880-0897
E-mail: fg@abc-advantage.com
Web site: http://www.abc-advantage.com.

†ABC-CLIO, Inc., *(0-87436; 0-903450; 1-57607; 1-85109; 1-59884)* 130 Cremona Dr., Santa Barbara, CA 93117 USA (SAN 301-5467) Tel 805-968-1911; Fax: 805-685-9685; Toll Free: 800-368-6868
E-mail: customerservice@abc-clio.com; service@abc-clio.com; salesuk@abc-clio.com
Web site: http://www.abc-clio.com
Dist(s): **Baker & Taylor Bks.**
Bookhouse, The
Follett Library Resources
Getty Pubns.
NetLibrary, Inc.; *CIP.*

Abccurate Business Ventures, *(0-9755341)* P.O. Box 2236, Smyrna, TN 37167 USA Tel 615-831-7100
E-mail: editor@abccurate.com
Web site: http://www.abccurate.com.

ABCDE Academic Bks. for Children's Development Through Education, *(0-9754008)* P.O. Box 374, Shrub Oak, NY 10588 USA.

ABCDMoon *See* **ABCDMoon Publishing**

ABCDMoon Publishing, *(0-9729216)* P.O. Box 910732, Lexington, KY 40591-0732 USA Tel 859-873-5031
E-mail: tex@charliethemonkey.com; amy@charliethemonkey.com
Web site: http://www.charliethemonkey.com
Dist(s): **Baker & Taylor Bks.**

ABConsulting, *(0-9669879)* P.O. Box 5806, SCC, FL 33571-5806 USA Tel 813-503-7213; Fax: 813-633-4315
E-mail: ActionBizConsult@aol.com.

ABCs Connection, Inc., *(0-9755475)* 1209 Caribou Crossing, Suite 101, Durham, NC 27713 USA Tel 919-451-4991; Fax: 919-484-1980
E-mail: casey_wallace@yahoo.com
Web site: http://www.abcsconnection.com.

ABC's Unlimited *See* **See abc's LC**

Abdiel Productions, *(0-9768088)* 4802 Nassau Ave., NE, No. 31, Tacoma, WA 98422-4632 USA.

ABDO & Daughters *Imprint of* **ABDO Publishing Co.**

ABDO & Daughters *Imprint of* **Spotlight**

Abdo & Daughters Publishing *See* **ABDO Publishing Co.**

†ABDO Publishing Co., *(0-939179; 1-56239; 1-57765; 1-59197; 1-59679; 1-59928; 1-59961; 1-60270; 1-60453)* Div. of ABDO Publishing Group, Orders Addr.: 8000 W. 78th St. Suite 310, Edina, MN 55439 USA (SAN 662-9172) Tel 952-831-2120; Fax: 952-831-1632; Toll Free: 800-800-1312 ; *Imprints:* ABDO & Daughters (ABDO & Dghtrs); Checkerboard Library (Checkerboard Library); SandCastle (SndCastle); Buddy Books (Buddy Bks); Super SandCastle (SuperSandcastle); Essential Library (EssentialLibrary)
E-mail: info@abdopublishing.com
Web site: http://www.abdopublishing.com; *CIP.*

Abednego's Free, *(1-934195)* 380-H Knollwood St. Suite #138, Winston-Salem, NC 27103 USA
E-mail: abednegosfree@yahoo.com
Web site: http://www.abednegosfree@yahoo.com.

Abedus Pr., *(0-9763091)* P.O. Box 8018, La Crescenta, CA 91224-0018 USA (SAN 256-2936)
E-mail: jadams@usc.edu.

Abel Publishing, *(0-9655739)* Orders Addr.: 3816 Rownd St., Cedar Falls, IA 50613-6144 USA; Edit Addr.: 3816 Rownd, Cedar Falls, IA 50613 USA Do not confuse with companies with the same or similar names in Santa Barbara, CA, Trinidad, CO, Los Angeles, CA
E-mail: Abel@UNI.edu.

Abernathy Hse. Publishing, *(0-9741940)* Orders Addr.: P.O. Box 1109, Yarmouth, ME 04096-1109 USA (SAN 255-4380) Tel 207-838-6170
E-mail: info@abernathyhousepub.com
Web site: http://www.abernathyhousepub.com
Dist(s): **Baker & Taylor Bks.**

Abidenme Bks., *(0-9714515)* P.O. Box 144, Island Heights, NJ 08732-0144 USA (SAN 254-1203) Fax: 732-573-0551; Toll Free: 888-540-8022
E-mail: info@abidenmebooks.com
Web site: http://www.abidenmebooks.com; http://www.unclesamskids.com
Dist(s): **Biblio Distribution.**

Abiding Life Ministries International, *(0-9670843)* Orders Addr.: P.O. Box 620998, Littleton, CO 80162-0998 USA (SAN 299-8629) Tel 303-972-0859; Fax: 303-973-2682; Edit Addr.: 8191 Southpark Ln. Unit 102, Littleton, CO 80120-4639 USA ; *Imprints:* Abiding Life Press (Abiding Life Pr)
E-mail: AbideLife@aol.com.

Abiding Life Pr. *Imprint of* **Abiding Life Ministries International**

Abiding Life Press *See* **Abiding Life Ministries International**

†Abingdon Pr., *(0-687; 1-4267)* Div. of United Methodist Publishing Hse., Orders Addr.: P.O. Box 801, Nashville, TN 37202-3919 USA (SAN 201-0054) Tel 615-749-6409; Fax: 615-749-6056; Toll Free: 800-627-1789; Edit Addr.: 201 Eighth Ave., S., Nashville, TN 37202 USA (SAN 699-9956) Toll Free: 800-627-1789
Web site: http://www.abingdonpress.com/
Dist(s): **CRC Pubns.**; *CIP.*

Abiogenesis Pr. (GBR) *(0-946790) Dist. by* **Diamond Book Dists.**

Abjad Bk. Designers & Builders, *(1-871031)* Subs. of Kazi Pubns., 3023-27 W. Belmont Ave., Chicago, IL 60618 USA Tel 773-267-7001; Fax: 773-267-7002.

AbleNet, Inc., *(0-9666667; 0-9764246)* 2808 Fairview Ave., N., Roseville, MN 55113 USA Tel 651-294-2200; Fax: 651-294-2222; Toll Free: 800-322-0956
E-mail: msagstetter@ablenetinc.com
Web site: http://www.ablenetinc.com
Dist(s): **Follett Library Resources.**

Abligio Bks., *(1-934437)* 4226 S. Rock St., Gilbert, AZ 85297-4536 USA (SAN 853-2362) Tel 480-272-6063
E-mail: publisher@abligio.com
Web site: http://abligio.com.

ABM Enterprises, Inc., *(0-9656688)* Orders Addr.: P.O. Box 123, Amelia Court House, VA 23002-0123 USA Tel 804-561-3655; Fax: 804-561-2065; Edit Addr.: 16311 Goodesbridge Rd., Amelia Court House, VA 23002 USA
E-mail: LarryDavies@SowingSeedsofFaith.com
Web site: http://www.SowingSeedsofFaith.com.

Abongold Bks., *(0-9668414)* 9444 Erwin Ave. Suite A, Orangevale, CA 95662 USA Tel 916-989-0388; Fax: 916-989-7303
E-mail: donanawalt@earthlink.net
Web site: http://www.abongoldbooks.com.

Aboriginal Studies Pr. (AUS) *(0-85575; 0-908097) Dist. by* **Intl Spec Bk.**

Abound Inc. Publishing, *(0-9676825)* Orders Addr.: P.O. Box 5930, Metairie, LA 70009-5930 USA Tel 504-259-0548; Fax: 504-887-7052; Edit Addr.: 2500 Houma Blvd., Suite 210, Metairie, LA 70001 USA
E-mail: Hdefraites@aol.com.

Abounding Love Ministries, Inc., *(0-9678519)* Orders Addr.: P.O. Box 425, Jackson, CA 95642 USA Tel 209-296-7264 (phone/fax); Edit Addr.: 225 Endicott Ave., Jackson, CA 95642-2512 USA
E-mail: alms@aboundinglove.org
Web site: http://www.aboundinglove.org.

About Comics, *(0-9716338; 0-9753958; 0-9790750)* 217 Red Oak Ln., Thousand Oaks, CA 91320-4028 USA Fax: 775 254-1022
E-mail: about@aboutcomics.com
Web site: http://www.aboutcomics.com
Dist(s): **Diamond Bk. Distributors.**

About Time Publishing, *(0-9791550)* 29792 Harper Rd., Junction City, OR 97448 USA Tel 541-954-6724
E-mail: michael@judeco.net
Web site: http://www.judeco.net.

Above the Clouds Publishing, *(1-60227)* P.O. Box 313, Stanhope, NJ 07874 USA (SAN 852-1328) Fax: 973-448-7789; Toll Free: 800-936-2319
E-mail: publisher@abovethecloudspublishing.com
Web site: http://abovethecloudspublishing.com.

Abovo Publishing, *(0-9762007)* P.O. Box 1231, Bonita, CA 91908 USA
E-mail: abovo@cox.net
Dist(s): **Baker & Taylor Bks.**
Biblio Distribution
Quality Bks., Inc.

Abrams Bks. for Young Readers *Imprint of* **Abrams, Harry N. , Inc.**

Abrams Gifts and Stationery *Imprint of* **Abrams, Harry N. , Inc.**

Abrams, Harry N. , Inc., *(0-8109; 1-4197)* 115 West 18th St., New York, NY 10011 USA (SAN 200-2434) Tel 212-206-7715; Fax: 212-519-1210 ; *Imprints:* Amulet Books (Amulet Bks); Abrams Books for Young Readers (ABYR); Abrams Gifts and Stationery (Abrams G & S); Abrams Image (Abrams Image)
E-mail: webmaster@abramsbooks.com
Web site: http://www.hnabooks.com
Dist(s): **Ediciones Universal**
Hachette Bk. Group.

Abrams Image *Imprint of* **Abrams, Harry N. , Inc.**

Abril BookStore & Publishing, *(0-9704131; 0-9772265; 0-9796842)* 415 E. Broadway, Suite 102, Glendale, CA 91205 USA Tel 818-243-4112; Fax: 818-243-4158
E-mail: info@abrilbooks.com; abrilbooks@earthlink.net
Web site: http://www.abrilbooks.com.

A-Brite Look Publishing, *(0-9714356)* 1125 NW. Sixth Pl., Moore, OK 73170 USA Tel 405-794-3504
E-mail: caw007@att.net.

Absecon Lighthouse, *(0-9779988)* 31 S. Rhode Island Ave., Atlantic City, NJ 08401 USA Tel 609-441-1360; Fax: 609-449-1919
E-mail: abseconlighthouse@verizon.net
Web site: http://www.abseconlighthouse.org.

Absey & Co., *(1-888842)* 23011 Northcrest, Spring, TX 77389 USA Tel 281-257-2340; Fax: 281-251-4676; Toll Free: 888-412-2739
E-mail: Abseyandco@aol.com
Web site: http://www.absey.biz
Dist(s): **Baker & Taylor Bks.**
Bibliotech, Inc.
BookMasters, Inc.
Brodart Co.
Follett Library Resources.

Abstract Studio, Inc., *(1-892597)* P.O. Box 271487, Houston, TX 77277-1487 USA Tel 713-666-0238 (phone/fax)
E-mail: sipnet@strangersinparadise.com
Web site: http://www.strangersinparadise.com
Dist(s): **Diamond Comic Distributors, Inc.**
Diamond Bk. Distributors
Koen-Levy Bk. Wholesalers LLC.

ABUAA, Inc., *(0-9760406)* Orders Addr.: P.O. Box 1542, Whitefish, MT 59937 USA Fax: 406-362-3407; Edit Addr.: 7347 Farm to Market Rd., Whitefish, MT 59937 USA ; *Imprints:* A Kidz World (Kidz Wrld)
Web site: http://www.akidzworld.com.

Abundant Answers Publishing Co., *(1-878110)* Orders Addr.: 369 - B Third St., Box 153, San Rafael, CA 94901 USA Tel 415-472-0735; Toll Free: 800-253-7303 (for California customers only)
E-mail: abunans@aol.com.

Abuzz Bks., *(0-9715865)* P.O. Box 15753, Scottsdale, AZ 85267 USA
E-mail: author@20umbrellas.com
Dist(s): **Quality Bks., Inc.**

AC Pubns. Group LLC, *(1-933302)* P.O. Box 260543, Lakewood, CO 80226 USA
E-mail: info@acpublicationsgroup.com
Web site: http://www.acpublicationsgroup.com
Dist(s): **Midpoint Trade Bks., Inc.**

Acacia Publishing, Inc., *(0-9666572; 0-9671187; 0-9762224; 0-9774306; 0-9788283; 0-9790826; 0-9792531; 0-9793273)* 1366 East Thomas Rd., Suite 305, Phoenix, AZ 85014 USA Tel 602-265 4553; Fax: 602-274-1598; Toll Free: 866-265-4553
E-mail: jason@hiredpen.com
Web site: http://www.acaciapublishing.com
Dist(s): **Baker & Taylor Bks.**
Book Clearing Hse.

Academic Coaching Services, Inc., *(0-9676641)* 3540 W. Sahara, PMB 129, Las Vegas, NV 89102-5816 USA Tel 702-876-3000; Fax: 702-693-4554
E-mail: academic@lvdi.net; academicoach@mgci.com
Web site: http://www.academic-coaching.com.

Academic Distribution Ctr., *(0-9640959)* 1216 Walker Rd., Freeland, MD 21053 USA Tel 410-343-0409.

Academic Edge, Inc., *(0-9754754)* Orders Addr.: P.O. Box 23605, Lexington, KY 40523-3605 USA Tel 859-221-3217; Fax: 812-331-8021; Edit Addr.: 216 E. Allen St., Suite 143, Bloomington, IN 47402 USA
E-mail: george@academicedge.com
Web site: http://www.academicedge.com.

Academic Multimedia Corporation *See* **Academic Multimedia, Inc.**

Academic Multimedia, Inc., *(0-9720535)* P.O. Box 425, Springfield, VA 22150-9998 USA Tel 703-440-0534
E-mail: wd@academicmultimedia.com
Web site: http://www.academicmultimedia.com.

Academic Power Ctr., *(0-9713992)* P.O. Box 215, Beaver, WA 98305-0215 USA
E-mail: apcpub@aol.com.

Academic Pr. *Imprint of* **Elsevier Science & Technology Bks.**

Academic Solutions, Inc., *(0-9635364; 0-9740200)* P.O. Box 102, Harvard, MA 01451 USA Tel 978-456-6829; Fax: 978-456-3053; Toll Free: 877-222-3765 (877-ACADSOL)
E-mail: asibooks@acadsol.com
Web site: acadsol.com.

Company

Academic Success for All Learners, *(0-9709686)* Utah State Univ. 6800 Old Main Hill, Logan, UT 84322-6800 USA Tel 435-797-3718; Fax: 435-797-3887
E-mail: read@cc.usu.edu
Web site: http://www.usu.edu/teach/read.

Academic Systems Corp., *(1-928962)* 2933 Bunker Hill Ln. Ste. 107, Santa Clara, CA 95054-1124 USA Toll Free: 800-694-6830
E-mail: info@academic.com
Web site: http://www.academic.com.

Academic Therapy Pubns., Inc., *(0-87879; 1-57128)* 20 Commercial Blvd., Novato, CA 94949-6191 USA (SAN 201-2111) Tel 415-883-3314; Fax: 415-883-3720; Toll Free: 800-422-7249
E-mail: sales@academictherapy.com; customerservice@academictherapy.com
Web site: http://www.academictherapy.com
Dist(s): **PCI Educational Publishing**
PRO-ED, Inc.
Saddleback Educational Publishing
Sopris West Educational Services.

Academics of Course!, *(0-9676692)* 1317 Arch St., Berkeley, CA 94708 USA Tel 510-845-9320; Fax: 510-845-9351
E-mail: academicsa@aol.com
Web site: http://www.academicsofcourse.com.

†Academy Chicago Pubs., Ltd., *(0-89733; 0-915864)* 363 W. Erie St., Chicago, IL 60610-3125 USA (SAN 213-2001) Tel 312-751-7300; Fax: 312-751-7306; Toll Free: 800-248-7323 (Orders, outside Illinois)
E-mail: info@academychicago.com
Web site: http://www.academychicago.com
Dist(s): **Baker & Taylor Bks.**
Brodart Co.
Chicago Distribution Ctr.; *CIP.*

Academy for Future Science, *(0-9603450; 1-892139)* Orders Addr.: P.O. Box 395, Ava, MO 65606 USA (SAN 222-2566) Tel 417-683-9636
E-mail: sales@affs.org
Web site: http://www.keysofenoch.org.

†Academy of American Franciscan History, *(0-88382)* 1712 Euclid Ave., Berkeley, CA 94709 USA (SAN 201-1964) Tel 510-548-1755; Fax: 510-549-9466
E-mail: acadafh@fst.edu
Web site: http://www.aafh.org; *CIP.*

Acadian Hse. Publishing, *(0-925417)* Orders Addr.: P.O. Box 52247, Lafayette, LA 70505 USA Tel 337-235-8851; Fax: 337-235-9925; Toll Free: 800-850-8851; Edit Addr.: 100 Asma Blvd., Suite 365, Lafayette, LA 70508 USA (SAN 253-1305)
E-mail: info@acadianhouse.com
Web site: http://www.acadianhouse.com
Dist(s): **Baker & Taylor Bks.**
Forest Sales & Distributing Co.

†Acanthus Pr. LLC, *(0-926494)* 54 W. 21st St. Rm. 408, New York, NY 10010 USA (SAN 256-999X) Tel 212-414-0108; Fax: 212-229-1959; Toll Free: 800-827-7614
E-mail: info@acanthuspress.com; orders@acanthuspress.com
Web site: http://www.acanthuspress.com; *CIP.*

Accelerated Pr., *(0-9703927)* Div. of Accelerated Success Strategies, 525 N. Belt, Suite 300, Houston, TX 77060 USA Tel 281-447-5222
E-mail: hgvetter@iamerica.net
Web site: http://www.acceleratedmind.com.

Accelerated Success Publisher *See* **Accelerated Pr.**

Accent On Success, *(0-9743700)* 29 Benton Pl., Saint Louis, MO 63104 USA Tel 314-664-6110; Fax: 314-664-6577
E-mail: jbishop@accentonsuccess.com
Web site: http://www.accentonsuccess.com.

Accent Pr. (GBR) *(0-9547092; 1-905170; 0-9548673) Dist. by* **Dufour.**

Accent Pubns., *(0-9708959; 0-9748426; 0-9787472)* Orders Addr.: P.O. Box 1171, Bay City, MI 48706 USA (SAN 851-433X) do not confuse with copanies with the same name in Nashville, TN
E-mail: dstevens2567@chartermi.net.

Access for Disabled Americans, *(1-928616)* 3685 Mt. Diablo Blvd., Suite 300, Lafayette, CA 94549 USA Tel 925-284-6444; Fax: 925-284-6448
E-mail: PSmither@aol.com
Web site: http://maxpages.com/disabledaccess; http://www.accessfordisabled.com.

Access Research Network, *(1-931796)* Orders Addr.: P.O. Box 38069, Colorado Springs, CO 80937-8069 USA Tel 719-633-1772; Fax: 719-268-9209; Toll Free: 888-259-7102; Edit Addr.: 2601 Rigel Dr., Colorado Springs, CO 80906 USA
E-mail: arn@arn.org
Web site: http://www.arn.org.

Access-4-All, Inc., *(0-9744908)* P.O. Box 220751, Sain Louis, MO 63122-0751 USA Tel 314-821-7011; Fax: 314-909-8086
E-mail: steve@access-4-all.com
Web site: http://www.access-4-all.com.

Accessibilities, *(0-9774546)* 1131 E. Spruce St., Sault Ste. Marie, MI 49783 USA
E-mail: geri.taeckens@isahealthfund.org
Web site: http://www.isahealthfund.org.

Acclaim Pr., Inc., *(0-9773198; 0-9790025; 0-9798802)* Orders Addr.: P.O. Box 238, Morley, MO 63767 USA Tel 573-262-2121 (phone/fax); Edit Addr.: 171 Co. Hwy. 430, Oran, MO 63771 USA
E-mail: dwsikes@cablerocket.com
Web site: http://www.StewardandWise.com
Dist(s): **Partners Bk. Distributing, Inc.**

Accord Publishing, Ltd., *(0-939251; 1-57939)* 1732 Wazee St., Suite 202, Denver, CO 80202 USA (SAN 663-5032) Tel 303-298-1300; Fax: 303-298-7111; Toll Free: 888-333-1676
E-mail: accordpublishing@msn.com; sales@accordpublishing.com
Web site: http://www.accordpublishing.com
Dist(s): **Baker & Taylor Bks.**
Bookmen, Inc.
Booksource, The
Simon & Schuster, Inc.

Accordian Bks., *(0-9754098)* Orders Addr.: P.O. Box 69912, West Hollywood, CA 90069 USA (SAN 256-0046); Edit Addr.: 69912 W. Hollywood, Hollywood, CA 90069 USA
E-mail: crystalilluminations@msn.com.

Ace Academics, Inc., *(1-57633; 1-881374)* 253 Closterdock Rd., Suite 6, Closter, NJ 07624 USA Tel 201-784-0001; Fax: 201-784-7704; Toll Free Fax: 800-352-7445; Toll Free: 888-378-8393 ; *Imprints:* Exambusters (Exambusters)
E-mail: highself@aol.com; acepub2@aol.com; info@exambusters.com
Web site: http://www.exambusters.com
Dist(s): **Baker & Taylor Bks.**
NACSCORP, Inc.

Ace Bks. *Imprint of* **Penguin Group (USA) Inc.**

Ace Hardcover *Imprint of* **Penguin Group (USA) Inc.**

Ace Reid Enterprises *See* **Cowpokes Cartoon Bks.**

Ace Trade *Imprint of* **Penguin Group (USA) Inc.**

Acen Press *See* **DNA Pr.**

Acervo Cultural (ARG) *(987-9333; 987-96277) Dist. by* **Latin Am Bk Source.**

Aceybee Publishing, *(0-9763958)* 285 W. Kootenai, No. 7, Richfield, ID 23349-5344 USA.

Achieve Pubns., *(0-615; 0-9727762)* Orders Addr.: 1216 Scobee Dr., Lansdale, PA 19446 USA Toll Free: 800-431-1579 (orders)
E-mail: achievepub@verizon.net
Web site: http://www.achievepublications.com
Dist(s): **Book Clearing Hse.**
Brodart Co.

Achieve3000, *(0-615; 1-932166)* 1091 River Ave., Lakewood, NJ 08701 USA Tel 732-367-5505; Fax: 732-367-2313; Toll Free: 877-803-6505
E-mail: kelly.tanko@achieve3000.com
Web site: http://www.achieve3000.com.

Achievers Technology Resource, Inc., *(0-9716113)* PMB No. 455, 442 Rte. 202-206 N., Bedminster, NJ 07921-1522 USA (SAN 254-2811)
Web site: http://www.achieversrus.com.

Achieving Corporate Excellence, Inc., *(0-9746262)* Orders Addr.: P.O. Box 651119, Vero Beach, FL 32965-1119 USA Toll Free: 877-656-8313; Edit Addr.: 8003 Kenwood Rd., Fort Pierce, FL 34951 USA
Web site: http://www.acespeaks.com.

Acid Test Productions *See* **Grateful Dead Productions**

ACME Pr., *(0-9629880)* Orders Addr.: P.O. Box 1702, Westminster, MD 21158 USA Tel 410-848-7577; Edit Addr.: 1116 E. Deep Run Rd., Westminster, MD 21158 USA.

Acmon Blue Publishing, *(0-9744792)* P.O. Box 475, Tujunga, CA 91043-0475 USA (SAN 255-5638) Tel 818-352-2551 (phone/fax)
E-mail: info@acmonblue.com
Web site: http://www.acmonblue.com
Dist(s): **Baker & Taylor Bks.**

Acorn Bks., *(0-9664470; 1-930472)* 7337 Terrace, Kansas City, MO 64114-1256 USA Tel 816-523-8321; Fax: 816-333-3843; Toll Free: 888-422-0320 Do not confuse with companies with the same or similar name in Springfield, IL, Bloomington, IN, St. Albans, VT
E-mail: jami.parkison@micro.com
Web site: http://www.acornbks.com.

Acorn Publishing, *(0-937921)* Div. of Vitesse Pr., PMB 367, 45 State St., Montpelier, VT 05601 USA (SAN 659-4840) Tel 802-229-4243; Fax: 802-229-6939 Do not confuse with companies with the same or similar name in Midvale, UT, Broomfield, CO, Battle Creek, MI, Sisters, OR, Suffern, NY,Saltlake City, UT, Portland, OR, Sping Lake, MI
E-mail: dick@vitessepress.com
Web site: http://www.vitessepress.com
Dist(s): **Hood, Alan C. & Co., Inc.**

Acorn Publishing *See* **ChoiceSkills, Inc.**

Acorn Publishing, *(0-9678801; 0-9710988; 0-9728969; 0-9774449)* Div. of Development Initiatives, 186 N. 23rd St., Battle Creek, MI 49015-1711 USA (SAN 854-6258) Tel 269-962-8184 (phone fax); Toll Free: 877-700-2219 (phone fax) Do not confuse with companies with the same or similar name in Broomfield, CO, Midvale, UT, Montpelier, VT, Sisters, OR, Suffern, NY, Salt Lake City, UT, Portland, OR, Sping Lake, MI
E-mail: editor@acornpublishing.com
Web site: http://www.acornpublishing.com
Dist(s): **Baker & Taylor Bks.**

Acoustic Learning Inc., *(0-9761435; 0-9800581)* 215 Prospect Ave., Highland Park, IL 60035-3357 USA
E-mail: eartraining@aruffo.com
Web site: http://www.acousticlearning.com.

Acres Publishing, *(0-9741081)* 311 Prospect St., Alton, IL 62002 USA.

Acrobatic Cats Publishing, *(0-9787864)* 325 Iliwahi Loop, Kailua, HI 96734 USA Tel 808-254-4691
Web site: http://www.rarehawaii.org/acrobaticcats.htm.

Acrospire Bk. Pubs., *(0-9658531)* P.O. Box 3472, Littleton, CO 80161 USA Tel 303-730-9689 (phone/fax)
E-mail: PsQsBook@aol.com.

ACT, *(0-937734; 1-56009)* Orders Addr.: P.O. Box 168, Iowa City, IA 52243-0168 USA (SAN 696-5075); Edit Addr.: 2201 N. Dodge St., Iowa City, IA 52243-0168 USA (SAN 204-8027) Tel 319-337-1410; Fax: 319-339-3020; 319-337-1014
E-mail: compass@act.org
Web site: http://www.act.org.

Act For Kids, *(1-930489)* 7 S. Howard St., Suite 200, Spokane, WA 99201 USA Tel 509-343-5010; Fax: 509-747-0609
E-mail: Sales@actforkids.org
Web site: http://www.actforkids.org.

ACTA Pubns., *(0-87946; 0-914070; 0-915388)* 5559 Howard St., Skokie, IL 60077-2621 USA (SAN 204-7489) Toll Free Fax: 800-397-0079; Toll Free: 800-397-2282
E-mail: actapublications@aol.com
Web site: http://www.actapublications.com
Dist(s): **Spring Arbor Distributors, Inc.**

Action Bks., *(0-9765692; 0-9799755)* Dept Of English, U. Of Notre Dame 356 O'shaughnessy Hall, Notre Dame, IN 46556 USA
Web site: http://www.actionbooks.org
Dist(s): **SPD-Small Pr. Distribution.**

Action Factor, Inc., *(0-9720763; 0-9754618)* PMB 218, 3195 Dayton-Xenia Rd., Suite 900, Beavercreek, OH 45434-6390 USA Tel 937-426-4364 (phone/fax)
E-mail: cgifford@actionfactor.com
Web site: http://www.actionfactor.com.

Action Organizing, *(0-9721964)* Div. of Successful Organizing Solutions, Orders Addr.: 406 Shato Ln., Madison, WI 53716 USA Tel 608-441-6767; Edit Addr.: P.O. Box 202, Milton, WI 53563 USA Tel 608-868-4079; Toll Free: 888-577-6655
E-mail: info@SOSorganize.net; sales@SOSorganize.net
Web site: http://www.actionorganizing.com.

Action Publishing, Inc., *(1-882210)* Div. of Action Products International, Inc., 344 Cypress Rd., Ocala, FL 34472-3108 USA Tel 352-687-2202; Fax: 352-687-4961; Toll Free: 800-772-2846 Do not confuse with companies with the same or similar name in Newport Beach, CA, Burlingame, CA, West Los Angeles, CA, Houstin, TX, Chicago, IL, Glendale, CA, Austin, TX.

Action Publishing, LLC, *(0-9617199; 1-883649; 1-888045)* P.O. Box 391, Glendale, CA 91209 USA (SAN 299-1802) Tel 323-478-1667; Fax: 323-478-1767; Toll Free: 800-705-7482 Do not confuse with companies with the same or similar name in Newport Beach, CA, Burlingame, CA, West Los Angeles, CA, Houstin, TX, Chicago, IL, Ocala, CA, Austin, TX
E-mail: sales@actionpublishing.com
Web site: http://www.actionpublishing.com
Dist(s): **Midpoint Trade Bks., Inc.**

Action Reading, Inc., *(1-928606)* Orders Addr.: P.O. Box 4944, Cave Creek, AZ 85327 USA Tel 623-465-1095; Fax: 623-465-0274; Toll Free: 800-378-1046; Edit Addr.: P.O. Box 4944, Cave Creek, AZ 85327-4944 USA
E-mail: reading@goodnet.com
Web site: http://www.actionreading.com.

Actionopolis *Imprint of* **Komikwerks, LLC**

Activated Ministries, P.O. Box 462805, Escondido, CA 92046-2805 USA Toll Free: 877-862-3228
E-mail: sales@activatedministries.org.

Active Images, *(0-9740567; 0-9766761)* 8910 Rayford Dr., Los Angeles, CA 90045 USA Tel 310-215-0362; Fax: 775-890-5787 do not confuse with Active Images, Incorporated in Sterling, VA
E-mail: richard@comicraft.com
Web site: http://www.activeimages.com
Dist(s): **Partners Pubs. Group, Inc.**

Active Learning Corp., *(0-912813)* P.O. Box 254, New Paltz, NY 12561 USA (SAN 282-7794) Tel 845-255-0844; Fax: 845-255-8796
E-mail: panmans@newpaltz.edu; info@activelearning.com
Web site: http://www.activelearningcorp.com.

Active Learning Systems, LLC, *(1-57652)* P.O. Box 254, Epping, NH 03042 USA Tel 603-679-3332; Fax: 603-679-2611; Toll Free: 800-644-5059
E-mail: info@iimresearch.com
Web site: http://www.iimresearch.com.

Active Media Publishing, LLC, *(0-9745645)* 362 Burleigh St., Orlando, FL 32824 USA (SAN 255-6545)
E-mail: wizbenny@aol.com
Web site: http://www.activemediapublishing.com.

Active Parenting Pubs., *(0-9618020; 1-880283; 1-59723)* 1955 Vaughn Rd. NW, Suite 108, Kennesaw, GA 30144-7808 USA (SAN 666-301X) Tel 770-429-0565; Fax: 770-429-0334; Toll Free: 800-825-0060
E-mail: cservice@activeparenting.com; ckeller@activeparenting.com
Web site: http://www.activeparenting.com
Dist(s): **National Bk. Network.**

Active Synapse, *(0-9677255)* Orders Addr.: 5336 Park Lane Dr., Columbus, OH 43231-4072 USA
E-mail: Info@ActiveSynapse.com; SalesHelp@ActiveSynapse.com
Web site: http://www.activesynapse.com
Dist(s): **Baker & Taylor Bks.**
Brodart Co.
Cold Cut Comics Distribution
Diamond Distributors, Inc.
Emery-Pratt Co.
Follett Library Resources
Midwest Library Service.

Activities Club, Inc., The, *(1-931042)* 220 Boylston St. Apt. 1516, Boston, MA 02116-3951 USA Toll Free: 800-873-5487
E-mail: taclub@earthlink.net
Web site: http://www.activitiesclub.com.

Activities for Learning, *(0-9609636; 1-931980)* 21374 York Rd., Hutchinson, MN 55350-6748 USA (SAN 283-2445) Toll Free: 800-593-7030
E-mail: joancott@hutchtel.net
Web site: http://www.alabacus.com/.

Activity Resources Co., Inc., *(0-918932; 1-882293)* Orders Addr.: P.O. Box 4875, Hayward, CA 94540 USA (SAN 209-0201) Tel 510-782-1300; Fax: 510-782-8172; Edit Addr.: 20655 Hathaway Ave., Hayward, CA 94541 USA
E-mail: info@activityresources.com
Web site: http://www.activityresources.com
Dist(s): **Delta Education, LLC**
Seymour, Dale Pubns.

ACTNew Bks., *(0-9762326)* 12687 Blue Star Memorial Hwy., South Haven, MI 49090 USA
E-mail: actnewbooks@yahoo.com
Web site: http://www.actnewbooks.com.

Ad Center, The *See* **Leathers Publishing**

Adage Pubns., *(1-879889)* Orders Addr.: P.O. Box 2377, Coeur d'Alene, ID 83816-2377 USA
Web site: http://wwwabcfeelings.com
Dist(s): **Baker & Taylor Bks.**
New Leaf Distributing Co., Inc.
Partners/West
Unique Bks., Inc.

Adair Business Institute & Publishing Company *See* **Innovative Products Plus**

Adam Enterprises *See* **Amberwood Pr.**

Adam Hill Pubns., *(0-9769360)* 2699 Stirling Rd., Suite B-301, Fort Lauderdale, FL 33312 USA Tel 954-983-5005
Web site: http://www.adamhilldesign.com.

Adamant Media, *(1-4021; 1-4212; 0-543)* Orders Addr.: 200 William Str. Suite 308, Port Chester, NY 10573 USA ; *Imprints:* Elibron Classics (Elibron Class)
E-mail: orders@elibron.com
Web site: http://www.elibron.com.

Adams, Evelyn, *(0-9761102)* 727 Virginia Ave., Midland, PA 15059-1429 USA Tel 724-643-9968; Fax: 724-775-8648
E-mail: rjb@timesnet.net
Web site: http://www.storiesfromvic.com.

Adams, Jeanette *See* **Camelot Tales**

†Adams Media Corp., *(0-937860; 1-55850; 1-58062; 1-59337; 1-59869)* Div.of F & W Publications, Inc., Orders Addr.: 57 Littlefield St., Avon, MA 02322 USA (SAN 215-2886) Tel 508-427-7100; Fax: 508-427-6790; Toll Free: 800-872-5627; F & W Publications, Inc. 4700 E. Galbraith, Cincinnati, OH 45236 Tel 513-531-2690; Toll Free: 800-289-0963
E-mail: Allison.Omeara@adamsmedia.com; orders@adamsmedia.com; FW_CIN_ORDERS@fwpubs.com; judy.bernardi@adamsmedia.com
Web site: http://www.adamsmedia.com
Dist(s): **Cranbury International**
Curreri, Michelle Morrow; *CIP.*

Adams Publishing *See* **Adams Media Corp.**

Adams Publishing, *(0-9729189)* 320 Lincoln Rd., Branchland, WV 25506 USA Tel 304-824-2504 (phone/fax) Do not confuse with companies with the same or similar name in Topanga, CA, Rainier, WA, Boston, MA
E-mail: Adamspublisher@zoominternet.net
Web site: http://www.geocities.com/daycarebook/index.html.

Adams-Crymes, Phyllis, *(1-930659)* 3916 Hearthstone Dr., Florissant, MO 63033-4029 USA.

Adams-Hall Publishing, *(0-944708)* P.O. Box 491002, Los Angeles, CA 90049 USA (SAN 244-9900) Tel 310-788-3809; Fax: 310-788-0175; Toll Free: 800-888-4452
E-mail: info@adams-hall.com
Web site: http://www.adams-hall.com.

Adamson, Bobby R., *(0-9720631)* Orders Addr.: P.O. Box 626, Palisade, CO 81526 USA; Edit Addr.: 323 W. Second St., Palisade, CO 81526 USA.

Adamson, Diane G., *(0-9673571)* 1926 Meadow Downs Way, Salt Lake Cty, UT 84121-3034 USA
E-mail: Diane50@juno.com.

Adamson, Mac, *(0-9779369)* P.O. Box 690, Midway, UT 84049 USA Tel 801-318-8544
E-mail: madamson@kids4fitkids.org
Web site: http://kids4fitkids.org.

Adams-Pomeroy Pr., *(0-9661009)* Orders Addr.: P.O. Box 189, Albany, WI 53502 USA Tel 608-862-3645; Fax: 608-862-3647; Toll Free: 877-862-3645; Edit Addr.: 103 N. Jackson St., Albany, WI 53502 USA
E-mail: adamspomeroy@ckhnet.com
Dist(s): **Baker & Taylor Bks.**

Adbeth Pr., *(0-9658468)* 617 Campbell St., Joliet, IL 60435 USA Tel 815-726-5113; Fax: 630-545-9514
E-mail: modelm@aol.com.

Addax Publishing Group, Inc., *(1-886110; 1-58497)* Orders Addr.: 15200 NBN Way, Blue Ridge Summit, PA 17214 USA Tel 717-794-3800 (Sales, Customer Service, MIS, Royalties, Inventory Mgmt., Dist. Credit & Collections); Fax: 717-794-3803 (Customer Service &/or orders only); 717-794-3857 (Sales & MIS; 717-794-3856 (Royalties, Inventory Mgmt. & Dist.; Toll Free Fax: 800-338-4550 (Customer Service &/or orders); Toll Free: 800-462-6420 (Customer Service &/or orders)
Web site: http://www.rlpgbooks.com
Dist(s): **Baker & Taylor Bks.**
Booksource, The
National Bk. Network.

Added Upon, Inc., *(0-9740319)* Orders Addr.: P.O. Box 65327, Vancouver, WA 98665 USA; Edit Addr.: 3018 NE 94th Way, Vancouver, WA 98665 USA Fax: 360-574-7115
E-mail: dunnjessel@msn.com.

†Addicus Bks., *(1-886039)* Orders Addr.: P.O. Box 45327, Omaha, NE 68145 USA Tel 402-330-7493; Fax: 402 330-1707; Toll Free: 800-352-2873
E-mail: addicusbks@aol.com
Web site: http://www.AddicusBooks.com
Dist(s): **Independent Pubs. Group**; *CIP.*

Addington Publishing, *(0-9640303)* 1339 Valencia Ave., Stockton, CA 95209-3029 USA Tel 209-951-5985; Fax: 209-477-6893
E-mail: balobet@aol.com.

Addison Wesley *Imprint of* **Benjamin-Cummings Publishing Co.**

Addison Wesley Schl., Orders Addr.: a/o Order Dept., 200 Old Tappan Rd., Old Tappan, NJ 07675 USA Toll Free Fax: 800-445-6991; Toll Free: 800-922-0579; Edit Addr.: 75 Arlington St., Boston, MA 02116 USA Tel 617-848-7500 ; *Imprints:* Scott Foresman (S-Foresman)
Web site: http://www.aw-bc.com.

Addison-Wesley Educational Pubs., Inc., *(0-321; 0-328; 0-673)* Div. of Addison Wesley Longman, Inc., 75 Arlington St., Boston, MA 02116 USA Tel 617-848-7500; Toll Free: 800-447-2226 ; *Imprints:* Scott Foresman (Scott Frsmn); Scott Foresman (S-Foresman)
Web site: http://www.awl.com.

†Addison-Wesley Longman, Inc., *(0-201; 0-321; 0-582; 0-673; 0-8013; 0-8053; 0-9654123)* Orders Addr.: 200 Old Tappan Rd., Old Tappan, NJ 07675 USA (SAN 299-4739) Toll Free: 800-922-0579; Edit Addr.: 75 Arlington St., Suite 300, Boston, MA 02116 USA (SAN 200-2000) Tel 617-848-7500; Toll Free: 800-447-2226
E-mail: pearsoned@eds.com; orderdeptnj@pearsoned.com
Web site: http://www.awl.com
Dist(s): **Continental Bk. Co., Inc.**
Pearson Education
Trans-Atlantic Pubns., Inc.; *CIP.*

Addison-Wesley Longman, Ltd. (GBR) *(0-582) Dist. by* **Trans-Atl Phila.**

Addison-Wesley Publishing Company, Incorporated *See* **Addison-Wesley Longman, Inc.**

Adelante Productions, Inc., *(0-9748017)* 600 Columbus Ave., 8G, New York, NY 10024 USA
E-mail: info@adelantepro.com
Web site: http://www.adelantepro.com.

Adelekan Publishing Co., *(0-9620036; 978-30056)* P.O. Box 5983, Garden Grove, CA 92846 USA (SAN 247-1809) Tel 310-885-4830; 213-309-0240
E-mail: ehof98@hotmail.com
Web site: http://www.angelfire.com/biz2/ehof.

AdHouse Bks., *(0-9721794; 0-9770304)* 1224 Greycourt Ave., Richmond, VA 23227-4042 USA
Dist(s): **Diamond Bk. Distributors.**

Adibooks.com, *(0-9728909; 0-9743872; 0-9748753; 0-9758993; 0-9760575; 0-9763465; 0-9764322; 0-9767424; 0-9772505; 0-9776044; 0-9778606; 0-9779682; 0-9787515; 0-9789741; 0-9791289; 0-9794769; 0-9797885)* 181 Industrial Ave., Lowell, MA 01852 USA Fax: 978-458-3026
Web site: http://www.adibooks.com
Dist(s): **Biblio Distribution.**

Adirondack Kids Pr., *(0-9707044)* 39 Second St., Camden, NY 13316 USA Tel 315-245-3614; Fax: 315-245-4861
E-mail: gvanriper@aol.com
Web site: http://www.adirondackkids.com.

Adisoft, Inc., *(0-9674897)* Orders Addr.: P.O. Box 2094, San Leandro, CA 94577-2094 USA Tel 510-483-3556; Fax: 510-483-3885; Edit Addr.: 664 Joaquin Ave., San Leandro, CA 94577 USA ; *Imprints:* Wawa Press (Wawa)
E-mail: information@adisoft-inc.com
Web site: http://www.adisoft-inc.com.

Adiva, Incorporated *See* **TEG Publishing**

Adjust Communications, *(0-9765973)* 905 Hwy. 321 NW, Suite No. 364, Hickory, NC 28601 USA Tel 828-850-3237; Fax: 866-334-4360
Web site: http://www.victoryafterhighschool.com.

Adler, Karen, *(0-9679772)* 34738 McDaniel Dr., Northfork, CA 93643 USA Tel 559-877-2033.

Adler's Foreign Bks., Inc., *(0-8417)* 915 Foster St., Evanston, IL 60201 USA (SAN 111-3089) Tel 847-864-0664; Fax: 847-864-0804; Toll Free: 800-235-3771
E-mail: info@afb-adlers.com
Web site: http://www.afb-adlers.com
Dist(s): **Distribooks, Inc.**

Admiral Nimitz Foundation, *(0-934841; 0-9790600)* Orders Addr.: 328 E. Main St., Fredericksburg, TX 78624 USA (SAN 201-1883) Tel 830-997-8600; Fax: 830-997-8092; Edit Addr.: 340 E. Main, Fredericksburg, TX 78624 USA (SAN 661-9312)
E-mail: vaugh@nimitz-museum.org
Web site: http://www.nimitz-museum.org.

Adonis Pr., *(0-932776)* 320 Rte. 21C, Ghent, NY 12075 USA (SAN 661-9320) Tel 518-392-8552; Fax: 518-392-9060
E-mail: adonis@taconic.net
Web site: http://www.adonispress.org/
Dist(s): **SteinerBooks, Inc.**

Adonoke Inc., *(0-9773180)* 1427 Graffenburg Rd., New Hartford, NY 13413 USA Tel 315-733-6445
E-mail: info@adonokebooks.com
Web site: http://www.adonokebooks.com.

Adoption Tribe Publishing, *(0-9747443)* Orders Addr.: 215 W. San Francisco, Suite 201, Santa Fe, NM 87501 USA Tel 505-988-5683
E-mail: sarahlbr@earthlink.net
Web site: http://www.adoptionmeanslove.com.

ADR BookPrint, *(0-9742743; 0-9761513; 0-9795033)* 2012 Northern Ave., Wichita, KS 67216 USA Tel 316-522-5599; Fax: 316-522-5445; Toll Free: 800-767-6066
Web site: http://www.adrbookprint.com.

ADV Manga, *(1-57813)* Div. of A. D. Vision, Inc., 5750 Bintliff, Suite 200, Houston, TX 77036 USA
Web site: http://ADVFilms.com.

ADVAN Pr., Inc. (CAN) *(0-9734496) Dist. by* **Biblio Dist.**

Advance Bks. *Imprint of* **Advance Bks. Co.**

Advance Bks. Co., *(0-9706224; 0-9746172)* P.O. Box 630634, Houston, TX 77263-0634 USA ; *Imprints:* Armadillo Books (Armadillo Bks); Advance Books (Advance Books) Do not confuse with Advance Books in San Francisco, CA
E-mail: staff@advancebooks.com
Web site: http://www.advancebooks.com
Dist(s): **Baker & Taylor Bks.**
Ingram Bk. Co.
Replica Bks.

Advance Cal Tech, Inc., *(0-943759)* 210 Clary Ave., San Gabriel, CA 91776-1375 USA (SAN 242-2603).

Advance Publishers, Incorporated *See* **Advance Pubs. LLC**

Advance Pubs. LLC, *(0-9619525; 1-57973; 1-885222)* 1060 Maitland Center Cmns Blvd. Ste. 365, Maitland, FL 32751-7499 USA (SAN 244-9226) Toll Free: 800-777-2041
E-mail: advpublish@aol.com; questions@adv-pub.com
Web site: http://www.advancepublishers.com.

Advance Publishing, Inc., *(0-9610810; 1-57537)* 6950 Fulton St., Houston, TX 77022 USA (SAN 263-9572) Tel 713-695-0600; Fax: 713-695-8585; Toll Free: 800-917-9630 Do not confuse with Advance Publishing, Brownburg, IN
E-mail: info@advancepublishing.com
Web site: http://www.advancepublishing.com
Dist(s): **Follett Library Resources**
Tandem Library Grp.

Advanced Learning Pr., *(0-9644955; 0-9709455; 0-9747343; 1-933196)* 317 Inverness Way S., Suite 150, Englewood, CO 80112 USA Tel 303-681-9995; Fax: 303-681-9996; Toll Free: 800-844-6599
E-mail: afenske@makingstandardswork.com
Web site: http://www.makingstandswork.com/
Dist(s): **National Bk. Network.**

Advanced Marketing, S. de R. L. de C. V. (MEX) *(970-718) Dist. by* **Bilingual Pubns.**

Advanced Marketing, S. de R. L. de C. V. (MEX) *(970-718) Dist. by* **Perseus Dist.**

Advanced Marketing Services, Incorporated *See* **Advantage Pubs. Group**

Advantage Books *See* **Advantage Bks., LLC**

Advantage Bks., LLC, *(0-9660366; 0-9714609)* 3268 Arcadia Pl NW, Washington, DC 20015-2330 USA (SAN 253-8237) Toll Free: 888-238-8588 Do not confuse with companies with the same or similar name in New Port Beach, CA, Longwood, FL
E-mail: advantagebooksdc@aol.com
Web site: http://www.addvance.com
Dist(s): **National Bk. Network.**

Advantage Pubs. Group, *(0-934429; 1-57145; 1-59223)* 5880 Oberlin Dr., San Diego, CA 92121 USA (SAN 630-8090) Toll Free: 800-284-3580 ; *Imprints:* Thunder Bay Press (Thunder Bay); Laurel Glen Publishing (Laurel Glen Pub); Silver Dolphin Books (Silver Dolph); Portable Press (Portable Pr)
E-mail: bernadetteb@advmkt.com
Web site: http://www.silverdolphinbooks.com; http://www.advantagebooksonline.com; http://www.laurelglenbooks.com; http://www.thunderbaybooks.com/; http://www.bathroomreader.com
Dist(s): **Learning Connection, The**
Perseus Distribution.

Adventure & Discovery Pr., *(0-9744672)* P.O. Box 11631, Syracuse, NY 13218 USA Toll Free: 800-682-2662.

Adventure Beyond The Horizon *See* **Omega Pr.**

Adventure Bks., Inc., *(0-9712217)* Orders Addr.: P.O. Box 5196, Fresno, CA 93755 USA Tel 559-294-8781 (phone/fax); Edit Addr.: 4909 N. Winery Cir., No. 106, Fresno, CA 93726 USA Do not confuse with companies with a similar name in Arvada, CO, Orange City, FL, Coeur d Alene, ID
E-mail: www.adventurebooks@juno.com
Dist(s): **Baker & Taylor Bks.**
Barnes & Noble, Inc.
Quality Bks., Inc.

Adventure in Discovery, *(0-9743414)* 18011 N. Hwy. A1A, Jupiter, FL 33477 USA Tel 561-575-4601.

Adventure Meadow, *(0-9662994)* 105 S. Sparks St., Burbank, CA 91506 USA Tel 818-848-4071; Fax: 818-848-1571
E-mail: pypdreams@earthlink.net; kenilworth@hotmail.com
Web site: http://www.pypdreams.com.

Adventure Medical Kits, *(0-9659768)* Orders Addr.: P.O. Box 43309, Oakland, CA 94624 USA Tel 510-261-7414; Fax: 510-261-7419; Toll Free: 800-324-3517; Edit Addr.: 5555 San Leandro St., Oakland, CA 94621 USA
E-mail: AMKUSA@aol.com.

Adventure Pr., *(0-9758654)* P.O. Box 40072, Casper, WY 82604 USA Tel 307-473-7483
E-mail: antelope85@hotmail.com.

Adventure Productions, Inc., *(0-9614904)* 3404 Terry Lake Rd., Fort Collins, CO 80524 USA (SAN 693-3955) Tel 970-493-8776; Fax: 970-484-5825 Do not confuse with Adventure Productions, Reno, NV.
E-mail: cjansen@wild-west.com.

Adventure Pubns., Inc., *(0-934860; 1-885061; 1-59193)* Orders Addr.: 820 Cleveland St., S., Cambridge, MN 55008 USA (SAN 212-7199) Tel 763-689-9800; Fax: 763-689-9039; Toll Free Fax: 877-374-9016; Toll Free: 800-678-7006
E-mail: orders@adventurepublications.net; custservice@adventurepublications.net
Web site: http://www.adventurepublications.net.

Adventures Galore, *(0-9759542)* Orders Addr.: P.O. Box 748, Lake George, CO 80827 USA Tel 719-748-8458; Fax: 719-748-8459; Edit Addr.: 35100 Hwy. 24, Lake George, CO 80827 USA
Web site: http://www.adventuresgalore.com.

Adventures In Books, *(0-9726541)* 4178 Mission St., San Francisco, CA 94112 USA (SAN 254-9638) Tel 415-469-9579 ext 201; Fax: 415-469-9481
E-mail: bohemio@ix.netcom.com
Web site: http://www.bohemionews.com
Dist(s): **Baker & Taylor Bks.**

Adventures in Ceramics, *(1-893502)* Div. of The Morrissey Company, Incorporated, 627 Venice Blvd., Venice, CA 90291 USA Tel 310-823-7712; Fax: 310-306-4702
E-mail: paulette@13sites.com; donsouth@cs.com
Web site: http://www.adventuresinceramics.com; http://www.morrisseydolls.com.

Adventures In Education, Inc., *(0-9767305)* 5N581 Hidden Springs Dr., Saint Charles, IL 60175 USA
Web site: http://www.adventures-in-education.com.

Adventures in Evergreen *See* **Evergreen Bks.**

Adventures Into Time, *(0-9601302)* P.O. Box 88, Independence, VA 24348 USA (SAN 210-6949) Tel 540-655-4523
Dist(s): **New Leaf Distributing Co., Inc.**

Company

Company

Adventures of Lady LLC, The, *(0-9789984)* 7657 Apple Tree Cir., Orlando, FL 32819 USA (SAN 852-1360) Tel 407-352-2684; Fax: 407-226-9148
E-mail: im@theadventuresoflady.com
Web site: http://www.theadventuresoflady.com.

Adventures Unlimited Pr., *(0-932813; 1-931882)* Orders Addr.: P.O. Box 74, Kempton, IL 60946 USA (SAN 630-1126) Tel 815-253-6390; Fax: 815-253-6300; Edit Addr.: 303 Main St., Kempton, IL 60946 USA (SAN 250-3484)
E-mail: auphq@frontiernet.net
Web site: http://www.adventuresunlimitedpress.com
Dist(s): **New Leaf Distributing Co., Inc.**
SCB Distributors.

Advice Pr., *(0-9650414; 1-881957; 1-889671)* 951 Old County Rd., Suite 103, Belmont, CA 94002-2760 USA Tel 650-321-2197; Fax: 650-321-2199
E-mail: orders@advicepress.com
Web site: http://www.advicepress.com
Dist(s): **Baker & Taylor Bks.**
Cromland
Kasper, Frank & Assocs.

Advocate Hse. *Imprint of* **A Cappela Publishing**

Aegean Design, *(0-9758803)* 5009 20th Ave., NW, Seattle, WA 98107 USA Tel 206-612-9698
E-mail: bdarling@handofzeus.com
Web site: http://www.aegeandesign.net.

Aegypan, *(1-59818; 1-60312)* Div. of Alan Rodgers Bks., 4750 Lincoln Blvd., No. 360, Marina del Rey, CA 90292-9303 USA.

Aenor Trust, The, *(0-9724251; 0-9766401; 0-9768128)* Orders Addr.: P.O. Box 4706, Salem, OR 97302 USA; Edit Addr.: 1286 Pressler Court S., Salem, OR 97306 USA
Web site: http://www.aenortrust.org; http://www.stellarlane.org.

Aeonian Pr. *Imprint of* **Amereon LTD.**

Aerial *Imprint of* **Farrar, Straus & Giroux**

Aerial Photography Services, Inc., *(0-936672; 1-880970; 0-9789603)* 2511 S. Tryon St., Charlotte, NC 28203 USA (SAN 214-2791) Tel 704-333-5143; Fax: 704-333-5148
E-mail: aps@aps-1.com
Web site: http://www.aps-1.com.

Aerie *Imprint of* **Doherty, Tom Assocs., LLC**

Aerie Hse., *(0-9627039)* Orders Addr.: P.O. Box 279, Bozman, MD 21612 USA Tel 410-745-2236 (phone/fax); Edit Addr.: 7711 Quaker Neck Rd., Bozman, MD 21612-0279 USA
E-mail: striper@shore.intercom.net
Dist(s): **Washington Bk. Distributors.**

Aerospace 1 Pubns., *(0-9705150)* 8 Brookstone Ct., Streamwood, IL 60107 USA
E-mail: aerospace1@aol.com.

AFCHRON, *(1-892824)* Orders Addr.: P.O. Box 11754, Minneapolis, MN 55411 USA ; *Imprints:* AFCHRON.COM (AFCHRON.COM)
E-mail: afchron5@aol.com
Web site: http://www.afchron.com
Dist(s): **Baker & Taylor Bks.**
Copyright Clearance Ctr., Inc.
EBSCO Media.

AFCHRON.COM *Imprint of* **AFCHRON**

Africa Community Publishing & Development Trust (ZWE) *(1-77936) Dist. by* **Mich St U Pr.**

Africa World Pr., *(0-86543; 1-59221)* 541 W. Ingham Ave., Suite B, Trenton, NJ 08638 USA (SAN 692-3925) Tel 609-695-3200; Fax: 609-695-6466
E-mail: awprsp@africanworld.com
Web site: http://www.africanworld.com.

African American Chronicle Software Publishing Corporation *See* **AFCHRON**

African American Images, *(0-913543; 0-9749000; 1-934155)* 1909 W. 95th St., Chicago, IL 60643 USA Tel 773-445-0322; Fax: 773-445-9844; Toll Free: 800-552-1991
E-mail: aai@africanamericanimages.com; customer@africanamericanimages.com
Web site: http://AfricanAmericanImages.com
Dist(s): **Independent Pubs. Group.**

African American Queen Hunt Production, Inc., *(0-9654517)* 118 Villa N. Ct., Warner Robins, GA 31093 USA Tel 912-923-6439; Fax: 912-825-6078.

African Artistic Ventures, *(0-9671238)* 1920 Pacific St., No. 3, Brooklyn, NY 11233 USA Tel 718-953-6811; Fax: 718-604-7483
E-mail: Wewedemping@yahoo.com.

African Sun Publishing, *(1-883701)* c/o First Presbyterian Church, 5555 S. Washington St., Grand Forks, ND 58201 USA
E-mail: africansun@igc.apc.org
Web site: http://www.igc.apc.org/africansunlink.

African Writers Series *Imprint of* **Heinemann**

Africana Homestead Legacy Pubs., *(0-9653308; 0-9770904; 0-9799537)* 100 Sprindale Rd. A3 No. 206, Cherry Hill, NJ 08003-3360 USA Tel 856-382-0629; Fax: 856-382-0630; Toll Free: 866-565-0471
E-mail: publisher@ahlpub.com; editors@ahlpub.com; accounting@ahlpub.com; book-orders@ahlpub.com
Web site: http://www.ahlpub.com; http://www.ahlpub.com/Order_Department.html
Dist(s): **BookMasters, Inc.**

Afro-Originals, *(0-9672356)* 12138 Central Ave., Suite 325, Mitchellville, MD 20721-1932 USA Tel 301-249-9070; Fax: 301-249-9058
E-mail: afrooriginals@hotmail.com.

Afton Historical Society Pr., *(0-9639338; 1-890434)* Orders Addr.: P.O. Box 100, Afton, MN 55001 USA Tel 651-436-8443; Fax: 651-436-7354; Toll Free: 800-436-8443; Edit Addr.: 3321 Saint Croix Trail, S., Afton, MN 55001 USA
E-mail: aftonpress@aftonpress.com
Web site: http://www.aftonpress.com
Dist(s): **Bookmen, Inc.**
Brodart Co.
Coutts Library Service, Inc.
Eastern Bk. Co.
Galda Library Services, Inc.

Afton Publishing, *(0-89359)* Orders Addr.: P.O. Box 1399, Andover, NJ 07821-1399 USA (SAN 692-2570) Tel 973-579-2442; Fax: 973-579-2842; Toll Free: 888-238-6665
E-mail: info3@aftonpublishing.com
Web site: http://www.aftonpublishing.com.

A-Game, LLC, *(0-9666764)* Orders Addr.: P.O. Box 34867, Los Angeles, CA 90034 USA Tel 310-567-6233; Fax: 310-559-9710; Toll Free: 800-356-9315; Edit Addr.: 1308 Amherst Ave., Suite 7, Los Angeles, CA 90025 USA
E-mail: marc.isenberg@gmail.com
Web site: http://moneyplayers.typepad.com
Dist(s): **Brodart Co.**
Quality Bks., Inc.

Agapy Publishing, *(0-9721328)* Wendy Williamson 1023 Woodberry Ln., Charleston, IL 61920 USA
E-mail: sales@agapy.com; custserv@agapy.com
Web site: http://www.agapy.com; http://www.agapy.com/cma
Dist(s): **Lightning Source, Inc.**

AGB Publishing, *(1-930908)* Div. of Mini Enterprises - M.E., 5415 Dunsmere St., Houston, TX 77091 USA Tel 713-686-6580; 281-788-5819 (cell); Fax: 713-680-4450 ; *Imprints:* Great Beginning-AGB, A (Great Begin); AGB/me (AGB-me)
E-mail: minienterprises@msn.com
Web site: http://www.minienterprises.net.

AGB/me *Imprint of* **AGB Publishing**

AGC Outreach Ministry, *(0-9774115)* 528 Starrett Ln., Ligonier, PA 15658 USA Tel 724-238-0341
E-mail: stevenjsmith799@adelphia.net
Web site: www.agcoutreach.com.

Ageless Treasures, *(0-9705726)* Orders Addr.: 3536 Saint Andrews Village Cir., Louisville, KY 40241-2664 USA (SAN 253-794X) Tel 502-412-5940; Fax: 502-327-6233
E-mail: dcw0810@insightbb.com; carlawebb@agelesstreasures.net.

Agency for Instructional Technology, *(0-7842; 0-941449; 0-9603244)* Box A, 1800 N. Stonelake Dr., Bloomington, IN 47402-0120 USA (SAN 668-954X) Tel 812-339-2203; Fax: 812-333-4218; Toll Free: 800-457-4509
E-mail: info@ait.net
Web site: http://www.ait.net.

Agents of Change, *(1-928992)* Div. of Granite Publishing, LLC, P.O. Box 1429, Columbus, NC 28722-1429 USA Tel 828-894-3088; Fax: 828-894-8454; Toll Free: 800-366-0264
E-mail: brian@5thworld.com
Web site: http://5thworld.com
Dist(s): **New Leaf Distributing Co., Inc.**

Age-Trotters Press *See* **Cameltrotters Publishing**

AGL Editions, *(0-9745629)* 1000 Bay Dr., No. 524, Niceville, FL 32578 USA.

Aglob Publishing, *(0-9708560; 1-59427)* P.O. Box 4036, Hallandale, FL 33008 USA Tel 954-456-1476; Fax: 954-456-3903
E-mail: info@aglobpublishing.com; info@aglob.com
Web site: http://www.aglobpublishing.com.

Agora Pubns., Inc., *(1-887250)* 17 Dean St., Millis, MA 02054 USA (SAN 851-8521) Tel 508-376-1073 (phone/fax)
E-mail: agorapub@comcast.net; info@agorapublication.com
Web site: http://www.agorapublications.com
Dist(s): **Philosophy Documentation Ctr.**

Agreka *Imprint of* **Agreka Bks., LLC**

Agreka Bks., LLC, *(1-888106; 0-9777072; 1-934243)* P.O. Box 14405, Scottsdale, AZ 85267-14405 USA Tel 480-767-1774; Toll Free Fax: 888-771-7758; Toll Free: 800-360-5284 ; *Imprints:* Agreka (Agreka)
E-mail: info@agreka.com
Web site: http://www.agreka.com; http://www.utahbooks.com; http://www.historypreserved.com
Dist(s): **Baker & Taylor Bks.**
Lightning Source, Inc.
Quality Bks., Inc.

Agua Caliente Pr., *(0-9768275)* 4352 Riley Rd., Gladwin, MI 48624 USA Tel 989-426-8400
E-mail: maryhansen4@hotmail.com.

Aguilar, Altea, Taurus, Alfaguara, S.A. de C.V (MEX) *(968-19) Dist. by* **Santillana.**

Aguilar Chilena de Ediciones, Ltd. (CHL) *(956-239) Dist. by* **Ediciones.**

Aguilar Editorial (MEX) *(968-19) Dist. by* **Lectorum Pubns.**

Aguilar Editorial (MEX) *(968-19) Dist. by* **Santillana.**

Aguilar, S. A. de Ediciones-Grupo Santillana (ESP) *(84-03) Dist. by* **Santillana.**

Aguirre Cox, Vicki & Ernest, *(0-9767994)* 10810 Lake Path Dr., San Antonio, TX 78217 USA Tel 210-364-8590; Fax: 210-653-3089
E-mail: vacemas@aol.com.

Aha! Elora Danan Productions, *(0-9786729)* P.O. Box 428, Estero, FL 33928 USA.

aha! Process, Inc., *(0-9647437; 1-929229; 1-934583)* P.O. Box 727, Highlands, TX 77562-0727 USA Tel 281-426-5300; Fax: 281-426-5600; Toll Free: 800-424-9484
Web site: http://www.ahaprocess.com.

Aha Punana Leo, *(0-9645646; 1-58191; 1-890270)* 3049 Ualena St. Ste. 402, Honolulu, HI 96819-1946 USA
E-mail: haawina@leoki.uhh.hawaii.edu
Web site: http://www.ahapunanaleo.org
Dist(s): **Booklines Hawaii, Ltd.**
Native Bks.

AH-HA Consulting Corp., *(0-9707864)* 32162 Caminito Osuna, Temecula, CA 92592 USA Tel 951-302-8128 (phone/fax)
E-mail: aaitcheson@earthlink.net
Web site: http://www.childrenscrusade.com.

Ahlman Publishing, *(0-9712906)* Div. of KODIAK Publishing, 9525 W. 230 St., Morristown, MN 55052 USA Tel 507-685-4247; Fax: 507-685-4280
E-mail: larryahlman@hotmail.com
Web site: http://www.ahlmans.com/mittens.html
Dist(s): **Baker & Taylor Bks.**
Partners Bk. Distributing, Inc.

Ahtreb, Inc., *(0-9676396)* 7402 Finch, Houston, TX 77028 USA Tel 713-633-2438; Fax: 713-633-2354
E-mail: wfrancois@compuserve.com.

Ahzar's Bk. Co. Publishing, *(0-9746130)* 3675 So. Rainbow Blvd No. 107, Las Vegas, NV 89103 USA Tel 702-391-1914; Fax: 702-871-8777
E-mail: croesus@joimail.com.

Aidan's Butterfly Pubns., *(0-9787341)* 4946 W. Laurie Ln., Glendale, AZ 85302 USA Fax: 623-776-9921
E-mail: eetagt@aol.com.

Aiglet Pr., *(0-9701944)* 308 W. Champion, Suite 503, Bellingham, WA 98225 USA Tel 360-671-4572 (phone/fax)
E-mail: readinguru@msn.com; readinguru1@yahoo.com.

AIL Newmedia Publishing, *(1-893798)* Div. of A. L. Labs, Orders Addr.: P.O. Box 147, Park Ridge, NJ 07656 USA (SAN 253-293X) Tel 201-300-0226; Fax: 201-300-0226
E-mail: publisher@newmediapublishing.com
Web site: http://www.newmediapublishing.com
Dist(s): **Baker & Taylor Bks.**
Lightning Source, Inc.

A.I.M. Enterprises, *(0-9772303)* 507 Grace - Stockham, Aurora, NE 68818-7019 USA
Web site: http://www.aim4theheart.com.

Aim Higher Bks., *(0-9713292)* 10556 Combie Rd., Suite 6242, Auburn, CA 95602 USA
E-mail: sales@aimhigherbooks.com
Web site: http://www.AimHigherBooks.com.

Aim Higher Publishing *See* **Aim Higher Bks.**

AIMS Education Foundation, *(1-881431; 1-932093; 1-60519)* Orders Addr.: P.O. Box 8120, Fresno, CA 93747-8120 USA Tel 559-255-4094; Fax: 559-255-6396; Toll Free: 888-733-2467; Edit Addr.: 5391 E. Home Ave., Fresno, CA 93727 USA
E-mail: aimsed@aimsedu.org
Web site: http://www.aimsedu.org
Dist(s): **Follett Media Distribution.**

AIMS Multimedia, *(0-8068)* 20765 Superior St., Chatsworth, CA 91311-4416 USA (SAN 687-3464) Toll Free: 800-367-2467
Web site: http://www.aimsmultimedia.com/
Dist(s): **Weston Woods Studios, Inc.**

Air To The Kingdom, *(0-9708486)* 67 Springfield Ave., Rochester, NY 14609-3607 USA Tel 716-288-3915; Fax: 716-784-1278
E-mail: info@airtothekingdom.org
Web site: http://www.airtothekingdom.org.

Airleaf *See* **Airleaf Publishing & Bookselling**

Airleaf Publishing *Imprint of* **Airleaf Publishing & Bookselling**

Airleaf Publishing & Bookselling, *(1-932301; 1-59453; 1-60002)* Orders Addr.: 35 Industrial Dr., Suite 104, Martinsville, IN 46151 USA Tel 765-342-2553; Fax: 765-342-7217; Toll Free: 800-342-6068 ; *Imprints:* Bookman Publishing (Bkman Pub); Airleaf Publishing (Arlf Pub)
E-mail: sales@airleaf.com; bdenton@airleaf.com
Web site: http://www.airleaf.com.

Airplane Reader Publishing, *(0-9702405; 0-9765485)* Div. of Pro Leisure Tour, Inc., 9260 E. Lake Pl., Greenwood Village, CO 80111 USA (SAN 253-6935) Fax: 303-221-2766 24-hour dedicated fax line; Toll Free: 877-611-6222 voice mail, 24 hours
E-mail: theo@12milestoparadise.com; tedsimendinger@comcast.net; ted@funnyted.com
Web site: http://www.proleisuretour.com; http:// www.piggychurch.com; http://www.12milestoparadise.com; http://www.richwithoutmoney.org; http:// www.jurassictrout.com; http://www.tukibanjo.com
Dist(s): **Baker & Taylor Bks.**

AK Pr. (GBR) *(1-873176; 1-902593; 1-904859) Dist. by* **Consort Bk Sales.**

AK Pr. Distribution, *(1-873176; 1-902593)* 674-A 23rd St., Oakland, CA 94612-1163 USA (SAN 298-2234) Tel 510-208-1700; Fax: 510-208-1701
E-mail: akpress@akpress.org
Web site: http://www.akpress.org
Dist(s): **Consortium Bk. Sales & Distribution**
SPD-Small Pr. Distribution.

a.k.a. Publishing, *(0-9663077)* 2828 Northwest Ave., Bellingham, WA 98225 USA Fax: 360-650-0500.

Akadine Pr., The, *(1-888173; 1-58579)* 141 Tompkins Ave., Pleasantville, NY 10570-3154 USA Tel 914-747-0777; Fax: 914-747-0778; Toll Free: 800-832-7323 ; *Imprints:* Common Reader Editions (Common Reader Eds)
E-mail: acr@akadine.com
Web site: http://www.acommonreader.com
Dist(s): **Trafalgar Square Publishing.**

Akashic Pr., Inc., The, *(0-913911)* 107 Lincoln Dr., W., Ambler, PA 19002 USA (SAN 286-8741) Tel 215-628-2291.

AKB Design, *(0-9748702)* 17640 Corkill Rd., No. 27, Sky Valley, CA 92241 USA Tel 760-861-5825.

Akebulan Ctr. of Excellence, *(1-891339)* Orders Addr.: P.O. Box 550512, Dallas, TX 75355 USA Tel 505-898-0735; Edit Addr.: 5555 Zuni Rd., SE, Albuquerque, NM 87108 USA.

AKMO Pubs., *(0-9745952)* P.O. Box 669, Odessa, FL 33556-9998 USA.

Akua Lani Enterprises, Inc., *(0-9657037)* P.O. Box 17630, Tucson, AZ 85731 USA (SAN 254-0843) Tel 520-290-1543; Fax: 520-290-1544
E-mail: webmaster@paewood-enterprises.com
Web site: http://www.paewood-enterprises.com.

Alaafia Kids Co., *(0-9788737)* 1020 Stonebrook Rd. Unit B, Sykesville, MD 21784-6173 USA.

Alabama Farmers Federation, *(0-9714419)* Orders Addr.: P.O. Box 11000, Montgomery, AL 36191 USA Tel 334-288-3900; Fax: 334-284-3957; Edit Addr.: 2108 East South Blvd., Montgomery, AL 36116 USA
E-mail: ptill@alfafarmers.org
Web site: http://alfafarmers.org
Dist(s): **Baker & Taylor Bks.**

Alabama Folklife Assn., *(0-9672672; 0-9772132)* Orders Addr.: c/o Alabama Center for Traditional Culture, 410 N. Hull St, Montgomery, AL 36104 USA Tel 334-242-3601; Fax: 334-269-9098
E-mail: joycecauthen@bellsouth.net
Web site: http://www.alabamafolklife.org.

Alaca Co., *(0-9641484)* a/o The Alaca Company & CottonsJourney.com, P.O. Box 55, Tranquillity, CA 93668 USA Fax: 559-698-5190; Toll Free: 800-698-1888
E-mail: admin@cottonsjourney.com
Web site: http://www.cottonsjourney.com.

Alacan Publishing, *(0-9749096)* P.O. Box 8623, Tarrytown, NY 10591 USA (SAN 255-8599)
E-mail: jim@comicmnemonics.com
Web site: http://www.comicmnemonics.com
Dist(s): **Beagle Bay Bks.**

Aladdin *Imprint of* **Simon & Schuster Children's Publishing**

Aladdin Library *Imprint of* **Simon & Schuster Children's Publishing**

Alan, Breck Music, *(0-9705382)* 704 Spruce B, Boulder, CO 80302 USA Tel 303-402-0225; Fax: 303-442-1794; Toll Free: 800-688-4212
E-mail: breck@breckalan.com
Web site: http://bodysinging.com.

Alaska Avenue Pr., *(0-9748091)* 5770 Alaska Ave., Alto, MI 49302-9714 USA Tel 616-868-0308
E-mail: stonehillis47657@aol.com.

Alaska Native Language Ctr., *(0-933769; 1-55500)* Univ. of Alaska, P.O. Box 757680, Fairbanks, AK 99775-7680 USA (SAN 692-9796) Tel 907-474-7874; Fax: 907-474-6586
E-mail: fntla@uaf.edu
Web site: http://www.uaf.edu/anlc
Dist(s): **Chicago Distribution Ctr.**
Todd Communications
Wizard Works.

Alaska Natural History Assn., *(0-930931; 0-9602876)* 750 W. Second Ave., Suite 100, Anchorage, AK 99501-1635 USA (SAN 223-5269) Tel 907-274-8440; Fax: 907-274-8343
Web site: http://www.alaskanha.org.

Alaska Northwest Bks. *Imprint of* **Graphic Arts Ctr. Publishing Co.**

Alaska Sea Grant College Program, *(1-56612)* Div. of Univ. of Alaska, Univ. of Alaska, P.O. Box 755040, Fairbanks, AK 99775-5040 USA Tel 907-474-6707; Fax: 907-474-6285; Toll Free: 888-789-0090
E-mail: fypubs@uaf.edu
Web site: http://www.uaf.edu/seagrant
Dist(s): **Chicago Distribution Ctr.**
Todd Communications
Univ. of Alaska Pr.
Wizard Works.

Alaska Zoo, The, *(0-9673915)* 4731 O'Malley Rd., Anchorage, AK 99516 USA.

Alaska-Siberia Research Ctr., *(0-9653891)* Orders Addr.: P.O. Box 34871, Juneau, AK 99803 USA Tel 907-789-3854 (phone/fax); Edit Addr.: 9216 Black Wolf Way, Juneau, AK 99803 USA
E-mail: adolitsky@gci.net
Web site: http://www.aksrc.org.

Alatyr Productions LLC, *(0-9743502)* 1680 York Ave., Suite 3D, New York, NY 10128-0766 USA Tel 212-570-9055; Fax: 212-570-4066
E-mail: alatyrprod@attglobal.net.

Alba Bk. Co., *(0-9662298)* Orders Addr.: P.O. Box 971, Evanston, IL 60204-0971 USA; Edit Addr.: 2244 Concord Ct., Springfield, IL 62704 USA
E-mail: books@albabookcompany.com.

†Alba Hse., *(0-8189)* Div. of Society of St. Paul, 2187 Victory Blvd., Staten Island, NY 10314-6603 USA (SAN 201-2405) Tel 718-761-0047; Fax: 718-761-0057; 718-698-8390; Toll Free: 800-343-2522 ; *Imprints:* Saint Pauls (Saint Pauls)
E-mail: albabooks@aol.com
Web site: http://www.albahouse.org; *CIP.*

Albatros (ARG) *(950-24) Dist. by* **Lectorum Pubns.**

Albee, Michael, *(0-9745405)* 1575 W. Mable, Anaheim, CA 92802 USA Tel 714-863-2149
E-mail: malbee@fairmontschools.net.

Albert Rene, Editions (FRA) *(2-86497) Dist. by* **Last Gasp.**

Albin-Michel, Editions (FRA) *(2-226) Dist. by* **Distribks Inc.**

Albright, Rachelle, *(0-9713435)* 5202 18th Ave., SW, Cedar Rapids, IA 52404 USA Fax: 319-390-5205.

ALCAPS, LLC, *(0-9769769)* 4004 Cibola Village Dr., NE, Albuquerque, NM 87111 USA
Web site: http://www.heartstohearts.net.

Alcazar AudioWorks, *(0-9724995; 0-9746806; 0-9755663; 0-9787553; 0-9793777)* 3032 Alcazar Dr., Burlingame, CA 94010-5814 USA Tel 650-692-1166; Fax: 650-692-7911
E-mail: bfrohman@pacbell.net
Web site: http://www.alcazaraudioworks.com.

Alchemy Bks., *(0-931290)* 1029 Solano Ave., No. E, Albany, CA 94706-1680 USA (SAN 111-3119).

ALCJR Enterprises, *(0-9752760)* P.O. Box 4067, Midlothian, VA 23112-0001 USA Tel 804-744-0100; Fax: 804-744-8961
E-mail: arthur@alcjr.com
Web site: http://www.alcjr.com.

Aldelo Systems Inc., *(0-9765992)* 4641 Spyres Way Ste. 4, Modesto, CA 95356-9802 USA
E-mail: sales@aldelo.com
Web site: http://www.aldelo.com.

Alderac Entertainment Group, *(1-887953; 1-59472)* 4045 Guasti Rd., No. 212, Ontario, CA 91761 USA
E-mail: kcarpenter@alderac.com
Web site: http://www.alderac.com
Dist(s): **PSI (Publisher Services, Inc.).**

Aldrich/Crow, *(0-615; 0-9706093)* 912 N. Hollywood Way, Suite D, Burbank, CA 91505 USA Fax: 818-841-0669
E-mail: vickieaIdrich@hotmail.com.

Alef Design Group, *(1-881283)* 4423 Fruitland Ave., Los Angeles, CA 90058 USA Tel 323-582-1200; Fax: 323-585-0327; Toll Free: 800-845-0662
E-mail: jane@torahaura.com
Web site: http://www.torahaura.com.

Alegra Hse. Pubs., *(0-933879)* Orders Addr.: P.O. Box 1443A, Warren, OH 44482 USA (SAN 692-7858) Tel 330-443-1706; Fax: 330-399-1619; Toll Free: 800-227-2591 (orders only)
E-mail: mineral9@theworks.com
Dist(s): **Baker & Taylor Bks.**
Brodart Co.
Paperbacks for Educators
Social Studies Schl. Service.

Alegria Hispana Pubns., *(0-944356)* Orders Addr.: P.O. Box 3765, Ventura, CA 93003 USA (SAN 243-4695) Tel 805-642-3969; Edit Addr.: 336 N. Ashwood, Ventura, CA 90003 USA (SAN 243-4709).

Alessi, Patricia, *(0-615)* 110 Fieldstone Cir., Ithaca, NY 14850-9497 USA
E-mail: pa31@cornell.edu.

Alethea In Heart, *(0-9719805; 1-932370)* 8071 Main St., Fenwick, MI 48834-9649 USA Tel 989-637-4179
E-mail: truthinheart@hotmail.com
Web site: http://www.truthinheart.com.

Alexander Art L.P., *(1-883576)* P.O. Box 1417, Beaverton, OR 97075-1417 USA Tel 503-362-7939; Fax: 503-361-7401; Toll Free: 800-896-4630
E-mail: sales@alexanderart.com
Web site: http://wwwalexanderart.com.

Alexander Productions, *(1-880534)* 9085 U. S. Hwy. 19 N., Pinellas Park, FL 33782 USA Tel 727-577-1391; Fax: 727-577-0134
E-mail: dalexan2@tampabay.rr.com
Web site: http://www.mayanreiki.com.

Alexander Pubns., *(0-9623078)* Orders Addr.: P.O. Box 518, Forney, TX 75126 USA Tel 972-552-9519; Edit Addr.: 806 E. Buffalo St., Forney, TX 75126 USA.

Alexander-Marcus Publishing, *(0-9760944)* 1115 Tunnel Rd., Santa Barbara, CA 93105 USA
E-mail: andreamarcuslaw@cox.net.

Alexie Bks., *(0-9679416)* Div. of Alexie Enterprises, Inc., P.O. Box 3843, Carmel, IN 46082 USA Tel 317-844-5638; Fax: 317-846-0788
E-mail: BusJobs@aol.com; alexie8@aol.com; sales@alexiebooks.com
Web site: http://www.alexieenterprises.com
Dist(s): **Baker & Taylor Bks.**
Distributors, The.

Alfaguara *Imprint of* **Santillana USA Publishing Co., Inc.**

Alfaguara, Ediciones, S.A.- Grupo Santillana (ESP) *(84-204; 958-704) Dist. by* **Lectorum Pubns.**

Alfaguara, Ediciones, S.A.- Grupo Santillana (ESP) *(84-204; 958-704) Dist. by* **Santillana.**

Alfaguara S.A. de Ediciones (ARG) *(950-511; 987-04) Dist. by* **Santillana.**

Alfaomega Grupo Editor (MEX) *(970-15) Dist. by* **IPG Chicago.**

Alfranpedoc, *(1-930502)* 4100 W. Coyote Ridge Tr., Tucson, AZ 85746 USA Tel 213-926-0762
E-mail: Waylandhi@aol.com
Web site: http://www.books-by-doc.com.

Alfred Publishing Co., Inc., *(0-7390; 0-88284)* Orders Addr.: P.O. Box 10003, Van Nuys, CA 91410-0003 USA; Edit Addr.: 123 Dry Rd., Oriskany, NY 13424 USA Tel 315-736-1572; Fax: 315-736-7281 ; *Imprints:* Warner Bros. Publications (Warner Bro)
E-mail: customerservice@alfred.com; permissions@alfred.com; submissions@alfred.com
Web site: http://www.alfred.com.

†Algonquin Bks. of Chapel Hill, *(0-7611; 0-912697; 0-945575; 1-56512)* Div. of Workman Publishing Co., Inc., Orders Addr.: 225 Varick St. Flr. 9, New York, NY 10014-4381 USA Toll Free Fax: 800-521-1832 (fax orders, customer sevice); Toll Free: 800-722-7202 (orders, customer service); Edit Addr.: P.O. Box 2225, Chapel Hill, NC 27515-2225 USA (SAN 282-7506) Tel 919-967-0108 (editorial, publicity, marketing); Fax: 919-933-0272 (editorial, publicity, marketing)
E-mail: dialogue@algonquin.com
Web site: http://www.algonquin.com; http://www.booksellerscorner.com
Dist(s): **Workman Publishing Co., Inc.**; *CIP.*

Algonquin Indian Arts & Culture Association, The, *(0-9748996)* P.O. Box 1518, Charlestown, RI 02813-1518 USA Tel 401-364-3880
E-mail: info@nativeamericancalendar.com
Web site: http://www.nativeamericancalendar.com.

Al-Huda Printing & Publishing Company *See* **Al-Huda Pubs.**

Al-Huda Pubs., *(0-9642101; 0-9763450)* Orders Addr.: 400 Industria Dr. Suite 100, Richardson, TX 75081 USA Tel 972-238-1050; Fax: 972-238-9240; Toll Free: 866-459-1052
E-mail: info@alhudapublishers.com
Web site: http://www.alhudapublishers.com.

Alianza Editorial, S. A. (ESP) *(84-206) Dist. by* **Continental Bk.**

Alianza Editorial, S. A. (ESP) *(84-206) Dist. by* **Lectorum Pubns.**

Alianza Editorial, S. A. (ESP) *(84-206) Dist. by* **AIMS Intl.**

Alianza Editorial, S. A. (ESP) *(84-206) Dist. by* **Distribks Inc.**

Alias Enterprises LLC, *(1-933428; 1-60039)* Orders Addr.: 8367 Lemon Ave., La Mesa, CA 91941-9194 USA Tel 619-589-1400
E-mail: burner@aliasenterprises.com
Web site: http://www.aliasenterprises.com
Dist(s): **Diamond Bk. Distributors.**

Alicubi Pubns., *(0-9668215)* Orders Addr.: 1658 Milwaukee Ave., Chicago, IL 60647 USA (SAN 299-7703) Tel 773-252-3181; Fax: 773-486-6993
E-mail: alicubi@earthlink.net.

Alien Time Treasure, *(0-9727309)* P.O. Box 2665, Newport, RI 02840 USA
E-mail: webmaster@alientimetreasure.com
Web site: http://alientimetreasure.com.

Alif Publishing Corp. *Imprint of* **Tractus Bks.**

Alisam Pr., *(0-9656442)* 6040 Camp Bowie, Suite 52, Fort Worth, TX 76116 USA Tel 817-735-8299; Fax: 817-377-0720; Toll Free: 888-458-5119
E-mail: dwelsh@flash.net
Dist(s): **Bookmen, Inc.**

Alisam Publishing *See* **Alisam Pr.**

Alixander Group, *(0-9665582)* 1901 N. Forsyth Rd., Orlando, FL 32807 USA Tel 407-380-6082; Fax: 407-679-2006
E-mail: alixhunter@aol.com.

Al-Kitaab & As-Sunnah Publishing, *(1-891229)* P.O. Box 2542, Arlington, TX 76004 USA Tel 817-801-6933
E-mail: al_jibaly@juno.com.

All About Kids Publishing, *(0-615; 0-9700863; 0-9710278; 0-9744446)* Orders Addr.: 117 Bernal Rd., #70 PMB 405, San Jose, CA 95119 USA (SAN 253-8601)
E-mail: mail@aakp.com
Web site: http://www.aakp.com.

All About Me, *(0-9668858)* Orders Addr.: 203 Alala Rd., Kailua, HI 96734 USA Tel 808-261-9316; Edit Addr.: P.O. Box 222420, Carmel, CA 93922 USA Tel 831-622-7155
E-mail: lynn@clallam.com
Web site: http://clallam.com/lynn.

All American Small Business Exporters Assn. (AASBEA), *(0-9703463)* 2300 M St., NW, Suite 800, Washington, DC 20037 USA Tel 202-332-5137; Fax: 202-293-3083
E-mail: larkhor@erols.com
Web site: http://www.aasbea.com.

All Enterprises *See* **TRANSFORMATIONS**

All For One Pr., *(0-9745951)* 29193 Northwestern Hwy, No. 658, Southfield, MI 48034 USA (SAN 255-6804) Tel 313-617-4012
E-mail: allforonepress@hotmail.com.

All Gold Publishing Co., *(0-9701519)* Orders Addr.: P.O. Box 13504, Dayton, OH 45413-0504 USA Tel 937-586-9804; Edit Addr.: 907 Reist, Dayton, OH 45408-1350 USA
E-mail: allgoldceo@netzero.net
Web site: http://www.allgoldpublishing.com.

All Health Chiropractic Ctrs. Inc., *(0-9770527)* 567 Church St., Royersford, PA 19468 USA (SAN 256-6443) Tel 610-948-4161
E-mail: susiequsie6@aol.com
Web site: http://www.drsnappy.com.

All MarCom, LLC *See* **Animal Humanity Bks., LLC**

All Nations Pr., *(0-9725110; 0-9777954)* P.O. Box 601, White Marsh, VA 23183 USA Do not confuse with companies with the same or similar name in Colorado Springs, CO, Southlake, TX
E-mail: editors@allnationspress.com
Web site: http://www.allnationspress.com.

All or Nothing Publishings *See* **Syntax Publishing**

All Over Creation, *(0-9788950)* P.O. Box 382, Madera, CA 93639 USA
E-mail: astorybytory@yahoo.com.

ALL Publishing Hse., *(1-929310; 1-59943)* 3191 Coral Way, Suite 114, Miami, FL 33145-3209 USA Tel 305-529-2224; Fax: 305-443-8538; Toll Free: 800-704-8181
E-mail: allpubh@aol.com; info@cclscorp.com
Web site: http://www.cclscord.com.

All Season Snowflakes, *(0-9664524)* 3238 W. Corinne Dr., South Jordan, UT 84095 USA Tel 801-240-5995; 801-254-8926; Fax: 801-254-8927
E-mail: allseasonsnowflakes@yahoo.com
Web site: http://www.allseasonsnowflakes.com
Dist(s): **Origin Bk. Sales, Inc.**

All That Productions, Inc., *(0-9679441)* Orders Addr.: P.O. Box 1594, Humble, TX 77347 USA Tel 281-878-2062; Edit Addr.: 5902 Thom Rd., Humble, TX 77346 USA
E-mail: dlur@aol.com.

All Things Southern Publishing Co., *(0-9712259)* 610 Schneider Ln., Lk Providence, LA 71254-2010 USA
E-mail: tomtom@allthingssouthern.com
Web site: http://www.allthingssouthern.com.

Allaf, Mashhad Al, *(0-9722722)* P.O. Box 2063, Chester, VA 23831-8440 USA.

Allcat Pr., *(0-9717451)* 3111 Camino del Rio N., Suite 400, San Diego, CA 92108 USA Tel 619-889-4372; Fax: 619-297-9962; 1286 University Ave., No. 109, San Diego, CA 92103 ; *Imprints:* Louisa May Allcat Children's Books (Louisa May Allcat)
E-mail: louisamay@allcatpress.com; alice21@abac.com
Web site: http://www.allcatpress.com
Dist(s): **Baker & Taylor Bks.**

Allecram Publishing, *(0-9764198)* P.O. Box 6003, Dayton, OH 45405 USA Tel 937-278-6630
E-mail: marcellaashe@sbcglobal.net
Web site: http://www.allecrampublishing.com.

Allegheny Pr., *(0-910042)* 19323 Elgin Rd., Corry, PA 16407 USA (SAN 201-2456) Tel 814-664-8504
E-mail: hjohn@tbscc.com.

Allen & Douglas Pubs., *(0-9674281)* 1536 Islamorada Blvd., Punta Gorda, FL 33955-1818 USA Tel 941-505-1135 (phone/fax, star 51)
E-mail: marstan@nut-n-but.net.

Allen & Unwin (AUS) *(0-04; 0-86861; 1-86373; 1-86448; 1-875680; 0-7299; 1-86508; 1-74114; 1-74115; 1-74175) Dist. by* **IPG Chicago.**

Allen, Evelyn W., *(0-9651123)* 4505 Edendale Ct., Austin, TX 78756 USA Tel 512-452-5324; Fax: 512-251-8152 ; *Imprints:* PyroWriters (PyroWriters)
E-mail: evwallen@aol.com
Dist(s): **Any Baby Can of Austin.**

Allen Innovations & Initiatives/AII, *(0-9708859)* P.O. Box 8973, Rocky Mount, NC 27804 USA.

Allen, Jeffrey S. & Roger J. Klein *See* **Inner Coaching**

Allen Publishing, USA, *(0-9724733)* Empire State Bldg., Suite 3304, 350 5th Ave., New York, NY 10018-0069 USA
E-mail: jenbvic@aol.com.

Allen, Tina R. *See* **E-Digital Bks., LLC**

Allen, Toi Operations, *(0-9753787)* 11300 E. 85th Terr., Raytown, MO 64138 USA Tel 816-737-5293; Fax: 816-923-2634
E-mail: itasca2001@aol.com.

Allen's Native Ventures, *(0-9718625)* 5070 Hwy. 399, Pitkin, LA 70656 USA Tel 337-328-2252
E-mail: native@camtel.net
Web site: http://www.nativeventures.net/.

AllensRusk Pr., *(0-9672246)* P.O. Box 100213, Nashville, TN 38134 USA Tel 615-365-0993
E-mail: allensrusk@aol.com.

Allergic Child Publishing Group, *(1-58628)* 425 W. Rockrimmon Blvd., Suite 202, Colorado Springs, CO 80919 USA Tel 719-338-0202; Fax: 719-633-0375
E-mail: nicole@allergicchild.com
Web site: http://www.allergicchild.com.

Allergy & Asthma Network-Mothers of Asthmatic, Inc., *(1-885543)* 2751 Prosperity Ave., Suite 150, Fairfax, VA 22031-4397 USA Tel 703-641-9595; Fax: 703-573-7794; Toll Free: 800-878-4403
E-mail: aanma@aol.com.

Allfit, *(0-9617796)* 106 Dickson Ave., Pittsburgh, PA 15202 USA (SAN 664-6468) Tel 412-761-0413
E-mail: labargesenior@aol.com.

Alli Kat Publishing, *(0-9788725)* 2353 Alexandria Dr., Suite 201, Lexington, KY 40504 USA Tel 859-264-7700; Fax: 859-264-7744
E-mail: eyemanjlh@aol.com.

Allied Crafts Pr., *(0-9632305)* 726 Bison Ave., Newport Beach, CA 92660 USA Tel 949-759-8156; Fax: 949-759-1426
E-mail: mm2yg@aol.com
Dist(s): **Baker & Taylor Bks.**

Allied Publishing, *(1-57755)* 107 Nob Hill Park Dr., Reisterstown, MD 21136 USA Tel 410-833-5278; Fax: 410-833-6193 ; *Imprints:* Flying Frog Publishing (Flyng Frog) Do not confuse with Allied Publishing, Irving, TX.

Alligator Boogaloo, *(0-9721416)* P.O. Box 20070, Oakland, CA 94620 USA
E-mail: business@alligatorboogaloo.com
Web site: http://www.alligatorboogaloo.com.

Allison & Busby, Ltd. (GBR) *(0-7490; 0-85031; 1-902809) Dist. by* **Intl Pubs Mktg.**

Allocca Biotechnology, LLC, *(0-9659987; 0-9769213)* 19 Lorraine Ct., Northport, NY 11768 USA Tel 631-757-3919; Fax: 631-757-3918
E-mail: john@allocca.com
Web site: http://www.allocca.com.

Allocca Technology & Healthcare Research *See* **Allocca Biotechnology, LLC**

Allosaurus Pubs., *(0-9620900; 1-888325)* Div. of North Carolina Learning Institute for Fitness & Education, Orders Addr.: P.O. Box 10245, Greensboro, NC 27404 USA (SAN 250-0906) Tel 336-292-6999
E-mail: ally@infionline.net
Web site: http://www.allosauruspublishers.com.

Allpet Roaches *Imprint of* **Elytra & Antenna**

Allure Pr., *(0-9702317)* 5305 Greenbrook Dr., Portsmouth, VA 23703-2015 USA Tel 757 484 6376
E-mail: olsen@pilot.infi.net.

AllWrite Advertising & Publishing, *(0-9744935)* P.O. Box 2363, Atlanta, GA 30301 USA
E-mail: editor@e-allwrite.com
Web site: http://www.e-allwrite.com.

†Allyn & Bacon, Inc., *(0-205; 0-321)* Div. of Pearson Education Corp. Commun, Orders Addr.: c/o Prentice Hall/Allyn & Bacon, 200 Old Tappan Rd., Old Tappan, NJ 07675 USA Toll Free Fax: 800-445-6991; Toll Free: 800-922-0579 (customer service); 800-666-9433 (ordering); 111 Tenth St., Des Moines, IA 50309 Tel 515-284-6751; Fax: 515-284-2607; Toll Free: 800-278-3525; Edit Addr.: 75 Arlington St., Suite 300, Boston, MA 02116 USA (SAN 201-2510)
E-mail: ab_webmaster@abacon.com
Web site: http://www.abacon.com
Dist(s): **Pearson Education**
Pearson Technology Group; *CIP.*

Alma Little *Imprint of* **Elva Resa Publishing, LLC**

Alma Pr., *(0-9746333)* 1204 Abbot Kinney Blvd., Venice, CA 90291 USA (SAN 255-6723) Fax: 310-314-3883
E-mail: info@almapress.com
Web site: http://www.almapress.com.

Almanac Publishing Co., *(1-928720)* Mt. Hope Ave., Lewiston, ME 04240 USA Tel 207-755-2246; Fax: 207-755-2422
E-mail: sandid@farmersalmanac.com;
peterg@farmersalmanac.com
Web site: http://www.farmersalmanac.com
Dist(s): **Biblio Distribution.**

Aloha Publications, *(0-9706062)* Orders Addr.: P.O. Box 1077, Oklahoma City, OK 73101 USA Tel 405-232-1400; Edit Addr.: P.O. Box 1077, Oklahoma City, OK 73101 USA
E-mail: alohapublishing@aol.com
Web site: http://www.catdetectives.com.

Aloha Publishing & Marketing, *(1-893455)* P.O. Box 55062, Valencia, CA 91385-5062 USA Tel 805-287-5852; Toll Free: 888-575-7853
E-mail: djeff613@ix.netcom.com
Web site: http://www.alohasales.com; http://www.rulesgame.com.

Alone Mill Publishing, *(0-9675205)* 1388 Turkey Hill Rd., Lexington, VA 24450 USA Fax: 540-997-0019
E-mail: artiii@earthlink.net.

Alpenhorn Pr., *(1-879056)* Orders Addr.: P.O. Box 1635, Uniontown, PA 15401 USA Tel 724-438-0992; Edit Addr.: 128 Roberta Dr., Uniontown, PA 15401 USA.

Alpenrose Pr., *(0-9603624; 1-889385)* Orders Addr.: P.O. Box 499, Silverthorne, CO 80498 USA (SAN 222-2612) Tel 970-468-6273; Fax: 970-468-2080
E-mail: orders@alpenrosepress.com; orders@zoebooks.com; zoebooks@cs.com
Web site: http://www.zoebooks.com; http://www.alpenrosepress.com
Dist(s): **Alpenbooks Pr. LLC**
Baker & Taylor Bks.

Alpha & Omega Publishing, *(0-9767778)* 3409 Daniel Place Dr., Charlotte, NC 28213 USA Tel 704-724-1683; Fax: 270-721-6019 Do not confuse iwth companies with the same name in Fremont, NE, Springfield, OR
E-mail: alphaomega@carolina.rr.com.

Alpha Behavior Consultants, *(0-9758755)* 12740 NW 11th St., Miami, FL 33172 USA
E-mail: info@alphbehc.com
Web site: http://www.alphabehc.com.

Alpha Bible Pubns., *(1-877917)* P.O. Box 155, Hood River, OR 97031 USA; P.O. Box 157, Morton, WA 98356 Tel 541-386-6634
Dist(s): **Pentecostal Publishing Hse.**

Alpha Bks. *Imprint of* **Penguin Group (USA) Inc.**

Alpha Connections, *(0-9715779; 0-9747610)* 530 W. Idaho Blvd., Emmett, ID 83617 USA
E-mail: contact@dragonsfuryseries.com
Web site: http://www.dragonsfuryseries.com
Dist(s): **Lightning Source, Inc.**

Alpha Heartland Press *See* **Heartland Foundation, Inc.**

Alpha Imagery, *(0-9703805)* Orders Addr.: P.O. Box 61, Edmonds, WA 98020 USA Tel 425-640-6606
E-mail: jimhauge@aol.com.

Alpha Omega Pubns., Inc., *(0-7403; 0-86717; 1-58095)* 300 N. McKemy Ave., Chandler, AZ 85226-2618 USA Tel 602-438-2717; Fax: 480-785-8034; Toll Free: 800-682-7391; 804 N. 2nd Ave. E., Rock Rapids, IA 51246 (SAN 853-2826) Tel 800-622-3070; Fax: 712-472-4856 ; *Imprints:* Lifepac (Lifepac); Horizons (Hrnzns AZ); Weaver (Weaver)
E-mail: cpatterson@aop.com
Web site: http://www.aop.com
Dist(s): **Appalachian Bk. Distributors**
Baker & Taylor Bks.
Spring Arbor Distributors, Inc.

Alpha OmeGa Publishing, *(0-9658073)* 1217 Cape Coral Pkwy., Cape Coral, FL 33904 USA Tel 941-542-3666; Fax: 941-945-7963; Toll Free: 800-542-3666; 4219 SE First Ct., Cape Coral, FL 33904
E-mail: GPMueller@aol.com
Web site: http://www.Floridawest.com/Liestorm.

Alpha Publishing Group, *(1-890549)* 12651 Briar Forest Dr., Suite 155, Houston, TX 77077 USA Tel 281-493-2993; Fax: 281-497-7786; Toll Free: 800-922-8846 Do not confuse with Alpha Publishing Group, Inc., Spanaway, WA
Web site: http://www.alphapublishing.com.

Alpha Run Pr., LLC, *(0-9761182; 1-933289)* Orders Addr.: P.O. Box 15079, Silver Spring, MD 20914-5079 USA Tel 202-508-3392; Edit Addr.: 1717 K St. NW, Suite 600, Washington, DC 20036 USA
E-mail: alpharp@aol.com
Web site: http://www.alpharunpress.com
Dist(s): **AtlasBooks Distribution**
BookMasters, Inc.

Alpha Shade, Inc., *(0-9768705)* 11850 85th Pl., N., Maple Grove, MN 55369 USA Tel 763-424-9316
E-mail: alphashade1@aol.com
Web site: http://www.alpha-shade.com.

Alpha Writers Ltd., *(0-9772018)* Orders Addr.: P.O. Box 561262, The Colony, TX 75056 USA (SAN 256-9256) Fax: 425-955-0859; Toll Free: 866-751-4340 Outside of Dallas
E-mail: source@alphawritersltd.com
Web site: http://www.alphawritersltd.com.

Alphabuddies, The *See* **Sonrose Pubs.**

Alpha-kidZ, *(0-9749220)* P.O. Box 1552, West Monroe, LA 71294-1552 USA Tel 318-372-2762; Fax: 318-396-4073
Web site: http://www.alphakidz.com.

AlphaLove Publishing, *(0-9764307)* P.O. Box 248, South Orange, NJ 07079 USA Fax: 973-275-3973.

Alpine Archaeological Consultants, Inc., *(0-9743137)* P.O. Box 2075, Montrose, CO 81402-2075 USA Tel 970-249-6761; Fax: 970-249-8482
E-mail: susan_chandler@alpinearchaeology.com
Web site: http://www.alpinearchaeology.com.

†Alpine Pubns., Inc., *(0-931866; 1-57779)* Orders Addr.: P.O. Box 120, Crawford, CO 81415 USA (SAN 255-2094) Tel 970-921-5005; Fax: 970-921-5081; Toll Free: 800-777-7257
E-mail: alpinecsr@alpinepub.com; alpine@paonia.com; alpinepubl@aol.com
Web site: http://www.alpinepub.com
Dist(s): **Baker & Taylor Bks.**
Partners/West; *CIP.*

Alpine Publishing, *(1-885624)* 1119 S. Mission Rd., No. 102, Fallbrook, CA 92028 USA Tel 760-728-3161; Fax: 760-728-3394 Do not confuse with Alpine Publishing, Monroe, OR.

Alta Book Center *See* **Alta Bk. Ctr. Pubs.**

Alta Bk. Ctr. Pubs., *(1-882483; 1-932383)* 14 Adrian Ct., Burlingame, CA 94010 USA (SAN 630-9240) Tel 650-692-1285; Fax: 650-692-4654; Toll Free: 800-258-2375
E-mail: info@altaesl.com
Web site: http://www.altaesl.com
Dist(s): **Continental Bk. Co., Inc.**

Alta Omnimedia, *(0-9726360)* 2 Valley View Ave., Ste. 116, San Jose, CA 95127 USA
Web site: http://www.altaomnimedia.com.

Alta Publishing LLC, *(0-9767120)* P.O. Box 108, Bellvue, CO 80512 USA (SAN 256-4874) Do not confuse with companies with the same name in Sandy, UT, Midvale, UT
Web site: http: www.digis.net ~tilden.

Alta Retreat Ctr., *(0-9746151)* 20 Alta School Rd., Alta, WY 83414 USA Tel 307-353-8200; Fax: 208-354-4002
E-mail: altacp@ida.net.

AltaMira Pr., *(0-7619; 0-910050; 0-942063; 1-884258; 0-7425; 0-7591)* Div. of Rowman & Littlefield Publishing Group, Orders Addr.: 15200 NBN Way, Blue Ridge Summit, PA 17214 USA Tel 717-794-3800 (Sales, Customer Service, MIS, Royalties, Inventory Mgmt., Dist., Credit & Collections); Fax: 717-794-3803 (Customer Service &/or orders only); 717-794-3857 (Sales & MIS); 717-794-3856 (Royalties, Inventory Mgmt., & Dist.); Toll Free Fax: 800-338-4550 (Customer Service &/or orders); Toll Free: 800-462-6420 (Customer Service &/or orders); 67 Mowat Ave., Suite 241, Toronto, ON M6K 3E3 Tel 416-534-1660; Fax: 416-534-3699; Edit Addr.: 1630 N. Main St., No. 367, Walnut Creek, CA 94596 USA Tel 925-938-7243; Fax: 925-933-9720 Short Discount, please contact rlpgsales@rowman.com
E-mail: explore@altamirapress.com; custserv@rowman.com
Web site: http://www.altamirapress.com; http://www.rlpgbooks.com
Dist(s): **National Bk. Network**
Rowman & Littlefield Pubs., Inc.
STL Distribution North America.

Altea, Ediciones, S.A. - Grupo Santillana (ESP) *(84-372) Dist. by* **Santillana.**

AlterLingo Bks. *Imprint of* **O'Hollow Publishing**

Alternative Comics, *(1-891867; 1-934460)* 503 NW 37th Ave., Gainesville, FL 32609-2204 USA Tel 352-373-6336 Do not confuse with companies with the same or similar name in Goleta, GA, Billerica, MA
E-mail: jmason@gator.net
Web site: http://www.indyworld.com/altcomics
Dist(s): **Diamond Bk. Distributors.**

Alternative Press, Incorporated *See* **Alternative Comics**

Alternative Publications *See* **Bookmark Publishing**

Althos, *(0-9728053; 0-9742787; 0-9746943; 1-932813)* 404 Wake Chapel Rd., Fuquay Varina, NC 27526 USA Tel 919-557-2260; Fax: 919-557-2261; Toll Free: 800-227-9681
E-mail: info@althos.com
Web site: http://www.althos.com.

Althouse Pr., *(1-59087)* 2251 Dick George Rd., Cave Junction, OR 97523 USA Tel 541-592-4142; Fax: 541-592-2597
E-mail: noah@oism.org
Web site: http://www.robinsonbooks.org.

Alton Museum of History & Art, Inc., *(0-9678461)* 2809 College Ave., Alton, IL 62002 USA Tel 618-463-1795.

Altruria Publishing Co., *(0-9708201)* Orders Addr.: P.O. Box 711, Clear Lake, SD 57226-0711 USA; Edit Addr.: 14204 Old Marlboro Pike, Upper Marlboro, MD 20772 USA
E-mail: djean@prodigy.net
Web site: ddiekman.tripod.com.

Alura Bks., *(0-9719766)* P.O. Box 130833, Ann Arbor, MI 48113-0833 USA Tel 734-426-9054; Fax: 734-426-9068
E-mail: wtheisenhalsey@hotmail.com.

Alvin Bks., Inc., *(0-9725022)* 3112 Nybeck Ave. S., Afton, MN 55001 USA.

Always Kids Publishing, *(0-9677118)* Orders Addr.: PMB 221, 18160 Hwy. 281 N., Suite 108, San Antonio, TX 78232 USA (SAN 253-3030); Edit Addr.: P.O. Box 701790, San Antonio, TX 78270 USA Tel 210-495-2246; Fax: 210-495-2232
E-mail: caramia@texas.net.

Alyson Bks. *Imprint of* **Alyson Pubns.**

Alyson Pubns., *(0-932870; 1-55583; 1-59350)* Div. of PlanetOut, Inc., Orders Addr.: P.O. Box 4371, Los Angeles, CA 90078 USA (SAN 213-6546) Toll Free: 800-283-3572; Edit Addr.: 6922 Hollywood Blvd., Suite 100, Los Angeles, CA 90028 USA; 245 W. 17th St., Suite. 1200, New York, NY 10011 Tel 212-242-8100; Fax: 212-727-7939 ; *Imprints:* Alyson Wonderland (Alyson Wonderland); Alyson Books (Alyson Bks)
E-mail: richard.fumosa@planetoutinc.com
Web site: http://www.alyson.com
Dist(s): **Consortium Bk. Sales & Distribution.**

Alyson Wonderland *Imprint of* **Alyson Pubns.**

†Amacom, *(0-7612; 0-8144)* Div. of American Management Association, Orders Addr.: 600 AMA Way, Saranac Lake, NY 12983 USA (SAN 227-3578) Tel 518-891-5510; Fax: 518-891-2372; Toll Free: 800-250-5308 (orders & customer service); Edit Addr.: 1601 Broadway, New York, NY 10019-7420 USA (SAN 201-1670) Tel 212-586-8100; Fax: 212-903-8168
E-mail: cust_serv@amanet.org
Web site: http://www.amacombooks.org
Dist(s): **NetLibrary, Inc.**
Productivity Pr.
Wybel Marketing Group; *CIP.*

Amadeus Press *Imprint of* **Leonard, Hal Corp.**

Amador Publishers, LLC, *(0-938513)* Orders Addr.: P.O. Box 12335, Albuquerque, NM 87195 USA (SAN 661-3055) Tel 505-877-4395; Edit Addr.: 607 Isleta Blvd., SW, Albuquerque, NM 87105 USA (SAN 661-3063)
E-mail: harry@amadorbooks.com
Web site: http://www.amadorbooks.com
Dist(s): **Books West**
Last Gasp of San Francisco.

amana pubns., *(0-915957; 1-59008)* Div. of amana corp., 10710 Tucker St., Beltsville, MD 20705-2223 USA (SAN 630-9798) Tel 301-595-5999; Fax: 301-595-5888; Toll Free: 800-660-1777
E-mail: amana@igprinting.com
Web site: http://www.amana-publications.com.

Amani Publishing, *(0-9752851; 0-9788937)* 2411 Wintergreen Rd., Tallahassee, FL 32308 USA Do not confuse with Amani Publishing in Pineville, LA
E-mail: amanipublishing@aol.com
Web site: http://www.amanipublishing.net.

Amaquemecan, Editorial (MEX) *(968-7205) Dist. by* **Continental Bk.**

Amaquemecan, Editorial (MEX) *(968-7205) Dist. by* **AIMS Intl.**

AMARA Entertainment, *(0-9760745)* 1024 Frans Rd., Westfield, NC 27053 USA Tel 336-351-3437 (phone/fax)
E-mail: rpitt@charlesthechef.com
Web site: http://www.charlesthechef.com.

Amaro Bks., *(0-9620556; 1-883203)* P.O. Box 126, Canal Point, FL 33438-0126 USA (SAN 249-2032)
E-mail: amarobooks@aol.com
Dist(s): **Book Warehouse.**

Amato, Frank Pubns., Inc., *(0-936608; 1-57188; 1-878175)* Orders Addr.: P.O. Box 82112, Portland, OR 97282 USA (SAN 214-3372) Tel 503-653-8108; Fax: 503-653-2766; Toll Free: 800-541-9498; Edit Addr.: 4040 SE Wister St., Milwaukie, OR 97222 USA
E-mail: wholesale@amatobooks.com; Lorraine@amatobooks.com
Web site: http://www.amatobooks.com
Dist(s): **Partners Bk. Distributing, Inc.**

Amaze Ink *Imprint of* **Slave Labor Bks.**

Amazing Dreams Publishing, *(0-9719628)* P.O. Box 1811, Asheville, NC 28802 USA
E-mail: contact@amazingdreamspublishing.com
Web site: http://www.amazingdreamspublishing.com
Dist(s): **BookSurge, LLC.**

Amazing Factory, The, *(0-9776282; 0-9788469; 0-9790302)* 5527 San Gabriel Way, Orlando, FL 32837 USA
E-mail: theamazingfactory@hotmail.com
Web site: http://www.theamazingfactory.com.

Amazing Herbs Pr., *(0-9742962)* 545 8th Ave., Suite 401, New York, NY 10018 USA Tel 770-982-0107; Fax: 770-982-0273; Toll Free: 800-241-9138 (orders)
E-mail: tnc100@bellsouth.net
Web site: http://www.amazingherbspress.com
Dist(s): **Baker & Taylor Bks.**

Amazing Minds, *(0-9714997)* 3350 Sweetwater Rd., No. 104, Lawrenceville, GA 30044-6562 USA Tel 770-925-4903
E-mail: bethes7@hellsouth.net
Web site: http://www.amazing-minds.com.

AMazing Pubns., *(0-9763434)* 337 W. Napa St., Sonoma, CA 95476 USA.

Ambassador Bks., Inc., *(0-9646439; 1-929039)* 91 Prescott St., Worcester, MA 01605 USA Tel 508-756-2893; Fax: 508-757-7055; Toll Free: 800-577-0909
E-mail: info@ambassadorbooks.com
Web site: http://www.ambassadorbooks.com
Dist(s): **Baker & Taylor Bks.**
Christian Bk. Distributors
Spring Arbor Distributors, Inc.

Ambassador International *Imprint of* **Emerald Hse. Group, Inc.**

Ambassador Pubns., *(1-58572)* 3110 E. Medicine Lake Blvd., Plymouth, MN 55441 USA Tel 763-545-5631; Fax: 763-545-0079
E mail: parishcd@aflc.org
Web site: http://www.aflc.org.

Ambassador-Emerald, International *Imprint of* **Emerald Hse. Group, Inc.**

Ambee Hse. Publishing, *(0-9675879)* P.O. Box 191893, Little Rock, AR 72219 USA Tel 501-847-9527
E-mail: RRoberts@Artistitle.net.

Amber Bks., *(0-9655064; 0-9702224; 0-9727519; 0-9749779; 0-9767735; 0-9790976)* Div. of Amber Communications Group, Inc., 1334 E. Chandler Blvd., Suite 5-D67, Phoenix, AZ 85048 USA Tel 480-460-1660; Fax: 480-283-0991
E-mail: amberbks@aol.com
Web site: http://www.amberbooks.com
Dist(s): **A & B Distributors & Pubs. Group**
African World Bks.
Baker & Taylor Bks.
Book Wholesalers, Inc.
Brodart Co.
D&J Bk. Distributors
Follett Library Resources
Independent Pubs. Group
Koen-Levy Bk. Wholesalers LLC
Midwest Library Service
Quality Bks., Inc.
Unique Bks., Inc.

Amber Lotus *See* **Amber Lotus Publishing**

Amber Lotus Publishing, *(0-945798; 1-56937; 1-885394; 1-60237)* P.O. Box 11329, Portland, OR 97211-1329 USA Toll Free: 800-326-2375
E-mail: info@amberlotus.com
Web site: http://www.amberlotus.com
Dist(s): **Banyan Tree Bks.**

Amber Trust, The *See* **Aenor Trust, The**

Amber Woods Publishing, *(0-9743717)* P.O. Box 280, Excelsior, MN 55331 USA Tel 952-476-1670
Web site: http://www.amberwoodspublishing.com.

Amberlin Group, The, *(1-58649)* Div. of the Amberlin Group, 791 Fir St., Pocatello, ID 83201 USA Tel 208-233-6689
E-mail: orders@amberlin.com; jwheeler@amberlin.com; btj@merrillandmerrill.com
Web site: http://www.amberlin.com; http://www.deep-magic.net
Dist(s): **Lightning Source, Inc.**

Amberock Pubns., *(0-9754636)* P.O. Box 491, Dallas, NC 28034 USA
Web site: http://www.meandmybassguitar.com.

Amberwaves, *(0-9708913)* P.O. Box 487, Becket, MA 01223 USA (SAN 256-4254) Tel 413-623-0012; 413-623-6042 (phone/fax); 305 Brooker Hill Rd., Becket, MA 01223 Tel 413-623-0012; Fax: 413-623-6042
E-mail: shenwa@bcn.net
Web site: http://www.amberwaves.org.

Amberwood Pr., *(0-9630243; 0-9776445)* 41 Hornbeck Ridge, Poughkeepsie, NY 12603 USA Tel 914-486-0244; Fax: 914-454-9751 Do not confuse with Amberwood Pr., in Ventura, CA
E-mail: nava@vegkitchen.com
Web site: http://www.vegkitchen.com
Dist(s): **Independent Pubs. Group.**

Ambition Studios *See* **Lexpress**

AMC World, LLC, *(0-9720750)* Orders Addr.: 3904 N. Druid Hills Dr., No. 211, Decatur, GA 30033 USA Tel 678-642-7396
Web site: http://www.amc-world.com.

Ameeramac Bks. *Imprint of* **Ameeramac Reporting, Inc.**

Ameeramac Reporting, Inc., *(0-9762911)* 168 Putnam Ave., Brooklyn, NY 11216-1606 USA Tel 917-353-1644; Fax: 718-636-8210 ; *Imprints:* Ameeramac Books (AmeeraBks)
E-mail: ameeramac@optonline.com.

Amelia Street Pr., *(0-9742602)* Orders Addr.: P.O. Box 87182, Baton Rouge, LA 70879 USA Tel 225-346-8811; Edit Addr.: 2135 Arlington Ave., Baton Rouge, LA 70808 USA
E-mail: ameliastreet@go.com.

Amenta Bks., *(0-9642831)* 1820 W. Lacey Blvd., No. 189, Hanford, CA 93230 USA Tel 209-583-6066; Fax: 209-583-6068; Toll Free: 800-774-9303
E-mail: kmativo@sprintmail.com
Web site: http://www.sprint.site.com.

Amereon LTD., *(0-8488; 0-88411; 0-89190)* Orders Addr.: P.O. Box 1200, Mattituck, NY 11952 USA (SAN 201-2413) Tel 631-298-5100; Fax: 631-298-5631 ; *Imprints:* Rivercity Press (Rivercity Pr); Aeonian Press (Aeonian Pr); American Reprint Company (Am Repr)
E-mail: amereon@aol.com.

America Sports Publishing, *(0-9721199)* Orders Addr.: P.O. Box 132, Brookfield, OH 44403 USA Tel 330-448-0866; Toll Free: 866-255-2267; Edit Addr.: 6881 Stewart Rd., Brookfield, OH 44403 USA Fax: 330-448-0936
E-mail: Info@AthleticScholarshipBook.com
Web site: http://www.AthleticScholarshipBook.com
Dist(s): **Baker & Taylor Bks.**
Cardinal Pubs. Group
Quality Bks., Inc.
Unique Bks., Inc.

American Academy of Pediatrics, *(0-910761; 0-915473; 1-58110)* 141 Northwest Point Blvd., Elk Grove Village, IL 60007-1098 USA (SAN 265-3540) Tel 847-434-4000; Fax: 847-434-8000; Toll Free: 888-227-1770
E-mail: pubs@aap.org
Web site: http://www.aap.org/bookstore
Dist(s): **Independent Pubs. Group**
Majors, J. A. Co.

American Antiquarian Society, *(0-912296; 0-944026; 1-929545)* 185 Salisbury St., Worcester, MA 01609 USA (SAN 206-474X) Tel 508-752-5221; Fax: 508-754-9069
E-mail: library@mwa.org
Web site: http://www.americanantiquarian.org
Dist(s): **Oak Knoll Pr.**

American Assn. for Clinical Chemistry, Inc., *(0-915274; 1-890883; 1-59425)* Orders Addr.: 1850 K St NW Ste. 625, Washington, DC 20006-2215 USA (SAN 214-2813) Toll Free: 800-892-1400 ; *Imprints:* AACC Press (AACC Pr)
E-mail: info@aacc.org
Web site: http://www.aaccdirect.org.

American Association for Counseling & Development *See* **American Counseling Assn.**

American Assn. of Veterinary Parasitologists, *(0-9770942)* 3915 S. 48th St. Terr., Saint Joseph, MO 64503 USA
Web site: http://www.aavp.org.

American Automobile Association *See* **AAA**

American Bar Assn., *(0-89707; 1-57073; 1-59031; 1-60442)* 321 N. Clark St. Ste. 1400, Chicago, IL 60610-7656 USA (SAN 211-4798) Toll Free: 800-285-2221
E-mail: service@abanet.org; packageplan@abanet.org
Web site: http://www.abanet.org
Dist(s): **National Bk. Network.**

American Basics, The, *(0-9706318)* P.O. Box 1530, Lake Havasu City, AZ 86405-1530 USA Tel 520-505-8197
E-mail: jdringer@uneedspeed.net
Web site: http://www.theramericanbasics.com.

American Bible Society, *(0-8267; 1-58516)* Orders Addr.: 844 NW Lowery Rd., Claremore, OK 74017-2116 USA (SAN 662-7129) Tel 918-342-3904; Toll Free Fax: 866-570-2877; Edit Addr.: 1865 Broadway, New York, NY 10023-9980 USA (SAN 203-5189) Tel 212-408-1200; Fax: 212-408-1305; 700 Plaza Dr., 2nd Flr., Secaucus, NJ 07094
E-mail: info@americanbible.org
Web site: http://www.bibles.org; http://www.americanbible.org
Dist(s): **Anchor Distributors.**

American Biography Service, Incorporated *See* **Reprint Services Co.**

American Bk. Co., *(1-932410; 1-59807)* 103 Executive Dr., Woodstock, GA 30188 USA Tel 770-928-2834 Toll Free: 888-254-5877 Do not confuse with companies with the same name in Chesterfield, VA, Knoxville, TN, Florence, AL
Web site: http://www.americanbookcompany.com.

American Book Publishing *See* **American Bk. Publishing Group**

American Bk. Publishing Group, *(1-930586; 1-58982)* P.O. Box 65624, Salt Lake City, UT 84165 USA (SAN 254-4725) Fax: 801-382-0881; Toll Free: 888-288-7413 ; *Imprints:* Bedside Books (Bedside Bks); Millennial Mind Publishing (Millennial Mind)
E-mail: orders@american-book.com; info@american-book.com; operations@american-book.com
Web site: http://www.american-book.com
Dist(s): **Seven Locks Pr.**

†American Camping Assn., *(0-87603)* 5000 State Rd. 67, N., Martinsville, IN 46151-7902 USA (SAN 201-2596) Tel 765-342-8456 (General Info.); Fax: 765-349-6357 (orders); Toll Free: 800-428-2267 (orders)
E-mail: bookstore@aca-camps.org
Web site: http://www.acacamps.org
Dist(s): **Independent Pubs. Group**; *CIP.*

American Cancer Society, Inc., *(0-944235; 1-60443)* 250 Williams St., Atlanta, GA 30303-1002 USA (SAN 227-6941) Tel 404-320-3333; Fax: 404-325-9341; Toll Free: 800-ACS-2345
Web site: http://www.cancer.org
Dist(s): **McGraw-Hill Cos., The**
McGraw-Hill Professional Publishing
Wiley-Blackwell.

American Carriage Hse. Publishing, *(0-9705734)* P.O. Box 1778, Penn Valley, CA 95946 USA Tel 530-432-8880; Fax: 530-265-9650 Do not confuse with Carraige House Publishing in Middleton, CA
E-mail: info@americancarriagehousepublishing.com; editor@americancarriagehousepublishing.com; research@americancarriagehousepublishing.com; assistant@americancarriagehousepublishing.com
Web site: http://www.americancarriagehousepublishing.com
Dist(s): **Baker & Taylor Bks.**
STL Distribution North America.

†American Chemical Society, *(0-8412)* 1155 16th St., NW, Washington, DC 20036 USA (SAN 201-2626) Tel 202-872-4600; Toll Free: 800-227-5558
E-mail: service@acs.org; help@acs.org
Web site: http://www.acs.org; http://www.ChemCenter.org
Dist(s): **AtlasBooks Distribution**
Oxford Univ. Pr., Inc.; *CIP.*

American Classical League, The, *(0-939507)* Miami Univ., Oxford, OH 45056 USA (SAN 225-8358) Tel 513-529-7741; Fax: 513-529-7742
E-mail: info@aclclassics.org
Web site: http://www.aclclassics.org.

American College Testing Program *See* **ACT**

American Correctional Assn., *(0-929310; 0-942974; 1-56991)* 206 N. Washington St. Ste. 200, Alexandria, VA 22314-2528 USA (SAN 204-8051) Toll Free: 800-222-5646 (ext. 1860)
E-mail: chantew@aca.org
Web site: http://www.corrections.com/aca.

American Counseling Assn., *(0-911547; 1-55620)* 5999 Stevenson Ave., Alexandria, VA 22304-3300 USA (SAN 291-9141) Tel 703-823-9800; Fax: 703-823-0252; Toll Free: 800-347-6647; 800-422-2648 (Book orders)
Web site: http://www.counseling.org.

American Dental Assn., *(0-910074; 1-932305; 1-60122)* 211 E. Chicago Ave., Chicago, IL 60611 USA (SAN 202-4519) Tel 312-440-2568; Fax: 312-440-7461
E-mail: survey@ada.org
Web site: http:/www.ada.org.

American Dog *Imprint of* **Ideate Prairie**

American Dream Series .. I Can Read!, *(0-9721529)* 14907 Claude Ln., Silver Spring, MD 20905 USA Tel 301-384-8979; Fax: 301-384-0486
E-mail: i4readsuccess@aol.com.

American Driving Society, *(0-9727292)* P.O. Box 278, Cross Plains, WI 53528-0278 USA Do not confuse with American Driving Society in Lakeville, CT
E-mail: ann@americandrivingsociety.org
Web site: http://www.americandrivingsociety.org.

American Education Publishing *Imprint of* **School Specialty Publishing**

American Fisheries Society, *(0-913235; 1-888569)* 5410 Grosvenor Ln., Suite 110, Bethesda, MD 20814-2199 USA (SAN 284-964X) Tel 301-897-8616; Fax: 301-897-5080
E-mail: main@fisheries.org; afspubs@pbd.com
Web site: http://www.fisheries.org
Dist(s): **PBD, Inc.**

American Forum For Global Education, *(0-944675)* 120 Wall St., Suite 2600, New York, NY 10005-4001 USA (SAN 236-364X) Tel 212-624-1300; Fax: 212-624-1412
E-mail: info@globaled.org
Web site: http://www.globaled.org/contact.html.

American Foundation Pubns., *(1-928596)* Orders Addr.: P.O. Box 355, Bridgewater, VA 22812 USA Tel 540-298-8964 (phone/fax); Fax: 540-298-1555; Toll Free: 888-298-8964
E-mail: afpub@rica.net
Web site: http://www.afpub.com.

American French Genealogical Society, *(1-929920; 1-932749; 1-60305)* Orders Addr.: P.O. Box 830, Woonsocket, RI 02895 USA; Edit Addr.: 78 Earle St., Woonsocket, RI 02895 USA
E-mail: RDBeaudry@afgs.org
Web site: http://www.afgs.org.

American Friends Service Committee, *(0-910082)* 1501 Cherry St., Philadelphia, PA 19102-1479 USA (SAN 153-4823) Tel 215-241-7048; Fax: 215-241-7275; Toll Free: 888-588-2372
E-mail: DLGibbs@afsc.org; afscinfo@afsc.org
Web site: http://www.afsc.org/.

Company

American Geological Institute, *(0-913312; 0-922152)* 4220 King St., Alexandria, VA 22302-1502 USA (SAN 202-4543) Tel 703-379-2480; Fax: 703-379-7563
E-mail: agi@agiweb.org
Web site: http://www.agiweb.org.

American Girl *Imprint of* **American Girl Publishing, Inc.**

†American Girl Publishing, Inc., *(0-937295; 1-56247; 1-58485; 1-59369)* Subs. of Mattel, Inc., Orders Addr.: P.O. Box 620991, Middleton, WI 53562-0991 USA Tel 608-836-4848; Toll Free Fax: 800-257-3865; Toll Free: 800-233-0264; Edit Addr.: 8400 Fairway Pl., Middleton, WI 53562-0998 USA (SAN 298-6337) Tel 608-836-4848; Fax: 608-831-7089 ; *Imprints:* American Girl (Amer Girl); Pleasant Company (Pleasnt Co)
Web site: http://www.pleasantcopublications.com/; *CIP.*

American Gita Society, *(0-9621099)* Div. of International Gita Society, 511 Lowell Pl., Fremont, CA 94536-1805 USA (SAN 250-4286) Tel 510-791-6993; 510-791-6953
E-mail: sanjay@gitainternational.com; prasad@gita-society.com
Web site: http://www.gita-society.com
Dist(s): **Quality Bks., Inc.**

American Ground Water Trust, *(0-9641186)* Orders Addr.: 16 Centre St., Concord, NH 03301 USA Tel 603-228-5444; Fax: 603-228-6557
E-mail: trustinfo@agwt.org
Web site: http://www.agwt.org.

American Guidance Service, Inc., *(0-7854; 0-88671; 0-913476; 0-942277; 1-56269)* 4201 Woodland Rd., Circle Pines, MN 55014-1796 USA (SAN 201-694X) Tel 763-786-4343; Fax: 763-786-9077; Toll Free: 800-328-2560
E-mail: ags@mr.net
Web site: http://www.agsnet.com.

American Health Pr., *(0-9664005)* 3717 Dixon St., Santa Barbara, CA 93105 USA Tel 805-563-8000.

American Health Publishing, *(0-9754443)* Orders Addr.: P.O. Box 282, Clarence, NY 14031 USA Tel 716-741-0177 Do not confuse with Amerricanhealth Publishing Company in Dallas, TX
E-mail: americahealthpub@aol.com
Web site: http://www.growingahealthyfamily.com.

American Heritage Publishing, *(0-9754859)* 5710 Mt. Repose Ln., NW, Norcross, GA 30092-1428 USA Tel 404-495-3720 (phone/fax)
E-mail: trjc@mindspring.com
Web site: http://www.privilegesofwar.com
Dist(s): **AtlasBooks Distribution.**

American Historical Pr., *(0-9654754; 1-892724)* 10755 Sherman Way, Suite 2, Sun Valley, CA 91352 USA Tel 818-503-0133; Fax: 818-503-9081; Toll Free: 800-550-5750
E-mail: ahp@amhistpress.com
Web site: http://www.amhistpress.com/
Dist(s): **Chicago Distribution Ctr.**

American Home-School Publishing, LLC, *(0-9667067; 0-9779000)* Orders Addr.: 6102 SE. State Rte. C, Cameron, MO 64429 USA (SAN 254-7244) Tel 816-632-1503; Fax: 816-632-1448; Toll Free Fax: 800-557-0234; Toll Free: 800-684-2121
E-mail: booklovers@ahsp.com
Web site: http://www.ahsp.com.

American Humanist Assn., *(0-931779)* 1777 T St., NW, Washington, DC 20009-7125 USA (SAN 266-9412) Tel 202-238-9088; Fax: 202-238-9047; Toll Free: 800-837-3792 ; *Imprints:* Humanist Press (Humanist Press)
E-mail: aelliott@americanhumanist.org
Web site: http://www.thehumanist.org; http://www.americanhumanist.org.

American Immigration Ctr., Inc., *(0-9663425; 0-9714586)* Orders Addr.: P.O. Box 45476, Rio Rancho, NM 87174 USA Tel 505-891-1555; Fax: 505-891-8887; Toll Free: 800-814-1555
E-mail: info@us-immigration.com
Web site: http://www.us-immigration.com.

American Institute of Ultrasound in Medicine, *(1-930047; 1-932962)* 14750 Sweitzer Ln., Suite 100, Laurel, MD 20707-5906 USA (SAN 224-4756) Tel 301-498-4100; Fax: 301-498-4450; Toll Free: 800-638-5352
E-mail: publications@aium.org
Web site: http://www.aium.org.

American International Distribution Corp., Orders Addr.: P.O. Box 574, Williston, VT 05495-0020 USA Tel 800-390-3149; Fax: 802-864-7626; Toll Free: 800-426-4742; Edit Addr.: 50 Winter Sport Ln., Williston, VT 05495 USA (SAN 630-2238) Toll Free: 800-488-2665
E-mail: jmacon@aidcvt.com
Web site: http://www.aidcvt.com/Specialty/Home.asp.

American International Printing & Marketing *See* **Graphix Network**

American LaserTechnic, *(0-9741805)* 1300 NE Miami Gardens Dr. Apt. 407, Miami, FL 33179-4731 USA
E-mail: dan-gregory@attbi.com
Web site: http://www.americanlasertechnic.com.

American Law Institute, *(0-8318)* 4025 Chestnut St., Philadelphia, PA 19104-3099 USA (SAN 204-756X) Tel 215-243-1600; 215-245-1654 (Library); 215-243-1700 (Customer Service); Fax: 215-243-0319; Toll Free: 800-253-6397
E-mail: publications@ali-aba.org
Web site: http://www.ali-aba.org; http://www.ali.org.

†American Library Assn., *(0-8389)* 50 E. Huron St., Chicago, IL 60611 USA (SAN 201-0062) Tel 312-280-2425; 312-944-8085; Fax: 770-280-4155 (Orders); Toll Free: 800-545-2433; 866-746-7252 (Orders)
E-mail: EditionsMarketing@ala.org
Web site: http://www.ala.org; http://www.alastore.ala.org; *CIP.*

American Literary Pr., *(1-56167; 1-934696)* 8019 Belair Rd., Suite 10, Baltimore, MD 21236 USA Tel 410-882-7700; Fax: 410-882-7703; Toll Free: 800-873-2003 ; *Imprints:* Shooting Star Edition (SSE); Five Star Special Edition (Five Star Spec Ed)
E-mail: amerlit@americanliterarypress.com
Web site: http://www.americanliterarypress.com.

American Map Corp., *(0-8416; 981-234)* Div. of Langenscheidt Pubs., Inc., P.O. Box 780010, Maspeth, NY 11378-0010 USA (SAN 202-4624) Toll Free: 800-432-6277
E-mail: customerservice@americanmap.com
Web site: http://www.americanmap.com
Dist(s): **Fujii Assocs.**
Langenscheidt Pubs Inc.

American Marine Publishing, Inc., *(0-9622134; 0-9773539)* 488 Bay East Dr., Traverse City, MI 49686 USA Tel 231-933-0827; Fax: 231-933-0887; Toll Free: 800-832-0038
E-mail: info@powerboatguide.net; edmck@charter.net
Web site: http://www.powerboatguide.com
Dist(s): **Hale, Robert & Co., Inc.**

†American Mathematical Society, *(0-8218)* Orders Addr.: 201 Charles St., Providence, RI 02904 USA (SAN 250-3263) Tel 401-455-4000; Fax: 401-331-3842; Toll Free: 800-321-4267
E-mail: cust-serv@ams.org
Web site: http://www.ams.org; *CIP.*

American Media Intl., *(0-9724462; 0-9724889; 1-932378; 1-933309)* 2609 Tucker St. Ext., Burlington, NC 27215 USA Tel 707-937-1225 Do not confuse with American Media International in Westport, CT
E-mail: audiobks@mcn.org
Dist(s): **Baker & Taylor Bks.**
Ingram Bk. Co.
National Bk. Network.

American Meteorological Society, *(0-933876; 1-878220)* 45 Beacon St, Boston, MA 02108-3693 USA (SAN 225-2139) Tel 617-227-2425; Fax: 617-742-8718
Web site: http://www.ametsoc.org/ams.

American Montessori Consulting, *(0-929487)* Orders Addr.: P.O. Box 5062, Rossmoor, CA 90721 USA (SAN 249-5651) Tel 562-598-2321 (phone/fax); Edit Addr.: 11961 Wallingsford Rd., Rossmoor, CA 90721-5062 USA (SAN 249-566X)
E-mail: amcnews1@aol.com; amonco@aol.com; amontessoric@earthlink.net
Web site: http://www.amonco.org
Dist(s): **Baker & Taylor Bks.**
Book Hse., Inc., The
Midwest Library Service.

American Museum of Natural History, *(0-913424)* Orders Addr.: Central Park West at 79th St., New York, NY 10024-5192 USA (SAN 208-2160) Tel 212-769-5000 (Museum Library); Edit Addr.: 256 Fifth Ave., New York, NY 10001 USA Tel 212-481-2997 (Micro Press only)
E-mail: mlwaxman@amnh.org
Web site: http://www.amnh.org.

American Poets Society *Imprint of* **Gem Printing**

†American Psychological Assn., *(0-912704; 0-945354; 1-55798; 1-59147; 0-9792125; 1-4338)* Orders Addr.: P.O. Box 92984, Washington, DC 20090-2984 USA (SAN 685-3137) Tel 202-336-6123; 202-336-5510 202-336-5502 (orders); Toll Free: 800-374-2721; Edit Addr.: 12884 Harbor Dr., Woodbridge, VA 22192-2921 USA (SAN 255-5921); P.O. Box 77318, Washington, DC 20013-8318 Toll Free: 800-374-2721 ; *Imprints:* Magination Press (Magination Press)
E-mail: ghughes@spa.org; jmacomber@apa.org; books@apa.org
Web site: http://www.apa.org; *CIP.*

American Quilter's Society *Imprint of* **Collector Bks.**

American Reprint Co. *Imprint of* **Amereon LTD.**

American Retrospects, LLC, *(0-9747666)* Orders Addr.: P.O. Box 352576, Toledo, OH 43635-2576 USA Tel 419-824-4500; Fax: 419-885-4255
E-mail: jkw@americanretro.net; jkw@bex.net; mds@bex.net; mds@americanretro.net
Web site: http://www.americanretro.net.

American Revolution Publishing, *(0-9760948)* 12514 Mustang Dr., Poway, CA 92064 USA Tel 858-842-1812 (phone/fax)
E-mail: amrevpub@cox.net
Web site: http://www.gwuh.com; http://www.amrevpub.com; http://www.americanrevolutionpublishing.com
Dist(s): **Baker & Taylor Bks.**
Book Clearing Hse.
Quality Bks., Inc.

American Schl. of Classical Studies at Athens, *(0-87661)* 6-8 Charlton St., Princeton, NJ 08540-5232 USA (SAN 201-1697) Tel 609-683-0800; Fax: 609-924-0578
E-mail: cwatkinson@ascsa.org
Web site: http://www.ascsa.edu.gr/publications
Dist(s): **Brown, David Bk. Co., The.**

American Society for Microbiology *See* **ASM Pr.**

American Success Institute, Inc., *(1-884864)* 5 N. Main St., Natick, MA 01760 USA Tel 508-651-3303; Fax: 508-653-2924; Toll Free: 800-585-1300
E-mail: info@Success.org
Web site: http://www.success.org.

American Technical Pubs., Inc., *(0-8269)* 1155 W. 175th St., Homewood, IL 60430 USA (SAN 206-8141) Tel 708-957-1100; Fax: 708-957-1137; Toll Free: 800-323-3471
E-mail: service@americantech.net
Web site: http://www.americantech.net.

American Trust Pubns., *(0-89259)* 745 McClintock Dr., Suite 114, Burr Ridge, IN 60521-0857 USA (SAN 664-6158)
Dist(s): **Islamic Bk. Service**
Kazi Pubns., Inc.

American Wind Power Ctr., *(0-9679480)* Div. of National Windmill Project, Inc., 1501 Canyon Lake Dr., Lubbock, TX 79403 USA Tel 806-747-8734; Fax: 806-740-0668
E-mail: charris@windmill.com
Web site: http://www.windmill.com.

American World Geographic Publishing *See* **Farcountry Pr.**

Americana Publishing, Inc., *(1-58807; 1-58943)* 195 Us Highway 9. Ste. 204, Englishtown, NJ 07726-8294 USA Toll Free: 888-883-8203
E-mail: editor@americanabooks.com
Web site: http://www.americanabooks.com.

Americana Souvenirs & Gifts, *(1-890541)* 206 Hanover St., Gettysburg, PA 17325-1911 USA (SAN 169-7366) Toll Free: 800-692-7436.

America's Choice *Imprint of* **National Ctr. on Education & The Economy**

Americas Group, The, *(0-935047)* Subs. of Harris/Ragan Management Group, 9200 Sunset Blvd., No. 404, Los Angeles, CA 90069-3506 USA (SAN 694-4698) Tel 310-278-8037; Fax: 310-271-3649; Toll Free: 800-966-7716
E-mail: hrmg@aol.com
Web site: http://www.americasgroup.com
Dist(s): **Penton Overseas, Inc.**

America's Young Heroes Pubns., *(0-9718197)* Orders Addr.: P.O. Box 810561, Boca Raton, FL 33481-0561 USA Tel 561-241-1169; Fax: 561-241-1567
E-mail: ameryoungheroes@aol.com
Web site: http://www.americasyoungheroes.org; http://www.publishershomepages.com/php/Americas_Young_Heroes_Publications.

Amerisearch, Inc., *(0-9653557; 0-9753455; 0-9778085)* Orders Addr.: P.O. Box 20163, Saint Louis, MO 63123 USA (SAN 254-6426) Tel 314-487-4395 (phone/fax); Fax: 314-487-4489; Toll Free: 888-872-9673 (888-872-WORD); Edit Addr.: 4346 Southview Way Dr., Saint Louis, MO 63129 USA
E-mail: wjfederer@aol.com
Web site: http://www.amerisearch.net.

Amerotica *Imprint of* **NBM Publishing Co.**

Ameya, LLC, 18115 NW Dustin Ln., Beaverton, OR 97006 USA Tel 503-645-6071
E-mail: ameya11@home.com.

Amherst Media, Inc., *(0-936262; 1-58428)* 175 Rano St., Suite 200, Buffalo, NY 14207 USA Tel 716-874-4450; Fax: 716-874-4508
E-mail: AmherstMedia@AmherstMedia.com; marketing@AmherstMedia.com; editing@AmherstMedia.com
Web site: http://www.amherstmedia.com
Dist(s): **Independent Pubs. Group.**

Amherst Pr., *(0-910122; 0-942495; 1-930596)* Div. of The Guest Cottage, Inc., Orders Addr.: P.O. Box 774, Saint Germain, WI 54558 USA (SAN 213-9820) Tel 715-477-0424; Fax: 715-477-0405; Toll Free: 800-333-8122; Edit Addr.: P.O. Box 774, Saint Germain, WI 54558 USA (SAN 666-6450) Do not confuse with companies with the same name in Amherst, NY, North Hampton, NH
E-mail: sales@theguestcottage.com
Web site: http://www.theguestcottage.com
Dist(s): **Partners Bk. Distributing, Inc.**

Amiaya Entertainment, *(0-9745075; 0-9777544)* 1154 E. 229 St., Apt. 12C, Bronx, NY 10466 USA.

Amicus Pr., *(0-914861)* 4201 Underwood Rd., Baltimore, MD 21218 USA (SAN 289-0518) Tel 301-889-5056.

Amicus Vitae Pr., *(0-9713926)* P.O. Box 15, Coldwater, OH 45828-0015 USA
E-mail: brunspj@bright.net.

AMIDEAST, *(0-913957)* 1730 M. St. NW, Suite 1100, Washington, DC 20036-4505 USA (SAN 286-7184) Tel 202-776-9600; Fax: 202-776-7000
E-mail: inquiries@amideast.org
Web site: http://www.amideast.org.

Amigos de Arizonac, Inc., *(1-887273)* Orders Addr.: P.O. Box 30124, Phoenix, AZ 85046 USA Tel 480-502-2450; Fax: 480-502-9470; Edit Addr.: 40502 N. Kearny Way, Phoenix, AZ 85086-1858 USA
E-mail: info@azamigos.com; dbuscher1@home.com
Web site: http://www.azamigos.com.

Amirah Publishing, *(1-889720)* Div. of IFNA, Orders Addr.: P.O. Box 541146, Flushing, NY 11354 USA; Edit Addr.: a/o IBTS, Inc., P.O. Box 5153, Long Island City, NY 11105 USA Tel 718-357-3872 (phone/fax)
E-mail: amirahpbco@aol.com
Web site: http://www.islamiceducation.net; http://www.ifna.net
Dist(s): **International Bks. & Tapes Supply.**

Amistad *Imprint of* **HarperCollins Pubs.**

AmityWorks, *(0-9678923)* 18 Pale Dawn Pl., Spring, TX 77381-6637 USA
Web site: http://www.amityworks.com.

Ammons Communications, Ltd., *(0-9651232; 0-9753023)* 29 Regal Ave., Sylva, NC 28779 USA (SAN 851-0881) Tel 828-631-4587 (phone/fax) ; *Imprints:* Catch the Spirit of Appalachia (CSA)
E-mail: v.ammons@mchsi.com
Web site: http://www.mousetrax.org; http://www.spiritofappalachia.org
Dist(s): **Baker & Taylor Bks.**

AMN Publishing, *(0-9728129)* P.O. Box 352, Massapequa, NY 11758 USA
E-mail: AMNPub@aol.com
Web site: http://amnpub.tripod.com.

Amnesty International USA, *(0-939994; 1-887204)* 5 Penn Plaza, New York, NY 10001 USA (SAN 225-6266) Tel 212-807-8400; Fax: 212-627-1451
Web site: http://www.amnestyusa.org.

Amnos Pubns., *(0-9623721)* c/o Holy Apostle Greek Orthodox Church, 2501 S. Wolf Rd., Westchester, IL 60153 USA Tel 708-562-2744; Fax: 708-562-2752
E-mail: harc@mediaone.net.

Amoeba Bks., *(0-9786473)* 5260 Rogers Rd., G-6, Hamburg, NY 14075 USA
E-mail: marketing@amoebabooks.com
Web site: http://www.amoebabooks.com.

Amon Carter Museum, *(0-88360)* 3501 Camp Bowie Blvd., Fort Worth, TX 76107-2695 USA (SAN 204-7608) Tel 817-738-1933; Fax: 817-336-1123; Toll Free: 800-573-1933
E-mail: teresa.tucker@cartermuseum.org
Web site: http://www.cartermuseum.org.

Amped Media, *(0-9742287)* 22 Shaw Pl., Walla Walla, WA 99362 USA.

Ampelon Publishing, LLC, *(0-9748825; 0-9786394; 0-9798104)* 119 E. 46th St. Suite 213, Boise, ID 83714 USA (SAN 850-2412)
E-mail: info@ampelonpublishing.com
Web site: http://www.ampelonpublishing.com
Dist(s): **Baker & Taylor Bks.**

Ampersand Pr., *(0-9702449)* P.O. Box 3827, Parker, CO 80134 USA Fax: 303-841-7350 Do not confuse with companies with same name in City Of Industry, CA, Bristol, RI, Princeton, NJ
E-mail: AmpersandPress@aol.com.

Amsco Music *Imprint of* **Music Sales Corp.**

AMSCO Schl. Pubns., Inc., *(0-87720; 1-56765)* 315 Hudson St., 5th Flr., New York, NY 10013-1085 USA (SAN 201-1751) Tel 212-886-6500; Fax: 212-675-7010; Toll Free: 800-969-8398; 800-676-6630 (ordering/return, Western U.S.); 800-447-7957 (ordering/returns, Florida); 866-902-6726 (ordering/returns, Eastern U.S.)
E-mail: amscopub.com
Web site: http://www.amscopub.com.

Amsea Group, Inc., *(0-9723044)* 441 N. Central Ave., Suite 1, Campbell, CA 95008 USA Tel 408-378-9200; Fax: 408-379-5621; Toll Free: 800-535-5363
E-mail: tuneman@aol.com
Web site: http://www.amseagroup.com.

AMSI Venture, Incorporated *See* **Sleep Garden, Inc.**

Amulet Bks. *Imprint of* **Abrams, Harry N. , Inc.**

Amulet Press *See* **Pensive Bks.**

AMY Pr., *(1-931730)* Div. of KidsBe Publishing, Inc., 254 West 54th St., 12th Flr., New York, NY 10019 USA Tel 212-247-1418; Fax: 212-247-1554 Do not confuse with The Amy Pr., in Walpole, NH
E-mail: motoyama@amypress.com
Web site: http://www.amypress.com.

Anacat Pubns., *(0-9674510)* 82 Fairview Farms, Shelby, NC 28150 USA Tel 704-482-8823; Fax: 704-482-0811.

Anacus Press *Imprint of* **Finney Co., Inc.**

Anadem Publishing, Inc., *(0-9646891; 1-890018)* 3620 N. High St., Suite 201, Columbus, OH 43214 USA Tel 614-262-2539; Fax: 614-262-6630; Toll Free: 800-633-0055
E-mail: anadem@erinet.com
Web site: http://www.anadem.com.

Anahata Pr., *(0-932177; 1-893099)* Div. of The Center of Timeless Being, P.O. Box 1673, Sebastopol, CA 95473 USA (SAN 686-5291) Tel 707-876-3380
E-mail: rmiller@nondual.com
Web site: http://www.nondual.com.

Anaiah, Ruth, *(0-9769675)* P.O. Box 2142, Brandon, FL 33509-2142 USA
E-mail: dozministry2001@yahoo.com.

Analytical Psychology Club of San Francisco, Inc., *(0-9611232)* Orders Addr.: 340 Howard Ave., Piedmont, CA 94611 USA (SAN 662-751X); Edit Addr.: 2411 Octavia St., San Francisco, CA 94109 USA (SAN 283-2461) Tel 415-547-3896.

Anamchara Bks. *Imprint of* **Harding Hse. Publishing Sebice Inc.**

Anancybooks.com, *(0-9753297)* P.O. Box 28677, San Jose, CA 95159-8677 USA Tel 408-286-0726; Fax: 408-947-0668
E-mail: info@anancybooks.com
Web site: http://www.anancybooks.com
Dist(s): **Biblio Distribution.**

Ananda Publications *See* **Crystal Clarity Pubs.**

Ananse Pr., *(0-9605670; 0-9749437)* Orders Addr.: P.O. Box 22565, Seattle, WA 98122-0565 USA (SAN 216-3292) Tel 206-325-8205; Fax: 206-328-4371; 1504 32nd Ave. S., Seattle, WA 98144-3918 (SAN 241-6123)
E-mail: gumbomedia@earthlink.net; gumbomedia@yahoo.com
Web site: http://home.usaa.net/~gumbomedia/ananse/index.htm.

Anar Bks. LLC, *(0-9748285)* 10266 Virginia Swan Pl., Cupertino, CA 95014-2025 USA
E-mail: anoopbusiness@yahoo.com
Web site: http://www.anarbooks.com.

Anatole Publishing Co., *(0-9666534)* 150 Rankin Way, Suite 24, Benicia, CA 94510-2130 USA Tel 707-326-3771; Fax: 707-746-6413
E mail: angclok@IX.netcom.com.

Anatomical Chart Co. *Imprint of* **Lippincott Williams & Wilkins**

Anaya Multimedia, S.A. (ESP) *(84-415; 84-7614) Dist. by* **Continental Bk.**

Anbeyond Pr., *(0-9744014)* 10420 NE 190th St., Bothell, WA 98011 USA (SAN 255-7886) Tel 425-483-9943; 22833 Bothell Everett Hwy. No. 102, PMB 1227, Bothell, WA 98021
E-mail: rm@anbeyond.com
Web site: http://www.anbeyond.com.

Ancestral Light Publishing, *(0-9718530)* 1969 S. Alafaya Trail, No. 322, Orlando, FL 32828 USA Tel 407-382-1707; Fax: 509-356-6971
E-mail: gigante@uaia.org.

Ancestral Tracks, *(0-9701266; 0-9754161)* P.O. Box 64, Forest Grove, OR 97116-0064 USA
E-mail: books@ancestraltracks.com
Web site: http://www.ancestraltrack.com.

Anchor *Imprint of* **Knopf Publishing Group**

Anchor Publishing Company *See* **BR Anchor Publishing**

Anchor Publishing Inc., *(0-9759335)* 945 Harpswell Neck Rd., Harpswell, ME 04079 USA Tel 207-833-5100
E-mail: bob@harpswellanchor.com
Web site: http://www.harpswellanchor.com.

Anchorage Foundation Pr., *(0-9795266)* 1518 Mohle Dr., Austin, TX 78703 USA
Dist(s): **Greenleaf Book Group Pr.**

Anchorage Museum of History & Art, *(1-885267)* Div. of Municipality of Anchorage, Cultural & Recreational Services, 121 W. Seventh Ave., Anchorage, AK 99501 USA Tel 907-343-6191; Fax; 907-343-6149
E-mail: BaldwinJO@ci.anchorage.ak.us
Dist(s): **Chicago Distribution Ctr.**

Anchorage Pr., *(0-87602)* Orders Addr.: 617 Baxter Ave., Louisville, KY 40204-1105 USA (SAN 203-4727) Tel 502-583-2288; Fax: 502-583-2288 ; *Imprints:* Anchorage Press Plays (Anchorage Pr Plays) Do not confuse with Anchorage Pr., Houston, TX
E-mail: applays@bellsouth.net.

Anchorage Press Plays *Imprint of* **Anchorage Pr.**

Ancient Days Pubs., *(0-9741405)* P.O. Box 356, Landisville, PA 17538 USA
E-mail: abrdl@ptd.net.

Ancient Studios, *(0-9744216)* 133 Iroquois Ave., Essex Jct, VT 05452-3572 USA
E-mail: ancientstudios@aol.com
Web site: http://www.ancientstudios.com; http://www.groovycomics.com
Dist(s): **Diamond Comic Distributors, Inc.**

And Bks., *(0-89708)* 702 S. Michigan, Suite 836, South Bend, IN 46601 USA (SAN 213-9502) Tel 574-232-3134; Fax: 574-288-4141
E-mail: andbooks@ripco.com
Dist(s): **Distributors, The.**

And Many More, *(0-9714047)* P.O. Box 40358, Austin, TX 78704 USA Tel 512-441-6439 (phone/fax)
Web site: http://www.andmanymore.com.

Andersen (GBR) *(0-86264; 0-905478; 1-84270) Dist. by* **Trafalgar.**

Andersen (GBR) *(0-86264; 0-905478; 1-84270) Dist. by* **IPG Chicago.**

Anderson, George, *(0-9743682)* 12301 Wilshire Blvd., Suite 418, Los Angeles, CA 90025 USA Tel 310-207-3591; Fax: 310-207-6234
E-mail: georgeandereson@aol.com
Web site: http://www.andersonservices.com.

Anderson House Foundation, *(1-890568)* 29W 424 Tanglewood Ln., Warrenville, IL 60555 USA Fax: 630-604-0490; Toll Free Fax: 888-508-5577 ; *Imprints:* A-BA-BA-HA-LA-MA-HA Publishers (A-BA-BA-HA-LA-MA-HA)
E-mail: interhouse@comcast.net
Web site: http:///www.snowqueen.us.

Anderson, Paul Youth Home, Inc., *(0-9772573; 0-9779679)* Orders Addr.: P.O. Box 525, Vidalia, GA 30475 USA (SAN 257-1277) Tel 912-537-7237; Fax: 912-537-8734; Toll Free: 877-537-7237; Edit Addr.: 1603 McIntosh St., Vidalia, GA 30475 USA
E-mail: rebecca@payh.org
Web site: http://www.payh.org.

Anderson Publishing, *(0-9718249)* Orders Addr.: P.O. Box 5544, Douglasville, GA 30154 USA Toll Free: 866-942-0790 (phone/fax); Edit Addr.: 5178 Holly Springs Dr., Douglasville, GA 30135 USA Do not confuse with companies with the same or similar name in Navato, CA, Saginawi, MI, Burley, ID, Cincinnati, MO, Anacortes, WA, Indio, CA
E-mail: canderson@andersonpub.com
Web site: http://www.andersonpub.com
Dist(s): **ACW Pr.**

ANDInternational, *(0-9762291)* 74 Woodcleft Ave., Freeport, NY 11520 USA Tel 516-546-2025; Fax: 516-546-6010; Toll Free: 800-229-2634
E-mail: orders@andihq.com; andihq@aol.com
Web site: http://www.andihq.com.

Andover Green Bk. Pubs., *(1-885934)* R.R. 1, Box 53, Alton, NH 03809 USA Tel 603-875-5200
E-mail: books@worldpath.net.

Andre Deutsch (GBR) *(0-233) Dist. by* **Trafalgar.**

Andre Deutsch (GBR) *(0-233) Dist. by* **IPG Chicago.**

Andre Deutsch (GBR) *(0-233) Dist. by* **Trans-Atl Phila.**

†Andrews McMeel Publishing, *(0-8362; 0-7407)* Orders Addr.: c/o Simon & Schuster, Inc., 100 Front St., Riverside, NJ 08075 USA Toll Free Fax: 1800-943-9831; Toll Free: 800-943-9839 (Customer Service); 800-897-7650 (Credit Dept.); Edit Addr.: 4520 Main St., Kansas City, MO 64111-7701 USA (SAN 202-540X) Tel 816-932-6600; Fax: 816.932.6684; Toll Free: 800-851-8923
Web site: http://www.AndrewsMcMeel.com
Dist(s): **AMCAL, Inc.**
Big River Distribution
Simon & Schuster, Inc.; *CIP.*

Andrews, Michael S. Publishing, LLC, *(0-9710450; 0-9777039; 0-9792565)* 7122 S. Sheridan Rd., Suite 2, No. 102, Tulsa, OK 74133 USA Tel 918-254-8874; Fax: 918-307-8738; Toll Free: 866-794-8577
E-mail: vision-quest@cox.net; MSAPublisher@cox.net; michaelsandrewsllc@cox.net
Web site: http://www.vision-questpublishing.com; http://www.michaelsandrews.com.

Andrus, Ashley, *(0-9772000)* 108 Deanna Dr., Lafayette, LA 70503-3716 USA
E-mail: ala@andrus.com.

Anela Publishing *See* **Abidenme Bks.**

Angel & Me Publishing, *(0-9709772)* P.O. Box 3337, Kalamazoo, MI 49008-2126 USA Fax: 616-344-1639
E-mail: everswell@acninc.net
Web site: http://angelandme.com.

Angel Bea Publishing, *(0-9717843; 0-9777790)* 9504 Bainsbrook Ct., Cincinnati, OH 45249 USA (SAN 255-1519) Tel 513-683-8592; Fax: 513-683-9523
E-mail: angelbeabooks@yahoo.com
Web site: http://www.angelbea.com
Dist(s): **Baker & Taylor Bks.**
Independent Pubs. Group.

Angel Eyes Publishing, *(0-9755346)* P.O. Box 2434, Streetsboro, OH 44241 USA (SAN 256-0542) Tel 404-423-5476
E-mail: dawnetteculp@yahoo.com
Web site: http://www.angeleyespublishingco.com
Dist(s): **Baker & Taylor Bks.**

Angel Fingers Foundation, *(0-9760160)* 6600 Plaza Dr., No.2000, New Orleans, LA 70127 USA.

Angel Gate *Imprint of* **Left Field Ink**

Angel Heart Children's Pr., *(0-9712124)* 58 Level Rd., Bennington, IN 47011 USA Tel 812-534-3912; Fax: 812-534-3983
E-mail: angelheartchildrnspress@hotmail.com; angelheartchildrenspress@hotmail.com
Web site: http://www.geocities.com/hs_mom2000.

Angel Heart Publishing, *(0-9671872)* 804 Bluffcreek Ln., No. 126, Arlington, TX 76006-3733 USA.

Angel Hse. Publishing, Inc., *(0-9675124)* 6584 Via Regina, Boca Raton, FL 33481 USA Tel 561-347-9788; P.O. Box 3447, Boca Raton, FL 33427-3447
E-mail: Laveni@bellsouth.net.

Angel Island Assoc., *(0-9667352)* P.O. Box 866, Tiburon, CA 94920 USA Tel 415-435-3522; Fax: 415-435-2950
E-mail: valaia@att.net
Web site: http://www.angelisland.org.

Angel Mind, *(0-9729866)* 5776-D Lindero Canyon Dr. #123, Westlake Village, CA 91362 USA Tel 818-424-2619; Fax: 818-780-8880
E-mail: bill@angelmind.net
Web site: http://www.angelmind.net
Dist(s): **Midpoint Trade Bks., Inc.**

Angel Pubns., *(1-889383)* 3111 Rte. 38, No. 11, Suite 124, Mount Laurel, NJ 08054 USA Tel 609-235-6896; Fax: 609-235-7167; 310 Timberline Dr., Mount Laurel, NJ 08054 Tel 609-235-6896; Fax: 609-235-7167
E-mail: angelpubs@aol.com
Web site: http://www.angelpubs.com
Dist(s): **Barnes&Noble.com.**

Angela's Bookshelf *See* **A B Publishing**

AngelBooks, *(0-9771749)* 4340 Janesville, Bel Aire, KS 67220 USA
Web site: http://www.whatheavenleftbehind.com; http://www.santasstray.org.

Angelic Enterprises, *(1-930303)* Div. of Ross & Assocs., Box 1327, Manhattan, KS 66505 USA Tel 785-539-4229 (phone/fax)
E-mail: 75042.2072@compuserve.com
Web site: http://www.gspbooks.com
Dist(s): **Good Shepherd Pubns.**

Angelina-Win Productions, *(0-9675940)* 39650 Us Highway 19 N. Apt. 583, Tarpon Spgs, FL 34689-3950 USA
E-mail: author@io114.com.

Angel's Boy Enterprises, *(0-9755352)* 8306 Wilshire Blvd., No. 3004, Beverly Hills, CA 90211 USA
Web site: http://www.angelboi.com.

Angelus Pr., *(0-935952; 1-892331)* Div. of Society of Saint Pius X, 2915 Forest Ave., Kansas City, MO 64109 USA (SAN 222-769X) Tel 816-753-3150; Fax: 816-753-3557; Toll Free Fax: 888-855-9022; Toll Free: 800-966-7337 (orders)
E-mail: info@angeluspress.org
Web site: http://www.angeluspress.org.

Angie Blue Bks., LLC, *(0-9677547)* 10910 Arabian Gate, San Antonio, TX 78254 USA
E-mail: info@AngieBlue.com
Web site: http://www.AngieBlue.com.

Angle Publishing Company, Incorporated *See* **Welcome Rain Pubs.**

Anglican Bk. Centre (CAN) *(0-919030; 0-919891; 0-921846; 1-55126) Dist. by* **Forward Movement.**

Anglophile Bks., *(0-9716612)* 1752 E. Ave. J, No. 176, Lancaster, CA 93535-4474 USA Tel 661-726-9745
E-mail: info@anglophilebooks.com
Web site: http://www.anglophilebooks.com.

Animagic Entertainment Group, Inc., *(0-9703338)* 410 Palm Ave. Apt. B7, Carpinteria, CA 93013-2466 USA
E-mail: jpoynor@webspan.net
Dist(s): **LPC Group**
DiIoia, Tony.

Animal Ark, Inc., *(0-9666535)* P.O. Box 16604, Tampa, FL 33687-6604 USA Tel 813-899-4373; Fax: 813-984-9088; Toll Free: 800-259-5272 (ext. 14)
E-mail: animalark@worldnet.att.net
Web site: http://www.light communications.com.

Animal Band Productions, Inc., The, *(0-9752619)* P.O. Box 392, Mount Juliet, TN 37121 USA Tel 615-754-8701
E-mail: info@theanimalband.com
Web site: http://www.theanimalband.com
Dist(s): **Baker & Taylor Bks.**

Animal Humanity Bks., LLC, *(0-9727585)* P.O. Box 3753, Portland, ME 04104 USA (SAN 255-0946) Tel 207-929-3858; Fax: 207-929-3896
E-mail: info@animalhumanity.com
Web site: http://www.animalhumanity.com.

Animal Place, *(0-9644062)* 3448 Laguna Creek Trail, Vacaville, CA 95688 USA Tel 707-449-4814; Fax: 707-449-8775
E-mail: porcilina@aol.com
Web site: http://www.envirolink.org/arrs/animal_place/ap_www.htm.

Animal Sounds, *(1-889276)* Orders Addr.: P.O. Box 7086, Asheville, NC 28802 USA
E-mail: kflynn62@hotmail.com.

Animal Teachers Enterprises, *(0-9788858)* 5902G Queenston St., Springfield, VA 22152 USA
E-mail: snork5902g@yahoo.com
Web site: http://funkman.org/animal/services/catalog.html.

Animal Tracks Pr., *(0-9760342)* P.O. Box 432, Cotah, CA 94931 USA (SAN 256-1808) Tel 707-776-8019; Fax: 707-795-2919
Web site: http://www.animaltrackspress.com.

Animalations, *(0-9776628; 1-933818)* 4186 Melodia Songo Ct., Las Vegas, NV 89135 USA (SAN 257-9111) Fax: 702-804-4220; Toll Free Fax: 866-670-8337; Toll Free: 866-670-8337
E-mail: info@animalations.com
Web site: http://Animalations.com
Dist(s): **Biblio Distribution.**

Animated Speech Corporation *See* **Fuzzy Bks.**

Anime Works *Imprint of* **Media Blasters, Inc.**

Company

AnimeVillage.com *See* **Bandai Entertainment**

AnJak Communications, Inc., *(0-9719408)* 468 N. Camden Dr., No. 200, Beverly Hills, CA 90210 USA (SAN 254-7457) Tel 310-273-1019; Fax: 310-247-9378; Toll Free: 800-204-2600
E-mail: mail@2jumpstartyourlife.com
Web site: http://www.2jumpstartyourlife.com.

Ankh Bks. (CAN) *(0-9738036) Dist. by* **Mtn Bk Co.**

Ann Arbor Media Group, LLC, *(1-58726)* P.O. Box 1007, Ann Arbor, MI 48106-1007 USA Tel 734-769-1004 ext 1267; Fax: 734-913-1249 ; *Imprints:* Mundus (Mundus); For Your Knowledge (For Your Knowledge); Sports Media Group (SMG); Mitten Press (Mitten Pr)
E-mail: tbudzinski@annarbormediagroup.com
Web site: http://www.annarbormediagroup.com; http://www.greatgolfbooks.com; http:// www.sports-mediagroup.com; http://www.mittenpress.com.

Ann Arrundell County Historical Society, Inc., *(0-9702355)* Orders Addr.: P.O. Box 385, Linthicum, MD 21090-0385 USA Tel 410-768-9518; Fax: 410-760-5206; Edit Addr.: 7101 Aviation Blvd., Linthicum, MD 21090 USA.

Annade Publishing, *(0-9761740)* 18964 Lauder, Detroit, MI 48235 USA
Web site: www.annade.com.

Annapolis Publishing Co., *(1-884878)* Orders Addr.: 921 E. Fort Ave. Ste. 300, Baltimore, MD 21230-5102 USA (SAN 631-4414) Toll Free: 800-536-1414
E-mail: Katherine@AnnapolisPublishing.com
Web site: http://www.AnnapolisPublishing.com; http://www.mewarren.com; http://www.AnnapolisBooks.com.

AnnArt Pr., *(0-9769719)* R R 1, Box 621, Richards, MO 64778 USA.

Anness Publishing (GBR) *(1-901688; 0-7548) Dist. by* **Natl Bk Netwk.**

Anness Publishing, Inc., *(1-886890)* 39 Sandy Ln., Eatontown, NJ 07724-2445 USA (SAN 299-0563) Toll Free: 800-354-9657 ; *Imprints:* Lorenz Books (Lorenz Bks)
E-mail: AFioravanti@anness.com
Dist(s): **National Bk. Network.**

Annick Pr., Ltd. (CAN) *(0-920236; 0-920303; 1-55037; 1-55451) Dist. by* **Firefly Bks Limited.**

Annie Mouse Bks., *(0-9793379)* P.O. Box 142, Harrisville, PA 16038 USA (SAN 853-1676)
E-mail: annesmike@zoominternet.net.

Annika Pubns., *(0-9670516)* Orders Addr.: P.O. Box 264, Fergus Falls, MN 56537 USA Tel 218-736-7735; Edit Addr.: R.R. 4, Box 50, Fergus Falls, MN 56537 USA
Web site: http://www.annikapublications.bigstep.com.

Annotation Pr., *(1-59977)* Orders Addr.: P.O. Box 428, Enumclaw, WA 98022 USA Tel 360-802-9758; Fax: 360-802-9992; Toll Free: 800-326-4674; Edit Addr.: 1730 Railroad St., Enumclaw, WA 98022 USA
E-mail: infosys@winepresspub.com
Web site: http://www.winepresspub.com.

Anoai Pr., *(0-9653971; 0-9702618)* P.O. Box 910, Aiea, HI 96701-0910 USA
E-mail: kukui@lava.net
Web site: http://www.anoaipress.com
Dist(s): **Booklines Hawaii, Ltd.**

Anointed Pubns., *(1-893853)* 269 Imperial Dr. Apt. 1, Pacifica, CA 94044-1737 USA.

Anointed Pubs., *(0-9763841)* Orders Addr.: P.O. Box 25215, Durham, NC 27702 USA Tel 919-806-0651; Edit Addr.: P.O. Box 25215, Durham, NC 27702 USA
E-mail: jainjie@msn.com
Web site: jainjie@msn.com
Dist(s): **Brown Enterprises, Inc.**

Anointed Word Pubns., *(0-9744024)* 611 N. Pennsylvania Ave., Lansing, MI 48912 USA Tel 517-372-3407.

Another Ep Publishing, *(0-615; 0-9740685)* Div. of Episodes By Wroe, P.O. Box 300, Walnut, CA 91788-0300 USA (SAN 253-2530) Tel 909-448-5356.

Another Language Pr., *(0-922852)* 7709 Hamilton Ave., Cincinnati, OH 45231-3103 USA Tel 513-521-5590; Fax: 513-521-5592; Toll Free: 800-733-2067
E-mail: aimsbooks@juno.com
Dist(s): **AIMS International Bks., Inc.**
Baker & Taylor Bks.

Anova Bks. (GBR) *(1-84411) Dist. by* **Trafalgar.**

Anova Bks. (GBR) *(1-84411) Dist. by* **Sterling.**

Anova Bks. (GBR) *(1-84411) Dist. by* **IPG Chicago.**

Answers in Genesis *See* **Answers in Genesis Ministries**

Answers in Genesis Ministries, *(1-893345; 1-60092)* Orders Addr.: P.O. Box 510, Hebron, KY 41048 USA Fax: 859-727-2299; Toll Free: 800-778-3390; Edit Addr.: 2800 Bullittsburg Church Rd., Petersburg, KY 41080 USA
E-mail: dzordel@answersingenesis.org
Web site: http://www.answersingenesis.org
Dist(s): **Master Bks.**
New Leaf Pr., Inc.

answers period, inc., *(0-917875)* Orders Addr.: P.O. Box 427, Goliad, TX 77963 USA (SAN 112-6431) Tel 361-645-2268; Toll Free: 800-852-4752
Web site: http://www.answersbook.com.

Antarctic Pr., Inc., *(0-930655; 0-9663588; 0-9728978; 1-932453; 0-9768043; 0-9776424; 0-9787725; 0-9792723; 0-9797719; 0-9801255)* Div. of Ben Dunn Corp., 7272 Wurzbach, Suite 204, San Antonio, TX 78240 USA Do not confuse with Antarctic Pr., Bellevue, WA
E-mail: apcog@texas.net; apcog@hotmail.com
Web site: http://www.antarctic-press.com
Dist(s): **Diamond Bk. Distributors.**

Antares Publishing, *(1-59002)* Orders Addr.: P.O. Box 387, Burlington, MA 01803-3807 USA (SAN 253-6706)
E-mail: books@antarespub.com
Web site: http://www.antarespub.com
Dist(s): **Baker & Taylor Bks.**

Anthem Distribution, 2748 Second Private, Flossmoor, IL 60422 USA Tel 708-798-9512
E-mail: ksood@wpcpress.com.

Anthem Publishing *Imprint of* **Gordon, Rev. Keith A.**

AntHill Publishing, *(0-9718544)* 5315 Clarendon Rd., Brooklyn, NY 11203 USA Tel 718-629-0294 (phone/fax) Do not confuse with Ant Hill Publishing in Gorman, TX
E-mail: anthillpublishing@hotmail.com.

Anthology of Poetry, Inc., *(1-883931)* Orders Addr.: P.O. Box 698, Asheboro, NC 27203 USA Tel 910-626-7762; Fax: 910-626-2622; Edit Addr.: 307 E. Salisbury, Asheboro, NC 27203 USA
E-mail: poetry@asheboro.com
Web site: http://www.anthologyofpoetry.com.

Anthony Publishing Co., *(0-9603832; 1-890764)* 206 Gleasondale Rd., Stow, MA 01775 USA (SAN 213-9073) Tel 978-897-7191; Fax: 978-897-0894
E-mail: ichingbooks@comcast.net
Web site: http://www.ichingoracle.com
Dist(s): **DeVorss & Co.**
New Leaf Distributing Co., Inc.

Anthro Co., The, *(1-878464)* 200 Carroll St., No. 21, Susanville, CA 96130 USA Tel 530-251-5712
E-mail: devajan@earthlink.net
Web site: http://www.ishifacts.com
Dist(s): **Social Studies Schl. Service.**

Anthroposophic Press, Incorporated *See* **SteinerBooks, Inc.**

Anticipation Pr., *(0-9754046)* 3563 Sueldo St. Ste. Q, Sn Luis Obisp, CA 93401-7332 USA Do not confuse with Anticipation Press in Cheyenne, WY
E-mail: doingbigbiz@aol.com
Web site: http://www.anticipationpress.com; http:// www.zacacreekdevelopment.com.

Antioch Media, *(0-9747772)* 37250 Kensington Dr., Madera, CA 93638-7600 USA Toll Free: 888-726-8462 (phone/fax)
E-mail: publishing@antiochmedia.com
Web site: http://www.antiochmedia.com.

Antioch Publishing Co., *(0-7824; 0-89954; 1-4017)* Div. of The Antioch Co., Orders Addr.: P.O. Box 28, Yellow Springs, OH 45387-0028 USA (SAN 654-7214) Tel 937-767-7379; Fax: 937-767-6137; Toll Free: 800-543-2397; 800-543-1515; Edit Addr.: 888 Dayton St., Yellow Springs, OH 45387 USA Do not confuse with Antioch Publishing Co., Torrance, CA
Web site: http://www.antioch.com.

Antipodes Bks. & Beyond, 9707 Fairway Ave., Silver Spring, MD 20901-3001 USA Tel 301-602-9519; Fax: 301-565-0160
E-mail: Antipode@antipodesbooks.com
Web site: http://www.antipodesbooks.com.

Antique Collectors' Club, *(0-902028; 0-907462; 1-85149)* Orders Addr.: Eastworks, 116 Pleasant St., Easthampton, MA 01027 USA (SAN 630-7787) Tel 413-529-0861; Fax: 413-529-0862; Toll Free: 800-252-5231 (orders)
E-mail: info@antiquecc.com; sales@antiquecc.com
Web site: http://www.antiquecollectorsclub.com.

Antiquity Publishing, *(0-9793284)* 4127 McLaughlin Ave., No. 15, Los Angeles, CA 90066-5445 USA Tel 310-390-9093 (phone/fax)
E-mail: Randwulf@humnet.ucla.edu
Dist(s): **Biblio Distribution.**

Antix Pr., Inc., *(0-9702052)* Orders Addr.: P.O. Box 97337, Raleigh, NC 27624-7337 USA Tel 910-256-2535; Fax: 910-256-9831; Edit Addr.: 3737 Benson Dr., Raleigh, NC 27609 USA
E-mail: BBSense@ik.netcom.com
Web site: http://AntixPress.com.

Anton Berkshire Publishing, *(0-9746330)* Orders Addr.: P.O. Box 372, Markle, IN 46770 USA (SAN 255-6618); Edit Addr.: 9374 N. Marzane Rd., Markle, IN 46770 USA
Web site: http://www.antonberkshirepublishing.com.

Antrim Hse., *(0-9662783; 0-9762091; 0-9770633; 0-9792226; 0-9798451)* 21 Goodrich Rd., Simsbury, CT 06070-1804 USA
Web site: http://www.antrimhousebooks.com
Dist(s): **Distributors, The.**

Antroll Publishing Co., *(1-877656)* 2616 Elmont St., Wheaton, MD 20902 USA Tel 301-942-0492.

Anubis Publishing, *(0-9707845)* 5122 Spencer Rd., Lyndhurst, OH 44124 USA Tel 440-461-3709; Fax: 440-446-9340 Do not confuse with Anubis Publishing in Manorville, NY
E-mail: piperdonaldwillis@yahoo.com; piperdbw@aol.com
Web site: http://members.aol.com/piperdbw.

Anup, A. B. *See* **ANUP Research & Multimedia LP**

ANUP Research & Multimedia LP, *(0-9657083; 1-60335)* 15 Lucia Ct., Aberdeen, NJ 07747 USA Tel 732-222-2006 (phone/fax)
E-mail: anupbooks@aol.com; dranup@aol.com
Web site: http://www.ab9help.com
Dist(s): **Majors, J. A. Co.**
Rittenhouse Bk. Distributors.

Anvil Bks., Ltd. (IRL) *(0-900068; 0-947962; 1-901737) Dist. by* **Dufour.**

ANXIETY Sup-Pr., *(0-9710538)* Orders Addr.: P.O. Box 19051, Cincinnati, OH 45219 USA Tel 513-965-0307
E-mail: lordofsecrets@hotmail.com
Web site: http://www.geocities.com/lordspacedog.

Anyone Can Write bks., *(0-9771470)* 2890 N. Hills Dr., NE, Atlanta, GA 30305-3210 USA Tel 404-261-1616
Web site: http://www.anyonecanwrite.com.

Anystar Publishing, *(0-9767047)* P.O. Box 621, Venus, TX 76084 USA
E-mail: anystarpublishing@yahoo.com
Web site: http://www.anystarpublishing.com.

Anything Bks. *Imprint of* **Random Hse. Value Publishing**

Anythings Possible, Inc., *(1-892186)* Orders Addr.: 1863 N. Farwell Ave., Milwaukee, WI 53202 USA Fax: 414-226-4901; Toll Free: 800-543-7153
E-mail: info@special-kids.com
Web site: http://www.special-kids.com.

Anytime Pubns., *(0-9646652)* Orders Addr.: P.O. Box 120, Retsof, NY 14539 USA (SAN 298-6167) Tel 716-243-4055 (phone/fax); Edit Addr.: 2518 Virginia Ave, Piffard, NY 14533 USA
E-mail: enethyme@aol.com
Web site: http://www.Enethyme@aol.com.

Anzalone, Frank, *(0-9770788)* P.O. Box 110422, Campbell, CA 95011 USA Tel 408-247-7572; Fax: 408-984-1519
E-mail: info@mckyfoto.com
Web site: http://www.mckyfoto.com.

Aoyama Publishing *See* **Marble House Editions**

Ap Amelia Pr., *(0-9766124)* 3403 12th St. S, Moorheah, MN 56560 USA
E-mail: awethern1@cableone.net
Web site: http://www.ameliapress.com
Dist(s): **Partners Bk. Distributing, Inc.**

A/P Pr., *(0-9715417)* P.O. Box 50402, Palo Alto, CA 94303 USA Tel 650-329-8986; Fax: 650-329-8614
E-mail: firstheroes@aol.com
Web site: http://www.firstheroes.com.

AP Publishing, *(0-9722906)* Orders Addr.: P.O. Box 160, Merrimac, WI 53561 USA
Web site: http://www.wildlife-trails.com
Dist(s): **Lightning Source, Inc.**

APA Publications Services (SGP) *(9971-925; 9971-982; 981-234; 981-4120; 981-246; 981-4137; 981-258; 981-268) Dist. by* **Langenscheidt.**

Ape Pen Publishing, *(0-9768779)* P.O. Box 691, Riverside, CA 92502 USA Toll Free: 800-506-7401
E-mail: donballard@comcast.net
Web site: http://www.apepenpublishing.com.

A-Peak Publishing, *(0-9667407)* Orders Addr.: P.O. Box 511, Johnstown, NY 12095 USA Tel 518-762-5309; Fax: 518-762-5317; Edit Addr.: 2533 State Hwy. 29, Johnstown, NY 12095 USA
E-mail: apeak@superior.net
Dist(s): **North Country Bks., Inc.**

Aperturas Foundation, *(0-9745220)* P.O. Box 25163, Chicago, IL 60625 USA Tel 773-478-7973
E-mail: aperturas@yahoo.com
Web site: http://www.aperturas.info.

Apex Pr., The, *(0-945257; 1-891843)* Div. of Council on International & Public Affairs, P.O. Box 337, Croton-on-Hudson, NY 10520 USA (SAN 246-2664) Tel 914-271-6500 (phone/fax); Toll Free: 800-316-2739 (orders)
E-mail: cipany@igc.org
Web site: http://www.cipa-apex.org.

Apex Publishing Services, *(0-9663809)* 30 Folkner Trail, Apex, NC 27523-7317 USA Tel 919-363-0007; Fax: 919-560-0296
E-mail: apex_ps@earthlink.net
Web site: http://home.earthlink.net/~apex_ps.

APG Sales and Fulfillment, Div. of Warehousing and Fulfillment Specialists, LLC (WFS, LLC), 7344 Cockrill Bend Blvd., Nashville, TN 37209-1043 USA (SAN 630-818X) Toll Free: 800-327-5113
E-mail: sswift@agpbooks.com
Web site: http://www.apgbooks.com.

Aplastic Anemia + MDS International Foundation, *(0-9755572)* Orders Addr.: P.O. Box 613, Annapolis, MD 21404-0613 USA Tel 410-867-0242; Fax: 410-867-0240; Toll Free: 800-747-2820; Edit Addr.: P.O. Box 310, Churchton, MD 20733-0310 USA
E-mail: help@aamds.org
Web site: http://www.aamds.org.

Aplus Bks. *Imprint of* **Capstone Pr., Inc.**

Apodixis Pr., *(0-9630539; 0-9703400; 1-933873)* Div. of Apodixis, Inc., Orders Addr.: P.O. Box 671053, Dallas, TX 75367 USA Tel 972-241-1366; Fax: 972-241-5345 (call first); Toll Free: 800-522-3341; Edit Addr.: 3975 High Summit Dr., Dallas, TX 75244 USA
E-mail: jillsmithusa@sbcglobal.net
Web site: http://www.learning-apodixis.com.

Apogee Components, Inc., *(0-9653620)* 3355 Fillmore Ridge Hts., Colorado Spgs, CO 80907-9024 USA
E-mail: tvm@apogeerockets.com
Web site: http://www.apogeerockets.com.

Apogee Publishing, *(0-9700035)* 2110 Slaughter Ln., Suite 115 PMB 184, Austin, TX 78749 USA Tel 512-280-1007; Fax: 512-292-1270 Do not confuse with companies with same or similar names in La Jolla, CA, Kerrville, TX, Gaithersburg, MD
E-mail: linda@claytonspath.com
Web site: http://www.claytonspath.com.

APOK Kreations, *(0-9664107)* P.O. Box 504, Broomfield, CO 80038-0504 USA Tel 303-469-6973; Fax: 818-348-2014.

Apollo Computer Systems, Inc., *(0-9610582)* 616 14th St., Arcata, CA 95521 USA (SAN 264-651X) Tel 707-822-0318.

Apollo Pubs., *(0-9718532; 0-9721368; 1-932832)* P.O. Box 9, Santa Cruz, CA 95063 USA Tel 831 479 9626 (phone/fax); 800-881-0181
E-mail: msc@greatcreations.net
Web site: http://www.apollopub.com.

Apologetics Pr., Inc., *(0-932859; 1-60063)* 230 Landmark Dr., Montgomery, AL 36117-2752 USA (SAN 688-9190) Tel 334-272-8558; Fax: 334-270-2002; Toll Free: 800-234-8558 (orders only)
E-mail: mail@apologeticspress.org
Web site: http://www.apologeticspress.org
Dist(s): **STL Distribution North America.**

Apologia Educational Ministries, Inc., *(0-9656294; 1-932012)* 1106 Meridian Plaza, Suite 220, Anderson, IN 46016 USA Tel 765-608-3280; Fax: 765-608-3290; Toll Free: 888-524-4724
E-mail: mailbag@apologia.com
Web site: http://www.apologia.com.

Appalachian Log Publishing Co., The, *(1-885935)* Orders Addr.: P.O. Box 20297, Charleston, WV 25362-1297 USA Tel 304-342-5789; Edit Addr.: 878 Anaconda Ave., Charleston, WV 25302 USA
E-mail: gregory@newwave.net.

†Appalachian Mountain Club Bks., *(0-910146; 1-878239; 1-929173; 1-934028)* 5 Joy St., Boston, MA 02108 USA (SAN 203-4808) Tel 617-523-0655; Fax: 617-523-0722; Toll Free: 800-262-4455
E-mail: bdavidson@outdoors.org; kbreunig@outdoors.org
Web site: http://www.outdoors.org
Dist(s): **Globe Pequot Pr., The**; *CIP.*

Appenzell Pr., *(0-9668328)* Orders Addr.: P.O. Box 270, Reeders, PA 18352 USA Tel 570-620-2906 (phone/fax); Toll Free: 877-620-2906; Edit Addr.: 307 Smith Hill Rd., Stroudsburg, PA 18360 USA
E-mail: peeps@ptd.net
Web site: http://www.appenzellpress.com.

Applause Theatre & Cinema *Imprint of* **Leonard, Hal Corp.**

Apple Bk. Ctr., *(0-9673591)* 18843 Gainsborough, Detroit, MI 48223 USA Tel 313-838-3117; Fax: 313-836-1640
E-mail: Appleoo1@aol.com
Web site: http://www.applebookcenter.com.

Apple Cover Books *See* **New Monic Bks.**

Apple Pie Pubs., *(0-9675123)* 5745 SW 75th St., PMB 325, Gainesville, FL 32608 USA Tel 352-472-2833 (phone/fax); Fax: 352-335-9080
E-mail: applepienow@aol.com
Web site: http://www.applepienow.com.

Appletree Pr., Ltd. (IRL) *(0-86281; 0-904651) Dist. by* **Irish Bks Media.**

AppleTree Press *See* **Lanton Haas Pr.**

†Applewood Bks., *(0-918222; 1-55709; 1-4290)* 1 River Rd., Carlisle, MA 01741-1820 USA (SAN 210-3419) Toll Free: 800-277-5312
E-mail: applewood@awb.com
Web site: http://www.awb.com
Dist(s): **Ingram Pub. Services**; *CIP.*

Applied Database Technology, Inc., *(0-9742610)* 8763-148th Ave. NE, Redmond, WA 98052 USA
Web site: http://www.applieddatabase.com.

Apprentice Shop Bks., LLC, *(0-9723410)* 18 Wentworth Dr., Bedford, NH 03110-4718 USA Fax: 603-472-2588
E-mail: mlduboi@aol.com.

Apricot Pr., *(1-885027)* P.O. Box 98, Nephi, UT 84648 USA Toll Free: 800-731-6145
E-mail: books@apricotpress.com
Web site: http://www.apricotpress.com.

April Arts Press & Productions, *(0-9650918)* P.O. Box 64, Morgan Hill, CA 95038-0064 USA
E-mail: books@aprilartspress.com
Web site: http://www.aprilartspress.com.

April Press *See* **April Arts Press & Productions**

AP's Travels *See* **Aunt Patty's Travels-London**

APTAC Publishing, *(1-887172)* Rte. 3, Box 60A, Duncan, OK 73533 USA Tel 580-252-1607; Fax: 580-252-5847.

APU Publishing Group, *(1-878647)* Orders Addr.: P.O. Box 1137, Edgewood, MD 21040 USA Tel 410-538-7400; Fax: 410-538-7468.

Aqua Quest Pubns., Inc., *(0-9623389; 1-881652)* Orders Addr.: P.O. Box 700, Locust Valley, NY 11560-0700 USA Tel 516-759-0476; Fax: 516-759-4519; Toll Free: 800-933-8989
E-mail: sales@aquaquest.com; info@aquaquest.com
Web site: http://www.aquaquest.com
Dist(s): **National Bk. Network.**

Aquamarine Pubns., *(1-885812)* 8001 Cattle Dr., Canyon, TX 79015-6540 USA Tel 806-655-7780.

Aqueduct Pr., *(0-9746559; 1-933500)* P.O. Box 95787, Seattle, WA 98145-2787 USA (SAN 256-131X)
Web site: http://www.aqueductpress.com
Dist(s): **Baker & Taylor Bks.**
Pathway Bk. Service.

Aquila Ink Publishing, *(0-9760789)* P.O. Box 160, Rio Nido, CA 95471 USA (SAN 850-9050) Tel 707-799-5981; 707-887-9090; Fax: 707-869-2973
E-mail: aquila@aquilaink.com
Web site: http://www.aquilaink.com.

Aquinnah Wampanoag Education Department, *(0-9725679)* 20 Black Brook Rd., Aquinnah, MA 02535 USA Tel 508-645-9265; Fax: 508-645-9820
E-mail: educate@wampanoagtribe.net
Web site: http://www.wampanoagtribe.net.

ARA IFA Publishing, Inc., *(0-9663132)* 10774 Capistrono Ave., Lynwood, CA 90262 USA Tel 310-488-4610
E-mail: ifa@artnet.net
Web site: http://www.araifa.com.

Aradiance Publishing, *(0-9715737)* P.O. Box 13855, Mill Creek, WA 98082 USA.

Arango-Duque, J. F. *See* **Arango's Publishing**

Arango's Publishing, *(0-9655750)* 1776 Polk St., No. 3K-032, Hollywood, FL 33020 USA (SAN 299-2078)
E-mail: arangoduke@aol.com
Dist(s): **Hispanic Bks. Distributors & Pubs., Inc.**
Lectorum Pubns., Inc.
Libros Sin Fronteras
Quality Bks., Inc.

Aranjo, Karl, *(0-9770667)* 16 Greenwood, Irvine, CA 92604 USA Tel 949-786-8765
E-mail: karlaranjo@yahoo.com
Web site: http://guitaru.com.

Arbiter Pr., *(0-9621385)* 1732 N. Lakemont Ave., Winter Park, FL 32792 USA (SAN 251-1282)
Dist(s): **Bookazine Co., Inc.**

Arbor Bks., *(0-9771870; 0-9777764; 0-9786107; 0-9790469; 0-9794118; 0-9800582)* 244 Madison Ave., No. 254, New York, NY 10016 USA Do not confuse with Arbor Books in Media, PA
Web site: http://www.arborbooks.com.

Arbor Hill Pr., *(0-9637547; 1-890156)* 4208 Stonehaven Way, Fredericksburg, VA 22408 USA Tel 540-710-2518
E-mail: Thanz3000@aol.com.

Arbutus Pr., *(0-9665316; 0-9766104; 1-933926)* Orders Addr.: 2364 Pinehurst Trail, Traverse City, MI 49686 USA Tel 231-946-7240; Fax: 231-946-4196
E-mail: editor@arbutuspress.com
Web site: http://www.arbutuspress.com
Dist(s): **Baker & Taylor Bks.**
Partners Bk. Distributing, Inc.

†Arcade Publishing, Inc., *(1-55970; 1-58996)* Orders Addr.: c/o Time Warner Trade Publishing, 3 Center Plaza, Boston, MA 02108 USA Toll Free Fax: 800-890-0875; Toll Free: 800-759-0190; Edit Addr.: 141 Fifth Ave., New York, NY 10010 USA (SAN 252-2012) Tel 212-475-2633; Fax: 212-353-8148
E-mail: arcadeinfo@arcadepub.com
Web site: http://www.arcadepub.com
Dist(s): **Hachette Bk. Group**
Time Warner Interactive; *CIP.*

Arcadia Bks. Ltd. (GBR) *(1-900850; 1-905147) Dist. by* **IPG Chicago.**

Arcadia Pr., *(1-881185)* Orders Addr.: P.O. Box 8697, Scottsdale, AZ 85252-8697 USA; Edit Addr.: 6270 N. 78th St., No. 340, Scottsdale, AZ 85250 USA Do not confuse with companies with the same name in New York, NY, Greenville, NH, Joshua Tree, CA
E-mail: crcjct@ix.netcom.com
Web site: http://www.vegsource.org/parenting.

Arcadia Publications *See* **Linden Hill Publishing**

Arcadia Publishing, *(0-7385; 1-58973)* Orders Addr.: 420 Wando Park Blvd., Mount Pleasant, SC 29464 USA (SAN 255-268X) Tel 843-853-2070; Fax: 843-853-0044; Toll Free: 888-313-2665
E-mail: sales@arcadiapublishing.com
Web site: http://www.arcadiapublishing.com.

Arcadiam Games, *(0-9769951)* 3106 NE 83rd Ave., Portland, OR 97220 USA
E-mail: travisbrown@crossroads-rpg.com
Web site: http://www.crossroads-rpg.com.

Arcadian Hse., *(0-9766666)* 3040 Rightmire Blvd., Columbus, OH 43221 USA
E-mail: lyn@arcadianhouse.com
Web site: http://www.arcadianhouse.com.

Arcana Studio, Inc., *(0-9763095)* 930 Winthrop Ln., Rockford, IL 61107 USA
Web site: http://www.arcanastudio.com.

Archaeological Ctr. Pubns. (ISR) *(965-90028; 965-90240; 965-7162) Dist. by* **Eisenbrauns.**

Archangel Studios, LLC, *(0-9714714)* 11042 Camarillo St., No. 9, North Hollywood, CA 91602 USA Tel 818-754-0802 (phone/fax)
E-mail: thredstar_hq@hotmail.com
Web site: http://www.theredstar.com
Dist(s): **Diamond Bk. Distributors.**

ArcheBooks *Imprint of* **ArcheBooks Publishing**

ArcheBooks Publishing, *(1-59507)* Subs. of Gelinas & Wolf, Inc., 9101 W. Sahara Ave., Suite 105-112, Las Vegas, NV 89117 USA Tel 702-253-1338 ; *Imprints:* ArcheBooks (ArchBks)
E-mail: publisher@archebooks.com
Web site: http://www.archebooks.com
Dist(s): **Baker & Taylor Bks.**

Archeological Assessments, Inc., *(0-9638956; 0-9794044)* P.O. Box 1631, Nashville, AR 71852 USA
E-mail: aaimjb@aol.com
Web site: http://www.arkansasstories.com.

Archer Fields, Inc., *(0-9627767; 1-56466)* 155 Sixth Ave., New York, NY 10013 USA Tel 212-627-1999; Fax: 212-627-9484; Toll Free: 800-338-2665
Dist(s): **D.A.P./Distributed Art Pubs.**

Archeworks, *(0-9753405)* 625 N. Kingsbury St., Chicago, IL 60610 USA Tel 312-867-7254; Fax: 312-867-7260
E-mail: info@archeworks.org
Web site: http://www.archeworks.org.

Archie Comic Pubns., Inc., *(1-879794)* 325 Fayette Ave., Mamaroneck, NY 10543-2318 USA Tel 914-381-5155; Fax: 914-381-2335
Web site: http://www.archiecomics.com
Dist(s): **Diamond Bk. Distributors.**

Archimede Editions (FRA) *(2-211) Dist. by* **Distribks Inc.**

Archipelago Pr., *(1-893335)* Orders Addr.: P.O. Box 1540, Los Gatos, CA 95031 USA (SAN 299-7541) Tel 408-354-5587 (phone/fax) Do not confuse with companies with the same name in Saint Thomas, VI, Friday Harbor, WA
E-mail: pelago2000@aol.com
Web site: http://www.rosswell.com.

Archival Services, Incorporated *See* **Red River Pr.**

Archives Pr. *Imprint of* **Media Assocs.**

Archives Press, The *See* **Media Assocs.**

Archon Bks. *Imprint of* **Shoe String Pr., Inc.**

Archstone Pr., LLC, *(1-929749)* Div. of JayMar Services, LLC, Orders Addr.: P.O. Box 210752, Nashville, TN 37221-0752 USA Tel 615-673-6938; Fax: 615-673-0540
E-mail: jaymarllc@aol.com
Web site: http://www.jaymarsvcs.com.

Arco *Imprint of* **Peterson's**

Arcoiris Records, Inc., *(1-57417)* P.O. Box 7428, Berkeley, CA 94707 USA Tel 510-527-5539
Dist(s): **Lectorum Pubns., Inc.**

Arctos Pr., *(0-9657015; 0-9725384)* 116 Cloud View Rd., Sausalito, CA 94965 USA Tel 415 331 2503
Web site: http://www.members.aol.com/runes/index.html
Dist(s): **Quality Bks., Inc.**
SPD-Small Pr. Distribution.

Arcturus Pubs., Inc., *(0-916877)* P.O. Box 606, Cherry Hill, NJ 08003 USA (SAN 653-9718) Tel 609-428-3863.

Ardara Hse., Pubs., *(0-9637647; 1-888676)* 1500 E. Johnson Ave., Suite 123, Pensacola, FL 32514 USA Tel 850-479-7962; Fax: 850-476-3377.

Arden Pr., Inc., *(0-912869)* Orders Addr.: P.O. Box 418, Denver, CO 80201 USA (SAN 277-6553) Tel 303-697-6766; Fax: 303-697-3443; Edit Addr.: 20723 Seminole Rd., Indian Hills, CO 80454 USA Do not confuse with Arden Pr. Inc., Cleveland, OH
E-mail: ardenpress@msn.com.

Ardent Fourth *See* **Ardent VI**

Ardent VI, *(1-929963)* Orders Addr.: P.O. Box 949, East Orange, NJ 07019 USA Tel 973-672-3484; Edit Addr.: 5 Woodland Ave., Whippany, NJ 07981-1121 USA
E-mail: jtw678@aol.com.

ARDI Research Pr., *(0-9640600)* 13571 Millpond Way, San Diego, CA 92129 USA (SAN 298-1866) Fax: 619-484-0377
E-mail: roger@rdooley.com.

Ardor Books.com *See* **Sadorian Pubns.**

Ardsley Pr., *(1-884417)* Div. of Ardsley Musical Instrument Service, Ltd., 219 Sprain Rd., Scarsdale, NY 10583 USA Tel 914-693-6639; Fax: 914-693-6974; Toll Free: 800-842-7286.

Area Fifty One Productions *See* **Media Blasters, Inc.**

Argee Pubs., *(0-917961)* 4453 Manitou, Okemos, MI 48864 USA (SAN 247-7858) Tel 517-349-1254.

Argentina Pubns., *(0-9670529)* Orders Addr.: 8 Spring Marsh Ln., Savannah, GA 31411-2947 USA
E-mail: jegrader@bellsouth.net
Web site: http://www.alli-gator.com.

Argonaut Publishing Co., *(0-9635118)* 284 Clearview Rd., Chuluota, FL 32766 USA (SAN 297-8199) Tel 407-977-5207 (phone) Do not confuse with companies with the same or similar name in Los Angeles, CA, Santa Barbara, CA
E-mail: spottedtail@spottedtail.com
Web site: http://www.spottedtail.com.

Argos Gameware *See* **H&M Systems Software, Inc.**

Argyle Bks., *(0-9642573)* 710 Old Justin Rd., Argyle, TX 76226 USA Tel 940-464-3368; Fax: 940-380-0151
E-mail: info@argylebooks.com
Web site: http://www.iglobal.net/argyle/
Dist(s): **Hervey's Booklink & Cookbook Warehouse.**

Argyropoulos, Paul & Phil Carpenter, *(0-9705144)* 4151 Galloway Dr., Pearland, TX 77584 USA
E-mail: bumchex@aol.com
Web site: http://members.aol.com/chokewagon/gallery2.htp.

Aries International (U.B.T.O.), *(0-615; 0-9653920)* Div. of Aries International, Orders Addr.: P.O. Box 541756, Merritt Island, FL 32954 USA; Edit Addr.: 821 Del Rio Way, No. 203, Merritt Island, FL 32954 USA
E-mail: sesolivan@earhtlink.net
Web site: http://www.performanceconsultants.co.uk/
Dist(s): **Lulu.com.**

Arimax, Inc., *(0-9634287)* 2865 S. Eagle Rd., No. 350, Newtown, PA 18940 USA Tel 215-862-5899; Fax: 215-862-9720
Web site: http://www.arimaxkids.com
Dist(s): **Koen-Levy Bk. Wholesalers LLC.**

Arimax Publishing Company *See* **Arimax, Inc.**

Aris & Phillips (GBR) *(0-85668) Dist. by* **David Brown.**

Arise Foundation, *(1-58614)* P.O. Box 2147, Jupiter, FL 33468-2147 USA (SAN 253-4835) Toll Free: 888-680-6100
E-mail: yisaacs@ariselife-skills.org
Web site: http://wwwariseife-skills.org.

Aristata Publishing, *(0-9754912)* 16429 Lost Canyon Rd., Santa Clarita, CA 91387 USA (SAN 256-6508) Tel 661-299-9478 (phone/fax)
E-mail: aristata@craigelliottgallery.com; celliottl@socal.rr.com
Web site. http://www.craigelliottgallery.com
Dist(s): **APG Sales and Fulfillment.**

Aristo Agon Brun Universal Union, *(1-58753)* 201 N. Dupont Pkwy., New Castle, DE 19720 USA Tel 435-508-0045 (phone/fax) ; *Imprints:* Martial Art-Org (Martial Art)
E-mail: aabuu-llc-de-usa@iname.com
Web site: http://www.martialart.org.

Arizona Blueberry Studios, *(0-9727894)* P.O. Box 5, Pasadena, CA 91102 USA Toll Free: 800-767-7186
E-mail: books@rossanthony.com
Web site: http://www.rossanthony.com/books.

Arizona Desert Ice Pr., *(0-9749846)* Orders Addr.: P.O. Box 27347, Tempe, AZ 85282-7347 USA; Edit Addr.: 2116 E. Balboa, Tempe, AZ 85282 USA
Dist(s): **Gem Guides Bk. Co.**

Arizona Highways, *(0-916179; 1-893860; 1-932082)* Div. of Arizona Dept. of Transportation, 2039 W. Lewis Ave., Phoenix, AZ 85009 USA (SAN 294-8974) Tel 602-712-2038; 602-712-2050; Fax: 602-254-4505
E-mail: aphares@azdot.gov
Web site: http://www.arizonahighways.com.

Arizona Sonora Desert Museum Pr., *(1-886679)* Arizona Sonora Desert Museum, 2021 N. Kinney Rd., Tucson, AZ 85743 USA Tel 520-883-3061; Fax: 520-883-3048
E-mail: asdmpress@desertmuseum.org; info@desertmuseum.org
Web site: http://www.desertmuseum.org
Dist(s): **Treasure Chest Bks.**

Arktika Publishing, *(0-9634578)* Div. of Arktika Publishing, Orders Addr.: 5730 W. Brookdale Dr., Reno, NV 89523 USA Tel 775-787-6797; Fax: 775-787-6798
E-mail: arktika@intercomm.com
Web site: http://www.cobrasoverthetundra.com.

Arledge, Judith, *(0-9720735)* 909 Gladis Dr., Missoula, MT 59804 USA.

Company

Arlene, Carmen Hibbs, *(0-9762567)* 584 Choctaw Dr., Madisonville, KY 42431 USA Tel 270-821-1968
E-mail: arlenehibbs@yahoo.com
Web site: http://www.heavenlyharborbooks.com.

Arlie Enterprises, *(1-880175)* Orders Addr.: P.O. Box 360933, Strongsville, OH 44136 USA (SAN 297-4665) Tel 440-238-9397 (phone/fax); Edit Addr.: 17035 Raccoon Trail, Strongsville, OH 44136 USA (SAN 297-4673)
E-mail: arlieentwarren@juno.com
Web site: http://www.arliebooks.com.

Arlington Pubns., *(0-9753611)* 2205 Manera St., Odessa, TX 79763 USA Tel 432-582-0272; Fax: 432-332-2499 Do not confuse with Arlington Publications Incorporated in Arlington, TX
E-mail: tommwhite@cableone.net.

Armadillo Bks. *Imprint of* **Advance Bks. Co.**

Armadillo Books *See* **Armadillo Publishing Corp.**

Armadillo Bks., *(0-9786132)* 232 Waller St., San Francisco, CA 94102 USA (SAN 851-0865) Do not confuse with Armadillo Books in Houston, TX
E-mail: patrick@armadillo-books.com.com
Web site: http://www.edgarfont.com.

Armadillo Niche, *(0-9626993)* 505 Pleasant St., Suite 202E, Saint Joseph, MI 49085 USA Tel 616-983-8787; Fax: 616-983-1502
Dist(s): **Baker & Taylor Bks.**

Armadillo Publishing Corp., *(1-891429)* Orders Addr.: P.O. Box 2052, Georgetown, TX 78627-2052 USA (SAN 851-8637) Tel 512-863-8660 (phone/fax); Edit Addr.: 120 Parque Vista Dr., Georgetown, TX 78626-4532 USA
E-mail: editor@armadillopublishing.com
Web site: http://www.fineliterature.com.

Armchair Pr., LLC, *(0-9744627)* P.O. Box 215, Ross, CA 94957-0215 USA Tel 415-460-9750; Fax: 415-460-0850
E-mail: ozzie@armchairpress.com
Dist(s): **Midpoint Trade Bks., Inc.**

Armelle Prod., *(0-615)* 640 28th Ave., Suite 1, San Francisco, CA 94121 USA Tel 415-387-7678; Fax: 415-379-3554
E-mail: info@armelle.com
Web site: http://armelle.com.

Armenian Missionary Assn. of America, *(1-883131)* 31 W. Century Rd., Paramus, NJ 07652 USA (SAN 226-0069) Tel 201-265-2607; Fax: 201-265-6015
E-mail: amaainc@aol.com
Web site: http://www.amaainc.org.

Armour of Light Publishing, *(0-9620604; 0-9788590)* P.O. Box 778, Chapel Hill, NC 27514 USA (SAN 249-4337)
E-mail: publisher@armourofflight.org; michael@focusedfire.com
Web site: http://armourofflight.org.

Armstrong Valley Publishing Co., *(1-928798)* Orders Addr.: P.O. Box 1275, Murfreesboro, TN 37133-1275 USA Tel 615-895-5445; Fax: 615-893-2688; Edit Addr.: 2568 Armstrong Valley Rd., Murfreesboro, TN 37128 USA
E-mail: rsanders@raider.net.

Arnica *See* **Big Sky Stories Publishing**

Arnica Publishing, Inc., *(0-9726535; 0-9745686; 0-9794771)* 3739 SE Eighth Ave., Suite 1, Portland, OR 97202 USA (SAN 255-0091) Tel 503-225-9900; Fax: 503-225-9901
E-mail: gloria@arnicacreative.com
Web site: http://www.arnicacreative.com
Dist(s): **American Wholesale Bk. Co.**
American West Bks.
Brodart Co.
Coutts Library Service, Inc.
Emery-Pratt Co.
Follett Library Resources
Midwest Library Service
New Leaf Distributing Co., Inc.
Partners/West.

Arnold, Patricia *See* **www.margaretmouse.com publishing co.**

Arnold Publishing Co., *(0-9746689)* 181 Branciforte Ridge, Santa Cruz, CA 95065 USA Tel 831-425-7618; Fax: 831-425-2342
E-mail: pat@california-maps.com.

Arnstein, Bennett, *(0-9620058)* 3049 W. Eighth St., No. 535, Los Angeles, CA 90005 USA (SAN 247-5162) Tel 213-388-3517
E-mail: b_arnstein@hotmail.com.

Aronson, Jason *Imprint of* **Rowman & Littlefield Pubs., Inc.**

ARose Bks. Publishing, *(0-9723970; 0-9740636)* 1779 Sample Rd., Allison Park, PA 15101 USA Toll Free Fax: 412-202-2861
E-mail: arosebooks_support@arosebooks.com
Web site: http://www.arosebooks.com.

Around The Globe Pr., *(0-9760573)* 11505 E. Calle Javelina, Tucson, AZ 85748-6339 USA Tel 520-290-8915
E-mail: aroundtheglobepress@earthlink.net
Web site: http://www.aroundtheglobepress.com.

Around The World Pubns., LLC, *(0-9772591)* P.O. Box 1024, Franktown, CO 80116-1024 USA Do not confuse with Around The World Publications in Seattle, WA
E-mail: bbrasier@etsgroup.com
Web site: http://www.worldthroughchildseyes.com.

arpr, inc., *(0-9660991; 0-9773839)* 1420 Centre Ave., Suite 2213, Pittsburgh, PA 15219 USA Tel 412-765-2020; Fax: 412-765-3672; Toll Free: 800-688-7435
E-mail: audrey@knowledgeinanutshell.com; sales@knowledgeinanutshell.com
Web site: http://www.knowledgeinanutshell.com.

Arrathoon-Davio Publishing Company, The *See* **Paint Creek Pr., Ltd.**

Arrest Me Not Publishing *See* **As Seen on the Internet / Arrest Me Not**

Arrinton Pubns., *(0-9754540)* Orders Addr.: P.O. Box 2573, Chesapeake, VA 23327 USA Tel 757-450-6068; Fax: 757-410-4215; Edit Addr.: 1601 Orchard Grove Dr., Chesapeake, VA 23320-1411 USA
E-mail: gobooks@cox.net.

Arrow Pubns., *(0-9715514; 0-9765849)* 16653 E. Kingstree Blvd., Fountain Hills, AZ 85268-5439 USA Tel 480-836-9855 Do not confuse with companies with the same or similar names in Cedar Rapids, IA, Kensington, MD
E-mail: arrowpublications@cox.net
Web site: http://www.arrowpublications.net.

Arrowhead Publishing, *(0-9640056)* 1238 Riva Rose Cir., Castle Rock, CO 80104-9650 USA Tel 303-663-9415 Do not confuse with companies with the same name in Lake Arrowhead, CA, Carlsbad, CA.

Arrowood Pr. *Imprint of* **BBS Publishing Corp.**

Arruzza, Richard *See* **Three Spots Productions**

Ars Poetica *Imprint of* **Skylands Writers & Artists Assn., Inc.**

Arsenal Pulp Pr. (CAN) *(0-88978; 1-55152) Dist. by* **Consort Bk Sales.**

Art & Creativity For Healing, Inc., *(0-9748462)* 26079 Getty Dr., Laguna Niguel, CA 92677 USA Tel 949-367-1902; Fax: 949-367-1904
E-mail: laurie@art4healing.org
Web site: http://www.art4healing.org.

Art & Soul Expressions, *(0-9729192)* P.O. Box 957, Mount Shasta, CA 96067 USA.

Art Barn, *(0-9658413)* 33 1/3 Fourth St., Crystal Falls, MI 49920 USA
E-mail: Peckola@uplogon.com.

Art In The Heartland, *(0-9725461; 0-9752839; 0-9762103; 0-9766587; 0-9778450)* 408 Washington St., Columbus, IN 47201 USA Tel 812-376-3465
E-mail: sbreeding@artintheheartland.com
Web site: http://www.breedingbooks.com; http://www.artintheheartlandbooks.com.

†Art Institute of Chicago, *(0-86559)* Orders Addr.: a/o Museum Shop Mail Order Dept., 950 N. North Branch St., Chicago, IL 60622-4276 USA; Edit Addr.: 111 S. Michigan Ave., Chicago, IL 60603-6110 USA (SAN 204-479X) Tel 312-443-3540; Fax: 312-443-1334
Web site: http://www.artic.edu
Dist(s): **D.A.P./Distributed Art Pubs.**
Univ. of Illinois Pr.
Univ. of Washington Pr.
Yale Univ. Pr.; *CIP.*

Art Night Bks., *(0-9794004)* 916 E. Townsend, Milwaukee, WI 53212 USA Tel 414-963-6111
E-mail: devintrudell@mac.com
Web site: http://artnightbooks.com.

Art of Living Books & Tapes, *(1-885289)* 607 W. Broadway, No. 168, Fairfield, IA 52556-3200 USA Tel 641-472-9892; Fax: 641-472-0671; Toll Free: 800-574-3001
E-mail: aolmailorder@lisco.com
Web site: http://www.artofliving.org.

Art of War Plus Bks. *Imprint of* **Clearbridge Publishing**

Art Official Media LLC, *(0-9768061)* Orders Addr.: P.O. Box 39323, Baltimore, MD 21212 USA Tel 443-629-0995; Edit Addr.: 1044 Radnor Ave., Baltimore, MD 21212 USA
Web site: http://www.artofficialmedia.com; http://www.UrbaniaMag.com
Dist(s): **A & B Distributors & Pubs. Group.**

Art With Heart Press, *(0-9715240)* Div. of Art with Heart, Orders Addr.: P.O. Box 94402, Seattle, WA 98124-6702 USA (SAN 850-2676)
E-mail: info@artwithheart.org
Web site: http://www.artwithheart.org
Dist(s): **Partners/West.**

ArtAnswer, *(0-9755413; 0-9771520)* P.O. Box 50387, Billings, MT 59105 USA Tel 406-672-8482
E-mail: artanswer@artanswer.com
Web site: http://www.artanswer.com.

ArtCan Drama Resources *Imprint of* **Promise Productions, Inc.**

†Arte Publico Pr., *(0-934770; 1-55885)* Univ. of Houston, 452 Cullen Performance Hall, Houston, TX 77204 USA (SAN 213-4594) Fax: 713-743-3080; 713-743-2847; Toll Free: 800-633-2783 ; *Imprints:* Piñata Books (Pinata Bks)
E-mail: bkorders@uh.edu; mtristan@uh.edu
Web site: http://www.artepublicopress.com; *CIP.*

†Artech Hse., Inc., *(0-89006; 1-58053; 1-59693)* Subs. of Horizon Hse., 685 Canton St., Norwood, MA 02062 USA (SAN 201-1441) Tel 781-769-9750; Fax: 781-769-6334; Toll Free: 800-225-9977; 46 Gillingham St, London, SW1V 1AH Tel 44 20 7596 8750; Fax: 44 20 7630 0166
E-mail: artech@artechhouse.com
Web site: http://www.artechhouse.com/
Dist(s): **NetLibrary, Inc.**; *CIP.*

Artel Publishing, *(1-889062)* P.O. Box 2123, Cary, NC 27512 USA Tel 919-387-8972; Fax: 919-387-3340
E-mail: artelpubs@worldnet.att.net.

Artemesia Publishing, LLC, *(1-932926)* Orders Addr.: 9 Mockingbird Hill Rd., Tijeras, NM 87059 USA Tel 505-286-0892; Fax: 505-821-3479 ; *Imprints:* Kinkajou Press (Kinkajou Pr)
E-mail: info@artemesiapublishing.com
Web site: http://www.apbooks.net; http://www.artemesiapublishing.com
Dist(s): **Books West.**

Artemisia Enterprises, *(0-9755416)* P.O. Box 59233, San Jose, CA 95159-0233 USA
E-mail: info@amazon-heart.com
Web site: http://www.amazon-heart.com.

Artesian Pr., *(1-58659)* Div. of R. F. Dawn, Inc., 7300 Artesia Blvd., Buena Park, CA 90621 USA (SAN 253-1259) Tel 714-562-0415; Fax: 714-562-0237; Toll Free Fax: 888-462-0226; Toll Free: 888-734-9355
E-mail: MillerEduc@aol.com
Web site: http://www.millereducational.com.

Article One *See* **Marsh Creek Pr.**

Artifact Wisdom *See* **New Books Publishing**

Artimo Foundation (NLD) *(90-75380) Dist. by* **Dist Art Pubs.**

Artisan, *(1-57965; 1-885183)* Div. of Workman Publishing Co., Inc., 225 Varick St. Flr. 9, New York, NY 10014-4381 USA Toll Free: 800-967-5630 Do not confuse with Artisan, Wheaton, IL
E-mail: artisan@workman.com
Dist(s): **Workman Publishing Co., Inc.**

Artisan House *See* **Artisan**

Artisan Pubs., *(0-934666)* P.O. Box 1529, Muskogee, OK 74402 USA (SAN 211-8408) Tel 918-682-8341; Fax: 918-682-1263.

Artisan Sales *See* **Artisan Pubs.**

Artist Designs, *(0-9760409)* P.O. Box 548, Webster, WI 54893 USA Tel 715-222-2362.

Artist Profile Publishing/Kedco Studios, *(1-878431)* P.O. Box 24302, Las Vegas, NV 89101 USA Fax: 702-471-1209
E-mail: kedro-ap@juno.com.

Artist Studios, Ltd., *(1-931037; 1-59487)* 111 Pine St. Ste. 1600, San Francisco, CA 94111-5618 USA.

Artistic Origins Pubns, *(0-9701137)* 228-A3 Eastwood Rd., Suite 103, Wilmington, NC 28403 USA (SAN 253-3413) Tel 910-392-5775; Fax: 910-392-8185
E-mail: artistic_origins@hotmail.com; dawnireland@prodigy.net
Web site: http://www.artistic-origins.com.

Artistic Ventures LLC, *(0-9771495)* Orders Addr.: P.O. Box 7096, Libertyville, IL 60048 USA; Edit Addr.: 701 Sedgwick Dr., Libertyville, IL 60048 USA
E-mail: dawn@artistic-ventures.com
Web site: http://www.artistic-ventures.com.

Artistry Press *See* **Artistry Pr. International**

Artistry Pr. International, *(0-9625023; 1-883474)* Div. of Artistry at the Piano, Inc., 10830 S 1000 E, Sandy, UT 84094-5928 USA Tel 801-553-1237
E-mail: mg@greywolf-artistry.com
Web site: http://www.greywolf-artistry.com.

Artists Looking Ahead, *(0-9749263)* 151 Surf Way, Suite 48, Monterey, CA 93940 USA
E-mail: adrea@artistslookingahead.com
Web site: http://www.artistslookingahead.com.

Artnik Media (GBR) *(1-903906; 1-905382; 1-905904) Dist. by* **V De Breff.**

Arts & Health Publishing, *(0-615)* 1 Shadowbrook Ln., Basking Ridge, NJ 07920 USA Tel 908-938-6079; Fax: 908-879-2552
E-mail: susan@artshealthpublishing.com
Web site: http://www.artshealthpublishing.com
Dist(s): **Lulu.com.**

Arts Colony Pubs., *(0-9712616)* 477 S. Main St., Pomona, CA 91766-1604 USA Tel 909-629-7560; Fax: 909-623-9515
E-mail: dfox@tstonramp.com.

Arts Pubns., *(0-9607458; 1-878079)* 5555 Paradise Dr., Corte Madera, CA 94925-1800 USA (SAN 238-003X) Do not confuse with ARTS Publications in Evansdale, IA
E-mail: babbadee@aol.com
Dist(s): **Educational Bk. Distributors**
Lectorum Pubns., Inc.

Arts Pubns., *(0-9766590)* P.O. Box 3006, Evansdale, IA 50707-0006 USA (SAN 256-4963) Do not confuse with Arts Publications in Corte Madera, CA
E-mail: adrianarubio@ciudad.com.ar; rcahoe@mchsi.com; ceremonypress@mchsi.com; infoartspublications@mchsi.com
Web site: http://www.artspublications.net.

art-SITES Pr., *(0-9667717; 1-931874)* 894 Waller St., San Francisco, CA 94117 USA Tel 415-437-2456; Fax: 415-701-0633
E-mail: info@art-sites.com
Web site: http://www.art-sites.com
Dist(s): **Baker & Taylor Bks.**

Artsource Publishing *See* **Markowitz Publishing**

Artspace Bks., *(0-9631095; 1-891273)* 33 Filbert Ave., Sausalito, CA 94965 USA Tel 415-331-3031; Fax: 415-332-7119
Dist(s): **D.A.P./Distributed Art Pubs.**

Artstreet LLC, *(0-9758971)* 211 Glenridge Ave., Montclair, NJ 07042 USA Tel 973-744-5800; Fax: 973-744-7373; Toll Free: 866-543-7878
E-mail: sjimenez@brandstretllc.com
Web site: http://www.brandstreetllc.com.

Artust Nasus Publishing, *(0-9763260)* 500 Rosita Ave., PO Box 1515, Westcliffe, CO 81252 USA
Web site: http://www.naturallybalancedhealth.com.

Artworks International, *(1-57938)* Orders Addr.: 3101 Clairmont Rd., Suite C, Atlanta, GA 30329 USA (SAN 255-6456) Tel 404-214-4331; Fax: 404-214-4390
E-mail: derek.adams@andersonpress.com
Web site: http://www.andersonpress.com.

Arty Facts Pr., *(1-892085)* Div. of Janet Hoelzel Ceramics, Orders Addr.: P.O. Box 36564, Albuquerque, NM 87107 USA Tel 505-344-2584; Fax: 505-341-4279; Edit Addr.: 906 Sandia Rd., NW, Albuquerque, NM 87107 USA.

Arundel Pr., *(1-933608)* P.O. Box 377, Warwick, NY 10990 USA (SAN 256-8195) Tel 845-988-6885 Do not confuse with Arundel Press in Seattle, WA
E-mail: slinnea@optonline.net.

Arutam Pr., *(0-9745477)* 62 Ave Maria, Monterey, CA 93940 USA Tel 831-375-6005
E-mail: emurray@sacredsite.com
Web site: http://www.elizabethmurray.com.

Arx Publishing, *(0-9644234; 1-889758)* 10 Canal St., Bristol, PA 19007 USA Tel 215-781-8600; Fax: 215-781-8602
E-mail: info@evolpub.com; info@arxpub.com
Web site: http://www.arxpub.com; http://www.evolpub.com.

Arzana, Inc., *(0-9770475)* Orders Addr.: P.O. Box 60473, Potomac, MD 20859 USA Tel 301-437-0017
E-mail: balance@arzanaworld.com
Web site: http://www.arzanaworld.com.

As Seen on the Internet / Arrest Me Not, *(0-9640336)* P.O. Box 608685, Cleveland, OH 44108-0685 USA Tel 440-487-8413; Fax: 425-963-3821
Web site: http://www.asseenontheinternet.tv.

As Simple As That Publishing, *(0-9728666)* P.O. Box 641, Montauk, NY 11954 USA Toll Free: 866-599-7246
Web site: http://www.simpleasthat.com.

As Sparkle Speaks & Informs/ASSI, *(0-9706187)* Orders Addr.: P.O. Box 1313, Madison, TN 37116-1313 USA Tel 615-860-9762; Fax: 615-870-0959; Edit Addr.: 1672 Liberty Hill Dr., Madison, TN 37115 USA
E-mail: searlessparkle@aol.com.

Ascending Realm Publishing, *(0-9762135)* P.O. Box 2223, Centennial, CO 80161-2223 USA
E-mail: brandon@ascendingrealm.com
Web site: http://www.ascendingrealm.com.

Ascension Education, *(0-9640837)* Orders Addr.: P.O. Box 504, Venice, CA 90294 USA Tel 310-254-4092; Edit Addr.: 1814 Pacific Ave., No. 17, Venice, CA 90291 USA
E-mail: ascension2020@comcast.net
Web site: http://www.ascension-education.com.

Ascension Lutheran Church, *(0-9715472)* 314 W. Main St., Danville, VA 24541 USA Tel 434-792-5795; Fax: 434-799-3900
E-mail: chrismon@gamewood.net
Web site: http://www.chrismon.org.

Ascension Pr., *(0-9659228; 0-9742238; 0-9744451; 1-932631; 1-932645; 1-932927; 1-934217)* Orders Addr.: W5180 Jefferson St., Necedah, WI 54646 USA (SAN 256-0224) Tel 608-565-2024; Fax: 608-565-2025; Toll Free: 800-376-0520; Edit Addr.: P.O. Box 1990, West Chester, PA 19341 USA Tel 610-696-7795; Fax: 610-696-7796; Toll Free: 800-376-0520; 20 Hagerty Blvd., Suite 3, West Chester, PA 19341
E-mail: mflickinger@ascensionpress.com
Web site: http://www.ascensionpress.com
Dist(s): **Midpoint Trade Bks., Inc.**

Asclepian Pr., *(1-893351)* 386 Quartz Cir., Bailey, CO 80421 USA Tel 303-816-9618; Fax: 303-816-9619
E-mail: pni@bewellnet.com
Web site: http://www.imeqinationheals.com.

ASE Media, *(0-9768890)* 5601 Brodie Ln., Suite 620-159, Austin, TX 78745 USA
E-mail: anne-easterling@earthlink.net
Web site: http://www.asemedia.com.

Ash Breeze Publishing, *(0-9715357)* 36 Kennedy Terr., Middletown, NY 10940 USA Tel 845-344-0074
E-mail: LGiordano@hvc.rr.com.

Ashay by the Bay, *(0-9704048)* Orders Addr.: P.O. Box 2394, Union City, CA 94587 USA Tel 510-477-0967; Edit Addr.: 39663 Leslie St. Apt. 387, Fremont, CA 94538-2240 USA
E-mail: poetashay@aol.com
Web site: http://www.ashaybythebay.com.

Ashcafe Publishing, *(0-9672699)* Div. of Maps N Books, Inc., Orders Addr.: 343 Soquel Ave., Suite 425, Santa Cruz, CA 95062 USA Tel 800-818-2180 (phone/fax) ; *Imprints:* Papillon Children's Books (Papillon Chldrns Bks)
E-mail: michael@mapsnbooks.com
Web site: http://www.ashcafe.com; http://www.mapsnbooks.com; http://www.surfmaps.com.

Ashe Street Hse., The, *(0-9723095)* Orders Addr.: P.O. Box 1582, West Jefferson, NC 28694 USA Tel 336-246-7558; Edit Addr.: 6 Ashe St., West Jefferson, NC 28694 USA
Web site: http://www.ashestreethouse.com.

Ashley & Taylor Publishing, Co., *(0-9745469)* P.O. Box 2793, Huntsville, AL 35804 USA Tel 256-430-1889
E-mail: AshleyTaylor4God@comcast.net.

Ashley Hse., *(0-9664337)* 614 47th St., Los Alamos, NM 87544 USA Tel 505-662-4926; Fax: 505-661-6300
E-mail: inezross@sisna.com
Web site: http://www.readsouthwest.com.

AshleyAlan Enterprises, *(0-9702171; 0-9710145)* Orders Addr.: P.O. Box 1510, Kyle, TX 78640-1510 USA Tel 512-405-3065; Fax: 512-405-3066; Edit Addr.: 115 Hogan, Kyle, TX 78640 USA
E-mail: celestem@kyle-tx.com
Web site: http://www.ashleyanlan.com.

Ashtabula County Genealogical Society, *(1-888851)* 860 Sherman St., Geneva, OH 44041-9101 USA Tel 440-466-4521; Fax: 440-466-0162
E-mail: acgs@ashtabulagen.org
Web site: http://www.ashtabulagen.org.

ASI, *(0-9759271)* 12 Brandywine Dr., Warwick, NY 10990 USA
Web site: http://www.asipublishing.com.

Asia for Kids *Imprint of* **Infini Pr., LLC**

Asia Pubn., *(0-9707435)* 1501 Glenwood Ave., Minneapolis, MN 55405 USA Tel 651-226-6099; 612-386-4017; Fax: 612-374-9542.

Asian Educational Services (IND) *(81-206) Dist. by* **S Asia.**

ASK Publishing, L.L.C., *(0-9742967)* 34046 Jefferson Ave., St Clr Shores, MI 48082-1162 USA (SAN 255-4976)
E-mail: admin@askpublishingllc.net
Web site: http://www.askpublishingllc.net
Dist(s): **Baker & Taylor Bks.**
Quality Bks., Inc.

Askeladd Pr., *(0-9619327)* 437 W. First St., Saint Charles, MN 55972 USA (SAN 243-7589) Tel 507-932-4099.

ASM Pr., *(0-914826; 1-55581)* Div. of American Society For Microbiology, 1752 N St., NW, Washington, DC 20036 USA (SAN 202-1153) Tel 202-737-3600; Fax: 202-942-9342
E-mail: books@asmusa.org
Web site: http://www.asmpress.org.

ASP Corp. Entertainment Group, Inc., *(0-9754147)* 3695 F Cascade Rd., Suite 229, Atlanta, GA 30331 USA Tel 404-349-1269; Fax: 404-346-0800
Web site: http://www.hannibaltrilogy.com.

Aspectos Culturales, *(0-9768474)* 1219 Luisa St., No. 2, Santa Fe, NM 87505 USA Tel 505-986-0799; Fax: 505-986-1499
E-mail: cultura@aspectosculturales.com
Web site: http://www.aspectosculturales.com.

Aspen Bks., *(1-56236)* Div. of Worldwide Pubs., Inc., P.O. Box 1271, Bountiful, UT 84011-1271 USA Toll Free: 800-748-4850
E-mail: jasay@qwest.net; prawlins@aspenbook.com
Dist(s): **Origin Bk. Sales, Inc.**

Aspen Light Publishing, *(0-9743620)* 13506 Summerport Village Pkwy. Suite #155, Windermere, FL 34786 USA Tel 407-342-4181
E-mail: orders@whycafe.com
Web site: http://www.aspenlightpublishing.com
Dist(s): **DeVorss & Co.**
New Leaf Distributing Co., Inc.
Southern Bk. Service
Why Cafe Institute, The.

Aspen Pubs. *Imprint of* **Wolters Kluwer Law & Business**

Asphodel Pr. *Imprint of* **Moyer Bell**

Aspirations Media, Inc., *(0-9776043; 0-9800034)* 7755 Lakeview Ln., Spring Lake Park, MN 55432 USA (SAN 257-7305)
E-mail: amteacolee@aol.com
Web site: http://www.aspirationsmediainc.com
Dist(s): **AtlasBooks Distribution**
BookMasters, Inc.

Aspiring Arts Publishing, *(0-9720579)* P.O. Box 832980, Richardson, TX 75083-2980 USA Tel 972-783-2364
E-mail: got2know@aspiringarts.com
Web site: http://www.aspiringarts.com.

ASQ Quality Pr., *(0-87389)* Div. of American Society for Quality, 600 N. Plankinton Ave., P.O. Box 3005, Milwaukee, WI 53203 USA (SAN 683-5244) Tel 414-272-8575; Fax: 414-270-8810; Toll Free: 800-248-1946
E-mail: cs@asq.org
Web site: http://www.qualitypress.asq.org/
Dist(s): **American Technical Pubs., Inc.**
Baker & Taylor Bks.

Assaca Pr., *(0-9667687)* 6719 Shadow Run, San Antonio, TX 78250-1742 USA Tel 210-260-5574; Fax: 210-681-2676
E-mail: mtezel@swbell.net
Web site: http://home.swbell.net/aliciavt/assaca.html.

Assessment Systems, Inc., *(0-15)* Subs. of The Psychological Corp., A Harcourt Brace Co., 3 Bala Plaza W., Suite 300, Bala Cynwyd, PA 19004-3481 USA (SAN 298-8852) Tel 610-617-9300; Fax: 610-617-9302; Toll Free: 800-274-3444; 888-204-6231
Web site: http://www.asisvcs.com.

Assimil France (FRA) *(2-7005) Dist. by* **Distribks Inc.**

Associated Pubns., *(0-9608806)* P.O. Box 728, Glendora, CA 91740 USA (SAN 238-2407)
E-mail: DivineMet@aol.com.

Associated Publishers Group *See* **APG Sales and Fulfillment**

Assocs. & Scribner-Trace Inc., *(0-9729221)* Orders Addr.: P.O. Box 2333, Marco Island, FL 34146 USA Tel 239-394-0399; Fax: 239-642-8250; Edit Addr.: 1757 Dogwood Dr., Marco Island, FL 34145 USA
E-mail: scribtrace@aol.com.

Assn. for Enterprise Opportunity, *(0-9708339; 0-9728985)* 1601 N. Kent St., Suite 1101, Arlington, VA 22209 USA Tel 703-841-7760; Fax: 703-841-7748
E-mail: slandry@assoceo.org
Web site: http://www.microenterpriseworks.org.

Association of American Laestadian Congregations *See* **Laestadian Lutheran Church**

Assn. of Christian Schls. International, *(1-58331)* Orders Addr.: P.O. Box 35097, Colorado Springs, CO 80935-3509 USA; Edit Addr.: 731 Chapel Hills Dr., Colorado Springs, CO 80920 USA (SAN 689-5751) Tel 719-528-6906; Fax: 719-531-0631; Toll Free: 800-367-0798 (orders only)
E-mail: webmaster@acsi.org; info@acsi.org
Web site: http://www.acsi.org.

Association of Ideas Publishing, *(0-9647119)* 433 N. Camden Dr., Suite 1128, Beverly Hills, CA 90210 USA Tel 310-205-0615; Fax: 310-275-3885
E-mail: brandiroth@yahoo.com
Web site: http://www.associationofideas.com.

Assn. of Waldorf Schls. of North America Pubns. (AWSNA), *(0-9623978; 1-888365)* 3911 Bannister Rd., Fair Oaks, CA 95628 USA Tel 916-961-0927; Fax: 916-961-0715; 1158 Quince Ave., Boulder, CO 80304 Tel 303-541-9244 (phone/fax)
E-mail: davidm@awsna.org
Web site: http://www.awsna.org; http://www.waldorfeducation.org; http://www.waldorfresearchinstitute.org
Dist(s): **SteinerBooks, Inc.**

Assouline (FRA) *(2-84323) Dist. by* **Perseus Dist.**

AS-Sunnah Foundation of America *See* **Islamic Supreme Council of America**

Astellas *See* **Astellas Pharma US, Inc.**

Astellas Pharma US, Inc., *(0-9702446)* 3 Parkway North Ctr., Deerfield, IL 60015 USA Tel 847-317-1077; Fax: 847-317-8229; Toll Free: 800-727-7003
E-mail: goldman-garrity@fujisawa.com
Web site: http://fujisawa.com.

Astonish Comics, *(0-9721259)* 10061 Riverside Dr., Suite No. 785, Toluca Lake, CA 91602 USA
Web site: http://www.theastonishfactory.com
Dist(s): **Diamond Bk. Distributors.**

Astor-Honor, Inc., *(0-8392)* 16 E. 40th St., Third Flr., New York, NY 10016 USA (SAN 203-5022) Tel 212-840-8800; Fax: 212-840-7246.

Astoria Productions, *(0-9662378; 0-9715876)* 8260 Eagle Ridge Dr., Concord, OH 44077 USA Tel 440-392-9041; Fax: 440-392-9042
E-mail: astoriaproductions@att.net.

Astral Publishing Co., *(0-9645867)* Orders Addr.: P.O. Box 3955, Santa Barbara, CA 93130-3955 USA (SAN 298-5705) Tel 805-967-7667; Edit Addr.: 333 Old Mill Rd., No. 324, Santa Barbara, CA 93110 USA
E-mail: wveigele@aol.com
Web site: http://www.astralpublishing.com
Dist(s): **Quality Bks., Inc.**

Astran, Inc., 6995 NW 82nd Ave. Ste. 40, Miami, FL 33166-2783 USA (SAN 169-1082) Toll Free: 800-431-4957
E-mail: sales@astranbooks.com
Web site: http://www.astranbooks.com.

Astrolog Publishing Hse. (ISR) *(965-494) Dist. by* **IPG Chicago.**

Astronaut Ink, *(0-9772727)* 2 Whispering Pines Rd., Wilton, NY 12831 USA
E-mail: joe@popartproperties.com
Web site: http://www.popartproperties.com.

Asylum Pr., *(0-9768509)* Orders Addr.: 101 Woodruff Ave., Watertown, CT 06795 USA
Web site: http://www.asylumpress.com
Dist(s): **Diamond Comic Distributors, Inc.**
FM International.

At Ease Pr., *(0-917921)* Div. of Be at Ease School of Etiquette, 9402 Dallum Dr., Austin, TX 78753-4517 USA (SAN 656-9900) Tel 512-821-2699; Fax: 512-821-8565
E-mail: schoolofetiquette@ateasepress.com
Web site: http://ateaspress.com
Dist(s): **Lulu.com.**

At Home Pubns., *(0-9754142)* 2834 Grier Nursery Rd., Forest Hill, MD 21050 USA Tel 410-420-2230 (phone/fax)
E-mail: athomepubs@juno.com
Web site: http://www.athomepubs.com.

At Peace Media, LLC, *(0-9742002)* 1117 E. Putnam Ave., No. 345, Riverside, CT 06878 USA Tel 203-698-2688; Fax: 203-698-3441; Toll Free: 800-575-7715
E-mail: john@atpeacemedia.com
Web site: http://www.atpeacemedia.com.

Athenaeum Music & Arts Library *Imprint of* **Library Assn. of La Jolla**

Athenean Pr., Inc., *(0-9701466; 1-932108)* 5005 Langford Pass., Old Hickory, TN 37138-1252 USA
E-mail: atheneanpress@aol.com
Web site: http://www.atheneanpress.com
Dist(s): **Ingram Bk. Co.**

Atheneum *Imprint of* **Simon & Schuster Children's Publishing**

Atheneum/Anne Schwartz Bks. *Imprint of* **Simon & Schuster Children's Publishing**

Atheneum/Richard Jackson Bks. *Imprint of* **Simon & Schuster Children's Publishing**

Athlete Network *See* **A-Game, LLC**

Athletic Edge, The, *(0-9708569)* 1328 E. 37th St., Long Beach, CA 90807 USA Tel 562-290-0119 (phone/fax)
E-mail: theathleticedge@wv1.net
Web site: http://www.theathleticedge.com.

ATInternational Pubs., *(0-9773816)* 227 Sunflower Ln., West Windsor, NJ 08550-2439 USA
E-mail: atinetus@yahoo.com.

Atkinson, Janet Irene, *(0-9653428)* Orders Addr.: P.O. Box 934, Sonora, CA 95370 USA Tel 209-532-2470; Fax: 209-532-0277; Edit Addr.: 19575 Roselyn Ln., Sonora, CA 95370 USA
E-mail: janirene@mlode.com.

Atlantic Bridge Publishing, *(0-9700930; 0-9706913; 1-931761; 1-59578)* 10509 Sedgegrass Dr., Indianapolis, IN 46235 USA Tel 317-826-8059 ; *Imprints:* Liquid Silver Books (Liquid Silver Bks) Do not confuse with Bridge Works Publishing Company, Inc. in Bridgehampton, NY
E-mail: linda@atlanticbridge.net
Web site: http://www.liquidsilverbooks.com; http://www.atlanticbridge.net.

Atlantic Monthly Pr. *Imprint of* **Grove/Atlantic, Inc.**

Atlantic Publishing Co., *(0-910627; 1-60138)* 1405 SW. 6th Ave., Ocala, FL 34471-0640 USA (SAN 268-1250) Toll Free: 800-814-1132 Do not confuse with companies with the same or similar name in Tabor City, NC , Aurora, IL , Lakeland, FL , Combs, KY , Neosho, MO
E-mail: info@atlantic-pub.com; sales@atlantic-pub.com
Web site: http://www.atlantic-pub.com.

Atlantida (ARG) *(950-08) Dist. by* **Lectorum Pubns.**

Atlantida (ARG) *(950-08) Dist. by* **AIMS Intl.**

Atlantida (ARG) *(950-08) Dist. by* **Libros Fronteras.**

Atlantida (ARG) *(950-08) Dist. by* **LD Bks Inc.**

Atlantis Productions, *(0-9639743; 0-9725423)* Orders Addr.: P.O. Box 700, Edgewater, FL 32132-0700 USA (SAN 631-0664) Tel 386-345-4208; Fax: 386-345-0709; Edit Addr.: 4502 U. S. Hwy. 1, Edgewater, FL 32132 USA
E-mail: rgvant@juno.com
Web site: http://www.airshiphistory.com.

Atlas Pr., *(0-9657960)* Orders Addr.: P.O. Box 7054, Boulder, CO 80306-7054 USA Tel 303-546-6529; Toll Free: 888-546-6520; Edit Addr.: 1735 Linden Ave., Boulder, CO 80304-1537 USA Do not confuse with Atlas Pr., Los Angeles, CA
E-mail: litgooroo@aol.com
Web site: http://www.littlegooroo.com.

AtlasBooks *See* **AtlasBooks Distribution**

AtlasBooks Distribution, Div. of BookMasters, Inc., Orders Addr.: 30 Amberwood Pkwy., Ashland, OH 44805 USA (SAN 631-936X) Tel 800-537-6727; Fax: 419-281-6883; Toll Free: 800-247-6553; 800-266-5564
E-mail: orders@atlasbooks.com
Web site: http://www.atlasbooksdistribution.com; http://www.bookmasters.com.

Atman Pr., *(0-9652900)* 2525 Auburn Ave., PMB 345, Columbus, GA 31906 USA (SAN 299-142X) Tel 706-323-6377; Fax: 706-321-1140; Toll Free: 800-563-4198
E-mail: turakhiasmita@yahoo.com; robertarnett@mindspring.com
Web site: http://www.atmanpress.com
Dist(s): **Baker & Taylor Bks.**
Brodart Co.
Mackin Bk. Co.

Atomic Fruit Pr., *(0-9753225)* 404 13th Ave., Huntington, WV 25701 USA
Web site: http://www.apocalyptictangerine.com.

Atori Publishing, Inc., *(0-9678459)* P.O. Box 125, Olyphant, PA 18447 USA Tel 570-383-2579; Fax: 570-383-6818
E-mail: readatori@aol.com.

Atria *Imprint of* **Simon & Schuster**

Atrium Publishing, Incorporated *See* **Trellis Publishing, Inc.**

Attack The Text / Magedo Publishing, *(0-9755923)* 1519 E. Chapman Ave., No. 3000, Fullerton, CA 92831 USA
Web site: http://www.attackthetext.com; http://www.magedo.com.

Attainment Co., Inc., *(0-934731; 1-57861)* Orders Addr.: P.O. Box 930160, Verona, WI 53593 USA (SAN 694-1656) Tel 608-845-7880; Fax: 608-845-8040; Toll Free: 800-327-4269; Edit Addr.: 504 Commerce Pkwy., Verona, WI 53953 USA (SAN 631-6174) ; *Imprints:* IEP RESOURCES (IEP RES)
E-mail: info@attainmentcompany.com; sue@attainmentcompany.com
Web site: http://www.attainmentcompany.com/
Dist(s): **Linx Educational Publishing, Inc.**
Sunburst Communications, Inc.

Attic Pr. (IRL) *(1-85594; 0-946211) Dist. by* **Intl Spec Bk.**

Attic Studio Pr. *Imprint of* **Attic Studio Publishing Hse.**

Attic Studio Publishing Hse., *(1-883551)* Orders Addr.: P.O. Box 75, Clinton Corners, NY 12514 USA (SAN 298-2838) Tel 845-266-8100; Fax: 845-266-5515; Toll Free: 800-974-5533 (orders); Edit Addr.: 564 Schultzville Rd., Clinton Corners, NY 12514 USA (SAN 298-2846) ; *Imprints:* Attic Studio Press (Attic Studio); Maple Corners Press (Maple Corners Pr)
E-mail: collegeavepress@aol.com; atticstudiopress@aol.com
Dist(s): **Baker & Taylor Bks.**
Spring Arbor Distributors, Inc.

Attica Press *See* **Nea Attiki Pr.**

Attitude Pr., Inc., *(0-9716631)* P.O. Box 16807, San Diego, CA 92176 USA Tel 619-665-1264
E-mail: cdamico@companiongroupinc.com
Web site: http://www.companiongroupinc.com
Dist(s): **Biblio Distribution.**

Attitude Publishing *Imprint of* **Moss, Renea L.**

Attitudes in Dressing, Inc., *(0-9766640)* 1350 Broadway, New York, NY 10018 USA Tel 212-279-3492; Fax: 212-564-3426; Toll Free: 800-899-0503
Web site: http://www.bodywrappers.com.

Atwood, Donna Design, *(0-9660293)* 1137 W. Culver St., Phoenix, AZ 85007-1908 USA Tel 602-254-7168; Fax: 602-258-7359
E-mail: Atwood@amug.org
Web site: http://www.atwooddesign.com; http://www.riatoz.com.

Auckland Univ. Pr. (NZL) *(1-86940) Dist. by* **IPG Chicago.**

Audio Bookshelf, *(1-883332; 0-9741711; 0-9761932)* Orders Addr.: 44 Ocean View Dr., Middletown, RI 02842 USA Tel 401-849-2333; Fax: 401-842-0440; Toll Free: 800-234-1713; Edit Addr.: P.O. Box 83, Belfast, ME 04915-0083 USA
E-mail: dd@audiobookshelf.com
Web site: http://www.audiobookshelf.com
Dist(s): **Baker & Taylor Bks.**
Landmark Audiobooks
Professional Media Service Corp.

Audio Craft Press *See* **AudioCraft Publishing, Inc.**

Audio Educators, *(0-9675050)* 769 Bevier Rd., Piscataway, NJ 08854 USA Tel 310-428-4871
E-mail: mc@audioeducators.com
Web site: http://www.audioeducators.com.

Audio Memory Publishing, *(1-883028)* 501 Cliff Dr., Newport Beach, CA 92663-5810 USA Tel 800-365-7464; Fax: 949-631-1150; Toll Free: 800-365-7464
E-mail: larry@audiomemory.com
Web site: http://www.audiomemory.com.

Audio Partners, Incorporated *See* **Audio Partners Publishing Corp.**

Audio Partners Publishing Corp., *(0-88690; 0-945353; 1-57270)* P.O. Box 6930, Auburn, CA 95604-6930 USA (SAN 253-4622) Tel 530-888-7803; Fax: 530-888-1840; Toll Free Fax: 800-882-1840; Toll Free: 800-231-4261 (orders only)
E-mail: info@audiopartners.com
Web site: http://www.audiopartners.com
Dist(s): **Baker & Taylor Bks.**
Landmark Audiobooks
Perseus Distribution.

AudioCraft Publishing, Inc., *(1-893699)* Orders Addr.: P.O. Box 281, Topinabee, MI 49791 USA Tel 231-238-0297; Fax: 231-238-0298; Toll Free: 888-420-4244; Edit Addr.: 1416 Patterson, Topinabee, MI 49791 USA
E-mail: boreas@mich.com
Web site: http://www.audiocraftpublishing.com; http://www.michiganchillers.com; http://www.americanchillers.com.

Audio-Forum *See* **Norton, Jeffrey Pubs., Inc.**

Audioscope, *(1-57375)* Div. of K-tel International (USA), Inc., 2605 Fernbrook Ln., N., No. H-O, Plymouth, MN 55447 USA Tel 612-559-6888; Fax: 612-559-6848; Toll Free: 800-328-6640
Web site: http://www.ktel.com.

Audisee Sound & Music, *(0-9666910; 1-930827)* 6736 38th, SW, Seattle, WA 98126 USA Tel 206-938-2347; Fax: 206-938-0163 ; *Imprints:* Car Tours (Car Tours)
E-mail: audisee@audisee.com
Web site: http://www.CarTours.org
Dist(s): **Lone Pine Publishing USA.**

Audrey Productions, *(0-9722673)* 7809 Paper Flower Ct., Las Vegas, NV 89128 USA Tel 702-228-4803 (phone/fax).

Augsburg Bks. *Imprint of* **Augsburg Fortress, Pubs.**

†**Augsburg Fortress, Pubs.,** *(0-8006; 0-8066)* Orders Addr.: P.O. Box 1209, Minneapolis, MN 55440-1209 USA (SAN 169-4081) Toll Free Fax: 800-722-7766; Toll Free: 800-328-4648 (orders only); Edit Addr.: 100 S. 5th St. Ste. 600, Minneapolis, MN 55402-1242 USA ; *Imprints:* Fortress Press (Fortress Pr); Augsburg Books (Augsburg Bks)
E-mail: customerservice@augsburgfortress.org; info@augsburgfortress.org; subscriptions@augsburgfortress.org; copyright@augsburgfortress.org; international@augsburgfortress.org
Web site: http://www.augsburgfortress.org; *CIP.*

Augsburg Fortress Publishers, Publishing House of The Evangelical Lutheran Church in America *See* **Augsburg Fortress, Pubs.**

Augsburg Youth & Family Institute of Augsburg College *See* **Youth & Family Institute, The**

†**August Hse. Pubs., Inc.,** *(0-87483; 0-935304)* 3500 Piedmont Rd. NE, Suite 310, Atlanta, GA 30305 USA (SAN 223-7288) Tel 501-404-4420; Fax: 501-404-4436; Toll Free: 800-284-8784; 201 E. Markham St., Little Rock, AR 72201 ; *Imprints:* August House Little Folk (Aug Hse Little Folk)
E-mail: ahinfo@augusthouse.com; order@augusthouse.com
Web site: http://www.augusthouse.com
Dist(s): **National Bk. Network**; *CIP.*

August Hse. Little Folk *Imprint of* **August Hse. Pubs., Inc.**

August Rose Publishing, *(1-879318)* Orders Addr.: 304 Northford Ct., Brandon, MS 39047 USA Tel 601-992-3245
E-mail: dleedavis@hotmail.com.

August Too Publishing, *(0-9767103)* 1346 E. Poinsettia St., Long Beach, CA 90805-3128 USA
E-mail: writeme@paulcarhart.com.

Augusta Win Publishing, *(0-9766597)* Orders Addr.: P.O. Box 53, Turin, NY 13473 USA; Edit Addr.: 6159 W. Main, Turin, NY 13473 USA
E-mail: augustawinpub@yahoo.com
Web site: http://www.augustawinpublishing.com.

Augustana College Geology Dept. Pr., *(0-9797015)* 639 38th St., Rock Island, IL 61201-2296 USA Tel 309-794-7318; Fax: 309-794-7564
Web site: http://www.augustana.edu.

Augustine Pr., *(0-9626431)* 900 Old Koenig Ln., No. 135, Austin, TX 78756 USA Tel 512-459-5194; Fax: 512-451-0755
E-mail: morganp@flash.net.

Augustinians of the Assumption *See* **Ambassador Bks., Inc.**

Augustus Publishing, *(0-9759453; 0-9792816)* Div. of Augustus Productions, 600 W. 218 St., Suite 3K, New York, NY 10034 USA Tel 646-526-7998
E-mail: jc@augustuspublishing.com; gfhood1@aol.com; aw@augustuspublishing.com
Web site: http://www.augustuspublishing.com
Dist(s): **A & B Distributors & Pubs. Group**
Biblio Distribution
Independent Pubs. Group.

Aum Pubns., *(0-88497)* Subs. of Agni Pr., 86-24 Parsons Blvd., Jamaica, NY 11432 USA (SAN 201-128X) Tel 718-291-9757; Fax: 718-523-1423; Toll Free: 800-739-2885 (Ext. 827) Do not confuse with AUM Pubns., Datil, NM
E-mail: amarkman@nyc.rr.com
Dist(s): **APG Sales and Fulfillment.**

Aunt Dee's Attic, Inc., *(0-9679437)* 415 Detroit St., Suite 200, Ann Arbor, MI 48104 USA Tel 734-668-6738; Fax: 734-668-0182; Toll Free: 800-352-6797
E-mail: dianne@elansys.com
Web site: http://www.auntdeesattic.com.

†**Aunt Lute Bks.,** *(0-918040; 0-933216; 1-879960)* Div. of Aunt Lute Foundation, Orders Addr.: P.O. Box 410687, San Francisco, CA 94141 USA Tel 415-826-1300; Fax: 415-826-8300; 2180 Bryant St., San Francisco, CA 94110-2128
E-mail: books@auntlute.com
Web site: http://www.auntlute.com
Dist(s): **Consortium Bk. Sales & Distribution**
SPD-Small Pr. Distribution; *CIP.*

Aunt Patty's Travels-London, *(0-9659668)* 4811 Wesleyan Woods Dr., Macon, GA 31210 USA.

Aunt Strawberry Bks., *(0-9669988)* Orders Addr.: P.O. Box 819, Boulder, CO 80306-0819 USA (SAN 299-9811) Tel 303-449-3574; Fax: 303-444-9221
E-mail: readasbs@hotmail.com
Dist(s): **Baker & Taylor Bks.**
Brodart Co.
Follett Library Resources.

Auntie B Publishing *See* **BaHart Pubns. / Eight Legs Publishing**

Aunty Ems Boutique, *(0-9742122)* P.O. Box 1963, Havasu Lake Landing, CA 92363 USA.

Aura Printing, Inc., *(0-911643)* 88 Parkville Ave., Brooklyn, NY 11230 USA (SAN 237-9317) Tel 718-435-9103; Fax: 718-871-9488
Dist(s): **Baker & Taylor Bks.**
Bookazine Co., Inc.

Auralog, Inc., *(1-893197)* 3710 E. University Dr. Ste. 1, Phoenix, AZ 85034-7292 USA Toll Free: 888-388-3535
E-mail: info@auralog.com
Web site: http://www.auralog.com.

Aurelia Pr., *(0-9670595)* P.O. Box 1426, Richland, WA 99352 USA (SAN 253-1003) Tel 509-627-0751; Fax: 509-627-0703 Do not confuse with Aurelia Press in Montague, TX
E-mail: info@aureliapress.com
Web site: http://www.aureliapress.com.

Aurelia Pr, *(0-615)* Orders Addr.: P.O. Box 13, Montague, TX 76251 USA Tel 940-894-2641; Fax: 940-894-2615; Edit Addr.: Hwy. 175 & Wall St., Montague, TX 76251 USA Do not confuse with Aurelia Press in Richland, WA
E-mail: pmfenoglio@earthlink.net.

Auriga, Ediciones S.A. (ESP) *(84-7281) Dist. by* **Continental Bk.**

Aurora Bks., *(0-9753508)* 512 Willow Branch Rd., Norman, OK 73072 USA
E-mail: aurorabooks@netzero.net.

Aurora Libris Corp., *(1-932233)* 40 E. 83rd St., Apt. 35, New York, NY 10028 USA Toll Free: 866-763-8411
E-mail: lavinia@laviniasworld.com
Web site: http://www.laviniasworld. com.

Aurora Metro Pubns. Ltd. (GBR) *(0-9515877; 0-9536757; 0-9542330; 0-9546912) Dist. by* **Consort Bk Sales.**

Aurora Production AG (CHE) *(3-905332) Dist. by* **Activated Mini.**

Aurora Pubs., Inc., *(0-9791758)* Orders Addr.: 5970 S.W. 18th St., No. 117, Boca Raton, FL 33433-7197 USA
E-mail: aurorapublishers@aol.com
Web site: http://www.aurorapublishers.com
Dist(s): **Independent Pubs. Group.**

Austin & Charlie Adventures *Imprint of* **Paw Print Pubns.**

Austin & Company, Inc., *(0-9657153)* 104 S. Union St., Suite 202, Traverse City, MI 49684 USA (SAN 631-1466) Tel 231-933-4649; Fax: 231-933-4659
E-mail: aandn@aol.com
Web site: http://www.austinandcompanyinc.com.

Austin & Nelson Publishing *See* **Austin & Company, Inc.**

Austin Christopher Swift, *(0-9764208)* 154 Golden Autumn Pl., Woodlands, TX 77384 USA Tel 956-421-5750; Fax: 956-421-5721
E-mail: john@toppmarketing.com.

Austin Energy Green Building Program, *(0-9679069)* Orders Addr.: P.O. Box 1088, Austin, TX 78767 USA Tel 512-322-6172; Fax: 512-505-3711; Edit Addr.: 721 Barton Springs Rd., Austin, TX 78704 USA
E-mail: dick.peterson@austinenergy.com
Web site: http://www.austinenergy.com.

Austin Publishing, *(0-9670001)* P.O. Box 1049, Clarkston, GA 30021 USA Tel 404-508-8200; Fax: 404-299-8622
E-mail: Helena2@bellsouth.com.

Australian Fishing Network (AUS) *(0-9587143; 1-86513) Dist. by* **Cardinal.**

Authentic Lifestyle *Imprint of* **Authentic Media**

Authentic Media, *(0-85364; 0-9630908; 1-884543; 0-903843; 0-948902; 1-85078; 1-86024; 1-932805; 1-934068)* Div. of Send the Light, Inc., Orders Addr.: P.O. Box 1047, Waynesboro, GA 30830 USA; Edit Addr.: 129 Mobilization Dr., Waynesboro, GA 30830-2047 USA Tel 706-554-5827; Fax: 706-554-7444; Toll Free: 866-732-6657; 9 Holdom Ave. Bletchley, Milton Keynes, MK1 1QR Tel 01908 364200; Fax: 01908 648592 ; *Imprints:* Authentic Lifestyle (AuthLifestyle)
E-mail: angela@omlit.om.org; info@authenticmedia.co.uk
Web site: http://www.authenticbooks.com
Dist(s): **Eisenbrauns, Inc.**
STL Distribution North America.

AuthorHouse, *(1-58500; 0-9675669; 1-58721; 1-58820; 0-7596; 1-4033; 1-4107; 1-4140; 1-4184; 1-4208; 1-4259; 1-4343)* Div. of Author Solutions, Inc., 1663 Liberty Dr., Suite 200, Bloomington, IN 47403 USA (SAN 253-7605) Tel 812-339-6000; Fax: 812-339-6554; Toll Free: 800-839-8640
E-mail: authorhouse@authorhouse.com
Web site: http://www.authorhouse.com.

Authors & Artists Publishers of New York, Inc., *(0-9708053; 0-9724922; 0-9740683; 0-9754298; 0-9763993; 0-9766716; 0-9771482; 0-9786211; 0-9787113)* Orders Addr.: 3 Kimberly Dr., Dryden, NY 13053 USA Tel 607-273-2870 ; *Imprints:* Ithaca Press (IthacaPress)
E-mail: quotes@ithacapress.com; authorsartists@aol.com
Web site: http://www.ithacapress.com.

Authors Choice Pr. *Imprint of* **iUniverse, Inc.**

Authors' Pr., The, *(0-9718099; 1-933505)* 588 Lindsey Way, Social Circle, GA 30025-2743 USA Tel 678-465-9058; Fax: 678-465-9097
E-mail: hclk@terracopiaepress.com
Web site: http://www.terracopiaepress.com.

Autism Asperger Publishing Co., *(0-9672514; 1-931282; 1-934575)* Orders Addr.: P.O. Box 23173, Overland Park, KS 66283-0173 USA Tel 913-599-3311; Fax: 913-492-2546; Edit Addr.: 15490 Quivira, Overland Park, KS 66221 USA
E-mail: kmcbr41457@aol.com
Web site: http://www.asperger.net.

Automobile Assn. (GBR) *(0-7495; 0-86145; 0-901088; 1-872163) Dist. by* **Trafalgar.**

Automobile Assn. (GBR) *(0-7495; 0-86145; 0-901088; 1-872163) Dist. by* **IPG Chicago.**

Automobiles-Memory Lane Publishing, *(0-9746667)* Orders Addr.: P.O. Box 228, Vicksburg, MI 49097 USA (SAN 255-7118) Tel 269-649-3614 (phone/fax); Edit Addr.: 2294 E. VW Ave., Vicksburg, MI 49097 USA.

Autonomedia, *(0-936756; 1-57027)* Orders Addr.: P.O. Box 568, Brooklyn, NY 11211-0568 USA; Edit Addr.: 55 S. 11th St., Brooklyn, NY 11211-0568 USA (SAN 221-3869) Tel 718-963-2603
E-mail: info@autonomedia.org
Web site: http://www.autonomedia.org
Dist(s): **AK Pr. Distribution**
SPD-Small Pr. Distribution.

Autumn Hse. Publishing, *(0-9637825)* Orders Addr.: P.O. Box 763833, Dallas, TX 75376 USA; Edit Addr.: 1535 Acapulco Dr., Dallas, TX 75232 USA Tel 214-376-8959 Do not confuse with the same or similar name in Lexington, KY, Hagerstown, MD
E-mail: millijp@earthlink.net.

Autumn Hse. Publishing Co., *(0-8127; 1-878951)* Div. of Review & Herald Publishing Assn., 55 W. Oakridge Dr., Hagerstown, MD 21740 USA Do not confuse with companies with the same name in Lexington, KY, Dallas, TX.

Autumn Light Pubns., *(0-9755173)* 5430 Lynx Ln., No. 298, Columbia, MD 21044 USA
E-mail: ellyh@comcast.net; publisher@autumnlight.net
Web site: http://www.autumnlight.net.

Autumn Publishing Group, LLC, *(1-890877)* Orders Addr.: P.O. Box 71604, Madison Heights, MI 48071 USA Tel 248-589-5249; Fax: 248-585-5715; Toll Free: 888-876-4114; Edit Addr.: 30755 Barrington Ave., Madison Heights, MI 48071 USA
Web site: http://www.wiredin.net/childcare
Dist(s): **Baker & Taylor Bks.**
Unique Bks., Inc.

AV Concepts Corp., *(0-931334; 1-55576)* Orders Addr.: 30 Montauk Blvd., Oakdale, NY 11769 USA (SAN 655-5888) Tel 631-567-7227; Fax: 631-567-8745
E-mail: info@edconpublishing.com
Web site: http://www.edconpublishing.com; http://www.acaresnet.com.

Avalon Publishing Group, *(0-7867; 0-88184; 0-929654; 0-931188; 0-938410; 0-941423; 1-56025; 1-56201; 1-56858; 1-56924; 1-58005; 1-878067; 1-60094)* Div. of Perseus Books Group, 161 William St., 16th Flr., New York, NY 10038 USA Tel 646-375-2570; Fax: 646-375-2571
Web site: http://www.thundersmouth.com; http://www.avalonpub.com; http://www.sealpress.com; http://www.carrollandgraf.com; http://www.marlowepub.com
Dist(s): **Bilingual Pubns. Co., The**
NetLibrary, Inc.
Perseus Distribution.

Avalon Travel Publishing, *(0-912528; 0-918373; 0-935701; 0-945465; 0-9603322; 1-56261; 1-56691; 1-57354; 1-59880)* Div. of Perseus Books Group, 1400 65th St., Suite 250, Emeryville, CA 94608 USA (SAN 221-7406) Tel 510-595-3664; Fax: 510-535-4228
Web site: http://www.avalonpub.com
Dist(s): **Perseus Distribution.**

Avant Garde Publishing, *(0-9754307; 0-9760129; 0-9763423; 0-9776554; 0-9788002)* 2330 Hickory Ridge, Ashland, KY 41101 USA Do not confuse with Avant-garde Publishing Company in Mableton, GA
E-mail: info@avantgardepublishing.com
Web site: http://www.avantgardepublishing.com.

Avant-garde Publishing Co., *(0-9743676)* Orders Addr.: P.O. Box 566, Mableton, GA 30126 USA Tel 770-739-5114 Do not confuse with Avant Garde Publishing in Ashland, KY
E-mail: avantgardeco@att.net
Web site: http://www.avantgardepublishing.com.

Avari Press, *(1-933770)* P.O. Box 285, Smoketown, PA 17576 USA (SAN 257-9413)
E-mail: editorial@avaripress.com
Web site: http://www.avaripress.com
Dist(s): **Biblio Distribution.**

Avatar Pr., Inc., *(0-9706784; 1-59291)* 9 Triumph Dr., Urbana, IL 61802 USA Tel 217-384-2211; Fax: 217-384-2216 Do not confuse with companies with the same or similar name in Sunnyside, NY, Atlanta, GA, Brick, NJ
E-mail: william@avatarpress.net
Web site: http://www.avatarpress.com
Dist(s): **Diamond Bk. Distributors.**

Avatar Pubns., Inc. (CAN) *(0-9735379; 0-9738442; 0-9737401; 0-9738555) Dist. by* **Baker & Taylor.**

Avatar Pubns., Inc. (CAN) *(0-9735379; 0-9738442; 0-9737401; 0-9738555) Dist. by* **New Leaf Dist.**

Ave Maria Pr., *(0-87061; 0-87793; 0-88347; 0-939516; 1-893732; 1-932057; 1-59471; 1-933495)* P.O. Box 428, Notre Dame, IN 46556-0428 USA (SAN 201-1255) Tel 574-287-2831; Fax: 574-239-2904; Toll Free Fax: 800-282-5681; Toll Free: 800-282-1865 ; *Imprints:* Forest of Peace Publishing (For Peace Pubng)
E-mail: avemariapress.1@nd.edu
Web site: http://www.forestofpeace.com; http://www.avemariapress.com; http://www.sorinbooks.com
Dist(s): **Fujii Assocs.**

Aventine Pr, *(0-9719382; 0-9722932; 1-59330)* 1023 Fourth Ave., No. 204, San Diego, CA 92101 USA Toll Free: 866-246-6142
E-mail: info@aventinepress.com
Web site: http://www.aventinepress.com
Dist(s): **Ingram Bk. Co.**

Avenue Publishing, *(0-9661306)* 603 Seagaze Dr., PMB 531, Oceanside, CA 92054 USA Tel 760-720-7189; Fax: 760-720-9544 Do not confuse with Avenue Publishing Co., Hamtramck, MI
E-mail: Nvlwritr13@aol.com
Web site: http://www.Avepub.com.

AverHill Pr., *(0-9766107)* 2545 SW Terwilliger Blvd., No. 807, Portland, OR 97201 USA.

AverStream Pr., *(0-9658740)* 13176 N. Dale Mabry Hwy. No. 444, Tampa, FL 33618 USA Tel 813-390-6258; Fax: 815-366-9705
E-mail: info@averstreampress.com
Web site: http://www.averstreampress.com
Dist(s): **Baker & Taylor Bks.**
Quality Bks., Inc.

Avery *Imprint of* **Penguin Group (USA) Inc.**

Avery Color Studios, Inc., *(0-932212; 1-892384)* 511 D Ave., Gwinn, MI 49841 USA (SAN 211-1470) Tel 906-346-3908; Fax: 906-346-3015; Toll Free: 800-722-9925
E-mail: avery@portup.com
Dist(s): **Partners Bk. Distributing, Inc.**
Hale, Robert & Co., Inc.

Avery Goode-Reid Pubs., *(0-9766620)* P.O. Box 702, Ormond Beach, FL 32175-0702 USA Tel 386-615-0493
E-mail: marianstomblin@aol.com
Web site: http://www.mariantomblin.com.

Avery's, Tom Totally Tennis, *(0-9727444)* 5771 12th Ave., NW, Naples, FL 34119 USA
Web site: http://tomavery.com.

AVI Communications, Inc., *(0-9663665)* 535 S. Nolen Dr. Ste. 100, Southlake, TX 76092-9194 USA (SAN 299-6944) Toll Free: 800-221-2842
E-mail: info@beatdepression.com
Web site: http://www.beatdepression.com.

Aviation Foundation of America, *(0-9725249)* 121 5th Ave. N.W., Suite 300, New Brighton, MN 55112 USA Tel 651-255-1999
Web site: http://www.nationalairtour.org.

Aviation Supplies & Academics, Inc., *(0-940732; 1-56027)* 7005 132nd Pl., SE, Newcastle, WA 98059-3153 USA (SAN 219-709X) Tel 425-235-1500; Fax: 425-235-0128; Toll Free: 800-272-2359
E-mail: asa@asa2fly.com
Web site: http://www.asa2fly.com
Dist(s): **Aviation Bk. Co.**
Independent Pubs. Group
Wing Aero.

Aviatrix Publishing, Inc., *(1-928760)* P.O. Box PO Box 485, Arlington Heights, IL 60006-0485 USA Tel 847-797-0170
E-mail: publisher@womanpilot.com
Web site: http://www.womanpilot.com.

Avisson Pr., Inc., *(1-888105)* Orders Addr.: P.O. Box 38816, Greensboro, NC 27438-8816 USA (SAN 298-8127) Tel 336-288-6989; Fax: 336-288-6989; Edit Addr.: 3007 Taliaferro Rd., Greensboro, NC 27408 USA (SAN 298-8097).

Avitable Pub., *(0-9769794)* P.O. Box 38, East Meadow, NY 11554 USA Fax: 516-826-6843
E-mail: milliemsrd@aol.com
Web site: CaloriestheBottomLine.com.

Avnner Publishing, *(0-9718952)* 11605 Glynshire Ct., Potomac, MD 20854 USA Tel 301-279-2224
E-mail: zivaa@hotmail.com.

Avocet Pr., Inc., *(0-9661072; 0-9677346; 0-9705049; 0-9725078)* 19 Paul Ct., Pearl River, NY 10965-1539 USA (SAN 299-4631) Fax: 845-735-6807; Toll Free: 877-428-6238
E-mail: books@avocetpress.com
Web site: http://www.avocetpress.com
Dist(s): **Bella Distribution.**

Avocus Publishing, Inc., *(0-9627671; 1-890765)* 4 White Brook Rd., Gilsum, NH 03448 USA (SAN 248-2223) Tel 603-357-0236; Fax: 603-357-2073; Toll Free: 800-345-6665
E-mail: info@avocus.com
Web site: http://www.avocus.com
Dist(s): **Baker & Taylor Bks.**
Pathway Bk. Service.

Avon *Imprint of* **HarperCollins Pubs.**

Avon Bks. *Imprint of* **HarperCollins Pubs.**

A.W.A. Gang *Imprint of* **Journey Stone Creations, LLC**

Awa Pr. (NZL) *(0-9582509; 0-9582538; 0-9582629) Dist. by* **IPG Chicago.**

Awaken Publishing, *(0-9729259)* Div. of 2211 Co., LLC, Orders Addr.: 8315 Lake City Way, NE, Seattle, WA 98115 USA; Edit Addr.: P.O. Box 25648, Seattle, WA 98165-1148 USA (SAN 255-2876) Do not confuse with Awaken Publishing in Houston, TX
E-mail: pub@awakenpublishing.com
Web site: http://www.awakenpublishing.com
Dist(s): **Baker & Taylor Bks.**
New Leaf Distributing Co., Inc.
Partners/West.

Awareness Pubns., *(0-9744163)* 310-A S. Alu Rd., Wailuku, HI 96793 USA Tel 808-244-3782 Do not confuse with companies with the same name in Greenfield, WI, Santa Maria, CA, Houston, TX, Pocomoke City, MD
E-mail: awarep@mauigateway.com
Web site: http://www.awarenesspublications.org
Dist(s): **New Leaf Distributing Co., Inc.**

Awesome Guides, Inc., *(0-9703694; 0-9723218)* 127 W. Fairbanks Ave., Suite No. 421, Winter Park, FL 32789 USA Fax: 407-678-4337; Toll Free: 866-311-5758
E-mail: sales@awesomeguides.com
Web site: http://www.awesomeguides.com.

Awe-Struck E-Books, Inc., *(1-928670; 1-58749)* 2458 Cherry St., Dubuque, IA 52001-5749 USA (SAN 854-4980) ; *Imprints:* Byte/Me Teen Book (Byte Me Teen); Earthling Press (Earthling Prss)
E-mail: kdstruck@mchsi.com; kdstruck@fastmail.fm
Web site: http://www.awe-struck.net
Dist(s): **Baker & Taylor Bks.**

AWP Ministries, *(0-9719852)* P.O. Box 292100, Sacramento, CA 95829 USA
E-mail: ladawp@aol.com
Web site: http://www.awpministries.org.

Axiom Hse., *(0-9760237)* P.O. Box 2901, Fairfax, VA 22031 USA
E-mail: orders@axiomhouse.com
Web site: http://www.axiomhouse.com/index.htm.

Axle Publishing Co., Inc., *(0-9755895)* 909 S. Drake, Perryton, TX 79070-0712 USA (SAN 256-3746) Tel 806-435-4802; Fax: 806-434-1032
E-mail: jody@axlegalench.com
Web site: http://www.axlegalench.com.

Aylen Publishing, *(0-9708623; 0-9765040)* Subs. of Master Planning Group International, P.O. Box 952499, Lake Mary, FL 32795-2499 USA Tel 407-330-2028; Fax: 407-330-4134; Toll Free: 800-443-1976
E-mail: info@masterplanninggroup.com; suzi@masterplanninggroup.com
Web site: http://www.masterplanninggroup.com; http://www.Aylen.com.

Ayn Rand Institute, *(0-9625336; 0-9794661)* 2121 Alton Parkway, Suite 250, Irvine, CA 92606 USA Tel 949-222-6550; Fax: 949-222-6558
E-mail: mail@aynrand.org
Web site: http://www.aynrand.org.

AYMN Pubns., *(1-893471)* Orders Addr.: 24507 Old River Rd., Junction City, OR 97448-9209 USA
E-mail: books@aywnpublications.com
Web site: http://www.aywnpublications.com.

Azalea Creek Publishing, *(0-9677934)* c/o Tom Kendrick, 308 Bloomfield Rd., Sebastopol, CA 95472 USA Tel 707-823-2911 (phone/fax)
E-mail: azalea@sonic.net
Web site: http://www.sonic.net/dragonfly/azaleaforth.html; http://www.sonic.net/dragonfly/adhtml.html; http://southwestdragonflies.net/Order_Form.html; http://southwestdragonflies.net/ColoringBook.html
Dist(s): **American West Bks.**
Bored Feet Pr.
Treasure Chest Bks.

Azel Publishing, *(0-9666642)* Orders Addr.: P.O. Box 6175, Ventura, CA 93006-6175 USA (SAN 299-7045) Tel 805-644-1884; Fax: 805-644-5396; Toll Free: 877-293-5783; Edit Addr.: 5301 Cliffside Cir., Ventura, CA 93003 USA
E-mail: gerry@azelpublishing.com
Web site: http://www.azelpublishing.com
Dist(s): **Spring Arbor Distributors, Inc.**

Azimuth Pr., *(0-9632074; 1-886218)* 4041 Bowman Blvd., Suite 211, Macon, GA 31210 USA Tel 770-994-9449; Fax: 770-996-6928 Do not confuse with companies with the same or similar name in Alexander, NC, Arnold, MD.

Azoka Co., The, *(0-9745560)* P.O. Box 323, Greenland, NH 03885 USA Tel 603-772-0181; Fax: 603-772-0550
Web site: http://www.seacoastcenter.com.

Azreal Publishing Co., *(0-9755566)* Orders Addr.: P.O. Box 21139, Tallahassee, FL 32312 USA; Edit Addr.: 280 John Knox Rd. 3155, Tallahassee, FL 32303 USA
Web site: http://www.azrealpublishing.com.

Azro Pr., Inc., *(0-9660239; 1-929115)* Orders Addr.: 1704 Llano St., Suite B, PMB 342, Sante Fe, NM 87505 USA Tel 505-989-3272; Fax: 505-989-3832
E-mail: gae@nets.com
Web site: http://www.azropress.com.

Aztec 5 Publishing, *(0-9769478)* Orders Addr.: P.O. Box 11693, Glendale, AZ 85318 USA Tel 623-537-4567 (phone/fax)
E-mail: aztec5publishing@aol.com.

Aztex Corp., *(0-89404)* P.O. Box 50046, Tucson, AZ 85703-1046 USA (SAN 210-0371) Tel 520-882-4656; Fax: 520-792-8501
E-mail: ac@aztexcorp.com
Web site: http://www.aztexcorp.com
Dist(s): **Baker & Taylor Bks.**

AZTexts Publishing, Inc., *(0-9677292)* P.O. Box 93487, Phoenix, AZ 85070-3487 USA Tel 480-283-0994 (phone/fax); 1043 E. Amberwood Dr., Phoenix, AZ 85048
E-mail: aztexts@cox.net
Web site: http://FrecklesFriends.org; http://www.aztexts.com
Dist(s): **Quality Bks., Inc.**

Azure Venture Publishing Co., *(0-9760089)* Orders Addr.: P.O. Box 541, Wilberforce, OH 45384 USA (SAN 256-1816) Tel 937-372-4267; Edit Addr.: 1523 Rte. 42 E., Wilberforce, OH 45384 USA
E-mail: essiepayne@aol.com.

AZURE/BMI, *(0-9643273)* Affil. of Broadcast Music, Inc., Orders Addr.: P.O. Box 3723, Santa Monica, CA 90408-3723 USA Tel 310-394-8463; Edit Addr.: 422 18th St., Santa Monica, CA 90402-2430 USA
E-mail: dbmrk@gte.net
Dist(s): **Partners/West.**

B.A.B., Ltd., *(1-928895)* Orders Addr.: P.O. Box 2327, Boston, MA 02107-2327 USA Tel 617-923-9553; 617-335-9817; Edit Addr.: 8 Westland Rd., Watertown, MA 02174 USA
E-mail: bostonart@hotmail.com
Web site: http://www.BostonArtBoutique.com.

B&B Publishing, *(1-885813)* 63418 Everett Rd., Coos Bay, OR 97420 USA Tel 541-269-9277 Do not confuse with companies with the same or similar name in Fort Collins, CO, Westminster, CO, Walworth, WI, Greenfield, IN
Dist(s): **Partners/West.**

B & R Samizdat Express, *(0-915232; 0-931968)* 33 Gould St., West Roxbury, MA 02132 USA (SAN 207-1037) Tel 617-469-2269
E-mail: seltzer@samizdat.com
Web site: http://www.samizdat.com; http://store.yahoo.com/samizdat.

B & S Publishing Corp., *(0-9765066)* 16540 El Lago Blvd., No. 6, Fountain Hills, AZ 85268-4730 USA
Dist(s): **AtlasBooks Distribution.**

BBI Publishing, *(0-9672580)* P.O. Box 12394, San Antonio, TX 78212 USA (SAN 299-9226) Tel 210-678-0811.

BBY Pubns., *(1-885775)* Div. of Head-Pollett Consultants, Inc., Orders Addr.: P.O. Box 726, Shelbyville, KY 40066-0726 USA Tel 502-633-7013; Edit Addr.: 1410 St. Andrew Dr., Shelbyville, KY 40065 USA
E-mail: randy@bbypublications.com
Web site: http://www.bbypublications.com.

BF Publishing, *(0-9653327)* 17503 Brushy River Ct., Houston, TX 77095-6905 USA Tel 281-256-1213 Do not confuse with B.F. Publishing, Huntington Beach, CA
E-mail: BFPub1@aol.com
Dist(s): **Origin Bk. Sales, Inc.**

B G & J Pubs., *(0-9678340)* Orders Addr.: P.O. Box 270634, Las Vegas, NV 89106 USA (SAN 254-0525) Tel 702-431-0604; Fax: 702-431-9905; Edit Addr.: 5829 Emerald Canyon, Las Vegas, NV 89142 USA
E-mail: billupsbrenda@hotmail.com.

B G R Publishing *See* **EMG Networks**

BOSC Publishing Co., Inc., *(0-9710283)* P.O. Box 1529, Austin, TX 78767 USA (SAN 253-9241) Toll Free Fax: 877-204-9955; Toll Free: 877-825-2182 Do not confuse with Bosc Publishing, Gaithersburg, MD
E-mail: information@boscpub.com; customerservice@boscpub.com
Web site: http://www.boscpub.com; http://www.calicobuffalo.com
Dist(s): **Baker & Taylor Bks.**

B.R. Publishing Co., *(0-9625593; 1-884538)* 1725 Pinebrook Dr., Knoxville, TN 37909 USA Tel 423-691-1990
Dist(s): **Baker & Taylor Bks.**

Company

Company

B S G Printing *See* **Bible Study Guide For All Ages**

B. T. Brooks, *(0-9772282)* Orders Addr.: P.O. Box 300087, Kansas City, MO 64130 USA Tel 816-810-1277
E-mail: btbrookspublish@aol.com
Web site: http://www.btbrookspublishing.com.

BV Wespat, *(0-9713342; 0-9788934)* 1641 N. Memorial Dr., Lancaster, OH 43130 USA
Dist(s): **Baker & Taylor Bks.**
Brodart Co.
Partners Bk. Distributing, Inc.

B2Z Publishing, Inc., *(0-9712070)* Orders Addr.: P.O. Box 307, Severna Park, MD 21146 USA (SAN 254-1068) Tel 410-431-8890; Fax: 410-431-5236
E-mail: towardcure@aol.com
Web site: http://www.mabcie.com.

B3 Publishing, *(0-9767849)* Div. of Dream Believer Factory, Inc., Orders Addr.: P.O. Box 360170, Strongsville, OH 44136 USA; Edit Addr.: 19428 Bennington Dr., Strongsville, OH 44136 USA
Web site: http://www.HaloRepair.com.

Babblins, *(0-9672966)* P.O. Box 351, Big Bend, WI 53103 USA Tel 414-662-0733; Fax: 414-662-4101
E-mail: SBabinat@aol.com.

Babcock Publishing Co., *(1-892161)* P.O. Box 8053, Saginaw, MI 48608 USA Tel 517-781-4830; Fax: 517-781-4610; 3505 Williamson, Saginaw, MI 48601
E-mail: jerrysps@aol.com
Web site: http://www.swiftsite.com/swm0164/books.htm.

Babu Bks., *(0-9722880)* P.O. Box 2449, Woburn, MA 01888-0849 USA
E-mail: ccryan@attbi.com
Web site: http://www.babubooks.com (under construction).

Baby Cat Books, *(0-9779518)* 605 E. 11th St., No. 1D, New York, NY 10009 USA.

Baby Einstein Co., LLC, The, *(1-892309; 1-931580)* Subs. of Walt Disney Productions, 1233 Flower St., Glendale, CA 91201 USA Tel 818-544-4842
E-mail: ellen.portantino@disney.com
Web site: http://www.babyeinstein.com
Dist(s): **Disney Publishing Worldwide**
Hachette Bk. Group
Penton Overseas, Inc.
Right Start, Inc.
Rounder Kids Music Distribution.

Baby Faye Bks. *Imprint of* **Northstar Entertainment Group, LLC**

Baby Hearts Pr., *(0-9652508)* Orders Addr.: 3910 Sierra Blanca, Temple, TX 76502 USA Tel 254-778-4770; Toll Free: 888-222-4649
E-mail: ajaworski@aol.com
Web site: http://www.babyhearts.com.

Baby Matters, Inc., *(1-888509)* 515 W. 29th St., Ground Flr., New York, NY 10001 USA Tel 212-242-7123; Fax: 212-366-9739
E-mail: ari@inch.com
Web site: http://www.inch.com/~ari/bm1.html
Dist(s): **Bookazine Co., Inc.**
Brodart Co.
Professional Media Service Corp.
Rounder Kids Music Distribution.

Baby Music Boom, Inc., *(0-9647786)* Orders Addr.: P.O. Box 62188, Minneapolis, MN 55426 USA Tel 612-470-1667; Fax: 612-474-1297; Toll Free: 888-470-1667; Edit Addr.: 19000 Maple Ln., Deephaven, MN 55331 USA
E-mail: babyboomms@aol.com
Web site: http://www.babymusicboom.com.

Baby School Company, Incorporated, The *See* **So Smart! Productions**

Baby Shadows, *(0-9744928)* 150 W. 56th St., Suite 4410, New York, NY 10019 USA (SAN 255-6367)
Web site: http://www.babyshadows.com.

Baby Shark Productions, *(0-9765125)* 15338 Roberts Ave., Jacksonville, FL 32218-1833 USA Tel 904-751-1564
E-mail: jackbradford90@aol.com
Web site: http://www.gregmoutafis.com.

Baby Star Productions, LLC, *(0-9705974)* 17847 W. Mequon Rd., Germantown, WI 53022 USA Tel 262-628-8939; Fax: 262-628-9647
E-mail: burczyk@execpc.com.

Baby Swan (AUS) *(0-9750325) Dist. by* **Biblio Dist.**

Baby Tattoo Bks., *(0-9729388; 0-9778949; 0-9793307)* 6045 Longridge Ave., Van Nuys, CA 91401 USA (SAN 255-2159) Tel 818-416-5314
E-mail: info@babytatto.com
Web site: http://www.babytattoo.com
Dist(s): **SCB Distributors.**

BabyStar Productions, *(0-9787296)* P.O. Box 1271, Dayton, OH 45401-1271 USA (SAN 851-4585)
E-mail: babystar@hughes.net
Web site: http://www.Latonyabranham.com; http://www.knowyourhistory.com.

Bacchae Pr., *(0-9637849; 1-890767)* c/o The Brown Financial Group, 10 Sixth St., Suite 215, Astoria, OR 97103 USA Tel 503-325-7972; Fax: 503-325-7959; Toll Free: 800-207-4358
E-mail: brown@pacifier.com
Web site: http://www.bacchaepress.com.

Bacchus, Noel Publishing, Inc., *(0-9624192)* 685 West End Ave., New York, NY 10025 USA Tel 212-663-8264
E-mail: jwbacchus@aol.com
Dist(s): **BookMasters, Inc.**

Back Bay *Imprint of* **Little Brown & Co.**

Back Channel Pr., *(0-9767590; 0-9789546; 1-934582)* 170 Mechanic St., Portsmouth, NH 03801 USA Tel 603-436-9485
E-mail: editor@backchannelpress.com
Web site: http://www.backchannelpress.com.

Back Home Industries, *(1-880045)* Orders Addr.: P.O. Box 22495, Milwaukie, OR 97269 USA Tel 503-654-2300; Fax: 503-659-9351; Edit Addr.: 8431 SE 36th Ave., Portland, OR 97222 USA
E-mail: backhome@integrity.com
Web site: http://webs.integrity.com/backhome.

Back In THE BRONX, *(0-9657221)* Orders Addr.: P.O. Box 141H, Scarsdale, NY 10583 USA Tel 914-592-1647; Fax: 914-592-4893; Toll Free: 800-727-6695; Edit Addr.: 40 Herkimer Rd., Scarsdale, NY 10583 USA
E-mail: info@backinthebronx.com
Web site: http://www.backinthebronx.com.

Back River Company, The, LLC, *(0-9672882)* 238 Robinson St. # 13, Wakefield, RI 02879-3549 USA.

Back Stage Bks. *Imprint of* **Watson-Guptill Pubns., Inc.**

Back to the Bible Publishing, *(0-8474)* Orders Addr.: P.O. Box 82808, Lincoln, NE 68501 USA (SAN 211-6901) Tel 402-464-7200; Fax: 402-464-7474; Toll Free: 888-559-7878; Edit Addr.: 6400 Cornhusker Hwy., Lincoln, NE 68507 USA
E-mail: books@backtothebible.org
Web site: http://www.backtothebible.org
Dist(s): **Vision Video.**

Back Yard Pub., *(0-9707560; 1-931934)* Div. of Wensel Enterprises, 7720 N. Moonwind Terr., Dunnellon, FL 34433 USA Tel 352-795-0844; Fax: 352-795-0813
E-mail: wwensel@backyardpublisher.com; wwensel@hughes.net; wensel@hughes.net
Web site: http://www.backyardpublisher.com.

Back2Life, Inc., *(0-9760151)* 8608 N. Richmond Ave., 1st Flr., Kansas City, MO 64157 USA Tel 816-835-4477; Fax: 816-891-7789
E-mail: ckehoe@back2life.us
Web site: http://www.back2life.us.

Back2Life Ministries *See* **Back2Life, Inc.**

Backinprint.com *Imprint of* **iUniverse, Inc.**

Backpack Bowie *See* **Educational Expertise, LLC**

Backroads Pr., *(0-9642371; 0-9724033)* Orders Addr.: P.O. Box 651, Mooresville, IN 46158 USA Tel 317-831-2815 (phone/fax); Edit Addr.: 452 Tulip Dr., Mooresville, IN 46158 USA
E-mail: wend@iquest.net
Web site:
http://www.publishershomepages.com/php/Backroads_Press
Dist(s): **Booksource, The.**

Backwaters Pr., The, *(0-9677149; 0-9726187; 0-9765231; 0-9785782; 0-9793934)* 3502 N. 52nd St., Omaha, NE 68104-3506 USA Tel 402-451-4052
E-mail: gkosmicki@cox.net
Web site: http://www.thebackwaterspress.homestead.com.

Backwoods Books *See* **Shore Pubns.**

Backwoods Publishing Co., *(0-9722501)* Rte. 1, Box 270, Boswell, OK 74727 USA Do not confuse with Backwoods Publishing in Logan, OH.

Backyard Ambassador Reader Publishing Co., *(0-9793808)* 2 New Grant Ct., Columbia, SC 29209 USA
E-mail: cbennett1@sc.rr.com
Web site: http://charleyscolumbiabackyard.com.

BackYard Bks., *(1-891596)* Orders Addr.: P.O. Box 1403, Rockland, ME 04841 USA Tel 207-594-4149; Edit Addr.: P.O. Box 1056, Camden, ME 04843 USA (SAN 299-6774) Tel 207-594-4149; Fax: 207-594-2773; Toll Free Fax: 800-837-0924; Toll Free: 877-669-7233
E-mail: david@imsafe.com; info@imsafe.com
Web site: http://www.imsafe.com
Dist(s): **Baker & Taylor Bks.**

Backyard Pub. Co., Inc., *(0-9646352)* Orders Addr.: P.O. Box 8343, Savannah, GA 31412 USA Tel 912-239-9300; Fax: 912-234-6009; Toll Free: 800-880-0446; Edit Addr.: 219 W. Bryan St., Savannah, GA 31401 USA.

Backyard Scientist, Inc., *(0-9618663; 1-888427)* P.O. Box 16966, Irvine, CA 92623 USA (SAN 219-1725) Tel 714-551-2392; Fax: 714-552-5351
E-mail: backyrdsci@aol.com.

Bad Cat Bks., *(0-9675214)* P.O. Box 1731, Lahaina, HI 96767-1731 USA Tel 808-661-1895; Fax: 808-667-5576
E-mail: badcat@aloha.net
Web site: http://www.surfdowns.com
Dist(s): **Diamond Comic Distributors, Inc.**

Bad Frog Art/SMG Bks, *(0-9795361)* Orders Addr.: 14931 251st Pl. SE, Issaquah, WA 98027 USA
E-mail: steve@badfrogart.com
Web site: www.badfrogart.com.

Bad Publishing, *(0-9765414)* 21522 5th Pl. S., DeMoines, WA 98198 USA Tel 206-824-6106
E-mail: edwardhl@hsd401.org.

BadCoaches, Incorporated *See* **Tony Franklin Cos., The**

Badger Bks., LLC, *(1-878569; 1-932542)* Orders Addr.: 1600 N. High Point Rd., Middleton, WI 53562 USA (SAN 297-9055) Tel 608-231-2556 (phone/fax); Toll Free: 800-928-2372
E-mail: books@badgerbooks.com
Web site: http://www.badgerbooks.com
Dist(s): **Midpoint Trade Bks., Inc.**
Partners Bk. Distributing, Inc.

Badger, David Alan *See* **Mailbox Pr.**

Badger Hse., LLC, *(1-931765)* 1452 Commanche Ave., Green Bay, WI 54313-5938 USA Toll Free Fax: 800-653-5163; Toll Free: 800-242-5585
E-mail: billbadgerhouse@aol.com.

Badgerland Bks. LLC, *(0-9765510)* Orders Addr.: 5407 Marsh Woods Dr., McFarland, WI 53558 USA
E-mail: sales@badgerlandbooks.com; joe_martino@uwbucky.com
Web site: http://www.badgerlandbooks.com; http://www.uwbucky.com.

Badi Publishing Corporation *See* **Changing-Times.net**

Badiru, Adedeji, *(0-9768100)* P.O. Box 31304, Knoxville, TN 37930-1304 USA.

Baen Bks., *(0-671; 1-55594; 0-7434)* Orders Addr.: c/o Simon & Schuster, 200 Old Tappan Rd., Old Tappan, NJ 07675 USA Fax: 800-445-6991; Toll Free: 800-223-2336; Edit Addr.: c/o Simon & Schuster, 1230 Ave. of the Americas, New York, NY 10020 USA (SAN 658-8417) Tel 212-698-7000; Toll Free: 800-223-2348 (customer service)
Web site: http://www.simonsays.com/
Dist(s): **Simon & Schuster**
Simon & Schuster, Inc.

Baggin's Books *See* **Tricorner Publishing**

BAGS' Baseball Co., LLC, *(0-9703780)* Orders Addr.: 3116 Atkins Rd., Mc Graw, NY 13101-9442 USA
E-mail: may@bluefrog.biz
Web site: http://www.bagsbaseball.com.

Baha'i Publishing Trust, U.S., *(0-87743)* 415 Linden Ave., Wilmette, IL 60091 USA
Dist(s): **Baha'i Distribution Service.**

BaHar Publishing, L.C., *(0-9718939)* P.O. Box 2201, Waterloo, IA 50704 USA Toll Free: 888-600-6033
E-mail: PhyllisDamico@AOnePublishing.com
Web site: http://www.baharpublishing.com.

BaHart Pubns. / Eight Legs Publishing, *(0-9760348)* PMB 70, PO Box 7000, Rolling Hills Estates, CA 90274 USA
E-mail: octopusrex@earthlink.net
Web site: http://www.octopusrex.com.

Bailey, Martha, *(0-9786448)* 6882 S. Peaceful Hills Rd., Morrison, CO 80465 USA Tel 303-697-4591 (phone/fax)
E-mail: nebjr@earthlink.net.

Bailey, Richard Harrison The Agency, *(0-9645495)* 121 S. Niles Ave., South Bend, IN 46617 USA Tel 219-287-8333; Fax: 219-287-5333.

Baker Academic, *(0-8010)* Div. of Baker Bk. Hse., Orders Addr.: P.O. Box 6287, Grand Rapids, MI 49516-6287 USA Toll Free Fax: 800-398-3111 (orders only); Toll Free: 800-877-2665 (orders only); Edit Addr.: 6030 Fulton Ave., Ada, MI 49301 USA Tel 616-676-9185; Fax: 616-676-9573
Web site: http://www.bakerbooks.com
Dist(s): **Baker Publishing Group.**

Baker & Taylor Bks., *(0-8480)* Orders Addr.: Commerce Service Ctr., 251 Mt. Olive Church Rd., Commerce, GA 30599-1100 USA (SAN 169-1503) Tel 404-335-5000; Toll Free: 800-775-1200 (customer service); 800-775-1800 (orders); Reno Service Ctr., 1160 Trademark Dr., Suite 111, Reno, NV 89511 (SAN 169-4464) Tel 775-850-3800; Fax: 775-850-3826 (customer service); Toll Free Fax: 800-775-1700 (orders); Edit Addr.: Bridgewater Service Ctr. 1120 US Hwy. 22, E., Bridgewater, NJ 08807-0885 USA (SAN 169-4901) Toll Free: 800-775-1500 (customer service); Momence Service Ctr., 501W. Gladiolus St., Momence, IL 60954-1799 (SAN 169-2100) Tel 815-472-2444 (international customers); Fax: 815-472-9886 (international customers); Toll Free: 800-775-2300 (customer service, academic libraries)
E-mail: btinfo@btol.com
Web site: http://www.btol.com.

Baker Book House, Incorporated *See* **Baker Publishing Group**

Baker Bks., *(0-8010; 0-913686)* Div. of Baker Bk. Hse., Orders Addr.: P.O. Box 6287, Grand Rapids, MI 49516-6287 USA (SAN 299-1500) Toll Free Fax: 800-398-3111 (orders only); Toll Free: 800-877-2665 (orders only); Edit Addr.: 6030 E. Fulton, Ada, MI 49301 USA (SAN 201-4041) Tel 616-676-9185; Fax: 616-676-9573 ; *Imprints:* New Kids Media (New Kids Media)
Web site: http://www.bakerbooks.com
Dist(s): **Baker Publishing Group**
CRC Pubns.
Twentieth Century Christian Bks.

Baker College Publishing Co., *(1-885545)* Div. of Baker College, 1050 W. Bristol Rd., Flint, MI 48507 USA Toll Free: 800-339-9879.

Baker, Helen Interiors, Inc., *(0-9743511)* Orders Addr.: P.O. Box 367, West Harwich, MA 02671 USA Tel 508-432-0287; Fax: 508-430-7744; Edit Addr.: 94 Main St., West Harwich, MA 02671 USA
E-mail: hbunce@attbi.com
Web site: http://www.shoppingthecape.com.

Baker Publishing Group, *(0-8007; 0-8010; 1-58743)* Orders Addr.: P.O. Box 6287, Grand Rapids, MI 49516-6287 USA Tel 616-676-9573; Toll Free Fax: 800-398-3111 (orders only); Toll Free: 800-877-2665 (orders only); Edit Addr.: 6030 E. Fulton, Ada, MI 49301 USA Tel 616-676-9185; Fax: 616-676-9573
Web site: http://www.bakerbooks.com
Dist(s): **Twentieth Century Christian Bks.**

Baker Trittin Concepts *See* **Baker Trittin Pr.**

Baker Trittin Pr., *(0-9729256; 0-9752880; 0-9787316)* P.O. Box 277, Winona Lake, IN 46590-0277 USA ; *Imprints:* Innovative Christian Publications (Innov Chris Pubns); Tweener Press (Tweener Pr)
E-mail: paul@btconcepts.com
Web site: www.bakertrittinpress.com; http://www.gospelstoryteller.com
Dist(s): **STL Distribution North America.**

Baker, Walter H. Company *See* **Baker's Plays**

Baker's Plays, *(0-87440)* Div. of Samuel French, Inc., 45 W. 25th St., New York, NY 10010 USA (SAN 202-3717) Tel 212-255-8085; Fax: 212-627-7754
E-mail: info@bakersplays.com
Web site: http://www.bakersplays.com.

Bakpak Travelers Guide, *(0-9669752; 0-9765910)* 91 A Front St., Nyack, NY 10960-1403 USA (SAN 254-2447)
E-mail: dbarish@bakpakguide.com
Web site: http://www.bakpakguide.com
Dist(s): **Baker & Taylor Bks.**

Balaam Books LLC, *(0-9785585)* 1825 W. Ave., Unit 11, Miami Beach, FL 33139-1441 USA (SAN 850-9972) Tel 305-531-9351; Fax: 305-531-9348
E-mail: Info@BalaamBooks.com
Web site: http://www.BalaamBooks.com.

Balance Bks., Inc., *(0-9743908)* P.O. Box 86, Des Plaines, IL 60016-0086 USA
Web site: http://www.balance-books.com
Dist(s): **Distributors, The.**

Balance Publishing Co., *(1-878298)* 1346 S. Quality Ave., Sanger, CA 93657 USA Tel 559-876-1577 phone/fax Do not confuse with companies with similar names in Naples, FL, Port Charlotte, FL
E-mail: service@balancepublishing.com
Web site: http://www.balancepublishing.com.

Balanced Families, *(0-9759468)* 432 N. 750 E., Lindon, UT 84042 USA Tel 801-380-3247; Fax: 801-785-3938
E-mail: info@starsofthesky.com.

Balanced Systems, Inc., *(0-9760037)* 995 Artdale, White Lake, MI 48383 USA.

Balboa Publishing Corp., *(0-935902)* 1323 San Anselmo Ave., San Anselmo, CA 94960-2244 USA (SAN 220-035X) Tel 415-453-8886; Fax: 415-453-8888
E-mail: shapedown@aol.com
Web site: http://www.just-for-kids.org.

Baldner, Jean V., *(0-9615317)* 1618 Burnett Ave., Ames, IA 50010-5337 USA (SAN 694-6526).

Balhund Entertainment, LLC, *(0-9743277)* 3018 Paulcrest Dr., Los Angeles, CA 90046 USA Tel 323-848-8778
Web site: http://www.magusgame.com.

Ball, Michael, *(0-9765750)* 237 S. Beaumont Ave., Russellville, AR 72801-4624 USA.

Ball Publishing, *(0-9626796; 1-883052)* Orders Addr.: P.O. Box 9, Batavia, IL 60510-0009 USA Tel 630-208-9080; Fax: 630-208-9350; Toll Free Fax: 888-888-0014; Toll Free: 888-888-0013 (U.S. & Canada only); Edit Addr.: 335 N. River St., Batavia, IL 60510 USA
E-mail: info@ballpublishing.com
Web site: http://www.ballbookshelf.com
Dist(s): **Independent Pubs. Group.**

Ball, Rulon Jay *See* **JBall Publishing**

Ballad Productions, *(0-9753663)* Orders Addr.: P.O. Box 4, North Miami Beach, FL 33164 USA Tel 786-285-3619; Edit Addr.: 163rd St., Suite No. 4, North Miami Beach, FL 33164 USA
E-mail: drlaz770@aol.com
Web site: http://www.drlaz.com.

Ballantine Bks. *Imprint of* **Random House Publishing Group**

Ballantine, Robert *See* **P.F.B. Publishing**

Ballard & Tighe Pubs., *(0-937270; 1-55501; 1-59989)* Div. of Educational Ideas, Inc., 480 Atlas St., Brea, CA 92821 USA (SAN 200-7991) Toll Free: 800-321-4332
Web site: http://www.ballard-tighe.com.

Ballenwyck Publishing Corp., *(0-9667780)* 20 Park Ln., E., Suite 8, Albany, NY 12204-1943 USA Tel 518-426-1637.

Ballindalloch Pr., *(1-893832)* Div. of Bananaboat Advertising Graphics, 620 Park St., Baraboo, WI 53913 USA Tel 608-356-1836 (phone/fax)
E-mail: info@ballindalloch-press.com
Web site: http://www.ballindalloch-press.com.

Ballinger Printing & Graphics, *(0-9754957)* 906 Hutchings Ave., Ballinger, TX 76821 USA Tel 325-365-8206; Fax: 325-365-2209; Toll Free: 888-915-8206
E-mail: michael.o.white@att.net.

Balloon Bks. *Imprint of* **Sterling Publishing Co., Inc.**

Balloon Magic, *(1-931084)* 928 W. 20 N., Orem, UT 84057-1918 USA ; *Imprints:* Penny's Publishing (Pennys Pubng)
E-mail: mlh@balloonmagic.com
Web site: http://www.balloonmagic.com.

Ballybunnion Bks., *(0-9726340)* Orders Addr.: P.O. Box 6357, Virginia Beach, VA 23456 USA; Edit Addr.: 833 Maitland Dr., Virginia Beach, VA 23454 USA
Web site: http://www.warrenmurphy.com.

Ballyhoo Books *See* **Ballyhoo BookWorks, Inc.**

Ballyhoo BookWorks, Inc., *(0-936335)* Orders Addr.: P.O. Box 534, Shoreham, NY 11786 USA (SAN 697-8487); Edit Addr.: 1 Sylvan Dr., Wading River, NY 11792 USA (SAN 698-2239) Tel 631-929-8148
E-mail: ballyhoo@optonline.net.

Balogh International, Inc., *(1-878762; 1-891770)* 1911 N. Duncan Rd., Champaign, IL 61822 USA (SAN 297-2344) Tel 217-355-9331; Fax: 217-355-9413
E-mail: balogh@balogh.com
Web site: http://www.balogh.com.

Balogh Scientific Books *See* **Balogh International, Inc.**

Balona Bks., *(0-9765479; 1-934376)* P.O. Box 690106, Stockton, CA 95269-0106 USA
E-mail: author@balona.com; jonathan@balona.com
Web site: http://www.balona.com.

Balticbard Publishing *Imprint of* **Leyva, Barbara**

Baltimore Sun, The, *(0-9649819; 1-893116)* Div. of Tribune Co., 501 N. Calvert St., Baltimore, MD 21278 USA Tel 410-332-6800; Fax: 410-332-6466; Toll Free: 800-829-8000 (ext. 6800)
E-mail: cari.pierce@baltsun.com; sunsource@baltsun.com
Web site: http://www.sunspot.net/sunsource
Dist(s): **Koen-Levy Bk. Wholesalers LLC**
Washington Bk. Distributors.

Balue Fox Publishing Co., *(0-9768663)* P.O. Box 61097, Denver, CO 80206 USA (SAN 257-5442) Tel 303-830-0171
E-mail: joan@peacefinder.com
Web site: http://www.peacefinder.com.

Bamboo Zoo, LLC, *(0-9774493)* 1637 Dahlia St., Denver, CO 80220 USA (SAN 257-5965) Tel 720-323-4955
E-mail: kim@bamboo-zoo.com
Web site: http://www.bamboo-zoo.com.

Banana Bunch Publishing, *(0-9761763)* 2260 Banana St., Saint James City, FL 33956 USA Tel 239-283-9306.

Banana Patch Pr., *(0-9715333; 0-9800063)* Orders Addr.: P.O. Box 950, Hanapepe, HI 96716 USA (SAN 254-3087) Tel 808-335-5944; Fax: 808-335-3830; Toll Free: 800-914-5944
E-mail: carolan@aloha.net
Web site: http://www.bananapatchpress.com
Dist(s): **Booklines Hawaii, Ltd.**
Islander Group.

Banana Peel Bks., *(0-9707509)* 30 River Ct., No. 1601, Jersey City, NJ 07310 USA
Web site: http://www.bananapeelbooks.com.

Bancroft Pr., *(0-9631246; 0-9635376; 1-890862)* P.O. Box 65360, Baltimore, MD 21209-9945 USA Tel 410-358-0658; Fax: 410-764-1967; Toll Free: 800-637-7377 Do not confuse with Bancroft Pr., San Rafael, CA
E-mail: bruceb@bancroftpress.com
Web site: http://www.bancroftpress.com
Dist(s): **Academic Bk. Ctr., Inc.**
Book Hse., Inc., The
Book Wholesalers, Inc.
Brodart Co.
Coutts Library Service, Inc.
Emery-Pratt Co.
Follett Library Resources
Mackin Library Media
Midwest Library Service
Yankee Bk. Peddler, Inc.

Banda Pr. International, Inc., *(0-9773175)* 6050 Stetson Hills Blvd., No. 313, Colorado Springs, CO 80922 USA
Web site: http://www.bandapress.com
Dist(s): **Biblio Distribution.**

Bandai Entertainment, *(1-58354; 1-59409)* Div. of Bandai Entertainment, Inc., 5551 Katella Ave., Cypress, CA 90630 USA Tel 714-816-9760; Fax: 714-816-6708
Web site: http://www.bandaient.com
Dist(s): **Diamond Bk. Distributors.**

B&H Bks. *Imprint of* **B&H Publishing Grp.**

†B&H Publishing Grp., *(0-8054; 0-87981; 1-55819; 1-58640; 0-8400; 1-4336)* Div. of LifeWay Christian Resources of the Southern Baptist Convention, 127 Ninth Ave. North, MSN 114, Nashville, TN 37234 USA (SAN 201-937X) Tel 615-251-2520; Fax: 615-251-5026 (Books Only); 615-251-2036 (Bibles Only); 615-251-2413 (Gifts/Supplies Only); Toll Free: 800-725-5416; 800-251-3225 (retailers); 800-296-4036 (orders/returns); 800-448-8032 (consumers); 800-458-2772 (churches) ; *Imprints:* B&H Books (B&H Bks.)
E-mail: broadmanholman@lifeway.com
Web site: http://www.bhpublishinggroup.com
Dist(s): **Baker & Taylor Bks.**; *CIP.*

Bangzoom Pubs., *(0-9728646; 0-9772927; 0-9779099)* Div. of Bangzoom Software, Inc., 14 Storrs Ave., Braintree, MA 02184 USA (SAN 256-6923) Toll Free: 800-589-7333
Web site: http://www.bangzoom.com
Dist(s): **Blu Sky Media Group.**

Bangzoom Software, Incorporated *See* **Bangzoom Pubs.**

Banis & Associates *See* **Science & Humanities Pr.**

Banks, A J & Associates, Incorporated *See* **BaHar Publishing, L.C.**

Banks Channel Bks., *(0-9635967; 1-889199)* 2314 Waverly Dr., Wilmington, NC 28403 USA Tel 910-762-4677
E-mail: bankschan@ec.rr.com
Dist(s): **Blair, John F. Pub.**

Banner of Truth, The, *(0-85151)* Orders Addr.: P.O. Box 621, Carlisle, PA 17013 USA Tel 717-249-5747; Fax: 717-249-0604; Toll Free: 800-263-8085; Edit Addr.: 63 E. Louther St., Carlisle, PA 17013 USA (SAN 112-1553)
E-mail: info@banneroftruth.org
Web site: http://www.banneroftruth.co.uk
Dist(s): **Spring Arbor Distributors, Inc.**

Bantam *Imprint of* **Bantam Bks.**

Bantam Bks. for Young Readers *Imprint of* **Random Hse. Children's Bks.**

†Bantam Bks., Div. of Bantam Dell Publishing Group, Orders Addr.: 400 Hahn Rd., Westminster, MD 21157 USA Tel 410-848-1900; Toll Free: 800-726-0600; Edit Addr.: 1745 Broadway, New York, NY 10019 USA Tel 212-354-6500, Fax: 212-492-8941; Toll Free Fax: 800-233-3294; Toll Free: 800-223-6834 (Bulk orders); 800-726-0600 (Orders/Customer service) ; *Imprints:* Spectra (Spectra); Bantam Classics (Bantam Classics); Bantam (Bant)
E-mail: bantampublicity@randomhouse.com
Web site: http://www.bantam.com
Dist(s): **Random Hse., Inc.**; *CIP.*

Bantam Classics *Imprint of* **Bantam Bks.**

†Bantam Dell Publishing Group, Div. of Random House, Inc., Orders Addr.: 400 Hahn Rd., Westminster, MD 21157 USA (SAN 201-3983) Tel 410-848-1900; Toll Free: 800-726-0600; Edit Addr.: 1745 Broadway, New York, NY 10019 USA (SAN 201-0097) Tel 212-782-9000; Fax: 212-492-8941
E-mail: bdpublicity@randomhouse.com
Web site: http://www.randomhouse.com/about/contact.html
Dist(s): **Giron Bks.**
Random Hse., Inc.; *CIP.*

Baptist International Missions, Inc. (BIMI), *(0-9641805)* P.O. Box 9215, Chattanooga, TN 37412 USA Tel 423-344-5050; Fax: 423-344-4774.

Baptist Publishing Hse., *(0-89114)* Div. of Baptist Missionary Assn. of America, P.O. Box 7270, Texarkana, TX 75505-7270 USA (SAN 183-6544) Tel 870-772-4550; Fax: 870-772-5451; Toll Free: 800-333-1442
E-mail: info@bph.org; pathway@bph.org
Web site: http://www.bph.org.

Barabara Pr., *(0-9719097)* 5929 S. Kolmar Ave., Chicago, IL 60629 USA Tel 773-735-1176 (phone/fax)
E-mail: captsma@comcast.net
Web site: http://www.barabarapress.com.

Barach Publishing, *(0-9767453)* 900 N. Walnut Creek, Suite 100, No. 280, Mansfield, TX 76063 USA
E-mail: lgonzalez@barachpublishing.com
Web site: http://www.barachpublishing.com.

Barbed Wire Publishing, *(0-9622940; 1-881325; 0-9678566; 0-9711930; 0-9723032)* 400 S. Compress Rd. Ste. D, Las Cruces, NM 88005-2772 USA Toll Free: 888-817-1990
E-mail: mschuster@barbed-wire.net
Web site: http://www.barbed-wire.net.

Barber, Mark D., *(0-9703731)* 538 Leta Ave., Flint, MI 48507 USA
E-mail: barbermk@hotmail.com
Web site: http://www.friendshipkeepers.com; http://www.friendshipkeeper.com.

Barbour & Company, Incorporated *See* **Barbour Publishing, Inc.**

Barbour Bks. *Imprint of* **Barbour Publishing, Inc.**

Barbour Publishing, Inc., *(0-916441; 1-55748; 1-57748; 1-58660; 1-59310; 1-59789; 1-60260)* Orders Addr.: P.O. Box 719, Uhrichsville, OH 44683 USA (SAN 295-7094) Tel 740-922-6045; Fax: 740-922-5948; Toll Free Fax: 800-220-5948; Toll Free: 800-852-8010 ; *Imprints:* Barbour Books (Barbour Bks)
E-mail: info@barbourbooks.com
Web site: http://www.barbourbooks.com
Dist(s): **Anchor Distributors**
Appalachian Bk. Distributors
Baker & Taylor Bks.
Spring Arbor Distributors, Inc.

Company

Barcelona Pubs., *(0-9624080; 1-891278)* Orders Addr.: 4 White Brook Rd., Lower Village, Gilsum, NH 03448 USA (SAN 298-6299) Tel 603-357-0236; Fax: 603-357-2073; Toll Free: 800-345-6665
E-mail: barcelonapublishers@comcast.net; pbs@pathwaybook.com
Web site: http://www.barcelonapublishers.com
Dist(s): **Pathway Bk. Service**
West Music Co.

Barcharts, Inc., *(1-57222; 1-4232)* 6000 Park of Commerce, Blvd. D, Boca Raton, FL 33487-8230 USA (SAN 299-5026) Tel 561-989-3666 ext.3054; Fax: 561-989-3722; Toll Free: 800-226-7799
E-mail: jmijares@barcharts.com
Web site: http://www.quickstudycharts.com.

Bard College Pubns. Office, *(0-941276; 1-931493)* Annandale Rd., Annandale-on-Hudson, NY 12504-5000 USA Tel 845-758-7872 (7418); Fax: 845-758-7554 ; *Imprints:* Center for Curatorial Studies (Ctr Curatorial Studies)
E-mail: rosasco@bard.edu; info@levy.org
Web site: http://www.levy.org; http://www.bard.edu
Dist(s): **D.A.P./Distributed Art Pubs.**

Bard, Frank, *(0-9767098)* Orders Addr.: 3801 Corbett Rd., North Lewisburg, OH 43060-9616 USA Tel 937-869-0235
E-mail: fbard@ctcn.net
Web site: http://www.ctcn.net/~febard.

Bardic Pr., *(0-9745667)* P.O. Box 761, Oregon House, CA 95962-0761 USA Tel 539-692-1180
E-mail: info@bardic-press.com; andrew@bardic-press.com
Web site: http://www.bardic-press.com.

Bardin & Marsee Publishing, *(0-9770169; 0-9792394)* 1112 N. Shadesview Ter, Birmingham, AL 35209 USA (SAN 854-6215) Tel 205-453-4361; Fax: 404-474-3086; Toll Free: 866-846-4338
E-mail: bobby@bardinmarseepublishing.com
Web site: http://www.bardinmarseepublishing.com.

BareBones Publishing, *(0-9779601)* Mountain View Drive Apt. 106 C Mt. View Apartments, Springfield, VT 05156 USA
Web site: http://www.tastethebook.com; http://www.nightairstudios.com.

Barefoot Bks., Inc., *(1-84148; 1-898000; 1-901223; 1-902283; 1-905236)* Orders Addr.: 2067 Mass Ave., 5th Fl., Cambridge, MA 02140 USA Tel 866-417-2369; Fax: 888-346-9138
E-mail: ussales@barefootbooks.com
Web site: http://www.barefootbooks.com
Dist(s): **Banta Packaging & Fulfillment.**

Barefoot Pr., *(1 882133)* Orders Addr.: P.O. Box 28514, Raleigh, NC 27611 USA (SAN 248-5656) Tel 919-834-1164; Edit Addr.: 700 W. Morgan St., Raleigh, NC 27603 USA (SAN 248-5664).

Barker Business Bks., Inc., *(0-9659606)* 4000 Town Ctr. Ste. 1750, Southfield, MI 48075-1411 USA
E-mail: jcap@caponigro.com
Dist(s): **Quality Bks., Inc.**
Unique Bks., Inc.

Barker Creek Publishing, Inc., *(0-9639307; 1-928961)* Orders Addr.: P.O. Box 2610, Poulsbo, WA 98370 USA (SAN 298-4628) Tel 360-692-5833; Fax: 360-613-2542; Toll Free: 800-692-5833
E-mail: marketing@barkercreek.com
Web site: http://www.barkercreek.com
Dist(s): **Appalachian Bk. Distributors**
Baker & Taylor Bks.
Koen-Levy Bk. Wholesalers LLC.

Barker, Lesley, *(0-9763211)* 12027 Charter Oak Pkwy., Saint Louis, MO 63146 USA
E-mail: asklesley@teamlesley.com
Web site: http://www.teamlesley.com.

Barksdale Hse. Pr., *(0-9703570)* 1 Tradd St., Charleston, SC 29401 USA Tel 843-722-3508
E-mail: hpgw@duke.edu
Dist(s): **Saturday Shop.**

Barmarle Pubns., *(0-9619463)* 735 Nardo Rd., Encinitas, CA 92024 USA (SAN 245-0070) Tel 760-753-6950.

Barn Owl Bks, London (GBR) *(1-903015) Dist. by* **IPG Chicago.**

Barnaby & Co., *(0-9642836)* P.O. Box 3198, Nantucket, MA 02584 USA Tel 508-228-5114; Fax: 508-325-0011
E-mail: barnaby@nantucket.net
Web site: http://www.barnabybear.com.

Barnaby Books *See* **Barnaby & Co.**

Company

Barnes & Noble, Inc., *(0-7607; 0-88029; 1-4028; 1-4351)* 122 Fifth Ave., New York, NY 10011 USA (SAN 141-3651) Tel 212-633-3300
E-mail: smcculloch@bn.com
Dist(s): **Bookazine Co., Inc.**
Sterling Publishing Co., Inc.

Barnesyard Bks., *(0-9674681)* P.O. Box 254, Sergeantsville, NJ 08557 USA Tel 609-397-6600; Fax: 609-397-3262
E-mail: info@barnesyardbooks.com
Web site: http://www.barnesyardbooks.com.

Barnett Educational Supplies, Inc., *(1-892250)* Orders Addr.: P.O. Box 22626, Savannah, GA 31403-2626 USA Tel 912-356-1878; Fax: 912-356-1808; Edit Addr.: 38 W. DeRenne Ave., Savannah, GA 31405 USA.

Barnette, Donald, *(0-9747816)* 591 Mira Vista Ave., Oakland, CA 94610-1928 USA.

Barney Publishing *See* **Lyrick Publishing**

Barnhardt & Ashe Publishing, Inc., *(0-9715402)* 444 Brickell Ave., Sutie 51, PMB 432, Miami, FL 33131-2492 USA Tel 410-707-6686; Toll Free: 800-283-6360
E-mail: barnhardtashe@aol.com
Web site: http://www.barnhardtashepublishing.com.

Barren Hill Bks., *(0-9769896)* 646 Highland Ave., South Portland, ME 04106 USA Tel 207-767-3268
E-mail: info@BarrenHillBooks.com
Web site: http://www.barrenhillbooks.com/.

Barrett Kendall Publishing, Ltd., *(1-58079; 1-889105)* Orders Addr.: P.O. Box 685168, Austin, TX 78768 USA; Edit Addr.: 9600 Great Hills Trl. Ste. 150W, Austin, TX 78759-6303 USA Toll Free: 800-677-3796
E-mail: sales@bkschoolhouse.com
Web site: barrettkendall.com
Dist(s): **Addison-Wesley Educational Pubs., Inc.**

Barrett's Bookshelf, *(0-9728731)* 16165 SW Inverurie Rd., Lake Oswego, OR 97035 USA Tel 503-697-4208.

Barrick, Sheila, *(0-9713414)* 1520 Delmont Dr., Raleigh, NC 27606 USA Tel 919-851-0330; Fax: 919-821-0998
E-mail: revbarrick@aol.com; donatojack@aol.com.

Barricks, Jeri Ministry, *(0-9743512)* P.O. Box 347, Buffalo, NY 14225 USA Fax: 716-685-6839
E-mail: jeribar37@hotmail.com
Web site: http://www.jeribarricks.net.

†Barron's Educational Series, Inc., *(0-7641; 0-8120)* Orders Addr.: 250 Wireless Blvd., Hauppauge, NY 11788-3917 USA (SAN 201-453X) Fax: 631-434-3723; 631-434-8067 (Sales Dept. Orders); Toll Free: 800-645-3476 (ext. 204 or 214 for Orders); a/o Georgetown Book Warehouse, 34 Armstrong Ave., Georgetown, ON L7G 4R9 (SAN 115-2033) Tel 905-458-5506; Fax: 905-877-5575; Toll Free Fax: 800-887-1594 Do not confuse with BARRONS, Monroe, WA
E-mail: barrons@barronseduc.com; info@barronseduc.com; orders@barronseduc.com
Web site: http://www.barronseduc.com
Dist(s): **NetLibrary, Inc.**; *CIP.*

Barsotti Bks., *(0-9642112)* 2239 Hidden Valley Ln., Camino, CA 95709-9722 USA Tel 530-622-4629; Fax: 530-642-9703
E-mail: jb@barsottibooks.com
Web site: http://www.barsottibooks.com
Dist(s): **Baker & Taylor Bks.**

Bartels, Christopher J., *(0-9715734)* 2978 Mildred Dr., Saint Paul, MN 55113 USA.

Barth Family Ministries, *(0-9624067; 1-891484)* 339 Parkhill Rd., Cornwall, VT 05753 USA Tel 802-462-2002; Fax: 802-462-2001.

Bartleby Pr., *(0-910155; 0-935437)* 9045 Maier Rd. Suite D, Silver Spring, MD 20823 USA (SAN 241-2098) Tel 301-949-2443; Fax: 301-949-2205; Toll Free: 800-953-9929
E-mail: Inquiries@bartlebythepublisher.com
Web site: http://www.BartlebythePublisher.com.

Bartlett Publishing, *(1-891210)* P.O. Box 56597, Sherman Oaks, CA 91413 USA Fax: 818-988-8376; Toll Free: 800-553-2061 Do not confuse with Bartlett Publishing in Broken Arrow, OK
E-mail: skreng@aol.com
Web site: http://members.aol.com/skreng.

Barton, D.C. Publishing, *(0-9759426)* P.O. Box 3057, Lakeland, FL 33801-6602 USA Tel 863-665-5986
E-mail: dfcbible@aol.com.

Bas Relief Publishing, *(0-9657472)* Orders Addr.: P.O. Box 645, Union, WV 24983 USA Tel 304-832-6647
E-mail: Barea@basrelief.org
Web site: http://www.basrelief.org.

Base Of The Bays, *(0-9708925)* 3301 Veterans Dr., Suite 213, Traverse City, MI 49684 USA Tel 231-929-3278; Fax: 231-929-5226.

Bases Loaded Bks. *Imprint of* **ChildrenzBks.**

†Basic Bks., *(0-201; 0-465; 0-7382)* A Member of Perseus Books Group, Orders Addr.: 5500 Central Ave., Boulder, CO 80301-2877 USA Fax: 303-449-3356 (customer service); Toll Free: 800-371-1669 (customer service); Edit Addr.: 387 Park Ave., S., New York, NY 10016 USA (SAN 201-4521) Tel 212-340-8100; Fax: 212-340-8135 ; *Imprints:* Nation Books (NationBks)
E-mail: perseus.orders@perseusbooks.com
Web site: http://www.perseusbooksgroup.com; http://www.perseusbooksgroup.com/basic/home.jsp
Dist(s): **Perseus Bks. Group**
Perseus Distribution; *CIP.*

Basic Educational Materials, Pubs., *(1-58532)* P.O. Box 36998, Rock Hill, SC 29732 USA Tel 803-327-9396; Fax: 803-329-1284
E-mail: bskarlinski@yahoo.com
Web site: http://www.bempub.com.

Basic Foundation Pr., *(0-9703205)* 1140 Hidden Oaks Dr., Menlo Park, CA 94025 USA Tel 650 328 7882; 650-328-7882
E-mail: kenemccarthy@mindspring.com
Web site: http://www.whythomascanread.com.

Basic Health Pubns., Inc., *(1-59120)* 28812 Top of the World Dr., Laguna Beach, CA 92651 USA Tel 949-715-7327; Fax: 949-415-7328; Toll Free: 800-575-8890 (orders only)
E-mail: ngoldfind@basicmediagroup.com
Web site: http://www.basichealthpub.com.

Basic Knowledge Publishing Co., *(1-885501)* 1024 Debbie Ln., Maryville, MO 64468 USA Tel 816-562-2665.

Basic Skills Assessment & Educational Services, *(1-888786)* 19146 S. Molalla Ave., Oregon City, OR 97045-8975 USA Tel 503-650-5282; Fax: 503-557-2953
E-mail: basicsk@MSN.COM
Web site: http://www.basicskills.net.

Baskerville Publishing *See* **Hound Pr.**

Basketball Fundamentals *See* **SportAmerica**

Bass Cove Bks., *(0-9630074)* 57 North St., Kennebunkport, ME 04046 USA Tel 207-967-4152
E-mail: amabee@adelphia.net.

Bass, Sheila, *(0-9766366)* 23 Conn. St., Woodsville, NH 03785 USA
E-mail: a_15bass@yahoo.com.

Bassan, Malca, *(0-9744039)* 9801 Collins Ave., Apt. 15Q, Bal Harbor, FL 33154 USA Tel 305-868-0365; Fax: 305-865-6992
E-mail: malcabass@hotmail.com.

Basswood Bks., *(0-9658455)* P.O. Box 23, Neenah, WI 54957-0023 USA (SAN 299-3600) Tel 920-725-9835 (phone/fax); Toll Free: 800-485-8719
E-mail: generalmanager@basswoodbooks.com
Web site: http://www.basswoodbooks.com
Dist(s): **Baker & Taylor Bks.**

Bastion Pr., Inc., *(0-9714392; 1-59263)* Orders Addr.: P.O. Box 46753, Seattle, WA 98146 USA; Edit Addr.: 8405 16th Ave., SW., Seattle, WA 98106-2365 USA Tel 206-763-3368; Fax: 206-763-3370 Do not confuse with Bastion Pr., Los Angeles, CA
E-mail: jim@bastionpress.com
Web site: http://www.bastionpress.com.

Bastos Bk. Co., *(1-883514)* Div. of Bastos Educational Group, Orders Addr.: P.O. Box 770-433, Woodside, NY 11377 USA (SAN 630-9291) Tel 718-997-7661; Fax: 718-997-6445; Toll Free: 800-662-0301; Edit Addr.: 66-32 Wetherole St., Forest Hills, NY 11374 USA
E-mail: bastos@bastosbooks.com
Web site: http://www.bastosbooks.com.

Bat Conservation International, Inc., *(0-9638248; 0-9742379)* Orders Addr.: P.O. Box 162603, Austin, TX 76716 USA Tel 512-327-9721; Fax: 512-327-9724; Edit Addr.: 500 N. Capital of Texas Hwy., N., Bldg. 1, Suite 100, Austin, TX 76716 USA
E-mail: pubs@batcon.org
Web site: http://www.batcon.org/
Dist(s): **Big Kids Productions, Inc.**
Univ. of Texas Pr.

Bat Wing Pr *Imprint of* **Harbor Hse.**

Bateman Pr., *(0-9665317)* 401 Cape Cod, Corpus Christi, TX 78412 USA Tel 512-993-8003; Fax: 512-993-3406.

Batfish Bks., *(0-9728653)* Div. of O'Neill, Michael P. Photography, Inc., P.O. Box 32909, Palm Beach Gardens, FL 33420-2909 USA (SAN 255-1780) Tel 305-333-7166; Fax: 561-840-1939
E-mail: mpo@msn.com
Web site: http://www.batfishbooks.com
Dist(s): **Baker & Taylor Bks.**
Southern Bk. Service.

†Battelle Pr., *(0-935470; 1-57477)* Div. of Battelle Memorial Institute, 505 King Ave., Columbus, OH 43201-2693 USA (SAN 213-4640) Tel 614-424-6393; Fax: 614-424-3819; Toll Free: 800-451-3543
E-mail: press@battelle.org
Web site: http://www.battelle.org/bookstore
Dist(s): **Univ. of Washington Pr.**
Univelt, Inc.; *CIP.*

Battle Creek Area Mathematics & Science Ctr., *(1-933281)* 765 Upton Ave., Battle Creek, MI 49015 USA Tel 269-965-9440
Web site: http://bcmsc.k12.mi.us.

Battler Pr., The, *(0-9678217)* 515 N. Bromley Ave., Scranton, PA 18504 USA.

Batyah & Assocs. Publishing, *(0-9749571)* P.O. Box 14756, Detroit, MI 48214 USA Fax: 313-822-2755
E-mail: alwaysbatyah@batyah.net.

Batyah Productions, Inc., *(0-9649608)* 6434 Saxet St., Houston, TX 77055-5317 USA.

BAU PUBLISHING GROUP, *(0-9766770)* 1201 Shakespeare Ave., Suite 1B, Bronx, NY 10452 USA
E-mail: tize@tize.biz; bau@baupublishinggroup.com
Web site: http://www.baupublishinggroup.com.

Baugrud, Kim, *(0-9715922)* 3435 Ascot Dr., Racine, WI 53406-5203 USA Tel 262-554-8995
E-mail: baugrud@asapnet.net
Web site: http://uwm.edu./~baugrud.

Baxter & Friends, *(0-9715864)* 3 Orchard Heights Rd., Essex, CT 06426 USA Tel 860-767-0246
Web site: http://www.baxterandfriends.com.

Baxter, Jason *See* **Morris Publishing**

Baxter Pr., *(1-888237)* 700 S. Friendswood Dr., Suite C, Friendswood, TX 77546 USA Tel 281-992-0628; Fax: 815-572-5115
E-mail: baxter2@flash.net
Web site: http://baxterpress.com
Dist(s): **Spirit Rising.**

Bay Area Explorers, *(0-9615635)* P.O. Box 519, San Ramon, CA 94583 USA (SAN 696-0782) Tel 510-828-4957.

Bay Books & Tapes, Incorporated *See* **Bay Soma Publishing**

Bay Horse Creations LLC, *(0-9749320)* 508 W. Irvine Rd., Phoenix, AZ 85086 USA Tel 602-818-7879
Web site: http://www.bayhorsecreations.com.

Bay Light Publishing, *(0-9670280; 0-9741817)* P.O. Box 3032, Mooresville, NC 28117 USA (SAN 299-9196) Tel 704-664-7541; Fax: 704-664-2712; Toll Free: 866-541-3895
E-mail: baylightpub@compuserve.com
Web site: http://www.baylightpub.com.

Bay Media, Inc., *(0-9665239; 0-9717047)* Orders Addr.: 550m Ritchie Hwy., #271 Severna Pk., Md 21146, Severna Park, MD 21146 USA Tel 410-647-8402; Fax: 410-544-4640
Web site: http://www.baymed.com.

Bay Mills Indian Community, *(0-9758801)* 12140 W. Lakeshore Dr., Brimley, MI 49715 USA
Web site: http://www.bmic.net.

Bay Oak Pubs., Ltd., *(0-9704692; 0-9741713; 0-9800874)* 34 Wimbledon Dr., Dover, DE 19904 USA Tel 302-674-5650 (phone/fax)
E-mail: bayoakpublishers@aol.com
Web site: http://www.bayoakpublishers@aol.com
Dist(s): **Washington Bk. Distributors.**

Bay Otter Pr., *(0-9778961)* Div. of New Spectrum, Inc, P.O. Box 20492, Palo Alto, CA 94309-0492 USA
Dist(s): **Independent Pubs. Group.**

Bay Shore Books *See* **Micah Publishing**

Bay Soma Publishing, *(0-912333; 1-57959)* Div. of Windmere Durable Holdings, Inc., 444 DeHaro St., Suite 130, San Francisco, CA 94107 USA (SAN 265-1246)
E-mail: info@baybooks.com
Web site: http://www.baybooks.com.

Bay Tree Enterprises, *(0-9701497)* 9360 Tonto Dr., Crystal River, FL 34428 USA Tel 352-795-7205
E-mail: maranda@citrus.infi.net.

Bay Villager, The, *(0-9769742)* 4923 43rd. St., Dickinson, TX 77539 USA
E-mail: lindalou36@hotmail.com.

Bayard Editions (FRA) *(2-227; 2-7009; 2-7470; 2-915480; 2-9518356) Dist. by* **Distribks Inc.**

Bayfield Street Publishing, Inc., *(0-9670683)* 405 W. Fifth St., Washburn, WI 54891 USA Tel 715-373-1040; Fax: 715-373-1080
E-mail: baypub@cheeq.net.net
Dist(s): **F & W Pubns., Inc.**

Bayliss, Erin, *(0-9778471)* 320 Roan Dr., Grants Pass, OR 97526 USA.

Baylor College of Medicine, *(1-888997)* Div. of Center for Educational Outreach, Orders Addr.: c/o Ctr. For Educational Outreach, One Baylor Plaze, Ms:Bcm411, Houston, TX 77030 USA Tel 713-798-8200; Fax: 713-798-8201; Toll Free: 800-798-8244 ; *Imprints:* BioEd (BioEd)
E-mail: edoutreach@bcm.tmc.edu
Web site: http://www.ccit.bcm.tmc.edu/ceo/; http://www.bcm.edu; http://www.bioedonline.org.

Bayou Publishing, *(1-886298)* 2524 Nottingham, Houston, TX 77005 USA Tel 713-526-4558; Fax: 713-526-4342; Toll Free: 800-340-2034 Do not confuse with Bayou Publishing, Longboat Key, FL
E-mail: info@bayoupublishing.com; orders@bayoupublishing.com; vloos@bayoupublishing.com
Web site: http://www.bayoupublishing.com
Dist(s): **Biblio Distribution**
Quality Bks., Inc.
Unique Bks., Inc.

Bayport Pr. *Imprint of* **Wellness Pubn.**

Bayshore Publishing Group, *(1-929727)* Div of Bayshore Publishing Group, Inc., Orders Addr.: P.O. Box 346, Pensacola, FL 32592-0346 USA Tel 850-434-1122; Fax: 850-434-2206; Edit Addr.: P.O. Box 346, Pensacola, FL 32591-0346 USA
E-mail: bayshore@pcola.gulf.net
Web site: http://bayshorepublishing.com.

†Baywood Publishing Co., Inc., *(0-89503)* 26 Austin Ave., P.O. Box 337, Amityville, NY 11701 USA (SAN 206-9326) Tel 631-691-1270; Fax: 631-691-1770; Toll Free: 800-638-7819 (orders only)
E-mail: baywood@baywood.com; info@baywood.com
Web site: http://baywood.com; *CIP.*

bazow, thomas, *(0-9777725)* 4845 Romaine Spring Dr., Fenton, MO 63026-5840 USA
Web site: http://www.inhistimepublishing.com.

Bazuji Publishing LLC, *(0-9761555)* 3843 53rd St., SE, Tappen, ND 58487 USA (SAN 256-2626) Toll Free: 800-615-7606
Web site: http://www.bazuji.com.

BB International Productions, Inc., *(0-9754329)* 1200 W. Ave., Suite 707, Miami Beach, FL 33139-4316 USA
Web site: http://www.bibiadventures.com.

BBC Audio (GBR) *(0-563; 0-7540; 1-84440; 1-4056; 1-84607) Dist. by* **BBC Audiobks.**

†BBC Audiobooks America, *(0-563; 0-7540; 0-7927; 0-89340; 1-55504; 1-60283)* Orders Addr.: P.O. Box 414190, Boston, MA 02241-4190 USA (SAN 208-4864) Tel 603-926-8744; Fax: 603-929-3890; Toll Free Fax: 877-492-0873; Toll Free: 800-621-0182; c/o Perseus, 1094 Flex Dr., Jackson, TN 38301; Edit Addr.: 42 Whitecap Dr., North Kingstown, RI 02852-7445 USA Toll Free: 800-621-0182 ; *Imprints:* Gunsmoke (Gunsmoke); Galaxy Children's Large Print (Galaxy Child Lrg Print); Chivers Children's Audio Books (Chivers Child Audio)
E-mail: vikkiwarner@bbcaudiobooksamerica.com
Web site: http://www.bbcaudiobooksamerica.com
Dist(s): **Perseus Distribution**; *CIP.*

BBC Worldwide (GBR) *(0-563) Dist. by* **Diamond Book Dists.**

BBC Worldwide Americas, *(0-563; 1-882335)* Subs. of BBC Enterprises, Inc., 747 Third Ave., 6th Flr., New York, NY 10017 USA Tel 212-705-9300; Fax: 212-888-0576; Toll Free Fax: 800-216-1222
Dist(s): **Diamond Bk. Distributors**
Diamond Distributors, Inc.
London Bridge
Trafalgar Square Publishing.

BBI Incorporated *See* **Bush Brothers & Co.**

BBM Pr., *(0-9722872)* P.O. Box 415, Carson City, NV 89702 USA Tel 775-883-4628 (phone/fax)
Dist(s): **AtlasBooks Distribution.**

BBR *Imprint of* **BBR: Books for Brilliance & Resilience**

BBR: Books for Brilliance & Resilience, *(0-9753245)* P.O. Box 5236, Takoma Park, MD 20913-5236 USA Toll Free: 888-898-2322 ; *Imprints:* BBR (B B R)
Web site: http://www.letscommunicate.org.

BBRACK Productions, Inc., *(0-9728837)* 1345-B Triad Ctr. Dr., No. 181, Saint Peters, MO 63376 USA Tel 636-936-2311
E-mail: 1stB@bbrack.com
Web site: http://www.bbrack.com.

BBS Publishing Corp., *(0-88365; 0-88394; 0-88486; 1-57866)* 252 W. 38th St., New York, NY 10018 USA (SAN 853-9529) Tel 212-842-0700; Fax: 212-842-1771 ; *Imprints:* Galahad Books (Galah Bks); Arrowood Press (Arrow Pr)
Dist(s): **Sterling Publishing Co., Inc.**

BC Publishing, *(0-9740511)* 633-1 Elk Ct., Fayetteville, NC 28301 USA Tel 910-578-2621 ; *Imprints:* Kids1st Books (Kids1st Bks) Do not confuse with BC Publishing in Tampa, FL
E-mail: dbradleyclarke@yahoo.com.

B-Dock Pr., *(0-9621728)* Orders Addr.: P.O. Box 8, Willingboro, NJ 08046 USA (SAN 252-1962); Edit Addr.: 16 Meadowbrook Pl., Willingboro, NJ 08046 USA (SAN 252-1970) Tel 609-877-6018.

Be A Dreamer Pubs., *(0-9628539)* Div. of Be A Dreamer Productions, Inc., P.O. Box 892, Riverview, FL 33568 USA Tel 813-238-5071
E-mail: info@beadreamer.com.

Be A Polyglot, Incorporated *See* **Sound Beginnings**

Be Family Bks., *(0-9728554)* 4011 Windward Dr., Fort Pierce, FL 34949 USA.

Be Sweet Pubns., Inc., *(0-9709105; 0-9796691)* 686 Ray Lively Rd., Collins, GA 30421 USA Tel 912-684-3716; Fax: 912-684-3307; Toll Free: 866-227-0653
E-mail: palex52@hotmail.com; ruby@besweetpublications.com.

Beach Front Bks., *(0-9651281)* P.O. Box 545, East Bridgewater, MA 02333 USA Tel 508-378-9319; Fax: 508-378-7621 Do not confuse with Beach Front Books in East Bridgewater, MA
E-mail: beachfrontbooks@aol.com.

Beach Lloyd Pubs., LLC, *(0-9743158; 0-9792778)* Orders Addr.: P.O. Box 2183, Southeastern, PA 19399-2183 USA (SAN 255-4992) Tel 610-407-0130; Fax: 775-254-0633; Toll Free: 866-218-3253; Edit Addr.: 40 Cabot Dr., Wayne, PA 19087-5619 USA
E-mail: beachlloyd@erols.com
Web site: http://www.beachlloyd.com
Dist(s): **Baker & Taylor Bks.**
MBS Textbook Exchange, Inc.

Beacham Publishing Corp., *(0-933833)* P.O. Box 830, Osprey, FL 34229-0830 USA (SAN 692-8730) Tel 941-480-9644; Fax: 941-485-5322; Toll Free: 800-466-9644
E-mail: beachampub@aol.com
Web site: http://www.beachampublishing.com
Dist(s): **Thomson Gale.**

Beachfront Publishing, *(1-892339)* Div. of Words, Words, Words, Inc., Orders Addr.: P.O. Box 811922, Boca Raton, FL 33481 USA
E-mail: info@beachfrontentertainment.com
Web site: http://www.beachfrontentertainment.com
Dist(s): **Biblio Distribution.**

BeachHouse Bks. *Imprint of* **Science & Humanities Pr.**

Beachhouse Publishing, LLC, *(0-9729905; 1-933067)* P.O. Box 2926, Ewa Beach, HI 96706-0926 USA
E-mail: beachhousepub@hawaii.rr.com
Dist(s): **Booklines Hawaii, Ltd.**
Islander Group.

BeachWalk Bks. Inc., *(0-9770158)* P.O. Box 446, Glenview, IL 60025 USA Tel 847-729-2222; Fax: 847-729-5215; Toll Free Fax: 866-720-3222; 2136 Fir St., Glenview, IL 60025
E-mail: amcdonald@beachwalkbooks.com
Web site: http://www.beachwalkbooks.com.

Beachwalker Pr., *(0-9727639)* 5557 SW Village Pl., Beaverton, OR 97007 USA Tel 503-799-6061; Fax: 503-644-9335
E-mail: beachwalkerpress@aol.com
Web site: http://www.beachwalkerpress.com.

Beachway Pr., *(1-882997)* Orders Addr.: P.O. Box 5981, Charlottesville, VA 22903 USA Tel 804-245-6800; Fax: 804-297-0569; Edit Addr.: 300 W Main St., Suite A, Charlottesville, VA 22903 USA
E-mail: scotta@beachway.com
Web site: http://www.beachway.com.

Beacon Hill Pr. of Kansas City, *(0-8341)* Div. of Nazarene Publishing Hse., 2923 Troost, Kansas City, MO 64109 USA (SAN 241-6328) Tel 816-931-1900; Fax: 816-753-4071; Toll Free: 800-877-0700 (orders only)
E-mail: nphdirect@nph.com; orders@nph.com; inquiry@bhillkc.com
Web site: http://www.nph.com; http://www.bhillkc.com.

Beacon Pr., *(0-8070)* 25 Beacon St., Boston, MA 02108-2892 USA (SAN 201-4483) Tel 617-742-2110; Fax: 617-723-3097
Web site: http://www.beacon.org
Dist(s): **Continental Bk. Co., Inc.**
Houghton Mifflin Co. Trade & Reference Div.
NetLibrary, Inc.

Beacon Street Girls *Imprint of* **B*tween Productions, Inc.**

Bead Man Pr., *(0-9663591)* P.O. Box 1423, Cannon Beach, OR 97110-1423 USA
E-mail: JDWilkens@aol.com
Dist(s): **Beadsmith, The/Helby Import Co.**

Beagle Bay Bks., *(0-9679591; 0-9749610)* Div. of Beagle Bay, Inc., 14120 Saddlebow Dr., Reno, NV 89511 USA Tel 775-827-8654; Fax: 775-827-8633
E-mail: info@beaglebay.com
Web site: http://www.beaglebay.com
Dist(s): **Baker & Taylor Bks.**
Brodart Co.

Bean Bk. Publishing, *(0-9761990)* 9246 E. Havasupai Dr., Scottsdale, AZ 85255 USA Tel 480-502-1257 (phone/fax)
E-mail: dawn.crichton@dcranch.com; Juliecrichton@cox.net
Web site: http://www.stringbeansorjellybeans.com; http://www.bean-books.com.

Bean Sprouts *Imprint of* **Standard Publishing**

Beanstalk Pubns, *(0-9785302)* 4762 Camino del Rey, Santa Barbara, CA 93110 USA Tel 805-448-0898
E-mail: mjmckechnie@beanstalkpublications.com
Web site: http://www.beanstalkpublications.com.

Bear & Co. *Imprint of* **Bear & Co.**

†Bear & Co., *(0-939680; 1-879181; 1-59143)* Orders Addr.: P.O. Box 388, Rochester, VT 05767-0388 USA; Edit Addr.: One Park St., Rochester, VT 05767 USA (SAN 216-7174) Tel 802-767-3174; Fax: 802-767-3726; Toll Free: 800-246-8648 ; *Imprints:* Bear Cub Books (Bear Cub Books); Bear & Company (Bear & Company)
E-mail: customerservice@innertraditions.com; info@innertraditions.com
Web site: http://www.innertraditions.com
Dist(s): **Baker & Taylor Bks.**
Book Wholesalers, Inc.
Bookazine Co., Inc.
Brodart Co.
Inner Traditions International, Ltd.
Integral Yoga Pubns.
New Leaf Distributing Co., Inc.
Nutri-Bks. Corp.
Partners Pubs. Group, Inc.
Partners/West
Phoenix Distributors
Quality Bks., Inc.
Ten Speed Pr.; *CIP.*

Bear & Company *See* **Boyds Collection Ltd., The**

Bear Cub Bks. *Imprint of* **Bear & Co.**

Bear Hug Bks. *Imprint of* **MidAmerica Publishing Co.**

Bear Hug Pr., *(0-9713567)* 111 Stark Hwy., S., Dunbarton, NH 03046 USA Fax: 603-774-7814
E-mail: bearhugpress@aol.com.

Bear Lake Publishing, *(0-9661132)* 201 Harrison St., Geneva, IL 60555 USA Tel 630-836-0127 (phone/fax); 31914 Village Green Blvd., Warrenville, IL 60555
E-mail: Blpub@aol.com.

Bear Path, The, *(0-9652211; 1-891317)* 3335 W. Desert Bend Loop, Tucson, AZ 85742-9382 USA Tel 520-744-6799.

Bear Paw Publishing, Incorporated *See* **WindRiver Publishing**

Bear Paw's Enterprises, *(0-9660271)* Orders Addr.: P.O. Box 1625, Lompoc, CA 93438 USA Tel 805-740-1842
E-mail: bearpawsenterprises@juno.com
Web site: http://www.bearpawsenterprises.com.

Bear Print (GBR) *(0-9528607) Dist. by* **Mountain Pr.**

Bear Star Pr., *(0-9657177; 0-9719607; 0-9793745)* 185 Hollow Oak Dr., Cohasset, CA 95973 USA Tel 530-891-0360
E-mail: bgumbo@aol.com
Web site: http://www.bearstarpress.com
Dist(s): **SPD-Small Pr. Distribution.**

Bear State Bks., *(1-892622)* Orders Addr.: P.O. Box 96, Exeter, CA 93221 USA Tel 559-592-6760; Fax: 559-592-5779; Edit Addr.: 199 E. Pine St., Exeter, CA 93221 USA
E-mail: 1718K@earthlink.net; bearstatebooks@verizon.net
Dist(s): **American West Bks.**

Bearly Cooking *Imprint of* **Mountain n' Air Bks.**

Bearport Publishing Co., Inc., *(1-59716)* 101 5th Ave., Suite 6-R, New York, NY 10003 USA (SAN 256-2103) Tel 212-337-8577 (phone/fax); Toll Free: 877-337-8577
E-mail: kenngoin@earthlink.net
Web site: http://www.bearportpublishing.com.

Bear's Designs Unlimited, *(0-9638473)* 7505 320th St., W., Northfield, MN 55057 USA Tel 507-645-9050; Toll Free: 800-497-8757.

Bearwallow Blessings Ministries, *(0-9768514)* HC 63 Box 77A-1 Rte. 637, Jewell Ridge, VA 24622 USA
Web site: http://www.bearwallowblessings.com.

Beascoa, Ediciones S.A. (ESP) *(84-488; 84-7546) Dist. by* **Lectorum Pubns.**

Beascoa, Ediciones S.A (ESP) *(84-488; 84-7546) Dist. by* **Distribks Inc.**

Beat The Test *Imprint of* **Trademark Universal, Inc.**

Beatstellar Bks. *Imprint of* **Essentials Educational Services**

Beau Francis Pr., *(0-9792147)* 4100 Newport Pl., Suite 400, Newport Beach, CA 92660 USA Tel 949-499-0679.

Beautiful America Publishing Co., *(0-89802)* Orders Addr.: P.O. Box 244, Woodburn, OR 97071-0244 USA (SAN 251-2548) Tel 503-982-4616; Fax: 503-982-2825; Toll Free: 800-874-1233; Edit Addr.: 2600 Progress Way, Woodburn, OR 97071 USA (SAN 211-4623)
E-mail: bapco@beautifulamericapub.com
Web site: http://www.beautifulamericapub.com
Dist(s): **Baker & Taylor Bks.**
Koen Pacific
Partners/West.

Beautiful Bks. (GBR) *(0-9549476; 1-905636) Dist. by* **Intl Pubs Mktg.**

Beautiful Feet Bks., *(0-9643803; 1-893103)* 1306 Mill St., San Luis Obispo, CA 93401-2817 USA Toll Free: 800-889-1978
E-mail: russell@bfbooks.com
Web site: http://www.bfbooks.com.

Beaver Island Arts, *(0-9708575)* P.O. Box 40, Bay City, MI 49708-0040 USA (SAN 253-8385) Tel 517-894-5925
E-mail: mblocksma@yahoo.com
Web site: http://beaverislandarts.com
Dist(s): **Partners Bk. Distributing, Inc.**

Beaver Meadow Publishing, *(0-9742085)* 11 Clarence Russell Rd., Thurman, NY 12885 USA Tel 518-623-9305; 352-463-3089
E-mail: PerkinFL@aol.com
Web site: http://www.persisgranger.com.

Beaver's Pond Pr., Inc., *(1-890676; 1-931646; 1-59298)* 7104 Ohms Ln., Suite 216, Edina, MN 55439 USA Tel 952-829-8818; Fax: 952-830-4000
E-mail: publishing@beaverspondpress.com
Web site: http://www.beaverspondpress.com
Dist(s): **Adventure Pubns., Inc.**

Becalm Publishing, *(0-9662759)* Orders Addr.: P.O. Box 725378, Berkley, MI 48072-5378 USA (SAN 299-5506) Tel 248-288-5637; Edit Addr.: 4235 Oakshire, Berkley, MI 48072 USA
E-mail: bbalok@rust.net
Web site: http://www.becalm-publishing.com.

Because Time Flies, Inc., *(0-9652652; 0-9754073)* 155 N. Harbor Dr., Concourse Suite 2, Chicago, IL 60601-7364 USA Tel 312-938-0938; Fax: 312-938-0029; Toll Free: 800-694-4786
E-mail: journals@covad.net
Web site: http://www.becausetimeflies.com.

Beck, John D., *(0-9714805)* 704 Spruce Dr., Hudson, WI 54016 USA
Web site: http://greasygrass.net.

Becker, Christie, *(0-9728116)* 16 Riverside Dr., Pawcatuck, CT 06379 USA Tel 860-599-5900
E-mail: beachbeckers@msn.com
Web site: http://www.cbeckerbooks.com.

becker&mayer! books, *(0-9700346; 0-9748486; 1-932855; 1-60380)* 11120 NE 33rd Pl. No. 101, Bellevue, WA 98004-1448 USA Toll Free: 866-319-5900
E-mail: cindyd@beckermayer.com; info@beckermayer.com
Web site: http://www.beckermayer.com; http://www.everydaywisdom.net
Dist(s): **Books Are Fun, Ltd.**
Chronicle Bks. LLC.

Beckett Publishing, Inc., *(0-9669923)* P.O. Box 2036, Short Beach, CT 06405 USA Tel 203-483-7296; Fax: 203-483-7298; Toll Free Fax: 888-576-2220; Toll Free: 888-568-3777
E-mail: magoopam@aol.com
Web site: http://www.beanieblessings.com.

Beckham House Publishers, Incorporated *See* **Beckham Pubns. Group, Inc.**

Beckham Pubns. Group, Inc., *(0-931761)* P.O. Box 4066, Silver Spring, MD 20914-4066 USA (SAN 683-2237) Tel 301-384-7995 phone; Toll Free Fax: 866-659-3306
E-mail: barry@beckhamhouse.com
Web site: http://www.beckhamhouse.com
Dist(s): **AtlasBooks Distribution.**

Become a Millionaire *See* **Grampa Jones's Publishing Co.**

Bed Bks., *(1-933652)* 101 Westgate Dr., Trinidad, CA 95570 USA
Web site: http://www.readinginbed.com; http://www.bedbooks.NET.

Bed Bug Publishing, Inc., *(0-9705588)* 44 Executive Blvd., Suite D, Farmingdale, NY 11735 USA (SAN 253-5165) Tel 516-822-5679; Fax: 631-454-0446
E-mail: littleal@littleal.com
Web site: http://www.littleal.com.

Bedazzled Ink Publishing Co., *(0-9759555; 1-934452)* 2137 Pennsylvania Ave., Fairfield, CA 94533 USA
E-mail: publisher@bedazzledink.com
Web site: http://www.bedazzledink.com.

Bedbug Pr., Inc., *(0-9771973)* Orders Addr.: P.O. Box 39, Brownsville, OR 97327-0039 USA (SAN 256-9396) Tel 541-466-5923 (phone/fax); Toll Free: 877-244-5928; Edit Addr.: 308 Averill, Brownsville, OR 97327 USA
E-mail: tony@bedbugpress.com
Web site: http://www.bedbugpress.com.

Bedell, Barbara F., *(0-9743731)* 307 Smith Neck Rd., South Dartmouth, MA 02748 USA Tel 508-993-3456
E mail: bb280z@yahoo.com.

Bedell, Jane M., *(0-9665837)* 1232 SE Bianca St., Hillsboro, OR 97123-5198 USA.

Bedford/Saint Martin's, *(0-312)* Div. of Holtzbrinck Publishers, Orders Addr.: 16365 James Madison Hwy., Gordonsville, VA 22942 USA Tel 540-672-7600; Toll Free Fax: 800-672-2054; Toll Free: 888-330-8477; Edit Addr.: 33 Irving Pl., New York, NY 10003 USA Tel 212-375-7000; Fax: 212-614-1885; Toll Free: 800-223-1715; 75 Arlington St., Boston, MA 02116 Tel 617-399-4000; Fax: 617-426-8582; Toll Free: 800-779-7440
E-mail: permissionsdept@bedfordstmartins.com; communication@bedfordstmartins.com
Web site: http://www.bfwpub.com
Dist(s): **Macmillan.**

Bedrick, Peter Bks. *Imprint of* **School Specialty Publishing**

Bedrock Books, Incorporated *See* **Dry, Paul Bks., Inc.**

Bedside Bks. *Imprint of* **American Bk. Publishing Group**

Bee at Ease Press *See* **At Ease Pr.**

Bee Smarter Study Kits *Imprint of* **Verde Publishing, Inc.**

Bee Unlimited, Inc., *(0-9662048)* Orders Addr.: P.O. Box 20364, Sedona, AZ 86341 USA Tel 928-567-4417; Fax: 928-567-4417; Toll Free: 888-321-1717; Edit Addr.: 425 Concho Dr., Sedona, AZ 86351 USA
E-mail: beeunltd@sedona.net
Web site: http://www.beeunlimited.com.

Beech River Bks., *(0-9776514; 0-9793778)* P.O. Box 62, Center Ossipee, NH 03814 USA Tel 603-539-3537
E-mail: banddmarion@earthlink.net
Web site: http://www.beechriver.com.

Beecher Scott, *(0-9763077)* 1128 Granada Way N., Saint Paul, MN 55128-7543 USA.

Beehive Bk. *Imprint of* **Pace Products, Inc.**

Beehive Pr., The, *(0-88322)* 321 Barnard St., Savannah, GA 31401 USA (SAN 201-7547) Tel 912-236-4870; Fax: 912-236-4747 Do not confuse with Beehive Pr., Las Vegas, NV
Web site: http://www.beehivepress.org.

Beekman & Hathaway, *(0-9758970)* P.O. Box 2355, Amherst, MA 01004-2355 USA
E-mail: cdc@beekmanandhathaway.com
Web site: http://www.beekmanandhathaway.com
Dist(s): **Independent Pubs. Group.**

Beekman Bks., Inc., *(0-8464)* 300 Old All Angels Hill Rd., Wappingers Falls, NY 12590 USA (SAN 170-1622) Tel 845-297-2690; Fax: 845-297-1002
E-mail: manager@beekmanbooks.com
Web site: http://www.beekmanbooks.com
Dist(s): **Biblio Distribution.**

Beeman Jorgensen, Inc., *(0-929758)* 7510 Allisonville Rd., Indianapolis, IN 46250 USA (SAN 250-1279) Tel 317-841-7677; Fax: 317-849-2001; Toll Free: 800-553-5319
Dist(s): **MBI Distribution Services Practice Ring.**

Beetle Bug Bks., *(0-9658365)* Orders Addr.: P.O. Box 4636, San Clemente, CA 92674 USA (SAN 299-3864) Tel 949-498-0162; Fax: 949-498-2531; Edit Addr.: 1504 Avenida Hacienda, San Clemente, CA 92672 USA (SAN 299-3872)
E-mail: BookOrders@BeetleBugBooks.com
Web site: http://www.BeetleBugBooks.com
Dist(s): **Baker & Taylor Bks. Unique Bks., Inc.**

Beevinwood, Inc., *(0-9652902)* Orders Addr.: 5748 Clark Rd., West Manchester, OH 45382 USA Tel 937-678-9910; Fax: 937-678-7715
E-mail: C1C2C3@aol.com.

Beex Art Bks., *(0-9724358)* P.O. Box 9143, Fountain Valley, CA 92728-9143 USA.

Before Christmas Pr., *(0-9759902)* Orders Addr.: 15170 State Rte. 550, Athens, OH 45701 USA
Web site: http://www.beforechristmaspress.com.

Beginnings Publishing Hse., *(0-9666578)* 328 Shady Ln., Alvaton, KY 42122 USA Tel 270-746-6651; Fax: 270-746-0607; Toll Free: 800-831-3570
E-mail: dcdobbins@aol.com
Web site: http://www.beginningspublishing.com.

Behavenkids Pr., *(0-9714405)* 10333 W. Center Rd., Omaha, NE 68124 USA Tel 402-926-4373; Fax: 402-926-3898
E-mail: janiep@behavenkids.com
Dist(s): **Book Clearing Hse.**

Behavioral Health & Human Development Ctr., *(0-9777672)* 4517 Lorino St., Suite 1, Metairie, LA 70006 USA Tel 504-454-3015
E-mail: carlos@littleduckyjr.com
Web site: http://littleduckyjr.com.

Behind the Scenes Bks., *(0-9770879)* 90 Windsor Dr., Pine Brook, NJ 07058 USA Tel 973-274-9472; Fax: 973-274-9272
E-mail: ma@behindthescenesmarketing.com.

Behr, D. J. Co., *(0-9660533)* Orders Addr.: P.O. Box 707, Northfield, MN 55057 USA Tel 612-435-7048; Fax: 612-898-0206; Edit Addr.: 211 Division St., Northfield, MN 55057 USA
E-mail: djbehr@viakids.com
Web site: http://www.viakids.com.

Behrman Hse., Inc., *(0-87441)* 11 Edison Pl., Springfield, NJ 07081 USA (SAN 201-4459) Tel 973-379-7200; Fax: 973-379-7280; Toll Free: 800-221-2755
E-mail: webmaster@behrmanhouse.com; orders@behrmanhouse.com
Web site: http://www.behrmanhouse.com; http://www.arepublish.com.

Beich Publications *See* **Beich Publishing Co.**

Beich Publishing Co., *(0-9631098)* 77-105 Shasta, Indian Wells, CA 92210-9050 USA Tel 760-345-3465; Fax: 760-360-8167
E-mail: ebeich@aol.com.

Beijing Language & Culture University Press, China (CHN) *(7-5619) Dist. by* **China Bks.**

Beil, Frederic C. Pub., Inc., *(0-913720; 1-929490)* Orders Addr.: 609 Whitaker St., Savannah, GA 31401 USA (SAN 240-9909) Tel 912-233-2446; Fax: 912-233-6456
E-mail: beilbook@beil.com
Web site: http://www.beil.com.

Belgrave Hse., *(0-9660643; 0-9741068)* 190 Belgrave Ave., San Francisco, CA 94117-4228 USA Tel 415-661-5025; Fax: 415-661-5703
E-mail: neff@belgravehouse.com
Web site: http://www.belgravehouse.com.

Believers Publishing, *(0-9795680)* 2245 N. Green Valley Pkwy., Suite 282, Henderson, NV 89014 USA
E-mail: believerspublishing@gmail.com
Web site: http://believerspublishing.com
Dist(s): **STL Distribution North America.**

Belisarian Bks., *(0-9658481)* Div. of Iconoclast, 6513 NW 30th Terr., Bethany, OK 73008 USA Tel 405-789-1030
E-mail: belisarianbooks@yahoo.com
Web site: http://www.belisarianbooks.tk/.

Belknap Digital Archives, *(0-9747471)* Orders Addr.: P.O. Box 1487, Meredith, NH 03253 USA Tel 603-279-8358; Edit Addr.: 20 True Rd., Unit No. 86, Meredith, NH 03253 USA
E-mail: apollock@worldpath.net
Web site: http://www.belknapdigital.com.

Belknap Publishing & Design, *(0-9723420)* P.O. Box 22387, Honolulu, HI 96823-2387 USA
Web site: http://www.calabashbooks.com
Dist(s): **Booklines Hawaii, Ltd.**

Bell, Alexander Graham Association for the Deaf *See* **Bell, Alexander Graham Assn. for the Deaf & Hard of Hearing, Inc.**

Bell, Alexander Graham Assn. for the Deaf & Hard of Hearing, Inc., *(0-88200)* 3417 Volta Pl., NW, Washington, DC 20007 USA (SAN 203-6924) Tel 202-337-5220; Fax: 202-337-8270
Web site: http://www.agbell.org.

Bell Buckle Pr., *(0-9624100; 1-882845)* P.O. Box 486, Bell Buckle, TN 37020 USA Tel 931-389-6878.

Bell Pond Bks. *Imprint of* **SteinerBooks, Inc.**

Bella Publishing *See* **Bellissima Publishing, LLC**

Bella Rosa Bks., *(0-9747685; 1-933523)* P.O. Box 4251, Rock Hill, SC 29732 USA
E-mail: info@bellarosabooks.com
Web site: http://www.bellarosabooks.com.

Bellaboozle Books, Inc., *(0-9765398)* 104 Lariat Dr., Canonsburg, PA 15317-3284 USA
E-mail: lkravec@adelphia.net.

Belle Lumiere Publishing *See* **MW International, Belle Lumiere**

Belle River Readers, Inc., *(0-9703548)* P.O. Box 1224, Lapeer, MI 48014 USA.

Belle Terre Pr., Inc., *(0-9649293)* 655-74 Belle Terre Rd., Port Jefferson, NY 11777 USA Tel 516-473-7630
E-mail: RWunder100@aol.com
Dist(s): **Brodart Co.**

BelleAire Pr., *(0-9640138; 0-9765234)* 5129 NW 57th St. Millhopper Forest, Gainesville, FL 32653-4079 USA Tel 352-377-1870
E-mail: belleairepress@earthlink.net
Dist(s): **BookMasters, Inc.**

BelleBks., *(0-9673035; 0-9768760)* Orders Addr.: P.O. Box 67, Smyrna, GA 30081 USA Tel 770-384-1348; Fax: 901-344-9068; Edit Addr.: 4128 Manson Ave., Smyrna, GA 30082 USA Tel 770-384-1348 (phone/fax)
E-mail: bellebooks@bellebooks.com; debbsmith@aol.com
Web site: http://www.BelleBooks.com.

Bellerophon Bks., *(0-88388)* Orders Addr.: P.O. Box 21307, Santa Barbara, CA 93121-1307 USA (SAN 254-7856) Tel 805-965-7034; Fax: 805-965-8286; Toll Free: 800-253-9943
E-mail: bellerophonbooks@bellerophonbooks.com
Web site: http://www.bellerophonbooks.com.

BelleTress Bks. *Imprint of* **Red Wheel/Weiser**

Bellissima Publishing, LLC, *(0-9768417; 0-9771916; 0-9776993; 0-9790449; 0-9793358; 0-9794006; 0-9794815)* Orders Addr.: P.O. Box 650, Jamul, CA 91935 USA
E-mail: pdweigandjd@aol.com
Web site: http://www.bellissimapublishing.com.

Bellman Publishing Co., *(1-884487)* Orders Addr.: P.O. Box 9118, Warwick, RI 02889 USA; Edit Addr.: 210 Bellman Ave., Warwick, RI 02889-2833 USA Tel 401-737-2058
E-mail: viewegdon@aol.com.

Bello, Andres (CHL) *(956-13) Dist. by* **Continental Bk.**

Bello, Andres (CHL) *(956-13) Dist. by* **AIMS Intl.**

Bellwether Media, *(1-60014)* P.O. Box 19349, Minneapolis, MN 55419 USA Fax: 952-974-0105.

BELLWORK Enterprises, Inc., *(0-934475; 1-932469)* Orders Addr.: P.O. Box 205, Stanton, CA 90680-0205 USA (SAN 693-8655) Tel 714-995-6977; Fax: 714-995-1181; Toll Free: 800-782-8869; Edit Addr.: 10529 Dale St., Stanton, CA 90680 USA
E-mail: sales@bellwork.com
Web site: http://www.bellwork.com.

Belshe, Judy, *(0-9655530)* 3145 Claremore Ave., Long Beach, CA 90808-4421 USA
E-mail: judybelshe@aol.com.

Belt, Robert L., *(0-9711519)* Orders Addr.: 639 Seville Dr., Hemet, CA 92543 USA Tel 951-929-5589
E-mail: rlbelt@aol.com
Web site: http://member.aol.com/rlbelt/index.

Beluga-Duga Pr., *(1-932176)* Orders Addr.: P.O. Box 923, Willits, CA 95490 USA; Edit Addr.: 700 E. Gobbi St., NO. 138, Ukiah, CA 95482 USA.

Be-Mused Pubns., *(0-9704868; 0-9740763)* P.O. Box 707, Grayland, WA 98547 USA (SAN 254-0215) Fax: 360-851-2820
E-mail: kristine@be-mused.com
Web site: http://www.be-mused.com.

Ben Franklin Pr., *(0-9772447)* 910 S. Hohokam Dr., Suite 104, Tempe, AZ 85281 USA Tel 480-968-7959
E-mail: rickburress@benfranklinpress.net.

BenBella Bks., *(1-932100; 1-933771; 0-9792331)* 6440 N. Central Expressway, Suite 617, Dallas, TX 77459 USA Tel 214-750-3600; Fax: 214-750-3645
E-mail: yara@benbellabooks.com
Web site: http://www.benbellabooks.com
Dist(s): **Independent Pubs. Group.**

Benchmark Bks. *Imprint of* **Cavendish, Marshall Corp.**

Benchmark Book Craft, *(0-9744015)* P.O. Box 19583, Colorado City, CO 81019 USA Tel 719-676-3009.

Benchmark Bks., *(0-9661592; 0-9709320)* 10623 Springmann Dr., Fairfax, VA 22030 USA Tel 703-273-6041; Fax: 703-293-9086 Do not confuse with companies with the same name , Benchmark Books in Estes Park, CO, San Marino, CA.

Benchmark Education Co., *(1-58344; 1-892393; 1-59000; 1-4108; 1-60437)* 629 Fifth Ave., Pelham, NY 10803 USA Tel 914-738-6977; Fax: 914-738-5063; Toll Free: 877-236-2465
E-mail: bhaggerty@benchmarkeducation.com
Web site: http://www.benchmarkeducation.com.

Benchmark Investigative Group, Div. Plumb Line Press, Incorporated, P.O. Box 717, Estes Park, CO 80517-0717 USA Tel 970-586-0760; Fax: 970-586-8208 Do not confuse with companies with the same name Benchmark Books in San Marino, CA, Fairfax, VA
E-mail: moses@88truthful.com
Web site: http://www.88truthful.com.

Benchmark Pr. *Imprint of* **Triumph Bks.**

Bendon Publishing International, *(1-932209; 1-59394; 1-60139)* 1840 Baney Rd., Ashland, OH 44805-3524 USA
E-mail: dwile@bendonpub.com
Web site: http://www.bendonpub.com.

Bendt Family Ministries, *(1-885814)* Orders Addr.: 333 W. Rio Vista Ct., Tampa, FL 33604 USA
E-mail: ValerieBendt@earthlink.net
Web site: http://www.ValerieBendt.com; http://www.ReadingMadeEasy.net; http://www.UnitStudiesMadeEasy.com.

Benefactory, Inc., The, *(1-58021; 1-882728)* 3 Baneberry Ln., Riverwoods, IL 60015-3534 USA Toll Free: 800-729-7251
E-mail: benefactry@aol.com.

Benei Yehudah Inc., *(0-9714772)* P.O. Box 172885, Hialeah, FL 33015 USA Tel 305-620-4946; Fax: 305-624-2546
E-mail: beneiyehudah@aol.com.

Bengal Pr., Inc., *(0-935650)* 20 Starshine Ln., Sedona, AZ 86351-7594 USA (SAN 213-7259)
E-mail: jilich1@msn.com.

Benjamin Pr., *(0-9663478; 0-9793431)* Div. of Elmwood Inn Fine Teas, P.O. Box 100, Perryville, KY 40468 USA Tel 859-332-2400; Fax: 859-332-7940; Toll Free: 800-765-2139 Do not confuse with Benjamin Pr., Northampton, MA
E-mail: BR@elmwoodinn.com
Web site: http://www.benjaminpress.com
Dist(s): **Cookbook Marketplace, The Partners Pubs. Group, Inc.**

†Benjamin-Cummings Publishing Co., *(0-201; 0-321; 0-582; 0-8053; 0-8465)* Subs. of Addison Wesley Longman, Inc., Orders Addr.: 75 Arlington St. Ste. 300, Boston, MA 02116-3988 USA (SAN 206-7862) Toll Free: 800-922-0579; Edit Addr.: 1301 Sansome St., San Francisco, CA 94111-1122 USA (SAN 200-2353) Tel 415-402-2500 ; *Imprints:* Addison Wesley (Add-West)
E-mail: question@aol.com
Web site: http://www.awl.com/bc/
Dist(s): **Pearson Education Pearson Technology Group;** *CIP.*

Bennerson, Denise, *(0-9646279)* Orders Addr.: P.O. Box 3164, Frederiksted, VI 00841 USA
E-mail: justdoit@viaccess.net
Web site: http://www.homelandcollections.com/children_books.htm
Dist(s): **Century Bk. Distribution.**

Bennett, Daina *See* **Educational Materials, Distributors**

Bennett, Joy *See* **Imagine Pr.**

Bennett, Robert *See* **Archeological Assessments, Inc.**

Bennett/Novak & Co., Inc., *(0-9713454)* 8500 Holloway Dr., Los Angeles, CA 90069 USA Tel 310-657-2975; Fax: 310-657-4006
Dist(s): **National Bk. Network.**

Bennington Pr., *(0-9671637)* 59 Hicks St., Brooklyn Heights, NY 11201 USA Tel 718-625-3416; Fax: 718-522-5445
E-mail: bernardo2@juno.com.

Bennovations Publishing Services, *(0-9721066)* P.O. Box 28906, San Diego, CA 92198 USA Tel 858-663-5302; Fax: 858-777-5779
E-mail: info@bennovations.com
Web site: http://www.bennovations.com.

Benoy Publishing, *(0-9720809; 1-932162)* 735 Bragg Dr., Unit H, Wilmington, NC 28412 USA Tel 910-796-0424 (phone/fax)
E-mail: bbppdodo@aol.com
Web site: http://www.benoypublishing.com.

Bensen, Rosie, *(0-9668325)* 33 Mills Rd., Newcastle, ME 04553 USA Tel 207-563-5842.

Benson, Queen M., *(0-615)* 106 James River Dr., Newport News, VA 23601 USA
E-mail: dbbenson@verizon.net
Web site: http://www.lactose-limited.com.

Benson, W. S. & Co., Inc., *(0-87443)* P.O. Box 1866, Austin, TX 78767 USA (SAN 202-3989) Tel 512-345-0732; Fax: 512-345-6837; Toll Free: 800-835-2197.

Bent Castle Workshops, *(0-9768848)* P.O. Box 10551, Rochester, NY 14610-0551 USA
E-mail: bent@skallywaggs.com
Web site: http://www.skallywaggs.com.

Bent Willow Publishing, *(0-9710627)* 2260 Towsgate Rd., Unit 2, Westlake Village, CA 91601 USA Tel 805-381-1033; Fax: 805-381-1334
Web site: http://www.bentwillowpublishing.com.

BentDaiSha, LLC, *(0-9749465)* 11020 E. Indigo Bush Pl., Tucson, AZ 85748-3558 USA
E-mail: bentdaisha@cox.net.

Bentivegna, Fred, *(0-9766228)* 445 W. 27th St., Chicago, IL 60616 USA Tel 312-225-5514 (phone/fax)
E-mail: fbentivegna@sbcglobal.net.

Bentle Bks., *(0-9746904)* Orders Addr.: P.O. Box 2274, Oakhurst, CA 93644 USA Fax: 559-683-6206; Edit Addr.: 42564 Buckeye Rd., Oakhurst, CA 93644 USA
E-mail: terrahulse@sierratel.com
Web site: http://www.bentlebooks.com.

Bentley, Trish, *(0-9774752)* 347 E. 6th St., Apt. 2B, New York, NY 10002 USA.

Benton, John Bks., *(0-9635411)* 127 S. El Molino Ave., Pasadena, CA 91101-2510 USA Tel 626-405-0950; Fax: 818-564-0952
Dist(s): **Baker & Taylor Bks. Spring Arbor Distributors, Inc.**

Berapa Pr. International, *(1-930187)* Orders Addr.: 12345 Lake City Way, NE, No. 224, Seattle, WA 98125-5401 USA Fax: 413-521-1901
E-mail: berapa@reciprocia.com
Web site: http://www.berapapress.com; http://www.reciprocia.com.

Berenger Co., *(0-9713356)* P.O. Box 408, Elmore, OH 43416 USA.

Beres, Nancy, *(0-9752801)* 6 Cardiff Ln., Athens, OH 45701-3715 USA.

Berg Pubs. (GBR) *(0-85496; 0-907582; 1-85973; 1-84520) Dist. by* **Macmillan.**

Bergstrom Bks., *(0-9787648)* 521 12th Ave. NE., Devils Lake, ND 58301 USA Tel 701-662-3320.

Berke Bks., *(0-9761463)* P.O. Box 862, Columbia, SC 29202 USA
E-mail: boykinbooks@yahoo.com.

Berkeley Major Publishing, *(0-9720691)* 8282 Skyline Cir., Oakland, CA 94605-4230 USA Fax: 419-791-7109
E-mail: dailon@progidy.net; BMP@berkeleymp.com
Web site: http://www.berkeleymp.com.

Berkeley Science Bks., *(0-9764138)* 529 Bonnie Dr., El Cerrito, CA 94530 USA Tel 510-524-8094
E-mail: wdflannery@aol.com.

Berkley *Imprint of* **Penguin Group (USA) Inc.**

Berkley Hardcover *Imprint of* **Penguin Group (USA) Inc.**

Berkley Trade *Imprint of* **Penguin Group (USA) Inc.**

Berkshire Hse. *Imprint of* **Countryman Pr.**

Berkshire Publishing Group, *(0-9743091; 0-9770159; 1-933782)* 314 Main St., Great Barrington, MA 01230 USA Tel 413-528-0206; Fax: 413-528-5241
E-mail: marcy@berkshirepublishing.com
Web site: http://www.berkshirepublishing.com.

Berlin, Theodore *See* **Theodore Berlin Publishing**

Berlitz International, Inc., *(2-8315; 1-59104)* 400 Alexander Park, Princeton, NJ 08540-6306 USA Tel 609-514-9650; Fax: 609-514-9649; Toll Free: 800-257-9449; Lincoln House 296-302 High Holborn, London, WC1V 7JH Tel 44.20.7611 9640; Fax: 44.20.7611 9656
Web site: http://www.berlitz.com
Dist(s): **Langenscheidt Pubs Inc.**
Libros Sin Fronteras.

Berlitz Publishing, *(2-8315; 981-234; 981-4120; 981-246)* 46-35 54th Rd., Maspeth, NY 11378 USA Tel 718-784-0055; Fax: 718-784-1216
E-mail: customerservice@langenscheidt.com
Web site: http://www.berlitzbooks.com
Dist(s): **Langenscheidt Pubs Inc.**

Bernson Pr., *(0-9720509)* Orders Addr.: P.O. Box 55563, Sherman Oaks, CA 91413 USA Tel 818-785-5290; Fax: 818-785-0948; Edit Addr.: 5530 Allot Ave., Sherman Oaks, CA 91401 USA
E-mail: bernsonpress@aol.com
Web site: http://www.thehealingartist.com.

Bernstein, Susan, *(0-9706596)* 31100 Northwestern Hwy., Farmington Hills, MI 48344-2519 USA Tel 248-737-8400; Fax: 248-737-4392; Toll Free: 800-225-5726
E-mail: les380414744@aol.com
Web site: http://www.epominonousepstein.com.

Berrett-Koehler Pubs., Inc., *(1-57675; 1-58376; 1-881052; 1-60509)* Orders Addr.: P.O. Box 565, Williston, VT 05495 USA Fax: 802-864-7626 (orders); Toll Free: 800-929-2929 (orders); Edit Addr.: 235 Montgomery St., Suite 650, San Francisco, CA 94104 USA Tel 415-288-0260; Fax: 415-362-2512
E-mail: bkpub@bkpubl.com; bkp.orders@AIDCVT.com
Web site: http://www.bkconnection.com
Dist(s): **American International Distribution Corp.**
Ingram Pub. Services
NetLibrary, Inc.

Berry Bks., *(0-9614746; 1-890579)* 814 Chelsea Way, Lake Wales, FL 33853-3462 USA (SAN 692-9214) Do not confuse with Berry Bks., Ltd., Columbus, OH
E-mail: bbbooks20@hotmail.com.

Berry Cove Publishing Co., *(0-9722679)* 17 Kitts Crossing, Lamoine, ME 04605 USA
E-mail: boats@flandersbayboats.com.

Berry Enterprises, *(0-9726091)* 484 E. Carmel Dr., No. 314, Carmel, IN 46032 USA Tel 317-581-9587 (phone/fax)
E-mail: vberryent@aol.com
Web site: http://www.berryent.com.

Bertelsman, Verlagsgruppe C. GmbH (DEU) *(3-570) Dist. by* **Distribks Inc.**

Beshqoy, Nisreen, *(0-9759181)* 25972 Limerick Ln., Lake Forest, CA 92630-8043 USA
E-mail: nisreenbeshqoy@hotmail.com
Web site: http://www.arabicandislamicbooksbynisreen.com.

Bess Pr., Inc., *(0-935848; 1-57306; 1-880188)* Orders Addr.: 3565 Harding Ave., Honolulu, HI 96816 USA (SAN 239-4111) Tel 808-734-7159; Fax: 808-732-3627; Toll Free: 800-910-2377
E-mail: kelly@besspress.com
Web site: http://www.besspress.com
Dist(s): **Baker & Taylor Bks.**
China Bks. & Periodicals, Inc.
Univ. of Hawaii Pr.

Best Books *See* **Library Reprints, Inc.**

Best Friends Bks., *(0-9662268)* Orders Addr.: P.O. Box 3880, Breckenridge, CO 80424 USA Tel 970-453-0410; Fax: 970-453-7375; Toll Free: 800-699-4541; Edit Addr.: 194 Wellington Rd., Breckenridge, CO 80424 USA
E-mail: ted@moozie.com
Dist(s): **Bibliotech, Inc.**

Best Friends Productions, *(0-9765140)* 131 Bank St., New York, NY 10014-2177 USA
Web site: http://www.bestfriendsproductions.com.

Best of East Texas Pubs., *(1-878096)* Div. of Bob Bowman & Assocs., 515 S. First, Lufkin, TX 75901 USA Tel 409-634-7444; Fax: 409-634-7750.

Best Practices in Action *Imprint of* **Scholastic, Inc.**

Best Seller *See* **Best Seller Pubns., Inc.**

Best Seller Pubns., Inc., *(0-9642997)* 12146 Island View Cir., Germantown, MD 20874 USA (SAN 253-4274) Tel 301-869-0072; Fax: 301-972-4456.

Bestmann, Nancy M., *(1-890398)* 61000 E. 265 Rd., Grove, OK 74344-7409 USA
E-mail: bestmann@bestmannbooks.com
Web site: http://www.bestmannbooks.com.

Bethany College Pr.-Kansas, *(0-916030)* 421 N. First St., Lindsborg, KS 67456-1897 USA (SAN 211-8882) Tel 785-227-3311.

†Bethany Hse. Pubs., *(0-7642; 0-87123; 1-55661; 1-56179; 1-57778; 1-880089; 1-59066)* Div. of Baker Book House, Inc., Orders Addr.: P.O. Box 6287, Grand Rapids, MI 49516-6287 USA Toll Free Fax: 800-398-3111 (orders); Toll Free: 800-877-2665 (orders); Edit Addr.: 11400 Hampshire Ave., S., Bloomington, MN 55438-2455 USA (SAN 201-4416) Tel 952-829-2500; Fax: 952-996-1393
E-mail: orders@bakerbooks.com
Web site: http://www.bethanyhouse.com
Dist(s): **Anchor Distributors**
Appalachian Bible Co.
Baker & Taylor Bks.
Baker Publishing Group
Brodart Co.
CRC Pubns.
Cambridge Univ. Pr.
Follett Library Resources
Permabound Bks.
Spring Arbor Distributors, Inc.
Beeler, Thomas T. Pub.; *CIP.*

Bethany Pr., LLC, *(0-9726299)* P.O. Box 151, Bethany, CT 06524 USA.

Bethlehem Bks., *(0-914869)* 2508 Dickens Rd., Richmond, VA 23230 USA (SAN 289-0607) Tel 804-282-4872; Fax: 804-285-9430 Do not confuse with Bethlehem Books in Bathgate, ND
E-mail: doug_mcmurry@pcusa.org
Web site: http://www.bethlehembooks.com.

Bethlehem Bks., *(1-883937; 1-932350)* Div. of Bethlehem Community, Orders Addr.: 10194 Garfield St. S., Bathgate, ND 58216-4031 USA Tel 701-265-3725; Fax: 701-265-3716; Toll Free: 800-757-6831 Do not confuse with bethlehem Books in Richmond, VA
E-mail: inquiry@bethlehembooks.com
Web site: http://www.bethlehembooks.com
Dist(s): **Ignatius Pr.**
Spring Arbor Distributors, Inc.

Betta Place, Inc., *(0-9723184)* 436 Ivy St., Jesup, GA 31545 USA Tel 912-427-2314.

Bettenhausen, Jo Anne *See* **CBM Publishing**

Better Chinese Limited (HKG) *(962-978) Dist. by* **Shens Bks.**

Better Comics, *(0-9728070)* P.O. Box 541924, Dallas, TX 75354-1924 USA
E-mail: JESmith@bettercomics.com
Web site: http://www.bettercomics.com.

Better Day Publishing Co., *(0-9767189; 0-9796763)* 11152 Westheimer No. 341, Houston, TX 77042-3222 USA Tel 281-550-7446
E-mail: contact@betterdaypublishing.com
Web site: http://www.betterdaypublishing.com.

Better Endings New Beginnings, *(0-9637072)* 6289 Brunswick Ave., N., Brooklyn Park, MN 55429-2306 USA
E-mail: jodee@connetworks.com
Web site: http//www.betterendings.org.

Better Homes & Gardens Bks. *Imprint of* **Meredith Bks.**

Better Homes & Gardens Books *See* **Meredith Bks.**

Better Me Bks., Inc., *(0-9770294)* P.O. Box 834, Marlton, NJ 08053 USA Tel 609-206-6318; Fax: 856-489-0234
E-mail: bettermebooks@aol.Com
Web site: http://www.bettermebooks.com.

Better Non Sequitur, *(0-9743235)* 11925 Via Zapata, El Cajon, CA 92019 USA Tel 619-246-5190
E-mail: steven@betternonsequitur.com
Web site: http://www.betternonsequitur.com.

Better Than One Publishing, *(0-9758958)* 27582 120th St., Staples, MN 56479 USA
Web site: http://www.creatingedumaterials.com.

Bette's Bks., *(0-9676360)* 8301 S. Pebble Creek Way, No. 48-102, Highlands Ranch, CO 80126 USA Tel 303-713-9805 (phone/fax); Toll Free: 877-236-7491
E-mail: heartfulloflove@earthlink.net.

Betts, Linda, *(0 9767802)* Orders Addr.: 6050 Pagenkopf Rd., Maple Plain, MN 55359 USA Tel 763-479-2789; Fax: 763-476-6508
E-mail: lynrae@hotmail.com.

Betty Crocker *Imprint of* **Wiley, John & Sons, Inc.**

Between the Lakes Group, LLC, *(0-9727403; 0-9766342; 0-9791000)* Orders Addr.: P.O. Box 13, Taconic, CT 06079-0013 USA Tel 860-824-0640
E-mail: geoff@betweenthelakes.com
Web site: http://www.betweenthelakes.com.

Beulah Fox, *(0-9714968)* P.O. Box 1065, Bishopville, SC 29010-3065 USA.

Beverly Hills Publishing, *(0-9758870; 0-9777074)* 291 S. La Cienega Blvd., Suites 107/108, Beverly Hills, CA 90211-3325 USA (SAN 850-0029) Tel 310-854-0705; Fax: 310-854-1840; Toll Free: 800-521-5669
E-mail: silvers@bevhillspub.com
Web site: http://www.bevhillspub,com.

Beyond Borders Bks., *(0-9715884)* 420 E. 120th Ave., B-2, No.206, Northglenn, CO 80233-1100 USA Tel 720-434-7032
E-mail: jk@beyondbordersbooks.com; jk@beyondbordersbooks.org
Web site: http://www.beyondbordersbooks.org.

Beyond Infinity Bks., Inc., *(1-930937)* 4340 Proctor Cove, Memphis, TN 31118 USA Tel 901-795-7168; Fax: 901-365-1901.

Beyond the Stars, Incorporated *See* **Beyond the Stars Pubns.**

Beyond the Stars Pubns., *(0-9763635)* 14902 Preston Rd., Suite 404-764, Dallas, TX 75254 USA
E-mail: rjohnson@beyondthestarsbooks.com
Web site: http://www.beyondthestarsbooks.com.

Beyond Words Publishing, Inc., *(0-941831; 1-58270; 1-885223)* 20827 NW Cornell Rd., Suite 500, Hillsboro, OR 97124-9808 USA (SAN 666-4210) Tel 503-531-8700; Fax: 503-531-8773; Toll Free: 800-284-9673
E-mail: info@beyondword.com; sales@beyondword.com
Web site: http://www.beyondword.com
Dist(s): **Simon & Schuster, Inc.**

Beyond Your Words, *(0-9788789)* P.O. Box 5842, Newport Beach, CA 92662-9266 USA
Web site: http://www.beyondyourwords.com.

Bezalel Bks., *(0-9792258; 0-9794976; 0-9800483)* P.O. Box 300427, Waterford, MI 48330 USA
Web site: http://www.bezalelbooks.com.

BFI Publishing (GBR) *(0-85170; 0-900212; 1-84457) Dist. by* **U CA Pr.**

B-52 Entertainment, LLC, *(0-9705015)* Orders Addr.: P.O. Box 25355, Honolulu, HI 96825 USA Tel 808-521-7934; Fax: 808-521-7935; Edit Addr.: 500 Ala Moana Blvd., Five Waterfront, Suite 350, Honolulu, HI 96825 USA
E-mail: ikt@worldquestllc.com.

Bhakta Program Institute *See* **Rupanuga Vedic College**

Bhaktivedanta Bk. Trust, *(0-89213; 0-912776; 91-7149; 0-902677)* Orders Addr.: 3764 Watseka Ave., Los Angeles, CA 90034 USA (SAN 203-8560) Tel 310-559-4455; Fax: 310-837-1056; Toll Free: 800-927-4152
E-mail: letters@harekrishna.com
Web site: http://www.harekrishna.com
Dist(s): **Biblio Distribution**
Torchlight Publishing.

BHB International, Incorporated *See* **Continental Enterprises Group, Inc. (CEG)**

BHouse Publishing Co., *(0-9653831)* Div. of SideView Concepts, 716 Fancy Bluff Rd., Brunswick, GA 31523 USA Tel 912-264-0660
E-mail: bhouse@darientel.net
Web site: http://www.sideviewconcepts.com.

Bible Based Studies, *(0-9797786)* 1134 SE 3rd St., Crystal River, FL 34429 USA Tel 352-795-5128
E-mail: info@biblebasedstudies.org
Web site: http://www.biblebasedstudies.org.

Bible Facts Pr., *(0-9762892; 0-9772942)* 631 Martin Ave. Suite 1, Rohnert Park, CA 94928 USA
Web site: http://www.biblefactspress.com.

Bible Game *Imprint of* **IMAGINEX, LLC**

Bible in Living Sound, The, *(1-57764)* Orders Addr.: P.O. Box 234, Nordland, WA 98358-0234 USA Tel 360-385-0234; Fax: 360-385-1124; Toll Free: 800-634-0234; Edit Addr.: 1510 E. Marrowstone Rd., Nordland, WA 98358 USA
E-mail: dean@bibleinlivingsound.org
Web site: http://www.bibleinlivingsound.org.

Bible League, *(1-882536)* Orders Addr.: P.O. Box 28000, Chicago, IL 60628 USA (SAN 297-8172) Tel 708-367-8573; Fax: 708-367-8922; Toll Free: 866-825-4636
E-mail: info@bibleleagueusa.com
Web site: http://www.bibleleagueusa.com.

Bible Pathway Ministries, *(1-879595)* Orders Addr.: P.O. Box 20123, Murfreesboro, TN 37133 USA Tel 615-896-4243; Fax: 615-893-1744; Toll Free: 800-598-7884; Edit Addr.: 810 W. Thompson Ln., Murfreesboro, TN 37129 USA
E-mail: mail@biblepathway.org
Web site: http://wwwbiblepathway.org
Dist(s): **STL Distribution North America.**

Bible Study Guide For All Ages, *(1-879614; 1-933396)* 118 N. Commerce Ave., Russellville, AR 72801 USA
E-mail: bsg@cei.net
Web site: http://www.biblestudyguide.com.

Bible Visuals International, Inc., *(1-932381; 1-933206)* P.O. Box 153, Akron, PA 17501-0153 USA
Web site: http://www.biblevisuals.org.

Bible-4-Life.com, *(0-9665124)* Div. of Sarah Keith of Creative Imaginations, 438 E. Ilex Dr., Lake Park, FL 33403-2606 USA Tel 561-281-5033
E-mail: orders@Bible-4-Life.com; orders@SundaySchoolNetwork.com; orders@christiancrafters.com
Web site: http://www.christiancrafters.com; http://www.Bible-4-Life.com; http://www.SundaySchoolNetwork.com; http://www.creativeimaginations.net.

Bibleco, Inc., *(0-9746058; 0-9754978)* 153 Pinehurst Dr., Easton, PA 18042 USA (SAN 256-0801) Fax: 610-438-3964 ; *Imprints:* Biblemania (Bibleman)
E-mail: biblemania@aol.com
Web site: http://www.biblemania.com.

Biblemania *Imprint of* **Bibleco, Inc.**

BibleRhymes *Imprint of* **BibleRhymes Publishing, L.L.C.**

BibleRhymes Publishing, L.L.C., *(0-9790605)* Orders Addr.: 54211 Horizon Dr., Shelby Township, MI 48316 USA (SAN 852-3207) ; *Imprints:* BibleRhymes (BibleRhymes USA)
E-mail: CustomerService@BibleRhymes.com
Web site: http://www.BibleRhymes.com.

BibleScope, *(0-9671417)* Div. of Multiscope, P.O. Box 5150, Spanaway, WA 98387 USA Tel 253-847-1876; Fax: 253-847-5772
E-mail: sambass@earthlink.net.

Biblesoft, Inc., *(1-56514)* 22014 Seventh Ave., S., Suite 105, Seattle, WA 98198-6235 USA (SAN 298-7473) Tel 206-824-0547; Fax: 206-824-2729
E-mail: rusty@biblesoft.com
Web site: http://www.biblesoft.com
Dist(s): **Anchor Distributors**
Appalachian Bk. Distributors
Spring Arbor Distributors, Inc.

BiblesPlus, *(0-9769109)* 13741 Annandale Dr., No. 20D, Seal Beach, CA 90740 USA Toll Free: 866-924-2537
E-mail: biblesplus7@yahoo.com
Web site: http://www.biblesplus.com.

Company

Biblical Perspectives, *(1-930987)* 4990 Appian Way, Berrien Springs, MI 49103 USA Tel 616-471-2915; Fax: 616-471-4013; Toll Free: 888-471-2915
E-mail: samuele@andrews.edu
Web site: http://www.biblicalperspectives.com.

Biblical Viewpoints Pubns., Inc., *(1-890133)* Div. of Round Oak Co., Inc., 63100 Cty. Rd. 111, Goshen, IN 46526 USA Tel 574-875-8007
E-mail: books@bibleviews.com
Web site: http://www.bibleviews.com.

Biblio Bks. International, *(0-9729545; 0-9741190; 0-9748524; 0-9766681; 0-9785565)* Kendall Tamiami Excutive Airport 14005 SW 127th St., Miami, FL 33186 USA
E-mail: info@bibliobooks.com
Web site: http://www.bibliobooks.com.

Biblio Distribution, Sister Company of National Book Network, Orders Addr.: 15200 NBN Way, Blue Ridge Summit, PA 17214 USA Toll Free Fax: 800-338-4550; Toll Free: 800-462-6420; Edit Addr.: 4501 Forbes Blvd., Suite 200, Lanham, MD 20706 USA (SAN 211-724X) Tel 301-459-3366; Fax: 301-429-5746
E-mail: custserv@nbnbooks.com
Web site: http://www.bibliodistribution.com.

Biblio Distribution Center *See* **Biblio Distribution**

Biblio Resource Pubn., *(1-934185)* 108 1/2 S. Moore St., Bessemer, MI 49911 USA Tel 906-364-2190
E-mail: race4hvn@hughes.net.

BiblioBazaar, *(1-4264; 1-4346)* Orders Addr.: 33 Cannon St., Charleston, SC 29403 USA Fax: 843-577-3240 11/15/05 Owner also owns Indigo, Inc. of Charleston, SC but the two companies are not connected. LT
E-mail: claire@bibliobazaar.com
Web site: http://www.bibliobazaar.com.

Bibliograf, S.A. (ESP) *(84-7153; 84-8332) Dist. by* **Continental Bk.**

Bibliograf, S.A. (ESP) *(84-7153; 84-8332) Dist. by* **Distribks Inc.**

Bibliographisches Institut & F. A. Brockhaus AG (DEU) *(3-411) Dist. by* **Continental Bk.**

Bibliographisches Institut & F. A. Brockhaus AG (DEU) *(3-411) Dist. by* **IBD Ltd.**

Bibliographisches Institut & F. A. Brockhaus AG (DEU) *(3-411) Dist. by* **Intl Bk Import.**

Bibliographisches Institut & F. A. Brockhaus AG (DEU) *(3-411) Dist. by* **Distribks Inc.**

Biblo & Tannen Booksellers & Pubs., Inc., *(0-8196)* P.O. Box 302, Cheshire, CT 06410 USA (SAN 202-4071) Tel 203-250-1647 (phone/fax); Toll Free: 800-272-8778
E-mail: biblo.moser@gte.net.

Bicast, Inc., *(0-9638258; 0-9701008; 0-9766753)* Orders Addr.: P.O. Box 2676, Williamsburg, VA 23187 USA Tel 757-229-3276; Fax: 757-253-2273; Toll Free: 800-767-8273; Edit Addr.: 231 K Parkway Dr., Williamsburg, VA 23185 USA
E-mail: bicastpub@aol.com; jogaertner@hughes.net
Web site: http://www.lighthousesusa.com.

Bick Publishing Hse., *(1-884158)* 307 Neck Rd., Madison, CT 06443 USA Tel 203-245-0073; 203 245 0073; Fax: 203-245-5990
E-mail: bickpubhse@aol.com
Web site: http://www.bickpubhouse.com
Dist(s): **Baker & Taylor Bks.**
Ingram Bk. Co.
Quality Bks., Inc.

Bickico Enterprises, Inc., *(0-9746508)* 19W042 Ave. Normandy E., Oak Brook, IL 60523 USA
E-mail: bickico@aol.com.

BICs Pr., *(0-9764253)* 1866 John F. Kennedy Blvd., No. B1, Jersey City, NJ 07305 USA.

Biddle Publishing Co., *(1-879418)* Orders Addr.: P.O. Box 1305, Brunswick, ME 04011 USA Tel 207-833-5016; Toll Free: 888-315-0582 (orders)
Web site: http://www.biddle-audenreed.com
Dist(s): **Baker & Taylor Bks.**

Bieler Pr. Monographs *Imprint of* **Bieler Pr.**

Bieler Pr., *(0-931460)* 4216 1/4 Glencoe Ave., Marina Del Rey, CA 90292 USA (SAN 209-7087) Tel 310-821-8269; Fax: 310-821-8440 ; *Imprints:* Bieler Press Monographs (Bieler Pr Monographs)
E-mail: Bieler@worldnet.att.net.

Bienes Ctr. for the Literary Arts. Broward County, *(0-9678858; 0-9762267)* 100 S. Andrews Ave, 6th Flr., Fort Lauderdale, FL 33301 USA Tel 954-357-8692; Fax: 954-357-6762
E-mail: jfindlay@browardlibrary.org
Web site: http://www.broward.org/bienes.

Bienestar, Inc., *(1-892039)* Orders Addr.: P.O. Box 47, Mount Tremper, NY 12457 USA Tel 914-688-2878; Fax: 914-688-5546; Toll Free: 888-692-4363; Edit Addr.: 1556 Wittenberg Rd., Mount Tremper, NY 12457 USA
E-mail: bienestar3@aol.com
Web site: http://www.bienestarinc.com.

Bier Brothers, Inc., *(0-9677238)* 147 Wild Dunes Way, Jackson, NJ 08527-4050 USA (SAN) ; *Imprints:* Sweet Dreams Press (Sweet Press)
E-mail: Dsb342@aol.com
Web site: http://www.newbreedcomics.com.

Big 8 Reviews *Imprint of* **N&N Publishing Co., Inc.**

Big Belly Bks., *(0-9749554)* P.O. Box 1254, Midland, MI 48641 USA
E-mail: sc@bigbellybooks.com
Web site: http://www.bigbellybooks.com.

Big Bks. for Little People *Imprint of* **Friendly Planet**

Big Bluestem Pr., *(0-9671386)* 12321 87th St., South, Wisconsin Rapids, WI 54494-9415 USA Tel 715-325-5749; Fax: 715-325-3109
E-mail: info@bigbluestempress.com
Web site: http://www.bigbluestempress.com.

Big Brain Publishing, LLC, *(0-9670636)* Orders Addr.: P.O. Box 8791, Silver Spring, MD 20907 USA Tel 301-587-7194; Fax: 301-588-8661; Edit Addr.: 8616 Second Ave., Silver Spring, MD 20910 USA
E-mail: bigbrainpb@aol.com.

Big Brown Box, Inc., The, *(0-9764647)* 443 Hill Rd., Douglassville, PA 19518-9530 USA Tel 610-385-7587
Web site: http://www.thebigbrownbox.com
Dist(s): **Book Clearing Hse.**
Ingram Bk. Co.

Big Cats Publishing, *(0-9670522)* 16 Linden Ln., Princeton, NJ 08540 USA Tel 609-683-8647
E-mail: tx2bigcats@aol.com
Web site: http://www.tx2bigcats.com/gayebookmain.html.

Big City Publishing, *(0-9762071)* P.O. Box 600576, Newtonville, MA 02460 USA
E-mail: m@bigcitypublishing.com
Web site: http://www.bigcitypublishing.com.

Big Creek Publishing, *(0-9742021)* Orders Addr.: P.O. Box 884, Sunbery, OH 43074 USA Tel 740-965-4127; Fax: 740-965-9541; Edit Addr.: 930 Joe Walker Rd., Sunbury, OH 43074 USA (SAN 255-4054) Tel 740-965-4127
E-mail: bigcreekpublishing@msn.com
Dist(s): **AtlasBooks Distribution**
Baker & Taylor Bks.

Big Dreams Publishing, *(0-9771868)* 8180 S. Allison Ct., Littleton, CO 80128 USA.

Big Drum Pr., *(1-890349)* P.O. Box 2406, Chapel Hill, NC 27515-2406 USA (SAN 253-9330) Tel 919-933-1805 (phone/fax)
E-mail: bdpnc@aol.com
Dist(s): **SPD-Small Pr. Distribution.**

†Big Earth Publishing, *(0-915024; 1-879483; 1-931599)* Orders Addr.: 3005 Ctr. Green Dr., Suite 200, Boulder, CO 80301 USA (SAN 209-2425) Fax: 608-259-8370; Toll Free: 800-258-5830; Edit Addr.: 923 Williamson St., Madison, WI 53703 USA ; *Imprints:* Trails Books (Trails Bks); Prairie Oak Press (Prairie Oak)
E-mail: books@bigearthpublishing.com
Web site: http://www.bigearthpublishing.com
Dist(s): **BPDI**
Baker & Taylor Bks.
Partners Bk. Distributing, Inc.; *CIP.*

Big Entertainment, Inc., *(0-9645175; 1-57780)* 2255 Glades Rd., Suite 237W, Boca Raton, FL 33431-7395 USA Tel 407-998-8000; Fax: 407-998-2974
Dist(s): **Kable Media Services.**

Big Foot Publishing, *(0-9645870)* P.O. Box 511, Liverpool, NY 13088 USA Tel 315-461-8402; Fax: 315-635-0829.

Big Guy Bks., Inc., *(1-929945)* 6359 Paseo Del Lago, Suite B, Carlsbad, CA 92009 USA (SAN 253-0392) Tel 760-804-0805; Fax: 760-804-0257; Toll Free: 800-536-3030
E-mail: info@bigguybooks.com; bernadette@bigguybooks.com
Web site: http://www.timesoldiers.com; http://www.bigguybooks.com
Dist(s): **Independent Pubs. Group.**

Big H Bks. *Imprint of* **Harvey, Alan**

Big Head Fish, *(0-9765007)* P.O. Box 121, New York, NY 10021 USA Tel 212-535-8705
E-mail: rafael_eugeniot@yahoo.com.

Big Kid Bks., *(0-9771990)* 6671 Sunset Blvd., No. 1585-101, Los Angeles, CA 90028 USA
Dist(s): **Midpoint Trade Bks., Inc.**

Big Kid Science, *(0-9721819)* 3015 10th St., Boulder, CO 80304 USA Tel 303-440-9313 (phone/fax)
E-mail: jbennett@indra.com
Web site: http://www.jeffreybennett.com
Dist(s): **Independent Pubs. Group.**

Big Kids Productions (Publishing), *(0-930249)* 85 Matthew Dr., Fairport (Rochester), NY 14450 USA (SAN 670-8617)
E-mail: pattiup@rochester.rr.com
Web site: http://www.rochesternyeats.com
Dist(s): **AtlasBooks Distribution**
North Country Bks., Inc.

Big Kids Publishing, Incorporated *See* **Big Kids Productions (Publishing)**

Big Lil' Bks., *(0-9749041)* Div. of ShadeTree Publishing, 3625 Tallman SE, Grand Rapids, MI 49508 USA
E-mail: janiceintheshade@msn.com.

Big River Distribution, *(0-9795944)* Orders Addr.: 9870 Big Bend Blvd., Suite D, Saint Louis, MO 63122-6573 USA (SAN 631-9114) Tel 314-918-9800; Fax: 314-909-6807
E-mail: info@bigriverdist.com; randy@bigriverdist.com
Web site: http://www.bifriverdist.com.

Big Rock Pr., *(0-9639377)* 801 W. Washington St., Athens, IL 62613 USA Tel 217-636-7790
E-mail: bharmeni@mail.state.il.us.

Big Secret, The, *(0-9724924)* P.O. Box 1994, Slidell, LA 70459 USA Tel 985-781-8704 (phone/fax)
Web site: http://www.thebigsecret.org.

Big Sky Stories Publishing, *(0-9728538)* Orders Addr.: P.O. Box 543, Choteau, MT 59422 USA; Edit Addr.: 3961 Hwy 89 S., Choteau, MT 59422 USA
E-mail: arnica@3rivers.net
Dist(s): **Big River Distribution.**

Big Smile, Inc., *(0-9761891)* P.O. Box 1042, Stroudsburg, PA 18360 USA Fax: 646-542-5319
E-mail: marcjohnjefferies@yahoo.com
Web site: http://www.marcjohnonline.com
Dist(s): **Midpoint Trade Bks., Inc.**

Big Tent Bks., *(1-60131)* 115 Bluebill Dr., Savannah, GA 31419 USA (SAN 851-1136)
E-mail: admin@dragonpencil.com
Dist(s): **Castlebridge Distribution.**

Big Tent Entertainment, Inc., *(1-59226)* 216 W. 18th St., New York, NY 10011 USA Tel 212-604-0064.

Big Tomato Pr., *(0-9791233)* Orders Addr.: 1126 2nd St. Suite 106, Sacramento, CA 95814 USA Tel 916-442-2993
E-mail: jocelyn@bigtomatopress.com
Web site: http://www.bigtomatopress.com
Dist(s): **Baker & Taylor Bks.**

Big Valley Pr., *(0-9765372)* S2104 Big Valley Rd, La Farge, WI 54639 USA Tel 608-489-3525; Fax: 866-627-1791
Web site: http://www.bigvalleypress.com.

Big Valley Publishing, *(0-9726004)* 516 N. Chinowth, Visalia, CA 93291 USA Do not confuse with company with similar name in Northridge, CA
E-mail: erkna@aol.com.

Big Wave Bks., *(0-9754979)* P.O. Box 108, Charlestown, RI 02813 USA Tel 401-322-8711
Web site: http://www.bigwavebooks.com.

Big Willz Records, *(0-9703881)* PMB 381, 23205 Gratiot Ave., Eastpointe, MI 48021 USA Tel 810-491-5646; Fax: 810-776-4471; Toll Free: 888-643-7083
E-mail: 6437083@skytel.com
Web site: http://www.bigwillz.iuma.com.

BIGfib Bks. (FRA) *(2-9524899) Dist. by* **Bookazine Co Inc.**

Bigfoot Books *See* **Bigfoot Bks. Society**

Bigfoot Bks. Society, *(0-9702362)* Orders Addr.: P.O. Box 30165, Edmond, OK 73003 USA Fax: 405-330-5372 (phone/fax); Edit Addr.: 1313 NW 197th St., Edmond, OK 73003 USA
E-mail: jgrelen@yahoo.com.

Bighorn Publishing, *(0-9722808)* Orders Addr.: 35 La Canada Way, Hot Springs Village, AR 71909 USA
E-mail: fboling@cox-internet.com; fboling@bighornpublishing.com
Web site: http://www.fredrickboling.com; http://www.bighornpublishing.com.

Bilingual *Imprint of* **Star Light Pr.**

Bilingual Educational Services, Inc., *(0-86624; 0-89075)* 2514 S. Grand Ave., Los Angeles, CA 90007 USA (SAN 218-4680) Tel 213-749-6213; Fax: 213-749-1820; Toll Free: 800-448-6032
E-mail: sales@besbooks.com
Web site: http://www.besbooks.com.

Bilingual Language Materials, *(0-9624096; 1-893447)* 130 East Grand Ave., South San Francisco, CA 94080 USA Tel 650-871-4449; Fax: 650-871-4551; Toll Free: 800-610-1565
E-mail: info@blmteachaids.com
Web site: http://blmteachaids.com/.

Bilingual Pr./Editorial Bilingue, *(0-916950; 0-927534; 1-931010)* Orders Addr.: Hispanic Research Ctr. Arizona State Univ. P.O. Box 875303, Tempe, AZ 85287-5303 USA (SAN 208-5526) Fax: 480-965-8309; Toll Free: 800-965-2280; Edit Addr.: Bilingual Review Pr. Administration Bldg. Rm. B-255 Arizona State Univ., Tempe, AZ 85281 USA
E-mail: brp@asu.edu
Web site: http://www.asu.edu/brp
Dist(s): **Baker & Taylor Bks.**
Libros Sin Fronteras
SPD-Small Pr. Distribution.

Bilingual Pubns., *(0-9644678)* P.O. Box 12678, Denver, CO 80212 USA Tel 303-433-0979 Do not confuse with Bilingual Pubns. Co., New York, NY.

Bilingual Pubns. Co., The, 270 Lafayette St., New York, NY 10012 USA (SAN 164-8993) Tel 212-431-3500; Fax: 212-431-3567 Do not confuse with Bilingual Pubns., in Denver, CO
E-mail: lindagoodman@juno.com; spanishbks@aol.com.

Bill Barry's Compass Bks., *(0-944099)* Subs. of Adventure Feature Syndicate, Orders Addr.: P.O. Box 2524, Waldport, OR 97394 USA (SAN 242-2999); Edit Addr.: 385 NW Grant St., No. 4, Waldport, OR 97394 USA Tel 541-563-7282
E-mail: barrytoons@hotmail.com
Web site: http://www.BlackBeard-the-Pirate.com
Dist(s): **Diamond Distributors, Inc.**

Bill of Rights Institute, The, *(1-932785)* 200 N. Glebe Rd. Ste. 200, Arlington, VA 22203-3756 USA Toll Free: 800-838-7870
E-mail: kash@billofrightsInstitute.org
Web site: http://www.billofrightsinstitute.org
Dist(s): **CLEARVUE/eav, Inc.**
Social Studies Schl. Service
Teacher's Discovery.

Billboard Bks. *Imprint of* **Watson-Guptill Pubns., Inc.**

Billiard Congress of America, *(1-878493)* 5 Piedmont Ctr NE Ste. 435, Atlanta, GA 30305-1509 USA
E-mail: amy@bca-pool.com; marketing@bca-pool.com
Web site: http://www.bca-pool.com.

Billings, David J., *(0-9789036)* 1499 Massachusetts Ave. NW, No. 1012, Washington, DC 20005 USA
E-mail: david@davidjbillings.com; david@roadtripbook.com
Web site: http://www.roadtripbook.com.

Billings Worldwide Brain, *(0-9654169)* P.O. Box 701, Addison, TX 75001 USA (SAN 299-2426)
E-mail: dave@hamr.com
Web site: http://www.hamr.com
Dist(s): **Distributors, The.**

Billinna Publishing Co., *(0-9712640)* 2620 S. Maryland Pkwy., Suite 517, Las Vegas, NV 89109 USA (SAN 254-4717) Tel 702-650-3468 (phone/fax).

Billion $ Baby Pubns., *(0-9707945)* 22817 Ventura Blvd., Suite 408, Woodland Hills, CA 91364 USA (SAN 254-3265) Toll Free Fax: 888-232-9022; Toll Free: 800-499-2771
E-mail: Djedra@BabyPublications.com; dottie@babypublications.com
Web site: http://www.BabyPublication.com.

Billiot, Wendy Wilson, *(0-9762592)* 2715 Bayou DuLarge Rd., Theriot, LA 70397 USA
E-mail: wendybilliot@charter.net
Web site: http://www.wetlandbooks.com.

Billy B Enterprises, *(0-9670394)* 357 W. Via Bacanora, Green Valley, AZ 85614 USA (SAN 299-8378) Tel 520-648-6163 (phone/fax)
E-mail: cuthbert21@aol.com.

Billy Bee Productions, *(1-886919)* 19 Grace Dr., Nashua, NH 03062 USA Toll Free Fax: 800-257-0907; Toll Free: 800-327-3227
E-mail: info@billybee.net
Web site: http://www.billybee.net.

Billy Jo Bks., *(0-9765088)* 9111 Oat Ave., Gerber, CA 96035-9723 USA Tel 530-385-1820
E-mail: biljoho@earthlink.net.

Billy the Bear & His Friends, Inc., *(0-9641338)* 1909 Munster Ave., Saint Paul, MN 55116 USA Tel 651-699-7636; Fax: 651-690-4815
Dist(s): **AtlasBooks Distribution**
STL Distribution North America.

Bimini Bks., *(0-9753118)* 9553 SW 189 Terr., Suite 200, Miami, FL 33157 USA Tel 305-256-0638
E-mail: biminibooks@aol.com.

Bimini Twist Adventures, Inc., *(0-9676853; 0-9728564)* 2911 NW 27th Ave., Boca Raton, FL 33434 USA Tel 561-451-3452; Fax: 954-964-3900; Toll Free: 800-558-5885
E-mail: pjm@biminitwist.com
Web site: http://www.biminitwist.com.

Bindu Bks. *Imprint of* **Inner Traditions International, Ltd.**

Binet International, *(0-942787)* P.O. Box 1429, Carlsbad, CA 92008 USA (SAN 667-7088) Tel 760-941-7929.

Binford & Mort Publishing, *(0-8323)* Orders Addr.: P.O. Box 91580, Portland, OR 97291 USA; Edit Addr.: 5245 NE Elam Young Pkwy., Suite C, Hillsboro, OR 97124 USA (SAN 201-4386) Tel 503-844-4960; Fax: 503-844-4959; Toll Free: 888-221-4514
Web site: http://www.binfordandmort.com/
Dist(s): **Baker & Taylor Bks.**
Maverick Distributors
Partners/West.

Binford & Mort Publishing; Metropolitan Press *See* **Binford & Mort Publishing**

Bing Note, Inc., *(0-9794323)* 300 Caldecott Ln., No. 215, Oakland, CA 94618 USA
E-mail: lisa@bingnote.com
Web site: http://www.bingnote.com.

Bing Puddlepot, *(0-9676148)* P.O. Box 390316, Minneapolis, MN 55439-0316 USA Fax: 612-942-8570
E-mail: Bing@Puddlepot.com
Web site: http://puddlepot.com
Dist(s): **Bookmen, Inc.**

Bingham Putnam Publishing, *(0-9760504)* 326 Newport Dr., No. 1710, Naples, FL 34114 USA.

Bingo Bks., Inc., *(1-933530)* P.O. Box 3355, Austin, TX 78763-3355 USA Toll Free: 877-246-4644
Web site: http://www.bingobooks.com.

Binnacle Kids *Imprint of* **Binnacle Publishing Group**

Binnacle Publishing Group, *(1-890493)* P.O. Box 3969, Santa Cruz, CA 95063 USA Tel 408-439-9710 (phone/fax); Toll Free: 800-223-1974 ; *Imprints:* Binnacle Kids (Binnacle Kids)
E-mail: binnacle@bpgx.com; analogp@ibm.net
Web site: http://www.bpgx.com
Dist(s): **BookMasters, Inc.**

Binney & Smith, Inc., *(0-86696)* P.O. Box 431, Easton, PA 18042 USA (SAN 216-5899).

BioEd *Imprint of* **Baylor College of Medicine**

Biographical Publishing Co., *(0-9637240; 1-929882)* 35 Clark Hill Rd., Prospect, CT 06712-1011 USA (SAN 298-2692) Tel 203-758-3661; Fax: 253-793-2618
E-mail: biopub@aol.com
Web site: http://members.aol.com/biopub/index.html.

BioImages, *(0-9707385)* Orders Addr.: P.O. Box 4537, Decatur, IL 62525 USA Tel 217-226-5413; Fax: 217-226-4424; Edit Addr.: 1004 E. Illinois St., Assumption, IL 62510 USA
E-mail: BioImages@aol.com
Web site: http://buffettimages.com.

Bios for Kids *Imprint of* **Panda Publishing, L.L.C.**

Biotech Publishing, *(1-880319)* Div. of Plant Something Different, Inc., Orders Addr.: P.O. Box 1032, Angleton, TX 77516-1032 USA Tel 281-369-2044; Toll Free: 800-659-3078
E-mail: services@biotechpub.com
Web site: http://www.biotechpub.com.

Birch Hill Pr., *(0-9656620)* 32 Clark Rd., Cummington, MA 01026-9708 USA Tel 413-634-5643
E-mail: lfpierce@javanet.com
Web site: http://www.javanet.com/~lfpierce.

Birchbark Bks. *Imprint of* **Farrar & Associates**

Birdcage Books *See* **Birdcage Pr.**

Birdcage Pr., *(1-889613; 1-59960)* 853 Alma St., Palo Alto, CA 94301 USA Tel 650-462-6300; Fax: 650-462-6305
E-mail: info@birdcagepress.com
Web site: http://www.birdcagepress.com
Dist(s): **National Bk. Network.**

Birdsall, Bonnie Thomas, *(0-9762679)* 3421 Lacewood Rd., Tampa, FL 33618 USA
E-mail: swimtaichibon@juno.com.

Birdseed Bks., *(0-9774142)* 520 17th St., Dallas, WI 54733 USA ; *Imprints:* Birdseed Books for Kids (Birdseed Books for Kids)
Web site: http://www.birdseedbooksforkids.com
Dist(s): **Independent Pubs. Group.**

Birdseed Books for Kids *Imprint of* **Birdseed Bks.**

Birdsong Bks., *(0-9662761)* Orders Addr.: 1322 Bayview Rd., Middletown, DE 19709 USA Tel 302-378-7274; Fax: 302-378-0339
E-mail: birdsongbooks@delaware.net
Web site: http://www.birdsongbooks.com
Dist(s): **Common Ground Distributors, Inc.**
Independent Pubs. Group.

Birlinn, Ltd. (GBR) *(1-874744; 1-84158; 1-84341) Dist. by* **Interlink Pub.**

BirlinnPolygon (GBR) *(1-84697) Dist. by* **Interlink Pub.**

†Birmingham Museum of Art, *(0-931394; 1-934774)* 2000 Eighth Ave., N., Birmingham, AL 35203 USA (SAN 278-2030) Tel 205-254-2565; Fax: 205-254-2710
E-mail: museum@artsbma.org
Web site: http://www.artsbma.org
Dist(s): **Antique Collectors' Club**
D.A.P./Distributed Art Pubs.
Univ. of Alabama Pr.; *CIP.*

Birthwrite Publishing, *(0-9670129)* 924 Fairway Dr., Waynesboro, VA 22980-3404 USA.

Bisham Hill Bks., *(0-9744281)* Orders Addr.: 25-13 Old Kings Hwy., No. 192, Darien, CT 06820 USA
E-mail: sales@bishamhill.com
Web site: http://www.bishamhill.com.

Bishop Museum Pr., *(0-910240; 0-930897; 1-58178)* 1525 Bernice St., Honolulu, HI 96817-2704 USA (SAN 202-408X) Tel 808-847-8260; 808-848-4135; Fax: 808-841-8968
E-mail: press@bishopmuseum.org
Web site: http://www.bishopmuseum.org
Dist(s): **Booklines Hawaii, Ltd.**
Islander Group.

Bishop, Susan Lynn, *(0-9772878)* Orders Addr.: P.O. Box 13, Onley, IL 62450 USA Tel 618-392-4011; Edit Addr.: P.O. Box 13, Olney, IL 62450-0013 USA
E-mail: suzyb@wabash.net.

Bisiar Music Publishing, *(0-9753091)* Orders Addr.: P.O. Box 424, Evergreen, CO 80437-0424 USA (SAN 256-0356) Tel 303-670-0752 (phone/fax); Edit Addr.: 3661 A Evergreen Pkwy., Evergreen, CO 80437-0424 USA
E-mail: bisiar@earthlink.net
Web site: http://www.eddiespaghettiusa.com.

Bison Bks. *Imprint of* **Univ. of Nebraska Pr.**

Bitty Book Pr., *(1-887270)* 851 Mt. Vernon Ct., Naperville, IL 60563 USA Tel 630-420-1887; Fax: 630-963-0341; Toll Free: 800-750-6649; 2736 Maple Ave., Downers Grove, IL 60515
E-mail: maryannako@aol.com
Web site: http://www.namepower101.com.

Bixie Gate Publishing, *(0-9773433)* 22694 SW Lincoln St., Sherwood, OR 97140 USA (SAN 257-3474)
E-mail: shannonk23@comcast.net
Web site: http://www.bixiegatepublishing.com; http://www.shannonkeegan.com.

Biz4Kids *Imprint of* **Round Cow Media Group**

Bjelopetrovich, Beba Foundation, *(0-9745724)* 5555 W. Howard St., Skokie, IL 60077-2621 USA Tel 847-679-6710; Fax: 847-679-6717.

BKB Group, Inc., The, *(0-9747628)* Orders Addr.: 11146 Harbour Springs Cr., Boca Raton, FL 33428 USA Tel 561-218-1215; Fax: 561-218-1214; Toll Free: 888-321-7664; Edit Addr.: 11146 HARBOUR SPRINGS CR., 11146 HARBOUR SPRINGS CR., BOCA RATON, FL 33428 USA
E-mail: rfproductions@adelphia.net
Web site: http://www.billybutterfly.com.

Bks. for Young Learners *Imprint of* **Owen, Richard C. Pubs., Inc.**

Black Alchemist Pr., Inc., *(0-9671082; 0-9709166)* P.O. Box 110569, Jamaica, NY 11411-0569 USA (SAN 253-3723) Fax: 718-977-7706 ; *Imprints:* Division of Words (Division of Wrds)
E-mail: marlena-gasper@hotmail.com; books@blackalchemistpress.com
Web site: http://www.blackalchemistpress.com.

Black Belt Pr. *Imprint of* **River City Publishing**

Black Belt Training, *(0-9759744)* 9109 Cochran Heights, Dallas, TX 75220 USA Tel 214-351-2234 (phone/fax)
E-mail: drted@wwwin.com
Web site: http://www.wwwin.com.

Black Bird Bks., *(0-9763238)* Orders Addr.: P.O. Box 901, Ankeny, IA 50021 USA; Edit Addr.: P.O. Box 901, Ankeny, IA 50021-0901 USA
E-mail: lizzie3blackbird@hotmail.com.

Black Cat Pubns., Inc., *(0-9712994)* Orders Addr.: P.O. Box 672, Plainview, NY 11803 USA Tel 631-273-3545
E-mail: cnamo@blackcatpublications.com
Web site: http://www.blackcatpublications.com.

Black, Clinton L., *(0-9620180)* Orders Addr.: P.O. Box 9096, Fort Lauderdale, FL 33310 USA Tel 954-722-0415; Fax: 954-720-7674
E-mail: thepurposeofhumanlife@yahoo.com
Dist(s): **Southern Bk. Service.**

Black Coat Pr. *Imprint of* **HollywoodComics.com, LLC**

Black Coffee Publishing, *(0-9745238)* Orders Addr.: 5543 Edmondson Pike, No. 213, Nashville, TN 37211-5808 USA Tel 615-969-5516
E-mail: bcpubl@aol.com
Web site: http://www.blackcoffeepublishing.com.

Black Death Bks. *Imprint of* **KHP Industries**

Black Dog & Leventhal Pubs., Inc., *(0-9637056; 1-57912; 1-884822)* 151 W. 19th St., New York, NY 10011-4116 USA Tel 212-647-9336; Fax: 212-647-9332
Dist(s): **Book Sales, Inc.**
Workman Publishing Co., Inc.

Black Dog Publishing Ltd. (GBR) *(0-9521773; 1-901033; 1-904772; 1-906155) Dist. by* **Perseus Dist.**

Black Dolphin Diving, *(0-9646281)* 5022 Two Harbors, Avalon, CA 90704-5022 USA Tel 310-510-2109
E-mail: bkdolphin@aol.com
Web site: http://www.divecatalina.com.

Black Dot Pubns., *(0-9649740)* Orders Addr.: P.O. Box 1068, Ojai, CA 93024 USA Tel 805-640-8825; Edit Addr.: 1208 Gregory St., Ojai, CA 93023 USA
E-mail: blackdotpubs@yahoo.com
Web site: http://www.backdotpubs.com; http://www.chuckhillig.com
Dist(s): **New Leaf Distributing Co., Inc.**

Black Falcon Publications *See* **LMW Works**

Black Forest Pr., *(1-58275; 1-881116)* Div. of Black Forest Enterprises, Orders Addr.: P.O. Box 6342, Chula Vista, CA 91909-6342 USA Fax: 619-482-8704; Toll Free: 800-451-9404 (General Information, Submission Inquiries and Acquisitions); 888-808-5440 (Book Sales, Marketing and Promotion); Edit Addr.: 1075 Hayuco Plz., Chula Vista, CA 91910-7006 USA (SAN 298-8445) ; *Imprints:* Segen Books (Segen Bks)
E-mail: bfp@blackforestpress.com
Web site: http://www.blackforestpress.com
Dist(s): **Ingram Bk. Co.**

Black Gate Publishing, *(0-9641722)* Orders Addr.: P.O. Box 1134, Portsmouth, VA 23705-1134 USA Tel 757-399-6478; Toll Free: 800-399-5816; Edit Addr.: 1633 Leckie St., Portsmouth, VA 23704-1717 USA.

Black Hat Pr., *(0-9614462; 1-887649)* Orders Addr.: P.O. Box 12, Goodhue, MN 55027-0012 USA (SAN 689-4259) Tel 651-923-4590; Edit Addr.: 508 Second Ave., Goodhue, MN 55027-0012 USA
E-mail: blackhatpress@yahoo.com.

Black Heron Pr., *(0-930773)* Orders Addr.: P.O. Box 95676, Seattle, WA 98145 USA (SAN 677-623X) Tel 206-363-5210 (phone/fax); Edit Addr.: 3032 NE 140th St., No. 407, Seattle, WA 98125 USA (SAN 241-9866)
Web site: http://mav.net/blackheron
Dist(s): **Midpoint Trade Bks., Inc.**

Black, Iris Pubns., *(0-9742214)* Orders Addr.: P.O. Box 5535, Bella Vista, AR 72714 USA Tel 479-855-1205; Edit Addr.: 17 Buckingham Dr., Bella Vista, AR 72714 USA
E-mail: iris@irisbp.com
Web site: http://www.irisbp.com.

Black Jasmine, *(0-9788802)* 46 Pleasant St., Sharon, MA 02067 USA
E-mail: deemajoan@yahoo.com
Web site: http://www.deemasglass.com.

Black, Judith Storyteller, *(0-9701073)* 33 Prospect St., Marblehead, MA 01941 USA Tel 781-631-4417
E-mail: jb@storiesalive.com
Web site: http://www.storiesalive.com.

Black Lab Publishing LLC, *(0-9742815)* Orders Addr.: P.O. Box 64, Alton, NH 03809 USA Tel 603-776-5007; 606-232-2170; Fax: 603-776-5011; P.O. Box 2223, Ashland, KY 41105-2223 Toll Free Fax: 606-327-0069
E-mail: loni@bearandkatie.com
Web site: www.bearandkatie.com.

Black Oak Pr., *(0-930674)* Box 4663, University Pl. Sta., Lincoln, NE 68504 USA (SAN 212-7261) Tel 402-467-4608 Do not confuse with companies with a similar name in Lambertville, NJ, Charleston, IL, Springfiled, MO.

Black Orb *See* **Angie Blue Bks., LLC**

Black Pearl Publishing, *(0-9667850)* Orders Addr.: P.O. Box 222088, Dallas, TX 75222 USA Tel 972-291-3160; Fax: 972-291-3310; Edit Addr.: 143 Hunter Dr., Cedar Hill, TX 75104 USA Do not confuse with Black Pearl Publishing in Southfield, MI
E-mail: clf@cyberramp.net.

Black Plum Bks., *(0-9785317)* Orders Addr.: 608 Jordan Trace, Chesapeake, VA 23323 USA
Web site: http://www.blackplumebooks.com.

Black River Trading Co., *(0-9649083; 0-9797492)* P.O. Box 7, Oxford, MI 48371 USA (SAN 854-2724) Tel 248-628-5150; Fax: 248-628-6422
E-mail: jane@whoopforjoy.com
Web site: http://www.whoopforjoy.com
Dist(s): **Bookmen, Inc.**

Black Sands Enterprises, *(0-9671781)* Orders Addr.: P.O. Box 4382, Canton, GA 30114-0017 USA
E-mail: admin@blacksands.com
Web site: http://www.blacksands.com.

Black Society Pages, Inc., *(0-9758611)* 228 S. Washington St., Alexandria, VA 22314 USA.

BlacKat Publishing, *(0-9677274)* 528 S. State St., No. 393, Ann Arbor, MI 48104 USA Do not confuse with Blackat Publishing, Edison, NJ
E-mail: EWiggins@BlacKat.net
Web site: http://BlacKat.net.

Blackberry Hill Pr., *(0-9792947)* Orders Addr.: 2860 Mohawk St., Sauquoit, NY 13456-3322 USA Tel 315-737-5147
Web site: http://dorothystacy.com/default.aspx
Dist(s): **North Country Bks., Inc.**

Blackberry Pubs., *(0-615)* 2545 Hwy. 76, Portland, TN 37148 USA Tel 615-325-3970
E-mail: fussellb@comcast.net
Web site: http://www.blackberrypublishers.com
Dist(s): **Sadler, Dale.**

Blackbirch Pr., Inc. *Imprint of* **Thomson Gale**

Blackbird's World Publishing Co., *(0-9789798)* Orders Addr.: P.O. Box 475, Clyde, TX 79510 USA Tel 325-201-2495; Edit Addr.: Box 475 212 Hunt St., Clyde, TX 79510 USA
E-mail: blackbird@blackbirdsworldpublishingcompany.net
Web site: http://blackbirdsworldpublishingcompany.net.

Blackfoot Burkino Cherokee Publishing, *(0-9722724)* Orders Addr.: P.O. Box 58074, Houston, TX 77258 USA; Edit Addr.: 1912 Trentwood Pl., Charlotte, NC 28216 USA
E-mail: ctdmysons@yahoo.com.

Blackfairs Pr., *(0-9745206)* 2319 Branner Dr., Menlo Park, CA 94025 USA.

BlacknBlue Pr. UK *Imprint of* **Blacknblue Pr.**

Blacknblue Pr., *(0-9677652)* 108 Benarr Ave., Fort Walton Beach, FL 32548 USA Tel 850-862-2874 (phone/fax); 13 Dellands Overton, Basingstoke, RG25 3LD Tel 1256 770736 (phone/fax) ; *Imprints:* BlacknBlue Press UK (BlacknBlue Pr UK)
E-mail: bobwick@cox.net; edddwicke@hotmail.com
Web site: http://www.blacknbluepress.info
Dist(s): **Lightning Source, Inc.**

Black-Out Media, *(0-9700319)* P.O. Box 600815, North Miami Beach, FL 33260 USA Tel 305-793-4352
E-mail: orpheus05@aol.com.

Blackstaff Pr., The (IRL) *(0-85640) Dist. by* **Dufour.**

Company

Blackstone Audio Books, Incorporated *See* **Blackstone Audio, Inc.**

Blackstone Audio, Inc., *(0-7861; 1-4332)* Orders Addr.: c/o Dept. LJ, P.O. Box 969, Ashland, OR 97520 USA Tel 541-482-9239; Fax: 541-482-9294; Toll Free: 800-729-2665; Edit Addr.: 31 Mistletoe Rd., Ashland, OR 97520 USA (SAN 173-2811)
E-mail: sales@blackstoneaudio.com
Web site: http://www.blackstoneaudio.com.

Blackstone Editions, *(0-9725017)* 11 S. Angell St. Pmb 2007, Providence, RI 02906 USA
E-mail: LynnGHughes@gmail.com
Web site: http://www.BlackstoneEditions.com.

Blacktypewriter Pr. *Imprint of* **Pittsburgh Literary Arts Network LLC**

Blackwell Publishers *See* **Blackwell Publishing, Inc.**

†Blackwell Publishing, Inc., *(0-631; 0-85012; 0-87993; 1-55786; 1-57718; 1-878975; 1-4051)* Orders Addr.: c/o AIDC, P.O. Box 20, Williston, VT 05495-0020 USA (SAN 680-5035) Tel 802-862-0095; Fax: 802-864-7626; Toll Free Fax: 800-864-7626; Toll Free: 800-216-2522; Edit Addr.: 350 Main St., 6th Flr., Malden, MA 02148-5018 USA (SAN 680-5035) Tel 781-388-8200; Fax: 781-388-8210
E-mail: books@blackwellpub.com; journalsrights@oxon.blackwellpublishing.com
Web site: http://www.blackwellpublishing.com
Dist(s): **American International Distribution Corp.**
Lightning Source, Inc.
Lippincott Williams & Wilkins
NetLibrary, Inc.; *CIP.*

Blackwell Publishing Ltd. (GBR) *(0-631; 0-632; 0-7279; 0-85238; 0-85520; 0-86216; 0-86542; 0-905774; 0-913848; 1-85075; 3-8263; 1-84127; 3-89412; 1-4051) Dist. by* **Blackwell Pubng.**

Blade Publishing, *(1-929409)* 110 W. C St. Ste. 1300, San Diego, CA 92101-3978 USA (SAN 254-7678)
E-mail: bladeinternational@yahoo.com.

BladeRunner Publishing, *(0-9785477)* P.O. Box 4298, Greenville, SC 29608 USA Tel 864-313-6182
E-mail: bladerunnerpublishing@charter.net.

Bladestar Publishing, *(0-9787931)* Orders Addr.: 1499 N. 950 W., Orem, UT 84057 USA Fax: 484-414-1674
E-mail: Promotion@BladestarPublishing.com
Web site: http://www.bladestarpublishing.com
Dist(s): **Brodart Co.**

Blair, John F. Pub., *(0-89587; 0-910244)* Orders Addr.: 1406 Plaza Dr., Winston-Salem, NC 27103 USA (SAN 201-4319) Tel 336-768-1374; Fax: 336-768-9194; Toll Free: 800-222-9796
E-mail: blairpub@blairpub.com
Web site: http://www.blairpub.com.

Blake, Edna, *(0-9668906)* 7 Babble Creek Ct., O Fallon, MO 63368-8321 USA.

Blake, John Publishing, Ltd. (GBR) *(0-905846; 1-85782; 1-903402; 1-904034; 1-84454) Dist. by* **IPG Chicago.**

Blake, Monica, *(0-9764155)* P.O. Box 475233, San Francisco, CA 94147 USA Tel 415-995-2515; Fax: 415-876-1002
E-mail: blakesfo@yahoo.com
Dist(s): **AtlasBooks Distribution.**

Blakk Phoxx Publishing *Imprint of* **RBC Publishing Co., Inc.**

Blancmange Publishing, *(0-9779488)* P.O. Box 17184, Memphis, TN 38187-7184 USA (SAN 850-7023).

Blandford Pr. (GBR) *(0-7137) Dist. by* **Sterling.**

Blanket Street Publishing, *(0-9760929)* 17278 Summit Hills Dr., Santa Clarita, CA 91387 USA
E-mail: kstrauss@socal.rr.com.

Blatant Times, *(0-9744376)* 608 Patton Rd., Great Bend, KS 67530 USA
Web site: http://www.cpcis.net.

Blaumond Pr., *(0-9789031)* 740 SE. Greenville Blvd., Suite 400, Box 283, Greenville, NC 27858 USA (SAN 851-9021) Tel 252-902-4509; Fax: 252-353-0732
E-mail: info@blaumondpress.com
Web site: http://www.blaumondpress.com.

Blaze, Ronan *See* **Medal Bks.**

Blessed Beginnings Publishing, *(0-9727201)* P.O. Box 241282, Milwaukee, WI 53223 USA Tel 414-351-6467
E-mail: pinksolitaire97@yahoo.com.

Blessing Our World, Inc., *(1-928777)* P.O. Box 185848, Fort Worth, TX 76181-0848 USA Toll Free: 800-729-1130 ; *Imprints:* BOW Books (BOW Bks)
E-mail: gerald@bowbooks.com; sales@blessworld.com
Web site: http://www.blessworld.com; http://www.bowbooks.com; http://www.markyseries.com; http://www.chrismouse.com; http://www.whatgoodis.com; http://www.whydaddywhy.com.

Blessings Unlimited, LLC, *(0-9742796)* P.O. Box 186, Highland Springs, VA 23075 USA Tel 804-640-7137 Do not confuse with Blessings Unlimited in Bloomington, MN
Web site: http://www.blessingsunlimited.info.

Blind Wolf Studios, *(0-9749941)* P.O. Box 465, Cross River, NY 10518 USA
Web site: http://www.blindwolfstudios.com.

Bliss on Tap, *(0-9763768)* 28326 Wellfleet Ln., Saugus, CA 91350 USA
E-mail: pephillipson@aol.com
Web site: http://www.godthedyslexicdog.com.

Blissful Biscuits, *(0-9702604)* 3083 Fallehn Dr., Cortland, OH 44410-9106 USA (SAN 254-5489) Toll Free: 888-880-8010
E-mail: bbiscuits@zomminternet.net; bbiscuits@zoominternet.com; blissfulbiscuits@netdotcom.com
Web site: http://www.blissfulbiscuits.com
Dist(s): **Ingram Bk. Co.**

Blizzard Publishing, Inc. (CAN) *(0-921368; 1-55215; 1-55331) Dist. by* **Consort Bk Sales.**

Bloch Publishing Co., *(0-8197)* 5875 Mining Ter. Ste. 104, Jacksonville, FL 32257-3225 USA (SAN 214-204X)
E-mail: BlochPub@worldnet.att.net
Web site: http://www.blochpub.com/.

Block, Jed, *(0-9672728)* 4300 Knollwood Ln., Appleton, WI 54915 USA Tel 920-735-6061; Fax: 920-735-6067
E-mail: jed@athenet.net
Web site: http://www.jedblock.com.

Block Publishing, *(0-9761625)* 1120 Forest Ave., No. 306, Pacific Grove, CA 93950 USA Fax: 831-655-4830
E-mail: blockpub@sbcglobal.net
Web site: http://www.blockpublishing.com.

Block System, The, *(0-9665545; 0-9800875)* 4619 Ranch View Rd., Fort Worth, TX 76109 USA Tel 817-732-2633; Fax: 817-732-0836
E-mail: andblock@gmail.com
Web site: http://www.blockcenter.com.

Bloess, Herman E., *(0-9716744)* Orders Addr.: P.O. Box 154, Warsaw, MO 65355 USA Tel 660-438-5131; Edit Addr.: 303 Seminary St., Warsaw, MO 65355 USA
E-mail: bloess@iland.net.

Blood Moon Productions, Ltd., *(0-9748118; 0-9786465)* 75 St. Marks Pl., Staten Island, NY 10301 USA Tel 718-556-9410; Fax: 718-816-4092
E-mail: DanforthPrince@hotmail.com
Web site: http://www.bloodmoonproductions.com
Dist(s): **Alamo Square Distributors**
Baker & Taylor Bks.
Bookazine Co., Inc.
Ingram Bk. Co.

Bloodaxe Bks. (GBR) *(0-906427; 1-85224) Dist. by* **Dufour.**

Blood-Horse, Inc., The, *(0-936032; 0-939049; 1-58150)* Div. of The Blood-Horse, Inc., 3101 Beaumont Centre Cir., Lexington, KY 40513 USA (SAN 203-5294) Tel 859-278-2361 (Retailers); Fax: 859-276-6868; Toll Free: 800-866-2361 (Retailers) ; *Imprints:* Eclipse Press (Eclip Press)
E-mail: info@eclipsepress.com
Web site: http://www.eclipsepress.com
Dist(s): **Ingram Pub. Services**
National Bk. Network
Western International, Inc.

Bloom & Grow Bks., *(1-931969)* Div. of Bloom & Grow, Inc., Orders Addr.: 149 S. Barrington Ave., #363, Los Angeles, CA 90049 USA Tel 310-472-0505; Fax: 310-472-1525
E-mail: stephanie@bloomandogrow.com; info@bloomandgrow.com
Web site: http://www.bloomandgrow.com; http://www.placetogrow.com
Dist(s): **BWI INC**
Baker & Taylor Bks.

Bloom & Grow, Incorporated *See* **Bloom & Grow Bks.**

Bloomberg Personal Bookshelf *Imprint of* **Bloomberg Pr.**

Bloomberg Pr., *(1-57660)* 731 Lexington Ave., New York, NY 10022 USA (SAN 298-6132) Tel 212-318-2000 ; *Imprints:* Bloomberg Personal Bookshelf (Blmbrg Pers Bkshlf)
E-mail: press@bloomberg.com
Web site: http://www.bloomberg.com/books
Dist(s): **Ingram Pub. Services.**

Bloomin' Tulip Studios, *(0-9672199)* 520 W. Foster Heights Rd., Rushville, IN 46173 USA Tel 765-938-1153
E-mail: jholland@lightbound.com
Web site: http://www.lightbound.com.

Blooming Tree Pr., *(0-9718348; 0-9769417; 1-933831)* Div. of Hees Enterprises, LLC, Orders Addr.: P.O. Box 140934, Austin, TX 78714-0934 USA Tel 512-921-8846; Fax: 512-873-7710; Edit Addr.: 10703 Jonwood Way, Austin, TX 78753 USA Tel 512-921-8846; Fax: 512-873-7710 ; *Imprints:* Ready Blade (Ready Blade)
E-mail: email@bloomingtreepress.com
Web site: http://www.bloomingtreepress.com
Dist(s): **Baker & Taylor Bks.**

Bloom's Literary Criticism *Imprint of* **Facts On File, Inc.**

Bloomsbury Children *Imprint of* **Bloomsbury Publishing**

Bloomsbury Pr., *(0-9667039)* 4340 Anza St., No. 6, San Francisco, CA 94121 USA Do not confuse with Bloomsbury Pr., Madison, WI.

Bloomsbury Publishing, *(1-58234; 1-59691; 1-59990)* Orders Addr.: 16365 James Madison Hwy., Gordonsville, VA 22942-8501 USA Toll Free: 888-330-8477; Edit Addr.: 175 Fifth Ave., Suite 300, New York, NY 10010 USA Toll Free: 888-330-8477 ; *Imprints:* Bloomsbury Children (Bloom Child)
E-mail: bloomsbury.kids@bloomsburyusa.com
Web site: http://www.bloomsburyusa.com
Dist(s): **Macmillan**
St. Martin's Pr.

Bloomsbury Publishing Plc (GBR) *(0-7475; 1-904970) Dist. by* **Trafalgar.**

Bloomsbury Publishing Plc (GBR) *(0-7475; 1-904970) Dist. by* **IPG Chicago.**

Bloomstreet Bks., *(0-9709750)* 2323 Huntington St., No. 904, Huntington Beach, CA 92648 USA Tel 714-434-8374
E-mail: bloomstreet@socal.rr.com.

BLPH, Inc., *(0-9759158; 0-9772425; 0-9791099)* P.O. Box 764, Springfield, OR 97477-0132 USA
E-mail: printing@bestlittleprinthouse.com
Web site: http://www.bestlittleprinthouse.com.

BLR Bks., *(0-9721839)* 94 Circle Dr., Waltham, MA 02452 USA
Dist(s): **Pathway Bk. Service.**

Blue Apple Bks., *(1-934706)* 515 Valley St., Suite 180, Maplewood, NJ 07040 USA (SAN 854-4727) Fax: 973-763-5944
E-mail: info@blueapplebooks.com
Web site: http://www.blueapplebooks.com
Dist(s): **Chronicle Bks. LLC.**

Blue Bear Publishing *See* **Beach Front Bks.**

Blue Begonia Pr., *(0-911287)* 225 S. 15th Ave., Yakima, WA 98902-3821 USA (SAN 268-3652) Tel 509-452-9748
E-mail: bodeen22@charter.net.

Blue Bk. Pubns., Inc., *(0-9625943; 1-886768)* 8009 34th Ave., S., Suite 175, Minneapolis, MN 55425 USA Tel 952-854-5229; Fax: 952-853-1486; Toll Free: 800-877-4867 Do not confuse with Blue Book Pubs., Inc. in La Jolla, CA
E-mail: bluebook@bluebookinc.com
Web site: http://www.bluebookinc.com
Dist(s): **Baker & Taylor Bks.**
Music Sales Corp.
Omnibus Pr.

Blue Boy Publishing Co., *(0-9742632)* P.O. Box 691, Camillus, NY 13031-0691 USA.

Blue Cat Bks, *(0-9779763)* P.O. Box 2818, Covina, CA 91722 USA Tel 626-339-1223
E-mail: info@bluecatpublishers.com
Web site: http://bluecatpublishers.com.

Blue Chip Publishing, *(0-9673970)* Orders Addr.: P.O. Box 26657, Austin, TX 78755 USA Tel 512-345-3021; Fax: 512-345-0181; Edit Addr.: 4119 Circletree Loop, Austin, TX 78731 USA Do not confuse with Blue Chip Publishing Corp., Keizer, OR
E-mail: MAMA19@aol.com.

Blue Cubicle Pr., LLC, *(0-9745900)* P.O. Box 250382, Plano, TX 75025-0382 USA Tel 972-824-0646 ; *Imprints:* Castle Builder Press (Castle Builder)
Web site: http://www.bluecubiclepress.com.

Blue Daylight Bks., *(0-9718849)* Orders Addr.: P.O. Box 805, Alpine, CA 91903 USA Tel 619-445-6033; Edit Addr.: 1829 Greenacres Dr., Alpine, CA 91901 USA.

Blue Devil Games, *(0-9763795)* P.O. Box 19359, Plantation, FL 33318 USA Tel 954-315-0920
Web site: http://www.bluedevilgames.com.

Blue Dog Productions, Inc., *(0-9627367)* 1690 Patrice Cir., Crofton, MD 21114-2919 USA.

Blue Dolphin Publishing, Inc., *(0-931892; 1-57733)* Orders Addr.: P.O. Box 8, Nevada City, CA 95959 USA (SAN 223-2480) Tel 530-265-6925; Fax: 530-265-0787; Toll Free: 800-643-0765; Edit Addr.: 12428 Nevada City Hwy., Grass Valley, CA 95945 USA (SAN 696-009X) ; *Imprints:* Papillon Publishing (Papillon Pubng)
E-mail: bdolphin@netshel.net; clemens@netshel.net
Web site: http://www.bluedolphinpublishing.com
Dist(s): **Baker & Taylor Bks.**
Koen-Levy Bk. Wholesalers LLC
Koen Pacific
New Concepts Bks. & Tapes Distributors
New Leaf Distributing Co., Inc.
Quality Bks., Inc.
Red Wheel/Weiser
Vision Distributors.

Blue Dragonfly Pubs., *(0-9648520)* 2400 E. Las Olas Blvd., PMB 310, Fort Lauderdale, FL 33301 USA Tel 954-525-6077; Fax: 954-522-7655
E-mail: bluedragonflypub@aol.com.

Blue Dream Studios, *(0-9789168)* 1133 Cedarview Ln., Franklin, TN 37067-4075 USA
Web site: http://www.bluedreamstudios.com
Dist(s): **Diamond Distributors, Inc.**

Blue Earth Bks. *Imprint of* **Capstone Pr., Inc.**

Blue Eyed Mayhem Publishing, *(0-9794545)* 6 Hopemont Dr., Mount Laurel, NJ 08054 USA Tel 609-781-0291.

Blue Fish, *(0-9703754)* 317 23rd, Galveston, TX 77550 USA Tel 409-750-8434
E-mail: jwk99@prodigy.net; jwk@my-freenet.com.

Blue Foot Pr. *Imprint of* **MidAmerica Publishing Co.**

Blue Fox Pr., *(0-9763119)* Pierce Arrow Bldg., 1685 Elmwood Ave., Suite 315, Buffalo, NY 14207-2407 USA Tel 716-447-1590; Fax: 716-837-7066
E-mail: bluefoxpress@yahoo.com
Web site: http://www.bluefoxpress.com.

Blue Heron Publishing, *(0-936085)* Orders Addr.: 1234 SW Stark St., Suite 1, Portland, OR 97205 USA Tel 503-223-2098; Fax: 503-223-9474; Edit Addr.: 4205 SW Washington St., Suite 303, Portland, OR 97204 USA (SAN 696-6446) Tel 503-221-6841; Fax: 503-221-6843 ; *Imprints:* West Coast Crime (West Coast Crime)
E-mail: pjt@blueheron.com
Web site: http://www.blueheron.com/.

Blue Heron Publishing Corporation *See* **Charnick Publishing Corp.**

Blue Horse Bks. *Imprint of* **Midwest Traditions, Inc.**

Blue Horse Mukwa Publishing, *(0-9707770)* 618 Hilltop W., Virginia Beach, VA 23451 USA Tel 757-425-7992; 757-425-7992; Fax: 757-425-2345
E-mail: yona@infi.net.

Blue Imp Bks. *Imprint of* **SterlingHouse Pubs., Inc.**

Blue Jay Bks. *Imprint of* **Crooked River Pr.**

Blue Jean Media, Incorporated *See* **Blue Jean Pr.**

Blue Jean Pr., *(0-9706609)* Div. of New Generation Media, Inc., Orders Addr.: P.O. Box 67111, Chestnut Hill, MA 02467 USA Tel 617-325-9852
E-mail: info@bluejeanpress.com
Web site: http://www.bluejeanpress.com
Dist(s): **Baker & Taylor Bks.**
Brodart Co.

Blue Kitty, The, *(0-9796814)* P.O. Box 254, Syracuse, NY 13214 USA
E-mail: info@thebluekitty.com.

Blue Lantern Books *See* **Laughing Elephant**

Blue Lantern Publishing, *(1-887303)* Orders Addr.: P.O. Box 5833, Kingwood, TX 77325-5833 USA Tel 281-358-2583; Fax: 281-361-5746; Edit Addr.: 4015 Pecan Pk., Kingwood, TX 77345 USA
E-mail: lanternblu@aol.com
Web site: http://www.geocities.com/SoHo/den/5463.

Blue Line Pro, *(1-888429)* Div. of Blue Line Productions, Orders Addr.: P.O. Box 6426, Florence, KY 41022 USA Tel 859-282-0096; Fax: 859-282-9412; Edit Addr.: 166 Mount Zion Rd., Florence, KY 41042-3272 USA
E-mail: info@bluelinepro.com
Web site: http://www.bluelinepro.com
Dist(s): **Diamond Bk. Distributors.**

Blue Line Pro Comics *See* **Blue Line Pro**

Blue Line Publishing, *(0-9657962)* 310 N. Park Dr., Raymore, MO 64083-9187 USA Do not confuse with companies with the same aor similar name in Chicago, IL, Lithonia, GA.

Blue Lion Productions, Ltd, *(0-9761132)* 302 Smith St., Freeport, NY 11520 USA Tel 516-546-4611
E-mail: info@bluelionproductions.com
Web site: http://www.bluelionproductions.com.

Blue Lobster Pr., *(0-9709569)* Orders Addr.: 3919 Union St., Levant, ME 04456-4358 USA
E-mail: books@bluelobsterpress.com; poet@robertpottle.com
Web site: http://www.bluelobsterpress.com.

Blue Marble Bks. *Imprint of* **Indigo Custom Publishing**

Blue Marlin Pubns., *(0-9674602; 0-9792918)* 823 Aberdeen Rd., West Bay Shore, NY 11706 USA Tel 516-666-0353 (phone/fax)
E-mail: jude@bluemarlinpubs.com
Web site: http://www.BlueMarlinPubs.com.

Blue Moon - Lee Pr., *(0-9667532)* 545 Terminal Ave., Modesto, CA 95350-5950 USA
E-mail: BluMoonP@aol.com.

Blue Mountain Arts Inc., *(0-88396; 1-58786; 1-59842)* Orders Addr.: P.O. Box 4549, Boulder, CO 80306 USA (SAN 299-9609) Tel 303-449-0536; Fax: 303-417-6434; Toll Free Fax: 800-943-6666; Toll Free: 800-525-0642 ; *Imprints:* Blue Mountain Press (Blue Mntn Pr); Rabbit's Foot Press (Rabb Ft Pr)
Web site: http://www.sps.com/
Dist(s): **Abingdon Pr.**

Blue Mountain Arts (R) by SPS Studios, Incorporated *See* **Blue Mountain Arts Inc.**

Blue Mountain Pr. *Imprint of* **Blue Mountain Arts Inc.**

Blue Mustang Pr., *(0-9759737)* 175B Mansfield Ave., Suite 240, Norton, MA 02766 USA Tel 206-350-2823 (phone/fax)
E-mail: info@bluemustangpress.com
Web site: http://www.bluemustangpress.com.

Blue Note Bks. *Imprint of* **Blue Note Pubns.**

Blue Note Pubns., *(1-878398)* Orders Addr.: 400 W. Cocoa Beach Cswy., Ste. 3, Cocoa Beach, FL 32931-5502 USA Toll Free: 800-624-0401 (order number) ; *Imprints:* Blue Note Books (Blue Note Bks)
E-mail: paul@bluenotebooks.com; editor@bluenotebooks.com
Web site: http://www.bluenotebooks.com
Dist(s): **American Wholesale Bk. Co.**

Blue Pig Productions, *(1-932545)* P.O. Box 691779, Orlando, FL 32869-1779 USA (SAN 255-4763) Tel 407-854-5679 (phone/fax)
E-mail: bluepigprod@aol.com
Web site: http://www.repunzal.com.

Blue Ribbon Publishing, *(0-9700993)* Div. of Blue Ribbon Commerical, 712 Bancroft Rd., Suite 513, Walnut Creek, CA 94598 USA Tel 925-202-3333; Toll Free Fax: 800-884-6685
E-mail: tomderkas@blueribboncommercial.com
Web site: http://www.franchiserealestate.com; http://www.retailrealestateexperts.com.

Blue River Publishing, Inc., *(1-884418)* 610 N. 23rd St., Colorado Springs, CO 80904 USA Tel 719-634-3918; Fax: 719-634-7559
E-mail: AKA.Jim@att.net.

Blue Shoe Publishing, *(0-9725552)* c/o Christine Merser, 38 W. 74th St., 3A, New York, NY 10023 USA Tel 212-579-0310
E-mail: inquiry@blueshoestrategy.com; inquiry@blueshoepublishing.com; LLim@BlueShoeStrategy.com
Web site: http://www.blueshoepublishing.com.

Blue Sky at Night Publishing, *(0-9768623)* 25679 360th Ave., Hillman, MN 56338-2431 USA
E-mail: polecatmb@yahoo.ca.

Blue Sky Ink, *(1-59475)* P.O. Box 1067, Brentwood, TN 37024-1067 USA (SAN 255-7401) Tel 805-677-6815
Dist(s): **STL Distribution North America.**

Blue Sky Pr., The *Imprint of* **Scholastic, Inc.**

Blue Sky Pr., *(0-9746896)* P.O. Box 6192, Malibu, CA 90264-6192 USA Tel 818-706-9814 Do not confuse with Blue Sky Press in San Jose CA, Placerville CO, Silver Spring MD, Berkeley CA, Dallas TX
E-mail: laura@lauralarsen.com
Web site: http://www.lauralarsen.com.

Blue State Pr., *(0-9773674)* 17771 Plumtree Ln., Yorba Linda, CA 92886 USA.

Blue Suit Bks., *(0-9748563)* P.O. Box 840057, New Orleans, LA 70184 USA (SAN 255-8998) Tel 504-450-4334
E-mail: bluesuit@imaginationmovers.com
Web site: http://www.imaginationmovers.com.

Blue Swan Bks., *(0-9703225)* Orders Addr.: P.O. Box 871388, Stone Mountain, GA 30087 USA; Edit Addr.: 984 Timbervale Ln., Lithonia, GA 30058 USA Tel 770-484-1121
E-mail: blueswanbooks@aol.com; blueswanpub@aol.com
Web site: http://www.blueswanbooks.com; http://cygnetbooks.com
Dist(s): **Baker & Taylor Bks.**
Brodart Co.

Blue Thistle Pr., *(0-9760505; 0-9786302)* P.O. Box 652, Van, TX 75790-0652 USA Tel 903-852-3032; Fax: 866-521-4068; Toll Free: 866-679-7323
Web site: http://www.lindaayers.com.

Blue Thunder One, Inc., *(0-9719284)* P.O. Box 2435, Riverview, MI 48192 USA.

Blue Tie Publishing, *(0-9777972)* 1 Hale Rd., East Hampton, CT 06424 USA Tel 860-267-0432
E-mail: tanner@sbcglobal.net.

Blue Tiger Publishing, *(0-9759903)* P.O. Box 3776, Glendale, CA 91221-0776 USA Tel 310-497-9291
E-mail: travis_english@charter.net.

Blue Unicorn Edition, LLC, *(1-891355; 1-58396)* 12300 NW 56th Ave., Gainesville, FL 32653 USA Toll Free Fax: 866-334-1497 (orders)
E-mail: blueunicorn@instabook.net
Web site: http://www.instabookpublisher.com.

Blue Unicorn Pr., Inc., *(0-9628584)* 5336 SE 17th Ave., Portland, OR 97202-4812 USA
E-mail: unicompapers@juno.com
Dist(s): **Baker & Taylor Bks.**
Brodart Co.

Blue Valley Bks., *(0-9661582)* 103 Johnstone St., Lexington, VA 24450-1817 USA
E-mail: maryskutt@earthlink.net.

Blue Vase Productions, *(0-9770125)* 3835 Cottonwood St., San Diego, CA 92113 USA (SAN 257-4454) Fax: 619-819-6311
E-mail: legal@eljarronazul.com; ventas@eljarronazul.com
Web site: http://www.eljarronazul.com.

Blue Willow Pr., *(0-9767473)* 197 Lamplight Ln., Bozeman, MT 59718 USA Tel 406-388-0272; Fax: 423-318-2329
E-mail: bluewillowpress@yahoo.com; obachs@juno.com
Web site: http://www.bluewillowpress.com.

Blue Windmill Bks., *(0-9670157)* Orders Addr.: P.O. Box 194, Blue Springs, MO 64013 USA; Edit Addr.: 1217 SW Arawak, Blue Springs, MO 64015 USA
E-mail: windmill@flash.net.

Blue Works *Imprint of* **Windstorm Creative**

Blue Zebra Entertainment, INc., *(0-9761350)* 4049 Madison Ave. Apt. 102, Culver City, CA 90232-3246 USA
Web site: http://www.nabiland.com.

Bluebird Meadows, *(0-9661776)* P.O. Box 0015, Stevensville, MI 49127 USA Tel 616-428-9919
E-mail: msbrown@qtm.net.

Bluebird Publishing, *(0-9718472)* 3768 W. Ben Holt, No. 16, Stockton, CA 95219 USA (SAN 254-4385) Tel 209-951-7686
E-mail: bluebirdpublish@aol.com
Dist(s): **American West Bks.**

Blue-Black Pr., *(0-9652827)* Div. of A & W Communications, Orders Addr.: P.O. Box 361765, Decatur, GA 30036 USA; Edit Addr.: 2724 Wesley Chapel Rd., Decatur, GA 30036 USA Do not confuse with Blue-Black, Inc., Avalon NJ
E-mail: Blueblackpress@aol.com
Dist(s): **Baker & Taylor Bks.**

Bluebonnet Classics, *(0-9708457)* 4216 Shadow Dr., Fort Worth, TX 76116 USA Tel 817-732-0787; Fax: 817-732-2075
E-mail: alex5u@airmail.net.

Bluebonnets, Boots & Bks., *(0-9645493; 0-9800061)* 11010 Hanning Ln., Houston, TX 77041-5006 USA
Web site: http://www.bluebonnetsbootsandbooks.com
Dist(s): **Book Marketing Plus**
Texas Connection Co.

Bluefish Bay Publishing, *(0-9707267; 0-9762251)* 5 N. Trident Pl., Saint Augustine, FL 32080 USA Tel 904-471-3142; Fax: 904-471-8463; Toll Free: 866-999-2583 (866-999-BLUE)
E-mail: dan@bluefishbay.com
Web site: http://www.bluefishbay.com.

Bluefish River Pr., *(0-9714701)* P.O. Box 1398, Duxbury, MA 02332 USA
E-mail: dpallao@aol.com
Web site: http://www.bluefishriverspress.com.

Bluegrass Publishing Inc., *(0-9745339; 0-9761925; 1-59978)* Orders Addr.: 318 S. 8th St., Mayfield, KY 42066 USA; Edit Addr.: P.O. Box 634, Mayfield, KY 42066 USA Tel 270-251-3600; Fax: 270-251-3603
E-mail: service@theultimateword.com; linda@theultimateword.com
Web site: http://www.bluegrasspublishing.com; http://www.theultimateword.com.

BlueLine Book Publishers *See* **Great American Pubs.**

BlueSky Publishing, *(0-9724386)* Div. of BlueSky Medical Group, Inc., 6965 El Camino Real Suite 105-602, Carlsbad, CA 92009 USA Tel 760-603-8130; 760-603-8331 (phone/fax)
E-mail: publishingdivision@blueskymedical.com
Web site: http://www.boypresident.com.

Bluestem Productions, *(0-9609064)* 381, Annapolis, MD 21404 USA (SAN 240-9747) Tel 410-849-2512; Fax: 410-849-2976
E-mail: cholsenius@aol.com
Dist(s): **Baker & Taylor Bks.**

Bluestocking Pr., *(0-942617)* Orders Addr.: P.O. Box 1014, Placerville, CA 95667 USA (SAN 667-2981) Tel 530-622-8586; Fax: 530-642-9222; Toll Free: 800-959-8586 (orders); Edit Addr.: 3333 Gold Country Dr., El Dorado, CA 95623 USA (SAN 667-299X)
E-mail: customerservice@BluestockingPress.com
Web site: http://www.BluestockingPress.com.

Bluestone Bks., *(0-9720046)* P.O. Box 761, Edmonds, WA 98020 USA
Web site: http://www.cmc.net/~jlwrig.

Bluewater Pubns., *(0-9719946; 1-934610)* 1812 CR 111, Killen, AL 35645 USA Tel 256-757-0829 Do not confuse with Heart Of Dixie Publishing Corporation in Foley, AL
E-mail: agapeed@aol.com; malcolm.broyles@gmail.com.

Bluewood Bks., *(0-912517)* Div. of The Siyeh Group, Inc., P.O. Box 689, San Mateo, CA 94010 USA (SAN 265-3214) Tel 650-548-0754; Fax: 650-548-0654
E-mail: Bluewoodb@aol.com
Dist(s): **LPC Group**
SCB Distributors.

Blume (ESP) *(84-89396; 84-932442; 84-95939)* *Dist. by* **IPG Chicago.**

Blumont Company, The, *(0-9776024)* 161 Great Rd., Littleton, MA 01460 USA (SAN 257-702X) Tel 781-899-6468
E-mail: slblu@netway.com.

Blushing Rose Publishing, *(1-884807)* P.O. Box 2238, San Anselmo, CA 94979-2238 USA Toll Free: 800-898-2263
Web site: http://www.blushingrose.com.

BMC Advertising, Incorporated *See* **BMCFerrell**

BMCFerrell, *(0-9764460; 0-9788242)* 2419 E. Skelly Dr., Tulsa, OK 74105 USA Tel 918-743-4600; Fax: 918-749-1895
Web site: http://www.bmcferrell.com.

BMF Pr., *(0-9659181)* Div. of BMF & Assocs., 613 Guy Walker Way, Durham, NC 27703 USA Tel 919-596-2245; Fax: 919-596-6009
Dist(s): **Baker & Taylor Bks.**

BMG, Incorporated *See* **RPM Publishing**

BNDC, *(0-9722647)* 21136 Nummer, Warren, MI 48089 USA Tel 646-286-5565
E-mail: bndcinfo@yahoo.com
Web site: http://www.bndc.info
Dist(s): **Lightning Source, Inc.**

Board Sports Management, *(0-9746953)* 503 Peregrine Dr., Indialantic, FL 32903 USA Tel 321-777-9935 (phone/fax)
E-mail: mvarnes@cfl.rr.com
Web site: http://www.hobgoods.com.

Bob Thomas Bks., *(0-9717682)* Orders Addr.: P.O. Box 853, Black Mountain, NC 28711 USA; Edit Addr.: P.O. Box 815, Kure Beach, NC 28449 USA Toll Free Fax: 866-615-0417.

Bobber Down Bks., LLC, *(0-9669961)* P.O. Box 46100, Madison, WI 53744-6100 USA Tel 608-845-3398; Fax: 608-831-6256
E-mail: bobbermike@aol.com.

Boca Raton Museum of Art, *(0-936859)* 501 Plaza Real, Mizner Park, Boca Raton, FL 33432 USA (SAN 278-2251) Tel 561-392-2500; Fax: 561-391-6410
E-mail: jkaminski@bocamuseum.org
Web site: http://www.bocamuseum.org
Dist(s): **Antique Collectors' Club**
RAM Pubns. & Distribution.

Bock, Stephen R. Publishing, *(0-9707513; 0-9764864)* 4615 Kugler Mill Rd., Cincinnati, OH 45236 USA Tel 513-791-0691
E-mail: srbock@fuse.net.

Bodkin Pointe Pr., *(0-9752684)* Orders Addr.: P.O. Box 654, Gibson Island, MD 21056 USA Tel 410-360-0838 (phone/fax)
E-mail: books@bodkinpointepress.com
Web site: http://www.bodkinpointepress.com.

Bodleian Library (GBR) *(1-85124; 0-900177)* *Dist. by* **Chicago Distribution Ctr.**

Body Tone Multimedia, *(0-9760650)* P.O. Box 580691, Elk Grove, CA 95758-0012 USA
E-mail: body_tone_multimedia@mac.com
Web site: http://www.bodytonemultimedia.com.

Bodycrafting Systems, Inc., *(0-9745265)* Orders Addr.: P.O. Box 1512, Nokomis, FL 34274 USA Fax: 941-484-9650
Web site: http://www.kidpowerfitness.com.

Boettcher, Ashley L., *(0-9768123)* Orders Addr.: P.O. Box 997, Southwick, MA 01077-0997 USA (SAN 256-5811) Tel 413-569-9492 available from 10am to 5pm m-f and 11am to 4pm sat; Edit Addr.: 45 Powder Mill Rd., Southwick, MA 01077 USA
E-mail: ljabphil413@juno.com
Web site: http://www.ALBbooks.com.

Bohemian Trash Studios, *(0-9767540)* 3322 Clearview, San Angelo, TX 76904 USA Tel 325-944-3282 ; *Imprints:* Star Cross'd Destiny (Star Cross)
Web site: http://www.bohemiantrash.com.

Bohobza Music, *(0-9744943)* P.O. Box 745, Teaneck, NJ 07666-0745 USA Tel 201-862-1692 (phone/fax)
E-mail: wetalkjazz@aol.com
Web site: http://www.ronibenhur.com.

Bois Pubns., *(0-9727967)* 5411 Colfax Pl., Oklahoma City, OK 73112 USA Tel 405-947 7988; Fax: 405-947-0977.

Bokmal Pr., *(0-9701441)* 2622 Fenwick Ct., Ann Arbor, MI 48104-6726 USA Tel 734 971 5823; 734-971-5823
E-mail: kuessner@wccnet.org.

†Bolchazy-Carducci Pubs., *(0-86516)* 1000 Brown St., Unit 101, Wauconda, IL 60084 USA (SAN 219-7685) Tel 847-526-4344; Fax: 847-526-2867; Toll Free: 800-392-6453
E-mail: jcull@bolchazy.com
Web site: http://www.bolchazy.com; *CIP.*

Bold Print, *(0-9647123)* P.O. Box 288, York, PA 17405-0288 USA Tel 717-846-5138; Fax: 717-843-3680; Toll Free: 800-551-8874.

Bold Venture Pr., *(0-9712246)* Orders Addr.: P.O. Box 64, Bordentown, NJ 08505 USA
E-mail: boldventurepress@aol.com
Web site: http://www.boldventurepress.com.

Bolder Bks. *Imprint of* **Random Hse. Children's Bks.**

Boldt.Entertainment, *(0-9662556)* 5867 Oakland Ave., Minneapolis, MN 55417 USA Tel 612-869-5999; Fax: 612-869-5995
E-mail: boldt@u-do.com
Web site: http://www.u-do.com.

Bollich, James J., *(0-9643275)* 128 Alabama Rd., Lafayette, LA 10501 USA Tel 318-235-0429.

Bollix Bks., *(1-932188)* 1609 W. Callender Ave., Peoria, IL 61606 USA
E-mail: staley.krause@insightbb.com
Web site: http://www.bollixbooks.com
Dist(s): **PSI (Publisher Services, Inc.).**

Bon Tiki Bks., *(0-9747072)* 8100 Thomas Dr., Panama City Beach, FL 32408 USA
E-mail: bontiki@knology.net
Web site: http://www.sparkythorne.com.

Bond, Ed Books *See* **Pulp Adventures, Inc.**

Bondcliff Bks., *(0-9657475; 1-931271)* Orders Addr.: P.O. Box 385, Littleton, NH 03561 USA Toll Free: 800-859-7581; Edit Addr.: 8 Bluejay Ln., Littleton, NH 03561 USA
E-mail: bondclif@ncia.net
Dist(s): **Peregrine Outfitters.**

Bonding with Baby Bks. *Imprint of* **Developing Hearts Systems, Inc.**

Company

Bongiorno Bks., *(0-9715819)* P.O. Box 83-2345, Richardson, TX 75083 USA Tel 972-671-6117; Fax: 972-671-0601
E-mail: info@bongiornobooks.com
Web site: http://www.tangledhearts.com; http://www.bongiornobooks.com
Dist(s): **Nonetheless Pr.**

Bonner, Larry, *(0-9747855)* 305 Chapwith Rd., Garner, NC 27529-4882 USA
Web site: http://www.bigrawhidebutte.com.

Bonneville Bks. *Imprint of* **Cedar Fort, Inc./CFI Distribution**

Bonnewitz, Roberta L., *(0-9700112)* 9717 Brook Ln., Raytown, MO 64133-6001 USA Tel 816-353-4023.

Bons Diversified Investment Co., *(0-9677864)* Orders Addr.: c/o Larry Umeh, P.O. Box 2031, Salt Lake City, UT 84110 USA Tel 801-359-3369 (phone/fax)
E-mail: Bonsobi@Yahoo.com.

Bonus Bks., Inc., *(0-929387; 0-931028; 0-933893; 1-56625)* 875 N. Michigan Ave., Suite 1416, Chicago, IL 60611 USA (SAN 630-0804) Tel 312-467-0580; Fax: 312-467-9271 ; *Imprints:* Volt Press (Volt Press)
E-mail: amanda@bonusbooks.com
Web site: http://www.bonusbooks.com
Dist(s): **National Bk. Network**
STL Distribution North America.

Boo Bks., Inc., *(1-887864)* 7628 S. Paulina, Chicago, IL 60620 USA Tel 312-873-1584; Toll Free: 800-205-1140.

Booger Red's Bks., Inc., *(0-9650751)* P.O. Drawer G, Clifton, CO 81520 USA Tel 970-434-4140
E-mail: booger-gj@att.net.

Book Bench, The, *(1-891142)* 617 Herschler Ave., Evanston, WY 82930 USA Tel 307-789-3642
E-mail: atterol@allwest.net.

Book Club of America, *(1-59384)* 1812 Front St., Scotch Plains, NJ 07076-1103 USA (SAN 255-3279) Do not confuse with Book Club of America in Mechanicsburg, PA
E-mail: dcarey@bookclubusa.com.

Book Co. Publishing Pty, Ltd., The (AUS) *(1-74047; 1-86309)* *Dist. by* **H Leonard.**

Book Co. Publishing Pty, Ltd., The (AUS) *(1-74047; 1-86309)* *Dist. by* **Penton Overseas.**

Book Ends, *(0-9677817)* 2001 N. Halsted St. Ste. 201, Chicago, IL 60614-4365 USA
E-mail: sacredflight@yahoo.com
Web site: http://www.sacredflight.com
Dist(s): **Independent Pubs. Group.**

Book Guild, Ltd. (GBR) *(1-85776; 0-86332; 1-84624)* *Dist. by* **Trans-Atl Phila.**

Book Her Publications *Imprint of* **Lyrically Korrect Publishing**

Book Jungle *Imprint of* **Standard Pubns., Inc.**

Book Nook Pr., *(0-9658983)* P.O. Box 598, Block Island, RI 02807 USA Tel 401-466-2993; Fax: 401-466-9936; Toll Free: 877-284-6665
E-mail: booknook@riconnect.com
Web site: http://www.booknookbi.com.

Bk. Nook Productions, *(0-9748990)* P.O. Box 101, Richmond, TX 77406 USA Tel 832-721-7655
E-mail: stephiemara@aol.com.

Book of Hope International, *(1-890525; 1-931940; 1-59480)* Div. of General Council of Assemblies of God, 3111 SW 10th St., Coral Springs, FL 33065 USA Tel 954-975-7777 Toll Free: 800-448-2425
E-mail: JodiEllis@bookofhope.net.

Book of Life International *See* **Book of Hope International**

Book of Signs Foundation, *(0-9773009)* 444 E. Roosevelt Rd., Suite 173, Lombard, IL 60148 USA.

Book Peddler, The *See* **Zeezok Publishing**

Book Peddlers, *(0-916773; 1-931863)* 2828 Hedberg Dr., Hopkins, MN 55305-3403 USA (SAN 653-9548) Toll Free: 800-255-3379
E-mail: vlansky@bookpeddlers.com
Web site: http://www.practicalparenting.com; http://www.bookpeddlers.com
Dist(s): **Gryphon Hse., Inc.**
Perseus Distribution
Skandisk, Inc.

Bk. Pubs. Network, *(1-887542; 0-9755407)* P.O. Box 2256, Bothell, WA 98041 USA Tel 425-483-3040; Fax: 425-483-3098
E-mail: sherynhara@earthlink.net
Web site: http://www.bookpublishersnetwork.com
Dist(s): **Seven Locks Pr.**

Book Pubs. of El Paso, *(0-944551)* a/o Book Publishers of El Paso, 1055-B Humble, El Paso, TX 79915 USA Tel 915-778-6670 (phone/fax) Do not confuse with Sundance Pr., Glen Carbon, IL
E-mail: bpep@ZiaNet.com.

†Book Publishing Co., The, *(0-913990; 1-57067; 0-9669317; 0-9673108)* P.O. Box 99, Summertown, TN 38483 USA (SAN 202-439X) Tel 931-964-3571; Fax: 931-964-3518; Toll Free: 888-260-8458 ; *Imprints:* Native Voices (Native Voices)
E-mail: bookpub@bookpubco.com
Web site: http://www.bookpubco.com
Dist(s): **Baker & Taylor Bks.**
Borders, Inc.
Four Winds Trading Co.
Integral Yoga Pubns.
New Leaf Distributing Co., Inc.
Nutri-Bks. Corp.
Partners Bk. Distributing, Inc.
Treasure Chest Bks.; *CIP.*

Book Sales, Inc., *(0-7858; 0-89009; 1-55521)* Orders Addr.: 114 Northfield Ave., Edison, NJ 08837 USA (SAN 169-488X) Tel 732-225-0530; Fax: 732-225-2257; 212-779-6058; Toll Free: 800-526-7257; Edit Addr.: 276 Fifth Ave., Suite 206, New York, NY 10001 USA (SAN 299-4062) Tel 212-779-4972; Fax: 212-779-6058 ; *Imprints:* Chartwell (Chrtwell)
E-mail: booksales@eclipse.net
Web site: http://www.booksales.com
Dist(s): **Continental Bk. Co., Inc.**

Bk. Shelf, *(0-9714160)* Orders Addr.: P.O. Box 946, Stratford, CT 06615 USA Tel 203-257-0158; Fax: 203-385-3481
E-mail: service@bookshelf123.com
Web site: http://www.bookshelf123.com.

Book Stops Here, *(0-9631612)* 1108 Rocky Point Ct., NE, Albuquerque, NM 87123 USA Tel 505-296-9047 (phone/fax)
E-mail: gldjvb@home.com
Web site: http://www.bookstopshere.com.

Book Street Pr., *(0-9628921)* Div. of Book Street, Inc., 230 E. Highland Ave., Philadelphia, PA 19118 USA Tel 215-247-2270.

Book Web Publishing, Ltd., *(0-9716567; 0-9795733)* P.O. Box 81, Bellmore, NY 11710 USA
E-mail: jeri@jerifink.com; donna@bookwebpublishing.com
Web site: http://www.bookwebpublishing.com.

Book Wholesalers, Inc., *(0-7587; 1-4046; 1-4131; 1-4155; 1-4156; 1-4287)* 1847 Mercer Rd., Lexington, KY 40511-1001 USA (SAN 135-5449) Toll Free: 800-888-4478
E-mail: jcarrico@bwibooks.com; lison@bwibooks.com
Web site: http://www.bwibooks.com.

Bookaroos Publishing, Inc., *(0-9678167)* Orders Addr.: P.O. Box 8518, Fayetteville, AR 72703 USA; Edit Addr.: 484 E. Pharris Dr., Fayetteville, AR 72703 USA
E-mail: books@bookaroos.com
Web site: http://www.bookaroos.com
Dist(s): **Baker & Taylor Bks.**
Follett Library Resources.

Bookazine Co., Inc., 75 Hook Rd., Bayonne, NJ 07002 USA (SAN 169-5665) Tel 201-339-7777; Fax: 201-339-7778; Toll Free: 800-221-8112.

BookBound Publishing, *(1-932367)* Orders Addr.: 26500 W. Agoura Rd., Suite 102-593, Calabasas, CA 91302 USA (SAN 256-3177) Tel 866-985-2665
E-mail: stacyquest@bookbound.net
Web site: http://www.bookbound.net; http://bookboundpublishing.com.

BookChamp LLC., *(0-9760111)* c/o Winter & Company P.C, 605 King Georges Post Rd., Fords, NJ 08863 USA
E-mail: info@bookchamp.net
Web site: http://www.bookchamp.net
Dist(s): **Chicago Review Pr., Inc.**
Independent Pubs. Group.

Bookcraft In Montclair *See* **Scribbulations LLC**

Bookcraft, Inc. *Imprint of* **Deseret Bk. Co.**

Bookends Pr., *(0-9724926; 0-9740922; 1-932667)* Orders Addr.: P.O. Box 14513, Gainsville, FL 32604 USA; 4130 NW 16th Blvd., Gainesville, FL 32604 Fax: 352-373-6905; Toll Free: 800-881-3208
E-mail: copyright@renaissance-printing.com
Web site: http://www.bookendspress.com
Dist(s): **Freeman Family Ministries**
Rosewood Foundation, The
StarCrossed Productions
Truth Pubns.

Bookhandler Pr., *(0-9700379)* 3597 Lomacitas Ln., Bonita, CA 91902 USA Tel 619-472-0471; Fax: 619-472-0418
E-mail: bookhandler@sprintmail.com
Web site: http://www.bookhandler.com.

Bookhaus Pubs., *(0-931613)* P.O. Box 691, Midlothian, VA 23113-0691 USA Tel 804-594-2887; Fax: 804-594-2886
E-mail: bookhaus@mich.com; bookhaus@bookhaus.com
Web site: http://www.bookhaus.com
Dist(s): **Perseus Distribution**
Quality Bks., Inc.

Book-Lab, *(0-87594)* Orders Addr.: P.O. Box 230206, New York, NY 10023-0206 USA Tel 212-874-5534; Fax: 212-874-3105; Toll Free: 800-654-4081
E-mail: BookLabpub@aol.com.

Booklines Hawaii, Ltd., *(1-929844; 1-58849; 1-60274)* Div. of Islander Group, 269 Pali'i St., Mililani, HI 96789 USA (SAN 630-6624) Tel 808-676-0116; Fax: 808-676-0634
E-mail: customerservice@booklines.com
Web site: http://www.booklineshawaii.com
Dist(s): **Islander Group.**

BOOKLINKS, *(0-9725800)* 983 Palmer Rd., Lithonia, GA 30058 USA Tel 770-482-1527
E-mail: booklinks4kids@yahoo.com.

Booklocker.com, Inc., *(1-929072; 1-931391; 1-59113; 1-60145)* P.O. Box 2399, Bangor, ME 04402 USA (SAN 254-363X) Fax: 207-262-5544
E-mail: booklocker@booklocker.com; writersweekly@writersweekly.com
Web site: http://www.booklocker.com; http://www.writersweekly.com.

Bookman Publishing *Imprint of* **Airleaf Publishing & Bookselling**

BookMann Pr. *Imprint of* **Mann Publishing Group**

Bookmark Bks., LLC, *(0-9764163)* P.O. Box 2996, Chester, VA 23831 USA Tel 804-706-6399 (phone/fax)
E-mail: bookmarkbooks@verizon.net
Dist(s): **Baker & Taylor Bks.**

Bookmark Pr., *(0-9672763)* Orders Addr.: P.O. Box 5162, Hauppauge, NY 11788 USA Tel 516-863-1215; Edit Addr.: 17 Acacia Rd., Kings Park, NY 11754 USA.

Bookmark Publishing, *(0-9653895)* Orders Addr.: P.O. Box 701413, San Antonio, TX 78270-1413 USA; Edit Addr.: 114 Donella Dr., San Antonio, TX 78232-1402 USA Tel 210-494-4439; Fax: 210-495-1423 Do not confuse with Bookmark Publishing, Phoenix, AZ
E-mail: bk@bookmarkpublishing.com
Web site: http://www.bookmarkpublishing.com.

Bookmark, The, *(0-930227)* Orders Addr.: 29021 Ave. Sherman, Unit 109, Santa Clarita, CA 91355 USA (SAN 694-6410) Tel 661-294-8022; Fax: 661-294-8027; Toll Free: 800-220-7767 Do not confuse with other companies with the same name in Marietta, GA, Knightstown, IN
E-mail: thebookmark@earthlink.net
Web site: http://www.thebookmark.com.

BookMasters, Inc., *(0-917889)* Orders Addr.: P.O. Box 388, Mansfield, OH 44903 USA (SAN 631-3566) Tel 419-281-1802; Fax: 419-281-6883; Toll Free: 800-247-6553; 30 Amberwood Pkwy., Ashland, OH 44805 Fax: 419-281-6886 Do not confuse with BookMasters, Burleson, TX
E-mail: info@bookmasters.com; order@bookmaster.com
Web site: http://www.bookmasters.com.

Bookmates *Imprint of* **Penny Laine Papers, Inc.**

BookMobile *See* **Syren Bk. Co.**

Book-On-Disc.Com, *(1-58519)* 3624 Simcoe Ct., Palm Harbor, FL 34684 USA Tel 727-785-2217
E-mail: Book@book-on-disc.com
Web site: http://www.book-on-disc.com.

BookPartners, Inc., *(0-9622269; 1-58151; 1-885221)* Orders Addr.: P.O. Box 345, Portland, OR 97205 USA; Edit Addr.: 620 SW Main, Portland, OR 97205 USA Tel 503-225-9900; Fax: 503-225-9901
Web site: http://www.arnicapublishing.com
Dist(s): **Arnica Publishing, Inc.**

Bookpublisher.com *See* **Wheatmark**

Books Are Fun, Ltd., *(0-9649777; 1-58209; 1-890409; 1-59795)* 1680 Hwy. 1 N., Fairfield, IA 52556 USA Tel 641-472-8301; Fax: 641-469-3915
E-mail: msmall@booksarefun.com
Web site: http://www.booksarefun.com
Dist(s): **Sandvik Publishing.**

Books By Anita, *(0-9662539)* 11453 Oceanspray Blvd., Englewood, FL 34224 USA Tel 941-474-2797; 941-474-4882; Fax: 941-474-4882
E-mail: Lancelot@myexcel.com.

Books By Byers, *(1-929663)* Orders Addr.: 321 Links Dr. Apt. 103, Lowell, AR 72745-8322 USA
E-mail: spbyers@booksbybyers.com
Web site: http://www.booksbybyers.com.

Bks. by Matt, *(0-9727660)* 33 Stoddard Way, Berkeley, CA 94708 USA Tel 510-849-2986; Fax: 510-849-1012
E-mail: mylamby@hotmail.com.

Books for Black Children, Inc., *(1-58521)* Orders Addr.: P.O. Box 13261, Reading, PA 19612 USA Tel 610-376-6996; Toll Free Fax: 610-375-0992; Edit Addr.: 1318 Pike St., Reading, PA 19612 USA
E-mail: bbc-inc@att.net
Web site: http://www.booksforblackchildren.com.

Books for Brats *Imprint of* **Little Redhaired Girl Publishing, Inc.**

Books for Children of the World, *(0-9661186; 0-9762078)* 6701 N. Bryant Ave., Oklahoma City, OK 73121 USA Tel 405-721-7417; Fax: 405-478-4352; Toll Free: 888-838-0003.

Bks. Leaving Footprints, *(0-9765432)* 861 W. US 10, Scottville, MI 49454 USA Tel 231-757-2205
E-mail: info@booksleavingfootprints.com
Web site: http://www.booksleavingfootprints.com.

Bks. of Slovenia, Div. of Delphi Assocs., 453 Rialto Ave., Venice, CA 90291 USA Tel 310-392-4843; Fax: 310-396-3574
E-mail: BooksofSlovenia@comcast.net
Web site: http://www.BooksofSlovenia.com.

Books of Truth, *(0-939399)* 1742 Orchard Dr., Akron, OH 44333-1853 USA (SAN 663-1312) Tel 330-666-3852
E-mail: ccrook@mango-bay.com.

Books on Tape, Inc., Div. of Random House, Inc., Orders Addr.: 400 Hahn Road, Westminster, MD 21157 USA Tel 410-848-1900; Toll Free: 800-726-0600 (customer service); Edit Addr.: 1745 Broadway, New York, NY 10019 USA (SAN 107-0460) Tel 212-782-9000; Toll Free: 800-626-3333
E-mail: botcs@booksontape.com
Web site: http://library.booksontape.com; http://www.booksontape.com.

Books on the Path, *(0-9743390)* P.O. Box 436, Barker, TX 77413-0436 USA Tel 281-492-6050; Fax: 832-201-7620; Toll Free: 866-875-7284
E-mail: info@patriarchspath.org
Web site: http://www.booksonthepath.com.

Books To Believe In *Imprint of* **Thornton Publishing**

Bks. To Enjoy.com, Inc., *(0-9707034)* 1114 23rd St., No. 3, Santa Monica, CA 90403 USA Tel 310-453-9493; Fax: 509-756-1161
E-mail: books@bookstoenjoy.com
Web site: http://www.bookstoenjoy.com.

Books To Remember *Imprint of* **Flyleaf Publishing**

Bks. Unbound E-Publishing Co., *(1-59201)* 1110 Kerwin St., Piscataway, NJ 08854-3323 USA
Web site: http://www.booksunbound.com.

Books2Go, *(1-59590)* 780 Reservoir Ave., Suite 243, Cranston, RI 02910 USA Tel 401-537-9175
E-mail: books2go@writerscollective.net
Web site: http://www.mybooks2go.com
Dist(s): **Baker & Taylor Bks.**

BooksbyDave Inc., *(0-9768867)* Orders Addr.: 5010 James loop, Killeen, TX 76542 USA Tel 254-628-1961
E-mail: project17us@yahoo.com
Web site: http://www.geocities.com/oilsbydave.

Booksforboys, *(0-9761440)* 8 Marigold Ct., Holtsville, NY 11742 USA
Web site: http://booksforboys.com.

Bookshelf Global Publishing, *(0-9755395; 0-9766954; 0-9779012; 0-9800430)* 3975 Hwy. 138 SW, Stockbridge, GA 30281 USA (SAN 850-4652) Tel 770-860-0168; Fax: 404-420-2420
E-mail: office@bookshelfglobal.com
Web site: http://www.bookshelfglobal.com.

Booksmart Pubns., *(0-9790896)* Orders Addr.: P.O. Box 4774, Mission Viejo, CA 92690 USA (SAN 852-4211) Tel 949-462-0076; Edit Addr.: 19 Bolero, Mission Viejo, CA 92692 USA
E-mail: b_smart@cox.net
Web site: http://www.booksmartpublications.com.

Booksmiles Pr., *(0-9671903)* P.O. Box 24140, Lexington, KY 40524-4140 USA (SAN 253-9683)
E-mail: booksmilespress@aol.com
Web site: http://www.booksmiles.com.

Booksmythe, *(0-945585)* 17216 Saticoy St., No. 360, Van Nuys, CA 91406-2103 USA (SAN 247-3585) Tel 818-343-1648; Fax: 818-343-0274; Toll Free: 800-788-0064
E-mail: russ@booksmythe.com
Web site: http://www.booksmythe.com
Dist(s): **Majors, J. A. Co.**
Rittenhouse Bk. Distributors.

booksonnet.com *Imprint of* **Pelican Pr.**

Booksource, The, *(0-7383; 0-911891; 0-9641084; 1-890760; 1-60446)* Orders Addr.: 1230 Macklind Ave., Saint Louis, MO 63110-1432 USA (SAN 631-8371); Edit Addr.: 1230 Macklind Ave., Saint Louis, MO 63110-1432 USA (SAN 169-4324) Tel 314-647-0600; Fax: 314-647-2422; Toll Free Fax: 800-647-1923; Toll Free: 800-444-0435
E-mail: vstadts@freewwweb.com
Web site: http://www.booksource.com.

Bookstand Publishing, *(1-58909)* 305 Vineyard Town Ctr., Suite 280, Morgan Hill, CA 95037 USA Tel 408-852-1832; Fax: 408-852-1812
E-mail: orders@bookstandpublishing.com
Web site: http://www.BookstandPublishing.com; http://.

BookSurge, LLC, *(1-58898; 1-59109; 1-59456; 1-59457; 1-4196; 1-4348)* Div. of Amazon.com, Orders Addr.: 7290 Investment Dr., #B, North Charleston, SC 29418-8302 USA (SAN 255-2132) Toll Free: 866-308-6235
E-mail: customerservice@booksurge.com; orders@booksurge.com
Web site: http://www.booksurge.com.

Bookworm Bks., *(0-9749423)* P.O. Box 77277, Washington, DC 20013 USA (SAN 255-8874) Fax: 202-387-5127; Toll Free: 877-302-0067
E-mail: info@bookwormbooks.biz
Web site: http://www.bookwormbooks.biz
Dist(s): **Independent Pubs. Group.**

BookWorm, The, *(1-57397)* Creativity Unlimited, Orders Addr.: P.O. Box 2176, Hot Springs, AR 71914-2176 USA Tel 501-622-0633; P.O. Box 2176, Hot Springs, AR 71914-2176 Tel 501-622-0633
E-mail: optimum@cablelynx.com; creativityunlimited@cablelynx.com
Web site: www.optimumpublishing.com.

Boom! Studios, *(1-934506)* 1800 Century Pk. E., Suite 200, Los Angeles, CA 90067 USA Tel 310-895-7746
E-mail: boomstudios@gmail.com; codydematteisboom@gmail.com
Web site: http://www.boom-studios.com
Dist(s): **Perseus Distribution.**

Boone, Angela, *(0-9745112)* P.O. Box 24982, Detroit, MI 48224 USA
E-mail: aboone@angelaboone.com
Web site: http://www.AngelaBoone.com.

Boone Bks., *(0-9765294)* P.O. Box 262147, Plano, TX 75026-2147 USA Toll Free: 800-755-6628
E-mail: cadprof@boonebooks.com
Web site: http: www.boonebooks.com.

Boot Prints, *(1-885548)* 701 College St., Spooner, WI 54801 USA Tel 715-635-2317 (phone/fax).

Boot the Mule & Company *See* **Glory to Glory Ministries**

Booth, John Harvey, *(0-9754291)* 246 Schilling St., West Lafayette, IN 47906 USA Tel 765-743-8728
E-mail: jhbooth2003@yahoo.com.

Bopar Bks., *(0-9759718)* 3375 Homestead Rd., Park City, UT 84098 USA Tel 435-640-4176
Web site: http://www.himynameisjack.com.

BOPO Biligual Bks., *(0-9665575)* P.O. Box 4713, Marietta, GA 30061-4713 USA Tel 770-432-9859 (phone/fax); Toll Free: 800-251-3423
E-mail: publisher@bopobooks.com
Web site: http://www.bopobooks.com.

Boptism Music Publications *See* **Boptism Music Publishing**

Boptism Music Publishing, *(0-9717983; 0-9726185; 0-9777503)* Orders Addr.: 23 Oakwood Rd., Candler, NC 28715 USA Tel 828-665-1405; Edit Addr.: 916 Union St., Apt. 2-C, Brooklyn, NY 11215 USA Tel 718-638-2767; Fax: 718-638-2613
E-mail: trbnplyr@aol.com; boptism@charter.net
Web site: http://www.boptism.com.

Border Pr., *(0-9650977)* 211 Celeste Dr., New Iberia, LA 70560 USA Tel 318-364-6730; Fax: 318-365-7427.

Borders Group, Inc., *(0-681)* 100 Phoenix Dr., Ann Arbor, MI 48108 USA Tel 734-477-1100
Web site: http://www.borders.com.

Borders Personal Publishing, *(1-4134)* a/o Pam Durant, 2 International Plaza, Suite 340, Philadelphia, PA 19113 USA Tel 610-915-5214; Fax: 610-915-0294; Toll Free: 888-795-4274
E-mail: dave@xlibris.com
Dist(s): **Xlibris Corp.**

Borders Pr., *(0-681)* Div. of Borders Group, Inc., 100 Phoenix Dr., Ann Arbor, MI 48108 USA
Web site: http://www.bordersstores.com; http://www.bordersgroupinc.com; http://www.borders.com.

Bordighera Incorporated, *(1-884419; 1-59954)* Orders Addr.: P.O. Box 1374, Lafayette, IN 47902-1374 USA; Edit Addr.: John D. Calandra Italian American Institute 25 W. 43rd St., 17th Flr., New York, NY 10036 USA Tel 212-642-2005
E-mail: dstarewich@verizon.net; anthony.tamburri@qc.cuny.edu
Dist(s): **SPD-Small Pr. Distribution.**

Borealis Bk. *Imprint of* **Minnesota Historical Society Pr.**

Borealis Pr., *(0-9632651)* 1935 Morgan Bay Crossroad, Surry, ME 04684 USA Tel 207-667-3700; Fax: 207-667-9649; Toll Free: 800-669-6845.

Born To Be Wild, LLC, *(0-9707002)* P.O. Box 1134, Truro, MA 02666 USA Tel 508-349-1795; Fax: 508-349-1754
E-mail: bewildtoys@aol.com.

Born to Blaze Ministries, *(0-9762910)* 2131 20th St SE, Buffalo, MN 55313-4813 USA
E-mail: info@borntoblaze.com
Web site: http://www.borntoblaze.com.

borntalking.com, *(0-9720892)* 34116 Blue Heron Dr., Solon, OH 44139-5641 USA
E-mail: david@borntalking.com
Web site: http://www.borntalking.com
Dist(s): **Baker & Taylor Bks.**

Borromeo Bks., *(0-9763098)* Orders Addr.: P.O. Box 7273, Saint Paul, MN 55107 USA
E-mail: borromeo.books@juno.com
Web site: http://www.borromeobooks.com.

Boshu Pr., *(0-9755624)* 3 Dogwood Ct., Greenville, NC 27858 USA
E-mail: boshucelli@earthlink.net.

Boss Paws Publishing, *(0-9769058)* 2536 Ridgewood Ave., Louisville, KY 40217 USA Tel 502-649-6864
E-mail: ag@animalgambill.org.

Bosse, Andre Ctr., *(0-9786128)* 302 Hanson St., Hart, MI 49420-1385 USA Tel 231-873-1707; Fax: 231-873-1456
E-mail: maltbie7@charter.net
Web site: http://www.andrebossecenter.org.

Boston Mills Pr. (CAN) *(0-919783; 0-919822; 1-55046) Dist. by* **Firefly Bks Limited.**

Botanical Society of Western PA, *(0-9710614)* 3333 Fifth Ave., Pittsburgh, PA 15213 USA Tel 412-578-6175; Fax: 412-578-8728
E-mail: mjhaywood@carlow.edu.

Botel, Morton Assocs., *(1-891564)* 3454 W. Penn St., Philadelphia, PA 19129 USA Tel 215-848-4646; Fax: 215-848-7255
E-mail: morton.botel@verizon.net
Web site: http://www.mortbotel.com.

Botero de Borrero, Beatriz & Martha Olga Botero de Gomez (COL) *(958-33) Dist. by* **Lectorum Pubns.**

Bottom Dog Pr., *(0-933087; 1-933964)* c/o Firelands College, P.O. Box 425, Huron, OH 44839 USA (SAN 689-5492) Fax: 419-433-9696
E-mail: LSmithDog@aol.com
Web site: http://www.members.aol.com/lsmithdog/bottomdog
Dist(s): **Baker & Taylor Bks.**
SPD-Small Pr. Distribution.

Boudelang Pr., *(0-9649742; 1-930124)* Orders Addr.: P.O. Box 12379, Portland, OR 97212-0379 USA Tel 310-821-2450; Fax: 310-821-5133; Edit Addr.: 1138 Grant Ave., Venice, CA 90291 USA
E-mail: Boudelang@aol.com
Web site: http://www.boudelang.com
Dist(s): **Baker & Taylor Bks.**
Partners/West.

Boudreaux Cajun General Store, *(0-9676002)* Orders Addr.: c/o Boudreaux Cajun General Store, 11033 Suncrest Ave., Baton Rouge, LA 70818-6920 USA
E-mail: cousin@boudreaux.com
Dist(s): **American Wholesale Bk. Co.**
Forest Sales & Distributing Co.

Bougie, Victoria *See* **Alvin Bks., Inc.**

Bouje Publishing, LLC, *(0-9779265)* 1101 Juniper St., Suite 602, Atlanta, GA 30309 USA.

Boulden Publishing, *(1-878076; 1-892421)* Div. of Turtle Pine, Inc., Orders Addr.: P.O. Box 1186, Weaverville, CA 96093-1186 USA Tel 530-623-5399; Fax: 530-623-5525; Toll Free: 800-238-8433
E-mail: ken@bouldenpublishing.com
Web site: http://www.bouldenpublishing.com
Dist(s): **MAR*CO Products, Inc.**
Social Studies Schl. Service
Sunburst Communications, Inc.

Bouncing Ball Bks., Inc., *(1-934138)* P.O. Box 6509, Spring Hill, FL 34611-6509 USA (SAN 851-6073)
E-mail: bouncingballbooks@yahoo.com
Web site: http://www.bouncingballbooks.com.

Bound & Determined Pubs., *(0-9704006)* Orders Addr.: P.O. Box 233, South Otselic, NY 13155 USA
E-mail: marcotte@kornet.net
Web site: http://www.sover.net/~niliacus/a&h/.

Bound By Faith Publishing, *(0-9741009)* 17333 Paoli Way, Parker, CO 80134 USA Tel 303-875-8742
E-mail: rhonda@boundbyfaith.biz
Web site: http://www.boundbyfaith.biz.

Boundaries Publishing Co., The, *(0-9672214)* Orders Addr.: 540 Mears St., Chadron, NE 69337 USA Tel 308-432-5676 (phone/fax)
E-mail: montanacabin@fastermac.net.

Bounty Project, The, *(0-9665861)* 6310 Georgetown Pike, McLean, VA 22101 USA Tel 703-442-7557
E-mail: kjackson@1771.org.

BOW Bks. *Imprint of* **Blessing Our World, Inc.**

Bow Historical Bks.,
Dist(s): **Oxford Univ. Pr., Inc.**

Bowden, Gill Consulting Services *See* **APTAC Publishing**

Bowden Music Co., *(0-9702219)* 1511 Grand Ave., Fort Worth, TX 76106 USA Tel 817-624-1547 (phone/fax)
E-mail: essieb@mindspring.com.

Bowman Communications, Inc., *(0-9670381)* P.O. Box 1626, Twin Falls, ID 83303-1626 USA Tel 208-735-0777; Fax: 208-734-0832
E-mail: bowcom@magiclink.com.

Bowmar/Noble Pubs., *(0-8107; 0-8372)* 220 E. Danieldale Dr., De Soto, TX 75115-2490 USA (SAN 201-4157).

BowTie Pr., *(0-9629525; 1-882770; 1-889540; 1-931993; 1-59378; 1-933958)* Div. of Fancy Pubns., Inc., Orders Addr.: P.O. Box 6050, Mission Viejo, CA 92690-0050 USA (SAN 298-5888) Tel 949-855-8822; Fax: 949-458-3856; Edit Addr.: 3 Burroughs, Irvine, CA 92618-2804 USA (SAN 298-5896)
Web site: http://www.bowtiepress.com
Dist(s): **MBI Publishing Co. LLC**
Perseus Distribution.

Box Girls, The, *(0-9769908)* 149 S. Barrington Ave, No. 126, Los Angeles, CA 90049 USA Fax: 310-440-0145
Web site: http://www.theboxgirls.com.

Boxer Bks., Ltd. (GBR) *(0-9547373; 1-905417) Dist. by* **Sterling.**

Boy Scouts of America, *(0-8395)* Orders Addr.: P.O. Box 7143, Charlotte, NC 28241-7143 USA (SAN 284-9801) Tel 704-588-4260; Fax: 704-588-5822; Toll Free: 800-323-0732; Edit Addr.: P.O. Box 152079, Irving, TX 75015-2079 USA (SAN 284-9798)
Web site: http://www.bsa.scouting.org.

Boyars, Marion Pubs., Inc., *(0-7145; 0-905223)* 237 E. 39th St., No. 1A, New York, NY 10016-2110 USA (SAN 284-981X) Tel 212-697-1599; Fax: 212-808-0664; Toll Free: 800-283-3572 (orders only)
Dist(s): **Consortium Bk. Sales & Distribution.**

Boyd Publications *See* **MEGA Corp.**

Boydell & Brewer, Inc., *(0-85115; 0-85991; 0-907239; 0-938100; 1-57113; 1-58046; 1-85566; 1-870252; 1-878822; 1-879751; 1-900639; 1-84384; 1-84383)* Div. of Boydell & Brewer Group, Ltd., Orders Addr.: 668 Mount Hope Ave., Rochester, NY 14620-2731 USA (SAN 013-8479) Tel 585-275-0419; Fax: 585-271-8778
E-mail: boydell@boydellusa.net; boydell@boydell.co.uk
Web site: http://www.boydellandbrewer.com.

Boyden Publishing, *(0-9655858)* 1520 Fennel Rd., Pennsburg, PA 18073 USA Tel 215-679-5433
E-mail: nona_ondra@hotmail.com; nona_ondra@yahoo.com
Web site: http://www.boydenpublishing.com.

Boyds Collection Ltd., The, *(0-9712840; 0-9713174)* 350 South St., McSherrystown, PA 17344 USA Tel 717-633-9898
E-mail: alana@boydsstuff.com
Web site: http://www.boydsstuff.com.

Boyds Mills Pr., *(1-56397; 1-878093; 1-886910; 1-59078; 1-932425)* Div. of Highlights For Children, Inc., 815 Church St., Honesdale, PA 18431-1877 USA (SAN 852-3177) Tel 717-253-1164; 570-251-4513; Fax: 570-253-0179; Toll Free: 800-490-5111 ; *Imprints:* Wordsong (Wordsong); Calkins Creek (Calkins Creek); Front Street (FrtSt); Lemniscaat (Lemnisca)
E-mail: admin@boydsmillspress.com
Web site: http://www.boydsmillspress.com
Dist(s): **Lectorum Pubns., Inc.**

Boynton/Cook *Imprint of* **Heinemann**

Boys Town, Nebraska Center, Public Service Division *See* **Boys Town Pr.**

Boys Town Pr., *(0-938510; 1-889322; 1-934490)* Div. of Father Flanagan's Boys' Home, Orders Addr.: 14100 Crawford St., Omaha, NE 68010 USA (SAN 215-8477) Tel 402-498-1320; Fax: 402-498-1310; Toll Free: 800-282-6657
E-mail: btpress@boystown.org
Web site: http://www.boystownpress.org
Dist(s): **Baker & Taylor Bks.**
Brodart Co.
Quality Bks., Inc.

Boyte, Jack O., *(0-9638262)* Orders Addr.: P.O. Box 6093, Charlotte, NC 28207 USA Tel 704-375-4243; Edit Addr.: 2222 Selwyn Ave., No. 503, Charlotte, NC 23207 USA
Web site: http://www.athomecharlotte.com/welcome/jack_orr_boyte.htm.

Boz Imagineering, *(0-9679395)* 2901 Clint Moore Rd., PMB 237, Boca Raton, FL 33496 USA (SAN 253-4096) Tel 561-912-9492; Fax: 561-893-9898
E-mail: cbosworthr@cs.com.

BPT Media, *(0-9772126)* P.O. Box 28663, Philadelphia, PA 19151-0663 USA
E-mail: bptmedia@aol.com.

BR Anchor Publishing, *(0-9627470; 1-888891)* 2044 Montrose Ln., Wilmington, NC 28405-6208 USA Tel 910-256-9598; Fax: 910-256-9579; Toll Free: 800-727-7691
E-mail: broman@branchor.com; questions@branchor.com
Web site: http://www.branchor.com.

Brad Smiley *See* **Kennesaw Publishing**

Bradford Pr., *(0-9705618)* Orders Addr.: P.O. Box 6802, South Bend, IN 46660-6802 USA Do not confuse with companies with same name in Bradford, MA, Palm Beach, FL, Chicago, IL
E-mail: BradfordPress@comcast.net.

Bradford Publishing Co., *(1-883726; 1-932779)* 1743 Wazee St., Denver, CO 80202 USA Tel 303-292-2500; Fax: 303-298-5014; Toll Free: 800-446-2831 Do not confuse with Bradford Publishing Company, San Francisco, CA
E-mail: candace@bradfordpublishing.com
Web site: http://www.bradfordpublishing.com.

Brady Computer Books *See* **Brady Publishing**

Brady GAMES, *(0-7440)* 800 E. 96th St., Indianapolis, IN 46240 USA Tel 317-428-3333
Web site: http://www.bradygames.com
Dist(s): **Dorling Kindersley Publishing, Inc.**
Pearson Education.

Brady Publishing, *(0-8359; 0-87618; 0-87619; 0-89303; 0-913486; 1-56686; 0-7440)* Div. of Prentice Hall, 201 W. 103rd St., Indianapolis, IN 46290 USA Tel 317-581-3500; Fax: 317-705-6290; Toll Free Fax: 800-835-3202; Toll Free: 800-428-5331 (orders); 800-571-5840
E-mail: janet.eshenour@bradygames.com
Web site: http://www.bradygames.com
Dist(s): **Alpha Bks.**
Dorling Kindersley Publishing, Inc.
Pearson Technology Group.

BradyBooks *See* **Nature Works Press**

Company

Bradybooks.biz, *(0-9754169)* 1888 County Road 72., Bailey, CO 80421-2175 USA
E-mail: readbradybooks@aol.com
Web site: http://bradybooks.biz.

Bragdon, Allen D. Pubs., Inc., *(0-916410)* Orders Addr.: Tupelo Rd., Bass River, MA 02664 USA; Edit Addr.: 252 Great Western Rd., South Yarmouth, MA 02664-2210 USA (SAN 208-5623) Tel 508-398-4440; Fax: 508-760-2397; Toll Free: 877-876-2787 ; *Imprints:* BrainWaves Books (BrainWaves)
E-mail: abragdon@brainwaves.com; admin@brainwaves.com
Web site: http://www.brainwaves.com.

Braided Image, *(0-9725170)* 3064 Old New Cut Rd., Springfield, TN 37172 USA ; *Imprints:* Braided Image Hair Briading (Braided Im Hair Br)
E-mail: masterbraider@mindspring.com
Web site: http://www.braidedimage.com.

Braided Image Hair Briading *Imprint of* **Braided Image**

BrailleInk, *(0-9769313)* 1704 Holly St., Austin, TX 78702-5424 USA Toll Free: 800-324-2919
E-mail: info@brailleink.org
Web site: http://www.brailleink.org.

Brain Child Bks., *(0-9771010)* 13324 Beckenham Dr., Little Rock, AR 72212-3710 USA
E-mail: phelan@aristotle.net.

Brain Injury Assn. of Kentucky, *(0-9709615)* 7410 New Lagrange Rd. Ste. 100, Louisville, KY 40222-4871 USA Toll Free: 800-592-1117
E-mail: director@braincenter.org
Web site: http://www.braincenter.org.

BrainBox, Ltd., *(0-9754539)* P.O. Box 26, Morris, AL 35116 USA
E-mail: saril@aol.com
Web site: http://www.infiniteodyssey.com
Dist(s): **Baker & Taylor Bks.**

Brainchild Publishing *See* **Mindfull Publishing**

Brainerd Enterprises, *(0-9747441)* 419 Old Clyde Pk. Rd., Livingston, MT 59047 USA Tel 406-222-8273
E-mail: sjbrainerd@ycsi.net.

BrainFriendly Learning, *(0-9759226)* 6801 6th St., NW, Washington, DC 20012-1911 USA Tel 202-723-7337; Fax: 202-726-6117
E-mail: stevecarroll@speakeasy.net
Web site: http://www.kathleencarroll.com.

Brainstorm Co., The, *(0-9728354)* Orders Addr.: 11684 Ventura Blvd., No. 970, Studio City, CA 91604 USA (SAN 255-5174) Tel 818-763-2674
E-mail: weddinggames@hotmail.com
Web site: http://www.TheBrainstormCompany.com
Dist(s): **Independent Pubs. Group.**

Brainstorm Pubns., Inc., *(0-9723429)* 24 NE 24th Ave., Pompano Beach, FL 33062 USA Tel 954-941-3329; Fax: 954-943-7708 Do not confuse with Brainstorm Publications in Lake Oswego, OR
E-mail: tditocco@brainstormpublications.com
Web site: http://www.brainstormpublications.com
Dist(s): **Biblio Distribution.**

BrainStorm 3000, *(0-9651174)* P.O. Box 42246, Barbara, CA 93140-2246 USA Tel 805-681-9810; 805-562-8601
Dist(s): **Educational Bk. Distributors.**

BrainWaves Bks. *Imprint of* **Bragdon, Allen D. Pubs., Inc.**

BrainX, Inc., *(0-9741604)* 1 Univ. Dr., Bldg. 55, Camarillo, CA 93012 USA Tel 805-384-1001; Fax: 805-484-8101
E-mail: info@brainx.com
Web site: http://www.brainx.com
Dist(s): **Majors, J. A. Co.**
Rittenhouse Bk. Distributors.

Braley & Thompson, Inc., *(1-883239)* P.O. Box 1396, Saint Albans, WV 25177-1396 USA Tel 304-722-1704; Fax: 304-722-1709; Toll Free: 800-258-5453.

Branch & Vine Pubs., LLC, *(0-9646990; 1-57688)* P.O. Box 1297, Radford, VA 24143-1297 USA (SAN 255-8335) Tel 540-230-5628; Fax: 540-639-3096 ; *Imprints:* Otherworlds Sci-Fi (Otherworlds Sci-Fi)
E-mail: branchandvine@aol.com; JSAdata@aol.com
Web site: http://www.branchandvinepublishers.com; http://www.ajalonpress.com
Dist(s): **Baker & Taylor Bks.**
BookSurge, LLC.

Branch Libraries *Imprint of* **New York Public Library**

Branch Springs Publishing, *(0-9727622)* 5731 Jones Valley Dr., Huntsville, AL 35802 USA
E-mail: fchap10220@aol.com.

Branching Leat Pubns., *(1-929589)* Orders Addr.: P.O. Box 803151, Valencia, CA 91380-3151 USA Tel 877-282-1457 (phone/fax); Edit Addr.: 36200 Paradise Ranch Rd., No. 15, Castaic, CA 91384 USA
E-mail: info@branchingleafpublications.com; orders@branchingleafpublications.com
Web site: http://www.branchingleafpublications.com.

Brand Nu Words *Imprint of* **Nunes Productions, LLC**

Branded Black Publishing, *(0-9746913)* P.O. Box 950781, Oklahoma City, OK 73195 USA
Web site: http://www.ebonymarshal.com; http://www.brandedblackpublishing.com.

Branden Bks., *(0-8283)* Div. of Branden Publishing Co., P.O. Box 812094, Wellesley, MA 02482 USA (SAN 201-4106) Tel 781-235-3634; Fax: 781-790-1056
E-mail: branden@brandenbooks.com; danteu@danteuniversity.org
Web site: http://www.brandenbooks.com; http://http:www.danteuniversity.org; http://http:/www.adolphcaso.com
Dist(s): **Baker & Taylor Bks.**
Brodart Co.
Follett Library Resources.

Branden Publishing Company *See* **Branden Bks.**

Brandworks Publishing, *(0-9715488)* Div. of Brandworks.net, Inc., Orders Addr.: 65 High Ridge Rd., No. 478, Stamford, CT 06905 USA (SAN 254-3060) Tel 203-356-9698; Toll Free Fax: 800-641-1282
E-mail: info@brandworks.net
Web site: http://www.brandworks.net; http://www.zaipubs.com; http://www.inkplaypress.com.

Brandylane Pubs., Inc., *(0-9627635; 1-883911)* Orders Addr.: 5 S. 1st St., Richmond, VA 23219-3716 USA Toll Free: 800-553-6922 (orders only)
E-mail: brandylanepublishersinc@yahoo.com; rhpruett@hotmail.com
Web site: http://www.brandylanepublishers.com
Dist(s): **Baker & Taylor International.**

Brass, Robin Studio, Inc. (CAN) *(1-896941) Dist. by* **Midpt Trade.**

BrassHeart Music, *(0-9673762; 0-9721478)* 256 S. Robertson Blvd., Suite 2288, Beverly Hills, CA 90211 USA Tel 323-932-0534; Fax: 323-937-6884; 323-933-4209 ; *Imprints:* Kid's Creative Classics (Kids Creative Classics)
E-mail: bunny@dreamaworld.com; brassheartmusic@aol.com
Web site: http://www.brassheartmusic.com; http://www.dreamaworld.com
Dist(s): **DeVorss & Co.**
Music Design, Inc.
New Leaf Distributing Co., Inc.

Braun Pubns., *(0-9774302)* 150 Clinton Ln., Spring Valley, NY 10977 USA.

Brave Ulysses Bks., *(0-615; 0-9700125)* P.O. Box 1877, Asheville, NC 28802 USA
E-mail: cecil@braveulysses.com; info@braveulysses.com
Dist(s): **Lulu.com.**

Braveheart Pr., LLC, *(0-9763935)* 23852 Pacific Coast Hwy., Suite 572, Malibu, CA 90265 USA Tel 310-770-7831; Fax: 310-456-5109 do not confuse with BraveHeart Press in Woodland Park, CO
E-mail: showrunnerbrv@aol.com
Web site: http://www.braveheartpressllc.com
Dist(s): **AtlasBooks Distribution.**

Braziller, George Inc., *(0-8076)* 171 Madison Ave., Suite 1103, New York, NY 10016 USA (SAN 201-9310) Tel 212-889-0909; Fax: 212-689-5405
Dist(s): **Norton, W. W. & Co., Inc.**

Brazos Pr., *(1-58743)* Div. of Baker Bk. Hse., Orders Addr.: P.O. Box 6287, Grand Rapids, MI 49516-6287 USA Toll Free Fax: 800-398-3111 (orders only); Toll Free: 800-877-2665 (orders only); Edit Addr.: 6030 E. Fulton, Ada, MI 49301 USA Tel 616-676-9185; Fax: 616-676-9573
E-mail: rclapp@brazospress.com
Web site: http://www.bakerbooks.com
Dist(s): **Baker Publishing Group.**

Brda, Tracy, *(0-9742355)* P.O. Box 510065, Saint Louis, MO 63129 USA Tel 314-293-0015; Fax: 636-343-0564
E-mail: info@power-twins.com.

Bread & Butter Bks., *(0-9800816)* 229 E. Ct. St., Cincinnati, OH 45202 USA Tel 513-884-0468
E-mail: jkiddielit@cinci.rr.com.

Bread For Life, *(0-9753922)* P.O. Box 7922, Athens, GA 30604 USA Tel 706-546-7214
E-mail: breadforlife@mindspring.com
Web site: http://www.breadforlife.net.

Break-A-Leg Bks., *(0-9668522)* 12332 Laurel Terr., Studio City, CA 91604 USA Tel 818-508-5585; Fax: 818-752-0682.

Breakaway Bks., *(1-55821; 1-891369)* P.O. Box 24, Halcottsville, NY 12438 USA Tel 607-326-4805; Fax: 212-898-0408; Toll Free: 800-548-4348 (voicemail) Do not confuse with Breakaway Bks., Albany, TX
E-mail: information@breakawaybooks.com
Web site: http://www.breakawaybooks.com
Dist(s): **Consortium Bk. Sales & Distribution.**

Breaking Cycles Bks., *(0-9741202)* Orders Addr.: P.O. Box 402, Severn, MD 21144-0402 USA Tel 410-519-6787
E-mail: BrCyBks@msn.com
Web site: http://www.breaking-cycles-visions-of-hope.com.

Breaking The Barrier, Inc., *(0-9712817; 0-9728570; 0-9758573; 0-9777987)* 63 Shirley Rd., Groton, MA 01450 USA Fax: 978-448-1237; Toll Free: 866-862-7325 Do not confuse with Breaking the Barrier Ministry, Inc. in Pennsauken, NJ
E-mail: info@tobreak.com
Web site: http://www.tobreak.com.

Breaking The Sounds' Barrier, Reading By Ear, *(0-9702826)* 309 Fourth St., Galena, IL 61036 USA Tel 815-777-3969 (phone/fax).

Breakout Publishing, *(0-9719762)* P.O. Box 5627, Gardena, CA 90249 USA Tel 708-352-0363; Fax: 310-970-1244
E-mail: lsimswill@msn.com
Web site: http://www.breakoutpublishing.com.

Breath & Shadows Productions, *(0-9720176)* P.O. Box 10557, Tampa, FL 33679 USA Tel 813-251-8187
E-mail: pstahel@aol.com.

Breau-Major, Germaine *See* **Les Editions Bleuts**

Brechin Bks., Ltd. (GBR) *(0-9540284) Dist. by* **Seven Locks Pr.**

Breckenridge Group & Assocs., *(0-9706099)* 4836 Sheffield Dr., Nashville, TN 37211-4510 USA Tel 615-837-9855; Fax: 615-834-2029
E-mail: p47skelton@home.com
Web site: http://breckenridge-group.com.

Breckling Pr., *(0-9721218; 1-933308)* 283 Michigan Ave., Elmhurst, IL 60126 USA
Web site: http://www.brecklingpress.com
Dist(s): **Independent Pubs. Group.**

Bree's Gift Publishing, *(0-9748512)* 3840 Listerman Rd., Howell, MI 48855 USA Tel 517-552-9184
E-mail: kimmie67@sbcglobal.net.

Bremer Press *See* **Zachmeyer, Mary L.**

Brenneman, Tim C. *See* **Grand Unification Pr., Inc.**

Brenner Publishing, LLC, *(0-9777203)* P.O. Box 584, Hicksville, NY 11802-0584 USA Tel 516-433-0804.

Brentwood Christian Pr. *Imprint of* **Brentwood Communications Group**

Brentwood Communications Group, *(0-916573; 1-55630; 1-59581)* 4000 Beallwood Ave., Columbus, GA 31904 USA (SAN 297-1895) Tel 706-576-5787 Toll Free: 800-334-8861 ; *Imprints:* Brentwood Christian Press (BrtwdChrist Pr) Do not confuse with Brentwood Communications Group in Vista, CA
E-mail: brentwood@knowlogy.net
Web site: http://www.brentwoodbooks.com; http://www.brentwoodreview.com; http://www.newchristianbooks.com
Dist(s): **Baker & Taylor Bks.**
Ingram Pub. Services.

Brentwood Home Video, *(0-7378; 0-924739; 1-57119; 1-879902)* Div. of Brentwood Communications, Inc., 810 Lawrence Dr., Suite 100, Newbury Park, CA 91320 USA Toll Free: 888-335-0528
E-mail: brentcom@earthlink.net
Web site: http://www.ssetsites.com/e-bci/default.htm.

Brentwood Music, Inc., *(0-7601; 1-55897)* 741 Cool Springs, Franklin, TN 37067 USA Tel 615-373-3950; Fax: 615-373-8612; Toll Free: 800-333-9000 (audio & video orders); 800-846-7664 (book orders)
Web site: http://www.providentmusic.com
Dist(s): **Appalachian Bible Co.**
Central South Christian Distribution
Leonard, Hal Corp.
New Day Christian Distributors
Provident Music Distribution
Spring Arbor Distributors, Inc.

Brentwood Productions, *(1-882091)* Orders Addr.: P.O. Box 1780, Sisters, OR 97759 USA (SAN 248-529X); Edit Addr.: 68928 Chestnut Dr., Sisters, OR 97259 USA (SAN 248-5303) Tel 541-549-2014.

Breslov Research Institute, *(0-930213; 1-928822)* P.O. Box 587, Monsey, NY 10952-0587 USA (SAN 670-7890) Tel 845-425-4258; Fax: 845-425-3018; Toll Free: 800-332-7375
E-mail: info@breslov.org
Web site: http://www.breslov.org
Dist(s): **Moznaim Publishing Corp.**

†Brethren Pr., *(0-87178)* Div. of Church of the Brethren, 1451 Dundee Ave., Elgin, IL 60120-1694 USA (SAN 201-9329) Tel 847-742-5100; 800-441-3712; Fax: 847-742-1407; Toll Free: 800-441-3712
E-mail: brethren_press_gb@brethren.org
Web site: http://www.brethrenpress.com; *CIP.*

Brethren Revival Fellowship, *(0-9745027; 0-9777766)* 26 United Zion Cir., Lititz, PA 17543-7956 USA Fax: 717-625-0511
E-mail: harpri@dejazzd.com
Web site: http://www.brfwitness.org.

Brevard Marketing, *(1-929554)* P.O. Box 410994, Melbourne, FL 32941 USA Tel 321-917-4300; Fax: 321-989-0209; Toll Free: 800-373-7625; 1125 Brook St NE, Palm Bay, FL 32905-4901
E-mail: chuck@brevardmarketing.com
Web site: http://www.djresource.com; http://www.allaboutchicks.com; http://www.chuckfresh.com.

Brewer, Neil, *(0-9771807)* 5290 Cedar Way Dr., NE, Corydon, IN 47112 USA Tel 812-952-3482
E-mail: 8oclock@aye.net
Web site: http://www.booksbybrewer.com.

Brewer's Historical Publications *See* **Bear State Bks.**

Brianna Nichole Enterprises, Inc., *(0-9670079)* 315 Third Ave., N., Columbus, MS 39701 USA Tel 662-329-1998
Dist(s): **Afrikan World Bk. Distributor.**

Briarwood Pubns., *(1-892614)* 150 W. College St., Rocky Mount, VA 24151 USA (SAN 299-8068) Tel 540-483-3606; Fax: 540-489-4692 ext 51 Do not confuse with Briarwood Pubns., Terre Haute, IN
E-mail: barbara@briarwoodva.com
Web site: http://www.briarwoodva.com.

Brickey E-Publishing, *(0-9758964)* 1029E Salisbury St., Kernersville, NC 27284-3063 USA
E-mail: mainoffice@brickey-epublishing.com
Web site: http://www.brickey-epublishing.com.

Bridge House *See* **Bridge Hse. Publishing, Inc.**

Bridge Hse. Publishing, Inc., *(0-9672215)* 3841 NE 2nd Ave. 4th Flr., Miami, FL 33137 USA Tel 786-871-4823; Fax: 305-531-6102
E-mail: publish@bridgehouse.net.

Bridge Ink, *(0-9641963)* 32580 SW Arbor Lake Dr., Wilsonville, OR 97070-8471 USA
E-mail: bob@bridgeink.com
Web site: http://www.bridgeink.com
Dist(s): **Far West Bk. Service**
Partners/West.

Bridge Pubns., Inc., *(0-88404; 1-57318; 1-4031)* 4751 Fountain Ave., Los Angeles, CA 90029 USA (SAN 208-3884) Tel 323-953-3320; Fax: 323-953-3328; Toll Free: 800-722-1733
E-mail: annarnow@bridgepub.com; daniellem@bridgepub.com; donarnow@bridgepub.com
Web site: http://www.bridgepub.com; http://www.clearbodyclearmind.com; http://www.scientology.org; http://www.dianetics.org; http://www.dianeticsbook.com
Dist(s): **Bookazine Co., Inc.**
Brodart Co.
Landmark Audiobooks.

Bridge Publishing Group, *(0-9728439)* P.O. Box 1673, Walnut, CA 91788-1673 USA Tel 626-290-1624; Fax: 909-595-9526
E-mail: info@schisandrae.com.

Bridge Publishing, Incorporated/LOGOS *See* **Bridge-Logos Pubs.**

Bridge Resources *Imprint of* **Curriculum Publishing, Presbyterian Church (U. S. A.)**

Bridge Resources, *(1-57895)* Div. of Presbyterian Church, 100 Witherspoon St., Louisville, KY 40202-1396 USA Fax: 502-569-8329; Toll Free Fax: 800-524-2612
Web site: http://www.bridgeresources.org
Dist(s): **CRC Pubns.**

Bridge To Life Ministries, Inc., *(0-9749490)* P.O. Box 2106, Lithonia, GA 30058 USA Tel 678-418-8733; Fax: 678-418-8578
E-mail: busresources1@yahoo.com
Web site: http://www.bridgetolife.net
Dist(s): **Baker & Taylor Bks.**

Bridge-Logos Pubs., *(0-88270; 0-912106)* Orders Addr.: P.O. Box 141630, Gainesville, FL 32614-1630 USA Toll Free Fax: 800-935-6467 (orders only); Toll Free: 800-631-5802 (orders only); Edit Addr.: P.O. Box 141630, Gainesville, FL 32614 USA (SAN 253-5254) Tel 352-472-7900; Fax: 352-472-7908
E-mail: info@bridgelogos.com; editor@bridgelogos.com; mail@bridgelogos.com; bevbrowning@bridgelogos.com
Web site: http://www.bridgelogos.com
Dist(s): **Anchor Distributors**
Appalachian Bible Co.
Baker & Taylor Bks.
Spring Arbor Distributors, Inc.

Bridgestone Bks. *Imprint of* **Capstone Pr., Inc.**

Bridgeway Bks., *(1-933538; 1-934454)* Div. of BookPros, LLC, 2100 Kramer Ln., Suite 300, Austin, TX 78758 USA Tel 512-478-2028
Web site: http://www.bridgewaybooks.net.

BR:IEFing Assocs. of New England, *(0-9706105)* Orders Addr.: P.O. Box 3159, Kingston, NY 12402-3159 USA Tel 845-339-0998; Edit Addr.: 289 Fair St., Suite 2A, Kingston, NY 12401-3844 USA.

Brigance Enterprises *See* **Brigance Publishing**

Brigance Publishing, *(0-9619971; 1-892467)* 275 Savannah Park Dr., Maryville, TN 37803-8874 USA (SAN 247-2988)
E-mail: brigance@usa.net
Web site: http://www.brigance.net
Dist(s): **Phoenix Learning Resources, LLC.**

Briggs, Sharon, *(0-615)* 109 Hope Way, Auburn, KY 42206 USA
E-mail: sharondeneice109@yahoo.com.

Brigham Young Univ., *(0-8425)* 205 UPB, Provo, UT 84602 USA (SAN 201-9337) Tel 801-422-2809; Fax: 801-422-0591
E-mail: diane_foerster@byu.edu
Web site: http://www.upb.byu.edu
Dist(s): **Brigham Young Univ. Print Services**
Chicago Distribution Ctr.
Indiana Univ. Pr.
Univ. of Chicago Pr.

Bright Cloud Publishing, *(0-9770727)* P.O. Box 214, Santa Fe, TX 77510 USA
E-mail: brightcloud77@aol.com
Web site: http://www.brightcloudpublishing.com.

Bright Eyes, Inc., *(0-9667718)* Orders Addr.: P.O. Box 2385, Madison, MS 39130-2385 USA Tel 601-856-1961; Edit Addr.: 486 St. Augustine Rd., Madison, MS 39110 USA.

Bright Eyes Pr., *(0-9728019)* 862 Congressional Rd., Simi Valley, CA 93065 USA Tel 805-579-0027
E-mail: kassie@kgraves.com
Web site: http://www.brighteyespress.com.

Bright Hill Pr., *(0-9646844; 1-892471)* Orders Addr.: P.O. Box 193, Treadwell, NY 13846-0193 USA Tel 607-746-7306; Fax: 607-746-7274; Edit Addr.: R.R. 1, Box 545, Delhi, NY 13753 USA
E-mail: wordthur@catskill.net
Web site: http://www.brighthillpress.org; http://www.nyslittree.org
Dist(s): **Baker & Taylor Bks.**
North Country Bks., Inc.
SPD-Small Pr. Distribution
Small Pr. Alliance.

Bright Ideas! Educational Resources, *(1-892427)* P.O. Box 333, Cheswold, DE 19936 USA Toll Free: 877-492-8081
E-mail: hogan@inet.net.

Bright Ideas Pr., LLC, *(0-9728730; 0-9740408; 0-9760153; 0-9772584; 1-934210)* Orders Addr.: P.O. Box 181243, Cleveland, OH 44118 USA Tel 216-832-5673; Fax: 216-382-5898; Edit Addr.: 1617 Sheridan Rd., South Euclid, OH 44121 USA Do not confuse with Bright Ideas Press in Springville, UT
Web site: http://www.SimpleSolutionsMath.com.

Bright Ideas Publishing *See* **Bright Ideas Pr., LLC**

Bright Ring Publishing, Inc., *(0-935607)* P.O. Box 31338, Bellingham, WA 98228-3338 USA (SAN 696-0537) Tel 360-592-9201; Fax: 360-592-4503; Toll Free: 800-480-4278
E-mail: maryann@brightring.com
Web site: http://www.brightring.com/books
Dist(s): **Gryphon Hse., Inc.**
Independent Pubs. Group.

Bright Sky Pr., *(0-9704729; 0-9709987; 1-931721; 1-933979)* Orders Addr.: P.O. Box 416, Albany, TX 76430 USA Tel 915-762-3909; Fax: 915-762-3690; Edit Addr.: 340 S. Second St., Albany, TX 76430 USA Do not confuse with Breakaway Bks., Halcottsville, NY
E-mail: carolcates@brightskypress.com
Web site: http://www.brightskypress.com
Dist(s): **Independent Pubs. Group**
Texas A&M Univ. Pr.

Bright Solutions for Dyslexia, LLC, *(0-9744343; 0-9755871)* 2059 Camden Ave., Suite 186, San Jose, CA 95124-2024 USA Tel 408-559-3652; Fax: 408-377-0503
E-mail: susan@brightsolutions.us
Web site: http://www.brightsolutions.us.

Bright Sparks *Imprint of* **Parragon, Inc.**

Bright Spots, *(0-9769150)* P.O. Box 3868, Rancho Santa Fe, CA 92067 USA Fax: 858-538-8866; Toll Free: 888-301-8880
E-mail: lmarneson@msn.com
Web site: http://www.brightspotsgames.com.

Bright Star Publishing, *(0-9662965)* P.O. Box 102, Midkiff, WV 25540 USA Tel 304-778-7549.

BrightBerry Pr., *(0-9720924)* 4262 Kennebec Rd., Dixmont, ME 04932 USA Tel 207-234-4225
E-mail: jeanhay@brightberrypress.com
Web site: http://www.brightberrypress.com.

Bright-Brights Media Co., The, *(0-9752553)* 1059 Briar Ave., Provo, UT 84604 USA Tel 801-375-3455.

Brighter Child *Imprint of* **School Specialty Publishing**

Brighter Child Interactive *See* **Brighter Minds Children's Publishing**

Brighter Horizons Publishing, *(1-929662)* P.O. Box 448, Littleton, CO 80160 USA Tel 303-347-2904; Fax: 303-795-5951
E-mail: brighterhorizons@earthlink.net
Web site: http://home.earthlink.net/~brighterhorizons; http://brighterhorizons@earthlink.net
Dist(s): **Baker & Taylor Bks.**
Book Wholesalers, Inc.

Brighter Minds Children's Publishing, *(1-57791)* Div. of Brighter Child Interactive, LLC, 600 D Lakeview Plaza Blvd., Worthington, OH 43085 USA Tel 614-430-3021; Fax: 614-430-3152 ; *Imprints:* Little Melody Press (Little Melody Pr); Penny Candy Press (Penny Candy Pr)
E-mail: ranf@brightermindsmedia.com; books@Brightermindspublishing.com
Web site: http://www.brightermindspublishing.com
Dist(s): **Perseus Distribution.**

Brighter Vision Pubns., *(1-55254)* P.O. Box 4104, Buffalo, NY 14240-4104 USA Toll Free: 888-343-9777 (in U.S. & Canada)
Dist(s): **Sony CONNECT, Inc.**

Brightside Co., *(0-9743720)* 5040 S. Elmira St., Greenwood Village, CO 80111-3608 USA (SAN 255-5573) Tel 303-694-6065; Fax: 303-694-1009
E-mail: cynthiadormer@msn.com
Dist(s): **Independent Pubs. Group.**

Brilliant Beginnings, LLC, *(0-9665815; 1-929651)* Orders Addr.: P.O. Box 13050, Long Beach, CA 90803 USA; Edit Addr.: 100 N. Studebaker Rd., No. 2, Long Beach, CA 90815-4949 USA Tel 562-498-6860; Fax: 562-498-1543; Toll Free: 800-432-1357
E-mail: jgoldfarb@brilliantbeginnings.com
Web site: http://www.brilliantbeginnings.com.

Brimax Books Ltd. (GBR) *(0-86112; 0-900195; 0-904494; 1-85854; 1-904952; 1-905279; 1-84656) Dist. by* **Byeway Bks.**

Brimfield Pubns., *(0-9653701)* P.O. Box 442, Brimfield, MA 01010 USA Tel 413-245-9329 (phone/fax); 508-764-4920
E-mail: brimfieldp@aol.com
Web site: http://www.brimfieldguide.com/.

Brimstone Ventures, *(0-9708337)* P.O. Box 894, Middlebury, CT 06762-0894 USA
E-mail: staff@brimstoneventures.com; kenborucki@yahoo.com
Web site: http://www.brimstoneventures.com.

BrimWood Pr., *(0-9770704)* 1941 Larsen Dr., Camino, CA 95709 USA Tel 530-644-7538; Fax: 530-647-9208 ; *Imprints:* Tools For Young Historians (Tools YngHist)
E-mail: marcia@brimwoodpress.com
Web site: http://www.brimwoodpress.com.

Brindle Pr., *(0-9749080)* 14121 Cardinal Ln., Houston, TX 77079 USA
Web site: http://www.brindlepress.com.

Bristol Classical Pr. (GBR) *(0-86292; 0-906515; 1-85399) Dist. by* **Intl Pubs Mktg.**

Bristol Fashion Publishing Co., *(1-892216)* Div. of Netpv Publishing, Orders Addr.: P.O. Box 560989, Rockledge, FL 32956 USA Tel 321-690-2224; Fax: 321-690-0853
E-mail: Publisher@WescottCovePublishing.com
Web site: http://www.wescottcovepublishing.com/.

Bristol Historical Society, *(0-9715501)* 98 Summer St., Bristol, CT 06010-5051 USA
E-mail: gailml@snet.net.

Bristol Hse., Ltd., *(0-917851; 1-885224)* P.O. Box 4020, Anderson, IN 46013 USA (SAN 225-4638) Tel 765-644-0856; Fax: 765-622-1045; Toll Free: 800-451-7323.

Bristol Publishing Co., *(0-9755667)* P.O. Box 3103, San Angelo, TX 76902-3103 USA Do not confuse with Bristal Publishing Company in San Jacinto, CA
E-mail: bristolpublishing@sbcglobal.net
Dist(s): **Alliance Bk. Co.**

Briston Hse. (CAN) *(1-894921) Dist. by* **IPG Chicago.**

Brite Bks., *(0-9726363)* Orders Addr.: P.O. Box 801, Ortonville, MI 48462 USA; Edit Addr.: 1580 Duck Creek Ln., Ortonville, MI 48462 USA
E-mail: twebb@britebooks.org; twebb@tawglobal.com
Web site: http://www.britebooks.org; http://www.tawglobal.com; http://www.promises-for-life.com.

Brite International *See* **Brite Music, Inc.**

Brite Music, Inc., *(0-944803)* Orders Addr.: P.O. Box 65688-0688, Salt Lake City, UT 84165 USA (SAN 244-948X) Tel 801-263-9191; Fax: 801-263-9198; Edit Addr.: P.O. Box 171076, Salt Lake Cty, UT 84117-1076 USA (SAN 244-9498)
Web site: http://www.britemusic.com.

Brite Pr., *(0-9743185)* 3447 Countyline Rd., Chalfont, PA 18914-3625 USA Tel 215-822-1659; Fax: 305-402-8163
E-mail: tntdns@aol.com.

British American Bks., *(0-89979)* P.O. Box 302, Willits, CA 95490 USA (SAN 201-9353) Tel 707-459-5424.

British Library, The (GBR) *(0-7123) Dist. by* **Chicago Distribution Ctr.**

Britt Allcroft Productions, *(0-9743690; 0-9767139; 0-9793343)* 2917 1/2 Main St., Santa Monica, CA 90405-5315 USA
E-mail: office@brittallcroftproductions.com
Web site: http://www.brittallcroftproductions.com.

Brittany's Bks, *(0-9778796)* 304 Gail Dr., Griffin, GA 30224 USA
E-mail: admin@brittanysbooks.com
Web site: http://www.brittanysbooks.com.

Broadcast Quality Productions, Inc., *(0-9716136)* 3199 Nottaway Ct., Atlanta, GA 30341 USA Tel 404-292-7777 (phone/fax)
Web site: http://www.bqproductions.com.

Broader Horizon Bks., *(0-9746849)* Orders Addr.: P.O. Box 2003, Centennial, CO 80161-2003 USA (SAN 256-3371) Tel 303-771-0991; Fax: 303-488-2665
E-mail: broaderhorizonbooks@msn.com
Dist(s): **Baker & Taylor Bks.**

Broadman & Holman Publishers *See* **B&H Publishing Grp.**

Broadnax, Cassandra A.L., *(0-9771608)* 295 Pannel Rd., Reidsville, NC 27320 USA.

BroadSword Comics/ Jim Balent Studios, *(0-9745367)* P.O. Box 596, Brodheadsville, PA 18322 USA
E-mail: tarot@jimbalent.com
Web site: http://www.jimbalent.com.

Broadway *Imprint of* **Broadway Bks.**

Broadway Ballplayers, Inc., *(0-9659091)* P.O. Box 597, Wilmette, IL 60091 USA Tel 847-570-4715; Fax: 847-570-0885
E-mail: maureen@bplayers.com
Web site: http://www.bplayers.com
Dist(s): **Baker & Taylor Bks.**

Broadway Bks., Div. of Doubleday Broadway Publishing Group, Orders Addr.: 400 Hahn Rd., Westminster, MD 21157 USA Tel 410-848-1900; Toll Free: 800-726-0600; Edit Addr.: 1745 Broadway, New York, NY 10019 USA Tel 212-354-6500; Fax: 212-782-8338; Toll Free: 800-223-6834 ; *Imprints:* Broadway (Broad); Main Street Books (MainStreet)
E-mail: bwaypub@randomhouse.com
Web site: http://www.bdd.com
Dist(s): **Random Hse., Inc.**

Broadway Cares, *(0-9754840)* 165 W. 46th St., 13th Flr., New York, NY 10036 USA Tel 212-840-0770; Fax: 212-840-0551
E-mail: viola@bcefa.org.

Broccoli Bks. *Imprint of* **Broccoli International USA, Inc.**

Broccoli Bks. Deluxe *Imprint of* **Broccoli International USA, Inc.**

Broccoli International USA, Inc., *(1-932480; 1-59741)* Orders Addr.: P.O. Box 66078, Los Angeles, CA 90066 USA Tel 310-815-0600; Fax: 310-815-0660; Edit Addr.: 1728 S. La Cienega Blvd., Los Angeles, CA 90035 USA ; *Imprints:* Broccoli Books (Broccoli Bks); Broccoli Books Deluxe (Broco Bks Delx)
E-mail: info@broccolibooks.com; ardith@bro-usa.com; wholesale@broccolibooks.com; books@animegamers.com; wholesale@bro-usa.com
Web site: http://www.bro-usa.com; http://www.broccolibooks.com; http://www.synch-point.com; http://www.boysenberrybooks.com
Dist(s): **Andrews McMeel Publishing**
Diamond Bk. Distributors
Perseus Distribution
Simon & Schuster, Inc.

Brockhaus, F. A., GmbH (DEU) *(3-325; 3-7653) Dist. by* **Intl Bk Import.**

Broderbund Software, Inc., *(0-922614; 1-55790; 1-57135; 1-57382; 1-57404)* 100 Pine St. Ste. 1900, San Francisco, CA 94111-5205 USA (SAN 264-8369) Toll Free: 800-527-6263
Web site: http://www.mattelinteractive.com.

Broken Bread Publishing, *(0-9769464)* 6417 S. Iris Way, Littleton, CO 80123-3135 USA
E-mail: books@brokenbreadpublishing.com
Web site: http://www.brokenbreadpublishing.com
Dist(s): **Spring Arbor Distributors, Inc.**

Broken Shackle Publishing, International, *(0-9759908)* P.O. Box 20312, Piedmont, CA 94620 USA
E-mail: jstickmon@msn.com.

Broken Wing Enterprises, Inc., *(0-9768948)* P.O. Box 368, Midlothian, VA 23113 USA Tel 804-378-0136; Fax: 804-378-2228
E-mail: dorothy@tateandtini.com
Web site: http://www.tateandtini.com.

Bromwell Bks., *(0-9753345)* 2500 E. Fourth Ave., Denver, CO 80206 USA Tel 303-388-5969; Fax: 303-764-7544
E-mail: steven_replogle@dpsk12.org
Web site: http://bromwell.dpsk12.org.

Bronner, Rivka D., *(0-9660684)* 21 Dr. Frank Rd., Spring Valley, NY 10977-2516 USA.

Bronze Bow Publishing, *(0-9724563; 1-932458)* 2600 E. 26th St., Minneapolis, MN 55406 USA Tel 612-724-8200; Fax: 612-724-8995; Toll Free: 866-724-8200
Dist(s): **STL Distribution North America.**

Bronze Medallion *Imprint of* **Medallion Pr., Inc.**

Brook Farm Bks., *(0-919761)* 479 U.S. Hwy. 1, P.O. Box 246, Bridgewater, ME 04735 USA (SAN 133-9095) Tel 506-375-4680 (phone/fax); Toll Free: 877-375-4680
E-mail: jean@brookfarmbook.com; jean@brookfarmbooks.com
Dist(s): **Brodart Co.**
Independent Pubs. Group.

Brooke-Richards Pr., *(0-9622652)* PMB 511, 9420 Reseda Blvd., Northridge, CA 91324 USA Tel 818-893-8126; Fax: 818-349-2558.

Brookes, C. Avery Ltd., *(0-9666246)* P.O. Box 7373, Saint Davids, PA 19087 USA Fax: 610-687-1807 ; *Imprints:* Bunny Express Press (Bunny Express)
E-mail: caverybrookes@bunnycousins.com
Web site: http://www.bunnycousins.com
Dist(s): **Baker & Taylor Bks.**

Brookes, Paul H. Publishing Co., *(0-933716; 1-55766; 1-59857)* Orders Addr.: P.O. Box 10624, Baltimore, MD 21285-0624 USA (SAN 212-730X) Tel 410-337-9580; Fax: 410-337-8539; Toll Free: 800-638-3775 (customer service/ordering/billing/fulfillment); Edit Addr.: 409 Washington Ave., Suite 500, Baltimore, MD 21204 USA (SAN 666-6485)
E-mail: custserv@brookespublishing.com
Web site: http://www.brookespublishing.com.

Company

Brookfield Reader, Inc., The, *(0-9660172; 1-930093)* 137 Peyton Rd., Sterling, VA 20165-5605 USA (SAN 299-4445) Tel 703-430-0202; Fax: 703-430-7315; Toll Free: 888-389-2741
E-mail: info@brookfieldreader.com; hbaggett@erols.com
Web site: http://www.brookfieldreader.com
Dist(s): **Book Wholesalers, Inc.**
Brodart Co.
International Publishers Marketing
Quality Bks., Inc.

Brookline Merrimac Pubs., *(0-9720871)* 47 Cypress St., Suite 100, Brookline, MA 02445 USA
Dist(s): **Baker & Taylor Bks.**

Brooklyn Pubs., *(1-930961; 1-931000; 1-931805; 1-932404; 1-60003)* 1841 Cord St., Odessa, TX 79762 USA Tel 915-550-5532; Fax: 915-368-0340; Toll Free: 888-473-8521
E-mail: brookpublishing@aol.com; brookpubl@aol.com
Web site: http://www.brookpub.com.

Brooklyn Publishing Company *See* **Brooklyn Pubs.**

Brooks & Brooks, *(0-9682530)* 5510 Owensmouth Ave. Apt. 102, Woodland Hls, CA 91367-7011 USA
E-mail: runningbrooks@hotmail.com.

Brooks, Andree Aelion, *(0-9702700)* 15 Hitchcock Rd., Westport, CT 06880 USA Tel 203-226-9834; Fax: 203-226-0814
E-mail: andreebrooks@hotmail.com.

Brooks Bks., *(0-9666869)* 5615 S. 77th St., Ralston, NE 68127 USA Tel 402-592-6552; Fax: 402-592-6568 Do not confuse with Brooks Bks. in Decatur, IL.

†Brooks/Cole, *(0-12; 0-15; 0-314; 0-534; 0-8185; 1-56527; 0-495)* Div. of Thomson Learning, Orders Addr.: 7625 Empire Dr., Florence, KY 41042-2978 USA Tel 606-525-2230; Toll Free: 800-354-9706 (orders); Edit Addr.: 511 Forest Lodge Rd., Pacific Grove, CA 93950 USA (SAN 202-3369) Tel 831-373-0728; Fax: 831-375-6414; 10 Davis Dr., Belmont, CA 94002 Tel 650-595-2350 ; *Imprints:* Brooks/Cole (Broks-Cole)
E-mail: info@brookscole.com
Web site: http://www.brookscole.com; http://www.duxbury.com
Dist(s): **CENGAGE Learning**; *CIP.*

Brooks/Cole *Imprint of* **Brooks/Cole**

Brooks/Cole Publishing Company *See* **Brooks/Cole**

Brookshire Pubns., Inc., *(1-880976)* 200 Hazel St., Lancaster, PA 17603 USA Tel 717-392-1321; Fax: 717-392-2078
E-mail: carla@brookshireprinting.com.

Brookteam Corp., *(0-9745864)* P.O. Box 276225, Boca Raton, FL 33427 USA Fax: 561-367-9976; Toll Free: 866-571-7878 ; *Imprints:* Shirt Tales (Shirt Tales)
E-mail: brookteam@worldnet.att.net
Web site: http://www.brookteam.com.

Brophy, Doris Anne, *(0-9745232)* 90 Bingham Ave., Rumson, NJ 07760 USA Tel 732-345-7276
E-mail: dambrophy@yahoo.com.

Broqueville Publishing, Inc., *(0-9669024; 0-9719413)* 1260 Logan Ave., Suite B3, Costa Mesa, CA 92626 USA (SAN 255-0083) Tel 714-624-6441; Fax: 714-668-9972
E-mail: bookorders@broqueville.com
Web site: http://www.broqueville.com.

Brosquil Edicions, S.L. (ESP) *(84-95620; 84-96154; 84-9795) Dist. by* **Lectorum Pubns.**

Bross Publishing, *(0-9763561)* 168 Island Pond Rd., No. 1, Manchester, NH 03109 USA (SAN 256-355X) Tel 603-623-2503 (phone/fax)
E-mail: brosspublishing@sunnyfla.us.

Brothers Heimberg Publishing *See* **Falls Media**

Brotman-Marshfield Curriculums, *(0-9762568)* 22 Howard St., Newton, MA 02458 USA Tel 617-332-5616; Fax: 617-332-9679
E-mail: brotmanco@aol.com.

Brown & Benchmark, *(0-936157)* Div. of Times Mirror Higher Education Group, Inc., 25 Kessel Ct., Madison, WI 53711 USA Tel 608-273-0040; Toll Free: 800-338-5578
E-mail: customer.service@mcgraw-hill.com
Web site: http://www.mhhe.com.

Brown Bag Bks, Inc., *(0-9720424)* Div. of World Holdings Group, Incorporated, 20 W. 20th St., Second Flr., New York, NY 10011-4213 USA Tel 212-822-8552; Fax: 212-822-8505 ; *Imprints:* Jacob & Victoria (Jacob & Victoria)
E-mail: frontdesk@brownbag-books.com
Web site: http://www.brownbag-books.com.

Brown Bag Productions, *(1-58193)* 2710 N. Stemmons Freeway, North Tower, Suite 600N, Dallas, TX 75207 USA Fax: 214-638-7747; Toll Free: 800-686-9484
E-mail: sweing@pcico.com
Web site: http://www.childrensplays.com.

Brown Barn Bks., *(0-9746481; 0-9768126; 0-9798824)* Div. of Pictures of Record, Inc., 119 Kettle Creek Rd., Weston, CT 06883 USA Toll Free: 888-227-3308
E-mail: editorial@brownbarnbooks.com
Web site: http://www.brownbarnbooks.com.

Brown Bear Books, *(0-9670861)* 325 High St., Santa Cruz, CA 95060 USA Tel 831-457-1135
E-mail: brwnbear@sasquatch.com.

Brown Bks. *Imprint of* **Olivo, Andy**

Brown, Bonnie M., *(0-9624705)* 548 Saint Johns Pl., Franklin, TN 37064-8901 USA
E-mail: bonnibear@aol.com.

Brown Bks., *(0-9668452; 0-9717197)* Div. of Personal Profiles, Inc., 16200 Dallas Pkwy. Ste. 170, Dallas, TX 75248-2616 USA Do not confuse with companies with the same or similar names in Allen, TX, Redway, CA, Montrose, CO, Plano, TX
Web site: http://www.brownbooks.com.

Brown Bks. Publishing, *(0-9708355)* Orders Addr.: P.O. Box 1545, Durant, OK 74702-1545 USA (SAN 254-1971) Tel 580-920-0400; Fax: 580-920-9117; Edit Addr.: 404 N. Washington, Durant, OK 74701 USA
E-mail: nkrieger@communicomm.com; publishing@brownbooks.com
Web site: http://www.brownbooks.com.

Brown Bks. Publishing Group, *(0-9713265; 0-9744597; 0-9753907; 1-933285; 1-934812)* 16200 N. Dallay Pkwy., No. 170, Dallas, TX 75248 USA Tel 972-381-0009; Fax: 972-248-4336
E-mail: natalie@brownbooks.com
Web site: http://www.brownbooks.com.

Brown County Historical Society, *(0-9641499)* Orders Addr.: P.O. Box 1411, Green Bay, WI 54305-1411 USA Tel 920-437-1840; Fax: 920-455-4518; Edit Addr.: 1008 S. Monroe Ave., Green Bay, WI 54301-3206 USA Do not confuse with Brown County Historical Society, Nashville, IN, New Ulm, MN
E-mail: bchs@netnet.net
Web site: http://www.browncohistoricalsoc.org.

Brown County Historical Society, *(0-9765095)* 2 N. Broadway, New Ulm, MN 56073 USA Do not confuse with Brown County Historical Society in Green Bay, WI.

Brown, David Bk. Co., The, *(0-9774094)* Div. of Oxbow Bks., Orders Addr.: P.O. Box 511, Oakville, CT 06779 USA (SAN 630-9461) Tel 860-945-9329; Fax: 860-945-9468; Toll Free: 800-791-9354
E-mail: david.brown.bk.co@snet.net
Web site: http://www.oxbowbooks.com
Dist(s): **Oxford Univ. Pr., Inc.**

Brown Dog Bks., *(0-9721967)* P.O. Box 2196, Flemington, NJ 08822 USA
E-mail: dar@darsart.com
Web site: http://www.browndogbooks.com
Dist(s): **Baker & Taylor Bks.**
Book Wholesalers, Inc.
Brodart Co.
Follett Media Distribution.

Brown, Harold *See* **Brown&Matthews**

Brown Hse. Bks., *(0-9767938)* 95 Sawyer Rd., Suite 400, Waltham, MA 02453 USA Tel 781-547-7600; Fax: 781-547-7610.

Brown, Nielsen, *(0-9725581)* 15 Washington, No. 306, Denver, CO 80206 USA
E-mail: kn9742@aol.com.

Brown, Samuel E., *(0-9770372)* P.O. Box 7009, Jackson, MS 39282 USA Tel 601-540-5470
E-mail: pcsandc@hotmail.com.

Brown Skin Girl Publishing, *(0-9719057)* Div. of Professional Resources, 10316 Kenworthy St., El Paso, TX 79924-2916 USA Tel 915-822-3490; Fax: 915-822-3287
E-mail: pcaves1@elp.rr.com.

Brown, Stephen *See* **Brown, Stephen R.**

Brown, Stephen R., *(0-9766150)* 3715 T St., NW, Washington, DC 20007 USA Tel 202-667-1965
E-mail: srb@srbphoto.com
Web site: http://www.jewelofthemall.com
Dist(s): **Baker & Taylor Bks.**

Brown Swan Pubs., *(0-9717993)* 760 Redriver Way, Corona, CA 92882 USA
E-mail: cdong@brownswan.com
Web site: http://www.brownswan.com.

Brown&Matthews, *(0-9759370)* 2923 E. Michigan St., Orlando, FL 32806 USA (SAN 256-2030)
E-mail: jkmatthews@cfl.rr.com
Web site: http://www.cafepress.com/sitm; http://www.janetmatthews.com.

Brownell, F. & Son, Pubs., *(0-9767409; 0-9789127)* P.O. Box 76, Montezuma, IA 50171 USA
Web site: http://www.brownells.com.

Brownian Bee Pr., *(0-9789688)* 1477 Grantham St., St. Paul, MN 55108 USA
E-mail: info@brownianbee.com
Web site: http://www.brownianbee.com
Dist(s): **Unique Bks., Inc.**

Brown-ROA *See* **Harcourt Religion Pubs.**

Brown's Graphics & Printing, *(0-9704872)* 3390 E. 137th St., Cleveland, OH 44120 USA Tel 216-921-3850; Fax: 216-561-6661
E-mail: tshdbro@hotmail.com.

Brownstone Monkey Productions, Inc., *(0-9785773)* 55 W. 84th St., No. 9, New York, NY 10024-1002 USA Tel 212-933-4168; Fax: 212-228-6149
E-mail: nicole@brownstonemonkey.com; kfiore@nyc.rr.com
Web site: http://brownstonemonkey.com; http://lenithepug.com.

BrownTrout Pubs., Inc., *(0-7631; 0-939027; 1-56313; 1-4216)* Orders Addr.: P.O. Box 280070, San Francisco, CA 94128-0070 USA (SAN 662-6505) Tel 650-340-9800; Fax: 650-340-9213; Toll Free: 877-950-7812; Edit Addr.: 2121 S. El Camino Real., Suite C-100, San Mateo, CA 94403 USA; P.O. Box 23031, Cambridge, ON N1S 4Z6 Tel 519-624-8617; Toll Free: 888-254-5842
E-mail: wendover@browntrout.com
Web site: http://www.browntrout.com.

Bruce & Lucky Story Bks., *(0-9712284)* 89 Undine Rd., Brighton, MA 02135 USA Tel 617-783-4060
E-mail: bruceandlucky@earthlink.net
Web site: http://bruceandlucky.com.

Brujo Film Production *See* **Pascualina Producciones S.A.**

Brumfield, Gordon R., *(0-9666482)* 525 W. Arlington Pl., Apt. 568, Chicago, IL 60614 USA Tel 773-525-8430
E-mail: caaaaab@aol.com.

Brunner/Mazel Publishers *See* **Brunner-Routledge**

†Brunner-Routledge, *(0-87630; 1-56032; 1-58391)* Div. of Taylor & Francis, Orders Addr.: 7625 Empire Dr., Florence, KY 41042 USA Toll Free Fax: 800-248-4724; Toll Free: 800-634-7064; Edit Addr.: 325 Chestnut St., 8th Flr., Philadelphia, PA 19106 USA (SAN 164-9167) Tel 215-625-8900; Fax: 215-625-2940
E-mail: info@taylorandfrancis.com; bkorders@taylorandfrancis.com
Web site: http://www.taylorandfrancis.com; http://www.brunner-routledge.com
Dist(s): **NetLibrary, Inc.**
Routledge
Sony CONNECT, Inc.
Taylor & Francis, Inc.; *CIP.*

Bruno, Elizabeth *See* **Uitti, Daniel**

Brunson Publishing, *(0-9758614)* Orders Addr.: P.O. Box 1133, Alamogordo, NM 88310 USA Tel 706-367-1334
E-mail: oldmaid4jesus@yahoo.com; oldmaid4jesus@yahoo.com; tim@teenpact.com
Web site: http://www.oldmaidministries.com; http://www.teenpact.com.

Brunswick Pr., *(1-888521)* Orders Addr.: P.O. Box 2244, Cathedral City, CA 92235 USA Tel 760-320-1448; Fax: 760-320-4019; Edit Addr.: 701 Panorama Dr., Palm Springs, CA 92262 USA
E-mail: brunswickp@aol.com
Web site: http://www.io.com/bpress.

Brunswick Publishing Corp., *(0-931494; 1-55618)* 593 Southlake Blvd., Richmond, VA 23236-3092 USA (SAN 211-6332)
E-mail: brunswickbooks@verizon.net; info@brunswickbooks.com
Web site: http://www.brunswickbooks.com/
Dist(s): **Baker & Taylor Bks.**

Bruño, Editorial (ESP) *(84-216) Dist. by* **Lectorum Pubns.**

Bryan Hse. Pubs., Inc., *(1-58232)* Orders Addr.: P.O. Box 791439, San Antonio, TX 78279-1439 USA (SAN 299-3678) Fax: 877-688-3226; Toll Free: 800-688-3224
E-mail: bryanhp@ix.netcom.com
Web site: http://www.bryanhouse.com.

Bryant, Carol, *(0-9706241)* 2402 W. Koenig St., Grand Island, NE 68803-5343 USA Tel 308-384-8084
E-mail: clbryant@kdsi.net.

Brzamo Publishing, *(0-9743580)* 887 Richart Ln., Greenwood, IN 46142 USA
Dist(s): **AtlasBooks Distribution.**

B'Squeak Productions, *(0-9746782)* P.O. Box 151, Menlo Park, CA 94026-0151 USA
E-mail: rights@bsqueak.com
Web site: http://www.bsqueak.com.

B*tween Productions, Inc., *(0-9746587; 0-9758511; 1-933566)* 1666 Massachusetts Ave., Suite 17, Lexington, MA 02420 USA Tel 781-863-8228; Fax: 781-863-8338 ; *Imprints:* Beacon Street Girls (B Street Girls)
E-mail: kblais@btweenproductions.com
Web site: http://www.beaconstreetgirls.com.

Bubba Bear Publishing, Inc., *(0-9663505)* 4894 Lone Mountain Rd., Suite 102, Las Vegas, NV 89130 USA Tel 702-645-4835.

Bubbi's Touch Pr., *(0-9748725)* 7529 W. Day Forest Rd., Empire, MI 49630 USA.

Bubble Gum Pr., *(0-9729833)* 416 4th St., SW, Jamestown, ND 58401-4030 USA Tel 701-252-9250
E-mail: bmehrmantraut@msn.com
Web site: http://www.bubblegumpress.com.

Bubblegum Bks., *(0-9754621)* P.O. Box 94106, Cleveland, OH 44101-6106 USA
E-mail: info@bubblegumbooks.com
Web site: http://www.bubblegumbooks.com
Dist(s): **Mariposa Pr.**
SCB Distributors.

Buccaneer Bks., Inc., *(0-89966; 0-89967; 0-89968; 1-56849)* P.O. Box 168, Cutchogue, NY 11935 USA (SAN 209-1542) Tel 631-734-5724; Fax: 631-734-7920 ; *Imprints:* Lightyear Press (Lghtyr Pr)
E-mail: BuccaneerBooks@aol.com
Web site: http://www.BuccaneerBooks.com.

Buchanan, George, *(0-9766421)* 110 30th Ave. N., Suite 4, Nashville, TN 37203 USA Tel 615-327-8100; Fax: 615-327-1004
E-mail: gobuch@aol.com.

Buchavina Pr., *(0-9725830)* 10979 Reed Hartman Hwy., Suite 107, Cincinnati, OH 45242 USA Tel 513-489-4446
E-mail: buchavinapress@hotmail.com.

Buck Engineering Company, Incorporated, Lab-Volt Systems Division *See* **Lab-Volt Systems, Inc.**

Buck Publishing, *(0-9725912)* Orders Addr.: P.O. Box 12231, Roanoke, VA 24023-2231 USA Tel 540-985-0618 (phone/fax); Edit Addr.: 710 Ferdinand Ave., No. 9, Roanoke, VA 24016 USA Do not confuse with companies with the same or similar name in Birmingham, AL, Fairbanks, AK.

Buckaroo Bks., *(1-885628)* Div. of Wade Cook Financial Corp., 14675 Interurban Ave., S., Seattle, WA 98168 USA Tel 206-901-3000; Fax: 206-901-3027 Do not confuse with Buckaroo Bks. in Huntsville, UT
Dist(s): **Origin Bk. Sales, Inc.**

Buckbeech Studios, *(0-9771494)* Orders Addr.: P.O. Box 430, Stanford, IN 47463-0430 USA
E-mail: publisher@buckbeech.com
Web site: http://www.buckbeech.com.

Bucket of Books *See* **Bimini Bks.**

Buckeye Publishing, *(0-9743844)* 3036 Quarry Rd., Maumee, OH 43537 USA
Web site: http://www.mortalmillionaire.com
Dist(s): **Biblio Distribution.**

Buckhead Pr., *(0-9664329)* 2025 Madison Grove Ln., Knoxville, TN 37922-9435 USA.

Bucknell Univ. Pr., *(0-8387)* 2010 Eastpark Blvd., Cranbury, NJ 08512-3514 USA
Web site: http://www.departments.bucknell.edu/univ_press/
Dist(s): **Associated Univ. Presses**
Baker & Taylor International
Replica Bks.

Buddha's Light Publishing, *(0-9715612; 0-9717495; 1-932293)* 3456 S. Glenmark Dr., Hacienda Heights, CA 91745 USA Tel 626-923-5144; 84 Margaret Street, London, Tel 020-7636-8394; Fax: 020-7580-6220
E-mail: info@blpusa.com
Web site: http://www.blpusa.com
Dist(s): **Greenleaf Book Group Pr.**
New Leaf Distributing Co., Inc.

Buddhi Pubns., *(0-9644226)* Orders Addr.: P.O. Box 208, Canyon, CA 94516 USA Tel 510-376-7796; Fax: 510-376-3503; Edit Addr.: 35 Pinehurst Rd., Canyon, CA 94516 USA.

Buddhist Text Translation Society, *(0-88139; 0-917512; 1-60103)* Affil. of Dharma Realm Buddhist Assoc., Orders Addr.: 4951 Bodhi Way, Ukiah, CA 95482 USA Tel 707-462-0939; Fax: 707-462-0949; Edit Addr.: 4951 Bodhi Way,, Ukiah, CA 95482 USA (SAN 281-3556) Tel 707-468-9112 (phone/fax)
E-mail: hchih@netzero.net; hengdzu@drba.org; bttsonline@snetworking.com
Web site: http://www.bttsonline.org.

Budding Artists, Inc., *(1-888108)* 200 Toyopa Dr., Pacific Plsds, CA 90272-4462 USA.

Budding Family Publishing, *(0-9741882)* P.O. Box 2078, Manhattan Beach, CA 90267-2078 USA Fax: 310-374-1030
E-mail: renee@buddingfamily.com
Web site: http://www.buddingfamily.com.

Buddy Bks. *Imprint of* **ABDO Publishing Co.**

Buenas Letra *Imprint of* **Rosen Publishing Group, Inc., The**

Buenaventura Pr., *(0-9766848; 0-9800039)* P.O. Box 23661, Oakland, CA 94623 USA
Web site: http://www.buenaventurapress.com
Dist(s): **D.A.P./Distributed Art Pubs.**
SCB Distributors.

Buffalo Creek Pr., *(1-885534)* Div. of CPU Computers, Inc., Orders Addr.: 603 N. Main, Cleburne, TX 76033-2424 USA Tel 817-641-4908; Fax: 817-641-0901; Toll Free: 800-610-4908
E-mail: micki@buffalo-creek-press.com
Web site: http://buffalo-creek-press.com.

Buffalo Fine Arts Academy *See* **Buffalo Fine Arts/ Albright-Knox Art Gallery**

†Buffalo Fine Arts/Albright-Knox Art Gallery, *(0-914782; 1-887457)* Albright-Knox Art Gallery, 1285 Elmwood Ave., Buffalo, NY 14222 USA (SAN 202-4845) Tel 716-882-8700; Fax: 716-882-1958; *CIP.*

Buffalo Free Pr., *(0-9678609)* Orders Addr.: 1888 Hertel Ave. Upper Left Apt., Buffalo, NY 14226 USA
E-mail: ron@ronchurchill.com; admin@ronchurchill.com; ronchurchill@yahoo.com
Web site: http://www.www.ronchurchill.com; http://www.bfp.ronchurchill.com.

Buffington, Peter M., *(0-9712084)* 2740 Holly Ct NW, Swisher, IA 52338-9425 USA
E-mail: pandj2000@netzero.net.

Buffington, Peter Michael *See* **Buffington, Peter M.**

Bugeye Bks., *(0-9722249)* 10645 N. Tatum Blvd., Suite 200-246, Phoenix, AZ 85028 USA Tel 602-980-7101; Fax: 480-483-3460
E-mail: insightstudios@cox.net
Web site: http://www.bugeyebooks.com.

Buggs Books *See* **Mogul Comics**

Build Your Story, *(0-9748416)* Orders Addr.: P.O. Box 6003, Midlothian, VA 23112 USA Fax: 810-592-2479; Toll Free: 866-807-8679; Edit Addr.: 2212 Water Horse Ct., Midlothian, VA 23112 USA
E-mail: oscar@buildyourstory.com
Web site: http://www.buildyourstory.com.

Build-a-Bk., *(0-9702807)* 564 Red Bridge Ct., Manchester, MO 63021 USA (SAN 253-6889) Tel 636-527-2085; Fax: 636-527-9700
E-mail: buildabook@onemain.com.

Building Blocks, LLC, *(0-943452)* 38 W. 567 Brindlewood Ln., Elgin, IL 60123 USA (SAN 240-6063) Tel 847-742-1013; Fax: 847-742-1054 (orders); Toll Free: 800-233-2448 Do not confuse with companies with similar and same name in Madison,NJ, Westbury NY
E-mail: dick@bblocksonline.com
Web site: http://www.bblocksonline.com
Dist(s): **Consortium Bk. Sales & Distribution**
Gryphon Hse., Inc.

Bujack Enterprises, Inc., *(0-615)* 13177 W. 3000 S., Cedar City, UT 84720 USA Tel 435-867-4671 (phone/fax)
E-mail: nichola3@swbell.net.

†Bulfinch Pr., *(0-8212)* Div. of Little Brown & Co., Orders Addr.: 3 Center Plaza, Boston, MA 02108-2084 USA Tel 617-227-0730; Fax: 617-263-2857; Toll Free Fax: 800-286-9471; Toll Free: 800-759-0190; Edit Addr.: Time & Life Bldg. 1271 Ave. of the Americas, New York, NY 10020 USA Toll Free: 800-343-9204 Do not confuse with Bullfinch Pr., Minnetonka, MN
E-mail: cust.service@twbg.com
Web site: http://www.twbookmark.com/arts/index.html
Dist(s): **Hachette Bk. Group**; *CIP.*

Bull, David Publishing, Inc., *(0-9649722; 1-893618)* 4250 E. Camelback Rd., Suite K150, Phoenix, AZ 85018 USA Tel 602-852-9500; Fax: 602-852-9503; Toll Free: 800-831-1758
E-mail: dbull@bullpublishing.com; sales@bullpublishing.com; tmoore@bullpublishing.com
Web site: http://www.bullpublishing.com.

Bull, John, *(0-9702615)* Div. of John Bull Bks., 1028 Beltline Blvd., Columbia, SC 29205 USA Tel 803-782-7799.

†Bull Publishing Co., *(0-915950; 0-923521; 0-945946; 1-933503)* Orders Addr.: P.O. Box 1377, Boulder, CO 80306-1377 USA Tel 303-545-6350; Fax: 303-545-6354; Toll Free: 800-676-2855; Edit Addr.: 1905 Mapleton Ave., Boulder, CO 80304 USA
E-mail: jim.bullpubco@comcast.net
Web site: http://www.bullpub.com
Dist(s): **Independent Pubs. Group**; *CIP.*

Bullard, Belinda *See* **A Blessed Heritage Educational Resources**

Bulldog Pr., *(0-9672710)* P.O. Box 620358, Woodside, CA 94062-0358 USA Tel 650-851-8218; Fax: 650-851-1753 Do not confuse with companies with the same name in Frankfort, IN, Whittier, CA
E-mail: dputnam555@aol.com
Web site: http://www.americanbulldogger.com.

Bullfrog Publishing *See* **Creative Publishing Services**

Bumble Bee Publishing, *(0-9754342; 1-933982)* Div. of Bumble Bee Productions, Inc., Orders Addr.: 725 Watch Island Reach, Chesapeake, VA 23320 USA (SAN 256-1611) Tel 757-410-9409 (phone/fax); Toll Free: 866-782-9533 (phone/fax); Edit Addr.: P.O. Box 1757, Chesapeake, VA 23327-1757 USA (SAN 256-162X) Tel 747-410-9409; 5721 M St., Lincoln, NE 68510 (SAN 256-1638)
E-mail: buzz707@bbpmail.com
Web site: http://www.yesterdaywehadahurricane.com; http://www.bumblebeepublishing.com; http://www.rubyleethebumblebee.com; http://www.bumblebeeproductions.com; http://www.bplusbooks.com.

Bumples, *(0-9700952)* 9 Shorefront Park., Norwalk, CT 06854-3752 USA
E-mail: bumples@aol.com; Bumples@aol.com
Dist(s): **Baker & Taylor Bks.**

Bumpy Bks Inc, *(0-9778736)* 9960 Third Ave., Brooklyn, NY 11209 USA (SAN 851-4321)
Web site: http://bumpybooks.com.

Bumpy Pumpkin, *(0-9754696)* 3405 Heather Dr., Augusta, GA 30909 USA
Web site: http://www.bumpypumpkin.com.

Bunim & Bannigan Ltd., *(1-933480)* PMB 157, 111 E. 14th St., New York, NY 10003-4103 USA Tel 646-414-2993; Fax: 212-217-0242
E-mail: greatblue2@rcn.com
Web site: http://www.bunim&bannigan.com
Dist(s): **Ingram Pub. Services.**

Bunker Hill Publishing, Inc., *(1-59373)* 285 River Rd., Piermont, NH 03779-3009 USA
E-mail: mail@bunkerhillpublishing.com
Web site: http://www.bunkerhillpublishing.com
Dist(s): **National Bk. Network.**

Bunny & The Crocodile Pr., The, *(0-938572)* 1821 Glade Ct., Annapolis, MD 21403-1945 USA Tel 410-267-7432 (phone/fax)
E-mail: gracecav@comcast.net
Web site: http://www.members.aol.com/grace7623/grace.htm.

Bunny Express Pr. *Imprint of* **Brookes, C. Avery Ltd.**

Bur Oak Pr., Inc., *(0-929326)* 8717 Mockingbird Rd., Platteville, WI 53818 USA (SAN 249-0463) Tel 608-348-8662
E-mail: buroakpress@yahoo.com
Web site: http://www.geocities.com/buroakpress.

Burbank, Luther Home & Gardens, *(0-9637883)* City of Santa Rosa, P.O. Box 1678, Santa Rosa, CA 95402 USA Tel 707-524-5445; Fax: 707-524-5827
E-mail: burbankhome@lutherburbank.org
Web site: http://www.lutherburbank.org.

Burd Street Pr. *Imprint of* **White Mane Publishing Co., Inc.**

Bureau of Education & Research, *(1-886397)* Orders Addr.: P.O. Box 96068, Bellevue, WA 98009-9668 USA Tel 425-453-2121; Fax: 425-453-1875; Toll Free: 800-735-3503; Edit Addr.: 915 118th Ave. SE, Bellevue, WA 98005 USA
Web site: http://www.ber.org.

Burke, John Gordon Pub., Inc., *(0-934272)* P.O. Box 1492, Evanston, IL 60204 USA (SAN 223-7083) Tel 847-866-8625; Fax: 847-866-6639
E-mail: info@jgburkepub.com
Web site: http://www.jgburkepub.com.

Burkhardt The Artist, *(0-9762996)* P.O. Box 35, Alexandria, KY 41001 USA Tel 859-694-6000
E-mail: rockyburk@hotmail.com
Web site: http://www.rockyburkhardt.com.

Burlington, David, *(0-9772136)* 513 Thurber Dr., Schertz, TX 78154 USA Tel 210-833-9417
E-mail: dave@bassfishingaskdave.com
Web site: http://www.bassfishingaskdave.com.

Burlington National, Inc., *(1-57706)* Orders Addr.: P.O. Box 732, Metairie, LA 70004 USA Tel 504-833-1792; Edit Addr.: 6301 Perrier, New Orleans, LA 70118 USA
E-mail: books@burlingtonnational.com
Dist(s): **Baker & Taylor Bks.**

Burman Books, Inc. (CAN) Dist. by IPG Chicago.

Burney Enterprises Unlimited, *(0-9745360)* P.O. Box 401402, Redford, MI 48240-9402 USA
Web site: http://www.mileafh.org.

BurnhillWolf, *(0-9645655)* 321 Prospect St., NW, Lenoir, NC 28645 USA Tel 704-754-0287
E-mail: Burnwolf@charter.net
Web site: http://www.burnhillwolf.com
Dist(s): **BookSurge, LLC.**

Burning Bk. Pr., The, *(0-9748280)* 1435 Newton St., NW, Suite 111, District of Columbia, DC 20010 USA
E-mail: brendan@burningbookpress.org
Web site: http://www.burningbookpress.org.

Burning Bush Creation, *(0-9768680; 1-60390)* 2114 Queen Ave. N., Minneapolis, MN 55411-2435 USA Tel 612-529-0198; Fax: 612-529-0199
E-mail: ron@mcconico.com
Web site: http://www.burningbushcreation.com.

Burns, Marilyn Education Associates *See* **Math Solutions Pubns.**

Burns, Nicholas K. Publishing, *(0-9713069; 0-9755224)* 130 Proctor Blvd., Utica, NY 13501 USA Tel 315-738-1890; Fax: 315-738-1891; Toll Free: 866-738-1890
E-mail: nkburns@adelphia.net
Dist(s): **Koen-Levy Bk. Wholesalers LLC**
Partners Bk. Distributing, Inc.

Burns, Phillys, *(0-9620065)* 7450 Olivetas Ave., No. 230, La Jolla, CA 92037 USA (SAN 247-526X).

BurnsBooks, *(0-9726099)* 50 Joe's Hill Rd., Danbury, CT 06811 USA Tel 203-744-0232
E-mail: burnsbookspub@aol.com
Web site: http://www.burnsbookspublishing.com.

Burnside Pubns., *(0-9766413)* 971 San Pascual Ave., Los Angeles, CA 90042-9004 USA
Web site: http://www.dwf-art.com.

Burt Creations, *(0-9649283; 0-9741407)* 29 Arnold Pl., Norwich, CT 06360 USA (SAN 253-925X) Tel 860-887-8312; 860-889-4066; Fax: 860 889-4068; Toll Free: 866-693-6936
E-mail: passtev@aol.com
Web site: http://www.burtcreations.com; http://www.achristmasdozen.com
Dist(s): **Baker & Taylor Bks.**
Biblio Distribution.

Burt, Steven E. *See* **Burt Creations**

Burton, Helen, *(0-9645769)* P.O. Box 50044, Austin, TX 78763 USA Fax: 512-452-7578.

Burton, Kenneth Hugh, *(0-9747043)* Orders Addr.: P.O. Box 38142, Atlanta, GA 30334 USA Tel 404-799-1908; Edit Addr.: 406 Collier Ridge Dr. NW, Atlanta, GA 30318-7312 USA
E-mail: notrub18@bellsouth.net.

Buscher, Julie W., *(0-9786352)* Orders Addr.: P.O. Box 627, Brighton, CO 80601-0627 USA (SAN 851-1802) Tel 303-659-7354
E-mail: julobush2@q.com
Web site: http://www.homerthehelicopter.com.

Bush, Bill *See* **Bush Publishing Inc.**

Bush Brothers & Co., *(0-9779308)* 1016 E. Weisgarber Rd., Knoxville, TN 37909-2683 USA.

Bush Publishing Inc., *(0-9723102; 0-9778728; 0-9798113)* 507 E. 2nd Ave., Owasso, OK 74055 USA Tel 918-272-2874; Fax: 918-272-2882
Web site: http://www.bushpublishing.com.

Business Bks. International, *(0-916673)* P.O. Box 1587, New Canaan, CT 06840 USA (SAN 297-1860) Tel 203-966-9645; Fax: 203-966-6018
E-mail: lesdv@businessbooksusa.com
Web site: http://www.businessbooksusa.com.

Business Bks., LLC, *(0-9723714)* 2709 Washington Ave., 21A, Evansville, IN 47714 USA
E-mail: mbussingbu@aol.com
Web site: http://www.bussinessbooksllc.com
Dist(s): **AtlasBooks Distribution.**

Business Cents Resources, *(1-889107)* Div. of Jo-Cid & Co., Inc., 3132 Millers Run Rd., Cecil, PA 15321-1208 USA Toll Free: 800-672-4639
E-mail: drcindy@cencentric.net
Web site: http://drcindy.com.

Business Jobs *See* **Alexie Bks.**

Business Pubns. Inc. (IND) *(81-86982; 81-7693) Dist. by* **St Mut.**

Business Word, The, *(0-9636745; 0-9655442; 1-891846)* 11211 E. Arapahoe Rd., Suite 101, Centennial, CO 80112 USA Tel 303-290-8500; Fax: 303-290-9025; Toll Free: 800-328-3211 ; *Imprints:* Twins Books (Twins Bks)
E-mail: Richard.Rhinehart@businessword.com
Web site: http://www.businessword.com; http://www.twinsmagazine.com/theBookshelf.shtml.

Buster B.B. Publishing, *(0-9726691)* 1530 Indian Springs Rd., Pine Beach, NY 12566 USA
E-mail: mirror38@aol.com
Web site: http://www.reflectionsseminars.com.

Busy Bee Bks., *(0-9759281)* 2160 110th St., SE, Delano, MN 55328 USA Tel 952-237-7218
E-mail: debbyanderson@juno.com.

Busy Bibles, Inc., *(0-9712022)* P.O. Box 2310, Goldenrod, FL 32733-2310 USA Tel 407-671-7972; Fax: 407-671-3039
E-mail: info@busybibles.com
Web site: http://www.busybibles.com
Dist(s): **STL Distribution North America.**

Busy Buddy Bks., *(0-9651598)* P.O. Box 337, Newport, RI 02840 USA Tel 401-845-2277; Fax: 401-845-2279; Toll Free: 800-690-9993
E-mail: busybuddy@aol.com
Web site: http://www.busybuddybooks.com.

Butler Ctr. for Arkansas Studies, *(0-9708574; 0-9800897)* c/o Central Arkansas Library System, 100 Rock St., Little Rock, AR 72201 USA
Web site: http://www.cals.org.

Butte Pubns., Inc., *(1-884362)* P.O. Box 1328, Hillsboro, OR 97123-1328 USA (SAN 299-8866) Tel 503-648-9791; Fax: 503-693-9526
E-mail: service@buttepublications.com
Web site: http://www.buttepublications.com.

Buttercup Media, *(0-9768152)* Orders Addr.: P.O. Box 222003, Dallas, TX 75222 USA Tel 214-890-6833
E-mail: corporate@buttercupmedia.com
Web site: http://www.buttercupmedia.com.

Butterfield Bks., Inc., *(1-886652)* Box 407, Lindsborg, KS 67456 USA Tel 785-227-2707; Fax: 785-227-2017
E-mail: linda@bookkansas.com
Web site: http://www.bookkansas.com
Dist(s): **Baker & Taylor Bks.**
Booksource, The
Skandisk, Inc.

Butterfly Bk. Makers, *(0-9754117)* 1450 W. 800 N., Orem, UT 84057 USA
E-mail: hatfiron@aol.com.

Company

Butterfly Creations, Inc., *(0-9650449)* 9 Laurel Cove, Greensboro, NC 27455-2495 USA (SAN 298-8984) Tel 366-288-6606
E-mail: eblloyd@bflycreations.com
Web site: http://www.funwithfreckles.com
Dist(s): **Baker & Taylor Bks.**

Butterfly Park Educational Materials, Inc., *(0-9744575)* 3126 Elmira Ct., Denver, CO 80238-2929 USA
E-mail: butterflypark@comcast.net
Web site: http://www.butterflyparkphonics.com.

Butterfly Pavilion, *(0-9729000)* 6252 W. 104th Ave., Westminster, CO 80020 USA Tel 303-469-5441; Fax: 303-657-5944
E-mail: ptennyson@butterflies.org
Web site: http://www.butterflies.org.

Butterfly Pr., *(0-9673550)* P.O. Box 264, Cochranville, PA 19330 USA Fax: 610-593-0399 Do not confuse with companies with the same or similar name in New York, NY, Worcester, MA, Houston, TX, Point Richmond, CA, Phoenix, AZ, Amherst, MA, Charleston, WV, Old Town, ME, Dayton, OH, Sedona, AZ Lenox, MA
E-mail: drnkmilk@epix.net
Web site: http://www.arjoyholsteins.com.

Butterfly Pr., *(0-9677692)* 18 Cedar St., Old Town, ME 04468-1302 USA Tel 207-827-5651 Do not confuse with companies with same name in New York, NY, Worcester, MA, Houston, TX, Cochranville, PA, Point Richmond, CA, Phoeniz, AZ, Amherst, MA, Stamford, Ct, Sedona, AZ Lenox, MA
E-mail: azames18@aol.com

Butterfly Press *See* **Butterfly Productions, LLC**

Butterfly Productions, LLC, *(0-9752936)* 165 Shadow Rock Dr., Sedona, AZ 86336 USA Tel 928-204-2811; Fax: 928-204-9118 Do not confuse with companies with the same or similar name in New York, NY, Worcester, MA, Houston, TX, Old Town, ME, Dayton, OH, Cochranville, PA, Princeton, NJ , Amherst, MA, Charston, WV, Pheonix, AZ
E-mail: butterfly@sedona.net
Web site: http://www.butterflyproductions.info.

Butterhouse Publishing, *(0-9763971)* 12251 N. 32nd St., Suite 4, Phoenix, AZ 85032 USA
E-mail: financialstories@juno.com.

Butters Pr., *(0-9754960)* 2047 Gale Rd., Eaton Rapids, MI 48827 USA
Web site: http://www.throughtheears.com.

Butterworth-Heinemann *Imprint of* **Elsevier Science & Technology Bks.**

Button Flower Pr., *(0-9747836)* 7422 Westview Dr., Boardman, OH 44512 USA.

Buttonweed Pr., L.L.C., *(0-9755675)* 204 7th St W. # 125, Northfield, MN 55057-2419 USA (SAN 256-1700)
E-mail: info@buttonweedpress.com
Web site: http://www.buttonweedpress.com
Dist(s): **Baker & Taylor Bks.**
Follett Library Resources
Partners Bk. Distributing, Inc.

Buttonwood Pr., *(0-9660685; 0-9742920)* Orders Addr.: P.O. Box 716, Haslett, MI 48840 USA Tel 517-339-9871; Fax: 517-339-5908; Edit Addr.: 5951 Buttonwood Dr., Haslett, MI 48840 USA Do not confuse with companies with the same name Champaign, IL, Potomac, MD, New York, NY, Solvang, CA
E-mail: rlbald@ave.com
Web site: http://www.buttonwoodpress.com
Dist(s): **Partners Bk. Distributing, Inc.**

Buy Books on the Web.Com *See* **Infinity Publishing**

Buy Rite, *(0-9723744; 1-60421)* 88 Vanderveer Rd., Freehold, NJ 07728 USA Tel 732-294-9000; Fax: 732-294-9363; Toll Free: 888-777-7952
Web site: http://www.buyriteinc.com.

Buz-Land Presentations, Inc., *(0-9766990)* 1082 Lenape Way, Scotch Plains, NJ 07076-2814 USA (SAN 256-5692) Tel 201-396-0200; Fax: 201-848-8999; 73 Harding Rd., Wyckoff, NJ 07481 Tel 201-848-0595
E-mail: buzi.bee@verizon.net
Web site: http://www.buz-land.com; www.WWRT.org
Dist(s): **Biblio Distribution.**

Buzzard Pr. International, *(0-9648488)* 506 W. Donna Dr., Merced, CA 95348 USA Tel 209-723-6738; Fax: 209-723-6253
E-mail: buzzard@buzzardpress.com
Dist(s): **Sunbelt Pubns., Inc.**

Buzzy's Bks., *(0-9719054)* P.O. Box 566, Grafton, MA 01519 USA Tel 508-839-2442; Fax: 508-839-7396
E-mail: buzzy@buzzysbooks.org
Web site: http://www.buzzysbooks.org
Dist(s): **Baker & Taylor Bks.**

By Faith Theatre Ministries, Inc., *(1-931785)* 364 W. Holmes Rd., Memphis, TN 38109 USA Tel 901-785-9036; Fax: 901-785-7596
E-mail: bftheatrem@msn.com.

By Grace Enterprises, *(0-9663629)* 9515 Twin Oaks Dr., Manvel, TX 77578-5307 USA
E-mail: huletteрl@aol.com
Web site: http://www.bygraceenterprises.com.

by shayne, *(0-9725593)* P.O. Box 221474, Santa Clarita, CA 91322 USA
Web site: http://www.byshayne.com.

By the Book Media, *(0-9726983)* Let's Get It Together, P.O. Box 590860, Houston, TX 77259 USA Tel 281-286-9512
E-mail: info@organizedtimes.com
Web site: http://www.organizedtimes.com.

BYE Publishing Services, *(0-9656739)* Orders Addr.: 915 L St., Suite 144, Sacramento, CA 95814 USA Tel 916-529-3119 Corporate Hq; Fax: 916-683-1476; Edit Addr.: 5245 College Ave., Suite 333, Oakland, CA 94618 USA Tel 510-272-0101
E-mail: byepublishing@comcast.net
Web site: http://www.byepublishing.com.

Byeway *Imprint of* **Byeway Bks.**

Byeway Bks., *(1-85997; 1-904586; 1-933581; 1-934004; 1-60176)* 10548 Lackman Rd., Lenexa, KS 66219 USA Tel 913-888-6790; Fax: 913-888-6759; Toll Free Fax: 866-426-3929; Toll Free: 866-429-3929 ; *Imprints:* Byeway (Byeway)
E-mail: customerservice@byewaybooks.com
Web site: http://www.byewaybooks.com/how_to_order.html.

Byrne, Susan K. *See* **R&R Pubns.**

Byte Me Enterprises *See* **Just For Children**

Byte/Me Teen Bk. *Imprint of* **Awe-Struck E-Books, Inc.**

C.A.P.E. Ctr., *(0-944454)* 4621 Ross Ave., YWCA Bldg., Dallas, TX 75204-4994 USA (SAN 243-7333) Tel 214-821-4784; Fax: 972-699-8147
E-mail: EBKRAUSE@prodigy.net.

C&C Educational Materials, LLC, *(0-9640524; 0-9747205)* 12514 Dermott Dr., Houston, TX 77065-2419 USA.

C & C Productions, *(0-9753273)* PMB 254, 330 SW 43rd St., No. K, Renton, WA 98055 USA.

C & C Publishing *See* **Cosmo Starr Bks.**

C&D Enterprises, *(0-9633231; 0-9765938)* P.O. Box 7201, Arlington, VA 22207-7201 USA Fax: 703-276-3033
E-mail: harryfp@comcast.net.

C&D International, *(0-937347)* 111 Ferguson Ct., Suite 105, Irving, TX 75062-7014 USA (SAN 659-1523) Toll Free: 800-231-0442.

C&D Productions JimMar, Inc., *(0-9629270)* 6369 C. Centennial Cir., Glen Burnie, MD 21061 USA
E-mail: Jameskdoran@earthlink.net.

C & H Pubns., *(0-9740882)* 31201 S. 596 Ln., Grove, OK 74344 USA.

C & R Enterprises, *(0-9702818)* 7772 Sunset Rd., Pittsville, WI 54466 USA Tel 715-884-6523.

C & R Productions, *(0-9728516)* P.O. Box 195, Henrico, NC 27842 USA
E-mail: comet-rainbow@starband.net
Web site: http://www.recipedujour.com.

†C&T Publishing, *(0-914881; 1-57120)* Orders Addr.: 1651 Challenge Dr., Concord, CA 94520 USA (SAN 289-0720) Tel 925-677-0373 (phone/fax); Toll Free: 800-284-1114
E-mail: ctinfo@ctpub.com
Web site: http://www.ctpub.com
Dist(s): **Macmillan**
Watson-Guptill Pubns., Inc.; *CIP.*

CBI Pr., *(0-9705812)* 6 Jeffrey Cir., Bedford, MA 01730 USA Do not confuse with C B I Press, Arlington, VA
E-mail: nancy_nugent@comcast.net
Web site: http://www.cbipress.com.

C. B. Publishing House, Incorporated *See* **Cubbie Blue Publishing**

CCLS Publishing Hse., *(1-928882; 0-7428)* 3191 Coral Way, Suite 114, Miami, FL 33145-3209 USA (SAN 254-4695) Tel 305-529-2224; Fax: 305-443-8538; Toll Free: 800-704-8181
E-mail: info@cclscorp.com
Web site: http://www.CCLSCORP.COM
Dist(s): **Continental Bk. Co., Inc.**

C C M Communications, *(0-9700821)* Synister Creative Systems, P.O. Box 86, Caldwell, NJ 07006-0086 USA
E-mail: thesynister@aol.com
Web site: http://www.synistercreative.com.

CDC Pr., *(0-935769)* 88 Bradley Rd., Woodbridge, CT 06525 USA (SAN 695-8338) Tel 203-387-8887; Fax: 203-387-7721.

CEC Pubs., *(1-892992)* P.O. Box 2906, Tampa, FL 33601-2906 USA; 220 E Madison St., Suuite 1218, Tampa, FL 33602 (SAN 256-8829) Tel 813-259-0303; Fax: 813-258-9383
E-mail: ferrara@cecconsultants.com; docfferrara@aol.com
Web site: http://www.cecconsultants.com.

CEF Pr., *(1-55976)* Div.of Child Evangelism Fellowship, Orders Addr.: P.O. Box 348, Warrenton, MO 63383 USA Tel 636-456-4321; Fax: 636-456-2078; Toll Free: 800-748-7710; Edit Addr.: 2300 E. Hwy. M, Warrenton, MO 63383 USA (SAN 211-7789)
E-mail: custserv@cefonline.com
Web site: http://www.cefonline.com; http://www.cefpress.com.

CEO Software Solutions, *(1-886292)* 30 Hudson Ave., Red Bank, NJ 07701-1931 USA Tel 732-933-4545; Fax: 732-933-4646
E-mail: ceo@tie2000.com; ceo@tienet.wf.

CES Industries, Inc., *(0-86711)* 130 Central Ave., Farmingdale, NY 11735 USA (SAN 237-9864) Tel 631-293-1420
E-mail: m.nesenoff@cesindustries.com
Web site: http://www.cesindustries.com.

CFKR Career Materials, Inc., *(0-934783; 1-887481)* P.O. Box 99, Meadow Vista, CA 95722-0099 USA (SAN 694-2547) Toll Free Fax: 800-770-0433; Toll Free: 800-525-5626
E-mail: requestinfo@cfkr.com; cfkr@cfkr.com; order@cfkr.com
Web site: http://www.cfkr.com.

CIS Communications, Inc., *(0-935063; 1-56062)* 180 Park Avenue, Lakewood, NJ 08701 USA (SAN 694-5953) Tel 732-905-3000; Fax: 732-367-6666.

CJH Enterprises, *(0-9643250; 1-890683)* 6064 Mayberry Ln., Milton, FL 32570-8875 USA Tel 850-626-2700; Fax: 850-626-7040; Toll Free: 888-258-2784
E-mail: altarvin@pcola.gulf.net
Web site: http://www.pcola.gulf.net/~altarvin
Dist(s): **Baker & Taylor Bks.**

C M J Associates, Incorporated, Publishers *See* **CMJ Marian Pubs.**

CMJ Marian Pubs., *(0-9648448; 1-891280)* Orders Addr.: P.O. Box 661, Oak Lawn, IL 60454 USA Tel 708-636-2995; Fax: 708-636-2855; Toll Free: 888-636-6799; Edit Addr.: 10745 S. Kolmar Ave., Oak Lawn, IL 60453 USA
E-mail: jwby@aol.com
Web site: http://www.cmjbooks.com.

CMSP Projects, *(0-942851)* School of Engineering, 51 Astor Pl., New York, NY 10003 USA (SAN 667-6731) Tel 212-228-0950.

CPI Pubs., *(0-9648363)* Div. of Christopher Productions, Inc., 1115 David Ave., Pacific Grove, CA 93950 USA Tel 818-831-9268; Fax: 818-845-2128
Dist(s): **Austin & Company, Inc.**

CPI Publishing, Inc., 311 E. 51st St., New York, NY 10022 USA (SAN 218-6896) Tel 212-753-3800
Dist(s): **Modern Curriculum Pr.**

CPM Educational Program, *(1-885145; 1-931287; 1-60328)* 1233 Noonan Dr., Sacramento, CA 95822 USA Tel 916-446-9936; Fax: 916-444-5263
E-mail: cpm@cpm.org; bradley@cpm.org
Web site: http://www.cpm.org.

†CRC Pr. LLC, *(0-8493; 0-87762; 0-87819; 0-935184; 1-56676; 1-57491; 1-58488; 1-58716; 1-4200)* Subs. of Taylor & Francis, Inc., Orders Addr.: 6000 Broken Sound Pkwy., NW, Suite 300, Boca Raton, FL 33487 USA Tel 800-272-7737; 561-361-6000; Fax: 800-374-3401 ; *Imprints:* Lewis Publishing (Lewis Pub); Parthenon Publishing (Parthenon Pbng)
E-mail: orders@crcpress.com
Web site: http://www.crcpress.com
Dist(s): **NetLibrary, Inc.**
Oxford Univ. Pr., Inc.
Sony CONNECT, Inc.
Taylor & Francis, Inc.; *CIP.*

†CRC Pubns., *(0-930265; 0-933140; 1-56212)* 2850 Kalamazoo Ave., SE, Grand Rapids, MI 49560 USA (SAN 212-727X) Tel 616-224-0724; Fax: 616-224-0834; Toll Free Fax: 888-642-8606; Toll Free: 800-333-8300; P.O. Box 5070, Burlington, ON L7R 3Y8 ; *Imprints:* Faith Alive Christian Resources (Faith Alive Christian)
E-mail: sales@crcpublications.org
Web site: http://www.crcpublications.org; *CIP.*

C R C World Literature Ministries *See* **C R C World Literature Ministries/Libros Desafio**

C R C World Literature Ministries/Libros Desafio, *(0-939125; 1-55883; 1-55955)* Subs. of CRC Pubns., 2850 Kalamazoo Ave., SE, Grand Rapids, MI 49560 USA (SAN 251-3269) Tel 616-224-0785 (customer service); Fax: 616-224-0834; Toll Free: 800-333-8300
E-mail: info@worldliterature.org
Web site: http://www.worldliterature.org/
Dist(s): **CRC Pubns.**

CRM, *(0-9713534; 1-933341)* Orders Addr.: P.O. Box 2124, Hendersonville, NC 28793 USA Tel 828-877-3356; Fax: 828-890-1511; Edit Addr.: 1916 Reasonover Rd., Cedar Mountain, NC 28218 USA
E-mail: crm@ciridmus.com
Web site: http://www.ciridmus.com
Dist(s): **Baker & Taylor Bks.**
STL Distribution North America.

†CSS Publishing Co., *(0-7880; 0-89536; 1-55673)* Orders Addr.: P.O. Box 4503, Lima, OH 45802-4503 USA (SAN 207-0707) Tel 419-227-1818; Fax: 419-228-9184; Toll Free: 800-537-1030 (Orders); 800-241-4056 (Customer Service); Edit Addr.: 517 S. Main St., Lima, OH 45804-4503 USA ; *Imprints:* Fairway Press (Fairway Pr) Do not confuse with CSS Publishing in Tularosa, NM
E-mail: editor@csspub.com; csr@csspub.com; info@csspub.com; orders@csspub.com
Web site: http://www.csspub.com
Dist(s): **Spring Arbor Distributors, Inc.**; *CIP.*

C T A, Inc., *(0-9712618; 0-9718985; 0-9728816; 0-9744640; 0-9747923; 0-9754499; 0-9759330; 1-933234)* P.O. Box 1205, Fenton, MO 63026-1205 USA Tel 636-305-3100; Toll Free Fax: 800-315-8713; Toll Free: 800-999-1874
Web site: http://www.ctainc.com.

C T L Publishing, *(0-9669116)* 12210 Fairfax Towne Ctr., Suite 18, Fairfax, VA 22033 USA Tel 703-631-8318; Fax: 703-849-0018
Dist(s): **Biblio Distribution.**

CTS Family Pr., *(1-930260)* c/o Concordia Theological Seminary, 6600 N.Clinton St., Fort Wayne, IN 46825 USA Tel 219-452-2100; Fax: 219-452-2246; Toll Free: 888-287-4338
E-mail: ctspress@mail.ctsfw.edu.

C. W. Historicals, LLC, *(0-9637745)* Orders Addr.: P.O. Box 113, Collingswood, NJ 08108 USA Tel 856-854-1290; Fax: 856-854-1290 (*69); Edit Addr.: 901 Lakeshore Dr., Westmont, NJ 08108 USA
E-mail: cwhist@erols.com.

C.W.R. Publishing, *(0-9678627)* 6106 Emerson Ave., N., Minneapolis, MN 55430 USA
E-mail: prollins@uswest.net
Web site: http://www.curpublish.faithweb.com.

C Z M Press *See* **Touchstones Discussion Project**

C2 (C squared) Publishing, *(0-9773115)* P.O. Box 5269, Vienna, WV 26105 USA
E-mail: noelclntn@yahoo.com.

Caballo Bks., *(1-59616)* P.O. Box 916392, Longwood, FL 32791-6392 USA Tel 407-756-5862.

Cabat Studio Pubns., *(0-913521)* 627 N. Fourth Ave., Tucson, AZ 85705 USA (SAN 285-1539) Tel 520-622-6362
E-mail: junecabat@hotmail.com.

Cabbage Patch Pr., *(0-9729044)* 841 Washington St., Suite 111, Franklin Square, NY 11010 USA Tel 516-437-8460; Fax: 516-483-7701
E-mail: cabbagepatchpress@hotmail.com
Web site: http://www.cabbagepatchpress.com.

CABI (GBR) *(0-85198; 0-85199) Dist. by* **OUP.**

Cabrilho Press *See* **LinguaText, Ltd.**

cactus annie pubns., *(0-9664997)* Orders Addr.: P.O. Box 5731, Carefree, AZ 85377 USA Tel 602-488-8472; Edit Addr.: 8028 E. Carefree Dr., Carefree, AZ 85377 USA.

Cactus Publishing, LLC, *(0-9766674)* 1235 S. Gilbert Rd., Suite 3-62, Mesa, AZ 85204 USA Do not confuse with companies iwht the same or similar name in East Perth, WA, Atlanta, GA, Peoria, AZ
E-mail: glsweetaz@msn.com.

Cadcim Technologies, *(0-9663537; 1-932709)* 525 St. Andrews Dr., Schererville, IN 46375 USA Tel 219-322-1001; Fax: 270-717-0185
E-mail: cadcim@yahoo.com; sales@cadcim.com
Web site: http//:www. cadcim.com.

Cadence Bks. *Imprint of* **Viz Media**

Cader Publishing, Ltd., *(1-885206; 1-58915)* 2886 Wagonwheel Dr., Troy, MI 48085-3756 USA
E-mail: info@cader.com
Web site: http://www.cader.com.

Cadmos Verlag GmbH (GBR) *(3-86127; 3-925760) Dist. by* **Trans-Atl Phila.**

Cadogan Guides (GBR) *(0-946313; 0-947754; 1-85744; 1-86011) Dist. by* **Globe Pequot.**

Cadron Creek Curriculum, *(0-9652511)* 4329 Pinos Altos Rd., Silver City, NM 88061 USA Tel 505-534-1496; Fax: 505-534-1499
E-mail: marigold@zianet.com
Web site: http://www.CadronCreek.com.

Cahill Publishing, *(0-9744027)* 1016-F Brentwood Way, Atlanta, GA 30350 USA
E-mail: e-diane@hotmail.com.

Cahill Publishing Company *See* **Advance Publishing, Inc.**

Cajun Prairie Habitat Preservation Society, *(0-9633191)* Dept. of Biology, NE Louisiana Univ., Monroe, LA 71209 USA Tel 318-342-1814; Fax: 318-342-1755; 721 Hill St., Eunice, LA 70535
E-mail: biallen@alpha.nlu.edu.

Calaca Pr., *(0-9660773; 0-9717035)* Orders Addr.: P.O. Box 2309, National City, CA 91951 USA Tel 619-434-9036 (phone/fax); Edit Addr.: 502 Rose Dr., National City, CA 91950 USA
E-mail: calacapress@cox.net
Web site: http://calacapress.com; http://redcalacartscollective.org
Dist(s): **Baker & Taylor Bks.**
SPD-Small Pr. Distribution
Sunbelt Pubns., Inc.

Calamus, *(0-9700689)* 1355 N. Laurel Ave., No. 4, Los Angeles, CA 90046 USA Tel 323-650-5384; Fax: 323-650-4963
E-mail: calamuspress@aol.com
Web site: http://www.calamuspress.com.

Cal-Asia Publishing, *(0-9662833)* Orders Addr.: P.O. Box 726, Temple City, CA 91780-0726 USA Tel 626-287-7538; Edit Addr.: 9662 Las Tunas Dr., Temple City, CA 91780 USA.

Calcar, Inc., *(0-9705167)* 122 S. El Camino Real, PMB 139, San Clemente, CA 92672 USA Tel 949-498-1100; Fax: 949-361-3759; Toll Free: 800-482-2522
E-mail: admin@calcarqt.com
Web site: http://sportdriving.com.

Caldwell, Judy, *(0-9774463)* 11216 Windy Peak Rdg., Sandy, UT 84094 USA Fax: 801-571-1422
E-mail: jlynncaldwell@msn.com.

Caleb Project, *(1-932329)* 10 W. Dry Creek Cir., Littleton, CO 80120 USA Tel 303-459-5400; Fax: 303-459-5401
E-mail: info@takeitglobal.com
Web site: http://www.takeitglobal.org.

Caleb's Pr., *(0-9729568)* 421 Seminole Ct., High Point, NC 27265-8631 USA Tel 336-887-6846; Fax: 888-726-9304
E-mail: calebspress@aol.com
Web site: http://www.calebspress.com
Dist(s): **Baker & Taylor Bks.**

Caleidoscope Creations, *(0-9723691)* 2850 Kilburn Ct., Rochester Hills, MI 48306 USA.

Cali Publishing, *(0-9793004)* 2875 NE 191st St., Suite 511, Aventua, FL 33180 USA Tel 786-200-9374; Fax: 305-937-4161
E-mail: lallouz@glmace.com
Web site: http://www.calipublishing.com.

Caliber Pubns., *(0-9673696)* 1295 Lincoln Dr., Marion, IA 52302 USA Tel 319-294-9468; Fax: 319-373-1370; Toll Free: 877-480-5790
E-mail: larson1965@aol.com
Web site: http://www.calpubs.com
Dist(s): **Biblio Distribution**
National Bk. Network.

Calicanto Assocs., *(0-9648362)* 6067 Aspinwall Rd., Oakland, CA 94611-2109 USA
Web site: http://www.linkdot.com.

Calico Connection, Inc., The, *(0-9767658)* 300 N. David Ln., Muskogee, OK 74403 USA Tel 918-687-6577 Do not confuse with Calico Publishing in Seabrook, TX
E-mail: calicoasay@cox.net.

Calico Publishing *See* **Calico Connection, Inc., The**

California Academic Pr. LLC, The, *(1-891557)* 217 La Cruz Ave., Millbrae, CA 94030 USA Tel 650-697-5628; Fax: 650-692-0141
E-mail: info@insightassessment.com
Web site: http://www.insightassessment.com.

California Capital Leasing Corp., *(0-9740309)* 122-A E. Foothill Blvd., No. 317, Arcadia, CA 91006 USA Tel 626-305-1053; Fax: 626-305-0019
E-mail: ted@acclease.com
Web site: http://www.cclease.com.

California Clock Company *See* **Joy Publishing**

California Street, *(0-915090)* 189 Pinehurst Rd., Canyon, CA 94516-0189 USA (SAN 207-673X) Tel 510-549-2461
E-mail: firefallmedia@worldnet.att.net
Web site: http://www.home.att.net/~firefallmedia.

California Weekly Explorer, Inc., *(0-936778)* 15052 Red Hill Ave. Ste. G, Tustin, CA 92780-6525 USA (SAN 217-0914)
E-mail: eurekacwe@aol.com
Web site: http://www.californiaweekly.com.

Calkins Creek *Imprint of* **Boyds Mills Pr.**

Callaway Editions, Inc., *(0-935112)* Div. of Callaway Arts & Entertainment, 19 Fulton St., 5th Fl., New York, NY 10038-2100 USA (SAN 213-2931) Fax: 212-929-8087
E-mail: info@callaway.com
Web site: http://www.callaway.com
Dist(s): **Holt, Henry & Co.**
Penguin Group (USA) Inc.
Simon & Schuster, Inc.
Simon & Schuster Children's Publishing.

Calling Crane Publishing, *(0-9619943)* Orders Addr.: 7605 Boston Harbor Rd. NE, Olympia, WA 98506 USA (SAN 246-9189)
E-mail: paula@callingcrane.com
Web site: http://www.callingcrane.com; http://www.readkilowatt.com.

Calliope Pr., *(0-9649241)* Orders Addr.: P.O. Box 2408, New York, NY 10108-2408 USA (SAN 298-9026) Tel 212-564-5068; Fax: 212-563-7859; Edit Addr.: 400 W. 43rd St., Apt. 34B, New York, NY 10036 USA Do not confuse with companies with same name in Silver Springs, MD, San Francisco, CA, North Hollywood, CA, Walnut Creek, CA
E-mail: Information@CalliopePress.com; Calliopenyc@aol.com
Web site: http://www.calliopepress.com
Dist(s): **Book Clearing Hse.**
Partners Bk. Distributing, Inc.

Calliope Pubns., *(0-9745249)* P.O. Box 251, Arabi, LA 70032 USA Do not confuse with Calliope Publishing in Steamboat Springs, CO
Web site: http://www.soundsdevine.com.

Callirobics, *(0-9630478)* Orders Addr.: P.O. Box 6634, Charlottesville, VA 22906 USA Tel 804-293-7055; Fax: 804-293-9008; Toll Free: 800-769-2891; Edit Addr.: 1616 King Mountain Rd., Charlottesville, VA 22901 USA
E-mail: cal-avir@cfw.com
Web site: http://www.callirobics.com.

Callis Editora Ltda (BRA) *(85-7416; 85-85642) Dist. by* **IPG Chicago.**

Cally Pr., *(0-9766199)* 3964 Loftlands Dr., Earlysville, VA 22936 USA
E-mail: callypress@aol.com.

Calm Flame Publishing Co., *(0-9745263)* 10745 Gilespie St., Las Vegas, NV 89123 USA.

CALs Ltd., *(0-9722212)* Orders Addr.: 418 Rye Creek Dr., Columbia, SC 29212 USA (SAN 254-749X)
E-mail: cflegette@sc.rr.com
Web site: http://www.calsltd.com.

Calvin College Alumni Assn., *(0-9703693)* 3201 Burton St., SE, Grand Rapids, MI 49546 USA Tel 616-526-6142; Fax: 616-526-7069
E-mail: alumni@calvin.edu; sbuist@calvin.edu
Web site: http://www.calvin.edu.

Calvin Partnership, LLC, *(1-891533)* 40 Ardmore Rd., Ho-Ho-Kus, NJ 07443-1008 USA Tel 201-670-8412; Fax: 201-670-0464
E-mail: jahelka@attglobal.net.

Cambria Creations, LLC, *(0-9770916)* 515 Main St., Johnston, PA 15901 USA Tel 814-535-5571; Fax: 814-535-1079
E-mail: djwlaw@wvdsl.net
Dist(s): **AtlasBooks Distribution.**

Cambridge Bks. *Imprint of* **ebooksonthe.net**

Cambridge Bk. Co., *(0-8428)* Div. of Simon & Schuster, Inc., 4350 Equity Dr., Box 249, Columbus, OH 43216 USA (SAN 169-5703) Toll Free: 800-238-5833
Web site: http://www.simonsays.com/.

Cambridge BrickHouse, Inc., *(1-59835)* 60 Island St., Lawrence, MA 01844 USA
E-mail: vmolina@cbhbooks.com
Web site: http://www.cambridgebh.com
Dist(s): **Ediciones Universal.**

Cambridge Educational Services, Inc., *(1-58894)* 2720 River Rd., Suite 36, Des Plaines, IL 60018 USA Tel 847-299-2930; Fax: 847-299-2933 Do not confuse with Cambridge Educational in Charleston, WV
Web site: http://www.cambridgeed.com.

Cambridge Hse. Publishing Co., LLC, *(0-9711359)* P.O. Box 383, Saddle River, NJ 07458 USA Fax: 973-777-8075
E-mail: cambridgehouse@verizon.net
Web site: http://www.cezanneismissing.com; http://www.cambridgehousepublishing.com
Dist(s): **Independent Pubs. Group.**

†Cambridge Univ. Pr., *(0-521; 0-511)* Orders Addr.: 100 Brook Hill Dr., West Nyack, NY 10994-2133 USA (SAN 281-3769) Tel 845-353-7500; Fax: 845-353-4141; Toll Free: 800-872-7423 (orders, returns, credit & accounting); 800-937-9600; Edit Addr.: 32 Avenue of the Americas, New York, NY 10013-2473 USA (SAN 200-206X) Tel 212-924-3900; Fax: 212-691-3239
E-mail: customer_service@cup.org; orders@cup.org; information@cup.org
Web site: http://www.cup.org
Dist(s): **Baker Bks.**
Baker Publishing Group
Thomson Gale
NetLibrary, Inc.; *CIP.*

Cambridge Way Publishing, *(0-9746976)* 149 Cambridge Way, Macon, GA 31220-8736 USA (SAN 255-8041) Tel 478-475-1763
E-mail: whwatson2@cox.net.

Camden Court Pubs., Inc., *(1-890828)* 2698 S. Redwood Rd., Suite O, West Valley City, UT 84119-2314 USA (SAN 299-3619)
E-mail: camdencourt@sisna.com
Dist(s): **Baker & Taylor Bks.**
Origin Bk. Sales, Inc.
Quality Bks., Inc.

Camden Hse. Publishing (CAN) *(0-920656; 0-921820; 0-944475; 1-55158) Dist. by* **Firefly Bks Limited.**

Camelot Publishing, *(0-9754063)* Orders Addr.: P.O. Box 500057, Lake Los Angeles, CA 93535 USA (SAN 256-0666)
E-mail: camelotpublishing@hotmail.com
Web site: http://www.camelotpublishing.com.

Camelot Publishing Co., *(0-89218)* P.O. Box 731138, Ormond Beach, FL 32173 USA (SAN 202-5035) Tel 386-672-5672; Fax: 386-672-3830.

Camelot Tales, *(0-9672375)* 4212 328th Ave., Burlington, WI 53105 USA
E-mail: tales@tds.net
Web site: http://www.talesfromwithin.com.

Cameltrotters Publishing, *(0-9666110; 0-9764475)* Orders Addr.: P.O. Box 3022, La Jolla, CA 92038-3022 USA Tel 619-235-9393 (phone/fax); Toll Free: 800-494-5341 (pager); Edit Addr.: 1455 Second Ave., No. 1113, San Diego, CA 92101-3026 USA
E-mail: ted@atborgeas.com
Web site: http://www.atborgeas.com.

Cameo Pubns., LLC, *(0-9715739; 0-9744149; 0-9744966; 0-9774659)* Orders Addr.: 2175 Deer Run Trl., Jacksonville, FL 32246-1068 USA
E-mail: info@cameopublications.com; publisher@cameopublications.com
Web site: http://www.cameopublications.com
Dist(s): **Baker & Taylor Bks.**
BookSurge, LLC
Bookazine Co., Inc.
Distributors, The
Independent Pubs. Group
New Leaf Pr., Inc.
Scholastic, Inc.

Camino Bks., Inc., *(0-940159; 1-933822)* P.O. Box 59026, Philadelphia, PA 19102 USA (SAN 664-225X) Tel 215-413-1917; Fax: 215-413-3255
E-mail: camino@caminobooks.com
Web site: http://www.caminobooks.com.

Camino E.E. & Bk. Co., *(0-940808; 1-55893)* Orders Addr.: a/o Jan Linzy, P.O. Box 6400, Incline Village, NV 89450 USA (SAN 219-841X) Tel 775-831-3078 (phone/fax); Fax: 775-831-3078 (phone/fax)
E-mail: info@camino-books.com
Web site: http://www.camino-books.com.

Camino Real Calendar LLC, *(0-9743501)* P.O. Box 17667, Anaheim, CA 92817 USA Toll Free: 800-200-6331
E-mail: support@caminosports.com
Web site: http://www.caminosports.com.

Camino Real Sports Marketing *See* **Camino Real Calendar LLC**

Camp Fire Boys & Girls *See* **Camp Fire Pr.**

Camp Fire Pr., *(0-9674529)* 4601 Madison Ave., Kansas City, MO 64112-1278 USA (SAN 675-0923) Tel 816-756-1950; Fax: 816-756-0258
E-mail: info@campfire.org
Web site: http://www.campfire.org.

Campanile Pr., *(1-892573)* Orders Addr.: P.O. Box 505, Fulton, MD 20759 USA Tel 301-604-4807; Edit Addr.: 11797 Limekiln Rd., Fulton, MD 20759 USA (SAN 299-5514)
E-mail: pronneberg@erols.com
Web site: http://www.campanilepress.com.

Campanita Bks. *Imprint of* **Editorial Campana**

Campbell & Lockwood Pubs., *(1-891180)* 55 Edgewater Dr., Pembroke, WA 02359 USA Tel 781-826-8763; Fax: 781-826-4635
E-mail: Lockwood@Lesley.edu.

Campbell Hse. Museum, *(0-9674867)* 1508 Locust St., Saint Louis, MO 63103-1816 USA (SAN 278-3320) Tel 314-421-0325; Fax: 314-421-0113
E-mail: campbellhousemuseum@worldnet.att.net
Web site: http://stlouis.missouri.org/501c/chm.

Campbell, Jean, *(0-9651833)* 940 Winter Ct., River Falls, WI 54022-1293 USA Tel 715-425-6384.

Campbell Road Pr., *(0-9625115; 1-882581)* 1129 Campbell Rd., Oklahoma City, OK 73111 USA Tel 405-427-7307; Fax: 405-427-1897.

Campbell, Terrie *See* **Sweet T. C. Campbell**

CampCrest Publishing, *(0-9763257)* 385 Hidden Hollow Ln., Chickamauga, GA 30707 USA
E-mail: sallyworland@mindspring.com.

Campfire Publishing Co., *(0-9617653)* 8107 Bayou Bend Blvd., Laurel, MD 20724-1958 USA (SAN 664-8932) Tel 301-498-4807
E-mail: rayh28@aol.com.

Camping Guideposts *See* **Wordshed**

Can Do Duck Publishing, *(0-9768384)* P.O. Box 1045, Voorhees, NJ 08043 USA Tel 856-816-5255; Fax: 856-429-0094
E-mail: ducktormorty@thecandoduck.com
Web site: http://www.the can do duck.com.

Can Family, The, *(0-9665043)* 12732 Hoven Ln., Bowie, MD 20716-1146 USA.

Can You Dig It?, Incorporated *See* **Little Spirit Publishing, Inc.**

Canadian Government Publishing (CAN) *(0-315; 0-660; 0-662) Dist. by* **Intl Spec Bk.**

Canadian Institute for Law, Theology & Public Policy, *(1-896363)* 33 Langlo Terr., Santa Barbara, CA 93105 USA Tel 780-465-4581 (phone/fax)
E-mail: ciltpp@cs.com
Web site: http://www.ciltpp.com.

Canady SW Publishing, *(1-929889)* Orders Addr.: P.O. Box 11361, Chandler, AZ 85248-0007 USA Tel 480-802-6623; Edit Addr.: 11132 E. Watford Ct., Sun Lakes, AZ 85248 USA
E-mail: grandmacc@uswest.com.

Canaima Pr., *(0-9632261)* 3817 Calle del Monte, NE, Albuquerque, NM 87110 USA Tel 505-256-0769.

Canal History & Technology Press *See* **Moore, Hugh Historical Park & Museums, Inc.**

Canal Side Pubs., *(0-9628208; 1-886623)* 3517 State Rd., No. 5, Schuyler, NY 13340 USA Tel 315-895-7535; Toll Free: 800-493-2501
Web site: http://www.canalsidepublishers.com.

Canary Connect Pubns., *(0-9643462)* Div. of SOBOLE, Inc., 605 Holiday Rd., Coralville, IA 52241-1016 USA Tel 319-338-3827; Fax: 612-435-3340 ; *Imprints:* Just Think Books (Just Think Bks)
E-mail: sondrak@canaryconnect.com
Web site: http://www.canaryconnect.com; http://www.justthinkbooks.com
Dist(s): **Follett Library Resources**
Integral Yoga Pubns.
Nutri-Bks. Corp.

Canasta Pr., *(0-9713075)* 223 N. Franklin St., Watkins Glen, NY 14891 USA Tel 607-535-541; 607-535-5411; Fax: 607-535-5413
E-mail: canasta@lightlink.com.

Candel Publishing, LLC, *(0-9620343)* Orders Addr.: P.O. Box 2505, Huntsville, AL 35804-2505 USA (SAN 248-1987) Tel 256-527-1800; Fax: 256-574-1745
E-mail: info@candel.net
Web site: http://candel.net
Dist(s): **BookMasters, Inc.**
Brodart Co.

Candle Fly Pr., *(0-9713551)* Orders Addr.: P.O. Box 4561, Spartanburg, SC 29305 USA Tel 864-585-7250; Edit Addr.: 815 Isom St., Spartanburg, SC 29303 USA
E-mail: candleflypress@aol.com.

Candle Light Pr., *(0-9743147; 0-9766053)* P.O. Box 10069, Iowa City, IA 52240-0002 USA Do not confuse with Candle Light Press in Martinez, CA.
E-mail: ding@candlelightpress.com
Web site: http://www.candlelightpress.com.

Candlelight Books *See* **Candlelight Publishing**

Candlelight Pr., *(0-9710667)* P.O. Box 110882, Campbell, CA 95011-0882 USA (SAN 254-3370) Do not confuse with companies with the same or similar name in Irvine, CA , New York, NY.
E-mail: candlelightpress@yahoo.com
Web site: http://www.giftsofgreatness.com.

Candlelight Publishing, *(0-9648090; 1-893096)* Orders Addr.: 3225 S. Pecos Rd. #105, Las Vegas, NV 89121 USA Do not confuse with companies with same or similar names in San Francisco, CA, South Bend, IN, Austin, TX, San Clemente CA
E-mail: marcia_mcdowell@yahoo.com
Web site: http://www.eaglesdisobey.net.

CandlePower Communications *See* **Candlepower, Inc.**

Candlepower, Inc., *(0-9677558; 1-932037)* Orders Addr.: P.O. Box 787, New Paltz, NY 12561 USA (SAN 255-2949) Tel 845-255-4076; Fax: 845-255-7645; Edit Addr.: 64 Plains Rd., New Paltz, NY 12561 USA
E-mail: david@candlepower.org
Web site: http://www.candlepower.org.

†**Candlewick Pr.**, *(0-7636; 1-56402)* Div. of Walker Bks., London, England, 2067 Massachusetts Ave., Cambridge, MA 02140 USA Tel 617-661-3330; Fax: 617-661-0565 Do not confuse with Candlewick Pr., Crystal Lake, IL
E-mail: bigbear@candlewick.com; salesinfo@candlewick.com
Web site: http://www.candlewick.com/
Dist(s): **Random Hse., Inc.**; *CIP.*

Candy Cane Pr. *Imprint of* **Ideals Pubns.**

Candy's Creations *See* **Fruitbearer Publishing**

Cane River Trading Co., Inc., *(0-9744189)* 1473 Cty. Rte. 26, Climax, NY 12042-2211 USA Tel 518-731-8598
E-mail: ny5kmagi@aol.com
Web site: http://members.aol.com/CaneR71456/.

Canh Nam Pubs., *(0-9749097; 0-9772129; 0-9799345)* 2607 Military Rd., Arlington, VA 22207 USA
E-mail: canhnam@dc.net.

Canis Lupus Productions, *(0-9661789)* Orders Addr.: P.O. Box 128262, San Diego, CA 92102-8262 USA; Edit Addr.: 1940 Third Ave., Unit 406, San Diego, CA 92101-2622 USA Tel 310-873-3232 (phone/fax).

Canisius College Pr., *(0-9671480; 0-9740936)* 2001 Main St., Buffalo, NY 14208-1098 USA Tel 716-888-2357; 716-888-3254; Fax: 716-888-3112
E-mail: bieron@canisius.edu
Dist(s): **Western New York Wares, Inc.**

Canmore Pr., *(1-887774)* Orders Addr.: P.O. Box 510794, Melbourne Beach, FL 32951-0794 USA Tel 321-729-0078; Fax: 321-724-1162 ; *Imprints:* Wynden (Wynden)
E-mail: publish@canmorepress.com
Web site: http://www.canmorepress.com.

Cannady, John, *(0-9754345)* 6126 Dunwoody Ct., Montgomery, AL 36117-5012 USA
E-mail: katphishe@starband.net
Web site: http://www.hopetkd.com.

Cannon, K. L., *(0-9675594)* 9412 Meadow Vale, Austin, TX 78758 USA Tel 512-837-6281; Fax: 512-837-7205
E-mail: cankl@msn.com.

Canon Pr., *(1-885767; 1-59128)* Div. of Christ Church, Orders Addr.: P.O. Box 8729, Moscow, ID 83843 USA (SAN 257-3792); 205 E. 5th St., Moscow, ID 83843 Do not confuse with companies with the same or similar names in Grand Rapids, MI, Centerville, UT
E-mail: ops@canonpress.org
Web site: http://www.canonpress.org.

Cantab Publishing, *(0-9745150)* P.O. Box 381591, Cambridge, MA 02238-1591 USA.

Cantemos-Bilingual Books and Music, *(0-9623930; 1-892306)* 15696 Altamira Dr., Chino Hills, CA 91709 USA Tel 909-393-8372; Fax: 909-393-1362; Toll Free: 800-393-1336
E-mail: jarjetb@writeme.com
Web site: http://www.cantemosco.com; http://simplespanishsongs.com
Dist(s): **Baker & Taylor Bks.**
Continental Bk. Co., Inc.
Follett Library Resources
Midwest Library Service.

Canterwine Pr., *(0-9764184)* 608 Longview Ave., Anacortes, WA 98221 USA Tel 360-941-4692
E-mail: canterwinepress@hotmail.com
Web site: http://www.canterwinepress.com.

Cantoo Records, *(0-9659936)* Orders Addr.: P.O. Box 8001, Ann Arbor, MI 48107 USA Tel 734-332-1641; Fax: 734-332-3357; Toll Free: 800-830-1919
E-mail: info@cantoorecords.com
Web site: http://www.cantoorecords.com.

Canyon Beach Visual Communications, *(0-9754221)* PMB 108, 10 St. Francis Way, Unit 9, Cranberry Township, PA 16066 USA Tel 724-612-5784
E-mail: info@canyonbeach.com
Web site: http://www.canyonbeach.com.

Cap & Compass, LLC, *(0-9717366)* 132 Chestnut St., Branford, CT 06405 USA Tel 203-483-7005
E-mail: jesse@capandcompass.com
Web site: http://www.capandcompass.com
Dist(s): **Biblio Distribution.**

Cape Fear Images, Inc., *(0-9729573)* 5621 Athens Ln., Wilmington, NC 28405-3716 USA Tel 910-392-5228; Fax: 910-313-2523; Toll Free: 888-755-0550 ; *Imprints:* Wilmington Today Publications (Wilmington Td Pubns)
E-mail: editor@wilmingtontoday.com
Web site: http://www.wilmingtontoday.com.

Capercaillie Bks., Ltd (GBR) *(0-9542905; 0-9545206; 0-9549625; 0-9551246) Dist. by* **Wlsn Assocs.**

Capital Media Enterprise, *(0-9721350)* P.O. Box 36706, Richmond, VA 23235 USA Tel 804-751-1295
E-mail: jody@rawley.com
Web site: http://www.rawley.com.

Capital Publishing, *(0-9773016)* 6311 10th Ave., Brooklyn, NY 11219 USA Tel 718-921-6400; Fax: 718-921-0160
E-mail: pommedia@pommedia.com.

Caponigro Public Relations, Incorporated *See* **Barker Business Bks., Inc.**

Cappella Publishing, A, *(0-9760271)* 20505 Yorba Linda Blvd., Suite 505, Yorba Linda, CA 92886 USA Tel 714-336-2350; Fax: 714-685-7773
E-mail: cgriffiths@acappellapublishing.com
Web site: http://www.acappellapublishing.com.

Capper's Bks., *(0-941678)* 1503 SW 42nd St., Topeka, KS 66608 USA (SAN 239-1694) Tel 295-274-4300; Fax: 913-274-4305; Toll Free: 800-678-5779
Web site: http://www.cappers.com.

Capri Publishing, *(0-9769132; 0-9788612)* 4401 NW 39th St., #518, Midwest City, OK 73112 USA Tel 405-623-7619
E-mail: capripub@aol.com
Web site: http://www.capripublishing.net.

Capriccio Publishing, *(0-9770076)* 11100 SW 93rd Ct. Rd., Suite 10-405, Ocala, FL 34481 USA Tel 352-873-1403.

Capricorn Publishing, *(0-9753970; 0-9774757)* 706 E. Brewster St., Appleton, WI 54911 USA Tel 920-475-0674; Fax: 920-954-9533
E-mail: getovd@yahoo.com
Web site: http://www.CapricornPublishing.com
Dist(s): **Baker & Taylor Bks.**
Ingram Bk. Co.

Capricorn Publishing, Incorporated *See* **Capricorn Publishing**

CAPS, LLC *See* **ALCAPS, LLC**

Capstone *Imprint of* **Wiley, John & Sons, Inc.**

Capstone Academics LLC, *(1-933557)* 3815 N. Brookfield Rd., Suite No. 104-122, Brookfield, WI 53045 USA (SAN 256-6761) Tel 262-754-4699; Toll Free: 888-922-7786
E-mail: contact@capstoneacademics.com
Web site: http://www.capstoneacademics.com.

Capstone Bks. *Imprint of* **Capstone Pr., Inc.**

Capstone Bks., *(0-9752843)* P.O. Box 7025, Greenwood, IN 46142 USA Tel 317-414-4770
Web site: http://www.capstonebooks.com.

Capstone High-Interest Bks. *Imprint of* **Capstone Pr., Inc.**

Capstone High/Low Bks. *Imprint of* **Capstone Pr., Inc.**

Capstone Pr., Inc., *(0-7368; 1-56065; 1-4296)* Div. of Coughlan Publishing, 1905 Lookout Dr., North Mankato, MN 55033 USA Tel 507-385-8215; Fax: 507-388-3752; Orders Addr.: 151 Good Council Dr., P.O. Box 669, Mankato, MN 56002-0669 USA (SAN 254-1815) Toll Free Fax: 888-262-0705; Toll Free: 800-747-4992; Edit Addr.: 7825 Telegraph Rd., Bloomington, MN 55438 USA Fax: 952-933-2410; Toll Free: 888-517-8977 ; *Imprints:* Pebble Books (Pebble Bks); Bridgestone Books (Bridgestone Bks); Capstone High/Low Books (Cpstone High Low); Blue Earth Books (Blue Earth Bks); A+ Books (Aplus Bks); LifeMatters Books (LifeMatters Bks); Capstone Books (Capstone Bks); Yellow Umbrella Books (Yell Umbrella); Capstone High-Interest Books (Caps Hight-Int); Edge Books (EdgeBks); Fact Finders (FactFind); First Facts (FirsFacts) Do not confuse with Capstone Pr., Inc. in Decatur, IL
Web site: http://www.capstone-press.com
Dist(s): **Continental Bk. Co., Inc.**
Lectorum Pubns., Inc.

Captain Caleb Communications, *(0-9703021)* 1250 Cynder Ct., Annapolis, MD 21401-7504 USA Tel 410 626 8904; 410-626-8904
E-mail: jcurtis@toad.net
Web site: http://www.oysterbook.com.

Captain Fiddle Pubns., *(0-931877)* 4 Elm Ct., Newmarket, NH 03857 USA (SAN 686-0508) Tel 603-659-2658
E-mail: cFiddle@tiac.net
Web site: http://www.captainfiddle.com.

Captain, Tamira R. *See* **Stories From Four Publishing Co.**

Captains Log Printing *Imprint of* **Mountain Hse. Publishing Co.**

Captio Corp., *(0-9766614)* 80 Santa Clara Ave., San Francisco, CA 94127 USA Tel 415-664-2700
Web site: http://www.captio.com.

Captured Light Distribution, LLC, *(0-9761074)* PMB 112 1201 Yelm Ave., Yelm, WA 98597 USA Tel 360-400-2537
E-mail: missbfc@msn.com
Web site: http://www.whatthebleep.com.

Capturing Memories, *(0-9727759)* 9228 SW 209th St, Vashon, WA 98070 USA Tel 206-463-5652; Toll Free: 866-595-9662
E-mail: roger@capturingmemories.com; stories@capturingmemories.com
Web site: http://www.capturingmemories.com.

Captus, LLC, *(0-9776627)* 32725 Ledge Hill Dr., Solon, OH 44139 USA Tel 440-498-9178; Fax: 440-238-2967
E-mail: cziance@yahoo.com
Web site: http://www.babyalmamater.com.

Car Tours *Imprint of* **Audisee Sound & Music**

Caravan of Dreams Productions, *(0-929856)* Div. of Caravan of Dreams, 512 Main St. Ste. 1500, Fort Worth, TX 76102-3922 USA (SAN 250-4855).

Carazona Creations LLC, *(0-9753724)* 957 Route 33, Suite 325, Hamilton Square, NJ 08690 USA Toll Free: 888-328-3300
E-mail: carazona@carazonacreations.com
Web site: http://www.carazonacreations.com
Dist(s): **Baker & Taylor Bks.**

Carden Jennings Publishing Co., Ltd., *(1-891524)* 375 Greenbrier Dr., No. 100, Charlottesvle, VA 22901-1618 USA
Web site: http://www.cjp.com.

Carderock Pr., *(0-938813)* Orders Addr.: P.O. Box 268, Cabin John, MD 20818 USA (SAN 662-5630) Tel 301-365-0768; Edit Addr.: 8305 Fenway Rd., Bethesda, MD 20817 USA (SAN 662-5649).

Cardinal Brands, Inc., *(1-932435)* 200 Jackson, Topeka, KS 66603 USA Tel 785-233-4101; Fax: 785-233-4291; Toll Free: 800-444-0038
Web site: http://www.witty-one.com; http://www.cardinalbrands.com.

Cardinal Enterprises of Florida, *(0-9639432)* 18721 S. Dixie Hwy., No. 106, Miami, FL 33157 USA Tel 305-232-5486; Fax: 305-253-0110; Toll Free: 888-222-6504
E-mail: info@cardinal-ent.com
Web site: http://cardinal-ent.com
Dist(s): **Great Outdoors Publishing Co.**
Mickler's Bks., Inc.
Mistco, Inc.

Cardinal Pubs. Group, *(0-9799240)* 2222 Hillside Ave., Suite 100, Carmel, IN 46218 USA (SAN 631-7936) Tel 317-879-0871; Fax: 317-879-0872
E-mail: tdoherty@in.net.

Cardinal Publishing Company *See* **Buckhead Pr.**

Cardinal Publishing Group, The, *(1-877784)* Div. of The Associate Group, L.L.C., Orders Addr.: P.O. Box 91079, Springield, MA 01139 USA; Edit Addr.: 181 Nursery St., No. E-9, Springfield, MA 01104 USA Tel 413-883-2527
E-mail: CardinalPubGroup@aol.com
Web site: http://www.theassociategroup.com.

Cardlings, *(0-9760108)* Orders Addr.: P.O. Box 931, Pueblo, CO 81002 USA; Edit Addr.: 815 W. 14th St., Pueblo, CO 81003 USA
E-mail: gnome@cardlings.com
Web site: http://www.cardlings.com.

Cardoza Publishing, *(0-940685; 0-9607618; 1-58042)* 857 Broadway., New York, NY 10003-1225 USA Tel 212-255-6661; Fax: 212-255-6671; Toll Free: 800-577-9467
E-mail: cardozapub@aol.com
Web site: http://www.cardozapub.com/
Dist(s): **Simon & Schuster, Inc.**

Career Communications, Inc., *(0-9653667)* 6701 W. 64th St., Suite 210, Overland Park, KS 66202 USA Tel 913-362-7788; Fax: 913-362-4864; Toll Free: 800-669-7795 Do not confuse with Career Communications, Inc., Harleysville, PA
E-mail: ccinfo@carcom.com
Web site: http://www.carcom.com.

Career Kids, *(1-929879)* 5043 Gregg Way, Auburn, CA 95602 USA Tel 916-624-7993; Fax: 916-624-7267; Toll Free: 800-537-0909
E-mail: linda@careerkids.com
Web site: http://www.careerkids.com
Dist(s): **JIST Publishing.**

Career Pr., Inc., *(1-56414; 1-60163)* Orders Addr.: P.O. Box 687, Franklin Lks, NJ 07417-0687 USA (SAN 694-3640) Toll Free: 800-227-3371 (outside New Jersey); Edit Addr.: P.O. Box 687, Franklin Lakes, NJ 07417 USA ; *Imprints:* New Page Books (New Page Bks)
E-mail: bbrienza@careerpress.com
Web site: http://www.newpagebooks.com; http://www.careerpress.com
Dist(s): **Ten Speed Pr.**

Career Publishing Co., *(0-918694)* 67 Melrose Ave., Haverhill, MA 01830 USA (SAN 250-9172) Tel 978-372-7957
E-mail: william100bond@yahoo.com.

Career Solutions Training Group, *(0-9714639)* 1199 Lancaster Ave., Berwyn, PA 19312-1243 USA Toll Free: 888-299-2784
E-mail: cstg@bellatlantic.net
Web site: http://www.careersolutionsgroup.com.

Carefree Publishing *Imprint of* **Milano, Jacque & Assocs.**

Carey, Kathleen, *(0-9769500)* 2 Dogwood Ln., North Oaks, MN 55127 USA.

Carey, William Library Pubs., *(0-87808)* Orders Addr.: 129 Mobilization Dr., Waynesboro, GA 30830 USA (SAN 208-2101) Tel 706-554-1594; Fax: 706-554-7444; Toll Free: 866-732-6657; Edit Addr.: P.O. Box 40129, Pasadena, CA 91114 USA
E-mail: inquiry@wclbooks.com
Web site: http://www.wclbooks.com
Dist(s): **Gabriel Resources.**

Cargill Consulting, Inc., *(0-9743780)* 19836 Linda Ln., Harrah, OK 73045-9351 USA
Web site: http://www.cargillconsulting.com.

Caribbean Books *See* **Mid-Prairie Bks.**

Caribbean Publishing *See* **Coconut Pr., LLC**

Caribbean Scene, *(0-9678030)* 5 Walnut Ave., East Norwich, NY 11732 USA.

Caring Communications, *(0-9706545)* P.O. Box 87, Days Creek, OR 97429 USA Tel 541-825-3438
E-mail: caring@pioneer-net.com
Web site: http://www.pioneer-net.com/~caring.

Caring People Pr., *(0-9635975)* Orders Addr.: 7108 127th Pl., SE, Newcastle, WA 98056 USA Tel 425-226-2350
E-mail: b_kbaugher@yahoo.com.

Caritas Communications, *(0-9668228; 0-9753259; 0-9799390)* 5526 W. Elmhurst Dr., Mequon, WI 53092-2010 USA Tel 262-242-5049 Do not confuse with Caritas Communications Incorporated in New York, NY, Rhinebeck, NY
E-mail: dgawlik@wi.rr.com.

Carle, Eric Museum of Picture Bk. Art, The, *(1-59288)* 125 W. Bay Rd., Amherst, MA 01002 USA
E-mail: shop@picturebookart.org
Web site: http://www.picturebookart.org.

Carleton Bks., *(0-9759738)* 335 N. Main Ave., Tucson, AZ 85701 USA.

Carlisle Pr.- Walnut Creek, *(0-9642548; 1-890050; 1-933753)* 2673 Township Rd., No. 421, Sugarcreek, OH 44681 USA Tel 330-852-1900; Fax: 330-852-3285; Toll Free: 800-852-4482 Do not confuse with companies with the same name in Mechanicsburg, PA, Sedona, AZ, Benbrook, TX
Dist(s): **Baker & Taylor Bks.**
Koen-Levy Bk. Wholesalers LLC.

CarLou Interactive Media & Publishing, *(0-9759325)* 12439 Magnolia Blvd., No. 170, Valley Village, CA 91607 USA
E-mail: tess@worldtrust.org
Web site: http://www.carloumedia.com.

Carlsbad Caverns Guadalupe Mountains Assn., *(0-916907)* P.O. Box 1417, Carlsbad, NM 88221-1417 USA (SAN 268-6627) Tel 505-785-2485.

Carlsbad Caverns Natural History Association *See* **Carlsbad Caverns Guadalupe Mountains Assn.**

Carlsen Verlag (DEU) *(3-551) Dist. by* **Distribks Inc.**

Carlson, Debra R., *(0-9765950)* 1705 N. 160th St., Omaha, NE 68118-2408 USA
Web site: http://www.cozykidspress.com.

Carlton Bks., Ltd. (GBR) *(1-85868; 1-84222; 1-84442; 1-84732) Dist. by* **Trafalgar.**

Carlton Bks., Ltd. (GBR) *(1-85868; 1-84222; 1-84442; 1-84732) Dist. by* **IPG Chicago.**

Carlton Bks., Ltd. (GBR) *(1-85868; 1-84222; 1-84442; 1-84732) Dist. by* **IngramPubServ.**

Carmel Concepts, Ltd., *(0-9646285)* 50 Mt. Tiburon Rd., Tiburon, CA 94920 USA Tel 415-435-8066; Fax: 415-435-3750.

Carnegie Learning, *(1-930804; 1-932409; 1-934239; 1-934800)* 437 Grant St., Frick Bldg., 20th Flr., Pittsburgh, PA 15219 USA Tel 412-690-2442 Toll Free: 888-851-7094
E-mail: manderson@carnegielearning.com
Web site: http://carnegielearning.com.

Carney Educational Services, *(1-930288)* 3441 Ocean View Blvd., Glendale, CA 91208-1508 USA Toll Free: 888-511-7737
E-mail: carneyed@aol.com
Web site: http://www.carneyed.com
Dist(s): **Sunbelt Pubns., Inc.**

Carnifex Pr., *(0-9759727; 0-9789583)* P.O. Box 1686, Ormond Beach, FL 32175 USA Tel 386-677-2980
E-mail: carnifexpress@hotmail.com
Web site: http://www.carnifexpress.net.

Carnivore Games, *(0-9749150)* Orders Addr.: P.O. Box 846, Londonderry, NH 03053-0846 USA; Edit Addr.: 12 Emerald Dr., Derry, NH 03038 USA
E-mail: brad@carnivoregames.com
Web site: http://www.carnivoregames.com/.

Carob Publishing, *(0-9669000)* 3222 Regent St., Dayton, OH 45409 USA Tel 937-299-7933.

Carolina Academic Pr., *(0-89089; 1-59460)* 700 Kent St., Durham, NC 27701 USA (SAN 210-7848) Tel 919-489-7486; Fax: 919-493-5668
E-mail: tim@cap-press.com.

Carolina Biological Supply Co., *(0-89278; 1-4350)* 2700 York Rd., Burlington, NC 27215-3398 USA (SAN 249-2784) Tel 336-584-0381; Fax: 910-584-3399; Toll Free Fax: 800-222-7112; Toll Free: 800-334-5551
E-mail: carolina@carolina.com
Web site: http://www.carolina.com.

Carolina Children, *(0-9794580)* P.O. Box 862, Mauldin, SC 29662 USA
Web site: http://carolinachildren.net.

Carolina Moon Publishing, *(0-9706358)* Orders Addr.: P.O. Box 99622, Raleigh, NC 27624 USA (SAN 253-5459) Tel 919-848-9144; Fax: 919-846-5488; Edit Addr.: 1033 Vestavia Woods Dr., Raleigh, NC 27615 USA
E-mail: carolinamoonpub@aol.com.

†**Carolina Wren Pr.**, *(0-932112)* 120 Morris St., Durham, NC 27701 USA (SAN 213-0327) Tel 919-560-2738; Fax: 919-560-2759
E-mail: carolinawrenpress@earthlink.net
Web site: http://www.carolinawrenpress.org
Dist(s): **Baker & Taylor Bks.**; *CIP.*

Carolkaydesigns, *(0-9707292)* 118 El Camino Dr., Ojai, CA 93023 USA Tel 805-646-1930; Fax: 805-646-1442
E-mail: carolkaydesigns@ojai.net.

Carolrhoda Bks. *Imprint of* **Lerner Publishing Group**

Carousel Pubns., Inc., *(0-9759382)* P.O. Box 225, Springfield, NJ 07081 USA
Web site: http://www.net2infinity/aplaceinthesky
Dist(s): **AtlasBooks Distribution.**

Carp Cove Pr., *(0-9703752)* P.O. Box 2991, Liverpool, NY 13089-2991 USA
E-mail: carpcovepress@holisticanimal.com; Colleen@holisticanimal.com
Web site: http://www.holisticanimal.com/.

Carpino Bks., *(1-928675)* 30 Park St., Coventry, RI 02816 USA Tel 401-828-5589
E-mail: topo4@myexcel.com; carpino@myexcel.com.

Carpino-Weller, Nancy *See* **Carpino Bks.**

Carriage House Publishing *See* **American Carriage Hse. Publishing**

Carrington Bks., *(0-9787143)* P.O. Box 451399, Los Angeles, CA 90045 USA Tel 310-628-5557
Web site: www.ASL911.com.

Carroll & Brown Pubs., Ltd. (GBR) *(1-903258; 1-904760) Dist. by* **IPG Chicago.**

Carroll Schl., The, *(1-893688)* Baker Bridge Rd., Lincoln, MA 01773 USA Tel 781-259-8342 ext 3032; Fax: 781-259-8852
E-mail: giftt@earthlink.net.

Carroll, Sherry, *(0-9752994)* P.O. Box 34603, Washington, DC 20774 USA
E-mail: carrollcom01@aol.com.

Carson, Tracy, *(0-9767077)* 1998 66th St., SE, Bismarck, ND 58504-3835 USA
Web site: http://www.grandmaisnowabutterfly.com.

Carson-Dellosa Publishing Co., Inc., *(0-88724; 1-59441; 1-60022; 1-60418)* Orders Addr.: P.O. Box 35665, Greensboro, NC 27425 USA Tel 336-632-0084; Fax: 336-808-3249; Toll Free: 800-321-0943
E-mail: kjones@carsondellosa.com; nbrown@carsondellosa.com
Web site: http://www.carsondellosa.com.

Carter Publishing Co., *(0-9705929)* 1709 Stearns Dr., Los Angeles, CA 90035 USA Tel 323-930-1290 Do not confuse with companies with the same name in Portland, OR, Baltimore, MD
E-mail: bsweet@mailandnews.com.

Cartoon Connections Pr., *(0-9657136)* P.O. Box 10889, White Bear Lake, MN 55110 USA (SAN 299-352X) Tel 651-429-1244; 651-429-7660
E-mail: CartoonC@aol.com
Web site: http://www.cartooningbasics.com; http://www.cartoonconnections.com.

Cartoonmario.com, *(0-9766755)* 5084 S. 65th St., Greenfield, WI 53220-4504 USA Tel 414-541-9221 (phone/fax)
E-mail: mdm@cartoonmario.com
Web site: http://www.cartoonmario.com.

Cartwheel Bks. *Imprint of* **Scholastic, Inc.**

Caruso, Kevin M. *See* **Aerospace 1 Pubns.**

Caruso, Tina Silvio, *(0-9706745)* 106 Parkhurst Rd., Dunstable, MA 01827 USA Tel 978-649-6271.

Caryn Solutions, LLC, *(0-9791046)* Orders Addr.: P.O. Box 635, Naples, FL 34106 USA (SAN 852-4726) Tel 239-404-5820
E-mail: caryn@carynsolutions.com
Web site: http://www.carynsolutions.com.

Casa Bautista de Publicaciones, *(0-311)* Div. of Southern Baptist Convention, Orders Addr.: P.O. Box 4255, El Paso, TX 79914 USA (SAN 220-0139) Tel 915-566-9656; Fax: 915-562-6502; Toll Free: 800-755-5958 ; *Imprints:* Editorial Mundo Hispano (Edit Mundo)
E-mail: epena@casabautista.org
Web site: http://www.casabautista.org.

Casa Creacion *Imprint of* **Strang Communications Co.**

Casa de Estudios de Literatura y Talleres Artisticos Amaquemecan A.C. (MEX) *(968-6465) Dist. by* **Lectorum Pubns.**

Casa de Periodistas Editorial, *(0-9743102)* Orders Addr.: P.O. Box 9021787, San Juan, PR 00902-1787 USA; Edit Addr.: Calle de la Luna, Esq. Calle de San José, San Juan, PR 00902-1787 USA
E-mail: multiser@coqui.net
Web site: http://www.asppro.org.

Casa Graphics, Inc., *(1-881474)* 1718 Rogers Pl., Suite 1A, Burbank, CA 91504 USA Tel 818-842-4278; Fax: 818-842-2960
Dist(s): **Best-Seller Bks.**

Casals Editorial (ESP) *(84-7684; 84-7864; 84-218; 84-9825; 84-88017) Dist. by* **Libros Fronteras.**

Cascabel Pr., *(0-9715484)* 5051 N. Blue Bonnet Rd., Tucson, AZ 85745 USA.

Cascade Design Publishing *See* **Cascade, Inc.**

Cascade, Inc., *(0-9726173)* 1085 Commonwealth Ave., PMB 253, Boston, MA 02215 USA Tel 617-558-1038 ; *Imprints:* Philograph (Philograph)
E-mail: info@philograph.com
Web site: http://www.philograph.com.

Cascade Pass, Inc., *(1-880599)* Orders Addr.: 4223 Glencoe Ave., Suite C-105, Marina del Rey, CA 90292 USA Tel 310-305-0210; Fax: 310-305-7850; Toll Free: 888-837-0704
E-mail: jlc@cascadepass.com
Web site: http://www.cascadepass.com
Dist(s): **Baker & Taylor Bks.**
Follett Library Resources.

Cascade Writing, *(0-9767519)* 1808 Lake Dr., Camano Island, WA 98282 USA Tel 360-387-8023
E-mail: dennisc@whidbey.net.

Casemate Pubs. & Bk. Distributors, LLC, *(0-9711709; 1-932033)* Orders Addr.: 1016c Warrior Rd., Drexel Hill, PA 19026-4818 USA; 22883 Quicksilver Dr., Herndon, VA 20166 (SAN 631-9386) Tel 703-661-1500
E-mail: casemate@casematepublishing.com
Web site: http://www.casematepublishing.com.

Caseys World Bks., *(0-9765872)* Orders Addr.: 5767 Monticello Way, Madison, WI 53719-1603 USA Tel 608-335-0401 Please call with any questions. Leave a voice message if no answer.
E-mail: kate@caseysworld.net
Web site: http://www.caseysworld.net.

Caslon Books *See* **Slangman Publishing**

Caslon Pr., *(0-9728144)* 315 Richards Ave., Portsmouth, NH 03801-5239 USA Tel 603-431-6823
E-mail: jbf@fergus.com
Web site: http://www.jbf.fergus.com.

Caso, George R., *(0-9719290)* 2445 Babylon Tpke., Merrick, NY 11566 USA Tel 516-379-9397.

Cassell Guides (GBR) *(1-84202; 1-84403) Dist. by* **Sterling.**

Cassette & Video Learning Systems *See* **Watch & Learn, Inc.**

Cassiopeia Pr., *(0-9761820)* P.O. Box 2564, Acton, MA 01720 USA Do not confuse with Cassiopeia Press, Morrison, CO
Web site: http://www.seymourstories.com.

Cassiquiare Press *See* **Really Alive Bks.**

Castellated Pr., *(0-9746416)* P.O. Box 4406, Warren, NJ 07059 USA
E-mail: scottzamek@castellatedpress.com
Web site: http://www.castellatedpress.com.

Casterman, Editions (FRA) *(2-203; 2-542) Dist. by* **Distribks Inc.**

Castillo, Ediciones, S. A. de C. V. (MEX) *(968-6635; 968-7415; 970-20) Dist. by* **Mariuccia Iaconi Bk Imports.**

Castillo, Ediciones, S. A. de C. V. (MEX) *(968-6635; 968-7415; 970-20) Dist. by* **Macmillan.**

Castle Builder Pr. *Imprint of* **Blue Cubicle Pr., LLC**

Castle Keep Pr. *Imprint of* **Rock, James A. & Co. Pubs.**

Castle Pacific Publishing, *(0-9653869; 0-9749305; 0-9774168)* P.O. Box 77089, Seattle, WA 98177 USA Tel 206-839-0984; Toll Free: 888-756-2665 (888-756-BOOK)
Web site: http://www.castlepacific.com.

Castlebay, Inc., *(0-9748145)* P.O. Box 168, Round Pond, ME 04564-0168 USA Tel 207-529-5438
E-mail: castlebay@castlebay.net.

Castleberry Farms Pr., *(1-891907)* Orders Addr.: P.O. Box 337, Poplar, WI 54864 USA Tel 715-364-8404
E-mail: cbfarmpr@centurytel.net
Web site: http://www.castleberryfarmspress.com; http://www.cbfarmpr.com.

Castleberry Toys, Inc., *(0-9706907)* 18185 Shore Line Ct., Northville, MI 48168 USA Fax: 248-344-4629; Toll Free: 800-861-6100
E-mail: gem7366@sbcglobal.net
Web site: http://www.supadupababee.com.

Castlebrook Pubns., *(0-9641697; 0-9798242)* Orders Addr.: P.O. Box 132, Camp Meeker, CA 95419 USA; 1535 Farmers Ln., Pmb #237, Santa Rosa, CA 95405 ; *Imprints:* You-Draw-It Books (You-Draw-It)
E-mail: castlebrookpub@aol.com
Web site: http://www.youdrawitbooks.com; http://www.printanddraw.com.

Castleconal Pr., *(0-9677348)* 1517 National Ave., Madison, WI 53716 USA Tel 608-222-6051; Fax: 608-221-5264
E-mail: dfleming@madison.k12.wi.us.

Castlegate Pr., *(0-9743588)* 457 Terraces Ct., Mesquite, NV 89027 USA Tel 303-550-3360; Fax: 702-346-2058.

Castlemarsh Pubns., *(0-942250)* P.O. Box 60728, Savannah, GA 31420-0728 USA (SAN 240-8708) Tel 912-232-6644; Fax: 912-232-6015; Toll Free: 800-353-8917
E-mail: cmpbooks@aol.com.

Castlemoyle Bks., *(1-888827)* Orders Addr.: P.O. Box 520, Pomeroy, WA 99347-0520 USA; Edit Addr.: 694 Main St., Pomeroy, WA 99347-0520 USA Tel 509-843-5009; Fax: 509-843-3183; Toll Free: 888-773-5586
E-mail: orders@castlemoyle.com
Web site: http://www.castlemoyle.com.

Castro, Shirley, *(0-9790307)* 25997 Maize Dr., Willits, CA 95490-5856 USA.

Catalpa Press *See* **Calling Crane Publishing**

Catalpa Pr., *(0-9745665; 0-9763810)* P.O. Box 27303, Oakland, CA 94602-0303 USA (SAN 256-4068)
E-mail: jack@jackschroder.com; staff@catalpapress.com
Web site: http://www.jackschroder.com; http://www.malpracticebooks.com.

Catalpa Pubns., *(0-9671616)* Orders Addr.: P.O. Box 291, Williamston, MI 48895 USA Tel 517-655-3505; Edit Addr.: 1498 Sherwood Rd., Williamston, MI 48895 USA Tel 517-655-2097 (phone/fax)
E-mail: lorielle.h@mailexcite.com.

Catalyst Publishing Co., *(0-9702199)* P.O. Box 959, Kihei, HI 96753-0959 USA Toll Free Fax: 877-676-6937 (phone/fax) Do not confuse with companies with same name in Yonkers, NY, New York, NY
E-mail: catalyst@newwinefreshskin.com
Web site: http://www.newwinefreshskin.com.

Catamount Publishing LLC, *(0-9752922)* P.O. Box 30015, Denver, CO 80218 USA Tel 303-839-1687 Do not confuse with Catamount Publishing LLC in Allenstown, NH.

Catapulta Pr., *(0-9762986)* 2242 Hemingway Dr., Suite H, Fort Myers, FL 33912 USA.

Catawba Publishing Co., *(1-59712)* 5945 Orr Rd. Ste. F, Charlotte, NC 28213-7314 USA
E-mail: grayscp@grayspublishing.com; info@catawbapublishing.com
Web site: http://www.catawbapublishing.com.

Catboat Assn., Inc., *(0-9715041)* P.O. Box 72, Middleboro, MA 02346-0072 USA
Web site: http://www.catboats.org.

Catch 22 Publishing Inc., *(0-9759691)* Orders Addr.: P.O. Box 471372, LAKE MONROE, FL 32747-1372 USA Tel 407-323-4884; Fax: 407-323-4882
E-mail: info@catch22publishing.com
Web site: http://www.catch22publishing.com.

Catch the Spirit of Appalachia *Imprint of* **Ammons Communications, Ltd.**

Catechesis of the Good Shepherd *Imprint of* **Liturgy Training Pubns.**

Cathedral Foundation Pr., *(1-885938)* Div. of Cathedral Foundation, Inc., Orders Addr.: P.O. Box 777, Baltimore, MD 21203 USA Tel 443-263-0248; Fax: 443-524-3155; Toll Free: 888-768-9555; Edit Addr.: 880 Park Ave., Baltimore, MD 21201 USA
E-mail: pmedinger@catholicreview.org
Web site: http://www.cathedralfoundation.org.

Cathedral of the Holy Spirit, *(0-917595)* Div. of Chapel Hill Harvester Church, 4650 Flat Shoals Rd., Decatur, GA 30034 USA (SAN 657-1484) Tel 404-243-5020; Fax: 404-243-5927; Toll Free: 800-241-4702.

Cathedrall Pr./Encycloware, *(0-9626554)* 2703 Townes Dr., Greenville, NC 27858 USA Tel 252-412-3974
E-mail: encycloware@cox.net
Web site: http://www.KabalyonKey.com.

Cathie, Kyle Ltd. (GBR) *(1-85626)* *Dist. by* **IPG Chicago.**

Cathier Pr., *(0-9720445)* 156 Gates Rd., Lizella, GA 31052 USA.

Catholic Answers, Inc., *(1-888992; 1-933919)* 2020 Gillespie Way, El Cajon, CA 92020 USA Tel 619-387-7200; Fax: 619-387-0042; Toll Free: 888-291-8000 (orders)
E-mail: jvercillo@catholic.com; mobrien@catholic.com
Web site: http://www.catholic.com.

Catholic Bk. Publishing Corp., *(0-89942; 0-9623410; 1-878718; 1-933066)* 77 West End Rd., Totowa, NJ 07512-1405 USA (SAN 204-3432) Tel 973-890-2400; Fax: 973-890-2410; Toll Free: 800-892-6657 ; *Imprints:* Resurrection Press (Resurrection Pr)
E-mail: resurpress@aol.com
Web site: http://www.catholicbkpub.com
Dist(s): **ACTA Pubns.**
Moshy Brothers, Inc.
Spring Arbor Distributors, Inc.

Catholic Heritage Curricula *See* **Little Way Pr.**

Catholic Heritage Curricula, *(0-9788376)* P.O. Box 125, Twain Harte, CA 95383 USA Fax: 209-586-1574; Toll Free: 800-490-7713
Web site: http://www.chcweb.com.

Catholic World Mission, *(0-9747571; 0-9765180; 1-933643)* 33 Rossotto Dr., Hamden, CT 06514 USA Tel 203-848-3323; Fax: 203-407-4823
E-mail: george.sirois@catholicworldmission.org
Web site: http://www.catholicworldmission.org.

Catholics Committed to Support the Pope, *(0-9672595)* 9402 Stateside Ct., Silver Spring, MD 20903 USA Tel 301-434-3245; Fax: 301-434-5486.

Catnip Press *See* **Lorgnette Bks.**

Cats Ink, *(0-9763441)* P.O. Box 387, Chagrin Falls, OH 44022 USA Tel 440-247-6486
Web site: http://www.lillieandrose.com
Dist(s): **Greenleaf Book Group Pr.**

Catskill Ctr. for Conservation & Development, Inc., *(0-9616712)* General Delivery, Arkville, NY 12406 USA (SAN 660-9953) Tel 914-586-2611; Fax: 914-586-3044; Rte. 28, Arkville, NY 12406 (SAN 660-9961)
E-mail: cccd@catskill.net
Web site: http://catskillcenter.org.

Catslip Arts, LLC, *(0-9729414)* 668 Cook St., Suite 200, Denver, CO 80206 USA Tel 303-322-9483; Fax: 303-758-6388
E-mail: books@catsliparts.com
Web site: http://www.catsliparts.com.

Catterfly Pr., *(0-9741074)* 122 Eagle Ridge Rd., Lake Orion, MI 48360-2612 USA Tel 248-789-2227; Fax: 248-393-2535
E-mail: frejen111@aol.com
Web site: http://www.catterflypress.com.

CattLeLogos Brand Management Systems, *(0-9745612)* 2522 Lombard St., Suite 300, Philadelphia, PA 19146-1025 USA Fax: 215-827-5578
E-mail: info@cattlelogos.com
Web site: http://www.cattlelogos.com.

Caution Bks., *(0-9754148)* P.O. Box 2235, Newport Beach, CA 92659 USA
Web site: http://www.cautionbooks.com.

Cavanagh, Dave Publishing, *(0-9765355)* P.O. Box 501, Clarksburg, CA 95612-0501 USA.

Cave Hollow Pr., *(0-9713497)* 304 Grover St., Warrensburg, MO 64093-2439 USA
E-mail: rmkinder@sprintmail.com
Web site: http://www.rmkinder.com.

Cavendish Children's Bks. *Imprint of* **Cavendish, Marshall Corp.**

†Cavendish, Marshall Corp., *(0-7614; 0-85685; 0-86307; 1-85435)* Member of Times Publishing Group, 99 White Plains Rd., Tarrytown, NY 10591-9001 USA (SAN 238-437X) Tel 914-332-8888; Fax: 914-332-8882; Toll Free: 800-821-9881 ; *Imprints:* Benchmark Books (Benchmark NY); Cavendish, Marshall Reference Books (M C Ref Bks); Cavendish Children's Books (Cav Child Bks)
E-mail: mmark@marshallcavendish.com
Web site: http://www.marshallcavendish.us
Dist(s): **Fujii Assocs.;** *CIP.*

Cavendish, Marshall Reference Bks. *Imprint of* **Cavendish, Marshall Corp.**

†Caxton Pr., *(0-87004)* Div. of Caxton Printers. Ltd., 312 Main St., Caldwell, ID 83605-3299 USA (SAN 201-9698) Tel 208-459-7421; Fax: 208-459-7450; Toll Free: 800-657-6465
E-mail: publish@caxtonprinters.com; wcornell@caxtonpress.com; sgipson@caxtonpress.com
Web site: http://www.caxtonprinters.com; http://www.caxtonpress.com; *CIP.*

Caxton Printers, Limited *See* **Caxton Pr.**

Caxton, Wm Ltd., *(0-940473)* P.O. Box 220, Ellison Bay, WI 54210-0220 USA (SAN 135-1303) Tel 920-854-2955.

CB Publishing & Design *See* **UBUS Communications Systems**

CB Publishing & Design *Imprint of* **UBUS Communications Systems**

CBM Publishing, *(0-9743988)* P.O. Box 6938, Lincoln, NE 68506 USA
E-mail: mvbettenhausen@alltel.net.

CCA & B, LLC, *(0-9769907)* 1590 N. Roberts Rd., Suite 105, Kennesaw, GA 30144 USA Fax: 678-990-1182; Toll Free: 877-919-4105
E-mail: sales@elfontheshelf.com
Web site: http://elfontheshelf.com.

CCC of America, *(1-56814)* P.O. Box 166349, Irving, TX 75016-6349 USA (SAN 298-7546) Toll Free: 800-935-2222
E-mail: customerservice@cccofamerica.com
Web site: http://www.cccofamerica.com
Dist(s): **Liguori Pubns.**

CCH Services, Inc., *(0-9768383)* 8862 Earhart Ave., Los Angeles, CA 90045 USA Tel 562-895-0682
Web site: http://www.realworldrecovery.com.

CCRiddles, *(0-9785118)* 878 Laramie Ct., Newbury Park, CA 91320 USA Tel 805-498-5613; Fax: 805-498-2901
E-mail: ccriddles@roadrunner.com
Web site: http://www.ccriddles.com.

CDA Publishing, *(0-9713985)* P.O. Box 1206, Lombard, IL 60148-1206 USA Tel 630-261-1884; Fax: 630-261-1886
E-mail: corporatedevelopement@corpdevelopmentassoc.com
Web site: http://www.corpdevelopmentassoc.com.

CDS Books *See* **Vanguard Pr.**

Ce Code Efficiency, Inc., *(0-9769931)* Orders Addr.: P.O. Box 1184, State College, PA 16804-1184 USA; Edit Addr.: 239 S. Fraser St., State College, PA 16801 USA.

CE National, Inc., *(0-9722278)* Orders Addr.: P.O. Box 365, Winona Lake, IN 46590-0365 USA Tel 574-267-6622; Fax: 574-269-7185; Edit Addr.: 1003 Presidential Dr., Winona Lake, IN 46590-0365 USA
E-mail: cenational@cenational.org
Web site: http://www.cenational.org.

Ceasar Bks., *(0-9706419)* 181 W. Hartsdale Ave., Hartsdale, NY 10530 USA Tel 914-946-1750; Fax: 718-584-7117.

Cebrano Publishing, *(0-9761366)* P.O. Box 27236, Barrigada, GU 96921 USA
E-mail: billyb1937@yahoo.com.

Cedar Bay Pr., L.L.C., *(1-57555)* P.O. Box 230084, Portland, OR 97281-0084 USA (SAN 298-6361)
E-mail: cedarbay@hotmail.com.

Cedar Chest Publishing, Inc., *(0-9704665)* P.O. Box 222, Wapiti, WY 82450 USA Tel 307-587-7560; Fax: 307-587-9267
E-mail: ashhome@cyberhighway.net.

Cedar Creek Pr., *(0-9653539)* 3380 Terra Dr., Suite 100, Boise, ID 83709 USA Tel 208-362-9892 Do not confuse with companies with the same name in Stillwater, OK, Columbus, OH, Macclenny, FL
E-mail: rickjust@rickjust.com
Web site: http://www.wizardchase.com; http://www.rickjust.com
Dist(s): **AllBooks**
Baker & Taylor Bks.

Cedar Fort, Inc. *Imprint of* **Cedar Fort, Inc./CFI Distribution**

Cedar Fort, Inc./CFI Distribution, *(0-88290; 0-934126; 1-55517; 1-59955)* 2373 West 700 South, Springville, UT 84663 USA (SAN 170-2858) Tel 801-489-4084; Fax: 801-489-1097; Toll Free: 800-759-2665 ; *Imprints:* Bonneville Books (Bonneville Bks); Horizon Publishers (HorPubs); Cedar Fort, Incorporated (Cedar Fort)
E-mail: skybook@cedarfort.com
Web site: http://www.cedarfort.com
Dist(s): **Todd Communications.**

Cedar Grove Bks., *(0-9740212)* 530 Divisadero St., No. 265, San Francisco, CA 94117 USA (SAN 255-3732) Tel 415-839-3595; Fax: 415-276-9858
E-mail: info@cedargrovebooks.com
Web site: http://www.cedargrovebooks.com.

Cedar Hill Bks., *(1-891812)* Div. of Cedar Hill Poetry Foundation, 3730 Arnyed Ave., San Diego, CA 92104 USA Fax: 619-294-4924; Toll Free: 800-869-7553
E-mail: cedarhill_bks@hotmail.com
Web site: http://www.cedarhillbooks.org
Dist(s): **SPD-Small Pr. Distribution.**

Cedar Hill Pr. *Imprint of* **Cedar Hill Publishing**

Cedar Hill Publications *See* **Cedar Hill Bks.**

Cedar Hill Publishing, *(1-932373; 1-933324)* Div. of Gaap Corp., Orders Addr.: 160 Timber Ridge Loop, Show Low, AZ 85901 USA Tel 928-225-2245 ; *Imprints:* Cedar Hill Press (Cdar Hill Pr)
E-mail: becky@cedarhillpublishing.com
Web site: http://www.cedarhillpublishing.com.

Cedar Hse. Pubs., *(0-9676289)* Orders Addr.: P.O. Box 399, Monroe, VA 24574 USA Tel 434-929-8002 (phone/fax); Fax: 434-929-1059; Edit Addr.: 407 Eastview Dr., Madison Heights, VA 24572 USA
E-mail: info@cedarhousepublishers.com
Web site: http://www.cedarhousepublishers.com
Dist(s): **STL Distribution North America.**

Cedar Tree Bks., *(0-9657328; 1-892142)* 208 E. Ayre St., Newport, DE 19804 USA Tel 302-998-4171; Fax: 302-998-4185
E-mail: books@ctpress.com
Web site: http://www.cedartreebooks.com.

Cedar Tree Publishing, *(0-9658075)* 201 Matilda St NE Ste. B, Grand Rapids, MI 49503-1593 USA Do not confuse with Cedar Tree Publishing, Cedaredge, CO
E-mail: georan@altinmo.com; georan@cpw.net
Web site: http://www.tapshoe.com
Dist(s): **Austin & Company, Inc.**
Partners Pubs. Group, Inc.

Cedar Valley Publishing, *(0-615)* P.O. Box 621, Jesup, IA 50648 USA Do not confuse with Cedar Valley Publishing in Cascade, WI.

Cedar Valley Publishing, *(1-933476)* N6854 Cedar Valley Rd., Fredonia, WI 53021 USA Tel 920-994-9906; Fax: 262-376-2991 Attn: Tracey Jackson Do not confuse with Cedar Valley Publishing in Cascade, WI, Jesup, IA
E-mail: stacey@cedarvalleypublishing.com
Web site: http://www.cedarvalleypublishing.com.

Cedartip Co., The, *(0-9771844)* Orders Addr.: P.O. Box 231, Manhattan, KS 66505-0231 USA; Edit Addr.: 3004 Pawnee Cir., Manhattan, KS 66502-1973 USA
E-mail: orders@cedartip.com
Web site: http://www.cedartip.com.

CEDCO Publishing, *(0-7683; 0-915865; 1-55912)* P.O. Box 9740, San Rafael, CA 94912-9740 USA (SAN 293-9495) Toll Free: 800-227-6162
E-mail: sales@cedco.com
Web site: http://www.cedco.com.

Cela Distribution Services, *(0-9662913; 1-893105)* 9131 Interline Ave. Ste. 3A, Baton Rouge, LA 70809-1957 USA Toll Free: 888-387-2200.

CelebrateU, *(0-9760144)* Orders Addr.: P.O. Box 3001, New York, NY 10163-3001 USA Tel 917-407-4990; 646-414-1020
E-mail: sue.tarlton@prodigy.net
Web site: http://www.celebrateu.com; http://www.mothertourista.com.

Celebration Pr., Orders Addr.: 135 South Mount Zion Rd. P.O. Box 2500, Lebanon, IN 46052 USA Toll Free Fax: 800-393-3156; Toll Free: 800-526-9907 ; *Imprints:* Good Year Books (GYB) Do not confuse with Celebration Press in Onalaska WI, Denver CO
Web site: http://www.aw-bc.com; http://www.pearsonlearning.com/rightsPerm.rtf.

Celebration Publishing, *(0-9613663; 0-9708081)* 230 S. Palace Gardens Dr., Tucson, AZ 85748 USA Tel 520-886-2769
E-mail: celebration@theriver.com
Web site: http://www.arnoldpatent.com
Dist(s): **Lightning Source, Inc.**
Spirit Support.

Celebrity Bks. *Imprint of* **Warehousing & Fulfillment Specialists, LLC (WFS, LLC)**

Celeste Ediciones, S.A. (ESP) *(84-8211; 84-87553)* *Dist. by* **Lectorum Pubns.**

Celestial Artisans Educational Productions, *(0-9719792)* Orders Addr.: P.O. Box 3732, Beverly Hills, CA 90212 USA; Edit Addr.: 100 N. Crescent Dr., No. 250, Beverly Hills, CA 90210 USA
E-mail: info@theoquest.com
Web site: http://www.theoquest.com.

Celestial Arts Publishing Company *Imprint of* **Ten Speed Pr.**

Celestial Commotion, *(0-9717698)* 5963 Hickory Meadow Ln., No. 8, Memphis, TN 38115 USA Tel 901-523-5628
E-mail: zeola42@cs.com.

Celestial Pr., *(0-9675368)* Orders Addr.: P.O. Box 1094, Dunkirk, NY 14048 USA; Edit Addr.: 11N. Pangolin St., Dunkirk, NY 14048 USA Tel 716-366-1143
E-mail: celestialpress@hotmail.com
Dist(s): **Baker & Taylor Bks.**

Celestine Pr., *(0-9749382)* 25 Ashland St., Rochester, NY 14620 USA (SAN 255-9927)
E-mail: hellerest@earthlink.net
Web site: http://www.celestinepress.com.

Celjon Bks., *(1-891612)* 325 Raymond Ln., Fredericksbrg, TX 78624-6028 USA (SAN 299-4976); 12470 Starcrest, No. 602, San Antonio, TX 78216-2980
E-mail: kgjz@aol.com; celjonbks@aol.com.

Celltrition, *(0-9746378)* 13472 Vidalia Rd., Pass Christian, MS 39571 USA Tel 228-586-2455.

Cellular Publishing, *(1-886358)* Div. of Lakeshore Business Services, P.O. Box 119, Sedona, AZ 86339-0119 USA Tel 520-300-7711; Fax: 413-825-8356.

Celo Valley Bks., *(0-923687)* 160 Ohle Rd., Burnsville, NC 28714 USA (SAN 251-7973) Tel 828-675-5918
E-mail: diatoday@msn.com.

Celstumo Publishing, *(0-9761041)* A Subs. of Celebration Studios of Missouri, Orders Addr.: P.O. Box 201, Glencoe, MO 63038 USA Tel 636-458-1819 (phone/fax)
E-mail: celstumo@celstumo.com
Web site: http://www.celstumo.com
Dist(s): **Baker & Taylor Bks.**

Celtic Cat Publishing, *(0-9658950)* P.O. Box 23694, Knoxville, TN 37933-1694 USA Tel 865-693-7678
E-mail: celtic01@comcast.net
Web site: http://www.celticcatpublishing.com
Dist(s): **Baker & Taylor Bks.**
Distributors, The.

Celtic Cross Communications, *(0-9740981)* 9039 W. XY Ave., Schoolcraft, MI 49087 USA
Web site: http://www.celticcrosscommunications.com
Dist(s): **STL Distribution North America.**

CEM Ventures, Ltd., *(0-9760072)* P.O. Box 1713, Harwich, MA 02645 USA Tel 508-896-4988; Fax: 508-896-2586; Toll Free: 866-246—7800; 112 Griffith's Pond Rd., Brewster, MA 02631
E-mail: cemventures@yahoo.com
Web site: http://www.jaysonthebluejay.com.

Cemetery Dance Pubns., *(1-881475; 1-58767)* Orders Addr.: 132-B Industry Ln., Unit 7, Forest Hills, MD 21050 USA Tel 410-588-5901; Fax: 410-588-5904
E-mail: cdancepub@aol.com; info@cemeterydance.com
Web site: http://www.cemeterydance.com.

CENGAGE Learning, Div. of The Thomson Corp., 10650 Toebben Dr., Independence, KY 41051 USA (SAN 631-2144) Tel 859-525-6620; Fax: 859-525-0978; Toll Free: 800-347-7707 (customer service); 800-842-3636 (orders); a/o Customer Service, P.O. Box 6904, Florence, KY 41022-6904 Toll Free Fax: 800 487 8488; Toll Free: 800 354 9706 ; *Imprints:* Thomson Learning (ThomLearning)
Web site: http://www.thomsonlearning.com
Dist(s): **Thomson Delmar Learning**
Ingenix, Inc.

Cengage Learning Australia (AUS) *(0-17) Dist. by* **Cheng Tsui.**

Centauro Publishing, *(1-893083; 958-33; 958-818)* 7230 NW 58th St., Miami, FL 33166 USA Tel 305-436-1159; Fax: 305-436-0974
E-mail: centauro.miami@ibm.net
Web site: http://www.centauropublishing.com
Dist(s): **Ediciones Universal.**

Ctr. for Adoption Support & Education, Inc., *(0-9711732)* 4000 Blackburn Ln. Ste. 260, Burtonsville, MD 20866-6147 USA
E-mail: caseadopt@erols.com
Web site: http://www.adoptionsupport.org.

Ctr. for Appalachian Trail Studies, *(0-9636342; 0-9707916)* Orders Addr.: 1800 Brandy Woods Trail, SE, Conyers, GA 30013 USA Tel 770-679-0633 (phone/fax)
E-mail: orders@trailplace.com
Web site: http://trailplace.com/orders.html.

Ctr. for Applications of Psychological Type, Inc., *(0-935652)* 2815 NW 13th St., Suite 401, Gainesville, FL 32609 USA (SAN 213-9162) Tel 352-375-0160; Fax: 352-378-0503; Toll Free: 800-777-2278
E-mail: development@capt.org
Web site: http://www.capt.org.

Center for Applied Psychology, Incorporated *See* **Childswork/Childsplay**

†Ctr. for Applied Research in Education, The, *(0-87628)* Orders Addr.: P.O. Box 11071, Des Moines, IA 50381-1071 USA (SAN 241-6492) Fax: 515-284-2607; Toll Free: 800-288-4745; Edit Addr.: 240 Frisch Ct., Paramus, NJ 07652-5240 USA (SAN 206-6424) Tel 201-909-6200
Web site: http://vig.prenhall.com/
Dist(s): **Continental Bk. Co., Inc.;** *CIP.*

Center for Basque Studies *See* **Univ. of Nevada, Reno-Center for Basque Studies**

Center for Cancer Treatment & Research of Richland Memorial Hospital *See* **Palmetto Richland Memorial Hospital**

†Ctr. for Chinese Studies Pubns., *(0-89264)* Univ. Michigan, 202 S. Thayer St., Ann Arbor, MI 48104-1608 USA (SAN 208-2772) Tel 734-998-7181; Fax: 734-998-7263
E-mail: ccs.publications@umich.edu; telf@umich.edu
Web site: http://www.umich.edu/~iinet/ccs/ccspubs.htm
Dist(s): **Chicago Distribution Ctr.**
Univ. of Michigan Pr.; *CIP.*

Ctr. For Cultural Leadership, *(0-9745948)* P.O. Box 70, La Grange, CA 95239 USA
Web site: http://www.christianculture.com.

Center for Economic Research & Social Change *See* **Haymarket Bks.**

Ctr. for Educational Media, *(1-888933)* Orders Addr.: P.O. Box 97, Westwood, NJ 07675 USA Tel 201-358-1504; Fax: 201-358-9013; Edit Addr.: 1221 Hanover St., Chatanooga, TN 37405 USA Tel 423-265-5556
E-mail: rpanzer@lovesmarts.org
Web site: http://www.lovesmarts.org; http://freeteens.org/stories/publications.htm
Dist(s): **Baker & Taylor Bks.**

Ctr. for Educational Policy Research, *(0-9729538)* 720 E. 13th Ave., Suite 201, Eugene, OR 97401 USA Tel 541-346-6153; Fax: 541-346-6154; Toll Free: 877-766-2279
E-mail: Terri_Heath@s4s.org
Web site: http://www.s4s.org.

Center for Information Technology *See* **Academic Success for All Learners**

Ctr. for International Training & Education, *(0-938960)* Orders Addr.: P.O. Box 337, Croton on Hudson, NY 10520 USA Tel 914-271-6500; Fax: 914-271-6500; Edit Addr.: 777 United Nations Plz. Suite 3C, New York, NY 10017 USA (SAN 217-0957) Tel 914-271-6500; Fax: 914-271-6500; Toll Free: 800-316-2739
E-mail: cipany@igc.apc.org
Web site: http://www.cipa-apex.org.

Ctr. for Leadership Studies, *(0-931619)* 230 W. Third Ave., Escondido, CA 92025 USA (SAN 683-7131) Tel 760-741-6595; Fax: 760-747-9384; Toll Free: 800-330-2840 Do not confuse with compamies with the same name in Centerville, MA, Virginia Beach, VA
E-mail: julene.burton@situational.com; info@situational.com
Web site: http://www.situational.com.

Ctr. for Learning, The, *(1-56077)* Orders Addr.: P.O. Box 910, Villa Maria, PA 16155 USA Tel 724-964-8083; Toll Free Fax: 888-767-8080; Toll Free: 800-767-9090 (ordering); Edit Addr.: 24600 Detroit Rd., Suite 201, Westlake, OH 44145 USA (SAN 248-2029) Tel 440-250-9341; Fax: 440-250-9715
Web site: http://www.centerforlearning.org.

Center for Loss & Life Transition *See* **Companion Pr.**

Ctr. for Self-Actualization, Inc., The, *(0-9758799; 0-9788389)* P.O. Box 98466, Atlanta, GA 30359-2166 USA Tel 404-327-5637; Fax: 404-321-4574
E-mail: selfactualized@earthlink.net
Web site: http://www.selfactualized.org.

Ctr. For Special Services, *(0-9717246)* Orders Addr.: P.O. Box 804, Thibodaux, LA 70301 USA Tel 985-449-1187; Fax: 985-449-1809; Toll Free Fax: 800-529-8671; Toll Free: 800-510-5235; Edit Addr.: 719 President St., Thibodaux, LA 70301 USA Tel 985-449-1795
E-mail: rjorgero@bellsouth.net
Web site: http://www.centerforspecialservices.com; http://www.sexccess.com.

Ctr. for Thanatology Research & Education, Inc., *(0-930194)* Orders Addr.: 391 Atlantic Ave., Brooklyn, NY 11217-1701 USA (SAN 210-7414) Tel 718-858-3026; Fax: 718-852-1846
E-mail: rhalporn@pipeline.com
Web site: http://www.thanatology.org.

Ctr. for the Affirmation of Responsible Education, *(0-9740071)* 496 Gold Ct., San Andreas, CA 95249 USA Tel 209-754-9218
E-mail: jnorton2@earthlink.net.

Ctr. for Understanding the Built Environment, *(0-9632033)* 8340 Mission Rd. Ste. B4, Shawnee Msn, KS 66206-1362 USA
E-mail: Ginny@cubekc.org
Web site: http://www.cubekc.org.

Ctr. for Victims of Torture, The, *(0-9759789)* 717 E. River Rd., Minneapolis, MN 55455 USA Tel 612-436-4800.

Center For Youth Issues, Incorporated *See* **National Center For Youth Issues**

Ctr. of SW Studies, Fort Lewis College, *(0-9727664)* 1000 Rim Dr., Durango, CO 81301 USA
E-mail: gulliford_a@fortlewis.edu
Web site: http://www.swcenter.fortlewis.edu.

Center Path Publishing *See* **Dr. Todd, LLC**

Center Point Large Print, *(1-58547; 1-60285)* Orders Addr.: P.O. Box 1, Thorndike, ME 04986-0001 USA Tel 207-568-3717; Fax: 207-568-3727; Toll Free: 800-929-9108; 600 Brooks Rd., Thorndike, ME 04986 ; *Imprints:* Premier (Premier)
E-mail: centerpoint@uninets.net
Web site: http://centerpointlargeprint.com.

Center Point Publishing *See* **Center Point Large Print**

Center Pr., The, *(0-9626888; 1-889198)* Orders Addr.: P.O. Box 6936, Thousand Oaks, CA 91360 USA; Edit Addr.: 2204 Kirsten Lee Dr., Westlake Village, CA 91361 USA Tel 818-889-7071; Fax: 818-889-7072 Do not confuse with The Center Pr., Grapevine, TX
E-mail: center@centerbooks.com
Web site: http://www.centerbooks.com
Dist(s): **Baker & Taylor Bks.**
Quality Bks., Inc.

Ctr. Stage Puppets, *(0-9795087)* P.O. Box 8279, Bend, OR 97708 USA Tel 541-420-7943
E-mail: info@centerstagepuppets.com
Web site: http://www.centerstagepuppets.com.

Centering Corp., *(1-56123)* P.O. Box 4600, Omaha, NE 68104-0600 USA (SAN 298-1815) Tel 402-553-1200; Fax: 402-553-0507
E-mail: j1200@aol.com; centering@centering.org
Web site: http://www.centering.org
Dist(s): **Baker & Taylor Bks.**

Centering Pubns., *(0-9713013; 0-9769175)* Div. of Centering Tools for Healing & Development, 9 Terrain Dr., Rochester, NY 14618 USA
E-mail: info@centeringtools.com; mbakerpr@rochester.rr.com
Web site: http://www.centeringtools.com.

CenterLine Media, *(0-9754212)* 7 N. Main St. # 7B, Ambler, PA 19002-5709 USA
E-mail: theresa@centerlinemedia.com
Web site: http://www.centerlinemedia.com.

Centerpunch Pr., *(0-9724882)* P.O. Box 43151, Cincinnati, OH 45243 USA Tel 513-561-3392 (phone/fax)
E-mail: info@centerpunchpress.com
Web site: http://www.centerpunchpress.com
Dist(s): **Biblio Distribution.**

Centerstage Pr., Inc., *(1-890298)* P.O. Box 36688, Phoenix, AZ 85067 USA Tel 602-242-1123; Fax: 602-861-2708; Toll Free: 888-836-3453
E mail: cstage@cstage.com
Web site: http://www.cstage.com.

Centerstream Publishing, *(0-931759; 1-57424)* Orders Addr.: P.O. Box 17878, Anaheim Hills, CA 92817 USA (SAN 683-8022) Tel 714-779-9390 (phone/fax)
E-mail: centerstrm@aol.com
Web site: http://www.pma-online.org
Dist(s): **Booklines Hawaii, Ltd.**
Leonard, Hal Corp.

Central America Resource Center *See* **Resource Ctr. of The Americas**

Central Coast Books *See* **Central Coast Pr.**

Central Coast Pr., *(0-9658776; 1-930401)* Orders Addr.: P.O. Box 3654, San Luis Obispo, CA 93403 USA (SAN 631-1547) Tel 805-534-0307 (phone/fax); Edit Addr.: 1181 17th St., Los Osos, CA 94302 USA (SAN 631-1539)
E-mail: ccbooks@surfari.net.

Central Conference of American Rabbis/CCAR Pr., *(0-88123; 0-916694)* 355 Lexington Ave., 18th Flr., New York, NY 10017-6603 USA (SAN 204-3262) Tel 212-972-3636; Fax: 212-692-0819; Toll Free: 800-935-2227
E-mail: ccarpress@ccarnet.org; info@ccarnet.org
Web site: http://ccarpress.org
Dist(s): **Fell, Frederick Pubs., Inc.**

Central Park Media Corp., *(1-56219; 1-57800; 1-887692; 1-58664)* 250 W. 57th St. Ste. 1723, New York, NY 10107-1708 USA (SAN 631-3191) Toll Free: 800-833-7456 ; *Imprints:* CPM Manga (CPM Manga); CPM Comics (CPM Comics); Manga 18 (Manga Eighteen); CPM Manhwa (CPM Manhwa)
E-mail: info@teamcpm.com
Web site: http://www.centralparkmedia.com/; http://www.cpmpress.com/
Dist(s): **Baker & Taylor Bks.**
Consortium Bk. Sales & Distribution
Hobbies Hawaii Distributors.

Central Valley Railroad Publications *See* **Signature Pr.**

Centre d'Art du Domaine de Kerguehennec (FRA) *(2-906574) Dist. by* **Dist Art Pubs.**

Centre Pointe Learning, Inc., *(1-930799)* 6749 Gilmore Rd. Apt. B, Hamilton, OH 45011-5392 USA Toll Free: 888-471-4545
E-mail: temrick@cplearning.com
Web site: http://www.cplearning.com.

Centro Bks., LLC, *(1-933572)* 200 E. 90th St., Suite 3D, New York, NY 10128 USA (SAN 256-7229)
Web site: http://www.centrobooks.com
Dist(s): **National Bk. Network.**

Centro de Informacion y Desarrollo de la Comunicacion y la Literatura (MEX) *(968-494) Dist. by* **Continental Bk.**

Centro de Informacion y Desarrollo de la Comunicacion y la Literatura (MEX) *(968-494) Dist. by* **Mariuccia Iaconi Bk Imports.**

Centro de Informacion y Desarrollo de la Comunicacion y la Literatura (MEX) *(968-494) Dist. by* **Lectorum Pubns.**

Centro de Informacion y Desarrollo de la Comunicacion y la Literatura (MEX) *(968-494) Dist. by* **AIMS Intl.**

Centurion Pubs., *(0-9673919)* Div. of Luthaire, Inc., Orders Addr.: P.O. Box 248, Hazel Green, AL 35750 USA (SAN 254-4245) Tel 256-881-2245 (phone/fax); Edit Addr.: 272 Approach Ln., Hazel Green, AL 35750 USA
E-mail: centurio@hiwaay.net
Web site: http://www.centurionpublishers.com.

Century Pr., *(0-9659417)* Div. of Conservatory of American Letters, P.O. Box 298, Thomaston, ME 04861 USA Tel 207-354-0998; Fax: 207-354-8953 Do not confuse with companies with the same name in Arroyo Seco, NM, Oklahoma City, OK
E-mail: cal@americanletters.org
Web site: http://www.americanletters.org.

Cepia LLC., *(0-9777241)* 121 Hunter Ave., Suite 103, Saint Louis, MO 63124 USA Tel 314-725-4900; Fax: 314-725-4919
E-mail: information@cepiallc.com
Web site: http://www.cepiallc.com
Dist(s): **Biblio Distribution.**

Ceres Pr., *(0-9606138; 1-886101)* P.O. Box 87, Woodstock, NY 12498 USA (SAN 217-0949) Tel 845-679-5573; Toll Free: 888-804-8848 Do not confuse with Ceres Pr., Stamford, CT
E-mail: cem620@aol.com
Web site: http://www.heathyhighways.com
Dist(s): **Baker & Taylor Bks.**
Integral Yoga Pubns.
New Leaf Distributing Co., Inc.
Nutri-Bks. Corp.
Partners Bk. Distributing, Inc.

Ceres Software, Incorporated *See* **Inspiration Software, Inc.**

Certified Firearms Instructors, LLC, *(0-9741480)* P.O. Box 131254, Saint Paul, MN 55113-1254 USA Tel 952-935-2414; Fax: 952-935-4122
E-mail: jolson@gw.hamline.edu
Web site: http://www.aacfi.com.

CeShore *Imprint of* **SterlingHouse Pubs., Inc.**

CET *Imprint of* **Greater Cincinnati TV Educational Foundation**

C E V Multimedia, Ltd., *(1-57078; 1-59535; 1-60333)* Orders Addr.: P.O. Box 65265, Lubbock, TX 79464 USA Tel 806-745-8820; Fax: 806-745-5300; Toll Free Fax: 800-243-6398; Toll Free: 800-922-9965; Edit Addr.: 1020 SE Loop 289, Lubbock, TX 79404 USA
E-mail: cev@cevmultimedia.com
Web site: http://www.cevmultimedia.com.

CF Bks. *Imprint of* **Don't Eat Any Bugs Prodns.**

CFM, *(0-9728620; 0-9769071)* 112 Greene St., New York City, NY 10012 USA Tel 212-966-3864; Fax: 212-226-1041
E-mail: info@cfmgallery.com
Web site: http://www.cfmgallery.com.

CG Star, L.L.C., *(0-9718151)* 230 S. Hamilton Dr. Unit 204, Beverly Hills, CA 90211 USA Tel 213-925-1535; Fax: 213-291-1473
E-mail: dennischristen@hotmail.com
Web site: http://www.booksnflicks.com.

CGS Communications, *(0-9650505)* P.O. Box 17485, Fort Worth, TX 76102-0509 USA Tel 817-589-7973; Fax: 817-413-9796
Dist(s): **Hervey's Booklink & Cookbook Warehouse.**

C.G.S. Pr., *(0-9660726)* P.O. Box 1394, Mountainside, NJ 07092 USA Tel 908-233-8293 (phone/fax)
E-mail: Gwynnic2000@aol.com
Dist(s): **Biblio Distribution.**

Chacmool Pr., *(0-9789391)* 849 W. University Pkwy., Baltimore, MD 21210 USA
E-mail: publisher@chacmoolpress.com
Web site: http://www.chacmoolpress.com
Dist(s): **Biblio Distribution.**

Chadko Publishing, *(0-9661451)* 20132 Bayview Ave., Newport Beach, CA 92660 USA Tel 714-475-1912; Fax: 714-640-6708.

Chagrin River Publishing Co., *(1-929821)* Orders Addr.: P.O. Box 173, Chagrin Falls, OH 44022 USA Tel 440-893-9250; Edit Addr.: 21 E. Summit St., Chargrin Falls, OH 44022 USA
E-mail: ephilipson@stratos.net.

Chairman Pubns., *(0-9658366)* Orders Addr.: P.O. Box 12066, Des Moines, IA 50312 USA (SAN 299-7185) Tel 515-279-0184; Fax: 515-279-2583; Edit Addr.: 701 55th St., Des Moines, IA 50312 USA
E-mail: chairpub@aol.com.

Chalfont Hse., *(0-9720111)* P.O. Box 84, Dumfries, VA 22026-3361 USA Tel 571-437-6163; Fax: 703-221-1303
E-mail: info@chalfonthouse.com
Web site: http://www.chalfonthouse.com.

Chalk Stream Publishing, *(0-9670607)* Orders Addr.: P.O. Box 4007, Temple, TX 76505 USA (SAN 299-822X) Tel 254-773-6112; Fax: 254-773-6240; Toll Free: 877-288-4606; Edit Addr.: 3215 Buckingham Ct., Temple, TX 76502 USA.

Chamberlain Hart Enterprises, Inc., *(0-9749756)* P.O. Box 1600, Fairfield, IA 52556 USA Tel 641-469-3717; Fax: 641-469-6647
E-mail: che@iowatelecom.net
Web site: http://www.chamberlainhart.com.

Chambers Harrap Pubs., Ltd. (GBR) *(0-245; 0-550) Dist. by* **HM Trade Div.**

Chameleon Designs, *(0-9701573)* P.O. Box 61855, North Charleston, SC 29419 USA Tel 843-761-7426
E-mail: yeleth@aol.com.

Chameleon Enterprises, Inc., *(0-9669801)* 6320 SW 34th Ave., Portland, OR 97201 USA Tel 503-892-3205; Fax: 503-231-0691; Toll Free: 877-235-5020
E-mail: dianeru@qwest.net.

Chamike Pubs., *(1-884876)* 9000 Doris Dr., Fort Washington, MD 20744 USA Tel 301-248-4034.

Champion Athlete Publishing Company *See* **National Assn. of Speed & Explosion**

Champion Pr., Ltd., *(1-891400; 1-932783)* 765 Main St., Belgium, WI 53004 USA (SAN 299-4607) Tel 262-285-4518; Fax: 262-285-4569 Do not confuse with Champion Pr., Inglewood CA
E-mail: sara@championpress.com
Web site: http://www.championpress.com
Dist(s): **Ingram Pub. Services**
Sourcebooks, Inc.

Championship Chess, *(0-9729456; 0-9772489)* Div. of Teachable Tech, Inc., Orders Addr.: 3565 Evans Rd., Atlanta, GA 30340 USA Toll Free: 888-328-7373
E-mail: dj@championshipchess.net
Web site: http://www.championshipchess.net.

Championship Debate Enterprises, *(1-889510)* P.O. Box Z, Taos, NM 87571 USA Tel 505-751-0514; Fax: 505-751-9788
E-mail: bennett@laplaza.org
Web site: http://www.cdedebate.com.

Chan, David, *(0-9754302)* 12511 Fox Trace Ln., Houston, TX 77066-4029 USA Tel 281-580-7042
E-mail: david@chancomputerhelp.com.

Chancellor Pr. (GBR) *(0-907486; 1-85152; 0-7537) Dist. by* **Sterling.**

Chandler Hse. Pr., *(0-9636277; 1-886284)* PO Box 20100 W. Side Sta. 34 Chiltern Hill Dr., Worcester, MA 01602 USA Fax: 508-753-7419
E-mail: chandlerhousepress@yahoo.com
Web site: http://www.chandlerhousebooks.com.

Chandler-Day, *(0-9677716)* 3587 Patton Hollow Rd., Watertown, TN 37184 USA Tel 615-286-2860
E-mail: labella@rectec.net.

Chandler/White Publishing Co., *(1-877804)* 517 W. Midvale Ave., Philadelphia, PA 19144-4617 USA
Dist(s): **Alliance Hse., Inc.**

Change Is Strange, Inc., *(0-9755902)* 3630 21st St., Boulder, CO 80304-1608 USA
E-mail: info@changeisstrange.com
Web site: http://www.changeisstrange.com
Dist(s): **Biblio Distribution.**

Changing Images Art Foundation, Inc., *(0-9665793)* 30 Forest Pl., Towaco, NJ 07082 USA Tel 973-402-0842; Fax: 973-263-0329
E-mail: ciaf97@aol.com
Web site: http://www.changingimages.org.

Changing Lives Changing The World, Incorporated *See* **Changing Lives Publishing**

Changing Lives Pr. *Imprint of* **Changing Lives Schl., Inc.**

Changing Lives Publishing, *(0-9653700; 0-9774513; 0-9798553)* Div. of Changing Lives Changing The World, Inc., Orders Addr.: P.O. Box 530733, Miami Shores, FL 33153 USA; Edit Addr.: P.O. Box 132, Sharpes, FL 32959 USA Tel 321-637-1128; Toll Free: 866-578-1900
E-mail: clcw1@bellsouth.net
Web site: http://www.print2publish.com.

Changing Lives Schl., Inc., *(0-9717682)* P.O. Box 853, Black Mountain, NC 28711 USA Fax: 866-615-0417 ; *Imprints:* Changing Lives Press (Chng Lives Pr)
E-mail: Thomasheart@aol.comTh
Dist(s): **Ingram Bk. Co.**

Changing-Times.net, *(0-9741930)* Orders Addr.: P.O. Box 39651, Phoenix, AZ 85069-9651 USA
Web site: http://www.changing-times.net.

ChannelOne.Com, Incorporated *See* **Trademark Universal, Inc.**

Chapel Hill Pr., *(1-880849; 1-59715)* 1829 E. Franklin St., Bldg. 300A, Chapel Hill, NC 27514-5863 USA Tel 919-942-8389; Fax: 919-942-2506
E-mail: publisher@chapelhillpress.com; dmcgill@chapelhillpress.com
Web site: http://www.chapelhillpress.com.

Chapelle *Imprint of* **Sterling Publishing Co., Inc.**

Chapin Hse. Bks., *(0-9771079)* 435 Brevard Ave., Cocoa, FL 32922 USA Tel 321-971-1971; Fax: 321-690-4388
E-mail: wynne@flahistory.net.

Chapman, Chris & Eric P. Hvolboll, *(0-9765061)* 2741 Cuerta Rd., Santa Barbara, CA 93105 USA Fax: 805-882-9897.

Chapman, Paul Publishing (GBR) *(1-85396; 1-4129) Dist. by* **SAGE.**

Chapman Pr., LLC, *(0-9725420)* 949 S. Josephine St., Denver, CO 80209 USA
E-mail: sales@chapmanpress.com; editor@chapmanpress.com
Web site: http://www.chapmanpress.com
Dist(s): **Baker & Taylor Bks.**

Chapman, Robert F. *See* **Cypress Trail Pr.**

Chapter & Verse Pr., *(0-9724549)* 7350 Detrick Jordan Pike, Springfield, OH 45502-9660 USA Tel 937-964-0294
E-mail: nashvila@bright.net.

Character Arts, *(0-9772259)* 37 Pond Rd., Bldg. 2, Wilton, CT 06897 USA Tel 203-834-0323.

Character Development Group *See* **Character Development Publishing**

Character Development Publishing, *(0-9653163; 1-892056)* Div. of Character Development Group, Inc., Orders Addr.: P.O. Box 35136, Greensboro, NC 27425-5136 USA Tel 336-668-9373; Fax: 336-668-9375; Edit Addr.: 8646 W. Market St. Suite 102, Greensboro, NC 27409 USA
E-mail: info@charactereducation.com; RESPECT96@aol.com
Web site: http://www.charactereducation.com.

Character Lines Publishing, *(0-9663522)* 1055 Brush Arbor Cir., Mcdonough, GA 30252-5594 USA.

Character-in-Action *Imprint of* **Quiet Impact, Inc.**

CharFaye Publishing, Incorporated *See* **FayeHouse. Pr. International**

Charisma Kids *Imprint of* **Strang Communications Co.**

CharismaLife Pubs., *(1-57405)* Div. of Strang Communications Co., 600 Rinehart Rd., Lake Mary, FL 32746 USA Tel 407-333-0600; Fax: 407-333-7100; Toll Free: 800-283-8494 ; *Imprints:* K.I.D.S. Church (KIDS Church); Cross Training (Cross Training).

Charles River Media, *(1-886801; 1-58450)* Orders Addr.: P.O. Box 960, Herndon, VA 20172 USA (SAN 254-1564) Fax: 703-996-1010; Toll Free: 800-382-8505; Edit Addr.: 25 Thomson Pl., Boston, MA 02210-1202 USA
E-mail: info@charlesriver.com
Web site: http://www.charlesriver.com
Dist(s): **CENGAGE Learning**
Thomson Delmar Learning.

Charles River Pr., *(0-9754913; 0-9791304; 0-9793844)* 37 Evergreen Rd., Norton, MA 02766 USA Fax: 508-285-3229; P.O. Box 1122, Mansfield, MA 02048 (SAN 256-2251) Tel 508-364-9851; Fax: 508-285-3229 ; *Imprints:* Gap Tooth Publishing (Gap Tooth Pubng)
E-mail: jwomack@charlesriverpress.com
Web site: http://www.charlesriverpress.com.

Charles Rivers Publishing Co., *(0-9648113)* Orders Addr.: P.O. Box 551623A, Dallas, TX 75355-1623 USA; Edit Addr.: 542 Haggard St., Suite 512, Plano, TX 75074 USA Tel 972-422-2322; Fax: 972-422-8030
E-mail: cmorris@aimforsuccess.org.

Charles Scribner's Sons *Imprint of* **Thomson Gale**

Charlesbridge Publishing, Inc., *(0-88106; 0-935508; 1-57091; 1-58089; 1-879085)* Orders Addr.: 85 Main St., Watertown, MA 02472 USA (SAN 240-5474) Tel 617-926-0329; Fax: 617-926-5720; Toll Free Fax: 800-926-5775; Toll Free: 800-225-3214
E-mail: orders@charlesbridge.com
Web site: http://www.charlesbridge.com
Dist(s): **Continental Bk. Co., Inc.**
Lectorum Pubns., Inc.

Charlie's Gift, *(0-9786795)* 920 York Rd., Suite 350, Hinsdale, IL 60521 USA Tel 630-399-8164.

Charlotte's Storybooks, *(0-9707920)* Orders Addr.: P.O. Box 1291, Apple Valley, CA 92307 USA Tel 760-961-2401 (phone/fax); Edit Addr.: 25404 Valley View, Apple Valley, CA 92307 USA
E-mail: charlottestories@aol.com
Web site: http://members.aol.com/charlottestories.

Charm Pubns., Inc., *(0-9701118)* P.O. Box 20318, Fountain Hills, AZ 85269 USA (SAN 253-2719) Tel 480-837-6449 (phone/fax)
E-mail: charminc@compuserve.com
Web site: http://www.charmpublications.com.

Charming Pubns., *(0-9773531)* Orders Addr.: P.O. Box 90792, Austin, TX 78709-0792 USA Tel 512-288-4803
E-mail: minia.lopez@gmail.com
Web site: http://www.happychildrenbooks.com.

Charnick Publishing Corp., *(0-9667954)* 10117 W. Oakland Pk. Blvd., Suite 311, Sunrise, FL 33351 USA Tel 954-748-9979; Fax: 954-748-1366; Toll Free: 800-661-5669.

Charta (ITA) *(88-8158; 88-86158) Dist. by* **Dist Art Pubs.**

Chartwell *Imprint of* **Book Sales, Inc.**

Chase Pubns., *(0-9665699)* 1171 Tellem Dr., Pacific Palisades, CA 90272 USA Tel 310-454-2344; Fax: 310-459-6021
E-mail: wlarsen421@aol.com.

Chaser Media LLC, *(0-9747447)* P.O. Box 99, Dorset, VT 05251 USA
Web site: http://www.chasermedia.com.

Chatman Pubs., *(1-886663)* Div. of Chatman & Assocs., P.O. Box 121121, Nashville, TN 37212 USA Tel 615-371-8203.

Chattanooga FuFu Factory, *(0-9711068)* 1225 Taft Hwy., Signal Mountain, TN 37377 USA Tel 423-756-3668; Fax: 423-886-1142
E-mail: rts9999999@aol.com
Web site: http://www.fufufactory.com.

Chauncey Park Pr., *(0-9667808)* Div. of Charles Chauncey Wells, Inc., 735 N. Grove Ave., Oak Park, IL 60302-1551 USA Tel 708-524-0695; Fax: 708-524-0742
E-mail: chauncey@wells1.com
Web site: http://www.wells1.com.

Cheadle Bks., *(0-9679622)* 3706 S. Acoma St., Englewood, CO 80110-3688 USA Tel 303-761-7906 ; *Imprints:* Desert Waters Publishing (Desert Wtrs Pub)
E-mail: trdcardguy@aol.com.

Checker Bk. Publishing Group, LLC, *(0-9710249; 0-9741664; 0-9753808; 1-933160)* 2044 S. Alex Rd. Ste. A, Dayton, OH 45449-4038 USA
Web site: http://www.checkerbpg.com
Dist(s): **Diamond Bk. Distributors.**

Checkerboard Library *Imprint of* **ABDO Publishing Co.**

†Checkerboard Pr., Inc., *(1-56288)* 1560 Revere Rd., Yardley, PA 19067-4351 USA; *CIP.*

Checkmark Bks. *Imprint of* **Facts On File, Inc.**

Cheerful Cherub, *(0-9753417)* Orders Addr.: P.O. Box 262238, Highlands Ranch, CO 80163 USA; Edit Addr.: 10071 S. Maples Ln., Highlands Ranch, CO 80129 USA
Web site: http://www.cheerfulcherub.com.

Chef John Folse & Co., *(0-9625152; 0-9704457)* Orders Addr.: 2517 S. Philippe Ave., Gonzales, LA 70737 USA Tel 504-644-6000; Fax: 225-647-0316
E-mail: folse@folse.com
Web site: http://www.jfolse.com.

Chelan Publishing, *(0-9672460)* Orders Addr.: 4 Gary Rd., Ithaca, NY 14850 USA
E-mail: dianeako@yahoo.com
Web site: http://www.makereallove.com; http://www.lightlink.com
Dist(s): **Baker & Taylor Bks.**
New Leaf Distributing Co., Inc.

Chelonian Pr, Inc., *(0-9676960)* 1420 Spring Hill Rd, No. 600, McLean, VA 22102 USA (SAN 253-0694) Tel 703-734-1160; Fax: 703-759-7378.

Chelsea Clubhouse *Imprint of* **Facts On File, Inc.**

Chelsea Green Publishing, *(0-930031; 1-890132; 1-931498; 88-86283; 1-933392; 1-60358)* Orders Addr.: P.O. Box 428, White River Junction, VT 05001 USA (SAN 669-7631) Tel 802-295-6300; Fax: 802-295-6444; Toll Free: 800-639-4099; Edit Addr.: 85 N. Main St., Suite 120, White River Junction, VT 05001 USA
E-mail: info@chelseagreen.com
Web site: http://www.chelseagreen.com.

Chelsea Hse. *Imprint of* **Facts On File, Inc.**

Chelsey Pr., *(0-9668448)* 39032 Gladiolus Ln., Palm Desert, CA 92211-5009 USA
E-mail: chelseyink@aol.com
Dist(s): **SteinerBooks, Inc.**

Chelsey Publishing, *(1-890869)* 1145 SW 23rd St., Suite 2, Oklahoma City, OK 73109-1603 USA Tel 405-632-5623
E-mail: lillianthorp@yahoo.com.

Cheng & Tsui Co., *(0-88727; 0-917056)* 25 West St., Boston, MA 02111-1213 USA (SAN 169-3387) Tel 617-988-2401; Fax: 617-426-3669
E-mail: service@cheng-tsui.com
Web site: http://www.cheng-tsui.com.

Cheng Chung Bk. Co., Ltd. (TWN) *(957-09) Dist. by* **Cheng Tsui.**

Cherish the Children, *(0-9679911)* P.O. Box 189, Cedar Bluff, AL 35959 USA Fax: 256-779-5203
E-mail: chrisdendy@mindspring.com
Web site: http://www.chrisdendy.com.

Cherished Books *See* **Riverpark Publishing Co.**

Cherniss, Bonnie, *(0-9700678)* 9641 Birmingham Ave., Riverside, CA 92509 USA Tel 951-681-6279; Fax: 951-681-6731; Toll Free: 888-752-7838
E-mail: HidenWrite4u@aol.com.

Cherokee Bks., *(0-9640458; 1-930052)* Orders Addr.: P.O. Box 463, Dover, DE 19964 USA Tel 302-734-8782; Fax: 302-734-3198; Edit Addr.: 231 Meadow Ridge Pkwy., Dover, DE 19904 USA Do not confuse with Cherokee Bks., Ponca City, OK
E-mail: milthanna@aol.com
Web site: http://www.cherokeebooks.com.

Cherokee Pubns., *(0-935741)* P.O. Box 430, Cherokee, NC 28719 USA (SAN 696-2785) Tel 828-488-8856; Fax: 828-488-6934
E-mail: cpubl@aol.com
Web site: http://www.cherokeepub.com
Dist(s): **Book Publishing Co., The.**

†Cherokee Publishing Co., *(0-87797)* Orders Addr.: P.O. Box 1730, Marietta, GA 30061-1730 USA (SAN 650-0404) Tel 404-467-4189; Fax: 404-237-1062; Toll Free: 800-653-3952; Edit Addr.: 800 Miami Cir., NE, Suite 100, Atlanta, GA 30324-3055 USA Do not confuse with Cherokee Publishing Co., Antioch, CA
E-mail: books@defoorcentre.com; *CIP.*

Cherokee Publishing Company *See* **Cherokee Bks.**

Cherry Lake Publishing, *(1-60279)* 1215 Overidgeview Ct., Ann Arbor, MI 48103 USA Tel 248-705-2045.

Cherry Lane Books *See* **Cherry Lane Music Co.**

†Cherry Lane Music Co., *(0-89524; 1-57560; 1-60378)* 6 E. 32nd St., 11th Flr., New York, NY 10016 USA (SAN 219-0788) Tel 212-561-3000; Fax: 212-251-0822
E-mail: print@cherrylane.com
Web site: http://www.cherrylane.com
Dist(s): **Leonard, Hal Corp.**; *CIP.*

Cherry Street Bks., *(0-9667567)* Div. of Levering Fruits, Inc., Orders Addr.: P.O. Box 1632, Mount Airy, NC 27030-1632 USA Tel 336-789-7400; Fax: 336-789-6401; Edit Addr.: 241 N. Main St., Mount Airy, NC 27030-1632 USA
E-mail: orchardgappress@advi.net.

Cherry Street Pr., *(0-9764921)* 139A N. 22nd St., Philadelphia, PA 19103 USA Fax: 215-568-4329
Dist(s): **Baker & Taylor Bks.**

Cherry Tree Bks., *(0-9666832; 0-9774665)* 433 Perkins Rd., Weybridge, VT 05753 USA Tel 802-545-2474
E-mail: idahw@pshift.com; lmwash@together.net
Web site: http://www.cherrytreebooks.net.

Cherry Tree Lane Publishing, *(0-9771858)* 125 Cobblestone Ct., Berea, OH 44017-1079 USA
E-mail: sharesom@wowway.com.

Cherry Tree Pr. LLC, *(0-9772771)* Orders Addr.: 525 W. 14th, Traverse City, MI 49684-4968 USA Tel 231-995-9221; Fax: 231-995-9223; Edit Addr.: 526 W. 14th St., No. 185, Traverse City, MI 49684-4968 USA Do not confuse with Cherry Tree Press in Palo Alto, CA
Dist(s): **Partners Bk. Distributing, Inc.**

Cherrytree Pubns., Inc., *(0-9677757)* 881 Ocean Dr., No. 18B, Biscayne, FL 33149 USA Tel 305-361-1828
Dist(s): **BookMasters, Inc.**

Cherubic Pr., *(0-9646576; 1-889590)* Orders Addr.: P.O. Box 5036, Johnstown, PA 15904-5036 USA Tel 814-535-4300; Fax: 814-535-4580; Edit Addr.: 412 Coleman Ave., Johnstown, PA 15902 USA
E-mail: CherubicPr@aol.com.

Cherubs Play, *(0-9706467)* Orders Addr.: 10 Wesley Ct., Napa, CA 94558-6700 USA Tel 707-319-3216
E-mail: kelly@ollietheotter.com
Web site: http://www.ollietheotter.com/.

Cheshire House Bks., *(0-9675073)* P.O. Box 2484, New York, NY 10021 USA Tel 212-861-5404 (phone/fax)
E-mail: Chershirehouse@webtv.net
Web site: http://www.samthecat.com.

Chesire Pr., *(0-9676870)* P.O. Box 7112, Alexandria, VA 22307-0112 USA Tel 703-768-9200; Fax: 703-768-9201; Toll Free Fax: 877-418-0801; Toll Free: 877-418-0800.

ChessDale Assocs., *(0-9700257)* 1031 Bernardo Oaks, Cat Spring, TX 78933 USA Tel 409-992-3295 (phone/fax)
E-mail: ragsdale@industryinet.com.

Chessmore Publishing, *(0-9659772)* 6902 River Birch Ct., Bradenton, FL 34202 USA Tel 941-358-5266; Fax: 941-358-5516
E-mail: jp@chessmorepublishing.com
Web site: http://www.chessmorepublishing.com.

Chester Music *Imprint of* **Music Sales Corp.**

Chestleigh's Bks. Publishing Co., *(1-893240)* Orders Addr.: P.O. Box 2014, Fond DuLac, WI 54936-2014 USA Tel 920-922-6670; Fax: 920-922-7311; Toll Free: 800-922-6670; Edit Addr.: 45 Sheboyan St., Suite 10, Fond Dulac, WI 54935 USA.

Cheval International, *(0-9640610; 1-885351)* P.O. Box 706, Black Hawk, SD 57718-0706 USA
E-mail: cheval@rapidnet.com
Web site: http://www.chevalinternational.com
Dist(s): **Barnes & Noble Bks.-Imports**
Baker & Taylor Bks.

Chia Pr., *(0-9672602)* 2875 N. Tucson Blvd., No. 25, Tucson, AZ 85716 USA Tel 520-327-0645
E-mail: achiasson1@aol.com.

Chiappetta, Joe, *(0-9644323)* 2209 Northgate, North Riverside, IL 60546 USA Tel 708-447-3437
E-mail: sillydaddy@redweb.com
Web site: http://www.wraithspare.com/sillydaddy
Dist(s): **Diamond Comic Distributors, Inc.**
Koen-Levy Bk. Wholesalers LLC
Last Gasp of San Francisco.

Chiappini, Lydia , *(0-9669355)* 60 Gaisler Rd., Blairstown, NJ 07825 USA Tel 908-362-5604
E-mail: lydiachiappini@yahoo.com.

Chiaramonti, Gregory, *(0-615)* 609 Mulberry St., Trenton, NJ 08638 USA Tel 609-865-3980
E-mail: gcmonti@yahoo.com
Web site: http://www.probie-thespaceprobe.com
Dist(s): **Lulu.com.**

Chicago Children's Museum, *(0-9759580)* Navy Pier, 700 E. Grand Ave., Chicago, IL 60611 USA Tel 312-527-1000; Fax: 312-527-9082
Web site: http://www.chichildrensmuseum.org
Dist(s): **Independent Pubs. Group.**

Chicago Distribution Ctr., Orders Addr.: 11030 S. Langley Ave., Chicago, IL 60628 USA (SAN 630-6047) Tel 773-702-7000 (International); Fax: 773-702-7212 (International); Toll Free Fax: 800-621-8476 (USA/Canada); Toll Free: 800-621-2736 (USA/Canada); 800-621-8471 (credit & collections)
E-mail: custserv@press.uchicago.edu; orders@press.uchicago.edu
Web site: http://www.press.uchicago.edu; http://www.press.uchicago.edu/presswide/cdc/.

†Chicago Historical Society, *(0-913820)* Clark St. at North Ave., Chicago, IL 60614 USA (SAN 203-6479) Tel 312-642-4600; Fax: 312-266-2077
E-mail: info@chicagohistory.org
Web site: http://www.chicagohistory.org; *CIP.*

Chicago Office of Fine Arts, Department of Cultural Affairs *See* **City of Chicago, Dept. of Cultural Affairs**

†Chicago Review Pr., Inc., *(0-914090; 0-914091; 1-55652; 1-56976)* 814 N. Franklin St., Chicago, IL 60610 USA (SAN 213-5744) Tel 312-337-0747; Fax: 312-337-5985; Toll Free: 800-888-4741 (orders only) ; *Imprints:* Hill, Lawrence Books (Lawrence Hill); Zephyr Press (ZephPr)
E-mail: frontdesk@ipgbook.com; orders@ipgbook.com
Web site: http://www.ipgbook.com
Dist(s): **AK Pr. Distribution**
Cobblestone Publishing Co.
Gryphon Hse., Inc.
Independent Pubs. Group; *CIP.*

Chicago Spectrum Pr., *(1-58374; 1-886094)* Div. of Evanston Publishing Inc., 4824 Brownsboro Ctr., Louisville, KY 40207 USA Tel 502-899-1919; Fax: 502-896-0246; Toll Free: 888-266-5780 (888-BOOKS-80); 800-594-5190
E-mail: Evanstonpublish@aol.com
Web site: http://www.EvanstonPublishing.com
Dist(s): **Baker & Taylor Bks.**
Partners/West.

Chicago Unzipped *Imprint of* **Nucorp**

Chick Pubns., Inc., *(0-937958; 0-7589)* P.O. Box 3500, Ontario, CA 91761-1019 USA (SAN 211-7770) Tel 909-987-0771; Fax: 909-941-8128; Toll Free: 800-932-3050
E-mail: orderdesk@chick.com
Web site: http://www.chick.com.

Chickadee Pr., *(0-9670743)* 697 County Rd., 480, Marquette, MI 49855 USA Tel 906-249-9210; Fax: 906-249-9487
E-mail: rhenry@hotbot.com.

Chickaloon Village Publishing, *(0-9767217)* P.O. Box 1105, Chickaloon, AK 99674 USA Tel 907-745-0707; Fax: 907-745-7154
E-mail: patricia@chickaloon.org
Web site: http://www.chickaloon.org.

Chicken Hse., The *Imprint of* **Scholastic, Inc.**

Chicken Socks *Imprint of* **Klutz**

Chicken Soup Pr., Inc., *(0-9646904; 1-893337)* Orders Addr.: P.O. Box 164, Circleville, NY 10919 USA (SAN 298-6787) Tel 845-692-6320; Fax: 845-692-7574; Edit Addr.: 17 Todd Dr., Middletown, NY 10941 USA
E-mail: poet@hvc.rr.com
Web site: http://www.freewebs.com/mcampi
Dist(s): **Baker & Taylor Bks.**
Brodart Co.
Follett Library Resources
Quality Bks., Inc.

Chicory Pr., *(0-9785886)* 49 Maple Ave., Morgantown, WV 26501 USA Tel 304-292-1115
E-mail: efaulkes@mail.wvu.edu.

Chidokai Personal Growth Center *See* **Esoteric Ink, LLC**

Chiffon Pubs., *(0-9642120)* Rt. 1, Box 3330, Elk City, OK 73644 USA Tel 580-225-3502
E-mail: chiffonpub@itlnet.net
Web site: http://www.CHIFFON-PUBLISHERS.com.

Chihuly, Dale *See* **Portland Pr., Inc.**

Chikara Kan, *(0-9707496; 0-9759491; 0-9796764)* P.O. Box 71644, Reno, NV 89570 USA
E-mail: books@chikara-kan.com
Web site: http://www.chikara-kan.com.

ChikChat' Ink, *(0-9766634)* P.O. Box 3302, Brentwood, TN 37024-3302 USA Tel 615-731-7422.

Child Access Center of Maryland,The *See* **Project Shalom**

Child Advocates, Inc., *(0-9754953)* 2401 Portsmouth, Suite 210, Houston, TX 77098 USA Tel 713-529-1396; Fax: 713-529-1390
Web site: http://www.childadvocates.org.

Child & Family Pr. *Imprint of* **Child Welfare League of America, Inc.**

Child Development Publishing Co., *(0-9678054)* 7 Snowberry Dr., Guild, NH 03754 USA Tel 603-863-3464.

Child LIfe Bks., LLC, *(0-9771143; 0-9791687)* 361 Van Ness Way, Suite 302, Torrance, CA 90501-6276 USA Fax: 310-781-7945
E-mail: liana@mannersicare.com.

Child Light, *(0-9677511)* P.O. Box 1563, Montpelier, VT 05602-1563 USA Tel 802-496-5962; Fax: 802-479-5437; Toll Free: 888-780-6258
E-mail: info@childlight.com
Web site: http://www.childlight.com.

Child Management, Incorporated *See* **ParentMagic, Inc.**

Child Safety Publishing, *(0-615)* 29254 Wellington W., Southfield, MI 48034 USA.

Child Scope Productions, *(0-9678778)* Div. of Moschea Promotions, 5016 N. Lydell Ave., White Fish Bay, WI 53217 USA Tel 414-332-1897; Fax: 414-332-1609
E-mail: mosch@execpc.com.

Child Sensitive Communication, LLC, *(0-9743197; 1-933803)* P.O. Box 40269, Nashville, TN 37204-0269 USA Toll Free: 888-573-3901; 888-573-3953 ; *Imprints:* Karyn Henley Resources (Krayn Henley)
Web site: http://www.karynhenley.com; http://www.ndxpress.com.

†Child Welfare League of America, Inc., *(0-87868; 1-58760)* Orders Addr.: P.O. Box 932831, Atlanta, GA 31193-2831 USA Tel 770-280-4164; Toll Free: 800-407-6273; Edit Addr.: 2345 Crystal Dr., Suite 250, Arlington, VA 22202 USA (SAN 201-9876) Tel 703-412-2400; Fax: 703-412-2401 (orders only); PBD 420 Eagleview Blvd., Exton, PA 19341 (SAN 851-2558) Tel 202-638-2952; Fax: 202-638-4004 ; *Imprints:* C W L A Press (CWLA Pr); Child & Family Press (Child-Family Pr)
E-mail: order@cwla.org
Web site: http://www.cwla.org/pubs
Dist(s): **Koen-Levy Bk. Wholesalers LLC**
Lectorum Pubns., Inc.; *CIP.*

Childcraft Education Corp., *(1-890275; 1-58669)* Div. of School Speciality, 2920 Old Tree Dr., Lancaster, PA 17603 USA Tel 717-391-4027; Fax: 717-397-7436; Toll Free: 800-631-5652
E-mail: kmyers@childcrafteducation.com
Web site: http://www.childcrafteducation.com/.

Childhood Anxiety Network *See* **Selective Mutism Anxiety Research & Treatment Ctr.**

Childhood Friends, Inc., *(1-930673)* Orders Addr.: P.O. Box 46, Phoenix, AZ 85032 USA Tel 480-585-2170; Fax: 480-585-2422; Toll Free: 877-520-2170; Edit Addr.: 4757 E. Greenway Rd., No. 103, Box 46, Phoenix, AZ 85032 USA
E-mail: childhoodfriends@aol.com
Web site: http://www.childhoodfriends.com.

Children *Imprint of* **Star Light Pr.**

Children Learning Awareness, Safety & Self-Defense, *(0-9768273)* Orders Addr.: 14620 Dickens St. #27, Sherman Oaks, CA 91403 USA Tel 818-990-9909 (phone/fax)
E-mail: janet@classeducation.org; janet@classpublications.com
Web site: http://www.classeducation.org; http://www.classpublications.com.

Children of Color/The Indra Collection, *(0-9746779)* P.O. Box 992, Great Falls, VA 22066 USA
Web site: http://www.childrenofcolor.com.

Children of the Future *See* **Smart Kids of the Future Publishing**

Children's Better Health Institute, *(1-885453)* Div. of Benjamin Franklin Literary & Medical Society, Inc., 1100 Waterway Blvd., Indianapolis, IN 46202 USA Tel 317-636-8881; Fax: 317-684-8094; Toll Free: 800-558-2376.

Childrens Bible Society, *(0-9777446)* Orders Addr.: P.O. Box 96, Hemet, CA 92546 USA Tel 951-652-9456; Edit Addr.: 1123 W. Acacia Ave., Hemet, CA 92543 USA
E-mail: kristy@actstracts.com
Web site: http://www.childrensbiblesociety.org/.

Children's Bk. Pr., *(0-89239)* 965 Mission St. Ste. 425, San Francisco, CA 94103-2961 USA (SAN 210-7864)
E-mail: orders@cbookpress.org; catalogs@cbookpress.org; info@cbookpress.org
Web site: http://www.cbookpress.org
Dist(s): **Baker & Taylor Bks.**
Continental Bk. Co., Inc.
Lectorum Pubns., Inc.
Libros Sin Fronteras
Perseus Distribution.

Children's Bookshoppe Stop, The, *(0-9728393)* P.O. Box 62261, Virginia Beach, VA 23466 USA Tel 757-671-7779 (phone/fax)
E-mail: seetcbs@exis.net
Web site: http://www.surftcbs.com.

Children's Classic Book Pubs., *(0-9794753)* Orders Addr.: 103 Josh Ln., Poolville, TX 76487 USA (SAN 853-5280)
E-mail: orders@snerfycat.com; ccbp@snerfycat.com; misterfish@snerfycat.com
Web site: www.SnerfyCat.com.

Children's Classics *Imprint of* **Random Hse. Value Publishing**

Children's Diabetes Foundation at Denver, The, *(0-9675398)* 777 Grant St., Suite 302, Denver, CO 80203 USA Tel 303-863-1200; Fax: 303-863-1122; Toll Free: 800-695-2873
E-mail: cdfregina@qwest.net
Web site: http://childrensdiabetesfdn.com.

Children's Health Care, Incorporated *See* **Children's Hospitals & Clinics**

Children's Heart Publishing Co., *(0-9786681)* P.O. Box 679005, Orlando, FL 32867 USA
E-mail: LHarris@chpublishing.org
Web site: http://www.chpublishing.org.

Children's Hospitals & Clinics, *(0-9644972)* Family Resource Ctr. 2525 Chicago Ave., S., Minneapolis, MN 55404 USA Tel 612-813-6816; Fax: 612-813-7926
E-mail: kendall.munson@childrenshc.org; kathi.rokke@childrenshc.org; frc@childrenshc.org
Web site: http://www.childrenshc.org.

Children's Legacy, *(0-9629365)* Orders Addr.: P.O. Box 300305, Denver, CO 80203 USA; Edit Addr.: 2553 Dexter St., Denver, CO 80207 USA Tel 303-830-7595.

Children's Literacy Pubns., *(0-9710432)* P.O. Box 3255, Riverview, FL 33568 USA Tel 813-677-2756; Fax: 813-671-7307
E-mail: jcdoolin@tampabay.rr.com
Web site: http://www.childrensliteracypublications.com
Dist(s): **Baker & Taylor Bks.**

Children's Literature, *(1-890920)* 7513 Shadywood Rd., Bethesda, MD 20817 USA Tel 301-469-2070; Fax: 301-469-2071; Toll Free: 800-469-2070
E-mail: marilyn@childrenslit.com
Web site: http://www.childrenslit.com.

Children's Nature Institute, The, *(0-9632753; 1-891927)* 2600 Franklin Canyon Dr., Beverly Hills, CA 90210-1600 USA (SAN 297-7796) Toll Free: 800-597-6799
E-mail: nurserynw@aol.com
Dist(s): **Baker & Taylor Bks.**
Quality Bks., Inc.
Sunbelt Pubns., Inc.

Children's Oncology Pubns., *(0-9668130)* 400 Andrews St., Suite 700, Rochester, NY 14604 USA Tel 716-546-3320; Fax: 716-546-5485
E-mail: vernol@worldnet.att.net.

Children's Pr. *Imprint of* **Scholastic Library Publishing**

Children's Psychiatric Ctr., Inc., The, *(0-9705111)* 15490 NW Seventh Ave., Suite 204, Miami, FL 33169-6231 USA Tel 305-687-2227; Fax: 305-681-4355
E-mail: cpcaacathy@aol.com.

Children's Psychological Health Ctr., Inc., The, *(0-9790846)* 2105 Divisadero St., San Francisco, CA 94115 USA Tel 415-292-7119; Fax: 415-749-2802
E-mail: gil.kliman@cphc-sf.org
Web site: http://www.cphc-sf.org.

Children's Publishing, *(0-9725803; 0-9789347)* Orders Addr.: 201 Woodland Park, Georgetown, TX 78628 USA (SAN 254-9328) Tel 512-864-7364; Fax: 512-864-1282; Toll Free: 877-864-7364
E-mail: carlson@childrenspublishing.com
Web site: http://www.childrenspublishing.com
Dist(s): **Quality Bks., Inc.**
Speech Bin, Inc., The.

Children's Village Foundation, Inc., *(0-9740481)* 1350 W. Hanley Ave., Coeur d'Alene, ID 83815 USA Tel 208-667-1189; Fax: 208-664-5735
E-mail: tinka@thechildrensvillage.org
Web site: http://www.thechildrensvillage.org.

ChildrenzBks., *(0-9748989)* PO Box 1431, Tucson, AZ 85702-1431 USA ; *Imprints:* Bases Loaded Books (Bases Loaded Bks)
E-mail: sales@childrenzbooks.com
Web site: http://www.childrenzbooks.com.

Child's Play International Ltd. (GBR) *(0-85953; 1-904550; 1-84643) Dist. by* **Childs Play.**

†Child's Play-International, *(0-85953)* Orders Addr.: 250 Minot Ave., Auburn, ME 04210 USA (SAN 216-2121) Tel 207-784-7252; Fax: 207-784-7358; Toll Free Fax: 800-854-6989; Toll Free: 800-639-6404
E-mail: chpmaine@aol.com; cplay@earthlink.net
Web site: http://www.childs-play.com
Dist(s): **Lectorum Pubns., Inc.**; *CIP.*

†Child's World, Inc., *(0-89565; 0-913778; 1-56766; 1-59296; 1-60253)* Orders Addr.: P.O. Box 326, Chanhassen, MN 55317-0326 USA (SAN 211-0032) Tel 952-906-3939; Fax: 952-906-3940; Toll Free: 800-599-7323; Edit Addr.: 7081 W. 192nd Ave., Eden Prairie, MN 55346 USA
E-mail: info@childsworld.com; mary.berendes@childsworld.com
Web site: http://www.childsworld.com; *CIP.*

Company

Childswork/Childsplay, *(1-882732; 1-58815)* Div. of The Guidance Channel, Orders Addr.: P.O. Box 760, Plainview, NY 11803-0760 USA Tel 516-349-5520; Fax: 516-349-5521; Toll Free Fax: 800-262-1886; Toll Free: 800-962-1141; 45 Executive Dr. Ste. 201, Plainview, NY 11803-1738
E-mail: karens@at-risk.com; info@childswork.com
Web site: http://www.childswork.com.

Chiliric Pubns., *(0-9755253)* 1423 6th St., Eureka, CA 95501 USA Tel 707-443-4046
Web site: http://www.geocities.com/harleysgreatadventures/; http://www.Geocities.com/harleys_great_adventures.

Chimera Publishing, LLC *See* **ShaGru Entertainment, LLC**

Chimera Pubns. (GBR) *(1-901388; 1-903931) Dist. by* **Perseus Dist.**

Chimeric, Incorporated *See* **Creations by You**

Chin & A Pr., *(0-9746341)* 2809 79th Ave., Brooklyn Park, MN 55444 USA Tel 763-549-8821
E-mail: jlodien@earthlink.net; ChinAndAPress@earthlink.net
Web site: http://www.allbeethere.com.

†**China Bks. & Periodicals, Inc.,** *(0-8351)* 360 Swift Ave., Suite 48, South San Francisco, CA 94080 USA (SAN 145-0557) Tel 800-818-2017; 650-872-7076; Fax: 650-872-7808
E-mail: info@chinabooks.com
Web site: http://www.chinabooks.com
Dist(s): **Biblio Distribution**; *CIP.*

Chinaberry Hse., *(0-9632180; 0-9742410)* Orders Addr.: P.O. Box 505, Anderson, IN 46015-0505 USA; Edit Addr.: 827 Myers Ave., Anderson, IN 46012 USA
E-mail: dliverett@aol.com
Web site: http://www.2lights.com.

Chinasoft (AUS) *(1-876739) Dist. by* **Cheng Tsui.**

Chinasprout, Inc., *(0-9707332; 0-9747302)* 110 W. 32nd St. Flr. 6, New York, NY 10001-3205 USA Toll Free: 800-644-2611
E-mail: info@chinasprout.com
Web site: http://www.chinasprout.com
Dist(s): **China Bks. & Periodicals, Inc.**

Ching Ying Center *See* **Manning, Laurie**

Chipendo, Veronica Scholarship Fund (VCSF), *(0-9676501)* 3690 N. Hwy. 38, Brigham City, UT 84302 USA Tel 435-734-2436
E-mail: peggyarogers@yahoo.com
Web site: http://www.hearttoheartafrica.org
Dist(s): **Aspen Bks.**

Chipman, Marilyn, *(0-9745857)* P.O. Box 441233, Aurora, CO 80044-1233 USA
Web site: http://www.marilynchipman.com.

Chippewa Valley Museum, *(0-9636191)* Orders Addr.: P.O. Box 1204, Eau Claire, WI 54702 USA Tel 715-834-7871; Fax: 715-834-6624; Edit Addr.: Carson Park Dr., Eau Claire, WI 54702 USA
E-mail: info@cvmuseum.com
Web site: http://www.cvmuseum.com
Dist(s): **Chicago Distribution Ctr.**
Univ. of Wisconsin Pr.

Chisholm, Juan, *(0-9755110)* 3720 McMillian Ave., Jacksonville, FL 32208 USA Tel 850-345-1622
E-mail: juan_chisholm@yahoo.com
Web site: http://www.younginvestors.org.

Chivers Children's Audio Bks. *Imprint of* **BBC Audiobooks America**

Chivers North America *See* **BBC Audiobooks America**

Chloe Pr., *(0-9679092)* 432 SW Ward Rd., No. 183, Lee's Summit, MO 64081 USA
E-mail: swwrites@excite.com
Web site: http://www.ChloePress.com
Dist(s): **Booksource, The.**

Choctaw Crafts & Bks., *(0-9710250)* Orders Addr.: P.O. Box 668, Durant, OK 74701 USA Tel 580-931-9144; Fax: 580-920-0864; Toll Free: 888-932-9199; Edit Addr.: 4202 S. Hwy. 69/75, Durant, OK 74701 USA
E-mail: sharbin@choctawcrafts.com
Web site: http://www.choctawcrafts.com.

Choicepoint Editions, *(0-9778774)* 7883 N. Pershing AVE., Stockton, CA 95207 USA Tel 209-952-7108; Fax: 209-951-3216
E-mail: choicepointeditions@inreach.com
Web site: http://www.choicepointeditions.com.

Choices Education Program, The, Watson Institute for International Studies, Brown University *See* **Choices Education Program, Watson Institute, Brown Univ.**

Choices Education Program, Watson Institute, Brown Univ., *(1-891306; 1-60123)* Box 1948, 111 Thayer St., Rm. 320 Brown Uni., Providence, RI 02912 USA Tel 401-863-9724; 401-863-3155; Fax: 401-863-1247
E-mail: choices@brown.edu
Web site: http://www.choices.edu.

Choices For Tomorrow, *(0-9748689)* 43H Meadow Pond Dr., Leominster, MA 01453 USA
E-mail: moniquehoude@yahoo.com.

Choices International, *(0-9768530)* Orders Addr.: P.O. Box 408, Berries Springs, MI 49103 USA Tel 269-471-9718 (phone/fax); Edit Addr.: P.O. Box 408, Berrien Sprgs, MI 49103-0408 USA
E-mail: pennyturner@sbcglobal.net; yourchoices@choicesinternational.info.

ChoiceSkills, Inc., *(0-938399)* Orders Addr.: P.O. Box 54, Midvale, UT 84047 USA; Edit Addr.: 7740 Chad Heights Ln., Midvale, UT 84047-5702 USA (SAN 659-6738) Tel 801-352-7141; Fax: 801-352-7145
E-mail: choiceskills@att.net
Web site: http://www.choiceskills.com.

Choo Choo Clan, *(0-9788670)* 1616 Brockton Ave., Apt. 104, Los Angeles, CA 90025 USA Tel 626-715-3342
E-mail: joey0724@hotmail.com
Web site: http://www.choochooclan.com.

Chooseco LLC, *(0-9745356; 1-933390)* Orders Addr.: P.O. Box 46, Waitsfield, VT 05673 USA (SAN 852-1131); P.O. Box 46, Waitsfield, VT 05673 USA (SAN 852-1158)
E-mail: jason@chooseco.com; gtroy@chooseco.com
Web site: http://www.cyoa.com; http://www.chooseco.com.

Choosing The Best Publishing, *(0-9724890)* 2625 Cumberland Pkwy., Suite 200, Atlanta, GA 30339 USA Tel 770-803-3100; Fax: 770-803-3110; Toll Free: 800-774-2378
E-mail: bcook@ctbpublishing.com; book@ctbpublishing.com
Web site: http://www.choosingthebest.org
Dist(s): **Independent Pubs. Group.**

Choristers Guild, *(1-929187)* 2834 W. Kingsley Rd., Garland, TX 75041-2498 USA (SAN 689-9188) Tel 972-271-1521; Fax: 972-840-3113
E-mail: choristers@choristersguild.org
Web site: http://www.choristersguild.org
Dist(s): **CRC Pubns.**
Lorenz Corp., The.

Chosen Bks., *(0-8007)* Div. of Baker Bk. Hse., Orders Addr.: P.O. Box 6287, Grand Rapids, MI 49516-6287 USA Toll Free Fax: 800-398-3111 (orders only); Toll Free: 800-877-2665 (orders only); Edit Addr.: 6030 E. Fulton, Ada, MI 49301 USA Tel 616-676-9185; Fax: 616-676-9573
E-mail: orders@bakerbooks.com; retail@bakerbooks.com
Web site: http://www.bakerbooks.com
Dist(s): **Baker Publishing Group**
CRC Pubns.

Chosen Collections, *(0-9679664)* 24 Kowal Ln., Westerlo, NY 12193-2428 USA
E-mail: choscollections@aol.com.

Chosen Word Publishing, *(0-9707536; 0-9748056; 0-9754779)* P.O. Box 481886, Charlotte, NC 28269 USA Tel 704-527-2177; Fax: 704-527-1677
E-mail: jeannette@chosenwordpublishing.com
Web site: http://www.chosenwordpublishing.com.

Chou-Chou Pr., *(0-9606140; 0-9716605; 0-9789152)* 26 Belvedere Ln., Bluffton, SC 29909 USA (SAN 220-2379)
E-mail: Chouchou@Hargray.com
Web site: http://www.bilingualkids.com.

Chouette Publishing (CAN) *(2-89450; 2-921198; 2-9800909) Dist. by* **IPG Chicago.**

Chouette Publishing (CAN) *(2-89450; 2-921198; 2-9800909) Dist. by* **Distribks Inc.**

Chouette Publishing (CAN) *(2-89450; 2-921198; 2-9800909) Dist. by* **Perseus Dist.**

Chris Paul USA, *(0-9715636)* 7802 S. James Rd., Tranquility, CA 93668 USA Tel 559-698-7647; Fax: 559-698-0012
E-mail: johnson1900@hotmail.com.

Christ Gospel Pr., *(1-58363)* Div. of Christ Gospel Churches International, Inc., Orders Addr.: P.O. Box 786, Jeffersonville, IN 47131 USA Tel 812-282-8458 ext 1320; Fax: 812-288-1570; Edit Addr.: 5900 Moser Knob Rd., Floyds Knobs, IN 47119 USA
E-mail: Printape@christgospel.org
Web site: http://www.christgospel.org.

Christ Inspired, Inc., *(1-4183)* 2263 Dicey Rd., Weatherford, TX 76085-3619 USA
Web site: http://www.christinspired.com.

Christ the Saviour Brotherhood Publishing, *(0-916700; 0-9678400)* P.O. Box 265, Ash Grove, MO 65604 USA (SAN 206-5037)
E-mail: magberry@att.net.

Christian Aid Ministries, *(1-885270)* Orders Addr.: P.O. Box 360, Berlin, OH 44610 USA Tel 330-893-2428; Fax: 330-893-2305; Edit Addr.: 4464 S.R. 39 E., Berlin, OH 44610 USA Tel 216-893-2428.

Christian Bible Studies, *(0-9763357)* P.O. Box 11155, Lansing, MI 48911 USA Tel 517-272-9076
E-mail: verseyawilliams@sbcglobal.net
Web site: http://www.christianstudies7.com.

Christian Bridge International *See* **Anderson House Foundation**

Christian Cottage Schls., *(0-9714671; 0-9768226)* 3560 W. Dawson Rd., Sedalia, CO 80135-8426 USA (SAN 254-8194) Tel 303-688-6626; Fax: 303-660-2015; Toll Free: 888-286-5494
E-mail: info@christiancottage.com
Web site: http://www.christiancottage.com.

Christian Crafters.com *See* **Bible-4-Life.com**

Christian Education Resources, *(1-933479)* P.O. Box 320099, Cocoa Beach, FL 32932 USA.

Christian Focus Pubns. (GBR) *(0-906731; 1-85792; 1-871676; 1-84550) Dist. by* **Spring Arbor Dist.**

Christian Focus Pubns. (GBR) *(0-906731; 1-85792; 1-871676; 1-84550) Dist. by* **STL Dist NA.**

Christian, Harvey Pubs. Inc., *(1-932774)* 3107 Hwy. 321, Hampton, TN 37658 USA Tel 423-768-2297
E-mail: books@harveycp.com
Web site: http://www.harveycp.com.

Christian History Institute, *(1-56364)* P.O. Box 540, Worcester, PA 19490 USA Tel 610-584-3500; Fax: 610-584-4610; Toll Free: 800-523-0226
E-mail: chglimpses@aol.com
Web site: http://www.chinstitute.org
Dist(s): **Spring Arbor Distributors, Inc.**
Vision Video.

Christian Liberty Pr., *(1-930092; 1-930367; 1-932971)* Div. of Church of Christian Liberty, 502 W. Euclid Ave., Arlington Heights, IL 60004 USA
E-mail: clplinak@starnetwx.net; ed.clp@db3mail.com; lina.clp@db3mail.com
Web site: http://www.christianlibertypress.com.

Christian Life Bks., *(0-9646289; 1-931393)* Subs. of River Revival Ministries, Inc., Orders Addr.: P.O. Box 36355, Pensacola, FL 32516-6355 USA Tel 850-457-7057; Fax: 850-458-9339
E-mail: riverofrevival@sofnet.com
Web site: http://www.rrmi.org.

Christian Life Workshops *See* **Noble Publishing Assocs.**

Christian Light Pubns., Inc., *(0-87813)* 1066 Chicago Ave., Harrisonburg, VA 22802 USA (SAN 206-7315) Tel 540-434-0768; Fax: 540-433-8896
E-mail: johnh@clp.org.

Christian Living Bks. *Imprint of* **Pneuma Life Publishing, Inc.**

Christian Logic, *(0-9745315)* PMB 168, 429 Lake Park Blvd., Muscatine, IA 52761 USA Tel 309-537-3641
E-mail: hans@christianlogic.com
Web site: http://www.christianlogic.com.

Christian Novel Studies, *(0-9707712)* 5208 E. Lake Rd., Saginaw, MN 55779 USA Tel 218-729-9733; Fax: 509-271-8614
E-mail: cnsroe@aol.com; chsroe@aol.com
Web site: http://www.christiannovelstudies.homestead.com.

Christian Publishing Services, Incorporated *See* **Victory Graphics & Media**

Christian Scholar's Pr., *(1-931230)* 1350 E. Flamingo Rd., Suite 97, Las Vegas, NV 89119-5263 USA Fax: 714-221-2108; Toll Free: 800-418-7842 (800-41-TRUTH) ; *Imprints:* Crescent Moon Publications (Crescent Moon)
E-mail: christianscholarspress@hotmail.com
Dist(s): **STL Distribution North America.**

Christian Science Publishing Society, The *See* **Eddy, The Writings of Mary Baker**

Christian Services Publishing, *(1-879854)* Div. of Christian Services Network, 1959 Longs Hill Rd., El Cajon, CA 92021 USA Tel 619-444-0695; Fax: 619-579-0685; Toll Free: 800-636-7276 Do not confuse with Christian Services, Damascus, MD.

Christian Sky, *(0-9762402)* 505 Cherry Dr., Souderton, PA 18964-1015 USA Tel 215-799-0641
Web site: http://www.christiansky.com.

Christian Visionary Communications, *(0-9746867)* P.O. Box 63, Sharon Center, OH 44274-0063 USA
E-mail: lorshir3@verizon.net
Web site: http://www.christianary.org.

Christian Visual Arts of California, *(0-9766584)* 64969 Pine St., Hume, CA 93628-9619 USA Tel 559-335-2797; Fax: 559-335-2107
E-mail: dajohnson@spiralcomm.net.

Christian Voice Publishing, A, *(0-9776747; 0-9786580; 1-934327)* 2031 W. Superior St. Ste. 1, Duluth, MN 55806-2036 USA.

Christiangela Productions, *(0-9720773)* 1955 Arapahoe St. Apt. 1610, Denver, CO 80202-1837 USA
E-mail: sandaij@hotmail.com.

Christine, Yates, *(0-9741210)* 13165 Oak Farm Dr., Woodbridge, VA 22192 USA
Web site: http://www.freekidcrafts.com.

Christine's Closet, *(0-9713405)* 10300 Grand Oak Dr., Austin, TX 78750 USA Tel 512-918-9255; Fax: 512-873-9818; Toll Free: 800-591-1165
E-mail: chrissy@chrissy.com
Web site: http://www.chrissy.com.

Christmas City Distribution, Inc., *(0-9723225)* PMB 352-1041, Honey Creek Rd., Conyers, GA 30013 USA Tel 770-679-0990 Toll Free: 866-786-4241
E-mail: info@santastories.biz
Web site: http://www.santastories.biz.

Christmas Classics Ltd., *(0-615)* Orders Addr.: P.O. Box 1184, North Cape May, NJ 08204 USA Tel 609-886-6540; Edit Addr.: 1626 Jennings Ave., Villas, NJ 08251 USA
E-mail: clancyrm@verizon.net
Web site: http://www.christmasclassics.com.

Christmas Organizing *See* **C.O. Publishing**

Christobe Publishing, *(0-9664973)* Orders Addr.: P.O. Box 1320, Mount Shasta, CA 96067 USA Tel 530-926-8855; Fax: 530-926-8866.

Christopher Lee Pubns., Inc., *(1-878383)* Orders Addr.: P.O. Box 6202, South Bend, IN 46660 USA Tel 219-277-3100; Fax: 219-271-0636; Toll Free: 800-822-6202; Edit Addr.: P.O. Box 1925, Johns Island, SC 29457-1925 USA
E-mail: clp@qtm.net.

Christopher Winkle Products *See* **First Stage Concepts**

Christopher-Gordon Pubs., Inc., *(0-926842; 1-929024; 1-933585; 1-933760)* 1502 Providence Hwy., Suite 12, Norwood, MA 02062-4643 USA Tel 781-762-5577; Fax: 781-762-7261; Toll Free: 800-934-8322
E-mail: cgpublish@aol.com
Web site: http://www.christopher-gordon.com.

†**Chronicle Bks. LLC,** *(0-8118; 0-87701; 0-938491; 1-58717)* Orders Addr.: 680 Second St., San Francisco, CA 94107 USA (SAN 202-165X) Tel 415-537-4200; Fax: 415-537-4460; Toll Free Fax: 800-858-7787; Toll Free: 800-722-6657 (orders only) ; *Imprints:* SeaStar Books (SeaStar Chronic)
E-mail: orders@chroniclebooks.com
Web site: http://www.chroniclebooks.com; *CIP.*

Chronicle Guidance Pubns., Inc., *(0-912578; 1-55631)* Orders Addr.: 66 Aurora St., Moravia, NY 13118-3569 USA Tel 315-497-0330; 315-497-3359; Toll Free: 800-622-7284
E-mail: CustomerService@ChronicleGuidance.com
Web site: http://www.chronicleguidance.com.

Chronos Press *See* **WingSpan Publishing**

Chrysalis Books *See* **Two Canoes Pr.**

Chrysalis Children's Bks. (GBR) *(1-85602; 1-903174; 1-903370; 1-903954; 1-84347; 1-84365; 1-904516) Dist. by* **Trafalgar.**

Chrysalis Education, *(1-929298; 1-930643; 1-931983; 1-932333; 1-59389)* Div. of Creative Company, The, 1980 Lookout Dr., North Mankato, MN 56003 USA Tel 507-388-6273; Fax: 507-388-2746; Toll Free: 800-445-6209
E-mail: schlichted@aol.com
Dist(s): **Creative Co., The**
Smart Apple Media.

Chrysalis Pr., *(0-9795933)* Orders Addr.: P.O. Box 13129, Newport Beach, CA 92658 USA (SAN 853-8514)
E-mail: amber@chrysalispress.com
Web site: http://www.Chrysalispress.com.

Chubasco Publishing Co., *(0-9640858)* Orders Addr.: P.O. Box 697, Cardiff, CA 92007 USA; Edit Addr.: 2387 Montgomery, Cardiff, CA 92007 USA Tel 760-753-4469.

Chucklebks. Publishing, *(0-9702730)* 27 Brown St., Andover, MA 01810 USA Tel 978-749-0674
E-mail: jeff@chucklebooks.com
Web site: http://www.chucklebooks.com; http://www.incredibleassemblies.com
Dist(s): **Baker & Taylor Bks.**
Partners Bk. Distributing, Inc.

Chung, Jo Anne *See* **Vision Unlimited Pr.**

†Church & Synagogue Library Assn., Inc., *(0-915324)* P.O. Box 19357, Portland, OR 97280-0357 USA (SAN 210-7872) Tel 503-244-6919; Fax: 503-977-3734; Toll Free: 800-542-2752
E-mail: csla@worldaccessnet.com
Web site: http://www.worldaccessnet.com/~csla; *CIP.*

Church Growth Institute, *(0-941005; 1-57052)* Div. of Ephesians Four Ministries, Orders Addr.: P.O. Box 9176, Oxnard, CA 93031 USA Fax: 805-644-4729; Toll Free: 800-553-4769; Edit Addr.: P.O. Box 7, Elkton, MD 21922-0007 USA Tel 434-525-0022; Fax: 434-525-0608
E-mail: cgimail@churchgrowth.org
Web site: http://www.churchgrowth.org
Dist(s): **Spring Arbor Distributors, Inc.**

Church Hse. Pubng. (GBR) *(0-7151) Dist. by* **Church Pub Inc.**

Church Hymnal Corporation *See* **Church Publishing, Historical Inc.**

Church of Jesus Christ of Latter Day Saints, Historical Dept., *(0-931300; 1-59297)* 50 E. North Temple., 25th Flr., Salt Lake City, UT 84150-3210 USA (SAN 220-469X)
Web site: http://www.lds.org.

Church Publishing, Inc., *(0-89869; 1-59627; 1-59628)* 445 Fifth Ave., New York, NY 10016-0109 USA Tel 212-592-1800; Fax: 212-779-3392; Toll Free: 800-242-1918
E-mail: churchpublishing@cpg.org
Web site: http://www.churchpublishing.org.

Church Without Walls Pubns., Inc., *(0-9755927)* P.O. Box 1473, LILBURN, GA 30047 USA
E-mail: segunmasha@yahoo.com.

Chuse, Patricia Jepsen, *(0-9667560)* Orders Addr.: P.O. Box 8830, Tucson, AZ 85738 USA Tel 520-825-7426; Fax: 520-825-7425
E-mail: patriciajepsen@earthlink.net
Web site: http://www.patriciajepsen.com
Dist(s): **DeVorss & Co.**
New Leaf Distributing Co., Inc.

Chuttani, Kabir, *(0-9749364)* 8 Nameloc Rd., Plymouth, MA 02360-1418 USA.

CicadaSun, *(0-9779808)* P.O. Box 90834, Austin, TX 78709-0834 USA
E-mail: service@cicadasun.com
Web site: http://www.cicadasun.com.

Cichlid Pr., *(0-9668255; 1-932892)* 417 Valplano Dr., El Paso, TX 79912-2706 USA Tel 915-845-1476; Fax: 915-585-1454
E-mail: infonbook@cichlidpress.com
Web site: http://www.cichlidpress.com.

Cideb (ITA) *(88-7754; 88-530) Dist. by* **Distribks Inc.**

Cider Mill Pr. Bk. Pubs. LLC, *(1-933662; 1-60433)* 12 Port Farm Rd., Kennebunkport, ME 04046 USA (SAN 257-1927) Tel 207-967-8232 ; Fax: 207-967-8233
E-mail: johnwhalen@cidermillpress.com
Web site: http://www.cidermillpress.com
Dist(s): **Sterling Publishing Co., Inc.**

Cidermill Bks., *(0-9748483)* P.O. Box 32250, San Jose, CA 95152-2250 USA
E-mail: info@cidermillbooks.com
Web site: http://www.cidermillbooks.com.

Cimino Publishing Group, *(1-878427)* P.O. Box 174, Carle Place, NY 11514 USA (SAN 630-3722) Tel 516-997-3721; Fax: 516-997-3420
E-mail: cimpub@juno.com
Dist(s): **CPG Publishing, Inc.**

Cincinnati Museum Ctr., The, *(0-911497; 1-882151)* 1301 Western Ave., Cincinnati, OH 45203 USA Tel 513-287-7000; Fax: 513-287-7029; Toll Free: 800-733-2077.

Cinco Puntos Pr., *(0 938317; 1-933693)* 701 Texas Ave., El Paso, TX 79901 USA (SAN 661-0080) Tel 915-838-1625; Fax: 915-838-1635; Toll Free: 800-566-9072
E-mail: leebyrd@cincopuntos.com
Web site: http://www.cincopuntos.com
Dist(s): **Consortium Bk. Sales & Distribution**
SPD-Small Pr. Distribution.

CineBook (GBR) *(1-905460) Dist. by* **Biblio Dist.**

Cinnamon Bay Entertainment Group, *(0-9727116)* 1300 W. Menlo Ave. SPC 113, Hemet, CA 92543-3779 USA
E-mail: rwdan@earthlink.net
Web site: http://www.delaneysrevenge.com.

Cipriani, Nicholas J., *(0-9653570)* 159-44 85th St., Howard Beach, NY 11414 USA Tel 718-848-4622; Fax: 718-962-1127; Toll Free: 800-464-6873
E-mail: nickc@inhouseinc.com.

Circelli, Kristina, *(0-9763728)* 854 Bobcat Trail, Port Orange, FL 32129 USA
Web site: http://www.geocities.com/helpinghands_2004.

Circle Journey, Ltd., *(0-9741104)* 22 East Gay St., Suite 801, Columbus, OH 43215 USA Fax: 614-564-7795; Toll Free: 877-247-2534
E-mail: connections@circlejourney.com
Web site: http://www.circlejourney.com.

Circle of Love Music *See* **Growing Up Great Productions**

Circle Pr., *(0-9651601; 0-9743661; 1-933271)* Circle Media, Inc., Orders Addr.: 33 Rossotto Dr., Hamden, CT 06514 USA Tel 203-230-3805; Fax: 203-230-3838; Toll Free: 888-881-0729; Edit Addr.: 432 Washington Ave., North Haven, CT 06473 USA Do not confuse with companies with the same name in Huntington Beach, CA, New York, NY, Itasca, IL
E-mail: victor@catholicformation.com.

Circumpolar Pr., *(1-878051)* Subs. of Wizard Works, P.O. Box 1125, Homer, AK 99603 USA Tel 907-235-8757 (phone/fax); Toll Free: 877-210-2665
E-mail: wizard@xyz.net
Web site: http://www.xyz.net/~wizard.

Cirrus Publishing, LLC, *(0-9755678)* Orders Addr.: P.O. Box 291724, Davie, FL 33329-1724 USA Fax: 954-965-2643
E-mail: cirruspublish@aol.com
Web site: http://www.yessy.com/wildImages.

Citadel Entertainment Group, *(0-9701849)* 1128 Mission St., South Pasadena, CA 91030 USA Tel 626-799-8334; Fax: 626-799-3976
E-mail: flora@citadelcapital.com
Web site: http://www.holidaymiracle.com.

Citadel Pr. *Imprint of* **Kensington Publishing Corp.**

Citapei Communications, Inc., *(0-9654604; 1-931111)* 2782 Marshall Lake Dr., Oakton, VA 22124-1148 USA Toll Free: 800-937-5571
E-mail: books@citapei.com
Web site: http://www.citapei.com.

Citizens Publishing, *(0-9755597)* 17636 W. Neuberry Ridge Dr., Lockport, IL 60441 USA
Web site: http://www.citizenspublishing.com.

Citlembik Pubns. (TUR) *(975-6663) Dist. by* **Biblio Dist.**

Cito/Birmingham, *(0-9677390)* 1424 Hamilton St., NW., Washington, DC 20011 USA Tel 202-882-3883 (phone/fax)
E-mail: bridBr@aol.com.

Citron Bay Pr., *(1-928595)* 77 Windstone Dr., San Rafael, CA 94903 USA (SAN 253-0260) Tel 415-472-1208
E-mail: publisher@citronbay.com; wakanpress@citronbay.com
Web site: http://www.citronbay.com; http://www.ruminator.com.

City Creek Pr., Inc., *(1-883841)* P.O. Box 8415, Minneapolis, MN 55408-0415 USA
E-mail: orders@citycreek.com
Web site: http://www.citycreek.com.

City of Chicago, Dept. of Cultural Affairs, *(0-938903)* 78 E. Washington St., Chicago, IL 60602 USA (SAN 661-8340) Tel 312-744-1424; Fax: 312-744-2089
E-mail: culture@cityofchicago.org
Web site: http://egov.cityofchicago.org.

City of Elmhurst, *(0-9708003)* 209 N. York St., Elmhurst, IL 60126 USA Tel 630-530-3000; Fax: 630-530-3014
E-mail: nancy.wilson@elmhurst.org
Web site: http://www.elmhurst.org.

City of God, St. Joseph's Hill of Hope, *(1-892957)* Orders Addr.: P.O. Box 1055, Brea, CA 92822 USA Tel 714-528-6962; Fax: 714-528-0707; Edit Addr.: 7351 Carbon Canyon Rd., Brea, CA 92823 USA
E-mail: mail@themiracleofstjoseph.org
Web site: http://www.themiralceofstjoseph.org.

City of Manassas Department of Social Services, *(0-9747385)* 8955 Center St., Manassas, VA 20110 USA Tel 703-361-8277.

City on a Hill, Inc., *(0-9779521)* 4085 Hancock Bridge Pkwy., Suite 111-269, North Fort Myers, FL 33903 USA Tel 614-488-6953
E-mail: info@cityonahillinc.org
Web site: http://www.cityonahillinc.org.

City Salvage Records, *(0-9713865)* 195 St. Marks Ave., No. 4, Brooklyn, NY 11238 USA Tel 718-857-6822
E-mail: andy@citysalvagerecords.com
Web site: http://citysalvagerecords.com.

CityWeb Corp., *(0-9719803)* P.O. Box 702216, Tulsa, OK 74170-2216 USA Tel 918-369-0544
E-mail: citywebcorporation@acken.com
Web site: http://www.citywebbooks.com.

CK Bks., *(0-9797580)* 395A S. Hwy. 65, No. 324, Lincoln, CA 95648 USA.

CKE Pubns., *(0-935133; 1-932327)* Div. of Carolyn Kyle Enterprises, Orders Addr.: P.O. Box 12869, Olympia, WA 98508-2869 USA (SAN 695-197X) Toll Free: 800-428-7402; Edit Addr.: P.O. Box 12869, Olympia, WA 98508-2869 USA
E-mail: ckepubs@aol.com
Web site: http://www.ckepublications.com.

CLADACH Publishing, *(0-9670386; 0-9759619)* P.O. Box 336144, Greeley, CO 80633 USA Tel 970-371-9530
E-mail: books@cladach.com
Web site: http://www.cladach.com
Dist(s): **Baker & Taylor Bks.**
Spring Arbor Distributors, Inc.

Claire Pubns. (GBR) *(1-871098; 1-904572) Dist. by* **Parkwest Pubns.**

Clairmont Pr., Inc., *(0-9623319; 1-56733)* Orders Addr.: P.O. Box 11743, Montgomery, AL 36111 USA Tel 334-874-8638; Edit Addr.: Rte. 2, Box 191, Selma, AL 36701 USA.

Clapper Publishing Co., *(0-930184)* Div. of Clapper Publishing Co., Inc., 2400 E. Devon, Suite 375, Des Plaines, IL 60018 USA (SAN 210-7104) Tel 847-635-5800; Fax: 847-635-6311 ; *Imprints:* Pack-O-Fun, Incorporated (Pack-O-Fun Inc).

Clarion Bks. *Imprint of* **Houghton Mifflin Co. Trade & Reference Div.**

Clarion Marketing Group, Inc., *(1-931317)* P.O. Box 1032, Lee's Summit, MO 64063 USA Tel 816-554-7772; Fax: 816-554-7297; Toll Free: 888-353-4668
E-mail: clarion@primary.net.

Clarity of Vision Writing & Design, *(0-9716712)* 3529 NE Simpson St., Portland, OR 97211 USA Tel 503-460-0014
E-mail: marilyn@clarityofvision.com
Web site: http://www.clarityofvision.com.

Clark, Arthur H. Co., The *Imprint of* **Univ. of Oklahoma Pr.**

Clark Bks., *(0-615; 0-9741677)* 599 Shapleigh Corner Rd., Shapleigh, ME 04076 USA (SAN 630-2017) Tel 207-636-1769 Do not confuse with Clark Books in Baton Rouge, LA
E-mail: clarkbooks@metrocast.net
Web site: http://www.clarkbooksmaine.com
Dist(s): **Baker & Taylor Bks.**

Clark, I. E. Pubns., *(0-88680)* P.O. Box 246, Schulenburg, TX 78956-0246 USA (SAN 282-7433) Tel 979-743-3232; Fax: 979-743-4765
E-mail: ieclark@cvtv.net
Web site: http://www.ieclark.com.

Clark, Jo Ann, *(0-9715835)* 2017 Lexington Ave., Owensboro, KY 42301-4688 USA Tel 270-691-6196; Fax: 509-351-0830
E-mail: jaashclark@aol.com.

Clark, Kenneth L., *(0-9720043)* 2301 Jerome Ln., Cahokia, IL 62206 USA.

Clark, Lance Publishing, *(0-9707491)* 17130 SE Naegeli Dr., No. 1, Portland, OR 97236 USA Tel 503-665-3854
E-mail: lclarkc@hotmail.com.

Clark, N. Laurie *See* **Clark Pubs.**

Clark Productions Ltd. Inc., *(0-9777289)* P.O. Box 583, Little Rock, AR 72203 USA Tel 501-280-9424
E-mail: ouida-clark56@yahoo.com.

Clark Pubs., *(0-9641197)* 133 Chestnut St., Amherst, MA 01002 USA Tel 413-549-0575; 941-255-0431
E-mail: ellusmith@aol.com
Dist(s): **Baker & Taylor Bks.**
Brodart Co.
North Country Bks., Inc.
Quality Bks., Inc.

Clark Publishing, Inc., *(0-931054)* P.O. Box 19240, Topeka, KS 66619-0240 USA Tel 785-862-0218; Fax: 785-862-8224; Toll Free: 800-845-1916 Do not confuse with companies with same or similar names in Tacoma, WA, Lexington, KY, Annapolis, MD
E-mail: custservice@clarkpub.com; clarkpub@clarkpub.com
Web site: http://www.clarkpub.com.

Clash Ministries, *(0-9667501)* P.O. Box 800554, Aventura, FL 33180 USA Tel 305-937-3774 (phone/fax)
E-mail: doug@clashradio.com
Web site: http://www.pitbullattitude.com.

Classic Bks., *(1-58201; 0-7426)* Orders Addr.: P.O. Box 130, Murrieta, CA 92564-0130 USA Tel 888-265-3547; Fax: 888-265-3550.

Classic Textbooks, *(1-4047)* Div of Classic Books, Orders Addr.: P.O. Box 130, Murrieta, CA 92564-0130 USA Tel 800-273-6635; Toll Free Fax: 888-265-3550; Edit Addr.: 26111 Ynez B14, Temecula, CA 92591 USA
E-mail: 4classic@gte.net.

Classical Academic Pr., *(1-60051)* 3920 Market St. Ste. 10, Camp Hill, PA 17011-4202 USA
Web site: http://www.classicalacademicpress.com.

Classical Connections, *(1-928908)* 1007 Larchmont Ave., Havertown, PA 19083 USA Tel 610-853-2130; Fax: 610-446-3467; Toll Free: 888-595-6511
E-mail: pdh50@aol.com.

Classical Home Education *See* **Pandia Pr.**

Classical Learning Universe, LLC, *(0-9721733; 0-9763376; 0-9793021)* 305 W. Broadway, Suite 184, New York, NY 10013 USA Tel 718-357-2431; Fax: 718-357-2432; Toll Free: 888-684-5922
E-mail: lindsay@classicallearning.com
Web site: http://www.classicallearning.com.

Classical Magic, Inc., *(0-9675997; 0-9794947)* P.O. Box 1809, Banner Elk, NC 28604 USA Tel 828-898-7764 (phone/fax); 828-898-9571
E-mail: comapers@skybest.com
Web site: http://www.classicalmagic.net
Dist(s): **Book Clearing Hse.**

Classics International Entertainment, Inc., *(1-57209)* 324 Main Ave., Suite 183, Norwalk, CT 06851 USA Tel 203-849-8977; Fax: 203-847-5746.

Classroom Enrichment Assocs., *(0-9748081)* P.O. Box 4023, Diamond Bar, CA 91765-0023 USA Tel 909-861-4837
E-mail: www.offleyharbahinc@cs.com.

Claudia Drumheller-Tomkiel & Julie Drumheller-Bushinski, *(0-9722959)* 644 Yorkshire Dr., Carlisle, PA 17013 USA
E-mail: twocrazedsisters@pa.net
Web site: http://www.twocrazedsisters.com.

Clawfoot Publishing, *(0-9747881)* 1236 S. Pekin Rd., Woodland, WA 98674 USA Tel 360-901-9932; Fax: 360-225-1311
E-mail: bobsbooks@zerfing.com
Web site: http://www.zerfing.com/bobsbooks.

†Claymont Communications, *(0-934254)* R.R. 1, Box 279, Charles Town, WV 25414-9765 USA (SAN 211-7010); *CIP.*

Clayro Corp., *(0-9709523)* P.O. Box 270605, Oklahoma City, OK 73137-0605 USA Tel 405-373-2347; Fax: 405-373-0923
E-mail: waderoddy@yahoo.com
Web site: http://tcpublishers.com.

Claystone Bks. *Imprint of* **Ingalls Publishing Group, Inc**

Clayton, Mike, *(0-9772622)* 639 Howard Rd., West Point, NY 10996-1510 USA
Web site: http://www.session6wrestling.com.

Clear Braces L.L.C., *(0-9790682)* 1530 Palisade Ave., Fort Lee, NJ 07024 USA Tel 201-947-6453
E-mail: drjfortlee@aol.com
Web site: http://www.pediatric-dentistry.com.

Clear Creek Pubs., *(0-9653543)* Orders Addr.: 115 Clear Creek Ct., Fayetteville, GA 30215 USA Tel 770-461-9460
E-mail: patcruzan@aol.com.

Clear Light Pubs., *(0-940666; 1-57416)* 823 Don Diego, Santa Fe, NM 87501 USA (SAN 219-7758) Tel 505-989-9590; Fax: 505-989-9519; Toll Free: 800-253-2747 Do not confuse with Clear Light Pub., Seattle, WA
E-mail: service@clearlightbooks.com
Web site: http://www.clearlightbooks.com.

Clear Water Pr., *(0-9742972)* 1909 S. Stagecoach Dr., Olathe, KS 66062 USA Do not confuse with Clear Water Press in Reno, NV
E-mail: editor@clearwaterpress.com
Web site: http://www.clearwaterpress.com
Dist(s): **STL Distribution North America.**

Clearbridge Publishing, *(1-929194)* Orders Addr.: P.O. Box 33772, Seattle, WA 98133 USA Tel 206-533-9357; Fax: 206-546-9756 ; *Imprints:* Art of War Plus Books (Art War Plus)
E-mail: garyg@clearbridge.com
Web site: http://www.clearbridge.com; http://www.booksonstrategy.com
Dist(s): **National Bk. Network.**

Clearing Skies Pr., *(0-9707937)* 4002 Dunbarton Way, Roswell, GA 30075 USA Tel 770-518-8931; Fax: 770-518-6278
E-mail: Walter@clearingskies.com
Web site: http://clearingskies.com
Dist(s): **Independent Pubs. Group.**

Clearwater Publishing, *(0-9769465)* 4300 NW 23rd Ave. Ate. 233, Gainesville, FL 32605 USA Toll Free: 866-766-5103.

Clearwater Publishing Co., Inc., *(0-9627815)* P.O. Box 778, Broomfield, CO 80038-0778 USA (SAN 297-3383) Fax: 917-386-2769
E-mail: wordguise@aol.com
Web site: http://www.clearwaterpublishing.com
Dist(s): **Brodart Co.**
Follett Library Resources
Mountain Bk. Co.
NACSCORP, Inc.
Nasco Math Eighty-Six.

Clearwood Pubs., *(0-9649997)* P.O. Box 52, Bella Vista, CA 96008 USA Tel 530-549-4129; Fax: 530-549-4598
E-mail: clrwood@c-zone.net.

Clem Publishing, *(0-9772225)* P.O. Box 246, Danvers, IL 61732 USA Tel 309-530-0710; 116 W. North St., Danvers, IL 61732
E-mail: josephclem@hotmail.com.

Clements, J. S. Corporation *See* **Clements, Jehan**

Clements, Jehan, *(0-9622500)* Orders Addr.: P.O. Box 543, Tarrytown, NY 10591 USA Tel 914-293-7884
E-mail: storyteller1@optonline.net
Web site: http://www.flipoverpicturebooks.com.

Cleo Cat Bks., *(0-9719483)* 3308 Oak Vista Dr., Port Orange, FL 32128 USA Tel 386-322-2260; Fax: 386-322-2260
E-mail: Cleocatbooks@mail.com
Web site: http://www.cleocatbooks.com.

Cleocat Books *See* **Cleo Cat Bks.**

Cleveland Clinic Pr., *(1-59624)* c/o Lawrence D. Chilnick, 9500 Euclid Ave., NA32, Cleveland, OH 44195 USA Tel 216-444-1158; Fax: 216-444-9385
E-mail: chilnil@ccf.org
Web site: http://www.clevelandclinicpress.org.

Cleveland, Shirley D., *(0-9671225)* 3121 Onyx Ct., Orlando, FL 32806 USA.

Cleveland Stock Images, *(0-9617637)* Two Bratenahl Pl., Suite 9 EF, Cleveland, OH 44108 USA (SAN 664-8533) Tel 216-681-5621; Fax: 216-249-5828
E-mail: jsjidc@aol.com.

Clevenger, Roy L., *(0-9720089)* 5208 Dee Alva Dr., Fairfield, OH 45014 USA Tel 513-863-1392
E-mail: rclevenger@cinci.rr.com.

Clever Concepts Publishing *See* **S.A.F.E. for Children Publishing, LLC**

Clever Factory, The, *(1-59277)* 545 Mainstream Dr., Suite 406, Nashville, TN 37228 USA.

Clever Hands Publishing, *(0-9651273; 1-892003)* Orders Addr.: P.O. Box 81224, Wellesley Hills, MA 02181 USA Tel 781-235-5856; Fax: 781-235-6263; Toll Free: 800-876-5223; Edit Addr.: 233 Glen Rd., Weston, MA 02193 USA
E-mail: phyllis@cleverhands.com
Web site: http://www.cleverhands.com.

Cleverley Created, Ltd., *(0-9675664)* 6368 Youngland Dr., Columbus, OH 43228 USA Tel 614-764-6255
E-mail: meredith_dean@oclc.org.

Client Distribution Services *See* **Perseus Distribution**

Cliff Notes *Imprint of* **Wiley, John & Sons, Inc.**

Cliffhanger *Imprint of* **DC Comics**

Clifton-Bennett Group, LLC, *(0-9700511)* 14050 Compton Heights Ct., Clifton, VA 20124-2610 USA Tel 703-502-0040; Fax: 703-815-8324; Toll Free: 888-848-0040
E-mail: dmetcalf@cbgpress.com
Web site: http://www.cbgpress.com.

Clo Iar-Chonnachta Teo (IRL) *(1-874700; 1-900693; 1-902420; 1-905560) Dist. by* **Dufour.**

ClockTower Pubns., *(0-9704280)* 203 Skyland Dr., Dept. I, Staunton, VA 24401-2358 USA Tel 540-885-6614
E-mail: trgww@ntelos.net.

CLOJ Publishing, *(0-9767711)* P.O. Box 1140, Venice, CA 90294-1140 USA (SAN 256-5129) Tel 310-869-5923
E-mail: publisher@clojpublishing.com
Web site: http://www.clojpublishing.com.

Cloonfad Pr., *(0-9744744; 0-9769404; 0-9797772)* Orders Addr.: P.O. Box 106, Cassville, NJ 08527 USA Tel 732-833-9800 (phone/fax)
E-mail: cloonfad@optonline.net
Web site: http://www.cloonfadpress.com
Dist(s): **Wilson & Assocs.**

Close Up Foundation, *(0-932765; 1-930810)* 44 Canal Ctr. Plaza, Alexandria, VA 22314 USA (SAN 679-1980) Tel 703-706-3559; Fax: 703-706-3564; Toll Free: 800-765-3131 (ext. 559)
E-mail: hoye@closeup.org
Web site: http://www.closeup.org/pubs.htm.

Closer Looks Bks., *(0-9763593)* 864 Horns Corners Rd., Cedarburg, WI 53012 USA
E-mail: sggk@wi.rr.com
Web site: http://home.wi.rr.com/acloserlookbooks.

Cloud 9 Ranch, *(0-9767690)* 231 Jung Blvd., E, Naples, FL 34120 USA Tel 239-353-6877; Fax: 239-353-7579
E-mail: nsfcloud9@aol.com
Web site: http://www.cloud9ranch.info.

Cloud Mountain Publishing *See* **Easter Island Foundation**

Cloud 9 Publishing, L L C, *(0-9710394)* 9545 Katy Freeway, Suite 350, Houston, TX 77024 USA Tel 713-722-8277; Fax: 713-722-0238 Do not confuse with companies with the same or similar name in Lincolnwood, IL, Highland, UT
E-mail: jdalton@zabbit.com; wdspies@zabbit.com.

Cloud Publishing, *(0-911981)* Div. of Cloud Assoc., Inc., P.O. Box 39016, Phoenix, AZ 85069 USA (SAN 264-6595) Tel 602-866-7820; Fax: 602-942-0557
E-mail: cloudassociates@aol.com.

Cloudland.net Publishing, *(1-882906)* Orders Addr.: HC 33, Box 50-A, Pettigrew, AR 72752-9501 USA Tel 870-861-5536; Fax: 870-861-5736; Toll Free: 800-838-4453
E-mail: tim@timernst.com
Web site: http://www.CLOUDLAND.NET.

Cloudmaker Entertainment, *(0-9743989)* 7654 195th Ave. Ct. E., Bonney Lake, WA 98390 USA Tel 253-862-1490 (phone/fax)
E-mail: trox@cloudmakerentertainment.com
Web site: http://www.cloudmakerentertainment.com.

Cloudstone, *(1-879846)* 10 Patchin Pl., New York, NY 10011 USA Tel 212-929-6871.

Cloudwalker Publications *See* **Working Title Publishing**

Clouse Publishing, *(0-9667555)* P.O. Box 32, Library, PA 15129 USA Fax: 412-831-7445
E-mail: clousepublishing@iol17.com.

Clove Pubns., *(1-889191)* 60 Falcon Hills Dr., Littleton, CO 80162 USA
E-mail: clovepublication@aol.com; sales@justinmatott.com
Dist(s): **Baker & Taylor Bks.**

Clover Pubns., *(0-9666581)* P.O. Box 28243, Fresno, CA 93729-8243 USA Tel 559-434-9359; Fax: 559-434-7751 Do not confuse with Clover Publications in Hamden, CT
E-mail: wwnugent@msn.com; julort@aol.com
Dist(s): **Sunbelt Pubns., Inc.**

Clover Pubns., *(0-9720243)* 31 Eaton Woods Rd., Hamden, CT 06518 USA Do not confuse with Clover Publications in Fresno, CA
E-mail: julort@aol.com.

Clown Ambassador of Health, The *See* **Clown of Natural Health**

Clown of Natural Health, *(0-9648663)* 3131 Palo Verde Ave., Long Beach, CA 90808-4056 USA Tel 562-377-1141
E-mail: holitte5353@aol.com.

Club Pro Products, *(0-9725721)* 153 Raquet Club Dr., Rancho Mirage, CA 92270 USA
E-mail: info@robstanger.com
Web site: http://www.robstanger.com.

ClueSearchPuzzles.com, *(0-9753879)* 7645 N. Union Blvd. #175, Colorado Springs, CO 80920-3863 USA Tel 719-659-9034
E-mail: books@cluesearchpuzzles.com
Web site: http://www.cluesearchpuzzles.com.

CMB Publishing Co., *(0-9722969)* 24 Appleton St., Suite 1, Boston, MA 02116 USA Tel 617-306-5581; Fax: 617-451-0168
E-mail: info@cmbpublishing.com
Web site: http://www.cmbpublishing.com/.

CMS Enterprises, *(0-9768170)* Orders Addr.: P.O. Box 8039, Van Nuys, CA 91409 USA (SAN 256-5226); Edit Addr.: 6429 Whitman Ave., Van Nuys, CA 91406 USA
E-mail: cms55@hotmail.com.

CMX *Imprint of* **DC Comics**

CNL PUBLISHING, *(0-9766921)* 105 Wedgewood Dr., Fairfield, AL 35064 USA Tel 205-835-5444; Fax: 205-923-3218.

C.O. Publishing, *(0-9715956)* Div. of Christmas Organizing, 20 Rebel Cove, Jackson, TN 37301 USA Tel 731-988-9946; Fax: 731-935-7497
E-mail: publishing@christmasorganizing.com
Web site: http://www.christmasorganizing.com.

Coach Enterprises, *(0-9636706)* 616 Munntown Rd., Finleyville, PA 15332 USA Tel 724-348-4843; Fax: 724-348-5549.

Coaches Choice, *(1-57167; 1-58518)* P.O. Box 1828, Monterey, CA 93942 USA Tel 831-393-0298; Fax: 831-372-6075
E-mail: info@coacheschoice.com
Web site: http://www.coacheschoice.com; http://www.healthylearning.com
Dist(s): **Partners Bk. Distributing, Inc.**

Coal Hole Productions, *(0-9709630)* 207 Hemlock Ln., Bloomsburg, PA 17815 USA Tel 570-784-4561
E-mail: ceo@coalhole.com
Web site: http://www.coalhole.com
Dist(s): **Partners Bk. Distributing, Inc.**

Coastal Carolina Pr., *(1-928556)* Orders Addr.: P.O. Box 9111, Chapel Hill, NC 27515-9111 USA
E-mail: books@coastalcarolinapress.org
Web site: http://www.coastalcarolinapress.org
Dist(s): **Baker & Taylor Bks.**
Blair, John F. Pub.
Parnassus Bk. Distributors.

Coastal Publishing Carolina, Inc., *(0-9705727; 1-931650)* 504 Amberjack Way, Summerville, SC 29485 USA Tel 843-870-9352; 843-821-6168; Fax: 843-851-6949
E-mail: coastalpublishing@earthlink.net
Web site: http://coastalpublishing.net/.

Coastal Publishing, LLC, *(0-9755573)* No. 226, 1133 Bal Harbor Blvd., Suite 1139, Punta Gorda, FL 33950-6574 USA Tel 941-505-5547.

Coastalfields, *(0-9785944)* 10120 W. 59th Ave., No. 201, Arvada, CO 80004 USA Tel 720-207-3642
E-mail: directors@coastalfields.com
Web site: http://www.coastalfields.com/coastalfieldspress.

Coastline Pubs., *(0-9679354)* 800 N. Harrison Ave., Campbell, CA 98005 USA Tel 408-378-5958.

Coastline Publishing Company *See* **Higher Consciousness Bks.**

Cobblestone Publishing Co., *(0-382; 0-942389; 0-9607638)* Div. of Cricket Magazine Group, 30 Grove St., Suite C, Peterborough, NH 03458 USA (SAN 237-9937) Tel 603-924-7209; Fax: 603-924-7380; Toll Free: 800-821-0115
E-mail: custsvc@cobblestone.mv.com
Web site: http://www.cobblestonepub.com
Dist(s): **Americana Publishing, Inc.**

Cochise County Juvenile Detention Ctr., *(0-9771011)* PO Drawer 208, Bisbee, AZ 85603 USA Fax: 520-432-7136
Web site: http://www.co.cochise.az.us/schools.

Cockburn Publishing, *(1-887461)* 1504 Mithra St., New Orleans, LA 70122-2018 USA.

Coconut Info, *(1-929317)* Orders Addr.: P.O. Box 75460, Honolulu, HI 96836 USA Tel 808-947-6543; Fax: 808-923-6544
E-mail: sales@coconutinfo.com; info@coconutinfo.com
Web site: http://www.coconutinfo.com
Dist(s): **Booklines Hawaii, Ltd.**

Coconut Pr., LLC, *(0-9702168; 0-9778913)* Div. of Puerto Rico Postcard Co., Inc, Orders Addr.: P.O. Box 309540, Saint Thomas, VI 00803 USA Tel 787-248-3774; Fax: 787-253-8449; Edit Addr.: P.O. Box 79710, Carolina, PR 00984 USA Do not confuse with companies with same or similar names in Coral Gables, FL, Missouri City, TX
E-mail: Angelaspenceley1@msn.com.

CodeBreak, Inc., *(0-9650450)* 255 Harlow Dr., Los Angeles, CA 90065 USA Tel 323-224-2734; Fax: 323-227-7877; Toll Free: 800-530-3350
Dist(s): **MBI Distribution Services.**

Cody & Co., *(0-9657343)* Orders Addr.: P.O. Box 426, Harrison, AR 72602 USA Tel 870-741-5625; Fax: 870-741-9818; Edit Addr.: Rte. 5, Box 346B, Harrison, AR 72601 USA.

Cody's Guide, *(0-9755305)* 3855 Humbug Creek Rd., Applegate, OR 97530 USA
Web site: http://www.codysguide.com.

Coffee Hse. Ink, *(0-9663176)* 32370 SE Judd Rd., Eagle Creek, OR 97022 USA Tel 503-637-3277; Fax: 503-423-7980
E-mail: donmilllll@aol.com
Web site: http://www.coffeehouseink.com.

Coffee Hse. Pr., *(0-918273; 1-56689)* 27 N. Fourth St., Suite 400, Minneapolis, MN 55401 USA (SAN 206-3883) Tel 612-338-0125; Fax: 612-338-4004
Web site: http://www.coffeehousepress.org
Dist(s): **Consortium Bk. Sales & Distribution**
SPD-Small Pr. Distribution.

Coffragants (CAN) *(2-921997; 2-89517; 2-89558) Dist. by* **Penton Overseas.**

Cogburn Enterprises, *(0-9644825)* 2718 Amelia Ave., Panama City, FL 32405 USA Tel 850-769-5968.

Cohen, Deanna Moreau, *(0-9747081)* 241 E. Mountain Dr., Santa Barbara, CA 93108 USA Tel 805-565-1181
E-mail: liftveil2@cs.com.

Cohen, Sonia *See* **Gigi Enterprises**

Cohn, Tricia, *(0-9743847)* 16158 Highgate Dr., Riverside, CA 92503-8718 USA Tel 714-272-6972
E-mail: triciacohn@beobi.com
Web site: http://www.beobi.com.

Cola, Arthur, *(0-9789423)* 425 Robins Run, Papa Adventures, Burlington, WI 53105 USA
E-mail: arthurcola@yahoo.com
Dist(s): **Partners Bk. Distributing, Inc.**

Colbert Hse., The, *(1-887399)* Orders Addr.: P.O. Box 150, Norman, OK 73070-0150 USA Tel 405-329-7999; Fax: 405-329-6977; Toll Free: 800-698-2644; Edit Addr.: P.O. Box 150, Norman, OK 73070-0150 USA
E-mail: customerservice@greatbargainbooks.com
Web site: http://www.greatbargainbooks.com
Dist(s): **Anchor Distributors**
Appalachian Bk. Distributors
Baker & Taylor Bks.

Cold Noses, *(0-9666117)* P.O. Box 67243, Topeka, KS 66667-0243 USA Tel 785-478-3186 (phone/fax)
E-mail: Gkurz007@aol.com
Web site: http://members.aol.com/gkurz007/.

Cold River Pubns., *(0-9712867)* P.O. Box 606, Long Lake, NY 12847-0606 USA Tel 518-624-3581
E-mail: criver@telenet.net; criver@telenent.net
Web site: http://www.coldriverwoodworks.com
Dist(s): **AtlasBooks Distribution.**

†Cold Spring Harbor Laboratory Pr., *(0-87969)* Orders Addr.: 500 Sunnyside Blvd., Woodbury, NY 11797 USA (SAN 203-6185) Tel 516-422-4100; Fax: 516-422-4097; Toll Free: 800-843-4388; Edit Addr.: c/o NBN International, Estover Rd., Plymouth, PL6 7PY GBR
E-mail: cshpress@cshl.org; cshpress@cshl.edu
Web site: http://www.cshlpress.com
Dist(s): **NetLibrary, Inc.**; *CIP.*

Cold Tree Pr., LLC, *(1-58385)* 214 Overlook Ct. #253, Brentwood, TN 37027 USA Tel 615-309-4984 Do not confuse with Four Winds Press in New York, NY, Tenafly, NJ, Malibu, CA
E-mail: inquiry@coldtreepress.com
Web site: http://www.coldtreepress.com.

Coldwater Pr., *(1-880384)* 2214 Forest Creek, Dallas, TX 75070 USA Fax: 214-320-2480
E-mail: neilaann@aol.com
Dist(s): **Baker & Taylor Bks.**

Cole Publishing, *(0-9678779; 0-9773973; 0-9787317)* 13428 Maxella Ave., Suite 701, Marina Del Rey, CA 90292 USA (SAN 256-856X) Fax: 310-209-2448
E-mail: candace@candacecole.com; ccpprod@aol.com
Web site: http://candacecole.com/.

Coleman, CJ, *(0-9773651)* 2191 Craig Springs Rd., Sturgis, MS 39769 USA Tel 662-312-4383
E-mail: cillycreations@hotmail.com
Web site: http://www.cillycreations.com.

Coleman, Kenneth, *(0-9715205)* 6689 Orchard Lake Rd., Suite 178, West Bloomfield, MI 48322 USA
Web site: http://www.interactiveeducationalsolutions.com.

Coleman, Omer, *(0-9720341)* Orders Addr.: P.O. Box 300165, Kansas City, MO 64130 USA; Edit Addr.: 5276 Spruce Ave, Kansas City, MO 64130 USA.

Coleman Ranch Pr., *(0-9677069)* Orders Addr.: P.O. Box 1496, Sacramento, CA 95812 USA Tel 916-393-9032; Toll Free Fax: 888-532-4190; Toll Free: 877-765-3225
E-mail: colemanranch@comcast.net
Web site: http://www.CRPRESS.com.

Cole's, C. Consultant & Pubns., *(0-9640459)* 4210 Farmdale Ave., N. Las Vegas, NV 89031 USA (SAN 298-1734) Tel 702-645-5786.

Colihue (ARG) *(950-581) Dist. by* **AIMS Intl.**

Collaboration for Literacy for All Children, *(0-9721591)* 5318 SW 16th Pl., Cape Coral, FL 33914 USA Tel 239-549-0748
E-mail: vinshirlmm@aol.com.

Collage Storybook Pr., *(0-9673408)* 359 Arno Way, Pacific Palisades, CA 90272 USA.

Collector Bks., *(0-89145; 1-57432; 1-60460)* Div. of Schroeder Publishing Co., Inc., Orders Addr.: P.O. Box 3009, Paducah, KY 42003 USA (SAN 157-5368) Tel 270-898-6211; 270-898-7903; Fax: 270-898-8890; 270-898-1173; Toll Free: 800-626-5420 (orders only); Edit Addr.: 5801 Kentucky Dam Rd., Paducah, KY 42003 USA (SAN 200-7479) ; *Imprints:* American Quilter's Society (Am Quilters Soc)
E-mail: Info@collectorbooks.com; info@AQSquilt.com
Web site: http://www.collectorbooks.com; http://www.americanquilter.com/.

Collector's Guide Publishing, Inc. (CAN) *(0-9695736; 1-896522; 1-894959) Dist. by* **IPG Chicago.**

Collectors Pr., Inc., *(0-9635202; 1-888054; 1-933112)* Orders Addr.: P.O. Box 230986, Portland, OR 97281 USA Tel 503-684-3030; Fax: 503-684-3777; Toll Free: 800-423-1848; Edit Addr.: P.O. Box 230986, Portland, OR 97281-0986 USA
E-mail: lperry@collectorspress.com; rperry@collectorspress.com
Web site: http://www.collectorspress.com
Dist(s): **Universe Publishing**
Worldwide Media Service, Inc.

College Assistance & Scholarship Help, Incorporated *See* **College Assistance, Inc.**

College Assistance, Inc., *(0-9760251)* Orders Addr.: 19510 Saturnia Lakes Dr., Boca Raton, FL 33498-6206 USA Toll Free: 866-346-7890
E-mail: thecollegebook@aol.com; librodereecy@aol.com
Web site: http://www.reecysbook.com; http://www.librodelauniversidad.com; http://www.thecollegebook.com.

College Hse. Enterprises, LLC, *(0-9655911; 0-9700675; 0-9723567; 0-9762413; 0-9792581)* 5713 Glen Cove Dr., Knoxville, TN 37919-8611 USA (SAN 253-5831) Tel 865-558-6111 (phone/fax)
Web site: http://www.collegehousebooks.com.

College Planning Network, *(1-880344)* 914 E. Jefferson, Campion Tower, Seattle, WA 98122 USA Tel 206-323-0624; Fax: 206-323-0623
E-mail: seaspn@collegeplan.org
Web site: http://www.collegeplan.org.

College Pr. Pubs. (NGA) Dist. by Mich St U Pr.

College Pr. Publishing Co., Inc., *(0-89900)* Box 1132, 223 W. Third St., Joplin, MO 64802-1132 USA (SAN 211-9951) Tel 417-623-6280; Fax: 417-623-8250; Toll Free: 800-289-3300
E-mail: info@collegepress.com
Web site: http://www.collegepress.com
Dist(s): **Spring Arbor Distributors, Inc.**

College Prowler, Inc., *(1-932215; 1-59658; 1-4274)* 5001 Baum Blvd. Ste. 750, Pittsburgh, PA 15213-1856 USA Toll Free Fax: 800-772-4972; Toll Free: 800-290-2682 ; *Imprints:* Off The Record (Off The Rcd)
E-mail: joey@collegeprowler.com; luke@collegeprowler.com
Web site: http://www.collegeprowler.com.

Collins *Imprint of* **HarperCollins Pubs.**

Collins Design *Imprint of* **HarperCollins Pubs.**

Collins, Janet, *(0-9674824)* 35-07 90th St., Apt A1, Jackson Heights, NY 11372 USA Tel 718-426-2705.

Collins Pr., The (IRL) *(0-9516306; 1-898256; 1-903464; 1-905172) Dist. by* **Dufour.**

Collins, Robert, *(0-9766426)* 865 Helke Rd., Vandalia, OH 45377 USA ; *Imprints:* Peregrine Communications (Peregrine Comm)
E-mail: adagio@gemair.com
Web site: http://www.ufoconspiracy.com/.

CollinwoodMedia, *(1-881786)* 7326 Presley Ave., Mentor, OH 44060 USA
E-mail: editor@collinwoodmedia.org
Web site: http://www.collinwoodmedia.org.

Colonel Davenport Historical Foundation, *(0-9755934)* P.O. Box 4703, Rock Island, IL 61204 USA
Web site: http://www.davenporthouse.org.

Colonial Pr., *(0-938991; 1-56883)* 5956 Lake Cyrus Dr., Birmingham, AL 35244 USA (SAN 662-6599) Tel 205-424-9585; Toll Free: 800-264-7541 (orders only) Do not confuse with Colonial Press, L.P., in Dallas, TX.

†Colonial Williamsburg Foundation, *(0-87935; 0-910412)* P.O. Box 3532, Williamsburg, VA 23187-3532 USA (SAN 128-4630) Fax: 757-565-8999 (orders only); Toll Free: 800-446-9240 (orders only)
Web site: http://www.colonialwilliamsburg.com
Dist(s): **Antique Collectors' Club**
Baker & Taylor Bks.
Koen-Levy Bk. Wholesalers LLC; *CIP.*

Colophon Hse., *(1-882539)* 17522 Brushy River Ct., Houston, TX 77095 USA Tel 281-304-9502; Fax: 281-256-3442
E-mail: marydwade@aol.com
Web site: http://www.wadeco.com/colophon.htm
Dist(s): **Baker & Taylor Bks.**
Brodart Co.
Follett Library Resources
Lectorum Pubns., Inc.

Color & Learn, *(0-9795190)* P.O. Box 1592, Saint Augustine, FL 32085-1592 USA (SAN 853-6023)
Web site: http://www.colorandlearn.com.

Color & Light, *(0-9671527)* 371 Drakes View Dr., Point Reyes Station, CA 94937 USA Tel 415-663-1615 (phone/fax)
E-mail: k@pointreyesvisions.com; kathrich@telescience.net
Web site: http://www.pointreyesvisions.com.

Color Cove Studio, *(0-9717629)* 165 Color Cove Rd., Sedona, AZ 86336 USA
Web site: http://www.colorcove.com.

Color Loco *See* **Color Loco, LLC**

Color Loco, LLC, *(0-9770652; 0-9788778)* 213 Woodland Dr., Downingtown, PA 19335-9335 USA
Web site: http://www.ColorLoco.com.

Color the Classics, *(1-881153)* 2611 Hwy. 39, W., Athens, TN 37303-6125 USA Tel 423-745-5788 (phone/fax)
Web site: http://www.colortheclassics.com.

Colorado Associated University Press *See* **Univ. Pr. of Colorado**

Colorado Mountain Club Pr., The, *(0-9671466; 0-9724413; 0-9760525; 0-9799663)* 710 10th St., No. 200, Golden, CO 80401 USA Tel 303-996-2743; Fax: 303-279-9690
E-mail: bear@cmc.org; starki@boulderbooks.com
Web site: http://www.cmc.org
Dist(s): **Books West**
Heinecken & Assoc., Ltd.
Mountaineers Bks., The.

Colorado Seminary, *(0-9715202)* 1981 S. Univ. Blvd., Denver, CO 80208 USA Tel 303-871-2531; Fax: 303-871-2566
Web site: http://extremecreativity.org.

ColorAnDraw, *(0-9669554)* Orders Addr.: P.O. Box 763, Sun Prairie, WI 53590 USA Tel 608-246-0039; Edit Addr.: 6251 Portage Rd., De Forest, WI 53532 USA
E-mail: mbelljac@gateway.net.

Colorful Bks. Pr., *(0-9746152)* 935 Ottawa Ave., Ypsilanti, MI 48198 USA.

Colorful Crayons For Kids Publishing, LLC, *(0-9744123)* P.O. Box 12393, Charlotte, NC 28220 USA
E-mail: ccfkpublishing@jebcoolkids.com
Web site: http://www.jebcoolkids.com.

Coloring Bk. Co., The, *(0-9664734)* 23411 Summerfield, Apt. 9H, Aliso Viejo, CA 92656-2825 USA
E-mail: mail@colorbook.com
Web site: http://www.colorbook.com.

Coloring Bks. 'N Stuff, *(0-9715160)* 1133 Grand Duke Way, Royal Palm Reach, FL 33411 USA Tel 561-795-7849 (phone fax)
E-mail: statecoloring@yahoo.com
Web site: http://members.tripod.com/coloringbooks0.

Colter Enterprises, Inc., *(1-929110)* PMB 183, 555 Rte. 18, S., East Brunswick, NJ 08816 USA
E-mail: gramelapam@aol.com.

†Columbia Univ. Pr., *(0-231)* Orders Addr.: 136 S. Broadway, Irvington-on-Hudson, NY 10533 USA (SAN 212-2480) Tel 914-591-9111; Fax: 914-591-9201; Toll Free Fax: 800-944-1844; Toll Free: 800-944-8648 (orders); Edit Addr.: 61 W. 62nd St., New York, NY 10023 USA (SAN 212-2472) Tel 212-459-0600; Fax: 212-459-3678
E-mail: cupbooks@columbia.edu
Web site: http://www.columbia.edu/cu/cup
Dist(s): **NetLibrary, Inc.**; *CIP.*

Columbine Pr., *(0-9651272; 0-9768570)* Orders Addr.: P.O. Box 1950, Cripple Creek, CO 80813 USA Tel 719-689-2141; Edit Addr.: 340 Colorado Ave., Cripple Creek, CO 80813 USA Do not confuse with companies with the same name in Bainbridge Island, WA, East Hampton, NY
E-mail: pkmacv@earthlink.net.

Column Hall Concepts, LLC, *(0-9786584)* P.O. Box 090263, Brooklyn, NY 11209 USA Tel 718-836-1072.

Combel Editorial, S.A. (ESP) *(84-7864; 84-9825) Dist. by* **IPG Chicago.**

Combel Editorial, S.A. (ESP) *(84-7864; 84-9825) Dist. by* **Libros Fronteras.**

Combs-Hulme Publishing, *(0-9769854)* 1720 Eldridge Ave. W., Saint Paul, MN 55113 USA Tel 651-631-2173 Do not confuse with Combs Publishing in Winston-Salem, NC
E-mail: lvhulme@aol.com.

Come & Get It Publishing, *(0-9653042; 0-9753883)* Orders Addr.: P.O. Box 1562, Madison, VA 22727 USA Tel 540-829-0516 Toll Free: 800-825-9008; Edit Addr.: 214 E. Spencer St., No. 1, Culpeper, VA 22701 USA
E-mail: hereme@aol.com
Dist(s): **Perseus Distribution.**

Comfort Tales, LLC, *(0-9741586)* Orders Addr.: 47 Watsons Way, Medford, NJ 08055 USA (SAN 255-464X) Tel 856-988-0884; Fax: 856-988-8499
E-mail: comforttales@aol.com.

Comic Art Publishing Company *See* **Bill Barry's Compass Bks.**

Comic Library International, *(1-929515)* 2049 Alfred St., Pittsburgh, PA 15212-1426 USA ; *Imprints:* Solovisions (Solovisions)
E-mail: gbstudios@comcast.net
Web site: http://www.geocities.com/SoHo/Cafe/9669/clipage.html
Dist(s): **Diamond Comic Distributors, Inc.**

Comical Sense Company, The *See* **Trevor Romain Co., The**

Comics Lit *Imprint of* **NBM Publishing Co.**

ComicsOne Corporation *See* **ComicsOne Corp./Dr. Masters**

ComicsOne Corp./Dr. Masters, *(1-58899)* P.O. Box 14232, Fremont, CA 94539-1532 USA
Web site: http://www.comicsone.com
Dist(s): **Diamond Bk. Distributors**
LPC Group.

Comicstories.com, *(0-9725925)* 168 E. Cascade Ct., Brea, CA 92821 USA Tel 714-529-3952
E-mail: kirkwerks@aol.com
Web site: http://www.comicstories.com.

Command Performance Language Institute, *(0-929724)* 1755 Hopkins St., Berkeley, CA 94707-2714 USA (SAN 250-1694) Tel 510-524-1191 (phone/fax)
E-mail: consee@aol.com
Web site: http://www.hometown.aol.com/commandperform1/myhomepage/
Dist(s): **Alta Bk. Ctr. Pubs.**
Applause Learning Resources
Athelstan Pubns.
Authors & Editors
Betty Segal, Inc.
BookLink
Calliope Bks.
Carlex
Continental Bk. Co., Inc.
Delta Systems Co., Inc.
Educational Showcase
Edumate-Educational Materials, Inc.
European Bk. Co., Inc.
Gessler Publishing Co., Inc.
International Bk. Ctr., Inc.
Midwest European Pubns.
Miller Educational Materials
Multi-Cultural Bks. & Videos, Inc.
Sky Oaks Productions, Inc.
SpeakWare
Teacher's Discovery
Tempo Bookstore
World of Reading, Ltd.

Commercial Communications Incorporated *See* **Great Lakes Design**

Commercial Transportation Consultants, LLC, *(0-9721289)* RR No. 1 Box 171, Rte. 467, Rome, PA 18837-9765 USA
Web site: http://www.1ctc.com.

Commission on Culture and Tourism, *(0-9759389)* 59 S. Prospect St., Hartford, CT 06106 USA Tel 860-566-3005; Fax: 860-566-5078
E-mail: kazkozlowski@snet.net.

Committee for Children, *(0-9741388)* 568 First Ave. S., Suite 600, Seattle, WA 98104-2804 USA Toll Free: 800-634-4449
Web site: http://www.cfchildren.org.

Common Courtesy, *(0-9746148)* 709 Uwharrie St., Asheboro, NC 27203 USA Tel 336-629-5274
E-mail: jjdortch@earthlink.net.

Common Reader Editions *Imprint of* **Akadine Pr., The**

Common Sense Pr., *(1-880892; 1-929683)* 8786 Hwy. 21, Melrose, FL 32666 USA Tel 352-475-5757; Fax: 352-475-6105 Do not confuse with companies with the same name in Purcellville, VA, Washington, DC, Neptune, NJ, Sun City, AZ or Common Sense Pr., Inc. in Escondido, CA
E-mail: inp@cspress.com; info@commomsensepress.com
Web site: http://www.cspress.com.

Commonwealth Editions, *(1-889833; 1-933212)* 266 Cabot St., Beverly, MA 01915 USA Tel 978-921-0747; Fax: 978-927-8195
E-mail: websterb@commonwealtheditions.com
Web site: http://www.commonwealtheditions.com.

Commonwealth Secretariat (GBR) *(0-85092) Dist. by* **Stylus Pub VA.**

Communicate! *See* **Rethinking Schls., Ltd.**

Communication Connection, *(0-9679353)* P.O. Box 1961, Davidson, NC 28036 USA Tel 704-896-3488; Fax: 704-896-3489
E-mail: mcintosh@vnet.net
Web site: http://users.vnet.net/mcintosh/.

Communication Counts, *(0-9645202)* 20 W. Fountain Ave., Delaware, OH 43015-1672 USA
Dist(s): **BookMasters, Inc.**

Communication Crossroads, *(0-9749343)* 222171, Carmel, CA 93922 USA Tel 831-333-9070; Fax: 831-375-0460
E-mail: info@commxroads.com
Web site: http://www.commxroads.com.

Communication Facilities & Services, Incorporated *See* **S&E Publishing Co.**

Communication Service Corporation *See* **Gryphon Hse., Inc.**

Community for Education Foundation, *(1-929393; 0-9755754)* 111 John St., Suite 1801, New York, NY 10038 USA Tel 212-406-7488; Fax: 212-406-7480; Toll Free: 888-840-9606
E-mail: mail@overcomingobstacles.org
Web site: http://www.overcomingobstacles.org.

Community Justice Foundation of Texas, *(0-9631028)* P.O. Box 720502, Dallas, TX 75372 USA Tel 214-828-4511
E-mail: apples@flash.net
Web site: http://www.appleseedbooks.com.

Community Partnership with Youth, Inc., *(0-9717497)* 6744 Falcon Ridge Ct., Indianapolis, IN 46278 USA
Web site: http://www.cpyinc.org.

Community Pr., *(0-9790878; 0-9797572)* Orders Addr.: 239 Windbrooke Ln., Virginia Beach, VA 23462 USA (SAN 852-4092) Tel 757-416-7272 Do not confuse with Community Press in San Francisco, CA
E-mail: contact@communitypresshome.com; editor@communitypresshome.com
Web site: http://www.communitypresshome.com.

Community Works!, *(0-9742213)* 13313 Country Way Cir., Fredericksburg, VA 22404 USA
E-mail: arayu1@comcast.net; carol@carolynnfitzpatrick.com
Web site: http://www.carolynnfitzpatrick.com
Dist(s): **New Leaf Distributing Co., Inc.**

Commuter's Library *See* **Sound Room Pubs., Inc.**

Companhia das Letras (BRA) *(85-7164; 85-85095; 85-85466) Dist. by* **Distribks Inc.**

Companhia Melhoramentos de Sao Paulo Industrias de Papel (BRA) *(85-06) Dist. by* **Lectorum Pubns.**

Compania Editorial Continental (MEX) *(968-26) Dist. by* **Fondo CA.**

Companion Group, The *See* **Attitude Pr., Inc.**

Company

Company

Companion Pr., *(1-879651)* Div. of Ctr. for Loss & Life Transition, 3735 Broken Bow Rd., Fort Collins, CO 80526 USA Tel 970-226-6050; Fax: 970-226-6051; Toll Free Fax: 800-922-6051 (orders only) Do not confuse with companies with the same name in Santa Barbara, CA, Aliso Viejo, CA
E-mail: wolfelt@centerforloss.com
Web site: http://www.centerforloss.com
Dist(s): **Independent Pubs. Group.**

Compass Books *See* **Lake Street Pubs.**

Compass Labs, *(1-931918)* Div. of Compass Marketing, 251 First Ave., N., Second Flr., Minneapolis, MN 55401 USA Tel 612-333-5300; Fax: 612-335-9580
E-mail: tlafrenz@compassmail.com.

Compass Point Bks., *(0-7565)* Div. of Coughlan Publishing, 3109 W. 50th St., No.115, Minneapolis, MN 55410 USA (SAN 254-2013) Toll Free Fax: 877-371-1539; Toll Free: 877-371-1536
E-mail: custserv@compasspointbooks.com
Web site: http://www.compasspointbooks.com
Dist(s): **Capstone Pr., Inc.**
NetLibrary, Inc.

Compass Publishing, *(0-9753102)* Orders Addr.: P.O. Box 280188, Lakewood, CO 80228-0188 USA (SAN 256-0186) Tel 303-989-8654 (phone/fax)
E-mail: billhowey@actorsmenu.com
Web site: http://www.actorsmenu.com
Dist(s): **Independent Pubs. Group.**

Compass Publishing Corp.,The, *(1-929804)* 140 Palm Dr., Alabaster, AL 35007 USA Tel 205-266-6919; Fax: 208-955-3828 ; *Imprints:* Compass Special Editions (Compass Spec Ed)
E-mail: Service@compassbooks.com; OurMail@compassbooks.com
Web site: http://www.compassbooks.com.

Compass Special Editions *Imprint of* **Compass Publishing Corp.,The**

Compassion Outreach Ministry, *(0-9755564)* P.O. Box 1168, Marcola, OR 97454 USA Tel 541-933-3338 (phone/fax)
E-mail: glorywalk1@aol.com.

Compassion Pets Publishing, *(0-615)* 34672 Hardtack Ln., Shingletown, CA 96088 USA Tel 530-474-1038
E-mail: compassionpet.pub@frontiernet.net
Web site: http://www.compassionpets.com.

Competitive Edge Dynamics, USA, *(0-9718689)* P.O. Box 486, Orefield, PA 18069-0486 USA Fax: 610-366-9680
Web site: http://www.travelsbyme.com.

Complete Mastery Learning Systems, *(0-9720169)* 413 Willis Rd., Spartanburg, SC 29301-1298 USA Tel 864-574-1896
E-mail: janice@completemastery.com
Web site: http://www.completemastery.com.

Comprecom, *(0-9772809)* 411 Hess Ave., Golden, CO 80401 USA.

Compsych Systems, Inc., Pubns. Div., *(0-929948)* Div. of Compsych Systems, Inc., P.O. Box 1568, Pacific Palisades, CA 90272 USA (SAN 250-8281) Tel 310-454-6426 (phone/fax)
Web site: http://www.jeanettegriver.com
Dist(s): **Baker & Taylor Bks.**

Compton's Encyclopedia & Yearbooks, *(0-944262)* Subs. of Success Publishing Group, Ltd., 310 S. Michigan Ave., 9th Flr., Chicago, IL 60604-4207 USA
Web site: http://www.comptonsbooks.com
Dist(s): **Honn, Joseph R.**
Proteus Enterprises, Inc.

Compton's Learning Company *See* **Compton's Encyclopedia & Yearbooks**

Computer Age Education *See* **Learning Net, The**

Computer Classics (R), *(0-9721216; 0-9748870)* 497 Elysian Fields Rd. Apt. A11, Nashville, TN 37211-4253 USA
E-mail: computerclassics@mindspring.com
Web site: http://www.computer-classics.com.

Computer Consultants Network, Inc., *(0-9726481)* 110 Waterwillow Rd., West Chester, PA 19380 USA Tel 610-692-3206; Fax: 610-692-0275
E-mail: jlhale@ccn1.com
Web site: http://www.ccn1.com.

Computer Literacy Pr., *(0-941681; 1-57426; 1-930938)* Orders Addr.: P.O. Box 562, Earlysville, VA 22936-0562 USA (SAN 666-3133)
E-mail: info@compLitpress.com
Web site: http://www.complitpress.com.

ComputerPREP, Inc., *(0-7423)* Div. of Drake Intl., 410 N. 44th St., Suite 600, Phoenix, AZ 85008 USA Tel 602-275-7700; Fax: 602-275-1603; Toll Free: 800-228-1027
Web site: http://www.computerprep.com.

ComQwest, LLC, *(0-9753454)* 1350 E. Flamingo Rd., Suite No. 265, Las Vegas, NV 89119 USA
Web site: http://www.comqwest.com.

Comstock Publishing Assocs. *Imprint of* **Cornell Univ. Pr.**

ComteQ Publishing, *(0-9674074; 0-9766889; 0-9793771)* Div. of ComteQ Communications, LLC, Orders Addr.: P.O. Box 3046, Margate, NJ 08402 USA (SAN 253-4088) Tel 609-487-9000; Fax: 609-822-4098; Edit Addr.: 7806 Marshall Ave., Margate, NJ 08402 USA
E-mail: publisher@comteqcom.com
Web site: http://www.comteqpublishing.com
Dist(s): **Baker & Taylor Bks.**

ConArtistE Pubng., *(0-9755386)* 6084 Churn Creek Rd., Redding, CA 96002 USA Tel 530-209-4338
E-mail: conartiste@msn.com
Web site: www.conartiste.com.

Conceivable Concepts, Inc., *(0-9629502)* 9363 Wilshire Blvd., Suite 200, Beverly Hills, CA 90210-5413 USA Tel 310-772-7744; Fax: 310-575-4290.

Concepcion, Jorge, *(0-9761779)* 9125 SW 56th Ter., Miami, FL 33173-1605 USA
E-mail: jconcepcion1@msn.com.

Conceptions, *(0-9661745)* P.O. Box 882153, San Diego, CA 92168 USA Tel 619-294-4770; Fax: 619-294-4410; Toll Free: 800-584-8188 Do not confuse with Conceptions in New York, NY; Conceptions.. in New York, NY
E-mail: sales@balloonascoop.com
Web site: http://www.balloonascoop.com/.

Concepts *See* **Developmental Vision Concepts**

Concepts 'N' Publishing, *(1-879940)* Orders Addr.: P.O. Box 1552, Seaside, CA 93955 USA Tel 831-899-1118; Edit Addr.: 582 Lighthouse Ave., Suite 7, Pacific Grove, CA 93950 USA.

Conceptual Research Corp., *(0-9722397)* P.O. Box 923156, Sylmar, CA 91392-3156 USA Tel 818-362-3546; Fax: 818-743-7483
E-mail: dprisbn@aircraftdesign.com
Web site: http://www.aircraftdesign.com
Dist(s): **AtlasBooks Distribution.**

Concerned Christians, *(0-9768352)* P.O. Box 18, Mesa, AZ 85211 USA Tel 480-833-2537; Fax: 480-833-4116
E-mail: jim@concernedchristians.org
Web site: http://www.concernedchristians.org.

Concerned Communications, *(0-936785; 1-58938)* Orders Addr.: P.O. Box 1000, Siloam Springs, AR 72761-1000 USA (SAN 699-8623) Tel 501-594-9000; Fax: 501-549-4002; Toll Free: 800-447-4332; Edit Addr.: 700 E. Granite St., Siloam Springs, AR 72761 USA (SAN 699-8631)
E-mail: lustwrt@areasonfor.com
Web site: http://www.areasonfor.com
Dist(s): **Project Patch.**

Conciliar Pr., *(0-9622713; 1-888212)* Orders Addr.: P.O. Box 76, Ben Lomond, CA 95005-0076 USA Tel 831-336-5118; Fax: 831-336-8882; Toll Free: 800-967-7377; Edit Addr.: 10090-A Hwy. 9, Ben Lomond, CA 95005 USA (SAN 175-8624)
E-mail: marketing@conciliarpress.com
Web site: http://www.conciliarpress.com
Dist(s): **Baker & Taylor Bks.**
Midpoint Trade Bks., Inc.
Spring Arbor Distributors, Inc.

Concordia Publishing Hse., *(0-570; 0-7586)* Subs. of Lutheran Church Missouri Synod, 3558 S. Jefferson Ave., Saint Louis, MO 63118-3968 USA (SAN 202-1781) Tel 314-268-1000; Fax: 314-268-1360; Toll Free Fax: 800-490-9889 (orders only); Toll Free: 800-325-3040 (orders only); 800-325-0191
E-mail: cphorder@cph.org
Web site: http://www.cph.org.

Conerly, Lawrence, *(0-9765669)* 85 Mt. Canaan Rd., Tylertown, MS 39667 USA
E-mail: augsept@bellsouth.net.

Conexion Educativa, *(0-9702021)* 900 Alameda St., Villa Granada, San Juan, PR 00923 USA Tel 787-766-4448; Fax: 787-250-8709
E-mail: conexion@coqui.net
Web site: http://home.coqui.net/conexion.

Confidence Sport Series, Incorporated *See* **Game Plan Pubns.**

Cong Bais Tziporah, *(0-9728849; 0-9767166; 1-934098)* 3 Harrison Ave., Spring Valley, NY 10977 USA.

Congregation Agudat Achim *See* **Congregation Agudat Achim**

Congregation Agudat Achim, *(0-9770172)* 2117 Union St., Schenectady, NY 12309 USA
Web site: http://www.divinekosher.com.

Congressional Publishing, Inc., *(0-9762916)* P.O. Box 1318, Leesburg, VA 20177 USA Tel 703-777-6737; Fax: 703-777-6272
E-mail: congressionalpub@verizon.net
Web site: http://www.congressionalpublishing.com.

Conjunctions, *(0-941964)* Bard College, Annandale-on-Hudson, New York, NY 12504 USA (SAN 239-5169) Tel 914-758-1539; Fax: 914-758-2660
E-mail: conjunctions@bard.edu
Web site: http://www.conjunctions.com
Dist(s): **D.A.P./Distributed Art Pubs.**
SPD-Small Pr. Distribution.

Connect With Your Kid Bks., *(0-9746094)* 106 Central Park Sq., No.150, Los Alamos, NV 87544 USA Toll Free: 888-388-5437
E-mail: DrSillyScience@comcast.net
Web site: http://www.DrSillyScience.com.

Connected 2 The Father Publishing, *(0-9745122)* 3203 Grace Ave., New York, NY 10469-3136 USA Tel 718-813-3363
E-mail: cttf03@aol.com
Web site: http://www.c2tf.com.

Connecticut Conference of Municipalities, *(0-9714608)* 900 Chapel St., 9th Flr., New Haven, CT 06510 USA Tel 203-498-3000; Fax: 203-562-6314
E-mail: ccm@ccm-ct.org
Web site: http://www.ccm-ct.org.

Connecticut Dept. of Environmental Protection, Environmental & Geographic Information Ctr., *(0-942085)* 79 Elm St., Store Level, Hartford, CT 06106-5127 USA (SAN 666-6388) Tel 860-424-3555; Fax: 860-424-4058
E-mail: nancy.mchone@po.state.ct.us
Web site: http://dep.state.ct.us.

Connecticut Department of Environmental Protection, Natural Resources Center *See* **Connecticut Dept. of Environmental Protection, Environmental & Geographic Information Ctr.**

Connection, *(0-9743687)* 601 Daniel Ct., Nashville, TN 37221-6512 USA.

Conner Prairie Pr., *(0-9614736; 0-9703951)* Div. of Conner Prairie Museum, Inc., 13400 Allisonville Rd., Fishers, IN 46060-4499 USA (SAN 692-7912) Tel 317-776-6000 ext 272; Fax: 317-776-6014; Toll Free: 800-966-1836
E-mail: bconn@connerprairie.org
Web site: http://connerprairie.org.

Connexions Unlimited, *(1-929785)* 1021 Silver Lake Blvd., Frankfort, KY 40601 USA Tel 502-695-5181.

Connors, E. W. Publishing Co., *(0-9635587)* P.O. Box 691, Buffalo, NY 14205-0691 USA Tel 716-851-1343.

Conquering Lion Enterprise, *(0-9701711)* P.O. Box 3553, Laurel, MD 20709-3553 USA
E-mail: david@conqlion.com
Web site: http://www.conqlion.com.

Conquerors Publishing, *(0-9648460; 0-9798241)* Div. of Victory Christian Ctr., Inc., 7224 Old Pineville Rd., Charlotte, NC 28217 USA.

Conroca Publishing, *(1-892617)* 132 Ridge Trail, Boerne, TX 78006 USA Tel 830-537-5917 (phone/fax); Toll Free: 877-762-2782 (phone/fax)
E-mail: conrocapub@yahoo.com
Web site: http://www.conrocoapub.com
Dist(s): **Baker & Taylor Bks.**

Consciousness-Based Education Association, *(0-9727877)* 1100 Univ. Manor Dr., B-24, Fairfield, IA 52556 USA Tel 641-472-1663; Fax: 641-472-3116; Toll Free: 888-472-1677
E-mail: info@cbeprograms.org
Web site: http://www.cbeprograms.org.

Consilient Pubns., *(0-9746242)* 8176 S. Centaur Dr., Evergreen, CO 80439 USA Tel 303-679-1538
E-mail: stephanie@cost-benefit-jr.com
Web site: http://www.cost-benefit-jr.com.

Consortium Bk. Sales & Distribution, Orders Addr.: 1045 Westgate Dr., Suite 90, Saint Paul, MN 55114-1065 USA (SAN 200-6049) Tel 651-221-9035; Fax: 651-917-6406; Toll Free: 800-283-3572 (orders)
E-mail: consortium@cbsd.com
Web site: http://www.cbsd.com.

Consortium of Collective Consciousness, *(1-888729)* 530 Eighth Ave., Unit 6, San Francisco, CA 94118 USA Tel 415-990-2122; Fax: 415-933-8132
E-mail: cccpublishing@juno.com
Web site: http://www.stompers.com; http://www.peacetour.org; http://www.cccpublishing.com; http://www.bradolsen.com
Dist(s): **Baker & Taylor Bks.**
Independent Pubs. Group.

Consortium Publishing, *(0-940139)* 640 Weaver Hill Rd., West Greenwich, RI 02817-2261 USA (SAN 664-2667) Tel 401-397-9838; Fax: 401-392-1926
E-mail: consortiumpublishing@cox.net.

Consortium Publishing Co., *(0-9644681; 0-9707173; 0-9748830)* Div. of Creative Ideas, Inc., Orders Addr.: P.O. Box 998, Jacksonville, IL 62651 USA; Edit Addr.: P.O. Box 1535, Jacksonville, IL 62651-1535 USA Tel 217-243-7628 (phone/fax); Toll Free: 800-419-8698; 888-456-7235; 4 Sunnydale Ave., Jacksonville, IL 62650
E-mail: consortm@aol.com
Web site: http://www.creativeideas.com.

Consortium, The *See* **Consortium Publishing Co.**

Constable & Robinson Ltd. (GBR) *(0-09; 0-948164; 1-85004; 1-85487; 1-84119; 1-84529) Dist. by* **IPG Chicago.**

Constellation Pr., *(0-9616620; 0-9794000)* 1790 Ogden Rd., Cambria, CA 93428 USA (SAN 661-0404) Tel 805-927-2202 (phone/fax)
E-mail: renshaw@mac.com
Web site: http://www.constellationpress.info.

Constitutional Rights Foundation, *(1-886253)* 601 S. Kingsley Dr., Los Angeles, CA 90005 USA (SAN 225-6401) Tel 213-487-5590; Fax: 213-386-0459; Toll Free: 800-488-4273 Do not confuse with Constitutional Rights Foundation Chicago in Chicago, IL
E-mail: crf@crf.usa
Web site: http://www.crftusa.org.

Consultant's Publishing Services, LLC, *(1-931829)* Orders Addr.: P.O. Box 11814, Kansas City, MO 64138 USA Tel 816-695-4897
E-mail: cps@cpsinfo.com
Web site: http://www.cpsinfo.com.

Consultant's Unlimited *See* **Schwarz Pauper Pr.**

Consumer Pr., The, *(0-9717119)* 6 Berkley Rd., Glenville, NY 12302 USA (SAN 254-5446)
E-mail: richesq@mindspring.com
Web site: http://www.theconsumerpress.com
Dist(s): **Biblio Distribution.**

Contemplation Corner Pr., *(0-9707979; 0-9758748)* 1229 Randy Rd., Ashland City, TN 37015 USA Tel 615-746-8220; Fax: 615-746-3697
E-mail: ccpress1@bellsouth.net
Web site: http://www.contemplationcornerpress.com.

Contemporary Bks. *Imprint of* **McGraw-Hill Trade**

Contemporary Publishing Co. of Raleigh, Inc., *(0-89892)* 6001-101 Chapel Hill Rd., Raleigh, NC 27607 USA (SAN 213-0424) Tel 919-851-8221; Fax: 919-851-6666
E-mail: ErikaCPC@aol.com; questions@comtemporarypublishing.com
Web site: http://www.contemporarypublishing.com.

Contender Entertainment Group (GBR) *(1-84357) Dist. by* **IPG Chicago.**

Continental Bk. Co., Inc., *(0-9626800)* Eastern Div., 80-00 Cooper Ave., Bldg. No. 29, Glendale, NY 11385 USA (SAN 169-5436) Tel 718-326-0560; Fax: 718-326-4276; Toll Free: 800-364-0350; Western Div., 625 E. 70th Ave., No. 5, Denver, CO 80229 (SAN 630-2882) Tel 303-289-1761; Fax: 303-289-1764 Do not confuse with Continental Book Company, Denver, CO
E-mail: hola@continentalbook.com; esl@continentalbook.com; bonjour@continentalbook.com; tag@continentalbook.com
Web site: http://www.continentalbook.com.

Continental Enterprises Group, Inc. (CEG), Orders Addr.: 302 West North 2nd St., Seneca, SC 29678 USA (SAN 631-0915) Tel 864-885-9444; Fax: 864-885-1090
E-mail: ContactUs@centerprisesgrp.com
Dist(s): **National Bk. Network.**

Continental Pr., Inc., *(0-8454)* Orders Addr.: 520 E. Bainbridge St., Elizabethtown, PA 17022 USA (SAN 202-182X) Tel 717-367-1836; Fax: 717-367-5660; Toll Free: 800-233-0759 ; *Imprints:* Seedling Publications (Seedlg Pubns)
E-mail: educationsales@continentalpress.com
Web site: http://www.continentalpress.com.

Continuum International Publishing Group, Ltd. (GBR) *(0-225; 0-264; 0-304; 0-485; 0-567; 0-7136; 0-7185; 0-7201; 0-7220; 0-8044; 0-8264; 0-86187; 1-56338; 1-85567; 1-85805; 1-84127; 0-223; 0-86012; 1-84371) Dist. by* **Chicago Distribution Ctr.**

Cook, Cheryl *See* **Heavenly C. Publishing**

Cook Communication, *(0-9726996)* P.O. Box 451, Dundee, IL 60118-0451 USA Tel 312-859-8090; Fax: 847-428-8974
E-mail: publish@author-me.com; cookcomm@gte.net
Web site: http://www.author-me.com
Dist(s): **AtlasBooks Distribution.**

Cook Communications Ministries *See* **Cook, David C. Publishing Co.**

Cook, David, *(0-9741629)* P.O. Box 657, Albemarle, NC 28001 USA Do not confuse with companies with the same name in Chapel Hill, NC, Boerne, TX
E-mail: info@dac-and.com
Web site: http://www.dac-and.com.

Cook, David C. Publishing Co., *(0-7814; 0-88207; 0-89191; 0-89693; 0-912692; 1-55513; 1-56476; 983-45026; 5-503; 983-45027; 983-45023; 983-45019; 983-45018; 983-45013; 983-45012; 983-45016; 983-45031; 1-4347)* 4050 Lee Vance View, Colorado Springs, CO 80918 USA (SAN 206-0981) Tel 719-536-0100; Fax: 719-536-3244; Toll Free: 800-708-5550; 800-323-7543 (Customer Service) ; *Imprints:* Faith Kidz (Faith Kidz)
E-mail: howella@cookministries.org
Web site: http://www.davidcook.com.

Cookbook Resources, LLC, *(0-9677932; 1-931294; 1-59769)* 541 Doubletree Dr., Highland Village, TX 75077 USA (SAN 253-5262) Tel 972-317-0245; Fax: 972-317-6404; Toll Free: 866-229-2665
E-mail: mary@cookbookresources.com
Web site: http://www.cookbookresourses.com
Dist(s): **Book Marketing Plus.**

Cookbooks by Morris Press *See* **Morris Publishing**

Cookie Bear Pr., Inc., *(0-9701155)* Orders Addr.: P.O. Box 5074, Buffalo Grove, IL 60089 USA (SAN 253-6579) Tel 847-955-0001; 847-478-9202; Fax: 847-955-0002; Edit Addr.: 205 Thompson Blvd., Buffalo Grove, IL 60089 USA
E-mail: info@cookiebearpress.com
Web site: http://www.cookiebearpress.com
Dist(s): **Baker & Taylor Bks.**
Distributors, The
Independent Pubs. Group.

Cookie Jar, *(1-933799; 1-60095)* Cookie Jar Entertainment, Inc., P.O. Box 35665, Greensboro, NC 27425 USA Fax: 336-808-3249; Toll Free: 800-321-0903
Web site: http://www.cinar.com/EN/
Dist(s): **Midpoint Trade Bks., Inc.**

Cool Grove Publishing, Inc., *(1-887276)* 512 Argyle Rd., Brooklyn, NY 11218 USA Tel 718-287-7221
E-mail: tej@coolgrove.com
Web site: http://www.coolgrove.com
Dist(s): **New Leaf Distributing Co., Inc.**
SPD-Small Pr. Distribution.

Cool, Kim @ Historic Venice Pr., *(0-9721655)* 312 Shore Rd., Venice, FL 34285 USA
Web site: http://www.historicvenicepress.com
Dist(s): **American Wholesale Bk. Co.**
Book Warehouse
Southern Bk. Service.

Cool Pubs., *(0-9715018)* Orders Addr.: P.O. Box 3328, Conroe, TX 77305 USA Tel 936-441-4244; Fax: 936-756-4973; Edit Addr.: 25831 Richards Rd., Spring, TX 77386 USA Tel 936-441-4244
E-mail: coolpublishers@aol.com.

Cool Springs Pr., *(0-9640392; 1-888608; 1-930604; 1-59186)* 402 Bna Dr., Bldg. 100, Suite 600, Nashville, TN 37217 USA Tel 615-277-5564
E-mail: dmilling@thomasnelson.com
Web site: http://www.coolspringspress.net
Dist(s): **Booksource, The**
Common Ground Distributors, Inc.
Hervey's Booklink & Cookbook Warehouse
Ingram Pub. Services
Nelson, Thomas Inc.
Parnassus Bk. Distributors.

Coole Schl., *(0-9678649; 0-9715800)* 1213 W. Loop N., Suite 100, Houston, TX 77055 USA Tel 713-552-1600; Fax: 713-812-9588; Toll Free: 800-364-1400
E-mail: lyi@cooleschool.com; jogg@cooleschool.com
Web site: http://www.cooleschool.com.

Coolmath.com, Inc., *(0-9791628)* P.O. Box 4386, Costa Mesa, CA, CA 92628-4386 USA
Web site: http://Coolmath.com.

Coomansingh Pubns., *(0-9665299)* 1717 Pulaski Pike, NW, Huntsville, AL 35816 USA Tel 256-539-2020; Fax: 256-539-7526.

Coon, Kathy, *(0-9741300)* P.O. Box 14267, Baton Rouge, LA 70898 USA
Web site: http://www.dogintelligencetest.com.

Cooper Publishing, *(1-59655)* Orders Addr.: P.O. Box 312, Bozrah, CT 06334 USA Tel 860-445-4949
E-mail: cooperpublishing@snet.net.

Cooper Publishing Co., *(0-9675037)* 1234 Powers Ferry Rd., Suite 104, Marietta, GA 30067 USA Tel 770-952-7681
E-mail: JTCooper35@aol.com.

Cooper, Robbi, *(0-9749643)* 9 Scott Crescent, Austin, TX 78703 USA
Web site: http://www.everythingfromthegarden.com.

Cooperfly Bks., *(0-9669504)* 3184 Plainfield NE PMB 248, Grand Rapids, MI 49525 USA Tel 616-364-5870; Fax: 616-364-5871; Toll Free: 877-986-6286
E-mail: kevin@tomatocollection.com; tomatocollection@charter.net
Web site: http://www.tomatocollection.com.

Copalis Publishing, *(0-9653703)* Orders Addr.: P.O. Box 339, Copalis Beach, WA 98535 USA Tel 360-289-0528; Fax: 360-289-4045; Toll Free: 800-286-4552; Edit Addr.: 3193 State Rte. 109, Copalis Beach, WA 98535 USA
Web site: http://www.copalis.com.

Copeland, Kenneth Pubns., *(0-88114; 0-938458; 1-57562; 1-60463)* Subs. of Eagle Mountain International Church, 14355 Morris-Dido- Rd., Newark, TX 76071 USA (SAN 211-7894) Tel 817-252-2700 Toll Free: 800-600-7395
E-mail: mjohnson@kcm.org
Web site: http://www.kcm.org.contact.html
Dist(s): **Anchor Distributors**
Appalachian Bible Co.
Central South Christian Distribution
Harrison Hse., Inc.
New Day Christian Distributors
Spring Arbor Distributors, Inc.

Copeland, P. Taylor *See* **Grammy Time Bks.**

Copernicus *Imprint of* **Springer**

Copernicus Pr., *(0-9741638)* 933 Dwyer Ave., Saint Louis, MO 63122 USA Tel 314-822-8597 Do not confuse with Copernicus Pr. in Atlanta, GA
E-mail: nikolom@slu.edu
Web site: http://www.Copernicuspress.com
Dist(s): **Baker & Taylor Bks.**
Unique Bks., Inc.

Copley Custom Publishing Group *Imprint of* **Copley Publishing Group**

Copley Publishing Group, *(0-87411; 1-58152; 1-58390)* 138 Great Rd, Acton, MA 01720 USA (SAN 687-4959) Tel 978-263-9090; Fax: 978-263-9190; Toll Free: 800-562-2147 ; *Imprints:* Copley Custom Publishing Group (Copley Custom Pub Grp)
E-mail: textbook@copleypublishing.com; publish@copleycustom.com
Web site: http://www.xanedu.com.

Coppenrath, F. Verlag KG (DEU) *(3-88547; 3-920192; 3-8157) Dist. by* **Distribks Inc.**

Copperleaf Publishing *See* **Dunhill Publishing**

Copyright Management Services *See* **Courier Custom Publishing, Inc.**

CopyRite Printing, *(0-9677268)* 30503 Gratiot Ave., Roseville, MI 48066-1775 USA Toll Free: 800-774-0012
E-mail: copyrite@teleweb.net
Web site: http://www.copyriteprinting.net.

Coram Deo Pr., *(0-9769054)* One Nelson Pkwy., 2400 FM 407, Highland Village, TX 75077 USA Tel 972-318-5222; Fax: 972-692-5140
E-mail: press@coramdeoacademy.org
Web site: http://www.coramdeopress.com.

Corbett Features, *(0-9762294)* Div. of Corbett Features, 2 Courthouse Ln., 14F, Chelmsford, MA 01824 USA Tel 978-459-1636; Fax: 978-459-1637 ; *Imprints:* Griffin Comics (Griffin Comics)
E-mail: cdesign.ma.ultranet@rcn.com
Web site: http://www.corbettfeatures.com.

Corbett, Glenn, *(0-9722604)* 136 Bergen Ave., Waldwick, NJ 07463 USA Fax: 201-652-0078
E-mail: gcorbet1@ix.netcom.com
Web site: http://www.greatpatersonfire.com.

Corbus Systems, *(0-9742347)* 20368 Forestwood, Southfield, MI 48706 USA Tel 248-356-9427
E-mail: info@corbus-systems.com
Web site: http://www.corbus-systems.com.

CORD Communications, *(1-55502; 1-57837)* Subs. of Ctr. for Occupational Research & Development, Orders Addr.: P.O. Box 21206, Waco, TX 76702-1206 USA Tel 254-776-1822; Fax: 254-776-3906; Toll Free: 800-231-3015; Edit Addr.: 324 Kelly Dr., Waco, TX 76710 USA
E-mail: webmaster@cord.org
Web site: http://www.cord.org/index.cfm.

Cordet Bks., *(0-9678378)* 2787 Kennedy Blvd., Suite 206, Jersey City, NJ 07306 USA Tel 201-659-8872
E-mail: cordetbooks@aol.com
Web site: http://www.outcry.com.

Cordova, Barbara Joy, *(0-9700181)* c/o Artists for a Better World, P.O. Box 11081, Glendale, CA 91226 USA
Web site: http://www.artistsforabetterworld.com.

Cordoves, Barbara & Gladys M., *(0-9637252)* 2800 SW 106th Ave., Miami, FL 33165-2748 USA.

Core Knowledge Foundation, *(1-890517; 1-933486)* 801 E. High St., Charlottesville, VA 22902 USA Tel 434-977-7550; Fax: 434-977-0021; Toll Free: 800-238-3233
E-mail: mford@coreknowledge.org
Web site: http://www.coreknowledge.org.

Core Publishing & Consulting, Inc., *(1-933079)* 13016 Bee St., Suite 208, Dallas, TX 75234 USA (SAN 256-1514) Tel 214-926-4742; Fax: 972-243-5854
E-mail: stan.peterson@sbcglobal.net
Web site: www.core-publishing.com
Dist(s): **AtlasBooks Distribution**
Baker & Taylor Bks.

Corey, C. L., *(0-9644698)* 9437 Haggerty Rd., Plymouth, MI 48170 USA Tel 248-474-4772; Fax: 313-455-9737.

Corimbo, Editorial S.L. (ESP) *(84-8470; 84-95150) Dist. by* **Mariuccia Iaconi Bk Imports.**

Corimbo, Editorial S.L. (ESP) *(84-8470; 84-95150) Dist. by* **Lectorum Pubns.**

Corimbo, Editorial S.L. (ESP) *(84-8470; 84-95150) Dist. by* **Distribks Inc.**

Corinthian Bks. *Imprint of* **Cote Literary Group, The**

Corinthian Enterprise Co., *(0-9711543)* 429 1/2 Sunlight Dr., Powell, WY 82435 USA Tel 307-532-8186 (phone/fax).

Cork Hill Pr., *(1-59408)* P.O. Box 117, Carmel, IN 46082-0117 USA
Web site: http://www.corkhillpress.com
Dist(s): **BookSurge, LLC**
Ingram Bk. Co.

Corman Productions, *(0-9655749)* 6729 Dume Dr., Malibu, CA 90265 USA Tel 310-457-7524; Fax: 310-457-5941
E-mail: Dikkybird@aol.com.

Cormier, Shawn *See* **Pine View Pr.**

Corn Tassel Pr., *(0-9752597)* 9655 Corn Tassel Ct., Columbia, MD 21046 USA Fax: 301-776-6538.

Cornell, A.J. Pubns., *(0-9727439)* 18-74 Corporal Kennedy St., Bayside, NY 11360 USA Tel 718-423-4082
Dist(s): **Biblio Distribution.**

†Cornell Maritime Pr., Inc., *(0-87033)* P.O. Box 456, Centreville, MD 21617 USA (SAN 203-5901) Tel 410-758-1075; Fax: 410-758-6849; Toll Free: 800-638-7641 ; *Imprints:* Tidewater Publishers (Tidewtr Pubs)
E-mail: editor@cornellmaritimepress.com
Web site: http://www.cornellmaritimepress.com/
Dist(s): **Hale, Robert & Co., Inc.**; *CIP.*

Cornell University, Cornell Cooperative Extension *See* **Resource Centre, The**

†Cornell Univ. Pr., *(0-8014; 0-87546)* Orders Addr.: P.O. Box 6525, Ithaca, NY 14851 USA (SAN 281-5680) Tel 607-277-2211; Toll Free Fax: 800-688-2877; Toll Free: 800-666-2211; Edit Addr.: Sage House, 512 E. State St., Ithaca, NY 14851 USA (SAN 202-1862) Tel 607-277-2338 ; *Imprints:* Comstock Publishing Associates (Comstock Pub); ILR Press (ILR Press)
E-mail: cupressinfo@cornell.edu; orders@nbninternational.com; cupress-sales@cornell.edu
Web site: http://www.cornellpress.cornell.edu
Dist(s): **CUP Services**; *CIP.*

Cornell Univ., Southeast Asia Program Pubns., *(0-87727)* Orders Addr.: 95 Brown Rd. Ste. 1004, Ithaca, NY 14850-1257 USA; Edit Addr.: 95 Brown Rd.,Box 1004, Rm 241, Ithaca, NY 14850 USA (SAN 241-6700) Tel 607-255-8038; Fax: 607-255-7534; Toll Free: 877-865-2432
E-mail: mdm44@cornell.edu; SEAP-Pubs@cornell.edu
Web site: http://www.einaudi.cornell.edu/southeastasia/publications.

Cornerstone Bk. Publishers *Imprint of* **Poll, Michael Publishing**

Cornerstone Curriculum Project, *(0-9656512)* 2006 Flat Creek Pl., Richardson, TX 75080 USA Tel 972-235-5149; Fax: 972-235-0236.

Cornerstone Enhancement, Incorporated *See* **Morning Star Media Group, Inc.**

Cornerstone Family Ministries/Lamplighter Publishing, *(1-58474)* Orders Addr.: P.O. Box 777, Waverly, PA 18471 USA Tel 717-585-1314; Fax: 717-587-4246; Toll Free: 888-246-7735; Edit Addr.: Waverly Community Ctr., Main St., S. Wing, 2nd Flr., Waverly, PA 18471 USA
E-mail: cfm@epix.net
Web site: http://www.agospel.com.

Cornerstone Pr. Chicago, *(0-940895)* 939 W. Willson, Chicago, IL 60640 USA (SAN 664-7200) Tel 773-561-2450; 773-989-4920; Fax: 773-989-2076; Toll Free: 888-407-7377
E-mail: cspress@jpusa.org
Web site: http://www.cornerstonepress.com
Dist(s): **Baker & Taylor Bks.**
Midpoint Trade Bks., Inc.

Cornerstone Press, Incorporated *See* **Patria Pr., Inc.**

Cornerstone Productions, Inc., *(1-883427; 1-58470)* P.O. Box 831955, Stone Mountain, GA 30083 USA.

Cornerstone Publishing & Distribution, Inc., *(1-929281)* P.O. Box 490, Bountiful, UT 84011-0490 USA Tel 801-295-9451; Fax: 801-295-0196; Toll Free: 800-453-0812
E-mail: rrhopkins@utah-inter.net.

Cornerstone Publishing, Inc., *(1-882185)* Orders Addr.: P.O. Box 1902, Griffin, GA 30223 USA (SAN 298-735X) Tel 267-975-7676 Do not confuse with companies with the same name in Decatur, GA, Altamonte Springs, FL, Wichita, KS
E-mail: books@cornerstonepublishing.com
Web site: http://www.cornerstonepublishing.com
Dist(s): **Book Clearing Hse.**

CornerWind Media, L.L.C., *(0-9741072)* Orders Addr.: 2635 Whitehall Ct., Rock Hill, SC 29732 USA Tel 803-329-7140; Fax: 803-329-7145
Web site: http://www.twiggyleaf.com; http://www.cornerwind.com
Dist(s): **Baker & Taylor Bks.**

Cornrows & Co., *(0-939183)* 5401 14th St., NW, Washington, DC 20011 USA (SAN 662-8303) Tel 202-726-3465; Fax: 202-882-3802; Toll Free: 800-543-3448
E-mail: talknhair@aol.com.

Corona Pr., *(1-891619)* 4535 Palmer Ct., Niwot, CO 80503 USA Tel 303-247-1455; Fax: 303-417-0355; Toll Free: 888-648-3877 Do not confuse with Corona Pr., Brooklandville, MD
E-mail: coronapress@aol.com.

Corona Publishing, Co., *(0-931722; 0-9720630)* Orders Addr.: P.O. Box 12407, San Antonio, TX 78212 USA (SAN 211-8491) Tel 210-828-9532; Fax: 210-828-4947; Edit Addr.: P.O. Box 12407, San Antonio, TX 78212-0407 USA Do not confuse with Corona Publishing in Long Beach, CA
E-mail: labatt@texas.net
Dist(s): **Hervey's Booklink & Cookbook Warehouse.**

Coronet Bks., *(0-89563; 91-7916)* 311 Bainbridge St., Philadelphia, PA 19147 USA (SAN 210-6043) Tel 215-925-2762; Fax: 215-925-1912 Do not confuse with Coronet Bks. & Pubns., Eagle Point, OR
E-mail: ronsmolin@earthlink.net; order@coronetbooks.com
Web site: http://www.coronetbooks.com.

Company

Coronet Bks. & Pubns., *(1-890609)* P.O. Box 957, Eagle Point, OR 97524 USA Tel 541-830-3040; Fax: 541-858-5595 ; *Imprints:* Lion's Paw Books (Lions Paw Bks) Do not confuse with Coronet Bks., Philadelphia, PA
E-mail: lions-paw@country.net.

Corporate Board Bks., *(0-9662445)* 7 Jennings Pond Rd., Natick, MA 01760 USA Tel 508-655-6170; Fax: 508-650-4091; Toll Free: 800-872-6097
E-mail: wmm47@aol.com.

Corpus Communications *See* **Caritas Communications**

Cortright Fellowship Pr., *(0-9706684)* P.O. Box 434, Allegan, MI 49010 USA
E-mail: ekklesia@accn.org
Web site: http://www.redbay.com/ekklesia.

Corunda, Ediciones, S.A. de C.V. (MEX) *(968-6044; 968-7444) Dist. by* **AIMS Intl.**

Corvina Books (HUN) *(963-13) Dist. by* **St Mut.**

Corvo Communications, *(0-9702366)* 551 Pearl St., Suite 209, Denver, CO 80203 USA Tel 303-722-6709
E-mail: dcdenver@aol.com
Web site: http://www.trailmixthebook.com.

Corwin Pr., *(0-7619; 0-8039; 1-57517; 1-879179; 1-4129)* Affil. of Sage Pubns., Inc., 2455 Teller Rd., Thousand Oaks, CA 91320-2218 USA Tel 805-499-9734; 805-499-9774 (customer service); Fax: 805-499-0871; 805-499-5323
E-mail: info@sagepub.com
Web site: http://www.corwinpress.com
Dist(s): **SAGE Pubns., Inc.**

Corwin Press, Incorporated *See* **Corwin Pr.**

Cosimo Classics *Imprint of* **Cosimo, Inc.**

Cosimo, Inc., *(1-59605; 1-60206; 1-60520)* P.O. Box 416, New York, NY 10011 USA Fax: 212-989-3662 ; *Imprints:* Cosimo Classics (CosClassics)
E-mail: adake@cosimobooks.com; info@cosimobooks.com
Web site: http://www.cosimobooks.com.

Cosley Production, *(0-9664588)* P.O. Box 5581, El Dorado Hills, CA 95762 USA Tel 530-626-6849; Fax: 530-676-0932; Toll Free: 888-706-6849
E-mail: cos2@foothill.net
Web site: http://www.cosleyprod.com
Dist(s): **Baker & Taylor Bks.**
Partners/West
Quality Bks., Inc.
Russell Dean & Co.

Cosmic Aye *Imprint of* **Hastings Ende Design Partners**

Cosmo Starr Bks., *(0-9650312; 1-930977)* Orders Addr.: P.O. Box 332, Taft, CA 93268 USA Tel 661-765-2484; Fax: 661-763-1262; Edit Addr.: 221 B St., Taft, CA 93268 USA.

Cosmos Publishing Co., Inc., *(0-9660449; 1-932455)* 262 River Vale Rd., River Vale, NJ 07675 USA (SAN 631-0486) Tel 201-664-3494; Fax: 201-664-3402 Do not confuse with companies with the same or similar names in Saint, Louis, MO, Loveland, CO
E-mail: greeceinprint@greeceinprint.com
Web site: http://www.greeceinprint.com.

Costume & Dressmaker Pr., *(0-9707242)* 1143 Bleistein Ave., Cody, WY 82414-3514 USA
E-mail: costumemag@costumemag.com; costumemaga@costumemag.com
Web site: http://www.costumemag.com.

Cote Literary Group, The, *(1-929175)* 483 Old Carolina Ct., Mount Pleasant, SC 29464 USA (SAN 850-4881) Tel 843-881-6080; Fax: 843-278-8456 ; *Imprints:* Corinthian Books (Corinthian Bks)
E-mail: editor@corinthianbooks.com; dickcote@earthlink.net
Web site: http://www.corinthianbooks.com
Dist(s): **Baker & Taylor Bks.**
Brodart Co.
Follett Library Resources
Parnassus Bk. Distributors
Quality Bks., Inc.
Sandlapper Publishing Co., Inc.

Cotler, Joanna Books *Imprint of* **HarperCollins Pubs.**

Cotsen Occasional Pr., *(0-9666084; 0-9745168)* Div. of Cotsen Family Foundation, 12100 Wilshire Blvd., Suite 905, Los Angeles, CA 90025 USA
E-mail: itrent@earthlink.net.

Cottonwood Graphics, Incorporated *See* **Cottonwood Publishing, Inc.**

Cottonwood Pr., Inc., *(1-877673)* 109-B Cameron Dr., Fort Collins, CO 80525 USA Tel 970-204-0715; Fax: 970-204-0761; Toll Free: 800-864-4297 Do not confuse with companies with same name in Novato, CA, Lawrence, KS, Wilsonville, OR
E-mail: cottonwood@cottonwoodpress.com
Web site: http://www.cottonwoodpress.com
Dist(s): **Independent Pubs. Group.**

CottonWood Publishing Co., *(0-9766804)* 840 W. Washington St., Ann Arbor, MI 48103 USA Do not confuse with Cottonwood Publishing Company in Saint George, UT Helena MT.

Cottonwood Publishing, Inc., *(0-9626999; 1-886370)* 120 Greenwood Dr., Helena, MT 59601-0374 USA Tel 406-495-1020; Fax: 406-495-1380; Toll Free: 800-937-6343 Do not confuse with Cottonwood Publishing in Saint George, UT Ann Arbor MI
E-mail: oldmt@mt.net
Web site: http://www.oldmontana.com
Dist(s): **Mountain Pr. Publishing Co., Inc.**

Coughlin Ranch Elementary's Finnell's Smart Little Minds, *(1-929544)* 4885 Village Green Pkwy., Reno, NV 89509 USA Tel 775-689-2600; Fax: 775-689-2535
E-mail: litlminds@aol.com.

Coulee Region Pubns., Inc., *(0-9650629)* 307 Twin Oak Dr., Altoona, WI 54720-1383 USA.

Counce, Paula, *(0-9762776)* 1628 Bob O Link Dr., Venice, FL 34293 USA
Web site: http://www.ajourneyremembered.com.

†**Council for Agricultural Science & Technology (CAST)**, *(1-887383)* 4420 W. Lincoln Way, Ames, IA 50014-3347 USA (SAN 225-7416) Tel 515-292-2125; Fax: 515-292-4512; Toll Free Fax: 800-375-2278; Toll Free: 800-762-4232
E-mail: cast@cast-science.org
Web site: http://www.cast-science.org; *CIP.*

Council for Indian Education, *(0-89992)* Orders Addr.: 1240 Burlington Ave., Billings, MT 59102-4224 USA Tel 406-248-3465; Fax: 406-248-1297
E-mail: cie@cie-mt.org
Web site: http://www.cie-mt.org.

Council for Spiritual & Ethical Education (CSEE), *(1-881678)* 10240 Groomsbridge Rd., Alpharetta, GA 30022-7314 USA (SAN 269-4247) Toll Free: 800-298-4599
E-mail: info@csee.org
Web site: http://www.csee.org.

Council Oak Bks., *(0-933031; 1-57178)* 2105 E. 15th St., Ste. B, Tulsa, OK 74104 USA (SAN 689-5522) Toll Free: 800-247-8850 (orders only); 2105 E. 15th St., Ste. B, Tulsa, OK 74104 (SAN 689-5522) Toll Free: 800-247-8850 (orders only) ; *Imprints:* PageMill Press (PageMll Pr)
E-mail: order@counciloakbooks.com; publicity@counciloakbooks.com
Web site: http://www.counciloakbooks.com
Dist(s): **New Leaf Distributing Co., Inc.**

Counseling Psychotherapy & Forensic Services, *(0-9700540)* 3214 Norway Pl., Norfolk, VA 23509 USA Tel 757-623-1939 (phone/fax)
Web site: http://www.psychologyinscripture.com.

Count On Learning, *(0-9771472)* 1406 Arlington Ave., Baton Rouge, LA 70808 USA
E-mail: admin@countonlearning.com
Web site: http://www.countonlearning.com.

Count Sheep Publishing, *(0-9668622)* 134 Mount Massive Way, Longmont, CO 80501-1966 USA
E-mail: loganleeh@aol.com; robjakoba@aol.com.

Counterpoint, *(1-59376)* 1400 65th St., Suite 250, Emeryville, CA 94608-1077 USA Tel 510-704-0230
E-mail: thoard@shoemakerhoard.com
Web site: http://www.shoemakerhoard.com/
Dist(s): **Perseus Distribution.**

Countertop Software *See* **TOPICS Entertainment**

Countinghouse Pr., Inc., *(0-9664732; 0-9786191)* 6632 Telegraph Rd., Suite 311, Bloomfield Hills, MI 48301 USA Tel 248-642-7191; Fax: 248-642-7192
E-mail: lcharla@comcast.net
Web site: http://www.countinghousepress.com.

Country Boy Publishing Co., *(0-9795574)* Orders Addr.: 300 Collier Dr., Winter Haven, FL 33884 USA
E-mail: dgreenl2@tampabay.rr.com
Web site: http://www.countryboypublishing.com.

Country Bumpkin Pubns, *(0-9677938)* 212 California Ave., Watertown, NY 13601 USA Tel 315-782-0941
E-mail: bsteve3@twcny.rr.com.

Country Home Pubs., *(0-9632513; 1-888831)* 6757 Cascade Rd SE, Grand Rapids, MI 49546-6849 USA (SAN 253-5807)
E-mail: cyndi@countryhomepublishers.com; cindi@countryhomepublishers.com
Web site: http://countryhomepublishers.com.

Country Lane Limited *See* **August Rose Publishing**

Country Place Bks., *(0-9643003)* Box 112, Weston, MA 02493 USA Tel 781-891-9530 (phone/fax)
E-mail: Nanfleming@comcast.net
Web site: http://www.missmouseshouse.com
Dist(s): **Baker & Taylor Bks.**

†**Countryman Pr.**, *(0-88150; 0-914378; 0-936399; 0-942440; 1-58157)* Div. of W. W. Norton & Co., Inc., P.O. Box 748, Woodstock, VT 05091-0748 USA (SAN 206-4901) Tel 802-457-4826 Toll Free: 800-245-4151 (Orders only) ; *Imprints:* Berkshire House (BerkHouse)
E-mail: countrymanpress@wwnorton.com
Web site: http://www.countrymanpress.com
Dist(s): **Norton, W. W. & Co., Inc.**; *CIP.*

County of Monroe, Michigan, *(0-615; 0-9722232)* 125 E. Second St., Monroe, MI 48161 USA Tel 734-240-7375; Fax: 734-240-7385; Toll Free: 888-354-5500
E-mail: royce_maniko@monroemi.org
Web site: http://www.co.monroe.mi.us.

Courage Bks. *Imprint of* **Running Pr. Bk. Pubs.**

Courage to Change *See* **CTC Publishing**

Courageous Kids, Inc., *(0-9742590)* P.O. Box 2322, County Club Hills, IL 60478 USA Tel 708-922-9233
E-mail: hesinme01@cs.com.

Courier Custom Publishing, Inc., *(1-58692)* Div. of Courier Corp., 15 Wellman Ave., North Chelmsford, MA 01863-1334 USA Tel 978-251-6133; Fax: 978-251-6240; Toll Free Fax: 877-516-2874; Toll Free: 800-487-4305
E-mail: info@coursepack.com
Web site: http://www.custombook.com.

Course Technology *Imprint of* **Thomson Course Technology, Inc.**

Course Technology, Incorporated *See* **Thomson Course Technology, Inc.**

Court Jester Ministries, Inc., *(0-9663002)* R.R. 7, Box 344, North Mankato, MN 56003-9015 USA Tel 507-947-3292.

Courtney Pr., *(0-9609108; 0-9795592)* Orders Addr.: Box 845, Aspen, CO 81612 USA (SAN 241-483X) Tel 970-379-2224; Fax: 970-925-6037; Edit Addr.: 121 Daniel Dr., Aspen, CO 81611 USA
E-mail: courtney@sopris.net
Web site: http://www.jillsheeleybooks.com.

Courtyard Publishing, LLC, *(0-9795260)* Div. of Alchemical Courtyard, LLC, 1688 Meridian Ave., 10th Flr., Miami Beach, FL 33139 USA Tel 305-695-9380
E-mail: ahorowitz@alchemicalcourtyard.com
Dist(s): **AtlasBooks Distribution.**

†**Covenant Communications**, *(0-9649122)* 1009 Jones St., Old Hickory, TN 37138 USA Tel 615-847-2066; Fax: 615-860-3601; Toll Free: 800-979-3882 Do nt oconfuse with Covenant Communications in Old Hickory, TN
Dist(s): **Quality Bks., Inc.**; *CIP.*

Covenant Communications, Inc., *(1-55503; 1-57734; 1-59156; 1-59811)* Orders Addr.: P.O. Box 416, American Fork, UT 84003-0416 USA (SAN 169-8540) Tel 801-756-9966; Fax: 801-756-1049; Toll Free: 800-662-9545; Edit Addr.: 920 E. State Rd., Suite F, American Fork, UT 84003 USA Do not confuse with Covenant Communications in American Fork, UT
E-mail: scottn@covenant-lds.com
Web site: http://www.covenant-lds.com.

Covenant of Light Publishing *See* **Sorcerer's Pr., The**

Covenant Publishing, Inc., *(1-892435)* Orders Addr.: P.O. Box 390, Webb City, MO 64870-0390 USA Tel 417-673-1015; Fax: 417-673-1065; Toll Free: 877-673-1015; Edit Addr.: P.O. Box 390, Webb City, MO 64870-0390 USA
E-mail: sdcable@covenantpublishing.com
Dist(s): **Twentieth Century Christian Bks.**

Covenant Support Network, *(0-9772313)* N7719 Maple Ridge Rd., Oconomowoc, WI 53066 USA
Web site: http://www.awhitestone.com.

Coventry Pool & Garden Houses *See* **Manor Hse. Publishing Co., Inc.**

Coventry Pr., LLC, *(0-9660774)* Div. of Owl Creek Assocs., 1214 Owl Creek Ranch Rd., Aspen, CO 81611 USA Tel 970-923-6629; Fax: 970-923-0263 Do not confuse with Coventry Pr., Columbus, OH
E-mail: Snodesert@aol.com
Dist(s): **Books West**
Quality Bks., Inc.

Covercraft *Imprint of* **Perfection Learning Corp.**

Covered Bridge Bks., *(0-9722027)* 336 Covered Bridge Rd., Cherry Hill, NJ 08034-2949 USA.

Covered Bridge Children's Books *See* **Covered Bridge Bks.**

Covered Bridge Pr. *Imprint of* **Douglas Charles, Ltd.**

Covered Wagon Publishing LLC, *(0-9723259)* P.O. Box 473038, Aurora, CO 80047 USA (SAN 254-7813) Tel 303-751-0992; Fax: 303-632-6794
E-mail: CoveredWagon@comcast.net
Web site: http://www.RockyMountainMysteries.com.

Covey Leadership Center, Incorporated *See* **Franklin Covey Co.**

Cow Heard Records, *(0-9763012)* 3622 Altura Ave., La Crescenta, CA 91214 USA
Web site: http://www.thesunflowers.com.

Cowboy Collector Pubns., *(0-9628078)* Orders Addr.: P.O. Box 7486, Long Beach, CA 90807 USA Tel 714-840-3942; Edit Addr.: 4677 Rio Ave., Long Beach, CA 90805 USA Tel 213-428-6972
Dist(s): **Hervey's Booklink & Cookbook Warehouse.**

Cowboy Magazine, *(0-9765969)* Orders Addr.: P.O. Box 126, La Veta, CO 81055 USA Tel 719-742-5250; Fax: 719-742-3034; Edit Addr.: 124 N. Main St., La Veta, CO 81055 USA
E-mail: workincowboy@amigo.net
Web site: http://www.cowboymagazine.com.

Cowgill, Ruth Moloney, *(0-9708761)* Orders Addr.: P.O. Box 31, Richwood, OH 43344 USA Tel 740-943-3851; Fax: 937-390-7798; Edit Addr.: 44 George St, Richwood, OH 43344 USA
E-mail: EACowgill@aol.com.

Cowgirl Peg Enterprises LLC, *(0-9721057)* Orders Addr.: P.O. Box 19899, Colorado City, CO 81019 USA; Edit Addr.: P.O. Box 56, Wheatland, WY 82201-0056 USA
E-mail: peg@cowgirlpeg.com
Web site: http://www.cowgirlpeg.com
Dist(s): **Baker & Taylor Bks.**
Books West
Follett Library Resources.

†**Cowley Pubns.**, *(0-936384; 1-56101)* Div. of Society of St. John the Evangelist, 4 Brattle St., Cambridge, MA 02138 USA (SAN 213-9987) Fax: 617-441-0300; Toll Free: 800-225-1534
E-mail: cowley@cowley.org
Web site: http://www.cowley.org
Dist(s): **Forward Movement Pubns.**
Ingram Pub. Services
National Bk. Network
Rowman & Littlefield Pubs., Inc.; *CIP.*

Cowpokes Cartoon Bks., *(0-917207)* P.O. Box 290868, Kerrville, TX 78029-0868 USA (SAN 656-089X) Tel 830-257-7446 (phone/fax); Toll Free: 800-257-7441 (phone/fax)
E-mail: cartoons@cowpokes.com
Web site: http://www.cowpokes.com.

Cowrie Bks. (AUS) *(0-646; 0-9581267) Dist. by* **UH Pr.**

Cox, Gene, *(0-9669672)* 2309 Limerick Dr., Tallahassee, FL 32308 USA Tel 850-893-1789
E-mail: gccox@mail.istal.com.

Cox, Julie, *(0-9742118)* P.O. Box 77966, Fort Worth, TX 76177 USA
E-mail: info@facereadingacademy.com
Web site: http://www.facereadingacademy.com.

Coyle, Arthur Pr., *(0-9665947)* Orders Addr.: P.O. Box 59435, Chicago, IL 60659 USA Tel 773-465-8418; Edit Addr.: 2730 W. Coyle Ave., Chicago, IL 60645 USA
Dist(s): **Independent Pubs. Group.**

Coyote Moon Pr., *(0-9661070)* P.O. Box 6867, Denver, CO 80206 USA Tel 303-316-4633; Fax: 303-321-3551
E-mail: wildlife_writer@msn.com
Dist(s): **Johnson Bks.**

Coyote Moon Publishing *See* **Cowgirl Peg Enterprises LLC**

CoZi Publishing LLC, *(0-9749151)* P.O. Box 211, Rutland, VT 05702-0211 USA
E-mail: publish@cozi.com
Web site: http://www.cozi.com.

Cozy Cottage Entertainment, *(0-9706321)* P.O. Box 206, Alton, MO 65606-0206 USA Tel 417-938-4259; Fax: 417-938-4935; Toll Free: 800-949-7664
E-mail: csigfus@ortrackm.missouri.org.

Cozy Graphics Corp., *(1-932002; 1-59343)* 61-20 G.C.P., Apt. B1204, Forest Hills, NY 11375 USA Tel 718-592-9782 (phone/fax) ; *Imprints:* Cozy House Publisher (Cozy Hse Pub)
E-mail: publisher@cozygraphics.com
Web site: http://www.cozygraphics.com.

Cozy Hse. Publisher *Imprint of* **Cozy Graphics Corp.**

CPCC Pr., *(1-59494)* P.O. Box 35009, Charlotte, NC 28235-5009 USA Tel 704-330-6789; Fax: 704-330-6720
Web site: http://www.cpccservicescorp.com.

CPG Publishing, Inc., *(1-931411)* Orders Addr.: c/o CPG Distribution, 7253 Grayson Rd., Harrisburg, PA 17111 USA Toll Free: 800-501-6883 (orders & customer service); Edit Addr.: P.O. Box 6142, New York, NY 10150 USA Tel 212-573-9180; Fax: 212-573-9181 Do not confuse with C P G Publishing Company in Gold Canyon, AZ
E-mail: cpgdistribution@juno.com.

CPM Comics *Imprint of* **Central Park Media Corp.**

CPM Manga *Imprint of* **Central Park Media Corp.**

CPM Manhwa *Imprint of* **Central Park Media Corp.**

CPR Pubng, *(0-9778597)* 740 13th St., Fennimore, WI 53809 USA.

CQ Pr. College *Imprint of* **CQ Pr.**

CQ Pr. Library Reference *Imprint of* **CQ Pr.**

†CQ Pr., *(0-7401; 0-87187; 0-87289; 0-9625531; 1-56692; 1-56802; 1-933116; 1-60426)* Div. of Congressional Quarterly, Inc., Orders Addr.: a/o Order Dept., 1255 22nd St. NW, Suite 400, Washington, DC 20037 USA (SAN 256-470X) Tel 202-729-1889 (customer service - orders); Fax: 202-729-1804 (customer service - orders); Toll Free: 866-427-7737 (customer service - orders) ; *Imprints:* C Q Press College (CQ Pr Coll); C Q Press Library Reference (CQ Pr Lib Ref)
E-mail: customerservice@cqpress.com
Web site: http://www.cqpress.com; *CIP.*

Crabtree, Linda F., *(0-9701581)* 980 NE Jacksonville Rd., Anthony, FL 32617 USA Tel 352-620-8454
E-mail: Lindwrite@aol.com.

Cracked Egg Brand Pr., *(1-882820)* Orders Addr.: P.O. Box 134, Stowell, TX 77661 USA Tel 409-296-2053; Fax: 409-835-5413; Edit Addr.: Main & Third, Stowell, TX 77661 USA.

Cracker the Crab LLC, *(0-9725560)* P.O. Box 80475, Simpsonville, SC 29680-0475 USA Do not confuse with Two Bear Publishing Company in Alpine, CA
E-mail: jillkcogdill@twobearproducts.com; jcogdill@crackerthecrab.com; jkcogdill@msn.com
Web site: http://www.crackerthecrab.com.

Crain, Suzanne, *(0-9763254)* 3585 New Saratoga Rd., Anna, IL 62906-4166 USA
E-mail: slcrain@hcis.net.

Cranberry Quill Publishing Co., *(0-9741406)* 439 Westwood Shopping Ctr., No. 138, Fayetteville, NC 28314-1532 USA
E-mail: dreneegibbs@aol.com; cranberryquill@aol.com
Web site: http://www.cranberryquill.com.

Crane & Rogers Pubs., *(0-9716515)* 6129 Vista Dr., Falls Church, VA 22041 USA Tel 703-715-6869.

Crane Bks., *(0-9647924)* Div. of Math in Motion, 668 Stony Hill Rd., No. 233, Yardley, PA 19067 USA Tel 215-321-5556; Fax: 215-310-9412
E-mail: info@mathinmotion.com
Web site: http://www.mathinmotion.com.

†Crane Hill Pubs., *(0-9621455; 1-57587; 1-881548)* 3608 Clairmont Ave., Birmingham, AL 35222-3508 USA Tel 205-714-3007; Fax: 205-714-3008
E-mail: cranemail@cranehill.com
Web site: http://www.cranehill.com
Dist(s): **Independent Pubs. Group**; *CIP.*

Crane Institute of America, Inc., *(0-9744279)* 3880 Saint Johns Pkwy., Sanford, FL 32771 USA Tel 407-322-6800; Fax: 407-330-0660; Toll Free: 800-832-2726
E-mail: megan@craneinstitute.com; info@craneinstitute.com
Web site: http://www.craneinstitute.com.

Crane Publishing, *(0-9753608)* 308 Trinity Rd., Venice, FL 34293 USA Do not confuse with companies with the same name in Paramus, New Jersey.
E-mail: jborza@josephborza.com; jborza@cranepublishing.net
Web site: http://www.cranepublishing.net.

Crane, Robert Publishing, *(1-891232)* Div. of The Robert Crane Corp., P.O. Box 440504, Jacksonville, FL 32222 USA Tel 904-276-4020; Fax: 904-276-1104
E-mail: Info@ClosetBooks.com
Web site: http://www.ClosetBooks.com.

CraneDance Pubns., *(0-9708895)* Div. of BGleason Design & Illustration, LLC, Orders Addr.: P.O. Box 50535, Eugene, OR 97405 USA Tel 541-345-3974 (phone/fax)
E-mail: barbdan@cranedance.com
Web site: http://www.bgleasondesign.com/sections/products.html.

Cranky Pants Publishing, LLC, *(0-9759627)* 2 Upland Rd., W., Arlington, MA 02474 USA
E-mail: sanzo@erols.com
Dist(s): **Biblio Distribution.**

Crawford, Quinton Douglass, *(0-615)* 225 Santa Ana Ct., Fairfield, CA 94533 USA
Web site: http://www.knowledgefortomorrow.com
Dist(s): **Lulu.com.**

Crayon Artist, LLC, The, *(0-9715441)* Orders Addr.: P.O. Box 50749, Denton, TX 76206 USA Tel 940-243-2248; Fax: 940-387-9390; Toll Free: 800-347-7774; Edit Addr.: 115 W. Hickory, Denton, TX 76206 USA
E-mail: thecrayonartist@aol.com
Web site: http://www.thecrayonartist.com.

Crazy Man Press, LLC, *(0-9743553)* 33 University Sq., Suite 254, Madison, WI 53715-1042 USA Tel 608-215-0532
E-mail: info@crazymanpress.com
Web site: http://www.crazymanpress.com.

Crazy Pet Pr., The, *(0-9744749)* 655 N. Azusa Ave., No. 104, Azusa, CA 91708 USA Tel 831-438-2730; Fax: 831-438-2764; Toll Free: 877-860-2100
E-mail: kpbooks@calcentral.com
Web site: http://www.crazydog.com; http://www.crazypetpress.com; http://www.kidoodlepetpress.com
Dist(s): **Biblio Distribution.**

Crazyfish/MJ-12, *(0-9700387)* 1632 N. Pepper St., Burbank, CA 91505 USA Tel 818-845-3818 (phone/fax)
E-mail: faustmorse@earthlink.net
Web site: http://www.crazyfish.net.

Creating Worlds Publishing Co., *(0-9669600)* Orders Addr.: P.O. Box 3014, Petersburg, VA 23805 USA Tel 804-862-2986 (phone/fax); Edit Addr.: 1847 Buckner St., Petersburg, VA 23805 USA.

Creation Bks. (GBR) *(1-84068; 1-871592) Dist. by* **Subterranean Co.**

Creation Hse. *Imprint of* **Strang Communications Co.**

Creation Instruction Publishing, *(1-928765)* Orders Addr.: P.O. Box 304, Plentywood, MT 59254 USA Tel 406-895-2689; Edit Addr.: 1770 S. Overland, Juniata, NE 68955 USA
E-mail: creation1@juno.com
Web site: http://www.creationinstruction.org/.

Creation of Celebration, Inc., *(1-929208)* 7 Dunnberry Ct., Greensboro, NC 27455 USA (SAN 253-6447) Tel 336-288-6354 (phone/fax); Toll Free: 877-587-2302 ; *Imprints:* Happy Tales Press (Happy Tales).

Creation Resource Foundation, *(0-9672713)* P.O. Box 570, El Dorado, CA 95667 USA Tel 530-626-4447; Fax: 530-626-3221; Toll Free: 800-497-1454
E-mail: info@creationresource.org
Web site: http://www.awesomeworks.com; http://www.creationresource.org/
Dist(s): **STL Distribution North America.**

Creations by Basia, *(1-890582)* 2219 E. Thousand Oaks Blvd., Suite 370, Thousand Oaks, CA 91362 USA Tel 818-707-7702; Fax: 818-707-7033
E-mail: creationsbybasia@msn.com
Web site: http://www.basia.com
Dist(s): **Sunbelt Pubns., Inc.**

Creations by You, *(0-9636796; 0-9753346; 0-9785879)* 1500 W. Hampden Ave., Suite 4E, Englewood, CO 80110 USA Toll Free: 800-706-8697
E-mail: nanthomas@creationsbyyou.com
Web site: http://www.creationsbyyou.com.

Creative 3, LLC, *(1-933815)* 2236 E Spring Hill Rd., Springfield, MO 65804 USA Tel 417-882-2145; Fax: 417-882-2145; Toll Free Fax: 800-866-1360; Toll Free: 800-866-1360 ; *Imprints:* Quirkles, The (The Quirkles)
E-mail: info@quirkles.com; thequirkles@aol.com
Web site: http://www.quirkles.com.

Creative Art Pr., *(0-9642712)* 6850 Brookshire Dr., West Bloomfield, MI 48322 USA Tel 248-669-7589; Fax: 248-669-6268
Dist(s): **APG Sales and Fulfillment.**

Creative Attic, Inc., The, *(0-9653955)* P.O. Box 187, Canterbury, NH 03224 USA Tel 603-783-9103; Fax: 603-783-0118; Toll Free: 888-566-6539
E-mail: the5kids@aol.com
Dist(s): **Baker & Taylor Bks.**

Creative Bk. Pubs., *(0-9754818; 0-9763093; 0-9765467; 0-9779662; 0-9795460)* 1912 Falcon Dr., Ridgefield, WA 98642 USA
Web site: http://www.creativebookpublishers.com.

Creative Communication, *(1-60050)* Orders Addr.: P.O. Box 303, Smithfield, UT 84335 USA Tel 435-713-4411; Fax: 435-713-4422; Edit Addr.: 1488 . 200 W., Logan, UT 84341 USA Do not confuse with companies with the same or similar name in Forest Grove, OR, Seattle, WA, Trabuco Canyon, CA, NIxa, MO, Chelan, WA, La Mesa, CA, Kalamazoo, MI
E-mail: drtom@poeticpower.com
Web site: http://www.poeticpower.com.

Creative Communication, Incorporated *See* **Poet Tree Pr.**

Creative Communications *See* **Sparkle Presentations**

Creative Co., The, *(0-87191; 0-88682; 1-56660; 1-56846)* 123 S. Broad St., P.O. Box 227, Mankato, MN 56001 USA Tel 507-388-6273; Fax: 507-388-2746; Toll Free: 800-445-6209 ; *Imprints:* Creative Editions (Creative Eds); Creative Education (Creat Educ); Creative Paperbacks (Creative Paperbks) Do not confuse with The Creative Co., Lawrenceburg, IN
E-mail: info@thecreativecompany.us
Web site: http://www.thecreativecompany.us
Dist(s): **Abraham Assocs. Inc.**

Creative Concepts for Children *See* **Arcadia Pr.**

Creative Connections, *(0-9668887)* 46629B Arapahoe, Indian Wells, CA 92210 USA Do not confuse the companies with a similar name in Santa Fe, NM, Nashville, TN .

Creative Continuum, Inc., *(0-9713804; 1-932252)* 2910 E. La Palma Ave. Ste. C, Anaheim, CA 92806-2618 USA
E-mail: info@creativecontinuum.com
Web site: http://www.creativecontinuum.com.

Creative Conversations, *(0-9768235)* 11767 W. Coal Mine Dr., Littleton, CO 80127 USA Tel 303-437-8533.

Creative Curriculum Initiatives, *(0-9786500; 1-60409)* 80 Fifth Ave., Suite 1503, New York, NY 10011 USA Tel 212-242-7827; Fax: 212-242-3523.

Creative Dreaming Ltd., *(0-615)* 6433 Topanga Canyon Blvd., No. 120, Woodland Hills, CA 91303 USA
Dist(s): **Lulu.com.**

Creative Editions *Imprint of* **Creative Co., The**

Creative Education *Imprint of* **Creative Co., The**

Creative Educational Video *See* **C E V Multimedia, Ltd.**

Creative Endeavors Publishing, *(0-9674768)* 844 Dodd Ct., Bay Point, CA 94565 USA
E-mail: comicmonkey@hotmail.com.

Creative Enigma Enterprises, *(0-9719943)* 215 W. MacArthur Blvd., No. 519, Oakland, CA 94611 USA Fax: 510-782-2572 (orders or requests)
E-mail: qtn2u2@yahoo.com
Web site: http://www.creativeenigma.com.

Creative Enterprises, *(1-880675)* 1040 Harvard Blvd., Dayton, OH 45406-5047 USA (SAN 253-5491) Tel 937-278-7159; Toll Free: 888-266-5777 Do not confuse with companies with the same or similar name in Mattapoisett, MA, Cordova, TN, Brooklyn, NY, Kittery, ME, Montgomery Village, MD
E-mail: allen45406@aol.com
Web site: http://creative-enterprises.org.

Creative Enterprises, *(1-893615)* Orders Addr.: P.O. Box 597, Kittery, ME 03904 USA Tel 207-438-9528 (phone/fax) Do not confuse with companies with the same or similar name in Dayton, OH, Mattapoisett, MA, Cordova, TN, Brooklyn, NY, Montgomery Village, MD.

Creative Expressions of America, *(0-9704231)* P.O. Box 665, Layton, UT 84041-0665 USA
E-mail: createxpressions@aol.com.

Creative Genius Pubns., *(0-9713539)* Orders Addr.: P.O. Box 5112, Woodridge, IL 60517 USA (SAN 254-0517) Tel 630-963-5681; Fax: 630-968-4154; Edit Addr.: 7000 Newport, No. 204, Woodridge, IL 60517 USA
E-mail: creategenius@sbcglobal.net
Web site: http://www.creategenius.com
Dist(s): **Baker & Taylor Bks.**

Creative Heart Media, *(0-9667583)* Orders Addr.: P.O. Box 229, Medford, NY 11763 USA Tel 516-654-0607; Toll Free: 888-816-2375; Edit Addr.: 28 Lace Bark Ln., Medford, NY 11763 USA
E-mail: creativeheartmedia@pastore.com.

†Creative Homeowner, *(0-932944; 1-58011; 1-880029)* Div. of Federal Marketing Corp., 24 Park Way, Upper Saddle River, NJ 07458-9960 USA (SAN 213-6627) Tel 201-934-7100; Fax: 201-934-8971; Toll Free: 800-631-7795
E-mail: info@creativehomeowner.com
Web site: http://www.creativehomeowner.com; *CIP.*

Creative Image Pubs., *(0-9742667)* 102 E. Main, Georgetown, KY 40324 USA
E-mail: Kathy@creativeimagepublishers.com
Web site: http://www.creativeimagepublishers.com.

Creative Imagery, *(0-9722040)* 22 Cleveland Way, West Yarmouth, MA 02673 USA
Web site: http://www.creativeImagery.biz.

Creative Learning Books *See* **Aradiance Publishing**

Creative Learning Consultants, Incorporated *See* **Pieces of Learning**

Creative Learning Exchange, *(0-9753169)* 27 Central St., Acton, MA 01720-3522 USA (SAN 850-8836) Tel 978-287-0070; Fax: 978-287-0080
E-mail: stuntzln@clexchange.org
Web site: http://www.clexchange.org.

Creative Learning Pr., Inc., *(0-936386; 1-931280)* Orders Addr.: P.O. Box 320, Mansfield Center, CT 06250 USA (SAN 298-4601) Tel 860-429-8118; Fax: 860-429-7783; Toll Free: 888-518-8004
E-mail: clp@creativelearningpress.com; customerservice@creativelearningpress.com
Web site: http://www.creativelearningpress.com.

Creative Links (JAM) *(976-610) Dist. by* **BookMasters.**

Creative Marketing Concepts, Inc., *(0-9761408)* 2775 Jade St., Mora, MN 55051 USA Tel 320-679-4105; Fax: 320-679-3349; Toll Free: 800-605-4280 Do not confuse with companies with the same name in Saint Louis, MO, Los Angeles, CA
E-mail: cmc@creativemk.com
Web site: http://www.creativemk.com.

Creative Nutrition & Wellness, *(0-615)* P.O. Box 7000-233, Redondo Beach, CA 90277 USA Fax: 310-792-0428
Web site: http://www.creativenutrition.com.

Creative Paperbacks *Imprint of* **Creative Co., The**

Creative Passages, Inc., *(0-9674467)* 568 Vinita Ave, Akron, OH 44320 USA Tel 330-836-5107; Fax: 330-836-3842
E-mail: creativepassages@hotmail.com.

Creative Pubns., *(0-7622; 0-88488; 1-56107)* Div. of Educational Publishing Corp., 2 Prudential Plaza, No. 1175, Chicago, IL 60601 USA (SAN 631-1024)
Dist(s): **Wright Group, The.**

Creative Publishing, *(0-9744833)* 2221 Justin Rd., No. 119-123, Flower Mound, TX 75028 USA Tel 281-251-1751 (phone/fax) Do not confuse with companies with the same or similar name in Roseboro, NC, Greenville, SC, Lawrenceville, GA, Shrevport, LA, College Station, TX, Tustin, CA
E-mail: support@creativekidsonthemove.com
Web site: http://www.creativekidsonthemove.com.

Creative Publishing International *Imprint of* **Quayside**

Creative Publishing Services, *(1-892774)* 25 Cordele Rd., Newark, DE 19711-5612 USA Tel 302-454-9041
E-mail: SBarb55@aol.com.

Creative Quill Publishing, Inc., *(0-9709906)* Orders Addr.: P.O. Box 4028, Salem, OR 97302 USA; Edit Addr.: 460 Myers S., Salem, OR 97302 USA Tel 503-363-2843
E-mail: mavist@aol.com; Creativequill@aol.com
Web site: http://www.creativequill.us.

Creative Realizations, Inc., *(0-9665086)* 7435 Blvd. E., Apt. 55, North Bergen, NJ 07047 USA Tel 201-861-0210; Fax: 201-861-3934
E-mail: greatstuff@worldnet.att.net.

Creative Services, *(0-9702584)* 1009 Paris Ave., Nashville, TN 37204 USA Tel 615-385-2881; Fax: 615-298-5309 Do not confuse with Creative Services in Carmichael, CA
E-mail: bose-tennessee@home.com.

Creative Sharp Presentations, Incorporated *See* **SHARP Literacy, Inc.**

Creative Sources, *(0-9759613)* 105 N. Harvest Crest Ct., Highland, IL 62249-3886 USA
E-mail: lls@empowering.com; info@creativesourcespublishing.com
Web site: http://www.creativesourcespublishing.com.

Creative Spirit Publishing Co., *(0-9706084)* 1034 E. Monroe St., Colorado Springs, CO 80907-7143 USA; P.O. Box 1041, Colorado Springs, CO 80907
E-mail: creative_spirit@netzero.com.

Creative Styles *See* **JFW, Ltd.**

Creative Success Works, *(0-9759551)* 752 E. Lake Lndg., Marietta, GA 30062-3876 USA
E-mail: creativesuccess@comcast.net
Web site: http://www.creativesuccessworks.com.

Creative Teaching Assocs., *(1-878669; 1-930818; 1-931474; 1-932918)* Orders Addr.: P.O. Box 7766, Fresno, CA 93747 USA (SAN 297-6803) Tel 559-294-2141 Toll Free: 800-767-4282 (800-767-4CTA); Edit Addr.: P.O. Box 7766, Fresno, CA 93747-7766 USA
Web site: http://www.mastercta.com.

Creative Teaching Pr., Inc., *(0-88160; 0-916119; 1-57471; 1-59198)* Orders Addr.: P.O. Box 2723, Huntington Beach, CA 92647-0723 USA Tel 714-895-5047; Fax: 714-895-6547; Toll Free Fax: 800-444-4287; Edit Addr.: 15342 Graham St., Huntington Beach, CA 92649-1111 USA (SAN 294-9180) Tel 714-895-5047; Toll Free Fax: 800-229-9929; Toll Free: 800-444-4287 ; *Imprints:* Learning Works, The (The Lrning Works)
E-mail: webmaster@creativeteaching.com; welisten@creativeteaching.com
Web site: http://www.creativeteaching.com; http://www.thelearningworks.com
Dist(s): **Abrams & Co. Pubs., Inc.**
Pacific Learning, Inc.

Creative Thinkers, Inc., *(1-58237)* 8 South St. Southfield, No. 10, Danbury, CT 06810 USA Tel 203-778-9749; Fax: 203-778-6492; Toll Free: 800-841-2883
E-mail: thinkkids@aol.com; sftierno@aol.com
Web site: http://www.thinkkids.com.

Creative Vision Publishing, *(0-9715166)* 1004 Carondelet Dr., Suite 330, Kansas City, MO 64114 USA Tel 913-631-6133; Fax: 816-941-6404 Do not confuse with Creative Vision Publishing LLC in Palm Beach Gardens, FL
E-mail: sdattel@aol.com.

Creative Well, The, *(0-9700108)* P.O. Box 2121, Ashtabula, OH 44005 USA Tel 440-964-0338.

Creative with Words Pubns., *(0-936945)* P.O. Box 223226, Carmel, CA 93922 USA (SAN 658-6961) Fax: 408-655-8627
E-mail: cwwpub@usa.net.

Creative Works, *(0-9727499)* 3747 Redwood Cir., Palo Alto, CA 94306 USA Tel 650-493-3747.

Creative World Enterprise, Inc, *(0-9701218; 0-9705631; 0-9715058; 0-9723405; 0-9729521; 1-933226)* 43 Candlewick Ct., Matawan, NJ 07747 USA Tel 732-441-1704
E-mail: practicalchinese@cs.com
Web site: http://practicalchinese.com.

Creative Writing & Publishing Co., *(1-887636)* P.O. Box 511848, Milwaukee, WI 53203-0311 USA
E-mail: Cbritt1@wi.rr.com.

Creative Writing Pr., Inc., *(0-9708382)* 1830 Stephenson Hwy., Troy, MI 48083-2173 USA Toll Free: 800-760-6397
E-mail: rodgers@mich.com
Web site: http://thepoetrylady.com.

Creatopia Productions - Lamy, New Mexico, *(0-9637467)* 31 Cerro Cir. # B, Lamy, NM 87540-9682 USA
E-mail: billyne@earthlink.net
Web site: http://www.members.tripod.com/~lyne4lyne/
Dist(s): **AK Pr. Distribution**
Adventures Unlimited Pr.
Barnes & Noble Bks.-Imports
Baker & Taylor Bks.
Free American, The
Greenleaf Pubns.
Truth Seeker Co., Inc.

Creator's creator, The, *(0-9713371)* P.O. Box 4542, Hampton Park, MD 20791-4542 USA Tel 301-567-3260.

Creatrix! LLC, *(0-9760604)* P.O. Box 366, Cottage Grove, WI 53527 USA.

Creed, Julie, *(0-9728181)* 17 Los Abitos, Rancho Santa Margarita, CA 92688 USA
E-mail: julie@qabranding.com
Web site: http://www.qabranding.com.

Creek Sound Bks., *(0-9743840)* 120 Misty Way, Cosby, TN 37722 USA Tel 606-523-5324
E-mail: rapowell7@msn.com.

Creekside Stories, *(0-9709843)* P.O. Box 46, Goveland, CA 95321 USA Tel 209-962-7634
E-mail: irene@zoo-phonics.com.

Creepy Little Productions, *(0-9704159)* 3726 W. Augusta Ave., Phoenix, AZ 85051 USA Tel 602-625-6596; Fax: 602-242-3046
E-mail: christy@atgproductions.com; madamem@creepylittlestories.com
Web site: http://www.creepylittlestories.com
Dist(s): **Baker & Taylor Bks.**
PSI (Publisher Services, Inc.).

Creevy, Anne *See* **ABC Bks.**

Creflo Dollar Ministries Pubns., *(1-931172; 1-59089)* Orders Addr.: P.O. Box 490124, College Park, GA 30349 USA Tel 770-210-5700; Fax: 770-210-5701; Edit Addr.: 2500 Burdett Rd., College Park, GA 30349 USA
E-mail: mfleming@worldchangers.org; mocarter@worldchangers.org; dfidler@worldchangers.org; tdavis@worldchangers.org
Web site: http://www.creflodollarministries.org
Dist(s): **Harrison Hse., Inc.**
STL Distribution North America.

CreoXimius Publishing Company, *(0-9776617)* 970 E. Smith Rd., Medina, OH 44256 USA
Web site: http://www.debrae.com.

Crescent *Imprint of* **Random Hse. Value Publishing**

Crescent Moon Pubns. *Imprint of* **Christian Scholar's Pr.**

Cress Co., The, *(1-929488)* 545 S. Main St., Elburn, IL 60119 USA Tel 630-365-8600; Fax: 630-365-8606; Toll Free: 800-637-2449
E-mail: eric@cressco.com
Web site: http://www.cressco.com.

CREST Pubns., *(0-9725546)* P.O. Box 481022, Charlotte, NC 28269 USA Do not confuse with Crest Publications, Richardson, TX
Web site: http://www.crestpub.com
Dist(s): **Baker & Taylor Bks.**

Crestmont Publishing, *(0-9642296)* 4 Schindler Dr., Sparta, NJ 07871-3563 USA
Dist(s): **Unique Bks., Inc.**

Creston Hall Pubns., *(0-9712971)* 7007 Almond Dr., Templeton, CA 93465-8558 USA
E-mail: editor@crestonhall.com
Web site: http://www.crestonhall.com.

Crew Pr., *(0-9762944)* 1298 Ann Arbor Trail, Plymouth, MI 48170 USA
E-mail: kielbaso@aol.com
Web site: http://www.crewpress.com.

Cribsheet Publishing *See* **Blue Shoe Publishing**

Cricket *Imprint of* **School Specialty Publishing**

Cricket Bks., *(0-8126)* Div. of Carus Publishing Co., 70 E. Lake St. Ste. 300, Chicago, IL 60601-5945 USA
Web site: http://www.cricketmag.com/home.asp
Dist(s): **Cobblestone Publishing Co.**
NetLibrary, Inc.
Perseus Distribution.

Cricket Productions, Incorporated *See* **Scrumps Entertainment, Inc.**

CrimethInc. Workers' Collective, *(0-9709101)* P.O. Box 1963, Olympia, WA 98507-1963 USA Tel 360-786-6924; Fax: 415-962-0773
E-mail: house@crimethinc.com
Web site: http://www.crimethinc.com
Dist(s): **AK Pr. Distribution**
Baker & Taylor Bks.

Crippen & Landru, Pubs., *(1-885941; 1-932009)* Orders Addr.: P.O. Box 9315, Norfolk, VA 23505-9315 USA Tel 757-622-6656 (phone/fax); Toll Free: 877-622-6656 (phone/fax); Edit Addr.: 533 W. 24th, Norfolk, VA 23517 USA Tel 757-622-6656 (phone/fax)
E-mail: info@crippenlandru.com
Web site: http://www.crippenlandru.com.

Criqueville Pr., *(0-9705404)* Orders Addr.: P.O. Box 1227, Princeton, NJ 08542-1227 USA Tel 908-359-7834; Edit Addr.: 2 Dogwood Ln., Princeton, NJ 08542-1227 USA (SAN 255-982X)
E-mail: criquevillepress@hotmail.com.

Crises Research Pr., *(0-86627)* 301 W. 45th St., New York, NY 10036 USA (SAN 238-9274).

Crispus Medical Pr., *(0-9640389)* 7923 Leschi Rd., SW, Lakewood, WA 98498 USA Toll Free: 877-464-6469.

Cristal Publishing Co., *(0-9779124)* P.O. Box 14-4828, Coral Gables, FL 33114-4828 USA
E-mail: cristal228@bellsouth.net
Dist(s): **Ediciones Universal.**

Criterion Publishing Co., Inc., *(1-887304)* Orders Addr.: P.O. Box 930698, Norcross, GA 30093 USA Tel 770-923-9053; Edit Addr.: 5917 MaryJo Ln., Norcross, GA 30093 USA.

Critical Path Publishing, *(0-9740605)* P.O. Box 1073, Clayton, CA 94517-9073 USA Do not confuse with Critical Path Publishing Company in Denville, NJ
E-mail: cpp@silcon.com
Dist(s): **Book Publishing Co., The.**

Critical Thinking Bks. & Software, *(0-89455; 0-910974; 1-60144)* Orders Addr.: P.O. Box 1610, Seaside, CA 93955 USA (SAN 207-0510) Toll Free: 800-458-4849; Edit Addr.: 1069 Broadway Ave., Seaside, CA 93955 USA
Web site: http://www.criticalthinking.com.

Critical Thinking Press & Software *See* **Critical Thinking Bks. & Software**

Critter Camp Inc., *(0-9772825)* 1190 Scenic Ave., Lummi Island, WA 98262 USA Tel 360-758-4269 (phone/fax)
E-mail: midiana@clearwire.net.

Critter Pubns., *(1-928972)* P.O. Box 413, Leicester, MA 01524-0413 USA
E-mail: del@critterp.com
Web site: http://www.critterp.com.

Critter Publishing, *(0-9754615)* Orders Addr.: P.O. Box 585, Readfield, ME 04355 USA Tel 207-685-5527 (phone/fax); Edit Addr.: 70 Walker Rd., Readfield, ME 04355 USA
E-mail: soniccomics@gwi.net
Web site: http://www.sonicpublishing.com.

Critters & Kids Publishing, Incorporated *See* **Froginhood & Friends, Inc.**

CrittersInc, *(0-9745997)* 19611 Longview Terr., Salinas, CA 93908 USA
Web site: http://www.crittersinc.com.

Crizmac, *(0-945666; 0-9796217)* P.O. Box 65928, Tucson, AZ 85728-5928 USA (SAN 667-1101) Tel 520-323-8555; Fax: 520-323-6194; Toll Free: 800-913-8555
E-mail: crizmacinc@aol.com; purchasing@crizmac.com
Web site: http://www.crizmac.com.

CRM Enterprises, *(0-615)* 411 Coram Avenue, Shelton, CT 06484 USA.

CRM Pubs., LLC, *(0-9746920)* P.O. Box 5706, Derwood, MD 20855 USA Tel 301-527-1667; Fax: 301-527-0771; Toll Free: 800-527-6991
Web site: http://www.crmpublishers.com
Dist(s): **Independent Pubs. Group.**

Crocodile Bks. *Imprint of* **Interlink Publishing Group, Inc.**

Croker Bks., *(0-9719034)* P.O. Box 6546, Fort Myers Beach, FL 33932 USA.

Cromer, J.T., *(0-9724895)* 249 Louisville Dr., Greenville, SC 29607-6527 USA.

Cronies, *(1-929566)* Div. of Reproductive Images, 22738 Roscoe Blvd., No. 225, Canoga Park, CA 91304-3350 USA Tel 818-773-4888; Fax: 818-773-8808; Toll Free: 800-232-8099
E-mail: SethJ@CRONIES.com.

Crooked Lane Productions, *(0-9743958)* 219 Wiltshire Ln., Severna Park, MD 21146-2038 USA.

Crooked River Pr., *(0-9778586)* P.O. Box 21, Cuyahoga Falls, OH 44221 USA Tel 330-701-3375 ; *Imprints:* Blue Jay Books (Blue Jay Bks)
E-mail: Books@CrookedRiverPress.com
Web site: http://www.CrookedRiverPress.com.

Crosam Pr., *(0-9774822)* 681 Beverly Dr., Lake Wales, FL 33853 USA Tel 863-676-5737 Toll Free: 877-676-2285
E-mail: winksampson22@aol.com
Web site: www.feathersandfur.com.

Cross Pointe Printing, *(0-9742154)* 8989 E. Via Linda, No. 118, Scottsdale, AZ 85258 USA Tel 480-860-2212; Fax: 480-860-2506
E-mail: dan@crosspointeprinting.com.

Cross Product Pubns., *(0-9793087)* 3222 Cascade Hills Dr., NW, Cleveland, TN 37312 USA.

Cross Reference Imprints, *(0-9725139)* 3607 Hycliffe Ave., Louisville, KY 40207 USA Tel 502-897-2719
E-mail: Pneuma@eclipsetel.com.

Cross Time *Imprint of* **Crossquarter Publishing Group**

Cross Training *Imprint of* **CharismaLife Pubs.**

Cross Training Publishing, *(1-887002; 1-929478)* Orders Addr.: P.O. Box 1541, Grand Island, NE 68802 USA (SAN 298-7406) Tel 308-293-3891; Fax: 308-338-2058; Toll Free: 800-430-8588; Edit Addr.: 101 Summerhaven, Kearney, NE 68847 USA
E-mail: gordon@crosstrainingpublishing.com
Web site: http://www.crosstrainingpublishing.com.

CrossGeneration Comics, Inc., *(1-931484; 1-59314)* 9030 Lake Chase Island Way, Tampa, FL 33626-1942 USA
E-mail: jbreitbeil@crossgen.com
Web site: http://www.crossgen.com
Dist(s): **Diamond Comic Distributors, Inc.**

Crossing Guard Bks. *Imprint of* **Longs Peak Publishing, Inc.**

Crossing Pr., Inc. *Imprint of* **Ten Speed Pr.**

Crossing Trails Pubns., *(0-9726095)* 4804 Kentwood Ln., Woodbridge, VA 22193 USA Tel 703-590-4449; Fax: 703-878-2119
E-mail: whnesbitt@compuserve.com
Web site: http://www.crossingtrails.com.

Cross-Lengua Productions *See* **KALEXT Productions, LLC**

CrossLife Expressions, *(0-9636049; 1-57838)* Div. of Exchanged Life Ministries, Inc., 10610 E. Bethany Dr., Suite A, Aurora, CO 80014 USA (SAN 169-0590) Tel 303-750-0440; Fax: 303-750-1228; Toll Free: 800-750-6818
E-mail: info@crosslifebooks.com
Web site: http://www.crosslifebooks.com.

Cross-Over, *(0-9749455)* FLC 7028, 1000 Rim Dr, Durango, CO 81301-3999 USA Tel 970-385-1809 (phone/fax); Toll Free: 866-385-1809
E-mail: crossover@ellison.net
Web site: http://crossover.ellison.net.

Crossover Comics, *(0-9748466)* 20-23 43 St., Astoria, NY 11105 USA
Web site: http://www.gavila.com.

Crossquarter Breeze Publishing *See* **Crossquarter Publishing Group**

Crossquarter Publishing Group, *(1-890109)* Div. of Earth Healers Inc., Orders Addr.: P.O. Box 23749, Santa Fe, NM 87502 USA Tel 505-690-3923 (phone); Fax: 214-975-9715 (fax); Edit Addr.: 510 Cr 71, Crookston, MN 56716 USA ; *Imprints:* Cross Time (Crosstime)
E-mail: t.francis@crossquarter.com
Web site: http://www.crossquarter.com.

Crossroad *Imprint of* **Crossroad Publishing Co.**

Crossroad Classic *Imprint of* **Crossroad Publishing Co.**

†Crossroad Publishing Co., *(0-8245)* 481 Eighth Ave., Suite 1550, New York, NY 10001 USA (SAN 287-0118) Tel 212-868-1801; Fax: 212-868-2171; Toll Free: 800-395-0690 (Orders Only) ; *Imprints:* Crossroad (Crsrd); Crossroad Classic (Crossroad Classic)
E-mail: ask@crossroadpublishing.com
Web site: http://www.crossroadpublishing.com
Dist(s): **ACTA Pubns.**
Abingdon Pr.
National Bk. Network; *CIP.*

Crossroads Pr., *(0-9714782)* P.O. Box 272817, Fort Collins, CO 80527-2817 USA Fax: 970-377-3826 Do not confuse with companies with the same or similar names in Edmore, MI, Washington, DC, Holyoke, MA, New Brunswick, NJ, Rowayton, CT, New York, NY, Honolulu, HI
E-mail: cforseth@crossroadspress.net; forseth@ideaspigot.com
Web site: http://www.crossroadspress.net; http://www.gentilegirl.com; http://www.arniehackett.com
Dist(s): **Riverside Distributors.**

Crossroads Publishing Company *See* **CrossroadsPub.com**

CrossroadsPub.com, *(1-58338)* Hc77 Box152, Laguna, NM 87026 USA Tel 505-836-5285 ; *Imprints:* CrossroadsPub.Org (CrossroadsPubOrg)
E-mail: brassminnie@peoplepc.com.

CrossroadsPub.Org *Imprint of* **CrossroadsPub.com**

Crosswalk Bks., *(0-9746269)* P.O. Box 176, American Fork, UT 84003 USA (SAN 255-7657)
Web site: http://www.crosswalkbooks.com.

Crossway Bibles *Imprint of* **Crossway Bks.**

†Crossway Bks., *(0-89107; 1-58134; 1-4335)* Div. of Good News Pubs., 1300 Crescent St., Wheaton, IL 60187 USA (SAN 211-7991) Tel 630-682-4300; 708-682-4300; Fax: 630-682-4785; Toll Free: 800-323-3890 (sales only) ; *Imprints:* Crossway Bibles (Crossway Bibles)
Web site: http://www.crosswaybooks.org; permissions@gnpcb.org
Dist(s): **LIM Productions, LLC**
Vision Video; *CIP.*

Crossways International, *(1-891245)* 7930 Computer Ave., S., Minneapolis, MN 55435-5415 USA Tel 952-832-5454; Fax: 952-832-5553; Toll Free: 800-257-7308
E-mail: info@crossways.org
Web site: http://www.crossways.org.

Crosswinds Bks., *(0-9726573)* P.O. Box 143, Keller, TX 76244 USA
E-mail: jroach35@earthlink.net.

Crouch, Valeria *See* **Zig the Pig**

Crouse, Donna J., *(0-9765339)* P.O. Box 250, Jersey, VA 22481 USA Tel 540-775-7787; Fax: 540-775-1682
E-mail: df_crouse@msn.com.

Crow, R.L. Pubns., *(0-9722958)* P.O. Box 262, Penn Valley, CA 95946 USA
E-mail: rlcrow@oro.net
Dist(s): **Baker & Taylor Bks.**
SPD-Small Pr. Distribution.

Crowder, Jack L., *(0-9616589)* Orders Addr.: P.O. Box 250, Bernalillo, NM 87004 USA (SAN 659-8064) Tel 505-867-5812 (phone/fax); Edit Addr.: 500 Beehive Ln., Bernalillo, NM 87004 USA (SAN 659-8072)
E-mail: crowdercon@aol.com.

Crowell, Peter T. Pubns., *(0-9740290)* 110 Woodside Ave. 1st Flr., Narberth, PA 19072 USA
E-mail: ptc@petertcrowell.com
Web site: http://www.petertcrowell.com
Dist(s): **Partners Bk. Distributing, Inc.**

Crowl, Tom & the Mrs., *(0-9707797)* P.O. Box 2131, Westminster, MD 21158 USA Tel 410-876-6771 (phone/fax)
E-mail: tom@crowlandthemrs.com
Web site: http://www.tomcrowlandthemrs.com.

Crown *Imprint of* **Crown Publishing Group**

Crown Books For Young Readers *Imprint of* **Random Hse. Children's Bks.**

Crown Financial Ministries, Inc., *(0-9651114; 1-56427; 1-893946)* 601 Broad St., SE, Gainesville, GA 30501 USA (SAN 298-752X) Tel 770-534-1000; Fax: 770-536-7226; Toll Free: 800-722-1976
E-mail: jarmstrong@crown.org
Web site: http://www.crown.org
Dist(s): **CRC Pubns.**

Crown Peak Publishing, *(0-9645663)* Orders Addr.: P.O. Box 317, New Castle, CO 81647 USA Tel 970-618-1748
E-mail: ann@methetree.com; ann@crownpeakpublishing.com
Web site: http://www.methetree.com; http://www.annlouiseramsey.com; http://www.crownpeakpublishing.

†Crown Publishing Group, Div. of Random Hse., Inc., Orders Addr.: 400 Hahn Rd., Westminster, MD 21157 USA Tel 410-848-1900; Toll Free Fax: 800-659-2436; Toll Free: 800-733-3000; 800-726-0600; Edit Addr.: 1745 Broadway, New York, NY 10019 USA (SAN 200-2639) Tel 212-751-2600; Toll Free Fax: 800-659-2436 ; *Imprints:* Crown (Crown); Three Rivers Press (Three River Pr); Harmony/Bell Tower (HarBellTow); Prima Lifestyles (PrimLife); Potter Craft (Pott Craft)
E-mail: customerservice@randomhouse.com; crownpublicity@randomhouse.com
Web site: http://www.randomhouse.com/
Dist(s): **Random Hse., Inc.**; *CIP.*

Crowood Pr., Ltd. (GBR) *(0-946284; 1-85223; 1-86126) Dist. by* **Trafalgar.**

Crowood Pr., Ltd. (GBR) *(0-946284; 1-85223; 1-86126) Dist. by* **MBI Dist Svcs.**

CrowsNest Publishing, *(0-9710225)* 11513 Crows Nest Rd., Clarksville, MD 21029-1601 USA Tel 410-531-3110
E-mail: hannon@erols.com.

Crowther, Debra, *(0-9741295)* P.O. Box 1870, Three Rivers, TX 78071 USA Tel 361-786-4703; Fax: 361-786-2579
Web site: http://www.jackthewestie.com.

Crucifiction Games, *(0-9778263)* P.O. Box 654, Selah, WA 98942 USA Tel 509-697-7393
E-mail: cweedin@crucifictiongames.com
Web site: http://www.crucifictiongames.com.

Cruising Companion Pubns., *(0-9715640)* P.O. Box 500441, Marathon, FL 33050-0441 USA Tel 305-731-7315
E-mail: captmarti@netzero.com
Web site: http://www.idiyachts.com
Dist(s): **Seaworthy Pubns., Inc.**

Crumb Elbow Publishing, *(0-89904)* P.O. Box 294, Rhododendron, OR 97049 USA (SAN 679-128X) Tel 503-622-4798 ; *Imprints:* Silhouette Imprints (Silhouette Imprints).

Crumly, Billie, *(0-9760577)* P.O. Box 281, Geraldine, AL 35974 USA.

Crunchpeep Media, *(0-9749469)* a/o Steven Merahn, 1700 Market St., 6th Flr., Philadelphia, PA 19103 USA Tel 215-832-0181
E-mail: smerahn@crunchpeep.com.

Crunchy Frog Enterprises, *(1-929332)* 4908 Valley Ridge Dr., Apt. 3027, Kenosha, TX 750627730 USA
E-mail: froggod@aol.com
Web site: http://www.teamfrog.com.

Cruzane Mountain Publishing, *(0-9711445; 0-9744465; 0-9761489)* P.O. Box 670132, Saltese, MT 59867-0132 USA Tel 406-678-4340; Fax: 406-678-4109
E-mail: hau4109@blackfoot.net
Web site: http://www.cruzanemountain.com.

Crysalis Publishing, Inc., *(0-9745190)* 10 Main St., Suite 4A, PMB 227, Woodbridge, NJ 07095 USA
Web site: http://www.chrysalispublishinc.com.

Crystal Ball Publishing, LLC., *(1-932277)* 107 Skiff Ave., Frankfort, NY 13340 USA
E-mail: Nerbo@msn.com; Sales@CrystalBallPublishing.com; Insight@CrystalBallPublishing.com
Web site: http://www.crystalballpublishing.com; http://www.gypsykids.com
Dist(s): **BookMasters, Inc.**

Crystal Clarity Pubs., *(0-916124; 1-56589; 1-878265)* 14618 Tyler-Foote Rd., Nevada City, CA 95959 USA (SAN 201-1778) Tel 530-478-7600 (intl. orders, cust. serv.); Fax: 530-478-7610 (orders); Toll Free: 800-424-1055
E-mail: sales@crystalclarity.com
Web site: http://www.crystalclarity.com
Dist(s): **Baker & Taylor Bks.**
Instructional Video
Koen Pacific
National Bk. Network
New Leaf Distributing Co., Inc.
Nutri-Bks. Corp.
Princeton Bk. Co. Pubs.

Crystal Dreams Publishing, *(0-9715658; 1-59146)* W1227 East County Rd A, Berlin, WI 54923 USA Tel 920-361-0961 (phone/fax)
E-mail: softails181@yahoo.com; sarahs@crystaldreamspub.com
Web site: http://www.crystaldreamspub.com
Dist(s): **Abyss Distribution.**

Crystal Journeys Publishing, *(1-880737)* 130 Cochise Dr., Sedona, AZ 86351-7927 USA Tel 520-284-5730
Dist(s): **Light Technology Publishing.**

Crystal Pr., *(0-9632123; 0-9670886; 0-9746109)* 1750 Orr Ave., Simi Valley, CA 93065 USA Tel 805-527-4369; Fax: 805-582-3949 Do not confuse with Crystal Pr. in Houston, TX
E-mail: crystalpress@aol.com
Web site: http://www.Crystalpress.org.

Crystal Productions, *(0-924509; 1-56290)* Orders Addr.: P.O. Box 2159, Glenview, IL 60025 USA; Edit Addr.: 1812 Johns Dr., Glenview, IL 60025 USA (SAN 653-2489) Tel 847-657-8144; Fax: 847-657-8149; Toll Free Fax: 800-657-8149; Toll Free: 800-255-8629
E-mail: custserv@crystalproductions.com
Web site: http://www.crystalproductions.com
Dist(s): **Getty Pubns.**

Crystal Springs Bks. *Imprint of* **Staff Development for Educators**

CS Media Resources, *(0-9764992)* Orders Addr.: 12 W. Willow Grove Ave. Suite 121, Philadelphia, PA 19118-3952 USA Toll Free: 877-866-8309
E-mail: csmr@csmediaresources.com
Web site: http://www.csmediaresources.com.

C.S. Publishing, *(0-9678386)* Div. of SPPT, PMB 154, 1319 Military Cut Off Rd., Wilmington, NC 28405 USA Fax: 910-350-0359
E-mail: Hoagan84@aol.com
Web site: http://www.clif-and-simmons.com.

CSE Publishing, *(0-9743567)* 706 Radcliffe Ave., Lynn Haven, FL 32444-3039 USA (SAN 255-5581) Fax: 850-271-9874; Toll Free: 866-262-8776
E-mail: tchardy@bellsouth.net
Dist(s): **STL Distribution North America.**

CSI Publishing *See* **Decere Publishing**

CSIRO Publishing (AUS) *(0-643) Dist. by* **Antipodes Bks.**

CTC Publishing, *(0-9747789; 1-934073)* 10431 Lawyers Rd., Vienna, VA 22181-2822 USA (SAN 851-7908) Toll Free: 800-942-0962
E-mail: pitts@ndmc.com
Web site: http://www.couragetochange.com/
Dist(s): **Baker & Taylor Bks.**
Follett Library Resources.

CTM Publishing, *(0-9660227)* P.O. Box 45, Lebanon, PA 17042 USA (SAN 299-8963) Tel 717-274-1695; Fax: 717-274-5567; 20 Berbec Ave., Lebanon, PA 17042.

CTO Bks., *(0-9724411)* Orders Addr.: 705 W. Walnut St., Kokomo, IN 46903 USA; Edit Addr.: 705 W. Walnut St., Kokomo, IN 46901 USA
Web site: http://www.schultze.org
Dist(s): **AtlasBooks Distribution.**

Ctr. for Curatorial Studies *Imprint of* **Bard College Pubns. Office**

Ctrl+Alt+Del Prodns., *(0-9764678)* P.O. Box 206392, New Haven, CT 06520 USA Tel 508-274-5804
E-mail: absath@ctrlaltdel-online.com
Web site: http://www.ctrlaltdel-online.com.

Cubbie Blue Publishing, *(0-9706341; 1-932824)* 21900 Marylee St., No. 290, Woodland Hills, CA 91367 USA Tel 818-883-3310; Fax: 818-883-3317
Dist(s): **National Bk. Network.**

Cubby Hole Tales, *(0-9754591)* 524 Moores Mill Rd., Pelzer, SC 29669 USA Tel 864-947-6426
E-mail: telvajo@bellsouth.net
Web site: http://www.talesfromtwocousins.com.

Cuccia, Louis, *(0-9727415)* 603 Winthrop, Smyrna, TN 37167 USA Tel 615-355-6821; Fax: 615-355-0171
E-mail: Lcuccia@aol.com.

Cued Speech for Integrated Communication, Inc., *(1-892917)* 23970 Hermitage Rd., Cleveland, OH 44122-4008 USA Tel 216-292-6213; Fax: 216-360-0359; Toll Free: 800-459-3529
E-mail: cuedspdisc@aol.com.

Cuisenaire Company of America, Incorporated *See* **ETA/Cuisenaire**

Culpepper, Felix International, Inc., *(0-9740435)* Orders Addr.: P.O. Box 70, Jefferson City, TN 37760-0070 USA (SAN 255-2752) Tel 865-475-4993; Fax: 914-470-1091; Edit Addr.: 2476 Tarr Rd., Talbott, TN 37877 USA
E-mail: gfac@cshore.com; peteculpepper@helpkidswhohavecancer.org; pete@felixculpepper.com
Web site: http://www.bigboxhead.com; http://www.felixculpepper.com
Dist(s): **American Wholesale Bk. Co.**

Cultural Connections, *(0-9636629; 1-57371)* P.O. Box 1582, Alameda, CA 94501 USA Toll Free: 888-234-5412
E-mail: info@culture-connect.org
Web site: http://www.culture-connect.org.

Culture Connection, The, *(0-9712383)* 6110 Twyckenham Dr., Indianapolis, IN 46236 USA
E-mail: erikadebarros@thecultureconnection.com
Web site: http://theculturеconnection.com.

Culture C.O.-O.P., The, *(0-9644655)* P.O. Box 463, Davis, CA 95616 USA (SAN 299-3260) Tel 530-792-1334; Fax: 530-753-8511
E-mail: info@CultureCo-Op.com
Web site: http://www.CultureCo-Op.com
Dist(s): **Baker & Taylor Bks.**
Follett Library Resources.

Culture Hse., *(0-9676080)* Orders Addr.: P.O. Box 293, Newton, IA 50208 USA; Edit Addr.: 3830 Harbor Ave., Newton, IA 50208-9040 USA
E-mail: museum@pcpartner.net.

Culture of Life, Inc., *(0-9761457)* 1054 Windy Knoll Rd., West Chester, PA 19382-7433 USA.

CultureGrams World Edition *Imprint of* **ProQuest CSA**

Culturelink Pr., *(0-9759276)* Orders Addr.: P.O. Box 3538, San Diego, CA 92163 USA (SAN 256-1174); Edit Addr.: 1435 Essex St., No.3, San Diego, CA 92103 USA
Web site: http://www.culturelinkpress.com.

Cumberland Hearthside *Imprint of* **Cumberland Hse. Publishing**

†Cumberland Hse. Publishing, *(1-58182; 1-888952)* Orders Addr.: 431 Harding Industrial Park Dr., Nashville, TN 37211-3105 USA (SAN 254-4172) Tel 615-832-1171; Fax: 615-832-0633; Toll Free Fax: 800-254-6716; Toll Free: 888-439-2665 ; *Imprints:* Cumberland Hearthside (Cumberland Hearthside) Do not confuse with Cumberland Hse. Publishing, Co., Inc. in Indianapolis, IN
E-mail: sbauerle@cumberlandhouse.com
Web site: http://www.CumberlandHouse.com; *CIP.*

Cummings Pr., *(0-9767063)* 1939 Mt. Vernon Pl., Dunwoody, GA 30338-4417 USA Tel 770-512-8115 (phone/fax).

Cummins, Judi, *(0-9760377)* Orders Addr.: P.O. Box 283, Victor, NY 14564 USA
E-mail: jc1965@frontiernet.net
Web site: http://www.Ginger-beagle.com.

Cumquat Publishing Company *See* **Floppinfish Publishing Co., Ltd.**

Cumuli, *(0-9709730)* Div. of Cumuli, Inc., P.O. Box 1174, Port Orchard, WA 98366 USA Tel 360-871-9493 (phone/fax)
E-mail: fletcher@cumuli.com; susan@cumuli.com
Web site: http://www.cumuli.com; http://www.cumulipress.com.

Cune *See* **Cune Pr., LLC**

Cune Pr., LLC, *(1-885942)* Div. of Scott Davis Co., P.O. Box 31024, Seattle, WA 98103 USA (SAN 298-3648) Tel 206-789-7055; Fax: 206-782-1330
E-mail: bowker@cunepress.com
Web site: http://www.cunepress.com; http://www.cunepress.net.

Cunha, Jacinto, *(0-9767572)* 31 Bryant St., Everett, MA 02149-1725 USA
E-mail: jessybcunha@aol.com
Web site: http://www.realidadenuaecrua.com.

Cupcake Pubns., *(0-9752786)* 318 Oak St., Ridgewood, NJ 07450 USA Tel 201-445-7795; Fax: 201-445-7402
E-mail: King_anthony2001@yahoo.com.

†Curbstone Pr., *(0-915306; 1-880684; 1-931896)* 321 Jackson St., Willimantic, CT 06226 USA (SAN 209-4282) Tel 860-423-5110; Fax: 860-423-9242
E-mail: info@curbstone.org
Web site: http://www.curbstone.org
Dist(s): **Consortium Bk. Sales & Distribution**
Lectorum Pubns., Inc.
SPD-Small Pr. Distribution; *CIP.*

Curcumin Bks. *Imprint of* **Davlaw Press**

Curen Enterprises, *(0-9667442)* P.O. Box 157, Oswego, IL 60543 USA Tel 310-791-0036; Fax: 310-791-6607; Toll Free: 888-238-3308
E-mail: cathicuren@earthlink.net.

Curio Pr., *(0-9661359)* 10201 Old Creedmoor Rd., Raleigh, NC 27613 USA Tel 919-848-1355.

Currach Pr. (IRL) *(1-85607) Dist. by* **Dufour.**

Curran, M.J., *(0-9768984)* 640 Gooseberry Dr., No. 1207, Longmont, CO 80503 USA Tel 720-206-9099
E-mail: mjcurran@hotmail.com.

Currency Pr. (AUS) *(0-86819; 0-9596937; 1-921428; 1-921429) Dist. by* **Antipodes Bks.**

Current Clinical Strategies Publishing, *(0-9626030; 1-881528; 1-929622; 1-934323)* P.O. Box 1753, Blue Jay, CA 92317 USA (SAN 298-4490) Tel 949-348-8404; Fax: 949-348-8405; Toll Free Fax: 800-965-9420; Toll Free: 800-331-8227
E-mail: info@ccspublishing.com
Web site: http://www.ccspublishing.com/ccs
Dist(s): **Baker & Taylor Bks.**
Majors, J. A. Co.
Matthews Medical Bk. Co.
Rittenhouse Bk. Distributors.

Current, Inc., *(0-944943; 1-58410)* Div. of Deluxe Corp., Orders Addr.: P.O. Box 2559, Colorado Springs, CO 80901 USA (SAN 246-0378) Tel 719-594-4100; Fax: 719-534-6259; Toll Free: 800-848-2848; Edit Addr.: 1005 E. Woodmen Rd., Colorado Springs, CO 80920 USA (SAN 246-0386).

Current Publishing Corp., *(1-878663)* 30151 Tomas St., Rancho Santa Margarita, CA 92688 USA Toll Free: 800-729-7234.

Curriculum Assocs., Inc., *(0-7609; 0-89187; 1-55915)* P.O. Box 2001, N Billerica, MA 01862-0901 USA (SAN 659-6304) Toll Free: 800-225-0248.

Curriculum Corporation (AUS) *(1-86366; 1-74200) Dist. by* **Cheng Tsui.**

Curriculum Publishing, Presbyterian Church (U. S. A.), *(1-57153)* 100 Witherspoon St., Louisville, KY 40202-1396 USA Tel 502-569-5090; Fax: 502-569-8329; Toll Free: 800-524-2612 ; *Imprints:* Bridge Resources (Bridge Res); Witherspoon Press (Witherspoon Pr)
Web site: http://www.pcusa.org/pcusa/currpub; http://www.bridgeresources.org.

Curriculum Solutions, Inc., *(0-9659517; 1-893206)* Orders Addr.: P.O. Box 3274, Lawrence, KS 66046 USA
E-mail: curriculumsolutions@yahoo.com
Web site: http://curriculumsolutions.org.

Currie & Smith Publishing *See* **T.Y.M. Publishing**

Currier, Alvin Alexsi, *(0-9723411)* 1880 E Shore Dr, Apt. 212, Saint Paul, MN 55109 USA Tel 651-772-2788; Fax: 651-772-3151
E-mail: a.currier@juno.com.

Currier Davis Publishing, *(0-930507)* 4791 Baywood Point Dr. S., Gulfport, FL 33711 USA (SAN 670-963X) Tel 727-327-9039; Fax: 727-323-9587
E-mail: jonmicocci@att.net
Web site: http://www.deathfromchildabuse.com.

Curry Brothers Publishing, *(0-9798364)* 608 Sandy Spring Trail, Madison, TN 37115 USA
E-mail: cbmpg@yahoo.com
Web site: http://currybrotherspublishing.com.

Cursack Bks., *(1-933439)* 31 Hubbard Rd., Dover, NH 03820 USA
E-mail: info@cursackbooks.com
Web site: http://www.cursackbooks.com
Dist(s): **Ediciones Universal.**

Curtis Elliott Designs, Ltd., *(0-9742438)* 5250 Franklin St., Unit C-1, Hilliard, OH 43026 USA Tel 614-771-7978
E-mail: info@creativecoloringbooks.com
Web site: http://www.creativecoloringbooks.com.

Curtis Publishing Co., *(0-9659419)* P.O. Box 17693, Richmond, VA 23226 USA Tel 804-285-1813 Do not confuse with companies with same or similar names in Hayward, CA, Anderson, IN, Indianapolis, IN
Dist(s): **Koen-Levy Bk. Wholesalers LLC.**

Custom Curriculum & Design LLC., *(0-9726495)* Orders Addr.: P.O. Box 742, Saint Charles, MN 55972 USA.

Customer Centered Consulting Group, Inc., *(0-9762493)* 5729 Lebanon Dr., Suite 144-222, Frisco, TX 75034 USA Tel 469-633-9833; Fax: 469-633-9843
E-mail: dreed@cccginc.com
Web site: http://www.cccginc.com.

Cute & Cuddly Productions, Inc., *(0-9761318)* 4401 Shallowford Rd., Suite 162-161, Roswell, GA 30075 USA Tel 678-478-6071 (phone/fax)
E-mail: cuteandcuddlyproductions@msn.com
Web site: http://www.bigbillandbuddies.com
Dist(s): **AtlasBooks Distribution.**

Cutt Publishing *See* **Hunnicutt Farris Publishing**

CVD Publishing, *(0-9743520)* 1254 Grizzly Flat Ct., Auburn, CA 95603 USA Tel 530-885-4988
E-mail: grizlyflat@jps.net
Web site: http://www.CVDbooks.com.

CWLA Pr. *Imprint of* **Child Welfare League of America, Inc.**

CWS Studios, Inc., *(0-9785827)* 5414 W. Barry Ave., Chicago, IL 60641 USA
Web site: http://www.cws-studios.com
Dist(s): **Biblio Distribution.**

Cyan Communications (GBR) *(0-9542829; 1-904879) Dist. by* **IPG Chicago.**

Cyber Haus, *(1-931373)* 159 Delaware Ave., #145, Delmar, NY 12054 USA Tel 518-478-9798
E-mail: cyhaus@msn.com
Web site: http://www.revolutionaryday.com/; http://www.cyhaus.com/
Dist(s): **Baker & Taylor Bks.**

Cyber Publishing Co., *(0-9637419; 0-9747870)* 421 Ave. De Teresa, Grants Pass, OR 97526 USA (SAN 255-691X) Tel 541-474-1077; Fax: 541-474-2829
E-mail: intrchild@aol.com.

Cybereditions Corp. Ltd. (NZL) *(1-877275) Dist. by* **Ingram Bk Co.**

Cyberlab Publishing, *(0-9746501)* P.O. Box 618, Dimondale, MI 48821-0618 USA Tel 517-974-8068; Fax: 517-887-9029
E-mail: ministerjd@yahoo.com
Web site: http://www.cyberlabpublishing.com.

Cyberosia Publishing, *(0-9709474; 0-9742713)* 101 Foreman Rd. Apt. C73, Mobile, AL 36608-6215 USA
E-mail: scott@cyberosia.com
Web site: http://www.cyberosia.com
Dist(s): **Diamond Distributors, Inc.**

Cyclops Pr., *(0-9740269)* 1342 Van Buren Ave., Saint Paul, MN 55104-1926 USA.

Cyclotour Guide Bks., *(1-889602)* Orders Addr.: P.O. Box 10585, Rochester, NY 14610-0585 USA; Edit Addr.: 160 Harvard St., Rochester, NY 14607-3115 USA
E-mail: cyclotour@cyclotour.com
Web site: http://www.cyclotour.com.

Cygnet Publishing Co., *(0-9636050)* 2153 Wealthy, SE, No. 238, East Grand Rapids, MI 49506 USA Tel 616-459-1258 Do not confuse with Cygnet Publishing, Montecito, CA
E-mail: bowman@grgig.net.

Cygnet Publishing Group, Inc./Coolreading.com (CAN) *(1-55305) Dist. by* **Orca Bk Pubs.**

Cymbal Technique 101, *(0-9762593)* 440 Ross Rd., Fort Walton Beach, FL 32547 USA
E-mail: edward_capps@cymbaltechnique101.com
Web site: http://www.cymbaltechnique101.com.

Cypress Bay Publishing, *(0-9746747)* 910 W. Harney Ln., Lodi, CA 95242 USA (SAN 255-6928) Tel 209-365-6114.

Cypress Communications, *(0-9636412)* 35 E. Rosemont Ave., Alexandria, VA 22301 USA Tel 703-548-0532 (phone/fax) Do not confuse with companies with similar names in Leawood, KS, Saint Paul, MN, Cypress, TX
E-mail: jcclifford@earthlink.net
Web site: http://www.lighthousehistory.info
Dist(s): **Baker & Taylor Bks.**
Partners Bk. Distributing, Inc.

Cypress Cove Publishing, *(0-9705868)* Orders Addr.: P.O. Box 2219, Lafayette, LA 70502-2219 USA (SAN 253-5343); Edit Addr.: 908 Amilcar Blvd., Lafayette, LA 70501 USA
Dist(s): **Forest Sales & Distributing Co.**

Cypress Knees Publishing, *(0-9745863; 0-9763757)* Div. of Top Brass Outdoors, Orders Addr.: P.O. Box 209, Starkville, MS 39760 USA Tel 662-323-1559; Fax: 662-323-7466; Edit Addr.: 312 Industrial Pk., Rd., Starkville, MS 39759 USA
E-mail: eric@topbrasstackle.com
Web site: http://www.topbrasstackle.com; http://www.outdooryouthadventures.com.

CyPress Pubns., *(0-9672585; 0-9776958)* P.O. Box 2636, Tallahassee, FL 32316-2636 USA
E-mail: iraymond@nettally.com
Web site: http://cypress-starpublications.com.

Cypress Publishing *See* **Cypress Communications**

Cypress Trail Pr., *(0-9644000)* 1610 Cypress Trail, Middleton, WI 53562 USA Tel 608-233-3080.

Cyr Design Publishing, *(0-9774543)* P.O. Box 1662, Nashua, NH 03061-1662 USA
Web site: http://cyrdesign.com.

Cyr, Joe, *(0-9713768)* 3723 Village Green Dr., Sarasota, FL 34239 USA Tel 941-925-3574; Fax: 941-927-9015
E-mail: echoplex@ieee.org
Web site: http://www.hoppingchristmastree.com.

D. A. M. Publisher *See* **Leapfrog Pr.**

D.A.P./Distributed Art Pubs., *(1-881616; 1-891024; 1-933045)* Orders Addr.: 155 Sixth Ave., 2nd Flr., New York, NY 10013-1507 USA (SAN 630-6446) Tel 212-627-1999; Fax: 212-627-9484; Toll Free Fax: 800-478-3128; Toll Free: 800-338-2665
E-mail: dap@dapinc.com
Web site: http://www.artbook.com/.

D A W Bks., Inc. *Imprint of* **Penguin Group (USA) Inc.**

D&J Arts Pubs., *(0-9634300)* Orders Addr.: P.O. Box 365, Sierra Vista, AZ 85636 USA; Edit Addr.: 5242 Laguna Ave., Sierra Vista, AZ 85635 USA Tel 602-378-6556; Fax: 520-378-2608
E-mail: shepj@primenet.com.

D&R Enterprises, *(0-911171)* 1101 W. Monte Cristo Rd, W., Edinburg, TX 78541 USA (SAN 269-557X) Tel 956-383-0372
E-mail: dskow@panam.edu.

D&S Marketing Systems, Inc., *(1-878621; 0-9787199)* 1205 38th St., Brooklyn, NY 11218-3705 USA Tel 718-633-8383; Fax: 718-633-8385; Toll Free: 800-633-8383
E-mail: dsmarketing@aol.com; info@dsmarketing.com
Web site: http://www.dsmarketing.com.

D&S Pubns., *(0-9672223)* 3073 Hwy. K ., E., Conover, WI 54519 USA Tel 715-545-8312; Fax: 715-545-2376 Do not confuse with D & S Pubns., Fort Myers, FL
E-mail: dspubl@mail.nnex.net
Web site: http://www.mortgage.maze.com.

D B W, Incorporated *See* **Just Like Me, Inc.**

D.C. Everest Schl. District, *(0-9708063)* 6500 Alderson St., Schofield, WI 54476 USA Tel 715-359-6561 ext 323; Fax: 715-355-7220
E-mail: paleckson@dce.k12.wi.us
Web site: http://www.dce.k12.wi.us.

DC Products, *(0-9672222)* 12527 Huston St., Valley Village, CA 91607 USA Tel 818-763-1200; Fax: 818-762-2553; Toll Free: 800-596-7114.

DDC Publishing, Inc., *(0-936862; 1-56243; 1-58577)* 31 E. 32nd St., Suite 610, New York, NY 10016 USA (SAN 223-5234) Tel 212-619-0200; Fax: 212-986-7302; Toll Free Fax: 800-528-3820; Toll Free: 800-964-6796.

DDDD Pubns., *(0-9635341; 1-885519)* 3407 Brown Rd., Saint Louis, MO 63114-4329 USA (SAN 631-2675)
Dist(s): **Baker & Taylor Bks.**

DEW Pubs., *(0-9704777)* Orders Addr.: P.O. Box 285, Saint Francis, KS 67756 USA Tel 785-332-2314; Fax: 785-332-2678; Edit Addr.: 512 E. Fourth St., Saint Francis, KS 67756 USA.

D J Enterprises, *(1-892196)* 296 John Pixley Rd., Homer, LA 71040 USA Tel 318-258-4922 (phone/fax)
E-mail: jenkinsdo@hotmail.com.

D K Ink *Imprint of* **Dorling Kindersley Publishing, Inc.**

D K Publishing, Incorporated *See* **Dorling Kindersley Publishing, Inc.**

D.R. Auten Music & Assocs., *(0-9669881)* P.O. Box 501, Alpine, CA 91903 USA Tel 858-558-1115
E-mail: dr@drauten.com
Web site: http://www.drauten.com.

DRL Bk., Inc., *(0-9665266; 0-9755859)* 12 W. 18th St., Suite 3E, New York, NY 10011 USA Tel 212-604-9637; Fax: 212-206-9329; Toll Free: 800-853-1057
E-mail: julie@drlbooks.com
Web site: http://www.drlbooks.com.

DSL, Ltd., *(1-889959)* 1218 Noridge, Port Washington, WI 53074-1367 USA Tel 414-284-2542; Fax: 414-284-7039
E-mail: ruthsova@execpc.com.

D. W. Ink, *(1-892313)* P.O. Box 5470, Huntsville, AL 35814 USA Fax: 205-721-1269.

D. W. Publishing, *(0-9741774)* 226 McFarland St., Grand Blanc, MI 48439 USA Tel 810-695-8985
E-mail: dan@dwpublishing.com
Web site: http://www.dwpublishing.com.

D3 *Imprint of* **Devil's Due Publishing, Inc.**

†Da Capo Pr., Inc., *(0-201; 0-306; 0-7382; 0-938289; 0-946771; 0-9627613; 1-55561; 1-58097; 1-873376; 1-882810; 1-885119)* A Member of Perseus Books Group, Orders Addr.: 5500 Central Ave., Boulder, CO 80301 USA Fax: 303-449-3356 (customer service); Toll Free: 800-371-1669 (customer service); Edit Addr.: 11 Cambridge Ctr., Cambridge, MA 02142 USA Tel 617-252-5200; Fax: 617-252-5285
E-mail: westview.orders@perseusbooks.com
Web site: http://www.perseusbooksgroup.com
Dist(s): **Perseus Bks. Group**
Perseus Distribution; *CIP.*

Da Trends Pubns., Inc., *(0-9719912)* Orders Addr.: P.O. Box 6929, Washington, DC 20032 USA; Edit Addr.: 3230 Guilford Dr., Waldorf, MD 20602 USA
E-mail: datrendzpublicationsinc@msn.com
Web site: http://msnusers.com/datrendzpublicationinc.

Da Wong Bks., *(0-9744360)* 4070 Cactus Rd., Shingle Springs, CA 95682 USA Tel 530-676-6060 (phone/fax)
E-mail: eslhotel@yahoo.com.

Dab Publishing Co., *(0-9662228; 0-9728089)* Orders Addr.: P.O. Box 5554, Fresno, CA 93755-5554 USA (SAN 254-1416) Tel 559-229-0038; Edit Addr.: 4711 N. Orchard, Fresno, CA 93726 USA
E-mail: phauck@dabpublishing.com
Web site: http://www.dabpublishing.com
Dist(s): **American West Bks.**
Baker & Taylor Bks.

DAC Educational Pubns., *(1-930731)* 4325 Carlton Pl., Yorba Linda, CA 92886 USA
E-mail: DACpublis@aol.com.

DaChosen Publishing, *(0-9762627)* 4278 Babette Ct., Stone Mountain, GA 30083 USA Toll Free: 866-301-8246
E-mail: dachosen@hotmail.com
Web site: http://www.dachosen.com.

Daddy's Heroes, Inc., *(0-9792111)* 4799 Baxter St., Santa Barbara, CA 93110 USA.

Dafina *Imprint of* **Kensington Publishing Corp.**

Dageforde Publishing, Incorporated *See* **Day of Grace Publishing Services**

Dahlin, Bill, *(0-9678028)* P.O. Box 233, Dent, MN 56528-0233 USA
E-mail: bdahlin@msn.com.

Dahomey Publishing Co., *(0-9723570)* Orders Addr.: 50 Hall Rd., Winchendon, MA 01475 USA (SAN 255-4542) Tel 978-297-1820; Fax: 978-297-2519
Web site: http://www.DahomeyPublishing.com.

Dailey International Pubs., *(0-9666251)* 500 Laurel Oaks Ln., Alpharetta, GA 30004-4508 USA
E-mail: franklyn@daileyint.com
Web site: http://www.daileyint.com
Dist(s): **Baker & Taylor.**

Dailey International Publishing *See* **Dailey International Pubs.**

Daily Racing Form Pr., *(0-9648493; 0-9700147; 0-9726401; 1-932910)* Div. of Daily Racing Form, Inc., 100 Broadway, 7th Flr., New York, NY 10005 USA Tel 212-366-7606; Fax: 212-366-7773; Toll Free: 800-537-1050
E-mail: dkeppler@drf.com
Web site: http://www.drf.com
Dist(s): **National Bk. Network.**

Daisy Hill Pr. International, *(0-9632799)* Orders Addr.: P.O. Box 1681, Rochester, MI 48308 USA (SAN 298-3524) Tel 248-651-0748; Fax: 810-752-3532; 248-652-8904; Edit Addr.: 165 Wimpole Dr., Rochester Hills, MI 48309-2147 USA (SAN 298-3532)
E-mail: amalgam13@worldnet.att.net
Dist(s): **Baker & Taylor Bks.**
Brodart Co.
Emery-Pratt Co.

Daisy Pubns., *(0-9704399)* PMB 237, 160 W. Camino Real, Boca Raton, FL 33432 USA (SAN 253-4371) Tel 561-417-7017
Web site: http://daisypublications.com.

Daisy Publishing, *(0-9740641)* P.O. Box 681171, Franklin, TN 37068 USA Do not confuse with Daisy Publishing in Massapequa Park, NY, Altoona, PA.

DaisyHill Press *See* **Daisy Hill Pr. International**

Daisyworld Pr., *(1-933609)* P.O. Box 105, Corning, NY 14830 USA (SAN 256-9671) Tel 607-330-2200 (phone/fax)
E-mail: jay@daisyworldpress.com
Web site: http://www.daisyworldpress.com
Dist(s): **Chelsea Green Publishing.**

Dakota Bks., *(0-9632861)* Orders Addr.: 2801 Daubenbiss, No. 1, Soquel, CA 95073 USA (SAN 630-9445) Tel 831-477-7174
E-mail: llogan@cruzio.com
Web site: http://www.dakota-books.com.

Dakota Publishing, *(0-9670116; 0-9670148)* P.O. Box 3204, Vista, CA 92085-0448 USA Tel 760-716-4342 Do not confuse with companies with the same or similar names in Scottsdale, AZ, Jamestown, ND, Sioux Falls, SD
E-mail: diamondsecret@home.com
Web site: http://www.gemsecrets.com.

Dakota Rose, *(0-9727056)* HC 74, No. 16, Okaton, SD 57562 USA Tel 605-669-2529
E-mail: dakrose@gwtc.net.

Dakota Skies Photography *See* **Johnny Sundby Photography**

Dale, Shelley *See* **Norman Bks.**

Dales Large Print Bks. (GBR) *(1-85389; 1-84262) Dist. by* **Ulverscroft US.**

Dally, James W. Associates *See* **College Hse. Enterprises, LLC**

Dalmatian Pr., *(1-57759; 1-888567; 1-4037)* 118 Seaboard Ln., Suite 118, Franklin, TN 37067-8218 USA Tel 615-370-9922; Fax: 615-370-8034; Toll Free: 800-815-8696 ; *Imprints:* Spirit Press (Spirit Press); Intervisual/Piggy Toes (Inter P Toes)
E-mail: bernadette.ahsam@dalmatianpress.com.

Dalton, Curt, *(0-9715702)* 2058 Ottello Ave., Dayton, OH 45414 USA
E-mail: cdalton@woh.rr.com.

Dalton, William, *(0-9764395)* 1338 N. Laurel Ave., West Hollywood, CA 90046 USA Tel 310-800-0811
E-mail: urban_mystic@yahoo.com.

Damien-Dutton Society for Leprosy Aid, Inc., *(0-9606330)* 616 Bedford Ave., Bellmore, NY 11710 USA (SAN 217-1694) Tel 516-221-5829; 516-221-9588; Fax: 516-221-5909.

Damon, Phyllis Associates *See* **Clever Hands Publishing**

Dan Il Pr., *(0-9703874)* Orders Addr.: P.O. Box 73, Ithaca, NE 68033 USA Tel 402-277-0030
E-mail: mprowe@alltel.net.

Dana, Charles A. Ctr., Univ. of Texas at Austin, *(0-9707948; 1-932371)* 2901 N. 1-H 35, Suite 2.200, Austin, TX 78722-2348 USA Tel 512-471-6190; Fax: 512-232-1855; Toll Free: 866-871-9995
E-mail: pswann@mail.utexas.edu
Web site: http://www.danacenter.org.

Dance Horizons *Imprint of* **Princeton Bk. Co. Pubs.**

Dancer's Publishing, *(0-9749848)* 2103 Harrison NW, Suite 2-336, Olympia, WA 98502 USA.

Dances With Horses, Inc., *(0-9763489)* P.O. Box 819, Rexburg, ID 83440 USA Tel 800-871-7635; Fax: 208-356-7817; Toll Free: 800-871-7635
E-mail: frankbell@horsewhisperer.com
Web site: http://www.horsewhisperer.com.

Dancing Crane Education & Illustration *See* **CraneDance Pubns.**

Dancing Crows Unlimited, *(0-9704420)* 97 Blodgett Ave., Duxbury, MA 02332 USA
E-mail: mewcsw@hotmail.com.

Dancing Force, The, *(0-9726119)* 2249 Reeves Creek Rd., Suite B, Selma, OR 97538 USA (SAN 255-156X) Tel 541-597-2093 (phone/fax)
E-mail: dancingforce@ureach.com
Dist(s): **DeVorss & Co.**

Dancing Hands Music, *(0-9638801)* 4275 Churchill Cir., Minnetonka, MN 55345 USA Tel 612-933-0781 (phone/fax); Toll Free: 800-898-8036
E-mail: al@dancinghands.com
Web site: http://www.dancinghands.com
Dist(s): **SCB Distributors.**

Dancing Magic Heart Bk., *(0-9790041)* Div. of Douglas/Steinman Productions, 1841 Broadway, Suite 1103, New York, NY 10023 USA Tel 212-765-9848; Fax: 212-765-9848
E-mail: faithdouglas@earthlink.net
Web site: http://www.douglas-steinman.com
Dist(s): **New Leaf Resources.**

Dancing Moon Pr., *(1-892076)* P.O. Box 832, Newport, OR 97365-0062 USA Tel 541-272-1484 (cell); 541-574-7708 (work)
E-mail: carla@dialoregon.net; carla@dancingmoonpress.com
Web site: http://www.dancingmoonpress.com.

Dancing Toad, *(0-9705625)* 5109 Washburn Ave., S., Minneapolis, MN 55410 USA Tel 612-920-5876; Fax: 612-927-5443
E-mail: marysusan@uswest.net
Web site: http://DancingToad.com.

Dancing Words Pr., Inc., *(0-9716346)* Orders Addr.: P.O. Box 1575, Severna Park, MD 21146 USA; Edit Addr.: 12 Sonneborn Ln., Severna Park, MD 21146 USA Tel 410-647-1441 (phone/fax)
E-mail: dwpinc@aol.com
Web site: http://www.dancingwordspress.com
Dist(s): **Biblio Distribution**
Quality Bks., Inc.

Dandelion Bks., LLC, *(1-893302; 0-9789611; 1-934280)* Div. of Dandelion Enterprises, Inc., 1133 W. Baseline Rd., Suite 178, Tempe, AZ 85283-5217 USA (SAN 852-4742) Tel 480-897-4452; Fax: 480-452-1580; Toll Free: 800-861-7899
E-mail: dandelionbooks@cox.net; info@dandelionbooks.com
Web site: http://www.dandelion-books.com; http://www.dandelionbooks.net
Dist(s): **Biblio Distribution**
BookSurge, LLC
NetSource Distribution.

Dandelion Pr., *(0-9643692)* 810 S. 12th St., Laramie, WY 82070 USA Tel 307-745-4134 Do not confuse with companies with the same name in Austin, TX, Olympia, WA, Stony Brook, NY
E-mail: guz@UWYO.edu.

Dandelion Productions, *(0-9721445)* 6013 Ogden Nash Way, Sacramento, CA 95842 USA.

Dandelion Publishing, *(0-9793930)* 6234 Eliza Ln., North Las Vegas, NV 89031 USA (SAN 853-330X)
E-mail: sand.d@cox.net
Web site: http://DandelionPublishing.com.

Dandle Pr., *(0-9704487)* 305 W. Magnolia, Suite 235, Fort Collins, CO 80521 USA Tel 970-482-4098.

Dandy Lion Pubns., *(0-931724; 1-883055)* P.O. Box 190, Sn Luis Obisp, CA 93406-0190 USA (SAN 211-5565) Toll Free: 800-776-8032
E-mail: dandy@dandylionbooks.come
Web site: http://www.dandylionbooks.com.

Dandy Productions, *(0-9672063)* 200 Clocktower Pl., Suite 201A, Carmel, CA 93923 USA Tel 831-622-5270; Fax: 831-375-4544.

Dangberg, Grace Foundation, Incorporated *See* **Sage Hill Pubs., LLC**

Daniels, Mitch for Governor Campaign, *(0-9766026)* 47 S. Meridian St., 2nd Flr., Indianapolis, IN 46204 USA Toll Free: 877-648-2448
Web site: http://www.mymanmitch.com.

DanMar Publishing, *(0-9749407)* 112 E. Pennsylvania Blvd., Feasterville, PA 19053 USA Tel 215-364-1112; Fax: 215-364-3231
E-mail: drlavanga@aol.com
Web site: http://www.drlavanga.com.

Dansu Pubs., LLC, *(0-9719328)* Orders Addr.: P.O. Box 17335, Euclid, OH 44117 USA; Edit Addr.: 1825 Braeburn Park Dr., Euclid, OH 44117 USA.

Dara's Canine Foundation, Inc., *(0-9700667)* 7507 Hampden Ln., Bethesda, MD 20814 USA Tel 301-652-9235; Fax: 301-652-3698
E-mail: finnie@erols.com.

†Darby Creek Publishing, *(0-87406; 1-58196)* Oxford Resources, Inc., 7858 Industrial Pkwy., Plain City, OH 43064 USA (SAN 687-4592) Tel 614-873-7955 ; *Imprints:* Willowisp Press (Willowisp Pr); Silver Elm Classic (Silver Elm)
E-mail: info@darbycreekpublishing.com
Web site: http://www.darbycreekpublishing.com
Dist(s): **Lerner Publishing Group**; *CIP.*

Darcey Pr., *(1-889079)* Orders Addr.: P.O. Box 5018, Vernon Hills, IL 60061 USA Tel 847-816-1468 (phone/fax); Edit Addr.: 27250 N. Meadowoods Ln., Mettawa, IL 60048 USA
E-mail: adriennemtindall@cs.com
Web site: darceypress.com.

d'ARCY LIAT, *(0-9612658; 0-9659078)* Orders Addr.: P.O. Box 1415, New York, NY 10276-1415 USA Tel 212-366-1408.

Dare 2 Dream Desktop Publishing *See* **Dare 2 Dream Publishing**

Dare 2 Dream Publishing, *(0-9716812; 0-9726444; 0-9741034; 0-9744037; 0-9744121; 0-9754922; 0-9755739; 0-9760769)* 100 Pin Oak Ct., Lexington, SC 29073-7911 USA (SAN 255-559X)
E-mail: limitless@alltel.net.

Dare to Dream Scholarship, Incorporated *See* **Cole Publishing**

Dargaud Publishing Co. (FRA) *(0-917201; 2-205) Dist. by* **Distribks Inc.**

Daring Child Pr., *(1-892885)* 2343 Timberidge Ln., SE, Rochester, MN 55904 USA Tel 507-254-1544; Fax: 507-281-4473
E-mail: nortung@aol.com
Dist(s): **Bookmen, Inc.**

Dark Carnival Games, L.L.C., *(0-9710905)* 3990 W. 12 Mile Rd., Suite 193, Berkley, MI 48072 USA Tel 248-426-0800; Fax: 248-426-6765
E-mail: questions@mortonslist.com
Web site: http://www.mortonslist.com.

Dark Forest Pr., *(0-9764226)* P.O. Box 9133, Arlington, VA 22210 USA (SAN 256-4475) Tel 202-368-4341; 1310 N. Oak St., Apt. 408, Arlington, VA 22209 Tel 202-368-4341 Do not confuse with Dark Forest Press in Denver, CO.

Dark Horse Comics, *(1-56971; 1-878574; 1-59307; 1-59582; 1-59617)* 10956 SE Main St., Milwaukie, OR 97222 USA Tel 503-652-8815; Fax: 503-654-9440
E-mail: info@darkhorse.com
Web site: http://www.darkhorse.com
Dist(s): **Diamond Bk. Distributors.**

Dark Horse Pr., *(0-9702308)* 4 Edgewood, Coto De Caza, CA 92672 USA
E-mail: obowazu@earthlink.net.

Dark Skull Studios, *(0-9797080)* 17711 Barker Bluff Ln., Cypress, TX 77433 USA (SAN 854-1922) Tel 832-220-6734
E-mail: richardleon@darkskullstudios.com
Web site: http://www.darkskullstudios.com.

Dark Woods Publishing, *(0-9665002)* 203 S. Elmont Dr., Apache Junction, AZ 85220 USA (SAN 299-6936) Tel 602-380-4073; 480-380-4073
E-mail: darkwoods@inficad.com.

Darker Intentiona Pr., *(0-9769612)* P.O. Box 569, Freehold Twp., NJ 07728-0569 USA Tel 732-879-1990 ; *Imprints:* Pixiefire (Pixiefire)
E-mail: jzdakota@hotmail.com
Web site: http://www.darkerintentionspress.com.

Darkerwood Publishing Group, *(0-9669788; 0-9788975)* P.O. Box 2011, Arvada, CO 80001 USA
E-mail: darkerwood@connollyweb.com; PMPress@cox.net; ofs.admin@gmail.com; darkerwoodpublishing@gmail.com
Web site: http://www.evvygarrett.com; http://www.ofs-demonolatry.org/dbpub.htm.

Darkstar Pubns., *(0-9712541)* 533 Plainview Rd., Lexington, KY 40517 USA Tel 859-266-5570
E-mail: kenleew@earthlink.net.

Darling & Co. *Imprint of* **Laughing Elephant**

Darling Pr. LLC, *(0-9765761)* Orders Addr.: 19740 SW 49th Ave., Tualatin, OR 97062 USA
Web site: http://www.darlingpress.com
Dist(s): **Bottman Design, Inc.**

Darnell Publishing, *(0-9755616)* P.O. Box 341825, Tampa, FL 33694 USA
Web site: http://www.abrink.com.

Daryl Ann Pubns., *(1-928641)* Orders Addr.: P.O. Box 7811, Warwick, RI 02887-7811 USA Tel 401-732-1676; Edit Addr.: 3524 W. Shore Rd., No. 205, Warwick, RI 02887 USA
E-mail: daryl_ann@yahoo.com.

Dashney, John *See* **Stage Within Your Mind, The**

Data Trace Legal Publishers, Incorporated *See* **Data Trace Publishing, Co.**

Data Trace Publishing, Co., *(0-9637468; 1-57400)* Orders Addr.: P.O. Box 1239, Brooklandville, MD 21022 USA Tel 410-494-4994; Fax: 410-494-0515; Toll Free: 800-342-0454; Edit Addr.: 110 West Rd., Suite 227, Towson, MD 21204 USA
E-mail: info@datatrace.com
Web site: http://www.datatrace.com/legal.

Databooks *See* **Chandler Hse. Pr.**

Data-Lynn Bk. Co., *(1-877983)* Div. of LaChic, Inc., Orders Addr.: P.O. Box 235, Prior Lake, MN 55372 USA Tel 952-237-1438; Fax: 952-226-4749
E-mail: jayrushing@techcertify.net; jayrushing@lindaacollections.com; jayr345@verizon.net
Web site: http://datalynnbooks.techcertify.net/.

Datobo Pr., *(0-9709860)* 1562 Carnation Ave., Ventura, CA 93004 USA Tel 805-647-4309
E-mail: roland.jacobus@att.net.

Dattel, Frederick Scott *See* **Creative Vision Publishing**

Daughter Culture Pubns., *(0-935281)* 1840 41st Ave., Suite 102-301, Capitola, CA 95010 USA (SAN 695-7447) Tel 408-476-0199.

Daughters Arise, LLC, *(0-9744178)* 2648 E. Workman Ave., Suite 314, West Covina, CA 91791 USA Tel 770-808-1199; Fax: 770-216-1626
E-mail: fhenley@daughtersarise.com
Web site: http://www.daughtersarise.com.

Daughters of St. Paul, 50 St. Paul Ave., Boston, MA 02130-3491 USA
Dist(s): **Pauline Bks. & Media.**

Dauntless Frog Publishing *See* **Laughing Peaches Pubns.**

Davenport, May Pubs., *(0-943864; 0-9603118; 0-9794140)* 26313 Purissima Rd., Los Altos Hills, CA 94022-4539 USA (SAN 212-467X) Tel 650-947-1325; Fax: 650-947-1373
E-mail: mdbooks@earthlink.net
Dist(s): **Todd Communications.**

Davenport, Sheena, *(0-9747625)* 3535 Riverview Approach, Ellenwood, GA 30294 USA Tel 404-241-3106
E-mail: dwgo@bellsouth.net.

David & Charles Children's Bks. (GBR) *(1-86233) Dist. by* **Sterling.**

David & Charles Pubs. (GBR) *(0-7153) Dist. by* **FandW Pubns Inc.**

David, Elizabeth A., *(0-9740170)* P.O. Box 766, Fairhaven, MA 02719-0700 USA Tel 508-979-5593
E-mail: yasny@comcast.net
Web site: http://www.zorena.com.

†David, Jonathan Publishers, Inc., *(0-8246)* 68-22 Eliot Ave., Middle Village, NY 11379 USA (SAN 169-5274) Tel 718-456-8611; Fax: 718-894-2818
E-mail: jondavpub@aol.com
Web site: http://www.jdbooks.com; *CIP.*

David Ladd Press, *(0-9774563)* 56 Collidge Ave., South Portland, ME 04106 USA Tel 207-767-2836
E-mail: davidladdpress@yahoo.com.

†Davidson, Harlan Inc., *(0-88295)* 773 Glenn Ave., Wheeling, IL 60090-6000 USA (SAN 201-2375) Tel 847-541-9720; Fax: 847-541-9830
E-mail: harlandavidson@harlandavidson.com
Web site: http://www.harlandavidson.com; *CIP.*

Davidson, Harrison Publishing Hse., *(0-9674105)* Div. of Pathway, Inc., 3001 Burnt Mill Rd., Charlotte, NC 28210 USA Tel 704-643-4407; Fax: 704-643-0584; Toll Free: 888-643-4407
E-mail: phillipmartz@email.msn.com
Web site: http://www.pathwayart.com.

Davidson Titles, Inc., *(1-884756)* Orders Addr.: 2345 Dr. F.E. Wright Dr., Jackson, TN 38303 USA; Edit Addr.: P.O. Box 3538, Jackson, TN 38303-3538 USA (SAN 255-9129) Tel 731-988-5333; Fax: 731-988-5080; Toll Free Fax: 800-787-7935; Toll Free: 800-433-3903 Do not confuse with companies of the same name in Sugar Hill NH, Windsor CT, Redmond & Kirkland WA, Newark NJ, Fairfield & Reddick FL, East Lansing MI, Rocklin CA, Tolono IL, MIssoula MT, Ann Arbor MI, Half Moon Bay CA
E-mail: brian@davidsontitles.com
Web site: http://www.davidsontitles.com.

Davis, A. S. Media Group, *(0-9666352; 0-9729150; 0-9759022; 0-9766013; 0-9776245; 0-9787719)* Orders Addr.: P.O. Box 590780, San Francisco, CA 94159 USA
E-mail: info@greenlinepub.com
Web site: http://www.greenlinepub.com
Dist(s): **Perseus Distribution.**

Davis Bks. LLC, *(0-9770142)* Orders Addr.: P.O. Box 6291, Cincinnati, OH 45206 USA Tel 513-687-1943
E-mail: georgedisselkamp@yahoo.com
Web site: http://www.davisbooks.cjb.net
Dist(s): **Docustar.**

Davis, James (Jim), *(0-9760960)* 125 Teal Dr., Chatham, IL 62629 USA Tel 217-483-4924.

Davis, Jenene L. *See* **Kidz Character, LLC**

Davis, Nancy, *(0-9653088)* 3122 Heather Ct., Springfield, MO 65804 USA Tel 703-978-4321; Fax: 703-978-1130
E-mail: drnancydavis@Juno.com
Web site: http://www.therapeutic-stories.com.

Davis, Paul *See* **Royal Hse. Publishing**

Davis Pubns., Inc., *(0-87192)* 50 Portland St., Worcester, MA 01608 USA (SAN 201-3002) Tel 508-754-7201; Fax: 508-753-3834; Toll Free: 800-533-2847
E-mail: maltobelli@davisart.com
Web site: http://www.davisart.com
Dist(s): **Sterling Publishing Co., Inc.**

Davis Publishing Co., *(1-888185)* 271 Sugar Creek Rd., Quitman, LA 71268 USA Tel 318-259-9677 Do not confuse with companies with same or similar names in Richfield, OH, Berkeley, CA, Clackamas, OR
E-mail: elladavis@colla.com.

Davis, Tamela, *(0-9772923)* 14572 Twin Oaks Dr., Carmel, IN 46032 USA
E-mail: tonyntamy@sbcglobal.net
Web site: http://www.adventuresingrammar.com.

davishooligans, *(0-9719268)* 1411 W. Corell Blvd., Suite 160 PMB 174, Davis, CA 95616 USA Tel 530-750-3322; 424 Russell Pk., No. 1, Davis, CA 95616.

Company

Davlaw Press, *(0-9776917)* Orders Addr.: P.O. Box 4317, Harrisburg, PA 17111 USA (SAN 257-9863) Tel 717-441-5451; Fax: 717-441-4925 ; *Imprints:* Curcumin Books (Curcumin Bks)
E-mail: larry@davlawpress.com
Web site: http://www.davlawpress.com.

Davus Publishing, *(0-915317)* P.O. Box 1101, Buffalo, NY 14213-7101 USA (SAN 289-9787) Tel 519-426-2077; Fax: 519-426-0105
E-mail: davus@kwic.com
Web site: http://www.kwic.com/~davus
Dist(s): **Coutts Library Service, Inc.**

Daw Enterprises, *(0-9628081)* 1338 Parrish St., Philadelphia, PA 19123-1817 USA Tel 215-424-2016.

DAW Hardcover *Imprint of* **Penguin Group (USA) Inc.**

Dawasoft, *(0-9764218)* 63 Forbell St., Brooklyn, NY 11208 USA Tel 718-541-5457
E-mail: dawasoft@yahoo.com.

†Dawn Horse Pr., *(0-913922; 0-918801; 1-57097)* 10336 Loch Lomond Rd., No. 305, Middletown, CA 95461 USA (SAN 201-3029) Tel 707-928-6590; Fax: 707-928-5068; Toll Free: 877-770-0772 (orders)
E-mail: dhp@adidam.org; *CIP.*

Dawn of a New Day Pubns., The *Imprint of* **Konkori International**

Dawn of Day Childrens Publishing Co., Inc., *(0-9666857)* 73 Ireland Pl., PMB 201, Amityville, NY 11757 USA (SAN 253-0198) Tel 631-225-5513; Fax: 631-225-5431; Toll Free: 800-575-7040
E-mail: information@dawnofday.com
Web site: http://www.dawnofday.com.

Dawn Pubns., *(0-916124; 1-878265; 1-883220; 1-58469)* 12402 Bitney Springs Rd., Nevada City, CA 95959 USA Tel 530-478-0111; Fax: 530-274-7778; Toll Free: 800-545-7475 Do not confuse with Dawn Pubns. in Pasadena, TX
E-mail: nature@dawnpub.com; info@dawnpub.com
Web site: http://www.dawnpub.com
Dist(s): **Baker & Taylor Bks.**
Booklines Hawaii, Ltd.
Brodart Co.
Common Ground Distributors, Inc.
Follett Library Resources
Hervey's Booklink & Cookbook Warehouse
Koen-Levy Bk. Wholesalers LLC
Territory Titles.

DawnSignPress, *(0-915035; 1-58121)* 6130 Nancy Ridge Dr., San Diego, CA 92121-3223 USA (SAN 289-9183) Tel 858-625-0600; Fax: 858-625-2336; Toll Free: 800-549-5350
E-mail: info@dawnsign.com
Web site: http://www.dawnsign.com
Dist(s): **Gryphon Hse., Inc.**
Independent Pubs. Group.

Dawson Bk. Shop, *(0-87093)* 535 N. Larchmont Blvd., Los Angeles, CA 90004 USA (SAN 201-3045) Tel 323-469-2186; Fax: 323-469-9553
E-mail: info@dawsonbooks.com
Web site: http://www.dawsonbooks.com
Dist(s): **Sunbelt Pubns., Inc.**

Daxton Wilde Fnd., *(0-9749834)* 155 N. 400 W., Suite 580, Salt Lake City, UT 84103 USA Tel 801-390-1603
E-mail: jeffdixon@daxtonwilde.com
Web site: http://www.daxtonwilde.org.

Day By Day, *(0-9674915; 1-934569)* P.O. Box 4215, Fairview, UT 84629 USA Tel 435-427-3501; 887-447-1683
E-mail: shelly@day-by-day.org
Web site: http://www.day-by-day.org.

Day, Donna, *(0-9726059)* 11014 19th Ave. SE, Everett, WA 98208 USA Tel 425-337-2969
E-mail: day.fam@verizon.net.

Day of Grace Publishing Services, *(0-9637515; 1-886225; 0-9753031)* 1155 Crestline Dr., Crete, NE 68333-1833 USA Toll Free: 800-216-8794
E-mail: info@dageforde.com
Web site: http://www.dageforde.com
Dist(s): **Baker & Taylor Bks.**
Quality Bks., Inc.
Unique Bks., Inc.

Day to Day Enterprises, *(1-890905)* Orders Addr.: 1721 Canoe Creek Rd., Oviedo, FL 32766-8533 USA (SAN 299-7118) Tel 407-359-9356; Fax: 407-359-4323 ; *Imprints:* Eco Fiction Books (Eco Fiction Bks)
E-mail: books@daytodayenterprises.com
Web site: http://www.daytodayenterprises.com
Dist(s): **Baker & Taylor Bks.**
Book Clearing Hse.

Daylight Pubs., *(0-9764103; 0-9792755)* 8255 S Wright Pl., Broken Arrow, OK 74014 USA Tel 918-357-1266
E-mail: kathy@daylightpublishers.com
Web site: http://www.daylightpublishers.com.

DayOne Pubns. (GBR) *(0-902548; 1-903087; 1-84625) Dist. by* **Gabriel Res.**

Days of Glory Publishing, *(0-9770206)* 28 Branden Way, Tolland, CT 06084 USA.

Daystar House *See* **Colbert Hse., The**

Day-Timers, Inc., *(1-58794)* Div. of Fortune Brands, Inc., 1 Willow Ln., East Texas, PA 18046 USA Tel 610-530-6089; Fax: 610-530-6004
E-mail: renae_bell@daytimer.com
Web site: http://www.daytimers.com.

Daz Unlimited, *(0-9708363)* 1093 Broxton Ave., Suite 523, Los Angeles, CA 90024 USA Tel 310-445-3118 (phone/fax)
E-mail: vickie@dazunlimited.com
Web site: http://www.dazunlimited.com.

Dazsling Inc., *(0-9749170)* P.O. Box 236, Allston, MA 02134 USA
Web site: http://www.rootfriends.com.

dbazza, Inc., *(0-9721677)* P.O. Box 71262, Pittsburgh, PA 15213 USA Tel 412-681-1180; Fax: 412-681-1106
E-mail: info@dbaza.com
Web site: http://www.dbaza.com.

DC Comics, *(0-930289; 1-56389; 1-4012)* Div. of Warner Bros.- A Time Warner Entertainment Co., 1700 Broadway, New York, NY 10019 USA Tel 212-636-5400; Fax: 212-636-5979 ; *Imprints:* Vertigo (Vertigo); Paradox (Paradox); Cliffhanger (Cliffhanger); A B C (A B C); Wildstorm (Wildstorm); CMX (CMX); Minx (Minx)
E-mail: booksales@dccomics.com
Web site: http://www.dccomics.com
Dist(s): **Diamond Comic Distributors, Inc.**
Eastern News Distributors
Hachette Bk. Group.

DCTS Publishing, *(0-9653904)* Div. of Hamilton Ministry, P.O. Box 40216, Santa Barbara, CA 93140 USA Tel 805-653-6064; Fax: 805-653-6522; Toll Free: 800-965-8150
E-mail: dennis@dctspub.com
Web site: http://www.dctspub.com.

De Armond, Garry, *(0-9676287)* 15590 92nd Ct N., West Palm Beach, FL 33412-1738 USA
E-mail: garry@bugaroos.com
Web site: http://www.bugaroos.com.

De Breff, Vanko, 3237 Yanceyville St., Greensboro, NC 27405 USA.

De Day Publishing, *(0-9664196)* 2973 HArbor Blvd., No. 326, Costa Mesa, CA 92626 USA Tel 714-432-9681; Fax: 714-545-6866
E-mail: cuddle1@ix.netcom.com
Web site: http://www/projectcuddle.org
Dist(s): **Biblio Distribution.**

De La Flor (ARG) *(950-515) Dist. by* **Edit Cultl.**

De La Luz Pubns., *(0-9748326)* 121 W. Hickory St., Denton, TX 76201 USA Tel 940-367-1651; Fax: 940-323-0488
E-mail: ccarrasco1@chater.net.

De Loach, George P., *(0-9768362)* 475 W. Fallen Leaf Cir., Wasilla, AK 99654 USA Tel 907-376-2680
E-mail: gdeloach@juno.com.

De Simonin Pubns., *(1-883100)* Orders Addr.: P.O. Box 57223, New Orleans, LA 70124 USA Tel 504-283-7463; Fax: 504-283-1337; Toll Free: 800-594-0611; Edit Addr.: 6841 Wuerpel St., New Orleans, LA 70124 USA
Dist(s): **Forest Sales & Distributing Co.**

De Sio, Anthony W. & Delores J. Foundation, *(0-9670347)* 18124 Wedge Pkwy., No. 434, Reno, NV 89511 USA Tel 775-849-1429; Fax: 775-849-1568
E-mail: awdesio2210@aol.com.

DeA Publishing Co., G., *(0-9712668)* 10405 Rushton Rd., South Lyon, MI 48178-9137 USA Tel 248-437-0375
E-mail: Sidorgeo@earthlink.com.

Deacon Denny Bks., *(0-9716330)* 3535 5th St., Suite T, Lewiston, ID 83501 USA
E-mail: deacondenny@hotmail.com.

Deaconess Press *See* **Fairview Pr.**

Deaf Life Pr. *Imprint of* **MSM Productions, Ltd.**

Deaf Missions, *(1-59799)* Orders Addr.: 21199 Greenview Rd., Council Bluffs, IA 51503-4190 USA
Web site: http://www.deafmissions.com.

Deal, Darlene, *(0-9747299)* P.O. Box 521, North Hollywood, CA 91603-0521 USA Tel 818-752-7065 (phone/fax).

DeAngelis, Anthony, *(0-9754853)* 101 Cypress Ave., San Bruno, CA 94066-5420 USA
E-mail: a.deangelis@worldnet.att.net.

Dean's Bks., Inc., *(0-9728607)* 1426 S. Kansas Ave., Topeka, KS 66612 USA Tel 785-357-4708
E-mail: contact@oilcanbook.com
Web site: http://www.oilcanbook.com.

Dearborn Publishing, *(1-891685)* Div. of The Mae Group LLC, Orders Addr.: P.O. Box 4456, Hammond, IN 46324 USA Tel 219-689-1286
E-mail: chermytalent@yahoo.com; johngraham@att.net.

Dearborn Resources, *(0-9644096)* P.O. Box 59677, Chicago, IL 60659 USA Fax: 773-262-5731.

Dearborn Trade, A Kaplan Professional Company *See* **Kaplan Publishing**

Deb on Air Bks., *(0-9727615)* Orders Addr.: P.O. Box 580055, Elk Grove, CA 95758 USA Tel 916-684-3551.

Debate, Editorial (ESP) *(84-7444; 84-8306) Dist. by* **AIMS Intl.**

Debate, Editorial (ESP) *(84-7444; 84-8306) Dist. by* **Libros Fronteras.**

Debbie-Lou Productions, *(0-9679561)* 5983 Rappahonnock Cir., Murray, UT 84123 USA Tel 801-266-9873; Fax: 801-268-0203
E-mail: debbieLou@earthlink.net
Web site: http://www.whataveg.com.

Debi, Kennedy *See* **nJoy Bks.**

DeCa Communications, LLC, *(0-9762262)* 300 Williamsburg Dr., Mandeville, LA 70471 USA
Web site: http://www.decacom.info.

Decere Publishing, *(0-9717013)* 5590 Bunky Way, Atlanta, GA 30338 USA Tel 404-474-2830; Fax: 770-399-5883 Do not confuse with CSI Publilshing in Monterey Park, CA
E-mail: mark@decere.com
Web site: http://www.decere.com.

Dedalus, Ltd., *(0-946626; 1-873982; 1-903517)* P.O. Box 160, Monroe, OR 97456 USA Tel 541-847-5274; Fax: 541-847-6018; 265 S. Fifth St., Monroe, OR 97456
E-mail: subco@clipper.net; dedaluslimited@compuserve.com
Dist(s): **SCB Distributors.**

Deep Dish Design, *(0-9755033)* 15012 Cherry Ln., Burnsville, MN 55306 USA
E-mail: jb@deepdishdesign.com
Web site: http://www.deepdishdesign.com.

Deep Roots Pubns., *(0-9671713)* Orders Addr.: P.O. Box 114, Saratoga, NY 12866 USA Tel 518-583-8920; Fax: 518-584-3919; Edit Addr.: 229 Lake Ave., Saratoga, NY 12866 USA
E-mail: drpalmer2002@yahoo.com
Web site: http//www.deeprootspublications.com
Dist(s): **North Country Bks., Inc.**

Deep Waters Pr., *(0-9748171)* Suite 100, 77 Court St., Laconia, NH 03246 USA (SAN 255-8777) Tel 603-520-1214; P.O. Box 452, Meredith, NH 03253 Tel 603-524-2585
E-mail: halclyon@yahoo.com; deepwaterspress@yahoo.com
Web site: http://www.DeepWaterspress.com
Dist(s): **Baker & Taylor Bks.**

Deeper Roots Pubns. & Media, *(1-930547)* 2100 Red Gate Rd., Orlando, FL 32818 USA Tel 407-293-8666; Fax: 407-293-8666
E-mail: deeperroots@aol.com
Web site: http://www.DeeperRoots.com.

Deepercalling Media, Inc., *(0-9726135; 1-59601)* 1200 Mt. Diablo Blvd., Suite 108, Walnut Creek, CA 94596 USA (SAN 254-9360) Fax: 925-939-4010
E-mail: info@deepercalling.com
Web site: http://www.deepercalling.com
Dist(s): **Whitaker Hse.**

Deer Creek Publishing, *(0-9651452)* Orders Addr.: P.O. Box 2594, Nevada City, CA 95959 USA Tel 530-478-1758; Fax: 530-478-1759 Do not confuse with Deer Creek Publishing, Provo, UT
Dist(s): **Baker & Taylor Bks.**

Deer Oaks, Inc., *(0-9764700)* P.O. Box 429, Barrington, IL 60011-0429 USA.

Deerbrook Editions, *(0-9712488)* P.O. Box 542, Comberland, ME 04021-0542 USA
E-mail: jeffwh@gpom.com; jeffwh@idesignbooks.com
Web site: http://www.idesignbooks.com
Dist(s): **Baker & Taylor Bks.**

Defense Research LLC, *(0-9749873)* 211 Kirkland Ave. Apt. 216, Kirkland, WA 98033-6578 USA
E-mail: sales@defenseresearch.org
Web site: http://www.defenseresearch.org.

Deffendall, Paul Vernon, *(0-9724477)* 28 W. Iowa St., Evansville, IN 47710 USA
E-mail: paul_deffendall@yahoo.com.

Defiance In Print, *(0-9771641)* 1139 Juniper Ct., Tavares, FL 32778 USA (SAN 256-9663) Tel 352-343-2554; Fax: 352-742-1442
E-mail: miller2554@embarqmail.com
Web site: http://www.carolmayomiller.com
Dist(s): **AtlasBooks Distribution.**

Defined Mind, Inc., *(0-9763767)* 580 Broadway, Suite 912, New York, NY 10012 USA Tel 212-925-5138 (Hours: M-F 9:30 am-5:30 pm)
E-mail: info@defmind.com
Web site: http://www.defmind.com.

DeForest Pr., *(0-9649922; 1-930374)* Orders Addr.: P.O. Box 383, Rogers, MN 55374 USA Tel 763-428-2997; Fax: 763-390-5919; Toll Free: 866-509-0604; Edit Addr.: P.O. Box 383, Rogers, MN 55374 USA
E-mail: shane@deforestpress.com
Web site: http://www.deforestpress.com
Dist(s): **Baker & Taylor Bks.**

DeForge Communincations, *(0-9677846)* 479 Dublin Ave., Eugene, OR 97404 USA Tel 541-688-5152; Fax: 541-461-1564
E-mail: ldeforge@ix.netcom.com.

DeFranco Entertainment, *(1-929845)* P.O. Box 1425, Thousand Oaks, CA 91358-1425 USA Fax: 805-376-2953
E-mail: tdefranco@vcnet.com.

Degenhardt, Scott, *(0-9765671)* P.O. Box 11182, Murfreesboro, TN 37129 USA Tel 615-890-9484
E-mail: anything@thedegshop.com
Web site: http://www.thedegshop.com.

Degner Pr., *(0-9668628)* 180 Grand Larry St., No. 10, Anchorage, AK 99504-5011 USA Tel 907-338-7769
E-mail: degner@alaska.net.

DeGraaf Publishing, *(0-9678385)* 903 W. Morse St., Plant City, FL 33563 USA Tel 813-752-2348; 813-967-7489 (Cell phone)
E-mail: robdegraaf@verizon.net
Web site: http://www.degraafpublishing.com.

Degree Network, LLC *See* **Marilux Pr.**

Dejohn Enterprises, *(0-9754528)* 1121 Elm St., Peekskill, NY 10566 USA
E-mail: dejohnenterprise@aol.com
Web site: http://www.thereturnofsf.com.

Deka Pr., *(0-9645045)* P.O. Box 812, Christmas Valley, OR 97641 USA Tel 541-576-3900; Fax: 541-576-3909
E-mail: katym@teleport.com.

DEKpress *See* **Parent Positive Pr.**

Del Gatto, Maria, *(0-9747509)* 2227 South 3rd St., Philadelphia, PA 19148 USA Tel 215-271-7165
Web site: http://www.shapettes.com.

Del Rey *Imprint of* **Random House Publishing Group**

Del Sol Pubns., *(0-9722936)* P.O. Box 1112, Ventura, CA 93002 USA Do not confuse with Del Sol Publications in Two River, WI
E-mail: info@delsolpublications.com
Web site: http://www.delsolpublications.com.

Del Sol Publishing, *(1-58186)* 29257 Bassett Rd., Westlake, OH 44145 USA (SAN 299-4178) Tel 440-892-5524; Fax: 440-892-5546; Toll Free: 888-335-7651
E-mail: delsolbooks@telocity.com
Dist(s): **Lectorum Pubns., Inc.**

Delacorte Bks. for Young Readers *Imprint of* **Random Hse. Children's Bks.**

Delacorte Pr. *Imprint of* **Dell Publishing**

Delancey Place Pr., *(1-58379)* 2129 Delancey Pl., Philadelphia, PA 19103 USA Tel 215-546-5206; Fax: 215-546-2733
Web site: http://www.sat-prep.com.

De'Languille Music & Poetry, *(0-9706776)* 950 Ashbridge Ln., Harbor City, CA 90710-1502 USA Tel 310-530-1487; Fax: 310-326-9391
E-mail: wubp1113@aol.com.

DeLaVega, T., *(0-9754328)* Orders Addr.: P.O. Box 760, Hanapepe, HI 96716 USA Tel 808-335-2704; Fax: 808-335-5469; Edit Addr.: 3691 Uwao St., Hanapepe, HI 96716 USA
E-mail: tim.delavega@verizon.net
Web site: http://www.napaliphoto.com.

Delirious Publishing, *(0-9674403)* P.O. Box 6202, Fishers, IN 46038 USA Tel 317-773-9750
E-mail: bga@deliriousbooks.com
Web site: http://deliriousbooks.com.

Delittle Storyteller Co., *(1-892633)* Orders Addr.: 1562 Pinehurst Dr., Casselberry, FL 32707 USA Tel 407-699-7769
E-mail: delittlestoryteller@yahoo.com
Web site: http://www.delittlestoryteller.com.

Dell *Imprint of* **Dell Publishing**

Dell Bks. for Young Readers (CAN) *(0-440)* *Dist. by* **Random.**

Dell Books for Young Readers *Imprint of* **Random Hse. Children's Bks.**

Dell, Jacob J., *(0-9744544)* 6518 Chasethorn Dr., San Antonio, TX 78249-4825 USA
E-mail: books@jacobjdell.com
Web site: http://www.jacobjdell.com/books.

†Dell Publishing, Div. of Bantam Dell Publishing Group, Orders Addr.: 400 Hahn Rd., Westminster, MD 21157 USA Tel 410-848-1900; Toll Free: 800-726-0600; Edit Addr.: 1745 Broadway, New York, NY 10019 USA Tel 212-782-9000; Fax: 212-492-9698; Toll Free: 800-223-6834 (Bulk orders); 800-223-5780 (Orders only); 800-323-9872 (Customer service) ; *Imprints:* Dell (Dll); Laurel (LE); Delta (Delta); Delacorte Press (Delacorte Pr); Island Books (IslandBks)
Web site: http://www.randomhouse.com
Dist(s): **Random Hse., Inc.**
Sony CONNECT, Inc.; *CIP.*

Delmar Learning *Imprint of* **Thomson Delmar Learning**

Delmar Thomson Learning *See* **Thomson Delmar Learning**

DeLorme, *(0-89933)* P.O. Box 298, Yarmouth, ME 04096 USA (SAN 220-1208) Tel 207-846-7000; Fax: 207-846-7051; Toll Free Fax: 800-575-2244 (orders); Toll Free: 800-335-6763 (orders only)
E-mail: reseller@delorme.com
Web site: http://www.delorme.com
Dist(s): **Hammond World Atlas Corp.**
Langenscheidt Pubs Inc.
Many Feathers Bks. & Maps
Map Link
Rand McNally.

DeLorme Mapping Company *See* **DeLorme**

Delphi Bks., *(0-9663397; 0-9765185)* Orders Addr.: P.O. Box 6435, Lee's Summit, MO 64064 USA Toll Free: 800-431-1579 (orders)
E-mail: DelphiBks@yahoo.com
Web site: http://www.DelphiBooks.us; http://www.FranBaker.com
Dist(s): **Baker & Taylor Bks.**
Brodart Co.
Emery-Pratt Co.
Ingram Bk. Co.
Midwest Library Service.

Delta *Imprint of* **Dell Publishing**

Delta Education, Incorporated *See* **Delta Education, LLC**

Delta Education, LLC, *(0-87504; 1-58356; 1-59242; 1-59821; 1-60395)* Div. of Wicks Learning, 80 Northwest Blvd., Nashua, NH 03063 USA (SAN 630-1711) Toll Free: 800-442-5444
E-mail: ngosselin@delta-edu.com
Web site: http://www.delta-education.com.

Delta Gamma Ctr., *(0-9748523)* 5030 McRee, Saint Louis, MO 63110 USA Tel 314-776-1300 (phone/fax); Toll Free: 800-341-4310
E-mail: info@dgckids.org
Web site: http://www.dgckids.org.

Demco, Inc., *(1-885360)* Orders Addr.: P.O. Box 7488, Madison, WI 53707-7488 USA Toll Free Fax: 800-245-1329; Toll Free: 800-962-4463 (customer service); 800-279-1586 (orders) Do not confuse with Demco Media, Ltd, Madison, WI
E-mail: custserv@demco.com; order@demco.com
Web site: http://www.demco.com.

DEMDACO, *(1-932139)* Div. of DD Traders, Inc., 7500 W. 160th St., Stilwell, KS 66085 USA Tel 913-402-6800 Toll Free: 888-336-3226
Web site: http://www.demdaco.com.

Demerest, Cheryl Carlisle, *(0-9714111)* 100 S. Sunrise Way, PMB 288, Palm Springs, CA 92262-6737 USA Tel 760-324-5629
E-mail: c.demerest@juno.com.

de.MO, *(0-9705768; 0-9742836; 0-9791800)* 123 Nine Partners Ln., Millbrook, NY 12545 USA
E-mail: mailbox@de-mo.org
Web site: http://www.de-mo.org
Dist(s): **Consortium Bk. Sales & Distribution.**

DeMosi *See* **DeMosi Publishing**

DeMosi Publishing, *(0-9708523)* Orders Addr.: P.O. Box 60606, Chicago, IL 60660 USA
E-mail: demosipublishing@email.com.

Dempsey Parr *Imprint of* **Parragon, Inc.**

Den Publishing Co., *(0-9742195)* P.O. Box 93336, Albuquerque, NM 87199-3336 USA Fax: 505-822-8035.

Dendy, Chris A. *See* **Cherish the Children**

DeNicest Concepts, *(0-9763973)* P.O. Box 1831, Buffalo, NY 14240 USA.

Denim Design Lab LLC, *(0-9773012)* P.O. Box 5853, San Clemente, CA 92674-9998 USA Tel 949-366-3307; Fax: 949-366-3304
E-mail: denimdesignlab@aol.com
Web site: http://www.denimdesignlab.com.

Denison, T. S. & Co., Inc., *(0-513)* Orders Addr.: P.O. Box 1650, Grand Rapids, MI 49501-5431 USA (SAN 201-3142) Tel 616-802-3000; Fax: 616-802-3009; Toll Free Fax: 800-543-2690; Toll Free: 800-253-5469
Dist(s): **Lectorum Pubns., Inc.**

Denlinger, Dennis, *(0-9742567)* Orders Addr.: 46 Purdy St., Harrison, NY 95821 USA; Edit Addr.: P.O. Box 60431, Sacramento, CA 95860-0431 USA Tel 916-488-9643 Phone/fax); Toll Free: 800-431-1579 fulfilment
E-mail: dennis@footarch.com
Web site: http://www.footarch.com
Dist(s): **Book Clearing Hse.**

Denlingers Pubs., Ltd., *(0-87714)* Orders Addr.: P.O. Box 1030, Edgewater, FL 32132-1030 USA (SAN 201-3150) Tel 386-416-0009; Fax: 386-236-0517; Toll Free Fax: 800-589-1191
E-mail: info@thebookden.com
Web site: http://www.thebookden.com
Dist(s): **Baker & Taylor Bks.**

Denney Literary Services, *(0-9654698; 0-9707469)* 2907 Noah St., Chattanooga, TN 37406-1928 USA Tel 423-622-0419 ; *Imprints:* DLS Books (DLS Bks)
E-mail: denney2907@earthlink.net.

Dennison, Donna, *(0-9760484)* 121 Tuxedo, San Antonio, TX 78209-3712 USA.

Densmore-Reid Pubns., *(0-9700827)* 67 S. 24th St., Richmond, IN 47374 USA Tel 765-939-2984 (phone/fax)
E-mail: ddgreens@netscape.net
Web site: htpp://www.demismorereid.com.

Denver Broncos, *(0-9759579)* INVESCO Field at Mile High, 1701 Bryant St., Suite 900, Denver, CO 80204 USA
Web site: http://www.denverbroncos.com.

DEO Consulting, Inc., *(0-9728793)* 16334 Boardwalk Terr., Orland Hills, IL 60477 USA
E-mail: dale@mbd2.com
Web site: http://www.mbd2.com.

DePalma, Vanessa, *(0-9728135)* 49 Tropez Point, Rochester, NY 14626 USA Tel 585-723-9699
E-mail: vdepalma@frontiernet.net.

Dept. of Chamorro Affairs, *(1-883488)* Dept. of Chamorro Affairs Research, Publication & Training P.O. Box 2950, Hagatna, GU 96932 USA Tel 671-477-6447
E-mail: dcarpt2@ite.net.

Depiction Bible, *(0-9719878)* 1452 Liho Liho St., No. 601, Honolulu, HI 96822 USA Tel 808-284-3577
E-mail: depictionbible@hotmail.msn.com.

Depot Bks., *(0-9717611)* Orders Addr.: 87 Throckmorton Ave., Mill Valley, CA 94941 USA; Edit Addr.: 8 Madrona St., Mill Valley, CA 94941 USA.

Dercum Audio, *(1-55656)* 1501 County Hospital Rd., Nashville, TN 37218 USA (SAN 658-7607) Tel 615-254-2408
E-mail: DawsonC@locc.com
Web site: http://www.bookcase.com/Dercum
Dist(s): **APG Sales and Fulfillment.**

Dercum Press/Dercum Audio *See* **Dercum Audio**

Derke, Connie, *(0-9747063)* 6418 W. 13100 S., Herriman, UT 84065 USA Tel 801-254-8711
E-mail: derke1904@msn.com.

Derrick, Paul, *(0-9744875)* Orders Addr.: 918 N. 30th St., Waco, TX 76707-2502 USA Tel 254-753-6920 (phone/fax)
E-mail: pjderrick@aol.com
Web site: http://stargazerpaul.com.

Derrydale *Imprint of* **Random Hse. Value Publishing**

Derrydale Pr., The, *(1-56416; 1-58667)* Div. of Rowman & Littlefield Publishing Group, Orders Addr.: 15200 NBN Way, Blue Ridge Summit, PA 17214 USA Tel 717-794-3800 (Sales, Customer Service, MIS, Royalties, Inventory Mgmt., Dist., Credit & Collections); Fax: 717-794-3803 (Customer Service &/or orders only); 717-794-3857 (Sales & MIS); 717-794-3856 (Royalties, Inventory Mgmt., & Dist.); Toll Free Fax: 800-338-4550 (Customer Service &/or orders); Toll Free: 800-462-6420 (Customer Service &/or orders); Edit Addr.: 4501 Forbes Blvd., Lanham, MD 20706 USA Tel 301-459-3366; Fax: 301-459-5748
E-mail: sdriver@derrydalepress.com
Web site: http://www.derrydalepress.com
Dist(s): **National Bk. Network.**

deRuyter-Nelson Pubns., Inc., *(0-9650848)* 1885 University Ave., Suite 110, Saint Paul, MN 55104 USA Tel 612-645-7045; Fax: 612-645-4780; Toll Free: 800-631-0973 ; *Imprints:* A Place to Remember (A Place to Remember).

†Deseret Bk. Co., *(0-87579; 0-87747; 1-57345; 1-59038)* Div. of Deseret Management Corp., Orders Addr.: P.O. Box 30178, Salt Lake City, UT 84130 USA (SAN 150-763X) Tel 801-517-3165 (Wholesale Dept.); 801-534-1515; Fax: 801-517-3338; Toll Free: 800-453-3876; Edit Addr.: 40 E. South Temple, Salt Lake City, UT 84111 USA ; *Imprints:* Shadow Mountain (Shadow Mount); Bookcraft, Incorporated (Bkcraft Inc)
E-mail: wholesale@deseretbook.com; dbwhsale@deseretbook.com
Web site: http://www.deseretbook.com; http://www.shadowmountain.com
Dist(s): **Simon & Schuster, Inc.**; *CIP.*

Desert Badger Pr., *(0-9767555)* 251 W. Calle del Estribo, Sahuarita, AZ 85629 USA Toll Free: 866-726-6677
Web site: http://www.elderlawtucson.com.

Desert Bear Publishing, *(0-9765389)* P.O. Box 72313, Phoenix, AZ 85050 USA Tel 480-538-0842; Fax: 602-926-2429.

Desert Bloom Pr., *(0-9621452)* P.O. Box 670, Cortaro, AZ 85652-0670 USA (SAN 251-3897) Tel 520-490-2571; Fax: 520-572-1597
E-mail: pub@desertbloompress.com; dbpress@wildblue.net
Dist(s): **Baker & Taylor Bks.**

Desert Discovery Pubns., *(0-9702963)* 124 Giralda Cir., Palm Desert, CA 92260 USA Tel 760-340-1280; Fax: 760-568-9558
E-mail: desdispub@aol.com.

Desert Song Productions, *(0-9743402)* P.O. Box 35052, Tucson, AZ 85740 USA
E-mail: brian@brianjharris.com
Web site: http://www.brianjharris.com.

Desert Stream Ministries, *(1-930159)* P.O. Box 17635, Anaheim, CA 92817-7635 USA Tel 714-779-6899; Fax: 714-701-1880
E-mail: info@desertstream.org
Web site: http://www.desertstream.org.

Desert Waters Publishing *Imprint of* **Cheadle Bks.**

DesertStar Communications, LLC, *(0-9769815)* Orders Addr.: P.O. Box 243988, Boynton Beach, FL 33424-3988 USA
Web site: http://www.desertstarcommunications.com.

Desiderata Institute, *(0-9740112)* 315 Oakwood Cove, Lavergne, TN 37086-4146 USA Tel 615-406-3404
E-mail: warriorsway@mindspring.com
Web site: http://www.warriorsway.com.

Design Pr. Bks. *Imprint of* **Savannah College of Art & Design**

Design Square (SGP) Dist. by Flanders.

Design to Printing, *(0-9653431)* 34 W. Morris Rd., Bantam, CT 06750-1512 USA
E-mail: design.to.printing@snet.net.

Design Vault, *(0-9768974)* P.O. Box 14314, Tulsa, OK 74159-1314 USA
E-mail: sales@designvault.net
Web site: http://www.designvault.net.

DesignAbility, *(0-9786425)* P.O. Box 9988, Salt Lake City, UT 84109 USA
Web site: http://www.design-ability.com.

Designed World Learning, LLC, *(0-9763351)* Suite 105-124, 1933 Hwy. 35, Wall, NJ 07719 USA
Web site: http://www.designedworldlearning.com.

Designs For Progress, Inc., *(0-9793902)* 24601 Milfay Rd., No. 5, Depew, OK 74028 USA
E-mail: dmccalment@aol.com.

Designs for Wellness Pr., *(0-9641952)* Div. of Vartabedian & Assocs., P.O. Box 1671, Carlsbad, CA 92018 USA Tel 760-804-5999; Fax: 760-804-5996
E-mail: healthdoc@nutripoints.com
Web site: http://www.nutripoints.com.

Desk Top Pubs., Inc., *(1-892455)* Orders Addr.: P.O. Box 4931, Topeka, KS 66604-0931 USA Tel 785-232-4810; Fax: 785-232-4610; Toll Free: 888-232-4812; Edit Addr.: 1019 Fillmore, Topeka, KS 66604 USA Do not confuse with Desk Top Pubs., Inc., Genoa, NV
E-mail: dalex@dtoppub.com
Web site: http://www.dtoppub.com.

Destination Pubs. *Imprint of* **Pulte, Therese Marie**

Destined For Greatness Publisher *See* **Empowering People Pub.**

Destiny Image Europe (ITA) *(88-900588; 88-89127)* *Dist. by* **Destiny Image Pubs.**

Destiny Image Pubs., *(0-7684; 0-914903; 1-56043; 0-9716036)* 167 Walnut Bottom Rd., Shippensburg, PA 17257 USA (SAN 253-4339) Tel 717-532-3040; Fax: 717-532-9291; Toll Free: 800-722-6774 ; *Imprints:* Treasure House (Treasure Hse)
E-mail: JLM@destinyimage.com
Web site: http://www.destinyimage.com
Dist(s): **Anchor Distributors**
Appalachian Bible Co.
Spring Arbor Distributors, Inc.

Destiny Publishing, *(0-9715735)* P.O. Box 101, Pacific Grove, CA 93950 USA Tel 831-915-3031; Fax: 831-626-3265 Do not confuse with companies with the same or similar names in Mt. Pocono, PA, Longdale, NV, North Little Rock, AR, Tucson, AZ, Brooksville, FL, Greensboro, NC
E-mail: ccoburn3@juno.com.

Destiny's Pr., *(0-9676139)* 325 Gonzales Dr., San Francisco, CA 94132 USA Tel 415-584-1451.

Destro Pubs., LLC, *(0-9670030)* Orders Addr.: 5118 N. Western Ave., Chicago, IL 60625 USA Tel 773-784-7358; Fax: 773-784-7278
E-mail: ellakop@ibm.net.

Details Creative, *(0-9679747)* 8175-A Sheridan Blvd., No. 362, Arvada, CO 80003-1928 USA Tel 303-467-2600; 6090 W. 83rd Pl., Arvada, CO 80003 Tel 303-467-2600; Fax: 303-467-0064
E-mail: details@uswest.net; details@qwest.net.

Determined Productions, Inc., *(0-915696)* P.O. Box 2150, San Francisco, CA 94126-2150 USA (SAN 212-7385) Tel 415-433-0660; Fax: 415-421-0929.

Detroit Free Pr., Inc., *(0-937247; 0-9605692)* 600 W. Fort St., Detroit, MI 48226 USA (SAN 239-6998) Tel 313-222-6457; Fax: 313-222-5982; Toll Free: 800-678-6400
E-mail: robinson@freepress.com
Dist(s): **Partners Bk. Distributing, Inc.**

Detroit International Pr., *(0-9766622)* 900 Wilshire Dr. Ste. 202, Troy, MI 48084-1600 USA
E-mail: vince@detroitip.com.

Detskaja Literatura (RUS) *(5-08)* *Dist. by* **Distribks Inc.**

Deutsche Buchhandlung-James Lowry, *(1-883453)* 13531 Maugansville Rd., Hagerstown, MD 21740 USA Tel 301-739-8542.

Deutscher Taschenbuch Verlag GmbH & Co KG (DEU) *(3-423)* *Dist. by* **Distribks Inc.**

Devamala Bks. Private, Ltd. (IND) *(81-7767)* *Dist. by* **Ameya LLC.**

Developing Hearts Systems, Inc., *(0-9721379)* 2048 Elm St., Stratford, CT 06615 USA ; *Imprints:* Bonding with Baby Books (Bond Baby Bks)
E-mail: mail@bondingwithbaby.org
Web site: http://www.BondingwithBaby.org.

Developmental Studies Ctr., *(1-57621; 1-885603; 1-59892)* 2000 Embarcadero, Suite 305, Oakland, CA 94606-5300 USA Tel 510-533-0213; Fax: 510-464-3670; Toll Free: 800-666-7270
E-mail: pubs@devstu.org
Web site: http://www.devstu.org.

Developmental Vision Concepts, *(0-9635507; 0-9747810)* Orders Addr.: P.O. Box 400, Tehachapi, CA 93581 USA Tel 661-822-3106; Edit Addr.: 316 S. Green, Tehachapi, CA 93581 USA
E-mail: stoebner@lightspeed.net.

†Devil Mountain Bks., *(0-915685)* P.O. Box 4115, Walnut Creek, CA 94596 USA (SAN 292-4803) Tel 925-939-3415; Fax: 925-937-4883
E-mail: cbsturges@aol.com
Dist(s): **SPD-Small Pr. Distribution**; *CIP.*

Devil's Due Publishing, Inc., *(1-932796; 1-934692)* 3759 N. Ravenswood Ave., No. 230, Chicago, IL 60613 USA ; *Imprints:* D3 (D3)
E-mail: swells@devilsdue.net; d.davis@devilsdue.net
Web site: http://www.devilsdue.net
Dist(s): **Diamond Bk. Distributors.**

†Devin-Adair Pubs., Inc., *(0-8159)* P.O. Box A, Old Greenwich, CT 06870 USA (SAN 112-062X) Tel 203-531-7755; Fax: 718-359-8568; *CIP.*

Devon Trading Corp., *(1-888765)* 5 Fairfield Rd., North Caldwell, NJ 07006 USA Tel 973-812-9190; Fax: 973-812-8384; Toll Free: 888-883-3866.

Devor, Nina, *(0-9676428)* 40178 Pleasant Ct., Oakhurst, CA 93644 USA Tel 559-683-4147
E-mail: ddevor@sierratel.com.

Devora Publishing *Imprint of* **Pitspopany Pr.**

DeVore & Sons, Incorporated *See* **Fireside Catholic Bibles**

DeVorss & Co., *(0-87516)* Orders Addr.: P.O. Box 1389, Camarillo, CA 93011-1389 USA (SAN 168-9886) Tel 805-322-9010; Fax: 805-322-9011; Toll Free: 800-843-5743; Edit Addr.: 553 Constitution Ave., Camarillo, CA 93012-8510 USA ; *Imprints:* Devorss Publications (Devorss Pubns)
E-mail: service@devorss.com
Web site: http://www.devorss.com
Dist(s): **Baker & Taylor Bks.**
Health and Growth Assocs.
New Leaf Distributing Co., Inc.

Devorss Pubns. *Imprint of* **DeVorss & Co.**

Devoted to You Bks., *(0-9677367)* 505 20th Ave., N., Sartell, MN 56377 USA Tel 320-202-5961; Fax: 320-654-9276
E-mail: info@devotedtoyoubooks.com
Web site: http://www.devotedtoyoubooks.com.

DewDrop Arts & Technology, *(1-928840)* Orders Addr.: 5002 Geetha Dr., Columbia, MO 65202 USA Tel 537-808-2011; 537-499-4800
E-mail: khansh@missouri.edu; sabihakhan@excite.com; thureen@yahoo.com
Web site: http://www.shwelumaung.org/DewDrop.

Dewey Does *See* **A B C-123 Publishing**

Dewey Pubns., Inc., *(0-9615053; 1-878810; 1-932612; 1-934651)* 2009 N. 14th St., Suite 705, Arlington, VA 22201 USA (SAN 694-1451) Tel 703-524-1355; Fax: 703-524-1463
E-mail: info@deweypub.com
Web site: http://www.deweypub.com.

Dewey's Good News Balloons, *(1-880215)* 1202 Wildwood Dr., Deer Park, TX 77536 USA Tel 281-479-2759; Fax: 281-476-9997; Toll Free: 888-894-6597
E-mail: balloonz@flash.net.

Dexcel Publishing, *(0-9704015)* P.O. Box 1049, Alief, TX 77411-1049 USA Tel 713-306-0874; Fax: 281-495-8767
E-mail: DexcelPublishing@aol.com
Web site: http://www.dexcelpublishing.com
Dist(s): **Baker & Taylor Bks.**

Dezaim Productions and Management, LLC, *(0-9770111)* 1385 Chancellor Cir., Bensalem, PA 19020 USA.

Deziner Media International, *(0-9743971)* P.O. Box 239, Marrero, LA 70073 USA
Web site: http://www.writeabc123.com
Dist(s): **Biblio Distribution.**

DFC Pubs., *(0-9793987)* 31 W. Smith St., Amityville, NY 11701 USA (SAN 853-3695)
E-mail: contactus@urbanclubbooks.com
Web site: http://www.urbanclubbooks.com.

DH Pr., *(1-59617)* 10956 SE Main St., Milwauke, OR 97222 USA Tel 503-652-8815; Fax: 503-654-9440
Dist(s): **Diamond Bk. Distributors.**

DH Publishing, Inc., *(0-9723124; 0-9745961; 1-932897)* c/o HKM Publisher Services, 4712 Admiralty Way., No. 123, Marina del Rey, CA 90292 USA; 2-31-16-903 Akabane-Kita, Kita-Ku, Tokyo, 115-0052 Tel 03-3515-2201; Fax: 03-3515-2210 Do not confuse with DH Publishing in Denver, CO, Issaquah, WA
E-mail: clive@dhp-online.com
Web site: http://www.dhp-online.com
Dist(s): **Diamond Bk. Distributors**
SCB Distributors.

†Dharma Publishing, *(0-89800; 0-913546)* 2910 San Pablo Ave., Berkeley, CA 94702 USA (SAN 201-2723) Tel 510-548-5407; Fax: 510-548-2230; Toll Free: 800-873-4276
E-mail: dp@dharmapublishing.com; order@dharma-publishing.com
Web site: http://www.dharmapublishing.com/
Dist(s): **New Leaf Distributing Co., Inc.**
Partners/West; *CIP.*

Di Capua, Michael *Imprint of* **Scholastic, Inc.**

Di Maggio, Richard *See* **Consumer Pr., The**

Dia Art Foundation *See* **Dia Ctr. for the Arts**

Dia Ctr. for the Arts, *(0-944521)* 542 W. 22nd St., New York, NY 10011 USA (SAN 243-8275) Tel 212-989-5566; Fax: 212-989-4055
E-mail: bfuncke@diacenter.org; kkelly@diacenter.org
Web site: http://www.diaart.org; http://www.diabooks.org; http://www.diabeacon.org
Dist(s): **D.A.P./Distributed Art Pubs.**

Diakonia Publishing, *(0-9676528; 0-9725609; 0-9747278; 0-9772483; 0-9800877)* P.O. Box 9512, Greensboro, NC 27429-0512 USA Tel 336-707-2610
E-mail: diakoniapublishing@hotmail.com
Web site: http://www.ephesians412.com.

Dial *Imprint of* **Penguin Group (USA) Inc.**

Dialogue Systems, Incorporated *See* **Metropolitan Teaching & Learning Co.**

Dialogus Play Service & Publishing, Incorporated *See* **Brown Bag Productions**

Diamond Bk. Distributors, Div. of Diamond Comic Distributors, Inc., Orders Addr.: 1966 Greenspring Dr., Suite 300, Timonium, MD 21093 USA (SAN 110-9502) Tel 410-560-7100; Fax: 410-560-2583; Toll Free: 800-452-6642
E-mail: books@diamondbookdistributors.com
Web site: http://www.diamondcomics.com; http://www.diamondbookdistributors.com/.

Diamond Book Distributors Inc. *See* **Diamond Comic Distributors, Inc.**

Diamond Comic Distributors, Inc., *(1-59396)* 1966 Greenspring Dr., Suite 300, Timonium, MD 21093 USA Tel 410-560-7100; Fax: 410-560-2583; Toll Free: 800-452-6642
E-mail: books@diamondcomics.com
Web site: http://www.diamondbookdistributors.com/
Dist(s): **Diamond Bk. Distributors.**

Diamond Creek Publishing, *(0-9713811)* P.O. Box 2068, Flagstaff, AZ 86003-2068 USA
Web site: http://www.apathways.com.

Diamond Cutter Pr., LLC, *(0-9765469)* 512 Newark Pompton Tpke., Pompton Plains, NJ 07444 USA Tel 973-835-6375; Fax: 973-835-6504
E-mail: jcerullo@diamondcutterpress.com
Web site: http://www.diamondcutterpress.com
Dist(s): **Continental Enterprises Group, Inc. (CEG).**

Diamond Dan Pubns., *(0-9678163)* P.O. Box 143, Manchester, NY 14504 USA Tel 716-289-4936
E-mail: ddan@eznet.net
Web site: http://home.eznet.net/~ddan/index.htm.

Diamond Event Planning, Inc., *(0-9766901)* 50-44 193rd St., Fresh Meadows, NY 11365 USA Tel 718-357-6144; Fax: 718-357-6685
E-mail: bridepro@aol.com
Web site: http://www.awedwitharedhead.com.

Diamond Farm Bk. Pubs., Div. of Yesteryear Toys & Books, Inc., Orders Addr.: P.O. Box 537, Alexandria Bay, NY 13607 USA (SAN 674-9054) Tel 613-475-1771; Fax: 613-475-3748; Toll Free Fax: 800-305-5138 (Order Line); Toll Free: 800-481-1353 (Order Line)
E-mail: info@diamondfarm.com
Web site: http://www.diamondfarm.com.

Diamond Peak Pr., *(0-9673697)* 6437 24th St., Greeley, CO 80634 USA Tel 970-330-8206 (phone/fax)
E-mail: mountainavenue@aol.com.

Diamond Select Toys & Collectibles, *(1-931724)* Div. of Diamond Comics Distributors, 1966 Greenspring Dr., Suite 300, Timonium, MD 21093 USA Tel 410-560-7100; Fax: 410-560-7589; Toll Free: 800-452-6642
E-mail: wjason@diamondcomics.com
Web site: http://www.diamondselecttoys.com
Dist(s): **Andrews McMeel Publishing**
Diamond Comic Distributors, Inc.
Simon & Schuster, Inc.

Diamond Springs Pr., *(0-9729940)* 8085 Diamond Springs Dr., Helena, MT 59602 USA Tel 406-458-9220
E-mail: sagewood@qwest.net.

Diamond Triple C Ranch, *(0-9790652)* 801 Floral Vale Blvd., Yardley, PA 19067 USA (SAN 852-324X) Tel 215-497-3188; Fax: 215-497-3190
Web site: http://www.diamondtriplecranch.com.

Diana Waring - History Alive! *See* **Diana Waring Presents**

Diana Waring Presents, *(1-930514)* Orders Addr.: 621 SR 9 NE PMB B-14, Lake Stevens, WA 98258 USA Tel 425-397-0631
E-mail: diana@dianawaring.com
Web site: http://www.dianawaring.com
Dist(s): **Appalachian Bk. Distributors.**

DIANE Publishing Co., *(0-7881; 0-941375; 1-56806; 0-7567; 1-4223; 1-4289)* Orders Addr.: P.O. Box 617, Darby, PA 19023-0617 USA (SAN 667-1217) Tel 610-461-6200; Fax: 610-461-6130; Toll Free: 800-782-3833; Edit Addr.: P.O. Box 617, Darby, PA 19023-0617 USA
E-mail: cfisher@dianepublishing.net
Web site: http://www.dianepublishing.net.

Dianoia Publishing, *(0-9760496)* Div. of XL Group, 5707 Santa Fe St., San Diego, CA 92109 USA
E-mail: dianoiapub@yahoo.com.

Diarmuid Inc., *(1-59347)* Orders Addr.: P.O. Box 357580, Gainesville, FL 32635 USA Toll Free: 877-475-3277; Edit Addr.: 2630 N.W. 41st St., Suite D-1, Gainesville, FL 32606 USA
E-mail: kuc49@aol.com; dalia@greatleaps.com
Web site: http://www.greatleaps.com.

DiaShah Pr., LLC, *(0-9761207)* Orders Addr.: P.O. Box 43804, Nottingham, MD 21236 USA
E-mail: diashahpress@yahoo.com
Web site: http://www.debrasawyer.com; http://www.diashahpress.com.

Diaz Educational Group, Inc., *(1-932554)* 1812 Commerce Dr., Suite 2, Laredo, TX 78041 USA (SAN 256-3436) Tel 956-753-6838; Fax: 956-753-6794.

Dibble Fund for Marriage Education, The, *(0-9652427; 0-9761349)* Orders Addr.: P.O. Box 7881, Berkeley, CA 94707-0881 USA Tel 510-528-7975 Main Office; Fax: 972-228-2624 Customer Service Fax; Toll Free: 800-695-7975 Customer Service; Edit Addr.: 728 Coventry Rd., Kensington, CA 94707 USA
E-mail: relationshipskills@dibblefund.org
Web site: http://www.buildingrelationshipskills.org.

Dickason, Linda, *(0-9710165)* 251 S. Orange Grove Blvd. Apt. 10, Pasadena, CA 91105-1767 USA
E-mail: ldickason@aol.com.

Dickow, Gregory Ministries, *(1-932833)* Orders Addr.: P.O. Box 7000, Chicago, IL 60680 USA Fax: 847-842-9904; Toll Free: 888-438-5433; Edit Addr.: 180 N. Hawthorne Rd., Barrington Hills, IL 60010 USA
E-mail: dt@changinglives.org
Web site: http://www.changinglives.org.

Dicmar Publishing Co., *(0-933165)* Subs. of Dicmar Trading Co., Inc., 4057 Highwood Ct., NW, Washington, DC 20007-2131 USA (SAN 692-2813) Tel 202-342-0145; Fax: 202-342-0773
E-mail: mpmpcarr@hotmail.com
Web site: http://www.dicmar.com.

Didax Educational Resources, Inc., *(1-58324; 1-885111)* 395 Main St., Rowley, MA 01969 USA Tel 978-948-2340 ext 350; Fax: 978-948-2813; Toll Free: 800-458-0024 ; *Imprints:* World Teachers Press (Wrld Teach Pr)
Web site: http://www.didaxinc.com.

Die Gestalten Verlag (DEU) *(3-931126; 3-89955) Dist. by* **Prestel Pub NY.**

DiEdwardo, Mary Ann P. Publishing, *(0-9641468)* 3435 Dartmouth Dr., Bethlehem, PA 18020 USA Tel 610-868-6820.

Diekman, Diane *See* **Altruria Publishing Co.**

Diesslin, Richard L., *(0-9702244)* 1366 Town Hall Rd., Beavercreek, OH 45432-2619 USA Tel 937-429-0139
E-mail: rldes@aol.com; rldiesslin@the-cartoonist.com
Web site: http://www.the-cartoonist.com; http://www.kampknots.com; http://www.cartoongospel.com.

Dietz Pr., *(0-87517)* Orders Addr.: 930 Winfield Rd., Petersburg, VA 23803-4748 USA Tel 804-733-0123; Fax: 804-733-3514; Toll Free: 800-391-6833
E-mail: rbeville@dietzpress.com; customerservice@dietzpress.com
Web site: http://www.dietzpress.com
Dist(s): **American Wholesale Bk. Co.**
Baker & Taylor Bks.
Barnes&Noble.com
Emery-Pratt Co.
Follett Library Resources.

Different Bks. *Imprint of* **Place In The Woods, The**

Different Friends, *(1-892750)* Orders Addr.: P.O. Box 40208, Cincinnati, OH 45240 USA Tel 513-825-1514; Edit Addr.: 703 Yorkhaven Rd., Cincinnati, OH 45246 USA.

Different Roads to Learning, LLC *See* **DRL Bk., Inc.**

Different Worlds Pubns., *(0-9753999)* 1600 Portola Dr., San Francisco, CA 94127-1402 USA (SAN 256-0577)
E-mail: info@diffworlds.com
Web site: http://www.diffworlds.com.

Digging Clams n Oregon, *(0-9767508)* P.O. Box 746, Newport, OR 97365 USA (SAN 850-9700) Tel 541-265-5847
E-mail: williamlackner001@msn.com.

Diginites Illustration, *(0-9678844)* 3060 Butte Ave., San Ramon, CA 94583 USA Tel 510-414-0816; Fax: 925-829-2337
E-mail: Brian@Diginites.com; brian@diginites.com
Web site: http://www.Diginites.com.

Digireads.com, *(0-9753222; 1-59625; 1-59674; 1-4209)* 16212 Riggs Rd., Stilwell, KS 66085 USA
E-mail: digireads@yahoo.com
Web site: http://www.digireads.com
Dist(s): **Ingram Pub. Services**
Lightning Source, Inc.

Digital Antiquaria, Inc., *(1-58057)* 2 Sand Hill Rd., Morristown, NJ 07960-5928 USA
E-mail: info@DigitalAntiquaria.com
Web site: http://digitalantiquaria.com.

Digital Commerce, Inc., *(0-9718649)* 12405 NW 83rd Ln., Ocala, FL 34482 USA
E-mail: mrsb@newsblues.com
Web site: http://www.newsblues.com.

Digital Edge, Incorporated *See* **Lucky Dog Publishing**

Digital Manga Distribution *See* **Digital Manga Publishing**

Digital Manga Publishing, *(1-56970)* Div. of Digital Manga, Inc., 1487 W. 178th St. Ste. 300, Gardena, CA 90248-3253 USA (SAN 111-817X) Toll Free: 866-897-7300
E-mail: contact@emanga.com
Web site: http://www.dmpbooks.com/
Dist(s): **Diamond Bk. Distributors.**

Digital Scanning, Inc., *(1-58218)* 344 Gannett Rd., Scituate, MA 02066 USA (SAN 299-8734) Tel 781-545-2100; Fax: 781-545-4908
E-mail: info@digitalscanning.com
Web site: http://www.digitalscanning.com
Dist(s): **Replica Bks.**
ebrary, Inc.

digital@batesjackson llc, *(1-932583)* 17-21 Elm St., Buffalo, NY 14203 USA Tel 716-854-3000; Fax: 716-847-1965
E-mail: mybook@batesjackson.com
Web site: http://www.batesjackson.com.

Digits International-Reflexology Institute, *(0-9623429; 1-884727)* 27636 Ynez Rd. L7, No. 232, Temecula, CA 92591 USA Tel 951-694-0225; Fax: 951-694-5910.

DiGuiseppi, Joseph, *(0-9768348)* 21 William St., Danbury, CT 06810 USA
E-mail: joedigspi@hotmail.com.

Diligence Woodwork & Design, *(0-9706453)* 95609 Marcola Rd., Marcola, OR 97454 USA Tel 541-933-2775
E-mail: ayala@fiberfanatics.com
Web site: http://www.fiberfanatics.com.

Dilligaf Publishing, *(0-9639070; 0-9701020; 1-931207)* Orders Addr.: 98 Main St., Ellsworth, ME 04605 USA Tel 207-667-5351
E-mail: studio3marty@acadia.net; vze277g4@verizon.net.

Dillingham Publishing, *(1-892071)* 3601 Meier St., Los Angeles, CA 90066 USA Tel 310-391-5794
E-mail: Babazaba@aol.com.

Dillman, George Karate International, Pubs., *(0-9631996; 1-889267)* 251 Mountain View Rd., Reading, PA 19607-9744 USA Tel 610-777-8444; Fax: 610-777-1557
E-mail: dillman@talon.net
Web site: http://www.dillman.com
Dist(s): **APG Sales and Fulfillment**
National Bk. Network.

Dilly Green Bean Games, *(0-9744698)* 33 Hillview Rd., Gorham, ME 04038 USA
E-mail: dillygreenbeangames@dillygreenbeangames.com
Web site: http://www.dillygreenbeangames.com.

Dimefast, Ltd., *(1-888417)* Orders Addr.: P.O. Box 291437, Fort Lauderdale, FL 33329 USA Tel 954-894-6188; Edit Addr.: 1821 N. 49th Ave., Hollywood, FL 33021 USA (SAN 298-9042)
E-mail: dimefast@aol.com
Web site: http://www.dimefast.com.

Dimension Five *See* **Granny Pr.**

Dimensions in Media, Inc., *(0-9762273)* 24191 N. Forest Dr., Lake Zurich, IL 60047 USA Tel 847-726-2093
E-mail: debbie@dimensionsinmedia.com
Web site: http://www.be-still.com.

DIMI Pr., *(0-931625)* 1340 SE 107th Ave., Suite 303, Portland, OR 97216-3216 USA (SAN 683-7271) Tel 503-580-0485; Fax: 503-327-8997
E-mail: dickbook@earthlink.net
Web site: http://home.earthlink.net/~dickbook
Dist(s): **Baker & Taylor Bks.**
Partners/West.

Dinah-Might Activities, Incorporated *See* **Dinah-Might Adventures, LP**

Dinah-Might Adventures, LP, *(1-882796)* P.O. Box 690328, San Antonio, TX 78269-0328 USA (SAN 298-7317) Tel 210-698-0123; Fax: 210-698-0095; Toll Free: 800-993-4624 (orders only)
E-mail: dma@dinah.com
Web site: http://www.dinah.com.

Dinamika, Ltd. (RUS) *(5-901257) Dist. by* **Intercont New Tech.**

Dingler, Jay *See* **BrainBox, Ltd.**

Dingles & Co., *(1-891997; 1-59646)* P.O. Box 508, Sea Girt, NJ 08750 USA ; *Imprints:* Treehouse Court (Treehse Ct)
E-mail: dinglesco@aol.com
Dist(s): **Central Programs**
Gumdrop Bks.

Dingman, Vera, *(0-9711814)* 3405 N. Higley Rd., Mesa, AZ 85215 USA.

Dings Bks., *(0-9748890)* 411 Schoolhouse Ln., Shippensburg, PA 17257 USA
E-mail: dingscenter@yahoo.com.

Dino Entertainment AG (DEU) *(3-89748; 3-932268) Dist. by* **Distribks Inc.**

Dino Tales, *(0-9667619)* P.O. Box 716, Hardin, TX 77561 USA Tel 409-298-2152.

Dinosaur Fund, *(0-9748618)* 711 E. St. SE, No. 104, Washington, DC 20003-2879 USA Tel 202-547-3326
E-mail: dinosaurfund@juno.com; shill@laser-image.com
Web site: http://www.dinosaurfund.org.

Dinoship, Inc., *(0-9728585; 1-933384)* 105 W. 73rd St., No. 1B, New York, NY 10023 USA Tel 212-721-5056; Fax: 212-595-0247; 299 Broadway, No. 1016, New York, NY 10007
E-mail: bob@dinoship.com
Web site: http://www.dinoship.com
Dist(s): **National Bk. Network.**

Dinosounds, Inc., *(0-9717154)* 11718 Barrington Ct., No. 732, Los Angeles, CA 90049 USA
E-mail: emron@worldnet.att.net
Web site: http://home.att.net/~emron/dinosounds.html.

DinRo, *(0-9744412)* 7545 Gladstone Dr., No. 205, Naperville, IL 60565 USA Fax: 630-305-3695.

Dinshah Health Society, *(0-933917)* P.O. Box 707, Malaga, NJ 08328 USA (SAN 693-0220) Tel 856-692-4686
E-mail: dinshahhealth@aol.com
Web site: http://www.wj.net/dinshah
Dist(s): **New Leaf Distributing Co., Inc.**

Diocese of Cleveland, *(0-9669580)* 1027 Superior Ave., Cleveland, OH 44114 USA Tel 216-696-6525; Fax: 216-621-7332.

Diogenes Verlag AG (CHE) *(3-257) Dist. by* **Intl Bk Import.**

Diogenes Verlag AG (CHE) *(3-257) Dist. by* **Distribks Inc.**

Diomo Square Bks., *(0-9765948)* 4911 SW 43rd Ave., Portland, OR 97206-5011 USA
E-mail: diomo@earthlink.net.

Dionis Bound Publishing, *(0-9667090)* 18 Bayberry Ln., Nantucket Island, MA 02554 USA Tel 508-228-5281
E-mail: holden@natucket.net.

Dion's Pubn., *(0-9795739)* 3002 Royston Rd., Charlotte, NC 28208 USA Tel 704-264-1640
E-mail: lokereke@carolina.rr.com.

Directions in Education, Training & Consultation, *(0-9664681)* Orders Addr.: P.O. Box 2478, Gig Harbor, WA 98335 USA Tel 253-858-7261; Edit Addr.: 4720 Birchtree Ln., NW, Gig Harbor, WA 98335 USA
E-mail: lbaker@HarborNet.com
Web site: http://www.pebblesinthepond.com.

DirkDesigns, LLC, *(0-9790923)* P.O. Box 3754, West Lafayette, IN 47996 USA.

Dis Voir Editions (FRA) *(2-906571; 2-914563) Dist. by* **Dist Art Pubs.**

Disciple Builder Media, *(0-9704641)* Div. of Strategic Endeavors, 5211 W. Caraway Pl., Lecanto, FL 34461 USA Tel 352-746-9997 (phone/fax); 352 746 9997; Toll Free: 877-463-5378 (phone/fax)
E-mail: info@smarterschools.org
Web site: http://www.smarterschools.org.

Disciple One Publishing, *(0-9791883)* Div. of DISCIPLE GROUP PRODUCTION, 10153 1/2 Riverside Dr., No. 467, Toluca Lake, CA 91602 USA Tel 323-654-8579
E-mail: baronjay@yourlittleblackbook.net
Web site: http://www.yourlittleblackbook.net
Dist(s): **Lushena Bks.**

Discipleship Pubns. International, *(1-57782; 1-884553)* 300 5th Ave. Ste. 5, Waltham, MA 02451-8749 USA Toll Free: 888-374-2665
E-mail: spjones@icoc.org; dpibooks@icoc.org
Web site: http://www.dpibooks.org
Dist(s): **AtlasBooks Distribution**
Independent Pubs. Group.

Discipleship Resources, *(0-88177)* Div. of Board of Discipleship of The United Methodist Church, Orders Addr.: P.O. Box 1616, Alpharetta, GA 30009-1616 USA (SAN 661-9932) Fax: 770-442-9742; Toll Free: 800-972-0433; Edit Addr.: P.O. Box 340003, 1908 Grand Ave., Nashville, TN 37203-0003 USA (SAN 264-0074)
E-mail: discipleshipresources@gbod.org
Web site: http://www.discipleshipresources.org
Dist(s): **Abingdon Pr.**
CRC Pubns.
Cokesbury
P.B.D., Inc.

Discover Writing Company *See* **Discover Writing Pr.**

Discover Writing Pr., *(0-9656574; 1-931492)* Orders Addr.: P.O. Box 264, Shoreham, VT 05770 USA Tel 802-897-7022; Fax: 802-897-2084; Toll Free: 800-613-8055; Edit Addr.: 1029 Richville Rd., Shoreham, VT 05770 USA
E-mail: register@discoverwriting.com; inservice@discoverwriting.com
Web site: http://www.discoverwriting.com
Dist(s): **Baker & Taylor Bks.**

Discovery Bks., *(0-679; 1-56331; 1-4000)* Orders Addr.: 400 Hahn Rd., Westminster, MD 21157 USA Tel 410-848-1900; Toll Free: 800-726-0600; Edit Addr.: Star Rte., Mountain View, Owls Heads, NY 12969 USA (SAN 206-9512)
Web site: http://www.discovery.com; http://www.randomhouse.com
Dist(s): **Libros Sin Fronteras**
Random Hse., Inc.

Discovery Channel *See* **Discovery Communications**

Discovery Comics, *(1-878181)* P.O. Box 1075, Doylestown, PA 18901 USA Tel 215-230-7540; Fax: 215-230-7848.

Discovery Communications, *(1-56331; 1-58738; 1-59527; 1-60288)* One Discovery Pl., Silver Spring, MD 20910 USA Toll Free: 888-892-3484
E-mail: megan.faller@discovery.com
Web site: http://www.discovery.com
Dist(s): **Explorations**
Insight Guides
Langenscheidt Pubs Inc.

Discovery Enterprises, Limited *See* **History Compass, LLC**

Discovery Hse. Pubs., *(0-929239; 1-57293)* Div. of R B C Ministries, Orders Addr.: P.O. Box 3566, Grand Rapids, MI 49501 USA (SAN 248-8949) Tel 616-942-9218; Fax: 616-957-5741; Toll Free: 800-653-8333; Edit Addr.: 3000 Kraft Ave., SE, Grand Rapids, MI 49512 USA (SAN 248-8957)
E-mail: dhp@rbc.org
Web site: http://www.dhp.org
Dist(s): **Barbour Publishing, Inc.**
Christian Literature Crusade, Inc.

Discovery Pr. Pubns., Inc., *(0-9645159)* 400 E. 3rd Ave., No. 901, Denver, CO 80203 USA (SAN 298-5691) Tel 303-355-9689; Fax: 303-733-3474
E-mail: discoverypresspub@comcast.net
Web site: http://www.discoverypresspub.com
Dist(s): **Baker & Taylor Bks.**
Brodart Co.
Quality Bks., Inc.

Discovery Pubns. (GBR) *(0-9538222; 0-9550458) Dist. by* **Irish Bks Media.**

Disc-Us Bks., Inc., *(1-58444)* 2570 Camino San Patricio, Santa Fe, NM 87505 USA Tel 505-474-9139
E-mail: books@disc-us.com
Web site: http://www.disc-us.com.

Disinformation Co. Ltd., The, *(0-9713942; 0-9729529; 1-932857; 1-934708)* 220 E. 23rd St., Suite 500, New York, NY 10010 USA
E-mail: books@disinfo.com
Dist(s): **Consortium Bk. Sales & Distribution.**

DiskUs Publishing, *(0-9667995; 1-58495; 0-7572)* Orders Addr.: P.O. Box 43, Albany, IN 47320 USA; Edit Addr.: PO Box 43, Albany, IN 47320 USA
E-mail: editor@diskuspublishing.com; DiskUsMail@aol.com
Web site: http://www.diskuspublishing.com
Dist(s): **NetLibrary, Inc.**

Disney Editions *Imprint of* **Disney Pr.**

Disney Educational Productions, *(0-89625; 1-932644; 1-59753)* Orders Addr.: 105 Terry Dr., Suite 120, Newtown, PA 18940 USA Toll Free: 800-295-5010; Edit Addr.: 3900 W. Alameda Ave., 20th Flr., Burbank, CA 91505 USA Tel 818-567-5684; 114 Fifth Ave., 12th Flr., New York, NY 10011 USA Tel 212-807-5422; Fax: 212-807-5435
E-mail: david.myer@disney.com; catherine.wood@disney.com.

†Disney Pr., *(0-7868; 1-56282; 1-4231)* Div. of Disney Bk. Publishing, Inc., A Walt Disney Co., 114 Fifth Ave., New York, NY 10011 USA Tel 212-633-4400; Fax: 212-633-4833; Toll Free: 800-759-0190 ; *Imprints:* Disney Editions (Disney Ed)
Web site: http://www.disney.com/disneybooks/index.html
Dist(s): **Hachette Bk. Group**
HarperCollins Pubs.
Libros Sin Fronteras
Little Brown & Co.; *CIP.*

Disney Publishing Worldwide, *(1-892309; 1-931580; 1-4231)* Subs. of Walt Disney Productions, 44 S. Broadway, 10th Flr., White Plains, NY 10601 USA Tel 914-288-4316
Web site: http://www.disney.go.com; http://www.hyperionbooksforchildren.com
Dist(s): **HarperCollins Pubs.**

Disneyland/Vista Records & Tapes *See* **Walt Disney Records**

Displays for Schls., Inc., *(0-9600962)* 1825 NW 22nd Terr., Gainesville, FL 32605 USA (SAN 157-9711) Tel 352-373-2030; Fax: 352-395-5102; Toll Free: 800-250-4645
E-mail: dupree6@hotmail.com
Web site: http://www.displaysforschools.com
Dist(s): **Baker & Taylor Bks.**

Disposition Sketch Bks. *Imprint of* **MacBride, E. J. Pubn., Inc.**

Dissertation.com, *(0-9658564; 1-58112; 1-59942)* 23331 Water Cir., Boca Raton, FL 33486-8540 USA (SAN 299-3635) Tel 561-750-4344; Fax: 561-750-6797; Toll Free: 800-636-8329
E-mail: publisher@dissertation.com; info4@univeral-publishers.com
Web site: http://www.dissertation.com; http://www.BrownWalker.com; http://www.universal-publishers.com.

Distant Waters Publishing & Designs, *(1-931015)* 26 Abner Point Rd., Bailey Island, ME 04003 USA Tel 207-833-7758
E-mail: distantwaterspublishing@yahoo.com
Web site: http://www.distantwaterspublishing.com.

Distribooks, Inc., Div. of Midwest European Pubns., Inc., 8120 N. Ridgeway, Skokie, IL 60076 USA (SAN 630-9763) Tel 847-676-1596; Fax: 847-676-1195
E-mail: info@distribooks.com.

Distribuidora Norma, Inc., *(1-881700)* Div. of Carvajal International, Orders Addr.: P.O. Box 195040, San Juan, PR 00919-5040 USA Tel 787-788-5050; Fax: 787-788-7161; Toll Free: 800-BOOKS58; Edit Addr.: Carretera 869 Km 1.5 Barrio Palmas Royal Industrial, Catano, PR 00962 USA
Web site: http://www.norma.com.

Diversified A+ Pubns., *(0-9773526)* P.O. Box 13, Winchendon, MA 01475 USA
E-mail: Dpipub@aol.com
Web site: http://www.dpublications.com.

Diversified Productions *Imprint of* **Williams Publishing Co.**

Diversity Foundation, The, *(0-9797193)* 505 W., 10200 S., South Jordan, UT 84095 USA Tel 801-553-4556; Fax: 801-553-4600; Toll Free: 888-216-2122
Web site: http://www.thediversityfoundation.org.

Diversity Ink Publishing, *(0-9767258)* P.O. Box 2414, Santa Maria, CA 93457 USA.

Diversity Pr., *(0-936715)* P.O. Box 25, Idabel, OK 74745 USA (SAN 699-9131) Tel 580-286-3148 Do not confuse with Diversity Pr., Cambridge, MA
E-mail: diversitypress@netscape.net
Web site: http://www.diversitypress.com.

Divine House Ministries *See* **Kingdom Sound Pubs.**

Divine Intertwine Publishing, *(0-9754489)* P.O. Box 4088, Ocean City, MD 21843 USA.

Divine Life Pubns., *(0-9679367; 0-9722620)* Div. of Divine Life Worship Center, Inc., 15205 Johnstone Ln., Bowie, MD 20721 USA Tel 301-218-9085 (phone/fax)
E-mail: willie.blount@verizon.net
Web site: http://www.divinelifeworship.org.

Divine Ministry of North Florida, Inc., *(0-9773356)* P.O. Box 5668, Gainesville, FL 32627-5668 USA (SAN 257-3652)
E-mail: ade0201@yahoo.com
Web site: http://www.divineministry.net.

Divine Mirror Pr. *Imprint of* **Remington Literary Assn., Inc.**

Divine Power Publishing, *(0-9708645)* P.O. Box 935, Chicopee, MA 01014-0935 USA
E-mail: JoyceAnnStevens@aol.com
Dist(s): **Baker & Taylor Bks.**

Divine Publishing *See* **Orchard Gang Publishing**

Divinity 7, *(1-892981)* P.O. Box 1564, Westborough, MA 01581 USA Tel 508-898-2093; Fax: 617-507-6208
E-mail: divinity7@hotmail.com
Web site: http://www.maxpages.com/divinity7.

Division of Words *Imprint of* **Black Alchemist Pr., Inc.**

DJ Blues Publishing, *(0-9743985)* 403 Dula Cir., Duncanville, TX 75116 USA
E-mail: hipdjblues@earthlink.net
Web site: http://www.djblues.com.

DK Novels & Playwrights, *(0-9798036)* P.O. Box 671254, Houston, TX 77267-1254 USA (SAN 854-4379) Tel 832-755-7458
E-mail: dking@dknovels.com
Web site: http://dknovels.com.

Dksmo-Press, Izdatel'skaja firma (RUS) *(5-04) Dist. by* **Distribks Inc.**

dLife - For Your Diabetes Life, *(0-9777463)* Div. of LifeMed Media, 101 Franklin St., Westport, CT 06880-0688 USA (SAN 850-1254) Tel 203-454-6985; Fax: 203-454-6986
E-mail: info@dlife.com
Web site: http://www.dlife.com.

DLS Bks. *Imprint of* **Denney Literary Services**

Dm Productions, *(0-615)* 10596 N. Washington Blvd., Indianapolis, IN 46280 USA
Web site: http://dmprod.blogspot.com/
Dist(s): **Lulu.com.**

DMCD Productions, Inc. *See* **DMcD Productions, Inc.**

DMcD Productions, Inc., *(0-9771521)* Orders Addr.: P.O. Box 40, Grand Rapids, MN 55744-0040 USA (SAN 256-9019) Tel 218-327-2129
E-mail: info@ohforsmart.com
Web site: http://www.ohforsmart.com.

DMT Publishing, *(0-9726189; 0-9749144; 0-9785553; 0-9800813)* 900 N. 400 W., Bldg. 12, North Salt Lake, UT 84054 USA
Web site: http://www.dmtpublishing.com.

Company

D-N Publishing, *(1-890424)* 596 Indian Trail Rd. S., No. 111, Indian Trail, NC 28079 USA Fax: 704-684-0698
E-mail: hhinsonrw@aol.com.

DNA Pr., *(0-9664027; 0-9748765; 1-933255)* P.O. Box 572, Eagleville, PA 19408-0572 USA (SAN 256-5005) Fax: 501-694-5495
E-mail: editors@dnapress.com
Web site: http://www.dnapress.com
Dist(s): **Baker & Taylor Bks.**
Independent Pubs. Group.

Do It Now Foundation, *(0-89230)* Orders Addr.: P.O. Box 27568, Tempe, AZ 85285 USA (SAN 225-9265) Tel 480-736-0599; Fax: 480-736-0771; Edit Addr.: P.O. Box 27568, Tempe, AZ 85285-7568 USA (SAN 669-0661)
E-mail: doitnow123@earthlink.net; info@doitnow.org
Web site: http://www.doitnow.org.

Dobbs Enterprises, *(0-9717664)* 2945 Waumpi Trail, Maitland, FL 32751 USA Tel 407-629-4820
E-mail: dobbsenterprises@cfl.rr.com.

Dobie Bk. Publishing, *(0-9710529)* 5074 Trott Cir. Unit 6, North Port, FL 34287-3406 USA
E-mail: storyteller2000@msn.com; storytellerjm@aol.com
Web site: http://dobiebookpublishing.com.

Doc Fizzix, *(0-9656674)* 1500 Laurel Oak Loop, Round Rock, TX 78664 USA Tel 512-218-0454
E-mail: docfizzix@docfizzix.com
Web site: http://www.docfizzix.com.

Dockter, Toni, *(0-9712201)* P.O. Box 1532, Soquel, CA 95073-1532 USA
E-mail: tonette101@aol.com
Web site: http://percyveerance.com.

Doctor Dolittle's Library *Imprint of* **PhotoGraphics Publishing**

Dodo Bks., *(0-9704850)* P.O. Box 8937, Houston, TX 77249-8937 USA Tel 713-284-2388; Fax: 713-228-0048
E-mail: dodobooks@yahoo.com
Web site: http://www.whosdodie.com.

Dodo Unlimited, Inc., *(0-9669447)* 239 Commonwealth Ave., Boston, MA 02116 USA Tel 617-262-4260; Fax: 617-262-4224; Toll Free: 800-436-3612
E-mail: Carole@dodo.com
Web site: http://www.dodo.com.

Dog & Pony Enterprises *See* **Dog & Pony Publishing**

Dog & Pony Publishing, *(0-9646970; 1-890479)* Orders Addr.: P.O. Box 3540, Kill Devil Hills, NC 27948 USA Tel 252-261-6905; Fax: 252-255-3236; Edit Addr.: 236 Hillcrest Dr., Southern Shores, NC 27949 USA
E-mail: marymadendogpony@interpath.com
Web site: http://www.marymaden.com
Dist(s): **Koen-Levy Bk. Wholesalers LLC**
Mistco, Inc.

Dog Days Publishing, *(0-9715065)* P.O. Box 5446, Hercules, CA 94547-1048 USA
E-mail: qoe4me@aol.com; NNBDdogdayspub@aol.com
Web site: http://www.nonobaddogs.com.

Dog Ear Publishing, LLC, *(0-9762173; 0-9766603; 1-59858)* 4010 W. 86th St., Suite H, Indianapolis, IN 46268 USA Tel 317-228-3656; Fax: 317-228-1401; Toll Free: 866-823-9613
E-mail: rayr@dogearpublishing.net
Web site: http://www.dogearpublishing.net
Dist(s): **Baker & Taylor Bks.**
Lightning Source, Inc.

Dog Soldier Pr., *(0-9718658)* P.O. Box 1782, Ranchos de Taos, NM 87557-1782 USA (SAN 254-4733) Tel 505-751-3781; Fax: 505-758-4071
E-mail: dogsoldier@newmexico.com
Web site: http://www.dogsoldierpress.com.

Dog-Eared Pubns., *(0-941042)* Orders Addr.: P.O. Box 620863, Middleton, WI 53562-0863 USA (SAN 281-6059) Tel 608-831-1410 (phone/fax); Toll Free: 888-364-3277; Edit Addr.: 4642 Toepfer Rd., Middleton, WI 53562 USA
E-mail: field@dog-eared.com
Web site: http://www.dog-eared.com
Dist(s): **Common Ground Distributors, Inc.**
Islander Group
Partners/West.

Doggerel Daze, *(0-9722820)* 10144 Riedel Pl., Cupertino, CA 95014 USA.

Doggie In The Window Pubns., *(0-9749876)* P.O. Box 1565, Duluth, GA 30096 USA Tel 770-680-1779; 2888 Winchester Ct., Duluth, GA 30096 (SAN 851-0466) Tel 770-680-1779
E-mail: doggieinthewindow@comcast.net
Web site: http://www.doggieinthewindow.biz.

DogHouse Pr., *(0-9761497)* 150 Chestnut St., Park Forest, IL 60466 USA Toll Free: 877-413-8997
E-mail: kimberly@rjsystems.us
Web site: http://www.doghousepress.com.

Doghouse Publishing, Incorporated *See* **Mess Hall Writers**

Dogs in Hats Children's Publishing Co., *(1-59445)* P.O. Box 182, Grand Haven, MI 49417 USA Tel 616-844-2220; Fax: 616-844-2922
E-mail: customerservice@dogsinhats.com
Web site: http://www.dogsinhats.com.

Dogs4dogs, *(0-9771265)* P.O. Box 675432, Rancho Santa Fe, CA 92067-5432 USA
Web site: http://www.dogs4dogs.com
Dist(s): **Biblio Distribution.**

Dogtown Artworks, *(0-9777126)* 341 Cty. Rd., 800 E, Pesotum, IL 61863 USA Tel 217-867-2486
E-mail: dogtownartworks@mac.com
Web site: http://www.dogtownartworks.com
Dist(s): **Independent Pubs. Group.**

Dogwalk Pr., *(0-9766846)* Div. of Dan Gersten & Assocs., LLC, 29636 Quail Run Dr., Agoura Hills, CA 91301 USA Tel 818-735-0280; Fax: 818-991-1838
Web site: http://www.askcurtisthedog.com.

Dogwise *See* **Dogwise Publishing**

Dogwise Publishing, *(1-929242)* Orders Addr.: P.O. Box 2778, Wentachee, WA 98807 USA (SAN 631-1415) Tel 509-663-9115; Fax: 509-662-7233; Toll Free: 800-776-2665; Edit Addr.: 701B Poplar, Wenatchee, WA 98801 USA
E-mail: mail@dogwise.com; charlenew@dogwise.com
Web site: http://www.dogwise.com.

Dohate Pr., *(0-9767003)* Orders Addr.: 1809 Brookhaven Dr., Austin, TX 78704 USA Tel 512-442-0576
E-mail: donbutlerbooks@earthlink.net.

Doherty, Tom Assocs., LLC, *(0-312; 0-7653; 0-8125)* Div. of Holtzbrinck Publishers, Orders Addr.: 16365 James Madison Hwy., Gordonsville, VA 22942-8501 USA Toll Free Fax: 800-672-2054; Toll Free: 888-330-8477; Edit Addr.: 175 Fifth Ave., New York, NY 10010 USA Tel 212-674-5151; Fax: 540-672-7540 (customer service) ; *Imprints:* Aerie (Aerie); Forge Books (Forge Bks); Tor Books (Tor Books); Tor Classics (Tor Class); Starscape (Starscape); Tor Kids (Tor Kids); Tor Teen (Tor Teen)
E-mail: inquiries@tor.com
Web site: http://www.tor.com/
Dist(s): **Cambridge Univ. Pr.**
Libros Sin Fronteras
Macmillan
Sony CONNECT, Inc.

Doing Good Ministries, *(0-9667054)* 217 Bayview Way, Chula Vista, CA 91910 USA Tel 619-476-7230
E-mail: moehlenpah@aol.com
Web site: http://www.doinggood.org.

Do-it's Proof Bks., *(0-9722935)* 10515 Churchill Ave., Chatsworth, CA 91311-2231 USA Tel 818-349-6810
E-mail: jerryJmontoya@aol.com.

Dolls Corp., *(1-889514)* P.O. Box 1245, Portsmouth, NH 03802-1245 USA Toll Free: 800-730-4891
E-mail: customerservice@idolls.com
Web site: http://www.idolls.com
Dist(s): **Baker & Taylor Bks.**
Bookman Bks.
Brodart Co.
Koen-Levy Bk. Wholesalers LLC.

Doll's Life, *(0-9720072)* Orders Addr.: P.O. Box 1336, Lakeville, CT 06039 USA; Edit Addr.: 31 Robin Hill Ln., Lakeville, CT 06039 USA
Web site: http://www.dollslife.com.

Dollworks, *(0-9760064; 1-60304)* 6693 Lake Shore Dr., Newport, MI 48166-9716 USA; P.O. Box 66075, Newport, MI 48166
E-mail: nanciejack@aol.com.

Dolly Dimple Ink Children's Bks., *(0-9773506)* 5484 Atlantic View, Saint Augustine, FL 32080 USA Tel 904-460-0997
E-mail: effiemaeshearin@aol.com
Web site: http://www.dollydimpleink.com.

Dolphin Paperbacks (GBR) *(1-85881; 1-84255) Dist. by* **Trafalgar.**

Dolphin Publishing, *(1-878400)* P.O. Box 16656, West Palm Beach, FL 33416-6656 USA Tel 561-585-8901; Toll Free: 800-547-7867 Do not confuse with companies with the same name in Richardson, TX, Mattawan, MI
E-mail: nicotinefree@bellsouth.net
Web site: http://www.davidcjones.com; http://www.self-helptherapy.com
Dist(s): **Baker & Taylor Bks.**

DolphinTrainer.com, *(0-9719853)* 1370 Trancas St., No. 402, Napa, CA 94558 USA Tel 707-224-8658
E-mail: dolphintrainer01@aol.com
Web site: https://www.dolphintrainer.com.

Dominick Pictures, *(0-9726092)* P.O. Box 1925, New York, NY 10013 USA.

Dominicus Publishing Co., *(1-893744)* 810 Woodview Dr., Stevens Point, WI 54481 USA Tel 715-341-5544.

Dominie Pr., Inc., *(0-7685; 1-56270)* Div. of Pearson Learning, 145 S. Mount Zion Rd., Lebanon, IN 46052-8186 USA (SAN 630-947X) Toll Free: 800-232-4570
E-mail: info@dominie.com
Web site: http://www.dominie.com.

DOMINIONHOUSE Publishing & Design, *(0-9755234)* Orders Addr.: P.O. Box 681938, Orlando, FL 32868 USA Tel 407-880-5790 (phone/fax)
E-mail: dominionhousepublishing@hotmail.com.

Domnick, Howard, *(0-9715419)* 6615 Coachman Dr., Springfield, VA 22152-2603 USA
E-mail: gankin@enid.com.

Don Cohen-The Mathman, *(0-9621674; 0-9779493)* Orders Addr.: 809 Stratford Dr., Champaign, IL 61821-4140 USA (SAN 251-866X) Tel 217-356-4555; Fax: 217-356-4593; Toll Free: 800-356-4559
E-mail: mathman@shout.net
Web site: http://www.shout.net/~mathman
Dist(s): **Baker & Taylor Bks.**
Rainbow Re-Source Ctr.

Don Pedro Enterprises, USA, Ltd., *(0-9656807)* Div. of A Place for Poets, 85 Fourth Ave., Suite 3JJ, New York, NY 10003 USA Tel 212-353-9114 (phone/fax)
E-mail: donpedrocookies@aol.com
Web site: http://www.donpedrocookies.com.

Don Quixote Publishing Co. Inc., *(0-9749196)* 905 Brickell Bay Dr., Unit 230, Miami, FL 33131 USA (SAN 255-884X) Tel 305-379-6151; Fax: 305-379-5156
E-mail: panza1209@aol.com; camote@manuelmartinezdreamer.com
Web site: http://www.manuelmartinezdreamer.com.

Don Rand's Classy Collectibles, *(0-9773775)* 7561 Center Ave., No. 4, Huntington Beach, CA 92647 USA.

Donalyn Bks., *(0-9654548)* 123 Harbor Ave., Madison, CT 06443-2815 USA Tel 203-245-2809
E-mail: dyroot@snet.net.

Donnellan, Martha, *(0-9791982)* 2870 Callie Still Rd., Lawrenceville, GA 30045 USA
E-mail: marty@donnellan.com
Web site: http://www.frendibles.com.

Donning Co. Pubs., *(0-89865; 0-915442; 1-57864)* Subs. of Walsworth Publishing Co., Inc., 184 Business Park Dr., Suite 209 Ste. 206, Virginia Bch, VA 23462-6533 USA (SAN 211-6316) Toll Free: 800-296-8572
E-mail: dcpr3@pilot.infi.net
Web site: http://www.donning.com
Dist(s): **Chicago Distribution Ctr.**
Schiffer Publishing, Ltd.

Donovan, Kevin M. *See* **Billy the Bear & His Friends, Inc.**

Donruss Playoff, L.P., *(1-931690; 1-931990)* 2300 E. Randol Mill, Arlington, TX 76011 USA Tel 817-983-0300; Fax: 817-983-0400; Toll Free: 800-852-8833
E-mail: bbondurant@donruss.com
Web site: http://www.scoreent.com
Dist(s): **Diamond Bk. Distributors.**

Don't Eat Any Bugs Prodns., *(0-9728177)* P.O. Box 291, Tehachapi, CA 93581 USA ; *Imprints:* CF Books (CF Books)
E-mail: ray@donteatanybugs.com
Web site: http://www.donteatanybugs.com
Dist(s): **Biblio Distribution.**

Don't Look Publishing, *(0-9728234)* P.O. Box 486, Moose Lake, MN 55767 USA.

Don't Run With Knives Publications *See* **Academic Solutions, Inc.**

Doo Productions *See* **Educational Media Enterprises, Inc.**

Doodle Publishing, *(0-9719518)* 2219 Tam-O-Shanter Ct., Carmel, IN 46032 USA Tel 317-538-6995
E-mail: adam10spro@aol.com.

Doodlebug Bks., *(0-9647756)* 850 Powell St. Apt. 500, San Francisco, CA 94108-2040 USA Do not confuse with Doodlebug Books in Tuscaloosa, AL
Dist(s): **Todd Communications**
Ammon, Von Studios.

Dooley Bks., Ltd, *(0-9786605)* 53 W. Jackson No. 1240, CHICAGO, IL 60604 USA
Web site: http://www.Dooleybooks.com.

Doorposts, *(1-891206)* 5905 SW Looking Glass Dr., Gaston, OR 97119-9241 USA Tel 503-357-4749; Fax: 503-357-4909 Do not confuse with Doorposts, Lansdale, PA
E-mail: admin@doorpost.net; orders@doorposts.net
Web site: http://www.doorposts.net.

Doral Publishing, Inc., *(0-944875; 0-9745407)* P.O. Box 6050, Mission Viejo, CA 92690 USA (SAN 245-4637) Toll Free: 800-633-5385; 3 Burroughs, Irvine, CA 92618
E-mail: doralpub@mindspring.com
Web site: http://www.doralpub.com.

Doran Productions *See* **C&D Productions JimMar, Inc.**

Dorcas Dezines, *(0-9771834)* 6333 N. 12th St., No.105, Phoenix, AZ 85014 USA
E-mail: dorcas@dorcasdezines.com
Web site: http://www.dorcasdezines.com.

Dorcas Pubns., LLC, *(0-9769829)* 890 Woodland Ave., Corydon, IN 47112 USA Tel 812-738-4361; Fax: 812-738-2259
E-mail: wfwilson@aol.com
Web site: http://www.dorcaspublications.com.

Dorcas Publishing, *(0-9762375)* 12101 N. MacArthur,, Suite 137, Oklahoma City, OK 73162-1800 USA Tel 405-751-3885 (phone/fax)
E-mail: buckboardquilts@cox.net
Web site: http://www.heavenlypatchwork.com.

Dorchester Publishing Co., Inc., *(0-505; 0-8439; 1-4285)* Orders Addr.: 200 Madison Ave., Suite 2000, New York, NY 10016 USA (SAN 264-0090) Tel 212-725-8811; Fax: 212-532-1054; 610-995-9274 (Single copy orders); Toll Free: 800-481-9191 ; *Imprints:* Love Spell (Love Spell); SMOOCH (Smooch)
E-mail: Dorchester@dorchesterpub.com
Web site: http://www.dorchesterpub.com; http://www.smoochya.com; http://www.hardcasecrime.com.

Dorie Bks., *(0-9703326)* P.O. Box 261, White Stone, VA 22578 USA Toll Free: 800-553-6922
E-mail: doriethurston@hotmail.com.

†Dorling Kindersley Publishing, Inc., *(0-7894; 1-56458; 1-879431; 0-7566)* Div. of The Penguin Group, 375 Hudson St., 2nd Flr., New York, NY 10014 USA (SAN 253-0791) Tel 212-213-4800; Fax: 212-213-5240; Toll Free: 877-342-5357 (orders only) ; *Imprints:* D K Ink (D K Ink)
E-mail: Annemarie.Cancienne@dk.com; customer.service@dk.com
Web site: http://www.dk.com
Dist(s): **Continental Bk. Co., Inc.**
Penguin Group (USA) Inc.
Hale, Robert & Co., Inc.
Sunburst Communications, Inc.; *CIP.*

Dormouse Productions, Inc., *(1-889300)* 25 NE 99th St., Miami, FL 33138-2338 USA Tel 305-379-4990; Fax: 305-379-7990
E-mail: dmouse@juno.com.

Dorn Enterprises *See* **Susy Dorn Productions, LLC**

Dorothy Payne & Virginia Letourneau, *(0-9747823)* 300 E. 33rd St., Apt. 7C, New York, NY 10016 USA
Web site: http://www.cityislandclamdigger.com.

Dorrance Publishing Co., Inc., *(0-8059; 1-4349)* 701 Smithfield St., Pittsburgh, PA 15222 USA (SAN 201-3363) Tel 412-288-4543; Fax: 412-288-1786; Toll Free: 800-788-7654 ; *Imprints:* RoseDog Books (RoseDog Bks)
E-mail: rpiotrowski@dorrancepublishing.com; dorrordr@dorrancepublishing.com
Web site: http://www.dorrancepublishing.com.

†Dorset Hse. Publishing, *(0-932633)* 353 W. 12th St., New York, NY 10014 USA (SAN 687-794X) Tel 212-620-4053; Fax: 212-727-1044; Toll Free: 800-342-6657
E-mail: info@dorsethouse.com; littlewest@dorsethouse.com
Web site: http://www.dorsethouse.com; http://www.littlewestpress.com
Dist(s): **Baker & Taylor Bks.**; *CIP.*

Dory Pr., *(0-9633240)* 13396 Wakefield Rd., Sedley, VA 23878 USA Tel 757-220-9206.

Dot E. Pubs., *(0-9671485)* P.O. Box 681, Corvallis, OR 97339-0681 USA.

Dothan Publishing *See* **Moriah Ministries**

Double B Pubns., *(0-929526)* 4123 N. Longview, Phoenix, AZ 85014 USA (SAN 249-6615) Tel 602-996-7129; Fax: 602-996-6928
E-mail: bfischerppg@aol.com.

Double Dagger Pr., *(0-9729293)* 625 Natural Dam Rd., Gettysburg, PA 17325-7134 USA (SAN 255-7517) Tel 717-334-5392
E-mail: mplank@doubledaggerpress.com
Web site: http://www.doubledaggerpress.com.

Double R Publishing, LLC, *(0-9713381; 0-9718696; 0-9770534)* 7301 W. Flagler St., Miami, FL 33144 USA Tel 305-262-4240; Fax: 305-262-4115; Toll Free: 877-262-4240
E-mail: abcsbook@abcsbook.com
Web site: http://www.abcsbook.com
Dist(s): **ABC'S Bk. Supply, Inc.**

Doubleday *Imprint of* **Doubleday Publishing**

Doubleday Bks. for Young Readers *Imprint of* **Random Hse. Children's Bks.**

Doubleday Canada, Ltd. (CAN) *(0-385; 0-7704) Dist. by* **Random.**

†Doubleday Publishing, Div. of Doubleday Broadway Publishing Group, Orders Addr.: 400 Hahn Rd., Westminster, MD 21157 USA (SAN 281-6083) Tel 410-848-1900; Toll Free: 800-726-0600; Edit Addr.: 1745 Broadway, New York, NY 10019 USA (SAN 201-0089) Tel 212-782-9000; 212-572-4961 Bulk orders; Toll Free Fax: 800-659-2436 Orders only; Toll Free: 800-669-1536 Electronic orders; 800-726-0600 Customer service ; *Imprints:* Doubleday (Double); Flying Dolphin Press (FDP)
E-mail: ddaypub@randomhouse.com
Web site: http://www.doubleday.com
Dist(s): **Random Hse., Inc.**; *CIP.*

DoubleStar, LLC, *(0-9742558)* 222 S. Central Ave., Suite 1006, Saint Louis, MO 63105 USA Tel 314-721-9199
E-mail: doublestarllc@sbcglobal.net
Web site: http://www.cogno.com.

Doughten, Russ Films, Inc., *(1-888568)* 5907 Meredith Dr., Des Moines, IA 50322-1204 USA Tel 515-278-4737; Fax: 515-278-4738; Toll Free: 800-247-3456
E-mail: marketing@rdfilms.com
Web site: http://www.rdfilms.com
Dist(s): **Anchor Distributors**
Appalachian Bible Co.
Christian Bk. Distributors
Pan De Vida Distributors
Spring Arbor Distributors, Inc.
Tapeworm Video Distributor, Inc.

Douglas, Bettye Forum, Inc., The, *(0-9703183)* 6608 N. Western Ave., No. 327, Oklahoma City, OK 73116 USA Tel 405-528-1773; Fax: 405-842-7541; Toll Free: 800-354-0680
E-mail: bettye_douglas@excite.com
Web site: http://www.bettyedouglas.com.

Douglas Charles, Ltd., *(0-924771; 1-58066)* 7 Adamsdale Rd., North Attleboro, MA 02760 USA Tel 508-761-5414; Fax: 508-761-6372 ; *Imprints:* Covered Bridge Press (Covered Brdge Pr)
E-mail: cdurang@naisp.net.

Doulos Christou Pr., *(0-9744796; 1-934406)* 57 N. Ruial St. Englewood Christian Church, Indianapolis, IN 46201-3330 USA
E-mail: douloschristoupress@yahoo.com
Web site: http://www.douloschristou.com.

DOVE Christian Fellowship International House to House Publications *See* **House to House Pubns.**

Dove Publishing, Inc., *(0-9766578)* P.O. Box 310326, Atlanta, GA 31131 USA Do not confuse with companies with the same or similar name in Houston, TX, Decatur, GA, Forest heights, MD, Lake Konkonkma, NY
Web site: http://www.dovepub.com.

†Dover Pubns., Inc., *(0-486)* Orders Addr.: 31 E. Second St., Mineola, NY 11501 USA (SAN 201-338X) Tel 516-294-7000; Fax: 516-742-5049 (orders only); Toll Free: 800-223-3130 (orders only)
E-mail: rights@doverpublications.com
Web site: http://www.doverdirect.com; http://www.doverpublications.com
Dist(s): **Continental Bk. Co., Inc.**
Beeler, Thomas T. Pub.; *CIP.*

DoveTail Hse., Inc., *(0-9706244; 0-9772935; 0-9800099)* P.O. Box 501995, San Diego, CA 92150 USA Tel 858-581-5954; Fax: 858-668-1771
E-mail: dovepub@san.rr.com.

Dovetail Publishing, *(0-9651284)* P.O. Box 19945, Kalamazoo, MI 49019 USA Tel 616-342-2900; Fax: 616-342-1012; Toll Free: 800-222-0070
E-mail: dovetail@mich.com
Web site: http://www.mich.com/~dovetail
Dist(s): **Baker & Taylor Bks.**
Independent Pubs. Group
Quality Bks., Inc.

Down East Bks., *(0-89272; 0-924357)* Div. of Down East Enterprise, Inc., P.O. Box 679, Camden, ME 04843 USA (SAN 208-6301) Tel 207-594-9544; Fax: 207-594-0147; Toll Free: 800-766-1670 Wholesale orders; 800-685-7962 Retail orders
E-mail: pblanchard@downeast.com; tbregy@downeast.com
Web site: http://www.countrysportpress.com; http://www.downeastbooks.com
Dist(s): **National Bk. Network.**

Down The Road Publishing, *(0-9754427)* 172 White Oak Dr., Batesville, IN 47006 USA (SAN 256-2227)
E-mail: timt@downtheroad.org
Web site: http://www.downtheroad.org
Dist(s): **AtlasBooks Distribution.**

Down The Shore Publishing, *(0-945582; 0-9615208; 1-59322)* Orders Addr.: 638 Teal St., West Creek, NJ 08092 USA Tel 609-978-1233; Fax: 609-597-0422; Edit Addr.: 638 Teal St., West Creek, NJ 08092 USA (SAN 661-082X)
E-mail: shore@att.net; info@down-the-shore.com; orders@down-the-shore.com
Web site: http://www.down-the-shore.com
Dist(s): **Baker & Taylor Bks.**

Downhome Enterprise, L. L. C., The, *(0-9669359)* 1533 Moores Point Rd., Suffolk, VA 23436 USA Tel 757-238-2089; Fax: 757-238-7027
E-mail: downhome1@aol.com
Web site: http://www.downhomeenterprise.com.

Downhome Publishing, *(0-9663952)* P.O. Box 260835, Hartford, CT 06126 USA Tel 860-655-6703; Fax: 860-521-6177
E-mail: Downhomebooks@aol.com
Web site: http://downhomebooks.com.

Down-To-Earth-Bks., *(1-878115)* P.O. Box 488, Ashfield, MA 01330 USA Tel 413-628-0227
E-mail: maryskole@aol.com
Web site: http://www.spinningl obe.net
Dist(s): **Baker & Taylor Bks.**

Dr. Gazebo Publishing *See* **Snow In Sarasota Publishing**

Dr. H Bks. *Imprint of* **Turtle Island Pr., Inc.**

Dr. Mac Productions, *(0-9724298)* 1435 School Hse Rd., Santa Barbara, CA 93108 USA
E-mail: drmac1@cox.net
Web site: http://www.apocketoftunes.com.

Dr. Mary's Bks., *(0-9765453)* 180 90th Ave. SE, Kensal, ND 58455 USA Tel 701-435-2388
E-mail: dwayneerickson@agristar.net
Web site: http://www.shopnd.com.

Dr. Mira of Healing *See* **Pleasanton Publishing**

Dr. Todd, LLC, *(0-9724022)* 14859 Embry Path, Apple Valley, MN 55124 USA (SAN 254-8054)
E-mail: drtodd@drtodd.com
Web site: http://www.centerpathpublishing.com.

Dragon Bks. *Imprint of* **Pacific View Pr.**

Dragon Dog Pr., Inc., *(0-9770121)* P.O. Box 5399, Godfrey, IL 62035 USA Tel 618-467-0738
E-mail: ryucope@sbcglobal.net
Web site: http://www.dragondogpress.com.

Dragon Tales Publishing, *(0-9675277)* Orders Addr.: P.O. Box 1949, Tustin, CA 92781 USA Tel 714-730-5386; Fax: 714-832-9487; Edit Addr.: 1192 Mitchell Ave., No. 70, Tustin, CA 92780 USA
E-mail: info@dragontalespublishing.com
Web site: http://www.dragontalespublishing.com.

Dragon Tree Pr., The, *(0-940918)* P.O. Box 1209, Guerneville, CA 95446 USA (SAN 217-3557) Tel 707-869-2747 Do not confuse with Dragon Tree Pr., Des Moines, IA
E-mail: mary@dragontree.com
Web site: http://www.dragontree.com.

Dragoneagle Pr., *(0-9787465)* P.O. Box 5431, North Branch, NJ 08876 USA Tel 732-861-0449
Web site: http://www.dragoneagle.com.

Dragonfly Bks. *Imprint of* **Random Hse. Children's Bks.**

Dragonfly Entertainment, *(0-9745213)* 1360 Winchester Ave., Glendale, CA 91201-1433 USA ; *Imprints:* Dragonfly Flipz (Dragonfly Flipz)
E-mail: dfly@earthlink.net
Web site: http://www.dragonflyent.net.

Dragonfly Flipz *Imprint of* **Dragonfly Entertainment**

Dragonfly Ministries, *(0-9788289)* 7 Andrews Ct., Parkton, MD 21120 USA
E-mail: info@dragonflyministries.com
Web site: http://www.dragonflyministries.com.

Dragonfly Publishing, *(0-9667820)* 277 Folly Brook Blvd., Wethersfield, CT 06109 USA Tel 860-257-7635; Fax: 860-563-1943 Do not confuse with companies with the same name in Mount Enterprise, TX , Sparks, OK , San Antonio, TX
E-mail: mklett@aol.com
Web site: http://www.dragonflypublishing.net.

Dragonfly Publishing, Inc., *(0-9710473; 0-9755888; 0-9765786; 0-9778651; 0-9787421; 0-9794660; 0-9797574)* 2440 Twin Ridge, Edmond, OK 73034 USA Do not confuse with companies with the same or similar name in Mount Enterprise, TX , Whethersfield, CT , San Antonio, TX ,
Web site: http://www.dragonflypubs.com.

Dragonflyer Pr., *(0-944933)* Div. of American Water Gardens, Inc., 2460 N. Euclid Ave., Upland, CA 91784-1184 USA (SAN 245-7660) Toll Free: 800-558-0676
E-mail: info@dragonflyerpress.com; cuber@uberadv.com
Web site: http://www.vnwg.com; http://www.dragonflyerpress.com
Dist(s): **Midpoint Trade Bks., Inc.**

Dragonhawk Publishing, *(1-888767)* Div. of Life Magic Enterprises, Inc., P.O. Box 1316, Jackson, TN 38302 USA Tel 901-987-3334; Fax: 901-987-2484
Dist(s): **Austin & Company, Inc.**
Baker & Taylor Bks.
New Leaf Distributing Co., Inc.
Partners Pubs. Group, Inc.

Dragonladies, Ltd., *(0-9744540)* P.O. Box 293, Alden, NY 14004 USA Tel 716-870-1117; Fax: 716-937-9526
E-mail: winningourway@aol.com
Web site: http://www.womenwow.com.

Dragonon, Inc., *(0-9763398)* 9378 Mason Montgomery Rd., Suite 108, Mason, OH 45040 USA (SAN 256-3398) Tel 513-227-9224
E-mail: dmeyer@dragonon.com.

Dragons Claw Pr., *(0-9716206)* P.O. Box 5557, Woodland Park, CO 80863 USA Tel 719-228-9376 (phone/fax)
E-mail: stein151@earthlink.net
Web site: http://home.earthlink.net~stein151.

Dragonseed Pr., *(0-9678115)* Orders Addr.: P.O. Box 23266, Chagrin Falls, OH 44023 USA
E-mail: dragonseedpress@aol.com.

Drake, Edwin, *(0-9743405)* R.R. 5, Box 5417, Saylorsburg, PA 18353 USA Tel 570-992-2914
E-mail: edrakee@enter.net.

Drake Univ., Anderson Gallery, *(0-9749296)* 25th St. & Carpenter Ave., Des Moines, IA 50311 USA Tel 515-271-1994; Fax: 515-271-2558
E-mail: cira.pascual-marquina@drake.edu
Web site: http//www.drake.edu/andersongallery.

Drama Tree Pr., *(0-9711777)* P.O. Box 1791, Bowling Green, KY 42101 USA
E-mail: yelittledramashop@hotmail.com.

Drama Tree Pr., *(0-9741670)* 150 Iota Ct., Madison, WI 53706 USA
E-mail: dramatree@mail.com
Web site: http://www.dramatree.com.

Dramaline Pubns., *(0-940669; 0-9611792)* 36851 Palm View Rd., Rancho Mirage, CA 92270-2417 USA (SAN 285-239X) Tel 760-770-6076; Fax: 760-770-4507
E-mail: drama.line@verizon.net
Web site: http://www.dramaline.com
Dist(s): **Distributors, The.**

DramaQueen, L.L.C., *(0-9766045; 1-933809; 1-60331)* Orders Addr.: P.O. Box 2626, Stafford, TX 77497 USA Fax: 281-498-4723; Toll Free: 800-883-1518 (ext. 2)
E-mail: orders@onedramaqueen.com; info@onedramaqueen.com
Web site: http://www.onedramaqueen.com
Dist(s): **AAA Anime Distribution**
Consortium Bk. Sales & Distribution.

Dramata Editions, *(0-9712092)* P.O. Box 1578, Winona, MN 55987 USA Tel 507-452-4693; Fax: 501-423-2988.

Dramatic Improvements Publishing, *(0-9768251)* 226 Perrine Ave., Auburn, NY 13021-1715 USA
E-mail: twoods@dramaimp.com
Web site: http://www.dramaimp.com.

Dramatic Publishing Co., *(0-87129; 1-58342)* Orders Addr.: 311 Washington St., Woodstock, IL 60098 USA Tel 815-338-7170; Fax: 815-338-8981; Toll Free Fax: 800-334-5302; Toll Free: 800-448-7469; Edit Addr.: 311 Washington St., Woodstock, IL 60098 USA (SAN 201-5676)
E-mail: plays@dramaticpublishing.com
Web site: http://www.dramaticpublishing.com.

Dramatists Play Service, Inc., *(0-8222)* 440 Park Ave., S., New York, NY 10016 USA (SAN 207-5717) Tel 212-683-8960; Fax: 212-213-1539
E-mail: postmaster@dramatists.com
Web site: http://www.dramatists.com.

Draumr Publishing, LLC, *(1-933157)* P.O. Box 428, Columbia, MD 21045-0428 USA Tel 410-290-6757
E-mail: robert@draumrpublishing.com
Web site: http://www.draumrpublishing.com.

Draw Three Lines Publishing, *(0-9749418)* P.O. Box 1522, Hillsboro, OR 97123-3954 USA Tel 503-648-9905
E-mail: hastings@draw3lines.com
Web site: http://www.draw3lines.com.

Drawn & Quarterly Pubns. (CAN) *(0-9696701; 1-896597; 1-894937; 1-897299) Dist. by* **Macmillan.**

DrDryland.Com, LLC, *(0-9766490)* P.O. Box 1281, Ashland, OR 97520 USA
Web site: http://www.DrDryland.Com.

Dream Bee Pubns., *(0-9661572)* 3325 C 1/2 Rd., Palisade, CO 81526 USA Tel 970-434-7501
E-mail: bee@dreambee.com
Web site: http://www.dreambee.com
Dist(s): **Books West**
Partners/West.

Dream Creek Pr., *(0-9771515)* 401 Taylor St., Ashland, OR 97520 USA
E-mail: bethart@mind.net
Web site: http://www.bbcreativecards.com.

Dream Dance Pubns., *(0-9769192)* P.O. Box 902, Redmond, WA 98073 USA Tel 425-898-9240
E-mail: briggs870@msn.com.

Dream Factory Bks., *(0-9701195)* Orders Addr.: P.O. Box 874, Enumclaw, WA 98022 USA (SAN 253-2611) Tel 360-663-0508; Fax: 360-825-7952; Toll Free Fax: 877-377-7030; Edit Addr.: 58402 114th St., E., Enumclaw, WA 98022-7305 USA
E-mail: sensel@earthlink.net
Web site: http://dreamfactorybooks.com
Dist(s): **Independent Pubs. Group.**

Dream Flight Productions, *(0-9656156; 0-9724962)* 1187 Coast Village Rd., No. 457, Santa Barbara, CA 93108 USA Tel 805-969-5654; Fax: 805-969-9294
E-mail: dreamflt@aol.com
Web site: http://www.dreamflt.com
Dist(s): **Follett Media Distribution.**

Dream Green, *(0-9740712)* P.O. Box 2347, Weirton, WV 26062 USA Tel 304-723-4553
E-mail: support@123oy.com
Web site: http://www.123oy.com.

Dream House Pr., *(0-9671555)* 2714 Ophelia Ct., San Jose, CA 95122 USA Tel 408-274-4574; Fax: 408-274-0786; Toll Free: 877-274-4574
E-mail: mr_art@prodigy.net; dreamhousepress@yahoo.com
Dist(s): **Baker & Taylor Bks.**
Biblio Distribution
Brodart Co.
Midwest Library Service
Milligan News Co., Inc.
Partners/West
Yankee Bk. Peddler, Inc.

Dream Image Pr., LLC, *(0-9744812)* P.O. Box 454, Northbrook, IL 60065-0454 USA Tel 847-480-8998
E-mail: drashley@dreamimagepress.com.

Dream On Pubns., *(0-9761151)* Orders Addr.: P.O. Box 190265, Fort Lauderdale, FL 33319 USA (SAN 256-2057)
E-mail: books@dreamonpublications.com.

Dream Pubns., I, Inc., *(0-9763596)* 111 Primrose Ln., Wyomissing, PA 19610 USA
E-mail: sukumar@idreampublications.com
Web site: http://www.idreampublications.com.

Dream Publishing, *(1-892073)* P.O. Box 1645, Blue Bell, PA 19422 USA Tel 610-279-7439; Fax: 610-279-1304 Do not confuse with Dream Publishing, Cartersville, GA
E-mail: Lynda27@aol.com.

Dream Publishing Co., *(0-9704861; 0-9728175)* 2306 Dexter Ave., Silver Spring, MD 20915-1747 USA Tel 301-592-8225; Fax: 301-592-8226; Toll Free: 877-537-3262 Do not confuse with companies with the same or similar names in Blue Bell, PA, Cartersville, GA, Louisville, KY
E-mail: dreampub@mindspring.com
Web site: http://www.sillweewobbert.com
Dist(s): **Baker & Taylor Bks.**
Quality Bks., Inc.

Dream Ridge Pr., *(0-9792084)* P.O. Box 5, Fonda, IA 50540 USA Tel 712-660-8409
E-mail: rainbowfarm2006@yahoo.com; trish@rainbowfarmbooks.com
Web site: http://www.lulu.com/trishacp; http://www.rainbowfarmbooks.com
Dist(s): **Lulu.com.**

Dream Scape Publishing, *(0-615; 0-9795519)* 805 Dunwood Ct., Chesapeake, VA 23322 USA Tel 757-717-2734
E-mail: dreamscape2@cox.net
Web site: http://www.dreamscapepublishing.com.

Dream Ship Publishing Co., *(0-9729155)* 1512 River Rock Trace, Woodstock, GA 30188 USA
E-mail: info@dreamshipbooks.com.

Dream Star Productions, *(0-9772027)* Orbisson Sq. 4306 S. Peoria Ave., Ste 705, Tulsa, OK 74105-3922 USA Tel 918-630-7580; Fax: 918-749-1717
Web site: http://www.kbaustin.com.

Dream Weaver Books *See* **Lighthouse Christian Publishing**

Dream Workshop Publishing Co., LLC, The, *(0-9786940)* 4421 Bachelor Creek Rd., Asheboro, NC 27205 USA (SAN 851-3635) Tel 336-879-8108
E-mail: info@dreamworkshoppub.com
Web site: http://www.dreamworkshoppub.com.

Dream-Catcher Pubns., *(0-9752878)* 22265 Petersburg, Eastpointe, MI 48021 USA.

DreamCatcherPress, Inc., *(0-9678810)* P.O. Box 5070, Zionsville, IN 46077-5070 USA Tel 317-733-9454; Fax: 317-733-9453
E-mail: ijcut@dreamcatcherpress.com; info@dreamcatcherpress.com
Web site: http://www.dreamcatcherpress.com.

DreamDog Pr., *(0-9666199)* 2308 Mount Vernon Ave., Alexandria, VA 22301-1328 USA
E-mail: rainey@dreamdog.com
Web site: http://www.dreamdog.com.

DreamerLand, *(0-9763250)* Orders Addr.: 1020 3rd St., Hermosa Beach, CA 90254 USA Tel 310-406-9371
E-mail: info@dreamerland.com; fanzan1@yahoo.com
Web site: http://www.Dreamerland.com; http://www.charlzfrommarz.com.

DreamHouse Publishing, Inc., *(0-9755516)* 2100 Blossom Way S., St. Petersburg, FL 33712 USA Fax: 727-906-4354
E-mail: linda@hgml.net
Web site: http://www.dreamhousepublishing.com
Dist(s): **Biblio Distribution.**

Dreams Due Media Group, Inc., *(0-9789202)* P.O. Box 1018, Firestone, CO 80520 USA Tel 303-241-3155 Toll Free: 877-462-1710
Web site: http://www.dreamsdue.com.

Dreamseekers, *(0-9668406)* P.O. Box 6212, Libertyville, IL 60048 USA Fax: 847-367-7623
E-mail: Rch4it@aol.com.

Dreamtime Publishing, *(0-9741726)* P.O. Box 834, Tahlequah, OK 74465 USA Tel 918-456-8639.

Dreamworks Publishing *See* **Dream Publishing**

Dressler, Avi, *(0-9744309)* 35 Old Brick Rd., East Hills, NY 11577-1816 USA.

Dressler, Craig, *(0-9778247)* 5341 NE Webster Ct., Portland, OR 97218 USA Tel 503-281-4214.

Drew Publishing Co., *(0-9658730)* Orders Addr.: 301 Birch St., Fircrest, WA 98466 USA Tel 253-302-5215
E-mail: kdrew@olympus.net.

Dreyer Pr., *(0-9669581)* Rte. 2, Box 309-A, Shiner, TX 77984 USA Tel 361-293-3148; Fax: 361-293-3847
E-mail: dreyerpress@dewittec.net
Web site: http://www.members.aol.com/boronia/illdobetter/htm.

Dried Fish Pubns., *(0-9709944)* 1412-B Camp Rd., Charleston, SC 29412 USA Tel 843-953-7629; Fax: 843-406-1552
E-mail: ainae@cofc.edu
Web site: http://www.cofc.edu/~ainael.

Driving Vision, Inc., *(0-9766329)* 2117 S. Ventura Dr., Tempe, AZ 85282 USA
Web site: http://www.drivingvision.com.

D.R.M. Publishing Co., *(0-9659677)* Div. of Historical Museum of Barbed Wire & Fencing Tools, Orders Addr.: P.O. Box 290, McLean, TX 79057-0010 USA Tel 806-779-2225; Edit Addr.: 100 Kingsley St., McLean, TX 79057 USA.

DrMaster Pubns. Inc., *(1-59796)* 48531 Warm Springs Blvd., Suite 408, Fremont, CA 94539 USA Tel 510-687-1388 (phone/fax)
Web site: http://www.drmasterpublications.com
Dist(s): **Diamond Bk. Distributors.**

Droemersche Verlagsanstalt Th. Knaur Nachf. - GmbH & Co. (DEU) *(3-426) Dist. by* **Distribks Inc.**

Drollery Pr., *(0-940920)* 1524 Benton St., Alameda, CA 94501-2420 USA (SAN 223-1808) Tel 510-521-4087.

DRT Pr., *(1-933084)* Orders Addr.: P.O. Box 427, Pittsboro, NC 27312 USA Tel 919-542-1763; Fax: 866-562-5040; Edit Addr.: 105 Beau Ln., Pittsboro, NC 27312 USA
E-mail: editorial@drtpress.com
Web site: http://www.drtpress.com.

Drumbeat *Imprint of* **Longman Publishing Group**

Drummond Publishing Group, The, *(0-9755080; 1-59763)* 4 Collins Ave., Plymouth, MA 02360-4809 USA Do not confuse with Rec#s 786442, 791375, 1194043
E-mail: f_allen@drummondpub.com
Web site: http://www.drummondpub.com
Dist(s): **Biblio Distribution.**

Drumstick Media, *(0-9764791)* Div. of Old Goats, Inc., 5805 Hwy. 93 S., Whitefish, MT 59937 USA Tel 406-862-8938; Fax: 406-862-8936; Toll Free: 800-404-8279
E-mail: robert@drumstickmedia.com; james@drumstickmedia.com
Web site: http://www.baxterowengraham.com; http://www.drumstickmedia.com.

Drunk Duck Comics, *(0-9748960)* 105 Market St., Pittston, PA 18640 USA
E-mail: rubbermallet@verizon.net
Web site: http://www.drunkduck.com.

Dry, Paul Bks., Inc., *(0-9664913; 0-9679675; 1-58988)* 117 S. 17th St., Suite 1102, Philadelphia, PA 19103 USA Tel 215-231-9939; Fax: 215-231-9942
E-mail: pdb@pauldrybooks.com
Web site: http://www.pauldrybooks.com
Dist(s): **Consortium Bk. Sales & Distribution**
Independent Pubs. Group.

Dry Store Publishing Co., The, *(0-9653572)* Rt. 2 Box 156B, Lanesboro, MN 55949 USA Tel 507-467-2928; Fax: 507-467-2694
E-mail: marytbell@drystore.com
Web site: http://www.drystore.com.

†Dryden Pr., *(0-03; 0-15; 0-8498)* Div. of Thomson Corp., The, Orders Addr.: 6277 Sea Harbor Dr., Orlando, FL 32887 USA Toll Free: 800-782-4479 (orders, inquires); 800-544-6678 (customer service); Edit Addr.: 301 Commerce St., Suite 3700, Fort Worth, TX 76012 USA (SAN 281-613X) Tel 817-334-7500; Fax: 817-334-7844; Toll Free: 800-447-9479 Do not confuse with Dryden Pr., Jackson Center, OH
Web site: http://www.thomson.com; *CIP.*

Dryden Publishing, *(0-9644370; 1-929204)* P.O. Box 482, Dryden, WA 98821-0482 USA
E-mail: dryden@csiconnect.com.

Dryland, David *See* **DrDryland.Com, LLC**

DSA Publishing & Design, Inc., *(0-9774451)* 6900 Edgewater Dr., Mckinney, TX 75070-5592 USA
Web site: http://www.dsapubs.com
Dist(s): **AtlasBooks Distribution.**

DS-Max USA, Inc., *(1-58805)* Orders Addr.: 19511 Pauling, Foothill Ranch, CA 92610 USA Tel 949-587-9207; Fax: 949-587-9024
E-mail: jennifer@dsmaxgroup.com; lizzas@dsmaxgroup.com.

DTJ, LLC, *(0-9765731)* P.O. Box 635, Sequim, WA 98382 USA.

D-Tower Pubns., *(0-9770386)* 8028 Pine St., Ethel, LA 70730-3853 USA Tel 225-335-0802
E-mail: swbloopers@yahoo.com.

Dualstar, Inc., *(1-892587)* 42-450 Bob Hope Dr., Suite 135, Palm Desert, CA 92270 USA
E-mail: cyberstories@earthlink.net
Web site: http://home.earthlink.net/~cyberstories.

Duchess Publications, Incorporated *See* **Fox Bks.**

Duckpond Publishing, Inc., *(0-9720350)* 130 Hillside Ln., Roswell, GA 30076 USA Tel 770-649-9947; Fax: 770-594-8058
E-mail: theducks@duckpondpublishing.com
Web site: http://www.duckpondpublishing.com.

Ducks Publishing, *(0-9666537)* 155 McCoy St., Winnemucca, NV 89445 USA Tel 702-623-2276
E-mail: mackenzie@the-onramp.net.

Ducks Unlimited, Inc., *(0-9617279; 1-932052)* One Waterfowl Way, Memphis, TN 38120 USA (SAN 269-7718) Tel 901-758-3962; Fax: 901-758-3909; Toll Free: 800-453-8257 (800-453-8257)
E-mail: sbrown@ducks.org
Web site: http://www.ducks.org
Dist(s): **Globe Pequot Pr., The.**

Duckworth, Gerald & Co., Ltd. (GBR) *(0-7156; 1-86176) Dist. by* **Intl Pubs Mktg.**

Dude Publishing *Imprint of* **National Professional Resources, Inc.**

Due Pubns., *(0-9746212)* Orders Addr.: P.O. Box 883, Loveland, CO 80539-0883 USA; Edit Addr.: 246 Alden Dr., Loveland, CO 80537 USA
Web site: http://www.dupepublications.com; http://www.committoyourself.com.

DUENDE Bks., *(0-615; 0-9777973)* Div. of DeCo Communications, 13900 Fiji Way, Apt. 306, Marina del Rey, CA 90292 USA Tel 310-486-0983
E-mail: denizr@verizon.net
Web site: http://www.duendebooks.blogspot.com
Dist(s): **Lulu.com.**

Duffy's Educational Resources, Inc., *(0-9754519)* P.O. Box 550537, Jacksonville, FL 32255 USA Tel 904-730-9676 Toll Free: 877-730-9676
Web site: http://www.readingreallyrocks.com.

†Dufour Editions, Inc., *(0-8023)* Orders Addr.: P.O. Box 7, Chester Springs, PA 19425-0007 USA (SAN 201-341X) Tel 610-458-5005; Fax: 610-458-7103; Toll Free: 800-869-5677
E-mail: info@dufoureditions.com
Web site: http://www.dufoureditions.com; *CIP.*

Dugmore, Heidi, *(0-9753888)* P.O. Box 64, Wray, CO 80758 USA
E-mail: thehappyhomemakernewsletter@yahoo.com.

Duke Publishing & Software Corp., *(0-9745406)* P.O. Box 3429, Los Altos, CA 94024 USA Tel 408-245-3853; Fax: 408-245-9289
E-mail: info@aboutthekids.org
Web site: http://www.aboutthekids.org.

†Duke Univ. Pr., *(0-8223)* P.O. Box 90660, Durham, NC 27708-0660 USA (SAN 201-3436) Tel 919-687-3600; Fax: 919-688-4574
E-mail: orders@dukepress.edu; subscriptions@dukepress.edu
Web site: http://www.dukeupress.edu; *CIP.*

Duke Univ. Talent Identification Program (T I P), *(0-9639756; 0-9744673)* 1121 W. Main St., Suite 100, Durham, NC 27701 USA Tel 919-668-9100; Fax: 919-668-9141
E-mail: eog@tip.duke.edu
Web site: http://www.tip.duke.edu.

Dukes World, Inc., *(0-9664506)* P.O. Box 85, Yonkers, NY 10704 USA Tel 917-403-7661
E-mail: dukesworldinc@aol.com
Web site: http://www.chillstreetgang.com.

Dulan & Assocs., *(0-9713093)* 1727 Holly Dr., Suite 306, Glendale, CA 91206 USA Tel 818-630-2340.

Duling Designs, *(0-9743445)* P.O. Box 1996, Marco Island, FL 34146-1996 USA
E-mail: jsduling87@aol.com.

Dume Publishing *See* **Corman Productions**

Dummer Publishing, *(0-9633479)* Orders Addr.: P.O. Box 253, Holmen, WI 54636 USA Tel 608-526-3493; Edit Addr.: N. 6595 Hwy. XX, Holmen, WI 54636 USA
E-mail: shuduhol@cs.com
Dist(s): **Badger Bks., LLC.**

Dummler's Ferd., Verlagsbuchhandlung (DEU) *(3-427) Dist. by* **Intl Bk Import.**

Dunamis Development, *(0-9767066)* 3972-J Barranca Pkwy., Suite 115, Irvine, CA 92606 USA Tel 949-263-0063.

Dunbar, Doctor Jay, *(0-9677560)* 15 Timberlyne Rd., Chapel Hill, NC 27514-1522 USA Tel 919-968-3936
E-mail: drjay@magictortoise.com
Web site: http://www.magictortoise.com.

Duncan & Duncan, Incorporated *See* **APU Publishing Group**

Duncan Baird Pubs. (GBR) *(1-900131; 1-903296; 1-904292; 1-84483) Dist. by* **Sterling.**

Duneside Pr., *(0-9712904)* 40 Hickory Point, Springfield, IL 62707 USA
Dist(s): **Partners/West.**

Dunhill Publishing, *(0-9701088; 1-931501)* 18340 Sonoma Hwy., Sonoma, CA 95476 USA Tel 707-939-0562; Fax: 707-938-3515 Do not confuse with Dunhill Publishing, Seattle, WA
E-mail: dunhillpublishing@pacbell.net
Dist(s): **SCB Distributors.**

Dunlap, J.A. & Sons Pubs., *(0-9712484)* 721 NW 15th St., Oklahoma City, OK 73103 USA Fax: 405-525-9963
E-mail: jadelaide@hotmail.com.

Dunlop, Edward, *(0-9785523)* 342 Meadow Green Dr., Ringgold, GA 30736 USA Tel 706-937-3798
E-mail: eddunlop@juno.com
Web site: http://www.dunlopministries.com.

Dunn, Charles Camaron, *(0-9663240)* Div. of Dunn Industries, Inc., 28917 Oak Springs Canyon Rd. # A, Canyon Cntry, CA 91387-2152 USA Toll Free: 800-961-7467
E-mail: cdunn@earthlink.net
Web site: http://www.leonardsworld.com.

Dunn, Hunter, *(0-9761732)* 410 Old Spring Rd., Danville, VA 24540-5206 USA.

Dunn, Michael *See* **Big Secret, The**

Dunne, Thomas Bks. *Imprint of* **St. Martin's Pr.**

Duomo Pr., *(0-9679456)* 6668 N. Sioux Ave., Chicago, IL 60646-2845 USA
E-mail: publisher@duomopress.com
Web site: http://www.duomopress.com.

Duplicates Printing, *(0-9749953)* Orders Addr.: P.O. Box 2398, Pawleys Island, SC 29585 USA Tel 843-237-3998; Edit Addr.: 14329 Ocean Hwy. Unit 115, Pawleys Isl, SC 29585-4816 USA
E-mail: slingshot@sc.rr.com.

Dupuis North Publishing, *(0-9749199)* 76 N. Church St., Clayton, GA 30525 USA Tel 828-524-9520; Fax: 828-349-1945.

Duracell & the National Ctr. for Missing & Exploited Children (NCMEC), *(0-9795307)* 415 Nadison Ave., New York, NY 10018 USA Tel 212-613-4904.

Durban Hse. Publishing Co., Inc., *(1-930754)* 7502 Greenville Ave., Suite 500, Dallas, TX 75231 USA Tel 214-890-4050; Fax: 214-890-9295 ; *Imprints:* Durban House (Durban)
E-mail: info@durbanhouse.com
Web site: http://www.durbanhouse.com
Dist(s): **Baker & Taylor Bks.**
BookMasters
Midpoint National, Inc.
Midpoint Trade Bks., Inc.
National Bk. Network.

Durban Hse. *Imprint of* **Durban Hse. Publishing Co., Inc.**

Durland Alternatives Library, *(0-9740184)* 127 Anabel Taylor Hall, Ithaca, NY 14853-1001 USA Tel 607-255-6486; Fax: 607-255-9985
E-mail: alt-lib@cornell.edu
Web site: http://www.alternativeslibrary.org.

Durst, Sanford J., *(0-915262; 0-942666; 1-886720)* 106 Woodcleft Ave., Freeport, NY 11520 USA (SAN 211-6987) Tel 516-867-3333; Fax: 516-867-3397
E-mail: sjdbooks@verizon.net.

Dust Bunny Games LLC, *(0-9747833)* Orders Addr.: 3744 Mistflower Ln., Naperville, IL 60564-5921 USA Tel 630-244-0335; Fax: 630-922-6995; Edit Addr.: 3744 Mistflower Ln., Naperville, IL 60564-5921 USA
E-mail: info@dustbunnygames.com
Web site: http://www.dustbunnygames.com.

Duthaluru, Vidhya, *(0-9797657)* 247 Levinberg Ln., Wayne, NJ 07470 USA.

Company

Earthen Vessel Production, Inc., *(1-887400)* 3620 Greenwood Dr., Kelseyville, CA 95451 USA Tel 707-279-9621; Fax: 707-279-8769
E-mail: books@earthen.com; request@earthen.com
Web site: http://www.earthen.com.

Earthen Vessel Publishing, *(0-9703296)* 289 Miller Ave., Mill Valley, CA 94941-2832 USA Tel 415-381-3061
E-mail: kentp@marinternet.com.

Earthkids Publishing, *(0-9704629)* Orders Addr.: 1042 Sayle St., Lady Lake, FL 32162-3792 USA (SAN 253-4592)
E-mail: mnewek@yahoo.com
Web site: http://www.earthkidspublishing.com
Dist(s): **Baker & Taylor Bks.**

Earthlight *See* **Light24**

Earthling Pr. *Imprint of* **Awe-Struck E-Books, Inc.**

Earthshaker Bks., *(0-9790357)* 400 Melville Ave., Saint Louis, MO 63130 USA (SAN 852-2545) Tel 314-862-8177
E-mail: albonnie@mindspring.com
Dist(s): **Biblio Distribution.**

EarthSpring Publishing, *(0-9705747)* P.O. Box 2086, Issaquah, WA 98027 USA Tel 425-391-4035; Fax: 425-391-1450
E-mail: n.atkins@home.com.

EarthTime Pubns., *(0-9663286)* Orders Addr.: 5662 Calle Real, #169, Santa Barbara, CA 93117 USA (SAN 299-5727) Tel 805-898-2263; Fax: 805-898-9460
E-mail: donna@seemamoon.com
Web site: http://www.seemamoon.com
Dist(s): **Midpoint Trade Bks., Inc.**

Earthwalk Pr., *(0-915749)* 5432 La Jolla Hermosa Ave., La Jolla, CA 92037-7613 USA (SAN 293-9258)
Dist(s): **Booklines Hawaii, Ltd.**

Earthways *See* **Earthways Guided Canoe Trips and School of Wilderness Living**

Earthways Guided Canoe Trips and School of Wilderness Living, *(0-9761714)* 159 Earthways Rd., Canaan, ME 04924 USA Tel 207-426-8138
E-mail: info@earthways.net
Web site: http://www.earthways.net.

Earthwing Pubns., *(0-9666720)* Orders Addr.: P.O. Box 187, Bonita Springs, FL 34133-0187 USA Tel 941-498-9369; Edit Addr.: 10255 Pennsylvania Ave., Bonita Springs, FL 34134 USA.

Ear Twiggles Productions, Inc., *(0-9762573)* 14610 Luna Media, San Diego, CA 92127 USA Tel 858-756-8644; Fax: 858-756-8235
E-mail: contactus@eartwiggles.com
Web site: http://www.eartwiggles.com.

Eas'l Pubns., *(1-57377)* Div. of The Idea Shop, Inc., Orders Addr.: P.O. Box 22088, Saint Louis, MO 63126 USA Tel 314-892-9222; Fax: 314-892-9607; Edit Addr.: 11150 Lindbergh Business Ct., Suite 107, Saint Louis, MO 63123 USA
E-mail: easlpub@I1.net
Web site: http://www.easlpublications.com.

East End Hospice, Inc., *(0-9754932)* Orders Addr.: P.O. Box 1048, Westhampton Beach, NY 11978 USA Tel 631-288-8400; Fax: 631-288-8492; Edit Addr.: 481 Westhampton River Head Rd., Westhampton Beach, NY 11978 USA
E-mail: info@eeh.org
Web site: http://www.eeh.org.

East Gate Bk. *Imprint of* **Sharpe, M.E. Inc.**

East Lake Publishing *See* **ESCO PR.**

East of the Sun Publishing, *(0-9668559)* Orders Addr.: P.O. Box 110063, Naples, FL 34108-0102 USA Tel 941-566-9676 (phone/fax); Edit Addr.: 75 Mentor Dr., Naples, FL 34110 USA
E-mail: sales@eastofthesun.biz
Web site: http://www.eastofthesun.biz.

East River Pr., *(0-9791283)* 455 FDR Dr., No. B1205, New York, NY 10002-5915 USA Do not confuse with companies with the same or similar name in Largo, MD, NEw YOrk, NY, Chester, NY.

East West Discovery Pr., *(0-9669437; 0-9701654; 0-9799339)* P.O. Box 2385, Manhattan Beach, CA 90266 USA Tel 310-545-3730; Fax: 310-545-3731
E-mail: info@eastwestdiscovery.com; icy@eastwestdiscovery.com
Web site: http://www.eastwestdiscovery.com
Dist(s): **American West Bks.**
Baker & Taylor Bks.
Master Communications, Inc.

Eastbank Publishing, *(0-9670911)* 325 Pennsylvania Ave., Washington, DC 20003 USA Tel 202-337-7898; Fax: 202-966-1179
E-mail: mary@firstdog.com
Web site: http://www.firstdog.com.

Easter Island Foundation, *(1-880636)* Orders Addr.: P.O. Box 6774, Los Osos, CA 93412-6774 USA Tel 805-528-8558; Fax: 805-534-9301
E-mail: rapanuibooks@worldnet.att.net
Web site: http://www.islandheritage.org.

Eastern Europe Aid Assn., *(1-893179)* P.O. Box 917, Waynesboro, PA 17268-0917 USA Tel 717-762-1086; Fax: 717-762-8103
E-mail: eeaa@genovieva.org
Web site: http://www.genovieva.org.

†Eastern National, *(0-915992; 1-888213; 1-59091)* 470 Maryland Dr., Suite 1, Fort Washington, PA 19034 USA (SAN 630-4044)
E-mail: erich@Easternnational.org
Web site: http://www.easternnational.org; *CIP.*

Eastern National Park & Monument Association *See* **Eastern National**

Eastern Slope Publisher, *(0-9746996)* Orders Addr.: P.O. Box 20357, Reno, NV 89515-0357 USA; Edit Addr.: 205 Urban Rd., Reno, NV 89509-3662 USA
E-mail: pdcafferata@sbcglobal.net.

Eastern Washington Univ. Pr., *(0-910055; 1-59766)* Orders Addr.: 705 W. 1st Ave., Spokane, WA 99201 USA (SAN 244-7967) Tel 509-623-4284; Fax: 509-623-4283; Toll Free: 800-508-9095; Edit Addr.: Eastern Washington Univ. EWU, MS-1, 705 W. First Ave., Spokane, WA 99201 USA (SAN 241-2977) Tel 509-623-4286; Fax: 509-623-4283
E-mail: ewupress@ewu.edu
Web site: http://www.ewu.edu/dcesso/press/
Dist(s): **Univ. of Washington Pr.**

Eastland Studios, *(0-9755635)* P.O. Box 670, Lompoc, CA 93438 USA Tel 805-735-5134
Web site: http://www.ideaship.com; http://www.wingedtiger.com
Dist(s): **Booklines Hawaii, Ltd.**

Easton Publishing Co., Inc., *(0-9714500)* 2011 Wind Valley Ct., Jefferson City, MO 65101-4474 USA Toll Free: 888-635-0609 Do not confuse with companies with the same or similar names in Rockfor, IL, Burlingame, CA
Web site: http://www.eastonpublishing.com.

EastWest Pr., *(0-9606090)* P.O. Box 14149, Minneapolis, MN 55414-0149 USA (SAN 216-809X) Tel 612-379-2049.

Eastword Publications Development, Incorporated *See* **Lincoln Library Press, The**

Eat Your Peas Publishing, *(0-9743210)* 330 Conestoga Rd., Wayne, PA 19087 USA Tel 610-995-0495; Fax: 610-995-0496
E-mail: lisa@richeyassociates.com
Web site: http://www.mannerstogo.com.

Eating Better Cookbooks *See* **Gregg, Sue Cookbooks**

Eaton, William, *(0-9713693)* 1241 Brookdale Ave., Bay Shore, NY 11706 USA Tel 631-348-2309; Fax: 516-539-2076
E-mail: weaton36@hotmail.com
Web site: http://www.childrensmoneybook.com.

EBA Creative, *(0-615)* 7346 Lake St., 1W, River Forest, IL 60305 USA Tel 708-366-0674
E-mail: author@alenabooks.com
Web site: http://www.alenabooks.com
Dist(s): **Lulu.com.**

Ebben, Willard, *(0-9719965)* 1605 Oakridge Ave., Kaukauna, WI 54130-3349 USA Fax: 920-766-1335.

Ebed Pr., *(0-9741927; 1-933484; 0-9774825; 1-934050)* 3103 Villa Ave., Bronx, NY 11468-1356 USA Tel 718-788-2484; Fax: 718-788-7760; Toll Free: 800-224-7808
E-mail: info@ebedpress.com
Web site: http://www.ebedpress.com.

Ebeemee Pubs., *(0-9678193)* Orders Addr.: P.O. Box 1235, Concord, MA 01742 USA Tel 978-369-2175; Edit Addr.: 2 Concord Greene, No. 7, Concord, MA 01742 USA
E-mail: ebeemeepond@aol.com.

Ebenezer A.M.E. Church, *(0-9748834)* 7707 Allentown Rd., Fort Washington, MD 20744 USA Tel 301-248-8833; Fax: 301-248-6894
Web site: http://www.ebenezerame.org.

Ebks. On The Net *Imprint of* **ebooksonthe.net**

EBL Coaching, *(0-9772110; 0-9778391)* 167 E. 82nd St., Suite 1A, New York, NY 10023 USA Tel 646-342-9380; Fax: 212-937-2305
E-mail: elevy@eblcoaching.com
Web site: http://www.eblcoaching.com.

Ebo Ink, *(0-9669230)* 331 Wende Way, Glen Burnie, MD 21061-6285 USA Tel 410-590-1937
E-mail: pohpoet@aol.com.

Ebon Research Systems *See* **Ebon Research Systems Publishing, LLC**

Ebon Research Systems Publishing, LLC, *(0-915960; 0-9648313)* 812 Sweetwater Club Blvd., Longwood, FL 32779 USA (SAN 254-6698) Tel 407-786-9200; Fax: 407-682-2384
E-mail: ebon@ebonresearchsystems.com
Web site: http://www.daretobebooks.com; http://www.ebonresearchsystems.com.

EbonyEnergy Publishing *See* **EbonyEnergy Publishing**

EbonyEnergy Publishing, *(0-9722795; 0-9755092; 1-59825)* Div. of The GEM Group, Orders Addr.: P.O. Box 43476, Chicago, IL 60643-0476 USA (SAN 255-3953) Tel 773-779-8129 (phone); 773-445-4948; Fax: 773-779-8139 (Fax); 773-233-5178; Toll Free: 877-447-1266 ; *Imprints:* Precious Gems (PreciousG)
E-mail: info@ebonyenergypublishing.com; books@ebonyenergy.com; books@ebonyenergypublishing.com
Web site: http://www.ebonyenergy.com; http://gemliteraryfoundation.org; http://ebonyenergybooks.com; http://ebonyenergykids.com; http://www.ebonyenergypublishing.com; http://highestgoodpublications.com; http://pocketbooksforyoursoul.com
Dist(s): **Biblio Distribution.**

Ebonylaw Publishing, *(0-9724284)* Unit 2709, Box 6, Apo, FL 34021-2709 USA
E-mail: caldans@ebonylaw.com.

E-Booksgen, *(1-893767)* 40 Sandy Pond South, East Wakefield, NH 03830 USA Tel 603-522-9951
E-mail: e-booksgen@e-booksgen.com
Web site: http://www.e-booksgen.com; http://www.e-booksgen.com/E-WW2DOC.html.

ebooksonthe.net *See* **Dilligaf Publishing**

ebooksonthe.net, *(0-9706152; 1-59431)* Div. of Write Words, Inc., 2934 Old Rte. 50, Cambridge, MD 21613 USA (SAN 254-0304) Fax: 410-221-7510 ; *Imprints:* Cambridge Books (CB); Ebooks On The Net (Ebks on the net) Do not confuse with The Write Words Inc., in Arlington, VA
E-mail: publisher@ebooksonthe.net
Web site: http://www.ebooksonthe.net; http://www.cambridgebooks.us
Dist(s): **Baker & Taylor Bks.**
BookSurge, LLC.

eBookstand Books *See* **Bookstand Publishing**

E-BookTime LLC, *(0-9717625; 1-932701; 1-59824)* 6598 Pumpkin Rd., Montgomery, AL 36108 USA Toll Free: 877-613-2665
E-mail: publishing@e-booktime.com
Web site: http://www.e-booktime.com.

Eborn Bks., *(1-890718)* Orders Addr.: P.O. Box 559, Roy, UT 84067 USA (SAN 174-4925) Fax: 801-773-2785; Edit Addr.: 3653 W. 4925 S., Roy, UT 84067 USA Tel 901-773-4708
E-mail: ebornbk@doitnow.com
Web site: http://www.ebornbooks.com.

Ebury Publishing (GBR) *(0-09; 0-7126; 0-85223) Dist. by* **Trafalgar.**

Ebury Publishing (GBR) *(0-09; 0-7126; 0-85223) Dist. by* **IPG Chicago.**

Ecce Homo Pr., *(0-9664689; 0-9797609)* 6401 Shrader Ln., La Grange, KY 40031 USA Toll Free Fax: 800-884-7649
E-mail: eccehomopr@aol.com
Web site: http://www.eccehomopress.com.

Echelon Press Publishing, *(1-59080)* Orders Addr.: 9735 Country Meadows Ln. 1-D, Laurel, MD 20723 USA Tel 410-878-7113; Fax: 410-878-7885
E-mail: admin@echelonpress.com; marketing@echelonpress.com
Web site: http://www.echelonpress.com
Dist(s): **Brodart Co.**
Lightning Source, Inc.

Echoes Joint Venture, *(0-9759995)* Intensive English Program, UD, 1845 E. Northgate Dr., Irving, TX 75062 USA.

Eckankar, *(1-57043)* Orders Addr.: P.O. Box 27300, Minneapolis, MN 55427 USA (SAN 253-7192) Fax: 952-380-2295; Toll Free: 800-568-3463
E-mail: eckbooks@eckankar.org
Web site: http://www.eckankar.org.

Eckerd College Leadership Development Institute, *(0-9764173)* 4200 54th Ave. S., St. Petersburg, FL 33711 USA Tel 727-864-8213; Fax: 727-864-7575; Toll Free: 800-753-0444
E-mail: ldi@eckerd.edu
Web site: http://www.eckerd.edu/ldi.

Eckl, Joseph J., *(0-9746686)* 346 Country Brook Ln., Harvard, IL 60033-7807 USA
E-mail: ecklindpil@aol.com.

Eclectic Dragon Pr., *(0-9746016)* PO Box 91, Laie, HI 96762-1294 USA.

Eclipse Pr. *Imprint of* **Blood-Horse, Inc., The**

Eco Fiction Bks. *Imprint of* **Day to Day Enterprises**

Eco Images, *(0-938423)* Orders Addr.: P.O. Box 61413, Virginia Beach, VA 23466-1413 USA (SAN 661-230X); Edit Addr.: 4132 Blackwater Rd., Virginia Beach, VA 23457 USA (SAN 661-2318) Tel 757-421-3929
E-mail: wildfood@cox.net
Web site: http://www.ecoimages-us.com.

Ecology Comics, *(0-9643421)* 465 B. Kawailoa Rd., Kailua, HI 96734 USA Tel 808-261-1018; Fax: 808-531-3177.

EconFun, LLC, *(0-9748368)* 11920 Dalkeith Ln., Richmond, VA 23233 USA Tel 804-360-0899 (phone/fax)
E-mail: econ.fun@verizon.net
Web site: http://www.econ-fun.com.

Eco-thumb Publishing Co., *(0-9778536)* 1212 S. Naper Blvd., Suite 119-337, Naperville, IL 60540 USA (SAN 850-4113) Tel 630-853-9758.

Ecotrust, *(0-9676364; 0-9779332)* 721 NW 9th Ave. Ste. 200, Portland, OR 97209-3448 USA
Web site: http://www.ecotrust.org
Dist(s): **Oregon State Univ. Pr.**

ECS Learning Systems, Inc., *(0-944459; 1-57022; 1-60539)* P.O. Box 433, Bulverde, TX 78163 USA (SAN 243-6167) Toll Free: 800-688-3224; 2709 Bulverde Rd., Bulverde, TX 78163
E-mail: lmammen@educyberstor.com
Web site: http://www.educyberstor.com.

Ectopic Publishing, *(0-9759695)* 3638 Lovejoy Ct. NE, Olympia, WA 98506 USA
E-mail: bryanrandall@ectopicpublishing.com
Web site: http://www.ectopicpublishing.com.

ECW Pr. (CAN) *(0-920763; 0-920802; 1-55022) Dist. by* **IPG Chicago.**

Ed. Acespanish S.A.C.- Lima, Peru, *(0-9762361)* 4806 Alta Loma Dr., Austin, TX 78749 USA Tel 512-784-6333
Web site: http://www.acespanish.com.

Ed D. Bear Enterprises, *(0-9664138)* Orders Addr.: P.O. Box 7510, Auburn, CA 95603 USA Tel 530-823-6641; Edit Addr.: 1329 Merry Knoll Rd., Auburn, CA 95604 USA.

E.D. Insight Bks., *(0-9761552)* P.O. Box 514, Beverly Hills, CA 90213-0514 USA
E-mail: brady@edinsight.com
Web site: http://www.edinsight.com.

Edah Bks., *(1-928903)* Orders Addr.: P.O. Box 514544, Los Angeles, CA 90051 USA; Edit Addr.: 16206 S. Denver Ave., Gardenia, CA 90248 USA Tel 310-532-4657
E-mail: markedah@aol.com
Web site: http://www.markedah.com.

Edamex, Editores Asociados Mexicanos, S. A. de C. V. (MEX) *(968-409; 970-661) Dist. by* **Giron Bks.**

EDC Publishing, *(0-7460; 0-86020; 0-88110; 1-58086; 0-7945; 1-60130)* Orders Addr.: P.O. Box 470663, Tulsa, OK 74147-0663 USA (SAN 658-0505); Edit Addr.: 10302 E. 55th Pl., Tulsa, OK 74146-6515 USA (SAN 107-5322) Tel 918-622-4522; Fax: 918-665-7919; Toll Free Fax: 800-747-4509; Toll Free: 800-475-4522 ; *Imprints:* Usborne (UsborneU)
E-mail: edc@edcpub.com
Web site: http://www.edcpub.com
Dist(s): **Continental Bk. Co., Inc.**
Lectorum Pubns., Inc.
Libros Sin Fronteras.

EDCO Publishing, Inc., *(0-9712692; 0-9749412; 0-9798088)* 2648 Lapeer Rd., Auburn Hills, MI 48326 USA (SAN 254-4261) Fax: 248-475-9122; Toll Free: 888-510-3326
E-mail: lynette@edcopublishing.com; martha@edcopublishing.com
Web site: http://www.edcopublishing.com
Dist(s): **Baker & Taylor Bks.**
Partners Bk. Distributing, Inc.

Eddie Crabtree Ministries, *(0-9765830)* Orders Addr.: P.O. Box 846, Salem, VA 24153 USA Tel 540-562-1500; Fax: 540-562-2695; Edit Addr.: 1928 Loch Haven Dr., Roanoke, VA 24019 USA
E-mail: eddiecrabtreeministries@valleywordministries.org.

Eddy, The Writings of Mary Baker, *(0-87510; 0-87952)* Orders Addr.: P.O. Box 1875, Boston, MA 02117 USA (SAN 203-6541); Edit Addr.: 175 Huntington Ave., A20-01, Boston, MA 02115 USA Tel 617-450-3537 Administration Queries (Paul Woodsum); Fax: 617-450-2054 Attn: Paul Woodsum, Production Manager; Toll Free Fax: 800-688-2017; Toll Free: 800-515-0160 (Science & Health Direct Orders)
E-mail: woodsump@twmbe.com; broadhurstg@twmbe.com
Web site: http://www.spirituality.com.

Edebé (ESP) *(84-236) Dist. by* **Baker & Taylor.**

Edebé (ESP) *(84-236) Dist. by* **Ediciones.**

Edebé (ESP) *(84-236) Dist. by* **Lectorum Pubns.**

Edelsa Grupo Didascalia, S.A. (ESP) *(84-389; 84-7711; 84-85786) Dist. by* **Continental Bk.**

Edelsa Grupo Didascalia, S.A. (ESP) *(84-389; 84-7711; 84-85786) Dist. by* **Distribks Inc.**

Edelson, Madelyn, *(0-9770131)* 69 Bay Ave., H, Huntington, NY 11743 USA
E-mail: mbedelson@optonline.net.

Eden Entertainment Ltd., Inc., *(0-9672819)* 1107 Key Plaza, Suite 195, Key West, FL 33040 USA Tel 305-294-7928
E-mail: Info@TrueSecretsOf.com
Web site: http://www.truesecretof.com.

Eden Studios, Inc., *(1-891153; 1-933105)* 6 Dogwood Ln., Londonville, NY 12211 USA Tel 518-331-2063; Fax: 425-962-2593
E-mail: edenprod@aol.com
Web site: http://www.edenstudios.net
Dist(s): **PSI (Publisher Services, Inc.).**

Edes Publishing Co., *(0-9788010)* 1224 E. Hadley, Las Cruces, NM 88001 USA (SAN 851-6561)
E-mail: publisher@edes.net
Web site: http://www.edes.net.

Edgar Gabriel Inc., *(0-9747842)* 732 S. Chestnut Ave., Arlington Heights, IL 60005 USA
Web site: http://www.edgargabriel.com.

Edge Bks. *Imprint of* **Capstone Pr., Inc.**

EDGEucation Publishing, *(1-932689)* Orders Addr.: P.O. Box 852013, Yukon, OK 73085-2013 USA; Edit Addr.: 1441 NW 47th St., Oklahoma City, OK 73085-2013 USA
E-mail: edgeucation@sbcglobal.net

EdgeWork Bks., *(1-931223)* 155 Cypress St., Fort Bragg, CA 95437 USA Tel 707-964-9520; Fax: 707-964-7531; Toll Free: 800-773-7782
E-mail: forms@cypresshouse.com
Web site: http://www.cypresshouse.com
Dist(s): **Baker & Taylor Bks.**
Partners/West.

Ediciones Alas, Inc., *(0-9753799)* Orders Addr.: P.O. Box 327495, Fort Lauderdale, FL 33332 USA; Edit Addr.: 6061 SW 195th Ave., Pembroke Pines, FL 33332 USA
E-mail: mm@miliymolo.com
Web site: http://www.miliymolo.com.

Ediciones B (ESP) *(84-406; 84-7735; 84-666) Dist. by* **Lectorum Pubns.**

Ediciones B (ESP) *(84-406; 84-7735; 84 666) Dist. by* **IPG Chicago.**

Ediciones B (ESP) *(84-406; 84-7735; 84-666) Dist. by* **Distribks Inc.**

Ediciones Cátedra (ESP) *(84-376) Dist. by* **Continental Bk.**

Ediciones de la Torre (ESP) *(84-7960; 84-85277; 84-85866; 84-86587) Dist. by* **AIMS Intl.**

Ediciones de la Torre (ESP) *(84-7960; 84-85277; 84-85866; 84-86587) Dist. by* **Libros Fronteras.**

Ediciones del Bronce (ESP) *(84-8453; 84-89854) Dist. by* **Planeta.**

Ediciones Destino (ESP) *(84-233; 84-9710) Dist. by* **Baker & Taylor.**

Ediciones Destino (ESP) *(84-233; 84-9710) Dist. by* **Continental Bk.**

Ediciones Destino (ESP) *(84-233; 84-9710) Dist. by* **Lectorum Pubns.**

Ediciones Destino (ESP) *(84-233; 84-9710) Dist. by* **AIMS Intl.**

Ediciones Destino (ESP) *(84-233; 84-9710) Dist. by* **Planeta.**

Ediciones El Salvaje Refinado *See* **Refined Savage Editions / Ediciones El Salvaje Refinado, The**

Ediciones Lerner *Imprint of* **Lerner Publishing Group**

Ediciones Libero, *(0-9601700)* 1657 Calle Adams., San Juan, PR 00920-4361 USA
E-mail: jsr@pop.dn.net.

Ediciones Norte, Inc., *(1-931928)* P.O. Box 29461, San Juan, PR 00929-0461 USA Tel 787-701-0909; Fax: 787-701-0922
Web site: http://www.edicionesnorte.com
Dist(s): **Independent Pubs. Group.**

Ediciones Nuevo Espacio, *(1-930879)* 53 Jackson St., Fair Haven, NJ 07704-3224 USA
E-mail: ednuevoespacio@aol.com; AcademicPressENE@aol.com
Web site: http://www.editorial-ene.com
Dist(s): **Baker & Taylor Bks.**
Book Wholesalers, Inc.
Brodart Co.
Ingram Bk. Co.

Ediciones Oniro S.A. (ESP) *(84-89920; 84-922523; 84-9754; 84-95456) Dist. by* **Bilingual Pubns.**

Ediciones Oniro S.A. (ESP) *(84-89920; 84-922523; 84-9754; 84-95456) Dist. by* **Lectorum Pubns.**

Ediciones Oniro S.A. (ESP) *(84-89920; 84-922523; 84-9754; 84-95456) Dist. by* **Latin Am Bk Source.**

Ediciones PayaLila, *(0-9726446)* P.O. Box 864, Gurabo, PR 00778 USA.

Ediciones Santillana, Inc., *(1-57581; 1-60484)* Div. of Santillana-S. A. (SP), P.O. Box 195462, San Juan, PR 00919-5462 USA Tel 809-781-9800; Fax: 809-782-6149; Toll Free: 800-981-9822
E-mail: molivera@santillanapr.net
Web site: http://www.gruposantillana.com
Dist(s): **Santillana USA Publishing Co., Inc.**

Ediciones Situm, Inc., *(1-59608)* 201 Calle Federico Costa Ste 22, San Juan, PR 00918-1305 USA Tel 787-753-1231; Fax: 787-753-1222
E-mail: valentin@biblioservices.com; anthony@biblioservices.com
Web site: http://www.biblioservices.com.

Ediciones Universal, *(0-89729; 1-59388)* Orders Addr.: P.O. Box 450353, Miami, FL 33245-0353 USA (SAN 658-0548); Edit Addr.: 3090 SW Eighth St., Miami, FL 33135 USA (SAN 207-2203) Tel 305-642-3355; Fax: 305-642-7978
E-mail: marta@ediciones.com; ediciones@ediciones.com
Web site: http://www.ediciones.com
Dist(s): **Lectorum Pubns., Inc.**

Ediciones Urano S. A. (ESP) *(84-7953; 84-95618; 84-95752; 84-86344; 84-95787; 84-96711) Dist. by* **Bilingual Pubns.**

Ediciones y Distribuciones Codice, S.A. (ESP) *(84-357) Dist. by* **Continental Bk.**

Edifytainment Bks., *(0-9753427)* P.O. Box 1566, Inglewood, CA 90308 USA Tel 310-677-9744
E-mail: edifytainmentbooks@prodigy.net
Web site: http://www.bobettejamison-harrison.com/EDIFYTAINMENTBOOKS.html.

E-Digital Bks., LLC, *(0-9672704; 0-9709364; 1-931792)* PMB 364, 1155 S. Havana St., No.11, Aurora, CO 80012 USA Tel 303-745-4997 (phone/fax)
E-mail: edigital@edigitalbooks.com
Web site: http://www.edigitalcatholic.com; http://www.edigitalbooks.com; http://www.edigitalbookstore.com.

Edimat Libros, S. A. (ESP) *(84-8403; 84-923200; 84-95002; 84-9764; 84-9794) Dist. by* **IPG Chicago.**

eDimples, Inc., *(0-9787759)* 9249 S. Broadway, 200-161, Highlands Ranch, CO 80129 USA Tel 303-284-1331 (phone/fax)
E-mail: greg@edimples.com
Web site: http://www.edimples.com.

Edinboro Bk. Arts Collective, *(0-9747001)* Orders Addr.: P.O. Box 77, Edinboro, PA 16412 USA; Edit Addr.: 103 Tarbell Ln., Edinboro, PA 16412 USA
E-mail: winterberger@edinboro.edu.

Edinborough Pr., *(1-889020)* P.O. Box 13790, Roseville, MN 55113-2293 USA (SAN 299-2825) Tel 651-415-1034; Toll Free Fax: 800-566-6145; Toll Free: 888-251-6336 (Orders Only)
E-mail: books@edinborough.com
Web site: http://www.edinborough.com
Dist(s): **Independent Pubs. Group.**

Edinburgh Univ. Pr. (GBR) *(0-7486; 0-85224) Dist. by* **Col U Pr.**

EDITER'S Publishing Hse., *(0-9706814; 0-9743743)* 654 Schafer Pl., Escondido, CA 92025 USA Tel 619-339-7030; Fax: 760-294-2685; 654 Schafer Pl., Escondido, CA 92025-3926
E-mail: books@editers.com
Web site: http://www.editers.com.

EDITER'S Publishing Hse. (MEX) *(968-6966; 968-5432) Dist. by* **EDITERS Pub Hse.**

Editex, Editorial S.A. (ESP) *(84-7131) Dist. by* **Lectorum Pubns.**

Edition Axel Menges GmbH (DEU) *(3-930698; 3-932565; 3-936681) Dist. by* **Natl Bk Netwk.**

Editions Alexandre Stanke (CAN) *(2-89558) Dist. by* **Penton Overseas.**

Editions Ango (CAN) *(1-894185) Dist. by* **Penton Overseas.**

Editions de la Paix (CAN) *(2-921255; 2-922565; 2-9800785; 2-89599) Dist. by* **World of Reading.**

Editions du Petit Music (FRA) *(2-84607) Dist. by* **Distribks Inc.**

Editions du Seuil (FRA) *(2-02) Dist. by* **Distribks Inc.**

Editions Fleurus (FRA) *(2-215; 2-250; 2-7289) Dist. by* **Distribks Inc.**

Editions Houde, *(0-9640475)* P.O. Box 82, Glencoe, IL 60022 USA
E-mail: editionshoude@cs.com.

Editions Memoire, *(1-58437)* 18324 NW 68th Ave., NO. P, Hialeah, FL 33015 USA Tel 305-825-1501; Fax: 305-623-3071; Toll Free: 888-576-1994
E-mail: ememoire@hotmail.com.

Editions Milan (FRA) *(2-7459; 2-84113; 2-86726) Dist. by* **Distribks Inc.**

Editores Mexicanos Unidos (MEX) *(968-15) Dist. by* **Ediciones.**

Editorial Betania *See* **Grupo Nelson**

Editorial Brief (ESP) *(84-931888) Dist. by* **IPG Chicago.**

Editorial Busqueda, *(0-9744408; 0-9760652; 0-9798461)* Calle Pinero, No. 113, San Juan, PR 00925-3612 USA.

Editorial Campana, *(0-9725611; 1-934370)* 19 W. 85th St., New York, NY 10024 USA (SAN 854-2791) Tel 212-721-4062 (phone/fax); *Imprints:* Campanita Books (Campanita Bks)
E-mail: gycultura@aol.com
Web site: http://www.editorialcampana.com
Dist(s): **Downtown Bk. Ctr., Inc.**

Editorial Chio *See* **Editorial Preparate**

Editorial Cultural, Inc., *(1-56758; 84-399)* Orders Addr.: P.O. Box 21056, San Juan, PR 00928 USA; Edit Addr.: Calle Robles, No. 51, San Juan, PR 00928 USA Tel 809-765-9767 (phone/fax)
E-mail: angiev@editorialculturalpr.com
Web site: http://www.editorialculturalpr.com.

Editorial Diana, S.A. (MEX) *(968-13) Dist. by* **Continental Bk.**

Editorial Diana, S.A. (MEX) *(968-13) Dist. by* **Lectorum Pubns.**

Editorial Diana, S.A. (MEX) *(968-13) Dist. by* **Giron Bks.**

Editorial El Antillano, Inc., *(0-9755661; 0-9793026)* 104 Jefferson St., Suite 5-B, Santurce, PR 00911 USA Tel 787-982-4060
E-mail: caribdig@mspr.net
Web site: http://www.elantillano.com.

Editorial Homagno, *(0-9727467)* Div. of Homagno Group, Inc., P.O. Box 960227, Miami, FL 33296 USA
Web site: http://www.homagno.com.

Editorial Humanitas, *(0-9650104)* Orders Addr.: 2006 23rd Ave., E., Seattle, WA 98112-2936 USA Tel 206-616-9394
E-mail: oberle@mindspring.com
Web site: http://www.mindspring.com/~oberle/PRbirds.htm
Dist(s): **Representaciones Borinquenas, Inc.**

Editorial John Louis von Neumann, Inc., *(0-9748297; 0-9779982)* Urb. Villa Fontana, 3NS-15 Via Lourdes, Carolina, PR 00983-4650 USA Tel 787-630-6330; Fax: 787-257-4979
E-mail: josejuandiaz@gmail.com
Web site: http://josejuandiaz.com
Dist(s): **Representaciones Borinquenas, Inc.**

Editorial Libros en Red, *(1-59754)* 5018 57th Ave., Apt. B8, Bladensburg, MD 20710 USA
E-mail: administracion@librosenred.com
Web site: http://www.librosenred.com
Dist(s): **Ediciones Universal.**

Editorial Lumen (ESP) *(84-264) Dist. by* **Lectorum Pubns.**

Editorial Lumen (ESP) *(84-264) Dist. by* **Distribks Inc.**

Editorial Miglo, *(0-9671705)* 1560 Grand Concourse, Apt. 504, Bronx, NY 10457 USA
E-mail: jcmalone01@aol.com
Web site: http://www.edimiglo.com.

Editorial Mundo Hispano *Imprint of* **Casa Bautista de Publicaciones**

Editorial Panamericana, *(1-881744; 1-934139)* Orders Addr.: P.O. Box 25189, San Juan, PR 00928-5189 USA Tel 787-753-7988; 787-753-7999; Fax: 787-764-7240; Edit Addr.: 7 Calle Acacia., San Juan, PR 00920-1512 USA.

Editorial Patmos, *(0-9673448; 1-58802)* Div. of Casa Publicadora A/D Brasil, Orders Addr.: P.O. Box 266585, Weston, FL 33326 USA Tel 954-452-9890; Fax: 954-452-4610; Toll Free: 877-452-9915; Edit Addr.: 450 SW. 130th Ave., Davie, FL 33325 USA
E-mail: patmos@editpatmos.com
Web site: http://www.editpatmos.com.

Editorial Pax (MEX) *(968-860; 968-461) Dist. by* **IPG Chicago.**

Editorial Plaza Mayor, Inc., *(1-56328)* Avenida Ponce De Leon 1527, Barrio El Cinco, Rio Piedras, PR 00926 USA Tel 787-764-0455; Fax: 787-764-0465
E-mail: patrigut@prtc.net
Dist(s): **Continental Bk. Co., Inc.**
Ediciones Universal
Lectorum Pubns., Inc.
Libros Sin Fronteras.

Editorial Porrua (MEX) *(968-432; 968-452; 970-07) Dist. by* **Continental Bk.**

Editorial Portavoz *Imprint of* **Kregel Pubns.**

Editorial Preparate, *(0-9719247)* 1201 Dons Dr., Mission, TX 78572 USA Tel 956-458-5554
E-mail: eneroenpoesia2@yahoo.com.

Editorial Resources, Inc., *(0-9745923)* 1031 Beckton Ln., Pearland, TX 77584-7741 USA
E-mail: anng@editorial-resources.com
Web site: http://www.editorial-resources.com.

Editorial Sendas Antiguas, LLC, *(1-932789)* 1730 Leffingwell Ave., Grand Rapids, MI 49525-4532 USA Tel 616-365-9073 (phone/fax); 616-365-0699; Fax: 616-365-1990
E-mail: info@sendasantiguas.com; sales@sendasantiguas.com; greendykbill@aol.com
Web site: http://www.sendasantiguas.com.

Editorial Sudamericana S.A. (ARG) *(950-07; 950-37) Dist. by* **Lectorum Pubns.**

Editorial Sudamericana S.A. (ARG) *(950-07; 950-37) Dist. by* **Random.**

Editorial Sudamericana S.A. (ARG) *(950-07; 950-37) Dist. by* **Distribks Inc.**

Editorial Sudamericana S.A. (ARG) *(950-07; 950-37) Dist. by* **Libros Fronteras.**

Editorial Unilit, *(0-7899; 0-945792; 1-56063)* Div. of Spanish Hse., Inc., 1360 NW 88th Ave., Miami, FL 33172-3093 USA (SAN 247-5979) Tel 305-592-6136; Fax: 305-592-0087; Toll Free: 800-767-7726
E-mail: sales1@unidial.com
Web site: http://www.editorialunilit.com/
Dist(s): **Bethany Hse. Pubs.**
Harrison Hse., Inc.
Lectorum Pubns., Inc.

Ed. Vida Abundante, *(0-9765828)* P.O. Box 1073, Fajardo, PR 00738 USA Tel 787-860-3555
E-mail: rema@coqui.net
Web site: http://www.vidaabundante.org.

Editorial Voluntad S.A. (COL) *(958-02) Dist. by* **Continental Bk.**

Editorial Voluntad S.A. (COL) *(958-02) Dist. by* **Distr Norma.**

Edivision Compania Editorial, S.A. de C.V. (MEX) *(968-890) Dist. by* **Continental Bk.**

EDR, *(0-9794615)* P.O. Box 22, Waterport, NY 14571 USA
E-mail: sakina@edrsinc.com
Web site: http://www.edrsinc.com; http://www.omariworld.com.

Company

Edsemco, Inc., *(0-9725238)* 3148 EdgeHill, Fort Worth, TX 76116 USA Tel 817-763-0029; Fax: 817-989-8189
E-mail: edsemco@msn.com.

Edu Designs, *(0-9795017)* P.O. Box 660518, Arcadia, CA 91066-0518 USA Tel 626-979-8417
E-mail: silverplume07@earthlink.net.

Educa Vision, *(1-881839; 1-58432)* 7550 NW 47th Ave., Coconut Creek, FL 33073 USA Tel 954-725-0701; Fax: 954-427-6739; Toll Free: 800-983-3822
E-mail: educa@aol.com
Web site: http://www.educavision.com.

Edu-Care *See* **Heron Publishing**

Educate US *Imprint of* **Fowler Publishing**

Education and More, Inc., *(0-9755809)* 1760 Clayton Cir., Cumming, GA 30040-7860 USA Tel 678-455-7667
E-mail: education@educationandmore.com
Web site: http://www.educationandmore.com.

Education Ctr., Inc., *(1-56234)* Orders Addr.: P.O. Box 9753, Greensboro, NC 27429 USA Tel 336-854-0309; Fax: 336-547-1590; Toll Free: 800-334-0298; Edit Addr.: 3515 W. Market St., Greensboro, NC 27403 USA (SAN 256-6311) Fax: 336-851-8218; 1411 Mill St., Greensboro, NC 27408 USA (SAN 256-632X) Tel 336-854-0309; Fax: 336-547-1587 ; *Imprints:* Mailbox Books, The (The Mailbox Bks)
E-mail: jmartin@theeducationcenter.com
Web site: http://theeducationcenter.com; http://www.themailbox.com
Dist(s): **Sharpe, M.E. Inc.**

Education Development Ctr., Inc., *(0-89292)* Orders Addr.: P.O. Box 1020, Sewickley, PA 15143-1020 USA Tel 412-741-1968 (orders); Fax: 412-741-0609 (orders); Toll Free: 800-793-5076 (orders); 800-225-3088 (inquiries); Edit Addr.: 55 Chapel St., Newton, MA 02458-1060 USA (SAN 207-821X) Fax: 617-969-5979; Toll Free: 800-225-4276
E-mail: dparker@edc.org
Web site: http://www.edc.org; http://www.edc.org/WomensEquity/
Dist(s): **Juvenile Justice Clearinghouse/NCJRS**
K E T Enterprise.

Education Express *Imprint of* **Nataco Publishing**

Educational Activities, Inc., *(0-7925; 0-89525; 0-914296; 1-55737)* Orders Addr.: P.O. Box 87, Baldwin, NY 11510 USA; Edit Addr.: 1937 Grand Ave., Baldwin, NY 11510 USA (SAN 207-4400) Tel 516-223-4666; Fax: 516-623-9282; Toll Free: 800-645-3739
E-mail: learn@edact.com
Web site: http://www.edact.com.

Educational Adventures, *(0-9765953; 0-9770455)* 3426 Toringdon Way Ste. 106, Charlotte, NC 28277-3497 USA Toll Free Fax: 877-723-3388 Do not confuse with companies with the same name in Dobbs Ferry, NY, Medofrd, OR, Lanett, AL
Web site: http://www.dangerrangers.com.

Educational Development Corporation *See* **EDC Publishing**

Educational Developmental Laboratories, Inc., *(1-55855; 1-56260; 1-928930)* Orders Addr.: P.O. Box 210726, Columbia, SC 29221 USA (SAN 247-3763) Tel 803-781-4416; Fax: 803-781-3627; Edit Addr.: 411 Western Ln., Irmo, SC 29063 USA
E-mail: east@conterra.com.

Educational Expertise, LLC, *(0-9713450)* 427 E. Belvedere Ave., Baltimore, MD 21212 USA
Web site: http://www.educationalexpertise.com.

Educational Impressions, *(0-910857; 1-56644)* Orders Addr.: P.O. Box 77, Hawthorne, NJ 07507 USA (SAN 274-4899) Tel 973-423-4666; Fax: 973-423-5569; Toll Free: 800-451-7450; Edit Addr.: 210 Sixth Ave., Hawthorne, NJ 07507 USA
E-mail: awpeller@word.net.att.net
Web site: http://www.awpeller.com
Dist(s): **Continental Bk. Co., Inc.**

Educational Innovations, Inc., *(0-9712857)* 4000 Gypsy Ln., Unit 242, Philadelphia, PA 19144-5513 USA Do not confuse with companies with the same name in Cos Cob, CT, Ormond Beach, FL, Laguna Niguel, CA
E-mail: magicsounds@msn.com.

Educational Insights, Inc., *(0-88679; 1-56767)* 18730 S. Wilmington Ave., Rancho Dominguez, CA 90220 USA (SAN 283-8745) Toll Free: 800-933-3277.

Educational Materials, Distributors, *(0-9777756)* Orders Addr.: 1424 - 4th Ave., Suite 4a, Seattle, WA 98101 USA Tel 206-371-7736; Fax: 206-624-8631
E-mail: bothbla@msn.com; bothbla@bothbla.com
Web site: http://www.bothbla.com.

Educational Media Corp., *(0-932796; 1-930572)* Orders Addr.: P.O. Box 21311, Minneapolis, MN 55421 USA (SAN 665-6919); Edit Addr.: 4256 Central Ave. NE, Minneapolis, MN 55421-2920 USA (SAN 212-4203) Tel 763-781-0088; Fax: 763-781-7753; Toll Free: 800-966-3382
E-mail: emedia@educationalmedia.com
Web site: http://www.educationalmedia.com
Dist(s): **Baker & Taylor Bks.**

Educational Media Enterprises, Inc., *(0-9656279)* Orders Addr.: 51 Whitesville Rd., Jackson, NJ 08527 USA Tel 732-905-1835; Fax: 732-367-6543
E-mail: thedooples@aol.com
Web site: http://www.dooples.com.

Educational Ministries, Inc., *(0-940754; 1-57438; 1-877871)* 165 Plaza Dr., Prescott, AZ 86303 USA (SAN 219-7316) Tel 520-771-8601; Fax: 520-771-8621; Toll Free: 800-221-0910
E-mail: edmin2@aol.com
Web site: http://www.educationalministries.com/index.html.

Educational Research & Applications, LLC, *(0-9762724)* P.O. Box 1242, Danville, CA 94526 USA.

Educational Solutions, Inc., *(0-87825)* 99 University Pl., 6th Flr., New York, NY 10003-4555 USA (SAN 205-6186) Tel 212-674-2988 Do not confuse with Educational Solutions, Stafford, TX.

Educational Testing Service, *(0-88685)* P.O. Box 6108, Princeton, NJ 08541-6108 USA (SAN 238-034X) Tel 609-771-7243; Fax: 609-771-7385 Do not confuse with Educational Testing Service in Washington, DC
E-mail: lsavadge@ets.org; cbrodsky@ets.org; j.womack@ets.org
Web site: http://www.ets.org
Dist(s): **Independent Pubs. Group.**

Educational Tools, Inc., *(0-9766802; 0-9774310; 1-933797)* 3500 Beachwood Ct., Suite 102, Jacksonville, FL 32224 USA Fax: 904-998-1941; Toll Free: 800-586-9940
E-mail: jashenfelder@educationaltools.org
Web site: http://www.educationaltools.org.

Educators for Social Responsibility, *(0-942349)* 23 Garden St., Cambridge, MA 02138 USA (SAN 667-0903) Tel 617-492-1764; Fax: 617-864-5164; Toll Free: 800-370-2515 Do not confuse with Educators for Social Responsiblity Metropolitan Area, NY. NY
E-mail: educators@esrnational.org
Web site: http://www.esrnational.org
Dist(s): **Gryphon Hse., Inc.**

Educators for the Environment *See* **Energy Education Group**

Educators Publishing Service, Inc., *(0-8388; 1-4293)* P.O. Box 9031, Cambridge, MA 02139-9031 USA (SAN 201-8225) Toll Free: 800-435-7728; 625 Mount Auburn St., Cambridge, MA 02138
E-mail: epsbooks@epsbooks.com
Web site: http://www.epsbooks.com.

Educ-Easy Bks., *(0-9664217)* P.O. Box 7054, Wilmington, NC 28406 USA Tel 910-798-5042
E-mail: educeay@bellsouth.net
Web site: http://www.educeasybooks.com
Dist(s): **Baker & Taylor Bks.**

EDUKIT, L.L.C., *(0-9765917)* P.O. Box 821, Suffern, NY 10901 USA
E-mail: edukitco@aol.com
Web site: http://www.edukit.biz.

Edupress, Inc., *(1-56472)* P.O. Box 800, Fort Atkinson, WI 53538-0800 USA Toll Free: 800-835-7978 Do not confuse with EduPress, Pittsburgh, PA
E-mail: info@edupressinc.com
Web site: http://www.edupressinc.com.

Edutech Learning Resource Ctr., *(0-9768208)* 1361 NE 158 St., North Miami Beach, FL 33162 USA Tel 305-947-6393
E-mail: edutech_learning@yahoo.com.

Ed-Venture Films/Bks., *(0-935873)* Orders Addr.: P.O. Box 23214, Los Angeles, CA 90023-0214 USA (SAN 696-530X); Edit Addr.: 1122 Calada St., Los Angeles, CA 90023 USA (SAN 696-3498) Tel 323-261-1885; Fax: 818-705-4241
E-mail: edventr@aol.com
Dist(s): **SCB Distributors.**

Edwards, J.W. Inc., *(0-910546; 1-886569; 1-930842)* 2500 S. State St., Ann Arbor, MI 48104 USA (SAN 223-0348) Tel 313-769-1000
Dist(s): **National Bk. Network.**

Edwards, Lorryann, *(0-9705459)* 94913 Kentuck Way Ln., Northbend, OR 97459 USA Tel 541-256-6180
E-mail: samoalll@earthlink.net.

Edwards, Michael, *(0-9720952)* 310 N. Front St., Suite No. 4, Box 248, Wilmington, NC 28401 USA
E-mail: neversanever@hotmail.com.

EE Publishing & Productions, Inc. *See* **ee publishing & productions, inc.**

ee publishing & productions, inc., *(0-9753843; 0-9798466)* P.O. Box 7006, Fairfax Station, VA 22039 USA Tel 703-256-1721 (phone/fax)
E-mail: info@eeppinc.com; lsaker@eepinc.com
Web site: http://www.eeppinc.com
Dist(s): **AtlasBooks Distribution.**

eeBoo Corp., *(1-59461)* P.O. Box 404, New York, NY 10025 USA Fax: 212-678-1922
E-mail: devo@eeboo.com
Web site: http://www.eeboo.com.

Eelman's Pr., *(0-9747053)* Orders Addr.: P.O. Box Box 359, South Orleans, MA 02662 USA Tel 607-277-0612; Edit Addr.: Davis Rd., South Orleans, MA 02662 USA.

Eepie Pr., *(0-9755606)* 1412 Greenbrier Pkwy., Suite 145-B, Norfolk, VA 23320 USA Tel 757-424-5868; Fax: 757-424-5845
E-mail: info@eepiepress.com
Web site: http://www.eepiepress.com
Dist(s): **Print and Ship.**

eeps media *Imprint of* **Epistemological Engineering**

Eerdmans Bks For Young Readers *Imprint of* **Eerdmans, William B. Publishing Co.**

†Eerdmans, William B. Publishing Co., *(0-8028)* 2140 Oak Industrial Dr. NE, Grand Rapids, MI 49505 USA (SAN 220-0058) Tel 616-459-4591; Fax: 616-459-6540; Toll Free: 800-253-7521 (orders) ; *Imprints:* Eerdmans Books For Young Readers (Eerdmans Bks)
E-mail: info@eerdmans.com; customerservice@eerdmans.com; npedersen@eerdmans.com
Web site: http://www.eerdmans.com
Dist(s): **CRC Pubns.**
Forward Movement Pubns.
Lightning Source, Inc.; *CIP.*

EFFE Bks., *(0-9773583)* P.O. Box 3448, Winter Park, FL 32790-23448 USA (SAN 257-3784) Tel 407-645-2326
E-mail: tfunaro@summittech.us
Web site: http://www.effebooks.com
Dist(s): **Midpoint Trade Bks., Inc.**

Effective Education Publishing, *(1-58460)* 7060 Hollywood Blvd., Suite 200, Los Angeles, CA 90028 USA Tel 323-962-2907; Fax: 323-962-9558; Toll Free: 800-424-5397
Dist(s): **Bridge Pubns., Inc.**

Effective Literacy Methods, *(0-9706094)* 57 Knollwood Dr., Rochester, NY 14618-3512 USA
E-mail: info@newphonics.com; rkb@newphonics.com
Web site: http://www.newphonics.com.

Effective Living Publishing, *(0-9643699; 0-9729173)* Orders Addr.: P.O. Box 232233, Sacramento, CA 95823 USA Tel 916-422-8435; Edit Addr.: 8343 Valley Lark Dr., Sacramento, CA 95823 USA
E-mail: elpbooks@aol.com
Web site: http://booksamerica.com/ELPBooks/
Dist(s): **Baker & Taylor Bks.**

Efforts Unified, *(0-9763523)* 244 Fifth Ave., No. N259, New York, NY 10001 USA.

Egap Gifa Bks. *Imprint of* **Leafcollecting.com Publishing Co.**

Egg Hill Pubns., *(0-9652351)* Orders Addr.: 113 Cottontail Ln., Centre Hall, PA 16828-8508 USA
E-mail: jandhfra2@yahoo.com
Dist(s): **Partners Bk. Distributing, Inc.**

Egger Publishing, Inc., *(1-886050; 1-934262)* P.O. Box 12248, Scottsdale, AZ 85267 USA Tel 480-596-5100; Fax: 480-951-2276; Toll Free: 888-937-7355
E-mail: regger@sittonspelling.com
Web site: http://www.sittonspelling.com
Dist(s): **Northwest Textbook Depository.**

EggShell Pr., *(0-9670647)* Div. of The Spence Foundation, P.O. Box 5, Cedar Grove, NJ 07009 USA Fax: 973-509-4543
E-mail: feminazi@home.com.

Egmont Bks., Ltd. (GBR) *(0-416; 0-603; 0-7497; 0-7498; 1-4052) Dist. by* **Trafalgar.**

Egmont Bks., Ltd. (GBR) *(0-416; 0-603; 0-7497; 0-7498; 1-4052) Dist. by* **IPG Chicago.**

Egner, Inc., *(0-9711711)* 88 Walden, Burnsville, MN 55337 USA Tel 612-991-8259; Fax: 952-894-3005
E-mail: su@woodfin.cc; marie@woodfin.cc
Web site: http://www.woodfin.cc
Dist(s): **Bookmen, Inc.**

Eiffel Pr, *(0-9679335)* P.O. Box 339, Osprey, FL 34229-0339 USA
E-mail: eiffelpress@home.com
Web site: http://www.gvieve.com.

Eight Dog Publishing, *(0-9721327)* Orders Addr.: 87 Hillcrest Rd., Warren, NJ 07059-5304 USA
E-mail: andreac@eightdogpublishing.com; info@eightdogpublishing.com
Web site: http://www.eightdogpublishing.com.

1873 Pr., *(0-594)* Div. of Barnes & Noble.com, 76 Ninth Ave., 9th Flr., New York, NY 10011 USA (SAN 253-0635) Tel 212-414-6000; Fax: 212-414-6320.

Eileen/Morris *See* **Shnoozles, LLC**

Eisch, Beverly, *(0-9724517)* W13211 Cty. C, Athelstane, WI 54104 USA Toll Free: 888-378-2512
E-mail: bgrandmasbooks@hotmail.com.

†Eisenbrauns, Inc., *(0-931464; 1-57506)* Orders Addr.: P.O. Box 275, Winona Lake, IN 46590-0275 USA (SAN 200-7835) Tel 574-269-2011; Fax: 574-269-6788; Edit Addr.: 600 N. Bay Dr., Warsaw, IN 46580 USA
E-mail: ghannah@eisenbrauns.com; Orders@eisenbrauns.com
Web site: http://www.eisenbrauns.com; *CIP.*

Eitel, Charles R., *(0-9700219)* 82 Blackland Rd NW, Atlanta, GA 30342-4421 USA
E-mail: ltimms@simmons.com.

EK Success Ltd., *(1-930232)* P.O. Box 1141, Clifton, NJ 07014-1141 USA Tel 973-458-0092; Fax: 973-594-0545; Toll Free: 800-524-1349
E-mail: success@eksuccess.com
Web site: http://www.eksuccess.com.

EKADOO Publishing Group, *(0-9747387)* Orders Addr.: P.O. Box 2286, North Redondo Beach, CA 90278 USA Toll Free: 877-252-3404; Edit Addr.: 123 West First St., Suite 675, Casper, WY 82601 USA
E-mail: info@ekadoo.com
Web site: http://www.ekadoo.com.

Ekare, Ediciones (VEN) *(980-257; 84-8351) Dist. by* **Baker & Taylor.**

Ekare, Ediciones (VEN) *(980-257; 84-8351) Dist. by* **Mariuccia Iaconi Bk Imports.**

Ekare, Ediciones (VEN) *(980-257; 84-8351) Dist. by* **Lectorum Pubns.**

Ekay Music, Inc., *(0-943748; 1-929009)* 333 Adams St., Bedford Hills, NY 10507 USA (SAN 241-0680) Tel 914-244-8500; Fax: 914-244-8560; Toll Free: 800-527-6300
E-mail: PianoToday@aol.com.

Eklektika Pr., *(0-9651672; 0-9765465)* Orders Addr.: P.O. Box 157, Chelsea, MI 48118 USA Tel 734-730-5161; Fax: 734-475-0125; Edit Addr.: 6401 Conway Rd., Chelsea, MI 48118 USA
E-mail: rebeccacolmer@sbcglobal.net
Web site: http://www.theseniorsguide.com
Dist(s): **Alliance Bk. Co.**
Distributors, The.

Ekwike Bks. & Publishing, *(0-9661598; 0-9789972)* Orders Addr.: P.O. Box 470, New York, NY 10034 USA Tel 718-798-5788 (phone/fax); Edit Addr.: 4417 Edson Ave., Bronx, NY 10466 USA Tel 917-306-7244 (cell)
E-mail: ikebezi@juno.com.

Ekwike Publications *See* **Ekwike Bks. & Publishing**

El Aleph Editores, S.A. (ESP) *(84-7669; 84-85501) Dist. by* **Ediciones.**

El Assali, Amira, *(0-9777650)* 23842 Alicia Pkwy Apt. 248, Mission Viejo, CA 92691 USA Tel 714-478-2114
E-mail: amiraalassaly@hotmail.com.

El Hogar y La Moda, S.A. (ESP) *(84-7183) Dist. by* **AIMS Intl.**

El Jefe, *(0-9742840)* P.O. Box 7871, Pueblo West, CO 81007 USA
E-mail: rearch145@aol.com.

El Zarape Pr., *(0-9789954)* 3815 N. Val Verde Rd., Donna, TX 78537-5276 USA (SAN 852-1514)
E-mail: wegotwords@hotmail.com
Web site: http://www.elzarapepress.com.

Elan Pr., *(0-9658891; 0-9706710)* 10721 W. Mission Ln., Sun City, AZ 85351 USA Tel 623-977-4515; Fax: 623-977-4493; Toll Free: 800-647-4175 Do not confuse Elan Press with Sunbury, PA Boulder, CO Kaneohe, HI and Toronto, ON.
E-mail: elanpress@aol.com
Web site: http://www.elanpress.com.

Elan Systems, Incorporated *See* **Aunt Dee's Attic, Inc.**

Elbo Elf, Inc., *(0-9704125)* 3652 N. Amblewood Cliff, Lima, OH 45806 USA Fax: 419-991-2886
E-mail: customerservice@elboelf.com.

Elder Pr., Inc., *(0-9677081)* P.O. Box 3435, Sedona, AZ 86340 USA (SAN 253-5521) Tel 928-204-1381
E-mail: info@caringspirit.com
Web site: http://www.caringspirit.com.

Elderberry Press, Inc., *(0-9658407; 1-930859; 1-932762)* Orders Addr.: 1393 Old Homestead Dr. Second Flr., Oakland, OR 97462 USA (SAN 254-6604) Tel 541-459-6043 PHONE; Fax: 270-458-6043 FAX Do not confuse with Elderberry Pr., Encinitas, CA
E-mail: editor@elderberrypress.com
Web site: http://elderberrypress.com.

Eldergivers, *(0-9742262)* 1755 Clay St., San Francisco, CA 94109 USA
E-mail: info@eldergivers.org
Web site: http://www.eldergivers.org.

Eldorado Ink, *(1-932904)* P.O. Box 100097, Pittsburgh, PA 15233-4842 USA Tel 412-688-0444; Fax: 412-688-8545; Toll Free: 800-783-6767
E-mail: info@eldoradoink.com
Web site: http://www.eldoradoink.com.

Electa (ITA) *(88-435; 88-370) Dist. by* **HachBkGrp.**

Electret Scientific Co., *(0-917406)* P.O. Box 4132, Star City, WV 26504 USA (SAN 206-4715) Tel 304-594-1639 (phone/fax)
E-mail: U1a00439@wvnet.edu.

Electric Paper (GBR) *(1-897584) Dist. by* **CPG Pub Inc.**

Electric Power Consultants, *(0-9717506)* 2933 Hamburg St. Ste. 3, Schenectady, NY 12303-4342 USA
E-mail: conrad@capital.net
Web site: http://epc-website.com.

Electrical Generating Systems Assn., *(0-9625949)* 1650 S. Dixie Hwy, Boca Raton, FL 33432-7462 USA (SAN 690-1441) Tel 561-750-5575; Fax: 561-395-8557
Web site: http://www.egsa.org.

Electronic Art & Publishing, *(0-9740110)* Orders Addr.: P.O. Box 1292, Duxbury, MA 02331 USA Tel 781-934-6909; Edit Addr.: 32 Abrams Hill Rd., Duxbury, MA 02331 USA
E-mail: vickers@gis.net
Web site: http://www.gis.net.

Electronic Bks. for Kids, *(1-889081)* 6387B Camp Bowie, No. 328, Fort Worth, TX 76116 USA Tel 817-737-7619 (phone/fax)
E-mail: gpr044@airmail.net
Web site: http://www.e-b-k.com
Dist(s): **Educational Software Institute.**

Electronic Bookshelf, Incorporated *See* **Scholastic Reading Counts**

Electronic Publishing Services, *(0-9711320)* Div. of eMedix, Inc., P.O. Box 10076, Hattiesburg, MS 39406 USA Fax: 601-266-5635
E-mail: kariesorrells@emedix.org.

Element Children's Bks., *(1-901881; 1-902618; 1-84207)* 160 N. Washington St., 4th Flr., Boston, MA 02114 USA Tel 617-598-6500; Fax: 617-248-0909
E-mail: publishers@elementboston.com
Dist(s): **National Bk. Network.**

Elemental Pubs., *(0-9765403)* 4404 Whistling Way, Raleigh, NC 27616 USA Tel 919-217-2092.

ElephantSide Pr., *(0-9716873)* 33 Bedford St., Suite 10, Lexington, MA 02420 USA (SAN 255-4062).

Elert Pubns., *(1-892217)* P.O. Box 7121, Grayslake, IL 60030 USA Tel 847-223-2284; Fax: 847-223-1184; Toll Free: 800-484-8030
E-mail: bigelert@aol.com
Web site: http://www.elert-publications.com.

Eleuthera Press *See* **Windsong Publishing Co.**

Elgar, Edward Publishing, Inc., *(1-84064; 1-85278; 1-85898; 1-84376; 1-84542)* Orders Addr.: c/o Custom Services, P.O. Box 574, Williston, VT 05495 USA Tel 800-390-3149; Fax: 802-864-7626; Toll Free: 800-426-4742; Edit Addr.: 9 Dewey Ct., Northampton, MA 01060-3815 USA (SAN 299-4615)
E-mail: eep.orders@aidcvt.com; rhenning@e-elgar.com; elgarinfo@e-elgar.com; tgorvine@e-elgar.com
Web site: http://www.e-elgar.com
Dist(s): **American International Distribution Corp.**
NetLibrary, Inc.

Elias Pubns., LLC, *(0-9726247)* P.O. Box 49704, Sarasota, FL 34230 USA Tel 941-556-5656; Fax: 720-920-7262
E-mail: eliaspublications@hotmail.com
Web site: http://www.eliaspublications.com.

eLiberty Pr., *(0-9755608)* 2250 N. University Pkwy. No. 4888, Provo, UT 84604 USA Tel 801-427-6630; Fax: 801-373-5999
E-mail: info@elibertypress.com; sales@elibertypress.com
Web site: http://www.elibertypress.com
Dist(s): **Alibris**
Baker & Taylor Bks.
Ingram Bk. Co.
Powells.com.

Elibron Classics *Imprint of* **Adamant Media**

Elijah Co., *(1-884098)* P.O. Box 2812, Crossville, TN 38557-2812 USA Toll Free: 888-235-4524
E-mail: elijahco@elijahco.com
Web site: http://www.elijahcompany.com.

Elim Publishing, *(0-9713711; 1-59919)* Div. of Elim Gospel Church, 1679 Dalton Rd., Lima, NY 14485 USA Tel 716-624-5560; Fax: 716-624-9677
E-mail: randy@elimpublishing.com
Web site: http://www.elimpublishing.com
Dist(s): **Lightning Source, Inc.**

Elin Grace Publishing, *(0-9729848)* N2143 Pine Beach Rd., N., Oostburg, WI 53070-1638 USA
E-mail: elingrace@wi.rr.com.

Elizabooks, *(0-9762839)* 5515 Catfish Ct., Waunakee, WI 53597 USA Tel 608-849-1984; Fax: 608-849-1985; Toll Free: 888-603-1984
E-mail: liz@kramerprinting.com
Web site: http://www.elizabooks.com.

Elk River Pr., *(0-9710389)* 1125 Central Ave., Charleston, WV 25302 USA Tel 304-342-1848; Fax: 304-343-0594 Do not confuse with companies with the same or similar name in Altamont, KS, Athens, AL.
E-mail: wvbooks@verizon.net
Web site: http://www.wvbookco.com
Dist(s): **West Virginia Book Co., The.**

Eller Books *See* **Brethren Pr.**

Ellingsworth Press, Limited, The *See* **Ellingsworth Pr., LLC**

Ellingsworth Pr., LLC, *(0-9605698)* 680 Main St., Suite 1, Watertown, CT 06795 USA (SAN 211-1519) Tel 860-274-7151; Fax: 860-274-9755; Toll Free: 877-355-7737
E-mail: ellpress@aol.com
Web site: http://www.ellpress.com; http://www.braininjurydragon.com.

Elliot's Bks., *(0-911830)* P.O. Box 6, Northford, CT 06472 USA (SAN 204-1529) Tel 203-484-2184; Fax: 203-484-7644
E-mail: outofprintbooks@mindspring.com.

Elliott, Jane, *(0-9741254)* 707 Country Club Rd., Schofield, WI 54476 USA ; *Imprints:* Dynagraphix (Dynagraphix).

Ellis Pr., The, *(0-933180; 0-944024)* Div. of Spoon River Poetry Pr., P.O. Box 6, Granite Falls, MN 56241 USA (SAN 214-008X) Tel 507-537-6463 Do not confuse with Ellis Pr., in Charlottesville, VA.
E-mail: pichaske@southwest.msus.edu
Web site: http://www.southwest.msus.edu/faculty/pichaske/plains.htm.

Ellison, Penny, *(0-9771121)* Orders Addr.: P.O. Box 510082, Miami, FL 33151 USA Tel 786-222-1443; Edit Addr.: 5574 Lavender Farms Rd., Powder Spgs, GA 30127-8350 USA.

Ellora's Cave, Incorporated *See* **Ellora's Cave Publishing, Inc.**

Ellora's Cave Publishing, Inc., *(0-9707169; 0-9712177; 1-84360; 0-9724377; 1-4199)* P.O. Box 37, Akron, OH 44309 USA (SAN 257-5612)
E-mail: orders@ellorascave.com; patty@ellorascave.com
Web site: http://www.ellorascave.com.

Elma Colletes & Sons, *(0-9719337)* 5895 Gardens Reach Cove, Memphis, TN 38120-2523 USA Fax: 901-747-0040
E-mail: mschnap1@midsouth.rr.com.

Elohim Bks., *(0-9768831)* Orders Addr.: P.O. Box 1027, Howell, MI 48844 USA.

Elora Pr., *(0-9786813)* Div. of Elora Media, LLC, PMB 112, 1201 Yelm Ave., Yelm, WA 98597-9859 USA (SAN 851-3228) Toll Free: 888-440-8972
E-mail: betsy@eloramedia.com
Web site: http://www.eloramedia.com.

Elsevier - Health Sciences Division, *(0-323; 0-443; 0-444; 0-7020; 0-7216; 0-7234; 0-7236; 0-7506; 0-8016; 0-8151; 0-920513; 0-932883; 1-55664; 1-56053; 84-8086; 84-8174; 1-898507; 1-932141; 1-4160)* Subs. of Elsevier Science, Orders Addr.: 11830 Westline Industrial Dr., Saint Louis, MO 63146 USA Tel 314-453-7010; Fax: 314-453-7095; Toll Free Fax: 800-535-9935; Toll Free: 800-545-2522; 800-460-3110 (Customers Outside US); Edit Addr.: The Curtis Center, Suite 300E, 3rd Flr. 170 S. Independence Mall W., Philadelphia, PA 19106 USA Tel 215-238-7800; Fax: 215-238-7362; Toll Free: 800-523-4069; 800-523-1649 ; *Imprints:* Mosby (MosElsHlth); Saunders (SaunElsHlth)
E-mail: usbkinfo@elsevier.com
Web site: http://www.elsevier.com; http://www.us.elsevierhealth.com/
Dist(s): **Elsevier.**

Elsevier Science *Imprint of* **Elsevier Science & Technology Bks.**

Elsevier Science - Health Sciences Division *See* **Elsevier - Health Sciences Division**

Elsevier Science & Technology Bks., Orders Addr.: 11830 Westline Industrial Dr., Saint Louis, MO 63146 USA Tel 314-453-7010; Fax: 314-453-7095; Toll Free Fax: 800-535-9935; Toll Free: 800-545-2522; 800-460-3110 (Customers Outside US); Edit Addr.: 525 B St., Suite 1900, San Diego, CA 92101 USA Toll Free: 1-800-894-3434; 200 Wheeler Rd., 6th Flr., Burlington, MA 01803 Tel 781-313-4700 ; *Imprints:* Academic Press (Acad Press); Butterworth-Heinemann (Butter Sci Hein); Elsevier Science (ElseSci); Focal Press (FocalSci); Newnes (NewSci)
E-mail: bookstore.orders@elsevier.com
Web site: http://www.syngress.com; http://www.elsevier.com/
Dist(s): **Elsevier**
LEXIS Publishing
NetLibrary, Inc.
Oxford Univ. Pr., Inc.

El-Shaddai Productions, *(0-9715945)* Orders Addr.: P.O. Box 4100, Fairview Heights, IL 62208-1815 USA Tel 618-394-1314; Fax: 618-394-1876; Edit Addr.: 49 Potomac Dr., Fairview Heights, IL 62208-1815 USA
E-mail: sherry@elshaddaiprodutcions.com
Web site: http://www.elshaddaiproductions.com.

Elsie & Darcy, Inc., *(0-9657352)* 354 14th St. Apt . 2, Brooklyn, NY 11215 USA.

Elva Resa Publishing, LLC, *(0-9657483; 1-934617)* 8362 Tamarack Village, Suite 119-106, Saint Paul, MN 55125 USA Tel 651-357-8770 orders & general info; Fax: 501-641-0777 orders accepted by fax ; *Imprints:* Alma Little (Alma Little)
E-mail: orders@elvaresa.com
Web site: http://www.elvaresa.com.

ELW Pubns., *(0-9766233)* 1831 Secretary's Rd., Scottsville, VA 24590 USA Tel 434-295-1678 ; *Imprints:* His Grace Is Sufficient (HGIS)
E-mail: bridgeministry@aol.com.

Elysian Editions *Imprint of* **Princeton Bk. Co. Pubs.**

Elysian Hills, *(0-9635589)* Orders Addr.: P.O. Box 40693, Albuquerque, NM 87196 USA Tel 505-897-2734; Fax: 505-897-4614; Edit Addr.: 919 Western Meadows, Albuquerque, NM 87114 USA
E-mail: EdDziczek@aol.com.

Elytra & Antenna, *(0-9719129)* 4663 Ruby Ln., Brunswick Hills, OH 44212 USA Tel 330-273-1918 ; *Imprints:* Allpet Roaches (Allpet Roaches)
E-mail: elytraandantenna@lycos.com
Web site: http://www.elytraandantenna.com.

ELZ Publishing, *(0-9772717)* 33 Sheridan Rd., Wellesley, MA 02481 USA Tel 781-237-7417; Fax: 781-237-7429
E-mail: elzahniser@mindspring.com
Web site: http://elzpublishing.com.

Emaculate Publishing, *(1-931855)* P.O. Box 1074, Woodbridge, VA 22195-1074 USA (SAN 254-2005)
E-mail: emaculatepublishing@yahoo.com; info@emaculatepublishing.com
Web site: http://www.emaculatepublishing.com.

Emaginit, *(1-886972)* 1025 W. 190th St., Suite 200, Gardena, CA 90248 USA Tel 310-630-1360; Fax: 310-630-1365; Toll Free: 877-633-4241
Dist(s): **Landmark Audiobooks**
Penton Overseas, Inc.

Embassy Court Productions *See* **Three Rivers Council, BSA, Inc.**

Embrace Communications, *(0-9668878)* 6887 Red Mountain Rd., Livermore, CO 80536 USA Tel 970-416-9076; Fax: 970-407-0083
E-mail: suengayReynolds@aol.com
Dist(s): **Spring Arbor Distributors, Inc.**

†EMC/Paradigm Publishing, *(0-7638; 0-8219; 0-88436; 0-912022; 1-56118)* Div. of EMC Corp., 875 Montreal Way, Saint Paul, MN 55102-4245 USA (SAN 201-3800) Tel 651-290-2800; Fax: 651-290-2828
E-mail: publish@emcp.com; educate@emcp.com
Web site: http://www.emcp.com
Dist(s): **Continental Bk. Co., Inc.**; *CIP.*

Emecé Editores S.A. (ARG) *(950-04; 950-519) Dist. by* **Lectorum Pubns.**

Emecé Editores S.A. (ARG) *(950-04; 950-519) Dist. by* **Libros Fronteras.**

Emecé Editores S.A. (ARG) *(950-04; 950-519) Dist. by* **Planeta.**

Emece Editores (ESP) *(84-95908) Dist. by* **Ediciones.**

Emece Editores (ESP) *(84-95908) Dist. by* **Lectorum Pubns.**

EMedia Corp., *(1-891155)* 664 NE Northlake Way, Seattle, WA 98105-6428 USA Toll Free: 888-363-3424
E-mail: custserv@emediamusic.com
Web site: http://www.emediamusic.com.

Emerald Bks., *(1-883002; 1-932096)* Orders Addr.: P.O. Box 635, Lynnwood, WA 98046 USA (SAN 298-7538) Tel 425-771-1153; Fax: 425-775-2383; Toll Free: 800-922-2143; Edit Addr.: 7825 230th St. SW, Edmonds, WA 98026 USA Do not confuse with Emerald Bks. in Westfield, NJ
E-mail: emeraldbooks@seanet.com
Web site: http://www.ywampublishing.com
Dist(s): **YWAM Publishing.**

Emerald Falcon Press *See* **Wandering Sage Bookstore & More, LLC**

Emerald Hse. Group, Inc., *(1-889893; 1-932307)* 427 Wade Hampton Blvd., Greenville, SC 29609 USA Tel 864-235-2434; Fax: 864-235-2491; Toll Free: 800-209-8570 ; *Imprints:* Ambassador-Emerald, International (Ambassador-Emerald); Ambassador International (Ambassador Intl)
E-mail: info@emeraldhouse.com
Web site: http://www.emeraldhouse.com
Dist(s): **Christian Bk. Distributors**
Spring Arbor Distributors, Inc.

Emerald Pademelon Pr., *(1-929704)* P.O. Box 381, Haddonfield, NJ 08033 USA Tel 856-795-2359
E-mail: sjdodgsn@ix.netcom.com
Web site: http://emeraldpademelon.com.

Emerald Productions, *(0-9666822, 1-929172)* 289 W. Weisheimer Rd., Columbus, OH 43235 USA Tel 614-262-4432; Fax: 614-261-9071 (to call first); Toll Free: 888-892-6338
E-mail: katina@qn.net.

Emergency Medical Planning, Incorporated *See* **MEDIC FIRST AID International, Inc.**

Emerson Pubns., *(0-9666697)* 4604 NE 49th St., Kansas City, MO 64119-3621 USA Tel 816-454-1112 Do not confuse with Emerson Publications in Houston, TX
E-mail: cemerson@kc.rr.com.

Emijo Pubns., *(0-9618303)* 1368 Beacon St., No. 108, Brookline, MA 02446 USA (SAN 667-1888) Tel 617-731-5767; 1368 Beacon Suite 108, Brookline, MA 02446
E-mail: judyosborne@earthlink.net
Web site: http://www.stepfamilyboston.com.

Eminent Pubn. Enterprises, *(0-936955)* P.O. Box 1026, Jeffersonville, IN 47131-1026 USA (SAN 658-6589) Tel 812-288-7298.

EMJ Collaborative *See* **JDW Collaborative**

EMK Pr., *(0-9726244)* Div. of EMK Group, LLC, 16 Mt. Bethel Rd., No. 219, Warren, NJ 07059 USA (SAN 255-0318) Tel 732-469-7544; Fax: 732-469-7861
E-mail: carriekitze@emkpress.com
Web site: http://www.emkpress.com
Dist(s): **Baker & Taylor Bks.**
Quality Bks., Inc.

Emma's Pantry, *(0-9648437)* 0373 Sopris Creek Rd., #7, Basalt, CO 81621 USA Tel 970-927-4661
E-mail: eewalling@yahoo.com
Web site: http://www.pages.prodigy.com/legends/.

Emmaus Pr., *(0-9624901)* Div. of Emmaus Hse. of Prayer, 1405 Newton St., NE, Washington, DC 20017-3010 USA Tel 202-488-3816 Do not confuse with Emmaus Pr. in Edmond, OK
E-mail: rtunison@home.com
Dist(s): **Chi Rho Pr.**

Company

Emmaus Pr., *(0-9707015)* P.O. Box 7703, Edmond, OK 73083-7703 USA (SAN 254-3273) Fax: 405-302-0008 Do not confuse with Emmaus Pr. in Washington, DC
E-mail: rtunison@cox.net
Web site: http://www.emmauspress.com.

Emmaus Road, International, *(1-880185)* 7150 Tanner Ct., San Diego, CA 92111 USA Tel 619-292-7020
E-mail: emmaus_road@eri.com
Web site: http://www.eri.org.

Emmaus Road Publishing, *(0-9663223; 1-931018)* 827 N. Fourth St., Steubenville, OH 43952 USA Tel 740-283-2484; Fax: 740-283-4011; Toll Free: 800-398-5470
E-mail: shughes@cuf.org
Web site: http://www.emmausroad.org.

Emmis Bks., *(0-9617367; 1-57860; 1-878208)* Orders Addr.: 1700 Madison Rd., The Old Firehouse, 2nd. Flr., Cincinnati, OH 45206 USA (SAN 255-478X) Tel 513-861-4045; Fax: 512-861-4430; Toll Free: 800-913-9563 ; *Imprints:* Guild Press of Indiana (GuilPr Indiana)
E-mail: info@emmisbooks.com; info@guildpress.com
Web site: http://www.emmisbooks.com.

Emnes Systems, *(0-9661636)* 7212 Antares Dr., Suite 100, Gaithersburg, MD 20879 USA Tel 240-683-8502
E-mail: ecfchang@msn.com
Web site: http://www.emnes.com.

Emotional Management Education, Inc., *(0-9635127; 1-885697)* P.O. Box 132, Rosemount, MN 55068 USA Toll Free: 800-496-4059 (phone/fax)
E-mail: Wmc@tcq.net.

Emp! Emp! Pr., *(0-9667677)* Div. of The Human Race Works, P.O. Box 90945, Washington, DC 20090-0945 USA.

Empak Publishing Co., *(0-922162; 0-9616156)* Subs. of Empak Enterprises, Inc., P.O. Box 8596, Chicago, IL 60680-8596 USA (SAN 699-9182) Tel 312-642-3434; Fax: 312-642-9657; Toll Free: 800-477-4554
E-mail: empak@email.msn.com
Web site: http://www.empakpub.com.

Empire Pr. Co., *(1-884535)* 550 Empire Blvd., Brooklyn, NY 11225 USA Tel 718-756-1473; Fax: 718-604-7633.

Empire Publishing, *(0-9766246)* 1117 Desert Ln., Suite 1362, Las Vegas, NV 89102 USA Fax: 413-714-5213.

Empire Publishing Group, *(0-9679989)* 3578 Cooper Island Rd., West Sacremento, CA 95691 USA
E-mail: randy@learnpianochords.com
Web site: http://www.desireofheart.com.

Empire Publishing Service, *(1-58690)* P.O. Box 1344, Studio City, CA 91614-0344 USA (SAN 630-5687) Tel 818-784-8918
E-mail: empirepubsvc@att.net.

Empowered Entertainment, *(0-9767076)* 2804 Hazelchase Ct., Indianapolis, IN 46268 USA
E-mail: sales@chameleonchronicles.com
Web site: http://www.chameleonchronicles.com.

Empowered Faith International, *(0-9768416)* P.O. Box 156, Marietta, GA 30060 USA Tel 770-218-6215
Web site: http://www.empoweredfaith.org.

Empowering People Pub., *(0-9762639)* Orders Addr.: P.O. Box 329, Rex, GA 30273 USA Tel 850-328-1698
E-mail: altrell@tinapipkin.com; info@tinapipkin.com; altrellpipkin@yahoo.com
Web site: http://www.tinapipkin.com; http://www.empoweringpeopleinc.com; http://www.altrellpipkin.com.

Empowerment in Action, *(0-9633195)* 24157 Saint Helena Ct., Ramona, CA 92065 USA Tel 760-788-7485; Fax: 760-788-8031
E-mail: jk@karlanthony.com.

Empress3 Publishing, *(0-9716419)* Div. of Empress3 Productions, Ltd., 2304 Glenmount Dr., NW, Canton, OH 44708 USA Fax: 330-477-6155.

Emprise Pubns., *(0-938129)* 910 Calle Angosta, thousand Oaks, CA 91360 USA (SAN 661-2423) Tel 805-498-9997
E-mail: reptilefamily@earthlink.net
Web site: http://www.reptilefamily.com
Dist(s): **Baker & Taylor Bks.**
Sunbelt Pubns., Inc.

Emprise Publishing *See* **Emprise Publishing & Media**

Emprise Publishing & Media, *(0-9717581; 0-9725121)* 3643 South Ave., Springfield, MO 65807 USA
E-mail: martyb@powermarkcomics.com.

Empty Sky *Imprint of* **Zeromayo Studios, LLP**

Enchanted Lion Bks., LLC, *(1-59270)* 45 Main St. Ste. 519, Brooklyn, NY 11201-1093 USA
E-mail: zoeclaud@earthlink.com; enchantedlionbooks@yahoo.com
Dist(s): **Farrar, Straus & Giroux**
Macmillan.

Enchanted Pen Publishing, LLC, *(0-9714344)* P.O. Box 140370, Broken Arrow, OK 74014 USA Fax: 918-251-3451
E-mail: wfnelson@msn.com.

Enchanted Quill Publications *See* **Stuart & Weitz Publishing Group**

Encore Performance Publishing, *(1-57514)* Orders Addr.: P.O. Box 692, Orem, UT 84059 USA Tel 801-785-9343; Fax: 801-785-9394
E-mail: encoreplay@aol.com
Web site: http://www.encoreplay.com.

Encore Software, Inc., *(1-58263)* 16980 S. Main St., Gardena, CA 90248 USA Tel 310-768-1800; Fax: 310-768-1822
Web site: http://www.encoresoftware.com
Dist(s): **Navarre Corp.**

Encuadernacion Geminis, S.A. de C.V. (MEX) *(968-7968) Dist. by* **Lectorum Pubns.**

Encyclopaedia Britannica, Inc., *(0-7826; 0-8347; 0-85229; 0-87827; 1-59339)* 331 North La Salle St., Chicago, IL 60610 USA (SAN 204-1464) Tel 312-347-7000; Fax: 312-294-2177; Toll Free Fax: 800-344-9624 (fax orders); Toll Free: 800-323-1229; 800-621-3900 (orders); 2nd Flr., Unity Wharf Mill St., London, SE1 2BH Tel 020 7500 7800; Fax: 020 7500 7878
E-mail: contact@eb.com; enquiries@britannica.co.uk
Web site: http://www.eb.com; http://www.britannica.co.uk
Dist(s): **Continental Bk. Co., Inc.**
Pearson Education
Pearson Technology Group.

End Of The Rainbow Projects, *(0-9706726)* Orders Addr.: P.O. Box 128, Reynoldsburg, OH 43068 USA Tel 614-806-6204; Edit Addr.: 3754 Eisenhower Rd., Columbus, OH 43224 USA
E-mail: joylynnjossel@aol.com
Web site: http://www.joylynnjossel.com
Dist(s): **Baker & Taylor Bks.**

End Times Children's Curriculm, The, *(0-9700603)* Div. of Radiant Life Lighthouse Publishing, Orders Addr.: P.O. Box 9073, Pittsburg, CA 94565 USA Tel 925-427-9584; Edit Addr.: 10 Lemonwood Pl., Pittsburgh, CA 94565 USA
E-mail: bkchance@aol.com
Dist(s): **Radiant Life Lighthouse Publishing.**

Endeavor Press *See* **Endeavor Publishing**

Endeavor Publishing, *(0-9743843)* 4204 E. Marshall Ave., Gilbert, AZ 85297 USA Tel 480-632-1306 (phone/fax) Do not confuse with Endeavor Press in Annapolis, MD
E-mail: endeavorpublishing@yahoo.com
Web site: http://www.dowkump.com.

Enders' Family Publishing, *(0-9719837)* Orders Addr.: P.O. Box 37, Gilbert, PA 18331 USA Tel 915-269-4036; Edit Addr.: Lot 2 Weir Mountain Rd., Gilbert, PA 18331 USA
E-mail: dave@endersfamily.com
Web site: http://www.endersfamily.com.

Endgame Entertainment, *(0-9710608)* 4031 12th St., Des Moines, IA 50313 USA Tel 515-283-1764
E-mail: 3devan@home.com.

Ends of the Earth Books.com, *(0-9636652)* P.O. Box 7702, Clearwater, FL 33758-7702 USA.

Endurance Entertainment *See* **Endurance Pubns., Inc.**

Endurance Pubns., Inc., *(0-9708805)* 675 Oak Run Trail, Unit 310, Oak Park, CA 91377 USA Fax: 818-880-8531
E-mail: j-lappin@msn.com
Dist(s): **Baker & Taylor Bks.**

Enduring Freedom Pr., *(0-9723945)* 139-12 Coolidge Ave., Briarwood, NY 11435-1119 USA
E-mail: efp@nypublish.com
Web site: http://www.efp.nypublish.com.

Eneke Pubns., *(1-929454)* 160-27 119th St., Jamaica, NY 11434-2111 USA Tel 718-723-1723; Fax: 718-723-4381; Toll Free: 888-758-9700
E-mail: EOseye@aol.com
Web site: http://www.EbeleOseye.com.

Energia *See* **Energia Pr.**

Energia Pr., *(0-9671207; 0-9712849)* P.O. Box 669306, Marietta, GA 30066 USA (SAN 253-9349) Tel 404-351-5001; Fax: 404-351-1801
E-mail: info@deweycolorsystem.com
Web site: http://www.deweycolorsystem.com
Dist(s): **National Bk. Network.**

Energy Education Group, *(0-9744765)* Div. of The California Study, Inc., Orders Addr.: 664 Hilary Dr., Tiburon, CA 94920 USA Tel 415-435-1527; Fax: 415-435-7737
E-mail: energyforkeeps@aol.com
Web site: http://www.energyforkeeps.org.

Enfield Publishing & Distribution Co., Inc., *(0-9656184; 1-893598)* Orders Addr.: P.O. Box 699, Enfield, NH 03748 USA Tel 603-632-7377; Fax: 603-632-5611; Edit Addr.: 234 May St., Enfield, NH 03748 USA
E-mail: info@enfieldbooks.com
Web site: http://www.enfielddistribution.com; http://www.enfieldbooks.com.

Enginuity, LLC, *(1-929645)* Orders Addr.: P.O. Box 20607, San Jose, CA 95160 USA Tel 408-268-9740; Toll Free Fax: 888-268-9740; Toll Free: 888-618-4263; Edit Addr.: 4183 Park Blvd., Palo Alto, CA 94306-4140 USA
E-mail: sales@enginuity.com; support@enqinuity.com
Web site: http://www.enginuity.com.

Englefield & Arnold, Incorporated *See* **Englefield & Assocs., Inc.**

Englefield & Assocs., Inc., *(1-884183; 1-59230)* Div. of Show What You Know Publishing, Orders Addr.: P.O. Box 341348, Columbus, OH 43234-1348 USA Tel 614-764-1211; Fax: 614-764-1311; Toll Free: 877-727-7464 (877-PASSING); Edit Addr.: 6344 Nicholas Dr., Columbus, OH 43235 USA
E-mail: eapub@eapublishing.com; marketing@eapublishing.com
Web site: http://www.showwhatyouknowpublishing.com/.

English Garden Talk Pr., *(0-9763572; 0-9779257)* 536 W. Hoptree Ct., Louisville, CO 80027 USA
E-mail: sanddollar5643@aol.com.

English Heritage (GBR) *(1-85074; 1-873592; 1-905624) Dist. by* **David Brown.**

Enhance Educational Services, *(0-9662971)* Orders Addr.: P.O. Box 25385, Fresno, CA 93729 USA Tel 559-277-9389; Fax: 559-276-8447; Edit Addr.: 7216 N. Belvedere, Fresno, CA 93722-3407 USA
E-mail: lilys@csufresno.edu
Dist(s): **Kituku & Assocs.**
Partners/West.

Enhancing Health, Inc., *(0-9744479)* P.O. Box 1882, Duluth, GA 30096 USA
E-mail: info@thefittgolfer.com.

ENHEART Publishing, *(0-9654899)* Orders Addr.: P.O. Box 620086, Charlotte, NC 28262 USA Tel 704-649-4313 (phone/fax)
E-mail: info@enheartpublishing.com
Web site: http://www.enheartpublishing.com
Dist(s): **Parnassus Bk. Distributors.**

Enisen Publishing, *(0-9702908; 0-9763070)* 2118 Wilshire Blvd., PMB 351, Santa Monica, CA 90403-5784 USA (SAN 253-3308) Tel 310-989-4069; Fax: 310-576-7278; Toll Free: 866-364-7367 Do not confuse with companies with the same name in Clermont, FL, Hollywood, CA, Otis Orchards, WA
E-mail: publishing@enisen.com
Web site: http://www.enisen.com
Dist(s): **Midpoint Trade Bks., Inc.**

Enlighten Learning, *(0-9755865)* 269 S. Beverly Dr., No. 139, Beverly Hills, CA 90212 USA Tel 310-358-2995.

Enlighten Pubns., *(0-9706226)* Orders Addr.: P.O. Box 525, Vauxhall, NJ 07088 USA Toll Free: 866-862-8626
E-mail: books@enlightenpublications.com
Web site: http://www.authorsden.com/jackiehardrick.

Enlightened Bks., *(0-9769541)* Orders Addr.: P.O. Box 7423, NewPort Beach, CA 92658 USA Tel 949-644-1376; Edit Addr.: 1 Belcourt Dr., Newport Beach, CA 92660 USA
E-mail: enlightenedbooks@aol.com.

Enlil, LLC, *(0-9776291)* 250 Pacific #421, Long Beach, CA 90802 USA
E-mail: jess.cortez@enlil-llc.com
Web site: http://www.booksforbeginningreaders.com
Dist(s): **Baker & Taylor Bks.**

enovel.com, *(1-58877)* 501 E. Franklin St., Richmond, VA 23219 USA Tel 804-783-0621
E-mail: jack@enovel.com
Web site: http://www.enovel.com.

EnRich Communications, *(0-615; 0-9720689)* P.O. Box 44213, Atlanta, GA 30336 USA
E-mail: contact_us@enrichcomm.com
Web site: http://www.realslamdunk.com
Dist(s): **Baker & Taylor Bks.**

Enricharamics, Inc., *(1-889654)* 8416-905 O'Connor Ct., Richmond, VA 23228 USA Tel 804-747-5826.

Enslow Elementary *Imprint of* **Enslow Pubs., Inc.**

†Enslow Pubs., Inc., *(0-7660; 0-89490; 1-59845)* Orders Addr.: P.O. Box 398, Berkeley Heights, NJ 07922-0398 USA (SAN 213-7518) Tel 908-771-9400; Fax: 908-771-0925; Toll Free: 800-398-2504; Edit Addr.: 40 Industrial Rd., Berkeley Heights, NJ 07922-0398 USA ; *Imprints:* MyReportLinks.com Books (MyRptLnks); Enslow Elementary (Enslow Elmntry)
E-mail: enslow@enslow.com; customerservice@enslow.com
Web site: http://www.enslow.com
Dist(s): **Follett Library Resources;** *CIP.*

Enterprise Inc., *(0-9752558)* 2 grant St., Montclair, NJ 07042 USA Tel 973-906-2814
E-mail: ugochuik@yahoo.com.

Enterprize Publishing Co., Inc., *(1-893490)* 1036 Parkway Blvd., Brookings, SD 57006 USA Tel 605-692-7778; Fax: 605-997-3194
E-mail: cfcecil@home.com.

Entertainment Ministry, The, *(0-9707798; 0-9717316; 0-9728003; 0-9765142; 0-9791259)* 609 Hidden Acres Dr., Madison, TN 37115-5626 USA Toll Free: 800-999-0101; 840 High Point Ridge Rd., Franklin, TN 37069 Tel 615-948-4005; Fax: 615-591-1550
E-mail: info@entertainmentministry.com
Web site: http://www.entertainmentministry.com
Dist(s): **STL Distribution North America.**

Entertainment Publications, Inc., *(1-880248; 1-58553; 1-59878)* Maple Corporate Ctr. 1414 E. Maple Rd., Troy, MI 48083 USA (SAN 253-2948) Tel 248-404-1000
E-mail: NationalRetail@entertainment.com
Web site: http://www.entertainment.com
Dist(s): **Waldenbooks, Inc.**

Entertainment Publications Operating Company, Incorporated *See* **Entertainment Publications, Inc.**

ENTRE Ink, *(0-9677854)* 4700 N. 76th St., Renaissance Ctr., Suite 1, Milwaukee, WI 53218-4731 USA Tel 414-438-9500; Fax: 414-355-8682
E-mail: mr_derek@execpc.com
Web site: http://www.execpc.com/~mr_derek.

Entry Way Marketing & Publishing, *(0-9785728; 0-9793944)* P.O. Box 868024, Plano, TX 75086-3507 USA (SAN 850-9344) Toll Free Fax: 866-223-7289
E-mail: entrywaypublish@aol.com
Web site: http://www.entrywaypublishing.com; http://www.digi-tall-media.com; http://www.entrywaymarketing.com; http://www.childrens-stor-e-books.com
Dist(s): **Digi-Tall Media.**

EniCare Consulting, Inc., *(0-9710925)* Orders Addr.: 2809 Blairmont Dr., Midland, MI 48642 USA Tel 989-839-9177; Fax: 989-839-4457
E-mail: bstrawter@chartermi.net
Web site: http://www.envicareinc.com.

Enviro Books *See* **Frederick Pr.**

Environmental Media Corp., *(1-56791)* 1008 Paris Ave., Port Royal, SC 29935-2304 USA Tel 843-986-9034; Fax: 843-986-9093; Toll Free: 800-368-3382
E-mail: bpendergraft@envmedia.com
Web site: http://www.envmedia.com.

Environmental Systems Research Institute *See* **ESRI, Inc.**

Environments, Inc., *(1-59794)* P.O. Box 1348, Beaufort, SC 29901-1348 USA Tel 843-846-8155; Fax: 843-846-2999; Toll Free Fax: 800-343-2987; Toll Free: 800-342-4453
E-mail: environments@eichild.com
Web site: http://www.eichild.com.

Envision EMI, Inc., *(0-9745760)* 1919 Gallows Rd. Ste. 700, Vienna, VA 22182-4007 USA.

EoH Publishing, *(0-9761322)* P.O. Box 676, Bowie, MD 20718 USA (SAN 256-257X) Tel 301-352-9263; Fax: 301-352-9262; Toll Free: 866-352-9263
E-mail: info@eohpublishing.com; wandascott@eohpublishing.com
Web site: http://www.eohpublishing.com.

Eos *Imprint of* **HarperCollins Pubs.**

Eos Publishing, *(0-9668718)* Orders Addr.: 3337 S. Bristol, Suite 332, Santa Ana, CA 92704 USA Tel 714-444-4425; Fax: 714-444-4472 Do not confuse with companies with the same or similar names in Columbus, OH, Leavenworth, WA
E-mail: dawn@dawnmartin.com
Web site: http://www.dawnmartin.com
Dist(s): **Biblio Distribution.**

EP PUBS., *(0-9678599)* 5142 La Subida, NW, Albuquerque, NM 87105 USA Tel 505-831-0387
E-mail: elizar34@yahoo.com.

EPEI Pr., *(0-9729065)* Orders Addr.: 1450 S. New Wilke Rd., Suite 102, Arlington Heights, IL 60005 USA Tel 847-670-6992; Fax: 847-670-7466; Toll Free: 877-670-7444; Edit Addr.: 1749 Golf Rd., No. 204, Mount Prospect, IL 60056 USA
E-mail: sara@getprepared.org
Web site: http://www.getprepared.org.

Epic Conversion Support, *(1-892365)* Orders Addr.: P.O. Box 113, Alpha, OH 45301-0113 USA Tel 937-426-8833; Toll Free: 888-420-5645; Edit Addr.: 2633 Valdina Dr., Beavercreek, OH 45434-6707 USA Tel 937-426-9850
E-mail: Epic@Coach-Builder.com
Web site: http://www.coach-builder.com.

EPIC Publishing Co., *(0-9674025; 0-9763870)* 1405 Ten Palms Ct., Las Vegas, NV 89117-1404 USA (SAN 253-2840) Do not confuse with companies with the same or similar name in Erie, PA, Canon City, CO, Greeley, CO
E-mail: rxl@epicpublishing.com
Web site: http://www.epicpublishing.com
Dist(s): **Baker & Taylor Bks.**
Biblio Distribution.

Epicenter Literary Software, *(0-9760222)* 6514 Seventh St., NW, Washington, DC 20012-2622 USA Tel 202-829-2427; Fax: 202-318-3012
E-mail: carolivia@epicenterliterarysoftware.com; carolivia@carolivia.org
Web site: http://www.epicenterliterarysoftware.com.

Epicenter Pr., Inc., *(0-945397; 0-9708493; 0-9724944; 0-9745014; 0-9790470; 0-9800825)* Orders Addr.: P.O. Box 82368, Kenmore, WA 98028 USA (SAN 246-9405); Edit Addr.: 6577 NE. 181st St., Kenmore, WA 98028 USA Do not confuse with companies with similar names in Kanehoe, HI, Long Beach, CA, Oakland, CA
E-mail: gksturgis@earthlink.com
Web site: http://www.epicenterpress.com
Dist(s): **Graphic Arts Ctr. Publishing Co.**
Wizard Works.

Epiphany Press *See* **Christ the Saviour Brotherhood Publishing**

Epiphany Pr., *(1-929010)* Orders Addr.: P.O. Box 427, Peoria, AZ 61601 USA Tel 623-878-7190; Fax: 623-412-9631; Edit Addr.: 7537 W. Dreyfus Dr., Peoria, IL 01601 USA Do not confuse with companies with the same name in Savannah, GA, Saginaw, MI
E-mail: ruth-rob@email.msn.com.

Epistemo Philiac's Delight, *(0-9663744)* 662 Payne Ave., Saint Paul, MN 55101 USA Tel 612-778-0050.

Epistemological Engineering, *(0-9648496)* 5269 Miles Ave., Oakland, CA 94618-1044 USA Tel 510-653-3377; Toll Free Fax: 866-879-7797 ; *Imprints:* eeps media (eeps media)
E-mail: publications@eeps.com
Web site: http://www.eeps.com; http://www.denofinquiry.com.

e-Pluribus Unum Publishing Co., *(0-9760045; 0-9779897)* Div. of Cronus College, P.O. Box 941, Lafayette, CA 94549 USA ; *Imprints:* Reluctant Reader Books (ReluctRead)
Web site: http://www.cronuscollege.com.

Epoca, Editorial, S.A. de C.V. (MEX) *(968-6769; 970-627) Dist. by* **Giron Bks.**

Epps-Alford Publishing, *(0-9631110; 0-9797931)* P.O. Box 504, Yellow Springs, OH 45387 USA Tel 937-767-1507
E-mail: info@epps-alford.com; julia.davis@epps-alford.com
Web site: http://www.epps-alford.com
Dist(s): **Baker & Taylor Bks.**

eProduction Services *See* **Kepler Pr.**

EQUALS *Imprint of* **Univ. of California, Berkeley, Lawrence Hall of Science**

Equidata Publishing, *(0-9714185)* Orders Addr.: P.O. Box 8116, Surprise, AZ 85174 USA
E-mail: jobrien6@cox.net
Web site: http://www.equidatapublishing.com.

Equimax USA, Inc., *(0-9668082)* HC65 Box 271, Alpine, TX 79830 USA Tel 432-371-2610; Fax: 432-371-2612; Toll Free: 800-759-9494
E-mail: employment@equimax.com
Web site: http://www.equixmax.com.

Equine Graphics Publishing Group, *(1-887932)* Div. of Equine Graphics, Orders Addr.: P.O. Box 8016, Zanesville, OH 43702-8016 USA Tel 740-588-0181; Fax: 740-588-0183; Toll Free: 800-659-9442; 800-375-9378; Edit Addr.: 7270 Forest Ln., Nashport, OH 43830-9045 USA ; *Imprints:* SmallHorse Press (SmallHorse Pr); New Concord Press (New Concord Pr)
E-mail: editor@newconcordpress.com; toniweeone@smallhorse.com; info@equinegraphicspublishing.com; sales@romancingthehorse.com
Web site: http://www.smallhorse.com; http://www.newconcordpress.com; http://www.equinegraphicspublishing.com; http://www.tonileland.com.

Equity Research Corp., *(0-9668560)* 2606 NW 67th Terr., Gainesville, FL 32606 USA Tel 352-376-6387 (phone/fax)
E-mail: jgaskin@ufl.edu.

Erazo, Carlos, *(0-9759757; 0-9796253)* P.O. Box 2111, Bayamon, PR 00960-2111 USA
E-mail: erazo2001@prtc.net
Web site: http://www.erazolabor.com
Dist(s): **Representaciones Borinquenas, Inc.**

Erda Publishing Co., *(0-9659942)* 529 W. Alder St., Sandpoint, ID 83864 USA Tel 208-263-1151
E-mail: erda@dmi.net.

ereads.com, *(1-58586; 0-7592)* 171 E. 74th St., New York, NY 10021 USA Tel 212-772-7363; Fax: 212-772-7393
E-mail: info@e-reads.com
Web site: http://www.e-reads.com
Dist(s): **EDC Publishing**
NetLibrary, Inc.
Replica Bks.

Erica Hse., *(0-9659308; 1-893162)* Orders Addr.: P.O. Box 151, Frederick, MD 21705-0151 USA Tel 301-631-0747; Fax: 301-631-9073; Edit Addr.: 230 E. Patrick St., Frederick, MD 21701 USA
E-mail: eribooks@ericahouse.com
Web site: http://www.ericahouse.com; http://www.eatyourselfslim.com
Dist(s): **Bookazine Co., Inc.**
Brodart Co.
Unique Bks., Inc.

Erickson Pr., *(1-60217)* Orders Addr.: P.O. Box 33, Yankton, SD 57078 USA (SAN 852-0402); Edit Addr.: 329 Broadway, Yankton, SD 57078 USA
Web site: http://www.ericksonpress.com.

Erickson, Rakel L., *(0-9744422)* P.O. Box 86, Fertile, MN 56540-0086 USA
E-mail: thomas_robinson@unl.nodak.edu.

Erickson, Tim, *(1-59492)* 8801 Fremont Ave S., Minneapolis, MN 55420-2642 USA
E-mail: terickson21@mn.rr.com
Web site: http://www.deathswhisper.com.

Erie Art Museum, *(0-9616623; 0-9709282)* 411 State St., Erie, PA 16501-1106 USA (SAN 661-2458) Tel 814-459-5477; Fax: 814-452-1744
E-mail: contact@erieartmuseum.org
Web site: http://www.erieartmuseum.org.

ErieKIDS, Inc., *(0-9779822)* 4544 W. Ridge Rd., Suite One, Erie, PA 16506 USA (SAN 850-668X) Tel 814-835-3430
Web site: http://www.eriekids.com.

E-Rights/E-Reads, Limited *See* **ereads.com**

†Eriksson, Paul S. Pub., *(0-8397)* P.O. Box 125, Forest Dale, VT 05745 USA (SAN 201-6702) Tel 802-247-4210; Fax: 802-247-4256
E-mail: paulerikss@AOL.com
Dist(s): **Independent Pubs. Group**; *CIP.*

Erinsillart, *(0-9779155)* 739 31 ave, san francisco, CA 94121 USA Tel 415-816-0766
E-mail: erin@erinsillart.com
Web site: http://www.erinsillart.com.

†Erlbaum, Lawrence Assocs., Inc., *(0-8058; 0-86377; 0-89859; 1-880393; 1-4106)* 270 Madison Ave. Flr. 4, New York, NY 10016-0601 USA (SAN 213-960X) Toll Free: 800-926-6579 (orders only)
E-mail: orders@erlbaum.com
Web site: http://www.erlbaum.com
Dist(s): **NetLibrary, Inc.**
Taylor & Francis, Inc.; *CIP.*

Ernie Publications, *(0-9716810)* 4125 Prescott St., Sarasota, FL 34232 USA Tel 941-724-4125
E-mail: eb4125@home.com; eb4125@comcast.net
Web site: http://www.extremelaserworks.com
Dist(s): **Book Clearing Hse.**

ERPublishing, LLC, *(0-9766568)* P.O. Box 152, Old Greenwich, CT 06870 USA
Web site: http://www.erpublishing.com.

Errepar (ARG) *(950-739; 950-9524; 987-9088) Dist. by* **Baker & Taylor.**

Ertl Co., Inc., *(1-887327)* Div. of U. S. Industries, Inc., 2021 9th St SE, Dyersville, IA 52040-2316 USA
Web site: http://www.rcertl.com.

Ervin, Imogene *See* **Finer Moments**

Ervin, Robert E., *(0-9746189)* 552 Keystone Station Rd., Jackson, OH 45640 USA Tel 740-286-2693; Fax: 740-286-0756
E-mail: multicominc@adelphia.net
Web site: http://johnhuntmorgan.com.

Escapr Pr., *(0-9667395)* 1310 Ponderosa Pine Ln., Carrollton, TX 75007 USA Tel 972-492-2512
E-mail: bonjo@escapepress.com.

Eschar Pubns., *(0-9623839; 1-929221)* Orders Addr.: P.O. Box 1196, Waynesboro, VA 22980 USA (SAN 297-6439) Tel 540-942-2171; Fax: 352-357-9695; Edit Addr.: 435 Alpha St., Waynesboro, VA 22980 USA
E-mail: escharpub@earthlink.net
Web site: http://www.vivianowens.com
Dist(s): **Baker & Taylor Bks.**
Brodart Co.

ESCO PR., *(1-930044)* Affiliate of ESCO Institute, Ltd., P.O. Box 521, Mount Prospect, IL 60056 USA Toll Free Fax: 800-546-3726; Toll Free: 800-726-9696
E-mail: mick@escoinst.com
Web site: http://www.escoinst.com/Publications.cfm.

Escuela de Musica, *(1-932637)* 2540 Crooked Trail Rd., Chula Vista, CA 91914-4142 USA
E-mail: escuelademusica@cox.net
Web site: http://escuelademusica.net.

Eslinger Hse. Publishing, *(0-9763033)* 17762 Neff Ranch Rd., Yorba Linda, CA 92886-9013 USA
E-mail: gilberstadt@earthlink.net.

Esmaili, Inc., *(0-9656185)* P.O. Box 421382, Dallas, TX 75342 USA Tel 214-521-9600; Fax: 214-526-9617.

ESOL Publishing, *(0-9793761)* 10305 Colony View Dr., Fairfax, VA 22032 USA (SAN 853-2796)
E-mail: ESOLPublishing@cox.net; mcpuginrodas@cox.net; mcpuginrodas@aol.com
Web site: http://www.TheEightBallClub.com
Dist(s): **Biblio Distribution**
Reading Matters, Inc.

Esoteric Ink, LLC, *(0-9721044)* Div. of M&M Ventures, 9318 N. 95th Way, Scottsdale, AZ 85258 USA
Web site: http://www.chidokai.org.

Espasa Calpe, S.A. (ESP) *(84-239; 84-339; 84-8326; 84-670) Dist. by* **Continental Bk.**

Espasa Calpe, S.A. (ESP) *(84-239; 84-339; 84-8326; 84-670) Dist. by* **Lectorum Pubns.**

Espasa Calpe, S.A. (ESP) *(84-239; 84-339; 84-8326; 84-670) Dist. by* **Distribks Inc.**

Espasa Calpe, S.A. (ESP) *(84-239; 84-339; 84-8326; 84-670) Dist. by* **Libros Fronteras.**

Espasa Calpe, S.A. (ESP) *(84-239; 84-339; 84-8326; 84-670) Dist. by* **Planeta.**

Especially Bks., *(1-892373)* 50 Montauk Ave., Stonington, CT 06378 USA Tel 860-535-1647; Fax: 860-535-2049.

Esperanza, J. Inc., *(0-615; 0-9719350)* Orders Addr.: 6749 S. Westnedge Ave., Suite K109, Portage, MI 49002 USA; Edit Addr.: 5041 Colony Woods, Kalamazoo, MI 49009 USA.

Esquire Publishing, Inc., *(0-9745045)* 5900 Harper Rd., Suite 107, Solon, OH 44139 USA Tel 440-528-0020; Fax: 440-528-0157
E-mail: contact@monsterbooks.net
Web site: http://www.monsterbooks.net.

ESRI, Inc., *(1-879102; 1-58948)* 380 New York St., Redlands, CA 92373-8100 USA Fax: 909-307-3082; Toll Free: 800-447-9778 ; *Imprints:* ESRI Press (ESRI Pr)
E-mail: esripress@esri.com
Web site: http://www.esri.com/esripress
Dist(s): **Thomson Gale**
Independent Pubs. Group
Ingram Pub. Services
Trans-Atlantic Pubns., Inc.

ESRI Pr. *Imprint of* **ESRI, Inc.**

Essential Book Publishers *See* **Writers Publishing Cooperative**

Essential Library *Imprint of* **ABDO Publishing Co.**

Essential Series, The *Imprint of* **Marvel Enterprises, Inc.**

Essentials Educational Services, *(0-9716290)* P.O. Box 2464, Springfield, MA 01101-2464 USA Tel 413-782-9670 (3 PM - 5PM) ; *Imprints:* Beatstellar Books (Beatstellar Bks)
E-mail: essedser@aol.com; renayjihad@verizonmail.com
Web site: http://www.eesplus.com.

et al Publishing *Imprint of* **Expert Publishing, Inc.**

†ETA/Cuisenaire, *(0-7406; 0-914040; 0-923832; 0-938587; 1-57162; 1-57452)* Div. of A. Daigger & Company, 500 Greenview Ct., Vernon Hills, IL 60061 USA (SAN 285-7553) Tel 847-816-5050; Fax: 847-816-5066; Toll Free: 800-445-5985
E-mail: info@etacuisenaire.com
Web site: http://www.etacuisenaire.com; *CIP.*

Eternal Covenant Pr., *(0-9711339)* P.O. Box 1364, Battle Ground, WA 98604 USA Tel 360-687-8335
E-mail: teaching@pacifier.com
Web site: http://www.pacifier.com/~teaching.

Eternal Foundations Curriculum, *(1-932505)* P.O. Box 1213, Atascadero, CA 93423 USA Tel 805-466-1910
E-mail: tsgaddis@tcsn.net.

Eternal Studios, *(1-887814)* 15235 Rainhollow, Houston, TX 77070 USA Tel 713-370-8384
Dist(s): **Diamond Comic Distributors, Inc.**

Eternity Pr., *(0-9758989)* 2828 Brannon Ave., Saint Louis, MO 63139-1438 USA Toll Free: 800-886-7587
Web site: http://www.cenveo.com.

Ethos Of Commerce Pubs., Ltd., *(0-9741412)* 3535 E. Coast Hwy. No. 216, Corona del Mar, CA 92625 USA Tel 949-862-5826
E-mail: ethosofcommerce@yahoo.com
Web site: http://www.geocities.com/EthosOfCommerce.

Ethridge, Gloria Jill *See* **Moondoggie Publishing**

eTreasures Publishing, *(0-9740537)* Orders Addr.: P.O. Box 71813, Newnan, GA 30271 USA Tel 770-683-8032
E-mail: publisher@etreasurespublishing.com
Web site: http://www.etreasurespublishing.com.

Ettinger, L. J., *(0-9614840)* 1991 Saddleback Rd., Reno, NV 89511 USA (SAN 693-1049) Tel 702-847-9303
E-mail: Mae@pyramid.net
Dist(s): **Gem Guides Bk. Co.**

Eudon Publishing, *(0-9765423)* P.O. Box 9, Goddard, KS 67052 USA Tel 316-210-4649; Fax: 316-233-1075
E-mail: gsmith@EudonPublishing.com
Web site: http://www.EudonPublishing.com
Dist(s): **BWI**
Brodart Co.
Follett Library Resources.

Eudy, Ellen, *(0-9717574)* P.O. Box 2024, Roanoke Rapids, NC 27870-4630 USA
E-mail: eudyel@schoollink.net.

Eumaeus Pr., *(0-9719704)* 60 West St., Suite 220, Annapolis, MD 21401 USA Tel 410-263-6161; Fax: 410-269-1665
E-mail: laweur@aol.com; jcll@peoplepc.com.

Euphema Press, *(0-9779600)* P.O. Box 2314, Bowie, MD 20718 USA
Web site: http://www.euphema.com.

Eureka Productions, *(0-9712464; 0-9746648; 0-9787919)* 8778 Oak Grove Rd., Mount Horeb, WI 53572 USA ; *Imprints:* Graphic Classics (Graphic Classics)
Web site: http://www.graphicclassics.com
Dist(s): **Diamond Bk. Distributors.**

Company

Company

EUROBOOKS Pubs., *(1-58750)* 7927 East Dr. Apt. 272, N Bay Village, FL 33141-3375 USA (SAN 253-2379)
E-mail: sales@eubooks.net
Web site: http://www.eubooks.net.

Europa Editions, Inc., *(1-933372)* Div. of Edizioni E/O (Rome, Italy), 116 E. 16th St., New York, NY 10003 USA; Italian Office, Via Gabriela Camozzi 1, Roma, 00195
E-mail: karinwessel@europaeditions.com
Web site: http://www.europaeditions.com/
Dist(s): **Consortium Bk. Sales & Distribution.**

European Language Institute (ITA) *(88-8148; 88-85148) Dist. by* **Midwest European Pubns.**

European Language Institute (ITA) *(88-8148; 88-85148) Dist. by* **Distribks Inc.**

Eurpsville USA, Inc., *(1-892522)* 5235 74th St., Elmhurst, NY 11373-4108 USA Toll Free: 800-932-3877
E-mail: makeurps@aol.com
Web site: http://www.eurps.com.

EV Publishing Corp., *(0-9727787)* 1628 E. Southern Ave., Suite 9, PMB 237, Tempe, AZ 85282 USA Fax: 480-966-8627
E-mail: info@evpub.com
Web site: http://www.evpub.com.

Eva Publishing, LLC, *(0-9786799)* 345 W. Broadway, Shelbyville, IN 46176 USA (SAN 851-321X) Tel 317-398-0231 (phone/fax)
E-mail: jmesser@lightbound.com.

EvangeCube International *See* **E3 Resources**

Evangel Author Services, *(1-933858)* Div. of Brethren in Christ Media Ministries, 2000 Evangel Way, P.O. Box 189, Nappanee, IN 46550 USA Tel 574-773-3164; Fax: 574-773-5934; Toll Free: 800-253-9315
E-mail: rearl@evangelpress.com; info@evangelpublishing.com
Web site: http://www.evangelpress.com; http://www.evangelpublishing.com
Dist(s): **Baker & Taylor Bks.**

Evangel Press *See* **Evangel Publishing Hse.**

Evangel Publishing Hse., *(0-916035; 1-891314; 1-928915; 1-934233)* Div. of Brethren in Christ Media Ministries, Orders Addr.: P.O. Box 189, Nappanee, IN 46550 USA (SAN 211-7940) Tel 574-773-3164; Fax: 574-773-5934; Toll Free: 800-253-9315 (order); Edit Addr.: 2000 Evangel Way, Nappanee, IN 46550 USA
E-mail: sales@evangelpublishing.com
Web site: http://www.evangelpublishing.com
Dist(s): **Anchor Distributors**
Appalachian Bk. Distributors
Baker & Taylor Bks.
Herald Pr.
Ingram Bk. Co.
Partners Bk. Distributing, Inc.
Spring Arbor Distributors, Inc.

Evangelical Formosan Church - Communication Ctr., *(0-9631789; 1-885216)* 9386 Telstar Ave., El Monte, CA 91731-2816 USA Tel 626-307-0030; Fax: 626-307-5557; Toll Free: 800-888-7796
E-mail: journal@efccc.org; efccc@efccc.org
Web site: http://www.ccim.org/Orgs/LOGOS/EFWN.

Evangelista, Susan, *(0-9769602)* 1261 W. Fulton Ave., Grand Rapids,, MI 49504 USA
Web site: http://micart.net.

Evan-Moor Educational Pubs., *(1-55799; 1-59673)* Sub. of Evan-Moor Corporation, 18 Lower Ragsdale Dr., Monterey, CA 93940 USA (SAN 242-5394) Tel 800-976-1915; 831-649-5901; Fax: 831-649-6256; Toll Free Fax: 800-777-4332; Toll Free: 800-777-4362
E-mail: customerservice@evan-moor.com
Web site: http://www.evan-moor.com
Dist(s): **Appalachian Bk. Distributors**
Spring Arbor Distributors, Inc.

Evans Book *See* **Evans Bk. Distribution & Pubs., Inc.**

Evans Bk. Distribution & Pubs., Inc., *(0-9654884; 1-56684)* 895 W. 1700 S., Salt Lake City, UT 84104 USA Tel 801-975-1315; Fax: 801-975-1343; Toll Free: 877-655-2665.

†Evans, M. & Co., Inc., *(0-87131; 1-59077)* 216 E. 49th St., New York, NY 10017 USA (SAN 203-4050) Tel 212-688-2810; Fax: 212-486-4544
E-mail: editorial@mevans.com
Web site: http://www.mevans.com/
Dist(s): **National Bk. Network**
Rowman & Littlefield Pubs., Inc.; *CIP.*

Evans Publishing Group (GBR) Dist. by IPG Chicago.

Evans, Robert, *(0-9766468)* 1065 Saint Helena Way, Sebastopol, CA 95472 USA
E-mail: rgevans@sonic.net.

EveEden Pr., *(0-9710127)* 1615 E. Boot Rd., Suite B 322, West Chester, PA 19380-6006 USA Tel 610-429-2202; Fax: 610-431-9712
E-mail: jawoodson@juno.com.

Evening Star Enterprise, Inc., *(0-9790210)* P.O. Box 254, Wilmore, KY 40390-1072 USA (SAN 852-2111)
E-mail: Director@Eveningstarenterprise.com
Web site: http://Evening Star Enterprise.com
Dist(s): **AtlasBooks Distribution.**

Evening Sun Pr., *(0-9726781)* 8332 Melrose Ave., West Hollywood, CA 90069 USA Tel 310-657-9092
E-mail: lc@pictureentertainment.com.

Evenson, Laurel, *(0-9666834)* 675 Moon Lake Dr., Cambridge, MN 55008 USA Tel 612-689-4093.

Event-Based Science Institute, Inc., *(0-9747576)* 6609 Paxton Rd., Rockville, MD 20852-3659 USA
Web site: http://www.eventbasedscience.com.

Eveott Enterprises, Inc., *(0-9674165)* P.O. Box 3696, Midland, TX 79702 USA Tel 915-689-7815; Fax: 915-682-7237
E-mail: linda@lindamcbride.com
Web site: http://www.lindamcbride.com.

EverCross Studios, *(0-9726100)* 112 Catlett Dr., Martinsburg, WV 25401 USA
E-mail: dustin@evercross.com
Web site: http://www.evercross.com.

Eveready Letter & Advertising Inc., *(0-9758714; 0-9777623)* 1817 Broadway, Nashville, TN 37203 USA
Dist(s): **Chicago Distribution Ctr.**

Everest de Ediciones y Distribucion, S.L. (ESP) *(84-241; 972-750) Dist. by* **Continental Bk.**

Everest de Ediciones y Distribucion, S.L. (ESP) *(84-241; 972-750) Dist. by* **Ediciones.**

Everest de Ediciones y Distribucion, S.L. (ESP) *(84-241; 972-750) Dist. by* **Lectorum Pubns.**

Everest Publishing, *(1-886295)* 7041 E. Orange Blossom Ln., Scottsdale, AZ 85253-7042 USA Tel 602-994-5024; Fax: 602-941-5561; Toll Free: 800-240-2332 Do not confuse with Everest Publishing Co., Costa Mesa, CA
E-mail: info@sourcebook.com
Web site: http://www.sourcebook.com
Dist(s): **Lectorum Pubns., Inc.**

Everett Sports Publishing & Marketing, *(1-891613)* Div. of the Everett Corp., 5 N. Greenwich Rd., Armonk, NY 10504-2311 USA
Web site: http://evernet.com.

Everette Publishing (EP), LLC, *(0-9672539)* 106 Tillerson Dr., Newport News, VA 23602 USA Tel 757-344-9092; 757-877-6943; Fax: 757-988-0909
E-mail: EverettePublish@cox.net
Web site: http://www.Webunlimted.com.

Evergreen Bks., *(0-9723010)* Orders Addr.: P.O. Box 186, Mohegan Lake, NY 10547 USA; Edit Addr.: 25 Hollow Brook Ln., Cortlandt Manor, NY 10567 USA
E-mail: info@evergreen-books.com
Web site: http://www.evergreen-books.com.

Evergreen Pr. *Imprint of* **Genesis Communications, Inc.**

Evergreen Press *See* **Genesis Communications, Inc.**

Evergreen Pr. of Brainerd, LLC, *(0-9661599; 0-9755252)* P.O. Box 465, Brainerd, MN 56401 USA; 201 W. Laurel St., Brainerd, MN 56401
E-mail: tenlee@evergreenpress.net
Web site: http://www.evergreenpress.net; http://lakecountryjournal.com.

EverRead Assocs., *(0-9744327)* 2824 Klein Rd., San Jose, CA 95148-2218 USA
Web site: http://www.everread.com.

Everwas Publishing, *(0-9777735)* 200 Broken Arrow Way S., Sedona, AZ 86351-8743 USA Tel 928-284-0457; Fax: 928-284-9225
E-mail: kroyce88@esedona.net.

Everydaysanctuary Pubns., *(0-9761900)* 12514 Maria Cir., Broomfield, CO 80020-5324 USA
Web site: http://www.everydaysanctuary.net.

Everyman Chess (GBR) *(1-85744) Dist. by* **Globe Pequot.**

Everyman's Library *Imprint of* **Knopf Publishing Group**

Evil Twin Pubns., *(0-9712972; 0-9763355)* P.O. Box 2, Livingston Manor, NY 12758 USA Tel 917-971-2450
E-mail: info@eviltwinpublications.com
Web site: http://www.eviltwinpublications.com
Dist(s): **AK Pr. Distribution.**

eVision, LLC, *(0-9768579)* Orders Addr.: 334 Sixth Ave. S., Birmingham, AL 35205 USA Tel 205-283-7690; Fax: 205-252-3090
Web site: http://www.eVisionLLC.net
Dist(s): **Parnassus Bk. Distributors.**

Evolution Publishing & Manufacturing *See* **Arx Publishing**

EvoraBooks, LLC, *(0-9725071)* P.O. Box 397, Canton, CT 06019 USA
E-mail: evorabooks@snet.net
Web site: http://www.booksbyevora.com.

Exambusters *Imprint of* **Ace Academics, Inc.**

Exams Unlimited, Inc., *(1-885343; 1-59132)* 1971 Western Ave., No. 191, Albany, NY 12203-5011 USA Tel 518-356-1486 (phone/fax)
E-mail: eui@eui.com
Web site: http://www.ebooks-etexts.com.

Exceed, LLC, *(0-9771722)* 715 E. 100 N., Lindon, UT 84042 USA (SAN 256-8519) Tel 801-785-7931
E-mail: kcooper@exceed.bz
Web site: http://www.exceed.bz.

Excel Digital Pr., Inc., *(0-9712249; 0-9718254; 0-9749202; 0-9786376)* Orders Addr.: P.O. Box 703978, Dallas, TX 75370-3978 USA Tel 469-892-2970; Fax: 469-892-2971; Edit Addr.: 2515 Daybreak Dr., Dallas, TX 75287 USA
E-mail: bookeagle@hotmail.com
Web site: http://www.exceldigitalpress.com.

Excel Publishing, *(0-9651100)* P.O. Box 1581, Troy, MI 48099 USA Tel 248-593-9070; Fax: 248-593-9071 Do not confuse companies with the same name in Woodside, NY, Napa, CA
E-mail: susan@childrengolfbooks.com
Web site: http://www.childrensgolfbooks.com.

Excellence Enterprises, *(0-9627735)* 3040 Aspen Ln., Palmdale, CA 93550-7985 USA Tel 818-367-8085; Fax: 818-361-2389.

Excellence Student Incentives, *(0-9789612)* 18942 Muirland, Detroit, MI 48221 USA (SAN 852-1107) Tel 313-646-6079; Fax: 313-449-0396
E-mail: beatthemeap@yahoo.com
Web site: http://www.beatthemeap.com.

Excellent Bks., *(0-9628014; 1-880780)* P.O. Box 131322, Carlsbad, CA 92013-1322 USA Tel 760-598-5069; Fax: 240-218-7601
E-mail: books@excellentbooks.com
Web site: http://www.excellentbooks.com.

Exceptional Innovations, Inc., *(1-931311)* P.O. Box 3853, Reston, VA 20195 USA Tel 703-709-0136; Fax: 703-435-2656
E-mail: mail@exinn.net
Web site: http://www.exinn.net.

Exclamation! Pubs., *(0-9710541; 0-9767183)* P.O. Box 664, Phoenixville, PA 19460-0664 USA
E-mail: dheap@deheap.com
Web site: http://www.deheap.com.

Exclusive Editions *Imprint of* **Parragon, Inc.**

Executive Performances, Inc., *(0-9748220)* P.O. Box 93, Palos Park, IL 60464 USA ; *Imprints:* Executive Performances Publishing (Exec Perform Pubng)
E-mail: magicriz@aol.com
Dist(s): **Baker & Taylor Bks.**

Executive Performances Publishing *Imprint of* **Executive Performances, Inc.**

Executive Pubs. International, *(0-9726075; 0-9796536)* 3525 Del Mar Heights, Suite 205, San Diego, CA 92154 USA Tel 619-671-9997; Fax: 619-671-9996
Web site: http://www.EPIBooks.com.

Exeter Pr., *(0-9700612; 0-9797407)* Orders Addr.: 223 Commonwealth Ave., Boston, MA 02116 USA Tel 617-267-7720; Fax: 617-262-6948; Edit Addr.: 223 Commonwealth Ave., Boston, MA 02116 USA (SAN 854-2554)
E-mail: davidburke@commonwealthfilms.com
Web site: http://www.exeterpress.com.

Exhibit A Pr., *(0-9633954)* 4657 Cajon Way, San Diego, CA 92115 USA Tel 619-286-6350; Fax: 619-286-1591
E-mail: jackieandbat@compuserve.com
Web site: http://www.edgeglobol.com/exhibit/
Dist(s): **Biblio Distribution.**

Exile Editions, Ltd. (CAN) *(0-920428; 1-55096) Dist. by* **IPG Chicago.**

Exit Studio, *(0-9640868)* 1466 N. Quinn St., Arlington, VA 22209 USA Tel 703-312-7121; Fax: 703-312-6217
E-mail: efontanez@exitstudio.com
Web site: http://www.exitstudio.com
Dist(s): **Independent Pubs. Group.**

Exley Giftbooks, 185 Main St. Apt. 2, Spencer, MA 01562-1755 USA Toll Free Fax: 800-453-5248; Toll Free: 800-423-9539
E-mail: exlgb@aol.com.

Exley, Helen Giftbooks (GBR) *(0-905521; 1-85015; 1-86187; 1-905130; 1-84634) Dist. by* **Exley Giftbooks.**

Expert Publishing, Inc., *(1-931945)* 14314 Thrush St., NW, Andover, MN 55304-3330 USA (SAN 255-3155) Tel 763-755-4966 Toll Free: 877-755-4966 ; *Imprints:* et al Publishing (et al Pubng)
E-mail: harry@expertpublishinginc.com
Web site: http://www.expertpublishinginc.com.

Expert Systems for Teachers *Imprint of* **Teaching Point, Inc.**

Explorer Editions, *(0-9719130)* 926 Commons Dr., Bloomington, IN 47401 USA Tel 812-339-3618
E-mail: volkova@indiana.edu.

Explorer Media *Imprint of* **Simon & Barklee, Inc./ ExplorerMedia**

Explorer's Bible Study, *(1-889015; 0-9787993)* 2652 Hwy. 46 S., Dickson, TN 37055 USA Tel 615-446-7316; Fax: 615-446-7951; Toll Free: 800-657-2874
Web site: http://www.explorerbiblestudy.org.

Exploring California Insects *Imprint of* **Quality Nature Displays by Eddie Dunbar**

Expressions of Grace, Incorporated *See* **Words of Grace, Inc.**

Expressions Woven, *(0-9668179)* P.O. Box 1004, Waterford, CT 06385 USA Tel 860-442-1332; Fax: 860-447-9916
E-mail: dreaminthelight@alum.rpi.edu
Web site: http://www.poetryin.com
Dist(s): **Baker & Taylor Bks.**
Lightning Source, Inc.

Expressive Ink, *(0-9759362)* Orders Addr.: P.O. Box 74, Foreston, MN 56330 USA; Edit Addr.: 305 Pheasant Ln., Foreston, MN 56330-5540 USA Tel 320-294-4022
E-mail: express@bctelco.net
Web site: http://www.natknows.com
Dist(s): **Baker & Taylor Bks.**

Expulsion Publications *See* **AverStream Pr.**

Extejt, Gabriele *See* **McGab Publishing**

Extreme Math *Imprint of* **McGuire, Nancy**

Eye Contact Media, *(0-9729187)* 1344 Disc Dr., No. 105, Sparks, NV 89436 USA
Web site: http://www.eyecontactmedia.com
Dist(s): **AtlasBooks Distribution.**

Eye of Newt, The, *(0-9762565)* 5203 Cedar Springs Rd, Dallas, TX 75235-8537 USA Tel 214-520-1739
Web site: http://www.theyeofnewt.com.

Eye of the Storm, *(0-9669585)* P.O. Box 18299, Cleveland Heights, OH 44118-0299 USA Tel 216-596-0535
E-mail: storme@animalhouse.com.

Eyes Wide Open Productions, *(0-9729479)* P.O. Box 2210, Kapaa, HI 96746 USA (SAN 255-2108) Tel 808 652-0180 (phone/fax); Fax: 808 823-6952
E-mail: mel@melbell-grey.com; jschwartz@melbell-grey.com
Web site: http://www.eyeswideopenproductions.com; www.meledelicious.com
Dist(s): **Booklines Hawaii, Ltd.**

Eyres, John, *(0-9769762)* 12713 Willowyck Dr., Saint Louis, MO 63146 USA.

EZ Comics, *(0-9795887)* 12, Pine Top Rd., Barrington, RI 02806-1706 USA
Web site: http://ezcomics.com, ez-comics.com.

E-Z Printing Pr., *(0-9657775)* 1600 S. Ogden Dr., Los Angeles, CA 90019-4903 USA Tel 213-931-3870.

Ezra's Earth Publishing, *(0-9727855)* P.O. Box 3036, South Pasadena, CA 91031 USA (SAN 255-0555)
E-mail: information@ezrasearth.com
Web site: http://www.ezrasearth.com
Dist(s): **Baker & Taylor Bks.**
Quality Bks., Inc.

Ezra's Engine Publishing *See* **Ezra's Earth Publishing**

F & S Music KS Publishing Co., *(0-9745630; 0-9765787)* Orders Addr.: P.O. Box 11805, Jackson, MS 39283 USA; Edit Addr.: 1902 Queens Road Ave., Jackson, MS 39213 USA
E-mail: lanniespann@yahoo.com
Web site: http://www.lanniespannmcbride.net.

Feral Pr., Inc., *(0-9649349; 1-930094)* 304 Strawberry Field Rd., Flat Rock, NC 28731 USA Tel 828-694-0438; Fax: 828-694-0438 ; *Imprints:* Rivet Books (Rivet Bks)
E-mail: gchet@feralpressinc.com
Web site: http://www.feralpressinc.com.

Fergus & Lady Publishing, *(0-9786975)* 2310 Del Mar Rd., No. 10, Montrose, CA 91020 USA.

Ferguson, Jennifer E. Pubns., *(1-892732)* 847-A Second Ave., Suite 251, New York, NY 10017 USA Tel 212-926-8825; Fax: 212-573-8362.

Ferguson, Linda, *(0-9755288)* 5825 Deermont Dr., Crestview, FL 32539-8171 USA Tel 850-682-6532
E-mail: lkinspire@yahoo.com
Web site: http://www.l-n-kinspirationalbooks.com/.

Ferguson, Melanie C. S. *See* **New Moon Publishing**

Ferguson Publishing Co. *Imprint of* **Facts On File, Inc.**

Ferguson, Suzanie Pamela, *(0-9658745)* 4609 Maplewood Dr., Suffolk, VA 23435 USA Tel 757-483-5721
E-mail: lferg72184@aol.com.

Fern Creek Pr., *(0-9625737; 1-893651)* P.O. Box 1322, Clayton, GA 30525 USA Tel 706-782-5379; Fax: 706-782-5379
E-mail: brian@ferncreekpress.com
Web site: http://rabun.net/boyd.

Fern Creek Publishing *See* **Fern Creek Pr.**

Fern Rock Falls Pr., *(0-9762409)* 22105 Fisk Rd., Noti, OR 97461-9718 USA Tel 541-935-3920
E-mail: dandq@rio.com.

Fernandez USA Publishing, *(968-416; 970-03)* 203 Argonne Ave., Suite B, PMB 151, Long Beach, CA 90803-1777 USA Tel 562-901-2370; Fax: 562-901-2372; Toll Free: 800-814-8080
Web site: http://www.fernandezusa.com
Dist(s): **Continental Bk. Co., Inc.**

Ferne Pr. *Imprint of* **Nelson Publishing & Marketing**

Fernhouse Pr., *(0-9759363)* P.O. Box 73, Woodstock, VT 05067 USA
Web site: http://www.fernhouse.com.

Fernwood Publishing Co., Ltd. (CAN) *(1-55266; 1-895686) Dist. by* **IPG Chicago.**

ferrocement.com, *(0-9748016)* P.O. Box 31 S. St., Bernardston, MA 01337-0133 USA Fax: 413-648-9098
E-mail: garrett@ferrocement.com.

Fetch! Publishing, *(0-9746324)* 27881 La Paz Rd., Suite G-124, Laguna Niguel, CA 92677 USA Fax: 877-426-3809; Toll Free Fax: 877-426-3809; Toll Free: 877-899-9454
Web site: http://fetchpublishing.com.

Fey, Sid Designs, Inc., *(0-9753530)* Box 184, 335 E. Geneva Rd., Carol Stream, IL 60188 USA Tel 630-668-6607; Fax: 630-668-6282
E-mail: zpdduda@earthlink.net
Web site: http://www.thebeinggame.com.

Fickling, David Bks. *Imprint of* **Random Hse. Children's Bks.**

FictionSpin, *(0-9724007)* P.O. Box 885, Pacific Palisades, CA 90272 USA (SAN 255-0431) Tel 310-456-5251; Fax: 310-456-0119
E-mail: FictionSpin@aol.com
Web site: http://www.fictionspin.com
Dist(s): **AtlasBooks Distribution.**

Fidelity Heart Publishing, *(0-9748522)* Orders Addr.: P.O. Box 1758, Houston, TX 77251 USA; Edit Addr.: 3923 Teal Run Pl., Ct, Fresno, TX 77545-7049 USA
E-mail: slmccraw@fidelityheart.com
Web site: http://www.fidelityheart.com.

Fidjus, *(0-9714964)* 4906 Pacifca Dr., San Diego, CA 92109 USA Tel 858-272-6237; Fax: 858-581-9336
E-mail: fidjis@myexcel.com.

Field Stone Pubs., *(0-9645272)* 331 Fields Hill Rd., Conway, MA 01341 USA Tel 413-369-4091; Fax: 413-369-4212
E-mail: fieldstn@crocker.com
Web site: http://www.crocker.com/fieldstn.

Fielder Group, *(0-9639986; 0-9789058)* Orders Addr.: P.O. Box 510, Benton, KY 42025 USA Tel 888-255-9248; Fax: 270-362-7130; Toll Free: 888-255-9248
E-mail: barbara@thefieldergroupusa.com
Web site: http://www.thefieldergroupusa.com.

Fielding Travel Books *See* **Fielding Worldwide, Inc.**

Fielding Worldwide, Inc., *(1-56952)* 4455 Torrance Blvd., No. 827, Torrance, CA 90503-4398 USA (SAN 201-4823)
E-mail: fielding@fieldingtravel.com
Web site: http://www.fieldingtravel.com.

Fields Communications & Publishing *See* **Fields Publishing, Inc.**

Fields Enterprises, Inc., *(1-930482)* Orders Addr.: P.O. Box 940, Douglas, WY 82633 USA Tel 307-358-4679; Edit Addr.: 219 Cold Springs Rd., Douglas, WY 82633 USA Do not confuse with Fields Enterprises, Inc., Raleigh, NC
E-mail: dosherry@coffey.com
Web site: http://www.molleymagrew.com.

Fields of Gold Publishing, Inc., *(0-9746296)* P.O. Box 965, Brentwood, TN 37027 USA Tel 615-335-2014
E-mail: tyra@foginc.com
Web site: http://www.foginc.com
Dist(s): **Baker & Taylor Bks.**

Fields Publishing, Inc., *(1-57843)* 8120 Sawyer Brown Rd. Ste. 108, Nashville, TN 37221-1410 USA
E-mail: Fieldsco@mindspring.com
Web site: http://www.fieldspublishing.com.

Fieldstone Hill Pr., *(0-9767762)* 321 Old Saluda Dam Rd., Easley, SC 29640 USA
Web site: http://www.fieldstone-hill.net.

Fiery Studios, *(0-9743110)* P.O. Box 51595, Kalamazoo, MI 49005-1595 USA
Web site: http://www.vogelein.com
Dist(s): **Diamond Bk. Distributors.**

Fiesta City Pubs., *(0-940076)* P.O. Box 5861, Santa Barbara, CA 93150-5861 USA (SAN 217-071X) Tel 805-681-9199
E-mail: fcooke3924@aol.com.

Fifth Ave Pr., *(0-9755390)* 413 Salt Pond Rd., Bethany Beach, DE 19930 USA Tel 302-537-9633; Fax: 302-537-0210; Toll Free: 800-862-6443 Do not confuse with Fifth Avenue Press in Fargo, ND and New York, NY.
E-mail: bethanybil@aol.com
Web site: http://www.e-studio8.com/fifthstreetpress.

Fifth Estate, Inc., *(0-9746336; 0-9760992; 0-9768233; 1-933580)* Orders Addr.: P.O. Box 116, Blountsville, AL 35031 USA Tel 205-237-9511; Toll Free: 888-734-2476; Edit Addr.: 2795 Cty. Hwy. 57, Blountsville, AL 35031 USA (SAN 852-6419) Tel 1-888-734-2476 Do not confuse with The Fifth Estate, Inc. in Providence, RI
E-mail: admin@fifth-estate.net
Web site: http://www.fifth-estate.net.

Fifth Hse. Pubs. (CAN) *(0-920079; 1-895618; 1-894004; 1-894856) Dist. by* **FandW Pubns Inc.**

Fifth Planet Pr., *(1-880855)* 268 Martha Ave., Atlanta, GA 30317 USA Tel 404-373-6919
E-mail: nisa@fifthplanetpress.com
Web site: http://www.fifthplanetpress.com
Dist(s): **SPD-Small Pr. Distribution.**

Figure 8 Pr., *(0-9630376)* P.O. Box 555, Belfast, ME 04915-0555 USA Tel 500-673-4448 (trade order)
E-mail: mreight@excite.com
Dist(s): **Pathway Bk. Service.**

Filaretos, William, *(0-9724520)* 220 W. Canton St. # 3, Boston, MA 02116-5814 USA
E-mail: william_filaretos@thepotionoftime.com
Web site: http://www.ThePotionofTime.com.

Filion, Rita-Anneliese, *(0-9749142)* 26 Elizabeth Ln., Saratoga Springs, NY 12866-2804 USA
E-mail: sirdino@noblebones.com
Web site: http://www.noblebones.com.

Filiquarian Publishing, LLC, *(0-9770505; 1-59986)* Orders Addr.: 110 W. Grant St. Unit 2c, Minneapolis, MN 55403 USA Tel 612-207-2335 ; *Imprints:* FQ Classics (FQ Classics).

Fillet Of Horn Publishing, *(0-9753077)* 35000 Muskrat Rd., Barnesville, OH 43713 USA Tel 740-758-5050; Fax: 740-758-5114
Web site: http://www.filletofhorn.com.

Films for the Humanities & Sciences *See* **Films Media Group**

Films Media Group, *(0-7365; 0-89113; 1-56950; 1-4213; 1-60467)* Div. of Primedia, Orders Addr.: P.O. Box 2053, Princeton, NJ 08543-2053 USA (SAN 653-2705) Tel 609-671-1000; Fax: 609-671-0266; Toll Free: 800-257-5126; Edit Addr.: 2572 Brunswick Pike, Lawrenceville, NJ 08648 USA
E-mail: custserv@films.com
Web site: http://www.films.com
Dist(s): **Cambridge Educational**
Follett Media Distribution
National Video Resources, Inc.

Filter Pr., LLC, *(0-86541; 0-910584)* P.O. Box 95, Palmer Lake, CO 80133 USA (SAN 201-484X) Tel 719-481-2420 (phone/fax); Toll Free: 888-570-2663
E-mail: info@filterpressbooks.com; doris@filterpressbooks.com
Web site: http://www.filterpressbooks.com
Dist(s): **Baker & Taylor Bks.**
Books West.

Finch Bks. Co., *(0-9661457)* Orders Addr.: P.O. Box 545, Tularosa, NM 88352 USA; Edit Addr.: 1418 Apple Ave., Tularosa, NM 88352 USA Tel 505-585-8037; Fax: 505-585-8039
Dist(s): **MBI Distribution Services.**

Findaway World, LLC, *(1-59895; 1-60252; 1-60514)* 3199 Aurora Rd., Solon, OH 44139 USA (SAN 853-8778)
E-mail: glamarca@playawaydigital.com
Web site: http://www.findawayworld.com; http://www.playawaydigital.com.

Findel Education, Ltd. (GBR) *Dist. by* **Schl Spec Pubng.**

Findhorn Pr. (GBR) *(0-905249; 1-899171; 0-906191; 0-9504268; 1-84409) Dist. by* **IPG Chicago.**

Fine Art Editions *Imprint of* **North American International**

Fine Communications, *(1-56731; 1-59308)* Div. of Fine Creative Media, Inc., 322 Eighth Ave., 15th Flr., New York, NY 10001 USA Tel 212-595-3500; Fax: 212-595-3779 ; *Imprints:* M J F Books (MJF Bks)
E-mail: mjf@mjfbooks.com; rebecca@mjfbooks.com
Dist(s): **Sterling Publishing Co., Inc.**

Fine Madness, *(0-9722988)* PO Box 31138, Seattle, WA 98103-1138 USA
E-mail: beastly@oz.net
Web site: http://www.finemadness.org.

Fine Media Group, *(0-9716826; 1-932008)* 9925 S. 76th Ave., Bridgeview, IL 60455 USA Tel 708-636-2003 Toll Free: 800-364-2000
E-mail: info@finemediagroup.com
Web site: http://www.finemediagroup.com.

Fine Print Publishing Co., *(0-9640713; 1-892951)* Orders Addr.: P.O. Box 916401, Longwood, FL 32791-6401 USA Tel 407-814-7777; Fax: 407-814-7677; Edit Addr.: 1350 Sheeler Rd., Apopka, FL 32703 USA
E-mail: books@fprint.net.

Finer Moments, *(0-9771549)* P.O. Box 22102, Robbinsdale, MN 55422 USA Tel 612-302-7830
E-mail: finermoments@earthlink.net
Web site: http://www.finermoments.net.

Fingerprint Bks., *(0-9709861)* P.O. Box 534, Redlands, CA 92373 USA (SAN 253-7923) Tel 909-307-9993 (phone/fax)
E-mail: mglis2t@earthlink.net.

Finial Publishing, *(1-933791)* P.O. Box 346, Mercer Island, WA 98040 USA
Web site: http://www.finialpublishing.com.

Fink, Andie, *(0-9715432)* 756 Wagonhound Rd., Douglas, WY 82633-9203 USA
E-mail: andie@ki7xh.com; andie_fink@hotmail.com.

FINK, Inc., *(1-930281)* P.O. Box 7562, Santa Monica, CA 90406-7562 USA Tel 310-384-1334
E-mail: info@studylab.com
Web site: http://www.studylab.com; http://www.finkadelic.com
Dist(s): **Diamond Comic Distributors, Inc.**

Finkelstein, Ruth, *(0-9628157)* 27 Saddle River Rd., Airmont, NY 10952-3034 USA.

Finlay Prints, Inc., *(0-9766998)* Orders Addr.: 74 Fifth Ave., 6D, New York, NY 10011 USA Tel 212-463-7173
E-mail: finlayprints@earthlink.net.

Finneran, Lisa, *(0-9777744)* 9709 River Rd., Newport News, VA 23601-2360 USA
E-mail: arkangels@cox.net.

Finney Co., Inc., *(0-89317; 0-912486; 0-933855; 0-9617767; 0-9639705; 1-880654; 1-893272)* Orders Addr.: 8075 215th St. W., Lakeville, MN 55044 USA (SAN 206-412X) Tel 952-469-6699; Fax: 952-469-1968; Toll Free Fax: 800-330-6232; Toll Free: 800-846-7027 ; *Imprints:* Windward Publishing (Windward Publng); Anacus Press (Anacus Press)
E-mail: feedback@finneyco.com; ecopress@peak.org
Web site: http://www.finneyco.com; http://www.ecopress.com; http://www.anacus.com; http://www.pogopress.com
Dist(s): **Baker & Taylor Bks.**
Book Wholesalers, Inc.
Brodart Co.
Follett Library Resources
Midpoint Trade Bks., Inc.
Southern Bk. Service.

Fiore, *(0-9661235)* Orders Addr.: P.O. Box 50663, Phoenix, AZ 85076 USA Tel 602-759-0048; Toll Free: 888-443-4677; Edit Addr.: 4030 E. Lavender Ln., Phoenix, AZ 85044 USA.

Fiorello's Pumpkin Patch *See* **Pumpkin Patch Publishing**

Fire Creek Publishing Corp., *(0-9715543)* 3685 S. Narcissus Way, Suite 500, Denver, CO 80237 USA Tel 303-691-6591 ; *Imprints:* Lil' Pardner Press (Lil Pard Pr)
E-mail: lilpardner@earthlink.net
Web site: http://www.firecreekpub.com
Dist(s): **Books West.**

Fire Flies Entertainment, LLC, *(0-9787302)* 1077 North Ave., Suite 114, Elizabeth, NJ 07208 USA Tel 212-561-1654; Fax: 908-351-1888.

Fire Mountain Pr., *(1-929374)* Orders Addr.: P.O. Box 3851, Hillsboro, OR 97123 USA Tel 503-846-9057 (phone/fax); 503-219-5643 (phone/fax)
Web site: http://www.firemountainpress.com.

Fire River Pr., *(0-9675089)* P.O. Box 397, Manzanita, OR 97130 USA (SAN 253-0007) Tel 503-368-6294
E-mail: fireriverpress@nehalemtel.net
Dist(s): **Baker & Taylor Bks.**

Firefly Bks., Ltd. (CAN) *(0-920668; 1-55209; 1-895565; 1-896284; 1-55297; 1-55407) Dist. by* **Firefly Bks Limited.**

Firefly Bks., Ltd., *(0-920668; 1-55209; 1-895565; 1-896284; 1-55297; 1-55407)* Orders Addr.: c/o Frontier Distributing, 1000 Young St., Suite 160, Tonawanda, NY 14150 USA (SAN 630-611X) Tel 203-222-9700; Toll Free Fax: 800-565-6034; Toll Free: 800-387-5085; Edit Addr.: 8514 Long Canyon Dr., Austin, TX 78730-2813 USA
E-mail: service@fireflybooks.com
Web site: http://www.fireflybooks.com/.

Firefly Games, *(0-9747671)* 4514 Marconi Ave., No. 3, Sacramento, CA 95821 USA Tel 916-487-9689
E-mail: patrick@firefly-games.com
Web site: http://www.firefly-games.com.

Firelight Press, Inc., *(0-9786555; 1-934517)* 550 Larchmont Dr., Cincinnati, OH 45215 USA (SAN 851-2353); P.O. Box 15758, Cincinnati, OH 45215 Tel 513-646-6803; Fax: 513-821-2830 Do not confuse with companies with the same name in Independence, MO, Solvang, CA
E-mail: books@firelightpress.com
Web site: http://firelightpress.com.

Firelight Publishing, Inc., *(0-9707206)* Orders Addr.: P.O. Box 444, Sublimity, OR 97385-0444 USA Toll Free: 866-347-3544; Edit Addr.: 226 Division St., SW, Sublimity, OR 97385-9637 USA Tel 503-767-0444; Fax: 503-769-8980; Toll Free: 866-347-3544
E-mail: info@firelightpublishing.com; editor@firelightpublishing.com; webmaster@firelightpublishing.com; orders@firelightpublishing.com
Web site: http://www.firelightpublishing.com
Dist(s): **Baker & Taylor Bks.**
Partners/West.

Firenze Pr., *(0-9711236)* Orders Addr.: P.O. Box 6892, Wyomissing, PA 19610-0892 USA (SAN 254-315X); Edit Addr.: 612 Museum Rd., Reading, PA 19610-0892 USA Tel 610-374-7048; Fax: 610-478-7992 Do not confuse with Leonardo Pr., Camden, ME
E-mail: hailejohnjr@msn.com; HaileJohnJr@msn.com; InkPenCJH@msn.com
Web site: http://caroljhaile.com.

Fireproof Ministries, *(0-9741849)* P.O. Box 150169, Grand Rapids, MI 49515 USA
E-mail: info@fireproofministries.com
Web site: http://www.fireproofministries.com.

Fireside *Imprint of* **Simon & Schuster**

Fireside Book Shop, Inc., *(0-9700846)* 29 N. Franklin St., Chagrin Falls, OH 44022 USA Tel 440-247-4050; Fax: 440-247-4310
Dist(s): **Replica Bks.**

Fireside Bks., *(0-9718282)* P.O. Box 157, Saint Marys, GA 31558 USA Tel 912-576-2257 Do not confuse with companies with the same name in St. Louis, MO, Boise, ID, Chicago, IL, Shingle Spring, CA
E-mail: cbyor33@yahoo.com.

Company

Fireside Catholic Bibles, *(1-55665)* Div. of Fireside Catholic Bibles, Orders Addr.: P.O. Box 780189, Wichita, KS 67278-0189 USA Tel 316-267-3211; Fax: 316-267-1850; Toll Free: 888-676-2040; Edit Addr.: 9020 E. 35th St., N., Wichita, KS 67226 USA (SAN 854-0780)
E-mail: info@firesidebibles.com; llear@devore.cc
Web site: http://www.firesidebibles.com
Dist(s): **Spring Arbor Distributors, Inc.**

Fireside Critters, *(0-9753248)* Orders Addr.: P.O. Box 283, Vermilion, OH 44089 USA; Edit Addr.: P.O. Box 283, Vermilion, OH 44089 USA
E-mail: FiresideCritters@AOL.com.

Fireweed Pr., *(0-9772528)* Orders Addr.: P.O. Box 31037, Seattle, WA 98103 USA; Edit Addr.: 1807 N. 36th St., Seattle, WA 98103 USA Do not confuse with Fireweed Press in Falls Church, VA Fairbanks, AK, Madison, WI, Evergreen, CO AJ
E-mail: fireweedpress@comcast.net
Dist(s): **AtlasBooks Distribution.**

First Act, Inc., *(0-9720533)* P.O. Box 811, Needham, MA 02494 USA Tel 781-453-2221 Toll Free: 800-551-1115
E-mail: info@firstact.com
Web site: http://www.firstact.com.

First Assist Pubns., *(0-9724865)* P.O. Box 608, Woodland Hills, CA 91365 USA Fax: 818-346-8988
E-mail: e21sherr@aol.com
Dist(s): **Baker & Taylor Bks.**

First Associates Publishing, *(0-9618835)* P.O. Box 1281, Richmond, VA 23218-1281 USA (SAN 242-5289) Tel 804-254-0662; Fax: 804-524-5138; Toll Free: 877-247-8343
E-mail: earl@fapbooks.com.

First Avenue Editions *Imprint of* **Lerner Publishing Group**

First Biographies *Imprint of* **Reynolds, Morgan Inc.**

First Bite Publishing, *(0-9668234)* 230 N. College Dr., No. H8, Santa Maria, CA 93454 USA Tel 805-348-0098; Fax: 805-349-8904
E-mail: firstbitep@aol.com
Dist(s): **BookMasters, Inc.**

First Bks., *(0-912301)* 6750 SW Franklin St., Suite A, Portland, OR 97223 USA (SAN 297-9063) Tel 503-968-6777; Fax: 503-968-6779
E-mail: customerservice@firstbooks.com
Web site: http://www.firstbooks.com
Dist(s): **Baker & Taylor Bks.**
Bookazine Co., Inc.
Koen-Levy Bk. Wholesalers LLC
Partners Bk. Distributing, Inc.

First Century Publishing, *(1-885273)* Div. of First Century Church Ministries, P.O. Box 130, Delmar, NY 12054 USA Tel 518-439-3544; Fax: 518-439-0105; Toll Free: 800-570-6060
E-mail: dnbubar1@nycap.rr.com; 1century@nycap.rr.com
Web site: http://www.firstcenturypublishing.com
Dist(s): **STL Distribution North America.**

First Choice Entertainment, *(1-884429)* Orders Addr.: P.O. Box 54502, Phoenix, AZ 85078-4502 USA
E-mail: firstchoiceent05@msn.com.

First Christmas Project, *(0-9769828)* 333 Brooks Bend, Brownsburg, IN 46112 USA
Web site: http://www.firstchristmaspresent.com
Dist(s): **STL Distribution North America.**

First Class Fitness Systems, Inc., *(0-9747008)* 23901 Civic Ctr. Way, Suite 342, Malibu, CA 90265 USA Tel 310-456-3043
E-mail: Mario@myfitfamily.com
Web site: http://myfitfamily.com.

First Facts *Imprint of* **Capstone Pr., Inc.**

First Intensity Pr., *(1-889960)* P.O. Box 665, Lawrence, KS 66044 USA
Dist(s): **SPD-Small Pr. Distribution.**

First Light Publishing, *(0-9754411)* 14402 Twickenham Pl., Chesterfield, VA 23832 USA Do not confuse with First Light Publishing in Chagrin Falls, OH
E-mail: briantherock@cs.com
Dist(s): **Baker & Taylor Bks.**
Parklane Publishing.

First Mom's Club, The, *(0-9704876; 0-9728180; 0-9764557)* 367 Eric Way, Grants Pass, OR 97526-8820 USA
E-mail: dianne@thefirstmomsclub.com
Web site: http://www.thefirstmomsclub.com
Dist(s): **Alliance Bk. Co.**

First Page Press *See* **Marblehead Publishing**

First Second Bks. *Imprint of* **Roaring Brook Pr.**

First Stage Concepts, *(0-9667719; 1-931430)* Orders Addr.: P.O. Box 3390, Redondo Beach, CA 90277-1390 USA Tel 310-371-6834; Fax: 310-370-3392; Edit Addr.: 5410 W. 190th St., No. 98, Torrance, CA 90503-1030 USA
E-mail: quickstartguitar@msn.com
Web site: http://www.QuickStartGuitar.com
Dist(s): **Baker & Taylor Bks.**
Ingram Bk. Co.

First Steps Pr., *(0-9659944)* Orders Addr.: P.O. Box 380122, Clinton Township, MI 48038-0060 USA Tel 810-463-5670; Edit Addr.: 38453 Gail, Clinton Township, MI 48036 USA.

First Story Pr., *(1-890326)* 1800 Business Park Dr., Clarksville, TN 37040-6023 USA Tel 931-572-0806; Fax: 931-552-3200; Toll Free: 888-754-0208.

First Word Learning Systems, Inc., *(0-9657752)* Div. of First Word Publishing, 2460 W. Main St., Unit D, No. 203, Saint Charles, IL 60175-1000 USA Tel 630-377-7766; Fax: 630-377-7703; Toll Free: 888-414-8881
E-mail: williamrussell@firstwordinc.com
Dist(s): **Quality Bks., Inc.**

First Word Publishing, The, *(0-9708590)* 305 Lind Ave., SW, No. 9, Renton, WA 98055 USA Tel 425-254-8575
E-mail: dejonfw@ayhoo.com.

FirstCompany Books *See* **1stCoBooks**

First-Sight Publishing, *(0-9770363)* 9636 Nevada Ave., Chatsworth, CA 91311 USA Tel 818-882-8915
E-mail: dextergstudio@aol.com.

Fischer, Carl LLC, *(0-8258)* Orders Addr.: 588 N. Gulph Rd. Ste. B, Kng Of Prussa, PA 19406-2831 USA Toll Free: 800-762-2328; Edit Addr.: 65 Bleeker St., New York, NY 10012-2420 USA (SAN 107-4245) Tel 212-772-0900; Fax: 212-477-6996; Toll Free: 800-762-2328
E-mail: cf-info@carlfischer.com
Web site: http://www.carlfischer.com.

Fischer Taschenbuch Verlag (DEU) *(3-596) Dist. by* **Distribks Inc.**

Fischl, Peter L., *(0-9677562)* 229 1/2 E. Cedar Ave., Burbank, CA 91502-1406 USA Tel 818-841-6633; Fax: 818-841-6639
E-mail: peterl.fischl@worlnet.at.net
Web site: http://www.Holocaust-trc.org.

Fish Decoy.com, Ltd., *(0-9748721; 0-9759386)* Orders Addr.: P.O. Box 321, Cross River, NY 10518 USA (SAN 256-1093) Tel 914-533-5181; Edit Addr.: 71 Conant Valley Rd., Pound Ridge, NY 10576 USA; 218 Honey Hallow Rd., Pound Ridge, NY 10576
Web site: http://www.fishdecoystore.com
Dist(s): **Antique Collectors' Club.**

Fish Head Pubns., LLC, *(1-934627)* 5013 W. Buckskin Tr., Glendale, AZ 85310 USA
Web site: http://www.fishheadpublications.com.

Fish Rock Publishing Co., *(0-9705329)* 33801 S. Hwy. 1, Gualala, CA 95445 USA Tel 707-884-3631 (phone/fax)
E-mail: soden@mcn.org.

Fish Tales Publishing, *(0-9795860)* Orders Addr.: 65 Glen Rd., PMB 128, Garner, NC 27529 USA (SAN 853-8344) Tel 919-320-7428
E-mail: Books@fishtales.org
Web site: http://www.fishtales.org.

Fishbowl International, Inc., *(0-9745188; 0-9765619)* Orders Addr.: P.O. Box 362, Roxie, MS 39661 USA Tel 601-384-0219; Fax: 601-384-1667
E-mail: fishbowlinternational@yahoo.com
Web site: http://www.fishbowlinternational.com.

Fisher & Hale Publishing, *(0-9742037)* Div. of Horizon Bks., Orders Addr.: 6525 Gunpark Dr. 370, #250, Boulder, CO 80301 USA; Edit Addr.: 18841 E. Cornell Ave., Aurora, CO 80013 USA
E-mail: slmclean@hotmail.com
Web site: http://www.fisherhale.com.

Fisher Enterprises, *(0-9767265)* P.O. Box 1342, Eagle, ID 83616 USA Tel 208-939-6650; Fax: 208-939-7480 Do not confuse with Fisher Enterprises, Inc. In Edmonds, WA
E-mail: ggfisher@earthlink.net.

Fisher Hill, *(1-878253)* 5267 Warner Ave., No. 166, Huntington Beach, CA 92649 USA (SAN 254-1289) Tel 714-377-9495; Fax: 714-377-9353; Toll Free: 800-214-8110
E-mail: fisher.k@mac.com
Web site: http://www.Fisher-Hill.com
Dist(s): **Baker & Taylor Bks.**
Continental Bk. Co., Inc.
Delta Systems Co., Inc.
Saddleback Educational Publishing.

Fisher, John Wilfred, *(0-9771093)* 25216 Arrow Highline Rd., Juliaetta, ID 83535 USA Tel 208-843-7159
E-mail: jwfisher@starband.net.

Fisher Wilcoxon *See* **Fisher Hill**

Fishman, Greg, *(0-9766153)* 824 Custer Ave., Evanston, IL 60202 USA
E-mail: greg1111@aol.com
Web site: http://www.gregfishmanjazzstudios.com.

Fit America, *(0-9706098)* 401 Fairway Dr., Deerfield Beach, FL 33441 USA Tel 954-570-3211; 954 570 3211; Fax: 954-570-8608; Toll Free: 800-221-1186
E-mail: maryannmorgan@fitamerica.com; chrisferris@fitamerica.com
Web site: http://www.fitamerica.com.

Fit Kids, *(0-9709301)* 175 W. 200 S., Suite 2012, Salt Lake City, UT 84101-1459 USA Tel 801-521-0109; Fax: 801-521-8360; Toll Free: 888-234-8543
E-mail: brucebellco@earthlink.net
Web site: http://www.fitkids.org.

Fit To Print, *(0-9672993)* 209 East Bloomfield Ave., Royal Oak, MI 48073 USA Tel 248-583-2847; Fax: 248-583-2837
E-mail: dcadman@f2p.com
Web site: http://f2p.com.

Fitch, Michele Marko, *(0-615)* 2103 Wilkerson St., South Boston, MA 24592 USA
E-mail: familyfitch@myembarg.com
Dist(s): **Lulu.com.**

Fithian Pr., *(0-931832; 1-56474)* Div. of Daniel & Daniel Pubs., Inc., P.O. Box 1525, Santa Barbara, CA 93102 USA (SAN 211-6103) Tel 805-962-1780; Fax: 805-962-8835; Toll Free: 800-662-8351 (orders only)
E-mail: dandd@danielpublishing.com
Web site: http://www.danielpublishing.com
Dist(s): **AtlasBooks Distribution**
SCB Distributors.

Fitness Information Technology, Inc., *(0-9627926; 1-885693)* Orders Addr.: P.O. Box 6116, Morgantown, WV 26506 USA; Edit Addr.: 262 Coliseium. WVU-PE, Morgantown, WV 26506-6116 USA Tel 304-293-6888; Fax: 304-293-6658; Toll Free: 800-477-4348
E-mail: ICPE@mail.wvu.edu
Web site: http://www.fitinfotech.com
Dist(s): **Unifacmanu International Trading Co., Inc.**

Fitzgerald Bks., *(1-887238; 1-59054; 1-4242)* Div. of Central Programs, Inc., Orders Addr.: P.O. Box 505, Bethany, MO 64424 USA Tel 660-425-7969; Fax: 660-425-3929; Toll Free: 800-821-7199; Edit Addr.: 802 N. 41st St., Bethany, MO 64424 USA
E-mail: wecare@gumdropbooks.com
Web site: http://www.gumdropbooks.com
Dist(s): **Gumdrop Bks.**

Fitzgerald, Clyde C. *See* **Ira Valley Ideas**

Fitzroy Dearborn Pubs., Inc., *(1-57958; 1-884964)* 425 W. Briar Pl. Apt. 1E, Chicago, IL 60657-4767 USA Toll Free: 800-850-8102
E-mail: fitzroy@aol.com
Web site: http://www.fitzroydearborn.com
Dist(s): **Sony CONNECT, Inc.**
Taylor & Francis, Inc.

Five Colors, *(0-9703248)* 403 Orchard Ave., Scottdale, PA 15683-1225 USA Tel 724-887-8099; Fax: 724-887-8097; Toll Free: 877-311-4233
E-mail: curt@five-colors.com
Web site: http://www.five-colors.com.

Five Degrees of Frannie, *(0-9679115)* P.O. Box 178, North Greece, NY 14515 USA Tel 716-467-9136
E-mail: ohfrannie@aol.com.

Five Oaks Pr., *(0-9779325)* P.O. Box 251, Lake Lure, NC 28746-0251 USA
E-mail: davidklett@bellsouth.net
Web site: http://www.lakelurechronicles.com.

Five O'clock Dog, *(0-9767887)* Orchid # 1170, Corona del Mar, CA 92625 USA Tel 949-422-5909
Web site: http://www.fiveodog.com
Dist(s): **Baker & Taylor Bks.**

Five Ponds Pr., *(0-9727156)* 14 Five Ponds Dr., Waccabuc, NY 10597 USA Tel 914-763-2323; Fax: 914-763-6328
E-mail: info@fivepondspress.com
Web site: http://www.fivepondspress.com.

Five Smooth Stones, *(0-9674492)* P.O. Box 578, Salem, VA 24153-0578 USA Tel 540-387-1072; Fax: 540-387-3599
E-mail: fivesmoothstones@earthlink.net
Web site: http://www.fivestonespublications.com.

Five Star *Imprint of* **Thomson Gale**

Five Star Christian Pubns., *(0-9740142; 0-9777291)* 312 SE 24th Ave., Cape Coral, FL 33990 USA Tel 239-574-1000
E-mail: info@5scp.com
Web site: http://www.gulfcoastbaptistchurch.com.

Five Star Pr., *(0-9673102)* Orders Addr.: P.O. Box 8454, Richmond, VA 23226 USA Tel 804-282-6069; Edit Addr.: 1910 Byrd Ave., Suite 12, Richmond, VA 23230 USA.

Five Star Pubns., Inc., *(0-9619853; 1-877749; 1-58985)* Orders Addr.: P.O. Box 6698, Chandler, AZ 85246-6698 USA (SAN 246-7429) Tel 480-940-8182; Fax: 480-940-8787; Edit Addr.: 4696 W. Tyson St., Chandler, AZ 85226-2903 USA
E-mail: info@fivestarpublications.com
Web site: http://www.fivestarpublications.com
Dist(s): **Baker & Taylor Bks.**
Quality Bks., Inc.
Unique Bks., Inc.

Five Star Special Edition *Imprint of* **American Literary Pr.**

Five Star Trade *Imprint of* **Thomson Gale**

Five Ways to Finish *Imprint of* **Team B Creative LLC**

Fivedegressbelowzero Pr., *(0-9708779)* 19 Winthrop Pl., Maplewood, NJ 07040 USA Tel 973-275-9370; Fax: 973-275-9372
Dist(s): **F & W Pubns., Inc.**

FizzBang Science, *(0-9718480)* 807 Murlay Dr., Plain City, OH 43064 USA Tel 614-873-8860 (phone/fax)
E-mail: blrohrig@worldnet.att.net
Web site: http://www.fizzbangscience.com.

Flaghouse, Inc., *(0-9713648; 1-932032)* 601 Rte. 46 W., Hasbrouck Heights, NJ 07604-3116 USA (SAN 631-3086) Tel 201-288-7600; Fax: 201-288-7887; Toll Free Fax: 800-793-7900
Web site: http://www.flaghouse.com.

Flagship Church Resources *Imprint of* **Group Publishing, Inc.**

Flaming Sparrow Press *See* **Foreworks**

Flammarion et Cie (FRA) *(2-08) Dist. by* **Distribks Inc.**

Flanders, Dean, P.O. Box 890, Crossville, TN 38557 USA Tel 931-456-6685.

Flash Blasters, Incorporated *See* **Ace Academics, Inc.**

Flashbacks, *(0-9703325)* 290 Sayles Rd., Duck Hill, MS 38925 USA Tel 662-226-5909
E-mail: mfondren@ayrix.net.

Flashlight Pr., *(0-9729225; 0-9799746)* 3709 13th Ave., Brooklyn, NY 11218 USA Tel 718-288-8300; Fax: 718-972-6307
E-mail: Editor@FlashlightPress.com; Publisher@FlashlightPress.com
Web site: http://www.flashlightpress.com/
Dist(s): **Independent Pubs. Group.**

FlashPaws Productions, *(0-9674929)* 7714 Rolling Fork Ln., Houston, TX 77040-3432 USA Tel 713-896-8484 (phone/fax)
E-mail: info@flashpaws.com
Web site: http://www.flashpaws.com
Dist(s): **Greenleaf Book Group.**

Flat Hammock Pr., *(0-9718303; 0-9758699; 0-9773725; 0-9795949)* 5 Church St., Mystic, CT 06355 USA Tel 860-572-2722; Fax: 860-572-2755
E-mail: info@flathammockpress.com
Web site: http://www.flathammockpress.com.

Flat Kids *Imprint of* **Smart Smiles Co., The**

Flatwater, Inc., *(0-9661672)* 3441 Archer Ct., Virginia Beach, VA 23452 USA Tel 757-631-8478
E-mail: thewhitehouse3@juno.com.

Flaxenfluff Pr., LLC, *(0-9743890)* P.O. Box 2287, Broken Arrow, OK 74013 USA
Web site: http://www.flaxenfluff.com.

Fleeting Moments Publishing, *(0-9725684)* Orders Addr.: P.O. Box 38, Brunswick, OH 44212 USA Tel 330-225-5512; Edit Addr.: 1177 Manitoulin Pk., Brunswick, OH 44212 USA.

Fletcher, C J Publishing LLC, *(0-9755255)* Orders Addr.: P.O. Box 784, Independence, KS 67301 USA (SAN 256-1050) Tel 620-331-5182; Fax: 620-331-5183; Toll Free: 800-814-8513; Edit Addr.: 212- 214 E. Myrtle, Independence, KS 67301 USA
E-mail: cjdcpa@cableone.net.

Fletcher, Elizabeth Byrd, *(0-9701870)* Orders Addr.: PUB 146, 3420 Pump Rd., Richmond, VA 23233-1111 USA Tel 757-249-8688; Fax: 757-247-0951
E-mail: elizabeth.fletcher@nn.k12.va.us
Web site: http://www.ss-united-states.com.

Fletcher, Robert *See* **Iron Mountain Pr.**

Fleur Art Productions, *(0-9741277)* 32 N. Goodwin Ave., Elmsford, NY 10523 USA Fax: 914-206-3558; Toll Free: 866-353-8727 ; *Imprints:* Fleur Publishing (Fleur Pubng)
E-mail: agents@fleur.ws
Web site: http://www.fleur.ws
Dist(s): **E-Pros DG.**

Fleur Publishing *Imprint of* **Fleur Art Productions**

Fleuve Noir (FRA) *(2-265) Dist. by* **Distribks Inc.**

Flinn Scientific, Inc., *(1-877991; 1-933709)* Orders Addr.: P.O. Box 219, Batavia, IL 60510 USA (SAN 630-1800) Fax: 866-452-1436; Toll Free: 800-452-1261; Edit Addr.: 770 N. Raddant Rd., Batavia, IL 60510 USA
E-mail: flinn@flinnsci.com.

Flip Publishing, *(0-9769342)* P.O. Box 1072, Hawthorne, CA 90251 USA
E-mail: flippublishing@yahoo.com
Web site: www.flippublishing.net
Dist(s): **Independent Pubs. Group.**

Flipp Sports, *(0-9744443)* 960 Turnpike St., Canton, MA 02021 USA Tel 781-821-8788; Fax: 781-821-4088
E-mail: jmarnikovic@flippsports.com
Web site: http://www.flippsports.com.

Flippin' Bks. LLC, *(0-9742500)* 25450 Williams Ridge, Warrenton, MO 63383 USA Tel 636-456-6224
E-mail: thw@flippinbooks.com
Web site: http://www.flippinbooks.com.

Floating Pr., *(1-887153)* Orders Addr.: 9305 Sandridge Rd., Long Beach, WA 98631-5102 USA Tel 360-642-8090
E-mail: booklady@pacifier.com.

FloBound Poems Publications, *(0-9705819)* Orders Addr.: P.O. Box 3101, Fredericksburg, VA 22402-3101 USA
E-mail: floboundpoems@aol.com; morningpoemsflog@aol.com
Web site: http://www.floboundpoems.com.

Flood Crest Pr., *(1-934130)* 604 E. Spring St., New Albany, IN 47150 USA Tel 812-944-5116; Fax: 812-944-5277
E-mail: ops@destinationsbooksellers.com
Web site: http://www.destinationsbooksellers.com.

Floodgate Publishing, *(0-9761355)* P.O. Box 1475, Castle Rock, WA 98611 USA.

Floppinfish Publishing Co., Ltd., *(0-9629124)* P.O. Box 4932, Saint Louis, MO 63108 USA Tel 314-567-8697
E-mail: wm4932@yahoo.com
Web site: http://www.JoeKeylon.com; http://www.pixofpeople.com
Dist(s): **Baker & Taylor Bks.**
Big River Distribution
Partners Bk. Distributing, Inc.

Flores, Travis, *(0-9759077)* P.O. Box 143, Newport, OH 45768 USA Tel 740-473-2999 (phone/fax)
E-mail: sparkeythespider@aol.com
Web site: http://www.sparkeythespider.com.

Floricanto Pr., *(0-915745; 0-9796457)* Div. of Inter American Development, 650 Castro St., Suite 120, No. 331, Mountain View, CA 94041-2055 USA (SAN 293-9169) Tel 415-552-1879; Fax: 415-793-2662; 702-995-1410
E-mail: info@floricantopress.com; rcabello@floricantopress.com
Web site: http://www.floricantopress.com.

Florida Classics Library, *(0-912451)* P.O. Drawer 1657, Port Salerno, FL 34992-1657 USA (SAN 265-2404) Tel 561-546-9380 (orders); Fax: 561-546-7545 (orders).

Florida Div. of Historical Resources, *(0-9642289; 1-889030)* Div. of Florida Dept. of State, c/o Bureau of Historic Preservation, 500 S. Bronough St., Tallahassee, FL 32399-0250 USA Tel 850-487-2333; Fax: 850-922-0496; Toll Free: 800-847-7278
Web site: http://www.dhrdos.state.fl.us/dhr/; http://www.flheritage.com.

Florida Literary Foundation, *(1-877978; 1-891855)* P.O. Box 711612, Herndon, VA 20121 USA Tel 703 856 5542 ; *Imprints:* STARbooks Press (STARbks Pr)
E-mail: info@flf.org; info@starbookspress.com
Web site: http://www.FLF.org; http://www.STARbooksPress.com
Dist(s): **Publishers Distributing Co.**

Florida Science Source, Inc., *(0-944961)* Orders Addr.: P.O. Box 8217, Longboat Key, FL 34228-8217 USA (SAN 245-6974); Edit Addr.: 2205 Harbourside Dr., Longboat Key, FL 34228-4108 USA (SAN 245-6982)
E-mail: FSSOURCE@aol.com
Web site: http://www.ultimacitrus.com/fssource.

Floris Bks. (GBR) *(0-86315; 0-903540) Dist. by* **SteinerBooks Inc.**

Floris Bks. (GBR) *(0-86315; 0-903540) Dist. by* **Gryphon Hse.**

Flo's Productions, *(0-9769645)* 4072 Grandview Dr., Flushing, MI 48433 USA Tel 810-720-5174 (phone/fax)
E-mail: flosproductions@comcast.net
Web site: http://www.flosproductions.biz.

Flournoy, Ronnie, *(0-9720330)* P.O. Box 100773, Fort Lauderdale, FL 33310-0773 USA Tel 954-560-3790
E-mail: rflourn3@bellsouth.net.

Flower Press *See* **Flowerfield Enterprises**

Flower Valley Pr., Inc., *(0-9620543; 1-886388)* P.O. Box 952, Glen Echo, MD 20812 USA (SAN 249-0277) Tel 301-654-1996; Fax: 301-654-1905; Toll Free: 800-735-5197
E-mail: dbress@flowervalleypress.com
Web site: http://www.dbress@flowervalleypress.com.

Flowerfield Enterprises, *(0-942256)* 10332 Shaver Rd., Kalamazoo, MI 49024-6744 USA (SAN 217-7358) Tel 269-327-0108; Fax: 269-327-7009
E-mail: nancy@wormwoman.com
Web site: http://www.wormwoman.com.

Flowerpress Bks. & Creative Hands, *(0-9667394)* Orders Addr.: P.O. Box 2217, Eugene, OR 97402 USA Tel 541-343-1562; Edit Addr.: 85281 Sarvisberry, Eugene, OR 97405 USA.

Fluckiger, Jay D. *See* **Harmony Hse. Publishing Co.**

Flugul Pubng, *(0-9779390)* P.O. Box 6090, Cincinnati, OH 45206 USA
E-mail: VLI@flugulpublishing.com
Web site: http://www.Flugulpublishing.com.

Fluharty, Linda Cunningham, *(0-9759097)* 833 Carnforth Dr., Baton Rouge, LA 70810 USA
E-mail: LCFlu@aol.com
Web site: http://www.lindapages.com.

Flutter-By Productions, *(0-9714734)* 1404 Goodlette Rd. N., Naples, FL 34102 USA Tel 941-240-1685; Fax: 239-262-2244
Web site: http://www.flutter-byproductions.com
Dist(s): **APG Sales and Fulfillment.**

Flux *Imprint of* **Llewellyn Pubns.**

Fly by Night Productions *Imprint of* **Interlight Studios, Inc.**

Flying Cloud Bks., *(0-615)* 123 Moore Rd., Sudbury, MA 01776 USA
E-mail: mail@paulgreenspan.com
Web site: http:www.paulgreenspan.com
Dist(s): **Lulu.com.**

Flying Dolphin Pr. *Imprint of* **Doubleday Publishing**

Flying Frog Publishing, *(0-9666647)* 567 Westcove Dr., Wasilla, AK 99654-7161 USA Tel 907-373-6994 (phone/fax); Toll Free: 888-673-6994 Do not confuse with Flying Frog Publishing, Reisterstown, MD
E-mail: jobshlh@corecom.net
Web site: http://www.galaxymall.com/children/alaskariddles
Dist(s): **Todd Communications**
Wizard Works.

Flying Frog Publishing *Imprint of* **Allied Publishing**

Flying Leap Music, *(1-930664)* 53599 N. Highway 245., Miramonte, CA 93641-9703 USA
E-mail: fleap@fleap.com
Web site: http://www.fleap.com.

Flying Pig Publishing, *(0-9746110)* P.O. Box 304, Harvard, MA 01451 USA
E-mail: douglee41@yahoo.com
Web site: http://deelee.net.

Flying Rhino Productions, Incorporated *See* **Flying Rhinoceros, Inc.**

Flying Rhinoceros, Inc., *(1-883772; 1-59168)* 1440 NW Overton St., Portland, OR 97209 USA Tel 503-552-8700; Fax: 503-221-7282; Toll Free: 800-537-4466
E-mail: flyingrhino@flyingrhino.com
Web site: http://www.flyingrhino.com.

Flying Snail Pr., *(1-892517)* P.O. Box 3157, South Pasadena, CA 91030 USA Tel 323-256-2600; Fax: 323-256-2227
E-mail: flyingsnailpress@worldnet.att.net.

Flying Squirrel Press *See* **Heritage Heart Farm**

Flyleaf Publishing, *(0-9658246; 1-929262; 1-60541)* Orders Addr.: P.O. Box 287, Lyme, NH 03768-0287 USA Toll Free: 800-449-7006 ; *Imprints:* Books To Remember (Bks To Remember)
E-mail: laura@flyleafpublishing.com
Web site: http://www.flyleafpublishing.com.

Flywheel Publishing Co., *(1-930826)* Orders Addr.: 1375 Sunnyhills Rd., Oakland, CA 94610 USA (SAN 253-2441) Tel 510-407-7577; Fax: 510-373-6060
E-mail: admin@flywheel.us
Web site: http://www.flywheel.us.

FM Rocks Kids, LLC *See* **Playdate Kids Publishing**

Focal Pr. *Imprint of* **Elsevier Science & Technology Bks.**

Focus Friends, LLC, *(0-9786028)* 5209 Black Bark Ct., Fort Collins, CO 80528 USA (SAN 851-0946)
Web site: http://www.focusfriends.com.

Focus Group, Inc., *(0-9766968)* 1800 Westlake Ave. N., No. 206, Seattle, WA 98109 USA Tel 206-281-8520; Fax: 206-281-8530
E-mail: pubs@focusgroupseattle.com.

†Focus on the Family Publishing, *(0-929608; 1-56179; 1-58997; 1-60482)* 8605 Explorer Dr., Colorado Springs, CO 80920-1051 USA (SAN 250-0949) Fax: 719-531-3356; Toll Free: 800-232-6459
Web site: http://www.family.org
Dist(s): **Gospel Light Pubns.**
Nelson, Tommy
Tyndale Hse. Pubs.
Zondervan; *CIP.*

Focus on Your Future, *(0-9678027)* P.O. Box 280823, Lakewood, CO 80228-0248 USA
E-mail: sandy-austin@worldnet.att.net
Web site: http://www.focusonyourfuture.net.

Focus Publishing, *(1-885904)* Orders Addr.: P.O. Box 665, Bemidji, MN 56619 USA Tel 218-759-9817; Fax: 218-751-7210; Toll Free: 800-913-6287; Edit Addr.: 502 Third St., NW, Bemidji, MN 56601 USA
Dist(s): **Appalachian Bk. Distributors**
Spring Arbor Distributors, Inc.

Focus Publishing/R. Pullins Co., Inc., *(0-941051; 1-58510)* P.O. Box 369, Newburyport, MA 01950 USA (SAN 665-2654) Tel 978-462-7288; 978-462-1378 (orders); Fax: 978-462-9035; Toll Free: 800-848-7236 (orders)
E-mail: pullins@pullins.com; kerri@pullins.com
Web site: http://www.pullins.com; http://www.focusbookstore.com.

Fodor's *Imprint of* **Fodor's Travel Pubns.**

Fodor's Travel Guides *See* **Fodor's Travel Pubns.**

Fodor's Travel Pubns., Div. of Random Hse., Information Group, Orders Addr.: 400 Hahn Rd., Westminster, MD 21157 USA Tel 410-848-1900; Toll Free: 800-726-0600; Edit Addr.: 1745 Broadway, New York, NY 10019 USA Tel 212-782-9000 ; *Imprints:* Fodor's (Fodor)
Web site: http://www.fodors.com
Dist(s): **Libros Sin Fronteras**
Random Hse., Inc.

Fog City Pr., *(1-875137; 1-887451; 1-892374; 1-929156; 1-74089)* Subs. of Weldon Owen, Inc., 2215-R Market St., No. 123, San Francisco, CA 94114 USA Tel 415-626-9636
E-mail: gilblock@sirius.com.

Foglestories, *(0-9716507)* Orders Addr.: P.O. Box 7714, Mesa, AZ 85277 USA; Edit Addr.: 1265 S. Meridian Lot, No. 24, Apache Junction, AZ 85220 USA
E-mail: dufogle49@aol.com.

Foglight Pr., *(0-9755848)* P.O. Box 22512, Sacramento, CA 95822 USA
E-mail: info@foglightpress.com
Web site: http://www.foglightpress.com.

folder leaf *Imprint of* **Story Time Stories That Rhyme**

Folse, John D. *See* **Chef John Folse & Co.**

Folsom Fallies Pr., *(0-9760790)* Orders Addr.: P.O. Box 348, Folsom, NM 88419 USA Tel 505-278-2520
E-mail: kristene@folsomfallies.com
Web site: http://www.folsomfallies.com.

Fondo de Cultura Economica (MEX) *(968-16) Dist. by* **Continental Bk.**

Fondo de Cultura Economica (MEX) *(968-16) Dist. by* **Lectorum Pubns.**

Fondo de Cultura Economica USA, *(968-16; 950-557; 956-7083; 9972-663)* 2293 Verus St., San Diego, CA 92154 USA Tel 619-429-0827; Fax: 619-429-0455; Toll Free: 800-532-3872
E-mail: sales@fceusa.com; fceusa@fceusa.com
Web site: http://www.fceusa.com
Dist(s): **Ediciones Universal**
Giron Bks.
Latin American Bk. Source, Inc.
Lectorum Pubns., Inc.
Libros Sin Fronteras
Trucatriche.

Font & Ctr. Pr., *(1-883280)* Orders Addr.: P.O. Box 95, Weston, MA 02493-0005 USA Tel 781-647-9756; Fax: 781-788-9643; Toll Free: 800-647-8658; Edit Addr.: 69 Pinecroft Rd., Weston, MA 02493 USA
E-mail: info@fontandcenter.com
Web site: http://www.fontandcenter.com.

Fontanel Bks., *(0-9709048)* P.O. Box 29234, Santa Fe, NM 87592 USA Tel 505-471-4102; Fax: 505-471-4202
E-mail: email@fontanelbooks.com; alansg@earthlink.net
Web site: http://www.fontanelbooks.com.

Food Allergy & Anaphylaxis Network, *(1-882541)* 11781 Lee Jackson Hwy. Suite 160, Fairfax, VA 22033 USA Tel 703-691-3179; Fax: 703-691-2713; Toll Free: 800-929-4040
E-mail: faan@foodallergy.org
Web site: http://www.foodallergy.org.

Food Allergy Network *See* **Food Allergy & Anaphylaxis Network**

Food Enhancement Enterprises, *(0-9747247)* Orders Addr.: P.O. Box 60581, Sacramento, CA 95680 USA; Edit Addr.: 2148 Bluebird Ln., Sacramento, CA 95821 USA
E-mail: hsdell@lanset.com
Web site: http://www.pizzareconsidered.com.

Food Marketing Consultants, Inc., *(0-9763307; 1-59949)* 2805 N. Commerce Pkwy., Miramar, FL 33025 USA Tel 954-322-2668 Toll Free: 877-493-2633
Web site: http://www.colorallabout.com.

Food Network Kitchens *Imprint of* **Meredith Bks.**

Foothill-Hydroponics, *(0-9669557)* 10705 Burbank Blvd., N., North Hollywood, CA 91601 USA Tel 818-760-0688; Fax: 818-760-4025
E-mail: mohsen@foothillhydroponics.com
Web site: http://www.foothill-hydroponic.com.

Footprints Pr., *(0-9679813)* 71 Hudson St., New York, NY 10013 USA Tel 212-267-9300; Fax: 212-267-9400.

For Children Only, *(0-9672224)* P.O. Box 522, Flossmoor, IL 60422 USA
E-mail: Hallfco@aol.com.

For Dummies *Imprint of* **Wiley, John & Sons, Inc.**

For His Glory Publishing, *(0-9749424)* P.O. Box 5956, Midlothian, VA 23112 USA.

For Kids' Sake Pr., *(1-930653)* 805 Rio Grande, Suite 1, Austin, TX 78701 USA Tel 512-263-3371 (phone/fax)
E-mail: claire@texas.net
Web site: http://www.for-Kids-Sake.com.

For Little Folks, *(0-9771236)* P.O. Box 571, Dresden, OH 43821 USA.

For Pete's Sake Publishing, *(0-9721472)* 7 Plymouth Dr., Saco, ME 04072 USA Tel 207-284-9848 (phone/fax)
E-mail: jvervill@maine.rr.com
Web site: http://www.readforpetessake.com.

For Such A Time As This Ministries, *(0-9725890)* 510 Swank Rd., Hollsopple, PA 15935-8116 USA Tel 814-479-7710; Fax: 814-479-4874; Toll Free: 877-378-4374
E-mail: jpstobaugh@aol.com
Web site: http://www.forsuchatimeasthis.com.

For The Love of Dog Bks., *(0-9761124)* 635 NE Buffalo, Portland, OR 97211 USA Tel 503-286-5351
E-mail: stelljes@aol.com
Web site: http//www.silvertonbobbie.com
Dist(s): **Far West Bk. Service**
Partners/West.

For Your Knowledge *Imprint of* **Ann Arbor Media Group, LLC**

Forbes Literary Ltd. Inc., *(0-9776284)* P.O. Box 494, Grover, MO 63040-1621 USA Tel 314-753-6142; Fax: 636-405-1963
E-mail: forbeslit@sbcgobal.net
Web site: http://www.forbesliterary.com.

Force of Faith Pubns., *(0-9747558)* P.O. Box 822, Broken Arrow, OK 74013-0822 USA Tel 918-259-3077; Fax: 918-259-3158 Do not confuse with Force of Faith Publications in Dublin CA
E-mail: admin@lhm.net
Web site: http://www.lhm.net
Dist(s): **Baker & Taylor Bks.**

Company

Ford, Vickie Lynn, *(0-9725878)* 2002 Yale Ave., Bradenton, FL 34207-5256 USA
E-mail: vford143@tampabay.rr.com.

Fore Angels Pr., *(0-9658920; 0-9799947)* 267 Woodbury Rd., Huntington, NY 11743 USA Tel 631-385-0336
E-mail: annaarts@verizon.net.

Foreign Languages Teaching & Research Pr. (CHN) *(7-5600) Dist. by* **Cheng Tsui.**

Foreign Media Books *See* **Mars Media Pubs.**

Foreign Policy Assn., *(0-87124)* 470 Park Ave. S., 2nd Flr., New York, NY 10016-6819 USA (SAN 212-9426) Tel 212-481-8100; Fax: 212-481-9275; Toll Free: 800-628-5754; 800-477-5836 (orders)
Web site: http://www.fpa.org.

Fore(In)Sight Foundation, *(0-9664283)* 4976 Oxford Rd., Macon, GA 31210-3059 USA Tel 478-474-3869; Fax: 478-474-5166
E-mail: foreinsight@foreinsight.org.

Forelle Graphics, *(0-9770918)* 1015 Atlantic Blvd., Suite 89, Atlantic Beach, FL 32233 USA
E-mail: forelle-graphics@yahoo.com.

Forerunner Pr., *(0-9674450)* P.O. Box 1768, Bonita, CA 91908-1768 USA Tel 619-267-6867; 619-479-4097; Fax: 619-479-3577; Toll Free: 888-558-4097 Do not confuse with Forerunner Press in Des Plaines, IL
E-mail: sales@forerunner-press.com.

Forest Hill Publishing, LLC, *(0-9759251; 0-9771113)* Orders Addr.: P.O. Box 12557, East Cleveland, OH 44112 USA; Edit Addr.: 13200 Forest Hill Ave., East Cleveland, OH 44112 USA Tel 216-761-8316 (phone/fax); Fax: 702-933-1605 ; *Imprints:* PlayGrnd (PlayGrnd OH) Do not confuse with Forest Hill Publishing in Downers Grove, IL
E-mail: books@foresthillpublishing.com; info@foresthillpublishing.com; info@fortunechildbooks.com
Web site: http://www.foresthillpublishing.com/ foresthillpublishing; http://www.fortunechildbooks.com
Dist(s): **Baker & Taylor Bks.**
Ingram Bk. Co.

Forest Hse. Publishing Co., Inc., *(1-56674; 1-878363)* P.O. Box 738, Lake Forest, IL 60045 USA Tel 847-295-8287; Fax: 847-295-8201; Toll Free: 800-394-7323 ; *Imprints:* H T S Books (HTS Bks)
Web site: http://www.forest-house.com.

Forest of Peace Publishing *Imprint of* **Ave Maria Pr.**

Forever *Imprint of* **Grand Central Publishing**

Forever Truth Publishing Company *See* **Windsor Hse. Publishing Group, The**

Forever Young Pubs., *(0-9774422)* Orders Addr.: P.O. Box 216, Niles, MI 49120 USA
E-mail: cheri@foreveryoungpublishers.com
Web site: http://www.foreveryoungpublishers.com
Dist(s): **Partners Bk. Distributing, Inc.**

Foreworks, *(0-943292)* P.O. Box 33493, Portland, OR 97292 USA (SAN 240-6519) Tel 503-653-2614
E-mail: info@fortuitouspress.com; eric@foreworks.com
Web site: http://www.foreworks.com; http://fortuitouspress.com.

Forge Bks. *Imprint of* **Doherty, Tom Assocs., LLC**

Fork in the Road Pubs., *(0-9740825)* 1883 145th Pl. SE, Bellevue, WA 98007-6019 USA Tel 425-644-4285
Web site: http://www.raincitycookingschool.com.

Formac Publishing Co., Ltd. (CAN) *(0-88780; 0-921921) Dist. by* **Casemate Pubs.**

Formosan Magazine Pr., Ltd. (CHN) *(957-632) Dist. by* **Shens Bks.**

Forouzan, Farid, *(0-9727609)* P.O. Box 16421, Knoxville, TN 37996 USA
E-mail: farforzan@yahoo.com.

Fortitude Graphic Design & Printing, *(0-9741611)* 841 Gibson St., Kalamazoo, MI 49001-2540 USA.

Fortress Pr. *Imprint of* **Augsburg Fortress, Pubs.**

Forum Gallery, *(0-9675826; 0-9744129)* 745 Fifth Ave., New York, NY 10051 USA Tel 212-355-4547; 212-355-4545; Fax: 212-355-4547
E-mail: gallery@forumgallery.com
Dist(s): **D.A.P./Distributed Art Pubs.**

Forward Communications *See* **NetNia Publishing Co.**

Forward Face, *(0-9666097)* 317 E. 34th St., Suite 901A, New York, NY 10016 USA Tel 212-684-5860; Fax: 212-684-5864; Toll Free: 800-393-3223
Web site: http://www.forwardface.com.

Forward Movement Pubns., *(0-88028)* 300 West Fourth St., Cincinnati, OH 45202 USA (SAN 208-3841) Tel 513-721-6659; Fax: 513-721-0729; Toll Free: 800-543-1813 (orders only)
E-mail: Orders@forwarddaybyday.com
Web site: http://www.forwardmovement.org.

Forword, *(0-9623937)* 16526 W. 78th St., Suite 335, Eden Prairie, MN 55346 USA Tel 612-944-7761; Fax: 612-944-8674
Dist(s): **Baker & Taylor Bks.**

Foster, Dennis, *(0-9771956)* P.O. Box 363, Millwood, VA 22646 USA.

Foster, Hicks & Assocs., *(0-9790709)* Orders Addr.: 4053 Harlan St., loft 201, Emeryville, CA 94608-9460 USA Tel 510-540-1241
E-mail: info@fosterhicks.com
Dist(s): **Biblio Distribution.**

Foster, Walter Publishing, Inc., *(0-929261; 1-56010; 1-60058)* Orders Addr.: Retail Order Dept., Quayside Publishing Group 18705 Lake Dr. E., Chanhassen, MN 55317 USA Tel 1-952-936-4700; Fax: 1-952-099-9101; Toll Free: 1-800-328-0590; Edit Addr.: 23062 La Cadena Dr., Laguna Hills, CA 92653 USA (SAN 249-051X) Tel 949-380-7510; Fax: 949-380-7575; Toll Free: 800-426-0099
E-mail: info@walterfoster.com; sales@creativepub.com
Web site: http://www.walterfoster.com
Dist(s): **Quayside.**

Foston Adolescent Workshop, Inc., *(0-9641709; 1-930362)* P.O. Box 726, Clarksville, TN 37041 USA Tel 931-906-4623; Fax: 931-645-3500; Toll Free: 800-418-0374
E-mail: minfoston@aol.com
Web site: http://www.drfoston.com.

Fotonovel Pubns., *(0-89752)* P.O. Box 691367, Los Angeles, CA 90069 USA Tel 310-659-8888
E-mail: fotonovel2@cs.com; info@fotonovel.com
Web site: http://www.fotonovel.com.

Foulsham, W. Co., Ltd. (GBR) *(0-572) Dist. by* **APG.**

Foundation for Advancements in Science & Education, *(1-932980)* 4801 Wilshire Blvd., Suite 250, Los Angeles, CA 90010 USA Tel 323-937-9911; Fax: 323-937-7440; Toll Free: 800-404-3273
E-mail: inquiries@fasenet.org
Web site: http://www.fasenet.org/store.

Foundation for Family Science, *(0-9748939)* 4614 SW Kelly Ave. Ste. 100, Portland, OR 97239-4277 USA
E-mail: familyscience@davidheil.com
Web site: http://www.familyscience.org.

Foundation for Global Evangelism, Incorporated, The *See* **Global Evangelism Ministries, Inc.**

Foundation for Religious Freedom, *(1-928575)* 1680 N. Vine St., Suite 415, Los Angeles, CA 90028 USA Tel 323-468-0567; Fax: 323-468-0562; Toll Free: 800-556-3055
E-mail: nomeara@pacbell.net
Web site: http://www.toleranceforall.org; http://www.forf.org
Dist(s): **Baker & Taylor Bks.**
Quality Bks., Inc.

Foundation, Pr. The, *(0-9765987)* P.O. Box 182, Westport, CT 06881 USA Do not confuse with companies with the same name in New York, NY, Anaheim, CA
Web site: http://www.thefoundationpress.com.

Foundation Publishing, *(0-9718774)* 2089 Simone Dr., North Canton, OH 44720 USA Do not confuse with companies with the same or similar names in Honolulu, HI, Burlington, VT, Katy, TX, Prior Lake, MN.

Foundation Pr., *(0-9767272)* 13832 Gimbert Ln., Santa Ana, CA 92705-2849 USA Do not confuse with companies with the same name in New York, NY, Westport, CT.

Foundations Behavioral Health, *(0-9676106)* 833 E. Butler Ave., Doylestown, PA 18901 USA Tel 215-345-0444; Fax: 214-340-1501
E-mail: nancydfbh@aol.com.

Foundations for Learning, LLC, *(0-9726479; 1-933546)* 246 W. Manson Hwy., PMB 144, Chelan, WA 98816 USA Toll Free: 800-553-5950
E-mail: info@gophonics.com
Web site: http://www.gophonics.com.

Foundations in Brass *See* **Cymbal Technique 101**

Foundry Bks. (GBR) *(1-901543) Dist. by* **Casemate Pubs.**

Fountain of Youth, *(0-9664750)* 1008 Wildlife Ln., Crowley, TX 76036 USA Tel 817-295-5321; Fax: 817-426-0888
E-mail: redfoy@aol.com
Dist(s): **Harrison Hse., Inc.**

Fountain Pen Press *See* **Buchavina Pr.**

Fountain Publishing, *(0-9659164; 0-9748423)* Orders Addr.: P.O. Box 80011, Rochester, MI 48306 USA (SAN 253-8571) Tel 248-651-2934; Fax: 248-656-4215; Toll Free: 877-736-8598; Edit Addr.: 375 Olivewood Ct., Rochester, MI 48306 USA Tel 810-651-1153 Do not confuse with Fountain Publishing in Pittsburgh, PA
E-mail: ftnpublish@aol.com; jk@fountainpublishing.com
Web site: http://www.fountainpublishing.com.

Fountain Pubs. Ltd. (UGA) *(9970-02) Dist. by* **Mich St U Pr.**

Fountain Square Publishing, *(0-9724421)* 786 Old Ludlow, Cincinnati, OH 45220 USA.

Fountain, The *Imprint of* **Light, Inc., The**

Fouque Publishers, Incorporated *See* **EUROBOOKS Pubs.**

Four Corners Publishing Co., Inc., *(1-893577)* 45 W. Tenth St., New York, NY 10011 USA Tel 212-673-5226; Fax: 516-771-1243
E-mail: RLutnick@aol.com
Dist(s): **Biblio Distribution.**

Four Dolphins Pr., *(0-9745746)* Orders Addr.: P.O. Box 93601, Los Angeles, CA 90093 USA (SAN 255-626X) Tel 323-304-2053; Edit Addr.: 2700 N. Cahuenga Blvd., E., Suite 1403, Los Angeles, CA 90068-2139 USA.

Four Dolphins Press/Smart Communications, Incorporated *See* **Four Dolphins Pr.**

Four Footed Friends, *(0-9707758)* P.O. Box 25736, Tempe, AZ 85285 USA Tel 480-730-5550; Fax: 480-730-5551
E-mail: whitedebraj@yahoo.com; tcameron@asu.edu
Web site: http://www.4-footedfriends.com.

415 TECH Media, *(0-9702960)* 140 Second St., Suite 602, San Francisco, CA 94102 USA Tel 415-243-8900; Fax: 415-284-1482
E-mail: info@sfdotcomdirectory.com
Web site: http://www.sfdotcomdirectory.com.

Four Panel Pr., *(0-9674102)* P.O. Box 50032, Eugene, OR 97405 USA Tel 541-343-6436; Fax: 541-684-0787
E-mail: tedlay@comcast.net
Web site: http://www.stonesoupcartoons.com
Dist(s): **Biblio Distribution.**

Four Seasons Bks., Inc., *(0-9666858; 1-893595)* P.O. Box 395, Ben Wheeler, TX 75754 USA Tel 903-963-1442; Fax: 903-963-1525; Toll Free: 800-852-7484
E-mail: hcmarlow@yahoo.com; editor@fourseasonsbookstore.com
Web site: http://www.herbmarlow.com; http:// www.fourseasonsbookstore.com.

Four Seasons Pubs., *(0-9656811; 1-891929; 1-932497)* Orders Addr.: P.O. Box 51, Titusville, FL 32781 USA Tel 321-632-2932; Fax: 321-632-2935; Edit Addr.: 4350 N. U.S. Hwy. 1, Cocoa, FL 32927 USA ; *Imprints:* Manatee Publishing (Manatee Publng)
E-mail: fseasons@bellsouth.net
Dist(s): **Baker & Taylor Bks.**
Follett Library Resources.

Four Sonkist Angels, *(0-9753117)* 4985 Wiltshire Ln., Suwanee, GA 30024 USA
E-mail: Michelle@FourSonkistAngels.com
Web site: http://www.FourSonkistAngels.com.

Four Sons Publishing, Inc., *(0-9712932)* 2900 Sand Rd., No. 67, Edwardsville, IL 62025 USA Tel 618-655-1622; 618-655-1621
E-mail: eunicejoyce@aol.com
Web site: http://www.foursonspublishing.com.

Four Winds Press, LLC *See* **Cold Tree Pr., LLC**

Fournier Media, *(0-9725243)* Orders Addr.: P.O. Box 83853, Phoenix, AZ 85071-3853 USA Fax: 602-997-2522; Toll Free: 800-446-3325; Edit Addr.: 1943 W N. Ln., Suite 1, Phoenix, AZ 85021-1932 USA
Web site: http://www.centerforempowerment.com.

Fourth Dimension Publishing Co., Ltd. (NGA) *(978-155; 978-156) Dist. by* **Mich St U Pr.**

Fourth Generation Pubs., *(0-9706186)* PMB 146,14625 Baltimore Ave., Laurel, MD 20707-4902 USA (SAN 253-5513) Tel 301-497-9948.

Fowema Publishing Co., *(0-9660136)* Orders Addr.: P.O. Box 51882, Provo, UT 84605-1882 USA Tel 801-377-6854; Edit Addr.: 86 S. 900 W., Provo, UT 84601 USA.

Fowler & Gooch, Incorporated *See* **Stringer, Alicia**

Fowler Cos., Inc., The, *(0-9661365)* 1417 Alford Ave., Birmingham, AL 35226 USA Tel 205-822-9252; Fax: 205-822-2140
E-mail: fowlerbook@aol.com.

Fowler Publishing, *(0-9673802)* 2219 Cascade Dr., Orofino, ID 83544 USA Tel 208-476-9724; Fax: 208-476-4071 ; *Imprints:* Educate US (Educate US)
E-mail: jfowler@orofino-id.com.

Fox Bks., *(0-9658180)* Orders Addr.: P.O. Box 150053, Cape Coral, FL 33915-0053 USA Tel 941-772-7849; Fax: 941-772-2269; Edit Addr.: 1909 SE Eighth Ave., Cape Coral, FL 33915 USA.

Fox Chapel Publishing Co., Inc., *(1-56523; 0-9777004)* 1970 Broad St., East Petersburg, PA 17520 USA Tel 717-560-4703; Fax: 717-560-4702; Toll Free Fax: 888-369-2885; Toll Free: 800-457-9112 (orders)
E-mail: sales@carvingworld.com
Web site: http://www.foxchapelpublishing.com/; http://www.scrollsawer.com/; http://www.carvingworld.com
Dist(s): **Independent Pubs. Group.**

Fox Den Bks., *(0-9708938)* Orders Addr.: P.O. Box 644, Concord, NH 03302-0644 USA Tel 603-226-5817; Edit Addr.: 120 Fisherville Rd., Unit 172, Concord, NH 03303 USA.

Fox Music Bks. (CAN) *(1-894997) Dist. by* **SCB Distributors.**

Fox Song Bks., *(0-9744989)* Orders Addr.: 8721 Santa Monica Blvd., No. 619, Los Angeles, CA 90069-4507 USA (SAN 255-593X) Toll Free Fax: 888-309-5063; Toll Free: 888-369-2769
E-mail: fox@foxsongbooks.com; orders@foxsongbooks.com
Web site: http://foxsongbooks.com
Dist(s): **Baker & Taylor Bks.**
Lightning Source, Inc.

FoxAcre Pr., *(0-9671783; 0-9709711)* 401 Ethan Allen Ave., Takoma Park, MD 20912 USA Fax: 301-560-2482
E-mail: info@foxacre.com
Web site: http://www.foxacre.com.

Foxglove Films, LLC, *(0-9700611)* 2339-I Fairview Ave., E., Seattle, WA 98102 USA Tel 206-323-9003 (phone/fax)
E-mail: lshelton@halcyon.com.

Foxglove Pr., *(1-882959)* P.O. Box 210602, Nashville, TN 37221-0602 USA Fax: 615-646-8188; 2606 Eugenia Ave., Nashville, TN 37211 Do not confuse with companies with the same name in Corte Mandera, CA, Bryn Mawr, PA
Dist(s): **Midpoint Trade Bks., Inc.**

Foxhaven Pr., *(0-9651747)* 2425 Foxhaven Dr., Franklin, TN 37069 USA Tel 615-661-9761; Fax: 615-287-6700; Toll Free: 800-937-8222 (ext. 3424)
E-mail: wibking@juno.com
Web site: http://www.Ingrambook.com
Dist(s): **New Leaf Distributing Co., Inc.**

Foxsong Enterprises, LLC, *(0-9677000)* c/o , 1769 Pine Creek Cir., Haslett, MI 48840 USA Tel 517-339-1869; Fax: 517-339-4784; Toll Free: 877-339-6918
E-mail: janeile.cannon@attbi.co
Web site: http://foxsong.com.

FP Hendriks Publishing, Ltd. (CAN) *(0-9682970; 0-9699619; 1-894380) Dist. by* **Baker & Taylor.**

FPI Publishing, *(0-9768215)* P.O. Box 247, Havre de Grace, MD 21078 USA Tel 410-459-9087
Web site: http://www.colourfulstitches.com.

FQ Classics *Imprint of* **Filiquarian Publishing, LLC**

Fragile X Assn. of Georgia, *(0-9727865)* Rood End Hse., 6 Stortford Rd., Great Dunmow, Essex CM6 1DA GBR Tel 01371 875100; 3161 W. Somerset Ct., Marietta, GA 30067-5045 Tel 770-988-9275; Fax: 770-988-8255
E-mail: info@fragilex.k-web.co.uk; frax@bellsouth.net
Web site: www.fragilex.org.uk; http:// www.myextraspecialbrother.com.

Fraley, David *See* **Player's Guide**

Francen World Outreach, *(0-9634878; 1-888079)* Orders Addr.: P.O. Box 701978, Tulsa, OK 74170 USA Tel 918-492-2493; Fax: 918-492-2495; Toll Free: 800-503-9355; Edit Addr.: P.O. Box 701978, Tulsa, OK 74170-1978 USA ; *Imprints:* F W O Books (FWO Bks)
E-mail: usafwo@aol.com
Web site: http://www.gofwo.org
Dist(s): **Double Blessing Productions.**

Frances Foster Bks. *Imprint of* **Farrar, Straus & Giroux**

Frances More International Teaching Systems, *(0-9768234)* Div. of Gray Squirrel, Inc., P.O. Box 26659, Collegeville, PA 19426 USA Tel 610-724-6331
E-mail: sales@graysquirrel.org; francesmore.hangingrock@xtra.co.nz
Web site: http://www.qwertyqik.com; http://www.fingerithmatic.com.

Francesca Studios, *(0-9741060)* 26 Dole Hill Rd., Holden, ME 04429 USA.

Frank, Paul, *(0-9741983)* 7361 NW 83 Way, Tamarac, FL 33321 USA
E-mail: Ifgolfballscouldtalk@comcast.net
Web site: http://www.Ifgolfballscouldtalk.com.

FrankenGeek Pr., *(0-9771182)* 311 Kenneth St., Greenwood, MS 38930 USA
E-mail: jrose@netdoor.com
Web site: http://themonstergrrls.blogspot.com; http://www.monstergrrls.com.

Benjamin Franklin Pr., *(0-9789827; 0-9795257; 0-9799941)* P.O. Box 222851, Carmel, CA 93923 USA Fax: 831-626-3734
E-mail: elliotsanders@benjaminfranklinpress.com
Web site: http://www.benjaminfranklinpress.com.

Franklin Covey Co., *(1-883219; 1-929494; 1-933976)* 2200 W. Pkwy. Blvd., Salt Lake City, UT 84119 USA
E-mail: harry.nelson@franklincovey.com
Web site: http://www.franklincovey.com
Dist(s): **Simon & Schuster, Inc.**
Simon & Schuster Audio.

Franklin Institute, *(0-9625622; 1-889939)* 222 N. 20th St., Philadelphia, PA 19103-1194 USA (SAN 166-1647) Tel 215-448-1239; Fax: 215-448-1364
E-mail: webteam@www.fi.edu
Web site: http://www.fi.edu.

Franklin, J.E., *(0-9746669)* P.O. Box 517, New York, NY 10031 USA Tel 212-283-8666
E-mail: je413@aol.com
Web site: http://www.geocities.com/haveplaywilltravel/playseries.html.

Franklin Mason Pr., *(0-9679227; 0-9760469)* Orders Addr.: P.O. Box 3808, Trenton, NJ 08629 USA (SAN 253-1828) Tel 609-291-5030; Fax: 609-291-7807; Edit Addr.: 415 Route 68, Columbus, NJ 08022 USA
E-mail: lwill0517@aol.com
Web site: http://www.franklinmasonpress.com.

Franklin Publishing, *(0-9708129)* 1917 Warrington Rd., SW, Roanoke, VA 24015-3037 USA Tel 540-982-1654 (phone/fax on demand) Do not confuse with Franklin Publishing, Tempe, AZ, Chandler, AZ
E-mail: ampaw@aol.com.

Franklin Street Books *See* **Inkwater Pr.**

Franklin-Sarrett Pubs., *(0-9637477)* 3761 Vinyard Trace, Marietta, GA 30062 USA (SAN 297-9918) Tel 770-578-9410; Fax: 770-973-4243
E-mail: kborden@mindspring.com; info@franklin-sarrett.com
Web site: http://www.franklin-sarrett.com.

Frayed Pages Publishing, *(0-9753397)* P.O. Box 1360, Pickens, SC 29671 USA
E-mail: writings@bellsouth.net
Dist(s): **Continental Enterprises Group, Inc. (CEG).**

Frazier, Jeffrey R. *See* **Egg Hill Pubns.**

Fred Pr., *(0-937393)* P.O. Box 333, Creston, OH 44217 USA (SAN 658-8573) Tel 330-435-4074
E-mail: dmz8@bright.net.

Frederic, Marc *See* **World of Whimsy Productions, LLC**

Frederick Pr., *(0-9653871; 1-931329)* Orders Addr.: P.O. Box 32593, Palm Beach Gardens, FL 33420-2593 USA Tel 561-625-4964 (phone/fax); Edit Addr.: 13329 Mallard Creek Dr., Palm Beach Gardens, FL 33418 USA
E-mail: fredpres@ix.netcom.com
Web site: http://www.frederickpress.com
Dist(s): **Baker & Taylor Bks.**
Brodart Co.
Follett Library Resources.

Free Assn. Bks. Ltd. (GBR) *(0-946960; 1-85343) Dist. by* **Intl Spec Bk.**

Free Indeed Pubns., *(0-9662438)* Orders Addr.: P.O. Box 232, Holton, MI 49425 USA Tel 616-821-0448; 4379 Holton-Whitehall Rd., Holton, MI 49425 Toll Free: 877-735-1427
E-mail: rjhcc@ncats.net.

Free Pr. *Imprint of* **Simon & Schuster**

Free Pr. Pubs., *(0-943751)* Orders Addr.: P.O. Box 4717, Monroe, LA 71211 USA (SAN 242-6242) Tel 318-388-1310; Fax: 318-388-2911
E-mail: RooseveltWright@prodigy.net
Web site: http://www.sermonideas.com.

F.R.E.E. Publishing House, *(0-86639; 0-9762472)* Div. of Friends of Refugees of Eastern Europe, 1383 President St., Brooklyn, NY 11213 USA Tel 718-467-0860; Fax: 718-467-2146
E-mail: info@russianjewry.org
Web site: http://www.russianjewry.org.

Free Song *Imprint of* **LeBlanc, Doreen**

Free Spirit Productions, *(0-9707748)* P.O. Box 1596, Ojai, CA 93024-1596 USA
E-mail: ridhwangirl@hotmail.com.

†Free Spirit Publishing, Inc., *(0-915793; 1-57542)* 217 Fifth Ave., N., Suite 200, Minneapolis, MN 55401-1299 USA (SAN 293-9584) Tel 612-338-2068; Fax: 612-337-5050; Toll Free: 800-735-7323
E-mail: help4kids@freespirit.com
Web site: http://www.freespirit.com
Dist(s): **Baker & Taylor Bks.**
Bookazine Co., Inc.
Booksource, The
Brodart Co.
Follett Library Resources
Heinecken & Assoc., Ltd.
Quality Bks., Inc.; *CIP.*

Free To Soar Enterprises, *(0-9700001)* Orders Addr.: P.O. Box 357, Pfafftown, NC 27040-0357 USA (SAN 254-3141) Fax: 336-765-9487
E-mail: freetosoar@triad.rr.com.

Free Will Pr., *(0-9701771)* P.O. Box 12130, San Francisco, CA 94112 USA Tel 415-337-5494; Fax: 415-586-3787; P.O. Box 12130, San Francisco, CA 94112-0130
E-mail: michael@freewillpress.com; michaelp@freewillpress.com
Web site: http://www.freewillpress.com.

Free Your Mind Publishing, *(0-9760056)* 1652 Ft. Dupont St. SE., Washington, DC 20020 USA (SAN 256-1883); P.O. Box 70, Boston, MA 02131 Fax: 617-327-2840 Do nopt confuse with Free Your Mind Publishing in Indianapolis, IN
E-mail: omekongo@omekongo.com
Web site: http://www.omekongo.com.

Freedom Archives, The, *(0-9727422; 0-9790789)* 522 Valencia St., San Francisco, CA 94110 USA Tel 415-863-9977
E-mail: info@freedomarchives.org
Web site: http://www.freedomarchives.org
Dist(s): **AK Pr. Distribution**
Consortium Bk. Sales & Distribution
SPD-Small Pr. Distribution.

Freedom Pr. (GBR) *(0-900384; 1-904491) Dist. by* **AK Pr Dist.**

Freedom Pr. Assocs., *(0-945069)* 18 Old Portland Rd., Freedom, NH 03836 USA (SAN 245-9558) Tel 603-539-2146; Fax: 603-539-5301; P.O. Box 460, Freedom, NH 03836
E-mail: gailh@usadatanet.net
Web site: http://www.riverhaven.org.

Freedom Publishing Co., *(0-9638152; 1-892946)* 2530 Crawford Ave. Ste. 102, Evanston, IL 60201-4954 USA Toll Free: 800-717-0770
E-mail: drj7777@megsinet.net
Web site: http://www.freedompub.com.

Freedom Voices Pubns., *(0-915117; 0-9625153)* Div. of Tenderloin Reflection & Education Ctr., P.O. Box 423115, San Francisco, CA 94142 USA
E-mail: info@freedomvoices.org; orders@freedomvoices.org
Web site: http://www.freedomvoices.org
Dist(s): **AK Pr. Distribution**
SPD-Small Pr. Distribution.

Freeland, Darlene, *(0-9771660)* 107 E. Charleston Blvd., Studio 203, Las Vegas, NV 89104 USA (SAN 256-839X)
E-mail: faceupstudio@aol.com
Web site: http://www.faceupstudio.com.

Freeman, Kimberly *See* **Keys For Kids Publishing Co.**

Freeman, Sharon T. *See* **All American Small Business Exporters Assn. (AASBEA)**

†Freeman, W. H. & Co., *(0-7167; 1-4292)* Div. of Holtzbrinck Publishers, Orders Addr.: 16365 James Madison Hwy., Gordonsville, VA 22942 USA Tel 540-672-7600; Toll Free Fax: 800-672-2054; Toll Free: 888-330-8477 (orders & customer service); Edit Addr.: 41 Madison Ave., 37th Flr., New York, NY 10010 USA (SAN 290-6864) Tel 212-576-9400; Fax: 212-689-2383; Toll Free: 800-903-3019
E-mail: webmaster@whfreeman.com
Web site: http://www.whfreeman.com
Dist(s): **Macmillan**
Oxford Univ. Pr., Inc.; *CIP.*

FreeStar Pr., *(0-9661315)* P.O. Box 54552, Cincinnati, OH 45254-0552 USA Toll Free: 800-441-6077 (phone/fax).

FreeStyle Pubns., Inc., *(0-9674171)* 32 Baymor Dr., East Longmeadow, MA 01028-2309 USA Tel 413-525-2989 (phone/fax)
E-mail: fstylepub@aol.com.

Freet Publishing, *(0-9676717)* Orders Addr.: P.O. Box 219, Willow Hill, PA 17271-0219 USA Tel 717-349-7873 (phone/fax); Edit Addr.: 18028 Pigeon Hill Rd., Willow Hill, PA 17271-0219 USA
E-mail: freepbl@pa.net.

Freethought Publishing Group, *(0-9704968)* 431 N. Galvin Rd., No. 315, Bellevue, NE 68005 USA
E-mail: yossarian@ftpg.net
Web site: http://www.ftpg.net.

Freeverse Enterprises Inc., *(0-9743789)* 1200 E. River Rd. C-35, Tucson, AZ 85718 USA.

Fremantle Pr. (AUS) *(1-86368; 0-909144; 0-949206; 1-920731; 1-921064; 1-921361) Dist. by* **Intl Spec Bk.**

French & European Pubns., Inc., *(0-320; 0-7859; 0-8288)* Rockefeller Ctr. Promenade, 610 Fifth Ave., New York, NY 10020-2497 USA (SAN 206-8109) Tel 212-581-8810; Fax: 212-265-1094
E-mail: frenchbookstore@aol.com
Web site: http://www.frencheuropean.com.

French, Samuel Inc., *(0-573)* 45 W. 25th St., New York, NY 10010-2751 USA Tel 212-206-8990; Fax: 212-206-1429
E-mail: samuelfrench@earthlink.net
Web site: http://www.samuelfrench.com.

French Workshop, The, *(1-931463)* P.O. Box 690, Pass Christian, MS 39571 USA Tel 228-452-1729 (phone/fax); Toll Free: 800-692-7409
E-mail: kelley@thefrenchworkshop.com
Web site: http://www.thefrenchworkshop.com.

Fresch Fruitz *Imprint of* **Got2Bfunki Artworks**

Fresh Baby LLC, *(0-9727227)* 616 Petoskey St., Suite 202, Petoskey, MI 49770 USA Tel 231-348-2706; Fax: 231-348-5374
E-mail: info@freshbaby.com
Web site: http://www.freshbaby.com
Dist(s): **Biblio Distribution.**

Fresh Word, *(0-9718012)* P.O. Box 10404, Westbury, NY 11590 USA Tel 718-804-0221
E-mail: freshword@onebox.com.

Freud, S. Romanian Translation & Pubn. Fund, Inc., *(1-883881)* One Marine Midland Plaza, E. Tower, 4th Flr., Binghamton, NY 13901-3216 USA.

Frick Art & Historical Ctr.,The, *(0-9703425)* 7227 Reynolds St., Pittsburgh, PA 15208 USA Tel 412-371-0600; Fax: 412-241-5393
E-mail: tsmart@frickart.org; info@frickart.org
Web site: http://www.frickart.org.

Fried, Scott *See* **TALKAIDS, Inc.**

Friedman, Michael Publishing Group, Inc., *(0-9627134; 1-56799; 1-58663; 1-4114)* Div. of Barnes & Noble, Inc., 122 Fifth Ave., Fifth Flr., New York, NY 10011 USA (SAN 248-9732) Tel 212-685-6610; Fax: 212-633-3327 ; *Imprints:* Friedman-Fairfax (Friedman-Fairfax); MetroBooks (MetroBooks)
E-mail: rlamarche@bn.com
Web site: http://www.metrobooks.com
Dist(s): **Hervey's Booklink & Cookbook Warehouse**
Sterling Publishing Co., Inc.

Friedman, Yuda, *(0-9677313)* 11 Quickway Rd. Unit 103, Monroe, NY 10950-8804 USA.

Friedman-Fairfax *Imprint of* **Friedman, Michael Publishing Group, Inc.**

Friedrich, Paul, *(0-9793676)* 323 W. Martin St., SPC 70, Raleigh, NC 27601 USA
Web site: http://onionheadmonster.com.

Friend Family Ministries, *(0-9767524)* 1601 Hamilton Richmond Rd., Hamilton, OH 45013 USA.

Friendly Isles Pr., *(0-9678979)* Orders Addr.: 11705 Darlington Ave., Bakersfield, CA 93312 USA Tel 661-587-0645
E-mail: ofalisiate@yahoo.com.

Friendly Math, *(1-929245)* P.O. Box 11061, Chicago, IL 60611 USA Fax: 312-787-0701
Web site: http://www.FRIENDLYMATH.com.

Friendly Planet, *(0-9742469)* 101 Third St., Cambridge, MA 02141 USA ; *Imprints:* Big Books for Little People (Big Bks)
E-mail: mike@friendlyplanet.org
Web site: http://www.friendlyplanet.org.

†Friendly Pr., *(0-938070)* Div. of Paradox Productions, Inc., 5120 Franklin Blvd., No.3, Eugene, OR 97403 USA (SAN 215-8671) Fax: 541-988-1002; Toll Free: 888-541-0336 Do not confuse with The Friendly Pr., McLean, VA
E-mail: info@friendlypress.com
Web site: http://www.friendlypress.com; *CIP.*

Friendly Universe Pr., *(0-9625385)* 2010 SW Sunset Blvd., Portland, OR 97201-2062 USA Tel 503-245-6774; Fax: 503-245-6759
E-mail: drardy4u@americaonline.com.

Friends & Co. Pubs., *(0-9716457)* Orders Addr.: P.O. Box 8504, Cranston, RI 02920-0504 USA (SAN 255-2574)
E-mail: info@fcpbooks.com
Web site: http://www.fcpbooks.com
Dist(s): **Baker & Taylor Bks.**

Friends & Company Publishing *See* **Friends & Co. Pubs.**

Friends General Conference *See* **Quaker Press of Friends General Conference**

Friends of Lulu, *(0-9740960)* 13210 Michigan Ave., Dearborn, MI 48126-3539 USA
E-mail: info@friends-lulu.org
Web site: http://www.friends-lulu.org/.

Friends Of The Goshen Grange, The, *(0-9771473)* P.O. Box 1016, Goshen, NH 03752-1016 USA.

†Friends United Pr., *(0-913408, 0-944350)* 101 Quaker Hill Dr., Richmond, IN 47374 USA (SAN 201-5803) Tel 765-962-7573; Fax: 765-966-1293; Toll Free: 800-537-8839
E-mail: friendspress@fum.org; barbaram@fum.org
Web site: http://www.fum.org; *CIP.*

Friends Without a Border, *(0-9653574)* 1123 Broadway Ste. 1210, New York, NY 10010-2007 USA
E-mail: fwab@fwab.org
Web site: http://www.fwab.org
Dist(s): **SCB Distributors.**

†Friendship Pr., *(0-377)* Subs. of National Council of the Churches of Christ USA, Orders Addr.: c/o Friendship Pr. Distribution Office, P.O. Box 37844, Cincinnati, OH 45222-0844 USA (SAN 201-5781) Tel 513-948-8733; Fax: 513-761-3722; Toll Free: 800-889-5733; Edit Addr.: 475 Riverside Dr., Rm. 860, New York, NY 10115 USA (SAN 201-5773) Tel 212-870-2496; Fax: 212-870-2550 Do not confuse with companies with the same name in Peoria, AZ, Santa Rosa, CA
Web site: http://www.ncccusa.org/; *CIP.*

Frog Bks. *Imprint of* **Kumarian Pr., Inc.**

Frog Ltd. *Imprint of* **North Atlantic Bks.**

Frog Pond Enterprises, *(0-615)* Orders Addr.: 1653 Frog Pond Rd., Sherman, TX 75092 USA Tel 903-564-6904; Fax: 903-564-7563
E-mail: fpent@earthlink.net
Web site: http:///www.joyforchurches.com.

F.R.O.G. the Rock Pubns., *(0-9727142)* 3524 Parkview Dr., Marietta, GA 30062 USA Tel 770-587-4902; Fax: 770-993-0394
E-mail: frogtherock@aol.com.

Froggie & Friends, LLC, *(0-9787456)* Orders Addr.: P.O. Box 240784, Saint Paul, MN 55124-0784 USA (SAN 851-5263)
E-mail: froggieandfriends@comcast.net
Web site: http://www.froggieandfriends.us/.

Company

Froggie Pr., *(0-9624260)* 2705 Fountain Ln., Plymouth, MN 55447 USA Tel 612-473-2619; Fax: 612-249-0765
E-mail: joyceB12@juno.com
Dist(s): **Bookmen, Inc.**

Froginhood & Friends, Inc., *(1-892812)* Orders Addr.: P.O. Box 1745, Safety Harbor, FL 34695 USA (SAN 299-9277) Tel 727-797-6343; Fax: 727-797-6453; Edit Addr.: P.O. Box 1745, Safety Harbor, FL 34695-1745 USA
E-mail: jonas@froginhood.com
Web site: http://www.froginhood.com.

From the Asylum Bks. & Pr., *(0-9715860)* P.O. Box 1516, Dickinson, TX 77539 USA
Web site: http://www.fromtheasylum.com.

From The Heart Bks., *(0-9726313)* P.O. Box 42036, Portland, OR 97242-0036 USA Tel 503-249-7853
E-mail: fromtheheartbook@aol.com.

From the Hse. of Ideas *Imprint of* **Marvel Enterprises, Inc.**

From the Lillypad Productions, *(0-9727770)* P.O. Box 5876, Oceanside, CA 92052 USA
E-mail: lillypadmktg@aol.com.

Frommers *Imprint of* **Wiley, John & Sons, Inc.**

Front Line Educ, *(0-9726522)* 3506 Hwy. 6 S., No. 335, Sugar Land, TX 77478 USA Tel 281-261-8844
E-mail: ace@sugarlandarea.com.

Front Porch Pr., *(0-9656086)* 1724 Vassar, Lansing, MI 48912 USA Tel 517-487-9295; Fax: 517-487-0888; Toll Free: 888-484-1997 Do not confuse with companies with the same or similar names in Elk, CA, Compton, CA
E-mail: styler@voyager.net
Dist(s): **Austin & Company, Inc.**
Baker & Taylor Bks.
Partners Pubs. Group, Inc.

Front Street *Imprint of* **Boyds Mills Pr.**

Front Street/Cricket Books *See* **Cricket Bks.**

Fronte, Kathy, *(0-9727725)* 5604 Greenwood Cir., Naples, FL 34112 USA.

Frontier Books *See* **Frontier Pr.**

Frontier Image Pr., *(0-9634309; 1-888571)* Orders Addr.: P.O. Box 3055, Silver City, NM 88061 USA Tel 505-534-4032; Fax: 505-590-1301
E-mail: frontr@cybermcs.com.

Frontier Pr., *(0-9768465)* 180 E. Ocean Blvd., Fl 4, Long Beach, CA 90802-9080 USA Tel 562-491-8331; Fax: 562-491-8791
E-mail: new_frontier@usw.salvationarmy.org.

Frontiera, Deborah *See* **Jade Enterprises**

Frontline Communications *See* **YWAM Publishing**

Frontline Pr., *(0-930201)* Orders Addr.: P.O. Box 764499, Dallas, TX 75376-4499 USA Tel 972-572-8336; Fax: 972-572-8335 Do not confuse with companies with the same or similar name in Washington, DC, Taylors, SC, Charlston, SC
E-mail: info@youthdirect.org
Web site: http://www.youthdirect.org.

Frost Hollow Pubs., LLC, *(0-9658523; 0-9720922; 0-9794273)* 411 Barlow Cemetery Rd., Woodstock, CT 06281 USA Tel 860-974-2081; Fax: 860-974-0813; Toll Free: 877-974-2081
E-mail: frosthollow@mindspring.com
Web site: http://www.frosthollowpub.com.

Frost Publishing, *(0-9714982)* Orders Addr.: P.O. Box 1877, Petersburg, VA 23805 USA (SAN 254-170X) Tel 804-733-6734 Do not confuse with Frost Publishing in Vero Beach, FL
E-mail: frostpublishing@yahoo.com
Web site: http://www.frostpublishing.net.

Frozen Field Pr., *(0-9720125)* 219 S. West St., Allentown, PA 18102 USA Tel 610-432-0158
E-mail: frozenfield@hotmail.com.

Frugal Bear Communications, *(0-9678694)* P.O. Box 5154, Inglewood, CA 90310 USA ; *Imprints:* FrugalBear.com (FrugalBear)
E-mail: regresa@hotmail.com; frugalbear@email.com
Web site: http://www.frugalbear.com.

FrugalBear.com *Imprint of* **Frugal Bear Communications**

Fruitbearer Publishing, *(1-886068)* Orders Addr.: P.O. Box 777, Georgetown, DE 19947 USA Tel 302-856-6649; Fax: 302-856-7742; Edit Addr.: 107 Elizabeth St., Georgetown, DE 19947 USA
E-mail: fruitbearer.publishing@verizon.net; candy.abbott@verizon.net
Web site: http://atlasbooks.com; http://www.fruitbearer.com
Dist(s): **AtlasBooks Distribution.**

Fruitgarden Pub., *(0-9646457)* 2647 Red Arrow Dr., Las Vegas, NV 89135-1607 USA
E-mail: Help@FruitgardenPublishing.com
Web site: http://www.FruitgardenPublishing.Com
Dist(s): **Baker & Taylor Bks.**
New Leaf Distributing Co., Inc.

Fruition Online Publishing, *(0-9712079)* Div. of Cherokee Ventures, 702 Oberlin Rd., Suite 150, Raleigh, NC 27605-2531 USA Tel 919-743-2500; Fax: 919-743-2501
E-mail: customersupport@fruitiononline.com
Web site: http://www.fruitiononline.com.

Frydenlund, Robert, *(0-9755594)* 1645 - 200th St., New Richmond, WI 54017 USA
E-mail: rbfarm@frontiernet.net
Web site: http://www.roundbarn.homestead.com.

FT Richards Publishing, *(0-9746561)* 41 Tailwinds Ln., North East, MD 21901 USA
Web site: http://www.fairwindsstables.com.

Ft. Valley Geology Study Ctr. *Imprint of* **InterPress**

FTD, *(0-9747637)* 3113 Woodcreek Dr., Downers Grove, IL 60515 USA Toll Free: 800-383-6659.

Fuel Media Group, Inc., *(0-9772047)* 15305 NW 60th Ave. Suite 100, Miami Lakes, FL 33014 USA Tel 305-822-7000
E-mail: bob@calvarywired.com
Web site: http://www.fuelmg.com.

†Fulcrum Publishing, *(0-912347; 1-55591; 1-56373)* Orders Addr.: 4690 Table Mountain Dr. Unit 100, Golden, CO 80403-1873 USA (SAN 200-2825) Toll Free Fax: 800-726-7112; Toll Free: 800-992-2908
E-mail: info@fulcrumbooks.com
Web site: http://www.fulcrumbooks.com
Dist(s): **Abraham Assocs. Inc.**
Alibris
Baker & Taylor Bks.
Copyright Clearance Ctr., Inc.; *CIP.*

Full Cast Audio, *(0-9717540; 1-932076; 1-933322; 1-934180)* 618 Westcott St., 1st Flr., Syracuse, NY 13210 USA Toll Free: 800-871-6809
Web site: http://www.fullcastaudio.com
Dist(s): **Harcourt Trade Pubs.**
Harcourt Children's Bks.

Full Circle Pr. *Imprint of* **WillowTree Pr., L.L.C.**

Full Effect Gospel Ministries, Inc, *(0-9679516)* 256 Brooklyn Ave., Brooklyn, NY 11213 USA Tel 718-774-1124; Fax: 718-774-0266
E-mail: ladymcinnis@aol.com.

Full Gospel Family Pubns., *(0-9745599)* 419 E. Taft Ave., Appleton, WI 54915-2079 USA Tel 920-734-6693
E-mail: character@characterbuildingforfamilies.com; pilgrims@juno.com
Web site: http://www.characterbuildingforfamilies.com.

Full Moon Creations, Incorporated *See* **LeLeu, Lisa Studios! Inc.**

Full Moon Publishing LLC, *(0-9666021; 0-9785402)* P.O. Box 408, Schererville, IN 46375 USA Tel 219-688-3093 Do not confuse with Full Moon Publishing, Norton, MA
E-mail: fullmoonpub@sbcglobal.net
Web site: http://www.fullmoonpub.com.

Full Moon Publishing LLCorp. *See* **Full Moon Publishing LLC**

Full Quart Pr. *Imprint of* **Holly Hall Pubns., Inc.**

Full Satchel Pr. (CAN) *(0-9731960) Dist. by* **Wlsn Assocs.**

Full Spectrum Information Library *Imprint of* **Windstorm Creative**

Fuller, Matt, *(0-9675849)* 36 Clear Pond Dr., Frisco, TX 75034-8581 USA
E-mail: mandmfull@msn.com
Web site: http://investingforkids.com.

Fullerton Bks., Inc., *(0-9652918)* Orders Addr.: P.O. Box 1, Waveland, MS 39576 USA Tel 972-412-3131; 228-457-5323; Fax: 509-278-0766
E-mail: info@vincevance.com
Web site: http://www.vincevance.com.

FullofPep Pubns., *(0-9760684)* P.O. Box 367, Columbia, SC 29202 USA
E-mail: fullofeppublications@yahoo.com.

Fullwood Marketing Communications Co., *(0-9667672)* Orders Addr.: P.O. Box 28083, Raleigh, NC 27611 USA Tel 919-857-4600; Fax: 919-857-4601; Toll Free: 800-274-4414; Edit Addr.: 1330 Pk. Glen Dr., No. 202, Raleigh, NC 27610 USA
E-mail: fmcc@bellsouth.net
Web site: http://www.fullwoodmedia.com
Dist(s): **Parnassus Bk. Distributors.**

Fulton, David Pubs. (GBR) *(1-85346; 1-84312) Dist. by* **Taylor and Fran.**

Fultus *See* **Fultus Corp.**

Fultus Bks. *Imprint of* **Fultus Corp.**

Fultus Corp., *(0-9744339; 1-59682)* P.O. Box 50095, Palo Alto, CA 94303 USA Fax: 650-745-0873 ; *Imprints:* Fultus Books (Fultus Bks); Fultus Publishing (Ful Pubng)
E-mail: production@fultus.com
Web site: http://www.fultus.com; http://www.elibrary.fultus.com; http://www.store.fultus.com; http://www.writers.fultus.com
Dist(s): **Lightning Source, Inc.**

Fultus Publishing *Imprint of* **Fultus Corp.**

Fumblefingers Press, Inc., *(0-9674227)* P.O. Box 7694, Algonquin, IL 60102 USA Tel 847-458-2787; Fax: 847-628-0187
E-mail: FFP100@aol.com
Web site: http://www.fumblefingerspress.com
Dist(s): **Baker & Taylor Bks.**
Quality Bks., Inc.

FUN 4 5 Pubns., *(0-9723719)* Div. of Sand Island Software, 137 Silverwood St., Mobile, AL 36607 USA
E-mail: doug_greene@bellsouth.net.

Fun Publishing Co., *(0-938293)* 2121 Alpine Pl., No. 402, Cincinnati, OH 45206 USA (SAN 661-1761) Tel 513-533-3636; Fax: 513-421-7269 Do not confuse with companies with the same or similar names in Scottsdale, AZ, Fort Lauderdale, FL, Indianapolis, IN
E-mail: funpublish@aol.com
Web site: http:/www.funpublishing.com
Dist(s): **Baker & Taylor Bks.**

Fun to Read Bks. with Royally Good Morals *Imprint of* **MKADesigns**

Fun With the Law, Inc., *(1-929905)* One Utah Ctr. 201 S. Main St., No. 900, Salt Lake City, UT 84111 USA Tel 801-535-4335 (phone fax); Fax: 801-621-6953
E-mail: Garth@orijins.com.

Fundacion Intermon (ESP) *(84-604; 84-8452; 84-89970; 84-921977) Dist. by* **Mariuccia Iaconi Bk Imports.**

Fundacion Intermon (ESP) *(84-604; 84-8452; 84-89970; 84-921977) Dist. by* **Lectorum Pubns.**

Fundamental Christian Endeavors, *(1-931787)* 49191 Cherokee Rd., Newberry Springs, CA 92365 USA Tel 760-257-3503; Fax: 760-257-3075
Web site: http://www.ironwood.org.

Fundamental Wesleyan Pubs., *(0-9629383; 0-9761003)* 2120 Culverson Ave., Evansville, IN 47714 USA Tel 812-476-2996
E-mail: victorpau@aol.com
Web site: http://www.fwponline.cc.

FUNdamentals in Education, *(0-9705117)* 19060 Pope Swamp Trail, Windsor, VA 23487 USA Tel 757-357-5409
E-mail: FUNed777@aol.com.

Fundangles, *(1-929992)* P.O. Box 1323, Burlingame, CA 94010-1323 USA Tel 650-342-2578; Fax: 650-342-3645; Toll Free: 800-305-1577
E-mail: fun@fundangles.com
Web site: http://www.fundangles.com.

Fundbuilder$, U.S.A., *(1-891989)* 2900 N. East St., Lansing, MI 48906 USA Tel 517-482-1955; Fax: 517-482-6627; Toll Free: 888-880-1955.

Fundcraft Publishing, *(1-931413)* Orders Addr.: P.O. Box 340, Collerville, TN 38027 USA Tel 901-853-7070; Fax: 901-853-6196; Edit Addr.: 410 Hwy. 72 W., Collierville, TN 38017 USA Tel 901-853-7070
E-mail: questions@cookbooks.com
Web site: http://www.fundcraft.com.

Funics Publishing, *(1-930676)* Orders Addr.: P.O. Box 582, Douglas, MI 49406 USA Tel 616-857-6108; Fax: 616-857-8708; Toll Free: 888-857-7304; Edit Addr.: 301 Union St., Douglas, MI 49406 USA; c/o Funics Publishing @ Riveer Company, 233 Veterans Blvd., South Haven, MI 49090 Tel 616-637-1997; Fax: 616-637-0177; Toll Free: 888-857-7304
E-mail: cpetter@funics.com
Web site: http://www.funics.com.

Funnel Cloud 9, Inc., *(0-9767297)* 545 Tom Treece Rd., Morristown, TN 37814 USA
Web site: http://www.fc9.net.

Funny Bone Bks., *(0-9771836; 0-9790240; 0-9799121)* 3435 Golden Ave., No. 302, Cincinnati, OH 45226 USA; 50 East Rd., Delray Beach, FL 33483
Dist(s): **AtlasBooks Distribution.**

Funny Friends, LLC, *(1-929758)* 48 Elm St., Meriden, CT 06450 USA Tel 203-235-2081; Fax: 203-235-2817; Toll Free: 800-656-6726
Web site: http://www.funnyfriends.com.

FunnyGuy.Comedy, *(0-9747398)* 123 N. Kings Rd., Los Angeles, CA 90048 USA
E-mail: dave@funnyguy.com
Web site: http://www.funnyguy.com.

FunStuff Productions, Inc., *(0-9660157)* 616 Highland Woods Dr., East Mobile, AL 36608 USA Tel 334-665-0100; Fax: 334-655-0155; Toll Free: 800-247-6553
E-mail: learn@funstuffinc.com
Web site: http://www.funstuffinc.com
Dist(s): **Baker & Taylor Entertainment**
Baker & Taylor Bks.
Educator's Resource
Quality Bks., Inc.
Streamwood Distribution
Tapeworm Video Distributor, Inc.

FunZone Co., *(0-9713153)* Orders Addr.: P.O. Box 5645, Newport Beach, CA 92662-5645 USA (SAN 254-5357) Tel 949-723-4141; Fax: 949-723-4085; Edit Addr.: 615 Carnation Ave., Corona Del Mar, CA 92625 USA
E-mail: funzone@pacbell.net
Web site: http://www.funzone.net.

Fur, George, *(0-9752985)* 165 Laurel Ave., Menlo Park, CA 94025 USA
E-mail: yfur@msn.com.

Futech Educational Products, Inc., *(0-9627001; 1-889192)* 2999 N. 44th St., Suite 225, Phoenix, AZ 85018-7248 USA Tel 602-808-8765; Fax: 602-278-5667; Toll Free: 800-597-6278.

Futech Interactive Products, Inc., *(1-58224; 1-879332)* Div. of Futech Interactive Products, 39 S. La Salle St. Ste. 1410, Chicago, IL 60603-1706 USA Toll Free: 800-541-2205.

Future Comics, *(0-9744225)* 220 W. Brandon Blvd., Brandon, FL 33511 USA Tel 813-655-1900; Fax: 813-662-3250; Toll Free: 877-226-6427
E-mail: info@futurecomicsonline.com
Web site: http://www.futurecomicsonline.com.

Future Education, Incorporated *See* **Future Horizons, Inc.**

Future Horizons, Inc., *(1-885477; 1-932565)* 721 W. Abram St., Arlington, TX 76013 USA Tel 817-277-0727; Fax: 817-277-2270; Toll Free: 800-489-0727
E-mail: kelly@fhautism.com
Web site: http://www.FHautism.com
Dist(s): **Ingram Pub. Services.**

Future of America Publishing *See* **Who You Are International, Inc.**

Future Publishing *See* **Future West Publishing**

Future West Publishing, *(1-891406)* Div. of Future Packaging & Preservation, 1580 W. San Bernardino Rd., Suite C, Covina, CA 91722-3457 USA Tel 626-966-1955; Fax: 626-966-5779; Toll Free: 800-786-6627
E-mail: editor@FutureWestPubs.com; graphics@futurewestpubs.com; pubs@futurepkg.com
Web site: http://www.FutureWestPubs.com/
Dist(s): **Independent Pubs. Group.**

Futurekids, Inc., *(1-58739)* 1000 N. Studebaker Rd. Ste. 3, Long Beach, CA 90815-4978 USA Toll Free: 800-765-8000
E-mail: sclifford@futurekids.com
Web site: http://www.futurekids.com; http://www.classroomcurrents.com.

Fuzzy Bks., *(0-9712714)* 617 Arroyo Seco, Santa Cruz, CA 95060 USA Tel 831-429-5300; Fax: 831-459-3519
E-mail: fuzzy_books@hotmail.com.

FUZZY DREAMS, Inc., *(0-9678352)* P.O. Box 2170, Saint Augustine, FL 32085 USA Tel 904-797-7707
E-mail: silb18@aol.com
Web site: http://www.fuzzythegreat.com.

FWDbks., *(0-9759152)* 347 McDonald Ave., Apt. B2, Brooklyn, NY 11218 USA Tel 347-439-4809
E-mail: blam@bway.net.

FWO Bks. *Imprint of* **Francen World Outreach**

FWOMP Publishing, *(0-9760096)* 935 Lighthouse Ave. No. 21, Pacific Grove, CA 93950 USA
Web site: http://www.fwomp.com
Dist(s): **Sunbelt Pubns., Inc.**

FX Digital Photo, *(0-9769009)* 9 Maison Way, Toms River, NJ 08757-6413 USA
Web site: http://www.fxdigitalphoto.com.

GAGA, *(0-9704202)* 3097 Roberts Ferry Rd., NE, Solon, IA 52333 USA Tel 319-848-7412
E-mail: jgokio@aol.com.

GA Publishing, *(0-9652894)* 2196 W. Park Ct., Stone Mountain, GA 30087 USA Tel 770-498-4091; Fax: 770-798-0691; Toll Free: 800-562-4091
E-mail: jeff_davis@graphatl.com
Web site: http://www.gapublishing.com
Dist(s): **Spring Arbor Distributors, Inc.**

G&R Publishing, *(1-56383)* 507 Industrial St., Waverly, IA 50677 USA Toll Free Fax: 800-866-7496; Toll Free: 800-383-1679; 800-887-4445
E-mail: gandr@gandrpublishing.com; gifts@cqproducts.com
Web site: http://www.cookbookprinting.com; http://www.cqproducts.com
Dist(s): **CQ Products.**

G C B Publishing *See* **Holly Hall Pubns., Inc.**

G. D. Stewart Publishing, *(0-9712332)* 3735 Mercedes Pl., Canfield, OH 44406 USA
E-mail: nstewart01@sceinet.com.

GEM/McCuen Pubns., Inc., *(0-86596)* 411 Mallalieu Dr., Hudson, WI 54016-1395 USA (SAN 691-909X) Tel 715-386-7113 (phone/fax); Toll Free: 800-290-6128
E-mail: gem@spacestar.net
Web site: http://www.spacestar.com/users/gem.

G F W C of South Dakota/Daughters of Dakota *See* **Sky Carrier Pr.**

GHB Publishers, LLC, *(1-892920)* P.O. Box 337, Ballwin, MO 63022-0337 USA Toll Free: 888-883-4427
E-mail: ghBPublishers@ghBPublishers.com
Web site: http://www.ghbpublishers.com.

GIA Pubns., Inc., *(0-941050; 1-57999)* 7404 S. Mason Ave., Chicago, IL 60638 USA (SAN 205-3217) Tel 708-496-3800; Fax: 708-496-3828; Toll Free: 800-442-1358
E-mail: custserv@giamusic.com
Web site: http://www.giamusic.com
Dist(s): **CRC Pubns.**
Independent Pubs. Group.

GJ & B Publishing, *(0-9635006)* 22442 University Ave., N., Cedar, MN 55011 USA Tel 612-434-0786.

G L B *See* **GLB Worldwide**

GMA Publishing & Inspiration Pr., *(0-9704650; 0-9720705; 1-59268)* 3399 Forestdale Dr., Newburgh, IN 47630 USA Tel 812-480-0249; Fax: 815-858-1787
E-mail: gmapublising@aol.com
Web site: http://www.GMAPublishing.com.

G.O.G. Enterprises, *(1-891503)* P.O. Box 2092, Beaufort, SC 29901-2092 USA Tel 803-986-9118; Fax: 803-524-9748; Toll Free: 888-464-7664
E-mail: gogent@ad.com
Web site: http://www.beaufortonline.com/ron-natalie
Dist(s): **Parnassus Bk. Distributors**
Sandlapper Publishing Co., Inc.

G O N U T S *See* **Imagine Nation Pr.**

G Publishing *See* **G Publishing LLC**

G Publishing LLC, *(0-9727582; 0-9773267; 0-9776780; 0-9788536; 0-9790691; 0-9796978)* P.O. Box 24374, Detroit, MI 48224-2348 USA; 4826 Harvard Rd., Detroit, MI 48224 Do not confuse with G Publishing in Sebastopol, CA
E-mail: jhun@gpublishingsuccess.com; juthegen@sbcglobal.net
Web site: http://www.gpublishingsuccess.com.

GRM Assocs., *(0-933813; 0-929093)* 290 W. End Ave., 16A, New York, NY 11111 USA Tel 212-874-5964; Fax: 212-874-6425 ; *Imprints:* Taylor Productions (Taylor Prods)
Dist(s): **Independent Pubs. Group.**

GR Publishing, *(0-9668530)* 460 Brookside Way, Felton, CA 95018 USA
E-mail: pub@grandmarose.com
Web site: http://www.grandmarose.com.

GRT Pubns., *(0-9678420; 0-9716906)* P.O. Box 1845, Provo, UT 84603 USA Tel 801-374-2587 (phone/fax)
E-mail: grtpublications@juno.com
Web site: http://www.rogerpminert.

G Schirmer, Inc. *Imprint of* **Leonard, Hal Corp.**

G Sharp Productions, *(0-9669852)* 220 Oak Meadow Dr., Los Gatos, CA 95032 USA Tel 408-354-0047; Fax: 408-399-5397
E-mail: gjkiii@aol.com; gikiii@aol.com
Web site: http://www.gsharpproductions.com.

GT Labs, *(0-9660106; 0-9788037)* P.O. Box 8145, Ann Arbor, MI 48107 USA Tel 734-994-0474; Fax: 734-764-4487 ; *Imprints:* General Tektronics Labs (Gnrl Tek Labs)
E-mail: info@gt-labs.com
Web site: http://www.gt-labs.com
Dist(s): **Diamond Bk. Distributors**
Koen-Levy Bk. Wholesalers LLC.

Gaap Publishing House *See* **Cedar Hill Publishing**

Gabann Enterprises, *(0-9714999)* 3 Russet Way, Cranston, RI 02920 USA Tel 401-946-6408; 401-944-0766; Fax: 401-943-4348
E-mail: annperlow@cox.net; gabann@home.com
Web site: http://www.gabann.com
Dist(s): **BookMasters, Inc.**

Gabriel Pr., *(0-9643475)* 12846 Glen Brae Dr., Saratoga, CA 95070 USA Tel 408-295-1270 Do not confuse with companies with same name in Phoenix, AZ, Ventura, CA, Ft. Lauderdale, FL, Sacramento, CA, Littleton, CO, San Juan, PR
E-mail: mjg827@aol.com.

Gabriel Pr., *(0-9721888)* 255 Calle San Sebastian, San Juan, PR 00901 USA Do not confuse with companies with the same name in Phoenix, AZ, Ventura, CA, Fort Lauderdale, FL, Saratoga, CA, Sacramento, CA, San Juan, PR, Littleton, CO
Web site: http://www.paolanogueras.net
Dist(s): **Lectorum Pubns., Inc.**

Gabriel Resources, Orders Addr.: P.O. Box 1047, Waynesboro, GA 30830 USA Tel 706-554-1594; Fax: 706-554-7444; Toll Free: 800-732-6657 (8MORE-BOOKS); Edit Addr.: 129 Mobilization Dr., Waynesboro, GA 30830 USA.

Gabriele Capelli Editore Sagl (CHE) *(88-87469) Dist. by* **SPD-Small Pr Dist.**

Gaff Pr., *(0-9619629)* Orders Addr.: P.O. Box 1024, Astoria, OR 97103 USA (SAN 245-8403); Edit Addr.: P.O. Box 1024, Astoria, OR 97103-1024 USA (SAN 245-8411)
E-mail: gaffpres@pacifier.com
Web site: http://www.gaffpress.com
Dist(s): **Baker & Taylor Bks.**

Gaffney, Linda, *(0-9787501)* Orders Addr.: PMB 2682 2103 Harrison Ave., NW, Olympia, WA 98502 USA Tel 360-584-8566
Web site: http://www.HomeplacePress.com.

Gagne International Pr., *(0-9666404; 0-9719053)* 1225 E. Sunset Dr., Suite 145, PMB 336, Bellingham, WA 98226 USA Tel 360-733-9500; Fax: 360-733-7595
E-mail: gagneint@aol.com
Web site: http://www.gagneint.com
Dist(s): **Baker & Taylor Bks.**
Diamond Bk. Distributors.

Gail's Guides, *(1-881005)* Orders Addr.: 134 West Canyonview Dr., Longview, WA 98632 USA
E-mail: guides@oz.net; info@gailsguides.com
Web site: http://www.gailsguides.com
Dist(s): **Anderson News - Tacoma**
Aramark
News Group, The
Partners/West.

Gaines, R. L. & Assoc., *(0-9645968)* 35626 Kensington, Sterling Heights, MI 48312 USA Tel 810-264-2111; Fax: 810-264-7473.

Galahad Bks. *Imprint of* **BBS Publishing Corp.**

Galahad Publishing, *(0-918483)* 6035 Vantage Ave., Suite 100, North Hollywood, CA 91606-4637 USA (SAN 657-680X) Tel 818-761-5198; Fax: 818-766-8645; Toll Free: 888-349-4878
Web site: http://www.GalahadPublishing.com.

Galaxia Publishing Group, LLC, *(0-9741657)* P.O. Box 61054, Phoenix, AZ 85082-1054 USA Tel 480-279-0836; Fax: 480-279-0863
E-mail: info@galaxiapg.com
Web site: http://www.galaxiapg.com.

Galaxsis Publishing, *(0-9723111)* 923 Cherry St., Santa Rosa, CA 95404-4208 USA (SAN 254-7511)
Web site: http://www.galaxsis.com.

Galaxy Bks., Inc., *(0-9652682)* Orders Addr.: P.O. Box 1421, Orange Park, FL 32067 USA Tel 904-264-0957 (phone/fax); Edit Addr.: 2018 Smith St., Orange Park, FL 32073 USA
E-mail: info@galaxybooksinc.com
Web site: http://www.galaxybooksinc.com
Dist(s): **Baker & Taylor Bks.**

Galaxy Children's Large Print *Imprint of* **BBC Audiobooks America**

Galaxy Publishing Co., *(1-879629)* 1320 Folsom St., Boulder, CO 80302 USA Tel 800-938-9848; Toll Free: 800-938-9848 Do not confuse with companies with the same or similar name in Saint Petersburg, FL Fresno, CA, Kansas City, KS, Redmond, WA; Houston, TX.

Galaxy Publishing Hse., *(0-9630409)* 7200 Sunshine Skyway Ln., No. 11-D, Saint Petersburg, FL 33711 USA Tel 727-866-2396 Do not confuse with companies with the same or similar name in Boulder, CO, Fresno, CA, Redmond, WA, Kansas City, KS
E-mail: fimlaid@yahoo.com
Web site: http://www.fimlaid.com
Dist(s): **American Federation of Astrologers, Inc.**
Bookazine Co., Inc.
New Leaf Distributing Co., Inc.

Galde Pr., Inc., *(1-880090; 1-931942)* Orders Addr.: P.O. Box 460, Lakeville, MN 55044-460 USA Tel 952-891-5991; Fax: 952-891-6091; Toll Free: 800-777-3454 (orders only) ; *Imprints:* Weasel Books (Weasel Bks)
E-mail: pgalde@galdepress.com
Web site: http://www.galdepress.com.

Gale Group *See* **Thomson Gale**

Gale Hill Bks., *(0-9645809)* 109 Irving St., Cambridge, MA 02138 USA Tel 617-491-3639.

Gale Research International, Ltd. (GBR) *(0-7876; 0-8103; 1-873477) Dist. by* **Gale.**

Galen Pr., Ltd., *(1-883620)* Orders Addr.: P.O. Box 64400, Tucson, AZ 85728-4400 USA (SAN 254-1823) Tel 520-577-8363; Fax: 520-529-6459; Toll Free: 800-442-5369 (orders only) Do not confuse with Galen Pr. in Madison, NJ
E-mail: galenpr@galenpress.com; sales@galenpress.com
Web site: http://www.galenpress.com
Dist(s): **Baker & Taylor Bks.**
Majors, J. A. Co.
Matthews Medical Bk. Co.
Rittenhouse Bk. Distributors.

Gali Girls, Inc., *(0-9773673)* 48 Cranford Pl., Teaneck, NJ 07666 USA Tel 201-862-1989
Web site: http://www.galigirls.com.

Galison, *(0-7353; 0-929648; 0-939456; 1-56155)* 28 W. 44th St., Suite 1411-12, New York, NY 10036 USA Tel 212-354-8840; Fax: 212-944-8682; Toll Free: 800-322-6663
E-mail: sales@galison.com
Web site: http://www.galison.com.

Gallagher, Carole M., *(0-9702197)* 431 S. Main St., Williamstown, NJ 08094 USA Tel 856-875-1575; Fax: 856-875-1998.

†Gallaudet Univ. Pr., *(0-913580; 0-930323; 1-56368)* 800 Florida Ave., NE, Washington, DC 20002-3695 USA (SAN 205-261X) Tel 202-651-5488; Fax: 202-651-5489; Toll Free Fax: 800-621-8476; Toll Free: 888-630-9347 (TTY)
E-mail: valencia.simmons@gallaudet.edu
Web site: http://www.gupress.gallaudet.edu/
Dist(s): **Chicago Distribution Ctr.**; *CIP.*

Galleon Distribution *See* **Quiltown**

Gallery of Diamonds Publishing, *(1-891665)* Div. of Gallery of Diamonds Jewelers, 1000 Bristol St. N. # 8, Newport Beach, CA 92660 USA (SAN 299-5492) Tel 949-476-2000; Fax: 949-222-2277; Toll Free: 800-667-4440
E-mail: info@galleryofdiamonds.com
Web site: http://www.galleryofdiamonds.com.

Gallery Press *See* **Gallery Press Publishing, Inc.**

Gallery Press Publishing, Inc., *(0-9717117)* 1301 Fraser St., Bellingham, WA 98229-5851 USA Toll Free: 800-237-4762
E-mail: bergsma@bergsma.com
Web site: http://www.bergsma.com
Dist(s): **Illumination Arts Publishing Co., Inc.**

Galletti, Barbara, *(0-9748737)* 2509 Lawnside Rd., Timonium, MD 21093-2605 USA Tel 410-252-6568
E-mail: gallettinotes@hotmail.com.

Gallimard, Editions (FRA) *(2-07) Dist. by* **AIMS Intl.**

Gallimard, Editions (FRA) *(2-07) Dist. by* **Distribks Inc.**

Gallopade International, *(0-635; 0-7933; 0-935326; 1-55609)* Orders Addr.: 665 Highway 74 South, Suite 600, Peachtree City, GA 30269 USA (SAN 213-8441) Tel 770-631-4222; Toll Free Fax: 800-871-2979; Toll Free: 800-536-2438 ; *Imprints:* Marsh, Carole Family CD-Rom (C Marsh); Marsh, Carole Books (C Mrsh Bks)
E-mail: sales@gallopade.com
Web site: http://www.gallopade.com.

Gallopade: Publishing Group *See* **Gallopade International**

Gallup Pr., *(1-59562)* 1251 Avenue of the Americas, 23rd Fl., New York, NY 10020 USA Tel 212-899-4709; Fax: 212-899-4899; Toll Free: 877-242-5587
Web site: http://www.gallup.com
Dist(s): **Perseus Distribution.**

Galore Park Publishing Ltd. (GBR) *(1-902984) Dist. by* **Coronet Bks.**

Galvan Pharmacy *See* **Galvart Publishing**

Galvart Publishing, *(0-9644836)* P.O. Box 15764, San Antonio, TX 78212-8964 USA Tel 210-732-2507 (phone/fax)
E-mail: galvart@hotmail.com
Web site: http://www.galvart.com.

Gambit Gameworks, Inc., *(0-9704213)* 9230 Vanalden Ave., Northridge, CA 91324 USA Tel 818-717-0345 (phone/fax)
E-mail: decaussin@socal.rr.com
Web site: http://www.gambitgameworks.com.

Gambit Pubns., Ltd. (GBR) *(1-901983; 1-904600) Dist. by* **Perseus Dist.**

Game Day Press *See* **Timberwood Pr.**

Game Designers' Workshop, *(0-943580; 1-55878)* 1418 N. Clinton Blvd., Bloomington, IL 61701 USA (SAN 240-656X) Tel 309-827-5534; Fax: 309-828-8170
E-mail: marcwmiller@aol.com
Dist(s): **PSI (Publisher Services, Inc.).**

Game Plan Pubns., *(0-9706421; 1-931377)* 588 Sutter St., No. 310, San Francisco, CA 94102 USA Tel 414-407-6313
E-mail: drwesley@earthlink.net
Web site: http://www.sportseries.org.

Games Workshop *Imprint of* **Simon & Schuster**

Gam-Jam Publishing Company *See* **Pendleton Publishing, Inc.**

Gamlin, Stephen, *(0-9767993)* P.O. Box 1696, Salem, NH 03079 USA Tel 603-560-3360; Fax: 603-774-8698; Toll Free: 877-560-3360
E-mail: dj@ramblinsounds.com
Web site: http://www.SteveGamlin.com.

Gamoke, John, *(0-9771290)* 6645 Humboldt Ave. S., Richfield, MN 55423 USA.

Gan Or, *(0-9652870)* 5850 Park St., Las Vegas, NV 89129 USA Tel 702-645-7997; Fax: 702-645-8002.

GanDale Associates Houston *See* **Holocaust Museum Houston**

Gander Educational Publishing *See* **Gander Publishing**

Gander Publishing, *(0-945856)* 412 Higuera St., Suite 200, San Luis Obispo, CA 93401 USA (SAN 247-9915) Tel 805-541-5523; Fax: 805-782-0488; Toll Free: 800-554-1819
E-mail: wcook@ganderpublishing.com
Web site: http://www.ganderpublishing.com.

G&V Publishing Company, Incorporated *See* **MedLife Publishing, Inc.**

Gant, Linda G. Gifted Creations *See* **Readers Are Leaders**

Gap Tooth Publishing *Imprint of* **Charles River Pr.**

Garborg's Heart 'n Home, Incorporated *See* **Garborg's, Inc.**

Garborg's, Inc., *(1-58375; 1-881830)* P.O. Box 1010, Siloam Spgs, AR 72761-1010 USA (SAN 299-8289) Toll Free: 800-678-5727
E-mail: deborahpeterson@garborgs.com
Dist(s): **Spring Arbor Distributors, Inc.**

Garcia, Cezanne, *(0-9728041)* 30405 Cupeno Ln., Temecula, CA 92592-2540 USA Tel 951-506-6407 (phone fax)
E-mail: stgarcia@fda.net.

Garden Fleetfoot Pr., *(0-9762544)* P.O. Box 1188, Okemos, MI 48805 USA
E-mail: info@gardenfleetfoot.com
Web site: http://gardenfleetfoot.com.

Garden, Randa, *(0-615)* 3503 Portia Pl., Norfolk, NE 68701 USA Tel 402-371-0544
E-mail: jrgarden@cableone.net
Web site: www.pennythepenguin.com.

Company

Gardenia Publishing, *(0-9678621)* Orders Addr.: P.O. Box 15, Arlington, TX 76004 USA Tel 817-507-6228; Fax: 817-652-9767; 2615 Nikos Pl. #82, Arlington, TX 76006 Tel 817-507-6228
E-mail: tcdanielbooks@aol.com
Web site: http://www.thesinadaniel.com.

Gardner, Colin, *(0-615; 0-9720348)* 1677 S. 75 E., Bouniful, UT 84010-5218 USA Tel 801-296-2109 (phone/fax)
E-mail: colingardner@juno.com.

Gardner, Garth Co., Inc. (GGC), *(0-9661075; 1-58965)* 5107 13th St., NW, Washington, DC 20011 USA Tel 202-541-9700; Fax: 202-541-9750
E-mail: gardner@ggcinc.com
Web site: http://www.ggcinc.com; http://www.gogardner.com
Dist(s): **Independent Pubs. Group.**

Garing, Bernard, *(0-9765809)* 1718 Sterling Oaks Dr., Sellersburg, IN 47172 USA.

Garland, Daniel, *(0-9768414)* 6247 Cascade Hwy., NE, Silverton, OR 97381 USA
E-mail: danielggarland@msn.com.

†Garland Publishing, Inc., *(0-8153; 0-8240)* Member of Taylor & Francis, Inc., 29 W. 35th St., Flr. 10, New York, NY 10001-2299 USA Tel 212-216-7800; Fax: 212-564-7854; Toll Free: 800-627-6273 (orders)
E-mail: info@garland.com
Web site: www.garlandscience.com
Dist(s): **NetLibrary, Inc.**
Sony CONNECT, Inc.
Taylor & Francis, Inc.; *CIP.*

Garland S T P M Press *See* **Garland Publishing, Inc.**

Garlic Pr., *(0-931993; 1-930820)* Orders Addr.: 605 Powers St., Eugene, OR 97402 USA (SAN 686-1105) Tel 541-345-0063; Fax: 541-683-8767; Edit Addr.: 1312 Jeppesen Ave., Eugene, OR 97401 USA Do not confuse with companies with the same name in Kirkwood, MO, New London, NH, Abingdon MD, Lenox MA, Kansas City, MO
E-mail: garlic.cecily@mindspring.com
Web site: http://www.garlicpress.com.

Garm Co., *(0-9665302)* 703 Highridge Ave., Greencastle, IN 46135 USA Tel 765-653-9498.

Garnett Publishing, Inc., *(0-9714150)* Orders Addr.: P.O. Box 409, Garnett, KS 66032-0409 USA Tel 785-448-3121; Fax: 785-448-6253; Edit Addr.: 112 W. Sixth Ave., Garnett, KS 66032-0409 USA Do not confuse with Garnett Publishing in Cleveland, OH
E-mail: review@garnett-ks.com
Web site: http://www.cybernovel.org.

Garr, Sherry B., *(0-9759866)* 3456 S. Mulberry Dr., Saint George, UT 84790 USA
Web site: http://www.gumfounded.com.

Garrelts, Christopher *See* **Squarey Head, Inc.**

Garrett County Pr., *(1-891053)* 614 S. 8th St. #373, Philadelphia, PA 19147 USA Tel 215-238-9893
E-mail: darby@gcpress.com
Web site: http://www.gcpress.com
Dist(s): **Biblio Distribution**
National Bk. Network.

Gaslight Pubns., *(0-934468)* P.O. Box 1344, Studio City, CA 91614-0344 USA Tel 818-784-8918
Dist(s): **Empire Publishing Service**
Players Pr., Inc.

GASLight Publishing, *(0-9754796; 1-933869)* P.O. Box 1025, Leander, TX 78646 USA Tel 512-528-1727; Fax: 512-259-8671
E-mail: ken@gaslightpublishing.com; kenschaefer@totalaccess.net
Web site: http://www.gsalightpublishing.com.

Gassett, John D., *(0-9671895)* 2119 S. Richmond, Tulsa, OK 74114 USA Tel 918-744-7142.

GateKeepers International, Incorporated, *(0-9745483)* 15245 Jessie Dr., Colorado Springs, CO 80921 USA
E-mail: gatekeepersinfo@cs.com
Web site: http://www.gatekeepersintl.org.

GateKeepers Ministries International, *(0-9754535)* 3600 Earl Ave., Pennsauken, NJ 08110 USA Toll Free: 866-910-2810
Web site: http://www.gkmi.org.

Gates & Bridges Inc., *(1-929953)* 4030 Tates Creek Rd., Apt. 2912, Lexington, KY 40517 USA Tel 203-426-5640; Fax: 203-426-7817
E-mail: hlomeyer@snet.net.

Gateway Learning Corporation *See* **HOP, LLC**

Gateway Pr. *Imprint of* **White-Bowden Assocs.**

Gateway Pubs., *(1-887646)* Orders Addr.: P.O. Box 1749, Newark, NJ 07101 USA Tel 973-824-7207; Fax: 973-824-1531; Toll Free: 800-511-2394; Edit Addr.: 10 Richmond St., Newark, NJ 07103 USA Do not confuse with companies with the same name or similar name in Louisville, CO, Charleston, SC
E-mail: modu@ix.netcom.com.

GATFPress, *(0-88362)* 200 Deer Run Rd., Sewickley, PA 15143-2600 USA (SAN 224-778X) Tel 412-741-6860; Fax: 412-741-2311; Toll Free: 800-910-4283 (800-910-GATF)
E-mail: AWoodall@piagatf.org; info@gain.net
Web site: http://www.gain.net.

Gathering Place Pubs., Inc., *(0-9754622)* P.O. Box 341, Kaysville, UT 84037-8403 USA (SAN 256-0658) Fax: 801-451-6008
E-mail: marketing@gatheringplacepublishers.com
Web site: http://www.gatheringplacepublisher.com; http://www.stonesquest.com.

†Gaunt, Inc., *(0-912004; 1-56169; 1-60449)* 3011 Gulf Dr., Holmes Beach, FL 34217-2199 USA (SAN 202-9413) Tel 941-778-5211; Fax: 941-778-5252; Toll Free: 800-942-8683 (US & Canada)
E-mail: info@gaunt.com; sales@gaunt.com
Web site: http://www.gaunt.com; *CIP.*

Gaunt, William W. & Sons, Incorporated *See* **Gaunt, Inc.**

Gauntlet, Inc., *(0-9629659; 1-887368; 1-934267)* 5307 Arroyo St., Colorado Springs, CO 80922 USA Tel 719-591-5566; Fax: 719-591-6676
E-mail: gauntlet66@aol.com; info@gauntletpress.com
Web site: http://www.gauntletpress.com
Dist(s): **Baker & Taylor Bks.**

Gaussian, Inc., *(0-9636769; 0-9727187)* 340 Quinnipiac St., Bldg. 40, Wallingford, CT 06492 USA Tel 203-284-2501; Fax: 203-284-2521
E-mail: isbn@gaussian.com
Web site: http://www.gaussian.com.

Gavin, Fred Enterprises, *(0-935668)* 96 Byron St., East Boston, MA 02128 USA (SAN 221-1629).

Gaviota Ediciones (ESP) *(84-392) Dist. by* **Lectorum Pubns.**

Gavlak, L.J. Publishing, *(0-9740357)* Orders Addr.: P.O. Box 72, Kylertown, PA 16847 USA Tel 814-345-6391; Edit Addr.: Rollingston Rd., Kylertown, PA 16847 USA
E-mail: largav@juno.com.

Gay, Lesbian & Straight Education Network, *(0-9722834; 1-934092)* 90 Broad St., Second Floor, New York, NY 10004 USA Tel 212-727-0135; Fax: 212-727-0354
E-mail: glsen@glsen.org
Web site: http://www.glsen.org.

Gayle Publishing Co., *(0-9678436)* 536 Santa Fe Trail, No. 253, Irving, TX 75063 USA Tel 972-401-1119 Do not confuse with Gayle Publishing, Houston, TX
E-mail: bridgetx@swbell.net
Web site: http://www.grandjuryconnections.com
Dist(s): **Baker & Taylor Bks.**
Hervey's Booklink & Cookbook Warehouse.

Gazebo Pr., The, *(0-9718587)* Div. of Emeritus Bks., 145 Woodhaven Ridge, Athens, GA 30606 USA.

gaZko Entertainment, *(0-9792694)* 19072 Florida St., Unit 12, Huntington Beach, CA 92648 USA (SAN 852-9779) Tel 949-246-4771
E-mail: greg@gazko.com
Web site: http://www.gazko.com.

Gazoobi Tales, *(0-9679364)* 320 W. Roy St., #301, Seattle, WA 98119 USA Tel 425-308-7249
E-mail: info@gazoobitales.com
Web site: http://www.gazoobitales.com.

GBGMusik *Imprint of* **General Board of Global Ministries, The United Methodist Church**

GDL Multimedia, LLC, *(1-60245)* 21801 26th St. E., Lake Tapps, WA 98391 USA
E-mail: greg@gdlmultimedia.com
Web site: http://www.gdlmultimedia.com.

GDM Consulting Services LLC, *(0-9763738)* 5 Alluvium Lakes Dr., Voorhees, NJ 08043 USA
Web site: http://www.gdmcs.com.

Gecko Publishing *See* **Two Geckos Music & Publishing**

Geckostufs, Incorporated *See* **Words & Pictures Publishing, Inc.**

Geddes & Grosset, Ltd. (GBR) *(1-84205; 1-85534) Dist. by* **CPG Pub Inc.**

Gee, Genese Celeste, *(0-9719935)* 3749 Greenmoor Gardens Ct., Florissant, MO 63034 USA
E-mail: aebballgirl@usa.com.

Gefen Bks., *(0-86343; 965-229)* 600 Broadway., Lynbrook, NY 11563-3908 USA Toll Free: 800-477-5257
E-mail: gefenny@gefenpublishing.com
Web site: http://www.israelbooks.com.

Gefen Publishing Hse., Ltd (ISR) *(965-229) Dist. by* **Gefen Bks.**

Gehring, James R., *(0-9709560)* 15090 Lakeside View Dr., No. 1502, Fort Myers, FL 33919-8481 USA Tel 941-482-7029
E-mail: flugehring@aol.com.

Gem Bk. Pubs., *(0-9633723; 1-887651)* Div. of Fred Ward Productions, Inc., Orders Addr.: 2575 Barrymore Dr., Malibu, CA 90265-2955 USA Tel 310-456-9949; Fax: 310-456-9799
E-mail: fred@fredwardgems.com
Web site: http://www.fredwardgems.com.

Gem Printing, *(0-9743429)* Orders Addr.: 600 Reisterstown Rd., Suite 200G, Baltimore, MD 21208 USA Tel 410-764-1617; Fax: 410-764-7471 ; *Imprints:* American Poets Society (Amer Poets)
E-mail: poetryamericaorders@yahoo.com
Web site: http://www.poetryamerica.com.

Gem Pubns., *(0-9742354)* 3520 McNally Ave., Altadena, CA 91001 USA
E-mail: gregmiddleton@earthlink.net
Web site: http://www.gempublications.com.

G.E.M. Publishing *Imprint of* **Global Evangelism Ministries, Inc.**

Gemini Mojo Pr., *(0-9752907)* 2343 W. Claremont St., Phoenix, AZ 85015 USA Toll Free Fax: 888-354-5794; Toll Free: 888-354-5794
E-mail: celise@geminimojopress.com
Web site: http://www.geminimojopress.com
Dist(s): **Lightning Source, Inc.**

Gemini Pr *Imprint of* **Project Publishing & Design**

GEMS *Imprint of* **Univ. of California, Berkeley, Lawrence Hall of Science**

Gems International Incorporated *See* **Gems International, LLC**

Gems International, LLC, *(0-9728626)* 640 S. Ave. Apt. I-8 Secane, Pa 19018, Secane, PA 19018 USA
Web site: http://www.myfaithbookclub.com.

Gemstone Publishing, Inc., *(0-911903; 1-888472; 1-60360)* Div. of Diamond Comic Distributors, Inc., 1966 Greenspring Dr., Suite 405, Timonium, MD 21093 USA Tel 410-427-9432; Fax: 410-252-4582 Do not confuse with companies with same or similar names in Thornville, OH, Lebanon, OR, Lauderdale Lakes, FL, Sugarland, TX
Web site: http://www.gemstonepub.com
Dist(s): **Diamond Bk. Distributors.**

General Board of Global Ministries, The United Methodist Church, *(1-890569; 1-933663)* 475 Riverside Dr. Rm. 1320, New York, NY 10115 USA Tel 212-870-3783; Fax: 212-870-3686 ; *Imprints:* GBGMusik (GBGMusik); WD/GBGM Books (WD GBGM)
E-mail: cscott@gbgm-umc.org
Web site: http://www.gbgm-umc.org
Dist(s): **Cokesbury**
Mission Resource Ctr.

General Tektronics Labs *Imprint of* **GT Labs**

Genesis Biotech, *(0-9710633)* 7 Anthony Ln., Bradford, PA 16701 USA Tel 814-362-8820; Fax: 814-368-6696
E-mail: soriano@penn.com
Web site: http://users.penn.com/soriano/index.html.

Genesis Communications, Inc., *(0-9637311; 1-58169)* P.O. Box 191540, Mobile, AL 36619 USA Tel 251-443-7900; Fax: 251-443-7090; Toll Free: 800-367-8203 ; *Imprints:* Evergreen Press (Evergrn Pr AL)
E-mail: Jeff@evergreen777.com
Web site: http://www.evergreenpress.com
Dist(s): **Spring Arbor Distributors, Inc.**

Genesis Group, *(0-9705317)* Orders Addr.: P.O. Box 382, Millville, NJ 08332 USA Tel 856-293-8176; Edit Addr.: N. High Street, Millville, NJ 08332 USA
E-mail: genesispub103800@aol.com.

Genesis Publishing Group, *(0-9749300; 1-933591)* 2002 Skyline Pl., Bartlesville, OK 74006-6137 USA Tel 918-333-9551; Fax: 918-333-9668
E-mail: lynncopeland@genesis-group.net
Web site: http://www.genesis-group.net
Dist(s): **STL Distribution North America.**

Geneva Lake Publishing, *(0-9711736)* N 1545 Willowbrook Dr., Lake Geneva, WI 53147 USA Tel 262-248-2785; Fax: 262-248-8630
E-mail: conlon@genevaonline.com.

Geneva Pr., *(0-664; 0-8042)* Div. of Presbyterian Publishing Corp., Orders Addr.: 100 Witherspoon St., Louisville, KY 40202-1396 USA Tel 502-569-5308; 502-569-5052 (outside U.S. for ordering); Fax: 502-569-5113 (outside U.S. for faxed orders); Toll Free Fax: 800-541-5113 (toll-free U.S. for faxed orders); Toll Free: 800-227-2872
Dist(s): **CRC Pubns.**
Presbyterian Publishing Corp.
Westminster John Knox Pr.

Genibrel Pubns., *(0-9669120)* 5318 E. Second St., Long Beach, CA 90803 USA Tel 562-434-3301
E-mail: genibrel@aol.com
Dist(s): **MBI Distribution Services.**

Genius In A Bottle Technology Corp., *(0-9768429)* 8241 SW 25th Ct., Miramar, FL 33025-2991 USA
E-mail: geniusinfo@geniusinabottle.net
Web site: http://www.geniusinabottle.net.

Gentle Giraffe Pr., *(0-9747921; 0-9777394)* 7405 Barra Dr., Bethesda, MD 20817 USA Tel 202-423-4205; Fax: 334-460-0724; Toll Free: 888-424-4723
E-mail: info@gentlegiraffe.com
Web site: http://www.gentlegiraffe.com.

Gently Worded Bks., LLC, *(0-9708940)* Orders Addr.: 211 Old Santa Fe Trail, Santa Fe, NM 87501 USA; Edit Addr.: P.O. Box 1326, Santa Fe, NM 87504-1326 USA Tel 505-983-6134; Fax: 505-984-7921
E-mail: chasjune@aol.com
Web site: http://www.gentlywordedbooks.com.

Geography Matters, Inc., *(0-9702403; 1-931397)* P.O. Box 92, Nancy, KY 42544 USA Tel 606-636-4678; Fax: 606-636-4697; Toll Free: 800-426-4650
E-mail: geomatters@geomatters.com
Web site: http://www.geomatters.com.

GeoPlaneta, Editorial, S. A. (ESP) *(84-320) Dist. by* **Lectorum Pubns.**

GeoQuest Pubns., *(0-9651101)* P.O. Box 1665, Lake Oswego, OR 97035-1212 USA Tel 971-242-1107
E-mail: info@geoquest.net
Web site: http://www.geoquest.net
Dist(s): **Baker & Taylor Bks.**
Far West Bk. Service
Partners/West.

George, H. Publishing, *(0-9728183)* Orders Addr.: 14513 Bayes Ave., Lakewood, OH 44107 USA Tel 216-319-4575
E-mail: ninthohio@sbcglobal.net.

George, Thomas Bks., *(0-9709829)* P.O. Box 861853, Los Angeles, CA 90086-1853 USA Tel 626-572-3544; Fax: 626-572-8772
E-mail: books@thomasgeorgebooks.com
Web site: http://www.thomasgeorgebooks.com
Dist(s): **Baker & Taylor Bks.**
Book Wholesalers, Inc.
National Bk. Network.

Georgetown Visitation Monastery, *(0-9705851)* Div. of Georgetown Visitation, 1524 35th St., NW, Washington, DC 20007-2785 USA Fax: 202-965-3845
E-mail: mcnabb@geoviscon.aol
Web site: http://www.ee.cua.edu.georgvis.

Georgia Public Broadcasting, *(1-892720)* Div. of Georgia Public Telecommunications Commission, 260 14th St., Atlanta, GA 30338 USA Tel 404-685-2550; Fax: 404-685-2556; Toll Free: 800-222-6006 (ext. 2550)
E-mail: bingram@gpb.org
Web site: http://www.gpb.org.

Geoscience Information Services, *(0-9777100)* Orders Addr.: P.O. Box 911, West Falmouth, MA 02574-0911 USA Tel 508-540-6490
E-mail: gis@cape.com.

Gequalsa, *(0-9792518)* 2710 Walnut St., Orlando, FL 32806 USA.

Gerard & Sarzin Publishing Co., *(0-9628467; 1-930080)* 28 Old Fulton St., Apt. TH-K, Brooklyn, NY 11201 USA Tel 718-858-6945
E-mail: cgerard@pipeline.com
Web site: http://www.changingtones.com/gerdsarz.htm/
Dist(s): **Music Sales Corp.**

Gerber, Judie *See* **Seachild**

Gerber Publishing Co., Inc., *(0-9623328)* P.O. Box 448, Glenbrook, NV 89413 USA Tel 775-882-4336; Fax: 775-883-1000
Dist(s): **Diamond Comic Distributors, Inc.**

Gere Publishing, *(0-9743995)* 113 Leonard Rd., Shutesbury, MA 01072-9783 USA (SAN 257-4594) Tel 413-259-1741
E-mail: info@gerepublishing.com
Web site: http://www.gerepublishing.com.

Geringer, Laura Book *Imprint of* **HarperCollins Pubs.**

Gerl, Perrine & Brasher Publishing *See* **Gerl Publishing**

Gerl Publishing, *(0-9663820)* 1230 Old Robeline Rd., Apt. C110, Natchitoches, LA 71457 USA Tel 318-356-0260; Fax: 318-352-2782
E-mail: euphoria@cp-tel.net.

Gernand, Linda, *(0-9755025)* 523 Oyster Creek Dr., Richwood, TX 77531 USA.

Gersten, Dan & Associates LLC *See* **Dogwalk Pr.**

Gerstenblatt, Judith Furedi *See* **Lucky & Me Productions, Inc.**

Gestalt Journal Pr., *(0-939266)* P.O. Box 278, Gouldsboro, ME 04607 USA (SAN 216-5317) Tel 207-963-7635; Fax: 866-460-8795 (Prefered order method)
E-mail: press@gestalt.org
Web site: http://www.gestaltjournalpress.com.

Gestalt Pubns., *(0-9764065)* 3828 Clinton Ave. S., Minneapolis, MN 55409-1314 USA Tel 612-822-4419.

Get Graphic Publishing, *(0-9711758)* Div. of Kymzinn, Inc., 23236 Lyons Ave., Suite 216, San Clarita, CA 91321 USA Tel 661-254-1000; Toll Free: 888-806-7827
E-mail: sales@kymzinn.com; info@kymzinn.com
Web site: http://www.kymzinn.com.

Get'n Even, *(1-928727)* Orders Addr.: P.O. Box 55, Clark, SD 57225 USA Tel 605-532-3553 (orders); Fax: 605-532-3553; Edit Addr.: 301 N. Commercial, Clark, SD 57225 USA
E-mail: tnickels@itctel.com.

Getting There, *(0-9707274)* P.O. Box 1412, Asheville, NC 28802-1412 USA Tel 828-645-5908
E-mail: bmayers@charter.net
Web site: http://www.paddlingasheville.com
Dist(s): **Appalachian Bk. Distributors**
Common Ground Distributors, Inc.

Getty, J. Paul Trust Publications *See* **Getty Pubns.**

†Getty Pubns., *(0-89236; 0-941103)* Orders Addr.: P.O. Box 49659, Los Angeles, CA 90049-0659 USA Tel 310-440-7333; Fax: 818-779-0051; Edit Addr.: 1200 Getty Ctr. Dr., Suite 500, Los Angeles, CA 90049-1682 USA (SAN 208-2276) Tel 310-440-7365; Fax: 310-440-7706; Toll Free: 800-223-3431 ; *Imprints:* J. Paul Getty Museum (J P Getty)
E-mail: pubsinfo@getty.edu
Web site: http://www.getty.edu/publications
Dist(s): **Lectorum Pubns., Inc.**
Libros Sin Fronteras
Oxford Univ. Pr., Inc.; *CIP.*

Geyer's Garten Cards & Bks., *(1-886123)* 19569 Hwy. 2, Monroe, WA 98272 USA Tel 360-794-7393; Fax: 360-794-4084.

GGMI Inc., *(0-9772647)* P.O. Box 1430, Dacula, GA 30019 USA (SAN 257-1528)
E-mail: office@godsglory.org
Web site: http://www.GodsGlory.org.

Ghim, John Yun, *(0-9656864)* 1139 Queen Anne Pl. Apt. 106, Los Angeles, CA 90019-7105 USA
E-mail: coolghim@yahoo.com
Dist(s): **Baker & Taylor Bks.**

GHL Publishing LLC, *(0-9726419)* P.O. Box 26462, Collegeville, PA 19426 USA (SAN 254-9875) Tel 610-831-1442; Fax: 610-831-1443
E-mail: c.lagunilla@att.net
Web site: http://www.GHLPublishing.com.

Ghost Hse. Bks (CAN) *(1-894877) Dist. by* **Lone Pine.**

Ghost Hunter Productions, *(0-9717234; 1-934307)* P.O. Box 1199, Helena, MT 59624 USA
E-mail: info@ibw-books.com
Web site: http://www.ibw-books.com.

G-Host Publishing, *(0-9649088)* Orders Addr.: 8701 Lava Pl., West Hills, CA 91304-2126 USA Tel 818-340-6676 (phone/fax)
E-mail: robanne@ix.netcom.com.

Ghost Town Pubns., *(0-933818)* P.O. Drawer 5998, Carmel, CA 93921 USA (SAN 209-4401)
E-mail: info@ghosttownpub.com; jbergez@earthlink.net
Web site: http://www.ghosttownpub.com.

Ghostdancer Press, Incorporated *See* **Grey Ghost Pr., Inc.**

Giant Robot Bks., *(0-9749492)* P.O. Box 641639, Los Angeles, CA 90064 USA Tel 310-479-7311
E-mail: books@giantrobot.com
Web site: http://www.giantrobot.com
Dist(s): **Trucatriche.**

†Gibbs Smith, Publisher, *(0-87905; 0-941711; 1-58685; 1-4236)* Orders Addr.: P.O. Box 667, Layton, UT 84041 USA (SAN 201-9906) Tel 801-544-9800; Fax: 801-544-5582; Toll Free Fax: 800-213-3023 (orders); Toll Free: 800-748-5439 (orders); 800-835-4993 (Customer Service order only); Edit Addr.: 1877 E. Gentile St., Layton, UT 84040 USA Tel 801-544-9800; Fax: 801-546-8853 ; *Imprints:* Wyrick (Wyri)
E-mail: info@gibbs-smith.com; text@gibbs-smith.com; tradeorders@gibbs-smith.com
Web site: http://www.gibbs-smith.com
Dist(s): **Publishers Group International, Inc.**; *CIP.*

Gibson Bks. *Imprint of* **Glory Days Group Publishing**

Gibson, C. R. Co., *(0-7667; 0-8378; 0-937970; 0-7053)* 401 BNA Dr., Bldg 200, Suite 600, Nashville, TN 37217 USA Toll Free: 800-243-6004 (ext. 2895)
E-mail: customerservice@crgibson.com
Web site: http://www.andersonpress.com.

Gibson, Cita, *(0-9727964)* P.O. Box 411236, Melbourne, FL 32941 USA Tel 316-210-6422; Fax: 321-757-7385
E-mail: maloon57@aol.com
Web site: http://www.citagibson.com.

Gibson Tech Ed, Inc., *(0-9712340)* 31516 Sagecrest Dr., Lake Elsinore, CA 92532 USA Tel 951-471-4932; Toll Free Fax: 866-367-6180; Toll Free: 800-314-3843
E-mail: gibsalsys@yahoo.com
Web site: http://www.gibsontron.com.

Giddy Up, LLC, *(1-932125; 1-59524)* 3630 Plaza Dr., Ann Arbor, MI 48108 USA (SAN 255-6847)
E-mail: stiehl@giddyup.com
Web site: http://www.giddyup.com.

Gifted Education Pr., *(0-910609)* Orders Addr.: P.O. Box 1586, Manassas, VA 20108 USA; Edit Addr.: 10201 Yuma Ct., Manassas, VA 20109 USA (SAN 694-132X) Tel 703-369-5017; Toll Free: 800-484-1406 (code 6857)
E-mail: mfisher345@home.com
Web site: http://GIFTEDEDPRESS.COM.

Gifted Psychology Press, Incorporated *See* **Great Potential Pr., Inc.**

Gigarjian, Ani & Linda Avedikian, *(0-9717799)* 169 S. Main St., Sherborn, MA 01770 USA
E-mail: gigarjian@comcast.net
Web site: http://www.armeniankids.com.

Giggles Group, Inc., The, *(1-892780)* 345 Middlesex Ave., Metuchen, NJ 08840-1510 USA (SAN 299-6995) Toll Free: 877-244-4453
E-mail: gigglesgr@aol.com
Web site: http://www.gigglesgroup.com.

Giggletins *Imprint of* **Le Bk. Moderne, LLC**

Giggling Gorilla Productions, LLC, *(0-9770700)* 12427 Caminito Brioso, San Diego, CA 92131 USA
E-mail: zoomanmike@earthlink.net
Web site: http://www.gigglinggorillaproductions.com.

GiGi Bks., *(0-9740847)* 17480 Old Waterford Rd., Leesburg, VA 20176 USA Tel 703-669-9781; Fax: 703-669-9782
E-mail: ganderson@gigiaudiobooks.com
Web site: http://www.gigiaudiobooks.com.

Gigi Enterprises, *(0-615)* P.O. Box 133, Irvington, NY 10533-0133 USA Fax: 914-591-9249
E-mail: sonia0904@aol.com.

GIL Pubns., *(0-9626035)* P.O. Box 80275, Brooklyn, NY 11208 USA
E-mail: kumasi@gilpublications.com
Web site: http://www.gilpublications.com
Dist(s): **Book Hse., Inc., The**
Quality Bks., Inc.

Gilbert Industries, Inc, *(0-937975)* 5611 Krueger Dr., Jonesboro, AR 72401-6818 USA (SAN 659-5049) Tel 870-932-6070; Fax: 870-932-5609; Toll Free: 800-643-0400
E-mail: mailbox@gilbertinc.com
Web site: http://www.gilbertinc.com/papp.htm.

Gilbert Research *See* **Gilbert Industries, Inc**

Gilbert Square Bks., *(0-9745308)* 2115 Plymouth SE, Grand Rapids, MI 49506 USA Tel 616-245-1050
E-mail: kvidro2003@yahoo.com
Web site: http://www.squarepears.com.

Gilboy Publishing, *(0-9774696)* 3521 River Narrows Rd., Hilliard, OH 43026-7833 USA.

Gilchrist & Guy Publishing, *(0-9747990)* 2112 Colina Vista Way, Costa Mesa, CA 92627 USA
E-mail: rguy2112@comcast.net.

Gilded Dog Enterprises LLC, *(0-9793483)* 106 High Point Dr., Churchville, PA 18966 USA (SAN 853-1943) Tel 215-322-5592; Fax: 215-396-6832
Web site: http://gildeddog.com.

Gilder Lehrman Institute of American History, The, *(0-9663843; 1-932821)* Orders Addr.: 19 W. 44th St., Suite 500, New York, NY 10036 USA Tel 646-366-9666; Fax: 646-366-9669
E-mail: rolon@gilderlehrman.org
Web site: http://www.gilderlehrman.org.

Gilderoy Pubns., *(0-9653132)* Orders Addr.: P.O. Box 7164, Capistrano Beach, CA 92624 USA
E-mail: Gilderoy@aol.com
Web site: http://www.gilderoypublications.com
Dist(s): **Bookazine Co., Inc.**

Gile, John Communications *See* **JGC/United Publishing Corps**

Gilead Pr, *(0-615)* P.O. Box 6835, Spartanburg, SC 29304 USA Do not confuse with Gilead Pr., Brookfield, WI.

Gilead Publishing *See* **Nottinghill Bks.**

Giles, Doug Productions *See* **Clash Ministries**

Giles, W. Marie, *(0-9728944)* Orders Addr.: P.O. Box 3757, Pensacola, FL 32516-3757 USA
Web site: http://www.hihenterprises.com/openmindandheart/index.htm.

Gilgit Pr., LLC, *(0-9746283)* P.O. Box 4881, Richmond, VA 23220 USA
Web site: http://www.gilgitpress.com.

Gill & MacMillan, Ltd. (IRL) *(0-7171) Dist. by* **Irish Bks Media.**

Gill & MacMillan, Ltd. (IRL) *(0-7171) Dist. by* **Pelican.**

Gill, Jim Music, *(0-9679038)* Subs. of Jim Gill, Inc., Orders Addr.: P.O. Box 2263, Oak Park, IL 60303-2263 USA Tel 708-763-9864; Fax: 708-763-9888; Edit Addr.: 835 N. Kenilworth Ave., Oak Park, IL 60303-9888 USA
Web site: http://www.jimgill.com.

Gilliam, T. & Associates, LLC, *(0-9762703)* 1696 Georgetown Rd., Unit B, Hudson, OH 44236 USA Tel 330-342-5940; Fax: 330-463-5730; Toll Free: 877-316-5097
E-mail: tgilliam@healthybodyweight.com
Web site: http://www.healthybodyweight.com.

Gilpatrick, Gil, *(0-9650507)* Orders Addr.: P.O. Box 461, Skowhegan, ME 04976 USA Tel 207-453-6959; Edit Addr.: 369 Middle Rd., Fairfield, ME 04937 USA
E-mail: gil@gilgilpatrick.com
Web site: http://www.gilgilpatrick.com.

Gimme Gimme Toys & Games Inc., *(0-9762524)* 1418 N. Clinton Blvd., Bloomington, IL 61701 USA
Web site: http://www.gimmegimme.ca
Dist(s): **PSI (Publisher Services, Inc.).**

Gina Designs, *(0-9665153)* 870 Sanitarium Rd., Deer Park, CA 94576 USA Tel 707-967-1044; Fax: 707-963-9799.

Gina's Ink, *(0-9740454)* P.O. Box 11650, Denver, CO 80211 USA
Web site: http://www.cassandrasangel.com.

Ginger Pr., The, *(0-9785151)* P.O. Box 45753, Omaha, NE 68145-0753 USA
Dist(s): **Greenleaf Book Group Pr.**

Gingerbread Hse., *(0-940112)* 602 Montauk Hwy., Westhampton Beach, NY 11978 USA (SAN 217-0760) Tel 631-288-5119; Fax: 631-288-5179 Do not confuse with Gingerbread House, The, Savannah GA
Web site: http://www.gingerbreadbooks.com
Dist(s): **Independent Pubs. Group.**

Gingham Dog Pr. *Imprint of* **School Specialty Publishing**

Gingko Pr., Inc., *(3-87439; 3-927258; 1-58423)* 5768 Paradise Dr., Suite J, Corte Madera, CA 94925-1229 USA (SAN 630-7418) Tel 415-924-9615; Fax: 415-924-9608 Do not confuse with Gingko Pr. in New York, NY
E-mail: Books@gingkopress.com
Web site: http://www.gingkopress.com.

Ginn, Don & Co., *(0-9755438)* 11228 Vista Sorrento Pkwy, Suite I-303, San Diego, CA 92130 USA Tel 859-720-8433; Fax: 858-720-8733; Toll Free: 888-357-7313
E-mail: donginn@sbcglobal.net.

Ginn Press *See* **Pearson Custom Publishing**

Ginne Seo Bks *Imprint of* **Simon & Schuster Children's Publishing**

GIP House *See* **Summit House Pubs.**

Giraffe Family Pr., *(0-9716882)* 6800 Iron Oak Dr., Bakersfield, CA 93312 USA
E-mail: gtrz100160@aol.com; GTrz100160@aol.com
Web site: http://www.oldmp.com/snowman.htm; http://www.oldmp.com/mr-giraffe.htm; http://www.oldmp.com/mrs-giraffe.htmmrs-giraffe.htm.

Girl Named Pants, Inc., A, *(0-9755959)* 8954 Stonebriar Dr., Clarence Ctr., NY 14032-9373 USA
Web site: http://www.agirlnamedpants.com.

Girl Pr., Inc., *(0-9659754)* P.O. Box 480389, Los Angeles, CA 90048-1389 USA
E-mail: gp@girlpress.com
Web site: http://www.girlpress.com.

Girl Scouts of the USA, *(0-88441)* 420 Fifth Ave., New York, NY 10018 USA (SAN 203-4611) Tel 212-852-8000; Fax: 212-852-6511
E-mail: bnelson@girlscouts.org
Web site: http://www.girlscouts.org/.

Girl Twirl Comics, *(0-9742450; 0-9766707; 0-9794207)* Orders Addr.: P.O. Box 88, Sebastopol, CA 95473 USA Tel 707-829-6383 Do not confuse with Jane's World in Seattle, WA
Web site: http://www.janesworldcomics.com; http://www.janecomics.com
Dist(s): **Diamond Bk. Distributors.**

Girls Explore *Imprint of* **Girls Explore LLC**

Girls Explore LLC, *(0-9749456)* Orders Addr.: P.O. Box 54, Basking Ridge, NJ 07920 USA (SAN 256-2677) Fax: 908-842-9166 ; *Imprints:* Girls Explore (GilExplore)
Web site: http://www.girls-explore.com
Dist(s): **Brodart Co.**

Girls In Da Game Publishing, *(0-9674454)* Orders Addr.: P.O. Box 13322, Richmond, VA 23225 USA
E-mail: contactus@corneliagail.com
Web site: http://www.corneliagail.com.

GIRLS KNOW HOW *Imprint of* **NouSoma Communications, Inc.**

Girls of Faith, *(0-9764304)* P.O. Box 535, Rogersville, MO 65742 USA
E-mail: orders@girlsoffaith.com
Web site: http://www.girlsoffaith.com.

GirlSource, Inc., *(0-9701056)* 2121 Bryant St., Suite 302N, San Francisco, CA 94110 USA Tel 415-824-9042; Fax: 415-821-0113
E-mail: lynn@girlsource.org
Web site: http://www.girlsource.org.

Giro Pr., *(1-878857)* Orders Addr.: P.O. Box 203, Croton-on-Hudson, NY 10520 USA Tel 914-271-8924; Fax: 914-271-6552; Edit Addr.: 44 Morningside Dr., Croton-on-Hudson, NY 10520 USA
E-mail: info@giropress.com
Web site: http://www.giropress.com.

Giro Publishing/Consultant Co., *(0-9664191)* 3724 Munson Rd., Falls Church, VA 22041 USA Tel 703-845-0169.

Giron Bks., *(0-9741393)* 2130 W. 21st. St., Chicago, IL 60608-2608 USA Tel 773-847-3000; Fax: 773-847-9197; Toll Free: 800-405-4276
E-mail: isbn_san@gironbooks.com
Web site: http://www.gironbooks.com.

Gish Creative, *(0-9728507)* 1940-A Fountainview, PMB 116, Houston, TX 77057 USA Tel 713-532-1173 (phone/fax)
Web site: http://www.gishcreative.com; http://www.thesummerbook.com.

Gita Press West *See* **American Gita Society**

Giunti, Gruppo Editoriale (ITA) *(88-09) Dist. by* **Distribks Inc.**

Company

Company

Gival Pr., LLC, *(1-928589)* P.O. Box 3812, Arlington, VA 22203 USA (SAN 852-9787) Tel 703-351-0079 (phone/fax)
E-mail: givalpress@yahoo.com
Web site: http://www.givalpress.com
Dist(s): **BookSurge, LLC**
BookMasters, Inc.
Ediciones Universal.

Givens, Florence Rosie *See* **FloBound Poems Publications**

Givinity Pr., *(0-9728654)* 3374 Maplewood Ct., Fargo, ND 58104-6224 USA (SAN 255-1527) Tel 701-235-4241; Fax: 701-280-2016; Toll Free: 866-221-5860
E-mail: ellen@givinity.com
Web site: http://www.givinity.com.

Gizicki-Lipson, Coryn *See* **In the Sky Publishing**

Gizmo Enterprises, Inc., *(0-9759638)* 4759 SW 51st St., Davie, FL 33314 USA
Web site: http://www.colorcutter.com.

Gladstone Publishing, *(1-928681)* Div. of Direct Konnections, Inc., Orders Addr.: P.O. Box 926, Voorhees, NJ 08043-0926 USA Tel 856-772-3820; Fax: 856-772-9596; Toll Free: 888-824-3810; Edit Addr.: 200 Federal St., Camden, NJ 08103-1015 USA (SAN 254-8410) Do not confuse with Gladstone Publishing, Prescott, AZ
E-mail: info@gladstonepublishing.com
Web site: http://www.gladstonepublishing.com; http://www.kidsbooks2000.com.

Glamorgan Bks., *(1-893120)* 65 Mitchell Rd., No. H2, Hackettstown, NJ 07840 USA Tel 908-813-2343; Fax: 973-366-9593
E-mail: docbell@bellatlantic.net
Web site: http://www.glamorganbooks.com.

Glas-Ra Products, Inc., *(0-9702066; 0-9710629)* 9950 Burghley Ln., Reno, NV 89521-6224 USA
E-mail: ray@glas-ra.com
Web site: http://www.glas-ra.com.

Glass, Michael B. & Assocs., Inc., *(0-940429)* 735 Calebs Path/Glaro Bldg., Hauppauge, NY 11788 USA (SAN 664-3574).

†Glastonbury Pr., *(0-944963)* Orders Addr.: 454 Las Gallinas Ave., No. 108, San Rafael, CA 94903 USA Tel 415-686-4150 Do not confuse with Glastonbury Pr., Whittier, CA
E-mail: starstone@comcast.net
Web site: http://www.glastonburypress.com
Dist(s): **BookSurge, LLC**; *CIP.*

GLB Worldwide, *(1-889823)* Orders Addr.: P.O. Box 6495, Kaneohe, HI 96744 USA Tel 808-239-1579; Toll Free Fax: 888-326-3701; Toll Free: 800-224-3701
E-mail: glb@glbworld.com
Web site: http://www.glbworld.com; http://www.anndarrow.com.

Glean Pubns., Ltd., *(1-885986)* 7205 Cessna Dr., Greensboro, NC 27409 USA Tel 910-668-7651; Fax: 910-668-7152; Toll Free: 800-454-6722.

Gleasner, Bill & Diana Inc., *(0-9651185)* 7994 Holly Ct., Denver, NC 28037 USA Tel 704-483-9301; Fax: 704-483-6309
E-mail: dgleasner@aol.com
Dist(s): **Booklines Hawaii, Ltd.**

Gleason, Anne V., *(0-9673900)* P.O. Box 640, Trappe, MD 21673-0640 USA.

Gleason Publishing, Inc., *(0-9655584)* P.O. Box G, Gwynn, VA 23066-9999 USA Tel 804-725-7700; Fax: 804-725-7400; Toll Free: 800-551-4478
E-mail: publishing@virginiamagazine.com
Dist(s): **Parnassus Bk. Distributors.**

Glenbridge Publishing, Ltd., *(0-944435)* 19923 E. Long Ave., Aurora, CO 80016 USA (SAN 243-5403) Tel 720-870-8381; Fax: 720-870-5598; Toll Free: 800-986-4135 (orders only)
E-mail: glenbr@eazy.net
Web site: http://www.glenbridgepublishing.com
Dist(s): **Baker & Taylor Bks.**

†Glencoe/McGraw-Hill, *(0-02; 0-07)* Div. of The McGraw-Hill Education Group, 8787 Orion Pl., Columbus, OH 43240-4027 USA Toll Free: 800-334-7344
E-mail: customer.service@mcgraw-hill.com
Web site: http://www.glencoe.com
Dist(s): **Libros Sin Fronteras**
McGraw-Hill Cos., The; *CIP.*

Glendale, *(0-9710246)* 192 Paris Ave., Northvale, NJ 07647-2016 USA Tel 201-767-0233; Fax: 201-767-3323; Toll Free: 800-653-5515 (phone/fax)
E-mail: wendy@glendale.com
Web site: http://www.glendale.com.

Glenda's Place, *(1-930457)* 2012 Briarcliff Dr., High Point, NC 27265 USA Tel 336-883-9639; Fax: 336-883-9648; Toll Free: 888-883-9639
E-mail: glendatees@northstate.net.

Glenhaven Pubns., *(0-9657061)* 4262 NE 125th St., Seattle, WA 98125 USA (SAN 299-2701) Tel 206-362-2265.

Glenn, Lauren, *(0-9772459)* 2436 Oakdale St., Tallahassee, FL 32308 USA.

Glenn, Peter Pubns., *(0-87314)* 824 E. Atlantic Ave. Ste. 7, Delray Beach, FL 33483-5300 USA (SAN 201-9930)
E-mail: gjames@pgdirect.com
Web site: http://www.pgdirect.com.

Glens Falls Printing LLC, *(1-933575)* 51 Hudson Ave., Glens Falls, NY 12801 USA (SAN 256-7148) Tel 518-793-0555; Fax: 518-793-8624; Toll Free: 866-793-0555
E-mail: bob@gfprinting.com
Web site: http://www.gfprinting.com.

Glitter Creek, Inc., *(0-9744520)* 2919 Westridge Ave., Cincinnati, OH 45238 USA Toll Free: 888-982-7335
Web site: http://www.glittercreek.com.

Glitterati, Inc., *(0-9721152; 0-9765851; 0-9777531; 0-9793384)* 225 Central Park W., No. 305, New York, NY 10024 USA Tel 212-362-9119 (phone/fax)
E-mail: glitterati@verizon.net
Web site: http://www.glitteratiincorporated.com
Dist(s): **National Bk. Network.**

Global 21 Foundation *See* **Sharif Enterprizes, Inc.**

Global Academic Publishing, *(0-9633277; 1-883058; 1-58684)* Institute of Global Cultural Studies, Binghamton Univ., Binghamton, NY 13902-6000 USA Tel 607-777-4495; 607-777-2745 (contact Barnes & Noble for orders); Fax: 607-777-6132
E-mail: gporders@binghamton.edu
Web site: http://www.academicpublishing.binghamton.edu
Dist(s): **Hesteria Records & Publishing Co.**

Global Age Publishing/Global Academy Pr., *(1-887176)* 16057 Tampa Palms Blvd., W., No. 219, Tampa, FL 33647 USA Tel 813-991-4982; Fax: 813-973-8166
Dist(s): **Baker & Taylor Bks.**

Global Alliances, *(0-9759126)* 82-09 166th St., Hillcrest, NY 11432 USA.

Global Authors Pubns., *(0-9728513; 0-9742161; 0-9766449; 0-9779680; 0-9798087)* P.O. Box 922, Crescent City, FL 32112-0922 USA; 2813 Bass Haven Ln., St. Augustine, FL 32092
E-mail: gapbook@yahoo.com
Web site: http://www.globalauthorspublications.com.

Global Awareness Publishing Co., *(1-885888)* 1102 Hickory St., Madison, WI 53715-1726 USA.

Global Commitment Publishing, *(1-884931)* Div. of Alpert & Assocs., 3544 Winfield Ln., NW, Washington, DC 20007 USA Tel 202-338-4975; Fax: 202-835-0668; 5505 Connecticut Ave., Washington, DC 20015.

Global Communications *See* **Inner Light - Global Communications**

Global Education Resources, LLC, *(1-934046)* 37 Station Rd., Madison, NJ 07940 USA (SAN 851-1012) Tel 973-410-0840; Fax: 973-410-1603
E-mail: myoshida@globaledresources.com
Web site: http://www.globaledresources.com.

Global Energy, *(1-893092)* P.O. Box 5617, Madison, WI 53705 USA Tel 608-238-6001; Fax: 608-238-6081
E-mail: ggiese@m9.sprynet.com
Web site: http://www.R2-D2.com.

Global Evangelism Ministries, Inc., *(0-9668907; 0-9749754)* P.O. Box 5040, Goodyear, AZ 85338 USA Toll Free: 877-552-4253; *Imprints:* G. E. M. Publishing (G E M Pubng)
E-mail: c.jacobs@avocon.com
Web site: http://www.swordbible.org.

Global Institute for Maximizing Potential, Incorporated, *(0-9772020)* 92 Mt. Zion Way, Ocean Grove, NJ 07756 USA Tel 732-776-7360
E-mail: richert@globalinst.com
Web site: http://www.globalinst.com.

Global Learning, Inc., *(0-928630)* 22 Mary Ann Dr., Brick, NJ 08723-5818 USA (SAN 270-5206)
E-mail: gljeff@verizon.net
Web site: http://www.globallearningnj.org; http://www.community.nj.com/cc/sustainableschools; http://www.ala.org/sustainablecommunities.

Global Learning, Inc., *(1-59867)* 1001 SE Water Ave., Suite 310, Portland, OR 97214 USA Toll Free: 888-548-2787 Do not confuse with Global Learning Inc. in Brielle, NJ
Web site: http://www.litart.com.

Global Light Network, *(0-9704176)* P.O. Box 654, Virginia Beach, VA 23451 USA Tel 757-437-8949; Fax: 757-437-2877
E-mail: russ.michael@vpn.at.

Global Perspectives in Education *See* **American Forum For Global Education**

Global Pr., *(0-9705547)* 2008 Q St., NW, No. 300, Washington, DC 20009 USA Tel 202-667-2855
E-mail: sales@thebigbreach.com
Web site: http://thebigbreach.com.

Global Publications (S S I P S) *See* **Global Academic Publishing**

Global Publishing, *(0-911649)* 51 Bell Rock Plaza, Suite A, PMB 511, Sedona, AZ 86351 USA (SAN 299-3627) Tel 928-284-5544; Fax: 928-284-5545 Do not confuse with companies with the same or similar name in Meimingham, MI, Costa Mesa, CA, Las Angeles, CA, Florence, MA, Memphis, TN, Sauk Rapids, MN, Fort Lauderdale, FL, Fort Worth, TX, Salt Lake City, UT
E-mail: minorwood@earthlink.net
Web site: http://www.wealthysoul.com
Dist(s): **Baker & Taylor Bks.**
New Leaf Distributing Co., Inc.

Global Rhyme Time, Inc., *(1-888228)* 12095 Dolphin Dr., Palm Beach Gardens, FL 33410-2401 USA Tel 561-799-2880; Fax: 561-626-0127; Toll Free: 888-467-4963
E-mail: GoRhyme@aol.com
Dist(s): **Baker & Taylor Bks.**
Norton, Jeffrey Pubs., Inc.
Teacher's Discovery.

Global Scholarly Pubns., *(1-59267)* 220 Madison Ave., Suite 11G, New York City, NY 10016 USA Tel 212-679-6410; Fax: 212-679-6424
E-mail: pmorewed@gsp-online.org
Web site: http://www.gsp-online.org.

Global Truth Publishing, *(0-9740465)* Orders Addr.: 1001 Bridgeway, Suite 474, Sausalito, CA 94965 USA Tel 415-331-1102; Fax: 415-331-2265
E-mail: sales@globaltruthpublishing.com
Web site: http://www.globaltruthpublishing.com.

Global Univ., *(0-7617; 1-56390)* Affil. of Assemblies of God, Div. of Foreign Missions, 1211 S. Glenstone Ave., Springfield, MO 65804 USA Tel 417-862-9533; Fax: 417- 862-5318; Toll Free: 800-443-1083
E-mail: sbush@globaluniversity.edu; info@globaluniversity.edu
Web site: http://www.globaluniversity.edu

Global Village Kids, LLC, *(0-9760472)* 4111 Calavo Dr., La Mesa, CA 91941-7051 USA Tel 619-303-0929; Fax: 925-888-8471
E-mail: seth.burns@globalvillagekids.com
Web site: http://www.globalvillagekids.com
Dist(s): **AV Cafe, Incorporated, The**
AtlasBooks Distribution
BWI
Iaconi, Mariuccia Bk. Imports
Wayland Audio-Visual.

Global Vision, LLC, *(0-9702765)* 50 B Peninsula Ctr., Dr., No. 262, Rolling Hills Estates, CA 90274 USA Tel 310-265-9777; Fax: 310-265-9888; Toll Free: 800-894-7054 Do not confuse with companies with the same or similar name in Leicester, MA, Ross, CA, Sarasota, FL
E-mail: ricki@icameo.com
Web site: http://www.tobesafe.org.

Globe Fearon Educational Publishing, *(0-13; 0-8224; 0-8359; 0-87065; 0-88102; 0-912925; 0-915510; 1-55555; 1-55675)* Div. of Pearson Education Corporate Communications, Orders Addr.: 4350 Equity Dr., P.O. Box 2649, Columbus, OH 43216-2649 USA Toll Free Fax: 800-393-3156; Toll Free: 800-848-9500; 800-321-3106 (customer service); Edit Addr.: One Lake St., Upper Saddle River, NJ 07458 USA
Web site: http://www.globefearon.com/
Dist(s): **Cambridge Bk. Co.**
IFSTA.

Globe Language Services, *(0-9631999)* 319 Broadway 2nd Floor, New York, NY 10007 USA Toll Free: 800-446-6228
E-mail: nfo@globelanguage.com
Web site: http://www.globelanguage.com.

†Globe Pequot Pr., The, *(0-7627; 0-87106; 0-88742; 0-914788; 0-933469; 0-934802; 0-941130; 1-56440; 1-57034; 1-58574; 1-59228; 1-59921)* Div. of Morris Communications Co., LLC, Orders Addr.: P.O. Box 480, Guilford, CT 06437-0480 USA (SAN 201-9892) Tel 888-249-7586; Toll Free Fax: 800-820-2329 (in Connecticut); Toll Free: 800-243-0495 (24 hours); Edit Addr.: 246 Goose Ln., Guilford, CT 06437 USA Tel 203-458-4500; Fax: 203-458-4604 ; *Imprints:* Lyons Press (Lyons); Falcon (Fal); Two Dot (Two-D)
E-mail: info@globepequot.com
Web site: http://www.globepequot.com; *CIP.*

Globe Pubs., *(0-9623663; 1-882614)* 724 Fair Meadows Dr., Saginaw, TX 76179-1017 USA.

Globe Publishing, *(0-9765168)* Orders Addr.: P.O. Box 3040, Pensacola, FL 32516-3040 USA Tel 850-453-3453; Fax: 850-456-6001; Edit Addr.: 8590 Hwy 98 W., Pensacola, FL 32506 USA Do not confuse with Globe Publishing in Salt Lake City, UT
Web site: http://www.gme.org.

Globo, Editora SA (BRA) *(85-217; 85-250) Dist. by* **Distribks Inc.**

Globo Libros, *(0-9706953)* Orders Addr.: P.O. Box 4025, Sunnyside, NY 11104 USA; Edit Addr.: 402 E. 64th St. Apt. 6C, New York, NY 10021-7826 USA
E-mail: dstockwell@globolibros.com
Web site: http://www.globolibros.com.

Globus Bks., *(0-9676869)* Orders Addr.: P.O. Box 203, Lake Worth, FL 33480 USA Tel 561-588-2713; Fax: 561-588-1427; Edit Addr.: 3360 S. Ocean Blvd., No. 1B1, Palm Beach, FL 33480 USA
E-mail: alanalanarl@aol.com.

Glolar Multimedia Productions, *(0-9707746)* P.O. Box 721452, San Diego, CA 92172-1452 USA
E-mail: info@Glolar.com; info@glolar.com
Web site: http://www.glolar.com.

Glory Be Collectibles, *(0-9795127)* 2169 Green Canyon Rd., Fallbrook, CA 92028 USA (SAN 853-6627) Tel 760-723-5222; Fax: 760-723-4433
E-mail: sales@glorybe.com
Web site: http://www.glorybe.com.

Glory Bound Bks., LTD. Las Vages, *(0-9766718; 0-9779654)* Orders Addr.: 838 Bare Branch Ave., Las Vegas, NV 89123-5349 USA (SAN 256-4564) Do not confuse with Glory Bound Books in Marlette, MI
E-mail: sherihauser@yahoo.com
Web site: http://www.fordreamers.com.

Glory Days Group Publishing, *(0-9755145)* P.O. Box 1869, Glen Burnie, MD 21060-1869 USA Tel 410-766-0005 (phone/fax) ; *Imprints:* Gibson Books (Gibson Bks)
E-mail: drgibson123@yahoo.com.

Glory Educational Resource, Inc., *(1-59022)* 3820 Packard St. Ste. 130, Ann Arbor, MI 48108-5000 USA Toll Free: 877-567-6244
Web site: http://www.k2college.com.

Glory Realm Pubns., *(0-9709315)* 10 N. 11th Ave., Yakima, WA 98902 USA Tel 509-575-8928
E-mail: patriciagamet@juno.com
Dist(s): **Elfin Cove Pr.**

Glory to Glory Ministries, *(0-9660753)* 1813 E. 45th St., Ashtabula, OH 44004 USA Tel 920-826-2557
E-mail: porkies@earthlink.net
Web site: http://www.glorytogloryministries.com.

Gloucester Crescent International, *(0-931151)* 1657a Ramblewood Way, Snellville, GA 30078-5632 USA (SAN 670-6681)
E-mail: robdunford@bellsouth.net.

Glo'worm (GBR) *(1-902172) Dist. by* **Last Gasp.**

Gnatcatcher Children'S Bks., *(0-9778005)* 1451 E. Armando Dr., Long Beach, CA 90807 USA Tel 562-427-1200
E-mail: maryhoch@excite.com
Dist(s): **AtlasBooks Distribution.**

GND Publishing, *(0-9728549)* P.O. Box 33288, Indianapolis, IN 46203 USA Tel 317-294-3423; Fax: 317-786-0323
E-mail: kchill24@aol.com
Dist(s): **Baker & Taylor Bks.**

Gnomon Pr., *(0-917788)* P.O. Box 475, Frankfort, KY 40602-0475 USA (SAN 209-0104) Tel 502-223-1858 (phone/fax)
E-mail: jgnomon@aol.com
Dist(s): **SPD-Small Pr. Distribution.**

Gnu Media Design Company *See* **Gnu Ventures Co.**

Gnu Ventures Co., *(0-9792419)* 341 Berry Dr., Naperville, IL 60540 USA Tel 630-548-1468
E-mail: don@gnumediadesign.com
Web site: http://www.gnumediadesign.com.

Go Ask Anyone, Inc., *(0-9742866)* 38 Irwin St., No.3, Winthrop, MA 02152 USA
Web site: http://www.goaskanyone.com.

Go Charts Marine LLC, *(0-9724583)* P.O. Box 460693, Fort Lauderdale, FL 33346 USA
E-mail: info@visualcruisingguide.com
Web site: http://www.visualcruisingguide.com.

Go Daddy Productions, Inc., *(0-9753938)* 2010 Ripley Point Ct., Odenton, MD 21113 USA Tel 443-226-4747
E-mail: mejagan@yahoo.com
Web site: http://www.go-daddyproductions.com.

Go Flag Football, *(0-9772203)* 1978 Shiloh Valley Trail, Kennesaw, GA 30144 USA
Web site: http://www.goflagfootball.com.

Go! Media Entertainment LLC, *(0-9768957; 1-933617; 1-60510)* 5737 Kanan Rd., No.591, Agoura Hills, CA 91301-1601 USA
Web site: http://www.gocomi.com/
Dist(s): **Diamond Bk. Distributors.**

GoalsGuy Learning Systems, Inc., *(1-889770)* 201 E. Jefferson St. Ste. 334, Syracuse, NY 13202-2510 USA Toll Free Fax: 800-731-4625; Toll Free: 877-462-5748
E-mail: info@goalsguy.com; order@goalsguy.com
Web site: http://www.goalsguy.com
Dist(s): **Koen-Levy Bk. Wholesalers LLC.**

GoalsGuy, The *See* **GoalsGuy Learning Systems, Inc.**

Goatee Graphics, *(0-9657257)* P.O. Box 591840, San Francisco, CA 94159-1840 USA (SAN 256-8985) Tel 415-272-6117
E-mail: goatee848@yahoo.com
Web site: http://www.undertherimbook.com
Dist(s): **AtlasBooks Distribution.**

Goblin Fern Pr., Inc., *(0-9647663; 0-9722099; 1-59598)* 6401 Odana Rd. Barkley Bldg., Suite B, Madison, WI 53719 USA Tel 608-442-0212; Fax: 608-442-0221; Toll Free: 888-670-2665
E-mail: kira@goblinfernpress.com
Web site: http://www.goblinfernpress.com
Dist(s): **Baker & Taylor Bks.**
New Leaf Distributing Co., Inc.
Quality Bks., Inc.

Goblinshead (GBR) *(1-899874) Dist. by* **Dufour.**

†Godine, David R. Pub., *(0-87923; 1-56792; 1-57423)* Orders Addr.: P.O. Box 450, Jaffrey, NH 03452 USA Tel 603-532-4100; Fax: 603-532-5940; Toll Free Fax: 800-226-0934; Toll Free: 800-344-4771; Edit Addr.: 9 Hamilton Pl., Boston, MA 02108-4715 USA (SAN 213-4381) Tel 617-451-9600; Fax: 617-350-0250
E-mail: info@godine.com; order@godine.com
Web site: http://www.godine.com
Dist(s): **Baker & Taylor International**; *CIP.*

Godinez-Hammermaster Design, *(0-9773205)* 122 Eugenia Dr., Ventura, CA 93003 USA (SAN 257-7127)
E-mail: artposter@sbcglobal.net.

Godiva Girl Records & Publishing, Incorporated *See* **Girls In Da Game Publishing**

Godly Writes Publishing, *(0-9704093)* 1215 Stuart St., Orangeburg, SC 29115-3423 USA Tel 803-516-8030
E-mail: GodlyWrites@aol.com
Web site: http://www.shanewall.com
Dist(s): **Spring Arbor Distributors, Inc.**

GoDriver, LLC, *(0-9720463)* 16400 Ventura Blvd, No.339, Encino, CA 91436 USA Tel 818-905-0015
E-mail: driver@godriver.com
Web site: http://www.godriver.com.

God's Bible School & College *See* **Revivalist Pr., The**

God's Daily Word Ministries, *(0-9708531)* P.O. Box 700113, San Antonio, TX 78270-0113 USA Tel 210-494-0702; Fax: 210-545-7758
E-mail: devotions@gdwm.org
Web site: http://www.godsdailyword.org.

God's Kids Publishing, *(1-929078)* 179 Forest Hill Dr., Asheville, NC 28803 USA
E-mail: godskids@mindspring.com

God's Word, *(0-9710476)* 5130 E. Charleston, Suite 5-517, Las Vegas, NV 89142 USA
E-mail: bonnie.thomason@verizon.net
Web site: http://www.godsword.pair.com.

God's World Publications *See* **God's World Pubns. Inc.**

God's World Pubns. Inc., *(1-882440)* 85 Tunnel Rd., Innsbruck Mall, Suite 12, Asheville, NC 28802 USA (SAN 254-1696) Fax: 828-232-5501; Toll Free: 800-951-4974
E-mail: service@gwbookclub.com
Web site: http://www.gwbc.com.

Godspeed Pr., *(0-9798250)* 430 Davis Dr., Suite 270, Morrisville, NC 27560 USA Tel 404-457-4097
E-mail: deanthewriter@gmail.com.

Godward Life Ministries, *(0-9677745)* 3904 Willowbend, Fort Worth, TX 76116 USA Tel 817-244-1363; Fax: 817-738-5021
E-mail: shasta1363@aol.com.

GoGo Pr., *(0-9769028)* Orders Addr.: 6007 Hickory Valley Rd., Nashville, TN 37205 USA (SAN 257-1412) Tel 615-356-6571; Fax: 615-356-9609
E-mail: info@gogopress.com; paul@pbuff.com
Web site: http://www.gogopress.com
Dist(s): **AtlasBooks Distribution.**

GoKnow, Incorporated *See* **GoKnow Learning**

GoKnow Learning, *(0-9762083; 0-9767504; 0-9786499)* 2084 S. State St., Ann Arbor, MI 48104-4608 USA Toll Free: 877-482-3439
Web site: http://www.goknow.com.

Golan, Hanna, *(0-9779723)* 17340 Hamlin St., Lake Balboa, CA 91406 USA (SAN 850-7732) Tel 818-342-4969
E-mail: hannagolan2000@yahoo.com
Web site: http://blessthechildren.com.

GO-LA-NV Pr., *(0-9741828)* P.O. Box 1897, Huntsville, TX 77342-1897 USA Tel 936-291-2906
E-mail: rhvann@sbcglobal.net.

Gold Angel Pr., *(0-9763354)* 4115-305 San Marino Blvd. Emerald Isle At Laguna Lakes, West Palm Beach, FL 33409 USA
E-mail: goldangelpress@earthlink.net
Web site: http://www.goldangelpress.com
Dist(s): **AtlasBooks Distribution**
BookMasters, Inc.

Gold Boy Music/Pubn., *(0-9761992)* 57-335 Pahi Pahi Alua St., Kahuku, HI 96731 USA (SAN 256-2499) Tel 808-638-2869
E-mail: westermar001@hawaii.rr.com
Web site: http://www.stardancermusic.com
Dist(s): **Booklines Hawaii, Ltd.**

Gold Charm Publishing, LLC, *(0-9744855)* Orders Addr.: P.O. Box 161, Nottingham, NH 03290 USA Tel 603-942-7925 (phone/fax); Edit Addr.: 82 Priest Rd., Nottingham, NH 03290 USA.

Gold Lace Publishing, LLC, *(0-9672074)* 8049 Rising Ridge Rd., Bethesda, MD 20817 USA Tel 301-767-0846; Fax: 301-767-0847
E-mail: acv1898@erols.com.

Gold Rush Entertainment, *(1-890305)* P.O. Box 2531, Elk Grove, CA 95759-2531 USA Tel 916-313-3575 (phone/fax); Fax: 0-870-120-6796 (UK - natl. call rate); 9529 Big Timber Dr., Elk Grove, CA 95758-1161 ; *Imprints:* Gold Rush Games (Gold Rush)
E-mail: GoldRushG@aol.com; GoldenPillarPub@aol.com
Web site: http://www.goldrushgames.com; http://www.goldenpillarpublishing.com
Dist(s): **Diamond Comic Distributors, Inc.**

Gold Rush Games *Imprint of* **Gold Rush Entertainment**

Golden Age Publishing, LLC, *(1-59090)* Orders Addr.: 342 Merrimac Rd., Hillsville, VA 24343 USA Tel 276-728-3598
E-mail: robert@gldnge.com
Web site: http://www.gldnge.com.

Golden Anchor Bks. *Imprint of* **Golden Anchor Pr.**

Golden Anchor Pr., *(1-886864)* 625 Elrod Rd., Bowling Green, KY 42104 USA Tel 270-780-9334 ; *Imprints:* Golden Anchor Books (Goldn Anchor Bks)
E-mail: smithdale2@aol.com; goldnanchr@aol.com
Web site: Everykidawinner.com
Dist(s): **Partners/West**
Quality Bks., Inc.
Unique Bks., Inc.

Golden Bks. *Imprint of* **Random Hse., Inc.**

Golden Bks. *Imprint of* **Random Hse. Children's Bks.**

Golden Bks. Adult Publishing Group *Imprint of* **St. Martin's Pr.**

Golden, Brian *See* **PastWays Inc.**

Golden Bunny Publishing, LLC, *(0-9712473)* Orders Addr.: P.O. Box 12315, Aspen, CO 81612 USA (SAN 254-0673) Tel 970-925-3900; 970-379-6500; Fax: 970-925-6767; Edit Addr.: 415 E. Hyman Ave., Suite 203, Aspen, CO 81611 USA
E-mail: alexis@sopris.net
Web site: http://www.goldenbunnypub.com.

Golden Eagle Publishing Hse., Inc., *(0-9744205; 0-9753533; 0-9759122; 0-9769364)* 9201 Wilshire Blvd., Suite 205, Beverly Hills, CA 90210 USA Tel 310-273-9176; Fax: 310-273-0954
E-mail: info@goldeneaglepublishing.com
Web site: http://www.goldeneaglepublishing.com
Dist(s): **AtlasBooks Distribution**
Greenleaf Book Group.

Golden Educational Ctr., *(1-56500)* 857 Lake Blvd., Redding, CA 96003 USA Tel 530-244-0101; Fax: 530-244-5939; Toll Free Fax: 888-755-7447; Toll Free: 800-800-1791
E-mail: info@goldened.com
Web site: http://www.goldened.com.

Golden Egg Bks., *(0-9667076)* 251 E. Crestwood Dr. Apt. B2, Camp Hill, PA 17011-1202 USA
Dist(s): **Baker & Taylor Bks.**

Golden Faith Pubng., *(0-9716689)* Orders Addr.: P.O. Box 703131, Tulsa, OK 74170 USA Tel 918-259-5000
E-mail: info@putyourarmor.org; info@ICriedToo.org; sheila@putonyourarmor.org
Web site: http://www.ICriedToo.org.

Golden Guides from Saint Martin's Pr. *Imprint of* **St. Martin's Pr.**

Golden Harvest Publishing Co., *(0-9747904)* 4849 Valley Rd., Rosedale, VA 24280 USA Tel 276-880-9862; Fax: 276-880-1146
E-mail: adda@mounet.com.

Golden Inspirational *Imprint of* **Random Hse. Children's Bks.**

Golden Master Mind Seminars, Incorporated *See* **More Heart Than Talent Publishing, Inc.**

Golden Monkey Publishing, LLC, *(0-9719632)* 24 Meadowood Ln., Old Saybrook, CT 06475 USA (SAN 254-5322)
Web site: http://www.goldenmonkeypublishing.com.

Golden Oak Pubs., *(1-929248)* Orders Addr.: P.O. Box 330385, Fort Worth, TX 76163-0385 USA Tel 817-292-0323; Fax: 817-292-3747; Edit Addr.: 4205 Wedgworth Rd., S., Fort Worth, TX 76133 USA
E-mail: leadergo@flash.net.

Golden Quill Pr., *(0-9676256)* Orders Addr.: P.O. Box 83, Troutville, VA 24175 USA Tel 540-591-9021 Do not confuse with Golden Quill Pr., Prescott, AZ
E-mail: thewritesource@pobox.com; goldenquillpress@mindspring.com
Web site: http://www.tellittothefuture.homestead.com; http://goldenquillpress.homestead.com; http://thewritesource.homestead.com
Dist(s): **Replica Bks.**

Golden Rain Tree Pr., *(0-9744107)* Div. of Leland Foerster Photography, 307 Fowles St., Oceanside, CA 92054 USA Tel 760-433-2554 (phone/fax)
E-mail: lelandfoerster@sbcglobal.net
Web site: http://www.lelandfoerster.com
Dist(s): **Sunbelt Pubns., Inc.**

Golden Sound Circles: Aunt Suzie's Books & Cd's *See* **Family Music Network: Bks. & CD's**

Golden State Dance Teachers Assn., *(0-932980)* Div. of Alterra Publishing, 10804 Woodruff Ave., Downey, CA 90241-3910 USA (SAN 212-6613) Tel 562-869-8949; Fax: 562-862-7129
E-mail: SkippyUUs@aol.com
Web site: http://www.skippyblair.com.

Golden Triangle Bks. *Imprint of* **Univ. of Pittsburgh Pr.**

Golden Valley Pr., *(0-9718053)* 24905 Mica Ridge Rd., Custer, SD 57730 USA
E-mail: horsted@dakotaphoto.com
Web site: http://www.goldenvalleypress.com.

Golden Voice Enterprises, *(0-9643301)* 8503 Summerdale Rd., No. 371, San Diego, CA 92126 USA.

†Golden West Pubs., *(0-914846; 1-885590; 1-58581)* 4113 N. Longview Ave., Phoenix, AZ 85014-4949 USA (SAN 207-5652) Tel 602-265-4392; Fax: 602-279-6901; Toll Free: 800-658-5830 Do not confuse with Golden West Pubs. Unlimited, Fresno, CA
E-mail: sherry@goldenwestpublishers.com
Web site: http://www.goldenwestpublishers.com; *CIP.*

Golden Wings Enterprises, *(0-9700103; 0-9749241; 0-9794340)* P.O. Box 468, Orem, UT 84059-0468 USA
E-mail: BJ@bjrowley.com; bjrowley@juno.com
Web site: http://www.bjrowley.com.

Golden Wood Studio, *(0-9672902)* Orders Addr.: P.O. Box 638, Ware, MA 01082 USA Tel 413-967-7733; Fax: 413-967-7035; Edit Addr.: 99 Church St., Ware, MA 01082 USA
Web site: http://www.ruthsanderson.com.

Golden Words Publishing, *(0-9726662)* Rte. 3, Box 3820, Toccoa, GA 30577 USA (SAN 255-3570).

Golden/Disney *Imprint of* **Random Hse. Children's Bks.**

Goldenrod Pr., *(0-9748333)* Orders Addr.: P.O. Box 71, Algona, IA 50511 USA Tel 515-295-7090; Edit Addr.: 2509 S. State St., Algona, IA 50511-7296 USA
E-mail: slotjm@yahoo.com.

Goldleaf Games, LLC, *(0-9748757)* P.O. Box 804, Lawrence, KS 66044 USA
E-mail: gary@goldleafgames.com
Web site: http://www.goldleafgames.com.

Goldmann, Wilhelm Verlag GmbH (DEU) *(3-442) Dist. by* **Distribks Inc.**

Goldner, Harriet LLC, *(0-9779676)* P.O. Box 480003, Delray Beach, FL 33448 USA
E-mail: hgoldnerbooks@bellsouth.net
Web site: JewishFamilyFun.com.

Goldsberry, Booty, *(0-9792875)* 10 Windsor Pl., Poland, ME 04274 USA Tel 207-998-5710
E-mail: elattanzi@bookmasters.com
Dist(s): **AtlasBooks Distribution.**

Goldstar Magic, *(0-9716488)* 611 Pennsylvania Ave., SE, No.121, Washington, DC 20003 USA Tel 202-675-0684
E-mail: terry@goldstarmagic.com
Web site: http://www.goldstarmagic.com.

Goldstar Publishing, Inc., *(1-58634)* P.O. Box 2032, Scottsdale, AZ 85252-2032 USA Tel 480-614-0555 (phone/fax); Toll Free: 877-569-2377 Do not confuse with Goldstar Publishing in Lexington, KY
E-mail: PattyDow@aol.com; melsauder@earthlink.net.

Goldwing Pubs., *(0-9674878)* P.O. Box 33652, Denver, CO 80233-0652 USA Tel 303-452-0523
E-mail: goldwingpublishers@excite.com.

GollyGee Software, Inc., *(0-9701391)* 1474 N. Port Village Ctr., PMB 304, Reston, VA 20194 USA Fax: 703-995-0381
E-mail: roland@gollygee.com
Web site: http://www.gollygee.com.

Golomb & Vavrichek Enterprises *See* **Writers' Cooperative of Greater Washington**

Gom Foxtail *Imprint of* **Gom Publishing, LLC**

Gom Publishing, LLC, *(0-9729197; 1-932966)* P.O. Box 211110, Columbus, OH 43221 USA (SAN 255-3988) Tel 614-876-7097; Toll Free Fax: 866-422-8292; Toll Free: 866-466-2608 ; *Imprints:* Gom Foxtail (Gom Foxtail)
E-mail: sfox@gompublishing.com
Web site: http://www.gompublishing.com.

Gonda Family Foundation, The, *(0-9675279)* 9350 Wilshire Blvd., Suite 400, Beverly Hills, CA 90212 USA Tel 310-247-8929; Fax: 310-247-9042
E-mail: fndmgmt@aol.com.

Gonzalez, David J. Ministries, *(0-9741561)* P.O. Box 847, Lake Delton, WI 53940 USA Tel 608-254-5150
E-mail: dgm@mountainfaith.org
Web site: http://www.mountainfaith.org.

Good 4U, Inc., *(0-9659426)* 533 S. Howard Ave., No. 801, Tampa, FL 33606-2063 USA Tel 813-765-4051; Fax: 770-988-9475
E-mail: Ann@lifepuzzle.com
Web site: http://www.lifepuzzle.com.

Company

†**Good Bks.,** *(0-934672; 1-56148)* Subs. of Good Enterprises, Ltd., Orders Addr.: P.O. Box 419, Intercourse, PA 17534 USA (SAN 693-9597) Tel 717-768-7171; Fax: 717-768-3433; Toll Free: 800-762-7171; Edit Addr.: 3510 Old Philadelphia Pike, Intercourse, PA 17534-0419 USA Do not confuse with the same or similar name in Farmington, MI, Los Angeles, CA
E-mail: mgood@goodbks.com; custserv@goodbks.com
Web site: http://www.goodbks.com; *CIP.*

Good Catch Publishing, *(0-9772383; 0-9785152; 0-9792475; 1-934635)* Orders Addr.: P.O. Box 6551, Aloha, OR 97007 USA (SAN 257-0289) Tel 503-475-2005; Fax: 503-356-9685; Toll Free: 877-967-3224; Edit Addr.: 4074 NW 169th Ave., Beaverton, OR 97006 USA
E-mail: nathanlindley@goodcatchpublishing.com
Web site: http://www.goodcatchpublishing.com.

Good Co. Players Educational Div., *(1-892405)* Div. of Good Company Players, 1105 N. Wishon Ave., Fresno, CA 93728 USA Tel 559-266-0211; Fax: 559-266-1342; Toll Free: 800-808-7344
E-mail: gcplayers@lightspeed.net; smarolf@lightspeed.net
Web site: http://www.gcplayers.com.

Good Earth Pubns., Inc., *(0-9624648)* 20 GreenWay Pl., Buena Vista, VA 24416 USA (SAN 297-8431) Tel 540-261-8874; Toll Free: 800-499-3201
E-mail: pat@goodearthpublications.com; andylee@ntelos.net
Web site: http://www.goodearthpublications.com; http://www.TinyHomes.com
Dist(s): **Chelsea Green Publishing.**

Good Ground Pr., *(1-885996)* 1884 Randolph Ave., Saint Paul, MN 55105 USA Tel 612-690-7011; Fax: 612-690-7039; Toll Free: 800-232-5533
E-mail: sales@goodgroundpress.com
Web site: http://www.goodgroundpress.com.

Good News Connections, *(0-9728900)* Orders Addr.: P.O. Box 66573, Austin, TX 78766 USA Toll Free: 888-899-3207 Do not confuse with The Good News Connections, Inc. in Orlando, FL
E-mail: stayton@xc.org
Web site: http://www.GoodNewsConnections.com.

Good News Fellowship Ministries, *(0-9629559; 1-888081)* 220 Sleepy Creek Rd., Macon, GA 31210-5720 USA Tel 478-757-8071; Fax: 478-757-0136; Toll Free: 800-300-9630
E-mail: goodnews@reynoldscable.net
Web site: http://www.goodnews.netministries.org
Dist(s): **Anchor Distributors.**

Good News Productions, International, *(1-59305)* Orders Addr.: P.O. Box 222, Joplin, MO 64802-0222 USA Tel 417-782-0060; Fax: 417-782-3999; Edit Addr.: 2111 N. Main, Joplin, MO 64802-0222 USA
E-mail: gnpi@gnpi.org
Web site: http://www.gnpi.org.

Good Reading Bks., *(1-888042)* Div. of Southern Printing, Imaging & Typography, Inc., 104 E. Shamrock Dr., Lafayette, LA 70508-4218 USA.

Good Roots Publishing, *(0-9745187)* Orders Addr.: P.O. Box 3493, Homer, AK 99603-3493 USA Tel 907-235-5283; Edit Addr.: 62315 Fireweed Ave., Homer, AK 99603-3493 USA
Dist(s): **Wizard Works.**

Good Stuff Desktop Publishing, *(0-9673627)* 850 South Rancho Dr., No. 4-376, Las Vegas, NV 89106 USA Tel 702-813-6302; Fax: 702-631-2008
E-mail: tamara@justimagine2000.com
Web site: http://www.justimagine2000.com/.

Good Turn Publishing, *(0-9794393)* 1 Bancroft Rd., Wellesley, MA 02481 USA
Web site: http://www.goodturnpublishing.com.

Good Works Pr., *(0-9634472; 1-888572)* 4121 Whitfield Ave., Fort Worth, TX 76109 USA Tel 817-927-8808.

Good Works Publishing Hse., *(0-9744733)* P.O. Box 52217, Houston, TX 77052-2217 USA Tel 713-708-8852.

Good Year Bks. *Imprint of* **Celebration Pr.**

Good Year Bks., *(1-59647)* P.O. Box 91858, Tucson, AZ 85752-1858 USA (SAN 854-4050) Toll Free Fax: 888-511-1501; Toll Free: 888-511-1530
E-mail: publisher@goodyearbooks.com; marketing@goodyearbooks.com; sales@goodyearbooks.com; orders@goodyearbooks.com
Web site: http://www.goodyearbooks.com.

Goodale Publishing, *(0-9662945)* 900 Fort Street Mall, No. 1725, Honolulu, HI 96813-3721 USA Do not confuse with Goodale Publishing, Minneapolis, MN
E-mail: info@goodalepublishing.com; jhgruenberg@aol.com
Web site: http://www.goodalepublishing.com
Dist(s): **Booklines Hawaii, Ltd.**
Univ. of Hawaii Pr.

Goodall, Barry, *(0-9763932)* 218 Tucker Sta. Rd, Louisville, KY 40243 USA Tel 502-817-8530
E-mail: bgoodal1@jefferson.k12.ky.us.

Goode, Ty *See* **Tytam Publishing**

Goodheart-Willcox Pub., *(0-87006; 1-56637; 1-59070; 1-60525)* Orders Addr.: 18604 West Creek Dr., Tinley Park, IL 60477-6243 USA (SAN 203-4387) Tel 708-687-5000; Fax: 708-687-5068; Toll Free Fax: 888-409-3900; Toll Free: 800-323-0440
E-mail: custserv@g-w.com
Web site: http://www.g-w.com.

Goodtimes Software *See* **GT Interactive Software**

Goodwin, Evelyn, *(0-615)* 1334 Akele St., Kailua, HI 96734 USA
Dist(s): **Lulu.com.**

Goodword Bks. Pvt. Ltd. (IND) *(81-85063; 81-87570; 81-7898)*
Dist. by **Lodhia Ctr.**

goodworksebooks.com, *(0-9773192)* 3084 CR 310, Brazoria, TX 77422 USA
Web site: http://goodworksebooks.com.

GoodyGoody Bks., *(0-9702546)* P.O. Box 1073, Sun City, AZ 85372-1073 USA
E-mail: goody4u@prodigy.net
Web site: http://charliethecat.com.

Goofy Foot Pr., *(1-885535)* P.O. Box 1719, Waldport, OR 97394-1719 USA
Web site: http://www.goofyfootpress.com
Dist(s): **National Bk. Network.**

Goofy Guru Publishing, *(0-9726130)* 405 Kiowa Pl., Boulder, CO 80303 USA.

Goon Dog Publishing, *(0-9791612)* 309 W. 14th, Suite 32, New York, NY 10014-0014 USA (SAN 852-6206) Tel 212-645-2096
E-mail: monk@ispwest.com
Web site: http://owenopolis.com.

Goose Creek Productions, *(0-9656758; 0-9711173)* Orders Addr.: 3025 Little Island Rd., Virginia Beach, VA 23456 USA Tel 757-721-0243
E-mail: ourhistory@aol.com
Web site: http://www.colonialamerica.us.

Goose Creek Pubs., *(1-59633)* 4227 Vermont Ave., Louisville, KY 40211 USA Tel 502-384-5109; Fax: 502-657-6326.

Goose River Pr., *(1-930648; 1-59713)* 3400 Friendship Rd., Waldoboro, ME 04572 USA Tel 207-832-6665; Fax: 207-832-6665
E-mail: dbenner@prexar.com
Web site: http://www.gooseriverpress.com.

Gooseberry Patch, *(0-9632978; 1-888052; 1-931890; 1-933494)* Orders Addr.: P.O. Box 190, Delaware, OH 43015 USA Toll Free: 800-854-6673; Edit Addr.: 600 London Rd., Delaware, OH 43201 USA Tel 740-369-1554
E-mail: Janie@gooseberrypatch.com
Web site: http://www.gooseberrypatch.com
Dist(s): **Andrews McMeel Publishing**
Bibliotech, Inc.
Gibson, Dot Pubns.
Simon & Schuster, Inc.
Southwest Cookbook Distributors.

Goosefoot Acres Pr., *(1-879863)* Div. of Goosefoot Acres, Inc., Orders Addr.: P.O. Box 18016, Cleveland, OH 44118-0016 USA (SAN 297-763X); Edit Addr.: 3283 E. Fairfax Rd., Cleveland, OH 44118 USA (SAN 297-7648) Tel 216-932-2145; Fax: 216-932-2187; Toll Free: 800-697-4858
E-mail: petergail@aol.com.

†**Gordon & Breach Publishing Group,** *(0-677; 0-905203; 1-872501; 2-88124; 2-88449; 2-903928; 2-919875; 3-364; 3-7186; 90-5699; 90-5700; 90-5701; 90-5702; 90-5703; 90-5704; 90-5708; 976-8097; 90-5755; 90-5706; 90-5707; 90-5709)* Div. of Taylor & Francis, Inc., Orders Addr.: 7625 Empire Dr., Florence, KY 41042 USA Toll Free Fax: 800-248-4724; Toll Free: 800-634-7064; Edit Addr.: 29 W. 35th St., New York, NY 10001 USA (SAN 201-6370) Tel 212-216-7800; Fax: 212-564-7854 ; *Imprints:* Harwood Academic Publishers (Harwood Acad Pubs)
E-mail: ncarter@taylorandfrances.com
Web site: http://www.gbhap.com
Dist(s): **CRC Pr. LLC;** *CIP.*

Gordon, Rev. Keith A., *(0-9720455)* 35 Montclair Ave., Batavia, NY 14020-1926 USA ; *Imprints:* Anthem Publishing (Ant Pub)
E-mail: reverendk@mondogordo.com
Web site: http://www.anthempopkult.com.

Gore Pubns., *(0-9701447)* P.O. Box 43561, Philadelphia, PA 19106-3561 USA Tel 215-545-1762.

Goretti Publishing, *(0-9778451)* Orders Addr.: 1150 N. Loop 1604 W., Ste. 108-410, San Antonio, TX 78248 USA (SAN 850-3176) Tel 210-274-2769; Fax: 210-493-6080 attn: 410
E-mail: publishedworks@aol.com
Web site: http://www.thetexasmermaid.com
Dist(s): **Book Marketing Plus.**

Gorgias Pr., LLC, *(0-9713097; 0-9715986; 1-931956; 1-59333)* 46 Orris Ave., Piscataway, NJ 08854 USA (SAN 853-0629) Tel 732-699-0343; Fax: 732-699-0342
E-mail: info@gorgiaspress.com; sales@gorgiaspress.com
Web site: http://www.gorgiaspress.com.

Gorilla Productions, *(0-9642721)* 44 Bayberry Ln., East Greenwich, RI 02818 USA Tel 401-884-2617.

Gormley Publishing, *(0-9794500)* Orders Addr.: 437 Woodie's Rd., Waynesburg, PA 15370-2677 USA
Web site: http://www.gormleypublishing.com.

Gorp Group Pr., The, *(0-9724249)* 4324 E. McDonald Dr., Ketchum, ID 83340 USA Tel 602-952-2774; Fax: 602-952-2007; Toll Free: 888-729-4677
E-mail: gorp2@earthlink.net
Web site: http://www.thegorp.com.

†**Gospel Advocate Co., Inc.,** *(0-89225)* Orders Addr.: P.O. Box 150, Nashville, TN 37202 USA (SAN 205-2792) Tel 615-254-8781; Fax: 615-254-7411; Toll Free: 800-251-8446; Edit Addr.: 1006 Elm Hill Pike, Nashville, TN 37210 USA (SAN 662-0213)
E-mail: kerry@gospeladvocate.com; keaton@gospeladvocate.com; haimericus@juno.com
Web site: http://www.gospeladvocate.com; *CIP.*

Gospel Communications International, *(1-55568)* 2735 E. Apple Ave., Muskegon, MI 49442 USA (SAN 653-3582) Tel 231-773-3361; Fax: 231-777-1847; Toll Free: 800-253-0413
Web site: http://www.gospelcom.net
Dist(s): **Christian Bk. Distributors.**

Gospel Films, Incorporated *See* **Gospel Communications International**

Gospel Light *Imprint of* **Gospel Light Pubns.**

Gospel Light Pubns., *(0-8307)* Orders Addr.: 1957 Eastman Ave., Ventura, CA 93003 USA (SAN 299-0873) Tel 805-644-9721; Fax: 805-289-0200; Toll Free: 800-446-7735 (orders only) ; *Imprints:* Gospel Light (Gospel Light); Regal Books (Regal Bks) Do not confuse with companies with similar names in Brooklyn, NY, Delight, AR
E-mail: info@gospellight.com; kyleloffelmacher@gospellight.com
Web site: http://www.gospellight.com
Dist(s): **CRC Pubns.**
Christian Bk. Distributors.

Gospel Missionary Union, *(0-9617490; 1-890940)* 10000 N. Oak Trafficway, Kansas City, MO 64155 USA (SAN 664-1830) Tel 816-734-8500; Fax: 816-734-4601
E-mail: info@gmu.org
Web site: http://www.gmu.org.

Gospel Projects Pr., *(0-929291)* P.O. Box 643, Milton, FL 32572 USA (SAN 249-101X) Fax: 850-983-0055
E-mail: childrensbibleclub@juno.com.

Gospel Puzzles, *(1-56998)* 3812 Laura Way, Bloomington, IN 47401 USA Tel 812-333-0339.

Gossamer Bks., *(0-9729016)* 444 Eastwood Dr., Petaluma, CA 94954 USA (SAN 255-2671) Tel 707-765-1992; Fax: 707-765-6507 Do not confuse with Gossamer Books LLC in Belmont, CA
E-mail: dcr530@cs.com.

Gossamer Bks., LLC, *(0-9742502)* P.O. Box 455, Belmont, CA 94002 USA Fax: 650-257-4058 Do not confuse with Gossamer Books in Petaluma, CA
E-mail: info@gossamerbooks.com
Web site: http://www.gossamerbooks.com.

Got It Goin' On, *(0-9651166)* 1221 Massachusetts Ave., NW, Suite 609, Washington, DC 20005-5315 USA Tel 202-829-2822
Dist(s): **African World Bks.**

Got2Bfunki Artworks, *(0-9713096)* 1250 E. Corson Ave., Apt. 3, Pasadena, CA 91106 USA Tel 626-792-5708 ; *Imprints:* Fresch Fruitz (Fresch)
E-mail: chozen4@yahoo.com.

Gotham *Imprint of* **Penguin Group (USA) Inc.**

Gough, Julie R., *(0-9714766)* 1491 Morris Rd., SE., Washington, DC 20020 USA
E-mail: julie.gough@mail.va.gov
Web site: http://www.formulamkt.com/bookmart/speakup.htm.

Goulasche Pr., *(0-9771466)* 1352 Ithilien, Excelsior, MN 55331 USA
Dist(s): **Itasca Bks.**

Gould, Marilyn *See* **Allied Crafts Pr.**

Gozo Bks., LLC, *(0-9776065)* 648 W. Wasatch St., Midvale, UT 84047 USA Tel 801-953-3793; Fax: 801-566-0265
E-mail: karlb@softcom.net
Web site: http://www.gozobooks.com.

GPKids *Imprint of* **Ideals Pubns.**

Grace & Mercy Publishing, *(0-9672049; 0-9764763)* Orders Addr.: P.O. Box 11531, Fort Wayne, IN 46857 USA; Edit Addr.: 7408 Mill Run, Suite B, Fort Wayne, IN 46819 USA.

Grace & Truth Bks., *(1-930133)* 3406 Summit Blvd., Sand Springs, OK 74063-3807 USA Tel 918-245-1500
E-mail: 76522.1451@compuserve.com
Web site: http://www.graceandtruthbooks.com.

Grace Communications Publishing *See* **Grace Publishing**

Grace Contrino Abrams Peace Education Foundation *See* **Peace Education Foundation**

Grace Hse. Publishing, *(0-9633633)* Div. of R. Allan McCauley Law Office, 6237 N. 15th St., Phoenix, AZ 85014 USA Tel 602-265-9151 Do not confuse with Grace House Publishing in Mahomet, IL.

Grace Pubns., LLC, *(1-59612)* P.O. Box 480, Johnson City, TN 37605-0480 USA Do not confuse with companies with the same or similar name in Albany OR, New York NY, Utopia TX
Web site: http://www.gracepublications.com.

Grace Publishing, *(1-893555)* Div. of Abundant Grace Fellowship, 11118 Robious Rd., Richmond, VA 23235-3724 USA Toll Free: 877-884-7223 Do not confuse with companies with the same name in Freeland, WA, Waldorf, MD, Woodinville, WA Seattle WA
E-mail: drmhunt@bellsouth.net; carylives@atthi.com; dremlenehunt@earthlink.net
Web site: http://www.abundantgrace.org; http://www.drmarlenehunt.com
Dist(s): **STL Distribution North America.**

Grace Publishing, *(0-9769985)* P.O. Box 17980, Seattle, WA 98123 USA (SAN 256-6257) Tel 206-818-9769 Do not confuse with Grace Publishing in Langley, WA- Woodinville, WA- Waldorf, MD, Los Angeles, CA, Elma, NY,
E-mail: vonukk@comcast.net
Web site: http://www.rcberg.com.

GraceMar Productions, Inc., *(0-9662234)* Orders Addr.: P.O. Box 23724, Eugene, OR 92402 USA Tel 541-344-7099; Fax: 541-344-7429; Toll Free: 800-800-7099; Edit Addr.: 90724 Dalewood Dr., Junction City, OR 97448 USA
E-mail: mbarker@medicfirstaid.com
Web site: http://www.graciedog.com
Dist(s): **Partners/West.**

GraceWorks Interactive, *(0-9760548)* P.O. Box 2613, Corvallis, OR 97339-2613 USA Toll Free: 877-785-3496 (phone/fax)
E-mail: tim@graceworksinteractive.com
Web site: http://www.graceworksinteractive.com.

Gracey, Everett L., *(0-9665842)* 3288 Alum Creek Ct., Reno, NV 89509-7117 USA Tel 775-324-3290; Fax: 775-324-3289
E-mail: gracey@eg.reno.nv.us
Web site: http://www.EverettGracey.com.

Graf Publishing, *(0-9674382)* 1820 Kristin Ln., South Milwaukee, WI 53172 USA Tel 414-764-4032
E-mail: grafpublishing@wi.rr.com
Web site: http://www.bookdrawer.com.

Grafco Bks. *Imprint of* **Grafco Productions, Inc.**

Grafco Productions, Inc., *(1-880719)* 291 Pat Mell Rd., Marietta, GA 30060 USA Tel 770-436-1500; Fax: 770-444-9357; Toll Free: 888-656-1500 ; *Imprints:* Grafco Books (Grafco Bks)
E-mail: jabo@mindspring.com
Web site: http://www.jackwboone.com.

grafixCORP, *(0-9778374)* Orders Addr.: P.O. Box 1441, Mount Vernon, WA 98273-9827 USA
Web site: http://www.grafixCORP.com.

Graham Bay, Jeanette, *(0-9771210)* 770 Victor Rd., Macedon, NY 14502 USA.

Graham Cracker Kids, *(0-615; 0-9716475)* 1661 Hunt Rd., El Cajon, CA 92019 USA Tel 619-258-7571; Fax: 619-258-5412
E-mail: grmcrkrkds@aol.com
Web site: http://www.grahamcrackerkids.com.

Gramercy *Imprint of* **Random Hse. Value Publishing**

Gramma Bks. Publishing Co., *(0-9669285)* Orders Addr.: P.O. Box 400, Oden, MI 49764 USA (SAN 299-8025) Tel 616-347-3562; Fax: 616-347-1130; Edit Addr.: 4630 Pangbuin St., Oden, MI 49764 USA
E-mail: wmct@freeway.net
Web site: http://www.grammabooks.com
Dist(s): **Quality Bks., Inc.**

Grammy Time Bks., *(0-9712675)* P.O. Box 639, San Luis Obispo, CA 93406 USA Tel 805-541-3515 (phone/fax)
E-mail: info@grammytimebooks.com
Web site: http://www.grammytimebooks.com
Dist(s): **Baker & Taylor Bks.**
Cogan Bks.

Grampa Jones's Publishing Co., *(0-615; 0-9748266)* P.O. Box 93, Heron, MT 59844-0093 USA (SAN 214-4700)
Web site: http://www.become-a-millionaire.com.

Grand Bks., Inc., *(0-930809)* P.O. Box 212, Crystal, MI 48818 USA (SAN 677-6361) Tel 517-875-4674; 517-235-4427
E-mail: jwrites@yahoo.com.

Grand Canyon Assn., *(0-938216; 1-934656)* Orders Addr.: P.O. Box 399, Grand Canyon, AZ 86023-0399 USA (SAN 215-7675) Tel 520-638-2481; Fax: 520-638-2484; Toll Free: 800-858-2808; Edit Addr.: 4 Tonto St., Grand canyon, AZ 86023 USA
E-mail: tberger@grandcanyon.org
Web site: http://www.grandcanyon.org
Dist(s): **Univ. of Arizona Pr.**
Yosemite Assn.

Grand Canyon Natural History Association *See* **Grand Canyon Assn.**

Grand Canyon Orphan, *(0-9764260)* P.O. Box 438, Mina, NV 89422 USA
E-mail: info@grandcanyonorphan.com
Web site: http://www.grandcanyonorphan.com.

†Grand Central Publishing, *(0-445; 0-446; 0-7595)* Orders Addr.: c/o Little Brown & Co., 3 Center Plaza, Boston, MA 02108-2084 USA Fax: 800-286-9471; Toll Free: 800-759-0190; Edit Addr.: 1271 Avenue of the Americas, New York, NY 10020 USA (SAN 281-8892) Tel 212-364-1200; Toll Free Fax: 800-286-9471 ; *Imprints:* Vision (VisionC); Forever (Forever); Sixth Avenue Books (SixthAveBks)
E-mail: renee.supriano@twbg.com
Web site: http://www.warnerbooks.com
Dist(s): **Hachette Bk. Group**
Lectorum Pubns., Inc.
Libros Sin Fronteras
Little Brown & Co.
Perelandra, Ltd.
Replica Bks.
Sony CONNECT, Inc.
Beeler, Thomas T. Pub.
Thorndike Pr.
iPublish.com; *CIP.*

Grand Hank Productions, Inc., *(0-9767236)* P.O. Box 23488, Philadelphia, PA 19143 USA Tel 215-724-5260
Web site: http://www.grandhank.com.

Grand Kidz, The *Imprint of* **Vertical Connect Pr.**

Grand Teton Natural History Assn., *(0-931895)* P.O. Box 170, Moose, WY 83012 USA (SAN 686-0303) Tel 307-739-3606; Fax: 307-739-3423
E-mail: gtnha@blissnet.com
Web site: http://www.grandtetonpark.org.

Grand Unification Pr., Inc., *(0-9700453)* 2380 Wayne St., Orrville, OH 44667 USA
E-mail: info@grandupress.com; grandupress@aol.com
Web site: http://www.grandupress.com.

Grandin Bk. Co., *(0-910523)* P.O. Box 2206, Provo, UT 84603-2206 USA (SAN 260-1931) Tel 801-225-2020; Fax: 801-222-0176; Toll Free: 800-292-2003.

Grandkidsandme, Inc., *(0-9741710)* 1764 Hampshire Ave., Saint Paul, MN 55116 USA (SAN 255-3902) Tel 651-695-1988; Fax: 651-699-5966
E-mail: don@grandkidsandme.com
Web site: http://www.grandkidsandme.com
Dist(s): **Independent Pubs. Group.**

Grandma Chubby's Bks., *(0-9728535)* P.O. Box 902308, Sandy, UT 84090-2308 USA Tel 801-571-6617; Fax: 801-571-2285
E-mail: lsashby@juno.com
Dist(s): **Granite Publishing & Distribution.**

Grandma's Attic, *(0-9714041)* 308 N. Main St. S1, Glassboro, NJ 08028 USA Tel 856-863-5627
E-mail: agracely@hotmail.com.

"Grandma's Hope Notes", *(0-9677477)* P.O. Box 868, Anchor Point, AK 99556 USA Tel 907-235-0502 (phone/fax).

Grandma's Stories, Inc., *(0-9722216)* P.O. Box 36357, Indianapolis, IN 46236 USA
E-mail: offset1@infi.net.

Grandoc Publishing, *(0-9761739)* 3923 Hidden Way NE, Rochester, MN 55906-5590 USA Tel 507-273-1695
E-mail: grandoc@mac.com; drjohngraner@mac.com.

Grandreams Bks., Inc., *(1-59340)* Div. of Robert Frederick, 360 Hurst St., Linden, NJ 07036 USA (SAN 254-9832) Fax: 908-523-0373
E-mail: ssullivan@grandreamsbooks.com.

Grandview Publishing Co., *(1-880114)* Orders Addr.: P.O. Box 2863, Jackson, WY 83001-2863 USA Fax: 307-734-0210; Toll Free: 800-525-7344
E-mail: kenthomasma@blissnet.com.

Grandy Pubns., *(0-9729237)* 290 E. Verdugo Ave., Stuite 105, Burbank, CA 91502 USA Tel 818-848-1313; Fax: 818-551-0305; Toll Free: 800-326-8953
E-mail: MannersA2Z@aol.com
Web site: http://www.youvegotmanners.com
Dist(s): **Independent Pubs. Group.**

Granite Publishing & Distribution, *(1-890558; 1-930980; 1-932280; 1-59936)* 868 N. 1430 W., Orem, UT 84057 USA (SAN 631-0605) Tel 801-229-9023; Fax: 801-229-1924; Toll Free: 800-574-5779 Do not confuse with companies with same or similar names in Madison, WI, Columbus, NC
E-mail: granitepd@aol.com; granite@granitepublishing.biz
Web site: http://granitepublishing.biz.

Granite Publishing, LLC, *(0-926524; 0-9632310; 1-893183)* P.O. Box 1429, Columbus, NC 28722 USA Tel 828-894-3088; Fax: 828-894-8454; Toll Free: 800-366-0264 Do not confuse with companies with same or similar names in Madison, WI, Orem, UT, Siloam Springs, AR
E-mail: brian@5thworld.com
Web site: http://www.5thworld.com
Dist(s): **Baker & Taylor Bks.**
New Leaf Distributing Co., Inc.

Granny Pr., *(0-945110)* 43 Forest Ridge Rd., Nyack, NY 10960-1754 USA
E-mail: estnelson@aol.com
Web site: http://www.grannypress
Dist(s): **Baker & Taylor Bks.**

Granny's Pub Co., *(0-9749950)* P.O. Box 1701, Granbury, TX 76048 USA Tel 817-605-9004; Fax: 817-605-1180
E-mail: granny@loralie.com
Web site: http://www.loralie.com.

Granville Island Publishing (CAN) *(1-894694) Dist. by* **Partners Bk Dist.**

Grape Elephant MarketPr., *(0-9760646)* 13025 Ct. Pl., Burnsville, MN 55337 USA Tel 612-281-2566
E-mail: jill@grapeelephant.com
Web site: http://www.grapeelephant.com.

Graphia *Imprint of* **Houghton Mifflin Co. Trade & Reference Div.**

Graphic Arts Ctr. Publishing Co., Orders Addr.: P.O. Box 10306, Portland, OR 97296-0306 USA (SAN 201-6338) Tel 503-226-2402; Fax: 503-223-1410 (executive & editorial); Toll Free Fax: 800-355-9685 (sales office); Toll Free: 800-452-3032 ; *Imprints:* Alaska Northwest Books (Alaska NW Bks); West Winds Press (West Winds Pr)
E-mail: sales@gacpc.com
Web site: http://www.gacpc.com.

Graphic Classics *Imprint of* **Eureka Productions**

Graphic Expressions *See* **Graphics North**

Graphic Planet *Imprint of* **Magic Wagon**

Graphic Publishing Company, Incorporated *See* **Stoyles Graphic Services**

Graphic Universe *Imprint of* **Lerner Publishing Group**

Graphically Speaking, Inc., *(0-9729975)* 15509 Lloyd St., Omaha, NE 68144 USA Tel 402-330-1144; Fax: 402-334-3311
E-mail: fontstudios@cox.net
Web site: http://www.fontstudios.com.

Graphics Atlanta *See* **GA Publishing**

Graphics North, *(0-9643452)* P.O. Box 218, Jay, NY 12941 USA Tel 518-946-7741
E-mail: mvf@charter.net.

Graphic-Sha (JPN) *(4-7661) Dist. by* **Diamond Book Dists.**

Graphis, U.S., Inc., *(1-888001; 1-931241; 1-932026)* Orders Addr.: c/o ABDI, Inc., Buncher Commerce Pk. Ave. A, Bldg. 16, Leetsdale, PA 15056-1304 USA Tel 412-741-3679; Fax: 412-741-0934; Toll Free: 800-209-4234 (for Canada & USA); Edit Addr.: 307 Fifth Ave., 10th Flr., New York, NY 10016 USA Tel 212-532-9387 ext 226; Fax: 212-213-3229; Toll Free: 800-209-4234
E-mail: graphisorders@abdintl.com; editors@graphis.com; custsvc_graphis@fulcoinc.com
Web site: http://www.graphis.com
Dist(s): **Macmillan**
Watson-Guptill Pubns., Inc.

Graphite Pr., *(0-9755810)* 2025 Lexington Parkway, Niskayuna, NY 12309-4205 USA (SAN 256-0712) Tel 206-222-2400; Fax: 206-222-2002
E-mail: publish@graphitepress.com
Web site: http://www.graphitepress.com.

Graphix *Imprint of* **Scholastic, Inc.**

Graphix Network, *(0-9740673; 0-9752832; 0-9762301; 0-9777043)* Orders Addr.: P.O. Box 2745, Evans, GA 30809 USA Tel 706-210-1000; Fax: 706-210-1111; Edit Addr.: 4104 Colben Blvd., Suite C, Evans, GA 30809 USA Tel 706-210-1000; Fax: 706-210-1111
E-mail: graphixnetwork@hotmail.com; sales@graphixnetwork.com
Web site: http://www.graphixnetwork.com.

Grass Lake Publishing, *(0-9673359)* 44 Kellar Dr., Bernhards Bay, NY 13028 USA (SAN 852-4521)
E-mail: dmmillerfoundation@earthlink.net
Web site: http://www.dmmillerfoundation.org.

Grass Root Enterprises, *(1-886075)* 16315 Forest Way Dr., Houston, TX 77090-4716 USA Tel 281-444-4103; Fax: 281-444-5804.

Grassdale Publishers, Incorporated *See* **Saxon Pubs., Inc.**

Grassfield Pr., Inc., *(0-9628514; 1-886438)* P.O. Box 398825, Miami Beach, FL 33239 USA Tel 305-538-1033
E-mail: grassfield@mindspring.com
Web site: http://www.grassfieldpress.com.

Grasshopper Bks. (CAN) *(0-9692641; 1-895910) Dist. by* **Orca Bk Pubs.**

Grasshopper Dream Productions, *(0-615)* Orders Addr.: P.O. Box 1831, Saint Petersburg, FL 33731-1831 USA Tel 813-382-4230; Edit Addr.: 121 E. Davis Blvd., No. 104, Tampa, FL 33731 USA
E-mail: kokopelli911@hotmail.com
Web site: http://www.kokopelli-butterfly.com.

Grassroots Educational Service *See* **Right On Programs, Inc.**

Grateful Dead Productions, *(1-888358)* P.O. Box X, Novato, CA 94948 USA Toll Free: 800-225-3323
Web site: http://www.dead.net.

Gratia et Veritas Press *See* **Papillon Publishing**

Gratitude Publishing & Printing, *(1-883583)* 302 N. Van Buren St., Auburn, IN 46706 USA Tel 219-925-0031.

Gravel Pit Pr., *(0-9678212)* N7790 535th St., Spring Valley, WI 54767 USA Tel 715-273-7762 (phone/fax)
E-mail: gravelpt@pressenter.com.

Graves, C. Werl Pubns., *(0-9664777)* 5465 Paradox Dr., Colorado Springs, CO 80918 USA Tel 719-460-2706; Fax: 719-380-9232; Toll Free: 800-410-2014
E-mail: werlgrvs@aol.com
Web site: http://www.germancooking.com.

Gravitas Pubns., Inc., *(0-9749149; 0-9765097; 0-9799459)* P.O. Box 4790, Albuquerque, NM 87196-4790 USA Tel 505-266-2761; Fax: 505-266-2762; Toll Free: 888-466-2761
E-mail: gravitaspublications@comcast.net.

Gravley, Debbie Bybee, *(0-9771793)* Orders Addr.: P.O. Box 268, Gaston, OR 97119 USA; Edit Addr.: 12320 S.W. Springhill Rd., Gaston, OR 97119 USA.

Gray & Co., Pubs., *(0-9631738; 1-886228; 1-59851)* Orders Addr.: 1588 E. 40th St., 3A, Cleveland, OH 44103 USA Tel 216-431-2665; Fax: 216-431-7933; Toll Free: 800-915-3609
E-mail: info@grayco.com
Web site: http://www.grayco.com.

Gray Company Publishing, *(0-9663901)* Orders Addr.: 12324 E. 86th St., N., Owasso, OK 74055-2543 USA Tel 918-272-7552; Fax: 918-272-9039; Toll Free: 888-834-2730
E-mail: dlhpe@fullnet.net.

Gray, D. H., *(0-9717227)* 1501 W. 39th Ave., Casper, WY 82604-5000 USA.

Gray Hse. Bks., *(0-9679046)* P.O. Box 920142, Snowbird, UT 84092 USA
Dist(s): **Baker & Taylor Bks.**
Evans Bk. Distribution & Pubs., Inc.

Gray, Susan *See* **Two's Company**

Grayson, Kate, *(0-9774357)* 2307 58th Ave. E., Bradenton, FL 34203 USA (SAN 257-5000)
E-mail: kgrayson1@aol.com.

Graziano, Claudia *See* **Meerkat's Adventures Bks.**

Great AD-Ventures, *(0-9665053)* P.O. Box 8011, Boise, ID 83707 USA Fax: 208-336-5797; Toll Free: 800-390-5687
E-mail: theplace@lesbois.com; book@freeread.com
Web site: http://www.freeread.com/.

Great Adventures Pubn., *(1-930120)* Div. of One Voice Ministries, 5351 S. 139th Plaza, Omaha, NE 68137-2964 USA Tel 402-896-6692; Fax: 402-891-9068
Dist(s): **DB & Assocs. Design & Distribution.**

Great Adventures Publishing, *(0-9747972)* 465 Hill St., Laguna Beach, CA 92651 USA Tel 949-494-5797
E-mail: paigeturner5@hotmail.com.

Great American Pr.,The, *(0-9777996; 0-9798776)* 8885 Monroe Rd., Houston, TX 77061 USA (SAN 850-2773) Toll Free: 800-292-4187
Web site: http://www.thegreatamericanpress.com.

Great American Pubs., *(0-9779053; 1-934817)* Orders Addr.: P.O. Box 1305, Kosciusko, MS 39090 USA Fax: 601-213-3843; Toll Free: 866-625-9241
E-mail: info@gapublishers.com; ssimmons@gapublishers.com
Web site: http://www.greatamericanpublishers.com.

Great Authors Online, *(0-9773869)* 16440 Monterey St., Lake Elsinore, CA 92530 USA Tel 951-674-3246; Fax: 951-245-3608
E-mail: rodgerolsen@yahoo.com
Web site: http://greatauthorsonline.com.

Great Beginning-AGB, A *Imprint of* **AGB Publishing**

Great Bks. Foundation, *(0-945159; 1-880323; 1-933147)* 35 E. Wacker Dr., Suite 2300, Chicago, IL 60601-2298 USA (SAN 205-3292) Tel 312-332-5870; Fax: 312-407-0334; Toll Free: 800-222-5870
E-mail: hurleyp@greatbooks.org
Web site: http://www.greatbooks.org.

Great Character Development Workbook, The, *(0-9728417)* P.O. Box 1852, Kingston, WA 98346 USA
Web site: http://www.thegreatcharacterdevelopmentworkbook.com.

Great Dog Publishing, *(0-9678057)* Orders Addr.: P.O. Box 1388, Claremont, CA 91711 USA Tel 909-621-6601; Fax: 909-621-9791; Toll Free: 877-621-8334; Edit Addr.: 786 Via Espirito Santos, Claremont, CA 91711 USA
E-mail: ltisopulos@aol.com
Web site: http://www.buddionline.com.

Great Expectations Bk. Co., *(1-883934)* P.O. Box 2067, Eugene, OR 07402 USA Tel 541-343-2647; Fax: 541-343-0568
E-mail: fred@pinehillgraphics.com.

Great House Publishers Grp., Inc., The, *(1-889448)* P.O. Box 278504, Miramar, FL 33027 USA (SAN 299-1764)
E-mail: keturaa@yahoo.com
Web site: http://www.amazonchristianbooks.com
Dist(s): **A & B Distributors & Pubs. Group**
Anchor Distributors
Spring Arbor Distributors, Inc.

Great I-AM Publishing Co., The, *(0-9762788)* Orders Addr.: P.O. Box 30412, Wilmington, DE 19805 USA Tel 302-888-0299; Fax: 302-888-2477; Edit Addr.: 25 Roselane Rosegate, New Castle, DE 19720 USA
E-mail: watkinstyree@aol.com.

Great Ideas for Teaching, Inc., *(1-886143)* Orders Addr.: P.O. Box 444, Wrightsville Beach, NC 28480-0444 USA Tel 910-256-4494; Fax: 910-256-4493; Toll Free Fax: 800-839-8498; Toll Free: 800-839-8339; Edit Addr.: 6800 Wrightsville Ave., No. 16, Wilmington, NC 28403 USA
E-mail: gift@wilmington.net
Web site: http://www.gift-inc.com.

Great Lakes Bks. *Imprint of* **Wayne State Univ. Pr.**

Great Lakes Design, *(0-9761274)* P.O. Box 511534, Milwaukee, WI 53203 USA
Web site: http://www.vikingadventure.net.

Great Lakes Press, Inc., *(0-9614760; 1-881018)* Orders Addr.: P.O. Box 550, Wildwood, MO 63040-0550 USA (SAN 692-9745) Tel 636-273-6016; Fax: 636-273-6086; Toll Free: 800-837-0201
E-mail: service@glpbooks.com
Web site: http://www.glpbooks.com.

Great Lakes Publishing Co., *(0-9620016)* Orders Addr.: P.O. Box 128, Emmett, MI 48022 USA (SAN 247-428X); Edit Addr.: 3079 Washington St., Emmett, MI 48022 USA (SAN 247-4298) Tel 810-384-6416; Fax: 810-384-6005.

Great Mastiff Corp., *(0-9759166)* 9945 E. Whitebirch Rd., Port wing, WI 54865 USA Tel 715-774-3247
E-mail: greatmastiff@hotmail.com
Web site: http://www.greatmastiff.com.

Great Northern Adventure Co., Inc., *(0-9763931)* 3860 Kula Vista Dr., Eagle River, WI 54521 USA
Web site: http://www.gnaco.com.

Great Ocean Publishers *See* **Great River Bks.**

†Great Outdoors Publishing Co., *(0-8200)* 4747 28th St., N., Saint Petersburg, FL 33714 USA (SAN 201-6273) Tel 727-525-6609; Fax: 727-527-4870; Toll Free: 800-869-6609
E-mail: info@floridabooks.com
Web site: http://www.floridabooks.com; *CIP.*

Great Persuader Publishing, The, *(0-9712581)* Orders Addr.: a/o , P.O. Box 1100, New York, NY 10030 USA Tel 646-271-2188
E-mail: greatpersuader@hotmail.com; Info@Poetryisalive.com
Web site: http://www.Poetryisalive.com.

Great Plains Pr., *(0-9632459)* 2532 W. Warren Blvd., #2, Chicago, IL 60612-2124 USA
E-mail: nancy@greatplainspress.com
Web site: http://www.greatplainspress.com/.

†Great Potential Pr., Inc., *(0-910707)* P.O. Box 5057, Scottsdale, AZ 85261 USA (SAN 260-2385) Tel 602-954-4200; Fax: 602-954-0185
E-mail: kristina@giftedbooks.com; info@giftedbooks.com
Web site: http://www.giftedbooks.com
Dist(s): **Baker & Taylor Bks.**
Bookmen, Inc.; *CIP.*

†Great River Bks., *(0-915556)* 121 M St., Salt Lake City, UT 84103 USA (SAN 207-527X) Tel 801-532-4833
E-mail: info@greatriverbooks.com
Dist(s): **Midpoint Trade Bks., Inc.**; *CIP.*

Great Smoky Mountains Natural History Assn., *(0-937207)* 115 Park Headquarters Rd., Gatlinburg, TN 37738 USA (SAN 658-7267) Tel 865-436-0120; Fax: 865-436-6884
E-mail: mail@smokiesaha.org
Web site: http://www.smokiesstore.org.

Great Source Education Group, Inc., *(0-669; 0-9638133; 1-57185)* Subs. of Houghton Mifflin Co., 181 Ballardvale St., Wilmington, MA 01887 USA Tel 978-661-1500; Fax: 978-661-1331; Toll Free Fax: 800-289-3994; Toll Free: 800-289-4490
Web site: http://www.greatsource.com.

Great Train Stores, The, *(0-9700383)* P.O. Box 93045, Southlake, TX 76092-1045 USA
E-mail: henry.rivas@greattrain.com.

Great Valley Bks. *Imprint of* **Heyday Bks.**

Great White Dog Picture Company *See* **Light-Beams Publishing**

Greater Cincinnati TV Educational Foundation, *(0-9744419)* 1223 Central Pkwy., Cincinnati, OH 45214-2812 USA Tel 513-381-4033; Fax: 513-381-7520 ; *Imprints:* CET (Cet)
E-mail: edtech@wcet.pbs.org
Web site: http://www.wcet.org.

Greater Mankato Area United Way, *(0-9668635)* 101 N. Second St., No. 202, Mankato, MN 56001 USA Tel 507-345-4551; Fax: 507-345-3724
E-mail: uwmnkto@mnic.net
Web site: http://www.nexus.mnic.net/~uwmnkto.

Greater Truth Pubs., *(0-9653078)* P.O. Box 4332, Lafayette, IN 47903 USA Do not confuse with Griffin Publishing, Glendale, CA
E-mail: gtp@ao-soft.com
Web site: http://www.ao-soft.com/gtpub/.

Greathall Productions, Inc., *(1-882513)* Orders Addr.: P.O. Box 5061, Charlottesville, VA 22905-5061 USA Tel 434-296-4288; Fax: 434-296-4490; Toll Free: 800-477-6234
E-mail: greathall@greathall.com
Web site: http://www.greathall.com
Dist(s): **Allegro Distribution**
Rounder Kids Music Distribution.

Greatland Graphics, *(0-936425)* Orders Addr.: P.O. Box 100333, Anchorage, AK 99510-0333 USA (SAN 698-1763); Edit Addr.: 2515 Wesleyan Dr., Anchorage, AK 99508 USA (SAN 698-1771) Tel 907-337-1234; Fax: 907-337-4567
E-mail: picturealaska@gci.net; info@alaskacalendars.com
Web site: http://www.alaskacalendars.com
Dist(s): **News Group, The**
Wizard Works.

Greek 'n' Stuff, *(1-931842; 1-933999)* P.O. Box 882, Moline, IL 61266-0882 USA Tel 309-796-2707; Fax: 309-796-2706
E-mail: workbooks@greekstuff.com
Web site: http://www.greeknstuff.com.

Green Angel Pr., *(0-9658065)* 7121 New Light Trail, Chapel Hill, NC 27516 USA Tel 919-933-9299; Fax: 919-968-9800
E-mail: greentfh@mindspring.com
Dist(s): **Baker & Taylor Bks.**
Follett Library Resources.

Green Hill Publishers *See* **Jameson Bks., Inc.**

Green Integer, *(1-892295; 1-931243; 1-933382)* Div. of Contemporary Arts Educational Project, Inc., 6022 Wilshire Blvd., Suite 200A, Los Angeles, CA 90036 USA Tel 323-857-1115; Fax: 323-857-0143
E-mail: info@greeninteger.com
Web site: http://www.greeninteger.com
Dist(s): **Consortium Bk. Sales & Distribution**
SPD-Small Pr. Distribution.

Green Irene, *(0-9742280)* P.O. Box 5, Huron, OH 44839 USA
E-mail: chager@buckeye-express.com
Web site: http://www.redandgreenchoices.com.

Green Key Bks., *(0-9705996; 1-932587; 1-60098)* 2514 Aloha Pl., Holiday, FL 34691 USA (SAN 254-4377) Tel 727-934-0927; Fax: 727-934-4241; Toll Free: 888-278-3300
E-mail: cseitz@greenkeybooks.com
Web site: http://www.greenkeybooks.com.

Green Light Readers *Imprint of* **Harcourt Children's Bks.**

Green Local Schl. District, *(0-9717616)* Orders Addr.: P.O. Box 218, Green, OH 44232 USA (SAN 512-0233) Tel 330-896-7500; Fax: 330-896-7529; Edit Addr.: 1900 Greensburg Rd., Green, OH 44232 USA
Web site: http://www.greensummit.k12.oh.us.

Green Magic Pubs. (GBR) *(0-9536631; 0-9542963; 0-9547230) Dist. by* **SCB Distributors.**

Green Mansion Pr. LLC, *(0-9714612; 0-9746457)* 501 E. 79th St., Suite 16A, New York, NY 10021-0773 USA (SAN 254-2684) Tel 212-396-2667; Fax: 212-937-4685
E-mail: info@greenmansionpress.com
Web site: http://www.greenmansionpress.com
Dist(s): **Baker & Taylor Bks.**
Ingram Bk. Co.

Green, Mary, *(0-9764639)* 159 Greene Ln., Cookeville, TN 38506-8223 USA
E-mail: greenma@multipro.com
Web site: http://www.bigfootlady.net.

Green Mountain Publishing, *(0-9664880)* Orders Addr.: P.O. Box 1291, Clovis, CA 93613 USA (SAN 299-6391) Tel 559-322-1668 (phone/fax); Edit Addr.: 3425 N. First St., Suite 205, Fresno, CA 93726 USA Do not confuse with Green Mountain Publishing, Williston, VT
E-mail: elidojau@yahoo.com; cterrence@hotmail.com.

Green Nest LLC, *(0-9772392)* P.O. Box 6117, Irvine, CA 92616 USA
Web site: http://www.greennest.com.

Green Pastures Pr., *(0-9627643; 1-884377)* HC 67, Box 91-A, Mifflin, PA 17058 USA Tel 717-436-9115.

Green Pastures Publishing, Inc., *(0-9664276; 0-9720580)* Orders Addr.: P.O. Box 804, Windsor, CO 80550 USA Tel 970-686-7242
Dist(s): **Independent Pubs. Group.**

Green Ridge Bks., *(0-9664376)* 98 Green Ridge Rd., Weaverville, NC 28787 USA Tel 828-645-6362; Fax: 828-254-7338
E-mail: hnewton@buncombe.main.nc.us.

Green Sheet Inc., The, *(0-9670947)* P.O. Box 6008, Petaluma, CA 94955-6008 USA Fax: 707-586-1738; Toll Free: 800-757-4441
E-mail: grnsht@aol.com
Web site: http://www.greensheet.com.

Green Tiger Pr. *Imprint of* **Laughing Elephant**

Green Troubadour Pr., *(0-9761000)* E8840 McCoy Rd., North Freedom, WI 53951 USA (SAN 256-5242) Tel 608-522-3362; Fax: 608-522-3361
E-mail: janedana@centurytel.net
Web site: http://www.greentroubadourpress.com.

Green Turtle Pr., *(0-9720198)* Orders Addr.: P.O. Box 1243, Paonia, CO 81428 USA Tel 970-527-4341 (phone/fax); Edit Addr.: 317 N. Fork Ave., Paonia, CO 81428 USA Do not confuse with Green Turtle Pr., in Waialua, HI
E-mail: greenturtlepress@lycos.com
Web site: http://members.tripod.com/greenturtlepress.

Greenberg, Scott *See* **Jump Start Performance Programs**

Greenbrier/Scentex, *(1-930355)* 300 Greenbrier Rd., Summersville, WV 26651 USA Tel 304-872-3000; Fax: 304-872-3033; Toll Free: 800-917-2368.

Greene, A.S. & Co., *(0-9761723)* 1828 Kings Hwy., Lincoln Park, MI 48146 USA Fax: 313-388-0447
E-mail: collegefundproductions@yahoo.com.

Greene Bark Pr., Inc., *(1-880851)* P.O. Box 1108, Bridgeport, CT 06601-1108 USA Tel 203-372-4861; Fax: 203-371-5856
E-mail: Greenebark@aol.com
Web site: http://www.greenebarkpress.com
Dist(s): **Baker & Taylor Bks.**

Greene, Brenda H. *See* **Three Willows Pr.**

Greene, Marjorie A., *(0-9741764)* 124 Caughman Park Dr., Columbia, SC 29209 USA Tel 803-783-5430; Fax: 803-783-5430
E-mail: remaininme@msn.com.

Greene Pubns., *(0-9608892)* 2820 Midwick Dr., Alhambra, CA 91803 USA (SAN 241-1180) Tel 213-413-2150 Do not confuse with Greene Pubns., Inc. in Alahambra, CA.

Greenfield Enterprises, Ltd. (HKG) *(962-563) Dist. by* **Cheng Tsui.**

Greenhaven Pr., Inc. *Imprint of* **Thomson Gale**

Greenhill Bks./Lionel Leventhal, Ltd. (GBR) *(0-947898; 1-85367) Dist. by* **MBI Dist Svcs.**

Greenhills Pr., *(0-9671160)* 1001 Capital of Texas Hwy., S., Bldg. L, Suite 200, Austin, TX 78746 USA Tel 512-347-8050; Fax: 512-347-8088.

Greenhouse Publishing Co., *(0-9616844)* P.O. Box 525, Marshall, VA 20116 USA (SAN 661-1729) Tel 540-987-8961; Fax: 540-987-3197
Web site: http://www.greenhouse_books.com.

Greenleaf Book Group, *(0-9665319; 1-929774)* Orders Addr.: 4425 S. Mopac, Suite 600, Longhorn Bldg, 3rd Fl., Austin, TX 78735 USA Tel 512-891-6100; Fax: 512-891-6150; Toll Free: 800-932-5420; Edit Addr.: 7600 Thistle Ln., Novelty, OH 44072 USA
E-mail: tanya@greenleafbookgroup.com
Web site: http://www.greenleafbookgroup.com
Dist(s): **Greenleaf Book Group Pr.**

Greenleaf Book Group Pr., *(1-929774; 0-9790842)* Div. of Greenleaf Book Group, 4425 S. Mopac, Suite 600 Longhorn Bldg., 3rd Flr., Austin, TX 78735 USA (SAN 631-9238) Tel 512-891-6100; 800-932-5420; Fax: 512-891-6150
E-mail: nathan@greenleafbookgroup.com; contact@greenleafbookgroup.com
Web site: http://www.greenleafbookgroup.com/.

Greenleaf Pr., *(1-882514)* 3761 Hwy. 109 N., Lebanon, TN 37087 USA (SAN 297-8555) Tel 615-449-1617; Fax: 615-449-4018; Toll Free: 800-311-1508 Do not confuse with Greenleaf Pr., Breckenridge, CO
E-mail: info@greenleafpress.com
Web site: http://www.greenleafpress.com.

Greenline Publications *See* **Davis, A. S. Media Group**

GreenPoint Computer Services *See* **GIL Pubns.**

Greenroom Bks., *(0-9712163)* 12 N. Juniper St., Hampton, VA 23669-2416 USA (SAN 254-2501) Tel 757-726-2651 (phone/fax)
E-mail: brad@greenroombooks.com; publisher@greenroombooks.com
Web site: http://www.greenroombooks.com
Dist(s): **Baker & Taylor Bks.**
Brodart Co.

Greensboro Historical Museum, Inc., *(0-9747456)* 130 Summit Ave., Greensboro, NC 27401-3016 USA Tel 336-373-2043; Fax: 336-373-2204
Web site: http://www.greensborohistory.org.

Greentown Glass Co., *(0-9723958)* Orders Addr.: P.O. Box 771, Westfield, IN 46074-0771 USA Tel 765-455-0595; Edit Addr.: 3703 Robin Dr., Kokomo, IN 46902 USA
Web site: http://www.greentownglasscompany.com.

Greenville Family Partnership, *(0-9759699)* P.O. Box 10203, Greenville, SC 29603-0203 USA Tel 864-467-4099; Fax: 864-467-4102
Web site: http://www.redribbonworks.org.

Greenwich Pr, *(0-9714078)* 1100 Cherokee St., Suite 303, Denver, CO 80204 USA Tel 303-573-7399; Fax: 303-573-7403 Do not confuses with companies witht he same name in New York, NY, Santa Rosa, CA
E-mail: nelson7402@aol.com; jj@parospress.com
Web site: Http://www.greenwichpress.com.

Greenwich Press, Limited *See* **Greenwich Workshop Pr.**

Greenwich Workshop Pr., *(0-86713)* Orders Addr.: P.O. Box 875, Seymour, CT 06483 USA (SAN 216-8170) Tel 203-881-3336; Fax: 203-881-9575; Toll Free: 800-243-4246; Edit Addr.: 151 Main St., Seymour, CT 06483 USA
E-mail: scottu@greenwichworkshop.com
Web site: http://www.greenwichworkshop.com
Dist(s): **Artisan**
Workman Publishing Co., Inc.

Greenwillow Bks. *Imprint of* **HarperCollins Pubs.**

Greenwood, Lori Ministries, Inc., *(0-9747956)* Orders Addr.: 17622 32nd Pl W., Lynnwood, WA 98037-7714 USA (SAN 255-8297)
E-mail: lgministries@cs.com
Web site: http://www.thevisionlink.com.

Greenwood Pr. *Imprint of* **Greenwood Publishing Group, Inc.**

Greenwood Press, Incorporated *See* **Greenwood Publishing Group, Inc.**

†Greenwood Publishing Group, Inc., *(0-275; 0-313; 0-8371; 0-86569; 0-89789; 0-89930; 1-56720)* Orders Addr.: P.O. Box 6926, Portsmouth, NH 03802 USA (SAN 213-2028) Fax: 603-431-2214 (customer service and sales) ; Toll Free: 800-225-5800 (orders only); Linacre House Jordan Hill Bus Pk, Banbury Rd, Oxford, OX2 8DP Tel 44 (0) 1865 888181; Fax: 44 (0) 1865 314981; Edit Addr.: 214 Bald Eagle Ln., Cary, NC 27518-9681 USA ; *Imprints:* Greenwood Press (Greenwood Pr); Praeger Publishers (Praeger Pubs); Oryx Press (Oryx); Middle School Reference (Mid Schl Ref) Do not confuse with Greenwood Publishing in Glenview, IL
E-mail: customer-service@greenwood.com; sales@greenwood.com; Greenwood.enquiries@harcourteducation.co.uk
Web site: http://www.greenwood.com
Dist(s): **International Specialized Bk. Services**
Libraries Unlimited, Inc.
NetLibrary, Inc.; *CIP.*

Greenwood Street Publishing. GSP, *(0-9745553)* 1539 W. Townley Ave., Phoenix, AZ 85021 USA Tel 602-997-4444; Fax: 602-997-5959 Do not confuse with Greenwood Publishing in Wixom, MI
E-mail: julie@gg-az.com; info@greenwoodstreet.com
Web site: http://www.greenwoodstreet.com.

Greer, Laura Jayne, *(0-615; 0-9724916)* 2400 S. Dixie Hwy., Suite 200, Miami, FL 33133 USA Tel 305-661-2482
E-mail: fosterbook@aol.com
Web site: http://www.fostercareguide.com.

Gregath Publishing Co., *(0-944619)* Orders Addr.: P.O. Box 505, Wyandotte, OK 74370 USA (SAN 630-0820) Toll Free: 800-955-5232
E-mail: fredrea@gregathcompany.com
Web site: http://www.gregathcompany.com.

Greger, Margaret, *(0-9613680)* 1425 Marshall, Richland, WA 99352 USA (SAN 670-8994) Tel 509-943-3951
E-mail: mggreg@gte.net
Web site: http://www.kitesforeveryone.com.

Gregg, Sue Cookbooks, *(1-878272)* 8830 Glencoe Dr., Riverside, CA 92503 USA Tel 951-687-5491; Toll Free: 800-998-2783
E-mail: suegregg@suegregg.com
Web site: http://www.suegregg.com.

For full information on wholesalers and distributors, refer to the Wholesaler and Distributor Symbol Index

Gregory, Charles, *(0-9745432)* 17697 Palmer St., Melvindale, MI 48122 USA (SAN 255-7991) Tel 313-389-2836
E-mail: charles_gregory@ameritech.net
Web site: http://www.charles_gregory/index.html.

Gregory, Charles Matthew, *(0-9766442)* P.O. Box 24733, Minneapolis, MN 55424-0733 USA.

Grenadier Pubns., *(0-9621020)* 1108 Farrington St., Saint Paul, MN 55117 USA (SAN 250-6602) Tel 651-489-4380
E-mail: jcluecke@skypoint.com.

Grendel Pr., *(0-9714988)* P.O. Box 238, Loveland, CO 80539-0238 USA Tel 970-461-9250; Fax: 970-461-9257; Toll Free: 866-473-6335
E-mail: sally@silverstories.com
Web site: http://www.silverstories.com.

Grendel Roleplaying, *(1-929928)* P.O. Box 4059, Lexington, KY 415044 USA
E-mail: questions@grendelrp.com
Web site: http://www.grendelrp.com.

Grenevitch, Betsy Coffman, *(0-9747113)* 1450 Hewatt Rd., Lilburn, GA 30047 USA Tel 678-344-6100 (phone/fax)
E-mail: blindangel@joimail.com.

Grenwood Publishing *See* **Greenwood Street Publishing. GSP**

Gresham, Joel, *(0-9708446)* 2201 Morgan Pl., Atlanta, GA 30324 USA Tel 404-633-4720
E-mail: jolgres@mindspring.com.

Grey Ghost Pr., Inc., *(1-887154)* P.O. Box 838, Randolph, MA 02368-0838 USA Tel 781-961-2050; Fax: 781-961-3909
E-mail: ghostgames@aol.com
Web site: http://www.members.aol.com.

†Grey Hse. Publishing, *(0-939300; 1-891482; 1-930956; 1-59237)* 185 Millerton Rd., Millerton, NY 12546 USA Tel 518-789-8700; Fax: 518-789-0556; Toll Free: 800-562-2139 ; *Imprints:* Universal Reference Publications (Universal Ref Pubns)
E-mail: books@greyhouse.com
Web site: http://www.greyhouse.com; *CIP.*

Grey Wolf Bks., *(0-9768259)* 4933 Grey Wolf Pl., Broomfield, CO 80020-3965 USA Tel 303-818-1876; Fax: 303-554-7434
E-mail: adamsons100@msn.com.

Greycat Tales, *(0-9717131)* 25 Lago Ct., Reno, NV 89506-5002 USA
E-mail: greycattales4u@aol.com.

GreyCore Pr., *(0-9671851; 0-9742074)* 3833 Hilton Ave NE, Albuquerque, NM 87110-1059 USA
E-mail: joan123@frontiernet.net
Dist(s): **Perseus Distribution.**

Greyhound Bks., *(0-9724136; 1-59677)* 2000 Stock Creek Rd., Knoxville, TN 37920 USA Tel 865-405-3002
E-mail: cynmob@aol.com; editor@bushidopress.com
Web site: http://www.dogbooks.org.

Griffin Comics *Imprint of* **Corbett Features**

Griffin, Curtis Monroe, *(0-9749583)* 3250 Oneal Cir., Boulder, CO 80301-1424 USA.

Griffin Publishing *See* **Greater Truth Pubs.**

Griffin Publishing Group, *(1-58000; 1-882180)* 18022 Cowan, Suite 202, Irvine, CA 92614-6811 USA Toll Free: 800-472-9741 Do not confuse with Griffin Publishing, Ogden, UT
E-mail: griffinbooks@earthlink.net; mvonarx@griffinpublishing.com
Web site: http://www.griffinpublishing.com
Dist(s): **BHB Fullfillment**
Bridgeport Bks.
Perseus Distribution
Teacher Created Materials, Inc.

Griffin, Sandi Zambarano, *(1-883838)* 10840 Kimberfyld Ln., Port Saint Lucie, FL 34986 USA Tel 561-461-6830
Dist(s): **Bookazine Co., Inc.**

Griffith, John *See* **Rosetta Stone Communications**

Griggs Music Co., *(0-9753385)* 228 Pope Bend Rd., Cedar Creek, TX 78612 USA Tel 512-303-2744
Web site: http://www.griggsmusic.net.

Grigore, Julius Jr., *(0-9715805)* 425 Harbor Dr., S., Venice, FL 34285-2809 USA
E-mail: scadta@home.com.

Grigsby, Cynthia, *(0-9786840)* 108 Eames Ave., Fort Benning, GA 31905-6542 USA
E-mail: cgrigsby6@yahoo.com.

Griha, *(0-9748503)* 23 iron Bark Ln., Aliso Viejo, CA 92656 USA
Web site: http://www.griha.com.

Grijalbo, Editorial (MEX) *(968-419; 970-05) Dist. by* **Continental Bk.**

Grijalbo, Editorial (MEX) *(968-419; 970-05) Dist. by* **AIMS Intl.**

Grijalbo Mondadori, S.A.-Junior (ESP) *(84-253; 84-397; 84-7419; 84-478; 84-7423) Dist. by* **Continental Bk.**

Grijalbo Mondadori, S.A.-Junior (ESP) *(84-253; 84-397; 84-7419; 84-478; 84-7423) Dist. by* **Lectorum Pubns.**

Grijalbo Mondadori, S.A.-Junior (ESP) *(84-253; 84-397; 84-7419; 84-478; 84-7423) Dist. by* **Random.**

Grijalbo Mondadori, S.A.-Montena (ESP) *(84-7515; 84-85297; 84-8441) Dist. by* **Lectorum Pubns.**

Grijalbo-Dargaud, S.A. Editores (ESP) *(84-7510) Dist. by* **Distribks Inc.**

Grimes, Richard, *(0-9770594)* 111 Lankford Dr., Georgetown, KY 40324 USA.

Grim, Gary & Assocs., *(1-56490)* 82 S. Madison St., Carthage, IL 62321 USA Tel 217-357-3401; Fax: 217-357-6763; Toll Free: 800-442-1614 ; *Imprints:* Turning Two-Thousand (Turning Two Thousand)
E-mail: gga@adams.net.

Gripper Products, *(0-916176)* 787 N. 24th St., Philadelphia, PA 19130-2540 USA (SAN 206-3816) Tel 215-765-9362
E-mail: cormo@iname.com.

Griz Innovations, *(0-9719681)* 53 Rolling Hills Dr., Holland, PA 18966 USA Tel 215-579-2575
E-mail: rginieczki@cbsd.org.

Grizzly Adams Productions, Inc., *(0-9667985; 1-929296; 1-931602; 1-933424; 1-934646)* Orders Addr.: P.O. Box 298, Baker City, OR 97814 USA; Edit Addr.: 2850 Myrtle St., Baker City, OR 97814 USA
Dist(s): **STL Distribution North America.**

Grizzly Bks Publishing, *(0-9747951; 0-9749634)* Orders Addr.: PMB Box 136, Dahlonega, GA 30533 USA Tel 706-864-2349 (phone/fax); Edit Addr.: 240 Wal-Mart Way, Dahlonega, GA 30533 USA
E-mail: ancient12@linkamerica.net
Web site: http://www.grizzlybookz.com.

Grizzly Ridge Publishing, *(0-9793963)* P.O. Box 294, West Glacier, MT 59936 USA.

Grolier *Imprint of* **Scholastic Library Publishing**

Grolier Interactive, Inc., Div. of Scholastic, Inc., 90 Sherman Tpke., Danbury, CT 06816 USA Tel 203-797-3530 (Customer Service); Fax: 203-797-3657; Toll Free: 800-371-3908
E-mail: giorders@grolier.com
Web site: http://www.gi.grolier.com
Dist(s): **Learn Technologies Interactive, LLC.**

Grolier Online *Imprint of* **Scholastic Library Publishing**

Grolier Publishing *See* **Scholastic Library Publishing**

Grosinger, Crain Publishing, *(0-9720054)* Orders Addr.: P.O. Box 55, Mandan, ND 58554 USA Tel 701-663-0846 Toll Free: 877-566-2665; Edit Addr.: 210 Collins Ave., Mandan, ND 58554 USA
Web site: http://www.johnsbook.net
Dist(s): **Baker & Taylor Bks.**
Partners Bk. Distributing, Inc.

Gross, H. H., *(0-9754699)* P.O. Box 122606, San Diego, CA 92112 USA
E-mail: hhgross@lycos.com
Web site: http://www.hhgross.net.

Grosset & Dunlap *Imprint of* **Penguin Group (USA) Inc.**

Grote Publishing, *(0-9663436)* Div. of Grote Deutsch, Inc., 802 W. Broadway, Suite 306, Madison, WI 53713-1890 USA
E-mail: grotepub@mailbag.com.

Groundbreaking Pr., *(0-9718562; 0-9745624; 0-9765821; 0-9773535; 0-9777795; 0-9793542)* 8305 Arboles Circle, Austin, TX 78737 USA Tel 512-657-8780
E-mail: brad@groundbreaking.com
Web site: http://www.groundbreaking.com.

Groundwood Bks. (CAN) *(0-88899) Dist. by* **Perseus Dist.**

Groundwork Ideas Pr., *(0-9668013)* P.O. Box 117, Cambridge, MA 02238-0117 USA Tel 617-623-8080
E-mail: timesizing@Timesizing.com
Web site: http://www.Timesizing.com.

Group Books *See* **Group Publishing, Inc.**

†Group Publishing, Inc., *(0-7644; 0-931529; 0-936664; 1-55945)* Orders Addr.: P.O. Box 485, Loveland, CO 80539 USA (SAN 214-4689) Tel 970-669-3836; Fax: 970-679-4373; Toll Free: 800-635-0404; 800-447-1070 (consumer orders only); 800-541-5200 (trade orders only); Edit Addr.: 1515 Cascade Ave., Loveland, CO 80538 USA (SAN 662-1376) ; *Imprints:* Group's Active Bible Curriculum (Grps Active Bible Curr); Flagship Church Resources (Flagship Church)
E-mail: cbuxman@grouppublishing.com
Web site: http://www.grouppublishing.com
Dist(s): **Appalachian Bible Co.**
CRC Pubns.
Spring Arbor Distributors, Inc.
Twentieth Century Christian Bks.; *CIP.*

Group's Active Bible Curriculum *Imprint of* **Group Publishing, Inc.**

Grove Creek Publishing, LLC, *(1-933963)* 1159 N. 950 E., Pleasant Grove, UT 84062 USA Tel 801-471-5652
E-mail: noonws@yahoo.com
Web site: http://www.grovecreekpublishing.com.

Grove Educational Technologies, *(0-936735)* 6435 Yamhill St., SE, Portland, OR 97215-2027 USA (SAN 699-9840); 27 Hy Pl., Lake Grove, NY 11755 (SAN 699-9859)
E-mail: geta@juno.com.

Grove Pr. *Imprint of* **Grove/Atlantic, Inc.**

†Grove/Atlantic, Inc., *(0-8021; 0-87113; 1-55584)* 841 Broadway, 4th Flr., New York, NY 10003-4793 USA (SAN 201-4890) Tel 212-614-7850; Fax: 212-614-7886; Toll Free: 800-521-0178 ; *Imprints:* Grove Press (Grove); Atlantic Monthly Press (Atlntc Mnthly)
Web site: http://www.groveatlantic.com/
Dist(s): **Continental Bk. Co., Inc.**
Perseus Distribution
Sony CONNECT, Inc.; *CIP.*

Growing Field Bks., *(0-9770391)* 311 Belview Ct., Longmont, CO 80501 USA (SAN 851-7193) Do not confuse with companies with the same or similar name in Lawrence, KS
E-mail: Mhoog@growingfield.com
Web site: http://www.Growingfield.com
Dist(s): **Blu Sky Media Group.**

Growing Home, *(0-9637696)* P.O. Box 4596, Saint Paul, MN 55104-0596 USA Toll Free: 800-736-8967
E-mail: krantzjl@growinghome.org
Web site: http://www.growinghome.org.

Growing Ideas, L.L.C., *(0-9670375)* 15809 Ouray Rd., Pine Grove, CO 80470-9015 USA
E-mail: rickm@ldsi.com
Web site: http://www.growingideas.com.

Growing Little Readers, *(0-9777150)* 1105 Kyle Ct., Chesapeake, VA 23322 USA
Web site: http://growinglittlereaders.com.

Growing Up Great Productions, *(0-9659094)* 2280 Allan Dr., Florissant, MO 63033 USA Tel 314-921-3227
E-mail: newglo39@aol.com
Web site: http://www.circleoflovemusic.com
Dist(s): **Childbirth Graphics, Ltd.**
Icea Bk. Ctr.
Lamaze Media Ctr.
MMB Music, Inc.

Growing Years *Imprint of* **Port Town Publishing**

Growth Publishing, *(1-893505)* Div. of Growth Central LLC, 750 Columbus Ave., Suite 9S, New York, NY 10025 USA Tel 212-749-3684; Fax: 212-749-7872
E-mail: growth@growthgroups.com
Web site: http://www.growthcentral.com/.

Growth Unlimited, Inc., *(0-916927; 0-9601334)* 2430 Timber Oak Dr., Hillsborough, NC 27278-9680 USA (SAN 210-8976) Toll Free: 800-441-7676
E-mail: artfettig@aol.com
Web site: http://www.imasource.com.

GROWTHco, *(0-9715507)* 48 Bluefield Rd., Ashburnham, MA 01430 USA (SAN 254-2692) Tel 978-827-3133
E-mail: jimd@growthco.com
Web site: http://www.growthco.com.

Gruber Enterprises, *(0-9770413)* 21521 Finlan, Saint Clair Shores, MI 48080 USA
Web site: http://www.thelegendofthebrog.com.

Grubish, Donald, *(0-9771179)* 1326 Goodwin Ave N., Saint Paul, MN 55128-6164 USA.

Gruler, Monica, *(0-9711111)* P.O. Box 2095, Petoskey, MI 49770-2095 USA Tel 231-347-8591; Fax: 231-347-0409
E-mail: portprac@freeway.net.

Grupo Anaya, S.A. (ESP) *(84-207; 84-667) Dist. by* **Continental Bk.**

Grupo Anaya, S.A. (ESP) *(84-207; 84-667) Dist. by* **Lectorum Pubns.**

Grupo Anaya, S.A. (ESP) *(84-207; 84-667) Dist. by* **AIMS Intl.**

Grupo Anaya, S.A. (ESP) *(84-207; 84-667) Dist. by* **Distribks Inc.**

Grupo Anaya, S.A. (ESP) *(84-207; 84-667) Dist. by* **Libros Fronteras.**

Grupo Nelson, *(0-8499; 0-88113; 0-89922; 1-60255)* Div. of Thomas Nelson, Inc., 501 Nelson Pl., Nashville, TN 37217 USA (SAN 240-6349) Tel 615-889-9000; Fax: 615-883-9376; Toll Free: 800-251-4000
Web site: http://www.editorialcaribe.com
Dist(s): **Ediciones Universal**
Libros Sin Fronteras
Luciano Bks.
Nelson, Thomas Inc.
Pan De Vida Distributors
Peniel Productions
Twentieth Century Christian Bks.

Gryphon Hse., Inc., *(0-87659; 1-58904)* Orders Addr.: P.O. Box 207, Beltsville, MD 20704-0207 USA (SAN 169-3190) Tel 301-595-9500; Fax: 301-595-0051; Toll Free: 800-638-0928; Edit Addr.: 10726 Tucker St., Beltsville, MD 20705 USA ; *Imprints:* Robins Lane Press (Robins Ln Pr)
E-mail: info@ghbooks.com
Web site: http://www.gryphonhouse.com
Dist(s): **Consortium Bk. Sales & Distribution.**

Gryphon Pr., The, *(0-940719)* 6808 Margarets Ln., Edina, MN 55439 USA Tel 952-941-5993; Fax: 952-941-6593
E-mail: eb6@earthlink.net
Dist(s): **Consortium Bk. Sales & Distribution.**

G.S. Enterprises of America Inc., *(0-9763141)* P.O. Box 776, Frankfort, KY 40602-0776 USA Tel 502-227-8226; Fax: 502-227-8223
E-mail: lstafford13@gmail.com
Web site: http://www.bedtimeboomer.com.

GS Publishers *See* **GSVQ Publishing**

GSD&M, *(0-9701853; 0-9722825; 0-9779211)* 828 W. Sixth St., Austin, TX 78703 USA (SAN 850-6388) Tel 512-242-4736
E-mail: maryellen_rasnick@gsdm.com
Web site: http://www.ideauniversitypress.com
Dist(s): **Greenleaf Book Group Pr.**

GSR Communications, *(0-9717507)* 6090 SW Elm Ave., Beaverton, OR 97005 USA
E-mail: gsr@teleport.com.

GSVQ Publishing, *(1-933156)* 1350 E. Flamingo Rd., Suite 50, Las Vegas, NV 89119-5263 USA Tel 866-347-9244 ; *Imprints:* VisionQuest Kids (VisionQuest Kids); Visikid Books (Visikid Bks)
E-mail: contactus@gsvisionquest.com
Web site: http://www.gsvisionquest.com; http://www.visikidbooks.com; herosallaround.com.

GT Bks. LLC, *(0-9765845)* 19 Housman Ct., Maplewood, NJ 07040-3006 USA
Web site: http://www.gtbooks.net.

GT Interactive Software, *(1-56893; 1-58869)* 417 Fifth Ave., New York, NY 10016 USA Tel 212-726-4243; Fax: 212-726-4204
E-mail: efierro@gtinteractive.com
Web site: http://gtinteractive.com.

Guardian Angel Publishing, *(0-9763990)* 415 Meadow View Dr., Lavon, TX 75166-1245 USA Do not confuse with companies with the same or similar name in Carby, OR, Saint Louis, MO
E-mail: admin@tommytellbooks.com
Web site: http://www.tommytellbooks.com.

Guardian Angel Publishing, Inc., *(1-933090)* 12430 Tesson Ferry Rd., No. 186, Saint Louis, MO 63128 USA Do not confuse with companies with same name in Canby, OR and Hubbard, OR., The Colony, TX
Web site: http://www.guardianangelpublishing.com.

Guardian of Truth Foundation, *(0-9620615; 1-58427)* Orders Addr.: P.O. Box 9670, Bowling Green, KY 42102 USA Tel 317-745-4708; Edit Addr.: 420 Old Morgantown Rd., Bowling Green, KY 42102 USA (SAN 249-4221)
E-mail: mikewillis1@compuserve.com.

Guardians of Order (CAN) *(0-9682431; 1-894525) Dist. by* **LPC Group.**

Guardians of Order (CAN) *(0-9682431; 1-894525) Dist. by* **PSI Ga.**

Guardsman Press *See* **Moondance Publishing**

Guastella Publications *See* **Tiny Paws Publishing**

Guernica Editions, Inc. (CAN) *(0-919349; 0-920717; 1-55071; 2-89135) Dist. by* **IPG Chicago.**

Company

Guevara, Alexis, *(0-9765663)* 1625 Palo Alto St., No. 208, Los Angeles, CA 90026 USA Tel 323-982-0032; Fax: 213-483-8573
E-mail: sa_guevara@msn.com.

Guia, Elizabeth, *(0-9764280)* 2956 Bird Ave. # 8, Miami, FL 33133-4542 USA
E-mail: eguiam@msn.com.

Guide to South Florida Off-Road Bicycling *See* **DeGraaf Publishing**

Guided Pen Pr., *(0-9701167)* 2937 Sombrero Ln., Fort Collins, CO 80525 USA (SAN 253-469X) Tel 970-225-1622 (phone/fax).

Guideline Pubns. Co., *(1-882951)* Div. of Marketing Support Services, Orders Addr.: P.O. Box 801094, Atlanta, GA 30101 USA Fax: 770-424-0778; Toll Free: 800-552-1076
E-mail: sales@guidelinepub.com
Web site: http://www.guidelinepub.com.

Guideposts *Imprint of* **Ideals Pubns.**

Guiding Horizons, *(0-9749763)* 2201 Heritage Crest Dr., Valrico, FL 33594-5120 USA
Web site: http://www.guidinghorizons.com.

Guidry Assocs., Inc., *(0-9724667)* P.O. Box 2280, Winchester, VA 22604 USA Tel 540-545-8800 ; *Imprints:* Who's Who In Sports (Who's Who In Sp)
E-mail: info@whoswhoinsports.com
Web site: http://www.whoswhoinsports.com.

Guild Pr. of Indiana *Imprint of* **Emmis Bks.**

Guild Press of Indiana, Incorporated *See* **Emmis Bks.**

Guilford Pubns., Inc., *(0-89862; 1-57230; 1-59385)* Orders Addr.: 72 Spring St., New York, NY 10012 USA (SAN 212-9442) Tel 212 431 9800; Fax: 212 966 6708; Toll Free: 800 365 7006
E-mail: info@guilford.com
Web site: http://www.guilford.com
Dist(s): **Red Toad Road Co.**
Sony CONNECT, Inc.

Guilty Mom Pr., *(0-9708415)* 172 Dolphin Cir., Marina, CA 93933 USA Tel 831-384-8459
E-mail: plumtckrd@aol.com
Dist(s): **One Small Voice Foundation.**

Guirard, Greg, *(0-9624778)* 1470A Bayou Mercier Rd., Saint Martinville, LA 70582 USA Tel 318-394-4631; Fax: 318-394-3536
E-mail: guirmart@bellsouth.net.

GuitarVoyager Inc., *(0-9785992)* 3616 Calvend Ln., Kensington, MD 20895 USA Tel 240-486-3849; Fax: 301-949-1647
E-mail: guitarvoyager@gmail.com
Web site: http://www.guitarvoyager.com.

Gulaab (ESP) *(84-86797) Dist. by* **LD Bks Inc.**

Gulf War Pr., *(0-9701105)* Cmr 451 Box 51, APO, NY 09708 USA Tel 354-421-4527 (phone/fax)
E-mail: johnfdubose@yahoo.com
Web site: http://www.yahoo.geocities/johnfrancys.com.

Gullah Heritage Consulting Services, *(0-9726597)* P.O. Box 22136, Hilton Head Island, SC 29926 USA Tel 843-681-3059; Fax: 843-681-5836
E-mail: eesjc@aol.com.

Gulliver Bks. *Imprint of* **Harcourt Children's Bks.**

GumShoe Press, *(0-9777538)* Orders Addr.: P.O. Box 227 Bentley Hill Dr, Reisterstown, MD 21136 USA Tel 410-526-6766; Edit Addr.: 227 Bentley Hill Dr., Reisterstown, MD 21136 USA (SAN 850-1769) Tel 410-526-6766
E-mail: sunbed007@aol.com
Web site: http://www.authorsden.com/tjperkins.

Gunsmoke *Imprint of* **BBC Audiobooks America**

Guppy Publishing LLC, *(0-9788553)* PMB 221, 6749 S. Westnedge, Suite K, Portage, MI 49002 USA Fax: 269-327-3168
E-mail: dkennis@charter.net
Web site: http://www.guppypublishing.com.

Gurevich, Leonid, *(0-9753458)* 254 Morris Ave., Providence, RI 02906-2424 USA Tel 401-751-1924
E-mail: lgurev3007@aol.com.

Gurnik, Karen, *(0-9708785)* Orders Addr.: 389 E. Essex Dr., Slidell, LA 70461 USA
E-mail: kgurnik@netzero.net
Web site: http://www.BigRedCraftBook.com.

Guru Graphics, *(0-9729759)* 500 Creekside Ct., Golden, CO 80403-1903 USA Tel 303-278-0177
E-mail: levropes@attbi.com.

Gurze Bks., *(0-936077)* Orders Addr.: P.O. Box 2238, Carlsbad, CA 92018 USA (SAN 697-0818) Tel 760-434-7533; Fax: 760-434-5476; Toll Free: 800-756-7533; Edit Addr.: 5145-B Avenida Encinas, Carlsbad, CA 92018 USA (SAN 697-0826)
E-mail: gurze@aol.com; qzcati@aol.com
Web site: http://www.gurze.com
Dist(s): **Perseus Distribution**
Quality Bks., Inc.

Gustav's Library, *(0-9758914)* 1011 E. High St., Davenport, IA 52803 USA Tel 563-323-2283
E-mail: gustav@gustavslibrary.com
Web site: http://www.gustavslibrary.com.

Gutenberg-Richter Pubns. *Imprint of* **NAPSAC Reproductions**

GW Publishing (GBR) *(0-9535397; 0-9546701; 0-9551564) Dist. by* **Wlsn Assocs.**

GWR Pr., *(1-928970)* 14220 SW Rochester Dr., Beaverton, OR 97008-4982 USA Tel 503-646-6322 (phone/fax)
E-mail: garyre@jps.net.

GW's Expeditions, *(0-9713621)* 1313 Darrow Ave., Evanston, IL 60201-4019 USA Tel 847-328-4227 (phone/fax)
E-mail: geowood_01@netzero.net
Web site: http://redeemingblood.org.

Gye Nyame Hse., *(1-886098)* Orders Addr.: P.O. Box 42248, Philadelphia, PA 19101 USA (SAN 299-0415) Tel 215 229 1751; Edit Addr.: 6810 Old York Rd., Philadelphia, PA 19126 USA Tel 215-548-2175
E-mail: gyenyamehouse@aol.com.

Gye Nyame Pr., *(0-9796679)* 860 Johnson Ferry Rd., Suite 140-345, Atlanta, GA 30342 USA (SAN 854-0535) Tel 404-808-0458.

Gypsy Hill Publishing Co., *(0-9742805)* 8300 Baron's Ct., Williamsburg, VA 23188 USA
Web site: http://www.bramblethicket.com
Dist(s): **AtlasBooks Distribution.**

H & H Design, *(0-9707705)* P.O. Box 2588, Wichita Falls, TX 76307 USA Tel 940-723-1110
E-mail: hesterputney@earthlink.net.

H&R Magic Bks., *(0-9727938)* 3839 Liles Ln., Humble, TX 77396 USA Tel 281-540-7229
Web site: http://www.magicbookshop.com.

HB&C Pr., *(0-9671864)* 405 Taylor Dr., Forsyth, GA 31029 USA Tel 912-994-4978
E-mail: AndyAdsit@aol.com.

HEC Software, Inc., *(0-928424)* 60 N. Cutler Dr., No. 101, North Salt Lake, UT 84054 USA (SAN 669-6201) Tel 801-295-7054; Fax: 801-295-7088; Toll Free: 800-333-0054
E-mail: info@readinghorizons.com
Web site: http://www.readinghorizons.com.

HH Krsna Balaram Swami, *(0-9631403)* Orders Addr.: P.O. Box 27127, Baltimore, MD 21230 USA; Edit Addr.: 1613 Webster St., Baltimore, MD 21230 USA Tel 301-752-7531.

H I N, Incorporated *See* **Health InfoNet, Inc.**

HLH Ministries, *(0-9700985)* P.O. Box 463, Candler, FL 32111-0463 USA Fax: 352-687-1164
E-mail: CandlerSL@aol.com.

HMS Pubns., Inc., *(1-888732)* P.O. Box 524, Niantic, CT 06357 USA Tel 860-739-3187; Toll Free: 888-739-3187
E-mail: hmspublications@earthlink.net
Dist(s): **Baker & Taylor Bks.**
Quality Bks., Inc.

HMW Pubns., *(0-9652173)* 3957 W. Greenwood St., Springfield, MO 65807 USA Tel 417-889-8416
E-mail: hiltrud@pcis.net
Web site: http://www.pcis.net/hwebber
Dist(s): **DDDD Pubns.**

H P Pubns., LTD, *(1-929771)* P.O. Box 24155, Hilton Head Island, SC 22925 USA Tel 843-816-6626
E-mail: dbmouser@adelphia.net; ffna@adelphia.net; louperella@hargray.com; ffna@hargray.com
Web site: http://www.harrypotterusa.com; http://www.flyfishingnorthamerica.com.

H R M Software *See* **Human Relations Media**

H. R. Publishing *See* **Urban Thought Bks., Inc.**

Haag Environmental Press *See* **Haag Pr.**

Haag Pr., *(0-9665497; 0-9710260; 0-9797511)* Div. of Haag Environmental Co., Inc., Orders Addr.: 315 E. Market St., Sandusky, OH 44870 USA (SAN 852-6583) Tel 419-621-9329; Fax: 419-621-8669
E-mail: haagpress@aol.com; help@haagpress.com
Web site: http://www.haagpress.com
Dist(s): **Ingram Bk. Co.**

Haan Graphic Publishing Services, Limited *See* **Southfarm Pr.**

Haber-Schaim & Associates *See* **Science Curriculum, Inc.**

Hability Solution Services, Inc., *(1-932062)* P.O. Box 2595, Kearney, NE 68848 USA Tel 308-338-9238; Fax: 308-338-9208; Toll Free: 888-814-3238
E-mail: info@habsol.com; info@ideamagicbooks.com
Web site: http://www.habsol.com; http://www.ideamagicbooks.com.

Habitat Pubns., *(0-9665625)* 599 Saint Leonards Rd., Southampton, PA 18966 USA Tel 215-860-7457; Fax: 215-860-5863.

Hachai Publications, Incorporated *See* **Hachai Publishing**

Hachai Publishing, *(0-922613; 1-929628)* 527 Empire Blvd., Brooklyn, NY 11225 USA (SAN 251-3749) Tel 718-633-0100; Fax: 718-633-0103 ; *Imprints:* Tzivos Hashem (Tzivos Hashem)
E-mail: info@hachai.com
Web site: http://www.hachai.com
Dist(s): **Kerem Publishing.**

Hachette Bk. Group, *(0-446)* Orders Addr.: 3 Center Plaza, Boston, MA 02108 USA (SAN 852-5463) Tel 617-263-1828; Toll Free Fax: 800-286-9471; Toll Free: 800-759-0190; Edit Addr.: 1271 Avenue of the Americas, New York, NY 10019 USA Tel 212-522-7200; Fax: 212-522-7991; Toll Free Fax: 800-477-5925; P.O. Box 2146, Johannesburg, 2196 Tel 2711 783-7565; Fax: 2711 883-6866
Web site: http://www.hbgusa.com
Dist(s): **Sony CONNECT, Inc.**

Hachette Groupe Livre (FRA) *(2-01) Dist. by* **Distribks Inc.**

†Hackett Publishing Co., Inc., *(0-87220; 0-915144; 0-915145; 1-60384)* Orders Addr.: P.O. Box 44937, Indianapolis, IN 46244-0937 USA (SAN 201-6044) Tel 317-635-9250; Fax: 317-635-9292; Toll Free Fax: 800-783-9213
E-mail: customer@hackettpublishing.com
Web site: http://www.hackettpublishing.com; *CIP.*

Hacking, Vickie, *(0-9753371; 1-933659)* 425 S. 400 E. BSMT, Orem, UT 84097 USA Tel 801-222-9705
E-mail: ywbooks@yahoo.com
Web site: http://www.1ds-yw.com.

Hackleman, Sharon, *(0-9715345)* 6291 Kipapa Rd., Kapaa, HI 96746 USA
Web site: http://www.marionthemagnet.com.

Hadassah Investments, Inc., *(0-9661602; 1-928654)* Orders Addr.: P.O. Box 641463, Chicago, IL 60664 USA Tel 773-928-0063; Fax: 773-264-0363; Edit Addr.: 118 E. 120th Pl., No. C, Chicago, IL 60664 USA.

Hadrosaur Pr., *(1-885093)* P.O. Box 2194, Mesilla Park, NM 88047-2194 USA Tel 505-527-4163 ; *Imprints:* LBF/Hadrosaur (LBF Hadrs)
E-mail: hadrosaur@zianet.com
Web site: http://www.hadrosaur.com.

Hafabanana Pr., *(0-9761128; 1-934486)* Div. of Three Post, Inc., Orders Addr.: 2400 Greenwood, Channing, TX 79018 USA Fax: 806-235-2436; P.O. Box 55, Channing, TX 79018 Tel 806-235-3796; Fax: 806-235-2436
E-mail: editor@hafabanana.com
Web site: http://www.hafabananabookstore.com; http://www.hafabanana.com.

Hagan, Theda *See* **Hagan, Theda Bks.**

Hagan, Theda Bks., *(0-9678032)* 47 Comer Dr., Madisonville, KY 42431 USA Tel 270-821-6968
E-mail: thedahagan@yahoo.com
Web site: http://www.heavenlyharborbooks.com/default.htm.

Hagen Publishing, *(0-9704303)* 403 N. Niagara St., Burbank, CA 91505 USA Fax: 213-489-1081
E-mail: khagen2@excite.com.

Hahn, Beverly, *(0-9722494)* Orders Addr.: P.O. Box 66, Hilmak, CA 95324 USA; Edit Addr.: 9613 Ailanthus Ave., Delhi, CA 95315 USA (SAN 254-7376).

Hairball Pr., *(0-9646781)* 2318 2nd Ave., Suite 591, Seattle, WA 98121 USA Tel 206-932-8173.

Hairston Enterprises, LLC, *(0-9762958)* 582 Bristol Ln., Birmingham, AL 35226 USA Tel 205-369-4022
E-mail: kchairston@yahoo.com
Web site: http://www.forgottenrules.com; http://www.forgottenrules.org; http://www.theforgottenrules.com; http://www.theforgottenrules.org
Dist(s): **Appalachian Bk. Distributors.**

Hairston, Rodney, *(0-9760689)* 132 Moses Milch Dr., Howell, NJ 07731 USA
E-mail: rhairston@jbmanagement.com.

Haislip, Allen, *(0-9767640)* Orders Addr.: 16 Saint Lawrence Dr., Florissant, MO 63031 USA Tel 314-838-4514.

Haiti World, *(0-9793039)* P.O. Box 5663, Vernon Hills, IL 60061 USA Tel 847-514-9967
E-mail: haitiworld@yahoo.com.

Halbur Publishing, *(0-9603520)* 142 Angela Dr., Santa Rosa, CA 95403-1702 USA (SAN 212-9469)
E-mail: dhalbur@sonic.net.

Halcyon Pr., *(0-941970)* 18-05 215 St., Flushing, NY 11360 USA (SAN 238-244X) Tel 212-631-9640 Do not confuse with companies with same or similar name in Hendersonville, NC, Dallas, TX, Houston, TX.

Halcyon Pr., Ltd., *(0-9706054; 1-931823)* 2656 South Loop West, Suite 440, Houston, TX 77054 USA (SAN 253-9934) Tel 713-774-5786; Fax: 713-774-5788; Toll Free: 866-774-5786 Do not confuse with companies with same or similar name in Hendersonville, NC, Flushing, NY, Dallas, TX
E-mail: david.raley@gmail.com
Web site: http://www.halcyonpress.com
Dist(s): **Book Marketing Plus.**

Hale & Iremonger Pty., Ltd. (AUS) *(0-908094; 0-86806; 0-949818) Dist. by* **Empire Pub Srvs.**

Hale Kuamo'o Hawaiian Language Ctr. at UHH, *(0-9665331; 1-930339; 0-9741580)* Div. of Ka Haka 'Ula o Ke'elikolani/College of Hawaiian Language at UH Hilo, 200 W. Kawili St., Hilo, HI 96720-4091 USA Tel 808-974-7339; Fax: 808-974-7686
E-mail: contact@ahapunanaleo.org
Web site: http://www.olelo.hawaii.edu; http://www.ahapunanaleo.org.

Hale Publishing, *(0-9636219; 0-9729583; 0-9772268)* 1712 N. Forest St., Amarillo, TX 79106 USA Tel 806-376-9900; Fax: 806-376-9901; Toll Free Fax: 800-378-1317
E-mail: books@ibreastfeeding.com
Web site: http://www.ibreastfeeding.com.

Hale, Robert Ltd. (GBR) *(0-7090; 0-7091; 0-7198; 0-85131) Dist. by* **Trafalgar.**

Hale, Robert Ltd. (GBR) *(0-7090; 0-7091; 0-7198; 0-85131) Dist. by* **IPG Chicago.**

Haley's, *(0-9626308; 1-884540)* Orders Addr.: P.O. Box 248, Athol, MA 01331 USA Tel 978-249-9400 (phone/fax); Toll Free: 800-215-8805 (phone/fax); Edit Addr.: 488 S. Main St., Athol, MA 01331 USA
E-mail: haley.antique@verizon.net
Web site: http://www.mattawasongcycle.com; http://www.haleysantiques.com
Dist(s): **Follett Library Resources.**

Half Halt Pr., *(0-939481)* Orders Addr.: P.O. Box 67, Boonsboro, MD 21713-0067 USA (SAN 663-270X) Tel 301-733-7119; Fax: 301-733-7408
E-mail: mail@halfhaltpress.com
Web site: http://www.halfhaltpress.com.

Half-Pint Kids, Inc., *(1-59256)* 820 Walnut Dr., Ellwood City, PA 16117 USA
Web site: http://halfpintkids.com.

Hall & Humphries Publishing Hse., *(0-9758521)* Orders Addr.: P.O. Box 371021, Decatur, GA 30037-1021 USA; Edit Addr.: 2652 Rainbow Pkwy., Decatur, GA 30034 USA Tel 404-625-4486.

Hall, Floriana, *(0-9701600)* 1232 Clifton Ave., Akron, OH 44310 USA Tel 330-928-8492
E-mail: HAFLORIA@cs.com
Web site: http://home.earthlink.net/~flossie102/flossiesbooknook.html.

Hall, G. K., & Co. *Imprint of* **Thomson Gale**

Hall, Monique P. Productions, *(0-9772634)* 8400 Stonebrook Pkwy. Apt. 434, Frisco, TX 75034-5571 USA; 167 Wyatt Earp Loop, Nolanville, TX 76559 (SAN 851-6391) Tel 254-698-5965
E-mail: m.hall777@earthlink.net; inhiscare777@comcast.net
Web site: httn://www.m.hall777.@rarthlink.net.

Hall, Nancy Inc., *(1-884270)* 7 W. 18th St., 6th Flr., New York, NY 10011 USA Tel 212-674-3408; Fax: 212-353-1521
E-mail: Nhallinc@aol.com.

Hall Press *See* **Hallcienda**

Hall, Stephen & Denise, *(0-9753305)* 404 Augusta Pl., Union, MO 63084-4468 USA
E-mail: wordsofahunter@cs.com.

Hallcienda, *(0-932218)* Orders Addr.: P.O. Box 5375, San Bernardino, CA 92412 USA (SAN 211-7061) Tel 909-887-3466; Edit Addr.: 17227 Hall Ranch Rd., San Bernardino, CA 92407 USA (SAN 665-7060).

Hallelujah Publishing Co., L.L.C., *(0-9743937)* Orders Addr.: P.O. Box 468, Norwood, CO 81423 USA Tel 970-327-0422 (phone/fax); Edit Addr.: 1533 Grand Ave., Norwood, CO 81423 USA
E-mail: rminc@telluridecolorado.net
Web site: http://www.teatwerps.com.

Haller Company, The, *(0-9743961)* Orders Addr.: P.O. Box 207, Burlingame, CA 94010 USA Tel 650-348-3900; Fax: 650-558-9012; Edit Addr.: 1325 Howard Ave., Burlingame, CA 94010 USA
Web site: http://www.hallercompany.com.

Hallmark Emporium, *(0-9665055)* 9201 Russell Ave., S., Bloomington, MN 55431 USA Tel 612-884-2601; Fax: 612-703-0218
E-mail: dead541@aol.com
Web site: http://members.aol.com/dead 541/index.html.

†Halo Bks., *(0-9622874; 1-879904)* 73691 Sawmill Canyon Way, Palm Desert, CA 92260 USA (SAN 200-3147)
E-mail: halobks@yahoo.com
Web site: http://www.teenagesurvivalmanual.com; *CIP.*

Halo Publishing International, *(0-9718350; 0-9797429)* 6415 Granger Rd., Independence, OH 44131 USA
Web site: http://www.halopublishing.com.

Hamill Publishing Co., *(0-9715134)* Orders Addr.: P.O. Box 1713, Collins, MS 39428 USA Tel 601-765-4329; Fax: 601-765-8900; Toll Free: 888-207-1596; Edit Addr.: 215 R. McQueen Rd., Collins, MS 39428 USA
E-mail: abobnett@aol.com.

Hamilton Assocs., *(0-9649954)* Orders Addr.: P.O. Box 681, Vienna, VA 22183 USA (SAN 298-8917) Tel 703-620-3960 (phone/fax); Edit Addr.: 11318 Hunt Farm Ln., Suite 200, Oakton, VA 22124 USA Do not confuse with companies with the same or similar name in Columbia, MD , Phoenix, AZ.

Hamilton Ministries *See* **DCTS Publishing**

Hamilton's, *(0-9608598; 1-883912)* Orders Addr.: P.O. Box 932, Bedford, VA 24523 USA (SAN 264-0759) Tel 540-586-5592; Fax: 540-586-6235; Edit Addr.: 155 W. Main St., Bedford, VA 24523 USA
E-mail: otterv@aol.com
Web site: http://www.peterv.com.

Hamish Hamilton *Imprint of* **Penguin Group (USA) Inc.**

Hamline Univ. Pr., *(0-9633686; 0-9723721; 1-934458)* 1536 Hewitt Ave., MS-C1916, Saint Paul, MN 55104-2490 USA
E-mail: bhansonhegg01@hamline.edu
Web site: http://www.hamline.edu.

Hammond, Incorporated *See* **Hammond World Atlas Corp.**

Hammond, Roger, *(0-9763822)* 4915 Avon Ln., Sarasota, FL 34238 USA
Web site: http://www.pelithepelican.com.

†Hammond World Atlas Corp., *(0-7230; 0-8437)* Subs. of Langenscheidt Pubs., Inc., 193 Morris Ave., Springfield, NJ 07081-1211 USA (SAN 202-2702)
E-mail: rstrung@americanmap.com
Web site: http://www.Hammondmap.com
Dist(s): **Langenscheidt Pubs Inc.**; *CIP.*

Hampshire Hse. Publishing, *(0-9636814)* 8 Nonotuck St., Florence, MA 01060 USA Tel 413-584-1706
E-mail: hamphouse@attbi.com
Web site: http://www.hampshirehousepub.com.

Hampton Roads Publishing Co., Inc., *(0-9624375; 1-57174; 1-878901)* Orders Addr.: 1125 Stoney Ridge Rd., Charlottesville, VA 22902 USA (SAN 299-8874) Tel 434-296-2772; Fax: 434-296-1441; Toll Free Fax: 800-766-9042; Toll Free: 800-766-8009
E-mail: hrpc@hrpub.com
Web site: http://www.hamptonroadspub.com.

Hampton-Brown Bks., *(0-7362; 0-917837; 1-56334)* Orders Addr.: P.O. Box 369, Marina, CA 93933 USA Tel 408-384-9695; Fax: 408-384-8940; Edit Addr.: 26385 Carmel Rancho Blvd., Suite 200, Carmel, CA 93923 USA (SAN 657-145X) Tel 408-625-3666; Fax: 408-625-8619; Toll Free: 800-933-3510
Web site: http://www.hampton-brown.com.

Hamster Huey Pr., *(0-9749090)* 7627 84th Ave., Ct., NW, Gig Harbor, WA 98335-6237 USA Tel 253-851-7839; Fax: 253-853-3493
E-mail: phs@oz.net
Web site: http://www.hamsterhueypress.com.

Hamster Pr., *(0-9645669; 0-9724630)* Orders Addr.: P.O. Box 27471, Seattle, WA 98125 USA Fax: 206-363-2878
E-mail: hamstrpres@aol.com
Web site: http://www.billschelly.com
Dist(s): **Diamond Comic Distributors, Inc.**
FM International
Syco Distribution.

†Hancock Hse. Pubs., *(0-88839; 0-919654)* 19313 Zero Ave., Surrey, BC V3S 9R9 CAN; 1431 Harrison Ave., Blaine, WA 98230-5005 (SAN 665-7079) Tel 604-538-1114; Fax: 604-538-2262; Toll Free Fax: 800-983-2262; Toll Free: 800-938-1114
E-mail: sales@hancockhouse.com
Web site: http://www.hancockhouse.com
Dist(s): **Baker & Taylor Bks.**; *CIP.*

Hancock Hse. Pubs., Ltd. (CAN) *(0-88839; 0-919654; 1-55205) Dist. by* **Hancock House.**

Hand Print Pr., *(0-9679846)* Orders Addr.: P.O. Box 576, Blodgett, OR 97326 USA Tel 541-438-4300; Edit Addr.: 395 Grant Creek Rd., Eddyville, OR 97343 USA
E-mail: kiko@handprintpress.com; potlatch@cmug.com
Web site: http://www.handprintpress.com
Dist(s): **Chelsea Green Publishing.**

Hand-In-Hand Bks. *Imprint of* **Introspect Bks.**

H&M Systems Software, Inc., *(1-885936)* 600 E. Crescent Ave., Suite 203, U Saddle Riv, NJ 07458-1846 USA Toll Free: 800-327-3713 ; *Imprints:* StudioLine Photo (StudioLine)
E-mail: Info@HM-Software.com
Web site: http://www.Gameware.com; http://www.HM-Software.com; http://www.StudioLine.biz
Dist(s): **Victory Multimedia.**

Handprint Bks., *(1-929766; 1-59354)* 413 Sixth Ave., Brooklyn, NY 11215-3310 USA
E-mail: publisher@handprintbooks.com
Web site: http://www.handprintbooks.com
Dist(s): **Chronicle Bks. LLC.**

Hands On Crafts For Kids, *(1-891514)* 7079 Navajo Trl., Solon, OH 44139-5845 USA
E-mail: info@craftsforkids.com
Web site: http://www.craftsforkids.com.

Hands to the Plow, Inc., *(1-930914)* P.O. Box 567, Webster, WI 54893 USA Tel 715-349-7185
E-mail: tomkelby@handstotheplow.org
Web site: http://www.handstotheplow.org.

Hands-On Pr., *(0-9669009)* 25060 Hancock Ave. ,103 Suite 385, Murrieta, CA 92562 USA
E-mail: haasmjbc@iinet.com.

Handwriting Without Tears *See* **Handwriting Without Tears, Inc.**

Handwriting Without Tears, Inc., *(1-891627; 1-934825)* 8001 Macarthur Blvd., Cabin John, MD 20818-1607 USA Tel 301-263-2700; Fax: 301-263-2707; Toll Free: 888-983-8409
Web site: http://www.hwtears.com.

Hanky Kids, *(1-929501)* 1070 Erica Dr., Wauconda, IL 60084 USA Tel 847-487-8440
E-mail: Beth@HankyKids.com
Web site: http://www.HankyKids.com.

Hann, David *See* **HannsKansasbooks**

Hanna Publishing, *(0-9650634)* 2315-10 N. Pearl St., Suite 160, Tacoma, WA 98406-2500 USA Tel 206-596-1634; Toll Free: 800-444-2524 (orders only).

Hannacroix Creek Bks., Inc., *(1-889262)* 1127 High Ridge Rd., No. 110, Stamford, CT 06905-1203 USA (SAN 299-9560) Tel 203-321-8674; Fax: 203-968-0193
E-mail: Hannacroix@aol.com
Web site: http://www.hannacroix.com
Dist(s): **Baker & Taylor Bks.**
Book Clearing Hse.
Book Hse., Inc., The
Brodart Co.
Follett Library Resources
Midwest Library Service
Quality Bks., Inc.
Replica Bks.
Unique Bks., Inc.

Hannah Mae Enterprises, Inc., *(0-9671111)* 50 Pondview Dr., Springfield, MA 01118-1145 USA Tel 413-737-3005.

Hannel Educational Consulting, *(0-9764776)* 1131 W. Palm Ln., Phoenix, AZ 85007-1536 USA Tel 602-524-7647; Fax: 602-253-2693
Web site: http://www.hannel.com.

Hannibal Bks., *(0-929292; 1-934749)* Div. of KLMK Communications, Inc., Orders Addr.: P.O. Box 461592, Garland, TX 75046-1592 USA Toll Free Fax: 888-252-3022; Toll Free: 800-747-0738
E-mail: hannibalbooks@earthlink.net; orders@hannibalbooks.com; louismoore@hannibalbooks.com
Web site: http://www.hannibalbooks.com
Dist(s): **Lightning Source, Inc.**
Spring Arbor Distributors, Inc.

HannsKansasbooks, *(0-9626038)* 1640 New Hampshire, Lawrence, KS 66044 USA Tel 913-843-2787.

Hanrow Pr., *(0-9703549; 0-9720075)* Div. of Hanrow House Corp., Orders Addr.: P.O. Box 502902, Ocala, FL 34477 USA Tel 352-236-5588; Fax: 858-756-2922; Toll Free: 800-235 5588; P.O. Box 770582, Ocala, FL 34477 Tel 352-236-5588; Edit Addr.: 12112F Royal Birkdale Row, San Diego, CA 92128 USA
E-mail: heg101@msn.com
Web site: http://www.hanrowpress.com; http://www.trialtechniques.com.

Hansen, Charles Educational Music & Bks., Inc., *(0-8494)* 1820 West Ave., Miami Beach, FL 33139 USA (SAN 205-0609) Tel 305-532-5461; Fax: 305-672-8729
E-mail: khansen507@aol.com
Web site: http://www.hansenpublications.com/
Dist(s): **Hansen Hse.**

Hansen, Diane, *(0-9761988)* P.O. Box 1051, Redondo Beach, CA 90278 USA Tel 310-379-8006
Web site: http://thosearemyprivateparts.com.

Hansen, Marc Stuff!, *(0-9794643)* P.O. Box 166, Statesville, NC 28625 USA
E-mail: marchansenstuff@gmail.com
Web site: http://www.marchansenstuff.com.

Happy About, *(0-9633302; 1-60005)* 21265 Stevens Creek Blvd., Suite 205, Cupertino, CA 95014 USA Tel 408-257-3000
E-mail: info@happyabout.info
Web site: http://www.happyabout.info
Dist(s): **Baker & Taylor Bks.**
Ingram Bk. Co.
National Bk. Network
NetLibrary, Inc.
OverDrive, Inc.

Happy Bks. Pr., *(0-9787826)* 29877 Westhaven Dr., Agoura, CA 91301 USA Tel 818-879-1268
E-mail: ghuyette@charter.net; happybookspress@vrillustration.com
Web site: http://www.vrillustration.com.

Happy Cat Bks. (GBR) *(1-899248; 1-903285; 1-905117) Dist. by* **Star Brght Bks.**

Happy Hamster Press, The *See* **Imagination Workshop, The**

Happy Heart Kids Publishing, *(0-9763143)* Orders Addr.: 2912 Beane Rd., Lenoir, NC 28645-8653 USA (SAN 256-3029) Tel 828-302-9500; 828-754-4126 (phone/fax); Fax: 828-758-8409
E-mail: mshelen@charter.net
Web site: http://www.happyheartkids.com.

Happy Horse Publishing, Ltd., *(0-9727849)* Orders Addr.: P.O. Box 15767, Chevy Chase, MD 20825 USA Tel 301-589-8888; Edit Addr.: 5910 Connecticut Ave., Chevy Chase, MD 70875 USA
E-mail: eashe@happyhorse.us
Web site: http://www.happyhorsekids.com.

Happy Tales Pr. *Imprint of* **Creation of Celebration, Inc.**

Happy Viking Crafts, *(0-9740175)* Orders Addr.: P.O. Box 35, Mahomet, IL 61853 USA; Edit Addr.: 1001 Sunrise Cir., Mahomet, IL 61853-3536 USA Tel 217-586-2497.

Happy Women Publishing Co., *(0-9745627)* 11487 57th St E., Parrish, FL 34219-5818 USA
E-mail: hwp@toerrific.com
Web site: http://toerrific.com
Dist(s): **Continental Enterprises Group, Inc. (CEG).**

Happyland Media, *(0-9726418)* Orders Addr.: P.O. Box 20398, Castro Valley, CA 94546 USA; Edit Addr.: 20283 Santa Marie Ave., Castro Valley, CA 94546 USA
E-mail: info@happylandmedia.com
Web site: http://www.happylandmedia.com.

Harambee Pr., *(0-9769846)* P.O. Box 353, Macatawa, MI 49434 USA
Web site: http://www.harambeepress.com.

Harbinger Pr., *(0-9674736; 0-9723998)* 2711 Buford Rd. PMB 383, Richmond, VA 23235-2423 USA (SAN 299-9994) Do not confuse with companies with the same or similar names in Woodland Hills, CA, Corte Madera, CA
E-mail: keith@harbpress.com
Web site: http://www.harbpress.com.

Harbor Branch Oceanographic Institution, Inc., *(0-9659686)* 5600 U.S. 1, N., Fort Pierce, FL 34946 USA Tel 772-465-2400; Fax: 772-468-0757
E-mail: mclark@hboi.edu
Web site: http://www.hboi.edu/marine/biolum.html.

Harbor Electronic Publishing, *(0-9669744; 0-9707039; 0-9740201; 1-932916)* c/o UNET 2 Corp., 80 E. 11th St., New York, NY 10003 USA Tel 212-777-5463; Fax: 212-777-5534; Toll Free: 800-269-6422
E-mail: JMonaco@UNET.net
Web site: http://www.readfilm.com; http://www.hepdigital.com; http://dvdlaser.com; http://peconic.org.

Harbor Hse., *(1-891799)* 111 Tenth St., Augusta, GA 30901 USA Tel 706-738-0354 (phone/fax) ; *Imprints:* Bat Wing Press (Bat Wing Pr)
E-mail: peggycheney@harborhousebooks.com; harborhouse@harborhousebooks.com
Web site: http://www.harborhousebooks.com.

Harbor Hse. Pubs., Inc., *(0-937360)* 221 Water St., Boyne City, MI 49712 USA (SAN 200-5751) Tel 616-582-2814; Fax: 616-582-3392; Toll Free: 800-491-1760
E-mail: harbor@harborhouse.com
Web site: http://www.harborhouse.com.

Harbor Island Bks., *(0-9741787)* 1214 W. Boston Post Rd., No. 245, Mamaroneck, NY 10543 USA (SAN 255-9137) Tel 914-420-9782; Fax: 914-835-7897
E-mail: publisher@lyingawake.net; hfurbush@earthlink.net
Web site: http://www.lyingawake.net/
Dist(s): **Baker & Taylor Bks.**
Partners/West.

Harbor Pr., Inc., *(0-936197)* Orders Addr.: P.O. Box 1656, Gig Harbor, WA 98335 USA (SAN 696-8953) Tel 253-851-5190; Fax: 253-851-5191; Edit Addr.: 5713 Wollochet Dr. NW, Gig Harbor, WA 98335 USA (SAN 696-8961) Do not confuse with companies with the same name in Friday Harbor, WA, Austin, TX, Ardmore, PA
E-mail: young2327@mindspring.com
Web site: http://www.harborpress.com
Dist(s): **National Bk. Network.**

Harbor View Publishing Co, *(0-9717984)* 71 Fort St., Fairhaven, MA 02719 USA Fax: 508-996-8403
E-mail: clopes7081@aol.com.

Harborseal Publishing Co., *(0-9652963; 0-9787308)* Orders Addr.: P.O. Box 126, Seal Cove, ME 04674-0126 USA Tel 207-244-7753; Edit Addr.: Rte. 102, Captain's Quarters Rd., Seal Cove, ME 04674 USA
Dist(s): **Magazines, Inc.**

HarborTown Histories, *(0-9710984)* 6 Harbor Way, Santa Barbara, CA 93109 USA
E-mail: baker@sbcc.net.

Harbour Arts, LLC, *(0-9778196)* 1790 Philippe Pkwy., Safety Harbor, FL 34695 USA
Web site: Harbourarts.com; mysite.verizon.net/resqx8xr.

Harbour Publishing Co., Ltd. (CAN) *(0-920080; 1-55017) Dist. by* **Gr Arts Ctr Pub.**

Harbourside Pr., *(0-9740552)* 7892 Sailboat Key Blvd., Suite 506, South Pasadena, FL 33707 USA Tel 727-543-5855
E-mail: harbours@harboursidepress.com
Web site: http://www.harboursidepress.com
Dist(s): **Baker & Taylor Bks.**
Greenleaf Book Group.

Harcourt Brace & Company *See* **Harcourt Trade Pubs.**

Harcourt Brace Jovanovich College Publishers *See* **Harcourt College Pubs.**

Harcourt Brace School Publishers *See* **Harcourt Schl. Pubs.**

Harcourt Children's Bks *Imprint of* **Harcourt Children's Bks.**

Harcourt Children's Bks., *(0-15)* Div. of Harcourt, Inc., Orders Addr.: 6277 Sea Harbor Dr., Orlando, FL 32887 USA Toll Free Fax: 800-235-0256; Toll Free: 800-543-1918; 465 S. Lincoln Dr., Troy, MO 63379 Toll Free Fax: 800-235-0266; Toll Free: 800-543-1918; Edit Addr.: 15 E. 26th St., 15th Flr., New York, NY 10010 USA Tel 212-592-1000; Fax: 212-592-1011; 525 B St., Suite 1900, San Diego, CA 92101 Tel 619-231-6616 ; *Imprints:* Green Light Readers (Green Light Read); Gulliver Books (Gulliver Bks); Harcourt Paperbacks (Harcourt Pbk); Harcourt Young Classics (Harcourt Young); Odyssey Classics (Odyssey Class); Red Wagon Books (Red Wagon Bks); Voyager Books/Libros Viajeros (Voyage Libros); Magic Carpet Books (Magic Carpet); Harcourt Children's Books (HCB)
E-mail: Andrew.porter@harcourt.com
Web site: http://www.HarcourtBooks.com
Dist(s): **Harcourt Trade Pubs.**

Harcourt College Pubs., *(0-03; 0-15)* Div. of Thomson Corp., The, Orders Addr.: 10650 Toebben Dr., Independence, KY 41051 USA (SAN 250-0086) Toll Free Fax: 800-487-8488 (customer service); Toll Free: 800-354-9706 (orders, inquiries); Edit Addr.: 801 Cherry St. Ste. 1300, Fort Worth, TX 76102-6810 USA (SAN 297-4789)
E-mail: wlittle@harbrace.com
Web site: http://www.harcourtcollege.com/
Dist(s): **CENGAGE Learning.**

†Harcourt Health Sciences Group, *(0-03; 0-15; 0-443; 0-7216)* Div. of Harcourt, Inc., 11830 Westline Industrial Dr., Saint Louis, MO 63146 USA Tel 314-872-8370; Toll Free Fax: 800-535-9935
Web site: http://www.harcourt-international.com
Dist(s): **Elsevier - Health Sciences Division**; *CIP.*

Harcourt Paperbacks *Imprint of* **Harcourt Children's Bks.**

Harcourt Religion Pubs., *(0-15; 0-936157)* Div. of Harcourt, Inc., Orders Addr.: 6277 Sea Harbor Dr., Orlando, FL 32887 USA Toll Free: 800-922-7696; Edit Addr.: 1665 Embassy W. Dr., Suite 200, Dubuque, IA 52002 USA Tel 319-557-3700; Fax: 319-557-3719; Toll Free: 800-922-7696
Web site: http://www.harcourtreligion.com
Dist(s): **ACTA Pubns.**

Harcourt Schl. Pubs., *(0-15)* Div. of Harcourt, Inc., 6277 Sea Harbor Dr., Orlando, FL 32887 USA (SAN 299-4585) Tel 407-345-2000; Fax: 407-352-3445; Toll Free Fax: 800-874-6418 (orders); Toll Free: 800-225-5425 (orders)
E-mail: hbspcs@harcourt.com
Web site: http://www.harcourtschool.com/.

†Harcourt Trade Pubs., *(0-15)* Div. of Harcourt, Inc., Orders Addr.: 6277 Sea Harbor Dr., Orlando, FL 32887 USA (SAN 200-285X) Tel 619-699-6707; Toll Free Fax: 800-235-0256; Toll Free: 800-543-1918 (trade orders, inquiries, claims); Edit Addr.: 525 B St., Suite 1900, San Diego, CA 92101-4495 USA (SAN 200-2736) Tel 619-231-6616; 15 E. 26th St., New York, NY 10010 Tel 212-592-1000; Fax: 212-592-1011 ; *Imprints:* Harvest Books (Harvest Bks); Silver Whistle (Silver Whistle)
E-mail: andrewporter@harcourt.com
Web site: http://www.HarcourtBooks.com
Dist(s): **Sony CONNECT, Inc.**; *CIP.*

Harcourt Young Classics *Imprint of* **Harcourt Children's Bks.**

hard girl bk. club, *(0-9748712)* 4143 S. Adelle, Mesa, AZ 85212 USA Tel 480-241-1351; Fax: 480-354-4727; Toll Free: 800-307-5261
E-mail: tkempton@cox.net
Web site: http://hardgirlbookclub.com.

Hard Pr. Editions, *(0-9638433; 1-889097)* Orders Addr.: P.O. Box 184, West Stockbridge, MA 01266 USA Tel 413-637-0079; Edit Addr.: 45 Walker St., West Stockbridge, MA 01240 USA
E-mail: jongams@cultureport.com
Web site: http://www.cultureport.com
Dist(s): **Antique Collectors' Club**
SPD-Small Pr. Distribution.

Hard Press, Incorporated *See* **Hard Pr. Editions**

Hard Shell Word Factory, *(1-58200; 0-7599)* Orders Addr.: P.O. Box 161, Amherst Junction, WI 54407 USA (SAN 631-4899) Tel 715-824-5542; Fax: 715-824-3875; Edit Addr.: 8941 Loberg Rd., Amherst Junction, WI 54407 USA
E-mail: books@hardshell.com; sales@hardshell.biz; support@hardshell.biz
Web site: http://www.hardshell.com
Dist(s): **Baker & Taylor Bks.**
BookSurge, LLC
News Group, The.

HardBound, Inc., *(0-9679662; 0-9719834; 0-9744237; 0-9749690)* 4280 Rider Trail N., Earth City, MO 63045 USA Tel 314-738-0303 (phone/fax)
Web site: http://www.bindabook.com
Dist(s): **Booksource, The.**

Hardenville SA (URY) *(9974-7799; 9974-7816; 84-96448; 84-933955) Dist. by* **IPG Chicago.**

Hardin Publishing, LLC, *(0-9742704)* 1380 W. Paces Ferry Rd., Suite 180, Atlanta, GA 30327 USA Tel 404-504-6619; Fax: 404-264-3583 Do not confuse with Hardin Publishing Company in Avera, GA
E-mail: proper@piedmont-atl.com; yntema@hardinpublishing.net
Web site: http://www.hardinpublishing.net.

Harding, A.R. Publishing Co., *(0-936622)* 2878 E. Main St., Columbus, OH 43209 USA (SAN 206-4936) Tel 614-231-9585.

Harding Hse. Publishing Sebice Inc., *(1-933630)* 201 Harding Ave., Vestal, NY 13850 USA Tel 607-785-1578; Fax: 607-786-9103 ; *Imprints:* Anamchara Books (Anamchara Bks)
E-mail: hardinghouse@stny.rr.com
Web site: http://www.hardinghousepages.com
Dist(s): **Baker & Taylor Bks.**

Harding Pr., Inc., *(0-9624779; 1-890450)* 123 Saratoga Rd., Box 323, Scotia, NY 12302 USA Tel 518-399-9955; Fax: 518-399-1673; Toll Free: 877-767-7114
E-mail: hardingpress@earthlink.net
Web site: http://www.hardingpress.com
Dist(s): **Baker & Taylor Bks.**

Hardman, Ann Ministries, Incorporated *See* **Hardman, Ann Publishings, LLC**

Hardman, Ann Publishings, LLC, *(0-9701937)* Div. of Ann Hardman Enterprises, LLC, P.O. Box 1512, Columbus, GA 31902-1512 USA Tel 706-323-6609; Fax: 706-323-9017
E-mail: ahardman@ahministries.net
Web site: http://www.faithtabernacle.net; http://www.ahministries.net; http://www.bishups.com.

Hardouin, Benny, *(0-9664731)* 2664 Arbor Chase Dr NE, Grand Rapids, MI 49525-9458 USA
E-mail: bhardouir@mcleodregional.org; safarislim@aol.com
Web site: http://mcleodregional.org; http://www.mcleodregional.org/safariscim/.

Hardtke Publishing Co., *(0-9718166)* 2217 Second Ave. E., No. 1, Hibbing, MN 55746-1966 USA (SAN 254-4601) Tel 218-262-6510
Web site: http://www.libertyandlove.com/.

Hardway Pr, *(0-9717148)* 16 W. Pacific Ave. No.3, Hendersen, NV 89015-7383 USA Tel 702-564-1665; Fax: 702-564-4190
Web site: http://www.brianrouff.com.

Hardy Hill Enterprises, Inc., *(1-890997)* P.O. Box 128, Syosset, NY 11791 USA Tel 516-921-4024; Fax: 516-364-5133
E-mail: JSchisgall@aol.com.

Hargroves, Ann *See* **Hargroves Publishing Co.**

Hargroves Publishing Co., *(0-9742277)* P.O. Box 985, Virginia Beach, VA 23451-0985 USA
Web site: http://www.annhhargroves.com.

Harlan Publishing Company *See* **Diakonia Publishing**

Harlem Writers Guild Pr. *Imprint of* **iUniverse, Inc.**

Harlequin Enterprises, Ltd. (CAN) *(0-373; 1-55166; 1-58314) Dist. by* **S and S Inc.**

Harlo Pr., *(0-8187)* 50 Victor Ave., Detroit, MI 48203 USA (SAN 202-2745) Tel 313-883-3600
Dist(s): **Mustard Seed Pubns.**

Harmony Hearth, LLC, *(0-9678871)* P.O. Box 341511, West Bethesda, MD 20827-1511 USA (SAN 253-3278)
E-mail: debbie@harmonyhearth.com
Web site: http://www.harmonyhearth.com.

Harmony Hse. Pubs., *(0-916509; 1-56469; 0-9677295)* Orders Addr.: P.O. Box 90, Prospect, KY 40059 USA (SAN 298-5446) Fax: 502-228-2010; Toll Free: 800-809-9334; Edit Addr.: 1008 Kent Rd., Goshen, KY 40026 USA (SAN 295-4257)
E-mail: harmonyhousepub@bellsouth.net
Web site: http://www.harmonyhousebooks.com.

Harmony Hse. Publishing Co., *(0-9725289)* P.O. Box 858, Rexburg, ID 83440 USA Tel 208-359-1595 (phone/fax)
E-mail: jaydef@cableone.net
Web site: http://www.debtfreestepbystep.com.

Harmony Institute, The, *(0-9701125)* Orders Addr.: P.O. Box 242, Jonesville, VT 05466 USA Fax: 518-338-0022 (Purchase orders)
E-mail: info@theharmonyinstitute.org
Web site: http://www.theharmonyinstitute.org/book
Dist(s): **New Leaf Distributing Co., Inc.**

Harmony Spirit Publishing Co., Inc., *(0-9762392)* 148 Westgate Dr., Saint Peters, MO 63376 USA
E-mail: lynowak@mail.win.org.

Harmony/Bell Tower *Imprint of* **Crown Publishing Group**

Harold, Elsie L., *(0-9764644)* 1701 Eleni Ct., Virginia Bch, VA 23453-2886 USA
E-mail: turtlelsie@aol.com.

Harold Pubns., Inc., *(0-9664638)* P.O. Box 189, Palm Beach, FL 33480-0189 USA Toll Free: 800-403-8850
E-mail: bonkers@goingbonkers.com
Web site: http://www.goingbonkers.com.

Harper, Angel Incorporated *See* **Heaven Sent Publishing**

Harper Entertainment *Imprint of* **HarperCollins Pubs.**

Harper Festival *Imprint of* **HarperCollins Pubs.**

Harper, Joel D., *(0-9714254)* P.O. Box 1123, Claremont, CA 91711-1123 USA
E-mail: freedomthree@hotmail.com
Web site: http://www.freedomthree.com.

Harper Paperbacks *Imprint of* **HarperCollins Pubs.**

Harper, Phyllis *See* **Fawn Grove Pr.**

Harper San Francisco *Imprint of* **HarperCollins Pubs.**

Harper Trophy *Imprint of* **HarperCollins Pubs.**

Harper, Vicky *See* **Little Bookstore Who Could, The**

Harper-Arrington Publishing, *(0-9764161)* 18701 Grand River Ave., 105, Detroit, MI 48223 USA Tel 313-283-4494; Fax: 248-281-0373; Toll Free: 888-435-9234
E-mail: info@harperarrringtonmedia.com
Web site: http://www.hapub.com/
Dist(s): **Baker & Taylor Bks.**

HarperChildren's Audio *Imprint of* **HarperCollins Pubs.**

HarperCollins *Imprint of* **HarperCollins Pubs.**

HarperCollins *Imprint of* **HarperCollins Pubs.**

†HarperCollins Pubs., *(0-00; 0-06; 0-380; 0-688; 0-690; 0-694; 0-7322; 0-87795; 1-55710)* Div. of News Corp., Orders Addr.: 1000 Keystone Industrial Pk., Scranton, PA 18512-4621 USA (SAN 215-3742) Tel 570-941-1500; Toll Free Fax: 800-822-4090; Toll Free: 800-242-7737 (orders only); Edit Addr.: 10 E. 53rd St., New York, NY 10022-5299 USA (SAN 200-2086) Tel 212-207-7000 ; *Imprints:* Julie Andrews Collection (Julie Andrews); Harper Trophy (HarperTrophy); Harper Festival (HarperFestival); Cotler, Joanna Books (JoCotler); Geringer, Laura Book (LauraGeringer); Greenwillow Books (GreenwillowBks); Avon (AvonChild); HarperCollins (HarperCollCh); HarperChildren's Audio (HarperChildAud); Tegen, Katherine Books (KTegenBooks); Harper San Francisco (HarperSanFran); Morrow, William &Company (WmMorrow); Avon Books (AvonBooks); Eos (Eos Harper); Harper Entertainment (HarperEntert); HarperCollins (HarperCollinsT); Harper Paperbacks (HarperPaper); Amistad (AmistadHarper); Rayo (Rayo Harper); ReganBooks (ReganBooks); Collins (Collins); Morrow Cookbooks, Wiillam (MorrowCookbks); Collins Design (CollinsDesign); HarperTeen (HarperTeen)
Web site: http://www.harpercollins.com; www.harpercollinschildrens.com
Dist(s): **Independent Pubs. Group**
NetLibrary, Inc.
Sony CONNECT, Inc.; *CIP.*

HarperCollins Pubs. (AUS) *(0-06; 0-207; 0-7322; 0-85835; 1-86256; 1-86371; 1-86378; 1-74050) Dist. by* **HarperCollins Pubs.**

HarperCollins Pubs. (AUS) *(0-06; 0-207; 0-7322; 0-85835; 1-86256; 1-86371; 1-86378; 1-74050) Dist. by* **Consort Bk Sales.**

HarperCollins Pubs. Ltd. (GBR) *(0-00; 0-06; 0-246; 0-261; 0-586) Dist. by* **Trafalgar.**

HarperCollins Pubs. Ltd. (GBR) *(0-00; 0-06; 0-246; 0-261; 0-586) Dist. by* **IPG Chicago.**

HarperCollins Pubs. New Zealand (NZL) *(1-86950) Dist. by* **Consort Bk Sales.**

HarperCollins Pubs. New Zealand (NZL) *(1-86950) Dist. by* **Antipodes Bks.**

HarperTeen *Imprint of* **HarperCollins Pubs.**

Harpswell Pr. *Imprint of* **Tilbury Hse. Pubs.**

Harrington, Denis J. Pub., *(0-9672290)* 6207 Fushsimi Ct., Burke, VA 22015-3451 USA.

Harrington Park Pr. *Imprint of* **Haworth Pr., Inc., The**

Harris, Candice *See* **Harris, K Publishing, Inc.**

Harris Communications, Inc., *(0-9727520)* 15155 Technology Dr., Eden Prairie, MN 55344-2277 USA (SAN 255-0512) Tel 952-906-1180; Fax: 952-906-1099; Toll Free: 800-825-6758
E-mail: mail@harriscomm.com
Web site: http://www.harriscomm.com.

Harris, H. E. & Company *See* **Whitman Publishing LLC**

Harris, K Publishing, Inc., *(0-9770331)* P.O. Box 3091, Brandon, FL 33509-3091 USA
Web site: http://www.khpinc.com.

Harris, Monica *See* **Keep Empowering Yourself Successfully**

Harris, Pleshette Communications Inc. Publishing, *(0-9754380)* P.O. Box 491282, Lawrenceville, GA 30049 USA Tel 678-910-6128; Fax: 770-237-9358
E-mail: contact@phc1.org
Web site: http://phc1.org.

Harris, Polly, *(0-9749375)* 6041 E Akron St., Mesa, AZ 85205 USA Tel 480-654-1213
E-mail: pollyharris@sbcglobal.net.

Harris, Samuel, *(0-9759253)* 9705 Mountain View Dr. #1105, Scottsdale, AZ 85258 USA
E-mail: sf864@aol.com; eharris864@aol.com
Dist(s): **Partners Bk. Distributing, Inc.**

Harrison, Bobby, *(0-9771752)* 444 Shooting Star Tr., Gurley, AL 35748 USA Tel 256-776-2003; Fax: 256-776-2003
E-mail: bnharri@aol.com; ivorybillwp@aol.com
Web site: http://www.bobbyharrison.com
Dist(s): **Impact Photographics**
Parnasas Bk. Distributors.

Harrison, Daniel B., *(0-9678139)* Orders Addr.: P.O. Box 137, Cordova, SC 29039 USA Tel 803-536-6354; Edit Addr.: 126 Frazier Ln., Cordova, SC 29039 USA
E-mail: tdkb@bellsouth.net.

†Harrison Hse., Inc., *(0-89274; 1-57794)* Orders Addr.: P.O. Box 35035, Tulsa, OK 74153 USA (SAN 208-676X) Tel 918-523-5700; Fax: 918-523-5747; Toll Free Fax: 800-830-5688; Toll Free: 800-888-4126; 877-663-1330; Edit Addr.: 2761 E. Skelly Dr. Ste. 703, Tulsa, OK 74105-6258 USA
E-mail: hh2@eaglemgmt.com
Web site: http://www.harrisonhouse.com
Dist(s): **Anchor Distributors**
Appalachian Bible Co.
Distributors, The
Spring Arbor Distributors, Inc.; *CIP.*

†Harrowood Bks., *(0-915180)* 3943 N. Providence Rd., Newtown Square, PA 19073 USA (SAN 207-1622) Tel 610-353-5585; Toll Free: 800-747-8356; *CIP.*

Harry and Stephanie Books, *(0-9760875)* P.O. Box 172, Bronxville, NY 10708 USA Tel 914-961-6601
E-mail: harryandstephanie@yahoo.com
Web site: http://www.harryandstephanie.com.

Harseal Publications *See* **Harborseal Publishing Co.**

Hart, Julien, *(0-9742418)* P.O. Box 943, Oregon House, CA 95962 USA Tel 530-692-9433
E-mail: julienhart@yahoo.com.

Hart Street Pubs., *(0-9793637)* 12157 Antibes St., Jacksonville, FL 32224 USA.

Hart-Burn Pr., *(0-9740318)* P.O. Box 99, Newton Junction, NH 03859-0099 USA
E-mail: stevehart7@earthlink.net
Web site: http://www.stevehartbooks.com.

Hartford Pubns., *(0-9653872)* 2687 Hartford Dr., Nashville, TN 37210-5418 USA Tel 615-333-6757.

Hartland Pubns., *(0-923309)* Div. of Hartland Institute of Health & Education, P.O. Box 1, Rapidan, VA 22733 USA (SAN 252-0834) Tel 540-672-3566; Fax: 540-672-3568; Toll Free: 800-774-3566
E-mail: jcarmouche@hartland.edu
Web site: http://www.hartlandpublications.com.

Hartley & Marks Publishers, Inc. (CAN) *(0-88179; 0-88930; 1-55156) Dist. by* **Perseus Dist.**

Hartman Publishing, *(0-9703490)* Orders Addr.: P.O. Box 183, Oracle, AZ 85623-0183 USA Tel 520-299-1611
E-mail: jeffhartman@n2books.com; jeffhartman55@hotmail.com.

Hartsuyker, Alice, *(0-9770441)* 20 Ponca Trail, Kirkwood, MO 63122-5112 USA
E-mail: info@insidedharma.org; info@alicememoir.com
Web site: http://www.insidedharma.org; http://www.alicememoir.com.

Hart-Whitlow Pubs., *(0-9637951)* 1845 Brandywine Dr., Lenoir City, TN 37772 USA Tel 865-986-8553
E-mail: dickins@utk.edu.

†Harvard Common Pr., *(0-87645; 0-916782; 1-55832)* 535 Albany St., Boston, MA 02118 USA (SAN 208-6778) Tel 617-423-5803; Fax: 617-695-9794; Toll Free: 888-657-3755
E-mail: orders@harvardcommonpress.com
Web site: http://www.harvardcommonpress.com
Dist(s): **National Bk. Network**; *CIP.*

Harvard Educational Review, *(0-916690)* Eight Story St., 5th Flr., Cambridge, MA 02138 USA (SAN 208-3426) Do not confuse with Harvard Education Letter, Cambridge, MA.

Harvard Perspectives in American Sports *Imprint of* **Harvard Perspectives Pr.**

Harvard Perspectives Pr., *(0-9715778)* P.O. Box 400827, Cambridge, MA 02140-0009 USA ; *Imprints:* Harvard Perspectives in American Sports (Harvard Pers Amer Sp)
E-mail: harvardperspecpr@aol.com.

Harvard Review of Philosophy, *(0-9753949)* c/o Philosophy Tutorial Office, Emerson Hall 303, Harvard University, Cambridge, MA 02138 USA
E-mail: hrp@hcs.harvard.edu
Web site: http://www.harvardphilosophy.com.

†Harvard Univ. Pr., *(0-674; 0-916724; 0-935617)* Orders Addr.: c/o Triliteral LLC, 100 Maple Ridge Dr., Cumberland, RI 02864 USA Tel 401-531-2800; Fax: 401-531-2801; Toll Free Fax: 800-406-9145; Toll Free: 800-405-1619; 800-448-2242; Edit Addr.: 79 Garden St., Cambridge, MA 02138 USA (SAN 200-2043) Tel 617-495-2600; Fax: 617-495-5898
E-mail: contact_hup@harvard.edu
Web site: http://www.hup.harvard.edu; *CIP.*

Harvest Bks. *Imprint of* **Harcourt Trade Pubs.**

Harvest Hill Pr., *(1-886862)* P.O. Box 55, Salisbury Cove, ME 04672 USA Tel 207-288-8900; Fax: 207-288-3611; Toll Free: 888-288-8900 Do not confuse with Harvest Hill Press, Chattanooga, TN
Dist(s): **Baker & Taylor Bks.**
Bryant Altman Map, Inc.
Univ. Pr. of New England.

Harvest Home Publishing, *(0-9713310)* 2023 Tenth St. Ct., Coralville, IA 52241 USA Tel 319-354-9465; Fax: 319-354-0991
E-mail: harvesthome@mybigfamily.org
Web site: http://www.mybigfamily.org.

Harvest Hse. Pubs., *(0-7369; 0-89081; 1-56507)* 990 Owen Loop, N., Eugene, OR 97402-9173 USA (SAN 207-4745) Tel 541-343-0123; Fax: 541-302-0731; Toll Free: 888-501-6991
E-mail: pat.mathis@harvesthousepublishers.com
Web site: http://www.harvesthousepublishers.com
Dist(s): **CRC Pubns.**
Twentieth Century Christian Bks.

Harvest Inspirational Publishing, Inc., *(0-9705225)* 421 Walton Way, Destin, FL 32550 USA Fax: 850-837-1696
E-mail: harpy1@cox.net.

Harvest Point Pr., *(0-9643763)* 2924 Ponkan Meadow Dr., Apopka, FL 32712 USA Tel 407-252-2383
E-mail: aprilrogers@earthlink.net.

Harvest Pubns., *(0-935797)* Div. of Baptist General Conference, 2002 S. Arlington Heights Rd., Arlington Heights, IL 60005 USA (SAN 696-8023) Tel 847-228-0200; Fax: 847-228-5376; Toll Free: 800-323-3885 Do not confuse with companies with the same name in Berkeley, CA, Fort Worth, TX, Minneapolis, KS, Jacksonville, TX
E-mail: bputman@baptistgeneral.org
Web site: http://www/Harvestbooks.org.

Harvest Pubns., *(0-9654272)* 1928 Oxbow Rd., Minneapolis, KS 67467 USA Tel 913-392-2750 Do not confuse with companies with same name in Berkeley, CA, Arlington Heights, IL, Fort Worth, TX, Jacksonville, TX
E-mail: Adharvest@juno.com
Web site: http://www.pma-online.org/list/7345.html.

Harvest Sun Pr., LLC, *(0-9743668)* Orders Addr.: P.O. Box 826, Fairacres, NM 88033 USA Tel 479-283-4000; Fax: 505-526-6930; Edit Addr.: 4109 Broken Arrow Cv., Springdale, AR 72764-7503 USA
E-mail: info@harvestsunpress.com
Web site: http://www.harvestsunpress.com.

Harvey, Alan, *(0-9766354)* P.O. Box 235, Chapel Hill, NC 27514 USA ; *Imprints:* Big H Books (Big H Bks)
Web site: http://www.lorneharvey.com.

Harwell, William, *(0-9728274)* HC 63 Box 1, Hanna, UT 84031 USA.

Harwood Academic Pubs. *Imprint of* **Gordon & Breach Publishing Group**

Hassan, Marian, *(0-9766616)* 430 Mendota Rd. W., Suite 219, West Saint Paul, MN 55118 USA
E-mail: mhassan1@yahoo.com.

Hastings Ende Design Partners, *(0-9700306)* 464 Wildwood Ln., Sewanee, TN 37375 USA Tel 931-598-0660; 615-598-0660; Fax: 931-598-5720 ; *Imprints:* Cosmic Aye (Cosmic Aye)
E-mail: janda@cafes.net.

HATCHBACK Publishing, *(0-9778155)* Orders Addr.: P.O. Box 480, Genesee, MI 48437 USA Tel 810-394-8612
E-mail: clynn@truevine.net
Web site: http://www.hatchbackpub.com.

Hatherleigh Co., Ltd., The, *(1-57826; 1-886330)* 5-22 46th Ave., Suite 200, Long Island City, NY 11101-5215 USA (SAN 298-878X) Tel 212-832-1584; Fax: 212-832-1502; Toll Free Fax: 800-621-8892; Toll Free: 800-367-2550 ; *Imprints:* Hatherleigh Press (Hath Pr)
E-mail: info@hatherleigh.com
Web site: http://www.hatherleigh.com; http://www.getfitnow.com
Dist(s): **Norton, W. W. & Co., Inc.**
Random Hse., Inc.

Hatherleigh Pr. *Imprint of* **Hatherleigh Co., Ltd., The**

Hatpin Press *See* **MusiKinesis**

Hats Off Bks. *Imprint of* **Wheatmark**

Haughton Publishing Co., *(0-914513)* Orders Addr.: P.O. Box 180218, Dallas, TX 75218-0218 USA (SAN 289-6338) Tel 972-661-1661; Fax: 972-661-2989; Toll Free: 800-669-3410; Edit Addr.: 3638 Executive Blvd., Mesquite, TX 75149 USA Tel 972-288-7511
E-mail: fte-book@juno.com.

Haus Publishing (GBR) *(1-904341; 1-904950) Dist. by* **Intl Pubs Mktg.**

Have Hope Publishing, *(0-9762044)* Orders Addr.: P.O. Box 20892, Baltimore, MD 21209 USA Tel 410-367-6179 (phone/fax); Edit Addr.: 5033 Yellowwood Ave., Baltimore, MD 21209 USA
E-mail: teachertalk@jhu.edu.

Have Vision Pubns., *(0-9718915)* Orders Addr.: P.O. Box 5146, Wheaton, IL 60189 USA Tel 630-668-8005; Edit Addr.: 1355 Brighton Dr., Wheaton, IL 60187 USA
E-mail: havevision2020@msn.com
Web site: http://www.notyourparentsprom.com; http://HaveVisionPublications.com
Dist(s): **Baker & Taylor Bks.**
Brodart Co.
Hervey's Booklink & Cookbook Warehouse.

Haven Bks., *(0-9659480; 1-58436)* 10153 1/2 Riverside Dr., Suite 629, North Hollywood, CA 91602 USA Tel 818-503-2518; Fax: 818-508-0299
E-mail: Havenbks@aol.com; reya@havenbooks.net; info@havenbooks.net
Web site: http://www.havenbooks.net
Dist(s): **Baker & Taylor Bks.**

Haven Harbor, *(0-9729863)* P.O. Box 2197, Huntington Beach, CA 92647-0197 USA
Web site: http://www.havenharbor.com.

HavenBound Publishing, *(0-9761733)* 174 Harrell Dr., Lake Junaluska, NC 28745 USA; 1305 Old Balsam Rd., Waynesville, NC 28786
E-mail: havenbound@earthlink.net; noah@dnet.net.

Haver, Nancy, *(0-9795696)* 19 Moorland St., Amherst, MA 01002 USA Tel 413-549-1337
E-mail: nhaver@crocker.com.

Havoc Publishing, *(1-57977; 0-7416)* 7909 Silverton Ave. Ste. 217, San Diego, CA 92126-6347 USA Toll Free: 800-222-2637
E-mail: mktg@havocpub.com
Web site: http://www.havocpub.com.

Hawaii Fishing News, *(0-944462)* 6650 Hawaii Kai Dr., No. 201, Honolulu, HI 96825 USA (SAN 243-6612) Tel 808-395-4499; Fax: 808-396-3474
E-mail: fishnews@pixi.com
Web site: http://www.hawaiifishingnews.com/hfn
Dist(s): **Booklines Hawaii, Ltd.**

Hawaii Natural History Assn., *(0-940295)* P.O. Box 74, Hawaii National Park, HI 96718 USA (SAN 664-2497) Tel 808-985-6050; Fax: 808-985-7333
E-mail: hnha@aloha.net
Dist(s): **Booklines Hawaii, Ltd.**

Hawaiian Publishing, *(0-9713838)* P.O. Box 390696, Keauhou, HI 96739 USA Toll Free: 877-355-5795
E-mail: admin@thewritersmentor.com
Web site: http://www.thewritersmentor.com.

Hawaiian Service, Inc., *(0-930492)* 94-527 Puahi St., Waipahu, HI 96797-4208 USA (SAN 205-0463) Tel 808-676-5026; Fax: 808-676-5156
Dist(s): **Booklines Hawaii, Ltd.**

Hawaya, Inc., *(0-9644149)* Orders Addr.: P.O. Box 300, Kailua, HI 96734 USA Tel 808-261-0589; Fax: 808-531-0957; Edit Addr.: 1564 Ulupii St., Kailua, HI 96734 USA
E-mail: ksullivan@pixi.com
Dist(s): **Booklines Hawaii, Ltd.**
Koen-Levy Bk. Wholesalers LLC.

Hawk Mountaintop Publishing, *(0-9672162)* P.O. Box 88, Piercy, CA 95587 USA Tel 707-247-3409
E-mail: hawk@saber.net.

Hawk Productions, *(1-881900)* 809 W. Maple St., Champaign, IL 61820-2810 USA Tel 217-359-5056
E-mail: llaque3605@aol.com; LLaque3605@aol.com
Dist(s): **Pursifull, Carmen M.**

HAWK Publishing Group, *(0-9673131; 1-930709)* 7107 S. Yale, No. 345, Tulsa, OK 74136 USA (SAN 299-9293) Tel 918-492-3677; Fax: 918-492-2120
E-mail: wb@hawkpub.com
Web site: http://www.hawkpub.com
Dist(s): **Biblio Distribution**
National Bk. Network.

Hawkeye Enterprises, *(0-9743061)* P.O. Box 252, Seal Rock, OR 97376-0252 USA Tel 541-563-4577
E-mail: hawkeye@oregonfast.net.

Hawkibinkler Pr., *(0-9721069)* 7725 N. Fowler, Portland, OR 97217 USA Tel 503-286-0945
E-mail: ruskin@streetfoodsecrets.com
Web site: http://www.streetfoodsecrets.com
Dist(s): **Biblio Distribution.**

Haworth, Margaret, *(0-9740313)* 1625 W. May St. Apt. 3, Wichita, KS 67213-3578 USA.

†Haworth Pr., Inc., The, *(0-7890; 0-86656; 0-917724; 1-56022; 1-56023; 1-56024)* Div. of Taylor & Francis Group, 10 Alice St., Binghamton, NY 13904-1580 USA (SAN 211-0156) Tel 607-722-5857 (Outside US/Canada); Fax: 607-722-6362; 607-722-1424; 607-771-0012 (Outside US/Canada); Toll Free Fax: 800-895-0582; Toll Free: 800-429-6784 ; *Imprints:* Pharmaceutical Products Press (Pharmctl Prods); Harrington Park Press (Harrington Park)
E-mail: orders@haworthpress.com; getinfo@haworthpress.com; barnold@haworthpress.com; docdelivery@haworthpress.com; tbronstein@haworthpress.com
Web site: http://www.haworthpress.com
Dist(s): **Barnes & Noble, Inc.**
Bookazine Co., Inc.
Borders, Inc.
Distributors, The
Koen-Levy Bk. Wholesalers LLC
Matthews Medical Bk. Co.
New Leaf Distributing Co., Inc.
Quality Bks., Inc.
Rittenhouse Bk. Distributors
SPD-Small Pr. Distribution
Unique Bks., Inc.
Waldenbooks, Inc.; *CIP.*

Hawthorn Pr. (GBR) *(0-9507062; 1-869890; 1-903458) Dist. by* **SteinerBooks Inc.**

Hawthorne Bks. & Literary Arts, Inc., *(0-9716915; 0-9766311; 0-9790188)* 1221 SW. 10th Ave., Suite 408, Portland, OR 97205 USA
E-mail: ksage@hawthornebooks.com
Web site: Http://hawthornebook.com
Dist(s): **Consortium Bk. Sales & Distribution**
Perseus Distribution.

†Hay Hse., Inc., *(0-937611; 0-945923; 1-56170; 1-891751; 1-58825; 1-4019)* Orders Addr.: P.O. Box 5100, Carlsbad, CA 92018-5100 USA (SAN 630-477X) Tel 760-431-7695 ext 112; Fax: 760-431-6948; Toll Free Fax: 800-650-5115 (orders only); Toll Free: 800-654-5126 (orders only); 2776 Loker Ave. W, Carlsbad, CA 92010 (SAN 257-3024) Tel 800-654-5126; Fax: 800-650-5115 ; *Imprints:* Hay House Lifestyles (Hay Hse Lifestyles)
E-mail: jkramer@hayhouse.com; kjohnson@hayhouse.com
Web site: http://www.hayhouse.com
Dist(s): **Lectorum Pubns., Inc.**; *CIP.*

Hay Hse. Lifestyles *Imprint of* **Hay Hse., Inc.**

Hayes, Jamie Gallery, LLC, *(0-9765720)* 903 Decatur St., New Orleans, LA 70116 USA Tel 504-596-2344
E-mail: jamiehayesart@aol.com
Web site: http://www.jamiehayes.com.

Haylett Publishing, *(0-9701025)* 1146 N. Central Ave., No. 310, Glendale, CA 91202-2502 USA (SAN 253-2522) Tel 818-500-0599; Fax: 818-247-2388
E-mail: jane@haylettpublishing.com
Web site: http://haylettPublishing.com
Dist(s): **Baker & Taylor Bks.**
Brodart Co.
Ingram Bk. Co.

Haymarket Bks., *(1-931859)* 4015 N. Rockwell, Chicago, IL 60618 USA Tel 773-583-7884
E-mail: orders@haymarketbooks.org
Web site: http://www.haymarketbooks.org
Dist(s): **Consortium Bk. Sales & Distribution.**

Haynes, Eva Johns, *(0-9679211)* 131 Avalon Dr., Warner Robins, GA 31093 USA Tel 912-923-3934
E-mail: evalore@aol.com.

Haynes Publishing PLC (GBR) *(0-85696; 0-900550; 1-56392; 1-85010; 1-85260; 1-85960; 1-84425) Dist. by* **MBI Dist Svcs.**

Hays, Peter D., *(1-885554)* 342 1/2 W. Eighth, Eugene, OR 97401 USA Tel 541-485-6254.

HazardousWeather Preparedness Institute, *(0-9742794)* 5203 N. Oaks Dr., Greensboro, NC 27455-1229 USA
E-mail: rjackson@weatherpreparedness.com
Web site: http://www.weatherpreparedness.com.

Hazel Street Productions, *(0-9786988)* 19831 Kittridge St., Winnetka, CA 91306 USA Tel 818-704-0153
Web site: http://www.hazelst.com.

Hazelden Information & Educational Services *See* **Hazelden Publishing & Educational Services**

†Hazelden Publishing & Educational Services, *(0-89486; 0-89638; 0-935908; 0-942421; 1-56246; 1-56838; 1-59285)* 15215 Pleasant Valley Rd., P.O. Box 176, Center City, MN 55012-0176 USA (SAN 209-4010) Fax: 651-213-4577; Toll Free: 800-328-9000 ; *Imprints:* Hazelden/Johnson Institute (HazeldenJohnson Inst)
E-mail: kbuzick@hazelden.org
Web site: http://www.hazelden.org
Dist(s): **Health Communications, Inc.**; *CIP.*

Hazelden/Johnson Institute *Imprint of* **Hazelden Publishing & Educational Services**

H.B.P., Inc., *(0-9753285; 0-9789617)* 952 Frederick St., Hagerstown, MD 21740 USA
Web site: http://www.hbp.com.

HCI Teens *Imprint of* **Health Communications, Inc.**

Head On Dialogue Publishing, *(0-9770550)* Orders Addr.: P.O. Box 11400, Oakland, CA 94611 USA; Edit Addr.: 509 El Dorado No. 309, Piedmont, CA 94611 USA Tel 510-677-3267
E-mail: headondialogue@yahoo.com.

Head Pr. Publishing, *(0-9758924)* 3804 Pk. Bend Dr., Flower Mound, TX 75022 USA Tel 817-410-9490
E-mail: headpresspublish@aol.com
Web site: http://www.headpress.info
Dist(s): **STL Distribution North America.**

Company

Headline Bk. Publishing (GBR) *(0-7472; 0-7553) Dist. by* **Trafalgar.**

Headline Bk. Publishing (GBR) *(0-7472; 0-7553) Dist. by* **IPG Chicago.**

Headline Bks., Inc., *(0-929915)* Orders Addr.: P.O. Box 52, Terra Alta, WV 26764 USA (SAN 250-8540); Edit Addr.: 5 Lake Rd., Terra Alta, WV 26764 USA (SAN 250-8559) Tel 304-789-3001 (phone/fax); Toll Free: 800-570-5951
E-mail: cathy@headlinebooks.com
Web site: http://www.headlinebooks.com; http://www.publisherpage.com; http://www.headlinekids.com
Dist(s): **Baker & Taylor Bks.**
Midwest Library Service
New Leaf Distributing Co., Inc.

Headrick, Gordon, *(0-9771385)* M. F. W. High School 1775 W. Lowell Ave., Tracy, CA 95376 USA.

Heads First (1st), *(0-9761969)* 4207 Magnolia Ln., Sugar Land, TX 77478 USA Tel 281-844-3719
E-mail: heads1st@aol.com
Web site: http://www.headsfirst.com.

Headway (GBR) *(0-340) Dist. by* **Trafalgar.**

Heagy, Wanda Powell, *(0-9712153)* P.O. Box 1143 CR 681, Saltillo, MS 38866 USA
E-mail: SaltilloAmerica@att.net.

Healing Arts Pr. *Imprint of* **Inner Traditions International, Ltd.**

Healing Flood Bks., Inc., *(0-9746497)* Orders Addr.: 3108 N. Longmore St., Chandler, AZ 85224 USA
E-mail: freebook@healingflood.com; prb@healingflood.com; marketing@healingflood.com; jerry@hospitalbooks.net; sales@hospitalbooks.net
Web site: http://www.healingflood.com; http://www.hospitalbooks.net.

Healing Hands Pr., *(0-9747686)* Div. of Holistic Home Health Care, 1329 N. Wembley Cir., Port Orange, FL 32128 USA Tel 386-322-4888
Web site: http://www.love-heals.com.

Healing Heart Communications, Inc., *(0-9716673)* 851 Arlington Pl., Atlanta, GA 30306 USA Tel 404-892-1476; Fax: 404-875-0824
E-mail: elke@mindspring.com; eleeds@coles2.kennesaw.edu; tony@tonyrooney.com
Web site: http://www.toolboxofhope.com.

Healing Path Foundation, *(0-9722617)* 8150 E. Douglas, Suite No. 40, Wichita, KS 67206-2362 USA Tel 316-579-6655.

Healing Society, Inc., *(0-9720282; 1-932843)* Orders Addr.: P.O. Box 4503, Sedona, AZ 86340-9978 USA; Edit Addr.: 6560 Hwy. 179, Suite 114, Sedona, AZ 86351 USA Toll Free: 877-504-1106
E-mail: dcrenshaw@hspub.com; moh@hspub.com
Web site: http://www.www.hspub.com; http://www.bodynbrain.com
Dist(s): **Baker & Taylor Bks.**
New Leaf Distributing Co., Inc.

Healing Species, The, *(0-9716164)* Orders Addr.: P.O. Box 1202, Orangeburg, SC 29116 USA Tel 803-535-6543 (phone/fax); Edit Addr.: 637 Farnum Rd., Orangeburg, SC 29118 USA
E-mail: cthomp9519@aol.com
Web site: http://www.healingspecies.com.

Healing Tree Arts, *(0-9779643)* P.O. Box 3398, Laguna Hills, CA 92654 USA (SAN 850-7775)
Web site: http://www.healingtreearts.com.

Health & Beauty Ctr., LLC, *(0-9747253)* P.O. Box 363, Oregon City, OR 97045 USA Toll Free: 888-648-7771
E-mail: support@healthnbeauty.com; support@perfect-prescription.com
Web site: http://www.healthnbeauty.com; http://www.perfect-prescription.com.

Health Circle Pubns., *(0-9755434)* P.O. Box 2442, Asheboro, NC 27205 USA Tel 336-267-3750
Web site: http://www.healthcircle.org.

†Health Communications, Inc., *(0-932194; 1-55874; 0-7573)* Orders Addr.: 3201 SW 15th St., Deerfield Beach, FL 33442-8190 USA (SAN 212-100X) Tel 954-360-0909; Fax: 954-360-0034; Toll Free: 800-441-5569 ; *Imprints:* Simcha Press (Simcha Press); HCI Teens (HCi Teens) Do not confuse with Health Communications, Inc., Edison, NJ
E-mail: hci@hcibooks.com; terryy@hcibooks.com; lorig@hcibooks.com
Web site: http://www.hcibooks.com
Dist(s): **Continental Bk. Co., Inc.**
Lectorum Pubns., Inc.
Landmark Audiobooks; *CIP.*

Health InfoNet, Inc., *(1-57810; 1-885274)* 231 Market Pl., No. 331, San Ramon, CA 94583 USA Tel 925-358-4370; Fax: 925-358-4377; Toll Free: 800-446-1947
E-mail: logo47@aol.com; HINBooks@aol.com
Web site: http://www.hinbooks.com.

Health 'n' Life Publishing (GBR) *(0-9531766) Dist. by* **Midpt Trade.**

Health New England, *(0-9777159)* One Monarch Pl., Springfield, MA 01144-1500 USA (SAN 850-0436) Tel 413-787-4000; Toll Free: 800-842-4464
Web site: http://www.hne.com; http://www.hnestore.com; http://www.hnewhizkidz.com.

Health Press *See* **Health Pr. NA, Inc.**

Health Pr. NA, Inc., *(0-929173)* P.O. Box 37470, Albuquerque, NM 87176 USA (SAN 248-5036) Tel 505-888-1394; Fax: 505-888-1521
E-mail: goodbooks@healthpress.com
Web site: http://www.healthpress.com.

Health Program Planning, Inc., *(0-9706867)* P.O. Box 60748, Harrisburg, PA 17106-0748 USA.

Health Trust International, Incorporated *See* **FUZZY DREAMS, Inc.**

Healthful Living Bks. *Imprint of* **Unique Executive Pubs.**

HealthMark Multimedia, *(0-9717399)* 1828 L St., NW, Suite 250, Washington, DC 20036 USA
E-mail: hm@healthmarkmultimedia.com; amcfarren@healthmarkmultimedia.com
Web site: http://www.HealthMarkMultimedia.com.

HealthSprings, LLC, *(0-9718120; 0-9740697; 0-9748263)* 1759 Grandstand, San Antonio, TX 78238 USA Tel 210-521-7650; Fax: 210-521-7141
E-mail: sabra@zoeyzones.com
Web site: http://www.zoeyzones.com.

Healthways, *(0-9630893)* 1300 Columbia Dr., SE, Albuquerque, NM 87106 USA Tel 505-268-5919
E-mail: panet@nmia.com
Web site: http://www.cowsareveg.com.

Healthy Life Pr., Inc., *(0-9727328)* 2667 Stellar Ct., Coquitlam, BC V3E 1H1 CAN Tel 604-682-5838; Fax: 604-468-1217; 1685 H St., PMB 860, Blaine, WA 98230-5107 Fax: 604-682-5817; Toll Free: 888-575-3173
E-mail: rszefler@shaw.ca; info@starthealthylife.com
Web site: http://www.starthealthylife.com
Dist(s): **Biblio Distribution.**

Healthy People Pr., *(1-930289)* 360 W. Ave., Canandaigua, NY 14424 USA Tel 716-396-2945; 585-396-2945; Fax: 716-393-1811
E-mail: sally@healthypeoplelearn.com.

Healthy Wealth, *(0-9722071)* 4795 Mile High Dr., Salt Lake City, UT 84124-4728 USA Tel 801-274-1999; Fax: 801-937-7029; Toll Free: 877-690-4800
E-mail: don@donchambers.com
Web site: http://www.healthywealth.com.

Hear & Play Music, *(0-9744845)* Orders Addr.: P.O. Box 91355, Long Beach, CA 90809 USA; Edit Addr.: 15771 Rockfield Blvd. Ste. 250, Irvine, CA 92618-2847 USA Toll Free: 877-856-4187
E-mail: webmaster@hearandplay.com
Web site: http://www.hearandplay.com.

†Hearst Bks., *(0-688; 0-87851; 0-910990; 0-910992; 1-58816)* Div. of Hearst Communications, Inc., Orders Addr.: P.O. Box 1219, Fairfield, NJ 07007 USA (SAN 202-5779) Tel 973-227-7200; Toll Free: 800-237-0657; Edit Addr.: 1350 Avenue of Americas, New York, NY 10019 USA (SAN 202-2842) Tel 212-261-6500; Fax: 212-261-6599
Dist(s): **Sterling Publishing Co., Inc.**; *CIP.*

Hearst Communications, Inc., *(0-87851; 1-58816)* 250 W. 55th St., New York, NY 10019-5288 USA
E-mail: jdeval@hearst.com
Web site: http://www.hearst.com
Dist(s): **Hearst Bks.**
Sterling Publishing Co., Inc.

Heart & Harp LLC, *(0-9742174)* P.O. Box 818, Walled Lake, MI 48390-0818 USA Tel 313-938-9847
E-mail: HeartandHarp@comcast.net.

Heart Arbor Bks., *(1-891452)* Orders Addr.: P.O. Box 542, Grand River, OH 44045 USA (SAN 299-6073) Tel 440-257-0722; Toll Free: 877-977-4422.

Heart Communications, *(0-9694176; 0-9747516)* P.O. Box 551, Fishers, IN 46038-0551 USA (SAN 116-404X) Tel 317-908-5635; Fax: 317-841-1879
E-mail: info@heartcommunications.com
Web site: http://www.HeartCommunications.com.

Heart Gallery Pr., *(1-928888)* 900 Central Ave., Saint Petersburg, FL 33705 USA
E-mail: mcurran@sagonet.net.

Heart Of Dixie Publishing *See* **Bluewater Pubns.**

Heart Path Publishing, *(0-9712305)* P.O. Box 44, Keene, TX 76059 USA Tel 817-681-3877 Do not confuse with Heart Path Publishing, Atlanta, GA
Web site: http://www.guidemagazine.org.

Heart to Heart Pr., *(0-9663602)* Orders Addr.: P.O. Box 427, Traverse City, MI 49685 USA Tel 231-933-6070; 231-437-0270; Fax: 231-933-8479; Toll Free: 800-831-3230
E-mail: jan@awakenedliving.com
Web site: http://www.soulsailing.com.

Heart to Heart Publishing, *(0-9742806)* 519 Muddy Creek Rd., Morgantown, KY 42261 USA Fax: 270-526-7489; Toll Free: 888-526-5589
E-mail: hawkinslindaj@logantele.com; hawkinslindaj@aol.com
Web site: http://www.lindajhawkins.com
Dist(s): **STL Distribution North America.**

Heart Warming Hse., *(0-9676367)* 83 Ward St., Manchester, NH 03104 USA Tel 603-627-7930
E-mail: rmalmquist@springmail.com.

Heartfelt Bks., *(0-9763933)* 149 Thunderbird Trail, Carol Stream, IL 60188-1982 USA.

Heartfelt Pubns., *(0-9671500)* 6789 SE 209th St., Holt, MO 64048 USA Do not confuse with companies with the same name in Bastrop, TX, Charlotte, NC
E-mail: nullclan@swbell.net.

HeartFelt Stories LLC, *(0-9778113)* P.O. Box 26094, Columbus, OH 43226 USA (SAN 850-3036) Toll Free: 866-494-3535
E-mail: heartfeltstories@hotmail.com
Web site: www.heartfeltstoriesllc.com
Dist(s): **Blu Sky Media Group.**

Heartful Loving Pr., *(0-9723639)* Div. of Illui International, 1450 Orange Grove Ave., Santa Barbara, CA 93105 USA Tel 805-687-7442; Fax: 805-687-3042
E-mail: howard@heartfullovingpress.com
Web site: http://www.heartfullovingpress.com; http://www.howtobeafamily.com; http://www.firstloveremembrances.com; http://www.howtobethebestlover.com
Dist(s): **Partners Bk. Distributing, Inc.**

Heartland Foundation, Inc., *(0-943177)* Orders Addr.: P.O. Box 887, Ames, IA 50010 USA Toll Free: 866-385-2027; Edit Addr.: 413 Northwestern Ave., Ames, IA 50010 USA (SAN 668-3010) Tel 515-232-1054
E-mail: lssn@att.net
Web site: http://mcmillenbooks.com
Dist(s): **McMillen Bk. Distributors.**

Heartlight, *(0-9641305)* 716 Turkey Oak Ln., Naples, FL 34108 USA Tel 239-596-1648
E-mail: heartlight3@comcast.net
Web site: http://www.uvm.edu/~afengler/
Dist(s): **New Leaf Distributing Co., Inc.**

Heartohopia Pr., *(0-9725184)* 2007 NE 59 Pl., Suite 105, Fort Lauderdale, FL 33308 USA
Web site: http://www.heartohopia.com
Dist(s): **Baker & Taylor Bks.**

HeartQuake Publishing, *(0-9630377)* 919 N. Alfred St., No. 205, Los Angeles, CA 90069 USA Tel 323-822-1719 (phone/fax)
E-mail: charleshunt3@dslextreme.com
Web site: http://www.insearchoftheperfectdiet.com; http://www.eatforyourbestlife.com.

Hearts 'N Tummies Cookbook Co., *(1-57166; 1-878488)* Div. of Quixote Pr., 1854-345th Ave., Wever, IA 52658-9597 USA Tel 319-372-7480; Fax: 319-372-7485; Toll Free: 800-571-2665
E-mail: heartsntummies@hotmail.com
Dist(s): **Bookmen, Inc.**

Heartsome Press *See* **Heartsome Publishing**

Heartsome Publishing, *(0-9726408)* 220 Norfolk St., Walpole, MA 02081 USA Tel 508-553-3858; Fax: 508-668-1998
E-mail: rrhearts@comcast.net
Web site: http://www.nolobsterplease.com/
Dist(s): **Baker & Taylor Bks.**

HeartStrings FiberArts, *(0-9726940)* 53 Parlange Dr., Destrehan, LA 70047-2133 USA Tel 985-764-8094 (phone/fax); Toll Free: 888-955-8094
E-mail: jackie@heartstringsfiberarts.com
Web site: http://www.heartstringsfiberarts.com.

Heartstrings Publishing, *(0-9760733)* Orders Addr.: P.O. Box 8255, Fernando Beach, FL 32035 USA; Edit Addr.: Marchette Burette Market, Amelia Island Plantation, Fernandina Beach, FL 32034 USA
E-mail: mledlen@aol.com.

Heart-to-Heart Pubns., *(0-9744565)* 18237 N. 51st Pl., Scottsdale, AZ 85254 USA Tel 602-485-0793
E-mail: cpruett1@cox.net.

Heartwings Publishing *See* **Spiritis Publishing**

Heath, Jonathan Publishing, *(0-9715837)* 10 Willowstream Dr., Vernon, CT 06066 USA Tel 860-875-8373
E-mail: lenpam@snet.net.

Heather & Highlands Publishing, *(1-58478)* Div. of Heather & Highlands Publishing, Orders Addr.: 2384 Tokay Ct., Paradise, CA 95969 USA (SAN 254-0932) Tel 530-876-8986; Fax: 530-876-8989; Toll Free: 888-999-2358 ; *Imprints:* Highland Children's Press (Hghlnd Child); Paw Prints Press (PawPrintsPr)
E-mail: pawprintsorders@pawprintspress.com; pawprints@pawprintspress.com; tew@tewatsononline.com
Web site: http://www.pawprintspress.com; http://www.tewatsononline.com
Dist(s): **Baker & Taylor Bks.**
Book Wholesalers, Inc.
Brodart Co.

Heaven on Earth Inspirational Trax Publishing *See* **Heaven on Earth Publishing**

Heaven on Earth Publishing, *(0-615)* Div. of Heaven on Earth Ministries, Orders Addr.: 1000 Valley Ct., Edmond, OK 73003 USA; Edit Addr.: P.O. Box 7496, Edmond, OK 73083 USA Tel 405-359-0937
E-mail: Castaneda0@aol.com.

Heaven Sent Publishing, *(0-9630551)* 1950 Tamarind Ave., Apt. 115, Los Angeles, CA 90068 USA Tel 323-467-7782; Fax: 323-467-7782 (phone/fax); Toll Free: 888-394-9221
E-mail: angelharper@earthlink.net
Web site: http://www.coldreading.com.

Heavenly C. Publishing, *(0-9746361)* P.O. Box 335, West Chester, OH 45071 USA
Web site: http://www.heavenlyCPublishing.com.

Heavenly Treasures, *(0-9724387)* 8816 SE 125th St., Valley Center, KS 67147 USA.

Heavy Metal Magazine, *(1-882931; 1-932413)* Div. of Metal Mammoth, Inc., 100 H. Village Ave., Suite IV, Rockville Centre, NY 11570-4801 USA Tel 516-594-2130; Fax: 516-594-2133
E-mail: juno@erots.com
Web site: http://www.heavymetal.com.

Hebe's International Pubs., *(0-9636510; 1-932110)* Orders Addr.: P.O. Box 20710, Jackson, MS 39289 USA Tel 601-371-1170 (phone/fax); Edit Addr.: 404 Parks Rd., Jackson, MS 39219 USA
E-mail: fesoguh@cs.com.

Hebler, Dave, *(0-9765392)* 5891 S. Military Trail, 5A-PMB, Lake Worth, FL 33463-6920 USA Tel 561-642-6696
E-mail: daveahebler@aol.com
Web site: http://www.protectingwomen.com.

Hedberg Maps, Inc., *(1-885508; 1-59353)* 1500 Jackson St., NE, Minneapolis, MN 55413-1561 USA (SAN 254-4970) Tel 612-706-9686; Fax: 612-706-9704; Toll Free: 800-933-6277
E-mail: thedberg@hedbergmaps.com
Web site: http://www.hedbergmaps.com
Dist(s): **Langenscheidt Pubs Inc.**
Rand McNally
Wilderness Pr.

Hedger, Ralph, *(0-9753880)* 208 Chaucer Rd., Charlottesville, VA 22901-2215 USA
E-mail: rehedger@aol.com.

Heersink, Roland, *(0-9770473)* 1212 E. Monte Cristo Ave., Phoenix, AZ 85022 USA
Web site: http://www.fairytunes.com.

Heflin & Thrall Language Pubns., Inc., *(0-9723341)* 2109 Stanford, Jacksonville, TX 75766 USA Toll Free: 888-313-3310
E-mail: jheflin@language-publications.com.

Hegemony Pr., *(0-9754114)* 5205 Pacific Ave., Tacoma, WA 98405 USA Tel 253-671-2665; Fax: 253-475-2665; Toll Free: 888-671-2665
Web site: http://www.hegemonypress.com.

Heian International Publishing, Inc., *(0-89346)* P.O. Box 8208, Berkeley, CA 94707-8208 USA (SAN 213-2036) Fax: 510-524-8711; Toll Free: 800-947-7271
E-mail: heianemail@earthlink.net
Web site: http://www.heian.com
Dist(s): **Cheng & Tsui Co.**
Consortium Bk. Sales & Distribution.

Heicron, Inc., *(0-9705435)* Orders Addr.: P.O. Box 1254, Palm Harbor, FL 34682-1254 USA Fax: 727-938-6455
E-mail: heicron@tampabay.rr.com
Web site: http://www.heicron.com.

†Heidelberg Graphics, *(0-918606)* 2 Stansbury Ct., Chico, CA 95928 USA (SAN 211-5654) Tel 530-342-6582 (phone/fax)
E-mail: service@HeidelbergGraphics.com
Web site: http://www.HeidelbergGraphics.com
Dist(s): **Baker & Taylor Bks.**; *CIP.*

Heiderer, Conrad, *(0-9746699)* P.O. Box 405, Glen Arbor, MI 49636 USA Tel 231-334-6680 Toll Free: 888-877-0994
E-mail: cehj1200@hotmail.com
Web site: http://www.twigma.com.

Heifer Project International, *(0-9755996; 0-9798439)* Orders Addr.: 1 World Ave., Little Rock, AR 72203-8058 USA Tel 800-422-1311; Fax: 501-907-2802
Web site: http://www.heifer.org.

†Heinemann, *(0-325; 0-434; 0-435; 1-59469)* Div. of Greenwood Publishing Group, Inc., Orders Addr.: P.O. Box 6926, Portsmouth, NH 03802 USA Toll Free: 800-225-5800; Edit Addr.: 361 Hanover St., Portsmouth, NH 03801 USA (SAN 210-5829) Tel 603-431-7894; Fax: 603-431-7840 ; *Imprints:* African Writers Series (African Write); Boynton/Cook (Boynton Cook)
E-mail: info@heinemann.com
Web site: http://www.heinemann.com
Dist(s): **Greenwood Publishing Group, Inc.**; *CIP.*

Heinemann Educational Books, Incorporated *See* **Heinemann**

Heinemann Kenya, Limited (East African Educational Publishers Ltd E.A.E.P.) (KEN) *(9966-46; 9966-45; 9966-25; 9966-9953) Dist. by* **Mich St U Pr.**

Heinemann Library, *(0-431; 1-57572; 1-58810; 1-4034; 1-4329)* Div. of Reed Elsevier, Orders Addr.: 1000 Hart Rd., 3rd Flr., Barrington, IL 60010-2627 USA Toll Free Fax: 888-844-5329; 847-620-7900 (Outside U.S.); Toll Free: 888-454-2279; 847-620-7500 (ext.: 3910, Outside U.S.); Edit Addr.: 100 N. LaSalle St., Suite 300, Chicago, IL 60602 USA Tel 312-324-5200; Fax: 312-845-1030; Toll Free: 888-475-7038
E-mail: sgafka@rigby-edue.com; sheryl.gafka@rigby.com
Web site: http://www.heinemannlibrary.com/
Dist(s): **Lectorum Pubns., Inc.**

Heiner, Garth *See* **Fun With the Law, Inc.**

Heinle *See* **Thomson Heinle**

Heins Pubns., *(0-9671762; 0-9748680)* 2016 Leonard Ct., Eau Claire, WI 54703 USA Toll Free: 800-554-3467
E-mail: revheins@wwt.net.

Heirloom Memories, Inc., *(0-9663273)* 351 Carrera Dr., Mill Valley, CA 94941 USA Tel 415-381-2900; Fax: 415-381-3160; Toll Free: 800-762-2986
E-mail: rubyshoe@sirius.com
Web site: http://www.heirloommemories.com.

Helen Darling *See* **My Darling-Tots Pubns.**

Heliand Publishing Corp., *(0-9770712)* P.O. Box 477, Pleasant Grove, UT 84062 USA
E-mail: submissions@heliandpublishing.com
Web site: http://www.heliandpublishing.com.

Heliograph, Inc., *(0-9668926; 1-930658)* 26 Porter St., Somerville, MA 02143-2215 USA Tel 617-776-3338; Fax: 617-776-2999
E-mail: info@heliograph.com
Web site: http://www.heliograph.com.

Heller, Andrew, *(0-9714951)* 5296 Lethbridge, Grand Blanc, MI 48439 USA Tel 810-694-1179
E-mail: andrewheller@compaq.net.

Helm Literary Publishing *See* **Helm Publishing**

Helm Publishing, *(0-9723011; 0-9760919; 0-9769193; 0-9778205; 0-9792328)* Orders Addr.: 3923 Seward Ave., Rockford, IL 61108 USA (SAN 254-7562) Tel 815-398-4660
E-mail: dianne@publishersdrive.com
Web site: http://www.publishersdrive.com
Dist(s): **Baker & Taylor Bks.**

Helms, Jo Publishing, *(0-9745319)* 824 S. Schaefer St., Appleton, WI 54915 USA
E-mail: cheesedawg@earthlink.net; ilovegrizz@earthlink.net
Web site: http://www.grizz.20megsfree.com.

H.E.L.P. for Self-Education, *(0-9766991)* 960 Perth Rd., Troutman, NC 28166 USA Tel 704-528-5866; Fax: 704-585-9397
E-mail: swedship@bellsouth.net
Web site: http://www.home.bellsouth.net/p/pwp-helpeducate.

Help Me 2 Learn Co., *(0-9741687; 1-932712)* 12033 4th St., Suite 3, Yucaipa, CA 92399-2755 USA Tel 909-797-2203; Fax: 909-797-4541; Toll Free: 800-460-7001
E-mail: sales@helpme2learn.com
Web site: http://www.helpme2learn.com.

Helping Hands Children's Bks., *(0-9762274)* 421 26th St., Marion, IA 52302 USA Tel 319-373-4169
E-mail: mary@mysak.com.

Helping Teens Succeed, Inc., *(0-9710666)* 1083 McConnell Dr., Decatur, GA 30033 USA Tel 404-929-0449; Fax: 404-325-8824
E-mail: helpingteens@mindspring.com
Web site: http://www.helpingteenssucceed.org.

†Hemisphere Publishing Corp., *(0-89116; 1-56032)* Member of Taylor & Francis Group, Orders Addr.: 325 Chestnut St., 8th Flr., Philadelphia, PA 19106 USA Fax: 215-269-0363; Toll Free: 800-821-8312
Dist(s): **McGraw-Hill Cos., The**; *CIP.*

Henderson Publishing, *(1-891029)* Orders Addr.: R.R. 1, Box 1018, Pounding Mill, VA 24637 USA Tel 276-964-2291.

Hendley, Jeff *See* **L'Edge Pr.**

†Hendrick-Long Publishing Co., *(0-937460; 1-885777)* Orders Addr.: 10635 Tower Oaks, Suite D, Houston, TX 77070 USA (SAN 281-7756) Toll Free: 800-544-3770; Edit Addr.: 10635 Tower Oaks Blvd. Ste. D, Houston, TX 77070-5927 USA (SAN 281-7748)
E-mail: hendrick-long@worldnet.att.net
Web site: http://www.hendricklongpublishing.com
Dist(s): **Baker & Taylor Bks.**
Book Wholesalers, Inc.
Brodart Co.
Follett Library Resources
Mackin Library Media; *CIP.*

†Hendrickson Pubs., Inc., *(0-913573; 0-917006; 0-943575; 1-56563; 1-59856)* Orders Addr.: P.O. Box 3473, Peabody, MA 01961-3473 USA (SAN 285-2772) Fax: 978-531-8146; Toll Free: 800-358-3111; Edit Addr.: 140 Summit St., Peabody, MA 01960 USA (SAN 663-6594) Fax: 978-573-8414 Do not confuse with Hendrickson Group, Sandy Hook, CT
E-mail: editorial@hendrickson.com
Web site: http://www.hendrickson.com; *CIP.*

Henrie, T. Books *See* **Keeping Track of Time**

Henry, Ian Pubns. (GBR) *(0-86025) Dist. by* **Players Pr.**

Henry, Ian Pubns. (GBR) *(0-86025) Dist. by* **Empire Pub Srvs.**

Henry Quill Pr., *(1-883960)* 7340 Lake Dr., Fremont, MI 49412-9146 USA Tel 231-924-3026; Fax: 231-928-2802.

Hensley, Michael, *(0-9747389)* P.O. Box 2952, Ranchos de Taos, NM 87557 USA
Web site: http://www.michaelmhensley.com.

Her Interactive, Inc., *(0-9672618; 0-9728336; 0-9753329; 0-9776966; 0-9788393)* 1150, 114th Ave. SE, Suite 200, Bellevue, WA 98004 USA
Web site: http://www.herinteractive.com.

Her Own Words, *(1-877933; 1-60118)* P.O. Box 5264, Madison, WI 53705-0264 USA Tel 608-271-7083; Fax: 608-271-0209
E-mail: herownword@aol.com
Web site: http://www.herownwords.com
Dist(s): **JIST Publishing.**

†Herald Pr., *(0-8361)* Div. of Mennonite Publishing Hse., Inc., 616 Walnut Ave., Scottdale, PA 15683-1999 USA (SAN 202-2915) Tel 724-887-8500; 412-887-8500; Fax: 724-887-3111; Toll Free: 800-245-7894 (orders only) Do not confuse with Herald Pr., Charlotte, NC
E-mail: hp@mph.org
Web site: http://www.mph.org
Dist(s): **Baker & Taylor Bks.**
CRC Pubns.
NetLibrary, Inc.
Spring Arbor Distributors, Inc.; *CIP.*

Herald Publishing Company *See* **Herald Source, Inc.**

†Herald Publishing Hse., *(0-8309)* Orders Addr.: P.O. Box 390, Independence, MO 64051-0390 USA Tel 816-521-3015; Fax: 816-521-3066 (customer services); Toll Free: 800-767-8181; Edit Addr.: 1001W. Walnut St., Independence, MO 64051-0390 USA (SAN 111-7556) Tel 816-257-0200
E-mail: sales@HeraldHouse.org
Web site: http://www.heraldhouse.org; *CIP.*

Herald Source, Inc., *(0-9648236)* 867 Neil Ave., Columbus, OH 43215 USA (SAN 298-6868) Tel 614-291-2477 (phone/fax) Do not confuse with companies with the same or similar name in Flushing, NY, Woodland, WA, Baton Rouge, LA
E-mail: falconmh@webtv.net.

Here & Now Publishing, *(0-9763491)* 5662 Calle Real, No. 139, Goleta, CA 93117 USA (SAN 256-3339) Fax: 805-683-8181
E-mail: info@hereandnowmeditation.com
Web site: http://www.hereandnowmeditation.com.

Here & There Pubns., *(0-9678482)* 858 Third Ave., No. 453, Chula Vista, CA 91911-1305 USA Tel 619-426-3898; Fax: 619-426-2047.

HerInteractive.com *See* **Her Interactive, Inc.**

Heritage Heart Farm, *(0-9706348)* Orders Addr.: 21387 Rd. 128, Oakwood, OH 45873 USA Tel 419-594-2258
E-mail: heritageheartfarm@tds.net; kohart@tds.net
Web site: http://www.heritageheartfarm.com.

Heritage Hse. Publishing Co., Ltd. (CAN) *(0-919214; 1-895811; 1-894384; 0-9690546; 1-894974) Dist. by* **Midpt Trade.**

Heritage Information Systems, *(0-9725784)* 166 Hilton Rd., Cochranville, PA 19330 USA Fax: 610-869-6369
E-mail: hertinfsys@aol.com
Web site: http://www.stallwritings.com.

Heritage Music Pr., *(0-89328)* Div. of The Lorenz Corp., Orders Addr.: 501 E. Third St., Dayton, OH 45401-0802 USA Tel 937-228-6118; Toll Free: 800-444-1144
E-mail: order@lorenz.com
Web site: http://www.lorenz.com.

Heritage Pr., *(0-9742970)* 1318 Burton Valley Rd., Nashville, TN 37215-4306 USA Tel 615-385-3922; Fax: 615-279-6903
E-mail: ussmindoro@juno.com.

Heritage Pubs., Inc., *(0-929690)* 5308 N. 12th St., Suite 400, Phoenix, AZ 85014 USA (SAN 249-9460) Tel 602-277-4780; Fax: 602-277-1659; Toll Free: 800-972-8507
E-mail: heritage@fastq.com; info@heritagepublishers.com
Web site: http://www.heritagepublishers.com.

Heritage Publishing, *(0-9672363)* 23507 E. State Rte. P, Pleasant Hill, MO 64080 USA Tel 816-540-4768; 913-338-3893 Do not confuse with companies with the same or similar names in Dallas, TX, Enumclaw, WA, Chicago, IL, Beverly Hills, CA, Loveland, CO, Valley Center, KS, Peabody, MA, Whitesboro, TX, Pleasant Hill, MO, Springdale, AR, Charlotte, NC, Thomasville, GA, North Little Rock, AR, Baton Rouge, LA, Stockton, CA, carthage, MO
E-mail: peggytucker@juno.com.

Heritage Youth, Inc., *(0-9740753)* 6245 Esplanade Ave., Baton Rouge, LA 70806-6144 USA.

Hermes Pr., *(0-9710311; 1-932563)* 2100 Wilmington Rd., New Castle, PA 16105-1931 USA Tel 724-652-0511; Fax: 724-652-5597 Do not confuse with companies with same or similar names in Brooks, ME, Vista, CA. Ferndale, MI
E-mail: geerherm@sgi.net
Dist(s): **Diamond Bk. Distributors.**

Hermes Pubs., Inc., *(0-9766543)* P.O. Box 186, Roselle Park, NJ 07207 USA (SAN 256-453X) Toll Free: 888-557-5527
E-mail: dollarnet@aol.com.

Hermit Chum Publishing, *(0-9760317)* 6901 S. McClieteck, No. 245, Tempe, AZ 89283 USA.

Hermit's Grove, The, *(0-9655687)* P.O. Box 0691, Kirkland, WA 98083-0691 USA Tel 425-828-4124; Fax: 425-803-2025
E-mail: paul@thehermitsgrove.org
Web site: http://www.thehermitsgrove.org
Dist(s): **New Leaf Distributing Co., Inc.**

Hermosa Creations, *(0-9667681)* P.O. Box 93593, Lubbock, TX 79424 USA Fax: 806-766-0525.

Hermosa Pubs., *(0-913478)* P.O. Box 9110, Albuquerque, NM 87119 USA (SAN 203-0012) Tel 505-866-5323 (phone/fax)
E-mail: hermosa@swcp.com
Web site: http://www.hermosa-pub.com/hermosa.

Hero Dog Pubns., *(0-9743659)* 14 Eastview Ave., Pleasantville, NY 10570 USA (SAN 255-545X) Tel 914-525-6483
E-mail: herodogpubl@msn.com
Web site: www.herodogpublications.com
Dist(s): **BCH Fulfillment & Distribution.**

Herodias, *(1-928746)* Orders Addr.: 1603 79th St., Brooklyn, NY 11214 USA; Edit Addr.: 346 First Ave., New York, NY 10009 USA Tel 212-995-5332 (phone/fax); Toll Free: 800-219-9116 (orders)
E-mail: greatblue@acninc.net
Web site: http://www.herodias.com
Dist(s): **Mercedes Distribution Ctr., Inc.**

Heron Bks., *(0-89739)* P.O. Box 503, Sheridan, OR 97378-9901 USA (SAN 678-4917) Tel 503-843-3834; Fax: 503-843-5129 Do not confuse with Heron Bks., Manchester, MI
E-mail: heronbooks@heronbooks.com
Web site: http://www.heronbooks.com.

Heron Publishing, *(1-880639)* 603 Seagaze St. , No. 180, Oceanside, CA 92054 USA (SAN 253-4673) Tel 760-754-5237; Fax: 760-754-5235
E-mail: orders@heronpub.com
Web site: http://www.heronpub.com.

Herrington, Nancy Publishing, *(0-9711299)* P.O. Box 7171, Daytona Beach Shores, FL 32116 USA Tel 386-304-1711; Fax: 386-304-6632
E-mail: nancyherrington@aol.com
Web site: http://www.roselearningbooks.com.

Herrington Publishing *See* **Herrington, Nancy Publishing**

Herrington Teddy Bears, *(0-9722343)* 8945 Research Dr., Irvine, CA 92618-4237 USA Toll Free: 866-482-2327
E-mail: chris@herringtonco.com
Web site: http://www.herringtonteddybears.com
Dist(s): **National Bk. Network.**

Herrle, David Joseph, *(0-9706843)* 1309 Freeport Rd., Cheswick, PA 15024 USA.

Herrod, Ron L. Evangelism Ministries Association (R.H.E.M.A), *(0-9763789)* 724 Sharp Rd., Sevierville, TN 37876 USA
Web site: http://ronherrod.org.

Hershberger, Ivan & Fannie, *(0-9725806)* 8219 CR 192, Holmesville, OH 44633 USA.

Hershenson, Bruce, *(1-887893)* Orders Addr.: P.O. Box 874, West Plains, MO 65775 USA Tel 417-256-9616; Fax: 417-257-6948
E-mail: mail@emovieposter.com
Web site: http://www.emovieposter.com
Dist(s): **Austin & Company, Inc.**
Partners Pubs. Group, Inc.

Heryin Publishing Corp., *(0-9762056; 0-9787550)* 1033 E. Main St., No. 202, Alhambra, CA 91801 USA Tel 626-289-2238; Fax: 626 289 3865
E-mail: info@heryin.com
Dist(s): **Independent Pubs. Group.**

Hesinme, Incorporated *See* **Courageous Kids, Inc.**

Hesperus Pr. (GBR) *(1-84391) Dist. by* **IPG Chicago.**

Hester Publishing, *(0-9789388)* 30 Kimball Ave., Suite. 301, S. Burlington, VT 05403 USA
E-mail: sales@hesterpublishing.com
Web site: http://hesterpublishing.com.

Heward Assocs., LLC, *(0-9755608)* 2250 N. University Pkwy., No. 4888, Provo, UT 84604-1500 USA Tel 801-427-6630; Fax: 801-705-3461; Toll Free: 877-439-2824
E-mail: info@elibertypress.com
Web site: http://www.elibertypress.com
Dist(s): **Baker & Taylor Bks.**
Ingram Bk. Co.

Hewitt Homeschooling Resources *Imprint of* **Hewitt Research Foundation, Inc.**

Hewitt Research Foundation, Inc., *(0-913717; 1-57896)* Orders Addr.: P.O. Box 9, Washougal, WA 98671 USA (SAN 286-1852) Tel 360-835-8708; Fax: 360-835-8697; Toll Free: 800-348-1750; Edit Addr.: 2103 B St., Washougal, WA 98671 USA ; *Imprints:* Hewitt Homeschooling Resources (Hewitt Homeschl Res)
E-mail: hewitths@aol.com
Web site: http://www.homeeducation.org.

Hewitt Research, Incorporated *See* **Hewitt Research Foundation, Inc.**

Hexagon Blue, *(0-9729958)* P.O. Box 1790, Issaquah, WA 98027-0073 USA (SAN 255-3406)
E-mail: mary@hexagonblue.com
Web site: http://www.hexagonblue.com
Dist(s): **Baker & Taylor Bks.**
Quality Bks., Inc.

Company

Heyday Bks., *(0-930588; 0-9666691; 1-890771; 1-59714)* Orders Addr.: P.O. Box 9145, Berkeley, CA 94709 USA (SAN 207-2351) Tel 510-549-3564; Fax: 510-549-1889; Edit Addr.: 2054 University Ave., Berkeley, CA 94704-2687 USA ; *Imprints:* Great Valley Books (Grt Valley Bks)
E-mail: joanne@heydaybooks.com
Web site: http://www.heydaybooks.com
Dist(s): **SPD-Small Pr. Distribution.**

Heyokah Publishing Co., *(0-9656124; 1-930910)* 7244 Lattigo Dr., Nampa, ID 83687 USA Tel 208-465-5809
E-mail: hiheyokah@aol.com
Dist(s): **New Leaf Distributing Co., Inc.**

Hez-N-Tales, *(0-9745349)* 11037 Hopewell Rd., Boaz, KY 42027 USA
Web site: http://www.feedinghislambs.org.

Hi.I.Que Publishing, *(0-9631333; 1-887492)* Div. of The Guthrie Studio, P.O. Box 508, Claremont, CA 91711 USA Tel 909-622-7501; Fax: 909-622-4942
E-mail: hiiquepublish@aol.com
Web site: http://www.hiiquepublishing.com.

Hi Willow Research & Publishing, *(0-931510; 1-933170)* Orders Addr.: P.O. Box 720400, San Jose, CA 95172-0400 USA (SAN 211-3945) Toll Free: 800-873-3043
E-mail: sales@lmcsource.com
Web site: http://www.lmcsource.com
Dist(s): **L M C Source.**

Hiawatha Island Software *See* **HiSoftware, Inc.**

Hibbard Pubns., Inc., *(1-931343)* P.O. Box 3091, Wilmington, DE 19804-0091 USA Fax: 302-992-0122
E-mail: info@hibbardpub.com.

Hibiscus Pr., *(0-9647763)* P.O. Box 77066, Coral Springs, FL 33077 USA (SAN 298-9506) Tel 813-528-8851; Fax: 813-528-8466; Toll Free: 800-356-9315
E-mail: bjd@aol.com
Dist(s): **Quality Bks., Inc.**
Unique Bks., Inc.

Hiccup Cottage Pubns., *(0-9718724)* 316 10th St., NE, Charlottesville, VA 22902 USA Tel 434-980-5347
E-mail: hiccupcottage@yahoo.com.

Hickle Pickle Publishing, *(1-881958)* 4450 Allison Dr., Michigan Center, MI 49254 USA Tel 517-764-1117
E-mail: hicklepickle@modempool.com
Web site: www.hicklepickle.com.

Hickory Bark Productions, *(0-9748047)* 3355 N. Five Mile Rd., Suite 332, Boise, ID 83713 USA Tel 208-322-7239.

Hickory Grove Pr., *(0-9679915)* 3135 Treeco Ln., Bellevue, IA 52031 USA Do not confuse with Hickory Grove Pr., Canton, OH
E-mail: challengemath@aol.com
Web site: http://www.challengemath.com.

Hickory Hse., *(1-886706)* Orders Addr.: P.O. Box 37, Eastville, VA 23347 USA Tel 804-678-7283; Fax: 804-678-7285; Edit Addr.: 15565 Courthouse Rd., Eastville, VA 23347 USA
E-mail: hickooryhouse@hickoryhouse.com
Web site: http://www.hickoryhouse.com.

Hickory Pubns., *(0-9700404)* 4 So. Grandview Dr., Latham, NY 12110 USA
E-mail: gturner@capital.net
Web site: http:/www.capital.net/com/gturner/.

Hickory Tales Publishing, *(0-9709104; 0-9787555)* Orders Addr.: 841 Newberry St., Bowling Green, KY 42103 USA Tel 270-791-3242
E-mail: jadonel@aol.com
Web site: http://www.hickorytales.com
Dist(s): **Baker & Taylor Bks.**
Book Clearing Hse.

Hidden Curriculum Education, *(0-9755103)* Orders Addr.: P.O. Box 222041, Hollywood, FL 33022 USA Tel 954-457-8098; Fax: 954-457-3331
Web site: http://www.collegefaqbook.com.

Hidden Forest Pubs., *(0-9755117)* 269 Co. Hwy. 250, Guin, AL 35563-2700 USA.

Hidden Lakes Pr., *(0-9715563)* P.O. Box 1240, Evergreen, CO 80437-1240 USA
E-mail: al@hiddenlakespress.com
Web site: http://www.hiddenlakespress.com.

Hidden Path Pubn., Inc., *(0-9711534)* 304 Briarwood Rd., Statesville, NC 28677 USA Tel 704-878-0716; 704-224-4832
E-mail: dkellysteele@aol.com.

Hidden Pictures, *(0-9678159)* Orders Addr.: P.O. Box 63, Tipp City, OH 45371-9103 USA (SAN 253-6862) Tel 937-667-6288; Fax: 937-669-4178
E-mail: hiddenpictures@aol.com
Web site: http://members.aol.com/HiddenPictures/.

Higginson Bk. Co., *(0-7404; 0-8328)* 148 Washington St., Salem, MA 01970 USA (SAN 247-9400) Tel 978-745-7170; Fax: 978-745-8025
E-mail: higginsn@cove.com
Web site: http://higginsonbooks.com.

High Country Publishers *See* **Ingalls Publishing Group, Inc**

High Desert Productions, *(0-9652920)* Orders Addr.: P.O. Box 5506, Bisbee, AZ 85603 USA Tel 520-432-5288; Edit Addr.: 511 Mance St., Bisbee, AZ 85603 USA
Dist(s): **Treasure Chest Bks.**

High Desert Publishing, *(0-9759110)* 6542 40th Ave., SW, Seattle, WA 98136-1810 USA Tel 206-938-4969 Do not confuse with High Desert Publishing in Elko, NV or Junction City, OR, Leneta, OR
E-mail: magazinesales@comcast.net; orders@bearmagsales.com
Web site: http://www.bearmagsales.com.

High Five *Imprint of* **Red Brick Learning**

High Ground Productions, Incorporated *See* **High Ground Pubns.**

High Ground Pubns., *(0-9720153)* 80 Supai Dr., Sedona, AZ 86351 USA (SAN 254-5748) Tel 360-945-2485
E-mail: Karen@amatteroftime.org
Web site: http://www.amatteroftime.org.

High Haven Music, *(0-9632621; 1-889686)* P.O. Box 246, Sonoita, AZ 85637-0246 USA Tel 520-455-5769
E-mail: sales@highhavenmusic.com
Web site: http://www.highhavenmusic.com
Dist(s): **Baker & Taylor Bks.**
Educational Record Ctr., Inc.
Professional Media Service Corp.

High Hopes Publishing, *(0-9708417)* Subs. of Communication Arts Multimedia, Inc., PMB 22, R.D. 4, Ligonier, PA 15658 USA Tel 724-238-1281; Fax: 724-238-1279; Toll Free: 888-742-0074
E-mail: mail@commartsmultimedia.com; cloud@BoTheCloud.com
Web site: http://commartsmultimedia; http://www.BoTheCloud.com.

High Impact Publishing, *(1-891793)* Div. of Touch Phoenix Ministries, Orders Addr.: P.O. Box 5003, Glendale, AZ 85312 USA Tel 623-979-3544; Fax: 623-486-7955; Toll Free: 800-729-6884; Edit Addr.: 8155 W. Thunderbird Rd., Suite 102, Peoria, AZ 85381 USA Do not confuse with High Impact Publishing, Guerneville, CA
E-mail: hiimpact@cellgroup.com; dawson@authorspublishing.com
Web site: http://www.cellgroup.com.

High Mountain Publishing, *(0-9718609)* Tarzana Karate Studio 19618 Ventura Blvd., Tarzana, CA 91356 USA Tel 818-645-8621
E-mail: uescher@hotmail.com
Web site: http://www.greatwarriorpak.com/store.htm; http://www.uescher.com/hmp; http://www.howtotrick.com
Dist(s): **AtlasBooks Distribution.**

High Noon Bks., *(0-87879; 1-57128)* Div. of Academic Therapy Pubns., Inc., 20 Commercial Blvd., Novato, CA 94949-6191 USA Tel 415-883-3314; Fax: 415-883-3720; Toll Free: 800-422-7249
E-mail: atpub@aol.com
Web site: http://www.atpub.com.

High Score, *(0-9664845)* 1014 Signal Hill Ln., Berwyn, PA 19312 USA Tel 610-408-9645; Fax: 610-408-0565
E-mail: reneemazer@aol.com
Dist(s): **Penton Overseas, Inc.**

High Standards Publishing, Incorporated *See* **True Exposures Publishing, Inc.**

High Tide Pr., *(0-9653744; 1-892696)* 3650 W. 183rd St., Homewood, IL 60430-2603 USA Tel 708-206-2054 Do not confuse with The Trinity Foundation, Hobbs, NM
E-mail: alex@hightidepress.com; mregan@hightidepress.com
Web site: http://www.hightidepress.com.

Higher Balance Institute, *(0-9759080)* 515 NW Saltzman Rd., No.726, Portland, OR 97229 USA Tel 503-646-4000; Toll Free: 800-935-4007
E-mail: publishing@higherbalance.com
Web site: http://www.higherbalance.com.

Higher Consciousness Bks., *(0-932927)* P.O. Box 2700, Oroville, WA 98844 USA (SAN 692-9508) Tel 250-446-2022; Toll Free: 800-336-6015 Do not confuse with Higher Consciousness Bks. in Spokane, WA
E-mail: office@HUMUH.org
Web site: http://www.humuh.org
Dist(s): **Baker & Taylor Bks.**
New Leaf Distributing Co., Inc.

Higher Education Ministries International, Inc., *(0-9706949; 0-9726512)* Orders Addr.: P.O. Box 4752, Marietta, GA 30061 USA Tel 770-333-8642; Fax: 770-333-8678; Edit Addr.: 1803 Silver Leaf Dr., Marietta, GA 30008 USA
E-mail: joabram@ephesians210.org; joabram@earthlink.net.

Higher Ground Pr., *(0-9766062)* P.O. Box 729, Allen, TX 75013 USA Tel 214-680-9779; Fax: 972-678-1121
E-mail: info@highergroundpress.com
Web site: Highergroundpress.com.

Highland Children's Pr. *Imprint of* **Heather & Highlands Publishing**

Highland Circle Publishing, *(0-9743126)* Orders Addr.: P.O. Box 3164, Silver Spring, MD 20918 USA Tel 301-587-6267; Fax: 301-587-6354; Edit Addr.: 720 Guilford Ct., Silver Spring, MD 20901-3218 USA
E-mail: cynthia@potomactalent.com
Web site: http://www.cynthiacathcart.net.

Highland Pr., *(0-910722)* 10108 Johns Rd., Boerne, TX 78006 USA (SAN 204-0522) Do not confuse with companies of the same name or similar in Birmingham, AL, Wilsonville, OR, Tonasket, WA, Bryson City, NC, San Rafael, CA, High Springs, FL.

Highland Publishing Group, *(0-945783)* Orders Addr.: P.O. Box 554, Los Gatos, CA 95031 USA (SAN 247-932X) Tel 408-353-5756; Fax: 408-353-3388; Edit Addr.: 25525 Mt. Bache Rd., Los Gatos, CA 95030 USA (SAN 247-9338) Do not confuse with companies with similar names in Edina, MN, Pittsburg, CA
E-mail: es@highlandpublishing.com
Web site: http://www.highlandpublishing.com
Dist(s): **Alta Bk. Co., Pubs.**
Delta Systems Co., Inc.

Highlight Publishing, *(0-9741734)* P.O. Box 27, Little Falls, MN 56345 USA Tel 320-630-1463; Toll Free: 866-336-6681
E-mail: books@highlightpublishing.com
Web site: http://www.highlightpublishing.com.

Highlights for Children, *(0-87534)* Orders Addr.: P.O. Box 269, Columbus, OH 43216-0269 USA (SAN 281-7810) Tel 614-486-0631; Fax: 614-876-8564; Toll Free: 800-255-9517; Edit Addr.: 803 Church St., Honesdale, PA 18431 USA (SAN 281-7802) Tel 570-253-1080; Fax: 570-253-1179
Web site: http://www.highlights.com
Dist(s): **Boyds Mills Pr.**

Highlights of Chicago Pr., *(0-9710487)* 4325 N. Central Park Ave., Chicago, IL 60618 USA Tel 773-509-0008 (phone/fax)
E-mail: bturner@highlightsofchicago.com
Web site: http://www.highlightsofchicago.com.

High-Lonesome Bks., *(0-944383)* Orders Addr.: P.O. Box 878, Silver City, NM 88062 USA (SAN 243-3079) Tel 505-388-3763; Fax: 505-388-5705; Toll Free: 800-380-7323 (orders only)
E-mail: Cherie@High-LonesomeBooks.com
Web site: http://www.high-lonesomebooks.com.

High-Pitched Hum Inc., *(0-9759818; 0-9777290; 0-9787995; 0-9792780; 1-934666)* 321 15th St., N., Jacksonville Beach, FL 32250 USA
E-mail: breynolds@jettyman.com
Web site: http://www.highpitchedhum.net.

HighPoint Publishing, Inc. *See* **HighPoint Publishing, Inc.**

HighPoint Publishing, Inc., *(1-933190)* Orders Addr.: 141 Loop 64, Suite E, Dripping Springs, TX 78620 USA (SAN 256-2952)
E-mail: kenc@highpointpublishing.com; milena@highpointpublishing.com
Web site: http://www.HighPointPublishing.com.

HighReach Learning, Inc., *(1-57332)* P.O. Box 35665, Greensboro, NC 27409 USA Tel 336-632-0084
E-mail: cstauffer@carsondellosa.com
Web site: http://www.highreach.com
Dist(s): **Midpoint Trade Bks., Inc.**

†High/Scope Pr., *(0-929816; 0-931114; 1-57379)* Div. of High/Scope Educational Research Foundation, 600 N. River St., Ypsilanti, MI 48198-2898 USA (SAN 211-9617) Tel 734-485-2000; Fax: 734-485-0704; Toll Free Fax: 800-442-4329 (orders); Toll Free: 800-407-7377 (orders only)
E-mail: info@highscope.org
Web site: http://www.highscope.org
Dist(s): **Thomson Delmar Learning**; *CIP.*

Highsmith Inc., *(0-913853; 0-917846; 1-57950; 1-932146; 1-59847; 1-60213)* W5527 State Rd.. 106 P.O. Box 800, Fort Atkinson, WI 53538 USA (SAN 159-8740) Tel 920-563-9571; Fax: 920-563-7395; Toll Free: 800-448-4887 ; *Imprints:* Upstart Books (Upstart Bks)
Web site: http://www.highsmith.com
Dist(s): **Rand McNally**
Women Ink.

Highsmith Press, LLC *See* **Highsmith Inc.**

Highwater Bks., *(0-9665363; 0-9700858; 1-932510)* P.O. Box 3115, Champlain, NY 12919-3115 USA
E-mail: tom@highwaterbooks.com
Web site: http://www.highwaterbooks.com
Dist(s): **LPC Group.**

Hignites, Tom Miracle Studio, *(1-934017)* Orders Addr.: 1977 Mayfield Rd., Richfield, WI 53076-5307 USA (SAN 850-9611) Tel 262-628-5577; Fax: 262-628-5580; Edit Addr.: 3070 Hwy. 145, Richfield, WI 53076-5307 USA
E-mail: jbrown@miracle-homes.com
Web site: http://tomhignitesmiraclestudios.com.

Hildebrand, Betty, *(0-9753729)* 116 Rosetta Ct., Springdale, OH 45246 USA
E-mail: deona@bethart.com
Web site: http://www.bethart.com.

Hiley, Matthew, *(0-9717970)* 2016 Misty Creek, Arlington, TX 76017 USA Tel 214-704-5027.

Hill & Wang *Imprint of* **Farrar, Straus & Giroux**

Hill, Lawrence Bks. *Imprint of* **Chicago Review Pr., Inc.**

Hill, Napoleon Foundation, *(1-880369)* Friends of Napoleon Hill, 19458 S. La Grange Rd., Mokena, IL 60448 USA Tel 847-998-0408; Fax: 847-998-6890; Toll Free Fax: 800-957-9124; Toll Free: 800-957-9114
E-mail: 70543.3377@compuserve.com
Web site: http://www.naphill.org.

Hill Publishing *See* **SunHill Pubs.**

Hill Publishing, *(0-9714042)* Orders Addr.: P.O. Box 279, Marina, CA 93933 USA Tel 831-384-4618 Do not confuse with Hill Publishing in Lawrenceville, GA
E-mail: hillpublishingcompany@msn.com
Web site: http://www.hillpublishingcompany.20m.com.

Hill, Stephanie & Clarissa, *(0-9785539)* P.O. Box 13212, Baltimore, MD 21203-3212 USA (SAN 850-9816) Tel 443-838-9426
E-mail: sachedesignsinc@yahoo.com
Web site: http://www.sachedesigns.com.

Hill Street Pr., LLC, *(1-892514; 1-58818)* 191 E. Broad St. Ste. 216, Athens, GA 30601-2848 USA Toll Free: 800-295-0365 ; *Imprints:* Hot Cross Books (Hot Cross Bks)
E-mail: info@hillstreetpress.com
Web site: http://www.hillstreetpress.com
Dist(s): **Gibbs Smith, Publisher**
Beeler, Thomas T. Pub.

HillHouse Publishing, *(0-9636071)* 91 Wood Rd., Centereach, NY 11720-1619 USA Tel 516-585-2592.

Hilliard & Harris, *(0-9704304; 1-59133)* P.O. Box 0275, Boonsboro, MD 21713-0275 USA Tel 301-432-7080; Fax: 301-432-7505; 301-432-7391
E-mail: sareilly@hilliardandharris.com; hilliardharris@aol.com
Web site: http://www.hilliardandharris.com.

Hillsboro Pr. *Imprint of* **Providence Hse Pubs.**

Hillsdale Educational Pubs., Inc., *(0-910726; 1-931466)* 39 North St., Box 245, Hillsdale, MI 49242 USA (SAN 159-8759) Tel 517-437-3179; Fax: 517-437-0531
E-mail: davestory@aol.com
Web site: http://www.michbooks.com; http://www.hillsdalepublishers.com.

Hillside Education, *(0-9766386; 0-9798469)* 475 Bidwell Hill Rd., Lake Ariel, PA 18436 USA (SAN 257-4446)
E-mail: sales@hillsideeducation.com; info@hillsideeducation.com
Web site: http://www.hillsideeducation.com.

Hillview Bks., *(0-9708131)* P.O. Box 3473, Los Altos, CA 94024 USA Tel 650-967-4933 (phone/fax)
E-mail: sumant@earthlink.net; sumant@best.com
Web site: http://www.hillviewbooks.com
Dist(s): **Baker & Taylor Bks.**
Quality Bks., Inc.

Hill-Ward, Robin, *(0-9677955)* 6 Harbor Way, Santa Barbara, CA 93103 USA Tel 805-966-3536.

Hilsman, Lenora N. & Connie Eberhart, *(0-9703305)* 8835 W. Wethersfield Rd., Peoria, AZ 85381 USA Tel 623-486-1731
E-mail: linty88@aol.com; comongoose@mindspring.com.

Himminbjorg Publishing, Inc., *(0-9749416)* P.O. Box 6493, Napa, CA 94581 USA Tel 707-251-9526 (phone/fax)
E-mail: himminbjorg@aol.com
Web site: http://www.wyrdsway.com.

Hindsight, Ltd., *(1-929031)* Orders Addr.: P.O. Box 46406, Eden Prairie, MN 55347 USA
E-mail: hindsightlimited@aol.com
Web site: http://www.hindsightlimited.com
Dist(s): **Baker & Taylor Bks.**
Bookmen, Inc.
Quality Bks., Inc.

Hinkler Bks. Pty, Ltd. (AUS) *(1-86515; 1-74121; 1-875980; 1-74157; 1-74181; 1-74182; 1-74183; 1-74184; 1-74185) Dist. by* **Penton Overseas.**

Hinman, Bobbie E. Inc., *(0-9632524; 0-9786791)* 1241 Chateau Green Ct., Bel Air, MD 21015 USA (SAN 851-2930) Tel 410-879-7578
E-mail: fairybooklady@aol.com
Dist(s): **Biblio Distribution.**

HinterWelt Enterprises, LLC, *(0-9740096)* 7504 W. Hickory Creek Dr., Frankfort, IL 60423-9094 USA
E-mail: winna@hinterwelt.com
Web site: http://www.hinterwelt.com.

Hip Hop Schl. House, *(0-9768674)* 8618 S. Constance, Chicago, IL 60617 USA Tel 793-218-4204
Dist(s): **AtlasBooks Distribution.**

Hippocratic Pr., The, *(0-9753516)* 281A Fairhaven Hill Rd., Concord, MA 01742 USA Tel 978-369-0739
E-mail: ccowanmd@hippocraticpress.com
Web site: http://www.hippocraticpress.com
Dist(s): **National Bk. Network.**

†Hippocrene Bks., Inc., *(0-7818; 0-87052; 0-88254)* 171 Madison Ave., New York, NY 10016-1002 USA (SAN 213-2060) Tel 718-454-2366 (sales); 212-685-4371 (editorial); Fax: 718-454-1391 (sales/order inquiry); 212-779-9338 (editorial)
E-mail: hippocre@ix.netcom.com
Web site: http://www.hippocrenebooks.com
Dist(s): **Continental Bk. Co., Inc.**; *CIP.*

Hippogryph *See* **Orange Avenue Publishing**

Hippoville Publishing, LLC, *(0-9722265)* 679 Boston Post Rd., Darien, CT 06820 USA Tel 203-606-4526
E-mail: hippopub@hotmail.com
Web site: http://www.hippoville.biz.

Hired Pen, Inc., The *See* **Acacia Publishing, Inc.**

Hirsch & Assocs., Inc., *(0-9674418)* 160 W. Carmel Dr. Ste. 216, Carmel, IN 46032-2531 USA Toll Free: 800-369-8926
E-mail: sales@hirschinc.com
Web site: http://www.hirschinc.com.

His Grace Is Sufficient *Imprint of* **ELW Pubns.**

His Hands, Inc., *(0-9720881)* Orders Addr.: P.O. Box 7063, Oak Ridge, TN 37831 USA Tel 865-482-9562; Edit Addr.: 82 E. Tennessee Ave., Apt. 117, Oak Ridge, TN 37830 USA (SAN 255-2930) Tel 865-482-9562
E-mail: hishandstn@netzero.com
Web site: http://www.hishands.org.

His Kids Publishing, Inc., *(0-9720417)* Orders Addr.: P.O. Box 72172, Marietta, GA 30007 USA Tel 770-998-3240; Fax: 770-998-4943; Edit Addr.: 1544 Sandpoint Dr., Roswell, GA 30075 USA
E-mail: management@intrag-publishing.com
Web site: http://www.intrag-publishing.com.

His Majesty's Pubns., *(0-9709986)* 322 S. Morton St., Waupaca, WI 54981 USA Tel 715-256-9110 (phone/fax)
E-mail: rodgerje@g2a.net.

His Seasons, *(0-9724287)* 8122 Datapoint Dr., Suite 1000, San Antonio, TX 78229 USA Tel 210-490-2101; Fax: 210-490-4102
E-mail: info@hisseasons.com
Web site: http://www.hisseasons.com.

His Sonshine, Inc., *(0-9758880)* 13214 Barwick Rd., Del Ray Beach, FL 33445 USA.

His Story, *(0-9766951)* 1409 Coolhurst, Sherwood, AR 72120 USA
Web site: http://www.hisstory.org.

His Work Christian Publishing, *(0-9778328; 0-9798290; 0-9799189)* Orders Addr.: P.O. Box 5732, Ketchikan, AK 99901 USA Tel 206-274-8474; Fax: 614-388-0664; Edit Addr.: 11385 N. Tongass Hwy. SPC 111, ketchikan, AL 99901 USA
E-mail: hiswork@hisworkpub.com; editor@hisworkpub.com
Web site: http://www.hisworkpub.com
Dist(s): **Lightning Source, Inc.**

HiSoftware, Inc., *(1-930616)* 6 Chenell Dr., Suite 280, Concord, NH 03301 USA Tel 603-229-3055; Fax: 603-223-9741; Toll Free: 888-272-2484
E-mail: ryonaitis@hisoftware.com
Web site: http://www.hisoftware.com.

Hispanic Publishing Works, Inc., *(0-922665)* 27-40 14th St., Astoria, NY 11102 USA (SAN 251-3757) Tel 718-932-1633
E-mail: hipuwo@nich.com.

Historic Carnton Plantation Assn., Inc., *(0-9667267)* 1345 Carnton Ln., Franklin, TN 37064 USA Tel 615-794-0903; Fax: 615-794-4275.

Historic Mint Co., The, *(0-9753767)* 36 Sandwedge Dr., Henderson, NV 89074-1714 USA Toll Free: 877-264-6266
Web site: http://www.historicmint.com.

Historic Pr.-South, *(0-9645990)* Orders Addr.: P.O. Box 407, Gatlinburg, TN 37738 USA Tel 423-436-4163; Toll Free: 800-279-2603; Edit Addr.: 367 Buckhorn Rd., Gatlinburg, TN 37738 USA.

Historic Tours of America, Inc., *(0-9752698)* 201 Front St., Suite 224, Key West, FL 33040 USA Tel 305-292-8920; Fax: 305-295-4999
E-mail: psmith@historictours.com
Web site: http://www.historictours.com.

Historical Pages Co., *(0-9772692)* 188 Main St., 3rd Flr., Poultney, VT 05764 USA (SAN 257-1625) Tel 802-287-2332; Fax: 802-287-2227
E-mail: historpg@sover.net
Web site: http://www.historicalpages.com
Dist(s): **Independent Pubs. Group.**

Historical Society of Michigan, The, *(0-9614344; 1-880311)* 1305 Abbott Rd., East Lansing, MI 48823 USA (SAN 687-8008) Tel 734-769-1828; Fax: 517-324-4370
E-mail: hsm@hsmichigan.org
Web site: http://www.hsmichigan.org.

†Historical Society of Rockland County, The, *(0-911183)* 20 Zukor Rd., New City, NY 10956 USA (SAN 211-4488) Tel 845-634-9629; Fax: 845-634-8690
E-mail: info@rocklandhistory.org
Web site: http://www.RocklandHistory.org; *CIP.*

History Co., The, *(0-941425)* P.O. Box 222612, Carmel, CA 93922-2612 USA (SAN 665-5564) Tel 831-624-2456 Do not confuse with History Company LLC in Ithaca, NY
E-mail: histryco@redshift.com
Web site: http://www.thehistorycompany.com.

History Compass, LLC, *(1-57960; 1-878668; 1-932663)* 25 Leslie Rd., Auburndale, MA 02466 USA (SAN 297-2611) Tel 617-332-2202; Fax: 617-332-2210
E-mail: info@historycompass.com; lisa@historycompass.com
Web site: http://www.historycompass.com
Dist(s): **Baker & Taylor Bks.**
Follett Library Resources
Social Studies Schl. Service.

Hither Creek Pr., *(0-9700555)* 14 Holman St., Laconia, NH 03246-3016 USA Do not confuse with Hither Creek Press in Nantucket, MA
E-mail: hithercreekpress@aol.com.

Hi-Time Pflaum *See* **Pflaum Publishing Group**

Hoard, W.D. & Sons Co., *(0-932147)* P.O. Box 801, Fort Atkinson, WI 53538-0801 USA (SAN 686-4341) Tel 920-563-5551; Fax: 920-563-7298 ; *Imprints:* Hoard's Dairyman (Hoards Dairyman)
Web site: http://www.hoards.com.

Hoard's Dairyman *Imprint of* **Hoard, W.D. & Sons Co.**

Hobar Pubns., *(0-89317; 0-913163; 0-933855; 0-9616847; 1-55797)* Div. of Finney Co., Orders Addr.: 8075 215th St. W., Lakeville, MN 55044 USA (SAN 283-1120) Tel 952-469-6699; Fax: 952-469-1968; Toll Free Fax: 800-330-6232; Toll Free: 800-846-7027
E-mail: feedback@finneyco.com
Web site: http://www.finney-hobar.com
Dist(s): **Baker & Taylor Bks.**
Book Wholesalers, Inc.
Brodart Co.
Follett Library Resources
Midpoint Trade Bks., Inc.
Southern Bk. Service.

Hobbs, Brenda F., *(0-9772970)* 14303 Greenview Rd., Detroit, MI 48223 USA
E-mail: bhobbs101@aol.com.

Hobby Hse. Pr., Inc., *(0-87588)* One Corporate Dr., Grantsville, MD 21536 USA (SAN 204-059X) Tel 301-895-3792; Fax: 301-895-5029; Toll Free: 800-554-1447
E-mail: email@hobbyhouse.com
Web site: http://www.hobbyhouse.com.

Hobby Hse. Publishing Group, *(0-9727179)* 48 Hickory Hill Rd., Box 1527, Jackson, NJ 08527 USA Fax: 732-886-7371
Web site: http://www.hobbyhousepublishinggroup.com.

Hodder Children's Division (GBR) Dist. by IPG Chicago.

Hodder Education (GBR) *(0-340; 0-412; 0-7506) Dist. by* **Trafalgar.**

Hodder Education (GBR) *(0-340; 0-412; 0-7506) Dist. by* **OUP.**

Hodder Education (GBR) *(0-340; 0-412; 0-7506) Dist. by* **Trans-Atl Phila.**

Hodder General Publishing Division (GBR) Dist. by Trafalgar.

Hodder General Publishing Division (GBR) Dist. by IPG Chicago.

Hoffman Enterprises, *(0-9718721)* 1064 Whytecliffe Rd., Palatine, IL 60067 USA
E-mail: rebebccahoffman@msn.com.

Hoffman, Mark *See* **Hramiec Hoffman Publishing**

Hoffmann Partnership, The, *(0-9753106)* 349 Martin Ln., Bloomingdale, IL 60108-1326 USA
E-mail: Catherine@WriteHappy.com; info@writehappy.com
Web site: http://www.writehappy.com.

Hogan Publishing LLC, *(0-9779504)* 2708 E. Edison, Tucson, AZ 85716 USA
E-mail: benjamin@madseadog.com
Web site: http://www.madseadog.com.

Hohm Pr., *(0-934252; 1-890772)* Div. of Hohm, Inc., P.O. Box 2501, Prescott, AZ 86302 USA (SAN 221-0924) Tel 520-778-9189; Fax: 520-717-1779; Toll Free: 800-381-2700 (orders only)
E-mail: staff@hohmpress.com; pinedr@goodnet.com
Web site: http://www.hohmpress.com
Dist(s): **SCB Distributors.**

Holbrook Studios, *(0-9762440)* Orders Addr.: P.O. Box 3064, Beverly Hills, CA 90212 USA; Edit Addr.: 754 E. S. Temple, Salt Lake city, UT 84102 USA
Web site: http://www.gingerbreadjimmi.com.

Hole in the Head Pr., *(0-615; 0-9761494)* P.O. Box 807, Bodega Bay, CA 94923 USA Tel 707-875-3928 (phone/fax)
E-mail: sestokes@sonic.net
Web site: http://www.holeintheheadpress.com
Dist(s): **Baker & Taylor Bks.**

Holes In My Socks Publishing, *(0-9771891)* P.O. Box 266, Paola, KS 66071 USA Tel 913-557-4508
Dist(s): **Midpoint Trade Bks., Inc.**

†Holiday Hse., Inc., *(0-8234)* Orders Addr.: 425 Madison Ave., New York, NY 10017 USA (SAN 202-3008) Tel 212-688-0085; Fax: 212-688-0395
E-mail: holiday@holidayhouse.com
Web site: http://www.holidayhouse.com; *CIP.*

Holiness.com, *(0-9743831)* 1271 Washington Ave., PMB 165, San Leandro, CA 94577 USA Tel 510-384-8082
E-mail: suppliers@holiness.com
Web site: http://www.holiness.com.

Holland, Gretchen, *(0-9768340)* 4437 Craig Dr., Fort Collins, CO 80526 USA Tel 970-282-1338.

Hollar, Cheryl Public Relations, *(0-9763826)* Orders Addr.: 218 S. Cheatham St., Franklinton, NC 27525 USA Tel 919-494-2150
E-mail: cherylfhollar@yahoo.com;
billythebunnybooks@yahoo.com.

Hollingsworth, Kenneth, *(0-9771572)* 2215 Janet Ct., Cedar Hill, TX 75104-1021 USA (SAN 256-8926)
Web site: http://www.hollingsworthtexas.com/plantingtheseeds.

Holloway Hse. Publishing Co., *(0-87067)* Orders Addr.: 8060 Melrose Ave., Los Angeles, CA 90046 USA (SAN 206-8451) Tel 323-653-8060; Fax: 323-655-9452 ; *Imprints:* Melrose Square (Melrose Sq)
E-mail: info@psiemail.com
Web site: http://www.hollowayhousebooks.com
Dist(s): **All America Distributors Corp.**

Holloway, J Company, *(0-9725086)* 280 W. Renner Rd., No. 1612, Richardson, TX 75080-1353 USA
Web site: http://www.charmbook.com.

Holly Hall Pubns., Inc., *(0-9645396; 1-888306)* P.O. Box 254, Elkton, MD 21922-0254 USA Tel 410-392-2300; Fax: 410-620-9877; Toll Free: 800-211-0719 ; *Imprints:* Home School Press (Home School Pr); Full Quart Press (Full Quart Pr)
Dist(s): **Spring Arbor Distributors, Inc.**

HollyBear Pr., *(0-9651067)* Orders Addr.: P.O. Box 4257, Prescott, AZ 86302-4257 USA Tel 928-776-4689; Edit Addr.: 910 Stevens Dr., Prescott, AZ 86305 USA
E-mail: monamc2@msn.com.

Hollybug, Polly Inc., *(0-9705740)* 6670 Vernon Ave., S, Minneapolis, MN 55436 USA Tel 952-935-9940; Fax: 952-938-3595.

Hollym International Corp., *(0-930878; 1-56591)* 18 Donald Pl., Elizabeth, NJ 07208 USA (SAN 211-0172) Tel 908-353-1655; Fax: 908-353-0255 Do not confuse with Hollym Corporation Pubs., New York, NY
E-mail: hollym2@optonline.net; contact@hollym.com
Web site: http://www.hollym.com.

Hollywood Jesus Bks., *(0-9759577; 0-9787554)* P.O. Box 48282, Burien, WA 98166 USA Tel 206-241-6149
E-mail: editor@hjbooks.com
Web site: http://www.hjbooks.com.

Hollywood Operating System, *(1-893899)* 400 S. Beverly Dr., Suite 307, Beverly Hills, CA 90212 USA Tel 310-289-9400; Fax: 310-277-3088
E-mail: hollywoodos@aol.com
Web site: http://www.HollywoodOS.com
Dist(s): **AtlasBooks Distribution.**

HollywoodComics.com, LLC, *(0-9740711; 1-932983; 1-934543)* P.O. Box 17270, Encino, CA 91416 USA (SAN 255-366X) Tel 818-995-7733 ; *Imprints:* Black Coat Press (Black Coat Pr)
E-mail: info@hollywoodcomics.com; info@riviereblanche.com; jean-marc@hollywoodcomics.com; info@blackcoatpress.com
Web site: http://www.hexagoncomics.com; http://www.blackcoatpress.com; http://www.riviereblanche.com.

Holman, Doris Anne, *(0-9667192; 0-9758630)* 5 Oak Ledge Rd., Harpswell, ME 04079 USA.

Holmlund Distributing, *(1-892661)* 1612 Tompy St., Miles City, MT 59301 USA Tel 406-232-6764; Fax: 406-232-6061; Toll Free: 877-846-7827
E-mail: holmlund@midrivers.com
Web site: http://www.earlbook.com.

Holocaust Museum Houston, *(0-9659781; 0-9773988)* 5401 Caroline St., Houston, TX 77004-6804 USA Tel 713-942-8000; Fax: 713-942-7953
E-mail: info@hmh.org
Web site: http://www.hmh.org
Dist(s): **Hervey's Booklink & Cookbook Warehouse.**

Holocaust Survivors' Memoirs Project, *(0-9760739)* c/o World Jewish Congress, 501 Madison Ave., New York, NY 10022 USA Fax: 212-717-1934
E-mail: jrosensaft@hvc.edu.

Holocene Press *See* **Hub City Writers Project**

Holofcener, Mark, *(0-9718626)* 7323 Island Cir., Boulder, CO 80301-3905 USA
E-mail: mark@evansadventure.com
Web site: http://www.evansadventure.com.

Holt, David, *(0-9658897)* Orders Addr.: P.O. Box 543, Goleta, CA 93116 USA Tel 805-569-9439
E-mail: holtrun@sprynet.com
Web site: http://www.runningbook.com; http://home.sprynet.com/~holtrun/10krun
Dist(s): **Distributors, The.**

Holt Enterprise, LLC, *(0-9740016)* Orders Addr.: P.O. Box 414, Riverside, NJ 08075 USA (SAN 255-2760) Tel 856-764-7043; Fax: 856-764-0851; Toll Free: 888-944-4658; Edit Addr.: 147 N. Fairview St., Riverside, NJ 08075 USA
E-mail: HoltEnterprise@comcast.net; holt109@comcast.net
Dist(s): **Quality Bks., Inc.**

Holt, Henry & Co. Bks. For Young Readers *Imprint of* **Holt, Henry & Co.**

Company

Company

†Holt, Henry & Co., *(0-03; 0-8050)* Div. of Holtzbrinck Publishers, Orders Addr.: 16365 James Madison Hwy., Gordonsville, VA 22942-8501 USA Toll Free Fax: 800-672-2054; Toll Free: 888-330-8477; Edit Addr.: 115 W. 18th St., 5th Flr., New York, NY 10011 USA (SAN 200-6472) Tel 212-886-9200; Fax: 540-672-7540 (customer service) ; *Imprints:* Owl Books (Owl); Metropolitan Books (Metropol Bks); Owlet Paperbacks for Young Readers (Owlet Pbks); Times Books (Times Bks); Holt, Henry & Company Books For Young Readers (HH Bks Yng Read); Holt Paperback (Holt Paperbck)
E-mail: info@hholt.com
Web site: http://www.henryholt.com
Dist(s): **Giron Bks.**
Lectorum Pubns., Inc.
Macmillan
Sony CONNECT, Inc.
Weston Woods Studios, Inc.; *CIP.*

Holt Paperback *Imprint of* **Holt, Henry & Co.**

Holt, Rinehart & Winston, *(0-03; 0-544)* Div. of Harcourt, Inc., Orders Addr.: 6277 Sea Harbor Dr., Orlando, FL 32887-0001 USA Tel 407-345-3800; Fax: 407-352-3395; Toll Free Fax: 800-235-0256; Toll Free: 800-544-6678; Edit Addr.: a/o School Div., 10801 N. Mopac Expressway, Bldg. 3, Austin, TX 78759-5415 USA (SAN 297-4711) Tel 512-721-7000 Toll Free: 800-992-1627
E-mail: holtinfo@hrw.com
Web site: http://www.gohrw.com
Dist(s): **Continental Bk. Co., Inc.**

Holt, Rinehart & Winston School Division *See* **Holt, Rinehart & Winston**

Holt, S. A. *See* **Holt, S.A. Publishing Inc.**

Holt, S.A. Publishing Inc., *(0-9701351; 0-9707405)* 5558 S. 79th East Pl., Tulsa, OK 74145 USA Tel 918-359-3343; Fax: 918-359-3344
E-mail: sanine@saholtpublishinginc.us.

Holtzbrinck Publishers *See* **Macmillan**

†Holy Cow! Pr., *(0-930100; 0-9779458)* P.O. Box 3170, Duluth, MN 55803 USA (SAN 685-3315) Tel 218-724-1653 (phone/fax)
Web site: http://www.holycowpress.org
Dist(s): **Consortium Bk. Sales & Distribution**
SPD-Small Pr. Distribution; *CIP.*

†Holy Cross Orthodox Pr., *(0-916586; 0-917651; 1-885652)* Div. of Hellenic College, Inc., 50 Goddard Ave., Brookline, MA 02445 USA (SAN 208-6840) Tel 617-731-3500 ext 1230; Fax: 617-850-1460; Toll Free: 800-245-0599
Dist(s): **Baker & Taylor Bks.**; *CIP.*

Holy Fire Publishing, *(0-9745212; 0-9761112; 0-9763756; 0-9766221; 0-9767211; 0-9769186; 0-9769957; 0-9772296; 0-9774242; 0-9774928; 1-933899; 1-60383)* 1525 D Old Trolley Rd., Unit 116, Summerville, SC 29485-8928 USA Tel 843-628-0319
E-mail: ed@christianpublish.com; vanessa@christianpublish.com.

Holy Ghost Writers Publishing, *(0-9662499)* PMB 208, 13146 Midlothian Tpke., Midlothian, VA 23113 USA Tel 804-379-1495; Fax: 804-379-4741
E-mail: ZoeHGWP@aol.com
Web site: http://www.galaxymall.com/religious/books.

Holy Macro! Bks. *Imprint of* **MrExcel.com Publishing**

Homa & Sekey Bks., *(0-9665421; 1-931907)* 3rd Floor, North Tower Mack-Cali Center III 140 East Ridgewood Ave, Paramus, NJ 07652 USA Tel 800-870-HOMA (4662) (Orders only); 201-261-8810; Fax: 201-261-8890
E-mail: info@homabooks.com
Web site: http://www.homabooks.com.

Homagno Group, Incorporated *See* **Editorial Homagno**

Home & Family Pubns., *(0-9723170; 0-9794658)* Orders Addr.: 3518 37th Ave., Moline, IL 61265 USA Tel 309-797-4149; Fax: 309-797-6323
E-mail: swpw@sbcglobal.net; fwpw@mchsi.com
Web site: http://hfp.bz; http://hfp.bz.

Home Discipleship Pr., *(0-9753133; 0-9785678)* 6645 W. Steger Rd., Monee, IL 60449 USA Tel 708-235-1901; Fax: 708-235-1904
E-mail: leaders@homediscipleship.orf
Web site: http://www.homediscipleshippress.org.

Home, Incorporated *See* **Cool Springs Pr.**

Home Planet Bks., *(0-9743712)* 2300 8th St., Encinitas, CA 92024-6565 USA Tel 760-634-4947.

Home Power, Inc., *(0-9629588; 0-9742385)* Orders Addr.: P.O. Box 275, Ashland, OR 97520-0010 USA Tel 541-944-5248; Fax: 541-512-0343; Edit Addr.: 312 N. Main St., Phoenix, OR 97535 USA Tel 916-475-3179; Fax: 916-475-0941; Toll Free: 800-707-6585
E-mail: karen.perez@homepower.com
Web site: http://www.homepower.com.

Home Run Publishing Company *See* **Santa's Publishing**

Home Sales Enhancements *See* **Castlebrook Pubns.**

Home Schl. in the Woods, *(0-9720265)* 3997 Roosevelt Hwy., Holley, NY 14470-9201 USA Tel 585-964-8188
E-mail: inwoods@rochester.rr.com
Web site: http://www.homeschoolinthewoods.com.

Home School Pr. *Imprint of* **Holly Hall Pubns., Inc.**

Home Team Pubns., *(1-893690)* 4240 Lost Hills, No. 2107, Agoura, CA 91301 USA Tel 818-876-8407; Fax: 818-876-8474
E-mail: kalli@netvip.com.

Homelight Pr., *(0-9749936)* P.O. Box 1901, Huntersville, NC 28070-1901 USA Toll Free: 877-438-6657
E-mail: homeligh@bellsouth.net.

Homer Historical Society, *(0-9770022)* 107 N. Main St., Homer, IL 61849 USA Tel 217-896-2549.

Homes for the Homeless, Inc., *(0-9641784; 0-9724425)* 36 Cooper Sq., Sixth Flr., New York, NY 10003 USA Tel 212-529-5252; Fax: 212-529-7698 ; *Imprints:* White Tiger Press (Wht Tiger Pr)
E-mail: info@homesforthehomeless.com
Web site: http://www.homesforthehomeless.com.

HomeScholar Bks., *(0-9754934)* 2311 Harrison Rd., Nashville, NC 27856 USA Tel 252-459-9279 ; *Imprints:* Literary Lessons (LitLessons)
Web site: http://www.homescholarbooks.com.

Homeschool Journey, *(0-9762918)* 4625 Devon, Lisle, IL 60532 USA Tel 630-969-1854
E-mail: mail@homeschooljourney.com
Web site: http://www.homeschooljourney.com.

Homespun Video, P.O. Box 340, Woodstock, NY 12498 USA Tel 914-246-2550; Fax: 914-246-5282; Toll Free: 800-338-2737
E-mail: hmspn@aol.com
Web site: http://www.homespuntapes.com
Dist(s): **Follett Media Distribution**
Leonard, Hal Corp.

Homestead Publishing, *(0-943972)* 1068 14th St., San Francisco, CA 94114 USA (SAN 241-029X) Tel 415-621-5039
E-mail: homesteadpublishing@mac.com
Web site: http://homesteadpublishing.net; http://www.homesteadpublishing.net.

Honey Bear Bks. *Imprint of* **Modern Publishing**

Honey Creek Publishing, Inc., *(0-9654436)* Orders Addr.: P.O. Box 265, North Lake, WI 53064 USA Tel 414-695-8815; Fax: 414-369-5605; Edit Addr.: 580 Foxtail Dr., No. 101, Pewaukee, WI 53072 USA Do not confuse with Honey Creek Publishing, Brimfield, IL
E-mail: HONEYCREEK@aol.com.

Honorable Pr., *(0-9719727)* 2432 Wilshire Ct., Decatur, GA 30035 USA.

Honoribus Pr., The, *(0-9622166; 1-885354)* Orders Addr.: P.O. Box 4872, Spartanburg, SC 29305 USA Tel 864-583-1307; Fax: 864-583-2046; Edit Addr.: 429 N. Church St., Spartanburg, SC 29304 USA Tel 864-597-4382; Fax: 864-597-4389
E-mail: halley@wofford.edu
Dist(s): **Baker & Taylor Bks.**
Barnes & Noble, Inc.
Hervey's Booklink & Cookbook Warehouse.

HonorNet, *(0-9753036; 0-9788726)* P.O. Box 910, Sapulpa, OK 74067 USA
E-mail: mail@honornet.net
Web site: http://honornet.net
Dist(s): **Destiny Image Pubs.**

Hood, Alan C. & Co., Inc., *(0-911469)* P.O. Box 775, Chambersburg, PA 17201 USA (SAN 270-8221) Tel 717-267-0867; Fax: 717-267-0572.

Hooker, Lou, *(0-9755106)* 6900 Chamberlain, Fremont, MI 49412 USA Tel 231-924-3555
E-mail: lvhook@ncats.net.

Hoopoe Bks. *Imprint of* **ISHK**

Hoosier Cider Pr., *(0-9639445)* Div. of Larry Reynolds Productions, Orders Addr.: P.O. Box 141, Fishers, IN 46038 USA Tel 317-849-1138; Fax: 317-849-4475; Edit Addr.: 9712 E. 116th St., Fishers, IN 46038 USA
Dist(s): **Baker & Taylor Bks.**

Hoot N' Cackle Pr., *(0-9659381)* 1928 S. Mayfair, Springfield, MO 65804 USA Tel 417-887-0837; Fax: 417-886-3994
E-mail: rlipe@usipp.net
Web site: http://www./mowrites4kids.drury.edu/authors/lipe/
Dist(s): **Booksource, The.**

Hoot Owl Bks. *Imprint of* **Maupin Hse. Publishing**

Hoot Owl Bks., *(0-9667043)* 720 N. Main St., Willard, UT 84340 USA Tel 435-734-2521
E-mail: zepher@utahlinx.com
Dist(s): **Baker & Taylor Bks.**
Windstorm Creative.

HOP, LLC, *(1-887942; 1-931020; 1-933863; 1-60143; 1-60242; 1-60498; 1-60499)* Educate, Inc., 1001 Fleet St., Baltimore, MD 21202 USA
Web site: http://www.hookedonphonics.com.

Hope Chest Legacy, Inc., *(1-59565)* P.O. Box 1398, Littlerock, CA 93543 USA Toll Free: 888-554-7292
E-mail: hopechestlegacy@aol.com
Web site: http://hopechestlegacy.com.

Hope Chest Publishing, *(0-615)* P.O. Box 3445, Camdenton, MO 65020-3445 USA
E-mail: jsfinks@socket.net; nhopejsf@mail.usmo.com.

Hope Farm Pr. & Bookshop, *(0-910746)* 252 Main St., Saugerties, NY 12477-1320 USA (SAN 204-0697) Tel 845-246-3522; Toll Free: 800-883-5778 (orders)
E-mail: hopefarm@hopefarm.com
Web site: http://www.hopefarm.com; http://www.hopefarmbooks.com
Dist(s): **North Country Bks., Inc.**

Hope for Families, Inc., *(0-9676489)* P.O. Box 238, Hatfield, PA 19440 USA Tel 215-280-5369
E-mail: ibmbam@fast.net.

Hope Harvest Ministries *See* **Hope Harvest Publishing**

Hope Harvest Publishing, *(0-9716523; 0-9763695; 0-9771318; 0-9779898)* Div. of H&H Bindery & Distribution Centre, P.O. Box 8353, Kentwood, MI 49518 USA Tel 616-248-7990; Fax: 616-248-0016
E-mail: hopeharvest@comcast.net
Web site: http://www.hopeharvest.com; http://www.blessly.com
Dist(s): **Anchor Distributors**
Anderson Merchandisers
Baker & Taylor Bks.
H & H Distribution
Spirit Filled Pr., Inc.
Spring Arbor Distributors, Inc.

Hope International Printshop, *(0-9748096)* Orders Addr.: P.O. Box 1182, Hobe Sound, FL 33475 USA; Edit Addr.: 8436 SE Bayberry Terr., Hobe Sound, FL 33475 USA.

Hope Publishing, LLC, *(0-9765532)* Orders Addr.: P.O. Box 260146, Highlands Ranch, CO 80163-0146 USA Do not confuse with companies with the same name in Carol Stream, IL, Birmingham, AL
E-mail: info@hopepublishing.org
Web site: http://www.hopepublishing.org
Dist(s): **Lightning Source, Inc.**

Hope Rekindled Pr. *See* **Risen Heart Pr.**

Hope Springs Pr., *(0-9639531)* 500 Hope Springs Ln., Manakin-Sabot, VA 23103 USA Tel 804-784-5025; Fax: 804-784-5484 Do not confuse with Hope Springs Press in West Babylon, NY
E-mail: robin.lind@webpointers.com
Web site: http://www.firstaidyourself.org; http://www.awty.webpointers.com.

Hopefulmonster Editore (ITA) *(88-7757) Dist. by* **Dist Art Pubs.**

Hope's Bks., *(0-9659993)* Orders Addr.: P.O. Box 6293, Buffalo Grove, IL 60089 USA Tel 874-883-8910; Fax: 874-478-9514
E-mail: hopesbooks@aol.com
Web site: http://www.hopesbooks.com.

Hopewell Pubns., LLC, *(0-9726906; 1-933435)* P.O. Box 11, Titusville, NJ 08560-0011 USA Tel 609-818-1049; Fax: 609-818-1913 Do not confuse with companies with the same or similar name in Longmont, CO, Austin, TX, Springdale, AZ
E-mail: publisher@hopepubs.com
Web site: http://www.hopepubs.com.

Hoppa Productions, Inc., *(1-891547)* 100 Horizon Dr., Denver, PA 17517 USA Tel 717-445-0313; Fax: 717-445-0860; Toll Free: 888-445-2824
E-mail: info@corncob.com
Web site: http://www.corncob.com.

Hoppenbrouwers, Toke *See* **Monte Nido Pr.**

HOPS Pr., LLC, *(1-892784)* Orders Addr.: 12 Quartz St., Pony, MT 59747-0697 USA Tel 406-685-3222
E-mail: orders@hollowtop.com
Web site: http://www.hopspress.com
Dist(s): **Mountain Pr. Publishing Co., Inc.**

Hopscotch, LLC, *(0-9724084)* 2425 NE Scruggs Rd., Lee's Summit, MO 64086 USA Tel 816-525-3737; Fax: 816-524-7981.

Horan Publishing, *(0-9769980)* P.O. Box 740485, Orange City, FL 32774-0485 USA
E-mail: horanpublishing@wmconnect.com.

Horizon Line Pr., *(0-9749426)* 77 N. River Dr., Roseburg, OR 97470 USA.

Horizon Pubs. & Distributors, Inc., *(0-88290)* Orders Addr.: P.O. Box 490, Bountiful, UT 84011-0490 USA.

Horizon Pubs. *Imprint of* **Cedar Fort, Inc./CFI Distribution**

Horizons *Imprint of* **Alpha Omega Pubns., Inc.**

Horley, Robert E., *(0-9701168)* 6466 State Rd., No. M-2, Parma, OH 44134 USA Tel 440-886-1931.

Horse & Dragon Publishing, *(0-9759488)* 241 Coast Hill Dr., Suite A, Indian Harbour Beach, FL 32937 USA Tel 321-821-2220; Fax: 321-821-2226; Toll Free: 877-374-6815
E-mail: bob@robertclark.us
Web site: http://www.robertclark.us.

Horse Creek Pubns., *(0-9722217)* 4500 Highland Hills Dr., Norman, OK 73026 USA Tel 405-364-9647
E-mail: sue.schrems@horsecreekpublications.com
Web site: http://www.horsecreekpublications.com
Dist(s): **Biblio Distribution.**

Horse Hollow Pr., Inc., *(0-9638814; 0-9795780)* P.O. Box 456, Goshen, NY 10924 USA Tel 845-651-2390; Fax: 845-651-2389; Toll Free: 800-414-6773
E-mail: info@horsehollowpress.com; jevers@warwick.net
Web site: http://www.horsehollowpress.com
Dist(s): **Independent Pubs. Group.**

Horsen Around Ranch, Incorporated *See* **Lucky Duck Pr., Inc.**

Horton, David, *(0-9763583)* P.O. Box 30126, Mableton, GA 30126 USA Fax: 770-948-2460
E-mail: supadave@negrointellect.com; dhhorton_2000@yahoo.com
Web site: http://www.negrointellect.com
Dist(s): **Baker & Taylor Bks.**
Culture Plus Bk. Distributors.

Horvath, Janet, *(0-9713735)* 122 Virginia St., Saint Paul, MN 55102 USA (SAN 255-5441) Tel 612-870-4200; Fax: 651-222-7420
E-mail: jhorvathcello@hotmail.com
Web site: http://www.playinglesshurt.com.

Ho's, Jane Children Bks., *(0-9619126)* 700 Kipling Ct., El Sobrante, CA 94803 USA (SAN 243-4954) Tel 510-222-2621.

Hosannah Pubns., *(0-9786031)* 507 W. Manheim St., Bldg.18 , Apt.D, Philadelphia, PA 19144-4859 USA Tel 215-991-6154; Fax: 215-991-0609
E-mail: fourhosannah@verizon.net.

Hospice & Community Care Pubns., *(0-9774691)* Orders Addr.: P.O. Box 993, Rock Hill, SC 29731 USA (SAN 257-6309) Tel 803-329-4663; Fax: 803-329-5935; Toll Free: 800-895-2273; Edit Addr.: 223 E. Main St., Suite 600, Rock Hill, SC 29731 USA
Web site: http://www.hospicecommunitycare.org.

Hospice of Saint John, The, *(0-9742849)* 1320 Everett Ct., Lakewood, CO 80215 USA.

Hot Biscuit Productions, Inc., *(1-880964; 0-9671667)* P.O. Box 111193, Memphis, TN 38111-1193 USA
E-mail: beecherhbp@aol.com
Web site: http://members.aol.com/beecherhbp/mfm1.html.

Hot Cross Bks. *Imprint of* **Hill Street Pr., LLC**

Hot off the Pr., *(0-933491; 0-9605904; 1-56231; 1-59776)* 1250 NW 3rd Ave., Canby, OR 97013 USA (SAN 216-3977) Toll Free: 800-227-9595
E-mail: info@hotp.com
Web site: http://www.craftpizazz.com.

HotComb Pr., *(0-9787940)* 6230 Wilshire Blvd., Suite 805, Los Angeles, CA 90048-5104 USA
E-mail: info@hotcombpress.com
Web site: http://hotcombpress.com.

HotDiggetyDog Pr., *(0-9741417)* P.O. Box 747, Shepherdsvilla, KY 40165 USA Tel 502-543-5315; Fax: 208-474-1227
E-mail: ronandleigh@alltel.net
Web site: http://www.ronflorence.com.

Houde, J. L. *See* **Editions Houde**

Houghton Mifflin College Div., *(0-395; 0-669; 0-618)* Orders Addr.: 181 Ballardvale St., Wilmington, MA 01887-7050 USA Tel 978-661-1300; Toll Free Fax: 800-458-9501; Toll Free: 800-225-1464; Edit Addr.: 222 Berkeley St., Boston, MA 02116-3764 USA Tel 617-351-5000
E-mail: college_cust_serv@hmco.com
Web site: http://www.hmco.com; http://college.hmco.com/booksellers/book_make_returns.html.

†Houghton Mifflin Co., *(0-395; 0-87466; 0-9631591; 1-57630; 1-881527; 0-618; 0-547)* Orders Addr.: a/o Orders for College, Trade & Great Source, 181 Ballardvale St., Wilmington, MA 01887-0750 USA Toll Free: 800-225-3362; Edit Addr.: 222 Berkeley St., Boston, MA 02116 USA (SAN 215-3793) Tel 617-351-5000
Web site: http://www.hmco.com
Dist(s): **Cheng & Tsui Co.**
Continental Bk. Co., Inc.
Houghton Mifflin Co. Trade & Reference Div.
Larousse Kingfisher Chambers, Inc.
Lectorum Pubns., Inc.
NetLibrary, Inc.
Perelandra, Ltd.
Replica Bks.; *CIP.*

Houghton Mifflin Company (College Division) *See* **Houghton Mifflin Co. Trade & Reference Div.**

Houghton Mifflin Co. (Schl. Div.), *(0-395; 0-669)* Orders Addr.: 1900 Batavia Ave., Geneva, IL 60134-3399 USA Toll Free Fax: 800-733-2098; Toll Free: 800-733-2828; 13400 Midway Rd., Dallas, TX 75244-5165 Toll Free: 800-733-2828; Edit Addr.: 222 Berkeley St., Boston, MA 02116 USA Tel 617-351-5000; Fax: 617-227-5409
E-mail: eduwebmaster@hmco.com
Web site: http://www.eduplace.com.

Houghton Mifflin Co. Trade & Reference Div., *(0-395; 0-89919; 0-618)* Orders Addr.: 181 Ballardvalle St., Wilmington, MA 01887 USA Tel 978-661-1300; Toll Free: 800-225-3362; Edit Addr.: 222 Berkeley St., Boston, MA 02116 USA (SAN 200-2388) Tel 617-351-5000; Fax: 617-227-5409; 215 Park Ave S. Flr. 12, New York, NY 10003-1621 ; *Imprints:* Clarion Books (Clarion Bks); Mariner Books (Mariner Bks); Walter Lorraine (W Lorraine); Kingfisher (Kingfisher); Graphia (Graphia)
E-mail: trade_sub_rights@hmco.com
Web site: http://www.hmco.com/; http://www.houghtonmifflinbooks.com
Dist(s): **NetLibrary, Inc.**

Hound Pr., *(0-9766030)* Div. of Baskerville Enterprises, LLC, Orders Addr.: P.O. Box 2328, Nevada City, CA 95959 USA (SAN 850-9069); Edit Addr.: 14937 Banner Lava Cap Rd., Nevada City, CA 95959 USA Tel 530-478-5709; Fax: 530-478-1108
E-mail: carole@houndpress.com
Web site: http://www.houndpress.com
Dist(s): **Independent Pubs. Group.**

HoundHut Pr., *(0-9675381)* 33 Southmar Ct., San Jose, CA 95138-1833 USA (SAN 253-0090) Tel 408-226-3956; Fax: 781-998-0310
E-mail: marie@houndhut.com
Web site: http://www.houndhut.com.

House, David, *(0-9777086)* 1652 Wiltsey Rd., SE No. 33, Salem, OR 97306 USA
Web site: http://www.space-worthy.com.

House Finch Pr., *(0-9712552)* P.O. Box 1461, Torrington, CT 06790-1461 USA
E-mail: housefinchpress@snet.net.

House of David, *(1-886987)* Orders Addr.: P.O. Box 700217, Saint Cloud, FL 34770 USA Tel 407-348-3770; Fax: 407-348-5577; Toll Free: 800-829-8777
E-mail: keyofdavid@mim.net
Web site: http://www.mim.net.

House of Mirth, *(0-9675506)* 403 E. Seventh St., Morris, MN 56267 USA Tel 320-589-3106
E-mail: nellisjg@mrs.umn.edu.

House of Prayer Ministries, Inc., *(1-882825)* 2428 Florian Ct., Decatur, IL 62526 USA Tel 217-428-7077 (phone/fax)
E-mail: vikischerer@insightbb.com
Web site: http://www.dramashare.org/hop.htm.

House of Stratus, Inc. (GBR) *(1-84232; 0-7551) Dist. by* **Midpt Trade.**

House of The Lord Fellowship, *(0-9673530)* Orders Addr.: P.O. Box 235, Lock Haven, PA 17745 USA Tel 570-748-6455; Fax: 570-748-6858; Edit Addr.: 201 W. Main St., Lock Haven, PA 17745 USA
E-mail: houseoflord235@yahoo.com
Web site: http://www.houseofthelordfellowship.com.

House of Usher, *(0-9747228)* 817 E. Mackinac Ave., Oak Creek, WI 53154 USA
E-mail: asala@mac.com
Web site: http://www.thehouseofusher.com.

House of White Birches, Inc., *(1-882138; 1-59217)* Div. of Dynamic Resources Group, 306 E. Parr Rd., Berne, IN 46711 USA (SAN 248-8310) Tel 219-589-4000; Fax: 219-589-8093
Web site: http://www.whitebirches.com
Dist(s): **National Bk. Network.**

House to House Pubns., *(1-886973)* 11 Toll Gate Rd., Lititz, PA 17543 USA Tel 717-627-1996; Fax: 717-627-4004; Toll Free: 800-848-5892
E-mail: karenr@dcfi.org
Web site: http://www.dcfi.org.

Houston Enterprises, *(0-9712861)* 5868 E. 71st St., No. 123, Indianapolis, IN 46220 USA Tel 317-726-1901; Fax: 317-726-1902; Toll Free: 888-826-8082
E-mail: info@scotthouston.com
Web site: http://www.scotthouston.com.

Houston Zoo, Inc., *(0-9762385)* 1513 N. MAcGregor, Houston, TX 77030 USA Tel 713-533-6500; Fax: 713-533-6755
E-mail: gwarfield@houstonzoo.org
Web site: http://www.houstonzoo.org.

HOW Bks. *Imprint of* **F & W Pubns., Inc.**

"How Do You Know", *(0-9675574)* Orders Addr.: P.O. Box 831172, Stone Mountain, GA 30083 USA Tel 404-296-7044; Edit Addr.: 944 Park Gate Pl., Stone Mountain, GA 30083 USA.

How Great Thou Art Pubns., *(0-9700405; 0-9717874)* Orders Addr.: P.O. Box 48, Mcfarlan, NC 28102-0048 USA Tel 704-851-3117; Fax: 704-851-3111; Toll Free: 800-982-3729; Edit Addr.: Hwy. 52, SR. 1003, Mcfarlan, NC 28102-0048 USA
E-mail: howgreat@vnet.net
Web site: http://www.howgreatthouart.com.

How I Learn & Grow, *(1-893886)* 120 Saint Mark's Ave., Brooklyn, NY 11217 USA
E-mail: Carola939@aol.com.

How To Books (GBR) *(1-85703; 1-84528) Dist. by* **Parkwest Pubns.**

Howard Bks. *Imprint of* **Simon & Schuster**

Howard, Emma Bks., *(1-886551)* P.O. Box 385, New York, NY 10024-0385 USA Tel 212-996-2590 (phone/fax)
E-mail: emmahowardbooks@verizon.net
Web site: http://www.EellGrassGirls.com
Dist(s): **Baker & Taylor Bks.**

Howe, Tina Field, *(0-9768585)* P.O. Box 762, Corning, NY 14830-4762 USA (SAN 256-8276)
Web site: http://www.tinafieldhowe.com.

Howell Bk. Hse. *Imprint of* **Wiley, John & Sons, Inc.**

Howell Canyon Pr., *(1-931210)* 1475 N Bundy Dr., Los Angeles, CA 90049 USA (SAN 255-3015) Toll Free: 888-252-0411 (Orders)
E-mail: info@HowellCanyonPress.com
Web site: http://www.AddisonTheDog.com; http://www.howellcanyonpress.com/; http://www.drdeanhowell.com/; http://www.TrishaHowell.com.

Howell, M Kay, *(0-9792499)* P.O. Box 1060, Rainier, OR 97048-1060 USA (SAN 852-8950)
Web site: http://fairyempire.biz.

Howie, C.J. Co., *(1-885275)* 1695 Quigley Rd., Columbus, OH 43227-3433 USA Tel 614-237-5474.

Howie Haus Bks., *(0-9703971)* Orders Addr.: P.O. Box 83911, Portland, OR 97283 USA (SAN 253-5793) Tel 866-894-9273 (866-8WIZARD); Fax: 503-289-1667; Edit Addr.: 7213 N. Alma, Portland, OR 97203 USA
E-mail: howiepro@aol.com; howie@howiehausbooks.com
Web site: http://www.howiehausbooks.com.

Howling at the Moon Pr., *(0-9654333)* P.O. Box 666, Jenks, OK 74037 USA Toll Free: 877-469-5464
E-mail: hatmpress@aol.com
Web site: http://www.howl4me.com.

Howling Oaks Studios, *(0-9713673)* 411 White Oak Rd., Somerset, PA 15501 USA Tel 814-443-0991
E-mail: howling-oaks@juno.com.

Howling Wolf Publishing, *(1-891423)* Orders Addr.: P.O. Box 1045, Pocatello, ID 83204 USA Tel 208-233-2708; Edit Addr.: 1611 City Creek Rd., Pocatello, ID 83204 USA
E-mail: kirb@ida.net; kirby@kirbyjonas.com
Web site: http://www.kirbyjonas.com.

Hoy, Marian A., *(0-9706943)* P.O. Box 158, Johnson City, TX 78636-0158 USA.

HP Trade *Imprint of* **Penguin Group (USA) Inc.**

HPH Publishing, *(0-9776281)* 333 W. N. Ave. Suite 289, Chicago, IL 60610-2586 USA (SAN 257-8271) Tel 312-335-1241; Fax: 312-276-4542
E mail: book_orders@hphpublishing.com
Web site: http://www.hphpublishing.com.

HPN Publishing, *(0-9768451)* 22902 Sonriente Trail, Trabuco Canyon, CA 92679 USA.

Hramiec Hoffman Publishing, *(0-9746901)* 6911 M-119 Hwy., Harbor Springs, MI 49740 USA Tel 231-526-1011
Dist(s): **Partners Bk. Distributing, Inc.**

HTS Bks. *Imprint of* **Forest Hse. Publishing Co., Inc.**

Huard Pubns., *(0-9661606)* 1549 E. Oriole Pl., Prescott, AZ 86303 USA Tel 520-717-0043.

Hub City Writers Project, *(0-9638731; 1-891885)* Orders Addr.: P.O. Box 8421, Spartanburg, SC 29305 USA Tel 864-577-9349; Fax: 864-577-0188; Edit Addr.: 149 S. Daniel Morgan Ave. Ste. 2, Spartanburg, SC 29306-3249 USA
E-mail: bteter@bellsouth.net
Web site: http://www.hubcity.org.

Hubbard Scientific, Inc., *(0-8331)* Orders Addr.: P.O. Box 760, Chippewa Falls, WI 54729-1468 USA (SAN 202-3121) Tel 715-723-4427; Fax: 715-723-8021; Toll Free: 800-323-8368; Edit Addr.: P.O. Box 760, Chippewa Fls, WI 54729-0760 USA
Web site: http://www.hubbardscientific.com.

Hubbell, Gerald, *(0-9762042)* 4127 Roanoke Rd., Kansas City, MO 64111 USA Tel 816-531-4427
Web site: http://www.malverack.com.

Huckleberry Pr., *(0-9653035; 1-890570; 1-58584)* Orders Addr.: P.O. Box 51772, Durham, NC 27707 USA Tel 646-205-8057 (phone/fax) Do not confuse with Huckleberry Pr., Gig Harbor, WA
E-mail: HucksPress@yahoo.com
Web site: http://www.huckleberrypress.com
Dist(s): **Baker & Taylor Bks.**

Hudson, Anna E., *(0-9703585)* 205 Putters Cir., Dillsburg, PA 17019-1562 USA
E-mail: DBHAES@aol.com.

Hudson Bks., *(0-9749860; 0-9762502; 0-9764459; 0-9767789; 0-9786296)* 244 Madison Ave., No. 254, New York, NY 10016 USA Tel 877-822-2504; Fax: 718-225-5556; Toll Free: 877-822-2500
Web site: http://www.thefloatinggallery.com.

Hudson Hills Press, Incorporated *See* **Hudson Hills Pr. LLC**

†Hudson Hills Pr. LLC, *(0-933920; 0-9646042; 1-55595)* Orders Addr.: P.O. Box 205, Manchester, VT 05254 USA; Edit Addr.: 74-2 Union St., Manchester, VT 05254 USA (SAN 213-0815) Tel 802-362-6450; Fax: 802-362-6459
E-mail: artbooks@hudsonhills.com
Web site: http://www.hudsonhills.com/
Dist(s): **Art Institute of Chicago**
National Bk. Network; *CIP.*

Hudson House Publishing & Productions, *(0-9778850)* 5658 NW Pioneer Cir., Norman, OK 73072 USA (SAN 850-5713)
E-mail: hudsonhousepub@yahoo.com.

Hudson Hse. Publishing & Productions *See* **Hudson House Publishing & Productions**

Hudson, Mary C., *(0-9627745; 0-9722937)* 1125 Karen Way, Mountainview, CA 94040 USA Tel 650-948-1270.

Hudson Park Pr., *(1-57641)* Orders Addr.: P.O. Box 774, Pine Plains, NY 12567-0774 USA Tel 212-929-8898; Edit Addr.: 232 Madsion Ave., Suite 1400, New York, NY 10016 USA
E-mail: hudpark@aol.com.

Hudson Street Pr. *Imprint of* **Penguin Group (USA) Inc.**

Huespin Productions, *(0-9701755)* 162-01 77th Rd., Flushing, NY 11366 USA Tel 718-591-9170; 718 591 9170
E-mail: kjoy7huesp@aol.com.

Huff, Gary, *(0-9715085)* 2920 Lee St., North Canton, OH 44720 USA.

Huffman, Wendie, *(0-9723016)* 316 Quincy Ave., Orange, CA 92867 USA Tel 714-348-5837
E-mail: adroit@prodigy.net.

Hufnagel Software, *(0-9743881)* P.O. Box 747, Clarion, PA 16214-0747 USA Tel 814-226-5600; Fax: 814-226-5551
Web site: http://www.hufsoft.com/books.

Hug Bandit & Co., LLC, *(0-9711776)* 7657 Winnetka Ave., No. 180, Canoga Park, CA 91306 USA Tel 818-998-8078; Fax: 818-773-0735
E-mail: nlalich@hugbandit.com
Web site: http://www.hugbandit.com.

Hugganite Publishing, *(0-9677987)* P.O. Box 147, Fairless Hills, PA 19030 USA
E-mail: info@hugganite.com
Web site: http://www.hugganite.com.

Hughes, Betty Barber *See* **Puwaii International, LLC**

Hughes, Bill, *(0-9746784)* 31 E. Bonneymead Cir., The Woodlands, TX 77381 USA
E-mail: bh@wondervista.com
Web site: http://www.wondervista.com.

Huia Pubs. (NZL) *(0-908975; 1-877266; 1-877241; 1-877283; 1-86969; 0-9582517) Dist. by* **UH Pr.**

Huia Pubs. (NZL) *(0-908975; 1-877266; 1-877241; 1-877283; 1-86969; 0-9582517) Dist. by* **Pacific Island Bks.**

Huiksi Music, *(1-879730)* P.O. Box 495, New York, NY 10024 USA (SAN 297-4037) Tel 212-724-3256; Fax: 212-724-3515; Toll Free: 800-484-1333 (access code 8400)
E-mail: juliehmus@aol.com
Web site: http://JulieLyonn.com
Dist(s): **Leonard, Hal Corp.**
Independent Pubs. Group.

†Human Kinetics Pubs., *(0-7360; 0-87322; 0-88011; 0-918438; 0-931250)* Orders Addr.: P.O. Box 5076, Champaign, IL 61825-5076 USA (SAN 211-7088) Tel 217-351-5076; Toll Free: 800-747-4457; Edit Addr.: 1607 N. Market St., Champaign, IL 61820 USA (SAN 658-0866) Tel 217-351-5076; Fax: 217-351-2674 ; *Imprints:* Y M C A of the U. S. A. (YMCA USA)
E-mail: humank@hkusa.com
Web site: http://www.humankinetics.com; http://www.hkusa.com; *CIP.*

Human Relations Media, *(1-55548)* 41 Kensico Dr., Mount Kisco, NY 10549 USA (SAN 287-4873) Tel 914-244-0486; Fax: 914-244-0485; Toll Free: 800-431-2050
Web site: http://www.hrmvideo.com.

Human Sciences Pubns., *(1-888733)* 4221 Capilla, Fort Worth, TX 76133 USA Tel 817-292-6758 Do not confuse with Human Sciences Pr., Inc. in New York, NY.

Human Service Associates *See* **Growing Home**

Humane Society Pr. *Imprint of* **National Assn. for Humane & Environmental Education**

Humanics, Limited *See* **Humanics Publishing Group**

†Humanics Publishing Group, *(0-89334)* Orders Addr.: P.O. Box 7400, Atlanta, GA 30357-0400 USA (SAN 208-3833) Tel 561-533-6231; Fax: 404-874-1976; Toll Free: 888-874-8844; Edit Addr.: 12 S. Dixie Hwy., Suite 203, Lake worth, FL 33460 USA (SAN 658-0882) Tel 561-533-6231; Fax: 561-533-6233; Toll Free Fax: 888-874-8844; Toll Free: 800-874-8844 Do not confuse with Humanics ErgoSystems, Inc., Reseda, CA
E-mail: humanics@mindspring.com
Web site: http://www.humanicspub.com; http://www.humanicslearning.com; http://www.humanicsdealer.com
Dist(s): **Baker & Taylor Bks.**
Borders, Inc.
New Leaf Distributing Co., Inc.; *CIP.*

Humanist Pr. *Imprint of* **American Humanist Assn.**

Humanities Iowa, *(0-9753751)* 100 Oakdale Campus, Northlawn, Iowa City, IA 52242-5000 USA Tel 319-335-4153; Fax: 319-335-4154
E-mail: info@humanitiesiowa.org
Web site: http://www.humanitiesiowa.org.

Company

Humanoids, Inc., *(0-9672401; 1-930652; 1-59465)* Div. of Humanoids Group, Orders Addr.: P.O. Box 931658, Hollywood, CA 90093 USA Tel 323-850-5802; Fax: 323-850-5804; Edit Addr.: P.O. Box 931658, Los Angeles, CA 90093-1658 USA
E-mail: cs@humanoids-publishing.com
Web site: http://www.humanoids-publishing.com.

Humming Meadow Ranch, *(0-9766431)* 47265 Twin Pines Rd., Banning, CA 92220-9656 USA Tel 951-849-1803; Fax: 951-849-9091
E-mail: elaine@hummingmeadowranch.com
Web site: http://www.hummingmeadowranch.com.

Hummingbird Mountain Pr., *(0-9746792)* P.O. Box 127, Midpines, CA 95345-0127 USA
Web site: http://www.sierratel.com/hummingbirdmountain.

Hummingbird Publishing *See* **MusicGem**

Humphreys, Kevin, *(0-9745727)* P.O. Box 10731, Spokane, WA 99220 USA; 1227 W. Nora Ave., Spokane, WA 99205.

Hundred Ways LLC, A, *(0-9789544)* 18034 Ventura Blvd., No. 491, Encino, CA 91316 USA Tel 818-708-0558
E-mail: admin@ahundredways.com
Web site: http://www.whenwordsdream.com.

Hundredth Munchy Books *See* **Hundredth Munchy Bks.**

Hundredth Munchy Bks., *(0-9656700)* P.O. Box 50927, Eugene, OR 97405 USA Tel 541-345-4491
E-mail: farouthippie@msn.com
Web site: http://www.AppreciateDiversity.com.

Hungry Bear Publishing, *(0-9754007)* Orders Addr.: 40 McClelland St., Saranac Lake, NY 12983 USA Tel 518-891-5559
Web site: http://www.hungrybearpublishing.com
Dist(s): **North Country Bks., Inc.**

Hungry Tiger Pr., *(0-9644988; 1-929527)* 5995 Dandridge Ln., Suite 121, San Diego, CA 92115-6575 USA
E-mail: books@hungrytigerpress.com
Web site: http://www.hungrytigerpress.com.

Hunnicutt Farris Publishing, *(0-9740232)* 128 Pamplin Ave., Florence, AL 35633 USA Tel 256-767-0612
E-mail: nhunnicutt@gmail.com
Web site: http://www.hfpublishing.com.

Hunt, J. L. Publishing, *(0-9769401)* Orders Addr.: 27881 La Paz Rd., Suite G-124, Laguna Niguel, CA 92677 USA Tel 949-751-7511; Fax: 949-363-8559
E-mail: james@chewnomore.com.

Hunt, J.L. Publishing *See* **Hunt, J. L. Publishing**

Hunt, John Publishing Ltd. (GBR) *(1-85608; 1-903019; 1-84298) Dist. by* **St Mut.**

Hunt, John Publishing Ltd. (GBR) *(1-85608; 1-903019; 1-84298) Dist. by* **APG.**

Hunt, John Publishing Ltd. (GBR) *(1-85608; 1-903019; 1-84298) Dist. by* **STL Dist NA.**

Hunter Hse., Inc., *(0-89793)* P.O. Box 2914, Alameda, CA 94501-0914 USA (SAN 281-7969) Tel 510-865-5282; Fax: 510-865-4295; Toll Free: 800-266-5592
E-mail: hhi@hunterhouse.com; info@hunterhouse.com
Web site: http://www.hunterhouse.com
Dist(s): **Gryphon Hse., Inc.**
Weiss, Paul G.
Perseus Distribution
Quality Bks., Inc.
Unique Bks., Inc.

Hunter Hse. Pubns., *(0-9662769)* Div. of Hunter & Assocs., 1132 21st St., SE, Cedar Rapids, IA 52403 USA Tel 319-362-4777; Fax: 319-369-9853
E-mail: lisa@hunterhouse.com.

Hunter, J. H. Publishing, *(0-9718274)* 8100 Schmuck Rd., Evansville, IN 47712 USA Tel 812-985-5013.

Hunter, Julius K. *See* **J.K.H. Enterprises**

Hunter Pubns., *(0-9654185)* P.O. Box 433, Vallejo, CA 94589 USA Tel 707-645-8714; Fax: 707-644-7880.

Hunter Publishing, Inc., *(1-55650; 1-58843)* Orders Addr.: 80 Northfield Ave., Edison, NJ 08837-3807 USA Toll Free: 800-255-0343 Do not confuse with Hunter Publishing, Inc., Hobe Sound, FL
E-mail: hunterp@bellsouth.net
Web site: http://www.hunterpublishing.com
Dist(s): **NetLibrary, Inc.**

HuntForMo Creations, *(0-9740182)* 3718 Brentford Rd., Randallstown, MD 21133 USA Toll Free: 800-327-9779
E-mail: monique@huntformo.com
Web site: http://www.huntformo.com.

Huntington Library Pr., *(0-87328)* Div. of Huntington Library, Art Collections & Botanical Gardens, 1151 Oxford Rd., San Marino, CA 91108 USA (SAN 202-313X) Tel 626-405-2172; Fax: 626-585-0794
E-mail: booksales@huntington.org
Web site: http://www.Huntington.org/HEHPubs.html
Dist(s): **California Princeton Fulfillment Services**
Univ. of California Pr.

Huntington Library Publications *See* **Huntington Library Pr.**

Huntington Ludlow Media Group, *(0-9789057)* 4925 Post Dr., Murfreesboro, TN 37128 USA (SAN 851-9080) Tel 615-907-6649
Web site: http://www.huntingtonludlow.com.

Hunton, Carroll & Wenonah, *(0-9758873)* 7608 American Heritage NE, Albuquerque, NM 87109 USA Tel 505-626-1871
E-mail: alan@excelstaff.com.

Huron River Pr., *(1-932399)* Orders Addr.: P.O. Box 310, Chelsea, MI 48118 USA Tel 734-913-9447; Fax: 734-332-4733; Edit Addr.: 320 N. Main St., Suite 100, Chelsea, MI 48118 USA
E-mail: info@huronriverpress.com
Web site: http://www.huronriverpress.com
Dist(s): **Partners Bk. Distributing, Inc.**

Hurst, Carol Consultants, *(0-9748509)* 41 Colony Dr., Westfield, MA 01085 USA Tel 413-562-3412
E-mail: carol@carolhurst.com
Web site: http://www.carolhurst.com.

Huseby, Kirby, *(0-9778494)* P.O. Box 8034, Kentwood, MI 49518 USA
E-mail: staytoond@aol.com.

Husky Trail Pr. LLC, *(0-9722918)* P.O. Box 705, East Lyme, CT 06333-0705 USA Tel 860-739-7644; Fax: 860-691-8066; Toll Free: 888-775-5211
Web site: http://www.huskytrailpress.com.

Hutchison, G.F. Pr., *(1-885631; 0-9796279)* 319 S. Block, Suite 17, Fayetteville, AR 72701-6484 USA Tel 479-587-1726 ; *Imprints:* Family Of Man Press, The (Family Of Man Pr)
E-mail: drwriterguy@netscape.net
Web site: http://www.thehappinessplace.com.

Hutman Productions, *(0-9702386)* P.O. Box 268, Linthicum, MD 21090 USA Tel 410-789-0930
E-mail: cbladey@mail.bcpl.net
Web site: http://www.bcpl.net/~cbladey/hutmanA.html.

Hutt, Sarah, *(0-9743417)* 1140 Washington St., No. 7, Boston, MA 02118 USA Tel 617-482-4722
Web site: http://www.mymotherslegacy.com.

Hutton Electronic Publishing, *(0-9742894; 0-9785171)* 160 N. Conpo Rd., Westport, CT 06880 USA
E-mail: cdubh@cptonline.net
Web site: http://www.huttonelectronicpublishing.com.

Hycliffe Publishing, *(0-9674662)* P.O. Box 7434, Louisville, KY 40207-0434 USA Fax: 502-852-4560
E-mail: jeconk01@athena.louisville.edu.

Hydra Publishing *See* **Hylas Publishing**

Hydrangea Pr., *(0-9768418)* 22 Plumer Rd., Epping, NH 03042 USA Tel 603-679-9544
E-mail: mswegles@comcast.net
Web site: http://www.plumercrest.com.

Hylas Publishing, *(1-59258)* 129 Main St., Irvington, NY 10533 USA Tel 917-478-6425; Fax: 914-591-3220
E-mail: hydrapublishing@mac.com
Dist(s): **St. Martin's Pr.**

Hyles Pubns., *(0-9709488; 0-9745499; 0-9764247; 0-9778936; 0-9800594)* 523 Sibley St., Hammond, IN 46320 USA Tel 219-932-0711
E-mail: info@hylespublications.com; chalifouxr@fbchammond.com
Web site: http://www.hylespublications.com.

Hynes Enterprises, Inc., *(0-9713900)* 8580 E. Bellewood Pl., Denver, CO 80237 USA Tel 303-221-7012; Fax: 303-221-7015; Toll Free: 800-841-7390
E-mail: thynes6958@aol.com
Web site: http://jimmpigg.com.

Hyperion Audio *Imprint of* **Hyperion Pr.**

†Hyperion Bks. for Children, *(0-7868; 1-56282)* Div. of Disney Bk. Publishing, Inc., A Walt Disney Co., Orders Addr.: 3 Center Plaza, Boston, MA 02108 USA Toll Free: 800-759-0190; Edit Addr.: 114 Fifth Ave., New York, NY 10011 USA Tel 212-633-4400; Fax: 212-633-4833 ; *Imprints:* Jump at the Sun (Jump at the Sun); Volo (Volo)
Web site: http://www.disney.com; http://www.hyperionbooksforchildren.com
Dist(s): **Disney Publishing Worldwide**
HarperCollins Pubs.
Little Brown & Co.; *CIP.*

†Hyperion Paperbacks for Children, *(0-7868; 1-56282)* Div. of Disney Bk. Publishing, Inc., A Walt Disney Co., 114 Fifth Ave., New York, NY 10011 USA Tel 212-633-4400; Fax: 212-633-4833
Web site: http://www.disney.com
Dist(s): **Hachette Bk. Group**
HarperCollins Pubs.
Little Brown & Co.; *CIP.*

†Hyperion Pr., *(0-7868; 1-56282; 1-4013)* Div. of Disney Bk. Publishing, Inc., A Walt Disney Co., Orders Addr.: 3 Center Plaza, Boston, MA 02108 USA Toll Free: 800-759-0190; Edit Addr.: 77 W. 66th St., 11th Flr., New York, NY 10023-6298 USA Tel 212-456-0100; Fax: 212-456-0108 ; *Imprints:* Hyperion Audio (Hyperion Audio)
Web site: http://www.hyperionbooks.com
Dist(s): **Hachette Bk. Group**
HarperCollins Pubs.
Sony CONNECT, Inc.; *CIP.*

Hypertext Publishing Group, *(0-9648010)* P.O. Box 420686, San Diego, CA 92142 USA (SAN 298-7651) Tel 619-627-9210; Toll Free: 800-754-9737
E-mail: HPGBooks@aol.com.

hyperwerks, *(0-9770213)* 1950 S. Sawtelle Blvd, No. 320, Los Angeles, CA 90025 USA Tel 310-312-2062
Web site: http://www.hyperwerks.com.

Hysolli Production Co., *(0-9645219)* 3169-C Chestnut Dr., Doraville, GA 30340 USA Tel 770-451-7498.

IAPS Bks., *(1-881448)* Orders Addr.: P.O. Box 117800, Gainesville, FL 32611-7800 USA Tel 352-392-1721 ext 492; Fax: 352-392-3698
E-mail: bilmarq@flmnh.ufl.edu
Dist(s): **Great Outdoors Publishing Co.**
Univ. Pr. of Florida.

I Am Your Playground LLC, *(0-9769580)* P.O. Box 301, Fanwood, NJ 07023-0301 USA Fax: 908-301-0777; Toll Free: 888-759-4736 (888-PLY-GRND)
E-mail: john@iamyourplayground.com
Web site: http://www.iamyourplayground.com
Dist(s): **Biblio Distribution.**

I & L Publishing, *(0-9661244; 1-930002)* 174 Oak Dr. Pkwy., Oroville, CA 95966 USA Tel 530-589-5048; Fax: 530-589-3551; Toll Free: 888-443-4722
E-mail: iolamoore@juno.com
Dist(s): **Morris Publishing.**

i.b.d., Ltd., *(0-88431)* 24 Hudson St., Kinderhook, NY 12106 USA (SAN 630-7779) Tel 518-758-1755; Fax: 518-758-6702
E-mail: lankhof@ibdltd.com
Web site: http://www.ibdltd.com.

I.B. Hoofinit Co., *(1-928890)* Orders Addr.: P.O. Box 136, Greenville, VA 24440 USA Tel 540-886-4415; Edit Addr.: 1746 Englewood Dr., Wakefield C-2, Staunton, VA 24401 USA
E-mail: ibhoofinit@earthlink.net.

I C A, *(0-9747506)* P.O. Box 910, Wayne, MI 48184-9998 USA Fax: 734-595-1869
E-mail: codemanray@aol.com
Web site: http://www.thefemalecode.com.

ICA Publishing Co., *(1-879774)* Div. of ICA, Inc., 1020 N. Commerce, Stockton, CA 95202 USA Tel 209-460-0622; Fax: 209-938-0416
E-mail: goss09@aol.com
Dist(s): **Academic Bk. Ctr., Inc.**
Baker & Taylor Bks.
Yankee Peddler Bookshop.

I C I University *See* **Global Univ.**

I Can Do All Things Productions, *(0-9745787)* 8 Loveland St., Madison, NJ 07940 USA Tel 973-377-5970; Fax: 973-377-5970
E-mail: seucony@optonline.net
Web site: http://www.perfectpraisebooks.com.

†I E E E * Standards, *(0-7803; 0-87942; 1-55937; 0-7381)* Div. of IEEE, Orders Addr.: P.O. Box 1331, Piscataway, NJ 08855-1331 USA (SAN 250-6130) Tel 732-981-0060; Fax: 732-981-0027; Toll Free: 800-701-4333; Edit Addr.: 445 Hoes Ln., Piscataway, NJ 08855-1331 USA Tel 732-981-0060; Fax: 732-981-1769
E-mail: confpubs@ieee.org
Web site: http://www.ieee.org
Dist(s): **IEEE**; *CIP.*

I E E E * Standards Department *See* **I E E E * Standards**

I E S Language Foundation, *(1-930866)* 7020 Koll Center Pkwy., Suite 127, Pleasanton, CA 94566 USA Tel 925-484-6028; Fax: 925-462-1692; Toll Free: 800-231-4703
E-mail: iesadmin@ieslanguages.org.

IFV, Inc., *(1-931861)* 1045 Coddington Rd., Ithaca, NY 14850 USA
E-mail: ifv@lightlink.com
Web site: http://www.classicalfencing.com.

I Have A Voice Enterprises, *(0-9746192)* P.O. Box 83, Peshtigo, WI 54157 USA
Web site: http://www.thehidersstory.com.

I M Printing, *(0-9747151)* 6912 41st Ave. SE, Lacey, WA 98503-7110 USA.

IOS Pr., Inc., *(90-407; 90-5199; 90-6275; 0-9673355; 1-58603; 90-298)* 5795-G Burke Centre Pkwy., Burke, VA 22015 USA Tel 703-323-5554; Fax: 703-323-3668
E-mail: iosbooks@iospress.com
Web site: http://www.iospress.nl.

ISHK, *(0-86304; 0-900860; 1-883536; 1-933779)* Div. of Institute for the Study of Human Knowledge, Orders Addr.: P.O. Box 381069, Cambridge, MA 02238-1069 USA (SAN 226-4536) Tel 617-497-4124; Fax: 617-876-2976; Toll Free Fax: 800-223-4200; Toll Free: 800-222-4745; Edit Addr.: P.O. Box 176, Los Altos, CA 94023 USA Tel 650-948-9428 ; *Imprints:* Malor Books (Malor Bks); Hoopoe Books (Hoopoe Books)
E-mail: ishkorders@aol.com; ishkbooks@aol.com
Web site: http://www.ishkbooks.com
Dist(s): **Baker & Taylor Bks.**
Borders, Inc.
New Leaf Distributing Co., Inc.

ISM Teaching Systems, Inc., *(1-56775)* 14132 Desert Willow, El Paso, TX 79938 USA Tel 915-856-6365; Fax: 915-856-6367; Toll Free: 800-453-4476
E-mail: Email4ism@aol.com
Web site: http://www16.inetba.com/ismteachingsystemsinc.

I S R P Press *See* **Sound Reading Solutions**

I Save A Tree, *(0-9714299; 0-9744670; 0-9745659)* Orders Addr.: P.O. Box 150277, Cape Coral, FL 33915 USA; Edit Addr.: 204 SE 10th Ave., Cape Coral, FL 33990 USA
Web site: http://www.garrettbooks.com; http://www.isaveatree.com.

I See Puppy, LLP, *(0-9774277)* Orders Addr.: 107 Richard Mine Rd., Dover, NJ 07801 USA (SAN 257-554X) Tel 973-361-8637; Fax: 973-361-8035
E-mail: info@iseepuppy.com
Web site: http://www.iseepuppy.com.

I Shine, Inc., *(0-9714403)* 3760 E. Sixth Ave., Hialeah, FL 33013 USA (SAN 254-2390) Toll Free: 877-474-4634
Web site: http://www.hippieandthebaldchick.com.

I Wanna Bee, *(0-9703609)* 2932 Maple Dr., Fairfax, VA 22031 USA Tel 703-277-7007
E-mail: www.yabahdo@yahoo.com
Web site: http//www.yabaho@yahoo.com.

i wantz Publishing, *(0-9727998)* P.O. Box 9305, Grand Rapids, MI 49509-0305 USA
E-mail: elizabeth@iwantz.com
Web site: http://www.iwantz.com.

IAC Publishing, *(0-9748383)* 3432 Denny St., No. 3, Pittsburgh, PA 15201 USA Toll Free: 877-592-0237
Web site: http://www.irishamericancatholic.com.

Iaconi, Mariuccia Bk. Imports, *(0-9628720)* P.O. Box 77023, San Francisco, CA 94107-0023 USA (SAN 161-1364) Toll Free: 800-955-9577
E-mail: mibibook@ixnetcom.com
Web site: http://www.mibibook.com
Dist(s): **Baker & Taylor Bks.**
Lectorum Pubns., Inc.

IAD Pr. (AUS) *(0-949659; 1-86465; 0-9596206) Dist. by* **Intl Spec Bk.**

IamCoach.com Publishing, *(0-9754761)* P.O. Box 60088, King of Prussia, PA 19406 USA Fax: 413-674-6078
E-mail: publishing@iamcoach.com
Web site: http://www.IamCoach.com/chess/publishing/.

IBD Pr., *(0-9714293)* 26889 Deer Creek Ln., Elkhart, IN 46514-6072 USA Tel 219-262-9906 (phone/fax)
E-mail: ibdpress@bridgesintime.com
Web site: http://www.bridgesintime.com.

IBEX Pubs., Inc., *(0-936347; 1-58814)* Orders Addr.: P.O. Box 30087, Bethesda, MD 20824 USA (SAN 696-866X) Tel 301-718-8188; Fax: 301-907-8707; Toll Free: 888-718-8188; Edit Addr.: 8014 Old Georgetown Rd., Bethesda, MD 20814 USA
E-mail: info@ibexpub.com
Web site: http://www.ibexpub.com.

ibooks, Inc., *(0-671; 0-7434; 1-58824; 1-59176; 1-59687)* 100 Jericho Quadrangle. Ste. 300, Jericho, NY 11753-2702 USA ; *Imprints:* Milk & Cookies (Milk-Cookie); ipicturebooks (Ipicbks)
Web site: http://www.ibooksinc.com
Dist(s): **National Bk. Network.**

ibooks, Incorporated/ipictures.com *See* **ibooks, Inc.**

I.B.Tauris & Co., Ltd. (GBR) *(1-85043; 1-86064; 1-84511) Dist. by* **Macmillan.**

I C Creative, Inc., *(0-9742714)* 2300 Michigan Ct., Suite B, Arlington, TX 76016 USA Tel 817-459-8079; Fax: 817-460-0430
E-mail: joi@stayintouchmail.com
Web site: http://www.stayintouchmail.com.

ICAN Press *See* **Black Forest Pr.**

ICanPublish, *(0-9711480)* Div. of Heckman Bindery, Inc., P.O. Box 89, North Manchester, IN 46962 USA (SAN 253-9500) Tel 260-982-2107; Fax: 260-982-1130; Toll Free: 800-334-3628
E-mail: dave_mcintyre@heckmanbindery.com.

Ice Age Park and Trail Foundation, Inc., *(0-9627079)* 2453 Atwood Ave. STOP 4, Madison, WI 53704-5682 USA
E-mail: iat@iceagetrail.org
Web site: http://www.iceagetrail.org.

Ice Cube Pr., *(1-888160)* 205 N. Front St., North Liberty, IA 52317 USA (SAN 298-9085) Tel 319-626-2055; Fax: 413-451-0223
E-mail: steve@icecubepress.com; steve@southslope.net
Web site: http://www.icecubepress.com
Dist(s): **Booklines Hawaii, Ltd.**
Distributors, The
Heinecken & Assoc., Ltd.
Quality Bks., Inc.

ICE Kunion (KOR) Dist. by Diamond Book Dists.

Ice Mountain Publishing, *(0-9748814)* P.O. Box 1418, Salida, CO 81201 USA
E-mail: nathanward@amigo.net.

Icecat Bks., *(0-9764308; 0-9768670)* 1243 Old Canyon Dr., Hacienda Heights, CA 91745 USA Tel 626-333-2430
E-mail: contact@icecatbooks.com
Web site: http://www.icecatbooks.com.

Iceni Bks. *Imprint of* **Wheatmark**

Ichabod Ink, *(0-9766641)* 418 Lake George Cir., West Chester, PA 19382 USA.

Ichneumon Pr., *(0-9670329)* 822 Candlewood Dr., Cupertino, CA 95014 USA Tel 408-996-2691; Fax: 408-873-9674
E-mail: ichneumon@tooch.com
Web site: http://www.tooch.com/ichneumon.

Icilcle Falls Publishing Co., *(0-9749360)* Orders Addr.: HC 31, Box 5118A, Wasilla, AK 99654 USA; Edit Addr.: 3420 E. Goderey Dr., Wasilla, AK 99654 USA.

Icorn/F3K Productions, Ltd., *(0-9664453)* Orders Addr.: P.O. Box 407, Mount Kisco, NY 10549 USA Tel 914-241-7780; Fax: 914-241-7749
E-mail: kidfoods@aol.com
Dist(s): **Baker & Taylor Bks.**

Idaho Bk. & Schl. Supply, *(0-9679086)* 5286 Chinden Blvd., Boise, ID 83714 USA Tel 208-375-5250; Fax: 208-376-6648.

Idaho State Journal, *(0-9749865)* Orders Addr.: P.O. Box 431, Pocatello, ID 83204 USA; Edit Addr.: P.O. Box 431, Pocatello, ID 83204-0431 USA
Web site: http://www.journalnet.com.

Idea & Design Works, LLC, *(0-9712282; 0-9719775; 1-932382; 1-933239; 1-60010)* 2645 Financial Ct., Suite E, San Diego, CA 92117 USA (SAN 255-1926) Tel 858-270-1315; Fax: 858-270-1308; 4411 Morena Blvd., Suite 106, San Diego, CA 92117 Tel 858-270-1315; Fax: 858-270-1308
E-mail: chris@idwpublishing.com
Web site: http://www.idwpublishing.com/
Dist(s): **Diamond Bk. Distributors**
LPC Group.

Idea, Inc., *(0-9701566)* 403 5th Pl NW, Austin, MN 55912-3051 USA Toll Free: 800-828-1231 (phone/fax)
E-mail: Idea_inc@smig.net
Web site: http://www.ccjournal.com.

Idea Network LA Inc., *(0-9773301)* 201 S. Santa Fe Ave. No. 105, Los Angeles, CA 90012 USA Tel 213-613-1252; Fax: 213-613-1440.

Ideal School Supply *Imprint of* **Schaffer, Frank Pubns.**

IdeaList Enterprises, Inc., *(0-9758794)* P.O. Box 101187, Chicago, IL 60610 USA.

Ideals *Imprint of* **Ideals Pubns.**

Ideals Children's Bks. *Imprint of* **Ideals Pubns.**

Ideals Pr. *Imprint of* **Ideals Pubns.**

Ideals Pubns., *(0-8249; 0-89542)* Div. of Guideposts, Orders Addr.: 535 Metroplex Dr., Suite 250, Nashville, TN 37211 USA Tel 615-333-0478; Fax: 615-781-1447 ; *Imprints:* Ideals (Ideals TN); Candy Cane Press (Candy Cane Pr); Ideals Children's Books (Ideals Chldrns Bks); Ideals Press (Ideals Pr); Williamson Books (Williamson Bks); Guideposts (Guideposts TN); GPKids (GPKids)
E-mail: dtimson@guideposts.org
Web site: http://www.idealsbooks.com
Dist(s): **Learning Connection, The.**

Ideals Publishing Corporation *See* **Ideals Pubns.**

Ideate Prairie, *(0-9762564)* P.O. Box 65, Genoa, IL 60135 USA Tel 815-986-6577 ; *Imprints:* American Dog (Am Dog)
Web site: http://www.americandogtales.com; http://www.ideate-prairie.com
Dist(s): **Biblio Distribution.**

Idee, LLC, *(0-9740012)* 812 Spanish Wells Dr., Melbourne, FL 32940 USA Tel 321-242-0307
E-mail: llwhill@aol.com
Dist(s): **Baker & Taylor Bks.**

Identity Pr., *(0-9753482)* P.O. Box 46224, Cincinnati, OH 45246-0224 USA Tel 513-313-5907 Do not confuse with companies with the same or similar name in Fountain Valley, CA, Cambridge, MA
E-mail: discovteenesteem@aol.com.

I.Design, *(1-929789)* 36 Santa Cruz Aisle, Irvine, CA 92606 USA Tel 949-838-4771
E-mail: imeedesign@yahoo.com
Web site: http://www.member.cox.net/imee/index_book_2.htm.

Idylls Pr., *(1-59597)* Orders Addr.: 970 Ratcliff Dr., SE, Salem, OR 97302-3241 USA; Edit Addr.: P.O. Box 3566, Salem, OR 97302-3566 USA (SAN 256-0232) Tel 503-269-4406; Fax: 503-345-0890
E-mail: info@idyllspress.com; orders@idyllspress.com; returns@idyllspress.com; dan@idyllspress.com; debra@idyllspress.com
Web site: http://www.catholicfiction.net; http://www.johnmurphyart.com; http://www.idyllspress.com; http://www.themysteryofthings.com; http://www.bardolatry.com; http://www.debramurphy.com.

Idyllworks, LLC, *(0-9794647)* 2904 Rippling Brook Ln., Dickinson, TX 77539-6199 USA
Web site: http://www.JamboNation.com.

IEP RESOURCES *Imprint of* **Attainment Co., Inc.**

IFLY Bks., *(0-9758888)* P.O. Box 894134, Temecula, CA 92589 USA.

I.Form Ink, Pub., *(0-9763274)* Div. of Insu-Form, Inc., 41921 Beacon Hill, Suite A, Palm Desert, CA 92211 USA Tel 760-779-0657; Fax: 760-779-5143
E-mail: john@hackergroup.org.

IGMI Publishing, *(0-9655933)* Div. of Professional Business Services, HC 69, Box 15A, Sapello, NM 87745-9602 USA.

Ignatius Pr., *(0-89870; 1-58617)* Orders Addr.: P.O. Box 1339, Fort Collins, CO 80522-1339 USA Tel 970-221-3920; Fax: 970-221-3964; Toll Free Fax: 800-278-3566; Toll Free: 800-651-1531 (credit card orders, no minimum, individual orders); 877-320-9276 (bookstore orders); Edit Addr.: 2515 McAllister St., San Francisco, CA 94118 USA (SAN 214-3887) Tel 415-387-2324; Fax: 415-387-0896
E-mail: info@ignatius.com
Web site: http://www.ignatius.com
Dist(s): **Baker & Taylor Bks.**
Midpoint Trade Bks., Inc.
Spring Arbor Distributors, Inc.

Ignite! Learning, *(0-9791935; 0-9798418; 1-934763)* 4030 W. Braker Ln., Suite 175, Austin, TX 78759 USA Tel 512-697-7000; Fax: 512-697-7001; Toll Free: 866-464-4648
E-mail: support@ignitelearning.com; sshen@ignitelearning.com; lbailey@ignitelearning.com
Web site: http://www.ignitelearning.com.

IGR Limited *See* **EKADOO Publishing Group**

Iguana Adventures Publishing *See* **Publish To Go Pubns., LLC**

IIEI Pr., *(0-9773098; 0-9797244)* 11225 N. 28th Dr., Suite B-201, Phoenix, AZ 85029 USA Tel 602-648-5750; Fax: 602-648-5755; Toll Free: 800-474-8013
E-mail: info@iiei.edu
Web site: http://www.iiei.edu.

Ijiwola Pr., Gregory *Imprint of* **Summit House Pubs.**

IJN Publishing, Inc., *(1-933894)* 2950 NE 190th St., No. 305, Aventura, FL 33180 USA (SAN 850-4474) Fax: 305-792-1387; P.O. Box 630577, Miami, FL 33163
E-mail: gerald@ijnpublishing.com
Web site: http://www.whatliesbeneaththebed.com; http://www.ijnpublishing.com.

IJustWantToSleep, Inc., *(0-9744357)* 18 Timothy Ln., Candler, NC 28715 USA
E-mail: store@ijustwanttosleep.com; author@ijustwanttosleep.com
Web site: http://www.ijustwanttosleep.com.

Ikarian Pr. Of America, *(0-9706247)* 142 Allegheny River Blvd., Oakmont, PA 15139 USA Tel 412-241-7511; Fax: 412-828-4330
E-mail: emamatas@wpahs.org
Web site: http://www.bymysidethebook.com.

Ike, J. Bks., *(0-937109)* 32 Bland Ave., Sumter, SC 29150-3816 USA (SAN 658-439X) Tel 803-778-6988
E-mail: bjustus@cpis.net
Dist(s): **Baker & Taylor Bks.**
Southern Bk. Service.

IKIDS *Imprint of* **Innovative Kids**

Ile Orunmila Communications, *(0-9644247; 0-9714949)* Orders Addr.: P.O. Box 2326, San Bernardino, CA 92405 USA Tel 909-475-5851; Fax: 909-475-5850; Toll Free: 888-678-6645; Edit Addr.: 515 W. 21st St., San Bernardino, CA 92405 USA
E-mail: fsorunmila@aol.com
Web site: http://www.IleOrunmila.com
Dist(s): **Original Pubns.**

Illui International *See* **Heartful Loving Pr.**

Illumination Arts Publishing Co., Inc., *(0-935699; 0-9701907; 0-9740190)* Orders Addr.: P.O. Box 1865, Bellevue, WA 98009 USA (SAN 696-2599) Tel 425-644-7185; Fax: 425-644-9274; Toll Free: 888-210-8216; Edit Addr.: 13256 Northup Way, No. 9, Bellevue, WA 98005 USA
E-mail: liteinfo@illumin.com
Web site: http://www.illumin.com
Dist(s): **Baker & Taylor Bks.**
DeVorss & Co.
Follett Library Resources
Koen Pacific
New Leaf Distributing Co., Inc.
Partners/West
Quality Bks., Inc.

Illumination Pubns., *(0-9789511)* 2802 Floore Ct., Louisville, KY 40299-1610 USA (SAN 852-0313) Tel 502-491-5664 Do not confuse with Illumination Publications in West Toluca lake, CA.

Illumination Studios, *(0-9741381)* 5924 Woodoak Dr., Dallas, TX 75249 USA
E-mail: contact@illuminationstudios.com
Web site: http://www.illuminationstudios.com.

Illusion Factory, The, *(0-9747331; 1-932949)* 21800 Burbank Blvd., Suite 225, Woodland Hills, CA 91367 USA (SAN 255-7096) Tel 818-598-8400; Fax: 818-598-8494
E-mail: ewong@illusionfactory.com
Web site: http://www.illusionfactory.com.

ILR Pr. *Imprint of* **Cornell Univ. Pr.**

ILT Publishing, *(0-9774409)* Div. of Integrated Learning Technology, Inc., P.O. Box 72420, Thorndale, PA 19372-0420 USA (SAN 257-4950) Tel 610-518-6860 (phone/fax)
E-mail: info@iltpublishing.com
Web site: http://www.iltpublishing.com; http://www.tommilance.com.

I.M. Enterprises, *(0-9777882)* P.O. Box 111, Rochester, MA 02770 USA (SAN 850-1645) ; *Imprints:* Light Works Publishing (Light Works)
E-mail: imenterprises@hotmail.com
Web site: http://www.imenterprises.org.

IM Pr., *(0-9654651; 0-9716911)* Orders Addr.: P.O. Box 5346, Takoma Park, MD 20913-5346 USA Tel 301-587-1202; Edit Addr.: 7214 Cedar Ave., Takoma Park, MD 20912 USA Do not confuse with companies with the same name in Cincinnati, OH, Fairfax Station, VA
E-mail: efaine@yahoo.com
Web site: http://www.takoma.com/ned/home.htm
Dist(s): **Book Clearing Hse.**

Imaajinn This, *(0-9767342)* P.O. Box 294, West Haven, CT 06516 USA (SAN 256-484X) Fax: 203-931-7177; Toll Free: 800-931-1177.

Image & Vision Builders, Inc., *(0-9704578)* 46356 166th St., Watertown, SD 57201 USA Tel 605-886-7379; Fax: 605-886-0477
E-mail: cdagel@yahoo.com
Web site: http://www.imageandvisionbuilders.com.

Image Cascade Publishing, *(0-9639607; 1-930009; 1-59511)* 720 Lovell Hill Rd., Marathon, NY 13803 USA (SAN 253-2972) Tel 607-849-4284; Fax: 607-849-4078; Toll Free: 800-691-7779
E-mail: JoyCan@aol.com
Web site: http://www.imagecascade.com.

Image Comics, *(1-58240; 1-887279)* 1942 University Ave. 3rd Floor, Suite 305, Berkeley, CA 94704 USA Tel 510-644-4980; Fax: 510-644-4988
E-mail: info@imagecomics.com
Web site: http://www.imagecomics.com/
Dist(s): **Diamond Bk. Distributors**
LPC Group
Trucatriche.

Image Connection America, Inc., *(0-9678238; 0-9702768; 1-931432)* 456 Penn St., Yeadon, PA 19050 USA (SAN 253-8709) Tel 610-626-7770; Fax: 610-626-2778; Toll Free: 800-227-8178 Do not confuse with Image Connection, Lomita, CA
E-mail: imageco@earthlink.net.

Image Express, Inc., *(0-9664634)* P.O. Box 66536, Austin, TX 78766 USA Tel 512-401-4900; Fax: 530-660-5783
E-mail: rmarston@greatday.com
Web site: http://www.greatday.com.

Image Formation, *(0-9763440)* 23233 N. Pima, No. 113-102, Scottsdale, AZ 85255 USA
E-mail: lance@themummymountainstory.com
Web site: http://www.themummymountainstory.com.

Image Maker Publishing Co., The, *(0-9644695)* 963 Blue Mountain Cir., Westlake Vlg, CA 91362-5482 USA
E-mail: imagemaker@netvip.com
Web site: http://www.malibu.org/imagemaker/.

Image Pr., Inc., *(1-891548)* Orders Addr.: P.O. Box 2407, Edmond, OK 73083-2407 USA Tel 405-844-6007; Fax: 405-348-5577; Edit Addr.: 247 N. Broadway, Suite 101, Edmond, OK 73034 USA.

Image Publishing, Ltd., *(0-911897)* Subs. of Roger Miller Photo, Ltd., 1411 Hollins St., Baltimore, MD 21223 USA (SAN 264-6781) Tel 410-566-1222; 410-233-1234; Fax: 410-233-1241 Do not confuse with companies with the same or similar names in Encino, CA, Wilton, CT
E-mail: rmpl.ipl@verizon.net
Web site: http://www.rogermillerphoto.com.

IMAGECRAFTERS, *(0-9773478)* Orders Addr.: 1644 Masters Ct., Naperville, IL 60563 USA (SAN 257-3709) Tel 630-355-1449
E-mail: imgcft@mc.net.

Imagenes Pr., *(0-939302)* P.O. Box 1150, Pine Valley, CA 91962 USA (SAN 220-1712) Tel 619-997-8676; 619-473-8676
E-mail: labrucheri@aol.com.

Imagery Pr., *(0-9754287)* P.O. Box 337, Carpinteria, CA 93014-0337 USA
E-mail: books@imagerypress.com.

Images and Pages, *(0-9788332)* P.O. Box 118120, Carrolton, TX 75007 USA
E-mail: deguzman@imagesandpages.com
Web site: http://imagesandpages.com.

Images Co., *(0-9677017)* 109 Woods of Arden Rd., Staten Island, NY 10312 USA
E-mail: john.iovine@verizon.net; imagesco@bellatlantic.net; imagesco@verizon.net
Web site: http://www.imagesco.com
Dist(s): **Baker & Taylor Bks.**

Images For Presentation, *(0-9749531)* 176 Second St., Saint James, NY 11780 USA Tel 631-361-7908
E-mail: imagesforpres@aol.com.

Company

Images Pr., *(1-891577)* 27920 Roble Alto St., Los Altos Hills, CA 94022 USA (SAN 299-4844) Tel 650-948-9251; 650-948-8251; Fax: 650-941-6114 Do not confuse with companies with the same name in San Leandro, CA, New York, NY
E-mail: bugsmom2@aol.com
Web site: http://www.images-press.com
Dist(s): **Baker & Taylor Bks.**
Quality Bks., Inc.

Images Unlimited, *(0-930643)* 124 N. Grand, Box 305, Maryville, MO 64468 USA (SAN 242-0163) Tel 660-582-4279; Toll Free: 800-366-1695
E-mail: imagesun@asde.net
Web site: http://www.imagesunlimitedpub.com; http://www.snaptail.com; http://www.snaptailpress.com; http://applecookbooks.com; http://www.imagesunlimitedpublishing.com
Dist(s): **Baker & Taylor Bks.**
Book Clearing Hse.
Brodart Co.
Finney Co., Inc.
Gluesing & Gluesing
Quality Bks., Inc.

Imaginart International, Inc., *(0-9609464; 1-883315)* 307 Arizona St., Bisbee, AZ 85603 USA (SAN 260-2067) Tel 520-432-5741; Fax: 520-432-5134
E-mail: imaginart@compuserve.com
Web site: http://www.imaginartonline.com.

Imaginart Press *See* **Imaginart International, Inc.**

Imaginary Lines, Incorporated *See* **Sally Ride Science**

Imagination Arts Pubns., *(0-9746119)* P.O. Box 103, Mahwah, NJ 07430 USA Tel 201-529-5105; Fax: 201-529-5105
E-mail: imaginationarts@optonline.net
Web site: http://www.iapbooks.com.

Imagination Development Group, LLC, *(1-931184)* 243 N. Highway 101, Ste. 22, Solana Beach, CA 92075-1168 USA
E-mail: coopermphd@aol.com
Dist(s): **Penton Overseas, Inc.**

Imagination Institute, The, *(0-9679157)* 13491 Romford Ave., Pt Charlotte, FL 33981-6148 USA
E-mail: billmarts@msn.com
Web site: http://www.imagination-institute.com
Dist(s): **Baker & Taylor Bks.**
DeVorss & Co.

Imagination Stage, Inc., *(0-9723729)* 4908 Auburn Ave., Bethesda, MD 20814 USA Tel 301-961-6060; Fax: 301-718-9526
E-mail: lagogliati@aol.com
Web site: http://www.imaginationstage.org.

Imagination Station Pr., *(0-9742575)* 4560 N. 25th Rd., Arlington, VA 22207-4147 USA Tel 703-528-5828
E-mail: epyatt1@comcast.net.

Imagination Workshop, The, *(0-9744437)* 4150 Abbott Ave., N., Minneapolis, MN 55422 USA
E-mail: imaginationworkshop@yahoo.com.

Imaginative Publishing, Ltd., *(0-9743335; 0-9767948)* P.O. Box 150008, Fort Worth, TX 76108 USA Tel 817-246-6436 (phone/fax); Toll Free: 877-246-6436 (phone/fax)
E-mail: publisher@imaginativepublishing.com
Web site: http://www.imaginativepublishing.com
Dist(s): **Baker & Taylor Bks.**

Imaginator Pr., *(0-9745603)* 6400 Baltimore National Pike, No. 194, Baltimore, MD 21228-3915 USA
E-mail: sruth@ImaginatorPress.com
Web site: http://www.ImaginatorPress.com
Dist(s): **Greenleaf Book Group Pr.**

Imagine Bks., *(0-9761317; 0-9764353; 0-9767913)* P.O. Box 16268, High Point, NC 27261 USA Tel 336-510-9629
E-mail: contact@artsimage.com
Web site: http://www.artsimagine.com.

Imagine Nation Pr., *(0-940411)* 6109 Peabody St., Long Beach, CA 90808 USA (SAN 664-4554)
E-mail: imaginenationpress@verizon.net
Web site: http://www.imaginenationpress.com.

Imagine Pr., *(0-9632649)* Orders Addr.: c/o Joy Bennett 2 Crownwood Cir., Pittsford, NY 14534 USA Do not confuse with Inagine Press, LLC in Kirkland, WA
E-mail: treepose1@yahoo.com.

Imagine Pubs., *(1-56491)* P.O. Box 26393, Santa Ana, CA 92799 USA (SAN 297-5041) Tel 714-641-4046; Fax: 714-966-5361; Toll Free: 800-826-3683
E-mail: info@imaginepublishers.com
Web site: http://www.imaginepublishers.com.

Imagine Publishing, *(0-9758899)* 7620 Dogleg Rd., Dayton, OH 45414 USA Fax: 937-890-7949
E-mail: skyblu40@earthlink.net.

Imagine That!, *(0-9671154)* 5225 Canyon Crest Dr., Suite 13, Riverside, CA 92507 USA Tel 951-784-0132; Fax: 951-784-7827
E-mail: RKRose@earthlink.net.

Imagine That Enterprises, *(0-9723067)* P.O. Box 29315, Saint Louis, MO 63126 USA
E-mail: underthedove@hotmail.com
Web site: http://www.underthedove.com.

Imagine the Possibilities, LLC *See* **Imagining Possibilities**

Imagineland, LTD, *(0-9765038)* P.O. Box 10134, College Station, TX 77842-0134 USA
Web site: http://www.imagineland.com.

IMAGINEX, LLC, *(0-9753620)* P.O. Box 1375, Frisco, TX 75034 USA ; *Imprints:* Bible Game (BibleGame)
Web site: http://www.imnex.net.

Imagining Possibilities, *(0-9747426)* P.O. Box 266, Gwynedd Valley, PA 19437-0266 USA.

Imago, *(0-9765179)* 14220 Duckett Rd., Brandywine, MD 20613-9343 USA Tel 856-812-0400; Toll Free Fax: 866-268-9003; Toll Free: 866-413-6864.

imaJen, Inc., 5530 Penn Ave., 1st Flr., Pittsburgh, PA 15206 USA Tel 412-441-4143; Fax: 412-441-4453.

ImaJinn Bks., *(1-893896; 0-9759653; 1-933417)* P.O. Box 545, Canon City, CO 81215-0545 USA Tel 719-275-0060; Fax: 719-276-0741; Toll Free: 877-625-3592
E-mail: orders@imajinnbooks.com
Web site: http://www.imajinnbooks.com.

Imani Enterprises, *(0-9704644)* P.O. Box 361379, Decatur, GA 30036-1379 USA Tel 770-323-1375
E-mail: ChikeA@bellsouth.net.

Imani-MCHS, *(0-9729586)* 3445 W. 66th Pl., Chicago, IL 60629 USA Tel 773-925-6473
E-mail: imanimchs@aol.com.

I-Mar, *(0-9741052)* 5500 Bolsa Ave., No. 200, Huntington Beach, CA 92649 USA Tel 714-901-5627; Fax: 714-901-4637
Web site: http://www.i-mar.net.

Immediex Publishing, *(1-932968)* 540 Evelyn Pl., Beverly Hills, CA 90210 USA Tel 310-273-1585
E-mail: rodney@immediex.com
Web site: www.immediex.com.

Immedium, *(1-59702)* 535 Rockdale Dr., San Francisco, CA 94127 USA
Web site: http://www.immedium.com
Dist(s): **Consortium Bk. Sales & Distribution.**

Immortality Pr., *(0-9795753)* 1005 Winthrope Chase Dr., Alpharetta, GA 30004 USA
E-mail: publisher@immortalitypress.com; order@immortalitypress.com
Web site: http://www.immortalitypress.com.

IMP Publishing *Imprint of* **International Management Group (International Merchandising Corporation)**

Impact *Imprint of* **F & W Pubns., Inc.**

Impact Films, *(1-892553)* 16614 Burbank Blvd., Suite 306, Sherman Oaks, CA 91411 USA Tel 818-994-7888; Fax: 818-994-0070
E-mail: impactfilms@jps.net.

Impact Pubns., *(0-942710; 1-57023)* Div. of Development Concepts, Inc., 9104 Manassas Dr., Suite N, Manassas Park, VA 20111-5211 USA (SAN 240-1142) Tel 703-361-7300; Fax: 703-335-9486 Do not confuse with companies with the same name in Evanston, IL, Mandeville, LA, Southfield, MI
E-mail: krannich@impactpublications.com
Web site: http://www.impactpublications.com
Dist(s): **National Bk. Network.**

Impact Publications, Incorporated *See* **Specialty Pr., Inc.**

†Impact Pubs., Inc., *(0-915166; 1-886230)* P.O. Box 6016, Atascadero, CA 93423 USA (SAN 202-6864) Tel 805-466-5917; Fax: 805-466-5919; Toll Free: 800-246-7228 ; *Imprints:* Little Imp Books (Little Imp Books); Rebuilding Books (Rebuilding Bks) Do not confuse with Impact Pubns. in Manassas Park, VA or Plantation, FL.
E-mail: publisher@impactpublishers.com
Web site: http://www.impactpublishers.com; *CIP.*

Impact Seminars, Inc., *(0-9630968)* Orders Addr.: P.O. Box 431, Brentwood, TN 37024-0431 USA Tel 615-373-3588; Edit Addr.: 6305 Murray Ln., Brentwood, TN 37027 USA
E-mail: john@impactseminars.come
Web site: http://www.impactseminars.com.

Imperius, *(1-889945)* Orders Addr.: P.O. Box 11388, Marina del Rey, CA 90295 USA (SAN 299-1365) Tel 310-392-9085; Edit Addr.: 1432 Elkgrove Cir., No. 4, Venice, CA 90291 USA.

Impossible Dreams Publishing Co., *(0-9786422)* 4123 Rancho Grande Pl., NW., Albuquerque, NM 87120 USA (SAN 851-139X)
E-mail: Quixote1818@aol.com
Web site: http://www.impossibledreamspub.com
Dist(s): **AtlasBooks Distribution.**

Impressions Ink, *(1-882626)* 3918 Peachtree Ln., Memphis, TN 38135-9115 USA Tel 901-388-5382; Fax: 901-385-0256; Toll Free: 800-388-5382.

Imprexions Publishing Co., *(0-9742922)* P.O. Box 1681, Thousand Oaks, CA 91358-1681 USA Tel 805-402-3079
E-mail: listinsky@hotmail.com.

Imprint Academic (GBR) *(0-907845; 1-84540) Dist. by* **IngramPubServ.**

Imprints, *(1-883986)* Div. of Spectrum Bks., Orders Addr.: P.O. Box 4365, Thousand Oaks, CA 91359 USA Tel 808-707-3336; Fax: 808-707-4446; Edit Addr.: 32151 Sailview Ln., Westlake Village, CA 91359 USA
Dist(s): **Continental Bk. Co., Inc.**

Impulse Surf, *(0-9744247)* Orders Addr.: 1106 Second St., PMB 823, Encinitas, CA 92024 USA Tel 760-431-6883; Fax: 760-436-7158; Edit Addr.: 7200 Ponto Dr., Carlsbad, CA 92009 USA
E-mail: franklinlives@yahoo.com
Web site: http://www.impulsesurf.com.

In Ardua Tendit Pr., *(0-9749673)* 464 Leton Dr., Columbia, SC 29210 USA Tel 803-796-4000
E-mail: jess@proprinters.com
Web site: http://www.jessmaccallum.com.

In Audio *Imprint of* **Sound Room Pubs., Inc.**

In Between Bks., *(0-935430)* P.O. Box 790, Sausalito, CA 94966 USA (SAN 213-6236) Tel 415-383-8447; Fax: 415-381-1938; 415-381-3513
E-mail: inbetweenbooks@atthebutterflytree.com
Web site: http://www.atthebutterflytree.com.

In Cahoots, *(0-9745990)* 105 Los Padres Way, Unit 6, Buellton, CA 93427 USA Do not confuse with In Cahoots in Marietta, GA
Dist(s): **SPD-Small Pr. Distribution.**

In Celebration *Imprint of* **Schaffer, Frank Pubns.**

In Cider Pr., *(0-9721716)* P.O. Box 228, Barton, VT 05822 USA Tel 802-754-8889.

In Hope Freedom Rings, Inc., *(0-9659488)* 8136 Old Keene Mill Rd., Suite A-312, Springfield, VA 22152 USA Tel 703-569-8600
E-mail: info@inhopefreedomrings.com
Web site: http://www.inhopefreedomrings.com
Dist(s): **Ingram Bk. Co.**

In the Desert, *(0-9744005)* 7990 E. Snyder Rd., No. 5106, Tucson, AZ 85750-9009 USA
Web site: http://www.inthedesert.biz.

In the Hands of a Child, *(1-60308)* 6222 Pierce St., Coloma, MI 49038 USA Fax: 269-849-0074; Toll Free: 866-426-3701
E-mail: niki@handsofachild.com; info@handsofachild.com; sales@handsofachild.com
Web site: http://www.Handsofachild.com.

In The Hse. Publishing Co., *(0-9760441)* 1122 N. 84th St., Seattle, WA 98103 USA
E-mail: projectfille@hotmail.com
Web site: http://www.projectgirl.com.

In The Lead Publishing, *(0-9741413)* 3588 Hwy. 138 S.E., No. 193, Stockbridge, GA 30281 USA Tel 678-284-1495
E-mail: nevlynn@nevjohnson.com
Web site: http://www.nevjohnson.com.

In the Sky Publishing, *(0-9740438)* Orders Addr.: 26300 Ford Rd., No. 407, Dearborn Heights, MI 48127 USA Tel 313-792-0694
E-mail: cmlipson@wideopenwest.com
Web site: http://www.intheskypublishing.com.

In the Think of Things, *(1-933407)* P.O. Box 391, Williamsfield, IL 61489 USA.

In Time Pubns. Inc., *(0-9762857)* P.O. Box 190537, Fort Lauderdale, FL 33319 USA
Web site: http://www.intimepublications.com.

In Unexpected Ways, *(1-930712)* Orders Addr.: P.O. Box 46716, Tampa, FL 33647 USA Tel 813-852-8856; Fax: 813-907-8498; Edit Addr.: 18013 Forest Retreat Ln., Tampa, FL 33647 USA
E-mail: Weyandsos@aol.com.

In Vision Pubs., *(1-929480)* Div. of Know It By Heart Enterprises, Orders Addr.: P.O. Box 2010, Helendale, CA 92342 USA Tel 760-952-2054; Fax: 760-245-9969; Edit Addr.: 14593 Ketch Ln., Helendale, CA 92342 USA
E-mail: IKIBH@aol.com
Web site: http://www.knowitbyheart.com.

Inaz Enterprises, *(0-9718640)* 1701 Van Ness Terr., Union, NJ 07083 USA
E-mail: inazenterprises@aol.com
Web site: http://inaz4husains.netfirms.com.

Incentive Pubns., Inc., *(0-86530; 0-913916)* 2400 Crestmoor Rd. Ste. 211, Nashville, TN 37215-2032 USA (SAN 203-8005) Toll Free: 800-421-2830
E-mail: info@incentivepublications.com
Web site: http://www.incentivepublications.com.

Incentives For Learning, *(1-56872)* 111 Center Ave., Suite I, Pacheco, CA 94553 USA Tel 925-682-2428; Fax: 925-682-2645; Toll Free: 888-238-2379.

Inch By Inch Pubns., LLC, *(0-9670941)* P.O. Box 15, Okemos, MI 48805 USA Tel 716-688-1515; Fax: 716-636-4058; Toll Free: 877-462-4967
E-mail: chofher@aol.com
Web site: http://www.inchbyinchbooks.com
Dist(s): **Biblio Distribution.**

Incite Insight, LLC, *(0-9714885)* 260 Avenida Vista Montana., San Clemente, CA 92672-9402 USA
E-mail: isq4change@aol.com.

Inclusive Books LLC, *(0-9778143)* 3027 New Natchez Trace, Nashville, TN 37215 USA Tel 615-383-1065
E-mail: estelle@estellecondra.com
Web site: http://www.inclusivebooks.com.

Inc. Trustees of the Gospel Worker Society, The, *(0-9617506; 1-59843)* Div. of Union Gospel Pr., 1980 Brookpark Rd., Cleveland, OH 44109 USA (SAN 664-2845) Toll Free: 800-638-9988
E-mail: berylcbidlen@uniongospelpress.com
Web site: http://www.uniongospelpress.com.

Incredible Kid, LLC, *(0-9755836)* 7095 Hollywood Blvd., Suite 461, Hollywood, CA 90028 USA.

Incredible Years Pr., *(1-892222)* 1411 Eighth Ave., W., Seattle, WA 98119 USA Tel 206-285-7565 (phone/fax)
E-mail: LisaStGeorge@comcast.net
Web site: http://incredibleyears.com.

in-D, *(1-893801)* P.O. Box 642556, Los Angeles, CA 90064 USA Fax: 310-694-0222
E-mail: info@in-d.com
Web site: http://www.in-d.com
Dist(s): **Baker & Taylor Bks.**
Book Hse., Inc., The
Yankee Bk. Peddler, Inc.

Independent Means, Inc., *(1-893215)* 126 E. Haley St. Ste. A16, Santa Barbara, CA 93101-2384 USA (SAN 299-7371) Toll Free: 800-350-1818
E-mail: mlittle@independentmeans.com
Web site: http://www.IndependentMeans.com.

Independent Pub., *(1-59975; 1-60402; 1-60461; 1-60530)* Div. of Bar Code Graphics, 444 N. Michigan Ave., Suite 3500, Chicago, IL 60611 USA Fax: 312-595-0725; Toll Free: 800-662-0701 Do not confuse with Independent Publishers in Bountiful, UT
E-mail: pubserv@barcode-us.com
Web site: http://www.publisherservices-us.com.

Independent Publisher Services, *(1-4243)* Orders Addr.: 444 N. Michigan Ave., #3500, Chicago, IL 60611 USA Toll Free: 800-662-0701
E-mail: sales@barcode-us.com
Dist(s): **Islander Group**
Miller Trade Bk. Marketing.

Independent Pubs. Group, Subs. of Chicago Review Pr., 814 N. Franklin, Chicago, IL 60610 USA (SAN 202-0769) Tel 312-337-0747; Fax: 312-337-5985; Toll Free: 800-888-4741
E-mail: frontdesk@ipgbook.com
Web site: http://www.ipgbook.com; http://www.trafalgarsquarepublishing.com.

Independent Spirit Publishing, *(0-9666919)* P.O. Box 462, Cannon Falls, MN 55009-0462 USA Tel 507-263-5158
E-mail: ispublish@aol.com
Web site: http://www.independentmysteries.com
Dist(s): **Baker & Taylor Bks.**

India Research Pr. (IND) *(81-87943; 81-901098)* *Dist. by* **IPG Chicago.**

Indian Hill Gallery of Fine Photography, *(0-9669079)* 671 River Rd., Wells, VT 05774 USA Tel 802-325-2274; Fax: 802-325-2276
E-mail: info@stephenschaub.com
Web site: http://www.indianhillgallery.com
Dist(s): **RAM Pubns. & Distribution.**

Indian Nations Publishing Co., *(0-9653874)* 701 W. Blair, Wilburton, OK 74578 USA Tel 918-465-5330 (phone/fax)
E-mail: ssh@cwis.net
Dist(s): **Hervey's Booklink & Cookbook Warehouse.**

Indian Territory Publishing, *(0-9727068)* P.O. Box 43, Bennington, OK 74723-0043 USA.

Indiana Career & Postsecondary Advancement Ctr. (ICPAC), *(1-892766)* 2805 E. Tenth St., Suite 150, Bloomington, IN 47408 USA Tel 812-855-8475; Fax: 812-855-4220; Toll Free: 800-992-2076
E-mail: gillies@indiana.edu
Web site: http://icpac.indiana.edu.

†Indiana Historical Society, *(0-87195)* 450 W. Ohio St., Indianapolis, IN 46202-3269 USA (SAN 201-5234) Tel 317-233-9557; 317-232-1882; Fax: 317-233-0857; Toll Free: 800-447-1830
E-mail: rvaught@indianahistory.org; cbennett@indianahistory.org
Web site: http://www.indianahistory.org
Dist(s): **Distributors, The**
Indiana Univ. Pr.; *CIP.*

†Indiana Univ. Pr., *(0-253)* 601 N. Morton St., Bloomington, IN 47404-3797 USA (SAN 202-5647) Fax: 812-855-7931; Toll Free: 800-842-6796
E-mail: iuporder@indiana.edu
Web site: http://www.Indiana.edu/~iupress
Dist(s): **Lightning Source, Inc.**
NetLibrary, Inc.
Transaction Pubs.; *CIP.*

IndieArtz, Inc., *(0-9753252)* 1650 Margaret St., Suite 302-131, Jacksonville, FL 32204-3869 USA
Web site: http://www.indieartz.com.

Indigenous Language Institute, *(0-9710315; 0-9753903)* 1601 Cerrillos Rd., Santa Fe, NM 87505-3551 USA
E-mail: ili@indigenous-language.org
Web site: http://www.indigenous-language.org.

Indigo Custom Publishing, *(0-9725951; 0-9762875; 0-9770912; 0-9776711; 1-934144)* 435 Second St., Suite 320, Macon, GA 31201 USA Toll Free: 866-311-9578 ; *Imprints:* Blue Marble Books (Blu Marble Bks)
E-mail: gpulliam@indigopublishing.us
Web site: http://www.indigopublishing.us
Dist(s): **American Wholesale Bk. Co.**
Parnassus Bk. Distributors.

Indigo Pr., LC, *(0-9676199)* 2560 Sanibel Blvd., Sanibel, FL 33957 USA (SAN 631-9327) Tel 239-472-0491; Fax: 239-472-1426 Do not confuse with Indigo Pr., West Fork, AR, Virginia Beach, VA
E-mail: indigocontact@earthlink.net
Web site: http://www.indigopress.net.

Individualized Education Systems/Poppy Lane Publishing, *(0-938911)* Orders Addr.: P.O. Box 5136, Fresno, CA 93755 USA (SAN 661-8405) Tel 559-299-4639; Edit Addr.: 134 Poppy Ln., Clovis, CA 93612 USA (SAN 661-8413)
E-mail: Bette1234@aol.com
Web site: http://www.poppylane.com
Dist(s): **American West Bks.**
Baker & Taylor Bks.

Indra Publishing (AUS) *(0-9587718; 0-9585805; 0-9578735; 1-920787)* *Dist. by* **Intl Spec Bk.**

Indulgence Pr., *(0-9742191)* 628 13th Ave NE, Minneapolis, MN 55413-1361 USA
Web site: http://www.indulgencepress.com.

IndyPublish.com, *(1-58827; 1-4043; 1-4142; 1-4219; 1-4280; 1-4353)* 170 Gore St. Suite 405, Cambridge, MA 02141 USA
E-mail: info@indypublish.com
Dist(s): **Baker & Taylor Bks.**
Lightning Source, Inc.
Replica Bks.

Indy-Tech Publishing *Imprint of* **Sams Technical Publishing, LLC**

Infant Learning Co., The, *(0-9657510; 1-931026)* 5009 Isle Royal Ct., Oceanside, CA 92057 USA Tel 760-630-6204; Fax: 760-630-3894; Toll Free: 888-463-2681
E-mail: brendan@infantlearning.com; lisa@infantlearning.com
Web site: http://www.infantlearning.com; http://www.yourbabycanread.com
Dist(s): **Penton Overseas, Inc.**

Infante Pubns., Inc., *(0-9661557)* Orders Addr.: P.O. Box 1475, New York, NY 10022 USA Tel 212-752-2885; Fax: 212-688-2183; Edit Addr.: 211 E. 53rd St., New York, NY 10022 USA
Web site: http://members.aol.com/lavoeinf/music12/index.htm
Dist(s): **Quality Bks., Inc.**

Infini Pr., LLC, *(1-932457)* Orders Addr.: P.O. Box 9096, Cincinnati, OH 45209-9096 USA Toll Free: 800-765-5885; Edit Addr.: 1120 Ave. of the Americas, Fourth Flr., New York, NY 10036 USA ; *Imprints:* Asia for Kids (Asia for Kids)
E-mail: info@infinipress.com
Web site: http://www.infinipress.com
Dist(s): **Master Communications, Inc.**

Infinite Discovery, *(0-9626535)* 3228 Wilshire Terr., Oklahoma City, OK 73116-3024 USA Tel 405-843-7308; Fax: 405-239-0741; Toll Free: 800-475-7308.

Infinite Possibilities Publishing Group, Inc., *(0-9729912; 0-9774243)* P.O. Box 150823, Altamonte Springs, FL 32715-0823 USA Tel 321-244-1329 ; *Imprints:* IP Books (IP Bks)
E-mail: IPpublishingGrp@aol.com
Web site: http://www.IPpublishingOnline.com
Dist(s): **Baker & Taylor Bks.**

Infinite Visions Forum, *(0-9770405)* Orders Addr.: P.O. Box 938, La Verne, CA 91750 USA Tel 909-593-7332 (phone/fax); Edit Addr.: 4095 Fruit St., SP 938, La Verne, CA 91750 USA
E-mail: ivforum@aol.com.

Infinity Publishing, *(0-9665678; 1-892896; 0-7414)* Div. of Buy Books On The Web.Com, 1094 New Dehaven St., Suite 100, West Conshohocken, PA 19428 USA Tel 610-941-9999; Fax: 610-941-9959; Toll Free: 877-289-2665
E-mail: info@infinitypublishing.com
Web site: http://www.buybooksontheweb.com.

Infinity Publishing *See* **Macro Publishing Group**

Infinity Studios LLC, *(1-59697)* 525 South 31st Street, Richmond, CA 94804 USA Fax: 510-215-5353 Do not confuse with companies with the same or similar name in Austin, TX
E-mail: info@infinitystudios.com
Web site: http://www.infinitystudios.com
Dist(s): **Diamond Bk. Distributors.**

InfoHi Publishing, *(0-9678605; 0-9717849)* P.O. Box 1688, Fremont, CA 94538 USA Tel 831-685-1063
E-mail: linda@infohi.com
Web site: http://www.infohi.com
Dist(s): **Booklines Hawaii, Ltd.**

INFORM, Inc., *(0-918780)* 120 Wall St., 14th Flr., New York, NY 10005 USA (SAN 210-4423) Tel 212-361-2400; Fax: 212-361-2412 Do not confuse with INFORM-International Forum for Management Systems, Inc., Montclair, VA
E-mail: inform@informinc.org
Web site: http://www.informinc.org.

Information Age Publishing, Inc., *(1-930608; 1-931576; 1-59311)* P.O. Box 4967, Greenwich, CT 06831 USA Tel 203-661-7602; Fax: 203-661-7952 Do not confuse with Information Age Publishing in Exeter, NH
E-mail: iap@infoagepub.com
Web site: http://www.infoagepub.com.

Information U.S.A., Inc., *(1-878346)* Orders Addr.: P.O. Box E, Kensington, MD 20895-0418 USA Tel 301-924-0556; Fax: 301-929-8907; Toll Free: 800-955-7693; Edit Addr.: 12081 Nebel St., Rockville, MD 20852 USA (SAN 256-5307) Fax: 301-469-8952; Toll Free: 800-871-8551
E-mail: mercedes@lesko.com
Web site: http://www.lesko.com
Dist(s): **Baker & Taylor Bks.**
Distributors, The.

Infusionmedia Publishing, *(0-9704852; 0-9718677; 0-9796586)* 140 N. 8th St., 205 The Apothecary, Lincoln, NE 68508-1327 USA (SAN 253-9136) Tel 402-477-2065 (phone/fax); Toll Free: 877-628-3845
E-mail: info@infusionmediapublishing.com
Web site: http://www.infusionmediapublishing.com
Dist(s): **Baker & Taylor Bks.**

Ingalls Publishing Group, Inc, *(0-9713045; 1-932158)* 197 New Market Ctr., No. 135, Boone, NC 28607 USA (SAN 254-3753) Tel 828-964-0590; 828-297-7127; Fax: 828-297-6884; Toll Free: 800-856-9099 ; *Imprints:* Caystone Books (Claystne Bks) Do not confuse with High Country Pubs., Lakewood, CO
E-mail: editor@highcountrypublishers.com
Web site: http://www.ingallspublishinggroup.com; http://www.highcountrypublishers.com
Dist(s): **Biblio Distribution.**

Ingleside Pr., *(0-9651345)* 200 W. Ramon Rd., Palm Springs, CA 92264 USA Tel 760-325-0046; Fax: 760-325-0710; Toll Free: 800-772-6655
Web site: http://www.ingleside/nn.com
Dist(s): **Sunbelt Pubns., Inc.**

Ingleside Pr., *(1-929883)* P.O. Box 30029, Baltimore, MD 21270 USA Fax: 320-205-6697; Toll Free: 877-378-7171 (ext. 592)
E-mail: inglesidepress@yahoo.com
Web site: http://www.geocities.com/athens/troy/5196.

Ingram Bk. Co., Subs. of Ingram Industries, Inc., Orders Addr.: 1 Ingram Blvd., P.O. Box 3006, La Vergne, TN 37086-1986 USA (SAN 169-7978) Tel 615-213-5000; Fax: 615-213-3976 (Electronic Orders); Toll Free Fax: 800-285-3296 (fax inquiry US & Canada); 800-876-0186 (orders); 877-663-5367 (Canadian orders); Toll Free: 800-937-8000 (orders only); 800-937-8200 (customer service US & Canada); 800-289-0687 (Canadian orders only customer service); 800-234-6737 (electronic orders US & Canada)) Do not confuse with Ingram Pr., Sacramento, CA
E-mail: customerservice@ingrambook.com; flashback@ingrambook.com; ics-sales@ingrambook.com
Web site: http://www.ingrambook.com.

Ingram Pub. Services, Orders Addr.: Customer Services, Box 512 1 Ingram Blvd., LaVergne, TN 37086 USA Toll Free Fax: 800-838-1149; Edit Addr.: 1 Ingram Blvd., LaVergne, TN 37086 USA (SAN 631-8630) Tel 615-793-5000; Fax: 615-213-5811
E-mail: customer.service@ingrampublisherservices.com; Publisher@ingrampublisherservices.com; Retailer@ingrampublisherservices.com
Web site: http://www.ingrampublisherservices.com.

Ingram's Nutrition Consultations, *(0-9769379)* 43889 Bayview Ave. Apt. 40107, Clinton Twp, MI 48038-7073 USA; 7701 Corporate Dr., No.212, Houston, TX 77036 (SAN 850-5179) Tel 281-513-4596; Fax: 713-771-2177
E-mail: dragonflysummersi@sbcglobal.net
Web site: http:// www.admin@ingramsnutritionconsultations.com; http://www.ingram's nutrition.com.

Inheritance Pr., Inc., *(0-9638086; 0-9749501)* Orders Addr.: P.O. Box 580, Trenton, NC 28585-0580 USA; Edit Addr.: 388 Henderson Ln., Trenton, NC 28585 USA.

Inherst, Marie, *(0-9749785)* 52670 TH 180, Beallsville, OH 43716-9226 USA.

Ink & Feathers Comics, *(0-9664974)* Div. of Ink & Feathers Calligraphy, Orders Addr.: 202 E. Grove St., Streator, IL 61364 USA Tel 815-672-1171 ; *Imprints:* Side Show Comics (Side Show Comics)
E-mail: nerwonduh@hotmail.com
Web site: http:///www.ifcomics.com
Dist(s): **Baker & Taylor Bks.**

Ink & Scribe, *(0-9679817; 1-931947)* Div. of Wise River Companies, Inc., 3101 Kintzley Ct. Unit J, Laporte, CO 80535-9393 USA Toll Free: 888-616-7720
E-mail: books@northfortynews.com
Web site: http://www.inkandscribe.com.

Ink Well, *(0-9767578)* P.O. Box 786, Winlock, WA 98596 USA ; *Imprints:* Ink Well Publishing (I W P) Do not confuse with Ink Well in Hermosa Beach, CA.

Ink Well Publishing *Imprint of* **Ink Well**

Inkberry Pr., *(0-9742148)* 15521 Shell Point Blvd., Fort Myers, FL 33908 USA Tel 239-466-2757
E-mail: wallykain@comcast.net.

Inkling Bks., *(1-58742)* 6528 Phinney Ave., N., Suite A, Seattle, WA 98103-5260 USA Tel 206-365-1624
E-mail: editor@inklingbooks.com
Web site: http://www.inklingbooks.com/
Dist(s): **Baker & Taylor Bks.**

Inkling Pr., *(0-9711039)* P.O. Box 2598, Menlo Park, CA 94026-2598 USA Tel 650-367-8794 Do not confuse with Inkling Press, Winsted, CT
E-mail: inkling@earthlink.net
Web site: http://www.inklingpress.com.

Inkwater Pr., *(0-9719414; 1-59299)* Div. of First Books, 6750 SW Franklin St., Suite A, Portland, OR 97223 USA Tel 503-968-6777; Fax: 503-968-6779
E-mail: customerservice@inkwaterpress.com; orders@inkwaterpress.com
Web site: http://www.inkwaterpress.com; http:// www.firstbooks.com.

Inkwell Productions, LLC, *(0-9658158; 0-9718155; 0-9728118; 0-9749701; 0-9766340; 0-9786202)* 101 N. 1st Ave. Ste. 150, Phoenix, AZ 85003-1913 USA Toll Free: 888-324-2665
E-mail: info@inkwellproductions.com
Web site: http://www.inkwellproductions.com.

Innate Foundation Publishing, *(0-9745866)* 9682 Sherwood Dr., Blaine, WA 98230 USA Tel 360-441-9156
E-mail: rca@robertclydeaffolter.com
Web site: http://www.innatefoundation.com.

Inner Circle Publishing, *(0-9770682)* 1407 Crane St., Schenectady, NY 12303 USA Tel 518-377-2508.

Inner Coaching, *(0-9636027)* 1108 Western Ave., Watertown, WI 53094 USA Tel 920-262-0439; Fax: 920-261-8801
E-mail: kids@readysetrelax.com
Web site: http://www.innercoaching.com
Dist(s): **Baker & Taylor Bks.**
Independent Pubs. Group
New Leaf Distributing Co., Inc.
Quality Bks., Inc.

Inner Learning, *(1-930640)* 349 N. Detroit St., Los Angeles, CA 90036 USA Tel 323-549-0279; 923-549-0279; Fax: 323-549-0289
Dist(s): **Feldheim Pubs.**

Inner Light - Global Communications, *(0-938294; 1-892062)* Orders Addr.: Box 753, New Brunswick, NJ 08903 USA (SAN 662-0191) Tel 212-685-4080
E-mail: mrufo@webtv.net
Dist(s): **Baker & Taylor Bks.**
Distributors, The
Distributors International
New Leaf Distributing Co., Inc.
Quality Bks., Inc.
Red Wheel/Weiser
Unique Bks., Inc.

Inner Peace Publishing, *(0-9720647)* P.O. Box 1538, Cedar Park, TX 78630-1538 USA Tel 512-415-5764 Do not confuse with Inner Peace Publishing, Spokane, WA
E-mail: info@innerpeacepublishing.com
Web site: http://www.innerpeacepublishing.com.

Inner Traditions *Imprint of* **Inner Traditions International, Ltd.**

†Inner Traditions International, Ltd., *(0-89281; 1-59477)* Orders Addr.: P.O. Box 388, Rochester, VT 05767-0388 USA Tel 802-767-3174; Fax: 802-767-3726; Toll Free Fax: 800-246-8648; Edit Addr.: One Park St., Rochester, VT 05767 USA (SAN 208-6948) Tel 802-767-3174; Fax: 802-767-3726 ; *Imprints:* Healing Arts Press (Heal Arts VT); Inner Traditions (Inner Trad); Bindu Books (Bindu Bks)
E-mail: customerservice@innertraditions.com; info@innertraditions.com
Web site: http://www.innertraditions.com
Dist(s): **Baker & Taylor Bks.**
Book Wholesalers, Inc.
Bookazine Co., Inc.
Brodart Co.
Integral Yoga Pubns.
Library Sales of N.J.
Lotus Pr.
New Leaf Distributing Co., Inc.
Nutri-Bks. Corp.
Partners/West
Quality Bks., Inc.
Ten Speed Pr.
Unique Bks., Inc.; *CIP.*

Inner Wisdom Pubns., *(0-9656741; 0-9774921)* 22850 Summit Rd., Los Gatos, CA 95033 USA (SAN 299-2450) Tel 408-353-2050; Fax: 408-353-4663; Toll Free: 888-468-4335
E-mail: 15minutemiracle@verizon.net
Web site: http://www.15MinuteMiracle.com.

InnerChamp Bks., *(0-9663949)* P.O. Box 11362, Santa Rosa, CA 95406 USA Tel 707-571-8023; Fax: 707-546-3764
E-mail: inrchamp@aol.com
Web site: http://www.innerchamp.com.

Innerchild Publishing, Inc., *(0-9768078)* Orders Addr.: P.O. Box 142317, Fayetteville, GA 30214-2317 USA.

Innerchoice Publishing, *(0-9625486; 1-56499)* 24426 S. Main, Carson, CA 90745 USA Tel 310-816-3085; Fax: 310-816-3092
Dist(s): **Jalmar Pr.**

Company

InnerCircle Publishing, *(1-882918; 0-9723191; 0-9755214; 0-9762924)* 522 Sadie St. Apt. 2, Laurens, IA 50554-1553 USA
E-mail: icpchad@longlines.com
Web site: http://www.innercirclepublishing.com; http://www.rev-press.com.

innertuber, *(0-9742742)* 2124 NE 7th St., Gainesville, FL 32609 USA.

Innes Bks., *(0-9702470)* P.O. Box 1254, Rancho Santa Fe, CA 92067-1254 USA Tel 858-756-5106
E-mail: jvinnes@aol.com
Web site: http://www.InnesBooks.com.

Innov8 Studios, *(0-9754544)* 16 Cedarwood Dr., Ballston Lake, NY 12019 USA
E-mail: innov8studios@nycap.rr.com.

Innovation Game, The, *(0-9643819)* 8509 Irvington Ave., Bethesda, MD 20817 USA Tel 301-530-4299
Web site: http://www.bethesdahistory.com.

Innovative Christian Pubns. *Imprint of* **Baker Trittin Pr.**

Innovative Cooking Enterprises - ICE, Inc., *(0-9629831; 1-891705)* Orders Addr.: P.O. Box 240888, Anchorage, AK 99524-0888 USA (SAN 297-441X) Tel 907-562-3131; Fax: 907-561-1835; Toll Free: 800-541-2733; Edit Addr.: P.O. Box 240888, Anchorage, AK 99524-0888 USA.

Innovative Kids, *(1-58476; 1-60169)* Div. of Innovative USA, Inc., 18 Ann St., Norwalk, CT 06854-2258 USA Tel 203-838-6400; Fax: 203-855-5582 ; *Imprints:* IKIDS (IKIDS)
E-mail: info@innovativekids.com
Web site: http://www.innovativekids.com
Dist(s): **Hachette Bk. Group.**

Innovative Language, LLC, *(0-9765236)* P.O. Box 1593, Eugene, OR 97440-1593 USA.

Innovative Products Plus, *(0-9659301)* Orders Addr.: P.O. Box 501846, San Diego, CA 92150 USA Tel 858-486-7622; Fax: 858-748-6296; Edit Addr.: 12936 Grimsley Ave., Poway, CA 92064 USA
E-mail: abinnovation@hotmail.com.

Innovative Training (I.T.) Works USA, Inc., *(0-9741425; 0-9791048)* Orders Addr.: 1138 Wilshire Blvd. Ste 2a, Los Angeles, CA 90017 USA (SAN 255-3805) Tel 949-351-2123; Fax: 213-250-9926
E-mail: techvalmonte@itworkscentral.com; info@itworkscentral.com
Web site: http://www.digitalwhizkids.com.

InQuest Ministries, Inc., *(0-9700652; 1-931548)* P.O. Box 1057, Burlington, NC 27216 USA Tel 336-222-1664; Fax: 336-222-1665; Toll Free: 800-776-1893
E-mail: inquest171@aol.com
Web site: http://www.inquest.org.

Insect Lore, *(1-891541)* Orders Addr.: P.O. Box 1535, Shafter, CA 93263 USA Tel 661-746-6047; Fax: 661-746-0334; Toll Free: 800-548-3284; Edit Addr.: 132 S. Beech St., Shafter, CA 93263 USA
E-mail: john@insectlore.com
Web site: http://www.insectlore.com.

Inside Out, Inc., *(0-9713562)* 2111 Woodward Ave., Suite 1010, Detroit, MI 48201 USA Tel 313-965-5332
E-mail: echoe@insideoutdetroit.org
Web site: http://www.insideoutdetroit.org.

Inside-OUT Corp., *(1-929157)* 631 N. Stephanie St., PMB 239, Henderson, NV 89014-2633 USA Tel 702-396-9083; Fax: 702-396-2354
E-mail: bookmktg@aol.com.

In-Sight Bks., Inc., *(1-892785; 0-9728165)* Orders Addr.: P.O. Box 42467, Oklahoma City, OK 73123 USA (SAN 850-1629) Tel 405-810-9501; Fax: 405-810-9504; Toll Free: 800-658-9262; Edit Addr.: 4141 NW Expressway, Suite 110, Oklahoma City, OK 73116 USA
E-mail: ordersinfo@insightbooks.com.

Insight Presentations, *(0-9635373)* Orders Addr.: P.O. Box 540367, Omaha, NE 68116 USA Tel 402-445-6071; Edit Addr.: P.O. Box 61, Waterloo, NE 68069-0061 USA.

†Insight Pr., *(0-935218)* 614 Vermont St., San Francisco, CA 94107-2636 USA (SAN 213-0955) Tel 415-826-3488; Fax: 415-821-2811 Do not confuse with companies with the same or similar name in San Jose, CA, Ocitillo, CA, New Orleans, LA
Dist(s): **Perseus Distribution**; *CIP.*

Insight Publishing Group, *(1-930027; 1-932503)* Div. of Insight International, Inc., 8801 S. Yale, Suite 410, Tulsa, OK 74137 USA Tel 918-493-1718; Fax: 918-493-2219; Toll Free: 800-924-8264 Do not confuse with companies with similar names in Parker, CO, Yreka,CA, Jacksonville, FL, Woodbridge, VA, Salt Lake City, UT
E-mail: info@freshword.com
Web site: http://www.freshword.com.

Insight Studios, *(1-889317)* 7844 Saint Thomas Dr., Baltimore, MD 21236 USA Tel 410-661-6897; Fax: 410-665-3597
Dist(s): **B T P Distribution**
Capital City
Diamond Bk. Distributors.

Insight Studios, LLC *See* **Bugeye Bks.**

Insomniac Pr. (CAN) *(1-895837; 1-894663; 1-897178) Dist. by* **Consort Bk Sales.**

Inspiration Software, Inc., *(0-928539; 1-932463; 1-933238; 1-934425)* 9400 SW Beaverton Hillsdale Hwy., No. 300, Beaverton, OR 97005 USA (SAN 670-8234) Toll Free: 800-877-4292
E-mail: jbrooks@inspiration.com
Web site: http://www.inspiration.com.

Inspirational Hse. of America, *(0-9768598)* 93 Jay Ln., Gasburg, VA 23857 USA.

Inspire Media, LLC *See* **Motivision Media**

Inspire Press, Inc., *(0-9741800)* P.O. Box 33241, Los Gatos, CA 95030 USA Tel 408-395-2003; Fax: 408-904-4662
E-mail: sharper@inspirepress.com
Web site: http://www.inspirepress.com.

Inspire Publications *See* **KITA Pubns.**

Inspire Pubns., *(0-9725292)* 13229 Middle Canyon Rd., Carmel Valley, CA 93924 USA (SAN 255-1225) Tel 831-917-6059; Fax: 831-659-8460
E-mail: larryhayes@mynamestartswith.com; lhayes@mynamestartswith.com
Web site: http://www.mynamestartswith.com
Dist(s): **AtlasBooks Distribution**
Baker & Taylor Bks.

Inspire U., LLC, *(0-9792361)* 30520 Rancho California Rd., Suite 107-64, Temecula, CA 92591 USA (SAN 852-8535).

Inspired By Family, *(0-9787074)* 1332 Westmore Ct., Stevens Point, WI 54481 USA
Web site: http://www.inspiredbyfamily.com.

Inspired By the Beach Publishing, *(0-9790415)* 7457 Broken Staff, Columbia, MD 21045 USA Tel 240-372-9194
Web site: http://www.26thingstoteach.com.

InspirEd Educators, *(1-933558)* 360 Waverly Hall Cir., Roswell, GA 30075 USA Tel 770-649-7571; Fax: 770-642-7568; Toll Free: 866-WE-INSPIRE (866-934-6774)
E-mail: sharon@inspirededucators.com
Web site: http://www.inspirededucators.com.

Inspired Idea, *(1-931203)* 185 Mark Twain Dr., Newport News, VA 23602-6622 USA
E-mail: business@inspiredidea.com; inquiry@inspiredidea.com; Eve@inspiredidea.com
Web site: http://www.inspiredidea.com.

Inspirio, *(0-310)* 5300 Patterson Ave., SE, Grand Rapids, MI 49530 USA Tel 1-800-727-3480
E-mail: zprod@zondervan.com
Web site: http://www.zondervan.com
Dist(s): **Zondervan.**

Instantpublisher.com, *(1-59196; 1-59872; 1-60458)* Orders Addr.: P.O. Box 985, Collierville, TN 38027 USA Tel 901-853-7070; Fax: 901-853-6196; Toll Free: 800-259-2592; Edit Addr.: 410 Hwy, 72 W., Collierville, TN 38017 USA
Web site: http://www.instantpublisher.com
Dist(s): **Dogwise Publishing.**

Institute for Advanced Physics Studies Press *See* **Stefan Univ. Pr., The**

Institute For Behavior Change Incorporated The, *(0-9770503)* 9900 W. Sample Rd., Suite 300, Coral Springs, FL 33065 USA Tel 954-755-6639; Fax: 954-755-4100
E-mail: rhall3318@acn.net
Web site: http:www.afterthestormchildrensbook.com.

Institute for Conscious Change, The, *(0-9743443)* Div. of BioPlan Associates, Inc., Orders Addr.: 481 W. Greys Rd., Oro Valley, AZ 85737 USA Tel 520-219-7009
E-mail: info@ConsciousChange.org
Web site: http://www.ConsciousChange.org.

Institute for Disabilities Research & Training, Inc., *(0-9667589; 0-9752933; 0-9760818; 0-9789373)* 11323 Amherst Ave., Wheaton, MD 20902 USA Tel 301-942-4326; Fax: 301-942-4439
E-mail: sales@idrt.com
Web site: http://www.idrt.com.

Institute for Preventative Sports Med., *(0-9745655)* P.O. Box 7032, Ann Arbor, MI 48107 USA Tel 734-434-3390; Fax: 734-572-4503
E-mail: admin@ipsm.org
Web site: http://www.ipsm.org.

Institute for Substance Abuse Research, *(0-935847)* Subs. of Security Consultant Services, Inc., 21124 Edinborough Pl., Leesburg, FL 34748-7523 USA (SAN 699-7759) Tel 352-315-0538
Dist(s): **Schaefer Education Foundation.**

Institute of Consumer Financial Education (ICFE), *(0-935451)* P.O. Box 34070, San Diego, CA 92163-4070 USA (SAN 693-2061) Tel 619-232-8811; 2515 Horton Ave., 2nd Flr., San Diego, CA 92101-1350 Tel 619-239-1401 (phone/fax)
E-mail: info@financial-education-icfe.org
Web site: http://www.financial-education-icfe.org.

Institute of Cultural Affairs, (USA), *(1-930913)* 4750 N. Sheridan Rd., Chicago, IL 60640 USA Tel 773-769-6363; Fax: 773-769-1144 Do not confuse with Institute of Cultural Affairs, Chicago, IL
E-mail: icachicago@iac.org
Web site: http://www.ica-usa.org.

Institute of Cybernetics Research, Inc., *(1-893375; 1-58578)* Orders Addr.: 15 W. 139th St. Apt. 10G, New York, NY 10037-1516 USA
E-mail: icri@usa.net; journal_of_amateur_computing-subscribe@yahoogroups.com
Web site: http://groups.yahoo.com/groups/journal_of_amateur_computing/
Dist(s): **American Heritage Magazine**
Analos Magazine
Theme Stream, Inc.
Wiley, John & Sons, Inc.

Institute of Physics Publishing, *(0-7503; 0-85274; 0-85498)* The Public Ledte Bldg., Suite 1035 150 S. Independence Mall, W., Philadelphia, PA 19106 USA (SAN 298-2315) Tel 215-627-0880; Fax: 215-627-0879; Toll Free: 800-632-0880; Dirac House Temple Back, Bristol, BS1 6BE Tel 44 (0) 117 929 7481; Fax: 44 (0) 117 930 1186
E-mail: book.enquiries@iop.org
Web site: http://bookmark.iop.org
Dist(s): **American International Distribution Corp.**
CRC Pr. LLC.

Instruction & Design Concepts, *(1-59199)* 441 Maple Springs Dr., Centerville, OH 45458-9232 USA (SAN 254-5144) Tel 937-439-2698; Fax: 937-439-5535.

Instructional Fair *Imprint of* **Schaffer, Frank Pubns.**

Instructional Resources Co., *(1-879478)* P.O. Box 111704, Anchorage, AK 99511-1704 USA Tel 907-345-6689 (phone/fax)
E-mail: susan@susancanthony.com
Web site: http://www.susancanthony.com.

Instructivision, Inc., *(0-929649; 0-938797; 1-56749)* P.O. Box 1970, Livingston, NJ 07039-7570 USA (SAN 661-5090)
E-mail: info@instructivision.com.

Instrument Society of America *See* **ISA**

Insu-Form, Incorporated *See* **I.Form Ink, Pub.**

Insurance Institute of America, Inc., *(0-89462; 0-89463)* 720 Providence Rd., Malvern, PA 19355 USA (SAN 210-2129) Tel 610-644-2100; Fax: 610-640-9576; Toll Free: 800-644-2101
E-mail: cserv@cpcuiia.org
Web site: http://www.aicpcu.org.

Intaglio, Inc., *(0-9748034)* P.O. Box 211296, Montgomery, AL 36109 USA Tel 706-593-2749; Fax: 334-260-9373
E-mail: sperez@intaglioinc.com
Web site: http://www.intaglioinc.com.

Intaglio Pr., *(0-944091)* Orders Addr.: P.O. Box 9952, College Station, TX 77842 USA (SAN 242-7133) Tel 409-696-7800; Toll Free: 800-768-5565; Edit Addr.: 8709 Bent Tree, College Station, TX 77845 USA (SAN 242-7141)
E-mail: HDETHL9414@aol.com.

†Integral Yoga Pubns., *(0-932040)* Satchidananda Ashram-Yogaville, Rte. 1, Box 1720, Buckingham, VA 23921 USA (SAN 285-0338) Tel 804-969-1706; Fax: 804-969-1463; Toll Free: 800-262-1008 (orders)
Web site: http://www.yogaville.org/pubs.html
Dist(s): **Biblio Distribution**
New Leaf Distributing Co., Inc.; *CIP.*

Intelligent Concepts, Inc., *(0-9740612)* 1889 N. Airport Dr., Lehi, UT 84043 USA Tel 801-766-0262
E-mail: joe@intelcon.biz
Web site: http://www.intelcon.biz.

Intellipop, LLC, *(0-9743805)* 2701 Troy Center Dr., Suite 275, Troy, MI 48084 USA Tel 248-269-6091; Fax: 248-269-6092
E-mail: info@intellipop.com
Web site: http://www.intellipop.com.

Interaction Pubs., Inc., *(1-57336)* Orders Addr.: P.O. Box 900, Fort Atkinson, WI 53538 USA; Edit Addr.: W5527 State Rd. 106, Fort Atkinson, WI 53538-0800 USA (SAN 631-2950) Tel 920-563-9571; Fax: 920-563-7395; Toll Free: 800-359-0961
E-mail: sales@interact-simulations.com; interact@highsmith.com
Web site: http://www.interact-simulations.com/; http://www.teachinteract.com.

Interactive Eye, L.L.C. *Imprint of* **Interactive Knowledge, Inc.**

Interactive Knowledge, Inc., *(0-9759464)* 142 High St., No. 618, Portland, ME 04101 USA Tel 207-775-2278; Fax: 413-778-6861 ; *Imprints:* Interactive Eye, L.L.C. (InterEye) Do not confuse with Interactive Knowledge, Inc., Charlotte, NC
E-mail: support@iknow.net
Web site: http://www.iknow.net.

Interactive Media Publishing, *(0-9744391; 1-934332)* Orders Addr.: P.O. Box 1407, Phoenix, OR 97535-1407 USA (SAN 256-095X) Tel 541-535-5552; Fax: 541-326-4239 ; *Imprints:* Once Upon A Time in a Classroom (OnceUponTime)
E-mail: orders@i-mediapub.com; accounts@i-mediapub.com; linda@i-mediapub.com
Web site: http://www.i-mediapub.com.

Intercollegiate Studies Institute, Incorporated *See* **ISI Bks.**

Intercontinental New Technologies, Inc., 3330 Dundee Rd., Suite C1, Northbrook, IL 60062 USA
E-mail: natasha@siscom.net.

Intercontinental Publishing, Inc., *(1-881164)* Orders Addr.: P.O. Box 7242, Fairfax Station, VA 22039 USA Tel 703-583-4800; Fax: 703-670-7825; Edit Addr.: 11681 Beacon Race Rd., Woodbridge, VA 22192 USA
E-mail: icpub@worldnet.att.net
Web site: http://home.att.net/~icpub/index.html.

Intercultural Center for Research in Education (I N C R E), *(1-58332)* 366 Massachusetts Ave., Suite 202, Arlington, MA 02474 USA Tel 781-643-2142; Fax: 781-643-1315; Toll Free: 888-462-7374
E-mail: mail@incre.org
Web site: http://www.incre.org.

Intercultural Communication Services, Inc., *(0-9741881; 0-9773359)* 2580 SW 76th Ave., Portland, OR 97225-3305 USA Fax: 503-292-6817
E-mail: jolinda@jolindaosborne.com
Web site: http://www.jolindaosborne.com.

Intercultural Development Research Assn., *(1-878550)* 5835 Callaghan Rd., Suite 350, San Antonio, TX 78228-1190 USA Tel 210-444-1710; Fax: 210-444-1714
E-mail: contact@idra.org
Web site: http://www.idra.org.

†Intercultural Pr., Inc., *(0-933662; 1-877864; 1-931930)* Div. of Nicholas Brealey Publishing, Ltd., P.O. Box 700, Yarmouth, ME 04096 USA (SAN 212-6699) Tel 617-523-3801; Fax: 617-523-3708; Toll Free: 866-372-2665; 888-273-2539
E-mail: books@interculturalpress.com; cdresner@nicholasbrealey.com
Web site: http://www.interculturalpress.com
Dist(s): **National Bk. Network**; *CIP.*

Interdata, *(1-58239)* 1741 Kekamek, NW, Poulsbo, WA 98370 USA Tel 360-779-1511; Fax: 360-697-4696; Toll Free: 800-818-0140
Web site: http://www.export-leads.com.

Interface Publishing, *(0-9709443; 0-9777121; 0-9799963)* 241 First Ave. N., Minneapolis, MN 55401 USA (SAN 854-1876) Tel 612-338-8973 Toll Free: 888-805-8973
E-mail: igi@igipublishing.com
Web site: http://www.igipublishing.com.

Interlight Studios, Inc., *(0-9674428)* Orders Addr.: P.O. Box 660237, Birmingham, AL 35266 USA Fax: 205-402-2684; Edit Addr.: 1586 Montgomery Hwy., Suite 1, Birmingham, AL 35216 USA ; *Imprints:* Fly by Night Productions (Fly by Night Prodns)
E-mail: interlight@earthlink.net
Web site: http://www.interlightstudios.com.

Interlink Bks. *Imprint of* **Interlink Publishing Group, Inc.**

Interlink Publishing Group, Incorporated *See* **Interlink Publishing Group, Inc.**

Interlink Publishing Group, Inc., *(0-940793; 1-56656)* 46 Crosby St., Northampton, MA 01060-1804 USA (SAN 664-8908) Tel 413-582-7054; Fax: 413-582-6731; Toll Free: 800-238-5465 ; *Imprints:* Crocodile Books (Crocodile Bks); Interlink Books (Interlink Bks)
E-mail: info@interlinkbooks.com; editor@interlinkbooks.com
Web site: http://www.interlinkbooks.com.

Interlink Resources International, *(0-9796411)* P.O. Box 12546, Reading, PA 19612 USA
E-mail: cjrempel@cs.com.

International Arts & Artists, *(0-9662859; 0-9767102)* 9 Hillyer Ct., NW, Washington, DC 20008 USA Fax: 202-333-0758
E-mail: katied@artsandartists.org
Web site: http://www.artsandartists.org.

International Black Writers & Artists, *(0-9640477)* Orders Addr.: P.O. Box 43576, Los Angeles, CA 90043 USA; Edit Addr.: 5472 S. Crenshaw Blvd., Los Angeles, CA 90043 USA Tel 213-964-3721.

International Bk. & Audio, *(1-892623)* Div. of Zins Design Studio, 30358 Baugh St., NW, Princeton, MN 55371-0421 USA Tel 763-893-2412 (phone/fax)
E-mail: zds@visi.com
Web site: http://www.citycart.com/iba.

†International Bk. Ctr., Inc., *(0-86685; 0-917062)* 2007 Laurel Dr., P.O. Box 295, Troy, MI 48099 USA (SAN 169-4014) Tel 248-879-8436; Fax: 810-254-7230
E-mail: ibc@ibcbooks.com
Web site: http://www.ibcbooks.com; *CIP.*

International Bk. Import Service, Inc., Orders Addr.: 161 Main St., P.O. Box 8188, Lynchburg, TN 37352-8188 USA (SAN 630-5679) Tel 931-759-7400; Fax: 931-759-7555; Toll Free: 800-277-4247
E-mail: IBIS@IBIService.com
Web site: http://www.IBIService.com.

International Business Pubns., USA, *(0-7397; 0-9646241; 1-57751; 1-4330)* Orders Addr.: P.O. Box 15343, Washington, DC 20003 USA Tel 202-546-2103; Fax: 202-546-3275; Edit Addr.: P.O. Box 15343, Washington, DC 20003-0343 USA Do not confuse with International Business Pubn., Inc. in Cincinnati, OH
E-mail: rusric@erols.com
Web site: http://world.mirhouse.com.

International Comics & Entertainment L.L.C., *(1-929090; 1-932575)* 1005 Mahone St., Fredericksburg, VA 22401 USA Tel 540-899-9186; Fax: 540-899-9196
E-mail: kblue@ic-ent.com
Web site: http://www.ic-ent.com
Dist(s): **Diamond Comic Distributors, Inc.**

International Council for Computers in Education *See* **International Society for Technology in Education**

International Council for Gender Studies, *(1-929656)* Orders Addr.: P.O. Box 702, Waxahachie, TX 75168 USA Fax: 972-937-9930; Toll Free: 800-317-6958
E-mail: rivilian@yahoo.com
Web site: http://www.fiveaspects.org.

International Debate Education Assn., *(0-9702130; 0-9720541; 1-932716)* 400 W. 59th St., New York, NY 10019 USA Tel 212-548-6932; Fax: 212-548-4610
E-mail: nselegzi@idebate.org
Web site: http://www.idebate.org
Dist(s): **Books International, Incorporated.**

International Design Library *Imprint of* **Stemmer Hse. Pubs., Inc.**

International Educational Improvement Ctr. Pr., *(1-884169)* Orders Addr.: c/o Dr. Archie W. Earl, Sr., Mathematics Dept. School of Science & Technology Norfork State University, Norfolk, VA 23504 USA Tel 757-823-9564
Web site: http://www.webspawner.com/users/ieicpress/index.html.

International Evangelism Crusades, Inc., *(0-933470)* 21601 Devonshire St., Suite 217, Chatsworth, CA 91311-8415 USA (SAN 203-8153) Tel 818-882-0039; Fax: 818-882-0047
Web site: http://www.nicufo.org.

International Fitness Professionals Assn., *(0-9714936)* 14509 University Point Pl., Tampa, FL 33613 USA Tel 813-979-1925; Fax: 813-979-1978; Toll Free: 800-785-1924
Web site: http://www.ifpa-fitness.com.

International Foundation of Employee Benefit Plans, *(0-89154)* Orders Addr.: P.O. Box 69, Brookfield, WI 53008-0069 USA (SAN 317-9214) Tel 262-786-6710; Fax: 262-786-8780; Toll Free: 888-334-3327
E-mail: books@ifebp.org
Web site: http://www.ifebp.org.

International Human Relations Consultants, Inc. (CAN) *(0-9681645) Dist. by* **Lone Pine.**

International Institute for Human Empowerment, Inc., *(0-9709461)* Orders Addr.: P.O. Box 3920, Albany, NY 12203 USA Tel 518-393-9491; Edit Addr.: 985 Avon Crest Blvd., Niskayuna, NY 12309 USA
E-mail: sshipe@humanempowerment.org
Web site: http://www.hunamempowerment.org.

International Language Centre, 1753 Connecticut Ave., NW, Washington, DC 20009 USA (SAN 209-1615) Tel 202-332-2894; Fax: 202-462-6657
E-mail: richard@newsinform.com; zisa@newsinform.com
Web site: http://www.newsinform.com.

International Learning Systems, Incorporated *See* **International Language Centre**

International Linguistics Corp., *(0-939990; 1-887371)* P.O. Box 17725, Kansas City, MO 64134-0025 USA (SAN 220-2573) Toll Free: 800-237-1830
E-mail: learn@accessus.net
Web site: http://www.learnables.com
Dist(s): **Appalachian Bk. Distributors.**

International Management Group (International Merchandising Corporation), *(0-9615344; 1-878843)* 1360 E. Ninth St., Suite 100, Cleveland, OH 44114 USA (SAN 695-1457) Tel 216-522-1200; Fax: 216-522-1145 ; *Imprints:* IMP Publishing (IMP Pubng)
Web site: http://www.imgworld.com
Dist(s): **Andrews McMeel Publishing**
Simon & Schuster, Inc.

International Marine/Ragged Mountain Pr. *Imprint of* **McGraw-Hill Professional Publishing**

International Masters Pubs., Inc., *(1-886614; 1-892207; 1-930560; 1-932013)* Div. of International Masters Publishers, AB, 225 Park Ave., 17th Flr., New York, NY 10003 USA Tel 212-353-6400; Fax: 212-353-7100
Web site: http://www.imponline.com.

International Merchandising Corporation *See* **International Management Group (International Merchandising Corporation)**

†International Monetary Fund, *(0-939934; 1-55775; 92-800; 1-58906)* c/o Publications Department, 700 19th St., NW, Hq1-7-124, Washington, DC 20431 USA (SAN 203-8188) Tel 202-623-7430; Fax: 202-623-7201
E-mail: publications@imf.org
Web site: http://www.imf.org/publications
Dist(s): **Bernan Assocs.**; *CIP.*

International Pacific Halibut Commission, *(0-9776931)* P.O. Box 95009, Seattle, WA 98145-2009 USA Tel 206-634-1838
E-mail: lauri@iphc.washington.edu
Web site: http://www.iphc.washington.edu.

International Preterist Assn., *(0-9621311; 1-932844)* 122 Seaward Ave., Bradford, PA 16701-1515 USA (SAN 251-0413) Tel 814-368-6578; Fax: 814-368-6030; Toll Free: 888-257-7023 (orders only) ; *Imprints:* I P A Logo (IPA Logo)
E-mail: preterist1@preterist.org
Web site: http://preterist.org.

International Publishers Marketing, Orders Addr.: 22883 Quicksilver Dr., Dulles, VA 20166 USA (SAN 253-3375) Toll Free: 800-758-3756; Edit Addr.: P.O. Box 605, Herndon, VA 20172-0605 USA Fax: 703-661-1501; Toll Free: 1-800-758-3756
E-mail: laureen@booksintl.com
Web site: http://www.internationalpubmarket.com
Dist(s): **Books International, Incorporated.**

International Publishing, *(1-889418)* Orders Addr.: P.O. Box 934, Eugene, OR 97440 USA (SAN 299-1020) Tel 541-688-9702; Fax: 541-688-7931; Edit Addr.: 295 Dean Ave., Eugene, OR 97404 USA
Web site: http://www.ipublishing.com.

†International Reading Assn., *(0-87207)* 800 Barksdale Rd., P.O. Box 8139, Newark, DE 19714-8139 USA (SAN 203-8218) Tel 302-731-1600 (main no.); Fax: 302-368-2449; Toll Free: 800-336-7323 (orders only)
E-mail: bzell@reading.org
Web site:
http://marketplace.reading.org/products/IRA_Book_Main.cfm
Dist(s): **Erlbaum, Lawrence Assocs., Inc.**; *CIP.*

International Reconciliation Coalition, *(0-9702590)* Orders Addr.: P.O. Box 3278, Ventura, CA 93006 USA Tel 805-642-5327; Fax: 805-642-2588; Edit Addr.: 1595 Walter St., Suite 2, Ventura, CA 93003 USA
E-mail: ircio@pacbell.net
Web site: http://reconcile.org.

International Rivers Network, *(0-9662771; 0-9718858)* 1847 Berkeley Way, Berkeley, CA 94703 USA Tel 510-848-1155; Fax: 510-848-1008
E-mail: info@irn.org
Web site: http://www.irn.org.

International Sephardic Leadership Council, *(0-9763226)* 45 John St., Suite 711, New York, NY 10038 USA Tel 917-207-4344
E-mail: email@sephardiccouncil.org; shelomo@alfassa.com
Web site: http://www.sephardiccouncil.org.

International Society for Sephardic Progress, Incorporated *See* **International Sephardic Leadership Council**

International Society for Technology in Education, *(0-924667; 1-56484)* 175 W. Broadway. Ste. 300, Eugene, OR 97401-3042 USA (SAN 296-7693) Toll Free: 800-336-5191
E-mail: iste@iste.org
Web site: http://www.iste.org.

International Society of Arboriculture, *(1-881956)* Orders Addr.: P.O. Box 3129, Champaign, IL 61826 USA Tel 217-355-9411; Fax: 217-355-9516; Toll Free: 888-472-8733; Edit Addr.: 1400 W. Anthony Dr., Champaign, IL 61821 USA
E-mail: isa@isa-arbor.com
Web site: http://www.isa-arbor.com.

International Specialized Bk. Services, 920 NE 58th Ave., Suite 300, Portland, OR 97213-3786 USA (SAN 169-7129) Tel 503-287-3093; Fax: 503-280-8832; Toll Free: 800-944-6190
E-mail: info@isbs.com
Web site: http://www.isbs.com.

International Storytelling Press *See* **Storytelling World Pr.**

International Tamil Language Foundation, *(0-9676212; 0-9793059)* 8417 Autumn Dr., Woodridge, IL 60517 USA Tel 630-985-3141; Fax: 630-985-3199
E-mail: Thiru@kural.org
Web site: http://www.kural.org.

International Training, Inc., *(1-931451)* 18 Elm St., Topsham, ME 04086 USA Tel 207-729-4201; Fax: 207-729-4453; Toll Free: 888-778-9073
E-mail: worldhq@tdisdi.com
Web site: http://www.tdisdi.com.

International Univ. Line, *(0-9636817; 0-9720774)* P.O. Box 2525, La Jolla, CA 92038 USA Tel 858-457-0595; Fax: 858-581-9073
E-mail: info@iul-press.com.

International Vaquero Productions, *(0-9761103)* 730 W. 8th St., Claremont, CA 91711 USA
E-mail: kurt@internationalvaquero.com
Web site: http://www.internationalvaquero.com.

International Wizard of Oz Club, The, *(1-930764)* P.O. Box 26249, San Francisco, CA 94126-6249 USA Fax: 510-642-7589 Do not confuse with International Wizard of OZ Club, Appleton, WI
E-mail: phanff@library.berkeley.edu
Web site: http://ozclub.org.

Internationalist Publishing Company *See* **Internationalist, The**

Internationalist, The, *(0-9633905; 1-891382)* 96 Walter St., Suite 200, Boston, MA 02131 USA Tel 617-354-7755; Fax: 617-354-7447
Web site: http://www.internationalist.com.

Internet Pubs., Inc., *(0-9701700)* 5000-18 Hwy. 17, No. 235, Orange Park, FL 32073 USA Tel 904-278-1053; Fax: 904-215-1302
E-mail: stories4children@mindspring.com
Web site: http://stories4children.com.

Interpact Pr., *(0-9628700)* 545 Westport Dr., Old Hickory, TN 37138-1115 USA
E-mail: sherra@tampabay.rr.com
Web site: http://www.interpactinc.com
Dist(s): **Baker & Taylor Bks.**

Interplay Productions, *(1-57629)* 16815 Von Karman Ave., Irvine, CA 92606-4920 USA Tel 714-553-6655; Fax: 714-252-2820.

InterPress, *(0-9744173)* 14056 Fort Valley Rd., Fort Valley, VA 22652 USA ; *Imprints:* Fort Valley Geology Study Center (Ft Valley)
E-mail: wjmelson@shentel.net
Web site: http://interpressusa.com.

InterRelations Collaborative, Inc., *(0-9761753)* P.O. Box 6280, Hamden, CT 06517-3503 USA.

Interset Pr., *(1-57433)* Orders Addr.: 56 Forest Rd., Wilton, NH 03086 USA Tel 603-654-2949
E-mail: artistafloat@earthlink.net.

Interstellar Productions, Inc., *(0-9678580)* 1758 N. Park St., Suite B, Castle Rock, CO 80104 USA Fax: 303-688-7936; Toll Free: 800-806-0023 ; *Imprints:* I P I Toys (IPI Toys)
E-mail: renaten@ipitoys.com
Web site: http://www.ipitoys.com.

Interstellar Publishing Co., *(0-9645957; 1-889599)* Orders Addr.: P.O. Box 7306, Beverly Hills, CA 90212 USA (SAN 298-5829) Tel 310-247-8154; Fax: 310-247-0622
E-mail: Interstlr@aol.com
Web site: http://www.interstellarpublishing.com
Dist(s): **Baker & Taylor Bks.**

Interstellar Trading & Publishing Company *See* **Interstellar Publishing Co.**

†InterVarsity Pr., *(0-8308; 0-87784)* Div. of InterVarsity Christian Fellowship of the USA, Orders Addr.: P.O. Box 1400, Downers Grove, IL 60515 USA (SAN 202-7089) Tel 630-734-4000; Fax: 630-734-4200; Toll Free: 800-843-7225 (other depts.); 800-843-9487 (orders); 800-843-1019 (customer service); 800-873-0143 (electronic ordering)
E-mail: email@ivpress.com
Web site: http://www.ivpress.com; *CIP.*

Intervisual/Piggy Toes *Imprint of* **Dalmatian Pr.**

InterWeave Corp., *(0-9771936)* Orders Addr.: 5364 Ehrlich Rd. #248, Tampa, FL 33624 USA Tel 813-933-4431; Fax: 813-933-4311
E-mail: info@interweavecorp.com; kking@wheredoyoufindgod.com
Web site: http://www.interweavecorp.com; http://www.wheredoyoufindgod.com.

Intes International (UK) Ltd. (GBR) *(0-9533178) Dist. by* **D C D.**

In-the-Valley-of-the-Wichitas Hse., *(0-941634)* P.O. Box 6741, Lawton, OK 73506 USA (SAN 239-2321) Tel 580-536-7118
E-mail: ecebrook@sirinet.net
Web site: http://www.wichitamountainsguide.com.

Intra America Beauty Network, *(1-928986)* 14 Commerce Dr., North Branford, CT 06471 USA Tel 203-484-2665; Fax: 203-484-4373; Toll Free: 800-634-8500
E-mail: inspire@connix.com
Web site: http://www.inspirequarterly.com.

INTRAG Int'l, *(0-9727432; 0-9749722; 1-933140)* 5715 Vineland Ave., Suite No. 5, North Hollywood, CA 91601 USA Tel 818-762-1665; Fax: 818-980-1696
E-mail: general@intrag-publishing.com; management@intrag-publishing.com
Web site: http://www.intrag-publishing.com.

Intralife Systems Publishing, *(0-9703102)* P.O. Box 1555, Layton, UT 84041 USA Tel 801-544-2470; Fax: 801-544-2518
E-mail: admin@frogbuster.com
Web site: http://www.frogbuster.com.

Intrepid Films, LLC, *(1-929931)* Orders Addr.: P.O. Box 566, Boulder, CO 80306-0566 USA Tel 303-443-2426; Fax: 303-541-9737; Toll Free: 800-279-0802
E-mail: sportinc@msn.com; marya@intrepidfilms.com
Web site: http://www.intrepidfilms.com.

Introspect Bks., *(1-890667)* Orders Addr.: P.O. Box 271615, Dallas, TX 75227 USA Tel 972-278-3265; Fax: 972-278-0306; Edit Addr.: 1521 Palm Valley Dr., Garland, TX 75043 USA ; *Imprints:* Hand-In-Hand Books (Hand-In-Hand Bks).

Intuitive Arts Pr., *(0-9741334)* 15 E. Northwest Hwy., Suite 15 B, Palatine, IL 60067 USA
E-mail: katychance@juno.com
Web site: http://www.peakperformanceliving.info
Dist(s): **AtlasBooks Distribution.**

invenTEAM, LLC, *(0-9729599)* 65064 Cline Falls Rd., Bend, OR 97701 USA (SAN 255-4593) Tel 541-948-0015
E-mail: e.wally@bendcable.com
Web site: http://www.e-wally.org.

Inventors' Place, *(0-9672613)* 2257 Via Blanca, Oceanside, CA 92054 USA (SAN 253-5874) Tel 760-439-1703 (phone/fax)
E-mail: tom@inventorsplace.com
Web site: http://www.inventorsplace.com.

Invisible Cities Pr., *(0-9679683; 1-931229)* 41 Northfield St., Montpelier, VT 05602-3407 USA
E-mail: editor@invisiblecitiespress.com
Web site: http://www.invisiblecitiespress.com
Dist(s): **Independent Pubs. Group.**

Invision Pubns., *(0-9767337)* 1136 Sherman Ave., Suite C4, Bronx, NY 10456 USA Tel 718-538-6102
E-mail: puzzles@puzzlesforus.com
Web site: http://www.puzzlesforus.com.

Inward Reflections, Inc., *(0-9746783)* P.O. Box 1747, Brockton, MA 02303-1747 USA
Web site: http://inwardreflections@homestead.com.

InWord Resources, *(1-931662)* P.O. Box 531, Middletown, OH 45042 USA Fax: 513-422-3178
E-mail: info@inword.org
Web site: http://www.inword.org.

Inyati Press, *(0-9777440)* P.O. Box 453, fulton, CA 95439 USA
E-mail: milton@webbellis.org
Web site: http://www.webbellis.org.

Ion Imagination Publishing, *(1-886184)* Div. of Ion Imagination Entertainment, Inc., Orders Addr.: P.O. Box 210943, Nashville, TN 37221-0943 USA (SAN 298-5411) Tel 615-646-3644; Fax: 615-646-6276; Toll Free: 800-335-8672; Edit Addr.: 133 Morton Mill Cir., Nashville, TN 37221 USA
E-mail: flumpa@aol.com
Web site: http://www.flumpa.com
Dist(s): **Brodart Co.**
Professional Media Service Corp.
Quality Bks., Inc.

Iowa City Pr.-Citizen, *(0-9712727)* Subs. of Gannett Co., Inc., Orders Addr.: P.O. Box 2480, Iowa City, IA 52244 USA Tel 319-337-3181; Fax: 319-339-7342; Edit Addr.: 1725 N. Dodge St., Iowa City, IA 55245 USA
E-mail: dbrown@press-citizen.com
Web site: http://www.press-citizen.com.

Iowa State Univ. Extension, *(0-9700528)* Iowa State Univ., 218 Beardshear Hall, Ames, IA 50011-2046 USA Tel 515-294-4576; Fax: 515-294-4715
Web site: http://www.extension.iastate.edu.

IP Bks. *Imprint of* **Infinite Possibilities Publishing Group, Inc.**

IPA Logo *Imprint of* **International Preterist Assn.**

IPI Toys *Imprint of* **Interstellar Productions, Inc.**

ipicturebooks *Imprint of* **ibooks, Inc.**

ipicturebooks, LLC, *(1-58824; 1-59019; 1-59155; 1-59173)* 24 W. 25th St., No. 12, New York, NY 10010 USA Tel 212-645-9870; Fax: 212-645-9874
E-mail: aandrade@ipicturebooks.com
Web site: http://www.ipicturebooks.com
Dist(s): **Hachette Bk. Group**
NetLibrary, Inc.

iPlayMusic, Inc., *(0-9760487; 0-9797683)* P.O. Box 391775, Mountain View, CA 94039 USA Tel 650-969-3387; Fax: 650-969-3680; Toll Free: 866-594-3344
E-mail: quincy@iplaymusic.com
Web site: http://www.iplaymusic.com
Dist(s): **Music Sales Corp.**

Ippolito, Eva Marie, *(0-615; 0-9705350)* 10316 W. Oakmont Dr., Sun City, AZ 85351-3528 USA.

IQRA International Educational Foundation, *(1-56316)* 7450 Skokie Blvd., Skokie, IL 60077-3374 USA Tel 847-673-4072; Fax: 847-673-4095; Toll Free: 800-521-4272
E-mail: kmohiuddin@iqra.org; pdc@iqra.org
Web site: http://www.iqra.org.

Ira Valley Ideas, *(0-9715874)* Orders Addr.: 112 Plain St., Rutland, VT 05701 USA Tel 802-235-2392
E-mail: ccf0005701@yahoo.com.

Iran Books *See* **IBEX Pubs., Inc.**

Irensia Pubns., *(0-9710385)* P.O. Box 56, Hagatna, GU 96932 USA Tel 671-828-8040 (phone/fax)
E-mail: judyflores@kuentos.guam.net; judyflores@guam.net
Web site: http://judyflores.com.

Irie Bks., *(0-9709112)* 12699 Cristi Way, Bokeelia, FL 33922 USA Tel 941-283-2561; Fax: 941-283-9305
E-mail: ghausman@compuserve.com
Web site: http://geraldhausman.com.

Iris Pallas-Luke E-Writings/E-Literature, *(0-9765637)* 12472 Lake Underhill Rd., Suite 267, Orlando, FL 32828 USA
E-mail: irispallasluke@msn.com; noir@noirpallasluke.com
Web site: http://www.irispallas-luke.com; http://www.barbarapallas-luke.com; http://www.vernninapallas-luke.com; http://www.noirpallas-luke.com
Dist(s): **AtlasBooks Distribution.**

Iris Publishing Group, Inc., The, *(0-916078; 1-60454)* 969 Oak Ridge Turnpike, No. 328, Oak Ridge, TN 37830-8832 USA Tel 865-483-0837; Fax: 865-481-3793; Toll Free: 800-881-2119
E-mail: rcumming@irisbooks.com
Web site: htt://irisbooks.com.

Irish American Bk. Co., Subs. of Roberts Rinehart Pubs., Inc., P.O. Box 666, Niwot, CO 80544-0666 USA Tel 303-652-2710; Fax: 303-652-2689; Toll Free: 800-452-7115
E-mail: irishbooks@aol.com
Web site: http://www.irishvillage.com.

Irish Bks. & Media, Inc., *(0-937702)* Orders Addr.: 2904 41st Ave S., Minneapolis, MN 55406-1814 USA (SAN 111-8870) Toll Free: 800-229-3505 Do not confuse with Irish Bks. in New York, NY
E-mail: Irishbook@aol.com
Web site: http://www.irishbook.com.

Irish Eyes Publishing, *(0-9675084)* 310 12th Ave., Green Bay, WI 54303 USA Tel 920-498-9178
E-mail: irisheyespubl@aol.com.

Irish Genealogical Foundation, *(0-940134)* Div. of O'Laughlin Pr., P.O. Box 7575, Kansas City, MO 64116 USA (SAN 218-4834) Tel 816-454-2410 (phone/fax)
E-mail: mike@Irishroots.com
Web site: http://www.IrishRoots.com
Dist(s): **Irish Bks. & Media, Inc.**

Irizarry-Ramos, Rafael, *(0-9705628)* 40 Helen Pl., Stratford, CT 06614 USA Tel 203-377-8769; Fax: 203-368-1949 ; *Imprints:* Remar Company (Remar Co).

Iron Arm International, *(0-9746989)* 1 Reid St., Amsterdam, NY 12010-3424 USA Tel 518-842-9299
E-mail: Ironarm1@aol.com
Web site: http://www.uechiryu-karate.com
Dist(s): **Tuttle Publishing.**

Iron Brigade Armory, Ltd., *(1-885633)* 100 Radcliffe Cir., Jacksonville, NC 28546 USA Tel 910-455-3834; Fax: 910-346-1134
E-mail: sales@ironbrigadearmory.com
Web site: http://www.ironbrigadearmory.com.

Iron Crown Enterprises, Inc., *(0-915795; 1-55806)* P.O. Box 1605, Charlottesvle, VA 22902-1605 USA (SAN 294-0272) Toll Free: 800-325-0479
E-mail: askice@aol.com
Web site: http://www.ironcrown.com.

Iron Mountain Pr., *(0-9722961)* Orders Addr.: P.O. Box 7, New Milford, NY 10959 USA (SAN 256-0097)
E-mail: info@ironmountainpress.com
Web site: http://www.ironmountainpress.com.

Ironbound Pr., *(0-9763857)* P.O. Box 250, Winter Harbor, ME 04693-0250 USA Tel 207-963-2355; Fax: 320-323-2434 Do not confuse with Ironbound Pr. in Scotch Plains, NJ
E-mail: sales@ironboundpress.com
Web site: http://www.ironboundpress.com
Dist(s): **Baker & Taylor Bks.**

Ironcreek Pr., *(0-9766017)* 530 S. Pk. St., Asheboro, NC 27203 USA
E-mail: crottycrotty@embarqmail.com.

IronDream, *(0-9708655)* 8602 NE Benton Dr., Vancouver, WA 98622 USA Tel 360-256-0375 (phone/fax)
E-mail: sargentpike@hotmail.com.

Ironhorse Publishing Co., *(0-9747039)* 308 B W. Market St., Gratz, PA 17030 USA Fax: 717-365-7399 do not confuse with Ironhorse Publishing in Hayden Lake, ID
E-mail: pennvalleyprint@epix.net.

Ironwood Pr., *(0-9662840)* P.O. Box 4651, Traverse City, MI 49685-4651 USA Tel 616-275-3505; Fax: 616-275-5606; Toll Free: 800-725-6565 Do not confuse with companeis with the same name in Darnestown, MD, Yuma, AZ, Tuscon, AZ
Dist(s): **Follett Library Resources**
Quality Bks., Inc.
Unique Bks., Inc.

†Irvington Pubs., *(0-512; 0-8290; 0-8422; 0-89197)* Orders Addr.: P.O. Box 286, New York, NY 10276-0286 USA Fax: 212-861-0998; Toll Free Fax: 800-455-5520; Toll Free: 800-472-6037; *CIP.*

Irwin, Esther L., *(0-9778462)* 3531 Grove Dr., Cheyenne, WY 82001 USA Tel 307-632-2060
E-mail: Elivroman@bresnan.net.

†ISA, *(0-87664; 1-55617; 0-9791330; 0-9792343; 1-934394)* 67 Alexander Dr., Research Triangle Park, NC 27709 USA (SAN 202-7054) Tel 919-549-8411; Fax: 919-549-8288
E-mail: info@isa.org; ebell@isa.org
Web site: http://www.isa.org; *CIP.*

Isaacs, John, *(0-9779606)* 643 N. Main St., Lawrenceburg, KY 40342 USA (SAN 850-6191) Tel 502-418-1521
E-mail: jisaacs@kheaa.com.

Isadore Pr., *(0-9602600)* c/o Triangle Tattoo & Museum, 356B N. Main St., Fort Bragg, CA 95437 USA Tel 707-964-8814; Fax: 707-964-1193
E-mail: chichi@mcntattoo.com
Web site: http://www.triangletattoo.com
Dist(s): **Baker & Taylor Bks.**
Quality Bks., Inc.
Unique Bks., Inc.

Isaiah's Promise Publishing Co., *(0-9717603)* P.O. Box 1612, Perry, GA 31069 USA
E-mail: starfishfoundationfund@yahoo.com
Web site: http://www.geocities.com/starfishfoundationfund/home.

Isha Enterprises, Inc., *(0-936981)* P.O. Box 25970, Scottsdale, AZ 85255 USA (SAN 658-7895) Tel 480-502-9454; Fax: 480-991-5635; Toll Free: 800-641-6015
E-mail: info@easygrammar.com
Web site: http://www.easygrammar.com.

Ishnuvu Publishing Co., *(0-9636906)* 963 Monroe Rd., Hattiesburg, MS 39401 USA Tel 601 583-2444
E-mail: ishnuvu@aol.com
Web site: http://members.aol.com/Ishnuvu/index.html.

ISI Bks., *(1-882926; 1-932236; 1-933859)* 3901 Centerville Rd., P.O. Box 4431, Wilmington, DE 19807-0431 USA Tel 302-652-4600; 773-702-7000 (orders from all other countries); Fax: 302-652-1760; 773-702-7212 (orders from all other countries); Toll Free Fax: 800-621-8476 (orders in the US & CAN); Toll Free: 800-526-7022; 800-621-2736 (orders M-F in the US & CAN)
E-mail: bookpub@isi.org
Web site: http://www.isibooks.org
Dist(s): **Chicago Distribution Ctr.**
Univ. of Chicago Pr.

ISIS Large Print Bks. (GBR) *(0-7531; 1-85089; 1-85695) Dist. by* **Transaction Pubs.**

ISIS Large Print Bks. (GBR) *(0-7531; 1-85089; 1-85695) Dist. by* **Ulverscroft US.**

Islamic Bk. Service, 1209 Cleburne, Hoston, TX 77004 USA (SAN 169-2453) Tel 713-528-1440; Fax: 713-528-1085.

Islamic Ctr. of Sacramento, The, *(0-9769245)* Div. of Sacramento Computers, c/o Sacramento Computers, 1710 Broadway, No. 133, Sacramento, CA 95818 USA
E-mail: shamdani@mindspring.com
Web site: http://www.hineaf.net.

Islamic Foundation, Ltd. (GBR) *(0-9503954; 0-86037) Dist. by* **Kazi Pubns.**

Islamic Pubns. International, *(1-889999)* Orders Addr.: Five Sicomac Rd., No. 302, North Haledon, NJ 07508 USA Fax: 201-326-5602; Toll Free Fax: 866-297-2307; Toll Free: 866-297-2307
E-mail: ipi@onebox.com
Web site: http://www.islampub.com.

Islamic Supreme Council of America, *(1-930409)* Orders Addr.: 17195 Silver Pkwy. #401 Fenton, Mi 48430, Fenton, MI 48430 USA Tel 810-593-1222; Fax: 810-815-0518; Toll Free: 800-278-6624; Edit Addr.: 17195 Silver Pkwy. #401 Fenton Michigan 48430, Fenton, MI 48430 USA
E-mail: staff@islamicsupremecouncil.org; aliyah@sunnah.org
Web site: http://www.worde.org.

Islamic Texts Society (GBR) *(0-946621; 1-903682) Dist. by* **IPG Chicago.**

Island Bks. *Imprint of* **Dell Publishing**

Island Flowers, Inc., *(0-9637712)* 2691 SW 110th Way, Davie, FL 33328-1006 USA.

Island Friends LLC, *(0-9729987)* 11 Promontory Ct., Hilton Head Island, SC 29928 USA
E-mail: benjo@adelphia.net
Web site: http://www.islandfriends.net
Dist(s): **Baker & Taylor Bks.**
Sandlapper Publishing Co., Inc.

Island Heritage Publishing, *(0-89610; 0-931548; 1-59700)* Div. of The Madden Corp., 94-411 Koaki St., Waipahu, HI 96797 USA (SAN 211-1403) Tel 808-564-8800; Fax: 808-564-8888; Toll Free: 800-468-2800
E-mail: vkitajima@welcometotheislands.com
Web site: http://www.welcometotheislands.com.

Island In The Sky Publishing Co., *(0-9760328)* P.O. Box 139, Eastsound, WA 98245-0139 USA
Web site: http://www.MemoriesOfWWII.com.

Island Ink, *(0-9657849)* Orders Addr.: P.O. Box 1818, Indiantown, FL 34956 USA Tel 561-597-3778; Fax: 561-597-4691.

Island Institute, *(0-942719)* 386 Main St., Box 648, Rockland, ME 04841-3345 USA (SAN 667-7274) Tel 207-594-9209; Fax: 207-594-9314
E-mail: inquiry@islandinstitute.org; publications@islandinstitute.org
Web site: http://www.islandinstitute.org
Dist(s): **Magazines, Inc.**

Island Moon Pr., *(0-9755605)* P.O. Box 956, Oaks, PA 19456-0956 USA Tel 610-935-2378; Toll Free: 877-252-8262
E-mail: islandquest@msn.com
Web site: http://www.IslandMoonPress.com
Dist(s): **Baker & Taylor Bks.**

Island Nation Pr., LLC, *(0-9657437; 1-892738)* Orders Addr.: 144 Rowayton Woods Dr., Norwalk, CT 06854 USA Tel 203-852-0028; Fax: 203-852-0528; Toll Free: 888-356-1450 [Direct Order Line]
E-mail: cvaleallen@earthlink.net
Web site: http://www.charlottevaleallen.com.

Islandport Pr., Inc., *(0-9671662; 0-9763231; 1-934031)* Orders Addr.: P.O. Box 10, Yarmouth, ME 04096 USA Tel 207-688-6290; Fax: 207-688-6291; Edit Addr.: 27 Gail Ln., Yarmouth, ME 04096 USA
E-mail: islandport@islandportpress.com
Web site: http://www.islandportpress.com.

Isle of Dogs Publishing, Co., *(0-9741321)* 4008 - 83rd Ave. SE, Snohomish, WA 98290 USA
E-mail: connieraestrain@msn.com; ConnieRaeStrain@IsleofDogsPublishing.com
Web site: http://www.isleofdogspublishing.com.

Isles of the Sea Pubs., *(0-9728126)* Orders Addr.: P.O. Box 51352, Provo, UT 84605-1352 USA Tel 801-427-5209; Edit Addr.: 2052 S. California Ave., No. 12, Provo, UT 84044 USA
E-mail: drrlesa@hotmail.com.

Islewest Publishing, *(0-9641919; 1-888461)* Div. of Carlisle Communications, Ltd., 4242 Chavenelle Dr., Dubuque, IA 52002-2650 USA (SAN 299-5018)
E-mail: mjgraham@carcomm.com
Web site: http://www.islewest.com.

Israel Bk. Shop, *(0-9670705; 1-931681; 1-60091)* 501 Prospect St., No. 97, Lakewood, NJ 08701 USA Tel 732-901-3009; Fax: 732-901-4012; Toll Free: 888-536-7427
E-mail: sales@israelbookshoppublications.com
Web site: http://www.israelbookshoppublications.com.

Israeli Trading Company *See* **Jewish Enrichment Pr.**

Istra (FRA) *(2-01; 2-219) Dist. by* **Distribks Inc.**

Italica Pr., *(0-934977; 1-59910)* 595 Main St., Suite 605, New York, NY 10044 USA (SAN 695-1805) Tel 212-935-4230; Fax: 212-838-7812
E-mail: inquiries@italicapress.com
Web site: http://www.italicapress.com.

Ithaca Pr. *Imprint of* **Authors & Artists Publishers of New York, Inc.**

Ithaca Pr., *(0-9679475)* 4042 Whipple Pl., Charlotte, NC 28215 USA Tel 704-567-7986; Fax: 704-383-7530 Do not confuse with Ithaca Pr. in Quincy, MA
E-mail: alexandria28215@yahoo.com; Ithacapress@yahoo.com
Web site: http://www.rallsoppublishing.com.

Ithuriel's Spear, *(0-9749502; 0-9793390)* 730 Eddy St., No. 304, San Francisco, CA 94109 USA Tel 415-440-3204
E-mail: Ithurielspear@att.net
Web site: http://www.ithuriel.com.

Itiya Publishing, Inc., *(0-9770312)* 217 Ave. Unvi. Interanericana PMB 161, San German, PR 00683 USA
E-mail: gpita@itiyainc.com
Web site: http://www.itiyainc.com.

ITRON Publishing, *(0-9786863)* 6510 LBJ Freeway, Suite 200, Dallas, TX 75240 USA (SAN 851-2817) Tel 972-934-2811; Fax: 972-934-1705.

It's a Girl Pubns., *(0-9660672)* 710 Riverside Ave., Whitefish, MT 59937 USA Tel 406-862-2418; Fax: 406-862-8740.

It's A Habit! Co., The, *(0-9713664)* 2238 Harwood St., Los Angeles, CA 90031-1238 USA Tel 323-254-7772
Web site: http://www.itsahabit.com.

It's About Time, Herff Jones Education Diiv., *(1-891629; 1-58591)* Orders Addr.: 84 Business Pk. Dr., Suite 307, Armonk, NY 10504 USA Tel 914-273-2233; Fax: 914-273-2227; Toll Free: 888-698-8463 Do not confuse with companies with the same name in Los Gatos, CA, Santa Monica, CA
E-mail: gerneralinfo@herffjones.com
Web site: http://www.its-about-time.com.

It's About Time, Incorporated *See* **It's About Time, Herff Jones Education Diiv.**

It's Me Briana, LLC, *(0-9793904)* P.O. Box 12386, Atlanta, GA 30355 USA
Web site: http://www.briananeighborhood.com.

ITSMEEE Industries, *(0-9677231)* 13918 E. Mississippi Ave., No 213, Aurora, CO 80012 USA Tel 303-696-0715.

Itsy Bitsy Entertainment Co., *(0-439; 0-590; 1-55268)* 555 Broadway, New York, NY 10012-3997 USA.

Itty Bitty Bks., *(0-9760691)* 1682 NW 785 Rd., Bates City, MO 64011 USA Tel 816-697-3617 (phone/fax)
E-mail: waynedyer@gmail.com.

Itty Bitty Witch Works, *(0-9768573)* P.O. Box 532, Kernville, CA 93238 USA Tel 760-376-3973 (phone/fax)
E-mail: ittybittywitch@sierranet.us
Web site: http://ittybittywitch.com.

iUniverse, Inc. *Imprint of* **iUniverse, Inc.**

iUniverse, Inc., *(0-9665514; 1-58348; 0-9668591; 1-893652; 0-595; 0-9795279; 1-60528)* Orders Addr.: 2021 Pine Lake Rd., Suite 100, Lincoln, NE 68512 USA (SAN 254-9425) Tel 402-323-7800; Fax: 402-323-7824; Toll Free: 800-AUTHORS (800-288-4677) ; *Imprints:* Writers Club Press (Writers Club Pr); Writer's Showcase Press (Writers Showcase); Backinprint.com (Backinprint); Harlem Writers Guild Press (Harlem Writers Guild); Authors Choice Press (Authors Choice Pr); People with Disabilities Press (People Disabilities Pr); Mystery Writers of America Presents (Myst Write Amer); Mystery & Suspense Press (Mystery & Suspense); Weekly Reader Teacher's Press (Weekly Rd Tch); Writers Advantage Press (Writers Adv Pr); iUniverse, Inc. (iUni Inc)
E-mail: post.production@iuniverse.com; book.orders@iuniverse.com; bethany.dirks@iuniverse.com
Web site: http://www.iUniverse.com.

iUniverse.com, Incorporated *See* **iUniverse, Inc.**

Iverson, Theodore, *(0-9747378)* P.O. Box 3671, Grand Canyon, AZ 86023-3671 USA.

Ivy Advising LLC, *(0-9771568)* 50 Livingston St., Brooklyn, NY 11201 USA (SAN 256-8934).

Ivy Bks. *Imprint of* **Random House Publishing Group**

Ivy Editorial Services, Inc., *(0-9667146)* 4 Susan Ct., Glen Cove, NY 11542 USA Tel 516-944-7340; Fax: 516-944-8663
E-mail: mspinter@aol.com
Dist(s): **Wimmer Cookbooks.**

Ivy Fund, The, *(0-9754003)* 33 Irving St., Waltham, MA 02451-0758 USA
E-mail: courtney@ivysplace.org
Web site: http://ivysplace.org.

Ivy Hill Bunch, LLC, *(0-9743619)* P.O. Box 1053, La Quinta, CA 92253 USA Tel 760-771-0834; Fax: 760-771-1910; Toll Free: 866-892-5795
E-mail: lynn@ivyhillbunch.com
Web site: http://www.saddyandgladdy.com.

Ivy House Publishing Group *Imprint of* **Pentland Pr., Inc.**

Ivystone Pr., *(0-9755771)* P.O. Box 50, Emmalena, KY 41740 USA
E-mail: hodson@tgtel.com
Web site: http://www.mountainrainbow.com.

iwishyouicecreamandcake, *(0-9792019)* 3871 W. Millers Bridge Rd., Tallahassee, FL 32312 USA Fax: 850-893-9616
E-mail: carolhmoore@yahoo.com
Web site: http://iwishyouicecreamandcake.com.

Iyengar, Malathi, *(0-9753912)* 14748 Morrison St., Sherman Oaks, CA 91403 USA
E-mail: msiyengar@yahoo.com
Web site: http://www.rangoli.org.

Iyengar, Uma *See* **UP**

iynx publishing (GBR) *(0-9535413; 0-9540583)* *Dist. by* **Dufour.**

IZA Publishing Co., *(0-9674241)* 253 Pvt. Rd. 2410, Uvalde County, TX 78801 USA Tel 361-946-3132; Fax: 361-946-2000
E-mail: smith-ma@swhell.net.

Izraeli, Elana, *(0-9722930)* 90 Canterbury, Rochester, MI 48309 USA.

IZS, Inc., *(0-9764684)* 34 E. Franklin St., Bellbrook, OH 45305-1746 USA Tel 937-848-8896
E-mail: pantherbay@aol.com
Web site: http://www.pantherbay.com.

JAFS, Inc., *(0-9709533)* 8846 Worthington Cir., Indianapolis, IN 46278 USA Tel 317-802-9784; Fax: 317-870-8772
E-mail: jmcclaine3@home.com
Dist(s): **Austin & Company, Inc.**
Partners Pubs. Group, Inc.

JAG Pubns., *(0-943327)* 11288 Ventura Blvd., No. 301, Studio City, CA 91604 USA (SAN 668-4157) Tel 818-505-9002 (phone/fax) Do not confuse with Jag Publications in Los Angeles, CA
E-mail: info@jagpublications-esl.com
Web site: http://www.jagpublications-esl.com.

J A Interests, Inc., *(0-9769648)* P.O. Box 1472, Versailles, KY 40383 USA.

JAS Pr., Inc., *(0-9666920; 0-9773316)* Orders Addr.: P.O. Box 1925, Bolingbrook, IL 60440 USA Tel 630-226-1635; Edit Addr.: 155 Ashcroft Dr., Bolingbrook, IL 60490 USA Tel 630-226-1635
E-mail: jaspress@mindspring.com.

J&J Collections, *(0-9628165)* 201 San Mateo Dr., Hot Springs, AR 71913 USA Tel 501-525-3190 ; *Imprints:* Park Press (Park Pr).

J & J Publishing Co., *(0-9759831)* Box 305, 9728 US Hwy. 277, Elgin, OK 73538 USA Do not confuse with companies with same or similar name in Los Angeles, CA, Buffalo, NY, Englewood, CO, Darien, IL, Frankfurt, IL MD
E-mail: djw73@aol.com.

J&S Publishing Co., Inc., *(0-9632873; 1-888308)* 1300 Bishop Ln., Alexandria, VA 22302 USA Tel 703-823-9833; Fax: 703-823-9834 Do not confuse with J&S Publishing in Prescott, AZ
E-mail: jandspub@ix.netcom.com
Web site: http://www.jandspub.com
Dist(s): **Majors, J. A. Co.**
Matthews Medical Bk. Co.
Rittenhouse Bk. Distributors.

JB Communications, Inc., *(1-55987)* 101 W. 55th St., No. 2D, New York, NY 10019-5346 USA Tel 212-246-0900 ; *Imprints:* Sunny Books (Sunny Bks).

J. B. J. Enterprises *See* **Morgan, E. A.**

J. Caro & Associates *See* **Cowboy Collector Pubns.**

J D V Publishing Company *See* **Booksmythe**

JJ Publishing, *(0-9604610)* 1312 Arthur St., Hollywood, FL 33019 USA (SAN 220-0090) Tel 954-929-3559 (phone/fax).

J. Kid Productions, Ltd., *(0-9662670)* 10412 E. Weaver Cir., Englewood, CO 80111 USA Tel 303-850-7740; Fax: 303-850-7727; Toll Free: 888-790-4673.

J L Publishing Co., *(0-9740774)* 669 Buzzard Roost Cutoff, Mountain Home, AR 72653 USA.

J M D's Business Services, *(0-9712641)* 52 Lee Ave., Wallingford, CT 06492-3610 USA
Web site: http://www.jmdsbusinessservices.com; http://www.liquidchariot.com.

JM Pubns., *(0-9638007)* Orders Addr.: P.O. Box 753427, Memphis, TN 38115 USA; Edit Addr.: 3830 Scottsdale Ave., Memphis, TN 38115 USA (SAN 255-0598) Tel 901-368-3414; Fax: 901-566-1978; Toll Free: 888-321-4747
E-mail: jmpub1@midsouth.rr.com
Web site: http://www.jmpublications.com
Dist(s): **Baker & Taylor Bks.**

JMT Pubns., *(0-9703045)* Orders Addr.: P.O. Box 64, Shirley, IN 47384 USA Toll Free: 800-341-5969; Edit Addr.: 501 N. White St., Shirley, IN 47384 USA Do not confuse with JMT Pubns., Silver Spring, MD
E-mail: jeantype@excite.com
Web site: http://jmtpubs.hypermart.net; http://jmtpubs.tripod.com
Dist(s): **Alibris**
Baker & Taylor Bks.

JNW Bks., *(0-9705482)* 905 Tanglewood Ct., Oconomowoc, WI 53066 USA Tel 262-569-7029
E-mail: jnw905@execpc.com.

J. Paul Getty Museum *Imprint of* **Getty Pubns.**

JRC Consulting, *(0-9672502)* 6671 W. Indiantown Rd., Suite 56-428, Jupiter, FL 33458 USA Tel 561-748-9429; Fax: 561-748-9430.

JR Pubs., *(0-9623694)* 4182 Ursa Course, Liverpool, NY 13090 USA Tel 315-652-8567.

JTC Sports, Inc., *(1-887791)* Orders Addr.: P.O. Box 3293, Burlington, NC 27215-0293 USA Tel 336-227-0000; Fax: 336-227-0426; Toll Free: 800-551-9721; Edit Addr.: 1714 Broadway Dr., Graham, NC 27253 USA
E-mail: socrnuz@netpath.net
Web site: http://www.jtcsports.com.

JVC Bks., *(1-878116)* 509 N. 12th Ave., Arcadia, FL 34266-8966 USA Tel 941-494-4819
E-mail: stormey@sunline.net.

J V T Publications *See* **JVT Pubns. & Creations**

Jacana Media (ZAF) *(1-874955; 1-919931; 1-919777)* *Dist. by* **IPG Chicago.**

Jacar Press Literary Community, *(0-9640528)* Orders Addr.: P.O. Box 2444, Raleigh, NC 27602 USA Tel 919-833-3004; Edit Addr.: 124 S. Salisbury St., Raleigh, NC 27601 USA ; *Imprints:* Voices Community Press (Voices Commun Pr).

Jack's Bookshelf, Inc., *(1-928907)* 224 Woodland Dr., Vista, CA 92083 USA.

Jackson Harbor Pr., *(0-9640210; 1-890352)* R.R. 1, Box 107AA, Washington Island, WI 54246 USA Tel 920-847-2463
E-mail: wolson@itol.com
Web site: http://home.att.net/~jacksonharbor
Dist(s): **Biblio Distribution.**

Jackson, Linda *See* **Jackson Publishing**

Jackson Press *See* **Jackson Pr. Corp.**

Jackson Pr. Corp., *(0-9769112)* P.O. Box 690344, Bronx, NY 10466 USA Do not confuse with Jackson Press in Carmel, CA
Web site: http://jacksonpress.net
Dist(s): **Biblio Distribution.**

Jackson Publishing, *(0-9716442)* 7661 Forstoria Cove, Southaven, MS 38672 USA Do not confuse with companies with the same name in Jackson, MS; Clarkston, MI
E-mail: luv2read@jacksonbooks.com
Web site: http://www.jacksonbooks.com.

Jackson, Robert, *(0-9761420)* 12807 Prospect Knolls Dr., Bowie, MD 20720 USA
E-mail: trebor_jackson@yahoo.com
Web site: http://www.amazingliberteens.com.

Jackson, Steve Games, Inc., *(1-55634)* P.O. Box 18957, Austin, TX 78760 USA (SAN 661-3292) Tel 512-447-7866; Fax: 512-447-1144
E-mail: sjgames@io.com
Web site: http://www.sjgames.com
Dist(s): **PSI (Publisher Services, Inc.).**

Jacob & Victoria *Imprint of* **Brown Bag Bks, Inc.**

Jacob's Magic Box Discovery Books *See* **Magic Box Pubns.**

Jacobs Publishing Co., *(0-918272)* 3334 E. Indian School Rd., Suite C, Phoenix, AZ 85018 USA (SAN 209-4525) Tel 602-954-6581 (phone/fax); Toll Free: 800-349-1063
E-mail: jacobs@jacobspublishing.com
Web site: http://www.jacobspublishing.com.

Jacpak Bks., *(0-9667429)* 17650 NW 22nd Ave., Miami, FL 33056 USA Tel 305-624-3346.

Jacqueline Beverly Hills, *(0-9664783)* 650 The Village. Unit 215, Redondo Beach, CA 90277-2734 USA
E-mail: jacquih3@yahoo.com
Web site: http://jbhbooks.com.

Jacquet-Acea, Russell, *(0-9771919)* 3645 Whitman Ave. N., Seattle, WA 98103 USA Tel 206-547-7026; Fax: 810-454-1721
E-mail: rjacquet2@msn.com
Web site: http://rjacquet.tripod.com.

Jacubbi Enterprises, *(0-9701667)* 5083 NE 46th St., Des Moines, IA 50317 USA (SAN 253-3006) Tel 515-266-5988; Fax: 515-265-1169
E-mail: jacubbienterprise@earthlink.net.

JADA Pr., *(0-9747501; 0-9761110; 0-9764115; 0-9771343; 0-9788724; 0-9800629)* Orders Addr.: 1403 Shadowood Pkwy. SE., Atlanta, GA 30339 USA
Web site: http://www.jadapress.com.

JadaStar *See* **Star Publish LLC**

Jade Enterprises, *(0-9753410)* 11807 S. Fair Hollow Ln., Suite 106, Houston, TX 77043-1033 USA Tel 713-690-7626
Web site: http://www.authorsden.com/deborahkfrontiera
Dist(s): **Baker & Taylor Bks.**

Jade Publishing Co., *(0-9709448)* 222 14th St NE Apt. 403, Atlanta, GA 30309-7683 USA Do not confuse with companies with the same name or similar names in Kirkland, VA, Carson City, NV
E-mail: jadepublishing@hotmail.com
Web site: http://www.jadepublishingcompany.com.

Jade Ram Publishing, *(1-877721)* 3003 Wendy's Way, No. 9, Anchorage, AK 99517-1466 USA Tel 907-248-0979; Fax: 907-272-8432
E-mail: jaderam@alaska.net
Dist(s): **Publication Consultants**
Todd Communications
Wizard Works.

Jadeda Pr., *(0-9672124)* 74 Main St., Framingham, MA 01702-2928 USA
E-mail: efriedlander1@yahoo.com
Web site: http://www.mrsdigger.com.

Jadenaila Publishing, *(0-615)* 7340 S. Union Creek Way 5G, Salt Lake City, UT 84047 USA Tel 801-916-1037
E-mail: kidsbooksbynaila@hotmail.com
Web site: http://www.kidsbooksbynaila.com.

Jades Publishing, *(0-9743352)* Orders Addr.: P.O. Box 485, Fayette, OH 43521 USA Tel 419-237-3128; Edit Addr.: 24022-T, Fayette, OH 43521 USA
E-mail: amadsj@bright.net; amadsj@bright.nett.

Jaffrey, Kamal, *(0-9753673)* 400 Technology Sq., Cambridge, MA 02139 USA.

Jahjep Bks., *(0-9727968)* 12707 Pleasant Grove Rd., Cypress, TX 77429 USA Tel 281-373-0998
E-mail: jahjepbooks@yahoo.com
Web site: http://www.jahjepbooks.com.

Jahs Publishing Group, *(0-9701144; 0-9747550)* Div. of Jahs Fitness & Jahs Active Wear, Orders Addr.: P.O. Box 1164, Riverdale, MD 20738-1164 USA Fax: 301-864-4595; Edit Addr.: 4206 Gallatin St., Hyattsville, MD 20781 USA Tel 301-804-2800
E-mail: info@jahsactivewear.com
Web site: http://www.jahsactivewear.com.

Jain Publishing Company, Inc., *(0-87573; 0-89581)* P.O. Box 3523, Fremont, CA 94539 USA (SAN 213-6503) Tel 510-659-8272; Fax: 510-659-0501
E-mail: mail@jainpub.com
Web site: http://www.jainpub.com
Dist(s): **Replica Bks.**

Jalali, Yassaman *See* **Saman Publishing**

Jalmar Pr., *(0-915190; 0-935266; 1-880396; 1-931061)* Subs. of B. L. Winch & Assocs., P.O. Box 370, Fawnskin, CA 92333-0370 USA (SAN 113-3640) Toll Free: 800-662-9662 (orders)
E-mail: jalmarpress@att.net
Web site: http://jalmarpress.com
Dist(s): **Winch, B. L. & Assocs.**
Baker & Taylor Bks.
Brodart Co.

JAM Publishers, *(0-615)* 1165 Manor Ln., Mount Pleasant, SC 29464 USA
Web site: http://www.mrgator.net.

JA-M Pubs., LLC, *(0-9728975)* 400 E. 33rd St., No. 1515, Chicago, IL 606016 USA Tel 312-842-7765 Do not confuse with companies with the same or similar name in Mount Pleasant, SC, Comstock Park, MI
E-mail: ednax4@yahoo.com; joycex4@msn.com.

Jamaldinian, Yousef, *(0-9766657)* 5207 Olley Ln., Burke, VA 22015 USA Tel 571-212-9471
E-mail: joedinian@yahoo.com.

Jameir Productions, *(0-9649198)* P.O. Box 2081, Glen Allen, VA 23058-2081 USA Tel 804-364-5279 (phone/fax)
Web site: http://www.whydoblacks.com
Dist(s): **Southern Bk. Service.**

James Dane Bks., *(0-9712798)* Div. of Gafner International Marketing, Inc., Orders Addr.: P.O. Box 3087, Dana Point, CA 92629 USA Tel 949-493-3202; Edit Addr.: 100 Terra Vista, Dana Point, CA 92629 USA Tel 949-289-9400
E-mail: jamesdane@hotmail.com
Web site: http://www.jamesdanebooks.com.

James, Hugo Publishing, *(0-9717436)* P.O. Box 1517, Greenwich, CT 06836-1517 USA
Web site: http://www.hugojames.com.

James, JoAnn, *(0-9764406)* P.O. Box 11459, Eugene, OR 97440 USA
E-mail: joann_james@comcast.net.

James Stevenson Pub., *(1-885852)* 1500 Oliver Rd., Suite K-109, Fairfield, CA 94533 USA Tel 707-469-0237; Fax: 206-350-2954
E-mail: ceo@jspub.com
Web site: http://www.jspub.com
Dist(s): **Baker & Taylor Bks.**
Marangio, Charles F. Distribution
Ingram Bk. Co.

†Jameson Bks., Inc., *(0-89803; 0-915463; 0-916054)* 722 Columbus St., P.O. Box 738, Ottawa, IL 61350 USA (SAN 281-7578) Tel 815-434-7905; Fax: 815-434-7907; Toll Free: 800-426-1357
E-mail: jamesonbooks@yahoo.com
Dist(s): **Midpoint Trade Bks., Inc.**; *CIP.*

Jamestown, *(0-07; 0-8092; 0-8442; 0-89061; 0-913327; 0-941263; 1-56943)* Div. of Glencoe/McGraw-Hill, Orders Addr.: P.O. Box 543, Blacklick, OH 43004-0543 USA Fax: 614-860-1877; Toll Free: 800-334-7344; Edit Addr.: P.O. Box 508, Columbus, OH 43216 USA Toll Free: 800-872-7323
Web site: jamestowneducation.com
Dist(s): **Libros Sin Fronteras**
McGraw-Hill Cos., The.

Jamison Publishing, *(0-9712359)* 176 Steamboat Ave., Wickford, RI 02852 USA
E-mail: lonjamison@home.com.

Jamondas Pr., *(0-9631035)* P.O. Box 2235, Ann Arbor, MI 48106 USA Tel 734-994-6289; Toll Free: 800-223-7873.

JamSum Limited, *(0-9770754)* 621 S. Main St., Bellefontaine, OH 43311-1725 USA Toll Free: 866-857-2061
E-mail: publish@jamsum.com
Web site: http://www.jamsum.com.

Jan & San, *(0-9729741)* 273 Roy Huie Rd., Riverdale, GA 30274 USA
E-mail: feedback@providerhouse.com
Web site: http://www.providerhouse.com.

Jandie Jams Music LLC, *(0-9796150)* 1036 Katy Ln., Longmont, CO 80504 USA (SAN 853-8999)
E-mail: jandiejams@comcast.net
Web site: http://www.kidcleveronline.com.

Jane & Street Pubs. Ltd., *(0-9745077)* 302-A W. 12th St., No. 197, New York, NY 10014 USA
Web site: http://www.janeandstreet.com.

Janella Pr., *(0-9709717)* 10118 W. Arizona Pl., Lakewood, CO 80232-5033 USA Tel 303-987-3595
E-mail: miltpackard@prodigy.net.

Janelle Pubns., Inc., *(0-9626739; 1-890265)* Orders Addr.: P.O. Box 811, De Kalb, IL 60115-0811 USA Tel 815-756-2300; Fax: 815-756-4799; Toll Free: 800-888-8834; Edit Addr.: 1189 Twombley Rd., De Kalb, IL 60115 USA
E-mail: info@janellepublications.com
Web site: http://www.janellepublications.com.

Jane's World *See* **Girl Twirl Comics**

Janis, Tim Ensemble, Inc., *(0-9773335)* P.O. Box 315, Kennebunk, ME 04043 USA (SAN 257-280X) Tel 207-985-3463.

Jan's Looks & Bks., *(0-9797139)* Orders Addr.: 1780 Phillips, Berkley, MI 48072 USA Tel 248-545-5160
Web site: http://www.janslooksandbooks.com.

Jansen, Marilyn, *(0-9761070)* P.O. Box 278, Makawao, HI 96768 USA Tel 808-572-0699 phone/fax
E-mail: jamarilyn2000@aol.com
Web site: http://amaryllisofhawaii.com
Dist(s): **Booklines Hawaii, Ltd.**

Janson Media Group, *(1-889131)* Orders Addr.: P.O. Box 7207, Port Richey, FL 34674 USA Tel 352-346-5997 Office
E-mail: bobbi@jansonmedia.com
Web site: http://www.jansonmedia.com.

Janus Publishing Co. (GBR) *(1-85756) Dist. by* **IPG Chicago.**

Japan Pubns. (U.S.A.), Inc., *(0-87040; 1-57883)* Subs. of Japan Pubns., Inc. (Tokyo, Japan), 160 Spruce Knob Rd., Middletown Springs, VT 05757-4432 USA (SAN 680-0513) Tel 802-235-2814
Dist(s): **Oxford Univ. Pr., Inc.**

Japan Pubn. Trading Co. (JPN) *(4-88996) Dist. by* **Kodansha.**

Japan Pubn. Trading Co. (JPN) *(4-88996) Dist. by* **OUP.**

Japanese American National Museum, *(1-881161)* 369 E. First St., Los Angeles, CA 90012 USA Tel 213-625-0414; Fax: 213-625-1770
Web site: http://www.janm.org
Dist(s): **RAM Pubns. & Distribution.**

Jappamation Studios, *(0-9720694)* Div. of Jappa Comics, P.O. Box 12702, Kansas City, KS 66112 USA Tel 816-560-9856 (phone/fax)
E-mail: jappa@swbell.net
Web site: http://jappacomics.tripod.com.

Jarndyce & Jarndyce Pr., *(0-9721916; 0-9772720)* Div. of PSA Consulting, Inc., 2449 Fairview Ave., Cincinnati, OH 45219 USA Tel 513-241-5777
E-mail: info@cincybooks.com
Web site: http://www.cincybooks.com.

Jarrett Press & Publications *See* **Pennyworth Pr.**

Jarvis, Dennis R., *(0-9670826)* 3620 Piermont Dr. Apt. C, Indianapolis, IN 46227-9666 USA.

Jasmine Pr., *(0-930069)* 2224 Ogden Ave., Bensalem, PA 19020 USA (SAN 669-9650) Tel 215-244-0525.

Jasnans Publishing Co., *(0-9761759)* P.O. Box 873633, Wasilla, AK 99687-3633 USA
E-mail: hallalfa@mtaonline.net
Web site: http://www.jasnanspublishing.com.

Jason & Nordic Pubs., *(0-944727)* P.O. Box 441, Hollidaysburg, PA 16648 USA (SAN 244-9374) Tel 814-696-2920; Fax: 814-696-4250 ; *Imprints:* Turtle Books (Turtle Books)
E-mail: turtlbks@nb.net
Web site: http://www.jasonandnordic.com.

Jason Foundation for Education *See* **JASON Project, The**

JASON Project, The, *(0-9763809; 0-9787574)* Subs. of National Geographic Society, 44983 Knoll Sq., Ashburn, VA 20147 USA Fax: 703-726-8366; Toll Free: 888-527-6600
E-mail: info@jason.org
Web site: http://www.jason.org.

javariBook, *(0-9679161)* P.O. Box 230551, New York, NY 10023 USA
E-mail: javaribook@javari.com
Web site: http://www.javaribook.com; http://www.globalwidetrade.com.

Jawbone Publishing Corp., *(0-9702959; 1-59094)* 2907 Paddington Way, Kissimmee, FL 34747 USA (SAN 253-5335) Tel 407-396-4245; Fax: 407-396-4247 ; *Imprints:* Top Shelf (Top); Jawbreakers for Kids (Jawbreakers)
E-mail: marketing@jawbonepublishing.com
Web site: http://www.jawbonepublishing.com
Dist(s): **Baker & Taylor Bks.**

Jawbreakers for Kids *Imprint of* **Jawbone Publishing Corp.**

Jay Street Pubs., *(0-9639999; 1-889534)* Div. of G-Communications, P.O. Box 230944, New York, NY 10023-0016 USA
E-mail: jaystpub@i-2000.com.

JayCee Productions, *(0-9705468)* 2280 MetroCenter Blvd., Suite 300, Nashville, TN 37228 USA Tel 615-742-9998; Fax: 615-742-9928; Toll Free Fax: 877-747-5685
E-mail: rchristuph@jayceeandfriends.com
Web site: http://www.jayceeand friends.com.

JayJo Bks., LLC, *(0-9639449; 1-891383)* Orders Addr.: P.O. Box 760, Plainview, NY 11803-0760 USA (SAN 178-5435) Tel 516-349-5520; Fax: 800-262-1886; Toll Free: 800-999-6884; Edit Addr.: 45 Executive Dr. Ste. 201, Plainview, NY 11803-1738 USA
E-mail: jayjobook@guidancechannel.com
Web site: http://www.jayjo.com
Dist(s): **Quality Bks., Inc.**
Unique Bks., Inc.

Jaylil Publishing Co., *(0-9748165)* Orders Addr.: P.O. Box 656551, Flushing, NY 11365 USA
E-mail: jaylilpublishing@aol.com
Web site: jaylilpublishing.com
Dist(s): **Culture Plus Bk. Distributors**
Seaburn Bks.

Jazwares Distribution, Inc., *(0-9724983; 0-9765714; 1-933752)* 1351 Sawgrass Corporate Pkwy., Suite 101, Sunrise, FL 33323 USA Tel 954-384-0800; Fax: 954-337-4658
E-mail: julio@jazwares.com
Web site: http://www.projectkitsforkids.com.

Jazz Path Publishing, *(0-9760977)* P.O. Box 381810, Cambridge, MA 02238 USA
Web site: http://www.jazzpath.com.

JazzKids, *(1-891679)* 21 Exeter St., Providence, RI 02906 USA Tel 401-331-0000; Fax: 401-383-0079
E-mail: email@jazzkids.com
Web site: http://www.jazzkids.com/; http://www.williemyette.com.

JB Information Station, *(0-934334)* P.O. Box 19333, Saint Louis, MO 63125 USA (SAN 213-4128) Tel 314-638-3404; 3888 Via Miralesta Dr., Saint Louis, MO 63125
E-mail: empoweredparenting@earthlink.net
Web site: http://www.JoanBramsch.com.

JBall Publishing, *(0-9764179)* P.O. Box 6621, Logan, UT 84321-6621 USA
Web site: http://pumpkinglow.com.

JBiRD iNK, Ltd., *(0-9715253)* 535 Moorland Rd., Suite 203, Madison, WI 53713 USA Tel 608-278-1880
E-mail: info@jbirdink.com
Web site: http://www.jbirdink.com
Dist(s): **Baker & Taylor Bks.**

JBT Publishing, *(0-9792059)* Orders Addr.: 1485 Christina Ln., Lake Forest, IL 60045 USA (SAN 852-7644) Tel 781-760-2357; Fax: 419-735-0603
E-mail: jtedesco@gis.net.

JCCJ Pr., *(0-9770207)* 81 River Rd., Norfolk, MA 02056 USA Tel 508-528-4767.

JCJoseph, Ltd., *(0-9715420)* 2865 S. Eagle Rd., PMB 324, Newtown, PA 18940-1546 USA Tel 215-497-0880
E-mail: solace@jcjoseph.com
Web site: http://www.jcjoseph.com.

JCTT, LLC, *(0-9766926)* 286 Cross Creek Rd., McGregor, TX 76657 USA
E-mail: linleyw@msn.com
Web site: http://www.mathemagicians.info.

JCW Enterprises, Inc., *(0-9673084)* P.O. Box 361, New York, NY 10035 USA (SAN 254-6795) Tel 212-996-6599 (phone/fax); Toll Free: 800-942-8623
E-mail: wr_rich@hotmail.com
Web site: http://www.wandathomasbooks.com.

JDB Publishing *See* **James Dane Bks.**

JDC Data Pubns., *(0-9715537)* Orders Addr.: c/o Data Duplicators, Inc., 8885 Monroe, Houston, TX 77061 USA Tel 713-944-4600; Fax: 713-944-8768; Edit Addr.: P.O. Box 548, Pattison, TX 77466 USA Tel 281-934-8477
E-mail: joelt@datadup.com
Web site: http://www.datadup.com.

JDW Collaborative, *(0-9767545)* 25176 Maplebrokke Dr., Southfield, MI 48034-5282 USA
Web site: http://www.jdwcollaborative.com.

JeaMei Publishing, *(0-9717299)* 1444 E. Vine Ave., West Covina, CA 91791 USA Tel 213-944-3888; Fax: 626-918-5181
E-mail: aminah@earthlink.net
Web site: http://www.mtdumpling.com.

Jeannie Deva Enterprises, Inc., *(1-882224)* Orders Addr.: P.O. Box 4636, Sunland, CA 91041-4636 USA Tel 818-446-0932; Fax: 818-353-9960; Toll Free: 800-920-8220 (orders only); Edit Addr.: 10257 Parr Avenue, Sunland, CA 91040 USA
E-mail: info@JeannieDeva.com
Web site: http://www.JeannieDeva.com
Dist(s): **Baker & Taylor Bks.**

Jeff & Gayle Farmer, *(0-9748728)* 447 Desert Lake Dr., Palm Springs, CA 92264 USA
E-mail: info@4showtime.com
Web site: http://www.4showtime.com.

Jeffers Pr., *(0-9745776; 0-9777618)* 2700 Neilson Way, Suite 1428, Santa Monica, CA 90405 USA Tel 310-450-4008; Toll Free: 877-450-4008
E-mail: mark@jefferspress.com
Web site: http://www.jefferspress.com
Dist(s): **National Bk. Network.**

Jelinck, Donald A., *(0-9704607)* 1942 University Ave., Suite 206, Berkeley, CA 94704-1023 USA Tel 510-841-4787; Fax: 510-841-3651
E-mail: don@donjelinek.com
Web site: http://donjelinek.com.

Jellyroll Productions *See* **Osborne Enterprises Publishing**

JEM Bks., Inc., *(0-9754317)* 10466 E. Sheena Dr., Scottsdale, AZ 85255-1742 USA
E-mail: rmahoney@jem-books.com
Web site: http://www.jem-books.com.

Jemima Creek Signature Bks., *(0-9726892)* P.O. Box 17596, Asheville, NC 28816 USA Tel 828-251-1564 Toll Free: 866-251-1564
E-mail: artisticventures@prodigy.net.

Jenkins-Simmons, Glenda, *(0-9758586)* 692 Mulberry Dr., Biloxi, MS 39532 USA Tel 228-388-7540
E-mail: res55472@cs.com.

Jennings, J. Publishing Co., *(0-9700038)* 5012 Kahn St., Carmichael, CA 95608 USA Tel 916-863-1638; Fax: 916-863-5807
E-mail: jane@jenningspub.com
Web site: http://www.jenningspub.com
Dist(s): **Omnibus Pr.**

Jennings Pond, LLC, *(1-893017)* 7 Jennings Pond Rd., Natick, MA 01760 USA Tel 508-655-6170; Fax: 508-650-4091
E-mail: WMM47@aol.com.

Jenpet Publishing, *(0-9726794)* P.O. Box 2542, Alameda, CA 94501 USA Tel 510-521-3582
E-mail: jj@jenpet.com
Web site: http://www.jenpet.com.

Jenrod, Inc., *(0-9664154)* 6107 Hopeton Ave., Baltimore, MD 21215 USA Tel 410-358-3360.

Jensen, Lissa, *(0-9666973)* 958 Summer Holly Ln., Encinitas, CA 92024 USA Tel 760-944-6345.

Jensen, Travis, *(0-9754439)* 209 23rd Ave., San Francisco, CA 94121-2008 USA
E-mail: thesfmasher@yahoo.com
Web site: http://www.sfmasher.cjb.net.

Jensonbooks, *(0-9794414)* P.O. Box 416, Greenfield, MA 01302-0416 USA (SAN 853-4322).

Jereleen Publishing, Inc., *(0-9643500)* 206 Laquinta Dr., Orangeburg, SC 29115 USA Tel 803-534-1992; Fax: 803-534-9200
E-mail: jereleen@bellsouth.com
Web site: http://www.jereleen.com.

Jeremy's Things, *(0-9747878)* 410 Fifth Ave., 2nd Flr., Brooklyn, NY 11215 USA Tel 718-788-3987
E-mail: jeremy@jeremybullis.com
Web site: http://www.jeremybullis.com.

Jeriger Pr., *(1-59810)* P.O. Box 1249, Stafford, TX 77477-1249 USA Tel 888-447-5495 (phone/fax)
E-mail: info@jeriger.com
Web site: http://www.jeriger.com.

Jersey Classic Publishing, *(0-9765261)* 75 Locust Ave., Wallington, NJ 07057 USA.

Jersey Shore Pubns., *(0-9632906; 0-9777077)* P.O. Box 176, Bay Head, NJ 08742-0176 USA Tel 732-892-1276; Fax: 732-892-3365
E-mail: JSVacation@aol.com
Web site: http://www.jerseyshorevacation.com
Dist(s): **Koen-Levy Bk. Wholesalers LLC.**

Jerusalem Pubns., *(0-9707572; 0-9743911; 0-9761862; 0-9773885; 0-9792230)* 2011 Pine Tree Ln., San Antonio, TX 78232 USA
E-mail: rapaport@netvision.net.il
Dist(s): **Feldheim Pubs.**

Jessel Gallery, *(0-9660381)* 1019 Atlas Peak Rd., Napa, CA 94558 USA Tel 707-257-2350; Fax: 707-257-2396
Dist(s): **Baker & Taylor Bks.**

JESSPress, *(0-9652546)* 4231 Wexford Way, Eagan, MN 55122 USA Tel 651-681-9537
E-mail: pyako@aol.com; jesspress@aol.com
Web site: http://www.jesspress.com.

Jester Bks., *(0-9723382)* 39 E. 12th St., 506, New York, NY 10003 USA Tel 212-529-9209 Do not confuse with companies with the same or similar names in Woodland Hills, CA, Orinda, CA
E-mail: davidmkorn@earthlink.net.

JETBAK Publishing, *(0-9713683)* 1258 S. Fenway, Casper, WY 82601 USA Tel 307-235-1171
E-mail: jetbakpub@yahoo.com
Web site: http://www.jetbakpublishing.com
Dist(s): **Baker & Taylor Bks.**
Books West
Follett Library Resources
Partners/West.

JetKor, *(0-9706612; 1-59208)* P.O. Box 33238, Reno, NV 89533 USA (SAN 254-5233) Tel 775-846-1185
E-mail: sdelsol@sbcglobal.net
Web site: http://www.jetkor.com
Dist(s): **Baker & Taylor Bks.**

JETM Publishing & Distribution *See* **I Am Your Playground LLC**

Jets Pr., *(0-9704189)* Orders Addr.: P.O. Box 260088, Bellerose, NY 11426-0088 USA Tel 718-740-2079; Fax: 718-740-5933
E-mail: patricerichardson@jjetspress.com
Web site: http://www.jjetspress.com
Dist(s): **Quality Bks., Inc.**

Jetway Geographer, LLC, *(0-9711640)* Orders Addr.: 431 S. Cooke, Helena, MT 59601 USA Tel 406-586-6879
E-mail: jgeographer@bresnan.net
Web site: www.jetwaygeographer.com.

Jewel Box & Friends, *(0-9672202)* 324 Lake Crest Dr., Andover, KS 67002 USA Tel 316-733-9654; Fax: 316-733-6520; Toll Free: 800-337-6827.

Jew-El Pr. Co., *(0-9767618)* 40022 Milkmaid Ln., Murrieta, CA 92562 USA Tel 951-600-7054 (phone/fax)
E-mail: jew-el-press@verizon.net
Web site: http://www.jew-el-press.com.

Jewel Publishing, *(0-9744944)* P.O. Box 38, Chino Hills, CA 91709 USA Fax: 909-606-1092 Do not confuse with companies with the same or similar name in Baltimore, MD, Denver, CO, Detroit, MI, Cincinnati, OH
E-mail: cmckee7721@aol.com.

Jewish Community Ctr. of Milwaukee, *(0-9713461)* 6255 N. Santa Monica Blvd., Whitefish Bay, WI 53217 USA (SAN 254-6140) Tel 414-967-8216; Fax: 414-964-0922; Toll Free: 888-644-1847
E-mail: sroth@jjcmilwaukee.org
Web site: http://www.jccmilwaukee.org.

Jewish Community Federation of Rochester, NY, Inc., *(0-9710686)* 441 East Ave., Rochester, NY 14607 USA Tel 585-461-0490; Fax: 585-461-0912
E-mail: bappelbaum@jewishrochester.org
Web site: http://www.jewishrochester.org
Dist(s): **Wayne State Univ. Pr.**

Jewish Continuity Foundation *See* **Torah Educational Software**

Jewish Educational Media, *(1-931607; 1-932349)* 784 Eastern Pkwy., Suite 403, Brooklyn, NY 11213 USA Tel 718-774-6000; Fax: 718-774-3402
E-mail: eli@jemedia.org
Web site: http://www.jemedia.org
Dist(s): **Kehot Pubn. Society.**

Jewish Educational Toys, *(1-889655)* 6135 N. Sacramento Ave., Chicago, IL 60659-2519 USA Toll Free: 800-695-6378
E-mail: ABJet@aol.com.

Jewish Enrichment Pr., *(1-880880)* Div. of Israeli Trading Co., c/o Rabbi Chaim Dalfin, 1721 45th St., Brooklyn, NY 11219 USA Tel 718-854-4139; Fax: 718438-7628
E-mail: hebook@erols.com.

†Jewish Lights Publishing, *(1-58023; 1-879045)* Div. of LongHill Partners, Inc., Orders Addr.: P.O. Box 237, Woodstock, VT 05091 USA (SAN 242-6439) Tel 802-457-4000; Fax: 802-457-4004; Toll Free: 800-962-4544 (orders)
E-mail: sales@jewishlights.com
Web site: http://www.jewishlights.com; *CIP.*

†Jewish Pubn. Society, *(0-8276; 965-7157)* Orders Addr.: 22883 Quicksilver Dr., Dulles, VA 20166 USA (SAN 253-9446) Tel 703-661-1165; 703-661-1529; Fax: 703-661-1501; Toll Free: 800-355-1165; Edit Addr.: 2100 Arch St., 2nd Flr., Philadelphia, PA 19103-1399 USA Tel 215-832-0600
E-mail: marketing@jewishpub.org
Web site: http://www.jewishpub.org; *CIP.*

Jews For The Preservation of Firearms Ownership, Inc., *(0-9642304)* P.O. Box 270143, Hartford, WI 53027 USA Tel 262-673-9745; Fax: 262-673-9746
E-mail: jpfo@execpc.com
Web site: http://www.jpfo.org.

JFA Productions, *(0-9723024)* 806 Homestead Ave., Maybrook, NY 12543 USA Tel 845-427-5008
E-mail: carrdero@warwick.net.

JFK Online Studios, LLC, *(0-9742249)* 293 2nd Ave., West Haven, CT 06516-5127 USA
Web site: http://www.jfkonlinestudios.com.

JFW, Ltd., *(0-9710071)* 400 N. Church St., Unit 602, Charlotte, NC 28202 USA Tel 704-277-8378 (phone/fax)
E-mail: create2000@earthlink.net; jfwbird@earthlink.com.

JGC/United Publishing Corps, *(0-910941)* 1710 N. Main St., Rockford, IL 61103 USA (SAN 270-5109) Tel 815-968-6601; Fax: 815-968-6600
E-mail: jgcmail@sbcglobal.net.

J.G.R. Enterprises, *(0-9758746)* 100 Oak St., Patchogue, NY 11772 USA Tel 631-790-0932
E-mail: joannros12@aol.com
Web site: Joannros12@aol.com.

JIA Publishing, *(1-929364)* 604 Meeting St., West Columbia, SC 29169 USA Tel 803-794-3908 (Phone & fax)
E-mail: oeyeC@aol.com
Web site: http://www.shurite.com.

Jimmyland Corp., *(0-9760140; 0-9792672)* Jimmyland Corp., Orders Addr.: 2804 E. Crosley Dr., Suite H, West Palm Beach, FL 33415 USA Tel 561-602-1400; Fax: 561-969-3329
E-mail: jimmydrobinson@adelphia.net; musicalstories2003@adelphia.net
Web site: http://peterkeilmuseum.comM/; http://jimmydrobinson.com; http://jimmylandpublishing.com
Dist(s): **AtlasBooks Distribution.**

Jinks, Elizabeth Schneider, *(0-9666312)* 7624 W. Mauna Loa Ln., Peoria, AZ 85381-4388 USA Tel 602-486-5362
E-mail: ee_jinks@qwest.net.

JINKS Studio Art & Publishing, *(0-9749672)* Orders Addr.: 864 Sunrise Rd., Petal, MS 39465 USA Tel 228-596-5529
E-mail: jinksstudio@comcast.net
Web site: http://www.jinksstudio.com.

Jireh & Assocs., Inc., *(0-9632669)* P.O. Box 1374, Wilmington, DE 19899-1374 USA Tel 302-325-4221; Fax: 302-325-4221
Dist(s): **Baker & Taylor Bks.**
Quality Bks., Inc.

Jireh Pubs., *(0-9653197)* P.O. Box 99003, Norfolk, VA 23509-9003 USA Tel 757-558-4964; Fax: 757-558-4965 Do not confuse with companies with the same or similar name in West Monroe, LA , Baltimore, MD.
E-mail: admin@jirehpublishers.com
Web site: http://www.jirehpublishers.com.

JIST Life *Imprint of* **JIST Publishing**

†JIST Publishing, *(0-942784; 1-56370; 1-57112; 1-59357)* 7321 Shadeland Sta. Ste 200, Indianapolis, IN 46256 USA (SAN 240-2351) Tel 317-613-4200 Toll Free Fax: 800-547-8329 ; *Imprints:* KIDSRIGHTS (Kidsrts); JIST Works (JIST Works); JIST Life (JIST Lfe)
E-mail: info@jist.com
Web site: http://www.jist.com
Dist(s): **Cardinal Pubs. Group**
Linx Educational Publishing, Inc.
NetLibrary, Inc.; *CIP.*

JIST Works *Imprint of* **JIST Publishing**

JIST Works, Incorporated *See* **JIST Publishing**

Jitterbug Bks., *(0-9763031)* 25 Whale Rock Rd., Jamestown, RI 02835 USA Tel 401-423-2823
E-mail: jitterbugbooks@cox.net.

J.K.H. Enterprises, *(0-9761422)* MSC 5033, Busch Student Center 20 N. Grand Blvd., Saint Louis, MO 63103 USA
E-mail: juliushunter@slu.edu
Web site: http://juliushunter.tripod.com.

JLM CD-ROM Publishing Co., *(0-9749905)* 150 Idora Ave., San Francisco, CA 94127-1016 USA (SAN 255-9552)
Web site: http://www.jlmcd-rompublishing.com.

JM2 Publishing Co., *(0-9767210)* 6316 Monte Cresta, Richmond, CA 94806 USA Fax: 510-237-4305
E-mail: jeanmock@comcast.net.

JMC Printing, *(0-9638586)* Div. of JMC Marketing, Orders Addr.: 6730 W. 84th Cir. Suite 88, Arvada, CO 80003 USA Tel 303-564-1606 mobile
E-mail: jmcpublishing@aol.com.

JMG Studio, *(0-9771117)* Div. of John-Marc Grob Studios, 6 Southwind Dr., Flanders, NJ 07836 USA (SAN 256-8691) Tel 973-347-5399
E-mail: johnmarc@jmgstudio.net
Web site: http://www.jmgstudio.net.

JMW Group, Inc., 1 West Ave. Ste. 219, Larchmont, NY 10538-2471 USA
E-mail: icct@net.att.net.

JoAnn Vergona Krapp & Gene Zaner, *(0-9722576)* 94 Sunset Ave., Farmingdale, NY 11735 USA
E-mail: jkrapp1940@aol.com.

Joanne Faye Pr., *(0-9747375)* c/o Goblin Fern Pr., Inc., 852 Hemlock Dr., Verona, WI 53593 USA Tel 608-835-5523; Fax: 608-442-0212
E-mail: jritland@mac.com
Web site: http://www.loveybooks.com.

Joanne Frances Pr., *(0-9777640)* Orders Addr.: 210 Piney Hill Rd., Oakland, MI 48363-1449 USA Toll Free: 800-960-2347
Web site: http://www.JoanneFrancesPress.com.

JoAnne/Horatio Bks., *(0-9762838)* P.O. Box 371641, Miami, FL 32821 USA
E-mail: srodriguez@lushenabks.com; Jeff@JeffRivera.com
Web site: http://www.JeffRivera.com
Dist(s): **NetSource Distribution.**

JoBen Bks., LLC, *(0-9776385)* 4206 Heartland Dr., W, Eau Claire, WI 54701 USA (SAN 257-8093) Tel 715-552-1494.

JoBiz!, Inc., *(0-9663567)* Orders Addr.: P.O. Box 910250, Saint George, UT 84791-0250 USA Tel 435-674-0056; Fax: 435-652-4290; Toll Free: 888-674-0056; Edit Addr.: 2970 Beech Cir., Saint George, UT 84790 USA
E-mail: jgriff@infowest.com
Web site: http://www.birth-mom.com.

Jodan Collections, *(0-9747181)* Orders Addr.: 2716 N. Univ. Rd., Spokane, WA 99206 USA Tel 509-927-1882; Edit Addr.: 6405 S. Dishman Mica Rd., Spokane, WA 99206 USA
E-mail: joanne@inlandbindery.com
Web site: http://www.inlandbindery.com.

Joe Girl Ink, *(0-9766080)* 111S. Morgan, No. 502, Chicago, IL 60607 USA.

Jo-Eric Pubns., *(0-9658113)* 528 Mallory Ave., Windsor, CA 95492-8884 USA Tel 707-838-6025; Toll Free: 888-838-2425
E-mail: joericpub@aol.com
Web site: http://www.dollysbooks.com.

Johannesen Printing & Publishing, *(1-881084)* Orders Addr.: P.O. Box 24, Whitethorn, CA 95589 USA Tel 707-986-7465; Fax: 707-986-1656
E-mail: books@johannesen.com
Web site: http://www.johannesen.com.

John Marshall High Schl. Alumni Assn., *(0-9759618)* 347 Pineview Cir., Berea, OH 44017 USA
E-mail: jmhalumni@ameritech.com
Web site: http://www.jmhalumni.com.

John Vincent Music, *(0-9709673)* 79 Lower Unionville Rd., Wantage, NJ 07461 USA Tel 973-702-8340.

Johnny Sundby Photography, *(0-9747152)* 4780 Easy St., Rapid City, SD 57702 USA Tel 605-343-5646; Fax: 605-342-0139
E-mail: dsp@rap.midco.net
Web site: http://www.johnnysundby.com.

†Johns Hopkins Univ. Pr., *(0-8018; 1-4214)* Div. of Johns Hopkins Univ., Orders Addr.: P.O. Box 50370, Baltimore, MD 21211-4370 USA; Edit Addr.: 2715 N. Charles St., Baltimore, MD 21218-4319 USA (SAN 202-7348) Fax: 410-516-4189
E-mail: webmaster@press.jhu.edu
Web site: http://muse.jhu.edu/; http://www.press.jhu.edu/books/
Dist(s): **NetLibrary, Inc.**; *CIP.*

Johnson, Anthony, *(0-9773760)* P.O. Box 731, Burbank, CA 91503-0731 USA (SAN 257-4187) Fax: 818-558-6771
E-mail: leedobug@hotmail.com.

Johnson, Bonnie, *(0-9769756)* Orders Addr.: 11 High Point Rd., Valley Center, KS 67147-6714 USA Tel 316-755-2842 (phone/fax).

Johnson Bks., *(0-917895; 0-933472; 1-55566)* Div. of Big Earth Publishing Co., Orders Addr.: 3005 Center Green Dr. Suite 220, Boulder, CO 80301 USA (SAN 201-0313) Tel 303-443-9766; Fax: 303-443-9687; Toll Free: 800-258-5830
E-mail: books@bigearthpublishing.com
Web site: http://www.johnsonbooks.com
Dist(s): **Big Earth Publishing.**

Johnson Bks., Inc., *(0-9709715)* 8312 Pepperidge Dr., Berkeley, MO 63134 USA Tel 314-522-1764; Fax: 314-524-3420
E-mail: johnsonbooksinc@hotmail.com.

Johnson, Colleen, *(0-9785002)* 2500 63rd St NW, Minot, ND 58703 USA Tel 701-839-5768
E-mail: gchristi@minot.com
Web site: http://icecreamforbreakfastbook.com.

Johnson, Gary, *(0-9791794)* 938 E. Lois Ln., Phoenix, AZ 85020-1189 USA (SAN 852-6931) Tel 602-944-7517 (phone/fax); Toll Free: 888-665-2762
E-mail: gjohnson@molarman.com
Web site: http://www.molarman.com.

Johnson, J LLC, *(0-9713224)* P.O. Box 910, Montrose, AL 36559 USA Tel 251-990-3358; Fax: 251-990-5966.

Johnson, James *See* **Strategies Publishing Co.**

Johnson, Janet L., *(0-9673389)* Orders Addr.: 160 Main St., Rockport, MA 01966 USA Tel 978-546-6431; Fax: 978-546-6783
E-mail: Darlcat@aol.com
Dist(s): **Baker & Taylor Bks.**

Johnson, Michael Presentations, *(1-893672)* Rte. 1, Box 234, Idabel, OK 74745 USA Tel 580-286-7784; Fax: 580-286-7476
E-mail: michaelspeaks@msn.com.

†Johnson Reprint Corp., *(0-384)* Subs. of Harcourt Brace & Co., 111 Fifth Ave., New York, NY 10003 USA (SAN 285-0362); *CIP.*

Johnson, W. Macaulay *See* **Lost Words Publishing**

JohnSong Music, *(1-892397)* Orders Addr.: P.O. Box 3646, Napa, CA 94558 USA Tel 707-251-0266; Fax: 707-251-0266; Edit Addr.: 4400 Linda Vista Ave., Napa, CA 94558 USA
E-mail: jeff@johnsong.com
Web site: http://www.johnsong.com.

Johnston, Don Inc., *(1-893376; 1-58702; 1-4105)* Orders Addr.: 26799 W. Commerce Dr., Volo, IL 60073 USA Tel 847-740-0749; Fax: 847-740-7326; Toll Free: 800-999-4660
Web site: http://www.donjohnston.com.

Johnston-Brown, Anne Publishing Co. *See* **Retriever Pr.**

Joint Committee on Printing *Imprint of* **United States Government Printing Office**

Joint Heirs Pubs., *(0-9660565)* Div. of the Joint Heirs Foundation, 800 Fifth Ave., Suite 101, Dept. 236, Seattle, WA 98104-3191 USA Tel 616-896-2000; Fax: 616-896-2002; Toll Free: 800-873-0596
E-mail: shiptooth@aol.com; rplekker@iserv.net
Web site: http://www.jointheirspub.org.

Joint Publishing Co. (HKG) *(962-04) Dist. by* **China Bks.**

Jolean Publishing Co., *(0-934284)* P.O. Box 920163, Far Rockaway, NY 11692 USA (SAN 212-9507) Tel 718-318-0039.

Jolly Geranium, Inc., *(0-9644524)* 2953 E. Pawnee Dr., Sierra Vista, AZ 85635-8511 USA Tel 520-321-4747.

Jolly Learning, Ltd. (GBR) *(1-870946; 1-903619; 1-84414) Dist. by* **Am Intl Dist.**

Jollyville Pr., *(0-9723394)* 9709 Grand Oak Dr., Austin, TX 78750-3837 USA.

Jona Bks., *(0-9657929; 0-9706725; 1-932673)* Orders Addr.: P.O. Box 336, Bedford, IN 47421 USA Tel 812-278-9512 (phone/fax); Fax: 812-278-9518; Toll Free: 800-824-0991; Edit Addr.: P.O. Box 336, Bedford, IN 47421-0336 USA
E-mail: jonabook@kiva.net
Web site: http://www.jonabooks.com
Dist(s): **Baker & Taylor Bks.**
Distributors, The.

Jonathan Stampf Design Services, *(0-9711471)* Div. of JSDS Interactive, 2784 Old Orchard Rd., Lancaster, PA 17601 USA
E-mail: publishing@jsds.com
Web site: http://www.jsds.com/interactive.

†Jones & Bartlett Pubs., Inc., *(0-7637; 0-86720)* 40 Tall Pine Dr., Sudbury, MA 01776-2256 USA (SAN 285-0893) Tel 978-443-5000; Fax: 978-443-8000; Toll Free: 800-832-0034
E-mail: info@jbpub.com
Web site: http://www.jbpub.com
Dist(s): **International Specialized Bk. Services**
National Bk. Network; *CIP.*

Jones, Augustine R., *(0-9743223)* 4213 N. Knoll Ridge Rd. Apt. B2, Peoria, IL 61614-7439 USA.

†Jones, Bob Univ. Pr., *(0-89084; 1-57924; 1-59166)* 1700 Wade Hampton Blvd., Greenville, SC 29614 USA (SAN 223-7512) Tel 864-242-5731; Fax: 864-298-8398; Toll Free Fax: 800-525-8398; Toll Free: 800-845-5731
E-mail: bjup@bjup.com
Web site: http://www.bjup.com; *CIP.*

Jones Bks., *(0-9721217; 0-9763539; 0-9790475)* 309 N. Hillside Terr., Madison, WI 53705 USA Tel 608-236-9259; Fax: 608-236-0225
E-mail: info@jonesbooks.com
Web site: http://www.jonesbooks.com
Dist(s): **Independent Pubs. Group.**

Jones, E. Payson, *(0-9729194)* 6604 Three Chopt Rd., Richmond, VA 23226 USA.

Jones, Edward-Lynne & Assocs., *(0-9602458; 1-881533)* 5517 17th Ave., NE, Seattle, WA 98105 USA (SAN 263-2195) Tel 206-524-9604; Fax: 206-525-3191; Toll Free: 800-594-7627
E-mail: EJones7280@aol.com
Web site: http://weber.U.Washington.edu/~jones.

Jones, Kirby K., *(0-9703968)* 4800 S. Chicago Beach Dr., Unit 2109 N., Chicago, IL 60618 USA Tel 773-285-0871; Fax: 773-884-3063
Dist(s): **Morris Publishing.**

Jones, Kirk, *(0-9759688)* P.O. Box 74702, Richmond, VA 23236 USA
E-mail: kirkjonesillustrations@juno.com.

Jones Publishing Network, *(0-9718857; 0-9765396)* P.O. Box 14011, Merrillville, IN 46411-4011 USA Tel 219-981-8185; Toll Free: 866-895-2268
E-mail: info@jpublishingnetwork.com
Web site: http://www.jpublishingnetwork.com.

Jon'taar Graphxs, *(0-9764385)* 75 Lantern Chase Dr., Delaware, OH 43015 USA Tel 740-972-6321
E-mail: msuplicki@jontaar.com; information@mirthburdz.com
Web site: http://www.jontaar.com; http://www.mirthburdz.com.

Jordan, Hellyn Lackey, *(0-9704474)* 139 Sweet Gum Ln., Winder, GA 30680-1789 USA.

Jordan Music Productions, Inc., *(1-895523; 1-894262; 1-55386)* M.P.O. Box 490, Niagara Falls, NY 14302-0490 USA
E-mail: sjordan@sara-jordan.com
Web site: http://www.sara-jordan.com; http://www.SongsThatTeach.com; http://www.edu-mart.com
Dist(s): **Baker & Taylor Bks.**
Follett Media Distribution
iLeon.

Jordan Publishing Hse., *(1-890875)* Orders Addr.: P.O. Box 671, Columbia, CA 95310 USA Fax: 209-532-5503; Edit Addr.: 22620 Parrotts Ferry Rd., Columbia, CA 95310 USA Do not confuse with companies with the same name in Las Vegas, NV, Nappanee, IN, Reston, VA, Phoenix, AZ, Prescott, AZ
E-mail: gpview@erli.net.

Jordan Valley Heritage Hse., *(0-939810)* P.O. Box 99, Stayton, OR 97383-0099 USA (SAN 216-7425) Tel 503-769-4236
E-mail: jvhh5@wvi.com.

Jorlan Publishing *See* **Jorlan Publishing, Inc.**

Jorlan Publishing, Inc., *(0-9710696; 1-933830)* P.O. Box 2882, Cedar City, UT 84721-2882 USA
Web site: http://www.jorlanpublishing.com.

Joseph Henry Pr. *Imprint of* **National Academies Pr.**

Joseph's Coat Publishing, *(0-9759784)* Orders Addr.: 12370 Whitechapel Way, Nampa, ID 83686-8030 USA (SAN 256-3762)
E-mail: customerservice@josephscoatpublishing.com
Web site: http://www.josephscoatpublishing.com.

Joseph's Heartprint, *(0-9787035)* 728 Creek Rd., Carlisle, PA 17013 USA Tel 717-258-8796; Fax: 717-243-4254
E-mail: george@catholicartworks.com
Web site: http://www.catholicartworks.com.

Joseph's Labor, *(0-9729800)* P.O. Box 176265, Covington, KY 41017-6265 USA Tel 859-578-8112
E-mail: JosephsLabor@aol.com.

Joshandra Publishing, Inc., *(0-9718518)* P.O. Box 1176-A, Pearland, TX 77581 USA.

Joshua Morris Publishing, Incorporated *See* **Reader's Digest Children's Publishing, Inc.**

Joshua Pr., Inc. (CAN) *(1-894400) Dist. by* **Gabriel Res.**

Jossey-Bass *Imprint of* **Wiley, John & Sons, Inc.**

Jostens Bks., *(0-9759530; 0-9788398)* 2400 Crownpoint Executive Dr., Suite No.100-6, Charlotte, NC 28227 USA Tel 704-847-5717; Fax: 704-844-0713; Toll Free: 800-458-0319
E-mail: sherry.clontz@jostens.com
Web site: http://www.jostens.com.

Journal Keepers, *(0-9674966)* 1756 Martingale Ave., Los Osos, CA 93402 USA Tel 805-528-8722
E-mail: JournlKeep@aol.com
Web site: http://JournalKeepers.com.

Journals Unlimited, Inc., *(1-892033)* 4151 Two Mile Rd., Bay City, MI 48706-2321 USA Tel 517-686-3377; Fax: 517-686-3380; Toll Free: 800-897-8528
E-mail: journals2u@aol.com
Web site: http://www.journalsunlimited.com.

Journey Pubns., LLC, *(0-9728716; 0-9748087; 0-9772078; 0-9798171)* Orders Addr.: P.O. Box 2442, Warminster, PA 18974-2442 USA (SAN 255-1675) Do not confuse with companies with the same or similar names in Woodstock, NY, Savannah, GA, Avon Park, FL, Metairie, LA, Lacey, WA
E-mail: journeypubs@aol.com
Web site: http://www.journeypublications.com
Dist(s): **Baker & Taylor Bks.**

Journey Stone Creations, LLC, *(0-9758709; 1-59958)* 3533 Danbury Rd., Fairfield, OH 45014 USA Tel 513-860-5616; Fax: 513-860-0176 ; *Imprints:* A.W.A. Gang (AWA Gang)
E-mail: pat@journeystonecreations.com
Web site: http://www.journeystonecreations.com
Dist(s): **STL Distribution North America.**

Jove *Imprint of* **Penguin Group (USA) Inc.**

Joy of my Youth Pubns., The, *(0-9774345)* P.O. Box 128702, Cincinnati, OH 45212 USA Tel 513-531-2709
E-mail: thejoyofmyyouth@netzero.net
Web site: http://www.thejoyofmyyouth.com.

J.O.Y. Pubns., *(0-9762975)* 186 Gatewood Ave., Rochester, NY 14624-1737 USA Do not confuse with companies with the same or similar name in Santa Maria, CA Gardena, CA, Pittsboro, NC, Woburn, MA
E-mail: rainbowvillagecc@yahoo.com; rainbowvillage@homewithGod.net
Web site: www.our.homewithGod.com/rainbowvillage/.

Joy Publishing, *(0-939513)* Div. of California Clock Co., P.O. Box 9901, Fountain Valley, CA 92708 USA (SAN 663-3544) Tel 714-545-4321; Fax: 714-708-2099; Toll Free: 800-454-8228 Do not confuse with Joy Publishing in College Station, TX,
E-mail: mail@joypublishing.com; plarke@tamu.edu
Web site: http://www.joypublishing.com
Dist(s): **Spring Arbor Distributors, Inc.**

JoyceHerzog.com, Inc., *(1-887225)* 1542 Norstar Ln., Fallbrook, CA 92028 USA Tel 760-451-0053
E-mail: joyceherzogcorp@aol.com.

Joyce's Books *See* **Divine Power Publishing**

Joyful Noise, *(0-9772109)* 312 Stonewall Rd., Concord, VA 24538 USA (SAN 257-0149)
E-mail: j.b.designs@att.net.

JoyRox, LLC, *(0-9754972)* 11585 Hooker St., Westminster, CO 80031-7121 USA
E-mail: info@joy-rox.com
Web site: http://www.joy-rox.com.

Joysong Creations, *(0-9753382)* 1487 Springside Dr., Weston, FL 33326 USA Tel 954-384-6018
E-mail: shirahpenn@yahoo.com
Web site: http://www.joysongcreations.com.

JoySoul Corp., *(0-9727786)* Orders Addr.: P.O. Box 71, Lisbon, ND 58054-0071 USA Tel 701-683-4859; Fax: 701-683-4950; Toll Free: 866-569-8486
E-mail: joysoul@joysoul.com; joysoul@earthlink.net; carol@joysoul.com
Web site: http://www.joysoul.com.

JPA Assocs., *(0-9727125)* 11026 Maple Rd., Lafayette, CO 80026 USA Tel 303-665-6764.

JRV Publishing, *(0-9771250)* P.O. Box 82, West Simsbury, CT 06092 USA
E-mail: jverney1@jrvpublishing.com.

JSP Bks., *(0-9728519)* 6886 Hickory Lake Cove, Memphis, TN 38119 USA Tel 901-757-0694
E-mail: contact@jspbooks.com
Web site: http://www.jspbooks.com.

Jubilation Creation, Inc., *(0-9676333)* 12800 University Dr., Suite 675, Fort Myers, FL 33907 USA Tel 904-415-0901; Fax: 941-415-0903
E-mail: jubicreations@aol.com.

Jubilee Day/Juneteenth Celebration, *(0-9701357)* 2121 Sycamore View, PMB 427, Memphis, TN 38134 USA Tel 901-481-6208; 901-785-1212; Fax: 901-547-9405
Web site: http://www.geocities.com/Juneteenthstory.

Jubilee, Incorporated *See* **Jubilee Publishing Group**

Jubilee Publishing Group, *(1-57727)* Orders Addr.: P.O. Box 30, Lebanon, TN 37088 USA Tel 615-443-3800; Fax: 615-443-8500; Toll Free: 800-474-0074.

Judah Bks., Inc., *(0-9767469)* 3535 W. Tierra Buena Ln., Apt. No. A273, Phoenix, AZ 85053 USA.

Judaica Pr., Inc., The, *(0-910818; 1-880582; 1-932443)* 123 Ditmas Ave., Brooklyn, NY 11218 USA (SAN 204-9856) Tel 718-972-6200; Fax: 718-972-6204; Toll Free: 800-972-6201 ; *Imprints:* Shayach Comics (Shayach Comics)
E-mail: info@judaicapress.com
Web site: http://www.judaicapress.com.

JuDe Publishing, *(0-9712585)* P.O. Box 88847, Los Angeles, CA 90009 USA Tel 310-519-8288
E-mail: judepublishing@yahoo.com
Dist(s): **Bookazine Co., Inc.**

†Judson Pr., *(0-8170)* Div. of American Baptist Churches, U.S.A., P.O. Box 851, Valley Forge, PA 19482-0851 USA (SAN 201-0348) Tel 610-768-2118; Fax: 610-768-2107; Toll Free: 800-331-1053
Web site: http://www.judsonpress.com
Dist(s): **A & B Distributors & Pubs. Group**
Afrikan World Bk. Distributor
Anchor Distributors
Appalachian Bible Co.
Baker & Taylor Bks.
Culture Plus Bk. Distributors
Partners Bk. Distributing, Inc.
Sociedad Biblica de Puerto Rico
Spring Arbor Distributors, Inc.
Wizard Works; *CIP.*

Judy *Imprint of* **Schaffer, Frank Pubns.**

Juice Gallery *See* **Juice Gallery Multimedia**

Juice Gallery Multimedia, *(1-58291)* 2042 Big Oak Ave., Chino Hills, CA 91709 USA Tel 909-597-0791; Toll Free: 800-710-0163
E-mail: info@juicegallery.com
Web site: http://www.juicegallery.com.

JukeJoint Publishing *See* **Downhome Publishing**

Julie Andrews Collection *Imprint of* **HarperCollins Pubns.**

Julson, D. K., *(0-615; 0-9746564)* 29996 U.S. Hwy. 14, Lone Rock, WI 53556 USA.

Ju'Mel Publishing, *(0-9714939)* 1716 E. Mechanic, Independence, MO 64050 USA
E-mail: elvistalk@yahoo.com.

Jump at the Sun *Imprint of* **Hyperion Bks. for Children**

Jump Start Performance Programs, *(1-893962)* P.O. Box 3448, Van Nuys, CA 91407 USA Toll Free Fax: 800-990-9667; Toll Free: 800-450-0432
E-mail: scott@scottgreenberg.com
Web site: http://www.scottgreenberg.com.

Jumping Jack Holidays, *(0-9713219)* 7420 N. Bell Rd., Milwaukee, WI 53217 USA Tel 414-351-0031
E-mail: jjholidays@aol.com
Web site: http://hometown.aol.com/jjholidays/myhomepage/business.html.

JumpRope Bks., *(0-9718411)* 496 N. Jefferson St., Danville, IN 46122-1144 USA Tel 317-745-7386 (phone/fax)
E-mail: timecastle@earthlink.net.

Junction Pr., *(1-881523)* P.O. Box F, New York, NY 10034 USA Tel 212-942-1985
E-mail: junction@earthlink.net
Web site: http://www.junctionpress.com
Dist(s): **Latin American Bk. Source, Inc.**
Lectorum Pubns., Inc.
SPD-Small Pr. Distribution.

Junebug Bks. *Imprint of* **NewSouth, Inc.**

Junebug Pr., *(0-9720493)* 575 Uhler Rd., Suite 100, Marion, OH 43302 USA Tel 740-387-1842
E-mail: tozphoto@aol.com.

JuneOne Publishing Hub, *(0-9763082)* 27762 Antonio Pkwy., L1-404, Ladera Ranch, CA 92694 USA Tel 949-364-6179; Fax: 757-299-4407 ; *Imprints:* A JuneOne Production (A JuneOne Prod)
E-mail: info@juneonehub.com
Web site: http://www.juneonehub.com.

Jung, Loretta, *(0-9724174)* 1738 Fifth Ave., NE, Jamestown, ND 58401 USA Tel 701-952-4741
E-mail: loretta@thejungs.com
Web site: http://www.crystalene.net; http://www.bowkerbios.com.

Jungle Communications, Incorporation *See* **Allergic Child Publishing Group**

Jungle Hse. Pubns., *(0-9769332)* Orders Addr.: 736 Cardium St., Sanibel, FL 33957-6704 USA Tel 239-395-4518
E-mail: junglehousepub@yahoo.com
Web site: http://junglehousepublications.com.

Junibird Productions, *(0-9725155)* 2321 Coldwater Canyon Dr., Beverly Hills, CA 90210 USA (SAN 254-895X) Tel 310-275-6029; Fax: 310-275-8748
E-mail: fumicum@earthlink.net.

Junior Golf of N.E. Pennsylvania, *(0-9716326)* Orders Addr.: P.O. Box 165, Olyphant, PA 18447 USA Tel 570-383-3689; Toll Free: 877-431-2195; Edit Addr.: 224 River St., Olyphant, PA 18447 USA
E-mail: don@juniorgolftips.com.

Junior History Pr., *(0-9744556)* Orders Addr.: P.O. Box 157, Summerville, SC 29484-0157 USA Tel 843-873-8117; Edit Addr.: 1311 Jahnz Ave., Summerville, SC 29485 USA
E-mail: gteaster@juniorhistory.com
Web site: http://www.juniorhistory.com.

Junior League of Charleston, South Carolina, Inc., *(0-9607854)* 51 Folly Rd., Charleston, SC 29407 USA (SAN 218-8031) Tel 843-763-5284; Fax: 843-763-1626
E-mail: office@jlcharleston.org
Web site: http://www.jlcharleston.org/.

Junior League of Grand Rapids Michigan, Inc., *(0-9611316; 0-9634927)* 25 Sheldon Blvd., Suite 124, Grand Rapids, MI 49503 USA (SAN 282-9452) Tel 616-451-0452; Fax: 616-451-1936
E-mail: juniorleague@iserv.net
Web site: http://www.juniorleagiegr.com.

Junior League of Houston, Inc., *(0-9632421)* 1811 Briar Oaks Ln., Houston, TX 77027 USA Tel 713-622-4191; Fax: 713-622-3160; Toll Free: 800-432-2665
E-mail: cookbook@juniorleaguehouston.org
Web site: http://www.juniorleaguehouston.org
Dist(s): **Baker & Taylor Bks.**
Booksource, The
Hervey's Booklink & Cookbook Warehouse
Koen-Levy Bk. Wholesalers LLC
Wimmer Cookbooks.

Junior League of Philadelphia, Inc., *(0-9626959)* 27 W. Lancaster Ave., Ardmore, PA 19003-1408 USA
E-mail: jlphila@atxmail.com
Web site: http://www.jphila.com.

Junior League of Tyler, Inc., The, *(0-9607122)* 1919 S. Donnybrook, Tyler, TX 75701 USA (SAN 238-9975) Tel 903-593-8141; Fax: 903-595-1362.

Juniper Berry Pr., *(0-9760076)* 6609 Cornelia Dr., Edina, MN 55435 USA Tel 952-285-4447
E-mail: gjudso@aol.com
Web site: http://www.juniperberrypress.com.

Juniper Grove, *(1-60355)* 2129 E. Stearns, Fayetteville, AR 72703 USA (SAN 853-5078)
E-mail: JuniperGrove@gmail.com
Web site: http://www.junipergrove.com
Dist(s): **BookSurge, LLC.**

Jupiter Coins *See* **Adventure in Discovery**

Jupiter Scientific Publishing Co., *(0-9655176)* c/o Gezhi Weng, 415 Moraga Ave., Piedmont, CA 94611 USA (SAN 299-4313)
E-mail: admin@jupiterscientific.org
Web site: http://www.jupiterscientific.org
Dist(s): **Baker & Taylor Bks.**
Bookmen, Inc.

Jurik, Cynthia L., *(0-9678807)* 210 Emerson Rd., Traverse City, MI 49686-8815 USA
E-mail: tcjuriks@aol.com.

Just Be Publishing, Inc., *(0-9668219)* 746 E. Rosemore Ct., Salt Lake City, UT 84107 USA (SAN 299-7479) Tel 801-265-3435 (phone/fax)
E-mail: bl_ehrler@att.net
Web site: http://www.justbepublishing.com
Dist(s): **Baker & Taylor Bks.**

Just Chill Pubns., *(0-9726548)* P.O. Box 5990, Chicago, IL 60680 USA
E-mail: chill1960@comcast.net; contact@justchill.org; contact@communityaccessresources.org
Web site: http://www.justchill.org; http://www.communityaccessresources.org.

Just Ducky Publishing, *(0-9717103)* P.O. Box 129, Edgefield, SC 29824 USA Tel 803-637-2007; Fax: 803-637-5825
E-mail: pam@boykinspaniel.com
Web site: http://www.justduckypublishing.com.

Just Enjoyable Memorable Story Bks., *(0-9724472)* 8258 Balsam Way, Arvada, CO 80005 USA
E-mail: jemsbooks@hotmail.com.

Just For Children, *(0-9670123)* 2470 S. Dairy Ashford, No. 152, Houston, TX 77077 USA Tel 281-638-5408; Toll Free: 888-840-9623
E-mail: kdnichols@hotmail.com.

Just Like Me, Inc., *(1-928889)* P.O. Box 4494, Washington, DC 20017 USA Tel 202-526-1725
E-mail: info@justlikemebooks.com
Web site: http://www.justlikemebooks.com.

Just My Best Bk. Publishing Co., *(0-9720344)* Div. of Just My Best, Inc., 1746 Dailey Rd., Wilmington, OH 45177 USA Fax: 937-987-9949 ; *Imprints:* Just My Book, Incorporated (Just My Bk Inc)
E-mail: jmbpub@justmybest.com; jst@jmbpub.com; jsueterry@yahoo.com
Web site: http://www.justmybest.com/Public/Default.htm; http://www.jmbpub.com.

Just My Best Publishing Company *See* **Just My Best Bk. Publishing Co.**

Just My Bk., Inc. *Imprint of* **Just My Best Bk. Publishing Co.**

Just Think Bks. *Imprint of* **Canary Connect Pubns.**

Just Us Bks., Inc., *(0-940975; 1-933491)* 356 Glenwood Ave., East Orange, NJ 07017 USA (SAN 664-7413) Tel 973-672-0304 ; *Imprints:* Sankofa Books (Sankofa Bks)
E-mail: justusbooks@mindspring.com
Web site: http://www.justusbooks.

Just Write Bks., *(0-9722839; 0-9766533; 0-9777614; 0-9788628)* Just Write Communications, 14 Munroe Ln., Topsham, ME 04086 USA
E-mail: jstwrite@jstwrite.com
Web site: http://www.jstwrite.com.

JUST-US Books *See* **Ike, J. Bks.**

Juvenescent Research Corp., *(0-9600148; 1-884996)* 807 Riverside Dr., Apt. 1F, New York, NY 10032 USA (SAN 206-7250) Tel 212-795-3749
Web site: http://www.juvenescent.qpg.com
Dist(s): **Barnes & Noble, Inc.**

Juventud, Editorial (ESP) *(84-261) Dist. by* **Continental Bk.**

Juventud, Editorial (ESP) *(84-261) Dist. by* **Mariuccia Iaconi Bk Imports.**

Juventud, Editorial (ESP) *(84-261) Dist. by* **Lectorum Pubns.**

Juventud, Editorial (ESP) *(84-261) Dist. by* **AIMS Intl.**

Juventud, Editorial (ESP) *(84-261) Dist. by* **Distribks Inc.**

JVED Publishing, *(0-9768833)* 18140 Zane St., NW No. 410, Elk River, MN 55330 USA
Web site: http://www.jvedpublishing.org.

JVT Pubns. & Creations, *(1-893812)* 885 Southwest Blvd., Coos Bay, OR 97420-1252 USA
E-mail: gyrojeff@aol.com
Web site: http://www.jvtpubs.com.

JWall Publishing, *(0-9760518)* 287 Jones Rd., Statham, GA 30666 USA Tel 770-725-7465.

J.W.A.N.D. Enterprises, *(1-883753)* Orders Addr.: P.O. Box 25313, Philadelphia, PA 19119 USA Tel 215-438-1809; Edit Addr.: 6215 Greene St., Philadelphia, PA 19144 USA
E-mail: niaebo@juno.com.

JYZ Bks., LLC, *(0-9743272)* 5816 White Pebble Path, Clarksville, MD 21029 USA Fax: 443-535-9664
E-mail: jianyi.zhang@chickensfirst.net
Web site: http://chickensfirst.net.

JZK Publishing, *(1-57873)* Div. of JZK, Inc., 14507 Yelm Hwy., SE, Yelm, WA 98597 USA Tel 360-458-5201 ext 36 editor; 360-458-5201 ext 35 Distribution Mgr.; Fax: 360-458-4449; Toll Free: 800-347-0439 customer service
E-mail: books@jzkpublishing.com; elaineb@ramtha.com
Web site: http://www.ramtha.com; http://www.jzkpublishing.com
Dist(s): **Baker & Taylor Bks.**
Bodhi Tree Bookstore
New Leaf Distributing Co., Inc.

K & B First Publishing Co., *(0-9729498)* 11446 SW French Glen Ct., Suite 3, Portland, OR 97070 USA.

K & D Limited, Incorporated *See* **Falling Star Publishing**

K&M International, *(1-890716)* Div. of K & M International, 1955 Midway Dr., Twinsburg, OH 44087 USA Tel 330-425-2550; Fax: 330-425-3777; Toll Free: 800-800-9678.

KCDI Publishing, *(0-9655719)* 674 E. Highway 80, Suite 303, Abilene, TX 79601 USA Tel 915-672-6476; Fax: 915-672-4202
Dist(s): **Hervey's Booklink & Cookbook Warehouse.**

KC Pubns., *(0-88714; 0-916122)* Orders Addr.: P.O. Box 94558, Las Vegas, NV 89193-4558 USA (SAN 201-0364) Tel 702-433-3415; Fax: 702-433-3420; Toll Free: 800-626-9673; Edit Addr.: 3245 E. Patrick Ln., Suite A, Las Vegas, NV 89120 USA (SAN 658-103X)
E-mail: kcp@kcpublications.com
Web site: http://www.kcpublications.com
Dist(s): **Anderson News, LLC**
Booklines Hawaii, Ltd.
Florida Flair Bks.

K. F. Enterprises *See* **Production Assocs., Inc.**

K M O S A 5 Media, Incorporated *See* **Black-Out Media**

KMTK Intelligence Agency, *(0-9712799)* 141 Glenridge Pl., C, Cincinnati, OH 45217 USA Tel 513-961-3763
E-mail: ceo_mitchell23@hotmail.com.

KRW International, Inc., *(0-9671611)* 9232 Eton Ave., Chatsworth, CA 91311 USA (SAN 254-6418) Tel 818-678-0000; Fax: 818-678-0005; Toll Free: 888-579-4685
E-mail: roni@krwintl.com
Web site: http://www.quizm.com.

K T Graphics, *(0-9755259)* 5300 Standing Rock Pl., Las Vegas, NV 89130 USA Tel 702-808-3773
Web site: http://www.ktgraphicsolutions.com.

K12, *(1-931728; 1-60153)* 2300 Corporate Park Dr., Herndon, VA 20171 USA Tel 703-483-7000; Fax: 703-483-7330
Web site: http://www.k12.com.

K-Twelve MicroMedia Publishing, Inc., *(0-943646; 1-56419)* 16 McKee Dr., Mahwah, NJ 07430 USA (SAN 286-990X) Tel 201-529-4500; Fax: 201-529-5282; Toll Free: 800-292-1997
E-mail: sales@k12mmp.com
Web site: http://www.k12mmp.com.

Kabel Pubs., *(0-930329; 1-57529)* 11225 Huntover Dr., Rockville, MD 20852-3613 USA (SAN 670-8323) Tel 301-468-6463 (phone/fax); Toll Free: 800-543-3167
E-mail: kabelcomp@erols.com
Web site: http://www.erols.com/kabelcomp/index2.html.

Kabet Pr. (GBR) *(0-948662) Dist. by* **Empire Pub Srvs.**

Kabouter Products, *(1-57909)* 1815 Highland Pl., Berkeley, CA 94709-1009 USA Tel 510-839-3931; Fax: 510-839-0954; Toll Free: 888-246-6637
Dist(s): **New Leaf Distributing Co., Inc.**
Sunbelt Pubns., Inc.

Kadar, Nicole Tokar, *(0-9745823)* 2465 McCleary Dr., Chambersburg, PA 17201 USA Tel 717-709-1813; Toll Free: 800-317-5673
E-mail: melkadar@yahoo.com.

Kadima Pr., *(0-9723229)* 410 Pine St. No., 802 C, Abilene, TX 79601-5163 USA Fax: 501-636-7425
E-mail: KadimaPress@juno.com
Web site: http://www.kadimapress.com; http://www.AuntLaya.com
Dist(s): **Books West.**

Kaeden Bks. *Imprint of* **Kaeden Corp.**

Kaeden Corp., *(1-57874; 1-879835)* Orders Addr.: P.O. Box 16190, Rocky River, OH 44116 USA Tel 440-617-1400; Fax: 440-617-1403; Toll Free: 800-890-7323; Edit Addr.: 806 Sharon Dr. Ste. F, Westlake, OH 44145-7701 USA ; *Imprints:* Kaeden Books (Kaeden)
E-mail: info@kaeden.com
Web site: http://www.kaeden.com.

Kagan Cooperative Learning *See* **Kagan Publishing**

Kagan Publishing, *(1-879097; 1-933445)* Orders Addr.: P.O. Box 72008, San Clemente, CA 92673 USA Tel 949-369-6310; Fax: 949-369-6311; Toll Free: 800-933-2667
Web site: http://www.kaganonline.com.

kahani.com, Inc., *(1-929981)* 31 Chase Ln., Ithaca, NY 14850 USA
Web site: http://kahani.com.

Kaimanu Prodns., Ltd., *(0-9764474)* 135-A Kaimanu Pl., Kihei, HI 96753 USA Tel 808-268-9092; Fax: 808-442-0013
E-mail: customerservice@kaimanu.net
Web site: http://www.kaimanu.net
Dist(s): **Booklines Hawaii, Ltd.**

KAIOS Bks., *(0-9714287)* P.O. Box 442, Helena, MT 59624 USA
E-mail: aqk@kaios.com.

Kairos Publishing, *(0-9665831)* Orders Addr.: P.O. Box 450, Clarence, NY 14031 USA Tel 716-759-1058; Fax: 716-759-0731; Toll Free: 800-519-4647; Edit Addr.: 10501 Main St., Clarence, NY 14031 USA Do not confuse with Kairos Publishing in Llano de San Juan, NM
E-mail: office@eagleswings.to
Web site: http://www.eagleswings.to
Dist(s): **Destiny Image Pubs.**
STL Distribution North America.

Kaiser Permanente Northwest/Health Education, *(0-9677134; 0-9744864)* 7201 N. Interstate Ave., Portland, OR 97217-55 USA Fax: 503-286-6881 Do not confuse with Kaiser Permanente, Portland OR
E-mail: erin.c.bruzda@kp.org.

Kalandraka Catalunya, Edicions, S.L. (ESP) *(84-95730) Dist. by* **IPG Chicago.**

Kalandraka Editora, S.L. (ESP) *(84-8464; 84-923553; 84-95123) Dist. by* **Mariuccia Iaconi Bk Imports.**

Kalandraka Editora, S.L. (ESP) *(84-8464; 84-923553; 84-95123) Dist. by* **Lectorum Pubns.**

Kalawantis Computer Services, Incorporated *See* **Kalawantis Publishing Services, Inc**

Kalawantis Publishing Services, Inc, *(0-9665909)* P.O. Box 10345, Charlotte, NC 28212 USA Tel 704-578-0475
E-mail: president@kalawantis.com
Web site: http://www.kalawantis.com
Dist(s): **Baker & Taylor Bks.**

Kalcolby, Pat, *(0-9675023)* Orders Addr.: P.O. Box 2206, Austin, TX 78768-2206 USA; Edit Addr.: 7312 S. Hwy. 183, Suite 101, Austin, TX 78744 USA.

Kalcom Publishing, *(0-9797530)* 84-01 Lefferts Blvd., Kew Gardens, NY 11415 USA Tel 718-805-5555
E-mail: yek@kalcom.com.

KALEXT Productions, LLC, *(0-9617451; 0-9748792)* 12795 75th Lane N., West Palm Beach, FL 33412 USA (SAN 664-0613) Tel 561-310-4338
E-mail: xela319@comcast.net; xela319@bellsouth.net
Web site: http://www.bilingualgames.com; http://www.biznizgames.com.

†Kalimat Pr., *(0-933770; 1-890688)* 1600 Sawtelle Blvd., Suite 310, Los Angeles, CA 90025 USA (SAN 213-7666) Tel 310-479-5668; Fax: 310-477-2840; Toll Free: 800-788-4067
E-mail: kalimatp@aol.com; orders@kalimat.com
Web site: http://www.kalimat.com; *CIP.*

Kaliyan Publishing, *(0-9762065)* P.O. Box 473, Stephens City, VA 22655-9998 USA.

Kallisti Music Pr., *(0-9645431)* 810 S. Saint Bernard St., Philadelphia, PA 19143-3309 USA Toll Free: 800-260-2881
E-mail: kallisti@ix.netcom.com
Web site: http://www.netcom.com/~kallisti/kallisti.html.

†Kalmbach Publishing Co., Bks. Div., *(0-8238; 0-89024; 0-89778; 0-913135; 0-933168)* Orders Addr.: P.O. Box 1612, Waukesha, WI 53187 USA (SAN 201-0399) Tel 414-796-8776; Fax: 414-798-6468; Toll Free: 800-533-6644 (customer sales); 800-446-5489 (customer service); 800-558-1544 (trade sales); Edit Addr.: 21027 Crossroads Cir., Waukesha, WI 53187 USA
E-mail: customerservice@kalmbach.com
Web site: http://corporate.kalmbach.com/
Dist(s): **Macmillan**
Watson-Guptill Pubns., Inc.; *CIP.*

Kalmia Publishing, *(0-9676620)* Orders Addr.: 826 Amiford Dr., San Diego, CA 92107 USA Tel 619-222-7074 (phone/fax)
E-mail: pixieh@mymailstation.com; folsom@islc.net
Web site: http://www.islc.net/~folsom/language.

Kalona Publishing, *(0-9700523)* Orders Addr.: P.O. Box 2707, Woodbridge, VA 22193 USA Tel 703-490-0405; Fax: 703-490-9019; Edit Addr.: 2499 Paxton St., Woodbridge, VA 22192 USA
E-mail: kalonapub@home.com; sjkalona@worldnet.att.net
Web site: http://www.geocities.com/sjkalona.

KAM Publishing, *(0-9795474)* Orders Addr.: 959 Knight Dr., Durant, OK 74701 USA
E-mail: sharonm@llibs.com
Web site: http://www.llibs.com
Dist(s): **Library Integrated Solutions & Assocs.**

Kamaron Institute Pr., Div. of Kamaron Institute for Rapid Business Results, 104 Strawflower Path, Peachtree City, GA 30269 USA
E-mail: info@kamaron.org; kamaroninstitute@earthlink.net
Web site: http://www.kamaron.org.

†Kamehameha Schools Pr., *(0-87336)* 1887 Makuakane St., Honolulu, HI 96817 USA Tel 808-842-8719; Fax: 808-842-8895; Toll Free: 800-842-4682 (ext. 8719)
E-mail: kspress@ksbe.edu
Web site: http://www.ksbe.edu/pubs/KSPress/catalog.html
Dist(s): **Bess Pr., Inc.**
Booklines Hawaii, Ltd.
Island Heritage Publishing
Native Bks.; *CIP.*

Kamishibai for Kids, *(1-893533)* Orders Addr.: P.O. Box 629, New York, NY 10025 USA Tel 212-663-2471; Fax: 212-662-5836; Toll Free: 800-772-1228
E-mail: kamishi@cybernex.net
Web site: http://www.kamishibai.com.

Kampupot Books *See* **Broader Horizon Bks.**

K&B Products, *(0-9646181; 0-9740841; 0-9772372)* P.O. Box 548, Yellville, AR 72687 USA Toll Free Fax: 888-871-5856; Toll Free: 800-700-5096
E-mail: brmp@aol.com; inquiry@thecompletepet.com
Web site: http://www.thecompletepet.com; http://www.whitehallpublishing.com
Dist(s): **Baker & Taylor Bks.**
Western International, Inc.

Kane Pr., The, *(1-57565)* 240 W. 35th St., Suite 300, New York, NY 10001-2506 USA Tel 212-268-1435; Fax: 212-268-2044
E-mail: ndmattia@kanepress.com
Web site: http://www.kanepress.com
Dist(s): **Baker & Taylor Bks.**
Bookmen, Inc.
Booksource, The
Brodart Co.
Lerner Publishing Group.

†Kane/Miller Bk. Pubs., Inc., *(0-916291; 1-929132; 1-933605)* Orders Addr.: P.O. Box 8515, La Jolla, CA 92038 USA (SAN 295-8945) Tel 858-456-0540; Fax: 858-456-9641; Toll Free: 800-968-1930; Edit Addr.: 7946 Ivanhoe Ave., Suite 203, La Jolla, CA 92037 USA Tel 858-456-0540
E-mail: kira@kanemiller.com; info@kanemiller.com
Web site: http://www.kanemiller.com; http://www.everyonepoops.com; *CIP.*

Kanlearn, Inc., *(0-9772077)* 8950 W. Olympic Blvd., No. 128, Beverly Hills, CA 90211 USA Tel 310-430-6806
E-mail: mattie3rd@yahoo.com
Web site: www.thekanlearnfoundation.com.

Kansas Alumni Assoc., *(0-9742918)* 1266 Oread Ave., Lawrence, KS 66044 USA
Web site: http://www.kualumni.org.

Kansas City Guidebooks, *(0-9763873)* P.O. Box 14082, Parkville, MO 64152 USA
Web site: http://www.kckidsguide.com.

Kansas City Star Bks., *(0-9604884; 0-9679519; 0-9709131; 0-9712920; 0-9717080; 0-9722739; 0-9740009; 0-9746012; 0-9754804; 0-9764021; 1-933466)* Cypress Media L L P, 1729 Grand Blvd., Kansas City, MO 64108 USA Tel 816-234-4292 ; *Imprints:* Rockhill Books (Rockhill Bks)
E-mail: dweaver@kcstar.com
Web site: http://www.thekansascitystore.com.

Kansas Heritage Ctr., *(1-882404)* Orders Addr.: P.O. Box 1207, Dodge City, KS 67801 USA Tel 316-227-1616; Fax: 316-227-1695; Edit Addr.: 1000 Second Ave., Dodge City, KS 67801 USA
E-mail: info@ksheritage.org
Web site: http://www.ksheritage.org.

Kansas State University, Beach Museum of Arts, The *See* **Kansas State Univ., Marianna Kistler Beach Museum of Art, The**

Kansas State Univ., Marianna Kistler Beach Museum of Art, The, *(1-890751)* 701 Beach Ln., Manhattan, KS 66506 USA Tel 785-532-7718; Fax: 785-532-7498
E-mail: bnorth@ksu.edu
Web site: http://www.ksu.edu/bma
Dist(s): **Univ. of Washington Pr.**

Kanto Productions, LLC, *(1-929956)* P.O. Box 630435, Simi Valley, CA 93063 USA Tel 805-584-9639; Fax: 310-507-0142; Toll Free: 800-335-2686
E-mail: info@atophill.com
Web site: http://www.atophill.com.

Kantourian Pr., *(0-9675888)* 3142 SW. Fairview Blvd., Portland, OR 97201 USA Tel 503-224-3331; Fax: 503-228-2290
E-mail: kanter@transport.com
Web site: http://www.transport.com/~kanter.

Kaplan Bks., *(0-684; 0-7432)* Orders Addr.: 100 Front St., Riverside, NJ 08075 USA Fax: 856-824-2289; Toll Free Fax: 800-943-9831; Toll Free: 800-223-2348; Edit Addr.: 1230 Avenue of the Americas, 1st Flr., New York, NY 10020 USA Tel 212-698-7000; Fax: 212-698-7007
E-mail: kaplan@simonandschuster.com
Web site: http://www.SimonSays.com
Dist(s): **Libros Sin Fronteras**
Simon & Schuster
Simon & Schuster, Inc.

Company

Kaplan Pr., *(0-9631833)* Orders Addr.: P.O. Box 6148, Chicago, IL 60680-6148 USA Tel 312-808-1497; Edit Addr.: 3124 S. Lowe Ave., Chicago, IL 60616 USA Do not confuse with Kaplan Pr., Inc. in Lewisville, NC
E-mail: skaplan@iit.edu.

†Kaplan Publishing, *(0-7931; 0-88462; 0-913864; 0-936894; 0-942103; 1-57410)* 1 Liberty Plaza, 24th Flr., New York, NY 10006 USA (SAN 211-2280) Tel 212-618-2400; Fax: 212-618-2498
E-mail: Charles.Holden@kaplan.com; Edwina.Lui@kaplan.com; Daniel.Russell@kaplan.com
Web site: http://www.kaplanpublishing.com
Dist(s): **Cranbury International**
Dearborn Financial Publishing, Inc.
JAGCO & Associates Inc.
MBI Distribution Services
Simon & Schuster
Simon & Schuster, Inc.; *CIP.*

Kaplan, Sheldon A. & Assocs,, *(0-9677993)* 730 Oakmount Ave., No. 905, Las Vegas, NV 89109 USA Tel 702-735-4935 (phone/fax); Toll Free: 888-527-5269
E-mail: skaplan33@hotmail.com
Web site: http://www.thecommitment.com.

Kar-Ben Copies, Incorporated *See* **Kar-Ben Publishing**

†Kar-Ben Publishing, *(0-929371; 0-930494; 1-58013)* Div. of Lerner Publishing Group, Orders Addr.: 1251 Washington Ave., N, Minneapolis, MN 55401 USA (SAN 201-7511) Tel 612-332-3344; Toll Free Fax: 800-332-1132; Toll Free: 800-452-7236
E-mail: info@lernerbooks.com
Web site: http://www.lernerbooks.com
Dist(s): **Lerner Publishing Group**; *CIP.*

Kardec, Allan Educational Society, *(0-9649907)* 5020 N. Eighth St., Philadelphia, PA 19120 USA Tel 215-329-4010 (phone/fax)
E-mail: akesbooks@cox.net
Web site: http://www.allan-kardec.org.

Karma Valley Music, *(0-9746011)* 505 Lovins Ln., Somerset, KY 42503 USA Tel 606-274-5194
E-mail: flo@floydlovins.com.

Karmichael Pr., *(0-9653966; 1-931770)* 440 Arrowhead Lake Trail, Westminster, SC 329693-6052 USA Tel 864-972-1618 (phone/fax); Toll Free: 888-443-9893
E-mail: books@karmichaelpress.com
Web site: http://www.karmichaelpress.com
Dist(s): **Baker & Taylor Bks.**
Book Wholesalers, Inc.
Brodart Co.
Follett Library Resources.

Karnak Co., *(0-9630951)* Orders Addr.: P.O. Box 497-158, Chicago, IL 60649-7158 USA Tel 773-684-5298; Edit Addr.: 1616 E. 50th Pl., No. 5-C, Chicago, IL 60615 USA
E-mail: tyrone.greer2@verizon.net.

Karosa Publishing, *(0-9706312)* 4636 Almond Ln., Boulder, CO 80301 USA Tel 303-484-8856 Do not confuse with companies with same or similar name in Lower Burnell, PA, Paradise Valley, AZ, Sheffield, PA, hailey, ID
E-mail: karpub@comcast.net
Web site: http://www.spadesbook.com.

Karsonkina, Tatiana, *(0-9779672)* P.O. Box 191, Brooklyn, NY 11223 USA.

Karuna Press *See* **Utopia Pr.**

Karyn Henley Resources *Imprint of* **Child Sensitive Communication, LLC**

Kasdan Communications, *(0-9673907)* 12200 Marion Ln.,W., No. 5125, Minnetonka, MN 55305-1312 USA Fax: 612-512-1820 ; *Imprints:* Kasdan Publishing (Kas Pubng)
E-mail: kasdan-comm@uswest.net
Web site: http://www.kasdancommunications.com.

Kasdan Publishing *Imprint of* **Kasdan Communications**

Kaseberg, W. G. Publishing, *(0-9761138)* 49 Red Bud Ln., Glen Carbon, IL 62034 USA Tel 618-288-5269; Fax: 618-288-0712
E-mail: wgkasebergpub@empowering.com.

Kashino Design *See* **Kashino Enterprises, Inc.**

Kashino Enterprises, Inc., *(0-9715709)* P.O. Box 27, Hailey, ID 83333 USA Tel 208-788-4500; Fax: 909-363-9765 ; *Imprints:* KEI Publishing (KEI Pub)
E-mail: mail@kashino.com
Web site: http://www.kashino.com.

Kasson Publishing, *(0-9729435)* 201 E. St., Elmo Rd., Austin, TX 78745-1217 USA Tel 512-447-1988 (phone/fax)
E-mail: publishing@kassonscastings.com
Web site: http://www.kassonscastings.com.

Kasten, Victoria, *(0-9788850)* 5465 Glencoe Ave., Webster, MN 55088 USA Tel 952-652-6065
E-mail: rkasten@integra.net
Web site: http://www.rosecrestalpacas.com.

Kat Tales Publishing, *(0-9744330)* 2515 Clarkson St., Denver, CO 80205 USA Tel 303-394-6380
E-mail: alluptojah@aol.com.

Katalin Media, *(0-9707619)* 236 E. 47th St., No. 33F, New York, NY 10017-2146 USA Tel 212-838-5191; Fax: 212-421-4606
E-mail: jreiser1@nyc.rr.com; jreiser@katalinmedia.com
Web site: http://www.katalinmedia.com
Dist(s): **Baker & Taylor Bks.**
Brodart Co.

KATastroPHE, *(0-9769698)* 6389 Florio St., Oakland, CA 94618 USA Tel 510-601-9631
E-mail: info@katastrophemusic.com
Web site: http://www.katastrophemusic.com.

Kathy's Pen, *(0-9777034)* 24 Ridgewood Pkwy, Newport News, VA 23608 USA Tel 757-872-6258
E-mail: regmcc@cox.net
Web site: http://www.kathyspen.com.

Kati Bee & Friends Publishing, *(0-9793760)* 8304 Limonite Ave. Suite D-3, Riverside, CA 92509 USA (SAN 853-2818) Tel 951-685-7256; Fax: 951-332-0436
E-mail: ContactKati@katibeeandfriends.com
Web site: http://www.katibeeandfriends.com.

Kat's Kids Kreation, A, *(0-9749516)* 413 Fairlawn Ave., Saint Louis, MO 63119-2614 USA Fax: 314-963-0494
E-mail: katbuck123@aol.com.

Katsoris, Nicholas C., *(0-9705100)* 235 W. 56th St., New York, NY 10019 USA Fax: 212-974-0786
E-mail: nkatsoris@aol.com
Dist(s): **Michigan State Univ. Pr.**

Kattan, Peter I., *(0-615)* 147-29 182nd St. Box AMM 2232, Springfield Gardens, NY 11413 USA Tel 718-553-8740
E-mail: pkattan@lsu.edu
Dist(s): **Lulu.com.**

Katydid Pubns., *(1-879945)* Orders Addr.: P.O. Box 526, Point Lookout, MO 65726 USA; Edit Addr.: Acacia Club Rd., Hollister, MO 65672 USA Tel 417-335-8134
E-mail: mgcameron@aol.com; kay@camerons-crag.com
Web site: http://www.katydid-publications.com.

Katydid Publishing LLC, *(0-9724272)* 5845 Eldorado, San Joaquin, CA 93660 USA Tel 559-693-4565 Do not confuse with Latydid Publishing in Mincie, IN.

Kaukini Ranch Pr., *(0-9643674)* P.O. Box 2462, Wailuku, HI 96793 USA Tel 808-244-3371; Fax: 808-395-0738.

Kav Bks. *Imprint of* **Royal Fireworks Publishing Co.**

Kav Books, Incorporated *See* **Royal Fireworks Publishing Co.**

Kawaida Publications *See* **Univ. of Sankore Pr., The**

Kawainui Pr., *(0-943357)* P.O. Box 163, Captain Cook, HI 96704 USA (SAN 668-6427) Tel 808-328-9126 (phone/fax)
E-mail: herbkane@kona.net
Web site: http://www.hitrade.com
Dist(s): **Booklines Hawaii, Ltd.**

Kay, Janet Consulting, *(0-9768786)* 115 Brighton Pk., Battle Creek, MI 49015 USA.

Kay Productions LLC, *(0-9707201)* Orders Addr.: 1115 W. Lincoln Ave., Suite 107, Yakima, WA 98902 USA Tel 509-853-0860; Fax: 509-853-0861; Toll Free: 800-619-4345; Edit Addr.: 732 Summitview Ave., Suite 628, Yakima, WA 98902 USA Do not confuse with Kay Productions, San Rafael, CA
E-mail: marketing@kayproductions.com
Web site: http://www.kayproductions.com.

Kay, Ronald, *(0-9745222)* P.O. Box 271, Hurricane, UT 84737 USA
E-mail: rangrron@infowest.com.

Kay-Dot Publishing Co., *(0-9663222)* 714 Manor Dr., Oxford, MS 38655 USA Tel 601-234-1970 (phone/fax)
E-mail: gowen2@teclink.net.

Kazi Pubns., Inc., *(0-933511; 0-935782; 1-56744; 1-871031; 1-930637)* 3023 W. Belmont Ave., Chicago, IL 60618 USA (SAN 162-3397) Tel 773-267-7001; Fax: 773-267-7002 ; *Imprints:* Library of Islam, Limited (Library of Islam); A B C International Group, Incorporated (A B C Intl)
E-mail: info@kazi.org
Web site: http://www.kazi.org.

KB Publishing, *(0-9768129)* 11 Running Fox Rd., Columbia, SC 29223 USA.

KBA, LLC, *(1-880931)* P.O. Box 3673, Carbondale, IL 62902 USA Tel 618-549-2893
E-mail: thriving@colorado.net
Web site: http://www.benziger.org.

KBCottontop Publishing, *(0-9719300)* 114 Lincoln Dr., Mayfield, KY 42066 USA
E-mail: kbcottontop@yahoo.com
Web site: http://www.kbcottontop.com.

KBR Mutti's Pubns., *(0-9762664)* P.O. Box 907431, Santa Barbara, CA 93190 USA
E-mail: kbrmuttis@cox.net
Web site: http://www.matthewsbox.com.

KBS, *(0-9710897)* 1089 Ruppert Rd., Marco Island, FL 34145-6806 USA Tel 239-394-9359; Fax: 239-389-0469
E-mail: richtuttle@earthlink.net
Web site: http://home.earthlink.net/~richtuttle.

K.C. Fox Publishing, *(0-9767078)* Div. of The Kerr Co., P.O. Box 5446, Takoma Park, MD 20913 USA Tel 301-434-9191
E-mail: publisher@kcfoxpublishing.com
Web site: http://www.poutorpurpose.com; http://www.kcfoxpublishing.com.

KCES *Imprint of* **Knowledge Concepts Pubns.**

KCI Sports, *(0-9758769; 0-9798729)* 3340 Whiting Ave., Suite 5, Stevens Point, WI 54481 USA Fax: 715-344-2668; Toll Free: 800-697-3756
Web site: http://www.kcisportsventures.com
Dist(s): **Advanced Marketing Services**
Partners Bk. Distributing, Inc.

KD Duet Publishing, *(0-9753192)* P.O. Box 652, Ashland, WI 54806 USA (SAN 255-9595) Tel 866-216-6459.

Keaster, Diane W. *See* **ZC Horses Series of Children's Bks.**

Keenan Tyler Paine, *(0-9740907)* 1715 Brae Burn Rd., Altadena, CA 91001 USA (SAN 255-3414)
E-mail: pmgoddard@earthlink.net.

Keene Publishing, *(0-9724853; 0-9766805; 0-9792371)* P.O. Box 54, Warwick, NY 10990-0054 USA (SAN 254-8631) Tel 845-987-7750; Fax: 845-987-7845 ; *Imprints:* Moo Press (Moo)
E-mail: dtinney@KeeneBooks.com; info@KeeneBooks.com; mbrowne@KeeneBooks.com
Web site: http://www.KeeneBooks.com
Dist(s): **Biblio Distribution.**

Keen's Martial Arts Academy, *(0-9702958; 1-60243)* Orders Addr.: 601 Upland Ave., Suite 209, Upland, PA 19015 USA (SAN 852-3002) Tel 610-872-4814 (phone/fax)
E-mail: LOHON6@msn.com
Web site: http://www.kmaa.info.

Keenspot Entertainment, *(0-9722350; 1-932775)* Orders Addr.: P.O. Box 110, Cresbard, SD 57435 USA Tel 605-324-3332; Toll Free: 888- 533-6776
E-mail: TeriCrosby@gmail.com
Web site: http://www.keenspot.com.

Keep Bks., *(1-893986)* Div. of The Ohio State Univ., 807 Kinnear Rd., Columbus, OH 43212 USA Tel 614-247-7878; Fax: 614-688-3980; Toll Free: 800-678-6484
E-mail: keepbooks@osu.edu
Web site: http://www.keepbooks.org.

Keep Coming Back *See* **Puddledancer Pr.**

Keep Empowering Yourself Successfully, *(0-9762009)* 5630 S. Division, Grand Rapids, MI 49548 USA Tel 616-261-3000; Fax: 616-261-3355
E-mail: monicaharris@grar.com
Web site: http://www.successfulkeys.com.

Keep Hope Alive, *(1-887831)* P.O. Box 270041, West Allis, WI 53227 USA Tel 414-545-6539; Fax: 414-329-0653
E-mail: khope@access4less.net
Web site: http://www.keephopealive.org
Dist(s): **New Leaf Distributing Co., Inc.**

Keep it Simple Bks., *(0-9630784; 0-9636255; 0-9710309)* P.O. Box 431, Murphys, CA 95247 USA (SAN 298-0061) Tel 209-728-0420; Fax: 209-728-0568
E-mail: kisjune@goldrush.com
Web site: http://www.keepitsimplebooks.com
Dist(s): **Independent Pubs. Group.**

Keep Me Company Publishing Co., *(0-9718632)* 214 Blue Ridge Rd., Plymouth Meeting, PA 19462 USA Tel 610-828-2641.

Keep Smiling, *(1-929146)* 245 Westhaven Cir., Geneva, IL 60134-4404 USA
E-mail: oldcoach77@aol.com
Web site: http://www.night.net/tucker/.

Keeping It Real Ministries *Imprint of* **Olive Print Pr. Ministry, The**

Keeping Track of Time, *(0-9667096; 0-9743784)* 4100 SW Temple, Suite 100, Salt Lake City, UT 84107 USA Tel 801-265-1400; Fax: 801-265-1771
E-mail: anchorapg@att.net
Web site: http://www.keepingtrackoftime.com.

Keepsafe, Inc., *(1-928772)* 1618 Main St., Baker, LA 70714 USA Tel 225-775-9421; Toll Free Fax: 888-213-9940; Toll Free: 888-300-7800
E-mail: keepsafe@ksafe.com
Web site: http://www.ksafe.com.

Keepsake Chronicles, *(0-9666156)* Orders Addr.: P.O. Box 156, Merrillan, WI 54754 USA Tel 715-333-7014; Edit Addr.: 501-10 N. Jackson, Merrillan, WI 54754-9048 USA
E-mail: hmb2@triwest.net.

Kegan Paul International, Ltd. (GBR) *(0-7103) Dist. by* **Col U Pr.**

Kehot Pubn. Society, *(0-8266)* Div. of Merkos L'Inyonei Chinuch, Orders Addr.: 291 Kingston Ave., Brooklyn, NY 11213 USA Tel 718-778-0226; Fax: 718-778-4148; Toll Free: 877-463-7567 (877-4MERKOS); Edit Addr.: 770 Eastern Pkwy., Brooklyn, NY 11213 USA (SAN 220-7060) Tel 718-604-2785
E-mail: orders@kehotonline.com
Web site: http://www.kehotonline.com.

KEI Publishing *Imprint of* **Kashino Enterprises, Inc.**

Kei-Vision, Inc., *(0-9754911)* P.O. Box 61524, Fort Myers, FL 33906 USA
Dist(s): **Biblio Distribution.**

Kell, Mary, *(0-9762303)* 1602 W. Easton St., Tulsa, OK 74127 USA Tel 918-382-9589
E-mail: bikegirl1602@cox.net
Web site: http://www.kellcalendars.com.

Keller, Christoph Revolver Verlag (DEU) *(3-936919; 3-934823; 3-9806326; 3-937577; 3-86588) Dist. by* **RAM Publications.**

Keller, J.J. & Assocs., Inc., *(0-934674; 1-57943; 1-877798; 1-59042; 0-9789130; 1-60287)* Orders Addr.: P.O. Box 368, Neenah, WI 54957-0368 USA (SAN 201-5056) Toll Free: 800-558-5011; Edit Addr.: 3003 W. Breezewood Ln., Neenah, WI 54957 USA
E-mail: sales@jjkeller.com
Web site: http://www.jjkeller.com.

Kelley, James *See* **Lypton Publishing**

KelleyGreenworks Publishing, *(0-9791029)* Orders Addr.: 607 Woodsman Way, Crownsville, MD 21032 USA
Web site: http://www.readysetgo-organic.com.

Kellum Cabin Pubs., *(0-9703191)* 37 Seton Dr., Bedford, NH 03110-5130 USA Tel 603-472-5966
E-mail: bosudary@aol.com.

Kelly, D Scott, *(0-9755442)* 208 W. Lincoln, Charlevoix, MI 49720 USA Tel 231-547-1144; Fax: 231-547-4970
E-mail: info@basesteencenter.org
Web site: http://www.basesteencenter.org.

Kelly, Kimberly, *(0-9747363)* 9801 E. Homestead Rd., Poplar, WI 54864 USA
E-mail: kimkellykimkelly@yahoo.com
Dist(s): **Partners Bk. Distributing, Inc.**

Kelsey Enterprises Publishing *See* **Cheval International**

Kelsey Publishing, *(0-944510; 0-9605824)* 456 E. 100 N., Provo, UT 84606-3208 USA (SAN 216-5775) Tel 801-373-3327 (phone/fax)
E-mail: mrkelsey2@attbi.com
Dist(s): **Adventurous Traveler Bookstore**
Alpenbooks Pr. LLC
Anderson News, LLC
Books West
Brigham Distribution
Canyon Country Distribution
Canyonlands Pubns.
Crown West Books
High Peak Bks.
Liberty Mountain
Nevada Pubns.
Peregrine Outfitters
Recreational Equipment, Inc.
Treasure Chest Bks.
Wide World of Maps, Inc.

Kemtec Educational Corp., *(1-877960)* 4780 Interstate Dr., Cincinnati, OH 45246-1112 USA Toll Free: 877-536-8321
E-mail: prekem@kemtecscience.com
Web site: http://www.kemtecscience.com.

Ken Pr., *(1-928771)* 4001 N. Paseo de los Rancheros, Tucson, AZ 85745 USA (SAN 299-9714) Tel 520-743-3200; Fax: 520-743-3210
E-mail: office@kenpress.com
Web site: http://www.kenpress.com
Dist(s): **Distributors, The.**

Kenamar, Inc., *(0-9753207)* P.O. Box 689, West Dundee, IL 60110-0689 USA
E-mail: kenamarpublish@aol.com
Dist(s): **Biblio Distribution.**

Kendall Publishing, *(0-9647633)* 6550 Delmonico Dr., No. 304, Colorado Springs, CO 80919 USA Tel 719-522-0880.

Kendall/Hunt Publishing Co., *(0-7872; 0-8403; 0-7575)* Orders Addr.: P.O. Box 1840, Dubuque, IA 52004-1840 USA; Edit Addr.: 4050 Westmark Dr., Dubuque, IA 52002 USA (SAN 203-9184) Tel 563-589-1000; Fax: 563-589-1046; Toll Free Fax: 800-772-9165; Toll Free: 800-228-0810
E-mail: orders@kendallhunt.com; kmalone@kendallhunt.com
Web site: http://www.kendallhunt.com.

Kendar Publishing Company *See* **Kendar Publishing, Inc.**

Kendar Publishing, Inc., *(1-889506)* 310 5th St., Suite 101, Racine, WI 53403 USA Tel 262-632-4070; Fax: 262-632-7089; Toll Free: 866-632-7040.

Kendrick, G. David Properties, *(0-9740227)* Orders Addr.: 534 Oakley Rd., Mountain Home, AR 72653 USA Fax: 870-404-7635
E-mail: gdavidkendrick@yahoo.com.

Kennedy, Byron & Company *See* **Southern Heritage Pr., Inc.**

Kennedy Christian Publishing, *(0-9743136)* P.O. Box 5385, Texarkana, TX 75505-5385 USA
E-mail: knndytgr@aol.com.

Kennel Club Bks. Inc., *(1-59378)* 308 Main St., Allenhurst, NJ 07711 USA Tel 732-531-1995; Fax: 732-531-2402
E-mail: dcalhoun@kennelclubbooks.com
Dist(s): **Perseus Distribution.**

Kennesaw Publishing, *(0-9664424)* 232 Rainbow Dr. # 13204, Livingston, TX 77399-2032 USA
E-mail: kenpub@worldnet.att.net.

Kensington Bks. *Imprint of* **Kensington Publishing Corp.**

Kensington Publishing Corp., *(0-7860; 0-8065; 0-8184; 0-8217; 1-55817; 1-57566; 0-7582; 1-4201; 1-59983; 1-60183; 1-60349)* 850 Third Ave., New York, NY 10022-6222 USA Tel 212-407-1500; Fax: 212-935-0699; Toll Free: 800-221-2647; 499 North Canon Dr., Beverly Hills, CA 90210 Tel 310-887-7082 ; *Imprints:* Citadel Press (Citadel Pr); Stuart, Lyle (L Stuart); Pinnacle Books (Pinncle Kensgtn); Kensington Books (Knsington); Dafina (Dafina)
E-mail: jmclean@kensingtonbooks.com
Web site: http://www.kensingtonbooks.com
Dist(s): **Penguin Group (USA) Inc.**
Sony CONNECT, Inc.
Worldwide Media Service, Inc.

Kent Fine Art *See* **Kent Gallery**

Kent Gallery, *(1-878607)* P.O. Box 684, New York, NY 10012-0013 USA
E-mail: kent@kentgallery.com
Web site: http:///www.kentgallery.com.

†Kent State Univ. Pr., *(0-87338)* Orders Addr.: c/o BookMasters, Inc., 30 Amberwood Pkwy., Ashland, OH 44805 USA Tel 419-281-1802; Fax: 419-281-6883; Toll Free: 800-247-6553; Edit Addr.: 307 Lowry Hall, Kent, OH 44242-0001 USA (SAN 201-0437) Tel 330-672-7913; Fax: 330-672-3104
E-mail: scash@kent.edu
Web site: http://www.kentstateuniversitypress.com
Dist(s): **BookMasters, Inc.**
Partners Bk. Distributing, Inc.; *CIP.*

Kepler Pr., *(0-9713770)* Orders Addr.: P.O. Box 400326, Cambridge, MA 02140 USA (SAN 255-6014) Tel 617-576-1577
E-mail: ealex@keplerpress.com
Web site: http://www.keplerpress.com
Dist(s): **New Leaf Distributing Co., Inc.**

KerbieKo, *(0-9664852)* 6212 Sierra Ct., Arlington, TX 76016 USA Tel 817-572-5920
E-mail: kerbieko@aol.com.

Kern-O'Neil Pubns., *(0-9664787)* P.O. Box 104, Sisters, OR 97759 USA Fax: 541-549-1057.

Kerpluggo Bks. LLC, *(0-9762429)* 1015 W. Webster Ave., Suite 3, Chicago, IL 60614 USA Tel 773-665-8075
E-mail: mbwillian2@yahoo.com.

Kerr, Alex, *(0-9753076)* 145 Lincoln Rd. Apt. 2L, Brooklyn, NY 11225-4017 USA
E-mail: alexkerr@earthlink.net.

Kerr, Charles H. Publishing Co., *(0-88286)* 1740 W. Greenleaf Ave., Chicago, IL 60626 USA (SAN 207-7043) Tel 773-465-7774 (orders); 847-328-2132 (orders); Fax: 773-472-7857 (orders)
E-mail: arcane@ripco.com
Web site: http://www.charleshkerr.net
Dist(s): **AK Pr. Distribution.**

Kerr Company, The *See* **K.C. Fox Publishing**

Kerr, Dana, 2740 Toro Vista Ct., Morgan Hill, CA 95037 USA Tel 407-778-8701.

Kerr, Justin & Shelley, *(0-9766408)* 10735 Atascadero Ave., Atascadero, CA 93422-5723 USA
Web site: http://www.kirraandrincon.com.

Kerr, Kimberly Pr., *(0-9672073)* P.O. Box 63, Sewickley, PA 15143 USA Tel 412-741-7720; Fax: 412-741-3656
E-mail: kkraindrop@aol.com.

Kessinger Publishing Company *See* **Kessinger Publishing, LLC**

Kessinger Publishing, LLC, *(0-7661; 0-922802; 1-56459; 1-4179; 1-4191; 1-4192; 1-4253; 1-4254; 1-4286; 1-4304; 1-4325; 1-4326; 0-548)* Orders Addr.: P.O. Box 1404, Whitefish, MT 59937 USA (SAN 251-4621)
E-mail: bip@kessinger.net
Web site: http://www.kessinger.net
Dist(s): **Lightning Source, Inc.**

Kesterson & Associates *See* **Big Valley Publishing**

Kestrel Pubns., *(0-9628472)* 1811 Stonewood Dr., Dayton, OH 45432-4002 USA Tel 937-426-5110; Fax: 937-320-1832; Toll Free: 800-314-4678 (orders only)
E-mail: invisiblei@aol.com
Web site: http://www.invink.com
Dist(s): **Baker & Taylor Bks.**

Ketab Corp., *(1-883819; 1-59584)* Orders Addr.: 1419 Westwood Blvd., Los Angeles, CA 90024 USA (SAN 107-7791) Tel 310-477-7477; Fax: 310-444-7176; Toll Free: 800-367-4726
E-mail: ketab@ketab.com
Web site: http://www.ketab.com
Dist(s): **Bookazine Co., Inc.**

Ketabe Gooya Publishing LLC, *(1-933429)* Orders Addr.: 6400 Canoga Ave., Suite 355, Woodland Hills, CA 91367 USA Tel 818-346-8338; Toll Free: 800-515-0069
E-mail: nasser@farrokh.us
Web site: http://www.ketabegooya.com.

Keter Sion, *(0-9760296)* 1914 E. 9th St., Brooklyn, NY 11223 USA.

Ketman Publishing *See* **Wooster Bk. Co., The**

Key Answer Products, Inc., *(0-9642823)* 108 S. Third St., Suite 4, Bloomingdale, IL 60108 USA (SAN 255-805X) Tel 630-893-4007; Fax: 630-893-4030; Toll Free: 800-539-1233
E-mail: dcowhey@ci-inc.com
Web site: http://www.ci-inc/what/what.htm.

Key Curriculum Pr., *(0-913684; 1-55953; 1-60440)* 1150 65th St., Emeryville, CA 94608 USA (SAN 202-6538) Tel 510-595-7000; Fax: 510-595-7045; Toll Free: 800-995-6284 (orders)
E-mail: editorial@keypress.com; customer.service@keypress.com; sales@keypress.com; hrudelitsch@keypress.com
Web site: http://www.keypress.com
Dist(s): **Springer.**

Key Porter Bks. (CAN) *(0-88619; 0-919493; 0-919630; 1-55013; 1-55263; 1-85375; 1-55356)* *Dist. by* **Perseus Dist.**

Key Publishers, Incorporated *See* **City Creek Pr., Inc.**

Key-A-Teese Production *Imprint of* **Word For Word Publishing Co.**

Keyboarding First, LLC, *(0-9768426)* 6919 Prairie Dr., Middleton, WI 53562-5356 USA Tel 608-836-4404 (phone/fax); Fax: 608-836-4405
E-mail: psm.janet@tds.net.

KEYGARD, *(0-9767086)* Orders Addr.: 7887 Broadway, Suite 506, San Antonio, TX 78209 USA Tel 210-829-5074; Fax: 210-829-5132
E-mail: bhkeyser@aol.com.

Keyhill Publishing Co., *(0-9718514)* N. 11069 Boatlanding 10 Rd., Athelstane, WI 54104 USA.

Keys For Kids Publishing Co., *(0-9725827)* 1256 Cranwood Square N., Columbus, OH 43229-1341 USA Tel 614-431-5311
E-mail: kfd43229@aol.com
Web site: http://www.keys.decisivenet.com.

Keysquake Music, *(0-9760837)* 42 Blackfoot Ct., Guilford, CT 06437 USA
E-mail: bgillie48@yahoo.com
Web site: http://www.briangillie.com.

Keytochange Publishing, Inc., *(0-9729798)* 7484 University Ave. Ste. T, La Mesa, CA 91941-6030 USA
E-mail: sjones@keytochange.com
Web site: http://www.keytochange.com.

Khanna, Rachel, *(0-9779568)* 163 John St., Greenwich, CT 06831 USA (SAN 850-7260).

KHP Industries, *(0-9679220; 0-9747680; 0-9767914; 0-9799881)* 306 Mountain Rd., Effort, PA 18330 USA; P.O. Box 588, Effort, PA 18330 ; *Imprints:* Black Death Books (Black Death Bks)
E-mail: blackdeath@khpindustries.com
Web site: http://www.khpindustries.com
Dist(s): **Baker & Taylor Bks.**

Kibo, *(0-9660593)* P.O. Box 19202, Reno, NV 89511 USA Toll Free Fax: 877-852-0390
E-mail: michellekibo@hotmail.com
Dist(s): **Smith Novelty Co., Inc.**

Kichita Productions, *(0-9672533)* 2227 Shadehill Ct., Tampa, FL 33612-5024 USA (SAN 254-3621) Tel 813-931-5148
E-mail: kichitaproductions@yahoo.com
Web site: http://www.sites.netscapes.net/kichita001.

KICK ASS Media, *(0-9762928)* 12358 Coit Rd., PMB No. 317, Dallas, TX 75251-2308 USA (SAN 256-3061) Tel 800-692-6652; Fax: 877-692-7441
E-mail: sales@kickassmedia.com.

Kid Beowulf *Imprint of* **Lexpress**

Kid by Kid, Incorporated, *(0-9745496)* 54249 Myrica Dr., Macomb, MI 48042 USA Tel 586-781-2345 (phone/fax)
E-mail: kidbykid@comcast.net
Web site: http://www.crystalkids.net.

Kid Concoctions Co., *(0-9661088; 0-9705976)* Orders Addr.: 14761 Pearl Rd., PMB 161, Strongsville, OH 44149 USA (SAN 299-4720) Tel 440-572-8486; Fax: 440-238-4453
E-mail: KidConcoct@aol.com; DanitaP@aol.com
Web site: http://www.kidconcoctions.com
Dist(s): **American Bk. Co.**
Baker & Taylor Bks.

Kid Galaxy, Incorporated *See* **Dolls Corp.**

Kid Prep, Inc., *(1-58312)* 6942 FM 1960 E-132, Humble, TX 77346 USA Tel 281-852-5261; Fax: 281-852-4901 ; *Imprints:* Little Chameleon Books (Little Chameleon)
E-mail: customerservice@kidprep.com
Web site: http://www.kidprep.com.

Kid Safety Plus, *(0-9676448)* 13031 Holmes Point Dr., NE, Kirkland, WA 98034 USA Tel 425-820-2971; Fax: 425-820-7633
E-mail: jimassea@aol.com.

KiD Sounds, *(0-9767650)* P.O. Box 13888, Las Vegas, NV 89112-1888 USA
Web site: http://www.kid-sounds.com.

KidBiz 3000 *See* **Achieve3000**

KidBoard, Inc., *(0-9658251; 1-891698)* 7416 Washington Ave., S., Eden Prairie, MN 55344 USA Toll Free: 800-926-3066
E-mail: kidboard@aol.com
Web site: http://www.kidboard.com.

Kidderature Publishing, *(0-9729703)* P.O. Box 612, Hammondsport, NY 14840 USA Tel 607-292-3026
E-mail: bobhicks@citlink.net
Web site: http://www.kidderature.com.

Kiddy Chronicles Publishing (CAN) *(0-9699203; 0-9733994)* *Dist. by* **Firefly Bks Limited.**

Kidhaven *Imprint of* **Thomson Gale**

Kidrich Corp., *(0-9761051)* 347 5th Ave., Suite 610, New York, NY 10016 USA Tel 718-767-5135; Toll Free: 800-231-7385
Web site: http://www.kidrich.com.

Kids 4 Ever, *(0-9764433)* P.O. Box 1784, Holland, MI 49422 USA Tel 616-566-1231
E-mail: kids4ever@charter.net
Web site: http://www.kids4everbooks.com.

Kids Ahead Bks. *Imprint of* **World Ahead Media**

Kids Bks., Pubs., *(0-9672972)* 1072 Via Bolzano, Goleta, CA 93117 USA Tel 805-967-0886; Fax: 805-964-0892
E-mail: maryrees@silcom.com.

Kids Can *Imprint of* **Proactive Publishing**

Kids Can Pr., Ltd. (CAN) *(0-919964; 0-921103; 1-55074; 1-55337; 1-55453)* *Dist. by* **Wybel Market.**

Kids Children & Teens World 2000 & Beyond, *(0-9747543)* Orders Addr.: P.O. Box 385, Brandywine, MD 20613 USA Fax: 301-372-9979; Edit Addr.: 8300 Belding Ct., Brandywine, MD 20613 USA
E-mail: djospeh301@aol.com.

K.I.D.S. Church *Imprint of* **CharismaLife Pubs.**

Kids Count, *(0-9704252)* 1155 Hillsboro Mile, Unit 201, Hillsboro Beach, FL 33062 USA Fax: 954-427-4535
E-mail: gpdearing@aol.com.

Kid's Creative Classics *Imprint of* **BrassHeart Music**

Kids, Critters & Country Publishing, *(0-9755200)* P.O. Box 866874, Plano, TX 75086-6874 USA
E-mail: jlarsen@chasewest.com
Web site: http://www.kidscrittersandcountry.com.

Kids Donate, Inc., *(0-9754131)* 221 Chesley Ln., Chapel Hill, NC 27514 USA Tel 919-967-0882.

Kids Eat Publishing, *(1-928883)* Div. of Studio Elizabeth Carpenter, Inc., 284 W. 12th St., No. 2, New York, NY 10014 USA Tel 212-929-0734; Fax: 212-989-5021
E-mail: kidseat@ix.netcom.com
Dist(s): **Koen-Levy Bk. Wholesalers LLC.**

Kids For Health, Inc., *(0-9759517; 1-933847)* P.O. Box 326, Springdale, AR 72763 USA Tel 479-756-9551; Fax: 479-756-0949.

Kid's Fun Pr., *(0-9772848)* 2708 Coastal Range Way, Lutz, FL 33559 USA (SAN 257-2168) Tel 813-786-9457
E-mail: kidsfunpress@verizon.net
Web site: http://ijbooks.com
Dist(s): **Independent Pubs. Group.**

Kids Go Europe, Inc., *(0-9772699)* P.O. Box 4014, Menlo Park, CA 94026 USA Tel 650-743-7404
E-mail: info@kidsgoeurope.com
Web site: http://www.kidsgoeurope.com.

Kids in Ministry International, *(0-9767647)* 511 S. Anderson St., Bismarck, ND 58504 USA
Web site: http://www.kidsinministry.com.

Kids in the Clouds, *(0-9723314)* 31602 37th Ave., SW, Federal Way, WA 98023 USA Tel 206-854-2623; Fax: 253-838-2696
E-mail: j102268@aol.com
Web site: http://www.kidsintheclouds.com.

Kids Life Pr., *(0-9755348)* P.O. Box 3020, Pismo Beach, CA 93448-3020 USA Fax: 920-757-9266; Toll Free: 800-262-8973
E-mail: tuzee@charter.net.

Kid's Literature Pr., *(0-9704069)* 4009 Old Deton Rd., No. 114-123, Carrollton, TX 75007-1021 USA
E-mail: sfetters@homemail.com
Web site: http://www.kidslit.com.

Kids Love Pubns., *(0-9663457; 0-9726854; 0-9774434)* 1985 Dina Ct., Powell, OH 43065 USA Tel 614-792-6451; Fax: 614-792-3595
E-mail: info@kidslovepublications.com
Web site: www.KidsLoveTravel.com
Dist(s): **Baker & Taylor Bks.**
Partners Bk. Distributing, Inc.

Kids Productions *See* **Midlands Marketing**

Kid's Shelf, *(0-9729339)* 19600 Baker Rd., Gambier, OH 43022 USA Tel 740-247-2427.

Kids1st Bks. *Imprint of* **BC Publishing**

Kidsafety of America, *(1-884413)* 17647 Buttercup Ct., Chino Hills, CA 91709-3263 USA
E-mail: peter@kidsafetystore.com
Web site: http://www.kidsafetystore.com.

Kidsbooks, Inc., *(0-942025; 1-56156; 1-58865)* Orders Addr.: P.O. Box 81388, Wellesley Hls, MA 02481-0004 USA; Edit Addr.: 230 5th Ave. Ste. 413, New York, NY 10001-7895 USA (SAN 666-3729)
E-mail: sales@kidsbooks.com
Web site: http://www.kidsbooks.com.

Company

Kidscope, Inc., *(0-9647798)* 2045 Peachtree Rd NE Ste. 150, Atlanta, GA 30309-1405 USA.

Kidskills America *Imprint of* **Kidskills International**

Kidskills International, *(0-9710641)* 1031 Cahoon Rd., Westlake, OH 44145-1232 USA Tel 440-835-5071 (phone/fax) ; *Imprints:* Kidskills America (Kidskills Amer)
E-mail: kidskills@wideopenwest.com; info@kidskills.com
Web site: http://www.kidskills.com.

KidSparks *Imprint of* **Trend Enterprises, Inc.**

KIDSRIGHTS *Imprint of* **JIST Publishing**

Kidsrights, 10100 Park Cedar Dr., Charlotte, NC 28210 USA (SAN 299-2809) Tel 704-541-0100; Fax: 704-541-0113; Toll Free: 888-970-5437 Do not confuse with Kidsrights, Mount Dora, FL.

Kidstalk, LLC, *(0-9776144)* P.O. Box 520, Sherman, TX 75091 USA (SAN 257-7992) Tel 903-436-0858; Fax: 903-893-1614
E-mail: kidstalk@cableone.net
Web site: http://www.kidstalkmag.com.

Kidstory Pr., *(0-9772231)* P.O. Box 75, Brighton, MI 48116-0075 USA Tel 517-204-9030; Fax: 484-346-4303
E-mail: kidstorypress@comcast.net
Web site: http://www.kidstorypress.home.comcast.net.

KidStreet LLC, *(0-615)* c/o Miriam Shankman, Brand Street, 211 Glen Ridge Ave., Montclair, NJ 07042 USA Tel 973-744-5800; Fax: 973-744-7373; Toll Free Fax: 866-543-7878.

Kid-Tech. Specialties, *(0-9708670)* 2607 Century Oaks Ln., Charlotte, NC 28262-3164 USA Tel 704-596-9792.

Kidwick Bks., *(0-9703809)* 363 S. Saltair Ave., First Fl., Los Angelas, CA 90049 USA Tel 310-471-2472; Fax: 310-861-8111
E-mail: mail@kidwick.com
Web site: http://www.kidwick.com
Dist(s): **National Bk. Network.**

Kidz & Katz Publishing Co., *(1-883371)* 752 Brandon Pl., Wheeling, IL 60090 USA Fax: 708-860-0513.

Kidz By Dezign Pr., Inc., *(0-9771030)* 1881 Kingston Way, Lawrenceville, GA 30044 USA (SAN 256-7121) Tel 770-962-2181; Fax: 678-615-2247; Toll Free: 800-719-5439
E-mail: info@slumbergirls.com
Web site: http://www.slumbergirls.com.

Kidz Character, LLC, *(0-9677751)* 1876 Pony Farm Rd., Jacksonville, NC 28540 USA Tel 910-346-7555
E-mail: sjdavis@gibralter.net; kidzcharacter@yahoo.com
Web site: http://www.kidzcharacter.com.

Kidz Krave Inc., *(0-9764144)* P.O. Box 88350, Houston, TX 77288 USA
Web site: http://www.prettypainful.com.

Kidzpoetz Publishing, *(0-9760220)* P.O. Box 621, New City, NY 10956 USA Tel 845-536-5505; Fax: 845-323-4272
E-mail: robertkurkela@kidzpoetz.com
Web site: http://www.kidzpoetz.com
Dist(s): **Baker & Taylor Bks.**
Quality Bks., Inc.

Kidzup Entertainment (CAN) *(1-894281; 1-894677) Dist. by* **Penton Overseas.**

Kidzup Productions, *(1-894281; 1-894677)* 555 VT Rte. 78, Suite 146, Box 717, Swanton, VT 05488 USA Toll Free: 888-321-5437 (888-321-KIDS)
E-mail: info@kidzup.com
Web site: http://www.kidzup.com
Dist(s): **Penton Overseas, Inc.**

Kienzle, Patricia Taylor, *(1-890798)* 3525 Northwood, Fayetteville, AR 72704 USA Tel 501-521-0076; Fax: 501-521-4973
E-mail: acotu@msn.com.

Kierstead, Nancy H., *(0-9668673)* P.O. Box 185, Waban, MA 02468-0002 USA.

Kies Publishing Co., *(0-9767437)* Orders Addr.: P.O. Box 923572, Sylmar, CA 91392-3572 USA Tel 818-367-8416
E-mail: kies@kies.org
Web site: http://www.kies.org.

Kilgore, Mark, *(0-9705365)* 712 Woodbriar Ln., Saint Charles, MO 63303-5439 USA.

Kilimanjaro Co., *(0-9708007)* 2890 Springhill Rd., Bozeman, MT 59718 USA Tel 406-586-3233; Fax: 406-582-0308.

Killer Sports Publishing, *(1-933135)* Orders Addr.: P.O. Box 862, Berea, OH 44017 USA Tel 440-239-1854; Edit Addr.: 201 S. Rocky River Rd., Berea, OH 44017 USA
Web site: http://www.killersports.com.

Killingbeck, Dale, *(0-9762758)* 18300 Tustin Rd., Tustin, MI 49677 USA Tel 231-829-3084.

Kilsby, Raymond *See* **RK Enterprises, Inc.**

Kim, Michael, *(0-9664003)* 216 Cotton Ridge Rd., Winchester, VA 22603 USA
E-mail: anthem1@usa.net.

Kimber Stories, *(0-9767773)* Orders Addr.: P.O. Box 143, Woodlake, CA 93286 USA; Edit Addr.: 37811 Millwood Dr., Woodlake, CA 93286 USA
E-mail: kimberstories@yahoo.com.

Kimberlite Publishing Co., *(0-9632675)* 44091 Olive Ave., Hemet, CA 92544-2609 USA Tel 951-927-7726 Do not confuse with Kimberlite Publishing, Ventura, CA
E-mail: frumpypapa@yahoo.com.

Kimberly Pr., LLC, *(0-9668611)* 100 Westport Ave., Norwalk, CT 06851 USA (SAN 251-2483) Tel 203-750-6101; Fax: 203-846-3472.

Kimble, George J., *(0-9767024)* 4941 Hickory Woods E., Antioch, TN 37013 USA
Web site: http://www.theroadpoet.com.

Kimbo Educational, *(0-937124; 1-56346)* Div. of United Sound Arts, Inc., Orders Addr.: P.O. Box 477, Long Branch, NJ 07740 USA (SAN 630-1592) Tel 732-870-3340 (phone/fax); Toll Free: 800-631-2187; Edit Addr.: 10 N. Third Ave., Long Branch, NJ 07740 USA
E-mail: kimboed@aol.com
Web site: http://www.kimboed.com
Dist(s): **Midwest Tape**
Rounder Kids Music Distribution.

Kind Critter Junction, *(0-9752842)* P.O. Box 30249, Indianapolis, IN 46220 USA Toll Free: 888-366-3525
E-mail: info@kindcritterjunction.com
Web site: http://www.kindcritterjunction.com.

KinderBach L.L.C., *(0-9773005)* P.O. Box 336, Hudson, IA 50643 USA (SAN 257-2397) Toll Free: 866-988-9814
E-mail: info@kinderbach.com
Web site: http://www.kinderbach.com.

Kindermusik International, *(0-945613; 1-931127; 1-58987)* Orders Addr.: P.O. Box 26575, Greensboro, NC 27415 USA (SAN 247-3747) Tel 336-273-3363; Fax: 336-273-2023; Toll Free: 800-628-5687; Edit Addr.: 6204 Corporate Park Dr., Browns Summit, NC 27214 USA (SAN 247-3755)
E-mail: info@kindermusik.com
Web site: http://www.kindermusik.com.

KinderWord, *(0-9642613)* 9218 Crownwood Rd., Ellicott City, MD 21042 USA Tel 410-750-3666
Dist(s): **Baker & Taylor Bks.**

Kindred Press *See* **Kindred Productions**

Kindred Productions, *(0-919797; 0-921788)* Orders Addr.: 315 S. Lincoln St., Hillsboro, KS 67063 USA Tel 316-947-3151; Fax: 316-947-3266; Toll Free: 800-545-7322
E-mail: kindred@mbconf.ca
Web site: http://www.mbconf.org/kindred.htm
Dist(s): **Spring Arbor Distributors, Inc.**

Kinfolk Research Pr., *(0-9712564)* P.O. Box 6303, Plymouth, MI 48170 USA Tel 734-454-1883
E-mail: KinfolkPress@aol.com
Web site: http://cheekfamilychronicles.homestead.com/CheekFamilyChronicles.html.

King Joe Educational Enterprises, Inc., *(0-9728596; 0-9773902)* Orders Addr.: P.O. Box 86, Los Alamitos, CA 90720 USA Tel 562-430-8600; Fax: 562-598-5940; Toll Free: 866-818-5464 (866-818-KING); Edit Addr.: 3112 Inverness Dr., Los Almitos, CA 90720 USA
E-mail: lindarodgers@kingjoe.com
Web site: http://www.kingjoe.com.

King, Joel, *(0-9787820)* 547 McLean Ave., Hopkinsville, KY 42240 USA
E-mail: joelk3@bellsouth.net.

King RIT - ACKS Pubs., *(0-9714446)* 5584 Hwy 41 S., Oconto, WI 54153 USA Tel 920-834-3927
E-mail: thekings12@juno.com.

King St Bks./Stabler-Leadbeater Apothecary Museum, *(0-9763945)* 410 S Fairfax St., Alexandria, VA 22314 USA Fax: 703-456-7890
Web site: http://apothecarymuseum.org.

King, Terri Ann *See* **Paulus Publishing**

Kingdom Ambassador Ministries, *(0-9714167)* P.O. Box 1196, Laurel, MD 20725-1196 USA Tel 301-651-1736; Fax: 801-327-5554
E-mail: hishands@kingdomambassador.com
Web site: http://www.kingdomambassador.com.

Kingdom Pr., *(0-9659952)* 1869 Top Rd., Mountain Grove, MO 65711 USA (SAN 254-1106) Tel 417-926-6420; 417-926-3340; Toll Free: 800-707-3640 (Pin 8126) Do not confuse with companies with the same name in Dublin, NH, Santa Rosa, CA, Stone Mountain, GA
E-mail: navajean@fidnet.com.

Kingdom Publications *See* **International Preterist Assn.**

Kingdom Publishers *See* **Cathedral of the Holy Spirit**

Kingdom Publishing Co., *(0-9765636)* 17100 Halsted St., Harvey, IL 60426-6131 USA.

Kingdom Publishing Group, Inc., *(0-9745324; 0-9772964; 0-9792074; 0-9796130)* P.O. Box 505, Ashland, VA 23005 USA Tel 804-515-9100; Fax: 804-515-9101; 6001 Lakeside Ave., Suite 25, Richmond, VA 23228
Web site: http://www.kingdompublishing.org.

Kingdom Sound Pubs., *(0-9662666)* Orders Addr.: P.O. Box 372428, Decatur, GA 30037 USA Tel 404-328-1166; Edit Addr.: 3622 Summit Trace, Suite 400, Decatur, GA 30034 USA
E-mail: kingdomsound@aol.com.

Kingdom Talk Publishing, Incorporated *See* **Rapha Publishing**

Kingfisher *Imprint of* **Houghton Mifflin Co. Trade & Reference Div.**

Kingfisher Bks., *(0-9662218)* Orders Addr.: P.O. Box 4628, Helena, MT 59604 USA Tel 406-442-2168; Toll Free: 800-879-4576; Edit Addr.: 2480 Broadway, No. 18D, Helena, MT 59601 USA
Dist(s): **Houghton Mifflin Co. Trade & Reference Div.**
Partners/West.

KingMaker Bks. LLC, *(0-9744870)* 13315 E. Cindy St., Chandler, AZ 85225 USA
E-mail: mbogumill@juno.com.

King's Bookshelf Pubns., *(0-9673806)* 35 Whitehall St., Belleville, PA 17004 USA Tel 717-483-6476
E-mail: Kingsbookshelf@juno.com.

King's High Way Ministries, Inc., The, *(0-9745177; 0-9752534; 0-9753593; 0-9760994; 0-9795136)* Orders Addr.: P.O. Box 3111, Coeur d'Alene, ID 83854 USA Tel 208-676-9796; Fax: 208-664-0086; Toll Free: 866-775-5464; Edit Addr.: 844 Third St., Coeur d'Alene, ID 83814 USA
E-mail: debbie@kingshighway.org
Web site: http://www.kingshighway.org.

King's Kids Trading Cards, Inc., *(0-9703880)* P.O. Box 923271, Sylmar, CA 91392-3271 USA Fax: 818-364-2443; Toll Free: 800-910-2690
E-mail: visioninprint@brandx.net
Web site: http://www.kingskidscards.com.

Kingsbridge Pr. *Imprint of* **Modern Learning Pr.**

Kingsway Pubns. (GBR) *(0-85476; 0-86065; 0-902088; 1-84291) Dist. by* **STL Dist NA.**

Kinkachoo Pr., The, *(0-9729285)* P.O. Box 9742, Newark, DE 19714-9742 USA
Web site: http://www.michaelmade.com/kinkachoo.

Kinkajou Pr. *Imprint of* **Artemesia Publishing, LLC**

Kinney Brothers Publishing, *(0-9702889)* 801 Range View Way, Knoxville, TN 37920 USA Tel 423-609-1672 (phone/fax)
E-mail: kinneybrothers@hotmail.com.

Kinte Kids, Inc, *(0-9707176)* 2900 Macon Ct., Suwanee, GA 30024-2891 USA
E-mail: kintekids@mindspring.com
Web site: http://www.kintekids.com.

Kip Kids of New York, *(0-9789384)* 85 Christopher St., Suite No. 5B, New York, NY 10014 USA
E-mail: KipKids@aol.com
Web site: http://www.KipKids.com.

Kip Kids of NY *See* **Kip Kids of New York**

Kirkbride, B.B. Bible Co., Inc., *(0-88707; 0-934854)* P.O. Box 606, Indianapolis, IN 46206-0606 USA (SAN 169-2372) Tel 317-633-1900; Fax: 317-633-1444; Toll Free: 800-428-4385
E-mail: hyperbible@aol.com
Web site: http://www.kirkbride.com
Dist(s): **Anchor Distributors**
Appalachian Bible Co.
Spring Arbor Distributors, Inc.

Kirkham, Sharon Birlson, *(0-9767100)* 1530 Michigan Ave., La Porte, IN 46350 USA.

Kisco Pubns., *(1-893566)* P.O. Box 405, Palermo, CA 95968 USA Tel 530-532-0953.

KISEIDO, *(4-906574)* 2255 29th St., Suite 4, Santa Monica, CA 90405 USA Toll Free: 800-988-6463
E-mail: sales@kiseido.com
Web site: http://www.kiseido.com/.

Kiss A Me Productions, Inc., *(1-890343)* 90 Garfield Ave., Sayville, NY 11782 USA Tel 516-589-4886; Fax: 516-218-8927; Toll Free: 888-547-7263.

Kissing Deer Pr., LLC, *(0-9703704)* 1223 Wilshire Blvd., No. 897, Santa Monica, CA 90403-5400 USA (SAN 253-410X) Tel 310-288-1655; Fax: 310-451-5921
E-mail: Cdiamondboyce@aol.com
Web site: http://www.littlehaha.com.

KIT (Koninklijk Instituut voor de Tropen) (NLD) *(90-6832; 90-74822) Dist. by* **Stylus Pub VA.**

KITA Pubns., *(0-9701301)* P.O. Box 13891, Scottsdale, AZ 85267 USA Tel 480-661-8199
Web site: http://www.kitakids.com.

Kitchen, Denis Publishing Co., *(0-9710080; 0-9788851)* P.O. Box 2250, Amherset, MA 01004-2250 USA (SAN 851-8467) Tel 413-259-1627; Fax: 413-259-1812
E-mail: info@deniskitchen.com; publishing@deniskitchen.com
Web site: http://www.deniskitchen.com.

Kitchen Table Pubs., *(0-9707685)* Orders Addr.: 136 Cook-McDonald Rd., Collins, MS 39428 USA Tel 601-765-8329; Edit Addr.: 802 S. Cherry St., Collins, MS 39428 USA Tel 601-765-8329
E-mail: knight3230@bellsouth.net.

Kitkooh Pubns., *(0-9718474)* 526 W. 775 N. Creekview, Centerville, UT 84014-1345 USA Tel 801-298-8631
E-mail: kitkooh@xmission.com
Web site: http://www.kitkooh.com.

KITS Publishing, *(0-9643177; 0-9778797)* 2359 E. Bryan Ave., Salt Lake City, UT 84108 USA Tel 801-582-2517; Fax: 801-582-2540
Dist(s): **Perseus Distribution**
Todd Communications.

Kitty Media *Imprint of* **Media Blasters, Inc.**

Kiva Publishing, Inc., *(1-885772)* 21731 E. Buckskin Dr., Walnut, CA 91789 USA Tel 909-595-6833; Fax: 909-860-5424; Toll Free: 800-634-5482
E-mail: kivapub@aol.com
Web site: http://www.kivapub.com
Dist(s): **Baker & Taylor Bks.**
Canyonlands Pubns.
New Leaf Distributing Co., Inc.
Quality Bks., Inc.
Treasure Chest Bks.

Kivel, Lee, *(0-9774999)* 6010 E. Paseo Santa Teresa, Tucson, AZ 85750 USA Tel 520-529-2802
E-mail: ghostriver@gainusa.com.

KiwE Publishing, Ltd., *(1-931195; 1-933973)* 2980 Glacier St., Anchorage, AK 99508 USA Tel 907-333-5493
E-mail: kiwe@kiwepublishing.com
Web site: http://www.kiwepublishing.com.

Kiwi Media Group, Inc., *(0-9743319)* P.O. Box 493, Hopkinton, MA 01748 USA Tel 508-435-4986; Fax: 508-435-0378
Web site: http://www.adventuresinsuburbia.com.

Kiwi Publishing *See* **Kiwi Media Group, Inc.**

KJ Pubns., *(0-9792383)* P.O. Box 243594, Boynton Beach, FL 33424-3594 USA
E-mail: contactus@thenutrigang.com
Web site: http://www.thenutrigang.com.

Kjelberg & Sons, Incorporated *See* **Kjellberg, Inc.**

Kjellberg, Inc., *(0-912868)* 805 W. Liberty Dr., Wheaton, IL 60187-4844 USA (SAN 201-5102) Tel 630-653-2244; Fax: 630-653-6233
E-mail: wsc@kjellbergprinting.com
Web site: http://kjellbergprinting.com.

Klare & Taylor Publishing Company *See* **Klare Taylor Pubs.**

Klare Taylor Pubs., *(0-9764403)* P.O. Box 637, Ashland, OR 97520 USA
Web site: http://www.klaretaylorpublishers.com; http://www.pacificwestcom.com/klare; http://www.pacificwestcom.com/amazon; http://www.pacificwestcom.com/shipsofchildren; http://www.pacificwestcom.com/richardpoem.

Kleidon Publishing, *(0-9712941)* 320 Springside Dr., Akron, OH 44333 USA Tel 330-666-5984; Fax: 330-666-6833
E-mail: redsky@kleidon.com
Web site: http://www.kleidon.com.

Klein, Arnold, Orders Addr.: 32782 Woodward Ave., Royal Oak, MI 48073 USA Tel 248-647-7709
E-mail: kak@tir.com
Web site: http://www.paperwasp.com.

Klemantaski Collection, The, *(0-9641689)* PMB 219, 65 High Ridge Rd., Stamford, CT 06905-3814 USA (SAN 253-956X) Tel 203-968-2970 (phone/fax)
E-mail: klemcoll@aol.com
Web site: http://www.klemcoll.com.

Klett, Ernst, Verlag GmbH (DEU) *(3-12) Dist. by* **Continental Bk.**

Klett, Ernst, Verlag GmbH (DEU) *(3-12) Dist. by* **Intl Bk Import.**

Klontz, Karl C. *See* **Klontz, K.C. Publishing**

Klontz, K.C. Publishing, *(0-9713500)* 4703 Chestnut St., Besthesda, MD 20814 USA (SAN 255-089X) Tel 301-656-0644
E-mail: kcklontz@aol.com.

Klutz, *(0-932592; 1-57054; 1-878257; 1-59174)* Div. of Scholastic, Inc., 450 Lambert St., Palo Alto, CA 94306 USA (SAN 212-7539) Tel 650-857-0888; Fax: 650-857-9110; Toll Free: 800-737-4123 ; *Imprints:* Chicken Socks (Chick Socks)
E-mail: thefolks@klutz.com
Web site: http://www.klutz.com
Dist(s): **Baker & Taylor Bks.**
Scholastic, Inc.

Klutz Latino (MEX) Dist. by IPG Chicago.

KMR Scripts, *(1-932240)* P.O. Box 189, Webster City, IA 50595 USA
Web site: http://www.kmrscripts.com.

KMT Enterprises *See* **KMT Pubns.**

KMT Pubns., *(0-9635645)* Orders Addr.: P.O. Box 881913, San Francisco, CA 94188-1913 USA Tel 415-822-5018; Fax: 415-822-7204; Edit Addr.: 86 Bayview St., San Francisco, CA 94124 USA
E-mail: kmtpub@juno.com
Web site: http://www.kmtpub.com
Dist(s): **NetLibrary, Inc.**

KnackPacks, Inc., *(0-9726619)* P.O. Box 3716, Oak Park, IL 60303-3716 USA Tel 708-358-1760
E-mail: comments@knackpacks.com
Web site: http://www.knackpacks.com.

KnausWorks, *(0-9758742)* 4160-87 Jade St., Capitola, CA 95010 USA
E-mail: ltrsfmspace@aol.com.

Knife in the Toaster Publishing Co., LLC, *(0-9719806)* Orders Addr.: P.O. Box 399, Cedar, MN 55011-0399 USA Tel 763-434-2422; Fax: 763-413-1181 ; *Imprints:* wee-speak (wee-speak)
Dist(s): **Baker & Taylor Bks.**
Partners/West
Quality Bks., Inc.

Knight, Kenneth J., *(0-9749544)* 198 Squire Canyon Rd., San Luis Obispo, CA 93401-8001 USA Tel 805-627-1778
E-mail: tri-books@peoplepc.com.

Knight Publishing, *(0-9740535)* P.O. Box 7452, Fremont, CA 94537-7452 USA Tel 209-743-7390; Fax: 510-818-1166
E-mail: knightpublishing@sbcglobal.net; childrenbooks@sbcglobal.net.

KNK Bks., *(0-9742010)* P.O. Box 23841, Alexandria, VA 22304 USA Tel 202-321-1425
E-mail: knkrecords@yahoo.com
Web site: http://www.knkrecords.com.

†Knoll, Allen A. Pubs., *(0-9627297; 1-888310)* 200 W. Victoria St., Santa Barbara, CA 93101 USA (SAN 299-0539) Tel 805-564-3377 (orders); Fax: 805-966-6657 (orders); Toll Free: 800-777-7623 (orders)
E-mail: bookinfo@knollpublishers.com
Web site: http://www.knollpublishers.com
Dist(s): **Baker & Taylor Bks.**
Brodart Co.; *CIP.*

Knopf *Imprint of* **Knopf Publishing Group**

†Knopf, Alfred A. Inc., Div. of The Knopf Publishing Group, Orders Addr.: 400 Hahn Rd., Westminster, MD 21157 USA Tel 410-848-1900; Toll Free: 800-726-0600 (orders); Edit Addr.: 1745 Broadway, New York, NY 10019 USA (SAN 202-5825) Tel 212-782-9000; Toll Free: 800-726-0600
E-mail: customerservice@randomhouse.com
Web site: http://www.randomhouse.com/knopf
Dist(s): **Libros Sin Fronteras**
Random Hse., Inc.; *CIP.*

Knopf Bks. for Young Readers *Imprint of* **Random Hse. Children's Bks.**

Knopf Canada (CAN) *(0-394; 0-676) Dist. by* **Random.**

Knopf Publishing Group, Orders Addr.: 400 Hahn Rd., Westminster, MD 21157 USA Tel 410-848-1900; Toll Free: 800-726-0600; Edit Addr.: 1745 Broadway, New York, NY 10019 USA Tel 212-782-9000 ; *Imprints:* Knopf (KnoG); Everyman's Library (Everymns Lib); Pantheon (Pantheon); Schocken (Schocken); Vintage (Vin Bks); Anchor (AncKPG)
Dist(s): **Random Hse., Inc.**

Knosis, LLC *See* **SkyMark Corp.**

Knot Garden Pr., *(0-9655018)* 7712 Eagle Creek Dr., Dayton, OH 45459 USA Tel 937-433-2592 (phone/fax)
E-mail: marthaboice@aol.com.

Knott, Joan, *(0-9779895)* 132 W. High St., Jackson, MI 49203 USA.

Know Me Pubn. LLC, *(0-9790934)* 1679 Valdosta Cir., Pontiac, MI 48340 USA Tel 248-462-2244
E-mail: kingbuilproduct@aol.com
Web site: http://knowmepub.com.

Knowing Pr., The, *(0-936927)* Orders Addr.: 400 Sycamore, McAllen, TX 78501 USA (SAN 658-361X) Tel 956-686-4033
E-mail: janseale@rgv.rr.com.

Knowledge Adventure, Inc., *(1-56997)* Div. of Vivendi Universal Interactive, 6060 Center Dr., Los Angeles, CA 90045 USA Tel 310-649-8000.

Knowledge College Planning, *(0-9761218)* P.O. Box 321, Stockbridge, GA 30281 USA Tel 770-331-0739
Web site: http://www.kcplan.com.

Knowledge Concepts Pubns., *(1-884331)* Orders Addr.: P.O. Box 973, Cedar Hill, TX 75106 USA (SAN 257-6163) Tel 972-223-1558; Fax: 972-223-1609; Toll Free: 800-269-6228; Edit Addr.: 136 Laurel Springs Dr., DeSoto, TX 75115 USA ; *Imprints:* KCES (KCES)
E-mail: ellapatterson5@att.net
Web site: http://www.ellap.com; http://www.msreal.com
Dist(s): **Baker & Taylor Bks.**
Hervey's Booklink & Cookbook Warehouse.

Knowledge Kids Enterprises, Incorporated *See* **LeapFrog Enterprises, Inc.**

Knowledge Quest, *(1-932786)* P.O. Box 474, Boring, OR 97009-0474 USA Tel 503-663-1210; Fax: 503-663-0670 Do not confuse with Knowledge Quest, Dieterich, IL
E-mail: orders@knowledgequestmaps.com; terri@knowledgequestmaps.com
Web site: http://www.knowledgequestmaps.com.

Knowledge Wand, LLC, *(0-9766680)* 100 Kennewyck Cir., Slingerlands, NY 12159 USA Tel 518-456-3110; Fax: 518-456-6990; Toll Free: 800-376-5669
E-mail: djahnel@gmail.com
Web site: http://www.knowledgewand.com.

KnowledgeGain Inc., *(0-9779844)* 3936 Hwy 52 N, Suite 121, Rochester, MN 55901 USA (SAN 850-802X) Tel 507-398-2384; Fax: 928-832-6568
E-mail: Publisher@KnowledgeGain.com
Web site: http://www.KnowledgeGain.com.

Knowtivate, LLC, *(0-9787021)* Orders Addr.: 116 Milton St., Lake Mills, WI 53551-5355 USA Tel 920-478-3936; Edit Addr.: N7894 Cty. Rd., O, Waterloo, WI 53594-5355 USA
Web site: http://www.knowtivate.com.

Knox, John Press *See* **Westminster John Knox Pr.**

Knox, Mark M., *(0-9713187)* 614 Saint Andrews Pl., Coppell, TX 75019 USA.

KO Kids Bks., *(0-9723946)* 502 Browning Ct., Mill Valley, CA 94941 USA Tel 415-380-8577
Web site: http://www.kokidsbooks.com
Dist(s): **Perseus Distribution.**

Koala Jo Publishing, *(0-9764698)* Orders Addr.: 352 N. El Camino Real, San Mateo, CA 94401 USA
Web site: http://www.koalajo.com.

Koala Music, P.O. Box 21168, Saint Petersburg, FL 37424 USA.

KOBZ, *(0-9772222)* 2230 Rockingham Dr., Maryville, TN 37803 USA Tel 865-980-7755.

Koch, Chris, *(0-9764338)* 8300 Running Spring Dr., Louisville, KY 40241 USA Tel 502-522-9503.

Kochevar, Steven, *(0-9763546)* 7 Beth Lee Dr., Grafton, MA 01519-1139 USA.

Kodak *Imprint of* **Tiffen Co. LLC, The**

†Kodansha America, Inc., *(0-87011; 1-56836)* 575 Lexington Ave., 23rd Flr., New York, NY 10022-6102 USA (SAN 201-0526) Tel 917-322-6200; Fax: 212-935-6929; Toll Free: 800-451-7556
E-mail: info@kodanshaamerica.com
Dist(s): **Oxford Univ. Pr., Inc.**; *CIP.*

Kodansha International (JPN) *(4-7700) Dist. by* **Cheng Tsui.**

Kodansha International (JPN) *(4-7700) Dist. by* **Kodansha.**

Kodansha International (JPN) *(4-7700) Dist. by* **OUP.**

Koenisha Pubns., *(0-9700458; 0-9718758; 0-9741685; 0-9759621; 0-9800098)* 3196-53rd St., Hamilton, MI 49419 USA
E-mail: koenisha@macatawa.org
Web site: http://www.koenisha.com
Dist(s): **Baker & Taylor Bks.**

Kofford, Greg Books, Inc., *(1-58958)* P.O. Box 1362, Draper, UT 84020 USA (SAN 253-5882) Tel 801-523-6063; Fax: 801-576-0583
E-mail: gregk@koffordbooks.com; agallup@koffordbooks.com; mcharrison@koffordbooks.com
Web site: http://www.koffordbooks.com
Dist(s): **Baker & Taylor Bks.**

Kokopelli Pr., *(0-9759270)* 9611 Paseo del Rey NE, Albuquerque, NM 87111-1649 USA Do not confuse with companies with the same name in Las Cruces, NM, Sedona, AZ.

Kokoro Kan *See* **Chikara Kan**

Koldarana Pubns., *(1-884993)* Orders Addr.: P.O. Box 973, Dover, AR 72837 USA; Edit Addr.: 958 SR 164 E., Dover, AR 72837 USA
E-mail: ctn47496@yahoo.com.

Kolowalu Bk. *Imprint of* **Univ. of Hawaii Pr.**

Komikwerks, LLC, *(0-9742803; 0-9778809; 1-933925)* 1 Ruth St., Worcester, MA 01602 USA ; *Imprints:* Actionopolis (Actionopolis)
E-mail: patrick@komikwerks.com
Web site: http://www.komikwerks.com; www.actionopolis.com
Dist(s): **Perseus Distribution.**

Kommon Cents, Inc., *(0-9745982)* Orders Addr.: P.O. Box 313274, Jamaica, NY 11431-3274 USA Tel 917-541-8568; Toll Free: 877-566-2368
E-mail: info@kommoncents.com
Web site: http://www.kommoncents.com.

Kommon Cents Publishing Company *See* **Kommon Cents, Inc.**

Konaa Publishing *See* **Smallbag Bks.**

Konecky & Konecky *Imprint of* **Konecky, William S. Assocs., Inc.**

Konecky, William S. Assocs., Inc., *(0-914427; 1-56852)* 72 Ayers Point Rd., Old Saybrook, CT 06475-4301 USA (SAN 663-2432) Tel 860-388-0878; Fax: 860-388-0273 ; *Imprints:* Konecky & Konecky (Konecky & Konecky)
E-mail: seankon@comcast.net.

Konemann, *(3-89508; 3-8290; 3-8331)* 137 W. 19th St., New York, NY 10011 USA Tel 212-367-8855; Fax: 212-367-8866; Toll Free: 888-317-8855
E-mail: mchin@konemann.com
Dist(s): **Bayside Entertainment Distribution**
Daedalus Bks.
Koen-Levy Bk. Wholesalers LLC
Lectorum Pubns., Inc.
Mel Bay Pubns., Inc.
Trucatriche.

Konkori International, *(0-9647012)* P.O. Box 102441, Denver, CO 80250 USA Tel 303-744-6318; Fax: 303-296-9113 ; *Imprints:* Dawn of a New Day Publications, The (Dawn of a New Day)
E-mail: dabdulai@yahoo.com
Dist(s): **Emery-Pratt Co.**

Kookalook Publishing, *(0-9706323)* 53 Garden Pl., Brooklyn, NY 11201-4501 USA
E-mail: kookypubs@hotmail.com.

Kookla KooksToy Co., *(0-9705347)* P.O. Box 140, Greens Farms, CT 06436 USA Fax: 203-255-4910
E-mail: blueskynut@aol.com
Web site: http://www.blueskynuts.com.

Kopacetic Ink, *(0-9619634)* P.O. Box 1117, Longview, WA 98632 USA (SAN 245-8330) Fax: 360-575-1820
E-mail: books@kalama.com
Web site: http://www.goodbooksink.com
Dist(s): **Partners/West.**

Korean Culture Research, Inc., *(0-9762990)* 38 W. 32nd St., Suite 1112, New York, NY 10001 USA Tel 212-563-5763; Fax: 212-563-6707
E-mail: leekle@sprynet.com
Web site: http://www.learnkoreannow.com.

Koroknay, Thomas, *(0-9749705)* 3718 Lindsey Rd., Lexington, KY 44904 USA Tel 419-884-0222.

Kotzig Publishing, Inc., *(0-9715411; 0-9767163)* 1109 NW 16th St., Delray Beach, FL 33444 USA
E-mail: susan@kotzigpublishing.com
Web site: htpp://www.kotzigpublishing.com
Dist(s): **Independent Pubs. Group.**

Kovalik, Susan & Assocs., *(1-878631)* 33506 10th Pl S., Federal Way, WA 98003-6306 USA
E-mail: skovalik@oz.net
Web site: http://www.kovalik.com
Dist(s): **Books for Educators, Inc.**

KP Books *See* **KP Bks.**

KP Bks., *(0-9748549)* 2430 Denby Way, Colorado Springs, CO 80919-3120 USA.

Kralor Incorporated *See* **Kralor Pr.**

Kralor Pr., *(1-887016)* P.O. Box 1867, Magdalena, NM 87825 USA Tel 505-854-3800
E-mail: kralorpress@gilanet.com.

Kramer, H.J. Inc., *(0-915811; 1-932073)* P.O. Box 1082, Tiburon, CA 94920 USA (SAN 294-0833) Fax: 415-435-5364; Toll Free: 800-972-6657
E-mail: hjkramer@jps.net
Web site: http://www.newworldlibrary.com
Dist(s): **New Leaf Distributing Co., Inc.**
New World Library
Perseus Distribution.

Krause, Claudia, *(0-9655689)* P.O. Box 7083, Capistrano Beach, CA 92624 USA Tel 714-492-7778.

KP Bks., *(0-87341; 0-87349; 0-89689; 0-930625; 0-934466; 1-58221)* Orders Addr.: 4700 E. Galbraith Rd., Cincinnati, OH 45236 USA Tel 513-531-2690; Edit Addr.: 700 E. State St., Iola, WI 54990-0001 USA (SAN 202-6554) Tel 715-445-2214; Fax: 715-445-4087; Toll Free: 888-457-2873 (Orders)
E-mail: bookorders@krause.com
Web site: http://www.fwpublications.com
Dist(s): **F & W Pubns., Inc.**
Marta Schooler, Michelle Morrow Curreri.

Kravec & Kravec & Associates *See* **Bellaboozle Books, Inc.**

KRBY Creations, LLC, *(0-9745715)* 2 Leeds Ct., Brick, NJ 08724-4011 USA
E-mail: krbyenterprises@comcast.net
Web site: http://www.krbycreations.com
Dist(s): **Midpoint Trade Bks., Inc.**

Kreations, *(0-9766621)* 19842 Needles St., Chatsworth, CA 91311 USA
E-mail: mbernal@netscape.net
Web site: www.skelanimals.com.

Kreativ Kaos, *(0-9790572)* P.O. Box 27955, Anaheim Hills, CA 92809 USA (SAN 852-310X)
E-mail: admin@kreativkaos.com
Web site: http://www.kreativkaos.com.

Kreative Character Kreations, Inc., *(0-9641381)* 9 Endicott Dr., Huntington, NY 11743 USA Tel 516-673-8230; Fax: 516-346-6620.

†Kregel Pubns., *(0-8254)* Div. of Kregel, Inc., Orders Addr.: P.O. Box 2607, Grand Rapids, MI 49501-2607 USA (SAN 206-9792) Tel 616-451-4775; Fax: 616-451-9330; Toll Free: 800-733-2607; Edit Addr.: 733 Wealthy St., SE., Grand Rapids, MI 49503-5553 USA (SAN 298-9115) ; *Imprints:* Editorial Portavoz (Edit Portavoz)
E-mail: kregelbooks@kregel.com; acquisitions@kregel.com
Web site: http://www.kregel.com
Dist(s): **Appalachian Bk. Distributors**
CRC Pubns.
STL Distribution North America
Spring Arbor Distributors, Inc.; *CIP.*

Kreizel Enterprises, Inc., *(0-9729232)* P.O. Box 224, Monsey, NY 10952 USA; 26 Charles Ln., Spring Valley, NY 10977-3330
E-mail: info@kreizelplating.com; books@kreizelplating.com.

Kremer Pubns, Inc., *(0-9707591; 0-9745631)* 12615 W. Custer Ave., Butler, WI 53007-1109 USA
E-mail: info@kremerpublications.com.

Kreyol Connection Pubns., *(1-892558)* P.O. Box 20813, West Palm Beach, FL 33416 USA Tel 561-533-7229; Fax: 561-434-8074
E-mail: kreyolconnection@hotmail.com.

Kringle Enterprises Co., *(0-9787129)* P.O. Box 394, San Clemente, CA 92674-0394 USA
E-mail: joe@moorewrites.com
Web site: http://www.santasbooks.com.

Krisaran Publishing Co., *(0-9773146)* 850 NC 55 E., Mount Olive, NC 28365 USA (SAN 257-3903)
E-mail: bjackson@esn.net
Web site: http://www.krisaran.com.

Krishnamurti Pubns. of America, *(1-888004)* Orders Addr.: P.O. Box 1560, Ojai, CA 93024-1560 USA Tel 805-646-2726; Fax: 805-646-6674
E-mail: kfa@kfa.org
Web site: http://www.kfa.org
Dist(s): **Biblio Distribution.**

KRISTOS LLC, *(0-9725288)* 3311 Goldsboro Pl., Falls Church, VA 22042 USA Fax: 703-533-3605
E-mail: tchrist@20r.rjf.com
Web site: http://www.atlasbooks.com
Dist(s): **AtlasBooks Distribution.**

KRO Publishing, *(0-9767008; 0-9770215)* P.O. Box 1159, Danville, CA 94526 USA
Web site: http://www.preschoolprepco.com.

Kruger, Wolfgang Verlag, GmbH (DEU) *(3-8105) Dist. by* **Intl Bk Import.**

Kruger, Wolfgang Verlag, GmbH (DEU) *(3-8105) Dist. by* **Distribks Inc.**

Krusi Reading, *(0-9707566)* 701 S. Fourth St., Raton, NM 87740 USA Tel 505-445-1321; Fax: 505-445-4009; Toll Free: 866-275-7874.

†Ktav Publishing Hse., Inc., *(0-87068; 0-88125; 1-60280)* Orders Addr.: 930 Newark Ave. 4th Flr., Jersey City, NJ 07306 USA (SAN 201-0038) Tel 201-963-9524; Fax: 201-963-0102; Toll Free Fax: 800-626-7517 (orders)
E-mail: orders@ktav.com; editor@ktav.com; questions@ktav.com
Web site: http://www.ktav.com
Dist(s): **Baker & Taylor Bks.**; *CIP.*

Kuffel Creek, *(0-9677587)* P.O. Box 2663, Riverside, CA 92516-2663 USA
E-mail: zzgrup@juno.com
Web site: http://www.kuffelcreek.tripod.com.

Kulupi Pr., *(0-9661867)* 5082 Warm Springs Rd., Glen Ellen, CA 95442-8753 USA Tel 707-996-1149
E-mail: kulupi@vom.com
Web site: http://www.kulupi.com.

†Kumarian Pr., Inc., *(0-931816; 1-56549; 1-887208)* 1294 Blue Hills Ave., Bloomfield, CT 06002 USA (SAN 212-5978) Tel 860-243-2098; Fax: 860-243-2867; Toll Free: 800-289-2664 ; *Imprints:* Frog Books (Frog Bks)
E-mail: Kpbooks@kpbooks.com
Web site: http://www.kpbooks.com; *CIP.*

Kumon Publishing North America, Inc., *(1-933241; 4-7743)* Goban-cho Grand, Bldg. 3F 3-1 Goban-cho Chiyoda-ku, Tokyo, 102-8180 JPN Tel 0081 0332343485; Fax: 0081 0332344018; Glenpointe Ctr. E., 5th Flr. 300 Frank W. Burr Blvd., Teaneck, NJ 07666 USA Tel 201-836-2105; Fax: 201-836-1559
E-mail: books@kumon.com
Web site: http://www.kumonbooks.com
Dist(s): **Baker & Taylor Bks.**
Bookazine Co., Inc.
Ingram Pub. Services.

Kumon U.S.A., Inc., *(0-9702092)* 300 Frank W. Burr Blvd., Teaneck, NJ 07666 USA Tel 201-928-0444 (phone/fax)
E-mail: falcbooks@home.com.

Kury Lane Inc., *(0-9768839)* 2514 Silver Maple Dr., Little Rock, AR 72210 USA
E-mail: kurylane@swbell.net.

Kurz, Ron, *(0-939829)* P.O. Box 95551, Las Vegas, NV 89193 USA (SAN 663-8333) Tel 702-837-6395 (phone/fax); 3060 Sunrise Heights Dr., Henderson, NV 89052 (SAN 663-8341) Tel 702-870-5968
E-mail: ronkurz@earthlink.net
Web site: http://www.ronkurz.com.

Kutie Kari Bks., Inc., *(1-884149)* 4189 Ethan Dr., Eagan, MN 55123 USA Tel 651-450-7427; Toll Free: 800-395-8843
E-mail: gharbo@garyharbo.com
Web site: http://www.garyharbo.com.

Kutscher, Martin, *(0-9726060)* 125 S. Broadway, White Plains, NY 10605 USA Tel 914-997-1692; Fax: 914-997-2253
E-mail: KutscherM@pol.net.

Kvale Good Natured Games LLC, *(0-9793583)* 771 Parkview Ave., Saint Paul, MN 55117-4045 USA Tel 651-204-6781; Fax: 651-204-6966
E-mail: admin@kvalegames.com
Web site: http://www.kvalegames.com.

Kwazy Kitty Publishing Co., *(0-9770012)* Orders Addr.: P.O. Box 178, Monkton, MD 21111-0178 USA.

Kwela Bks. (ZAF) *(0-7957) Dist. by* **IPG Chicago.**

Kwist, Karla, *(0-9795046)* 2420 Golden Arrow, Las Vegas, NV 89120 USA Tel 702-768-8406
E-mail: karlakk@aol.com
Web site: http://www.karlakwist.com.

Kyoodoz, *(0-9771172)* Orders Addr.: P.O. Box 5431, Beaverton, OR 97006-0431 USA
E-mail: customerservice@kyoodoz.com; sales@kyoodoz.com
Web site: http://www.kyoodoz.com.

LA 411 Publishing Co., *(0-9614276; 1-879930; 1-931625; 0-9764027)* 5700 Wilshire Blvd., Suite 120, Los Angeles, CA 90035 USA (SAN 687-3944) Toll Free: 800-545-2411
Web site: http://www.la411.com
Dist(s): **SCB Distributors.**

L. A. Eng Bks., *(0-9748598)* 231 W. Hillcrest Blvd., Inglewood, CA 90301 USA
E-mail: luis_arevalo@lennox.k12.ca.us.

L & L Enterprises, *(0-9760046)* 808 Fairfield Ave., Elmhurst, IL 60126 USA Tel 630-832-7141; Fax: 630-833-3401
Web site: https//:www.latinandlanguage.com.

L & M Creations, *(0-9710749)* P.O. Box 415, Round Top, NY 12473 USA Tel 518-622-8105
E-mail: cjmeyer@mhonline.net
Web site: http://www.thetouchofkidness.com; http://www.toothfairylegend.com.

L.C.D., *(0-941414)* 663 Calle Miramar, Redondo Beach, CA 90277 USA (SAN 239-0035) Tel 310-375-6336
E-mail: lenduncan@earthlink.net
Web site: http://www.phonicsplus.com.

LED Publishing, *(1-885674)* Div. of Logical Expression In Design, 1730 M St. NW, Suite 407, Washington, DC 20036 USA Tel 703-558-0100; Fax: 703-558-4970.

L E J Poetic Expressions, *(1-893719)* Orders Addr.: P.O. Box 700333, San Antonio, TX 78270 USA Tel 210-497-0054 (phone/fax); Edit Addr.: 2335 Encino Point, San Antonio, TX 78259 USA
E-mail: lindamoye@aol.com.

L G Productions, *(0-9768486)* Orders Addr.: P.O. Box 351444, Detroit, MI 48235-9998 USA Tel 313-516-6920
E-mail: admin@lgproductions.info
Web site: http://www.lgproductions.info.

LIM Productions, LLC, *(1-929617)* 3553 Northdale St., NW, Uniontown, OH 44685-8004 USA Toll Free: 877-628-4532
E-mail: customerservice@limproductions.com
Web site: http://www.limproductions.com.

L L Teach, *(0-9676545; 1-931104)* 709 Country Club Rd., Bridgewater, NJ 08807-1601 USA Tel 908-575-8830; Fax: 908-704-1730; Toll Free: 800-575-7670
E-mail: ann4480@aol.com; llteach5757670@aol.com
Web site: http://www.LLteach.com.

L. Lemon O'Pea Productions, *(0-9700250)* 31 Dunham Rd., Billerica, MA 01821 USA Fax: 978-964-0587
E-mail: lynne@llemonopea.com
Web site: http://www.llemonopea.com.

LMW Works, *(1-889584)* 211 Green Tree Rd., Tonawanda, NY 14150 USA
E-mail: lmwworks@netzero.net
Web site: http://www.classicalhack.com.

LNA Publishing, *(0-9653635)* 4939 Woods Edge Rd., Wilmington, NC 28409-3964 USA.

LNR Pubns., *(0-9627894)* 318 Cooper Rd., Marion, NC 28752 USA (SAN 254-7546) Fax: 828-652-6802; Toll Free: 877-652-6802
E-mail: elfis@wnclink.com
Web site: http://www.geocities.com.

L O M A (Life Office Management Association) *See* **Life Office Management Assn.**

LPC Group, c/o CDS, 193 Edwards Dr., Jackson, TN 38305 USA (SAN 630-5644) Fax: 731-423-1973; 731-935-7731; Toll Free Fax: 800-351-5073; Toll Free: 800-343-4499
E-mail: lpc-info@lpcgroup.com
Web site: http://www.lpcgroup.com.

LWS Bks., *(0-9704361)* 227 Bayshore Dr., Hendersonville, TN 37075 USA Tel 615-826-3871; Fax: 615-826-3883; Toll Free: 800-643-4718
E-mail: clazzy@mindspring.com
Web site: http://www.janethan.com; http://www.imsonofman.com.

L W S Publishers *See* **LWS Bks.**

La Caille Nous Publishing Co., *(0-9647635; 0-9718191)* 328 Flatbush Ave, Suite 240, Brooklyn, NY 11238 USA Tel 212-726-1293; Fax: 212-591-6465
E-mail: gcadet@lcnpub.com.

La Clase Divertida, Inc., *(0-9710190)* 1703 Anniston Ave., Holly Hill, FL 32117 USA Tel 386-677-0421
E-mail: funclase@bellsouth.net
Web site: http://www.funclase.com.

La Galera, S.A. Editorial (ESP) *(84-246; 84-7515; 84-85297) Dist. by* **Lectorum Pubns.**

La Galera, S.A. Editorial (ESP) *(84-246; 84-7515; 84-85297) Dist. by* **AIMS Intl.**

†La Leche League International, *(0-912500; 0-9768969)* 1400 N. Meacham Rd., Schaumburg, IL 60173 USA (SAN 201-0585) Tel 847-519-7730; Fax: 847-519-0035; Toll Free: 800-525-3243
E-mail: llli@llli.org; orderdepartment@llli.org
Web site: http://www.lalecheleague.org; *CIP.*

La Luz comics, *(0-9755193)* 1516 10th Ave. S., No. 6, Minneapolis, MN 55404-1795 USA
E-mail: sam@samhiti.com
Web site: http://www.samhiti.com.

La Montagne Secrete (CAN) *(2-923163) Dist. by* **Natl Bk Netwk.**

La Oferta Publishing Co., *(0-9665876; 0-9791624)* 1376 N. Fourth St., San Jose, CA 95112 USA Tel 408-436-7850; Fax: 408-436-7861; Toll Free: 800-336-7850
E-mail: sales@laoferta.com; mary@laoferta.com
Web site: http://www.laoferta.com
Dist(s): **Bilingual Pubns. Co., The**
Lectorum Pubns., Inc.
Libros Sin Fronteras
SPD-Small Pr. Distribution.

La Villita Pubns., *(0-9624727; 1-928792)* 5520 Homerlee Ave., East Chicago, IN 46312 USA Tel 219-397-4649
E-mail: lavillita@webtv.net.

Laasya Design, *(0-9774147)* 400 N. Catalina St., Burbank, CA 91505 USA
E-mail: info@laasyadesign.com
Web site: http://www.laasyadesign.com.

Lab-Aids, Inc., *(1-887725; 1-933298; 1-60301)* 17 Colt Ct., Ronkonkoma, NY 11779 USA Tel 631-737-1133; Fax: 631-737-1286; Toll Free Fax: 800-381-8003
E-mail: lab-aids@lab.aids.com.

Labarco, *(0-9762439)* P.O. Box 1734, Alief, TX 77411 USA
Web site: http://www.cushcity.com; http://www.Amazon.com.

Label Buster, Incorporated *See* **Block System, The**

Labor, Editorial S. A. (ESP) *(84-335) Dist. by* **Continental Bk.**

Labosh Publishing, *(0-9744341)* P.O. Box 588, East Petersburg, PA 17520-0588 USA Tel 717-898-3813 (phone/fax)
E-mail: laboshpublishing@msn.com
Web site: http://laboshpublishing.com.

Lab-Volt Systems, Inc., *(0-86657; 1-60533)* Orders Addr.: P.O. Box 686, Farmingdale, NJ 07727 USA (SAN 238-7050) Tel 732-938-2000 Toll Free: 800-522-8658
E-mail: us@labvolt.com; lvanbrug@labvolt.com
Web site: http://www.labvolt.com.

Lacewing Pr., *(0-9659698)* 15889 Woodlake Dr., College Station, TX 77845 USA Tel 409-690-7251.

Lacey Productions, *(0-9771076)* 611 Druid Rd., Suite 705, Clearwater, FL 33767 USA
E-mail: sherry@laceyproductions.com
Web site: http://www.laceyproductions.com.

Lacey Publishing Co., *(0-9709249)* 29 Bounty Rd W., Benbrook, TX 76132-1003 USA
E-mail: jamesb50@earthlink.net.

LaChrisAnd Productions, *(0-9765063)* P.O. Box 969, Desert Hot Springs, CA 92240 USA Tel 760-309-2263
Web site: http://www.lachrisandproductions.com.

Lacis Pubns., *(0-916896; 1-891656)* 3163 Adeline St., Berkeley, CA 94703 USA (SAN 202-9901) Tel 510-843-7178; Fax: 510-843-5018
E-mail: jules@lacis.com
Web site: http://www.lacis.com.

Lackner, William *See* **Digging Clams n Oregon**

Lacret Publishing Co., *(0-943144)* 601 12th St., P.O. Box 8231, Union City, NJ 07087 USA (SAN 240-3927) Tel 201-867-6465 (phone/fax)
E-mail: subirat@verizon.net.

LaDow Publishing, *(0-9723623)* 308 Reynolds Ln., West Chester, PA 19380-3300 USA Tel 219-689-4565; Fax: 610-918-9571
E-mail: wmladow@aol.com
Web site: http://www.wmladow.com.

Lady Illyria Pr., *(0-9765572)* 30 Lamprey Ln., Lee, NH 03824 USA Tel 603-659-3826
E-mail: patricia.emison@unh.edu.

LadyBug Pr., *(0-9650296)* P.O. Box 7249, Albuquerque, NM 87194-7249 USA Tel 505-890-2656; Toll Free: 800-244-1761
Do not confuse with companies with the same name in Dallas, TX, San Carlos, CA, Sequim, WA.

Laestadian Lutheran Church, *(1-887034)* 279 N. Medina St. Ste. 150, Loretto, MN 55357-4714 USA.

Lafferty, *(0-9707840)* 33 Cherrydale Rd., Glen Mills, PA 19342 USA Tel 610-455-0553
E-mail: Jlaf5@aol.com
Web site: http://www.testprepcollegeprep.com.

Laffin Minor Pr., *(0-9770516)* P.O. Box 273, Alma, CO 80420 USA Tel 970-409-8857; Fax: 207-967-5492
E-mail: lydia@laffinminorpress.com
Web site: http://www.laffinminorpress.com.

Lagesse Stevens *Imprint of* **Martell Publishing Co**

Laguna Pr./BTI, *(0-916309)* HC-71 Box 121-1, Thornfield, MO 65762 USA (SAN 295-9461) Tel 417-679-4748
E-mail: lagunapress@braintypes.com
Web site: http://www.braintypes.com.

Lake 7 Creative, *(0-9774122)* 530 Pk. St., S., Mora, MN 55051-5505 USA (SAN 257-5167) Tel 763-639-5553.

Lake Claremont Pr., *(0-9642426; 1-893121)* P.O. Box 25291, Chicago, IL 60625 USA Tel 773-728-1600; Fax: 773-728-1613
E-mail: lcp@lakeclaremont.com
Web site: http://www.lakeclaremont.com
Dist(s): **Partners Bk. Distributing, Inc.**

Lake Isle Pr., Inc., *(0-9627403; 1-891105)* 16 W. 32nd St., Suite 10B, New York, NY 10001 USA Tel 212-273-0796; Fax: 212-273-0198; Toll Free: 800-462-6420 (Orders only)
E-mail: lakeisle@earthlink.net; hiroko@lakeislepress.com
Web site: lakeislepress.com
Dist(s): **National Bk. Network.**

Lake Limericks, *(0-9761711)* P.O. Box 478, Lake Waccamaw, NC 28450 USA Tel 910-646-4998; Fax: 910-371-1133
E-mail: aldrich@weblnk.net.

Lake Street Pubs., *(1-58417)* Orders Addr.: 4537 Chowen Ave S., Minneapolis, MN 55410-1364 USA
E-mail: compass@sd.cybernex.net.

Lake Superior Port Cities, Inc., *(0-942235)* Orders Addr.: P.O. Box 16417, Duluth, MN 55816-0417 USA Tel 218-722-5002; Fax: 218-722-4096; Toll Free: 888-244-5253; Edit Addr.: 310 E. Superior St. #125, Duluth, MN 55802-3134 USA (SAN 666-9980)
E-mail: reader@lakesuperior.com
Web site: http://www.lakesuperior.com
Dist(s): **Partners Bk. Distributing, Inc.**

Lakefront Research LLC, *(0-9764665)* P.O. Box 667, East Hampstead, NH 03826-0667 USA.

Lakeshore Curriculum Materials Company *See* **Lakeshore Learning Materials**

Lakeshore Learning Materials, *(1-929255; 1-58970; 1-59746)* Orders Addr.: 2695 E. Dominguez St., Carson, CA 90895 USA (SAN 630-0251) Toll Free: 800-421-5354; Edit Addr.: 2695 E. Dominguez St., Carson, CA 90895 USA Tel 310-537-8600; Fax: 310-632-8314
E-mail: lwininger@lakeshorelearning.com
Web site: http://www.lakeshorelearning.com.

Lakeview Pr., *(0-9749677)* c/o Jan Devereux, 255 Lakeview Ave., Cambridge, MA 02138 USA Do not confuse with Lake View Press in New Orleans, LA, Mooresville, NC, Lake Oswego, OR.

Lakewalk Publishing, *(0-9658821)* Orders Addr.: P.O. Box 3045, Duluth, MN 55811 USA; Edit Addr.: 2729 Jean Duluth Rd., Duluth, MN 55804 USA
E-mail: kisola@cpinternet.com.

Lakota Language Consortium, Inc., *(0-9761082)* 2233 N. Browncliff Ln., Bloomington, IN 47408 USA Tel 812-340-3517; Fax: 812-339-3135
E-mail: orders@lakhota.org
Web site: http://www.lakhota.org.

Lamar, Mel Ministries *See* **Lamar, Melvin Productions, Inc.**

Lamar, Melvin Productions, Inc., *(0-9716068)* 3400 Kent Ave., No. D204, Metairie, LA 70006 USA
E-mail: mllamar@aol.com.

Lamb, Wendy *Imprint of* **Random Hse. Children's Bks.**

Lambers, Bill, *(0-9656520; 0-9724629; 0-9797464)* 821 Neeb Rd., Unit 5, Cincinnati, OH 45233 USA Tel 513-347-7344; Fax: 513-347-7747
Web site: http://www.lamberspublications.com.

Lambert Bk. Hse., Inc., *(0-89315)* 4139 Parkway Dr., Florence, AL 35630-6347 USA (SAN 180-5169) Tel 256-764-4098; 256-764-4090; Fax: 256-766-9200; Toll Free: 800-551-8511
E-mail: Info@lambertbookhouse.com
Web site: http://www.lambertbookhouse.com.

LaMear, Arline *See* **Lucky Cat Publishing**

LaMothe, Karin, *(0-9728763)* P.O. Box 672, Belleville, MI 48112-0672 USA
Web site: http://www.angelslullaby.com.

Lamp Post Publishing, Inc., *(1-892135)* 1741 Tallman Hollow Rd., Montoursville, PA 17754 USA (SAN 253-4681) Tel 570-435-2804; Fax: 570-435-2803; Toll Free: 800-326-9273
E-mail: lamppostp@aol.com
Web site: http://www.lamppostpublishing.com; http://www.beyondthegloesmur.com; http://www.heartstringsbio.com.

Lamplight Ministries, Inc. *Imprint of* **Lamplight Pubns.**

Lamplight Pubns., *(0-915445)* Orders Addr.: P.O. Box 1307, Dunedin, FL 34697 USA (SAN 291-4719) Fax: 727-733-8467; Toll Free: 800-540-1597; Edit Addr.: 2182 Marquita Dr., Dunedin, FL 34698-2921 USA Tel 727-784-2688 ; *Imprints:* Lamplight Ministries, Incorporated (Lamplight Ministries)
E-mail: judyann@tampabay.rr.com
Web site: http://www.lamplight.net.

Lampo Group Inc., The, *(0-9635712; 0-9718554; 0-9720044; 0-9726323; 0-9753033; 0-9769630; 0-9777767)* 1749 Mallory Ln., Suite 100, Brentwood, TN 37027 USA Tel 615-371-8881; Fax: 615-371-5007
Web site: http://www.daveramsey.com.

Lamprecht, Edith Hertel, *(0-9704468)* 31 Chris Dr., Uncasville, CT 06382 USA Tel 860-848-4505
Dist(s): **BookMasters, Inc.**

LaMuth Publishing Company *See* **Fairhaven Bk. Pubs.**

Land Information Access Assn., *(0-9671861)* 322 Munson Ave., Traverse City, MI 49686 USA Tel 616-929-3696; Fax: 616-929-3771
E-mail: jvander@liaa.org
Web site: http://www.liaa.org.

Landauer Corp., *(0-9646870; 1-890621; 0-9770166; 0-9793711; 0-9800688)* Div. of Landauer Corp., 3100 NW. 101st St., Suite A, Urbandale, IA 50322 USA Fax: 515 276 5102; Toll Free: 800-557-2144
E-mail: info@landauercorp.com
Web site: http://www.landauercorp.com
Dist(s): **Abingdon Pr.**
American Wholesale Bk. Co.
BPDI
Baker & Taylor Bks.
Bookazine Co., Inc.
Brodart Co.
Spring Arbor Distributors, Inc.

Landfall Co., The, *(0-9747445)* 18640 Mack Ave., P.O. Box 36551, Grosse Pointe Farms, MI 48236 USA Tel 313-886-6250
E-mail: mhslandfall@landfallcompany.com.

Landmark Editions, Inc., *(0-933849)* 1949 Foxridge Dr., Kansas City, KS 66106-4733 USA (SAN 692-6916) Toll Free: 800-653-2665
E-mail: sales@landmarkeditions.com
Web site: http://www.landmarkeditions.com
Dist(s): **Baker & Taylor Bks.**
Brodart Co.
Childswork/Childsplay
Follett Library Resources.

Landmark Foundation *See* **Landmark Schl., Inc.**

Landmark Publishing Inc., *(0-9726738)* P.O. Box 46403, Minneapolis, MN 55446 USA (SAN 254-9689) Tel 763-694-8907; Fax: 763-694-8909
E-mail: info@brainerdbound.com
Web site: http://www.brainerdbound.com.

Landmark Schl., Inc., *(0-9624119; 0-9713297)* 429 Hale St., Prides Crossing, MA 01965 USA Tel 978-236-3216; Fax: 978-927-7268
E-mail: outreach@landmarkschool.org
Web site: http://www.landmarkschool.org.

Landon Pubns., *(0-9679973)* Div. of Abydos Enterprises, P.O. Box 12523, Wichita, KS 67277 USA Tel 719-845-1021; Fax: 316-942-3699; Toll Free: 888-373-2752 Do not confuse with Landon Pubns., Harrisonburg, VA
E-mail: abydos@angelfeather.com
Web site: http://www.angelfeather.com.

Land's End Publishing *See* **Tusktown Publishing**

Lane, Sondra Corp., *(0-9743874)* 2436 N. Federal Hwy., No. 300, Lighthouse Point, FL 33064 USA
Web site: http://www.hallelujahkids.com.

Lane, Veronica Bks., *(0-9637597; 0-9762743)* 513 Wilshire Blvd., No. 282, Santa Monica, CA 90401 USA (SAN 298-1157)
E-mail: info@veronicalanebooks.com
Web site: http://www.veronicalanebooks.com.

Lang Graphics, Ltd., *(0-933617; 1-55962; 1-57832; 0-7412)* 514 Wells St., Delafield, WI 53018 USA (SAN 692-4689) Tel 414-646-3399; Fax: 414-646-2224; Toll Free: 800-262-2611
E-mail: support@shop.lang.com
Web site: http://www.lang.com.

Lang, Peter (CHE) *(3-906750; 3-906751; 3-906752; 3-906753; 3-906754; 3-906755; 3-906756; 3-906757; 3-906758; 3-906759; 3-906760; 3-906761; 3-906762; 3-906763; 3-906764; 3-906765; 3-906766; 3-906767; 3-906768; 3-906769; 3-906770) Dist. by* **P Lang Pubng.**

†Lang, Peter Publishing, Inc., *(0-8204; 1-4331)* Subs. of Verlag Peter Lang AG (SZ), 29 Broadway, New York, NY 10006 USA (SAN 241-5534) Tel 212-647-7700; 212-647-7706 (Outside USA); Fax: 212-647-7707; Toll Free: 800-770-5264
E-mail: customerservice@plang.com
Web site: http://www.peterlangusa.com; *CIP.*

Langenscheidt Pubs Inc., *(0-88729; 3-468; 1-58573; 3-526; 3-324; 981-258)* Subs. of Langenscheidt KG, Orders Addr.: 15 Tyger River Dr., Duncan, SC 29334 USA Fax: 888-773-7979; Toll Free: 800-432-6277; Edit Addr.: 36-36 33rd St., Long Island City, NY 11106 USA
Web site: http://www.americanmap.com; http://www.langenscheidt.com
Dist(s): **Bilingual Pubns. Co., The.**

Langenscheidt Publishing Group *See* **Langenscheidt Pubs Inc.**

Lange-Patton, Lorraine, *(0-9752874)* P.O. Box 96811, Las Vegas, NV 89193-6811 USA.

Langley, Jan, *(0-9724777)* 1625 16th Ave., S., Escanaba, MI 49829 USA Tel 906-786-2053.

LangMarc Publishing, *(1-880292)* Orders Addr.: P.O. Box 90488, Austin, TX 78709 USA (SAN 297-519X) Tel 512-394-0989; Fax: 512-394-0829; Toll Free: 800-864-1648 (orders only); Edit Addr.: 7500 Shadowridge Run, No. 28, Austin, TX 78749 USA
E-mail: langmarc@booksails.com
Web site: http://www.langmarc.com
Dist(s): **Baker & Taylor Bks.**
STL Distribution North America.

Langtry Pubns., *(0-915369)* 9555 Owensmouth Ave., Chatsworth, CA 91311-4811 USA (SAN 291-2473)
E-mail: langtrypub@aol.com.

Language 911, Inc., *(1-933451)* 12924 Calais Cir., Palm Beach Gardens, FL 33410 USA.

Language Adventure Pubns., *(0-9671053)* 2311 E. Stadium Blvd., Suite 204, Ann Arbor, MI 48104 USA Tel 734-763-8378; Fax: 734-769-8409
E-mail: andrearojo@aol.com.

Language Experience, Inc., *(0-9672448)* Orders Addr.: P.O. Box 17403, Plantation, FL 33318 USA Tel 954-791-4964; Fax: 954-791-5086; Edit Addr.: 100 NW 76th Ave., No. 306-2, Plantation, FL 33324 USA
E-mail: resavain@konpitek.com.

Language for Little Ones, *(0-9718409)* P.O. Box 161, LaVergne, TN 37086 USA Toll Free: 877-755-5402
Web site: http://www.littlelanguage.com.

Language Literacy Links, L. C., *(0-615; 0-9711372; 1-932239)* 448 S. 1470 E., Springville, UT 84663 USA Tel 801-489-0386 (phone/fax); Toll Free Fax: 888-489-9593; Toll Free: 888-489-9592
E-mail: lllinks@airswitch.net
Web site: http://www.lllinks.com.

Language Resource Manual for Schools *Imprint of* **Language Treasures**

Language Transformer Bks. *Imprint of* **Velichko, Vera**

Language Treasures, *(0-9765293)* 2141 SE 113th Ave., Portland, OR 97216 USA ; *Imprints:* Language Resource Manual for Schools (L R M S)
E-mail: vrisk@comcast.net
Web site: http://www.languagetreasures.com.

Language Workshop for Children, The, *(0-9754205; 0-9755659; 0-9759664)* 888 Lexington Ave., 2nd Flr., New York, NY 10021 USA (SAN 256-0704) ; *Imprints:* Professor Toto Language Education Series (Prof Toto)
E-mail: info@professortoto.com
Web site: http://www.professortoto.com.

Languages For Kids, *(0-9723849)* 841 Harrison St., Denver, CO 80206-4041 USA Toll Free: 866-421-7010 Do not confuse with Language For Kids in brooklyn, NY
E-mail: langbks@earthlink.net
Web site: http://www.langbks.com.

LANIUS Software, *(0-9679338)* 5055 Business Ctr. Dr. Suite 108, Box #110, Fairfield, CA 94534 USA (SAN 254-4326) Tel 707-864-8279 ; *Imprints:* Wings-on-Disk (Wings Disk)
E-mail: logshrike@comcast.net
Web site: http://www.OnMyMountain.com.

Lanphier Pr., *(0-9762151; 0-9786039; 1-934570)* Div. of Corporate Chaplains of America, 2018 S. Main St., Suite 804, Wake Forest, NC 27587 USA
E-mail: rcrabtree@iamchap.org.

Lansing, Richard D. *See* **Purple Gorilla, LLC, The**

Lantern Bks., *(1-930051; 1-59056)* Div. of Booklight, Inc., One Union Sq., W., Suite 201, New York, NY 10003-3303 USA Tel 212-414-2275; Fax: 212-414-2412
E-mail: martin@booklightinc.com
Web site: http://www.booklightinc.com
Dist(s): **SteinerBooks, Inc.**

Lantern Pr., *(0-9703433)* P.O. Box 10771, Bainbridge Island, WA 98110 USA
E-mail: jjpsr2@aol.com
Web site: http://pillarquest.com.

Lanton Haas Pr., *(0-9702482)* Orders Addr.: P.O. Box 276, Old Bethpage, NY 11804 USA Tel 516-367-3984; Fax: 516-367-6344; P.O. Box 333, Harrington, WA 99134; Edit Addr.: 37 Juneau Blvd., Woodbury, NY 11797 USA
E-mail: appletreepress@aol.com.

Lapcat Pubns., *(0-9641998)* Orders Addr.: P.O. Box 20465, Juneau, AK 99801-9213 USA Tel 907-789-0325 (phone/fax); Edit Addr.: 8305 Gladstone St., Juneau, AK 99801 USA
E-mail: pdavis@ptialaska.net
Dist(s): **Todd Communications.**

Lapp, Susan E., *(0-615)* 1007 W. Princess St., York, PA 17404 USA Tel 717-843-5777
E-mail: yellowstone12@cs.com.

Laramie, Charles, *(0-9769536)* 11 W. St., Fair Haven, VT 05743 USA Tel 802-265-3538
E-mail: chucklaramie@adelphia.net.

†Laredo Publishing Co., Inc., *(1-56492)* 8907 Wilshire Blvd., No. 102, Beverly Hills, CA 90211 USA Tel 310-358-5288; Fax: 310-358-5282; Toll Free: 800-547-5113
E-mail: info@laredopublishing.com
Web site: http://www.laredopublishing.com; *CIP.*

Large Print Bk. Co., The, *(1-59688)* P.O. Box 970, Sanbornville, NH 03872-0970 USA Tel 603-569-4215.

Large Print Pr. *Imprint of* **Thorndike Pr.**

Largesse Publishing, Inc., *(0-9670675)* Orders Addr.: P.O. Box 626, Spring Lake, NJ 07762 USA (SAN 254-2617) Tel 732-449-9040; 732-449-7211; Fax: 732-449-7162; 732-449-1389; Fulfillment Addr.: 555 Wall Rd., Spring Lake, NJ 07762 USA
E-mail: largessepi@aol.com
Web site: http://www.largessepublishing.com.

Lariat Pubns., *(0-9748459)* P.O. Box 364, Plympton, MA 02364 USA (SAN 255-8521) Tel 781-582-0700; Fax: 781-585-6328; Toll Free: 800-829-0715
E-mail: lisa@usstablingguide.com
Web site: http://www.usstablingguide.com
Dist(s): **Independent Pubs. Group.**

Lark Bks., *(0-937274; 1-57990; 1-887374; 1-60059)* Div. of Sterling Publishing Co., Inc., 67 Broadway St., Asheville, NC 28801-2919 USA (SAN 219-9947)
E-mail: info@larkbooks.com
Web site: http://www.larkbooks.com
Dist(s): **Hearst Bks.**
Sterling Publishing Co., Inc.

Lark Enterprising *See* **Master Maker Productions**

†Larksdale, *(0-89896)* P.O. Box 801222, Houston, TX 77280 USA (SAN 220-0643) Tel 713-461-7200; Fax: 713-467-4770 (purchase orders); Toll Free: 877-461-7200; *CIP.*

Larousse, Ediciones, S. A. de C. V. (MEX) *(968-6042; 968-6147; 968-6347; 970-607; 970-22) Dist. by* **Continental Bk.**

Larousse, Ediciones, S. A. de C. V. (MEX) *(968-6042; 968-6147; 968-6347; 970-607; 970-22) Dist. by* **AIMS Intl.**

Larousse, Ediciones, S. A. de C. V. (MEX) *(968-6042; 968-6147; 968-6347; 970-607; 970-22) Dist. by* **HM Trade Div.**

Larousse, Ediciones, S. A. de C. V. (MEX) *(968-6042; 968-6147; 968-6347; 970-607; 970-22) Dist. by* **Giron Bks.**

Larousse, Editions (FRA) *(2-03) Dist. by* **HM Trade Div.**

Larry Huch Ministries, *(0-9745301)* Orders Addr.: P.O. Box 2197, Mansfield, TX 76063-0039 USA
E-mail: cory@larryhuchministries.com
Web site: http://www.larryhuchministries.com
Dist(s): **Anchor Distributors.**

Larsen's Outdoor Publishing, *(0-936513)* 2640 Elizabeth Pl., Lakeland, FL 33813 USA (SAN 697-8975) Tel 863-644-3381; Fax: 863-644-3288
E-mail: lop@larsenoutdoors.com
Web site: http://www.larsenoutdoors.com.

Larson Learning, Inc., *(0-9639121; 1-58123; 1-887050)* Div. of Larson Texts, Inc., 1762 Norcross Rd., Erie, PA 16510-3838 USA Tel 814-824-6365; Fax: 814-824-6377; Toll Free: 800-530-2355
Web site: http://www.larsonlearning.com.

Laser Productions *See* **Global Publishing**

Lash & Assocs. Publishing/Training, Inc., *(1-931117)* 708 Young Forest Dr., Wake Forest, NC 27587 USA Tel 919-562-0015 (phone/fax)
E-mail: mlyn@lapublishing.com
Web site: http://www.lapublishing.com.

Last Gasp Eco-Funnies, Incorporated *See* **Last Gasp of San Francisco**

Last Gasp of San Francisco, *(0-86719)* Orders Addr.: 777 Florida St., San Francisco, CA 94110 USA (SAN 216-8308); Edit Addr.: 777 Florida St., San Francisco, CA 94110-2025 USA (SAN 170-3242) Tel 415-824-6636; Fax: 415-824-1836; Toll Free: 800-366-5121
E-mail: colin@lastgasp.com
Web site: http://www.lastgasp.com
Dist(s): **SCB Distributors**
Trucatriche.

Last Play Publishing, *(0-9760181)* 17931 Inverness Ave., Baton Rouge, LA 70810 USA Tel 225-751-6419
E-mail: djones@dow.com.

Lasting Bks. Publishing Co., *(0-9767511)* 8433 Briggs Dr., Roseville, CA 95747-5951 USA
E-mail: director@lastingbooks.com
Web site: http://www.lastingbooks.com.

Late For The Sky Production Co., *(1-932150; 0-9795778)* 3000 Robertson Ave., Cincinnati, OH 45209 USA (SAN 631-7456) Tel 513-531-4400; Fax: 513-458-8484; Toll Free: 800-422-3434
E-mail: lfts@fuse.net
Web site: http://www.lateforthesky.com.

Latin American Bk. Source, Inc., 289 Third Ave., Chula Vista, CA 91910 USA Tel 619-426-1226; Fax: 619-426-0212
Web site: http://www.latinbooks.com.

Company

†**Latin American Literary Review Pr.,** *(0-935480; 1-891270)* P.O. Box 17660, Pittsburgh, PA 15235 USA (SAN 215-2142) Tel 412-824-7903; Fax: 412-824-7909
Web site: http://www.lalrp.org
Dist(s): **Bilingual Review Press * Hispanic Research Center**
Continental Bk. Co., Inc.
SPD-Small Pr. Distribution; *CIP.*

Latino, Frank Publishing Co., *(0-9640474)* 6806 Newport Lake Cir., Boca Raton, FL 33496 USA Tel 561-241-3880; Fax: 561-995-6975; Toll Free: 800-922-8565
E-mail: frank@hollyboy.com
Web site: http://www.hollyboy.com.

Latino Literacy Press *See* **Lectura Bks.**

Latitude 20 Bks. *Imprint of* **Univ. of Hawaii Pr.**

Laughing Elephant, *(0-9621131; 1-883211; 1-59583)* Orders Addr.: 3645 Interlake Ave., N., Seattle, WA 98103 USA Tel 206-447-9229; Fax: 206-447-9189; Toll Free: 800-354-0400 (orders only); Edit Addr.: 4649 Sunnyside Ave., N., Seattle, WA 98103 USA (SAN 250-7722) Tel 206-632-7075; Fax: 206-632-0466 ; *Imprints:* Darling & Company (Darling & Comp); Green Tiger Press (Grn Tiger Pr)
E-mail: laughingelephant@laughingelephant.com
Web site: http://www.laughingelephant.com
Dist(s): **Abingdon Pr.**
Ingram Pub. Services.

Laughing Gull Pr., *(0-9726699)* P.O. Box 23272, Brooklyn, NY 11202-3272 USA
E-mail: laughinggullpress@earthlink.net.

Laughing Peaches Pubns., *(0-9643004)* P.O. Box 28458, Saint Paul, MN 55128 USA Tel 651-702-9399
E-mail: dane@laughingpeaches.com
Web site: http://www.laughingpeaches.com
Dist(s): **Bookmen, Inc.**

Laughing Sun Productions, *(0-9674849)* 1845 Cromwell Dr., Nashville, TN 37215-5615 USA
E-mail: Laughinsun@aol.com.

Laurel *Imprint of* **Dell Publishing**

Laurel & Herbert, Inc., *(0-9619155)* P.O. Box 440266, Sugarloaf Shores, FL 33044 USA (SAN 243-4687) Tel 305-745-3506; Fax: 305-745-9070.

Laurel Glen Publishing *Imprint of* **Advantage Pubs. Group**

Laurel Leaf *Imprint of* **Random Hse. Children's Bks.**

Laurel Press *See* **Laurel & Herbert, Inc.**

Laurel Valley Graphics, Inc., *(0-9717475)* P.O. Box 498, Latrobe, PA 15650 USA Fax: 724-532-1957
Web site: http://www.lvgraphics.net.

Lauren Elizabeth Design, *(0-9779594)* 2002 Duboin Rd, New Iberia, LA 70560 USA
E-mail: chad@turnkeybid.com.

Lauria, David C., *(0-9676600)* 8024 Lindbergh Blvd., Philadelphia, PA 19153-1601 USA Tel 215-365-0997.

Laurily Productions, *(0-9678585)* 7 Markus Dr., Kendall Park, NJ 08824 USA (SAN 253-1348) Tel 732-297-8487; Fax: 732-398-1246
E-mail: Laurilypro@aol.com.

Laurob Pr., *(0-9787376)* 4204 Anjou Ct., Chico, CA 95973 USA.

Lava Pubns., *(0-9638838; 0-9714261; 0-9761449; 0-9792400)* Div. of Field O Dreams Farm, Orders Addr.: P.O. Box 182, Webb, AL 36376 USA (SAN 255-2027)
E-mail: lavainc@centurytel.net.

Lavender Moon, Inc., *(1-891551)* 3225 S. MacDill Ave., No. 129-257, Tampa, FL 33629 USA Tel 813-251-2923; Fax: 813-254-7117.

Lavender Bks., *(0-9742739)* Orders Addr.: P.O. Box 3555, Culver City, CA 90231-3555 USA; Edit Addr.: 11111 Jefferson Blvd., Culver City, CA 90230 USA
E-mail: lavender_books33@aol.com; kc_kang@yahoo.com; lavenderbooks33@aol.com.

Lavoe & Infante, Incorporated *See* **Infante Pubns., Inc.**

LaVonKeish Pubs., *(0-9672684)* 1355 NW 93rd Ct., Suite A-106, Miami, FL 33172 USA Tel 242-373-7861; Fax: 242-373-4011
E-mail: Berbooks@batelnet.bs.

Law Offices of Harry Glick, *(0-9717419)* 100 Quentin Rossevelt Blvd. No. 511, Garden City, NY 11530 USA Tel 516-456-1088; Fax: 805-473-9025
Web site: http://www.harryglick.com
Dist(s): **Baker & Taylor Bks.**
BookMasters, Inc.

Lawder, Ursula, *(0-9703905)* 147 Armory St., Hamden, CT 06517-4005 USA Tel 203-562-4648; Fax: 203-782-2442
E-mail: manimal165@aol.com.

Lawe Street Bks., *(0-9713179)* 1818 S. Lawe St., Appleton, WI 54915 USA Tel 920-739-4577
E-mail: stedjee@aol.com.

Lawells Publishing, *(0-934981)* P.O. Box 1338, Royal Oak, MI 48068-1338 USA (SAN 694-602X) Tel 248-543-5297
E-mail: lawells@tm.net
Web site: http://www.lawells.net
Dist(s): **AtlasBooks Distribution**
Baker & Taylor Bks.

Lawrence Educational Services, Inc., *(1-932959; 1-59699)* Orders Addr.: P.O. Box 6256, Bridgewater, NJ 08807 USA Tel 908-575-8830; Fax: 908-704-1730; Toll Free: 800-575-7670; Edit Addr.: 674 Rte. 202-206 N, Suite 4, Bridgewater, NJ 08807 USA
E-mail: llteach5757670@aol.com
Web site: http://www.llteach.com.

Lawrence Hse. Pubs., *(0-9609436; 1-891707)* One Washington Sq., Suite 3C, Larchmont, NY 10538 USA (SAN 260-0935) Tel 914-833-7300; Fax: 914-833-0627; Toll Free: 800-533-8681
E-mail: budbooks@mindspring.com.

Lawrence Publishing, *(0-9716039)* Div. of Educational Services & Publications, 2935 E. Rose Ln., Phoenix, AZ 85016 USA Tel 602-912-9553 Do not confuse with companies with the same or similar names in Flower Mound, TX, Van Nuys, CA, Los Angeles, CA, Wichita, KS, Baton Rouge, LA
E-mail: llawre2222@aol.com; walton90@alltel.net.

Lawson, Archie B., *(0-9762660)* 1168 Shashas Way, Riverton, UT 84065-4111 USA Tel 801-302-0440
E-mail: archiebl@msn.com.

Layman Bks., *(0-9679235)* P.O. Box 4702, Austin, TX 78765-4702 USA Tel 512-306-9065 ext 2254
E-mail: layman@laymanbooks.com
Web site: http://www.laymanbooks.com
Dist(s): **Baker & Taylor Bks.**

Layman Press *See* **Layman Bks.**

Layne Morgan Media, Inc., *(0-9762904; 0-9772007; 0-9774803; 1-4265)* 2101 W. Chesterfield Blvd. Ste. A102, Springfield, MO 65807-8672 USA
E-mail: kimberlym@laynemorgan.com
Web site: http://www.laynemorgan.com.

LB Bks. *Imprint of* **Liberty Bell Productions**

LB Collection *See* **LB Collection Custom Bks.**

LB Collection Custom Bks., *(1-890113)* Orders Addr.: 173 W. Main St., Orange, VA 22960-1539 USA
E-mail: bookstore@lbcbooks.com
Web site: http://www.lbcbooks.com.

LBF/Hadrosaur *Imprint of* **Hadrosaur Pr.**

L. C. Enterprises, Inc., *(0-9712515)* 7150 E. Camelback Rd., Suite 300, Scottsdale, AZ 85251 USA Tel 480-423-7744; 402-203-3243 [mobile]; Fax: 480-423-7099 Do not confuse with L.C. Enterprises, San Diego, CA
E-mail: GMahloch@aol.com.

L'Chaim Pubns., *(0-9766946)* 521 Fifth Ave., Suite 1740, New York, NY 10175 USA
E-mail: lchaim@att.biz
Web site: http://lchaimpublications.com/.

LD Bks., Inc., *(0-9772669; 0-9785897)* 8313 NW. 68th St., Miami, FL 33166 USA (SAN 631-8088) Tel 305-406-2292; Fax: 305-406-2293
E-mail: ldbventas@bellsouth.net
Web site: http://www.sinlimites.net.

LD Coach, LLC, *(0-9745938; 0-9764112)* 1401 Johnson Ferry Rd., Suite 328-C13, Marietta, GA 30062-5241 USA Toll Free: 888-848-6224
E-mail: bill.allen@ldcoach.com
Web site: http://www.ldcoach.com.

LDinfo Publishing, *(0-9701735)* 4208 Colfax Ave., S, Minneapolis, MN 55409 USA Tel 612-988-4821; Fax: 763-764-2387
E-mail: mail@ldinfo.com
Web site: http://www.ldinfo.com.

LDS & Assocs., LLC, *(1-883574)* No. 354, 13681 Newport Ave., Suite 8, Tustin, CA 92780 USA Fax: 714-573-0314; Toll Free: 800-331-3610
E-mail: info@ldsaassoc.com
Web site: http://www.ldsassoc.com.

LDS Family Travels, *(0-9720782)* 641 S. 150 W., Orem, UT 84058 USA.

ldscrafts.com, *(0-9726557)* P.O. Box 736, Provo, UT 84603-0736 USA Tel 801-375-0456
Web site: http://www.ldscrafts.com.

Le Bonheur Club, Inc., *(0-9722730)* 1047 Cresthaven, Memphis, TN 38119 USA Tel 901-682-9905; Fax: 901-682-9926
Web site: http://www.lebonheur.org
Dist(s): **Wimmer Cookbooks.**

Le Bk. Moderne, LLC, *(0-9768450)* 2849 W. 23rd Ave., Denver, CO 80211 USA Tel 303-523-6401 ; *Imprints:* Giggletins (Gigglet)
E-mail: michael@lebookmoderne.com
Web site: http://www.lebookmoderne.com.

Le Jam Bks., *(0-9665060)* 1000 Oakview Ave., Clearwater, FL 33756 USA Tel 727-447-8034.

Le Petit Chien, *(0-9717019)* 2415 Daybreaker Dr., Park City, UT 84098 USA.

Le Robert (FRA) *(2-85036; 2-84902) Dist. by* **Continental Bk.**

Le Robert (FRA) *(2-85036; 2-84902) Dist. by* **Distribks Inc.**

Lead Life Pr., LLC, *(0-9762408)* The Lead Life Institute, 2111 Deerfield Dr., New Hope, PA 18938 USA Tel 215 794 8516; Fax: 215 794 8532
E-mail: mdec@leadlifeinstitute.com.

Leaderbrook, *(0-9719079)* P.O. Box 864, Amherst, OH 44001-0864 USA Tel 440-985-5844
E-mail: timothy@clevelandceo.com
Web site: http://www.leaderbrook.com
Dist(s): **STL Distribution North America.**

Leadership Horizons, LLC, *(0-9668868)* 959 Keystone Way, Carmel, IN 46032-2823 USA Tel 317-844-5587; Fax: 317-581-9226; Toll Free: 888-262-2477
E-mail: ron@leadershiphorizons.com.

Leadership Loft, The, *(0-9727273)* 304 Copperline Dr. Apt. A, Chapel Hill, NC 27516-0421 USA (SAN 255-0679)
E-mail: info@theleadershiploft.com
Web site: http://www.theleadershiploft.com.

Leadership Pub., Inc., *(0-911943)* Orders Addr.: P.O. Box 8358, Des Moines, IA 50301-8358 USA (SAN 251-2599); Edit Addr.: 4030 39th Pl., Des Moines, IA 50310-2801 USA (SAN 264-1712) Tel 515-278-4765; Fax: 515-270-8303; Toll Free: 800-814-3757
Web site: http://www.LeadershipPublishere.com
Dist(s): **Baker & Taylor Bks.**
Creative Learning Pr., Inc.

Leading Edge, *(1-891432)* 1574 Coburg Rd., Suite 141, Eugene, OR 97401 USA Tel 541-461-9819; Fax: 541-461-3364
E-mail: klw@continet.com
Web site: http://www.safetykidsclub.com.

Leaf Critters, *(0-9703241)* P.O. Box 3516, Huntersville, NC 28070-3516 USA Tel 704-947-0515 (phone & fax).

Leafcollecting.com Publishing Co., *(0-9747654)* 189 N. Jefferson Ave., Bradley, IL 60915-1829 USA Tel 815-932-0850 ; *Imprints:* Egap Gifa Books (Egap Gifa Bks)
E-mail: Darlene@leafcollecting.com; Thegreatlakes189@yahoo.com
Web site: http://www.leafcollecting.com.

League for The Hard of Hearing, *(0-9677843)* 50 Broadway. Flr. 5, New York, NY 10004-1607 USA Toll Free: 877-544-4327 (877-LHH-HEAR)
Dist(s): **Sterling Publishing Co., Inc.**

Lean Pr., *(1-932475)* Div. of Hopefuls, Inc., Orders Addr.: P.O. Box 80334, Portland, OR 97280-1334 USA (SAN 255-6286) Tel 503-708-4415; Fax: 503-626-9098
E-mail: sean@leanpress.com; mike@leanpress.com
Web site: http://www.leanpress.com
Dist(s): **Baker & Taylor Bks.**

Leap Forward Pubns., *(0-9743664)* 12108 Scribe Dr., Austin, TX 78759-3133 USA
E-mail: mjanthony@sbcglobal.net.

L.E.A.P. (Learning through an Expanded Arts Program, Inc), *(0-9713649)* 441 W. End Ave., Suite 2G, New York, NY 10024 USA Tel 212-769-4160; Fax: 212-724-4479
E-mail: leap@leapnyc.org
Web site: http://www.leapnyc.org.

LeapFrog Enterprises, Inc., *(1-58605; 1-932256; 1-59319)* 6401 Hollis St., Suite 125, Emeryville, CA 94608 USA Tel 510-420-5000; Fax: 510-596-6821 ; *Imprints:* LeapFrog School House (LeapSchHse)
Web site: http://www.leapfrog.com.

Leapfrog Pr., *(0-9654578; 0-9679520; 0-9728984)* Orders Addr.: P.O. Box 1495, Wellfleet, MA 02667-1495 USA Tel 508-349-1925; Fax: 508-349-1180; Edit Addr.: 95 Commercial St., Wellfleet, MA 02667-1495 USA Do not confuse with Leapfrog Pr., Wyandotte, MI
E-mail: books@leapfrogpress.com
Web site: http://www.leapfrogpresscom
Dist(s): **Consortium Bk. Sales & Distribution**
SPD-Small Pr. Distribution.

Leapfrog Pr., *(0-9679412)* 1031 Hazel, Wyandotte, MI 48192 USA Tel 734-281-1332 Do not confuse with Leapfrog Pr., Wellfleet, MA.

Leapfrog Press, Incorporated, The *See* **Leapfrog Pr.**

LeapFrog Schl. Hse. *Imprint of* **LeapFrog Enterprises, Inc.**

Leaping Antelope Productions, *(0-9659222; 0-9762059)* Div. of Armadillo Pr., Orders Addr.: 1331c Old County Rd., Belmont, CA 94002-3922 USA (SAN 253-7974) Toll Free: 888-909-5327
E-mail: print123@leapingantelope.com
Web site: http://www.leapingantelope.com
Dist(s): **Baker & Taylor Bks.**
Distributors, The
Quality Bks., Inc.

Leaping Dog Pr., *(1-58775)* P.O. Box 90473, Raleigh, NC 27675-0473 USA (SAN 254-0126) Toll Free: 877-570-6873 (phone/fax)
E-mail: editor@leapingdogpress.com; sales@leapingdogpress.com; webmaster@leapingdogpress.com
Web site: http://www.leapingdogpress.com/.

Learn & Sign Funtime *See* **Learn and Sign Funtime Bks.**

Learn and Sign Funtime Bks., *(0-9753717)* Div. of Barfell Productions, Inc., P.O. Box 457, Wanatah, IN 46390-9689 USA
E-mail: learnandsign@aol.com; jujub121@aol.com
Web site: http://www.learnandsignfuntime.com.

Learn, Inc. *Imprint of* **Oasis Audio**

Learn Quickly, *(1-889434)* P.O. Box 336, Boulder, CO 80306-0336 USA Fax: 303-642-8395; Toll Free: 888-576-3278
E-mail: janet@learnquickly.com
Web site: http://www.learnquickly.com.

Learn2study, *(0-9729557)* 1935 Columbia Pike No. 24, Arlington, VA 22204 USA
Web site: http://www.learn2study.org.

Learning Abilities Bks., *(0-9658853; 0-9720267)* 166 Glyndale Cir., Brunswick, GA 31520 USA (SAN 850-3087) Tel 912-264-5308; Fax: 775-305-0063; Toll Free: 800-779-5088
E-mail: contactlab@gate.net
Web site: http://www.gate.net/~labooks.

Learning All About Me, LLC, *(0-9763961)* Orders Addr.: P.O. Box 161923, Boiling Springs, SC 29316 USA; Edit Addr.: 8 Montford Ave., Boiling Springs, SC 29316 USA.

Learning Challenge, Inc., *(1-59203)* 36 Washington St., Wellesley, MA 02481 USA Tel 781-239-9900; Fax: 781-239-3273
Web site: http://www.learningchallenge.com.

Learning Co. Bks., *(0-7630)* 100 Pine St. Ste. 1900, San Francisco, CA 94111-5205 USA
E-mail: lstarr@riverdeep.net
Web site: http://www.riverdeep.net
Dist(s): **Perseus Distribution.**

Learning Connection, The, *(1-56831)* Orders Addr.: 1901 Longleaf Blvd., Suite 300, Lake Wales, FL 33859 USA Tel 863-676-4246; Fax: 863-676-5216; Toll Free: 800-218-8489
Web site: http://www.tlconnection.com.

Learning Curve International, LLC *See* **RC2 Corp.**

Learning Fasten-Ations, Inc., *(0-9673268; 0-9729476)* 5014-16th Ave., Suite 195, Brooklyn, NY 11204 USA Tel 718-854-3808; Fax: 718-854-9436; Toll Free: 800-252-8152
Web site: http://www.velcroboards.com.

Learning Horizons, Inc., *(1-58610; 1-59545)* Div. of American Greetings, One American Rd., Cleveland, OH 44144 USA (SAN 853-0717) Toll Free: 800-532-8876 ; *Imprints:* McClanahan Book (McClanahan Book)
E-mail: theresa.gamble@amgreetings.com; professortrex@amgreetiings.com
Web site: http://www.learninghorizons.com
Dist(s): **Levy Home Entertainment.**

Learning in Motion, *(1-889775)* 497 Lake Ave., Santa Cruz, CA 95062-3938 USA Toll Free: 800-560-5670 Do not confuse with Learning in Motion, Mount Laurel, NJ
Web site: http://www.learn.motion.com.

Learning Links Inc., *(0-7675; 0-88122; 0-934048; 1-56982)* Orders Addr.: 2300 Marcus Ave., New Hyde Park, NY 11042 USA (SAN 241-3302) Tel 516-437-9071; Fax: 516-437-5392; Toll Free: 800-724-2616
E-mail: learninglx@aol.com
Web site: http://www.learninglinks.com.

Learning Management Systems *See* **Active Learning Corp.**

Learning Materials *Imprint of* **School Specialty Publishing**

Learning Net, The, *(1-887946)* 567 Catnip Rd., Cullowhee, NC 28723 USA Tel 828-293-2542.

Learning Parent, The, *(0-9708770; 0-9777685; 0-9785859)* 2430 Sunnymeade Rd., Rustburg, VA 24588 USA Tel 434-845-8345; Fax: 434-845-3020
E-mail: learningparent@aol.com
Web site: http://www.thelearningparent.com.

Learning Plus, Inc., *(0-9639614)* Orders Addr.: P.O. Box 713, Corvallis, OR 97339-0713 USA; Edit Addr.: 3635 NW Roosevelt Dr., Corvallis, OR 97330 USA Tel 541-757-7049.

Learning Props, *(0-9741549; 0-9768706)* P.O. Box 774, Racine, WI 53401 USA Toll Free: 877-776-7750
E-mail: bev@learningprops.com
Web site: http://www.learningprops.com.

Learning Pubns., Inc., *(0-918452; 1-55691)* Orders Addr.: P.O. Box 1338, Holmes Beach, FL 34218-1338 USA (SAN 688-3990) Toll Free: 800-222-1525; Edit Addr.: P.O. Box 1338, Holmes Beach, FL 34218-1338 USA (SAN 208-1695)
E-mail: info@learningpublications.com
Web site: http://www.learningpublications.com
Dist(s): **Herdman PhD P.C., John W.**

Learning Research Associates, Incorporated *See* **National Reading Styles Institute, Inc.**

Learning Resources, Inc., *(1-56911)* 380 N. Fairway Dr., Vernon Hills, IL 60061 USA (SAN 630-057X) Tel 847-573-8400; Fax: 847-573-8425
E-mail: info@learningresources.com
Web site: http://www.learningresources.com.

Learning Seed Co., *(0-917159)* 330 Telser Rd., Lake Zurich, IL 60047 USA (SAN 287-6647) Tel 847-540-8855; Fax: 847-540-0854; Toll Free Fax: 800-998-0854; Toll Free: 800-634-4941
E-mail: info@learningseed.com
Web site: http://www.learningseed.com.

Learning Series Pr., *(0-9769701)* P.O. Box 590812, Fort Lauderdale, FL 33359 USA (SAN 256-6060) Tel 954-552-4855
E-mail: mdgeddes@comcast.net
Web site: http://www.learningtodream.com.

Learning Strategies, *(0-9630773)* Orders Addr.: P.O. Box 709, Rye Beach, NH 03871 USA Tel 603-964-2356 (phone/fax); Edit Addr.: 10 Richard Rd., Rye Beach, NH 03871 USA Tel 603-964-6195
E-mail: lrnstrat@aol.com
Web site: http://www.helpkidsread.com.

Learning Through Adventure Co., The, *(0-9706634)* 3265 East Ave., Rochester, NY 14618-3508 USA Toll Free: 800-477-7977
E-mail: LTAC@ooeygooey.com
Web site: http://www.ooeygooey.com.

Learning to Give, *(0-9774155)* 630 Harvey St., Muskegon, MI 49442 USA
Web site: http://www.learningtogive.org.

Learning Together, *(1-931840)* 5509b W. Friendly Ave. Ste. 201, Greensboro, NC 27410-4279 USA
E-mail: wtlecl@aol.com.

Learning Tools Co., *(0-938017)* Orders Addr.: P.O. Box 657, Berkeley Springs, WV 25411 USA (SAN 692-7297) Tel 304-258-1304; Edit Addr.: 714 Rockwell St., Berkeley Springs, WV 25422 USA.

Learning Works, The *Imprint of* **Creative Teaching Pr., Inc.**

Learning Wrap-Ups, *(0-943343; 1-59204)* 1660 West Gordon Ave., No. 4, Layton, UT 84041 USA (SAN 668-3975) Tel 801-479-0050; Fax: 801-497-0063; Toll Free: 800-992-4966
E-mail: info@learningwrapups.com
Web site: http://www.learningwrapups.com.

Learning ZoneXpress, *(1-57175)* Orders Addr.: P.O. Box 1022, Owatonna, MN 55060 USA Tel 507-455-9076; Fax: 507-455-3380; Toll Free: 888-455-7003
E-mail: customerservice@learningzonexpress.com
Web site: http://www.learningzonexpress.com.

LearningExpress, LLC, *(1-57685)* 55 Broadway. Flr. 8, New York, NY 10006-3754 USA Toll Free: 800-295-9556
E-mail: info@learnatest.com; customerservice@learnatest.com
Web site: http://www.learnatest.com
Dist(s): **National Bk. Network.**

LearningSuccess Pr., *(0-9772350)* 1590 E. Main St., Ventura, CA 93001 USA (SAN 257-0726) Tel 805-648-1739
Web site: http://www.learningsuccessinstitute.com.

Learnovation, LLC, *(0-9705790; 0-9796434)* Orders Addr.: P.O. Box 502150, Indianapolis, IN 46250 USA (SAN 255-4577); Edit Addr.: 10831 Thristle Ridge, Fishers, IN 46038 USA Tel 317-577-1190; Fax: 317-598-0816; Toll Free: 888-577-1190
E-mail: anna@learnovation.com
Web site: http://learnovation.com
Dist(s): **Baker & Taylor Bks.**

Leatherman, Diane *See* **Bounty Project, The**

Leathers Publishing, *(0-9646898; 1-890622; 1-58597)* Div. of Ad Ctr., 4500 College Blvd., Overland Park, KS 66211-1760 USA Tel 913-498-2625; Fax: 913-498-1561; Toll Free: 888-888-7696
E-mail: leatherpub@aol.com
Web site: http://www.leatherspublishing.com
Dist(s): **AtlasBooks Distribution**
Baker & Taylor Bks.
Booksource, The.

Leatherwood Pr., *(1-933317; 1-59992; 1-934393)* 8160 S. Highland Dr., Suite 109, Sandy, UT 84093-6492 USA Tel 801-438-1088; Fax: 801-733-4007
E-mail: editorial@leatherwoodpress.com
Web site: http://www.leatherwoodpress.com
Dist(s): **Independent Pubs. Group.**

Leatherwood Publishing, *(0-9741725)* 20395 Cty. 86, Long Prairie, MN 56347 USA Tel 320-732-2879
E-mail: leasman@rea-alp.com
Web site: http://www.alexweb.net/whimsy/index.htm.

Leba Hse. Pubs., *(0-9677902)* 13002 Edina Ct., Suite A, Poway, CA 92064-1120 USA (SAN 253-5327) Fax: 858-485-9521
E-mail: althea@san.rr.com.

†Lebhar-Friedman Bks., *(0-86730; 0-912016)* Subs. of Lebhar-Friedman, Inc., 425 Park Ave., New York, NY 10022 USA (SAN 201-9744) Tel 212-756-5248; Fax: 212-756-5128
Web site: http://www.lfbooks.com
Dist(s): **National Bk. Network**; *CIP.*

LeBlanc, Doreen, *(0-9704581)* 109 Egerton Dr., Mount Holly, NC 28120 USA ; *Imprints:* Free Song (Free Song)
E-mail: freesongbooks@aol.com
Dist(s): **Unique Bks., Inc.**

LeBlanc, Terry Leonard, *(0-9755913)* Orders Addr.: P.O. Box 387, Loyalton, CA 96118 USA; Edit Addr.: 805 Mill St., Loyalton, CA 96118 USA
E-mail: terrythetrashman@cwo.com.

Lectern Publishing, *(1-880150)* Div. of Gower Group, Inc., Orders Addr.: P.O. Box 1065, Toccoa, GA 30577-1065 USA Tel 706-886-0090; Fax: 706-886-0465; Toll Free: 800-242-7404; Edit Addr.: 8529 Walton Creek Dr., Toccoa, GA 30577 USA Do not confuse with Lectern Publishing, Canton MA.
E-mail: srng@stephengower.com
Web site: http://www.stephengower.com.

Lectorum Pubns., Inc., *(0-9625162; 1-880507; 1-930332; 1-933032)* Subs. of Scholastic, Inc., 205 Chubb Ave., Lyndhurst, NJ 07071-3520 USA Tel 212-965-7322; Fax: 212-727-3035; Toll Free Fax: 877-532-8678; 877-532-8676; Toll Free: 800-345-5946
E-mail: info@lectorum.com
Web site: http://www.lectorum.com
Dist(s): **Libros Sin Fronteras.**

Lectorum, S.A. de C.V. (MEX) *(968-7748; 968-5270; 970-732)* *Dist. by* **LD Bks Inc.**

Lectura Bks., *(0-9716580; 0-9772852; 1-60448)* 1107 Fair Oaks Ave., Suite 225, South Pasadena, CA 91030 USA
E-mail: info@lecturabooks.com
Web site: http://www.lecturabooks.com.

L'Edge Pr., *(0-9762014)* P.O. Box 2567, Boone, NC 28607 USA
E-mail: jeffhendley@charter.net
Web site: http://www.upsidedownministries.com.

LeDor Publishing, *(0-9747382)* 4885 McKnight Rd., No. 350, Pittsburgh, PA 15237 USA Tel 888-624-9094; Fax: 412-421-1628; Toll Free: 888-624-9094
E-mail: drichman@ledorgroup.com
Web site: http://www.ledorgroup.com
Dist(s): **AtlasBooks Distribution.**

Lee & Low Bks., Inc., *(1-880000; 1-58430; 1-60060)* 95 Madison Ave., New York, NY 10016 USA Tel 212-779-4400 (General info./Editorial); Fax: 212-683-1894 (orders); Toll Free: 888-320-3190 (ext. 28, orders)
E-mail: clow@leeandlow.com
Web site: http://www.leeandlow.com
Dist(s): **Lectorum Pubns., Inc.**

Lee, Howard, *(0-9766137)* 191 Lorraine Dr., Berkeley Heights, NJ 07922 USA.

Lee Instruments, *(0-9704913)* Orders Addr.: P.O. Box 460-999, Leeds, UT 84746 USA; Edit Addr.: 1050 N. Main, Leeds, UT 84746 USA Tel 435-879-6907; 555 E. 900 N., Leeds, UT 84746
E-mail: violguy@infowest.com
Web site: http://www.leeinst@infowest.com; http://kevinleeluthier.com.

Lee, J.& L. Co., *(0-934904)* P.O. Box 5575, Lincoln, NE 68505 USA (SAN 213-8557) Tel 402-488-4416; Fax: 402-489-2770; Toll Free: 888-665-0999
E-mail: leebooks@radiks.net
Web site: http://www.leebooksellers.com
Dist(s): **Big River Distribution.**

Lee, James V. *See* **Salado Pr., LLC**

Lee, Keith Russel/ Publishing, *(0-9768684)* 325 Illinois Blvd., Hoffman Estates, IL 60194-0000 USA Tel 847-885-2908; Fax: 847-885-0646
E-mail: kcith@kcithrlcc.com
Web site: http://www.keithrlee.com.

Lee, Kenneth M., *(0-9711850)* 152 Mills Branch Rd., Sylva, NC 28779 USA Tel 828-631-3904
Web site: http://www.godshelpnow.com.

Lee, Shelley, *(0-9786757)* Orders Addr.: 441 Frazee Ave., Suite A, Bowling Green, OH 43402-1834 USA Tel 419-354-4673
E-mail: bgpc@wcnet.org
Web site: http://BeforeIKnewYou.com.

Leeman, Linda, *(0-9668001)* 6311 288th St., S., Roy, WA 98580 USA Tel 253-843-2929 (phone/fax).

Leeway Pubs., *(0-9744929)* Div. of Leeway Artisans, Orders Addr.: P.O. Box 1577, Laurel, MD 20707 USA Tel 301-404-3355
E-mail: info@LeewayArtisans.com
Web site: http://www.LeewayArtisans.com.

Lefall and Co., Inc., *(0-9761778)* 2020 Edmondson Ave., Baltimore, MD 21223 USA (SAN 256-2596)
E-mail: lefallandco@aol.com
Web site: http://www.jockobook.com.

Left Field Ink, *(0-9664737; 1-932431; 1-59559)* 1010 N. Central Ave., Glendale, CA 91202 USA (SAN 255-3082) Tel 818-558-5838; Fax: 818-347-3263; Toll Free: 800-768-6181 ; *Imprints:* Angel Gate (Angel Gate CA)
E-mail: sales@angelgatepress.com; leftfieldink@earthlink.net
Web site: http://www.angelgatepress.com
Dist(s): **Diamond Comic Distributors, Inc.**
National Bk. Network.

Left Field Productions *See* **Left Field Ink**

Left Hand Publishing Co., *(0-9744799)* P.O. Box 253, Moose Lake, MN 55767 USA
E-mail: nemadji@computerpro.com
Web site: http://computerpro.com/~nemadji.

Legacy *Imprint of* **WordWright.biz, Inc.**

Legacy Bk. Publishing, Inc., *(0-9655835; 0-9716705)* 348 W. 2660 N., Lehi, UT 84043 USA Tel 801-766-5585 (phone/fax)
E-mail: treehouse07@juno.com
Dist(s): **Baker & Taylor Bks.**

Legacy Bks. & Resources, *(0-9666054)* Orders Addr.: P.O. Box 770768, Steamboat Springs, CO 80477 USA Tel 970-879-2500; Edit Addr.: 528 Laurel St., Steamboat Springs, CO 80477 USA
E-mail: stowler@csn.net.

Legacy, Esther, *(0-9667332)* Orders Addr.: P.O. Box 53, Brainardsville, NY 12915 USA Tel 518-425-9956; Edit Addr.: Rte. 374, Brainardsville, NY 12915 USA.

Legacy Group Productions, LLC, *(0-9740585)* 3980 Greenmount Rd., Harrisonburg, VA 22802-0504 USA Toll Free: 877-227-6027
E-mail: cheryl@legacymatters.org
Web site: http://www.legacymatters.org.

Legacy Kids *Imprint of* **Yeva Corp.**

Legacy Pr. *Imprint of* **Rainbow Pubs. & Legacy Pr.**

Legacy Pubns., *(0-933101)* Subs. of Pace Communications, Inc., Orders Addr.: 1301 Carolina St., Greensboro, NC 27401 USA (SAN 662-2852) Tel 336-378-6065; Fax: 336-378-8265 ATTN: Dena Caulder Do not confuse with companies with the same or similar name in Tumon GU, Overland KS, Brentwood TN, Canyon TX, Irving TX, Lilburn GA, Midlothian, VA
E-mail: dena.caulder@paceco.com.

Legacy Pubs., *(1-932957)* 2386 Clower St., Bldg. G, Suite 101, Snellville, GA 30078-6134 USA Tel 770-979-7899; Fax: 770-979-5939; Toll Free: 800-290-8055 Do not confuse with Legacy Publishers in Natural Bridge, VA, Austin, TX
E-mail: mrcofer@aol.com
Web site: http://www.eeinc.org.

Legacy Pubs. International, *(1-880809)* 1301 South Clinton St., Denver, CO 80247 USA (SAN 257-0718) Tel 303-283-7480; Fax: 303-283-7536
E-mail: Michele@LegacyPublishersInternational.com; dmiller@hccweb.org
Web site: http://www.LegacyPublishersInternational.com
Dist(s): **Destiny Image Pubs.**

Legacy Publishing Services, Inc., *(0-9628733; 0-9708395; 0-9764982; 0-9776777; 1-934449)* 602 N. Wymore Rd., Winter Park, FL 32789 USA Tel 407-657-3787; Fax: 407-647-7597 Do not confuse with companies with the same or similar name in Ojai, CA, Berkeley, CA, Atlanta, GA, West Chester, OH, Birmingham, AL, Daty, TX, Fort Meyers, Fl, Baton Rouge, LA
E-mail: legacypublishing@earthlink.net
Web site: http://www.legacypublishingservices.com.

Legend eXpress Publishing, *(0-9773648)* 3831 E. Clovis Ave., Mesa, AZ 85206-8520 USA Tel 480-664-1047; Fax: 480-641-6043; Toll Free Fax: 866-458-2808
E-mail: jana@legendexpress.biz
Web site: http://www.legendexpress.biz.

Legendary Publishing Co., *(0-9625040; 1-887747)* Orders Addr.: P.O. Box 7706, Boise, ID 83707-1706 USA (SAN 297-231X) Tel 208-376-9814 (phone/fax); Toll Free: 877-909-1016 (orders only)
E-mail: dproctor@rmci.net
Web site: http://www.legendarypublishing.com
Dist(s): **New Leaf Distributing Co., Inc.**
Partners/West
Sunbelt Pubns., Inc.
Unique Bks., Inc.

Legenderry.com, *(0-9776967)* 6154 Meadowbrook Dr., Morrison, CO 80465 USA Fax: 720-222-0490
Web site: http://www.legenderry.com.

LegendMaker Scriptoria, *(0-9759355)* 25 Robin St., East Longmeadow, MA 01028 USA Tel 413-313-9127
E-mail: business@legendmaker.com
Web site: http://legendmaker.com; http://sevenlockspublishing.com
Dist(s): **Seven Locks Pr.**

Legends of the West Publishing Co., *(0-9786904)* 174 Santa Rosa Ave., Sausalito, CA 94965-2060 USA (SAN 851-2825) Do not Copnfuse with Know DeFeet Publishing Company 2 Different companies. LD
E-mail: knowdefeet@aol.com.

Legler, Caroline, *(0-9771233)* Orders Addr.: 1930 Bonanza Ct., Winter Park, FL 32792 USA
E-mail: glegler@cfl.rr.com.

Lego Media International, Inc., *(1-893018; 1-903276)* 555 Taylor Rd., Enfield, CT 06082 USA Tel 860-749-2291; Fax: 860-763-7773; Toll Free: 800-344-5346
Web site: http://www.lego.com
Dist(s): **Perseus Distribution.**

Lehman Publishing, *(0-9792686)* 15997 Hough, Allenton, MI 48002 USA
E-mail: dlehman@iwarp.net; dana@lehmanpublishing.com
Web site: http://www.lehmanpublishing.com
Dist(s): **Partners Bk. Distributing, Inc.**

Lehua, Inc., *(0-9647491)* P.o. Box 25548, Honolulu, HI 96825-0548 USA
E-mail: lehua@ohia.com
Web site: http://www.lehuainc.com
Dist(s): **Booklines Hawaii, Ltd.**

Leicester Hill Bks., *(0-9620313)* 1134A Grafton St., Worcester, MA 01604 USA (SAN 248-7543) Tel 508-756-6368.

Leigh, Kimbra *See* **Leigh, Kimbra Inc.**

Leigh, Kimbra Inc., *(0-9718851)* Orders Addr.: 406 S. Main St., Muncy, PA 17756 USA; Edit Addr.: P.O. Box 113, Muncy, PA 17756 USA Tel 570-546-7512
E-mail: kimbraleigh@suscom.net
Web site: http://www.kimbraleigh.com.

Leigh, Tina Illustrator, *(0-9715673)* P.O. Box 7, Higganum, CT 06441 USA
E-mail: tleighillustrator@snet.net.

Leihuna Enterprises, *(0-9709866)* 5205 Dobrot Way, Central Point, OR 97502 USA
E-mail: leihuna@cdsnet.net
Web site: http://home.internetcds.com/~leihuna.

Leisure Arts, Inc., *(0-942237; 1-57486; 1-60140)* Orders Addr.: 5701 Ranch Dr., Little Rock, AR 72223 USA (SAN 666-9565) Tel 501-868-8800; Fax: 501-868-1001; Toll Free Fax: 877-710-5603; Toll Free: 800-643-8030 (customer service); 800-526-5111
E-mail: hermine_linz@leisurearts.com; nicholsonl@sunset.com
Web site: http://www.leisurearts.com.

Lekha Pubs., LLC, *(0-9725901)* 4204 Latimer Ave., San Jose, CA 95130 USA
Web site: http://www.lekhapublishers.com.

LeLeu, Lisa Puppet Show Bks. *Imprint of* **LeLeu, Lisa Studios! Inc.**

LeLeu, Lisa Studios! Inc., *(0-9710537; 0-9770299)* 100 Mechanics St., Doylestown, PA 18901 USA Tel 215-345-1233; Fax: 215-348-5378 ; *Imprints:* LeLeu, Lisa Puppet Show Books (L LeLeu Puppet)
E-mail: lisa.leleu@lisaleleustudios.com; Frederic.Leleu@LisaLeLeuStudios.com
Web site: http://www.LisaLeLeuStudios.com
Dist(s): **Baker & Taylor Bks.**

Lem Publishing & Production, *(0-9612948)* Orders Addr.: P.O. Box 18045, Louisville, KY 40261 USA (SAN 291-2759) Tel 502-479-8020
E-mail: mary_meena@hotmail.com
Web site: http://www.bookstohave.com.

Lemieux International, Ltd., *(0-9667269; 0-9719323)* P.O. Box 170134, Milwaukee, WI 53217-0134 USA Tel 414-962-2844 (phone/fax); Toll Free: 800-950-7723
E-mail: lemintld@aol.com
Web site: http://www.publishingbookservices.com.

Lemniscaat *Imprint of* **Boyds Mills Pr.**

Lemon Shark Pr., *(0-9741067)* 1604 Marbella Dr., Vista, CA 92081-5463 USA Tel 760-727-2850 [phone after 9AM PCT]
E-mail: lemonsharkpress@yahoo.com
Web site: http://www.lemonsharkpress.com
Dist(s): **Coutts Library Service, Inc.**
Eastern Bk. Co.
Yankee Bk. Peddler, Inc.

Lemonflavor Productions, *(0-9740169)* 100 Pk. Ave., 18th Flr. (Dept. MSM), New York, NY 10017 USA Tel 212-316-4278; Fax: 212-937-2211
E-mail: info@lemonflavor.com
Web site: http://www.lemonflavor.com.

LemonTree Pr., *(0-9644846)* P.O. Box 841, Santa Cruz, CA 95061 USA (SAN 254-1610) Tel 831-457-2298 ()phone/fax)
E-mail: Postmaster@lmntreepress.com
Dist(s): **Baker & Taylor Bks.**

Lems-Dworkin, Carol Pubs., *(0-9637048)* Orders Addr.: Box 1646, Evanston, IL 60204-1646 USA Tel 847-328-1029; Fax: 847-869-4239; Edit Addr.: 2305 Brown Ave., Evanston, IL 60201 USA
E-mail: lemsdworkn@aol.com
Web site: http://members.aol.com lemsdworkn.

Lemur Conservation Foundation, *(0-9766009)* P.O. Box 249, Myakka City, FL 34251 USA Tel 941-322-8494; Fax: 941-322-9264
Web site: http://www.lemurreserve.org.

Lenroc Publishing, Inc., *(0-9671869)* 23 Lenroc Dr., White Plains, NY 10607-2421 USA Tel 914-592-4355; Toll Free: 888-909-0047
E-mail: lenrocpub@aol.com.

Leo, Mabel R. *See* **MIBS Publishing**

Leon, Ines Publishing Network, *(0-9707974)* 455 Grant Ave., Suite 10, Palo Alto, CA 94306 USA (SAN 253-7648) Tel 650-325-7272 (phone/fax)
E-mail: inesleon@compaq.net.

Leonard, Dennis Publications *See* **Legacy Pubs. International**

†Leonard, Hal Corp., *(0-634; 0-7935; 0-87910; 0-87930; 0-88188; 0-931340; 0-9607350; 1-56516; 1-57467; 1-4234)* Orders Addr.: P.O. Box 13819, Milwaukee, WI 53213-0819 USA Tel 414-774-3630; Fax: 414-774-3259; Toll Free: 800-524-4425; Edit Addr.: 7777 W. Bluemound Rd., Milwaukee, WI 53213 USA (SAN 239-250X) ; *Imprints:* G Schirmer, Incorporated (G Schirmer); Amadeus Press (AmadeusPress); Applause Theatre & Cinema (ApplauseTheatr)
E-mail: halinfo@halleonard.com
Web site: http://www.halleonard.com
Dist(s): **Giron Bks.**
Perseus Distribution; *CIP.*

Leonard Pr., *(0-9769114; 1-934223)* P.O. Box 752, Bolivar, MO 65613-0752 USA Tel 417-326-5001
Web site: http://www.leonardpress.com.

Leonardo Pr., *(0-914051)* P.O. Box 1326, Camden, ME 04843 USA (SAN 287-542X) Tel 207-236-8649 (phone/fax) Do not confuse with Leonardo Press, Reading, PA
E-mail: Leonardo@spellingdoctor.com; inkpencjh@msn.com
Web site: http://www.spellingdoctor.com.

Leonardo Press *See* **Firenze Pr.**

Leonard's Pubns., *(0-9703402)* 3902 W. Little York, No. 1410, Houston, TX 77091 USA Tel 281-447-7509 (phone/fax)
Web site: http://www.forbiddendestiny.com.

Leonard's, Stew Holdings, LLC *See* **Kimberly Pr., LLC**

†Lerner Publishing Group, *(0-7613; 0-8225; 0-87614; 0-929371; 0-930494; 1-57505; 1-58013)* Orders Addr.: 1251 Washington Ave. N., Minneapolis, MN 55401 USA (SAN 256-0283) Tel 612-332-3344; Fax: 612-204-9208; Edit Addr.: 241 First Ave., N., Minneapolis, MN 55401 USA (SAN 201-0828) Tel 612-332-3344; Fax: 612-215-6230; Toll Free Fax: 800-332-1132; Toll Free: 800-328-4929 ; *Imprints:* First Avenue Editions (First Ave Edns); Lerner Publications (Lerner Publctns); LernerSports (LernerSports); Carolrhoda Books (Carolrho Bks); Ediciones Lerner (EdiciLerner); Millbrook Press (Millbrok Pr); Twenty-First Century Books (TwentFrstCent); Graphic Universe (Graphic Univ)
E-mail: info@lernerbooks.com; custserve@lernerbooks.com
Web site: http://www.lernerbooks.com; http://www.karben.com; *CIP.*

Lerner Pubns. *Imprint of* **Lerner Publishing Group**

LernerSports *Imprint of* **Lerner Publishing Group**

LERN-LEARN, *(0-9763195)* 340 Vallejo Dr., Suite 82, Millbrae, CA 94030 USA.

Les Editions Bleuts, *(0-9701316)* 10227 Gifford Dr., Spring Hill, FL 34608-2727 USA Tel 352-686-0416
E-mail: grbreau@juno.com.

Les Lurn Pubs., *(0-9792000)* 5451 Bancroft Ave., Oakland, CA 94601 USA (SAN 852-7512).

Les Penseurs, *(0-9764999)* 309 Weatherstone Ln., Marietta, GA 30068 USA Tel 678-575-7052; Fax: 678-560-1580
E-mail: ssands@lespenseurs.com
Web site: http://www.lespenseurs.com.

Lesen Pub., *(0-9767200)* 2207 Shermont Pl., Brandon, FL 33511 USA Tel 813-857-6629; Fax: 813-684-7876
E-mail: jem2207@aol.com.

Leslie, Beverly J., *(0-9769722)* 1911 Patton Pl., Lithonia, GA 30058 USA Tel 770-987-8769; Fax: 770-987-8018
E-mail: bjleslie1@comcast.net; Beverly@lesliegraphicdesigns.com
Web site: http://LeslieGraphicDesigns.com.

Les-Man Pubns., *(0-9676736)* Orders Addr.: P.O. Box 411172, Kansas City, MO 64141 USA Fax: 816-941-7485; Edit Addr.: 2632 Spruce Ave., Kansas City, MO 64127-4155 USA
E-mail: lk5754@aol.com.

Less Pr., *(0-9657367)* 100 Hannah Niles Way, Braintree, MA 02184-7261 USA Tel 781-848-0555.

Let Me Learn Enterprises, *(1-892385)* 2 Tiverstock Dr.; Pittsgrove, NJ 08318 USA Tel 609-358-0039; Fax: 609-358-6998
E-mail: gcdainton@compuserve.com
Web site: http://www.letmelearn.edu.

LeTay Publishing, *(0-9753434)* Div. of LeTay Corp., P.O. Box 170233, Atlanta, GA 30317 USA Tel 404-667-2810
E-mail: booksales@letaypublishing.com; publisher@letaypublishing.com
Web site: http://www.letaypublishing.com
Dist(s): **Lightning Source, Inc.**

Let's Get It Together *See* **By the Book Media**

Let's Learn Library of Knowledge Series, *(0-9771015)* P.O. Box 9910, Canoga Park, CA 91309-9910 USA (SAN 256-7849)
E-mail: letslearn@letslearnlibrary.net
Web site: http://www.letslearnlibrary.net.

Letter People, The, *(0-7665; 0-8073; 0-89796; 0-914876)* Div. of Abrams & Co. Pubs., Inc., P.O. Box 10025, Waterbury, CT 06725 USA (SAN 207-7078) Tel 203-756-3580; Fax: 914-592-4257; Toll Free: 800-227-9120.

Level 4 Press, Inc., *(0-9768001; 1-933769)* 13518 Jamul Dr., Jamul, CA 91935 USA Tel 619-669-3100; Fax: 619-374-7311
E-mail: sales@level4press.com
Web site: http://www.level4press.com
Dist(s): **Baker & Taylor Bks.**
Midpoint Trade Bks., Inc.

Level Ground Pr., *(0-9773461)* 2810 San Paula Ave., Dallas, TX 75228 USA Tel 214-796-2135
Web site: http://www.levelgroundfilms.com.

Levenger Pr., *(1-929154)* 420 S. Congress Ave., Delray Beach, FL 33445 USA Tel 561-276-2436; Fax: 561-276-3584
E-mail: mvogel@levenger.com
Web site: http://www.levenger.com
Dist(s): **Consortium Bk. Sales & Distribution.**

Leverage Factory, *(0-9773000)* 4 Davie Cir., Chapel Hill, NC 27514-5900 USA (SAN 257-2710)
E-mail: info@leveragefactory.com
Web site: http://www.beawriter.us; http://www.leveragefactory.com
Dist(s): **Independent Pubs. Group.**

Levin, Hugh Lauter Assocs., *(0-88363)* 9 Burr Rd., Westport, CT 06880-4220 USA (SAN 201-6109)
E-mail: inquiries@hlla.com
Web site: http://www.hlla.com.

Levine, Arthur A. Bks. *Imprint of* **Scholastic, Inc.**

Levinson Bks. Ltd. (GBR) *(1-86233; 1-899607) Dist. by* **Sterling.**

Lewis & Clark Bicentennial Corps of Discovery Arch, *(0-9763970)* 1907 NE 75th Ave., Portland, OR 97213 USA Tel 503-201-2494
E-mail: faith.ruffing@bicencorpsarchive.com
Web site: http://www.bicencorpsarchive.com.

Lewis & Clark Interpretive Assn., *(1-883844)* Orders Addr.: P.O. Box 2848, Great Falls, MT 59403 USA Tel 406-453-6248; Fax: 406-453-6157
Dist(s): **Graphic Arts Ctr. Publishing Co.**

Lewis, C. Deanna, *(0-9665911)* 1045 N. Utah St., No. 702, Arlington, VA 22201 USA Tel 703-522-9363; Fax: 703-522-6733.

Lewis International, Inc., *(0-9666771; 1-930983)* 2201 NW 102nd Pl., No. 1, Miami, FL 33172 USA Tel 305-436-7984; Fax: 305-436-7985; Toll Free: 800-259-5962.

Lewis Lynn Bks., *(0-9745544)* 1143 N. Carey Ave., Clovis, CA 93611-7371 USA Fax: 559-322-9038
E-mail: cconn@cwnet.com
Web site: http://www.borainiansector.com.

Lewis, Nancy Erickson, *(0-9716363)* Orders Addr.: P.O. Box 1163, Sanger, CA 93657 USA Tel 559-875-5561 ext 289; Edit Addr.: 1655 Tollhouse Ln., Clovis, CA 93611 USA
E-mail: lilla51@aol.com.

Lewis Publishing *Imprint of* **CRC Pr. LLC**

Lewis-Thornton, Rae, *(0-9747983)* 1507 E. 53rd St., Suite 315, Chicago, IL 60615 USA Tel 773-643-4316; Fax: 773-643-4356
E-mail: rae_lewis_thornton@hotmail.com
Web site: http://www.raelewisthornton.org.

Lexford Expression, *(0-9722207)* 2017 Woodland Blvd., Flower Mound, TX 75022 USA.

Lexico, *(1-929450)* Orders Addr.: 1616 Pinion Cir., Price, UT 84501-2216 USA
E-mail: publishing@lexico.net; lexico@lexico.net
Web site: http://www.lexico.net.

Lexicon Marketing Corp., *(1-59172)* 640 S. San Vicente Blvd., Los Angeles, CA 90048 USA Tel 323-782-7400; Fax: 323-782-7570
E-mail: kperatt@lexiconmarketing.com.

Lexicus Pr., *(0-9727484)* P.O. Box 1691, Palo Alto, CA 94301 USA (SAN 255-5123) Tel 650-799-5602; Fax: 650-325-8537
E-mail: jstewart@lexicuspress.com
Web site: http://www.lexicuspress.com
Dist(s): **Baker & Taylor Bks.**
Distributors, The
Cook, Marilyn
Partners Bk. Distributing, Inc.

Lexikon Services, *(0-944601)* Orders Addr.: 3241 Boulder Creek Way, Antelope, CA 95843 USA (SAN 244-5174) Tel 916-331-3046
E-mail: Luminquest@aol.com
Web site: http://www.Luminquest.com.

Lexington Bks., *(0-7391)* Div. of Rowman & Littlefield Publishing Group, Orders Addr.: 15200 NBN Way, Blue Ridge Summit, PA 17214 USA Tel 717-794-3800 (Sales, Customer Service, MIS, Royalties, Inventory Mgmt., Dist., Credit & Collections); Fax: 717-794-3803 (Customer Service &/or orders only); 717-794-3857 (Sales & MIS); 717-794-3856 (Royalties, Inventory Mgmt., & Dist.); Toll Free Fax: 800-338-4550 (Customer Service &/or orders); Toll Free: 800-462-6420 (Customer Service &/or orders); 67 Mowat Ave., Suite 241, Toronto, ON M6K 3E3 Tel 416-534-1660; Fax: 416-534-3699; Edit Addr.: 4501 Forbes Blvd., Blvd. 200, Lanham, MD 20706 USA Tel 301-459-3366; Fax: 301-429-5748 Short Discount, contact rlpgsales@rowman.com
E-mail: custserv@rowman.com
Web site: http://www.lexingtonbooks.com; http://www.rlpgbooks.com
Dist(s): **National Bk. Network**
Rowman & Littlefield Pubs., Inc.
STL Distribution North America
Transaction Pubs.

Lexington Pubs., *(1-933361)* P.O. Box 750018, Alrlington Heights, MA 02475 USA
E-mail: lexingtonpublishers@gmail.com.

Lexpress, *(0-9746000)* 269 Divisadero St., San Francisco, CA 94117 USA Tel 415-613-6110 ; *Imprints:* Kid Beowulf (Kid Beowulf); Swampfox (Swampfox)
E-mail: lex@kidbeowulf.com
Web site: http://www.kidbeowulf.com; http://www.platosrepublic.com
Dist(s): **Diamond Comic Distributors, Inc.**

Leyva, Barbara, *(0-9729056)* 1120 NE 15 St., Homestead, FL 33030 USA ; *Imprints:* Balticbard Publishing (Balticbard Pub)
E-mail: balticbard@yahoo.com
Web site: http://www.geocities.com/balticbard/index.html.

LG Fun Learning Pubns., *(0-9716539)* 2919 Miles Ave., Bronx, NY 10465 USA.

LGE Performance Systems, Inc., *(0-9778776)* 9757 Lake Nona Rd., Orlando, FL 32827 USA (SAN 850-5055) Tel 407-438-9911; Fax: 407-438-6667.

LGR Productions *See* **LGR Publishing, Inc.**

LGR Publishing, Inc., *(0-9657610)* 3219 NW C St., Richmond, IN 47374 USA Tel 765-939-8924 (phone/fax)
E-mail: jwilde@indiana.edu; mcphd@infocom.com
Web site: http://www.angerchillout.com
Dist(s): **Baker & Taylor Bks.**

Loguez Ediciones (ESP) *(84-85334; 84-89804) Dist. by* **Baker & Taylor.**

Loguez Ediciones (ESP) *(84-85334; 84-89804) Dist. by* **Lectorum Pubns.**

LH Pubns. & Productions, *(0-9749013)* Orders Addr.: P.O. Box 914, Center Harbor, NH 03226 USA
E-mail: mcat_lh@yahoo.com
Web site: http://www.laurahickey.com.

LHA Bks., *(0-9656945)* Div. of Linda Hardy & Assocs., 16816 Second Ave., SW, Seattle, WA 98166 USA Tel 206-244-0339; Fax: 206-244-5574
E-mail: hardyrl@comcast.net
Web site: http://www.home1.gte.net/lhabooks/index.htm.

Li, Richard T., *(0-9675988)* 4554 Rose Tree Ct., Fort Worth, TX 76137 USA Tel 817-656-5178; Fax: 817-656-4138.

LiArt-Literature & Art, *(1-931481)* P.O. Box 245686, Pembroke Pines, FL 33024-5686 USA Tel 954-986-6886 (phone/fax)
E-mail: liartpe@aol.com.

Liberty Artists Management, *(0-9785427)* Orders Addr.: 31 Liberty St., Catskill, NY 12414-1442 USA
E-mail: admin@libertyartists.com
Web site: http://www.beckyblume.com; http://www.libertyartists.com.

Liberty Bell Productions, *(1-890963)* 740 S. Burnside Ave. Apt. 117, Los Angeles, CA 90036-3890 USA ; *Imprints:* LB Books (LB Bks)
Dist(s): **APG Direct.**

Liberty Communications House *See* **JB Information Station**

Liberty Publishing Group, *(1-893095)* Div. of The Holton Consulting Group, Inc., Orders Addr.: 1405 Autumn Ridge Dr., Durham, NC 27712-2680 USA Tel 919-767-9620; Toll Free Fax: 866-500-7697; Toll Free: 877-819-7489
E-mail: bil@holtonconsulting.com
Web site: http://www.holtonconsulting.com.

Libie Alone Pubns., *(0-9678821)* Orders Addr.: 580 East Ave., Pawtucket, RI 02860 USA Tel 401-726-8630
E-mail: libiealone@earthlink.net
Dist(s): **Baker & Taylor Bks.**
Brodart Co.
Follett Media Distribution.

Librairie du Liban Pubns. (FRA) Dist. by Intl Bk Ctr.

Librairie Larousse (FRA) *(2-03) Dist. by* **Distribks Inc.**

†Libraries Unlimited, Inc., *(0-313; 0-87287; 1-56308; 1-59158)* Div. of Greenwood Publishing Group, Orders Addr.: a/o Customer Service Group, Dept. 2229, P.O. Box 5007, Westport, CT 06881 USA Fax: 603-431-2214; Toll Free: 800-225-5800; Edit Addr.: 88 Post Rd W., Westport, CT 06880-4208 USA ; *Imprints:* Teacher Ideas Press (TIP)
E-mail: lubooks@lu.com
Web site: http://www.lu.com
Dist(s): **Greenwood Publishing Group, Inc.**
NetLibrary, Inc.; *CIP.*

Library Assn. of La Jolla, *(0-9744804)* 1008 Wall St., La Jolla, CA 92037-4418 USA Tel 858-454-5872; Fax: 858-454-5835 ; *Imprints:* Athenaeum Music & Arts Library (Athenaeum Music)
E-mail: Athlibrary@pacbell.net.

Library of America, The, *(0-940450; 1-883011; 1-931082; 1-59853)* Div. of Literary Classics of the U. S., Inc., 14 E. 60th St., New York, NY 10022 USA (SAN 286-9918) Tel 212-308-3360; Fax: 212-750-8352
E-mail: info@loa.org
Web site: http://www.loa.org
Dist(s): **Penguin Group (USA) Inc.**

Library of Islam, Ltd. *Imprint of* **Kazi Pubns., Inc.**

Library of New Atlantis *See* **Scientists of New Atlantis**

Library Professional Pubns. *Imprint of* **Shoe String Pr., Inc.**

Library Reprints, Inc., *(0-7222)* Orders Addr.: P.O. Box 893520, Temecula, CA 92589-3520 USA (SAN 254-0258) Toll Free Fax: 888-265-3540; Toll Free: 888-265-3531; Edit Addr.: 26111 Ynez B14, Temecula, CA 92592 USA
E-mail: sales@thebooks.net.

Library Sales of N.J., *(1-888032)* Orders Addr.: P.O. Box 335, Garwood, NJ 07027-0335 USA Tel 908-232-1446; Edit Addr.: 607 S. Chestnut St., Westfield, NJ 07090-1369 USA
E-mail: Librarysalesofnj@aol.com.

Library Solutions Pr., *(1-882208)* 2137 Oregon St., Berkeley, CA 94705 USA Tel 916-939-2018; Fax: 916-939-9626
E-mail: sales@library-solutions.com
Web site: http://www.library-solutions.com.

LIBRI Bks.,#A Division of Seasons & A Muse#Inc. *See* **LIBRI Pubs.**

LIBRI Pubs., *(0-9763952)* P.O. Box 5849, Playa Del Rey, CA 90296-5849 USA Tel 310-827-6495; Fax: 310-827-8166
E-mail: libri@seasonsandamuse.com
Web site: http://www.seasonsandamuse.com.

Libros, Encouraging Cultural Literacy, *(0-9675413; 0-9710860)* Orders Addr.: P.O. Box 453, Long Beach, NY 11561 USA Tel 516-889-6077; Fax: 516-889-6365; Toll Free: 800-260-9915; Edit Addr.: 160 LaFayette Blvd., Long Beach, NY 11561 USA (SAN 253-374X)
E-mail: librospress@msn.com
Web site: http://www.librospress.com.

Libros Para Ninos *Imprint of* **Simon & Schuster Children's Publishing**

Libros Sin Fronteras, P.O. Box 2085, Olympia, WA 98507 USA Tel 360-357-4332; Fax: 360-357-4964
E-mail: info@librossinfronteras.com
Web site: http://www.librossinfronteras.com.

Libros-Latin American Treasures For Kids *See* **Libros, Encouraging Cultural Literacy**

Librujas, *(0-9771566)* 4335 Van Nuys Blvd., Suite 117, Sherman Oaks, CA 91403 USA (SAN 256-887X) Tel 818-905-7221
E-mail: jamie@librujas.com; patricia@librujas.com
Web site: http://www.librujas.com
Dist(s): **Quality Bks., Inc.**

Libsa, Editorial S.A. (ESP) *(84-7630; 84-662) Dist. by* **Continental Bk.**

Libsa, Editorial S.A. (ESP) *(84-7630; 84-662) Dist. by* **Lectorum Pubns.**

Licensing by Loren, Inc., *(1-889151)* Orders Addr.: P.O. Box 936, Marshalls Creek, PA 18335-0936 USA.

Life Action Publishing, *(0-940110; 0-9667124; 1-934718)* Orders Addr.: P.O. Box 31, Buchanan, MI 49107 USA Tel 269-697-8600; Fax: 269-695-2974; Toll Free: 800-321-1538; Edit Addr.: 2727 Niles Buchanan Rd., Buchanan, MI 49107 USA (SAN 220-2859)
Web site: http://www.lifeaction.org; http://www.ReviveOurHearts.com.

Life Assurance Ministries, *(0-9627546; 0-9747679)* Orders Addr.: P.O. Box 11587, Glendale, CA 85318 USA; Edit Addr.: 20427 N. 87th Dr., Peoria, AZ 85382 USA Tel 623-572-9549 (phone/fax); Fax: 623-572-3035; Toll Free: 800-355-7073
E-mail: dale@ratzlaf.com
Web site: http://www.ratzlaf.com.

Life Athletes Pr., *(0-9676435)* 400 Plaza Bldg., 210 S. Michigan St., South Bend, IN 46601 USA Tel 574-237-9000; Fax: 574-237-0902; Toll Free: 888-635-5433
E-mail: info@lifeathletes.org
Web site: http://www.lifeathletes.org.

Life by Design Youth Leadership Resources *See* **Youthleadership.com**

Life Changers International Church *See* **Dickow, Gregory Ministries**

Life Education Ctr., USA, *(1-931028)* 601 S. York St., Elmhurst, IL 60126-4434 USA
E-mail: jackie55@aol.com
Web site: http://www.lec.com.

Life Engineering Foundation, *(0-9672814)* 2953 Delta Ave., Bridgewater, IA 50837-8015 USA Tel 515-369-2391; Fax: 515-369-4961; Toll Free Fax: 800-852-5072
E-mail: office@lifeengineering.org
Web site: htttp://www.lifeengineering.org.

Life Innovations, Inc., *(0-9671983)* 2660 Arthur St., Roseville, MN 55113 USA Tel 651-635-0511; Fax: 651-635-0716; Toll Free: 800-331-1661
E-mail: kolson@lifeinnovation.com
Web site: http://www.lifeinnovation.com.

Life Letters Publishing, *(0-9746022)* P.O. Box 360111, Strongsville, OH 44136 USA
E-mail: lifeletter@aol.com
Web site: http://www.lifeletter.net.

Life Line, Inc., *(0-9647089)* P.O. Box 7990, New York, NY 10116-8715 USA Tel 212-947-0661; Fax: 212-947-0681 Do not confuse with Life Lines, Rimrock, AZ
E-mail: lifel@aol.com.

Life Line Publishing, *(0-9761604)* P.O. Box 1482, Bridgeport, CT 06601-1482 USA Do not confuse with Life Line Publishing in Franklin, VA.

Life Link Worldwide Pubs., *(1-880608)* 350 Marley Dr., College Park, GA 30349 USA Tel 770-994-1683.

Life Management, Inc., *(0-9701093)* 718 Griffin Ave., No. 239, Enumclaw, WA 98022 USA Tel 206-780-4165; Fax: 360-802-4521; Toll Free: 800-545-4384 Do not confuse with companies with the same or similar name in Marietta, GA, Westland, MI
E-mail: inwdjrny@aol.com
Web site: http://www.Life-Management.net.

Life Mission Assocs., *(0-9631262)* P.O. Box 182, Ojai, CA 93024 USA Tel 805-640-9709; Fax: 805-640-9707; Toll Free: 800-957-8888
E-mail: info@lifemissionassociates.com
Web site: http://www.lifemissionassociates.com
Dist(s): **Distributors, The**
New Leaf Distributing Co., Inc.

Life Office Management Assn., *(0-915322; 0-939921; 1-57974)* 2300 Windy Ridge Pkwy., Suite 600, Atlanta, GA 30339-8443 USA (SAN 207-2548) Tel 770-951-1770; Fax: 770-984-0441
E-mail: education@loma.org
Web site: http://www.loma.org
Dist(s): **PBD, Inc.**

Life Pubs. International, *(0-7361; 0-943258; 1-890219)* 1625 N. Robberson Ave., Springfield, MO 65803 USA (SAN 213-5817) Tel 417-831-7766; Fax: 417-831-6445; Toll Free: 888-776-2425
E-mail: info@lifepublishers.org.

Life Support System Publishing, Inc., *(1-929664)* 2223 Blue Mesa Dr., Box 237, Divide, CO 80814 USA (SAN 253-6625) Tel 719-686-8921; Fax: 413-431-3499
E-mail: office@lifesupportsystem.com
Web site: http://www.lifesupportsystem.com.

Lifebridge Bks., *(0-9740880; 0-9755311; 0-9770398; 0-9774223; 0-9786581; 0-9793192)* P.O. Box 49428, Charlotte, NC 28277 USA Fax: 704-846-8965
Dist(s): **STL Distribution North America.**

LifeCom, *(0-9615722)* Orders Addr.: P.O. Box 1832, Saint Cloud, MN 56302 USA (SAN 242-0724) Tel 320-252-9866; Edit Addr.: 1248 N. 13th Ave., Saint Cloud, MN 56303 USA (SAN 696-2572)
E-mail: Robertjoyce@charter.net.

Life-Enhancing Publishing, *(0-9722720)* Orders Addr.: P.O. Box 681427, Riverside, MO 64168 USA Fax: 816-505-9111; Edit Addr.: 4400 N. Mulberry Dr., Kansas City, MO 64116 USA
Dist(s): **AtlasBooks Distribution.**

Lifelight Bks., *(0-9743801)* 2629 262nd Pl SE, Sammamish, WA 98075-7900 USA (SAN 850-8070)
E-mail: lynne@lifelightbooks.com
Web site: http://www.lifelightbooks.com.

LifeLine Bks., *(1-891041)* Orders Addr.: P.O. Box 38, Hot Springs, NC 28743 USA Tel 704-622-3323; Fax: 704-622-7221; Toll Free: 800-453-8732; Edit Addr.: 1145 Bainey Lusk Rd., Hot Springs, NC 28743 USA
E-mail: wellth@onvillage.net
Web site: http://www.ear4strength
Dist(s): **Remnant Pubns.**
Spring Arbor Distributors, Inc.

LifeLine Studios, Inc., *(0-9714753)* 1390 W. Main St., Lancaster, TX 75146 USA Tel 972-275-0468; Fax: 972-275-0469
E-mail: afoutsjr@lifelinestudios.com
Web site: http://www.lifelinestudio.com.

LifeMatters Bks. *Imprint of* **Capstone Pr., Inc.**

Lifepac *Imprint of* **Alpha Omega Pubns., Inc.**

Life's Footprints, Inc., *(1-892458)* 905 Long Rd., Centralia, WA 98531 USA Tel 360-807-8850
E-mail: Lfbooks@quik.com.

Life's Journey of Hope Pubns., *(0-9747815)* Orders Addr.: P.O. Box 1277, Groton, MA 01450 USA (SAN 255-7789) Tel 978-448-1252; Edit Addr.: 90 Martins Pond Rd., Groton, MA 01450 USA
E-mail: LLeonard@lifesjourneyofhope.com; lifesjourneyofhope@hotmail.com
Web site: http://www.lifesjourneyofhope.com.

Life's Reflections, Incorporated *See* **Heritage Pubs., Inc.**

Lifesighs Cards, *(0-9657012)* Orders Addr.: P.O. Box 19446, San Diego, CA 92159 USA Tel 619-697-6026; Fax: 619-697-1712; Toll Free: 800-747-6026; Edit Addr.: 8265 Commercial St., No. 15, La Mesa, CA 91942 USA.

LifeSong Pubs., *(0-9718306; 0-9799116)* Orders Addr.: P.O. Box 183, Somis, CA 93066-0183 USA Tel 805-504-3916; Fax: 614-455-5030; Toll Free: 866-266-6917
Web site: http://www.lifesongpublishers.com.

Lifetime Relationship Center *See* **Intralife Systems Publishing**

Lifetrack Resources, *(0-9743826)* 709 Univ. Ave. W., Saint Paul, MN 55104-4804 USA Tel 651-227-8471; Fax: 651-227-0621
E-mail: familiestogether@lifetrackresources.org
Web site: http://www.lifetrackresources.org.

Lifevest *Imprint of* **Lifevest Publishing, Inc.**

Lifevest Publishing, Inc., *(0-9724680; 1-932338; 1-59879)* 4910 E. Dry Creek Rd., Suite 170, Centennial, CO 80122 USA Tel 303-221-1007; Fax: 303-771-1166; Toll Free Fax: 877-843-1007 ; *Imprints:* Lifevest (Livevst)
E-mail: ric.simmons@lifevestpublishing.com; publisher@lifevestpublishing.com
Web site: http://www.lifevestpublishing.com.

LifeWay Christian Resources, *(0-7673; 0-633; 1-4158; 1-4300)* Div. of The Southern Baptist Convention, One Lifeway Plaza, Nashville, TN 37234 USA Fax: 615-277-8221 (product info., ordering, order tracking); 615-251-2626 (shipping/transportation); Toll Free: 888-227-9493 (product info., ordering)
E-mail: customerservice@lifeway.com
Web site: http://www.lifeway.com; http://www.lifewaystores.com
Dist(s): **Spring Arbor Distributors, Inc.**

Liffey Pr., The (IRL) *(1-904148; 1-905785) Dist. by* **Dufour.**

Lift Every Voice *Imprint of* **Moody Pubs.**

Lift Every Voice, *(0-9635885; 1-891657)* 16 Park Ln., Newton Centre, MA 02459-1731 USA Tel 617-244-9808; Fax: 617-964-5432
E-mail: liftever@gis.net
Web site: http://www.qis.net/~liftever/.

Light & Life Publishing Co., *(0-937032; 1-880971; 1-933654)* 4808 Park Glen Rd., Minneapolis, MN 55416 USA (SAN 213-8565) Tel 952-925-3888; Fax: 952-925-3918
E-mail: info@light-n-life.com
Web site: http://www.light-n-life.com.

Light Bugs Publishing, *(0-9765514)* 1400 Champions Green Dr., Gulf Breeze, FL 32563 USA Tel 850-932-9325
E-mail: allen911@bellsouth.net; russ@lightbugspublishing.com; jan@lightbugspublishing.com
Web site: http://www.lightbugspublishing.com.

Light Energy Bks., *(0-9740480)* 731 Mandana Blvd., Oakland, CA 94610 USA Tel 510-268-9999.

Light in Glass Publishing, *(0-9719384)* 8706 206th St. SE, Snohomish, WA 98296-7909 USA Tel 360-668-9142
E-mail: deveriea@hotmail.com
Web site: http://www.deveriewood.com.

Light, Inc., The, *(0-9720654; 1-932099; 1-59784)* 26C Worlds Fair Dr., Somerset, NJ 08873 USA Tel 732-868-0210; Fax: 732-868-0211 ; *Imprints:* Fountain, The (The Fount) Do not confuse with Light, Inc., in Lemont, IL
E-mail: info@thelightinc.com
Web site: http://www.thelightinc.com
Dist(s): **Independent Pubs. Group.**

Light Line, *(0-9773244)* 353 E. Pittsfield St., Pennsville, NJ 08070 USA (SAN 257-2540) Toll Free: 877-427-8271
E-mail: jildadf@comcast.net.

Light Messages, *(0-9679937; 0-9800756)* 5216 Tahoe Dr., Durham, NC 27713 USA Tel 919-361-5041; Toll Free Fax: 866-585-4635
E-mail: books@lightmessages.com
Web site: http://www.lightmessages.com.

Light Sword Publishing LLC, *(0-9792030; 0-9800733)* P.O. Box 851556, Westland, MI 48185-9461 USA
E-mail: admin@lightswordpublishing.com; mslldaly@lightswordpublishing.com
Web site: http://www.lightswordpublishing.com.

Light Way Pubns., The, *(0-9702821)* P.O. Box 10123, Jackson, TN 38308-0102 USA Tel 731-660-5057; Fax: 731-668-6957; Toll Free: 888-815-0445
E-mail: earlemu@aol.com
Web site: http://www.earlemu.com.

Light Works Publishing *Imprint of* **I.M. Enterprises**

Light Years Ahead, *(0-9700121)* 4107 Scarborough Dr., Richfield, WI 53076 USA Tel 262-628-3674; Fax: 262-628-4023
E-mail: polo@execpc.com.

Light24, *(0-9700002)* Orders Addr.: 85-42 160th St., Jamaica Queens, NY 11432 USA Tel 718-526-7021 Do not confuse with companies with the same name in Worthington, OH, Kirkland, WA.

Light-Beams Publishing, *(0-9708104; 0-9766289)* Orders Addr.: 10 Toon Ln., Lee, NH 03824 USA Tel 603-659-1300; Fax: 603-659-3399; Toll Free: 800-397-7641
E-mail: mforman@light-beams.com; info@light-beams.com
Web site: http://www.light-beams.com
Dist(s): **Baker & Taylor Bks.**
Book Wholesalers, Inc.
Brodart Co.
Library Video Co.
Midwest Tape
New Leaf Distributing Co., Inc.
NewSound, LLC.

Lighted Lamp Pr., *(1-888350)* Orders Addr.: P.O. Box 1234, Wheat Ridge, CO 80034 USA; Edit Addr.: 4945 Gray St., Denver, CO 80212 USA (SAN 298-8348)
E-mail: robertjinye@msn.com
Web site: http://www.lightedlamp.com/
Dist(s): **Baker & Taylor Bks.**

Lighthearted Press Inc., *(0-9659225)* Orders Addr.: P.O. Box 90125, Portland, OR 97290 USA Tel 503-786-3085; Fax: 503-786-0315; Edit Addr.: 10585 SE Fairway Dr., Portland, OR 97266 USA
E-mail: davis@lightheartedpress.com
Web site: www.lightheartedpress.com.

Lighthouse Bk. Publishing, *(0-9791168)* Orders Addr.: P.O. Box 310534, Houston, TX 77231 USA Toll Free: 800-247-9100
E-mail: foxcity22@hotmail.com
Web site: http://www.journeytoseetheking.com.

Lighthouse Christian Products Co., *(0-9712894)* 1050 Remington Rd., Schaumburg, IL 60173-4518 USA
Web site: http://lcpgifts.com.

Lighthouse Christian Publishing, *(0-9621392)* P.O. Box 505, Norman, OK 73070-0505 USA (SAN 251-236X) Fax: 405-329-3857
E-mail: Lighthcp@aol.com.

Lighthouse Literary Pr., Inc., *(0-9668780)* P.O. Box 421, Chesterland, OH 44026 USA
E-mail: Lthsepress@aol.com.

LightHouse Ministries, *(0-9668763)* 2214 Baker Terr., NW, Atlanta, GA 30318 USA Tel 404-249-9000; Fax: 404-249-6620 Do not confuse with companies with the same name in Ferndale, MI & Claypool, AZ.

Lighthouse Point Pr., *(0-9637966; 0-9792998)* Div. of Yearick-Millea, Inc., 100 First Ave., Suite 525, Pittsburgh, PA 15222-1504 USA Tel 412-323-9320; Fax: 412-323-9334
E-mail: info@yearick-millea.com
Web site: http://lighthousepointpress.com
Dist(s): **Ingram Bk. Co.**

LightHouse Pr., *(0-9703823; 0-9724442; 0-9747189; 0-9762898; 0-9791372)* Orders Addr.: P.O. Box 281375, Nashville, TN 37228 USA Tel 615-300-1195; Edit Addr.: 2053 Williams Valley Dr., Madison, TN 37115 USA Do not confuse with companies with the same or similar names in Culver City, CA, Millersburg, OH, York, ME, Marblehead, MA, Deerfield Beach, FL, La Junta, CO, Rochester, NY, San Mateo, CA
E-mail: lighthousepress1@yahoo.com.

Lighthouse Pr., Inc., *(0-9677347; 0-9795392)* 35 Ryans Run, Rochester, NY 14624-1160 USA (SAN 253-0961) Tel 716-594-0311; Fax: 716-594-4207 Do not confuse with companies with the same or similar names in York, ME, Marblehead, MA, La Junta, CO, Deerfield Beach, FL, San Mateo, CA, Sanford, MI, Minneapolis, MN, Millersburg, OH
E-mail: swagner@lighthouse-press.com
Web site: http://www.lighthouse-press.com
Dist(s): **Biblio Distribution.**

Lighthouse Productions, Inc., *(0-9656957)* 542 CR 2073, Eureka Springs, AR 72632 USA Tel 501-253-5008 Do not confuse with Lighthouse Productions, Lancaster, PA
E-mail: av1cadet@arkansas.net
Web site: aviationcadet.com.

Lightly Pr., *(0-9794452)* 26 Quay Ct., No. 65, sacramento, CA 95831-1540 USA Tel 916-427-7840
E-mail: regdown@hotmail.com.

Lightning Bug Flix, *(1-933262)* 1126 S. 70th St., Suite N601, Milwaukee, WI 53214 USA Tel 414-475-4445; Fax: 414-475-3621
E-mail: vicky@lightningbugflix.com
Web site: http://www.lightningbugflix.com.

Lightning Creek *See* **Perceval Pr.**

Lightning Rod Pubs. *Imprint of* **Windstorm Creative**

Lightning Source, Inc., 1246 Heil Quaker Blvd., LaVergne, TN 37086 USA (SAN 179-6976) Tel 615-213-4595; Fax: 615-213-4426.

LightningBolt Pr., *(0-9746398)* 1481 Applegate Dr., Suite 101, Naperville, IL 60565-1225 USA Tel 630-778-7310; Fax: 630-778-7890
E-mail: info@lightningboltpress.com
Web site: http://www.lightningboltpress.com.

Lightport Bks., *(0-9712425)* P.O. Box 7112, Berkeley, CA 94707 USA
E-mail: haconrad@earthlink.net
Web site: http://www. lightportbooks.com
Dist(s): **Baker & Taylor Bks.**

Lightstream Pubns., *(1-892713)* 44999 Cree Ct., Fremont, CA 94539-6513 USA Tel 510-657-2912; Fax: 510-657-1750; Toll Free: 800-651-9644
E-mail: nancyr@thegrid.net
Web site: http://www.mypage.goplay.com/nancym88/books.html.

Lightwatcher Publishing, *(0-9718600)* P.O. Box 2643, Friday Harbor, WA 98250-2643 USA Tel 360-378-6047
E-mail: lightman@lightwatcher.com
Web site: http://www.lightwatcher.com; http://www.lightwatcher.com/LW_pub/public_html/index.html.

Lightyear Pr. *Imprint of* **Buccaneer Bks., Inc.**

Liguori Lifespan *Imprint of* **Liguori Pubns.**

Liguori Pubns., *(0-7648; 0-89243)* One Liguori Dr., Liguori, MO 63057-9999 USA (SAN 202-6783) Tel 636-464-2500; Fax: 636-464-8449; Toll Free Fax: 800-325-9526; Toll Free: 800-325-9521 (orders) ; *Imprints:* Liguori Lifespan (Liguori Lifespan)
E-mail: liguori@liguori.org
Web site: http://www.liguori.org
Dist(s): **ACTA Pubns.**
Baker & Taylor Bks.

LikeMinds Pr., *(0-9764724)* 1400 Balsam Ave., San Diego, CA 92064 USA Tel 858-679-7157; Fax: 858-679-7157
E-mail: shendl@cox.net
Web site: http://www.likemindspress.com.

Lil' Pardner Pr. *Imprint of* **Fire Creek Publishing Corp.**

Lilac Pr., *(0-9662568)* Orders Addr.: P.O. Box 1356, Scottsdale, AZ 85252-1356 USA Fax: 480-368-5551; Edit Addr.: 6268 N. 85th St., Scottsdale, AZ 85250 USA
E-mail: lilacp@cholesterolnodiet.com; lilacp@frontiernet.net
Web site: http://www.cholesterolnodiet.com.

Lilith & Co., *(0-9717860)* 31185 Blue Springs Rd., Meadowview, VA 24361-2441 USA Tel 276-475-5208
E-mail: pendragon@naxs.net
Web site: http://www.lilithandcompany.com.

Lillenas Publishing Co., *(0-8341)* Div. of Nazarene Publishing Hse., P.O. Box 419527, Kansas City, MO 64141 USA (SAN 298-7619) Tel 816-931-1900; Fax: 816-753-4071; Toll Free: 800-877-0700 (Orders Only)
E-mail: music@lillenas.com
Web site: http://www.lillenas.com
Dist(s): **Spring Arbor Distributors, Inc.**

Lillian Press *See* **Smith & Assocs.**

Lilliput Pr., Ltd., The (IRL) *(0-946640; 1-874675; 1-901866; 1-84351) Dist. by* **Dufour.**

Lillis, Holly, *(0-9762733)* P.O. Box 1082, Aptos, CA 95001-0000 USA.

Lill-Till Pr., *(0-9742808)* 15305 Walvern Blvd., Maple Heights, OH 44137 USA.

Lily & Co. Publishing, *(1-929265)* 231 Old County Rd., Smithfield, RI 02917 USA
E-mail: lilyandco@aol.com
Web site: http://www.lilycopublishing.com.

Lily Wish Factory, *(0-9792472)* 44 W. Main St., Mystic, CT 06355 USA (SAN 852-8861) Tel 860-245-0629
E-mail: shipandshimmer@aol.com
Web site: http://shipandshimmer.com.

Lima Bean Pr., Inc., *(0-9711349)* 630 Shore Rd., Apt. 505, Long Beach, NY 11561 USA Tel 516-431-7292; Fax: 516-431-1907; Toll Free: 800-972-9480
E-mail: growingup@earthlink.net.

Lima Bear Pr LLC, The, *(1-933872)* 2305 MacDonough Rd., Wilmington, DE 19805 USA
E-mail: lbp.books@yahoo.com
Web site: http://www.limabearpress.com.

Limac Publishing, *(0-9713258)* 2811 Aster Pl., Onalaska, WI 54650 USA Tel 608-781-3687
E-mail: limacpublishing@aol.com
Web site: http://www.mouseconnections.com.

Limerock Bks., *(0-9746589)* 15 Mechanic St., Thomaston, ME 04861 USA Tel 207-354-8191 Do not confuse with Limerock Books, Inc., New Canaan, CT
E-mail: limebks@midcoast.com
Web site: http://www.ChristopherFahy.com
Dist(s): **Baker & Taylor Bks.**
Brodart Co.

Limestock Pr. *Imprint of* **Moonlight on the Wabash Publishing**

Limpid Butterfly Productions, The, *(0-9668781; 0-9709119)* P.O. Box 83942, San Diego, CA 92138 USA Fax: 858-679-4180; Toll Free: 800-837-7336
E-mail: booksbymaryo@hotmail.com; look@limpidbutterfly.com
Web site: http://www.booksbymaryo.com; http://www.limpidbutterfly.com
Dist(s): **Baker & Taylor Bks.**

Lincoln, Frances Ltd. (GBR) *(0-7112; 0-906459; 1-84507) Dist. by* **Antique Collect.**

Lincoln, Frances Ltd. (GBR) *(0-7112; 0-906459; 1-84507) Dist. by* **St Mut.**

Lincoln, Frances Ltd. (GBR) *(0-7112; 0-906459; 1-84507) Dist. by* **Star Brght Bks.**

Lincoln, Frances Ltd. (GBR) *(0-7112; 0-906459; 1-84507) Dist. by* **Perseus Dist.**

Lincoln Library *Imprint of* **Lincoln Library Press, The**

Lincoln Library Press, The, *(0-912168)* Div. of Eastword Publications Development, Incorporated, Orders Addr.: 812 Huron Rd., SE, Suite 401, Cleveland, OH 44115-1126 USA (SAN 205-5953) Tel 216-781-9559 (phone/fax); Toll Free: 800-516-2656 ; *Imprints:* Lincoln Library (Lincoln Lib)
E-mail: tgall@thelincolnlibrary.com
Web site: http://www.thelincolnlibrary.com.

Lincoln Public Schls., *(0-9671920)* P.O. Box 82889, Lincoln, NE 68501 USA (SAN 508-9964) Tel 401-436-1628; Fax: 401-436-1638
E-mail: dpeters@lps.org
Web site: http://www.lps.org.

Linda Hall Library, *(0-9763590)* 5109 Cherry St., Kansas City, MO 64110-2498 USA Tel 816-363-4600; Fax: 816-926-8790
E-mail: bradleyb@lindahall.org
Web site: http://www.lindahall.org.

Linda Kaye's Birthdaybakers, Partymakers, *(0-9759161)* 195 East 76th St., New York, NY 10021 USA Tel 212-288-7112; Fax: 212-879-6785
E-mail: lindak@partymakers.com
Web site: http://www.partymakers.com.

Linden Hill Publishing, *(0-9704754)* Subs. of Arcadia Productions, 11923 Somerset Ave., Princess Anne, MD 21853 USA Tel 410-651-0757 (phone/fax)
E-mail: lh123@comcast.net
Web site: http://www.lindenhill.net.

Linden Pubs., *(0-89642; 0-7949)* 1750 N. Sycamore, Suite 305, Hollywood, CA 90028-8662 USA (SAN 206-7218) Tel 323-876-5190.

Linden Publishing Co., Inc., *(0-941936; 1-933502)* 2006 S. Mary, Fresno, CA 93721 USA (SAN 238-6089) Tel 559-233-6633 (phone/fax); Toll Free: 800-345-4447 (orders only) Do not confuse with LInden Publishing in Avon, NY
E-mail: richard@lindenpub.com
Web site: http://www.lindenpub.com
Dist(s): **Baker & Taylor Bks.**
Independent Pubs. Group
Quality Bks., Inc.

Linder Pubns., *(1-929167)* Orders Addr.: P.O. Box 250231, West Bloomfield, MI 48322 USA Tel 248-737-1395; Fax: 248-865-0472; Edit Addr.: 4175 Breckenridge Dr., West Bloomfield, MI 48322 USA
E-mail: Treg714@aol.com.

Lindos Bks, *(0-9672875)* 10510 W. Tumblewood Dr., Sun City, AZ 85351-1631 USA Toll Free: 877-773-8884
E-mail: dad@worlddad.com
Web site: http://www.worlddad.com.

Lindsay Pubns., Inc., *(0-917914; 1-55918)* Orders Addr.: P.O. Box 12, Bradley, IL 60915 USA (SAN 209-9462) Tel 815-935-5353; Fax: 815-935-5477.

Line of Promise Pr., *(0-9705251; 0-9744240)* P.O. Box 1242, Sunnyside, WA 98944 USA (SAN 255-7061) Tel 509-837-2229; Fax: 509-837-2292
E-mail: covenant@lineofpromise.com
Web site: http://www.lineofpromise.com.

Lingenfelser, Lynda L., *(0-615)* 3284 Spruce Creek Glen, Daytona Beach, FL 32198 USA; P.O. Box 290714, Port Orange, FL 32129
Dist(s): **Lulu.com.**

Lingo Pr. LLC, *(0-9777419)* 1020 Janet Dr., Lakeland, FL 33805 USA (SAN 850-119X) Tel 863-868-5996 (phone/fax)
E-mail: customerservice@lingopress.com
Web site: http://www.lingopress.com.

Linguatechnics Publishing, *(0-9767837)* 2114 Pauline Blvd., Ann Arbor, MI 48103 USA Tel 734-662-0434; Fax: 734-662-0248
E-mail: info@linguatechnics.com
Web site: http://www.linguatechnics.com.

LinguaText, Ltd., *(0-936388; 0-942566; 1-58871; 1-58977)* Orders Addr.: 270 Indian Rd., Newark, DE 19711-5204 USA (SAN 238-0307) Tel 302-453-8695; Fax: 302-453-8601; Toll Free: 800-784-4938
E-mail: linguatext@juno.com
Web site: http://www.LinguatextLtd.com; http://www.EuropeanMasterpieces.com; http://www.JuandelaCuesta.com.

LinguiSystems, Inc., *(0-7606; 1-55999)* 3100 Fourth Ave., East Moline, IL 61244-9700 USA Tel 309-755-2300; Fax: 309-755-2377; Toll Free: 800-776-4332; 800-577-4555
E-mail: kgeorge@linguisystems.com
Web site: http://www.linguisystems.com.

Linham, Stephen V., *(0-9704084)* 1165 Normandy Dr., Newark, OH 43055-9021 USA
E-mail: stevel5355@aol.com.

Linive Kreyol Publishing, *(0-9720954)* 339 Howell Dr. SE, Suite 3-F, Atlanta, GA 30316 USA.

Link & Rosie Pr., *(0-9762434)* Orders Addr.: c/o Goblin Fern Press, Inc., 1118 Sequoia Trail, Madison, WI 53713 USA Tel 608-335-0542; Fax: 608-210-7235
E-mail: ssharron@sbcglobal.net
Web site: http://www.linkandrosie.com.

Linker, F. Ephraim, *(0-9718132)* P.O. Box 670732, Flushing, NY 11367 USA
E-mail: froyam@yahoo.com
Web site: http://www.HebrewPrayersLearningSeries.com.

Linky & Dinky Enterprises, *(0-9768588)* P.O. Box 418, Oldsmar, FL 34677 USA
E-mail: uncle-url@linkydinky.com
Web site: http://www.linkydinky.com.

Linmore Publishing, Inc., *(0-916591; 1-934472)* Orders Addr.: P.O. Box 1545, Palatine, IL 60078 USA (SAN 662-2291) Fax: 612-729-9125; Toll Free: 800-336-3656
E-mail: linmore@linmore.com
Web site: http://www.linmore.com.

Linnet Bks. *Imprint of* **Shoe String Pr., Inc.**

Linnet Professional Pubns. *Imprint of* **Shoe String Pr., Inc.**

Lintel, *(0-931642)* 24 Blake Ln., Middletown, NY 10940 USA (SAN 213-6325) Tel 845-342-5224 (phone/fax).

Linville, Dorothy, *(0-9701551)* 10 Wildbird Ln., Hilton Head, SC 29926-2766 USA
E-mail: dorlinville@msn.com.

Linwood Hse. Publishing, *(0-9753098)* 843 Cypress Pkwy., No. 338, Kissimmee, FL 34759 USA Tel 407-595-6220
E-mail: zippityzern@comcast.net.

Linworth Publishing, Inc., *(0-938865; 1-58683)* 3650 Olentangy River Rd., Suite 250, Columbus, OH 43214 USA (SAN 662-5800) Tel 614-884-9995; Fax: 614-884-9993; Toll Free: 800-786-5017
E-mail: linworth@linworthpublishing.com
Web site: http://www.linworth.com
Dist(s): **Thomson Gale.**

Linx Educational Publishing, Inc., *(1-891818; 0-9797510)* P.O. Box 50009, Jacksonville Beach, FL 32240 USA Tel 904-241-1861; Fax: 904-241-3279; Toll Free Fax: 888-546-9338; Toll Free: 800-717-5469
E-mail: mimi@lixedu.com; info@linxedu.com
Web site: http://www.linxedu.com
Dist(s): **American Assn. for Vocational Instructional Materials**
Films Media Group
JIST Publishing
S V E & Churchill Media.

†Lion Bks., *(0-87460)* 235 Garth Rd. Apt. D5A, Scarsdale, NY 10583-3994 USA (SAN 241-7529)
Dist(s): **BookMasters, Inc.;** *CIP.*

Lion Hudson plc (GBR) *(0-7459; 0-85648) Dist. by* **Trafalgar.**

Lion Hudson plc (GBR) *(0-7459; 0-85648) Dist. by* **Kregel.**

Lion Hudson plc (GBR) *(0-7459; 0-85648) Dist. by* **IPG Chicago.**

Lion Stone Bks., *(0-9658486)* Orders Addr.: 4921 Aurora Dr., Kensington, MD 20895 USA Tel 301-949-3204; Fax: 301-949-3860
E-mail: lionstone@juno.com
Dist(s): **Baker & Taylor Bks.**
Book Wholesalers, Inc.
Brodart Co.
Follett Library Resources.

Lionel L.L.C., *(1-892136)* 50625 Richard W Blvd., Chesterfield, MI 48051 USA Tel 810-949-4100; Fax: 810-949-1013
Web site: http://www.lionel.com.

Lionheart Foundation, The, *(0-9644933; 0-9799338)* P.O. Box 194, Boston, MA 02117 USA Tel 781-444-6667; Fax: 781-444-6855
E-mail: judith@lionheart.org
Web site: http://www.lionheart.org.

Lionheart Television International, Incorporated *See* **BBC Worldwide Americas**

Lions & Tigers & Bears Publishing, Inc., *(1-893459)* 612 Hidden Valley Ln., Jefferson City, MO 65101 USA Tel 573-496-3600; Toll Free: 866-628-6463
E-mail: me@meandunclemike.com
Web site: http://www.MeAndUncleMike.com; http://www.particlemechanics.com; http://www.tadtron.com.

Lion's Crest Pr., *(0-9763798)* 1900 S. Rock Rd., Suite 5205, Wichita, KS 67207 USA Tel 316-305-5813.

Lion's Heart Publishing *See* **Lion's Heart Publishing, LLC**

Lion's Heart Publishing, LLC, *(0-9677117)* Orders Addr.: 6336 Mock Orange Dr., Charlotte, NC 28277 USA Tel 704-759-8119
E-mail: charper@carolina.rr.com
Web site: http://www.lionsheartpublishing.com.

Lion's Paw Bks. *Imprint of* **Coronet Bks. & Pubns.**

Lion's Paw Pr., LLC, *(0-9712400)* 4039 NE 57th St., Seattle, WA 98105 USA Tel 206-526-5164
E-mail: svandergrift@msn.com
Web site: http://lionspawpress.com.

Company

Little Ones *Imprint of* **Port Town Publishing**

Little Pee-Wee Publishing Co., *(0-9667210)* 751 Rabbit Rd., Wimberley, TX 78676-9780 USA Tel 830-833-0306; Fax: 830-833-5694
E-mail: preston@littlepeewee.com
Web site: http://www.littlepeewee.com.

Little Pemberley Pr., *(0-9763359)* Orders Addr.: 1528 Tulane St., Suite F, Houston, TX 77008-4146 USA Tel 713-862-8542; Fax: 713-862-6399
E-mail: littlepemberleypress@hotmail.com
Web site: http://www.giraffeofmontana.com; http://www.littlepemberleypress.com.

Little People Bks., *(0-9764114)* 2 Victor Ave., Worcester, MA 01603 USA Tel 508-963-2004.

Little Petals *Imprint of* **Roses Are READ Productions**

Little Petoskey Press *See* **Mackinac Island Pr., Inc.**

Little Red Cat Publishing, *(0-9726375)* 939A Terra Bella Ave., Mountainview, CA 94043 USA (SAN 254-9549) Tel 650-960-4040; Fax: 650-960-1040
E-mail: email@comprintingco.com; e-mail@comprintingco.com.

Little Redhaired Girl Publishing, Inc., *(0-9729264)* P.O. Box 9013, Miramar Beach, FL 32550-1848 USA ; *Imprints:* Books for Brats (Books for Brats)
E-mail: booksforbrats@aol.com
Web site: http://www.booksforbrats.net.

Little River Bookshelf, *(0-9769856)* 2707 Silver Leaf Ct., Grapevine, TX 76051 USA Tel 817-308-2510
E-mail: mark.storer@usa.net.

Little Rose Publishing *See* **3D Pr., Inc.**

Little Scribblers Bks., LLC, *(0-9747689)* 2545 NW 55th Pl., Oklahoma City, OK 73112-7101 USA Tel 405-615-8662
E-mail: littlescribblers@cox.net
Web site: http://www.littlescribblers.com.

Little Shepherd *Imprint of* **Scholastic, Inc.**

Little Shepherd Bks. *Imprint of* **White Stone Co., The**

Little Simon *Imprint of* **Simon & Schuster Children's Publishing**

Little Simon Inspirations *Imprint of* **Simon & Schuster Children's Publishing**

Little Soundprints *Imprint of* **Soundprints**

Little Spirit Publishing, Inc., *(0-9619482)* 5410 Poncha Pass Ct., Colorado Springs, CO 80917 USA (SAN 244-9269) Tel 719-597-5733
E-mail: digthefun@canyoudigitgarden.com
Web site: http://www.canyoudigitgarden.com.

Little Sprout Publishing Hse., *(0-9779194)* Orders Addr.: 520 Berry Way, La Habra, CA 90631 USA
Web site: http://psalmsforkidz.com.

Little Teacher Bks., *(0-615; 0-9744338)* 635 E. Golf Rd., Des Plaines, IL 60016 USA (SAN 255-0938).

Little Thoughts For Little Ones Publishing, Inc., *(0-9748884)* Orders Addr.: P.O. Box 665, Tavernier, FL 33070 USA
E-mail: vhandelsman@bellsouth.net
Web site: http://www.littlethoughtspublishing.com.

Little Tiger Pr., *(1-888444; 1-58431)* Div. of Futech Interactive Products, 39 S. La Salle St. Ste. 1410, Chicago, IL 60603-1706 USA Toll Free: 800-541-2205 Do not confuse Little Tiger Press in San Francisco, CA
E-mail: jody@futechsales.com
Dist(s): **Futech Educational Products, Inc.**
Lectorum Pubns., Inc.

Little Treasure Pubns., Inc., *(0-9639838)* Orders Addr.: P.O. Box 937, Ocean City, NJ 08226 USA Tel 609-398-5252; Fax: 609-398-5039
E-mail: bgltp@comcast.net
Web site: http://www.littletreasurebooks.com.

Little Trucker Bks., *(1-892388)* P.O. Box 733, Hampstead, NC 28445 USA Tel 910-328-6281; Toll Free: 888-547-6281
Web site: http://www.littletruckerbooks.com.

Little Tule Bks., *(0-9773133)* P.O. Box 549, Carmel Valley, CA 93924-0549 USA (SAN 257-2311) Tel 831-659-0107; Fax: 831-659-0106
E-mail: bill@littletulebooks.com
Web site: http://www.littletulebooks.com.

Little Vegan Monsters Publishing, *(0-9787590)* P.O. Box 9258, New Haven, CT 06533 USA
E-mail: Lourdes@littleveganmonsters.com
Web site: http://www.littleveganmonsters.com.

Little Way Pr., *(0-9764691)* 18252 Little Fuller Rd., Twain Harte, CA 95383 USA
Web site: http://www.littlewaypress.com
Dist(s): **Catholic Heritage Curricula.**

Little Wooden Bks., *(0-929949)* 11001 S. Degray Ln., Spokane, WA 99224 USA (SAN 250-7943) Tel 509-932-4729.

LittleJeanie Publishing Co., *(0-9700101)* P.O. Box 31183, Phoenix, AZ 85046 USA Tel 602-200-8255; Fax: 602-212-0340
E-mail: JSFlipdDip@aol.com.

LittleKid Pr., *(1-891806)* 646 S. Barrington, No. 107, Los Angeles, CA 90049 USA Tel 310-471-7861; Fax: 310-471-3998.

Littleton Coin Co., Inc., *(0-9644591; 1-930848; 1-933256)* Div. of Littleton Stamp & Coin Company, Inc., 1309 Mount Eustis Rd., Littleton, NH 03561 USA (SAN 855-109X) Toll Free: 877-512-2923
Web site: http://www.littletoncoin.com.

Liturgical Pr. Bks. *Imprint of* **Liturgical Pr.**

†Liturgical Pr., *(0-8146; 0-916134)* Div. of Order of St. Benedict, Inc., Orders Addr.: a/o St. Johns Abbey, P.O. Box 7500, Collegeville, MN 56321-7500 USA (SAN 202-2494) Tel 320-363-2213; 612 363 2326; Fax: 320-363-3299; Toll Free Fax: 800-445-5899; Toll Free: 800-858-5450 ; *Imprints:* Liturgical Press Books (Liturg Pr Bks)
E-mail: sales@litpress.org
Web site: http://www.litpress.org; http://sjbible.org; http://cistercianpublications.com; *CIP.*

Liturgy Training Pubns., *(0-929650; 0-930467; 1-56854)* Div. of Archdiocese of Chicago, 1800 N. Hermitage Ave., Chicago, IL 60622 USA (SAN 670-9052) Tel 773-486-8970 (editorial); Fax: 773-486-7094 (editorial); Toll Free Fax: 800-933-7094 (orders); Toll Free: 800-933-1800 (orders) ; *Imprints:* Catechesis of the Good Shepherd (Catechesis Good Shepherd)
E-mail: marketing@ltp.org; orders@ltp.org
Web site: http://www.ltp.org
Dist(s): **Baker & Taylor Bks.**
CRC Pubns.

Live Oak Games, *(0-9764394)* P.O. Box 780932, Orlando, FL 32878 USA Toll Free Fax: 800-214-4632 (phone/fax)
E-mail: sales@liveoakgames.com
Web site: http://www.liveoakgames.com.

Live Oak Media, *(0-87499; 0-941078; 1-59112; 1-59519; 1-4301)* Orders Addr.: P.O. Box 652, Pine Plains, NY 12567-0652 USA (SAN 217-3921) Tel 518-398-1010; Fax: 518-398-1070; Toll Free: 800-788-1121
E-mail: info@liveoakmedia.com
Web site: http://www.liveoakmedia.com
Dist(s): **BBC Audiobooks America**
Greathall Productions, Inc.
Lectorum Pubns., Inc.

Live Wire Pr., *(0-9672885; 0-9727531)* 103 Birdwood Ct., Charlottesville, VA 22903 USA Toll Free: 866-579-3850
E-mail: padler@cstone.net
Web site: http://www.livewirepress.net; http://www.mondaynightmeditation.com/distribution
Dist(s): **Conley, John C.**
New Leaf Distributing Co., Inc.

†Liveright Publishing Corp., *(0-87140)* Subs. of W. W. Norton Co., Inc., 500 Fifth Ave., New York, NY 10110 USA (SAN 201-0976) Tel 212-354-5500; Fax: 212-869-0856; Toll Free Fax: 800-458-6515; Toll Free: 800-233-4830
Web site: http://www.wwnorton.com
Dist(s): **Norton, W. W. & Co., Inc.**; *CIP.*

Liverpool Academic Pr. (GBR) *(1-872807; 1-903499; 1-903500) Dist. by* **Intl Spec Bk.**

Liverpool Univ. Pr. (GBR) *(0-85323; 1-84631) Dist. by* **Chicago Distribution Ctr.**

Living Gold Pr., *(0-9651377; 0-9768321)* Orders Addr.: P.O. Box 2, Klamath River, CA 96050 USA; Edit Addr.: 18341 Hgwy. 96, Klamath River, CA 96050 USA
E-mail: jandk@livinggoldpress.com
Web site: http://www.livinggoldpress.com
Dist(s): **American West Bks.**
Baker & Taylor Bks.

Living History Pr., *(0-9664925)* 7426 Elmwood Ave., Middleton, WI 53562 USA Tel 608-836-7426; Fax: 608-836-0176 Do not confuse with Living History Pr., Bellevue, WA
E-mail: pferd@itis.com
Web site: http://www.inwave.com/Milton/MiltonHouse/.

Living in Grace, *(0-9659319)* 10051 Siegen Ln., Baton Rouge, LA 70810 USA Tel 504-769-8844; Fax: 504-767-5655; Toll Free: 800-484-2046 ext. 9506
E-mail: QRBC@aol.com.

Living Language *Imprint of* **Random Hse. Information Group**

Living Life Publishing Co., *(0-9768773; 0-9769166; 0-9774499; 1-934796)* 24165 IH-10, W., Suite 217-474, San Antonio, TX 78257 USA (SAN 256-5684) Tel 210-698-6392; Fax: 210-698-6394
E-mail: livinglifepublishing@msn.com
Web site: http://www.livinglifepublishing.com
Dist(s): **AtlasBooks Distribution**
BookMasters.

Living Ministry, Inc., *(0-9763167)* 800 Prospect Blvd., Pasadena, CA 91103 USA Tel 626-356-9491; Fax: 626-584-0290
Web site: http://www.livingministry.com.

Living Room Games, *(1-55560; 0-9704191; 0-9755206)* 12241 Cox Ln., Dallas, TX 75244-7020 USA Fax: 214-233-3086
E-mail: pr@lrgames.com
Web site: http://www.lrgames.com.

Living Stone Arts, *(0-9763901)* 3806 Owl Dr., Rolling Meadows, IL 60008 USA
Web site: http://www.livingstonearts.com.

Living Stream Ministry, *(0-7363; 0-87083; 1-57593)* 2431 W. La Palma Ave., Anaheim, CA 92801 USA (SAN 253-4266) Tel 714-236-6001; 714-991-4681; Fax: 714-991-4685
E-mail: books@lsm.org
Web site: http://www.lsm.org
Dist(s): **Anchor Distributors**
Spring Arbor Distributors, Inc.

Living the Good News, *(0-8192; 1-889108; 1-931960)* Div. of The Morehouse Group, Orders Addr.: P.O. Box 1321, Harrisburg, PA 17105 USA Tel 717-541-8130; Fax: 717-541-8128; Toll Free: 800-877-0012; Edit Addr.: 600 Grant St., Suite 400, Denver, CO 80203 USA Tel 303-832-4427; Fax: 303-832-4971
E-mail: dirk@livingthegoodnews.com
Dist(s): **Spring Arbor Distributors, Inc.**

Living Water Pubns., *(1-59521)* P.O. Box 4653, Rockford, IL 61110-4653 USA Fax: 815-394-0140 Do not confuse with Living Water Publications in Edwardsville, KS
E-mail: lwministry@aol.com
Web site: http://www.livingwaterpublications.org.

Living Waters, Inc., *(0-9718292)* Div. of Lake Regional Conference Of Seventh Day Adventist, 8787 Southside Blvd., Suite 314, Jacksonville, FL 32256 USA Tel 904-538-9356.

Living Waters Publishing Co., *(0-9798154)* 1221 N. 2nd St., West Monroe, LA 71291 USA Tel 318-387-3899
E-mail: administration@livingwaterspc.com
Web site: http://www.livingwaterspc.com
Dist(s): **Lightning Source, Inc.**

Living Well Publishing Co., *(0-9725307)* 89 Auburn St., No. 1139, Portland, ME 04103 USA.

Livingston Pr., *(0-930501; 0-942979; 1-931982; 1-60489)* Div. of Univ. Of West Alabama, Univ. of West Alabama, Sta. 22, Livingston, AL 35470 USA (SAN 851-917X) Tel 205-652-3470; Fax: 205-652-3717; Toll Free: 800-959-3245 Do not confuse with Livingston Pr., Anaheim, CA
E-mail: jwt@uwa.edu
Web site: http://www.livingstonpress.uwa.edu.

LivnLern Pr., *(0-9656414)* 416 Fourth St., Langley, WA 98260 USA Tel 360-221-8842; Fax: 360-221-6946
E-mail: mathman@whidbey.com
Web site: http://www.MarkWahl.com
Dist(s): **Wahl, Mark Learning Services.**

Livraria Martins Editora (BRA) *(85-336) Dist. by* **Distribks Inc.**

LizStar Bks, *(0-9779753)* 2648 Jolly Acres Rd., White Hall, MD 21161 USA Tel 410-557-9388
E-mail: tracy@lizstarbooks.com
Web site: http://www.lizstarbooks.com.

LJK Publishing LLC, *(0-9771476)* P.O. Box 993, Springer, NM 87747 USA Tel 505-483-2451 (fax as well - phone to turn on)
E-mail: chieftalkjaw@aol.com.

L'Kayle, *(0-9676387)* 2479 Big Creek Terr., Stone Mountain, GA 30087 USA Tel 770-469-1264
E-mail: lkayle@juno.com
Dist(s): **Baker & Taylor Bks.**
Brodart Co.
Spring Arbor Distributors, Inc.

L/L Research, *(0-945007)* Orders Addr.: P.O. Box 5195, Louisville, KY 40255-0195 USA; Edit Addr.: 1504 Hobbs Park Rd., Louisville, KY 40223 USA (SAN 245-775X)
E-mail: carla.l.rueckert@llresearch.org; jim@llresearch.org
Web site: http://www.llresearch.org
Dist(s): **New Leaf Distributing Co., Inc.**

†Llewellyn Pubns., *(0-7387; 0-87542; 1-56718)* Div. of Llewellyn Worldwide, Ltd., Orders Addr.: 2143 Wooddale Dr., Woodbury, MN 55125-2989 USA Tel 651-291-1970; Fax: 651-291-1908; Toll Free: 800-843-6666 ; *Imprints:* Flux (Flux Llew)
E-mail: sales@llewellyn.com
Web site: http://www.llewellyn.com; http://www.midnightinkbooks.com
Dist(s): **Ingram Bk. Co.**
Koen-Levy Bk. Wholesalers LLC
Lectorum Pubns., Inc.
Libros Sin Fronteras
Llewellyn Worldwide Ltd.
New Leaf Distributing Co., Inc.
Partners/West
Perrone; *CIP.*

Llinks, Co. *See* **Language Literacy Links, L. C.**

Llumina Christian Bks. *Imprint of* **Media Creations, Inc.**

Llumina Pr. *Imprint of* **Media Creations, Inc.**

LM Digital, *(0-9760770)* 207 Eaton Ct., Benicia, CA 94510 USA Tel 707-373-4350; Fax: 707-751-0613
E-mail: luke@lm-digital.com
Web site: http://www.lm-digital.com.

LM Pubns., *(0-935596)* Orders Addr.: 885 E. 900 N., Mapleton, UT 84664-3716 USA (SAN 213-0653) Toll Free: 877-407-1858
E-mail: learta@vitalvillage.net
Web site: http://www.vitalvillage.net
Dist(s): **QW, Inc.**

L.M.N. Publishing International, Inc., *(0-9665786)* HC 04, Box 94-C, Saint Maries, ID 83861-9403 USA Tel 208-245-5388; Fax: 208-245-3280
E-mail: lmnpubint@nidlink.com
Web site: http://www.lmn.org.

LMS Bks., *(0-9764185)* 1007 Manor Dr., Ripon, CA 95366 USA Tel 209-599-4685.

Lobster Cove Publishing Co., *(0-9669946)* c/o Bannon, 728 Washington St., Gloucester, MA 01930 USA Tel 978-281-5098; Fax: 978-524-3734
E-mail: kandk2@flash.net
Web site: http://www.gordon.edu/faculty/yonder_mountain.

Lobster Pr. (CAN) *(1-894222; 1-897073) Dist. by* **Natl Bk Netwk.**

Local History Co., The, *(0-9711835; 0-9744715; 0-9770429)* Orders Addr.: 112 N. Woodland Rd., Pittsburgh, PA 15232 USA (SAN 257-5264) ; *Imprints:* Towers Maguire Publishing (Towers Mag)
E-mail: Sales@TheLocalHistoryCompany.com; Sales@TowersMaguire.com
Web site: http://www.TheLocalHistoryCompany.com; http://www.TowersMaguire.com.

Lockett, Hazel, *(0-9678877)* Orders Addr.: P.O. Box 1292, Philadelphia, PA 19105 USA Tel 215-567-0147 (phone/fax); Edit Addr.: 2042 Ranstead St., Philadelphia, PA 19103 USA.

Lockman, Vic, *(0-936175)* 233 Rogue River Hwy No. 360, Grants Pass, OR 97527 USA (SAN 697-2063) Fax: 541-472-1083
E-mail: vlockman@budget.net.

Locust Hill Pr., *(0-933951; 0-9722289)* P.O. Box 260, West Cornwall, CT 06796 USA (SAN 693-0646) Tel 860-672-0060; Fax: 860-672-4968; 419 Main St., Goshen Tpke., West Cornwall, CT 06796
E-mail: locusthill@optonline.net
Dist(s): **Syracuse Univ. Pr.**

Lodestone Pr., *(0-9678922)* 17 Appleby Rd., Suite B-2, Wellesley, MA 02482 USA
E-mail: books@lodestone.nu
Web site: http://www.lodestone.nu.

Lodhia Ctr., The, 4405 International Blvd., Suite C-101, Norcross, GA 30093 USA Tel 770-564-4000; Fax: 770-564-2500
E-mail: rafiq@thelodhiacenter.org
Web site: http://www.thelodhiacenter.org.

Loew-Cornell, Inc., *(0-9776925; 0-9794445)* Div. of Jarden Corporation, 400 Sylvan Ave., 2nd Flr., Englewood Cliffs, NJ 07632 USA Fax: 201-836-4878
E-mail: joleary@loew-cornell.com
Web site: http://www.loew-cornell.com
Dist(s): **Watson-Guptill Pubns., Inc.**

Loewe Verlag GmbH (DEU) *(3-7855) Dist. by* **Distribks Inc.**

Log Cabin Bks., *(0-9755548)* P.O. Box 8, Earlville, NY 13332 USA Tel 315-750-9157
Web site: http://www.logcabinbooks.com/; http://www.logcabinbooks.us/.

Logan Bks., *(0-9728691)* P.O. Box 21451, Columbia Heights, MN 55421 USA
Web site: http://www.loganbooks.com.

Logan Hse., *(0-9674123; 0-9769935)* Orders Addr.: Rte. 1, Box 154, Winside, NE 68790 USA Tel 402-286-4891; Edit Addr.: Rte. 1 Box 154, Winside, NE 68790 USA
E-mail: jim@loganhousepress.com
Web site: http://www.loganhousepress.com.

Login Fulfillment Services *See* **LPC Group**

Logos Christiam College & Graduate Schls., Inc., *(1-58897)* 9000 Regency Sq Blvd., Jacksonville, FL 32211-8115 USA ; *Imprints:* Logos Publishing (Logos FL)
E-mail: rj.gosselin@logos.edu
Web site: http://www.logos.edu.

Logos Productions, Inc., *(0-9618891; 1-885361)* 6160 Carmen Ave., E., Inver Grove Heights, MN 55076-4422 USA Tel 612-451-9945; Fax: 612-457-4617; Toll Free: 800-328-0200 Do not confuse with Logos Productions, Carmel, CA
E-mail: lpstaff@mn.uswest.net
Web site: http://www.1logos.com.

Logos Publishing *Imprint of* **Logos Christiam College & Graduate Schls., Inc.**

Logos Schl., *(1-930443)* 110 Baker St., Moscow, ID 83843 USA Tel 208-883-3199; Fax: 208-883-8292
E-mail: logosschool@turbonet.com
Web site: http://www.logosschool.com
Dist(s): **Canon Pr.**
Veritas Pr., Inc.

LOGOS System Assocs., *(0-9727146; 0-9752605; 0-9768168)* 1405 Frey Rd., Pittsburgh, PA 15235 USA Tel 412-372-1341; Fax: 412-372-8447; Toll Free: 877-937-2572
E-mail: patjanssen@logos-system.org
Web site: http://www.logos-system.org.

Logos-Rhema Publishing *See* **Triumph Publishing**

Lollipop Publishing, LLC, *(0-9709793; 1-931737)* P.O. Box 6354, Chesterfield, MO 63006-6354 USA Tel 314-434-6011; Fax: 314-434-6040; Toll Free: 800-383-7767
E-mail: jbenigas@aol.com
Web site: http://www.lollippoppublishing.com.

Lolot Pr., *(0-9650824)* 207 Jacob Cir., Talent, OR 97540 USA Tel 541-535-4942.

Loma, LLC, *(0-9769460)* 6 Bryan Valley Ct., O'Fallon, MO 63366-3465 USA
E-mail: dudleytg@aol.com.

Londa Signs, *(0-9701674)* P.O. Box 32, Crabtree, OR 97335-0032 USA Tel 541-259-3857
E-mail: anklambs@proaxis.com
Web site: http://www.proaxis.com/~londa.

London Publishing Co., *(0-9613262)* 1010 Massachusetts Ave., NW, Suite 410, Washington, DC 20001-5402 USA (SAN 296-5976).

London Town Pr., *(0-9666490; 0-9766134; 0-9799759)* 2026 Hilldale Dr., La Canada, CA 91011 USA
E-mail: martin@londontownpress.com
Web site: http://www.londontownpress.com
Dist(s): **Perseus Distribution.**

Lone Butte Pr., *(0-9666860)* 32 S. Fork Extended, Santa Fe, NM 87508 USA Tel 505-424-3574; Fax: 505-473-1227
E-mail: wbaxter@ix.netcom.com.

Lone Oak Pr., Ltd., *(0-9627860; 1-883477)* 1412 Bush St., Red Wing, MN 55066 USA (SAN 254-5241) Tel 651-388-3730; Toll Free: 877-315-2746
E-mail: info@loneoak.org
Web site: http://www.loneoak.org
Dist(s): **Baker & Taylor Bks.**
Bookmen, Inc.
Partners Bk. Distributing, Inc.

Lone Pine Publishing *See* **Lone Pine Publishing USA**

Lone Pine Publishing USA, *(0-919433; 1 55105)* 1808 B St., NW, Suite 140, Auburn, WA 98001 USA Tel 425-204-5965; Fax: 253-394-0405; Toll Free Fax: 800-548-1169; Toll Free: 800-518-3541
E-mail: rtruppner@lonepinepublishing.com
Web site: http://www.lonepinepublishing.com
Dist(s): **American West Bks.**
Baker & Taylor Bks.
Bookmen, Inc.
Koen-Levy Bk. Wholesalers LLC
Partners Bk. Distributing, Inc.
Partners/West
Sunbelt Pubns., Inc.

Lone Star Bks., *(1-58907)* Orders Addr.: 15200 NBN Way, Blue Ridge Summit, PA 17214 USA Tel 717-794-3800 ((Sales, Customer Service, MIS, Royalties, Inventory Mgmt., Dist., Credit & Collections); Fax: 717-794-3803 (Customer Service &/or orders only); 717-794-3857 (Sales & MIS); 717-794-3856 (Royalties, Inventory Mgmt., & Dist.); Toll Free Fax; 800-338-4550 (Customer Service &/or orders); Toll Free: 800-462-6420 (Customer Service &/or orders); Edit Addr.: 4501 Forbes Blvd., Suite 200, Lanham, MD 20706 USA Toll Free Fax: 301-459-5748; Toll Free: 301-459-3366
Dist(s): **National Bk. Network.**

Lone Star Pubns., *(0-9766157)* P.O. Box 810872, Dallas, TX 75381 USA Do not confuse with Lone Star Publication in Dallas, TX
E-mail: info@lonestarpublications.com
Web site: http://www.lonestarpublications.com.

Lone Star Publishing Co., *(0-9777274)* 906 SW St., Lucie W. Blvd., Port Saint Lucie, FL 34986 USA Tel 772-486-3214; Fax: 772-785-8496 do not confuse with companies with the same name in Paradise, TX, Amarillo, TX, Bryan, TX.

Lone Wolf Enterprises, Ltd., *(1-892518)* P.O. Box 801, Fort Fairfield, ME 04742 USA
E-mail: lonewolf@mfx.net.

Lone Wolf Productions *See* **Canis Lupus Productions**

Lonejack Mountain Pr., *(0-9729101)* P.O. Box 28424, Bellingham, WA 98228-0424 USA.

Lonely Blue Coyote, Inc., *(0-9667227)* P.O. Box 3642, Champaign, IL 61821 USA (SAN 299-8831) Tel 217-355-5308 (phone/fax); Toll Free: 888-522-6968
E-mail: TerBatCole@aol.com
Web site: http://www.lbcoyote.com/Bio/Teresa/silent.html.

Lonely Planet Pubns., *(0-86442; 0-908086; 1-55992; 1-86450; 1-74059; 1-74104; 1-74179)* Orders Addr.: 150 Linden St., Oakland, CA 94607 USA (SAN 659-6541) Tel 510-893-8555; Fax: 510-893-8572; Toll Free: 800-275-8555 (orders, 9am - 5pm Pacific Time)
E-mail: orders@lonelyplanet.com; customerservice@lonelyplanet.com
Web site: http://www.lonelyplanet.com.

Lonestar Abilene Publishing *Imprint of* **LoneStar Abilene Publishing, LLC**

LoneStar Abilene Publishing, LLC, *(0-9749725)* 402 Cedar St., Suite 208, Abilene, TX 79601 USA Tel 325-676-9800; Fax: 325-676-2790 ; *Imprints:* Lonestar Abilene Publishing (LoneStarAbil)
E-mail: michael@yrbks.com
Web site: http://www.yrbks.com/LoneStar.html.

Long Beach City Schl. District, *(0-9677925)* 235 Lido Blvd., Lido Beach, NY 11561 USA Tel 516-897-2104; Fax: 516-897-2107
E-mail: RLF@li.net.

Long Hill Productions, Inc., *(0-9701450; 1-931179)* 6446 S. Western Ave., Clarendon Hills, IL 60514 USA (SAN 253-2883) Tel 630-920-8168; Fax: 630-920-8169
E-mail: info@long-hill.com
Web site: http://www.long-hill.com.

Long Life Publishing Co., *(0-9725836)* P.O. Box 1564, Escondido, CA 92033 USA.

Long River Pr., *(1-59265)* Orders Addr.: 360 Swift Ave., Suite 48, South San Francisco, CA 94080 USA Tel 650-872-7718; Fax: 650-872-7808 Do not confuse with Long River Pr., in Grass Lake, MI
E-mail: info@longriverpress.com
Web site: http://www.longriverpress.com
Dist(s): **Baker & Taylor Bks.**
China Bks. & Periodicals, Inc.
Consortium Bk. Sales & Distribution.

Long Wind Publishing, *(0-9658128; 1-892695)* 108 N. Depot Dr., Box 13024, Fort Pierce, FL 34950 USA Tel 561-595-0268; Fax: 561-595-6246
E-mail: LongWndPub@aol.com
Web site: http://www.longwindpub.com
Dist(s): **Midpoint Trade Bks., Inc.**

Longacre Pr. (NZL) *(0-9583405; 1-877135; 0-9583465; 1-877361) Dist. by* **Pacific Island Bks.**

Longhorn Creek Pr., *(0-9714358; 0-9764026)* 2438 10th St., Irving, TX 75060 USA Tel 972-790-4708
E-mail: editor@longhorncreekpress.com; Ron@longhorncreekpress.com
Web site: http://www.longhorncreekpress.com
Dist(s): **Wilson & Assocs.**

Longman Publishing, *(0-02; 0-06; 0-13; 0-201; 0-205; 0-321; 0-582; 0-673; 0-7248; 0-8013; 1-57322; 0-7339)* 75 Arlington St., Boston, MA 02116 USA Tel 617-848-7500
Web site: http://www.aw-bc.com
Dist(s): **Giron Bks.**
Libros Sin Fronteras
Pearson Education.

†Longman Publishing Group, *(0-13; 0-201; 0-321; 0-582; 0-8013)* Div. of Addison Wesley Longman, Inc., The Longman Bldg., 10 Bank St., White Plains, NY 10606-1951 USA (SAN 202-6856) Tel 914-993-5000; Fax: 914-997-8115 800-922-0579 (college, bkstores, customer service only) ; *Imprints:* Drumbeat (Drumbeat)
Web site: http://store.awl.com
Dist(s): **Coronet Bks.**
Giron Bks.
Pearson Education
Pearson Technology Group
Sourcebooks, Inc.
Trans-Atlantic Pubns., Inc.; *CIP.*

Longoria, Eugene R., *(0-9796818)* 2222 W. Central Ave., Coolidge, AZ 85228 USA (SAN 854-1116) Tel 520-723-4106
E-mail: ElJunior@ElJunior.com
Web site: http://eljunior.com.

Longs Peak Publishing, Inc., *(0-9770141)* Orders Addr.: P.O. Box 1792, Loveland, CO 80538 USA Tel 970-663-2665; Fax: 970-663-7600 ; *Imprints:* Crossing Guard Books (CrossGrdBks)
E-mail: info@longspeakpublishing.com
Web site: http://www.longspeakpublishing.com.

Longseller S.A. (ARG) *(987-550; 987-9481; 987-98516) Dist. by* **Bilingual Pubns.**

Longseller S.A. (ARG) *(987-550; 987-9481; 987-98516) Dist. by* **Libros Fronteras.**

Longstreet Pr., Inc., *(0-929264; 1-56352)* Subs. of Cox Newspapers, Inc., 325 N. Milledge Ave., Athens, GA 30601-3805 USA (SAN 248-7640) Toll Free: 800-927-1488
E-mail: rrichardson@longstreetpress.net
Dist(s): **National Bk. Network**
STL Distribution North America.

Look, Learn & Do Pubns., *(1-893327)* 24 Highland Blvd., Kensington, CA 94707 USA Fax: 510-524-7577
E-mail: professor@lldkids.com
Web site: http://www.looklearnanddo.com
Dist(s): **Ten Speed Pr.**

Looking Glass Library *Imprint of* **Magic Wagon**

Lookout Pr., *(1-882405)* Orders Addr.: 900 53rd St., Sacramento, CA 95819 USA Tel 916-456-6991.

Looney Laboratories, Inc., *(1-929780)* Orders Addr.: P.O. Box 761, College Park, MD 20740 USA Tel 301-441-1019; Fax: 301-441-4871; Edit Addr.: 5003 Geronimo St., College Park, MD 20740 USA
E-mail: us@looneylabs.com
Web site: http://www.looneylabs.coml.

Loonfeather Pr., *(0-926147)* Orders Addr.: P.O. Box 1212, Bemidji, MN 56619 USA Tel 218-444-4869; Edit Addr.: 2709 Beltrami Ave., Bemidji, MN 56601 USA
E-mail: brossi@paulbunyan.net
Web site: http://www.loonfeatherpress.com.

Loose Cannon Pr., *(1-888034)* 598 Shore Rd., Cape Elizabeth, ME 04107-1017 USA.

Loose Change, *(0-944707)* 936 Sixth St., Los Banos, CA 93635 USA (SAN 244-9692) Tel 209-826-3797; Fax: 209-826-1514
E-mail: nco4242@sbcglobal.net.

Loose In The Lab, *(0-9660965; 1-931801)* 9462 S. 560 W., Sandy, UT 84070 USA Tel 801-568-9596; Fax: 801-568-9586; Toll Free: 888-403-1189
E-mail: mail@looseinthelab.com
Web site: http://www.looseinthelab.com.

Looseleaf Law Pubns., Inc., *(0-930137; 1-889031; 1-932777)* Orders Addr.: P.O. Box 650042, Fresh Meadows, NY 11365-0042 USA Tel 718-359-5559; Fax: 718-539-0941; Toll Free: 800-647-5547; Edit Addr.: 43-08 162nd St., Flushing, NY 11358 USA (SAN 135-0099)
E-mail: llawpub@erols.com
Web site: http://www.looseleaflaw.com
Dist(s): **Austin & Company, Inc.**
Partners Pubs. Group, Inc.

Lopez, David, *(0-9744097)* 3441 Twinberry Ct., Bonita Springs, FL 34134 USA Tel 239-947-2532 (phone/fax)
E-mail: jazzpop@aol.com
Web site: http://www.maddiesmagicmarkers.com.

Lopez, Hilda, *(0-9729299)* 45 Urb Vista Verde, Camuy, PR 00627-3304 USA ; *Imprints:* Vida Devocional (Vida Dev).

LoPopolo, Carlos, *(1-58707)* Orders Addr.: P.O. Box 1198, Los Lunas, NM 87031 USA Tel 505-865-8992 (phone/fax); Edit Addr.: 10 Servis Farm Rd., Los Lunas, NM 87031 USA
E-mail: clopopolo@hotmail.com.

Loquacious Publishing Co., *(0-9763811)* 2115 Wintermere Pointe Dr., Winter Garden, FL 34787-5439 USA
Dist(s): **AtlasBooks Distribution.**

Lord, William H., *(0-9606320)* 9210 N. College Ave., Indianapolis, IN 46240 USA (SAN 214-0497) Tel 317-846-3907; Fax: 317-581-9013
E-mail: stagecrafter@aol.com; whlord@aol.com
Web site: http://www.stagecrafter.com.

Lorenz Bks. *Imprint of* **Anness Publishing, Inc.**

Lorenz Educational Pubs., *(1-885564)* P.O. Box 146340, Chicago, IL 60614-6340 USA Tel 773-929-9847 (phone/fax); Fax: 501-423-4158
E-mail: lorenz@megsinet.net
Web site: http://www.shkspr.com
Dist(s): **Baker & Taylor Bks.**

Loreto Pubns., *(1-930278)* Orders Addr.: P.O. Box 603, Fitzwilliam, NH 03447 USA Tel 603-239-6671; Fax: 603-239-6127; Edit Addr.: 139 Tully Brook Rd., Richmond, NH 03470 USA
E-mail: sharonrose@loretopubs.org.

Lorgnette Bks., *(0-9668894)* 405 Chapelwood Ct., Houston, TX 77024 USA (SAN 299-8009) Tel 713-468-2585; Fax: 713-650-1211.

Loridad, *(0-9667002)* P.O. Box 158, Ramona, CA 92065 USA Tel 760-788-2861; Fax: 760-788-9840
E-mail: quantumspirits@yahoo.com.

Lorimer, James & Co., Ltd., Pubs. (CAN) *(0-88862; 1-55028) Dist. by* **Casemate Pubs.**

Lormax Communications, *(0-9641239)* P.O. Box 40304, Raleigh, NC 27629 USA Tel 919-878-9108.

†Los Alamos Historical Society, *(0-941232)* Orders Addr.: P.O. Box 43, Los Alamos, NM 87544 USA (SAN 276-9603) Tel 505-453-7909; Fax: 505-662-6312; Edit Addr.: 1921 Juniper, Los Alamos, NM 87544 USA (SAN 241-9025)
E-mail: jess7780@aol.com; *CIP.*

Los Andes Publishing Co., *(0-9637065; 1-57159)* P.O. Box 190, Chino Hills, CA 91709 USA Tel 562-789-1540; Toll Free: 800-532-8872
E-mail: losandes@losandes.com
Web site: http://www.losandes.com.

Los Angeles Times, *(0-9619095; 0-9653061; 1-883792)* Div. of Times Mirror Co., 202 W. First St., Los Angeles, CA 90012 USA (SAN 243-1998) Tel 213-237-5982; Fax: 213-237-0782; Toll Free: 800-528-4637
Web site: http://www.latimes.com
Dist(s): **Angel City Pr.**
Sunbelt Pubns., Inc.

Los Cabos Guide to Good Eating *See* **One Step Productions**

Los Perros Publishing Co., *(0-9764685)* 3565 Parches Cove, Union Grove, AL 35175-8422 USA
E-mail: mrgsd@hiwaay.net; jr@losperros.com
Web site: http://www.mrgsd.com.

Lost Candy Bar Pr., LLC, *(0-9786794)* P.O. Box 5193, Madison, WI 53705-0193 USA Tel 608-233-5690; Fax: 608-231-2312
Web site: http://www.lostcandybarpress.com.

Lost Classics Bk. Co., *(0-9652735; 1-890623)* Orders Addr.: P.O. Box 1756, Fort Collins, CO 80522 USA Tel 970-493-3793 (Distribution Center); Toll Free Fax: 888-211-2665 (Wholesale, Libraries & Schools); Toll Free: 888-611-2665 (credit card orders only); Edit Addr.: P.O. Box 3429, Lake Wales, FL 33859-3429 USA Tel 863-676-1920; Fax: 863-676-1707; Toll Free: 888-611-2665
E-mail: lcbci@gte.net; lcbc@gte.net
Web site: http://lcbcbooks.com
Dist(s): **Applewood Bks.**
Consortium Bk. Sales & Distribution
Ingram Pub. Services.

Lost Coast Pr., *(1-882897)* 155 Cypress St., Fort Bragg, CA 95437 USA Tel 707-964-9520; Fax: 707-964-7531; Toll Free: 800-773-7782
E-mail: forms@cypresshouse.com
Web site: http://www.cypresshouse.com
Dist(s): **Baker & Taylor Bks.**
Continental Bk. Co., Inc.
Cypress Hse.
New Leaf Distributing Co., Inc.
Partners/West.

Lost Scout Pr., *(0-9741310)* P.O. Box 86, Loveland, OH 45140-0086 USA (SAN 255-7193) Fax: 719-457-5952; 1283 Sand Trap Ct., Loveland, OH 45140-6060
E-mail: hq@lostscout.com
Web site: http://www.lostscout.com.

Lost Words Publishing, *(0-9740538)* Orders Addr.: P.O. Box 703, Shreveport, LA 71162 USA; Edit Addr.: 260 1/2 Wyandotte, Shreveport, LA 71101 USA.

LOTI Publishing, *(0-9715793)* Div. of The LOTI Group, Inc., 146 Christmasville Rd., Trenton, TN 38382-8406 USA Toll Free: 866-746-4229 ; *Imprints:* Singing Is Easy (Singing Is Easy)
E-mail: scott@thesingingspot.com
Web site: http://www.affordablesingingvoicelessons.com; http://www.youcansingwithimpact.com; http://www.affordablesinginglessons.com; http://www.singingiseasy.com
Dist(s): **Dumont, Charles Son, Inc.**

Lotti, Marc, *(1-932341)* P.O. Box 5841, Carefree, AZ 85377-5841 USA
E-mail: mlotti@mandragore.com.

Lotus Lights Publications *See* **Lotus Pr.**

Lotus Petal Publishing, *(0-9787672)* Div. of Lotus Petal, 75 S. Jefferson, Nashville, IN 47448-1394 USA Tel 812-988-1250; Fax: 801-515-8663
E-mail: info@lotuspetalpublishing.com
Web site: http://www.lotuspetalpublishing.com.

Lotus Pond Media, *(0-9791021)* 176 Broadway, Suite 9C, New York, NY 10038 USA Tel 212-608-3329
E-mail: scgrant@goatkids.net
Web site: http://www.goatkids.net.

Lotus Pr., *(0-910261; 0-914955; 0-940676; 0-940985; 0-941524)* Div. of Lotus Brands, Inc., P.O. Box 325, Twin Lakes, WI 53181 USA (SAN 239-1120) Tel 262-889-2461; Fax: 262-889-8591; Toll Free: 800-824-6396 Do not confuse with companies with the same or similar name in Lotus, CA, Westerville, OH, Bokeelia, FL, Brattleboro, VT, Detroit, MI, Tobyhanna, PA
E-mail: lotuspress@lotuspress.com
Web site: http://www.lotuspress.com
Dist(s): **National Bk. Network.**

Lotus Publications, *(0-9649645; 0-9779024)* Orders Addr.: P.O. Box 870165, Saintne Mountain, GA 30087 USA Tel 678-476-3950 new as of 6/2006; Fax: 678-476-3951 new as of 6/2006; Toll Free: 800-795-6887; Edit Addr.: 5353 Pounds Dr. N., Saintne Mountain, GA 30087 USA
E-mail: photos@lotuspub.com
Web site: http://www.lotuspub.com
Dist(s): **MBI Distribution Services.**

Louck, Cheryl, *(0-9744230)* 2708 Avalon Ln., Montgomery, IL 60538 USA Tel 630-853-0653
Web site: http://www.cheryllouck.com.

Louisa May Allcat Children's Bks. *Imprint of* **Allcat Pr.**

Louisiana Ladybug Pr., *(0-9753435)* 210 Pinecrest Rd., Arcadia, LA 71001 USA
Web site: http://www.LouisianaPotpourriFromAtoZ.com.

†Louisiana State Univ. Pr., *(0-8071)* Orders Addr.: 3990 W. Lakeshore Dr., Baton Rouge, LA 70808 USA Tel 225-578-6295; Fax: 225-578-6461; Toll Free Fax: 800-305-4416; Toll Free: 800-861-3477
E-mail: lsupress@lsu.edu
Web site: http://www.lsu.edu/lsupress; *CIP.*

Love & Blessings, *(0-9644765)* P.O. Box 55116, Valencia, CA 91385 USA Tel 661-288-1711; Toll Free: 800-906-3629
E-mail: vloveland@babybonding.com; vloveland@earthlink.net
Web site: http://www.babybonding.com
Dist(s): **New Leaf Distributing Co., Inc.**

Love Buddies *Imprint of* **MW International, Belle Lumiere**

Love Bug Bks., *(0-9787174)* 1117 Ariana Rd., Suite 102, San Marcos, CA 92069-8122 USA Tel 760-798-9415; Fax: 760-798-9415
E-mail: rolwink@cox.net
Web site: http://www.lovebugbooks.com.

Love Cultivating Editions, *(0-9744999)* 2665 Reed Rd., Hood River, OR 97031-9609 USA
Web site: http://www.lovecultivatingeditions.com.

Love Language Pubns., *(0-9749924)* 2111 E. Santa Fe, No. 268, Olathe, KS 66062 USA
E-mail: anne@lovelanguageforbabies.com
Web site: http://www.lovelanguageforbabies.com.

Love Publishing Co., *(1-892212)* Orders Addr.: P.O. Box 1358, Belmont, NC 28012-1358 USA Tel 704-829-9500; Fax: 704-829-9555; Edit Addr.: 28 Alice Ave., Belmont, NC 28012-1358 USA Do not confuse with companies with the same name in Indiantown, FL, Denver, CO, Bossier, LA.

Love Song Publishing (AUS) *(0-9757001) Dist. by* **AtlasBooks.**

Love Spell *Imprint of* **Dorchester Publishing Co., Inc.**

LOVE TO READ Bks., *(0-9665222)* P.O. Box 270056, Littleton, CO 80127-0001 USA.

Love Works International, *(0-9705806)* 726 Lincoln Blvd., Suite C, Marion, IN 46953 USA Tel 765-664-4742; Fax: 765-664-0447
E-mail: kandy@comteck.com.

Love Your Life, *(0-9664806; 0-9798554)* Orders Addr.: P.O. Box 2, Red Lion, PA 17356 USA (SAN 256-1387) Tel 717-200-2852; Fax: 310-496-0716; Edit Addr.: 755 Conndly Dr., Red Lion, PA 17356 USA Tel 717-200-2852; Fax: 310-496-0716
E-mail: publish@loveyourlife.com
Web site: http://www.loveyourlife.com.

Lovegifts Publishing, *(0-9702601)* P.O. Box 201388, Denver, CO 80220 USA Tel 303-537-7338; Fax: 303-537-7339
E-mail: lovegiftspublishing@aol.com.

Loveland Pr., *(0-9662696; 0-9744851)* P.O. Box 7001, Loveland, CO 80537-0001 USA Tel 970-593-9557 Toll Free: 800-593-9557
E-mail: info@lovelandpress.com
Web site: http://www.lovelandpress.com
Dist(s): **Books West.**

Love's Creative Resources, *(1-929548)* Orders Addr.: P.O. Box 35114, Charlotte, NC 28235-5114 USA Tel 704-563-7469
E-mail: mjet64@aol.com.

Loving Guidance, Inc., *(1-889609)* P.O. Box 622407, Oviedo, FL 32762 USA Tel 407-366-0233; 407-977-8862; Fax: 407-366-4293; Toll Free: 800-842-2846; 50 Smith St., Oviedo, FL 32765-9608
E-mail: bryan@lovingguidance.com; kate@lovingguidance.com
Web site: http://www.beckybailey.com; http://www.consciousdiscipline.com
Dist(s): **Gryphon Hse., Inc.**

Loving, William M., *(0-9708193)* 5205 Lucas Ln., Austin, TX 78731 USA Tel 512-451-1739; Fax: 512-451-5400.

Lovstad, Joel Publishing, *(0-9749058)* 701 Henry St., No. 203, Waunakee, WI 53597 USA
E-mail: jlfred@chorus.net
Web site: http://www.joellovstad-books.com.

Low Fat Express, Incorporated *See* **Learning ZoneXpress**

Low Lively Productions, *(0-9708804)* 2000 E. Lamar Blvd., Suite 600, Arlington, TX 76006 USA Tel 817-275-5663; Fax: 817-860-1793; Toll Free: 866-746-5428 (866-pinkhat)
E-mail: pinkhatdiaries@yahoo.com
Web site: http://www.pinkhatdiaries.com.

Lowcountry Literature, *(0-9675841)* 12 B Rutledge Ave., Charleston, SC 29401 USA Tel 843-853-6720; Fax: 843-937-0610
E-mail: bcsanford@charleston.net.

†Lowell Hse., *(0-7373; 0-8092; 0-929923; 1-56565)* 2020 Avenue of the Stars, Suite 300, Los Angeles, CA 90067-4704 USA (SAN 250-863X) Tel 310-552-7555; Fax: 310-552-7573 ; *Imprints:* Roxbury Park (Roxbury Park)
Dist(s): **McGraw-Hill Trade**; *CIP.*

Lowell Hse. Juvenile, *(0-7373; 0-929923; 1-56565)* 2020 Avenue of the Stars, No. 300, Los Angeles, CA 90067 USA Tel 310-552-7555; Fax: 310-552-7573 ; *Imprints:* Roxbury Park Juvenile (Roxbury Pk Juvenile)
Web site: http://www.lowellh.com
Dist(s): **McGraw-Hill Trade.**

†Lowell Pr., The, Gallion Communications, *(0-913504; 0-932845)* Orders Addr.: P.O. Box 411877, Kansas City, MO 64141-1877 USA (SAN 207-0774) Tel 816-753-4545; Fax: 816-753-4057; Toll Free: 800-736-7660 Do not confuse with Lowell Pr. in Eugene, OR
E-mail: plowell@accessus.net
Web site: http://www.thelowellpress.com; *CIP.*

Lowell, Shelley, *(0-9765344)* Orders Addr.: c/o Montage Gallery, 925 South Charles St., Baltimore, MD 21230 USA.

Lower Kuskokwim Schl. District, *(1-58084)* Orders Addr.: P.O. Box 305, Bethel, AK 99559 USA Tel 907-543-4928; Fax: 907-543-4935
E-mail: catalog@fc.lksd-do.org
Web site: http://www.lksd.org/catalog.

Lowry Hse. Pubs., *(0-9629591)* P.O. Box 1014, Eugene, OR 97440-1014 USA Tel 541-686-2315
E-mail: LowryHousePub@aol.com
Web site: http://www.LowryHousePublishers.com
Dist(s): **Baker & Taylor Bks.**
Left Bank Distribution.

Lowry Pr. (GBR) *(1-902970) Dist. by* **Antique Collect.**

Loyal Pubs. *Imprint of* **WaterBrook Pr.**

†Loyola Pr., *(0-8294)* 3441 N. Ashland Ave., Chicago, IL 60657 USA (SAN 211-6537) Tel 773-281-1818; Fax: 773-281-0555; Toll Free: 800-621-1008
E-mail: customerservice@loyolapress.com
Web site: http://www.loyolabooks.org
Dist(s): **Baker & Taylor Bks.**
Spring Arbor Distributors, Inc.; *CIP.*

L.Patrick Publishing, *(0-9774418)* 2710 W. 76th St., Inglewood, CA 90305 USA.

LRS, *(1-58118)* 14214 S. Figueroa St., Los Angeles, CA 90061-1034 USA Tel 310-354-2610; Fax: 310-354-2601; Toll Free: 800-255-5002
E-mail: lrsprint@aol.com
Web site: http://www.lrs-largeprint.com
Dist(s): **Beeler, Thomas T. Pub.**

LSG Pubns., *(1-933532)* 1065 Bay Ave., East Marion, NY 11939 USA
E-mail: lisagaljanic@optonline.net
Web site: http://www.lsgpublications.com.

LTDBooks (CAN) *(1-55316) Dist. by* **Baker & Taylor.**

LTI Publishing, *(0-9743048)* Div. of Let's Talk Interactive, Inc., P.O. Box 371, Huntersville, NC 28070 USA
E-mail: art@LTIPublishing.net
Web site: http://www.FathersTouch.com; http://www.letstalkinterctive.com; http://www.SexualAbuse.ws; http://www.ChildHoodItShouldNotHurt.com; http://www.ChildHoodShouldNotHurt.com; http://www.AgainstSexualAbuse.org; http://www.LetsTalkCounseling.com.

Lu, Melissa Productions, *(0-9726832)* 5356 Rose Ridge Ln., Colorado Springs, CO 80917 USA Fax: 719-594-6993
E-mail: patsy@melissalu.com
Web site: http://www.melissalu.com.

Lua Publishing, *(0-9746304)* P.O. Box 3250, Fairfield, CA 94533 USA Tel 707-426-9480
E-mail: info@luapublishing.com
Web site: http://www.luapublishing.com
Dist(s): **New Leaf Distributing Co., Inc.**

Luath Pr. Ltd. (GBR) *(0-946487; 1-84282; 1-905222) Dist. by* **IngramPubServ.**

Lubbers, Theresa *See* **Mr. Emmett Publishing**

Lucas Co., *(0-9715916)* P.O. Box 9245, Moscow, ID 83843 USA
Web site: http://www.lucasco.com.

Lucas Educational Systems, *(1-930853)* P.O. Box 701629, Dallas, TX 75370-1629 USA
Web site: http://doctormemory.com.

Lucas Enterprises, *(0-9770611)* P.O. Box 9201, Chico, CA 95927 USA
E-mail: lucasent1@earthlink.net.

Lucas, Kimberly *See* **Trout-Tail, LLC**

Lucas, Mattie, *(0-9762456)* P.O. Box 47070, Windsor Mills, MD 21244 USA Fax: 410-944-2597
E-mail: bishop@digc.org.

LucasBooks for Young Readers *Imprint of* **Random Hse. Children's Bks.**

Lucent Bks. *Imprint of* **Thomson Gale**

Lucia Pubs., *(0-9762297)* Orders Addr.: P.O. Box 3, Churubusco, IN 46723-0003 USA Tel 260-693-0852; Fax: 260-693-0082; Edit Addr.: 209C S. Main St., Churubusco, IN 46723 USA
E-mail: diannegg@peoplepc.com; giannakeff@iquest.net
Web site: http://www.luciapublishers.com.

Lucid Solutions, *(0-9716827)* Orders Addr.: P.O. Box 32141, Mesa, AZ 85275-2141 USA; Edit Addr.: 2939 E. Nance St., Mesa, AZ 85213 USA
E-mail: questions@auditionmonologues.com; lucidsolutions@cox.net
Web site: http://www.auditionmonologues.com.

Luckman, Phyllis, *(0-9669810)* 668 Fairmount Ave., Oakland, CA 94611-5033 USA Tel 510-652-9821 (phone/fax)
E-mail: info@cellohandbook.com
Web site: http://www.cellohandbook.com.

Lucky & Me Productions, Inc., *(0-9721256)* Orders Addr.: 410 East 74th St., 6H, New York, NY 10021-3918 USA (SAN 255-0873) Tel 212-288-7203; Fax: 401-783-7815 call before faxing/not always on
E-mail: writermyst@aol.com
Web site: http://www.dearjohnlennon.com.

Lucky Cat Publishing, *(0-9720394)* 288 Franklin Ave., Astoria, OR 97103 USA Tel 503-338-6883
E-mail: cliff.arline@charter.net.

Lucky Dog Publishing, *(0-9778546)* Div. of Digital Edge, Inc., 2108 S. Blvd., Suite 300, Charlotte, NC 28203-2820 USA (SAN 850-4172) Tel 704-371-7222
Web site: http://www.luckydogpublishing.com.

Lucky Duck Designs, *(0-9790632)* P.O. Box 2192, Petaluma, CA 94953-2192 USA
E-mail: stuart@lucky-duck.com
Web site: http://www.lucky-duck.com.

Lucky Duck Pr., Inc., *(0-9715699)* 11120 Tyler Dr., Port Richey, FL 34668 USA
E-mail: pubprof@tampabay.rr.com
Web site: http://www.luckyduckpress.org
Dist(s): **BookMasters.**

Lucky Pr., LLC, *(0-9676050; 0-9706377; 0-9713318; 0-9760576; 0-9776300)* 126 S. Maple St., Lancaster, OH 43130 USA (SAN 850-9697) Tel 740-689-2950; Fax: 740-689-2951
E-mail: books@luckypress.com; janice@luckypress.com
Web site: http://www.luckypress.com
Dist(s): **Baker & Taylor Bks.**

Lucky Publications *See* **Covered Wagon Publishing LLC**

Lucky Red Pr., LLC, *(0-9790690)* 10061 Riverside Dr., Suite 812, Toluca Lake, CA 91602 USA Tel 818-795-2388; Fax: 818-566-4995
E-mail: Susan@frankiespals.com
Web site: http://www.frankiespals.com.

Lucky 3 Ranch, Inc., *(1-928624)* 2457 S. County Rd. 19, Loveland, CO 80537-9044 USA Tel 970-663-0066; Fax: 970-663-0676; Toll Free: 800-816-7566
E-mail: meredith@luckythreeranch.com
Web site: http://www.luckythreeranch.com/
Dist(s): **MediaTech Productions.**

Lucy Rose Publishing LLC, *(0-9789386)* P.O. Box 2371, Ewa Beach, HI 96706 USA Tel 808-689-4037; Fax: 808-689-4657
E-mail: admin@lucyrosepublishing.com
Web site: http://www.lucyrosepublishing.com.

Lueck Studios, *(0-9774547)* 8353 11th Ave. NW, Seattle, WA 98117 USA (SAN 257-6023)
E-mail: jenny@lueckstudios.com
Web site: http://www.chicabee.com
Dist(s): **AtlasBooks Distribution**
BookMasters, Inc.

Lugano Books *See* **Hanrow Pr.**

Luke & Lori Bks., *(0-9747792)* Orders Addr.: 5908 90th St., Lubbock, TX 79424 USA Tel 806-783-9941; Fax: 806-783-3099
E-mail: Melissa@lukeandlori.com
Web site: http://www.LukeAndLori.com.

Lulilite Productions, *(0-9759631)* P.O. Box 20847, Sedona, AZ 86341-0847 USA Tel 928-284-5442 (phone/fax)
E-mail: ariamagi@npgcable.com
Web site: http://www.lulilites.com.

LuLu Bks Ltd., *(0-9724929)* 1215 Ridgewood Dr., Cincinnati, OH 45140 USA.

LuLubelle Bks., *(0-9747058)* Orders Addr.: 264 Cromesett Point, Wareham, MA 02571 USA Fax: 508-291-3300
E-mail: www.angels@lulubellebooks.com
Web site: http://www.lulubellebooks.com.

Lulu.com, *(1-4116; 1-84728; 1-4303; 1-84753; 1-4357)* 860 Aviation Pkwy., Suite 300, Morrisville, NC 27560 USA Fax: 919-459-5867; Goldencross Hse. 8 Duncannon St., London, WC2N 4JF Tel 0207 484 6262
Web site: http://www.lulu.com
Dist(s): **Booklines Hawaii, Ltd.**
Copyright Clearance Ctr., Inc.
Lightning Source, Inc.

Lumen (ARG) *(950-724; 950-9017; 987-00) Dist. by* **Lectorum Pubns.**

LUMEN-US Pubns., *(0-9703611; 0-9787788; 0-9794862)* 234 Main St., Park Forest, IL 60466-2098 USA Toll Free: 866-219-9637
E-mail: Lumenuspubl@aol.com
Web site: http://www.lumen-us.com.

Lumina Pr. LLC, *(0-9708442)* P.O. Box 1106, Wrightsville Beach, NC 28480-1106 USA Do not confuse with Lumina Press in Springfield, MO
E-mail: david@luminapress.com.

Luminary Media Group *Imprint of* **Pine Orchard, Inc.**

Lumpkin, Carol *See* **Peace Rug Company, Inc., The**

Luna Publishing, *(0-9791785)* Orders Addr.: 5815 82nd St., No. 145, PMB 137, Lubbock, TX 79424 USA Tel 806-687-3479; Fax: 806-687-3401 Do not confuse with Luna PUblishing Company in Los Angeles, CA
E-mail: ccrmgr2@nts-online.net
Web site: http://www.lunapublish.com.

Luna, Rachel Nickerson *See* **Howard, Emma Bks.**

Luna Rising *Imprint of* **Northland Publishing**

Lunar Donut Pr., *(0-9725638)* P.O. Box 692625, Orlando, FL 32869 USA Tel 407-298-7779; Fax: 407-298-7779
E-mail: caricatureconnection@cfl.rr.com
Web site: http://www.caricatureconnection.com.

Lunchbox Pr., *(0-9678285)* 3929 Marlowe St., Houston, TX 77005-2045 USA
E-mail: info@lunchboxpress.com
Web site: http://www.lunchboxpress.com
Dist(s): **National Bk. Network.**

Luquer St. Pr., *(0-9729735)* 199 Luquer St., Brooklyn, NY 11231-4518 USA Tel 718-237-4456; Fax: 718-488-7574
E-mail: editors@luquerstreet.org; events@luquerstree.org
Web site: http://www.luquerstreet.org
Dist(s): **SPD-Small Pr. Distribution.**

Luthers, *(1-877633)* 1009 N. Dixie Freeway, New Smyrna Beach, FL 32168-6221 USA (SAN 200-3961) Tel 386-423-1600 (phone/fax)
E-mail: publish@lutherspublishing.com
Web site: http://www.lutherspublishing.com.

Lutz, William G., *(0-615)* 10248 Ramm Rd., Whitehouse, OH 43571 USA
Dist(s): **Lulu.com.**

Luv U Bks., *(0-9715322)* P.O. Box 42037, Cincinnati, OH 45242-0037 USA
E-mail: luvubooks@fuse.net
Web site: http://www.luvubooks.com.

LuvLife, Incorporated *See* **Museum of Living History**

Luvlife Publishing, *(0-9764316)* Orders Addr.: 69 Shore Dr., Old Lyme, CT 06371 USA Tel 860-434-0723
E-mail: mistilove@earthlink.net
Web site: http://www.snakesofnewengland.com.

L.W. Communications, *(0-9723378)* 16815 Victory Blvd. #226, Van Nuys, CA 91406-5550 USA Tel 818-787-9550 (phone, fax - call first)
E-mail: lancecoach@aol.com
Web site: http://www.lancecoach.com.

LWCD, Inc., *(0-9648724)* 38 Overhills Dr., Saint Louis, MO 63124-1532 USA
E-mail: lwcdinc@aol.com.

Lyandy Pr., *(0-9705957)* Orders Addr.: 7012 Hopewood St., Bethesda, MD 20817 USA Tel 301-320-2693; Fax: 301-320-2694
E-mail: lya@ix.netcom.com.

Lynch, Marietta & Patricia Perry, *(0-9610962)* 240 Atlantic Rd., Gloucester, MA 01930 USA (SAN 265-2722) Tel 508-283-6322.

Lyndel Pubns., *(0-9650690)* Orders Addr.: P.O. Box 87304, Vancouver, WA 98687 USA; Edit Addr.: 505 SE Hearthwood Blvd., Vancouver, WA 98684-7426 USA Tel 360-260-1358
E-mail: lyndel@prodigy.net.

LynHawk Publishing Co., Inc., *(1-885005)* 809 Ranch Rd., Florence, SC 29506 USA Tel 803-667-0103.

Lynn Tyner Mitchum & James Rogers, *(0-9745191)* P.O. Box 5799, Sevierville, TN 37864 USA
Web site: http://jamesrogersonline.com.

Lynne Ellen, Inc., *(0-9748889)* 670 N. Stiles Dr., Charleston, SC 29412 USA Tel 843-817-2530
E-mail: lynne@metoomommy.com.

Lynn's Bookshelf, *(0-9618608)* Orders Addr.: P.O. Box 2224, Boise, ID 83701 USA (SAN 667-1314) Tel 208-331-1987 (phone/fax); Edit Addr.: 3423 Scenic Dr., Boise, ID 83703 USA
E-mail: lynnsbooks@cableone.net.

Lynnx Ink, *(0-9710143)* 6 Burke Loop, Silver City, NM 88061-8700 USA Tel 505-388-3813
E-mail: lynnx@writeme.com
Web site: http://www.writerscenter.com.

†Lynx Hse. Pr., *(0-89924)* 420 W. 24th Ave., Spokane, WA 99203-1922 USA (SAN 250-3344) Tel 309-624-4594; Fax: 309-623-4238
E-mail: cnhowell@mail.ewu.edu
Dist(s): **SPD-Small Pr. Distribution**; *CIP.*

Lyon, Ernest Media Productions, *(0-9741328)* P.O. Box 26101, San Francisco, CA 94126-6101 USA (SAN 255-7460) Tel 415-387-5569 (phone/fax)
E-mail: davidlyon@mindspring.com.

Lyons Group, The *See* **Lyrick Studios**

Lyons Media Group.com *See* **Cleveland, Shirley D.**

Lyons Pr. *Imprint of* **Globe Pequot Pr., The**

Lypton Publishing, *(0-9752780)* 35409 S. Fairbank Point, Drummond Island, MI 49726 USA (SAN 256-0143).

Lyrical Learning, *(0-9646367; 0-9741635)* 8008 Cardwell Hill, Corvallis, OR 97330 USA Tel 541-754-3579 (phone/fax); Toll Free: 800-761-0906
Web site: http://www.lyricallearning.com.

Lyrically Korrect Publishing, *(0-9727776)* 5402 Belle Vista Ave., Baltimore, MD 21206 USA ; *Imprints:* Book Her Publications (Bk Hr Pubns)
Web site: http://www.lyricallykorrect.com
Dist(s): **Baker & Taylor Bks.**

Lyrick Publishing, *(1-57064; 1-58668)* Subs. of HIT Entertainment, 830 S. Greenville Ave., Allen, TX 75002 USA Tel 972-390-6068; Fax: 972-390-6030; Toll Free: 800-418-2371
E-mail: customerservice@HITEntertainment.com; koliveri@Hitentertainment.com
Web site: http://www.HITEntertainment.com
Dist(s): **Lectorum Pubns., Inc.**

Lyrick Studios, *(0-7829; 0-89505; 0-913592; 1-55924; 1-57132)* Subs. of HIT Entertainment, 830 S. Greenville Ave., Allen, TX 75002 USA Tel 972-390-6002; 214-424-6630; Fax: 972-390-6030; Toll Free: 800-418-2371
E-mail: customerservice@HITEntertainment.com
Web site: http://www.HITEntertainment.com
Dist(s): **Midwest Tape**
Rounder Kids Music Distribution.

Lytton Publishing Co., *(0-915728)* Orders Addr.: P.O. Box 1212, Sandpoint, ID 83864 USA (SAN 207-4257) Tel 208-263-3564; Edit Addr.: 2026 Janelle Way, Sandpoint, ID 83864 USA (SAN 241-757X)
E-mail: jlpayne@netw.com
Web site: http://www.lyttonpublishing.com.

M & B Publishing, *(0-9758580)* 930 Edgecliffs Dr., Langley, WA 98260 USA
E-mail: wistful@whidbey.com.

M & D Publishing, Inc., *(0-9768667)* '2980 SE Fairway W., Stuart, FL 34997 USA Tel 772-286-9781; Fax: 772-286-5169 Do not confuse with M & D Publishing in Phoeniz, AZ
E-mail: manddpublishing@bellsouth.net.

M & JP Publishing, *(0-9720816)* Orders Addr.: P.O. Box 1154, Decatur, IL 62522 USA Tel 217-412-0321; Fax: 217-865-2213; Edit Addr.: 1870 S. Wyckles Rd., Suite 102, Decatur, IL 62522 USA
E-mail: marshasykes@hotmail.com
Web site: http://www.marshaandjohnsplace.com.

M & M Bk. Publishing Co., *(0-9716704)* 9 Janice Cir., Natchez, MS 39120 USA
Web site: http://www.mandmbooks.natchez.ms.us.

MDCT Publishing, *(0-9674491)* 31990 SW Village Crest Ln., Wilsonville, OR 97070-8427 USA
E-mail: mdundy@teleport.com
Dist(s): **Partners/West.**

M E P Productions *See* **M.E.P. Pubns.**

M.E.P. Pubns., *(1-892516)* Div. of Daya Kay Communications, 477 Arlington St., San Francisco, CA 94131 USA Tel 415-587-9264; Fax: 415-337-8532; Toll Free: 800-484-2665 (ext. 9066) Do not confuse with M E P Pubns., Minneapolis, MN
E-mail: mepleasant@aol.com
Web site: http://www.mepleasant.com.

MGLS, Inc., *(0-9601682; 1-888833)* 700 S. First St., Marshall, MN 56258 USA (SAN 212-2170) Tel 507-532-4311; Fax: 507-532-4313
E-mail: carberry@mgls.com

MIR, *(0-935352)* Div. of Dr. Ilija Poplasen, Orders Addr.: P.O. Box 962, Pittsburgh, PA 15230 USA (SAN 213-5833) Tel 412-322-1319; Fax: 412-322-1856; Edit Addr.: 835 Suismon Dr., Pittsburgh, PA 15212 USA (SAN 213-5825) Do not confuse with MIR, Ogden, UT
E-mail: vladar@webtv.net.

M K L Publishing, *(0-9746204)* Orders Addr.: P.O. Box 407, Ballston Spa, NY 12020 USA; Edit Addr.: 5019 Fairground Ave., Ballston Spa, NY 12020 USA
E-mail: mklpublishing@aol.com.

MM Co., *(1-883473)* 15007 Avon St., Independence, MO 64055 USA Tel 816-246-6365.

MND Publishing, Inc., *(0-940847)* 1290 County Road 13., Clanton, AL 35045-4911 USA (SAN 665-1720)
E-mail: mnd@mndbooks.com; orders@mndbooks.com
Web site: http://www.mndbooks.com
Dist(s): **New Leaf Distributing Co., Inc.**

MP Publishing, *(0-9645487)* 6045 E. Edison St., Tucson, AZ 85712 USA Tel 602-885-3570.

M Press *See* **M Pr. Publishing**

M Pr., *(1-59617)* 10956 SE Main St., Milwaukie, OR 97222 USA Tel 503-652-8815
Dist(s): **Diamond Bk. Distributors.**

M Pr. Publishing, *(0-9707495)* 157 Riviera Dr., San Rafael, CA 94901 USA Do not confuse with companies with the same or similar names in Billings, MT, Washington, DC, Milwaukee, WI, Kihei, HI.

M Q Pubns. (GBR) *(1-84072; 1-897954; 1-84601; 0-9797400) Dist. by* **IngramPubServ.**

MRL, Inc., *(1-892860)* 1445 Cannon St., Louisville, CO 80027-1453 USA Tel 303-666-8164
E-mail: moyazena@aol.com.

MSM Productions, Ltd., *(0-9634016; 0-9705876)* 1095 Meigs St., Rochester, NY 14620 USA Tel 716-442-6370 (TTY); Fax: 716-442-6371 ; *Imprints:* Deaf Life Press (Deaf Life Pr)
E-mail: deaflife@deaflife.com
Web site: http://www.deaflife.com.

M S S Publishing *See* **Sentinel Pr. L.L.C.**

MTE, Ltd., *(1-888679)* 3095 S. Trenton St., Denver, CO 80231-4164 USA Tel 303-696-0839.

M. T. Wall Publishing Co., *(1-891203)* 769 Mindy Sue, Medford, OR 97501 USA Tel 541-779-5777; Fax: 541-899-2255.

MVM Bks., *(1-931135)* 4200 Lafayette Ctr. Dr., Suite A, Chantilly, VA 20151 USA (SAN 253-6919) Tel 703-263-9505; Fax: 703-263-9509
E-mail: sylviefed@aol.com
Web site: http://www.jhoonrhee.com.

MVM Pubs., *(0-9637279)* 707 Sumner Ave., Syracuse, NY 13210 USA Tel 315-475-0398 (phone/fax).

M2M Partners, *(0-9768884)* P.O. Box 60923, Phoenix, AZ 85082-0923 USA Toll Free: 800-658-8790
Web site: http://www.mamaroses.com; http://www.printserve.net; http://www.nonnieskitchen.com
Dist(s): **Baker & Taylor Bks.**
Partners/West.

Maas Presentations, LLC, *(0-9712140)* 6 Sunset, W., Ithaca, NY 14850 USA Tel 607-347-4590; Fax: 607-347-6561
E-mail: jbm1@cornell.edu
Web site: http://www.remmyweb.com
Dist(s): **National Bk. Network.**

Mabbul Publishing Co., *(0-9762860)* 915 Hunting Horn Way, Evans, GA 30809 USA
Web site: http://www.mabbul.com.

MAC Productions, *(1-878591)* 15320 279th Pl., NE, P.O. Box 84, Duvall, WA 98019 USA Tel 425-844-8406; Fax: 425-844-9245
E-mail: mac.productions@gte.net
Web site: http://www.mac.productionsgolf.com
Dist(s): **Baker & Taylor Bks.**
Partners/West.

Mac3publishing, *(0-9767796)* P.O. Box 1177, Rowlett, TX 75030 USA
E-mail: mac3publishing@verizon.net
Web site: http://www.mac3publishing.com.

MacAdam/Cage Publishing, Inc., *(0-9673701; 1-931561; 1-59692)* 155 Sansome St., Suite 550, San Francisco, CA 94104 USA (SAN 299-9730) Tel 415-986-7502; Fax: 415-986-7414; Toll Free: 866-986-7470
E-mail: elizabeth@macadamcage.com
Web site: http://www.macadamcage.com.

Macalester Park Publishing Co., Inc., *(0-910924; 0-930286; 1-886158)* 24558 546th Ave., Austin, MN 55912 USA (SAN 110-8077) Tel 507-396-0135; Toll Free: 800-407-9078
E-mail: macalesterpark@macalesterpark.com
Web site: http://www.macalesterpark.com
Dist(s): **Baker & Taylor Bks.**
Bookmen, Inc.
Spring Arbor Distributors, Inc.

Macaronic Pr., *(0-9766859; 1-59864)* P.O. Box 1542, Sebastopol, CA 95473-1542 USA Tel 707-813-7047; Toll Free: 888-364-8253
E-mail: vivienka@msn.com
Web site: http://www.macaronicpress.com
Dist(s): **Midpoint Trade Bks., Inc.**

MacBride, E. J. Pubn., Inc., *(1-892511)* 129 W. 147th St., No. 20B, New York, NY 10039 USA ; *Imprints:* Disposition Sketch Books (Disposition Sketch).

MacDonald Sward Publishing Co., *(0-945437)* RD 3, Box 104A, Greensburg, PA 15601 USA (SAN 247-1973) Tel 724-832-7767
Dist(s): **Baker & Taylor Bks.**

Macedon Production Co., *(0-939965)* Orders Addr.: P.O. Box 60773, Oklahoma City, OK 73146 USA (SAN 663-8821) Tel 405-842-5259; Fax: 405-842-0583; Edit Addr.: 3000 United Founders Blvd., Suite 125, Oklahoma City, OK 73112 USA (SAN 663-883X)
E-mail: jimann@ionet.net.

MacGill, William V. & Company, *(0-9744720)* 1000 N. Lombard Rd., Lombard, IL 60148-1232 USA Tel 800-323-2841; Toll Free Fax: 800-727-3433
E-mail: macgill@macgill.com
Web site: http://www.macgill.com.

MacGregor, Doug, *(0-9654843)* 1578 Rosada Way, Fort Myers, FL 33901 USA Tel 941-337-3980
E-mail: dmacgregor@news-press.com.

MacHillock Publishing, *(0-9744996)* 2537 Pine Cove Dr., Tucker, GA 30084 USA
E-mail: sdh@mindspring.com
Dist(s): **Independent Pubs. Group.**

Mackenzie Smiles, *(0-9790347)* 659 Broderick St., San Francisco, CA 94117 USA Tel 415-519-9054
E-mail: christinasturner@yahoo.com
Dist(s): **Ingram Pub. Services.**

Mackin, Dan, *(0-615)* 8395 SE Palm St., Hobe Sound, FL 33455 USA Tel 772-546-3008; Fax: 772-546-5374
E-mail: danmackinartist@aol.com
Web site: http://www.danmackin.com.

Mackinac Island Pr., Inc., *(0-9749145; 1-934133)* 216 E. Front St., Suite 205, Traverse City, MI 49684 USA Fax: 231-946-7754
Web site: http://www.mackinacislandpress.com.

Mackinac Island State Park Commission *See* **Mackinac State Historic Parks**

Mackinac State Historic Parks, *(0-911872)* Orders Addr.: P.O. Box 873, Mackinaw City, MI 49701 USA; Edit Addr.: 207 W. Sinclair, Mackinaw City, MI 49701 USA (SAN 202-5981) Tel 231-436-5564; Fax: 231-436-4210
Dist(s): **Michigan State Univ. Pr.**

MackStorm Productions, Inc., *(0-9753078)* 1410 Prairie Crossing Dr., West Chicago, IL 60185 USA Tel 630-231-3998
E-mail: marilee@americanslidechart.com.

Company

Company

MacMenamin Pr., *(0-9761414)* P.O. Box 133, Zionsville, PA 18092 USA Tel 610-739-9527
E-mail: sales@macmenaminpress.com
Web site: http://www.macmenaminpress.com.

Macmillan, *(0-374)* Orders Addr.: 16365 James Madison Hwy., Gordonsville, VA 22942 USA (SAN 631-5011) Tel 540-672-7600; Fax: 540-672-7664; 540-672-7540 (Customer Service); Toll Free Fax: 800-672-2054 (Order Dept.); Toll Free: 888-330-8477; Edit Addr.: 175 Fifth Ave., New York, NY 10010 USA Tel 212-674-5151; Fax: 212-677-6487; Toll Free Fax: 800-258-2769; Toll Free: 800-488-5233; 16365 James Madison Hwy., Gordonsville, VA 22942 (SAN 852-5587) Tel 540-672-7761
Web site: http://www.macmillan.com
Dist(s): **Sony CONNECT, Inc.**

Macmillan Caribbean (GBR) *(0-333; 1-4050) Dist. by* **Interlink Pub.**

Macmillan College *Imprint of* **Prentice Hall PTR**

Macmillan Education Australia (AUS) *(0-333; 0-7329; 0-86859; 0-7330; 1-4202) Dist. by* **Paul & Co Pubs.**

Macmillan Education, Ltd. (GBR) *(0-333; 1-4050) Dist. by* **Players Pr.**

Macmillan Publishers Ltd. (GBR) *(0-330; 0-333; 1-4050) Dist. by* **Trafalgar.**

Macmillan Publishers Ltd. (GBR) *(0-330; 0-333; 1-4050) Dist. by* **IPG Chicago.**

Macmillan Publishers Ltd. (GBR) *(0-330; 0-333; 1-4050) Dist. by* **Trans-Atl Phila.**

Macmillan Reference USA *Imprint of* **Thomson Gale**

Macmillan Reference USA, *(0-02; 0-13; 0-7838; 0-7862)* .

Macmillan/McGraw-Hill Schl. Div., *(0-02)* Div. of The McGraw-Hill Education Group, Orders Addr.: 220 E. Daniel Dale Rd., DeSoto, TX 75115 USA Fax: 972-228-1982; Toll Free: 800-442-9685.

Macro Publishing Group, *(0-9702699; 0-9754130)* 16781 S. Torrence, Suite 103, Lansing, IL 60438 USA Toll Free: 888-854-8823 (phone/fax)
Web site: http://www.macropublishing.com
Dist(s): **National Bk. Network.**

Macromedia Education *Imprint of* **Macromedia, Inc.**

Macromedia, Inc., *(0-9742273; 1-932719)* 600 Townsend St., San Francisco, CA 94103 USA Tel 415-252-2000; Fax: 415-832-5555; Toll Free: 800-457-1774 ; *Imprints:* Macromedia Education (Macromedia Educ) Do not confuse with Macromedia, Inc. in Lake Placid, NY
Web site: http://www.macromedia.com/education.

MacroPrintBooks *Imprint of* **Science & Humanities Pr.**

Mad Yak Pr., *(0-9717995)* 8232 Styers Ct., Laurel, MD 20723-2100 USA Tel 301-317-8817
Dist(s): **Diamond Bk. Distributors.**

Madame Fifi Pubns., *(0-9667418; 0-9762900)* P.O. Box 310967, Newington, CT 06131-0967 USA
Web site: http://www.madamefifi.com.

Madden Publishing Co., Inc., *(0-9645819)* 673 E. Lakeside Dr., Monticello, IN 47960-4106 USA (SAN 255-0733)
E-mail: wmadden@peoplepc.com
Web site: http://www.baseballstoriesforsoul.homestead.com.

Madison Bks., Inc., *(0-8128; 0-8191; 0-911572; 1-56833; 1-879511)* Div. of Rowman & Littlefield Publishers, Inc., Orders Addr.: 15200 NBN Way, Blue Ridge Summit, PA 17214 USA Tel 717-794-3800 (Sales, Customer Service, MIS, Royalties, Inventory Mgmt., Dist., Credit & Collections); Fax: 717-794-3803 (Customer Service &/or orders only); 717-794-3857 (Sales & MIS); 717-794-3856 (Royalties, Inventory Mgmt. & Dist.); Toll Free Fax: 800-388-4550 (Customer Service &/or orders); Toll Free: 800-462-6420 (Customer Service &/or orders); Edit Addr.: 200 Park Ave., S., Suite 1109, New York, NY 10003-1503 USA Tel 212-529-3888; Fax: 212-529-4223
Web site: http://www.univpress.com/
Dist(s): **National Bk. Network**
Rowman & Littlefield Pubs., Inc.

Madison Claire Publishing Co., *(0-9669385)* 4723 Bayou Black Dr., Gibson, LA 70356-3314 USA Tel 504-575-2612; Fax: 504-868-8369
E-mail: Warnke38@aol.com.

Madison, Dr. Ron *See* **Ned's Head Productions**

Madjec Jet Publishing Co., *(1-892589)* P.O. Box 120, North Freedom, WI 53951 USA Tel 608-522-4385; Fax: 608-522-4141
E-mail: madjecjet@jvlnet.com
Web site: http://www.madjecjet.com.

Maelstrom Pr, *(0-9710552)* P.O. Box 403, Silverado, CA 92676-0403 USA Tel 714-649-0651; Fax: 714-649-4456 Do not confuse with maelstrom Press in New Milford, CT
E-mail: maelstrompress@aol.com; Kingsword@aol.com
Web site: http://www.maelstrompress.com.

Maerkle Pr., *(0-9721966)* 66 East Shore Blvd., Timberlake, OH 44095 USA Tel 440-269-8653; Fax: 440-269-8035
Web site: http://www.maerklepress.com.

Maestro Learning, *(0-9740533)* 1 Brook St., Watertown, MA 02472-2364 USA
E-mail: peter@maestrolearning.com
Web site: http://www.maestrolearning.com.

MaestroMedia Pr., *(0-9773731)* 408 Pearl St., Richmond, IN 47374 USA Tel 765-962-8380
E-mail: rosecitysp@msn.com.

MAETA, *(1-889168)* P.O. Box 6012, Metairie, LA 70009-6012 USA Tel 504-833-4428; Fax: 504-833-5272; Toll Free: 888-577-4428
E-mail: maeta@flash.net
Web site: http://www.maeta.com.

Magabala Bks. (AUS) *(0-9588101; 1-875641) Dist. by* **Intl Spec Bk.**

Mage Pubs., Inc., *(0-934211; 1-933823)* 1032 29th St., NW, Washington, DC 20007 USA (SAN 693-0476) Tel 202-342-1642; Fax: 202-342-9269; Toll Free: 800-962-0922 (orders only)
E-mail: as@mage.com
Web site: http://www.mage.com
Dist(s): **Baker & Taylor Bks.**

Magee, Burke & Glenna, *(0-9748424)* Orders Addr.: P.O. Box 581, Carnation, WA 98014 USA; Edit Addr.: 2015 290th Ave., NE, Carnation, WA 98014 USA
E-mail: rtg@returntogod.com
Web site: http://www.returntogod.com.

Maggie's D.O.G. Co., *(0-9703795)* Orders Addr.: 517 E. 58th St., Savannah, GA 31405 USA Tel 912-354-2948; Edit Addr.: 2210 E. 59th St., Savannah, GA 31404 USA
E-mail: AlbieFlea@aol.com.

Magic Box Pubns., *(0-9700386; 0-9704908)* Orders Addr.: P.O. Box 910760, Saint George, UT 84791-0760 USA (SAN 253-7168) Tel 435-628-3845; Fax: 435-628-3849; Toll Free Fax: 888-771-1860; Edit Addr.: 1554 W. Bloomington Dr., S., Saint George, UT 84790 USA
E-mail: magicboxpub@aol.com
Web site: http://www.magicboxpub.com.

Magic Carpet Bks. *Imprint of* **Harcourt Children's Bks.**

Magic Lamp Pr., *(1-56891; 1-882629)* Div. of Magic Lamp Productions, 1838 Washington Way, Venice, CA 90291-4704 USA (SAN 256-1670) Tel 310-822-2985; Fax: 310-827-9123; Toll Free: 800-367-9661
E-mail: videopage@earthlink.net
Web site: http://www.magiclamppress.com
Dist(s): **Baker & Taylor Bks.**

Magic Lamp Productions *See* **Magic Lamp Pr.**

Magic Penny Publishing Co., The, *(0-9673735)* 7770 Regent Rd., NO. 113-577, San Diego, CA 92122-1967 USA (SAN 299-9439)
E-mail: cliff@magicpenny.com; cynthia@magicpenny.com
Web site: http://www.magicpenny.com.

Magic Picture Frame Studio, LLC, *(0-9749269)* Orders Addr.: P.O. Box 2603, Issaquah, WA 98027 USA Tel 425-222-7562
E-mail: publisher@magicpictureframe.com; mvm@magicpictureframe.com; class@magicpictureframe.com
Web site: http://www.magicpictureframe.com
Dist(s): **BookMasters, Inc.**

Magic Propaganda Mill, *(0-9760117)* Please Send All Correspondence To: Info@mpmill.com, Brooklyn, NY 11238 USA
E-mail: info@mpmill.com
Web site: http://www.magicpropagandamill.com.

Magic Shoes Pr., *(0-9670934)* Orders Addr.: P.O. Box 1076, Capitola, CA 95010 USA Fax: 831-464-7348
E-mail: kmaltbie@aol.com.

Magic Tails Pr., *(0-9712596)* P.O. Box 817, Flagstaff, AZ 86002-0817 USA Tel 520-714-1361
E-mail: thothmaat1@aol.com; admin@magictails.com
Web site: http://www.magictails.com.

Magic Valley Pubs., *(0-9716681; 0-9774833; 0-9785509; 0-9800879)* 6390 E. Willow St., Long Beach, CA 90815 USA Tel 562-795-0289; Fax: 562-795-0490 Do not confuse with Magic Valley Publishers in Burly, ID
Web site: http://www.magicvalleypub.com.

Magic Wagon, *(1-60270)* Div. of ADBO Publishing Group, Orders Addr.: P.O. Box 398166, Minneapolis, MN 55439-8166 USA Fax: 952-831-1632; Toll Free: 800-458-8399; Edit Addr.: 8000 W. 78th St. Ste 310, Edina, MN 55439 USA Toll Free: 800-458-8399 ; *Imprints:* Looking Glass Library (LookngGlassLib); Graphic Planet (Graphic Planet)
E-mail: info@abdopub.com
Web site: http://www.abdopublishing.com
Dist(s): **ABDO Publishing Co.**

Magic Woman Pubns., *(0-9760062)* 1527 Veteran Ave., Suite 7, Los Angeles, CA 90024-5566 USA Tel 310-478-7743; Fax: 310-478-9892
E-mail: artdivin@yahoo.com
Web site: http://www.magicwomanpublications.com.

Magic Wordweaver Pr., *(0-615; 0-9754116)* Orders Addr.: P.O. Box 1315, Conifer, CO 80433 USA (SAN 255-8459) Tel 303-838-7515 (phone/fax); Edit Addr.: 29580 S. Sunset Trail, Conifer, CO 80433 USA
E-mail: premalee108@yahoo.com.

Magical Concepts, *(0-9717815)* Orders Addr.: 24211 Elrond Ln., Lake Forest, CA 92630 USA Tel 949-583-7783; 949-554-5497
E-mail: Michael@Magical-Concepts.com; magicalconcepts@earthlink.net
Web site: http://www.MichaelVarma.com; http://www.Magical-Concepts.com/.

Magical Creations, *(0-9744879)* P.O. Box 324, Chicago Park, CA 95712 USA Tel 530-477-7429
E-mail: doris_rainville@hotmail.com.

Magical Graphics *See* **Magical Pubns.**

Magical Mischief Maker, *(0-9754004)* P.O. Box 1075, Douglasville, GA 30133 USA
Web site: http://www.magicalmischiefmaker.com.

Magical Pubns., *(1-880852)* 23361 McKim Ave., Port Charlotte, FL 33980 USA Tel 941-764-9881; Fax: 941-255-0945
E-mail: magical_publications@email.com
Web site: http://www.magicalpublications.com.

Magician's Ink, *(0-9706331)* California Sisters, LLC, P.O. Box 12, Ramona, KS 67475 USA Tel 785-965-7110
E-mail: patandjess@CaliforniaSisters.com
Web site: http://www.CaliforniaSisters.com.

Magill's Choice *Imprint of* **Salem Pr., Inc.**

Magination, *(1-881597)* 3579 E. Foothill Blvd., No. 330, Pasadena, CA 91107 USA Tel 626-306-1190; Fax: 626-306-1193.

Magination Pr. *Imprint of* **American Psychological Assn.**

Magna Large Print Bks. (GBR) *(0-7505; 0-86009; 1-84137; 1-85057) Dist. by* **Ulverscroft US.**

Magnatic Music, *(0-9719897)* 13806 Delaney Rd., Dale City, VA 22193 USA
E-mail: alstonsongs@aol.com.

Magner Publishing *See* **Magner Publishing & American Binding & Publishing**

Magner Publishing & American Binding & Publishing, *(1-929416; 1-60080)* P.O. Box 60049, Corpus Christi, TX 78466 USA Tel 361-658-4221; Toll Free: 800-863-3708
E-mail: rmmagner@pyramid3.net
Web site: http://www.americanbindingpublishing.com.

Magni, *(1-882330)* 7106 Wellington Point Rd., McKinney, TX 75070 USA Tel 972-540-2050; Fax: 972-540-1057
E-mail: sales@magnico.com
Web site: http://www.magnico.com
Dist(s): **Book Publishing Co., The.**

Magnolia Street Pubs., *(0-9613309; 1-890374)* 1250 W. Victoria, Chicago, IL 60660 USA (SAN 653-8843) Tel 773-561-2121; Fax: 773-506-0735
E-mail: kserah@attglobal.net
Web site: http://magnoliastreetpublishers.com.

Magnus Media Sales & Services, LLC *See* **Ann Arbor Media Group, LLC**

Magnus Pr., *(0-9654806; 0-9724869)* Orders Addr.: P.O. Box 2666, Carlsbad, CA 92018 USA Tel 760-806-3743; Fax: 760-806-3689; Toll Free: 800-463-7818; Edit Addr.: 1647 Shire Ave., Oceanside, CA 92057 USA
E-mail: magnuspress@aol.com
Web site: http://www.magnuspress.com
Dist(s): **Baker & Taylor Bks.**
Quality Bks., Inc.
Spring Arbor Distributors, Inc.
Unique Bks., Inc.

Magpie Enterprise *See* **Holmlund Distributing**

Magpie Press *See* **Magpie Pr., Pine Mtn Club, CA**

Magpie Pr., Pine Mtn Club, CA, Orders Addr.: P.O. Box 6434, Pine Mountain Club, CA 93222-6434 USA Tel 661-242-1265 (phone/fax) Do not confuse with Magpie Pr. in Wallington, NJ
E-mail: MagSmith1265@msn.com
Web site: www.magpiepress.com
Dist(s): **Baker & Taylor Bks.**

Magpie Pubns., *(0-936480)* P.O. Box 636, Alamo, CA 94507 USA (SAN 221-4091) Tel 925-838-9287 (phone/fax); Toll Free: 800-624-7435 (phone/fax)
Web site: http://www.pp.ph.ic.ac.uk/~magpie.

Magrane, Etna International, *(0-9741167)* 8 Hill Point Ave., San Francisco, CA 94117 USA Tel 415-681-5157; Fax: 415-681-5820
E-mail: emagrane@aol.com.

Magsimba Pr., *(1-932956)* 1821 Bruce Rd., NE, Atlanta, GA 30329-2508 USA Tel 404-633-9153
E-mail: info@magsimba.org
Web site: http://www.magsimba.org; http://www.tagalog1.com/Ordinary/Learn_Filipino.jsp
Dist(s): **Quality Bks., Inc.**

Mailbox Bks., The *Imprint of* **Education Ctr., Inc.**

Mailbox Pr., *(0-9650793)* 202 S. Plum, Havana, IL 62644 USA Tel 309-543-4644; Fax: 309-543-2053; 106 Laurel Ln., Seneca, SC 29678 Tel 864-882-8574; Toll Free: 800-398-6613.

Main Asset Pubns., *(0-9667617)* P.O. Box 1153, Teaneck, NJ 07666 USA Tel 201-837-6400; Fax: 201-837-8842
E-mail: mathispublishing@aol.com
Web site: http://www.whyarentumarried.com.

Main Event Pr., *(0-9774129)* 1714 Boxwood Cir., Saint Cloud, MN 56303-0148 USA.

Main St. Bks. *Imprint of* **Broadway Bks.**

Main Street Books *See* **Cherry Street Bks.**

Main Street Pubns., *(0-9745033)* 4850 Rayner Pk. Dr., Orion, MI 48359 USA.

Main Street Publishing, Inc. *See* **Main St Publishing, Inc.**

Main St Publishing, Inc., *(0-9666676; 0-9710470; 0-9741294; 0-9748591; 0-9760414; 0-9765369; 0-9776480; 0-9785934; 0-9791154; 1-934615)* 206 E. Main, Suite 207, Jackson, TN 38301 USA Fax: 731-427-7380; Toll Free: 866-457-7379 ; *Imprints:* MSP (MSP) Do not confuse with companies with same or similar names in Kingston, NJ, Shorewood, WI, Osage Beach MO,
E-mail: netster66@yahoo.com; mspsupport@charterinternet.com
Web site: http://www.mainstreetpublishing.com.

Main Street Rag Publishing Co., *(0-9663293; 1-930907; 1-59948)* Orders Addr.: P.O. Box 690100, Charlotte, NC 28227-7001 USA Tel 704-573-2516
E-mail: editor@mainstreetrag.com
Web site: http://www.mainstreetrag.com.

Maine Writers & Pubs. Alliance, *(0-9618592)* P.O. Box 9301, Portland, ME 04104-9301 USA (SAN 224-2303).

Mainstay Church Resources, *(1-57849)* Div. of The Chapel of the Air Ministries, P.O. Box 30, Wheaton, IL 60189-0030 USA Toll Free: 800-224-2735
Web site: http://www.teamsundays.org.

Mainstream Connections, Inc., *(1-60336)* 10103 Queens Cir., Ocean City, MD 21842 USA Tel 410-430-3844
E-mail: barb.esham@mainstreamconnections.org; lisa.spielman@mainstreamconnections.org
Web site: http://www.mainstreamconnections.org.

Mainstreet Systems & Software Inc., *(0-9726871)* P.O. Box 577, Harleysville, PA 19438-0577 USA (SAN 255-335X) Toll Free: 800-257-4535
E-mail: epwhelan@netcarrier.com
Web site: http://www.promotecopyrights.com.

Maire, Lucy Bedoya, *(0-9768436)* Orders Addr.: P.O. Box 2632, Westport, CT 06880 USA Tel 203-454-5204; Fax: 203-454-5204; Edit Addr.: 19 River Oak Rd., Westport, CT 06880 USA
E-mail: twelvetreasures@yahoo.com
Dist(s): **Raimond Graphics Inc.**

Maison, Karen M., *(0-9671421)* 32615 N. North Valley Pkwy. Apt. 337, Phoenix, AZ 85085-4220 USA
E-mail: kmaison@qwest.net.

Majestic Eagle Publishing, *(0-9797495)* Div. of James J. Brown & Assoc., Inc., 6649 Navajo, Lincolnwood, IL 60712 USA Tel 847-679-3447; Fax: 847-679-6191
E-mail: jola1@aol.com.

Majestic Publishing, *(0-9679065)* 1303 Hixson Pike, Suite A, Chattanooga, TN 37405 USA Tel 423-756-0102; Fax: 423-756-0144
E-mail: ellen1068@aol.com.

Majestic Publishing, LLC, *(0-9755314)* Orders Addr.: P.O. Box 1560, Lithonia, GA 30058 USA Tel 770-482-9129; Fax: 770-482-1295 Do not confuse with Majestic Publishing, LLC in Santa Barbara, CA
E-mail: majpublish@bellsouth.net
Web site: http://www.majesticpublishing.net.

Majestic Scholar Publishing Co., *(1-892818)* P.O. Box 2892, Broken Arrow, OK 74013-2892 USA Tel 918-355-4349; Fax: 918-665-1157
E-mail: mjscholar@aol.com
Web site: http://www.simplyphonics.com.

Majesty Publishing, *(0-9754839)* 12 Paddock Ln., Hampton, VA 23669 USA
E-mail: customerservice@faithfrontier.com
Web site: http://www.faithfrontier.com.

Major for Minors Publishing Co., *(1-892092)* 1234 Lexington Pkwy., Ypsilanti, MI 48198-3136 USA
Dist(s): **Independent Pubs. Marketing.**

Majority Pr., Inc., The, *(0-912469)* Orders Addr.: 46 Development Rd., Fitchburg, MA 01420 USA (SAN 249-3012) Tel 978-342-9676; Fax: 978-348-1233; Edit Addr.: P.O. Box 538, Dover, MA 02030 USA (SAN 265-2757) Tel 508-744-6097 (phone/fax)
E-mail: tmpress@earthlink.net
Web site: http://www.themajoritypress.com
Dist(s): **A & B Distributors & Pubs. Group**
Koen-Levy Bk. Wholesalers LLC
Lexicon Pubns., Inc.

Majzik, Bill *See* **Mill Creek Metro Publishing**

Makai Concepts, LLC, *(0-9744035)* Orders Addr.: 3 King Willilam Ct., Hilton Head Island, SC 29926 USA (SAN 255-6219)
E-mail: betsys@hargray.com.

Make Believe Ideas (GBR) *(1-905051; 1-84610) Dist. by* **IngramPubServ.**

Make Believe Publishing, *(0-9675994)* Orders Addr.: P.O. Box 608817, Orlando, FL 32860-8817 USA Tel 407-599-4988; Fax: 407-599-4989; Toll Free: 800-509-5796; Edit Addr.: 1099 Henry Balch Dr., Orlando, FL 32810 USA
E-mail: monte222@aol.com.

Make Me A Story Pr., *(1-878847)* 1737 N. 2580 E. Rd., Sheldon, IL 60966 USA Tel 815-429-3501 (phone/fax)
E-mail: info@earlthesquirrel.com
Web site: http://www.earlthesquirrel.com
Dist(s): **Baker & Taylor Bks.**

Make Pretend, Inc., *(1-891883)* 2502 Church St., Fort Wayne, IN 46809 USA Tel 219-478-8697; Fax: 219-478-8604; Toll Free: 800-779-8697.

Makinson, R. B., *(0-9654228; 0-9720590)* Orders Addr.: P.O. Box 605, Brooklyn, NY 11217 USA Tel 718-855-5057; Edit Addr.: 419 State St., Brooklyn, NY 11217-1706 USA
E-mail: makinsonrobert@hotmail.com.

Mala Vision, *(0-9704307)* 120 Dunmore St., Throop, PA 18512 USA Tel 570-489-1026
E-mail: malavision@aol.com.

Malamute Pr., *(0-9722180)* Orders Addr.: P.O. Box W, Aspen, CO 81612 USA; Edit Addr.: P.O. Box W, Aspen, CO 81612-7424 USA
E-mail: malamutepress@aol.com; sales@malamutepress.com
Web site: http://www.malamutepress.com.

Malbrough, Michael, *(0-9758883)* 163-167 N. Pk. St., Apt. 5, East Orange, NJ 07019 USA
Web site: http://www.fireprovesiron.com.

Malibu Bks. for Children, *(1-929084)* Div. of Malibu Films, Inc., 48 Broad St., No. 134, Red Bank, NJ 07701 USA Tel 732-933-0446 (phone/fax); Toll Free: 888-629-9947 (phone/fax)
E-mail: malibuinc@aol.com
Web site: http://www.malibubooks.com.

Malik, Sakinah A. *See* **EDR**

Mal-Jonal Productions, Inc., *(0-9648271; 0-9715031)* 16713 SW. 107th Pl., Miami, FL 33157-2965 USA Tel 305-253-4061; Fax: 305-235-2600
E-mail: alicejohnsonmj@aol.com.

Mallinckrodt Communications & Research, *(0-931227)* 498 Schell Rd., Augusta, MO 63332-1628 USA (SAN 682-8752) Tel 636-228-4821 (phone/fax).

Malone, J. C. *See* **Editorial Miglo**

Malone-Ballard Book Publishers, *(0-9729484)* 160 S. Third St., Lansing, IA 52151 USA Tel 319-389-7174 (phone/fax)
Web site: http://www.malone-ballard.com
Dist(s): **Partners Bk. Distributing, Inc.**

Malor Bks. *Imprint of* **ISHK**

Mama Incense Publishing, *(0-9761523)* P.O. Box 4635, Long Beach, CA 90804-9998 USA Tel 310-490-9097
E-mail: mama@mamaincense.com
Web site: http://www.mamaincense.com.

Mama Specific Productions, *(0-9749480)* P.O. Box 110393, Cleveland, OH 44111-0393 USA Tel 440-396-1963; Fax: 801-640-2494 ; *Imprints:* MSPpress (MSPpr)
E-mail: info@msppress.com; trula@MSPpress.com
Web site: http://www.msppress.com.

Mamag Publishing, *(0-9722728)* Orders Addr.: 14 Melrose Terr., Linden, NJ 07036 USA Tel 908-925-9068; Fax: 908-925-9367
E-mail: vitagreco@aol.com
Web site: http://hometown.aol.com/vitagreco/myhomepage/profile.html.

Mama's Boyz, Inc., *(0-9796132)* PMB 114; 304 Main Ave., Norwalk, CT 06851 USA (SAN 854-1914)
E-mail: jerrycraft@aol.com
Web site: http://www.mamasboyz.com.

Mammoth Bks. *Imprint of* **Mammoth Pr., Inc.**

Mammoth Pr., Inc., *(0-9666028; 0-9718059; 1-59539)* 7 S. Juniata St., DuBois, PA 15801 USA Tel 814-371-7066 ; *Imprints:* Mammoth Books (Mammoth Bks) Do not confuse with companies with the same or similar name in Rochester, NY, Culver City, CA
E-mail: avallone@psu.edu
Web site: http://www.mammothpressinc.org
Dist(s): **SPD-Small Pr. Distribution.**

Mamoo Hse., *(1-933014)* 17 W. Browning Rd., Collingswood, NJ 08108 USA Tel 856-858-6616
E-mail: melisma@earthlink.net
Web site: http://www.mamoohouse.com.

MAMP Creations, *(0-9772210)* P.O. Box 4253, Hopkins, MN 55343 USA Tel 952-938-9320 (phone/fax)
E-mail: mampcreations@aol.com.

Man For All Seasons, A, *(1-892088)* P.O. Box 58517, Philadelphia, PA 19102-8517 USA Tel 215-927-2028; Fax: 215-686-0169.

Management Services, *(0-9747418)* 302 S. 2nd St. Apt. 711, Champaign, IL 61820-4141 USA Do not confuse with Managment Services Incorporated in Atlantta, GA
E-mail: aepelbaum@yahoo.com
Web site: http://moscowtechchicago.com.

Manassas Museum, The, *(1-886826)* Orders Addr.: P.O. Box 560, Manassas, VA 20108 USA Tel 703-368-1873; Edit Addr.: 9101 Prince William St., Manassas, VA 201110-5615 USA
Web site: http://www.manassasmuseum.org.

Manatee Publishing *Imprint of* **Four Seasons Pubs.**

Manchester Univ. Pr. (GBR) *(0-7190) Dist. by* **Macmillan.**

Mandala Publishing, *(0-945475; 1-886069; 1-932771; 1-60109)* 17 Paul Dr., San Rafael, CA 94903 USA Tel 415-526-1380; Fax: 415-532-3281; Toll Free: 800-688-2218 (orders only)
E-mail: info@mandala.org
Web site: http://www.mandala.org
Dist(s): **Perseus Distribution.**

Mandala Publishing Group *See* **Mandala Publishing**

Mandell, Ted, *(0-9749156)* 2232 Pine Creek Ct., South Bend, IN 46628 USA Tel 574-631-6953
E-mail: tmandell@nd.edu.

Mandeville, Terry M., *(0-9762475)* 7933 NE 124th St., Kirkland, WA 98034 USA
E-mail: terrymand@aol.com.

M&J Southwest, Inc., *(0-9744534)* 4402 E. Desert Willow Rd., Phoenix, AZ 85044 USA Tel 480-940-4046
E-mail: michaelc@gotwords.com
Web site: http://www.gotwords.com.

Mandolin Hse., *(1-893731)* 2800 N. Pine Grove, Chicago, IL 60657 USA Tel 773-296-6228
E-mail: esmith334@comcast.net
Web site: http://www.~recyellow.com/members6.

M&R Publishing, *(0-9703444)* 1836 Ashley River Rd., Suite 250, Charleston, SC 29407 USA Fax: 205-892-5602
E-mail: MandRYessick@home.com.

Mandracchia Bks. *Imprint of* **Mandracchia, Charles**

Mandracchia, Charles, *(0-9721957)* 316 95th St., Brooklyn, NY 11209 USA Tel 917-805-8347 ; *Imprints:* Mandracchia Books (Mandracchia Bks)
E-mail: charlesmandracchia@yahoo.com
Web site: http://www.kungfoogrannys.com; http://www.showtoonz.com.

Mandy & Andy Bks., Inc., *(0-9772757)* 124 Meridian Ave., Poinciana, FL 34759-3241 USA (SAN 257-1765) Tel 863-427-4643; 407-319-3880
E-mail: wadams23@cfl.rr.com
Web site: http://mandyandandybooks.com
Dist(s): **AtlasBooks Distribution.**

Manga 18 *Imprint of* **Central Park Media Corp.**

Manga Punk, *(0-9748966)* P.O. Box 966, Meadows of Dan, VA 24120 USA
Web site: http://www.mangapunk.com.

MANGACANDY, LLC, *(0-9785891)* 13937 W. 73rd St., Shawnee, KS 66216 USA Tel 913-638-9940
E-mail: nami.bunny@gmail.com
Web site: http://www.mangacandy.com.

Mango (FRA) *(2-7404; 2-84270; 2-910635) Dist. by* **Distribks Inc.**

Mango Tree Pr., *(0-9708571)* Orders Addr.: P.O. Box 853, Mackinaw City, MI 49701 USA Tel 231-627-7322 (phone/fax); Edit Addr.: 2562 Pinewood Cir., Cheboygan, MI 49721 USA
E-mail: ids@mangotreepress.com; lds@mangotreepress.com
Web site: http://www.mangotreepress.com
Dist(s): **Partners Bk. Distributing, Inc.**

Mangrum-Strichart Learning Resources, *(0-9745999; 0-9797723)* 2634 Glendale Dr., Loveland, CO 80538 USA Tel 970-593-1586; Fax: 970-962-0057; Toll Free: 866-409-0585
E-mail: study@mangrum-strichart.com
Web site: http://www.mangrum-strichart.com.

Manhattan Toy, *(0-9676292; 1-931912)* 430 First Ave., N., Suite 500, Minneapolis, MN 55401 USA Toll Free: 800-541-1345
Web site: http://www.manhattantoy.com.

Manifest Pubns., *(0-9627896; 1-929354)* Orders Addr.: P.O. Box 429, Carpinteria, CA 93014 USA Tel 805-684-4905; Fax: 805-684-3100; Edit Addr.: P.O. Box 429, Carpinteria, CA 93014-0429 USA
E-mail: editor@manifestpub.com; publisher@manifestpub.com
Web site: http://www.manifestpub.com
Dist(s): **Sunbelt Pubns., Inc.**

Maninge Mali, *(0-9729698)* 204 Garden Pl., Radnor, PA 19087 USA (SAN 255-4623) Tel 610-254-0846
E-mail: maningemali@aol.com.

Manitowish River Pr., *(0-9656763)* 4245 Hwy. 47, Mercer, WI 54547 USA Tel 715-476-2828; Fax: 715-476-2818
E-mail: manitowish@centuryinter.net
Dist(s): **Adventure Pubns., Inc.**

Mankamyer, Laura, *(0-9728431)* 828 Wheatland Cir., Bridgeville, PA 15017 USA.

Mann Publishing Group, *(0-9726888; 1-932577; 1-933673)* 710 Main St., 6th Flr., Rollinsford, NH 03869 USA (SAN 255-5409) Tel 603-601-0325; Fax: 603-601-0334; Toll Free: 877-877-6266 ; *Imprints:* BookMann Press (BkMann Pr)
E-mail: tmann@mannpublishing.com
Web site: http://www.askopus.com; http://www.rationalpress.com; http://www.agilitypress.com; http://www.incpress.com; http://www.mannpublishing.com.

Mann Publishing Inc. *See* **Mann Publishing Group**

Mannheim Steamroller, LLC, *(0-9754149)* 9130 Mormon Bridge Rd., Omaha, NE 68152 USA Tel 402-457-4341; Fax: 402-457-4332
E-mail: jcarr@americangramaphone.com
Web site: http://www.mannheimsteamroller.com.

Manning, Laurie, *(1-892686)* Orders Addr.: 2640 Violet, Glenview, IL 60025 USA
E-mail: chinaqi888@aol.com.

Manoa Pr., *(1-891839)* 2702 Menoa Rd., Honolulu, HI 96822 USA Tel 808-988-4904
Dist(s): **Native Bks.**

Manoa Valley Publishing Co., The, *(0-9646885)* P.O. Box 5009, Balboa Island, CA 92662 USA Tel 949-675-1340; Fax: 949-720-2069
E-mail: tcleedom@aol.com
Web site: http://www.thelightside.com.

Manor Hse. Pubns., *(0-9648261)* 3501 Newberry Rd., Philadelphia, PA 19154 USA Tel 215-632-7951; 215-637-9255; Fax: 215-632-2176; Toll Free: 800-343-8464 Do not confuse with Manor Hse. Pubns., Alexandria, VA
E-mail: medmanor@bellatlantic.net
Dist(s): **Baker & Taylor Bks.**
Distributors, The
Koen-Levy Bk. Wholesalers LLC
Quality Bks., Inc.

Manor Hse. Publishing Co., Inc., *(0-9645844; 0-9796239)* 880 Louis Dr., Warminster, PA 18974-2819 USA Tel 215-259-1700 Toll Free: 800-768-3222
E-mail: rdean@mgadvertising.com
Web site: http://www.poolspaliving.com.

Mansfield, J. Hse. Publishing Co., *(0-9707428)* P.O. Box 191575, Los Angeles, CA 90019 USA Fax: 323-935-6169
E-mail: jlmansfield@usa.net.

Mansfield, Scott, *(0-9708636)* 626 E. Roses Rd., San Gabriel, CA 91775 USA Tel 626-285-9609 (phone/fax)
E-mail: smansfield7@mindspring.com.

†Manson Western Corp., *(0-87424)* 12031 Wilshire Blvd., Los Angeles, CA 90025 USA (SAN 205-8820) Tel 310-478-2061; Fax: 310-478-7838; Toll Free: 800-648-8857
E-mail: custsvc@wpspublish.com
Web site: http://www.wpspublish.com; *CIP.*

Manta Vision, *(0-9764146)* P.O. Box 1101, Bountiful, UT 84011-1101 USA
Web site: http://www.manta-vision.com.

Mantle Ministries, *(1-889128)* 228 Still Ridge, Bulverde, TX 78163 USA Tel 830-438-3777; Fax: 830-438-3370; Toll Free: 877-548-2327
E-mail: mantleministries@cs.com
Web site: http://www.mantlemin.com
Dist(s): **STL Distribution North America.**

Mantra Publishing, Ltd. (GBR) *(1-85269; 0-947679; 1-84444; 1-84611) Dist. by* **AIMS Intl.**

Manual In Truth, A, *(0-9763252)* P.O. Box 541486, Miami, FL 33054 USA
E-mail: customersupport@amanualintruth.com
Web site: http://www.amanualintruth.com.

Many Kites Pr., *(0-9618469; 0-9729002)* 2203 Elmhurst Dr., Rapid City, SD 57702 USA Tel 605-341-4232 (phone/fax); Toll Free: 800-486-8940
E-mail: info@oyate.com
Web site: http://www.manykites.com
Dist(s): **Independent Pubs. Group.**

ManyTracks Publishing, *(0-9652036; 0-9707024)* 770N Fox Rd., Cooks, MI 49817 USA Toll Free: 877-644-2598
E-mail: mt@manytracks.com
Web site: http://www.manytracks.com.

Manzanita Falls Pubs., *(0-9763916)* P.O. Box 991920, Redding, CA 96099-1920 USA (SAN 256-3347)
Web site: http://www.manzanitafallspublishers.com.

Maple Bend Farms Pr., *(0-9740799)* 4804 Laurel Canyon Blvd., Suite 224, Valley Village, CA 91607 USA
E-mail: ocsage@aol.com
Web site: http://www.maplebend.com.

Maple Canyon Co., *(0-9669760; 0-9787164)* P.O. Box 565, Mapleton, UT 84663 USA Tel 801-489-8948
E-mail: chuckclifton@maplecanyon.com; customerservice@maplecanyon.com
Web site: http://www.maplecanyon.com.

Maple Corners Press *Imprint of* **Attic Studio Publishing Hse.**

Maple Hill Pr., Ltd., *(0-930545)* 174 Maple Hill Rd., Huntington, NY 11743 USA (SAN 677-105X) Tel 631-549-3748; Fax: 631-427-8473; Toll Free: 800-743-3748.

Maple Leaf Ctr., *(0-9759850)* 167 N. Main St., Wallingford, VT 05773 USA Tel 802-446-3601; Fax: 802-446-3801
E-mail: mapleleaf@vermontel.net
Web site: http://www.mapleleafcenter.com.

Maple Leaf Publishing *See* **Spreeda Publishing**

Maple Tree Pr. (CAN) *(0-919872; 0-920775; 1-895688; 1-894379; 1-897066; 1-897349) Dist. by* **Firefly Bks Limited.**

Company

Maple Tree Pr. (CAN) *(0-919872; 0-920775; 1-895688; 1-894379; 1-897066; 1-897349) Dist. by* **Perseus Dist.**

Maps For Kids Inc., *(0-9759433)* 1550 Poly Dr., Billings, MT 59102 USA Tel 406-238-7131; Fax: 406-259-4021; Toll Free: 877-897-7131
E-mail: banjo@floberg.com
Web site: http://www.mapsforkids.com.

Maps.com, *(1-930194)* 120 Cremona Dr. Ste. H, Goleta, CA 93117-5564 USA (SAN 254-4180) Toll Free: 800-929-4627
E-mail: info@maps.com
Web site: http://www.maps.com
Dist(s): **Cram, George F. Co., Inc.**

Marandu, Thobias L., *(0-9767605)* 2915 A Columbiana Rd., Vestavia Hills, AL 35216 USA
E-mail: tlekundayo@yahoo.com.

Mar-Bear Publishing, *(0-9725452)* 606 Mary Hughes Dr., Houma, LA 70363 USA Tel 985-872-3897; Fax: 985-876-4507
E-mail: mgresale@bellsouth.net.

Marble House Editions, *(0-9677047; 0-9786745)* 96-09 66th Ave., Suite 1d, Rego Park, NY 11374 USA (SAN 253-6536) Tel 718-896-4186
E-mail: dougeliz@att.net
Web site: http://www.marble-house-editions.com/.

Marble Mountain Pr., *(0-9748552)* PMB 214, 2019 Aero Way, Suite 103, Medford, OR 97504 USA Tel 530-926-2473
E-mail: marblemountain@snowcrest.net
Web site: http://www.rvinnz.com
Dist(s): **Baker & Taylor Bks.**

Marblehead Publishing, *(0-943335)* 315 Blueridge Rd., Carrboro, NC 27510 USA (SAN 668-5471) Tel 919-929-1719; Fax: 919-933-2209
E-mail: smadon315@aol.com
Dist(s): **Parnassus Bk. Distributors.**

Marcasa Bks., *(0-9763015)* Paloma del Lago No. 67, Campolago, Cidra, PR 00739-9361 USA Tel 787-739-0815 (phone/fax)
E-mail: MarcasaBooks@ElPoderDeLaPalabra.net
Web site: http://www.ElPoderDeLaPalabra.net.

March Forth Pubns., *(1-930506)* Orders Addr.: P.O. Box 17413, Sugar Land, TX 77496-7413 USA Tel 281-313-1231; Edit Addr.: 3130 Grant Lake Blvd., Sugar Land, TX 77496 USA
E-mail: h_langlais@hotmail.com.

March 4th Publishing Co., *(1-887018)* P.O. Box 322, Huron, OH 44839 USA
E-mail: johnbg@bgnet.bgsu.edu
Dist(s): **Baker & Taylor Bks.**

March Media, Inc., *(0-9634824)* 1114 Oman Dr., Brentwood, TN 37027 USA Tel 615-377-1146; Fax: 615-373-1705
E-mail: etta.wilson@comcast.net.

March Street Pr., *(0-9624453; 1-882983; 0-9745909; 1-59661)* 3413 Wilshire Dr., Greensboro, NC 27408-2923 USA Fax: 336-282-9754 prefer orders by email (rbixby@aol.com)
E-mail: rbixby@aol.com
Web site: http://www.marchstreetpress.com
Dist(s): **Baker & Taylor Bks.**

Marcia's Menagerie, *(0-9777359)* 2960 W. Stuart St., A-203, Fort Collins, CO 80526 USA Tel 970-493-6373
E-mail: tangome27@hotmail.com.

MAR*CO Products, Inc., *(1-57543; 1-884063)* Orders Addr.: 1443 Old York Rd., Warminster, PA 18974 USA Tel 215-956-0313; Fax: 215-956-9041; Toll Free: 800-448-2197
E-mail: csfunk@marcoproducts.com; marcoproducts@comcast.net
Web site: http://www.store.yahoo.com/marcoproducts; http://www.marcoproducts.com.

Marcus Institute of Commercial Modeling, *(0-9653585)* 3505 Shelburne Rd., Suite 100, Baltimore, MD 21208 USA Tel 410-764-0511; Fax: 410-764-5636; Toll Free: 800-626-6335
E-mail: aaron@howtomodel.com
Web site: http://www.howtomodel.com/
Dist(s): **Baker & Taylor Bks.**

Mardi Gras Publishing, LLC, *(0-9787262; 0-9789024; 0-9789986; 0-9790649; 0-9791570; 1-934329)* .

Marduk Publishing Inc., *(1-893138)* Orders Addr.: a/o Marduk Publishing Inc., P.O. Box 480608, Delray Beach, FL 33448 USA (SAN 256-3053) Tel 561-638-6070; 516 695-8077; Toll Free: 888-462-7385 (phone/fax)
E-mail: docbloc@marduk1.com; docbloc@marpub.com; docbloc@hotmail.com
Web site: http://www.marpub.com; http://www.marduk1.com; http://www.all-a.us; http://www.all-ace.com.

Mare Rich Studios *See* **Marianne Richmond Studios, Inc.**

Marn Green Publishing, Inc., *(1-934277)* 5525 Memorial Ave. N., Suite 6, Oak Park Heights, MN 55082 USA (SAN 852-4920) Tel 651-439-4500; Fax: 651-439-4532; Toll Free: 800-287-1512
E-mail: toddsnow@marengreen.com
Web site: http://www.marengreen.com
Dist(s): **Crabtree Publishing.**

Maresca, Wendi, *(0-9772897)* 6130 Murifield Dr., Gurnee, IL 60031-5357 USA.

Margolis, Amy Publishing, *(0-9776692)* Orders Addr.: 31 Saddle Ln., Old Brookville, NY 11545 USA (SAN 257-9294)
E-mail: Amy@ButterfliesandMagicalWings.com
Web site: http://www.ButterfliesandMagicalWings.com.

Margolis, Marion, *(0-9753184)* 1 W. 72nd St., Apt. No. 95, New York, NY 10023 USA Tel 212-595-7555
E-mail: chasmargolis@aol.com
Dist(s): **Xlibris Corp.**

Marhouse, Inc., *(0-9752703)* Orders Addr.: a/o Marhouse Inc., P.O. Box 150605, Altamonte Springs, FL 32715 USA Tel 407-499-5307 (phone/fax)
E-mail: customerservice@adventurefox.com
Web site: http://www.adventurefox.com
Dist(s): **Biblio Distribution.**

Marian Pr., *(0-944203; 1-932773; 1-59614)* Marian Helpers Ctr., Eden Hill, Stockbridge, MA 01263-0004 USA (SAN 243-1548) Tel 413-298-3691; Fax: 413-298-1356; Toll Free: 800-462-7426
E-mail: mromaniak@marian.org
Web site: http://www.marian.org
Dist(s): **STL Distribution North America.**

Marianne Richmond Studios, Inc., *(0-9652448; 0-9741465; 0-9753528; 0-9763101; 0-9769522; 0-9770000; 0-9774651; 1-934082)* 3900 Stinson Blvd. NE., Minneapolis, MN 55421 USA (SAN 255-6200) Tel 612-305-1130
E-mail: jim@mariannerichmond.com
Web site: http://www.mariannerichmond.com
Dist(s): **Baker & Taylor Bks.**
Ingram Bk. Co.
Partners Bk. Distributing, Inc.

Marilux Pr., *(0-9710281)* 4100 Corporate Sq., Suite 161, Naples, FL 34104 USA Tel 239-398-7018; Fax: 917-591-0387
E-mail: sales@mariluxpress.com
Web site: http://www.MariluxPress.com.

Mariner Bks. *Imprint of* **Houghton Mifflin Co. Trade & Reference Div.**

Mariner Publishing, *(0-9768238; 0-9776841)* Div. of Mariner Companies, Inc., 212 E. 21st St., Buena Vista, VA 24416-2716 USA Tel 540-264-0021 (phone/fax); Fax: 540-264-0021 Do not confuse with Mariner Publishing in Tampa, FL Oklahoma City, OK
E-mail: info@marinermedia.com
Web site: http://www.marinermedia.com
Dist(s): **Eastern National.**

Marion Institute, *(958-692)* 3 Barnabas Rd., Marion, MA 02738 USA
E-mail: info@marioninstitute.org
Web site: http://www.marioninstitute.org/matriarch/default.asp
Dist(s): **Chelsea Green Publishing.**

Marion Street Pr., *(1-892082)* 901 Bryan Ct., Silverton, OR 97381-1187 USA Do not confuse with Marion Street Pr., Inc., Oak Park, IL.

Maritime Kids Quest Pr., *(0-9761178)* P.O. Box 700, Manteo, NC 27954 USA Tel 252-473-6933
E-mail: maritimekidsquest@earthlink.net.

Maritime Museum Assn. of San Diego, *(0-944580)* 1492 N. Harbor Dr., San Diego, CA 92101 USA (SAN 279-5027) Tel 619-234-9153; Fax: 619-234-8345
E-mail: museumstore@sdmaritime.com
Web site: http://www.sdmaritime.com/mains'lhaul
Dist(s): **Sunbelt Pubns., Inc.**

Marker, Margaret Penfield, *(0-9716721)* 625 Hospitalilty Dr., Rancho Mirage, CA 92270 USA Fax: 760-320-3037
E-mail: tmlrmarker@aol.com.

Market 1 Group Inc., *(0-9748109)* 118 Worthington Business Ctr. 1550 Douglas Ave., Charleston, IL 61920 USA Tel 217-345-8281
E-mail: bmcelwee@consolidated.net
Web site: http://www.familyjourneys.net
Dist(s): **Booksource, The.**

MarketCorp International. Inc., *(0-9761996)* 4819 Highpoint Dr., Marietta, GA 30066 USA Tel 770-924-7997 (phone/fax)
Web site: http://www.godlight.org.

Marketing by Design, *(0-9662634)* 328 Kerr Dr., Johnstown, PA 15904 USA Tel 814-266-6980
E-mail: skylim2485@aol.com.

Marketing Dynamics, Inc., *(0-9676006)* Orders Addr.: 2701 Drakestone Ave., Oklahoma City, OK 73120-4527 USA Fax: 405-842-7834
E-mail: jimh@marketingdynamicsinc.com; guesthester@hotmail.com
Web site: http://www.marketingdynamicsinc.com.

Marketing Magic, Inc., *(0-9675551)* 55 Oceanview Dr., Mastic Beach, NY 11951-1507 USA.

Markets Global Publishing, *(0-9723007)* Div. of Markets Global, LLC, Orders Addr.: P.O. Box 1076, Spruce Pine, NC 28777-1076 USA Tel 828-765-1851; Fax: 828-766-8448; Toll Free: 877-765-1851; Edit Addr.: 16 Fairway Ln., Suite 2, Spruce Pine, NC 28777 USA
E-mail: info@marketsglobal.net
Web site: http://www.marketsglobal.net.

Markins Enterprises, *(0-937729)* 2039 SE 45th Ave., Portland, OR 97215 USA (SAN 659-3224) Tel 503-235-1036.

Markowitz Publishing, *(0-9655890)* 769 Luakini St., Lahaina, HI 96761-1533 USA.

Marks, William *See* **MPC Pr. International**

Markwin Pr., *(0-9740793)* Orders Addr.: P.O. Box 19898, Reno, NV 89511 USA Tel 775-849-0676; Fax: 775-849-3162; Edit Addr.: 3190 Ophir Hill Rd., Washoe Valley, NV 89704-9567 USA
E-mail: softgaits@aol.com.

MarLin Bks., *(0-9713839)* P.M.B. 444, 1001 S. Tenth, Suite G, McAllen, TX 78501 USA Tel 956-668-1516; Fax: 956-668-7580
E-mail: LMMR13@aol.com.

Marlor Pr., Inc., *(0-943400; 1-892147)* 4304 Brigadoon Dr., Saint Paul, MN 55126 USA (SAN 240-7140) Tel 651-484-4600; Fax: 651-490-1182; Toll Free: 800-669-4908
E-mail: marlor@minn.net
Dist(s): **Independent Pubs. Group.**

Marmardesign, *(0-9714438)* 745 Clymer St., Philadelphia, PA 19147-2813 USA
E-mail: carolnoel2@aol.com; marmardesign@comcast.net.

Maroma Bks., *(0-9796465)* 5615 Kirby Dr., Suite 820, Houston, TX 77005 USA Toll Free Fax: 800-525-0910; Toll Free: 888-627-6628
E-mail: molly@maromabooks.com
Web site: http://www.maromabooks.com
Dist(s): **Lightning Source, Inc.**

Marquette Bks., LLC, *(0-922993)* 3107 E. 62nd Ave., Spokane, WA 99223 USA (SAN 251-5261) Tel 509-443-7057; Fax: 509-448-2191
E-mail: books@marquettebooks.org
Web site: http://www.marquettebooks.org
Dist(s): **Ambassador Bks. & Media**
Baker & Taylor Bks.
Book Hse., The
Brodart Co.
Coutts Library Service, Inc.
Eastern Bk. Co.
Emery-Pratt Co.
Levant USA, Inc.
Midwest Library Service
Blackwell North America.

Marquise Publishing, *(0-9745264)* Orders Addr.: P.O. Box 43821, Richmond Heights, OH 44143 USA Tel 216-261-7733
E-mail: admin@marquisepublishing.com
Web site: http://www.marquisepublishing.com.

Marrero, Rafael, *(0-9747569)* 2121 Red Rd., Ave., Coral Gables, FL 33155-2232 USA Tel 305-267-0163
E-mail: rafelitomarrero@hotmail.com.

Marriage Education *See* **Dibble Fund for Marriage Education, The**

Marriwell Publishing, *(0-9742891)* P.O. Box 116, Center Valley, PA 18034 USA Tel 610-282-6807; Fax: 610-282-0909
Web site: http://www.marriwell.com.

Mars Media Pubs., *(1-60136)* Div. of Mars Media Enterprises, Inc., P.O. Box 119, Franklin Park, NJ 08823 USA (SAN 851-0776) Tel 732-940-4286; Fax: 732-940-0534
E-mail: mgladishev@hotmail.com
Dist(s): **National Bk. Network.**

Marsh, Carole Bks. *Imprint of* **Gallopade International**

Marsh, Carole Family CD-Rom *Imprint of* **Gallopade International**

Marsh Creek Pr., *(0-937750)* Div. of Don Aslett, Inc., Orders Addr.: P.O. Box 700, Pocatello, ID 83204 USA (SAN 216-1028) Tel 208-232-3535; Fax: 208-235-5481; Edit Addr.: 311 S. Fifth Ave., Pocatello, ID 83201 USA
E-mail: Tobih@aol.com
Web site: http://www.aslett.com
Dist(s): **Aspen West Publishing**
F & W Pubns., Inc.

Marsh Media, *(0-925159; 1-55942)* Div. of Marsh Film Enterprises, Inc., P.O. Box 8082, Shawnee Mission, KS 66208 USA Tel 816-523-1059; Fax: 816-333-7421; Toll Free: 800-821-3303 (for orders/customer service only)
E-mail: info@marshmedia.com
Web site: http://www.marshmedia.com
Dist(s): **Baker & Taylor Bks.**

Marsh, Thomas E. Inc., *(0-9633682)* 914 Franklin Ave., Youngstown, OH 44502 USA Tel 216-743-8600; Toll Free: 800-845-7930.

Marshall, Barry L., *(0-9714409)* 121 Quail Rd., Perrysburg, OH 43551 USA Tel 419-874-4673
E-mail: blmarshall50@hotmail.com.

Marshall Consulting, *(0-9664540)* 720 Appaloosa Dr., Walnut Creek, CA 94596 USA Tel 925-945-6051; Fax: 925-945-1461
E-mail: marshallconsult@aol.com.

Marshall, George Publishing, *(0-9729403)* P.O. Box 375, Bedford, VA 24523 USA.

Marshfilm Enterprises, Incorporated *See* **Marsh Media**

Martain Pubs., *(0-9646489)* 16 Dalewood, Searcy, AR 72143 USA Tel 501-268-7391; Toll Free: 877-445-3397.

Martell Publishing Co, *(1-893181; 1-930200)* 3333 Midway Dr., Dept. 104, San Diego, CA 92110 USA Tel 619-224-4400; Toll Free Fax: 800-805-3329; Toll Free: 800-240-9695 (order) ;
Imprints: Lagesse Stevens (LageseS)
E-mail: martell@martellpublishing.com.

Martella, Liz, *(0-615)* 393 Lathrop Rd., Lathrop, CA 95330 USA
E-mail: lizmartella@yahoo.com
Dist(s): **Lulu.com.**

Marti Bks., *(0-9766006)* Orders Addr.: P.O. Box 603, West Tisbury, MA 02575 USA Tel 508-696-7496 (phone/fax); Edit Addr.: 635 State Rd., West Tisbury, MA 02575 USA
E-mail: fferr2@aol.com
Web site: http://www.martibooks.com.

Martial Art-Org *Imprint of* **Aristo Agon Brun Universal Union**

Martin & Brothers, *(0-9719842; 0-9767500)* Orders Addr.: P.O. Box 122, Abbott, TX 76621 USA Tel 254-235-8588; Edit Addr.: 101 Bordon, Abbott, TX 76621 USA
E-mail: martinbrothers@aol.com.

Martin, Carolyn, *(0-9746808)* 1890 N. 36th St., Galesburg, MI 49053-9528 USA Tel 269-665-9953 Do not confuse with Carolyn Martin in Philadelphia, PA
E-mail: carmartin@earthlink.net
Web site: http://www.finefrets.com/metalhorses.

Martin Graphics, *(0-615)* 4030 Sherwood Dr., York, PA 17404 USA Tel 717-792-4474; 717-792-3551 (work)
E-mail: martingraphics@aol.com.

Martin, Jack & Assocs., *(0-9649530)* Orders Addr.: 9422 S. Saginaw, Grand Blanc, MI 48439 USA Tel 810-694-5698; Fax: 810-694-7851
E-mail: jdmart@tir.com
Web site: http://www.Pre-Apprenticetraining.com.

Martin, Liz *See* **Mayden Publishing Corp.**

Martin Publishing, *(0-9753992)* 1600 S. 30th, Lot 36, Escanaba, MI 49829 USA Do not confuse with companies with the same or similar name in Fort Morgan, CO; Tampico, IL; La Mesa, CA; Perry, OK; Cowpens, SC; Lincoln, ME.

Martinez, Leroy F., *(0-9748002)* 4045 E. 3rd St. Unit 111, Long Beach, CA 90814-2883 USA
Web site: http://leroymartinez.com.

†**Martingale & Co.,** *(0-943574; 1-56477; 1-60468)* Orders Addr.: 20205-144th Ave., NE, Woodinville, WA 98072-8478 USA (SAN 665-7923) Tel 425-483-3313; Fax: 425-486-7596; Toll Free: 800-993-9444; Edit Addr.: 20205-144th Ave., NE, Woodinville, WA 98072-8478 USA (SAN 240-7876) Toll Free: 800-426-3126 ; *Imprints:* That Patchwork Place (That Patchwrk Pl)
E-mail: scorley@martingale-pub.com
Web site: http://www.martingale-pub.com; *CIP.*

Martin-Ola Pr., *(0-9659125)* 2464 Taylor Rd., Suite 131, Wildwood, MO 63040 USA (SAN 299-4771) Tel 636-273-0404 (phone/fax)
E-mail: editor@ParentToParent.com
Web site: http://www.parenttoparent.com
Dist(s): **Baker & Taylor Bks.**
Ingram Bk. Co.

Martin's *See* **Green Pastures Pr.**

Marvel Enterprises, Inc., *(0-7851; 0-87135; 0-939766; 0-9604146)* 417 5th Ave. Flr. 2, New York, NY 10016-2204 USA (SAN 216-9088); c/o Marvel Enterprises Japan, Inc., Hill House B, 9-10 Hachiyama-cho Sibuya, Tokyo, 150-0034 ; *Imprints:* Marvel's Finest (Marvels Finest); Essential Series, The (Essential Series); From the House of Ideas (From the Hse); Visionaries (Visionaries)
E-mail: mail@marvel.com
Web site: http://www.marvel.com
Dist(s): **Diamond Bk. Distributors.**

Marvel Entertainment Group, Incorporated *See* **Marvel Enterprises, Inc.**

Marvelous Dream, *(0-9771016)* Div. of Marvelous World LLC, P.O. Box 252, Bloomfield, NJ 07003-9998 USA (SAN 256-7857).

Marvel's Finest *Imprint of* **Marvel Enterprises, Inc.**

MarWel Enterprises, Inc., *(0-9759582)* P.O. Box 31227, Washington, DC 20030 USA
E-mail: marwel@earthlink.net.

Marx Group, The, *(0-9773962)* 2111 Jefferson Davis Hwy. 303N., Arlington, VA 22202 USA Tel 703-418-1956; Fax: 703-418-0224
E-mail: don@themarxgroup.com
Web site: http://www.the marxgroup.com.

Marx, Jeff, *(0-9667824; 0-9793134)* 3160 N. 35th St., Hollywood, FL 33021-2630 USA (SAN 853-1021)
E-mail: JeffMarx@schoolelection.com
Web site: http://www.schoolelection.com
Dist(s): **Independent Pubs. Group.**

Mary, Inc., *(1-929411)* 9211 S. Oak Park, Oaklawn, IL 60453 USA Tel 708-430-4742; Fax: 708-430-9754 Do not confuse with Mary, Inc., Providence, RI.

Maryknoll Fathers & Brothers *See* **Maryknoll Missioners**

Maryknoll Missioners, *(0-941395)* P.O. Box 308, Maryknoll, NY 15054-0308 USA (SAN 219-3752) Tel 914-941-7590; Toll Free: 800-227-8523
E-mail: jgoldbeck@maryknoll.org.

Maryknoll World Productions, *(0-941395)* P.O. Box 308, Maryknoll, NY 10545-0308 USA Tel 914-941-7636; Fax: 914-762-6567; Toll Free: 800-227-8523
E-mail: jdemm@maryknoll.org
Web site: http://www.maryknoll.org.

MaryKnoll World Video & Film Library/Maryknoll Media Relations *See* **Maryknoll World Productions**

Maryland Historical Pr., *(0-917882)* 2364 Sandell Dr., Dunwoody, GA 30338 USA (SAN 202-6147) Tel 770-671-0740; Fax: 770 481-0661
E-mail: rollovera@bellsouth.net
Dist(s): **Barnes & Noble Bks.-Imports**
Baker & Taylor Bks.
Book Wholesalers, Inc.
Brodart Co.
Coutts Library Service, Inc.
Eastern National
Follett Library Resources
S&L Sales Co., Inc.

†**Maryland Historical Society,** *(0-938420)* 201 W. Monument St., Baltimore, MD 21201 USA (SAN 203-9788) Tel 410-685-3750; Fax: 410-385-2105
E-mail: rcottom@mdhs.org; jwouters@mdhs.org
Web site: http://www.mdhs.org
Dist(s): **Hood, Alan C. & Co., Inc.**; *CIP.*

Maryruth Bks., Inc., *(0-9713518; 0-9720295; 0-9746475; 1-933624)* 2938 Green Rd., Shaker Heights, OH 44122 USA Tel 216-491-9029; P.O. Box 221143, Beachwood, OH 44122 Tel 216-491-0261 (phone/fax)
E-mail: robcoulton@cs.com
Web site: http://www.maryruthbooks.com.

Marzetta Bks., *(0-9657033)* P.O. Box 274, Lombard, IL 60148 USA Tel 630-424-1403
E-mail: marzetta@concentric.net
Dist(s): **Midpoint Trade Bks., Inc.**

Masalai Pr., *(0-9714127)* 368 Capricorn Ave., Oakland, CA 94611-2058 USA
E-mail: THSlone@yahoo.com
Web site: http://THSlone.tripod.com/masalaipress.html.

Mascari & Co., *(1-930413)* 1125 Linda Vista Dr. Ste. 105, San Marcos, CA 92078-3819 USA Toll Free Fax: 800-464-6490; Toll Free: 800-464-6420
E-mail: jmascari@volonet.com.

Mascot Bks., Inc., *(0-9743442; 1-932888)* P.O. Box 220157, Chantilly, VA 20153-0157 USA Tel 703-437-3584; Fax: 703-437-3554
E-mail: info@mascotbooks.com
Web site: http://www.mascotbooks.com; http://www.mascotavenue.com.

Mascots for Kids, *(0-9762636)* Div. of Wells Yeager Best Co., Inc., 400 S. 7th St., Lafayette, IN 47901 USA Tel 765-742-7648; Fax: 765-742-1049
E-mail: aklink@nlci.com
Web site: http://www.mascotsforkids.com.

Mask Flight Pr., *(0-9664035)* 16383 Bolsa Chica, Huntington Beach, CA 92649 USA Tel 714-846-0679
E-mail: maskflight@aol.com.

Mason Crest Pubs., *(1-59084; 1-59482; 1-4222)* Orders Addr.: 370 Reed Rd., Suite 302-Dept. MC6, Broomall, PA 19008-0914 USA Tel 610-543-6200; Fax: 610-543-3878; Toll Free: 866-627-2665 (866-MCP-Book)
E-mail: gbaffa@masoncrest.com
Web site: http://www.masoncrest.com
Dist(s): **Biblio Distribution.**

Mason, E. Design, Inc., *(1-933075)* P.O. Box 10043, Glendale, AZ 85318 USA Toll Free: 800-211-9692 (phone/fax)
Web site: http://www.emasondesigninc.com.

MassAward Publishing, Inc., *(0-9669902)* Div. of MassAward, Incorporated, 963 Leahy Cr., Des Plaines, IL 60016 USA Tel 847-258-3305 (phone/fax)
E-mail: jwardz@wwa.com.

Massey Publishing, *(0-9640883)* P.O. Box 8945, Atlanta, GA 31106-0945 USA Tel 404-406-5034 (phone/fax)
E-mail: galemassey7@aol.com
Web site:
http://hometown.aol.com/galemassey7/myhomepage/business.html
Dist(s): **New Leaf Distributing Co., Inc.**

Master Bks., *(0-89051)* P.O. Box 726, Green Forest, AR 72638-0726 USA (SAN 205-6119) Tel 870-438-5288; Fax: 870-438-5120; Toll Free: 800-999-3777
E-mail: nlp@newleafpress.net
Web site: http://www.masterbooks.net
Dist(s): **Spring Arbor Distributors, Inc.**

Master Communications, Inc., *(1-888194; 1-60480)* 4480 Lake Forest Dr., Suite 302, Cincinnati, OH 45242 USA (SAN 299-2140) Tel 513-563-3100; Fax: 513-563-3105; Toll Free: 800-765-5885
E-mail: sales@master-comm.com
Web site: http://www.familiesoftheworld.com; http://www.master-comm.com.

Master Design, The, *(0-9665424; 1-930285)* Orders Addr.: P.O. Box 569, Union City, TN 38281 USA Tel 270-838-7060
E-mail: Finley@masterdesign.org; publisher@masterdesign.org
Web site: http://www.masterdesign.org
Dist(s): **STL Distribution North America.**

Master Maker Productions, *(0-9673957)* 17 Providence Blvd., Kendall Park, NJ 08824 USA
E-mail: comments@themastersclassroom.com
Web site: http:///www.themastersclassroom.com.

Master Publishing, Inc., *(0-945053)* 6125 W. Howard Ave., Niles, IL 60714 USA (SAN 245-8829) Tel 847-763-0916; Fax: 847-763-0918
E-mail: pete@w5yi.com
Web site: http://www.MasterPublishing.com; http://www.ForrestMims.com; http://www.w5yi.org
Dist(s): **WFiveYI Group, Inc., The.**

Master Strategies Publishing, *(0-9766485)* 5806 Chatsworth Ct., Arlington, TX 76018 USA Toll Free: 888-792-5105.

MasterArts Pr. LLC, *(0-9720778)* 701 Renner Rd., Wilmington, DE 19810 USA Tel 609-927-9528
E-mail: jimpix@netvision.net.il; lisehk@comcast.net
Web site: http://www.masterartspress.com; http://hollanderart.com.

Master-Player Library, The, *(1-877873)* Div. of William Grant Still Music, Orders Addr.: P.O. Box 3044, Flagstaff, AZ 86003-3044 USA Tel 928-526-9355; Fax: 928-526-0321; Edit Addr.: 809 W. Riordan Rd., Suite 100, Box 109, Flagstaff, AZ 86001 USA
E-mail: wsmusic@bigplanet.com.

MasterVision, *(1-55919)* 969 Park Ave., New York, NY 10028 USA Tel 212-879-0448
E-mail: stadin1@aol.com
Web site: http://www.mastervision.com/.

Mastery Education Corporation *See* **Charlesbridge Publishing, Inc.**

Mastery For Strings Pubns., *(0-9753919)* 1005 Meriden Ln., Austin, TX 78703 USA Tel 512-474-8196
E-mail: musipro@aol.com.

Mastery Learning Systems, *(1-888976)* 532 N. School St., Ukiah, CA 95482 USA Fax: 707-462-9307; Toll Free: 800-433-4181 (phone/fax)
E-mail: mastery@pacific.net
Web site: http://www.masterylearningsystems.com.

Masthof Pr., *(1-883294; 1-930353; 1-932864; 1-60126)* 219 Mill Rd., Morgantown, PA 19543-9701 USA Tel 610-286-0258; Fax: 610-286-6860
E-mail: mast@masthof.com
Web site: http://www.masthof.com.

Mateboer, Johannes Aart, *(0-9759487)* Div. of Captain's Publishing, 6410 Wakehurst Rd., Charlotte, NC 28226 USA Tel 704-540-7617 (phone/fax)
E-mail: hlmateboer@hotmail.com.

Math Concepts, Inc., *(1-893632)* 445 State Rte. 13, N. No. 26-372, Jacksonville, FL 32259 USA (SAN 253-1089) Tel 904-287-5051; Fax: 904-287-0363; Toll Free: 800-574-9936
E-mail: mathconcepts@leading.net
Web site: http://www.mathconcepts.com.

Math in Motion *See* **Crane Bks.**

Math Solutions Pubns., *(0-941355)* Div. of Marilyn Burns Education Assocs., 150 Gate 5 Rd., Suite 101, Sausalito, CA 94965 USA (SAN 665-5424) Tel 415-332-4181; Fax: 415-331-1931; Toll Free: 800-868-9092
E-mail: msp@mathsolutions.com
Web site: http://www.mathsolutions.com.

Math Studio, The, *(1-929362)* 81 Washington St. Ste. 6, Salem, MA 01970-3514 USA
E-mail: cdraper@mathstudio.com
Web site: http://www.mathstudio.com.

Math Teachers Pr., Inc., *(0-933383; 1-891192; 1-931106; 1-59167)* 4850 Park Glen Rd., Minneapolis, MN 55416 USA (SAN 691-6813) Tel 952-545-6535 Toll Free: 800-852-2435
Web site: http://www.movingwithmath.com.

Mathcounts Foundation, *(0-9674453)* 1420 King St., Alexandria, VA 22314-2794 USA Tel 703-684-2828; Fax: 703-836-4875
E-mail: mathcounts@nspe.org
Web site: http://mathcounts.org.

Mathematical Assn. of America, *(0-88385)* Orders Addr.: P.O. Box 91112, Washington, DC 20090-1112 USA; Edit Addr.: 1529 18th St., NW, Washington, DC 20036 USA (SAN 203-9737) Tel 301-617-7800; Fax: 301-206-9789; Toll Free: 800-331-1622
E-mail: epedreira@maa.org
Web site: http://www.maa.org.

Mathematical Solutions Publishing Co., *(0-9718019)* P.O. Box 36365, Grosse Pointe Farms, MI 48236-0365 USA Fax: 313-881-4277.

Mathis-Njie, Joan J. *See* **Anointed Pubs.**

MATHSTORY.COM, *(0-9702641)* Div. of Rak Productions, P.O. Box 20226, New York, NY 10025-1511 USA Tel 212-864-5462
E-mail: mathstory2000@aol.com
Web site: http://mathstory.com.

Matinicus Pr., *(0-9765689)* 734 Cleveland Ave., Brackenridge, PA 15014-1501 USA.

Matou Communications, *(0-9660596)* 1404 Corey Way S., South Pasadena, FL 33707 USA Tel 727-344-3062 (phone/fax)
E-mail: jackieclarke@yahoo.com
Dist(s): **South Bay Bks.**

Matter of Africa America Time, *(0-9760523)* 2114 Vincent Ave. N., Minneapolis, MN 55411 USA.

Matting Leah Publishing Co., *(0-9761528)* P.O. Box 265, Warwick, NY 10990-0265 USA
Web site: http://www.fatherlikeatree.com.

Matzah Ball Bks., *(0-9753629)* 4652 Via Marina. Apt. 305, Marina Dl Rey, CA 90292-7213 USA
E-mail: info@matzahballbooks.com
Web site: http://www.matzahballbooks.com.

Mau, C. Publishing Co., *(0-9778843)* Orders Addr.: P.O. Box 30084, Edmond, OK 73003-0002 USA
E-mail: cmaupublishing@cox.net.

Maui Arthoughts Co., *(0-945045)* P.O. Box 967, Wailuku, HI 96793-0967 USA (SAN 245-8799) Tel 808-244-0156; Toll Free: 800-403-3472
E-mail: books@maui.net
Web site: http://www.booksmaui.com
Dist(s): **Baker & Taylor Bks.**
Quality Bks., Inc.

Maupin Hse. Publishing, *(0-929895; 1-934338)* Orders Addr.: P.O. Box 90148, Gainesville, FL 32607-0148 USA (SAN 250-7676) Tel 352-373-5588; Fax: 352-373-5546; Toll Free: 800-524-0634 (orders); Edit Addr.: 32 SW 42nd St., Gainesville, FL 32607 USA (SAN 250-7684); 2416 NW 71st Pl., Gainesville, FL 32653 Tel 352-373-5588; Toll Free: 800-524-0634 ; *Imprints:* Hoot Owl Books (Hoot Owl Bks)
E-mail: info@maupinhouse.com
Web site: http://www.maupinhouse.com.

Maval Medical Education *See* **Maval Publishing, Inc.**

Maval Publishing, Inc., *(1-884083; 1-59134)* Div. of Maval Printing Co., 5335 Victoria Cir., Firestone, CO 80504 USA Tel 303-682-9424
E-mail: info@jejerre.com
Web site: http://www.jejerre.com
Dist(s): **Majors Scientific Bks., Inc.**
Matthews Medical Bk. Co.

Maven Of Memory, *(0-9768042)* P.O. Box 398, Hurst, TX 76053-0398 USA
Web site: http://www.sateinstein.com.

Maverick Bks., Inc., *(0-916941; 0-9608612; 1-59188)* Orders Addr.: Box 549, Perryton, TX 79070 USA (SAN 240-7183) Tel 806-435-7611; Fax: 806-435-2410; Edit Addr.: 402 S. Amherst, Suite 1, Perryton, TX 78070 USA Do not confuse with Maverick Books, Woodstock, NY
E-mail: hank1@ptsi.net
Web site: http://www.hankthecowdog.com
Dist(s): **Baker & Taylor Bks.**
Ingram Pub. Services.

Maverick Publishing Co., *(0-9651507; 1-893271)* P.O. Box 6355, San Antonio, TX 78209 USA (SAN 299-0547) Tel 210-828-5777; Fax: 210-828-7874 Do not confuse with companies with the same or similar name in Fulton, OH, New London, MO
E-mail: maverickpub@earthlink.net
Web site: http://www.maverickpub.com.

Mawi, Incorporated, *(0-9743901)* 1746 N. Rockwell St. Apt. 3, Chicago, IL 60647-6525 USA
E-mail: info@mawispeaks.com
Web site: http://www.mawispeaks.com.

Max Media, Inc., *(1-931319)* 471 Arsenal St., No. 14, Watertown, MA 02472 USA Tel 617-721-5581
E-mail: storymaster@grandstories.com
Web site: http://www.grandstories.com.

Max Pubn., Inc., *(0-9633577; 0-9799882)* 825 Malvern Hill, Alpharetta, GA 30022 USA Tel 770-851-0935; Fax: 770-754-7828
E-mail: debra.levinson@gmail.com
Web site: http://www.levinsontravel.com.

Max Publications *See* **Max Pubn., Inc.**

Max-A-Million Guidance Pubns., *(0-9705677)* 1243 Basswood Ct., Chesapeake, VA 23320 USA Tel 757-549-4456.

Maxim Pr., *(0-9767096)* 6947 Coal Creek Pkwy. SE, No. 137, Newcastle, WA 98059-3159 USA
E-mail: lg@maximpress.com
Web site: http://www.maximpress.com/.

Maximilian Pr. Pubs., *(0-9668650; 1-930211)* Orders Addr.: P.O. Box 64841, Virginia Beach, VA 23467-4841 USA Tel 757-482-2273; Fax: 757-482-0325; Edit Addr.: 920 S. Battlefield Blvd., No. 100, Chesapeake, VA 23322 USA
E-mail: mp-publishing@inter-source.org
Web site: http://www.aom-~aom.com.

Maximum Potential, Inc., *(0-9759305)* 10525 Wren Ridge Rd., Alpharetta, GA 30022 USA Tel 404-993-5570.

Maximum Publishing Co., *(0-9740308)* 8405 Spinnaker Cove, Rowlett, TX 75088 USA Tel 972-412-0218 (phone/fax)
E-mail: mmorales@gisd.net.

Maximus Publishing, *(0-9792439)* P.O. Box 4455, Whitefish, MT 59937-4455 USA (SAN 852-8829)
E-mail: MaximusPublishing@bresnan.net
Web site: http://www.maximuspublishing.com.

Maxit Publishing, Inc., *(0-9700174; 0-9708904)* P.O. Box 700', Lompoc, CA 93436 USA (SAN 253-6811) Tel 805-735-6758 (for orders, bills & invoices); Fax: 805-735-6768; Toll Free: 866-686-5100
E-mail: info@maxitpublishing.com
Web site: http://www.maxitpublishing.com.

Maxwell, Joseph, *(0-9758988)* 5328 Runnymede Rd., Jackson, MS 39211 USA Tel 601-978-3478
E-mail: maxwell@thewellpublishing.org.

May, Cynthia D., *(0-615)* 7720 W. 14 Rd., Mesick, MI 49668-9792 USA.

May Maisey Moo *Imprint of* **Paula Pr. Pubs.**

May Maisey Moo, LLC *See* **Paula Pr. Pubs.**

Maya Ventures & Publishing, *(0-9769069)* Div. of Strategic Visions, Inc., Orders Addr.: 337 Turnberry Rd., Birmingham, AL 35244 USA Tel 205-995-8495; Fax: 205-995-8484
E-mail: john@wonderwhippet.com; jom@strategicvisionsinc.com
Web site: http://www.wonderwhippet.com.

Mayden Publishing Corp., *(0-9770603)* P.O. Box 17433, Louisville, KY 40217 USA
E-mail: mart2707@bellsouth.net
Web site: http://www.louisvilleatoz.com.

Mayer-Johnson, Incorporated *See* **Mayer-Johnson LLC**

Mayer-Johnson LLC, *(0-9609160; 1-884135)* Orders Addr.: P.O. Box 1579, Solana Beach, CA 92075-7579 USA (SAN 241-4007) Tel 858-550-0084; Fax: 858-550-0449; Edit Addr.: 6650 Flanders Dr., Suite F, San Diego, CA 92121 USA Tel 858-550-0084; 800-588-4548
E-mail: mayerj@mayer-johnson.com
Web site: http://www.mayer-johnson.com.

Mayfield, Ruth, *(0-9701193)* 3501 Sycamore School Rd., Suite 125-194, Fort Worth, TX 76133 USA Tel 817-294-0802 (phone/fax)
E-mail: rbar10633@aol.com.

Mayhaven Publishing, *(1-878044; 1-932278)* Orders Addr.: P.O. Box 557, Mahomet, IL 61853 USA Tel 217-586-4493; Edit Addr.: 803 Buckthorn Cir., Mahomet, IL 61853 USA ; *Imprints:* Wild Rose (Wld Rose)
E-mail: mayhavenpublishing@mchsi.com
Web site: http://www.mayhavenpublishing.com
Dist(s): **Baker & Taylor Bks.**
Beyda for Bks., LLC
Booksource, The
Brodart Co.
Distributors, The
Forest Sales & Distributing Co.
Mumford Library Bks., Inc.
Quality Bks., Inc.
Unique Bks., Inc.

Mayhem Bks., *(0-9770055)* P.O. Box 313, Bon Secour, AL 36511 USA
E-mail: sweetzer@gulftel.com.

Maylin, Grace, *(0-9792384)* 204 S. Roycroft Blvd., Cheektowaga, NY 14225 USA
E-mail: gmds@adelphia.net.

Maynestream Pr., *(0-9715183)* 3189 Cocoplum Cir., Coconut Creek, FL 33063 USA
E-mail: contact@maynestream.com
Web site: http://www.weirdthings.com
Dist(s): **Biblio Distribution.**

Mayo, Johnny, *(0-9765918)* P.O. Box 5484, Columbia, SC 29250 USA Tel 803-767-6756
E-mail: k9heroes@att.net
Web site: http://www.bucksheroes.com.

Maytag Messerschmitt Media Concern, *(0-9768470)* 931 W. 19th St., Santa Ana, CA 92706 USA.

Maze Creek Studio, *(0-9742285)* 1495 E. Thirteenth St., Carthage, MO 64836-9507 USA Tel 417-359-8787
E-mail: mazecreek@cox-internet.com
Web site: http://www.andythomas.com.

Mazeology, *(0-9793043)* 284 W. 12th St., No. 2, New York, NY 10014-6000 USA Tel 212-929-0734
E-mail: mazeology@yahoo.com
Web site: http://www.mazeology.net.

Mazie, Bernard *See* **Pangus Publishing**

Mazur, Kathy *See* **Spring Ducks Bks., LLC**

Mazz Marketing, Inc., *(0-9663557; 0-9792896)* 287 Courtland Ave., Bridgeport, CT 06605-3238 USA Tel 203-260-4932; Toll Free Fax: 866-209-1305
E-mail: wmazz22@aol.com
Web site: http://www.waynemazzoni.com.

MB Publishing, LLC, *(0-9624166)* 7831 Woodmont Ave., PMB No. 312, Bethesda, MD 20814 USA Toll Free: 866-530-4732
Web site: http://www.mbpublishing.com
Dist(s): **BWI**
Baker & Taylor Bks.

MBAR Publishing, *(0-9650298)* Orders Addr.: P.O. Box 2164, Roswell, NM 88202-2164 USA (SAN 298-9077) Tel 505-625-9327 (phone/fax); Edit Addr.: 5 Bayou Ct., Roswell, NM 88201 USA
E-mail: mbar@rt66.com
Web site: http://www.rt66.com/~mbar
Dist(s): **Sunbelt Pubns., Inc.**

MBE Pubns., *(0-9726499)* 61 Driggs St., Staten Island, NY 10308 USA
E-mail: emonreale@aol.com
Web site: http://www.memoirsbyeileen.com.

MBI Distribution Services, *(0-7603; 0-87938; 0-912612; 1-85010)* Div. of MBI Publishing Co. LLC, Orders Addr.: 729 Prospect Ave., Osceola, WI 54020 USA (SAN 169-9164) Tel 715-294-3345; Fax: 715-294-4448; Toll Free: 800-458-0454; Edit Addr.: 380 Jackson St., Suite 200, Saint Paul, MN 55101-3885 USA Tel 651-287-5000; Fax: 651-287-5001
Web site: http://www.motorbooks.com.

MBI Publishing Co. LLC, *(0-7603; 0-87938; 0-912612)* Orders Addr.: 729 Prospect Ave., Osceola, WI 54020 USA (SAN 699-5462) Tel 715-294-3345; Fax: 715-294-4448; Toll Free: 800-458-0454; Edit Addr.: 380 Jackson St., Suite 200, Saint Paul, MN 55101-3885 USA Tel 651 287 5000; Fax: 651 287 5001 ; *Imprints:* Motorbooks (Motorbks); Zenith Press (Zenith Press)
E-mail: mbibks@motorbooks.com
Web site: http://www.motorbooks.com; http://www.mbipublishing.com
Dist(s): **MBI Distribution Services**
Johnson, Warren A.

MBT, *(0-9768419)* P.O. Box 215, Guilford, CT 06437 USA.

MC Math Comics, *(0-9728453)* 720 Sutton Dr., Carlisle, PA 17013 USA Tel 717-243-4470
E-mail: clarkcherry@aol.com
Web site: http://plusman.org.

MC123, *(0-9765321)* P.O. Box 9556, Michigan City, IN 46361-9556 USA
E-mail: info@mc123.com
Web site: http://www.mc123.com.

McArdle, Donald, *(0-615)* 3867 Berkshire Ct., palm Harbor, FL 34684 USA
Web site: http://www.santaandbugsy.com
Dist(s): **Lulu.com.**

McArthur & Co. (CAN) *(1-55278) Dist. by* **Natl Bk Netwk.**

McBook Pubs., LLC, *(0-9705777)* Orders Addr.: P.O. Box 35513, Tulsa, OK 74005 USA Tel 918-671-6656
E-mail: jdokla@cableone.net
Dist(s): **Baker & Taylor Bks.**

McBrown Songs & Stories, *(1-891721)* Orders Addr.: P.O. Box 1868, Hillsboro, OR 97123-1868 USA; Edit Addr.: 697 NE Terry Ct., Hillsboro, OR 97124 USA Tel 503-648-2695.

McCall Bks., *(0-9701531)* 4748-B La Villa Marina, Marina Del Ray, CA 90292 USA Tel 310-867-1441
E-mail: mccallbooks@juno.com
Web site: http://www.amazon.com/exec/obidos/ASIN/0970153112/qid%3D1028866963/sr%3D1-2/ref%3Dsr%5F1%5F2/104-9128908-3959146; http://www.amazon.com/exec/obidos/ASIN/0970153120
Dist(s): **Baker & Taylor Bks.**
Blackwell Corp.

McCarthy, Maria Skantzaris, *(0-9755844)* P.O. Box 1308, Westford, MA 01886 USA
E-mail: msmccarthy@mindspring.com.

McClain Printing Co., *(0-87012)* P.O. Box 403, Parsons, WV 26287-0403 USA (SAN 203-9478) Tel 304-478-2881; Fax: 304-478-4658; Toll Free: 800-654-7179
E-mail: Mcclain@access.mountain.net
Web site: http://www.McClainPrinting.com.

McClanahan Bk. *Imprint of* **Learning Horizons, Inc.**

McClanahan Publishing Hse., Inc., *(0-913383)* P.O. Box 100, Kuttawa, KY 42055 USA (SAN 285-8371) Tel 270-388-9388; Fax: 270-388-6186; Toll Free: 800-544-6959
E-mail: books@kybooks.com
Web site: http://www.kybooks.com
Dist(s): **Partners Bk. Distributing, Inc.**

McCleery & Sons Publishing, *(0-9700624; 0-9712027; 1-931916)* Div. of J & M Printing, Inc., Orders Addr.: P.O. Box 248, Gwinner, ND 58040-0248 USA Tel 701-678-2461; Fax: 701-678-2264; Toll Free: 800-437-1033; Edit Addr.: 407 Hwy. 13, E., Gwinner, ND 58040-0248 USA
E-mail: janderson@jmcompanies.com; kgallagher@jmcompanies.com
Web site: http://www.jmcompanies.com
Dist(s): **AtlasBooks Distribution.**

McClelland & Stewart (CAN) *(0-396; 0-7710) Dist. by* **Random.**

McClenney Publishing *See* **First Associates Publishing**

McCloud Publishing, *(0-9670275)* Orders Addr.: P.O. Box 93, Romeo, MI 48065 USA (SAN 299-8483) Tel 586-752-3188; Edit Addr.: P.O. Box 1015, Romeo, MI 48065 USA Toll Free Fax: 877-644-2845
E-mail: director@books4hearts.com
Web site: http://www.books4hearts.com
Dist(s): **Baker & Taylor Bks.**

McCourtie, Anne, *(0-9744448)* 15700 154th Rd., Mayetta, KS 66509 USA.

McCray, Kathy *See* **Kathy's Pen**

McCuen, Gary E. Publications *See* **GEM/McCuen Pubns., Inc.**

McDaniel, Megan Faux, *(0-9768019)* Div. of Faux Publishing Concepts, P.O. Box 11474, Marina del Rey, CA 90295 USA
E-mail: meganmcdaniel@sbcglobal.net.

McDonald & Woodward Publishing Co., The, *(0-939923)* 431-B E. College St., Granville, OH 43023-1319 USA (SAN 663-6977) Tel 740-321-1140; Fax: 740-321-1141; Toll Free: 800-233-8787
E-mail: mwpubco@mwpubco.com
Web site: http://www.mwpubco.com
Dist(s): **Partners Bk. Distributing, Inc.**

McDonald, Diane, *(0-9721681)* P.O. Box 622, Sublette, IL 61367 USA.

McDonald Publishing Co., *(1-55708; 1-934256)* 567 Hanley Industrial Ct., Saint Louis, MO 63144 USA (SAN 249-5813) Tel 314-781-7400; Toll Free: 800-722-8080
E-mail: lisa@mcdonaldpublishing.com.

McDougal Littell Inc., *(0-395; 0-8123; 0-86609; 0-88343; 0-618)* Subs. of Houghton Mifflin Co., Orders Addr.: 1900 S. Batavia Ave., Geneva, IL 60134 USA Toll Free: 888-872-8380; Edit Addr.: P.O. Box 1667, Evanston, IL 60204 USA (SAN 202-2532) Toll Free: 800-323-5435; 800-462-6595 (customer service); 909 Davis St., Evanston, IL 60201 Tel 847-869-2300; Fax: 847-869-0841
Web site: http://www.mcdougallittell.com.

McDougal Publishing Co., *(1-58158; 1-884369)* Orders Addr.: P.O. Box 3595, Hagerstown, MD 21742-3595 USA Tel 301-797-6637; Fax: 301-733-2767; Toll Free: 800-962-3684 ; *Imprints:* Parable Publications (Parable Pubns)
E-mail: publishing@mcdougal.org
Web site: http://www.mcdougalpublishing.com
Dist(s): **Anchor Distributors**
Appalachian Bk. Distributors
Spring Arbor Distributors, Inc.

McDowell Health-Science Bks., LLC, *(0-9741238)* P.O. Box 81, Lafayette, CO 80026 USA Tel 303-570-7231; Fax: 303-604-0773
E-mail: McDPubCo@mcdowellpublishing.com; McDPubCo@aol.com; healthscience@mcdowellpublishing.com
Web site: http://www.mcdowellpublishing.com.

McElderry, Margaret K. *Imprint of* **Simon & Schuster Children's Publishing**

McElreath, K.M., *(0-9769271)* 10420 Rivertown Rd., Fairburn, GA 30213 USA Tel 770-969-1718; Fax: 770-969-0183
E-mail: tmcelreath@bellsouth.net.

McElroy & Assocs., *(0-9673917)* 6651 Avignon Blvd., Falls Church, VA 22043-1724 USA Tel 703-237-5993; Fax: 703-237-5994
E-mail: roland@mcelroyassoc.com
Web site: http://www.mcelroyassoc.com.

McFadden, Charles B. Company, Incorporated *See* **Waterview Pr., Inc.**

McFadden, Rebecca, *(0-9725913)* 276 Atkins Ave., Brooklyn, NY 11208 USA
E-mail: iwjccd@aol.com.

†McFarland & Co., Inc. Pubs., *(0-7864; 0-89950)* Orders Addr.: P.O. Box 611, Jefferson, NC 28640 USA (SAN 215-093X) Tel 336-246-4460; Fax: 336-246-5018; 336-246-4403; Toll Free: 800-253-2187 (orders only); Edit Addr.: 960 Hwy., 88 W., Jefferson, NC 28640 USA
E-mail: info@mcfarlandpub.com
Web site: http://www.mcfarlandpub.com; *CIP.*

McFarlin Memorial United Methodist Church, *(0-9672095)* P.O. Box 6390, Norman, OK 73070 USA Tel 405-321-3484
Web site: http://www.okld.com/MCFARLIN.

McGab Publishing, *(0-9788092)* 12438 Prather Ave., Pt Charlotte, FL 33981-1352 USA.

McGauley, Patrick, *(0-9724209)* 2808 5th Ave. W., Hibbing, MN 55746 USA
E-mail: shatiferin@aol.com
Dist(s): **Partners Bk. Distributing, Inc.**

McGovern, Matthew /700acres Communications, *(0-9749445)* 27 McGovern Dr., Buxton, ME 04093 USA
E-mail: matt@mattmcgovern.com
Web site: http://www.mattmcgovern.com.

McGraw, Jason A., *(0-615)* 254 Westminster Rd., Rochester, NY 14607 USA Tel 585-771-7777
E-mail: jaymcgraw18@aol.com
Dist(s): **Lulu.com.**

McGraw-Hill Children's Publishing *See* **School Specialty Publishing**

†McGraw-Hill Cos., The, *(0-07)* 6480 Jimmy Carter Blvd., Norcross, GA 30071-1701 USA (SAN 254-881X) Tel 614-755-5637; Fax: 614-755-5611; Orders Addr.: 860 Taylor Station Rd., Blacklick, OH 43004-0545 USA (SAN 200-254X) Fax: 614-755-5645; Toll Free: 800-722-4726 (orders & customer service); 800-338-3987 (college); 800-525-5003 (subscriptions); 800-352-3566 (books - US/Canada orders); P.O. Box 545, Blacklick, OH 43004-0545 Fax: 614-759-3759; Toll Free: 877-833-5524
E-mail: customer.service@mcgraw-hill.com
Web site: http://www.mcgraw-hill.com; http://www.ebooks.mcgraw-hill.com/
Dist(s): **Libros Sin Fronteras**
McGraw-Hill Osborne
McGraw-Hill Primis Custom Publishing
NetLibrary, Inc.
Sams Technical Publishing, LLC
Sony CONNECT, Inc.; *CIP.*

McGraw-Hill Education (GBR) *(0-07) Dist. by* **McGraw.**

McGraw-Hill Higher Education, *(0-07)* Orders Addr.: P.O. Box 545, Blacklick, OH 43004-0545 USA Toll Free: 800-338-3987; Edit Addr.: 1333 Burr Ridge Pkwy., Burr Ridge, IL 60521 USA ; *Imprints:* WCB/McGraw-Hill (WCB McGr Hill); McGraw-Hill/Dushkin (Dshkn McG-Hill); McGraw-Hill Humanities, Social Sciences & World Languages (Mc-H Human Soc); McGraw-Hill Science, Engineering & Mathematics (McG-H Sci Eng)
E-mail: customer.service@mcgraw-hill.com
Web site: http://www.mhhe.com
Dist(s): **McGraw-Hill Cos., The**
Oxford Univ. Pr., Inc.

McGraw-Hill Humanities, Social Sciences & World Languages *Imprint of* **McGraw-Hill Higher Education**

McGraw-Hill Osborne, *(0-07; 0-88134; 0-931988)* Div. of The McGraw-Hill Professional, 160 Spear St. Flr. 7, San Francisco, CA 94105-1544 USA (SAN 274-3450) Toll Free: 800-227-0900
E-mail: customer.service@mcgraw-hill.com
Web site: http://www.osborne.com
Dist(s): **McGraw-Hill Cos., The**
NetLibrary, Inc.

McGraw-Hill Professional Book Group *See* **McGraw-Hill School Education Group**

McGraw-Hill Professional Publishing, *(0-07)* Div. of McGraw-Hill Higher Education, Orders Addr.: P.O. Box 545, Blacklick, OH 43004-0545 USA Fax: 614-755-5645; Toll Free: 800-722-4726; Edit Addr.: 2 Penn Plaza, New York, NY 10121-2298 USA Tel 212-904-2000 ; *Imprints:* McGraw-Hill Scientific, Technical & Medical (M-H Sci Tec Med); McGraw-Hill/Appleton & Lange (M-H Apple & Lange); International Marine/Ragged Mountain Press (Inter Mar/Rag)
Dist(s): **Amacom**
American Pharmacists Assn.
Berrett-Koehler Pubs., Inc.
Entrepreneur Pr.
Harvard Business Schl. Pr.
McGraw-Hill Cos., The
McGraw-Hill Medical Publishing Div.
McGraw-Hill Trade
NetLibrary, Inc.
Sony CONNECT, Inc.

McGraw-Hill School Education Group, *(0-07; 0-7602; 0-8306; 0-911314; 0-917253; 1-55738)* Div. of The McGraw-Hill Companies, Orders Addr.: P.O. Box 545, Blacklick, OH 43004-0545 USA Fax: 614-755-5645; Toll Free: 800-442-9685 (customer service); 800-722-4726; Edit Addr.: 8787 Orion Pl., Columbus, OH 43240 USA Tel 614-430-4000; c/o Grand Rapids Distribution Center, 3195 Wilson NW, Grand Rapids, MI 49544 (SAN 253-6420) Fax: 614-755-5611
E-mail: customer.service@mcgraw-hill.com
Web site: http://www.accessmedbooks.com; http://www.pbg.mcgraw-hill.com/
Dist(s): **McGraw-Hill Cos., The**
NetLibrary, Inc.
Urban Land Institute.

McGraw-Hill Science, Engineering & Mathematics *Imprint of* **McGraw-Hill Higher Education**

McGraw-Hill Scientific, Technical & Medical *Imprint of* **McGraw-Hill Professional Publishing**

McGraw-Hill Trade, *(0-07; 0-658; 0-8442)* Div. of McGraw-Hill Professional, Orders Addr.: P.O. Box 545, Blacklick, OH 43004-0545 USA Tel 800-722-4726; Fax: 614-755-5645; Edit Addr.: 2 Penn Plaza, New York, NY 10121 USA Tel 212-904-2000 ; *Imprints:* Contemporary Books (Contemporary); Teach Yourself (Tch Yourself); VGM Career Books (VGM Career Bks); Passport Books (Passport Bks)
E-mail: Jeffrey_Krames@mcgraw-hill.com
Web site: http://www.books.mcgraw-hill.com
Dist(s): **McGraw-Hill Cos., The**
NetLibrary, Inc.

McGraw-Hill/Appleton & Lange *Imprint of* **McGraw-Hill Professional Publishing**

McGraw-Hill/Contemporary, *(0-658; 0-8092; 0-8325; 0-8442; 0-88499; 0-89061; 0-913327; 0-940279; 0-941263; 0-9630646; 1-56626; 1-56943; 1-57028)* Div. of McGraw-Hill Higher Education, Orders Addr.: P.O. Box 545, Blacklick, OH 43004-0545 USA Toll Free Fax: 800-998-3103; Toll Free: 800-621-1918; Edit Addr.: 4255 W. Touhy Ave., Lincolnwood, IL 60712 USA (SAN 169-2208) Tel 847-679-5500; Fax: 847-679-2494; Toll Free Fax: 800-998-3103; Toll Free: 800-323-4900 ; *Imprints:* National Textbook Company (Natl Textbk Co)
E-mail: ntcpub@tribune.com
Web site: http://www.ntc-cb.com
Dist(s): **Continental Bk. Co., Inc.**
Giron Bks.
Libros Sin Fronteras
McGraw-Hill Cos., The
NetLibrary, Inc.

McGraw-Hill/Dushkin *Imprint of* **McGraw-Hill Higher Education**

McGuire, Nancy, *(0-9728148)* 325 Glendale Ave., San Marcos, CA 92069 USA Tel 760-798-1493 (phone/fax) ; *Imprints:* Extreme Math (Ext Mth)
E-mail: nancy@extrememathgames.com
Web site: http://www.extrememathgames.com.

McIntyre, Connie, *(0-9677685; 0-9793296)* P.O. Box 11343, Saint Louis, MO 63105 USA Tel 314-863-0775; Fax: 314-863-0813 ; *Imprints:* Thumbprint Press (Thumbprint Pr MO)
E-mail: cmciwrite@aol.com
Web site: http://www.BooksFromTheHeart.com; http://www.UpsideDownside.net.

McJA-ESFA, *(0-9671196)* Orders Addr.: P.O. Box 3183, Erie, PA 16508 USA Tel 814-838-1431; Fax: 814-838-6620; Edit Addr.: 4108 Zuch Rd., Erie, PA 16508 USA
Web site: http://greatlakesgrimsby.com.

McKatlib Pr., *(0-9745440)* P.O. Box 76693, Atlanta, GA 30358-1693 USA
Web site: http://www.bethanyadventures.com.

†**McKay, David Co., Inc.,** *(0-679; 0-88326; 0-89440)* Subs. of Random Hse., Inc., Orders Addr.: 400 Hahn Rd., Westminster, MD 21157 USA Tel 410-848-1900; Toll Free: 800-733-3000 (orders only); Edit Addr.: 201 E. 50th St., MD 4-6, New York, NY 10022 USA (SAN 200-240X) Tel 212-751-2600; Fax: 212-872-8026
Dist(s): **Libros Sin Fronteras**; *CIP.*

McKellen-Caffey, *(0-9794191)* 15543 Sprig St., Chino Hills, CA 91709-2853 USA (SAN 853-4144) Tel 909-393-0894
E-mail: mckellencaffey@yahoo.com
Web site: http://chiselhedgehog.com.

McKenna, Mark, *(0-9727681)* P.O. Box 633, Florida, NY 10921 USA.

McKenna Publishing Group, *(0-9713659; 1-932172)* 425 Poa Pl., San Luis Obispo, CA 93405 USA Tel 805-550-1667; Fax: 805-783-2317
E-mail: ric@mckennapubgrp.com
Web site: http://www.mckennapubgrp.com
Dist(s): **Booklines Hawaii, Ltd.**
Ingram Bk. Co.

McLean News Service, Inc., *(0-9727628)* 13232 Fox Farm Rd., De Soto, MO 63020-4424 USA Tel 636-337-3026
E-mail: johnell@nothnbut.net.

McLellan Bks., *(0-9747536)* Orders Addr.: P.O. Box 341, Claymont, DE 19703-0341 USA Tel 302-798-4006; Fax: 302-798-2567
E-mail: richardmclellan@dca.net; richard@mclellanbooks.com
Web site: http://www.mclellanbooks.com.

MCM Prime, Inc., *(0-9742351)* 6355 E. Duke Ranch Rd., Pearce, AZ 85625-6113 USA Tel 520-824-4051; Fax: 775-249-9133
E-mail: paulmc@vtc.net
Web site: http://www.mcmprime.pair.com/mcmpindx.htm.

McMillan Assocs., *(0-9708885)* 680 N. Lake Shore Dr. Apt. 523, Chicago, IL 60611-4489 USA
E-mail: mikem@mcmillandesign.com
Web site: http://www.mcmillandesign.com.

McMillen Publishing, *(0-9635812; 1-888223)* Orders Addr.: 304 Main St., Ames, IA 50010 USA (SAN 254-9085) Tel 515-232-0208; Fax: 515-232-0402 (orders); Toll Free: 800-750-6997 (In Iowa); 800-453-3960 (Outside Iowa)
E-mail: denise.sunvold@sigler.com
Web site: http://www.mcmillenbooks.com.

McMurtrey, Martin A., *(0-9623961)* 808 Camden, San Antonio, TX 78215 USA Tel 210-223-9680.

McMyr Publishing, *(1-893849)* Orders Addr.: 7931 Miller Ave., No. 152, Gilroy, CA 95020 USA; Edit Addr.: 777 First St., No. 142, Gilroy, CA 95020 USA
E-mail: krisandi@earthlink.net.

McNally Songs & Stories *See* **McBrown Songs & Stories**

Mcnarn Group, The, *(0-9678933)* 815 W. Pine St., Centralia, WA 98531 USA Tel 360-451-1384; Fax: 360-807-0221
E-mail: mcnarn@thoughtdairy.com
Web site: http://www.thoughtdairy.com/mcnarn.

McPhaul Bks., *(0-9655777)* Div. of McPhaul, Inc, 583 Scarborough Rd., P.O. Box 2594, Ellenwood, GA 30294 USA Fax: 678-418-6845
E-mail: mcphaul@bellsouth.net
Web site: http://www.mcphaulbooks.netfirms.com.

McPugh, Kathleen, *(0-9742062)* Orders Addr.: P.O. Box 8372, Fresno, CA 93747 USA; Edit Addr.: 5556 E. Madison Ave., Fresno, CA 93727 USA
Web site: http://home.att.net/~kathfreeman/book.html; http://home.att.net/~kathfreeman
Dist(s): **Lightning Source, Inc.**

McQuaid Jesuit High Schl., *(0-9703109)* 1800 S. Clinton Ave., Rochester, NY 14618 USA Tel 585-256-6121; Fax: 585-256-6171
E-mail: jcarriero@mcquaid.org.

McQueen Publishing Co., *(0-917186)* 1211 S. Osceola Ave., Orlando, FL 32806-2223 USA (SAN 203-9516).

McRae, Lee, *(0-9626075)* 2130 Carleton St., Berkeley, CA 94704 USA Tel 510-848-5591 (phone/fax)
E-mail: lmcr@aol.com.

Mcruffy Pr., *(1-59269)* P.O. Box 212, Raymore, MO 64083 USA Tel 816-331-2500; Fax: 816-331-3868; Toll Free Fax: 888-967-1300; Toll Free: 888-967-1200
E-mail: brian@mcruffy.com
Web site: http://www.mcruffy.

McSweeney's Books *See* **McSweeney's Publishing**

McSweeney's Publishing, *(0-9703355; 0-9719047; 1-932416; 1-934781)* Orders Addr.: 849 Valencia St., San Francisco, CA 94110-1736 USA (SAN 254-3184)
E-mail: heidi@mcsweeneys.net
Web site: http://www.mcsweeneys.net
Dist(s): **Perseus Distribution.**

MCW Publishing, *(0-9753773)* 50 Brookdale Ave., Rochester, NY 14621 USA Tel 585-317-5780
E-mail: itm2000@hotmail.com.

McWitty Pr., Inc., *(0-9755618)* 110 Riverside Dr., No. 1A, New York, NY 10024 USA Tel 212-595-4161
E-mail: elliemcgra@aol.com
Web site: http://www.mcwittypress.com
Dist(s): **Perseus Distribution.**

m.d. hughes, *(0-9788541)* 9 Pasadena Rd., Branford, CT 06405 USA
Web site: http://www.cryofthefalcon.com.

ME Media LLC, *(1-58925)* Orders Addr.: P.O. Box 411037, Kansas City, MO 64141-1037 USA Fax: 913-362-7401; Toll Free: 888-454-0097; Edit Addr.: 202 Old Ridgefield Rd., Wilton, CT 06897 USA (SAN 253-6382) Tel 203-834-0005; Fax: 203-834-0004 ; *Imprints:* tiger tales (tiger tales)
E-mail: etprial@tigertalesbooks.com
Web site: http://www.tigertalesbooks.com
Dist(s): **Fujii Assocs.**

Mead, Brian Publishing, *(0-9717509)* 203 E. Grove Rd., Long Grove, IA 52756 USA (SAN 255-2329)
E-mail: meadpub@juno.com; mattedeye@aol.com.

Meadow Bks. (GBR) *(0-9515655; 1-905363; 1-84685) Dist. by* **Ingram Bk Co.**

Meadow Brook Pubns., *(0-9634281)* Div. of Mind Over Media, 11328 28th Ave., NE, Seattle, WA 98125 USA Tel 206-367-2219.

Meadow Geese Pr., *(0-9665564)* P.O. Box 345, Marshfield Hills, MA 02051 USA Tel 781-834-3957; Fax: 781-834-3578
E-mail: gander@ids.net
Web site: http://www.MeadowGeesePress.com.

†**Meadowbrook Pr.,** *(0-88166; 0-915658)* 5451 Smetana Dr., Minnetonka, MN 55343 USA (SAN 207-3404) Tel 612-930-1100; Fax: 612-930-1940; Toll Free: 800-338-2232
E-mail: mballard@meadowbrookpress.com
Web site: http://www.meadowbrookpress.com
Dist(s): **Simon & Schuster**
Simon & Schuster, Inc.
Simon & Schuster Children's Publishing; *CIP.*

Meanma Pr., *(0-9651136; 1-893882)* 63 Silver St., South Hadley, MA 01075 USA Tel 413-533-4507 (phone/fax)
E-mail: mmcmenam@mtholyoke.edu; meanma@earthlink.net
Web site: http://www.hometown.aol.com/mamca/myhomepage/index.html; http://www.phoenicia.org/press.html.

Mear Pubs., *(0-9707132)* 6140 W. Fifth St., Los Angeles, CA 90048-4724 USA Fax: 323-934-1089
E-mail: slfactor@pacbell.net
Web site: http//www.baseballtao.com.

MEC Publishing, *(0-9746865)* 1923 W. 17th St., Santa Ana, CA 92706 USA (SAN 256-405X)
E-mail: mecpublishing@aol.com
Web site: http://www.mecpublishing.com.

Mechanech Pubns., *(0-9702861)* 4 Kaser Terr., Monsey, NY 10952 USA Tel 914-352-1926.

Mechling Bookbindery, *(0-9703825; 0-9744657; 0-9760563; 0-9793772)* Div. of Mechling Associates, Inc., 1124 Oneida Valley Rd., Chicora, PA 16025-3820 USA Tel 724-287-2120; Fax: 724-285-9231; Toll Free: 800-941-3735
E-mail: sales@mechlingbooks.com
Web site: http://www.mechlingbooks.com
Dist(s): **Partners Bk. Distributing, Inc.**

Meckley Publishing Co., *(1-892464)* P.O. Box 1251, Bowie, MD 20715-1251 USA Tel 301-262-2039; Fax: 410-741-1083; Toll Free: 800-383-2039
E-mail: kidgifts@puff.dsport.com.

Medal Bks., *(0-9764300; 0-9785667)* P.O. Box 7231, Clearwater, FL 33758-7231 USA
E-mail: ronan@ronanblaze.com
Web site: http://www.ronanblaze.com.

Medallion Pr., Inc., *(0-9743639; 1-932815; 1-933836; 1-934755; 1-60542)* Orders Addr.: 937 Four Seasons Blvd., Aurora, IL 60504 USA (SAN 255-5360); Edit Addr.: 1020 Cedar Ave., Suite 2N, Saint Charles, IL 60174 USA ; *Imprints:* Bronze Medallion (Bronze Medallion)
Web site: http://www.medallionpress.com
Dist(s): **Baker & Taylor Bks.**
Independent Pubs. Group
Levy Home Entertainment.

Medernach, T.K., *(0-615)* 14785 kay Ln., Atlanta, GA 30306 USA
E-mail: medernach@bellsouth.net
Web site: http://www.kenmedernach.com
Dist(s): **Lulu.com.**

Media Alert!, *(0-9676616)* P.O. Box 735, Littleton, CO 80160-0735 USA Toll Free: 800-986-5560 (code 02)
E-mail: CNFsueLS@aol.com.

Media Angels, Inc., *(0-9700385; 1-931941)* Orders Addr.: 15720 S. Pebble Ln., Fort Myers, FL 33912-2341 USA
E-mail: felice@mediaangels.com; mediaangels@comcast.net
Web site: http://www.mediaangels.com
Dist(s): **STL Distribution North America.**

Media Assocs., *(0-918501)* P.O. Box 46, Wilton, CA 95693 USA (SAN 657-3207) Toll Free: 800-373-1897 ; *Imprints:* Archives Pr. (Archives Pr) Do not confuse with Media Assocs., Marina Del Rey, CA
E-mail: arkivz10@aol.com.

Media Blasters, Inc., *(1-890228; 1-58655; 1-59883)* 519 8th Ave., 14th Fl., New York, NY 10018 USA Tel 212-868-0991; Fax: 212-868-3315 ; *Imprints:* Anime Works (Anime Works); Kitty Media (Kitty Med); Shriek Show (Shriek Show); Tokyo Shock (Tokyo Shock); Media Blasters Press (MeBlast)
E-mail: info@media-blasters.com
Web site: http://www.media-blasters.com; http://www.kittymedia.com
Dist(s): **Diamond Bk. Distributors.**

Media Blasters Pr. *Imprint of* **Media Blasters, Inc.**

Media Consultants, Inc., *(1-890123)* 3908 East Valley Crt., Raleigh, NC 27606 USA Tel 919-821-2190; Fax: 919-821-3444; Toll Free: 800-392-4434
E-mail: carlg@mediaconsultants.com
Web site: http://www.mediaconsultants.com.

Media Creations, Inc., *(0-9713099; 0-9718509; 1-932047; 1-932303; 1-932560; 1-59526; 1-933626)* Orders Addr.: P.O. Box 772246, Coral Springs, FL 33077-2246 USA Tel 954-726-0902; Fax: 954-726-0903; Toll Free: 866-229-9244; 8055 W. McNab Rd., Tamarac, FL 33321; Edit Addr.: 7970 NW 4th Pl., Plantation, FL 33324-1950 USA ; *Imprints:* Llumina Christian Books (LluminaChrist); Llumina Press (Llumina Pr)
E-mail: diane@llumina.com
Web site: http://www.llumina.com
Dist(s): **Baker & Taylor Bks.**

Media For Life, *(0-9675068)* P.O. Box 1214, Little Falls, NJ 07424 USA Fax: 603-250-8553
E-mail: EduFun@aol.com.

Media Magic New York, *(0-9744211)* 15 W. 39th St., 13th Flr., New York, NY 10018 USA Tel 212-926-5575
E-mail: mediamagicny@aol.com; info@mediamagic-ny.com.

Media Rodzina (POL) *(83-7278; 83-85594) Dist. by* **Distribks Inc.**

Medias & Co., Inc., *(1-893993)* 5107 N. Mesa Dr., Castle Rock, CO 80104 USA Tel 303-688-2624; Fax: 303-660-5053
E-mail: medias@uswest.net
Web site: http://www.zoooo.com.

MEDIC FIRST AID International, Inc., *(0-940430)* 1450 Westec Dr., Eugene, OR 97402-9189 USA (SAN 217-1732)
E-mail: response@medicfirstaid.com
Web site: http://www.medicfirstaid.com.

Medical Alternative Pr., *(0-9660882)* 4173 Fieldbrook Rd., West Bloomfield, MI 48323 USA Tel 248-851-3372; Fax: 248-851-0421; Toll Free: 888-647-5616 Do not confuse with Medical Alternative Pr., Colleyville, TX
E-mail: info@drbrownstein.com
Web site: http://www.drbrownstein.com.

Medical Multimedia Learning Series, *(0-9763371)* Orders Addr.: 2439 De Ovan Ave., Stockton, CA 95204 USA Fax: 209-462-6771
E-mail: bowker@medicalmultimedia.com
Web site: http://www.medicalmultimedia.com.

Medici Publishing, Inc., *(0-9743791)* P.O. Box 562, Pueblo, CO 81002 USA
E-mail: judithfodor@medicibooks.org
Web site: http://www.medicibooks.org.

Medicine Woman Inc., The, *(0-9771906)* Orders Addr.: P.O. Box 613, Cascade, ID 83611 USA Tel 208-382-6653; Edit Addr.: 843 S. Main Hwy. 55, Cascade, ID 83611 USA
E-mail: tmw@ctcweb.net
Web site: http://www.themedicinewoman.com.

Medio Media *See* **Medio Media Publishing**

Medio Media Publishing, *(0-9666941; 0-9725627; 1-933182)* 627 N. 6th Ave., Tucson, AZ 85705-8330 USA Toll Free: 800-324-8305
E-mail: JoeD846136@aol.com; meditate@mediomedia.org
Web site: http://www.mediomedia.org
Dist(s): **Continuum International Publishing Group, Inc.**

Meditapes, *(1-893868)* Div. of Euphogenia, Inc. , 5860 SW 117th St., Miami, FL 33156 USA Fax: 305-669-4694; Toll Free: 888-234-5005
E-mail: meditapes@usa.net
Web site: http://www.meditapes.bitshop.com.

Medley, *(1-890034)* 1620 Los Alamos, SW, Albuquerque, NM 87104 USA Tel 505-247-3921 ; *Imprints:* Medley Publications (Medley Pubns)
E-mail: litchman@unm.edu.

Medley Pubns. *Imprint of* **Medley**

MedLife Publishing, Inc., *(0-9768150)*
E-mail: ceo@medlifepublishing.com
Web site: http://www.medlifepublishing.com.

MedPress & Quality Publishers *See* **Quality Pubs.**

Medusa Road Pr., *(0-9779295)* 6 Rte. 75, Norton Hill, NY 12083 USA Tel 518-966-5281
E-mail: MedusaRoadStudio@aol.com
Web site: http://CarolynsWebsite.net.

Medved, Denise *See* **Tiny Kitchen Publishing**

Medwag Publishing, *(0-9654963)* P.O. Box 36037, Richmond, VA 23235 USA Tel 804-794-8186
E-mail: alrx1@juno.com.

Meehl Foundation Pr., *(0-9767049)* P.O. Box 2089, Brazoria, TX 77422-2089 USA
E-mail: meehlfou@meehlfoundation.org
Web site: http://www.meehlfoundation.org.

Meeko Tin Pr., *(0-9666212)* 1035 W. Lubbock St., Slaton, TX 79364 USA Tel 806-828-6487; Fax: 806-828-4952
E-mail: meekotin@aol.com.

Meena, Nicholas *See* **Lem Publishing & Production**

MeeRa Pubns., *(0-9635539)* P.O. Box 812129, Wellesley, MA 02482 USA Tel 781-235-7441
E-mail: info@meerapublications.com
Web site: http://www.meerapublications.com.

Meerkat's Adventures Bks., *(0-9778072)* 510 Diamond St, Suite A, San Francisco, CA 94114 USA (SAN 850-2862)
Web site: http://www.meerkatsadventures.com
Dist(s): **Biblio Distribution.**

Meet the Author *Imprint of* **Owen, Richard C. Pubs., Inc.**

Mefford, David, *(0-9762143)* 274 W. 700 N., American Fork, UT 84003 USA
E-mail: david@mefford.org.

MEGA Corp., *(1-890436)* Orders Addr.: P.O. Box 92460, Nashville, TN 37209 USA Tel 615-350-8011; Fax: 615-350-8012; Edit Addr.: 3813 Cleghorn Ave., Nashville, TN 37215 USA.

Megasent Pr., *(0-9712234)* Orders Addr.: P.O. Box 1691, Johnson City, TN 37605 USA Tel 423-929-8476
E-mail: megasent@cs.com.

Megaverse City Studios, *(1-929914)* 299 Newport Ave., Quincy, MA 02170 USA Tel 617-773-9449; Fax: 617-773-9440 ; *Imprints:* Ruf-fur Publications (Ruf-Fur Pubns)
E-mail: megaversecity@netzero.net.

Megyeri, Graham Bks., *(0-9711971; 0-9791994)* 439 Lakeview Blvd., Albert Lea, MN 56007 USA Tel 507-377-1255; Toll Free: 866-755-5942
E-mail: minnmemory@aol.com
Web site: http://www.minnesotamemories.com
Dist(s): **Partners Bk. Distributing, Inc.**

Mehr Iran Publishing Co. *See* **Mehriran Publishing Co.**

Mehriran Publishing Co., *(0-9633129)* 14900 Talking Rock Ct., Suite B, N. Potomac, MD 20878 USA Tel 301-279-6778; Fax: 301-738-2174
E-mail: Pirnia1@aol.com
Web site: http://www.pirnia.com.

MEIER Enterprises Inc., *(0-9726808)* 8697 Gage Blvd., Kennewick, WA 99336 USA Tel 509-735-1589; Fax: 509-783-5075; Toll Free: 800-239-7589
E-mail: sranderson@meierinc.com; info@learningtowrite.com
Web site: http://www.meierinc.com; http://www.learningtowrite.comw.

Meisha Merlin Publishing, Inc., *(0-9658345; 1-892065; 1-59222)* Orders Addr.: P.O. Box 7, Decatur, GA 30031 USA Tel 404-634-1702 (phone/fax); Edit Addr.: P.O. Box 7, Decatur, GA 30031-0007 USA
E-mail: email@meishamerlin.com
Web site: http://www.meishamerlin.com
Dist(s): **Diamond Bk. Distributors.**

Meister-Home, Inc., *(0-9702497)* P.O. Box 471250, Charlotte, NC 28247-1250 USA (SAN 256-1794) Tel 704-968-6741; Fax: 704-544-2034 ; *Imprints:* Meister-Home Press (Meister-Home Pr)
E-mail: ragilmartin@hotmail.com; rgilmartin@meister-home.com
Web site: http://www.meister-home.com.

Meister-Home Pr. *Imprint of* **Meister-Home, Inc.**

Mel Bay Pubns., Inc., *(0-7866; 0-87166; 1-56222)* Orders Addr.: #4 Industrial Dr., Pacific, MO 63069-0066 USA (SAN 657-3630) Tel 636-257-3970; Fax: 636-257-5062; Toll Free: 800-863-5229
E-mail: connie@melbay.com; email@melbay.com
Web site: http://www.melbay.com
Dist(s): **Baker & Taylor Bks.**
Ingram Bk. Co.

Melcher Media, *(0-9717935; 1-59591)* 124 W. 13th St., New York, NY 10011 USA Tel 212-727-2322; Fax: 212-627-1973
E-mail: greatbooks@melcher.com
Dist(s): **Dorling Kindersley Publishing, Inc.**
Simon & Schuster, Inc.

MELJAMES, Inc., *(0-9755195; 1-933419)* 107 Suncreek Dr., Suite 300, Allen, TX 75013 USA
Web site: http://www.meljamesinc.com.

†Mellen, Edwin Pr., The, *(0-7734; 0-88946; 0-935106; 0-7799)* Orders Addr.: P.O. Box 67, Queenston, ON L0S 1L0 CAN; Edit Addr.: P.O. Box 450, Lewiston, NY 14092-0450 USA (SAN 207-110X) Tel 716-754-2266; 716-754-2788; Fax: 716-754-1860
E-mail: mellen@wzrd.com; sales@mellenpress.com
Web site: http://www.mellenpress.com; *CIP.*

Melo, Irene, *(0-9678631)* 111b Prospect Ave., Hartford, CT 06106-2941 USA
E-mail: melo_121@yahoo.com.

Melpomene Institute, *(0-9651137)* 1010 University Ave., Saint Paul, MN 55104 USA Tel 651-642-1951; Fax: 651-642-1871
E-mail: health@melpomene.org
Web site: http://www.melpomene.org.

Melrose Square *Imprint of* **Holloway Hse. Publishing Co.**

Melzee's Production, *(0-9722738)* P.O. Box 394, Hawthorne, CA 90251-0394 USA Tel 310-263-7804
E-mail: melzee3@juno.com.

Me+Mi Publishing, *(0-9679748; 1-931398)* 128 S. County Farm Rd., Suite E, Wheaton, IL 60187 USA Tel 630-752-9951; Fax: 630-588-9804; Toll Free: 888-251-1444
E-mail: m3@memima.com
Web site: http://www.memima.com
Dist(s): **Baker & Taylor Bks.**
Lectorum Pubns., Inc.
Quality Bks., Inc.

Memoria Pr., *(1-930953)* 4605 Poplar Level Rd., Louisville, KY 40213-2337 USA Toll Free: 877-862-1097
E-mail: magister@memoriapress.com
Web site: http://www.memoriapress.com.

Memories Publishing, *(0-9748984)* P.O. Box 82516, Austin, TX 78708 USA Tel 512-907-1821
E-mail: mindyred@aol.com.

Memory Makers Bks. *Imprint of* **F & W Pubns., Inc.**

Memory Matters, LLP, *(0-9724494)* 18437 Piers End Dr., Noblesville, IN 46060-6650 USA Tel 317-774-0502
E-mail: cmargenau@insightbb.com
Web site: http://www.stores.ebay.com/moneymattersllp.

MENC - The National Assn. for Music Education, *(0-940796; 1-56545)* 1806 Robert Fulton Dr., Reston, VA 20191-4348 USA (SAN 676-8733) Tel 703-860-4000; Fax: 703-860-9443; Toll Free: 800-336-3768
E-mail: francesp@menc.org
Web site: http://www.menc.org
Dist(s): **Rowman & Littlefield Pubs., Inc.**

Mennonite Pr. Inc., *(0-9772745)* Orders Addr.: P.O. Box 867, Newton, KS 67114 USA Tel 316-283-4680; Fax: 316-283-2068; Toll Free: 800-536-4686; Edit Addr.: 532 N. Oliver Rd., Newton, KS 67114 USA
E-mail: reliability@mennonitepress.com
Web site: http://www.mennonitepress.com.

Mensch Makers Pr., *(0-9619880)* 1588 Northrop, Saint Paul, MN 55108 USA (SAN 246-9138) Tel 651-644-8533; Fax: 651-645-8340
E-mail: Warkx001@maroon.tc.umn.edu
Web site: http://www.menschmakers.com.

Mental Health Historic Preservation Society Of Central Illinois, *(0-9748742)* 209 Arnold Ave., East Peoria, IL 61611 USA Tel 309-699-3051
E-mail: aparr12345@aol.com
Dist(s): **Partners Bk. Distributing, Inc.**

Mental Interactive Systems, *(0-9668491)* 1172 S. Dixie Hwy., PMB Suite 423, Coral Gables, FL 33146 USA Tel 305-662-5025; Fax: 305-662-1969
E-mail: CliffhangerKidz@aol.com; info@cliffhangerseries.com; kimt924@aol.com
Web site: http://www.cliffhangerseries.com.

Mental Truth Inc., *(0-9744047)* 10637 Redbud Land, Jonesboro, GA 30238 USA Tel 770-210-8732
E-mail: mentaltruth@hotmail.com
Web site: http://www.mentaltruth.com.

Mental Wellness Publishing House *See* **Mental Wellness Pub. Hse.**

Mental Wellness Pub. Hse., *(1-933559)* 12822 Slade Castle Ct., Charlotte, NC 28273 USA (SAN 256-6753)
E-mail: writer@chrisstroble.com
Web site: http:// www.chrisstroble.com.

Mentoring Minds, LP, *(0-9763559; 0-9767940)* P.O. Box 8843, Tyler, TX 75711 USA Fax: 800-838-8186; Toll Free: 800-585-5258
Web site: http://www.mentoring-minds.com.

MentorSource, LLC, *(0-9773324)* P.O. Box 24436, Minneapolis, MN 55424 USA Tel 612-269-8242
E-mail: gianna_bl@msn.com
Web site: http://www.rosyproses.com.

Mentzer Printing Ink, *(0-9746705; 0-9786276; 0-9797502)* 1037 Shelby St., Indianapolis, IN 46203 USA Tel 317-261-1000; Fax: 317-261-1005; Toll Free: 800-514-6017
E-mail: info@m2print.com
Web site: http://www.m2print.com.

Mercer Mayer First Readers *Imprint of* **School Specialty Publishing**

†Mercer Univ. Pr., *(0-86554; 0-88146)* 1400 Coleman Ave., Macon, GA 31207 USA (SAN 220-0716) Tel 478-301-2880; Fax: 478-301-2585; Toll Free: 800-342-0841 (Ext. 2880 in Georgia); 800-637-2378 (Ext. 2880 orders only)
E-mail: mupressorders@mercer.edu
Web site: http://www.mupress.org
Dist(s): **Baker & Taylor Bks.**
Ingram Pub. Services; *CIP.*

Mercersburg Historical Society, *(0-9702361)* Orders Addr.: P.O. Box 115, Mercersburg, PA 17236 USA; Edit Addr.: 5711 Oakwood Dr., Mercersburg, PA 17236 USA.

Mercier Pr., Ltd., The (IRL) *(0-85342; 1-85635; 1-86023) Dist. by* **Irish Bks Media.**

Mercury Bks. Ltd. (GBR) *(1-904668; 1-84560) Dist. by* **Intl Pubs Mktg.**

Mercury Publishing *See* **Muse Press**

Mercury/Hula Babe Productions, *(0-9707594)* c/o Easy Rider Productions, P.O. Box 864, Kilauea, HI 96754 USA Tel 866-263-7287
E-mail: info@mercuryworld.org
Web site: http://www.mercuryprods.com; http://www.santatakesaholiday.com; http://www.bandofpirates.com
Dist(s): **Booklines Hawaii, Ltd.**

Mercy Place, Inc., *(0-9677402; 0-9707919)* P.O. Box 134, Shippensburg, PA 17257 USA Tel 717-532-6899; Fax: 717-532-8646; Toll Free: 800-722-6774
E-mail: mpm@reapernet.com
Web site: http://mercyplace.com
Dist(s): **Destiny Image Pubs.**

†Meredith Bks., *(0-696; 0-89721; 0-917102)* Div. of Meredith Corp., Orders Addr.: 1716 Locust St., LN-110, Des Moines, IA 50309-3023 USA (SAN 202-4055) Tel 515-284-2363; 515-284-2126 (sales); Fax: 515-284-3371; Toll Free: 800-678-8091 ; *Imprints:* Better Homes & Gardens Books (Better Homes); Food Network Kitchens (Food Net) Do not confuse with Meredith Pr. in Skaneateles, NY
E-mail: John.OBannon@meredith.com
Web site: http://www.bhgstore.com; *CIP.*

Meredith Group Ltd., The, *(0-9765341)* Orders Addr.: 24 N. Bryn Mawr Ave., Box117, Bryn Mawr, PA 19010 USA (SAN 256-4920) Tel 610-642-0199; Edit Addr.: 71 Eden View Rd. # 6, Elizabethtown, PA 17022-3124 USA
E-mail: mmbellamy1@verizon.net
Web site: http://www.goldiesbook.com.

Meredith International, LLC, *(0-9706254)* Continental Rd., Tuxedo Park, NY 10987 USA Tel 845-351-3490; Fax: 845-351-2624; Toll Free: 800-697-6111
E-mail: meredithintl@qed.net.

Meridian Creative Group *See* **Larson Learning, Inc.**

Meridian Education Corp., *(0-936007; 1-56191; 1-877844)* Orders Addr.: P.O. Box 911, Monmouth Junction, NJ 08852-0911 USA Toll Free Fax: 888-340-5507; Toll Free: 800-727-5507; Edit Addr.: P.O. Box 1309, Charleston, WV 25325 USA (SAN 696-6012) Tel 304-744-9323; Fax: 304-744-9351
E-mail: meridian@meridianeducation.com; customerservice@meridianeducation.com
Web site: http://www.meridianeducation.com
Dist(s): **Films Media Group**
JIST Publishing
Linx Educational Publishing, Inc.

Merit Publishing International, Inc., *(1-873413)* 1095 Jupiter Park Dr. Ste. 7, Jupiter, FL 33458-8972 USA
E-mail: meritpi@aol.com; merituk@aol.com
Web site: http://www.meritpublishing.com
Dist(s): **Midpoint Trade Bks., Inc.**

Meritage Publishing, *(0-9769866)* Orders Addr.: 12339 Meritage Ct., Rancho Cucamonga, CA 91739 USA
E-mail: meritagepub@charter.net
Dist(s): **Baker & Taylor Bks.**
Quality Bks., Inc.

Meriwether Publishing, Ltd., *(0-916260; 1-56608)* Orders Addr.: P.O. Box 7710, Colorado Springs, CO 80933 USA (SAN 208-4716) Tel 719-594-4422; Fax: 719-594-9916; Toll Free Fax: 888-594-4436; Toll Free: 800-937-5297; Edit Addr.: 885 Elkton Dr., Colorado Springs, CO 80907 USA
E-mail: mzapel@aol.com; merpcds@aol.com
Web site: http://www.contemporarydrama.com; http://www.meriwetherpublishing.com.

Merkos L'Inyonei Chinuch, *(0-8266)* 291 Kingston Ave., Brooklyn, NY 11213 USA Tel 718-778-0226; Fax: 718-778-4148
E-mail: yonason@kehot.net
Web site: http://www.kehotonline.com.

Merlin, Debbi, *(0-9793568)* 12339 Scarcella Ln., Stafford, TX 77477-1609 USA (SAN 853-232X)
E-mail: merlin@merlinmagic.cc
Web site: http://www.merlinmagic.cc.

Merlin Enterprises, *(0-9761017)* 346 N. Grandstaff Dr., No.178, Auburn, IN 46706 USA
Web site: http://cafepress.com/npuff.

Merlyn's Pen, Inc., *(1-886427)* P.O. Box 2550, Providence, RI 02906-0550 USA Toll Free: 800-247-2027
E-mail: merlynspen@aol.com
Web site: http://www.merlynspen.com.

Mermaid Utopia, Inc., *(0-9721276)* 1618 El Rito Ave., Glendale, CA 91208 USA
E-mail: staff@mermaidutopia.com
Web site: http://www.mermaidutopia.com.

Meroe Publishing, *(0-9768306)* P.O. Box 664, Cusseta, GA 31805 USA
E-mail: tonieshort@meroepublishing.com
Web site: http://www.meroepublishing.com.

Merriam-Webster, Inc., *(0-87779)* Subs. of Encyclopaedia Britannica, Inc., Orders Addr.: 47 Federal St., Springfield, MA 01102 USA (SAN 202-6244) Tel 413-734-3134; Fax: 413-731-5979; Toll Free: 800-828-1880
E-mail: tbishop@Merriam-Webster.com; sales@Merriam-Webster.com; orders@Merriam-Webster.com
Web site: http://www.WordCentral.com; http://www.Merriam-Webster.com
Dist(s): **Thomson Delmar Learning.**

Merril Pr., *(0-936783)* 12500 NE Tenth Pl., Bellevue, WA 98005 USA (SAN 699-9387) Tel 425-454-7009; Fax: 425-451-3959
E-mail: editor@merrilpress.com
Web site: http://www.merrilpress.com
Dist(s): **Midpoint Trade Bks., Inc.**

Merritt Park Pr., *(0-9666677)* 910 N. Elm St., Greenville, IL 62246 USA Tel 618-664-2207
E-mail: dslarsen@merrittpark.com
Web site: http://www.merrittpark.com
Dist(s): **Bookmen, Inc.**

Merritt Publishing *See* **Silver Lake Publishing**

Merriwell, Frank Inc., *(0-8373)* Subs. of National Learning Corp., 212 Michael Dr., Syosset, NY 11791 USA (SAN 209-259X) Tel 516-921-8888; Toll Free: 800-645-6337.

Merry Lane Pr., *(0-9744307)* 18 E. 16th St., 7th Flr., New York, NY 10003 USA Tel 212-633-6505; Fax: 212-242-6077
E-mail: alan@merrylanepress.com
Web site: http://www.merrylanepress.com
Dist(s): **Biblio Distribution.**

Merryant Pubs., *(1-877599)* 10920 Palisades Ave SW, Vashon, WA 98070-3049 USA Toll Free: 800-228-8958
E-mail: jmboule@aol.com.

Merrybooks & More, *(0-9615407; 1-882607)* 1214 Rugby Rd., Charlottesville, VA 22903 USA (SAN 695-5053) Tel 804-979-3658; Fax: 804-296-8446; Toll Free: 800-959-2665.

Mertz, Kenneth, *(0-9717300)* 2750 Jean LaFitte Dr., Fernandina Beach, FL 32034 USA
E-mail: k_a_mertzjr@hotmail.com.

Mesorah Pubns., Ltd., *(0-89906; 1-57819; 1-4226)* 4401 Second Ave., Brooklyn, NY 11232 USA (SAN 213-1269) Tel 718-921-9000 Toll Free: 800-637-6724
Web site: http://mesorah.com.

Mesquite Tress Pr., LLC, *(0-9729835)* Orders Addr.: P.O. Box 17513, Louisville, KY 40217 USA; Edit Addr.: 212 W. Ormsby Ave, Louisville, KY 40203 USA
Web site: http://www.onetinytwig.com; http://www.mesquitetreepress.com; http://bluegrassbreeze.com.

Mess Hall Writers, *(1-885531)* P.O. Box 1551, Jeffersonville, IN 47130 USA Tel 812-288-9888; Fax: 812-288-9695
E-mail: fooddudes2@aol.com.

Message In a Bottle Translators *See* **Pangloss Publishing**

Messiah Publishing - Pearables, *(0-9792446)* P.O. Box 272000, Fort Collins, CO 80527 USA (SAN 852-8837) Tel 719-549-0662
Web site: http://www.pearables.com.

Messianic Jewish Perspective *See* **Purple Pomegranate Productions**

Messianic Perspectives, *(0-9674319)* Orders Addr.: P.O. Box 345, San Antonio, TX 78292-0345 USA Tel 210-226-0421; Fax: 210-226-2140; Toll Free: 800-926-5397; Edit Addr.: 611 Broadway St., San Antonio, TX 78215 USA
E-mail: orderline@cjf.org
Web site: http://www.cjf.org.

Messineo, David, *(0-9676066)* Orders Addr.: P.O. Box 90, Glen Ridge, NJ 07028 USA ; *Imprints:* Snake Hill Press (Snake Hill Pr)
E-mail: messineo@concentric.net
Web site: http://www.sensationsmag.com.

Mestas, Jorge A. Ediciones Escolares La Escuela Nueva y Alinorma, S.L. (ESP) *(84-89163; 84-95311; 84-95994) Dist. by* **Continental Bk.**

Mestas, Jorge A. Ediciones Escolares La Escuela Nueva y Alinorma, S.L. (ESP) *(84-89163; 84-95311; 84-95994) Dist. by* **Distribks Inc.**

Mestas, Jorge A. Ediciones Escolares La Escuela Nueva y Alinorma, S.L. (ESP) *(84-89163; 84-95311; 84-95994) Dist. by* **Fondo CA.**

Meta Adventures *See* **Meta AdventuresPublishing & DIA Publishing**

Meta AdventuresPublishing & DIA Publishing, *(0-9721202)* Orders Addr.: P.O. Box 1894, Sedona, AZ 86339 USA (SAN 254-6183) Tel 928-204-1560
E-mail: info@dreamsinaction.us; publishing@dreamsinaction.us; orderinfo@dreamsinaction.us
Web site: http://www.dreamsinaction.us; http://www.MrSedona.com
Dist(s): **Dreams in Action Distribution.**

Metalmark Pr., *(0-9767239)* 7116 New Sharon Church Rd., Rougemont, NC 27572 USA
E-mail: birdcr@concentric.net
Web site: http://www.rlephoto.com.

Metamedix, Incorporated *See* **Science2Discover, Inc.**

Metaphrog (GBR) *(0-9534932; 0-9545984) Dist. by* **Diamond Book Dists.**

Metapublishing, *(0-9654522)* 500 Center Ave. Apt. 211, Westwood, NJ 07675-1677 USA Do not confuse with Metapublishing, North Miami Beach, FL
Dist(s): **New Leaf Distributing Co., Inc.**

Metchnikoff, Elie Memorial Library, *(0-9634067)* 230 Orange St., No. 6, Oakland, CA 94610-4139 USA Tel 510-444-3435; Fax: 510-642-7175
E-mail: jbibel@arg.org.

Methuen Publishing Ltd. (GBR) *(0-413; 0-415; 0-416; 0-423) Dist. by* **Consort Bk Sales.**

Metric Moon Press *See* **Graphite Pr.**

MetroBooks *Imprint of* **Friedman, Michael Publishing Group, Inc.**

Metropolitan Bks. *Imprint of* **Holt, Henry & Co.**

Metropolitan Museum of Art, The, *(0-87099; 1-58839)* 1000 Fifth Ave., New York, NY 10028 USA (SAN 202-6279) Tel 212-879-5500; Fax: 212-396-5062
Web site: http://www.metmuseum.org
Dist(s): **Chicago Distribution Ctr.**
Continental Bk. Co., Inc.
Random Hse., Inc.
Yale Univ. Pr.

Metropolitan Teaching & Learning Co., *(0-928415; 1-58120; 1-58830)* 317 Madison Ave., New York, NY 10017 USA Tel 212-475-8826; Fax: 212-475-8311; Toll Free: 800-235-6931
Web site: http://metrotlc.com.

Meyer & Meyer Sport, Ltd. (GBR) *(1-84126) Dist. by* **Lewis Intl Inc.**

Meyer & Meyer Sport, Ltd. (GBR) *(1-84126) Dist. by* **Perseus Dist.**

Meyer Enterprises *See* **Western New York Wares, Inc.**

Meyer, Tjaden, *(0-9744536)* Orders Addr.: P.O. Box 230015, Saint Louis, MO 63123 USA Tel 314-352-2253; Edit Addr.: 7045 Parkwood St., Saint Louis, MO 63116 USA
E-mail: klmeyer@worldnet.att.net.

MF Unlimited, *(0-9712278)* P.O. Box 55346, Atlanta, GA 30308 USA
Web site: http://www.mfunews.com
Dist(s): **C & B Book Distribution.**

Mfg Application Konsulting Engineering, *(0-9762208)* 1071 E. 425 N., Ogden, UT 84404 USA.

M-Graphics Publishing, *(0-9753075; 0-9777003; 0-9792808)* One Dead Eye Run, Swampscott, MA 01907 USA Tel 781-595-6863; Fax: 206-770-7492
E-mail: mgraphics@comcast.net.

Mia Sharon, Inc., *(0-9759098)* 600 Academy Dr., No. 130, Northbrook, IL 60062 USA Tel 847-826-8196
Web site: http://www.miasharon.com.

Miami Univ. Pubns., *(0-918761)* Subs. of Miami Univ., Pubns. Office, Miami Univ., Oxford, OH 45056 USA (SAN 657-6567) Tel 513-529-7596; Fax: 513-529-1950.

MIBS Publishing, *(0-9650787)* Orders Addr.: P.O. Box 17413, Phoenix, AZ 85011-0413 USA
E-mail: mibbles1274@msn.com
Web site: http://www.booksbyleo.com.

Micah Publishing, *(1-889018)* 16727 Hutchinson Dr., Lakeville, MN 55044 USA Tel 612-953-4466; Fax: 612-953-4417 Do not confuse with companies with same name in Hartford, CT, Bridgeville, PA
Dist(s): **Baker & Taylor Bks.**
Koen-Levy Bk. Wholesalers LLC.

MiceWorks, *(0-9764719)* 544 13th Ave., W., Kirkland, WA 98033 USA.

Michael Neugebauer Bks. *Imprint of* **North-South Bks., Inc.**

Michael-Christopher Bks., *(0-9710398)* P.O. Box 75313, Washington, DC 20013-0313 USA Tel 703-671-2484
E-mail: mc@michael-christopher.com
Web site: http://www.livedlife.com.

MichaelsMind LLC, *(0-9704597; 1-932317)* 5600 Claire Rose Ln., Atlanta, GA 30327 USA
E-mail: satiller@bellsouth.net
Web site: http://www.michaelsmind.com.

Michaelson Entertainment, *(0-9727702; 1-932530)* 1134 Euclid St., Santa Monica, CA 90403 USA Tel 310-899-3739 (phone/fax) ; *Imprints:* 101 Book (101 Bk); 123 Book (123 Bk)
E-mail: bradepstein@michaelsonentertainment.com
Web site: http://www.michaelsonentertainment.com
Dist(s): **Baker & Taylor Bks.**
Partners Bk. Distributing, Inc.

Michalek, Curtis, *(0-9786177)* P.O. Box 403, Montezuma, IA 50171 USA Tel 641-623-3368
E-mail: c.a.michalek@hotmail.com
Web site: www.aluris.com.

Michelle Designs, *(0-615)* 268 Village Run, W., Encinitas, CA 92024 USA Tel 760-942-9537
E-mail: michelledesigns@msn.com.

Michelle's A & E (KOR) *(89-954869) Dist. by* **APG.**

Michelle's Bks. & More, Ltd. Co., *(0-9763080)* 800 Fabric X-Press Way, Dallas, TX 75234 USA Tel 972-625-1444; Fax: 972-406-1321
E-mail: michelle@michellesbooks.com
Web site: http://www.michellesbooks.com.

Michelle's Designs, *(0-9789694)* 3702 Sandpoint Ct, Carlsbad, CA 92010 USA Tel 760-720-4335; Fax: 802-609-2629
E-mail: patterns@michelles-designs.com
Web site: http://www.michelles-designs.com.

Michelson, Bettie E., *(0 9709436)* 2100 Grayfox Ct., Waukesha, WI 53188 USA Tel 262-896-9741.

Michigan State University, Cooperative Extension Service/Outreach Communications *See* **Michigan State Univ. Extension**

Michigan State Univ. Extension, *(1-56525)* c/o MSU Bulletin Office, 10B Agriculture Hall, East Lansing, MI 48824-1039 USA Tel 517-355-0240; Fax: 517-353-7168
E-mail: fettig@pilot.msu.edu
Web site: http://www.msu.edu/bulletin/ctlgmast.html.

Michigan State Univ., Julian Samora Research Institute, *(0-9650557)* 301 Nisbet Bldg., 1407 S. Harrison, East Lansing, MI 48823-586 USA Tel 517-432-1317; Fax: 517-432-2221
E-mail: info@jsri.msu.edu
Web site: http://jsri.msu.edu.

†Michigan State Univ. Pr., *(0-87013; 0-937191)* Orders Addr.: 1405 S. Harrison Rd. Suite 25, East Lansing, MI 48823 USA (SAN 202-6295) Tel 517-355-9543; Fax: 517-432-2611; Toll Free: 800-678-2120
E-mail: msupress@msu.edu
Web site: http://www.msupress.msu.edu; *CIP.*

Microphonic Pr., *(0-9700576)* 500 2nd St., No. 3, Brooklyn, NY 11215-2503 USA Tel 718-499-9211
E-mail: drewg@unidial.com
Web site: http://www.microphonicpress.com.

†Microsoft Pr., *(0-7356; 0-914845; 0-925550; 1-55615; 1-57231; 1-879021)* Orders Addr.: 3 Center Plaza, Boston, MA 02108-2084 USA Toll Free: 800-677-7377; Edit Addr.: One Microsoft Way, Redmond, WA 98052-6399 USA (SAN 264-9969) Tel 425-882-8080; 206-882-8080; 425-703-0942; Fax: 425-936-7329 Do not confuse with Microsoft Pr., Dunmore, PA
E-mail: msporder@msn.com; duanedr@microsoft.com; chriscai@microsoft.com
Web site: http://www.microsoft.com/mspress/
Dist(s): **Hachette Bk. Group**; *CIP.*

MidAmerica Publishing Co., *(0-9754728; 1-933732)* 40120 Industrial Pk. Cir. Suite C, Georgetown, TX 78626 USA Tel 512-863-0641 ; *Imprints:* Blue Foot Press (Blue Foot Pr); Bear Hug Books (Bear Hug Bks); Round Rock Chapter Books (Round Rock Chpt Bks)
E-mail: info@mapubco.com
Web site: http://www.mapubco.com.

Midas Entertainment, Inc., *(0-9672540)* 23679 Calabasas Rd., No. 186, Calabasas, CA 91302 USA Tel 818-591-8143; Fax: 818-876-0133
E-mail: uncleted@midaskids.com
Web site: http://www.MidasKids.com
Dist(s): **Baker & Taylor Bks.**

Mid-Atlantic Highlands Publishing *Imprint of* **Publishers Place, Inc.**

Middelhauve Verlags GmbH (DEU) *(3-7876) Dist. by* **Distribks Inc.**

†Middle Atlantic Pr., *(0-912608; 0-9705804; 0-9754419)* 400 Pond View Dr., Moorestown, NJ 08057 USA Tel 856-273-9062; Fax: 856-273-7526
E-mail: blake@middleatlanticpress.com; info@middleatlanticpress.com
Web site: http://www.middleatlanticpress.com
Dist(s): **Partners Bk. Distributing, Inc.**; *CIP.*

Middle School Reference *Imprint of* **Greenwood Publishing Group, Inc.**

Middleburry Hse. Publishing, *(0-9792067)* 3225 Middleburry Ln., Charleston, SC 29414 USA
Web site: http://www.rwridley.com.

Middlefork Pr., *(0-9670466)* 1009 Madrone Rd., Austin, TX 78746 USA Tel 512-347-1915; Fax: 512-347-1914
E-mail: nndzn@aol.com
Dist(s): **P S I Fulfillment.**

Middleway Pr., *(0-9674697; 0-9723267; 0-9779245)* Div. of SGI-USA, 606 Wilshire Blvd., Santa Monica, CA 90401 USA Tel 310-260-8900; Fax: 310-260-8910
E-mail: dmcneill@sgi-usa.org
Web site: http://www.middlewaypress.org
Dist(s): **Independent Pubs. Group.**

Midlands Marketing, *(0-9674995; 0-9723006)* Div. of Omaha World-Herald Co., 5847 N. 90th St., Omaha, NE 68134-1856 USA Toll Free: 800-800-9060
E-mail: kristine.gerber@own.com; kristine.gerber@owh.com
Web site: http://www.midlandsmarketing.com
Dist(s): **Booksource, The.**

Midnight Oil Publishing Co., *(0-9633488)* P.O. Box 134, New Kingston, NY 12459 USA.

Midnight Pr., *(0-9721872)* Orders Addr.: P.O. Box 91, Jarrettsville, MD 21084 USA; Edit Addr.: 3842 Salem Church Rd., Jarrettsville, MD 21084 USA Do not confuse with Midnight Pr., in West Hampton Beach, NY
Dist(s): **Book Clearing Hse.**

Midpoint Trade Bks., Inc., Orders Addr.: 1263 Southwest Blvd., Kansas City, KS 66103 USA (SAN 631-3736) Tel 913-831-2233; Fax: 913-362-7401; Toll Free: 800-742-6139 (consumer orders); Edit Addr.: 27 W. 20th St., No. 1102, New York, NY 10011 USA (SAN 631-1075) Tel 212-727-0190; Fax: 212-727-0195
E-mail: info@midpointtrade.com
Web site: http://www.midpointtrade.com; http://www.midpointtradebooks.com/.

Mid-Prairie Bks., *(0-931209)* 801 Fourth Ave., Parkersburg, IA 50665 USA (SAN 681-9680) Tel 319-346-2048; Fax: 319-346-1420
E-mail: neymeyer@forbin.com
Dist(s): **Bookmen, Inc.**

MidRun Pr., *(0-9664095)* 90 Larch Row, Wenham, MA 01984-1624 USA
E-mail: Petrlik@aol.com
Web site: http://www.midrunpress.com.

Midtown Publishing Corp., *(0-9660768)* 1349 W. Peachtree St., Suite 1680, Atlanta, GA 30309 USA Tel 404-881-1111; Fax: 404-881-8040.

Midwest Christian Center *See* **Family Harvest Church**

Midwest Cylinder Management, Inc., *(0-9729026)* 1203 Paramount Pkwy., Batavia, IL 60510-1458 USA Tel 630-673-9770; Fax: 630-406-9922
E-mail: prminalt@yahoo.com
Web site: http://www.kidsmenus.com.

Midwest European Pubns., 915 Foster St., Evanston, IL 60201 USA (SAN 169-1937) Tel 847-866-6289; Fax: 847-866-6290; Toll Free: 800-380-8919
E-mail: info@mep-eli.com
Web site: http://www.mep-eli.com.

Midwest Graphics, Inc., *(0-9776893)* 180 N. Wacker Dr., Suite 104, Chicago, IL 60606 USA Tel 312-641-2236; Fax: 312-641-2256
E-mail: mark@mwgchicago.com
Web site: http://www.mwgchicago.com.

Midwest History Pr., *(0-9671787)* P.O. Box 432, Northfield, MN 55057 USA Tel 507-663-7845; Fax: 507-663-8804; Toll Free: 800-833-8808
E-mail: MHP@rconnect.com
Dist(s): **Chicago Distribution Ctr.**
Univ. of Wisconsin Pr.

Midwest Screen and Media Production, *(0-9719665)* P.O. Box 133, Greeley, KS 66033 USA (SAN 254-5527)
Web site: http://www.msmediaproduction.com.

Midwest Traditions, Inc., *(1-883953)* 3147 S. Pennsylvania Ave., Milwaukee, WI 53207 USA Tel 414-294-4319 (phone/fax); Toll Free: 800-736-9189 ; *Imprints:* Blue Horse Books (Blue Horse Bks)
E-mail: info@bluehorsebooks.org
Web site: http://www.bluehorsebooks.org
Dist(s): **Austin & Company, Inc.**
Partners Pubs. Group, Inc.

Company

Company

Mielcarek, David, *(0-9785480)* 3387 Ocean Beach Hwy, Longview, WA 98632 USA
E-mail: thebook@timeforyourmind.com
Web site: http://timeforyourmind.com.

Mihelakis, Laura, *(0-9725414)* P.O. Box 323, Bloomingburg, NY 12721 USA Fax: 845-386-1576.

Mijade Editions (BEL) *(2-87142)* *Dist. by* **Distribks Inc.**

Mikaya Pr., *(0-9650493; 1-931414)* 12 Bedford St., New York, NY 10014 USA Tel 212-647-1831; Fax: 212-727-0236
E-mail: Waldman@Mikaya.com
Web site: http://www.mikaya.com
Dist(s): **Firefly Bks., Ltd.**

Mike-Auri Bks., *(0-9747587)* P.O. Box 420966, Del Rio, TX 78842 USA Tel 830-774-2789
E-mail: dfitzgibbon@stx.rr.com
Web site: http://www.texasredhen.com; http://www.mikeauri.com.

Mike-Mike Distribution, *(0-9741043)* 1003 N., Fifth St., Champaign, IL 61820 USA Tel 217-352-4215.

Milano, Jacque & Assocs., *(0-9728432)* 700 N. Dobson Rd., No. 15, Chandler, AZ 85224 USA ; *Imprints:* Carefree Publishing (Carefree Pubng)
Web site: http://www.carefreepublishing.com.

Mile Oak Publishing, Inc. (CAN) *(1-896819)* *Dist. by* **Partners Pubs Grp.**

Miles and Associates, *(0-9778623)* P.O. Box 15566, Phoenix, AZ 85060 USA Tel 386-446-9291
E-mail: drlinda03@aol.com
Web site: http://www.thenewmarriage.com.

Miles Kelly Publishing, Ltd. (GBR) *(1-902947; 1-84236)* *Dist. by* **Natl Bk Netwk.**

Miles, Linda *See* **Miles and Associates**

Miles Music, *(0-9710446)* Div. of Miles Enterprises, 3060 Larson Rd., Weippe, ID 83553 USA Tel 208-435-4600; Fax: 208-435-1116
E-mail: milesmusic@idamall.com
Web site: http://www.idamall.com.

Miles Publishing, *(0-9675463)* PMB 194 825 College Blvd., Suite 102, Oceanside, CA 92057 USA Tel 760-758-6152
E-mail: dorothy@iolink.com
Web site: http://www.milespublishing.com.

Milestone *Imprint of* **Schaffer, Frank Pubns.**

Milestone Pr., Inc., *(0-9631861; 1-889596)* Orders Addr.: P.O. Box 158, Almond, NC 28702 USA Tel 828-488-6601 (phone/fax)
E-mail: maryellenhammond@milestonepress.com
Web site: http://www.milestonepress.com
Dist(s): **Alpenbooks Pr. LLC**
America's Cycling Pubns.
Appalachian Bk. Distributors
Bright Horizons Specialty Distributors, Inc.
Common Ground Distributors, Inc.
Parnassus Bk. Distributors.

Milestones Publishing, *(0-9786154)* P.O. Box 1556, Wylie, TX 75098 USA Tel 214-403-9852; Fax: 972-442-1613
E-mail: kaylasadams@hotmail.com
Web site: http://www.kaylaadams.net.

Milet Publishing, *(1-84059)* 333 N. Michigan Ave., Suite 530, Chicago, IL 60601 USA
E-mail: info@milet.com
Web site: http://www.milet.com
Dist(s): **Independent Pubs. Group**
Tuttle Publishing.

Milk & Cookies *Imprint of* **ibooks, Inc.**

Milk Mug Publishing, *(0-9721882)* 9190 W. Olympic Blvd., Suite 253, Beverly Hills, CA 90212 USA Tel 310-278-1153 (phone/fax)
E-mail: orders@thehoopsterbook.com
Web site: http://www.thehoopsterbook.com
Dist(s): **SCB Distributors.**

Milken Family Foundation, *(0-9646425)* 1250 Fourth St., 4th Flr., Santa Monica, CA 90404-1353 USA Tel 310-998-2825; Fax: 310-998-2899
E-mail: jboone@mff.org
Web site: http://www.milkenexchange.org.

Milkweed Editions, *(0-915943; 1-57131)* 1011 Washington Ave. S., Suite 300, Minneapolis, MN 55415-1246 USA (SAN 294-0671) Tel 612-332-3192; Fax: 612-215-2550; Toll Free: 800-520-6455
E-mail: market@milkweed.org
Web site: http://www.milkweed.org; http://www.worldashome.org
Dist(s): **Consortium Bk. Sales & Distribution**
Perseus Distribution.

Mill City Pr., Inc., *(1-934248; 0-9798246; 0-9798467; 0-9799120)* 212 3rd Ave. N. Suite 570, Minneapolis, MN 55401-2420 USA Toll Free: 888-645-2489
E-mail: info@millcitypress.net; anna@millcitypress.net
Web site: http://www.millcitypress.net.

Mill Creek Metro Publishing, *(0-9741989)* P.O. Box 90134, Youngstown, OH 44509 USA Tel 330-797-0024
E-mail: ianjcue@ianjcue.com
Web site: http://www.ianjcue.com
Dist(s): **Book Clearing Hse.**

Mill Park Publishing, *(0-9728225)* E & M Group, LLC, Orders Addr.: P.O. Box 1932, McCall, ID 83638 USA Tel 208-634-1358; Fax: 208-634-3785 (call first)
Web site: http://www.MillParkPublishing.com.

Mill Street Forward, The, *(0-9654628)* 15 1/2 Van Houten St., Apt. 117, Paterson, NJ 07505 USA Tel 973-345-9539.

Millbrook Pr. *Imprint of* **Lerner Publishing Group**

Millennial Mind Publishing *Imprint of* **American Bk. Publishing Group**

Millennium Assocs., *(0-9671934)* P.O. Box 440, South Orleans, MA 02662 USA Tel 508-240-6873; Fax: 508-240-6874; 66 Winslow Dr., South Orleans, MA 02662
E-mail: jstewart@millenniumassoc.com
Web site: http://www.millenniumassoc.com.

Millennium Marketing & Publishing, *(1-886161)* 2455 Glen Hill Dr., Indianapolis, IN 46240-3460 USA Tel 317-815-9828; Fax: 317-815-9829
E-mail: MMPbooks@comcast.net
Web site: http://www.chicksguidetofootball.com
Dist(s): **Cardinal Pubs. Group**
Independent Pubs. Group
Journey Pubns., LLC
Quality Bks., Inc.

Millennium Pubns., *(0-9627610)* Orders Addr.: P.O. Box 501, Bloomfield, CT 06002 USA Tel 860-243-2663; Fax: 860-242-5649; Edit Addr.: 166 Albany Tpke., Canton, CT 06019 USA Tel 860-693-6763 Do not confuse with companies with similar names in East Brunswick, NJ, Denver, CO.

Millennium Publishing *See* **American Health Pr.**

Millennium Workshop Production, *(0-9725344)* 11501 Maple Ridge Rd., Reston, VA 20190-3604 USA (SAN 255-1624) Tel 703-925-0610 (phone/fax)
E-mail: victor@millenniumworkshop.com
Web site: http://www.millenniumworkshop.com.

Miller, Ann *See* **Jaylil Publishing Co.**

Miller, Bruce, *(0-9765598)* 10011 Bridgeport Way SW., Suite 1500 PMB128, Lakewood, WA 98499 USA Tel 253-227-2292
E-mail: warofpowers@comcast.net.

Miller, Deanna, *(0-9725424)* http://www.deannamiller.com, Merrifield, VA 22116 USA
E-mail: info@deannamiller.com
Web site: http://www.deannamiller.com.

Miller, Don G., *(0-615)* 5051 S. 172nd. St., Omaha, NE 68135 USA.

Miller, J. Garnet Ltd. (GBR) *(0-85343)* *Dist. by* **Empire Pub Srvs.**

Miller, Larry, *(0-9720961)* 25 Stevens Ave., West Lawn, PA 19609 USA Tel 610-670-9000; Fax: 610-670-9901
E-mail: millerlawgroup@earthlink.net
Web site: http://www.millerlawgroup.net.

Miller, Michael, *(0-9723474; 0-9743522)* 2418 Hagerman St., Colorado Springs, CO 80904 USA Tel 719-635-0017; Fax: 501-421-1495
E-mail: michael@mail.sabineundmichael.com
Web site: http://www.sabineundmichael.com.

Miller, Peter Mitchell *See* **Silver Print Pr., Inc.**

Miller, Randy, *(0-9770530)* 17 N. Rd., Alstead, NH 03602 USA Tel 603-835-7889
E-mail: jrmiller@sover.net
Web site: http://www.randymillerprints.com.

Miller, Smit Enterprises, *(0-9769433)* 112 Misty Creek Dr., Colorado Springs, CO 80132-6032 USA
E-mail: dawn@dawnsmit.com.

MillerWrite, Inc., *(0-9723948)* 2875-F Northtowne Ln., No. 302, Reno, NV 89512-2062 USA Tel 775-673-2152
E-mail: chrisshelton78@msn.com; jmiller@millerwrite.com
Web site: http://www.millerwrite.com.

Milligan Bks., Inc., *(1-881524; 0-9719749; 0-9725941; 0-9742811; 0-9753504; 0-9759654; 0-9764690; 0-9767678; 0-9771082; 0-9786032; 0-9792016)* 1425 W. Manchester Ave., Suite C, Los Angeles, CA 90047 USA (SAN 852-7563)
E-mail: milliganbooks.com; drrosie@aol.com
Web site: http://www.milliganbooks.com
Dist(s): **Baker & Taylor Bks.**

Millman, Selena, *(0-615; 0-9793058; 0-9794584; 0-9795756; 0-9798417; 0-9798603)* 4984 Ridgebury, Lyndhurst, OH 44124 USA
Web site: http://www.freewebs.com/heal4michael.

Mills & Morris Publishing Corporation *See* **Bluebonnets, Boots & Bks.**

Mills, Joy & Assocs., LLC, *(0-9671280)* Div. of LightSource Pubns., 2615 Wykeham Dr., Saint Charles, MO 63303 USA Tel 636-947-4265; Fax: 636-925-1878
E-mail: joymmills@aol.com
Web site: http://www.joymills.com.

Milner, Sally Publishing Pty, Ltd. (AUS) *(1-86351)* *Dist. by* **Sterling.**

MiMar Publishing, *(0-615; 0-9754241)* 714 Enchanted Rock Trail, Georgetown, TX 78633 USA
Web site: http://www.bakerstreetbunch.com
Dist(s): **Lulu.com.**

Mimi Bee Pubns., *(0-9745944)* Orders Addr.: P.O. Box 188, Accord, NY 12404 USA
E-mail: mimibee@att.com
Web site: http://mrallergyhead.com.

Minardi Photography, *(1-878444)* 5501 Harvest Scene Ct., Columbia, MD 21044 USA Tel 410-964-5403; Fax: 410-964-5643.

Minch, John & Assocs., Inc., *(0-9631090)* P.O. Box 4244, Mission Viejo, CA 92690-4244 USA Tel 949-367-1000; Fax: 949-367-0117; Toll Free: 800-367-2995
E-mail: jmainc@earthlink.net.

Mind - Stretch, *(0-9676409)* 3124 Landrum Rd., Columbus, NC 28722 USA Tel 828-863-4235; Fax: 828-863-2584; Toll Free: 888-538-8911
E-mail: marklevin@alltel.net
Web site: http://www.mindstretch.com.

Mind Body Health Bks., *(0-9711176)* Orders Addr.: P.O. Box 8519, Calabasas, CA 91372 USA (SAN 253-9020) Tel 310-289-9545; Fax: 818-880-0607
E-mail: mschoen11111@yahoo.com
Web site: http://marcschoen.com.

Mind Set Pr., *(0-9672018)* 531 Eastwood Shores, Traverse City, MI 49684 USA Tel 616-943-9214; 616-933-0445.

Mind/Body Workshops, *(0-9748548)* 131 S. Euclid, Westfield, NJ 07090 USA Tel 718-273-3682
Web site: http://www.kickoutstress.com.

Mindcastle Bks., Inc., *(0-9677204)* Orders Addr.: P.O. Box 3005, Woodinville, WA 98072 USA Tel 425-424-8860; Fax: 425-398-1354
E-mail: vanessa@mindcastle.com
Web site: http://www.mindcastle.com.

MindCatcher Pr., *(0-9724113)* 284 Mattison Dr., Concord, MA 01742 USA Tel 978-369-7868
E-mail: marian@mindcatcherpress.com
Web site: http://www.mindcatcherpress.com; http://www.readylady.com.

MindFlight Publishing, *(0-9711983)* Orders Addr.: P.O. Box 1738, Hamilton, MT 59840 USA Fax: 406-821-3905; Toll Free: 866-737-7860; Edit Addr.: 234 Forest Hill Rd., Hamilton, MT 59840 USA
E-mail: info@mind-flight.com; info@TeachersMind.com
Web site: http://www.mind-flight.com; http://www.TeachersMind.com.

Mindfull Publishing, *(0-9669551)* 177 W. Norwalk Rd., Norwalk, CT 06850 USA Tel 203-831-0855
E-mail: mindfullpub@hotmail.com
Web site: http://www.homestead.com/mindfullpublishing/.

Mindfull Publishing Co., *(0-9720308)* Orders Addr.: P.O. Box 34, Clairton, PA 15025 USA Toll Free: 888-946-0816; Edit Addr.: 329 Mitchell Ave., Clairton, PA 15025 USA
Web site: http://www.georgebberry.bigstep.com
Dist(s): **Baker & Taylor Bks.**

Mindgoal Publishing, *(0-9720797; 0-9766776)* P.O. Box 86011, St Petersburg, FL 33738-6011 USA
E-mail: jeff@mindgoal.com
Web site: http://www.mindgoal.com.

MindMaze Publishing Co., *(0-9747668)* P.O. Box 251278, Woodbury, MN 55125 USA
E-mail: mindmaze@comcast.net
Dist(s): **Biblio Distribution.**

MindMotion *Imprint of* **Trend Enterprises, Inc.**

Mindo Pr., *(0-9747971)* P.O. Box 34, Danielsville, PA 18038-9754 USA
E-mail: rshade@fast.net.

MindOH! Foundation, The, *(0-9773689)* 2525 Robinhood St., Houston, TX 77005 USA (SAN 257-3741) Tel 713-533-1138 Toll Free: 866-646-3641
Web site: http://www.mindohfoundation.org.

MindsOrb, Inc., *(0-9741877)* P.O. Box 162706, Austin, TX 78716 USA
Web site: http://www.mindsorb.com.

MindWare Holdings, Inc., *(0-9648481; 1-892069; 1-933054)* 2100 County Rd. C W., Roseville, MN 55113 USA Tel 651-582-0555; Fax: 651-582-0556; Toll Free: 800-999-0398
Web site: http://www.mindwareonline.com.

Mindwing Concepts, Inc., *(0-9761393; 0-9769527; 0-9791307; 0-9792917; 0-9793185)* 1 Federal St., Bldg. No. 101-R, Springfield, MA 01105-1222 USA Tel 413-734-7476; Fax: 413-734-0075; Toll Free: 888-228-9746
E-mail: bswelch@mindwingconcepts.com
Web site: http://www.mindwingconcepts.com.

MindWorks Pr., *(1-886554)* 4019 Westerly Pl., Suite 108, Newport Beach, CA 92660 USA (SAN 850-4873) Tel 949.266.3714; Fax: 949.266.3770; Toll Free: 800-626-2720
E-mail: mindworkspress@aol.com; sposs@amenclinic.com
Web site: http://www.mindworkspress.com.

Minedition *Imprint of* **Penguin Group (USA) Inc.**

Minerva Bks., *(0-9620125)* Div. of Hulbert Performance Rating, Inc., 316 Commerce St., Alexandria, VA 22314 USA (SAN 247-493X) Tel 703-683-5905 Do not confuse with companies with the same or similar name in Palo Alto, CA, New York, NY, Louisville, KY.

Minerva Bks., Ltd., *(0-8056)* 30 W. 26th St., New York, NY 10010 USA (SAN 205-8367) Tel 212-675-0465; Fax: 212-675-0573 Do not confuse with companies with the same or similar name in Alexandria, VA, Palo Alto, CA, Louisville, KY
Dist(s): **Continental Bk. Co., Inc.**
Lectorum Pubns., Inc.

MinervaPress, *(0-9637795)* Div. of Heartmates, Inc., Orders Addr.: P.O. Box 16202, Minneapolis, MN 55416 USA
E-mail: rachael@womenslegacies.com
Web site: http://www.heartmates.com.

Mines Road Bks., *(1-889064)* P.O. Box 3185, Fremont, CA 94539-9989 USA (SAN 298-9557) Tel 510-656-2240
E-mail: minesrb@pacbell.net
Web site: http://cmug.com/~minesroad/.

Mini DayTrip Bks., *(0-929198)* 24287 Buccaneer Blvd., Punta Gorda, FL 33955 USA (SAN 248-448X) Tel 941-639-5034; Fax: 941-505-8463.

Mini Enterprises - M.E. *See* **AGB Publishing**

Minikin Pr., *(0-9772320)* P.O. Box 528, Barrington, RI 02806-0280 USA (SAN 257-0076) Tel 401-245-7960
E-mail: jill@minikinpress.com
Web site: http://www.minikinpress.com.

Minnesota Department of Economic Security *See* **Minnesota Dept. Employment & Economic Development**

Minnesota Dept. Employment & Economic Development, *(0-9670505)* 332 Minnesota St. Ste. E200, Saint Paul, MN 55101-1349 USA Toll Free: 888-234-1114
E-mail: Amy.yerkes@state.mn.us
Web site: http://www.mnworkforcecenter.org.

†Minnesota Historical Society Pr., *(0-87351)* Orders Addr.: 11030 S. Langley Ave., Chicago, IL 60628 USA Toll Free Fax: 800-621-8476; Toll Free: 800-621-2736; Edit Addr.: 345 Kellogg Blvd., W., Saint Paul, MN 55102-1906 USA (SAN 202-6384) Tel 651-297-2221; Fax: 651-297-1345; Toll Free: 800-647-7827 ; *Imprints:* Borealis Book (Borealis Book)
E-mail: greg.britton@mnhs.org
Web site: http://www.mnhs.org/mhspress
Dist(s): **Chicago Distribution Ctr.**; *CIP.*

Minnesota Humanities Commission, *(0-9629298; 1-931016)* 987 E. Ivy Ave., Saint Paul, MN 55106-2046 USA Tel 612-774-0105 ext 112; Fax: 651-774-0205
E-mail: leant@thinkmhc.org
Web site: http://www.thinkmhc.org.

Minnesota's Bookstore, *(0-9647451; 0-9754338)* 660 Olive St., Saint Paul, MN 55155 USA Tel 651-297-3000; Fax: 651-215-5733; Toll Free: 800-657-3757
E-mail: mnbookstore@state.mn.us
Web site: http://www.minnesotasbookstore.com.

Minnie Troy Pubs., *(0-9727480)* Div. of Historically Speaking, 309 Union St., Murfreesboro, NC 27855 USA Tel 252-398-5098; Fax: 252-398-5098 ext 51
E-mail: lion5098@aol.com.

Minon, S.A. (ESP) *(84-355) Dist. by* **Continental Bk.**

Minon, S.A. (ESP) *(84-355) Dist. by* **Lectorum Pubns.**

Minotauro Ediciones (ESP) *(84-450) Dist. by* **Lectorum Pubns.**

Minotauro Ediciones (ESP) *(84-450) Dist. by* **Distribks Inc.**

Minotauro Ediciones (ESP) *(84-450) Dist. by* **Planeta.**

MinRef Pr., *(0-9624394; 1-930322)* 2248 SW Vista Pk. Dr., Oak Harbor, WA 98277 USA Tel 360-240-9059; Fax: 815-550-2832
E-mail: minref@gmail.com
Web site: http://www.minref.com
Dist(s): **Baker & Taylor Bks.**
Quality Bks., Inc.

Minuteman Pr. of Green Bay, *(0-9772315)* 513B S. Military Ave., Green Bay, WI 54303-2209 USA Tel 920-499-7767; Fax: 920-499-0907.

Minx *Imprint of* **DC Comics**

Mira Pr., The, *(0-9762947)* P.O. Box 590207, Newton Centre, MA 02459 USA.

Miracle Distrbution Ctr., Inc., *(0-9618309)* 3947 E. La Palma Ave., Anaheim, CA 92807-1714 USA (SAN 667-4143) Toll Free: 800-359-2246.

Miracle Pr., *(0-929889)* 2808 W. Lexington Way, Edmond, OK 73003-4224 USA (SAN 250-975X) Tel 405-359-0369; Fax: 703-883-1861
E-mail: miraclepress@cox.net.

MiracleLand Publishers, *(0-9714994)* Orders Addr.: P.O. Box 1485, Morgan City, LA 70380 USA Tel 985-384-6992; Fax: 985-384-3348; Edit Addr.: 1418 Bernice St., Morgan City, LA 70380 USA
E-mail: madise@teche.net.

Miraculous Fingerprints Pubs., *(1-886134)* 74565 Dillon Rd., MH 15, Desert Hot Springs, CA 92241 USA Tel 760-251-3037.

Miramax Bks., *(0-7868; 1-4013)* Div. of Walt Disney Productions, 11 Beach St., 5th Flr., New York, NY 10013 USA Tel 212-941-3800; Fax: 212-625-5075
Web site: http://www.miramax.com
Dist(s): **Disney Publishing Worldwide**
Hachette Bk. Group
HarperCollins Pubs.
Hyperion Pr.

Mirasol/Libros Juveniles *Imprint of* **Farrar, Straus & Giroux**

Mirhady, Farhad, *(0-9760323)* 1414 SW 3rd Ave., Suite 2503, Portland, OR 97201 USA Tel 503-243-3319; Fax: 503-227-3654
E-mail: fmirhady@comcast.net
Web site: http://www.poeticliterature.com.

Miroglyphics, *(0-9773064; 0-9801073)* Orders Addr.: 1581 W. 49th St. Pmb 309, Hialeah, FL 33012 USA; Edit Addr.: P.O. Box 22877, Hialeah, FL 33002 USA (SAN 257-2451) Tel 786-368-8742
E-mail: romoulous2005@yahoo.com
Web site: http://www.miroglyphics.net
Dist(s): **Lightning Source, Inc.**

Mirror Pond Publishing, *(0-9777683)* 63090 Casey Pl., Bend, OR 97701 USA Tel 541-385-6927
E-mail: speedyread@hotmail.com.

Mirror Publishing, *(0-9796519)* 6434 W. Dixon St., Milwaukee, WI 53214-1750 USA Tel 414-763-1034
E-mail: info@pagesofwonder.com
Web site: http://www.pagesofwonder.com
Dist(s): **Lightning Source, Inc.**

Mirrorstone *Imprint of* **Wizards of the Coast**

MirthMarks Publishing, *(0-9789591)* 675 Deis Dr., STE 123, Fairfield, OH 45014 USA
E-mail: flymaster@coppershoo.com.

Mishe-Mokwa Design Prepress & Publishing, *(0-9719283)* 6091 Milnes Rd., Jonesville, MI 49250 USA Tel 734-355-8545; 517-849-2912; Fax: 517-849-9019
E-mail: christina@mishe-mokwa.com
Web site: http://www.mishe-mokwa.com.

Mishe-Mokwa Pubns., *(0-934372)* Orders Addr.: P.O. Box 458, Old Greenwich, CT 06870 USA Tel 203-363-0806; Edit Addr.: 11211 Scenic Rd. (summer address), Honor, MI 49640 USA (SAN 221-377X) Tel 616-325-2067
Dist(s): **Partners Bk. Distributing, Inc.**

MISS Foundation Publishing, *(0-9717266)* Orders Addr.: P.O. Box 5333, Peoria, AZ 85385 USA Tel 623-979-1000; Fax: 623-979-1001; Edit Addr.: 8448 W. Aster Dr., Peoria, AZ 85381 USA
E-mail: info@misschildren.org
Web site: http://www.misschildren.org/.

Missing Piece Pr., *(0-9703729)* 18816 230th Ave E., Orting, WA 98360-9682 USA Toll Free: 877-56-THINK
E-mail: Questions@MissingPiecePress.com
Web site: http://www.missingpiecepress.com
Dist(s): **Reveal Entertainment, Inc.**

Mission City Pr., Inc., *(1-928749; 1-934306)* 202 2nd Ave S., Franklin, TN 37064 USA Toll Free: 800-840-2641
E-mail: busaffair@missioncitypress.com
Web site: http://www.alifeoffaith.com
Dist(s): **Zondervan.**

Mission Creek Studios, *(0-929702)* 1040 Mission Canyon Rd., Santa Barbara, CA 93105-2122 USA (SAN 249-9630) Tel 805-682-6724; Fax: 805-682-6761
E-mail: dave@missioncreek.com
Web site: http://www.missioncreek.com.

Mission Manuscripts, Inc., *(0-9768880)* 1000 Jorie Blvd., Suite 206, Oak Brook, IL 60523 USA Tel 630-990-0220; Fax: 630-990-2556
E-mail: kathy.hill@arends-inc.com.

Mission Mill Museum, *(0-9753484)* 1313 Mill St., SE, Salem, OR 97301 USA Tel 503-585-7012; Fax: 503-588-9902
E-mail: info@missionmill.org
Web site: http://www.missionmill.org.

Mision Ridge Pr., *(0-9763956)* 4660 Eastus Dr., San Jose, CA 95129 USA.

Missionaries of the Blessed Sacrament, *(0-9723512; 0-9762324)* Orders Addr.: P.O. Box 1701, Plattsburgh, NY 12901 USA Tel 518-561-8193; Edit Addr.: 12 Brinkerhoff St., Plattsburgh, NY 12901 USA
Web site: http://www.acfp2000.com.

Missions & Forts Pr., Inc., *(0-9700418)* P.O. Box 222, Wapiti, WY 82450 USA Fax: 210-738-1559
E-mail: missionsandforts@hotmail.com.

†Mississippi Museum of Art, *(1-887422)* 380 S. Lamar St., Jackson, MS 39201-4007 USA (SAN 279-6198)
E-mail: rpb@netdoor.com
Web site: http://www.msmuseumart.org; *CIP.*

Missouri Historical Society Pr., *(1-883982)* Orders Addr.: P.O. Box 11940, Saint Louis, MO 63112-0040 USA Tel 314-746-4557; Fax: 314-746-4548
E-mail: jstevens@mohistory.org
Web site: http://www.mohistory.org
Dist(s): **Booksource, The**
SPD-Small Pr. Distribution
Univ. of Missouri Pr.
Univ. of New Mexico Pr.
Wayne State Univ. Pr.

Mister C Music, *(0-9755333)* P.O. Box 28, Rochester, PA 15074 USA Toll Free: 877-687-4258
E-mail: misterc437@aol.com
Web site: http://www.mistercmusic.com.

†MIT Pr., *(0-262; 0-89706)* Orders Addr.: c/o Triliteral LLC, 100 Maple Ridge Dr., Cumberland, RI 02864 USA Tel 401-531-2800; Fax: 401-531-2801; Toll Free Fax: 800-406-9145; Toll Free: 800-405-1619; Edit Addr.: 55 Hayward St., Cambridge, MA 02142-1315 USA (SAN 202-6414) Tel 617-253-5646; Fax: 617-253-6779
E-mail: mitpress-orders@mit.edu
Web site: http://mitpress.mit.edu
Dist(s): **NetLibrary, Inc.**; *CIP.*

Mitchell, Karan, *(0-9763793)* 79 Baruch Dr., Apt.5E, New York, NY 10002-3659 USA Tel 212-982-7977
E-mail: mtchllkrn@aol.com.

Mitchell, Kathleen Riley, *(0-9669648)* Orders Addr.: P.O. Box 853, Block Island, RI 02807-0853 USA Tel 401-466-5403; Fax: 401-466-5401; Toll Free: 800-379-1875
Web site: http://www.blockisland.com/islandadventure.

Mitchell Lane Pubs., Inc., *(1-883845; 1-58415)* Orders Addr.: P.O. Box 196, Hockessin, DE 19707 USA Tel 302-234-9426; Fax: 302-234-4742; Toll Free: 800-814-5484
E-mail: mitchelllane@mitchelllane.com
Web site: http://www.mitchelllane.com.

Mitchell Publishing, Inc., *(0-938188)* 160 Spear St. Ste. 700, San Francisco, CA 94105-1562 USA (SAN 215-7896) Toll Free: 800-435-2665 Do not confuse with companies with the same or similar names in Spokane, WA, Medina, NY, Medicine Lodge, KS.

Mitchell Publishing, Incorporated *See* **Teaching & Learning Co.**

Mitre's Touch Gallery, The, *(0-9764384)* 1414 Adams Ave., La Grande, OR 97850 USA Tel 541-963-3477
E-mail: weframe@eoni.com.

Mitten Pr. *Imprint of* **Ann Arbor Media Group, LLC**

Mixta Publishing Co., *(0-9675951)* 3179 San Francisco Ave., Long Beach, CA 90806 USA Tel 562-427-4270
E-mail: michael.archuleta@gte.net; michael@mixtapublishing.com
Web site: http://www.mixtapublishing.com; http://www.mixtapublishing.net
Dist(s): **Leonard, Hal Corp.**

Mixx Entertainment, Inc., *(1-892213; 1-931514; 1-59182)* 5900 Wilshire Blvd., Suite 2000, Los Angeles, CA 90036 USA Tel 323-692-6700; Fax: 323-692-6701 ; *Imprints:* Mixx Manga (Mixx Manga); Pocket Mixx (Pocket Mixx)
E-mail: info@tokyopop.com
Web site: http://www.tokyopop.com
Dist(s): **Diamond Comic Distributors, Inc.**

Mixx Manga *Imprint of* **Mixx Entertainment, Inc.**

MJ Licensing LLC, *(0-9768891)* Subhash Kataria Office 1515 E. Captain Dreyfus Ave., Phoenix, AZ 85002 USA
E-mail: info@mj-licensing.com
Web site: http://www.mj-licensing.com.

MJF Bks. *Imprint of* **Fine Communications**

MJS Music Pubns., *(0-9762917)* 611 NE 5th Ter. Unit 3, Crystal River, FL 34428-3971 USA Toll Free: 866-463-9247 Do not confuse with comapnies with the same or similar name in Boyertown, PA, Searsport, ME
E-mail: msternal@mjspublications.com; wriverroad@aol.com
Web site: http://www.mjspublications.com
Dist(s): **Baker & Taylor Bks.**
Ingram Bk. Co.
Southcoast Music.

MJS Publications *See* **MJS Music Pubns.**

MJS Publishing Group LLC, *(0-9764336)* P.O. Box 6582, Evanston, IL 60204-6582 USA Tel 847-869-5901; Fax: 847-745-0219
E-mail: mjspg@ameritech.net
Web site: http://www.mjspub.com
Dist(s): **AtlasBooks Distribution.**

MK Publishing, *(0-9720484; 0-9747147; 0-9760534; 0-9763271; 0-9770933; 0-9785081)* 25123 22nd Ave. S., Saint Cloud, MN 56301 USA; P.O. Box 945, St Cloud, MN 56302 USA (SAN 256-4092) Tel 320-252-1023; Fax: 320-252-4574
Web site: http://www.yourbookpublisher.net
Dist(s): **Closet Case Bks.**
J & N Creations, LLC
JMS Distribution
Main Trail Productions
Ozark Bk. Distributors
Perfume River Pubns.
Puzzle Piece Pubns.

MKADesigns, *(0-9745839)* 131 Frankie Ln., Madison, AL 35757-6922 USA Tel 256-721-0200 ; *Imprints:* Fun to Read Books with Royally Good Morals (Fun to Read Bk)
E-mail: mike.dozier@mkadesigns.com
Web site: http://www.mkadesigns.com.

Mkuki na Nyoka Pubs. (TZA) *(9976-973) Dist. by* **Mich St U Pr.**

ML Publishing, *(0-9768347)* Div. of MIHP, 31500 Dequindre Rd., Warren, MI 48092-1057 USA Tel 586-268-6942
E-mail: smclaughlin@mihp.net
Web site: http://mlpublishing.com.

Mladinska Knjiga Zalozba, d.d. (SVN) *(86-11) Dist. by* **Bks of Slovenia.**

MLM Ranch Publishing, *(0-9743098)* P.O. Box 910251, St. George, UT 84791 USA.

MLML Assocs., *(0-9754930)* P.O. Box 492034, Los Angeles, CA 90049 USA.

MMG Technology Corp., *(0-9754886)* 379 Amherst St., Suite 204, Nashua, NH 03063 USA
Web site: http://www.the-common.com.

M-m-mauleg Publishing, *(0-9790111)* Orders Addr.: P.O. Box 5258, Mangilao, GU 96923 USA; Edit Addr.: 303 University Dr., Mangila, GU 96923-5258 USA
E-mail: millhoff@uog.edu.

MMP *See* **Millennium Marketing & Publishing**

MMS Publishing, *(0-922658)* Div. of Nadel Worldwide, Inc., 5429 McConnell Ave., Los Angeles, CA 90066 USA (SAN 251-4729) Tel 310-823-5755; Fax: 310-823-1272; Toll Free: 800-541-3533
E-mail: mmspub@earthlink.net
Web site: http://www.4perfectgifts.com.

MNMC, *(0-9728518; 0-9763532)* 17 Old Shelter Rock Rd., Danbury, CT 06810 USA Tel 203-798-6936; Toll Free: 866-210-0004
E-mail: order@muslimplanet.com
Web site: http://www.muslimpublisher.com.

Mobius Communications, Ltd., *(1-891304; 1-928583)* Div. of Publication Services, Inc., 1802 S. Duncan Rd., Champaign, IL 61822-5222 USA Fax: 217-398-3923; Toll Free: 800-662-4875
Web site: http://www.8-mobius.com.

Mocha Enterprises, *(0-9707163)* 6322 Chesapeake Cir., Stockton, CA 95219 USA (SAN 253-620X) Tel 209-478-0635 (phone/fax); 209-946-3064
E-mail: mochaenterprises@aol.com
Web site: http://www.welcometotheprofessionalwork.com.

†Modern Curriculum Pr., *(0-7652; 0-8136; 0-87895)* Div. of Pearson Education, Orders Addr.: P.O. Box 2500, Lebanon, IN 46052-3009 USA (SAN 206-6572) Toll Free: 800-526-9907 (Customer Service)
Web site: http://www.pearsonlearning.com
Dist(s): **Lectorum Pubns., Inc.**; *CIP.*

Modern Evil Pr., *(1-934516)* 2713 E. Aire Libre Ave., Phoenix, AZ 85032-2911 USA Tel 602-999-6449
E-mail: teel@modernevil.com
Web site: http://modernevil.com/.

Modern Learning Pr., *(0-935493; 1-56762)* P.O. Box 167, Rosemont, NJ 08556 USA Tel 609-397-2214; Fax: 845-277-3548; Toll Free Fax: 888-558-7350; Toll Free: 800-627-5867 ; *Imprints:* Kingsbridge Press (Kingsbridge Pr)
E-mail: Rlow@tasa.com.

Modern Library *Imprint of* **Random House Publishing Group**

Modern Living Media, *(0-9729815)* P.O. Box 10653, Newport Beach, CA 92658 USA (SAN 255-3899)
E-mail: raymond@modernlivingmedia.com
Web site: http://www.modernlivingmedia.com.

Modern Publishing, *(0-7666; 0-87449; 1-56144)* Div. of Unisystems, Inc., 155 E. 55th St., New York, NY 10022 USA (SAN 253-2921) Tel 212-826-0850; Fax: 212-759-9096 ; *Imprints:* Honey Bear Books (Honey Bear Bks)
E-mail: info@modernpublishing.com; rvreeland@modernpublishing.com
Web site: http://www.modernpublishing.com
Dist(s): **Worldwide Media Service, Inc.**

Modern Rock Entertainment *See* **Brevard Marketing**

Modern Star Bks., *(1-928694)* 6167 N. Broadway Ave., Suite 169, Chicago, IL 60660 USA Tel 773-728-5063
Dist(s): **Alliance Hse., Inc.**

Moffatt Business Research, *(0-9704695)* 5000 S. Himes Ave., Suite 514, Tampa, FL 33611 USA Tel 813-835-1255 (phone/fax)
E-mail: emekw@aol.com; emekw@ao.com.

Mogdrmombooks, *(0-9706232)* 3307 Herbert St., Mogadore, OH 44260 USA Fax: 330-628-2384
E-mail: mogdrmom@aol.com
Web site: http://mogdrmombooks@aol.com.

MoGho Bks., LLC, *(0-615; 0-9712559)* Box 200, 9801 Hartley Rd., Hallsville, MO 65255 USA Tel 573-696-3537 (phone/fax)
E-mail: moghobks@tranquility.net
Dist(s): **Booksource, The**
Cowley Distributing, Inc.
Univ. of Missouri Pr.

Mogul Comics, *(0-9657723)* 102 6th Ave. 2nd Flr., WaterVliet, NY 12189 USA.

Mogzilla (GBR) *(0-9546576) Dist. by* **IPG Chicago.**

Mohawk River Pr., *(0-9662100)* Orders Addr.: P.O. Box 4095, Clifton Park, NY 12065-0850 USA Tel 518-383-2254; Fax: 518-373-8018; Edit Addr.: 57 Carriage Rd., Clifton Park, NY 12065 USA
E-mail: Jimlabate@hotmail.com
Web site: http://www.mohawkriverpress.com.

Molino, Editorial (ESP) *(84-272) Dist. by* **Continental Bk.**

Molino, Editorial (ESP) *(84-272) Dist. by* **Lectorum Pubns.**

Molino, Editorial (ESP) *(84-272) Dist. by* **Santillana.**

Molino, Editorial (ESP) *(84-272) Dist. by* **AIMS Intl.**

Molino, Editorial (ESP) *(84-272) Dist. by* **Distribks Inc.**

Momentary Pleasures Pr., *(0-9648133)* Div. of New Thought Journal, P.O. Box 1494, Pickens, SC 29671 USA Tel 864-878-5859
E-mail: edw@innova.net
Web site: http://www.rockmusicgroup.com.

Momentpoint Media, *(0-9710448)* 2385 Friesian Rd., York, PA 17406 USA Tel 717-848-4528 (phone/fax) Do not confuse with Moment Point Press Inc. of NH/ME.
E-mail: momentpoint@suscom.net
Web site: http://www.momentpointmedia.com.

MomGeek.com *Imprint of* **Wood Designs, Inc.**

Mommy Has Tattoos, *(0-9770232)* P.O. Box 231059, New York, NY 10023-0023 USA
E-mail: info@mommyhastattoos.com
Web site: http://www.mommyhastattoos.com
Dist(s): **AtlasBooks Distribution.**

Momotombo Pr., *(0-9710465; 0-9797446)* Institute for Latino/University of Notre Dame, Notre Dame, IN 46556 USA; Inst. for Latino Studies Univ. of Notre Dame 230 McKenna Hall, Notre Dame, IN 46556
E-mail: faragon@nd.edu
Web site: http://www.momotombopress.com
Dist(s): **SPD-Small Pr. Distribution.**

Mom's Pride Enterprises, *(0-9720549)* 16521 N. 69th Dr., Peoria, AZ 85382 USA Tel 623-487-7589; Fax: 623-487-1504
E-mail: mrsb4kids@yahoo.com
Web site: http://www.mrsbstorytime.com.

Monarch Baby Publishing, *(0-9749499)* Orders Addr.: P.O. Box 24365, New Orleans, LA 70184 USA Tel 504-669-1044; Edit Addr.: 100 Kimball Ave., Apt. E51, Salem, VA 24153 USA
E-mail: monarchbaby@blackbutterflyrecords.com
Web site: http://blackbutterflyrecords.com
monarch_baby_publishing.thml.

Monarch Pubs., *(0-615; 0-9774038)* Orders Addr.: 400 N. Main St., No. 405, Greenville, SC 29601 USA
E-mail: vhollinger@aol.com
Web site: http://www.monarchpublishers.com
Dist(s): **Follett Library Resources**
Parnassus Bk. Distributors
Bryan, R. L.

Mondadori (ITA) *(88-04; 88-356; 88-86372; 88-520; 88-521) Dist. by* **Distribks Inc.**

Monday Morning Bks., Inc., *(0-912107; 1-57612; 1-878279)* Orders Addr.: P.O. Box 1680, Palo Alto, CA 94302 USA (SAN 264-7656) Tel 650-327-3374; Toll Free: 800-255-6049; Edit Addr.: P.O. Box 1134, Inverness, CA 94937-1134 USA
E-mail: mmbooks@aol.com
Web site: http://www.mondaymorningbooks.com
Dist(s): **Quality Bks., Inc.**
Unique Bks., Inc.

Mondial, *(1-59569)* 203 W 107th St., No. 6C, New York, NY 10025 USA
E-mail: contact@mondialbooks.com
Web site: http://www.mondialbooks.com
Dist(s): **Ingram Bk. Co.**

Mondo Fax Publishing, *(0-9710095)* 26235 Ravenhill Rd., Suite M, Santa Clarita, CA 91350-4754 USA Tel 661-250-0990; Fax: 661-251-4452
E-mail: argapc@socal.rr.com
Web site: http://mondofax.com
Dist(s): **Baker & Taylor Bks.**

Mondo Publishing, *(1-57255; 1-879531; 1-58653; 1-59034; 1-59336; 1-60201)* Div. of Music Plus, Inc., 980 Ave. of the Americas, New York, NY 10018 USA Toll Free Fax: 888-532-4492; Toll Free: 888-55-66636
Web site: http://www.mondopub.com.

Money Counsel, Inc., *(0-9648316)* Orders Addr.: P.O. Box 441227, Indianapolis, IN 46202 USA Tel 317-634-8049; Fax: 317-634-0266; Edit Addr.: 902 N. Market St. Apt. 521, Wilmington, DE 19801-3048 USA Do not confuse with Money Counseling, Edina, MN
E-mail: aletahodge@email.msn.com
Web site: http://www.moneycounsel.com.

Money Management Books *See* **Prism Hse. Media**

Monique Patrice Hall *See* **Hall, Monique P. Productions**

Monjeu Pr., Inc., *(0-9662738)* P.O. Box 64353, Tucson, AZ 85728-4353 USA Tel 520-293-4908; Fax: 520-622-2959
E-mail: monyhc@mindspring.com
Web site: http://www.ozstarnet.com/~mony
Dist(s): **Gryphon Hse., Inc.**

Monkey Business *See* **Monkeying Around**

MonkeyGod Enterprises, *(0-9708094; 0-9717729; 0-9728197)* Div. of Face 2 Face Games Publishing, 36 The Arcade, 65 Weybosset St., Providence, RI 02903 USA Tel 401-351-0362 (phone/fax)
E-mail: fmf@pipeline.com
Web site: http://www.monkeygodenterprses.com.

Monkeying Around, *(0-9700437; 0-9799753)* P.O. Box 10131, Rochester, NY 14610 USA Tel 585-256-2660; Fax: 585-442-2965
E-mail: info@monkeyingaround.com
Web site: http://www.monkeyingaround.com.

Monkeyshines Publishers *See* **Allosaurus Pubs.**

Monkeytoes Pr., *(0-615)* 49 Beckford Farm Rd., Hannover, MA 02339 USA
E-mail: jvgandkdlarson@comcast.net
Web site: http://www.monkeytoespress.com.

Monogram Aviation Pubns., *(0-914144)* P.O. Box 223, Sturbridge, MA 01566 USA (SAN 206-5983) Tel 508-347-5574 9-5, M-F; Fax: 508-347-5772 24/7
E-mail: monogram@meganet.net
Web site: http://www.monogramaviation.com.

Monogram Booklets, *(0-9706782; 0-9776014)* P.O. Box 428017, Evergreen Park, IL 60805 USA
E-mail: monogrambooklets@yahoo.com.

Monolith Graphics, *(0-9675756; 0-9788857)* Orders Addr.: 4377 W. 60th St., Cleveland, OH 44144 USA Tel 440-843-1378 (main number); Fax: 440-845-2164 (24-hour dedicated fax)
E-mail: goth@monolithgraphics.com; nox@noxarcana.com
Web site: http://www.monolithgraphics.com; http://www.noxarcana.com
Dist(s): **Diamond Comic Distributors, Inc.**

Monroe Educational Media, *(0-9721146)* 2965 Taylor Rd., Reynoldsburg, OH 43068 USA Tel 614-866-4289; Fax: 740-927-9131
E-mail: jon@gooddebt.com
Web site: http://www.monroemedia.com.

Monroe, Guy, *(0-9742443)* P.O. Box 2325, Newport, OR 97365-0171 USA Toll Free: 877-562-3866.

Monroe Media *See* **Monroe Educational Media**

Monsoon Bks. Pte. Ltd. (SGP) *(981-05) Dist. by* **Biblio Dist.**

Montage Publishing International, *(0-9768589)* P.O. Box 162621, Altamonte Springs, FL 32714 USA
E-mail: montagepi@yahoo.com
Web site: http://www.michaeltowens.com.

Montana Historical Society Pr., *(0-917298; 0-9721522; 0-9759196; 0-9801292)* P.O. Box 201201, Helena, MT 59620 USA (SAN 208-7693) Toll Free: 800-243-9900
E-mail: mholz@mt.gov
Web site: http://www.montanahistoricalsociety.org
Dist(s): **Globe Pequot Pr., The.**

Montanha Pr., *(0-9743380)* 1547 Palos Verdes Mall , Suite 139, Walnut Creek, CA 94597 USA.

Monte Nido Pr., *(0-9742663)* Rm 9L19, 1240 Mission Rd., Los Angeles,, CA 90033 USA Tel 323-226-3406; Fax: 323-226-3440
E-mail: hoppenbrou@earthlink.net
Web site: http://www.toke.hoppenbrouwers.net.

Monte Ávila Editores Latinoamericana CA (VEN) *(980-01) Dist. by* **Lectorum Pubns.**

Montemayor Pr., *(0-9674477; 1-932727)* P.O. Box 526, Millburn, NJ 07041 USA Tel 973-761-1341
E-mail: mail@montemayorpress.com
Web site: http://www.montemayorpress.com.

†Monterey Bay Aquarium, *(1-878244)* 886 Cannery Row, Monterey, CA 93940 USA Tel 831-648-4942; 408-648-4800; 831-648-4847; Fax: 831-644-7568; Toll Free: 877-665-2665
E-mail: mmckenzie@mbayaq.org
Web site: http://www.montereybayaquarium.org*; CIP.*

Monterey Bay Sancturary Foundation, *(0-9742810)* 299 Foam St., Monterey, CA 93940 USA
E-mail: info@mbnmsf.org
Web site: http://www.mbnmsf.org
Dist(s): **Sunbelt Pubns., Inc.**

Monterey Pacific Institute *See* **Monterey Pacific Pubs.**

Monterey Pacific Pubs., *(1-880710)* P.O. Box 1619, Bandon, OR 97411 USA Tel 650-994-6570; Fax: 650-994-6579
E-mail: ingram@uci.net
Dist(s): **Baker & Taylor Bks.**

Monterey Publishing, *(0-9640537)* Div. of Communicating Images, P.O. Box 1411, Bellaire, TX 77402-1411 USA
E-mail: DonEddy@DonEddy.org.

Montessori Advantage, *(0-9766453)* Orders Addr.: P.O. Box 272, Wickatunk, NJ 07765 USA Toll Free: 888-946-2114; Edit Addr.: 257 Rt. 79N, Wickatunk, NJ 07765 USA.

Montevallo Historical Pr., Inc., *(0-9658624)* 1727 West 17th St., Davenport, OH 52804 USA Tel 563-343-1372
E-mail: dean@mhpress.com
Web site: http://www.mhpress.com.

Montevista Pr., *(0-931551)* P.O. Box 327, Winthrop, WA 98862-0327 USA (SAN 682-191X)
E-mail: joroe@verizon.net
Dist(s): **Hancock Hse. Pubs.**
Partners/West
Todd Communications.

Montgomery County Historical Society, *(0-9720965)* 1000 Carillon Blvd., Dayton, OH 45409-2023 USA Do not confuse with Montgomery County Historical Society in Rockville MD, Fort Johnson NY
Web site: http://www.daytonhistory.org.

†Monthly Review Pr., *(0-85345; 1-58367)* Div. of Monthly Review Foundation, Inc., 146 W. 29th St. Rm. 6FW, New York, NY 10001-8202 USA (SAN 202-6481) Toll Free: 800-670-9499
E-mail: promo@monthlyreview.org
Web site: http://www.monthlyreview.org
Dist(s): **New York Univ. Pr.***; CIP.*

Montrose Training & Pubn., *(0-9724354)* P.O. Box 2048, Warrendale, PA 15086 USA Tel 724-776-0483
E-mail: kmontros@greenbriar.net
Web site: http://www.greenbriartraining.com.

Montville Pr., *(0-9706527)* P.O. Box 4304, Greensboro, NC 27410-4304 USA Tel 336-292-8268; Fax: 336-218-0410
E-mail: bas236@aol.com.

Moo Pr. *Imprint of* **Keene Publishing**

Moo Press, Incorporated *See* **Keene Publishing**

Moodoo Productions, Inc., *(0-9762454)* P.O. Box 6461, Altadena, CA 91003 USA Tel 626-296-6956
E-mail: michael@drawingpower.org
Web site: http://www.drawingpower.org
Dist(s): **Book Wholesalers, Inc.**
Library Video Co.

†Moody Pubs., *(0-8024)* Div. of Moody Bible Institute, Orders Addr.: 210 W. Chestnut, Chicago, IL 60610 USA; Edit Addr.: 820 N. LaSalle, Chicago, IL 60610 USA (SAN 202-5604) Tel 312-329-2101; Fax: 312-329-2144; Toll Free: 800-678-8812 ; *Imprints:* Lift Every Voice (LEV)
E-mail: mpcustomerservice@moody.edu
Web site: http://www.moodypublishers.com
Dist(s): **Jones, Bob Univ. Pr.**
Tyndale Hse. Pubs.*; CIP.*

Moody, William, *(0-9762556)* 301 Willard Hall, Univ. of Delaware, Newark, DE 19711 USA Tel 302-831-1658; Fax: 302-831-0591
E-mail: wmoody@udel.edu
Web site: http://www.udel.edu/educ/solveit.htm.

Moombaya Bks., *(0-9766799)* 2118 Wilshire Blvd., Suite 528, Santa Monica, CA 90403-9040 USA
E-mail: diponzagroup@aol.com.

Moon, Alice *See* **PeachMoon Publishing**

Moon Smile Pr., *(0-9660346)* 11038 27th Ave., NE, Seattle, WA 98125 USA Tel 206-365-4116; Fax: 206-365-1124; Toll Free: 800-561-3039
E-mail: author@feedingfamily.com
Web site: http://www.feedingfamily.com
Dist(s): **Baker & Taylor Bks.**
New Leaf Distributing Co., Inc.
Nutri-Bks. Corp.
Partners/West.

Moon Travel Handbooks *See* **Avalon Travel Publishing**

Moon Valley Productions, *(0-934290)* P.O. Box 1342, Healdsburg, CA 95448 USA (SAN 221-2900) Tel 707-823-9340; 707-523-8525
E-mail: zaksartandsoul@yahoo.com
Web site: http://www.zakzaikine.com.

Moonation, *(0-9722899)* 5513 Eagle Lake Dr., Palm Beach Gardens, FL 33418-1548 USA
Web site: http://www.moonation.com/.

Moonbow Pr., LLc, *(0-9789092)* P.O. Box 95, Bethel, OH 45106 USA (SAN 851-9110).

Moonchpa Pubns. (AUS) *(0-9578408; 0-9580240; 0-9750111) Dist. by* **Potters Hse.**

Moondance Publishing, *(0-9671865; 1-931524)* Orders Addr.: P.O. Box 16, Upper Black Eddy, PA 18972 USA Tel 610-442-1951; Fax: 610-982-5331; Edit Addr.: 1525 Oak Ln., Upper Black Eddy, PA 18972 USA (SAN 254-5101) Tel 610-442-1951
E-mail: caravan@moondancepublishing.com
Web site: http://www.moondancepublishing.com
Dist(s): **Baker & Taylor Bks.**

Moondoggie Publishing, *(0-9711773)* P.O. Box 5917, Destin, FL 32540 USA Tel 850-897-1149
E-mail: sissyandscooter@cox.net
Web site: http://sissyandscooter.com.

Moonjar, LLC, *(0-9724282; 0-9764231)* 612 19th Ave., E., Seattle, WA 98112 USA Tel 206-325-6331; Fax: 206-726-0769; Toll Free: 888-323-0001
E-mail: contact@moonjar.com
Web site: http://www.moonjar.com
Dist(s): **Ten Speed Pr.**

Moonlight on the Wabash Publishing, *(0-9744810)* 5928 Martel Ave., Dallas, TX 75206-5708 USA ; *Imprints:* Limestock Press (Limestock)
Web site: http://www.lespoir-corp.com.

Moonlight Publishing, *(0-9723422; 0-9779603)* 2528 Lexington St., Lafayette, CO 80026 USA Do not confuse with companies with the same or similar name in Hickley, OH, Mount Holly, VT, Portland, OR, Isle of Palms, SC
Web site: http://www.moonlight-publishing.com
Dist(s): **Graphic Arts Ctr. Publishing Co.**
National Bk. Network.

Moonlight Rose Pubns., *(1-56479)* Orders Addr.: P.O. Box 154, Huntington, NY 11743 USA; Edit Addr.: 47 Pearwood Dr., Huntington Station, NY 11746 USA Tel 516-421-2231; Fax: 516-421-1050
E-mail: JaniceKidMusic@worldnet.att.net
Web site: http://www.JaniceBuckner.com.

MoonRattles, *(0-9790920)* P.O. Box 939, Carmel, CA 93921 USA; 70 Dapplegray Rd., Bell Canyon, CA 91307 (SAN 854-2201) Fax: 818-932-9631; Toll Free: 800-961-6073
E-mail: info@moonrattles.com
Web site: http://www.moonrattles.com.

Moons & Stars Publishing For Children, *(1-929063)* Div. of Moon Star Unlimited, Inc., , Pasadena, TX 77505 USA Tel 713-473-7120; Fax: 713-473-1105
E-mail: services@dorpexpress.com
Web site: http://www.dorpexpress.com.

MoonStar Pr., *(0-9672107)* 4360 E. Main St., Suite 408, Ventura, CA 93003 USA Tel 805-648-7753
E-mail: toutzhag@earthlink.net
Dist(s): **New Leaf Distributing Co., Inc.**

Moonstone, *(0-9710129; 0-9712937; 0-9721668; 0-9726443; 0-9748501; 1-933076)* Div. of Amazing Fantasy Comic Shop Ltd., 582 Torrence Ave., Calumet City, IL 60409 USA Fax: 708-891-0644
E-mail: afbooks_frankfort@sbcglobal.net
Web site: http://www.moonstonebooks.com
Dist(s): **Diamond Bk. Distributors.**

Moonstone Pr., *(0-9707768; 0-9727697; 0-9769542)* 7820 Oracle Pl., Potomac, MD 20854 USA (SAN 852-5625) Tel 301-765-1081; Fax: 301-765-0510
E-mail: mazeprod@erols.com
Web site: http://www.moonstonepress.net
Dist(s): **Independent Pubs. Group**
Lectorum Pubns., Inc.
PSI (Publisher Services, Inc.).

Moonwater Products, *(0-9769033)* 63 Roycroft Dr., Rochester, NY 14621 USA
E-mail: djed_ra_maat@yahoo.com.

Moore, Ammanuel, *(0-9744060)* P.O. Box 3295, Baltimore, MD 21228 USA Tel 410-788-7271
E-mail: info@acmoorebooks.com
Web site: http://www.acmoorebooks.com.

Moore Bks., *(1-891635)* Orders Addr.: P.O. Box 324, Somerville, IN 47683 USA Tel 812-795-2502; Fax: 812-795-2665; Edit Addr.: 202 E. Illinois St., Somerville, IN 47683 USA
E-mail: moorebooks@hotmail.com.

Moore, Evans, *(0-9709762)* P.O. Box 30311, Washington, DC 20030 USA Tel 202-889-3648
E-mail: evansmoore@hotmail.com.

Moore, Greg Publishing, *(0-9639495)* Orders Addr.: 6202 Wallina Ct., SE, Salem, OR 97309 USA Tel 503-749-1393; Fax: 503-588-7707
E-mail: yoyo@tdn.com.

†Moore, Hugh Historical Park & Museums, Inc., *(0-930973)* 30 Centre Sq., Easton, PA 18042-7743 USA (SAN 678-8831) Tel 610-559-6617; 610-559-6613; Fax: 610-559-6690
E-mail: ncm@canals.org
Web site: http://www.canals.org; *CIP.*

Moore, Hullihen, *(0-9785775)* P.O. Box 116, Oldhams, VA 22529 USA (SAN 850-9468).

Moore, Kelly D., *(0-9755613)* P.O. Box 9021, San Pedro, CA 90734 USA
E-mail: kdgmoore@aol.com.

Moore, Lonnie W. *See* **I & L Publishing**

Moose Country Pr., *(0-9642213; 1-893863)* 73 Zerah Fiske Rd., Shelburne, MA 01370 USA Tel 413-625-9569; Fax: 413-774-3077; Toll Free: 800-346-6673
E-mail: moose@moosecountry.com
Web site: http://moosecountry.com.

Moose Run Productions, *(0-9766315)* 22010 Highview, Clinton Township, MI 48036 USA Tel 586-718-7700
Web site: http://www.moose-run.com.

Mora Art Studio, *(0-9671753)* Orders Addr.: P.O. Box 8494, Kansas City, MO 64114-0494 USA Tel 816-313-0370; Edit Addr.: 5309 Crisp Ave., Raytown, MO 64133 USA
E-mail: eddy4art@yahoo.com; eddy@moraartstudio.com; info@moraartstudio.com
Web site: http://www.moraartstudio.com.

Morals & Values Pr., *(0-9754191)* P.O. Box 29110, Baltimore, MD 21205 USA
Web site: http://www.inthenameofluv.com.

Morari Specialties Inc., *(0-9770618)* 13901 SW 22nd St., Miami, FL 33175-7006 USA
Web site: http://www.moraríspecialties.com.

Morcan, Dorina, *(0-9763663)* P.O. Box 1564, Malvern, AR 72104 USA Fax: 501-262-4127
E-mail: dmorcan@ix.netcom.com.

M.O.R.E., *(0-9719984; 0-9758549)* Div. of St. Louis Writing & Performing Guild, Inc., P.O. Box 294, Hazelwood, MO 63042-0294 USA (SAN 255-1055) Fax: 314-385-7474; 314-895-4153; 6614 W. Florissant Ave., Suite 2B, Saint Louis, MO 63136-3646
E-mail: stlouiswpguild@aol.com; MOREPublishers@AOL.com
Web site: http://www.morepublishers.com.

More, Frances International Teaching Systems *See* **Frances More International Teaching Systems**

More, Francisco J., *(0-9747851)* 221 Majorca Ave., No. 207, Coral Gables, FL 33134-4429 USA Tel 305-448-5081.

More Heart Than Talent Publishing, Inc., *(0-9740924)* 6507 Pacific Ave., Suite 329, Stockton, CA 95207-3717 USA (SAN 255-2639) Fax: 209-467-3260; Toll Free: 800-208-2260
E-mail: gms@goldenmastermind.com
Web site: www.MoreHeartThanTalentPublishing.com
Dist(s): **AtlasBooks Distribution.**

More Pr., *(0-9743394)* Div. of More Consulting Co., 1634 E. 53rd St., Chicago, IL 60615-4389 USA
E-mail: shaharimoore@aol.com.

More Than a Card, Inc., *(0-922589)* 2 Canal St., Suite 2344, New Orleans, LA 70130-1501 USA (SAN 251-3331) Tel 504-822-7594; Fax: 504-822-8594; Toll Free: 800-635-9672.

More to Life Publishing, *(0-9632564; 0-9766971)* Orders Addr.: P.O. Box 113, Coxsackie, NY 12051 USA Tel 518-731-2179; Edit Addr.: 85 Washington Ave., Coxsackie, NY 12051 USA
E-mail: morelife33@mhcable.com; michaels@mhcable.com
Web site: http://www.askrealjesus.com.

†Morehouse Publishing, *(0-8192)* Orders Addr.: P.O. Box 1321, Harrisburg, PA 17105-1321 USA Fax: 717-541-8136; Toll Free: 800-242-1918; Edit Addr.: 4775 Linglestown Rd., Harrisburg, PA 17112 USA Fax: 717-541-8136
E-mail: morehouse@morehousegroup.com
Web site: http://morehousepublishing.org
Dist(s): **Church Publishing, Inc.**; *CIP.*

Morelmasters LLC, *(0-615)* Orders Addr.: 6294 Reynolds Ridge Rd., Potosi, WI 53820 USA Tel 608-732-2175; Fax: 608-763-2799
E-mail: morelmasters@tds.net
Web site: http://www.morelmasters.com.

Moreno, Fanny, *(0-9718874)* 9061 SW 156th St., A203, Miami, FL 33157-1954 USA Tel 305-234-5339
E-mail: fannito@msn.com.

Morgan, E. A., *(0-9631975)* Orders Addr.: P.O. Box 7452, Naples, FL 34101 USA Fax: 941-598-9809
E-mail: rhymetime@mailstation.com
Dist(s): **AtlasBooks Distribution.**

Morgan Foundation Pubs.: International Published Innovations, *(1-885679)* Orders Addr.: 14730 Gold Creek Ct. Apt. B, Grass Valley, CA 95949-9411 USA Tel 530-273-1009; Fax: 815-550-4456
E-mail: morganfoundation@earthlink.net
Web site: http://www.morganfoundationpublishers.com.

Morgan Hse. Publishing, *(0-9711970)* 6510 N. Leonardo DeVinci, Tucson, AZ 85704 USA Tel 520-229-3183; Fax: 520-229-3124
E-mail: sales@morganthedog.com
Web site: http://www.morganthedog.com.

Morgan James Publishing, LLC, *(0-9746133; 0-9758570; 0-9760901; 0-9768491; 1-933596; 1-60037)* Orders Addr.: 1225 Franklin Ave. Suite 325, Garden City, NY 11530 USA Tel 516-620-2528; Fax: 516-908-4496
E-mail: david@morganjamespublishing.com
Web site: http://www.morganjamespublishing.com
Dist(s): **Ingram Pub. Services**
Lightning Source, Inc.

Morgan Publishing Co., *(0-9639940)* Orders Addr.: P.O. Box 28718, San Jose, CA 95159 USA (SAN 298-1432) Fax: 408-637-1674; Edit Addr.: 338 Fifth St., Hollister, CA 95023 USA Tel 408-637-7031.

Morgan Publishing, Incorporated *See* **Augustine Pr.**

Morganstern, Mimi, *(0-9700522)* 7235 Fairfax Dr., Tamarac, FL 33321-4308 USA Tel 954-720-3362; Toll Free: 800-484-8729 (code 0995)
E-mail: mmorganste@cs.com.

Moriah Ministries, *(0-9728454; 0-9774836)* P.O. Box 23823, Chagrin Falls, OH 44023 USA Tel 440-543-9304 (phone/fax)
E-mail: info@davidicdance.com; info@moriahministries.org
Web site: http://www.davidicdance.com; http://www.moriahministries.org.

Moriarty, Timothy K., *(0-9650519)* 901 SE 14th Ter., Cape Coral, FL 33990-3423 USA.

Morley Pr., *(0-9662888)* Orders Addr.: P.O. Box 864472, Plano, TX 75086 USA Tel 972-618-0491; Fax: 972-643-4540; Edit Addr.: 6732 Manitowoc Dr., Plano, TX 75023 USA.

Mormon Comics, *(0-9764965)* 435 N. 150 W., Blackfoot, ID 83221 USA Tel 208-785-4558 (phone/fax)
E-mail: info@mormoncomics.com
Web site: http://www.mormoncomics.com.

Mornin' Light Media, *(0-9763534)* Orders Addr.: 31203 N. Course View, Franklin, TN 37067 USA ; *Imprints:* Mornin'Light Media (MorninLight)
E-mail: shawnsurber@comcast.net; hopebook@bellsouth.net
Web site: http://www.thehopebook.com.

†Morning Glory Pr., Inc., *(0-930934; 1-885356; 1-932538)* 6595 San Haroldo Way, Buena Park, CA 90620 USA (SAN 211-2558) Tel 714-828-1998; Fax: 714-828-2049; Toll Free: 888-612-8254 Do not confuse with Morning Glory Press in Nashua, NH
E-mail: jwl@morninggloryppress.com
Web site: http://www.morninggloryppress.com
Dist(s): **Independent Pubs. Group**; *CIP.*

Morning Glory Pubns., *(0-9762929)* Orders Addr.: 1104 Blue ridge Dr., Clarkston, MI 48348 USA
E-mail: klinejane@hotmail.com.

Morning Joy Publishing, *(0-9637811)* Div. of MA BAYBE Christian Greetings, Orders Addr.: P.O. Box 702, Vandalia, OH 45377-0702 USA; Edit Addr.: 5322 Silverdome Dr., Dayton, OH 45414 USA.

Morning Star, *(0-9713685)* Orders Addr.: P.O. Box 450, Hatch, UT 84735 USA Tel 435-648-2228; Edit Addr.: 38 Ouray Cir., Glendale, UT 84729 USA
E-mail: info@beautybrainsandtalent.com.

Morning Star Media Group, Inc., *(0-9623791)* 850 Maury Rd. Unit 17, Orlando, FL 32804-3651 USA
Web site: http://www.morningstartv.com.

Morning Star Music Pubs., *(0-944529)* 1727 Larkin Williams Rd., Fenton, MO 63026 USA (SAN 243-8496)
E-mail: morningstar@morningstarmusic.com
Web site: http://www.morningstarmusic.com.

Morning Sun Bks., Inc., *(0-9619058; 1-58248; 1-878887)* 9 Pheasant Ln., Scotch Plains, NJ 07076 USA (SAN 243-1157) Tel 908-755-5454; Fax: 908-755-5455
E-mail: morningsunbooks@comcast.net
Web site: http://www.morningsunbooks.com
Dist(s): **Walthers, William K. Inc.**

MorningGlory Publishing, *(0-9705090)* Orders Addr.: P.O. Box 15523, Plantation, FL 33318-5523 USA Tel 954-370-7205; Fax: 954-370-6817; Edit Addr.: 9951 NW Sixth Ct., Plantation, FL 33324 USA
E-mail: tandtsm@aol.com.

Morningstar Christian Chapel, *(0-9715733; 0-9729477)* 16241 Leffingwell Rd., Whittier, CA 90603 USA Tel 562-943-0297; Fax: 562-943-3608
E-mail: mrngstr@morningstarcc.org
Web site: http://www.morningstarcc.org.

MorningStar Pubns., Inc., *(1-878327; 1-929371; 1-59933)* Div. of MorningStar Fellowship Church, Orders Addr.: P.O. Box 440, Wilkesboro, NC 28697 USA Fax: 336-651-2430; Toll Free: 800-542-0278 (orders only); Edit Addr.: 1605 Industrial Dr., Wilkesboro, NC 28697 USA Do not confuse with Morningstar Pubns., Boulder, CO
E-mail: info@morningstarministries.org
Web site: http://www.morningstarministries.org
Dist(s): **Anchor Distributors**
Destiny Image Pubs.
Whitaker Hse.

Morningtide Pr., *(0-9790395)* P.O. Box 312, St. Augustine, FL 32085-0312 USA
Web site: http://www.morningtidepress.com
Dist(s): **Midpoint Trade Bks., Inc.**
Quality Bks., Inc.

Mornin'Light Media *Imprint of* **Mornin' Light Media**

Moro Management, Inc., *(1-893714)* Orders Addr.: P.O. Box 520-A, Villanova, PA 19085 USA Tel 610-525-5118; Fax: 610-525-5279; Edit Addr.: 835 Mount Moro Rd., Villanova, PA 19085 USA
E-mail: sbarbacane@comcast.com
Web site: http://www.patcroce.com.

Morris Communications, *(0-9668242)* P.O. Box 598, Lawai, Kauai, HI 96765 USA Tel 808-332-0065; Fax: 808-332-7754 Do not confuse with companies with the same or similar name in Augusta, GA, Topeka, KS, Ft. Lee, NJ
E-mail: slammit@aloha.net; creativ@aloha.net
Web site: http://www.slammit.com.

Morris Publishing, *(0-7392; 0-9631249; 1-57502; 1-885591)* Subs. of Morris Pr. & Office Supplies, 3212 E. Hwy. 30,, Kearney, NE 68847 USA Tel 308-236-7888; Fax: 308-237-0263; Toll Free: 800-650-7888 Do not confuse with companies with the same Wesley Chapel, FL, Elkhart, IN
E-mail: kimmyw414@yahoo.com; snowgers@mcn.org; publish@morrispublishing.com
Web site: http://morrispublishing.com.

Morris Publishing, *(0-9714841)* 5235 New Savannah Cir., Wesley Chapel, FL 33544 USA Do not confuse with companies with the same in Kearney, NE, Elkhart, IN
E-mail: jason_m_baxter@yahoo.com
Dist(s): **Morris Publishing.**

Morris, Tami *See* **2B Pr.**

Morrissey Company, Incorporated, The *See* **Adventures in Ceramics**

Morrow Cookbooks, Wiillam *Imprint of* **HarperCollins Pubs.**

Morrow, William &Co. *Imprint of* **HarperCollins Pubs.**

Morten Moore Publishing, *(0-9672576)* Div. of K & M Marketing, 415 E. Mohawk, Flagstaff, AZ 86001 USA Tel 520-779-2209; Fax: 520-779-0126
Dist(s): **Canyonlands Pubns.**

Morton Bks., *(1-929188)* 47 Stewart Ave., Irvington, NJ 07111 USA Tel 973-374-8327; Fax: 973-374-1125
E-mail: rmo1033555@aol.com
Web site: http://www.mortonbooks.com.

MOS, Inc., *(0-9778570)* P.O. Box 100, Pekin, IN 47165-0100 USA Tel 812-967-2530; Fax: 812-967-2980; Toll Free: 800-451-3993
E-mail: info@moscompany.com
Web site: http://www.moscompany.com.

Mosaic Pr., *(0-88962)* Orders Addr.: PMB 145, 4500 Witmer Industrial Estates, Niagara Falls, NY 14305 USA Tel 905-825-2130 (phone/fax); Toll Free: 800-387-8992; Edit Addr.: 1252 Speers Rd., Units 1 & 2, Oakville, ON L6L 5N9 CAN
E-mail: mosaicpress@on.aibn.com
Web site: http://www.mosaic-press.com
Dist(s): **Midpoint Trade Bks., Inc.**

Mosaic Publishing *See* **Branded Black Publishing**

Mosby *Imprint of* **Elsevier - Health Sciences Division**

†Mosby, Inc., *(0-323; 0-7234; 0-8016; 0-8151; 0-88416; 0-941158; 1-55664; 1-56375; 1-56815)* Div. of Harcourt, Inc., A Harcourt Health Sciences Co., Orders Addr.: 6277 Sea Harbor Dr., Orlando, FL 32887 USA Toll Free Fax: 800-235-0256; Toll Free: 800-545-2522; Edit Addr.: 11830 Westline Industrial Dr., Saint Louis, MO 63146 USA (SAN 200-2280) Tel 314-872-8370; Toll Free: 800-325-4177
E-mail: usbkinfo@elsevier.com
Web site: http://www.mosby.com/
Dist(s): **Elsevier - Health Sciences Division**
Elsevier
PennWell Corp.; *CIP.*

Mosby-Year Book, Incorporated *See* **Mosby, Inc.**

Moscow Ballet *Imprint of* **Sports Marketing International, Inc.**

Mosdos Pr., *(0-9671009; 0-9742160)* Div. of Mosdos Ohr Hatorah, 1508 Warrensville Ctr. Rd., Cleveland, OH 44121 USA Tel 216-291-4158; Fax: 216-291-4169
E-mail: mosdospress@mohi.org; mospress@mohi.org
Web site: http://www.mosdospress.com.

Mosely, Winifred, *(0-9769610)* 6600 E. River Rd., Tucson, AZ 85750 USA Tel 520-327-3681
E-mail: njmosely@comcast.net.

Mosley, Kim, *(0-9663215)* 4120 Parker Rd., Florissant, MO 63033 USA Tel 314-831-1243; Fax: 314-831-4749; Toll Free: 888-524-3276
E-mail: kmosley@stlnet.com
Web site: http://www.stlcc.cc.mo.us/fv/users/kmosley.

Mosley Publishing Group, *(1-886185)* P.O. Box 586502, Oceanside, CA 92058-6502 USA (SAN 298-4113) Tel 760-233-1183; Toll Free: 866-566-7539
E-mail: info@mosleypublishing.com
Web site: http://www.mosleypublishing.com.

Moss, Michael, *(0-9763003)* 610 Prestwick Dr., Frankfort, IL 60423 USA Tel 312-437-7827 (312-437-STAR)
Web site: http://www.5starpc.com.

Moss Portfolio, The, *(0-9665198)* 1 Poplar Grove Ln., Mathews, VA 23109 USA (SAN 630-4303) Tel 804-725-7378; Fax: 804-725-3040; Toll Free: 800-430-1320
E-mail: mossportfolio@ccsinc.com
Web site: http://www.p-buckley-moss.com.

Moss, Renea L., *(0-9678805)* 11921 NW 15th Ave., North Miami, FL 33167 USA; 20533 Biscayne Blvd., No. 428, Aventura, FL 33180 ; *Imprints:* Attitude Publishing (Attitude Pubng)
E-mail: reneasworld@yahoo.com
Web site: http://www.reneasworld.com.

Mostats, Marie C., *(0-9742848)* Orders Addr.: P.O. Box 230053, Las Vegas, NV 89123-0001 USA; Edit Addr.: 1921 Steven Ave. Apt. 460, Bedford, IN 47421-3669 USA.

Mother Goose Programs, *(0-9753985)* 256 Haywood Rd., Chester, VT 05143 USA
E-mail: debbi@mothergooseprograms.org
Web site: http://www.mothergooseprograms.org.

Mother List Publishing Co., The, *(1-891687)* 4477A Valley Steppe Dr., Buhl, ID 83316 USA
Web site: http://www.motherlist.com.

Mother Moose Pr., *(0-9724570)* Orders Addr.: 21010 Southbank St., PMB No. 435, Potomac Falls, VA 20165 USA Tel 571-223-6472
E-mail: books@mothermoosepress.com
Web site: http://www.mothermoosepress.com
Dist(s): **STL Distribution North America.**

M.O.T.H.E.R. Publishing Co., Inc., The, *(0-9718431)* Orders Addr.: P.O. Box 477, Rock Springs, WY 82902 USA Tel 307-382-5027; Fax: 307-382-6492; Edit Addr.: 616 Elias Ave., Rock Springs, WY 82901 USA
E-mail: motherpublishing@wyoming.com
Web site: http://www.motherpublishing.com.

Mother Tongue Ink, *(0-9510661; 1-890931)* Orders Addr.: P.O. Box 1395, Estacada, OR 97023-1395 USA
E-mail: mothertongue@wemoon.ws
Web site: http://www.wemoon.ws
Dist(s): **Baker & Taylor Bks.**
New Leaf Distributing Co., Inc.
Partners/West
Phoenix Distributors
Timeline Market Group, LLC.

Motherboard Bks., *(0-9749653)* P.O. Box 430041, Saint Louis, MO 63143 USA
E-mail: info@motherboardbooks.com
Web site: http://motherboardbooks.com.

Motherly Way Enterprises, *(0-9671428)* P.O. Box 11, Marylhurst, OR 97036-0011 USA Tel 503-723-2879; Toll Free: 877-666-7929
E-mail: julie@motherlyway.com
Web site: http://www.motherlyway.com.

Mother's Hse. Publishing, *(0-9743869; 0-9773990; 0-9792704; 0-9797144)* 2814 E. Woodmen Rd., Colorado Springs, CO 80920 USA Toll Free: 800-266-0999
E-mail: my2bits@earthlink.net; mothershouse@earthlink.net.

Mother's Love Publishing, A, *(0-9777022)* 4962 Bristol Rock Rd, Florissant, MO 63033 USA (SAN 257-9707)
Dist(s): **Lushena Bks.**

Mothwing Pr. *Imprint of* **Mothwing.com**

Mothwing.com, *(0-9724528)* 80 Sheffield Rd., Waltham, MA 02451-2374 USA Tel 781-899-8153 ; *Imprints:* Mothwing Press (Mothwng Pr)
E-mail: mothwingpress@mothwing.com; andylevesque@rcn.com
Web site: http://www.mothwing.com/mothwingpress.

Motion Fitness LLC, *(0-9744568)* P.O. Box 2179, Palatine, IL 60078-2179 USA
E-mail: sales@motionfitness.com
Web site: http://www.motionfitness.com.

Motion Pubns., *(0-9679446; 0-9768492)* P.O. Box 2551, Elk Grove, CA 95759 USA Toll Free: 866-552-2211
E-mail: motionpublishing@email.com
Web site: http://www.terryoneal.com.

Motivated Proformance, *(0-9676942)* Div. of Consignment Trust, Orders Addr.: P.O. Box 701774, Dallas, TX 75370 USA Tel 972-731-8486; Fax: 469-633-0687; Edit Addr.: 1653 Parson Ln., Frisco, TX 75034 USA
E-mail: sales@motivatedpro.com
Web site: http://www.getumotivated.com
Dist(s): **Hervey's Booklink & Cookbook Warehouse.**

Motivation Basics, *(0-9661993)* P.O. Box 6327, Diamondhead, MS 39525 USA Tel 228-255-5019 (phone/fax)
E-mail: will01@aol.com
Dist(s): **Quality Bks., Inc.**

Motivision Media, *(0-9722332)* 9528 Blossom Valley Rd., El Cajon, CA 92021 USA
E-mail: dehaven@motivisionmedia.com
Web site: http://www.motivisionmedia.com.

Motorbooks *Imprint of* **MBI Publishing Co. LLC**

Motorbooks International Wholesalers & Distributors *See* **MBI Distribution Services**

Mottley, William, *(0-9769216)* 428 N. Genito Rd., Burkeville, VA 23922 USA Tel 434-767-5594
E-mail: emottley@ceva.net
Web site: http://www.narrowstrip.com.

Mount de Sales Academy, *(0-9715386)* 700 Academy Rd., Catonsville, MD 21228 USA Tel 410-744-8498; Fax: 410-747-5105
Web site: http://www.mountdeslaes.org.

Mount Olive College Pr., *(0-9627087; 1-880994; 1-59761)* Mount Olive College, Administration Bldg. 634 Henderson St., Mount Olive, NC 28365 USA (SAN 297-7729) Tel 919-658-2502; Toll Free Fax: 800-653-0854.

Mount Rushmore History Assn., *(0-9646798; 0-9752617; 0-9798823)* Div. of Mount Rushmore National Memorial Society, 13000 Hwy. 244, Bldg. 31, Suite 2, Keystone, SD 57751 USA Tel 605-574-3161; Fax: 605-574-3144; Toll Free: 800-699-3142
E-mail: moru_mrha@nps.gov
Web site: http://www.mtrushmorebookstore.com.

Mountain Bk. Co., P.O. Box 778, Broomfield, CO 80038-0778 USA Tel 303-436-1982; Fax: 917-386-2769
E-mail: wordguise@aol.com
Web site: http://www.mountainbook.org.

Mountain Breeze Publishing, *(0-9675128)* Div. of The Snyder Group, Inc., P.O. Box 4641, Crofton, MD 21114-4641 USA Tel 410-721-9196; Fax: 410-721-0660
E-mail: johnsnyder@johnsnyder.net
Web site: http://www.thegoldenring.com; http://www.johnsnyder.net
Dist(s): **American Wholesale Bk. Co.**

Mountain Empire Pubns., *(0-9664709; 0-9707800)* Orders Addr.: P.O. Box 480, Clifton Forge, VA 24422-3512 USA Tel 540-862-2557 (phone/fax, call first); Edit Addr.: 300 Evans Ln., Clifton Forge, VA 24422 USA
E-mail: gnoma@aol.com; Mepubl@aol.com.

Mountain Hse. Publishing Co., *(0-9653084; 1-891658)* Div. of Mountain House LLC, P.O. Box 445, Polson, MT 59860-0445 USA ; *Imprints:* Captains Log Printing (Captains Log) Do not confuse with Mountain Hse. Publishing, Inc., Waitsfield, VT
E-mail: grannyraz@yahoo.com.

Mountain Maid *See* **Light Messages**

Mountain Meadow Pr., *(0-9702267)* 133 Canvasback Rd., Sheridan, WY 82801 USA Tel 307-672-7795; Fax: 307-672-6317 Do not confuse with companies with the same name in Kooshia, ID, Pittsburgh, PA
E-mail: djrodell@cyberhighway.net.

Mountain Memories Bks. *Imprint of* **Quarrier Pr.**

Mountain Ministries, *(0-9787761)* 18055 100th St., Lindsay, OK 73052-3308 USA Do not confuse with Mountain Ministries Sitka, Alaska.

Mountain n' Air Bks., *(1-879415)* Div. of Mountain n' Air Sports, Inc., Orders Addr.: P.O. Box 12540, La Crescenta, CA 91224 USA (SAN 630-5598) Tel 818-248-9345; Toll Free Fax: 800-303-5578; Toll Free: 800-446-9696; Edit Addr.: 2947-A Hololulu Ave., La Crescenta, CA 91214 USA (SAN 631-4198) ; *Imprints:* Bearly Cooking (Bearly Cooking)
E-mail: books@mountain-n-air.com
Web site: http://mountain-n-air.com
Dist(s): **Alpenbooks Pr. LLC**
BookSurge, LLC
Partners/West.

Mountain Path Pr., *(0-9653149)* 664-A Freeman Ln., PMB 888, Grass Valley, CA 95949 USA Toll Free: 888-224-9997 (phone/fax)
E-mail: Info@MountainPathPress.com
Web site: http://www.mountainpathpress.com
Dist(s): **Books West**
Integral Yoga Pubns.
New Leaf Distributing Co., Inc.
Partners Bk. Distributing, Inc.

Mountain Path Publications *See* **Mountain Path Pr.**

†Mountain Pr. Publishing Co., Inc., *(0-87842)* Orders Addr.: P.O. Box 2399, Missoula, MT 59806-2399 USA (SAN 202-8832) Tel 406-728-1900; Fax: 406-728-1635; Toll Free: 800-234-5308; Edit Addr.: 1301 S. Third West, Missoula, MT 59801 USA (SAN 662-0868)
E-mail: jrimel@mtnpress.com; mtnpress@montana.com; info@mtnpress.com
Web site: http://www.mountain-press.com
Dist(s): **Booklines Hawaii, Ltd.**
Lone Pine Publishing USA; *CIP.*

Mountain States Specialties, *(0-9726022)* 1671 Valtec Ln., Boulder, CO 80301 USA Tel 303-444-6186 Toll Free: 800-353-2147.

Mountain Voices Pubs., *(0-9671908)* Orders Addr.: 2 Junaluska Rd., Andrews, NC 28901 USA Tel 828-321-5553; Fax: 828-321-2446
E-mail: MountainTeller@mountainvoice.com
Web site: http://www.mountainvoice.com.

Mountain Watch Pr., *(1-930439)* Orders Addr.: 1919 Augusta Valley Ln., SE, Ada, MI 49301 USA Tel 616-897-7479; Toll Free: 888-875-5856
E-mail: jeff@spriggles.com
Web site: http://www.spriggles.com.

Mountain World Media LLC, *(0-9763309)* Orders Addr.: P.O. Box 506, Norwood, CO 81426-8142 USA Tel 970-327-4192 (phone/fax); Edit Addr.: 1240 Spruce St., Norwood, CO 81423 USA
E-mail: nfo@mountainworldmedia.com; books@mountainworldmedia.com
Web site: http://www.mountainworldmedia.com.

Mountaintop Pr., *(0-9711106)* Orders Addr.: P.O. Box 550, Cary, NC 27512-0550 USA Tel 919-567-9550; Fax: 919-567-9694; Edit Addr.: 201-D Foliage Cir., Cary, NC 27511 USA
Dist(s): **STL Distribution North America.**

MountainView *Imprint of* **Treble Heart Bks.**

Mountcastle Co., *(0-913063)* Two Annabel Ln., Suite 214, San Ramon, CA 94583 USA (SAN 285-6689) Toll Free: 800-585-7323
E-mail: mntcastle@earthlink.net
Web site: http://www.readinglesson.com
Dist(s): **Independent Pubs. Group.**

Mourning Dove Studio, *(0-9701089)* 65 Buckingham Pl., Lebanon, NH 03677-2612 USA Tel 603 448 5274; 603-448-5274
E-mail: glaurie@juno.com.

Mouse Works, *(0-7364; 1-57082)* Div. of Disney Bk. Publishing, Inc., A Walt Disney Co., 114 Fifth Ave., New York, NY 10011 USA (SAN 298-0797) Tel 212-633-4400; Fax: 212-633-4811
Web site: http://www.disneybooks.com
Dist(s): **Random Hse., Inc.**

Mousetime Bks. *Imprint of* **Mousetime Media LLC**

Mousetime Media LLC, *(0-9723213)* 7960-B Soquel Dr., No. 297, Aptos, CA 95003 USA ; *Imprints:* Mousetime Books (Msetime Bks)
E-mail: books@mousetime.com
Web site: http://www.mousetime.com.

Mousetrap Bks., *(0-9673723)* Orders Addr.: P.O. Box 13833, Columbus, OH 43213 USA Tel 614-231-1947; Edit Addr.: 172 S. James Rd., Columbus, OH 43213 USA.

Move It Math, *(0-941530)* P.O. Box 17416, Sugar Land, TX 77496-7416 USA (SAN 239-1279) Tel 512-572-0541; Fax: 512-572-3973.

Movement Makers International, *(0-9766930)* P.O. Box 3940, Broken Arrow, OK 74013-3940 USA
Web site: http://www.j12.com.

†Moyer Bell, *(0-918825; 1-55921)* 549 Old North Rd., Kingston, RI 02881-1220 USA (SAN 630-1762) Tel 401-783-5480; Fax: 401-284-0959; Toll Free: 888-789-1945 ; *Imprints:* Asphodel Press (Asphodel Pr); Papier-Mache Press (Papier-Mache); Olmstead Press (Olmstead)
Web site: http://www.moyerbellbooks.com/
Dist(s): **Acorn Alliance**
Midpoint Trade Bks., Inc.
Perseus Distribution; *CIP.*

Moznaim Publishing Corp., *(0-940118; 1-885220)* 4304 12th Ave., Brooklyn, NY 11219 USA (SAN 214-4123) Tel 718-438-7680; Fax: 718-438-1305; Toll Free: 800-364-5118.

MP2ME Enterprise, *(0-9717947; 0-9776679)* 16754 SE 45th St., Issaquah, WA 98027 USA Tel 425-957-9459
E-mail: mpighin1@msn.com
Dist(s): **Lightning Source, Inc.**

MPC Pr. International, *(0-9628453; 0-9715541)* P.O. Box 26142, San Fransisco, CA 94126-6142 USA
E-mail: info@laughingcookiejar.com
Web site: http://www.laughingcookiejar.com.

MPG Pr., *(0-9714649)* Orders Addr.: P.O. Box 1631, San Marcos, TX 78667-1631 USA Tel 512-353-3971
Web site: http://www.MargaretFrench.com; http://www.MargaretGlendinning.com.

Mr Do It All, Inc., *(0-9722038)* 2212 S. Chickasaw Trail, No. 220, Orlando, FL 32825 USA Toll Free: 800-425-9206
E-mail: info@planet-heller.com
Web site: http://www.planet-heller.com.

Mr. Emmett Publishing, *(0-9759346)* 37 Harleston Pl., Charleston, SC 29401 USA Tel 843-853-5728
E-mail: talubbers@comcast.net.

Mracek, Ann, *(0-9766488)* 22 Morwood Ln., Creve Coeur, MO 63141 USA (SAN 257-0009) Tel 314-432-5713; Fax: 314-569-2202
E-mail: anmracek@springmail.com.

MrExcel.com Publishing, *(0-9724258; 1-932802)* 13386 Judy Ave., NW, Uniontown, OH 44685 USA Tel 330-715-2875; Fax: 707-220-4510 ; *Imprints:* Holy Macro! Books (Holy Macro Bks)
E-mail: consult@mrexcel.com
Web site: http://www.holymacrobooks.com
Dist(s): **Independent Pubs. Group.**

MRG Professional Services, *(0-9760310)* 6255 Cherry Ln. Farm Dr., West Chester, OH 45069 USA.

Mrs. L's Reading Room, *(0-9767278)* Orders Addr.: 110 Wedgefield Dr., Hilton Head Island, SC 29926 USA Tel 843-682-2820 (telephone/fax)
Web site: http://www.readroom.com.

M.S.C. Bks *Imprint of* **Mustard Seed Comics**

MSJ Music Publighing, *(0-9764521)* P.O. Box 3185, Rancho Santa Fe, CA 92067-3185 USA.

MSP *Imprint of* **Main St Publishing, Inc.**

MSPpress *Imprint of* **Mama Specific Productions**

MsRevenda.com, *(0-9768538)* P.O. Box 370109, Decatur, GA 30037 USA
Web site: http://www.msrevenda.com.

M.T. Publishing Co., Inc., *(1-932439; 1-934729)* Orders Addr.: P.O. Box 6802, Evansville, IN 47719-6802 USA Toll Free: 888-263-4702; Edit Addr.: 2425 U.S. Hwy., 41 N. Suite 139, Evansville, IN 47711 USA
Web site: http://www.mtpublishing.com.

MTV *Imprint of* **Simon & Schuster**

MTW Investments, *(0-9723929)* 13133 Parker, Grandview, MO 64030 USA Tel 816-763-4817
E-mail: twilson2@kc.rr.com
Web site: http://www.carpetdweller.net.

Mu Alpha Theta, National High Schl. Mathematics Club, *(0-940790)* 601 Elm Ave., Rm. 423, Norman, OK 73019 USA (SAN 204-0077) Tel 405-325-4489; Fax: 405-325-7184
E-mail: matheta@ou.edu
Web site: http://www.mualphatheta.org.

MU Pr., *(1-883847)* 1505 SW Alaska, Seattle, WA 98106 USA Tel 206-923-2972; Fax: 425-702-9287
E-mail: edd@jetcity.com.

Mucsu.net, *(0-9718333)* P.O. Box 2054, H54, Westminster, CA 92684 USA Tel 714-531-1620
E-mail: info@mucsu.net
Web site: http://www.mucsu.net.

Mud Pie Pr., *(0-9714941)* 4201 Morrow Ave., Waco, TX 76710 USA Tel 254-716-3193
E-mail: bjelmore@msn.com; belmore1@hot.rr.com
Web site: http://www.mudpiepress.com
Dist(s): **Baker & Taylor Bks.**
Quality Bks., Inc.

Mud Puddle, Inc., *(1-59412; 1-60311)* 54 W. 21st St., Suite 601, New York, NY 10010 USA Tel 212-647-9168.

Mueller, Pamela Bauer *See* **Pinata Publishing**

Muffin & Co., *(0-9665686)* P.O. Box 25754, Honolulu, HI 96825-0754 USA Fax: 808-395-8556; Toll Free: 888-396-8261
E-mail: muffinco@lava.net
Web site: http://www.dogonnet.com/muffin
Dist(s): **Booklines Hawaii, Ltd.**

Muggli Graphics, *(1-57665)* Orders Addr.: P.O. Box 897, Estacada, OR 97023 USA Tel 503-630-2535; Edit Addr.: 788 Edgehill Dr., Estacada, OR 97023-0576 USA
E-mail: muggligr@cascadeaccess.com; muggligr@netzero.net; info@gloriannemuggli.com
Web site: http://www.muggligraphics.com.

Muh-He-Con-Neew Pr., *(0-935790)* Affil. of Arvid E. Miller Memorial Library, Mohican Nation Reservation, N9136 Big Lake Rd., Gresham, WI 54128 USA Tel 715-787-4427
Dist(s): **Miller, Arvid E. Memorial Library Museum.**

Mukund Pubns., *(0-9663831)* 3033 Arbor Bnd., Birmingham, AL 35244-1573 USA
E-mail: pratibhakhare@hotmail.com
Web site: http://www.learnhindi.com.

Mullings Media, *(0-9767657)* P.O. Box 934, Woodbridge, NJ 07095 USA.

Multables, Inc., *(0-9645004)* 6398 S. Louthan St., Littleton, CO 80120 USA Tel 303-794-0786; Toll Free: 800-320-6857.

Multicultural Pubns., *(0-9634932; 1-884242)* 936 Slosson St., Akron, OH 44320 USA Tel 330-865-9578; Fax: 330-734-0737; Toll Free: 800-238-0297
E-mail: multiculturalpub@prodigy.net
Web site: http://www.multiculturalpub.net
Dist(s): **Brodart Co.**
Follett Library Resources.

Multifaceted Productions, *(0-9659511)* 5214-F Diamond Heights Blvd., PMB 130, San Francisco, CA 94131-2118 USA Tel 415-282-7448
E-mail: jblagden@aol.com
Web site: http://www.jewelsandthegems.com
Dist(s): **Margatuck Productions**
Sparkling Records.

Multi-Language Pubns., *(0-9703210; 1-931891)* 2500 George Dieter, El Paso, TX 79936 USA Tel 915-857-5852; Fax: 915-857-7644; Toll Free: 800-876-1388
E-mail: luterano@whc.net.

Multi-Language Publications Program *See* **Multi-Language Pubns.**

Multnomah *Imprint of* **WaterBrook Pr.**

Multnomah Fiction *Imprint of* **WaterBrook Pr.**

Multnomah Gift Bks. *Imprint of* **WaterBrook Pr.**

Multnomah Kidz *Imprint of* **WaterBrook Pr.**

Mumblefish Bks., *(0-9759649)* Orders Addr.: P.O. Box 139, Point Pleasant, PA 18950-0139 USA Tel 215-297-5002; Fax: 215-297-5299
E-mail: info@mumblefishbooks.com
Web site: http://mumblefishboooks.com
Dist(s): **Baker & Taylor Bks.**

Munchweiler Pr., *(0-7940)* Orders Addr.: P.O. Box 2529, Victorville, CA 92393-2529 USA Tel 760-245-9215; Fax: 760-245-9418; Edit Addr.: 13940 Okesa Rd., Apple Valley, CA 92307-7220 USA
E-mail: publisher@munchweilerpress.com
Web site: http://www.munchweilerpress.com.

Mundania Pr., *(0-9723670; 1-59426)* 6470A Glenway Ave., No. 109, Cincinnati, OH 45211 USA (SAN 255-013X) Tel 513-574-8902; Fax: 513-598-6800
E-mail: bob@mundania.com
Web site: http://www.mundania.com; http://www.phaze.com
Dist(s): **Baker & Taylor Bks.**
Lightning Source, Inc.

Mundus *Imprint of* **Ann Arbor Media Group, LLC**

Murdock, Bob E., *(0-9754363)* 352 Carly Ln., Rock Hill, SC 29732-7750 USA Tel 803-366-2666 (phone/fax)
E-mail: pbmurdock@comporium.net
Web site: http://www.sermonsforchildren.com.

Murdock Publishing Co., *(0-9743359; 1-934102)* Orders Addr.: 127 Belk Ct., Clayton, NC 27520 USA Tel 919-934-2393; Fax: 919-938-2394
Web site: http://www.murdockmedia.com.

Murlin Pubns., *(1-892218)* P.O. Box 433, Orefield, PA 18069-0433 USA
E-mail: party4@fast.net.

Murlin Publishing Company *See* **Murlin Pubns.**

Murphy, Janice Ferebee *See* **Got It Goin' On**

Murray, David M., *(0-9729807)* Orders Addr.: ., Seekonk, MA 02916 USA; Edit Addr.: 30 Wnterberry Ln., Seekink, MA 02771-4816 USA.

Murray Hill Bks., LLC, *(0-9719697)* 220 Madison Ave., Suite 10H, New York, NY 10016 USA (SAN 256-3622) Tel 212-689-5232
E-mail: rsegal@nyc.rr.com
Web site: http://www.massagemassage.com; http://www.murrayhillbooks.com
Dist(s): **Learning Connection, The.**

Murray, John (GBR) *(0-7195) Dist. by* **Trafalgar.**

Murray, Regina Waldron, *(0-9636918; 0-9664042)* 900 Hollinshead Spring Rd. Apt. H108, Skillman, NJ 08558-2068 USA
E-mail: reginawmurray@yahoo.com.

Murray's Pubns., *(0-9718812)* Div. of R.H.M. Enterprises, P.O. Box 19948, Houston, TX 77224 USA Tel 281-493-1828; 722 G Country Pl., Houston, TX 77079
E-mail: webhost@houston.rr.com
Web site: http://www.murrayspublications.com.

Muscatello Publishing, *(0-9722774)* P.O. Box 620011, Orlando, FL 32862-0011 USA Tel 407-888-3060; Fax: 407-650-3222; Toll Free: 877-888-3060
E-mail: info@muscatellopublishing.com
Web site: http://www.muscatellopublishing.com.

Muse Eek Publishing Co., *(0-9648632; 1-890944; 1-59489)* P.O. Box 509, New York, NY 10276 USA (SAN 253-4215) Tel 212-473-7030; Fax: 212-473-4601
E-mail: sales@muse-eek.com
Web site: http://www.muse-eek.com
Dist(s): **Lightning Source, Inc.**

Muse Press, *(1-892137)* P.O. Box 493, Lake Toxaway, NC 28747 USA Tel 954-614-0089 Do not confuse with Mercury Publishing, Woodside, CA
E-mail: info@witchmart.com
Web site: http://www.witchmart.com
Dist(s): **Abyss Distribution**
New Leaf Distributing Co., Inc.

Museum Mania, *(1-892240)* 2412 Springbrook St., Thousand Oaks, CA 91362 USA Tel 805-552-9147; Fax: 818-552-9148; Toll Free: 888-707-4289
E-mail: camuseum@museummania.com
Web site: http://www.museummania.com.

†Museum of Fine Arts, Boston, *(0-87846)* 465 Huntington Ave., Boston, MA 02115-4401 USA (SAN 202-2230) Tel 617-369-3438; Fax: 617-369-3459
E-mail: kmullins-mitchell@mfa.org
Web site: http://www.mfa.org
Dist(s): **Brown, David Bk. Co.**
Brown, David Bk. Co., The
D.A.P./Distributed Art Pubs.; *CIP.*

Museum of Glass, *(0-9726649)* 1801 Dock St., Tacoma, WA 98402 USA Toll Free: 866-468-7386 (866-4-MUSEUM)
Web site: http://www.museumofglass.org
Dist(s): **Univ. of Washington Pr.**

Museum of Glass: International Center for Contemporary Art *See* **Museum of Glass**

Museum of Living History, *(0-9667336)* Orders Addr.: P.O. Box 1460, Gadsden, AL 35902 USA Tel 256-549-1534; 256-547-5333; Fax: 256-549-1539; Edit Addr.: 1136 Seventh Ave., Gadsden, AL 35901 USA
E-mail: luvlife@internetpro.net.

Museum of Modern Art, *(0-87070)* 11 W. 53 St., New York, NY 10019-5497 USA (SAN 202-5809) Tel 212-708-9700; Fax: 212-333-1127; Toll Free: 800-447-6662 (orders)
E-mail: MoMA_Publications@moma.org
Web site: http://www.moma.org/publications
Dist(s): **D.A.P./Distributed Art Pubs.**

Museum of New Mexico Foundation, *(0-9623304; 0-9677409)* Orders Addr.: P.O. Box 2065, Santa Fe, NM 87504-2087 USA; Edit Addr.: 113 Lincoln, Santa Fe, NM 87501 USA Tel 505-982-8594.

Museum of New Mexico Pr., *(0-89013)* Div. of New Mexico Department of Cultural Affairs, Orders Addr.: 1312 Basehart Rd SE, Albuquerque, NM 87106-4363 USA (SAN 202-2575) Toll Free: 800-249-7737; Edit Addr.: P.O. Box 2087, Santa Fe, NM 87504-2087 USA
E-mail: custserv@upress.unm.edu
Web site: http://www.mnmpress.org
Dist(s): **Univ. of New Mexico Pr.**

Museum of Science, *(0-918866; 0-9774084; 1-933758)* 1 Science Pk., Boston, MA 02114 USA (SAN 210-4687) Tel 617-589-0230
E-mail: mhiggins@mos.org
Web site: www.mos.org/eie.

Museum of Texas Tech Univ., *(0-9640188; 1-929330)* Div. of Texas Tech Univ., 3301 4th St., Box 43191, Lubbock, TX 79409-3191 USA Tel 806-742-2442; Fax: 806-742-1136
E-mail: museum.texastech@ttu.edu
Web site: http://www.museum.ttu.edu.

Museum of the Rockies, Inc., *(0-933819)* 600 W. Kagy Blvd., Bozeman, MT 59717-2730 USA (SAN 692-8870) Tel 406-994-5283; Fax: 406-994-2682
E-mail: sfischer@montana.edu
Web site: http://www.montana.edu/wwwmon/.

Mushroom Cloud Pr. of Orlando, *(0-9679552)* 278 Leslie Ln., Lake Mary, FL 32746 USA Tel 407-328-7311
E-mail: mushroomcloudpress@hotmail.com.

Music Awareness, *(0-9753599)* P.O. Box 188, Amherst, MA 01004 USA Tel 413-253-4216; Fax: 413-253-1397
E-mail: pwb@valinet.com
Web site: http://www.musicawareness.com.

music bks. & games, *(0-9744427)* P.O. Box 97, McNeil, TX 78651 USA
E-mail: info@musicbooksandgames.com
Web site: http://www.musicbooksandgames.com/.

Music City Publishing, *(1-933215)* P.O. Box 41696, Nashville, TN 37204-1696 USA (SAN 256-288X)
E-mail: manager@musiccitypublishing.com
Web site: http://www.musiccitypublishing.com.

Music Educators National Conference *See* **MENC - The National Assn. for Music Education**

Music for Little People, Inc., *(1-56628; 1-877737)* 390 Lake Benbow Dr., No. C, Garberville, CA 95542 USA Tel 707-923-3991; Fax: 707-923-3241; Toll Free: 800-346-4445
Web site: http://www.mflp.com
Dist(s): **Educational Record Ctr., Inc.**
Goldenrod Music, Inc.
Linden Tree Children's Records & Bks.
Music Design, Inc.
New Leaf Distributing Co., Inc.
Rounder Kids Music Distribution
Western Record Sales.

Music, Inc., *(1-929140)* 2603 Elm Hill Pike. Ste. G, Nashville, TN 37214-3156 USA
E-mail: minc@mindspring.com.

Music Institute of California, *(0-9624062; 1-883993)* Orders Addr.: P.O. Box 3535, Vista, CA 92085-3535 USA (SAN 297-5955) Tel 760-891-0226
Dist(s): **Baker & Taylor Bks.**
Brodart Co.

Music Magic of Colorado, *(1-930031)* 1935 Ashland Mine Rd., Ashland, OR 97520 USA.

Music Resources International *See* **Kindermusik International**

Music Sales Corp., *(0-7119; 0-8256; 1-84609)* Orders Addr.: 445 Bellvale Rd., P.O. Box 572, Chester, NY 10918 USA (SAN 662-0876) Tel 845-469-2271; Fax: 845-469-7544; Toll Free Fax: 800-345-6842; Toll Free: 800-431-7187; Edit Addr.: 257 Park Ave., S., 20th Flr., New York, NY 10010 USA (SAN 282-0277) Tel 212-254-2100; Fax: 212-254-2103 ; *Imprints:* Amsco Music (Amsco Music); Chester Music (Chester Music); Schirmer Trade Books (Schirmer Trade Bks)
E-mail: info@musicsales.com
Web site: http://www.musicroom.com; http://www.musicsales.com
Dist(s): **Baker & Taylor Bks.**
Dumont, Charles Son, Inc.
Chesbro Music Co.
Leonard, Hal Corp.
Quality Bks., Inc.

Musical Linguist, The, *(0-9706829)* Orders Addr.: 14419 Greenwood Ave. N., Suite A, No. 354, Seattle, WA 98133 USA Fax: 509-693-4160; Toll Free: 866-297-2128
E-mail: mlinguist@aol.com
Web site: http://www.musicalspanish.com.

MusicGem, *(0-9643073)* Orders Addr.: P.O. Box 4777, Downey, CA 90241-1777 USA Tel 562-927-7536 Do not confuse with Hummingbird Publishing Co. in Kingwood, TX
E-mail: gem777@earthlink.net
Web site: http://home.earthlink.net/~gem777/
Dist(s): **Bookmen, Inc.**
Harris Teller, Inc.

MusicKit.COM, *(0-9713194)* 778 Western Dr., Point Richmond, CA 94801 USA Tel 510-237-5551 ; *Imprints:* MusicTales (MusicTales)
E-mail: kit@musickit.com
Web site: http://www.musickit.com.

MusicTales *Imprint of* **MusicKit.COM**

Musictech College Pr., *(0-9729879)* 19 Exchange St., E., Saint Paul, MN 55101 USA Tel 651-291-0177; Fax: 651-291-0366; Toll Free: 800-594-9500
E-mail: dsmith@musictech.com
Web site: http://www.musictech.com.

MusicWorks, *(0-9763194)* Orders Addr.: P.O. Box 1492, Maryland Heights, MO 63043 USA; Edit Addr.: 13233 Amiot Dr., Saint Louis, MO 63146 USA Do not confuse with MusicWorks in Marietta, GA
Web site: http://www.the-music-works.com
Dist(s): **HardBound, Inc.**

MusiKinesis, *(0-9701416)* 3734 Cross Bow Ct., Ellicott City, MD 21042 USA Fax: 410-465-8472
E-mail: monicadale@musikinesis.com
Web site: http://www.musikinesis.com
Dist(s): **Biblio Distribution.**

Muslim Writers Publishing, *(0-9767861; 0-9793577)* P.O. Box 27362, Tempe, AZ 85285 USA Tel 480-894-6014
E-mail: woodad@mindspring.com
Web site: http://www.muslimwriterspublishing.com.

Mustafa, Malik, *(1-893727)* Orders Addr.: P.O. Box 3224, New York, NY 10027-9998 USA
E-mail: zzzigzag@hotmail.com.

Mustang BKS, *(0-9766270)* P.O. Box 1193, Crooked River Ranch, OR 97760 USA Tel 541-504-9620.

Mustard Seed Comics, *(0-9769819)* 3667 Madrid Dr., Augusta, GA 30906 USA Tel 706-793-0926 ; *Imprints:* M.S.C. Books (MSC Bks)
E-mail: benitomsc@hotmial.com
Web site: http://www.mustardseedcomics.com.

Mustard Seed Press *See* **Silver Fox Marketing**

Mustard Seed Pr., *(0-9797703)* 263 Northampton Rd., Amherst, MA 01002 USA
Web site: http://www.bagelsbuddyandme.com.

Musterion Pr. *Imprint of* **VMI Pubs.**

Muszynski, James A., *(0-9766461)* 1446 Yoder Rd., Manister, MI 49660 USA Tel 231-723-6500 (phone/fax)
E-mail: lsmuszyk@hotmail.com
Web site: http://www.jaminjimbooks.com.

Mutual Publishing LLC, *(0-935180; 1-56647)* 1215 Center St., Suite 210, Honolulu, HI 96816 USA (SAN 222-6359) Tel 808-732-1709; Fax: 808-734-4094
E-mail: mutual@lava.net
Web site: http://www.mutualpublishing.com
Dist(s): **Booklines Hawaii, Ltd.**
Islander Group.

MVCD, Inc., *(0-9753617)* 4711 E. Falcon Dr., Suite 251, Mesa, AZ 85215 USA.

MW Enterprises, *(0-9654136)* 207 W. Green Forest Dr., Cary, NC 27511-9305 USA
E-mail: mwe@evenstar.net
Web site: http://www.starfishy.com/mwe/
Dist(s): **Baker & Taylor Bks.**

MW International, Belle Lumiere, *(0-9703419; 1-60361)* Div. of Belle Lumiere, Orders Addr.: 3500 Briarwood Ct., Antioch, CA 94509 USA Toll Free: 888-473-1555 ; *Imprints:* Love Buddies (Love Buddies)
E-mail: holmesbookshop@yahoo.com.

MX No Fear, *(0-9766918)* 2251 Faraday Ave., Suite A, Carlsbad, CA 92008 USA Toll Free: 866-787-3691
Web site: http://www.mxnofear.com.

My Darling-Tots Pubns., *(0-9797674)* 8593 Pantherburn Trace, Cordova, TN 38018 USA
E-mail: hdarling30@yahoo.com
Web site: http://www.helendarling.com.

My Grandma & Me Pubs., *(0-9742732)* 1275 E. Parks Rd., Saint Johns, MI 48879 USA
E-mail: info@mygrandmaandme.com
Web site: http://www.mygrandmaandme.com
Dist(s): **Partners Pubs. Group, Inc.**

My Heart Yours Publishing, *(1-932721)* P.O. Box 4975, Wheaton, IL 60187 USA (SAN 255-6774)
E-mail: tanya@myheartyours.com; jeannine@myheartyours.com
Web site: http://www.myheartyours.com.

My Journey Bks., *(0-9766295)* P.O. Box 1169, Olney, MD 20830-1169 USA Toll Free: 877-965-2665
E-mail: KGF@billiesworld.com; KGF@myjourneybooks.com
Web site: http://www.billiesworld.com; http://www.myjourneybooks.com.

My Journey With Jesus *See* **Webster, Jennifer Hope**

My Kids' Bk. Co., *(0-9671080)* Orders Addr.: P.O. Box 486, Westminster, CA 92684-0486 USA Tel 714-901-5003; Edit Addr.: 6225 E. Allison Cir., Orange, CA 92869 USA.

My Little Jessie Pr., *(0-9740743)* Orders Addr.: P.O. Box 529, Bethel, VT 05032 USA (SAN 255-321X) Tel 802-234-9725; Edit Addr.: One Cushing Ave., Bethel, VT 05032 USA
E-mail: jhaywardburnham@aol.com.

My Lyric's Hse., *(0-9761446)* 593 Vanderbilt Ave., No. 135, Brooklyn, NY 11238 USA Tel 347-408-7786
E-mail: itsmeisha@yahoo.com.

My Special Thoughts, *(0-9743019)* P.O. Box 150747, Nashville, TN 37215 USA Fax: 615-297-3138
Web site: http://www.myspecialthoughts.com.

My Student-Athlete, Inc., *(0-9767250)* P.O. Box 15, Redan, GA 30074 USA Tel 770-981-3000
Web site: http://www.morethanvictories.com.

My Stuff Planner, *(0-9712804)* P.O. Box 38, Novi, MI 48375-0038 USA
E-mail: coco01@earthlink.net.

Company

Company

My Sunshine Bks., *(0-9749561)* 1370 Little Brier Creek Rd., Warrenton, GA 30828 USA Toll Free: 800-765-4663.

My World Pr., *(0-9662153)* Orders Addr.: P.O. Box 196, Delta, OH 43515 USA Tel 419-822-9562; Edit Addr.: 514 1/2 Main St., Delta, OH 43515 USA
E-mail: jmaz@powernet.net.

Myers, Jack Ministries, Inc., *(0-9720928)* P.O. Box 158, Orland Park, IL 60462-0158 USA
E-mail: jmm.revival@juno.com
Web site: http://www.jackmyersministries.com
Dist(s): **STL Distribution North America.**

Myers, Joy, *(0-9716456)* P.O. Box 1502, Castle Rock, CO 80104 USA Tel 303-643-8914; Fax: 303-740-7709
E-mail: joybmyers@yahoo.com.

Myers Publishing Co., *(0-9745210; 0-9745929)* Orders Addr.: 207 Shelley Ct., Roseville, CA 95747 USA Tel 916-987-7668 (phone/fax) Do not confuse with Myers Publishing Company in Tarpon Springs, FL
E-mail: myerspubco@myerspublishing.com
Web site: http://www.myerspublishing.com.

Myers, Ralph, *(0-9724047)* 323 River Point Dr., McDonough, GA 30252 USA (SAN 254-9379)
E-mail: ralphmyers@charter.net.

MyHandiwork, *(0-9742555)* 7520 Walker St., Saint Louis Park, MN 55426-4042 USA Fax: 952-935-2840
E-mail: myhandiwork@earthlink.net
Web site: http://www.myhandiwork.com.

MYHRECO, *(0-9753704)* 9033 1/2 Hubbard St., Culver City, CA 90232-2508 USA.

Myles Music Corp., *(0-9634218)* 10313 S. Lockwood Ave., Oak Lawn, IL 60453 USA Tel 708-857-8420
E-mail: mylesmusic@aol.com.

Myoushi Enterprises, *(0-9703537)* Div. of My Perfect Image, 15820 SW 98th Ct, Miami, FL 33157 USA Tel 305-378-5583; Fax: 305-378-5732
E-mail: Myoushi@aol.com.

MyReportLinks.com Bks. *Imprint of* **Enslow Pubs., Inc.**

Myrin Institute, Incorporated *See* **Orion Society, The**

Myrtle Learns, *(1-930694)* Orders Addr.: P.O. Box 3645, Rancho Cucamonga, CA 91729 USA Fax: 909-428-2401 (phone/fax); Edit Addr.: 14034 Fort Ross Ct., Fontana, CA 92336 USA Tel 909-428-2401
E-mail: jaajdeem@aol.com
Web site: http://myrtlelearns.com.

Myrtle-Seal Publishing, *(1-929456)* P.O. Box 2484, Hayden, ID 83835-2193 USA
Web site: http://www.toontakes.com/Products.html.

Mysteries by Vincent, LLC, *(1-932169)* 3207 Mill House Run, Missouri City, TX 77459 USA Tel 281-778-7167; Fax: 281-778-7168; Toll Free: 866-946-3864 1-866-WHODUNIT
E-mail: robert@mysteriesbyvincent.com
Web site: http://www.mysteriesbyvincent.com.

Mystery & Suspense Pr. *Imprint of* **iUniverse, Inc.**

Mystery Writers of America Presents *Imprint of* **iUniverse, Inc.**

Mystic Arts, LLC, *(0-9771700)* P.O. Box 1110, Riverton, UT 84065 USA (SAN 256-8217)
Web site: http://www.reading-with-kids.com.

Mystic Night Bks. *Imprint of* **Pink Stucco Pr.**

Mystic Publishing, *(0-9747454)* 16613 195th Ave., Mystic, IA 52574-8678 USA Do not confuse with Mystic Publishing in North, VA
E-mail: mysticpublish@iowatelecom.net; sharon@freddiethefrogbooks.com.

Mystic Ridge Bks., *(0-9672182; 0-9742845)* Div. of Mystic Ridge Productions, Inc., 6104 Whisper Ridge Dr. NW, Albuquerque, NM 87193-6930 USA (SAN 852-4548); 222 Main St., Sutie 142, Famington, CT 06032 (SAN 853-9898)
E-mail: mysticridge@comcast.net
Web site: http://www.mysticridgebooks.com; http://www.blackjacktoday.com; http://www.baringit.com
Dist(s): **Baker & Taylor Bks.**
Quality Bks., Inc.
Unique Bks., Inc.

Mystic Seaport Museum Stores, Inc., *(0-939510)* 47 Greenmanville Ave., Mystic, CT 06355 USA (SAN 216-6062) Tel 860-572-5357; Fax: 860-572-5321; Toll Free: 800-248-1066
E-mail: rae_anna@mysticseaport.org; wholesale@mysticseaport.org
Web site: http://www.mysticseaport.org.

Mystical Willow Productions, *(0-9763205)* P.O. Box 95, Wheaton, IL 60189 USA
E-mail: mysticalwillow@comcast.net.

Mystique International, Ltd., *(0-9745333)* 2533 N. Carson St., Suite 593, Carson City, NV 89706-0147 USA
E-mail: metamind@eznet.net.

Myth Breakers *See* **Happy About**

Mythic Rain Productions *See* **Mythic Rain Publishing, Inc.**

Mythic Rain Publishing, Inc., *(0-9672982)* P.O. Box 11840, Saint Paul, MN 55111 USA Toll Free: 888-698-7362 (phone/fax)
E-mail: mythicrain@aol.com
Web site: http:///www.mythicrain.com.

Mythopoeic Pr., The, *(1-887726)* Orders Addr.: c/o D & B Russell Books, 129 Kings Hwy., Shreveport, LA 71104 USA Toll Free: 888-215-6944
E-mail: russells@shreve.net
Web site: http://www.mythsoc.org
Dist(s): **Baker & Taylor Bks.**

Mythopoeic Society, The *See* **Mythopoeic Pr., The**

Mythos Bks., LLC, *(0-9659433; 0-9728545; 0-9789911)* 351 Lake Ridge Rd., Poplar Bluff, MO 63901-2177 USA (SAN 253-2735) Tel 573-785-7710 (phone/fax)
E-mail: dwynn@LDD.net
Web site: http://www.mythosbooks.com
Dist(s): **Baker & Taylor Bks.**
Ingram Pub. Services.

MythSeries, *(0-9776472)* P.O. Box 211, Millville, MN 55957 USA (SAN 257-8743) Tel 507-798-2450
E-mail: lisa@mythseries.com
Web site: http://mythseries.com.

Mz. Rosa Notions, *(0-9740267)* P.O. Box 114, Turlock, CA 95380 USA
E-mail: ninarule62@aol.com.

MZW, Ink *See* **MZW Ink**

MZW Ink, *(0-9708711)* Orders Addr.: P.O. Box 484, Hessel, MI 49745-0484 USA Tel 906-484-2708; Edit Addr.: 661 S. Pointe Brulee Rd., Hessel, MI 49745 USA
E-mail: moirazw@cedarville.net
Web site: http://www.cedarville.net/mzwink/
Dist(s): **Partners Bk. Distributing, Inc.**

N A L *Imprint of* **Penguin Group (USA) Inc.**

N A L Hardcover *Imprint of* **Penguin Group (USA) Inc.**

N A L Trade *Imprint of* **Penguin Group (USA) Inc.**

NAPSAC Reproductions, *(0-934426; 1-932747)* Rte. 4, Box 646, Marble Hill, MO 63764 USA (SAN 222-4607) Tel 573-238-4846; Fax: 573-238-2010 ; *Imprints:* Gutenberg-Richter Publications (Gutenberg-Richter)
E-mail: napsac@clas.net.

N&N Publishing Co., Inc., *(0-9606036; 0-935487)* 18 Montgomery St., Middletown, NY 10940 USA (SAN 216-4221) Tel 845-342-1677; Fax: 845-342-6910; Toll Free: 800-664-8398 ; *Imprints:* STAReviews (STAReviews); Big 8 Reviews (Big Eight Rev)
E-mail: info@nandnpublishing.com; sales@nandnpublishing.com
Web site: http://www.nandnpublishing.com; http://www.nn4text.com; http://www.starreview.com; http://www.big8review.com.

NERO International Holding Co., Inc, *(0-9700563)* Orders Addr.: P.O. Box 744, Mahopac, NY 10541-0744 USA Tel 914-628-9497; Edit Addr.: 29 Tulip Rd., Mahopac, NY 10541 USA
E-mail: neroint@aol.com
Web site: http://www.nerolarp.com.

NGOB Assn. Inc., *(0-9674901)* 12241 Tilney Ct., Woodbridge, VA 22192-6611 USA
E-mail: NGOB1@aol.com
Web site: http://NGOB.net.

N His Will Ministries, *(1-929127)* 3040 Lebanon Rd., Nashville, TN 37214 USA Tel 615-902-0471 (phone/fax)
E-mail: inhiswill@email.msn.com.

N2Print *Imprint of* **New Age World Publishing**

N8TIVE, *(0-9769575)* 620 S. 19th St., Philadelphia, PA 19146 USA
Web site: http://www.n8tve.com.

Na Kamalei Koolauloa Early Education Program, *(0-9773495; 0-9760892)* Orders Addr.: P.O. Box 900, Hauula, HI 96717 USA Tel 808-237-8500; Fax: 808-237-8501
E-mail: nkpublishing@hawaii.rr.com; executivedirector@nakamalei.org
Web site: http://www.nakamalei.org.

Nadel Worldwide, Incorporated *See* **MMS Publishing**

Nadir Pubn., *(0-9659592)* 831 NW 18th Pl., Miami, FL 33125 USA Tel 305-642-6926
E-mail: Cjuliocon@aol.com.

Nafziger Collection, Inc., The, *(1-58545)* Orders Addr.: P.O. Box 1522, West Chester, OH 45069-1522 USA Tel 513-777-8734
E-mail: nafziger@fuse.net
Web site: http://www.home.fuse.net/nafziger.

Nags Head Art, Inc., *(0-9616344; 1-878405)* Orders Addr.: P.O. Box 2149, Manteo, NC 27954 USA (SAN 200-9145) Tel 252-441-7480; Fax: 252-475-9893; Toll Free Fax: 800-246-7014; Toll Free: 800-541-2722; Edit Addr.: 7728 Virginia Dare Trail, Manteo, NC 27954 USA (SAN 658-8107)
E-mail: suzannetate@yahoo.com
Web site: http://www.suzannetate.com
Dist(s): **Florida Classics Library**
Mistco, Inc.

NAHSH M'ISTAH Pub., *(0-9665427)* 8614 E. Dahlia Dr., Scottsdale, AZ 85260 USA Tel 480-998-8189
E-mail: nashmista@aol.com.

Naim, Deborah, *(0-9762828)* 20801 Biscayne Blvd., Suite 403, Aventura, FL 33180 USA
E-mail: dnaim@mercadoecologico.com.

Nam Pubs., *(1-930531)* 1500 Evergreen Manor, Apt. 80, Mission, TX 78572 USA Tel 956-584-5590; Fax: 956-519-3012
E-mail: nampub@swbell.net.

Nambennett Publishing, *(0-9742208)* 11748 Fremont Ave. N., Seattle, WA 98133 USA
E-mail: kelly@nambennett.com
Web site: http://www.nambennett.com.

Namuk International, Inc., *(0-933057)* Orders Addr.: Colesville, Silver Spring, MD 20914 USA (SAN 689-7738) Tel 301-622-4744 (phone/fax); Edit Addr.: 1011 Brantford Ave., Silver Spring, MD 20904-2010 USA
E-mail: shaque@howard.edu.

Nancy's Artworks, *(0-9748074)* Orders Addr.: 6185 Faxon Ct., Colorado Spgs, CO 80922-1839 USA
E-mail: sales@nancyweb.com
Web site: http://www.multcamp.com; http://www.nancyweb.com; http://www.seanotes.net.

Nantucket Cobblestones, Ltd., *(0-9653674)* One Saint Matthews Dr., Barrington, NH 03825 USA Tel 603-942-9274.

NAPNAP, *(0-9749769)* 20 Brace Rd., Suite 200, Cherry Hill, NJ 08034-2634 USA Tel 856-857-9700; Fax: 856-857-1600
E-mail: info@napnap.org
Web site: http://www.napnap.org.

Napoleon Publishing/Rendezvous Pr. (CAN) *(0-929141; 1-894917) Dist. by* **AtlasBooks.**

Napue & Tucker Publishing, L.L.C. *See* **NT Publishing, L.L.C.**

Narragansett Graphics, *(0-615)* 641 Arnold Rd., Coventry, RI 02816 USA Tel 401-823-0022; 401-823-9000; Fax: 401-823-0022
E-mail: lsousa@narragansettgraphics.com
Web site: http://www.narragansettgraphics.com.

NASW Pr. *Imprint of* **National Assn. of Social Workers/NASW Pr.**

Nataco Publishing, *(1-891769)* Orders Addr.: P.O. Box 35A, Concord, NH 03302-0035 USA Tel 603-485-6109; Fax: 603-485-7860; Edit Addr.: 6 Sherwood Meadows, Pembroke, NH 03275 USA ; *Imprints:* Education Express (Educ Express)
E-mail: natacopub@aol.com
Web site: http://www.members.aol.com/natacopub.

Natavi Guides, *(0-9719392; 1-932204)* 44 Pine St., West Newton, MA 02465-1425 USA
E-mail: info@nataviguides.com
Web site: http://www.nataviguides.com.

Nate's Tennis, Inc., *(0-9703486)* 660 Wellingborough Ct., Alpharetta, GA 30005 USA Tel 770-326-7784; Fax: 770-263-1730
E-mail: nateindks@hotmail.com
Web site: http://www.natestennis.com
Dist(s): **Hervey's Booklink & Cookbook Warehouse.**

Nathan, Fernand (FRA) *(2-09) Dist. by* **Distribks Inc.**

Nathanael Publishing, *(1-930442)* Orders Addr.: P.O. Box 205, Liverpool, NY 13088-0205 USA Tel 315-457-7551; Edit Addr.: 214 Third St., Liverpool, NY 13088 USA
E-mail: jcoud72159@msn.com
Dist(s): **STL Distribution North America.**

Nathaniel Max Rock, *(0-9749392; 1-59980)* 1418 S. Orange Ave., Monterey Park, CA 91755 USA
Web site: http://rockmath.com.

Nation Bks. *Imprint of* **Basic Bks.**

Nation Builders Network Publishers Group, Incorporated, The *See* **Great House Publishers Grp., Inc., The**

Nation of Imagi, LLC, The, *(0-9672652)* 8155 E. Fairmount Dr. Unit 1935, Denver, CO 80230-6837 USA.

†National Academies Pr., *(0-309)* Orders Addr.: 8700 Spectrum Dr., Landover, MD 20785 USA; Edit Addr.: 500 Fifth St., NW, Washington, DC 20001 USA (SAN 202-8891) Tel 202-334-3313; Fax: 202-334-2451; Toll Free: 888-624-7654 ; *Imprints:* Joseph Henry Press (Joseph Henry Pr)
E-mail: zjones@nas.edu
Web site: http://www.nap.edu
Dist(s): **NetLibrary, Inc.**
ebrary, Inc.; *CIP.*

National Academy Press *See* **National Academies Pr.**

†National Archives & Records Administration, *(0-911333; 1-880875)* Orders Addr.: 700 Pennsylvania Ave., NW, Washington, DC 20408 USA (SAN 210-363X) Tel 301-713-6800; Fax: 310-713-6169; Toll Free: 800-234-8861
E-mail: katherine.coram@nara.gov
Web site: http://www.nara.gov; *CIP.*

National Assn. for Humane & Environmental Education, *(0-941246)* Div. of Humane Society of the U.S., P.O. Box 362, East Haddam, CT 06423 USA (SAN 285-0680) Tel 860-434-8666; Fax: 860-434-9579 ; *Imprints:* Humane Society Press (Humane Soc Pr)
E-mail: nahee@nahee.org
Web site: http://www.nahee.org.

National Assn. for Visually Handicapped, *(0-89064)* 3201 Balboa St., San Francisco, CA 94121 USA (SAN 202-0971) Tel 415-221-3201; Fax: 415-221-8754; 22 W. 21st St., 6th Flr., New York, NY 10010 (SAN 669-1870) Tel 212-889-3141
E-mail: staff@navh.org
Web site: http://www.navh.org.

†National Assn. of Social Workers/NASW Pr., *(0-87101)* Orders Addr.: P.O. Box 431, Annapolis Junction, MD 20701 USA Fax: 301-206-7989; Toll Free: 800-227-3590; Edit Addr.: 750 First St., NE, Suite 700, Washington, DC 20002-4241 USA (SAN 202-893X) Tel 202-408-8600; Fax: 202-336-8312; Toll Free: 800-638-8799 ; *Imprints:* N A S W Press (NASW Pr)
E-mail: press@naswdc.org
Web site: http://www.naswpress.org; *CIP.*

National Assn. of Speed & Explosion, *(0-938074)* P.O. Box 1784, Kill Devil Hills, NC 27948 USA (SAN 215-6148) Tel 252-441-1185; Fax: 252-449-4125
E-mail: naseinc@aol.com.

National Bk. Network, Div. of Rowman & Littlefield Pubs., Inc., Orders Addr.: 15200 NBN Way, Blue Ridge Summit, PA 17214 USA (SAN 630-0065) Tel 717-794-3800; Fax: 717-794-3828; Toll Free Fax: 800-338-4550 (Customer Service); Toll Free: 800-462-6420 (Customer Service); a/o Les Petriw, 67 Mowat Ave., Suite 241, Toronto, ON M6P 3K3 Tel 416-534-1660; Fax: 416-534-3699
E-mail: lpetriw@nbnbooks.com; custserv@nbnbooks.com
Web site: http://www.nbnbooks.com.

National Braille Pr., *(0-939173)* Orders Addr.: 88 St. Stephen St., Boston, MA 02115 USA (SAN 273-0952) Tel 617-266-6160; Fax: 617-437-0456; Toll Free: 800-548-7323
E-mail: orders@nbp.org
Web site: http://www.nbp.org.

National Campaign to Prevent Teen Pregnancy, *(1-58671)* 1776 Massachusetts Ave., NW, Suite 200, Washington, DC 20037 USA Tel 202-478-8500; Fax: 202-478-8588
E-mail: campaign@teenpregnancy.org
Web site: http://www.teenpregnancy.org.

National Catholic Educational Assn., *(1-55833)* 1077 30th St., NW, Suite 100, Washington, DC 20007-3852 USA (SAN 676-8636) Tel 202-337-6232; Fax: 202-333-6706
E-mail: pubs@ncea.org
Web site: http://www.ncea.org.

National Center for Financial Education *See* **Institute of Consumer Financial Education (ICFE)**

National Center For Youth Issues, *(1-931636)* Orders Addr.: P.O. Box 22185, Chattanooga, TN 37422-2185 USA Tel 423-899-5714; Fax: 423-899-4547; Toll Free: 800-477-8277; Edit Addr.: 6101 Preservation Dr., Chattanooga, TN 37416 USA ; *Imprints:* Students Taking a Right Stand, (STARS) (STARS)
E-mail: info@ncyi.org
Web site: http://www.ncyi.org
Dist(s): **MAR*CO Products, Inc.**
Youthlight, Inc.

National Ctr. on Education & The Economy, *(0-9627063; 1-889630; 1-931954; 1-932230; 1-932976; 1-59896)* 555 13th St. NW, Suite 500 W., Washington, DC 20004 USA Fax: 202-783-3672; Toll Free: 888-361-6233 ; *Imprints:* America's Choice (Americas Choice)
Web site: http://www.ncee.org.

National Children's Book Project *See* **Public Square Bks.**

National Council of State Boards of Nursing, Inc., *(0-9720273; 0-9745768; 0-9779066; 0-9796795)* 11 E. Wacker Dr., Suite 2900, Chicago, IL 60601-2921 USA
E-mail: dkappel@ncsbn.org
Web site: http://www.ncsbn.org.

†National Council of Teachers of English, *(0-8141)* Orders Addr.: 1111 W. Kenyon Rd., Urbana, IL 61801-1096 USA (SAN 202-9049) Tel 217-328-3870 Main Switchboard; Fax: 217-328-0977 Editorial Fax; 217-328-9645 Customer Service Fax; Toll Free: 800-369-6283 Main Switchboard Toll Free Tel; 877-369-6283 Customer Service Toll Free Tel
E-mail: kaustin@ncte.org; orders@ncte.org
Web site: http://www.ncte.org*; CIP.*

†National Council of Teachers of Mathematics, *(0-87353)* 1906 Association Dr., Reston, VA 20191-9988 USA (SAN 202-9057) Tel 703-620-9840; Fax: 703-476-2970; Toll Free Fax: 800-220-8483; Toll Free: 800-235-7566 (orders only)
E-mail: info@nctm.org
Web site: http://www.nctm.org*; CIP.*

National Crime Prevention Council, *(0-934513; 1-929888; 1-59686)* 1000 Connecticut Ave., NW, 13th Flr., Washington, DC 20036-1356 USA (SAN 693-8574) Tel 202-466-6272; Fax: 202-296-1356; Toll Free: 800-627-2911 (orders only) Do not confuse with The National Crime Prevention Assn., also in Washington, D.C.
E-mail: kirby@ncpc.org; demenno@ncpc.org; shunt@ncpc.org
Web site: http://www.weprevent.org; http://www.ncpc.org.

National Dance Education Organization, *(1-930798)* 4948 St. Elmo Ave., Suite 301, Bethesda, MD 20814-6013 USA Tel 301-657-2880; Fax: 301-657-2882
E-mail: ndeo@erols.com
Web site: http://www.ndeo.org.

National Deacons Association *See* **Tommy Bks. Pubng.**

†National Education Assn., *(0-8106)* Orders Addr.: P.O. Box 404846, Atlanta, GA 30384-4846 USA (SAN 203-7262) Tel 202-822-7208; Fax: 202-822-7377; Toll Free: 800-229-4200; Edit Addr.: 1201 16th St., NW. Suite 514, Washington, DC 20036 USA Tel 770-280-4080; Fax: 770-280-4134
E-mail: nea-orders@pbd.com
Web site: http://www.nea.org/books*; CIP.*

National Educational Service *See* **Solution Tree**

National Educational Systems, Inc., *(1-893493)* P.O. Box 691450, San Antonio, TX 78269-1450 USA Toll Free: 800-442-2604.

National Family Resiliency Ctr., Inc., *(0-9729415)* 10632 Little Patuxent Pkwy., Suite 121, Columbia, MD 21044 USA Tel 410-740-9553; Fax: 301-596-1677
E-mail: info@divorceabc.com
Web site: http://www.divorceabc.com.

National Federation of the Blind, *(0-9624122; 1-885218)* 1800 Johnson St., Baltimore, MD 21230 USA (SAN 224-2729) Tel 410-659-9314; Fax: 410-685-5653
E-mail: nfb@iamdigex.net
Web site: http://www.nfb.org.

National Film Network LLC, *(0-8026)* Orders Addr.: 4501 Forbes Blvd., Lanham, MD 20706 USA (SAN 630-1878) Tel 301-459-8020 ext 2066
E-mail: info@nationalfilmnetwork.com
Web site: http://www.nationalfilmnetwork.com.

National Foundation for Teaching Entrepreneurship, The, *(1-890859)* Orders Addr.: 120 Wall St., 29th Flr., New York, NY 10005 USA Tel 212-232-3333; Fax: 212-232-2244; Toll Free: 800-367-6383
E-mail: nfte@nfte.com
Web site: http://www.nfte.com.

National Gallery of Australia (AUS) *(0-642) Dist. by* **U of Wash Pr.**

National Gallery of Victoria (AUS) *(0-7241) Dist. by* **Antique Collect.**

National Gardening Assn., Inc., The, *(0-915873)* 1100 Dorset St., South Burlington, VT 05403-8000 USA (SAN 294-0086) Tel 802-863-5251; Fax: 802-864-6889; Toll Free: 800-538-7476
E-mail: valeriek@kidsgardening.com
Web site: http://www.garden.org; http://www.kidsgardening.com; http://www.nationalgardening.com.

National Geographic *Imprint of* **National Geographic Society**

National Geographic Children's Bks. *Imprint of* **National Geographic Society**

†National Geographic Society, *(0-7922; 0-87044; 1-4262; 1-4263)* 1145 17th St., NW, Washington, DC 20036 USA (SAN 202-8956) Tel 202-857-7000; Fax: 301-921-1575; Toll Free: 800-647-5463; 800-548-9797 (TTD users only) ; *Imprints:* National Geographic Children's Books (NGCB); National Geographic (NatlGeo)
E-mail: rgraham@ngs.org
Web site: http://nationalgeographic.com
Dist(s): **Andrews McMeel Publishing**
Follett Media Distribution
Lectorum Pubns., Inc.
Map Link
Rand McNally
Random Hse., Inc.
Simon & Schuster, Inc.
Sony CONNECT, Inc.*; CIP.*

National Honor Roll, LLC, *(0-9714201; 0-9721652; 0-9729406; 1-932654)* 777 Sunrise Hwy. Ste. 300, Lynbrook, NY 11563-2950 USA Toll Free: 800-416-2185
Web site: http://www.nationalhonorroll.org.

National Horseman Publishing Inc., The, *(0-9762854)* 16101 N. 82nd St., Suite 10, Scottsdale, AZ 85260-1830 USA Tel 480-922-5202
Web site: http://www.tnh1865.com.

National Institute for Trauma & Loss in Children, The/TLC, *(1-931310)* Div. of Childrens Home of Detroit, 900 Cook Rd., Grosse Pointe Woods, MI 48236 USA Tel 313-885-0390; Fax: 313-885-1861; Toll Free: 877-306-5256
E-mail: steele@hcinst.org
Web site: http://www.hcinst.org.

National Learning Corp., *(0-8293; 0-8373)* 212 Michael Dr., Syosset, NY 11791 USA (SAN 206-8869) Tel 516-921-8888; Fax: 516-921-8743; Toll Free: 800-645-6337 ; *Imprints:* Passbooks (Passbooks)
E-mail: sales@passbooks.com.

National Maritime Museum (GBR) *(0-905555; 0-948065; 0-9501764) Dist. by* **Casemate Pubs.**

†National Museum of Women in the Arts, *(0-940979)* 1250 New York Ave., NW, Washington, DC 20005 USA (SAN 664-7421) Tel 202-783-5000; Fax: 202-393-3235; Toll Free: 800-222-7270
Web site: http://www.nmwa.org
Dist(s): **Univ. of Washington Pr.***; CIP.*

National Professional Resources, Inc., *(1-887943; 1-934032)* 25 S. Regent St., Port Chester, NY 10573 USA Tel 914-937-8879; Fax: 914-937-9327; Toll Free: 800-453-7461 ; *Imprints:* Dude Publishing (Dude Pubng)
E-mail: ncassone@nprinc.com; ahanson@NPRinc.com
Web site: http://www.NPRinc.com.

National Reading Styles Institute, Inc., *(0-929192; 1-883186; 1-933533)* Orders Addr.: P.O. Box 737, Syosset, NY 11791 USA (SAN 248-8191) Tel 516-921-5500; Fax: 516-921-5591; Toll Free: 800-331-3117; Edit Addr.: 179 Lafayette Dr., Syosset, NY 11791 USA (SAN 248-8205)
E-mail: readingstyle@nrsi.com
Web site: http://www.literacy.org; http://www.nrsi.com.

National Rehabilitation Services *See* **Northern Speech Services**

National Review, Inc., *(0-9627841; 0-9758998)* 215 Lexington Ave., 4th Flr., New York, NY 10016 USA (SAN 226-1685) Tel 212-679-7330; Fax: 212-696-0340
E-mail: jfowler@nationalreview.com
Web site: http://www.nationalreview.com.

National Science Resources Ctr., *(1-933008)* 901 D St. SW, Suite 704B, Washington, DC 20024 USA
E-mail: nsrcinfo@si.edu
Web site: http://www.nsrconline.org
Dist(s): **Carolina Biological Supply Co.**

†National Science Teachers Assn., *(0-87355; 1-933531)* 1840 Wilson Blvd., Arlington, VA 22201 USA (SAN 203-7173) Tel 703-243-7100; Fax: 703-243-7177; Toll Free Fax: 888-433-0526 (orders); Toll Free: 800-277-5300 (orders)
E-mail: pubsales@nsta.org
Web site: http://www.nsta.org*; CIP.*

National Self-Esteem Resources & Development Ctr., *(0-9632276)* 851 Irwin St., Suite 205, San Rafael, CA 94901-3343 USA Tel 415-457-4411; Fax: 415-457-0356.

National Society of Professional Engineers, *(0-915409)* 1420 King St., Alexandria, VA 22314-2715 USA (SAN 225-168X) Tel 703-684-2800; Fax: 703-836-4875; Toll Free: 888-285-6773
E-mail: customer.service@nspe.org
Web site: http://www.nspe.org.

National Speleological Society, Inc., *(0-9615093; 1-879961)* 2813 Cave Ave., Huntsville, AL 35810-4431 USA (SAN 273-8619) Tel 256-852-1300; Fax: 256-851-9241
Web site: http://www.caves.org
Dist(s): **Quality Bks., Inc.**

National Textbook Co. *Imprint of* **McGraw-Hill/Contemporary**

National Textbook Co., *(0-8442)* .

National Training Network, Inc., *(1-57290)* Orders Addr.: P.O. Box 36, Summerfield, NC 27358 USA
Web site: http://www.algebraicthinking.com.

National Writers Pr., The, *(0-88100)* Div. of National Writers Assn., 17011 Lincoln Ave., No. 421, Parker, CO 80134 USA (SAN 240-320X) Tel 720-851-1944; Fax: 303-841-2607
E-mail: natlwriterspress@hotmail.com
Web site: http://www.nationalwriters.com.

National Writing Institute, *(1-888344)* PMB 248, 624 W. University Dr., Denton, TX 76201-1889 USA Tel 940-382-0044; Fax: 940-383-4414; Toll Free Fax: 888-663-7855; Toll Free: 800-688-5375
E-mail: info@writingstrands.com
Web site: http://www.writingstrands.com.

Nations Hope, Inc., The, *(0-9761415)* P.O. Box 691446, Orlando, FL 32869-1446 USA
Web site: http://www.nationshope.org.

Native American Genealogical Research & Publishing Company *See* **NativeStudy.com**

Native American Pubns., *(0-9745867)* Orders Addr.: P.O. Box 9, Dulac, LA 70353-0009 USA Tel 985-223-3857; Edit Addr.: 443 Ashland Dr., Houma, LA 70363-7283 USA
E-mail: ccbilliot@aol.com.

Native Discovery Publishing, *(0-9716000)* P.O. Box 62657, Colorado Springs, CO 80962 USA (SAN 254-203X) Tel 719-282-7747; Fax: 719-282-4113
E-mail: djvanas@earthlink.net
Web site: http://www.nativediscovery.com.

Native Nature, *(0-9726628)* 3310 Bexley Park Rd., Columbus, OH 43213 USA Tel 614-338-0783; Fax: 614-338-0816
E-mail: svpmba@aol.com
Web site: http://www.nativenature.us.

Native Sun Pr., *(0-9746848)* Orders Addr.: P.O. Box 1139, Summerland, CA 93067 USA (SAN 255-6839) Tel 805-969-2234 (phone/fax); Edit Addr.: 2240 Banner Ave., Summerland, CA 93067 USA.

Native Voices *Imprint of* **Book Publishing Co., The**

NativeStudy.com, *(0-9712423)* P.O. Box 908, Hixson, TN 37343 USA Tel 423-421-1901; Fax: 423-875-3895
E-mail: NativeStudy@nativestudy.com; jbowen61@comcast.net
Web site: http://www.nativestudy.com.

Natural Genius Bks., *(0-9765070)* P.O. Box 191088, Sacramento, CA 95819 USA Toll Free: 800-917-9321
E-mail: mjsee3@earthlink.net
Web site: http://www.naturalgeniusbooks.com.

Natural Heritage/Natural History, Inc. (CAN) *(0-920474; 1-896219; 1-897045) Dist. by* **Cardinal.**

Natural High Bks., *(0-9666603)* 5557 W. Oakland Pk. Blvd., Lauderhill, FL 33313 USA Tel 954-748-6459; Fax: 954-321-8513.

Naturally You Can Sing, *(0-9708397)* 3026 South St., East Troy, WI 53120 USA (SAN 255-4712)
E-mail: mary@flowformsamerica.com
Web site: http://www.maturallyyoucansing.com
Dist(s): **SteinerBooks, Inc.**

Nature Sense Pr., *(0-9727675)* 7010 Skyland Dr., Warrenton, VA 20187 USA
E-mail: nmarx@erols.com.

Nature Study Guild, *(0-912550)* Orders Addr.: P.O. Box 10489, Rochester, NY 14610-0489 USA (SAN 203-722X) Tel 585-482-6090; Toll Free: 800-954-2984
E-mail: Naturebooks@worldnet.att.net
Web site: http://www.naturestudy.com
Dist(s): **Common Ground Distributors, Inc.**
Wilderness Pr.

Nature Works Press, *(0-915965)* Orders Addr.: P.O. Box 469, Talent, OR 97540 USA (SAN 293-9738) Tel 541-535-3189; Fax: 541-535-5728
E-mail: irene@natureworkspress.com
Web site: http://www.natureworkspress.com
Dist(s): **Books West**
Partners/West.

Naturegraph Pubs., Inc., *(0-87961; 0-911010)* Box 1047, 3543 Indian Creek Rd., Happy Camp, CA 96039 USA (SAN 202-8999) Tel 530-493-5353; Fax: 530-493-5240; Toll Free: 800-390-5353
E-mail: nature@sisqtel.net
Web site: http://www.naturegraph.com
Dist(s): **American West Bks.**
Gem Guides Bk. Co.
New Leaf Distributing Co., Inc.
Sunbelt Pubns., Inc.

NaturEncyclopedia *Imprint of* **Stemmer Hse. Pubs., Inc.**

Natures Beauty Publishing, *(0-9754701)* P.O. Box 107, Oxford, MI 48371-0107 USA Tel 248-546-0100
E-mail: Ron@Naturesbeautyphotography.com
Web site: http://www.naturesbeautyphotography.com.

Natures Medicine Chest *See* **LM Pubns.**

Nature's Nest Bks., *(1-930130)* 10139 NE Campbell Rd., Fayetteville, AR 72701 USA Fax: 501-443-0025; Toll Free: 888-464-2665
E-mail: naturesnestbooks@aol.com.

Nature's Tools, Inc., *(0-9702494)* 222 Purchase St., Suite 145, Rye, NY 10580 USA Tel 914-967-7768; Fax: 914-967-3125; Toll Free: 888-662-7768
E-mail: mamy555559@aol.com
Web site: http://www.gemsacs.com.

Natures Trail, *(0-9713132)* 10640 Egypt Rd., Weedsport, NY 13166 USA Tel 315-626-2019
E-mail: contact@naturestrail.net
Web site: http://www.naturestrail.net.

†Nautical & Aviation Publishing Co. of America, Inc., The, *(0-933852; 1-877853)* 2055 Middleburg Ln., Mount Pleasant, SC 29464-4433 USA (SAN 213-3431) Tel 843-856-0561; Fax: 843-856-3164
E-mail: nauticalaviationpublishing@att.net
Web site: http://www.nauticalaviation.com*; CIP.*

Nava Pubns., *(0-9723488)* 1792 Saunders Ave., Saint Paul, MN 55116 USA Tel 651-695-9166
E-mail: mike78452@aol.com
Web site: http://www.navapublications.com.

†Naval Institute Pr., *(0-87021; 1-55750; 1-59114)* Orders Addr.: 2062 Generals Hwy., Annapolis, MD 21401 USA (SAN 662-0930) Tel 410-268-6110; Fax: 410-571-1703; Toll Free: 800-233-8764; Edit Addr.: 291 Wood Rd., Beach Hall, Annapolis, MD 21402-5034 USA (SAN 202-9006)
E-mail: psappington@usni.org
Web site: http://www.navalinstitute.org
Dist(s): **Fujii Assocs.***; CIP.*

Navigator Publishing *See* **NavPublishing, LLC**

Navigator Systems, Inc., *(1-58220)* 845 Yale Ln., Highland Park, IL 60035-2331 USA Tel 847-266-7043; Fax: 847-266-7044; Toll Free Fax: 888-757-4539; Toll Free: 800-717-4539 ; *Imprints:* PowerTools for Kids (PowerTools for Kids)
E-mail: navsysptk@aol.com.

NavPress Publishing Group, *(0-89109; 1-57683; 1-60006)* 3820 N. 30th St., Colorado Springs, CO 80904 USA Toll Free Fax: 800-343-3902; Toll Free: 800-366-7788 ; *Imprints:* Th1nk Books (Th1nk Bks)
E-mail: toby.lorenc@navpress.com; eric.helus@navpress.com
Web site: http://www.navpress.com
Dist(s): **CRC Pubns.**

NavPublishing, LLC, *(1-879932)* P.O. Box 1289, Kingston, WA 98346 USA Fax: 360-738-6642; Toll Free: 800-355-8832 Do not confuse with Navigator Publishing in Portland, ME
E-mail: contact@navpublishing.com
Web site: http://www.navpublishing.com
Dist(s): **Baker & Taylor Bks.**
Follett College Stores Corp.
Follett Library Resources
Quality Bks., Inc.

Naxos of America, Inc., *(962-634; 1-930838)* Cambridge House, Suite 7 1260 N. Forest Rd., Williamsville, NY 14221 USA (SAN 253-407X) Tel 716-634-3215; Fax: 716-634-3051
E-mail: inquiries@naxosusa.com
Web site: http://www.naxosaudiobooks.com.

Naynay Bks *See* **Naynay Bks.**

Naynay Bks., *(0-9769589)* 122 Arbor Rd., NW, Minerva, OH 44657 USA
E-mail: naynaybooks@aol.com
Web site: http://www.naynaybooks.com.

Naypree Enterprises, *(0-9786565)* P.O. Box 522, Aurora, CO 80040-0522 USA (SAN 851-237X) Tel 303-343-0818; Fax: 303-343-0780
E-mail: napreeewpu@aol.com.

Nazarene Publishing Hse., *(0-8341)* Orders Addr.: 2923 Troost Ave., Kansas City, MO 64109 USA (SAN 253-0902); Edit Addr.: P.O. Box 419527, Kansas City, MO 64141 USA (SAN 202-9022) Tel 816-931-1900; Fax: 816-531-0923; Toll Free Fax: 800-849-9827; Toll Free: 800-877-0700
E-mail: Darren@nph.com
Web site: http://www.bhillkc.com
Dist(s): **Spring Arbor Distributors, Inc.**

NBI:Necessity Breeds Invention *See* **Necessity Breeds Invention**

NBK Publishing, *(0-9718796)* 4400 Thirty-sixth St., NW, Washington, DC 20008 USA
Web site: http://www.shimmeringsword.com.

NBM Publishing Co., *(0-918348; 1-56163)* Orders Addr.: 40 Exchange Pl., Suite 1308, New York, NY 10005 USA (SAN 210-0835) Tel 212-643-5407; Fax: 212-643-1545; Toll Free: 800-886-1223 ; *Imprints:* Comics Lit (Comics Lit); Amerotica (Amerotica)
E-mail: catalog@nbmpublishing.com
Web site: http://www.nbmpub.com.

N'Deeo Beauty, *(0-9724203; 0-9753811)* Orders Addr.: P.O. Box 460574, Aurora, CO 80046 USA Tel 303-617-4829; Edit Addr.: 20511 E. Union Ave., Aurora, CO 80015 USA
E-mail: info@ndeeobeauty.com
Web site: http://www.ndeeobeauty.com.

Ndegwa, Catherine W., *(0-9742688)* Orders Addr.: P.O. Box 220411, Saint Louis, MO 63122-0411 USA; Edit Addr.: 119 Oakside Ln., Saint Louis, MO 63122-0411 USA
E-mail: catherine@varietystl.com.

NdueCzon Publishing Group, *(0-9755679)* P.O. Box 341825, Tampa, FL 33694 USA Tel 813-269-9351; Fax: 813-968-1941
E-mail: ndueczon@aol.com
Dist(s): **Baker & Taylor Bks.**
Culture Plus Bk. Distributors.

Nea Attiki Pr., *(0-9638051)* c/o Marilyn Rouvelas, 1200 N. Nash St., No. 1126, Arlington, VA 22209 USA Tel 703-528-0088
E-mail: dgpapadop@yahoo.com
Web site: http://www.greektraditions.org.

Neal, Ann-Marie F, *(0-9747734)* P.O. Box 122, Portsmouth, RI 02871-3109 USA
E-mail: clarence@clarencethefrog.com
Web site: http://www.clarencethefrog.com.

Neal Morgan Publishing, *(0-9786117)* 51 Arrowgate Dr., Randolph, NJ 07869 USA Tel 973-598-9601; Fax: 973-927-8722
E-mail: Daleb6@aol.com.

†Neal-Schuman Pubs., Inc., *(0-918212; 1-55570)* 100 William St., Suite 2004, New York, NY 10038 USA (SAN 210-2455) Tel 212-925-8650; Fax: 212-219-8916; Toll Free Fax: 800-584-2414
E-mail: info@neal-schuman.com
Web site: http://www.neal-schuman.com; *CIP.*

Neatly Chiseled Features, *(0-9745967)* N1870 Loramoor Ln., Lake Geneva, WI 53147 USA Tel 262-248-9460; Fax: 262-248-3431
E-mail: mrboffo@mrboffo.com
Web site: http://www.mrboffo.com.

Nebbadoon Pr., *(1-891331)* Div. of Nebbadoon, Inc., Orders Addr.: P.O. Box 333, Etna, NH 03750 USA Tel 603-643-0400; Fax: 603-643-0404; Toll Free: 800-500-9086; Edit Addr.: 23 Old Kings Hwy., Lebanon, NH 03766-2742 USA
E-mail: george@sover.net
Web site: http://www.nebbadoon.com.

Nebe, Charles, *(0-9773091)* Orders Addr.: P.O. Box 631143, Irving, TX 75063-1143 USA
Web site: http://www.boonefiles.com.

Nebeker-Peirce Enterprises *See* **Nebeker's**

Nebeker's, *(0-9720137)* 642 E. 660 N., Orem, UT 84097 USA
E-mail: NebekerJohnRC@MSN.com.

Nebraska Wealth.com, *(0-9746206)* 1803 Stagecoach Rd., Grand Island, NE 68801 USA
Web site: http://www.nebraskawealth.com.

Necessity Breeds Invention, *(0-9670338)* P.O. Box 351058, Los Angeles, CA 90035 USA Tel 323-936-3528
E-mail: orders@privateschooladmissions.com
Web site: http://www.privateschooladmissions.com.

Necro Pubns., *(1-889186)* Orders Addr.: 5139 Maxon Terrace, Sanford, FL 32771 USA Tel 407-443-6494; Fax: 407-551-0216 ; *Imprints:* Little Devil Books (Little Devil Bks)
E-mail: dave@necropublications.com
Web site: http://www.necropublications.com.

Needer, E.T. Publishing, *(1-893757)* Orders Addr.: 9121 E. Tanque Verde, Suite 105, Tucson, AZ 85749-8390 USA Fax: 520-798-1514; Edit Addr.: 13620 E. Lookout Ln., Tucson, AZ 85749-8112 USA Tel 520-760-2742; Fax: 520-760-5883; Toll Free: 877-817-2742
E-mail: ernie@nedder.com
Web site: http://www.nedderpublishing.com
Dist(s): **Theological Bk. Service.**

Ned's Head Productions, *(1-887206)* 307 State St., Apt. B3, Johnstown, PA 15905 USA (SAN 253-8059) Tel 814-255-6646 (phone/fax)
E-mail: drron@charter.net
Dist(s): **APG Sales and Fulfillment.**

Need of the Times Publishers *See* **Westminster Literature Resources, Inc.**

Neely, Judy, *(1-893968)* 54505 NW Scofield Rd., Buxton, OR 97109 USA Tel 503-324-8222; Fax: 503-324-8252
E-mail: jneely@neelyranch.com
Web site: http://www.neelyranch.com.

Neema's Children Literature Assn., Inc., *(0-9740653)* Orders Addr.: P.O. Box 440073, Chicago, IL 60644-1937 USA Tel 773-378-0607; Fax: 773-378-0042; Edit Addr.: 5345 W. Ferdinand, Chicago, IL 60644-1937 USA
E-mail: nclapub@aol.com.

Neff, Lisi A., *(0-9719396)* Hc 60 Box 576., Ruby Valley, NV 89833-9802 USA.

NEHA Training LLC, *(0-944111)* 720 S. Colorado Blvd. Ste. 1000N, Denver, CO 80246-1926 USA
E-mail: support@nehatraining.com
Web site: http://www.nehatraining.com.

Neighborhood Pr. Publishing, *(0-9655340; 1-893108)* 459 Kingsley Ave., Suite H, Orange Park, FL 32073-4827 USA (SAN 253-8091) Tel 904-215-0150; Fax: 904-215-8885; Toll Free: 888-303-7958
E-mail: nppubs3@aol.com
Web site: http://www.members.aol.com/NPPubs/; http://neighborhoodpress.com.

Nelanie Kroupa Bks. *Imprint of* **Farrar, Straus & Giroux**

Nelsbok Publishing, *(0-9763072)* 2551 38th Ave NE Unit 221, Minneapolis, MN 55421-5009 USA
Web site: http://www.nelsbok.com.

Nelson Building Block Bks., *(0-9673943)* Orders Addr.: P.O. Box 23, Lynn Center, IL 61262 USA Tel 309-799-7531; Fax: 309-799-5349; Edit Addr.: 1718 340th St., Lynn Center, IL 61262 USA
E-mail: nlsn@mnic.net.

Nelson Publishing & Marketing, *(1-933916; 0-9785075)* 366 Welch Rd., Northville, MI 48167-1160 USA Tel 248-767-8559 ; *Imprints:* Ferne Press (Ferne Press)
E-mail: marian@nelsonpublishingandmarketing.com; Julayne@nelsonpublishingandmarketing.com
Web site: http://nelsonpublishingandmarketing.com
Dist(s): **Partners Pubs. Group, Inc.**

Nelson, R. E. & Assoc., *(0-9749636)* 1535 SW Plass Ave., Topeka, KS 66604 USA Tel 785-235-3041
Web site: http://www.renelson.com.

Nelson, Roy *See* **Nelson, R. E. & Assoc.**

†Nelson, Thomas Inc., *(0-529; 0-7852; 0-8407; 0-8499; 0-86605; 0-88113; 0-89840; 0-89922; 0-918956; 1-4002; 1-4003; 1-59145; 1-59554; 1-59555; 1-59951; 1-60255)* Orders Addr.: P.O. Box 141000, Nashville, TN 37214-1000 USA (SAN 209-3820) Fax: 615-902-1866; Toll Free: 800-251-4000; Edit Addr.: 501 Nelson Pl., Nashville, TN 37214 USA
E-mail: info@thomasnelsonpublishers.com
Web site: http://www.thomasnelson.com
Dist(s): **Christian Bk. Distributors**
Twentieth Century Christian Bks.; *CIP.*

Nelson Thornes Ltd. (GBR) *(0-17; 0-7487; 0-85950; 1-871402; 1-873732; 1-237) Dist. by* **Intl Spec Bk.**

Nelson Thornes Ltd. (GBR) *(0-17; 0-7487; 0-85950; 1-871402; 1-873732; 1-237) Dist. by* **Trans-Atl Phila.**

NEMESIS Enterprises, *(0-9713230)* P.O. Box 8292, North Brattleboro, VT 05304-8292 USA Toll Free: 877-636-8646
E-mail: nemesis@gophergo.com
Web site: http://www.gophergo.com.

Nemsi Bks., *(0-9718164; 0-9766400; 0-9794855)* Div. of Morphtek.com, Inc., P.O. Box 191, Pierpont, SD 57468-0191 USA; 307 3rd St., Pierpont, SD 57468
Web site: http://www.nemsi-books.net.

Neon Rose Productions *Imprint of* **Smart Alternatives, Inc.**

Nesak International, *(1-890095)* 6772 Casa Grande Way, Delray Beach, FL 33446-2347 USA
E-mail: nesak@ix.netcom.com
Web site: http://www.nesak.com.

NESFA Pr. *Imprint of* **New England Science Fiction Assn., Inc.**

Neshee Pubn., *(0-9747017; 0-9770907; 0-9785794)* P.O. Box 48028, Philadelphia, PA 19144 USA
E-mail: info@nesheepublicaiton.com
Web site: http://www.nesheepublication.com.

Neshui Publishing, Inc., *(0-9652528; 1-931190)* 3420b Cherokee St., Saint Louis, MO 63118-2702 USA
E-mail: neshui62@hotmail.com
Web site: http://www.neshui.com
Dist(s): **Baker & Taylor Bks.**
Booksource, The
Raven West Coast Distribution.

Net Works Publishing, *(0-9711818)* Div. of E-Wally, Inc., 15699 NW 12th Rd., Pembroke Pines, FL 33028 USA (SAN 253-9314) Tel 954-439-6409
E-mail: wendy_schulz@msn.com; invteam@bellsouth.net
Web site: http://www.e-wally.com.

NetClinger, *(0-9760308)* P.O. Box 38144, Houston, TX 77238-8144 USA
Web site: http://www.netclinger.com.

Netcomics, *(1-60009)* P.O. Box 16484, Jersey City, NJ 07306 USA
Dist(s): **Ingram Pub. Services.**

Netherfield Creations, Inc., *(0-9671255)* 19 Rowlands Rd., Flemington, NJ 08822 USA Tel 908-231-0484; Fax: 908-704-1112
E-mail: limezink@aol.com.

Nethope Publishing, *(0-9677054)* P.O. Box 23, Rocklin, CA 95677 USA Tel 916-300-9939; Fax: 781-240-1258
E-mail: nethope@nethope.com
Web site: http://www.nethope.com.

NetNia Publishing Co., *(1-884163)* 7311 Caillet St., Dallas, TX 75209 USA
E-mail: publishing@netnia.com
Web site: http://www.howtogrowdreadlocks.com; http://www.netnia.com; http://www.africanamericanchildrenplays.com
Dist(s): **Lightning Source, Inc.**

netpoets.com, *(0-9715646)* P.O. Box 392, Colon, MI 49040-0392 USA
E-mail: books@netpoets.com
Web site: http://www.netpoets.com/.

NETroplex Books *See* **Yankee Cowboy**

Network CPU Learning Technologies, *(1-932257)* 172 Fifth Ave., Suite 37, Brooklyn, NY 11217-3504 USA (SAN 254-9298)
E-mail: roxceyluv@yahoo.com.

NETWORK Inc., The, *(1-878234)* Div. of NETWORK, Inc., 136 Fenno Dr., Rowley, MA 01969-1004 USA Tel 978-948-7764; Fax: 978-948-7836; Toll Free: 800-877-5400
E-mail: info@thenetworkinc.org
Web site: http://www.thenetworkinc.org.

Network 3000 Publishing, *(0-9635085; 0-9709321; 1-934266)* Orders Addr.: 3432 Denmark, No. 108, Eagan, MN 55123 USA Tel 612-616-0732; Fax: 651-365-0524; Toll Free: 800-398-4642
E-mail: khogan1652@aol.com; meta@ix.netcom.com
Web site: http://www.kevinhogan.com; http://www.network3000publishing.com
Dist(s): **Baker & Taylor Bks.**
Ingram Pub. Services.

Neuburger Publishing, *(0-9762419)* Orders Addr.: P.O. Box 3928, Taulatin, OR 97062-3928 USA Tel 503-925-0400; Edit Addr.: 24386 SW Baker Rd., Sherwood, OR 97140 USA
Web site: http://www.takethefearoutofmath.com.

Neugard, S.L., *(0-615)* 141 Tabby Creek Cir., Summerville, SC 29483 USA Tel 843-821-1120
E-mail: slneugard@yahoo.com
Dist(s): **Lulu.com.**

Neumann Pr., The, *(0-911845; 1-930873)* 21892 Cty. 11, Long Prairie, MN 56347 USA (SAN 264-2425) Tel 320-732-6358; Fax: 320-732-3858; Toll Free: 800-746-2521
E-mail: sales@neumannpress.com
Web site: http://www.neumannpress.com.

Neva's Arts & Crafts, *(0-9721303)* 5625 N. Quincy, Kansas City, MO 64119 USA.

Never Stop Reading Never Stop Learning, *(0-9741750)* 3221 S. Indiana St., Lakewood, CO 80228 USA Tel 303-829-8699
E-mail: neverstopreading@aol.com
Web site: http://www.jdmcdoil.com.

New Age World Pr. *Imprint of* **New Age World Publishing**

New Age World Publishing, *(1-59405)* 4071 San Pablo Dam Rd. # 141, El Sobrante, CA 94803-2903 USA Toll Free Fax: 888-739-6129; Toll Free: 877-411-8744 ; *Imprints:* New Age World Press (New Age World Pr); N2Print (N2Print)
E-mail: NAWP@comcast.net
Web site: http://www.nawpublishing.com.

New Amsterdam Publishing, Incorporated *See* **Intercontinental Publishing, Inc.**

New & Living Way Publishing Co., *(0-910003)* P.O. Box 830384, Tuskegee, AL 36083-0384 USA (SAN 241-2314) Tel 334-727-5372
E-mail: nlwpc@bellsouth.net; clgpgt@bellsouth.net
Web site: http://www.clgpgt.org/NLW/nlw1.html.

New & Living Way Publishing House *See* **New & Living Way Publishing Co.**

New Art & Vision, LLC, *(0-9742322)* 1360 E. 300 N., Layton, UT 84040 USA Tel 801-543-3383
E-mail: bnybo@elmojackson.com
Web site: http://www.elmojackson.com.

New Atlantean Pr., *(1-881217)* Orders Addr.: P.O. Box 9638, Santa Fe, NM 87504 USA (SAN 297-617X) Tel 505-983-1856 (phone/fax); Edit Addr.: 1 Camino Delilah, Santa Fe, NM 87506 USA
E-mail: global@thinktwice.com
Dist(s): **Baker & Taylor Bks.**
Midpoint Trade Bks., Inc.
New Leaf Distributing Co., Inc.
Nutri-Bks. Corp.

New Bee-ginnings, *(0-9676383)* 2722 Village Pkwy., San Antonio, TX 78251 USA.

New Beginnings Publishing, *(0-9705862; 0-9788278)* Subs. of Morrill Corporation, 3217 N. Mason Ave., Tacoma, WA 98407 USA Tel 253-383-5757; Toll Free: 888-663-5757 ; *Imprints:* Transitions, Incorporated (Transitions WA) Do not confuse with New Beginnings Publishing in Crosby, TX
E-mail: delmorrill@hypnocenter.com.

New Birth Publishing, *(0-9755489)* 1900 Preston Rd., No. 267, PMB 264, Plano, TX 75093 USA
Web site: http://www.newbirthpublishing.com.

New Books Publishing, *(0-9679861)* P.O. Box 260572, Boston, MA 02126 USA Tel 617-296-5242; Fax: 617-296-6786; Toll Free: 877-902-2775
E-mail: khinds6363@aol.com.

New Canaan Publishing Co. LLC, *(1-889658)* 2384 N. Hwy. 341, Rossville, GA 30741 USA Tel 203-966-3408; Toll Free: 800-705-5698
E-mail: djm@newcanaanpublishing.com
Web site: http://www.newcanaanpublishing.com
Dist(s): **STL Distribution North America.**

New Castle Bks., *(0-9674484)* P.O. Box 5193, Winston-Salem, NC 27103 USA Tel 336-760-3529.

New Castle Publishing Co., *(0-9740195)* 512 Wadsworth Dr., Richmond, VA 23236 USA
E-mail: newcastlepubl@aol.com.

New Century Pr., *(1-890035)* Orders Addr.: 1055 Bay Blvd., Suite C, Chula Vista, CA 91911-1628 USA Tel 619-476-7400; Fax: 619-476-7474; Toll Free: 800-519-2465 (orders) Do not confuse with companies with the same or similar name in Bermuda Dunes CA, New York NY
E-mail: sales@newcenturypress.com; authorservices@newcenturypress.com
Web site: http://www.newcenturypress.com.

†New City Pr., *(0-911782; 1-56548)* Div. of Focolare Movement, 202 Cardinal Rd., Hyde Park, NY 12538-2903 USA (SAN 203-7335) Tel 845-229-0335; Fax: 845-229-0351; Toll Free: 800-462-5980 (orders only) Do not confuse with New City Press in Philadelphia, PA
E-mail: info@newcitypress.com
Web site: http://www.newcitypress.com
Dist(s): **STL Distribution North America**; *CIP.*

New Classics Pr., *(0-9755704)* 2400 Ridgecroft SE, Grand Rapids, MI 49546 USA.

New Concepts Publishing, *(1-891020; 1-58608; 1-60394)* 5202 Humphreys Rd., Lake Park, GA 31636 USA Tel 229-257-0367; Fax: 229-219-1097
E-mail: newconcepts@newconceptspublishing.com; service@newconceptspublishing.com
Web site: http://www.newconceptspublishing.com
Dist(s): **Baker & Taylor Bks.**

New Concord Pr. *Imprint of* **Equine Graphics Publishing Group**

New Dawn Publishing, *(0-9721948)* P.O. Box 11151, Portland, ME 04104 USA Tel 207-839-8809 Do not confuse with companies with the same or similar name in Elk Mills, MD, Dexter, NY
Web site: http://www.mynewdawn.com.

New Dawn Publishing Co., *(0-9621408)* P.O. Box 2601, Pasadena, CA 91102-2601 USA (SAN 251-2068) Tel 626-459-9079 Do not confuse with companies with the same or similar name in Elk Mills, MD, Dexter, NY, Saint Paul, MN, Gorham, ME.

New Day Enterprises, Ltd., *(0-9675011)* 81 Park Ave., Arlington, MA 02476-5962 USA Tel 781-646-2929; Fax: 781-646-9292
E-mail: newday007@peoplepc.com.

New Day Pr., *(0-913678)* c/o Karamu Hse., 2355 E. 89th St., Cleveland, OH 44106 USA (SAN 279-2664) Tel 216-795-7070 ext 228; Fax: 216-795-7073 Do not confuse wtih New Day Press in Southlake, TX
E-mail: editor@newdaypress.com.

New Day Publishing, *(0-9743259)* P.O. Box 24233, Winston-Salem, NC 27114 USA Do not confuse with companies with the same or similar name in Phoenis, AZ, North Miami, FL, Greensboro, NC
Web site: http://www.Cocktailbooks.com
Dist(s): **Independent Pubs. Group.**

New Day Publishing, Inc., *(0-9789056; 0-9798247)* 26 Bluff Ridge Ct., Greensboro, NC 27455 USA Tel 336-545-1545; Fax: 336-545-1640; Toll Free: 866-763-2977 Do not confuse with companies with the same or similar name in Winston-Salem, NC, Phoenix, AZ, North Miami, FL
E-mail: ateich@newdaypublishing.net
Web site: http://www.newdaypublishing.net.

New Dimensions in Education *See* **Letter People, The**

†New Directions Publishing Corp., *(0-8112)* 80 Eighth Ave., New York, NY 10011 USA (SAN 202-9081) Tel 212-255-0230; Fax: 212-255-0231; Toll Free: 800-233-4830
E-mail: nd@ndbooks.com
Web site: http://www.ndpublishing.com
Dist(s): **Continental Bk. Co., Inc.**
Norton, W. W. & Co., Inc.
SPD-Small Pr. Distribution; *CIP.*

†New England Pr., Inc., The, *(0-933050; 1-881535)* Orders Addr.: P.O. Box 575, Shelburne, VT 05482 USA (SAN 213-6376) Tel 802-863-2520; Fax: 802-863-1510
E-mail: nep@together.net
Web site: http://www.nepress.com; *CIP.*

New England Science Fiction Assn., Inc., *(0-915368; 1-886778)* P.O. Box 809, Framingham, MA 01701-0809 USA (SAN 223-8187) Tel 617-588-9350; Fax: 617-776-3243 ; *Imprints:* N E S F A Press (NESFA Pr)
E-mail: press@nesfa.org
Web site: http://www.nesfa.org/press/.

New Family Pr., *(0-9742008)*
Dist(s): **Book Wholesalers, Inc.**

New Forums Pr., *(0-913507; 1-58107)* Orders Addr.: P.O. Box 876, Stillwater, OK 74076 USA (SAN 285-8673) Tel 405-372-6158; Fax: 405-377-2237; Toll Free: 800-606-3766; Edit Addr.: 1018 S. Lewis, Stillwater, OK 74074 USA
E-mail: dougdollar@provalue.net; dougdollar@newforums.com
Web site: http://www.newforums.com
Dist(s): **Baker & Taylor Bks.**
Booksource, The.

New Future Publishing, *(0-9654507)* 2222 Fuller Ct., Suite 505A, Ann Arbor, MI 48105 USA Tel 313-668-7897; Fax: 313-996-1427.

New Global Publishing, *(0-9762292; 0-9770043; 0-9785609; 0-9791748)* 1209 K St. SW, Cedar Rapids, IA 52404 USA Tel 319-364-0194
Web site: http://www.newglobalpublishing.com.

New Harbinger Pubns., *(0-934986; 1-57224; 1-879237)* Orders Addr.: 5674 Shattuck Ave., Oakland, CA 94609 USA (SAN 205-0587) Tel 510-652-2002; 510-652-0215; Fax: 510-652-5472; Toll Free: 800-652-1613
E-mail: customerservice@newharbinger.com
Web site: http://www.newharbinger.com.

New Holland Pubs., Ltd. (GBR) *(1-85368; 1-85974; 1-84330; 1-84636; 1-84537) Dist. by* **Sterling.**

New Holland Pubs. Pty, Ltd. (AUS) *(1-86436; 1-875580; 1-876334; 1-877069; 1-74110; 1-921024; 1-921073; 1-921072) Dist. by* **Natl Bk Netwk.**

New Hope *See* **Woman's Missionary Union**

New Hope Pr., *(0-9634826; 0-9724101)* 125 22nd Ave., Apalachicola, FL 32320-1549 USA Do not confuse with companies with the same name in New Hope, PA, La Jolla, CA, Littleton, CO
E-mail: cronkite@gtcom.net.

New Hope Pubns., *(1-892875)* Div. of Saint Martin de Porres Lay Dominican Community, 3050 Gap Knob Rd., New Hope, KY 40052 USA Tel 270-325-3061; Fax: 270-325-3091; Toll Free: 800-352-7153 Do not confuse with companies with the same or similar names in Durham, NC, Columbus, MS, Lafayette, LA
E-mail: roi@scrtc.com; djmusk@earthlink.net
Web site: http://www. member.aol.com/newhopelc.

New Hope Pubns., LLC, *(0-9726129)* 4211 S. Alston Ave., Durham, NC 27713 USA Tel 919-405-2326; Fax: 919-544-2796 Do not confuse with companies with the same or similar names in New Hope, KY, Columbus, MS, Lafayette, LA
E-mail: TDEP02@aol.com
Web site: http://www.thomasday.net.

New Hope Pubs., *(1-56309)* Orders Addr.: P.O. Box 830010, Birmingham, AL 35283 USA Tel 205-991-8100; Fax: 205-995-4825; Toll Free: 800-968-7301 Do not confuse with New Hope Publishers in New Hope, MN
E-mail: info@newhopepublishers.com
Web site: http://www.newhopepublishers.com
Dist(s): **B&H Publishing Grp.**

New Horizon Pr. Pubs., Inc., *(0-88282)* Orders Addr.: P.O. Box 669, Far Hills, NJ 07931 USA (SAN 677-119X) Tel 908-604-6311; Fax: 908-604-6330; Toll Free: 800-533-7978 (orders only) ; *Imprints:* Small Horizons (Small Horizons)
E-mail: nhp@newhorizonpressbooks.com
Web site: http://www.newhorizonpressbooks.com
Dist(s): **Kensington Publishing Corp.**
Penguin Group (USA) Inc.
Perseus Distribution.

New Horizons Book Publishing Company *See* **World Citizens**

New Horizons Christian Ctr., *(0-9728532)* 16 Foxbriar Rd., Hilton Head, SC 29926 USA.

New Horizons Press *See* **Apex Pr., The**

New Horizons Pr., *(0-9667770)* P.O. Box 2161, Leesburg, VA 20177-7545 USA Fax: 703-777-2695 Do not confuse with companies with the same name in Marietta, GA, Lake Mary, FL, Chico, CA, Ferrisburgh, VT., Orlando, FL.

New Horizons Publishing Co., *(1-884687)* Orders Addr.: P.O. Box 226, New Wilmington, PA 16142 USA Tel 724-946-3604; Fax: 412-946-2097; Toll Free: 800-995-7746; Edit Addr.: 129 W. Neshannock Ave., New Wilmington, PA 16142 USA Tel 412-946-3501 Do not confuse with companies with the same or simliar names in Santa Barbara, CA, Romance, AR, Oklahoma City, OK
Dist(s): **Princeler Publishing, Don C.**

New Horizons Software, Inc., *(0-9669293)* 660 Suffolk St., Suite 200, Lowell, MA 01854 USA Tel 978-934-9193; Fax: 978-934-9176
E-mail: info@nhsiusa.com
Web site: http://www.nhsiusa.com.

New Issues Poetry & Prose, Western Michigan Univ., *(0-932826; 1-930974)* 1903 West Michigan Ave. Western Michigan University, Kalamazoo, MI 49008 USA (SAN 276-6299) Tel 269-387-2592; 269-387-8185; Fax: 269-387-2562
E-mail: new-issues@wmich.edu
Web site: http://www.wmich.edu/newissues
Dist(s): **Austin & Company, Inc.**
Partners Pubs. Group, Inc.
SPD-Small Pr. Distribution.

New Kids Media *Imprint of* **Baker Bks.**

New Leaf Bks. *Imprint of* **WigWam Publishing Co.**

New Leaf Communications, *(0-9726611)* 70 W. Tietan, Walla Walla, WA 99362 USA Tel 509-529-0188 Do not confuse with New Leaf communications in San Jose, CA.

New Leaf Distributing Co., Inc., *(0-9627209)* Div. of Al-Wali Corp., 401 Thornton Rd., Lithia Springs, GA 30122-1557 USA (SAN 169-1449) Tel 770-948-7845; Fax: 770-944-2313; Toll Free Fax: 800-326-1066; Toll Free: 800-326-2665
E-mail: santoshk@msn.com; alimt@bellsouth.net
Web site: http://www.NewLeaf-dist.com.

New Leaf Education, Inc. *See* **New Leaf Educ., Inc.**

New Leaf Educ., Inc., *(0-9722452; 0-9764217; 1-933655)* Orders Addr.: P.O. Box 16230, Baltimore, MD 21210 USA Tel 410-467-7835; Fax: 410-951-0419; Edit Addr.: 2050 Rockrose Ave., Baltimore, MD 21211 USA
E-mail: contactus@newleafeducation.com
Web site: http://www.newleafeducation.com.

New Leaf Pr. *Imprint of* **New Leaf Pr., Inc.**

New Leaf Pr., Inc., *(0-89221)* P.O. Box 726, Green Forest, AR 72638 USA (SAN 207-9518) Tel 870-438-5288; Fax: 870-438-5120 Toll Free: 800-643-9535 ; *Imprints:* New Leaf Press (NLP) Do not confuse with companies with the same or similar name in Los Angeles, CA
E-mail: nlp@newleafpress.net
Web site: http://www.newleafpress.net
Dist(s): **Spring Arbor Distributors, Inc.**

New Learning Publishing, *(0-9793576)* 123 Wolcott Ave., Rochester, NY 14606 USA (SAN 853-2273) Tel 585-426-9454
E-mail: callen10@rochester.rr.com.

New Library Press.Net, *(0-7950)* P.O. Box 130, Murrieta, CA 92564 USA Toll Free Fax: 888-265-3550; Toll Free: 888-265-3547
E-mail: New.Library@Verizon.Net.

New Life Gospel Productions, Inc., *(0-9675738)* 610 N.W. 186 St., Miami, FL 33169 USA Tel 305-651-9955; Fax: 305-651-9931.

New Life Pubns., *(0-935379)* 2730 Lapey, Rockford, IL 61109 USA (SAN 696-3234) Tel 815-397-4563 Do not confused with companies with the same name in Sedona, AZ, Mount Dora, FL.

New Life Two Thousand Publications *See* **NewLife Pubns.**

New Light Leadership Coalition, Inc., *(0-9716696)* Orders Addr.: 28 Allegheny Ave. Suite 503, Baltimore, MD 21204 USA Tel 410-494-1588; Fax: 410-494-1517; Toll Free: 866-655-2462
E-mail: info@nllc.org
Web site: http://www.nllc.org.

New Line Bks., *(1-57717; 1-880908; 1-59764)* 245 Eighth Ave., No. 180, New York, NY 10011-1607 USA Toll Free Fax: 888-719-7723; Toll Free: 888-719-7722
E-mail: info@newlinebooks.com
Web site: http://www.newlinebooks.com.

New Media *See* **Random House Foreign Language Publishing**

New Media German Language *Imprint of* **Random House Foreign Language Publishing**

New Mill Publishing, *(0-9711335)* P.O. Box 101, Meadow Vista, CA 95722 USA.

New Millenium Pr., The, *(0-9706728)* 311 E. Seventh St., Tama, IA 52339 USA Tel 515-484-2313 Do not confuse with New Millennium Press in Augusta, GA.

New Millennium Bks., *(0-9672333)* 1320 NW Frazier Ct., Portland, OR 97229 USA Tel 503-332-8537 Do not confuse with New Millennium Bks., Petersburg, VA
E-mail: gem@mathabane.com
Web site: http://www.mathabane.com.

New Millenium Bks., *(0-9674014)* P.O. Box 171, Wadsworth, OH 44281-0171 USA Tel 330-336-4790; Fax: 330-334-1784 Do not confuse with New Millenium Bks., Petersburg, VA
E-mail: jneumann@neo.rr.com.

New Millennium Entertainment, *(1-893224; 1-931056; 1-59007)* 15233 Ventura Blvd., Sherman Oaks, CA 91403-2201 USA ; *Imprints:* New Millennium Press (New Millenn Pr).

New Millennium Pr. *Imprint of* **New Millennium Entertainment**

New Missions, Inc., *(0-9653234)* 8054 Presidents Dr., Orlando, FL 32809 USA Tel 407-240-4058; Fax: 407-240-1962
Web site: http://www.newmissions.org.

New Monic Bks., *(0-9652422)* Orders Addr.: P.O. Box 511314, Punta Gorda, FL 33951-1314 USA Toll Free: 800-741-1295; Edit Addr.: P.O. Box 511314, Punta Gorda, FL 33951 USA
E-mail: bburchers@earthlink.net
Dist(s): **Baker & Taylor Bks.**

New Moon Publishing, *(0-9638202)* 9900 Rathburn Ave., Northridge, CA 91325 USA Tel 818-576-1455 Do not confuse with companies with the same name in San Antonio, TX, Duluth, MN, Ormond Beach, FL
E-mail: melaniesilos@hotmail.com.

New Mouth from the Dirty South, *(0-9666469)* P.O. Box 19742, New Orleans, LA 70179-0742 USA Tel 504-948-2228
E-mail: books@newmouthfromthedirtysouth.com
Web site: http://www.newmouthfromthedirtysouth.com
Dist(s): **Biblio Distribution**
SPD-Small Pr. Distribution.

New Orleans Stories, *(0-9758996)* 7301 Burnet Rd., Suite 102 PMB 107, Austin, TX 78757 USA Tel 512-923-5015
E-mail: sean@neworleansstories.com
Web site: http://neworleansstories.com
Dist(s): **Forest Sales & Distributing Co.**
Greenleaf Book Group Pr.

New Page Bks. *Imprint of* **Career Pr., Inc.**

New Paradigm Bks., *(1-892138)* 22491 Vistawood Way, Boca Raton, FL 33428 USA Tel 561-482-5971; Fax: 561-852-8322; Toll Free: 800-808-5179
E-mail: darbyc@earthlink.net
Web site: http://www.newpara.com
Dist(s): **Baker & Taylor Bks.**
New Leaf Distributing Co., Inc.

New Pathways Publishers, *(1-890002)* 40 Coopers Beach Rd., Owls Head, ME 04854 USA Tel 207-596-5794; Fax: 207-594-1757; Toll Free: 800-373-0960
E-mail: js@ReConnectingWorks.com.

New Philosopher Pr., *(0-945741)* Orders Addr.: P.O. Box 162, Unionville, IN 47468 USA; Edit Addr.: 5156 N. Brummetts Creek Rd., Bloomington, IN 47408 USA (SAN 247-7130) Tel 812-333-4288; Fax: 815-550-0392
E-mail: newphilosopherpress@home.com; joeweisman@home.com; franweisman@home.com; jamespbridges@home.com
Web site: http://www.newphilosopherpress.bigstep.com.

New Pr., The, *(1-56584; 1-59558)* 38 Greene St., 4th Flr., New York, NY 10013 USA Tel 212 629 8802; Fax: 212 629 8617; Toll Free Fax: 800 458 6515; Toll Free: 800 233 4830
E-mail: newpress@thenewpress.com
Web site: http://www.thenewpress.com
Dist(s): **Norton, W. W. & Co., Inc.**

New Readers Pr., *(0-88336; 1-56420)* Div. of Laubach Literacy International, Orders Addr.: 1320 Jamesville Ave., Syracuse, NY 13210 USA (SAN 202-1064) Tel: 315-422-6369; Toll Free: 800-448-8878
E-mail: nrp@proliteracy.org
Web site: http://www.newreaderspress.com
Dist(s): **CRC Pubns.**

†New Riders Publishing, *(0-7357; 0-934035; 1-56205; 1-57870)* Div. of Pearson Technology Group, 1249 8th St., Berkeley, CA 94710-1413 USA Toll Free: 800-428-5331 (orders)
Web site: http://www.newriders.com
Dist(s): **Alpha Bks.**
Pearson Technology Group; *CIP.*

Company

Company

New River Pr., *(1-891724)* 645 Fairmount St., Woonsocket, RI 02895-4012 USA (SAN 255-5344) Tel 401-765-4948; Fax: 401-356-0913; Toll Free: 800-244-1257 Do not confuse with New River Pr., Boone, NC
E-mail: books@newriverpress.com
Web site: http://www.newriverpress.com; http://www.newenglandghosts.com; http://www.turninghome.net; http://www.genialhistory.com; http://www.footstepsintheattic.com; http://www.41signsofhope.com; http://www.10famousmen.net
Dist(s): **Baker & Taylor Bks.**

New Song Publishing Co., *(0-942925)* Div. of Al Menconi Ministries, Orders Addr.: P.O. Box 131147, Carlsbad, CA 92013 USA (SAN 667-8475) Tel 760-591-4696; Fax: 760-591-4698; Toll Free: 800-786-8742; Edit Addr.: 1635 S. Rancho Santa Fe Rd., Suite 105, San Marcos, CA 92069 USA (SAN 667-8483)
E-mail: adina@almenconi.com; al@almenconi.com
Web site: http://www.AlMenconi.com.

New Spectrum Incorporated *See* **Bay Otter Pr.**

New Star Bks., Ltd. (CAN) *(0-919573; 0-919888; 0-921586; 1-55420) Dist. by* **SPD-Small Pr Dist.**

New Start Publishing, LLC, *(0-9671807)* Orders Addr.: P.O. Box 256, Plymouth, CT 06782 USA Tel 860-283-9324; Edit Addr.: 268 Lake Plymouth Blvd., Plymouth, CT 06782 USA.

New Sweden Pr., *(0-9702646)* 10509 Schmidt Ln., Manor, TX 78653 USA Fax: 512-278-1251 Do not confuse with New Sweden Pr., South Saint Paul, MN
E-mail: shrout@mail.utexas.edu.

New Thought Journal Press *See* **Momentary Pleasures Pr.**

New Traditions Pr., Inc., *(0-9662813)* Orders Addr.: P.O. Box 1567, New York, NY 10028 USA Tel 212-535-2955; Fax: 212-585-1687
E-mail: nycvoice@pipeline.com.

New Tribes Mission, Inc., *(1-890040)* 1000 E. First St., Sanford, FL 32771-1487 USA Tel 407-323-3430; Fax: 407-330-0376; Toll Free: 800-321-5375
E-mail: ntm@ntm.org
Web site: http://www.ntm.org.

New Underground Railroad Publishing Co., The, *(0-9702762)* Orders Addr.: 8004 NW 154th St., No. 376, Miami Lakes, FL 33016 USA Toll Free: 866-201-4292; Edit Addr.: 14411 Commerce Way, Suite 320, Miami Lakes, FL 33016 USA
E-mail: Finance@netside.net
Web site: http://www.newundergroundrailroad.com.

New Underground Railroad, The *See* **New Underground Railroad Publishing Co., The**

†New Victoria Pubs., Inc., *(0-934678; 1-892281)* Orders Addr.: P.O. Box 13173, Chicago, IL 60613-0173 USA (SAN 212-1204)
E-mail: newvicpub@aol.com
Web site: http://www.newvictoria.com*; CIP.*

New Vision Ent, *(0-9778310)* Orders Addr.: 30 Estuary Trail, Clearwater, FL 33759 USA
E-mail: jim@newvisionentertainment.us.

New Voices Publishing Co., *(1-931642)* Div. of KidsTerrain, Inc., P.O. Box 560, Wilmington, MA 01887 USA (SAN 253-9047) Tel 978-658-2131; Fax: 978-988-8833 Do not confuse with companies with the same or similar names in Sarasota, FL, Flushing, NY
E-mail: egilmartin@kidsterrain.com
Web site: http://www.newvoicespublishing.com; http://www.kidsterrain.com.

New Wave Bks. & CD, *(0-9727753; 0-9741493)* Orders Addr.: 7850 S. Normandie Ave., Apt. 69, Los Angeles, CA 90044 USA; Edit Addr.: 11050 Bryant St., No. 292, Yuacaipa, CA 92399 USA.

New Wave Internet Services Incorporated *See* **Healthy Life Pr., Inc.**

New Wave Pubns., *(0-9749674; 0-9786660; 0-9800452)* 1419 New York Ave., Rm 3A, New York, NY 11210-1221 USA Do not confuse with New Wave Publications in Lincoln, NE.

†New Win Publishing, *(0-8329; 0-87691)* 9682 Telstar Ave., Suite 110, El Monte, CA 91731 USA (SAN 217-1201) Tel 626-448-4422 ; *Imprints:* Z Health Books (Z Hlth Bks)
E-mail: info@AcademicLearningCompany.com
Web site: http://www.newwinpublishing.com
Dist(s): **Continental Bk. Co., Inc.***; CIP.*

†New World Library, *(0-931432; 0-945934; 1-57731; 1-880032)* 14 Pamaron Way, Novato, CA 94949 USA (SAN 211-8777) Tel 415-884-2100; Fax: 415-884-2199; Toll Free: 800-972-6657 (retail orders only) Do not confuse with New World Library Publishing Co., Los Altos, CA
E-mail: escort@nwlib.com
Web site: http://www.newworldlibrary.com
Dist(s): **Islander Group**
Landmark Audiobooks
NetLibrary, Inc.
New Leaf Distributing Co., Inc.
Perseus Distribution*; CIP.*

New World Media, Inc., *(0-9707954; 1-931633; 1-932581; 1-934020)* 801 N. Pitt St., Suite 123, Alexandria, VA 22314 USA (SAN 253-9802) Tel 703-684-6895; Fax: 703-684-0639
E-mail: info@americanbookpress.com
Web site: http://www.edenplaza.com.

New World Pubns., Inc., *(1-878348)* 1861 Cornell Rd., Jacksonville, FL 32207 USA (SAN 298-4768) Tel 904-737-6558; Fax: 904-731-1188; Toll Free: 800-737-6558
E-mail: eric@fishid.com; orders@fishid.com
Web site: http://www.fishid.com
Dist(s): **Baker & Taylor Bks.**
Great Outdoors Publishing Co.
Mickler's Bks., Inc.
Sunbelt Pubns., Inc.

New World Publishing, *(0-9771939; 0-9776818; 0-9787112; 0-9796815)* 4540 State Rd., Cleveland, OH 44109 USA Tel 216-635-1671 Do not confuse with New World Publishing in Riverdale, GA, Scottsdale, AZ and Auburn, CA
E-mail: rkisner5@sbcglobal.net
Web site: http://www.silverquillpoetry.net.

New World Revelation Pr., *(0-9762105)* Orders Addr.: P.O. Box 839, Ellijay, GA 30540 USA Tel 706-635-7720; Fax: 706-635-8170
E-mail: fess1944@etcmail.com; office@awakeandlive.org
Web site: http://www.awakeandlive.org
Dist(s): **Lightning Source, Inc.**

New Year Publishing, *(0-9760095; 0-9799885)* 144 Diablo Ranch Ct., Danville, CA 94506 USA Tel 925-838-9806; Fax: 925-984-7256 Do not confuse with New Year Publishing in Oceanside, CA
E-mail: dmorris@newyearpublishing.com
Web site: http://www.newyearpublishing.com.

New York City Publishing Co., *(0-9614772; 1-881939)* 143 Hoyt St., No. 2B, Stamford, CT 06905 USA (SAN 696-0758) Tel 203-327-4443
Dist(s): **Feldheim Pubs.**

New York Labor News, *(0-935534)* P.O. Box 218, Mountain View, CA 94042-0218 USA (SAN 202-0947) Tel 408-280-7266; Fax: 408-280-6964
E-mail: socialists@slp.org
Web site: http://www.slp.org
Dist(s): **Socialist Labor Party.**

†New York Public Library, *(0-87104)* Pubns. Office, 6th Flr., 8 W. 40th St., New York, NY 10018 USA (SAN 202-926X) Tel 212-512-0202; Fax: 212-704-8620 ; *Imprints:* Branch Libraries (Branch Libraries)
E-mail: mciccone@nypl.org; syoung@nypl.org; sharrison@nypl.org
Web site: http://www.nypl.org*; CIP.*

New York Review of Bks., Inc., The, *(0-940322; 1-59017)* 1755 Broadway, 5th Flr., New York, NY 10019-3780 USA (SAN 220-3448) Tel 212-757-8070; Fax: 212-333-5374 ; *Imprints:* NYR Children's Collection (NY Rev Child); NYRB Classics (NYRB Class)
E-mail: mail@nybooks.com
Web site: http://www.nyrb.com
Dist(s): **Random Hse., Inc.**

†New York Univ. Pr., *(0-8147)* Div. of New York Univ., Orders Addr.: 838 Broadway, 3rd Flr., New York, NY 10003-4812 USA (SAN 658-1293) Tel 212-998-2575; Fax: 212-995-3833; Toll Free: 800-996-6987 (ordering)
E-mail: orders@nyupress.org
Web site: http://www.nyupress.org*; CIP.*

Newbury Hse. *Imprint of* **Thomson Heinle**

Newburyport Pr., *(1-882266)* Orders Addr.: P.O. Box 389, Newburyport, MA 01950 USA Tel 978-465-5751; Fax: 978-462-2043; Toll Free: 800-491-4700 (in Massachusetts only); Edit Addr.: 80 Hanover St., Newbury, MA 01951 USA
E-mail: mail@newburyportpress.com
Dist(s): **D.A.P./Distributed Art Pubs.**

Newburyport Press, Incorporated *See* **Newburyport Pr.**

NeWest Pubs., Ltd. (CAN) *(0-920316; 0-920897; 1-896300; 1-897126) Dist. by* **Strauss Cnslts.**

NewLife Pubns., *(1-56399)* Affil. of Campus Crusade for Christ International, Orders Addr.: P.O. Box 620877, Orlando, FL 32862-0877 USA Tel 407-826-2145; Fax: 407-826-2149; Toll Free Fax: 800-514-7072; Toll Free: 800-235-7255; Edit Addr.: 100 Lake Hart Dr., Orlando, FL 32832-0100 USA Do not confuse with New Life Pubns. in Rockford, IL
Web site: http://www.newlifepubs.com
Dist(s): **CRC Pubns.**

Newman Educational Publishers *See* **Newman Educational Publishing Co.**

Newman Educational Publishing Co., *(0-938990)* P.O. Box 461, Glen Ellyn, IL 60138 USA (SAN 239-8273) Tel 630-668-7027
E-mail: bizfootstep@aol.com
Web site: http://www.ugrr.illinois.com.

Newman, Jill, *(0-9674262)* 9201 Lime Bay Blvd. Apt. 202, Tamarac, FL 33321-8682 USA
E-mail: JAN778@aol.com.

Newmark Pr., *(0-9673859)* 425 Riverside Dr. Apt. 12K, New York, NY 10025-7732 USA
E-mail: tnschott@aol.com.

Newmarket Pictorial Moviebooks *Imprint of* **Newmarket Pr.**

†Newmarket Pr., *(0-937858; 1-55704)* Div. of Newmarket Publishing & Communications Corp., 18 E. 48th St., New York, NY 10017 USA (SAN 217-2585) Tel 212-832-3575; Fax: 212-832-3629; Toll Free Fax: 800-458-6515 (trade orders); Toll Free: 800-233-4830 (trade orders) ; *Imprints:* Newmarket Shooting Scripts (Newmarket Shooting); Newmarket Pictorial Moviebooks (Newmarket Pictorial)
E-mail: mailbox@newmarketpress.com
Web site: http://www.newmarketpress.com
Dist(s): **Norton, W. W. & Co., Inc.**
Worldwide Media Service, Inc.*; CIP.*

Newmarket Shooting Scripts *Imprint of* **Newmarket Pr.**

Newnes *Imprint of* **Elsevier Science & Technology Bks.**

NewRoad Publishing, *(1-931109)* Div. of Triangle Concierge, Inc., Orders Addr.: 3650 Rogers Rd., #328, Wake Forest, NC 27587 USA Tel 919-453-2850; Fax: 919-453-2851
E-mail: ron@newroadpublishing.com; newroad@nc.rr.com; rgiovanni@triangleconcierge.com
Web site: http://www.triangleconcierge.com; http://www.newroadpublishing.com; http://katharinegiovanni.com.

NewSound, LLC, 81 Demeritt Pl., Waterbury, VT 05676 USA Tel 802-244-7858; Fax: 802-244-1808; Toll Free: 800-342-0295 (wholesale orders)
E-mail: sales@newsoundmusic.com.

NewSouth Bks. *Imprint of* **NewSouth, Inc.**

NewSouth, Inc., *(1-58838; 1-60306)* P.O. Box 1588, Montgomery, AL 36102-1588 USA Tel 334-834-3556; Fax: 334-834-3557; Toll Free: 866-639-7688 ; *Imprints:* NewSouth Books (NewSouth AL); Junebug Books (Junebug Bks)
E-mail: info@newsouthbooks.com
Web site: http://www.newsouthbooks.com
Dist(s): **Blair, John F. Pub.**

New-Swan Bks., *(0-9667511)* Orders Addr.: P.O. Box 1005B, Livingston, MT 59047 USA Tel 406-222-0044; Fax: 406-222-0022.

Newton, J. Britt *See* **Twelve Stones Publishing**

Newtonian Golf & Particle Physics, Inc., *(0-9725355)* 107 Bordeaux Ln., Cary, NC 27511 USA Tel 919-469-0180
E-mail: sales@saintmulligan.com
Web site: http://www.stmulligan.com.

Next Page Pr., The, *(0-9749826)* Orders Addr.: 1915 W. Wakeham Pl., Santa Ana, CA 92704-7147 USA Tel 714-432-1729
E-mail: raday@pngusa.net
Web site: http://www.womeninrailroading.com.

Next Step Magazine, Inc., The, *(0-9752926)* 86 W. Main St., Victor, NY 14564 USA Tel 585-742-1260; Fax: 585-742-1263; Toll Free: 800-771-3117
Web site: http://www.nextstepmagazine.com.

Next Step Pr., *(1-892876)* Sub. of New Wisdom, Inc., 1201 Delta Glen Ct., Vienna, VA 22182-1320 USA Tel 703-757-7945; Fax: 703-757-7946
E-mail: Wyattwooodsmall@compuserve.com
Web site: http://www.peoplepatterns.com; http://www.mindcoach.org.

Nextpos Corporation *See* **Aldelo Systems Inc.**

NF Publishing *See* **SouthWest Pubns.**

Nguyen, Talia, *(0-9655943)* 45 Daro Dr., Enfield, CT 06082 USA Tel 703-690-9615.

Niagara Frontier Chapter NRHS, Inc., *(0-9703552)* Orders Addr.: P.O. Box 178, Alexander, NY 14005 USA Tel 716-694-9588; 716-864-4074; Fax: 585-547-3822
E-mail: publications@nfcnrhs.com; nfcnrhs@aol.com
Web site: http://www.niagarafrontier.railfan.net.

Nicewood Imagined, *(0-9720334)* 6823 NW 52nd Ln., Gainesville, FL 32653 USA Tel 352-271-3306 (phone/fax)
E-mail: nicewoodimagined@yahoo.com
Web site: http://www.macecora.com.

NicheMarket.com *See* **Passion Profit Co., The/NicheMarket**

Nichols Schwartz Publishing, *(1-882269)* Orders Addr.: P.O. Box 254, Honesdale, PA 18431-0254 USA Tel 570-253-9362; Toll Free: 800-732-4334; Edit Addr.: 315 15th St., Honesdale, PA 18431 USA
E-mail: nspmath@aol.com.

Nicholson, Ed, *(0-9720828)* P.O. Box 689, Covington, VA 24426-0689 USA.

Nickel Pr., *(1-57122; 1-879424)* Div. of S.R. Jacobs & Assocs., 107 Knob Hill Pk. Dr., Reisterstown, MD 21136 USA Do not confuse with Nickel Press, Inc., Enterprise, AL.

Nicolin Fields Publishing, Inc., *(0-9637077; 1-892066)* 861 Lafayette Rd. Unit 2A, Hampton, NH 03842-1232 USA Toll Free: 800-431-1579 (orders only)
E-mail: nfp@nh.ultranet.com
Web site: http://www.nicolinfields.com
Dist(s): **Alpenbooks Pr. LLC**
Peregrine Outfitters
Quality Bks., Inc.
Univ. Pr. of New England.

Nicoll Creations, *(0-9747527)* 5608 Evergreen, Midland, MI 48642 USA Tel 989-839-8293
E-mail: hgnicoll@sbcglobal.net.

Nicolosi, Gaetano, *(0-9763828)* 74 W. Fountain Ave., Delaware, OH 43015-1629 USA
E-mail: ciaogaetano@yahoo.com.

Nielsen, Lester *See* **Eaglesquest Publishing**

Night Howl Productions, *(0-9702176)* P.O. Box 1, Clay Center, NE 68933 USA Tel 402-984-2566
E-mail: dirtytricksforchicks@yahoo.com
Dist(s): **AK Pr. Distribution**
Baker & Taylor Bks.

Night LIght Pubns., LLC, *(0-9740418; 0-9743785)* 6101 E. Wethersfield Rd., Scottsdale, AZ 85254 USA Tel 480-948-2607; Fax: 480-948-9921
E-mail: reg@nightlightpublications.com
Web site: http://www.nightlightpublications.com.

Night of Psalms, *(0-9723373)* P.O. Box 300786, Austin, TX 78703-0014 USA
E-mail: night_of_psalms@yahoo.com.

Night Sky Bks., *(1-59014)* Div. of North-South Books, Inc., 11 E. 26th St., 17th Flr., New York, NY 10010 USA Tel 212-706-4545; Fax: 212-706-4546; Toll Free: 800-282-8257 Do not confuse with companies with the same name in Santa Fe, NM
E-mail: nightsky@northsouth.com
Web site: http://www.northsouth.com
Dist(s): **Chronicle Bks. LLC**
Lectorum Pubns., Inc.

Nightengale Pr., *(0-9743348; 0-9761289; 1-933449)* 10936 N. Port Washington Rd. Suite 206, Mequon, WI 53092 USA Tel 847-810-8498; Toll Free Fax: 866-830-2624
E-mail: publisher@nightengalepress.biz
Web site: http://www.nightengalepress.com.

Nightscape Publishing Company *See* **Painted Sky Productions**

nightwares Bks., *(0-9742549)* 2711 Western, Kingman, AZ 86401 USA
E-mail: nw-ebooks@nightwares.com
Web site: http://www.nightwares.com/ebooks/.

Nightwares Ebooks *See* **nightwares Bks.**

Nightwood Editions (CAN) *(0-88971) Dist. by* **Gr Arts Ctr Pub.**

NIIS Publishing, *(0-615; 0-9745013)* 7349 Milliken, No. 140164, Rancho Cucamonga, CA 91730 USA.

Nile Publishing, *(0-9768485)* 213 Hancock St., Brooklyn, NY 11216 USA Tel 718-810-1148 Do not confuse with Nile PUblishing in Cincinnati, OH
E-mail: wale1@hotmail.com.

Nilsson Media, *(0-9724771)* Box 1371, Brentwood, TN 37024-1371 USA Tel 615-776-2593; Fax: 615-776-3193; Toll Free: 888-801-5190 ; *Imprints:* Nilsson, Troy (Troy Nilsson)
E-mail: books@nilssonmedia.org
Web site: http://www.nilssonmedia.com.

Nilsson, Troy *Imprint of* **Nilsson Media**

Nimble Bks. LLC, *(0-9754479; 0-9765406; 0-9777424; 0-9788138; 0-9799205; 1-934840)* 1521 Martha Ave., Ann Arbor, MI 48103 USA
E-mail: wfz@nimblebooks.com
Web site: http://www.nimblebooks.com.

Nimbus Publishing, Ltd. (CAN) *(0-919380; 0-920852; 0-921054; 1-55109) Dist. by* **Natl Bk Netwk.**

90's Pr., *(1-883070)* 524 Orleans St., Saint Paul, MN 55107 USA Tel 612-291-2652
Dist(s): **Ally Pr.**

Ninos Aprenden Ingles Corp., *(1-934665)* 15476 NW 77 Ct., No. 360, Miami Lakes, FL 33016 USA (SAN 854-249X)
E-mail: ar@childrenlearninglanguages.com
Web site: http://www.ChildrenLearningLanguages.com.

Nintendo of America, Inc., *(1-930206; 1-59812)* 4820 150th Ave., NE, Redmond, WA 98052 USA Tel 425-882-2040; Fax: 425-882-3585; Toll Free: 800-633-3236
Web site: http://www.nintendo.com
Dist(s): **Diamond Comic Distributors, Inc.**
Eastern News Distributors.

Ninth Judicial Circuit Historical Society, *(0-9635086)* 125 S. Grand Ave., Pasadena, CA 91105 USA Tel 626-795-0266 Do not confuse with Ninth Judicial Historical Society & U. S. District Court for the Northern District of California Historical Society, also in Pasadena, CA (a joint venture).

Nistraman Consulting, *(0-9706387)* P.O. Box 1314, Brookline, MA 02446 USA
E-mail: alex_belenky@lycos.com
Web site: http//www.asbbooks.com.

Nite Owl Bks., *(0-9661105)* 4040 E. Camelback Rd., Suite 101, Phoenix, AZ 85018 USA (SAN 299-6413) Tel 602-840-0132; Fax: 602-957-1671; Toll Free: 888-927-9600
E-mail: theniteowl@juno.com
Dist(s): **Independent Pubs. Group**
KCS.

Nittany Pubs., LLC, *(0-9613823)* Orders Addr.: P.O. Box 80362, Phoenix, AZ 85060 USA Fax: 602-482-0515; Toll Free: 888-404-7927; Edit Addr.: 888 E. Clinton St., No. 1006, Phoenix, AZ 85020 USA (SAN 679-1824)
E-mail: carlynm@aol.com.

NJL College Preparation, *(0-9753913)* 880 Willis Ave., Albertson, NY 11507 USA Tel 516-741-3550
E-mail: njlcp@aol.com.

nJoy Bks., *(0-9769959)* Orders Addr.: 18 S. 2nd St., Madison, WI 53704 USA
E-mail: office@njoybooks.com
Web site: http://www.njoybooks.com.

NLAlex Publishing *See* **Joe Girl Ink**

N-Mas, *(1-929640)* Orders Addr.: P.O. Box 6441, Fort Myers Beach, FL 33932 USA Tel 941-418-4154; Fax: 941-463-3410; Edit Addr.: 16900 S. Tamiami Trail, No. W25, Fort Myers, FL 33908 USA Tel 239-267-0351 (phone/fax)
E-mail: cheapeasy@yahoo.com
Web site: http://www.geocities.com/cheapeasy.

NMS Enterprises Ltd. - Publishing (GBR) *(0-948636; 0-900733; 1-901663; 1-905267) Dist. by* **Antique Collect.**

No Dead Lines *See* **Fithian Pr.**

No Exit Pr. (GBR) *(0-948353; 1-874061; 1-901982; 1-84243) Dist. by* **IPG Chicago.**

No Limits Communications, *(0-9712842)* P.O. Box 220, Horsham, PA 19044 USA Tel 215-675-9133; Fax: 215-675-9376.

No Limitz Productions, Inc., *(0-9766942)* 3257 Primera Ave., Los Angeles, CA 90068 USA Tel 323-876-7149
E-mail: nolimitz@aol.com
Web site: http://www.suzannelopez.com.

No Starch Pr., Inc., *(1-886411; 1-59327)* 555 De Haro St., Suite 250, San Francisco, CA 94107 USA Tel 415-863-9900; Fax: 415-863-9950; Toll Free: 800-420-7240 Do not confuse with No Starch Pr., in Berkeley, CA
E-mail: info@nostarch.com
Dist(s): **Ingram Pub. Services**
NetLibrary, Inc.
O'Reilly Media, Inc.

No Stress Pr., *(1-890641)* Div. of SageCreek Assocs., 1807 N. Elm, Suite 238, Denton, TX 76201 USA Tel 940-243-5125; Fax: 940-380-1105
E-mail: sagecrk@iglobal.net
Web site: http://www.iglobal.net/sagecreek.

No Voice Left Behind Publishing, *(0-9773513)* P.O. Box 1109, Ceres, CA 95307 USA Tel 209-968-3425
E-mail: fernando_pena@sbcglobal.net
Web site: http://www.nvlb.net.

Noah's Children, Inc., *(0-9674273)* 5008 Monument Ave., Richmond, VA 23230-3620 USA
E-mail: info@noahschildren.org
Web site: http://www.noahschildren.org.

Noble Endeaver, *(0-9700692)* P.O. Box 770, Prospect, KY 40059 USA Fax: 502-228-6771
E-mail: jilljacks@worldnet.att.net
Web site: http://www.jill1jackson.com.

Noble Hero Pr., *(0-9768410)* 3754 Salem Walk, No. A1, Northbrook, IL 60062 USA
E-mail: mike@nobleheropress.com
Web site: http://www.nobleheropress.com.

Noble, John A. Collection *See* **Noble Maritime Collection, The**

†Noble Maritime Collection, The, *(0-9623017)* 1000 Richmond Terr., Staten Island, NY 10301-1114 USA Tel 718-447-6490
E-mail: erinurban@earthlink.net; *CIP.*

Noble Publishing Assocs., *(0-923463; 1-56857)* 1300 NE 131st Cir., Vancouver, WA 98685 USA (SAN 251-656X) Tel 360-258-3119; Fax: 360-258-3122; Toll Free: 800-225-5259; 1300 NE 131st St., Vancouver, WA 98685-3164
E-mail: noblebooks@noblepublishing.com
Web site: http://www.noblepublishing.com.

Nubod Concept, Inc., *(0-9740485)* 6965 El Camino Real, PMB 634, Carlsbad, CA 92209 USA.

Noel Studio, Inc., *(0-9652531)* 75 N. Main St., Zionsville, IN 46077-1547 USA Toll Free: 800-444-6635
E-mail: info@nanoel.com
Web site: http://www.nanoel.com.

Noesis, Inc., *(0-9742091)* 10530 Linden Lake Plaza, Manassas, VA 20109 USA Tel 703-369-2924; Fax: 703-392-7978
E-mail: fstilley@noesis-inc.com
Web site: http://www.noesis-inc.com/drydockhistory.

Noesis Publishing, *(0-9794328)* Div. of Noesis Communications International, 5777 W. Century Blvd., Suite 200, Los Angeles, CA 90045 USA Tel 310-645-5604; Fax: 310-215-3018
E-mail: diana@cmsbiz.com
Web site: http://noesispublishing.com.

Noguer y Caralt Editores, S. A. (ESP) *(84-217; 84-279) Dist. by* **Lectorum Pubns.**

Noixia's Reading Circle, *(0-9749122)* 8002 Avenida Navidad, San Diego, CA 92122 USA Tel 858-550-9519
E-mail: contact@noixia.com
Web site: http://www.noixia.com.

Noller, Gail, *(0-9744877)* 1416 Oakwood Dr., Anoka, MN 55303 USA Tel 763-427-6897
E-mail: nolle005@tc.umn.edu.

Nomad Pr., *(0-9668289)* P.O. Box 484, Fort Collins, CO 80522-0484 USA (SAN 256-5110) Tel 970-226-3590; Fax: 970-282-3467 Do not confuse with Nomad Press, Clewiston, FL, White River Junction, VT
E-mail: nomad@nomad-press.com; robson@frii.com
Web site: http://www.nomad-press.com
Dist(s): **National Bk. Network.**

Nomad Pr., *(0-9659258; 0-9722026; 0-9749344; 0-9771294; 0-9785037; 0-9792268; 1-934670)* Div. of Nomad Communications, Inc., 2456 Christian St., White River Junction, VT 05001 USA Tel 802-649-1995; Fax: 802-649-2667 Do not confuse with Nomad Pr., Clewiston, FL, Fort Collins, CO
E-mail: rachel@nomadcom.com
Web site: http://www.nomadpress.net
Dist(s): **Independent Pubs. Group.**

Non Sequitur Pr., *(0-9662448)* Div. of Meteora Pub., Orders Addr.: P.O. Box 5043, Champaign, IL 61825 USA Tel 217-344-2903; Fax: 217-344-1439; Edit Addr.: 906 E. Washington St., Urbana, IL 61801 USA Tel 217-384-7657
E-mail: lfay@prairienet.org
Web site: http://www.nonsequiturpress.com.

Nonetheless Pr., *(1-932053)* 20332 W. 98th St., Lenexa, KS 66220-2650 USA Tel 913-254-7266; Fax: 913-393-3245
E-mail: mschutte@nonethelesspress.com
Web site: http://www.nonethelesspress.com; http://www.lookingglasspress.com
Dist(s): **Baker & Taylor Bks.**
Bookazine Co., Inc.
Brodart Co.
Greenleaf Book Group
Midwest Library Service.

Noodle Pr., *(0-9601022)* Orders Addr.: P.O. Box 42542, Washington, DC 20015 USA; Edit Addr.: P.O. Box 42542, Washington, DC 20015 USA (SAN 208-7871) Tel 202-363-5078; Fax: 202-364-0090
E-mail: Noodleprss@aol.com
Dist(s): **Baker & Taylor Bks.**

Noon Productions, *(0-9670024)* P.O. Box 62005, Virginia Beach, VA 23462 USA Tel 757-486-7879
E-mail: onuora@aol.com.

Nooni Publishing, *(0-9796832)* 1211 Garden Lake Dr., Riverdale, GA 30296 USA
E-mail: Nooni-pub@hotmail.com.

Noor Foundation-International, *(0-9632067; 0-9766972)* P.O. Box 758, Hockessin, DE 19707 USA (SAN 854-3712) Tel 302-234-8860; Fax: 208-279-5341; Toll Free: 888-937-2665; 249 Peoples Way, Hockessin, DE 19707
E-mail: cyrusomar@hotmail.com; alnoorfoundation@hotmail.com
Web site: http://www.islamusa.org.

Noorart, Inc., *(1-933269)* 577 Sterling Dr., Richardson, TX 75081 USA Tel 972-234-9108
E-mail: asaadeh1@hotmail.com
Web site: http://www.noorart.com.

NooVoo Publishing LLC, *(0-9767513)* 28257 Thornybrae, Farmington Hills, MI 48331 USA Tel 248-762-4858
E-mail: glennrader@noovoo.com.

Norcor Enterprises, *(0-9622469)* 6147 N. Sheridan Rd., Chicago, IL 60660 USA Tel 773-743-6792
E-mail: norcorent@juno.com.

Norfleet Pr., Inc., *(0-9649934)* 1 Gracie Ter. Apt. 4C, New York, NY 10028-7956 USA
Dist(s): **Continental Enterprises Group, Inc. (CEG)**
North Country Bks., Inc.

Norilana Bks., *(1-934169; 1-934648)* Orders Addr.: P.O. Box 2188, Winnetka, CA 91396 USA (SAN 851-8556); Edit Addr.: 6615 Winnetka Ave., Winnetka, CA 91306-4346 USA
E-mail: service@norilana.com
Web site: http://www.norilana.com/.

Norma S.A. (COL) *(958-04) Dist. by* **Bilingual Pubns.**

Norma S.A. (COL) *(958-04) Dist. by* **Continental Bk.**

Norma S.A. (COL) *(958-04) Dist. by* **Lectorum Pubns.**

Norma S.A. (COL) *(958-04) Dist. by* **AIMS Intl.**

Norma S.A. (COL) *(958-04) Dist. by* **Distr Norma.**

Norma S.A. (COL) *(958-04) Dist. by* **Libros Fronteras.**

Norman & Globus, Inc., *(1-886978)* Orders Addr.: P.O. Box 20533, El Sobrante, CA 94803 USA; Edit Addr.: 3820 San Pablo Dam Rd. Ste. B, El Sobrante, CA 94803-2812 USA
E-mail: info@electrowiz.com
Web site: http://www.electrowiz.com.

Norman Bks., *(0-9708617)* 900 Euclid St., Suite 302, Santa Monica, CA 90403 USA Tel 310-899-9310; Fax: 503-961-9523
E-mail: normanbooks@adelphia.net
Web site: http://www.normanbooks.com
Dist(s): **Baker & Taylor Bks.**
Book Wholesalers, Inc.
Follett Library Resources
Lectorum Pubns., Inc.
Iaconi, Mariuccia Bk. Imports
Quality Bks., Inc.
Sunbelt Pubns., Inc.
Treasure Chest Bks.

Norman ID, *(0-9706212)* 466 Branch St., San Luis Obispo, CA 93401 USA
E-mail: info@helpwithenglish.com
Web site: http://www.helpwithenglish.com.

Norman, Iris A., *(0-9668509)* 6202 Lincolnton Rd., Lincolnton, GA 30817 USA Tel 706-293-4222; Fax: 706-293-4230.

Normand, Don Ministries, Inc., *(1-931137)* Orders Addr.: P.O. Box 813, Melrose, FL 32666 USA Tel 352-475-1847; Fax: 352-475-1277; Edit Addr.: 651 SE 28th St., No. 12, Melrose, IL 32666 USA
E-mail: Donnorm@aol.com
Web site: http://www.bibl@sermons.com.

Norris, George W. Foundation, Inc., *(0-9725927)* P.O. Box 884, McCook, NE 69001 USA Tel 308-345-3212.

Norseman Publishing Co., *(0-9613202)* 781 Lehigh Rd., Venice, FL 34293 USA (SAN 295-7507) Tel 941-497-2750; Toll Free: 800-843-0213.

Norsemen Ventures, *(1-893186)* Orders Addr.: P.O. Box 820203, Vancouver, WA 98682 USA Tel 360-892-4066
E-mail: jddavis@rocketmail.com
Web site: http://www.ghostsandcritters.com
Dist(s): **Partners/West.**

Nortex Pr. *Imprint of* **Eakin Pr.**

North American Bear, *(0-9665277)* 1200 W. 35th St., Chicago, IL 60609-1368 USA Toll Free: 800-682-3427.

North American International, *(0-88265)* P.O. Box 251, Penn Laird, VA 22846 USA (SAN 202-9200) Tel 540-435-6454 ; *Imprints:* Fine Art Editions (Fine Art Edtns)
E-mail: naibooks@yahoo.com.

North American Mission Board, SBC, *(1-59312)* 4200 North Point Pkwy, Alpharetta, GA 30022-4176 USA Tel 770-410-6100; Fax: 770-410-6051; Toll Free: 866-407-6262
E-mail: marketing@namb.net
Web site: http://www.namb.net.

North American Training Institute, A Div. of Minnesota Council on Compulsive Gambling, Inc., *(1-930467)* 314 W. Superior St. Ste. 508, Duluth, MN 55802-1824 USA Toll Free: 888-989-9234
E-mail: info@nati.org
Web site: http://www.wannabet.org; http://www.nati.org.

North American Vexillological Assoc. (NAVA), *(0-9747728)* 101 Belair Dr., New Milford, CT 06776 USA
E-mail: tmealf@aol.com
Web site: http://www.nava.org.

†North Atlantic Bks., *(0-913028; 0-938190; 0-942941; 1-55643; 1-883319)* Div. of The Society of the Study of Native Art & Science, Orders Addr.: P.O. Box 12327, Berkeley, CA 94712 USA (SAN 203-1655) Fax: 510-559-8277; Toll Free: 800-337-2665 (orders only); Edit Addr.: 1435 4th St. # A, Berkeley, CA 94710-1335 USA ; *Imprints:* Frog Limited (Frog Ltd)
E-mail: orders@northatlanticbooks.com
Web site: http://www.northatlanticbooks.com
Dist(s): **Nutri-Bks. Corp.**
Random Hse., Inc.
SPD-Small Pr. Distribution; *CIP.*

North Bay Bks., *(0-9725200; 0-9749098)* Orders Addr.: P.O. Box 21234, El Sobrante, CA 94820-1234 USA Tel 510-758-4276; Fax: 510-758-4659; Toll Free: 800-870-3194; Edit Addr.: 3110 Whitecliff Ct., Richmond, CA 94803 USA Do not confuse with companies with the same name in El Sobrante, CA, Richmond, CA
Web site: www.northbaybooks.com
Dist(s): **Midpoint Trade Bks., Inc.**

North Bks., *(0-939495; 1-58287)* P.O. Box 1277, Wickford, RI 02852 USA (SAN 663-4052) Tel 401-294-3682; Fax: 401-294-9491.

North Cape Pubns., Inc., *(1-882391)* P.O. Box 1027, Tustin, CA 92781 USA Tel 714-832-3621; Fax: 714-832-5302; Toll Free: 800-745-9714
E-mail: ncape@ix.netcom.com
Web site: http://www.northcapepubs.com.

North Carolina Division of Archives & History *See* **North Carolina Office of Archives & History**

North Carolina Office of Archives & History, *(0-86526)* Orders Addr.: Historical Publications Section 4622 Mail Service Ctr., Raleigh, NC 27699-4622 USA (SAN 203-7246) Tel 919-733-7442 ext. 223; Fax: 919-733-1439
Web site: http://www.ncpublications.com.

North Carolina State University, Humanities Extension Publications *See* **North Carolina State Univ. Humanities Extension Pubns./Program**

North Carolina State Univ. Humanities Extension Pubns./Program, *(1-881507; 1-885647)* North Carolina State Univ., Box 8101 026 Winston Hall, Raleigh, NC 27695 USA Tel 919-515-1334; Fax: 919-515-8738
Web site: http://www.ncsu.edu/chass/extension.

North Carolina Symphony Society, Inc., The, *(0-9618952)* 4361 Lassiter At North Hills A. Ste. 105, Raleigh, NC 27609-5781 USA (SAN 242-5378).

North Coast Cued Speech Services *See* **Cued Speech for Integrated Communication, Inc.**

†**North Country Bks., Inc.,** *(0-925168; 0-932052; 0-9601158; 1-59531)* 311 Turner St., Utica, NY 13501 USA (SAN 110-828X) Tel 315-735-4877
E-mail: ncbooks@adelphia.net
Web site: http://www.northcountrybooks.com; *CIP.*

North Dakota Institute for Regional Studies *See* **North Dakota State Univ., Institute for Regional Studies**

North Dakota State Univ., Institute for Regional Studies, *(0-911042)* Orders Addr.: P.O. Box 5075, Fargo, ND 58105-5075 USA (SAN 203-1574) Tel 701-231-8338; Fax: 701-231-1047
E-mail: cathy.heiraas@ndsu.edu; thomas.riley@ndsu.edu
Web site: http://www. ndirs.ndsu.nodak.edu
Dist(s): **Big River Distribution**
Partners/West.

North Gap Publishing, *(0-9677379)* 636 Golden Hill St., Cheyenne, WY 82009 USA Tel 307-778-8761
E-mail: twalkwyo@hotmail.com.

North Harbor Publishing, *(0-9670205; 0-9788898)* 528 E. Arch St. No. 1, Marquette, MI 49855 USA Tel 906-226-3984; Fax: 906-226-0663; Toll Free: 877-906-3984
E-mail: jharju@chartermi.net
Web site: http://jerryharju.com
Dist(s): **Partners Bk. Distributing, Inc.**

North Light Bks. *Imprint of* **F & W Pubns., Inc.**

North Pine, Ltd., *(0-9665991)* Div. of Valmet International, Ltd., 3220 N. St., NW, Suite 162, Washington, DC 20007 USA Tel 202-333-5151; Fax: 202-965-7745.

North Pole Chronicles, *(0-9636442)* 7306 Park Ln., Dallas, TX 75225-2462 USA Tel 214-696-1717; Fax: 214-696-5288.

North River Press *See* **Meadow Geese Pr.**

North River Press, Incorporated *See* **North River Pr. Publishing Corp., The**

†**North River Pr. Publishing Corp., The,** *(0-88427)* P.O. Box 567, Great Barrington, MA 01230 USA (SAN 202-1048) Tel 413-528-0034; Fax: 413-528-3163; Toll Free Fax: 800-266-5329; Toll Free: 800-486-2665
E-mail: agallagher@northriverpress.com
Web site: http://www.northriverpress.com; *CIP.*

North Shore Records, Inc., *(0-9746229)* Orders Addr.: P.O. Box 1118, Felton, CA 95018 USA (SAN 257-3733) Tel 800-771-7531
E-mail: info@jacirae.com
Web site: http://www.winningromance.com; http://www.christmaswithlove.com; http://www.theindieguide.com; http://www.winningpoints.net; http://www.jacirae.com.

North Star Bks., *(0-9712336)* P.O. Box 3106, Saint Charles, IL 60174 USA Do not confuse with North Star Bks. in Lancaster, CA
E-mail: northstarbooks@avenew.com.

†**North Star Pr. of St. Cloud,** *(0-87839)* P.O. Box 451, Saint Cloud, MN 56302-0451 USA (SAN 203-7491) Tel 320-558-9062; Fax: 320-558-9063; Toll Free: 888-820-1636
E-mail: nspress@cloudnet.com
Dist(s): **Adventure Pubns., Inc.**
Partners Bk. Distributing, Inc.
Skandisk, Inc.; *CIP.*

North Star Pubns., *(1-930458)* 1474 E. Springdell Dr., Provo, UT 84604 USA Tel 801-221-0040 (phone/fax) Do not confuse with North Star Publications, Inc., East Sandwich, MA.

North Star Publishing, *(0-9704437)* 1514 E. 19th Ave., Spokane, WA 99203 USA Tel 509-532-9566; Fax: 509-532-9568 Do not confuse with companies with the same name in Boulder, CO, Amherst, MA, Newport Beach, CA
E-mail: cmurphy@ior.com
Web site: http://www.ior.com/~cmurphy.

North Valley Pubns., *(1-60171)* 3530 De La Cruz Blvd., Santa Clara, CA 95054-2111 USA Tel 408-988-8881
Web site: http://www.nvpublications.org.

North Woods Enterprises, *(0-9709294)* P.O. Box 107, Wevertown, NY 12886 USA Tel 518-251-0818
E-mail: northwoodsent@aol.com
Web site: http://www.northwoodsguides.com.

Northbooks, *(0-9653074; 0-9720604; 0-9789766)* 17050 N. Eagle River Loop, No. 3, Eagle River, AK 99577-7804 USA Tel 907-696-8973; Fax: 907-696-0084
E-mail: rjh@northbooks.com; ertg@northbooks.com
Web site: http://www.northbooks.com.

Northeast Foundation for Children, Inc., *(0-9618636; 1-892989)* Orders Addr.: P.O. Box 718, Turners Falls, MA 01376 USA (SAN 668-3835) Tel 413-863-8288; Fax: 413-863-8310; Toll Free Fax: 877-206-3952; Toll Free: 800-360-6332
E-mail: info@responsiveclassroom.org
Web site: http://www.responsiveclassroom.org.

†**Northern Illinois Univ. Pr.,** *(0-87580)* 310 N. Fifth St., DeKalb, IL 60115-2854 USA (SAN 202-8875) Tel 815-753-1826; Fax: 815-753-1845
E-mail: bberg@niu.edu
Web site: http://www.niu.edu/univ_press/; *CIP.*

Northern Lights, ND Pr., *(0-9717181)* 2112 Grimsrud Dr. Apt. 108, Bismarck, ND 58501-8124 USA.

Northern Lights Publishing *See* **Pocket Guides Publishing, Inc.**

Northern Publications, Incorporated *See* **Northern Publishing**

Northern Publishing, *(0-9639869; 0-9741684)* P.O. Box 871803, Wasilla, AK 99687 USA Tel 907-376-6474
E-mail: tony@tonyruss.com
Web site: http://www.tonyruss.com
Dist(s): **News Group, The**
Partners Bk. Distributing, Inc.
Partners/West.

Northern Speech Services, *(0-9708947; 0-9761967; 0-9765497; 0-9785581; 0-9799245)* 117 N. Elm, Gaylord, MI 49735 USA Toll Free Fax: 888-696-9655; Toll Free: 888-337-3866; P.O. Box 1247, Gaylord, MI 49734
E-mail: tslominski@nss-nrs.com
Web site: http://www.nss-nrs.com.

Northern Star Publishing, *(0-9662018)* Div. of Thomasson International Corp., 181 Springbrook Tr., Sparta, NJ 07871 USA Tel 973-729-9508; Fax: 973-729-9538
E-mail: info@uslawbooks.com
Web site: http://www.uslawbooks.com.

Northern State Univ. Pr., *(1-883120)* Div. of NSU Foundation, Orders Addr.: Northern State Univ., Box 740, Aberdeen, SD 57401 USA Fax: 605-622-3022; Edit Addr.: 12th & Jay Sts., Aberdeen, SD 57401 USA Tel 605-622-2456.

Northern Virginia Writing Project, *(0-9759524)* GMU, MSN3E4, 4400 University Dr., Fairfax, VA 22030 USA Tel 703-993-1168; Fax: 703-993-1184
E-mail: mfarring@gmu.edu
Web site: http://www.nvwp.org.

Northland Press *See* **Northland Publishing**

Northland Pr., *(0-9620280)* Orders Addr.: P.O. Box 62, Boon, MI 49618-0062 USA (SAN 248-5818); Edit Addr.: 4198 S. 27th Rd., Cadillac, MI 49601 USA (SAN 248-5826).

†**Northland Publishing,** *(0-87358)* Orders Addr.: P.O. Box 1389, Flagstaff, AZ 86002-1389 USA Tel 928-774-5251; Fax: 928-774-0592; Toll Free Fax: 800-257-9082; Toll Free: 800-346-3257; Edit Addr.: 2900 N. Fort Valley Rd., Flagstaff, AZ 86001 USA (SAN 854-2392) ; *Imprints:* Rising Moon Books for Young Readers (Rising Moon Bks); Luna Rising (Luna Rising) Do not confuse with companies with the same or similar name in Memomonie, WI, Cleveland, OH
E-mail: info@northlandpub.com
Web site: http://www.northlandbooks.com; http://www.risingmoonbooks.com
Dist(s): **Fujii Assocs.**
Lectorum Pubns., Inc.
Libros Sin Fronteras
Learning Connection, The
National Bk. Network; *CIP.*

Northlight Communications, *(0-9668367; 1-932354)* Div. of Sign2Me, 12125 Harbour Reach Dr., Suite D, Mukilteo, WA 98275 USA (SAN 850-7902) Tel 425-493-1903; Fax: 425-493-1904 ; *Imprints:* Sign2Me (Sign Two Me)
E-mail: vkiteley@sign2me.com; btarcea@sign2me.com
Web site: http://www.sign2me.com
Dist(s): **American Wholesale Bk. Co.**
Baker & Taylor Bks.
Ingram Pub. Services.

†**North-South Bks., Inc.,** *(0-7358; 1-55858)* 350 7th Ave. Rm. 1400, New York, NY 10001-5013 USA ; *Imprints:* Michael Neugebauer Books (M Neugebauer Bks)
E-mail: mnavarro@northsouth.com
Web site: http://www.northsouth.com/privacy/index.html
Dist(s): **Chronicle Bks. LLC**
Continental Bk. Co., Inc.
Lectorum Pubns., Inc.
Libros Sin Fronteras; *CIP.*

Northstar Entertainment Group, LLC, *(0-9741544)* 6042 Hillvale Ct., Lithonia, GA 30058 USA ; *Imprints:* Baby Faye Books (Baby Faye)
E-mail: northstarent2003@yahoo.com
Web site: http://www.northstarent.net.

Northstar Publishing, Inc., *(0-9702071)* Orders Addr.: P.O. Box 1166, Medina, OH 44258-1166 USA Tel 330-721-9126; Fax: 330-723-6598 Do not confuse with companies with the same or similar names in Blue Island, IL, Las Vegas, NV, San Jose, CA, Riverview, FL, Boca Raton, FL
Web site: http://www.northstarguides.com.

Northstone Publishing, Inc. (CAN) *(1-55145; 1-896836) Dist. by* **Pilgrim OH.**

Northwest Media, Inc., *(1-892194; 1-933848)* 326 W. 12th Ave., Eugene, OR 97401 USA Toll Free: 800-777-6636
E-mail: laurie@northwestmedia.com; betty@northwestmedia.com
Web site: http://www.sociallearning.com; http://www.northwestmedia.com
Dist(s): **Baker & Taylor Bks.**
Koen Pacific
Partners/West.

Northwest Parent Publishing, *(0-9614626; 0-9715644)* 733 17th Ave. E, Seattle, WA 98112 USA (SAN 691-8999) Tel 206-910-0138
Web site: http://www.booksforparents.com.

Northwestern Publishing Hse., *(0-8100)* 2949 N. Mayfair Rd., Suite 200, Milwaukee, WI 53222 USA (SAN 206-7943) Tel 414-454-2100; Fax: 414-454-2170
E-mail: kuehlt@nph.wels.net; johnsonr@nph.wels.net
Web site: http://www.nph.net.

Northwind Sailing, Inc., *(0-9752700)* P.O. Box 973, Grand Marais, MN 55604-0973 USA.

NorthWord Bks. for Young Readers *Imprint of* **T&N Children's Publishing**

Norton, Frances M., *(0-9632938)* 1012 N. Wheaton Ave., Wheaton, IL 60187 USA Tel 630-665-0249.

Norton, Jeffrey Pubs., Inc., *(0-88432; 1-57970)* 1 Orchard Park Rd., Madison, CT 06443-2272 USA (SAN 213-957X) Toll Free Fax: 888-453-4329; Toll Free: 800-243-1234
E-mail: info@audioforum.com
Web site: http://www.audioforum.com.

Norton Paperbacks *Imprint of* **Norton, W. W. & Co., Inc.**

†**Norton, W. W. & Co., Inc.,** *(0-393; 0-920256)* Orders Addr.: 800 Keystone Industrial Pk., Scranton, PA 18512 USA (SAN 157-1869) Tel 570-346-2020; Fax: 570-346-1442; Toll Free Fax: 800-458-6515 (credit card orders only); Toll Free: 800-233-4830 (book orders only); Edit Addr.: 500 Fifth Ave., New York, NY 10110-0017 USA (SAN 202-5795) Tel 212-354-5500; Fax: 212-869-0856; Toll Free: 800-223-2584 ; *Imprints:* Norton Paperbacks (Norton Paperbks)
E-mail: webmaster@wwnorton.com
Web site: http://www.wwnorton.com; http://www.wwnorton.com/trade
Dist(s): **Continental Bk. Co., Inc.**
NetLibrary, Inc.
Peoples Publishing Group, Inc., The; *CIP.*

Norwood Hse. Pr., *(1-59953; 1-60357)* P.O. Box 316598, Chicago, IL 60631 USA (SAN 257-1552) Tel 773-467-0837; Fax: 773-467-9686
E-mail: customerservice@norwoodhousepress.com
Web site: http://www.norwoodhousepress.com
Dist(s): **National Bk. Network.**

Nostalgia Pubns., *(0-9660599)* 2816 Lotus Hill Dr., Las Vegas, NV 89134 USA Tel 702-363-4534 (phone/fax) Do not confuse with companies with a similar name in River Edge, NJ, Springfield, TN.

Not Available Comics, *(0-9744767)* P.O. Box 12038, Hamtramck, MI 48212 USA Tel 313-365-5929
E-mail: cynicalman@aol.com
Web site: http://www.cynicalman.com.

Not So Plain Jane Publishing, *(1-59664)* 4322 Declaration Cir., Suite 101, Belcamp, MD 21017 USA Tel 443-866-9672.

Notebook Pubns., Inc., *(0-9673287)* 1606 Dogwood Ct., Fort Collins, CO 80525 USA Tel 970-224-4097; Fax: 970-224-4113
E-mail: info@notebookpublications.com
Web site: http://www.notebookpublications.com
Dist(s): **Booklocker.com, Inc.**

Nothing Sacred Press *See* **Freethought Publishing Group**

Nottingham Publishing, *(0-9664960)* 12839 Glengary Dr., Fishers, IN 46038 USA Tel 317-595-9350; Fax: 317-845-4186
E-mail: Tnottingham@usa.net
Web site: http://tedn.hypermart.net
Dist(s): **Baker & Taylor Bks.**

Nottinghill Bks., *(0-9638648; 1-892477)* 1269 E. Guinevere Ct. # 30, Springfield, MO 65804-3626 USA
E-mail: retathewriter@sbcglobal.net.

NouSoma Communications, Inc., *(0-9743604)* 35 Founders Way, Downingtown, PA 19335-4520 USA Tel 610-458-1580; Fax: 610-458-1556 ; *Imprints:* GIRLS KNOW HOW (Girls Know How)
Web site: http://www.nousoma.com
Dist(s): **Baker & Taylor Bks.**
Book Wholesalers, Inc.
Brodart Co.
Koen-Levy Bk. Wholesalers LLC.

Nova Blue, Inc., *(0-9725584)* 14403 Little Blue Rd., Kansas City, MO 64136 USA Tel 816-737-8895
E-mail: novablueco@aol.com.

Nova Media, Inc., *(0-9618567; 1-884239)* 1724 N. State St., Big Rapids, MI 49307-9073 USA (SAN 668-0372) Tel 231-796-4637 (phone/fax)
E-mail: trund@netonecom.net
Web site: http://www.novamediainc.com.

Nova Pr., *(0-9637371; 1-889057)* Orders Addr.: 11659 Mayfield Ave., Suite 1, Los Angeles, CA 90049 USA Tel 310-207-4078; Fax: 310-571-0908; Toll Free: 800-949-6175
E-mail: novapress@aol.com
Web site: http://www.novapress.net
Dist(s): **NetLibrary, Inc.**

†**Nova Science Pubs., Inc.,** *(0-941743; 1-56072; 1-59033; 1-59454; 1-60021; 1-60456)* 400 Oser Ave., Suite 1600, Hauppauge, NY 11788-3619 USA (SAN 666-0266)
E-mail: novascience@earthlink.net; novapublishers@earthlink.net
Dist(s): **Baker & Taylor Bks.**; *CIP.*

Novel Approach Pubns., LLC, *(0-9701013)* P.O. Box 11747, Kansas City, MO 64138 USA
E-mail: read2me@novel-approach.com
Web site: http://www.novel-approach.com.

Novel Units, Inc., *(1-56137; 1-58130)* Orders Addr.: 2709 Bulverde Rd., Bulverde, TX 78163 USA (SAN 253-9276) Tel 830-438-4262; Fax: 830-438-4263; Toll Free Fax: 877-688-3226; Toll Free: 800-688-3224
E-mail: editors@educyberstor.com
Web site: http://www.educyberstor.com
Dist(s): **Lectorum Pubns., Inc.**
Perma-Bound Bks.

Novello Festival Pr., *(0-615; 0-9708972; 0-9760963)* Div. of Public Library of Charlotte & Mecklenburg County, 310 N. Tryon St., Charlotte, NC 28202 USA (SAN 254-3206) Tel 704-432-0153
Dist(s): **Blair, John F. Pub.**

Novice Nomad Publishing, *(1-928693)* P.O. Box 940825, Simi Valley, CA 93094 USA Tel 805-527-6752 (phone/fax)
E-mail: nomadpublg@aol.com
Web site: http://www.novicenomad.com.

Novosel, Scott, *(0-9768353)* P.O. Box 541, Lawrence, KS 66044 USA
E-mail: novosel@getcreactive.com
Web site: http://www.getcreactive.com.

Noware Bks., *(0-9656985; 1-893159)* Div. of Noware Productions, Inc., 140 Charles St., No. 16D, New York, NY 10014 USA Fax: 212-255-4458
E-mail: beckstein@hombeez.com
Web site: http://www.hombeez.com.

Noware Productions, Incorporated *See* **Noware Bks.**

Noyes, Alice Daley, *(0-9621964)* 144 Exchange Ave., Manchester, NH 03104 USA Tel 603-644-5100.

NPG Newpapers, Inc., *(0-9724933)* Orders Addr.: P.O. Box 29, St Joseph, MO 64502-0029 USA Tel 816-271-8500; Fax: 816-271-8631; Toll Free: 800-779-6397; Edit Addr.: 825 Edmond St., St Joseph, MO 64502-0029 USA
E-mail: brucek@npgco.com.

NQSBks., *(0-9793168)* 477 Brentview Hills Dr., Nashville, TN 37220 USA Tel 615-832-1125
E-mail: nqsbooks@comcast.net
Web site: http://www.nqsbooks.com.

N.R. Etc, *(0-9676216)* 25060 Hancock Ave., No. 103-330, Murrieta, CA 92562 USA Tel 951-698-7158; Fax: 951-698-7608; Toll Free: 877-639-7735
E-mail: NRetc@aol.com.

NRG Pubns., *(0-9741647)* 3510 Plum Brook, Missouri City, TX 77459 USA
E-mail: info@nrgpublications.com
Web site: http://www.nrgpublications.com.

NSR Pubns., *(0-9761724)* 1482 51st Rd., Douglass, KS 67039 USA Tel 620-986-5472; Toll Free: 866-677-2624
E-mail: gumm@wheatstate.com
Web site: http://www.nsrpublications.com.

NT Publishing, L.L.C., *(0-9741864; 0-9787123)* P.O. Box 461540, Aurora, CO 80047 USA Tel 303-484-1071; Fax: 303-484-1072
E-mail: questions@ntpublishing.net
Web site: http://www.ntpublishing.net.

NTC/Contemporary Publishing Company *See* **McGraw-Hill/Contemporary**

Nu Energy Horizons, *(1-930216)* P.O. Box 22, Rumney, NH 03266-0022 USA Tel 603-786-9316
E-mail: bruce.perreault@nuenergy.org
Web site: http://www.nuenergy.org.

Nu, Inc., *(0-9665844)* 965 NW Wildrose Dr., Corvallis, OR 97330 USA Tel 541-754-1134; Fax: 541-766-1112.

NUA Multimedia, *(0-9777573)* Orders Addr.: 2657-g Annapolis Rd. Suite 233, Hanover, MD 21076 USA
E-mail: nua_llc@hotmail.com
Web site: http://www.soniahayes.com; http://www.myspace.com/soniahayes.

NuAngel, Inc., *(0-9626614)* 14717 Friend Rd., Athens, AL 35611 USA Tel 256-729-5000; Fax: 256-729-5111
E-mail: sales@nuangel.com
Web site: www.nuangel.com.

NuBaby, Incorporated *See* **NuAngel, Inc.**

Nubiangodess Publishing, *(0-9744291)* P.O. Box 12224, Columbus, GA 31917-2224 USA
E-mail: ngpublishing@cs.com; admin@nubiangodesspublishing.com
Web site: http://www.nubiangodesspublishing.com.

Nubiano Project, Inc., The, *(0-9762837)* P.O. Box 371, Chapel Hill, NC 27514 USA
E-mail: info@thenubianoproject.com.

Nucorp, *(0-9771699)* 1801 Maple Ave., Evanston, IL 60208-3135 USA ; *Imprints:* Chicago Unzipped (Chic Unzip)
Web site: http://www.chicagounzipped.com.

Numa, Jean Ricard Rosarion, *(0-9650069)* Urbana Buena Vista, Calle C, No. 68, Ponce, PR 00731 USA Tel 787-284-0637.

Numbskull Pr., *(0-9704366)* P.O. Box 148, South Deerfield, MA 01373 USA
E-mail: numbskull@gutwallow.com
Web site: http://www.gutwallow.com.

Nu-Nature, *(0-9759008)* 858 Heritage Valley Rd., Norcross, GA 30093 USA Tel 404-376-8917
E-mail: nunatureinfo@aol.com
Web site: http://www.nu-nature.com.

Nunes Productions, LLC, *(0-9748142)* 1314 Fairmont St., NW, Washington, DC 20009 USA Tel 202-387-1314 ; *Imprints:* Brand Nu Words (Brand Nu)
E-mail: charisse@nunesproductions.com
Web site: http://www.nunesproductions.com; http://www.brandnuwords.com
Dist(s): **Biblio Distribution.**

Nu-Nu & You, *(0-9661959)* 15020 Lost Canyon Ct., No. 202, Woodbridge, VA 22191 USA Tel 703-670-7094
E-mail: lowkie_1@hotmail.com.

Nur Pubns., *(0-9764947)* Orders Addr.: 562 Sawmill River Rd., Millwood, NY 10546 USA
E-mail: s_nadimi@yahoo.com
Web site: http://www.nurpublications.com.

Nurchey Pr., *(0-9712768)* 1129 Royal Palm Beach Blvd., Royal Palm Beach, FL 33411-1641 USA Tel 877-362-8705; 561-791-3308; Fax: 561-795-6463; Toll Free Fax: 800-669-6279
E-mail: publicrelations@rickcane.com.

Nursery Nature Walks *See* **Children's Nature Institute, The**

Nurturing Your Children Pr., *(0-9767198)* P.O. Box 5066, Larkspur, CA 94977-5066 USA Tel 415-927-4839 (phone/fax)
E-mail: nurturingpress@aol.com
Web site: http://nurturingyourchildren.com
Dist(s): **Independent Pubs. Group.**

Nutcracker Publishing Co., *(0-9705752)* P.O. Box 486, Hutchinson, MN 55350 USA Tel 320-234-8941; 20066 248 Cir., Hutchinson, MN 55350
E-mail: nutpubco@hutchtel.net
Web site: http://www.nutcrackerpublishing.com
Dist(s): **Baker & Taylor Bks.**
Brodart Co.

Nutmeg Pubns., *(1-890537)* P.O. Box 9335R, Moscow, ID 83843 USA Tel 208-882-5251 Do not confuse with Nutmeg Pubs., New London, CT
E-mail: nutmeg@moscow.com.

Nutrishare Publishing, *(0-9764116)* 10519 E. Stockton Blvd., Suite 110, Elk Grove, CA 95624 USA.

Nutshell Publishing *See* **Enisen Publishing**

NuVISIONS *See* **NuVISIONS & Assocs., Inc.**

NuVISIONS & Assocs., Inc., *(0-9678295)* Div. of The Writers Block, Orders Addr.: 8306 Wilshire Blvd., Suite 7021, Beverly Hills, CA 90211 USA Tel 510-532-5999
E-mail: mrnecless@yahoo.com
Web site: http://www.anuvisionsdream.com.

Nuway Products *See* **Nuway Youth Sports**

Nuway Youth Sports, *(1-890527)* 9936 E. Cinnabar Ave., Scottsdale, AZ 85258 USA Tel 480-661-6643; Toll Free: 888-676-8929
E-mail: info@youth-sports.com; youthsports@cox.net
Web site: http://www.youth-sports.com.

NxLevel Training Network, *(1-890730)* c/o University of Colorado at Denver, Campus Box 128 P.O. Box 173364, Denver, CO 80217-3364 USA Tel 303-620-4665
E-mail: mledoux@carbon.cudenver.edu
Web site: http://www.nxlevel.org.

Nye Products, *(0-9746665)* P.O. Box 177, Wexford, PA 15090-0177 USA Tel 724-935-8710
E-mail: nyeproducts@stargate.net
Web site: http://nyeproducts.com; http://www.beverlynye.com/.

NYR Children's Collection *Imprint of* **New York Review of Bks., Inc., The**

NYRB Classics *Imprint of* **New York Review of Bks., Inc., The**

Nystrom, *(0-7825; 0-88463)* Div. of Herff Jones, 4719 W. 62nd St., Indianapolis, IN 46268-2593 USA (SAN 203-5529) Toll Free: 800-621-8086 Do not confuse with Nystrom Publishing, Inc., Maple Grove, MN
Web site: http://www.nystromnet.com.

O.A.T.S., Inc. (Offering Alternative Therapy With Smiles), *(0-9717627)* 3090 Weidemann Dr., Clarkston, MI 48348 USA Tel 248-620-0505; 248-620-1775
E-mail: oatssmiles@aol.com
Web site: http://www.oatshrh.org.

O Bks. (GBR) *(1-903816; 1-905047; 1-84694) Dist. by* **Natl Bk Netwk.**

OSS Publishing Co., *(0-9660286)* Orders Addr.: P.O. Box 610, White Plains, NY 10603 USA Tel 914-946-6521; Fax: 914-949-5380; Toll Free: 888-677-6521
E-mail: OSSpublishing@att.net
Web site: http://www.osspublishing.com.

O.T.S., *(0-9656252)* P.O. Box 17166, Sarasota, FL 34276 USA Tel 941-918-9215; Fax: 941-918-0265
E-mail: otsf@aol.com
Web site: http://www.otsf.org.

Oak Court Pr., *(0-9767696)* 34612 Oak Ct., Elizabeth, CO 80107 USA Tel 303-703-6633
E-mail: oakcourtpress@msn.com.

Oak Hammock Publishing, *(0-9672616)* P.O. Box 651373, Vero Beach, FL 32965-1373 USA Tel 561-567-0119; Fax: 603-299-5702
E-mail: Info@oakhammockbooks.com.

Oak Hill Bks., *(0-9616701)* Orders Addr.: P.O. Box 5308, Coeur d' Alene, ID 83814 USA (SAN 661-3020) Tel 208-676-1845.

Oak Hill Pr., *(0-9675045)* 2407 Laguna Vista, Novato, CA 94945 USA Fax: 415-892-5748
E-mail: nancydgill@aol.com.

†Oak Knoll Pr., *(0-938768; 1-884718; 1-58456; 1-872116)* 310 Delaware St., New Castle, DE 19720 USA (SAN 216-2776) Tel 302-328-7232; Fax: 302-328-7274; Toll Free: 800-996-2556 Do not confuse with Oak Knoll Press in Hardy, VA
E-mail: oakknoll@oakknoll.com
Web site: http://www.oakknoll.com; *CIP.*

Oak Lake Pr., *(0-9744115)* Orders Addr.: 1432 Higuera, San Luis Obispo, CA 93406 USA Tel 916-791-2309; Edit Addr.: P.O. Box 529, Loomis, CA 95650 USA
E-mail: abowler@surewest.net
Web site: http://www.annmartinbowler.net.

Oak Manor Publishing, Inc., *(0-9747361; 0-9791757)* 161 Boutwell St., Manchester, NH 03102-2933 USA Tel 603-860-5551
E-mail: customerservice@aokmanorpublishing.com
Web site: http://www.oakmanorpublishing.com.

Oak Tree Pubs., *(0-9646602)* P.O. Box 345, Cherry Hill, NJ 08003-0345 USA Tel 609-354-8129.

Oak Tree Publishing, *(1-892343)* Orders Addr.: 140 E. Palmer St., Taylorville, IL 62568-2569 USA Do not confuse with companies with the same or similar name in Virginia Beach, VA, Seminole, FL
E-mail: oaktreepub@aol.com; info@oaktreebooks.com
Web site: http://www.oaktreebooks.com.

Oak Woods Media, *(0-88196)* P.O. Box 19127, Kalamazoo, MI 49019 USA (SAN 264-6285) Tel 616-375-5621; Fax: 616-375-7526
E-mail: oakwoods@net.link.net.

Oakana Hse., *(0-9762197)* Orders Addr.: 231 E. Grand Ave., Escondido, CA 92025 USA (SAN 257-5418)
Dist(s): **Baker & Taylor Bks.**

Oakbrook Publishing Hse., *(0-9649939)* 8279 S. Franklin Ct., Littleton, CO 80122 USA Tel 303-738-1733; Fax: 303-797-1995; Toll Free: 888-738-1733
E-mail: oakbrook@whatdoidobooks.com
Web site: http://www.whatdoidobooks.com
Dist(s): **Independent Pubs. Group**
Quality Bks., Inc.

Oakdale Pr., *(0-9656364)* Orders Addr.: P.O. Box 555, Caulfield, MO 65626 USA Tel 417-284-3512; Fax: 417-284-3623 Do not confuse with companies with the same name in Lincoln., MA, Tallahassee, FL
E-mail: oakdale@webound.com
Web site: http://www.oakdalepress.com.

Oaklawn Marketing, Inc., *(0-9764628)* P.O. Box 190615, Dallas, TX 75219 USA Tel 713-542-7642; Fax: 832-550-2079
E-mail: admin@bookofcontext.com.

Oakleaf Pr., *(0-9663251)* 920 Vesper Rd., Ann Arbor, MI 48103-3015 USA Tel 734-668-8579; Fax: 734-668-8538
E-mail: oakleaf@provide.net
Web site: http://www.oakleaf-press.com.

Oakwood Publishing, *(1-59165)* P.O. Box 403, Dayton, OH 45409 USA Tel 937-298-1998 Do not confuse with companies with the same or similar names in Great Neck, NY, Maywood, IL, Neponsit, NY
Web site: http://oakwoodpublishing.com.

Oakwood Solutions, LLC, *(1-893806; 1-933093)* 1789 N. Oakwood Rd., Oshkosh, WI 54904-8446 USA
E-mail: bschmitz@conovercompany.com; conover@execpc.com
Web site: http://www.conovercompany.com.

Oasis Audio, *(1-55536; 1-886463; 1-58926; 1-59859)* Div. of Domain Communications, 289 S. Main Pl., Carol Stream, IL 60188 USA (SAN 854-3534) Tel 630-668-5300; Fax: 630-668-0158; Toll Free: 800-323-2500 ext. 110 ; *Imprints:* Learn, Incorporated (Lrn Inc)
E-mail: info@oasisaudio.com; jelwell@oasisaudio.com
Web site: http://www.oasisaudio.com
Dist(s): **Baker & Taylor Bks.**
TNT Media Group
Tyndale Hse. Pubs.

Oasis, Producciones Generales de Comunicacion, S.L. (ESP) *(84-7871; 84-7901; 84-85351) Dist. by* **Lectorum Pubns.**

Oasis Pubns., *(0-9652736)* 2344 Cambridge Dr., Sarasota, FL 34232 USA Tel 941-371-2223; Fax: 941-342-1228
E-mail: oasis.dianne@juno.com
Web site: http://www.nutrikid2.com
Dist(s): **Nelson's Bks.**
New Leaf Distributing Co., Inc.
Teva Nature.

Oasis Studios Inc, *(0-9785605)* Orders Addr.: 7701 Witherspoon Dr., Baltimore, OH 43105 USA Tel 740-862-8620
E-mail: ekayzer@hotmail.com
Web site: http://www.championoasisstudios.com
Dist(s): **STL Distribution North America.**

Obelisco, Ediciones S.A. (ESP) *(84-7720; 84-86000; 84-9777) Dist. by* **Lectorum Pubns.**

†Oberlin College Pr., *(0-932440)* 50 N. Professor St., Oberlin, OH 44074 USA (SAN 212-1883) Tel 440-775-8408; Fax: 440-775-8124
E-mail: oc.press@oberlin.edu
Web site: http://www.oberlin.edu/ocpress
Dist(s): **CUP Services**; *CIP.*

Oberon Bks. *Imprint of* **Theatre Communications Group, Inc.**

Oberon Bks., Ltd. (GBR) *(0-948230; 1-84002; 1-870259) Dist. by* **Consort Bk Sales.**

Oblagon, Inc., *(0-929463)* 728 Burleigh Dr., Pasadena, CA 91105 USA (SAN 249-5392) Tel 626-441-3737; Fax: 626-441-3739
E-mail: oblagon@worldnet.att.net
Web site: http://www.sydmead.com
Dist(s): **Diamond Bk. Distributors.**

Oblate Media & Communication Corp., *(0-9674408; 0-9701363; 1-932142)* Sub. of U. S. Province of the Oblates of Mary Immaculate, 1509 Washington Ave., Suite 550, Saint Louis, MO 63103 USA Tel 314-621-1509; Fax: 314-621-5810; Toll Free: 800-233-4629
E-mail: vidwithval@birch.net
Web site: http://www.videoswithvalues.org.

O'Block Bks., *(0-9726743)* P.O. Box 126, Irwin, PA 15642 USA Tel 412-559-3384
E-mail: oblockbooks@worldnet.att.net
Web site: http://oblockbooks.home.att.net; http://www.oblockbooks.com.

O'Brien, Gerard, *(0-9743850)* 115 Essex St., Indian Orchard, MA 01151-1409 USA Tel 413-543-5939
E-mail: gob@ifriendly.com.

O'Brien, James P. Publishing, *(1-886348)* Orders Addr.: P.O. Box 12580, Pittsburgh, PA 15241 USA Tel 412-221-3580; Edit Addr.: 1603 Terphin Dr., Pittsburgh, PA 15241 USA
E-mail: jpobrien@stargate.net
Dist(s): **Renaissance News**
United Magazine Co.

O'Brien Pr., Ltd., The (IRL) *(0-86278; 0-905140; 0-9502046; 1-84717) Dist. by* **Irish Bks Media.**

Ocean Front Bk. Publishing, Inc., *(1-934190)* Orders Addr.: 9101 W. Sahara Ave. Suite 105-130, Las Vegas,, NV 89117 USA (SAN 852-0046) Tel 702-499-0608; 9101 W. Sahara Ave. Suite 105-130, Las Vegas,, NV 89117 (SAN 852-0046) Tel 702-499-0608
E-mail: jhorowitz@oceanfrontbooks.com
Web site: http://www.oceanfrontbooks.com.

Ocean Publishing, *(0-9717641; 0-9767291)* Div. of Gromling Group, Inc., The, P.O. Box 1080, Flagler Beach, FL 32136-1080 USA (SAN 254-8755) Tel 386-517-1600; Fax: 386-517-2564; Toll Free: 800-690-2455 Do not confuse with companies with the same or similar names in Key West, FL, Belmar, NJ
E-mail: info@ocean-publishing.com
Web site: http://www.ocean-publishing.com
Dist(s): **Baker & Taylor Bks.**
Ingram Pub. Services
Quality Bks., Inc.

Ocean View Publishing, *(0-9704614)* Orders Addr.: P.O. Box 222317, Carmel, CA 93922 USA Toll Free: 800-592-1248
E-mail: coastbooks@aol.com; bookcities@aol.com
Web site: http://www.alcatrazhistory.com.

Ocean World Photography, *(0-9766749)* 6461 Running Brook Rd., Manassas, VA 20112 USA
E-mail: wgregorybrown@comcast.net
Web site: http://www.wgregorybrown.com.

Ocean-Hose, *(0-9651140)* P.O. Box 444, Willits, CA 95490 USA Tel 707-459-2333
E-mail: oceanhose@pacific.net
Web site: http://www.pacificsites.com/~oceanhose.

Oceano Grupo Editoria, S.A. (ESP) *(84-494; 84-7069; 84-7505; 84-7555; 84-7764; 84-85317; 84-9719) Dist. by* **Gale.**

O'Connor Hannon Pubns., *(1-893877)* Orders Addr.: P.O. Box 943, Longmont, CO 80502-0943 USA Tel 303-682-2558; Fax: 303-684-8689; Edit Addr.: 1251 Ptarmigan Dr., Longmont, CO 80501-8661 USA.

O'Connor, Ilett K., *(0-9717003; 0-9725968)* 164 Mayfair Ave., W Hempstead, NY 11552-1514 USA.

OCRS, Inc., *(0-9725796)* P.O. Box 551627, Jacksonville, FL 32255-1627 USA (SAN 850-5098) Tel 904-563-6277; Fax: 904-940-5178
E-mail: sharron@ocrsinc.net
Web site: http://www.somestillserve.com; http://www.orcsinc.net.

Octagon Pr., Ltd. (GBR) *(0-86304; 0-900860) Dist. by* **ISHK.**

Company

Company

Octagon Pr./ISHK Bk. Service *See* **ISHK**

Octameron Assocs., *(0-917760; 0-945981; 1-57509)* 1900 Mount Vernon Ave., Alexandria, VA 22301-1302 USA (SAN 282-0714) Tel 703-836-5480; Fax: 703-836-5650
E-mail: info@octameron.com
Web site: http://www.thinktuition.com.

Octopus Publishing Group (GBR) *(1-84091) Dist. by* **Sterling.**

Oculus Pr., The, *(0-9678775)* RR 1, Box 690, Grafton, NH 03240 USA Tel 603-523-7997
E-mail: oculuspress@valley.net.

Odd Duck Ink, Inc., *(1-933069)* P.O. Box 533, Norwell, MA 02061-0533 USA
E-mail: jennifer@oddduckink.com
Web site: http://www.oddduckink.com.

Odditeas, Inc., *(0-9702128)* P.O. Box 1155, Bluffton, SC 29910-1155 USA Fax: 843-757-7070
E-mail: tamelafleetwood@aol.com.

Oddo Publishing, Inc., *(0-87783)* Storybook Acres, Box 68, Fayetteville, GA 30214 USA (SAN 282-0757) Tel 770-461-7627.

Odds Bodkin Storytelling Library, The *Imprint of* **Rivertree Productions, Inc.**

Oden, Rachel, *(0-9729914)* 133 E. Graham Ave., Council Bluffs, IA 51503 USA Tel 712-323-7222 (phone/fax)
E-mail: cbmarketadmin@juno.com.

Odenwald Pr., *(0-9623216; 1-884363)* P.O. Box 27727, Panama City, FL 32411 USA Tel 850-234-5911; Fax: 850-234-2900
E-mail: CSho777@aol.com
Dist(s): **Career Dynamics International.**

Odyssey Classics *Imprint of* **Harcourt Children's Bks.**

Odyssey Mind Institute (AUS) *(0-646; 0-9577945) Dist. by* **Dana Kerr.**

Odyssey Tales, LLC, *(0-9666841)* Orders Addr.: 1631 Tanglewood Dr., Fort Collins, CO 80525 USA Tel 970-493-0262; Fax: 970-416-7827; Toll Free: 888-363-9773
E-mail: greg@odysseytales.com
Web site: http://www.odysseytales.com.

Oehler, Janet, *(0-9671159)* 1 Oak Park Ct., Saint Louis, MO 63141 USA
Dist(s): **Booksource, The.**

Off Beat Books *See* **Thornton Hse.**

Off The Porch Productions, *(0-9719051)* Orders Addr.: P.O. Box 1222, Enid, OK 73702 USA Tel 580-233-3301; Fax: 580-233-3639; Edit Addr.: 2734 N. Oakwood Rd., Enid, OK 73706 USA
E-mail: tjgigi@us.inter.net; Tracy@offtheporchproductions.com
Web site: http://www.greengutsandgigi.com; http://www.ijustknow.com.

Off The Record *Imprint of* **College Prowler, Inc.**

Office Max, *(1-930503)* 416 Aspen St., Vandenberg AFB, CA 93437 USA Tel 805-734-0343 Do not confuse with Office Max in Dearborn, MI
E-mail: KHar934191@aol.com
Web site: http://hometown.aol.com/khar934191/myhomepage/index.

Officer Byrd Publishing Co., *(0-9787322)* 15730 Williams Cir., Lake Mathews, CA 92570 USA (SAN 851-4712) Tel 951-334-6111
E-mail: officerbyrd@aol.com.

Oglethorpe Pr., Inc., *(1-891495)* 326 Bull St., Savannah, GA 31401 USA Tel 912-231-9900; Fax: 912-234-7258
E-mail: sjackel@comcast.net
Dist(s): **Baker & Taylor Bks.**
Parnassus Bk. Distributors.

Ogma Pr., *(0-9785853)* 4717 Broad Rd., Syracuse, NY 13215 USA Tel 315-491-9339
E-mail: bernie@ogmapress.com
Web site: http://www.ogmapress.com.

Oh! Yes I Can! Bks., *(0-615)* 3540 W. Sahara Ave., No. 219, Las Vegas, NV 89102 USA Tel 702-492-1420; Fax: 509-752-9130
E-mail: books@jeffrivera.com
Web site: http://www.jeffrivera.com.

Oh, You Girls!, *(0-9668728)* Div. of The Silly Sisters, 1360 University Ave. W., No. 318, Saint Paul, MN 55104 USA Tel 612-882-2084.

OHC Group LLC, *(0-9763213)* P.O. Box 7839, Westlake Village, CA 91359 USA Tel 805-384-4800
Web site: http://www.onlyheartsclub.com.

Ohe Bks., *(0-9713877)* Div. of Beamer, Keola Productions, Inc., 843 Wainee St., F5, Suite 685, Lahaina, HI 96761-1685 USA Tel 808-661-0090; Fax: 808-667-7069; Toll Free: 800-945-5651
E-mail: books@kbeamer.com
Web site: http://www.kbeamer.com
Dist(s): **Booklines Hawaii, Ltd.**

Ohio Biological Survey, *(0-86727)* Div. of Ohio State Univ College of Biological Sciences, c/o Ohio State Univ., Museum of Biological Diversity, 5530 Olentangy River Rd., Columbus, OH 43235-3444 USA (SAN 217-0787)
Web site: http://www.obs.biosci.ohio-state.edu.

Ohio Poetry Cooperative *See* **CollinwoodMedia**

Ohio State Univ., Ohio Agricultural Education Curriculum Materials Service, *(1-56502)* Orders Addr.: 254 Agricultural Administration Bldg., 2120 Fyffe Rd., Columbus, OH 43210-1067 USA Tel 614-292-4848; Fax: 614-292-4919; Toll Free Fax: 800-292-4919
E-mail: cms@osu.edu
Web site: http://www.ohcms.org.

†**Ohio State Univ. Pr.,** *(0-8142)* 1070 Carmack Rd., Columbus, OH 43210 USA (SAN 202-8158) Tel 614-292-6930; 773-568-1550 (orders); Fax: 614-292-2065; Toll Free Fax: 800-621-8476 (orders); Toll Free: 800-621-2736 (orders)
E-mail: ohiostatepress@osu.edu
Web site: http://www.ohiostatepress.org
Dist(s): **Chicago Distribution Ctr.**
Partners Bk. Distributing, Inc.
Univ. of Chicago Pr.; *CIP.*

†**Ohio Univ. Pr.,** *(0-8214)* Orders Addr.: 11030 S. Langley Ave., Chicago, IL 60628 USA Tel 773-702-7000; Fax: 773-702-7212; Toll Free Fax: 800-621-8476; Toll Free: 800-621-2736; Edit Addr.: 19 Circle Dr. The Ridges, Athens, OH 45701 USA (SAN 282-0773) Tel 740-593-1154; Fax: 740-593-4536
Web site: http://www.ohiou.edu/oupress/
Dist(s): **Chicago Distribution Ctr.**
NetLibrary, Inc.
Univ. of Chicago Pr.
Univ. of Hawaii Pr.; *CIP.*

Ohnick Enterprises, *(0-9746222)* Orders Addr.: P.O. Box 969, Meade, KS 67864-0969 USA Tel 620-873-2900; Fax: 620-873-2603; Toll Free: 800-794-2356; Edit Addr.: 102 N. Fowler, Meade, KS 67864-0969 USA
E-mail: nancy@prairiebooks.com
Web site: http://backroomprinting.com.

o-ho-lee-ab Publishing, *(0-9720790)* Div. of Big Bones, Inc., 428 Laurel Ave., Romeoville, IL 60446 USA
E-mail: caleblandesign@aol.com
Web site: http://www.ohpub.com.

O'Hollow Publishing, *(0-9669645)* Orders Addr.: P.O. Box 942, Price, UT 84501-0942 USA Tel 435-613-9413; Fax: 435-636-8272; Edit Addr.: 1010 W. 2060 N., Helper, UT 84526 USA ; *Imprints:* AlterLingo Books (AlterLingo)
E-mail: ohollow@afnetinc.com.

Oka, Joseph *See* **Joseph's Labor**

Okasan & Me, *(0-9743613)* 829 N. Sixth St., San Jose, CA 95112 USA
Web site: http://www.okasanandme.com.

OKey-Doke Productions, Inc., *(0-9660933)* 49 W. 55th St., No. 3R, New York, NY 10019 USA Tel 212-765-1051; Fax: 718-488-9772.

Oki, Blessed, *(0-9721336)* 2465 Heaton Dri., Suite A, East Point, GA 30344 USA
E-mail: blessiebeke@yahoo.com.

Oklahoma Dept. of Libraries, *(1-880438)* 200 NE 18th St., Oklahoma City, OK 73105 USA Tel 405-521-2502; Fax: 405-348-0886; Toll Free: 800-522-8116
E-mail: annhamilton@cox.net
Web site: http://www.odl.state.ok.us.

Oklahoma Heritage Assn., *(1-885596)* 1400 Classen Dr., Oklahoma City, OK 73106 USA Tel 405-235-4458; Fax: 405-235-2714; Toll Free: 888-501-2059
E-mail: gmc@oklahomaheritage.com
Web site: http://www.oklahomaheritage.com.

Oktopus Publishing, *(0-9667725)* 11814 Coursey Blvd., Suite 263, Baton Rouge, LA 70816 USA Tel 504-293-0609; Toll Free: 800-705-3962
E-mail: cir.jon@usa.net
Web site: http://pmschool.com.

Olandar Pr. Ltd., *(0-9729502)* Orders Addr.: 2222 Parview Rd., Middleton, WI 53562 USA Tel 608-831-1222; Fax: 608-831-1647
Web site: http://www.leighmccloskey.com.

Olas, *(0-9764788)* P.O. Box 919, Dana Point, CA 92629 USA (SAN 256-4688) Tel 949-715-9534; Fax: 207-669-8899; Toll Free: 866-238-7759
Web site: http://www.olaspanama.com
Dist(s): **Booklines Hawaii, Ltd.**

Ola's Hanalei LTD, *(0-9763907)* P.O. Box 488, Hanalei, HI 96714 USA
E-mail: olashanalei@hawaiiantel.net.

Old Bess Publishing Co., *(0-9631912; 0-9762132)* Orders Addr.: P.O. Box 277, Brunswick, ME 04011 USA Tel 207-725-8575; P.O. Box P.O. Box 277, Brunswick, ME 04011
E-mail: sbutcherr@mcn.net.

Old Canyon Pr., *(0-9667834)* 2865 Marquette Dr., Topanga, CA 90290 USA Tel 310-455-3834; Fax: 310-455-1087
E-mail: angel@netwood.net.

Old Cove Pr., *(0-9675424)* 445 Bristol Rd., Lexington, KY 40502 USA Tel 859-266-6374; Fax: 859-268-5405.

Old Farm Pr., *(0-9788227)* P.O. Box 20894, Oklahoma City, OK 73156-0894 USA (SAN 851-6995) Tel 405-748-7072; Fax: 405-748-7073
E-mail: spi@mbo.net
Web site: http://www.BobbyBrightBooks.com.

Old Fort 4 Assocs., *(0-9622471)* Orders Addr.: P.O. Box 1336, Charlestown, NH 03603 USA Toll Free: 888-367-8284; Edit Addr.: 267 Springfield Rd., Rte. 11, Charlestown, NH 03603 USA Tel 603-826-5700; Fax: 603-826-3368
E-mail: floyd@fortat4.org
Web site: http://www.fortat4.org.

Old Hogan Publishing Co., *(0-9638851)* Orders Addr.: P.O. Box 91978, Tucson, AZ 85752 USA Tel 520-579-9321; Fax: 520-579-0502; Toll Free: 800-867-1506; Edit Addr.: 3600 W. Mesa Ridge Trail, Tucson, AZ 85742 USA
E-mail: mgaraway@juno.com
Web site: http://www.oldhogan.com
Dist(s): **Hispanic Bks. Distributors & Pubs., Inc.**
Treasure Chest Bks.

Old Hundred & One Pr. Publishing Co., The, *(0-9721613; 0-9763676)* 2220 Leota St., North Platte, NE 69101-6910 USA Tel 308-532-1748
E-mail: billielee@inebraska.com
Web site: http://www.theold101press.com
Dist(s): **Baker & Taylor Bks.**

Old Maps, *(0-911653; 0-9747639)* P.O. Box 54, West Chesterfield, NH 03466 USA (SAN 264-2689)
E-mail: daven@sover.net
Web site: http://www.old-maps.com.

Old Mountain Pr., *(1-884778; 1-931575)* 2542 S. Edgewater Dr., Fayetteville, NC 28303 USA Tel 910-484-5887
E-mail: omp4u@mail.com
Web site: http://www.oldmp.com.

Old Soldier Publishing, *(0-9764167)* Orders Addr.: P.O. Box 1113, Richmond, TX 77469 USA Tel 281-341-0781 (phone/fax); Edit Addr.: 1110 Pioneer Dr., Richmond, TX 77469 USA.

Oldcastle Publishing, *(0-932529)* Orders Addr.: P.O. Box 1193, Escondido, CA 92033 USA (SAN 297-9039) Tel 760-489-0336; Fax: 760-747-1198; Edit Addr.: 3415 Laredo Ln., Escondido, CA 92025 USA (SAN 297-9047) ; *Imprints:* Earth Rider (Earth Rider)
E-mail: abcurtiss@cox.net
Web site: http://www.abcurtiss.com; http://www.depressionisachoice.com
Dist(s): **Biblio Distribution.**

Olde Springfield Shoppe *See* **Masthof Pr.**

Olde Town Publishing, *(0-9755906)* 703 W. Main, Jonesborough, TN 37659 USA
Web site: http://www.drisbell.com.

Oleson, Susan, *(0-9779251)* 511 E Iowa St, Monona, IA 52159 USA
Web site: http://sammytails@netins.net.

Olive Branch Publishing, LLC, *(0-9793147)* P.O. Box 940725, Plano, TX 75094-0725 USA (SAN 853-0955) Tel 972-977-4881
E-mail: theolivebranch@tx.rr.com.

Olive Grove Publishing, *(0-9676474)* P.O. Box 5486, Santa Monica, CA 90409 USA Tel 310-396-1500; Fax: 310-399-1277; Toll Free: 877-396-1500; Fulfillment Addr.: 4322 Wilshire Blvd. , 3rd Flr., Los Angeles, CA 90010 USA (SAN 253-0805) Toll Free: 877-396-1500
E-mail: Olivegrovepub@aol.com; h.hunter@verizon.net
Web site: http://www.olivegrovepublishing.com
Dist(s): **Baker & Taylor Bks.**
Quality Bks., Inc.

Olive Leaf Pubns., *(0-9761583)* 782 San Gabriel Loop, New Braunfels, TX 78132 USA (SAN 256-6206) Tel 830-626-7671
E-mail: sharon@oliveleafpublications.com
Web site: http://www.oliveleafpublications.com
Dist(s): **Lightning Source, Inc.**

Olive Media Services, *(0-9707831)* 2501 Molton Way, Windsor Mill, MD 21244-1923 USA
E-mail: olivemediaserv@aol.com.

Olive Pr., The, *(0-9769298)* Orders Addr.: P.O. Box 2056, Saintllwater, MN 55082 USA Tel 651-251-3063 Do not confuse with Olive Press i Ann Arbor, MI West Orange, NJ Estes Park, CO
E-mail: olivepressinc@yahoo.com
Web site: http://jumpstartfuture.com.

Olive Print Pr. Ministry, The, *(0-9711016)* c/o The New Olivet Baptist Church, 3084 Southern Ave., Memphis, TN 38111 USA Tel 901-454-7777; Fax: 901-454-4990 ; *Imprints:* Keeping It Real Ministries (Keeping It Real)
E-mail: pastor@olivetbc.com
Web site: http://www.olivetbc.com.

Olive Tree of Life, *(0-9768182)* P.O. Box 344, Tijeras, NM 87059 USA
Web site: http://www.olivetreeoflife.com.

Oliver Pr., Inc., *(1-881508; 1-934545)* 5707 W. 36th St., Minneapolis, MN 55416-2510 USA Tel 952-926-8981; Fax: 952-926-8965; Toll Free: 800-865-4837
E-mail: info@oliverpress.com
Web site: http://www.oliverpress.com.

Oliver, Wade, *(0-9768030)* P.O. Box 1605, Logan, UT 84322-1605 USA
E-mail: wademan@cache.net
Web site: http://www,dovepage.com.

Olivo, Andy, *(0-9743376)* 1807 Glengarry St., Carrollton, TX 75006 USA Tel 972-242-0924; Fax: 972-242-1754 ; *Imprints:* Brown Books (Brown BksTX).

OLLY Publishing Co., *(0-9720427)* 4335 Lake Michigan Dr., NW Suite H, Grand Rapids, MI 49544 USA (SAN 254-587X) Tel 616-735-0553
E-mail: diane@ollypublishing.com
Web site: http://www.ollypublishing.com
Dist(s): **Baker & Taylor Bks.**

Olmstead LLC, *(0-9667696; 1-934194)* Orders Addr.: 1631 Rock Springs Rd., Apopka, FL 32712-2229 USA Tel 954-559-0192 (phone); Fax: 407-814-8771
E-mail: olmsteadllc@usa.com.

Olmstead Pr. *Imprint of* **Moyer Bell**

Olowotot Productions, *(0-9710121)* P.O. Box 250697, New York, NY 10025 USA Tel 212-252-2253
E-mail: qpurdie@yahoo.com; purdie@yahoo.com.

Olsen, Mary Bks., *(0-9715374)* P.O. Box 882, Eastsound, WA 98245-0882 USA
E-mail: mary@maryolsenbooks.com
Dist(s): **Biblio Distribution.**

Olszewski, Zbigniew & Janis, *(0-9708198)* 1760 Campbell Rd., No. 20, Houston, TX 77080 USA
E-mail: jolsz@pdq.net
Web site: http://freeweb.pdq.net/jolsz.

Oma Publishing Co., *(0-9747175)* 325 River Springs Dr., Seguin, TX 78155-0179 USA.

Omaha Bks., *(0-9745410; 0-9788429)* Div. of Eventive Marketing, 9312 Leavenworth St., Omaha, NE 68114 USA Tel 402-614-0056; Toll Free: 866-332-3866
E-mail: kristine.gerber@cox.net; eventive.marketing@cox.net
Dist(s): **Partners Bk. Distributing, Inc.**

O'Mara, Michael Bks., Ltd. (GBR) *(1-85479; 0-946429; 0-948397; 1-84317; 1-903840; 1-904613) Dist. by* **IPG Chicago.**

O'Mara, Michael Bks., Ltd. (GBR) *(1-85479; 0-946429; 0-948397; 1-84317; 1-903840; 1-904613) Dist. by* **Trans-Atl Phila.**

O'Mara, Michael Bks., Ltd. (GBR) *(1-85479; 0-946429; 0-948397; 1-84317; 1-903840; 1-904613) Dist. by* **IngramPubServ.**

Omega House Publishing, *(0-9672519)* Div. of Spectrum Group, Inc., Orders Addr.: P.O. Box 68, Three Rivers, MI 49093 USA Tel 616-273-7070; Fax: 616-273-7026; Edit Addr.: 58690 US 131, Three Rivers, MI 49093 USA
E-mail: zendra@omega777.com.

Omega Pr., *(0-9626087; 0-9754923; 1-933951)* 5823 N. Mesa, No. 823, El Paso, TX 79912-3340 USA Tel 915-584-6844; Toll Free: 888-560-1243 Do not confuse with companies with the same name in Tustin, CA
E-mail: ken@kenhudnall.com
Web site: http://www.omegapress.us; http://www.kenhudnall.com; http://shop.kenhudnall.com.

Omega Publishing, *(0-9748494)* P.O. Box 53626, Lubbock, TX 79453 USA (SAN 255-8815) Tel 806-748-9880; Fax: 806-748-9870; Toll Free: 877-842-9880 do not confuse with companies iwth the same or similar name in Madisonville, KY, Stockton, GA, Snohomish, WA, Norcross, GA
E-mail: jpartin@omega-pub.com
Web site: http://www.omega-pub.com.

Omega Publishing Hse., *(1-886297)* Subs. of B. C. & G. Graphics, 4870 Brookwood Rd., No. 2, Boardman, OH 44512 USA.

Omen Sky Pubns., *(0-9744192)* 3600 Brookewind Way, No. 1201, Lexington, KY 40515 USA Tel 859-543-2026 (phone/fax)
E-mail: omensky@qx.net.

Omma Publishing, *(0-9659436)* Orders Addr.: P.O. Box 151284, Austin, TX 78715-1284 USA.

Omni Arts Publishing, Incorporated *See* **Read Street Publishing, Inc.**

Omnibus Pr., *(0-7119; 0-8256; 0-86001; 1-84449)* Div. of Music Sales Corp., Orders Addr.: 445 Bellvale Rd., Chester, NY 10918-0572 USA Tel 845-469-4699; Fax: 845-469-7544; Toll Free Fax: 800-345-6842; Toll Free: 800-431-7187; Edit Addr.: 257 Park Ave., S., 20th Flr., New York, NY 10010 USA Tel 212-254-2100; Fax: 212-254-2013 Do not confuse with Omnibus Pr., Menasha, WI
E-mail: info@musicsales.com
Web site: http://www.musicsales.com
Dist(s): **Music Sales Corp.**

Omnibus Publishing, *(0-9740599)* 3402 Beresford Ave., Belmont, CA 94002 USA Tel 650-622-9702; Fax: 650-240-3586
E-mail: yuhogan@omnibuspublishing.com
Web site: http://www.omnibuspublishing.com.

†Omnigraphics, Inc., *(0-7808; 1-55888)* Orders Addr.: P.O. Box 625, Holmes, PA 19043 USA Toll Free Fax: 800-875-1340 (orders & customer service); Toll Free: 800-234-1340 (orders & customer service); Edit Addr.: P.O. Box 311640, Detroit, MI 48231-1640 USA (SAN 249-2520)
E-mail: info@omnigraphics.com
Web site: http://www.omnigraphics.com
Dist(s): **Visible Ink Pr.**; *CIP.*

Omniland Bks., *(0-9786593)* 9535 Fairdale Ln., Houston, TX 77063-3841 USA Tel 713-783-7599; P.O. Box 631052, Houston, TX 77063-3841
E-mail: sjdimaggio@sbcglobal.net; admin@omnilandbooks.com
Web site: http://www.omnilandbooks.com.

O'More Publishing, *(0-9717444; 0-9800285)* 423 S. Margin St., Franklin, TN 37064 USA Tel 615-794-4254; Fax: 615-790-1662
E-mail: mhilliard@omorecollege.edu
Web site: http://www.omorecollege.edu.

On Cape Pubns., *(0-9653283; 0-9719547; 0-9758502; 0-9785766)* Orders Addr.: P.O. Box 218, Yarmouth Port, MA 02675 USA Tel 508-385-2108 Toll Free: 877-662-5839; Edit Addr.: 41 Janall Dr., Dennis, MA 02638 USA
Web site: http://www.oncapepublications.com
Dist(s): **Commonwealth Editions.**

On The Fly International LLC, *(0-9721697)* 22 47th St., Suite 1, Weehawken, NJ 07086 USA Tel 917-566-0634; Fax: 201-223-5072
E-mail: arkush@attglobal.net
Web site: http://www.popupcreations.com.

On the Spot! Bks., *(0-9652998)* 1492 Tipperary St., Boulder, CO 80303 USA Tel 303-666-0550
E-mail: onthespotbooks@msn.com
Web site: www.kerryleemaclean.com
Dist(s): **Baker & Taylor Bks.**
Books West
New Leaf Distributing Co., Inc.

On Tour Publishing, *(0-9767234)* Orders Addr.: 512 Northampton St., 151, 303, Edwardsville, PA 18704 USA
E-mail: otp@ontourpublishing.com.

ON Words Publishing, LLC, *(0-9787589)* 8720 Ferguson Ave., Savannah, GA 31406 USA.

Once Upon A Time in a Classroom *Imprint of* **Interactive Media Publishing**

Oncology Nursing Press, Incorporated *See* **Oncology Nursing Society**

Oncology Nursing Society, *(1-890504)* Subs. of Oncology Nursing Society, 125 Enterprise Dr., Pittsburgh, PA 15275-1214 USA (SAN 689-8041) Tel 412-859-6100
E-mail: jholmes@ons.org
Web site: http://www.ons.org.

One Arm Publishing, *(0-9746024)* 3344 Via La Selva, Palos Verdes Estates, CA 90274 USA
E-mail: mariana1969@hotmail.com
Web site: http://www.onearmpublishing.com.

One Armed Operation *See* **One Arm Publishing**

One Faithful Harp Publishing Co., *(0-9666701)* 138 N. 2nd St., Catawissa, PA 17820-1210 USA
E-mail: info@onefaithfulharp.com
Web site: http://www.onefaithfulharp.com.

One Feather Publishing, *(0-9665833)* 6979 Speas Rd., Casper, WY 82604-9148 USA
E-mail: ahill@ajoutfitters.com; sandy@hughes-designs.com.

One Horse Pr., *(0-9725650)* 23 Mechanic St., Girard, PA 16417 USA Tel 814-774-3010
E-mail: onehorsepress@adelphia.net
Web site: http://www.onehorsepress.net
Dist(s): **Partners Bk. Distributing, Inc.**

One Hundred Best Co., LLC, *(0-9706876)* Orders Addr.: 19782 MacAurther Blvd., No. 280, Irvine, CA 92612 USA Tel 949-752-8881; Fax: 947-752-8883; Toll Free Fax: 877-314-0544; Edit Addr.: 4521 Campus Dr., No. 274, Irvine, CA 92612 USA (SAN 253-7915)
E-mail: brierlee@juno.com
Web site: http://find100best.com.

One Little Miracle, *(0-9743948)* 1449 Highland Ct., Stillwater, MN 55082 USA Tel 651-439-3250
E-mail: allieschield@hotmail.com
Web site: http://www.onelittlemiracle.com.

One Love Assn. Books, *(0-9776603)* 306 Trillick Ct., Rolesville, NC 27571 USA (SAN 257-8654)
E-mail: ras@newkemet.com; gerald@newkemet.com
Web site: http://www.newkemet.com/gerald.

One Monkey Books, *(0-9777082)* 156 Diamond St., San Francisco, CA 94114-2414 USA (SAN 850-0320).

One of a Kind Books, Incorporated *See* **Webster Henrietta Publishing**

One Peaceful World Pr., *(0-9628528; 1-882984)* Orders Addr.: P.O. Box 10, Becket, MA 01223 USA (SAN 631-2519) Tel 413-623-2322; Fax: 413-623-6042; Toll Free: 888-322-4095; Edit Addr.: 308 Leland Rd., Becket, MA 01223 USA
E-mail: opw@macrobiotics.org
Web site: http://www.macrobiotics.org.

One Pink Rose, *(0-9722991)* 111921 Rawson Rd., Red Bluff, CA 96080 USA
E-mail: pinkwhirlwind@cablespeed.com; squallsknight@yahoo.com
Web site: http://www.darkfedora.com.

One Reed Pubns., *(0-9628031)* P.O. Box 561, Amherst, MA 01004-0561 USA Tel 413-253-9450
E-mail: ninewind@juno.com
Web site: http://www.onereed.com
Dist(s): **New Leaf Distributing Co., Inc.**

One Rib Pubns., *(0-9722625; 0-9746191)* Orders Addr.: 2001 NW 51st St., Fort Lauderdale, FL 33309 USA Tel 954-489-0141; Edit Addr.: PMB 826, 2001 NW 51st St., Ft. Lauderdale, FL 33309 USA.

1 Sleeve Publishing, *(0-9729153)* Orders Addr.: P.O. Box 1865, North Mankato, MN 56002-1865 USA; Edit Addr.: 442 Belgrade Ave., No. 13, North Mankato, MN 56003 USA
E-mail: onesleeve@hotmail.com.

One Source Publishing, LLC, *(0-9779374)* 63 Gates St, White River Junction, VT 05001 USA Fax: 802-295-5338
E-mail: hphipps@onesourcefg.com.

One Step Productions, *(0-9708674)* P.O. Box 1666, Studio City, CA 91614 USA Tel 818-762-1624; Fax: 818-763-1955
E-mail: judychaikin@yahoo.com
Web site: http://loscabosrestaurantguide.com.

One Voice Recordings, *(0-9708022)* 16835 Halper St., Encino, CA 91436 USA Tel 818-501-8145 (phone/fax)
E-mail: ddavies858@aol.com.

One Way Out, *(0-9742738)* Orders Addr.: P.O. Box 881, Radcliff, KY 40159 USA Tel 270-352-0013; 270-319-3100 (cell)
E-mail: onewayout@bbtel.com.

One Way St., Inc., *(1-58302)* Orders Addr.: P.O. Box 5077, Englewood, CO 80155-5077 USA Tel 303-790-1188; Fax: 303-790-2159; Toll Free: 800-569-4537
E-mail: webmaster@onewaystreet.com
Web site: http://www.onewaystreet.com.

One World Publishing, *(0-9704516)* 695 E. Kingsley Ave., Pomona, CA 91767 USA Tel 900-868-0995; Fax: 900-620-4003 Do not confuse with companies with the same name in New Orleans, LA, Notre Dame, IN, Fountain Valley, CA, Glen Oaks, NY
E-mail: mythra@earthlink.net
Web site: http://www.1worldmusicandpuppets.com.

ONeill, Gene & Assoc., *(0-9747797)* 10163 Potter Rd., Des Plaines, IL 60016 USA.

O'Neill, Hugh & Assocs., *(0-9675919)* Orders Addr.: P.O. Box 1297, Nevada City, CA 95959 USA Tel 530-265-4196; Edit Addr.: 227 Prospect St., Nevada City, CA 95959 USA
E-mail: info@bydb.com
Web site: http://www.bydb.com.

O'Neill, Jan, *(0-9746409)* 5505 Rives Junction, Jackson, MI 49201 USA.

O'Neill Publishing, *(0-9678874)* 1843 S. St. Paul St., Denver, CO 80210 USA Tel 303-757-8842; Fax: 303-757-8841
E-mail: oneillpub@qwest.net.

One-More-Cast for KIDS, *(0-9702117)* P.O. Box 16, Waterville, MN 56096 USA Toll Free: 800-737-0633
E-mail: spatenka@frontiernet.net.

OneShare Educational Pr., *(0-9788438)* 3450 Third St. Bldg. 1-D, San Francisco, CA 94124 USA (SAN 851-7487) Tel 415-777-1777; Fax: 415-777-1677; Toll Free: 888-777-6919
Web site: http://www.oneshare.com.

Onesti Online, *(0-9717022)* P.O. Box 1345, Fall City, WA 98024 USA
E-mail: info@onestionline.com
Web site: http://www.onestionline.con.

Oni Pr., Inc., *(0-9667127; 1-929998; 1-932664)* 6336 SE Milwaukie Ave., PMB 30, Portland, OR 97202 USA Tel 503-233-1377; Fax: 503-233-1477
E-mail: oni1@onipress.com
Web site: http://www.onipress.com
Dist(s): **Diamond Bk. Distributors.**

Onion River Pr., *(0-9657144)* 23 Wildbery Ln., Underhill, VT 05489 USA
E-mail: information@onionriverpress.com
Web site: http://www.onionriverpress.com.

Onjinjinkta Publishing, *(1-892714)* Div. of Onjinjinkta Enterprises, Orders Addr.: 909 SE Everett Mall Way, No. A-120, Everett, WA 98208 USA Tel 425-290-7809; Fax: 425-290-7789; Toll Free: 800-433-8978
E-mail: peter@onjinjinkta.com; jaydavis@onjinjinkta.com
Web site: http://www.rippleon.com; http://www.onjinjinkta.com
Dist(s): **National Bk. Network.**

Onoma Enterprises, *(0-9701184)* P.O. Box 14251, Arlington, TX 76094 USA Tel 817-276-0761
E-mail: onomaenterprises@netscape.net
Web site: http//www.owpetcoff.com.

Onondaga Hill Publishing, *(0-9794908)* 4586 Bloomsbury Dr., Syracuse, NY 13215 USA Tel 315-498-6342
E-mail: matthew@matthewdunn.net; mdunn@imsolv.com
Web site: http://www.matthewdunn.net.

Onstage Publishing, LLC, *(0-9700752; 0-9753367; 0-9790857)* Orders Addr.: 190 Lime Quarry Rd., Suite 106 J, Madison, AL 35758 USA Tel 256-461-0661; Fax: 256-772-3437
E-mail: onstage123@knology.net
Web site: http://www.onstagepublishing.com
Dist(s): **American Wholesale Bk. Co.**
Baker & Taylor Bks.
Southern Bk. Service.

ONTRAK, *(0-9765502)* P.O. Box 205, Bethel, CT 06801-0153 USA Do not confuse with Ontrak in Yorba Linda, CA
E-mail: plumtrees@snet.net.

Onyx Pubns., *(0-9702628)* 2002 Tioga Pass Way, Antioch, CA 94531 USA Do not confuse with Onyx Publications, Inglewood, CA
E-mail: onyxpub04@aol.com.

OPA Publishing, *(0-911041)* Div. of Optimum Performance Associates, 777 W. Chandler Blvd., No. 1322, Chandler, AZ 85244-1764 USA (SAN 254-9255) Tel 480-275-5270; 480-393-1646 (phone/fax); Toll Free: 866-466-6643
E-mail: pmcneese@yahoo.com
Web site: http://www.opapublishing.com
Dist(s): **OPA Publishing & Distributing.**

Opal Creek Pr., LLC, *(1-931105)* 1675 Fir St., S., Salem, OR 97302 USA Tel 866-375-9015; Fax: 503-363-6228
E-mail: kristi@opalcreekpress.com
Web site: http://opalcreekpress.com.

Open Arms Publishing, *(0-9770841)* 607 Knob Ct., Fayetteville, NC 28303 USA Tel 910-258-3941
E-mail: sallymander66@earthlink.net; thoglenrn@yahoo.com
Web site: http://www.oaim.net.

Open Bk. Publishing, *(0-9719167; 0-9740321; 1-932621)* Rte. 2, Box 2607, Birch Tree, MO 65438 USA Tel 573-292-3368; Fax: 573-292-8115 Do not confuse with Open Book Publising Company in Huntington beach, CA
E-mail: lfann@socket.net; ifann@socket.net
Web site: http://www.openbookpublishing.com.

Open Bk. Publishing Co., *(0-9753349)* P.O. Box 3602, Huntington Beach, CA 92649 USA Tel 714-264-7284; Fax: 714-846-6782 Do not confuse with Open Book Publishing in Birch Tree, MO
E-mail: k.cutt@verizon.net
Web site: http://www.openbookpublishingcompany.com.

Open Court Publishing Co., *(0-8126; 0-87548; 0-89688; 0-912050)* Div. of Carus Publishing Co., Orders Addr.: c/o Publishers Group West, 1700 Fourth St., Berkeley, CA 94710 USA Fax: 510-528-3444; Toll Free: 800-788-3123; Edit Addr.: 70 E. Lake St. Ste. 300, Chicago, IL 60601-5945 USA Toll Free: 800-815-2280
E-mail: opencourt@caruspub.com
Web site: http://www.opencourtbooks.com
Dist(s): **Perseus Distribution.**

Open Gate Publishing, *(0-9717036)* Div. of Open Gate Sangha, Inc., Orders Addr.: P.O. Box 782, Los Gatos, CA 95030 USA; Edit Addr.: 647 N. Santa Cruz Ave., Suite A, Los Gatos, CA 95030 USA
E-mail: jerilyn@zen-satsang.org
Web site: http://www.zen-satsang.org
Dist(s): **New Leaf Distributing Co., Inc.**

Open Gate Sangha Publishing *See* **Open Gate Publishing**

Open Hand Publishing, LLC, *(0-940880)* P.O. Box 20207, Greensboro, NC 27420 USA (SAN 219-6174) Tel 336-292-8585; Fax: 336-292-8588
E-mail: info@openhand.com
Web site: http://www.openhand.com.

Open Heaven Pubns., *(0-9752622)* P.O. Box 799, Dallas, GA 30132 USA
Web site: http://www.garyoates.com.

Open Mind Pr., *(0-9755157)* P.O. Box 1241, Stanton, CA 90680-1241 USA Tel 714-322-3049 Do not confuse with Open Mind Press in Garner, NC
E-mail: openmindpress@albalagh.net
Web site: http://www.openmindpress.com.

Open Pages Publishing, *(0-9785937)* Orders Addr.: P.O. Box 420788, Houston, TX 77242 USA (SAN 851-0822); Edit Addr.: 3130 Walnut Bend Ln., Unit No. 317, Houston, TX 77042-4778 USA
E-mail: goodstory@openpagespublishing.com.

Open Spaces Publishing (Rupen), LLC, *(0-9768752)* P.O. Box 496812, Garland, TX 75049-6812 USA Tel 214-770-6673
E-mail: SGTROK@comcast.net.

Open Vision Entertainment Corp., *(0-9721825)* 48 Summer St., Stoneham, MA 02180 USA Tel 781-438-7939; Fax: 781-438-8115
Web site: http://www.open-visions.com
Dist(s): **Fell, Frederick Pubs., Inc.**
STL Distribution North America.

OpenBook Learning, Inc., *(1-893586)* 10945 State Bridge Rd. Suite 401, Rm. 341, Alpharetta, GA 30022-5676 USA Tel 770-325-0300; Fax: 770-325-0301; Toll Free: 877-719-1804
E-mail: tcopeland@openbooksoftware.com; kenny@schoolteam.net
Web site: http://www.openbookenglish.com; http://www.openbooklearning.com; http://www.schoolteam.net.

Openvein, *(0-9764033)* 3760 SE Morrison St., Portland, OR 97214-3210 USA
Web site: http://www.openvein.com/.

Oppelt Pubns., *(0-9662845)* 2218 25th St., Greeley, CO 80631 USA Tel 970-352-8280.

Company

Oppenheim Toy Portfolio, Inc., *(0-9664823; 0-9721050)* 40 E. Ninth St., Suite 14M, New York, NY 10003 USA (SAN 255-2175) Tel 212-598-0502; Fax: 212-598-9709
E-mail: stephanie@toyportfolio.com
Web site: http://www.toyportfolio.com
Dist(s): **Baker & Taylor Bks.**
Brodart Co.

Opposable Thumb Pr., *(0-9786570)* P.O. Box 409107, Chicago, IL 60640 USA
E-mail: Dawn@opposablethumbpress.com
Web site: http://opposablethumbpress.com.

Optimum Publishing *See* **BookWorm, The**

Optiview Publishing, *(0-9723066)* 7725 Martin Mill Pike, Knoxville, TN 37920 USA
E-mail: mmediajohn@ao.com
Web site: http://www.optiviewpubs.com.

Optometric Extension Program Foundation, *(0-943599)* 1921 Carnegie Ave., Suite 3L, Santa Ana, CA 92705-5510 USA (SAN 274-3094) Tel 949-250-8070; Fax: 949-250-8157
E-mail: smc.oep@worldnet.att.net
Web site: http://www.oep.org.

OPUS II Bks., *(0-9796210)* Orders Addr.: 1216 Purple Sage Loop, Castle Rock, CO 80104 USA (SAN 853-9367) Tel 720-371-1872
E-mail: egualberto@opusiibooks.com
Web site: http://www.opusiibooks.com.

Oracle *See* **Dansu Pubs., LLC**

Oracle Institute Press, LLC, The, *(0-9773929)* Div. of The Oracle Institute, Orders Addr.: P.O. Box 368, Hamilton, VA 20159 USA (SAN 257-4780) Tel 540-882-9252 (phone/fax)
E-mail: laura@TheOracleInstitute.org
Web site: http://www.TheOracleInstitute.org.

Orage Publishing, *(0-9740901)* 1460 Wren Ct., Punta Gorda, FL 33950 USA Tel 941-639-6144
E-mail: ntoupsschmitt@comcast.net.

Orange Avenue Publishing, *(0-9772660; 0-9790173; 0-9800732)* 35 Stillman St., Suite 121, San Francisco, CA 94107 USA ; *Imprints:* Zest Books (Zest Bks)
Web site: http://www.orangeavenue.com
Dist(s): **Independent Pubs. Group.**

Orange Boy Bks., *(0-9724803)* P.O. Box 1343, Chapel Hill, NC 27514-1343 USA Tel 910-322-6335
E-mail: anthonystokes@unc.edu.

Orange Cty. Historical Society, Inc., *(1-932547)* 130 Caroline St., Orange, VA 22960 USA Tel 540-672-5366 (Wednesday afternoon)
E-mail: info@orangecohist.org
Web site: http://www.orangecohist.org.

Orange Creations, Inc., *(0-9704613)* P.O. Box 26121, Overland Park, KS 66225 USA Tel 913-927-9027
E-mail: hojax@swbell.net.

Orange Frazer Pr., *(0-9619637; 1-882203; 1-933197)* Orders Addr.: P.O. Box 214, Wilmington, OH 45177 USA (SAN 245-9299)
E-mail: ofrazer@erinet.com
Web site: http://www.orangefrazer.com
Dist(s): **Baker & Taylor Bks.**

Orange, Michael Nicholas, *(0-9758877)* Orders Addr.: P.O. Box 236, Half Moon Bay, CA 94019 USA; Edit Addr.: Pobox 236, Half Moon Bay, CA 94019 USA.

OrangeFoot Publishing Co., *(0-9760651)* P.O. Box 3694, Pittsburgh, PA 15230-3694 USA
E-mail: orangefootpublishing@zoominternet.net; info@orangefootpublishing.com.

Orbigo, *(0-9708398)* 9728 Third Ave., Suite 426, Brooklyn, NY 11209 USA Tel 718-621-0225 (phone/fax)
E-mail: support@orbigo.com
Web site: http://www.orbigo.com.

Orbin Publishing, Ltd., *(0-9676205)* 118 Sunnymeadow Ln., Reisterstown, MD 21136 USA Tel 410-526-5210; Fax: 202-783-6947
E-mail: lgitomer@erols.com.

†Orbis Bks., *(0-88344; 1-57075)* Div. of The Catholic Foreign Mission Society of America, Inc., Orders Addr.: P.O. Box 308, Maryknoll, NY 10545-0308 USA (SAN 202-828X) Tel 914-941-7590 ext 2487; Fax: 914-945-0670; Toll Free: 800-258-5838
E-mail: orbisbooks@maryknoll.org
Web site: http://www.orbisbooks.com; *CIP.*

Orca Bk. Pubs. USA, *(0-920501; 1-55143)* Orders Addr.: P.O. Box 468, Custer, WA 98240-0468 USA (SAN 630-9674) Tel 250-380-1229; Fax: 250-380-1892; Toll Free: 800-210-5277
E-mail: orca@orcabook.com
Web site: http://www.orcabook.com.

Orchard Academy Pr. *Imprint of* **Windstorm Creative**

Orchard Bks. *Imprint of* **Scholastic, Inc.**

Orchard Gang Publishing, *(0-9700157)* Box 103, Rte. 1, Box 91A1, Lindside, WV 24951 USA Tel 304-753-4037 (phone/fax)
E-mail: apporga@gva.net
Web site: http://geocities.com.

Orchid Isle Publishing Co., *(1-887916)* 131 Halai St., Hilo, HI 96720 USA.

Orchid Publishing Co., *(0-9740898)* 14906 SW 104 St., Miami, FL 33196 USA.

†Orchises Pr., *(0-914061; 1-932535)* P.O. Box 20602, Alexandria, VA 22320-1602 USA (SAN 287-4962) Fax: 703-993-1161
E-mail: lathbury@gmu.edu
Web site: http://mason.gmu.edu/rlathbur
Dist(s): **Washington Bk. Distributors;** *CIP.*

Oregon Catholic Pr., *(0-915531; 0-915903; 1-57992)* 5536 NE Hassalo, Portland, OR 97213 USA (SAN 291-316X) Tel 503-281-1191; Toll Free Fax: 800-462-7329; Toll Free: 800-548-8749; 800-977-5397
E-mail: liturgy@ocp.org
Web site: http://www.ocp.org
Dist(s): **Spring Arbor Distributors, Inc.**

Oregon Ctr. for Applied Science, Inc., *(1-933898)* 260 E. 11th Ave., Eugene, OR 97401-3291 USA (SAN 850-5284) Toll Free: 888-349-5472
E-mail: orcas@orcasinc.com
Web site: http://www.orcasinc.com.

†Oregon Historical Society Pr., *(0-87595)* 1200 SW Park Ave., Portland, OR 97205-2483 USA (SAN 202-8301) Tel 503-222-1741; Fax: 503-221-2035
E-mail: press@ohs.org
Web site: http://www.ohs.org
Dist(s): **Univ. of Washington Pr.;** *CIP.*

Oregon Institute of Science & Medicine, *(0-942487)* 2251 Dick George Rd., Cave Junction, OR 97523 USA (SAN 667-3163) Tel 541-592-4142; Fax: 541-592-2597
E-mail: art@oism.org
Web site: http://www.oism.org.

Oregon Sea Grant, *(1-881826)* 322 Kerr, Admin. Bldg., Corvallis, OR 97331-2134 USA Tel 541-737-2716; Fax: 541-737-7958; Toll Free: 800-375-9360
E-mail: sea.grant.communications@orst.edu
Web site: http://www.seagrant.orst.edu.

Oregon State Univ. Extension Service, *(1-931979)* Extension & Station Communications 422 Kerr Administration, Corvallis, OR 97331 USA Fax: 541-737-0817
Web site: http://eesc.orst.edu.

†Oregon State Univ. Pr., *(0-87071)* 500 Kerr Administration Bldg., Corvallis, OR 97331-2122 USA (SAN 202-8328) Tel 541-737-3166; Fax: 541-737-3170; Toll Free: 800-426-3797
E-mail: osu.press@oregonstate.edu
Web site: http://osu.orst.edu/dept/press
Dist(s): **American Society of Civil Engineers**
Partners Bk. Distributing, Inc.
Univ. of Arizona Pr.; *CIP.*

Oregon Treasure Publishing, *(0-9759475)* 64830 Grande Loop, Bend, OR 97701-8823 USA
E-mail: otrc@aol.com
Web site: http://www.oregontreasure.com
Dist(s): **Partners/West.**

O'Reilly & Associates, Incorporated *See* **O'Reilly Media, Inc.**

O'Reilly Media, Inc., *(0-937175; 1-56592; 3-89721; 3-930673; 4-900900; 0-596; 4-87311; 1-60033)* Orders Addr.: 1005 Gravenstein Hwy. N., Sebastopol, CA 95472 USA (SAN 658-5973) Tel 707-827-7000; Fax: 707-829-0104; Toll Free: 800-998-9938; Edit Addr.: 10 Fawcett St. Ste. 4, Cambridge, MA 02138-1175 USA Toll Free: 800-775-7731; 4 Castle St, Farnham, GU9 7HR Tel 01252 71 17 76; Fax: 01252 73 42 11
E-mail: order@oreilly.com; information@oreilly.co.uk; nuts@ora.com
Web site: http://www.oreilly.com; http://www.editions-oreilly.fr; http://oreilly.co.uk; http://oreilly.com.tw; http://www.ora.com; http://www.oreilly.fr/; http://www.oreilly.com.cn/; http://www.orielly.de
Dist(s): **Ingram Pub. Services**
NetLibrary, Inc.

OREP Edition & Communication (FRA) *(2-912925; 2-915762) Dist. by* **Casemate Pubs.**

Oresjozef Pubns., *(1-885566)* 167 Canton St., Randolph, MA 02368 USA Tel 781-961-5855; Toll Free: 617-851-0100
E-mail: ojozef@massed.net
Dist(s): **Educa Vision**
Haitiana Pubns., Inc.

Original Pubns., *(0-942272)* Subs. of Maximo, Inc., 59 Central Ave. Ste. 4, Farmingdale, NY 11735-6902 USA (SAN 133-0225) Toll Free: 888-622-8581.

Originals by Ellsworth E., *(0-9640483)* 9706 Dublin Dr., Manassas, VA 20109 USA Fax: 703-530-0559
E-mail: Miw25ees@aol.com
Dist(s): **A.F. Eurotool, Inc.**

Orion Bks. Ltd. (GBR) *(0-7528; 1-85797; 1-85881; 1-905619) Dist. by* **Trafalgar.**

Orion Bks. Ltd. (GBR) *(0-7528; 1-85797; 1-85881; 1-905619) Dist. by* **Sterling.**

Orion Children's Bks. (GBR) *(1-85881; 1-84255) Dist. by* **Trafalgar.**

Orion Children's Bks. (GBR) *(1-85881; 1-84255) Dist. by* **IPG Chicago.**

Orion Publishing Group, Ltd. (GBR) Dist. by Trafalgar.

Orion Publishing Group, Ltd. (GBR) Dist. by Sterling.

Orion Publishing Group, Ltd. (GBR) Dist. by IPG Chicago.

Orion Society, The, *(0-913098)* 187 Main St., Great Barrington, MA 01230-1601 USA (SAN 204-0182) Tel 413-528-4422; Fax: 413-528-0676; Toll Free: 888-909-6568
E-mail: orion@orionsociety.org
Web site: http://www.oriononline.org
Dist(s): **Biblio Distribution**
SteinerBooks, Inc.

Orion-Cosmos, *(0-9752725)* 3609 Candleknoll Cir., San Antonio, TX 78244 USA
E-mail: customerservice@orion-cosmos.com
Web site: http://www.orion-cosmos.com.

Orison Pubs., *(0-9763800)* P.O. Box 188, Grantham, PA 17027 USA Tel 717-433-7985; Fax: 717-427-1525
E-mail: marshablessing@comcast.net.

Orphan Pr., *(1-58265)* Orders Addr.: P.O. Box 324, Croton Falls, NY 10519 USA; Edit Addr.: 2 Avery Rd., Carmel, NY 10512 USA.

Orphan Train Heritage Society of America, Inc. (OTHSA), *(0-9635902)* Orders Addr.: P.O. Box 496, Johnson, AR 72741-0496 USA Fax: 501-756-0769; Edit Addr.: 4912 Trout Farm Rd., Springdale, AR 72762 USA Tel 501-756-2780.

Orpheus Bks., Ltd. (GBR) *(1-901323) Dist. by* **CPG Pub Inc.**

Ortells, Alfredo Editorial S.L. (ESP) *(84-7189) Dist. by* **Continental Bk.**

Oryx Pr. *Imprint of* **Greenwood Publishing Group, Inc.**

Osage Bend Publishing Co., *(0-9626245; 1-58389)* 213 Belair Dr., Jefferson City, MO 65109 USA Tel 573-635-5580; Toll Free: 888-243-9772
E-mail: OBPC@Socket.net
Dist(s): **Follett Library Resources.**

Osborne Enterprises Publishing, *(0-932117)* P.O. Box 255, Port Townsend, WA 98368 USA (SAN 242-7567) Tel 360-385-1200; Fax: 360-385-6572; Toll Free: 800-246-3255 (orders only)
E-mail: jpo@olympus.net
Web site: http://www.jerryosborne.com.

Osborne Pr., *(1-928856)* Div. of David M. Osborne, Inc., 16726 Comstock, Livonia, MI 48154 USA Tel 734-464-7002; Fax: 734-464-6837
E-mail: osborne@mich.com
Web site: http://www.mich.com/~osborne.

Osborne/McGraw-Hill *See* **McGraw-Hill Osborne**

Oshkosh B'Gosh, Inc., *(1-929174)* Orders Addr.: P.O. Box 300, Oshkosh, WI 54903-0300 USA; Edit Addr.: 112 Otter Ave., Oshkosh, WI 54902-0300 USA Tel 920-232-4272; Fax: 920-232-4434
E-mail: bnancy@bgosh.com
Web site: http://www.oshkoshbgosh.com.

Osmer, Harold L. Publishing, *(0-9659533)* Orders Addr.: P.O. Box 4741, Chatsworth, CA 91313 USA Tel 818-999-1878; Edit Addr.: 7400 Liz Ct., West Hills, CA 91304 USA
E-mail: laracing@value.net
Web site: http://www.zoomie.com.

Osmosis, LLC, *(0-9727886)* 8 Findlay Ave., Hartsdale, NY 10530-2613 USA Tel 914-328-8898; Fax: 914-328-1124; Toll Free: 866-676-6747
E-mail: osmosis@earthlink.net
Web site: http://www.learningbyosmosis.com; http://www.osmosis.tv.

Osprey Pr., *(0-9673711)* 2107 Ibis Dr., Buffalo, MN 55313 USA Tel 763-682-4558 Do not confuse with companies with the same or similar names in St. Johnsbury, VT, Wiscasset, ME
E-mail: ospreypress@charter.net
Web site: http://www.planetearthhome.com
Dist(s): **Random Hse., Inc.**

Osprey Publishing, Ltd. (GBR) *(0-540; 0-85045; 1-85532; 1-84176; 1-84603) Dist. by* **Random.**

Osteogenesis Imperfecta Foundation, *(0-9642189)* 804 W. Diamond Ave., Suite 210, Gaithersburg, MD 20878 USA Tel 301-947-0083; Fax: 301-947-0456; Toll Free: 800-981-2663
E-mail: bonelink@oif.org
Web site: http://www.oif.org.

Ostrageous Publishing, *(0-9785144)* P.O. Box 2867, Hot Springs, AK 71914 USA Tel 501-525-4245.

Otakorp, Inc., *(0-9770461)* 620 Bishop Pl., Northampton, PA 18067-9563 USA Tel 646-853-5226
E-mail: publications@otakon.org
Web site: http://www.otakon.org.

Otherworlds Sci-Fi *Imprint of* **Branch & Vine Pubs., LLC**

Otis & Randolph Pr., *(0-9752516)* 1229 Bishop's Lodge Rd., Santa Fe, NM 87501 USA.

Otis, Dorcas Marie *See* **Zion Publishing**

Otter Creek Pr., Inc., *(1-890611)* 3154 Nautilus Rd., Middleburg, FL 32068 USA Tel 904-264-0465; Fax: 904-264-0465; Toll Free: 800-378-8163
E-mail: otterpress@aol.com; whill73528@aol.com
Web site: http://www.otterpress.com
Dist(s): **AtlasBooks Distribution.**

Otter Run Bks. LLC, *(0-9760796)* 16965 Nicolet Rd., Townsend, WI 54175 USA Tel 715-276-6515 (phone/fax)
E-mail: kathiemarsh@yahoo.com
Web site: http://www.otterrunbooks.com.

OTTN Publishing, *(1-59556)* 16 Risler Street, Stockton, NJ 08559 USA Tel 609-397-4005; Fax: 609-397-4007
E-mail: jgallagher@ottnpublishing.com
Web site: http://www.ottnpublishing.com.

†Our Child Pr., *(0-9611872; 1-893516)* P.O. Box 4379, Philadelphia, PA 19118 USA (SAN 682-272X) Tel 610-308-8988
E-mail: ourchildpress@aol.com
Web site: http://www.ourchildpress.com; *CIP.*

Our Companions, Inc., *(0-9753257)* 84 N. Acoma Blvd., No. 100-33, Lake Havasu City, AZ 86403 USA Tel 928-486-4508.

Our Kids Pubn., Inc., *(1-892089)* Orders Addr.: P.O. Box 59790, Chicago, IL 60659-0790 USA Tel 847-398-1041; Fax: 847-398-0058.

Our Lady of Victory Schl., *(1-931555)* 103 E. Tenth Ave., Post Falls, ID 83854 USA Tel 208-773-7265; Fax: 208-773-1951
E-mail: lepanto@olvs.org
Web site: http://www.olvs.org.

Our Little Secret Pr., *(0-9720978)* 1524 E. Park Rd., Grand Island, NY 14072 USA Tel 716-773-4866.

Our Story Pubns., *(0-9765554)* P.O. Box 7514, Round Rock, TX 78683 USA Tel 512-663-1471
E-mail: nicoleeutsey@ourstorypublications.com
Web site: http://www.ourstorypublications.com.

Our Sunday Visitor, Publishing Div., *(0-87973; 0-9707756; 1-931709; 1-59276)* 200 Noll Plaza, Huntington, IN 46750 USA (SAN 202-8344) Tel 260-356-8400; Fax: 260-359-9117; Toll Free: 800-348-2440
E-mail: osvbooks@osv.com; ntopp@osv.com
Web site: http://www.osv.com
Dist(s): **Baker & Taylor International**
Spring Arbor Distributors, Inc.

Our World of Books, *(0-9777979; 1-60219)* P.O. Box 218, Yarmouth Port, MA 02675 USA Toll Free: 877-662-5839; 41 Janall Dr., Dennis, MA 02638
E-mail: adam@goodnightourworld.com
Web site: http://www.goodnightourworld.com
Dist(s): **Independent Pubs. Group**
Islander Group.

OurRainbow Pr., LLC, *(0-9752860; 1-934214)* 2600 Penrick Dr., Marietta, GA 30064-1809 USA Tel 770-514-8794; Fax: 603-761-5863
E-mail: publisher@ourrainbow.com; ameadows@ourrainbow.com
Web site: http://www.ourrainbowpress.com.

Out in Left Field, *(0-9704258)* 13879 Phelps Rd., Charlevoix, MI 49720 USA Tel 231-547-9944; Fax: 231-547-9799
E-mail: kimleft@northlink.net
Web site: http://www.kimleft.com.

Out of Our Mind, Incorporated *See* **Mora Art Studio**

Out of the Box, *(0-9726849)* P.O. Box 24234, Minneapolis, MN 55424 USA Tel 612-822-5151; Fax: 612-823-4164
E-mail: info@ootbooks.com
Web site: http://www.ootbooks.com
Dist(s): **Baker & Taylor Bks.**
Brodart Co.
Follett Library Resources
Quality Bks., Inc.

Out of the Box Publishing, Inc., *(0-9664517; 0-9708554; 0-9716729; 1-932359)* P.O. Box 521, Richland Center, WI 53581 USA (SAN 760-5269) Toll Free: 800-540-4201 Do not confuse with Out of the Box Publishing, Cinncinati, OH
E-mail: mark@otb-games.com; brad@otb-games.com
Web site: http://www.otb-games.com.

Outback Publications *See* **OutbackUSA, LLC**

OutbackUSA, LLC, *(1-878261)* Orders Addr.: P.O. Box 470309, Aurora, CO 80047-0309 USA Tel 303-910-7647
E-mail: Sales@OutbackUSA.com
Web site: http://www.outbackusa.com.

Outdoor Communications Co., *(0-9678156)* P.O. Box 5851, Aloha, OR 97007-5851 USA Tel 503-642-1185 (phone/fax)
E-mail: RobRutt@msn.com.

Outdoor Originals LLC, *(0-9762971)* 1052 California Ave. W., Saint Paul, MN 55117 USA.

Outdoor Writing & Photography, Limited *See* **Visions Of Nature**

Outland Communications, LLC, *(0-9714102; 1-932820)* Orders Addr.: P.O. Box 534, Skaneateles, NY 13152 USA; Edit Addr.: 4022 Mill Rd., Skaneateles, NY 13152-9319 USA
Web site: http://www.outlandbooks.com
Dist(s): **Perseus Distribution.**

Outlaw Bks., *(0-9656946)* 419 Centre St., Hereford, TX 79045 USA Tel 806-364-2838; Fax: 806-364-5522; Toll Free: 888-583-9408 Do not confuse with Outlaw Books, Bozeman, MT
Dist(s): **Hervey's Booklink & Cookbook Warehouse.**

Outlaw Pubns., *(1-886709)* Orders Addr.: P.O. Box 1424, Red Oak, TX 75154 USA Tel 972-504-6608; Edit Addr.: P.O. Box 3043, Desoto, TX 75115 USA.

Outlet Book Company, Incorporated *See* **Random Hse. Value Publishing**

Outlook Publishing, Inc., *(0-9711667)* Orders Addr.: P.O. Box 278, Laurel, MT 59044 USA Tel 406-628-4412; Fax: 406-628-8260; Edit Addr.: 415 E. Main St., Laurel, MT 59044 USA
E-mail: publisher@laureloutlook.com.

Out-of-Body Travel Foundation, The, *(0-615)* 25 E. Andrew Ln., Cortez, CO 81321 USA
E-mail: marilynhughes@outofbodytravel.org
Web site: http://www.outofbodytravel.org
Dist(s): **Lulu.com.**

Out-of-the-Mist Pr., *(0-9664864)* P.O. Box 3766, Danbury, CT 06813 USA
E-mail: theMist@SBCglobal.net; walker113@mac.com
Web site: http://quickmist.com.

Outskirts Press, Inc., *(0-9725874; 1-932672; 1-59800; 1-4327)* 10940 S. Parker Rd.- 515, Parker, CO 80134 USA (SAN 256-5420) Toll Free: 888-672-6657 (toll free phone/fax)
E-mail: jeanine@outskirtspress.com
Web site: http://www.outskirtspress.com
Dist(s): **AtlasBooks Distribution.**

Oval Window Pr., Inc., *(0-9669474)* 4650 Lake Forest Dr., Suite 580, Cincinnati, OH 45252 USA (SAN 299-8491)
E-mail: ovalwin@aol.com
Web site: http://www.bugtales.com.

Ovation Bks., *(1-933538; 0-9790275)* 2100 Kramer Ln., Suite 300, Austin, TX 78758 USA Tel 512-478-2028; Fax: 512-478-2117
E-mail: awillis@bookpros.com
Dist(s): **National Bk. Network.**

Over the Rainbow Productions, *(0-9661330)* 1715 Rosedale, Suite B, Houston, TX 77004 USA Tel 713-523-1276; Fax: 713-526-0571
E-mail: apb3@prodigy.net
Web site: http://www.imneecie.com.

Overcomer Pr., *(0-9718999)* P.O. Box 37764, Rock Hill, SC 29732 USA.

Overdue Bks., *(0-9786850)* P.O. Box 259462, Madison, WI 53725 USA Do not confuse with Overdue Books in West Linn, OR
E-mail: theoverduebooks@yahoo.com.

Overdue Media LLC, *(0-9740353)* 2518 Royal Ct., E., Seattle, WA 98112-2248 USA
E-mail: unshelved@overduemedia.com
Web site: http://www.overduemedia.com
Dist(s): **Diamond Bk. Distributors.**

Overeaters Anonymous, Inc., *(0-9609898; 1-889681)* Orders Addr.: P.O. Box 44020, Rio Rancho, NM 87174-4020 USA (SAN 237-2134) Tel 505-891-2664; Fax: 505-891-4320; Edit Addr.: 6075 Zenith Ct., NE, Rio Rancho, NM 87124-6424 USA
E-mail: nlippel@oa.org
Web site: http://www.overeatersanonymous.org
Dist(s): **Hazelden Publishing & Educational Services.**

†Overlook Pr., The, *(0-87951; 1-58567; 1-59020)* 141 Wooster St., 4th Flr., New York, NY 10012 USA (SAN 202-8360) Tel 212-673-2210; Fax: 212-673-2296
Web site: http://www.overlookpress.com
Dist(s): **Penguin Group (USA) Inc.**; *CIP.*

Overmountain Pr., *(0-932807; 0-9644613; 1-57072)* P.O. Box 1261, Johnson City, TN 37605 USA (SAN 687-6641) Tel 423-926-2691; Fax: 423-232-1252; Toll Free: 800-992-2691 (orders only) ; *Imprints:* Silver Dagger Mysteries (Silver Dagger)
E-mail: beth@overmtn.com
Web site: http://www.silverdaggermysteries.com; http://www.overmountainpress.com
Dist(s): **Independent Pubs. Group.**

Overstreet, Mae *See* **Overstreet Pub. & Mktg.**

Overstreet Pub. & Mktg., *(0-9746253)* P.O. Box 3808, Yountville, CA 94599 USA
Web site: http://www.bettyoverstreet.com.

Overview Publishing, *(0-9760685)* 1081 Crown River Pkwy., McDonough, GA 30252 USA Tel 678-583-0898
E-mail: cindy@overviewpublishing.com
Web site: http://www.overviewpublishing.com
Dist(s): **Baker & Taylor Bks.**
Quality Bks., Inc.

Owen, Peter Ltd. (GBR) *(0-7206) Dist. by* **Dufour.**

Owen, Richard C. Pubs., Inc., *(0-913461; 1-57274; 1-878450)* P.O. Box 585, Katonah, NY 10536 USA (SAN 285-1814) Tel 914-232-3903; Fax: 914-232-3977; Toll Free: 800-336-5588 (orders) ; *Imprints:* Meet the Author (Meet Author); Books for Young Learners (Bks Yng Learn)
Web site: http://www.RCOwen.com.

Owen, V., *(0-9653334)* P.O. Box 1692, Aptos, CA 95001-1692 USA Tel 831-688-3154.

Owens Pubns., *(0-9649393)* 8525 Dewey St., Crown Point, IN 46307 USA Tel 219-365-1113 Do not confuse with Owens Pubns., Wilsonville, OR.

Owensby, Legertha, *(0-9742789)* 6820 Chiffview Dr., No. E, Indianapolis, IN 46214 USA
E-mail: legethao@yahoo.com
Web site: http://earvino.tripod.com.

Owl Bks. *Imprint of* **Holt, Henry & Co.**

Owl Creek Farm Bks. *Imprint of* **Owl Tree Pr.**

Owl Hollow Publishing, *(0-9726826)* 13704 Lawrence 2187, Verona, MO 65769 USA Tel 417-498-6964
E-mail: zona@mo-net.com.

Owl of Minerva Press *See* **Minerva Bks.**

Owl Tree Pr., *(1-929424)* P.O. Box 292, Saint Helens, OR 97051 USA Tel 503-397-3667; Fax: 503-397-3684 ; *Imprints:* Owl Creek Farm Books (Owl Creek Farm Bks)
E-mail: jdnyberg@ados.com
Web site: http://www.owltreepress.com.

Owlet Paperbacks for Young Readers *Imprint of* **Holt, Henry & Co.**

Owlink Media, *(1-57994)* Orders Addr.: 210 SE Cedar Hill Ln., Shelton, WA 98584 USA Tel 425-788-6155 (info, ordering)
E-mail: debbie@owlink.net
Web site: http://www.owlinkmedia.com; http://www.wildernessawareness.org.

Owl's Hse. Pr., *(1-891992)* 40951 Fremont Blvd., Fremont, CA 94538-4307 USA Toll Free: 888-848-6957
E-mail: hoot@owlshouse.com
Web site: http://www.owlshouse.com.

Oxbow Bks., *(0-9771129)* 76 Presidio Dr., Novato, CA 94949 USA
E-mail: dchaller@horizoncable.com.

Oxcart Pubns, *(0-9717147)* 4910 Rock Valley, Marietta, GA 30066-1147 USA Tel 770-926-3334
E-mail: oxcarat1212@aol.com; oxcart1212@aol.com.

Oxen Bks., *(0-9713773)* N. 3748 Bowers Rd., Lake Geneva, WI 53147 USA Tel 262-248-4710.

Oxfam Publishing (GBR) *(0-85598; 971-91752) Dist. by* **Stylus Pub VA.**

Oxford Museum Pr., *(1-930127)* 5790 Stillwell-Beckett Rd., Oxford, OH 45056 USA Tel 513-756-9386; Fax: 513-756-9123; Toll Free: 877-127-1941
E-mail: omp@oxfordmuseumpress.com
Web site: http://www.oxfordmuseumpress.com.

Oxford Univ. Pr., Inc., *(0-19)* Orders Addr.: 2001 Evans Rd., Cary, NC 27513 USA (SAN 202-5892) Tel 919-677-0977 (general voice); Fax: 919-677-1303 (customer service); Toll Free: 800-445-9714 (customer service - inquiry); 800-451-7556 (customer service - orders); Edit Addr.: 198 Madison Ave., New York, NY 10016-4314 USA (SAN 202-5884) Tel 212-726-6000 (general voice); Fax: 212-726-6440 (general fax)
E-mail: custserv@oup-usa.org; orders@oup-usa.org
Web site: http://www.oup.com/us
Dist(s): **Chicago Distribution Ctr.**
Hancock Hse. Pubs.
NetLibrary, Inc.
World Bank Pubns.

Oxfordshire Publishing Co., *(0-9745895)* 900 Lincoln Hwy., Box 180, East Mckeesport, PA 15035 USA Tel 412-823-1700
E-mail: blissman@pghmail.com.

Oxmoor Hse., Inc., *(0-8487)* Orders Addr.: Leisure Arts 5701 Ranch Dr., Little Rock, AR 72223 USA; Edit Addr.: 2100 Lakeshore Dr., Birmingham, AL 35209 USA Tel 205-445-6000; Fax: 205-445-6078; Toll Free: 800-633-4910
E-mail: nicholsonl@sunset.com
Web site: http://www.oxmoorhouse.com/
Dist(s): **Leisure Arts, Inc.**

Oxton Hse., Pubs., *(1-881929)* Orders Addr.: P.O. Box 209, Farmington, ME 04938 USA Tel 207-779-1923; Fax: 207-779-0623; Toll Free: 800-539-7323
E-mail: info@oxtonhouse.com
Web site: http://www.oxtonhouse.com.

Oyate, *(0-9625175)* 2702 Matthews St., Berkeley, CA 94702 USA Tel 510-848-6700; Fax: 510-848-4815
E-mail: oyate@oyate.org
Web site: http://www.oyate.org
Dist(s): **SPD-Small Pr. Distribution.**

Ozark Publishing, *(1-56763; 1-59381)* P.O. Box 228, Prairie Grove, AR 72753 USA (SAN 298-4318) Tel 214-649-0188; Fax: 501-846-2853; Toll Free: 800-321-5671
E-mail: srg304@aol.com
Web site: http://www.ozarkpublishing.com
Dist(s): **Central Programs**
Gumdrop Bks.

Ozone Publishing, Corp., *(0-9773285)* PMB 500, RR-8 Box 1995, Bayamon, PR 00956-9676 USA Tel 787-562-5200; Fax: 787-730-0987
E-mail: info@ozonepublishing.net
Web site: http://www.ozonepublishing.net.

Ozten, *(0-9752966)* 347 NW 87th St., Seattle, WA 98117 USA
E-mail: shout@ozten.com
Web site: http://www.ozten.com.

P & R Publishing, *(0-87552; 1-59638)* Orders Addr.: 1102 Marble Hill Rd., Harmony, Phillipsburg, NJ 08865 USA (SAN 658-1463) Tel 908-454-0505; Fax: 908-859-2390; Toll Free: 800-631-0094 Do not confuse with P & R Publishing Co. in Sioux Center, IA
E-mail: tara@prpbooks.com; jesse@prpbooks.com
Web site: http://www.prpbooks.com
Dist(s): **CRC Pubns.**
Christian Literature Crusade, Inc.

P B M Global, Publishing, *(0-9673649)* P.O. Box 1625, Newport Beach, CA 92659 USA
E-mail: edie1950@mac.com.

PCI Educational Publishing, *(1-884074; 1-58804)* 4560 Lockhill-Selma, Suite 100, San Antonio, TX 78265-4270 USA Tel 210-377-1999; Fax: 210-377-1121; Toll Free Fax: 888-259-8284; Toll Free: 800-594-4263
E-mail: lboulet@pcieducation.com
Web site: http://www.pcieducation.com
Dist(s): **Attainment Co., Inc.**

P E A Pr. *Imprint of* **Phillips Exeter Academy Pr., The**

PJN & Assocs., *(0-9715198)* 1537 Gibson Rd., Waxahachie, TX 75165 USA Tel 972-935-9031; Fax: 419-818-8005
E-mail: rebelssong@aol.com
Web site: http://www.breakthroughpromotions.com.

P K I Ds, *(1-929524)* P.O. Box 5666, Vancouver, WA 98668 USA Tel 360-695-0293; Fax: 360-695-6941; Toll Free: 877-557-5437
E-mail: pkids@pkids.org
Web site: http://www.pkids.org.

PLC Pubns., *(0-9652602; 0-9703772)* Div. of Presbyterian Lay Committee, Orders Addr.: P.O. Box 2210, Lenoir, NC 28645 USA Tel 828-758-8716; Edit Addr.: 136 Tremont Pk. Dr., Lenoir, NC 28645 USA Fax: 828-758-0920; Toll Free: 800-368-0110
E-mail: laymanletters@layman.org
Web site: http://www.layman.org.

PLC Publishing, *(0-9672309)* 6 Glaize View Dr., Town & Country, MO 63017-8410 USA Tel 314-878-7801.

P L P *Imprint of* **Pro Lingua Pr.**

PL Studio, *(0-9667652)* 142-10 58th Ave., Flushing, NY 11355 USA Tel 718-886-0102.

P.O.W. (Pubns. of Worth), *(1-877898)* 2561 E. 1980 N., Layton, UT 84040-7928 USA.

P R I Publishing, *(0-9703269)* 53 CR 2575, Lakeville, OH 44638 USA (SAN 253-3693) Tel 419-827-2304; Fax: 419-827-2410 Do not confuse with PRI Publishing, Tampa, FL
E-mail: proreach@aol.com
Dist(s): **Baker & Taylor Bks.**

P4K Publishing, *(0-9744570)* 5699 Kanan Rd., Suite 373, Agoura Hills, CA 91301 USA Toll Free: 866-744-4948
E-mail: publishing@prosperity4kids.com
Web site: http://www.prosperity4kids.com.

Paarmann, Al International, *(0-9715963)* 368 El Gaucho Rd., Santa Barbara, CA 93111 USA Tel 805-964-2830 (phone/fax)
E-mail: alpaarmann@aol.com.

Pace Products, Inc., *(1-58295; 1-880592)* P.O. Box 470970, Lake Monroe, FL 32747-0970 USA Toll Free. 800-541-7670 ; *Imprints:* Beehive Book (Beehive Book)
E-mail: PaceProd@aol.com
Web site: http://www.paceplace.com.

PaceSetter Direct, Inc., *(1-893053)* P.O. Box 12637, Oregon, UT 84412 USA
E-mail: pacesetter@sisna.com.

Pacific Bks., *(1-885375)* Orders Addr.: P.O. Box 3562, Santa Barbara, CA 93130 USA (SAN 630-2548) Tel 805-687-8340; Fax: 805-687-2514; Edit Addr.: 2573 Treasure Dr., Santa Barbara, CA 93105 USA ; *Imprints:* Shore Line Press (Shore Line Pr).

Pacific Heritage Bks., *(0-9635906; 1-928753)* Orders Addr.: P.O. Box 998, Palos Verdes, CA 90274 USA Tel 310-541-8818; Fax: 310-791-9069; Toll Free: 888-810-9891; Edit Addr.: 532 Via del Monte, Palos Verdes Estates, CA 90274 USA
E-mail: amawong@worldnet.att.net
Web site: http://wind-water.com
Dist(s): **Distributors, The**
Quality Bks., Inc.

Pacific Island Bks., 2802 E. 132nd Cir., Thornton, CO 80241 USA Fax: 603-368-6628; Toll Free: 888-492-6657 (888-49-BOOKS)
E-mail: pacificbks@aol.com
Web site: http://www.pacificislandbooks.com.

Pacific Isle Publishing Co., P.O. Box 827, Makawao, HI 96768 USA
E-mail: hanalei@maui.net.

Pacific Northwest Ballet, *(0-9745415)* 301 Mercer St., Seattle, WA 98109 USA Tel 206-441-9411; Fax: 206-441-2440
E-mail: kaolivier@mac.com
Web site: http://www.pnb.org.

Pacific Pr. Pubns., *(0-9678122)* 3260 Monument, Ann Arbor, MI 48108 USA Tel 734-975-1877 (phone/fax)
E-mail: hailstormx@aol.com.

Company

Company

†**Pacific Pr. Publishing Assn.,** *(0-8163)* P.O. Box 5353, Nampa, ID 83653-5353 USA (SAN 202-8409) Tel 208-465-2500; Fax: 208-465-2531; Toll Free: 800-447-7377
E-mail: donlay@pacificpress.com
Web site: http://www.AdventistBookCenter.com; *CIP.*

Pacific Pubs., *(0-936521; 1-933120)* P.O. Box 480, Bolinas, CA 94924 USA (SAN 697-9335) Tel 415-868-2909; Fax: 415-868-9040
E-mail: tideguy@fastmail.fm
Web site: http://www.tidelog.com.

Pacific Sunset Publishing, Inc., *(0-9633582)* Orders Addr.: R.R. 3, Redlands, CA 92373-8710 USA; Edit Addr.: 30320 Live Oak Canyon Rd., Redlands, CA 92373 USA
E-mail: info@pacificsunset.com
Web site: http://www.pacificsunset.com.

Pacific View Pr., *(1-881896)* 2864 Harrison St., San Francisco, CA 94110 USA Tel 415-285-8538; 510-849-4216; Fax: 415-285-2620; 510-843-5835 ; *Imprints:* Dragon Books (Dragon Bks)
E-mail: pvp2@mindspring.com
Web site: http://www.pacificviewpress.com
Dist(s): **Cheng & Tsui Co.**
China Bks. & Periodicals, Inc.

Pacifica Military History, *(0-935553; 1-890988)* 1149 Grand Teton Dr., Pacifica, CA 94044 USA Tel 650-355-6678
E-mail: hammel1149@comcast.net.

Pacifica Press *See* **Pacifica Military History**

Packard, Boyle & Jackson *See* **Apollo Pubs.**

Pack-O-Fun, Inc. *Imprint of* **Clapper Publishing Co.**

Padah Pr., *(0-9721269)* Orders Addr.: P.O. Box 231285, Gresham, OR 97281 USA Tel 971-219-1861
E-mail: eileen@padah.net; eileen@eileenscott.com
Web site: http://www.eileenscott.com
Dist(s): **STL Distribution North America.**

Paddle Wheel Publishing, *(0-9657612)* Div. of Arabia Steamboat Museum, 400 Grand Blvd., Kansas City, MO 64106 USA Tel 816-471-1856; Fax: 816-471-1616; Toll Free: 800-471-1856
E-mail: greghawley@comcast.net
Web site: http://www.1856.com
Dist(s): **Booksource, The.**

Padwolf Publishing, Inc., *(1-890096)* P.O. Box 117, Yulan, NY 12792-0117 USA Toll Free: 800-484-7284 ext. 7239
E-mail: padwolf@padwolf.com
Web site: http://www.padwolf.com
Dist(s): **Koen-Levy Bk. Wholesalers LLC.**

Paewood Enterprises, Incorporated *See* **Akua Lani Enterprises, Inc.**

PageFree Publishing, Inc., *(1-929077; 1-930252; 1-58961)* P.O. Box 60, Otsego, MI 49078-0060 USA Toll Free: 1-866-GO BOOKS
E-mail: pagefreepublish@aol.com; publisher@pagefreepublishing.com
Web site: http://www.pagefreepublishing.com
Dist(s): **Ingram Bk. Co.**
Lightning Source, Inc.
Midpoint Trade Bks., Inc.
Univ. of Hawaii Pr.

PageMill Pr. *Imprint of* **Council Oak Bks.**

PAGES Publishing Group *See* **Darby Creek Publishing**

Pageturner Bks., *(0-9704678)* P.O. Box 171, Vineburg, CA 95487 USA Tel 707-933-8608; Fax: 707-938-0601
E-mail: pageturner@hotmail.com.

Pageturners Publishing Co., *(0-9755102)* Orders Addr.: P.O. Box 6, Jacksonville, FL 32234-0006 USA (SAN 256-1719) Tel 904-266-3393; Fax: 904-266-3394
E-mail: publisher@pageturnerspublishing.com
Web site: http://www.pageturnerspublishing.com.

Paginas de Espuma (ESP) *(84-95642; 84-931243) Dist. by* **Lectorum Pubns.**

Paidea Classics, *(0-9749900)* P.O. Box 46, Edwards, CA 93523 USA
E-mail: paideaclassics@aol.com
Web site: http://paideaclassics.org.

Paige Publishing, *(0-9662064)* P.O. Box 95, Lexington, OK 73051 USA Tel 405-527-3245 Do not confuse with companies with the same or similar name in La Habra, CA, Mesa, AZ, San Antonio, TX Downers Grove, IL.

Paige Publishing, *(0-9769375)* 5708 Washington St., Downers Grove, IL 60516 USA Do not confuse with companies with the same or similar name in Lexington, OK, Mesa, AZ La Harba, CA San Antonio, TX .

Paine Wolf Productions, *(0-9669240)* P.O. Box 531, Eastham, MA 02642-0531 USA Tel 508-247-9539
E-mail: storyteller@c4.net
Web site: http://www.storyteller@c4.net.

Paint Creek Pr., Ltd., *(0-9648564; 1-893047)* 620 Miller St., Rochester, MI 48307 USA Tel 248-656-9888; Fax: 248-656-9777; Toll Free: 888-275-5639
E-mail: leigh2@worldnet.att.net
Dist(s): **Baker & Taylor Bks.**

Paintbox Pr., *(0-9669433; 0-9777905)* 208 Glandon Dr., Chapel Hill, NC 27514 USA Tel 919-969-7512; Fax: 919-933-4199; Toll Free: 877-969-7512
E-mail: ppease@paintboxpress.com
Web site: http://www.paintboxpress.com.

Painted Horse Pubns., Inc., *(0-9708066; 0-9729482)* 45 Wingate St., Haverhill, MA 01835 USA Tel 978-521-1740
E-mail: sully@stopforastory.com
Dist(s): **Baker & Taylor Bks.**

Painted in the Corner Productions, L.L.C., *(1-893397)* 707 Plymouth, E., Grand Rapids, MI 49506 USA Tel 616-245-0835; Fax: 616-248-5691.

Painted Pony, Inc., *(0-9759806)* Orders Addr.: P.O. Box 661, Fort Washakie, WY 82514 USA Tel 307-335-7330; Fax: 307-335-7332; Edit Addr.: 47 N. Fork Rd., Fort Washakie, WY 82514 USA Do not confuse with companies with similar name in Atlanta, GA and La Conner, WA.
E-mail: ppi@wrdf.org.

Painted Sky Productions, *(0-9675082)* Orders Addr.: P.O. Box 30585, Seattle, WA 98113 USA Tel 206-364-1680 (phone/fax); advance notice for fax required Do not confuse with A Class Act, Sierra Madre, CA
E-mail: chiefhighliner@yahoo.com.

Painted Turtle *Imprint of* **Wayne State Univ. Pr.**

Painted Wood Studios, *(0-9721845)* P.O. Box 1606, Crosby, TX 77532-1606 USA Tel 281-456-8810 Toll Free: 866-241-7510
E-mail: paintedwordstudios@gmail.com
Web site: http://www.paintedwordstudios.com.

Painter, Annie & Assocs., *(1-928875)* P.O. Box 2135, Sisters, OR 97759 USA Tel 541-549-9539 (phone/fax)
E-mail: painterannie@msn.com.

Painting With Words, *(0-9743080)* 10 B State St., Windsor, VT 05089 USA Tel 802-674-5514; Fax: 802-674-9810.

Pair'a Spurs Pr., *(0-9749518)* Rt. 2 Box 20, Hollis, OK 73550 USA.

Pair'o'Docs Pr., *(0-9723884)* 9205 Lansbrook Ln., Oklahoma City, OK 73132-2220 USA Tel 405-728-2833
E-mail: personalpastor@sbcglobal.net.

Paisley Publishing, *(0-9761710)* 7240 Sagebrush Dr., Parker, CO 80138 USA Fax: 303-841-5229 Do not confuse with Paisley Publishing in Anchorage, AK
E-mail: mlheinze11@aol.com.

Paizo Publishing, LLC, *(0-9770071; 0-9776778; 1-60125)* 2700 Richards Rd., Suite 201, Bellevue, WA 98005-4200 USA
Web site: http://www.paizo.com
Dist(s): **Diamond Bk. Distributors.**

Pajaro, *(0-9672459)* 3343 Las Huertas Rd., Lafayette, CA 94549 USA (SAN 299-9218) Tel 925-283-7793; Fax: 925-284-2642; Toll Free: 877-725-2764
E-mail: info@pajaro.com
Web site: http://www.pajaro.com
Dist(s): **Acorn Group, The**
Common Ground Distributors, Inc.

PAJE Publishing Co., *(0-9753200)* 267 Henley Rd., Wynnewood, PA 19096 USA Tel 610-642-1729; Fax: 610-642-9891; Toll Free: 877-561-1377
E-mail: jay.scott@verizon.net
Dist(s): **Biblio Distribution**
Quality Bks., Inc.

Pajo Publishing Co., *(0-9700756)* 808 E. Main St., Ada, OK 74820-5616 USA
E-mail: pajoseany@aol.com.

Pakkins Presents, *(0-9700241)* Orders Addr.: P.O. Box 10503, Salinas, CA 93912 USA Tel 831-422-3442; Edit Addr.: 637 Carmelita Dr., No. 23, Salinas, CA 93901 USA
E-mail: Pakkins-Land@worldnet.att.net
Web site: http://www.pakkinsland.com.

Pak's Tang Soo Do Studio *See* **High Mountain Publishing**

Pal Toys, LLC, *(0-9726170; 0-9763648)* P.O. Box 2531, Palos Verdes Peninsula, CA 90274 USA Tel 310-938-6125; 26 Santa Bella Rd., Rolling Hills Estates, CA 90274
E-mail: info@paltoys.com
Web site: http://www.paltoys.com.

Palabra, Ediciones S.A. (ESP) *(84-7118; 84-8239) Dist. by* **Lectorum Pubns.**

Paladin Timeless *Imprint of* **Twilight Times Bks.**

Palasades Publishing *See* **We Publish Bks.**

Palazzo Editions, Ltd. (GBR) *(0-9545103) Dist. by* **Trafalgar.**

Palazzo Editions, Ltd. (GBR) *(0-9545103) Dist. by* **IPG Chicago.**

Pale Silver Rainplop Pr., *(0-615; 0-9794396)* P.O. Box 1285, Sioux City, IA 51102 USA
Web site: http://www.katieandkimbleblog.com
Dist(s): **Lulu.com.**

Palgrave *See* **Palgrave Macmillan**

Palgrave Macmillan, *(0-312; 0-333; 1-4039)* Div. of Saint Martin's Press, LLC, Orders Addr.: 16365 James Madison Hwy., Gordonsville, VA 22942-8501 USA Toll Free Fax: 800-672-2054; Toll Free: 888-330-8477; Edit Addr.: 175 Fifth Ave., New York, NY 10010 USA Tel 212-982-9300; Fax: 212-777-6359; Toll Free Fax: 800 672-2054 (Customer Service); Toll Free: 800-221-7945; 888-330-8477 (Customer Service) ; *Imprints:* Palgrave Macmillan (PalgMac)
E-mail: customerservice@vhpsva.com
Web site: http://www.palgrave.com
Dist(s): **Libros Sin Fronteras**
Macmillan
NetLibrary, Inc.
Trans-Atlantic Pubns., Inc.

Palgrave Macmillan *Imprint of* **Palgrave Macmillan**

PALH, *(0-9719458)* P.O. Box 5099, Santa Monica, CA 90409 USA
E-mail: palh@aol.com
Web site: http://www.palhbooks.com
Dist(s): **Baker & Taylor Bks.**

Palila Bks., *(0-9674183)* 1314 S. King St. Ste. 1160, Honolulu, HI 96814-1946 USA
E-mail: hansloff@lava.net
Dist(s): **Booklines Hawaii, Ltd.**

Palladium Bks., Inc., *(0-916211; 1-57457)* 12455 Universal Dr., Taylor, MI 48180-4077 USA (SAN 294-9504) Tel 734-946-2900; Fax: 734-946-1238
E-mail: palladiumbooks@palladiumbooks.com
Web site: http://www.PalladiumBooks.com.

Palmae Publishing, *(1-930167)* 14423 S. 24th Pl., Phoenix, AZ 85048-9015 USA (SAN 253-049X) Toll Free: 800-993-0040.

Palmer, Barbara A., *(0-9728228)* 486 Manitou Beach Rd., Hilton, NY 14468 USA Tel 585-392-3391; Fax: 585-392-1322
E-mail: bpforlkart@aol.com.

Palmer Lake Historical Society, *(0-9755989)* P.O. Box 662, Palmer Lake, CO 80133 USA.

Palmer, Lina, *(0-9676090)* 6456 W.. 81st St., Los Angeles, CA 90045 USA Tel 310-649-6130.

Palmer Publications, Incorporated/Amherst Press *See* **Amherst Pr.**

Palmer Publishing, *(0-9744410)* 604 4th N.W., Ardmore, OK 73401 USA Tel 580-504-2609 Do not confuse with companies with the same or similar name in Palmer, AK, Ocala, FL
E-mail: charlsie@duracom.net.

Palmer-Pletsch Assocs., *(0-935278)* P.O. Box 12046, Portland, OR 97212-0046 USA (SAN 209-1933) Tel 503-274-0687; Fax: 503-274-1377; Toll Free: 800-728-3784
E-mail: info@palmerpletsch.com
Web site: http://www.palmerpletsch.com
Dist(s): **Independent Pubs. Group.**

Palmetto Conservation Foundation, *(0-9679016; 0-9745284)* Orders Addr.: 1314 Lincoln St. Suite 305, Columbia, SC 29201 USA
E-mail: sanderson@palmettoconservation.org
Web site: http://www.palmettoconservation.org
Dist(s): **Parnassus Bk. Distributors**
Sandlapper Publishing Co., Inc.

Palmetto Richland Memorial Hospital, *(1-889863)* 7 Richland Medical Pk. Dr., Columbia, SC 29203 USA Tel 803-434-4760; Fax: 803-434-7291 (orders); 803-434-3095; Toll Free: 800-775-2287
Web site: http://www.sccancercenter.org.

Palmetto Tree Pr., *(0-9742532)* 821 Coulmbus St., Columbia, SC 29201 USA (SAN 255-5832) Tel 803-771-9300; Fax: 803-407-0766
E-mail: follybeech@aol.com.

Palmland Publishing, *(0-9666942; 1-933678)* Orders Addr.: 7881 Barrancas Ave., Bokeelia, FL 33922 USA (SAN 299-7835) Tel 239-283-3975; Fax: 941-870-2589; Toll Free: 877-725-6782; P.O. Box 478, Pineland, FL 33922 Toll Free: 877-725-6782
Web site: http://www.palmlandpublishing.com.

Palmore, Julie, *(0-9722653)* 3203 Harwood, Tyler, TX 75701-7642 USA.

Palmtree Publishing, *(0-9708721)* 131 W. 500 S., P.O. Box 501, Bountiful, UT 84010 USA.

Palmtree Publishing, Inc., *(0-9722655; 0-9777802)* 318 Marcy Ave., Brooklyn, NY 11211 USA Tel 718-599-2634 Do not confuse with companies with the same or similar name in Baltimore, MD, Bountiful, UT.

Palomina Publishing, *(0-9763393)* 338 Napa Rd., Sonoma, CA 95476 USA.

Palson Publishing, *(0-9663965)* P.O. Box 2090, Upland, CA 91785-2090 USA.

Pamacheyon Publishing, *(0-9655081)* 305 Saint Louis Ave., Rockford, IL 61104-1522 USA.

Pampa Publishing, *(0-615; 0-9744675)* Orders Addr.: P.O. Box 3481, Olympia, WA 98509-3481 USA; Edit Addr.: 4613 Shincke Rd. NE, Olympia, WA 98506 USA
E-mail: pampapublishing@comcast.net; ma2ka@home.com.

Pam's Pages, *(0-9669201)* Orders Addr.: P.O. Box 191, Rockville, IN 47872 USA Tel 765-344-7603; Edit Addr.: R.R. 1, Box 404, Raccoon Lake, Rockville, IN 47872 USA
E-mail: psbacon@aol.com.

Pan Asia Pubns. (USA), Inc., *(1-57227)* 29564 Union City Blvd., Union City, CA 94587 USA (SAN 173-685X) Tel 510-475-1185; Fax: 510-475-1489; Toll Free: 800-909-8088
E-mail: sales@panap.com
Web site: http://www.panap.com
Dist(s): **Lectorum Pubns., Inc.**

Pan Macmillan (GBR) *(0-283; 0-312; 0-330; 0-333; 0-7522; 1-85283; 1-4050) Dist. by* **Trafalgar.**

Pan Macmillan (GBR) *(0-283; 0-312; 0-330; 0-333; 0-7522; 1-85283; 1-4050) Dist. by* **Trans-Atl Phila.**

Panacea Publishing, *(0-9743432)* P.O. Box 395, Bloomfield Hills, MI 48303-0395 USA Tel 248-854-1692 Do not confuse with Panacea Publishing in North Attleboro MA, South Yarmouth MA
E-mail: panaceapublishing@yahoo.com
Dist(s): **Baker & Taylor Bks.**
Quality Bks., Inc.

Pan-American Publishing Co., *(0-932906)* P.O. Box 1505, Las Vegas, NM 87701 USA (SAN 212-5366).

Panamericana Editorial (COL) *(958-30) Dist. by* **Lectorum Pubns.**

Panamericana Editorial (COL) *(958-30) Dist. by* **AIMS Intl.**

Panamericana Editorial (COL) *(958-30) Dist. by* **Libros Fronteras.**

Panda Bear Pr., *(0-9724699)* Orders Addr.: 612 Museum Rd., Reading, PA 19611-1427 USA (SAN 255-5328) Tel 610-374-7048; Fax: 610-478-7992
E-mail: HaileJohnJr@msn.com
Web site: http://www.caroljhaile.com
Dist(s): **Firenze Pr.**

Panda Publishing, L.L.C., *(0-9740180; 1-932724)* Orders Addr.: P.O. Box 670608, Dallas, TX 75367 USA (SAN 255-8165) Toll Free: 800-807-1776; Edit Addr.: 6215 Rex Dr., Dallas, TX 75230 USA ; *Imprints:* Bios for Kids (Bios for Kids)
E-mail: info@biosforkids.com.

Pandia Pr., *(0-9766057; 0-9798496)* 18400 SE Hwy.42, Weirsdale, FL 32195 USA
Web site: http://www.PandiaPress.com.

Pandora Pr. (GBR) *(0-04; 0-86358; 1-85489) Dist. by* **IPG Chicago.**

P&P Studios, Inc., *(0-9726029)* 110 Lenox Ave., Suite 210, Stamford, CT 06906 USA Tel 203-359-9292 Toll Free: 888-937-7638
E-mail: ppstudios@weproduce.com
Web site: http://www.wherestheplay.com.

PANGAEA, *(0-9630180; 1-929165)* 226 Wheeler St., S., Saint Paul, MN 55105-1927 USA
E-mail: info@pangaea.org
Web site: http://www.pangaea.org
Dist(s): **Baker & Taylor Bks.**
Follett Library Resources
Lectorum Pubns., Inc.

Pangaea Publishing *See* **PANGAEA**

Pangea Software, Inc., *(0-9761505)* 12405 John Simpson Ct., Austin, TX 78732-2112 USA Tel 512-266-9991
Web site: http://www.pangeasoft.net.

Pangloss Publishing, *(0-615; 0-9768586)* 3904 Becker Ave., Austin, TX 78751-5209 USA Fax: 512-453-1486
E-mail: candide@grandecom.net.

Pangus Publishing, *(0-9769715)* Orders Addr.: 1637 S. Iseminger St., Philadelphia, PA 19148 USA; Edit Addr.: P.O. Box 15763, Philadelphia, PA 19148 USA.

Pankratz Creations, *(0-9742637)* 355 S. Fairlane Dr., Tooele, UT 84074-2623 USA
E-mail: customerservice@pankratzcreations.com; pankratz@mstar2.net
Web site: http://www.pankratzcreations.com.

Panline U.S.A., Inc., *(0-9713507)* 251 Union St., Northvale, NJ 07647 USA Tel 201-750-8010; Fax: 201-750-8030; Toll Free: (800-666-2539) (800-666-ALEX)
E-mail: info@alextoys.com
Web site: http://www.alextoys.com.

Pannonia Pr., *(0-9657793)* P.O. Box 1062, Palatine, IL 60078-1062 USA Tel 847-277-0806; Fax: 847-228-6847
E-mail: pannoniapress2000@sbcglobal.net
Web site: http://www.pannoniapress.com
Dist(s): **Baker & Taylor Bks.**

Pannycake Pubn., *(0-9769538)* 1710 Vallejo St., Unit B, Seaside, CA 93955 USA Tel 831-393-1358; Fax: 831-753-6085
E-mail: carmelalayne@yahoo.com.

Panola Publishing Co., *(0-9661531)* 3281 Boulder Dr., SW, Stockbridge, GA 30281 USA (SAN 299-7037) Tel 770-860-8456; Fax: 770-385-1561.

Panorama Editorial (MEX) *(968-38) Dist. by* **Giron Bks.**

Panterra Publishing, Inc., *(1-892680)* 177 Telegraph Rd., No. 654, Bellingham, WA 98226 USA
Web site: http://www.bcfirst.com/notes.html.

Pantheon *Imprint of* **Knopf Publishing Group**

Panther Creek Pr., *(0-9678343; 0-9718361; 0-9747839; 0-9771797)* Orders Addr.: P.O. Box 130233, Spring, TX 77393-0233 USA (SAN 253-8520); Edit Addr.: 116 Tree Crest Cir., Spring, TX 77381 USA
E-mail: panthercreek3@hotmail.com; guidamj@juno.com
Web site: http://www.panthercreekpress.com
Dist(s): **Baker & Taylor Bks.**

Panzerwrecks, *(0-9754183)* P.O. Box 2332, Monroe, NY 10950-2332 USA
E-mail: billauer@optonline.net
Web site: http://www.panzerwrecks.com.

Paon Pubns., *(0-9711721)* 608 S. Webik Ave, Clawson, MI 48017 USA Tel 248-288-5621.

Papa & Noelle Stories *Imprint of* **Seven Locks Pr.**

PaPa Fuzz Pubns., *(1-928597)* 1408 W. Danny St., Claremore, OK 74017-8618 USA
E-mail: papafuzzbk@aol.com.

Papaloizos Pubns., Inc., *(0-932416)* 11720 Auth Ln., Silver Spring, MD 20902-1645 USA (SAN 220-9853) Tel 301-593-0652
E-mail: info@greek123.com
Web site: http://www.greek123.com.

Paper Crane Pr., *(0-9650833)* P.O. Box 29292, Bellingham, WA 98228-1292 USA Tel 360-676-0266; Toll Free: 800-356-9315
E-mail: carolrj@nas.com
Dist(s): **Baker & Taylor Bks.**
Brodart Co.
New Leaf Distributing Co., Inc.
Unique Bks., Inc.
Upper Access, Inc.

Paper Jam Publishing, *(1-888345)* Orders Addr.: P.O. Box 435, Eastsound, WA 98245 USA Tel 360-376-3200 (phone/fax); Toll Free: 877-757-2665; Edit Addr.: 531 Fern St., Eastsound, WA 98245 USA
E-mail: paperjam@rockisland.com
Web site: http://www.rockisland.com/~paperjam.

Paper Kite Pr., *(0-9725942; 0-9798470)* 443 Main St., Kingston, PA 18704 USA
E-mail: wordpainting@comcast.net
Web site: http://www.wordpainting.com.

Paper Posie, *(0-9707944; 0-9774763)* 817 Vincente Way, Santa Barbara, CA 93105 USA Tel 805-569-2398; Fax: 805-563-0166; Toll Free: 800-360-1761
Web site: http://www.paperposie.com.

Paper Studio Pr., *(0-9790668; 0-9795053)* Orders Addr.: P.O. Box 14, Kingfield, ME 04947-4947 USA; Edit Addr.: 46 Narrow Gauge St., Kingfield, ME 04947-4947 USA
Web site: http://paperstudiopress.com
Dist(s): **Greenleaf Book Group Pr.**

Paper Tale Pr., *(0-9726065)* Orders Addr.: 6132 W. Townley Ave., Glendale, AZ 85302-4516 USA; Edit Addr.: 9201 N. 29th Ave., Suite 154-63, Phoenix, AZ 85051-3472 USA Tel 602-373-5442 (cell); 623-931-0913
E-mail: wynnie@2n4o.com; ellen@exacom.net
Web site: http://www.2n4o.com; http://www.papertale.com
Dist(s): **Baker & Taylor Bks.**

Paperbacks for Educators, *(0-9702376; 1-59721)* 426 W. Front St., Washington, MO 63090 USA (SAN 103-3379) Tel 636-239-1999; Fax: 636-239-4515; Toll Free Fax: 800-514-7323; Toll Free: 800-227-2591
E-mail: paperbacks@usmo.com
Web site: http://www.any-book-in-print.com.

Papercutz, *(1-59707)* 40 Exchange Pl., Suite 1308, New York, NY 10005 USA (SAN 850-9670) Tel 212-643-5407
E-mail: papercutz@speakeasy.net
Web site: http://www.papercutz.com
Dist(s): **Macmillan.**

Papergraphics Printing, *(0-9773322)* 4 John Tyler St., Suite 1, Merrimack, NH 03054-3054 USA Tel 603-880-1835; Fax: 603-880-1751; Toll Free: 800-499-1835
E-mail: prepress@papergraphics.biz
Web site: http://www.papergraphics.biz.

Papier-Mache Pr. *Imprint of* **Moyer Bell**

Papillon Children's Bks. *Imprint of* **Ashcafe Publishing**

Papillon Pr., Inc., *(0-9667476)* 23 Seagull Pl., Vero Beach, FL 32960-5212 USA
Dist(s): **New Leaf Distributing Co., Inc.**

Papillon Publishing *Imprint of* **Blue Dolphin Publishing, Inc.**

Papillon Publishing, *(0-9651048)* P.O. Box 12044, Dallas, TX 75225 USA Tel 214-722-1297 (phone/fax) Do not confuse with Papillon Publishing in Rochester, MN
E-mail: ford.lawrence@sbcglobal.net.

Papito Publishing, *(0-9622849; 1-887653)* Orders Addr.: P.O. Box 75535, Los Angeles, CA 90075-0535 USA Tel 213-920-2305; Fax: 323-737-5403; Edit Addr.: 4517 S. Figueroa St., Los Angeles, CA 90037 USA
E-mail: anoble@aol.com
Web site: http://www.papito.com.

PAPO Brand *Imprint of* **Planet Bronx Productions**

Papyrus Publishing, Inc., *(0-9675581)* Orders Addr.: 7409 Edgewood Ave. N., Brooklyn Park, MN 55428 USA Tel 763-560-0760 ; Fax: 763-560-0548 Do not confuse with Papyrus Publishing in Missouri City, TX
E-mail: PapyrusPublishing@msn.com.

†Para Publishing, *(0-915516; 1-56860)* P.O. Box 8206, Santa Barbara, CA 93118-8206 USA (SAN 215-8981) Tel 805-968-7277; Fax: 805-968-1379; Toll Free: 800-727-2782 (800-PARA-PUB)
E-mail: info@parapublishing.com; onfo@parapublishing.com
Web site: http://www.parapublishing.com
Dist(s): **Baker & Taylor Bks.**
National Bk. Network
Quality Bks., Inc.; *CIP.*

†Parable Pr., *(0-917250)* P.O. Box 51, Vinalhaven, ME 04863-0051 USA (SAN 208-4449); *CIP.*

Parable Publishing House *See* **Barth Family Ministries**

Parable Pubns. *Imprint of* **McDougal Publishing Co.**

Parable Venture Partners, LLC, *(0-9728501)* 12946 SW 133 Ct., Suite B, Miami, FL 33186 USA Tel 305-252-0905; Fax: 305-245-9974
E-mail: info@ethansparables.com
Web site: http://www.ethansparables.com
Dist(s): **STL Distribution North America.**

Parabola Bks., *(0-930407)* 656 Broadway, Suite 615, New York, NY 10012-2317 USA (SAN 219-5763) Tel 212-505-6200; Fax: 212-979-7325; Toll Free: 800-560-6984
E-mail: ads-promo@parabola.org; orders@parabola.org; JoeKulin@aol.com; editors@parabola.org
Web site: http://www.parabola.org/; http://www.cinemaofthespirit.org
Dist(s): **Baker & Taylor Bks.**
Independent Pubs. Group
New Leaf Distributing Co., Inc.
Perseus Distribution.

Parabola Magazine/Society for Study of Myth & Tradition *See* **Parabola Bks.**

Parachute Press, Incorporated *See* **Parachute Publishing, LLC**

Parachute Publishing, LLC, *(0-938753; 1-57351)* 156 Fifth Ave., New York, NY 10010 USA (SAN 661-5554) Tel 212-691-1421; Fax: 212-645-8769
E-mail: ppibooks@aol.com.

Paraclete Pr., Inc., *(0-941478; 1-55725)* Orders Addr.: P.O. Box 1568, Orleans, MA 02653 USA (SAN 282-1508) Fax: 508-255-5705; Toll Free: 800-451-5006; Edit Addr.: 36 Southern Eagle Cartway, Brewster, MA 02631 USA (SAN 664-6239) Do not confuse with companies with the same or similar names in Indianapolis, IN, Pentwater, MI
E-mail: srmercy@paracletepress.com; miao@paracletepress.com
Web site: http://www.paracletepress.com
Dist(s): **Forward Movement Pubns.**

Paraclete Publishing, *(0-9721946)* 1581 Garland Ave., Tustin, CA 92780-3932 USA Tel 714-832-3327 Do not confuse with companies with the same or similar names in Ventura, CA, Provo, UT, Pembroke Pines, FL
E-mail: Rec_Room@Hotmail.com
Web site: http://www.paracletepublishing.org.

Paraclete Publishing, Inc., *(0-9724820)* P.O. Box 245876, Pembroke Pines, FL 33024-0114 USA Tel 954-436-0220 Do not confuse with companies with the same or similar name in Ventura, CA, Tustin, CA, Provo, UT
Web site: http://www.paracletepub.com.

Paradigm Accelerated Curriculum, *(1-928629; 1-59476)* Div. of Paradigm Alternatives Centers, Inc., Orders Addr.: P.O. Box 200, Dublin, TX 76446-0200 USA Tel 254-445-4272; Fax: 254-445-3947; Edit Addr.: 112 S. Grafton, Dublin, TX 76446-0200 USA
E-mail: learn@pacworks.com
Web site: http://www.pacworks.com.

Paradigm Alternatives Centers, Incorporated *See* **Paradigm Accelerated Curriculum**

Paradigm Co., *(0-941995)* P.O. Box 45161, Boise, ID 83711 USA (SAN 682-8019) Tel 208-322-4440; Fax: 208-322-7781
E-mail: phonics@howtotutor.com
Web site: http://www.howtotutor.com.

Paradigm Publishing, *(0-9746013)* Orders Addr.: P.O. Box 872, LaPorte, CO 80535 USA; Edit Addr.: 3106 Kintzley Ct., D, LaPorte, CO 80535 USA Do not confuse with companies with the same or similar name in Oklahoma City OK, San Dimas CA, Chicago IL, McFarland WI, Saint Paul MN, Midvale UT, Pembroke Pines FL, Pocatello ID, Brookline MA, Boulder CO, Laguna Park, TX , Washington, DC
E-mail: sales@paradigmpublish.com
Web site: http://www.paradigmpublish.com.

†Paradigm Publishing, Inc., *(0-7638; 1-56118)* 300 York Ave., Saint Paul, MN 55101 USA Do not confuse with companies with the same or similar names in Oklahoma City, OK, Laguna Park, TX, Chicago, IL, Midvale, UT, Saint Cloud, FL, MacFarland, WI, LaPorte, CO, Washington, DC; *CIP.*

Paradise Pr. & Assocs., LLC, *(0-9755970)* P.O. Box 680759, Orlando, FL 32868-0759 USA Tel 407-905-6296 (phone/fax)
E-mail: ppallc@earthlink.net
Web site: http://www.paradisepressallc.net.

Paradise Pr., Inc., *(1-57657; 1-884907; 1-4194)* 1575 N. Park Dr., Suite 100, Weston, FL 33326-3230 USA Tel 954-349-9474; Fax: 954-349-7217 Do not confuse with companies with the same or similar names in Crested Butte, CO Corte Madera, CA, Santa Monica, CA, Ridgefield, CA, Chicago, IL, Herdon, VA, Temple Terrace, FL
E-mail: buybooks@paradisepress.us.

Paradise Research Pubns., Inc., *(1-885803)* Orders Addr.: P.O. Box 837, Kihei, HI 96753-0837 USA Tel 808-874-4876 (phone/fax)
E-mail: dickb@dickb.com
Web site: http://www.dickb.com/index.html
Dist(s): **Good Bk. Publishing Co.**

Paradox *Imprint of* **DC Comics**

Paradoxal Pr., *(0-9766132)* 28916 NE 34th Ct., Redmond, WA 98053-9114 USA
Web site: http://www.paradoxalpress.com
Dist(s): **Biblio Distribution.**

Paraglyph, Inc., *(1-932111; 1-933097)* 3533 E. Friess Dr., Phoenix, AZ 85032-5318 USA; 3533 E. Friess Dr., Phoenix, AZ 85032-5318 ; *Imprints:* Paraglyph Press (Paraglyph Pr)
E-mail: ccaldwell@paraglyphpress.com; stevesayre@paraglyphpress.com
Web site: http://www.paraglyphpress.com
Dist(s): **Ingram Pub. Services**
O'Reilly Media, Inc.

Paraglyph Pr. *Imprint of* **Paraglyph, Inc.**

Paragon Agency, Pubs., The *Imprint of* **Paragon Agency, The**

Paragon Agency, The, *(1-891030)* Orders Addr.: P.O. Box 1281, Orange, CA 92856 USA Tel 714-771-0652 ; *Imprints:* Paragon Agency, Publishers, The (The PAP)
E-mail: ParagonA@pacbell.net
Web site: http://www.SpecialBooks.com.

†Paragon Hse. Pubs., *(0-88702; 0-89226; 0-913729; 0-943852; 1-55778)* Orders Addr.: 1925 Oakcrest Ave., Suite 7, Saint Paul, MN 55114-1635 USA (SAN 286-1704) Tel 651-644-3087; Fax: 651-644-0997; Toll Free Fax: 800-494-0997; Toll Free: 800-447-3709
E-mail: paragon@paragonhouse.com
Web site: http://www.paragonhouse.com
Dist(s): **Continuum International Publishing Group, Inc.**; *CIP.*

Paragon Publishing, *(0-9721426)* P.O. Box 5354, Chubbuck, ID 83202 USA Tel 208-237-9620 (phone/fax); 5120 Kay Ave., Chubbuck, ID 83202 Do not confuse with companies with the same or similar name in Palos Verdes Esta, CA Red BLuff, CA, Santa Rosa, CA, Sidney, ID
E-mail: lisalete@cableone.net.

Parallax, Inc., *(1-928982)* 599 Menlo Dr., No. 100, Rocklin, CA 95765-3708 USA Tel 916-624-8333; Fax: 916-624-8003; Toll Free: 888-512-1024
E-mail: info@parallaxinc.com
Web site: http://www.parallaxinc.com.

Parallax Pr., *(0-938077; 1-888375)* Orders Addr.: P.O. Box 7355, Berkeley, CA 94707 USA (SAN 663-4494) Tel 510-525-0101; Fax: 510-525-7129; Toll Free: 800-863-5290; Edit Addr.: 2236 6th St. # B, Berkeley, CA 94710-2219 USA ; *Imprints:* Plum Blossom Books (Plum Blossom)
E-mail: parallax@parallax.org
Web site: http://www.parallax.org
Dist(s): **Perseus Distribution**
SPD-Small Pr. Distribution.

Para-Troop Publishing, *(0-9672306)* 8056 Redlands St., No. 5, Playa Del Rey, CA 92093 USA
E-mail: mayberry@melonpool.com
Web site: http://www.melonpool.com.

Paratwa Partnership, Inc., *(0-9724917)* 419 Plateau Dr., Florissant, CO 80816 USA Tel 719-689-9752
E-mail: cornellcolbert@hotmail.com
Web site: http://www.wanderingbrothers.com; http://www.achievingprofits.com.

Pardy Chick Pubns., *(0-9705332)* 59-361 Wilinau Rd., Haleiwa, HI 96712-9654 USA Tel 808-638-8619
E-mail: dapardy@compuserve.com.

Pardy, DA *See* **Pardy Chick Pubns.**

Parent 2 Child Bks., *(0-9700939)* 6213 Cty. Rd. 14, Orland, CA 95963 USA Tel 530-865-5295
E-mail: p2c@parent2child.com; lyntonsmith@yahoo.com
Web site: http://www.parent2child.com.

Parent Brigade Company, The, *(0-9774998)* 530 New Los Angeles Ave., Suite 115-332, Moorpark, CA 93021 USA Fax: 805-523-0119.

Parent Child Pr., Inc., *(0-939195; 0-9601016)* Orders Addr.: P.O. Box 675, Hollidaysburg, PA 16648-0675 USA (SAN 208-4333) Tel 814-696-7512; Fax: 814-696-7510; Toll Free: 866-727-3683; Edit Addr.: 129 Summit Dr., Hollidaysburg, PA 16648 USA (SAN 662-7331)
E-mail: pcp@nb.net
Web site: http://www.parentchildpress.com.

Parent Positive Pr., *(0-9721502)* 446 Willis Ave., No. 118, Williston Park, NY 11596-0118 USA (SAN 257-4438) Tel 516-997-0051
E-mail: Info@parentpositive.com
Web site: http://www.girlsonlyweightloss.com
Dist(s): **Independent Pubs. Group.**

Parental Interventional Tools, Inc, *(0-9778274)* P.O. Box 547, Southbury, CT 06488 USA Tel 203-264-1054
E-mail: pittools@aol.com
Web site: http://www.drketch.com; http://www.pit-inc.com.

†Parenting Pr., Inc., *(0-943990; 0-9602862; 1-884734)* Orders Addr.: P.O. Box 75267, Seattle, WA 98175 USA (SAN 215-6938) Tel 206-364-2900; Fax: 206-364-0702; Toll Free: 800-992-6657; Edit Addr.: 11065 Fifth Ave. NE, Suite F, Seattle, WA 98125 USA (SAN 699-5500)
E-mail: office@parentingpress.com; cthreadgill@ParentingPress.com
Web site: http://www.parentingpress.com
Dist(s): **Baker & Taylor Bks.**
Brodart Co.
Follett Library Resources
Midwest Library Service
Penton Overseas, Inc.; *CIP.*

ParentMagic, Inc., *(0-9633861; 1-889140)* 800 Roosevelt Rd., Glen Ellyn, IL 60137 USA Tel 630-469-0484; Fax: 630-469-4571; Toll Free: 800-442-4453
Web site: http://www.thomasphelan.com
Dist(s): **Independent Pubs. Group**
MAR*CO Products, Inc.

Parents Choice Pr., *(0-9717570)* 7461 Steeplechase Dr., Saline, MI 48176 USA Tel 734-944-3328
E-mail: patkilbane@aol.com; patkilbane@parenteschoicepress.com; patkilbane@abcanybodycan.com
Web site: http://www.parentschoicepress.com; http://www.abcanybodycan.com
Dist(s): **Baker & Taylor Bks.**

Parent-Wise Solutions, Inc., *(0-9714532; 1-932740)* 2130 Cheswick Ln., Mount Pleasant, SC 29466 USA Fax: 843-388-2692
E-mail: gezzo@gfi.org.

Parity Pr., *(0-9762015)* 1450 W. Horizon Ridge Pkwy, B-304-226, Henderson, NV 89012-4480 USA Tel 702-260-8989; Fax: 702-364-8988; Toll Free: 877-260-8989
E-mail: info@paritypress.biz
Web site: http://www.ShiftingRings.com
Dist(s): **Baker & Taylor Bks.**

Pariyatti Publishing, *(0-9649484; 81-7414; 1-928706)* Div. of Pariyatti, 867 Larmon Rd., Onalaska, WA 98570 USA Tel 360-978-4998; Fax: 360-978-4557
E-mail: wholesale@pariyatti.com; marketing@pariyatti.com
Web site: http://www.pariyatti.com
Dist(s): **Independent Pubs. Group.**

Park Hse. Bks., *(0-9755097)* 838 N. 6th St., Saint Clair, MI 48079 USA
E-mail: parkhousebooks@yahoo.com; mmerkau@yahoo.com
Web site: http://www.familyunity.us.

Park Pr. *Imprint of* **J&J Collections**

Park Pr., Inc., *(0-9652044; 1-892740)* P.O. Box 475, Waite Park, MN 56387 USA Tel 612-255-8937
E-mail: ppress@cloudnet.com.

Park Publishing, *(0-9651202)* 444 S. State St., No. 207, Bellingham, WA 98225 USA Do not confuse with companies with the same or similar names in New Richmond, WI, Scottsdale, AZ, San Antonio, TX
E-mail: Park.publishing@gte.net
Web site: http://www.Parkpublishingbooks.com.

Park Street Pr., LLC, *(0-9703346)* 6757 Cascade Rd., SE, Suite 149, Grand Rapids, MI 49546 USA Fax: 616-676-01533
E-mail: parkstreetpress@hotmail.com
Web site: http://www.geocities.com.

Park Tutor Schl., *(0-9612740)* 7200 N. College Ave., Indianapolis, IN 46240 USA (SAN 289-7903) Tel 317-415-2700; Fax: 317-254-2714; Toll Free: 888-782-5861
E-mail: info@parktudor.pvt.org
Web site: http://www.parktudor.org.

Parker Publishing Co., *(0-9654700; 1-893091)* Orders Addr.: P.O. Box 8654, Fort Lauderdale, FL 33310 USA; Edit Addr.: P.O. Box 8654, Fort Lauderdale, FL 33310 USA
E-mail: thebusiness2@yahoo.com.

Parkhurst Brook Pubs., *(0-9615664)* 303 Perrin Rd., Potsdam, NY 13676 USA (SAN 695-9121) Tel 315-265-9037
E-mail: mhcharle@northnet.org.

Parkhurst, R.M., *(0-9770323)* Orders Addr.: P.O. Box 1033, Redwood City, CA 94064 USA; Edit Addr.: P.O. Box 1013, Atascadero, CA 93423-1013 USA
E-mail: parkhurst@bigfoot.com.

Parklane Publishing, *(1-59384)* Div. of Book Club of America, 100 Marcus Blvd. Ste. 8, Hauppauge, NY 11788-3749 USA
E-mail: lbaumert@bookclubusa.com
Web site: http://www.parklanepublishing .com.

Parkside Pubns., Inc., *(0-9617266)* 999 Third Ave., Suite 3210, Seattle, WA 98104 USA (SAN 663-4907) Tel 206-839-1191; Fax: 206-839-1192 Do not confuse with Parkside Pubns., Inc., Davis, SD
E-mail: info@parksidepublications.com
Web site: http://www.parksidepublications.com
Dist(s): **Partners Bk. Distributing, Inc.**

Parkstone Pr. USA, Ltd., *(1-85995)* Orders Addr.: P.O. Box 605, Herndon, VA 20172-6105 USA; Edit Addr.: 10 E. 39th W., Suite 518, New York, NY 10016 USA Tel 212-807-7755; Fax: 212-620-0901; Toll Free: 800-844-2905
E-mail: parkstone@mindspring.com
Web site: http://www.parkstone-international.com
Dist(s): **Perseus Distribution.**

Parkstone Publishing, *(0-9679350)* 44 Bullough Pk., Newton, MA 02460 USA Tel 617-332-7317; Fax: 617-332-6205
E-mail: parkstone@aol.com.

Parkway Pubs., Inc., *(0-9635752; 1-887905; 1-933251)* 421 Fairfield Ln., Blowing Rock, NC 28605 USA Tel 828-265-3993 (phone/fax); Toll Free: 800-821-9155
E-mail: parkwaypub@hotmail.com
Web site: http://www.parkwaypublishers.com
Dist(s): **Baker & Taylor Bks.**
Blair, John F. Pub.

Parkwest Pubns., Inc., *(0-88186)* P.O. Box 310251, Miami, FL 33231 USA (SAN 264-6846) Tel 305-256-7880; Fax: 305-256-7816
E-mail: parkwest@parkwestpubs.com; info@parkwestpubs.com
Web site: http://www.parkwestpubs.com.

Parlance Publishing, *(0-9721032)* Orders Addr.: P.O. Box 841, Columbus, MS 39703-0841 USA (SAN 255-0806) Tel 662-327-4064; Fax: 662-327-4504; Edit Addr.: 1099 Southdown Pkwy., Columbus, MS 39701 USA
E-mail: parlancepub@aol.com
Web site: http://www.parlancepublishing.com.

Parra, Beverly, *(0-615)* 20412 Tufts Cir., Walnut, CA 91789 USA
E-mail: mrsparra@charter.net
Dist(s): **Lulu.com.**

Parragon, Inc., *(0-7525; 1-85813; 1-4054)* Div. of Parragon Publishing, 440 Pk. Ave. S, 13th Flr., New York, NY 10016 USA (SAN 256-7385) Tel 212-629-9773; Fax: 212-629-9756 ; *Imprints:* Dempsey Parr (Dempsey); Exclusive Editions (Exclusive Editions); Bright Sparks (Bright Sparks)
Dist(s): **Central Programs.**

Parramon Ediciones S.A. (ESP) *(84-342) Dist. by* **Continental Bk.**

Parramon Ediciones S.A. (ESP) *(84-342) Dist. by* **Lectorum Pubns.**

Parramon Ediciones S.A. (ESP) *(84-342) Dist. by* **Distr Norma.**

Parrhesia Pr. *Imprint of* **Listening Chamber**

Parrott Pr., The, *(0-9718006)* Orders Addr.: R.R. No. 3, Box 262B, DuBois, PA 15801 USA Fax: 814-371-2361; Edit Addr.: 601 Juniata St., DuBois, PA 15801 USA Do not confuse with Parrott Press, Lancaster, MA
Web site: http://www.parrottpress.com.

PARSEC Ink, *(0-615; 0-9743231)* P.O. Box 3681, Pittsburgh, PA 15230-3681 USA Tel 412-344-0456
Web site: http://www.trfn.clpgh.org/parsec
Dist(s): **Lulu.com.**

PARSEC Publishing *See* **PARSEC Ink**

Parsons Technology, *(1-57264)* Subs. of The Learning Co., Orders Addr.: P.O. Box 100, Hiawatha, IA 52233-0100 USA (SAN 665-6161) Tel 319-395-9626; Fax: 319-378-0335; Toll Free: 800-833-3241
Dist(s): **Spring Arbor Distributors, Inc.**

Partae Pr., *(0-9662608)* 703 Ivinson Ave., Laramie, WY 82070 USA (SAN 254-1688) Tel 307-745-6893
E-mail: press@partae.com
Web site: http://www.partae.com.

Partera Pr., *(0-9659873)* 2741 Indian School Rd NE, Albuquerque, NM 87106-2653 USA Toll Free: 800-717-6813
Dist(s): **Independent Pubs. Group.**

Parthenon Pr., *(0-9718398)* 4839 Fullmoon Dr., El Sobrante, CA 94803-2139 USA Tel 510-223-6850 Do not confuse with Parthenon Pr., in New York, NY
E-mail: wakingthetiger@yahoo.com
Web site: http://expage.com/tigerspirit
Dist(s): **Biblio Distribution.**

Parthenon Publishing *Imprint of* **CRC Pr. LLC**

Partner Productions, *(0-9665148)* Orders Addr.: P.O. Box 612, Albany, OR 97321 USA Tel 541-926-9794; Edit Addr.: 4283 Cabrillo Pl., SE, Albany, OR 97321 USA
Web site: http://www.nwcities.com/keiko.

Partners Book Distributing, Incorporated *See* **Partners Pubs. Group, Inc.**

Partners Bk. Distributing, Inc., Orders Addr.: P.O. Box 580, Holt, MI 48842 USA; Edit Addr.: 2325 Jarco Dr., Holt, MI 48842 USA (SAN 630-4559) Tel 517-694-3205; Toll Free: 800-336-3137 (orders).

Partners in Development, *(1-933835)* 2040 Bachelot St., Honolulu, HI 96817 USA Tel 808-524-7633; Fax: 808-524-7514
E-mail: admin@pidfoundation.net
Web site: http://www.pidfoundation.net.

Partners Pubs. Group, Inc., Orders Addr.: 2325 Jarco Dr., Holt, MI 48842 USA (SAN 631-3418) Tel 517-694-3205; Fax: 517-694-0617; Toll Free: 800-336-3137
Web site: http://www.partnerspublishersgroup.com.

Partnership Publishing, *(0-9668747)* 296 Hermosa Ave., Apt. C, Hermosa Beach, CA 90254 USA Tel 310-784-5676.

Pasco Scientific, *(1-886998)* 10101 Foothills Blvd., Roseville, CA 95678-8905 USA Tel 916-786-3800; Fax: 916-786-8905.

Pascualina Producciones S.A., *(956-8222)* 150 42nd Ave. E., Seattle, WA 98112 USA Tel 206-940-5412; Fax: 206-621-7956
E-mail: magdelenarossa@aol.com
Dist(s): **Independent Pubs. Group.**

Pasiteles Publishing Co., *(0-9785270)* 743 Belmont St., Belmont, MA 02478 USA
Web site: http://www.pasiteles.com.

Passage Publishing, *(0-9715926; 0-9724619)* Div. of Up Country Creations, 2711 Glenoaks, Nashville, TN 37214 USA Tel 615-525-6098 Do not confuse with Passage Publishing in Seattle, WA
E-mail: upcountrygirl@comcast.net
Web site: http://www.upcountrycreations.com.

Passageway Pubns., LLC, *(0-9722326)* P.O. Box 872243, New Orleans, LA 70187-2243 USA Tel 504-248-5295 (phone/fax)
E-mail: goalkpr@bellsouth.net
Web site: http://www.passagewaypublishing.com.

Passbooks *Imprint of* **National Learning Corp.**

Passeggiata Pr., *(1-57889)* 420 W. 14th St., Pueblo, CO 81003-2708 USA
E-mail: Passeggiata@compuserve.com.

Passion Profit Co., The/NicheMarket, *(0-9629202; 0-9745313)* Div. of A Company Called W, Orders Addr.: P.O. Box 618, New York, NY 10008 USA Tel 646-219-3565; Fax: 212-658-9232
E-mail: orders@passionprofit.com; passionprofit@aol.com
Web site: http://www.passionprofit.com.

Passion Works, LLC, *(0-9708027)* 704 228th Ave., NE, No. 334, Sammamish, WA 98074 USA (SAN 253-6676) Tel 425-868-1281 (phone/fax)
E-mail: dchristiansen@passionworks.net
Web site: http://www.passionworks.net.

Passport Bks. *Imprint of* **McGraw-Hill Trade**

Pastime Pr., *(0-9711632; 1-932046)* Div. of CICA Industries, Inc., P.O. Box 741084, Boynton Beach, FL 33474 USA Tel 561-740-9007; Toll Free: 800-370-1174 Do not confuse with Pastime Press in Seattle, WA
E-mail: drudow@pastimepress.com
Web site: http://www.pastimepress.com.

Pastime Pubns., *(0-9760276)* 1370 Trancas St., No. 372, Napa, CA 94558 USA Do not confuse with Pastime Publications in Walnut Creek, CA; Oakhill, VA; Herndon, VA
Web site: http://napavalleypastime.com.

PastWays Inc., *(0-9671075)* Orders Addr.: P.O. Box 551, Farmington, MI 48332-0551 USA Tel 248-701-8112; Edit Addr.: 33414 Oakland, Suite 2, Farmington Hills, MI 48335-3571 USA
E-mail: bgolden@pastways.info
Web site: http://www.pastways.info.

Pat & Sunny Pr., *(0-9721080)* P.O. Box 3296, Blue Jay, CA 92317-3296 USA Tel 909-337-8934
E-mail: sunny888@worldnet.att.net.

Patagonia Pr., *(1-882695)* P.O. Box 284, Bagdad, FL 32530 USA Tel 904-623-5790 Do not confuse with Patagonia Pr., Inc., Patagonia AZ
E-mail: Patagoniapress@aol.com.

Paternoster Publishing USA *See* **Authentic Media**

Paterson Museum for Italian Girls Press *See* **Mill Street Forward, The**

Path of Peace Inc., The, *(0-9766702)* 6610 Dorel St., Suite B, Philadelphia, PA 19142 USA Tel 215-681-6592
E-mail: blessbango@yahoo.com
Web site: http://www.thepathofpeace.net.

Path Publishing, Inc., *(0-9639132; 1-891774)* 4302 W. 51st Ave., Apt. 121, Amarillo, TX 79109-6159 USA
E-mail: path2@pathpublishing.com
Web site: http://www.pathpublishing.com.

Pathway Pr., *(0-87148; 1-59684)* Div. of Church of God Publishing Hse., Orders Addr.: P.O. Box 2250, Cleveland, TN 37320-2250 USA (SAN 665-7567); Edit Addr.: 1080 Montgomery Ave., Cleveland, TN 37311 USA (SAN 202-8727) Tel 423-476-4512; Fax: 423-478-7616; Toll Free: 800-546-7590 (music only); 800-553-8506 (trade only) Do not confuse with Pathway Press, San Rafael, CA
E-mail: bill_george@pathwaypress.org
Web site: http://www.pathwaypress.org.

Pathways Publishing, *(1-58303)* P.O. Box 267, Hudson, MA 01749-0267 USA Toll Free: 888-333-7284 Do not confuse with Pathways Publishing Gulfport, MS
E-mail: sblair@pathwayspub.com
Web site: http://www.pathwayspub.com.

Patmos, Inc., *(0-9741748)* P.O. Box 124, Maple Hill, KS 66507-0124 USA
Web site: http://www.patmos.us.

Patmos Publishing, *(0-9768545)* 4360 Ponderosa Rd., Milton, FL 32583 USA Do not confuse with Patmos Publications in Bristol GBR
E-mail: notes@patmospublishing.com
Web site: http://www.patmospublishing.com.

Patou Bks., LLC, *(0-9767756)* 1550 Larimer St., Suite 459, Denver, CO 80202-1602 USA.

Patria Pr., Inc., *(1-882859)* P.O. Box 752, Carmel, IN 46082 USA (SAN 153-7504) Tel 317-577-1321; Fax: 413-215-8030; Toll Free: 877-736-7930 ; *Imprints:* Young Patriots Series (Yng Patriots)
E-mail: info@patriapress.com
Web site: http://www.patriapress.com
Dist(s): **Independent Pubs. Group**
NetLibrary, Inc.

Patricia M. Mote Publisher *See* **Quixote Pubns.**

Patrick Henry College Pr., *(0-9714458)* 1 Patrick Henry Cir., Purcelville, VA 20132 USA Tel 540-338-1776; Fax: 540-338-8707
E-mail: info@phc.edu
Web site: http://www.phc.edu.

†Patrick's Pr., *(0-944322; 0-9609412)* Orders Addr.: P.O. Box 5189, Columbus, GA 31906 USA (SAN 274-466X) Tel 706-322-1584; Fax: 706-322-5806; Toll Free: 800-654-1052; Edit Addr.: 2218 Wynnton Rd., Columbus, GA 31906 USA (SAN 243-2773)
E-mail: quizbowl@aol.com
Web site: http://www.patrickspress.com
Dist(s): **Peller, A. W. & Assocs.**; *CIP.*

Patriot Publishing, *(0-9789936)* Ernest Beath, III, 2216 Horn Point Rd., Cambridge, MD 21613-3379 USA Tel 410-228-5771
E-mail: docprb@bluecrab.org.

Patsher Pr., *(0-9718808)* 40 Roberta St., Farmingdale, ME 04344 USA Tel 207-582-5023.

Patten Point Marketing Services, Inc., *(0-9710748)* Orders Addr.: P.O. Box 453, Rumson, NJ 07760 USA Tel 732-842-3000; Fax: 732-741-5820; Toll Free: 877-842-2100; Edit Addr.: P.O. Box 453, Rumson, NJ 07760-0453 USA
Web site: http://www.libertyservicesgroup.com.

Pattern Pr., *(0-9729248)* Orders Addr.: P.O. Box 2737, Fallsbrook, CA 92088 USA; Edit Addr.: 40521 De Luz Rd., Fallbrook, CA 92028 USA
E-mail: patternpr@aol.com
Web site: http://www.members.aol.com patternpr.

Patty Cake Bks., *(0-9664794)* P.O. Box 852, Cotaro, AZ 85652-0852 USA
E-mail: jd-cromwell@juno.com; PattyCakeBooks@juno.com.

Paul & Co. Pubs. Consortium, Inc., Div. of Independent Publishers Group, Orders Addr.: 814 N. Franklin St., Chicago, IL 60610 USA Tel 312-337-0747; Fax: 312-337-5985; Toll Free: 800-888-4741
E-mail: frontdesk@ipgbook.com
Web site: http://www.ipgbook.com
Dist(s): **Independent Pubs. Group.**

Paula Pr. Pubs., *(1-929745)* Div. of Country Cow Corp., Orders Addr.: P.O. Box 5057, Clinton, NJ 08809-0057 USA Tel 908-735-3838; Fax: 908-735-1474; Toll Free: 877-870-2697 (877-870-COWS); Edit Addr.: 7 Colt Rd., Pittstown, NJ 08867 USA ; *Imprints:* May Maisey Moo (May Maisey Moo)
E-mail: maymaisey@aol.com
Web site: http://www.maymaiseymoo.com.

†Pauline Bks. & Media, *(0-8198)* 50 St. Paul's Ave., Boston, MA 02130-3491 USA (SAN 203-8900) Tel 617-522-8911; Fax: 617-524-8035; Toll Free: 800-876-4463 (orders only)
E-mail: editorial@pauline.org; lmacauley@paulinemedia.com
Web site: http://www.PAULINE.org
Dist(s): **Alba Hse.**; *CIP.*

†Paulist Pr., *(0-8091; 1-58768)* 997 MacArthur Blvd., Mahwah, NJ 07430-2096 USA (SAN 202-5159) Tel 201-825-7300 ext 232; Fax: 201-825-8345; Toll Free Fax: 800-836-3161; Toll Free: 800-218-1903
E-mail: info@paulistpress.com
Web site: http://www.paulistpress.com
Dist(s): **Baker & Taylor Bks.**
Bookazine Co., Inc.
Spring Arbor Distributors, Inc.; *CIP.*

Paulus Publishing, *(0-9744863)* 6115 E. Hillview St., Mesa, AZ 85205 USA.

Paupieres Publishing Co., *(0-944064)* P.O. Box 707, Houma, LA 70361-0707 USA (SAN 242-8334) Tel 504-876-9223.

Pavillion, Ltd., *(0-9657077)* 4524 Curry Ford Rd., Suite 237, Orlando, FL 32812 USA Tel 407-420-2538; Fax: 407-370-0530.

Paw Impressions, Inc., *(0-9673095)* 405 El Camino Real, PMB 120, Menlo Park, CA 94025 USA Tel 650-328-8255; Fax: 650-321-1630; Toll Free: 888-767-7797
E-mail: paws@pawimpressions.com
Web site: http://www.pawimpressions.com.

Paw Island Entertainment, Inc. *Imprint of* **PetCare, Inc.**

Paw Press *See* **Guided Pen Pr.**

Paw Print Pubns., *(0-9785473)* Orders Addr.: 226 SE Douglas, Suite 201, Lees Summit, MO 64063 USA (SAN 850-9573) Tel 816-525-5084; Fax: 816-525-5094; Toll Free: 877-267-9482 ; *Imprints:* Austin & Charlie Adventures (Austin & Charlie Adventures)
E-mail: lparker154@aol.com; pawfacts@aol.com; linda8000@sbcglobal.net
Web site: http://www.austincharlieadventures.com
Dist(s): **Book Clearing Hse.**

Paw Print Publishing, *(0-9770898)* Orders Addr.: P.O. Box 48309, Cumberland, NC 28331-8309 USA
Web site: www.k9fluffy.com.

Paw Prints Pr. *Imprint of* **Heather & Highlands Publishing**

Paw Prints Press *See* **Heather & Highlands Publishing**

Pawpress, *(1-880882)* Orders Addr.: P.O. Box 492213, Los Angeles, CA 90049 USA Tel 310-471-5048; Fax: 310-471-7528; Toll Free: 877-293-8047 (on prompt, security code: 0314)
E-mail: InaPaw@aol.com
Web site: http://www.InasPawprints.com
Dist(s): **Baker & Taylor Bks.**

Paws IV Publishing, *(0-934007)* P.O. Box 2364, Homer, AK 99603 USA (SAN 692-7890) Tel 907-235-7697; Fax: 907-235-7698; Toll Free: 800-807-7297
E-mail: pawsiv@ptialaska.net.

Paws In the Sand Publishing, *(0-9790057)* Orders Addr.: 4644 Pepper Mill St., Moorpark, CA 93021-9302 USA (SAN 852-193X) Fax: 805-553-9253
Web site: http://pawsinthesand.com.

Paycock Pr., *(0-931181; 0 9602421)* 3819 N. 13th St , Arlington, VA 22201 USA (SAN 212-5420) Tel 703-525-9296 phone/fax
E-mail: gargoyle@gargoylemagazine.com
Web site: http://www.gargoylemagazine.com.

Payne, Christine, *(0-9740643)* P.O. Box 951, Mountain Home, AR 72654-0951 USA.

Payne, Yadira V. Publishing, *(0-9747350)* 341 Lamplighter Ln., Martinez, GA 30907 USA Tel 706-414-9566
E-mail: yvppublishing@knology.net.

PAZ Publishing, *(0-942253)* Div. of PAZ Percussion, Orders Addr.: 2415 Bevington St. NW, North Canton, OH 44709-2221 USA (SAN 666-8100) Tel 330-493-6661 (phone/fax)
E-mail: PAZPublishing@aol.com
Web site: http://www.PAZPublishing.com.

PB&J OmniMedia *Imprint of* **Takahashi & Black**

PBL Stories LLC, *(0-9792379)* Orders Addr.: P.O. Box 393, Lynn Haven, FL 32444-4272 USA Tel 850-348-0718; Fax: 850-265-9815; Edit Addr.: 1812 S. Hwy. 77, Suite. 115, Lynn Haven, FL 32444-4272 USA
E-mail: booksales@pblstories.com
Web site: http://www.pblstories.com.

PC Treasures, Inc., *(1-933796; 1-60072)* 2765 Metamora Rd., Oxford, MI 48371 USA Tel 248-969-7800; Fax: 248-969-7801
E-mail: lthomas@pctreasures.com; jbrandt@pctreasures.com; jadams@pctreasures.com
Web site: http://www.pctreasures.com.

PCS Edventures, Inc., *(0-9753193)* 345 Bobwhite Ct., Suite 200, Boise, ID 83706 USA Tel 208-343-3110; Fax: 208-343-1321; Toll Free: 800-429-3110
E-mail: rmwright@pcsedu.com; rgrover@pcsedu.com
Web site: http://www.edventures.com.

PDG *Imprint of* **Publishers Design Group, Inc.**

Peace B Still Ministries Pr., *(0-9752665)* 205 Joel Blvd., Suite 107, Lehigh Acres, FL 33972-0202 USA
E-mail: gduncan316@aol.com
Web site: peacebstillministries.com.

PEACE By Piece Publishing, *(0-9672640)* Orders Addr.: P.O. Box 523, Beverly Hills, CA 90213 USA Tel 310-446-3988; Edit Addr.: 10833 Wilshire Blvd., Suite 510, Los Angeles, CA 90213 USA
E-mail: neda@najibi.com.

Peace Education Foundation, *(1-878227; 1-934760)* 1900 Biscayne Blvd., Miami, FL 33132-1025 USA Tel 305-576-5075; Fax: 305-576-3106; Toll Free: 800-749-8838
Web site: http://www.peaceeducation.com.

Peace Education International, *(1-890276)* Div. of Fran Schmidt, Inc., 221 Palm Ave., Miami Beach, FL 33139 USA Tel 305-534-0031; Fax: 305-673-9303.

Peace Evolutions, LLC, *(0-9753837)* P.O. Box 458, Glen Echo, MD 20812-0458 USA (SAN 256-2146) Fax: 301-263-9280
E-mail: info@peace-evolutions.com; julie@peace-evolutions.com
Web site: http://www.peace-evolutions.com.

Peace Hill Pr., *(0-9714129; 0-9728603; 1-933339)* 18021 The Glebe Ln., Charles City, VA 23030-3828 USA (SAN 254-1726)
E-mail: ptbuff@peacehillpress.net
Web site: http://www.peacehillpress.com
Dist(s): **Norton, W. W. & Co., Inc.**

Peace Love Karma Publishing, *(0-9743540)* 607 Elmira Rd., No. 266, Vacaville, CA 95687 USA
E-mail: Carol@peacelovekarma.com; mail@peacelovekarma.com
Web site: http://www.peacelovekarma.com
Dist(s): **New Leaf Distributing Co., Inc.**

Peace Rug Company, Inc., The, *(0-9763949)* 407 W. Emery St., Dalton, GA 30720 USA Tel 706-272-0200; Fax: 706-226-2296; Toll Free: 888-732-2378
E-mail: info@peacerug.com
Web site: http://www.peacerug.com.

Peace Vision Bks. *Imprint of* **Peace Vision Publishing**

Peace Vision Publishing, *(1-931144)* Div. of One Earth One People Peace Vision, Inc., P.O. Box 813, San Juan Bautista, CA 95045-0813 USA Tel 831-623-2379; Fax: 831-623-1807 ; *Imprints:* Peace Vision Books (Peace Vision Bks)
E-mail: bluebirdwoman@iname.com
Web site: http://peacevision.net.

Peaceable Kingdom Pr., *(1-56890; 1-59395)* 950 Gilmain, Suite 200, Berkeley, CA 94710 USA Tel 510-558-2051; Fax: 510-558-2052; Toll Free: 800-444-7778 Do not confuse with Peaceable Kingdom Press in Greenville, VA
E-mail: djaffe@pkpress.com
Web site: http://www.pkpress.com.

Peaceable Productions, *(0-9709187)* Orders Addr.: P.O. Box 708, Center Hill, FL 33514 USA (SAN 254-4946) Tel 352-793-7516; Edit Addr.: 6698 SE 57th Rd., Center Hill, FL 33514 USA Tel 352-793-7516; Fax: 775-514-8681
E-mail: yvonne@atlantic.net.

Peaceful Thoughts Pr., *(0-9725118)* 510 Falls Watch Cir., Alpharetta, GA 30022 USA
Web site: http://www.peacefulthoughts.net
Dist(s): **Biblio Distribution.**

Peaceful Village Publishing, *(0-9658061)* Orders Addr.: P.O. Box 7032, Snowmass Village, CO 81615 USA Tel 608-770-1441 Toll Free: 608-770-1441
E-mail: mfhumphrey@juno.com.

Peacemakers Press *See* **Positive Spin Pr.**

Peach Blossom Pubns., *(0-941367)* 120 E. Beaver Ave. Apt. 212, State College, PA 16801-4991 USA (SAN 665-4800)
E-mail: inezwaterson@prodigy.net
Dist(s): **Baker & Taylor Bks.**
Quality Bks., Inc.

Peacham Press *See* **Republic Policy Institute Pr.**

PeachMoon Publishing, *(0-9795831)* 3915 Bonnett Creek Ln., Hoschton, GA 30548-6204 USA (SAN 853-814X)
Web site: http://luckythelizard.com.

Peachpit Pr., *(0-201; 0-321; 0-938151; 1-56609)* Div. of Pearson Education, 1249 Eighth St., Berkeley, CA 94710 USA (SAN 630-110X) Tel 510-524-2178; Fax: 510-524-2221; Toll Free: 800-283-9444
E-mail: mimiv@peachpit.com
Web site: http://www.peachpit.com
Dist(s): **Addison-Wesley Longman, Inc.**
Baker & Taylor Bks.
Bookazine Co., Inc.
Koen-Levy Bk. Wholesalers LLC
Koen Pacific
Partners/West
Pearson Education
Pearson Technology Group.

Peachtree Junior *Imprint of* **Peachtree Pubs., Ltd.**

†Peachtree Pubs., Ltd., *(0-931948; 0-934601; 1-56145)* 1700 Chattahoochee Ave., Atlanta, GA 30318-2112 USA (SAN 212-1999) Tel 404-876-8761; Fax: 404-875-2578; Toll Free Fax: 800-875-8909; Toll Free: 800-241-0113 ; *Imprints:* Peachtree Junior (Peachtree)
Web site: http://www.peachtree-online.com
Dist(s): **Heinecken & Assoc., Ltd.**
Lectorum Pubns., Inc.; *CIP.*

Peacock Publishing, *(0-9671047)* 14781 Pomerado Rd., Suite 127, Poway, CA 92064 USA Tel 858-653-0822; Fax: 858-485-7806 Do not confuse with companies with the same name in Englewood, CO, Watersmeet, MI
E-mail: adgoldc21@aol.com.

Peak Writing, LLC, *(0-9717330; 0-9767961)* Orders Addr.: P.O. Box 14196, Savannah, GA 31416 USA Tel 912-398-2987; Toll Free Fax: 888-226-4811; Edit Addr.: 12 Mercer Rd., Savannah, GA 31411 USA Do not confuse with Peak Writing in Frisco, CO
E-mail: info@peakwriting.com
Dist(s): **Quality Bks., Inc.**
STL Distribution North America
Spring Arbor Distributors, Inc.

Peanut Butter Publishing, *(0-89716; 1-59849)* 2207 Fairview Ave. E., Houseboat No. 4, Seattle, WA 98102 USA (SAN 212-7881) Tel 206-860-4900 Toll Free: 800-328-4348
E-mail: ewolfpub@aol.com
Web site: http://www.peanutbutterpublishing.com.

Peapod Publishing, Inc., *(0-9729507)* P.O. Box 951599, Lake Mary, FL 32795-1599 USA Toll Free: 888-473-2763
E-mail: info@peapodpublishing.com
Web site: http://www.adventureswithpawpaw.com; http://www.pawpawspals.org; http:// www.peapodpublishing.com.

Pearce-Evetts Publishing, *(0-936823)* 414 Foothills Rd., Greenville, SC 29617-7008 USA (SAN 699-9271) Tel 864-294-9494; Fax: 864-294-9696; Toll Free: 800-842-9571
E-mail: nicole@veenet.net
Web site: http://www.tonjaweimer.com
Dist(s): **Baker & Taylor Bks.**

Pearl & Dotty, *(0-9772441)* Orders Addr.: P.O. Box 2162, Seattle, WA 98111-2162 USA
E-mail: holler@pearlanddotty.com; pearlanddotty@gmail.com
Web site: http://www.pearlanddotty.com.

Pearl Line Press *See* **Pearl Line Pr., Inc.**

Pearl Line Pr., Inc., *(0-9705823; 1-932388)* P.O. Box 39, Zuni, VA 23898 USA
E-mail: info@pearllinepress.com
Web site: http://www.pearllinepress.com.

Pearl Pr., *(0-9741332)* 3104 O St., No. 175, Sacramento, CA 95816 USA Do not confuse with Pearl Press in Nazareth PA, Eastport MI
E-mail: info@pearlpress.net
Web site: http://www.pearlpress.net
Dist(s): **Baker & Taylor Bks.**
Quality Bks., Inc.

Pearl Street Publishing, LLC, *(0-9673867; 0-9722688)* Orders Addr.: 1515 S. Pearl St., Denver, CO 80210 USA (SAN 255-8025)
E-mail: pearlstpub@aol.com
Web site: http://www.pearlstreetpublishing.com.

Pearlman, Beth, *(0-9767522)* 1773 Diane Rd., Mendota Heights, MN 55118 USA.

Pearson Custom Publishing, *(0-536; 0-8087)* Div. of Simon & Schuster Higher Education Publishing Group, 75 Arlington St., Suite 300, Boston, MA 02116 USA (SAN 214-0225) Tel 617-848-6300; Fax: 617-848-6333; Toll Free: 800-428-4466 (orders only)
E-mail: pcp@pearsoncustom.com
Web site: http://www.pearsoncustom.com.

Pearson Education, *(0-582)* Orders Addr.: 200 Old Tappan Rd., Old Tappan, NJ 07675 USA (SAN 200-2175) Tel 201-767-5000 (Receptionist); Toll Free Fax: 800-445-6991; Toll Free: 800-428-5331; 800-922-0579; Edit Addr.: One Lake St., Upper Saddle River, NJ 07458 USA Tel 201-236-7000; 201-236-5321; Fax: 201-236-6549
E-mail: communications@pearsoned.com
Web site: http://www.pearsoned.com
Dist(s): **Gaunt, Inc.**
Trans-Atlantic Pubns., Inc.

Pearson Education Australia (AUS) *(0-7248; 0-7342; 0-7339; 1-74009; 1-74103; 1-74091; 1-74206; 1-4425) Dist. by* **Cheng Tsui.**

Pearson ESL, *(0-582)* Div. of Pearson International, 75 Arlington St., Boston, MA 02116 USA
Dist(s): **Pearson Education.**

Pearson Learning, *(0-7652; 1-4284)* Div of Pearson Education, Orders Addr.: P.O. Box 2500, Lebanon, IN 46052 USA Toll Free Fax: 800-393-3156; Toll Free: 800-321-3106; Edit Addr.: 299 Jefferson Rd., Parsippany, NJ 07054 USA Tel 973-739-8000; Fax: 973-739-8505; Toll Free: 800-526-9907 (Customer Service)
E-mail: jeff.hoitsma@pearsonlearning.com
Web site: http://www.pearsonlearning.com.

Peartree, *(0-935343)* P.O. Box 14533, Clearwater, FL 33766 USA Tel 727-531-4973; Fax: 727-803-2667
E-mail: martree@aol.com
Dist(s): **Baker & Taylor Bks.**
Book Wholesalers, Inc.
Brodart Co.
Hamakor Judaica, Inc.
Koen-Levy Bk. Wholesalers LLC
Ner Tamid Bk. Distributors
Quality Bks., Inc.

Pease Publishing, *(0-9655648)* 682 Miramar Ave., San Francisco, CA 94112 USA Tel 415-334-2072; Fax: 408-721-2233
E-mail: rap@galaxy.nsc.com
Dist(s): **Baker & Taylor Bks.**

Peasepod Bks., *(0-9702275)* 4334 Vinca Ct., Boulder, CO 80304 USA Tel 303-447-9509
E-mail: ryspease@yahoo.com
Dist(s): **Books West.**

Pebble Beach Pr., Ltd., *(1-883740)* P.O. Box 1171, Pebble Beach, CA 93953-1171 USA Tel 408-372-5559; Fax: 408-375-4525.

Pebble Bks. *Imprint of* **Capstone Pr., Inc.**

Pebbleton Pr., *(0-9760011)* P.O. Box 1894, Duxbury, MA 02331 USA
E-mail: pebbletonpress@yahoo.com
Web site: http://www.pebbletonpress.com.

Peckhaven Publishing, *(0-9714620)* 178 Wagman's Ridge, Saratoga Springs, NY 12866-6620 USA Tel 518-584-4129; Fax: 518-226-0096
E-mail: joe@joepeckonline.com; ppeck1@juno.com
Web site: http://www.joepeckonline.com.

Pedroni, L T, *(0-9710011)* 1903 Emerald Dr., Calistoga, CA 94515-1178 USA Tel 707-942-8269
E-mail: ralincal@webtv.net.

Peduncle Pr., Inc., *(0-9665778)* Orders Addr.: P.O. Box 846, Waldport, OR 97394 USA Tel 541-563-5560; Edit Addr.: 5250 Flansberg Ave., Waldport, OR 97394 USA
E-mail: peduncle@fbo.com.

Company

Peebco Publishing Hse., The, *(0-9644758)* P.O. Box 45333, Saint Louis, MO 63145 USA (SAN 298-6760) Tel 636-386-5925
E-mail: Info@PeebcoPublishing.com
Web site: http://www.PeebcoPublishing.com
Dist(s): **Baker & Taylor Bks.**

Peek, T.H. Pub., *(0-917962)* Orders Addr.: P.O. Box 50123, Palo Alto, CA 94303-0123 USA (SAN 693-9708) Toll Free: 800-962-9245; Edit Addr.: 897 Independence Ave., Suite 1A, Mountain View, CA 94043 USA (SAN 202-1382) Tel 650-962-1010; Fax: 650-962-1211; Toll Free: 800-962-9245 (orders & customer service)
E-mail: thpeek@aol.com.

Peek-A-Boo Publishing, *(0-9670821)* 5700 Barfield Rd., Suite 100, Memphis, TN 38120 USA Tel 901-685-2571; Fax: 901-383-9218 Do not confuse with Peek-a-boo Publishing LLC in Stillwater ME
E-mail: scott@jamesongibson.com.

Peek-A-Bks., *(0-9700318)* PMB 234, 1669-2 Hollenbeck Ave., Sunnyvale, CA 94087 USA Tel 408-732-4535; Fax: 408-739-7231
E-mail: peekabooks@mindspring.com.

Peel Productions, Inc., *(0-939217)* 9415 NE Woodridge, Vancouver, WA 98664 USA
E-mail: xwkmw0lrul001@sneakemail.com
Web site: http://www.drawbooks.com; http://www.peelbooks.com; http://www.abcriddles.com; http://www.123draw.com; http://www.1-2-3.draw.com
Dist(s): **F & W Pubns., Inc.**
Pathway Bk. Service.

Peeper & Friends *See* **Tree Of Life Publishing**

Peeper & Friends *Imprint of* **Tree Of Life Publishing**

Peer Tutor Press, Incorporated *See* **Stretching Charts, Inc.**

Peerless Publishing, L.L.C., *(0-9666076)* Orders Addr.: P.O. Box 20466, Ferndale, MI 48220 USA Tel 248-542-1930; Fax: 248-542-3895; Edit Addr.: 414 W. Lewiston, Ferndale, MI 48220 USA
E-mail: peerlesspublishing@ameritech.net
Web site: http://www.spannet.org/peerless/index.html.

Pefecting Parenting Pr., *(0-9790420)* 3943 Jefferson Ave, Emerald Hills, CA 94062-3437 USA Tel 650-369-8032; Fax: 650-364-2299
Web site: http://www.perfectingparentingpress.com.

Pegasus Graphics, *(0-942559)* P.O. Box 72, Cahone, CO 81320 USA (SAN 667-2698) Tel 970-562-4495
E-mail: dunmire@fone.net
Dist(s): **D & L Distribution.**

Pegasus Pubns., *(0-9747023)* 1055 E., 16th St., Brooklyn, NY 11230 USA Do not confuse with companies with the same name in Point Reyes Statio, CA, San Antonio, TX.

Peiffer, Trisha Cousineau *See* **Dream Ridge Pr.**

Pelaganty Bks., Inc., *(1-883261)* 2310 S. Green Bay Rd., Suite C238, Racine, WI 53406-4954 USA Tel 414-632-5025.

Pelican Island Publishing, *(0-9710332)* P.O. Box 671, Lebanon, NJ 08833-2146 USA (SAN 254-072X) Tel 908-227-0991; Fax: 908-236-9873
E-mail: dianperf@rcn.com; pelicanislandpublishing@rcn.com
Web site: http://www.alcatrazdoc.com
Dist(s): **American West Bks.**
Baker & Taylor Bks.

Pelican Lake Pr., *(0-9649139)* Div. of Healthy Lifestyle, Inc., P.O. Box 2599, Sun Valley, ID 83353 USA Tel 208-726-8150
E-mail: info@aspenrg.org
Web site: http://www.aspenrg.org
Dist(s): **Baker & Taylor Bks.**

Pelican Pr., *(1-888562; 0-9675540)* Div. of Shoestring Productions, 134 Hernandez Ave., Palm Coast, FL 32137 USA Tel 386-503-0380 ; *Imprints:* booksonnet.com (bksonnet) Do not confuse with companies with the same name in Prather CA, Santa Barbara CA, Aptos CA, Belvedere CA, Albion CA, Pensacola, FL
E-mail: shannona444@hotmail.com
Dist(s): **Lightning Source, Inc.**

Pelican Pr., *(0-9652561)* Orders Addr.: P.O. Box 1766, Aptos, CA 95001-1766 USA Tel 831-688-5561; Edit Addr.: 544 Beach Dr., Aptos, CA 95003 USA Do not confuse with companies with the same name in Prather CA, Santa Barbara CA, Belvedere CA, Saint Augustine FL, Albion CA
E-mail: pelicanpress@altavista.com.

†Pelican Publishing Co., Inc., *(0-88289; 0-911116; 1-56554; 1-58980)* Orders Addr.: 1000 Burmaster St., Gretna, LA 70053-2246 USA Tel 504-368-1175; Fax: 504-368-1195; Toll Free: 800-843-1724 Do not confuse with companies with the same or similar names in Lowell, MA, Dallas, TX
E-mail: Sales@pelicanpub.com; promo@pelicanpub.com
Web site: http://www.bedandbreakfastguide.com; http://www.pelicanpub.com; http://www.epelican.com; http://www.eirishbooks.com
Dist(s): **Continental Bk. Co., Inc.**; *CIP.*

Pella Publishing Co., Inc., *(0-918618; 0-933824)* 337 W. 36th St., New York, NY 10018-6401 USA (SAN 210-6183) Tel 212-279-9586; Fax: 212-594-3602.

Peller, A. W. & Associates, Incorporated *See* **Educational Impressions**

Pemberley Pr *See* **Pemberley Pr.**

Pemberley Pr., *(0-9702727; 0-9771913)* P.O. Box 1027, Corona del Mar, CA 92625 USA Fax: 949-675-6431 Do not confuse with Pemberly Press, New York, NY
E-mail: pat@pemberleypress.com
Web site: http://www.pemberleypress.com
Dist(s): **Independent Pubs. Group.**

Pemblewick Pr., *(0-9656557; 0-9718507)* Orders Addr.: P.O, Box 321, Lincoln, MA 01773 USA (SAN 254-0886); Edit Addr.: 155 S. Great Rd., Lincoln, MA 01773 USA Tel 781-259-8832 (phone/fax); 617-259-8389; 617 259 8389
E-mail: pemblewick@aol.com
Web site: http://www.pemblewickpress.com.

Pen & Pad Publishing, *(0-9769050)* P.o. Box 2995, Orcutt, CA 93457-2995 USA Tel 805-938-1307
E-mail: jenpete@aol.com.

Pen & Paper Publishing, *(0-9703876)* 5450 Saluson Ave., PMB 15, Culver City, CA 90230 USA Fax: 323-933-3851; Toll Free: 800-662-9066 Do not confuse with Pen & Paper Publishing in Horn Lake, MS
E-mail: sixrags@earthlink.net
Web site: http://www.penandpaper.net.

Pen & Publish Inc., *(0-9768391; 0-9779530; 0-9790446; 0-9800429)* 4735 S. State Rd., 446, Bloomington, IN 47401 USA Tel 812-837-9226; Toll Free: 866-326-7768
E-mail: info@penandpublish.com; paul@penandpublish.com
Web site: http://www.penandpublish.com.

Pen & Sword Bks. Ltd. (GBR) *(0-7232; 0-85052; 1-84415; 1-84468) Dist. by* **Casemate Pubs.**

Pen & Sword Publishing Co., The, *(0-9745798)* 522 N. Holly St., Philadelphia, PA 19104 USA
E-mail: nk81dove@yahoo.com; melodicg2003@hotmail.com; nancy@theaalamgroup.com.

Pen Notes, Inc., *(0-939564)* 70 S. Main St. Apt. 2A, Freeport, NY 11520-3853 USA (SAN 107-3621)
E-mail: pennotes@worldnet.att.net.

Pen of A Ready Writer *Imprint of* **Zoe Life Publishing**

Pen Poised Pr., *(0-615)* P.O. Box 233, Saintfford, VA 22555 USA Tel 540-242-9165
E-mail: writekj@kamichijackson.com
Web site: http://www.kamichijackson.com.

Pen Row Productions, *(0-9766695)* 9461 Charleville Blvd., No. 506, Beverly Hills, CA 90212 USA Tel 310-924-9167
E-mail: bwasz1@verizon.net
Web site: http://www.penrowproductions.com.

PenArtProductions, Incorporated *See* **Dandelion Bks., LLC**

Pencil Point Pr., Inc., *(1-58108; 1-881641)* P.O. Box 634, New Hope, PA 18938-0634 USA Toll Free: 800-356-1299
E-mail: penpoint@ix.netcom.com
Web site: http://www.pencilpointpress.com.

Pendle Hill Pubns., *(0-87574)* 338 Plush Mill Rd., Wallingford, PA 19086 USA (SAN 202-8794) Tel 610-566-4507; Fax: 610-566-3679; Toll Free: 800-742-3150
E-mail: bob@pendlehill.org
Web site: http://www.pendlehill.org
Dist(s): **Morehouse Publishing.**

Pendleton Bks., *(1-893221)* 666 Fifth Ave., Suite 365, New York, NY 10103 USA Toll Free: 800-690-7090
E-mail: editor@pendletonbooks.com
Web site: http://www.pendletonbooks.com.

Pendleton Publishing, Inc., *(0-9654480; 0-9711564)* Orders Addr.: P.O. Box 5004, Laurel, MD 20726 USA Tel 301-604-4076; Fax: 301-317-5746; Edit Addr.: 3113 Burning Springs Rd., No.1A, Laurel, MD 20724 USA
E-mail: newauthorsandartists@msn.com; gamjampublishing@yahoo.com.

†Pendragon Pr., *(0-918728; 0-945193; 1-57647)* Div. of Camelot Publishing Co., Inc., P.O. Box 190, Hillsdale, NY 12529-0190 USA (SAN 213-1463); 52 White Hill Ln., Hillsdale, NY 12529-5839 Tel 518-325-6100; Fax: 518-325-6102
E-mail: penpress@Taconic.net
Web site: http://www.pendragonpress.com; http://www.bmtsinc.com/pdragon; *CIP.*

Pendulum Pr., *(0-9673951)* 20 Pennypacker Ln., Palm Coast, FL 32164-7464 USA Toll Free: 800-226-9326 Do not confuse with companies with same or similar names in West Haven CT, Jacksonville FL, Minneapolis, MN
E-mail: gh@perfectimpact.com.

Pendulum Pr., Inc., *(0-87232; 0-88301)* Academic Bldg., Saw Mill Rd., West Haven, CT 06516 USA (SAN 202-8808) Tel 203-933-2551 Do not confuse with companies with same or similar names in Jacksonville, FL, Palm Coast, FL, Minneapolis, MN.

Penfield Pr., *(0-941016; 0-9603858; 1-57216)* 215 Brown St., Iowa City, IA 52245 USA (SAN 221-6671) Tel 319-337-9998; Fax: 319-351-6846; Toll Free: 800-728-9998
E-mail: penfield@penfieldpress.com
Web site: http://www.penfieldpress.com
Dist(s): **Bookmen, Inc.**

PenGame Publishing LLC, *(0-9771444)* Orders Addr.: P.O. Box 341361, Jamaica, NY 11434 USA (SAN 256-8802)
E-mail: PenGameLLC@aol.com.

Penguin AudioBooks *Imprint of* **Penguin Group (USA) Inc.**

Penguin Bks., Ltd. (GBR) *(0-14; 0-563; 1-4059) Dist. by* **Penguin Grp USA.**

Penguin Classics *Imprint of* **Penguin Group (USA) Inc.**

Penguin Family Publishing, *(0-9637985)* P.O. Box 471, Orland, CA 95963 USA.

Penguin Global *Imprint of* **Penguin Group (USA) Inc.**

Penguin Group (USA) Inc., *(0-14; 0-399; 0-525; 1-933438; 1-4295; 1-934511; 1-4362)* Orders Addr.: 405 Murray Hill Pkwy., East Rutherford, NJ 07073-2136 USA (SAN 282-5074) Fax: 201-933-2903 (customer service); Toll Free Fax: 800-227-9604; Toll Free: 800-526-0275 (reseller sales); 800-631-8571 (reseller customer service); 800-788-6262 (individual consumer sales); Edit Addr.: 375 Hudson St., New York, NY 10014 USA Tel 212-366-2000; Fax: 212-366-2666; 405 Murray Hill Pkwy., East Rutherford, NJ 07073 (SAN 852-5455) Tel 201-933-9292 ; *Imprints:* Ace Trade (AceTrade); Minedition (Minedition); Ace Books (Ace Bks); Ace Hardcover (Ace HC); Alpha Books (Alph Bks); Avery (Avr); Berkley (BerkBks); Berkley Hardcover (BerkleHC); Berkley Trade (BrkTrade); DAW Hardcover (DAWHC); D A W Books, Incorporated (D A WBksInc); Dial (Dial); Dutton Adult (Dut); Dutton Juvenile (DuttJuv); Warne (Warne); Putnam Adult (Putnam Adult); Putnam Juvenile (PutnaJuv); Gotham (GotBksHard); Grosset & Dunlap (Gross-Dun); HP Trade (HPTrade); Hamish Hamilton (Hamish Ham); Hudson Street Press (HudSt Pr); Jove (JovPG); ROC Trade (RocTrade); N A L (NewAmLib); N A L Hardcover (NALHC); N A L Trade (NewTrade); Penguin AudioBooks (PengAudBks); Penguin Classics (PenClassics); Penguin (Non-Classics) (PeNonClass); Perigee Trade (PeriTrade); Philomel (PhilPG); Planet Dexter (PlanDext); Plume (PlumPG); Portfolio Trade (PortfolTrade); Price Stern Sloan (PSS); Puffin (PufBks); Penguin Global (PenGlobal); Roc (Roc); Razorbill (Razrbil); Riverhead Books (Hardcover) (RivhdHC); Riverhead Trade (Paperbacks) (RiverTrade Pap); ROC Hardcover (ROCHC); Signet (SigBks); Signet Classics (SigClassics); Tarcher (Tarch-Peng); Penguin Press HC, The (The Penguin Pr); Viking Adult (VikiPG); Viking Juvenile (VCB); Studio (PStudio)
E-mail: customer.service@us.penguingroup.com; us.penguingroup.com
Web site: http://penguingroup.custhelp.com; http://booksellers.penguingroup.com; http://www.penguinputnam.com
Dist(s): **NetLibrary, Inc.**
Pearson Education
Sony CONNECT, Inc.
Viking Penguin.

Penguin (Non-Classics) *Imprint of* **Penguin Group (USA) Inc.**

Penguin Pr. HC, The *Imprint of* **Penguin Group (USA) Inc.**

Penguin Putnam, Incorporated *See* **Penguin Group (USA) Inc.**

Penman Publications *See* **Voice & Vision Pubns.**

Penman Publishing, Inc., *(0-9700486; 0-9707646; 0-9712808; 0-9720775; 1-932496)* Div. of Pathway Pr., Orders Addr.: P.O. Box 2250, Cleveland, TN 37320-2250 USA; Edit Addr.: 1080 Montgomery Ave., Cleveland, TN 37311 USA Tel 423-478-7613
Web site: http://www.penmanpublishing.com.

Pen-Mar News Distributors *See* **Americana Souvenirs & Gifts**

Penn, John, *(0-9720785)* P.O. Box 1344, Antioch, TN 37011-1344 USA
E-mail: parkerpenn61@aol.com.

Penner/Lynn Publishing, *(0-9763025)* P.O. Box 7393, Naples, FL 34104 USA
E-mail: pennerlynn@msn.com
Web site: http://www.pennerlynn.com.

Penniman Publishing Co., *(1-929974)* 2091 Norma St., Westland, MI 48185 USA Tel 734-722-9445.

Pennington Family Publishers *See* **Terpsichore Pubns.**

†Penns Valley Pubs., *(0-931992)* Div. of PVP, Inc., Orders Addr.: 154 E. Main St., Lansdale, PA 19446 USA (SAN 202-1455) Tel 215-855-4948; Fax: 215-855-7238; Toll Free: 800-422-4412; Edit Addr.: 800 W. Church Rd., Mechanicsburg, PA 17055 USA Toll Free: 800-524-3232 (ext. 2417)
E-mail: info@pennsvalleypub.com
Web site: http://www.pennsvalleypub.com/; *CIP.*

Pennsylvania Coalition Against Rape, *(0-615; 0-9743845)* 125 N. Enola Dr., Enola, PA 17025 USA Tel 717-728-9740 Toll Free: 800-692-7445
E-mail: stop@pcar.org
Web site: http://www.pcar.org.

Pennsylvania Forestry Assn., The (PFA), *(0-9661896)* 56 E. Main St., Mechanicsburg, PA 17055 USA Tel 717-766-5371; Fax: 717-697-4274
Web site: http://www.cas.psu.edu/docs/casdept/forest/PFA.html.

Penny Bear Co., Inc., The, *(1-893356)* 25 Clark's Rd., No. 308, Amesbury, MA 01913 USA Fax: 978-388-7520; Toll Free: 877-887-2828 ; *Imprints:* Penny Bear Publishing (Penny Bear Pubng)
E-mail: ElissaAmal@aol.com
Web site: http://www.worksofhope.com
Dist(s): **Baker & Taylor Bks.**

Penny Bear Publishing *Imprint of* **Penny Bear Co., Inc., The**

Penny Candy Pr. *Imprint of* **Brighter Minds Children's Publishing**

Penny Laine Papers, Inc., *(1-890703)* 2211 Century Center Blvd. Ste. 110, Irving, TX 75062-4960 USA Toll Free: 800-456-6484 ; *Imprints:* Bookmates (Bkmates)
E-mail: cardwhiz1@mindspring.com.

Penny Lane Pubns., Inc., *(0-911211)* P.O. Box 3005, New York, NY 10012-0009 USA (SAN 274-4961) Tel 212-570-9666.

Penny Pr. *Imprint of* **Penny Pubns., LLC**

Penny Press, Incorporated *See* **Penny Pubns., LLC**

Penny Pubns., LLC, *(0-944422; 1-55956; 1-59238)* 6 Prowitt St., Norwalk, CT 06855 USA (SAN 243-6485) ; *Imprints:* Penny Press (Penny Pr)
E-mail: ltrutnau@pennypublications.net
Web site: http://www.pennypress.com; http://www.dellmagazines.com; http://www.analogsf.com; http://www.asimovs.com; http://www.themysteryplace.com; http://www.dellhoroscope.com; http://www.thecrosswordsclub.com.

For full information on wholesalers and distributors, refer to the Wholesaler and Distributor Symbol Index

Penny-Farthing Pr., Inc., *(0-9673683; 0-9719012)* 2000 W. Sam Houston Pkwy., S., Suite 550, Houston, TX 77042 USA Tel 713-780-0300; Fax: 713-780-4004; Toll Free: 800-926-2669
E-mail: corp@pfpress.com
Web site: http://www.pfpress.com
Dist(s): **Baker & Taylor Bks.**
Diamond Comic Distributors, Inc.

Pennypack Productions, Inc., *(0-9704184)* 21 Tree Farm Ct., Glen Arm, MD 21057 USA Tel 410-420-3828; Fax: 410-420-2243
E-mail: ppennypack@comcast.net
Web site: http://www.kinderfun.net.

PennyRoyal Bks., *(0-9654197)* Orders Addr.: P.O. Box 324, Royal Oak, MI 48068 USA Tel 248-548-4931; Fax: 248-548-5125; Toll Free: 800-247-6553; Edit Addr.: 1211 Irving, Royal Oaks, MI 48067 USA
E-mail: Proyalbook@aol.com.

Penny's Publishing *Imprint of* **Balloon Magic**

Pennywhistler's Pr., *(0-9623456; 0-9727516)* Orders Addr.: P.O. Box 2473, New York, NY 10108 USA Tel 212-247-3231 (phone/fax); Edit Addr.: 467 W. 46th St., New York, NY 10036 USA
E-mail: info@pennywhistle.com
Web site: http://www.pennywhistle.com
Dist(s): **Book Clearing Hse.**
Mel Bay Pubns., Inc.

Pennywise Pubns., Inc., *(0-9702944)* 10550 St. Rd. 84, L98, Davie, FL 33324 USA Tel 954-472-8776 (phone/fax)
E-mail: filmpeny@bellsouth.net.

Pennywood Pr., *(0-9679514)* 1338 Mountain Rd., Manheim, PA 17545 USA Tel 717-664-5089; Fax: 717-665-4651
E-mail: hevener@desupernet.net; Pennywood@dejazzd.com
Web site: http://www.ronhevener.com.

Pennyworth Pr., *(1-888701)* P.O. Box 25176, Ashville, NC 28813 USA Tel 828-335-6112
E-mail: pennyworthpress@aol.com
Dist(s): **Parnassus Bk. Distributors.**

Penrod/Hiawatha Co., *(0-942618; 1-893624)* 10116 M140, Berrien Center, MI 49102 USA (SAN 238-5546) Tel 269-461-6993; Fax: 269-461-4170; Toll Free: 800-632-2823
Web site: http://www.penrodhiawatha.com.

Pensive Bks., *(1-893213)* 6000 Gunn Rd., Springfield, TN 37172 USA Tel 615-384-2534
E-mail: chris@pensivebooks.com
Web site: http://www.pensivebooks.com.

Pentacle Pr., *(0-9604760; 0-9763500)* Orders Addr.: P.O. Box 9400, Scottsdale, AZ 85252 USA (SAN 255-4860) Tel 480-922-2759; Fax: 480-443-8333; Edit Addr.: 5432 E. Desert Jewel Dr., Paradise Valley, AZ 85253 USA
E-mail: djm543@cox.net
Web site: http://www.missionscalifornia.com; http://www.pentacle-press.com
Dist(s): **Sunbelt Pubns., Inc.**
Univ. of New Mexico Pr.

Pentland Pr., Inc., *(1-57197)* 5122 Bur Oak Cir., Raleigh, NC 27612 USA (SAN 298-5063) Tel 919-782-0281; Fax: 919-781-9042; Toll Free: 800-948-2786 ; *Imprints:* Ivy House Publishing Group (Ivy Hse Pubng Grp)
E-mail: janetevans@mindspring.com
Web site: http://www.pentlandpressusa.com
Dist(s): **AtlasBooks Distribution**
Baker & Taylor Bks.
Midpoint Trade Bks., Inc.

Penton Kids *Imprint of* **Penton Overseas, Inc.**

Penton Overseas, Inc., *(0-939001; 1-56015; 1-59125; 1-60379)* 1958 Kellogg Ave., Vista, CA 92008 USA (SAN 631-0826) Tel 760-431-0060; Fax: 760-431-8110; Toll Free: 800-748-5804 ; *Imprints:* Penton Kids (Penton Kids); Smart Kids (Smrt Kds)
Web site: http://www.pentonoverseas.com.

People Bks. *Imprint of* **Time, Inc. Home Entertainment**

People with Disabilities Pr. *Imprint of* **iUniverse, Inc.**

People's Literature Publishing Hse. (CHN) *(7-02) Dist. by* **China Bks.**

People's Pr., The, *(0-9658432; 0-9710139)* Div. of National Tax Ctr., Inc., 4810 Norwood Ave., Baltimore, MD 21207-6839 USA Toll Free: 800-517-4475 (phone/fax) Do not confuse with companies with the same name in Birmingham, AL, Pittsburgh, PA.

PeopleScapes, *(0-9673485)* 1208 S. Aberdeen Ave., Sioux Falls, SD 57106-4920 USA
E-mail: glatza@dakota.net
Web site: http://www.dakota.net~glatca.

Peponi, Inc., *(0-9662990)* Orders Addr.: P.O. Box 1260, Lake Havasu City, AZ 86405 USA Tel 520-855-8822; Fax: 520-855-8898; Toll Free: 800-314-4750; Edit Addr.: 1980 Centers Ave., Lk Havasu Cty, AZ 86403-1982 USA Do not confuse with peponi, Incorporated in Seattle, WA
E-mail: peponi@interworldnet.net
Web site: http://www.fatdragons.com.

Peppertree Pr., The, *(0-9778525; 0-9787740; 1-934246)* 4017 Swift Rd., Sarasota, FL 34231 USA
Web site: http://www.peppertreepress.com.

Peppery Pr., *(0-9764813)* 504 Springcreek Dr., Longwood, FL 32779 USA Tel 407-786-6113
E-mail: pruben@cfl.rr.com
Web site: http://www.pepperypress.com.

Peralt Montagut (ESP) *(84-87650; 84-86154; 84-8214) Dist. by* **imaJen.**

Perc Publishing, *(0-9653203)* Div. of Personal Energies, Resources & Capabilities, Inc., P.O. Box 351030, Toledo, OH 43635 USA Tel 419-531-0088; Fax: 419-531-8866; Toll Free: 888-438-7372
E-mail: GetPerc@aol.com
Web site: http://www.joniarredia.com.

Perceval Pr., *(0-9721436; 0-9747078; 0-9763009; 0-9774869)* 1223 Wishire Blvd. No. F, Santa Monica, CA 90403 USA
E-mail: info@percevelpress.com
Web site: http://www.percevalpress.com.

Peregrine Communications *Imprint of* **Collins, Robert**

Peregrine Fund, The, *(0-9669569)* Orders Addr.: c/o Hawaiian Endangered Bird Conservation Program, P.O. Box 39, Volcano, HI 96785 USA Tel 808-985-7218; Fax: 808-985-7034; Edit Addr.: Keauhou Bird Conservation Ctr., Volcano, HI 96785 USA
E-mail: HTSU21A@prodigy.com
Web site: http://www.peregrinefund.org.

Peregrine Publishing, *(1-930432)* P.O. Box 343, Glen Head, NY 11545 USA (SAN 253-0821) Tel 516-759-1089; Fax: 516-759-1034 Do not confuse with Peregrine Publishing, Mckinney, TX
E-mail: sgmuth@gateway.net; peregrinepub@aol.com.

Peregrino Pr., *(0-9754545)* 4421 Berenice Ave., Los Angeles, CA 90031-1409 USA
E-mail: jmichael@allthesaints.com.

Perfect 4 Preschool, *(0-9769239)* 428 N. Nelson St., Arlington, VA 22203 USA (SAN 850-0614) Tel 703-351-5843
E-mail: bjmischel@aol.com
Web site: http://www.perfect4preschool.

Perfect Bks., *(0-9720854)* 6652 S. Minerva Ave. Apt. 2, Chicago, IL 60637-4378 USA
E-mail: niambi@projectbutterfly.com
Web site: http://www.projectbutterfly.com
Dist(s): **Baker & Taylor Bks.**

Perfect Praise Publishing, *(0-9679240)* 1228 Fourth Ave., E., Williston, ND 58801 USA
E-mail: perfectpraise@dia.net
Web site: http://www.perfect-praise.com.

Perfection Form Company, The *See* **Perfection Learning Corp.**

Perfection Learning Corp., *(0-7807; 0-7891; 0-89598; 1-56312; 0-7569)* 1000 N. Second Ave., Logan, IA 51546 USA (SAN 221-0010) Tel 712-644-3553; Fax: 712-644-2122; Toll Free: 800-831-4190 ; *Imprints:* Covercraft (Covercraft)
E-mail: rfetter@logan.phonline.com
Web site: http://www.perfectionlearning.com.

Performance Consultants International, Limited *See* **Aries International (U.B.T.O.)**

Peri Tales *See* **2 Brian's Pr.**

Perigee Trade *Imprint of* **Penguin Group (USA) Inc.**

Perinatal Loss, *(0-9615197; 0-9724241)* Div. of Metanoia Peace Community United Methodist Church, 2116 NE 18th Ave., Portland, OR 97212 USA (SAN 694-2911) Tel 503-284-7426; Fax: 503-282-8985
E-mail: grieving@tearsoup.com
Web site: http://www.griefwatch.com
Dist(s): **ACTA Pubns.**

Perio Reports, *(0-9659236)* Orders Addr.: P.O. Box 30367, Flagstaff, AZ 86003-0367 USA Tel 520-526-2523; Fax: 520-526-0852; Edit Addr.: 1640 N. Spyglass Way, Flagstaff, AZ 86004 USA
Dist(s): **Jenkins Group, Inc.**

Periplus Editions (HK), Ltd. (HKG) *(0-945971; 962-593; 0-7946) Dist. by* **Tuttle Pubng.**

PeriplusEdition *Imprint of* **Tuttle Publishing**

Periscope Pr., *(0-9718546)* 15736 Horton Ln., Overland Park, KS 66223-3491 USA (SAN 254-9700)
Web site: http://www.hearthisorg.com
Dist(s): **Baker & Taylor Bks.**
Midwest Library Service
Quality Bks., Inc.

Periwinkle Park Educational Productions, *(1-893919)* Orders Addr.: P.O. Box 21, Woodstock, GA 30188-0021 USA Tel 770-592-3436; Fax: 770-924-8748; Edit Addr.: 3217 Eagle Watch Dr., Woodstock, GA 30189 USA ; *Imprints:* Sing to Read Adventure, The (Sing Read Ad)
E-mail: peripark@bellsouth.net
Web site: http://www.cris.com/~peripark.

Periwinkle Studios, *(0-9759385)* P.O. Box 5134, Roselle, IL 60172 USA
E-mail: periwinklestudios@comcast.net.

Perkins Crawford, *(0-9762935)* 2605 Treyburne Ln., Owens Crossroads, AL 35763 USA Tel 256-536-5391
E-mail: e_vroom@bellsouth.net
Web site: http://www.perkinscrawford.com.

Perkins Miniatures, *(0-9759198)* 1708-59th St., Des Moines, IA 50322 USA Tel 515-279-6639
E-mail: gladon@earthlink.net.

Perkins Schl. for the Blind, *(0-9657170; 0-9743510)* a/o Publications Dept., 175 N. Beacon St., Watertown, MA 02472 USA Tel 617-924-3434; Fax: 617-972-7334 (purchases)
E-mail: Publications@Perkins.org
Web site: http://www.Perkins.org.

Perkins-Stell, Crystal, *(0-9740705)* P.O. Box 8044, Edmond, OK 73013-8044 USA Tel 405-216-0224; Fax: 405-216-0224
E-mail: cleva@crystalstell.com
Web site: http://www.crystalstell.com.

Perlycross Pubs., *(0-9741743)* Orders Addr.: a/o Bryce D. Gibby, P.O. Box 9725, Ogden, UT 84409 USA Tel 801-732-8600; Fax: 801-732-8602; Edit Addr.: 2711 Centerville Rd., Suite 120, PMB 5544, Wilmington, DE 19808 USA.

PermaGrin Publishing, *(0-9717464)* 27758 Santa Margarita Pkwy. No. 379, Mission Viejo, CA 92691 USA (SAN 254-4148) Tel 949-766-1545; Fax: 949-766-0937
E-mail: r2ktrahan@cox.net
Web site: http://www.permagrinpublishing.com
Dist(s): **Independent Pubs. Group.**

Permanent Pr., The, *(0-932966; 1-57962; 1-877946)* Affil. of Second Chance Pr., 4170 Noyac Rd., Sag Harbor, NY 11963 USA (SAN 212-2995) Tel 631-725-1101; Fax: 631-725-8215 Do not confuse with companies with the same name in Santurce, PR, San Francisco, CA, Brooklyn, NY, Santa Fe, NM
E-mail: info@thepermanentpress.com
Web site: http://www.thepermanentpress.com.

PERMEDHIST *Imprint of* **Wing, Thomas Publishing**

Permiso Por Favor Publishing Co., *(0-9747272)* 8568 Riverwood Farms, Cordova, TN 38016 USA Tel 901-756-0663
E-mail: permisoporfavor@hotmail.com.

Perpendicular Pr., *(0-9740234)* 64 Estabrook Rd., Carlisle, MA 01741-1724 USA
E-mail: info@perpendicularpress.com
Web site: http://www.perpendicularpress.com.

Perri Tales Pubns., *(0-9763442)* Orders Addr.: 45 W. 132nd St., Suite 12K, New York City, NY 10037-3123 USA; Edit Addr.: 19601 Kings Hwy., Warrensville Heights, OH 44122 USA
E-mail: perrigaffney@aol.com
Web site: http://www.perritales.com.

Perrin & Kabel Publishing, *(0-9725364)* 145 Waverly Dr., Pasadena, CA 91105 USA Tel 626-577-1023; Fax: 626-577-1024
E-mail: perrinkabel@earthlink.net.

Perry Enterprises, *(0-941518)* 3907 N. Foothill Dr., Provo, UT 84604 USA (SAN 171-0281) Tel 801-226-1002.

Perry Heights Pr., *(0-9630181)* 610 Nod Hill Rd., Wilton, CT 06897-1305 USA Tel 203-767-6509; Fax: 309-403-4827 ; *Imprints:* A Road to Discovery Series Guide (Rd Discovery)
E-mail: contact@perryheightspress.com; contact@cttrips.com
Web site: http://www.cttrips.com.

Perry Publishing, *(0-9643728; 1-891043)* 5087 Columbia Rd., Columbia, MD 21044 USA Tel 410-997-2731; Fax: 410-730-6092; Toll Free: 888-247-3779 Do not confuse with companies of same name in Thompson Falls, MT, Hallowell, ME
E-mail: perry2@home.com
Web site: http://www.perrypublishing.com
Dist(s): **Baker & Taylor Bks.**
Quality Bks., Inc.

Pers Publishing, *(1-932179)* Div. of Pers Corp., 5255 Stevens Creek Blvd., No. 232-5, Santa Clara, CA 95051-6664 USA (SAN 254-7716) Toll Free Fax: 800-505-7377
E-mail: info@pers.com
Web site: http://www.pers.com; http://www.pers.com/wholesale
Dist(s): **APG Sales and Fulfillment**
Baker & Taylor Bks.
Brodart Co.
Emery-Pratt Co.
Quality Bks., Inc.

†Persea Bks., Inc., *(0-89255)* 853 Broadway, Suite 604, New York, NY 10003 USA (SAN 212-8233) Tel 212-260-9256; Fax: 212-260-1902
E-mail: info@perseabooks.com
Web site: http://www.perseabooks.com
Dist(s): **Norton, W. W. & Co., Inc.**; *CIP.*

Perseus Bks. Group, *(0-7382; 0-938289; 1-58097; 1-882810)* Orders Addr.: 2465 Central Ave., Suite 200, Boulder, CO 80301-5728 USA Toll Free: 800-343-4499 (customer service); Edit Addr.: 387 Park Ave., S., 12th Flr., New York, NY 10016-8810 USA Tel 212-340-8100; Fax: 212-340-8105
E-mail: perseus.orders@perseusbooks.com
Web site: http://www.perseusbooksgroup.com
Dist(s): **Perseus Distribution.**

Perseus Distribution, Orders Addr.: 1700 4th St., Berkeley, CA 94710 USA (SAN 760-5129) Fax: 510-528-3614; Toll Free: 800-788-3123; Edit Addr.: 387 Park Avenue South, New York, NY 10016 USA (SAN 631-760X) Tel 212-340-8100; Fax: 212-340-8195
E-mail: skail@cds.aeneas.com; tflowers@cdsbooks.com
Web site: http://www.cdsbooks.com/.

Personal Best Motivional Sciences, Inc., *(0-9769988)* P.O. Box 562, Social Circle, GA 30025-0562 USA
Web site: http://www.babysimplerecipe.com/.

Personal Genesis Publishing, *(0-9747395)* 110 Pacific Ave., No. 204, San Francisco, CA 9411 USA Toll Free: 888-337-7776
Web site: http://www.ForgottenFaces.org.

Personal Power Pr., *(0-9616046; 0-9772321)* Div. of Institute for Personal Power, P.O. Box 547, Merrill, MI 48637 USA (SAN 698-0155) Tel 989-643-5059; Fax: 989-643-5156; Toll Free: 877-360-1477
E-mail: ipp57@aol.com
Web site: http://www.chickmoorman.com
Dist(s): **Austin & Company, Inc.**
Partners Pubs. Group, Inc.

Personal Promise Bible, *(0-9759578)* 164 Riverwood St., Richland, WA 99352 USA Tel 509-627-2607; Fax: 775-402-2106; Toll Free: 866-968-7242
Web site: http://www.personalpromisebible.com.

Personal Security, *(0-9675357)* 24366 Falcon, Lake Forest, CA 92630 USA Tel 949-461-9552; Fax: 949-472-8018
E-mail: xwordshicklers@hotmail.com.

Personality Press *See* **Laguna Pr./BTI**

Personality Wise *See* **Uniquely You Resources**

Personalized Books & Journals, *(0-9743782)* Orders Addr.: P.O. Box 465, Alcoa, TN 37701 USA Tel 865-681-2161; Fax: 865-983-2594; Edit Addr.: 1410 Remsen St., Alcoa, TN 37701 USA
E-mail: pbjtn@att.net
Web site: http://www.pbjtn.home.att.net.

Personhood Pr., *(1-932181)* P.O. Box 370, Fawnskin, CA 92333 USA Tel 909-866-2912; Fax: 909-866-2961; Toll Free: 800-662-9662
E-mail: blwjalmar@att.net; catwinch@att.net; personhoodpress@att.net
Web site: http://www.personhoodpress.com
Dist(s): **Independent Pubs. Group.**

Perspective Bks., LLC, *(0-9701736)* 7 Nehemiah Rd., Shirley, MA 01464 USA
E-mail: rsaganich@perspective-books.com.

Perspective Publishing, Inc., *(0-9622036; 1-930085)* 2528 Sleepy Hollow Dr., No. A, Glendale, CA 91206 USA Tel 818-502-1270; Fax: 818-502-1272; Toll Free: 800-330-5851 Do not confuse with Perspective Publishing, Memphis, TN
E-mail: books@familyhelp.com
Web site: http://www.familyhelp.com
Dist(s): **Independent Pubs. Group**
Quality Bks., Inc.

Perspectives Pr., Inc., *(0-944934; 0-9609504)* P.O. Box 90318, Indianapolis, IN 46290-0318 USA (SAN 262-5059) Tel 317-872-3055
E-mail: patjohnston@perspectivespress.com
Web site: http://www.perspectivespress.com.

Perth Pubns., Ltd., *(0-9660758)* Orders Addr.: P.O. Box 2996, Sanford, NC 27330 USA Tel 919-499-6081; Fax: 919-499-2781; Edit Addr.: 526 Perth Dr., Sanford, NC 27330 USA
Web site: http://www.alltel.net/~docorr.

PES, Inc., *(0-9766962)* P.O. Box 5501, Virginia Bch, VA 23471-0501 USA
E-mail: sailingthroughbusiness@cox.net
Web site: http://www.sailingthroughbusiness.com.

Peta Pubns., *(0-9622101)* 501 Front St., Norfolk, VA 23510-9800 USA Tel 757-622-7382; Fax: 757-628-0783; Toll Free: 800-483-4366
Dist(s): **Book Publishing Co., The.**

PetCare, Inc., *(1-890145)* 168 E. Highland Ave., Elgin, IL 60120-5507 USA Tel 847-622-9920; Fax: 847-622-0219; Toll Free: 800-729-4753 ; *Imprints:* Paw Island Entertainment, Incorporated (Paw Island Ent)
Web site: http://www.PawIsland.com.

Peter Pauper Pr. Inc., *(0-88088; 1-59359)* Orders Addr.: 202 Mamaroneck Ave., Suite 400, White Plains, NY 10601 USA (SAN 204-9449) Tel 914-681-0144; Fax: 914-681-0389; Toll Free: 800-833-2311
E-mail: orders@peterpauper.com; customerservice@peterpauper.com
Web site: http://www.peterpauper.com.

Peterman, Melvin G., *(0-9722058; 0-9755280)* 13410 NE 92nd St., Vancouver, WA 98682 USA Tel 360-604-9333
Web site: http://www.insightteched.com.

Peters & Pardee Pubs., *(0-9626279)* Orders Addr.: 1039 NW Hwy. 101, Lincoln City, OR 97367 USA.

Petersburg Museums, The, *(0-9744824)* 15 W. Bank St., Petersburg, VA 23803 USA Tel 804-733-2402 Toll Free: 800-368-3595.

Peterson *Imprint of* **Peterson's**

Peterson Publishing Co., Inc., *(0-9709033)* 1574 Sherwood Dr., N., Mankato, MN 56003 USA Tel 507-625-4803 Do not confuse with Peterson Publishing Co. in Gunnison, CO.

Peterson-Boyce, Linda, *(0-9766034)* P.O. Box 2942, North Babylon, NY 11703 USA.

†Peterson's, *(0-02; 0-7689; 0-87866; 1-56079)* Div. of Nelnet, Orders Addr.: P.O. Box 67005, Lawrenceville, NJ 08648-6105 USA (SAN 200-2167); Edit Addr.: 2000 Lenox Dr., 3rd Flr., Lawrenceville, NJ 08648 USA (SAN 297-5661) Tel 609-896-1800; Fax: 609-896-1811; Toll Free: 800-338-3282 X5660;Customer Service ; *Imprints:* Arco (Arco); Peterson (Peter)
E-mail: custsvc@petersons.com
Web site: http://www.petersons.com
Dist(s): **Simon & Schuster**
Simon & Schuster, Inc.; *CIP.*

Petra Publishing *See* **Petra Publishing Co.**

Petra Publishing Co., *(0-9712429)* 385 S. Lemon Ave., Suite E314, Walnut, CA 91789 USA Tel 404-452-3374
E-mail: admin@petrapublishingcompany.com
Web site: http://www.petrapublishingcompany.com; http://www.positivemag.com
Dist(s): **Baker & Taylor Bks.**

Petra Publishing Corp., *(1-880015)* 4319 Scottsville Rd., Charlottesville, VA 22902-7800 USA Tel 804-244-3358 Do not confuse with companies with similar or same names in Fountain Hills, AZ, Berrien Springs,MI, Wilmington, OH
Dist(s): **Revolution Booksellers.**

Petrie Pr., *(0-9711638)* 9 Card Ave., Camden, NY 13316 USA Tel 315-245-2408
E-mail: lettiegus@aol.com
Dist(s): **North Country Bks., Inc.**

Petunia Pr., Inc., *(0-9662399)* 407 Bridge St., Charlevoix, MI 49720 USA Tel 616-547-7323; Fax: 616-547-0416.

Peutral Publications *See* **Peytral Pubns., Inc.**

Pex Castle, *(0-9676844)* 33111 SE Wood Dr., Washougal, WA 98671 USA Tel 360-835-9608 (phone/fax).

Pex Publishing Co., *(0-933767)* 8625 Boysenberry Dr., Tampa, FL 33635 USA (SAN 692-7645).

Peytral Pubns., Inc., *(0-9644271; 1-890455)* P.O. Box 1162, Minnetonka, MN 55345 USA (SAN 298-4733) Tel 952-949-8707; Fax: 952-906-9777; Toll Free: 877-739-8725
E-mail: peggy@peytral.com
Web site: http://www.peytral.com
Dist(s): **Baker & Taylor Bks.**
Ingram Bk. Co.

P.F.B. Publishing, *(0-9741273)* P.O. Box 149, Warren, OH 44482-0149 USA Fax: 330-373-0211
E-mail: pat@southparktitle.com.

PFC Publishing, *(0-9728449)* 16503 Governor Bridge Rd., No. 302, Bowie, MD 20716 USA Do not confuse with PFC Publishing in Tulsa, OK.

Pfeiffer *Imprint of* **Wiley, John & Sons, Inc.**

Pfeiffer, Florise C. & Henry B., *(0-9721752)* P.O. Box 654, Pine Island, NY 10969 USA.

Pflaum Publishing Group, *(0-89837; 0-937997; 1-933178)* 2621 Dryden Rd., Dayton, OH 45439 USA (SAN 661-2539) Tel 937-293-1415; Fax: 937-293-1310; Toll Free Fax: 800-543-4383; Toll Free: 800-543-4383
E-mail: service@pflaum.com
Web site: http://www.pflaum.com
Dist(s): **ACTA Pubns.**

Phaelos Bks. *Imprint of* **Phaelos Publishing**

Phaelos Publishing, *(0-9700209; 0-9787991)* Orders Addr.: 860 N. Mcqueen Rd., Unit 1171, Chandler, AZ 85225-8104 USA (SAN 253-8008) Tel 602-325-7432; Fax: 509-479-8415 ; *Imprints:* Phaelos Books (Phaelos Bks)
E-mail: info@phaelos.com
Web site: http://www.phaelos.com
Dist(s): **New Leaf Distributing Co., Inc.**
NorthCountry Distributors.

Phaidon Pr. (GBR) *(0-7148; 1-904563) Dist. by* **HachBkGrp.**

Phaidon Pr., Inc., *(0-7148)* 180 Varick St., 14th Flr., New York, NY 10014-4606 USA (SAN 253-3367) Tel 212-652-5400; Fax: 212-652-5410; Toll Free Fax: 800-286-9471 (Orders only); Toll Free: 800-759-0190 (Orders only); 877-742-4366 (Editorial)
E-mail: ussales@phaidon.com
Web site: http://www.phaidon.com
Dist(s): **Hachette Bk. Group.**

Phantom Pubns., Inc., *(0-9625372)* 9451 Page Rd., Wattsburg, PA 16442-2005 USA
Dist(s): **Empire Publishing Service.**

Phantom Publishing, Inc., *(0-9660292)* P.O. Box 169, Chapman, AL 36015 USA Tel 334-376-9169; Fax: 334-376-9541 Do not confuse with Phantom Publishing in Santa Clarita, CA
E-mail: ogsf@earthlink.net.

Pharmaceutical Products Pr. *Imprint of* **Haworth Pr., Inc., The**

Pharmasoft Publishing *See* **Hale Publishing**

Phat Art 4, *(0-9706581)* Orders Addr.: P.O. Box 711, Stratham, NH 03885-0711 USA Tel 603-778-9990; Fax: 603-778-9669; Toll Free: 888-682-6837; Edit Addr.: 149 Winnicutt Rd., Stratham, NH 03885 USA
E-mail: sibley@phatart4.com; abby@phatart4.com
Web site: http://www.phatart4.com.

Phelps Publishing, *(1-887627)* P.O. Box 22401, Cleveland, OH 44122 USA Tel 216-752-4938; Fax: 216-752-4941
E-mail: earl@phelpspublishing.com
Web site: http://www.phelpspublishing.com
Dist(s): **Baker & Taylor Bks.**
Brodart Co.
Independent Pubs. Group
Quality Bks., Inc.

Phelps Publishing Company *See* **Phelps Publishing**

Phi Sigma Omega, Alpha Kappa Alpha Sorority, Inc., *(0-9785269)* P.O. Box 1784, Gonzales, LA 70707-1784 USA Tel 225-936-1665
Web site: http://phisigmaomega2000.org.

Phidal Publishing, Inc./Editions Phidal, Inc. (CAN) *(2-89393; 2-920129; 2-7643) Dist. by* **AIMS Intl.**

Philadelphia Folklore Project, *(0-9644937)* 735 S. 50th St., Philadelphia, PA 19147 USA Tel 215-726-1106; Fax: 215-726-6250
E-mail: pfp@folkloreproject.org
Web site: http://www.folkloreproject.org.

Philadelphia Inquirer, The, *(1-58822)* Div. of Philadelphia Newspapers, Inc., 400 N. Broad St., Philadelphia, PA 19101 USA Tel 215-854-2000
Web site: http://www.philly.com.

Philipp, Cathy Publishing, *(0-9655848)* P.O. Box 1954, Thousand Oaks, CA 91358-1954 USA Tel 805-498-0611; Fax: 805-498-7331
E-mail: philifam@adelphia.net.

Philippine American Literary House *See* **PALH**

†Phillips Collection, The, *(0-943044)* 1600 21st St., NW, Washington, DC 20009 USA (SAN 321-2297) Tel 202-387-2151; Fax: 202-387-2436
E-mail: kschneider@phillipscollection.org
Web site: http://phillipscollection.org
Dist(s): **Univ. of Washington Pr.**; *CIP.*

Phillips Exeter Academy Pr., The, *(0-939618)* 13 Spring St., Exeter, NH 03833-1104 USA (SAN 216-4353) Tel 603-772-5181; Fax: 603-777-4398; Toll Free: 800-743-5181 ; *Imprints:* P E A Press (PEA Pr)
E-mail: info@exeterbook.com
Web site: http://www.exeterbook.com.

Phillips, Lavearne Products, *(1-930058)* P.O. Box 70650, Memphis, TN 38107 USA Tel 901-525-4837; Toll Free: 800-213-7553 (ext. 01)
E-mail: lavearnep@lavearneproducts.com
Web site: http://www.lavearneproducts.com.

Phillips, S.G. Inc., *(0-87599)* P.O. Box 416, Ghent, NY 12075 USA (SAN 293-3152) Tel 518-392-3068; Fax: 518-392-6493
E-mail: sgp@taconic.net.

Philograph *Imprint of* **Cascade, Inc.**

Philomel *Imprint of* **Penguin Group (USA) Inc.**

†Philosophical Library, Inc., *(0-8022)* P.O. Box 1789, New York, NY 10010 USA (SAN 201-999X) Tel 212-886-1873; Fax: 212-873-6070
Dist(s): **Kensington Publishing Corp.**; *CIP.*

Phlare, Inc., *(0-9741147)* 9565 W. 52nd Ave., Arvada, CO 80002 USA Tel 303-513-1565; Toll Free: 888-731-2398
Web site: http://www.phlare.com.

Phoenix Color Corp., *(0-9702653)* 317 Madison Ave., 4th Flr., Suite 415, New York, NY 10017 USA (SAN 179-6550); 18249 Phoenix Rd., Hagerstown, MD 21742-1351 (SAN 179-6569).

Phoenix Films & Video, *(0-7919)* 2349 Chaffee Dr., Saint Louis, MO 63146 USA (SAN 653-5224) Tel 314-569-0211; Fax: 314-569-2834; Toll Free: 800-221-1274
E-mail: phoenixfilm@worldnet.att.net
Web site: http://www.phoenix-bfa-coronet.com
Dist(s): **Weston Woods Studios, Inc.**

Phoenix Literary Productions, *(0-9665612)* 111 Miss Ellie Cir., Belton, MO 64012-4546 USA.

Phoenix Publishing, *(1-928812)* Orders Addr.: P.O. Box 8231, Missoula, MT 59807 USA Fax: 406-721-6195; Toll Free: 800-549-8371; Edit Addr.: 309 SW Higgins, Missoula, MT 59803 USA Do not confuse with companies with the same or similar names in Redmond, WA, W. Kennebunk, ME, Rocklin, CA, Bloomington, IN, Miami, FL, Fairfield, FL, Tolono, IL, Newark, NJ, Lansing, MI, Alpharetta, GA, Custer, WA, Marina del Ray, CA, Half Moon Bay, CA, New York, NY
E-mail: phoenixi@phoenixpub.com
Web site: http://www.phoenixpub.com.

PhotoGraphics Publishing, *(0-9643844; 0-9793813)* 23 Cool Water Ct., Palm Coast, FL 32137 USA Tel 386-246-3672; Fax: 386-445-7365 ; *Imprints:* Doctor Dolittle's Library (Doctor Dolittle)
E-mail: bestdives@hotmail.com
Web site: http://www.photographicspublishing.com.

Photon Pubns., *(0-615; 0-9744128)* 7532 Mason Dells Dr., Dallas, TX 75230-3246 USA
E-mail: j1jagger@aol.com
Dist(s): **BookMasters, Inc.**

Photosensitive, *(1-889252)* Div. of Birth Of America Audiobooks, Orders Addr.: P.O. Box 7008, Hemet, CA 92545 USA Tel 951-765-0950 (phone/fax); Toll Free: 877-742-6241
E-mail: photosensitive@worldnet.att.net
Web site: http://www.home.att.net/~photosensitive.

Phred's Pharm Pr., *(0-9754346)* RR 1, Box 109, Tallula, IL 62688-9748 USA.

Pi Communication Materials, Inc., *(0-9639415)* Orders Addr.: 1510 Professor Ct., Richmond, VA 23228-3331 USA
Web site: http://www.picommunication.com.

Pi Pr., *(0-9677074)* P.O. Box 4161, New Orleans, LA 70178-4161 USA Tel 504-258-0618
E-mail: gridmatics@ontele.com.

Piano Pr, *(0-9673325; 1-931844)* Orders Addr.: P.O. Box 85, Del Mar, CA 92014-0085 USA Tel 619-884-1401; Fax: 858-755-1104; Edit Addr.: 1425 Ocean Ave., No. 17, Del Mar, CA 92014 USA
E-mail: eaxford@aol.com; lizaxford@pianopress.com; pianopress@pianopress.com
Web site: http://www.pianopress.com
Dist(s): **Baker & Taylor Bks.**
Book Wholesalers, Inc.
Coutts Library Service, Inc.
Blackwell North America
Wayland Audio-Visual.

Piñata Books *Imprint of* **Arte Publico Pr.**

Picador, *(0-312)* Div. of Holtzbrinck Publishers, Orders Addr.: 16365 James Madison Hwy., Gordonsville, VA 22942-8501 USA Fax: 800-672-2054; Toll Free: 888-330-8477; Edit Addr.: 175 Fifth Ave., New York, NY 10010 USA Tel 212-674-5151; Fax: 540-672-7540 (customer service)
Web site: http://www.picadorusa.com
Dist(s): **Libros Sin Fronteras**
Macmillan.

Piccadilly Bks., Ltd., *(0-941599)* P.O. Box 25203, Colorado Springs, CO 80936 USA (SAN 665-9969) Tel 719-550-9887
E-mail: info@piccadillybooks.com
Web site: http://www.piccadillybooks.com
Dist(s): **Nutri-Bks. Corp.**

Pickering, Todd, *(0-615)* P.O. Box 907, Pt Reyes Sta, CA 94956-0907 USA
E-mail: todd@toddpickering.com
Web site: http://www.toddpickering.com.

Pickled Eggs Pr., *(0-9725311)* Div. of E-Compass Communications, Inc., P.O. Box 9177, Rochester, MN 55903 USA Tel 507-280-1794; Fax: 507-280-4440 (Attn: Pickled Eggs Pr.)
E-mail: pickledeggspress@aol.com
Web site: http://www.pickledeggspress.com
Dist(s): **e-Compass Communications, Inc.**

Pickled Herring Pr., *(0-9778276)* 2380 W. Hill Dr., Madison, WI 53711 USA.

Picklesisters, *(0-9767542)* 1257 Mills St., No. 4, Menlo Park, CA 94025 USA
E-mail: editor@picklesisters.com
Web site: http://www.picklesisters.com.

Pickup, Terry Lowey *See* **Terry Lowey's Children's Stories, LLC**

Picton Pr., *(0-89725; 0-912274; 0-929539; 0-9614281)* Div. of Picton Corp., P.O. Box 250, Rockport, ME 04856-0250 USA (SAN 249-6321) Tel 207-236-6565; Fax: 207-236-6713
E-mail: sales@pictonpress.com
Web site: http://www.pictonpress.com.

Pictorial Legends, *(0-939031)* Subs. of Event Co., 435 Holland Ave., Los Angeles, CA 90042 USA (SAN 662-8486) Tel 213-254-4416
Dist(s): **Igram Pr.**

Picture Bk Learning, Inc., *(0-9760725)* P.O. Box 270075, Louisville, CO 80027 USA
E-mail: todd@picturebooklearning.com
Web site: http://www.picturebooklearning.com.

Picture Entertainment *See* **Evening Sun Pr.**

Picture Me Books, Incorporated *See* **Playhouse Publishing**

Picture Me..! Pubns. *Imprint of* **Picture Me Reading!**

Picture Me Reading!, *(0-9742951; 0-9743916)* 3899 Kenwood Dr., Spring Valley, CA 91977-1024 USA Tel 619-462-3938 (phone/fax); Toll Free: 800-235-6822 ; *Imprints:* Picture Me..! Publications (Picture Me)
E-mail: picturemereading@mindspring.com
Web site: http://www.picturemereading.com.

Picture Window Bks., *(1-4048)* Div. of Coughlan Publishing, 151 Good Counsel Dr., P.O. Box 669, Mankato, MN 56002-0669 USA (SAN 254-8828) Toll Free Fax: 877-787-2746; Toll Free: 877-845-8392
E-mail: gbeer@capstone-press.com
Web site: http://www.picturewindowbooks.com
Dist(s): **Capstone Pr., Inc.**

Pie in the Sky Publishing, LLC, *(1-893815)* 8031 E. Phillips Cir., Centennial, CO 80112 USA
E-mail: PieintheSkyPublishing@msn.com
Web site: http://www.pieintheskypublishing.com.

Pieces of Learning, *(0-9623835; 1-880505; 1-931334; 1-934358)* Div. of Creative Learning Consultants, Inc., 1990 Market Rd., Marion, IL 62959 USA (SAN 298-461X) Tel 618-964-9426; Fax: 618-964-1897; Toll Free Fax: 800-844-0455; Toll Free: 800-729-5137
E-mail: piecesoflearning@verizon.net
Web site: http://www.piecesoflearning.com.

Piemme (ITA) *(88-384)* *Dist. by* **Distribks Inc.**

Pier Avenue Publishing, *(0-9779768)* 1250 6th St., Hermosa beach, CA 90254 USA Tel 310-530-0770
Web site: educatingamerica.us.

Pier Media, *(0-9715980)* Div. of Pier Video, Inc., P.O. Box 190, Gardiner, NY 12525 USA Tel 212-481-0031; Fax: 212-481-0892
E-mail: joe514@aol.com
Web site: http://www.marcusantebi.com.

Pieras Inc. Editorial, *(0-9729719)* Div. of Pieras Inc., Y-9 México Ave. and Colorado St. Parkville Extension, Guaynabo, PR 00962-3923 USA (SAN 255-3112) Tel 787-299-4486
E-mail: jorge@elbien.org
Web site: http://www.elbien.org.

Pieras Incorporated *See* **Pieras Inc. Editorial**

Pierce, Paul, *(0-9741819)* 1400 15th St., Columbus, GA 31901 USA
E-mail: prpierce@mindspring.com
Dist(s): **Parnassus Bk. Distributors.**

Pig Iron Pr., *(0-917530)* Orders Addr.: P.O. Box 237, Youngstown, OH 44501 USA (SAN 209-0937) Tel 330-747-6932; Fax: 330-747-0599; Edit Addr.: 26 N. Phelps, Youngstown, OH 44503 USA (SAN 241-8193)
E-mail: pigironpress@cboss.com.

Pigtail Publishing, *(0-9677548)* 18 Banbury Dr., Westford, MA 01886-3518 USA Do not confuse with Pigtail Publishing, Coral Springs, FL.

PigTale Pr., *(0-9679638)* 6611 W. Surrey Ave., Glendale, AZ 85304 USA Tel 623-412-0706; Fax: 623-412-2432 Do not confuse with PigTale Press in San Pedro CA,
E-mail: tororoy@msn.com
Web site: http://pigtales.com.

Pikkdata, *(0-9718414)* 124 Tamalpais Rd., Fairfax, CA 94930 USA
E-mail: pikkdata@yahoo.com; GPikkara@msn.com.

Pik-Ware Publishing, *(0-9744190)* P.O. Box 110, Crisfield, MD 21817 USA Tel 410-968-3873 (phone/fax)
E-mail: pat@funkyseagull.com
Web site: http://www.pik-ware.com.

PIL Kids *Imprint of* **Publications International, Ltd.**

Pilate, Victoria, *(0-9759665)* P.O. Box 75433, Washington, DC 20013 USA.

Pilgrim Press *See* **Kinfolk Research Pr.**

Pilgrim Pr., The/United Church Pr., *(0-8298)* Div. of United Church Board for Homeland Ministries, Orders Addr.: 230 Sheldon Rd., Berea, OH 44017 USA Fax: 216-732-3713; Toll Free: 800-537-3394; Edit Addr.: 700 Prospect Ave. E., Cleveland, OH 44115-1100 USA Tel 216-736-3764; Fax: 216-736-2207
E-mail: ucpress@ucc.org; pilgrim@ucc.org
Web site: http://www.ucpress.com;
http://www.pilgrimpress.com
Dist(s): **CRC Pubns.**
Women Ink.

Pilgrim Way Pr., The, *(0-9623785)* 350 Pearl St., No. 1108, Eugene, OR 97401 USA Tel 541-686-9594
E-mail: westernprinters@mailcity.com.

Pilgrim's Tales, Inc., *(0-9770536)* Orders Addr.: P.O. Box 791613, Paia, HI 96779 USA Tel 760-494-7537 (phone/fax); Toll Free: 866-829-0820
E-mail: pilgrimstales@hawaii.rr.com; pilgrimstales@yahoo.com
Web site: http://www.yakbutterblues.com;
http://www.PilgrimsTales.com
Dist(s): **Baker & Taylor Bks.**

Pilinut Pr., Inc., *(0-9779576)* 5089 Old Auburn Rd., Warrenton, VA 20187 USA.

Pill Bug Pr., *(0-9761623)* 1868 Bridgeport Ave., Claremont, CA 91711 USA Tel 909-624-9985 (phone/fax).

Pillar of Enoch Ministry Bks., *(0-9759131)* 1708 N. 77th Ave., Elmwood Park, IL 60707-4107 USA
E-mail: helena@pillar-of-enoch.com
Web site: http://www.pillar-of-enoch.com
Dist(s): **Lightning Source, Inc.**

Pillar Rock Publishing, *(0-9764109)* P.O. Box 86571, Portland, OR 97286 USA
Web site: http://www.zoppa.com.

Pinata Pubns., *(0-934925)* P.O. Box 13252, Oakland, CA 94611 USA (SAN 694-6062) Tel 510-336-0819 (phone/fax)
E-mail: bsalinas@ousd.k12.ca.us
Dist(s): **Lectorum Pubns., Inc.**
Libros Sin Fronteras
Teacher's Discovery.

Pinata Publishing, *(0-9685097)* 626 Old Plantation Rd., Jekyll Island, GA 31527-0724 USA Tel 912-635-9402 (phone/fax)
E-mail: pam@kiskalore.com
Web site: http://www.pinatapub.com
Dist(s): **Partners Pubs. Group, Inc.**

Pince Nez Pr. *Imprint of* **Pince-Nez Pr.**

Pince-Nez Pr., *(0-9648757; 1-930074)* 1459 18th St., PMB 175, San Francisco, CA 94107-2801 USA Tel 415-267-5978; Toll Free Fax: 800-579-3614 ; *Imprints:* Pince Nez Press (Pince Nez)
E-mail: susan@pince-nez.com
Web site: http://www.pince-nez.com
Dist(s): **Books West**
Partners/West.

Pine Hill Graphics, *(0-9714103; 0-9727279; 1-933150)* 85334 Lorane Hwy., Eugene, OR 97405 USA Tel 541-343-1364; Fax: 541-343-0568
E-mail: fred@pinehillgraphics.com.

Pine Hill Pr., Inc., *(1-57579)* 4000 W. 57th St., Sioux Falls, SD 57106 USA Tel 605-362-9200; Fax: 605-362-9222 Do not confuse with Pine Hill Pr., Lafayette, CA8
E-mail: print@pinehillpress.com
Web site: http://www.pinehillpress.com.

Pine Orchard, Inc., *(0-9645727; 1-930580)* Orders Addr.: 2850 Hwy 95 South. P.O. box 9184, Moscow, ID 83843 USA (SAN 253-4258) Tel 208-882-4838; Fax: 208-882-4845; Toll Free: 877-354-7433 ; *Imprints:* Ulyssian Publications (Ulyssian Pubns); Luminary Media Group (Luminary Media)
E-mail: orders@pineorchard.com; pineorch@pineorchard.com
Web site: http://www.pineorchard.com
Dist(s): **Baker & Taylor Bks.**
Brodart Co.
Ingram Bk. Co.

Pine Orchard Press *See* **Pine Orchard, Inc.**

Pine View Pr., *(0-9740151)* Orders Addr.: 42 Central St., Southbridge, MA 01550 USA (SAN 255-3309) Tel 508-764-4961; Fax: 508-765-1963
E-mail: shawnpcormier@aol.com
Web site: http://www.pineviewpress.com
Dist(s): **Baker & Taylor Bks.**
Partners Bk. Distributing, Inc.

Pineapple Pr., Inc., *(0-910923; 1-56164)* P.O. Box 3889, Sarasota, FL 34230-3889 USA (SAN 285-0850) Tel 941-739-2219; Fax: 941-739-2296; Toll Free: 800-746-3275 Do not confuse with companies with same or similar names in Saint Johns, MI, Middletown, RI, Northampton, MA, Wimberley, TX
E-mail: info@pineapplepress.com;
editorial@pineapplepress.com
Web site: http://www.pineapplepress.com
Dist(s): **American Wholesale Bk. Co.**
Baker & Taylor Bks.

Pinefield Publishing, *(0-9746397)* 9801 Fall Creek Rd., Suite 318, Indianapolis, IN 46256 USA Tel 317-258-6211; Fax: 317-576-9154
E-mail: Pinefieldpublishing@comcast.net
Web site: http://www.Pinefieldpublishing.com.

Pines Publishing, *(0-9766820)* 9896 Lincoln Rd., Morrison, KY 61270-9498 USA
E-mail: info@pinespublishing.com
Web site: http://www.pinespublishing.com.

Pinetree Pubns., *(0-9709408)* 6523 Oregon Chickadee Rd., Weeki Wachee, FL 34613-8353 USA Tel 352-592-5292 (phone/fax)
E-mail: lwnorris@hitter.net; lwnorris@bellsouth.net.

Pink Elephant Pr. The, *(0-9772975)* P.O. Box 1153, Jonesboro, GA 30236-1153 USA (SAN 257-2532) Toll Free: 800-583-1439 (phone/fax)
E-mail: info@thepinkelephantpress.com
Web site: http://www.thepinkelephantpress.com.

Pink Flamingo, *(0-9704761)* 4498 Kindlewood Dr., Ladson, SC 29456 USA Tel 843-709-1026.

Pink Granite Pr., *(0-9766737)* P.O. Box 231, Thousand Island Park, NY 13692-0231 USA Tel 613-549-6575.

Pink Hse. Pr., *(0-9648284)* 1197 Chapel Park Blvd., Cordova, TN 38018 USA Tel 901-756-7388; Fax: 901-756-0386
E-mail: info@marypadron.com
Web site: http://www.marypadron.com.

Pink Hyacinth Pr., *(0-9773481)* 4203 Cty. Rd., 3100, Lubbock, TX 79403-7869 USA
E-mail: kellyall@nts-online.net
Web site: http://www.pinkhyacinthpress.com.

Pink Stucco Pr., *(0-9717796)* 36 Dexter St., Waltham, MA 02453-5017 USA ; *Imprints:* Mystic Night Books (Mystic Night Bks)
E-mail: publishing@pinkstucco.net
Web site: http://www.pinkstucco.net/psp/.

Pinkney Wilcox, JoAnn, *(0-9764191)* 3900 George Busbee Pkwy., #1313, Kennesaw, GA 30144 USA Tel 678-768-5644
E-mail: jpwconnect@gmail.com
Web site: http://www.joannpinkneywilcox.com.

Pinkston Publishing, *(0-9671708)* Orders Addr.: P.O. Box 1964, Rowlett, TX 75030-1964 USA Tel 972-816-3848; Edit Addr.: 7609 Dockside Dr., Rowlett, TX 75088 USA Tel 972-475-3923; Fax: 214-670-4980
E-mail: badge5591@cs.com
Dist(s): **Hervey's Booklink & Cookbook Warehouse.**

Pinnacle Bks. *Imprint of* **Kensington Publishing Corp.**

Pinnacle Press *See* **Mountaintop Pr.**

Pinnacle-Syatt Pubns., *(1-886580)* Div. of Pinnacle-Syatt Enterprises, 535 Calle Capistrano, San Marcos, CA 92069-8306 USA (SAN 299-1179) Tel 760-598-9896; Fax: 760-598-9897
E-mail: gwenevans@msn.com
Web site: http://www.pinnadesyatt.com.

Pinninti Pubs., *(0-9703474)* 86 Sycamore Ct., Lawrenceville, NJ 08648-4836 USA Tel 609-912-0737 (phone/fax)
E-mail: pkrao@dr.com
Web site: http://www.pinnintipublishers.com.

Pinpoint Color *See* **Pinpoint Printing**

Pinpoint Printing, *(0-9702324)* 5115 E. Highland Dr., Jonesboro, AR 72401 USA Tel 870-931-6200; Fax: 870-931-5800
E-mail: dkelley@mkbmarketing.com
Web site: http://www.pinpointprinting.com.

Pinto Pr., *(0-9632476; 0-9755677)* 35 Stewart Pl., Suite 503, Mount Kisco, NY 10549 USA Tel 914-241-8549 (phone/fax)
E-mail: pintopot@optonline.net
Dist(s): **Koen-Levy Bk. Wholesalers LLC**
North Country Bks., Inc.

Pinz, Shelley Music, *(0-9700251)* Orders Addr.: P.O. Box 275, Atlantic Beach, NY 11509 USA Tel 516-371-4437; Fax: 516-371-4437 (*51); Edit Addr.: 2100 Atlantic Blvd., Atlantic Beach, NY 11509 USA.

Pioneer Heritage, *(0-9708289)* P.O. Box 450982, Westlake, OH 44145 USA Tel 440-835-3354.

Pioneer Valley Educational Pr., Inc., *(1-58453)* P.O. Box 9375, North Amherst, MA 01059-9375 USA Tel 413-548-3906; Fax: 413-548-4914
E-mail: dufresne@oitunix.oit.umass.edu; richard@pvep.com
Web site: http://www.pvep.com.

Piper Bks., *(0-330; 0-9722819)* P.O. Box 60625, Santa Barbara, CA 93160 USA Fax: 270-458-6712
E-mail: dhatchell@cox.net
Dist(s): **Biblio Distribution.**

Piper, Susie Sansom, *(0-9618280)* 5904 Coolbrook Dr., Austin, TX 78724 USA (SAN 667-027X) Tel 512-928-1740.

Piper Verlag GmbH (DEU) *(3-492; 3-89029; 3-8225; 3-89521; 3-921909)* *Dist. by* **Distribks Inc.**

Pipevine Pr., *(0-9676839)* 9516 Graton Rd., Sebastopol, CA 95472 USA Tel 707-823-8924
E-mail: pipevineps@aol.com.

Pippin Pr., *(0-945912)* Orders Addr.: P.O. Box 1347, New York, NY 10028 USA (SAN 247-8366) Tel 212-288-4920; Fax: 732-225-1562; Edit Addr.: 229 E. 85th St., New York, NY 10028 USA.

Pirate Publishing International, *(0-9674081)* 6323 St. Andrews Cir., No. 5, Fort Myers, FL 33919-1719 USA Tel 941-939-4845
E-mail: SuperK@juno.com.

P.I.T. Pubns., *(0-9760608)* 120 Deweese Dr., Waggaman, LA 70094-2480 USA Tel 504-436-7012.

Pitambar Publishing (IND) *(81-209)* *Dist. by* **St Mut.**

Pitcher, Jan, *(0-9795877)* 208 Tait Ave., Los Gatos, CA 95030 USA
E-mail: janpitcher@verizon.net.

Pitman Publishing (GBR) *(0-272; 0-273)* *Dist. by* **Trans-Atl Phila.**

Pitsco, Incorporated *See* **Pitsco/Pitsco LEGO Dacta**

Pitsco/Pitsco LEGO Dacta, *(0-9657261; 1-58651)* 1004 E. Adams, Pittsburg, KS 66762 USA; 915 E. Jefferson, Pittsburg, KS 66762 Tel 620-231-0000; Fax: 620-231-6737; Toll Free: 800-835-0686
E-mail: mtremain@pitsco.com
Web site: http://www.pitsco.com.

Pitspopany Pr., *(0-943706; 965-465; 1-930143; 1-932687; 965-483; 1-934440)* Orders Addr.: 40 E. 78th St., Suite 16D, New York, NY 10021-1830 USA (SAN 238-373X) Tel 212-472-4959; 212-444-1657; Fax: 212-472-6253; 866-205-3966; Toll Free: 800-232-2931 ; *Imprints:* Devora Publishing (Devora Pubng)
E-mail: pitspop@netvision.net.il; popany@netvision.net.il; pitspopany@aol.com
Web site: http://www.pitspopany.com;
http://www.devorapublishing.com
Dist(s): **Baker & Taylor Bks.**
Bookazine Co., Inc.

Pittsburgh Literary Arts Network LLC, *(0-9727319)* P.O. Box 226, Oakmont, PA 15139 USA Tel 412-820-2507 ; *Imprints:* Blacktypewriter Press (Blacktypewriter Pr)
E-mail: info@blacktypewriter.com
Web site: http://www.blacktypewriter.com.

Pivotal Bks., *(0-9700686; 1-931062)* Orders Addr.: P.O. Box 10161, Daytona Beach, FL 32120-0161 USA Tel 386-258-7824; Fax: 386-258-0809; Edit Addr.: 1202 David Dr., Holly Hill, FL 32117 USA
E-mail: pivotalbooks@worldnet.att.net
Web site: http://www.pivotalbooks.com.

Pivotal Force, *(0-9740473)* 632 Skyview Rd., Bellville, TX 77418 USA (SAN 256-4319) Tel 979-865-9213
E-mail: pivotalforce@evl.net
Web site: http://www.pivotalforce.com.

Pixelpics Publishing, *(0-9747826)* 4801 Secret Harbor Dr., Jacksonville, FL 32257 USA
Web site: http://www.pixelpics.net.

Pixels Publishing, *(0-9728743)* P.O. Box 10, La Fox, IL 60147 USA
E-mail: customerservice@pixelspublishing.com
Web site: http://www.pixelspublishing.com.

Pixie Stuff LLC, *(0-9761421; 0-9795832)* Orders Addr.: 5257 Shaw Ave. Suite 207, Saint Louis, MO 63110 USA Tel 314-446-6344; Fax: 314-446-6345; Toll Free: 866-749-4378
E-mail: kris@thumbsupjohnnie.com
Web site: http://www.thumbsupjohnnie.com.

Pixiefire *Imprint of* **Darker Intentiona Pr.**

PixyJack Pr., LLC, *(0-9658098; 0-9773724)* Orders Addr.: P.O. Box 149, Masonville, CO 80541 USA Tel 303-810-2850; Fax: 801-904-8747
E-mail: info@pixyjackpress.com
Web site: http://www.pixyjackpress.com.

Pizzazz Publishing, *(0-9744936)* Orders Addr.: P.O. Box 415, Victoria, MN 55386 USA Tel 952-368-1903; Fax: 952-944-0399
E-mail: psimenson@aol.com
Web site: http://www.pizzazzpublishing.com
Dist(s): **Baker & Taylor Bks.**
Biblio Distribution
Quality Bks., Inc.

PJR Assocs., Ltd., *(0-9790796)* Orders Addr.: P.O. Box 2482, Alexandria, VA 22301 USA Fax: 703-683-4348; Edit Addr.: 910 Junior St., Alexandria, VA 22301 USA
E-mail: patrichards@pjrassociates.com
Web site: http://www.pjrassociates.com.

PJs Corner, *(0-9745615; 1-933158)* P.O. Box 39, Taft, CA 93268 USA Tel 661-765-7216; Fax: 661-770-8608 ; *Imprints:* Twiglet The Little Christmas Tree (Twiglet)
E-mail: memories@pjscorner.net
Web site: http://www.pjscorner.net.

PJS Publishing, *(0-9743177)* P.O. Box 981, Yosemite, CA 85389 USA Tel 209-372-4766.

†Place In The Woods, The, *(0-932991)* 3900 Glenwood Ave., Golden Valley, MN 55422-5302 USA (SAN 689-058X) Tel 763-374-2120; Fax: 952-593-5593 ; *Imprints:* Different Books (Different Bks)
E-mail: placewoods@aol.com; differentbooks@aol.com
Dist(s): **Baker & Taylor Bks.**
Social Studies Schl. Service; *CIP.*

Placenames Press *See* **Back Channel Pr.**

Plaidswede Publishing, *(0-9626832; 0-9755216; 0-9790784)* P.O. Box 269, Concord, NH 03302-0269 USA Tel 603-226-1020; Toll Free: 800-267-9044
E-mail: gnews@empire.net
Web site: http://www.plaidswede.com.

Plain View Pr., *(0-911051; 1-891386)* Orders Addr.: P.O. Box 42255, Austin, TX 78704 USA (SAN 264-3073) Tel 512-441-2452
E-mail: sb@plainviewpress.net; jcapvp@hotmail.com
Web site: http://www.plainviewpress.net
Dist(s): **Baker & Taylor Bks.**
Yankee Peddler Bookshop.

Plainsong Publishing, *(0-9709718)* 174 Rd. P W. 20, Ogallala, NE 69153 USA Tel 308-352-4161
E-mail: dwhitejone@aol.com.

Plair, James B., *(0-9718770)* Rt. 1 Box 80 A-5 Slick Rock Mountain, Brevard, NC 28712 USA Tel 828-885-2906; Fax: 828-885-2987 Do not confuse with Serendipity Press in Millburn, NJ, Wilmington, DE, Troy, VA, AU
E-mail: citgrad1950@brinet.com
Web site: http://www.jamesbplair.com.

Plan B Bks, *(0-9785798)* P.O. Box 300307, University City, MO 63130 USA
E-mail: abby@planbbooks.com
Web site: http://www.planbbooks.com.

Plan Nine Publishing, Inc., *(0-9660676; 1-929462)* 1237 Elon Pl., Elon Hse., High Point, NC 27263 USA Tel 336-454-8028; Fax: 336-454-7766; Toll Free: 888-454-0098
E-mail: plan9@plan9.org
Web site: http://www.plan9.org.

Planet Bronx Productions, *(0-9765566)* P.O. Box 672146, Bronx, NY 10467-0803 USA ; *Imprints:* PAPO Brand (PAPO)
E-mail: ivanvelezjr@planetbronx.com; admin@planetbronx.com
Web site: http://www.planetbronx.com.

Planet Crea, Inc., *(1-893264)* 25 East 22nd St., New York, NY 10010 USA Tel 212-228-4901; Fax: 212-228-4916
E-mail: planetc@planetcrea.com
Web site: http://www.planetcrea.com.

Planet Dexter *Imprint of* **Penguin Group (USA) Inc.**

Planeta Mexicana Editorial S. A. de C. V. (MEX) *(968-406; 970-690) Dist. by* **Lectorum Pubns.**

Planeta Publishing Corp., *(0-9715256; 0-9719950; 0-9748724; 1-933169; 0-9795042)* 2057 NW 87th Ave., Miami, FL 33172 USA Tel 305-470-0016; Fax: 305-470-6267
E-mail: mnorman@planetapublishing.com
Web site: http://www.planeta.es
Dist(s): **Ediciones Universal.**

Plankton Pr., *(0-9774074)* 5692 Kalanianaole Hwy., Honolulu, HI 96821 USA Tel 808-373-1016; Fax: 808-373-5381
Web site: www.planktonpress.com.

†Planned Parenthood Federation of America, Inc., *(0-934586; 1-930996)* 434 W. 33rd St., New York, NY 10001 USA (SAN 205-1281) Fax: 212-868-4649; Toll Free: 877-478-7732
E-mail: communications@ppfa.org
Web site: http://www.plannedparenthood.org/store; *CIP.*

Planned Parenthood of Greater Northern New Jersey, Inc., *(0-9609366)* Affil. of Planned Parenthood Federation of America, 196 Speedwell Ave., Morristown, NJ 07960-3889 USA (SAN 260-2482) Tel 973-539-9580 ext 149
E-mail: edu345@eclipse.net
Web site: http://www.plannedparenthoodnj.com.

Planned Parenthood of Northwest New Jersey, Incorporated *See* **Planned Parenthood of Greater Northern New Jersey, Inc.**

Planning/Communications, *(0-9622019; 1-884587)* 7215 Oak Ave., River Forest, IL 60305-1935 USA (SAN 253-8717) Tel 708-366-5200; Fax: 708-366-5280; Toll Free: 888-366-5200 (orders only)
E-mail: info@planningcommunications.com; dl@planningcommunications.com
Web site: http://jobfindersonline.com; http://planningcommunications.com; http://dreamitdoit.net
Dist(s): **SCB Distributors.**

Plant Pr., *(0-9664245)* 1290 Three Meadows Ln., Friday Harbor, WA 98250 USA Do not confuse with Plant Pr., Halifax, MA
E-mail: JFRMO@acad1.alaska.edu.

Plant the Seed Publishing, *(0-9759790)* 4361 Fiesta Ln., Houston, TX 77004 USA Tel 713-747-0026
E-mail: rr4361@aol.com
Web site: http://hometown.aol.com/rr4361/myhomepage/business.

Plateau Pubns., *(0-9644033)* Orders Addr.: 4807 S. Helena St., Spokane, WA 99223 USA
E-mail: grizzkid@aol.com
Dist(s): **Baker & Taylor Bks.**
Brodart Co.

Plath, C. North American Division of Litton Systems, Incorporated *See* **Weems & Plath, Inc.**

Platinum Bks., *(0-9746503)* P.O. Box 660876, Arcadia, CA 91066-0876 USA (SAN 255-7525) Do not confuse with companies with the same name in Alpharetta, GA, Washington, DC
E-mail: hongdenise@yahoo.com
Web site: http://www.happierkids.com.

Platinum Medallion Children's Bks., *(1-929489)* Div. of EDS Design & Animation, 2705 Ridge Rd., Huntingtown, MD 20639 USA Tel 410-535-6992; Fax: 410-535-7643
E-mail: doug@dougweb.com; edsdesign@dsmith.com
Web site: http://www.platinum-medallion.com
Dist(s): **Baker & Taylor Bks.**

Platinum Rose Publishing, *(0-9742948)* 16619 W. Sierra Hwy., Canyon Country, CA 91351 USA
Web site: http://www.platinumrose.com.

Platypus Media, L.L.C., *(1-930775)* Orders Addr.: 627 A St., NE, Washington, DC 20002 USA Tel 202-546-1674; Fax: 202-546-2356; Toll Free: 877-752-8977
E-mail: info@platypusmedia.com
Web site: http://www.platypusmedia.com
Dist(s): **National Bk. Network.**

Play Bac Publishing, USA, *(1-60214)* 225 Varick St., New York, NY 10014 USA (SAN 852-0356) Tel 212-614-7736
Web site: http://Workman.com
Dist(s): **Workman Publishing Co., Inc.**

Play Bks., *(0-9766086)* Div. of NK Enterprises, P.O. Box 88731, Indianapolis, IN 46208 USA Tel 317-724-8926
E-mail: nicoleckearney@yahoo.com
Web site: http://www.nicolekearney.com.

Playbooks, Inc., *(0-9718565; 1-60476)* 111 Corporate Dr. Ste. 240, Ladera Ranch, CA 92694-1158 USA Toll Free: 800-375-2926
E-mail: info@eplaybooks.com
Web site: http://www.eplaybooks.com.

Playco Editores, C.A., *(980-6437)* Orders Addr.: 950 S. Pine Island Rd, Suite A150-126, Plantation, FL 33324 USA Tel 954-727-8116; Fax: 954-727-8426
E-mail: info@playcobooks.com
Web site: http://www.playcobooks.com
Dist(s): **Lectorum Pubns., Inc.**
Iaconi, Mariuccia Bk. Imports.

Playdate Kids Publishing, *(1-933721)* 1901 Main St., Santa Monica, CA 90405 USA (SAN 257-571X) Toll Free: 800-587-1501
E-mail: info@fmrockskids.com
Web site: http://theplaydatekids.com/
Dist(s): **Biblio Distribution.**

Player Pr., *(0-9623966)* 139-22 Caney Ln., Rosedale, NY 11422 USA Tel 718-528-3285 Do not confuse with Player Press LLC in New York, NY.

Player's Guide, *(0-9724773)* 10321 Yellow Pine Dr., Vienna, VA 22182-1344 USA
Web site: http://www.playersguide.biz.

Players Pr., Inc., *(0-88734)* P.O. Box 1132, Studio City, CA 91614-0132 USA (SAN 239-0213) Tel 818-789-4980
E-mail: Playerspress@att.net
Dist(s): **Empire Publishing Service.**

Playful Harmonies, Inc., *(0-9705088)* 8502 W. Main, Belleville, IL 62223 USA Tel 618-394-1482; Fax: 618-398-1912; Toll Free: 800-257-1088
E-mail: kathy@playfulharmonies.com
Web site: http://www.playfulharmonies.com.

Playful Pr., Inc., *(0-9663762)* 302 E. Carson, Suite 508, Las Vegas, NV 89101 USA Tel 702-254-6525; Fax: 702-388-4151
E-mail: teachplay@aol.com
Web site: http://www.quikpage.com/c/childrenlst.

PlayGround *Imprint of* **Forest Hill Publishing, LLC**

Playground Pr., *(0-9790033)* 1951 W. Rochelle Ave., Glendale, WI 53209 USA (SAN 852-1832) Tel 414-352-1590
E-mail: trishwilliams@trishwilliams.net
Web site: http://www.trishwilliams.net.

Playgroup Pr., *(0-9674572)* P.O. Box 10219, Aspen, CO 81612-7318 USA
E-mail: playgrouppress@carolina.rr.com
Web site: http://www.playgrouppress.com
Dist(s): **National Bk. Network.**

Playhouse Publishing, *(1-57151; 1-878338)* 1566 Akron Peninsula Rd., Akron, OH 44313 USA Tel 330-762-6800; Fax: 330-762-2230; Toll Free: 800-762-6775
E-mail: info@playhousepublishing.com
Web site: http://www.nibble-me-books.com; http://www.playhousepublishing.com; http://www.littlelucyandfriends.com
Dist(s): **Baker & Taylor Bks.**

Playing Pig Pr., *(0-9788324)* 922 S. 87th Ave., Omaha, NE 68114 USA (SAN 851-7452) Tel 402-399-0516
E-mail: bettyhan@cox.net
Web site: http://FrecklesandMaya.com.

PlayinTime Productions, Inc., *(1-932895; 1-59860)* 19525 Valdez Dr., Tarzana, CA 91356-4946 USA Toll Free: 800-310-0087
E-mail: playintime@aol.com
Web site: http://www.playintime.com.

Playmore, Incorporated, Publishers *See* **Waldman Publishing Corp.**

Playoff Corporation *See* **Donruss Playoff, L.P.**

Playor, Editorial, S.A. (ESP) *(84-359) Dist. by* **Continental Bk.**

Plaza & Janes Editories, S.A. (ESP) *(84-01) Dist. by* **AIMS Intl.**

Plaza & Janes Editories, S.A. (ESP) *(84-01) Dist. by* **Distribks Inc.**

Plaza Joven, S.A. (ESP) *(84-7655) Dist. by* **Lectorum Pubns.**

Pleasant Co. *Imprint of* **American Girl Publishing, Inc.**

Pleasant Company Publications *See* **American Girl Publishing, Inc.**

Pleasant Plains Pr., *(0-9790906)* 366 Kingsberry Dr, Suite 100, Annapolis, MD 21409 USA Tel 410-757-1318
E-mail: boaterbrenda@comcast.net
Web site: http://www.pleasantplainspress.com.

Pleasant St. Pr., *(0-9792035)* P.O. Box 520, Raynham Center, MA 02768 USA (SAN 852-7598) Tel 508-822-3075; Fax: 508-977-2498
Web site: http://www.pleasantstpress.com.

Pleasant Word, *(1-4141)* Div. of WinePress Publishing, Orders Addr.: P.O. Box 428, Enumclaw, WA 98022 USA Tel 360-802-9758; Fax: 360-802-9992; Toll Free: 800-326-4674; Edit Addr.: 1730 Railroad St., Enumclaw, WA 98022 USA
E-mail: info@pleasantword.com; athena@winepresspub.com; judy@winepresspub.com
Web site: http://www.pleasantword.com
Dist(s): **Appalachian Bk. Distributors**
Spring Arbor Distributors, Inc.

Pleasanton Publishing, *(0-9677174)* Orders Addr.: P.O. Box 1257, Pleasanton, CA 94566 USA (SAN 253-1410) Tel 925-249-9112; Fax: 925-249-1807; Edit Addr.: 25 Colby Ct., Pleasanton, CA 94566 USA Tel 925-249-9112
E-mail: mira@Drmira.com; mira@drmira.com
Web site: http://www.DrMira.com.

Pleasure Boat Studio *See* **Pleasure Boat Studio: A Literary Pr.**

Pleasure Boat Studio: A Literary Pr., *(0-912887; 0-9651413; 1-929355)* 201 W. 89th St., No. 6F, New York, NY 10024 USA Tel 212-362-8563; Toll Free: 888-810-5308; 721 Mt. Pleasant Rd., Port Angeles, WA 98362 (SAN 299-0075)
E-mail: pleasboat@nyc.rr.com
Web site: http://www.pleasureboatstudio.com
Dist(s): **Baker & Taylor Bks.**
Brodart Co.
Midwest Library Service
Partners/West
SPD-Small Pr. Distribution.

Pleiades Publishing, *(0-9662777)* Orders Addr.: P.O. Box 917, Captain Cook, HI 96704 USA Tel 808-322-1778; Fax: 808-322-1861; Edit Addr.: Aloha Theatre Bldg., Mamalahoa Hwy., Kainaliu, HI 96750 USA Do not confuse wtih companies with the same or similar name in Sandy, UT, Pittsford, NY
E-mail: hokukona@gfe.net.

Pleiness Publishing, *(0-9742472)* 45937 Duke Dr., Chesterfield Township, MI 48051 USA
E-mail: cpbusy@comcast.net.

PLEO, *(0-9660617)* 302 Park Tree Terr Bldg. 1311, Orlando, FL 32825-3474 USA Tel 407-277-3776; 321-297-5531.

pleo leonard productions *See* **PLEO**

Plexus Publishing, Inc., *(0-937548; 0-9666748)* 143 Old Marlton Pike, Medford, NJ 08055 USA (SAN 212-436X) Tel 609-654-6500; Fax: 609-654-4309 Do not confuse with Plexus Publishing, Limited in London, United Kingdom
Web site: http://www.plexuspublishing.com
Dist(s): **Independent Pubs. Group**
Information Today, Inc.

Pluegl Bks., *(0-9760868)* Orders Addr.: P.O. Box 16622, Chapel Hill, NC 27516-6622 USA; Edit Addr.: 114 Waverly Forest Ln., Chapel Hill, NC 27516 USA.

Plum Blossom Bks. *Imprint of* **Parallax Pr.**

Plum Tree Pr., *(0-9653535; 1-892476)* 531 Silcott Rd., Clarkston, WA 99403 USA Tel 509-758-2820; 509-332-1520 (Pine Orchard Distributors)
E-mail: bookinfo@pineorchard.com
Web site: http://www.pineorchard.com/plumtree
Dist(s): **Baker & Taylor Bks.**
Partners/West
Pine Orchard, Inc.

Pluma Productions, *(1-889848)* Div. of Southern Dominican Province, USA, Orders Addr.: P.O. Box 1138, Los Angeles, CA 90078-1138 USA Tel 213-463-6488; Fax: 213-466-6645; Edit Addr.: 1977 Carmen Ave., Los Angles, CA 90068 USA
E-mail: pluma@eatrhlink.net.

Plume *Imprint of* **Penguin Group (USA) Inc.**

Pluto Pr. (GBR) *(0-7453; 0-86104; 0-902818; 0-904383; 1-85305) Dist. by* **U of Mich Pr.**

Pluto Project, *(0-9662982)* 601 Van Ness, No. E3801, San Francisco, CA 94102-3200 USA Tel 415-647-5501; Fax: 415-840-0060; Toll Free: 888-227-5886
E-mail: walter@plutoproject.com
Web site: http://www.plutoproject.com
Dist(s): **New Leaf Distributing Co., Inc.**
Quality Bks., Inc.

Plymouth Press, Limited *See* **Plymouth Toy & Book**

Plymouth Toy & Book, *(1-882663)* 101 Panton Rd., Vergennes, VT 05491 USA Tel 802-877-2150; Fax: 802-877-2116; Toll Free: 800-350-1007 Do not confuse with Plymouth Pr. in Miami Beach, FL
E-mail: plymouth@together.net
Web site: http://www.plymouthtoyandbook.com.

PM, INK, *(0-9753852)* 522 aNDERSON aVE., Rockville, MD 20850 USA (SAN 256-0275) Tel 301-424-0638 (phone/fax)
E-mail: pm.ink@verizon.net
Web site: http://www.pmink.net.

PM Moon Pubs., *(0-615)* 3308 W. 111th St., West Park, OH 44111-3642 USA
Dist(s): **Lulu.com.**

PMK Press *See* **Dancer's Publishing**

Pneuma Life Publishing, Inc., *(1-56229)* P.O. Box 9176, Oxnard, CA 93031 USA (SAN 297-3057) Fax: 805-644-4729; Toll Free: 800-727-3218 (orders) ; *Imprints:* Christian Living Books (Christian Livng)
E-mail: customer-service@pneumalife.com
Web site: http://www.pneumalife.com
Dist(s): **Anchor Distributors**
Appalachian Bk. Distributors
GL Services
Lightning Source, Inc.
Spring Arbor Distributors, Inc.

Pneumatikos Publishing, *(0-9720681; 1-932710)* P.O. Box 595351, Dallas, TX 75359 USA
E-mail: info@pneumatikos.com
Web site: http://www.pneumatikos.com.

Pocahontas Pr., Inc., *(0-936015)* Orders Addr.: P.O. Box Drawer F, Blacksburg, VA 24063-1020 USA (SAN 630-124X) Tel 540-951-0467; Fax: 540-961-2847; Toll Free: 800-446-0467; Edit Addr.: 832 Hutcheson Dr., Blackburg, VA 24063-1020 USA
E-mail: mchollim@vt.edu
Dist(s): **Baker & Taylor Bks.**
Coutts Library Service, Inc.
Koen-Levy Bk. Wholesalers LLC
Quality Bks., Inc.

Pocket *Imprint of* **Simon & Schuster**

Pocket Guides Publishing, Inc., *(0-9711007; 1-931676)* 2031 San Antonio Pl., Santa Rosa, CA 95405 USA (SAN 253-8784) Tel 707-525-9847; Fax: 707-525-9848
E-mail: ghess@sonic.net
Web site: http://www.pocketguides.net
Dist(s): **Adventure Pubns., Inc.**
Baker & Taylor Bks.
Books West.

Pocket Mixx *Imprint of* **Mixx Entertainment, Inc.**

Pocket of Sanity, *(0-9663019)* P.O. Box 5241, Fresno, CA 93755-5241 USA Tel 559-298-6181; Fax: 559-225-3670; Toll Free: 800-497-4909 (orders only)
E-mail: posanity@aol.com
Dist(s): **American West Bks.**

Pocket Poetry Publishing, *(0-9710316)* Orders Addr.: P.O. Box 6084, Christiansburg, VA 24068-6084 USA
E-mail: sonji@romanticpoetry.com; sonji@romanticpoetry.com
Web site: http://www.romanticpoetry.com.

Pocket Pr., Inc., *(1-884493)* P.O. Box 25124, Portland, OR 97298 USA Toll Free Fax: 877-643-3732; Toll Free: 888-237-2110
E-mail: sales@pocketpressinc.com
Web site: http://www.pocketpressinc.com.

Pocket Publication, A, *(0-9721333)* 6701 Democracy Blvd., Suite 300, Bethesda, MD 20817 USA Tel 301-468-4905 Do not confuse with Pocket Publications in York, PA
E-mail: david_new@msn.com
Web site: http://www.home.talkcity.com/LibertySt/davidwnew.

Pocket Star *Imprint of* **Simon & Schuster**

Pockets of Learning, *(1-888074; 1-58405)* Orders Addr.: 30 Cutler St., Suite 101, Warren, RI 02885 USA Tel 401-247-1991; Fax: 401-247-7860; Toll Free Fax: 800-370-1580; Toll Free: 800-635-2994
E-mail: pocketsofl@aol.com
Web site: http://www.pocketsoflearning.com.

PockitBook Publishing, Inc., *(0-9761716)* P.O. Box 6753, Athens, GA 30604-4120 USA Tel 706-354-8380
E-mail: pockitbook@bellsouth.net
Web site: http://www.pockitbook.com.

Pocol Pr., *(1-929763)* Orders Addr.: 6023 Pocol Dr., Clifton, VA 20124-1333 USA (SAN 253-6021) Tel 703-830-5862; Fax: 703-830-5862
E-mail: chrisandtom@erols.com
Web site: http://www.pocolpress.com
Dist(s): **Baker & Taylor Bks.**

Pocono Mountain Music Publishing, Inc., *(1-58918)* 208 Drexel Rd., Tobyhanna, PA 18466-8921 USA Toll Free: 800-215-1880
E-mail: pmmp@ptd.net
Web site: http://www.poconomusic.com.

podbooks.com, LLC, *(1-893939)* 18724 Cox Ave., Saratoga, CA 95070-4195 USA (SAN 253-4819) Tel 408-378-7841; Fax: 408-378-7891
Web site: http://www.packet-level.com.

Poet Tree Pr., *(1-58876)* Orders Addr.: P.O. Box 303, Smithfield, UT 84335 USA (SAN 253-6587) Fax: 435-713-4422; Toll Free: 800-618-8444; Edit Addr.: 90 N. 100 E., Logan, UT 84321-4649 USA Tel 800-618-8444
E-mail: editor@poettreepress.com; editor@poetreepress.com
Web site: http://www.poettreepress.com
Dist(s): **Midpoint Trade Bks., Inc.**

Poet Tree Pubns., *(0-9658926)* P.O. Box 571444, Salt Lake City, UT 84157-1444 USA Tel 801-685-9398; Fax: 801-262-2324
Dist(s): **Tree Hse. Distribution.**

Poets' Refuge, *(0-9623968)* 3131 Grand Concourse, Bronx, NY 10468 USA Tel 718-367-0780 (phone/fax).

Pohl, J. Assocs., *(0-939332)* 307 N. Shady Ave., Houston, PA 15342 USA (SAN 220-181X) Tel 724-746-1178
E-mail: judepohl@comcast.net.

Pohl, Linda Perelman, *(0-9625453)* 69 Forestview Ct., Williamsville, NY 14221 USA Tel 716-688-3838
E-mail: annabula1@hotmail.com.

Pohrte, Dorey Publishing, Inc., *(0-9722296)* 917 Maple Rd., Buffalo, NY 14221 USA Tel 716-631-1256
E-mail: kathysue1@adelphia.net.

Poimen Pr, *(0-9717919)* P.O. Box 141651, Spokane, WA 99214 USA Tel 509-928-1703
E-mail: billgoth@att.net
Web site: http://www.poimenpress.com.

Point E Publishing, *(1-59151)* 280 Park Ave. S., Suite 15F, New York, NY 0010-6131 USA Tel 917-312-8873; Fax: 212-473-0846
E-mail: info@pointepublishing.com; phillip@pointepublishing.com
Web site: http://www.pointepublishing.com/
Dist(s): **Cold Cut Comics Distribution.**

Point of Life, Inc., *(0-9668069)* 3032 E. Commercial Blvd., Ft. Lauderdale, FL 33308 USA
E-mail: mikmikl@aol.com
Web site: http://www.pointoflife.com.

Point Pubns., *(0-9620888)* Orders Addr.: P.O. Box 145, Point Lookout, NY 11569 USA (SAN 250-0434); Edit Addr.: 59 Cedarhurst Ave., Point Lookout, NY 11569 USA (SAN 250-0442) Tel 516-889-3526 Do not confuse with companies with the same or silimar name in, Wayzata, MN, Snowmass, CO
E-mail: pointpub@aol.com.

Point To Point Publishing, *(0-9714147)* 5108 Brittany Dr., Old Hickory, TN 37138 USA Fax: 615-758-8495.

Pokemon Player Pocket Guide *See* **H P Pubns., LTD**

Polaire Pubns., *(0-9708500; 0-9795218)* Div. of Polaire Entertainment Group, Inc., 422 Wolf Run Rd., Bartonville, TX 76226 USA (SAN 254-8291)
E-mail: chmeezepal@earthlink.net
Web site: http://www.animalcompanionsandtheirpeople.com
Dist(s): **Baker & Taylor Bks.**
DeVorss & Co.

Polar Bear & Co., *(1-882190)* Orders Addr.: P.O. Box 311, Solon, ME 04979 USA Tel 207 643-2795; Edit Addr.: 8 Brook St., Solon, ME 04979 USA
E-mail: mythodem@yahoo.com
Web site: http://www.polarbearandco.com
Dist(s): **Baker & Taylor Bks.**
Biblio Distribution
Magazines, Inc.

Polaris Bks., *(0-9741443)* 11111 W. 8th Ave., Unit A, Lakewood, CO 80215-5516 USA Tel 303-980-0890; Fax: 303-980-0753
E-mail: zubrin@aol.com
Web site: http://www.polarisbooks.net.

Political Status Education Coordinating Commission *See* **Dept. of Chamorro Affairs**

Politico's Publishing Ltd. (GBR) *(1-902301; 1-84275)* *Dist. by* **Consort Bk Sales.**

Polka Dot Pr., *(1-58646)* N16 W23390 Stoneridge Dr., Waukesha, WI 53188 USA Tel 414-544-2001; Fax: 414-544-2022; Toll Free: 800-541-2205 Do not confuse with Polka Dot Press, Mountainside, NJ
Web site: http://www.okid.com.

Polka Dot Pr. Corp., The, *(1-930248)* P.O. Box 471, Alpine, NJ 07620-0471 USA Tel 201-750-0372; Fax: 201-750-9372
E-mail: info@muffles.org.

Poll, Michael Publishing, *(1-887560)* 2700 Ambassador Caffery Pkwy. #53, Lafayette, LA 70506 USA Tel 337-706-8244 ; *Imprints:* Cornerstone Book Publishers (Cstone Bk Pubs)
E-mail: mpoll@lostword.com; mike@cornerstonepublishers.com
Web site: http://www.cornerstonepublishers.com.

Pollyanna Publishing, *(0-9774603)* 3773 Coconut Palm Cir., Oviedo, FL 32765 USA (SAN 257-6139) Tel 407-359-0556; Fax: 407-971-6821
E-mail: pollyanna711@bellsouth.net.

PollyRhythm Productions, *(0-9701249)* Orders Addr.: P.O. Box 7707, New York, NY 10150 USA Tel 212 688 3900; Toll Free Fax: 800 701 7981
E-mail: prprd@attglobal.net
Web site: http://www.pollyrhythm.com.

Polt Mountain Pr., *(0-9717964)* P.O. Box 241, Califon, NJ 07830 USA (SAN 254-4032)
E-mail: carter@poltmountainpress.com
Web site: http://www.poltmountainpress.com.

Polychrome Publishing Corp., *(1-879965)* 4509 N. Francisco, Chicago, IL 60625-3808 USA Tel 773-478-4455; Fax: 773-478-0786
E-mail: polypub@earthlink.net
Web site: http://www.home.earthlink.net/~polypub.

Polyglot Pr., Inc., *(1-931927; 1-4115)* 1523 Pine St., Philadelphia, PA 19102 USA Tel 267-319-1149; Fax: 267-319-1956 Do not confuse with Polyglot Press in Fairfax, VA
E-mail: david@polyglotpress.com
Web site: http://www.polyglotpress.com.

Polytope Pr., *(0-9670526)* Div. of Tarescent Synductions, Orders Addr.: P.O. Box 1349, Phoenix, AZ 85001 USA Tel 602-271-9922; Fax: 602-230-1991; Edit Addr.: 321 E. Portland, No. 6, Phoenix, AZ 85004 USA
E-mail: polytope@hotmail.com.

Pom Publishing, *(0-9708533)* 28 Zickafoose Ln., Chillicothe, OH 45601 USA Tel 740-775-1104.

Pomegranate Communications, Inc, *(0-7649; 0-87654; 0-917556; 1-56640)* Orders Addr.: P.O. Box 808022, Petaluma, CA 94975 USA (SAN 211-0857) Tel 707-782-9000; Fax: 707-782-9810; Toll Free: 800-227-1428; Edit Addr.: 775A Southpoint Blvd., Petaluma, CA 94954 USA Tel 707-782-9000; Fax: 707-782-9810; 707-782-9820; Toll Free: 800-227-1428
E-mail: info@pomegranate.com
Web site: http://www.pomegranate.com.

Pomegranate Publishing, *(0-9767377)* PO Box 43, Carpinteria, CA 93014 USA Do not confuse with Pomegranate Publishing in Loma Linda, CA
Web site: http://www.pomegranatepublishing.com.

POMNI Publishing, *(0-9727202)* 31 Hampton Rd., Suffern, NY 10901 USA
E-mail: pomni@optonline.net
Web site: http://pomni@optonline.net.

Ponder Bks., *(0-9623922)* P.O. Box 792, Mason, TX 76856-0792 USA Tel 915-347-6539.

Ponent Mon, S.L. (ESP) *(84-933409; 84-933093; 84-933992; 84-96427)* *Dist. by* **Biblio Dist.**

Pontrelli, Jeany, *(0-9778456)* 6156 Solstice Dr., Sparks, NV 89436 USA.

PONY *Imprint of* **Stabenfeldt Inc.**

Pony Rock Pr., *(0-9759598)* 23484 150th Ave. NE, Thief River Falls, MN 56701 USA.

Poodle Suit Publishing, *(0-9728429)* P.O. Box 9844, Phoenix, AZ 85068 USA (SAN 255-1608) Tel 602-943-6766 Toll Free: 800-547-8247
E-mail: lougold@cox.net
Web site: http://www.poodlesuit.com.

Poolbeg Pr. (IRL) *(0-905169; 0-907085; 1-85371; 1-84223)* *Dist. by* **Dufour.**

Poole & Smith Publishing, *(0-9669658; 1-930392)* 1152 Wilkinson Rd., Richmond, VA 23227 USA Fax: 804-262-3494.

Poor Magazine, *(0-9742007)* 255 9th St., 3, San Francisco, CA 94103 USA Tel 415-863-6306; Fax: 415-865-1932
E-mail: alex@poormagazine.org
Web site: http://www.poormagazine.org.

Pop the Cork Publishing, *(0-9741854)* 1629 McGilvra Blvd., E., Seattle, WA 98112 USA Tel 206-720-9779; Fax: 206-720-9771
E-mail: sallyv@isomedia.com
Dist(s): **AtlasBooks Distribution**
Hara Publishing Group.

Popol Vuh Press *See* **Talisman Pr.**

Poppel Pr., *(0-9724193)* 1114 Sandstone Ct., Green Bay, WI 54313 USA Tel 920-499-9695 (phone/fax)
Web site: http://www.poppelpress.com.

Poppin & Co. Communication Materials, *(1-886498)* Orders Addr.: P.O. Box 176, Unity, ME 04988 USA Tel 207-437-2746; Fax: 207-437-2404
E-mail: poppin@uninets.net.

Poppy *Imprint of* **Little, Brown Bks. for Young Readers**

Popular Bk. Co. (Canada) Ltd. (CAN) *(0-9698843; 1-896477; 1-894810; 1-897164)* *Dist. by* **AtlasBooks.**

Popular, Editorial S.A. (ESP) *(84-7884; 84-85016; 84-86524)* *Dist. by* **AIMS Intl.**

Popular Kinetics Pr., *(0-9627752)* 6005 Yale Ave., Glen Echo, MD 20812 USA Tel 301-229-2213
E-mail: cbarton@mindspring.com
Web site: http://www.popularkinetics.com
Dist(s): **Independent Pubs. Group.**

Popular Truth, Inc., *(0-9631547)* P.O. Box 40656, Indianapolis, IN 76260 USA Toll Free: 888-342-8156
E-mail: anyike@netscape.net.

Popular Weasel Pr., *(0-9715781)* Div. of McDonald Communications, Orders Addr.: P.O. Box 247, South Hill, VA 23970 USA Tel 804-955-2478; Fax: 804-955-2479; Toll Free: 866-268-1361; Edit Addr.: 25412 Herring Creek Dr., Chantilly, VA 20152-4404 USA
E-mail: popularweasel@netscape.net
Web site: http://www.popularweaselpress.com.

Popular Woodworking Bks. *Imprint of* **F & W Pubns., Inc.**

Port Ludlow Bks., *(0-9729884)* 20 Keefe Ln., Port Ludlow, WA 98365 USA
E-mail: gldyerjr@waypt.com.

Port Town Publishing, *(0-9700544; 0-9716239; 0-9725990; 0-9740833; 1-59466)* 5909 Tower Ave., Superior, WI 54880 USA Tel 715-392-6843 ; *Imprints:* Little Ones (Little Ones); Growing Years (Growing Years)
E-mail: porttownpublish@aol.com
Web site: http://www.porttownpublishing.bigstep.com
Dist(s): **Ingram Bk. Co.**

Port Washington Public Library, *(0-9615059)* 1 Library Dr., Port Washington, NY 11050 USA (SAN 694-163X) Tel 516-883-4400.

Portable Pr. *Imprint of* **Advantage Pubs. Group**

Portal Pr., *(1-933454)* 1327 Irving St., NE, Washington, DC 20017 USA Do not Confuse with Portal Press in Port Washington, NY, Glandale, AZ, Queens Village, NY
E-mail: editor@theportalpress.com
Web site: http://www.theportalpress.com
Dist(s): **SPD-Small Pr. Distribution.**

Porteous, David Editions (GBR) *(1-870586)* *Dist. by* **Parkwest Pubns.**

Portfolio Pal Press, L C, *(0-9712002)* P.O. Box 116, Oldhams, VA 22529 USA
E-mail: nmoore1146@aol.com.

Portfolio Press *See* **Portfolio Pr. Corp.**

Portfolio Pr. Corp., *(0-942620)* Orders Addr.: 130 Wineow St., Suite 3, Cumberland, MD 21502 USA Tel 301-724-2795; Fax: 301-724-2796; Toll Free: 877-737-1200; Edit Addr.: 1107 Broadway, 12th Flr., New York, NY 10010 USA (SAN 238-5554) Tel 212-989-8700; Fax: 212-691-3073
E-mail: portfolio@hereintown.net
Web site: http://www.portfoliopress.com.

Portfolio Trade *Imprint of* **Penguin Group (USA) Inc.**

Portico Bks., *(0-9664867)* Orders Addr.: P.O. Box 6094, Chesterfield, MO 63006 USA Tel 636-527-2822 (phone/fax); Toll Free: 888-641-5353 (phone/fax); Edit Addr.: 1316 Rusticview Dr., Manchester, MO 63011 USA
E-mail: info@grammarandmore.com
Web site: http://www.grammarandmore.com.

Portland Pr., Inc., *(0-9608382; 1-57684)* Orders Addr.: P.O. Box 70856, Seattle, WA 98127 USA (SAN 240-3579) Tel 206-632-8165; 206-297-1304; Fax: 253.274-8188; Toll Free: 800-574-7272 (trade orders) Do not confuse with Portland Pr., Inc., Chapel Hill, NC
E-mail: info@portlandpress.net
Web site: http://www.chihuly.com; http://www.portlandpress.net
Dist(s): **Baker & Taylor Bks.**
Partners/West.

Portland State Univ., Continuing Education Pr., Extended Studies, *(0-87678)* Orders Addr.: P.O. Box 1394, Portland, OR 97207-1394 USA (SAN 221-9719) Tel 503-725-4891; Fax: 503-725-4715; Toll Free: 866-647-7377
E-mail: steveg@pdx.edu; scholza@pdx.edu; press@pdx.edu
Web site: http://www.cep.pdx.edu
Dist(s): **Baker & Taylor Bks.**

Portos Publishing Co., *(0-9663651)* Orders Addr.: P.O. Box 2009, Saratoga, CA 95070-0009 USA Tel 408-867-7946; Edit Addr.: 19375 Portos Ct., Saratoga, CA 95070 USA.

Portunus Publishing Co., *(0-9641330; 1-886440)* 27875 Berwick Dr., Carmel, CA 93923 USA Tel 831-622-0604; Fax: 310-399-5644
E-mail: service@portunus.net
Dist(s): **Lectorum Pubns., Inc.**

Poseidon Publishing Co., *(0-9673483)* 530 W. 4th St., Apt. 2W, Dulth, MN 55806 USA Tel 218-722-3057 Do not confuse with Poseidon Publishing, LLC in New York, NY
E-mail: benfondrk@safcoproducts.com.

Company

Positive Action For Christ, *(1-929784; 0-9719491; 1-59557)* Orders Addr.: P.O. Box 1948, Rocky Mount, NC 27802-1948 USA Tel 252-977-9977 Toll Free: 800-688-3008; Edit Addr.: 833 Falls Rd., Rocky Mount, NC 27804 USA ; *Imprints:* ProTeens (ProTeens)
Web site: http://www.positiveaction.org.

Positive Children's Programming Corp., *(1-890571)* 69 Skyland Dr., Roswell, GA 30075 USA Tel 770-993-6607; Fax: 770-518-5831; Toll Free: 800-866-8337.

Positive Power Publishing, *(0-9668378)* P.O. Box 2644, Merrifield, VA 22116 USA Tel 703-241-2375 (phone/fax)
E-mail: PosPower@aol.com
Web site: http://www.PositivePowerPublishing.com.

Positive Productions, *(1-928726)* 934 E. 84th Pl., Suite A, Chicago, IL 60619 USA Tel 773-846-6131; Fax: 773-846-6555; Toll Free: 800-306-3064
Web site: http://www.positiveproductions.com.

Positive Purpose Pr., *(0-9711291)* 10714 S.Wood St., Chicago, IL 60643 USA Tel 773-779-6826
E-mail: judigp107@compuserve.com.

Positive Spin Pr., *(0-9773096)* P.O. Box 653, Warren, MI 02885-9998 USA
E-mail: info@positivespinpress.com; lisa@studiocvr.com
Web site: http://www.thehalloweenfairy.com
Dist(s): **Independent Pubs. Group.**

Positive Strokes, *(0-9673490)* Orders Addr.: P.O. Box 9552, Fayetteville, NC 28311 USA
E-mail: pstrokes@aol.com; healheartsbooks@aol.com
Web site: http://www.PStrokes.com.

Positively for Kids, Inc., *(0-9634650; 0-9765722; 0-9778237; 0-9786838)* P.O. Box 3283, Kirkland, WA 98083-3283 USA Toll Free: 800-600-5437
E-mail: customerservice@positivelyforkids.com
Web site: http://www.positivelyforkids.com
Dist(s): **American West Bks.**
BWI INC
Baker & Taylor Bks.
Brodart Co.
Ingram Bk. Co.
Mackin Bk. Co.

Possibilities Publishing, *(0-9722928)* Orders Addr.: P.O. Box 364, Milford, CT 06460-2307 USA; Edit Addr.: West River St., Milford, CT 06460 USA Do not confuse with companies with the same or similar name in Orem, UT, Gloversville, NY
E-mail: fbaker@optonline.net.

Possibilities Unlimited, *(0-9711577)* 49 S. Kingsboro Ave., Gloversville, NY 12078 USA Tel 518-725-3565 Do not confuse with companies with the same or similar name in Oren, UT, Milford, CT
E-mail: arobbin1@nycap.rr.com.

Possibilities W/MCSS (Mary Chloe Schoolcraft Saunders), *(0-9662892)* Div. of Saunders Enterprizes, 2400 Rio Grande Blvd., NW, PMB 156, Albuquerque, NM 87104-2100 USA Tel 505-343-2100; Fax: 505-344-3259.

Possum Products, *(0-615)* 712 Warren Dr., Annapolis, MD 21403 USA Fax: 410-510-1003; 410-263-4473 (call 410-263-1847 first)
E-mail: possumpalette@aol.com.

Post Oak Hill, *(0-9636122)* 235 Shady Hill Ln., Double Oak, TX 75067-8270 USA Tel 817-430-1182.

Posterity Pr., Inc., *(1-889274)* P.O. Box 71081, Chevy Chase, MD 20813 USA Tel 301-652-2384; Fax: 301-652-2543 Do not confuse with companies with the same name in Emerald Isle, NC, Buffalo, NY
E-mail: Publisher@PosterityPress.com
Web site: http://www.PosterityPress.com
Dist(s): **Koen-Levy Bk. Wholesalers LLC.**

Pota Pr., *(1-887963)* 112 Surfside Ave., Santa Cruz, CA 95060 USA Tel 831-423-4806 (phone/fax)
E-mail: jackpot@cruzio.com
Web site: http://www.cruzio.com/~nikan/index.htm.

Potenial Psychotherapy Counseling & Remedial Serv., *(0-9759889)* 1525 E. 53rd St., Suite 516, 11-2, Chicago, IL 60615 USA.

Potential Developing Ministries, Inc., *(0-9745554)* 455 Grason Hwy., Suite 111 Box 153, Lawrenceville, GA 30045 USA
E-mail: pdm@winning.com.

Potential Unlimited Publishing, *(0-9740003)* 7634 Sawyer Rd., Darien, IL 60561 USA Tel 630-325-8552
E-mail: bigbrotherdp@yahoo.com.

Potomac Conference of Seventh-Day Adventists, *(0-9708717; 0-9710965)* 2850 Oak Forest Ln., Luray, VA 22835 USA Tel 540-743-7875 (phone/fax)
E-mail: barbaraw@shentel.net.

Potser, T.T. , Inc., *(0-9670198)* 328 Flatbush Ave., Suite 167, Brooklyn, NY 11238 USA Toll Free: 877-413-2979
E-mail: ttpotser@ttpotser.com
Web site: http://www.ttpotser.com
Dist(s): **Baker & Taylor Bks.**
Book Wholesalers, Inc.
Brodart Co.

Potter Craft *Imprint of* **Crown Publishing Group**

Potter's Hse. Bookservice, *(1-928717)* 1658 Columbia Rd., NW, Washington, DC 20009 USA Tel 202-232-5483; Fax: 202-328-7483
E-mail: pottershse@aol.com
Web site: http://www.pottershousebooks.com.

Potter's House Church *See* **Potter's Hse. Bookservice**

PottyMD LLC, *(0-9762877)* 2216 White Ave., Knoxville, TN 37916 USA Tel 865-525-0000; Fax: 865-525-0262; Toll Free: 877-769-8963
E-mail: support@pottymd.com
Web site: http://www.pottymd.com
Dist(s): **Baker & Taylor Bks.**
SCB Distributors.

Poudre Landmarks Foundation, *(0-9753849)* 108 N. Meldrum St., Fort Collins, CO 80521 USA Tel 970-221-4220; 970-221-0553
Web site: http://www.poudrelandmarks.com.

Pounce To Success International, Inc., *(0-9776074)* 608 1/2 W. Park St., Lamar, CO 81052 USA (SAN 257-7364) Tel 719-201-7470; Toll Free: 800-768-6238.

Pouring the Oil: Poetic Praise Pubns., *(0-9760734)* Orders Addr.: P.O. Box 944, Brewster, NY 10509 USA Tel 203-300-5152 (phone/fax)
E-mail: spoken_word03@yahoo.com; pouringtheoil@aol.com; info@pouringtheoilpublications.com
Web site: http://www.pouringtheoilpublications.com.

Powell Hill Pr., *(0-9760648)* 8 Packett's Glen, Fairport, NY 14450 USA Tel 585-388-8622
E-mail: scoopwrite@aol.com
Web site: http://www.spiritwolf.info; http://www.powellhillpress.com
Dist(s): **North Country Bks., Inc.**

Power Community Church *See* **Power Living Ministries**

Power for Kids Pr. *Imprint of* **Rust Foundation for Literacy, Inc., The**

Power Living Ministries, *(0-9626910; 1-929571)* 22653 Old Canal Rd., Yorba Linda, CA 92887-4601 USA Toll Free: 800-435-2627.

Power Play Media, *(0-9724003; 0-9741394; 1-934230)* P.O. Box 423, Brandywine, MD 20613 USA Tel 240-375-6908; Fax: 301-579-9913
E-mail: tressa428@cs.com
Web site: http://www.nvisionpublishing.com/.

Power Pr., *(0-9748508)* P.O. Box 622, Tyrone, GA 30290 USA Tel 770-486-0758; Fax: 770-486-6687 Do not confuse with Power Press in Torrance CA, Chico CA, Sonoma CA
E-mail: ratto@mindspring.com.

Power Pubns., Inc., *(0-9724194)* 1004 Ridge Pointe Cove, Longwood, FL 32750 USA (SAN 254-6817) Fax: 407-261-0278 Do not confuse with companies with the same or similar names in Staten Island, NY, Tyler, TX, Appleton, WI, Phoenix, AZ, Mountain City, GA
E-mail: igilbert@cfl.rr.com
Web site: http://www.peakpowermarketing.com.

Power Publishing, *(0-9717623)* 1627 E. Manhatton Dr, Tempe, AZ 85282 USA Tel 480-491-6646; Fax: 480-491-6418 Do not confuse with companies with the same or similar names in Franklin, IN, St. Augstine, FL, Houston, TX, Conroe, TX, Bethpage, NY, Camby, IN, Culver City, CA
Web site: http://www.powerpublishing.us.

Power Through Faith, *(0-9707320)* 1702 Capps St., Durham, NC 27707 USA Tel 919-596-7753.

Powerband, LLC, *(0-9746445)* 16199 Kennedy Rd., Los Gatos, CA 95032-9503 USA Fax: 408-402-0617; 16199 Kennedy Rd., Los Gatos, CA 95032-9503
E-mail: clelliott@mac.com
Web site: http://www.powerbandllc.com
Dist(s): **Greenleaf Book Group Pr.**

Power-Glide Foreign Language Courses, *(1-58204)* 1682 W. 820 N., Provo, UT 84601 USA Tel 801-373-3973; Fax: 801-343-3912; Toll Free: 800-596-0910
E-mail: deloyh@power-glide.com
Web site: http://www.power-glide.com.

powerHouse Bks. *Imprint of* **powerHouse Cultural Entertainment, Inc.**

powerHouse Cultural Entertainment, Inc., *(1-57687)* 37 Main St., Brooklyn, NY 11201 USA (SAN 850-5845); Mercedes Distribution Ctr. Bldg. 3 Brooklyn Navy Yard, Brooklyn, NY 11205 Tel 212-604-9074; Fax: 212-366-5247 ; *Imprints:* powerHouse Books (pwerHse Bks); PowerHouse Kids (PowerKids)
E-mail: info@powerhousebooks.com
Web site: http://www.powerhousebooks.com
Dist(s): **Perseus Distribution.**

PowerHouse Kids *Imprint of* **powerHouse Cultural Entertainment, Inc.**

PowerKids Pr. *Imprint of* **Rosen Publishing Group, Inc., The**

PowerMark Productions, *(0-9705669; 0-9713412; 0-9717876; 0-9729135; 0-9747026; 0-9749339; 0-9795833)* Div. of Quest Ministries International, 380 E. Hwy. Cc Suite E104, Nixa, MO 65714 USA Tel 417-724-1222; Fax: 417-724-0119; Toll Free: 877-769-2669
E-mail: stefanie@qminternal.com
Web site: http://www.powermarkcomics.com
Dist(s): **Appalachian Bk. Distributors**
New Day Christian Distributors.

PowerMoves, *(0-9748298)* P.O. Box 92907, Washington, DC 20090 USA Tel 301-568-9111
Web site: http://www.powermoves.org.

PowerPartners, USA, Inc., *(0-9720839)* 1155 Camino Del Mar, Suite 209, Del Mar, CA 92014 USA Tel 760-630-9535; Fax: 310-919-3081; Toll Free: 800-462-4421
Web site: http://www.powerpartnersusa.com.

Powerstart Pr. *Imprint of* **Rosen Publishing Group, Inc., The**

PowerTools for Kids *Imprint of* **Navigator Systems, Inc.**

PR Product Research, LLC, *(0-9727906)* P.O. Box 729, Stanwood, WA 98292 USA.

P.R.A. Enterprises Incorporated *See* **P.R.A. Publishing**

P.R.A. Publishing, *(0-9727703)* Div. of Phoenix Rising Art Enterprises, Inc., Orders Addr.: P.O. Box 211701, Martinez, GA 30917 USA Tel 706-855-6173; P.O. Box 211701, Martinez, GA 30917
E-mail: info@prapublishing.com; lclark@phoenixrisingarts.com
Web site: http://www.prapublishing.com.

Practical Christianity Foundation *See* **Green Key Bks.**

Praeger Pubs. *Imprint of* **Greenwood Publishing Group, Inc.**

Prairie Arts, Inc., *(0-9725382)* 3100 Birch Bark Ln., Oklahoma City, OK 73120 USA Tel 405-755-5432; 405-728-1350; Fax: 405-728-9813
E-mail: dgordonart@aol.com.

Prairie Designs of Califórnina, *(0-615; 0-9724559)* Orders Addr.: P.O. Box 886, Brisbane, CA 94005-0886 USA Tel 415-468-5319; Fax: 415-468-6634; Edit Addr.: 24 Kings Rd., Brisbane, CA 94005 USA
E-mail: dennis@prairiedesigns.com
Web site: http://prairiedesigns.com.

Prairie Heart Publishing, *(0-9793668)* 8967 W. Driftwood Dr., Coeur d'Alene, ID 83814 USA Tel 208-777-8079 (phone/fax)
E-mail: aprairieheart@earthlink.net; sdianewood@earthlink.net
Web site: http://www.prairievirtuedolls.com.

Prairie Oak Pr. *Imprint of* **Big Earth Publishing**

Prairie Shore Creative, Inc., *(0-9740542)* 2500 S. Corbett, Chicago, IL 60608 USA
E-mail: PSCreative@AOL.come
Web site: http://www.Prairieshorecreative.com.

Prairie View Publishing LLC, *(0-9744991; 1-933276)* P.O. Box 45, New Carlisle, IN 46552-0045 USA
E-mail: prairieviewbooks@earthlink.net
Web site: http://www.prairieviewpublishing.com
Dist(s): **Lightning Source, Inc.**

Prairie Winds Publishing, *(0-9778240)* 15154 W. 231st St., Spring Hill, KS 66083 USA Tel 913-592-5002
E-mail: cyndi@gertrudemccluck.com
Web site: http://www.gertrudemccluck.com.

Prairieland Pr., *(0-9759829)* P.O. Box 2404, Fremont, NE 68026-2404 USA Toll Free: 800-721-1670
E-mail: info@prairielandpress.com
Web site: http://www.prairielandpress.com
Dist(s): **Biblio Distribution.**

Praise Pubns., *(1-930338)* 188 Trail Rider Way, Georgetown, TX 78628 USA Do not confuse with companies with the same name in Channelview, TX, Schererville, IN.

Prakash, Shamsher Foundation, *(0-9641737)* Anandkutir, 1111 Duane Ave., Rolla, MO 65401 USA Tel 573-364-5572; Fax: 573-341-4729.

Prakken Pubns., Inc., *(0-911168; 0-9703398)* Orders Addr.: P.O. Box 8623, Ann Arbor, MI 48107-8623 USA (SAN 204-9112) Tel 734-975-2800 ext 200; Fax: 734-975-2787 ext 206, editorial; Toll Free: 800-530-9673 ext 200, orders; Edit Addr.: 832 Phoenix Dr., Ann Arbor, MI 48108-2221 USA ; *Imprints:* Tech Directions Books (Tech Directions)
E-mail: tdbooks@techdirections.com; sp@techdirections.com
Web site: http://www.techdirections.com/html/tdbooks.html.

Pranayama Institute, Inc., The, *(0-9724450)* Orders Addr.: P.O. Box 40731, Albuquerque, NM 87196 USA Tel 706-889-5035 (phone/fax); Fax: 505-212-0097
E-mail: ssaranam@pranayama.org; publicity@pranayama.org
Web site: http://www.pranayama.org; http://www.godwithoutreligion.com
Dist(s): **Midpoint Trade Bks., Inc.**

Prancing Pony, The, *(0-9763555)* Orders Addr.: 104802 W. Foisy Rd., Prosser, WA 99350 USA
Web site: http://www.herbleonhard.com.

Prather, Cathy, *(0-9666959)* P.O. Box 13927, Detroit, MI 48213 USA Tel 313-693-3108
E-mail: cathypcute@yahoo.com
Web site: http://www.carolsgreetings.com.

Pratt Ctr. The, *(0-9772835)* Orders Addr.: Four Main St., Suite 210, Los Altos, CA 94022 USA Tel 650-949-2997; Fax: 650-949-2442
E-mail: prattcenter@covad.net.

Praxis Music Pubns., Inc., *(1-884848)* 2708 Shady Grove, Bedford, TX 76021 USA Tel 817-283-6349
Dist(s): **Music Sales Corp.**

Praxis Pr., Inc., *(0-9754305; 1-934278)* 1515 Skelton Rd.5-100, Gainesville, GA 30504 USA Tel 770-846-5978
Web site: http://www.praxispress.com.

Prayer Bk. Pr., Inc., *(0-87677)* Subs. of Media Judaica, Inc., Orders Addr.: 1363 Fairfield Ave., Bridgeport, CT 06605 USA (SAN 207-0022) Tel 203-384-2284; Edit Addr.: 304 E. 49th St., New York, NY 10017 USA (SAN 282-1788) Tel 212-319-6666.

Prayer Point Pr., *(1-57892)* Orders Addr.: 2100 N. Carrolton Dr., Muncie, IN 47304 USA Tel 765-759-0215; Fax: 765-759-5857; Toll Free: 888-656-6067 (orders only); Edit Addr.: 10 Coralberry, The Woodlands, TX 77381 USA Tel 281-292-1220
E-mail: jangof@aol.com; lponder@swbell.net
Web site: http://www.prayerpointpress.com
Dist(s): **CRC Pubns.**
Spring Arbor Distributors, Inc.

Precept Ministries, *(1-888655)* Orders Addr.: P.O. Box 182218, Chattanooga, TN 37422 USA Tel 423-892-6814; Fax: 423-894-2449; Edit Addr.: 7324 Noah Reid Rd., Chattanooga, TN 37412 USA
E-mail: info@precept.org
Web site: http://www.precept.org.

Precious Gems *Imprint of* **EbonyEnergy Publishing**

Precious Life Bks., Inc., *(1-889733)* Orders Addr.: P.O. Box 1948, Lewisburg, TN 37091 USA Tel 615-270-1921; Toll Free: 800-728-5945; Edit Addr.: 1448 New Columbia Hwy., Lewisburg, TN 37091 USA.

Precious Little Bks., *(0-9787235)* 9353 SE. Yardarm Terr., Hobe Sound, FL 33455-3214 USA (SAN 851-3813) Tel 561-307-2367; Fax: 772-545-4944
E-mail: clarke@preciouslittlebooks.com
Web site: http://www.preciouslittlebooks.com.

Precious Resources, *(0-937836)* 349 S. Jackson St., Bluffton, OH 45817 USA (SAN 213-3512) Tel 419-358-0334
E-mail: precious@wcoil.com.

Precioustymes Entertainment, LLC, *(0-9729325; 0-9776507)* 229 Governors Pl., No. 138, Bear, DE 19701 USA Tel 866-773-8963 (office line); Fax: 302-455-0808
E-mail: PrecioustymesEnt@aol.com
Web site: http://www.precioustymes.com
Dist(s): **A & B Distributors & Pubs. Group**
Afrikan World Bk. Distributor
Lushena Bks.

Precision Cad/Cam Systems, Inc., *(0-9707464)* 9564 Deereco Rd., Luthvle Timon, MD 21093-2119 USA
E-mail: info@cadcam4u.com
Web site: http://www.cadcam4u.com.

Predestinarian, The, *(0-9706376)* 1159 County Rd. 420, Quitman, MS 39355 USA Tel 601-776-6056
E-mail: stanley@mississippi.net.

Preferred Enterprises, *(1-885143)* P.O. Box 848, Lakewood, NJ 08701-0848 USA.

Preferred Marketing *See* **American Historical Pr.**

Pregnancy & Infant Loss Ctr., Inc., *(1-892254)* 1421 E. Wayzata Blvd., No. 30, Wayzata, MN 55391 USA Tel 612-473-9372; Fax: 612-473-8978.

Prell Bks. & Multimedia, *(1-889406)* Orders Addr.: P.O. Box 191, Sparta, WI 54656-8104 USA Fax: 608-269-3744; Edit Addr.: 14446 Janus Ave., Sparta, WI 54656-8187 USA
E-mail: prellpubl@centurytel.net.

Prell Publishing *See* **Prell Bks. & Multimedia**

Prem Rawat Foundation, The, *(0-9740627; 1-933717)* P.O. Box 241498, Los Angeles, CA 90024 USA Tel 310-392-5700
E-mail: tprf.info@tprf.org
Web site: http://www.tprf.org.

PremaNations Publishing, *(1-892176)* Div. of PremaNations, Inc., P.O. Box 321447, Cocoa Beach, FL 32932-1447 USA (SAN 299-5808) Tel 310-417-9195; Fax: 407-784-5372; Toll Free Fax: 877-372-4660; Toll Free: 877-372-4664
E-mail: Paradigm@PremaNations.com
Web site: http://www.PremaNations.com
Dist(s): **Baker & Taylor Bks.**
New Leaf Distributing Co., Inc.
Quality Bks., Inc.

Prematurely Yours, *(0-9614786)* Orders Addr.: P.O. Box 9141, Chesapeake, VA 23321 USA (SAN 692-9907) Tel 757-483-9879; Fax: 757-484-8267; Toll Free: 800-767-0023
E-mail: kbryant@prematurelyyours.com
Web site: http://www.prematurelyyours.com.

Premier *Imprint of* **Center Point Large Print**

Premier Publishing *See* **Futech Interactive Products, Inc.**

Premier Schl. Agendas, *(1-884272; 1-59923)* 2000 Kentucky St., Bellingham, WA 98229 USA Tel 360-734-1153; Fax: 360-734-3014; Toll Free Fax: 800-880-3287; Toll Free: 800-447-2034
E-mail: wkanis@premieragendas.com
Web site: http://www.premier.us.

Prentice Hall *Imprint of* **Prentice Hall PTR**

Prentice Hall Pr., *(0-13; 0-7352)* Orders Addr.: 200 Old Tappan Rd., Old Tappan, NJ 07675 USA; Edit Addr.: 240 Frisch Ct., Paramus, NJ 07652 USA Tel 201-909-6200; Fax: 201-909-6360; Toll Free: 800-288-4745; 800-223-2336 (customer service); a/o Prentice Hall Direct, P.O. Box 11075, Des Moines, IA 50336 Tel 515-284-6719; Toll Free: 800-947-7700
E-mail: pearsoned@eds.com
Web site: http://www.phdirect.com
Dist(s): **Pearson Education**
Penguin Group (USA) Inc.

†Prentice Hall PTR, *(0-13; 0-201; 0-672)* Div. of Pearson Technology Group, Orders Addr.: 200 Old Tappan Rd., Old Tappan, NJ 07675 USA Fax: 416-447-2819 (orders - Canada); Toll Free Fax: 800-835-5327 (individual single copy orders - US); 800-445-6991 (government orders); Toll Free: 800-922-0579 (government orders); 800-282-0693 (individual single copy orders - US); 800-567-3800 (orders - Canada); Edit Addr.: 405 Murray Hill Pkwy., E Rutherford, NJ 07073-2136 USA ; *Imprints:* Macmillan College (Macmillan Coll); Prentice Hall (Prentice Hall)
Web site: http://www.phptr.com/
Dist(s): **Cambridge Bk. Co.**
Continental Bk. Co., Inc.
IFSTA
NetLibrary, Inc.
Pearson Education
Pearson Technology Group
Trans-Atlantic Pubns., Inc.; *CIP.*

Prentice Hall (Schl. Div.), *(0-13)* P.O. Box 2500, Lebanon, IN 46052-3009 USA Toll Free: 800-848-9500; P.O. Box 2649, Columbus, OH 43216-2649; Edit Addr.: 160 Gould St. (Northeast Region), Needham Heights, MA 02194-2310 USA Tel 617-455-1300; 8445 Freeport Pkwy., Suite 400 (South Central Region), Irving, TX 75063 Tel 214-915-4255
Web site: http://www.phschool.com/
Dist(s): **Pearson Education.**

Prentice-Hall *See* **Prentice Hall PTR**

Prentice-Hall, Orders Addr.: a/o Prentice Hall Corporate Sales Dept., One Lake St., Upper Saddle, NJ 07458 USA Tel 800-382-3419; Fax: 201-236-7141
E-mail: corpsales@pearsontechgroup.com
Web site: http://www.prenticehall.com
Dist(s): **NetLibrary, Inc.**
South Asia Bks.

PrepWorks Publishing, *(0-9660694)* Orders Addr.: P.O. Box 292239, Dayton, OH 45429 USA Tel 937-294-5057; Fax: 937-294-9442; Toll Free: 800-773-6825; Edit Addr.: 3525 Blossom Heath Rd., Kettering, OH 45419 USA
E-mail: smprice315@aol.com
Web site: http://www.prepworks.com
Dist(s): **Baker & Taylor Bks.**

Presbyterian & Reformed Publishing Company *See* **P & R Publishing**

Presbyterian Publishing Corporation *See* **Curriculum Publishing, Presbyterian Church (U. S. A.)**

Presbyterian Publishing Corp., *(0-664)* 100 Witherspoon St., Louisville, KY 40202-1396 USA Tel 502-569-5052; Fax: 502-569-8308; Toll Free Fax: 800-541-5113; Toll Free: 800-227-2872
E-mail: rpinotti@presbypub.com; customer_service@presbypub.com
Web site: http://www.ppcbooks.com.

Presence Publishing, *(0-9729676)* P.O. Box 1806, Denham Springs, LA 70727 USA
E-mail: presencepub@bellsouth.net.

Present Testimony Ministry, *(0-9666657; 0-9789019)* Orders Addr.: P.O. Box 140370, Gainesville, FL 32614 USA
E-mail: fviola3891@aol.com; FAVBHS@aol.com
Web site: http://www.home-church.org/present/
Dist(s): **Destiny Image Pubs.**
Seedsowers, The.

Preserving Memories, *(0-9742576)* 5809 Stonebridge Ln., Waxhaw, NC 28173 USA
E-mail: yakobo@excite.com
Web site: http://www.preservememories.net.

Presidential Christmas, A, *(0-9657684)* 16612 Millan de Avila, Tampa, FL 33613-1043 USA Tel 813-968-2020; Fax: 813-968-5694; Toll Free: 800-738-7838
E-mail: MLS42@aol.com
Web site: http://www.whitehousechristmas.com.

Presidential Publishing, *(0-9729095)* Orders Addr.: P.O. Box 221834, Sacramento, CA 95822 USA (SAN 255-1977) Tel 916-447-2460
E-mail: contactus@presidentialcookies.com; contactus@presidentialpublishing.com
Web site: http://www.presidentialcookies.com; http://www.presidentialpublishing.com.

Press Release Group Corp., *(0-9764633)* P.O. Box 30052, New York, NY 10011 USA Tel 718-303-9093; Fax: 718-228-4040
E-mail: info@prgroup.info
Web site: http://www.prgroup.info.

Presses Pocket (FRA) *(2-266) Dist. by* **Distribks Inc.**

PressMark Publishing, *(0-9711726)* 5105 E. Los Angeles Ave., No. 120, Simi Valley, CA 93063 USA Tel 805-584-6964
E-mail: jwwendling@earthlink.net.

Prestel Publishing, *(3-7913)* Orders Addr.: c/o VNU, 575 Prospect St., Lakewood, NJ 08701 USA Tel 732-363-5679; Fax: 732-363-0338; Toll Free Fax: 877-227-6564; Toll Free: 888-463-6110; Edit Addr.: 900 Broadway, Suite 603, New York, NY 10003 USA Tel 212-995-2720; Fax: 212-995-2733
E-mail: sales@prestel-usa.com
Web site: http://www.prestel.com; http://www.die-gestalten.de; http://www.scalo.com
Dist(s): **VNU.**

Prestige Pubns., *(1-888224)* Div. of Continental Ventures, Inc., 6820 Veterans Memorial Blvd. # 200, Metairie, LA 70003-4417 USA Toll Free: 800-831-4030
Dist(s): **Hervey's Booklink & Cookbook Warehouse.**

Prestige Publishing, *(0-9705235)* 2665 Balfour St., Eugene, OR 97408-1645 USA Tel 541-343-6607 (phone/fax) Do not confuse with companies with the same or similar names in Dunkirk, MD, Southgate, MI, Webster, NY, North Little Rock, AR, Fort Calhoun, NE.

Preston-Speed Pubns., *(1-887159; 1-931587)* 51 Ridge Rd., Mill Hall, PA 17751 USA Tel 570-726-7844; Fax: 570-726-3547
E-mail: doug@prestonspeed.com
Web site: http://www.prestonspeed.com.

Prestwick Hse., Inc., *(1-58049; 1-60389)* Orders Addr.: P.O. Box 246, Cheswold, DE 19936 USA Tel 302-736-2665; Fax: 302-734-0549; Toll Free: 800-932-4593; Edit Addr.: 58 Artisan Dr., Smyrna, DE 19977 USA (SAN 154-5523) Tel 302-659-2070; Fax: 302-659-2792
E-mail: books@prestwickhouse.com; info@prestwickhouse.com
Web site: http://www.prestwickhouse.com.

Pretty Paper Pr., *(0-9746315)* 14 Everett St., East Orange, NJ 07017 USA
Web site: http://www.moodyholiday.com.

Pretty Please Pr., Inc., *(0-9759378)* 105 E. 29th St., 6th Flr., New York, NY 10016 USA.

Prevention Through Puppetry, Inc., *(0-9768827)* 468 Boyle Rd., Port Jefferson Station, NY 11776 USA Tel 631-476-3099; Fax: 631-476-7680
Web site: http://www.sunshinepreventionctr.org.

Price Stern Sloan *Imprint of* **Penguin Group (USA) Inc.**

Priceless Ink Publishing Co., Inc., *(0-9778937)* Orders Addr.: P.O. Box 218538, Nashville, TN 37221 USA
E-mail: apricelessgiftcom@yahoo.com; audreylprice@yahoo.com or apricelessgiftcom@yahoo.com
Web site: http://apricelessgift.com.

Prickly Pear Pr., *(0-9764323)* P.O. Box 69, Sahuarita, AZ 85629-0069 USA Tel 520-625-1587; Fax: 520-625-3655 Do not confuse with Pricly Pear Press in San Francisco CA, Cedar Park TX, Scottsdale AZ, Tucson AZ.
E-mail: pricklypearpress@msn.com
Web site: http://pricklypearpress.info.

Prickly Pr., *(1-893463)* 7911 W. 92nd Terr., Overland Park, KS 66212 USA Tel 913-648-2034 (phone/fax)
E-mail: ikesmith@kc.rr.com
Web site: http://www.readwest.com/flouncesmith.thm.

Priddy Bks. *Imprint of* **St. Martin's Pr.**

Priest, Gerald L., *(0-9743871)* 4801 Allen Rd., Allen Park, MI 48101 USA Toll Free: 800-866-0111.

Prima Games *Imprint of* **Random Hse. Information Group**

Prima Lifestyles *Imprint of* **Crown Publishing Group**

Primary Concepts/Concepts to Go, *(1-893791; 1-60184)* 1338 Seventh St., Berkeley, CA 94710 USA Toll Free: 800-660-8646
Web site: www.primaryconcepts.com.

Primary Sources, *(1-881849)* 16442 SE 42nd Pl., Issaquah, WA 98027 USA Tel 425-865-0409 (phone/fax)
E-mail: info@primary-sources.com
Web site: http://www.primary-sources.com/.

Primordia, *(0-9759007)* P.O. Box 2455, Santa Barbara, CA 93120 USA (SAN 256-1018).

Primrose Pr., *(0-9673171)* Orders Addr.: P.O. Box 2577, Prescott, AZ 86302 USA (SAN 299-9331) Tel 520-445-4567; Fax: 520-445-0517; Edit Addr.: 815 Bertrand Ave., Prescott, AZ 86303 USA Do not confuse with companies with the same name in Antelope, CA, Alhambra, CA, San Francisco, CA.

Prince, L.B. Co., Inc., *(1-879295)* 6621C Electronic Dr., Springfield, VA 22151-4302 USA Tel 703-560-2100.

Princess Ring, LLC, *(0-9745991)* 15721 Bernardo Heights Pkwy., Suite B-30, San Diego, CA 92128 USA.

Princeton Architectural Pr., *(0-907259; 0-910413; 0-9636372; 1-56898; 1-878271; 1-885232; 90-77620)* 37 E. Seventh St., New York, NY 10003 USA (SAN 260-1176) Tel 212-995-9620; Fax: 212-995-9454; Toll Free: 800-722-6657
E-mail: sales@papress.com
Web site: http://www.papress.com
Dist(s): **Chronicle Bks. LLC.**

Princeton Bk. Co. Pubs., *(0-87127; 0-916622)* Orders Addr.: P.O. Box 831, Hightstown, NJ 08520-0831 USA (SAN 630-1568) Tel 609-426-0602; Fax: 609-426-1344; Toll Free: 800-220-7149; 614 Rte. 130, Hightstown, NJ 08520 (SAN 244-8076) ; *Imprints:* Dance Horizons (Dance Horizons); Elysian Editions (Elysian Editions)
E-mail: pbc@dancehorizons.com; elysian@aosi.com
Web site: http://www.dancehorizons.com
Dist(s): **Independent Pubs. Group.**

Princeton Design Group, *(0-9708284; 0-9717549; 0-9728780)* 80 W. End Ave., Somerville, NJ 08876-1824 USA
E-mail: pdg123@rcn.com; jreed@floridatrust.com
Web site: http://www.themissingpeace.net.

Princeton Health Pr., *(0-933665)* 711 Westchester Ave., West Harrison, NY 10604-3504 USA (SAN 692-5391) Toll Free: 800-636-3415
E-mail: sales@phplifeskills.com
Web site: http://www.lifeskillstraining.com.

Princeton Review *Imprint of* **Random Hse. Information Group**

†Princeton Univ. Pr., *(0-691)* Orders Addr.: California-Princeton Fulfillment Services, 1445 Lower Ferry Rd., Ewing, NJ 08618 USA Tel 800-777-4726; Fax: 800-999-1958; Edit Addr.: 41 William St., Princeton, NJ 08540 USA (SAN 202-0254) Tel 609-258-4900; Fax: 609-258-6305; 3 Market Place, Woodstock, OX20 1SY Tel (0) 1993 814501; Fax: (0) 1993 814504
E-mail: webmaster@pupress.princeton.edu
Web site: http://www.pup.princeton.edu
Dist(s): **California Princeton Fulfillment Services**
NetLibrary, Inc.; *CIP.*

Principle Woods, Inc., *(0-9700601; 0-9719228; 0-9796954)* One San Jose Pl., Suite 11, Jacksonville, FL 32257 USA Tel 904-260-8735; Fax: 904-260-8492
E-mail: dcm@pwimpact.com; susan@principlewoods.com
Web site: http://www.principlewoods.com.

Prindle House *See* **Prindle Hse. Publishing Co.**

Prindle House Publishing Co. *Imprint of* **Prindle Hse. Publishing Co.**

Prindle Hse. Publishing Co., *(0-9759527)* Orders Addr.: P.O. Box 18761, Jacksonville, FL 32229 USA Tel 904-751-9125; Fax: 904-751-9338; Toll Free: 866-877-4635; Edit Addr.: 1019 Ashton Cove Terr., Jacksonville, FL 32218 USA ; *Imprints:* Prindle House Publishing Company (PrinHsePubCo)
E-mail: tp@prindlehouse.com; twylaprindle@yahoo.com
Web site: http://www.prindlehouse.com; http://www.twylaprindle.com.

Prinit Pr., *(0-932970)* 211 NW Seventh St., Richmond, IN 47374-4051 USA (SAN 212-680X) Tel 765-966-7130; Fax: 765-966-7131; Toll Free: 800-478-4885
Web site: http://www.printpress.com.

PrinnyWorld Pr., *(0-9668005)* Orders Addr.: P.O. Box 248, Saraland, AL 36571 USA Tel 334-675-5967; Fax: 334-675-6909; Edit Addr.: 10385K Army Rd., Ext. S, Chunchula, AL 36521 USA
E-mail: prinnywrld@aol.com
Web site: http://members.aol.com/prinnywrld/intro.html
Dist(s): **Baker & Taylor Bks.**

Print Place, *(0-9647151)* 1943 N. Coolidge Ave., Altadena, CA 91001 USA Tel 626-797-0184; Fax: 626-795-5774
Dist(s): **Quality Bks., Inc.**
Supreme Co., The
Tal San Distributing
Unique Bks., Inc.

Printing Systems, *(0-9767595; 1-59916)* Orders Addr.: 540 S. Main St. #115, Akron, OH 44311 USA Toll Free: 800-231-0521
E-mail: info@48HrBooks.com
Web site: http://www.48HrBooks.com.

Printmedia Bks., *(0-9778591; 0-9788447; 0-9790999; 1-934379)* Div. of Niedle and Perry, Ent., 3355 E. Miraloma Ave., Bldg. 165, Anaheim, CA 92806 USA Tel 714-729-0729; Fax: 714-729-0730; Toll Free: 866-774-6893
E-mail: peter@printmedia.com; books@printmediabooks.com
Web site: http://www.printmediabooks.com.

printONDEMANDpublisher.com, *(0-9765725)* 325 W. Belden Ave., Chicago, IL 60614-3817 USA Tel 773-988-8619; Fax: 773-935-9967
E-mail: george@georgevalko.com
Web site: http://www.printondemandpublisher.com.

Prints By Mail, *(0-9740173)* 33 Jose I Garica Rd., Belen, NM 87002 USA; 33 Jose I Garcia Rd., Belen, NM 87002
E-mail: books@printsbymail.com
Web site: http://www.printsbymail.com.

Printstar Bks., *(0-9702518; 0-9706531)* 633 W. Wisconsin Ave., Suite 1008, Milwaukee, WI 53203 USA Tel 414-640-9377; Fax: 414-272-7802
E-mail: nick@ppub.com; insignificance@netscape.net
Web site: http://www.ppub.com.

Prion (GBR) *(1-85375) Dist. by* **IPG Chicago.**

Priority Multimedia Group, Inc., *(0-9667483)* 2339 W. Lomita Cir., Mesa, AZ 85202-6458 USA Tel 602-831-5557; Fax: 602-831-7373; Toll Free: 800-546-8879
E-mail: gottry@prioritymm.com
Web site: http://www.prioritymm.com
Dist(s): **Macalester Park Publishing Co., Inc.**

Company

Company

Prioritybooks Pubns., *(0-9753634; 0-9792823)* P.O. Box 2535, Florissant, MO 63033 USA (SAN 853-0130) Tel 314-741-6789 (phone/fax); 314-306-2972; Fax: 314-741-6789
E-mail: rosbeav03@yahoo.com
Web site: http://www.prioritybooks.com
Dist(s): **Lightning Source, Inc.**
Lushena Bks.

Prism Comics, *(0-9759164)* 2621 E. Madison, Seattle, WA 98122-4711 USA Fax: 206-770-6137
Web site: http://www.prismcomics.org.

Prism Hse. Media, *(0-9748088)* Orders Addr.: 1163 Charming St., Maitland, FL 32751 USA
E-mail: pwpelley@moneymanagementbooks.com
Web site: http://www.moneymanagementbooks.com
Dist(s): **Review & Herald Publishing Assn.**

Pristine Pubs., Inc., *(0-9716633)* 18 Buckthorn Cove, Jackson, TN 38305 USA (SAN 254-2420) Tel 731-660-3333 Toll Free: 866-565-3311
E-mail: Kathy@pristinepublishers.com
Web site: http://www.readysetgofitness.com; http://www.questforasdin.com; http://www.pristinepublishers.com; http://www.gabrielsmagicornament.com
Dist(s): **Biblio Distribution.**

†Pritchett & Hull Assocs., Inc., *(0-939838; 1-933638)* 3440 Oakcliff Rd., NE, Suite 110, Atlanta, GA 30340 USA (SAN 216-9258) Tel 770-451-0602; Fax: 770-454-7130; Toll Free: 800-241-4925
E-mail: phsales@p-h.com
Web site: http://www.p-h.com/; *CIP.*

Privacy Council, Inc., *(1-932214)* Div. of Stone Investments, Inc., 8150 N. Central Expy. Ste. 1900, Dallas, TX 75206-1833 USA Toll Free: 866-726-8624
E-mail: info@privacycouncil.com
Web site: http://www.privacycouncil.com.

Privacy Trust Group, The, *(0-9777457)* Div. of JR The Trust Group Inc., P.O. Box 10, Elbert, CO 80106 USA (SAN 850-122X) Tel 303-648-3496 Toll Free: 877-648-0119
Web site: http://www.privacytrustgroup.com.

Privateer Pr., Inc., *(0-9706970; 1-933362)* 13434 NE 16th St. Ste. 120, Bellevue, WA 98005-2335 USA Do not confuse with Privateer Pr. in New Orleans, LA
E-mail: mw@privateerpress.com
Web site: http://www.privateerpress.com
Dist(s): **PSI (Publisher Services, Inc.).**

Privatgaeste Verlag, *(0-9712545)* c/o Ute Kruedewagen, 3168 Harrison St., No. 106, Oakland, CA 94611 USA
Web site: http://www.privatgaeste.com.

Privitera, Vincent J., *(0-9675172)* Orders Addr.: P.O. Box 580545, Houston, TX 77258 USA Tel 281-333-3429; Edit Addr.: 1426 Antigua Ln., Houston, TX 77058-4003 USA.

PRL Publishing, *(0-9743957)* 2245 E. Colorado Blvd., No. 104 PMB 243, Pasadena, CA 91107 USA Tel 626-255-1743
E-mail: info@prldesigns.com
Web site: http://www.prlpub.com
Dist(s): **Baker & Taylor Bks.**

†Pro Lingua Assocs., Inc., *(0-86647)* Orders Addr.: P.O. Box 1348, Brattleboro, VT 05302 USA (SAN 216-0579) Tel 802-257-7779; Fax: 802-257-5117; Toll Free: 800-366-4775; Edit Addr.: P.O. Box 1348, Brattleboro, VT 05302-1348 USA
E-mail: info@prolinguaassociates.com; orders@prolinguaassociates.com
Web site: http://www.prolinguaassociates.com; http://www.lexicarry.com
Dist(s): **Hood, Alan C. & Co., Inc.**; *CIP.*

Pro Lingua Pr., *(1-879870)* Div. of European American R.E. Inv., Inc., Orders Addr.: P.O. Box 24368, Los Angeles, CA 90024 USA Tel 310-472-8396; Fax: 310-472-0770 ; *Imprints:* P L P (P L P)
E-mail: kaufmann-plp@prodigy.net
Web site: http://www.prolinguapress.com
Dist(s): **Baker & Taylor Bks.**
Book Wholesalers, Inc.
Brodart Co.
Follett Library Resources.

Pro Se Publishing Company *See* **Eagle Publishing Co.**

Pro Star Sports, Inc., *(0-9708678)* P.O. Box 1280, Littleton, CO 80160 USA Tel 303-972-4113; Fax: 303-972-8639
E-mail: prostr@attglobal.net
Web site: http://paintballnation.com.

Pro-Action Publishing, *(0-9615126; 1-890378)* Div. of Pro-Action Sports, Inc., Orders Addr.: P.O. Box 26657, Los Angeles, CA 90026 USA (SAN 694-1826) Tel 323-666-7789; Fax: 323-666-3225; Toll Free: 888-567-7789; Edit Addr.: 1717 N. Glendale Blvd., Los Angeles, CA 90026 USA.

Proactive Publishing, *(0-9767324)* 260 Gateway Dr., Suite 21-C, Bel Air, MD 21014 USA Tel 410-893-9016; Fax: 410-893-9380 ; *Imprints:* Kids Can (Kids Can)
Web site: http://www.proactive-solutions.net.

Process Inc U. S. *See* **Process Transition International, Inc.**

Process Transition International, Inc., *(0-9646008)* P.O. Box 1988, Annapolis, MD 21404 USA Tel 301-261-9921; Fax: 410-295-5037
E-mail: spi@processtransition.com
Web site: http://www.processtransition.com.

Product Information & Analysis, *(0-9621865)* Orders Addr.: P.O. Box 25226, Saint Paul, MN 55125-0226 USA; Edit Addr.: 7601 Carillon Plaza E., Woodbury, MN 55125 USA Tel 612-731-9789.

Production 101, Inc., *(0-9729706; 0-9767765)* P.O. Box 150141, Nashville, TN 37215 USA Tel 615-383-0955; Fax: 615-383-6655
E-mail: julie@smartkids101.com
Web site: http://www.babysittingvideo.com
Dist(s): **Big Kids Productions, Inc.**

Production Assocs., Inc., *(1-887120)* 1206 W. Collins Ave., Orange, CA 92867 USA Tel 714-771-6519; Fax: 714-771-2456; Toll Free: 800-535-8368
E-mail: mikec@production-associates.com
Web site: http://www.production-associates.com
Dist(s): **Baker & Taylor Bks.**
Brodart Co.
Educational Insights, Inc.

Products With A Purpose, *(0-9641134)* 16430 N. 34th Pl., Phoenix, AZ 85032 USA Tel 602-595-1188
E-mail: maryalice@ev1.net.

Profane Existence, *(0-9662035)* P.O. Box 8722, Minneapolis, MN 55408-0722 USA
E-mail: blackened@visi.com
Web site: http://www.propaneexistence.com
Dist(s): **AK Pr. Distribution.**

Professional Associates *See* **Professional Assocs. Publishing**

Professional Assocs. Publishing, *(0-9657911; 0-9716233; 0-9787042)* P.O. Box 28056, Austin, TX 78755-8056 USA Toll Free: 866-335-1460
E-mail: info@kingore.com
Web site: http://www.kingore.com.

Professional Business Consultant *See* **Milligan Bks., Inc.**

Professional Pr., *(1-57087; 1-880365)* Orders Addr.: P.O. Box 4371, Chapel Hill, NC 27515-4371 USA Fax: 919-942-8020; Toll Free: 800-277-8960; Edit Addr.: 314 Warren Way, Chapel Hill, NC 27516 USA Do not confuse with Professional Pr., New York, NY
E-mail: tag@geldermann.com
Dist(s): **AtlasBooks Distribution**
Sunbelt Pubns., Inc.

Professional Publishing Services *See* **WayaMedia**

Professional Resource Pubns., *(0-9639023)* Div. of New Perspectives of Indiana, Inc., Orders Addr.: P.O. Box 501485, Indianapolis, IN 46256 USA Tel 317-465-9688; Fax: 317-465-9689; Edit Addr.: 6308-B Rucker Rd., Indianapolis, IN 46220 USA.

Professor Toto Language Education Series *Imprint of* **Language Workshop for Children, The**

Profile Bks. Ltd. (GBR) *(1-86197; 1-84668) Dist. by* **Trafalgar.**

Profile Entertainment, Inc., *(0-88013; 0-931064; 0-934551)* 475 Park Ave., S., 8th Flr., New York, NY 10016 USA (SAN 212-1247) Tel 212-689-2830; Fax: 212-889-7933
E-mail: dee.erwine@starloggroup.com
Dist(s): **Kable Media Services.**

Profitable Publishing *Imprint of* **Thornton Publishing**

Profound Impact Group, *(0-9760564)* Orders Addr.: P.O. Box 370567, Denver, CO 80237 USA Tel 303-797-3982; Fax: 303-680-0472; Toll Free: 877-797-3982
Web site: http://www.profoundgroup.com
Dist(s): **Baker & Taylor Bks.**
Books West.

Profound Promises, *(0-9708195)* Orders Addr.: P.O. Box 1599, Fairfax, VA 22038 USA (SAN 254-282X) Tel 703-449-7751
E-mail: fite@ix.netcom.com
Web site: http://www.profoundpromises.com.

Progeny Pr., *(1-58609)* Div of MG Publishers Group LLC, Orders Addr.: P.O. Box 223, Eau Claire, WI 54702-0223 USA Tel 715-838-0171; Fax: 715-836-0176; Toll Free: 877-776-4369; Edit Addr.: 133 S. State St., Box 100, Fall Creek, WI 54742 USA
E-mail: progeny@progenypress.com
Web site: http://www.progenypress.com.

Programming Concepts, Incorporated *See* **PCI Educational Publishing**

Progressive Language, Inc., *(0-9758759)* 5804 Lost Dutchman Ave NE, Albuquerque, NM 87111-5901 USA
Web site: http://www.progresssivelangauge.com.

Project Amigo, Inc., *(0-9704776)* 4236 Longridge Ave., Penthouse 302, Studio City, CA 91604-1816 USA Fax: 323-525-0870
E-mail: mail@projectamigo.com.

Project Publishing & Design, *(0-915082)* c/o The Cowans, 176 Warren Dr., Vacaville, CA 95687 USA (SAN 207-1150) Tel 707-451-2879; Fax: 707-451-3861 ; *Imprints:* Gemini Press (Gmni Pr)
E-mail: thecowans@mindspring.com.

Project Shalom, *(0-9677266)* P.O. Box 32834, Pikesville, MD 21282-2834 USA Tel 410-358-0383; Fax: 410-764-8382
E-mail: projectshalom1@aol.com
Web site: http://www.projectshalom2.org.

Prologo Pubns., *(0-9764264)* 4109 N. O Connor Rd., Irving, TX 75062-3748 USA
E-mail: layne@msu.edu; prologo@comcast.net
Web site: http://www.prologopublications.com.

Prom Girl Publishing. Inc., *(0-9726917)* 808 Broadway, Penthouse C, New York, NY 10003 USA
Web site: http://www.promgirl.com.

†Prometheus Bks., Pubs., *(0-87975; 1-57392; 1-59102)* Orders Addr.: 59 John Glenn Dr., Amherst, NY 14228-2197 USA (SAN 202-0289) Tel 716-691-0133; Fax: 716-691-0137; Toll Free: 800-421-0351 ; *Imprints:* Pyr Books (Pyr Bks)
E-mail: marketing@prometheustbooks.com
Web site: http://www.prometheusbooks.com; *CIP.*

Promise Productions, Inc., *(1-887710)* Orders Addr.: P.O. Box 927, Glen Rose, TX 76043 USA Tel 254-897-4341; Fax: 254-897-3388; Toll Free: 800-687-2661; Edit Addr.: 114 NE Barnard St., Glen Rose, TX 76043 USA ; *Imprints:* ArtCan Drama Resources (ArtCan Drama)
E-mail: drama@thepromise.org
Web site: http://www.thepromise.org
Dist(s): **Dramatic Publishing Co.**

Promise Pubns., *(0-9656498)* Orders Addr.: PMB 117 6632 Telegraph Rd., Bloomfield Hills, MI 48301-3013 USA Tel 248-865-9345; Fax: 248-538-0403 Do not confuse with Promise Pubns., Plano, TX
E-mail: sherea@realisticallyspeaking.net
Dist(s): **Baker & Taylor Bks.**

PromiseGarden.com, *(0-9723773)* P.O. Box 638, Warrenville, IL 60555 USA Tel 630-393-6516
E-mail: info@promisegarden.com
Web site: http://www.promisegarden.com.

Promocion Editorial Inca S.A., PEISA (PER) *(9972-40; 9972-721) Dist. by* **Mariuccia Iaconi Bk Imports.**

ProNailTech.com, *(0-9748796)* P.O. Box 260515, Lakewood, CO 80226 USA Tel 720-935-1761
Web site: http://www.pronailtech.com.

Pronghorn Pr., *(0-9714725; 1-932636)* Orders Addr.: P.O. Box 707, Greybull, WY 82426 USA Toll Free: 877-765-2979; Edit Addr.: 335 2nd Ave., N., Greybull, WY 82426 USA
Web site: http://www.pronghornpress.org.

Propeller Pr., *(0-9678577)* P.O. Box 729, Fort Collins, CO 80522 USA (SAN 253-1704) Tel 970-482-8807; Fax: 970-493-1240
E-mail: propress@frii.com
Web site: http://www.propellerpress.com.

Prophecy Pubns., *(0-941241)* P.O. Box 7000, Oklahoma City, OK 73153 USA (SAN 665-5319) Tel 405-634-1234; Fax: 405-636-1054; Toll Free: 800-245-5577
Dist(s): **STL Distribution North America.**

Prophecy, The *Imprint of* **Simon & Son Publishing**

ProQuest CSA, *(0-608; 0-7837; 0-8357; 0-591; 0-9702937; 0-599; 1-931694; 1-59399; 0-496; 0-542; 1-4247; 0-9778091; 1-4345; 0-549)* Div. of ProQuest Company, 5252 N. Edgewood Dr., Suite 125, Provo, UT 84604 USA Tel 801-765-1737; 789 Eisenhower Pkwy., Ann Arbor, MI 48106-1346 Tel 734-761-4700 Toll Free: 800-521-0600 ; *Imprints:* CultureGrams World Edition (CultureGram Wrld)
Web site: http://www.culturegrams.com.

ProQuest Information and Learning *See* **ProQuest CSA**

Prospect Hill Co., *(0-9664050)* Div. of A.W. McMullen Co., Inc., 12 Field St., Brockton, MA 02301-2416 USA (SAN 299-710X).

Prosperity & Profits Unlimited, Distribution Services, P.O. Box 416, Denver, CO 80201-0416 USA (SAN 200-4682) Tel 303-575-5676; Fax: 303-575-1187
E-mail: mail@breadpudding.net; mail@contentprovidermedia.com
Web site: http://www.breadpudding.net; http://www.contentprovidermedia.com; http://www.gumbomedia.com.

Prospero's Pr., *(0-9727315)* P.O. Box 4616, Boulder, CO 80306-4616 USA (SAN 255-0121) Tel 303-817-5622
Web site: http://www.ahouseforamouse.com.

Protar Hse., LLC, *(0-9720910)* 829 Ann St., East Lansing, MI 48823 USA Tel 517-974-7993
E-mail: info@protarhouse.com
Dist(s): **Partners Bk. Distributing, Inc.**

Protecting Our Diversity (POD), *(0-9727714)* P.O. Box 231598, Encinitas, CA 92023-1598 USA Tel 760-944-0852
E-mail: email@kidspod.com
Web site: http://www.kidspod.com.

ProTeens *Imprint of* **Positive Action For Christ**

Proteus, *(0-9620541; 0-9722030; 0-9778480)* 4457 Coldwater Canyon Ave., No. 1, Studio City, CA 91604 USA (SAN 248-8760) Tel 818-761-2026; Fax: 818-761-2029 Do not cinfuse with the same or similar name in College Park, MD, Arlington, VA, Albany, NY, Aptos, CA
E-mail: proteusla@proteusla.com
Web site: http://www.proteusla.com
Dist(s): **Replica Bks.**

Prothro, James S. *See* **Robot Publishing**

ProTips(TM) Media, *(0-9740600)* 810 Adair Pl., Del Rey Oaks, CA 93940 USA
E-mail: tom@rivelli.com
Web site: http://www.protipsmedia.com.

Proton Arts, *(0-9752647)* 10261 Brookstone Ct., Manassas, VA 20109-3168 USA
E-mail: info@protonarts.com
Web site: http://www.protonarts.com.

Proud to be Good! Charitable Trust *See* **Pelican Pr.**

Proud 2-B Me Publishing!, *(0-9655726)* 3653-F Flakes Mill Rd., PMB-F188, Decatur, GA 30034 USA Tel 770-808-2301.

Prous, J. R. S.A. (ESP) *(84-499; 84-300; 84-401; 84-86973) Dist. by* **Continental Bk.**

Providence Foundation, *(1-887456)* Orders Addr.: P.O. Box 6759, Charlottesville, VA 22906 USA Tel 434-978-4535; Fax: 434-973-0329; Edit Addr.: 609 E. Market St., Charlottesville, VA 22902 USA
E-mail: info@providencefoundation.com
Web site: http://www.providencefoundation.com.

Providence Hse Pubs., *(1-57736; 1-881576)* 238 Seaboard Ln., Franklin, TN 37067 USA Tel 615-771-2020; Fax: 615-771-2002; Toll Free: 800-321-5692 ; *Imprints:* Hillsboro Press (Hillsboro Pr); Providence House Publishers (ProvHousePubs)
E-mail: books@providencehouse.com
Web site: http://www.providence-publishing.com.

Providence Hse. Pubs. *Imprint of* **Providence Hse Pubs.**

Providence Publishing, *(0-9651661; 0-9753004)* 5744 Bowling Dr., Watauga, TX 76148-3422 USA Do not confuse with companies with the same or similar name in Salt Lake City, UT, Martinez, CA
E-mail: info@providencepublishing.com
Web site: http://www.providencepublishing.com
Dist(s): **Wilson & Assocs.**

Providence Publishing Corporation *See* **Providence Hse Pubs.**

Provident Music Group *See* **Provident-Integrity Distribution**

Provident-Integrity Distribution, 741 Cool Springs Blvd., Franklin, TN 37067 USA (SAN 249-6836)
E-mail: tmarshall@providentmusicgroup.com.

Provine Pr., *(1-889883)* 832 Cerrito St., Albany, CA 94706 USA Tel 510-528-7055
E-mail: jmbartlett@sbcglobal.net.

Provo Craft, *(1-58050)* 151 E. 3450 N., Spanish Fork, UT 84600 USA Tel 801-794-9000; Fax: 801-794-9001; Toll Free: 800-937-7686
E-mail: beckyk@provocraft.com
Web site: http://www.provocraft.com.

PRPublishing, *(0-9712258)* 2830 N. Fifth St., Kalamazoo, MI 49009 USA Tel 616-375-5909; Fax: 616-375-7649
E-mail: freelanceediting@ameritech.net.

PRS Inc., *(0-9768441)* PRS Ctr. Suite 200, PO Box 852, Latrobe, PA 15650 USA Tel 724-539-7820; Fax: 724-539-1388; Toll Free: 800-338-3688
E-mail: prsinfo@prsrx.com; alexr@prsrx.com
Web site: http://www.prsrx.com.

†Pruett Publishing Co., *(0-87108)* P.O. Box 2140, Boulder, CO 80306-2140 USA (SAN 205-4035) Toll Free: 800-592-9727 (orders)
Web site: http://www.pruettpublishing.com
Dist(s): **Books West**; *CIP.*

Prufrock Pr., *(1-882664; 1-59363)* Orders Addr.: P.O. Box 8813, Waco, TX 76714-8813 USA Tel 254-756-3337; Fax: 254-756-3339; Toll Free Fax: 800-240-0333; Toll Free: 800-998-2208; Edit Addr.: 100 N. 6th St., Suite 400, Waco, TX 76701 USA (SAN 851-9188)
E-mail: info@prufrock.com
Web site: http://www.prufrock.com
Dist(s): **Sourcebooks, Inc.**

PSI (Publisher Services, Inc.), 1554 Litton Dr., Stone Mountain, GA 30083 USA Tel 678-382-3887; Toll Free: 800-755-9653.

Psychological Associates *See* **Davis, Nancy**

PTO Pr., *(0-9760187)* P.O. Box 5394, Snowmass Village, CO 81615 USA.

P2 Educational Services, Inc., *(1-885964)* 4915 S. 146th Cir., Omaha, NE 68137-1402 USA Tel 712-727-3772.

Puarose Publishing, *(1-933593)* P.O. Box 1597, Gilroy, CA 95021 USA Tel 408-846-0116
E-mail: admin@puarosepublishing.com
Web site: http://www.puarosepublishing.com.

Public Affairs Research Council of Louisiana, Inc., *(0-9667795)* Orders Addr.: P.O. Box 14776, Baton Rouge, LA 70898-4776 USA (SAN 237-8191) Tel 225-926-8414; Fax: 225-926-8417; Edit Addr.: 4664 Jamestown Ave., Suite 300, Baton Rouge, LA 70898-4776 USA
E-mail: parbrla@aol.com
Web site: http://www.la-par.org.

Public Management Associates *See* **Fellows, RE Publishing**

Public Relations Outreach, Inc., *(0-9677531)* 12138 Central Ave., Suite 559, Mitchellville, MD 20721 USA Tel 301-249-7083; Fax: 301-249-7692
E-mail: asampson@erols.com
Web site: http://lsampson@proinc.net.

Public Space Program (I.C.E.R.) Corporation, *(0-9724484)* P.O. Box 1931, Lillington, NC 27546-1931 USA Tel 910-890-3024; Toll Free: 800-205-0687 (Pin Code 6834).

Public Square Bks., *(1-59497)* 307 Seventh Ave., Suite 1601, New York, NY 10001 USA (SAN 255-8149) Tel 212-604-0415; Fax: 212-604-0390; Toll Free: 800-732-3321
Web site: http://www.publicsquarebooks.com
Dist(s): **Diamond Bk. Distributors**
National Bk. Network.

Publicaciones Citem, S.A. de C.V. (MEX) *(970-656; 968-6792; 968-7668) Dist. by* **Lectorum Pubns.**

Publicaciones Cultural, S.A. de C.V. (MEX) *(968-439; 970-16) Dist. by* **Ediciones.**

Publicaciones Educativas, Inc., *(0-9767623; 0-9767624; 0-9779806)* Orders Addr.: P.O. Box 192337, San Juan, PR 00919-2337 USA Tel 787-250-8252; Fax: 787-274-1671; Edit Addr.: 1117 Ave. Munoz Rivera, San Juan, PR 00925 USA Do not confuse with Publicaciones Educativas, Inc. in Hato Rey, PR, Rio Piedras, PR
E-mail: peduc@coqui.net
Web site: http://www.libreriaeducativapr.com.

Publicaciones Fher, S.A. (ESP) *(84-243) Dist. by* **AIMS Intl.**

Publicaciones Papelandia, *(0-9759194; 0-9765805)* 843 Waukee Pass, San Antonio, TX 78260-1919 USA
E-mail: wjconaway@yahoo.com
Web site: http://www.mexicowalkingtours.com.

Publicaciones Puertorriquenas, Inc., *(0-929441; 1-881713; 1-881720; 1-932243; 1-933485; 1-934630)* Orders Addr.: P.O. Box 195064, San Juan, PR 00919 USA; Edit Addr.: 44 Mayaguez St., San Juan, PR 00918 USA (SAN 249-4272) Tel 787-759-9673; Fax: 787-250-6498
E-mail: pubpr@coqui.net
Web site: http://www.publicacionespr.com.

Publicaciones y Ediciones Salamandra, S.A. (ESP) *(84-7888; 84-86033) Dist. by* **Ediciones.**

Publicaciones y Ediciones Salamandra, S.A. (ESP) *(84-7888; 84-86033) Dist. by* **Lectorum Pubns.**

PublicAffairs, *(1-891620; 1-58648)* A Member of Perseus Books Group, 250 W. 57th St., Suite 1321, New York, NY 10107 USA Tel 212-397-6666; Fax: 212-397-4277; Toll Free: 877-782-1234
E-mail: westview.orders@perseusbooks.com
Web site: http://www.publicaffairsbooks.com
Dist(s): **Perseus Distribution.**

Publication Consultants, *(0-9644809; 1-888125; 1-59433)* 8370 Eleusis Dr., Anchorage, AK 99502 USA Tel 907-349-2424; Fax: 907-349-2426 ; *Imprints:* Publishing Consultants (Pubng Consultants)
E-mail: evan@publicationconsultants.com
Web site: http://www.publicationconsultants.com
Dist(s): **Baker & Taylor Bks.**
News Group, The
Todd Communications
Wizard Works.

Publications International, Ltd., *(0-7853; 0-88176; 1-56173; 1-4127)* Orders Addr.: Suite 701, 6 Help Street, Chatswood, NSW 2067 AUS Tel 02 9413 4088; Fax: 02 9413 4055; Edit Addr.: 7373 N. Cicero Ave., Lincolnwood, IL 60712 USA (SAN 263-9823) Tel 847-676-3470; Fax: 847-676-3671; Toll Free: 800-595-8484 ; *Imprints:* PIL Kids (PIL Kids)
E-mail: customer_service@pubint.com
Web site: http://www.pilbooks.com
Dist(s): **Pan American Publishing, Inc.**
Penguin Group (USA) Inc.
Publishers Clearing Hse.

Publish For Christ, Incorporated *See* **Nathaniel Max Rock**

Publish To Go Pubns., LLC, *(0-9669289; 0-9728923; 0-9745110)* Orders Addr.: P.O. Box 272392, Boca Raton, FL 33427 USA; Edit Addr.: 21539 E. Hollandaire Dr., Boca Raton, FL 33433 USA Tel 561-392-4390 (phone/fax); Fax: 561-392-6774
E-mail: mark@publishtogo.com
Web site: http://www.publishtogo.com.

PublishAmerica, Inc., *(1-893162; 1-58851; 1-59129; 1-59286; 1-4137; 1-4241; 1-60441; 1-60474)* Div. of America Hse. Bk. Pubs., Orders Addr.: P.O. Box 151, Frederick, MD 21705 USA Fax: 301-631-9073; Edit Addr.: 111/113 E. Church St., Frederick, MD 21701 USA
E-mail: pratherm@publishamerica.com; alicek@publishamerica.com; support@publishamerica.com
Web site: http://www.publishamerica.com
Dist(s): **America Hse. Bk. Pubs.**

Publisher Media Services *See* **Independent Publisher Services**

Publisher Plus, *(1-888537)* Div. of Montana Ole Store, Orders Addr.: 200 Choteau St., Sun River, MT 59483 USA Tel 406-264-5953; Fax: 406-264-5672
E-mail: rebeccahel2000@yahoo.com
Web site: http://www.montanaolestore.com.

Publishers Design Group, Inc., *(1-929170)* Orders Addr.: P.O. Box 37, Roseville, CA 95678 USA Tel 916-784-0500; Fax: 916-773-7421; Toll Free: 800-587-6666; Edit Addr.: 1655 Booth Rd., Roseville, CA 95747 USA ; *Imprints:* PDG (PDG)
E-mail: books@publishersdesign.com; orders@publishersdesign.com; admin@publishersdesign.com; marketing@publishersdesign.com
Web site: http://www.publishersdesign.com; http://www.tearoomguide.com
Dist(s): **Biblio Distribution**
Quality Bks., Inc.
STL Distribution North America.

Publishers' Graphics, L.L.C., *(0-9663402; 1-930847; 1-933556; 1-934703)* 140 Della Ct., Carol Stream, IL 60188 USA Toll Free: 888-404-3769
Web site: http://www.pubgraphics.com.

Publishers Place, Inc., *(0-9676051; 0-9744785; 0-9771978)* 945 Fourth Ave., Suite 200A, Huntington, WV 25701 USA Tel 304-697-3236; Fax: 304-697-3399 ; *Imprints:* Mid-Atlantic Highlands Publishing (Mid Atlantic WV)
E-mail: publish@cloh.net; kris.publish@verizon.net
Web site: http://www.publishersplace.org.

Publishers' Pr., *(0-943592)* Orders Addr.: P.O. Box 86421, Portland, OR 97286 USA (SAN 240-7558) Do not confuse with Publishers Pr., Salt Lake City, UT.

Publishers@TreeHouse, The, *(0-9708816)* 2658 Patapsco Rd., Finksburg, MD 21048 USA Tel 410-848-9306
E-mail: pix4u@qis.net.

Publishing Assocs., Inc., *(0-942683)* Subs. of Financial & Commercial Printing Services, 5020 Montcalm Dr., Atlanta, GA 30331 USA (SAN 667-2183) Tel 404-349-4678; Fax: 404-629-5533
E-mail: fcpublish@aol.com.

Publishing by Devon, *(1-891809)* Div. of Jacquelyn Donald Publishing, 10900 Research Blvd., Suite 160C-25, Austin, TX 78759 USA Tel 512-468-4414
E-mail: drjackie2000@yahoo.com.

Publishing Consultants *Imprint of* **Publication Consultants**

Publishing Cooperative, The *Imprint of* **Publishing Factory, The**

Publishing Designs, Inc., *(0-929540)* Orders Addr.: P.O. Box 3241, Huntsville, AL 35810 USA (SAN 249-6372) Tel 256-533-4301; Fax: 256-533-4302; Edit Addr.: 517 Killingsworth Cove Rd., Gurley, AL 35748 USA (SAN 249-6380) Tel 205-859-9372
E-mail: info@publishingdesigns.com
Dist(s): **STL Distribution North America**
Twentieth Century Christian Bks.

Publishing Factory, The, *(0-9722741)* 1836 Blake St., Suite 200, Denver, CO 80202 USA Tel 303-297-1233; Fax: 303-297-3997 ; *Imprints:* Publishing Cooperative, The (Publishing Coop)
E-mail: editorinchief@penclay.com.

Publishing Hse. Gelany, *(0-9712665; 0-9728301; 0-9747248; 0-9777566)* Orders Addr.: P.O. Box 61472, Staten Island, NY 10306 USA Tel 718-668-1375; Edit Addr.: 34 Maple Terr., Staten Island, NY 10306 USA
E-mail: gelany@juno.com
Web site: http://www.zagorizontom20megsfree.com.

Publishing International, 1454 Enderby Way, Sunnyvale, CA 94086-0790 USA Tel 408-738-4311 Do not confuse with companies with the same name in Williamsville, TX, Chicago, IL, Stafford, TX.

PublishingWorks, *(0-9744803; 1-933002)* 60 Winter St., Exeter, NH 03833 USA Tel 603-778-9883; Fax: 603-772-1980; Toll Free: 800-333-9883; 60 Winter St., Exeter, NH 03833 (SAN 850-4806) Tel 603-778-9883; Fax: 603-772-1980 Do not confuse with The Publishing Works in Waldport, OR
E-mail: bookpub@worldpath.net
Web site: http://www.publishingworks.com; http://www.revolutionbooksellers.com
Dist(s): **Revolution Booksellers.**

Pucker Art Pubns. *Imprint of* **Pucker Gallery**

Pucker Gallery, *(0-9635318; 1-879985)* 171 Newbury St., Boston, MA 02116-2897 USA Tel 617-267-9473; Fax: 617-424-9759 ; *Imprints:* Pucker Art Publications (Pucker Art)
E-mail: contactus@puckergallery.com
Web site: http://www.puckergallery.com
Dist(s): **Syracuse Univ. Pr.**
Univ. Pr. of New England
Univ. of Washington Pr.

Pucker Safrai Gallery *See* **Pucker Gallery**

Puckett Publishing, Inc., *(0-9764938)* P.O. Box 528, Columbia, IL 62236 USA.

Puddingstone Pubns., *(0-9678040)* 3 Sadler Dr., Brunswick, ME 04011 USA Tel 207-725-1202.

Puddle Jump Pr. Ltd. *See* **Puddle Jump Pr., Ltd.**

Puddle Jump Pr., Ltd., *(0-9726487)* 763 Route 9W, Nyack, NY 10960 USA Tel 845-359-4085 (phone/fax)
E-mail: puddlejumppress@optonline.net
Web site: http://www.puddlejumppress.com
Dist(s): **Baker & Taylor Bks.**

Puddledancer Pr., *(0-9647349; 1-892005; 1-934336)* Orders Addr.: P.O. Box 231129, Encinitas, CA 92023-1129 USA Toll Free: 877-367-2849; Edit Addr.: 3245 Rim Rock Cir., Encinitas, CA 92024 USA
E-mail: email@puddledancer.com; neill@puddledancer.com; meiji@puddledancer.com
Web site: http://www.puddledancer.com; http://www.nonviolentcommunication.com
Dist(s): **Baker & Taylor Bks.**
Independent Pubs. Group.

Puddleduck Music & Publishing, *(0-9675577)* 224 Emery Dr., Nashville, TN 37214 USA Tel 615-391-2222; Fax: 615-391-3770; Toll Free: 800-828-0999
E-mail: info@puddleduckmusic.com.

Puddleduck Publishing *See* **Puddleduck Music & Publishing**

Puffin *Imprint of* **Penguin Group (USA) Inc.**

Puffin Press, Greatland Graphics *See* **Greatland Graphics**

Pug House Pr., *(0-9717900)* 250 E. Wynnewood Rd., No. E-13, Wynnewood, PA 19096 USA
E-mail: amyunbounded@yahoo.com
Web site: http://www.amyunbounded.com.

Puget Sound Pr., *(0-9660092; 1-930809)* 6523 California Ave., SW, PMB 292, Seattle, WA 98136-1833 USA Tel 206-763-2415
Dist(s): **Baker & Taylor Bks.**
Partners/West
Quality Bks., Inc.

Puget Sound Pubns., *(0-9723537)* 7702 S. Junett St., Tacoma, WA 98409 USA.

PugTale Publishing, *(0-9766390)* 1601 W. Main St. Suite 90 #403, Willimantic, CT 06226 USA Tel 860-456-7847; Fax: 860-456-9173; Toll Free: 877-456-7847
E-mail: admin@pugtalepublishing.com
Web site: http://www.pugtalepublishing.com
Dist(s): **Continental Enterprises Group, Inc. (CEG).**

Pulley Pr., *(0-9707672)* 1160 Camino Cruz Blanca, Sante Fe, NM 87501-4599 USA
E-mail: walba@pulleypress.com
Web site: http://www.pulleypress.com.

Pulp Adventures, Inc., *(1-891729)* P.O. Box 45495, Madison, WI 53744-5495 USA (SAN 254-5500)
E-mail: pulpadventures@charter.net
Web site: http://www.pulpadventures.com
Dist(s): **Baker & Taylor Bks.**
Diamond Comic Distributors, Inc.

Pulte, Therese Marie, *(0-9746557)* 1278 Glenneyre St., Suite 39, Laguna Beach, CA 92651 USA ; *Imprints:* Destination Publishers (Destin Pubs)
Web site: http://www.destinationpublishers.com.

Pumpkin Hill Productions, *(0-9793602)* P.O. Box 165, Hawleyville, CT 06440 USA
E-mail: nmroddas@aol.com

Pumpkin House Company *See* **Pumpkin Hse., Ltd.**

Pumpkin Hse., Ltd., *(0-9646010)* 3508 La Rochelle Dr., Columbus, OH 43221 USA (SAN 255-0644) Fax: 614-557-9635
E-mail: pumpkinhouse@columbus.rr.com
Web site: http://www.pumpkinhouse.net
Dist(s): **Independent Pubs. Group.**

Pumpkin Patch Publishing, *(0-9646300; 0-9708400)* 4232 Riva De Tierra Ln., Las Vegas, NV 89135 USA Tel 702-304-0938 (phone/fax)
E-mail: sfiorello@cox.net
Web site: http://www.pumpkinpatchpublishing.com.

Pumpkin Patch Publishing, *(0-9754823)* 10911 E. Skinner Dr., Scottsdale, AZ 85262 USA.

Pumpkin Pr., *(0-9661631)* 1463 W. Conway Rd., Suite 119, Harbor Springs, MI 49740 USA Tel 616-347-6048.

Pumpkin Ridge Publishing, *(0-9754459)* P.O. Box 1668, North Plains, OR 97113-6157 USA (SAN 256-1379) Tel 503-647-5970
E-mail: prpublish@msn.com
Web site: http://www.factoryride.com.

Pumpkin Seed Pr., *(0-9700273)* 68335 355th Ave., Humphrey, NE 68642 USA Tel 402-923-1682; Fax: 402-923-9110; Toll Free Fax: 877-923-1682
E-mail: rjnoona@megavision.com; rjnoona@magavision.com
Web site: http://www.usedhomeschoolbooks.com/bgh.htm.

Pumpkins Pansies Bunnies & Bears, *(0-9747367)* 3900 RR 620 W., Suite 120, Austin, TX 78738 USA Tel 512-922-9182; Fax: 512-372-8895
E-mail: paklppbh@aol.com
Web site: http://www.tricialowenfield.com.

Punkin Poo Publishing, *(0-9719896)* P.O. Box 654, Duplessis, LA 70728 USA.

Company

Punkin Pr., *(1-60149)* 1221 S. Sherbourne Dr., Apt. No. 5, Los Angeles, CA 90035 USA
E-mail: punkinpress@hotmail.com
Web site: http://www.punkinpress.net.

Punto de Lectura *Imprint of* **Santillana USA Publishing Co., Inc.**

Pupfish Ltd. (GBR) *(1-904637) Dist. by* **Penton Overseas.**

Puppetry in Practice, *(0-9720183)* 1923 Haring St., Brooklyn, NY 11229-3713 USA
E-mail: tovaa@aol.com
Web site: http://www.puppetryinpractice.com.

Puptattle Pr., Inc., *(0-9786947)* 21813 S. Embassy Ave., Carson, CA 90810 USA
Web site: http://www.puptattle.com.

Pura Vida Publishing Co., *(1-891569)* 10705 NE 193rd St., Bothell, WA 98011 USA (SAN 299-4933) Tel 425-670-1346; Fax: 425-744-0563; Toll Free: 888-670-1346
Dist(s): **Baker & Taylor Bks.**
New Leaf Distributing Co., Inc.

†Purdue Univ. Pr., *(0-911198; 1-55753)* Orders Addr.: P.O. Box 388, Ashland, OH 44805 USA Toll Free: 800-247-6553; Edit Addr.: 1207 SCC-E, West Lafayette, IN 47907-1207 USA (SAN 203-4026) Tel 765-494-2038; Fax: 765-496-2442 Do not confuse with Purdue Univ. Pubns., same address
E-mail: mchunt@purdue.edu
Web site: http://www.thepress.purdue.edu/
Dist(s): **AtlasBooks Distribution**
NetLibrary, Inc.; *CIP.*

Pure & Simple Productions, *(1-893401)* 936 Lido Cir., Discovery Bay, CA 94514-9462 USA Toll Free: 888-782-9739
E-mail: sribar@jps.net
Web site: http://www.rexruby.com.

Pure Joy Pubns., *(0-9749578)* P.O. Box 482, Wheat Ridge, CO 80034-0482 USA
E-mail: purejoypublicatrions@comcast.net.

Pureplay Pr., *(0-9714366; 0-9765096)* 11353 Missouri Ave., Los Angeles, CA 90025-5553 USA (SAN 852-5404) Tel 310-479-8773; Fax: 310-473-9384
E-mail: editor@pureplaypress.com
Web site: http://www.pureplaypress.com
Dist(s): **BookMasters, Inc.**

pureplaypress.com *See* **Pureplay Pr.**

Purfect Promises, *(0-9759343)* 149 Summerhill Dr., Rockwall, TX 75032 USA Tel 972-771-9528; Fax: 972-772-5403
E-mail: purfectpromises@aol.com.

Purgatory Publishing Inc., *(1-932867)* P.O. Box 657, Sadsburyville, PA 19369 USA Fax: 610-857-9849 ; *Imprints:* West End Games (W End Games)
Web site: http://www.westendgames.com; http://www.purgatorypublishing.com
Dist(s): **Century Pr.**
Diamond Distributors, Inc.

Purity Pr. Pubs., *(0-9728797)* P.O. Box 2896, Decatur, GA 30031 USA.

Purple Bear Bks., Inc., *(1-933327)* 300 Park Ave., Suite 1700, New York, NY 10022 USA
Dist(s): **Perseus Distribution.**

Purple Chickie Pr., *(0-9674363)* 5049 Wornall Rd., No. AB, Kansas City, MO 64112 USA Tel 816-931-8093; Fax: 816-931-8094 ; *Imprints:* Rainy Day Books (Rainy Day)
E-mail: gammyK@aol.com.

Purple Crayon Studios, *(0-9706491)* 0-115 Luce, SW, Grand Rapids, MI 49055 USA Tel 616-822-3186; Toll Free Fax: 877-710-2368
E-mail: beryl@pca3d.com
Web site: http://www.mushtons.com.

Purple Gorilla, LLC, The, *(0-9661844)* 393 Toilsome Hill Rd., Fairfield, CT 06825-1624 USA Tel 203-367-5040; Fax: 203-367-3459
E-mail: Purple_Gorilla@excite.com.

Purple Hse. Pr., *(1-930900)* Orders Addr.: P.O. Box 787, Cynthiana, KY 41031 USA; Edit Addr.: 8100 Us Highway 62 E., Cynthiana, KY 41031-6796 USA
E-mail: jimorgan@earthlink.net
Web site: http://www.purplehousepress.com.

Purple Hse. Productions, *(0-9673036)* 936 Live Oak Pk. Rd., Fallbrook, CA 92028 USA (SAN 253-1852) Tel 760-723-9256 (phone/fax)
E-mail: gamini@tfb.com
Web site: http://222.biohaven.com/ratnavira.

Purple Lady Productions, *(0-9714506)* P.O. Box 1277, Tiburon, CA 94920-4277 USA Tel 415-435-0720
E-mail: purpleladybythebay@earthlink.net.

Purple Lizard Pr. LLC, *(0-9762902)* 10467 N. Calle Verano Seco, Tucson, AZ 85737-7076 USA Tel 520-991-1771
Web site: http://www.purplelizardpress.com.

Purple Mountain Pr., Ltd., *(0-916346; 0-935796; 1-930098)* Orders Addr.: P.O. Box 309, Fleischmanns, NY 12430-0309 USA (SAN 222-3716) Tel 845-254-4062; Fax: 845-254-4476; Toll Free: 800-325-2665; Edit Addr.: 1060 Main St., Fleischmanns, NY 12430 USA Do not confuse with Purple Mountain Pr., Carson City, NV
E-mail: purple@catskill.net
Web site: http://www.catskill.net/purple
Dist(s): **Baker & Taylor Bks.**
Partners Pubs. Group, Inc.

Purple Penguin Publishing, *(0-9765473)* 3929 Hummingbird Ln., Roanoke, VA 24018 USA Tel 540-400-7220; Toll Free: 800-788-3196
E-mail: tanyapenguin@aol.com
Web site: http://www.underragingskies.tanyaadams.com.

Purple People, Inc., *(0-9707793)* P.O. Box 3194, Sedona, AZ 86340-3194 USA Tel 928-204-6400; Fax: 928-282-1662
E-mail: info@purplepeople.com
Web site: http://www.purplepeople.com.

Purple Pig Publishing, *(0-9700380)* Orders Addr.: P.O. Box 1083, Bethel, CT 06801 USA Tel 203-797-1857; Edit Addr.: 7 Wixon Rd., Danbury, CT 06811 USA
E-mail: jshaboo@att.net.

Purple Plume Pr., *(0-9744923)* 5980 Peach Ave., Manteca, CA 95337 USA Tel 209-825-7602
E-mail: purpleplumepress@cs.com; purpleplumeprss@cs.com.

Purple Pomegranate Productions, *(0-9616148; 1-881022)* Div. of Jews for Jesus, Orders Addr.: 80 Page St., San Francisco, CA 94102-5914 USA Fax: 415-864-3995; Toll Free: 800-366-5521; Edit Addr.: 60 Haight St., San Francisco, CA 94102-5895 USA (SAN 699-8240) Tel 415-864-2600; Fax: 415-552-8325
E-mail: purplepome@aol.com; trperk@jewsforjesus.org
Web site: http://www.store.jewsforjesus.org.

Purple Rhinoceros Publishing Co., *(0-9679868)* P.O. Box 2157, Sells, AZ 85634 USA Tel 520-909-9023; Fax: 520-327-0746
E-mail: tjull@earthlink.net; bnagy@earthlink.net
Web site: http://www.purplerhinoceros.com.

Purple Sky Publishing, *(0-9769017)* P.O. Box 12013, Parkville, MO 64152 USA
E-mail: sjb2faa@yahoo.com
Web site: http://www.purpleskypublishing.com.

PUSH *Imprint of* **Scholastic, Inc.**

Pushkin Pr., Ltd. (GBR) *(1-901285) Dist. by* **Natl Bk Netwk.**

Putnam Adult *Imprint of* **Penguin Group (USA) Inc.**

Putnam Juvenile *Imprint of* **Penguin Group (USA) Inc.**

Putumayo World Music & Crafts, *(1-885265; 1-58759)* Div. of Putumayo, Inc., 324 Lafayette St., 7th Flr., New York, NY 10012 USA Tel 212-625-1400; Fax: 212-460-0095; Toll Free: 800-995-9588
E-mail: info@putumayo.com
Web site: http://www.putumayo.com
Dist(s): **Recorded Bks., LLC**
Rhino Entertainment Co, A Warner Music Group Co.
Rounder Kids Music Distribution.

Puumakaa Pr., *(0-9762387)* Orders Addr.: P.O. Box 500, Na'Alehu, HI 96772 USA; Edit Addr.: 94-6448 Mamalahoa Hwy., Na'Alehu, HI 96772 USA
E-mail: elizabeth@fastnethi.com
Web site: http://www.inka-online.com.

Puwaii International, LLC, *(0-9787949)* 7326 N. 61 St., Paradise Valley, AZ 85253 USA
E-mail: jvanier@clinefineart.com.

Puzzler's Guides, *(0-9714226)* P.O. Box 1719, Boulder, CO 80306-1719 USA
Web site: http://www.puzzlerguides.com.

PXL Media, LLC, *(0-9749322)* P.O. Box 99, LeClaire, IA 52753-0099 USA
E-mail: pxlmedia@aol.com.

Pyle, Robert Associates *See* **Avocus Publishing, Inc.**

Pyr Bks. *Imprint of* **Prometheus Bks., Pubs.**

Pyradyne Publishing, *(0-9740311)* Orders Addr.: 1278 Glenneyre, Suite 305, Laguna Beach, CA 92651 USA Tel 949-499-2603; Fax: 949-499-5788; Toll Free: 800-729-2603; Edit Addr.: 3275 Laguna Canyon Rd., Suite R-2, Laguna Beach, CA 92651 USA
E-mail: sales@pyradyne.com; slaes@pyradyne.com
Web site: http://www.pyradyne.com.

Pyramid Dancer Pubns., *(0-9659913)* 7473 Fortman Ave., Fountain, CO 80817-1403 USA
E-mail: rjb@phoenixbonsai.com
Web site: http://www.phoenixbonsai.com.

Pyramid Educational Products, Inc., *(1-928598)* Div of Pyramid Educational Consultants, Incorporated, 13 Garfield Way, Newark, DE 19713-3450 USA
E-mail: dbittner@pyramidproducts.com
Web site: http://www.pyramidproducts.com.

Pyramid Media, *(1-55981)* Orders Addr.: P.O. Box 1048, Santa Monica, CA 90406 USA (SAN 218-2807) Tel 301-828-7577; Fax: 301-453-9083; Toll Free: 800-421-2304; Edit Addr.: 2801 Colorado Ave., Santa Monica, CA 90404 USA
E-mail: info@pyramidmedia.com; sales@pyramidmedia.com
Web site: http://www.pyramidmedia.com
Dist(s): **National Video Resources, Inc.**

Pyramid Publishing, Inc., *(1-885920; 1-934008)* Orders Addr.: P.O. Box 129, Zenda, WI 53195-0129 USA Tel 414-275-3384; Fax: 414-275-3584; P.O. Box 129, Zenda, WI 53195 Do not confuse with companies with the same name in Utica, NY, Montgomery, AL
E-mail: pyramid2mail@gmail.com.

Pyramid Publishing (PTY), Ltd. (BWA) Dist. by Mich St U Pr.

PyroWriters *Imprint of* **Allen, Evelyn W.**

Pyxie Moss Pr., *(0-9762483)* 13 Taunton Rd., Medford, NJ 08055 USA Tel 609-953-7885 (phone/fax)
E-mail: jeyre2@comcast.net
Web site: http://www.janeeyre-art.com.

Pyxis Pr., *(0-9700809)* 2100 Ashcraft Ln., Louisville, KY 40242-3304 USA Tel 502-412-2308; Fax: 502-253-0796 Do not confuse with Pyxis Press, San Diego, CA
E-mail: pyxispress@pyxispress.win.net
Web site: http://pyxispress.com.

QEB Publishing Inc., *(1-59566)* 23062 La Cadena Dr., Irvine, CA 92653 USA
E-mail: stevee@quarto.com
Web site: http://www.qeb-publishing.com.

QED Publishing *See* **QEB Publishing Inc.**

Quackenbush, Robert Studios, *(0-9612518; 0-9712757)* Orders Addr.: 460 E. 79th St., Suite 14E, New York, NY 10021 USA (SAN 656-0458) Tel 212-744-3822; Fax: 212-861-2761
E-mail: rqstudios@aol.com
Web site: http://www.rquackenbush.com.

Quackenworth Publishing, *(1-933211)* P.O. Box 4747, Culver City, CA 90230-4747 USA Tel 310-945-5634; Fax: 310-945-5709
E-mail: info@quackenworth.com
Web site: http://www.quackenworth.com.

Quadradrillion, llc, *(0-9771802)* 5517 E St., Sacramento, CA 95819 USA
E-mail: contact@quadradrillion.com
Web site: http://www.quadradrillion.com/.

Quadre Enterprises, Ltd., *(1-928719)* 11408 Orchard Pk. Ln., Suite No.316, Glen Allen, VA 23060 USA Tel 804-273-1297; Fax: 804-273-0468; Toll Free: 800-899-7233.

Quadrillion Media LLC, *(1-58185)* 10105 E. Via Linda Rd., Suite 103-390, Scottsdale, AZ 85258 USA Tel 602-905-5600; Fax: 602-905-5602; Toll Free: 888-795-9494 ; *Imprints:* Tessloff Publishing (Tessloff Publishing).

Quadrillion Publishing, *(1-84100)* 1160 Mclester St. Ste. 3, Elizabeth, NJ 07201-2917 USA
E-mail: nyquadpub@aol.com.

Quail Ridge Pr., Inc., *(0-937552; 1-893062; 1-934193)* Orders Addr.: P.O. Box 123, Brandon, MS 39043 USA (SAN 257-8794) Tel 601-825-2063; Fax: 601-825-3091; Toll Free Fax: 800-864-1082; Toll Free: 800-343-1583
E-mail: info@quailridge.com; dwalker@quailridge.com
Web site: http://www.quailridge.com
Dist(s): **Booklines Hawaii, Ltd.**
Gibson, Dot Pubns.
Forest Sales & Distributing Co.
Islander Group
Southwest Cookbook Distributors.

Quaker Press of Friends General Conference, *(0-9620912; 1-888305)* 1216 Arch St., 2B, Philadelphia, PA 19107 USA (SAN 225-4484) Tel 215-561-1700; Fax: 215-561-0759; Toll Free: 800-966-4556
E-mail: bookstore@fgc.quaker.org; barbarah@fgcquaker.org
Web site: http://www.fgcquaker.org.

Quality Medical Publishing, Inc., *(0-942219; 1-57626)* 2248 Welsch Industrial Ct., Saint Louis, MO 63146 USA (SAN 666-8755) Tel 314-878-7808; Fax: 314-878-9937; Toll Free: 800-348-7808 (customer service)
E-mail: qmp@qmp.com
Web site: http://www.qmp.com
Dist(s): **Elsevier - Health Sciences Division**
Majors Scientific Bks., Inc.
Matthews Medical Bk. Co.
Rittenhouse Bk. Distributors.

Quality Nature Displays by Eddie Dunbar, *(0-9764454)* 5209 Congress Ave., Oakland, CA 94601-5405 USA ; *Imprints:* Exploring California Insects (Ex CA In)
E-mail: qnd@aol.com
Web site: http://www.bugpeople.org.

Quality of Life Publishing Co., *(0-9675532)* 6210 Shirley St. Ste. 112, Naples, FL 34109-6258 USA Toll Free: 877-513-0099
E-mail: info@QoLpublishing.com
Web site: http://www.QoLpublishing.com
Dist(s): **Biblio Distribution.**

Quality Pubs., *(0-9671107)* Orders Addr.: P.O. Box 691546, San Antonio, TX 78269 USA Tel 210-699-9007; Fax: 210-641-6334; Edit Addr.: 11238 Jade Green, San Antonio, TX 78249 USA Toll Free: 888-633-9898
E-mail: aroman@qualitypublishers.com
Web site: http://www.medpress.com
Dist(s): **Baker & Taylor Bks.**
Ingram Bk. Co.

Quality Publishing Inc., *(0-9745741; 0-9759309)* 1005 E. Highland Ave., Rome, GA 30161 USA Fax: 706-290-1223; Toll Free: 800-262-4404
E-mail: bbmonday@comcast.net.

Quality Sports Pubns., *(1-885758)* 24 Buysse Dr., Coal Valley, IL 61240 USA Tel 309-234-5016; Fax: 309-234-5019; Toll Free: 800-464-1116
E-mail: duane@qualitysportsbooks.com
Web site: http://www.qualitysportsbooks.com
Dist(s): **Baker & Taylor Bks.**

Quantum Group, *(0-9725769)* Orders Addr.: 1270 Hillcrest Ave., Pasadena, CA 91106 USA (SAN 254-9506) Tel 213-500-8806; Fax: 626-795-4334
E-mail: ryan.capalbo@quantumstore.net
Web site: http://www.quantumgrp.net.

Quantum Leap S.L.C Pubns., *(0-9705455)* 2740 Greenbriar Pkwy., Suite 201, Atlanta, GA 30331 USA Toll Free: 877-571-9788
E-mail: distribution@blackamericanhandbook.com
Web site: http://www.blackamericanhandbook .com.

Quantum One Publishing, *(0-9755681)* 1728 Spruce Ln., Linton, IN 47441 USA Tel 812-847-8708; Fax: 812-847-8712
E-mail: jdsapara@iglide.net.

Quarrier Pr., *(0-938985; 0-9646197; 1-891852)* 1125 Central Ave., Charleston, WV 25302 USA Tel 304-342-1848; Fax: 304-343-0594; Toll Free: 888-982-7472 ; *Imprints:* Mountain Memories Books (Mtn Memories Bks)
E-mail: wvbooks@ntelos.net
Web site: http://www.wvbookco.com
Dist(s): **West Virginia Book Co., The.**

Quarry Pr., *(0-9613111)* P.O. Box 176, Hallowell, ME 04347 USA (SAN 294-1007) Tel 207-622-7131 Do not confuse with Quarry Press in Philadelphia, PA
E-mail: dumphrey@mail.smu.edu.

Quarrystone Bond, *(0-9712297)* 4017 Dutch Harbor Ct., Raleigh, NC 27606-8604 USA Tel 919-387-9939
E-mail: bob@sas.com.

Quarter Milestones Publishing, *(0-9748216)* Orders Addr.: P.O. Box 441, Milligan College, TN 37682-0441 USA Tel 423-542-0159; Fax: 423-542-9532; Edit Addr.: 1682 Powder Branch Rd., Johnson City, TN 37601-6220 USA
E-mail: qmp@preferred.com
Web site: http://www.quartermilestones.com
Dist(s): **Overmountain Pr.**

Quarter-Inch *See* **Quarter-Inch Publishing**

Quarter-Inch Publishing, *(0-9653422; 0-9740932)* 33255 Stoneman St., No. B, Lake Elsinore, CA 92530 USA Tel 951-609-3309; Fax: 951-609-3369 ; *Imprints:* Quarter-Inch Publishing (Quarter-In Pubng)
E-mail: quarteri@aol.com
Web site: http://www.quarterinchpublishing.com
Dist(s): **Sunbelt Pubns., Inc.**

Quarter-Inch Publishing *Imprint of* **Quarter-Inch Publishing**

Quartz Pr., *(0-911455)* 392 Taylor St., Ashland, OR 97520-3058 USA (SAN 274-9246) Tel 541-482-8119 Do not confuse with Quarts Press in Temple Terrace, FL
E-mail: spira@mind.net.

Quatemion Pr., *(0-9672535)* P.O. Box 700564, San Antonio, TX 78270 USA Tel 210-497-1096.

Quayside, *(0-86573; 1-58923)* Orders Addr.: 18705 Lake Dr., E., Chanhassen, MN 55317 USA Tel 952-936-4700; Fax: 952-988-0201; Toll Free: 800-328-0590; Edit Addr.: 100 Cummings Ctr. Ste. 406L, Beverly, MA 01915-6101 USA ; *Imprints:* Creative Publishing International (Creativ Pub)
E-mail: sales@creativepub.com
Web site: http://www.rockpub.com; http://www.quaysidepublishers.com; http://www.quiverbooks.com; http://www.walterfoster.com
Dist(s): **Creative Publishing International, Inc.**

Que, *(0-7897; 0-88022; 1-56529)* Div. of Pearson Technology Group, 201 W. 103rd St., Indianapolis, IN 46290-1094 USA Tel 317-581-3500; Toll Free: 800-428-5331 (orders); 800-858-7674 (customer service) Do not confuse with Que Software, also a division of Macmillan Computer Publishing, same address
E-mail: customerservice@macmillanUSA.com
Web site: http://www.quepublishing.com
Dist(s): **Alpha Bks.**
Pearson Education
Pearson Technology Group
Sams Technical Publishing, LLC.

Quebla, *(0-9772738)* P.O. Box 958073, Duluth, GA 30095 USA Tel 404-245-9055
E-mail: support@quebla.com
Web site: http://www.quebla.com.

Queen Enterprises, Inc., *(1-930272)* 117 Lafayette Dr., Riverdale, GA 30296 USA Fax: 770-719-4931
E-mail: Lilbuddie@msn.com.

Queen's Knight, *(0-9752810)* 8741 Saline Waterwirks Rd., Saline, MI 48176 USA.

Quentin Road Ministries *See* **Victory In Grace Ministries**

Quercus Pr., *(0-9793444)* P.O. Box 46163, Plymouth, MN 55446-0163 USA (SAN 853-1773)
Web site: http://www.windingoak.com.

Quest Comics, *(0-9715206)* 29 Stuart Ave., Wappingers Falls, NY 12590 USA Tel 845-297-1697
E-mail: xquestcmxx@aol.com.

Questmarc Publishing, *(0-9634251; 0-9755801)* Orders Addr.: P.O. Box 340, Yankton, SD 57078 USA Tel 605-660-0335; Fax: 605-260-6873; Edit Addr.: 811 W. 8th, Yankton, SD 57078 USA Tel 605-660-0335
E-mail: questmarc@mail.com
Web site: http://www.questmarc.com.

Quick American, *(0-932551)* Div. of Quick Trading Co., Orders Addr.: 1635 E. 22nd St., Oakland, CA 94606-4047 USA (SAN 687-4843) Tel 510-533-0605; Fax: 510-535-0437
E-mail: snewhart@juno.com
Web site: http://www.quicktrading.com
Dist(s): **Bookpeople**
Last Gasp of San Francisco
Perseus Distribution.

Quick American Publishing Company *See* **Quick American**

Quick Bk. Publishing, *(0-9659891)* 77635 Malone Cir., Palm Desert, CA 92211 USA Tel 760-772-6628; Fax: 760-772-0169
E-mail: odyssey@odysseyofthesoul.org
Web site: http://www.odysseyofthesoul.org
Dist(s): **New Leaf Pr., Inc.**

Quick Books *See* **Quick Bk. Publishing**

Quick Quest Pubns. LLC, *(0-9760372)* Orders Addr.: P.O. Box 57485, tucson, AZ 85732 USA Toll Free Fax: 800-682-6576; Edit Addr.: P.O. Box 57485, Tucson, AZ 85732 USA Tel 978-726-5713
E-mail: nathanialportis@yahoo.com
Web site: http://www.quickquestpub.com
Dist(s): **Lushena Bks.**

Quick Wisdom Publishers *See* **Aylen Publishing**

Quickpresspublishing Incorporated *See* **Quick Quest Pubns. LLC**

Quiet Impact, Inc., *(0-9713749; 0-9754629)* 140 Cherry St., No. 388, Hamilton, MT 59840 USA Tel 406-375-9378; Fax: 406-363-5234 ; *Imprints:* Character-in-Action (Character-in-Action)
E-mail: elhamilton@quietimpact.com; elhamilton@character-in-action.com
Web site: http://www.character-in-action.com; http://www.quietimpact.com.

Quiet Man, *(0-9744251)* 28 W. 44th St., Suite 2105, New York, NY 10036-6600 USA (SAN 255-7150) Tel 212-921-4444; Fax: 212-921-4504
E-mail: dawn@quietman.net
Web site: http://www.quietman.net.

Quiet Man Publishing, *(0-9742829)* 27542 Berkshire Hills Pl., Valencia, CA 91354 USA
E-mail: jh1429@yahoo.com
Web site: http://www.Quietmanpublishing.com
Dist(s): **Baker & Taylor Bks.**

Quiet Storm Publishing Group, *(0-9714296; 0-9728819; 0-9744084; 0-9749608; 0-9758571; 0-9770070; 0-9787528)* Orders Addr.: P.O. Box 1666, Martinsburg, WV 25401 USA; Edit Addr.: 1045 Needmore Rd., Martinsburg, WV 25401 USA
E-mail: quietstormbooks@yahoo.com
Web site: http://www.quietstormpublishing.com
Dist(s): **Baker & Taylor Bks.**

Quiet Vision Publishing, *(1-57646; 1-891595; 1-60545)* Orders Addr.: 12155 Mountain Shadow Rd., Sandy, UT 84092-5812 USA Tel 801-572-4018; Fax: 801-571-8625; Toll Free: 800-442-4018
E-mail: john@quietvision.com; info@quietvision.com
Web site: http://www.quietvision.com
Dist(s): **Baker & Taylor Bks.**

Quiet Waters Productions, *(0-9721392)* 11045 Ketchum Rd., North Collins, NY 14111 USA Tel 716-337-2337
E-mail: quietwaters@juno.com.

Quiet Waters Pubns., *(0-9663966; 1-931475)* Orders Addr.: P.O. Box 0034, Bolivar, MO 65613-0034 USA Tel 417-326-5001; Fax: 617-249-0256; Edit Addr.: 1228 Northwood Cir., Bolivar, MO 65613 USA
E-mail: qwp@usa.net
Web site: http://www.quietwaterspub.com; http://www.fromthescholarsdesk.com.

Quill To Pen Publishing, *(0-9717586)* 9892 V Hwy., Mount Vernon, MO 65712 USA Tel 417-466-4105
E-mail: bugsy@sofnet.com.

Quill Works, *(0-9712785)* 15683 Hazel Rd., Morrison, IL 61270 USA Tel 815-772-3144
E-mail: vavra@essex1.com.

Quillpen, *(0-9673504)* 1520 Waverly Dr., Trenton, MI 48183 USA Tel 734-676-1285; Fax: 734-676-9822
E-mail: bfquillpen@msn.com.

Quilt in a Day, *(0-922705; 1-891776)* 1955 Diamond St., Unit A, San Marcos, CA 92069 USA (SAN 251-5644) Tel 760-591-0081; Fax: 760-591-4424; Toll Free: 800-777-4852
E-mail: qiad@quilt-in-a-day.com
Web site: http://www.quilt-in-a-day.com.

Quiltown, *(0-9729001)* 520 E. Central Pkwy., Plano, TX 75074 USA Tel 972-422-6996; Fax: 972-517-1820
E-mail: quiltown@msn.com
Web site: http://www.quiltown.com
Dist(s): **STL Distribution North America.**

Quincannon Publishing Group, *(1-878452)* P.O. Box 8100, Glen Ridge, NJ 07028 USA Tel 973-669-8367 (phone/fax) ; *Imprints:* Tory Corner Editions (Tory Corner)
E-mail: editors@quincannongroup.com
Web site: http://www.quincannongroup.com
Dist(s): **Alibris.**

Quinlan Pr., *(0-933341; 0-9611268; 1-55770)* 1 Devonshire Pl., No. 3108, Boston, MA 02109-3515 USA (SAN 226-4641).

Quinn Entertainment, *(0-9773099)* 7535 Austin Harbour Dr., Cumming, GA 30041 USA (SAN 257-2575) Tel 770-356-3847; Fax: 770-886-1475
E-mail: stephaniequinn@bellsouth.net
Web site: http://www.startabusinessteachingkids.com.

Quinn Micheal Publishing, Incorporated *See* **Rhapsody Branding, Inc.**

Quint, Steven, *(0-9721150)* 208 W. 85th St., No. 5E, New York, NY 10024 USA
E-mail: extra@thenewyorkrhymes.com
Web site: http://www.thenewyorkrhymes.com.

Quintessential Corp., *(0-9715298)* P.O. Box 9224, Mclean, VA 22102 USA Tel 703-734-4900
E-mail: info@qproductsarchery.com
Web site: http://qproductsarchery.com.

Quirk Bks., *(1-931686; 1-59474)* 215 Church St., Philadelphia, PA 19106 USA Tel 215-627-3581; Fax: 215-627-5220
E-mail: general@quirkbooks.com
Web site: http://www.quirkbooks.com
Dist(s): **Chronicle Bks. LLC.**

Quirkles, The *Imprint of* **Creative 3, LLC**

Quist, Harlin Bks., *(0-8252)* 608 Ninth St., S., Virginia, MN 55792 USA
Dist(s): **Alliance Hse., Inc.**
Perseus Distribution.

Quixote Pr., *(1-57166; 1-878488)* 1854 345th Ave., Wever, IA 52658-9597 USA Tel 319-372-7480; Fax: 319-372-7485; Toll Free: 800-571-2665 Do not confuse with Quixote Pr., Houston, TX, Los Angeles, CA
E-mail: heartsntummies@hotmail.com
Dist(s): **Bookmen, Inc.**

Quixote Press *See* **Padwolf Publishing, Inc.**

Quixote Pubns., *(0-9633083; 0-9677583)* 490 Merrimak Dr., Berea, OH 44017 USA Tel 440 234-4244; Fax: 440-234-1141
E-mail: PatMote@aol.com
Web site: http://www.quixotepub.com
Dist(s): **Baker & Taylor Bks.**

QuizQuester Pr. LLC, *(0-9718432)* 127 Edgewood Ave., Baltimore, MD 21228-4354 USA Tel 410-747-0003
E-mail: brocato.one@verizon.net
Web site: http://www.quizquester.com
Dist(s): **STL Distribution North America.**

Quool Publishing, *(0-615)* 4707 Highway 61, No. 245, White Bear Lake, MN 55110 USA
Web site: http://www.thestarkfiles.com
Dist(s): **Lulu.com.**

QuotationWorld Pubns., *(0-9741868)* 3035 Shannon Lakes Dr., N., Tallahassee, FL 32309 USA Tel 850-894-1903 (phone/fax)
E-mail: admin@quotationworld.com
Web site: http://www.quotationworld.com.

Qur'an Society of America, *(0-9630687)* c/o Khalfon, 80-10 51st Ave., Elmhurst, NY 11373 USA Tel 718-446-6472; Fax: 718-446-4370.

Quranic Educational Society, *(0-9760681)* Orders Addr.: P.O. Box 597969, Chicago, IL 60659 USA; Edit Addr.: 6355 N Claremont Ave., Chicago, IL 60659 USA Tel 773-743-9345
E-mail: qeschicago@sbcglobal.net
Web site: http://www.qesonline.org.

R & D Educational Ctr., *(0-9725365; 0-9774432)* 301 Immigrant TL, Windsor, CO 80550 USA
Web site: http://www.rdeducation.home.att.net.

R & D Publishing of Lakeland, Florida, *(0-9797566)* 5709 LaSerena Ave., Lakeland, FL 33809-4262 USA Tel 863-859-2984.

R & R Advertising, *(0-9765225)* 3409 Executive Ctr. Dr., No. 202, Austin, TX 78731 USA Tel 512-342-0110; Fax: 512-342-0142
E-mail: info@rradinc.com
Web site: http://www.rradinc.com.

R & R Publishing, LLC, *(0-9764845)* Orders Addr.: 446 N. Wells, Suite 254, Chicago, IL 60610 USA Tel 312-371-4442; Fax: 312-276-8001 Do not confuse with companies with the same or similar name in Torrance, CA, Brimingham, AL, Shelton, WA, San Antonio, TX, Washington, DC, Baldwin City, KS
E-mail: info@rnrpublishing.com
Web site: http://www.glutenfreepassport.com; http://www.rnrpublishing.com; http://www.allergyfreepassport.com
Dist(s): **Integral Yoga Pubns.**

R & S Bks. (SWE) *(91-29) Dist. by* **Macmillan.**

RBC Publishing Co., Inc., *(0-9703178; 0-9721547)* Orders Addr.: P.O. Box 1330, Elk Grove, CA 95759 USA Tel 916-685-5578; Fax: 916-685-5958; Edit Addr.: 9107 Voos Ct., Elk Grove, CA 95624 USA ; *Imprints:* Ramona's Book Company (Ramonas Bk); Blakk Phoxx Publishing (Blakk Phoxx)
E-mail: scituate@citlink.net
Web site: http://www.rbcpublishingco.com
Dist(s): **Baker & Taylor Bks.**

R D R Books *See* **RDR Bks.**

R. E. Farrellbooks, LLC, *(0-9759116)* 9217 W. Sierra Pinta Dr., Peoria, AZ 85382-0983 USA
E-mail: info@refarrellbooks.com
Web site: http://www.refarrellbooks.com.

REP Pubs., *(0-9604876)* Orders Addr.: 733 Turrentine Trail, St. Louis, MO 63141 USA (SAN 239-3786) Tel 314-434-1833
E-mail: Richard@reppublishers.com
Web site: http://www.reppublishers.com
Dist(s): **Booksource, The**
Unique Bks., Inc.

R F T Publishing Company *See* **aha! Process, Inc.**

R.H. Boyd Publishing Corp., *(1-58942)* 6717 Centennial Blvd., Nashville, TN 37209-1049 USA Tel 615-350-8000; Fax: 615-350-9018
Web site: http://www.rhboydpublishing.com.

R H W Publishing, *(0-9716835)* 7811 Fussells Ridge Dr., Richmond, VA 23231 USA Tel 804-795-2432
E-mail: rwright@rhwpublishing.com
Web site: http://www.rhwpublishing.com.

R I C C Productions, *(0-9678741)* P.O. Box 1160, Boston, MA 02117 USA Tel 617-287-2005
E-mail: Ronald1102@aol.com.

R in R Ink *See* **Move It Math**

R J Communications, LLC, *(0-9700741; 1-59664)* 51 E. 42nd St., Suite 1202, New York, NY 10017-5404 USA Tel 212-867-1331; Fax: 212-681-8002; Toll Free: 800-621-2556 (New York)
E-mail: ron@rjcom.com
Web site: http://www.selfpublishing.com; http://www.booksjustbooks.com.

R. N. M., Incorporated *See* **Onion River Pr.**

RRP Pubs., *(0-9607034)* 5 N. Bank St., Easton, PA 18042 USA (SAN 239-0264) Tel 610-252-1199.

RSVP Pr., *(0-930865; 1-60209)* 514 Cabin Dr., Irmo, SC 29063-7860 USA (SAN 657-6346)
E-mail: writernet@aol.com
Web site: http://www.rsvpbooks.com; http://members.aol.com/writernet/rsvp.htm.

RVS Bks., Inc., *(0-9634257)* P.O. Box 683, Lebanon, TN 37088-0683 USA (SAN 298-7325) Tel 615-449-6725; Fax: 615-449-6910.

Rabbit Ears Pr. & Co., *(0-9748922)* Orders Addr.: P.O. Box 1952, Davis, CA 95617 USA Tel 530-220-3289
Web site: http://www.rockythemudhen.com
Dist(s): **Partners Bk. Distributing, Inc.**

Rabbit's Foot Pr. *Imprint of* **Blue Mountain Arts Inc.**

Rach, W. Dennis, *(0-9792579)* 9965 Portofino Dr., Orlando, FL 32832 USA (SAN 852-9299) Tel 407-625-8528
E-mail: dennis@rachfamily.com.

Rachel's Records, *(1-886673)* 217 Silo Ct., Nashville, TN 37221-3544 USA Tel 615-646-3220; Fax: 615-662-6550
E-mail: rachel@rachelsumner.com
Web site: http://www.rachelsumner.com
Dist(s): **Follet Higher Education Grp**
Professional Media Service Corp.
Wayland Audio-Visual.

Raconteurs, Inc., *(0-9621758)* 1305 W. Wisconsin Ave., No. 114, Oconomowoc, WI 53066-2646 USA (SAN 252-080X) Tel 414-567-4009.

Rafka Pr. LLC, *(0-9779628)* P.O. Box 8507, Surprise, AZ 85374 USA
Web site: http://www.rafkapress.com.

Rafter Five Pr., *(0-9673497)* Orders Addr.: P.O. Box 65618, Tucson, AZ 85728-5618 USA Tel 520-742-9978; Fax: 520-797-5618; Edit Addr.: 6811 N. Camino de Fray Marcos, Tucson, AZ 85718 USA
E-mail: rafter5@azstarnet.com.

Rag Mag *See* **Black Hat Pr.**

Ragged Bears USA, *(1-929927)* Div. of Ragged Bears Publishing, Ltd., 413 Sixth Ave., Brooklyn, NY 11215-3310 USA Tel 718-768-3696; Fax: 718-369-0844
E-mail: publisher@raggedbears.com
Web site: http://www.raggedbears.com
Dist(s): **Chronicle Bks. LLC.**

Ragged Edge Pr. *Imprint of* **White Mane Publishing Co., Inc.**

Ragged Sky Pr., *(0-9633092; 1-933974)* 270 Griggs Dr., Princeton, NJ 08540 USA
E-mail: ellen_foos@pupress.princeton.edu.

Raider Publishing International, *(0-9772054; 0-9790799; 1-934360)* 9 Farview Terr., Suffern, NY 10901 USA Tel 845-228-8757
E-mail: johnraider@hotmail.com; jraider@raiderpublishing.com
Web site: http://www.raiderpublishing.com.

Raiff, Angela *See* **Bear Lake Publishing**

Company

Company

Railroad Pr., The, *(0-9657709; 1-931477)* Orders Addr.: P.O. Box 444, Hanover, PA 17331-0444 USA Tel 717-637-3852; Fax: 717-632-7312; Edit Addr.: 1150 Carlisle St., PMB 444, Hanover, PA 17331 USA
E-mail: trp@alco628.com; trpmail@sun-link.com
Web site: http://www.alco628.com.

Rain, Blue, & The Crew Pubs., *(1-929396)* P.O. Box 3773, Easton, PA 18043-3773 USA
E-mail: thiswarisover@msn.com
Web site: http://www.rainblueandthecrew.com.

Rain Tree Bks., *(0-9764129)* Orders Addr.: P.O. Box 1290, DeQueen, AR 71832 USA; Edit Addr.: 146 Treating Plant Rd., DeQueen, AR 71832 USA Tel 870-582-3565.

Rainbow Angel Pubns., *(0-9675187)* 700 Karlaney Ave., Cayce, SC 29033 USA Tel 803-796-7755 (phone & fax)
E-mail: rainbowangel@bellsouth.net
Web site: http://www.rainbowangel.com.

Rainbow Arch Publishing, *(0-9673492)* Orders Addr.: P.O. Box 23192, Glade Park, CO 81523 USA Tel 970-256-0504; Edit Addr.: 891 DS Rd., Glade Park, CO 81523 USA.

Rainbow Bks., Inc., *(0-935834; 1-56825)* P.O. Box 430, Highland City, FL 33846-0430 USA (SAN 213-5515) Tel 863-648-4420; Fax: 863-647-5951 Do not confuse with companies with the same or similar name in Middleburg, VT, Amstgerdam, NY, New York, NY, Sparks, NV
E-mail: RBIbooks@aol.com
Web site: http://www.RainbowBooksInc.com
Dist(s): **Baker & Taylor Bks.**
Book Clearing Hse.

Rainbow Bridge Publishing, *(1-887923; 1-932210)* Orders Addr.: P.O. Box 571470, Salt Lake City, UT 84157-1470 USA Tel 801-268-8887; Fax: 801-268-2770; Toll Free: 800-598-1441; Edit Addr.: P.O. Box 571470, Salt Lake Cty, UT 84157-1470 USA
E-mail: danell@rbpbooks.com
Web site: http://www.rbpbooks.com
Dist(s): **Baker & Taylor Bks.**
Midpoint Trade Bks., Inc.

Rainbow Communications, *(0-9725479; 0-9728737)* 417 NW Hemlock Ave., Corvallis, OR 97330 USA Tel 541-753-3335
E-mail: varsell4@attbi.com.

Rainbow Dancer *See* **Redwoods Pr.**

Rainbow Educational Media, Inc., *(0-942669; 1-56701)* Div. of Charles Clark Co., Inc., 1020 Falls Bridge Dr., Raleigh, NC 27614-8938 USA (SAN 667-1683) Toll Free: 800-331-4047
E-mail: rb@rainbowedumedia.com
Web site: http://www.rainbowedumedia.com.

Rainbow Educational Video, Incorporated *See* **Rainbow Educational Media, Inc.**

Rainbow Hse. Publishing, *(1-893659)* Orders Addr.: P.O. Box 5360, Bridgeport, CT 06604 USA; Edit Addr.: 690 W. Jackson Ave., Bridgeport, CT 06604 USA (SAN 299-8211) Tel 203-334-0646; Fax: 203-368-4012; Toll Free: 800-361-2609
E-mail: rainbow.house@snet.net
Web site: http://www.RainbowHousePublishing.com
Dist(s): **Baker & Taylor Bks.**
Quality Bks., Inc.

Rainbow Morning Music Alternatives, *(0-938663; 0-9615696)* 2121 Fairland Rd., Silver Spring, MD 20904 USA (SAN 218-2963) Tel 301-384-9207; Fax: 312-337-5985; Toll Free: 800-881-4741
E-mail: barrylou@ziplink.net
Web site: http://www.barrylou.com
Dist(s): **Independent Pubs. Group.**

Rainbow Pony Publishing, *(0-9728871)* 368 S. McCaslin Blvd., PMB No. 226, Louisville, CO 80027 USA.

Rainbow Pony Publising *See* **Rainbow Pony Publishing**

Rainbow Pr., *(0-9665140)* 215 Maple St., Bangor, ME 04401-4087 USA Do not confuse with ompanies with the same name in Southhampton, NY, Snover, MI, Sparta NJ, Fayetteville, NY, Saco, ME, Montgomery, MN, Clackamas, OR, Snover, MI, Independence, WI.

Rainbow Pride Pr., *(0-9703988)* 6525 Gunpark Dr., Suite 150-117, Boulder, CO 80301 USA Tel 303-267-2155; Fax: 303-543-0026
E-mail: editorrpp@aol.com; EditorRPP@aol.com
Web site: http://www.RainbowPridePress.com
Dist(s): **Baker & Taylor Bks.**

Rainbow Project, Inc., The, *(1-931273)* 831 E. Washington Ave., Madison, WI 53703 USA Tel 608-255-7356; Fax: 608-255-0457
E-mail: darren@rainbowproject.bizland.com
Web site: http://www.rainbowproject.bizland.com.

Rainbow Publishers *See* **Rainbow Pubs. & Legacy Pr.**

Rainbow Pubs. & Legacy Pr., *(0-937282; 1-885358; 1-58411)* Orders Addr.: P.O. Box 261129, San Diego, CA 92196 USA (SAN 256-4718) Tel 858-668-3260; Fax: 858-668-3328; Toll Free Fax: 800-331-0297; Toll Free: 800-323-7337; Edit Addr.: P.O. Box 70130, Richmond, VA 23255-0130 USA ; *Imprints:* Legacy Press (Lgacy Pr)
E-mail: rainbowed@earthlink.net; drmiley@juno.com
Web site: http://www.rainbowpublishers.com; http://www.shipping via media mail or using your shipper number
Dist(s): **Appalachian Bible Co.**
Spring Arbor Distributors, Inc.

Rainbow Star Publishing, *(0-9718538)* P.O. Box 1485, Monroe, NC 28111 USA Tel 704-226-1013 (phone/fax)
E-mail: rainbowstar11111@msn.com.

Rainbow Valley Publishing Co., *(0-9748558)* 2189 Hwy. 90 W., Sulphur, LA 70663 USA Tel 337-528-1157.

Rainbow Write! Publishing, *(0-9666317)* P.O. Box 211805, Royal Palm Beach, FL 33421 USA Tel 561-682-9884; Fax: 561-682-9826.

RainbowBrush, LLC (CAN) *(0-9734981) Dist. by* **Biblio Dist.**

Raincoast Bk. Distribution (CAN) *(0-920417; 1-55192; 1-895714) Dist. by* **Perseus Dist.**

Raindrop Bks., *(0-9766129)* 423 Hicks St., No. 6-H, Brooklyn, NY 11201 USA Tel 718-855-2918
E-mail: lgliessner@aol.com.

Raining Popcorn Media, *(0-9797304)* P.O. Box 91244, San Antonio, TX 78209 USA Tel 210-320-0548; Toll Free: 866-503-3088
E-mail: lisa@rainingpopcorn.com; info@rainingopcorn.com
Web site: http://www.RainingPopcorn.com.

Raintree, *(1-4109)* Orders Addr.: 6277 Sea Harbor Dr. 5th Flr., Orlando, FL 32887 USA Toll Free Fax: 877-578-2638; 888-801-8299 (Online Orders); Toll Free: 888-363-4266; 888-677-7357 (Online Orders) Do not confuse with Raintree in Memphis, TN
E-mail: heinemanninfo@hil.com
Web site: http://www.raintreelibrary.com/; http://www.heinemannlibrary.com.

Raintree Steck-Vaughn Publishers *See* **Steck-Vaughn**

Rainy Day Bks. *Imprint of* **Purple Chickie Pr.**

Rainy Day Women Pr., *(1-879082)* Orders Addr.: P.O. Box 1085, Willits, CA 95490-1085 USA; Edit Addr.: 60 S. Humboldt, Willits, CA 95490 USA Tel 707-459-6349.

Rairarubia Bks., *(0-9712206)* 1000 San Diego Rd., Santa Barbara, CA 93103 USA Fax: 805-966-4697
E-mail: raira@silcom.com
Web site: http://www.rairarubia.com.

Raise Giant Frogs Publishing, *(0-9722885)* 211 Alplaus Ave., Alplaus, NY 12008 USA (SAN 255-139X)
E-mail: ben@raisegiantfrogs.com
Web site: http://www.raisegiantfrogs.com.

Rakowski, Diane, *(0-9760194)* 9100 Tejon St., No. 2, Denver, CO 80260-6728 USA
E-mail: dsjsit@juno.com.

Raku Bks., *(0-615)* Orders Addr.: P.O. Box 51954, Palo Alto, CA 94303 USA
E-mail: rapimus@yahoo.com.

Rallsop Publishing Company *See* **Ithaca Pr.**

RAM Pubns. & Distribution, *(0-9630785; 0-9703860)* Bergamot Sta., 2525 Michigan Ave., No. A2, Santa Monica, CA 90404 USA (SAN 298-2641) Tel 310-453-0043; Fax: 310-264-4888
E-mail: rampub@gte.net.

Rama Pr., Inc., *(1-892316)* Orders Addr.: 5455 Wilshire Blvd., Suite 1011, Los Angeles, CA 90036 USA; Edit Addr.: 1114 23rd St., Apt. 3, Los Angeles, CA 90036 USA Tel 213-939-3544; Fax: 213-939-7730; Toll Free: 888-695-4886; c/o Stern, Hammer, Shaldino & Associates, 15255 Venture Blvd., Suite 850, Encino, CA 91436-2394
E-mail: ramapress@kitto.com
Web site: http://www.kitto.com.

Ramona's Bk. Co. *Imprint of* **RBC Publishing Co., Inc.**

Rams Horn Bks., *(1-879911)* Orders Addr.: Rams Horn Mountain, Box 20622, Estes Park, CO 80511 USA Tel 970-586-3509; Edit Addr.: 1460 Front Nine Dr., Unit D, Fort Collins, CO 80525 USA Tel 970-223-6981.

Ranch Gate Bks., *(0-9618660)* 2409 Dormarion, Austin, TX 78703 USA (SAN 668-4033) Tel 512-476-2185.

Ranch Works, *(1-892221)* Orders Addr.: P.O. Box 23565, Columbia, SC 29224-3565 USA Tel 803-736-9797; Fax: 803-736-5362; Edit Addr.: 204 Beaver Dam Rd., Columbia, SC 29223 USA
E-mail: ranchworks@sciencespiders.com
Web site: http://www.sciencespiders.com
Dist(s): **Baker & Taylor Bks.**

Rancho Santa Ana Botanic Garden, *(0-9605808)* 1500 N. College Ave., Claremont, CA 91711-3157 USA (SAN 220-1836) Tel 909-625-8767; Fax: 909-626-7670
E-mail: richard.chute@cgu.edu
Web site: http://www.rsabg.org.

†RAND Corp., The, *(0-8330)* Orders Addr.: P.O. Box 2138, Santa Monica, CA 90407-2138 USA (SAN 218-9291) Tel 310-393-0411; Fax: 310-393-4818; Edit Addr.: 1776 Main St., Santa Monica, CA 90407-2138 USA (SAN 665-763X)
E-mail: jwarren@rand.org; correspondence@rand.org; randell@rand.org
Web site: http://www.rand.org
Dist(s): **National Bk. Network**
NetLibrary, Inc.; *CIP.*

†Rand McNally, *(0-528)* Orders Addr.: P.O. Box 1906, Skokie, IL 60076 USA Fax: 847-329-6139; Toll Free Fax: 800-934-3479 (Orders); Toll Free: 800-333-0136 (ext. 4771); 800-678-7263 (Orders)
E-mail: Education@randmcnally.com
Web site: http://www.randmcnally.com
Dist(s): **Bryant Altman Map, Inc.**
Map Link; *CIP.*

Randall, Cheri, *(0-9767213)* P.O. Box 2176, Belton, TX 76513 USA Tel 254-939-8776 (phone/fax)
E-mail: hrandallmail@aol.com
Web site: http://www.harveyrandall.org.

Randall Fraser Publishing *See* **RandallFraser Publishing**

Randall Hse. Pubns., *(0-89265)* 114 Bush Rd., Nashville, TN 37217 USA (SAN 207-5040) Tel 615-361-1221; Fax: 615-367-0535; Toll Free: 800-877-7030
E-mail: keith@randallhouse.com
Web site: http://www.randallhouse.com.

†Randall, Peter E. Pub., *(0-914339; 1-931807)* Orders Addr.: P.O. Box 4726, Portsmouth, NH 03802 USA; Edit Addr.: 5 Greenleaf Woods Dr. #102, Portsmouth, NH 03801 USA (SAN 223-0496) Tel 603-431-5667; Fax: 603-431-3566
E-mail: deidre@perpublisher.com
Web site: http://www.perpublisher.com
Dist(s): **Biblio Distribution**
Enfield Publishing & Distribution Co., Inc.; *CIP.*

RandallFraser Publishing, *(0-9745143)* 2082 Business Ctr. Dr., Suite 163, Irvine, CA 92612 USA Fax: 949-250-9020; Toll Free: 866-339-3999
E-mail: algreen51@comcast.net
Web site: http://www.Deweydooit.com
Dist(s): **National Bk. Network.**

R&B Trading Co., *(0-9718784)* 7619 Belmont Stakes Dr., Midlothian, VA 23112 USA (SAN 254-4741) Tel 804-739-8073; Fax: 775-243-6578
E-mail: dwindsofdestiny@aol.com
Web site: http://www.RnBtradingco.net/home.html
Dist(s): **Baker & Taylor Bks.**

Randell Productions, Inc., *(0-9677781)* P.O. Box 788, Ponca City, OK 74602-0788 USA Tel 580-767-1512
E-mail: info@randellproductions.com.

Randle, Ian Pubs., Inc., *(0-9729358; 0-9742155; 0-9753529)* 25 SE Second Ave., Suite 1105, Miami, FL 33131 USA Tel 305-358-1588; Fax: 305-358-1589
E-mail: info@ianrandlepublishers.com
Web site: http://www.ianrandlepublishers.com.

Randolph Publishing, *(0-9712158)* 9531 SW 189th Ct., Dunnellon, FL 34432 USA Tel 352-489-6104 Do not confuse with companies with the same or similar names in Good Hope, GA, Dallas, TX, Indianapolis, IN, Princeton, TX.

Randolph Publishing, *(1-932258)* Orders Addr.: P.O. Box 160, Good Hope, GA 30641-160 USA (SAN 254-9522) Tel 770-356-0655; Fax: 404-627-2322 Do not confuse with companies with the same or similar names in Dunnellon, FL, Dallas, TX, Indianapolis, IN, Princeton, TX
E-mail: randolphpublishing@EarthLink.net
Web site: http://www.RandolphPublishing.com
Dist(s): **Baker & Taylor Bks.**

Random House *Imprint of* **Random House Publishing Group**

Random House Adult Trade Publishing Group *See* **Random House Publishing Group**

Random Hse. Audio Publishing Group, Div. of Random House, Inc., Orders Addr.: 400 Hahn Rd., Westminster, MD 21157 USA (SAN 201-3975) Tel 410-848-1900; Toll Free: 800-726-0600; Edit Addr.: 1745 Broadway, New York, NY 10036 USA Tel 212-782-9000 ; *Imprints:* Listening Library (Listening Lib)
Web site: http://www.randomhouse.com/audio
Dist(s): **Random Hse., Inc.**

Random Hse. Children's Bks., Div. of Random Hse., Inc., Orders Addr.: 400 Hahn Rd., Westminster, MD 21157 USA Tel 410-848-1900; Toll Free: 800-726-0600; Edit Addr.: 1745 Broadway, 10th Flr., New York, NY 10019 USA Tel 212-782-8491; 212-782-9000; Fax: 212-782-9577; Toll Free: 800-200-3552 ; *Imprints:* Delacorte Books for Young Readers (Delacorte Bks); Lamb, Wendy (Wendy Lamb); Fickling, David Books (D Fickling Bks); RH Para Ninos (ParaNinos); Crown Books For Young Readers (CBYR); LucasBooks for Young Readers (LucasBks Young); Dell Books for Young Readers (DBYR); Knopf Books for Young Readers (Knop); RH/Disney (RH Disney); Golden Books (Gold Bks); Random House Books for Young Readers (RHBYR); Bantam Books for Young Readers (BBYngRead); Doubleday Books for Young Readers (Doubleday Bk Yng); Yearling (Year); Dragonfly Books (Dragonfly Bks); Laurel Leaf (LaurelLeaf); Skylark (SkylarkRH); Starfire (Starfire); Bolder Books (BolderBks); Schwartz & Wade Books (Schwartz & Wade); Golden/Disney (Gold Disney); Robin Corey Books (Robin Corey); Golden Inspirational (Gold Inspir)
E-mail: pmuller@randomhouse.com; kids@random.com
Web site: http://www.randomhouse.com/kids/
Dist(s): **Libros Sin Fronteras**
Random Hse., Inc.

Random House Foreign Language Publishing, Orders Addr.: 400 Hahn Rd., Westminster, MD 21157 USA Tel 410-848-1900; Toll Free: 800-726-0600 (customer service); Edit Addr.: 1745 Broadway, New York, NY 10019 USA Tel 212-782-9000 ; *Imprints:* New Media German Language (NewMed German)
Dist(s): **Random Hse., Inc.**

†Random Hse., Inc., *(0-307; 0-345; 0-375; 0-385; 0-394; 0-440; 0-449; 0-517; 0-553; 0-593; 0-609; 0-676; 0-679; 0-7364; 0-7366; 0-7615; 0-7679; 0-7704; 0-8041; 0-8052; 0-8129; 0-87637; 0-87665; 0-87788; 0-88070; 0-913369; 0-914629; 0-930014; 0-945564; 1-57082; 1-57673; 1-57856; 1-878867; 1-884536; 1-885305; 1-58836; 1-4000; 1-59052; 1-4159)* Div. of Bertelsmann AG, Orders Addr.: 400 Hahn Rd., Westminster, MD 21157 USA (SAN 202-5515) Tel 410 848 1900; Toll Free Fax: 800 659 2436; Toll Free: 800 726 0600 (customer service/orders); Edit Addr.: 1745 Broadway, New York, NY 10019 USA (SAN 202-5507) Tel 212 782 9000; Fax: 212 302 7985 ; *Imprints:* Golden Books (Golden Books)
E-mail: customerservice@randomhouse.com
Web site: http://www.randomhouse.com
Dist(s): **Giron Bks.**
Libros Sin Fronteras
NetLibrary, Inc.
Sony CONNECT, Inc.; *CIP.*

Random Hse. Information Group, Div. of Random Hse., Inc., Orders Addr.: 400 Hahn Rd., Westminster, MD 21157 USA Tel 410-848-1900; Toll Free: 800-726-0600; Edit Addr.: 1745 Broadway, New York, NY 10019 USA Tel 212-751-2600; Toll Free: 800-726-0600 ; *Imprints:* Random House Puzzles & Games (RHPG); Prima Games (PrimGames); Living Language (LivingLang); Princeton Review (Prince Review)
E-mail: customerservice@randomhouse.com
Web site: http://www.randomhouse.com/
Dist(s): **Bilingual Pubns. Co., The**
Ediciones Universal
Libros Sin Fronteras
Random Hse., Inc.

Random Hse. Large Print, Div. of Random House, Inc., Orders Addr.: 400 Hahn Rd., Westminster, MD 21157 USA Tel 410-848-1900 Toll Free: 800-726-0600 (customer service); Edit Addr.: 1745 Broadway, New York, NY 10019 USA Tel 212-782-9000 ; *Imprints:* Random House Large Print (RHLP)
E-mail: editor@randomhouse.com; customerservice@randomhouse.com
Web site: http://www.randomhouse.com
Dist(s): **Libros Sin Fronteras**
Random Hse., Inc.
Thorndike Pr.

Random House Large Print *Imprint of* **Random Hse. Large Print**

Company

Random House Mondadori (ESP) Dist. by Random.

Random House Publishing Group, Orders Addr.: 400 Hahn Rd., Westminster, MD 21157 USA (SAN 852-5471) Tel 410-848-1900; 410-386-7560; Toll Free: 800-726-0600; Edit Addr.: 1745 Broadway, New York, NY 10019 USA Tel 212-751-2600; Fax: 212-572-4949; Toll Free: 800-726-0600 ; *Imprints:* Modern Library (Mod Lib); Villard Books (Villard Books); Random House (Random House); Del Rey (Del Rey); Ballantine Books (Ballantine Bks); Fawcett (Fawcett); Ivy Books (Ivy)
E-mail: lstark@randomhouse.com
Dist(s): **Libros Sin Fronteras**
Random Hse., Inc.

Random House Reference & Information Publishing *See* **Random Hse. Information Group**

†Random Hse. Value Publishing, Div. of Random House, Inc., Orders Addr.: 400 Hahn Rd., Westminster, MD 21157 USA Tel 410-848-1900 Toll Free: 800-726-0600 (Customer Service); Edit Addr.: 280 Park Ave., 11th Flr., New York, NY 10017 USA Tel 212 572 2400 ; *Imprints:* Gramercy (Gram); Testament (Test); Anything Books (AnyBks); Children's Classics (Chld Class); Crescent (Crescnt); Derrydale (Derry)
Web site: http://www.randomhouse.com
Dist(s): **Random Hse., Inc.**; *CIP.*

Random Hse. (GBR) *(0-09; 0-224; 0-7126; 1-86046; 1-84657; 1-84655) Dist. by* **Trafalgar.**

Random Hse. (GBR) *(0-09; 0-224; 0-7126; 1-86046; 1-84657; 1-84655) Dist. by* **IPG Chicago.**

Random Hse. Bks. for Young Readers *Imprint of* **Random Hse. Children's Bks.**

Random Hse. Children's Bks. (GBR) Dist. by Trafalgar.

Random Hse. Children's Bks. (GBR) Dist. by Random.

Random Hse. Children's Bks. (GBR) Dist. by IPG Chicago.

Random Hse. of Canada, Ltd. (CAN) *(0-09; 0-307; 0-375; 0-394; 0-676; 0-679; 0-7704; 1-4000) Dist. by* **Random.**

Random Hse. Puzzles & Games *Imprint of* **Random Hse. Information Group**

R&R Endeavors, Inc., *(0-9740444)* Orders Addr.: P.O. Box 301, Indianapolis, IN 46217 USA; Edit Addr.: 1350C W. Southport Rd., Indianapolis, IN 46217 USA
E-mail: editor@writerpublishing.com
Web site: http://www.writerpublishing.com.

R&R Pubns., *(0-9723652)* 13129 Arthur Wall, Grass Valley, CA 95949 USA Tel 530-268-2334; Fax: 530-888-7899.

Ransom Publishing Ltd. (GBR) *(1-84167; 1-900127; 1-84671) Dist. by* **Intl Pubs Mktg.**

RAPC - Sparkle & Shine Project, *(0-9760282)* 116 Jackson St., Sylva, NC 28779 USA Tel 828-586-0661; Fax: 828-586-0663
Web site: http://www.sparkle-shine.com.

RAPHA, Inc., *(0-9740081)* Orders Addr.: P.O. Box 1184, Groton, CT 06340 USA Tel 860-938-2599; Edit Addr.: 45 South Rd., Apt. 9A, Groton, CT 06340 USA Tel 860-514-7266
E-mail: joyindamornin@earthlink.net.

Rapha Publishing, *(0-9763686)* 431 Beechwood Ave., Carnegie, PA 15106 USA Tel 412-249-0669
E-mail: raphapublishing@yahoo.com
Web site: http://www.raphapublishing.com/.

Raphael, Morris Bks., *(0-9608866)* 1404 Bayou Side Dr., New Iberia, LA 70560 USA (SAN 241-0737) Tel 337-369-3220
Dist(s): **Cajun Country Distributors**
Forest Sales & Distributing Co.

Rapids Christian Pr., Inc., *(0-915374)* P.O. Box 717, Ferndale, WA 98248-0717 USA (SAN 205-0986) Tel 360-384-1747
E-mail: gundersonwv@aol.com.

Rare Bird Pr., *(0-9665281)* 240 Pennsylvania Ave., Yonkers, NY 10707-2219 USA Tel 914-779-4881; Fax: 914-395-1636
Web site: http://starry.com/rarebird/
Dist(s): **Baker & Taylor Bks.**

R.A.R.E. TALES, *(0-9760303)* 14120 River Rd., Fort Myers, FL 33905-7436 USA
E-mail: kphchance@comcast.net
Web site: http://www.raretales.net.

Rarecity Pr., *(0-9760959)* 17 Yardley Dr., Medford, NJ 08055 USA Tel 201-788-9746
E-mail: jason@rarecity.com.

Rasa Music Co., *(0-9766219)* 409 Glenview Rd., Glenview, IL 60025-3262 USA Tel 847-486-0416; Fax: 847-657-9459
E-mail: lleifer@northpark.edu
Web site: http://www.admin.northpark.edu/lleifer/.

Rascal Publishing, *(0-9671996)* HC 84 Box 50, Canyon City, OR 97820-9701 USA Tel 541-575-0545; Fax: 541-575-2915.

Rascal Treehouse Publishing, *(0-9759321)* 1523 Morris St. - Suite 330, Lincoln Park, MI 48146 USA
E-mail: lscoffman@lscoffman.com
Web site: http://www.lscoffman.com.

Raspberry Pr., Ltd., *(0-929568)* Orders Addr.: P.O. Box One, Dixon, IL 61021-0001 USA (SAN 250-2194) Tel 815-288-4910; Edit Addr.: 1989 Grand Detour Rd., Dixon, IL 61021 USA (SAN 250-2208)
E-mail: raspberrypresslimited@yahoo.com
Dist(s): **Baker & Taylor Bks.**
Brodart Co.
Quality Bks., Inc.

Ratliff, Thomas G., *(0-9704865)* 190 Ethelrob Cir., Carlisle, OH 45005 USA Tel 937-746-9948
E-mail: tdratliff@netzero.net.

Rattle OK Pubns., *(0-9626210; 1-883965)* Orders Addr.: P.O. Box 5614, Napa, CA 94581 USA (SAN 297-5475) Tel 707-253-9641; Edit Addr.: 296 Homewood Ave., Napa, CA 94558-5617 USA
Dist(s): **Gryphon Hse., Inc.**

Ratway, Michael, *(0-9724698)* 9 Clover Rd., Apalachin, NY 13732-2553 USA
E-mail: yawtar@earthlink.net
Web site: http://www.earthlink.net/~yawtar.

Raven Bks. *Imprint of* **Raven Productions**

Raven Productions, *(0-9764091)* 325 E. 2550 N, Suite 117, North Ogden, UT 84414 USA Tel 801-782-0872 ; *Imprints:* Raven Books (RavenBks) Do not confuse with companies with the same or similar name in Delta Junction, AK
E-mail: gshaw@post.harvard.edu.

Raven Productions, Inc., *(0-9677057; 0-9766264; 0-9794202; 0-9801045)* P.O. Box 188, Ely, MN 55731 USA Fax: 218-343-3423 Do not confuse with companies with the same or similar name in Delta Junction, AK, North Ogden, UT
E-mail: raven@ravenwords.com
Dist(s): **Adventure Pubns., Inc.**

Raven Publishing *See* **Raven Publishing Inc. of Montana**

Raven Publishing Inc. of Montana, *(0-9714161; 0-9772525)* Orders Addr.: P.O. Box 2866, Norris, MT 59745 USA (SAN 254-5861) Tel 406-685-3545; Fax: 406-685-3599; Toll Free: 866-685-3545; Edit Addr.: 121 Cherry Creek Rd., Norris, MT 59745 USA Do not confuse with companies with the same or similar name in Bronx, NY, Pittsfield, MA
E-mail: info@ravenpublishing.net
Web site: http://www.ravenpublishing.net
Dist(s): **Baker & Taylor Bks.**
Books West
Distributors, The
Follett Library Resources
Partners/West
Quality Bks., Inc.
Wolverine Distributing, Inc.
Western International, Inc.

Raven Rocks Pr., *(0-9615961)* 53650 Belmont Ridge, Beallsville, OH 43716 USA (SAN 696-5679) Tel 740-926-1481 (phone/fax)
E-mail: jmrpress@1st.net.

Raven Tree Pr., *(0-9701107; 0-9720192; 0-9724973; 0-9741992; 0-9770906; 0-9794462; 0-9795477)* Div. of Delta Systems Co., Inc., 1400 Miller Pkwy., Mc Henry, IL 60050 USA (SAN 253-6005) Toll Free: 877-256-0579
E-mail: dawn@raventreepress.com
Web site: http://www.raventreepress.com
Dist(s): **Baker & Taylor Bks.**
Follett Media Distribution.

Ravenhawk Bks., *(1-893660)* Div. of The 6DOF Group, 7739 E. Broadway Blvd. Suite 95, Tucson, AZ 85710 USA Tel 520-886-9885 (phone/fax); Toll Free: 800-520-9885
E-mail: 76673.3165@compuserve.com
Web site: http://www.ravenhawk.org.

RavenMark, *(0-9713998)* 26 State St. Ste. 10, Montpelier, VT 05602-2943 USA
E-mail: basho@together.net.

Ravensburger Buchverlag Otto Maier GmbH (DEU) *(3-473) Dist. by* **Distribks Inc.**

Ravenscroft Pr., *(0-9638603)* Orders Addr.: P.O. Box 270, Winchester, MA 01890 USA Tel 617-512-2264; Fax: 781-729-4710; Edit Addr.: 9 Ravenscroft Rd., Winchester, MA 01890 USA
E-mail: tmarotta@comcast.net
Web site: http://www.terrymarotta.com; http://www.thetrailofbreadcrumbs.com.

Ravenstone Pr., *(0-9659712)* Orders Addr.: P.O. Box 6382, Sun City Center, FL 33571-6382 USA Tel 813-633-5759; Fax: 813-633-6347; Edit Addr.: 2056 Berry Roberts Dr., Sun City Ctr, FL 33573-6130 USA
E-mail: raven@ravenstonepress.com
Web site: http://www.ravenstonepress.com.

RavensYard Publishing, Ltd., *(0-9667883; 1-928928)* Orders Addr.: 9900 Timmark Ct., Vienna, VA 22181 USA
E-mail: rtcjr@bellatlantic.net
Web site: http://www.ravensyard.com.

Ravette Publishing, Ltd. (GBR) *(0-948456; 1-85304; 0-906710; 1-84161) Dist. by* **Parkwest Pubns.**

Ray Greer, Mary Lou, *(0-9749161)* P.O. Box 1740, Eagar, AZ 85925 USA Tel 520-850-6209.

Rayles, Jason, *(0-9725651)* 322 Summer St., 5th Flr., Boston, MA 02210-1705 USA
E-mail: jason@23grand.com
Web site: http://www.23grand.com.

Raynestorm Bks. *Imprint of* **Silver Rose Publishing**

Rayo *Imprint of* **HarperCollins Pubs.**

Rays of Hope, *(0-9658766)* P.O. Box 336, Angwim, CA 94508 USA Tel 707-965-9400
E-mail: Romigram@aol.com.

Rayve Productions, Inc., *(1-877810)* Orders Addr.: P.O. Box 726, Windsor, CA 95492 USA (SAN 248-4250) Tel 707-838-6200; 707-838-2740 (phone/fax); Fax: 707-838-2220; Toll Free: 800-852-4890
E-mail: rayvepro@aol.com
Web site: http://www.rayveproductions.com; http://www.rayvepro.com; http://www.foodandwinebooks.com
Dist(s): **Baker & Taylor Bks.**
Book Wholesalers, Inc.
Brodart Co.
Follett Library Resources
Majors, J. A. Co.
Quality Bks., Inc.
Sunbelt Pubns., Inc.
Unique Bks., Inc.

Razorbill *Imprint of* **Penguin Group (USA) Inc.**

RBA Libros, S.A. (ESP) *(84-89662; 84-7871; 84-7901; 84-85351) Dist. by* **Lectorum Pubns.**

RBA Libros, S.A. (ESP) *(84-89662; 84-7871; 84-7901; 84-85351) Dist. by* **Santillana.**

RC2 Corp., *(1-890647)* 314 W Superior, 6th Flr., Chicago, IL 60610 USA Tel 312-470-7700; Fax: 312-470-9400; Toll Free: 800-704-8697
E-mail: rcs@rc2corp.com; credit@rc2corp.com
Web site: http://www.learningtoys.com; http://www.learningcurve.com.

RDM, *(1-931984; 1-60382)* Div. of General Council of the Assemblies of God, 1722 S. Glenstone W-163, Springfield, MO 65804 USA Tel 417-881-4698; Fax: 417-881-1037
E-mail: rdmlit@rdmlit.org; office@rdmlit.org
Web site: http://www.rdmlit.org.

RDM Publishing, *(0-9766038)* 605 CR 1040E, Norris City, IL 62869 USA Tel 618-265-3225
E-mail: earthart@midwest.net.

RDR Bks., *(0-9636161; 1-57143)* 1487 Glen Ave., Muskegon, MI 49441-3101 USA; 960 S. Sherman, Muskegon, MI 49441
E-mail: books@rdrbooks.com
Web site: http://www.rdrbooks.com
Dist(s): **Alpen Bks**
American West Bks.
Baker & Taylor Bks.
Book Wholesalers, Inc.
Bookazine Co., Inc.
Brodart Co.
Follett Library Resources
Koen-Levy Bk. Wholesalers LLC
New Leaf Distributing Co., Inc.
Quality Bks., Inc.
Sunbelt Pubns., Inc.
Unique Bks., Inc.
Yankee Bk. Peddler, Inc.

Reach Pr., *(0-9660148)* Orders Addr.: P.O. Box 764, Hershey, PA 17033 USA Tel 717-838-2904; Fax: 717-838-7260; Toll Free: 888-707-3224; Edit Addr.: 64 Palmyra Rd., Campbelltown, PA 17010 USA
Dist(s): **Baker & Taylor Bks.**

Reaching Beyond, Inc., *(0-9741893)* Orders Addr.: P.O. Box 12364, Columbus, GA 31917-2364 USA Tel 706-573-5942; Fax: 706-562-0487; Edit Addr.: P.O. Box 12364, Columbus, GA 31917-2364 USA
E-mail: nccjohnson@hotmail.com
Web site: http://www.reachingbeyond.net
Dist(s): **Baker & Taylor Bks.**
Book Clearing Hse.

Reachment Pubns., *(1-888141)* 79 Whittington Dr., Palm Coast, FL 32164 USA Tel 386-447-0324; Fax: 386-446-7579
E-mail: Reachment@msn.com
Web site: http://www-gout-haters.com.

Read 2 Children, *(0-9755839)* P.O. Box 4113, Warren, NJ 07059 USA Tel 732-805-9073
Web site: http://www.read2children.com.

Read All Over Publishing, *(0-9728779)* 17705 Ingleside Rd., Cleveland, OH 44119 USA Tel 216-486-8615 ext. 3
E-mail: readallover@sbcglobal.net.

Read & Write Pr., *(0-9723511)* 730 W. 28th Ave., Eugene, OR 97405 USA Tel 541-686-0800
Web site: http://www.readandwrite.net.

Read It Again Books *See* **Read-It-To-Me Publishing**

Read Publishing, *(0-9762868)* Orders Addr.: 3918 Dorcas Dr., Nashville, TN 37215 USA Tel 615-279-9988; Fax: 615-385-2651
E-mail: snea5001@bellsouth.net; jennie0120@aol.com.

Read Street Publishing, Inc., *(0-942929)* Div. of Tropical Dining Inc., 133 W. Read St., Baltimore, MD 21201 USA (SAN 667-8505) Tel 410-837-1116; Fax: 410-727-3174
E-mail: editor@omnititles.com; editor@tablespr.com; editor@readstreetpublishing.com
Web site: http://www.omnititles.com; http://www.tablespr.com; http://www.readstreetpublishing.com.

Readers Are Leaders, *(0-9673625)* 908 Ashland Dr., Mesquite, TX 75149 USA Tel 972-288-5806 (phone/fax)
E-mail: rlgant@airmail.net.

Readers Are Leaders U.S.A., Inc., *(0-9768035; 0-9800397)* 2315 SW 5th Ave., Miami, FL 33129-1939 USA (SAN 855-0557)
Web site: http://www.readersareleadersusa.net.

†Reader's Digest Assn., Inc., The, *(0-7621; 0-89577; 0-86438)* Orders Addr.: Reader's Digest Rd., Pleasantville, NY 10570 USA (SAN 282-2091) Toll Free: 800-463-8820; 800-334-9599 (Magazines); 800-635-5006 (Customer Service)
Web site: http://www.readersdigest.com
Dist(s): **Penguin Group (USA) Inc.**
Simon & Schuster
Simon & Schuster, Inc.; *CIP.*

Reader's Digest Children's Bks. *Imprint of* **Reader's Digest Children's Publishing, Inc.**

Reader's Digest Children's Publishing, Inc., *(0-276; 0-7621; 0-88705; 0-88850; 0-89577; 1-57584; 1-57619; 0-7944)* Subs. of Reader's Digest Assn., Inc., Reader's Digest Rd., Pleasantville, NY 10570-7000 USA (SAN 283-2143) Tel 914-244-4800; Fax: 914-244-4841 ; *Imprints:* Reader's Digest Children's Books (RD Childrens); Reader's Digest Young Families, Incorporated (RDYF)
Web site: http://www.readersdigestkids.com
Dist(s): **Continental Bk. Co., Inc.**
Simon & Schuster, Inc.
Simon & Schuster Children's Publishing.

Reader's Digest Young Families, Inc. *Imprint of* **Reader's Digest Children's Publishing, Inc.**

Reader's Digest Young Families, Inc., *(1-59939)* One Reader's Digest Rd., Pleasantville, NY 10570-7000 USA (SAN 256-9116) Tel 914-244-4872; Fax: 914-244-4890
E-mail: sharon_yates@rd.com
Web site: http://rd.com.

Reader's Pr., *(0-9638494)* 214 S. Adams, Hillsboro, KS 67063 USA Tel 316-947-5702; Fax: 316-947-5940
E-mail: psdirect@southwind.net; joel@hillsborofreepress.com
Web site: http://www2.southwind.net/~psdirect/.

Reader's Writes, *(0-9679979)* R. R. 2, Box 23, Ashton, NE 68817 USA Tel 308-745-1536
E-mail: garvel@micrord.com.

Reading & O'Reilly/Wilton Art Programs, *(0-924041)* P.O. Box 646, Botsford, CT 06404-0646 USA (SAN 252-1172) Tel 203-270-6536; Fax: 203-270-5569; Toll Free: 800-458-4274
E-mail: ror@wiltonart.com
Web site: http://www.Wiltonart.com.

Reading Co., The *Imprint of* **Rhoades & Assocs.**

Reading Gems, *(0-915988)* P.O. Box 806, Madison, WI 53701-0806 USA (SAN 207-6934).

Reading Matters, Inc., *(1-930654)* 806 Main St., Akron, PA 17501 USA Tel 717-859-5608; Fax: 717-859-3469; Toll Free: 888-255-6665 Do not confuse with companies with the same name in Brookline, MA, Denver, CO
E-mail: office@readingmatters.net
Web site: http://readingmatters.net.

Reading Reading Bks., LLC, *(1-933727)* P.O. Box 6654, Reading, PA 19610 USA
E-mail: service@readingreadingbooks.com; orangetabbycat2000@yahoo.com
Web site: http://www.readingreadingbooks.com.

Reading Realm, *(0-9665568)* Orders Addr.: P.O. Box 570245, Houston, TX 77257-0245 USA Tel 713-993-0254; Fax: 713-993-0258; Edit Addr.: 5342 Navarro St., Houston, TX 77056 USA
E-mail: babsbh@aol.com.

Reading Resc., *(0-9755561; 0-9795648)* 314 Knowles Hill Rd., Alexandria, NH 03222 USA (SAN 853-7771) Tel 603-744-5803 Do not confuse with Reading Resources, Inc. in Worthington, OH
E-mail: maglaberge@yahoo.com; readingrescources@metrocast.net.

Reading Rock Books *See* **Reading Rock, Inc.**

Reading Rock, Inc., *(1-929591)* P.O. Box 67, Athens, MI 49011 USA Tel 616-729-9440
Web site: http://www.Readingrockbook.com.

Reading Room Collection *Imprint of* **Rosen Publishing Group, Inc., The**

Reading Studio Pr., *(0-9767506)* 250 W. 90th St., Suite 12F, New York, NY 10024 USA Tel 212-724-6232
E-mail: readingstudio@aol.com
Web site: http://www.alphieandthealphabets.com.

Reading Wade Ink *See* **Hole in the Head Pr.**

Reading's Fun/Books are Fun, Limited *See* **Books Are Fun, Ltd.**

Read-It-To-Me Publishing, *(0-9700870)* P.O. Box 986, North Myrtle Beach, SC 29582 USA (SAN 253-2492) Tel 843-280-6875 Do not confuse with Read It Again Books, Hoover, AL
E-mail: readittome333@aol.com
Web site: http://www.read-it-to-me.com.

Ready Blade *Imprint of* **Blooming Tree Pr.**

Ready Writer Publishing, LLC, *(0-9748748)* P.O. Box 18197, Shreveport, LA 71138 USA Tel 318-636-1542
E-mail: readywriterpublishing@hotmail.com; satbeau1@bellsouth.net
Web site: http://www.Readywriterpublishing.com.

Reagent Pr. Echo *Imprint of* **Reagent Pr.**

Reagent Pr. Signature Editions *Imprint of* **Reagent Pr.**

Reagent Pr., *(1-57545)* Div. of RP Bks., Orders Addr.: P.O. Box 362, East Olympia, WA 98540 USA Fax: 360-413-7108 (orders) ; *Imprints:* Ruin Mist Publications (Ruin Mist Pubns); Reagent Press Signature Editions (Reagent Pr Sig Edns); Reagent Press Echo (Reagent Pr Echo)
E-mail: reagentpress@aol.com; rpressorders@aol.com
Web site: http://www.tvpress.com/; http://www.reagentpress.com/; http://www.ruinmist.com/; http://books.reagentpress.com/; http://audio.reagentpress.com/
Dist(s): **Baker & Taylor Bks.**
Lightning Source, Inc.

Reaktion Bks., Ltd. (GBR) *(0-948462; 1-86189) Dist. by* **Chicago Distribution Ctr.**

R.E.A.L. Pubns., *(0-9724503; 0-9748003)* 109 La Costa Dr., Georgetown, KY 40324 USA (SAN 255-867X) Tel 859-539-2463
E-mail: james.french@roadrunner.com
Web site: http://www.arealeducation.com.

R.E.A.L. Publishing *See* **R.E.A.L. Pubns.**

Realistically Speaking Publishing Co., *(0-9727874)* P.O. Box 3566, Cerritos, CA 90703-3566 USA Tel 562-674-2955
E-mail: info@realisticallyspeaking.net
Web site: http://www.realisticallyspeaking.net.

Reality Living Publishing, Inc., *(0-9643021; 1-888220)* 8720 E. 55th St., Kansas City, MO 64129 USA Tel 816-358-1515 ext 2062; Fax: 816-358-3439 ext 2062
E-mail: sehle@kcbt.org
Web site: http://www.realityliving.org.

Really Alive Bks., *(0-9648834)* P.O. Box 1669, Nederland, CO 80466 USA Tel 303-258-1900; Fax: 303-258-7726
E-mail: reallyalivebooks@earthlink.net.

Really Big Coloring Bks., Inc., *(0-9727833; 0-9729753; 0-9763186)* 224 N. Meramec, Saint Louis, MO 63105 USA Tel 314-725-1452; Fax: 314-725-3553; Toll Free: 800-244-2665 (1-800-Big-Book)
E-mail: wayne@bigcoloringbooks.com; ken@bigcoloringbooks.com
Web site: http://www.bigcoloringbook.com.

RealWord Pubns., *(0-9743088)* Orders Addr.: P.O. Box 931461, Norcross, GA 30093-1461 USA Fax: 678-406-9178; Edit Addr.: 6450 Indian Acres Trail, Norcross, GA 30093 USA
E-mail: wrcomm@comcast.net
Web site: http://www.climbeveryobstacle.com.

Rebecca's Bks., *(0-9744346)* P.O. Box 644, Watertown, WI 53094 USA.

Rebecca's Hse. Publishing, *(1-892263)* 2549 Waukegan Rd., Suite 111, Bannockburn, IL 60015 USA Tel 847-520-9976
E-mail: rebecca@rebeccashouse.com
Web site: http://www.rebeccashouse.com.

Rebel Butterfly Pr., *(0-9627986)* 1241 N. 3rd Ave., Tucson, AZ 85705 USA (SAN 254-4830) Tel 520-245-1544; Fax: 520-326-1956
E-mail: nico@rebelbutterflypress.com
Web site: http://www.rebelbutterflypress.com
Dist(s): **Baker & Taylor Bks.**

Rebel Press *See* **Little Dixie Publishing Co.**

Rebel Publishing, *(0-9705593)* 3560 Broadway, No. 902, Kansas City, MO 64111 USA Tel 816-529-3262; Fax: 816-254-2405
E-mail: writer401@aol.com
Web site: http://www.soulseternal.com.

Rebuilding Bks. *Imprint of* **Impact Pubs., Inc.**

Reclam, Philip jun., Verlag GmbH (DEU) *(3-15) Dist. by* **Intl Bk Import.**

Reconciliation Pr. *Imprint of* **Trinity Rivers Publishing, Inc.**

Recorded Bks., LLC, *(0-7887; 1-55690; 1-84197; 1-4025; 1-4193; 1-84505; 1-4281; 1-4361)* 270 Skipjack Rd., Prince Frederick, MD 20678 USA (SAN 111-3984) Toll Free: 800-638-1304
E-mail: recordedbooks@recordedbooks.com; mgarber@recordedbook.com
Web site: http://www.recordedbooks.com
Dist(s): **NetLibrary, Inc.**

Rector Pr., Ltd., *(0-7605; 0-934393; 1-57205)* Orders Addr.: 130 Rattlesnake Gutter Rd., Leverett, MA 01054-9726 USA (SAN 693-8108) Tel 413-367-0303 (International Book Sales)
E-mail: info@rectorpress.com
Web site: http://www.rectorpress.com.

Recursos, Ediciones (ESP) *(84-89984; 84-921663) Dist. by* **IPG Chicago.**

Red Barn Reading Inc., *(0-9753059)* P.O. Box 540, Alanson, MI 49706 USA
E-mail: thecathy@tm.net.

Red Bird Publishing, *(0-9665072)* Div. of Darlene Trew Crist Writing & Editorial Services, 54 Church Ln., Wickford, RI 02852-5004 USA Tel 401-295-1356; Fax: 401-295-2793.

Red Bird Publishing (GBR) *(1-902626) Dist. by* **Perseus Dist.**

Red Brick Learning, *(0-7368)* Div. of Coughlan Publishing, 151 Good Counsel Dr., P.O. Box 669, Mankato, MN 56002-0669 USA Toll Free Fax: 888-574-5570; Toll Free: 888-262-6135 ; *Imprints:* High Five (High Five)
Dist(s): **Capstone Pr., Inc.**

Red Bud Publishing, *(0-9759421)* 2425 Lakeshore Ct., Lebanon, IN 46052 USA.

Red Carpet Publishing, *(0-9719657; 0-9722829)* P.O. Box 309, Noblesville, IN 46061-0309 USA (SAN 255-755X) Tel 317-847-9553; Fax: 317-773-5375
Web site: http://www.redcarpetpublishing.com.

†Red Crane Bks., Inc., *(1-878610)* Orders Addr.: P.O. Box 33590, Santa Fe, NM 87954 USA; Edit Addr.: 2008 Rosina St., Suite C, Santa Fe, NM 87505 USA Tel 505-988-7070; Fax: 505-989-7476; Toll Free: 800-922-3392
E-mail: publish@redcrane.com
Web site: http://www.redcrane.com
Dist(s): **Consortium Bk. Sales & Distribution**
Continental Bk. Co., Inc.
Libros Sin Fronteras; *CIP.*

Red Cygnet Pr., *(1-60108)* 11858 Stoney Peak Dr., No. 525, San Diego, CA 92128 USA Tel 858-674-1500; Fax: 858-674-1511
E-mail: info@redcygnet.com
Web site: http://www.redcygnet.com
Dist(s): **Soundprints.**

Red Deer Pr. (CAN) *(0-88995) Dist. by* **FandW Pubns Inc.**

Red Door Pr., *(0-9763770)* 6 Aqueduct Ct., Potomac, MD 20854 USA Tel 240-354-9641 Do not confuse with Red Door Press in San Francisco, CA
E-mail: gvistica@comcast.net.

Red Earth Publishing, *(0-9767748)* P.O. Box 1477, Ponca City, OK 74602-1477 USA Tel 580-763-7003
E-mail: info@redearthpub.com
Web site: http://www.redearthpub.com.

Red Engine Pr., *(0-9663276; 0-9743758; 0-9745652; 0-9785158; 0-9800064; 0-9800332)* 18942 State Hwy. 13, Suite F107, Branson West, MO 65737 USA Tel 417-230-5555
E-mail: riverroadpress@yahoo.com
Web site: http://www.redenginepress.com
Dist(s): **Biblio Distribution.**

Red Fox Publishing Co., *(0-9677953)* 1839 NE 14th St., No. 615, Portland, OR 97212-4348 USA Tel 503-288-1007 Do not confuse with companies with the same or similar name in Belleuve, WA, Middletown, DE, Conifer, CO.

Red Giant Publishing, *(0-9767661)* P.O. Box 5, San Mateo, CA 94401 USA
E-mail: questions@redgiantpublishing.com
Web site: http://www.redgiantpublishing.com.

†Red Hen Pr., *(0-931093)* P.O. Box 454, Big Sur, CA 93920 USA (SAN 678-9420) Tel 831-667-2726 (phone/fax) Do not confuse with Red Hen Pr., Casa Grande, AZ
E-mail: HopeHen@aol.com
Dist(s): **Baker & Taylor Bks.**
Book Wholesalers, Inc.
Brodart Co.
Follett Library Resources; *CIP.*

Red Hen Pr., *(1-888996; 1-59709)* P.O. Box 3537, Granada Hills, CA 91394 USA Tel 818-831-0649; Fax: 818-831-6659
E-mail: editors@redhen.org
Web site: http://www.redhen.org
Dist(s): **SPD-Small Pr. Distribution**
Valentine Publishing Group.

Red Hill Pr., *(0-9708217)* Orders Addr.: P.O. Box 2053, Carbondale, CO 81623 USA Tel 970-963-4968; Fax: 970-947-9266; Edit Addr.: 335 Los Adobes Dr., Carbondale, CO 81623 USA.

Red Hills Writers Project, *(0-9759339)* 1509 Hasosaw Nene, Tallahassee, FL 32301 USA Tel 850-216-2016; Fax: 831-308-3285
E-mail: info@redhillswritersproject.org
Web site: http://www.redhillswritersproject.org.

Red Ink Pr., *(0-9788401)* 1805 N. Roan St., B-2, No. 223, Johnson City, TN 37601 USA (SAN 851-724X) Tel 423-202-3518.

Red Jacket Pr., *(0-9748895)* 3099 Maqua Pl., Mohegan Lake, NY 10547-1054 USA
E-mail: info@redjacketpress.com
Web site: http://www.redjacketpress.com
Dist(s): **Pathway Bk. Service.**

Red Lake Pr., *(0-9671068)* Orders Addr.: P.O. Box 951, Navajo, NM 87328 USA Tel 520-724-3638; Fax: 520-724-3605; Edit Addr.: 953 F Old Red Lake Rd., Apache County, AZ 85220 USA
E-mail: avrum@navcha.navajo.ihs.gov.

†Red Letter Pr., *(0-932323)* 4710 University Way NE, No. 100, Seattle, WA 98115 USA (SAN 686-8045) Tel 206-985-4621; Fax: 206-985-8965 Do not confuse with Red Letter Pr., Columbia, SC
E-mail: RedLetterPress@juno.com
Web site: http://www.RedLetterPress.org
Dist(s): **Alamo Square Distributors**
Partners/West
SPD-Small Pr. Distribution; *CIP.*

Red Letter Publishing & Media Group *See* **Potential Unlimited Publishing**

Red Maple Publishing, *(1-893309)* P.O. Box 291, Jefferson, OH 44047 USA Tel 440-576-9483.

Red Men Interprises, *(0-9744682)* 8 Boton Rd., Lloyd Harbor, NY 11743 USA Tel 516-769-9720
E-mail: jason@drugfreeteen.com
Web site: http://www.drugfreeteen.com.

Red Mountain Creations, *(0-9795858)* P.O. Box 172, High Ridge, MO 63049 USA Tel 636-677-3088; Toll Free: 866-732-4857
E-mail: redmountain@swbell.net
Web site: http://www.byronvonrosenberg.com.

Red Mud Pr., *(0-9672996)* Orders Addr.: P.O. Box 1257, Sedona, AZ 86336-4357 USA Tel 520-282-5285; Edit Addr.: 51 Remuda Rd., Sedona, AZ 86336 USA
E-mail: Crawford@sedora.net.

Red Note Records, *(1-886146)* Div. of Smilin' Atcha Music, 5049 Orange Port Rd., Brewerton, NY 13029 USA Tel 315-676-5516; Fax: 315-676-2709; Toll Free: 800-824-2980
E-mail: carol@redgrammer.com
Web site: http://www.redgrammer.com.

Red Pebble Bks. *Imprint of* **Red Rock Pr., Inc.**

Blue Pheonix Bks., *(0-9726290)* 809 W. Dike St., Glendora, CA 91740 USA
E-mail: Service@redphoenixbooks.com
Web site: http://www.redphoenixbooks.com.

Red Pumpkin Pr., *(0-9711572)* P.O. Box 40, Rutledge, TN 37861 USA Tel 865-828-3362; Fax: 865-828-4578
E-mail: centar123@aol.com.

Red Reef Publishing, Inc., *(0-9711768)* 5380 NW 55th Blvd., Suite 305, Coconut Creek, FL 33073 USA Tel 954-481-2285 Do not confuse with Red Reef Pubns., Boynton Beach, FL
E-mail: irenevosburgh@redreefpublishing.com
Web site: http://www.redreefpublishing.com.

Red River Pr. *Imprint of* **Red River Pr.**

Red River Pr., *(0-910653)* Div. of Archival Services, Inc., 3900 Roy Rd., Suite 37, Shreveport, LA 71107 USA (SAN 270-1774) Fax: 318-929-2106 ; *Imprints:* Red River Press (Red River Pr)
E-mail: Buddy_RRP@PeoplePC.com
Web site: http://www.ArchivalServices.com
Dist(s): **American Bk. Ctr.**

Red Rock Pr., Inc., *(0-9669573; 0-9714372; 1-933176)* 459 Columbus Ave., Suite 114, New York, NY 10024 USA Tel 212-362-8304; Fax: 212-362-6216; Toll Free: 800-488-8040 ; *Imprints:* Red Pebble Books (Red Pebble Bks)
E-mail: info@redrockpress.com
Web site: http://www.redrockpress.com
Dist(s): **National Bk. Network.**

Red Rose Pr., *(0-9701534)* 8237 E. Indianola, Scottsdale, AZ 85251 USA Tel 480-949-7598; Fax: 480-481-3442 Do not confuse with Red Rose Press, Granada Hills,CA
E-mail: Epauling@aol.com.

Red Sea Pr., *(0-932415; 1-56902)* Affil. of Africa World Pr., 541 W. Ingham Ave., Suite B, Trenton, NJ 08638 USA (SAN 630-1983) Tel 609-695-3200; Fax: 609-695-6466
E-mail: awprsp@verizon.net
Web site: http://www.africanworld.com/.

Red Tail Publishing, *(0-9635757)* P.O. Box 1477, Anderson, CA 96007 USA Tel 530-365-5863; Toll Free: 800-473-3824
E-mail: livingston@redtail.com; info@redtail.com
Web site: http://www.redtail.com.

Red Wagon *See* **Magic Wagon**

Red Wagon Bks. *Imprint of* **Harcourt Children's Bks.**

Red Wheel *Imprint of* **Red Wheel/Weiser**

†Red Wheel/Weiser, *(0-87728; 0-943233; 1-57324; 1-57863; 1-59003)* Div. of Weiser Bks., Orders Addr.: P.O. Box 612, York Beach, ME 03910-0612 USA (SAN 255-8610) Tel 207-363-4393; Fax: 207-363-5799; Toll Free Fax: 877-337-3309; Toll Free: 800-423-7087 (orders only) ; *Imprints:* Red Wheel (Red); Weiser Books (Weise); BelleTress Books (BelleTress Bks)
E-mail: customerservice@redwheelweiser.com
Web site: http://www.redwheelweiser.com
Dist(s): **Abyss Distribution**
Baker & Taylor Bks.
Koen-Levy Bk. Wholesalers LLC
NetLibrary, Inc.
New Leaf Distributing Co., Inc.
Ten Speed Pr.; *CIP.*

Red Wolf Publications *See* **Red Wolf Publishing**

Red Wolf Publishing, *(0-9661687)* 2319 Merton, No. 3, Los Angeles, CA 90041 USA Tel 213-257-8559; Fax: 213-255-5900
E-mail: vozeta@loop.com.

Redbird Bks. *Imprint of* **Redbird Enterprises**

Redbird Enterprises, *(0-9664657)* 171 E. Granada Blvd., Suite 222, Ormond Beach, FL 32176 USA Fax: 904-615-1424 ; *Imprints:* Redbird Books (Redbird Bks).

Redbud Pr., *(0-9646370)* Orders Addr.: P.O. Box 200, Almont, MI 48003 USA Tel 810-798-3412; Edit Addr.: 8200 Tiffany, Almont, MI 48003 USA Do not confuse with Redbud Pr., Sebastopol, CA.

Redbud Publishing Co., *(0-9720293)* P.O. Box 1267, Sidney, MT 59270 USA Tel 406-742-8717 (phone/fax); 406-742-8717 (phone/fax) Do not confuse with Redbud Publishing Company in Tulsa, OK
E-mail: ccr-firebirds@juno.com; sylvia@redbudpublishing.com
Web site: http://www.redbudpublishing.com
Dist(s): **Wilson & Assocs.**

Redding Pr., *(0-9658879)* Orders Addr.: c/o Mary Mahony, P.O. Box 366, Belmont, MA 02178 USA Fax: 617-489-9476; Toll Free: 800-267-6012; Edit Addr.: P.O. Box 366, Belmont, MA 02178 USA
E-mail: mary@reddingpress.com
Web site: http://www.channel.com/users/msmahony; http://http//www.reddingpress.com
Dist(s): **Baker & Taylor Bks.**
Koen-Levy Bk. Wholesalers LLC
Quality Bks., Inc.

Redel, Nicole, *(0-9769738)* 2125 David Dr., Florissant, MO 63031-4321 USA Tel 314-839-3242
E-mail: gospelpitbull@sbcglobal.net
Web site: http://www.gospelpitbull.com.

Redemptorists Marriage Preparation Resources, *(0-9677223)* 1617 Iowa St., San Antonio, TX 78203-1819 USA Tel 210-534-1129; Fax: 210-534-1280
E-mail: ruhnke@flash.net
Web site: http://www.marriagepreparation.com.

Redhawk Publishing, *(0-9641861; 0-9769267)* Orders Addr.: 602 Pompa St., Carlsbad, NM 88220 USA Tel 505-885-1748 ; *Imprints:* RWP Books (RWP Bks)
E-mail: randy@rwpbooks.com
Web site: http://rwpbooks.com
Dist(s): **BookSurge, LLC.**

RedJack, *(1-892619)* P.O. Box 633, Bayside, CA 95524 USA Tel 707-825-7817
E-mail: heidi@redjack.us
Web site: http://www.redjack.us
Dist(s): **Baker & Taylor Bks.**

Redleaf Pr., *(0-934140; 1-884834; 1-929610; 1-933653)* Div. of Resources for Child Caring, Inc., 10 Yorkton Ct., Saint Paul, MN 55117-1065 USA (SAN 212-8691) Toll Free Fax: 800-641-0115; Toll Free: 800-423-8309
Web site: http://www.redleafpress.org
Dist(s): **Consortium Bk. Sales & Distribution**
Gryphon Hse., Inc.
Lectorum Pubns., Inc.

Redline Bks., *(0-9727440)* 2280 Jones Creek Rd., White Bluff, TN 37187 USA Tel 615-797-3043 (phone/fax)
E-mail: redlinebooks@bardyoung.com; bardyoung@bardyoung.com.

RedMEDIA, *(0-9721708)* 41 Schermerhorn St., No. 147, Brooklyn, NY 11201 USA Tel 718-857-6638; Fax: 718-857-6427
E-mail: rmedia3@aol.com
Web site: http://www.tgoodlife.com; http://www.ibrooklyn.com/redmedia.

Redmond, Pamela, *(0-9760767)* P.O. Box 169, Topping, VA 23169-0169 USA.

Redwoods Pr., *(0-9631046)* 906A Stockton Ct., Lansdale, PA 19446 USA Tel 215-361-3197 (phone/fax)
E-mail: Redwoodspress@aol.com.

Reece, Kim Taylor Prodns. LLC, *(0-9660395; 1-59779)* 53-866 Kamehameha Hwy., Hauula, HI 96717 USA Tel 808-293-2000; Fax: 808-293-2136; Toll Free: 800-657-7966
E-mail: info@kimtaylorreece.com
Web site: http://www.kimtaylorreece.com
Dist(s): **Booklines Hawaii, Ltd.**
Islander Group.

Reece, Robert *See* **Dark Horse Pr.**

Reed, Robert D. Pubs., *(1-885003; 1-931741; 1-934759)* P.O. Box 1992, Bandon, OR 97411 USA Tel 541-347-9882; Fax: 541-347-9883
E-mail: 4bobreed@msn.com
Web site: http://www.rdrpublishers.com
Dist(s): **Midpoint Trade Bks., Inc.**
Todd Communications.

Reed's Apiary, *(0-9722462)* Orders Addr.: P.O. Box 658, Bisbee, AZ 85603 USA Tel 520-432-2938 (phone/fax); Edit Addr.: 15 Main St., Bisbee, AZ 85603 USA
E-mail: killerbeeguy@earthlink.net
Web site: http://www.killerbeeguy.net; http://www.killerbeeguy.com.

Reedswain, Inc., *(0-9651020; 1-890946; 1-59164)* Orders Addr.: 562 Ridge Rd., Spring City, PA 19475-9681 USA Toll Free: 800-331-5191
E-mail: bryan@reedswain.com
Web site: http://www.reedswain.com
Dist(s): **Cardinal Pubs. Group.**

Reedy Pr., *(0-9753180; 1-933370)* P.O. Box 5131, Saint Louis, MO 63139 USA
E-mail: mheidenry@reedypress.com; jstevens@reedypress.com
Web site: http://www.reedypress.com
Dist(s): **Big River Distribution**
Partners Pubs. Group, Inc.

Reel Productions, LLC, *(0-9675010; 0-9707422)* P.O. Box 1069, Monument, CO 80132 USA Toll Free: 800-964-0439
E-mail: support@reelproductions.net; jolene@explorationfilms.com
Web site: http://www.explorationfilms.com; http://www.reelproductions.net
Dist(s): **Exploration Films**
STL Distribution North America.

Reeve, Phyllis, *(0-9725590)* 829 Park Ln., Grosse Pointe Park, MI 48230 USA Tel 313-331-2378
E-mail: mpreeve@msn.com.

Reference Service Pr., *(0-918276; 1-58841)* 5000 Windplay Dr., Suite 4, El Dorado Hills, CA 95762 USA (SAN 210-2633) Tel 916-939-9620; Fax: 916-939-9626
E-mail: findaid@aol.com; info@rspfunding.com
Web site: http://www.rspfunding.com.

ReferencePoint Pr., Inc., *(1-60152)* P.O. Box PO Box 27779, San Diego, CA 92198 USA Tel 858-618-1314
E-mail: dan@referencepointpress.com; orders@referencepointpress.com
Web site: http://www.referencepointpress.com.

Refined Savage Editions / Ediciones El Salvaje Refinado, The, *(0-9713175; 0-9746855; 0-9761940; 0-9768868; 0-9791011)* 124 Meadow Dr., Scott Depot, WV 25560-9670 USA Tel 304-206-1612
E-mail: salvajerefinado@yahoo.com
Web site: http://www.esrefinado.net.

Reflection Pr., *(0-9671543)* 4245 Boardwalk Dr, Unit D1, Fort Collins, CO 80525 USA Tel 970-207-1918 Do not confuse with companies with the same name in Huntsville, AL, Berkeley, CA
E-mail: msmith@fcgov.com.

Reflection Publishing Company *See* **Imprints**

Reflection Publishing Co., *(0-9657561; 0-9712142)* 1813 4th St W., Palmetto, FL 34221-4303 USA (SAN 299-2787) Toll Free: 888-677-0101
E-mail: lakepm@msn.com
Web site: http://www.reflectionpublishing.com
Dist(s): **Baker & Taylor Bks.**
Brodart Co.
Spring Arbor Distributors, Inc.

Reflections Publishing, *(0-9721791)* 2719 Piscataway Run Dr., Suite 102, Odenton, MD 21113 USA Do not confuse with companies with the same or similar names in Livingston, TX, Cove, OR, Idaho Falls, ID, Dallas, TX, Hume, CA
E-mail: valmcmanus@yahoo.com
Web site: http://www.reflectionspublishing.com.

Reformation Herald Publishing Assn., *(0-9745295; 1-934308)* P.O. Box 7240, Roanoke, VA 24019-0240 USA
Web site: http://www.sdarm.org.

Reformation Heritage Bks., *(1-892777; 1-60178)* 2965 Leonard St. NE., Grand Rapids, MI 49525-5828 USA
E-mail: jay.collier@heritagebooks.org
Web site: http://www.heritagebooks.org.

Reformation Pubs., *(1-933304; 1-60416)* 242 University Dr., Prestonsburg, KY 41653-1058 USA Tel 606-886-7222; Fax: 606-886-8222; Toll Free Fax: 800-765-2464
E-mail: rpublisher@aol.com
Web site: http://www.reformationpublishers.com
Dist(s): **Lightning Source, Inc.**

Reformed Church Pr., Reformed Church in America, *(0-916466)* 4500 60th St., SE, Grand Rapids, MI 49512-9670 USA Tel 616-698-7071; Fax: 616-698-6606; Toll Free: 800-968-7221 (orders); 475 Riverside Dr., 18th Flr., New York, NY 10115 (SAN 207-4508)
Dist(s): **CRC Pubns.**

Reformed Free Publishing Assn., *(0-916206)* 1894 Georgetown Center Dr., Jenison, MI 49428-7137 USA Tel 616-457-5970; Fax: 616-457-5980
E-mail: mail@rfpa.org
Web site: http://www.rfpa.org.

Regal Bks. *Imprint of* **Gospel Light Pubns.**

Regal Enterprises, *(0-9727771; 0-9729960)* 16310 Garfield Ave., Paramount, CA 90723-4806 USA (SAN 255-2477)
Dist(s): **Timberwolf Pr., Inc.**

Regal Publications *See* **University Publishing Hse., Inc.**

Regal Publishing, Inc., *(0-9717355)* 2 Burbank Blvd., Savannah, GA 31419 USA Toll Free: 866-849-4058
E-mail: regalpublishing1@hotmail.com
Web site: http://www.regalpublishing.com.

ReganBooks *Imprint of* **HarperCollins Pubs.**

ReGeJe Pr., *(0-9639147)* Div. of Banks Communications, Orders Addr.: P.O. Box 293442, Sacramento, CA 95829-9998 USA; Edit Addr.: 7515 Bruno Way, Sacramento, CA 95828 USA Tel 916-689-9683
E-mail: regejepress@comcast.net
Web site: http://www.regejepress.com
Dist(s): **Baker & Taylor Bks.**

Regency Hse., Ltd., *(0-9716923)* 6538 Pardee, Taylor, MI 48180-1771 USA Tel 313-291-9242
Dist(s): **AtlasBooks Distribution**
BookMasters, Inc.

Regenold Publishing, *(0-9773085)* P.O. Box 621967, Littleton, CO 80162-1967 USA (SAN 257-2583) Tel 303-797-8881
Web site: http://www.regenoldpublishing.com
Dist(s): **Books West.**

Regent Music & Bk. Publishing, *(0-9712885)* Div. of Regent Asset Management, Inc., 115 D Maunalua Ave., Honolulu, HI 96821 USA Tel 808-396-8410; Fax: 808-396-7762; Toll Free: 800-636-2080 (phone/fax)
E-mail: williamcrowe@hawaii.rr.com
Web site: http://www.exploringlosthawaii.com
Dist(s): **Island Heritage Publishing**
Univ. of Hawaii Pr.

Regina Orthodox Pr., *(0-9649141; 1-928653)* Orders Addr.: P.O. Box 5288, Salisbury, MA 01952 USA Fax: 978-462-5079; Toll Free: 800-636-2470; Edit Addr.: 6 Second St., Salisbury, MA 01952 USA
E-mail: Rop@seacoast.com
Web site: http://www.reginaorthodoxpress.com
Dist(s): **National Bk. Network.**

Regina Pr., Malhame & Co., *(0-88271)* Orders Addr.: P.O. Box 608, Melville, NY 11747-0608 USA (SAN 203-0853) Tel 631-694-8600; Edit Addr.: 10 Hub Dr., Melville, NY 11747 USA
E-mail: customerservice@malhame.com
Web site: http://www.malhame.com/.

Region IV Education Service Ctr., *(1-932524; 1-932797; 1-933049; 1-933521)* 7145 W. Tidwell, Houston, TX 77092-2096 USA Tel 713-744-6592; Fax: 713-744-6514
Web site: http://www.esc4.net.

Regional Laboratory for Educational Improvement of the Northeast & Islands *See* **NETWORK Inc., The**

Regnery Gateway, Incorporated *See* **Regnery Publishing, Inc., An Eagle Publishing Co.**

†Regnery Publishing, Inc., An Eagle Publishing Co., *(0-89526; 1-59698)* Subs. of Phillips Publishing International, One Massachusetts Ave., NW, Suite 600, Washington, DC 20001 USA (SAN 210-5578) Tel 202-216-0600
Web site: http://www.regnery.com
Dist(s): **Continental Bk. Co., Inc.**
Perseus Distribution
STL Distribution North America
Sony CONNECT, Inc.; *CIP.*

Regnig Mountain Pr., *(0-9676207)* 3007 16th St., NW, Saint Paul, MN 55112-1761 USA
E-mail: jalfs@attbi.com
Web site: http://regnig.com.

†Regular Baptist Pr., *(0-87227; 1-59402)* Div. of General Assn. of Regular Baptist Churches, 1300 N. Meacham Rd., Schaumburg, IL 60173-4806 USA (SAN 205-2229) Tel 847-843-1600 (foreign orders); 708-843-1600; Fax: 847-843-3757; Toll Free: 800-727-4440 (orders only)
E-mail: rbporders@garbc.org
Web site: http://www.regularbaptistpress.org; *CIP.*

Reiki Blessings, *(0-9743679)* P.O. Box 2000, Byron, GA 31008-2000 USA (SAN 255-7045) Fax: 801-705-1802
E-mail: reikiblessings@earthlink.net
Web site: http://www.rbpress.com.

Reilly Enterprises, *(0-9669497)* 763 Mouton St., Baton Rouge, LA 70806 USA Tel 504-924-3568; Fax: 850-456-0649.

Reiman Gardens, *(0-9710093)* 1407 Elwood Dr., Ames, IA 50011 USA Tel 515-294-2710; Fax: 515-294-4817
E-mail: tmcl@foundation.iastate.edu; reimangardens@iastate.edu
Web site: http://reimangardens.iastate.edu.

Rein Designs, Inc., *(0-9758704)* 2400 Central Ave. Ste. I, Boulder, CO 80301-3099 USA Toll Free: 800-432-7346 (phone/fax)
E-mail: ricd@reindesigns.com
Dist(s): **Baker & Taylor Bks.**

Reinoso, Marta, *(0-9676203)* World Educational Guild, Inc. 1330 E. 223rd., Suite 501, Carson, CA 90745 USA Tel 310-816-1100; Fax: 310-816-1103
E-mail: wegi@earthnet.com.

Reivers Pr., *(0-9663764)* 3553 Eugene Pl., San Diego, CA 921166 USA Tel 619-584-1841.

Rejoyce Pubns., *(0-9661564)* 5205 Aryshire Dr., Dublin, OH 43017 USA Tel 614-766-2771; Fax: 614-766-1731.

Relationship Resources, Inc., *(0-9721728)* P.O. Box 63383, Colorado Springs, CO 80962 USA
E-mail: gaylyn@relationshipresources.org
Web site: http://www.relationshipresources.org.

Relde Publishing, *(0-9701863)* Subs. of Solutions Training & Development LLC, P.O. Box 21304, Jackson, MS 39289 USA Tel 601-926-4375; Fax: 601-926-4374; Toll Free: 800-489-3439
E-mail: solut2000@aol.com.

Relevant Media Group, Inc., *(0-9714576; 0-9729276; 0-9746942; 0-9760357; 0-9763642; 0-9768175; 0-9776167; 0-9777480)* 1220 Alden Rd., Orlando, FL 32803-2546 USA; 600 Rinehart Rd., Lake Mary, FL 32746
E-mail: nick@relevantmediagroup.com
Web site: http://www.relevantbooks.com/
Dist(s): **Strang Communications Co.**

Relevant Ventures, LLC, *(0-9760259)* 4279 Roswell Rd., Suite 102-273, Atlanta, GA 30342-4145 USA (SAN 256-4483) Tel 404-842-1930; Fax: 404-842-1021
E-mail: td3@mac.com; tom@relevantventures.com
Web site: http://www.relevantventures.com.

Reliance Pr., *(0-9619639; 1-889683)* 3904 Taylor Ln., Yukon, OK 73099-2906 USA (SAN 245-7172)
E-mail: bonny@oklahoma.net
Dist(s): **Baker & Taylor Bks.**
Hervey's Booklink & Cookbook Warehouse
Quality Bks., Inc.

Reliant Energy, *(0-9791383)* 1000 Main St., Houston, TX 77002 USA
E-mail: jmolholt@reliant.com.

Religion Res. Institute, *(0-9765024)* P.O. Box 7505, Prospect Heights, IL 60070 USA Tel 773-396-0147
E-mail: info@religionresearchinstitute.org
Web site: http://www.religionresearchinstitute.org.

Reluctant Reader Bks. *Imprint of* **e-Pluribus Unum Publishing Co.**

Remar Co. *Imprint of* **Irizarry-Ramos, Rafael**

RemarkableMe, *(0-9776642)* 3905 W 10260 N, CEDAR HILLS, UT 84062 USA Tel 801-796-6486; Fax: 801-796-6486
E-mail: charless@utahweb.com
Web site: http://www.remarkableme.com.

Remedia Pubns., *(1-56175; 1-59639)* 15887 N. 76th St., Ste. 120, Scottsdale, AZ 85260-1696 USA Tel 602-661-9900; Fax: 602-661-9901; Toll Free: 800-826-4740
E-mail: sara@rempub.com
Web site: http://www.rempub.com.

Reminders Of Faith, Inc., *(0-9748160; 0-9763691)* 518 Overhead Dr., Moon Township, PA 15108 USA Fax: 412-264-7857
E-mail: kathyb@remindersoffaith.com
Dist(s): **STL Distribution North America.**

Remington Literary Assn., Inc., *(0-9678780)* 2228 Cliffrose Ln., Louisville, CO 80027 USA ; *Imprints:* Divine Mirror Press (Divine Mirror Pr)
E-mail: remlit@aol.com.

Remnant Pr., The, *(1-890740)* Div. of The Remnant Newspaper, 336 280th St., Osceola, WI 54020 USA Tel 715-294-4139; Fax: 715-294-2795
E-mail: Remnant@centurytel.net; Remnant@Compuserve.com
Web site: http://www.remnantBookstore.com.

Remnant Pubns., *(1-883012; 1-933291)* 649 E. Chicago Rd., Coldwater, MI 49036-9497 USA Tel 517-279-1304; Fax: 517-279-1804
E-mail: remnant@charter.net
Web site: http://www.remnantpublications.com
Dist(s): **Spring Arbor Distributors, Inc.**

Renaissance Bks. *Imprint of* **St. Martin's Pr.**

Renaissance Books *See* **New Millennium Bks.**

Renaissance Learning, Inc., *(0-9646404; 1-893751; 0-9708138; 1-931731; 1-931819; 1-932299; 1-59455)* 2911 Peach St., Wisconsin Rapids, WI 54494 USA Tel 715-424-3636; Fax: 715-424-4242; Toll Free: 800-656-6740; P.O. Box 8036, Wisconsin Rapids, WI 54495-8036
E-mail: answers@renlearn.com
Web site: http://www.renlearn.com.

Renaissance Pr., *(0-9712169; 0-9796052)* P.O. Box 5060, Harrisburg, PA 17110 USA Do not confuse with companies with the same or similar name in Richmond, VA, New Orleans, LA, Morristown, TN, Chicago, IL, Charlotte, NC, Macon, GA, Brooklyn, NY, San Francisco, CA, Las Vegas, NV, Tucson, AZ
E-mail: kgownley@excite.com; Kgownley@ameliarules.com; jimmygownley@excite.com
Web site: http://www.ameliarules.com.

Renaissance Printing *See* **Bookends Pr.**

Renaissance Pubns., *(1-929473)* Div. of Mission Renaissance, 800 W. Doran St., Glendale, CA 91203 USA Tel 818-243-9696; Fax: 818-243-9697; Toll Free: 800-430-4278 Do not confuse with Renaissance Publications, Worthington, OH .

Renaissance Publishing Co., *(0-9671455)* P.O. Box 9490, Longview, TX 75608-9490 USA Tel 903-297-4434 Do not confuse with companies with the same or similar names in Sonoma, CA, Omaha, NE, Redmond, WA, Tempe, AZ, Taylor, MI, Indianapolis, IN
E-mail: renpub@texramp.net
Web site: http://www.texramp.net/~renpub.

Renaissance-Atlantic Films, *(0-9667475)* 8383 Wilshire Blvd. Ste. 835, Beverly Hills, CA 90211-2420 USA (SAN 299-7290)
E-mail: FEWARD49@aol.com.

Renaud & Co., *(0-9711805)* 1017 Bucida Rd., Delray Beach, FL 33483 USA (SAN 254-2862) Tel 561-441-4674; Fax: 561-243-9658
E-mail: mprenaud@bellsouth.net

Renegade Publishing, *(0-9704050)* Orders Addr.: P.O. Box 544, Camp Verde, AZ 86322 USA Tel 970-882-4922; Edit Addr.: 2300 Squaw Peak Dr., Camp Verde, AZ 86322 USA
E-mail: books@renegadepublishing.com
Web site: http://www.renegadepublishing.com.

RENEW: Ctr. for Personal Recovery, Inc., *(0-9719569)* Orders Addr.: P.O. Box 125, Berea, KY 40403 USA (SAN 254-6752) Tel 859-986-7878 (phone/fax); Edit Addr.: P.O. Box 125, Berea, KY 40403-0125 USA
E-mail: renew@mis.net
Web site: http://www.renew.net.

Reney Editions, Inc., *(0-9752688)* 35 Sands Brook Dr., New Hemstead, NY 10977 USA Tel 845-548-4029
E-mail: ethan@reney.com
Web site: http://www.reney.com.

Renown Publishing Co., *(0-9643378)* 3655 Elizabeth Way, Redding, CA 96001 USA Tel 916-246-2406
E-mail: renown@shasta.com.

Repko, Marya, *(0-9716006)* Orders Addr.: P.O. Box 5033, Everglades City, FL 34139 USA Tel 239-695-2905.

Replay Publishing, *(0-9700351)* P.O. Box 91, Ohiopyle, PA 15470 USA Tel 724-329-4646
E-mail: replaybb@hotmail.com
Web site: http://www.replaybb.com.

Replica Bks., *(0-7351)* Div. of Baker & Taylor, Orders Addr.: 1120 Us Hwy., 22 E., Bridgewater, NJ 08807 USA Tel 908-541-7392; Fax: 908-541-7875; Toll Free: 800-775-1800; Edit Addr.: P.O. Box 6885, Bridgewater, NJ 08807-0885 USA
E-mail: btinfo@baker-taylor.com.

†Reprint Services Co., *(0-7812; 0-932051)* P.O. Box 890820, Temecula, CA 92589-0820 USA (SAN 686-2640) Fax: 951-767-0133; Toll Free Fax: 888-265-3540; Toll Free: 800-273-6635
E-mail: M.gille@verizon.net; *CIP.*

Repristination Pr., *(1-891469)* Rte. 1, Box 285, Malone, TX 76660-9720 USA Tel 254-533-2710; Fax: 254-533-2357
E-mail: Hunnius@aol.com.

Reptile Education & Research Publishing, *(0-9673958)* P.O. Box 901422, Kansas City, MO 64190-1422 USA (SAN 254-8275) Tel 816-468-5609; Fax: 816-468-8441; 8816 N. Charlotte, Kansas City, MO 64155
E-mail: nieves4@attglobal.net
Web site: http://www.reptilesupclose.com.

Republic of Texas Pr. *Imprint of* **Wordware Publishing, Inc.**

Republic Policy Institute Pr., *(0-9654296)* Div. of The Walker Group, Orders Addr.: P.O. Box 789, Lancaster, CA 93584-0789 USA Tel 805-948-4900; Fax: 805-949-6788; Toll Free: 800-244-7196; Edit Addr.: 44519 Foxton Ave., Lancaster, CA 93535 USA.

Research & Education Assn., *(0-7386; 0-87891)* Orders Addr.: 61 Ethel Rd., W., Piscataway, NJ 08854 USA (SAN 204-6814) Tel 732-819-8880; Fax: 732-819-8808; Toll Free: 800-822-0830
E-mail: jcording@rea.com; info@rea.com
Web site: http://www.rea.com.

Research Ctr. for Children, Youth, & Families/Achenbach System of Empirically Based Assessment (ASEBA), *(0-938565; 0-9611898; 1-932975)* 1 S. Prospect St., Burlington, VT 05401-3456 USA (SAN 286-2123) Tel 802-264-6432; Fax: 802-264-6433
E-mail: mail@aseba.org
Web site: http://www.aseba.org.

†Research Centre of Kabbalah, *(0-924457; 0-943688; 1-57189)* 83-84 115th St., Richmond Hill, NY 11418 USA (SAN 210-9484) Tel 718-805-9122; Fax: 718-805-5899; Toll Free: 888-522-2252
Web site: http://www.kabbalah.com/kabbalah/
Dist(s): **Perseus Distribution**; *CIP.*

Research Evaluation & Statistics *See* **Image Cascade Publishing**

Research Pr., *(0-87822)* Orders Addr.: P.O. Box 9177, Champaign, IL 61826-9177 USA (SAN 282-2490) Toll Free: 800-519-2707; Edit Addr.: 2612 N. Mattis Ave., Champaign, IL 61822 USA (SAN 282-2482) Tel 217-352-3273; Fax: 217-352-1221 Do not confuse with Research Pr., Prairie Village, KS
E-mail: rp@researchpress.com
Web site: http://www.researchpress.com.

Resort Gifts Unlimited, Incorporated *See* **RGU Group, The**

Resource Ctr. of The Americas, *(0-9617743; 1-893440)* 3019 Minnehaha Ave., Minneapolis, MN 55406-1931 USA (SAN 664-7782)
E-mail: info@americas.org
Web site: http://www.americas.org.

Resource Centre, The, *(1-57753)* Div. of Cornell Cooperative Extension, Media Services Resource Ctr., 7 Business & Technolgy Park, Ithaca, NY 14850 USA Tel 607-255-2080; Fax: 607-255-9946
E-mail: resctr@cornell.edu
Web site: http://www.cce.cornell.edu/publications/catalog.html.

ReSource Guides, Inc., *(0-9755370)* 13110 Vista del Mundo, San Antonio, TX 78216-2200 USA Tel 210-493-3974
E-mail: resource@resourceguides.com
Web site: http://www.resourceguides.com.

†Resource Pubns., Inc., *(0-89390)* 160 E. Virginia St., No. 290, San Jose, CA 95112-5876 USA (SAN 209-3081) Tel 408-286-8505; Fax: 408-287-8748; Toll Free: 888-273-7782 Do not confuse with Resource Pubns. in Los Angeles, CA
E-mail: info@rpinet.com
Web site: http://www.rpinet.com
Dist(s): **Empire Publishing Service**
Feldheim Pubs.; *CIP.*

Resource Publishing, *(0-9706429)* 3736 Brookwood Rd. Birmingham, Al 35223, Birmingham, AL 35223 USA Tel 205-967-3446 Do not confuse company with same or similar name in Greensboro, NC, Baton Rouge, LA, San Francisco, CA
E-mail: hoytwilson1@charter.net.

Resource Pubns. *Imprint of* **Wipf & Stock Pubs.**

Resources for Children with Special Needs, Inc., *(0-9678365; 0-9755116)* 116 E. 16th St., 5th Flr., New York, NY 10003 USA
E-mail: dlittwin@resourcesnyc.org
Web site: http://www.resourcesnyc.org.

Resources on the Net Publishing, *(0-9722803)* 250 32 St., No. 307, Bellingham, WA 98225-0943 USA.

Respect, Inc., *(0-945745)* Orders Addr.: P.O. Box 349, Bradley, IL 60915 USA (SAN 247-6509); Edit Addr.: 231 E. Broadway, Hoover Bldg., Bradley, IL 60915 USA (SAN 247-6517) Tel 815-932-8389; Fax: 815-933-9919
E-mail: respect@keynet.net
Web site: http://www.respectincorporated.com.

RESPONDER911, Inc., *(0-9746186)* 17011 Beach Blvd., Suite No. 900, Huntington Beach, CA 92647 USA Tel 714-375-6693; Fax: 714-375-6694
Web site: http://www.responder911.com.

Resting Place Pubns., *(0-9715225)* P.O. Box 10211, Greensboro, NC 27404-0211 USA Tel 336-665-1105
E-mail: rest@northstate.net.

Resurrection Pr. *Imprint of* **Catholic Bk. Publishing Corp.**

Resurrection Resources LLC, *(0-9653723; 0-9710950; 0-9792338)* 10050 Powers Lake Cir., Woodbury, MN 55129-8579 USA Tel 651-578-1581; Fax: 651-739-3285; Toll Free: 866-578-1581 M-F 9:30am - 5:00pm (orders/customer service)
E-mail: editor@thefathersbooks.com; sales@thefathersbooks.com
Web site: http://www.thefathersbooks.com.

Rethinking Schls., Ltd., *(0-942961)* Orders Addr.: P.O. Box 2222, Williston, WI 05495 USA; Edit Addr.: 1001 E. Keefe Ave., Milwaukee, WI 53212 USA (SAN 667-9633) Tel 414-964-9646; Fax: 802-864-7626; Toll Free: 800-669-4192
E-mail: rsbusiness@aol.com
Web site: http://www.rethinkingschools.org
Dist(s): **American International Distribution Corp.**

Retriever Pr., *(0-9760718)* 3689 Ridge Line Dr., San Bernardino, CA 92407 USA.

Retro Recess, *(0-9785425)* 3939 Lavista Rd., Suite E, PMB 327, Tucker, GA 30084 USA
E-mail: retrorecess@comcast.net
Web site: http://www.retrorecess.net.

Retrouvaille Pubg., *(0-9672895)* 7200 France Ave., S., Suite 224, Edina, MN 55435 USA Tel 612-921-9421; Fax: 612-921-9420; Toll Free: 888-467-9421
E-mail: Paul@impressionmanagement.com
Web site: http://www.impressionmanagement.com.

Return To The Word, *(0-9709763)* Div of LIFE Fellowship Family Bible Church, 11500 Sheridan Blvd., Westminster, CO 80020 USA Tel 303-451-5433; Fax: 303-469-1787
E-mail: truthquester@aol.com
Web site: http://www.returntotheworld.org.

Revelation Communications, *(1-930035)* Div. of The Entrepreneurs Network, 13957 S. Marquette, Burnham, IL 60633 USA Fax: 708-891-0785; Toll Free: 877-468-1060
E-mail: sotobesure@yahoo.com.

Revelation of Hymn Ministries *See* **Revelation Pubns.**

Revelation Pubns., *(0-9668482)* P.O. Box 700, Tontitown, AR 72770 USA Fax: 479-361-2517; Toll Free: 800-952-4457 Do not confuse with Revelation Publications, Mountain View, CA
E-mail: ROHM@juno.com
Web site: http://www.RevelationPublications.com.

†Revell, *(0-8007)* Div. of Baker Bk. Hse., Orders Addr.: P.O. Box 6287, Grand Rapids, MI 49516-6287 USA Toll Free Fax: 800-398-3111; Toll Free: 800-877-2665; Edit Addr.: 6030 E. Fulton, Ada, MI 49301 USA Tel 616-676-9185; Fax: 616-676-9573 ; *Imprints:* Spire (Spire)
E-mail: sharlow@bakerbooks.com
Web site: http://www.bakerbooks.com
Dist(s): **Baker Publishing Group**; *CIP.*

Revell, Fleming H. Company *See* **Revell**

Reverence for Life, *(1-880757)* P.O. Box 222, Rectortown, VA 20140 USA Tel 540-364-1282; Fax: 540-364-7636
E-mail: sananda@erols.com
Web site: http://www.1spirit.com/sananda.

Reverie Publishing Co., *(1-932485)* Orders Addr.: 130 South Wineow St., Suite 3, Cumberland, MD 21502 USA Tel 301-722-2373; Fax: 301-722-2374; Toll Free: 888-721-4999; Edit Addr.: 127 West 96th St., 6-D, New York, NY 10025 USA Tel 212-662-7627
E-mail: info@reveriepublishing.com
Web site: http://www.reveriepublishing.com.

†Review & Herald Publishing Assn., *(0-8127; 0-8280)* 55 W. Oak Ridge Dr., Hagerstown, MD 21740 USA (SAN 203-3798) Tel 301-393-3000
E-mail: smulkern@rhpa.org
Web site: http://www.reviewandherald.com/
Dist(s): **Spring Arbor Distributors, Inc.**; *CIP.*

Revival Fires Publishing, *(1-932744)* Rd1 Box 940, Claysburg, PA 16625 USA
Web site: http://www.revivalfirespub.org.

Revivalist Pr., The, *(0-9749186)* Div. of God's Bible School & College, 1810 Young St., Cincinnati, OH 45202 USA
E-mail: president@gbs.edu
Web site: http://www.gbs.edu.

Revolutionary Strategies, *(0-9769354)* P.O. Box 900, Dripping Springs, TX 78620 USA Tel 512-858-0974
Web site: http://www.rickgreen.com.

†Reymont Assocs., *(0-918734)* P.O. Box 114, New York, NY 10276-0114 USA (SAN 204-6857) Tel 212-473-8031; Fax: 212-677-5048
E-mail: webtextwriter@aol.com; *CIP.*

Reynolds & Hearn (GBR) *(1-903111; 1-905287) Dist. by* **Trafalgar.**

Reynolds & Hearn (GBR) *(1-903111; 1-905287) Dist. by* **IPG Chicago.**

Reynolds, Morgan Inc., *(1-883846; 1-931798; 1-59935)* 620 S. Elm St., Suite 223, Greensboro, NC 27406 USA Tel 336-275-1311; Fax: 336-275-1152; Toll Free Fax: 800-535-5725; Toll Free: 800-535-1504 ; *Imprints:* First Biographies (First Biographies)
E-mail: sales@morganreynolds.com; editorial@morganreynolds.com
Web site: http://www.morganreynolds.com.

Reyomi Publishing Co., *(0-9670712)* P.O. Box 51928, Durham, NC 27717 USA Tel 708-906-4036; Fax: 919-489-3913
E-mail: Reyomi@aol.com
Web site: http://www.reyomi.com
Dist(s): **Baker & Taylor Bks.**
Book Hse., The
Brodart Co.

RGC Pr., *(0-9728876; 0-9779886)* P.O. Box 2921, Indianapolis, IN 46206-2921 USA (SAN 255-4747) Tel 317-631-0605; Fax: 775-667-0027
E-mail: info@RGCPress.com
Web site: http://www.RGCPress.com.

RGU Group, The, *(1-891795)* 560 W. Southern Ave., Tempe, AZ 85282 USA (SAN 299-9366) Tel 480-736-9862; Fax: 480-736-9863; Toll Free: 800-266-5265
E-mail: mpagnozzi@theRGUgroup.com
Web site: http://www.thergugroup.com
Dist(s): **STL Distribution North America.**

RH Para Ninos *Imprint of* **Random Hse. Children's Bks.**

Rhapsody Branding, Inc., *(0-9667232)* Orders Addr.: 14027 N. Miami Ave., Miami, FL 33168 USA Tel 305-681-0489
E-mail: pumba66@yahoo.com; Don@notw8.com; Don@nightofthewitches.com
Web site: http://www.nightofthewitches.com
Dist(s): **Baker & Taylor Bks.**
Book Warehouse Distributors, The
Southern Bk. Service.

RH/Disney *Imprint of* **Random Hse. Children's Bks.**

Rhette Enterprises, Inc., *(0-9702319)* 3316 Shorewood Ave., Fort Gratiot, MI 48059 USA Tel 810-385-9416; Fax: 810-385-2304
E-mail: bobjan@futureone.com.

Rhino Entertainment Co, A Warner Music Group Co., *(0-7379; 0-930589; 1-56826; 0-9797278)* 3400 W. Olive Ave., Burbank, CA 91505 USA (SAN 677-5454) Tel 818-238-6110; Fax: 818-562-9239
E-mail: gladys.sanchez@wmg.com; tracie.bowers@wmg.com
Web site: http://www.rhino.com.

Rhizoo Publishing, *(0-9762723)* P.O. Box 1249, Stephenville, TX 76401 USA.

Rhoades & Assocs., *(1-930006)* 8070 19th St., No. 326, Alta Loma, CA 91701 USA Tel 909-945-1715; Fax: 909-945-3147; Toll Free: 888-221-1715 ; *Imprints:* Reading Company, The (Reading Co)
E-mail: info@reading-company.net
Web site: http://www.reading-company.com; http://www.rhoadestoreading.net.

Rhode Island State Council, International Reading Assn., *(0-9664455)* 4 Gardner Ave., North Providence, RI 02911 USA.

Rhode,, Steve Incorporated *See* **Rhode, Steve Inc.**

Rhode, Steve Inc., *(0-9742781; 1-59840)* 310 Watkins Pond Blvd., Rockville, MD 20850 USA
E-mail: steve@steverhode.com
Web site: http://www.steverhode.com.

Rhodes & Easton, *(0-9649401; 1-890394)* 400 W. Front St., 4th Flr., Traverse City, MI 49684 USA Tel 231-933-0445; Fax: 231-933-0448; Toll Free: 800-706-4636 ; *Imprints:* Sage Creek Press (Sage Creek)
E-mail: mclweley@bookpublishing.com
Web site: http://www.bookpublishing.com
Dist(s): **Baker & Taylor Bks.**
TSBI, Inc.

Rhodes Educational Pubns., *(0-9743214)* P.O. Box 501155, Dallas, TX 75250 USA
Web site: http://www.nativeamericanrhymes.com.

Rhoman Bks., *(0-9721438)* P.O. Box 1181, Castle Rock, CO 80104 USA
E-mail: info@rhomanbooks.com
Web site: http://www.rhomanbooks.com.

Rialp, Ediciones, S.A. (ESP) *(84-320; 84-321)* *Dist. by* **Lectorum Pubns.**

Ribbitt Productions, *(0-9679713)* Orders Addr.: P.O. Box 33474, Indialantic, FL 32903-0474 USA Tel 321-727-3921; Toll Free: 888-279-7640; Edit Addr.: 1620 Pineapple Ave., Melbourne, FL 32935-6543 USA
E-mail: pac@iv.net; pac@iu.net
Web site: http://www.sciencefairproject.com.

R.I.C. Publications Asia Co, Inc. (JPN) *(4-902216)* *Dist. by* **CEG.**

R.I.C. Pubns. (AUS) *(1-86311; 1-74126)* *Dist. by* **SCB Distributors.**

Ricara Features, *(0-911737)* Div. of Mohawk Nation Publishing Co., P.O. Box 664, Sanborn, NY 14132 USA (SAN 264-3472) Tel 519-445-2748; Fax: 519-445-1235
E-mail: ricara@attglobal.net
Dist(s): **Baker & Taylor Bks.**
Brodart Co.
Greenfield Review Literary Ctr., Inc.

Rich Pr., *(1-933914)* 6611 N 64th Pl., Paradise Valley, AZ 85253 USA (SAN 850-5209)
Dist(s): **Perseus Distribution.**

Rich Publishing, *(0-9726670)* 4175 W. 5345 S., Salt Lake City, UT 84118 USA Tel 801-965-6200; Fax: 801-965-6199; Toll Free: 800-224-3221 Do not confuse with companies with the same or similar name in Houston, TX, Temecula, CA
E-mail: milton@zeestlouis.com
Web site: http://www.miltonrich.com.

RICH University *See* **Changing Lives Schl., Inc.**

Richards Studio, *(0-9675623)* 39 River View Terr., Kingston, NY 12401-6959 USA Tel 845-336-4617; 5110 Sun Cir., Sarasota, FL 34234
E-mail: Richardsjh@aol.com
Web site: http://www.richardsstudio.net.

Richardson Production, Inc., *(0-9761222)* Orders Addr.: P.O. Box 543, Marietta, OH 45750 USA Tel 740-373-0861; Edit Addr.: 177 Acme St., Marietta, OH 45750 USA
Web site: http://www.richardsonproductions.tv.

Riches Publishing Co., *(0-9728219)* P.O. Box 02232, Detroit, MI 48202 USA
E-mail: klrich@sbcglobal.net
Web site: http://www.klrich.com.

Richlyn Publishing, *(0-9722264)* 12373 W. Tufts Ave., Morrison, CO 80465-1748 USA Tel 303-979-8609; Fax: 303-932-1257
E-mail: richlyn2@msn.com
Web site: http://www.richlynpublishing.com
Dist(s): **Baker & Taylor Bks.**

Richmond *Imprint of* **Santillana USA Publishing Co., Inc.**

Rickshaw Press *See* **Ragged Sky Pr.**

Riddering, Marggie, *(0-9765977)* P.O. Box 770, Hormigueros, PR 00660 USA Fax: 787-833-2260.

Riddle Creek Publishing, *(0-9725894)* 232 Cty. Rd. 19, Haleyville, AL 35565-7416 USA
E-mail: riddlecreek@centurytel.net.

Rider Franklin Reynolds Publishing *See* **Belisarian Bks.**

Riders Elite Academy, Inc., *(0-9741628)* 23120 Garrison Rd., Corcoran, MN 55340-9103 USA Tel 763-498-6565 (phone/fax)
E-mail: books@riderselite.com
Web site: http://www.riderselite.com.

Ridge Rock Pr., *(0-9670177)* Div. of Ridge Rock, Inc., Orders Addr.: P.O. Box 255, Healy, AK 99743 USA (SAN 253-6595) Tel 907-322-8185 (cell); 907-683-7737 (phone/fax); Edit Addr.: Mile 261 Parks Hwy., Box 255, Healy, AK 99743 USA
E-mail: ridgerock@gtemail.net
Dist(s): **Baker & Taylor Bks.**
Todd Communications.

Ridgeview Publishing Co., *(0-917930; 0-924922)* Box 686, Atascadero, CA 93423 USA (SAN 209-9993).

†Ridgeway Pr., *(1-56439)* P.O. Box 120, Roseville, MI 48066 USA Tel 313-577-7713; Fax: 586-296-3303 Do not confuse with companies with the same name in Los Alamitos, CA, Dayton, OH
E-mail: mlliebler@aol.com
Dist(s): **Baker & Taylor Bks.**; *CIP.*

Ridgewood Group, The, *(0-9716907)* P.O. Box 8011, Manchester, CT 06040 USA (SAN 254-3419) Tel 860-432-4537 (phone/fax) ; *Imprints:* Ridgewood Publishing (Ridgewd Pub)
E-mail: info@theridgewoodgroup.com
Web site: http://www.hermanthecrab.com.

Ridgewood Pr., *(0-9650434)* 2160 Aztec Dr., dyersburg, TN 38024 USA Do not confuse with Ridgewood Pr., Jefferson City, MO
E-mail: bartonsn@mac.com.

Ridgewood Publishing *Imprint of* **Ridgewood Group, The**

Ridyl Publishing, *(1-889736)* 2118 Wilshire Blvd., Suite 467, Santa Monica, CA 90403 USA Tel 310-392-9544; Toll Free: 800-390-9920.

Rieder, Ruth, *(0-9674360; 0-9723182)* Orders Addr.: P.O. Box 15252, Rio Rancho, NM 87174 USA; Edit Addr.: 1608 13th St SE, Rio Rancho, NM 87124-0755 USA
E-mail: rieder5@juno.com
Web site: http://www.positivepowerofholiness.com.

†Rienner, Lynne Pubs., Inc., *(0-89410; 0-931477; 1-55587; 1-58826)* 1800 30th St., Suite 314, Boulder, CO 80301-1026 USA (SAN 683-1869) Tel 303-444-6684; Fax: 303-444-0824
E-mail: cservice@rienner.com; sglover@rienner.com; questions@rienner.com
Web site: http://www.rienner.com; *CIP.*

Rigby Education, *(0-7635; 0-7578; 1-4189)* Orders Addr.: 6277 Sea Harbor Dr., 5th Flr., Orlando, FL 32887 USA Toll Free Fax: 877-578-2638; Toll Free: 888-363-4266; Edit Addr.: 10801 N. Mopac Expressway, Bldg. 3, Austin, TX 78759 USA Toll Free Fax: 800-699-9459; Toll Free: 800-531-5015
Web site: http://www.harcourtachieve.com.

Rigby Interactive Library *See* **Heinemann Library**

Riggott, Ann, *(0-9777641)* 321 14th St. NE, Rochester, MN 55906 USA Tel 507-286-8727
E-mail: annrigg@netzero.com.

Riggott, Dean Photography, *(0-9659875)* 831 10 1/2 St., SW, Rochester, MN 55902 USA Tel 507-285-5076; Fax: 253-540-6093
Web site: http://www.riggottphoto.com
Dist(s): **Partners Bk. Distributing, Inc.**

Riggs, Theresia, *(0-9746132)* 8910 Dogwood Dr., Tomball, TX 77375 USA Tel 281-351-2329 (phone/fax)
E-mail: Ohringen@aol.com
Web site: http://Cosmic Sisters.com.

Right On Programs, Inc., *(0-933426)* 522 E. Broadway, Suite 101, Glendale, CA 91205 USA (SAN 212-5099) Tel 818-240-1683; Fax: 818-240-2858.

Right Track Reading LLC, *(0-9763290)* P.O. Box 1952, Livingston, MT 59047 USA
E-mail: mmgagen@earthlink.net.

Righter Publishing Co., Inc., *(0-9706823; 0-9747735; 0-9766032; 0-9778948; 0-9796209)* P.O. Box 105, Timberlake, NC 27583 USA Tel 336-503-8881; Fax: 336-597-8881
E-mail: righterpub@esinc.net
Web site: http://www.righterpublications.com
Dist(s): **Ingram Bk. Co.**

Right-Side-Up Stories, *(0-9667455)* 260 S. Lake Ave., No. 185, Pasadena, CA 91101 USA Tel 818-957-8822; Fax: 818-957-5335; Toll Free: 800-369-9230
E-mail: astory4u@earthlink.net
Web site: http://www.astory4u.com.

Riker, Dale, *(0-9771621)* 6937 W. Country Club Dr. N, Unit 152, Sarasota, FL 34243-3507 USA.

Riley, Jocelyn Productions *See* **Her Own Words**

Riley Pr., *(0-9728958)* P.O. Box 202, Eagle, MI 48822 USA Tel 517-626-7027
E-mail: rileypress@yahoo.com
Web site: httt://rileypress.hypermart.net.

Rimwalk Pr., *(0-9720696)* 4249 S. Whitehill Dr., Cedar, MI 49621 USA Tel 231-256-2237; Fax: 231-256-9236
E-mail: rimwalkpress@aol.com
Web site: http://www.rimwalkstudio.com
Dist(s): **Partners Bk. Distributing, Inc.**

Rinchen, Inc., *(0-9714554)* 20 John St. Kingston, Ny 12401, Kingston, NY 12401 USA
Web site: http://www.rinchen.com
Dist(s): **Baker & Taylor Bks.**

Rincon Publishing Co., *(0-9660858)* 1465 W. 1700 N., Provo, UT 84604 USA Tel 801-377-7657; Fax: 801-356-2733
E-mail: RinconPub@Utahtrails.com
Web site: http://www.utahtrails.com
Dist(s): **Alpenbooks Pr. LLC**
Books West
Partners/West
Treasure Chest Bks.

Rind, Sherry, *(0-9674729)* Orders Addr.: 959 Evonshire Ln., Great Falls, VA 22066 USA; Edit Addr.: 19636 Derby Ct., West Linn, OR 97068-2207 USA
E-mail: AIREBIRD@hotmail.com; KCBROOM@erols.com
Web site: http://www.airedaleterriers.org.

Rinehart, Roberts International *Imprint of* **Rinehart, Roberts Pubs.**

Rinehart, Roberts Pubs., *(0-911797; 0-943173; 1-57098; 1-57140; 1-879373; 1-58979)* Div. of Rowman & Littlefield Pubs., Inc., Orders Addr.: 15200 NBN Way, Blue Ridge Summit, PA 17214 USA Tel 717-794-3800 (Customer Service &/or orders); Fax: 717-794-3803 (Customer Service &/or orders only); 717-794-3857 (Sales & MIS); 717-794-3856 (Royalties, Inventory Mgmt., & Dist.); Toll Free Fax: 800-338-4550 (Customer Service &/or orders); Toll Free: 800-462-6420 (Customer Service &/or orders); Edit Addr.: 4501 Forbes Blvd., Suite 200, Lanham, MD 20706 USA Tel 301-459-3366; Toll Free: 800-462-6420 ; *Imprints:* Rinehart, Roberts International (R Rinehart Intl)
E-mail: nrothschild@rowman.com
Web site: http://www.robertsrinehart.com
Dist(s): **National Bk. Network**
NetLibrary, Inc.
Rowman & Littlefield Pubs., Inc.

Rio Nuevo Pubs. *Imprint of* **Treasure Chest Bks.**

Rio Wildflower Pubns., *(0-9786168)* P.O. Box 246, Almont, CO 81210 USA Tel 970-642-0272
E-mail: wildflowercd@peoplepc.com.

Rip Squeak, Inc., *(0-9672422; 0-9747825)* 840 Capitolio Way Ste. B, Sn Luis Obisp, CA 93401-7130 USA Toll Free: 800-251-0654
E-mail: Info@RipSqueak.com
Web site: http://www.RipSqueak.com
Dist(s): **Parklane Publishing.**

Ripley Entertainment, Inc., *(1-893951)* Div. of The Jim Pattison Group, 7576 Kingspointe Pkwy., Suite. 188, Orlando, FL 32819-6510 USA (SAN 299-9498)
E-mail: meyer@ripleys.com; dula@ripleys.com
Dist(s): **Mint Pubs. Group**
Perseus Distribution.

Ripple, Wilhelminia *See* **Oakbrook Publishing Hse.**

Riptide Pr., Inc., *(0-9723456)* 233 Walnut Creek Dr., Clayton, NC 27520 USA Tel 919-359-2852; Fax: 919-882-9924 Do not confuse with companies with the same or similar name in New York, NY, Fredericksburg, VA
E-mail: info@riptidebooks.com; info@riptidepress.com
Web site: http://www.riptidebooks.com; http://www.riptidepress.com.

Risa Publications, *(0-9771404)* 8424-A Santa Monica Blvd., Suite 175, West Hollywood, CA 90069 USA
Web site: http://www.lisahaisha.com.

Risen Heart Pr., *(0-9764497)* 554 Bruns Dr., Rossford, OH 43460 USA Tel 419-666-6269
E-mail: rjbaden@wcnet.org.

Rising Bks., *(0-9644456)* P.O. Box 1408, Conyers, GA 30012 USA (SAN 298-5438) Tel 404-378-7464; Fax: 770-761-9865
E-mail: chadfoster@mindspring.com
Web site: www.chadfoster.com.

Rising Lyons Pr., *(0-9793492)* 400 E. 56th St., Apt. 33H, New York, NY 10022 USA Tel 619-964-1990
E-mail: layne@risinglyonspress.com
Web site: http://www.risinglyonspress.com.

Rising Moon Bks. for Young Readers *Imprint of* **Northland Publishing**

Rising Star Publishers *See* **WeWrite LLC**

Rising Sun Ctr. for Loss & Renewal, *(0-9652410)* 2848 Windsor Oaks Trace, Marietta, GA 30066 USA Tel 770-928-1027; Fax: 770-592-4428
E-mail: sharonrugg@aol.com
Dist(s): **Book Bin - Pacifica, The.**

Rising Sun Publishing, Inc., *(1-880463)* P.O. Box 70906, Marietta, GA 30007-0906 USA Tel 770-518-0369; Fax: 770-587-0862; Toll Free: 800-524-2813 Do not confuse with Rising Sun Pubng in Fairfield, OH
E-mail: info@rspublishing.com; sholland@rspublishing.com
Web site: http://www.rspublishing.com.

Rising Tide Pr., *(0-913844)* Div. of American-Canadian Pubs., Inc., P.O. Box 6136, Santa Fe, NM 87502-4595 USA (SAN 298-217X) Do not confuse with Rising Tide Pubs., Tucson, AZ.

Ritchie Unlimited Pubns., *(0-939656)* 1427 Anderson Rd., Springfield, OR 97477 USA (SAN 216-6461) Tel 541-741-0794 (phone/fax)
E-mail: ralph-ritchie@comcast.net
Web site: http://www.ritchieunlimitedpublications.com.

Rivendell Bk. Factory, *(0-944353)* 217 Country Club Park Crestline Village, PMB321, Mountain Brook, AL 35213 USA Tel (205) 871-5915; Fax: (205) 871-5945
Dist(s): **Cardinal Pubs. Group.**

River by Night, *(0-9727435)* P.O. Box 126, Liberty Hill, TX 78642 USA
Web site: http://www.riverbynight.com.

River City Kids *Imprint of* **River City Publishing**

River City Pr., *(0-9706962; 0-9764232; 0-9776713)* 4301 Emerson Ave. N., Minneapolis, MN 55412 USA Tel 612-521-9633 (phone/fax); Toll Free: 888-234-3559 Do not confuse with River City Pr. in New Orleans, LA
E-mail: bwolf@rivercitypress.net
Web site: http://www.rivercitypress.net.

River City Publishing, *(0-913515; 0-9622815; 1-57966; 1-880216; 1-881320)* 1719 Mulberry St., Montgomery, AL 36106 USA (SAN 631-4910) Tel 334-265-6753; Fax: 334-265-8880; Toll Free: 877-408-7078 ; *Imprints:* Black Belt Press (Black Belt); River City Kids (River City Kids) Do not confuse with companies with the same or similar names in Richland, WA, South Bend, IN
E-mail: sales@rivercitypublishing.com
Web site: http://www.rivercitypublishing.com.

River Of Life Publishing, *(0-9710709)* P.O. Box 1085, Kremmling, CO 80459-1085 USA Do not confuse with River of Life Publishing in Kremmling, CO.
Web site: http://www.gospelstore.com.

River of Life Publishing, *(0-9746345)* 3700 Chestnut Lake Ct., Jonesboro, GA 30236-5502 USA Do not confuse with River of Life Publishing in Kremmling, CO.

River Pointe Pubns., *(0-9758805)* P.O. Box 130143, Ann Arbor, MI 48105 USA Tel 734-439-8031
E-mail: riverptpub@sbcglobal.net.

River Road Pubns., Inc., *(0-938682)* 830 E. Savidge St., Spring Lake, MI 49456 USA (SAN 253-8172) Tel 616-842-6920; Fax: 616-842-0084; Toll Free: 800-373-8762
E-mail: socialstudies@riverroadpublications.com
Web site: http://www.riverroadpublications.com.

Riverbank Publishing, *(0-9753320)* 1917 Winterport Cluster, Reston, VA 20191 USA
Web site: http://www.riverbankpublishing.com.

Riverbend Publishing, *(1-931832)* Orders Addr.: P.O. Box 5833, Helena, MT 59604 USA Tel 406-449-0200; Fax: 406-449-0330; Toll Free: 866-787-2363; Edit Addr.: 1660 B St., Helena, MT 59601 USA (SAN 254-5020) Do not confuse with companies with the same or similar names in Elizabeth, CO, Marion, KY, Knoxville, TN
Web site: http://www.riverbendpublishing.com
Dist(s): **Books West**
High Peak Bks.
Partners Bk. Distributing, Inc.
Wolverine Distributing, Inc.

Rivercity Pr. *Imprint of* **Amereon LTD.**

RiverCreek Bks., Inc., *(0-9745171)* Orders Addr.: P.O. Box 1146, Buies Creek, NC 27506 USA Tel 910-893-8853.

Riverdale Bks. *Imprint of* **Riverdale Electronic Bks.**

Riverdale Electronic Bks., *(0-9712207; 1-932606)* P.O. Box 962085, Riverdale, GA 30296 USA ; *Imprints:* Riverdale Books (RiverdBks)
E-mail: jtm@riverdalebooks.com
Web site: http://www.riverdaleebooks.com.

Company

Riverdeep, Inc., *(0-7630; 1-930106)* 100 Pine St. Ste. 1900, San Francisco, CA 94111-5205 USA Toll Free: 800-223-6925; 125 Cambridgepark Dr., Cambridge, MA 02140-2329
E-mail: info@riverdeep.net; international@riverdeep.net
Web site: http://www.riverdeep.com
Dist(s): **Perseus Distribution.**

RiverEarth, *(0-9787722)* Orders Addr.: P.O. Box 245, Southern Pines, NC 28388 USA (SAN 851-5824) Tel 910-695-0989; Edit Addr.: 124 NW. Broad St., No. 1, Southern Pines, NC 28387 USA
E-mail: bernie@riverearth.com
Web site: http://riverearth.com

Riverhead Bks. (Hardcover) *Imprint of* **Penguin Group (USA) Inc.**

Riverhead Trade (Paperbacks) *Imprint of* **Penguin Group (USA) Inc.**

Riverpark Publishing Co., *(0-915029)* 3680 Little Rock Dr., Provo, UT 84604 USA (SAN 289-8217) Toll Free: 800-224-1606
E-mail: garyjoy@itsnet.com
Dist(s): **Baker & Taylor Bks.**

RiverPlace Development Corp., *(0-9785538)* Orders Addr.: 201 Washington St., Suite 541, Reading, PA 19601 USA Tel 610-736-3900; Fax: 610-736-3988
E-mail: info@RiverPlacePA.com
Web site: http://www.RiverPlacePA.com.

Rivers, Swannee *See* **Swannee Rivers**

Riverside Museum Pr., *(0-935661)* 3580 Mission Inn Ave., Riverside, CA 92501 USA (SAN 280-2740) Tel 951-782-5273; Fax: 951-369-4970
Web site: http://www.ci.riverside.ca.us/museum.

Riverstone Group Publishing, *(0-9706117; 0-9763092)* 1245 Scott Rd., Canton, GA 30114 USA; 1245 Scott Rd., Canton, GA 30115 Tel 770-720-1008
E-mail: epulleu@riverstonegroup.com
Web site: http://www.riverstonegroup.com.

Riverstone Publishing, *(0-9721928)* Orders Addr.: P.O. Box 270852, Saint Paul, MN 55127 USA Tel 651-775-2192
E-mail: contact@AmericanYouth.net
Web site: http://www.AmericanYouth.net.

Rivertree Productions, Inc., *(1-882412)* P.O. Box 410, Bradford, NH 03221 USA Tel 603-938-5120; Fax: 603-938-5616; Toll Free: 800-554-1333 ; *Imprints:* Odds Bodkin Storytelling Library, The (Odds Bodkin)
E-mail: rivertree@conknet.com
Web site: http://www.oddsbodkin.com
Dist(s): **Penton Overseas, Inc.**

Riverview Foundation, *(0-9771639)* Orders Addr.: P.O. Box 310, Topsham, ME 04086 USA (SAN 256-8357) Tel 207-729-7399; Fax: 207-797-5676; Edit Addr.: 610 Augusta Rd., Tomsham, ME 04086 USA
E-mail: office@riverviewfoundation.com
Web site: http://www.riverviewfoundation.com.

Riverwise, Inc., *(0-9653950; 0-9716904)* Orders Addr.: P.O. Box 204, Winona, MN 55987 USA Tel 507-454-5949; Fax: 507-454-2133; Toll Free: 800-303-8201; Edit Addr.: 70 E. 4th St., Winona, MN 55987-3508 USA
E-mail: editors@big-river.com
Web site: http://www.riverwise.com.

Rivet Bks. *Imprint of* **Feral Pr., Inc.**

Riviera Pubns., *(1-888771)* 370 Ledroit St., Laguna Beach, CA 92651-1349 USA.

†Rizzoli International Pubns., Inc., *(0-8478)* Subs. of RCS Rizzoli Editore Corp., 300 Park Ave., S., 3rd Flr., New York, NY 10010 USA (SAN 111-9192) Tel 212-387-3400; Fax: 212-387-3535 ; *Imprints:* White Star (White Star NY); Rizzoli Universe Promotional Books (RUPB)
Web site: http://www.rizzoliusa.com/
Dist(s): **Random Hse., Inc.**; *CIP.*

Rizzoli Universe Promotional Bks. *Imprint of* **Rizzoli International Pubns., Inc.**

R.J. Bob Chavez Images, *(0-9778110)* 10037 W. 68th Pl., Arvada, CO 80004 USA Tel 303-423-6982
E-mail: rjbcimages@aol.com.

RJ Pubns., *(0-9769277; 0-9786373)* 290 Dune St., Far Rockaway, NY 11691-2714 USA (SAN 256-5919)
Web site: http://www.richardjeanty.com
Dist(s): **Biblio Distribution.**

RJS Pubns., *(1-892291)* 3784 Grouse Haven Rd., Oregon, WI 53575 USA Tel 608-455-1478
E-mail: sschmidt@nfcna.com
Web site: http://www.rjspublications.com.

RK Enterprises, Inc., *(0-9743775)* 22581 NE State Route 3., Belfair, WA 98528-9303 USA
E-mail: rkilsby@wavecable.com
Web site: http://www.gooshu.com.

RKO Enterprises, *(0-9718034)* P.O. Box 117, LaGrange, IL 60525-0117 USA
E-mail: oshea928@earthlink.net.

Road Tunes Media, *(0-9721725)* Orders Addr.: 534 Hidden Way, Homer, AK 99603 USA (SAN 852-5188)
E-mail: roadtunes@gci.net
Web site: http://www.berniejones.com
Dist(s): **Follett Library Resources.**

Roadracing World Publishing, Inc., *(0-9749615)* P.O. Box 1428, Lake Elsinore, CA 92531 USA Tel 951-245-6411 Toll Free: 800-464-8336
E-mail: custsvc@roadracingworld.com
Web site: http://www.roadracingworld.com.

Roadrunner Pr., *(0-9636346)* Orders Addr.: P.O. Box 1034, Michigan City, IN 46361-1034 USA Tel 219-879-0133; Fax: 219-874-7413; Toll Free: 888-662-7786; Edit Addr.: 2815 Lake Shore Dr., Michigan City, IN 46360 USA
E-mail: roadrunnerpress@comcast.net
Web site: http://www.halhigdon.com.

Roaninn Pubns., *(0-9664797)* Orders Addr.: 751 N. Jasmine Pl., Tucson, AZ 85710 USA Fax: 520-885-0353
E-mail: roaninn@theriver.com.

Roaring Brook Pr., *(0-7613; 1-59643)* 115 West 18th Street, New York, NY 10011 USA Tel 212-886-1030 ; *Imprints:* First Second Books (First Second)
Web site: http://www.henryholt.com
Dist(s): **Macmillan.**

Roark, Candice, *(0-9677184)* 13186 Elderberry Ct., Saint Paul, MN 55124-4236 USA
E-mail: croark42@juno.com.

Robbie Dean Pr., *(0-9630608; 1-889743)* 2910 E. Eisenhower Pkwy., Ann Arbor, MI 48108 USA Tel 734-973-9511; Fax: 734-973-9475
E-mail: fairyha@aol.com.

Robert Welch Univ., *(1-892647)* 700 Westhill Blvd., Appleton, WI 54914 USA Toll Free: 800-241-2882
E-mail: rwu@robertwelchuniversity.org
Web site: http://www.robertwelchuniversity.org.

Roberts, Cindy, *(0-9706660)* 13910 Bond St., Overland Park, KS 66221-2800 USA
E-mail: mrsatalker@aol.com.

Roberts, Michele, *(0-9760188)* P.O. Box 271611, Houston, TX 77277-1611 USA.

Roberts Publishing, *(0-9727046)* 197 Woodland Pkwy., No. 104-529, San Marcos, CA 92069 USA Tel 760-233-1460 (phone/fax) Do not confuse with companies with the same or similar names in Sacramento, CA, Grand Rapids, MI, Great Lake, WI, Blaine, WA
E-mail: mystavalon@aol.com
Web site: http://www.robertspublishing.com.

Roberts Publishing Co., *(0-931764)* 738 32nd St., S. E., Grand Rapids, MI 49548 USA Tel 616-245-1560; Fax: 616-245-1561 (orders can be sent by fax) Do not confuse with companies with the same or similar names in Sacramento, CA, San Marcos, CA, Great Lake, WI, Blaine, WA
E-mail: robertspublishingco@juno.com
Web site: http://www.scoliosishelp.com; http://www.scoliosishelp.org; http://www.robertsbookshelf.comw
Dist(s): **Baker & Taylor Bks.**

Robertson, Oscar Media Ventures, *(0-9662483)* 500 N. Rossmore Ave. Apt. 214, Los Angeles, CA 90004-2436 USA Toll Free: 888-327-1401
E-mail: orders@thebigo.com
Web site: http://www.thebigo.com.

Robertson Publishing, *(0-9727721; 0-9796251; 0-9798633)* 59 N. Santa Cruz Ave., Suite B, Los Gatos, CA 95030 USA Fax: 408-354-5957
E-mail: alicia.r@robertsonpubblishing.com
Web site: http://www.RobertsonPublishing.com.

Robin Corey Bks. *Imprint of* **Random Hse. Children's Bks.**

Robin Thompson Charm Schl., *(0-9675318)* 17298 Lake Knolls Rd., Pekin, IL 61554 USA Tel 309-925-3157
E-mail: robin@etiquette-network.com
Web site: http://www.etiquette-network.com.

Robinbk., Ediciones S.L. (ESP) *(84-7927)* *Dist. by* **Lectorum Pubns.**

Robins Lane Pr. *Imprint of* **Gryphon Hse., Inc.**

Robinson, Consuelo, *(0-9786767)* P.O. Box 8662, Delray Beach, FL 33482 USA (SAN 851-2868)
E-mail: math1on1@math1on1.com
Web site: www.math1on1.com.

Robinson, Francesca *See* **Francesca Studios**

Robinson Pubs., *(0-9718091)* P.O. Box 189, New London, NC 28127-0189 USA Tel 704-463-0213
E-mail: robinson@vnet.net
Web site: http://www.australiancowboy.com.

Robison Gamble Creative, *(1-933497)* 1420 W. Skyline Ave., Ozark, MO 65721 USA Tel 417-581-6008; Fax: 417-581-4542; Toll Free: 877-335-2735
E-mail: carrie@robisongamble.com
Web site: http://www.robisongamble.com.

Robot Publishing, *(0-9662919; 1-930505)* Div. of JADDPRECRYS Enterprise, Orders Addr.: P.O. Box 961840, Riverdale, GA 30296 USA Tel 770-460-7092; Fax: 770-719-4315; Edit Addr.: 125 Morning Springs Walk, Fairburn, GA 30213 USA Do not confuse with Robot Publishing Co., in Pasadena, CA.

Robus, Debbie, *(0-9762034)* 2403 Elmwood Dr., Heber Springs, AR 72543-6303 USA
E-mail: firecrackerbaby57@yahoo.com
Web site: http://firecrackerbaby57.blogspot.com; http://www.workamper.com
Dist(s): **Workamper Bookstore.**

Robyn Z Moon Publishing, *(0-615)* 3021 Eads Ave., Saint Lois, MO 63104 USA Tel 877-544-0102
E-mail: robynzmoon@gmail.com
Dist(s): **Lulu.com.**

Roc *Imprint of* **Penguin Group (USA) Inc.**

ROC EdTech Publishing, Incorporated *See* **Olmstead LLC**

ROC Hardcover *Imprint of* **Penguin Group (USA) Inc.**

ROC Trade *Imprint of* **Penguin Group (USA) Inc.**

Roca Editorial De Libros (ESP) *(84-96284; 84-96544)* *Dist. by* **Ediciones.**

Rocco, Editora, Ltda (BRA) *(85-325)* *Dist. by* **Distribks Inc.**

Rochester Institute of Technology, Cary Graphic Arts Pr., *(0-9713459; 0-9759651; 1-933360)* 90 Lomb Memorial Dr. Rochester Institute of Technology, Rochester, NY 14623-5604 USA Tel 585-475-6766
E-mail: ahfwml@rit.edu
Web site: http://library.rit.edu/carypress.

Rochford & Assocs., Inc., *(1-886618)* 104 New Hampshire St., Long Beach, NY 11561-1336 USA
E-mail: rochfordinc@yahoo.com
Web site: http://www.baileygirl.com.

Rock & Learn Educational Products *See* **Rock 'N Learn, Inc.**

Rock Cliff Media, *(0-9791384)* 553 Staci Ct., Ogden, UT 84404 USA
E-mail: info@rockcliffmedia.com
Web site: http://www.rockcliffmedia.com.

Rock Hill Press *See* **RockHill Communications**

Rock Ink, *(0-9726979)* 2826 Cory Creek Rd., Oroville, CA 95965 USA Tel 530-894-7743; Fax: 530-892-8293
E-mail: mlrock@mariarock.com
Web site: http://www.mariarock.com.

Rock, James A. & Co. Pubs., *(0-918736; 1-59663)* 12403 Sanit James Rd., Rockville, MD 20850 USA (SAN 211-4690) Fax: 301-294-1683; Toll Free: 800-411-2230; 9710 Traville Gateway Dr., No. 305, Rockville, MD 20850 ; *Imprints:* Castle Keep Press (Castle Keep Pr); Sense of Wonder Press (Sense of Wonder)
E-mail: jarrock@sprintmail.com
Web site: http://www.rockpublishing.com; http://www.senseofwonderpress.com
Dist(s): **Baker & Taylor Bks.**

Rock 'N Learn, Inc., *(1-878489; 1-934312)* Orders Addr.: P.O. Box 3595, Conroe, TX 77305-3595 USA Tel 936-539-2731; Fax: 936-539-2659; Toll Free Fax: 800-801-5481; Toll Free: 800-348-8445; Edit Addr.: 105 Commercial Cir., Conroe, TX 77304 USA
E-mail: info@rocknlearn.com
Web site: http://www.rocknlearn.com
Dist(s): **Big Kids Productions, Inc.**
Rounder Kids Music Distribution.

Rock Song Publishing, *(0-9673750)* 900 S. Boardman H-81, Gallup, NM 87301 USA
E-mail: rocksong@juno.com
Web site: http://www.geocities.com/mxgpix/mg3.

Rock Village Publishing, *(0-9674204; 0-9721389; 0-9766356; 1-934400)* 41 Walnut St., Middleborough, MA 02346 USA Tel 508-946-4738
E-mail: rockvillage@verizon.net.

Rockbott'm *See* **Spring Hollow Bks., LLC**

Rockhill Bks. *Imprint of* **Kansas City Star Bks.**

RockHill Communications, *(1-890604)* Div. of Bagnell & Socha, P.O. Box 522, Bala Cynwyd, PA 19004-0522 USA Toll Free: 888-762-5445
E-mail: info@rockhillcommunications.com
Web site: http://www.webfeetguides.com.

Rockmill Publishing Co., *(0-9764012)* Rockmill Management, Inc., 17360 Hunter Ct., Lake Oswego, OR 97035 USA (SAN 256-5722) Tel 503-989-2590 (phone/fax); 503-806-3970
E-mail: energiesinc@msn.com; tammystarnermotsch@msn.com.

Rockon Publishing, *(0-9726255)* 210 Hy Rd., Buda, TX 78610 USA Tel 512-295-4889
E-mail: wermundj@mail.utexas.edu.

Rocky Mountain Bks. (CAN) *(0-921102; 0-9690038; 1-894765)* *Dist. by* **Midpt Trade.**

Rocky River Pubs., LLC, *(0-944576)* P.O. Box 1679, Shepherdstown, WV 25443 USA (SAN 243-9409) Tel 304-876-2711; Fax; 304-263-2949; Toll Free: 800-343-0686
E-mail: rockyriv@intrepid.net
Web site: http://www.rockyriver.com
Dist(s): **Academic Bk. Ctr., Inc.**
Baker & Taylor Bks.
Follett Library Resources
Waldenbooks, Inc.

Rod & Staff Pubs., Inc., *(0-7399)* P.O. Box 3, 14193 Hwy. 172, Crockett, KY 41413 USA (SAN 206-7633) Tel 606-522-4348; Fax: 606-522-4896; Toll Free Fax: 800-643-1244.

†Rodale Pr., Inc., *(0-87596; 0-87857; 1-57954; 1-4050; 1-59486; 1-60529)* Orders Addr.: 16365 James Madison Hwy., Gordonsville, VA 22942-8501 USA Toll Free Fax: 800-672-2054; Toll Free: 888-330-8477; Edit Addr.: 33 E. Minor St., Emmaus, PA 18098-0099 USA (SAN 200-2477) Tel 610-967-5171; Fax: 215-967-8961; Toll Free: 800-222-4997
E-mail: info@rodale.com
Web site: http://www.rodalepress.com
Dist(s): **Bilingual Pubns. Co., The**
Lectorum Pubns., Inc.
Macmillan
STL Distribution North America
St. Martin's Pr.; *CIP.*

Rodeo Chaps (CAN) *(1-55142)* *Dist. by* **Orca Bk Pubs.**

Rodgers & Nelsen Publishing Company *See* **Loveland Pr.**

Rodopi, *(90-5183; 90-420; 90-6203)* Orders Addr.: 295 N. Michigan Ave., Suite 1b, Kenilworth, NY 07033 USA Toll Free: 800-225-3998 (within the U.S.)
E-mail: orders-queries@rodopi.nl
Web site: http://www.rodopi.nl.

Rodriguez, Estela, *(0-9772631)* Orders Addr.: 2050 NW 16th Terr., Apt. E111, Miami, FL 33125 USA Tel 305-549-3039; Edit Addr.: Jose Marti Stat. 27 & 4th St., Miami, FL 33135 USA
E-mail: colorama@bellsouth.net.

Rodro, *(0-9744770)* 52 Richmond Blvd., No. 3B, Ronkonkoma, NY 11779-3629 USA
Web site: http://www.rodro.com.

Roehm, Nancy Jean, *(0-9745591)* 545 Dogleg Ct., Roswell, GA 30076-3912 USA
E-mail: njroehm4116@aol.com.

Roehm Pubs., *(1-929792)* 7864 S. One 1/2 Rd., Wellston, MI 49689 USA Tel 248-628-6203
E-mail: roehm-pub@mindspring.com.

Rogers, Al M. Jr., *(0-9760159)* 48151 N. Laura Rogers Rd., Tickfaw, LA 70466 USA
Web site: http://www.lasttrumpgathering.com.

Rogers, Josephine H., *(0-9679975)* Orders Addr.: P.O. Box 186, Cottondale, AL 35456 USA Tel 205-556-8544; Edit Addr.: 8750 Canyon Lake, Cottondale, AL 35456 USA.

Rogers, Peggy A. *See* **Chipendo, Veronica Scholarship Fund (VCSF)**

Rogue Bear Pr., *(0-9789512)* 703 Pondside Dr. White Plains, New York, NY 10607 USA (SAN 852-0275)
Web site: http://monsterdetectiveagency.com
Dist(s): **Partners Pubs. Group, Inc.**

Rogue Wave Publishing *See* **Tonepoet Publishing**

Rohrer Design, *(0-9721138)* 725-17th St., Kenosha, WI 53140-1329 USA
Web site: http://www.rohrer-design.com.

Roland & Eleanor Bergthold, *(0-9741193)* 9133 N. Stoneridge Ln., Fresno, CA 93720 USA Tel 559-434-4137
E-mail: rolbergthold@prodigy.net; embergthold@prodigy.net.

Rolfe Leadership Institute, *(1-890984)* 9201 Jadecrest Dr., Las Vegas, NV 89134 USA Tel 702-363-9740; Fax: 702-363-9795.

Roll, Renee, *(0-9727995)* 4089 Five Mile Dr., Stockton, CA 95219 USA
E-mail: reneeroll@comcast.net.

Rolla Fine Arts Museum *See* **Westphalia Publishing**

Rolling Fork Publications *See* **Rolling Fork Publishing**

Rolling Fork Publishing, *(0-9722584)* 2485 Linebaugh Rd., Xenia, OH 45385 USA Tel 937-372-1217
E-mail: sboonern@aol.com.

Rolling Hills Pr., *(0-943978)* 17 Olive Ave., Novato, CA 94945-3428 USA (SAN 282-2601) Do not confuse with Rolling Hills Pr., in Alexandria, VA
E-mail: rhpressllc@aol.com.

Roman Catholic Bks., *(0-912141; 1-929291; 0-9793540)* Div. of Catholic Media Apostolate, Orders Addr.: P.O. Box 2286, Fort Collins, CO 80522 USA Fax: 970-493-8781; Edit Addr.: P.O. Box 993, Ridgefield, CT 06877 USA (SAN 264-7877); 1331 Red Cedar Cir., Dort Collins, CO 80524
Web site: http://www.booksforcatholics.com.

Roman, Inc., *(0-937739)* P.O. Box 552, Lombard, IL 60148-0552 USA Toll Free: 800-729-7662
Web site: http://www.roman.com.

Romancing Cathay, *(1-932592)* 10050 Montgomery Rd., No. 315, Cincinnati, OH 45242 USA Tel 513-290-7419; Fax: 949-266-8395
E-mail: business@romancingcathay.com
Web site: http://www.romancingcathay.com.

Romoulous Enterprises *See* **Miroglyphics**

Ronan, Anne M. *See* **Polka Dot Pr. Corp., The**

Ronin Publishing, *(0-914171; 1-57951)* P.O. Box 22900, Oakland, CA 94609 USA (SAN 287-5365) Tel 510-420-3669; Fax: 510-420-3672; Toll Free: 800-858-2665 (orders) Do not confuse with Ronin Publishing in Cambridge, MA
E-mail: orders@roninpub.com
Web site: http://www.roninpub.com
Dist(s): **New Leaf Distributing Co., Inc.**
Perseus Distribution.

RonJon Publishing, Inc., *(1-56870)* 3728 Arapaho Rd., Addison, TX 75001-4311 USA Toll Free: 800-262-3060
E-mail: sales@ronjonpublishing.com
Web site: http://www.ronjonpublishing.com
Dist(s): **AtlasBooks Distribution.**

Roo Pubns., *(0-9652579)* 6021 Kipps Colony Dr., E, Gulfport, FL 33707 USA Tel 727-347-7007 (phone/fax)
E-mail: hiphopmob@aol.com
Web site: http://www.roopublications.com.

Roof Publishing Co., *(0-9662025)* P.O. Box 3675, Redwood City, CA 94064 USA
Web site: http://www.roofpublishing.com.

Root, A.I. Co., *(0-936028)* Div. of Root Candle Co., Orders Addr.: P.O. Box 706, Medina, OH 44258-0706 USA (SAN 205-230X) Tel 330-725-6677; Fax: 330-725-5624; Toll Free: 800-289-7668; Edit Addr.: 623 W. Liberty St., Medina, OH 44256 USA (SAN 241-838X) Tel 216-725-6677; Toll Free: 800-768-3394
E-mail: Kim@BeeCulture.com; Sharon@BeeCulture.com
Web site: http://www.BeeCulture.com.

Roots & Wings, *(0-9703319)* 20114 Illinois Rte. 16, Nokomis, IL 62075 USA Tel 217-594-7300; Fax: 217-563-2111 Do not confuse with companies with the same name in Lake Forest, IL, New Paltz, NY, Boulder, CO
E-mail: beltpulley@ccipost.net.

Roots, Robert, *(0-9715336)* P.O. Box 171186, Miami, FL 33017 USA
E-mail: rbroots22@yahoo.com; rr@robertroots.com
Web site: http://www.robertroots.com.

Rope Ferry Pr., *(0-9759264)* 16 Rope Ferry Rd, Hanover, NH 03755 USA Tel 603-643-0922
E-mail: krusi@dartmouth.edu
Dist(s): **Biblio Distribution.**

Roque-Velasco, Dr. Ismael, *(0-9706319)* P.O. Box 432804, Miami, FL 3243 USA Tel 305-667-6230; 305-740-6724
E-mail: northernismael@aol.com
Web site: http://www.cubaforkids.com
Dist(s): **Lectorum Pubns., Inc.**

Rorschach Entertainment, *(0-9748654)* 15806 18th Ave W. Apt. F203, Lynnwood, WA 98087-8755 USA
E-mail: info@rorschachentertainment.com
Web site: http://www.rorschachentertainment.com.

Rorval Pubns., *(0-9641033)* 560 Mount Hope Ave., Rochester, NY 14620-2235 USA Tel 716-271-7127; Fax: 716-546-4788.

Rosado Arts, Inc., *(0-9664101)* Orders Addr.: P.O. Box 186, Lima, OH 45805 USA Tel 419-991-0907; Fax: 419-991-8803; Edit Addr.: 4360 Fort Amanda Rd., Lima, OH 45805 USA.

Rose Art Industries, Inc., *(1-57041)* 6 Regent St., Livingston, NJ 07039 USA Toll Free: 800-272-9667.

Rose International Publishing Hse., Inc., *(1-930574)* 3580 W. Hwy 44, Inverness, FL 34453 USA Tel 352-637-7237
E-mail: publisher@ladyliterature.com
Web site: http://www.ladyliterature-films.com; http://www.roseinternational-graphicartsdesignpublishing.com.

Rose Publishing, *(0-9655082; 1-890947; 1-59636)* 4733 Torrance Blvd., No. 259, Torrance, CA 90503-4100 USA (SAN 253-0120) Tel 310-353-2100; Fax: 310-353-2116; Toll Free: 800-532-4278 Do not confuse with companies with same or similar names in Flagtown, NJ, Arcadia, CA, Keystone Heights, FL, Salem, OR, Santa Cruz, CA, Tucson, AZ, Alameda, CA, Grand Rapids, MI, Little Rock, AR, Boulder, CO
Web site: http://www.rose-publishing.com
Dist(s): **Appalachian Bk. Distributors**
Spring Arbor Distributors, Inc.

Rose River Publishing Co., *(0-9707976)* P.O. Box 19864, Alexandria, VA 22320 USA Tel 703-768-2380 (phone/fax)
E-mail: herbpuscheck@cs.com.

Rose, Robert Inc. (CAN) *(1-896503; 0-7788) Dist. by* **Firefly Bks Limited.**

Rose Valley Publishing, *(0-9765905)* 53762 Kristin Ct., Shelby Township, MI 48316 USA
E-mail: manitoumagic@aol.com
Web site: http://www.rosevalleypublishing.com.

Rose Wind Pr., *(0-9631232)* Div. of Compass Rose Corp., 1701 Broadway, No. 345, Vancouver, WA 98663 USA Tel 360-693-7742; Fax: 360-693-0950
E-mail: galenahk@aol.com
Web site: http://www.compassart.

Rosebird Publishing, *(0-9716170)* Orders Addr.: P.O. Box 32, Weimar, CA 95736 USA Tel 530-637-5033; Edit Addr.: 20500 Natures Way, Weimar, CA 95736 USA
E-mail: rcrb@infostations.com.

Rosebriar Publishing, *(0-9653918)* 11304 1st Pl W., Everett, WA 98204-4923 USA
E-mail: rosebripub@aol.com
Web site: http://www.pms-online.org/list/5683.html
Dist(s): **Partners/West.**

Rosebrooke Co., The, *(1-879611)* Orders Addr.: 343 W. 19th St., Deer Park, NY 11729 USA Tel 631-667-6795; Toll Free Fax: 888-474-6040
E-mail: support@rosebrooke.com
Web site: http://www.rosebrooke.com.

Rosebrooke Publishing Corporation *See* **Rosebrooke Co., The**

RoseDog Bks. *Imprint of* **Dorrance Publishing Co., Inc.**

RoseFountain Pr., LLC, *(0-9768051)* 65 High ridge Rd., No. 163, Stamford, CT 06905-3814 USA
Dist(s): **Enfield Publishing & Distribution Co., Inc.**

RoseKnows, Inc., *(0-9755889)* P.O. Box 5448, McLean, VA 22103-5448 USA
Web site: http://www.playgeist.com.

Rosell, Emily, *(0-9672388)* 12311 N. E. 147th Ct., No. 1B, Kirkland, WA 98034 USA Tel 425-488-6315.

Rosemaling & Crafts, *(0-9674583)* Orders Addr.: 3208 Snowbrush Pl., Fort Collings, CO 80521 USA Tel 970-229-9846; Fax: 970-229-5683
E-mail: diaedwards@cs.com
Web site: http://www.nordic-arts.com.

Rosemont, Ltd., *(0-9635811)* 1620 Belmont St., Jackson, MS 39202-1203 USA Tel 601-355-1233.

Rosen & Assocs., Inc., *(0-9746811; 0-9778973)* P.O. Box 17173, Chapel Hill, NC 27516 USA Tel 919-264-5976; Fax: 919-929-7119
E-mail: info@cashworkbooks.com
Web site: http://www.cashworkbooks.com.

Rosen Central *Imprint of* **Rosen Publishing Group, Inc., The**

†Rosen Publishing Group, Inc., The, *(0-8239; 1-4042; 1-4358)* a/o Dept. C234561, 29 E. 21st St., New York, NY 10010 USA (SAN 203-3720) Tel 212-777-3017; Fax: 212-358-9588; Toll Free Fax: 888-436-4643; Toll Free: 800-237-9932 ; *Imprints:* PowerKids Press (PowerKids Pr); Rosen Central (Rosen Central); Buenas Letra (Buenas Letra); Powerstart Press (Powerstart Pr); Reading Room Collection (RRC)
E-mail: info@rosenpub.com; customerservice@rosenpub.com; deang@rosenpub.com
Web site: http://www.rosenpublishing.com; http://www.rosenpublishing.com/index.cfm
Dist(s): **Lectorum Pubns., Inc.**; *CIP.*

Rosen Publishing, Inc., *(1-881930)* 3000 Chestnut Ave., Suite 300, Baltimore, MD 21211 USA Tel 800-237-9932; Fax: 410-889-1320.

Rosenbach Museum & Library, The, *(0-939084)* 2010 DeLancey Pl., Philadelphia, PA 19103 USA (SAN 211-9749) Tel 215-732-1600; Fax: 215-545-7529
E-mail: rosenb1@libertynet.org; inforosenbach@rosenbach.org
Web site: http://www.rosenbach.org.

Rosenberg Publishing Pty, Ltd. (AUS) *(1-877058) Dist. by* **Intl Spec Bk.**

Rosenberger, Matthew, *(0-9760047)* Div. of ABC Publishing for Kids, One Summit St., Philadelphia, PA 19118 USA Tel 215-242-4011; Fax: 215-242-9421
E-mail: mgr@kidstravelguides.com
Web site: http://www.kidstravelguides.com.

Roses Are READ Productions, *(0-9703489; 0-9755093)* P.O. Box 7844, Saint Paul, MN 55107 USA Tel 651-686-8418; Fax: 651-340-5333 ; *Imprints:* Little Petals (Little Petals)
E-mail: admin@rosesareread.cc.

Rosetta Stone Communications, *(0-9759331)* 1971 N. Nowak Ave., Thousand Oaks, CA 91360 USA (SAN 256-1549) Tel 805-370-0010; Fax: 805-435-1541
E-mail: johngriffith@maggio-associates.com
Web site: http://www.scientificgolfer.com.

Rosmen-Izdat (RUS) *(5-8451) Dist. by* **Distribks Inc.**

Rosmen-Izdat (RUS) *(5-8451) Dist. by* **Russia Online.**

Ross, Alan Publications *See* **Ross Pubns.**

Ross & Perry, Inc., *(1-931641; 1-931839; 1-932080; 1-932109)* 3 South Haddon Avenue, Suite 43 South Haddon Avenue, Suite 43 S. Haddon Ave., Suite 4, Haddonfield, NJ 08003 USA (SAN 253-8555) Tel 856 427-6135; Fax: 856-427-6136
E-mail: jstevenson@rossperry.com
Web site: http://www.rossperry.com; http://www.gporeprints.com
Dist(s): **Baker & Taylor Bks.**
Replica Bks.

†Ross Bks., *(0-89496; 0-931272)* P.O. Box 4340, Berkeley, CA 94704 USA (SAN 209-5912) Tel 510-841-2474; Fax: 510-295-2531
E-mail: franzross@comcast.net; sales@rossbooks.com
Web site: http://www.rossbooks.com; http://www.baldar.com; *CIP.*

Ross, Cathy, *(0-9797832)* 1509 Cypress Rd., Olney, IL 62450 USA Tel 618-393-7732; Fax: 618-395-0123
E-mail: devspecinc@yahoo.com.

Ross, James, *(0-9762497)* 2634 Apache Dr., Las Cruces, NM 88007 USA Do not confuse with James Ross in Marshall, TX
Web site: http://www.geocities.com/majaross/
Dist(s): **Baker & Taylor Bks.**
Ingram Bk. Co.

Ross Pubns., *(0-9617038)* 1438 W. Lantana Rd., No. 401, Lantana, FL 33462 USA (SAN 662-8230)
E-mail: alanross@aol.com
Web site: http://www.thegenuinejesus.com
Dist(s): **Baker & Taylor Bks.**

Ross-Back Roads Pr. *See* **Ross Bks.**

Rossi, Debra, *(0-9758982)* 813 Wentwood, Southlake, TX 76092 USA.

Rotaplast Pr., *(0-9706901)* Orders Addr.: P.O. Box 1100, Kennebunkport, ME 04046 USA Tel 207-967-0118; Edit Addr.: 4 East Ave., Kennebunkport, ME 04046 USA.

Rotire, Inc., *(0-9719222)* P.O. Box 7184, Boulder, CO 80304 USA Tel 303-440-7194
E-mail: rotire@earthnet.net.

Round Cow Media Group, *(0-9745218)* Orders Addr.: P.O. Box 87, Alpharetta, GA 30009-0087 USA Tel 678-762-9053; Edit Addr.: 2822 Ashleigh Ln., Alpharetta, GA 30004 USA ; *Imprints:* Biz4Kids (Biz4Kids)
E-mail: christian@biz4kids.com
Web site: http://www.biz4kids.com.

Round Rock Chapter Bks. *Imprint of* **MidAmerica Publishing Co.**

Round Top Pr., *(0-9642160)* P.O. Box 275, Sedona, AZ 86336 USA Tel 520-282-1449; Fax: 520-204-2015.

Round Tower Pr., *(0-9765964)* P.O. Box 2942, Paradise, CA 95969-2942 USA Tel 530-872-9705; Fax: 530-872-7732; Toll Free: 888-737-9705
E-mail: thor@roundtowerpress.com
Web site: http://www.roundtowerpress.com.

Rounder Bks., *(1-57940)* 1 Rounder Way, Burlington, MA 01803-5157 USA Toll Free: 800-768-6337
E-mail: info@rounderbooks.com
Web site: http://www.rounderbooks.com/
Dist(s): **National Bk. Network.**

Roundsquare Pr., *(0-9717280)* 295 Marble St., Suite 303, Broomfield, CO 80020-2171 USA
E-mail: rs_press@msn.com.

Rourke Publishing, LLC, *(0-86592; 0-86593; 0-86625; 1-55916; 1-57103; 1-58952; 1-59515; 1-60044; 1-60472)* Orders Addr.: P.O. Box 3328, Vero Beach, FL 32963 USA Fax: 772-234-6622; Toll Free: 800-394-7055
E-mail: rourke@rourkepublishing.com; rkbrady@rourkepublishing.com
Web site: http://www.rourkepublishing.com.

Roussan Pubs., Inc./Roussan Editeur, Inc. (CAN) *(1-896184; 2-921212; 2-9800915) Dist. by* **Orca Bk Pubs.**

Route 66 Publishing, Ltd., *(0-9644293)* Orders Addr.: P.O. Box 25222, Albuquerque, NM 87125-5222 USA Tel 505-266-6128; Fax: 505-341-2608; Toll Free: 800-687-2665
E-mail: brenric@aol.com.

†Routledge, *(0-04; 0-413; 0-415; 0-7100; 0-86861; 0-87830)* Mem. of Taylor & Frances Group, Orders Addr.: 7625 Empire Dr., Florence, KY 41042 USA Toll Free Fax: 800-248-4724 (orders, customer serv.); Toll Free: 800-634-7064 (orders, customer serv.); Edit Addr.: 270 Madison Ave. # 3, New York, NY 10016-0601 USA (SAN 213-196X) ; *Imprints:* Theatre Arts Books (Thtre Arts Bks); Spon Press (Spon)
E-mail: cserve@routledge-ny.com; info@routledge-ny.com
Web site: http://www.routledge-ny.com
Dist(s): **NetLibrary, Inc.**
Oxford Univ. Pr., Inc.
Sony CONNECT, Inc.
Taylor & Francis, Inc.
Women Ink; *CIP.*

RoutledgeFalmer (GBR) *(0-415) Dist. by* **Taylor and Fran.**

Rowe, Kysha, *(0-9769339)* 2560 Yocumshire Ct., Lithonia, GA 30058 USA Tel 678-485-9266; 770-573-9325
E-mail: kysha_r@yahoo.com
Web site: http://www.whatcreaturesteachus.com; http://www.focusontheyouth.com.

Rowfant Pr., *(1-929731)* 2401 W. 27th St., N., Wichita, KS 67204 USA Tel 316-832-0309
E-mail: rowfant@hotmail.com
Web site: http://www.expage.com/RowfantPress
Dist(s): **Booksource, The.**

Rowles, Louis, *(0-9708748)* 204 12th Ave., N., Amory, MS 38821-1206 USA Tel 662-256-3865
E-mail: glrowles@network-one.com.

Rowman & Littlefield Education, *(0-8108; 1-56676; 1-57886)* Orders Addr.: 15200 NBN Way, Blue Ridge Summit, PA 17214 USA Tel 717-794-3800 (Sales, Customer Service, MIS, Royalties Inventory); Fax: 717-794-3803 (Customer Service & orders only); 717-794-3857 (Sales & MIS); 717-794-3856 (Royalties, Inventory Mgmt. & Distribution); Toll Free Fax: 800-338-4550 (Customer Service & orders); Toll Free: 800-462-6420 (Customer Service & orders); Edit Addr.: 4501 Forbes Blvd., Suite 200, Lanham, MD 20706 USA Tel 301-459-3366; Fax: 301-459-5748 Short Discount, contact rlpgsales@rowman.com
Web site: http://www.rlpgbooks.com; http://www.scarecroweducation.com
Dist(s): **National Bk. Network**
Rowman & Littlefield Pubs., Inc.

†Rowman & Littlefield Pubs., Inc., *(0-8476; 0-87471; 0-7425)* Mem. of Rowman & Littlefield Publishing Group, Inc., Orders Addr.: 15200 NBN Way, Blue Ridge Summit, PA 17214 USA Tel 717-794-3800 (Sales, Customer Service, MIS, Royalties, Inventory; Fax: 717-794-3803 (Customer Service & orders only); 717-794-3857 (Sales & MIS); 717-794-3856 (Royalties, Inventory Mgmt. & Distribution); Toll Free Fax: 800-338-4550 (Customer Service & orders); Toll Free: 800-462-6420 (Customer Service & orders); Edit Addr.: 4501 Forbes Blvd., Suite 200, Lanham, MD 20706 USA Tel 301-459-3366; Fax: 301-459-5748 ; *Imprints:* Scholarly Resources, Incorporated (ScholRes); Aronson, Jason (J Aronson); Sheed & Ward (SheWard) Short Discount, please contact rlpgsales@rowman.com
E-mail: Rogers@univpress.com; rlpgsales@rowman.com
Web site: http://www.rowmanlittlefield.com; http://www.rlpgbooks.com/bookseller/index.shtml
Dist(s): **AK Pr. Distribution**
National Bk. Network
National Film Network LLC
STL Distribution North America; *CIP.*

Rowohlt Taschenbuch Verlag GmbH (DEU) *(3-499) Dist. by* **Continental Bk.**

Rowohlt Taschenbuch Verlag GmbH (DEU) *(3-499) Dist. by* **Distribks Inc.**

Roxbury Park *Imprint of* **Lowell Hse.**

Roxbury Park Juvenile *Imprint of* **Lowell Hse. Juvenile**

Roy, Caesar A., *(0-9716138)* P.O. Box 8261, Jacksonville, TX 75766-8261 USA
E-mail: croy1934@aol.com.

Royal College of Psychiatrists (GBR) *(0-902241; 1-901242) Dist. by* **Balogh.**

Royal Fireworks Publishing Co., *(0-88092; 0-89824)* Orders Addr.: P.O. Box 399, Unionville, NY 10988 USA (SAN 240-2394) Tel 845-726-4444; Fax: 845-726-3824; Edit Addr.: 1 First Ave., Unionville, NY 10988 USA ; *Imprints:* Kav Books (Kav Bks)
E-mail: rfpress@frontiernet.net
Web site: http://www.rfwp.com/
Dist(s): **Baker & Taylor Bks.**

Royal Flush *See* **Papito Publishing**

Royal Hse. Publishing, *(0-9772671)* 2315 Market Pl., Suite E, Huntsville, AL 35801 USA Tel 256-519-2291 ; Fax: 256-519-2292.

Royal Limited Partnership, *(0-9714798)* P.O. Box 448, Eugene, OR 97440-0448 USA
E-mail: fun@funnix.com
Web site: http://www.funnix.com.

Royal Regal Bks., *(0-9719490)* Orders Addr.: P.O. Box 973, Englewood Cliffs, NJ 07632-0973 USA; Edit Addr.: 18 Old Quarry Rd., Englewood, NJ 07631 USA
E-mail: athenderson@mac.com
Web site: http://www.royalregalbooks.com
Dist(s): **Baker & Taylor Bks.**

Royal Society of Chemistry, The (GBR) *(0-85186; 0-85404; 0-85990; 0-901886; 1-870343) Dist. by* **Spri.**

Royall World Productions, *(0-9768115)* 1608 N. 13th St., Kansas City, KS 66102 USA Toll Free: 800-331-7668
E-mail: royallworldproductions@unoi.org.

Royalty Bks. International, *(0-9705458)* Orders Addr.: P.O. Box 494, Lake Charles, LA 70602 USA
E-mail: royaltybooks@email.com.

Royalty Company Two-Thousand, The *See* **Royalty Bks. International**

Royalty Publishing Co., *(0-910487)* P.O. Box 2125, Bedford, IN 47421 USA (SAN 260-1265) Fax: 812-278-8785
E-mail: nscoggan@insightbb.com
Web site: http://www.the-maximum-zone.com.

RPG Objects, *(0-9724826; 0-9743067)* 9275 Cedar Forest Rd., Eden Prairie, MN 55347 USA
E-mail: chris@rpgobjects.com
Web site: http://www.rpgobjects.com.

RPM Publishing, *(0-9764085; 0-9795126)* P.O. Box 1417, Maple Valley, WA 98038 USA Tel 425-281-8045; Fax: 425-996-0614
E-mail: sarahg@bmginc.com
Web site: http://www.sarahgerdes.com.

RS Art Studio, *(0-9787729)* 1602 Mitchell Ave., Tustin, CA 92780 USA Tel 714-724-1480
E-mail: rsart@aol.com
Web site: http://www.rsartstudio.com.

RS Publishing, *(0-9772240)* 7291 Southdale Ave., Brighton, MI 48116 USA
E-mail: directorrsp@yahoo.com
Web site: http://www.rspublish.com
Dist(s): **Partners Bk. Distributing, Inc.**

RTH ENT, *(0-9704504)* 3309 St. Catherines Way, Virginia Beach, VA 23452 USA Tel 757-486-5422; Fax: 757-493-8266; Toll Free Fax: 888-472-4462
E-mail: RTHENT@aol.com
Dist(s): **National Bk. Network.**

RTI Publishing, LLC, *(0-9769086)* 5685 S. Topaz Pl., Chandler, AZ 85249-5804 USA (SAN 256-6338)
E-mail: rtipublishing@cox.net.

RTMC Organization, LLC, *(1-934316)* P.O. Box 15105, Baltimore, MD 21282 USA (SAN 852-6923) Tel 410-900-7834
E-mail: Sales@RTMC.org
Web site: http://www.rtmc.org.

Ruach Publishing, *(0-9669910)* 1507 Central Ave., Deerfield, IL 60015 USA Tel 847-945-6421; Fax: 847-607-0217; Toll Free: 877-647-8224
E-mail: larry@ruachbooks.com
Web site: http://www.ruachbooks.com
Dist(s): **Independent Pubs. Group.**

Rubbers Bros. Comics, The AIDS Prevent Pubns. & Seminars, *(1-880058)* Orders Addr.: c/o Peter Mozeleski, 601 Starkey Rd., No. 77, Largo, FL 33771-2862 USA Tel 727-531-8410; Edit Addr.: c/o Paul Mozeleski, 72 Grand Ave., Vernon, CT 06066 USA Tel 860-870-3804.

Rubicon Bks., *(0-9771676)* P.O. Box 1167, Silver City, NM 88062-1167 USA Tel 505-388-4585 Do not confuse with companies with the same name in Montrose, CA, Glendale, AZ
E-mail: badarmstrong@signalpeak.net.

Rubicon Publishing, Inc. (CAN) *(0-921156; 1-894915) Dist. by* **Intl Pubs Mktg.**

Ruf-Fur Pubns *Imprint of* **Megaverse City Studios**

Rufio Enterprises *See* **d'ARCY LIAT**

Rugg, Sharon *See* **Rising Sun Ctr. for Loss & Renewal**

Rugg's Recommendations, *(0-9608934; 1-883062)* P.O. Box 417, Fallbrook, CA 92088-0417 USA (SAN 237-9694) Tel 760-728-4558; Fax: 760-728-4467
E-mail: frugg@thegrid.net
Web site: http://www.ruggsrecommendations.com.

Rugrups Publishing, *(0-9703487)* P.O. Box 932, Crescent City, CA 95531-0932 USA
E-mail: guyds@cs.com; Guyds@cs.com
Web site: http://www.rugrupspublishingwom.com.

Ruin Mist Pubns. *Imprint of* **Reagent Pr.**

Ruiz, Efrain, *(0-9768636)* 15 Gill Ln., Stockbridge, GA 30281 USA Tel 770-841-7774
E-mail: ltceruiz@aol.com
Web site: http://www.otoaocigars.com.

Rule of Thumb Publishing, *(0-9669794)* Orders Addr.: P.O. Box 11001, Terre Haute, IN 47801 USA Tel 812-665-4256; 812-237-2647 (day); Fax: 812-299-3397; Edit Addr.: 1325 Clover Ct., Terre Haute, IN 47802 USA
E-mail: thumb@ruleofthumb.net
Web site: http://www.ruleofthumb.com.

Rumsey Family Ministries, *(0-9719108)* 2112 Macy Ln., Greensburg, IN 47240 USA Tel 812-663-5656
E-mail: rumseyfamilyministries@juno.com.

Run With Me Publishing, *(0-9776835)* 15447 W. Monterey Ln., Kerman, CA 93630 USA Tel 559-846-6432
E-mail: runwithmepublishing@yahoo.com.

RuneStone Publishing, LLC, *(1-59648)* P.O. Box 946, Dover, NH 03821 USA
Web site: http://www.runestonepublishing.com.

Running Moose Publications, *(0-9777210)* 42400 Garfield Road, Clinton Township, MI 48038 USA
Dist(s): **Biblio Distribution.**

Running Pr. *Imprint of* **Running Pr. Bk. Pubs.**

Running Pr. Kids *Imprint of* **Running Pr. Bk. Pubs.**

Running Pr. Minature Editions *Imprint of* **Running Pr. Bk. Pubs.**

†Running Pr. Bk. Pubs., *(0-7624; 0-89471; 0-914294; 1-56138)* Div. of Perseus Books Group, 125 S. 22nd St., Philadelphia, PA 19103-4399 USA (SAN 204-5702) Tel 215-567-5080; Fax: 215-568-2919; Toll Free Fax: 800-453-2884; Toll Free: 800-345-5359 customer service ; *Imprints:* Courage Books (Courage); Running Press (RunPr); Running Press Kids (RunningKids); Running Press Miniature Editions (RunMinEdns)
E-mail: support@runningpress.com
Web site: http://www.runningpress.com
Dist(s): **Perseus Bks. Group**
Perseus Distribution
Zondervan; *CIP.*

Rupa & Co. (IND) *(81-7167; 81-291) Dist. by* **S Asia.**

Rupanuga Vedic College, *(0-9650899; 0-9728372; 1-934405)* Div. of Iskcon Krishnafest, Inc., 5201 Paseo, Kansas City, MO 64110 USA Tel 816-924-5619; Fax: 816-924-5640
E-mail: info@rvc.edu
Web site: http://www.rvc.edu.

Rural Farm Productions, *(0-9753542)* 6538 Germanton Rd., Rural Hall, NC 27045 USA Tel 336-969-2202.

RUSA, Incorporated *See* **Six Generations Publishing**

RUSH Pubns. & Educational Consultancy, LLC, *(0-9748222; 0-9748868)* 220 E. 31st St., Apt. 1D, Baltimore, MD 21218 USA Tel 443-756-1532
E-mail: maylani@superonline.com
Web site: http://www.rushsociety.com
Dist(s): **Cardinal Pubs. Group.**

Rush, Ricki, *(0-9674292)* 123 Gregory Dr., Fairfax, CA 94930 USA Tel 415-457-6422; Fax: 415-456-4459
E-mail: rickicoach@aol.com
Web site: http://lifeworks-coaching.com.

Russell, James, *(0-916367)* Orders Addr.: 205 Rainbow Dr., No. 10585, Livingston, TX 77399 USA (SAN 295-852X)
E-mail: jrpub2002@yahoo.com
Web site: http://www.jamesrussellpublishing.com.

Russell, James Publishing *See* **Russell, James**

Russia Online, Inc., Orders Addr.: P.O. Box 558, Kensington, MD 20895 USA; Edit Addr.: 3800 Howard Ave., Kensington, MD 20895 USA Tel 301-933-0607; Fax: 240-363-0598
E-mail: james@russia-on-line.com
Web site: http://russianbooks.safeshoper.com.

Russian Information & Business Center, Incorporated *See* **International Business Pubns., USA**

Rust Foundation for Literacy, Inc., The, *(1-885848)* 12021 Wilshire Blvd., No. 924, Los Angeles, CA 90025 USA Tel 818-386-1383; Fax: 818-784-1325; Toll Free: 800-676-9951 ; *Imprints:* Power for Kids Press (Power for Kids)
E-mail: PowerforKids@aol.com
Dist(s): **Penton Overseas, Inc.**

Rust, Patricia Productions *See* **Rust Foundation for Literacy, Inc., The**

†Rutgers Univ. Pr., *(0-8135)* 100 Joyce Kilmer Ave., Piscataway, NJ 08854-8099 USA (SAN 253-2115) Tel 732-445-7762; Fax: 732-445-7039; Toll Free Fax: 888-471-9014; Toll Free: 800-446-9323 (orders)
Web site: http://rutgerspress.rutgers.edu
Dist(s): **NetLibrary, Inc.**; *CIP.*

Ruth, A. Creations, *(0-9656306)* 1860 Winnewood Ln., Cincinnati, OH 45237 USA Tel 513-821-9027; Fax: 513-821-7762
E-mail: artist@annieruth.com
Web site: http://www.annieruth.com.

Rutherford Pr. (GBR) Dist. by David Brown.

Rutigliano, Joe, *(0-9767769)* 178 Ramona Ave., Staten Island, NY 10312-2717 USA.

Ruwanga Trading, *(0-9615102; 0-9701528)* P.O. Box 1027, Puunene, HI 96784 USA (SAN 694-2776)
Dist(s): **Booklines Hawaii, Ltd.**

RWP Bks. *Imprint of* **Redhawk Publishing**

RWP Interests, LLC, *(0-9679195)* 855 Harbour Pl., Sugar Land, TX 77478 USA Tel 281-491-4723; Fax: 281-491-0427
E-mail: zoolady@neosoft.com.

Rx for Reading Success..Publisher Consultant *See* **American Dream Series .. I Can Read!**

Rx Humor, *(0-9639002; 1-892157)* 2272 Vistamont Dr., Decatur, GA 30033 USA Tel 404-321-0126; Fax: 404-633-9198
E-mail: nshulma@emory.edu.

Ryan Ave Publishing, *(0-9760759)* Div. of J. C. Melvin Seminars, Inc., 5738 Hedgeford Ct., Las Vegas, NV 89120 USA Tel 702-454-9822; Fax: 702-454-9821.

Ryan Hse. Publishing, *(0-9705201)* 5125 E. Paddington Ct., Unit C, Orange, CA 92867 USA.

Ryan, Perry T., *(0-9625504)* 100 Maplewood Dr., Georgetown, KY 40324-2630 USA
E-mail: mail@ryandomain.com.

Ryan, Shirley, *(0-9754196)* 1343 Canyon Dr., Petaluma, CA 94952-4806 USA
E-mail: shirley@workingtogether1.com
Web site: http://www.workingtogether1.com.

Ryherd, Tim Publishing, *(0-9749974)* 21479 FM 365, Beaumont, TX 77705 USA.

Ryland, John B. Publishing *See* **DJ Blues Publishing**

Rymer Bks., *(0-934723; 0-9600792)* P.O. Box 153, Tollhouse, CA 93667-0153 USA (SAN 207-1010) Tel 209-298-8845.

Ryton Pubns., *(0-9633824)* P.O. Box 2306, Bellingham, WA 98227 USA Tel 360-733-7351.

Ryton Publishing *See* **Ryton Pubns.**

Ryzewski, Deborah, *(0-9765302)* 240 Crabapple Ln., Valparaiso, IN 46383 USA.

R.Z. Enterprises of Florida, *(0-9792031)* 7640 Prospect Hill Cir., New Port Richey, FL 34654-6376 USA
E-mail: rze@sanctum.com
Web site: http://www.rhymetimebob.com.

SAT Pubs., *(0-9717917)* P.O. Box 713, Grants Pass, OR 97528-0062 USA
E-mail: orders@satpub.com
Web site: http://www.satpub.com.

S & A Assocs., Inc., *(0-9702421)* 3720 E. 62nd St., Indianapolis, IN 46220 USA Tel 317-251-2008; Fax: 317-257-6170.

S&E Publishing Co., *(0-9657239)* 5 Beaver Dam Rd., Pomona, NY 10970 USA Tel 845-362-1800; Fax: 845-362-3252
E-mail: sd@scoutpatch.com
Web site: http://www.scoutpatch.com
Dist(s): **Baker & Taylor Bks.**
Barnes & Noble, Inc.
Midwest Library Service
Quality Bks., Inc.

S & S Pr., *(0-615)* 35221 SE Kinsey, Suite 101, Snoqualmie, WA 98065 USA
Web site: http://www.gloriabond.com
Dist(s): **Lulu.com.**

S&V Publishing Co., *(0-9717114)* 107 Vermont St., Travis, CA 94535 USA Tel 707-437-4579; 925-366-3934
E-mail: gutenappetite@hotmail.com.

S B C Publishing, *(0-9666843)* 9121 E. Tangue Verde, Suite 105-107, Tucson, AZ 85749 USA
Dist(s): **Origin Bk. Sales, Inc.**

SBP Collaboratioin Works, *(1-889664)* 1414 Forest Ave. Apt. 16, Portland, ME 04103-1161 USA.

SCW Pubns., *(1-877882)* 1011 Boren Ave., Suite 155, Seattle, WA 98104 USA Tel 206-682-1268
E-mail: info@poetswest.com
Web site: http://www.poetswest.com
Dist(s): **Partners/West.**

S D Enterprises, *(0-9769947)* Orders Addr.: 323 Holley Ln., Ridgeland, MS 39157 USA Tel 601-856-0060
E-mail: sdent@jam.rr.com
Web site: http://www.neverceese.com.

SIDS Educational Services, Inc., *(0-9641218)* 2905 64th Ave., Cheverly, MD 20785 USA Tel 301-773-9671; Fax: 301-322-9822
E-mail: sidses@aol.com
Dist(s): **Baker & Taylor Bks.**

S.I.E., *(1-881400)* 788 Eastern Pkwy., Brooklyn, NY 11213 USA Tel 718-778-5436; Fax: 718-735-4139
Dist(s): **Kehot Pubn. Society.**

SMC Publishing (Strategic Marketing Concepts), *(0-9663140)* Orders Addr.: P.O. Box 1178, Corona, CA 91718-1178 USA Tel 951-549-6751; Fax: 951-785-1666; Edit Addr.: 2049 Fairmont Dr., Corona, CA 91720 USA
E-mail: smcpub@aol.com.

S M G *See* **SMG Pubns.**

SMS Cos., Inc., *(0-9669595)* P.O. Box 1184, Smyrna, GA 30081 USA Tel 678-339-0626; Fax: 678-339-0726
E-mail: JMBryant@bellsouth.net
Web site: http://www.smsbooks.com
Dist(s): **Baker & Taylor Bks.**
Follett Library Resources.

S.O.C.O. Pubns., *(0-910119)* 276 Ward Rd., Mohawk, NY 13407 USA (SAN 241-5720) Tel 315-866-7445
E-mail: copress@borg.com.

SPD-Small Pr. Distribution, *(0-914068)* 1341 Seventh St., Berkeley, CA 94710-1409 USA (SAN 204-5826) Tel 510-524-1668; Fax: 510-524-0852; Toll Free: 800-869-7553 (orders)
E-mail: orders@spdbooks.org
Web site: http://www.spdbooks.org.

SPI Bks., *(0-944007; 1-56171)* 99 Spring St., 3rd Flr., New York, NY 10012 USA Tel 212-431-5011; Fax: 212-431-8646
E-mail: ian@spibooks.com
Web site: http://www.spibooks.com
Dist(s): **APG Sales and Fulfillment**
Perseus Distribution.

SPIE-International Society for Optical Engineering, *(0-8194; 0-89252)* Orders Addr.: P.O. Box 10, Bellingham, WA 98227-0010 USA (SAN 224-1706) Tel 360-676-3290; Fax: 360-647-1445; Edit Addr.: 1000 20th St., Bellingham, WA 98225 USA (SAN 669-1323)
E-mail: spie@spie.org
Web site: http://www.spie.org/bookstore.

S.Q. Productions, Inc., *(0-86562)* P.O. Box 248, Columbus, NJ 08022 USA (SAN 222-965X) Tel 609-298-5111; Fax: 609-298-0525 (orders); Toll Free: 800-648-4789 (orders)
E-mail: salq1@comcast.net
Web site: http://www.sqpinc.com
Dist(s): **Diamond Comic Distributors, Inc.**

S T A T S Publishing, *(0-9625581; 1-884064; 1-931584)* 8130 Lehigh Ave., Morton Grove, IL 60053 USA Tel 847-583-2100; Fax: 847-470-9140; Toll Free: 800-637-8287
E-mail: balock@stats.com
Web site: http://www.stats.com.

S V E & Churchill Media, *(0-7932; 0-89290; 1-56357)* 6465 N. Avondale Ave., Chicago, IL 60631-1909 USA (SAN 208-3930) Toll Free Fax: 800-624-1678; Toll Free: 800-829-1900
E-mail: custserv@svemedia.com
Web site: http://www.svemedia.com
Dist(s): **Video Project, The**
Weston Woods Studios, Inc.

†SYDA Foundation, *(0-911307; 0-914602; 1-930939)* 371 Brickman Rd., South Fallsburg, NY 12779 USA (SAN 206-5649) Tel 845-434-2000 Toll Free Fax: 888-422-2339 (ordering); Toll Free: 888-422-3334 (ordering); P.O. Box 600, South Fallsburg, NY 12779 ; *Imprints:* Siddha Yoga Publication (Siddha Yoga Pubs)
Web site: http://www.siddhayoga.org
Dist(s): **Bookpeople**
Independent Pubs. Group
New Leaf Distributing Co., Inc.; *CIP.*

S2 Services, *(0-9770928)* 9006 Friars Rd., Bethesda, MD 20817 USA (SAN 257-3377) Tel 301-493-4982
E-mail: socrtwo@s2services.com
Web site: http://www.cafepress.com/simplysilly/481903; http://www.socrtwo.info/portfolio.htm; http://people.lulu.com/users/index.php?fHomepage=179563
Dist(s): **CafePress.com**
Lulu.com.

S.A. Kokinos (ESP) *(84-88342; 84-96629) Dist. by* **Lectorum Pubns.**

Sabi Wiri Inc., *(0-9760961)* 796 Jefferson Ave., Brooklyn, NY 11221 USA Tel 718-919-9279
E-mail: info@going-natural.com
Web site: http://going-natural.com.

Sable Creek Pr. LLC, *(0-9766823)* P.O. Box 12217, Glendale, AZ 85318 USA
E-mail: sablecreekpress@cox.net
Web site: http://www.sablecreekpress.com.

Sabledrake Enterprises, *(0-9702189; 0-9771005)* P.O. Box 30751, Seattle, WA 98113 USA Tel 425-317-9241; Fax: 772-673-2381
E-mail: tim@sabledrake.com
Web site: http://www.sabledrake.com.

Sabre Publishing Hse., Inc., *(0-9746213)* 201 Huff Lake Ct., Ortonville, MI 48462 USA Tel 248-627-1112; Fax: 248-627-1113
E-mail: mikeatsabre@aol.com.

Sabyr Pr., *(0-9746463)* 2999 Allmon Ln., Missouri Vly, IA 51555-5057 USA
E-mail: info@sabyr.com
Web site: http://www.sabyr.com.

Sacred Mountain Foundation, A California Non Profit Public Pubns. *(0-9726639)* Nine Penninsula Rd., Belvedere, CA 94920 USA (SAN 255-0768) Tel 415-751-3200; Fax: 415-751-3233
E-mail: sacred-mountain@att.net.

Sacred Scales Publishing, *(0-9710772)* Orders Addr.: P.O. Box 7073, Loveland, CO 80537 USA Tel 970-663-1171
E-mail: rogerjames@yahoo.com
Web site: http://www.sacredscales.com.

Saddle & Bridle, Inc., *(0-9655501)* 375 Jackson Ave., Saint Louis, MO 63130-4243 USA Tel 314-725-9115; Fax: 314-725-6440
E-mail: saddlebr@saddleandbridle.com
Web site: http://www.saddleandbridle.com
Dist(s): **Baker & Taylor Bks.**

Saddle Pal Creations *See* **Saddle Pal Creations, Inc.**

Saddle Pal Creations, Inc., *(0-9663495; 1-931353)* Orders Addr.: P.O. Box 872127, Wasilla, AK 99687-2127 USA Tel 907-357-3235; Fax: 907-357-3446
Web site: http://www.alaskachildrensbooks.com
Dist(s): **Partners Bk. Distributing, Inc.**
Partners/West
Wizard Works.

Saddle Tree Pr., *(0-9666433)* Orders Addr.: P.O. Box 26565, Fraser, MI 48026 USA Tel 586-293-5855; Fax: 586-293-5542; Edit Addr.: 31721 Northwood, Fraser, MI 48026 USA Tel 810-293-5855
E-mail: info@saddletreepress.com
Web site: http://www.saddletreepress.com; http://www.littlehorseybook.com.

Saddleback Educational Publishing, *(1-56254; 1-59905; 1-60291)* Three Watson, Irvine, CA 92618-2716 USA Tel 949-860-2500; Fax: 949-860-2508; Toll Free: 888-735-2225
E-mail: cpizer@sdlback.com; jgrexton@sdlback.com
Web site: http://www.sdlback.com.

Saddleback Publishing, Incorporated *See* **Saddleback Educational Publishing**

Saddlebag Pr., *(0-9716703)* 6848 NW 25 Way, Fort Lauderdale, FL 33309-1417 USA Tel 954-973-1195
E-mail: hjohn80@aol.com.

Sadlier *Imprint of* **Sadlier, William H. Inc.**

Sadlier, William H. Inc., *(0-8215; 0-87105; 1-4217)* 9 Pine St., New York, NY 10005-1002 USA (SAN 204-0948) Tel 212-227-2120; Fax: 212-267-8696; Toll Free: 800-221-5175 ; *Imprints:* Sadlier-Oxford (Sadlier-Oxford); Sadlier (Sadlier)
Web site: http://www.sadlier.com.

Sadlier-Oxford *Imprint of* **Sadlier, William H. Inc.**

Sadorian Pubns., *(0-9700102; 0-9718148; 0-9741714)* P.O. Box 2443, Durham, NC 27715 USA (SAN 253-7834) Tel 919-599-3038; Fax: 309-431-4387
E-mail: sadorianllc@aol.com
Web site: http://www.sadorianonline.com
Dist(s): **Baker & Taylor Bks.**
Brodart Co.
Culture Plus Bk. Distributors
Midwest Library Service
Yankee Bk. Peddler, Inc.

Safari, Ltd., *(1-881469)* Orders Addr.: P.O. Box 630685, Miami, FL 33163 USA Tel 305-621-1000; Fax: 305-621-6894; Toll Free: 800-554-5414; Edit Addr.: 1400 NW 159th St., Miami, FL 33169 USA
Web site: http://www.toydirectory.com.

S.A.F.E. for Children Publishing, LLC, *(0-9711735)* 1814 E. Second St., Scotch Plains, NJ 07076 USA (SAN 254-606X) Tel 908-490-9090
Web site: http://www.safeforchildren.com
Dist(s): **Independent Pubs. Group.**

Safe Harbor Pr., *(0-9715840)* 3222 Robin's Trace, Akron, OH 44319 USA Tel 330-644-6489 Do not confuse with Safe harbor Press in Lancaster, CA
E-mail: caanje@msn.com.

Safe Harbor Pubns., *(0-9760416)* P.O. Box 396, Titusville, FL 32781 USA
E-mail: admin@rikerbooks.com
Web site: http://www.rikerbooks.com
Dist(s): **Baker & Taylor Bks.**

Safe Harbour Pr., *(0-9631050; 1-929895)* Div. of Interprel Corp., 738 Martin Blvd., Glenwillard, PA 15046-0331 USA Tel 724-457-7753.

Safer Society Pr., *(1-884444)* Div. of Safer Society Foundation, Inc., Orders Addr.: P.O. Box 340, Brandon, VT 05733-0340 USA Tel 802-247-3132; Fax: 802-247-4233; Edit Addr.: 8-10 Conant Sq., Brandon, VT 05733-1121 USA
E-mail: Theream@saver.net
Web site: http://www.safersociety.org.

Safety Always Matters, Inc., *(0-9620584; 1-883994)* 222 Wildwood Ct., Bloomingdale, IL 60108 USA (SAN 248-9759) Tel 630-894-1229
Dist(s): **Syndistar, Inc.**

Safety Ctr., *(1-888241)* 5775 North Bay Road, Miami Beach, FL 33140 USA.

Safeworld Publishing Co., *(0-9655604)* Orders Addr.: P.O. Box 425, Owings Mills, MD 21117 USA; Edit Addr.: 10733 Hewitt Farms Rd., Owings Mills, MD 21117 USA Tel 410-581-8958
Dist(s): **Baker & Taylor Entertainment**
Baker & Taylor Bks.

Sagamore Publishing, L.L.C., *(0-915611; 1-57167; 1-58382)* 804 N. Neil St., Champaign, IL 61820-3015 USA (SAN 292-5788) Tel 217-359-5940; Fax: 217-359-5975; Toll Free: 800-327-5557 (orders only)
E-mail: books@sagamorepub.com
Web site: www.recreationprogramming.com; http://www.sagamorepub.com.

Sagaponack Bks., *(0-9668845)* 7324 A1A S., Saint Augustine, FL 32080-8111 USA Tel 904-471-5376; Toll Free: 800-450-7383
E-mail: Publisher@SagBooks.com
Web site: http://www.SagaponackBooks.com.

Sage Creek Pr. *Imprint of* **Rhodes & Easton**

Sage Hill Pubs., LLC, *(0-913205)* Orders Addr.: P.O. Box 866, Yerington, NV 89447 USA (SAN 283-0493) Tel 775-463-4188 (phone/fax)
E-mail: booksbysagehill@aol.com.

Sage, Joan, *(0-9669813)* 914 Kimball St., Philadelphia, PA 19147 USA.

†SAGE Pubns., Inc., *(0-7619; 0-8039; 1-4129)* 2455 Teller Rd., Thousand Oaks, CA 91320-2218 USA (SAN 204-7217) Tel 805-499-9774; 800-818-7243; Fax: 800-583-2665; 805-499-0871
E-mail: info@sagepub.com
Web site: http://www.sagepub.com; http://www.sagepub.co.uk; http://www.pineforge.com
Dist(s): **Ambassador Bks. & Media**
Baker & Taylor Bks.
Coutts Library Service, Inc.
Cranbury International
Emery-Pratt Co.
MBS Textbook Exchange, Inc.
Midwest Library Service
Blackwell North America
NACSCORP, Inc.
Yankee Bk. Peddler, Inc.; *CIP.*

Sagebrush Education Resources *See* **Tandem Library Bks.**

Sagebrush Entertainment, Inc., *(0-9766557)* P.O. Box 261187, Encino, CA 91426-1187 USA Toll Free Fax: 800-881-4577; Toll Free: 800-711-4677
E-mail: info@hopalong.com
Web site: http://www.hopalong.com.

SageBrush Exchange, *(0-9762728)* P.O. Box 525, Buckner, MO 64016 USA Tel 816-305-6916
E-mail: toby@homeisp.com
Web site: http://www.prairielabyrinth.com; http://www.chakralabyrinth.com.

SageWorks Pr., *(0-9634618; 0-9790503)* P.O. Box 441, Fairfax, CA 94978 USA Tel 415-258-9924 Do not confuse with companies with the same name in Phoenix, AZ, Oklahoma City, OK, or Glenwood Springs, CO
E-mail: mw@sageworks.net
Web site: http://www.making-a-difference.com
Dist(s): **SCB Distributors.**

SageWorks Press of San Anselmo *See* **SageWorks Pr.**

St. Alban Pr., San Diego, *(0-935461)* Div. of Liberal Catholic Church, 741 Cerro Gordo Ave., San Diego, CA 92102 USA (SAN 695-8664)
E-mail: info@stalbanpress.com
Web site: http://www.liberalcatholic.org; http://www.StAlbanPress.com.

St. Anthony Messenger Pr. & Franciscan Communications, *(0-86716; 0-912228)* Subs. of Franciscan Friars (St. John Baptist Province), 28 W. Liberty St., Cincinnati, OH 45202 USA (SAN 204-6237) Tel 513-241-5615; Fax: 513-241-1197; Toll Free: 800-488-0488 ; *Imprints:* Servant Books (ServBks)
Web site: http://www.AmericanCatholic.org
Dist(s): **Appalachian Bk. Distributors**
Baker & Taylor Bks.
Forward Movement Pubns.
Spring Arbor Distributors, Inc.

St. Augustine's Pr., Inc., *(1-890318; 1-58731)* P.O. Box 2285, South Bend, IN 46680 USA Tel 574-291-3500; Fax: 574-291-3700; Toll Free: 888-997-4994
E-mail: bruce@staugustine.net
Web site: http://www.staugustine.net
Dist(s): **Chicago Distribution Ctr.**
Univ. of Chicago Pr.

St. Charles Enterprises, *(0-9651394)* 19807 First Ave., S., Seattle, WA 98148-2493 USA Tel 206-878-3329; Fax: 206-824-4377
Dist(s): **Northwest Archery Co., Inc.**

St. John of Kronstadt Pr., The, *(0-912927; 1-928920)* Div. of Russian Orthodox Church Outside Russia, 1180 Orthodox Way, Liberty, TN 37095 USA (SAN 283-3980) Tel 615-536-5239; Fax: 615-536-5945; Toll Free Fax: 800-581-7340
E-mail: info@kronstadt.org; sales@kronstadt.org
Web site: http://www.kronstadt.org.

St. Johns Pr., *(0-9676067)* 400 Old Orchard Rd., Baltimore, MD 21229 USA Tel 410-362-4347.

St. Joseph Media, *(0-9715061)* Subs. of Mount Saint Michael, P.O. Box 186, Wayne, MI 48184 USA Fax: 734-729-9350
Web site: http://www.stjosephschurch.net/media.htm.

Saint Joseph's Catholic Church *See* **St. Joseph Media**

St. Lucie Pr., *(0-9634030; 1-57444; 1-878205; 1-884015)* Div. of CRC Pr., 2000 Corporate Blvd., NW, Boca Raton, FL 33431-7372 USA (SAN 297-9489) Tel 561-274-9906; Fax: 561-274-9927; Toll Free: 800-272-7737
E-mail: information@slpress.com
Web site: http://www.slpress.com.

St. Mark's Community Ctr., *(0-9708184)* 1130 N. Rampart St., New Orleans, LA 70116 USA Tel 504-529-1681 ext 12; Fax: 504-522-9987.

St. Mary's Pr., *(0-88489; 1-59982)* 702 Terrace Heights, Winona, MN 55987-1320 USA (SAN 203-073X) Tel 507-457-7900; Toll Free Fax: 800-344-9225; Toll Free: 800-533-8095
E-mail: smpress@smp.org
Web site: http://www.smp.org.

St. Nectarios Pr., *(0-913026)* 10300 Ashworth Ave., N., Seattle, WA 98133-9410 USA (SAN 203-3542) Tel 206-522-4471; Fax: 206-523-0550; Toll Free: 800-643-4233
E-mail: orders@orthodoxpress.org
Web site: http://www.stnectanospress.com.

St. Nicholas Monastery, *(0-9773579)* 1340 Piney Rd., North Fort Myers, FL 33903-3822 USA.

Saint Paul Books & Media *See* **Pauline Bks. & Media**

St. Vincent Archabbey Pubns., *(0-9708216; 0-9773909)* 300 Fraser Purchase Rd., Latrobe, PA 15650-2690 USA Tel 724-805-2601; Fax: 724-805-2775
E-mail: kim.metzgar@email.stvincent.edu
Web site: http://www.stvincentstore.com.

St. Vincent College Ctr. for Northern Appalachian Studies, *(1-885851)* 300 Fraser Purchase Rd., Latrobe, PA 15650 USA Tel 724 539-9761 ext 2316; Fax: 724-537-4554
E-mail: rwissolik@stvincent.edu
Web site: http://www.facweb.stvincent.edu/academics/english/faculty/wissolik/center.htm.

†St. Vladimir's Seminary Pr., *(0-88141; 0-913836; 0-9622536)* 575 Scarsdale Rd., Yonkers, NY 10707 USA (SAN 204-6296) Tel 914-961-2203; Fax: 914-961-5456; Toll Free: 800-204-2665
E-mail: deborah@svots.edu; dhickman@svots.edu
Web site: http://www.svspress.com
Dist(s): **Orthodox Christian Pubns. Ctr.**; *CIP.*

Saints Alive Pr., *(0-9650704)* 4707 Mount Hood Dr., Bakersfield, CA 93309 USA Tel 805-398-8571; Fax: 805-398-8608.

Saints Of Glory Church, *(0-9673342)* Orders Addr.: P.O. Box 8957, Anaheim, CA 92812-0957 USA Tel 714-846-0401; Fax: 714-846-3395; Edit Addr.: 16102 Warmington Ln., Huntington Beach, CA 92649 USA
E-mail: sgcgow@aol.com.

Sakthi Bks., Inc., *(0-9752586)* P.O. Box 1466, Fairfield, IA 52556 USA
E-mail: sakthibooks@yahoo.com
Web site: http://www.matrixjourney.com; http://www.journeytothesource.com.

Sakura Pr., *(0-9660583)* Hesta Roach 227 Croatan Dr., Oriental, NC 28571 USA Tel 252-249-1929 (phone/fax) Do not confuse with Sakura Pr., Pleasant Hill, OR
E-mail: roachdj@hotmail.com.

Salado Pr., LLC, *(0-9663870)* Orders Addr.: P.O. Box 941006, Plano, TX 75094-1006 USA Tel 972-437-9131; Fax: 972-437-9710
E-mail: lee@saladopress.com
Web site: http://www.salaodpress.com
Dist(s): **Baker & Taylor Bks.**

Salamander Group, Inc., The, *(1-890616)* Orders Addr.: P.O. Box 52628, Boston, MA 02205 USA Tel 313-549-8950 Do not confuse with companies with similar names in Evanston, IL, Yazoo City, MS
E-mail: info@littlesalamander.com; pam@littlesalamander.com
Web site: http://www.littlesalamander.com.

Salamander Press, Incorporated *See* **Salamander Group, Inc., The**

Salani (ITA) *(88-7782) Dist. by* **Distribks Inc.**

Salaud Publishing, *(0-9713167)* P.O. Box 11681, Portland, OR 97211 USA Tel 919-963-9135
E-mail: jesse@hastardrecords.com; jesse@bastardrecords.com; jordan_lari@highcountrystudentpublishers.org
Web site: http://www.highcountrystudentpubishers.org; http://www.bastardrecords.com/salaud.htm.

Salch, Megan F., *(0-9776154)* 3106 Lawrence St., Houston, TX 77018 USA Tel 713-864-1344
Dist(s): **AtlasBooks Distribution.**

†Salem Pr., Inc., *(0-89356; 1-58765)* Orders Addr.: Two University Plaza, Suite 121, Hackensack, NJ 07601 USA (SAN 241-841X) Tel 201-968-9899; Fax: 201-968-1411; Toll Free: 800-221-1592 ; *Imprints:* Magill's Choice (Magills Choice)
E-mail: csr@salempress.com
Web site: http://www.salempress.com
Dist(s): **NetLibrary, Inc.**; *CIP.*

Sales Effectivness, Inc., *(0-9676255)* 570 W. Crossville Rd., Suite 103, Roswell, GA 30075 USA Tel 770-552-6612; Fax: 770-643-8205
E-mail: info@saleseffectiveness.com
Web site: http://www.saleseffectiveness.com.

Salina Bookshelf, *(0-9644189; 1-893354)* 1254 W. University Ave., Suite 130, Flagstaff, AZ 86001 USA (SAN 253-0503) Tel 928-527-0070; Fax: 928-526-0386; Toll Free: 877-527-0070
E-mail: sales@salinabookshelf.com
Web site: http://www.salinabookshelf.com
Dist(s): **National Bk. Network.**

Sally Ride Science, *(0-9753920; 1-933798)* 9191 Towne Centre Dr. Ste. L101, San Diego, CA 92122-6204 USA Tel 858-638-1432; Fax: 858-638-1419; Toll Free: 800-561-5161
E-mail: tam@sallyridescience.com; bleck@sallyridescience.com
Web site: http://www.sallyridescience.com.

Salmon Hole Poetry Pr., *(0-9742516)* 406 Colchester Ave., Burlington, VT 05401 USA Tel 802-865-9603
E-mail: marcawodey@mac.com.

Salmon Publishing (IRL) *(0-948339; 1-897648; 1-903392) Dist. by* **Dufour.**

Salmon Run Pr., *(0-9634000; 1-887573)* Orders Addr.: P.O. Box 672130, Chugiak, AK 99567-2130 USA Tel 907-688-4268
E-mail: salmonrp@aol.com
Dist(s): **Partners/West**
SPD-Small Pr. Distribution
Todd Communications
Wizard Works.

Salmon Run Publishing Company *See* **Salmon Run Pr.**

Salt City Books, *(0-9776332)* P.O. Box 6, Farmington, UT 84025-0006 USA (SAN 257-8522) Tel 801-309-7820
E-mail: saltcitybooks@msn.com
Web site: http://www.saltcitybooks.com
Dist(s): **Baker & Taylor Bks.**

Salt City Systems *See* **Salt Pubs.**

Salt Marsh Pubns., *(1-929202)* 163 Grand Oak Cir., Venice, FL 34292 USA Tel 941-484-9953; Toll Free: 888-441-2436
E-mail: smp@coastalnet.com
Dist(s): **Baker & Taylor Bks.**
Parnassus Bk. Distributors
Southern Bk. Service.

Salt Productions, Inc., *(0-9746001)* P.O. Box 306, Grapevine, TX 76051 USA Tel 817-858-0998; Fax: 817-354-4195; Toll Free: 877-430-7258
E-mail: info@shakeandlearn.com
Web site: http://www.shakeandlearn.com.

Salt Pubs., *(0-9709940; 0-9725804)* 6163 E. Molloy Rd., East Syracuse, NY 13057 USA Tel 315-437-1139; Fax: 315-463-2055; Toll Free: 800-324-2607
E-mail: salt@twcny.rr.com.

Salt Publishing (GBR) *(1-876857; 1-901994; 1-84471) Dist. by* **SPD-Small Pr Dist.**

Salt River Press *See* **Summerland Pr.**

Salty DeSK Pubns., *(0-9668263)* 5454 Oley Tpke. Rd., Reading, PA 19606-9572 USA Tel 610-779-1848
E-mail: deb_sk@juno.com.

Salvo Pr., *(0-9664520; 1-930486)* Orders Addr.: P.O. Box 7396, Beaverton, OR 97007-7396 USA
E-mail: schmidt@salvopress.com
Web site: http://www.salvopress.com
Dist(s): **Baker & Taylor Bks.**
Ingram Bk. Co.
Seven Locks Pr.

Saman Publishing, *(0-9728020)* 751 Lemonwood Ct., San Jose, CA 95120 USA.

Samara Pr., *(0-9577556)* c/o Trillium Hse., 241 Bonita, Los Trancos Woods, Portola Valley, CA 94028-8103 USA Tel 650-851-1847.

Sampson, Lynda Owens *See* **Public Relations Outreach, Inc.**

Sams, *(0-672; 0-8104)* Div. of Pearson Technology Group, 800 E. 96th St. Ste. 300, Indianapolis, IN 46240-3759 USA Toll Free Fax: 800-882-8583; Toll Free: 800-428-5331 (orders)
Web site: http://www.samspublishing.com
Dist(s): **Alpha Bks.**
Pearson Education
Pearson Technology Group
Sams Technical Publishing, LLC.

Sams, II, Carl R. Photography, Inc., *(0-9671748; 0-9770108)* 361 Whispering Pines, Milford, MI 48380-3807 USA Tel 248-685-2422; Fax: 248-685-1643; Toll Free: 800-552-1867
E-mail: carlsams@ameritech.net
Web site: http://www.carlsams.com; http://www.strangerinthewoods.com
Dist(s): **Partners Bk. Distributing, Inc.**

Sams Technical Publishing, LLC, *(0-7906)* 9850 E. 30th St., Indianapolis, IN 46229 USA Toll Free Fax: 800-552-3910; Toll Free: 800-428-7267 ; *Imprints:* Indy-Tech Publishing (Indy-Tech Pubng)
E-mail: samstech@samswebsite.com
Web site: http://www.samswebsite.com
Dist(s): **Cardinal Pubs. Group.**

Samson Pr., *(0-9721166)* 20610 Jayhawk Dr., Chugiak, AK 99577-5888 USA Tel 907-688-9068; Fax: 907-688-9069; Toll Free: 866-688-9068
E-mail: leebee@mtaonline.net
Dist(s): **Todd Communications.**

Samuels, Ami, *(0-9715430)* 21931 Canterbury, Grosse Ile, MI 48138 USA Tel 734-675-9393
E-mail: asamuels9@home.com.

San Diego Business Accounting Solutions a Non CPA Firm, *(0-9746093; 0-9794124)* Orders Addr.: P.O. Box 1128, Lakeside, CA 92040 USA Tel 619-312-0454; Fax: 619-312-0510
E-mail: julieaydlott@cox.net
Web site: http://www.sdbas.biz.

San Diego County Regional Airport Authority, *(0-9745294)* P.O. Box 82776, San Diego, CA 92138-2776 USA Tel 619-400-2400; Fax: 619-400-2866
Web site: http://www.san.org.

San Francisco Art Commission, The, *(1-888048)* 800 Chestnut St., San Francisco, CA 94133 USA Tel 415-771-7020; Fax: 415-252-2595 ; *Imprints:* WritersCorps Books (WrtrsCorps Bks).

San Francisco Story Works, *(0-9774227)* 386 Union St., San Francisco, CA 94133-3516 USA (SAN 257-5248)
Web site: http://www.pengey.com.

San Francisco Study Ctr., *(0-936434; 1-888956)* 1095 Market St., Rm. 602, San Francisco, CA 94103 USA (SAN 214-4654) Tel 415-626-1650; Fax: 415-626-7276; Toll Free: 888-281-3757 ; *Imprints:* Study Center Press (Study Ctr Pr)
E-mail: marjorie@studycenter.org
Web site: http://www.studycenter.org.

San Gabriel Pr., *(0-9721501)* Orders Addr.: P.O. Box 40279, Pasadena, CA 91114 USA (SAN 254-6345) Tel 626-797-9272; Fax: 626-797-4230; Edit Addr.: 1927 E. Washington Blvd., Pasadena, CA 91104 USA
E-mail: fdw@sbcglobal.net
Web site: http://www.sangabrielpress.com.

San Juan Publishing, *(0-9707399)* Orders Addr.: P.O. Box 923, Woodinville, WA 98072 USA
E-mail: sanjuanbooks@yahoo.com
Dist(s): **Partners Bk. Distributing, Inc.**

Sananda Publications *See* **Reverence for Life**

Sancho Storybooks, *(0-9773243)* P.O. Box 356, N. Pomfret, VT 05053 USA Tel 802-763-7523.

Sanctuary Bks., *(0-9753334)* P.O. Box 1623, New York, NY 10028 USA Do not confuse with companies with the same or similar name in Mount Juliet, TN, Tampa, FL
E-mail: sanctuarybooks@earthlink.net
Web site: http://www.sanctuarybks.com.

Sanctuary Pr., *(0-9676438)* 11566 S. Newman Rd., Maple City, MI 49664 USA Tel 616-228-4262 Do not confuse with companies with the same name in Lenoir, NC, Franklin, NC.

Sandbox Bks., *(0-9755184)* 6561 Portage Rd., DeForest, WI 53532-0000 USA
Web site: http://www.sandboxbooks.com.

SandCastle *Imprint of* **ABDO Publishing Co.**

Sandcastle Publishing, *(0-9627756; 1-883995)* Orders Addr.: P.O. Box 3070, South Pasadena, CA 91031-6070 USA Fax: 323-255-3616; Edit Addr.: 1723 Hill Dr., South Pasadena, CA 91030 USA Tel 213-255-3616 Do not confuse with Sandcastle Publishing, Orleans, MA
E-mail: info@sandcastle-online.com; rwhatley@sandcastle-online.com
Web site: http://www.sandcastle-online.com
Dist(s): **Baker & Taylor Bks.**
Quality Bks., Inc.
Unique Bks., Inc.

Sanders, Cheryl *See* **Jollyville Pr.**

Sandhaus, Paul Assocs., Inc., *(1-893266)* 965 5th Ave. # 12C, New York, NY 10021-1709 USA
E-mail: psandhaus@aol.com.

†Sandlapper Publishing Co., Inc., *(0-87844)* Orders Addr.: P.O. Box 730, Orangeburg, SC 29115 USA (SAN 203-2678) Toll Free Fax: 800-337-9420 (orders); Toll Free: 800-849-7263 (orders); Edit Addr.: 1281 Amelia St., NE., Orangeburg, SC 29116 USA Tel 803-533-1658; Fax: 803-534-5223
Web site: http://www.sandlapperpublishing.com
Dist(s): **Baker & Taylor Bks.**
Parnassus Bk. Distributors; *CIP.*

Sandner-Petersen International Bks., *(0-9744852)* 5112 Coronado Pkwy., No.11, Cape Coral, FL 33904 USA Tel 739-549-3028; Fax: 239-549-5547.

Sandvik Innovations, LLC, *(1-932915)* 460 E. Swedesford Rd., Suite 2030, Wayne, PA 19087 USA Tel 610-975-3585; Fax: 610-975-3587
Web site: http://www.sandvikinnovations.com
Dist(s): **National Bk. Network.**

Sandvik Publishing, *(1-58048; 1-881445)* Div. of Sandviks Bokforlag, Norway, 3729 Knights Rd., Bensalem, PA 19020-2908 USA Toll Free: 800-843-2445
E-mail: Nicole@sandvikpublishing.com; cust-serv@sandvikpublishing.com
Web site: http://www.sandviks.com
Dist(s): **National Bk. Network.**

Sandwich Islands Publishing, *(0-9624676; 1-884364)* Orders Addr.: P.O. Box 10669, Lahaina, HI 96761 USA (SAN 297-9551) Tel 808-661-8177; Fax: 808-661-2715; Edit Addr.: P.O. Box 10669, Lahaina, HI 96761-0669 USA
E-mail: gamebooks@aol.com
Web site: http://www.gamebooks.com
Dist(s): **Distributors, The**
Gamebooks.com.

Sandwight Publishing Co., *(0-9706671)* 2241 Buchanan Ct., Westland, MI 48186 USA Tel 734-595-6066 (phone/fax)
E-mail: dwight_whitfield@ameritech.net.

Sandy Bay Publishing, *(0-9701285)* Orders Addr.: P.O. Box 580, Hatteras, NC 27943-0580 USA Tel 252-986-2195; Fax: 252-986-2372; Edit Addr.: 56187 Pamlico Dr., Hatteras, NC 27973-0580 USA Tel 252-986-2195
E-mail: joannewhale@earthlink.net.

Sandy Convertible, LLC, *(0-9670749)* 1326 Cool Creek Dr, Carmel, IN 46033 USA Tel 317-848-4840; Fax: 317-848-4841.

SangFroid Pr., *(0-917939)* 34 Water St., Excelsior, MN 55331 USA (SAN 657-0178) Tel 952-474-6220; Fax: 952-474-6221 Do not confuse with Sang Froid in New York, NY
Dist(s): **Independent Pubs. Group.**

Sanguine Productions, Ltd., *(0-9704583; 1-932592)* 2692 Madison Rd. No.279, Cincinnati, OH 45208 USA Tel 312-803-1961 (phone/fax)
E-mail: biz@ironclaw.gs
Web site: http://www.ironclaw.gs
Dist(s): **Wizard's Attic, The.**

Sankofa Bks. *Imprint of* **Just Us Bks., Inc.**

Sankofa Publishing Co., *(0-9667215)* Orders Addr.: P.O. Box 20066, Lansing, MI 48901-0666 USA Tel 517-394-4023; Fax: 517-394-4544; Edit Addr.: 4817 Bristol, Lansing, MI 48910 USA
E-mail: sshule2@aol.com.

SanPaul Group, LLC, The, *(0-9670875)* 17704 Wormer St., Detroit, MI 48219 USA (SAN 253-6013) Tel 313-533-7383; Fax: 313-533-1559
E-mail: gtpspg@cs.com
Web site: http://www.qtpieworld.com.

Sanpitch Pr., *(0-9760607)* 141 S. Main, Manti, UT 84642 USA Tel 435-835-6271; Fax: 435-835-8431; Toll Free: 800-748-4660
E-mail: sanman@horseshoetrader.com.

Sanron Educ. Enterprises, Inc., *(0-9727748; 0-9774584)* 5140 SW 109 Ave., Fort Lauderdale, FL 33328-4726 USA Tel 954-680-6052; Fax: 954-680-3270; Toll Free: 888-604-8063
E-mail: sanroned@aol.com
Web site: http://www.teachmewriting.com.

Santa Ana River Pr., *(0-9747638)* P.O. Box 5473, Norco, CA 92860 USA (SAN 255-7568)
E-mail: admin@santaanariverpress.com
Web site: http://www.santaanariverpress.com
Dist(s): **Sunbelt Pubns., Inc.**

Santa Ines Pubns., *(0-9644386)* 330 W. Hwy 246, No. 232, Buellton, CA 93427 USA Tel 805-688-7862
E-mail: hernan@solvang.sbceo.k12.ca.us.

Santa Monica Pr., *(0-9639946; 1-891661; 1-59580)* Orders Addr.: P.O. Box 1076, Santa Monica, CA 90406 USA (SAN 298-1459) Tel 310-230-7759; Fax: 310-230-7761; Toll Free: 800-784-9553; Edit Addr.: 513 Wilshire Blvd., No. 321, Santa Monica, CA 90401 USA
E-mail: books@santamonicapress.com
Web site: http://www.santamonicapress.com
Dist(s): **Independent Pubs. Group.**

Santa's Publishing, *(0-9642311)* 668 Potomac Ct., San Jose, CA 95136 USA Tel 408-629-3051; Fax: 408-229-8092
E-mail: brucemcguy@hotmail.com
Web site: http://www.santasholidystore.com.

Santa's Secret Creations, *(0-9660336)* 6223 Hwy. 90, Suite 300, Milton, FL 32570 USA Tel 850-994-6078; Toll Free: 888-295-0960; 4746 Live Oak Ln., Milton, FL 32571.

Santiago, Claribel, *(0-9744726)* P.O. Box 25345, Tamarac, FL 33320 USA
E-mail: claribel_santiago@hotmail.com
Web site: http://www.claribelsantiago.com.

Santillana (COL) *(958-24) Dist. by* **Santillana.**

Santillana S. A. (URY) *(9974-590; 9974-671) Dist. by* **Santillana.**

Santillana, S.A. de C.V., Editorial (MEX) *(970-29; 970-770) Dist. by* **Santillana.**

Santillana USA Publishing Co., Inc., *(0-88272; 1-56014; 1-58105; 84-294; 1-58986; 1-59437; 1-59820; 1-60396)* Div. of Grup Santillana De Ediciones, S.A., 2105 NW 86th Ave., Doral, FL 33122 USA (SAN 205-1133) Tel 305-591-9522; Fax: 305-591-9145; Toll Free Fax: 888-248-9518 (orders); Toll Free: 800-245-8584 ; *Imprints:* Richmond (Richmond); Alfaguara (Alfaguara); Punto de Lectura (Punto de Lectura)
E-mail: dpena@santillanausa.com; esanta@santillanausa.com
Web site: http://www.santillanausa.com/
Dist(s): **Baker & Taylor Bks.**
Barnes & Noble, Inc.
Bilingual Pubns. Co., The
Continental Bk. Co., Inc.
EMC/Paradigm Publishing
Follett Library Resources
Lectorum Pubns., Inc.
Libros Sin Fronteras.

Santoon Bks., *(0-9744905)* 13533 1/2 Village Dr., Cerritos, CA 90703 USA Tel 562-926-3361; Fax: 562-802-7680
E-mail: santoon@santoon.com
Dist(s): **Baker & Taylor Bks.**

Santoon Productions, Incorporated *See* **Santoon Bks.**

Santos-Santos Pubns., *(0-9616484)* 4815 E. River Rd., Tucson, AZ 85718 USA (SAN 659-3399) Tel 520-577-3596.

Saptuary, The, *(0-9722100)* Orders Addr.: 815 W. Boynton Beach #10203, Boynton Beach, FL 33426 USA Tel 954-382-5387
E-mail: saptuary7@aol.com.

Saqi Bks. (GBR) *(0-86356) Dist. by* **Consort Bk Sales.**

Sarah & David LLC, *(0-9761648; 0-9796785)* P.O. Box 5894, Englewood, NJ 07631-5894 USA Fax: 201-221-7879
Web site: http://www.sarahdavid.com.

SarahRose Children's Bks. *Imprint of* **SarahRose Publishing**

SarahRose Publishing, *(0-9745865)* Orders Addr.: 5044 N. Highland St., Ruston, WA 98407-3118 USA; Edit Addr.: 8925 Timber Loop SE, Lacey, WA 98513 USA Tel 360-455-7172 ; *Imprints:* SarahRose Children's Books (SarahRose Child Bks)
E-mail: jbeletz@innovial.net; mel.curtiss@innovial.net; sarahrosepublishing@innovial.net; jamie.beletz@innovial.net
Web site: http://www.innovial.net/sarahrosepublishing.

Sarah's Daughters Publishing *See* **Fidelity Heart Publishing**

Sarajames Poetry, Inc., *(0-9767395)* 88 Lawrence Ave., Brooklyn, NY 11230 USA Tel 718-972-2944
E-mail: jamestronan@yahoo.com.

Saranjon Publishing, *(0-9665282)* Orders Addr.: P.O. Box 980, Homer, AK 99603-0980 USA Tel 907-235-8200; Fax: 907-235-8699; Edit Addr.: 385 E. Fairview St., Homer, AK 99603-0980 USA
E-mail: saranjon@alaska.net
Dist(s): **Wizard Works.**

Sarto Hse., *(0-9639032; 1-930959)* Div. of Angelus Press, Orders Addr.: P.O. Box 270611, Kansas City, MO 64127-0611 USA; Edit Addr.: 2918 Tracy Ave., Kansas City, MO 64109 USA
Dist(s): **Spring Arbor Distributors, Inc.**

Sasquatch Bks., *(0-912365; 1-57061)* 119 S. Main St. Ste. 400, Seattle, WA 98104-2555 USA (SAN 289-0208) Toll Free: 800-775-0817
E-mail: custserv@SasquatchBooks.com
Web site: http://www.sasquatchbooks.com
Dist(s): **Perseus Distribution.**

SAT1600 Manhasset LLC, *(0-9742305)* 55 Northern Blvd., Suite 210, Greenvale, NY 11548 USA Tel 516-625-3000
E-mail: profdrfikar@sat1600.org
Web site: http://www.sat1600.org.

Satellite Dynamica Pub., Inc., *(0-9727010)* Orders Addr.: P.O. Box 17081, Philadelphia, PA 19105 USA Tel 215-231-7642
E-mail: admin@satellitedynamics.com
Web site: http://satellitedynamics.com
Dist(s): **Baker & Taylor Bks.**

Satellite Studio, *(0-9743968)* P.O. Box 32457, Knoxville, TN 37930-2457 USA Tel 865-691-1450; Fax: 865-691-2464
E-mail: dwilson@dannywilson.com.

Saturn International, *(0-9764957)* 126 Herricks Rd., Mineola, NY 11501 USA Fax: 516-214-0154.

SATwords.com, *(0-9720583)* 1000 Johnson Ferry Rd., Suite B-100, Marietta, GA 30068 USA Toll Free: 888-498-8223
E-mail: info@satwords.com
Web site: http://www.satwords.com.

Sauerlander AG (CHE) *(3-7941) Dist. by* **Distribks Inc.**

Saulsman, Helen L., *(0-9663051)* 6455 Anita Dr., Dallas, TX 75214 USA Tel 214-826-5535; Fax: 972-216-7576.

Saunders *Imprint of* **Elsevier - Health Sciences Division**

†Saunders College Publishing, *(0-03)* Orders Addr.: 6277 Sea Harbor Dr., Orlando, FL 32887 USA Tel 407-345-2525; Toll Free: 800-782-4479 (orders); 800-544-6678 (customer service); Edit Addr.: The Public Ledger Bldg., 150 S. Independence Mall W., Suite 1250, Philadelphia, PA 19106-3412 USA (SAN 282-2768) Tel 215-238-5500
Web site: http://www.hbcollege.com; *CIP.*

Savage Bks., *(0-9673000)* 7510 W. Sunset Blvd., No. 277, Los Angeles, CA 90046 USA Toll Free: 888-777-4631 Do not confuse with Savage Bks., in Honolulu, HI
E-mail: d@savage1.com
Web site: http://SAVAGE1.com.

Savage Bks., *(0-9719168)* Div. of Lancelot Illustration, P.O. Box 235788, Honolulu, HI 96823-3513 USA Do not confuse with Savage Bks., in Los Angeles, CA
E-mail: michel@savage-books.com; michelangelo@hawaii.rr.com
Web site: http://www.savage-books.com.

Savage, Derek Productions *See* **Savage Bks.**

Savage Parks Pr., *(0-9669130)* 25985 Genesee Trail Rd., K-322, Golden, CO 80401 USA Tel 303-778-1695; Fax: 303-526-1132
E-mail: nancy@nickelbuffalo.com
Web site: http://www.nickelbuffalo.com
Dist(s): **Baker & Taylor Bks.**
Biblio Distribution
Books West.

Savage Pr., *(1-886028)* P.O. Box 115, Superior, WI 54880 USA Tel 715-394-9513 (phone/fax); Toll Free: 800-732-3867 (orders only)
E-mail: mail@savpress.com
Web site: http://www.savpress.com
Dist(s): **Partners Bk. Distributing, Inc.**

Savanna Pr., *(0-9759440)* Orders Addr.: P.O. Box 777, Monte Vista, CO 81144 USA Tel 719-850-2255; Fax: 719-852-2211; Edit Addr.: 67 Gold Cir., Pagosa Springs, CO 81147 USA; P.O. Box 1806, Vryburg, 8600
E-mail: riovista@rmi.net
Dist(s): **AtlasBooks Distribution.**

Savannah Butterfly Bks., *(0-9705781)* P.O. Box 13274, Savannah, GA 31416-0274 USA
E-mail: savbutrfly@aol.com; savbutrfly.com@aol.com.

Savannah College of Art & Design, *(0-9654682; 1-893974; 0-9797440)* Orders Addr.: P.O. Box 3146, Savannah, GA 31401-3146 USA Tel 912-525-5287; Fax: 912-5254952; Edit Addr.: 212 W. Hall St., Garden Apt., Savannah, GA 31401 USA ; *Imprints:* Design Press Books (Design Press Bks)
E-mail: asalgado@scad.edu
Web site: http://www.scadexhibitions.com.

Savas, Bachtsoglou, *(0-9771020)* 139-02 97th Ave., Jamaica, NY 11435 USA Tel 718-793-0107
E-mail: avipremlall@gmail.com.

Savas Beatie, *(1-932714)* P.O. Box 4527, El Dorado Hills, CA 95762 USA
Web site: http://www.savasbeatie.com
Dist(s): **Casemate Pubs. & Bk. Distributors, LLC**
MBI Publishing Co. LLC.

Savor Publishing Hse., Inc., *(0-9708296)* 6020 Broken Bow Dr., Citrus Heights, CA 95621 USA Tel 718-846-7277
E-mail: Smarties@SavorPublishing.com; SavorPubHouse@aol.com
Web site: http://www.savorpublishing.com
Dist(s): **Baker & Taylor Bks.**
Book Clearing Hse.
Book Wholesalers, Inc.
Follett Library Resources.

Savory Palate, Inc., *(1-889374)* 8174 S. Holly, No. 404, Centennial, CO 80122-4004 USA Tel 303-741-5408; Fax: 303-741-0339; Toll Free: 800-741-5418
E-mail: info@savorypalate.com
Web site: http://www.savorypalate.com
Dist(s): **Baker & Taylor Bks.**
Brodart Co.
New Leaf Distributing Co., Inc.
Quality Bks., Inc.
Royal Pubns., Inc.

Sawmill Publishing, *(0-9749915)* 6444 E. Spring St., No. 215, Long Beach, CA 90815 USA.

Sawmill Ridge Publishing, *(0-9761924)* 183 Post Oak Dr., Roanoke, VA 24019 USA Tel 540-966-5706.

Saxon Pubs., Inc., *(0-939798; 1-56577; 1-59141)* Div. of Harcourt Achieve, Orders Addr.: 6277 Sea Harbor Dr., 5th Flr., Orlando, FL 32887 USA Toll Free Fax: 877-578-2638; Toll Free: 888-363-4266; Edit Addr.: 10801 N. Mopac Expressway, Bldg. 3, Austin, TX 78759 USA (SAN 216-8960) Toll Free: 800-531-5015
Web site: http://www.saxonpublishers.com.

Saxton Pubns., *(0-9716858)* 1809 Richmond St., Sacramento, CA 95825-2110 USA.

Say It Right, *(0-9723457; 0-9760490; 0-9770418; 1-934701)* Orders Addr.: P.O. Box 651, Tybee Island, GA 31328 USA Tel 912-228-4556; Fax: 912-480-4214; Toll Free: 888-811-0759
E-mail: jim@sayitright.org
Web site: http://www.sayitright.org.

Sayger Company *See* **Sayger, Jack**

Sayger, Jack, *(0-9711403)* P.O. Box 1754, Ridgeland, SC 29936 USA Tel 843-726-6330
E-mail: flgator@hargray.com.

SB Mandolin Publishers *See* **Mandolin Hse.**

Sblendido, Barbara, *(0-9722555)* 330 George Rd., Ghent, NY 12075 USA.

Scala Pubs., Ltd. (GBR) *(1-85759; 1-870248) Dist. by* **Antique Collect.**

Scandia Pubs., *(0-937242)* Orders Addr.: 11594 Willamette Meridian, NW, Silverdale, WA 98383 USA (SAN 282-2806) Tel 360-337-7662 8 AM- 5PM Mon-Fri Pacific; Fax: 360-337-7688 8 Am - 5 PM Pacific; Toll Free: 888-891-1893 Order line only
E-mail: Drercksn@aol.com.

Scandinavia Publishing Hse. (DNK) *(87-7247; 87-87732) Dist. by* **Am Bible.**

Scandinavia Publishing Hse. (DNK) *(87-7247; 87-87732) Dist. by* **Natl Bk Netwk.**

Scarabosio, Holly S. *See* **Dandelion Productions**

†Scarecrow Pr., Inc., *(0-8108; 1-57886)* Div. of Rowman & Littlefield Publishing Group, Orders Addr.: 15200 NBN Way, Blue Ridge Summit, PA 17214 USA Tel 717-794-3800 (Sales, Customer Service, MIS, Royalties, Inventory Mgmt., Dist., Credit & Collection); Fax: 717-794-3803 (Customer Service &/or orders); 717-794-3857 (Sales & MIS); 717-794-3856 (Royalties, Inventory Mgmt. & Dist.); Toll Free Fax: 800-338-4550 (Customer Service &/or orders); Toll Free: 800-462-6420 (Customer Service &/or orders); Edit Addr.: 4501 Forbes Blvd., Suite 200, Lanham, MD 20706-4310 USA Tel 301-459-3366; Fax: 301-429-5747 Short Discount, please contact rlpgsales@rowman.com
E-mail: custserv@rowman.com
Web site: http://www.scarecrowpress.com; http://www.rlpgbooks.com
Dist(s): **National Bk. Network**
Rowman & Littlefield Pubs., Inc.; *CIP.*

ScarecrowEducation *See* **Rowman & Littlefield Education**

Scars Pubns. & Design, *(1-891470)* 829 Brian Ct., Gurnee, IL 60031 USA
E-mail: Editor@scars.tv
Web site: http://scars.tv.

SCB Distributors, Orders Addr.: 15608 S. New Century Dr., Gardena, CA 90248-2129 USA (SAN 630-4818) Tel 310-532-9400; Fax: 310-532-7001; Toll Free: 800-729-6423 (orders only)
E-mail: info@scbdistributors.com
Web site: http://www.scbdistributors.com.

Scenic Art, *(0-9718567; 0-9797447)* Div. of Danita Enterprises, Orders Addr.: 43980 Mahlon Vail Cir., No. 301, Temecula, CA 92592-9602 USA Toll Free Fax: 800 283-8765; Toll Free: 800 283-8765
E-mail: dan@mirrokoat.com.

Schaefer's Publishing, *(0-9658132)* 6864 Stahelin, Detroit, MI 48228 USA Tel 313-441-6135; Fax: 313-982-1806.

Schafer-Post Entomology Pubns., *(0-9766855)* Entomology Dept. Hultz Hall, North Dakota State Univ., Fargo, ND 58105 USA Tel 701-231-7582; Fax: 701-231-8557
E-mail: david.rider@ndsu.edu.

Schaffer, Frank *Imprint of* **Schaffer, Frank Pubns.**

Schaffer, Frank Pubns., *(0-7647; 0-7682; 0-8224; 0-86653; 0-88012; 0-911019; 0-911925; 0-916456; 1-56417; 1-56451; 1-56822; 0-7424)* 3195 Wilson Dr. NW, Grand Rapids, MI 49544 USA ; *Imprints:* Fearon Teacher Aids (FTA); Ideal School Supply (ISS); In Celebration (In Celeb); Instructional Fair (Inst Fair); Judy (Ju); Milestone (Milest); Schaffer, Frank (Schaf); Totline Publications (Totline)
Dist(s): **NetLibrary, Inc.**
School Specialty Publishing.

Schaub, Stephen M. Photography *See* **Indian Hill Gallery of Fine Photography**

Scheer Delight Publishing, *(0-9671761)* 4030 E. Christy, Wichita, KS 67220-2540 USA (SAN 253-908X) Tel 316-683-2001; Fax: 316-636-1268
E-mail: schdelight@cox.net
Web site: http://scheerdelightpub.com.

Scheewe, Susan Pubns., Inc., *(1-56770)* 13435 NE Whitaker Way, Portland, OR 97230 USA Tel 503-254-9100; Fax: 503-252-9508; Toll Free: 800-796-1953
E-mail: scheewepub@aol.com
Web site: http://www.painting-books.com.

Schema Pr., Ltd., *(0-9638925; 0-9711203)* 7101 Lake Powell Dr., Suite 100, Arlington, TX 76016-3517 USA Tel 817-572-6254; Fax: 817-478-1048
E-mail: schema@krii.com
Web site: http://www.krii.com.

Scherer, Bonnie, *(0-9622421)* 1021 Alderson, Billings, MT 59102 USA Tel 406-245-7289
E-mail: jbscherer@mcn.net.

Schiavi, Sherry *See* **Celltrition**

Schiffer Publishing, Ltd., *(0-7643; 0-88740; 0-916838)* Orders Addr.: 4880 Lower Valley Rd., Atglen, PA 19310 USA (SAN 208-8428) Tel 610-593-1777; Fax: 610-593-2002 ; *Imprints:* Whitford Press (Whitford)
E-mail: info@schifferbooks.com
Web site: http://www.schifferbooks.com
Dist(s): **Booklines Hawaii, Ltd.**

Schiffner, Frederick A., *(0-9765782)* P.O. Box 1047, Spring Mt., PA 19478 USA Tel 610-287-5827
E-mail: fschiffner@fast.net.

Schilling, Mickey, *(0-9663885)* 1910 W. 23rd St., Loveland, CO 80538 USA Tel 970-667-0849; Fax: 970-669-3231.

Schirmer Trade Bks. *Imprint of* **Music Sales Corp.**

Schlabach Printers, *(0-9667622)* 2881 SR 93, Sugarcreek, OH 44681 USA Tel 330-852-4687; Fax: 330-852-2689; Toll Free: 888-406-2005
E-mail: sprint@tusco.net.

Schleich, James, *(0-615)* 105 Woodland Dr., Zelienople, PA 16063-9316 USA
E-mail: james@the-soundman.org
Web site: http://www.the-soundman.org.

Schlessinger Media, *(1-57225; 1-879151)* Div. of Library Video Co., Orders Addr.: P.O. Box 580, Wynnewood, PA 19096 USA Tel 610-645-4000; Fax: 610-645-4050; Toll Free: 800-843-3620; Edit Addr.: 7 Wynnewood Rd., Wynnewood, PA 19096 USA
E-mail: sales@libraryvideo.com
Web site: http://www.libraryvideo.com
Dist(s): **Library Video Co.**
Video Project, The.

Schlessinger Video Productions *See* **Schlessinger Media**

Schley, Michael, *(0-9759645)* 2 Oak Pk. Ave., Darien, CT 06820 USA
E-mail: mike_schley@yahoo.com.

Schlifer, Sherry, *(0-9700375)* 239 Ash Ln., Lafayette Hill, PA 19444-2101 USA Tel 610-828-6427
E-mail: sherbook@aol.com.

Schmidt-Cannon International, *(1-884344; 0-9674289)* Div. of Aspen Marketing Group, 4700 E. Airport Dr., Ontario, CA 91761 USA Tel 909-390-9000; Fax: 909-390-6251; Toll Free: 800-669-3733
E-mail: name@aspenmg.com
Web site: http://aspenmg.com.

Schmul Publishing Co., Inc., *(0-88019)* Orders Addr.: P.O. Box 716, Salem, OH 44460-0716 USA (SAN 180-2771) Tel 330-222-2249; Fax: 330-222-0001; Toll Free: 800-772-6657; Edit Addr.: 3583 Newgarden Rd., Salem, OH 44460 USA
E-mail: spchale@valunet.com
Web site: http://www.wesleyanbooks.com.

Schocken *Imprint of* **Knopf Publishing Group**

Schoenhof's Foreign Bks., Inc., *(0-87774)* Subs. of Editions Gallimard, 76a Mount Auburn St., Cambridge, MA 02138-5051 USA (SAN 212-0062)
E-mail: info@schoenhofs.com
Web site: http://www.schoenhofs.com.

Schofield & Sims Ltd. (GBR) *(0-7217) Dist. by* **St Mut.**

Scholarly Resources, Inc. *Imprint of* **Rowman & Littlefield Pubs., Inc.**

†Scholars' Facsimiles & Reprints, *(0-8201)* P.O. Box 5934, Carefree, AZ 85377 USA (SAN 203-2627) Tel 480-575-9451
E-mail: n.mangouni@att.net*; CIP.*

Scholastic *Imprint of* **Scholastic, Inc.**

Scholastic Canada, Ltd. (CAN) *(0-439; 0-590; 0-7791) Dist. by* **Firefly Bks Limited.**

Scholastic en Espanol *Imprint of* **Scholastic, Inc.**

Scholastic, Inc. *Imprint of* **Scholastic, Inc.**

†Scholastic, Inc., *(0-439; 0-590; 0-545)* Orders Addr.: c/o HarperCollins, 1000 Keystone Industrial Pk., Scranton, PA 18512 USA Toll Free: 800-242-7737; Edit Addr.: 557 Broadway, New York, NY 10012-3999 USA (SAN 202-5442) Tel 212-343-6100; Fax: 212-343-6802; Toll Free: 800-325-6149 (customer service) ; *Imprints:* Cartwheel Books (Cartwheel); Scholastic Reference (Scholastic Ref); Blue Sky Press, The (Blue Sky Press); Scholastic (Scholastic); Levine, Arthur A. Books (A A Levine); Orchard Books (Orchard Bks); Scholastic Press (Scholastic Pr); Chicken House, The (Chick Hse); PUSH (PUSH); Scholastic en Espanol (Scholastic en Espanol); Scholastic Nonfiction (Schol Nonfic); Scholastic Paperbacks (Schol Pbk); Sidekicks TM (Sidekicks); Tangerine Press (Tang Pr Sch); Teaching Resources (Teach Res Sch); Graphix (Graphx); Scholastic, Incorporated (SchInc); SideKicks TM Baby (SideBaby); Teaching Strategies (TeachStrategi); Theory & Practice (Theory & Prac); Little Shepherd (Little Shepard); Best Practices in Action (BP in AC); Di Capua, Michael (Michael DiCapua)
E-mail: info@scholastic.com
Web site: http://www.scholastic.com
Dist(s): **Hachette Bk. Group**
NetLibrary, Inc.*; CIP.*

Scholastic Library Publishing, *(0-516; 0-531; 0-7172)* 90 Old Sherman Tpke., Danbury, CT 06816 USA (SAN 253-8865) Tel 203-797-3500; Fax: 203-797-3657; Toll Free: 800-621-1115 ; *Imprints:* Grolier Online (Grolier Online); Children's Press (Childrens Pr); Grolier (Grolier Schol); Watts, Franklin (Frank Watts)
E-mail: agraham@grolier.com
Web site: http://librarypublishing.scholastic.com
Dist(s): **Lectorum Pubns., Inc.**

Scholastic Nonfiction *Imprint of* **Scholastic, Inc.**

Scholastic Paperbacks *Imprint of* **Scholastic, Inc.**

Scholastic Pr. *Imprint of* **Scholastic, Inc.**

Scholastic Reading Counts, *(0-935325; 1-55749)* 555 Broadway, New York, NY 10012 USA Tel 212-343-6100
Dist(s): **Lectorum Pubns., Inc.**

Scholastic Reference *Imprint of* **Scholastic, Inc.**

Schonwalder, Helmut, *(0-9763287)* P.O. Box 1390, Monterey, CA 93940 USA Tel 831-375-7737
E-mail: helmut@schonwalder.org; helmut@schonwalder.com
Web site: http://www.schonwalder.com; http://www.gastronomical.net; http://www.kaufhouse.info.

†School Age Notes, *(0-917505)* P.O. Box 476, New Albany, OH 43054 USA (SAN 656-1004) Tel 614-855-9315; Fax: 614-855-9325; Toll Free: 800-410-8780
E-mail: info@schoolagenotes.com
Web site: http://www.schoolagenotes.com*; CIP.*

School Days, *(0-9744302)* Orders Addr.: P.O. Box 454, North Carrollton, MS 38947 USA
E-mail: schooldaysmemorybook@yahoo.com
Web site: http://www.schooldaysmemorybook.com
Dist(s): **Wimmer Cookbooks.**

School of Color Publishing, *(0-9679628; 1-931780)* Div. of The Michael Wilcox School of Color, Inc., 5116 N. Armenia Ave., Tampa, FL 33603-1406 USA Toll Free: 888-794-5269
E-mail: wilcoxschool@earthlink.net; anne.m.gardner@worldnet.att.net
Web site: http://www.schoolofcolor.com
Dist(s): **F & W Pubns., Inc.**

School of Music Publishing Hse. (RUS) *(5-9500) Dist. by* **Coronet Bks.**

Schl. Services of California, Inc., *(0-9708628; 0-9748487)* 1121 L St., No. 1060, Sacramento, CA 95814 USA Tel 916-446-7517; Fax: 916-446-2011
E-mail: susanm@sscal.com
Web site: http://www.sscal.com.

School Specialty Publishing, *(0-7647; 0-7682; 0-7696; 0-86653; 0-88012; 1-56417; 1-56451; 1-56822; 1-57029; 1-57768; 0-7424; 1-58845)* 8720 Orion Pl., Suite 200, Columbus, OH 43240-2111 USA (SAN 256-0925) Tel 614-880-6787; 614-430-4487; Fax: 614-880-6745; 614-430-6482; Toll Free Fax: 800-543-2690; Toll Free: 800-253-5469 ; *Imprints:* Cricket (Cricket); Bedrick, Peter Books (Peter Bedrick); Mercer Mayer First Readers (Mercer Mayer); Learning Materials (Learn Mate); American Education Publishing (Am Educ Pubng); Gingham Dog Press (Gingham Dog); Waterbird Books (Waterbird); Brighter Child (Brighter Chld); Spectrum (Spectrum USA)
E-mail: barbara-boggs@mcgraw-hill.com; baboggs@childrens-publishing.com
Web site: http://www.schoolspecialtypublishing.com/
Dist(s): **NetLibrary, Inc.**

Schl. Tools, *(0-9754578)* 23418 28th Ave. W, Brier, WA 98036 USA.

School Zone Publishing Co., *(0-88743; 0-938256; 1-58947; 1-60041; 1-60159)* P.O. Box 777, Grand Haven, MI 49417 USA (SAN 289-8314) Tel 616-846-5030; Fax: 616-846-6181; Toll Free: 800-253-0564; 1819 Industrial Dr., Grand Haven, MI 49417
E-mail: Bobb@schoolzone.com
Web site: http://www.schoolzone.com.

Schoolhouse Publishing, *(0-9758543)* Orders Addr.: 659 Schoolhouse Rd., Telford, PA 18969-2449 USA
Web site: http://www.shpublishing.com.

Schoolhouse Secrets Unlimited, *(0-9661968)* 4305 Kenwood Dr., Grapevine, TX 76051-6711 USA Tel 817-481-8293
E-mail: molly@schoolhousesecrets.com.

Schoolside Pr, *(0-9785100)* 20950-40 Oxnard St., Woodland Hills, CA 91367 USA Tel 818-884-7349; Fax: 818-884-6226
E-mail: EAMartonyi@schoolsidepress.com
Web site: http://Schoolsidpress.com
Dist(s): **STL Distribution North America.**

Schoolyard Pr., *(0-9725229)* P.O. Box 6453, Bakersfield, CA 93386-6453 USA Tel 661-872-5328; Fax: 661-872-2851.

Schooner Pubns., *(1-929234)* 1610-D Church St. Coastal Ctr., PMB 360, Conway, SC 29526 USA Tel 843-347-9792.

Schoppe Bookcrafters Pubs., *(0-9666712)* 2317 SE 146th Ave., Portland, OR 97233 USA Tel 503-760-1879 (phone/fax)
E-mail: CSchoppe@msc.com.

Schott Musik International GmbH & Co. KG (DEU) *(3-7957) Dist. by* **H Leonard.**

Schrader, Richard A., *(0-9622987; 1-930381)* 2 G Calquohoun, P.O. Box 39, Kingshill, Saint Croix, VI 00851-0039 USA Tel 340-778-0477
E-mail: michaelala1@aol.com.

Schroeder, Patrick A. Publications: Civil War Books *See* **Schroeder Pubns.: Civil War Bks.**

Schroeder Pubns.: Civil War Bks., *(1-889246)* Orders Addr.: 131 Tanglewood Dr., Lynchburg, VA 24502 USA Tel 434-525-4431; Fax: 434-525-7293
E-mail: civilwarbooks@yahoo.com
Web site: http://www.civilwar-books.com.

Schroeder, Robert, *(0-9746974)* 4453 Summerglen Ct., Moorpark, CA 93021 USA Tel 805-529-3927.

Schryver Enterprises, LLC, *(0-9712300)* 10316 Little Cir., Minneapolis, MN 55437-2821 USA
E-mail: sewrld@aol.com
Web site: http://www.schryverenterprises.com.

Schuerholz Graphics, *(0-9715665)* 3540 Marshall Rd., Kettering, OH 45429 USA (SAN 631-7073) Tel 937-294-5218.

Schwarcz, Editora Ltda, Companhia das Letrinhas (BRA) *(85-7406) Dist. by* **Distribks Inc.**

Schwartz & Wade Bks. *Imprint of* **Random Hse. Children's Bks.**

Schwartz, Arthur & Company, Incorporated/Woodstocker Books *See* **Woodstocker Books/Arthur Schwartz & Company**

Schwartz, Joel, *(0-9785885)* 1315 Cinnamon Dr., Fort Washington, PA 19034-2818 USA
E-mail: jshrink@comcast.net
Web site: http://www.stresslessshrink.com.

Schwarz Pauper Pr., *(0-9621505)* 88 Winwood Dr., Barnstead, NH 03225 USA (SAN 251-4540) Tel 603-776-5680
E-mail: Granitesunset@aol.com.

Schwarz Publishing, *(1-887417)* c/o Aletheia Institute, P.O. Box 2400, Mendocino, CA 95460-2400 USA Tel 707-937-0602; Fax: 707-937-0624
E-mail: aletheia@mcn.org
Web site: http://www.holisticu.org
Dist(s): **New Leaf Distributing Co., Inc.**

Sci Fi-Arizona, Inc., *(1-929381)* 1931 E. Libra Dr., Tempe, AZ 85283 USA Tel 480-838-6558 ; *Imprints:* Third Millennium Publishing (Third Millen Pubng)
E-mail: mccollum@scifi-az.com
Web site: http://www.scifi-az.com; http://www.3mpub.com.

Science Academy Software, *(0-9623926)* 600 Baychester Ave., Apt 5B, Bronx, NY 10475-4457 USA Tel 718-561-4048.

Science & God, Inc., *(0-9745861)* P.O. Box 2036, Labelle, FL 33975-2036 USA Tel 239-218-4543.

Science & Humanities Pr., *(1-888725; 1-59630)* Subs. of Banis & Assocs., Orders Addr.: P.O. Box 7151, Chesterfield, MO 63006-7151 USA (SAN 299-8459) Tel 636-394-4950; Fax: 636-394-1381; Edit Addr.: 1023 Stuyvesant Ln., Manchester, MO 63011-3601 USA Tel 636-394-4950; Fax: 636-394-1381 ; *Imprints:* MacroPrintBooks (MacroPrintBks); BeachHouse Books (BeachHouse Bks)
E-mail: sales@sciencehumanitiespress.com; pub@macroprintbooks.com; banis@banis-associates.com
Web site: http://www.banis-associates.com; http://www.sciencehumanitiespress.com; http://www.macroprintbooks.com; http://www.stressmyth.com; http://www.normajeanebook.com; http://www.route66book.com; http://www.accessible-travel.com
Dist(s): **Beeler, Thomas T. Pub.**

Science Curriculum, Inc., *(1-882057)* Orders Addr.: 200 Union Blvd. Ste. G18, Lakewood, CO 80228-1845 USA (SAN 248-3637) Toll Free: 888-501-0957; 24 Stone Rd., Belmont, MA 04278
E-mail: marketing@sci-ips.com
Web site: http://www.sci-ips.com.

Science Educator's Ink, *(0-9715268)* Orders Addr.: P.O. Box 731, Glen Carbon, IL 62034 USA Tel 618-659-9714
E-mail: pkeck@siue.edu.

Science Kids, *(1-891418)* Div. of Caroline Publishing, 7016 Kentwood Ave., Los Angeles, CA 90045 USA Tel 626-934-0649; Fax: 310-379-5065
E-mail: Scikids@hotmail.com.

Science, Naturally!, *(0-9678020; 0-9700106)* 627 A St., NE, Washington, DC 20002 USA Tel 202-465-4798; Fax: 202-558-2132; Toll Free: 866-724-9876
E-mail: dia@sciencenaturally.com
Dist(s): **National Bk. Network.**

Science of Knowledge Pr., *(1-59620)* P.O. Box 324, Little Falls, NJ 07424 USA Fax: 973-272-1102
Web site: http://www.scienceok.com
Dist(s): **Majors, J. A. Co.**

Science of Mind Publishing, *(0-911336; 0-917849; 0-9727184)* Div. of United Church of Religious Science, Orders Addr.: P.O. Box 75127, Los Angeles, CA 90075-0127 USA (SAN 203-2570); Edit Addr.: 2600 W. Magnolia Blvd., Burbank, CA 91505-3031 USA Tel 818-526-7757; Fax: 818-556-2253
Web site: http://www.scienceofmind.com; http://www.spirituallivingpress.com
Dist(s): **DeVorss & Co.**

Science Square Publishing, *(0-9740861)* 2845 Bowen St., Graton, CA 95444-9347 USA
E-mail: info@sciencesquare.com
Web site: http://www.sciencesquare.com.

Science Topics LLC, *(0-9718117)* 4403 N. County Line, Whitewater, WI 53190 USA Tel 608-883-6574 (phone/fax)
E-mail: biotopics@jvlnet.com
Dist(s): **Carolina Biological Supply Co.**
Nasco Math Eighty-Six.

Science2Discover, Inc., *(0-9673811)* P.O. Box 2435, Del Mar, CA 92014-1735 USA Fax: 858-793-0410; Toll Free: 888-359-6075; 2015 Seaview Ave., Del Mar, CA 92014 Do not confuse with MetaMetrix, Inc., Norcross, GA
E-mail: info@science2discover.com
Web site: http://www.science2discover.com.

Scientific Publishing, Ltd., *(1-930633; 1-932922)* 129 Joey Dr., Elk Grove Village, IL 60007-1303 USA Tel 847-788-9100; Fax: 847-788-9124
E-mail: charts@scientificpublishing.com
Web site: http://www.scientificpublishing.com.

Scientists of New Atlantis, *(1-57179; 1-883147)* P.O. Box 1210, Pahrump, NV 89041 USA (SAN 159-4168)
E-mail: orders@sona-inc.com
Web site: http://www.sona-inc.com
Dist(s): **SONA, Inc.**

SciTech Publishing, Inc., *(1-884932; 1-891121)* 911 Paverstone Dr., Suite B, Raleigh, NC 27615 USA (SAN 256-6672) Tel 919-847-2434; Fax: 919-847-2568; Toll Free: 866-510-4724 Do not confuse with Scitech Pubs., Inc., Cliffside Park, NJ
E-mail: info@scitechpub.com
Web site: http://www.scitechpub.com.

SCM-Canterbury Pr. Ltd. (GBR) *(0-334) Dist. by* **Presbyterian Pub.**

Scobre Pr. Corp., *(0-9708992; 0-9741695; 0-9741997; 0-9766240; 1-933423; 1-934713)* 2255 Calle Clara, La Jolla, CA 92037 USA
Web site: http://www.scobre.com.

Scoop Press *See* **Eastbank Publishing**

SCOPE Pubns., *(0-9759955)* Orders Addr.: 100 Lawrence Ave., Smithtown, NY 11787 USA Tel 631-360-0800; Fax: 631-360-8489 Do not confuse with Scope Publications, Fairfax, OK
E-mail: bkauffman@scopeonline.us
Web site: http://www.scopeonline.us.

Scott & McCleary Publishing Co., *(0-9636225)* Orders Addr.: 2482 11th St., SW, Akron, OH 44314 USA Tel 702-566-8756; Fax: 702-568-1378; Toll Free: 800-765-3564
E-mail: scottmccleary@lvcm.com
Web site: http://www.scottmccleary.com.

Scott, Carlton T. *See* **Ends of the Earth Books.com**

Scott, D.&F. Publishing, Inc., *(0-941037; 1-930566)* Orders Addr.: P.O. Box 821653, North Richland Hills, TX 76182-1653 USA (SAN 665-2875) Tel 817-788-2280; Fax: 817-788-9232; Toll Free: 888-788-2280; Edit Addr.: P.O. Box 821653, N Richlnd Hls, TX 76182-1653 USA ; *Imprints:* WestWind Press (WstWind)
E-mail: info@dfscott.com
Web site: http://www.dfscott.com.

Scott Foresman *Imprint of* **Addison-Wesley Educational Pubs., Inc.**

Scott Foresman *Imprint of* **Addison-Wesley Educational Pubs., Inc.**

Scott Foresman *Imprint of* **Addison Wesley Schl.**

Scott, J & N Pubs., *(0-9719868)* 10461 NW 20 St., Pembroke Pines, FL 33026 USA Tel 954-432-6578
E-mail: nscott2000@aol.com.

Scott, James *See* **Scott, J & N Pubs.**

Scott, Josephine, *(0-9718582; 0-9746600)* P.O. Box 55127, Bridgeport, CT 06610 USA
E-mail: jartist@optonline.net
Web site: http://www.ethnuicitycards.com.

†Scott Pubns., Inc., *(0-916809; 1-893625; 0-9787419)* 801 W. Norton Ave., Suite 200, Muskegon, MI 49441 USA Toll Free: 866-733-9382 Do not confuse with Scott Pubns. in Indianapolis, IN
E-mail: contactus@scottpublications.com
Web site: http://www.scottpublications.com*; CIP.*

Scottish Children's Pr. (GBR) *(1-898218; 1-899827) Dist. by* **Wlsn Assocs.**

Scottish Christmas, *(0-9726114)* 2369 Joslyn Ct., Lake Orion, MI 48360 USA.

Scottwall Assocs., *(0-942087; 0-9612790)* 95 Scott St., San Francisco, CA 94117 USA (SAN 289-8322) Tel 415-861-1956; Fax: 415-863-7273
E-mail: scotwall@pacbell.net
Web site: http://www.scottwallpub.com
Dist(s): **Baker & Taylor Bks.**
Sunbelt Pubns., Inc.
Todd Communications.

Scott-Waters, Marilyn, *(0-9759884)* 1589 Baker St., Costa Mesa, CA 92626 USA
E-mail: msw@scottwatersdesign.com
Web site: http://www.thetoymaker.com.

Scoty 1 Publishing, *(0-9668006)* 113 Strawberry Ln., Wisconsin Rapids, WI 54494 USA Tel 715-423-1023.

SCR Books LLC *See* **SCR Pubns.**

SCR Pubns., *(0-9747582)* P.O. Box 144, Brooklyn, NY 11224 USA (SAN 255-7509)
E-mail: scrbooks@yahoo.com
Web site: http://www.caffeineawareness.org
Dist(s): **Independent Pubs. Group.**

S.C.R.A.P. Gallery, *(0-9708135)* 46-350 Arabia St., Indio, CA 92201 USA Tel 760-863-7777; Fax: 760-863-8973; Toll Free: 866-717-2727 (866-71-SCRAP)
E-mail: scrapgallery@earthlink.net
Web site: http://www.infoteam.com/nonprofit/scrapgallery.

Scrap Paper Pr., *(0-9745493)* 6 Manor Dr., Goldens Bridge, NY 10526 USA Tel 914-997-1692; Fax: 914-997-2253.

Scratch & Scribble Pr., Inc., *(0-933675)* P.O. Box 490, Ridge, NY 11961 USA Tel 631-345-2100; Fax: 631-345-5463
E-mail: jjones@scratchandscribblepress.com
Web site: http://www.scratchandscribblepress.com.

Screamin' Mimi Pubns., *(0-9652770)* 1789 Woodland Ct., Concord, CA 94521 USA (SAN 299-0652) Tel 510-676-5132
E-mail: smimipub@aol.com.

ScribbleBooks Co., The, *(0-9706406)* 3000 Kathleen Ct., Homewood, IL 60430-2850 USA
E-mail: mail@scribblebooks.com
Web site: http://www.scribblemonster.com.

Scribbler's Sword, *(0-9761186)* 1640 Halfacre Rd., Newberry, SC 29108 USA.

Scribbulations LLC, *(0-9629311)* Orders Addr.: P.O. Box 3027TCB, W. Orange, NJ 07052 USA Tel 973-325-1648 Do not confuse with Bookcraft, Inc. in West Valley, UT
E-mail: info@scribbulations.com
Web site: http://www.scribbulations.com.

Scribe Agency Press-Advantage International *See* **Scribe Pr.**

Scribe Pr., *(1-882833)* 1830 Sequoia Ave., No. D, Burlingame, CA 94010 USA Tel 650-692-7946
E-mail: sinclair888@yahoo.com.

Scribner *Imprint of* **Simon & Schuster**

Scribner Paper Fiction *Imprint of* **Simon & Schuster**

Scribolin, *(0-9746226)* 10107 Copeland Dr., Manassas, VA 20109 USA Tel 703-257-7683
E-mail: books@scribolin.com
Web site: http://www.scribolin.com.

†Scrimshaw Pr., *(0-87155)* P.O. Box 1795, Mashpee, MA 02649-1795 USA (SAN 206-9253) Tel 508-539-2833
E-mail: pgiam@comcast.net
Web site: http://www.giambarba.com; http://www.scrimshawpress.com; http://www.vinehill.com; *CIP.*

Scripts Publishing, *(1-889826)* Orders Addr.: 638 Hennepin Ter., Mcdonough, GA 30253-5965 USA
E-mail: AtaxiaBooks@aol.com
Web site: http://www.hometown.aol.com/pathamilto/myhomepage/profile.html.

Scripture Mastery Resources!, *(1-933589)* 6810 Gillings Rd., Springfield, VA 84404 USA
E-mail: scripturemastery@kenalford.com
Web site: http://www.kenalford.com.

Scripture Memory Fellowship International, *(1-880960)* Orders Addr.: P.O. Box 411551, Saint Louis, MO 63141 USA Tel 314-569-0244; Fax: 314-569-0025; Toll Free: 888-569-2560; Edit Addr.: 70 Weldon Pkwy., Maryland Heights, MO 63043 USA
E-mail: memorize@stlnet.com
Web site: http://www.scripturememory.com.

Scripture On The Go, *(1-930350)* 23272 Vista Grande, Suite A, Laguna Hills, CA 92653 USA Tel 949-457-1323; Fax: 949-457-1888; Toll Free: 888-700-9285.

Scripture Union (GBR) *(0-85421; 0-86201; 1-85999; 1-873824; 0-949720; 1-84427) Dist. by* **STL Dist NA.**

Scripture Union (GBR) *(0-85421; 0-86201; 1-85999; 1-873824; 0-949720; 1-84427) Dist. by* **Gabriel Res.**

Scripture Union, USA, *(0-913585)* 150 Strafford Ave., Suite 215, Wayne, PA 19087 USA (SAN 285-3817) Tel 610-341-0830; Fax: 610-341-0836; Toll Free: 800-621-5267
E-mail: suusa@aol.com.

†Scroll Pr., Inc., *(0-87592)* 2858 Valerie Ct., Merrick, NY 11566 USA (SAN 206-796X) Tel 516-379-4283; *CIP.*

Scrumps Entertainment, Inc., *(0-9672279)* 19320 NW. 47th Ave., Miami, FL 33055 USA Tel 305-624-7231
E-mail: climbcrick@aol.com.

Se7enth Swan Publishing Group, LLC, *(0-615)* P.O. Box 16874, Chapel Hill, NC 27516 USA
Web site: http://www.se7enthswan.com
Dist(s): **Lulu.com.**

Sea Challengers, Inc., *(0-930118)* Four Sommerset Rise, Skyline Forest, Monterey, CA 93940 USA (SAN 210-5446) Tel 831-373-6306; Fax: 831-373-4566
E-mail: seachall@aol.com
Dist(s): **Lectorum Pubns., Inc.**
Sunbelt Pubns., Inc.

Sea Chest Bks., *(0-9742909)* 11573 Viking Ave., Northridge, CA 91326 USA
E-mail: sales@seachestbooks.com
Web site: http://www.seachestbooks.com.

Sea Critters, *(0-9665692)* Div. of Fashion Formulas by Ecoly, 9232 Eton Ave., Chatsworth, CA 91311 USA Tel 818-718-6982; Fax: 818-718-9353; Toll Free: 888-333-1277.

Sea Dog Pr., *(0-9672110)* Div. of William Rucker Enterprises, Ltd., 1708 S. Elm St., Pine Bluff, AR 71601 USA.

Seabird Publishing International, LLC, *(1-893551)* 1093 A1A Beach Blvd., Suite 165, Saint Augustine, FL 32084 USA Tel 904-631-0226; Fax: 904-827-0061; Toll Free: 800-274-1282
E-mail: seabird01@aol.com
Web site: http://augweb.com/seabird.

Seaburn Pubs., *(1-885778; 1-59232)* Orders Addr.: P.O. Box 2085, Astoria, NY 11102 USA Tel 718-274-1300; Fax: 718-274-3353; Edit Addr.: 41-19 31st Ave., Astoria, NY 11103 USA
E-mail: info@seaburn.com
Web site: http://www.seaburn.com
Dist(s): **A & B Distributors & Pubs. Group**
Baker & Taylor Bks.
Bookazine Co., Inc.
Distributors, The
Hervey's Booklink & Cookbook Warehouse
Ingram Bk. Co.
Koen-Levy Bk. Wholesalers LLC
Lectorum Pubns., Inc.
New Leaf Distributing Co., Inc.
Quality Bks., Inc.

Seachild, *(0-9787881)* P.O. Box 2600, Petaluma, CA 94952 USA (SAN 851-6499) Tel 707-762-7316
E-mail: judiegerber@earthlink.net
Web site: http://www.seachild.net.

Seacoast Publishing, Inc., *(1-878561; 1-59421)* Orders Addr.: P.O. Box 26492, Birmingham, AL 35260 USA Tel 205-979-2909; Fax: 205-979-3706; Edit Addr.: 1149 Mountain Oaks Dr., Birmingham, AL 35226 USA Do not confuse with companies with the same name in Monterey, CA, East Hampton, NY
E-mail: seacoast@charter.net
Dist(s): **Booksource, The**
Hervey's Booklink & Cookbook Warehouse.

Seaforth Publishing, *(0-9725706)* 5818 Three Ponds Ct., West Bloomfield, MI 48324-3124 USA.

Seagull Bks. (IND) *(81-7046) Dist. by* **S Asia.**

Seagull Pr., *(0-9753709)* 375-A Maxham Rd., No. 414, Austell, GA 30168 USA Fax: 770-944-3799 Do not confuse with companies with the same name in Oakland, CA, Owings, MD.

Seal Pr, *(0-931188; 1-58005; 1-878067)* Div. of Persues Bks. Grp., 387 Park Ave., S., 12th Flr., New York, NY 10016-8810 USA Tel 212-340-8100
Dist(s): **Perseus Distribution.**

Seal Publishing, LLC, *(0-9774062)* P.O. Box 435, Odessa, FL 33556 USA
Web site: http://www.sealswimschool.com.

Seal Rock Publishing, LLC, *(0-9763778)* 2660 Heidelberg Dr., Boulder, CO 80305 USA Fax: 720-304-8923
E-mail: sealrockpub@yahoo.com.

Sealing Touch End - Time Memory Fellowship, *(0-9717734)* P.O. Box 314, Thomas, OK 73669-0314 USA Tel 580-661-3837
E-mail: sealingtouch@pldi.net
Web site: http://www.sealingtouch.org.

Seaman, P. David, *(0-9755066)* 4221 E. White Aster St., Phoenix, AZ 85044-6780 USA Tel 480-759-0969.

Sean & I Publishing, *(1-929319)* 22626 Sunset Ave., Panama City, FL 32413 USA Tel 850-230-1919.

Search Institute, *(1-57482)* 615 First Ave. NE, Suite 125, Minneapolis, MN 55413 USA Tel 612-376-8955; Fax: 612-376-8956; Toll Free: 800-888-7828
Web site: http://www.search-institute.org
Dist(s): **Independent Pubs. Group.**

Search Pr., Ltd. (GBR) *(0-85532; 1-903975; 1-84448) Dist. by* **IPG Chicago.**

Search Pr., Ltd. (GBR) *(0-85532; 1-903975; 1-84448) Dist. by* **Search Press.**

Search Pr. USA, 1338 Ross St., Petaluma, CA 94954 USA Tel 707-762-3362; Fax: 707-762-0335; Toll Free: 800-289-9276 (orders); Wellwood North Farm Rd, Tunbridge Wells, TN2 3DR Tel 01892 510850; Fax: 01892 515903
E-mail: searchpressusa@aol.com; searchpress@searchpress.com
Web site: http://www.searchpress.com
Dist(s): **Midpoint Trade Bks., Inc.**

Sears, M.A., *(0-9639785)* 16809 Superior, North Hills, CA 91343 USA; 555 W. Sierra Hwy., Acton, CA 93510 Tel 818-891-8632.

Sears, Stanley, *(0-9770067)* Rte. 1 Box 215, Hickman, NE 68372-9686 USA.

SeaScape Pr., Ltd., *(0-9669741)* 1010 Roble Ln., Santa Barbara, CA 93103-2046 USA (SAN 299-8386) Tel 805-965-4646; Fax: 805-963-8188; Toll Free: 800-929-2906 do not confuse with Seascape Press in Jekyll Island, GA
E-mail: seapress@aol.com
Web site: http://www.seascapepress.com.

Seascay Productions, *(0-9764152)* 11 Ventnor Dr. Suite 906, Edison, NJ 08820 USA Tel 732-242-3902
E-mail: corporate@seascay.com
Web site: http://www.seascay.com.

Seashell Pr., The, *(0-9768866)* P.O. Box 1236, Edgartown, MA 02539 USA
E-mail: editorial@theseashellpress.com
Web site: http://www.theseashellpress.com.

Seashop Pr., *(0-9718825)* P.O. Box 1974, Thousand Oaks, CA 91358 USA Tel 805-341-8895; Fax: 805-241-5470
E-mail: pscelia@gte.net; scelia@seashoppress.com
Web site: http://www.seashoppress.com
Dist(s): **Mistco, Inc.**

Seaside Books *See* **David Ladd Press**

Seasoning Quilting (Arts & Crafts), *(1-888413)* 806 Elvie St., Wilson, NC 27893-6116 USA Tel 919-291-7705.

SeaStar Bks. *Imprint of* **Chronicle Bks. LLC**

Seastory Pr., *(0-9673704; 0-9768370)* 305 Whitehead St., Key West, FL 33040 USA Tel 305-296-5762; Fax: 305-296-9516; Toll Free: 877-454-6282
E-mail: sheri@seastorypress.com
Web site: http://www.seastorypress.com.

Sea-To-Sea Pubns., *(1-932889; 1-59771)* Div. of Creative Co., 2140 Howard Dr., W., North Mankato, MN 56003 USA
Dist(s): **Creative Co., The.**

Seattle's Child Publishing *See* **Northwest Parent Publishing**

SeaWorld Bks. for Young Learners *Imprint of* **SeaWorld, Inc.**

SeaWorld Education Dept. *Imprint of* **SeaWorld, Inc.**

SeaWorld, Inc., *(1-893698)* Div. of Anheuser-Busch Adventure Parks, 500 SeaWorld Dr., San Diego, CA 92109 USA (SAN 255-576X) Tel 619-225-4275; Fax: 619-226-3634; Toll Free: 800-237-4268 ; *Imprints:* SeaWorld Education Department (SeaWorld Educ); SeaWorld Books for Young Learners (SeaWorld Bks)
E-mail: swc.education@seaworld.com; debbie.nuzzolo@seaworld.com
Web site: http://www.seaworld.org
Dist(s): **Baker & Taylor Bks.**
Book Wholesalers, Inc.
Brodart Co.
Carolina Biological Supply Co.

Second Ark Pubns., *(1-889667)* 2907 Kevin Lane, Houston, TX 77043 USA.

Second Helping Foundation, The, *(0-9712134)* 16741 W. Park Cir. Dr., Chagrin Falls, OH 44023 USA (SAN 253-9373) Tel 330-995-3228; Fax: 330-995-3229
E-mail: bksaurora@aol.com.

Second Star Creations, *(0-9725977)* 12120 State Line Rd., No. 190, Leawood, KS 66209 USA Tel 913-681-2252
E-mail: jan@secondstar.us
Web site: http://www.secondstar.us
Dist(s): **Biblio Distribution.**

Second Story Pr. (CAN) *(0-921299; 0-929005; 1-896764; 1-897187) Dist. by* **Orca Bk Pubs.**

Second Wish Pr., *(0-9791887)* P.O. Box 139, Clarkston, MI 48347 USA Tel 248-705-3619; Toll Free: 866-544-3058
E-mail: information@secondwishpress.com
Web site: http://www.secondwishpress.com/; http://www.thesecretzoo.com
Dist(s): **Biblio Distribution.**

Seconds Out, Inc., *(1-932835)* 2800 Leprechuan Ln., Palm Harbor, FL 34683 USA (SAN 256-0054) Tel 727-771-6783
E-mail: johngraden@martialartsbusiness.com
Web site: http://www.martialartsbookstore.com
Dist(s): **Independent Pubs. Group.**

Secret Garden Bookworks, *(0-9766283)* Orders Addr.: P.O. Box 1506, Oak Bluffs, MA 02557-1506 USA Tel 508-693-4759; Fax: 508-693-4867; Edit Addr.: 41 Circuit Ave., Oak Bluffs, MA 02557-1506 USA
E-mail: secretgardenmv@peoplepc.com
Web site: http://www.secretgardenbookworks.com.

Secret Passage Pr., *(1-888695)* 26 Tucker Hollow Rd., North Scituate, RI 02857 USA Tel 401-647-0440; Toll Free: 877-863-4622 (Orders Only)
E-mail: lucindalandon@verizon.net
Web site: http://www.megmackintosh.com
Dist(s): **Baker & Taylor Bks.**
Enfield Publishing & Distribution Co., Inc.
Independent Pubs. Group
Koen-Levy Bk. Wholesalers LLC.

Secretaria de Educacion Publica (MEX) *(968-29; 970-18) Dist. by* **Santillana.**

Secretarius MEMPS Pubns., *(1-884855)* Orders Addr.: 12685 Dorsett Rd. 187, Maryland Heights, MO 63043 USA
E-mail: secmm@sbcglobal.net
Web site: http://www.memps.com.

Secretarius Publications *See* **Secretarius MEMPS Pubns.**

See abc's LC, *(1-890566)* Orders Addr.: P.O. Box 276, Smithfield, UT 84335 USA; Edit Addr.: 9 S. 490 E., Smithfield, UT 84335 USA.

See See Bks., *(0-9723427)* 1013 Carden Dr., Franklin, TN 37069 USA Tel 615-591-9642
E-mail: bill1@clcarter.com
Web site: http://www.clcarter.com.

SEEBIC Publishing Co., *(1-885037)* Orders Addr.: P.O. Box 1738, Broken Arrow, OK 74013-1738 USA; Edit Addr.: 4906 S. Hickory Ave., Broken Arrow, OK 74011-4607 USA.

SeeDEGA, *(0-9746586)* P.O. Box 588, Rhinebeck, NY 12572 USA
E-mail: info@seedega.com
Web site: http://seedega.com.

Seedling Pubns. *Imprint of* **Continental Pr., Inc.**

Seelcraft Publishing, *(0-9728380)* 63 Church St., Suite 201, High Bridge, NJ 08829-1516 USA
Web site: http://www.seelcraft.com.

See-More's Workshop, *(1-882601)* Div. of Shadow Box Theatre, 325 West End Ave., New York, NY 10023 USA Tel 212-724-0677; Fax: 212-724-0767
E-mail: sbt@shadowboxtheatre.org
Web site: http://www.shadowboxtheatre.org
Dist(s): **Baker & Taylor Bks.**
Follett Library Resources
Professional Media Service Corp.

Segal, Berty Inc., *(0-938395)* 1749 E. Eucalyptus St., Brea, CA 92821 USA (SAN 630-0553) Tel 714-529-5359; Fax: 714-529-3882
E-mail: bertytprsource@earthlink.net
Web site: http://www.tprsource.com
Dist(s): **Continental Bk. Co., Inc.**

Segal, Robin *See* **Murray Hill Bks., LLC**

Segarra, Angelo, *(0-9752664)* 9 Calle De Sol., Rnch De Taos, NM 87557-7920 USA
Dist(s): **Greenleaf Book Group.**

Segen Bks. *Imprint of* **Black Forest Pr.**

Seglie, Susan M., *(0-9747243)* 1 Deer Run Ln., Pittsburg, KS 66762 USA Fax: 620-232-5819.

Segue Pubs., *(0-9671796)* P.O. Box 89, Jenkintown, PA 19046 USA Tel 215-663-0797 phone
E-mail: seguepublishing@aol.com.

Selah Publishing Group, LLC, *(0-9679371; 1-58930)* 16238 W. Young St., Surprise, AZ 85374-5744 USA Toll Free Fax: 866-777-8909; Toll Free: 877-616-6451 Do not confuse with the same name in Kingston, NY, Berkley, MI
E-mail: garlen@selahbooks.com
Web site: http://www.selahbooks.com.

Selah Publishing, Incorporated *See* **Selah Publishing Group, LLC**

Company

Selby Dean Ventures, Inc., *(0-9716479)* P.O. Box 246, Kure Beach, NC 28449 USA (SAN 852-7539) Tel 910-279-2486
E-mail: fishinstructor@aol.com
Web site: http://www.gullswatch.com; http://www.SelbyDeanVentures.com.

Selby, Marie Botanical Gardens Pr., *(0-9701613)* 811 S. Palm Ave., Sarasota, FL 34236 USA Tel 941-955-7553; Fax: 941-951-1474
E-mail: bholst@selby.org.

Selective Mutism Anxiety Research & Treatment Ctr., *(0-9714800)* 1130 Herkness Dr., Meadowbrook, PA 19046 USA Tel 215 -887-5748; Fax: 215-827-5722
E-mail: dreshiponblum@aol.com
Web site: http://www.selectivemutismcenter.org.

Selecto Publishing, *(0-9662898)* 1406 E. Orange Grove Rd., Tucson, AZ 85718 USA Tel 520-575-4679
E-mail: jdavid7837@aol.com.

Selector, S.A. de C.V. (MEX) *(968-403; 970-643) Dist. by* **Bilingual Pubns.**

Selector, S.A. de C.V. (MEX) *(968-403; 970-643) Dist. by* **Lectorum Pubns.**

Selector, S.A. de C.V. (MEX) *(968-403; 970-643) Dist. by* **AIMS Intl.**

Selector, S.A. de C.V. (MEX) *(968-403; 970-643) Dist. by* **Libros Fronteras.**

Self-Esteem Adventures Pr., *(0-9747597)* P.O. Box 2145, Universal City, TX 78148 USA Tel 210-595-6952
E-mail: daddybooks@grandecom.net
Web site: http://www.daddybooks.com.

Self-Mastery Press *See* **Love & Blessings**

Self-Realization Fellowship Pubs., *(0-87612)* Orders Addr.: 3208 Humboldt St., Los Angeles, CA 90031 USA (SAN 204-5788) Tel 323-276-6002; Fax: 323-276-6003; Toll Free: 888-773-8680; Edit Addr.: 3880 San Rafael Ave., Los Angeles, CA 90065 USA Tel 323-276 6000; 215 K. St., Encinitas, CA 92024 Tel 760-753-2888 ext 471; Fax: 323-276-6003
E-mail: sales@srfpublishers.org
Web site: http://www.srfpublishers.org
Dist(s): **Distributors, The.**

Sellers, Amy, *(0-9787632)* 5151 Round Lake Rd., Apopka, FL 32712 USA (SAN 851-5425)
E-mail: amycsellers@yahoo.com
Web site: http://www.amysellers.com.

Sellers Publishing, Inc., *(1-56906; 1-4162)* Orders Addr.: P.O. Box 818, Portland, ME 04104 USA Tel 207-772-6833; Fax: 207-772-6814; Toll Free: 800-625-3386 (800-MAKE-FUN); Edit Addr.: 81 W. Commercial St., Portland, ME 04101 USA
E-mail: rsp@rsvp.com
Web site: http://www.rsvp.com
Dist(s): **Baker & Taylor Bks.**
Bookazine Co., Inc.
MBI Distribution Services
MBI Publishing Co. LLC
New Leaf Distributing Co., Inc.
Partners Bk. Distributing, Inc.

Sellers, Ronnie Productions, Incorporated *See* **Sellers Publishing, Inc.**

Selwyn & Ross Pubs., *(0-9677406)* 4525 Laclede, Unit 12, Saint Louis, MO 63108 USA Tel 314-454-9075
E-mail: psychBev@aol.com.

Sem Fronteiras Pr., Ltd., *(0-9642333)* 1530 Palisade Ave., Suite 2F, Fort Lee, NJ 07024 USA (SAN 253-4959) Toll Free Fax: 800-433-5193
E-mail: semfront@superlink.net.

Sem, Gilmore, *(0-9742299)* 1822 Carl St., Lauderdale, MN 55113-5203 USA.

Seminole Tribe of Florida, Dept. of Anthropology & Genealogy, *(0-9659981)* 6300 Stirling Rd., Room 421, Hollywood, FL 33024 USA Tel 954-966-6300; Fax: 954-967-3423; Toll Free: 800-683-7800 Do not confuse with Seminole Tribe of Florida, Inc., Commns. Dept., at same address
E-mail: semgenes@semtribe.com
Web site: http://www.seminoletribe.com.

Semper Studio, *(0-9778420)* 4416 Rte. 47, Delmont, NJ 08314 USA (SAN 850-3885) Tel 609-501-3341
E-mail: Catherine@semperstudiosus.com
Web site: http://www.semperstudiosus.com.

Seneca Mill Pr. LLC, *(0-9768986)* P.O. Box 1423, Great Falls, VA 22066 USA
E-mail: senecamillpress@aol.com.

Senegalpress, *(0-9758594)* P.O. Box 1613, Venice, CA 90294 USA
E-mail: elke@senegalpress.com
Web site: http://www.senegalpress.com.

Sensational Bks., *(0-9770054)* P.O. Box 261085, Lakewood, CO 80226 USA (SAN 256-6265) Tel 303-238-4760; Fax: 303-205-0614
Web site: http://www.sensationalbooks.com.

Sense of Wonder Pr. *Imprint of* **Rock, James A. & Co. Pubs.**

Sensory Resources, *(1-893601; 1-931615)* Div. of Future Horizons, Inc., 2690 Chandler Ave. Ste. 8, Las Vegas, NV 89120-4088 USA (SAN 253-8288) Toll Free: 888-357-5867
E-mail: orders@sensoryresources.com
Web site: http://www.sensoryresources.com.

Sentient Pubns., *(0-9710786; 1-59181)* 1113 Spruce St., Boulder, CO 80302 USA Tel 303-443-2188; Fax: 303-447-1511; Toll Free: 866-588-9846
E-mail: cshaw@sentientpublications.com; dialagzone@aol.com
Web site: http://www.sentientpublications.com/
Dist(s): **National Bk. Network.**

Sentinel Group, The, *(1-930612)* Orders Addr.: P.O. Box 6334, Lynnwood, WA 98036 USA Tel 425-672-2989; Fax: 425-672-3028; Toll Free: 800-668-5657; Edit Addr.: 19217 36th Ave. W, Suite 106, Lynnwood, WA 98036 USA (SAN 179-1931)
E-mail: info@sentinelgroup.org
Web site: http://www.transformnations.com; http://www.sentinelgroup.org; http://www.transformationsvideo.org.

Sentinel Pr. L.L.C., *(0-9705290)* 83 Gallmeier Rd., Frenchtown, NJ 08825 USA Tel 908-713-8795; Fax: 908-996-6390
E-mail: info@sentinelpressllc.com
Web site: http://www.sentinelpressllc.com; http://www.sntllc.com; http://www.sentinelpress.net.

Sentinel Publishing, *(0-9666559)* P.O. Box 13406, Ogden, UT 84412-3406 USA Tel 801-393-9575; Fax: 801-627-5080 Do not confuse with Sentinel Publishing Co., Lubbock, TX , Wayne, PA
E-mail: cphaid@aol.com.

Sentinel Publishing, *(0-9728291)* 1131 Rossiter Ln., Wayne, PA 19087-2812 USA Tel 610-687-5908; Fax: 610-687-5909 Do not confuse with Sentinel Publishing in Ogden, UT
E-mail: orchidman@snip.net
Web site: http://www.linenpostcards.com.

Sentry Pr., Inc., *(1-889574)* 424 E. Call St., Tallahassee, FL 32301-7693 USA
E-mail: wrogers@fsu.edu
Dist(s): **Polk County Historical Assn.**

Separate Star, Inc., *(0-9712872)* 400 E. 77th St., Apt. 14D, New York, NY 10021 USA Tel 212-861-2768; Fax: 212-249-7887 ; *Imprints:* Separate Star Publishing (Separate Star Pubng)
E-mail: publish@separate-star.com
Web site: http://www.separate-star.com.

Separate Star Publishing *Imprint of* **Separate Star, Inc.**

Separating Sickness Foundation *See* **Anoai Pr.**

SepSha Publishing, *(0-9727885)* P.O. Box 462075, Aurora, CO 80046 USA (SAN 255-3007)
Web site: http://www.endtimebooks.com.

Sepulveda, Wilfredo, *(0-9747787)* P.O. Box 30851, San Juan, PR 00929-1851 USA
E-mail: wsepulveda@yahoo.com.

Sequent Media, Inc., *(0-9746531)* P.O. Box 126325, San Diego, CA 92112 USA
Web site: http://www.sequentmedia.com.

Sequoia Natural History Assn., *(1-878441)* 47050 Generals Hwy. #10, Three Rivers, CA 93271-9599 USA Tel 559-565-3759
E-mail: mark_tilchen@sequoiahistory.org
Web site: http://www.sequoiahistory.org
Dist(s): **American West Bks.**

Sequoyah Literacy Systems, LLC *See* **OpenBook Learning, Inc.**

Seraphemera Bks, *(0-9778989)* P.O. Box 73562, houston, TX 77273-7727 USA Tel 832-515-9539; Fax: 832-515-9539; Toll Free Fax: 832-515-9539.

Seraphic Pr., *(0-9754382)* 1531 Cardiff Ave., Los Angeles, CA 90035 USA (SAN 256-0496) Tel 310-557-0132; Fax: 310-286-9534
E-mail: robert@seraphicpress.com; rjaprod@aol.com
Web site: http://www.seraphicpress.com
Dist(s): **David, Jonathan Publishers, Inc.**

Seren Bks. (GBR) *(0-907476; 1-85411) Dist. by* **IPG Chicago.**

Serena Bocchino/In His Perfect Time Collection, *(0-9767674)* 82 Haas Rd., Basking Ridge, NJ 07920 USA Tel 908-542-1987 (phone/fax)
E-mail: serena@serenabocchino.com
Web site: http://www.serenabocchino.com.

Serenade *Imprint of* **Sierra Raconteur Publishing**

Serendipity Press *See* **Plair, James B.**

Serendipity Pubns., *(0-9715395)* 21721 SR 47, West Mansfield, OH 43358 USA Tel 937-358-2190; Fax: 614-451-2406 Do not confuse with Serendipity Publications, Boca Raton, FL
E-mail: ams108@msn.com
Web site: http://www.magicalmac.com.

Serendipity Publishing Company *See* **Blue Dragonfly Pubs.**

Serendipity Publishing Co., *(0-9678709)* P.O. Box 932, Mims, FL 32754 USA Tel 321-268-9336; Fax: 321-268-4088
E-mail: rvpitoni@digital.net.

Serene Sounds, *(0-9718866)* 10308 Metcalf Ave., PMB 109, Overland Park, KS 66209-2814 USA
E-mail: serenesnd@aol.com.

Serenity Pr., *(0-9669436)* RFD 3, Box 21E, Plymouth, NH 03264 USA Tel 603-536-3442 Do not confuse with companies with the same name in Grants Pass, OR, Plainfield, CT
E-mail: owls4golf@aol.com.

Serenity Pr., *(0-9787981)* 500 SW. 21st Terr., Fort Lauderdale, FL 33312 USA (SAN 851-6251)
E-mail: marty@mwpr.com
Web site: http://www.mwpr.com/Splash.html.

Serpent's Tail Ltd. (GBR) *(1-85242) Dist. by* **Consort Bk Sales.**

Serpent's Tale Natural History Bk. Distributors, Inc., *(1-885209)* Orders Addr.: P.O. Box 405, Lanesboro, MN 55949-0405 USA (SAN 630-6101) Tel 507-467-8734; Fax: 507-467-8735
E-mail: zoobooks@acegroup.cc
Web site: http://www.zoobooksales.com.

Serres, Ediciones, S. L. (ESP) *(84-88061; 84-95040; 84-8488) Dist. by* **Lectorum Pubns.**

Serres, Ediciones, S. L. (ESP) *(84-88061; 84-95040; 84-8488) Dist. by* **Libros Fronteras.**

Servano Style Gaming, *(0-9679972)* P.O. Box 1516, N Little Rock, AR 72115-1516 USA
E-mail: ssg@itisthetale.com; SSG@itisthetale.com
Web site: http://www.itisthetale.com.

Servant Bks. *Imprint of* **St. Anthony Messenger Pr. & Franciscan Communications**

Servant Ministries, Inc., *(0-9702375)* Orders Addr.: P.O. Box 1120, Tioga, LA 71477 USA Tel 318-640-6993; Fax: 318-640-5511; Edit Addr.: 57 Robin Hood Rd., Dry Prong, LA 71423-3547 USA Do not confuse with Servant Ministries in Kirkland, WA
E-mail: ira@iamerica.net.

Serve Man Pr., *(0-9768517)* 117 Franklin St., Northampton, MA 01060 USA Tel 413-586-7089
E-mail: rokaril@hotmail.com
Web site: http://www.seanwang.com.

Servilibro Ediciones, S.A. (ESP) *(84-7971) Dist. by* **Giron Bks.**

Session Family, *(0-9658006)* Orders Addr.: P.O. Box 841, Florissaint, MO 63033 USA Tel 314-972-7705 (phone/fax); Edit Addr.: 16856 Heather Moor Dr., Florissant, MO 63034 USA
E-mail: denise.session@att.net
Web site: http://www.sessionfamily.com
Dist(s): **Baker & Taylor Bks.**

Sessions, William Ltd. (GBR) *(0-900657; 1-85072) Dist. by* **St Mut.**

Seth Enterprises *See* **Incredible Years Pr.**

Seton St. Clare Bks., *(1-890236)* Orders Addr.: P.O. Box 8543, Waco, TX 76714-8543 USA Tel 254-776-1794; Fax: 254-776-4498; Edit Addr.: 4906 Lake Englewood, Waco, TX 76710 USA
E-mail: setonbooks@aol.com
Dist(s): **Book Marketing Plus**
Booksource, The.

Setubandh Pubns., *(0-9623674)* 1 Lawson Ln., Great Neck, NY 11023 USA Tel 516-482-6938
Web site: http://www.setubandh.com.

Seven Arrows Publishing, *(0-9622341)* Winter Harbor Haven, Rte. 608, Port Hollywood, VA 23138 USA Tel 804-725-0355; Fax: 804-725-0002 Do not confuse with Seven Arrows Publishing House, Saint Peters, MO
E-mail: dickbozung@hotmail.com
Web site: http://www.guitarsimplified.com.

Seven Coin Pr., *(0-9700974)* P.O. Box 477, Spruce Head, ME 04859-0477 USA
E-mail: publisher@sevencoinpress.com; bookw@midcoast.com
Web site: http://www.sevencoinpress.com
Dist(s): **Baker & Taylor Bks.**

†Seven Locks Pr., *(0-929765; 0-932020; 0-9615964; 1-931643; 0-9790950; 0-9795852; 0-9801270)* 3100 W. Warner Ave., Suite 8, Santa Ana, CA 92704 USA (SAN 211-9781) Tel 714-545-2526; Fax: 714-545-1572; Toll Free: 800-354-5348 ; *Imprints:* Papa & Noelle Stories (Papa & Noelle)
E-mail: sevenlocks@aol.com
Web site: http://www.sevenlockspublishing.com
Dist(s): **Baker & Taylor Bks.**
Koen-Levy Bk. Wholesalers LLC; *CIP.*

Seven Rivers Publishing, *(0-9728768)* P.O. Box 682, Crowley, TX 76036-0682 USA Toll Free: 800-544-3770 (Order line: Hendrick-Long)
E-mail: hendrick-long@att.net; djls@sevenriverspublishing.com; sales@sevenriverspublishing.com
Web site: http://www.hendricklongpublishing.com; http://www.sevenriverspublishing.com
Dist(s): **Hendrick-Long Publishing Co.**

Seven Seas Entertainment, LLC, *(1-933164)* 718 N. Kings Rd., No. 303, West Hollywood, CA 90069 USA Tel 323-377-6545
E-mail: dallas@sent.com
Web site: http://www.gomanga.com
Dist(s): **Diamond Bk. Distributors.**

Seven Stars Trading Co., *(0-9743999)* 3543 Marvin St., Annandale, VA 22003 USA Tel 703-573-2939.

Seven Stories Pr., *(1-58322; 1-888363)* 140 Watts St., New York, NY 10013 USA Tel 212-226-8760; Fax: 212-226-1411; Toll Free: 800-596-7437
E-mail: info@sevenstories.com
Web site: http://www.sevenstories.com
Dist(s): **Consortium Bk. Sales & Distribution**
Continental Bk. Co., Inc.
Libros Sin Fronteras.

Seventh Generation Design, *(0-9653169)* 8295 SW Ridgeway Dr., Portland, OR 97225 USA Tel 503-292-2356.

Seventh Seal Publishing, LLC, *(0-9712228)* Orders Addr.: P.O. Box 689, Darby, PA 19023 USA; Edit Addr.: 266 W. 4020 N., Provo, UT 84604 USA Tel 801-227-0232
E-mail: cotedwar@ihc.com
Web site: http://www.millennialglory.com.

Seventh Street Pr., Div. of Malone-Ballard Book Pubs., 2215 6th Ave. Apt D, Moline, IL 61265 USA
E-mail: bookwoman1110@hotmail.com.

Seventh Sun Productions, *(0-9706412)* 212 3rd St. Ste. 4, Tracy, MN 56175-1267 USA Toll Free: 888-293-4384
E-mail: Info@dream-chasers.net; jmarks@seventhsunproductions.com
Web site: http://www.seventhsunproductions.com.

Seventy Fourth Street Productions, *(0-9655702)* 350 N. 74th St., Seattle, WA 98103 USA Tel 206-781-1447
E-mail: info@74thstreet.com
Web site: http://www.74thstreet.com
Dist(s): **Baker & Taylor Bks.**
Brodart Co.
Partners/West.

Severn Hse. Pubs., Ltd., *(0-7278)* Orders Addr.: c/o Chivers North America, P.O. Box 1450, Hampton, NH 03843-1450 USA Tel 603-926-8744; Fax: 603-929-3890; Toll Free: 800-830-3044; Edit Addr.: 595 Madison Ave., 15th Flr., New York, NY 10022 USA Tel 212-888-4042; Fax: 212-759-5422; Toll Free: 800-830-3044 (customer service)
E-mail: chivers@rcn.com
Dist(s): **BBC Audiobooks America**
Mercedes Distribution Ctr., Inc.

Severn Hse. Pubs., Ltd. (GBR) *(0-7278) Dist. by* **IngramPubServ.**

SEView Publishing, *(0-9707353)* 3610 W. Cromwell Dr., Tucson, AZ 85741 USA Tel 520-744-8077
E-mail: svaterlaus@earthlink.net.

Sextant Pr., Inc., *(0-9658769)* Orders Addr.: P.O. Box 1416, Chicago, IL 60690-1416 USA Tel 312-346-7863; Fax: 312-346-2531; Toll Free: 800-399-7533 Do not confuse with companies with the same or similar name in Slidell, LA, Portland, OR.

Seymour, Dale Pubns., *(0-201; 0-7690; 0-86651; 1-57232)* Div. of Pearson Learning, Orders Addr.: P.O. Box 2500, Lebanon, OH 43216 USA Toll Free Fax: 800-393-3156; Toll Free: 800-321-3106 (Customer Service); Edit Addr.: 10 Bank St., White Plains, NY 10602-5026 USA (SAN 200-9781) Toll Free Fax: 800-393-3156; Toll Free: 800-237-3142
E-mail: pearson_learning2@prenhall.com
Web site: http://www.pearsonlearning.com; http://www.pearsonlearning.com/rightsPerm.rtf
Dist(s): **Addison-Wesley Educational Pubs., Inc.**

Sgian Enterprises, *(0-615; 0-9771197)* 4349 W. Tomahawk Dr., Beverly Hills, FL 34465-4871 USA.

Shades of Me Publishing, *(0-9718307)* 3969 Strandhill Rd., Cleveland, OH 44128 USA
E-mail: marybury1927@msn.com.

Shades of White, *(0-9796834)* 301 Tenth Ave., Crystal City, MO 63019 USA Tel 314-740-0361
Web site: http://www.handcraftedpagan.com.

Shadow Mountain *Imprint of* **Deseret Bk. Co.**

Shadow Pubns., *(0-9771424)* P.O. Box 1151, Valley Forge, PA 19482-1151 USA
Web site: http://www.olliedude.com.

Shadowbox Media, *(0-9668126)* 10061 Riverside Dr., Suite 770, Toluca Lake, CA 91602 USA Tel 818-846-2322
E-mail: ringletred@aol.com
Web site: http://www.shadowbox-media.com.

ShadowPlay Pr., *(0-9638819)* P.O. Box 647, Forreston, IL 61030 USA Tel 815-938-3151; Fax: 815-371-1440
E-mail: sheilawelch@juno.com; ericwelch2@juno.com
Web site: http://www.shadowplay.userworld.com.

Shaffer, Dale E., *(0-915060)* 437 Jennings Ave., Salem, OH 44460 USA (SAN 206-9067) Tel 330-337-3348.

Shaffner, Randolph P. *See* **Faraway Publishing**

ShaGru Entertainment, LLC, *(0-9724621)* P.O. Box 689, Darby, PA 19023 USA
E-mail: sag@shawnagrundy.com
Web site: http://www.shawnagrundy.com.

Shah, Meera, *(0-9774219)* 7003 Westminster Ln., Germantown, TN 38138 USA Tel 901-754-7197
E-mail: meeds_46@yahoo.com
Web site: merra.meeds46@gmail.com.

Shakalot High Entertainment, *(0-9721067; 0-9796219)* 20687 White Dove Ln., Bend, OR 97702 USA Tel 541-788-4011 ; *Imprints:* Writing Wild & Crazy (Writing Wild)
E-mail: shakalothighentertainment@yahoo.com
Web site: http://www.shakalothigh.com.

Shake It, *(0-9777651)* 4156 Hamilton Ave., Cintcinnatti, OH 45223-3012 USA (SAN 850-1408)
Dist(s): **AK Pr. Distribution**
Perseus Distribution.

Shakti for Children, *(0-9651722)* P.O. Box 99350, Durham, NC 27708 USA Tel 919-956-9606; Fax: 919-683-3194.

Shalhout, Ahlam LLC *See* **Expressions Woven**

Shamber Pubns., *(0-9771326)* P.O. Box 470321, Lake Monroe, FL 32747-0321 USA
E-mail: unbrokencirclebymcghee@gmail.com.

Shambhala Publications, Incorporated *See* **Shambhala Pubns., Inc.**

†Shambhala Pubns., Inc., *(0-8348; 0-87773; 1-56957; 1-57062; 1-59030)* Horticultural Hall, 300 Massachusetts Ave., Boston, MA 02115 USA (SAN 203-2481) Tel 617-424-0030; Fax: 617-236-1563 ; *Imprints:* Weatherhill, Incorporated (Weathill); Trumpeter (Trumpeter)
E-mail: editors@shambhala.com
Web site: http://www.shambhala.com
Dist(s): **Random Hse., Inc.**
Sounds True, Inc.; *CIP.*

Shamrock Hse., The, *(0-9702985)* 990 Forest Pond Ct., Marietta, GA 30068 USA
E-mail: sales@shamrockpublishing.com
Web site: http://www.shamrockpublishing.com.

Shamrock Pr., *(0-9675410)* Rte. 2, Box 340, Charleston, WV 25314 USA Tel 304-744-4259 (phone/fax) Do not confuse with Shamrock Pr. in Chattanooga, TN
E-mail: shamrock.press@worldnet.att.net.

Shamrock Publishing, Inc., *(0-9743244; 0-9759703)* 400 Corey Ave., Wachovia Bldg., 2nd Flr., Saint Pete Beach, FL 33706 USA Tel 727-363-4747; Fax: 727-363-4848; 1220 S. State St., Chicago, IL 60605 Tel 312-212-1143; Fax: 708-371-9576 Do not confuse with Shamrock Publishing, Incorporated in New Orleans, LA
E-mail: tpmac@sprynet.com; bksemmer@blueshamrockpublishing.com.

Shamus B. Publishing, *(0-9753671)* 18533 Pond Dr., Abingdon, VA 24211 USA.

Shanahan, John Francis Publishing, *(0-9618275)* 6727 N. Lightfoot Ave., Chicago, IL 60646 USA (SAN 667-0490) Tel 773-631-6344; Fax: 773-631-6372
E-mail: REPSbooks@aol.com.

Shangri-La Pubns., *(0-9677201; 0-9714683; 0-9719496)* Orders Addr.: P.O. Box 65, Warren Center, PA 18851-0065 USA Toll Free: 866-966-6288; Edit Addr.: 3 Coburn Hill Rd., PMB 65, Warren Center, PA 18851 USA Tel 570-395-3423; Fax: 570-395-0146
E-mail: gosline@egypt.net; shangrila@egypt.net; shangri_la_book@hotmail.com
Web site: http://www.shangri-la.0catch.com/.

Shapeland Publishing, *(0-9712677)* 1935 Acacia Pkwy., Box 1086, Spring Branch, TX 78070 USA Tel 830-885-2554; Fax: 830-885-2285
E-mail: wnjhunt@gvtc.com; amy@shapelandpub.com
Web site: http://www.shapelandpub.com.

Share & Care Society, *(0-9722025)* 2105 55th Ln., NW, Olympia, WA 98502 USA Tel 760-819-9174
E-mail: london_pain@hotmail.com
Web site: http://www.shareandcaresociety.org.

Share Publishing, *(0-9633705)* Orders Addr.: 313 Laurel Ave., Menlo Park, CA 94025 USA Tel 650-321-5947 (phone/fax)
E-mail: pamelalaw@sbcglobal.net
Web site: http://sharepublishing.com.

Sharif Enterprizes, Inc., *(0-9637036)* P.O. Box 51282, Phoenix, AZ 85076-1282 USA
E-mail: asus@ix.netcom.com.

Sharif, Mboya, *(0-9754024)* 6008 S. Bishop, Chicago, IL 60636 USA
E-mail: dosesofreality@yahoo.com.

Shark Press *See* **Lemon Shark Pr.**

Sharon's Small Pr., *(1-929453)* 7 Elizabeth Dr., Bethpage, NY 11714-6005 USA Tel 516-796-2144; Fax: 516-579-3919
E-mail: SDockweiler@juno.com.

†Sharp & Dunnigan, *(0-918495)* 2700 Richards Rd., Suite 110, Bellevue, WA 98005 USA (SAN 657-3029) Tel 425-467-6565; Fax: 425-467-6564
E-mail: ecovepress@aol.com
Web site: http://elfincovepress.com
Dist(s): **Baker & Taylor Bks.**
Elfin Cove Pr.
Ingram Bk. Co.; *CIP.*

Sharp & Dunnigan, Publications, Incorporated *See* **Sharp & Dunnigan**

Sharp, Diana Consulting, *(0-9762626)* 5954 Fishhawk Crossing Blvd., Lithia, FL 33547-5878 USA.

SHARP Literacy, Inc., *(0-9770816)* 750 N. Lincoln Memorial Dr., Milwaukee, WI 53202 USA Tel 414-270-3388
Web site: http://www.creativesharp.org.

Sharpe, Jeannie W., *(0-9763117)* 373 Langford Rd., Blythewood, SC 29016 USA Fax: 803-786-4557
E-mail: jws415@aol.com
Dist(s): **AtlasBooks Distribution.**

†Sharpe, M.E. Inc., *(0-7656; 0-87332; 1-56324)* 80 Business Park Dr., Armonk, NY 10504 USA (SAN 202-7100) Tel 914-273-1800; Fax: 914-273-2106; Toll Free: 800-541-6563 ; *Imprints:* East Gate Book (East Gate Bk); Sharpe Reference (Sharpe Ref)
Web site: http://www.mesharpe.com
Dist(s): **Women Ink**; *CIP.*

Sharpe Reference *Imprint of* **Sharpe, M.E. Inc.**

Shartec Systems, Incorporated *See* **Mountcastle Co.**

Shauger, Daniel, *(0-9746114)* 12438 Moorpark St., No. 241, Studio City, CA 91605 USA Tel 818-693-6231
E-mail: dan@aperfectswing.com
Web site: http://dan@aperfectswing.com.

Shavatt Enterprises, *(0-9678630)* 1716 Greentree Ct., Crofton, MD 21114 USA Tel 410-721-2559
E-mail: DShavatt@aol.com.

Shaw *Imprint of* **WaterBrook Pr.**

Shaw, Dana, *(0-9791091)* Orders Addr.: P.O. Box 91, Franklin, ME 04634 USA (SAN 852-4815) Tel 207-565-4445; Edit Addr.: 206 Georges Pond Rd., Franklin, ME 04634 USA
E-mail: myfriendzundel@yahoo.com
Web site: http://myfriendzundel.com.

Shawangunk Pr., Inc., *(1-885482)* 181 Parker Hill Rd., Springfield, VT 05156-9338 USA
Dist(s): **New Leaf Distributing Co., Inc.**

Shawkey, Gary International, Inc., *(0-9720609)* 12468 Spring Hill Dr., Spring Hill, FL 34609 USA (SAN 255-3090) Tel 352-684-9216; Fax: 352-684-9244; Toll Free: 800-727-6815
E-mail: gshawkey@garyshawkey.com
Web site: http://www.garyshawkey.com.

Shayach Comics *Imprint of* **Judaica Pr., Inc., The**

Shaymaa Publishing Corp., *(0-9719581)* P.O. Box 501, Lodi, NJ 07644-0501 USA (SAN 255-738X) Fax: 973-472-6045
E-mail: elhewiemf@juno.com; todaysgy@todaysgym.com; elhewie@lift-4-life.com
Web site: http://www.lift-4-life.com; http://www.todaysgym.com; http://www.shaymaa-publishing.com.

Shayne Publishing, *(0-9771192)* 4895 SE 40th St., Des Moines, IA 50320 USA (SAN 256-7997) Tel 515-263-2784
E-mail: dlhuston01@aol.com.

Shazak Productions *Imprint of* **Torah Excel**

She Bear Publishing, *(0-9658876)* 4493 E. Cedar Lake Dr., Greenbush, MI 48738 USA Tel 517-739-8636
E-mail: SheBear@mail.theenchantedforest.com
Web site: http://www.theenchantedforest.com/SheBearPublishing.

Shedd Aquarium Society, *(0-9611074; 0-9701035)* 1200 S. Lake Shore Dr., Chicago, IL 60605 USA (SAN 283-4359) Tel 312-692-3266; Fax: 312-939-3430
E-mail: rschlegel@sheddaquarium.org
Web site: http://sheddaquarium.org.

Sheed & Ward *Imprint of* **Rowman & Littlefield Pubs., Inc.**

Sheeley, Barbara, *(0-9672077)* 31 Chinaberry Cir., Hilton Head, SC 29926-1293 USA.

Sheepdog Pr., *(0-9742205)* P.O. Box 60, Onancock, VA 23417 USA Tel 888-787-1951; Fax: 888-787-2675
E-mail: publisher@sheepdogpress.com
Web site: http://www.sheepdogpress.com.

Sheepdog Publishing, *(0-9721164)* P.O. Box 9964, Philadelphia, PA 19118 USA Tel 215-438-4212 (phone/fax)
E-mail: kidzofking@comic.com
Web site: http://www.kidzoftheking.com.

Sheer Bliss Communications, LLC, *(0-9679436)* P.O. Box 186, Newport, RI 02840 USA Fax: 401-848-2551
E-mail: gloria@wurman.com.

Sheets, Judy, *(0-9726451)* 2526 Brune Rd., Farmington, MO 63640 USA Tel 573-756-6254
E-mail: judys@i1.net.

Shekinah Publishing Hse., *(0-9700976)* Orders Addr.: P.O. Box 156423, Ft. Worth, TX 76155 USA Tel 877-538-1363; Edit Addr.: P.O. Box 156423, Fort Worth, TX 76155 USA Tel 877-538-1363 ; *Imprints:* Shekinah Publishing House (Shek Pub Hse) Do not confuse with companies with the same or similar names in Cameron, NC, Cameron, NC
E-mail: patadams@ureach.com
Web site: www.patriciaadams.us; http://www.geocities.com/sheknh
Dist(s): **Baker & Taylor Bks.**

Shekinah Publishing Hse. *Imprint of* **Shekinah Publishing Hse.**

Shelby, Lloyd *See* **Painted Wood Studios**

Shelbykay Pubilshing Co., *(0-9744407)* 525 Greenhill Ln., Philadelphia, PA 19128 USA Tel 215-483-6688
E-mail: cdkae@aol.com.

Sheldrake Pr. (GBR) *(1-873329) Dist. by* **Interlink Pub.**

Shelf-Life Bks., *(1-880042)* Div. of M.A.P.S., Inc., 2132 Fordem, Madison, WI 53704-0599 USA Tel 608-244-7767; Fax: 608-244-8394.

Shell Beach Publishing, LLC, *(0-9706732)* 677 Shell Beach Dr., Lake Charles, LA 70601-5732 USA Tel 433-439-2110
E-mail: kkblake@compuserve.com.

Shelle, Carole Creative Arts, *(0-9792641)* P.O. Box 52972, Irvine, CA 92619 USA (SAN 852-9493) Toll Free: 800-929-1634.

Shelter of Flint, Inc., *(0-9740929)* 902 E. 6th St., Flint, MI 48503-2787 USA
E-mail: sof@shelterofflint.com
Web site: http://www.shelterofflint.com.

†Shelter Pubns., Inc., *(0-936070)* Orders Addr.: P.O. Box 279, Bolinas, CA 94924 USA (SAN 122-8463) Tel 415-868-0280; Fax: 415-868-9053; Toll Free: 800-307-0131; Edit Addr.: 285 Dogwood Rd, Bolinas, CA 94924 USA
E-mail: shelter@shelterpub.com
Web site: http://www.shelterpub.com
Dist(s): **Book Express**
Bookmen, Inc.
Distributors, The
Koen-Levy Bk. Wholesalers LLC
Koen Pacific
Partners/West
Perseus Distribution; *CIP.*

shelterpetsink, *(0-9740980)* 16457 Gledhill St., North Hills, CA 91343 USA Fax: 818-892-2112
E-mail: shelterpetsink@shelterpetsink.com; remilove2002@yahoo.com
Web site: http://www.shelterpetsink.com.

Shenanigan Bks., *(0-9726614; 1-934860)* 129 W. End Ave., Summit, NJ 07901 USA
E-mail: patriciaollom@shenaniganbooks.com
Web site: http://www.shenaniganbooks.com
Dist(s): **Biblio Distribution.**

Shen's Bks., *(1-885008)* 40951 Fremont Blvd., Fremont, CA 94538 USA (SAN 138-2926) Tel 510-668-1898; Fax: 510-668-1057; Toll Free: 800-456-6660
E-mail: info@shens.com
Web site: http://www.shens.com
Dist(s): **Lectorum Pubns., Inc.**
Quality Bks., Inc.

Shepard Pubns., *(0-938497)* 1102 Olympia Ave NE, No. 18, Olympia, WA 98506 USA (SAN 661-0536) ; *Imprints:* Skyhook Press (Skyhook Pr)
Web site: http://www.shepardpub.com
Dist(s): **Lightning Source, Inc.**
Replica Bks.

Shepherd Mountain Pr., *(0-9749282)* 21 Cargill Rd., LIberty, ME 04949 USA Tel 207-589-4772.

Shepherd Pr. Inc., *(0-9663786; 0-9723046; 0-9767582)* Orders Addr.: P.O. Box 24, Wapwallopen, PA 18660 USA Fax: 570-379-2071; Toll Free: 800-338-1445; Edit Addr.: 45 Eagle Ridge Ln., Wapwallopen, PA 18660 USA Do not confuse with companies with the same or similar names in Tappan, NJ, S. Hackensack, NJ, Birmingham, AL, Amityville, NY
E-mail: info@shepherdpress.com
Web site: http://www.shepercdpress.com.

Shepherd's Workshop, LLC, The, *(0-9752895)* 8213 Otis Ct., Arvada, CO 80003 USA Toll Free: 888-257-4673
E-mail: info@tsworkshop.com
Web site: http://www.tsworkshop.com
Dist(s): **STL Distribution North America.**

Sheppard Publishing, *(0-9725286)* 3371 Old Forge Rd., Kent, OH 44240 USA Tel 330-325-9658
E-mail: sheppardpublishing@neo.rr.com.

Sher-A-Craft, *(0-9670612)* Div. of Bell Blueprint Co., Inc., 7888 Othello Ave., San Diego, CA 92111 USA Tel 619-278-4830; Fax: 619-278-6830; Toll Free: 877-235-5877.

Sheridan Books *See* **KEYGARD**

Sherian County Historical Society Pr., *(0-9792871)* Orders Addr.: 850 Sibley Cir., Sheridan, WY 82801-9626 USA
Web site: http://www.sheridancountyhistory.org
Dist(s): **Greenleaf Book Group Pr.**

Sherman Asher Publishing, *(0-9644196; 1-890932)* P.O. Box 31725, Santa Fe, NM 87594-1725 USA
E-mail: westernedge@santa-fe.net
Web site: http://www.shermanasher.com
Dist(s): **Baker & Taylor Bks.**
Koen-Levy Bk. Wholesalers LLC
Partners/West
SCB Distributors.

SherMar Pubns., *(0-9705693)* 11679 Sherman, Northglenn, CO 80233 USA (SAN 254-1130) Tel 303-452-7183 (phone/fax)
E-mail: mfrflower@earthlink.net.

Sheron Enterprises, Inc., *(1-891877)* 1035 S. Carley Ct., N Bellmore, NY 11710-2051 USA
E-mail: sheron@concentric.net.

Sherrill, Carolyn, *(0-9674618)* 3 Pensacola Heights, Arden, NC 28704 USA Tel 828-684-2544.

Sherry Gansle *See* **Little Big Tomes**

Sheryl Da Pearl Productions, *(0-9795862)* P.O. Box 640173, Pike Road, AL 36064 USA
Web site: http://www.thecandylady.us.

Sheryl Lynn's, *(0-615; 0-9703678)* 4349 Clearwood Rd., Moorpark, CA 93021 USA Tel 805-523-0900 (phone/fax)
E-mail: sheryllynn@aol.com.

Sheva, Marie, *(0-9741736)* 301 Main St., Apt. 8, East Greenwich, RI 02818 USA
E-mail: mariesheva@yearofthedogs.com
Web site: http://www.yearofthedogs.com.

Shifflett, Christa, *(0-9740367)* 305 Huntersridge Rd., Winchester, VA 22602-6835 USA
E-mail: erizac@adelphia.net.

Shilo Publishing, *(0-9708726)* 5505 Valmont Rd., Suite 35, Boulder, CO 80301 USA Tel 303-447-9074
E-mail: shilopublishing@aol.com; raine@tryreading.com
Web site: http://www.tryreading.com.

Shiloh Group, *(0-9777923)* P.O. Box 4274, Missoula, MT 59806-4274 USA Tel 406-244-2780; Fax: 406-244-2780
E-mail: oxman@blackfoot.net.

Shiloh Publishing Hse., Inc., *(1-891879)* P.O. Box 100, Woodburn, OR 97071 USA Tel 503-981-4328; Toll Free: 800-607-6195.

Shine On Pubns., *(0-9749806)* 747 Camden Ave., Suite A, Campbell, CA 95008 USA; 12325 Kosich Pl., Saratoga, CA 95070
Web site: http://www.shineonpublications.com.

Shine Pubns., *(0-9705188)* P.O. Box 318, Issaquah, WA 98027-0013 USA (SAN 253-7532) Tel 425-254-0030; Fax: 425-254-9742
E-mail: hatleyco@nwlink.com
Web site: http://www.shinepublications.com.

Shine Publishing Hse., *(0-9749467)* 1811 Abbey Oak Dr., Suite 12879, Vienna, VA 22182 USA (SAN 255-9269) Tel 571-432-8922; Fax: 703-448-8443
E-mail: sales@shinepublishing.com
Web site: http://www.shinepublishing.com
Dist(s): **BookSurge, LLC**
Global Bk. Distributors.

Shine Time Records & Bks., *(0-9712398)* Orders Addr.: P.O. Box 331941, Nashville, TN 37203 USA Tel 615-242-9857 (phone/fax); Toll Free: 888-807-4463 (888-80-SHINE); Edit Addr.: 113 17th Ave., S., Suites 5 & 6, Nashville, TN 37203 USA
E-mail: chucwhit@usit.net; info@shinetime.com
Web site: http://www.shinetime.com; http://www.littleststar.com
Dist(s): **STL Distribution North America.**

Shining Tramp Pr., *(0-9749352)* 38 Garden St., Wethersfield, CT 06109 USA Tel 860-563-1899
E-mail: kevin.murphy38@sbcglobal.net.

Shiny Red Ball Publishing, *(0-9773608)* 105 Lakeover Dr., Athens, GA 30607 USA
Web site: http://www.shinyredball.com.

Shiny Star Productions, *(0-9706975)* 4972 Woodmark Dr., Liverpool, NY 13088 USA Tel 315-451-2586
E-mail: shinystarbooks@aol.com.

Shirt Tales *Imprint of* **Brookteam Corp.**

Shively, Lisa Cookbooks, *(0-9766756)* P.O. Box 2123, Eden, NC 27289 USA
E-mail: loopi3@earthlink.net
Web site: http://www.fromourhometoyours.net.

Shiver Hill Bks., *(0-9747417)* 18 Sunset W. Cir., Ithaca, NY 14850 USA
E-mail: shiver@twcny.rr.com.

Shnoozles, LLC, *(0-9768852; 0-9770292)* 8 Canyon Ridge, Irvine, CA 92603 USA
Web site: http://www.shnoozles.com
Dist(s): **AtlasBooks Distribution.**

†Shoe String Pr., Inc., *(0-208)* 2 Linsley St., North Haven, CT 06473-2517 USA (SAN 213-2079) ; *Imprints:* Library Professional Publications (Lib Prof Pubns); Archon Books (Archon Bks); Linnet Books (Linnet Bks); Linnet Professional Publications (Linnet Prof Pubns); *CIP.*

Shoe String Pubns., *(0-9713249)* P.O. Box 35021, Juneau, AK 99803 USA Tel 907-586-2076; Fax: 907-780-6322
E-mail: glaesman@alaska.net.

Shoemaker & Hoard *See* **Counterpoint**

Shoemaker Bks., *(0-9720150)* P.O. Box 8, Ringgold, GA 30739-9998 USA.

Shoestring Press *See* **Marion Street Pr.**

Shoetree Publishers, Inc., *(0-9785521)* P.O. Box 2122, Chandler, AZ 85244 USA (SAN 850-9859) Fax: 480-812-0182
Web site: http://www.shoetreepublishers.com.

Shooting Star Edition *Imprint of* **American Literary Pr.**

Shooting Star Publishing, *(0-615)* Div. of Primary Colors Inc., Orders Addr.: 3319 Greenfield Rd., PMB 310, Dearborn, MI 48120 USA Tel 313-865-1874; Fax: 313-865-1416 Do not confuse with companies with the same name in Ocala, FL, Moses Lake, WA
E-mail: yburton@primefun.com
Web site: http://www.primefun.com
Dist(s): **Baker & Taylor Bks.**

Shooting Star Publishing, *(0-9762835)* 1305 E. Fort King St. # 100, Ocala, FL 34471-2443 USA Do not confuse with companies with the same name in Dearborn, MI, Moses Lake, WA
Web site: http://www.shottingstarpublishing.com.

Shope, E. Raymond *See* **Flutter-By Productions**

Shore Line Pr. *Imprint of* **Pacific Bks.**

Shore Pubns., *(0-938833)* Orders Addr.: P.O. Box 908, Chestertown, MD 21620 USA (SAN 661-700X) Tel 410-778-9249
E-mail: marci@dcl.net
Web site: http://www.ohiopyle.com/author.

Shorebird Media, *(0-9745737)* Orders Addr.: P.O. Box 372, Mukiltel, WA 98275-0372 USA (SAN 255-6359)
E-mail: jeanie.james@verizon.net.

Shorefront N.F.P., *(0-9765232)* Orders Addr.: P.O. Box 1894, Evanston, IL 60204 USA; Edit Addr.: 2121 Church St., evanston, IL 60201 USA
Web site: http://shorefrontj.net.

Shore Publishing Co., *(0-9746846)* PMB 123, 7485 Rush River Dr., Suite 710, Sacramento, CA 95831-5260 USA Tel 916-442-4883; Fax: 916-428-9542.

Shorey Publications *See* **Shorey's Bookstore**

Shorey's Bookstore, *(0-8466)* P.O. Box 77316, Seattle, WA 98177-0316 USA (SAN 204-5958) Tel 206-633-2990
E-mail: shorey@serv.net
Web site: http://www.serv.net/shorey.

Short Bks., Ltd. (GBR) *(1-904095; 1-904977) Dist. by* **IPG Chicago.**

Short Books *See* **Half-Pint Kids, Inc.**

Short Term Mission Language Program, *(0-9746182)* 3612 Mary Elizabeth Church Rd., Waxhaw, NC 28173-9273 USA
E-mail: info@missionlanguage.com
Web site: http://www.missionlanguage.com.

Shortfuse Publishing Co., *(0-9667947)* 30 Hilltop Terr., Barstow, CA 92312 USA Tel 760-256-6141
E-mail: dottiemn@aol.com
Dist(s): **Gem Guides Bk. Co.**

Shortland Pubns. (U. S. A.) Inc., *(0-7699; 1-57257)* 19201 120th Ave NE Ste. 100, Bothell, WA 98011-9507 USA
Dist(s): **Heinemann Library**
Wright Group, The.

Showboard, Inc., *(1-891022)* 1251 S. Lincoln Ave., Clearwater, FL 33756-8203 USA Toll Free: 800-323-9189
E-mail: Oleksak@Showboard.com
Web site: http://www.showboard.com.

Showcase Pubs., *(0-9660720)* Orders Addr.: 1729 Monument Dr., Lincoln, CA 95648 USA (SAN 299-6545)
E-mail: czstars@aol.com; OrdersSCP@aol.com
Web site: http://www.geocities.com/athens/creke/502.

Showcase Writers, *(0-9753340)* P.O. Box 13757, Richmond, VA 23225 USA Tel 804-398-1138
E-mail: editor@showcasewriters.com
Web site: http://www.showcasewriters.com.

Shrewsbury Publishing, *(0-9678182)* 3624 Livingston, New Orleans, LA 70118 USA Tel 504-488-5249.

Shriek Show *Imprint of* **Media Blasters, Inc.**

Shuffling Papers, *(0-9724086)* 9200 Montgomery Rd., No. 8A, Cincinnati, OH 45242 USA (SAN 255-0695) Tel 513-793-6550; Fax: 513-793-2191
E-mail: erl223@aol.com.

Shug' n Spice Press *See* **Pen Poised Pr.**

Shulemite Christian Crusade, *(0-9714361)* 1420 Armstrong Valley Rd., Halifax, PA 17032-8383 USA (SAN 254-3931) Tel 717-896-8383; Fax: 717-896-8386
E-mail: sherrerd@epix.net
Web site: http://www.chrissherrerd.com.

Shulenberger Publishing, *(0-9767355)* 3912 NE 127th St., Seattle, WA 98125 USA (SAN 256-5935) Tel 206-367-5886
E-mail: ericshul@u.washington.edu.

Shulsinger Sales, Inc., *(0-914080)* 799 Hinsdale St., Brooklyn, NY 11207-7603 USA (SAN 205-9851) Toll Free: 800-548-0085
E-mail: uugam@aol.com.

ShuNu Publishing, *(0-9742329)* P.O. Box 2636, Saintfford, TX 77497 USA Tel 281-208-1687
E-mail: kmitchellthomas@aol.com.

Shure Products, Inc., *(1-58286)* 2129 W. North Ave., Chicago, IL 60647-5415 USA
E-mail: shureprds@aol.com.

Shurley Instructional Materials, Inc., *(1-881940; 1-58561)* 366 Sim Dr., Cabot, AR 72023 USA Tel 501-843-3869; Fax: 501-843-0583; Toll Free: 800-566-2966; Ballad Rd., Cabot, AR 72023
E-mail: shurley@shurley.com
Web site: http://www.shurley.com.

Sick Mind Pr., *(0-9701814)* 77 Kilsyth Rd., Brighton, MA 02135 USA Tel 617-713-3719
E-mail: sheba@ici.net
Web site: http://www.shebacomic.com
Dist(s): **Diamond Comic Distributors, Inc.**

Siddha Yoga Pubn. *Imprint of* **SYDA Foundation**

Side Show Comics *Imprint of* **Ink & Feathers Comics**

Sidedoor Publishing LLC, *(0-9770248)* 740-F Sierra Vista Ave., Mountain View, CA 94943-2576 USA Tel 650-903-9400; Fax: 650-903-9411
E-mail: isbn@sidedoorpublishing.com
Web site: http://www.sidedoorpublishing.com.

Sidekicks TM *Imprint of* **Scholastic, Inc.**

SideKicks TM Baby *Imprint of* **Scholastic, Inc.**

Sidewalk Publishing, *(0-9766418)* Inform Design, 2809 Forest Hill Cir., SE, Olympia, WA 98501 USA Tel 360-570-9398
E-mail: informbarb@qwest.net
Web site: http://www.sidewalkpublishing.net.

Sidewalk Univ. Pr., *(0-9759962)* 1739 Springfield Ave., Maplewood, NJ 07040 USA Tel 973-885-0860
E-mail: sidewalku@msn.com
Web site: http://www.sidewalkuniversity.org.

Sidewinder Publishing LLC, *(0-914001)* 4609 Kinney St. SE, Albuquerque, NM 87105 USA Tel 505-998-8000
Web site: http://www.sidewinderpublishing.com/.

Sidran Institute Pr., *(0-9629164; 1-886968)* Div. of Sidran Institute, 200 E. Joppa Rd., Suite 207, Baltimore, MD 21286 USA Tel 410-825-8888; Fax: 410-337-0747; Toll Free: 888-825-8249 (orders only)
E-mail: sidran@sidran.org
Web site: http://www.sidran.org
Dist(s): **Baker & Taylor Bks.**
New Leaf Distributing Co., Inc.
Quality Bks., Inc.

Siedon Pubns., *(0-9704470)* 3721 Wilkens Ave., Baltimore, MD 21229 USA Tel 410-646-0753
E-mail: sierram101@msn.com; sierraM101@msn.com.

Siemers, Robert, *(0-9744723)* P.O. Box 549, Koloa, HI 96756-0549 USA Toll Free: 888-233-8365
Web site: http://www.teok.com.

Sierra Club Bks. for Children, *(0-87156; 1-57805)* Div. of Sierra Club Bks., 85 Second Street, San Francisco, CA 94105 USA Tel 415-977-5500; Fax: 415-977-5792
E-mail: Books.Publishing@sierraclub.org
Web site: http://www.sierraclub.org/books
Dist(s): **Gibbs Smith, Publisher**
Perseus Distribution.

Sierra Nevada Publishing Hse., *(0-9765697)* P.O. Box 50366, Henderson, NV 89016 USA Tel 702-991-1383; Fax: 702-953-8973; Toll Free: 800-254-6266
Web site: http://www.climbonsuccess.com.

Sierra Press *See* **Sierra Pr.**

Sierra Pr., *(0-939365; 0-9617651; 1-58071)* Div. of Panorama International Productions, Inc., Orders Addr.: 4988 Gold Leaf Dr., Mariposa, CA 95338 USA (SAN 662-6955) Tel 209-966-5071; Fax: 209-966-5073; Toll Free: 800-745-2631 ; *Imprints:* Wish You Were Here (Wish You Were Here)
E-mail: siepress@sti.net
Web site: http://www.nationalparksusa.com.

Sierra Raconteur Publishing, *(1-58365; 1-58582)* Orders Addr.: P.O. Box 452, Greenfield, IN 46140 USA Tel 317-462-0037 ; *Imprints:* Timeless Romance (Timeless Romance); Serenade (Serenade)
E-mail: LASoard@aol.com; LoriSoard@aol.com.

Sierra Vista Junior High *See* **Sierra Vista Pubns.**

Sierra Vista Pubns., *(0-615; 0-9711314)* Alpine Sports, Orders Addr.: P.O. Box 55391, Valencia, CA 91385 USA Fax: 661-259-8941; Toll Free: 800-330-7734; Edit Addr.: P.O. Box 186, Crystal Bay, NV 89402 USA (SAN 411-5961)
E-mail: alpinesport@earthlink.net
Web site: http://www.alpinebasketball.com
Dist(s): **American West Bks.**
Brigham Distribution.

Sights Productions, *(0-9629978; 1-886366)* Orders Addr.: 15130 Black Ankle Rd., Mount Airy, MD 21771 USA Tel 410-795-4582; Fax: 410-795-5054
E-mail: eric@sights-productions.com
Web site: http://sights-productions.com
Dist(s): **Baker & Taylor Bks.**
Brodart Co.
Follett Library Resources
Kamkyi Bks.
New Leaf Distributing Co., Inc.
Quality Bks., Inc.

Sigil Publishing, *(0-9728461; 0-9785642)* P.O. Box 824, Leland, MI 49654- USA (SAN 255-1667)
E-mail: dave@sigilpublishing.com
Web site: http://www.knightscares.com
Dist(s): **Baker & Taylor Bks.**
Partners Bk. Distributing, Inc.
Quality Bks., Inc.

Sigler Printing & Publishing, Incorporated *See* **McMillen Publishing**

Sigmar (ARG) *(950-11) Dist. by* **Continental Bk.**

Sigmar (ARG) *(950-11) Dist. by* **Mariuccia Iaconi Bk Imports.**

Sigmar (ARG) *(950-11) Dist. by* **Lectorum Pubns.**

Sigmar (ARG) *(950-11) Dist. by* **AIMS Intl.**

Sign2Me *Imprint of* **Northlight Communications**

Signal Fire Pr., *(0-9764128)* 25260 Terr. Grove Rd., Los Gatos, CA 95033 USA (SAN 256-4351)
Web site: http://www.signalfirepress.com
Dist(s): **Ingram Bk. Co.**

Signator Publishing Group Inc., *(0-9728472)* 1725 I St. NW., Suite 300, Washington, DC 20006 USA Tel 202-349-3896; Fax: 202-349-3915
E-mail: info@signatorpublishing.com
Web site: http://www.signatorpublishing.com.

†Signature Bks., LLC, *(0-941214; 1-56085)* 564 West 400 N., Salt Lake City, UT 84116-3411 USA (SAN 217-4391) Tel 801-531-1483; Fax: 801-531-1488; Toll Free: 800-356-5687 (orders only)
E-mail: people@signaturebooks.com
Web site: http://www.signaturebooks.com
Dist(s): **Baker & Taylor Bks.**; *CIP.*

Signature Pr., *(0-9633791; 1-930013)* 11508 Green Rd., Wilton, CA 95693 USA Tel 510-540-6538; Fax: 510-540-1937; Toll Free: 800-305-7942 Do not confuse with Signature Pr., in Peekskill, NY
E-mail: info@signaturepress.com; chuccaro@aol.com
Web site: http://www.signaturepress.com
Dist(s): **Sunbelt Pubns., Inc.**

Signet *Imprint of* **Penguin Group (USA) Inc.**

Signet Classics *Imprint of* **Penguin Group (USA) Inc.**

Sigueme, Ediciones, S.A. (ESP) *(84-301) Dist. by* **Augsburg Fortress.**

Sijama Publishing, *(0-615)* Orders Addr.: P.O. Box 946, Mulino, OR 97402 USA Tel 503-829-7588; Edit Addr.: 15100 Howards Mill Rd., Mulino, OR 97042 USA.

Sikh Foundation, *(0-9700363)* 580 College Ave., Palo Alto, CA 94806 USA Tel 650-494-7454; Fax: 650-494-3316
E-mail: info@sikhfoundation.org
Web site: http://www.sikhfoundation.org.

Sikh Research Institute, *(1-60411)* P.O. Box 690504, San Antonio, TX 78269 USA (SAN 854-0403)
E-mail: info@sikhri.org
Web site: http://www.sikhri.org.

Sikorski, Lorna D. & Associates *See* **LDS & Assocs., LLC**

Silbert & Bress Pubns., *(0-89544)* P.O. Box 68, Mahopac, NY 10541 USA (SAN 210-5020) Tel 845-628-7910; Fax: 845-628-6027; Toll Free: 888-378-7664.

Silent Devil Productions, *(0-9752582; 0-9786451; 0-9789281; 0-9791192; 0-9796902)* 3777 Center Way, Fairfax, VA 22033 USA
E-mail: silentdevilproductions@hotmail.com
Web site: http://www.silentdevil.com.

Silent Moon Bks., *(0-9721457)* P.O. Box 1280, Seeley Lake, MT 59868 USA
E-mail: bschieber@yahoo.com.

Silesia Companies, Inc., *(1-887188)* Orders Addr.: P.O. Box 441110, Fort Washington, MD 20749 USA Tel 301-292-1970; Fax: 301-292-1787; Edit Addr.: 619 Broadcreek Dr., Fort Washington, MD 20749 USA
E-mail: animag@lattmag.com.

Silhouette Imprints *Imprint of* **Crumb Elbow Publishing**

Silhouette Pond Productions, *(0-9761169)* P.O. Box 778, Palm Harbor, FL 34682-0778 USA (SAN 256-3886) Tel 727-771-1691
E-mail: ceceenter@tampabay.rr.com
Web site: http://www.silhouettepond.com.

Silk Label Bks., Inc., *(1-928767)* Orders Addr.: First Ave., P.O. Box 399, Unionville, NY 10988-0399 USA Tel 845-726-3434; Fax: 845-726-3824
E-mail: rfpress@frontiernet.net
Dist(s): **Royal Fireworks Publishing Co.**

Silk Waters Mooney, *(0-9776608)* 316 E. El Paso St., Brackettville, TX 78832 USA Tel 830-563-3443; P.O. Box 393, Brackettville, TX 78832
E-mail: swmooney@pukathemoose.com.

Silly Goose Productions, LLC, *(0-9711500)* 24701 Magic Mountain Pkwy, Ste 2833 P.O. Box 800252, Valencia, CA 91355 USA
E-mail: sallysue678@yahoo.com; sally@onmyown.com
Web site: http://www.starfishpublishing.com; http://www.onmyown.com
Dist(s): **Baker & Taylor Bks.**
Follett Library Resources.

Siloam Publishing, *(0-9668358)* P.O. Box 174, Jarrettsville, MD 21084 USA Tel 410-557-0311 (phone/fax).

Silver Bells Publishing Hse., *(0-9793517)* 19415 150th Ave., Tustin, MI 49688 USA Tel 231-829-3898
E-mail: dgbelleville@yahoo.com.

Silver Boat Productions, *(0-9678498)* 393 Timberlake Ln., Eureka Springs, AR 72631 USA Tel 479-253-6795; Fax: 479 253-0298
E-mail: ajn@arkansas.net
Web site: http://mywebpage.netscape.com/annadamsusa.

†Silver, Burdett & Ginn, Inc., *(0-382; 0-663; 1-4182)* Orders Addr.: P.O. Box 2500, Lebanon, IN 46052 USA Toll Free Fax: 800-841-8939; Toll Free: 800-552-2259; Edit Addr.: P.O. Box 480, Parsippany, NJ 07054 USA (SAN 204-5982); 108 Wilmot Rd., Suite 380, Midwest Div., Deerfield, IL 60015 (SAN 111-6517) Tel 708-945-1240
E-mail: customerservice@scottforesman.com
Web site: http://www.scottforesman.com/; *CIP.*

Silver Cloak Pubns., *(0-9777677)* P.O. Box 1027, Carpinteria, CA 93014-1027 USA
E-mail: SilverCloak@aol.com.

Silver Dagger Mysteries *Imprint of* **Overmountain Pr.**

Silver Dolphin Bks. *Imprint of* **Advantage Pubs. Group**

Silver Elm Classic *Imprint of* **Darby Creek Publishing**

Silver Fox Marketing, *(1-891797)* Div. of ConCenSys Group, Inc., P.O. Box 39703, Fort Lauderdale, FL 33339-9703 USA Do not confuse with companies with the same name in Palos Verdes Peninsula, CA, Washington, DC, New York, NY, San Antonio, TX, Dodgeville, WI
E-mail: DLJeay1103@aol.com
Web site: http://www.concensysgroup.com.

Silver Lake Mill, *(0-9706322)* Div. Of L D A Creations, Inc., 2328 Silver Lake Rd., Dayton, VA 22821 USA Tel 540-879-2800
E-mail: LDA@LDAcreate.com; karen@ldacreate.com
Web site: http://www.silverlakemill.com.

Silver Lake Publishing, *(0-930868; 1-56343)* 1119 N. Broadway St., Aberdeen, WA 98520-2433 USA (SAN 203-8110) Toll Free: 800-663-3091 Do not confuse with Silver Lake Publishing, Morton, PA
E-mail: publisher@silverlakepublishing.com; SCRIBERE@aol.com; mthorpe@silverlakepub.com
Web site: http://www.silverlakepub.com
Dist(s): **SCB Distributors.**

Silver Lake Publishing, *(1-931095; 1-933511)* 11 S. Mansfield Rd., Lansdowne, PA 19050 USA Do not confuse with Silver Lake Publishing, Los Angeles, CA
E-mail: publisher@silverlakepublishing.com
Web site: http://www.silverlakepublishing.com.

Silver Leaf Bks., LLC, *(0-9744354; 0-9787782)* Orders Addr.: P.O. Box 6460, Holliston, MA 01746 USA Tel 508-740-6270; Toll Free: 888-823-6450; Edit Addr.: 13 Temi Rd., Holliston, MA 01746 USA
E-mail: Sales@SilverLeafBooks.com
Web site: http://www.silverleafbooks.com
Dist(s): **Baker & Taylor Bks.**

Silver Moon Pr., *(1-881889; 1-893110)* 381 Park Ave S. Rm. 1121, New York, NY 10016-8806 USA Toll Free: 800-874-3320
E-mail: mail@silvermoonpress.com
Web site: http://www.silvermoonpress.com.

Silver Pr. Co., *(0-9640442)* 69 E. Wilson Bridge Rd., No. A, Worthington, OH 43085-2357 USA Tel 614-459-1999; Fax: 614-457-8741.

Silver Print Pr., Inc., *(0-9628064; 0-9749890)* Div. of Actionpix, Inc., 20 Crossroad, Colbyville, VT 05676 USA (SAN 299-0350) Tel 802-244-5339; Fax: 802-244-6813
E-mail: info@silverprintpress.com
Web site: http://www.silverprintpress.com
Dist(s): **Baker & Taylor Bks.**
Koen-Levy Bk. Wholesalers LLC.

Silver Rim Pr., *(1-878611)* 2759 Park Lake Dr., Boulder, CO 80301 USA Tel 303-666-4290 (phone/fax)
E-mail: Sybilset@aol.com.

Silver Rose Publishing, *(0-9778211)* P.O. Box 462174, Aurora, CO 80046 USA Tel 303-946-2183; Toll Free: 800-431-1579 ; *Imprints:* Raynestorm Books (Raynestorm Bks)
E-mail: contact@silverrosepublishing.com
Web site: http://www.silverrosepublishing.com; http://www.bookch.com
Dist(s): **BCH Fulfillment & Distribution.**

Silver Snowflake Publishing, *(0-9778476)* P.O. Box 1256, East Greenwich, RI 02818 USA (SAN 850-394X)
E-mail: exteriordesigner@cox.net
Web site: http://www.themagicsceptre.com; http://www.silversnowflakepublishing.com.

Silver Strong & Assocs., *(1-58284)* 227 1st St., Ho Ho Kus, NJ 07423-1534 USA Toll Free: 800-962-4432 ; *Imprints:* Thoughtful Education Press, The (Thoughtful Educ)
E-mail: mperini@silverstrong.com
Web site: http://www.silverstrong.com.

Silver Whistle *Imprint of* **Harcourt Trade Pubs.**

SilverBear, *(0-9778070)* Orders Addr.: 9 Westminster Shopping Ctr. No. 333, Westminster, MD 21157 USA (SAN 850-2870) Tel 410-374-0128; Fax: 410-374-1742
E-mail: info@silverbeargraphics.com
Web site: http://www.silverbeargraphics.com.

SilverhawkCorp., *(0-9772933)* 618 Draper Heights Way, Draper, UT 84020 USA.

Silverhawke Pubns., *(0-9651406)* 514 Seminole Trl., Danville, KY 40422-1743 USA.

†Silverleaf Pr., *(0-915591)* 19 Harding Ln., Westport, CT 06880 USA (SAN 292-6660) Tel 203-227-5727
Dist(s): **Independent Pubs. Group**; *CIP.*

Silverman, Toby, *(0-9793475)* 1611 Hemlock Farms, Lords Valley, PA 18428 USA
E-mail: tsilverman@noln.com.

Silvey Bk. Publishing, *(0-9762446)* P.O. Box 5171, Goodyear, AZ 85338-5171 USA Fax: 623-853-9172
E-mail: silveybooks@earthlink.net.

Simakan Group, The, *(0-9767812)* P.O. Box 492496, Atlanta, GA 30349 USA Fax: 770-981-1046
E-mail: info@playingyouragame.com
Web site: http://www.playingyourAgame.com.

Simba Publishing Co., *(0-9765982)* 5413 Whistler Dr., Tallahassee, FL 32317 USA (SAN 256-4270) Tel 850-878-7741
E-mail: gladys_gikiri@simbapublishingcompany.com
Web site: http://www.simbapublishingcompany.com.

Simcha Pr. *Imprint of* **Health Communications, Inc.**

Simmons, Kristina, *(0-9769843)* 40 Christopher Cir., Middletown, CT 06457 USA.

Simmons, Sukether Williams *See* **Shrewsbury Publishing**

Simon & Barklee, Inc./ExplorerMedia, *(0-9704661; 0-9714502)* 2280 E. Whidbey Shores Rd., Langley, WA 98260 USA Tel 360-730-2360; Fax: 360-730-2355 ; *Imprints:* Explorer Media (Explorer Media)
E-mail: cwsch@whidbey.com
Web site: http://simonandbarklee.com
Dist(s): **Baker & Taylor Bks.**
Quality Bks., Inc.

Simon & Northrop of Cal, Incorporated *See* **Martell Publishing Co**

Simon & Schuster, *(0-671; 0-684; 0-689; 0-914676; 0-7432; 1-4165)* Div. of Simon & Schuster, Inc., Orders Addr.: 100 Front St., Riverside, NJ 08075 USA (SAN 200-2442) Toll Free Fax: 800-943-9831; Toll Free: 800-223-2336 (ordering); 800-223-2348 (customer service); Edit Addr.: a/o Subsidiary Rights, 11th Flr., 1230 Avenue of the Americas, New York, NY 10020 USA (SAN 200-2450) Tel 212-698-7000; Fax: 212-698-7007; 212-632-8099 (Rights & Permissions); 212-698-1269 (Pocket Bks. Rights & Permissions); Toll Free: 800-897-7650 (customer financial services); 100 Front St., Riverside, NJ 08075 (SAN 256-6044) Tel 856-461-6500; Fax: 856-824-2287 ; *Imprints:* Games Workshop (GameWork); Atria (Atria); MTV (MTV Bks); Pocket (PB); Pocket Star (Pocket Star Bks); Star Trek (Star Trek); Washington Square Press (Wash Sq Pr); Fireside (Fireside); Free Press (Free Pr); Scribner (Scribner); Scribner Paper Fiction (ScriPapFic); Simon & Schuster (SimSchu); Touchstone (Touchstone); Simon Spotlight Entertainment (SSpotEnt); Howard Books (Howard Bks)
E-mail: ssonline_feedback@simonsays.com; consumer.customerservice@simonandschuster.com
Web site: http://www.simonsays.com; http://www.oasis.simonandschuster.com; http://www.simonandschuster.com/ebooks
Dist(s): **Thomson Gale**
Giron Bks.
Libros Sin Fronteras
Replica Bks.
Simon & Schuster, Inc.
Sony CONNECT, Inc.
Thorndike Pr.

Simon & Schuster *Imprint of* **Simon & Schuster**

Simon & Schuster Children's Publishing, *(0-02; 0-671; 0-684; 0-689; 0-7434; 1-4169)* Orders Addr.: 100 Front St., Riverside, NJ 08075 USA Toll Free Fax: 800-943-9831; Toll Free: 800-223-2336; Edit Addr.: a/o Subsidiary Rights, 4th floor, 1230 Avenue of the Americas, New York, NY 10020 USA Tel 212-698-7200; Fax: 212-698-2797 (Rights & Permissions) ; *Imprints:* Aladdin (AlaChild); Aladdin Library (AlaLib); Atheneum (AthenSS); Atheneum/Anne Schwartz Books (Anne Schwart); Atheneum/Richard Jackson Books (Rich Jack); Little Simon (Little Simon); McElderry, Margaret K. (McElderry); Simon & Schuster Children's Publishing (SSChildren); Simon & Schuster/Paula Wiseman Books (Paula Wise); Simon Pulse (SPulse); Simon Spotlight (SSpot); Simon Spotlight/Nickelodeon (SiSpNick); Libros Para Ninos (Libros ParNin); Little Simon Inspirations (LSI); Simon Scribbles (Sim Scribbles); Ginne Seo Books (Ginne Seo Bks)
Web site: http://www.simonsays.com
Dist(s): **Simon & Schuster**
Simon & Schuster, Inc.
Sony CONNECT, Inc.

Simon & Schuster Children's Publishing *Imprint of* **Simon & Schuster Children's Publishing**

†Simon & Schuster, Inc., *(0-671)* Div. of Viacom Co., Orders Addr.: 100 Front St., Riverside, NJ 08075 USA Toll Free Fax: 800-943-9831; Toll Free: 800-223-2336 (orders); 800-223-2348 (customer service); Edit Addr.: 1230 Ave. of the Americas, New York, NY 10020 USA
E-mail: Consumer.CustomerService@simonandschuster.com
Web site: http://www.simonsays.com; *CIP.*

Simon & Schuster, Ltd. (GBR) *(0-671; 0-684; 0-689; 0-7432; 0-7434; 1-84738) Dist. by* **Trafalgar.**

Simon & Schuster, Ltd. (GBR) *(0-671; 0-684; 0-689; 0-7432; 0-7434; 1-84738) Dist. by* **IPG Chicago.**

Simon & Schuster Trade *See* **Simon & Schuster**

Simon & Schuster/Paula Wiseman Bks. *Imprint of* **Simon & Schuster Children's Publishing**

Simon & Son Publishing, *(0-9773665)* 4995 Paist Rd., Doylestown, PA 18901 USA ; *Imprints:* Prophecy, The (Prophecy)
E-mail: frankfsp1@comcast.net
Web site: http://www.simonsonpublishing.com
Dist(s): **Biblio Distribution**
National Bk. Network.

Simon, Les, *(0-9761914)* Orders Addr.: P.O. Box 57274, Washington, DC 20037-0274 USA Tel 202-659-3639; Fax: 202-457-1155; Edit Addr.: 1400 20th St., NW, No. 805, Washington, DC 20036 USA
E-mail: lessim2003@yahoo.com.

Simon Pulse *Imprint of* **Simon & Schuster Children's Publishing**

Simon Scribbles *Imprint of* **Simon & Schuster Children's Publishing**

Simon Spotlight *Imprint of* **Simon & Schuster Children's Publishing**

Simon Spotlight Entertainment *Imprint of* **Simon & Schuster**

Simon Spotlight/Nickelodeon *Imprint of* **Simon & Schuster Children's Publishing**

Simpatico Bks., *(0-9771322)* P.O. Box 201, Heber Springs, AR 72543 USA Tel 501-362-2858
Web site: http://www.simpaticobooks.com.

Simple Books/Cardinal Publishing *See* **Cardinal Publishing Group, The**

Simple Learning, *(0-9713301)* HC 74, Box 3147, Chapmanville, WV 25508 USA Tel 304-855-3139
E-mail: information@simplelearninginc.com; customerservice@simplelearninginc.com
Web site: http://www.simplelearninginc.com.

Simple Life Corp., *(0-9661063)* Orders Addr.: P.O. Box 1529, Elkhart, IN 46515-1529 USA Tel 574-848-0180 [phone/fax]; Edit Addr.: 20613 CR 2, Bristol, IN 46507 USA
E-mail: patti@simplelifecorp.com
Web site: http://www.simplelifecorp.com.

Simple Productions *See* **Shepard Pubns.**

Simple Publishing *See* **Motivated Proformance**

Simple Thoughts Pr., LLC, *(0-9768557)* Orders Addr.: P.O. Box 759, Northfield, MN 55057 USA; Edit Addr.: 14345 Falk Ave., Northfield, NJ 55057 USA
Web site: http://www.backandforthjournal.com.

Simplemente Maria Pr., *(0-9766811)* 914 Santa Barbara St., Studio 6, Santa Barbara, CA 93101 USA Tel 805-962-2497
E-mail: mary@maryheebner.com
Web site: http://www.maryheebner.com.

Simpler Life Pr., *(0-9619806)* 1599 S. Uinta Way, Denver, CO 80231 USA (SAN 246-5809) Tel 303-751-2454; Fax: 303-671-5200
E-mail: avs@vansteenhouse.com
Web site: http://www.vansteenhouse.com
Dist(s): **Baker & Taylor Bks.**

Simplex Pubns., *(0-9623113; 1-929304)* Orders Addr.: 575 Larkspur Plaza Dr., Unit 4, Larkspur, CA 94939-1476 USA
E-mail: gosmith@pacbell.net
Web site: http://www.simplexpublications.com
Dist(s): **Bookpeople.**

Simplified Learning *See* **JoyceHerzog.com, Inc.**

SimpliFun Studios, *(1-932839)* 2070 Stratford Dr., Milpitas, CA 95035 USA Tel 408-946-8632; Toll Free: 800-850-4-FUN
E-mail: mail@simplifun.com
Web site: http://www.childrenspartygames.com.

Simply Angels Creative Pr. & Design, *(0-9651678)* Orders Addr.: P.O. Box 644, Cambria, CA 93428 USA Tel 805-927-2824; Fax: 805-927-2825; Toll Free: 800-914-7577; Edit Addr.: 821 Cornwall St., Cambria, CA 93428 USA
E-mail: starhall@aol.com
Web site: http://www.simplyangels.com.

Simply Kid's Publishing, *(0-9671987)* Orders Addr.: P.O. Box 482, New Hope, PA 18938 USA Tel 215-598-9918; Edit Addr.: 6178 Pidcock Creek Rd., New Hope, PA 18938 USA.

Company

Simply Read Bks. (CAN) *(0-9688768; 1-894965)* *Dist. by* **Perseus Dist.**

Simpson, Charles B., *(0-9703818)* 234 Faulkner Ave., Hazard, KY 41701 USA Tel 606-436-4652
E-mail: cngsimpson@earthlink.net
Web site: http://www.appalachianwriter.com.

Simpson, J.R. & Assocs., Inc., *(0-9703086)* 2175 Huntington Dr., Florissant, MO 63033-1227 USA Tel 314-921-4419
E-mail: JRSiminc@aol.com
Web site: http://littleriverbooks.com.

Simsand Publishing, *(0-9765580)* 8 Huntington Pl. Dr., Atlanta, GA 30350 USA Tel 678-458-0759
E-mail: timsanders01@aol.com.

Sinanan, Cindy, *(0-9769004)* 10169 New Hampshire Ave., No. 155, Silver Spring, MD 20903 USA
E-mail: mybook@mris.com.

Sing to Read Adventure, The *Imprint of* **Periwinkle Park Educational Productions**

SingaporeMath.com, Inc., *(0-9741573; 1-932906)* 404 Beavercreek Rd., No. 225, Oregon City, OR 97045 USA (SAN 255-6510) Tel 503-557-8100; Fax: 503-557-8103
E-mail: customerservice@singaporemath.com
Web site: http://www.singaporemath.com.

Singing Is Easy *Imprint of* **LOTI Publishing**

Singing River Pubns., *(0-9709575; 0-9759953; 0-9774831; 0-9789870)* Orders Addr.: P.O. Box 72, Ely, MN 55731 USA (SAN 254-136X) Tel 218-365-3498; Fax: 218-365-5792; Edit Addr.: 3365 Wolf Lake Rd., Ely, MN 55731 USA
E-mail: cmoroni@singingriverpublications.com
Web site: http://www.singingriverpublications.com
Dist(s): **Adventure Pubns., Inc.**
Partners Bk. Distributing, Inc.

Singing Tree Pr., *(0-9708005)* P.O. Box 722, Auburn, CA 95604 USA (SAN 255-4011) Tel 530-823-9284
E-mail: editor@mail.singingtreepress.com; orders@singingtreepress.com
Web site: http://www.singingtreepress.com.

Singing Turtle Pr., *(0-9659113)* 942 Vuelta Del Sur., Santa Fe, NM 87507-7755 USA Toll Free: 888-308-6284; 942 Vuelta del Sur, Santa Fe, NM 87505
E-mail: kathy@mathkits.com
Web site: http://www.mathkits.com
Dist(s): **Blessing Way Publishing Co.**
Midpoint Trade Bks., Inc.

Single Vision Pubns., *(0-9608960; 1-892541)* Orders Addr.: P.O. Box 804, Lebanon, OR 97355 USA (SAN 241-2519) Tel 541-258-5888; Edit Addr.: 2485 Stoltzhill Rd., Lebanon, OR 97355 USA
E-mail: singlevision@proaxis.com
Web site: http://www/proaxis.com/~singlevision.

Sinolingua (CHN) *(7-80052)* *Dist. by* **China Bks.**

Sinsinawa Dominicans, Inc., *(0-9774934)* 585 Cty. Rd., Z, Sinsinawa, WI 53824-9701 USA Tel 608-748-4411; Fax: 608-748-4491
E-mail: communication@sinsinawa.org
Web site: http://www.sinsinawa.org.

Sioux City Lewis & Clark Interpretive Ctr., The, *(0-9753860; 0-9785063)* 900 Larsen Pk. Rd., Sioux city, IA 51103 USA Tel 712-224-5242; Fax: 712-224-5244
E-mail: mpoole@siouxcitylcic.com
Web site: http://www.siouxcitylcic.com.

Sir Fir Bks. & Music *Imprint of* **Sir Fir Enterprises, LLC**

Sir Fir Enterprises, LLC, *(0-9670160)* 1468 Shadowrock Heights, Marietta, GA 30062 USA Tel 770-565-7020; Fax: 770-565-6885; Toll Free: 877-565-7020 ; *Imprints:* Sir Fir Books & Music (Sir Fir Bks)
E-mail: rrwrites@mindspring.com
Web site: http://sirfirbooksandmusic.com
Dist(s): **Baker & Taylor Bks.**

Sir Wrinkles Pr., *(0-9766639)* P.O. Box 11627, Newport Beach, CA 92658 USA
Web site: http://www.sirwrinklesthebulldog.com.

Sirio, Editorial S.A. (ESP) *(84-7808; 84-86221)* *Dist. by* **Lectorum Pubns.**

Sirius Entertainment, Inc., *(1-57989)* Orders Addr.: P.O. Box X, Unadilla, NY 13849 USA Tel 607-369-2620; Fax: 607-369-2623; Edit Addr.: P.O. Box X, Unadilla, NY 13849-0723 USA
E-mail: sirent@aol.com
Dist(s): **Diamond Bk. Distributors.**

Sirius Pubns., *(1-930889)* Orders Addr.: 1704 Knollwood Ave., K102, Kalamazoo, MI 49006 USA
E-mail: sirius@sirius-books.com; editor@sirius-books.com
Web site: http://www.sirius-books.com.

SIRS Mandarin *See* **SIRS Publishing, Inc.**

†SIRS Publishing, Inc., *(0-89777; 0-9678914)* Div. of ProQuest Information and Learning, 5201 Congress Ave., Suite 250, Boca Raton, FL 33487 USA (SAN 222-8920) Tel 561-994-0079; Fax: 561-995-4074; Toll Free: 800-521-0600
Web site: http://www.proquestK12.com; *CIP.*

Siruela, Ediciones S.A. (ESP) *(84-7844; 84-85876)* *Dist. by* **Lectorum Pubns.**

Sistemas Tecnicos de Edicion, S.A. de C.V. (MEX) *(968-6579; 970-629; 968-6048; 968-6135; 968-6394)* *Dist. by* **AIMS Intl.**

Sisterlove Productions/Time To Build Records & Publishing, *(1-893926)* Orders Addr.: P.O. Box 546, Jackson, MS 39205-0546 USA
E-mail: thepoetwarrior@hotmail.com.

Sisters Three Publishing Inc., *(0-9787375)* 5026 SW. 94th Ave., Cooper City, FL 33328 USA Fax: 954-885-8007
Web site: http://www.sistersthreeseries.com.

Sitare, Ltd., *(0-940178)* Orders Addr.: 1101 N. Rainbow Blvd., No 44, Las Vegas, NV 89108 USA (SAN 217-0833) Tel 702 878-1252 (phone/fax)
E-mail: starstreamworld@netzero.net.

Six Generations Publishing, *(0-9760418)* 9048 Little Brook St., Anchorage, AK 99507-4922 USA Fax: 907-522-9433
E-mail: soloview@gci.net
Web site: http://www.sixgenerations.com.

Six Seconds, *(0-9629123; 0-9716772; 0-9797343)* 316 Seville Way, San Mateo, CA 94402 USA Tel 650-685-9885; Fax: 650-685-9880
E-mail: staff@6seconds.org
Web site: http://www.6seconds.org.

Six Suns Publishing, *(0-9654200)* P.O. Box 112852, Anchorage, AK 99511 USA Tel 907-344-2905
Dist(s): **Todd Communications**
Wizard Works.

Sixth Avenue Bks. *Imprint of* **Grand Central Publishing**

Sixth House Press, Incorporated, The *See* **Akashic Pr., Inc., The**

Sixth&Spring Bks., *(1-931543; 1-933027)* 233 Spring St., 8th Flr., New York, NY 10013 USA
Web site: http://www.vogueknitting.com/books/
Dist(s): **Sterling Publishing Co., Inc.**

SK Publications *See* **St Kitts Pr.**

Skandisk, Inc., *(0-9615394; 1-57534)* 6667 W. Old Shakopee Rd., Suite 109, Bloomington, MN 55438-2622 USA (SAN 695-4405) Tel 952-829-8998; Fax: 952-829-8992; Toll Free: 800-468-2424 (orders)
E-mail: lhamnes@skandisk.com; tomten@skandisk.com
Web site: http://www.skandisk.com.

Skeete, D., *(0-9769012)* P.O. Box 737, New York, NY 10030 USA
E-mail: msdss@aol.com
Web site: http://www.hiphopwordsearch.com.

Skeeter Hill Pr., *(0-9667007)* Orders Addr.: P.O. Box 4, Bethel Park, PA 15102 USA Tel 412-851-9273; Edit Addr.: 4789 Criss Rd., Bethel Park, PA 15102 USA
E-mail: shp@bellatlantic.net.

Skeezel Pr., *(0-9747217)* 2624 Lakeside Dr., Erie, PA 16511 USA
E-mail: pmerski@adelphia.net; pmerski@gmail.com
Web site: http://www.roaringboringalice.com
Dist(s): **Independent Pubs. Group.**

Skeptical Guitarist Pubns., *(0-9665029; 0-9788609)* Orders Addr.: P.O. Box 5824, Raleigh, NC 27650-5824 USA Tel 919-834-2031; Edit Addr.: 714 Faircloth St., Raleigh, NC 27607-4013 USA
E-mail: bruceemery@mindspring.com
Web site: http://www.skepticalguitarist.com/.

Sketch Publishing, *(0-9726764)* 414 S. 43rd St, Philadelphia, PA 19104 USA Tel 215-243-0644
E-mail: msand227@aol.com.

Sketches From The Heart Publishing, *(0-9759300)* P.O. Box 3431, Boulder, CO 80307 USA
Web site: www.sketchesfromtheheart.com
Dist(s): **Baker & Taylor Bks.**
Books West
Common Ground Distributors, Inc.
Partners/West
Quality Bks., Inc.

Skinder-Strauss Assocs., *(1-57741)* Orders Addr.: P.O. Box 50, Newark, NJ 07101 USA Tel 973-642-1440; Fax: 973-242-1905; Toll Free: 800-444-4041; Edit Addr.: 240 Mulberry St., Newark, NJ 07101 USA
E-mail: ed@elaw.com
Web site: http://lawdiary.com; http://elaw.com.

Skinner Hse. Bks. *Imprint of* **Unitarian Universalist Assn.**

Skinny Lamb Publishing, *(0-9662900)* Orders Addr.: Rte. 3, Box 521H, Wichita Falls, TX 73608 USA Tel 940-696-5735; Fax: 940-696-5380; Edit Addr.: 521H 3-Way Rd., Wichita Falls, TX 76308 USA
E-mail: skinnylamb@aol.com.

Skirball Cultural Ctr., *(0-9651640; 0-9704295)* 2701 N. Sepulveda Blvd., Los Angeles, CA 90049 USA Tel 310-440-4600; 310-440-4500; Fax: 310-440-4595
E-mail: aburke@skirball.org; lhuey@skirball.org; tgozani@skirball.org
Web site: http://www.skirball.org
Dist(s): **Univ. of Washington Pr.**
Wayne State Univ. Pr.

Skirvan, Pamela, *(0-9742943)* P.O. Box 484, New Harbor, ME 04554-0484 USA.

Skutt, Mary S. *See* **Blue Valley Bks.**

Sky Blue Pr., *(0-9652364; 0-9774851)* 3438 Kilmer, Troy, MI 48083 USA Tel 248-619-9918
E-mail: orders@skybluepress.com; skybluepress@skybluepress.com
Web site: http://www.skybluepress.com.

Sky Carrier Pr., *(1-880589)* P.O. Box 442, Fayetteville, NY 13066 USA Tel 605-486-4310; 315-637-9511
E-mail: swagner711@aol.com.

Sky Media, *(1-892114)* 12999 E. Jamison Cir., No. 230, Englewood, CO 80112-4167 USA
E-mail: info@sky-media.com
Web site: http://www.sky-media.com
Dist(s): **Discovery Hse. Pubs.**

Sky Oaks Productions, Inc., *(0-940296; 1-56018)* P.O. Box 1102, Los Gatos, CA 95031 USA (SAN 217-5843) Tel 408-395-7600; Fax: 408-395-8440
E-mail: TRPWorld@aol.com
Web site: http://www.tpr-world.com.

†Sky Publishing, *(0-933346; 1-931559)* Div. of New Track Media, 90 Sherman St. Ste. D, Cambridge, MA 02140-3264 USA (SAN 212-4556) Toll Free: 800-253-0245
E-mail: bjackson@skyandtelescope.com; orders@SkyandTelescope.com
Web site: http://www.skyandtelescope.com
Dist(s): **Sterling Publishing Co., Inc.**; *CIP.*

Sky Publishing Corporation *See* **Sky Publishing**

Sky Rocket Pr., *(0-9724637)* Orders Addr.: 2104 Old York Dr., Keller, TX 76248-5497 USA Tel 817-498-4300; Fax: 757-299-3608
E-mail: robert@rocketvilletexas.com
Web site: http://www.rocketvilletexas.com.

sky-dog, *(0-9721831)* 7948 Freehollow Dr., Falls Church, VA 22042 USA
Web site: http://www.skydogcomics.com
Dist(s): **Diamond Bk. Distributors.**

Skyhook Pr. *Imprint of* **Shepard Pubns.**

Skylands Writers & Artists Assn., Inc., *(1-886841)* 57 Montague St., Box 8G, Brooklyn, NY 11201-3356 USA Tel 973-786-7947; Fax: 973-328-5425 ; *Imprints:* Ars Poetica (Ars Poetica)
E-mail: daniela@garden.net
Web site: http://www.NJPoets.com.

Skylark *Imprint of* **Random Hse. Children's Bks.**

SkyLight Paths Publishing, *(1-893361; 1-59473)* Div. of LongHill Partners, Inc., Sunset Farm Offices, Rte. 4 P.O. Box 237, Woodstock, VT 05091 USA Tel 802-457-4000; Fax: 802-457-4004; Toll Free: 800-962-4544 (orders)
E-mail: editorial@skylightpaths.com
Web site: http://www.skylightpaths.com
Dist(s): **Baker & Taylor Bks.**
Jewish Lights Publishing
New Leaf Distributing Co., Inc.
Spring Arbor Distributors, Inc.

Skylight Publishing, *(0-9654853; 0-9727055)* Orders Addr.: 9 Bartlet St., Suite 70, Andover, MA 01810-3655 USA Tel 978-475-1431 (phone/fax); Toll Free: 888-476-1940
E-mail: support@skylit.com
Web site: http://www.skylit.com.

Skyline Pr., Div. of David White, Inc., One Pleasant Ave., Port Washington, NY 11050 USA (SAN 678-9021)
Dist(s): **Independent Pubs. Group.**

Skyline Publishing, *(0-918981)* Orders Addr.: P.O. Box 1118, Columbia Falls, MT 59912 USA (SAN 669-8662) Tel 406-892-5560; Fax: 406-892-1922; Toll Free: 800-821-6784; Edit Addr.: a/o Skyline Publishing, 3101 Hwy. 206, Columbia Falls, MT 59912 USA Do not confuse with companies with similar names in Londonderry, NH, Saint George, UT
E-mail: jane@rolandcheek.com
Web site: http://www.rolandcheek.com
Dist(s): **Baker & Taylor Bks.**
Partners/West.

SkyMark Corp., *(0-9769873)* 7300 Penn Ave., Pittsburgh, PA 15208 USA Tel 412-371-0680; Fax: 412-371-0681
E-mail: marie.routledge@skymark.com
Web site: http://www.theseus.biz.

Skyward Publishing Co., *(1-881554)* Div. of Paragon Media Corp., 813 Michael St., Kennett, MO 63857 USA (SAN 297-9705) Tel 573-888-5589
E-mail: nfo@skywardpublishing.com
Web site: http://www.skywardpublishing.com; http://www.bransonozarks.com; http://www.brandywineswar.com
Dist(s): **Biblio Distribution.**

Skyword Pr., *(0-9740202)* Orders Addr.: P.O. Box 1714, Hood River, OR 97031 USA; Edit Addr.: 555 Highline Rd., Hood River, OR 97031 USA.

SLACK, Inc., *(0-913590; 0-943432; 1-55642)* 6900 Grove Rd., Thorofare, NJ 08086-9447 USA (SAN 201-8632) Tel 856-848-1000; Fax: 856-853-5991; Toll Free: 800-257-8290
E-mail: orders@slackinc.com; lplummer@slackinc.com
Web site: http://www.slackbooks.com
Dist(s): **Barnes & Noble Bks.-Imports**
Baker & Taylor Bks.
Coutts Library Service, Inc.
Emery-Pratt Co.
Holt, Henry & Co.
Majors, J. A. Co.
Macmillan
Matthews Medical Bk. Co.
Rittenhouse Bk. Distributors.

Slangman Publishing, *(1-891888)* Orders Addr.: 12206 Hillslope St., Studio City, CA 91604 USA Tel 818-752-6462; Fax: 413-647-1589
E-mail: info@slangman.com
Web site: http://www.slangman.com
Dist(s): **Delta Systems Co., Inc.**

Slater Software. Inc., *(0-9743149)* 351 Badger Ln., Guffey, CO 80820-9106 USA Tel 719-479-2255 Toll Free: 877-306-6968
E-mail: jim@slatersoftware.com
Web site: http://www.slatersoftware.com.

Slator, Laraine, *(0-9707575)* 3170 Holiday Springs Blvd., Bldg. 6-103, Margate, FL 33063 USA Tel 954-346-2765
E-mail: LALO0926@aol.com.

Slave Labor Bks., *(0-943151; 1-59362)* 577 S. Market St., San Jose, CA 95113 USA (SAN 668-1204) Tel 408-971-8929; Fax: 408-279-0451; Toll Free: 800-866-8929 ; *Imprints:* Amaze Ink (Amaze Ink); Slave Labor Graphics (Slave Labor Graph)
E-mail: dan@slavelabor.com
Web site: http://www.slavelabor.com
Dist(s): **Diamond Bk. Distributors.**

Slave Labor Graphics *Imprint of* **Slave Labor Bks.**

Slavens Enterprises & Marketing Services, LLP *See* **Slavens Enterprises, LLC.**

Slavens Enterprises, LLC., *(0-9740348)* 14314 SW Allen Blvd., PMB 229, Beaverton, OR 97005 USA Tel 503-526-0904 Toll Free: 877-526-0904 ; *Imprints:* Special Editions — Customized Biographies (Special Edns)
E-mail: ricks@slavensmarketing.com.

Sleep Garden, Inc., *(0-9752988)* P.O. Box 2365, Menlo Park, CA 94025-2365 USA Toll Free: 877-475-3376
E-mail: marykelley@amsiventures.com
Web site: http://www.zzonesleep.com.

Sleeping Bear Pr., *(1-57504; 1-886947; 1-58536)* Div. of Gale Group, Orders Addr.: P.O. Box 20, Chelsea, MI 48118 USA (SAN 253-8466) Tel 734-475-4411; Fax: 734-475-0787; Toll Free: 800-487-2323; Edit Addr.: 310 N. Main, Suite 300, Chelsea, MI 48118 USA
E-mail: customerservice@sleepingbearpress.com
Web site: http://www.sleepingbearpress.com
Dist(s): **Baker & Taylor Bks.**
Booklines Hawaii, Ltd.
Thomson Gale
Keith Distributors
Partners Pubs. Group, Inc.
Southern Bk. Service
Urban Land Institute.

Sleepy Creek Music, *(0-9754633)* P.O. Box 2652, Bloomington, IN 47402-2652 USA Tel 812-334-9901
E-mail: grey@greylarsen.com
Web site: http://www.greylarsen.com.

Sleepy D Publishing, *(0-9721833)* 5505 E. McLellan, No. 120, Mesa, AZ 85205 USA
E-mail: grdixon1@cox.net
Web site: http://www.maxwellsociety.net.

SLG, *(0-615)* 128 C Main St., Agawam, MA 01001 USA
E-mail: slg_gallery@yahoo.com
Web site: http://geocities.com/slg_gallery/about.

Slhoetree Publishers, Incorporated *See* **Shoetree Publishers, Inc.**

Sloan Publishing, *(0-9724147)* 522 Fisk Rd., Cookville, TN 38501 USA
E-mail: donnathorne@charter.net
Web site: http://www.buzzandollie.com; http://www.childrens-book.com.

Sloane Pubns., *(0-9664248)* Orders Addr.: P.O. Box 7712, Portland, ME 04102 USA Tel 207-774-8733; Edit Addr.: 225 York St., Portland, ME 04102 USA Do not confuse with Sloane Pubns., Sun Lakes, AZ
E-mail: sloane@maine.rr.com.

Slusser, Jan *See* **RiverCreek Bks., Inc.**

SM Ediciones (ESP) *(84-348; 84-404; 84-398; 84-675) Dist. by* **Continental Bk.**

SM Ediciones (ESP) *(84-348; 84-404; 84-398; 84-675) Dist. by* **Mariuccia Iaconi Bk Imports.**

SM Ediciones (ESP) *(84-348; 84-404; 84-398; 84-675) Dist. by* **Lectorum Pubns.**

SM Ediciones (ESP) *(84-348; 84-404; 84-398; 84-675) Dist. by* **AIMS Intl.**

SM Ediciones (ESP) *(84-348; 84-404; 84-398; 84-675) Dist. by* **IBD Ltd.**

SM Ediciones (ESP) *(84-348; 84-404; 84-398; 84-675) Dist. by* **Distribks Inc.**

SM Ediciones (ESP) *(84-348; 84-404; 84-398; 84-675) Dist. by* **Libros Fronteras.**

Small Beer Pr., *(1-931520)* 176 Prospect Ave., Northampton, MA 01060 USA
E-mail: info@lcrw.net
Web site: http://www.lcrw.net; http://www.smallbeerpress.com
Dist(s): **Baker & Taylor Bks.**
Consortium Bk. Sales & Distribution.

Small Fry Productions, *(0-9651690; 1-892703)* Affil. of LightVision Films, Inc., 1200 Alpha Dr., Suite B, Alpharetta, GA 30004-3923 USA Tel 678-339-1990; Fax: 678-339-1991
E-mail: smfryprod@aol.com
Web site: http://www.small-fry.com
Dist(s): **Baker & Taylor Bks.**
Ingram Entertainment, Inc.
VPD, Inc.
Valley Media, Inc.

Small Gate Media, *(0-9643389)* Orders Addr.: P.O. Box 675754, Marietta, GA 30006 USA Tel 770-420-3964
E-mail: wxdude1@juno.com; nick@wxdude.com
Web site: http://www.wxdude.com.

Small Group Consultant Firm *See* **McPhaul Bks.**

Small Horizons *Imprint of* **New Horizon Pr. Pubs., Inc.**

Small Miracles Pr., *(0-9673794)* 972 Somerset Ln., York, PA 17403 USA Tel 717-845-9647 (phone/fax) Do not confuse with Small Miracles Pr, in Ojai, CA
E-mail: yopeggy@aol.com
Web site: http://www.goose.ycp.edu/~swojciec.

Small People Publishing, *(0-9709736)* 340 E. 93rd St., Suite 24E, New York, NY 10128 USA Tel 212-369-0891; Fax: 212-369-2239
E-mail: khalsagfx@aol.com.

Small Planet Communications, Inc., *(0-9656211; 1-931376)* 15 Union St., Lawrence, MA 01840 USA Tel 978-794-2201; Fax: 978-794-8062; Toll Free: 800-475-9486 (orders only)
E-mail: lisa@smplanet.com
Web site: http://www.smplanet.com; http://www.PlanetBookClub.com/.

Small Potatoes Pr., *(0-9661200)* 401 Collings Ave., Collingswood, NJ 08108 USA Tel 856-869-5207; Fax: 856-869-5247 Do not confuse with Small Potatoes Pr., San Clemente, CA
E-mail: info@smallpotatoespress.com; cuizine1@aol.com
Web site: http://www.smallpotatoespress.com.

Small Press Distribution *See* **SPD-Small Pr. Distribution**

Small Rain Pr., *(0-9655317)* Orders Addr.: P.O. Box 400, Lincoln, MA 01773 USA (SAN 299-3309) Tel 781-259-9656 (phone/fax); Edit Addr.: 63 Bedford Rd., Lincoln, MA 01773 USA (SAN 299-3317)
E-mail: info@smallrainpress.com.

Small Secrets Unlimted, Inc., *(0-9700943)* Div. of Dweebz, 17051 SE 272nd St., Suite 43, No. 22, Covington, WA 98042-4955 USA Tel 253-740-1314
E-mail: nllovejoy@dweebz.com
Web site: http://www.dweebz.com.

Small Ventures, *(1-930165)* 1618 Kendolph, Denton, TX 76205 USA Tel 940-566-6123 (phone/fax)
E-mail: lhspublisher@aol.com
Web site: http://www.inhissteps.com.

Small Waters Publishing, *(0-9765621)* 14251 75th Ave. SE, Atwater, MN 56209 USA Tel 320-894-7904; Fax: 320-235-6418
E-mail: markp@lakesideprintingandadvertising.com.

Small Wonders Enterprises, *(0-9741888)* 12210 Fairfax Towne Ctr., PMB No. 901, Fairfax, VA 22033 USA Tel 703-352-0226 Do not confuse with Small Wonders Enterprises in Farmingron, NM
E-mail: snickerdoodle@erols.com
Web site: http://www.snickerdoodleforkids.com
Dist(s): **Biblio Distribution.**

Small World Toys, *(0-9774677; 0-9776034; 0-9795081)* P.O. Box 3620, Culver City, CA 90231-3620 USA
Web site: http://www.smallworldtoys.com.

Smallbag Bks., *(0-9761631)* Orders Addr.: 2000 Del Sol, Bowie, MD 20721 USA
E-mail: konaapub@yahoo.com
Web site: http://www.younganddebtfree.com.

Smallfellow Pr. *Imprint of* **Tallfellow Pr.**

SmallHorse Pr. *Imprint of* **Equine Graphics Publishing Group**

Smallwood, Edward, *(0-9741282)* 1609 Mountain Ashe Ct., Matthews, NC 28105 USA
Web site: http://www.jfrankles.com.

Smarr Pubs., *(0-9663784; 1-929579)* 4917 High Falls Rd. Ste. 201, Jackson, GA 30233-6654 USA Toll Free: 888-366-7627
E-mail: order@smarrpublishers.com
Web site: http://www.smarrpublishers.com/.

Smart Alec Toys Publishing, *(0-9670091)* P.O. Box 880, Andover, MA 01810 USA Tel 978-442-4892; Fax: 978-686-9444
E-mail: smatoys@aol.com
Web site: http://www.marsmartians.com; http://www.smartalectoys.com.

Smart Alternatives, Inc., *(0-9636140)* Orders Addr.: P.O. Box 5849, Austin, TX 78763 USA Tel 512-445-0602; Fax: 512-445-0210; Toll Free: 800-453-9226; Edit Addr.: 311 Le Grand Ave., Austin, TX 78704 USA ; *Imprints:* Neon Rose Productions (Neon Rose).

Smart & Smarter Publishing, *(0-9713530)* P.O. Box 475, Orondo, WA 98802 USA (SAN 255-3104)
E-mail: MaryRemley@smartandsmarter.com; customerservice@smartandsmarter.com
Web site: http://www.smartandsmarter.com.

Smart Apple Media, *(1-58340; 1-887068; 1-59920)* Div. of Black Rabbit Bks., Orders Addr.: P.O. Box 3263, Mankato, MN 56002 USA; Edit Addr.: 123 S. Broad Stree, Mankato, MN 56001 USA
E-mail: info@blackrabbitbooks.com; aschwab@blackrabbitbooks.com
Web site: http://www.blackrabbitbooks.com
Dist(s): **Creative Co., The.**

Smart Data Processing, Inc., *(0-9718439)* 14 Molly Pitcher Dr., Manalapan, NJ 07726 USA Tel 732-598-4027; Fax: 732-409-1364
E-mail: info@smartdataprocessing.com
Web site: http://www.smartdataprocessing.com.

Smart Kids *Imprint of* **Penton Overseas, Inc.**

Smart Kids of the Future Publishing, *(1-928540)* Orders Addr.: P.O. Box 72043, Marietta, GA 30007-2043 USA Tel 678-822-2198 (phone/fax); Edit Addr.: 4233 Singing Post Ln., Roswell, GA 30075 USA Tel 770-645-8912
E-mail: smartkids.publishing@yahoo.com.

Smart Kids Publishing, *(1-891100)* 8403 Cliffridge Ln., La Jolla, CA 92037-2119 USA Tel 619-668-0570; Fax: 760-728-5309
Dist(s): **APG Sales and Fulfillment**
Penton Overseas, Inc.

Smart Kids Studio Productions *Imprint of* **Literary Assocs. Pr.**

smart Life Ministries, Inc., The, *(0-9741091)* 1649 Springhill St., Chillicothe, MO 64601 USA.

Smart Picks, Inc., *(0-9764785)* P.O. Box 771440, Lakewood, OH 44107 USA Tel 216-226-6173; Fax: 216-226-5413
E-mail: games@smartpicks.com.

Smart Publishing, *(0-9761819)* P.O. Box 410894, Chicago, IL 60641 USA Tel 773-616-0267
E-mail: halfbakedsistas@aol.com
Web site: http://www.halfbakedsistas.com.

Smart Smiles Co., The, *(0-9722792; 0-9723727; 0-9762740; 0-9763328)* 380 S. Mizner Blvd., No. 1709, Boca Raton, FL 33432 USA Tel 561-347-3075 ; *Imprints:* Flat Kids (Flat Kids)
Web site: http://www.smartsmilescompany.com.

Smartinbooks, Inc., *(0-9761765)* Orders Addr.: P.O. Box 729, Paducah, KY 42002-0729 USA; Edit Addr.: 1441 HC Mathis Dr., Paducah, KY 42001 USA
E-mail: hmartin@paducah.com
Web site: http://www.smartinbooks.com.

SmartiPantz Publishing, *(0-9747563)* P.O. Box 24014, Minneapolis, MN 55424 USA (SAN 256-0720).

SMARTseeds Co., LLC, The, *(0-9790931)* P.O. Box 100028, Cudahy, WI 53110 USA (SAN 852-4068) Tel 414-433-0500
E-mail: carlos@thesmartseedscompany.com; info@thesmartseedscompany.com
Web site: http://www.thesmartseedscompany.com.

SmartSong, Inc., *(1-882500)* 150 W. 55th St., New York, NY 10019 USA Tel 212-246-8282; Fax: 212-541-9477; Toll Free: 800-317-8383 (orders & customer service)
E-mail: slemberg@nyc.rr.com
Dist(s): **Baker & Taylor Bks.**
Bookazine Co., Inc.

Smarty Pants Bks., *(0-9718074)* 24 Rosedale Rd., Wynnewood, PA 19096-3524 USA Do not confuse with Smarty Pants, Lakewood, OH.

Smartypants Bks., *(0-9773550)* P.O. Box 1014, Logandale, NV 89021-1014 USA (SAN 257-3423)
Web site: http://www.smartypants-books.com.

Smartypants Publishing, *(0-9792897)* Orders Addr.: P.O. Box 1548, Buckley, WA 98321 USA Tel 253-278-6612
E-mail: christa@smartypantspublishing.com
Web site: http://smartypantspublishing.com.

SMC Publishing, *(0-9729546)* P.O. Box 2684, Branchville, NJ 07826 USA Tel 973-948-7441 (phone/fax) Do not confuse with companies with the same name in Houston, TX, Garden Grove, CA, Corona, CA, West Long Branch, NJ
E-mail: magic@mercurylink.net
Web site: http://www.magi-call.com.

SMG Pubns., *(0-9705342)* Orders Addr.: 175 San Angelo Ave. Apt. E, Santa Barbara, CA 93111-2244 USA (SAN 253-7052)
E-mail: kallona@verizon.net
Web site: http://www.drstix.com
Dist(s): **Baker & Taylor Bks.**

Smile Time Publishing, *(0-9785961)* P.O. Box B, Del Mar, CA 92014 USA
E-mail: ps@peterstrunk.com
Web site: http://www.smile-time.com.

Smile-a-Lot, LLP, *(0-9785132)* 1050 Walnut St. #201, Boulder, CO 80302 USA Tel 303-443-2006; Fax: 303-443-9475 ; *Imprints:* Smiletown Books (Smiletown Bks)
E-mail: chris@smiletownbooks.com
Web site: http://smiletownbooks.com.

SMiles Productions (SMP), LLC, *(0-9768456)* 14241 NE Woodinville-Duvall Rd., Woodinville, WA 98072 USA Tel 425-481-8817; Fax: 425-481-8179
E-mail: language@smilesprod.com
Web site: http://www.smilesprod.com.

Smiletime Publishing, *(0-9702565)* Orders Addr.: P.O. Box 11614, Jackson, WY 83002 USA Tel 307-739-9872; Edit Addr.: 4265 Fallen Leaf Ln., Jackson, WY 83002 USA.

Smiletown Bks. *Imprint of* **Smile-a-Lot, LLP**

Smiley Co., *(0-9629001)* 401 Anglin St., Smiley, TX 78159-0099 USA (SAN 297-4045) Tel 830-587-6623; Fax: 830-587-6113; Toll Free: 800-584-3655
E-mail: npattesonsmiley@the-cia.net
Dist(s): **Baker & Taylor Bks.**

Smiley Originals *See* **Smiley Co.**

Smiling Butterfly Pubns., *(0-9709083)* 41 Hollister St., Dundee, NY 14837 USA Tel 607-243-5713
E-mail: smbfly@linkny.com.

Smirk Productions, *(0-9665637)* 240 Blooming Grove Rd., Hanover, PA 17331 USA Tel 717-632-0556
E-mail: jgcoulson@netrax.net.

Smith & Assocs., *(0-9790817)* 70 Goodwin Cir., Hartford, CT 06105 USA (SAN 852-3886) Tel 860-543-0279; Fax: 860-586-8718
Web site: http://www.morningdovepress.com
Dist(s): **Connecticut River Pr.**

Smith & Daniel, *(0-9630463; 1-889668)* P.O. Box 8097, Jacksonville, FL 32239-0097 USA Toll Free: 800-330-1325.

Smith and Kraus Publishers, Incorporated, *(0-9622722; 1-57525; 1-880399)* Orders Addr.: P.O. Box 127, Lyme, NH 03768 USA (SAN 255-1454) Tel 603-669-7032 IDS Customer Service; 603-647-4369 IDS (returns only); Fax: 603-669-7945 IDS Customer Service Fax; Toll Free: 888-282-2881
E-mail: sandk@sover.net; jantonivich@tds.net
Web site: http://www.smithandkraus.com
Dist(s): **Baker & Taylor Bks.**

Smith, Andrea Joy, *(0-9764396)* 2447 Mission Ave, Suite B, Carmichael, CA 95608 USA
E-mail: smithfamdent@aol.com.

Smith, Brenda J. Few *See* **Tall Through Bks.**

Smith, C. Brandt, *(0-9768020)* 1910 Scenic Rd., Jonesboro, AR 72401-0220 USA Tel 870-933-1908
E-mail: brandt@walnutstreetbaptist.org.

Smith, Deanna *See* **Annade Publishing**

Smith, Ernest, *(0-9729154)* Orders Addr.: 7549 Bevy Ridge Cv., Memphis, TN 38125-3456 USA
E-mail: ernest725@Hotmail.com.

Smith, Florence B. *See* **Prickly Pr.**

Smith, George Publishing, *(0-9740434)* Orders Addr.: 11 Amberwinds Ct., Lakewood, NJ 08701 USA (SAN 255-3716)
E-mail: customer_support@georgesmithpublishing.com
Web site: http://www.georgesmithpublishing.com
Dist(s): **Mountain Bk. Co.**

Smith, Gibbs Publisher *See* **Gibbs Smith, Publisher**

Smith, Hilary, *(0-9621110)* Box 72, Alumni Hse., Peacham, VT 05862 USA (SAN 250-5509) Tel 802-592-3500.

Smith Island Foundation, *(0-9754170)* 44108 Bristow Cir., Ashburn, VA 20147 USA Tel 703-729-4462 Phone/Fax
E-mail: books@smithislandfoundation.org; heather@pneumabooks.com
Web site: http://www.smithislandfoundation.org.

Smith, Joseph L., *(0-9754985)* 38118 Village 38, Camarillo, CA 93012 USA
E-mail: cayusekid@earthlink.net.

Smith, Josephine Petra *See* **Universal Express**

Smith, Judith Grand Pre *See* **Positive Purpose Pr.**

Smith, Kasper, *(0-9744519)* 4251 Fischer, Detroit, MI 48214 USA Tel 313-922-1728
E-mail: pastorsmith@dominionintl.org
Web site: http://www.dominionintl.org.

Smith, Keith Bks., *(0-9637682; 0-9740764)* 1115 E. Main St., Suite 219, Box 8, Rochester, NY 14609 USA Tel 585-473-6776; Fax: 585-482-2496
E-mail: keith@keithsmithbooks.com
Web site: http://www.keithsmithbooks.com.

Smith Lane Pubs., *(0-9672639)* Orders Addr.: P.O. Box 54, Cotuit, MA 02635 USA Tel 508-420-9258; Fax: 508-420-1688; Toll Free: 888-338-6566; Edit Addr.: 215 Lewis Pond Rd., Cotuit, MA 02635 USA
E-mail: SLPublishers@cs.com.

Smith, Michael *See* **East West Discovery Pr.**

Smith, Mildred C., *(0-9778641)* 4200 Cathedral Ave, NW, Apt. 610, Washington, DC 20016 USA Tel 202-363-5352
E-mail: mcs29@georgetown.edu.

Smith Novelty Co., Inc., *(0-938765; 1-59099)* Div. of Smith News Co., Inc., 460 Ninth St., San Francisco, CA 94103 USA (SAN 216-2326) Tel 415-861-4900 ext 615; Fax: 415-861-5683
E-mail: michellesnco@hotmail.com.

Smith, Peter Pub., Inc., *(0-8446)* Five Lexington Ave., Magnolia, MA 01930 USA (SAN 206-8885) Tel 978-525-3562; Fax: 978-525-3674.

Smith, Ronald J. Sr., *(0-9749390)* Orders Addr.: 1123 S. Thomas St., Apt. 22, Arlington, VA 22204-3640 USA
E-mail: rjngds@yahoo.com
Dist(s): **Morris Publishing.**

Smith, S. Pubns., *(0-9769320)* P.O. Box 122, Severna Park, MD 21146 USA Tel 410-271-0837; Fax: 410-544-0059
E-mail: stew@stewsmith.com
Web site: http://www.ebookmerchant.com.

Smith, Tyjauna, *(0-9760112)* Orders Addr.: P.O. Box 2230 Misty Woods Rd., Lake Cormorant, MS 38641 USA
E-mail: tyjauna0344@bellsouth.net
Web site: http://www.freewebs.com/tyjauna.

Smith, Viveca Publishing, *(0-9740551)* PMB No. 131, 3001 S. Hardin Blvd., Suite 110, McKinney, TX 75070-9028 USA Tel 214-793-0089; Fax: 972-562-7559
E-mail: vsmithpublishing@aol.com
Web site: http://www.vivecasmithpublishing.com
Dist(s): **AtlasBooks Distribution.**

Smithfield Capital Corp., *(0-9764670)* 219 S. D. St., Hamilton, OH 45013 USA
E-mail: smithfieldcap@msn.com.

Smithfield Press *See* **Princeton Health Pr.**

†Smithsonian Institution Pr., *(0-87474; 1-56098; 1-58834)* Div. of Smithsonian Institution, Orders Addr.: 22883 Quicksilver Dr., Dulles, VA 20166 USA (SAN 253-3383); Edit Addr.: 750 Ninth St. NW, Suite 4300, Washington, DC 20560-0950 USA (SAN 206-8044) Tel 202-275-2300; Fax: 202-275-2245; 202-275-2274; Toll Free: 800-233-4830 (orders)
Web site: http://www.sipress.si.edu/
Dist(s): **HarperCollins Pubs.**
NetLibrary, Inc.
Rowman & Littlefield Pubs., Inc.
Wittenborn Art Bks.; *CIP.*

SMOOCH *Imprint of* **Dorchester Publishing Co., Inc.**

Smooth Sailing Pr., *(1-933660)* Orders Addr.: P.O. Box 1439, Tomball, TX 77377 USA (SAN 257-2680) Tel 281-251-0830 (phone/fax); Edit Addr.: P.O. Box 1439, Tomball, TX 77377-1439 USA ; *Imprints:* Tadpole Press 4 Kids (Tadpole Pr)
E-mail: smoothsailingpress@houston.rr.com; leebee3@peoplepc.com.

SMPR, *(0-9767898)* 4800 S. Westshore Blvd., Suite 411, Tampa, FL 33611 USA Tel 813-831-8206 (phone/fax); Toll Free Fax: 866-958-1323 (phone/fax)
E-mail: sonja.moffett@smpr.info
Web site: http://www.smpr.info.

†Smyth & Helwys Publishing, Inc., *(0-9628455; 1-57312; 1-880837)* 6316 Peake Rd., Macon, GA 31210-3960 USA (SAN 298-7732) Tel 478-757-0564; Fax: 478-757-1305; Toll Free: 800-747-3016
E-mail: griff@helwys.com
Web site: http://www.helwys.com; *CIP.*

Smythe, Colin Ltd. (GBR) *(0-85105; 0-86140; 0-900675; 0-901072) Dist. by* **Dufour.**

Snake Country Publishing, *(0-9635828)* 16748 W. Linden St., Caldwell, ID 83607-9270 USA Tel 208-459-9233
E-mail: snakecountry@mindspring.com
Dist(s): **Caxton Pr.**

Snake Goddess Bks., *(0-9744910)* 11431/2 Gladsy Ave., Long Beach, CA 90804 USA.

Snake Hill Pr. *Imprint of* **Messineo, David**

Sneaky Snake Pubns., *(1-889967)* 2807 Saint Francis Forest Dr., Lake Charles, LA 70605-7900 USA
E-mail: ssnopub@aol.com.

Snelsonbks.com, *(0-9723935)* 355 N. Diamond Ave., Canon City, CO 81212 USA
E-mail: bs@ris.net
Web site: http://www.snelsonbooks.com.

Snojoy Publishing, *(0-9743913)* 4509 14th St., Greeley, CO 80634 USA
E-mail: snojoy1@hotmail.com; gnojoy1@hotmail.com.

Snow In Sarasota Publishing, *(0-9663335)* 5170 Central Sarasota Pkwy., No.309, Sarasota, FL 34238 USA Tel 941-923-9201; Fax: 941-926-8739
E-mail: sarasota58@aol.com.

†Snow Lion Pubns., Inc., *(0-937938; 1-55939)* Orders Addr.: P.O. Box 6483, Ithaca, NY 14851-6483 USA (SAN 250-328X) Tel 607-273-8519; Fax: 607-273-8508; Toll Free: 800-950-0313; Edit Addr.: 605 W. State St., Ithaca, NY 14851 USA
E-mail: tibet@snowlionpub.com
Web site: http://www.snowlionpub.com
Dist(s): **National Bk. Network**
New Leaf Distributing Co., Inc.; *CIP.*

Snow Tree Bks., *(0-9749006)* Orders Addr.: P.O. Box 546, Peabody, MA 01960-7564 USA (SAN 255-965X) Tel 781-592-9866
E-mail: info@snowtreebooks.com
Web site: http://snowtreebooks.com
Dist(s): **Biblio Distribution.**

Snowbound Bks., *(0-9722570)* Orders Addr.: P.O. Box 281327, Lamoille, NV 89828 USA; Edit Addr.: 1291 Country Ln., Lamoille, NV 89828 USA.

Snowbound Pr. *See* **Snowbound Pr., Inc.**

Snowbound Pr., Inc., *(1-932362)* P.O. Box 698, Littleton, CO 80160-0698 USA Tel 303-347-2869; Fax: 303-386-3232
E-mail: info@snowboundpress.com
Web site: http://www.snowboundpress.com
Dist(s): **Independent Pubs. Group**
Quality Bks., Inc.

Snowflakes *See* **All Season Snowflakes**

Snowman Learning Center, The, *(0-9674666)* 6 Carver St., Plymouth, MA 02360-3301 USA Tel 508-746-5993; Fax: 508-746-8097
E-mail: S.Snowmanph.d@worldnet.att.net.

Snyder, Tom Productions, Inc., *(0-926891; 1-55998; 1-57809; 1-59009)* Div. of Scholastic, Inc., 100 Talcott Ave. # 6, Watertown, MA 02472-5714 USA (SAN 285-6441) Toll Free Fax: 800-304-1254; Toll Free: 800-342-0236
E-mail: ask@tomsnyder.com
Web site: http://www.tomsnyder.com.

Snyder, Vicki, *(0-9773187)* 4349 Cimarron Ct., NW, Rochester, MN 55901 USA
E-mail: cctraining@prodigy.net.

Snyder, William Foundation for Animals, The, *(0-9674058)* 3600 Clipper Mill Rd., Suite 224, Baltimore, MD 21211 USA Tel 410-366-0787; Fax: 410-366-0789
E-mail: croll@wsfanimals.org
Web site: http://www.wsfanimals.org.

Snyder-Winston Pr., *(0-9752749)* 23679 Calabasas Rd., No. 186, Calabasas, CA 91302 USA Tel 818-876-0188; Fax: 818-876-0133
E-mail: tedafed@earthlink.net
Web site: http://www.midaskids.com.

SNZ Publishing, *(0-9758815)* P.O. Box 32190, Cincinnati, OH 45232 USA (SAN 256-1255)
E-mail: doug@snzpublishing.com
Web site: http://www.snzpublishing.com.

So Simple Learning, *(0-9772158)* 12463 Rancho Bernardo Rd., PMB 253, San Diego, CA 92128 USA Tel 858-530-5055
E-mail: info@sosimplelearning.com
Web site: http://www.sosimplelearning.com.

So Smart! Productions, *(0-9660151; 0-9713747; 0-9717936; 1-932189)* 320 North High St., West Chester, PA 19380 USA Tel 610-918-1888; Fax: 610-918-1205
E-mail: info@sosmart.com
Web site: http://www.sosmart.com
Dist(s): **Big Kids Productions, Inc.**
Follett Media Distribution
Rounder Kids Music Distribution
Tapeworm Video Distributor, Inc.
Valley Media, Inc.

Soaring Sparrow Pr., *(1-891262)* 11795 SW Crater Loop, Beaverton, OR 97008 USA Tel 503-644-5960
E-mail: sparrowman@earthlink.net
Web site: www.marvinmallard.com.

†Social Science Education Consortium, Inc., *(0-89994)* P.O. Box 21270, Boulder, CO 80308-4270 USA (SAN 213-1684) Tel 303-492-8154; Fax: 303-449-3925
E-mail: singletl@stripe.colorado.edu
Web site: http://www.ssecinc.org; *CIP.*

Social Studies Schl. Service, *(1-56004)* Orders Addr.: 10200 Jefferson Blvd., P.O. Box 802, Culver City, CA 90232-0802 USA (SAN 168-9592) Tel 310-839-2436; Fax: 310-839-2249; Toll Free: 800-421-4246
E-mail: access@socialstudies.com
Web site: http://socialstudies.com.

Sociedad de San Pablo (COL) *(958-607) Dist. by* **Alba.**

Sociedad de San Pablo (ESP) Dist. by Alba.

Sociedad General Espanola de Libreria (ESP) *(84-7143; 84-9778) Dist. by* **Continental Bk.**

Sociedad General Espanola de Libreria (ESP) *(84-7143; 84-9778) Dist. by* **Distribks Inc.**

Society for Developmental Education *See* **Staff Development for Educators**

Society for Visual Education, Incorporated *See* **S V E & Churchill Media**

Society of Actuaries, *(0-938959; 0-9759337)* 475 N. Martingale Rd., Suite 600, Schaumburg, IL 60173-2226 USA (SAN 224-8387) Fax: 847-273-8507
E-mail: bhaynes@soa.org; Jarce@soa.org
Web site: http://www.soa.org.

Society of St. Teresa of Jesus, *(0-9638041)* 18080 Saint Joseph Way, Covington, LA 70435-5623 USA Tel 985-893-1470; Fax: 985-893-2476
E-mail: judyroxstj@aol.com; mlgstj@aol.com
Web site: http://www.teresians.org/.

Sociometrics Corp., *(0-9666901)* 170 State St., Suite 260, Los Altos, CA 94022 USA Tel 650-949-3282 ext 232; Fax: 650-949-3299
E-mail: socio@socio.com
Web site: http://www.socio.com.

Soft Saints, Inc., *(0-9769519)* 5753-G Santa Ana Canyon Rd., No. 378, Anaheim Hills, CA 92807 USA Tel 714-505-3127; Fax: 714-838-5857
E-mail: teri@softsaints.com
Web site: http://www.softsaints.com.

Soft Stuff, *(0-9664799)* 500 E. 29th Ave., Apt. 304, Spokane, WA 99203 USA Tel 509-990-2391
E-mail: kiefersands@comcast.net
Web site: http://www.softstuff4kids.com.

SoftPlay, Inc., *(1-931312; 1-59292)* 3535 W. Peterson Ave., Chicago, IL 60659 USA Tel 773-509-0707; Fax: 773-509-0404
E-mail: sales@softplayforkids.com
Web site: http://www.softplayforkids.com.

SoftTouch, Inc., *(1-59321)* Orders Addr.: 17117 Oak Dr., Ste. C, Omaha, NE 68130 USA Tel 402-334-8477; Fax: 402-334-8478; Toll Free: 877-763-8868
E-mail: brenda@softtouch.com
Web site: http://www.softtouch.com.

Sohn, Mark F. Pubns., *(0-9616911; 1-883207)* 103 Honeysuckle Dr., Pikeville, KY 41501 USA (SAN 661-5228) Tel 606-437-6467; Fax: 606-437-7837
E-mail: sohn@kymtnnet.org.

Soho Pr., Inc., *(0-939149; 1-56947)* 853 Broadway, New York, NY 10003 USA (SAN 662-5088) Tel 212-260-1900; Fax: 212-260-1902
E-mail: bdevendorf@sohopress.com
Web site: http://www.sohopress.com/
Dist(s): **Consortium Bk. Sales & Distribution.**

Soho Publishing Company *See* **Sixth&Spring Bks.**

SoJam Pr., *(0-9761477)* P.O. Box 25163, Woodbury, MN 55125-9998 USA (SAN 256-2359)
E-mail: sojam@comcast.net
Web site: http://www.sojampress.com.

Sol de Oro Pubns., *(0-9754261)* 1004 S. Quinn Ct., Gilbert, AZ 85296-8818 USA Tel 480-892-0582
E-mail: SoldeOroPublications@yahoo.com
Web site: http://www.SoldeOroPublications.50megs.com.

Solar, Kay, *(0-9666945)* 6280 Sevenoaks, Baton Rouge, LA 70806 USA Tel 225-201-2068; Fax: 225-201-2111
E-mail: kays@lwha.com.

Solar Publishing LLC, *(0-9785326)* P.O. Box 1448, Owings Mills, MD 21117 USA (SAN 850-8089) Tel 410-493-1872
E-mail: robyn@solarpub.com
Web site: http://www.solarpub.com.

Solel Pubns., *(0-9748332)* 309 Concord Ave., Oceanside, NY 11572 USA Tel 516-678-9778.

Soli Deo Gloria Pubns., *(1-57358; 1-877611)* Div. of Soli Deo Gloria Ministries, Inc., Orders Addr.: P.O. Box 547500, Orlando, FL 32854 USA (SAN 298-7589) Tel 407-333-4244; Fax: 407-333-4233; Toll Free: 800-435-4343; Edit Addr.: 400 Technology Park Dr., Lake Mary, FL 32746 USA
E-mail: craig@sdgbooks.com
Web site: http://www.SDGbooks.com.

Solibros, *(0-9755945)* 2215 Peachtree N. Ct., Atlanta, GA 30338 USA
Web site: http://www.solibros.com.

Solid Ground Christian Bks., *(0-9710169; 1-932474; 1-59925)* Orders Addr.: P.O. Box 660132, Vestavia Hills, AL 35266 USA Tel 205-443-0311; Fax: 775-822-5917; Toll Free: 877-666-9469; Edit Addr.: 715 Oak Grove Rd., Birmingham, AL 35209-6503 USA
E-mail: solid-ground-books@juno.com; solid_ground_books@yahoo.com; sgcb@charter.net; scgbclassics@juno.com
Web site: http://www.solid-ground-books.com.

Solid Rock Bks. *Imprint of* **Trumpet In Zion Publishing**

Solid Rock Publishing *See* **Trumpet In Zion Publishing**

SolidA, Inc., *(0-9677328)* 9339 Paradise Rd., Kewaskum, WI 53040 USA Tel 262-692-9609
E-mail: deanne@solida.net
Web site: http://www.solida.net.

SolidGumboWorks, *(1-889851)* Orders Addr.: P.O. Box 41889, Philadelphia, PA 19101-1889 USA Tel 215-281-1040; Toll Free: 888-843-1084; Edit Addr.: 10825 E. Keswick Rd., Unit 241, Philadelphia, PA 19154 USA.

Solitude Pr., *(1-928874)* 212 Brooks St., Williamsburg, VA 23185 USA Tel 757-564-1365
E-mail: zander67@cox.net.

Sollil Productions, *(0-9711342)* 40 Frothingham Crossing, Lenox, MA 01240 USA Tel 413-637-2064
E-mail: sollil@yahoo.com.

†Solomon Pr., The, *(0-934623)* Subs. of Publishers Creative Services, 98-12 66th Ave., Suite 2, Rego Park, NY 11374 USA (SAN 693-9252) Tel 718-830-9112; *CIP.*

SoloProse Publishing, *(0-9663142)* 46-9 Raintree Island, Tonawanda, NY 14150-2779 USA Tel 716-695-2463
E-mail: rdeneen@aol.com; soloprose@aol.com
Web site: http://www.soloprose.com.

Solovisions *Imprint of* **Comic Library International**

Solsidan Hse., *(0-9741620)* Orders Addr.: 104 7th St., Colorado Springs, CO 80906 USA; Edit Addr.: 475 Sunnyside Ave., Eugene, OR 97404 USA
E-mail: solsidanhouse@yahoo.com
Web site: http://www.solsidanhouse.com.

Solution Tree, *(1-879639; 1-932127; 1-934009)* 304 W. Kirkwood Ave., Suite 2, Bloomington, IN 47404-5132 USA Toll Free: 800-733-6786
E-mail: susan.pigg@solution-tree.com
Web site: http://www.solution-tree.com.

Solutions for Human Services, LLC, *(0-9764802)* 25 Vernon Dr., Warren, PA 16365 USA Tel 814-726-1228
E-mail: lindab@westpa.net.

Solving Light Bks., *(0-9705438)* 727 Mountalban Dr., Annapolis, MD 21409-4646 USA Tel 410-757-4630
E-mail: rbowiej@comcast.net; nancygjohnson@comcast.net
Web site: http://www.solvinglight.com; http://www.theparthenoncode.com
Dist(s): **Biblio Distribution**
STL Distribution North America.

Soma Pr., *(0-9720464)* 1930 Cherry Tree Ln., Fairfield, IA 52556 USA Tel 641-472-7734; Fax: 641-472-1048
E-mail: fredg@lisco.com.

Some Kids I Know, *(0-9768230)* Div. of Some Kids I Know, LLC, W323 N8164 Northcrest Dr., Hartland, WI 53029 USA Tel 262-966-2582
E-mail: thorst@wi.rr.com.

Someone Special Foundation, *(0-9673179)* 1750 Kalakaua Ave., Suite 103 Century Center, PMB 3774, Honolulu, HI 96826 USA Tel 808-942-3786
E-mail: MCampaniel@aol.com.

†Somerset Pubs., Inc., *(0-403)* 1532 State St., Santa Barbara, CA 93101 USA (SAN 204-6105) Toll Free: 800-937-7947
Web site: http://www.somersetpubl.com
Dist(s): **North American Bk. Distributors**; *CIP.*

Somerville Hse. Bks., Ltd. (CAN) *(0-921051; 1-58184; 1-895897; 1-55286; 1-894042) Dist. by* **Penguin Grp USA.**

Sonata Publishing, *(0-9642529)* Orders Addr.: 1277 S. Adams St., Glendale, CA 91205 USA Tel 818-380-7155; Fax: 818-242-5551
E-mail: buttwinick@earthlink.net.

Song Revival Fellowship & Ministries, *(0-9673093)* Div. of LaVerne Tripp Ministries, Orders Addr.: P.O. Box 899, Gallatin, TN 37066 USA Tel 615-230-7577; Fax: 615-230-7939; Edit Addr.: 2105 Cages Bend Rd., Gallatin, TN 37066 USA
E-mail: laverne@lavernetripp.com
Web site: http://www.lavernetripp.com.

Songadh, Jain Swadhyay Mandir, *(0-9748681)* 304 Tall Oak Trail, Tarpon Springs, FL 34688 USA Tel 602-863-1073; 727-376-7290; Fax: 602-863-3557; 727-843-8157
E-mail: kahanguru@hotmail.com.

Songbird Pr., *(0-9720913)* Orders Addr.: P.O. Box 99, Freeport, ME 04032 USA Fax: 207-373-1128
Web site: http://www.songbirdpress.biz.

Songs & Stories Children Love, *(0-934591)* 123 Valentine Ln., Yonkers, NY 10705 USA (SAN 694-0609) Tel 914-423-7045; Fax: 914-423-0722
E-mail: fdil@bestweb.net.

SonLife Publishing, *(0-9658103)* 405 W. Scott Ave., Willcox, AZ 85643 USA Tel 520-384-9232
E-mail: sonlife@vtc.net
Web site: http://www.sonlifepub.com.

Sono Nis Pr. (CAN) *(0-919203; 0-919462; 0-9690282; 1-55039)* *Dist. by* **Orca Bk Pubs.**

Sonora Environmental Research Institute, Inc., *(1-892816)* 3202 E. Grant Rd., Tucson, AZ 85716 USA Tel 520-321-9488; Fax: 520-577-6954
E-mail: sonoraen@flash.net
Web site: http://www.flash.net/~sonoraen.

Sonrel Pr., *(0-9717284)* 7 Sonrel St., Woburn, MA 01801 USA Tel 781-933-0838
E-mail: jmcelhiney94@comcast.net
Web site: http://www.sonrelpress.com.

SonRise Pubns., *(0-615)* Orders Addr.: 9127 Don Ramon Dr., Stockton, CA 95210 USA Tel 209-476-8982 Do not confuse with Sonrise Pubns., Coopersville, MI
E-mail: sonrise@iexalt.net
Web site: http://www.hebrewmadeeasy.com.

Son-Rise Pubns. & Distribution Co., *(0-936369)* 51 Greenfield Rd., New Wilmington, PA 16142 USA (SAN 698-0031) Tel 724-946-9057; Fax: 724-946-8700; Toll Free: 800-358-0777
Web site: http://www.sonrisepublications.com;
http://www.softspace.com/steelvalley
Dist(s): **Baker & Taylor Bks.**

Sonrise Publishing, *(0-9724458)* 131 Galleon St. # 2B, Marina Dl Rey, CA 90292-5973 USA (SAN 254-8348) Do not confuse with companies with the same or similar names in Corte Madera, CA, Ashland, OH
E-mail: annsonrise@aol.com
Web site: http://www.sonrisepublishing.com;
http://www.annhamiltonwallace.com
Dist(s): **AtlasBooks Distribution**
Baker & Taylor Bks.
BookMasters, Inc.

SonRises Bk. Publishing, *(1-929486)* Div. of SonRises Catholic Bookstore, Orders Addr.: P.O. Box 130, Ludlow, MA 01056 USA Tel 413-583-4014; Edit Addr.: 200 Center St., Unit 14, Ludlow, MA 01056 USA
E-mail: sonrises@aol.com.

Sonrose Pubs., *(0-9715405)* P.O. Box 188, Pismo Beach, CA 93448-0188 USA
E-mail: SonrosePublish@aol.com
Web site: http://www.thealphabuddies.com
Dist(s): **STL Distribution North America.**

Sonship Pr. *Imprint of* **21st Century Pr.**

Sonship Publishing, *(0-9725007)* P.O. Box 627, Kernersville, NC 27285-0627 USA
E-mail: lrecord@pol.net.

†Sophia Institute Pr., *(0-918477; 1-928832; 1-933184)* Orders Addr.: P.O. Box 5284, Manchester, NH 03108 USA (SAN 657-7172) Tel 603-641-9344; Fax: 603-641-8108; Toll Free: 800-888-9344 Do not confuse with Sophia Pr., Durham, NH
E-mail: production@sophiainstitute.com; sipress@grolen.com
Web site: http://www.sophiainstitute.com; *CIP.*

Sopris West *See* **Sopris West Educational Services**

Sopris West Educational Services, *(0-944584; 1-57035; 1-59318; 1-60218)* 4093 Specialty Pl., Longmont, CO 80504 USA (SAN 243-945X) Tel 303-651-2829; Fax: 303-907-8694; Toll Free: 800-547-6747 (orders only)
E-mail: publishing@sopriswest.com
Web site: http://www.sopriswest.com.

Sora Publishing, *(0-9765756)* 1800 Atlantic Blvd., A-405, Key West, FL 33040-5708 USA (SAN 256-4157) Tel 305-296-6699
E-mail: sorapublishing@comcast.net
Web site: http://www.sorapublishing.com.

Sorcerer's Pr., The, *(0-9667747)* 6 Berks St., Catasauqua, PA 18032-1532 USA.

Sorella Bks., *(0-9767351)* P.O. Box 454, Plantsville, CT 06479 USA
E-mail: sorellabooks@yahoo.com
Web site: http://www.sorellabooks.com.

Sotter Engineering Corp., *(0-9676030)* 26705 Loma Verde, Mission Viejo, CA 92691-6055 USA Tel 959-582-0889 (phone/fax)
E-mail: sottergeo@aol.com.

Soul Pubns., *(0-937327)* 232 Rockford St., Mt. Airy, NC 27030 USA (SAN 658-8050)
E-mail: Rthorne3@rjia.net.

Soul Publishing, Inc., *(1-929606)* Orders Addr.: P.O. Box 81806, Conyers, GA 30013 USA Tel 770-602-9966; Edit Addr.: 2364 Brentmoore Point, Conyers, GA 30013 USA
Web site: http://www.soulpublishing.com.

Soul Vision Works Publishing, *(0-9659538)* 1185 E. 96th St., Brooklyn, NY 11236 USA Tel 718-257-0456.

Soulful Pen Publishing +, *(0-9767592)* P.O. Box 70878, Rochester, MI 48309 USA
E-mail: brook@brookblander.com
Web site: http://www.niaradesigns.com.

SoulSong Publishing, *(0-9793113)* Div. of SoulSong Enterprises, Orders Addr.: P.O. Box 715, Crestone, CO 81131 USA
E-mail: soulsongpublishing@yahoo.com
Web site: http://www.soulsong.org.

Sound Beginnings, *(1-885278)* 3102 Beverly Dr., Dallas, TX 75205-2923 USA Tel 972-680-4443; Fax: 972-403-7685; Toll Free: 800-460-6802
E-mail: world@onramp.net
Web site: http://www.soundbeginnings.com
Dist(s): **Penton Overseas, Inc.**

Sound Concepts, Inc., *(1-887938; 1-933057)* 15 E. 400 S., Orem, UT 84058-5428 USA Tel 801-225-9520; Fax: 800-459-8420; Toll Free: 800-544-7044
E-mail: mjo@soundconcepts.com; cto@soundconcepts.com; jca@soundconcepts.com; jason@soundconcepts.com
Web site: http://www.soundconcepts.com.

Sound Craft Designs, *(0-9771357)* P.O. Box 1563, Poway, CA 92074-1563 USA Tel 858-842-1985
E-mail: info@exploreguitar.com
Web site: http://www.exploreguitar.com.

Sound Reading *Imprint of* **Sound Reading Solutions**

Sound Reading Solutions, *(0-9704183; 0-9742485; 0-9743384)* 379 Turkey Hill Rd., Ithaca, NY 14850 USA Tel 607-273-1370 (phone/fax); Toll Free: 800-801-1954 ; *Imprints:* Sound Reading (Sound Read)
E-mail: b7howlett@aol.com
Web site: http://www.soundreading.com.

Sound Room Pubs., Inc., *(1-883049; 1-58472)* Orders Addr.: P.O. Box 3168, Falls Church, VA 22043 USA Tel 540-722-2535; Fax: 540-722-0903; Toll Free: 800-643-0295; Edit Addr.: 100 Weems Ln., Winchester, VA 22601 USA ; *Imprints:* In Audio (In Aud)
E-mail: commuterslib@worldnet.att.net
Web site: http://www.inaudio.biz/
Dist(s): **Baker & Taylor Bks.**
Distributors, The
Follett Media Distribution.

Soundprints, *(0-924483; 1-56899; 1-931465; 1-59249)* Div. of Trudy Corp., 353 Main Ave., Norwalk, CT 06851 USA Tel 203 838 6009 Toll Free: 800-228-7839 ; *Imprints:* Little Soundprints (Little Sound)
Web site: http://www.soundprints.com
Dist(s): **Thomson Gale**
Learning Connection, The.

Sounds, Michelle, *(0-9741584)* 176-25 Union Tpke, No. 398, Queens, NY 11366 USA.

Sounds Write Productions, Inc., *(0-9626286; 1-890161)* 6685 Norman Ln., San Diego, CA 92120 USA Tel 619-697-6120; Fax: 619-697-6124; Toll Free: 800-976-8639
E-mail: soundswrite@aol.com; info@soundswrite.com
Web site: http://www.soundswrite.com.

Source Bk. Pubns., *(1-887137)* 1814 Franklin St., Suite 820, Oakland, CA 94612 USA Tel 510-839-5471; Fax: 510-547-3245
Dist(s): **Perseus Distribution.**

Source Bks., *(0-940147; 0-85650)* Orders Addr.: 204 E. Fourth St., Suite O, Santa Ana, CA 92701 USA (SAN 248-2231) Tel 714-558-8944 (phone/fax); Toll Free: 800-695-4237 Do not confuse with Source Bks., Nashville, TN
E-mail: studio185@earthlink.net.

Sourcebook Project, The, *(0-915554; 0-9600712)* P.O. Box 107, Glen Arm, MD 21057 USA (SAN 201-7652) Tel 410-668-6047
Web site: http://www.science-frontiers.com.

†Sourcebooks, Inc., *(0-942061; 0-9629162; 0-9629803; 1-57071; 1-57248; 1-883518; 1-887166; 1-4022)* 1935 Brookdale Rd., Suite 139, Naperville, IL 60563 USA (SAN 666-7864) Tel 630-961-3900; Fax: 630-961-2168; Toll Free: 800-727-8866 ; *Imprints:* Sourcebooks MediaFusion (MediaFusion); Sourcebooks Jabberwocky (Srcbks Jabber)
E-mail: info@sourcebooks.com
Web site: http://www.sourcebooks.com/; *CIP.*

Sourcebooks Jabberwocky *Imprint of* **Sourcebooks, Inc.**

Sourcebooks MediaFusion *Imprint of* **Sourcebooks, Inc.**

South Asia Bks., *(0-8364; 0-88386)* P.O. Box 502, Columbia, MO 65205 USA (SAN 207-4044) Tel 573-474-0116; Fax: 573-474-8124
E-mail: sabooks@juno.com
Web site: http://www.southasiabooks.com.

South Carolina Dept. of Archives & History, *(1-880067)* 8301 Parklane Rd., Columbia, SC 29223 USA Tel 803-896-6100; Fax: 803-896-6198
Web site: http://www.state.sc.us/scdah.

South Carolina Geographic Alliance, *(0-9768247)* Ctr. of Excellence for Geographic Education, Orders Addr.: Department of Geography, Univ. of S. C., Columbia, SC 29208 USA Toll Free: 888-895-2023
Web site: http://www.cas.sc.edu/cege/.

South Dakota State Historical Society, *(0-9622621; 0-9715171; 0-9749195; 0-9777955; 0-9798940)* Dept. of Tourism and State Development, State of South Dakota, 900 Governors Dr., Pierre, SD 57501 USA ; *Imprints:* South Dakota State Historical Society Press (S Dak St Hist Soc Pr)
E-mail: sdshspress@state.sd.us
Web site: http://www.sdshspress.com.

South Dakota State Historical Society Pr. *Imprint of* **South Dakota State Historical Society**

South Florida Art Ctr., Inc., *(0-9719492)* 924 Lincoln Rd., Suite 205, Miami Beach, FL 33139-2609 USA
Web site: http://www.artcentersf.org.

South Hadley Publishing, *(0-9761844)* Orders Addr.: P.O. Box 681, South Hadley, MA 01075 USA Tel 413-538-9658; Edit Addr.: 18 Maria Dr., South Hadley, MA 01075 USA
E-mail: price@southhadleypublishing.com
Web site: http://southhadleypublishing.com.

South Jetty Publishing, *(0-9669637)* 7243 Viar Ave., San Diego, CA 92120 USA Tel 619-286-8689; Fax: 619-280-3004
E-mail: sojetty@aol.com.

South River Pr., *(0-9770764)* P.O. Box 392, Indianola, IA 50125-5012 USA (SAN 256-6982) Tel 515-962-9375.

Southall, Twyla, *(0-9765501)* 5837 Karric Sq. Dr., Dublin, OH 43016 USA
E-mail: twyla@tsouthall.com
Web site: http://www.tsouthall.com.

Southeastern Guide Dogs, Inc., *(0-9672071)* 4210 77th St., E., Palmetto, FL 34221 USA Tel 941-729-5665; Fax: 941-729-6646; Toll Free: 800-944-3647
E-mail: webmaster@guidedogs.org
Web site: http://www.guidedogs.org.

Southern Girl Media, *(0-9744423)* P.O. Box 1764, Oceanside, CA 92051 USA Tel 760-535-2640
Web site: http://www.masonweaver.com
Dist(s): **Executive Bks.**

Southern Heritage Pr., Inc., *(0-941072)* P.O. Box 10937, Saint Petersburg, FL 33733 USA (SAN 217-3875) Tel 813-823-1938; Fax: 813-821-2379; Toll Free: 800-282-2823
E-mail: byronkennedy@hotmail.com
Web site: http://www.southernheritagepress.com
Dist(s): **Southern Bk. Service.**

†Southern Illinois Univ. Pr., *(0-8093)* Div. of Southern Illinois Univ., Orders Addr.: P.O. Box 3697, Carbondale, IL 62902-3697 USA (SAN 203-3623) Tel 618-453-6610; Fax: 618-453-1221; Toll Free: 800-346-2680; Edit Addr.: 1915 University Press Dr., Carbondale, IL 62901 USA Toll Free Fax: 800-346-2681
E-mail: angmoore@siu.edu
Web site: http://www.siu.edu/~siupress
Dist(s): **Chicago Distribution Ctr.**; *CIP.*

†Southern Methodist Univ. Pr., *(0-87074)* Orders Addr.: c/o Texas A&M Univ. Pr., 4354 TAMU, College Sta., TX 77843-4354 USA Toll Free Fax: 888-617-2421; Toll Free: 800-826-8911; Edit Addr.: P.O. Box 750415, Dallas, TX 75275-0415 USA (SAN 203-3615) Tel 214-768-1432; Fax: 214-768-1428
Web site: http://www.tamu.edu/upress
Dist(s): **Texas A&M Univ. Pr.**; *CIP.*

Southern Pub., *(1-929228)* 19 Woodland Sq., Petal, MS 39465 USA Tel 601-544-7740
E-mail: DavidMyra@aol.com.

Southern Washington Pr., *(0-9724172)* 425 NE Fourth Ave., Camas, WA 98607 USA Tel 360-834-2141; Fax: 360-834-3423; Toll Free: 800-765-1343.

Southfarm Pr., *(0-913337)* Div. of Haan Graphic Publishing Services, Ltd., P.O. Box 1296, Middletown, CT 06457 USA (SAN 283-4146) Tel 860-346-8798
E-mail: southfar@ix.netcom.com
Web site: http://www.war-books.com; http://www.wandahaan.com.

Southland Specialty Publications Companies *See* **OPA Publishing**

Southpaw Books LLC, *(0-9777720)* Southpaw Books LLC, Maplewood, NJ 07040 USA (SAN 850-1017) Tel 973-313-0843; Fax: 973-313-0843
E-mail: info@southpawbooks.com
Web site: http://southpawbooks.com.

Southpaw Publishing, *(0-9718539)* 1327 Mitchell Rd., NW, Suite 200, Cullman, AL 35055 USA Tel 256-734-0140 Do not confuse with Southpaw Publishing, San Marcos, CA
E-mail: pattivalin@hotmail.com.

Southport Historical Society, Inc., *(1-892444)* P.O. Box 10014, Southport, NC 28461-0014 USA Tel 910-457-6940
E-mail: Furstenau@earthlink.net.

Southwest guns & stuff, *(0-9747407)* 4212 Lanshire Ct., Grand Prairie, TX 75052-3164 USA.

Southwest Legal Services, *(0-9644908)* Div. of Charlynn Publishing Co., Inc., Orders Addr.: P.O. Box 57091, Tucson, AZ 85732 USA Tel 520-795-1414; Edit Addr.: 4152 E. Fifth St., Tucson, AZ 85711 USA
E-mail: larry@southwestlegalservices.com
Web site: http://www.southwestlegalservices.com
Dist(s): **Baker & Taylor Bks.**
Charlynn Publishing Co., Inc.

Southwest Parks & Monuments Association *See* **Western National Parks Assn.**

SouthWest Pubns., *(1-934345)* Div. of NF Publishing, P.O. Box 782, Kingsport, TN 37662 USA Tel 423-765-1416; Fax: 800-807-9203; Toll Free Fax: 800-807-9203; Toll Free: 800-807-9203
Web site: http://www.southwestpublications.net.

South-Western *See* **Thomson South-Western**

Souvenir Pr. Ltd. (GBR) *(0-285)* *Dist. by* **IPG Chicago.**

Sovereign Grace Pubs., Inc., *(1-878442; 1-58960)* 4427 E. 200 N., Lafayette, IN 47905 USA (SAN 299-6847) Tel 765-429-4122; Fax: 765-429-4142; Toll Free: 800-447-9142 Do not confuse with Sovereign Grace Pubns., Lexington, KY
E-mail: jaygreenxx@iquest.net
Web site: http://www.sovgracepub.com.

Sovereign Pr., *(1-931567)* 431 Broad St., Lake Geneva, WI 53147 USA Fax: 262-249-0769 Do not confuse with Sovereign Pr. in Rochester, WA
E-mail: dperrin@sovstone.com
Web site: http://www.sovstone.com
Dist(s): **PSI (Publisher Services, Inc.).**

Sowash, Rick Publishing Co., *(0-9762412)* 338 Milton St. # 1, Cincinnati, OH 45202-0971 USA Toll Free: 888-255-2764
E-mail: rick@sowash.com
Web site: http://www.sowash.com.

SP Family Productions, LLC, *(0-9773134)* 5 Knute Drive, Andover, NJ 07821-3912 USA Tel 973-479-6111
E-mail: seancanning@hotmail.com
Web site: http://www.seancanning.com.

Spallone, Joseph *See* **CTM Publishing**

Spanish Hse. Distributors, 1360 NW 88th Ave., Miami, FL 33172-3093 USA (SAN 169-1171) Tel 305-592-6136; Fax: 305-592-0087; Toll Free: 800-767-7726.

Spanish Language Texts, Inc., *(0-9710710)* Orders Addr.: P.O. Box 1088, New York, NY 10040 USA; Edit Addr.: 19 Seaman Ave. 2M, New York, NY 10034 USA
Web site: http://www.spanishlanguagetexts.com
Dist(s): **Lectorum Pubns., Inc.**

Spann Productions, *(0-9772209)* P.O. Box 10412, Bakersfield, CA 93389 USA Tel 661-832-2135 (phone/fax)
E-mail: spannlake@aol.com.

SpanPr., Inc., *(1-58045; 1-887578)* 5722 S. Flamingo Rd., Suite 277, Cooper City, FL 33330 USA Tel 305-592-7913; Fax: 305-477-5632; Toll Free: 800-585-8384
Dist(s): **Continental Bk. Co., Inc.**
Lectorum Pubns., Inc.

Spark Publishing Group, *(1-58663)* Div. of Spark Notes, LLC, 120 5th Ave., 8th Flr., New York, NY 10011 USA Tel 212-414-6535; Fax: 212-414-6018
Web site: http://www.soarknotes.com
Dist(s): **Sterling Publishing Co., Inc.**

Sparkle Presentations, *(1-880878)* P.O. Box 2373, La Mesa, CA 91943-2373 USA (SAN 253-7672) Tel 858-569-6555; Fax: 858-569-5924; Toll Free: 800-932-0973
E-mail: sheryl@sparklepresentations.com
Web site: http://www.sparklepresentations.com; http://www.SherylRoush.com.

Sparkledoll Productions, *(0-9747832)* P.O. Box 56173, Virginia Beach, VA 23456 USA Tel 757-718-3095
E-mail: books@sparkledoll.com
Web site: http://www.sparkledoll.com/publishing
Dist(s): **Baker & Taylor Bks.**

Sparklesoup Studios, Inc., *(0-9714776; 1-932379; 1-59748)* P.O. Box 142003, Irving, TX 75014 USA
E-mail: sparklesoup@aol.com
Web site: http://www.sparklesoup.com; http://www.teenagetart.com; http://www.giftedgirls.net; http://www.discountdonna.com; http://www.queenbseries.com; http://www.kailingow.com
Dist(s): **Baker & Taylor Bks.**
BookSurge, LLC
Lightning Source, Inc.
PageFree Publishing, Inc.

Sparkling Pr., *(0-9774855)* 137 E. Curtice St., St. Paul, MN 55107 USA Tel 651-227-5248.

Sparks Fly, *(0-9789445)* 555 Washington Ave., Suite 1K, Brooklyn, NY 11238-2742 USA Tel 866-556-2432; Fax: 866-556-2432; Toll Free Fax: 866-556-2432; Toll Free: 866-556-2432
E-mail: info@can-i-have-some-money.com
Web site: http://www.can-i-have-some-money.com.

Sparrow, L.T. Publishing, *(0-9670171)* Orders Addr.: P.O. Box 2675, Arnold, CA 95223 USA Tel 209-795-6311; Edit Addr.: 936 Smokehouse Rd., La Conner, WA 98223 USA
E-mail: ltsparrow@earthlink.net.

Sparrow Media Group, Inc., *(0-9719304; 0-9786018)* P.O. Box 44272, Eden Prairie, MN 55344-4272 USA Tel 952-953-9166
Web site: http://www.sparrowmediagroup.com.

Sparrowgrass Chapbooks, *(1-930695)* Orders Addr.: P.O. Box 193CB, Sisterville, WV 26175-0193 USA Tel 304-652-1920; Edit Addr.: 609 Main St., Sisterville, WV 26175-0193 USA.

Sparrowgrass Poetry Forum, Inc., *(0-923242; 1-930695)* Orders Addr.: P.O. Box 193, Sistersville, WV 26175 USA (SAN 251-7302) Tel 304-652-1449; Fax: 304-652-1148; Toll Free: 800-685-0848; Edit Addr.: P.O. Box 162, Sistersville, WV 26175-0162 USA (SAN 251-7310)
E-mail: SPFpoetry@aol.com
Web site: http://www.tinplace.com/sparrow.

SPCK Publishing (GBR) *(0-281; 0-7459; 0-85969; 1-902694)* *Dist. by* **Pilgrim OH.**

Speak-Easy Publishing, LLC, *(0-9714433; 0-9754977)* Orders Addr.: P.O. Box 11377, Takoma Park, MD 20913 USA Tel 202-723-1317
E-mail: jgduarte@speakeasypublishing.com; info@speakeasypublishing.com
Web site: http://www.speakeasypublishing.com
Dist(s): **Lyrical Liquor Productions.**

Special Child Pubns., *(0-87562)* 5208 33rd Ave., W., Everett, WA 98203-1349 USA (SAN 203-2317).

Special Edition Studios, Inc., *(0-9759013)* P.O. Box 7606, Sebring, FL 33872 USA
Web site: http://www.sestudios.com.

Special Editions — Customized Biographies *Imprint of* **Slavens Enterprises, LLC.**

Spedial Editions Pr., *(1-893467)* Orders Addr.: 65 Cheyenne Trl., Sparta, NJ 07871-2925 USA Tel 973-726-5126; Fax: 973-726-6146
E-mail: beth@specialeditionspress.com.

Special Ideas, *(1-888547)* P.O. Box 9, Heltonville, IN 47436 USA Tel 812-834-5691 (phone/fax); Toll Free: 800-326-1197
E-mail: karen@special-ideas.com.

Special Kids Company, Incorporated *See* **Anythings Possible, Inc.**

Special Me!, *(0-9666964)* 7474-200 Creedmoor Rd., Raleigh, NC 27613-1665 USA Tel 919-743-6233.

Special Pubns., Inc., *(0-9636339; 1-892937)* Orders Addr.: P.O. Box 4649, Ocala, FL 34478 USA Tel 352-622-2995; Fax: 352-622-9200; Edit Addr.: 743 SE Fort King St., Ocala, FL 34471 USA Tel 904-622-2995
E-mail: todaymag@earthlink.net
Web site: http://www.ocalamagazine.net.

Special Reads for Special Needs, *(0-9702698; 0-9795922)* 12025 Merganser Dr., Cincinnati, OH 45246-1542 USA Tel 513-541-7617; Fax: 513-541-2543; Toll Free: 866-553-2042
E-mail: specialreads@aol.com
Web site: http://www.specialreads.com.

Specialized Quality Pubns., *(0-9634906; 0-9789582)* 921 11th St., S., Wisconsin Rapids, WI 54494 USA (SAN 299-299X) Tel 715-423-7476 ; *Imprints:* SQP (SQP)
Web site: http://www.specializedqualitypublications.com/index.htm.

Specialty Educational Pubs., *(0-9718488)* P.O. Box 161, New Oxford, PA 17350 USA
E-mail: specialtypublishers@hotmail.com.

Specialty Pr., Inc., *(0-9621629; 1-886941)* 300 NW 70th Ave., Suite 102, Plantation, FL 33317 USA (SAN 251-6977) Tel 954-792-8100; Fax: 954-792-8545; Toll Free: 800-233-9273 Do not confuse with Specialty Pr., Inc., in Ocean, NJ
E-mail: sales@addwarehouse.com
Web site: http://www.addwarehouse.com
Dist(s): **Baker & Taylor Bks.**
Independent Pubs. Group.

Specialty Publishing Co., *(0-9755199)* 135 E. Saint Charles Rd., Caol Stream, IL 60188 USA (SAN 256-0569) Tel 630-933-0844; Fax: 630-933-0845
Web site: http://www.specialtypub.com.

Spectacle Films, Inc., *(0-9767771)* 163 3rd Ave., Suite 200, New York, NY 10003 USA Tel 212-807-0290
E-mail: jim@monk.com
Web site: http://www.Rumpleville.com; http://www.SpectacleFilms.com.

Spectra *Imprint of* **Bantam Bks.**

Spectrum *Imprint of* **School Specialty Publishing**

Spectrum Bks., Ltd. (NGA) *(978-029; 978-2-265)* *Dist. by* **Mich St U Pr.**

Spectrum Films Inc., *(0-9760906)* 4319 Salisbury Rd., Suite 4, Jacksonville, FL 32216 USA
Web site: http://www.spectrumfilms.tv.

Speech Bin, Inc., The, *(0-937857)* 1965 25th Ave., Vero Beach, FL 32960 USA (SAN 630-1657) Tel 772-770-0007; Fax: 772-770-0006
E-mail: info@speechbin.com
Web site: http://www.speechbin.com.

Speech Kids Texas Pr., *(1-933319)* 3802 Beaconsdale Dr., Austin, TX 78727-2951 USA (SAN 256-4122)
E-mail: info@speechkidstexaspress.com
Web site: http://www.speechkidstexaspress.com.

Speech Place Publishing, The, *(0-9794102)* 1810-A York Rd., No. 432, Lutherville, MD 21093 USA (SAN 853-3679) Tel 410-517-9026
E-mail: cs@thespeechplace.com
Web site: http://www.thespeechplace.com.

Speech Publishing Hse., *(0-9770483)* 1115 Cordova St., Suite 318, Pasadena, CA 91106-3013 USA Tel 626-372-1195
E-mail: jonandspeech@prodigy.net
Web site: http://www.jasonpost.net.

Speedwitch Media, *(0-9749508)* 645 Tanner Marsh Rd., Guilford, CT 06437-2106 USA
Web site: http://www.speedwitch.com.

Speer Publishing, *(0-9711241)* P.O. Box 6256, Bloomington, IN 47407-6256 USA Tel 812-876-6256; Toll Free: 800-604-4277
E-mail: dspeer@indiana.edu.

†Speller, Robert & Sons, Pubs., Inc., *(0-8315)* Orders Addr.: P.O. Box 411, New York, NY 10159 USA (SAN 203-2295) Tel 212-473-0333; P.O. Box 461, New York, NY 10108 (SAN 203-2309); *CIP.*

Spence, Stephen Mark, *(0-9705324)* 211 Moore Ave., Buffalo, NY 14223 USA Tel 716-836-5178
E-mail: spence@buffalo.edu
Web site: http://www.FollowTheStag.com.

Spencer, Russell & Kathlynn, *(0-9664055)* Orders Addr.: 2484 Dewberry Ln., Oxnard, CA 93030 USA Tel 805-981-2820
E-mail: RSpencer@windshieldadventures.com
Web site: http://www.windshieldadventures.com
Dist(s): **Gem Guides Bk. Co.**

Spencer's Mill Pr., *(0-9771666)* 7804 Fairview Rd., No. 210, Charlotte, NC 28226 USA (SAN 256-8225) Tel 615-792-6727 (phone/fax)
Web site: http://www.spencersmillpress.com
Dist(s): **Pathway Bk. Service.**

Spending Solutions Pr., *(0-9729732)* 4347 W. NW Hwy., Suite 120, PMB 283, Dallas, TX 75220-3864 USA
Web site: http://www.spendingsolutions.com.

Spica Bks., *(0-9728531)* 9742 N. 105th Dr., Sun City, AZ 85351 USA Tel 623-583-6764 (phone/fax)
E-mail: marilyn@dreamlady.com
Web site: http://www.dreamlady.com.

Spicka, Jana Incorporated *See* **Tree of Life Pr.**

Spiegel, Allen Fine Arts, *(0-9642069; 1-934298)* 221 Lobos Ave., Pacific Grove, CA 93950 USA Tel 831-372-4672
E-mail: asfa@redshift.com
Web site: http://www.asfa.biz.

Spiegel Publishing Co., *(0-9673977)* 12815 Coral Tree Pl., Los Angeles, CA 90066 USA Tel 310-301-0721; Fax: 310-823-0673
E-mail: april01@earthlink.net.

Spike Enterprises, *(0-9665995)* 20725 Shaker Blvd., Shaker Heights, OH 44122 USA Tel 216-371-8234; Fax: 216-371-8276
E-mail: susiecargile@aol.com.

Spilled Candy Pubns., *(1-892718)* Orders Addr.: 32 Southwind Ct., Niceville, FL 32578 USA Tel 850-897-4644
E-mail: orders@spilledcandy.com; staff@spilledcandy.com
Web site: http://www.spilledcandy.com
Dist(s): **New Leaf Distributing Co., Inc.**

Spilled Milk, *(0-9709707)* P.O. Box 260258, Highlands Ranch, CO 80163-0258 USA
E-mail: psmart@spilledmilk.com
Web site: http://www.spilledmilk.com.

Spineless Bks., *(0-9724244)* P.O. Box 515, Urbana, IL 61803 USA Tel 217-337-6237; Fax: 217-344-0059
E-mail: william@spinelessbooks.com
Web site: http://www.spinelessbooks.com.

Spinelli, Patti, *(0-9742328)* 21 Fairway Dr., Dover, NH 03820 USA Tel 603-749-2293
E-mail: pasbug1010@aol.com.

Spinifex Pr. (AUS) *(1-875559; 1-876756)* *Dist. by* **IPG Chicago.**

Spinner Pubns., Inc., *(0-932027)* 164 William St., New Bedford, MA 02740-6022 USA (SAN 686-0826) Tel 508-994-4564; Fax: 508-994-6925; Toll Free: 800-292-6062
E-mail: spinner@spinnerpub.com
Web site: http://www.spinnerpub.com.

SpinSmart Software, *(0-9743434)* Orders Addr.: 4717 S. Hydraulic, Wichita, KS 67216 USA
E-mail: support@spinsmart.com
Web site: http://www.spinsmart.com.

Spiral Publishing, Inc., *(0-9755403; 0-9765687)* Orders Addr.: P.O. Box 616826, Orlando, FL 32861 USA
E-mail: starr@spiralpublishinginc.com
Web site: http://www.spiralpublishinginc.com.

Spire *Imprint of* **Revell**

Spirit Arm Publishing, *(0-9759717)* 2225 E. Main St., C-13, Murfreesboro, TN 37130 USA Tel 615-895-4116
E-mail: chadblanchard@essenceandlonging.com
Web site: http://www.essenceandlonging.com.

Spirit Bear, *(1-889401)* Div. of Spirit Bear Productions, 727-15th Ave. S.E., No. 9, Minneapolis, MN 55414 USA Tel 612-624-5251
E-mail: bluapache@yahoo.com; mahto002@umn.edu.

Spirit Pr. *Imprint of* **Dalmatian Pr.**

Spirit Publishing LLC, *(0-9770967)* 819 Marcy Ave., Brooklyn, NY 11216 USA (SAN 256-7636) Tel 718-230-5605.

Spirited Presentations, *(0-9790017)* 3384 EAgle Creek Ct. NE, Grand Rapids, MI 49525 USA
E-mail: Kathey@spiritedpresentations.com
Web site: http://Spiritedpresentations.com.

Spirited Publishing, LLC, *(0-9768513)* Orders Addr.: P.O. Box 1796, Appleton, WI 54912-1796 USA Tel 920-419-3340; Fax: 920-968-4571
E-mail: kris@spiritedpublishing.com
Web site: http://www.spiritedpublishing.com
Dist(s): **Quality Bks., Inc.**

Spiritis Publishing, *(0-9666623)* Orders Addr.: P.O. Box 239, Sedona, AZ 86339 USA Tel 928-204-1665; Fax: 928-204-1836; Toll Free: 888-453-6324; Edit Addr.: 21 Pine Tree Ln., Sedona, AZ 86336 USA Tel 928-204-1665 Do not confuse with Spiritis Publishing in Southfield, MI
E-mail: care@lovewithoutend.com; star@lovewithoutend.com
Web site: http://www.lovewithoutend.com
Dist(s): **Baker & Taylor Bks.**
New Leaf Pr., Inc.

Spiritpoint Press *See* **Bitty Book Pr.**

Spiritual Hse. Pr., The, *(0-9656847)* 24 Old Milford Rd., Brookline, NH 03033 USA Tel 603-673-4845
E-mail: blueskies24@charter.net
Web site: http://www.spiritual-house.com.

Spit & A Half *See* **Chiappetta, Joe**

Spitwad Studios, *(0-9714445)* 2410 Parkview Cir., Conway, AR 72034 USA.

Spizzirri Pr., Inc., *(0-86545)* P.O. Box 9397, Rapid City, SD 57709 USA (SAN 215-2851) Tel 605-348-2749; Fax: 605-348-6251 (orders); Toll Free: 800-322-9819; 800-325-9819
E-mail: spizzpub@aol.com
Web site: http://www.spizzirri.com.

Splendors Publishing, *(0-9717228)* P.O. Box 1155, Soquel, CA 95073 USA Fax: 831-464-1854
E-mail: lalo@lalofiorelli.com
Web site: http://www.lalofiorelli.com.

Splish Splash Pubns., *(0-9656352)* 1100 Alameda Dr., Tallahassee, FL 32311-9580 USA Tel 904-878-4073
E-mail: ssplash@talbiz.com; splishsplash@talbiz.com
Web site: http://www.talbiz.com/splishsplash.

Split Level of the Blessed Suburbs Publishing, *(0-9761515)* 56 Arbor St., Hartford, CT 06106-1201 USA Tel 860-586-8448 (phone/fax)
Web site: http://www.tedpaulsen.com.

Spoken Arts, Inc., *(0-8045)* 195 S. White Rock Rd., Holmes, NY 12531-5406 USA (SAN 205-079X) Toll Free: 800-326-4090
Web site: http://www.spokenartsmedia.com/Home.htm
Dist(s): **Follett Media Distribution**
Lectorum Pubns., Inc.
Weston Woods Studios, Inc.

Spoken Word, The, *(0-9637644)* 1031 Michigan Ave. NE, No. 205, Washington, DC 20017 USA Tel 202-832-2368 Do not confuse with Spoken Word, The, Arlington , TX.

SpokenVizions Entertainment Group, LLC, *(0-9773834)* P.O. Box 373, Florissant, MO 63032 USA Tel 314-517-8764
E-mail: info@spokenvizions.com
Web site: http://www.spokenvizions.com.

Spokesman Bks. (GBR) *(0-85124; 0-902917; 0-9500300)* *Dist. by* **Coronet Bks.**

Spon Pr. *Imprint of* **Routledge**

Spoon Publishing Hse., *(0-615)* Div. of A Corpus Polymedia Monolith, 440 E. Broadway, Executive Suite 51, Salt Lake City, UT 84111-2651 USA
E-mail: spoonpublishing@corpuspolymedia.com
Web site: http://www.corpuspolymedia.com/spoonpublishing/; http://www.spoonpublishing.com.

Spoonbender Bks., *(0-9725750)* Div. of Holahan, Inc., 419 N. Larchmont Blvd., No. 4, Los Angeles, CA 90004 USA (SAN 254-9123) Tel 323-933-0253 (phone/fax)
E-mail: jgrist@mac.com; publisher@spoonbenderbooks.com
Web site: http://www.spoonbenderbooks.com
Dist(s): **Baker & Taylor Bks.**
Follett Library Resources
Quality Bks., Inc.
SCB Distributors.

Spooners Publishing, *(0-9766179)* 98 Onteora Ct., Shokan, NY 12481-5610 USA Tel 845-657-8737
E-mail: ecurtis@hvc.rr.com.

Sport Logbooks, *(0-9754827)* 6009 Camelot Ct., Midland, MI 48640 USA Fax: 989-835-3766; Toll Free: 888-283-3766
E-mail: info@sportlogbooks.com
Web site: http://www.sportlogbooks.com.

Sport Source, Inc., The, *(0-9631148; 1-893588)* 1845 Summit Ave., Suite 402, Plano, TX 75074 USA Tel 972-509-5707; Fax: 972-516-1754; Toll Free: 800-862-3092 Do not confuse with Sport Source, Inc., Seattle, WA
E-mail: sports@thesportsource.com
Web site: http://www.thesportsource.com
Dist(s): **Baker & Taylor Bks.**

Sport Story Publishing, *(0-9702216)* 740 Lakeview Dr., Palm Harbor, FL 34683 USA Fax: 727-447-3587
E-mail: thoover@tampabay.rr.com.

Sport Workbooks, *(0-9787458)* P.O. Box 1623, Pacifica, CA 94044 USA (SAN 851-5093) Tel 650-270-3200
E-mail: baseballmath@hotmail.com.

Sport Your Stuff Corp., *(1-931746)* 5025 Longbrook Rd., Winston Salem, NC 27105 USA.

SportAmerica, *(1-879498)* P.O. Box 95030, South Jordan, UT 84095 USA Tel 801-253-3360; Fax: 801-253-3361; Toll Free: 800-467-7885
Web site: http://www.sportamerica.com.

Sporting News Publishing Co., *(0-89204)* 14500 S. Outer 40. Ste. 300, Chesterfield, MO 63017-5781 USA (SAN 699-5616)
Web site: http://www.sportingnews.com/books
Dist(s): **Andrews McMeel Publishing**
Simon & Schuster, Inc.

Sports Illustrated For Kids, *(0-316; 0-553; 1-886749; 1-930623)* Div. of Time, Inc., 135 W. 50th St. ., New York, NY 10020-1393 USA Tel 212-522-1212; Fax: 212-522-0926
E-mail: joe_nunziata@sikids.com
Web site: http://www.sikids.com.

Sports In Mind, *(0-9745066; 0-9765074)* 3603 Palm Harbor Blvd., Unit C, Palm Harbor, FL 34683 USA Fax: 727-942-3339
Web site: http://www.ravesystems.com.

Sports Marketing International, Inc., *(0-9743082)* 27 E. Housatonic St., Pittsfield, MA 01201-4121 USA Tel 413-499-1733; Fax: 413-499-3820; Toll Free: 800-320-1733 ; *Imprints:* Moscow Ballet (Moscow Ballet)
E-mail: smi@nutcracker.com
Web site: http://www.nutcracker.com.

Sports Media Group *Imprint of* **Ann Arbor Media Group, LLC**

Sports On The Edge, LLC, *(0-9676408)* P.O. Box 931, Mays Landing, NJ 08330 USA Tel 609-576-0549; Fax: 240-384-1942
E-mail: jason@sportsontheedge.com
Web site: http://www.sportsontheedge.com.

Sports Pubns., Inc., *(0-9647782)* 90 Bell Rock Plz. Ste. 200, Sedona, AZ 86351-9040 USA Toll Free: 800-345-7946; 2710 W. Hwy. 89A, Suites D & E, Sedona, AZ 86336
E-mail: swimworld@aol.com.

Sports Publishing, LLC, *(1-57167; 1-58261; 1-58382; 1-59670)* 804 N. Neil St., Champaign, IL 61820 USA Tel 217-363-2072; Fax: 217-353-2073; Toll Free: 877-424-2665 Do not confuse with Sports Publishing, Champaign, IL
E-mail: info@sportspublishingllc.com
Web site: http://www.sportspublishingllc.com
Dist(s): **Ingram Pub. Services**
MBI Publishing Co. LLC.

Sports Reference Publishing *See* **Sport Source, Inc., The**

Sports Touch *See* **Sports Touch/Kate Montgomery**

Sports Touch/Kate Montgomery, *(1-878069)* 1625 E. Jackson Blvd., Elkhart, IN 46516 USA
E-mail: orders@sportstouch.com; info@sportstouch.com
Web site: http://www.sportstouch.com.

SportsKid, *(0-9705115)* 4607 White Blossom Blvd., Mason, OH 45040 USA Tel 513-235-1806; Fax: 513-459-9506
E-mail: pzeltwanger@cinci.rr.com
Web site: http://www.sportskid.net.

Sportsman's Connection, *(1-885010)* Div. of Sportsman's Marketing, Inc., Orders Addr.: P.O. Box 852, Lake Elmo, MN 55042 USA Tel 800-264-0474; Fax: 651-773-3320; Toll Free: 800-777-7461; Edit Addr.: 1423 N. Eighth St., Superior, WI 54880 USA
E-mail: info@sportsmansconnection.com
Web site: http://www.sportsmansconnection.com
Dist(s): **Partners Bk. Distributing, Inc.**

Spotlight, *(1-59961)* Div. of ABDO Publishing Group, Orders Addr.: P.O. Box 398166, Edina, MN 55439-8166 USA Fax: 952-831-1632; Toll Free: 877-877-5939; Edit Addr.: 8000 W. 78th St., Suite 310, Edina, MN 55439 USA ; *Imprints:* ABDO & Daughters (ABDO & Dghtrs)
E-mail: info@abdopublishing.com
Web site: http://www.abdopublishing.com
Dist(s): **ABDO Publishing Co.**

Spotlight Books *See* **Hannacroix Creek Bks., Inc.**

Spotlight News Publications *See* **Autumn Hse. Publishing**

Spreeda Publishing, *(0-9748979)* Div. of SPREEDA, 15941 W. 65th St., No. 165, Shawnee, KS 66217 USA Do not confuse with Maple Leaf Publishing in Minneapolis, MN
E-mail: karen@spreeda.com
Web site: http://www.spreeda.com.

Spriitelee Enterprises, *(0-9773460)* P.O. Box 207, Westwood, MA 02090 USA.

Spring Arbor Distributors, Inc., Subs. of Ingram Industries Inc., 4271 Edison Ave., Chino, CA 91710 USA; 7315 Innovation Blvd., Fort Wayne, IN 46818-1371; Edit Addr.: 1 Ingram Blvd., La Vergne, TN 37086-1976 USA Fax: 615-213-5192; Toll Free: 800-395-4340; 800-395-7234 (customer service)
E-mail: orders@springarbor.com.

Spring Creek Bk. Co., *(1-932898)* P.O. Box 50355, Provo, UT 84606-0355 USA Tel 801-375-4442 Toll Free: 877-375-4442
Web site: http://www.springcreekbooks.com
Dist(s): **Midpoint Trade Bks., Inc.**

Spring Ducks Bks., LLC, *(0-9761076)* Orders Addr.: P.O. Box 44847, Madison, WI 53744-4847 USA Toll Free: 800-342-4404; Edit Addr.: 222 Carillon Dr., Madison, WI 53705 USA
E-mail: kathy@springducks.com
Web site: http://www.springducks.com
Dist(s): **Greenleaf Book Group Pr.**

Spring Hollow Bks., LLC, *(0-9665389)* P.O. Box 115, Cave Spring, GA 30124-0115 USA Tel 706-235-5113; Fax: 706-235-0742 Do not confuse with Spring Hollow Bks., Richfield, MN
E-mail: jbcjmc@aol.com.

Spring Hse. Bks., *(1-892570)* Orders Addr.: P.O. Box 129, Wadmalaw Island, SC 29487 USA Tel 843-559-9307; Fax: 843-559-4759; Toll Free: 877-559-4759; Edit Addr.: 6697 Bears Bluff Rd., Wadmalaw Island, SC 29487 USA
E-mail: springhouse@charleston.net.

Spring Tree Pr., *(0-9785007)* P.O. Box 461, Atlantic Highlands, NJ 07716 USA (SAN 850-8429) Tel 732-872-8002; Fax: 732-872-6967
E-mail: info@janinekimmel.com
Web site: http://janinekimmel.com.

†Springer, *(0-387; 0-8176; 3-211; 3-540; 3-7908; 4-431; 1-85233; 1-84628)* Subs. of Springer-Verlag GmbH & Co. KG, Orders Addr.: P.O. Box 2485, Secaucus, NJ 07096-2485 USA (SAN 203-2228) Tel 201-348-4033; Fax: 201-348-4505; Toll Free: 800-777-4643; Edit Addr.: 233 Spring St., New York, NY 10013 USA Tel 212-460-1500; Fax: 212-473-6272 ; *Imprints:* Copernicus (Copernicus) Thomson Delmar Learning Distributes Blanchard & Loeb Nursing Videos Only
E-mail: Slu@Springer-ny.com
Web site: http://www.springeronline.com
Dist(s): **NetLibrary, Inc.**; *CIP.*

Springer-Verlag New York, Incorporated *See* **Springer**

Sprite Pr., *(0-9706654; 0-9764295)* 5400 Mountville Rd., Glouster, OH 45732-9508 USA Tel 740-767-2470
E-mail: spritepress@aol.com
Web site: members.aol.com/spritepress.

SpritSBo, *(0-9643029)* 125 N. Seventh St., McLoud, OK 74851 USA Tel 405-964-5169
E-mail: glendakuhn@myexcel.com.

Sproing Books *See* **Gripper Products**

Sprout Of Jessie Pubns., *(0-9719888)* P.O. Box 603, Germantown, MD 20875-0603 USA Tel 301-938-6046; Fax: 202-645-8693
E-mail: sproutofjessie@aol.com
Web site: http://www.sproutofjessie.com.

Spruce Gulch Pr., *(0-9625714)* Orders Addr.: P.O. Box 4347, Rome, NY 13442-4347 USA (SAN 297-3014) Tel 315-337-1968
E-mail: SprGulch@aol.com
Dist(s): **North Country Bks., Inc.**

Spuyten Duyvil, *(1-881471; 0-9720662; 1-933132)* Orders Addr.: P.O. Box 1852, New York, NY 10025 USA (SAN 237-9481) Toll Free: 800-886-5304 (phone/fax); Edit Addr.: 42 St. John's Pl., Garden, Brooklyn, NY 11217 USA
E-mail: editors@spuytenduyvil.net
Web site: http://www.spuytenduyvil.net
Dist(s): **SPD-Small Pr. Distribution.**

SPYMYTHS, Inc., *(0-9708834)* 15439 Fallow Ridge Dr., San Antonio, TX 78248-1822 USA (SAN 253-7273) Tel 210-408-0396
E-mail: txburch@aol.com.

SQP *Imprint of* **Specialized Quality Pubns.**

Square Circle Pr., LLC *See* **Square Circle Pr. LLC**

Square Circle Pr. LLC, *(0-9789066)* 137 Ketcham Rd., Voorheesville, NY 12186 USA (SAN 851-9145) Tel 518-432-6657 Do not confuse with Square Circle Press in Corte Madera, CA
E-mail: bookinfo@squarecirclepress.com
Web site: http://www.squarecirclepress.com
Dist(s): **BCH Fulfillment & Distribution.**

Square Deal Pr., *(0-9754941)* 368 S. McCaslin Blvd., Box 206, Louisville, CO 80027 USA.

Square Fish, 175 Fifth Ave., New York, NY 10010 USA Tel 646-307-5770
E-mail: squarefish.market@hbpub.com
Web site: http://www.squarefishbooks.com
Dist(s): **Macmillan.**

Square Halo Bks., *(0-9658798; 0-9785097)* Orders Addr.: P.O. Box 18954, Baltimore, MD 21206 USA Tel 410-485-6227; Edit Addr.: 4310 Southern Ave., Baltimore, MD 21206 USA
E-mail: square_halo@yahoo.com; ned@squarehalobooks.com
Web site: http://www.squarehalobooks.com.

Square 1 Pubns., *(0-9619321)* 2721 N. Windsor Ave., Altadena, CA 91001 USA (SAN 243-8135) Tel 626-791-9403.

Square One Publishers, *(0-9664202; 0-7570; 0-9792746)* 115 Herricks Rd., Garden City Park, NY 11040 USA Tel 516-535-2010; Fax: 516-535-2014 ; *Imprints:* Vital Health Publishing (Vital Hlth)
E-mail: sq1info@aol.com
Web site: http://squareonepublishers.com
Dist(s): **Athena Productions, Inc.**

Squarey Head, Inc., *(0-9742003)* 6362 W. Cross Dr., Littleton, CO 80123 USA Tel 303-798-1877; Fax: 303-794-4639.

Squid Works, *(0-9755041)* P.O. Box 480463, Denver, CO 80248-0463 USA
Web site: http://www.squidworks.com.

SR Publishing Co., *(0-9773406)* 1159 N.Poinsettia Pl., No. 3, West Hollywood, CA 90046-5753 USA (SAN 257-3350)
E-mail: stvrox@sbcglobal.net
Web site: http://stevenrox.com.

SRA/McGraw-Hill, *(0-07; 0-383)* Div. of The McGraw-Hill Education Group, Orders Addr.: 220 E. Daniel Dale Rd., DeSoto, TX 75115-2490 USA Fax: 972-228-1982; Toll Free: 800-843-8855; Edit Addr.: 8787 Orion Pl., Columbus, OH 43240-4027 USA Tel 614-430-6600; Fax: 614-430-6621; Toll Free: 800-468-5850
E-mail: sra@mcgraw-hill.com
Web site: http://www.mcgraw-hill.com/education/sra.html
Dist(s): **Libros Sin Fronteras**
Weston Woods Studios, Inc.

Sri Ramakrishna Math (IND) *(81-7120; 81-86465; 81-7823) Dist. by* **Vedanta Pr.**

Sroda, George, *(0-9604486)* P.O. Box 97, Amherst Junction, WI 54407 USA (SAN 210-8607) Tel 715-824-3868; Fax: 715-824-5344.

SRT Publishing, *(0-9771248)* 530 Moon Clinton Rd., Moon Township, PA 15108 USA Tel 412-741-0581; Fax: 412-264-1103
E-mail: merch@silverringthing.com
Web site: http://www.silverringthing.com.

Ssorgsoft, LLC, *(0-9765240)* P.O. Box 771192, Orlando, FL 32877 USA.

St. Bernard Publishing, LLC, *(0-9741269)* P.O. Box 2218, Bay City, MI 48707-2218 USA Tel 989-892-1348 (phone/fax)
E-mail: bcgirl@charter.net
Web site: http://www.lifeongrannysfarm.com/.

St. Hope Academy, *(0-9759548)* Orders Addr.: P.O. Box 5447, Sacramento, CA 95817 USA Tel 916-649-7900; Fax: 916-452-7177; Edit Addr.: 3400 3rd Ave., Sacramento, CA 95817 USA
Web site: http://40acresartgallery.org.

St Kitts Pr., *(0-9661879; 1-931206)* Div. of SK Pubns., Orders Addr.: P.O. Box 8173, Wichita, KS 67208 USA Tel 316-685-3201; Fax: 316-685-6650; Toll Free: 888-705-4887; Edit Addr.: 4200 E. 24th, Wichita, KS 67220 USA Do not confuse with SK Pubns., Northfield, OH
E-mail: stkitts@skpub.com
Web site: http://www.stkittspress.com
Dist(s): **Baker & Taylor Bks.**
Book Wholesalers, Inc.
Brodart Co.
Coutts Library Service, Inc.
Emery-Pratt Co.
Follett Library Resources.

St. Martin's Griffin *Imprint of* **St. Martin's Pr.**

St. Martin's Minotaur *Imprint of* **St. Martin's Pr.**

St. Martin's Paperbacks *Imprint of* **St. Martin's Pr.**

†St. Martin's Pr., *(0-312; 0-8050; 0-940687; 0-9603648; 1-55927; 1-58063; 1-58238; 1-4299)* Div. of Holtzbrinck Pubs., Orders Addr.: 16365 James Madison Hwy., Gordonville, VA 22942 USA Tel 540-672-7600; Fax: 540-672-7540 (customer service); Toll Free Fax: 800-672-2054; Toll Free: 888-330-8477; Edit Addr.: 175 Fifth Ave., New York, NY 10010 USA (SAN 200-2132) Tel 212-674-5151 (Trade Div.); 212-726-0200 (College Div.); Fax: 212-674-3179 (Trade Div.); 212-686-9491 (College Div.); Toll Free: 800-221-7945 (Trade Div.); 800-470-4767 (College Div.) ; *Imprints:* Saint Martin's Griffin (St Martin Griffin); Saint Martin's Paperbacks (St Martins Paperbacks); Dunne, Thomas Books (Thomas Dunne); Saint Martin's Minotaur (Minotaur); Golden Books Adult Publishing Group (Golden Adult); Golden Guides from Saint Martin's Press (Gldn Guides); Priddy Books (Priddy); Renaissance Books (Rena Bks)
E-mail: webmaster@stmartins.com; enquiries@stmartins.com
Web site: http://www.stmartins.com; http://www.smpcollege.com
Dist(s): **Comag Marketing Group**
Ediciones Universal
Libros Sin Fronteras
Macmillan
Sony CONNECT, Inc.; *CIP.*

St Mary's Church, *(0-9763902)* 429 Central Ave., Sandusky, OH 44870 USA Tel 419-625-7465
Web site: http://www.stmarysandusky.org.

St. Michael's Abbey, *(0-9742298)* 19292 El Toro Rd., Silverado, CA 92676-9710 USA
E-mail: frnorbertw@yahoo.com
Web site: http://www.abbeynews.com.

St. Padraic Pr., *(0-9704155)* P.O. Box 43351, Cincinnati, OH 45243-0351 USA Fax: 513-985-9316
E-mail: mgray64632@aol.com
Web site: www.cathalliam.com.

St. Pauls *Imprint of* **Alba Hse.**

St Pauls Pubns. (AUS) *(0-909986; 0-949080; 1-875570; 1-876295; 1-921032) Dist. by* **Alba.**

St. Roux Pr., *(0-9718433)* 308 Montmartre St., Folsom, LA 70437 USA
E-mail: faucheux@msn.com.

Stabenfeldt Inc., *(1-933343)* 457 N. Main St., Suite 3C, Danbury, CT 06811 USA Tel 203-205-2332; Fax: 203-730-1631; Toll Free: 800-410-4145 ; *Imprints:* PONY (Pny)
E-mail: info@pony.us
Web site: http://www.pony.us.

Stacey International Pubs. (GBR) *(0-905743; 0-9503304; 1-900988; 0-9533300) Dist. by* **Interlink Pub.**

Stacey International Pubs. (GBR) *(0-905743; 0-9503304; 1-900988; 0-9533300) Dist. by* **David Brown.**

†Stackpole Bks., *(0-8117)* 5067 Ritter Rd., Mechanicsburg, PA 17055 USA (SAN 202-5396) Tel 717-796-0411; Fax: 717-796-0412; Toll Free: 800-732-3669
E-mail: pmoran@stackpolebooks.com
Web site: http://www.stackpolebooks.com; *CIP.*

Staff Development for Educators, *(0-9627389; 1-884548; 1-934026)* Div. of Highlights for Children, Orders Addr.: P.O. Box 577, Peterborough, NH 03458 USA Tel 603-924-9621; Fax: 603-924-6688; Toll Free Fax: 800-337-9929; Toll Free: 800-321-0401; Edit Addr.: 10 Sharon Rd., Peterborough, PA 03458 USA ; *Imprints:* Crystal Springs Books (Crystal Spgs)
E-mail: dfredericks@sde.com
Web site: http://www.sde.com; http://www.crystalsprings.com.

Stage Harbor Pr., *(0-9676082)* Orders Addr.: P.O. Box 460, Orleans, MA 02653 USA; Edit Addr.: 20 Salt Marsh Way, Eastham, MA 02642 USA Tel 508-945-9004 (phone/fax)
E-mail: SHP@thunderball.com
Web site: http://www.stageharbor.com.

Stage Within Your Mind, The, *(0-9633236)* 1932 Chemeketa St., NE, Salem, OR 97301 USA Tel 503-364-5825 ; *Imprints:* Wicklewood Books (Wicklewood Bks)
E-mail: dashney7@msn.com.

Stagecast Software, Inc., *(1-929721)* 580 College Ave., Palo Alto, CA 94306 USA Tel 650-354-0735; Fax: 650-354-0739; Toll Free: 888-782-4322
E-mail: info@stagecast.com
Web site: http://www.stagecast.com.

Stagecoach Publishing, *(0-9660053; 0-9747551)* 5360 Campcreek Loop, Roseville, CA 95747 USA Tel 916-771-8166 (phone/fax)
E-mail: stagecoach@surewest.net
Web site: http://stagecoachpublishing.com
Dist(s): **Booklines Hawaii, Ltd.**

Stages Learning Materials, *(0-9668008)* P.O. Box 27, Chico, CA 95927-0027 USA Tel 530-892-1112; Fax: 530-892-0281; Toll Free Fax: 888-735-7791; Toll Free: 888-801-8880
E-mail: angela@stageslearning.com
Web site: http://www.stageslearning.com.

Stagger Lee Bks., *(0-9791006)* Orders Addr.: P.o. Box 442, W. Thunderbird, Ste. 1, Peoria, AZ 85351 USA (SAN 852-4300)
E-mail: michael.lalumiere@gmail.com
Web site: http://staggerleebooks.com
Dist(s): **Partners/West.**

Stahl Pubns., *(0-9755174)* P.O. Box 201, Ashley, IN 46705-0201 USA.

Staige Productions, *(0-9641375)* 290 Orrin St., Winona, MN 55987-2083 USA Tel 507-452-3627.

Stairway Pubns., *(0-9740061)* P.O. Box 518, Huntington, NY 11743-0518 USA (SAN 255-3422) Fax: 631-351-2142
E-mail: publisher@stairwaypub.com
Web site: http://www.stairwaypub.com
Dist(s): **Quality Bks., Inc.**
STL Distribution North America.

Stairway Publishing, *(0-9761953)* 230 E Pedregosa St., Santa Barbara, CA 93101 USA (SAN 256-761X) Tel 805-451-5070; Fax: 805-962-1404; 1332 Anacapa St., Suite 200, Santa Barbara, CA 93101 Do not Confuse with Shoreline Publishing in Bayside, NY
E-mail: pumoff@seedmackall.com.

Stampley, C.D. Enterprises, Inc., *(0-915741; 1-58087)* Orders Addr.: P.O. Box 33172, Charlotte, NC 28233 USA (SAN 294-1325) Tel 704-333-6631; Fax: 704-336-6932; Edit Addr.: 1135 N. Tryon St., Charlotte, NC 28206 USA
E-mail: info@stampley.com; rick@stampley.com
Web site: http://www.stampley.com
Dist(s): **Giron Bks.**

Standard Pubns., Inc., *(0-9709788; 0-9722691; 1-59462; 1-60424)* P.O. Box 2226, Champaign, IL 61825 USA Tel 217-898-7825; Fax: 630-214-0564 ; *Imprints:* Book Jungle (Book Jungle)
E-mail: spi@standardpublications.com.

†Standard Publishing, *(0-7847; 0-87239; 0-87403; 0-933657; 1-58170)* 8805 Governors Hill Dr. Ste. 400, Cincinnati, OH 45249-3319 USA (SAN 110-5515) Toll Free Fax: 877-867-5751 (customer service); Toll Free: 800-543-1353 (customer service); 800-543-1301 ; *Imprints:* Bean Sprouts (Bean Sprouts) Do not confuse with Standard Publishing Corp., Boston, MA
E-mail: customerservice@standardpub.com; trolfes@standardpub.com; dlewis@standardpub.com
Web site: http://www.standardpub.com; *CIP.*

Standard Publishing Company *See* **Standard Publishing**

Standing For Christ, Inc., *(0-9754834)* P.O. Box 28468, Cleveland, OH 44128 USA Tel 216-299-4523
E-mail: kelvinsfc@yahoo.com
Web site: http://www.standingforchrist.org.

Stanek, Mary Beth, *(0-9747556)* 291 Lothrop Rd., Grosse Pointe, MI 48236 USA.

Stanford Center for Research in Disease Prevention (S C R D P) *See* **Stanford Prevention Research Ctr.**

Stanford Prevention Research Ctr., *(1-879552)* Div. of Stanford Univ. Schl. of Medicine, Hoover Pavilion, Rm. N 229 211 Quarry Rd., Stanford, CA 94305-5705 USA Tel 650-723-0003; Fax: 650-498-4828
E-mail: askhprc@med.stanford.edu
Web site: http://hprc.stanford.edu.

†Stanford Univ. Pr., *(0-8047)* Orders Addr.: Stanford University Press Chicago Distribution Center 11030 South Langley Ave., Chicago, IL 60628 USA Tel 773-702-7000; Toll Free Fax: 800-621-8471; Toll Free: 800-621-2736; Edit Addr.: 1450 Page Mill Rd., Palo Alto, CA 94304 USA (SAN 203-3526) Tel 650-723-9434; Fax: 650-725-3457
E-mail: custserv@press.uchicago.edu; info@sup.org
Web site: http://www.sup.org
Dist(s): **Chicago Distribution Ctr.**
Univ. of Hawaii Pr.; *CIP.*

Stanger, Robert *See* **Club Pro Products**

Stanley Bks., *(0-9707181)* 721 S. Weller Ave., Springfield, MO 65802 USA Tel 417-865-8234
E-mail: sasher@drury.edu.

Stanley, Donna Lacy, *(0-9766894)* 244 Sunset Dr., Waynesboro, VA 22980 USA Tel 540-949-5474
E-mail: dlstanle@yahoo.com.

Stansbury Publishing, *(0-9708922; 0-9766269)* Div. of Heidelberg Graphics, Orders Addr.: 2 Stansbury Ct., Chico, CA 95928 USA
E-mail: spublishing@heidelberggraphics.com
Web site: http://www.heidelberggraphics.com
Dist(s): **Baker & Taylor Bks.**

Star Bible & Tract Corp., *(0-933672; 0-940999; 1-56794)* Orders Addr.: P.O. Box 821220, Fort Worth, TX 76182 USA (SAN 203-3518) Tel 817-416-5889; Fax: 817-251-0129; Toll Free: 800-433-7507; Edit Addr.: P.O. Box 821220, N Richlnd Hls, TX 76182-1220 USA (SAN 664-6247)
E-mail: starbible@starbible.com
Web site: http://www.starbible.com
Dist(s): **Twentieth Century Christian Bks.**

Star Bright Bks., Inc., *(1-887734; 1-932065; 1-59572)* Orders Addr.: 30-19, 48th Ave., Long Island City, NY 11101 USA (SAN 254-5225) Tel 718-784-9112; Fax: 718-784-9012; Toll Free: 800-788-4439
E-mail: info@starbrightbooks.com
Web site: http://www.starbrightbooks.com.

Star Chaser Pr., *(0-9649539)* 719 Cornwallis Dr., Mount Holly, NJ 08054 USA Tel 856-642-6443; Fax: 856-642-1675
E-mail: aecannon@att.net
Dist(s): **Baker & Taylor Bks.**
Quality Bks., Inc.

Star Cross'd Destiny *Imprint of* **Bohemian Trash Studios**

Star Dome Publishing, LLC, *(0-9766662)* P.O. Box 411300, Melbourne, FL 32941 USA
E-mail: fcavalli@bellsouth.net
Web site: http://www.stardomepublishing.com.

Star Light Pr., *(1-879817)* 1811 S. First St., Austin, TX 78704-4299 USA Tel 512-441-0588; 512-441-0062 (phone/fax) ; *Imprints:* Bilingual (Bilingual); Children (Children)
E-mail: info@starlightpress.com
Web site: http://www.starlightpress.com
Dist(s): **Book Wholesalers, Inc.**
iLeon.

Star Press *See* **Star Pr., The**

Star Pr., The, *(0-9676189)* Div. of Indiana Newspapers, Inc., Orders Addr.: P.O. Box 2408, Muncie, IN 47307-0408 USA (SAN 169-2437) Tel 765-213-5799; Fax: 765-213-5703; Toll Free: 800-783-7827; Edit Addr.: 345 S. High St., Muncie, IN 47305 USA
E-mail: rfarmer@thestarpress.com
Web site: http://www.thestarpress.com.

Star Publish LLC, *(1-932993)* 450 Hillside Dr., Pmb #283, Mesquite, NV 89027 USA
E-mail: starpublish04-info@yahoo.com
Web site: http://www.starpublish.com.

Star Quest Publishing Phx, *(0-9767035)* 3030 E. Shangri-La Rd., Phoenix, AZ 85028 USA Tel 602-482-1568; Fax: 602-926-2484
E-mail: karen@starquestpublishing.com
Web site: http://www.starquestpublishing.com.

Star Root Pr., *(0-9717180)* P.O. Box 112, Austerlitz, NY 12017 USA Tel 518-392-3860
E-mail: starrootpress@aol.com
Web site: http://www.starrootpress.com
Dist(s): **BreakThrough Productions.**

Star Spangled Baby, Ltd., *(0-9726762)* P.O. Box 513, Douglassville, PA 19518 USA
Web site: http://www.starspangledbabyltd.com
Dist(s): **Baker & Taylor Bks.**
Quality Bks., Inc.

Star Trek *Imprint of* **Simon & Schuster**

Star Write Creations, *(0-9743851)* P.O. Box G, Birnamwood, WI 54414 USA Toll Free: 888-999-6609.

Starad, Inc., *(0-9647556)* 828 S. Broadway., Tarrytown, NY 10591-6602 USA.

Starbell Bks., *(0-9747774)* 2507 LaBrecque Dr., Plainfield, IL 60544 USA Tel 815-254-9495
E-mail: starbellbooks@comcast.net
Web site: http://www.starbellbooks.com.

STARbooks Pr. *Imprint of* **Florida Literary Foundation**

Starborne Hse., *(0-9671701)* Orders Addr.: 15590 Pleasant View Rd., Mount Vernon, OH 43050 USA Tel 740-369-4952; Fax: 740-548-5996; Edit Addr.: P.O. Box 767, Delaware, OH 43015 USA (SAN 254-4024) Tel 740-501-4792 (cell phone); 740-392-1565; Fax: 801-437-1888
E-mail: starbourne@axom.com
Web site: http://www.davidredding.com.

Starbound Bks. *Imprint of* **Wheatmark**

Starbound Publishing Company *See* **Collectors Pr., Inc.**

StarBright Pubs., *(0-9650838)* 350 W. Ninth Ave., Suite L, Escondido, CA 92025-5053 USA Tel 760-745-1802; Fax: 760-745-0537.

Starbucks Coffee Co., *(0-9726394)* 2401 Utah Ave. S., Seattle, WA 98134 USA Tel 206-447-1575; Toll Free: 800-235-2883
E-mail: info@starbucks.com
Web site: http://www.starbuckscollectibles.com.

Starburst Company *See* **Starburst Pubs.**

Starburst Pubs., *(0-914984; 1-892016)* Orders Addr.: P.O. Box 4123, Lancaster, PA 17604 USA Tel 717-293-0939; Fax: 717-293-1945; Toll Free: 800-441-1456 (orders only)
E-mail: starburst@starburstpublishers.com
Web site: http://www.starburstpublishers.com
Dist(s): **Anchor Distributors**
Appalachian Bible Co.
Baker & Taylor Bks.
Brodart Co.
National Bk. Network
Nutri-Bks. Corp.
Quality Bks., Inc.
STL Distribution North America
Spring Arbor Distributors, Inc.
Unique Bks., Inc.

Starcatcher Pr., *(0-9700164)* 256 Tudor Cir., Ashland, OR 97520 USA Tel 541-488-4230; Fax: 541-488-4354
E-mail: malcolm@wherewelive.com; starcatcherpress@aol.com
Web site: http://www.starcatcherpress.com.

Starden, Ltd., *(0-9672390)* Orders Addr.: P.O. Box 36, Englewood, CO 80151-0036 USA Tel 303-771-4524; Fax: 303-771-4523; Toll Free: 877-782-7336; Edit Addr.: 5734 S. Ivanhoe St., Greenwood Village, CO 80111 USA
E-mail: starden@starden.com
Web site: http:///www.starden.com.

STAReviews *Imprint of* **N&N Publishing Co., Inc.**

Starfall Education, *(1-59577)* P.O. Box 359, Boulder, CO 80306 USA Toll Free Fax: 800-943-6666; Toll Free: 888-857-8990
Web site: http://www.starfall.com.

Starfall Publications *See* **Starfall Education**

StarFestival, Inc., *(1-929724)* P.O. Box 401025, Cambridge, MA 02140-0011 USA Tel 617-492-5594; Toll Free Fax: 877-492-5594
E-mail: info@starfestival.com
Web site: http://www.starfestival.com.

Starfire *Imprint of* **Random Hse. Children's Bks.**

Starfish Adoption Funding Foundation, The *See* **Isaiah's Promise Publishing Co.**

Starfish Press *See* **Starfish Specialty Pr., LLC**

Starfish Specialty Pr., LLC, *(0-9666529; 1-932784)* P.O. Box 799, Higganum, CT 06441-0799 USA (SAN 254-590X) Tel 860-345-2155; Fax: 860-345-4471; Toll Free: 877-782-7347
E-mail: info@starfishpress.com
Web site: http://www.starfishpress.com.

Stargate Electronic Library, Inc., *(1-931457)* P.O. Box 79765, Houston, TX 77279-9765 USA (SAN 254-2544) Tel 713-466-4725
E-mail: stargate@e-shoppe.org
Web site: http://store.yahoo.com/ebooks4kids/index.html; http://www.e-shoppe.org.

Stargazer, *(0-9668846)* 455 Eastwood Dr., Stevens Point, WI 54481 USA
E-mail: broman@coredcs.com.

Stargazer Bks., *(1-932799; 1-59604)* 123 S. Broad St., Mankato, MN 56001 USA Tel 507-388-6273; Fax: 507-388-2746; Toll Free: 800-445-6209
E-mail: schlichte@aol.com
Dist(s): **Creative Co., The.**

Stargazer Publishing Co., *(0-9643853; 0-9713756; 1-933277)* Orders Addr.: P.O. Box 77002, Corona, CA 92877-0100 USA Tel 951-898-4619; Fax: 951-898-4633; Toll Free: 800-606-7895; Edit Addr.: 958 Stanislaus Dr., Corona, CA 92881 USA (SAN 298-6566) Do not confuse with Stargazer Publishing in Neenah, WI
E-mail: stargazer@stargazerpub.com
Web site: http://www.stargazerpub.com.

StarHeart Productions, *(0-9713181)* 1927 Bay Crest Dr., Santa Ana, CA 92704 USA Tel 714-436-1428; Fax: 714-546-4604
E-mail: mytlady@flash.net
Web site: http://www.starheart.com.

Starks, Shirley *See* **Inspirational Hse. of America**

Starlight Communications, *(0-9658331)* 2025 Windsor Rd., Cayce, SC 29033 USA Tel 803-796-6856; Fax: 803-796-2012.

StarLineage Pubns., *(1-885226)* P.O. Box 1630, McCloud, CA 96057-1630 USA Tel 530-964-2496.

Starlog Group, Incorporated *See* **Profile Entertainment, Inc.**

StarMist Development, Inc., *(1-892403)* Orders Addr.: P.O. Box 6006, Torrance, CA 90504-0006 USA Tel 310-640-7236; Edit Addr.: 540 E. Imperial Ave., El Segundo, CA 90245 USA.

StarProse Corp., *(0-9721071)* P.O. Box 320, Hemlock, MI 48626 USA
E-mail: webmaster@starprose.com
Web site: http://www.starprose.com.

Starry Puddle Publishing, *(0-9672839)* 1923 N. Granery Pl., Los Angeles, CA 90068 USA Tel 323-468-0370; Fax: 323-468-0371
E-mail: jjillwright@earthlink.net.

Starry-Eyed Pubns., *(0-9614627)* Orders Addr.: P.O. Box D, Culdesac, ID 83524 USA (SAN 691-8913) Tel 208-843-2886
E-mail: starry_eyed12@hotmail.com.

Starscape *Imprint of* **Doherty, Tom Assocs., LLC**

Starshell Pr., Ltd., *(0-9707110)* 210 Ridge Rd., Watchung, NJ 07069 USA Tel 908-755-7050; Fax: 212-983-5271
E-mail: starshellpress@yahoo.com
Web site: http://www.starshellpress.com
Dist(s): **Biblio Distribution.**

Start America Coloring *See* **Crayon Artist, LLC, The**

Startheme Pubns., *(0-9667312; 0-9745209)* 4411 N. 23rd St., Phoenix, AZ 85016 USA Tel 602-265-8668; Fax: 602-265-7667; c/o Madeline Rosenstein, 12645 SW 9th, Beaverton, OR 97005 Tel 503-671-9072; Fax: 503-671-0682
Web site: http://www.drturi.com
Dist(s): **Truth Seeker Co., Inc.**

Starving Writers Publishing, *(1-932996)* 4791 CR 4700, Athens, TX 75752 USA Tel 214-669-8766
E-mail: sales@starvingwriters.net
Web site: http://www.starvingwriters.net.

State Champion Wrestling Co., *(0-9726395)* 1404 W. St., Naperville, IL 60563 USA
Web site: http://www.statechampwrestling.com.

State Historical Society of North Dakota, *(1-891419)* 612 E. Boulevard Ave., Bismarck, ND 58505 USA Tel 701-328-2666; Fax: 701-328-3710
E-mail: histsoc@state.nd.us
Web site: http://www.state.nd.us/hist.

State Historical Society of Wisconsin *See* **Wisconsin Historical Society**

State Hse. Pr., *(0-938349; 1-880510; 1-933337)* S. 14th & Sayles Blvd., Austin, TX 79697 USA (SAN 660-966X); McMurry University, Box 637, Abilene, TX 79697-0637 Tel 325-793-4697; Fax: 325-793-4754 Do not confuse with State House Publishing in Madison, WI
E-mail: ckahl@mcm.edu
Web site: http://www.mcwhiney.org
Dist(s): **Encino Pr.**
Texas A&M Univ. Pr.

State Mutual Bk. & Periodical Service, Ltd., *(0-7855; 0-89771)* Orders Addr.: P.O. Box 1199, Bridgehampton, NY 11932-1199 USA.

State of Growth Publishing Co., *(0-9740289)* P.O. Box 38633, Colorado Springs, CO 80937 USA
Web site: http://www.stateofgrowth.com.

State Street Pr., *(0-9715387)* 13 Summit Sq., Langhorne, PA 19047 USA Do not confuse with State Street Press, Pittsford, NY.

†State Univ. of New York Pr., *(0-7914; 0-87395; 0-88706)* Orders Addr.: c/o CUP Services, P.O. Box 6525, Ithaca, NY 14851 USA (SAN 203-3496) Tel 607-277-2211; Fax: 607-277-6292; Edit Addr.: 194 Washington Ave. Suite 305, Albany, NY 12210 USA (SAN 658-1730) Tel 518-472-5000; Fax: 518-472-5038
E-mail: info@sunypress.edu
Web site: http://www.sunypress.edu
Dist(s): **Baker & Taylor Bks.**
CUP Services
NetLibrary, Inc.
Pegasus Pr.; *CIP.*

Stationery Office, The (GBR) *(0-10; 0-11; 0-337; 0-338; 0-339; 1-872236) Dist. by* **Balogh.**

Stay Connected, *(0-9709081)* Orders Addr.: P.O. Box 88418, Los Angeles, CA 90009 USA Tel 310-281-8429; Edit Addr.: Airport Blvd, Los Angeles, CA 90009 USA.

Stay, Play & Learn, *(0-9672430)* P.O. Box 645, Lake Bluff, IL 60044 USA
E-mail: staynplay@ync.net.

Staying Healthy Media, Inc., *(0-9763237)* 4409 Summer Grape Rd., Pikesville, MD 21208 USA Tel 410-484-0457
E-mail: healthy@stayinghealthymedia.com
Web site: http://www.stayinghealthymedia.com.

STE Pubs. (ZAF) *(1-919855) Dist. by* **IPG Chicago.**

Stealth Medialabs, INc., *(0-9770583)* 70 S. Lively Blvd., Elk Grove Village, IL 60007 USA (SAN 256-646X) Tel 847-483-8956; Fax: 312-896-9235
E-mail: howard@stealthmedialabs.com
Web site: http://www.stealthmedialabs.com.

Steam Crow Pr., *(0-9774173)* 7233 W. Cottontail Ln., Peoria, AZ 85383 USA
E-mail: sales@steamcrow.com
Web site: http://www.steamcrow.com.

Steam Passages Pubns., *(0-9758584)* 508 Lakeview Ave., Wake Forest, NC 27587 USA
E-mail: sdegaetano@steampassages.com
Web site: http://www.dlrcad.com/book.

†Steck-Vaughn, *(0-8114; 0-8172; 0-8393; 0-7398; 1-4190)* Div. of Harcourt, Inc., Orders Addr.: 6277 Sea Harbor Dr., 5th Flr., Orlando, FL 32887 USA Toll Free Fax: 877-578-2638; Toll Free: 888-363-4266; Edit Addr.: 10801 N. Mopac Expressway, Bldg. 3, Austin, TX 78759 USA (SAN 658-1757) Toll Free: 800-531-5015
E-mail: ecare@harcourt.com
Web site: http://www.harcourtachieve.com; *CIP.*

Stedjee Publishing *See* **Lawe Street Bks.**

Steel Bridge Pr., *(0-9764415)* 610 Briarcliff, Bardstown, KY 40004-8941 USA Tel 502-348-7447; Fax: 502-350-1126
E-mail: john@steelbridgepress.com

Steele, Eugene *See* **E-BookTime LLC**

Steele Studios, *(0-9716811)* Orders Addr.: P.O. Box 3093, Glenwood Springs, CO 81602 USA (SAN 254-3230); Edit Addr.: 125 Ctr. Dr., No.18, Glenwood Springs, CO 81601 USA.

Steeple Ridge Press *See* **Steeple Ridge Publications**

Steeple Ridge Publications, *(0-9762862)* Div. of Steeple Ridge Press, Orders Addr.: 7220 Hillside Dr., Clarkston, MI 48346-1474 USA Tel 248-342-6678
E-mail: info@steepleridgepress.com
Web site: http://www.steepleridgepress.com
Dist(s): **Partners Bk. Distributing, Inc.**

Steerforth Italia *Imprint of* **Steerforth Pr.**

Steerforth Pr., *(0-944072; 1-58195; 1-883642; 1-58642)* 25 Lebanon St., Hanover, NH 03755 USA Tel 603-643-4787; Fax: 603-643-4788 ; *Imprints:* Steerforth Italia (Steerforth Italia); Zoland Books, Incorporated (Zoland)
E-mail: helga@steerforth.com; info@steerforth.com
Web site: http://www.steerforth.com
Dist(s): **Random Hse., Inc.**

Stefan Univ. Pr., The, *(1-889545)* Div. of La Jolla International Schl. of Science, Inc., P.O. Box 2946, La Jolla, CA 92038-2946 USA Tel 619-456-0379; Fax: 619-456-0373
E-mail: Press@Stefan-University.edu
Web site: http://www.stefan-university.edu/S-U-PRESS/.

Steiner, Lili Pubns., *(1-891397)* 2160 Century Pk., E., No. 1508, Los Angeles, CA 90067 USA (SAN 299-4569) Tel 310-553-5520; Fax: 310-553-4340
E-mail: lilily@earthlink.net.

†SteinerBooks, Inc., *(0-8334; 0-88010; 0-89345; 0-910142; 1-58420; 1-85584; 0-9701097)* Orders Addr.: P.O. Box 960, Herndon, VA 20172-0960 USA Tel 703-661-1594 (orders); Fax: 702-661-1501; Toll Free Fax: 800-277-7947 (orders); Toll Free: 800-856-8664 (orders); Edit Addr.: 610 Main St., Great Barrington, MA 01230 USA Tel 413-528-8233; Fax: 413-528-8826; Fulfillment Addr.: 22883 Quicksilver Dr., Dulles, VA 20166 USA (SAN 253-9519) Tel 703-661-1529; Fax: 703-996-1010 ; *Imprints:* Bell Pond Books (Bell Pond)
E-mail: service@steinerbooks.org
Web site: http://www.steinerbooks.org; http://www.lindisfarne.org; http://www.bellpondbooks.com
Dist(s): **New Leaf Distributing Co., Inc.**
Red Wheel/Weiser; *CIP.*

Steingart, Nathan Publishing, *(0-9769321)* 617 N. Kensington Dr., No. 1, Appleton, WI 54915 USA
E-mail: nathansteingart@new.rr.com
Web site: http://www.santastories.net.

Steinschneider, Bernadetta, *(0-9790026)* 205 Georgetown Rd., Weston, CT 06883 USA Tel 203-454-8907; Fax: 203-227-0184
E-mail: swigutb@gmail.com.

Stejskal, Susan M., *(0-615)* 15095 S. 18th St., Vicksburg, MI 49097 USA.

Stella Bks, Inc., *(0-9746932)* P.O. Box 4707, Edwards, CO 81632-4707 USA Tel 970-926-7827 (phone/fax)
E-mail: info@astellabook.com
Dist(s): **Partners/West.**

Stellar Learning, *(0-9763833)* P.O. Box 64, Guildrlnd Ctr, NY 12085-0064 USA
E-mail: admin@stellarlearn.com
Web site: http://www.stellarlearn.com.

Stellar Pr., *(0-9708422; 1-932860)* Div. of Stellar Management, L.L.C., 634 N. Grand Blvd., Suite 10C, Saint Louis, MO 63103 USA Do not confuse with Stellar Press in Berkeley, CA
E-mail: info@stellarpress.com
Web site: http://www.booksonstlouis.com; http://www.stellarpress.com/
Dist(s): **Booksource, The.**

Stellar Pubns., *(0-9761224)* 3767 Forest Ln., Suite 124 - MBX 1231, Dallas, TX 75244 USA Toll Free: 866-840-4378
E-mail: info@stellarpublishers.com; maymathis@msn.com
Web site: http://www.stellarpublishers.com.

Stellinga, Mark, *(0-9762011; 0-9796421)* Orders Addr.: 42 Lancester Pl., Iowa City, IA 52240 USA Tel 319-354-7287
E-mail: billiard@avalon.net
Web site: http://www.billiard-antiques/books/index.html.

Stelucan Pr., *(0-9601454)* 2129 State Hwy. 79 S., Wichita Falls, TX 76302 USA (SAN 221-3176).

†Stemmer Hse. Pubs., Inc., *(0-88045; 0-916144)* P.O. Box 89, Gilsum, NH 03448 USA (SAN 207-9623) Tel 603-357-0236; Fax: 603-357-2073 ; *Imprints:* International Design Library (Intl Design); NaturEncyclopedia (Naturencyclop)
E-mail: pbs@pathwaybook.com
Web site: http://stemmer.com
Dist(s): **Pathway Bk. Service**; *CIP.*

Stenhouse Pubs., *(1-57110)* Div. of Highlights for Children, Orders Addr.: 480 Congress St., Portland, ME 04104-7020 USA (SAN 298-1580) Tel 207-253-1600; Fax: 207-253-5121; Toll Free Fax: 800-833-9164; Toll Free: 800-988-9812 (orders)
E-mail: info@stenhouse.com; nbutler@stenhouse.com
Web site: http://www.stenhouse.com.

Stensland Bks., *(0-9759456)* 3121 S. 102 St., Omaha, NE 68124 USA
E-mail: info@stenslandbooks.com
Web site: http://www.stenslandbooks.com.

Stephens Pr. LLC, *(1-932173)* Div. of Stephens Media Group, Orders Addr.: P.O. Box 1600, Las Vegas, NV 89125-1600 USA (SAN 255-044X) Tel 702-387-5260; Fax: 702-387-2997; Edit Addr.: 1111 W. Bonanza Rd., Las Vegas, NV 89106 USA Do not confuse with Stephens Pr. in Spokane, WA
E-mail: cuber@stephenspress.com
Web site: http://www.stephenspress.com
Dist(s): **Midpoint Trade Bks., Inc.**

SteppingStones BookCard Pubns., LLC, *(1-931006)* 13 Ranalet Dr., Hampton, VA 23664 USA Tel 757-851-2262; Fax: 757-851-5727
E-mail: steppingstones@aol.com
Web site: http://www.steppingstonesbookcardpublications.com; http://www.BookCards.com.

Steps To Literacy, LLC, *(0-9728803; 1-59564; 1-60015)* Orders Addr.: P.O. Box 6737, Bridgewater, NJ 08807 USA Toll Free: 800-895-2804
Web site: http://www.stepstoliteracy.com.

Sterling House Publishing *See* **SterlingHouse Pubs., Inc.**

Sterling Innovation *Imprint of* **Sterling Publishing Co., Inc.**

Sterling Pr., Inc., *(0-9637735)* 6811 Old Canton Rd., Apt. 3802, Ridgeland, MS 39157-1248 USA Tel 602-957-9265 Do not confuse with companies with similar names in Bulverde, TX, Chicago, IL, Marysville, WA, Bedford, TX, Kihei,HI.

Sterling Publishing, *(0-9625183)* 833A S. Main, 192, Fallbrook, CA 92028 USA Tel 760-728-1756; Fax: 760-728-1982 Do not confuse with companies with the same name in Falls Church, VA, Lewisville, TX, New York, NY.

†Sterling Publishing Co., Inc., *(0-8069; 1-4027)* 387 Park Ave., S., New York, NY 10016-8810 USA (SAN 211-6324) Tel 212-532-7160 212-213-2495; Toll Free Fax: 800-775-8736 (warehouse) ; *Imprints:* Sterling/Main Street (Sterling-Main St); Chapelle (Chapelle); Balloon Books (Balloon Books); Sterling/Pinwheel (SterPin); Sterling Innovation (SterInnov) Do not confuse with companies with similar names in Falls Church, VA, Fallbrook, CA, Lewisville, TX
E-mail: custservice@sterlingpub.com; tradesales@sterlingpub.com
Web site: http://www.sterlingpub.com
Dist(s): **Booklines Hawaii, Ltd.**
Partners Bk. Distributing, Inc.; *CIP.*

Sterling Ties Pubns., *(0-9642420)* 5989 Sterling Dr., Boise, ID 83703 USA Tel 208-853-0507
E-mail: sterling@integrityonline4.com.

SterlingHouse Pubs., Inc., *(1-56315; 1-58501)* Div. of CYNTOMEDIA Corporation, 7436 Washington Ave., Suite 200, Pittsburgh, PA 15218 USA Tel 412-436-3100; Fax: 412-437-1606; Toll Free: 888-542-2665 ; *Imprints:* CeShore (CeShore); Blue Imp Books (Blue Imp Bks)
E-mail: info@sterlinghousepublisher.com
Web site: http://www.sterlinghousepublisher.com.

Sterling/Main St. *Imprint of* **Sterling Publishing Co., Inc.**

Sterling/Pinwheel *Imprint of* **Sterling Publishing Co., Inc.**

Stern & Weiss Publishing *See* **Lyandy Pr.**

Sternkopf, Susan, *(0-9677130)* Orders Addr.: 404 Cottonwood Ave., Hartland, WI 53029-2302 USA; Edit Addr.: 2701 SW 13th St., Suite M-22, Gainesville, FL 32608 USA.

Sternlight, Phyllis Paulson, *(0-9673505)* Orders Addr.: P.O. Box 877, Sandwich, MA 02563-0877 USA Fax: 508-833-5033; Edit Addr.: P.O. Box 877, Sandwich, MA 02563-0877 USA
E-mail: papsternlight@hotmail.com.

†Stevens, Gareth Inc., *(0-8368; 0-918831; 1-55532; 1-4339)* Subs. of WRC Media, Inc., Orders Addr.: P.O. Box 360140, Strongsville, OH 44136-0140 USA Fax: 877-542-2596; Toll Free Fax: 800-542-2595; Edit Addr.: 1 Reader's Digest Rd., Pleasantville, NY 10570 USA (SAN 696-1592) Toll Free: 800-542-2595 ; *Imprints:* World Almanac Library (Wrld Almanac Lib); Weekly Reader Early Learning Library (Weekly Reader)
E-mail: info@gspub.com; customerservice@gspub.com
Web site: http://www.garethstevens.com
Dist(s): **Lectorum Pubns., Inc.**; *CIP.*

Stevenson, James D. Publisher *See* **James Stevenson Pub.**

Stevenson Language Skills, Incorporated *See* **Stevenson Learning Skills, Inc.**

Stevenson Learning Skills, Inc., *(0-941112)* 8 Commonwealth Ave., Attleboro Falls, MA 02763-1014 USA (SAN 217-4413) Tel 508-643-3002; Fax: 508-699-4279; Toll Free: 800-343-1211
E-mail: slsol@ICI.NET.

Steward & Wise Publishing *See* **Acclaim Pr., Inc.**

Stewart Education Services, *(0-9764154)* 3722 Bagely Ave., No. 19, Los Angeles, CA 90034-4113 USA Tel 310-838-6247; Fax: 310-838-6769
E-mail: info@stewarteducationservices.com
Web site: http://www.stewarteducationservices.com.

†Stewart, Tabori & Chang, *(0-941434; 0-941807; 1-55670; 1-899791; 1-58479)* Div. of Harry N. Abrams, Inc., 115 W. 18th St., 5th Flr., New York, NY 10011 USA (SAN 293-4000) Tel 212-519-1200; Fax: 212-519-1210
E-mail: trudi@stcbooks.com
Web site: http://www.abramsbooks.com
Dist(s): **Abrams, Harry N. , Inc.**
Hachette Bk. Group; *CIP.*

Stick to The Word Publishing, *(0-9644282)* Div. of Stick To The Word, Inc., 6326 E. Livingston Ave., No. 142, Reynoldsburg, OH 43068-2754 USA Tel 614-216-7026; Fax: 614-920-0367
E-mail: Rapdnsozo@aol.com.

Stickysoft Corp., *(0-9740384)* Orders Addr.: P.O. Box 7855, Buffalo Grove, IL 60089 USA Tel 847-229-9999; Fax: 847-808-8777; Toll Free: 800-366-8448; Edit Addr.: 620 Silver Rock Ln., Buffalo Grove, IL 60089 USA
E-mail: euclid@stickysoft.com
Web site: http://www.blackjack678.com.

Still Water Publishing, *(0-9740855)* Orders Addr.: 1093 Kiva Cir., Windsor, CO 80550 USA
E-mail: chein8@attbi.com
Web site: http://www.stillwaterpublishing.com.

Still Waters Press *See* **Tinwood Bks.**

Stillman, Steve, *(0-9740508)* 251 Green St., Shrewsbury, MA 01545-4708 USA.

Stillsonworks, *(0-9723009)* 5515 Keokuk Ave., Woodland Hills, CA 91367 USA Tel 818-884-4284; Fax: 818-592-6472
E-mail: stillson@jps.net.

Stillwater Publishing, *(0-9709754)* Div. of Stillwater Enterprises, Inc., P.O. Box 500, Lionville, PA 19335 USA (SAN 253-7931) Tel 610-458-4000; Fax: 610-458-4001 ; *Imprints:* Take a Walk Book (Take a Walk Bk) Do not confuse with companies with the same or similar name in Stillwater,MN
E-mail: jane@takeawalk.com
Web site: http://www.takeawalk.com
Dist(s): **Baker & Taylor Bks.**
Common Ground Distributors, Inc.
Independent Pubs. Group.

Stilts, *(0-9708080)* 1228 N. Dearborn Pkwy., 3rd Flr., Chicago, IL 60610 USA
E-mail: robertfrederick@mac.com
Web site: http://www.wiltsonstilts.com.

Stinky Dog Press *See* **Pivotal Bks.**

Stipes Publishing L.L.C., *(0-87563; 1-58874)* Orders Addr.: P.O. Box 526, Champaign, IL 61824 USA (SAN 206-8664) Tel 217-356-8391; Fax: 217-356-5753; Edit Addr.: 202-204 W. University Ave., Champaign, IL 61824 USA
E-mail: stipes@soltec.net
Web site: http://www.stipes.com.

Stirling, H. Publishing, *(0-9700757)* 43165 Ambro Cir., Banning, CA 92220 USA Tel 951-849-3774; Fax: 951-849-7344; Toll Free Fax: 800-454-3795; Toll Free: 800-814-8863.

STL Distribution North America, *(1-932805)* Orders Addr.: 129 Mobilization Dr., Waynesboro, GA 30830 USA (SAN 631-8894) Tel 706-554-5827; Toll Free Fax: 877-323-4551; Toll Free: 877-323-4550; Edit Addr.: 9247 Hunterboro Dr., Brentwood, TN 37027 USA Tel 615-221-6442 (phone/fax) Do not confuse with Faithworks in Bronx NY
E-mail: custserv@faithworksonline.com
Web site: http://www.faithworksonline.com.

Stockwell Publishing, *(0-9785594)* 84 State St. Suite 300, Boston, MA 02109 USA Tel 617-290-3039; Fax: 617-720-0761
E-mail: pel.stockwell@lpl.com
Web site: http://www.followthefox.com.

Stoddard, Michael Eugene, *(0-9675924)* 536 S. Palm Dr., Brea, CA 92821-6641 USA Tel 626-821-3911; Fax: 714-990-5110
E-mail: webmaster@rockymesa.com
Web site: http://www.Rockymesa.com.

Stoecklein Publishing, *(0-922029; 1-931153; 1-933192; 1-933790)* Orders Addr.: Tenth St. Ctr., Suite A1, Ketchum, ID 83340 USA; Edit Addr.: P.O. Box 856, Ketchum, ID 83340 USA (SAN 251-1002)
Web site: http://www.drsphoto.net
Dist(s): **Globe Pequot Pr., The**
Sunbelt Pubns., Inc.
Western International, Inc.

Stokes Publishing Co., Inc., *(0-914534)* 1292 Reamwood Ave., Sunnyvale, CA 94089 USA (SAN 206-5789) Tel 408-541-9145; Fax: 408-541-9149; Toll Free: 800-550-5254
E-mail: stokesco@aol.com
Web site: http://www.stokesco.com.

Stone Acres Publishing Co., *(0-9765478)* P.O. Box 407, Waverly, PA 18471-0407 USA (SAN 850-0940) Fax: 570-563-2993
E-mail: gmiltony@yahoo.com.

Stone & Scott Pubs., *(0-9627031; 1-891135)* Orders Addr.: P.O. Box 56419, Sherman Oaks, CA 91413-1419 USA (SAN 297-3030) Tel 818-904-9088; Fax: 818-787-1431
E-mail: Friday@StoneandScott.com; BostonLesPaul@adelphia.net
Web site: http://www.stoneandscott.com.

Stone Arch Bks., *(1-59889; 1-4342)* Div. of Coughlan Publishing, Orders Addr.: 151 Good Counsel Dr., Mankato, MN 56001 USA (SAN 257-3148) Tel 800-421-7731; Fax: 877-245-4902; Edit Addr.: 7825 Telegraph Rd., Minneapolis, MN 55438 USA Fax: 952-933-2410; Toll Free: 1-888-517-8977; P.O. Box 669, Mankato, MN 56001 Do not confuse with Stone Arch Books in Afton, MN
E-mail: m.gregoire@stonearchbooks.com; g.beer@coughlanpublishing.com; info@stonearchbooks.com
Web site: http://stonearchbooks.com.

†Stone Bridge Pr., *(0-9628137; 1-880656; 1-933330)* P.O. Box 8208, Berkeley, CA 94707 USA Tel 510-524-8732; Fax: 510-524-8711; Toll Free: 800-947-7271 (orders) Do not confuse with Stone Bridge Press in Naples, FL
E-mail: sbpsales@stonebridge.com
Web site: http://www.stonebridge.com
Dist(s): **Art Media Resources, Inc.**
Consortium Bk. Sales & Distribution
SPD-Small Pr. Distribution; *CIP.*

Stone Cloud Phonics, *(0-9678068)* Orders Addr.: P.O. Box 84281, San Diego, CA 92138-4281 USA Tel 619-295-2015; Fax: 619-255-4857; Edit Addr.: 1860 Fort Stockton Dr., San Diego, CA 92138-4281 USA.

Stone Publishing Co., *(1-880991)* Orders Addr.: P.O. Box 711, Mendocino, CA 95460 USA Tel 707-937-0239; Edit Addr.: 10491 Wheeler St., Mendocino, CA 95460 USA.

†Stone Wall Pr., Inc., *(0-913276)* 6644 John Marshall Hwy., The Plains, VA 20198-2226 USA (SAN 203-3402)
Dist(s): **Pathway Bk. Service**; *CIP.*

Stonechester, Inc., *(0-9759014)* 4894 Lone Mountain Rd., No. 311, Las Vegas, NV 89130-2239 USA.

Stonecrest Industries, *(0-9712057; 0-9786219)* Orders Addr.: 152 Starheim Rd., Stamford, NY 12167 USA; Edit Addr.: RR 1, Box 120 C, Decker Rd., Stamford, NY 12107 USA Tel 607-652-2665; Fax: 607-330-8005
E-mail: gerrys@genericcomp.com
Web site: http://www.stonecrestindustries.com; http://www.genericcomp.com.

StoneGarden.net Publishing, *(0-9765426; 1-60076)* 3851 Cottonwood Dr., Danville, CA 94506 USA Tel 925-984-7867
E-mail: theshop@stonegarden.net
Web site: http://www.stonegarden.net.

Stonehill Publishing, *(0-9650769)* Orders Addr.: P.O. Box 250, Ephraim, WI 54211 USA Tel 920-854-9506; Fax: 920-854-6845; Edit Addr.: 9962 S. Dane St., Ephraim, WI 54211 USA Do not confuse with Stonehill Publishing Co., Traverse City, MI.

Stonehorse Publishing, LLC, *(0-9764199)* Orders Addr.: 6528 E. 101st St. S., Ste D1 Rm. 296, Tulsa, OK 74133 USA (SAN 256-3797) Toll Free Fax: 888-867-1927; Toll Free: 888-867-1927
E-mail: generalinfo@stonehorsepublishing.com
Web site: http://www.stonehorsepublishing.com
Dist(s): **Educational Distribution Corp.**

Stoneleigh Pr., *(0-9789174)* P.O. Box 9673, Seattle, WA 98109-9673 USA
E-mail: anne@annieseries.com
Web site: http://www.annieseries.com
Dist(s): **Biblio Distribution.**

Stones Point Pr., *(1-882521)* Orders Addr.: P.O. Box 384, Belfast, ME 04915-0384 USA (SAN 297-8024) Tel 207-338-1921; Fax: 207-338-8379; Edit Addr.: 71 Congress St., Belfast, ME 04915 USA
E-mail: stonespt@mint.net; haaron@mint.net
Dist(s): **Baker & Taylor Bks.**

StonesThrow Publishing LLC, *(0-9793823)* P.O. Box 1898, Mount Dora, FL 32756 USA Tel 208-610-0431.

Stoney Creek Pr., *(0-9700487)* P.O. Box 70, Trabuco Canyon, CA 92678 USA (SAN 253-4401) Tel 949-858-3021; 21022 Horsetree Cir., Trabuco Canyon, CA 92679 Tel 949-858-1561
E-mail: yod@home.com; yod@cox.net
Web site: http://www.firestories.com
Dist(s): **Baker & Taylor Bks.**
Partners/West
Quality Bks., Inc.

Stoneydale Pr. Publishing Co., *(0-912299; 1-931291)* Orders Addr.: P.O. Box 188, Stevensville, MT 59870 USA Tel 406-777-2729; Fax: 406-777-2521; Toll Free: 800-735-7006; Edit Addr.: 523 Main St., Stevensville, MT 59870 USA (SAN 265-3168)
E-mail: daleburk@montana.com
Web site: http://www.stoneydale.com.

Stony Meadow Publishing, *(0-9787925)* 2020 W. 10th Ave. #103, Broomfield, CO 80020-1076 USA Tel 303-960-9072
E-mail: stan@stonymeadowpublishing.com
Web site: http://www.stonymeadowpublishing.com; http://www.inspiration4songwriters.net; http://www.books4songwriters.com.

Stop & Smell the Roses, L.L.C., *(0-9666903)* 152 Congressional Ln., No. 118, Rockville, MD 20852 USA Tel 301-468-7673 (phone/fax)
E-mail: stopandsmelltheroses@erols.com
Web site: http://www.stopandsmelltheroses.com/.

Storer, Mark *See* **Little River Bookshelf**

Storey Books *See* **Storey Publishing, LLC**

Storey Kids *Imprint of* **Storey Publishing, LLC**

†Storey Publishing, LLC, *(0-88266; 1-58017; 0-9674717; 1-60342)* Subs. of Workman Publishing Co., Inc., Orders Addr.: 210 Mass Moca Way, North Adams, MA 01247 USA (SAN 203-4158) Fax: 413-346-2198; Toll Free Fax: 800-865-3429; Toll Free: 800-827-7444; c/o Workman Publishing, 225 Varick St., New York, NY 10014-4381 Tel 212-614-7700; Toll Free Fax: 800-521-1832; Toll Free: 800-722-7202 ; *Imprints:* Storey Kids (Storey Kids)
E-mail: info@storey.com; sales@storey.com
Web site: http://www.storey.com
Dist(s): **MBI Publishing Co. LLC**
Workman Publishing Co., Inc.; *CIP.*

Stori Tyme Huggggs, Inc., *(1-890925)* Div. of T.L.B. Publishing, 827 N. Hollywood, #202, Burbank, CA 91505 USA Tel 770-987-5547; 894 Roberts Way, Lawrenceville, GA 30043
E-mail: tenabrown@thejpak.com.

Storie Tree, Inc., The, *(0-9679014)* Orders Addr.: P.O. Box 441048, Aurora, CO 80044-1048 USA Tel 303-690-6493; Fax: 303-758-7792; Edit Addr.: 3952 S. Joplin Way, Aurora, CO 80044-1048 USA.

Stories From Four Publishing Co., *(0-9742288)* 558 N. Nash St., Hortonville, WI 54944 USA Tel 920-779-9995
E-mail: fourinspirations@aol.com
Web site: http://www.storiesfromfour.com.

Stories of My Life, The, *(0-9741215)* Div. of Frontsiders Marketing Strategists, P.O. Box 1478, Summerland, CA 93067 USA Tel 805-969-3597
Web site: http://www.thestoriesofmylife.com.

Storitime Publishing, *(0-9708489)* Div. of Storitime.com, 10513 Fawn Dr., NW, Gig Harbor, WA 98332-9510 USA (SAN 253-6994) Tel 253-853-3661; Fax: 253-853-3861
E-mail: liz@storitime.com
Web site: http://www.storitime.com.

Storm Peak Pr., *(0-9641357; 1-928990)* 2502 4th Ave N., Seattle, WA 98109-2149 USA
Dist(s): **Baker & Taylor Bks.**

Story Line Pr., *(0-934257; 1-885266; 1-58654)* Orders Addr.: P.O. Box 1240, Ashland, OR 97520-0055 USA (SAN 242-0465) Tel 541-512-8792; Fax: 541-512-8793; Edit Addr.: Three Oaks Farm, Ashland, OR 97520 USA
E-mail: mail@storylinepress.com
Web site: http://www.storylinepress.com
Dist(s): **Consortium Bk. Sales & Distribution.**

Story of Your Life Publishing Co., The, *(0-9771667)* 528 Palisades Dr., No. 711, Pacific Palisades, CA 90272 USA (SAN 256-8241) Tel 310-230-8510.

Story Place, The, *(0-9671660)* 1326 SW 22nd Ave., Cape Coral, FL 33991-2215 USA
E-mail: help@thestoryplace.com
Web site: http://www.thestoryplace.com.

Story Reader, Inc., *(0-9720158; 0-9720651)* 5050 Quorum Dr., Suite 315, Dallas, TX 75240 USA Tel 214-415-9200; Fax: 972-620-0715
E-mail: admin@storyreaders.com
Web site: http://www.storyreaders.com.

Story Store Collection Publishing, *(0-9764798)* 11040 Hickman Rd. # 226, Clive, IA 50325-3740 USA.

Story Stuff, Inc., *(1-928811)* P.O. Box 501372, Indianapolis, IN 46250-6372 USA Fax: 317-913-1777
E-mail: jmferrone@storystuff.com
Web site: http://www.storystuff.com.

Story Teller, The, *(1-929098)* P.O. Box 1174, Sterling Heights, MI 48311-1174 USA Tel 810-977-0411 (phone/fax)
E-mail: storezby1@aol.com.

Story Time Stories That Rhyme, *(1-56820)* P.O. Box 416, Denver, CO 80201-0416 USA Tel 303-575-5676 ; *Imprints:* folder leaf (folder leaf)
E-mail: starsuccess@excite.com; mail@storytimestoriesthatrhyme.net
Web site: http://www.storytimestoriesthatrhyme.net; http://www.storytimestoriesthatrhyme.com/; http://www.storytimestoriesthatrhyme.org; http://www.storiesforschools.com; http://www.kidsrhymenewsletter.com.

Storybook Acres, *(0-9761675)* 4309 Creek Rd., Conneaut, OH 44030 USA (SAN 256-2219) Tel 440-593-2780 (phone/fax)
E-mail: storybookacres@adelphia.net
Web site: http://storybookacres.org.

Storybook Meadow Publishing, *(0-9704621)* 7700 Timbers Trail, Traverse City, MI 49684 USA
E-mail: gbower@microagetc.com; garybower@charter.net
Web site: http://www.bowerbooks.com.

Storybook Pr. & Productions, *(1-887683)* 467 Central Park W., Apt. 6E, New York, NY 10025 USA Tel 212-975-2473; 212-749-7178 (phone/fax); Fax: 212-975-2026; Toll Free: 800-779-4341
E-mail: storybookp@aol.com
Dist(s): **Baker & Taylor Bks.**

Storycraft Publishing, *(0-9638339)* Orders Addr.: P.O. Box 205, Masonville, CO 80541-0205 USA Tel 970-669-3755 (phone/fax); Edit Addr.: 8600 Firethorn Dr., Loveland, CO 80538 USA
E-mail: Vivian@storycraft.com
Web site: http://www.storycraft.com
Dist(s): **Baker & Taylor Bks.**
Book Wholesalers, Inc.
Brodart Co.
Follett Library Resources
Quality Bks., Inc.
Unique Bks., Inc.

Storydog, Inc., *(0-9722690)* 3510 N. Bell Ave., Chicago, IL 60618 USA (SAN 254-9786) Tel 773-327-1588
Web site: http://www.storydog.com.

StoryGirl Productions, LLC, *(0-9762587)* 213 W. Montebello, Phoenix, AZ 85013 USA
E-mail: jaime@ding-a-lings.net
Web site: http://www.ding-a-lings.net.

StoryLoft Publishing, *(0-9651396)* 304 W. Church St., Bishopville, SC 29010-1008 USA.

Storyplus, Inc., A, *(0-9778477)* P.O. Box 1174, Pine Lake, GA 30072-1174 USA (SAN 850-3907) Tel 770-970-8607
E-mail: astoryplu@comcast.net
Web site: astoryplus.com.

Storytellers Ink, Inc., *(0-9623072; 1-880812; 1-930767)* Orders Addr.: a/o Quinn Currie, P.O. Box 33398, Seattle, WA 98133-0398 USA Tel 206-365-8265; Fax: 206-363-0830 Do not confuse with Storytellers Ink, Inc. in Kansas City, MO
E-mail: publisher@storytellers-Ink.com
Web site: http://www.storytellers-ink.com.

Storytelling World Pr., *(1-884624)* 108 Oak Grove Blvd., Suite 201, Johnson City, TN 37601 USA Tel 423-542-8425; Fax: 423-929-4235.

Storytime Ink International, *(0-9628769)* P.O. Box 470505, Broadview Heights, OH 44147 USA Tel 440-838-4881; Fax: 408-580-5967; 10001 Gatewood Dr., Brecksville, OH 44141
E-mail: storytimeink@att.net.

Storytime Pr., Inc., *(0-9754942)* 427 W. Main, Suite D, Brighton, MI 48116 USA
E-mail: storytimepress@yahoo.com
Web site: http://www.storytimepress.com
Dist(s): **Ann Arbor Media Group, LLC.**

StoryTime World Publishing Hse., *(0-9792800)* 152 Congressional Ln., No. 303, Rockville, MD 20852-5306 USA Tel 301-672-4296
Web site: http://storytimeworld.com.

StoryTyme Publishing, *(0-9753699)* 7909 Walergra Rd., Suite 112, PMB 178, Antelope, CA 95843 USA (SAN 256-0763)
Web site: http://www.storytymepublishing.com
Dist(s): **Biblio Distribution.**

Storywriter Pr., *(0-9712952)* 330 Clayton Oaks Dr., Ellisville, MO 63011 USA Tel 636-391-6734
E-mail: storywriter@mindspring.com.

Stourbridge Distributors, Inc., *(0-9753758)* 910 Church St. Ste. 3, Honesdale, PA 18431-1965 USA
E-mail: rich@stourbridgedist.com
Web site: http://www.stourbridgedist.com.

Stout, William Inc., *(0-9712716; 0-9743838)* 1468 Loma Vista St., Pasadena, CA 91104-4709 USA Tel 626-798-6490; Fax: 626-798-3756
E-mail: wmstout@altrionet.com
Web site: http://www.williamstout.com.

Stover Engineering, *(0-9716912)* 2121 N. Aurora Dr., Palm Springs, CA 92262 USA Tel 760-322-0618 (phone/fax)
E-mail: stovereng@earthlink.net
Web site: http://www.jazznart.com; http://www.jeffstover.com.

Stoyles Graphic Services, *(0-89279)* P.O. Box 1564, Mason City, IA 50401-1564 USA Tel 641-424-4341; Fax: 641-424-9687; Toll Free: 800-247-5986 Do not confuse with Graphic Publishing Co., Atlanta, GA
E-mail: bstoyles@stoyles.com
Web site: http://www.stoyles.com.

Straight Edge Pr., The, *(1-883043)* Subs. of Straight Edge, Inc., 296 Court St., Brooklyn, NY 11231 USA (SAN 254-9395) Tel 718-643-2794; Fax: 718-403-9582; Toll Free: 800-732-3628
E-mail: info@straightedgeinc.com
Web site: http://www.straightedgeinc.com
Dist(s): **Ingram Bk. Co.**

Straight Forward Technologies, *(0-9718515)* P.O. Box 102, Valley Center, KS 67147 USA Tel 316-207-3211; Toll Free Fax: 877-766-8566
E-mail: info@straightforwardtech.com
Web site: http://www.bakingwithmommy.com; http://www.straightforwardtech.com; http://www.gardeningwithmommy.com.

Straight Paths Pr., *(0-9759871)* 17450 SW Viking St., Beaverton, OR 97007 USA (SAN 256-1468) Tel 503-259-9764 (phone/fax); Toll Free: 800-348-2346 ext. 23
E-mail: info@straightpathspress.com
Web site: http://www.straightpathspress.com.

Strang Communications Co., *(0-88419; 0-930525; 1-59185; 1-59979)* Div. of Creation House Pr., 600 Rinehart Rd., Lake Mary, FL 32746 USA (SAN 677-5640) Tel 407-333-0600; Fax: 407-333-7100; Toll Free: 800-283-8494 ; *Imprints:* Casa Creacion (Casa Cre); Creation House (CreatHse); Charisma Kids (Charisma Kids)
Web site: http://www.strang.com/
Dist(s): **Dake Publishing.**

StrangeDays Publishing, *(0-9747581)* P.O. Box 587, Merton, WI 53056 USA.

Strategic Dreamers, LLC., *(0-9765358)* 4766 E. Eden Dr., Cave Creek, AZ 85331-3870 USA
E-mail: erikauthor@aol.com.

Strategies Publishing Co., *(0-9769662)* Orders Addr.: P.O. Box 5588, Cary, NC 27512 USA Do not confuse with companies with the same or similar name in Sahuarita, AZ, Tampa, FL, New Augusta, MS
E-mail: jjohnson0710@yahoo.com; strategiespublishing@nc.rr.com.

Stratford Road Pr., Ltd., *(0-9743221)* 128 S. Camden Dr., Suite 201, Beverly Hills, CA 90212-3232 USA Fax: 310-550-8926
E-mail: peasonions@aol.com
Dist(s): **AtlasBooks Distribution.**

Strathmoor *Imprint of* **Tabby Hse. Bks.**

Strathmoor Pr., *(0-9740718)* 1710 Tyler Pkwy., Louisville, KY 40204 USA Tel 502-479-3287.

Stratten, Lou, *(0-9747173)* Orders Addr.: 3144 S. Barrington Ave. #c, Los Angeles, CA 90066 USA; Edit Addr.: 3144 S. Barrington Ave. Apt. C, Los Angeles, CA 90066-1146 USA.

Strauss Consultants, 48 W. 25th St., 11th Flr., New York, NY 10010-2708 USA Toll Free Fax: 888-528-8273; Toll Free: 800-236-7918
E-mail: strausscon@aol.com.

Strawberry Laine LLC, *(0-9678111)* 440 Belle Vue, Lockport, LA 70374 USA Tel 504-532-6324; Fax: 504-532-3363
E-mail: blj7@aol.com; eblinky@aol.com.

Stray Dog Pr., *(0-9664082)* P.O. Box 1099, Calistoga, CA 94515 USA Tel 707-963-8364 do not confuse with the same or similar name in springfield, IL, Portland, OR
E-mail: mickiv@napanet.net
Web site: http://www.dogchefs.com.

Street Saint Pubns., *(0-615; 1-931090)* 441 Brighton Rd., Pacifica, CA 94044 USA Tel 650-355-4296
E-mail: lynnruth@pacbell.net
Web site: http://www.lynnruthmiller.com.

Streetside Stories, Inc., *(0-9646977; 0-9710606)* 1360 Mission St., Suite. 200, San Francisco, CA 94103 USA Tel 415-864-5221; Fax: 415-864-5628
E-mail: contact@streetside.org
Web site: http://www.streetside.org.

StreetTalk Publishing Co., *(0-9770009)* 7261 Brooke Blvd., Reynoldsburg, OH 43068 USA
E-mail: amazingteistreet@aol.com.

Strelecky, John *See* **Aspen Light Publishing**

Stress Management Technologies, *(0-9664007)* 3507 Tully Rd., Bldg. F, Suite E1, Modesto, CA 95356 USA Tel 209-525-8740; Fax: 209-525-3776.

Stretching Charts, Inc., *(1-929343)* 11003 A St., S., Tacoma, WA 98444 USA Tel 253-536-4922; Fax: 253-536-4944; Toll Free: 800-356-0709
E-mail: ann@vhikits.com
Web site: http://www.peertutorpress.com.

Strickland, Wilton, *(0-9747035)* 618 Pk. Ave., Goldsboro, NC 27530 USA (SAN 255-8114) Tel 919-734-2830 (phone/fax)
E-mail: wilton@esn.net
Web site: http://www.wiltonstrickland.com.

Strike Publishing, *(0-9674612)* 866 S. Gretna Green Way, Los Angeles, CA 90049 USA
E-mail: joshstrike@earthlink.net
Web site: http://www.home.earthlink.net/~joshstrike.

Striking Presence Pubns., *(0-9724935)* Orders Addr.: P.O. Box 475, Moorestown, NJ 08057 USA Tel 609-936-7278; Fax: 609-936-9651; Edit Addr.: 49-13 Quail Ridge Dr., Plainsboro, NJ 08536 USA
E-mail: jc@strikingpresence.com
Web site: http://www.strikingpresence.com.

String of Beads Pubns., *(0-9672012)* 9297 Avignon Pl., West Jordan, UT 84088 USA Fax: 801-566-0406
E-mail: jepp@fiber.net
Web site: http://www.stringofbeads.com.

Stringer, Alicia, *(0-9651588)* 411 Bastin Rd., Kings Mountain, KY 40442 USA.

Strombosky, Jerome D., *(0-9665579)* P.O. Box 4018, Westford, MA 01886-0032 USA.

Strong Corner Publishing, LCC, *(0-9754755)* 5331 Talavero Pl., Parker, CO 80134-2799 USA
E-mail: spencerj@broncos.nfl.com.

Strong, Louise dev, *(0-9770950)* P.O. Box 197, Morristown, NY 13664 USA Tel 315-375-4238
E-mail: riverstrong@gisco.net.

Structured Learning, *(0-9787800)* 27062 Lost Colt, Laguna Hills, CA 92653 USA
Web site: http://www.structuredlearning.net.

Struggle Against the Odds, *(0-9778318)* 3929 Clay Pl., NE, Washington, DC 20019 USA Tel 202-397-5310 (phone/fax)
E-mail: satocommunications@rcn.com
Web site: http://www.satocommunication.com.

Struik Pubs. (ZAF) *(0-86977; 0-86978; 0-86966; 1-86825; 1-86872; 1-875015; 1-86870; 1-86809; 1-86823; 1-77007) Dist. by* **Intl Pubs Mktg.**

Stuart & Weitz Publishing Group, *(0-9769949)* Div. of EQ Pubns., Orders Addr.: 32412 Lake Pleasant Dr., Westlake Village, CA 91361 USA
Web site: http://www.enchantedquillpublications.com; http://www.stuartweitzpublishing.com.

Stuart, Jesse Foundation, The, *(0-945084; 1-931672)* Orders Addr.: P.O. Box 669, Ashland, KY 41105 USA (SAN 245-8837) Tel 606-326-1667; Fax: 606-325-2519; Edit Addr.: 1645 Winchester Ave., Ashland, KY 41101 USA (SAN 245-8845)
E-mail: jsf@inet99.net
Web site: http://www.jsfbooks.com.

Stuart, Lyle *Imprint of* **Kensington Publishing Corp.**

Student Pr. Initiative, *(1-932948)* 509 W. 121st St., Suite 406, New York, NY 10027 USA Tel 212-678-8339; Fax: 212-678-3746
E-mail: epg10@columbia.edu.

Students Taking a Right Stand, (STARS) *Imprint of* **National Center For Youth Issues**

Studies From The Herbarium, *(0-9726953; 0-9761774)* Orders Addr.: 400 W. 1st St., Chico, CA 95929-0515 USA Tel 530-898-5381; Fax: 530-898-4363; Edit Addr.: California State Univ., Chico, Chico, CA 95929-0515 USA
E-mail: ljaneway@csuchico.edu
Web site: http://www.csuchico.edu/biol/Herb/studies.html.

Studio *Imprint of* **Penguin Group (USA) Inc.**

Studio 403, *(0-9633943; 1-933129)* 399 Shoreland Dr., Lopez Island, WA 98261-8412 USA Tel 360-468-4347
E-mail: mark@studio403.com
Web site: http://www.studio403.com.

Studio 9 Bks. and Music, 162 Margaret St., Plattsburgh, NY 12901 USA Tel 518-298-8595
E-mail: studio9@rdppub.com
Dist(s): **Booksource, The**
Koen-Levy Bk. Wholesalers LLC.

Studio Editions *See* **Studio Editions/TC Pubs**

Studio Editions/TC Pubs, *(1-893592)* 2000 N. Prairie Ave., Roswell, NM 88201 USA (SAN 299-8246) ; *Imprints:* TC Pubs (TC Pubs)
E-mail: martha_keltz@yahoo.com; JForbes@studioeditions.com
Web site: http://www.tcpubs.com; http://www.studioeditions.com.

Studio Five/Fourteen, *(1-891736)* Orders Addr.: 4429 Limerick Ln., Frisco, TX 75034-8436 USA Tel 214-618-4226 (phone/fax)
E-mail: robinh@vxiv.com
Web site: http://www.artietheairplane.com.

Studio Foglio, LLC, *(1-889061; 1-890856)* 2400 NW 80th St., Suite 129, Seattle, WA 98117-4449 USA (SAN 254-5128) Tel 206-782-8739; Fax: 206-783-3931
E-mail: foglio@studiofoglio.com; savannah@studiofoglio.com; foglio@xxxenophile.com
Web site: http://www.studiofoglio.com
Dist(s): **Berkeley Game Distributors**
Chessex
Cold Cut Comics Distribution
Diamond Comic Distributors, Inc.
Diamond Bk. Distributors
FM International
Rip Off Pr., Inc.
Syco Distribution.

Studio Indiana, *(0-9745186)* 430 N. Sewell Rd., Bloomington, IN 47408 USA Tel 812-223-5073 (phone/fax)
E-mail: john@studioindiana.com
Web site: http://www.studioindiana.com.

Studio Ironcat L.L.C. *See* **International Comics & Entertainment L.L.C.**

Studio Loplop, *(0-9677459)* 3522 Green Vista Dr., Encino, CA 91436 USA Fax: 818-505-1199
E-mail: nasdaquero@aol.com; clerid@aol.com.

Studio Mouse LLC, *(1-59069)* 353 Main Ave., Norwalk, CT 06851 USA Tel 203-846-2274; Fax: 203-846-1776; Toll Free: 800-228-7839
E-mail: chelsea.shriver@soundprints.com
Dist(s): **Soundprints.**

Studio 17, *(0-9700777)* 17 Shakerag St., Mineral Point, WI 53565 USA Tel 608-987-3573
E-mail: mgrow@fammed.wisc.edu.

StudioLine Photo *Imprint of* **H&M Systems Software, Inc.**

Studios West Publications *See* **Ritchie Unlimited Pubns.**

Study Ctr. Pr. *Imprint of* **San Francisco Study Ctr.**

Study Systemizer, Inc., *(1-886695)* 9700 Lamar Ave., Overland Park, KS 66207 USA Tel 913-648-6666; Fax: 913-648-1166; Toll Free: 800-788-3954
E-mail: study@studysystemizer.com
Web site: http://www.studysystemizer.com.

Studymates Ltd. (GBR) *(1-84285) Dist. by* **Trans-Atl Phila.**

Stull, Judy, *(0-9765738)* 16401 96th St., Lexington, OK 73051-8208 USA Tel 405-527-7467
E-mail: puppetlady@valornet.com.

Stump Hse. Bks., *(0-9707334)* 11411 N. Pinecrest Dr., Spokane, WA 99218 USA Tel 509-466-5449
E-mail: stien@mail.whitworth.edu.

Stunt Publishing, *(0-9745930)* 22287 Mulholland Why, No. 281, Calabasas, CA 91302 USA Tel 818-312-5157
E-mail: stuntpublishing@earthlink.net
Dist(s): **Independent Pubs. Group.**

Stunz, Ruth S., *(0-9720322)* 1933 S. Ridgewood Dr., Wichita, KS 67218 USA.

Stupar, Robert, *(0-9715142)* Orders Addr.: P.O. Box 3311, Pueblo, CO 81005 USA Tel 719-561-3176; Edit Addr.: 2531 Begonia, Pueblo, CO 81005 USA.

Stylewriter Pubns., *(0-9718288; 0-9721653; 0-9729411; 0-9748771)* Div. of Stylewriter, Inc., 4395 N. Windsor Dr., Provo, UT 84604-6301 USA Toll Free: 866-802-7888
E-mail: customerservice@spllc.rog
Web site: http://www.spllc.org.

Stylus Publishing, LLC, *(1-57922)* Orders Addr.: P.O. Box 605, Herndon, VA 20172-0605 USA; Edit Addr.: 22883 Quicksilver Dr., Sterling, VA 20166-2012 USA (SAN 299-1853) Tel 703-661-1581; Fax: 703-661-1501 Do not confuse with companies with the same name in Sunnyvale, CA, Quakertown, PA
E-mail: stylusmail@presswarehouse.com
Web site: http://www.styluspub.com
Dist(s): **Books International, Incorporated.**

Suanne Tastica Creations Inc. *See* **Tastica, Suanne Creations Inc.**

Subiaco Abbey, *(0-9665080)* 405 N. Subiaco Ave., Subiaco, AR 72865-9700 USA Tel 501-934-4295; Fax: 501-934-4328
E-mail: abbeydevelop@subi.org
Web site: http://www.subi.org/abbey.htm.

Sub-Saharan Pubs. & Traders (GHA) *(9988-550) Dist. by* **Mich St U Pr.**

Subterranean Co., Orders Addr.: P.O. Box 160, Monroe, OR 97456 USA Fax: 541-847-6018
E-mail: subco@clipper.net.

Success Empowering Techniques, Inc., *(0-9753415)* 5500 S. Eastern Ave., Las Vegas, NV 89119 USA Tel 702-893-0042
E-mail: set@setsuccess.com
Web site: http://www.setsuccess.com.

Success for All Foundation, *(0-9767850)* 200 W. Towsontown Blvd., Baltimore, MD 21204 USA Tel 800-548-4998; Fax: 410-324-4458
Web site: http://www.successforall.net.

Suckerfish Bks., *(0-9764659)* 23700 NW Skyline Blvd., North Plains, OR 97133 USA Tel 503-957-1554
Web site: http://www.suckerfishbooks.com.

Suffering Servant Scriptorium, *(0-9703996)* 9634 Boyett Ct., Fairfax, VA 22032 USA Tel 703-978-6230; Fax: 703-978-6025
E-mail: christine@haapala.clom; christine@haapala.com
Web site: http://www.sufferingservant.com.

Sugar Ducky Bks., Inc., *(0-9727388)* P.O. Box 56954, Jacksonville, FL 32241-6954 USA (SAN 255-1403)
E-mail: service@sugarduckybooks.com
Web site: http://www.sugarduckybooks.com.

Suitcase Pr.,The, *(0-9675567)* P.O. Box 6107, Orange, CA 92863-6107 USA (SAN 253-0163) Tel 714-317-1989; Fax: 949-713-5032; Toll Free: 800-796-1989
E-mail: CMShubeck@aol.com.

SuiteOne Design Group *See* **Mindgoal Publishing**

Sullivan, Kelley Enterprises, *(0-9728556)* c/o L. Leon, KSE, P.O. Box 1843, Lemon Grove, CA 91946-1843 USA
E-mail: info@mykse.com
Web site: http://www.mykse.com.

Sultemeier, Annette, *(0-9662426)* P.O. Box 6907, Crp Christi, TX 78466-6907 USA.

Sulu Arts & Books *See* **T'Boli Publishing & Distributors**

Suma de Letras, S.L. (ESP) *(84-663; 84-95501; 84-96463) Dist. by* **Distribks Inc.**

Sumach Pr. (CAN) *(1-894549) Dist. by* **Orca Bk Pubs.**

Sumeria, Inc., *(1-57047)* P.O. Box 194145, San Francisco, CA 94119-4145 USA
E-mail: info@sumeria.com
Web site: http://www.sumeria.com
Dist(s): **Sunburst Communications, Inc.**

Summa Bks., *(0-932423)* P.O. Box 2095, Darien, IL 60561-6895 USA (SAN 687-4096).

Summa Publishing Company *See* **Summa Bks.**

Summer Day Publishing, LLC, *(0-9768653)* 14747 San Marsala Ct., Tampa, FL 33626 USA Tel 727-224-9874; Fax: 813-926-8215
E-mail: baflorida@aol.com
Web site: http://www.thebreakawaykid.com.

Summer Street Pr., *(0-9766367)* 460 Summer St., Stamford, CT 06901 USA Tel 203-325-2217 Do not confuse with Summer Street Press in Santa Barbara, CA
E-mail: nick@summerstreetpress.com
Web site: http://www.summerstreetpress.com.

Summer Sun Publishing, *(0-9710809)* Orders Addr.: P.O. Box 6009, Newport News, VA 23606 USA Tel 757-930-3369; Edit Addr.: 31 Deep Creek Rd., Newport News, VA 23606 USA Tel 757 930 3369
E-mail: ads@summersunpublishing.com; aseward300@aol.com
Web site: http://www.summersunpublishing.com
Dist(s): **Baker & Taylor Bks.**

Summerbook Co., *(1-933055)* 305 Lyndale Dr., Hartsville, SC 29550 USA Tel 843-383-5554 (phone/fax)
E-mail: angela@summerbookcompany.com
Web site: http://www.summerbookcompany.com.

Summerland Pr., *(1-882021)* Div. of The Summerland Group, Inc., 3451 SE Court Dr., Stuart, FL 34997 USA (SAN 248-2967).

Summerland Publishing, *(0-9794585; 0-9794863; 0-9795444)* P.O. Box 1006, Buellton, CA 93427 USA (SAN 853-4497) Tel 805 736-8359; Fax: 805-365-0526
E-mail: SummerlandPubs@aol.com
Web site: http://www.SummerlandPublishing.com.

Summerside Lane, *(0-9777570)* 179 Highlands Dr., Williston, VT 05495 USA (SAN 850-1793)
Web site: http://www.Summersidelane.com.

Summertime Bks. & Comics, *(0-9716357)* 24727 Airville Ave., Newhall, CA 91321 USA
Web site: http://www.summertimebooks.com.

Summerwind Marketing, Inc., *(0-9704447)* Orders Addr.: 44831 Milestone Sq., No. 404, Ashburn, VA 20147 USA Tel 703-850-3733; Fax: 703-783-0449; Edit Addr.: 1927-F E. Huntington Dr., Duarte, CA 91010 USA (SAN 253-4509) Tel 213-305-8688; Toll Free: 888-820-8140 (phone/fax)
E-mail: jimmoseley@wwdb.org
Web site: http://www.birbal.net
Dist(s): **Biblio Distribution.**

Summit House Pubs., *(0-9746735)* P.O. Box 964, Morton Grove, IL 60053-0964 USA Tel 847-731-3177 (phone/fax) ; *Imprints:* Ijiwola Press, Gregory (G Ijiwola Pr)
Web site: http://www.summitpublishers.com.

Summit Lighthouse Library, The *Imprint of* **Summit Univ. Pr.**

Summit Pr., *(0-9612378)* P.O. Box 131, Volcano, HI 96785 USA (SAN 289-5013) Tel 808-967-7512.

Summit Univ. Pr., *(0-916766; 0-922729; 1-932890)* Orders Addr.: P.O. Box 5000, Gardiner, MT 59030-5000 USA Tel 406-848-9500; Fax: 406-848-9605; Toll Free: 800-245-5445 ; *Imprints:* Summit Lighthouse Library, The (Summit Lghthse)
E-mail: info@summituniversitypress.com
Web site: http://www.summituniversitypress.com
Dist(s): **National Bk. Network.**

†Summy-Birchard, Inc., *(0-87487; 1-58951)* Div. of Warner/Chappell, 15800 NW 48th Ave., Miami, FL 33014 USA (SAN 202-7461) Tel 305-620-1500; Fax: 305-621-1094; Toll Free: 800-327-7643
Web site: http://www.lentine.com/bo/sebsum.stm; *CIP.*

Sun Circle Pr., *(0-9729612)* 7600 Franklin Dr., El Paso, TX 79915 USA (SAN 255-2795) Tel 915-779-5161
E-mail: jaimeoperez@yahoo.com; suncirclepress@yahoo.com
Web site: http://www.casajaguar.com; http://www.socialsyntaxjournal.com.

Sun Coast Communications, Inc., *(0-9705383)* 205 White Harbor Rd., Long Beach, MS 39560-5611 USA Tel 228-863-3558; Fax: 228-868-6366
E-mail: suncoastcom@earthlink.net.

Sun R.A.Y.S., LLC, *(0-9702880)* 417 Clover Ln., Fort Collins, CO 80521 USA Tel 970-495-9782; Fax: 970-495-6863
E-mail: emsunco@aol.com
Web site: http://iwant2learn.com.

Sun Rose Pubs., *(0-9712781)* P.O. Box 2314, East Orange, NJ 07019 USA
E-mail: carolineilo@yahoo.com; eph-llogienboh@worldnet.att.net.

Sun Sings Pubns., *(0-9721429)* 4144 LaFayette Pl., Culver City, CA 90232 USA Tel 323-732-4701; Fax: 802-609-2959
E-mail: alan@alan-lindgren.org
Web site: http://www.alan-lindgren.org.

Sun Sprite Publishing, *(0-9745712)* 19 Milton Ave, Cranston, RI 02905 USA Toll Free: 877-883-4798
E-mail: kwanyin@ureach.com
Web site: http://www.mykwanyin.com/sunsprite.html.

Sun Star Magic Entertainment, *(0-9716311)* Orders Addr.: P.O. Box 31878, Seatt;e, WA 98103 USA; Edit Addr.: 2212 N. 80th St., Seattle, WA 98103 USA
E-mail: sunstarmagic@hotmail.com
Web site: http://www.sunstarmagic.com.

Sunbelt Media, Incorporated *See* **Eakin Pr.**

†Sunbelt Pubns., Inc., *(0-916251; 0-932653; 0-9606704; 0-9620402)* 1256 Fayette St., El Cajon, CA 92020-1511 USA (SAN 630-0790) Tel 619-258-4911; Fax: 619-258-4916; Toll Free: 800-626-6579
E-mail: sunbeltpub@prodigy.net
Web site: http://www.sunbeltpub.com; http://www.sunbeltbooks.com
Dist(s): **Baker & Taylor Bks.**
Pacific Bks.
Quality Bks., Inc.; *CIP.*

Sunburst *Imprint of* **Farrar, Straus & Giroux**

Sunburst Communications, Inc., *(0-7805; 0-911831; 1-55636; 1-55826)* 400 Columbus Ave., Valhalla, NY 10595-1335 USA (SAN 213-5620) Toll Free: 800-431-1934
E-mail: webmaster@nysunburst.com
Web site: http://www.sunburst.com
Dist(s): **Follett Media Distribution**
JIST Publishing
Linx Educational Publishing, Inc.

Suncrest Pubns., *(0-9701589)* P.O. Box 236, Las Cruces, NM 88004 USA Tel 505-527-5527 (phone/fax)
E-mail: jlsmith@zianet.com.

Sundance Entertainment, *(0-9729847)* P.O. Box 418, New York, NY 10035 USA Tel 646-431-9334.

Sundance Media Group, Inc./VASST, *(0-9762380)* P.O. Box 3, Stockton, UT 84071 USA Tel 435-882-8494; Fax: 435-882-8508
E-mail: info@sundancemediagroup.com
Web site: http://www.vasst.com.

SunDance Press *See* **Book Pubs. of El Paso**

Sundance/Newbridge Educational Publishing, *(0-7608; 0-88741; 0-940146; 1-56784; 1-56801; 1-58273; 1-4007; 1-4207)* Div. of Haights Cross Communications, P.O. Box 740, Northborough, MA 01532 USA (SAN 169-3484) Tel 508-571-6500; Fax: 508-571-6502; Toll Free: 800-343-8204
E-mail: asterling@sundancepub.com; info@sundancepub.com
Web site: http://www.newbridgeonline.com; http://www.sundancepub.com.

Sunday Paper, The, *(0-9614022)* 19 Colony Rd., New Haven, CT 06511 USA (SAN 683-6259) Tel 203-624-2520
E-mail: sundaypaper@snet.net.

Sunday School Board of the Southern Baptist Convention *See* **LifeWay Christian Resources**

Sunday School Publishing Board *See* **Townsend Pr. - Sunday Schl. Publishing Board**

Sundback, Ruth, *(0-9776850)* 10430 Perla Bello Ct., Las Vegas, NV 89135 USA (SAN 850-9719)
E-mail: ruthslv@earthlink.net.

Sundog, Ltd., *(1-932203; 1-59744)* Orders Addr.: 1505 Stratton Ave., Nashville, TN 37206 USA
E-mail: booksales@sundogltd.com; ascameron@SundogLtd.com
Web site: http://www.sundogltd.com
Dist(s): **Express Media.**

Sundown Publishing Co., *(1-893691)* Div. of Bandera Enterprises, Orders Addr.: P.O. Box 397, Glen Carbon, IL 62034 USA Tel 618-288-6452 (phone/fax); Toll Free: 800-327-2897; Edit Addr.: 18 Hansen Dr., Glen Carbon, IL 62034 USA Do not confuse with Sundown Publishing Co., Mesa, AZ
E-mail: sundown@the-word.net; info@mustangcorral.com.

Sunergos Bible Studies, *(1-932934)* 2485 Morse Rd., Sebastopol, CA 95472 USA Tel 707-829-2956
E-mail: jan@sunergos.org; rich@sunergos.org
Web site: http://www.sunergos.org.

Sunfleur Pubns., Inc., *(0-9653729)* 421 Westchester Rd., Statesville, NC 28677 USA Tel 704-873-5516; Fax: 704-873-3850
E-mail: hdarden@i-america.net
Web site: http://www.booksbyhunter.com
Dist(s): **Parnassus Bk. Distributors.**

Sunflower Pr., *(0-9616586; 0-9768507)* P.O. Box 750733, Forest Hills, NY 11375 USA (SAN 659-7785) Fax: 718-830-9616
E-mail: order@chutaichi.com.

Sunflower Pr., *(0-9647783)* Div. of Sunflower Foods, 109 Pine Cone Ln., Elgin, TX 78621-9727 USA Do not confuse with companies with the same or similar names in Boise, ID, Meridian, ID, Newton, MA, Lafayette, LA
E-mail: info@sfpressaustin.com.

Sunflower Promotions, L.L.C., *(0-9662934)* P.O. Box 48, Great Cacapon, WV 25422-0048 USA Tel 410-974-4177; Fax: 410-974-0301; Toll Free: 800-660-2630
E-mail: susansunflower@aol.com
Dist(s): **Quality Bks., Inc.**

Sunflower Publishing *See* **Growing Field Bks.**

Sunflower Publishing Company *See* **Sunfleur Pubns., Inc.**

Sunflower Seeds Pr., *(0-9743627)* 9470 Hwy 96 W., Franklin, TN 37064 USA
E-mail: bill@sunflowerseedspress.com
Web site: http://www.sunflowerseedspress.com; http://www.downonfriendlyacres.com.

Sunflower Univ. Pr., *(0-89745)* Subs. of Journal of the West, Inc., 2961 Nevada St., Manhattan, KS 66502-2355 USA (SAN 218-5075) Toll Free: 800-258-1232 (orders)
E-mail: pub@sunflower-univ-press.org
Web site: http://www.sunflower-univ-press.org.

SunHill Pubs., *(0-9673189)* Orders Addr.: P.O. Box 464955, Lawrenceville, GA 30042 USA Tel 770-513-1417; Fax: 770-513-2450 Do not confuse with Hill Publishing in Marina, CA
E-mail: ehill111@charter.net
Web site: http://www.SunHillPublishers.com.

Sunlight Bks., *(0-9678081)* P.O. Box 385, Forked River, NJ 08731-0385 USA (SAN 253-651X) Tel 609-242-7881; Fax: 609-693-0491; 321 Lacey Rd., Forked River, NJ 08731-0385 Tel 609-693-9167
E-mail: sunlightbooks@molecadv.com
Web site: http://www.molecadv.com
Dist(s): **Baker & Taylor Bks.**
BookMasters, Inc.

Sunny & The Chocolate Dog, LLC, *(0-9725945)* 5 Palm Row, Saint Augustine, FL 32084 USA Tel 904-808-7144; Fax: 904-808-7142
E-mail: josh@sunnyandthechocolatedog.com
Web site: http://www.sunnyandthechocolatedog.com.

Sunny Bks. *Imprint of* **JB Communications, Inc.**

Sunny Future Pr., *(0-9754980)* 890 Bruce Dr., Wantagh, NY 11793-1116 USA
E-mail: canivan@optonline.net
Web site: http://www.jc-solarhomes.com.

Sunny Hollow Pr., *(0-9755818)* 2517 N. 62nd St., Mesa, AZ 85215 USA Tel 480-830-7634; Toll Free: 800-442-0046
E-mail: rjvb@sunnyhollowpress.com
Web site: http://www.sunnyhollowpress.com.

Sunphone, Ltd., *(0-9652458)* 427 Sippewissett Rd., Falmouth, MA 02540 USA Tel 508-540-6899; Fax: 508-540-8226
E-mail: sunfal@aol.com.

SunRaSon Production Co., *(0-9677644)* 882 E. 57th St., Brooklyn, NY 11234 USA
E-mail: info@sunrason.com
Web site: http://www.sunrason.com.

Sunrise Publications *See* **Prematurely Yours**

Sunrise Pubns., *(0-9670790)* 4000 Greenwood Way, Mansfield, TX 76063-5560 USA Do not confuse with companies with same name in Kingston, NH, Cincinnati OH, Hewitt NJ, San Antonio, TX
E-mail: sunrise@digitalexp.com
Web site: http://www.users.digitalexp.com/~users/sunrise/.

SunRise Publishing, *(0-9644552; 1-57636)* Orders Addr.: P.O. Box 1001, Orem, UT 84059 USA Tel 801-860-2665; Fax: 801-705-0124; Edit Addr.: P.O. Box 1001, Orem, UT 84059-1001 USA Do not confuse with companies with the same or similar names in Lake Forest, IL, Niagara Falls, NY, Lincoln City, OR, Santa Barbara, CA, Hatfield, PA, Maryland Heights, MD, Austinburg, OH, Inman, SC, Fort Lauderdale, FL, Albuquerque, NM
E-mail: brian@sunrisebooks.com
Web site: http://www.sunrisebooks.com
Dist(s): **Granite Publishing & Distribution**
Village Marketing.

Sunrise Selections, *(0-9656307)* Orders Addr.: P.O. Box 51602, Provo, UT 84605-1602 USA Tel 801-852-6141; Fax: 801-489-9517; Edit Addr.: 1102 N. Main, Mapleton, UT 84664 USA
E-mail: bbriggs@provo.utah.gov
Web site: http://www.sunrise-selections.com
Dist(s): **Granite Publishing & Distribution.**

SunriseHouse Pubs., *(0-9770783)* 5181 Blackpool Rd., Westminster, CA 92683 USA
E-mail: dawn@dawnwilliams.net
Web site: http://www.sunrisehousepublishers.com.

Sunseeker Designs LLC, *(0-9714347)* P.O. Box 1562, Evanston, WY 82931-1562 USA
E-mail: mcgraw_21069@msn.com
Web site: http://www.sunseekerdesigns.com.

Sunset Beach Music, *(0-9639279)* P.O. Box 159, Haleiwa, HI 96712 USA
E-mail: msmusic@hula.net.

Sunset Bks./Sunset Publishing Corp., *(0-376)* Orders Addr.: Leisure Arts 5701 Ranch Dr., Little Rock, AR 72223 USA; Edit Addr.: 80 Willow Rd., Menlo Park, CA 94025-3691 USA Tel 650-321-3600; Fax: 650-324-1532; Toll Free: 800-227-7346 (except California); 800-321-0372 (in California)
E-mail: nicholsonl@sunset.com
Web site: http://sunsetbooks.com
Dist(s): **Leisure Arts, Inc.**

Sunset Readers Publishing, *(0-9749333)* 220 W., 400 N., American Fork, UT 84003-1567 USA
E-mail: beb1@sisna.com
Web site: http://www.bennetthbracken.com.

Sunshine Bks. for Children, *(0-9745116)* 8127 E. Weldon Ave., Scottsdale, AZ 85251 USA.

Sunshine Center, Incorporated *See* **Prevention Through Puppetry, Inc.**

Sunshine Pr., LLC, *(0-9668072)* Div. of Sharin' Sunshine, LLC, 2101 Tallman Ln., Longmont, CO 80501-4187 USA Tel 970-586-3317; Fax: 303-684-0654
E-mail: shards2@juno.com.

Sunshine Pubs., *(0-9715753)* P.O. Box 7261, Fremont, CA 94537 USA
E-mail: sunshinepublish@aol.com
Web site: http://www.sunshinepublishers.com.

Sunshine Publishing, *(0-9749844)* 1421 Washington St., Lincoln, NE 68502-2455 USA Do not confuse with companies with the same or similar names in Carthage, NY, Buffalo Grove, IL , Bristol, TN, Columbus, GA, Raleigh, NC, Ft Worth, TX.

Sunstar Publishing *Imprint of* **1st World Publishing, Inc.**

†Sunstone Pr., *(0-86534; 0-913270)* Div. of The Sunstone Corporation, Orders Addr.: 239 Johnson St., Santa Fe, NM 87504-2321 USA; Edit Addr.: P.O. Box 2321, Santa Fe, NM 87504-2321 USA (SAN 214-2090) Tel 505-988-4418; Fax: 505-988-1025; Toll Free: 800-243-5644 (Orders Only)
E-mail: jsmith@sunstonepress.com
Web site: http://www.sunstonepress.com
Dist(s): **Baker & Taylor Bks.**
Brodart Co.
Lightning Source, Inc.
New Leaf Distributing Co., Inc.
Quality Bks., Inc.
Treasure Chest Bks.; *CIP.*

Super Dentists, The, *(0-9798506)* 2226 Otay Lakes Rd., Chula Vista, CA 91915 USA (SAN 854-5650)
Web site: http://www.thesuperdentists.com.

Super Duper Pubns., *(1-58650)* Div. of Super Duper, Inc., Orders Addr.: P.O. Box 24997, Greenville, SC 29616 USA Tel 864-288-3536; Fax: 864-288-3380; Toll Free: 800-277-8737; Edit Addr.: 5201 Pelham Rd., Greenville, SC 29615-5723 USA
E-mail: custserv@superduperinc.com
Web site: http://www.superduperinc.com.

Super SandCastle *Imprint of* **ABDO Publishing Co.**

Supercat Pr., Ltd., *(0-9718499)* 165 Hillcrest Ave., Athens, GA 30606 USA (SAN 254-556X) Fax: 706-548-0766
E-mail: info@supercatpress.com
Dist(s): **Baker & Taylor Bks.**

Sur Mar Publishing, *(0-9711901)* P.O. Box 219, Yorkville, IL 60560 USA Fax: 630-553-2531
E-mail: surmarprod@aol.com; sumarprod@aol.com.

Surber, Shawn-Michelle *See* **Mornin' Light Media**

Surfing Group, The, *(0-9770730)* Primedia, 950 Calie Amanecer, Suite C, San Clemente, CA 92673 USA
E-mail: ross.garrett@primedia.com.

Sur-Mount Pubs., *(0-9673517; 0-9740107)* P.O. Box 99396, Emeryville, CA 94662-9396 USA Tel 510-559-8797
E-mail: cs@surmountpublishersincorporated.com; sales@surmountpublishersincorporated.com
Web site: http://www.surmountpublishersincorporated.com
Dist(s): **Baker & Taylor Bks.**

Suromex, Ediciones, S.A. (MEX) *(968-855) Dist. by* **Giron Bks.**

Surrey Bks., *(0-940625; 0-9609516; 1-57284)* 1501 Madison St., Evanston, IL 60202-2033 USA (SAN 275-8857) Toll Free: 800-326-4430
E-mail: seibold@agatepublishing.com
Web site: http://www.agatepublishing.com
Dist(s): **Perseus Distribution.**

Survival Bks. (GBR) *(0-9516528; 0-9519804; 1-901130; 1-905303) Dist. by* **Natl Bk Netwk.**

Susaeta Ediciones, S.A. (ESP) *(84-305) Dist. by* **Lectorum Pubns.**

Susaeta Ediciones, S.A. (ESP) *(84-305) Dist. by* **AIMS Intl.**

Susaeta Ediciones, S.A. (ESP) *(84-305) Dist. by* **Giron Bks.**

Susi B. Marketing, Inc., *(0-9773653)* 188 Wentworth St., Charleston, SC 29401 USA Tel 843-822-7676; Fax: 843-958-8444
E-mail: keri@susibmarketing.com
Web site: http://www.susibmarketing.com.

Susquehanna Univ. Pr., *(0-941664; 0-945636; 1-57591)* Affil. of Associated Univ. Presses, Orders Addr.: 2010 Eastpark Blvd., Cranbury, NJ 08512 USA Tel 609-655-4770; Fax: 609-655-8366
Web site: http://www.susqu.edu/su_press
Dist(s): **Baker & Taylor International**
Replica Bks.

Sussex Academic Pr. (GBR) *(1-898723; 1-902210; 1-903900; 1-84519) Dist. by* **Intl Spec Bk.**

Susy Dorn Productions, LLC, *(0-9764010)* P.O. Box 111393, Campbell, CA 95011-1393 USA
Web site: http://www.juguemosenespanol.com.

Suthernsky, *(1-893709)* 801 Benefit Rd., Chesapeake, VA 23322 USA Tel 757-421-7963; Fax: 757-421-2860
E-mail: misl@aol.com.

Sutton Publishing, *(0-7509; 0-86299; 0-904387)* Subs. of Sutton Publishing, Ltd., 260 Fifth Ave., 6th Flr., New York, NY 10001 USA Do not confuse with companies with same names in Old Greenwich, CT, Eugene, OR
E-mail: Suttonus@mindspring.com
Web site: http://www.suttonpublishing.co.uk/
Dist(s): **MBI Distribution Services**
National Bk. Network.

Sutton Publishing, Ltd. (GBR) *(0-7509; 0-86299; 0-904387) Dist. by* **Natl Bk Netwk.**

Sutton, Robin, *(0-9755098)* P.O. Box 79174, Saginaw, TX 76179 USA
Web site: http://www.therobinsnestbooks.com.

Suttons Bay Pubns., *(0-9621466)* Box 361, Suttons Bay, MI 49682 USA (SAN 251-4222) Tel 616-271-6821; Fax: 616-271-4749.

Suzalooz Pr., *(0-9660350)* 139 S. Eighth St., Brooklyn, NY 11211 USA Tel 718-387-3384; Fax: 212-475-4442
E-mail: zhour@inx.net.

Susy & Livy Pubns., *(0-9727757)* Orders Addr.: P.O. Box 449, Virginia City, NV 89440 USA Tel 775-847-0454; Fax: 775-847-9010; Edit Addr.: 111 S. C St., Virginia City, NV 89440-0449 USA
E-mail: info@marktwainbooks.com
Web site: http://www.marktwainbooks.com.

Suzy's Zoo, *(0-9643588; 0-9726147; 0-9765108)* Orders Addr.: P.O. Box 85490, San Diego, CA 92186-5490 USA (SAN 298-7481) Tel 619-282-9401; Fax: 619-285-5730; Toll Free: 800-777-4846; Edit Addr.: 2355 Northside Dr., Suite 202, San Diego, CA 92108 USA
Web site: http://www.suzyszoo.com.

Svoboda, David *See* **BooksbyDave Inc.**

Swak Pak, LLC, *(0-9707420)* 9417 S. 157th Pl., Gilbert, AZ 85234 USA (SAN 253-9527) Tel 480-557-6749; Fax: 480-557-6709; Toll Free: 866-792-5725 (866-SWAK-PAK)
E-mail: eileen@swakpak.com; gstrange@strangeview.com
Web site: http://swakpak.com.

†Swallow Pr., *(0-8040)* Ohio Univ. Pr., Scott Quadrangle, Athens, OH 45701 USA (SAN 202-5663) Tel 740-593-1158; Fax: 740-593-4536; Toll Free: 800-621-2736
E-mail: arnold@ohio.edu
Web site: http://www.ohio~.edu/oupress/
Dist(s): **Chicago Distribution Ctr.**
Ohio Univ. Pr.
Univ. of Chicago Pr.; *CIP.*

Swami Shivom Tirth Ashram, Inc., *(0-9676306)* 124 Rock Harbor Ln., Foster City, CA 94404 USA Tel 415-806-1007 (For Orders and all other communication); Fax: 650-506-5439
E-mail: drathi@yahoo.com
Web site: http://www.shivomtirthashram.org.

Swampfox *Imprint of* **Lexpress**

Swampland Publishing Co., *(0-9754785)* P.O. Box 1311, Larose, LA 70373 USA
E-mail: alces@cajunswampland.com.

Swan Creek Pr., *(0-9753216)* 3736 Linden Green Dr., Toledo, OH 43614 USA Tel 419-381-0115; Fax: 419-381-8696
E-mail: swancreekpress@buckeye-express.com.

Swan-Jones Production, *(1-882238)* 3801 Normandy, Dallas, TX 75205-2106 USA Tel 214-528-2732; Fax: 214-637-4572; Toll Free: 800-736-5663.

Swann, Alexandra, *(0-9623611)* 310 Thunderbird, No. 3, El Paso, TX 79912 USA Tel 915-584-7420; Fax: 915-584-2512.

Swann, Francine Pubns., *(0-9645451; 1-890770)* 10063 Smitherman Dr., Shreveport, LA 71115-2924 USA Tel 318-795-9391 (phone/fax) ; *Imprints:* Swann Publications (Swann Pubns)
E-mail: francine@prysm.net
Dist(s): **Denston, Richard O.**

Swann Pubns. *Imprint of* **Swann, Francine Pubns.**

Swannee Rivers, *(0-9749216)* 1629 Index Ave. Se, Suite No. 400, Renton, WA 98058 USA Fax: 425-277-2950
E-mail: swanneerivers@mindspring.com
Web site: http://www.swanneerivers.com.

Swansbury, Inc., *(0-9656745)* Orders Addr.: P.O. Box 117, Aberdeen, MD 21001 USA Tel 410-272-0836; Fax: 410-297-9767; Edit Addr.: 111 Beards Hill Rd., Aberdeen, MD 21001 USA.

SWC Editions *Imprint of* **Wayne, Steven Co.**

Sweeney Gulch Pr., *(0-9727469)* P.O. Box 26, Pomeroy, WA 99347 USA Tel 509-843-6138
E-mail: huntington@pomeroy-wa.com.

Sweet Apple Pr., *(0-9702465)* 153 Prospect St., Norwell, MA 02061 USA; P.O. Box 770, Norwell, MA 02061 Fax: 781-659-6761
E-mail: sweetapplepress@aol.com.

Sweet Dreams Bilingual Pubs., *(0-9673032)* 1713 NW 97th Ter., Coral Springs, FL 33071-5904 USA
E-mail: librosbp@earthlink.net
Web site: http://www.bilingualpublishers.com.

Sweet Dreams Pr. *Imprint of* **Bier Brothers, Inc.**

Sweet Legacy *Imprint of* **Yeva Corp.**

Sweet Potato Brown, *(0-9788158)* 3619 Saint Marys Ln., Saint Louis, MO 63121 USA
E-mail: sofiapenelopebrown@sbcglobal.net
Web site: http://www.at3619.com.

Sweet Punkin Pr., *(0-9755078)* 43 Riverside Ave., No. 405, Medford, MA 02155-4605 USA Tel 781-389-0693; Fax: 781-396-8052
E-mail: cvenez@aol.com
Web site: http://www.sweetpunkinpress.com.

Sweet Sommer Productions, *(0-9714378)* P.O. Box 1537, Healdsburg, CA 95448-1537 USA (SAN 254-2943) Tel 707-433-4304; Fax: 707-433-9185
E-mail: karen@littleamp.com
Web site: http://www.littleamp.com.

Sweet Success Pr., *(0-9700127)* 10012 Bryant Ct., Denver, CO 80260 USA Tel 303-469-2640 (phone/fax)
E-mail: Vkrudwig@aol.com
Web site: http://www.members.aol.com/vkrudwig
Dist(s): **Books West.**

Sweet T. C. Campbell, *(0-9761560)* 130 Lenox Ave., No. 1005, New York, NY 10026-2578 USA.

Sweetgrass Pr., L.L.C., *(0-9702630; 0-9714272; 0-9723376; 0-9745434)* P.O. Box 1862, Merrimack, NH 03054-1862 USA Do not confuse with Sweetgrass Press in Salem, OR
E-mail: info@sweetgrasspress.com
Web site: http://www.sweetgrasspress.com.

Sweetwater Pr., *(0-9615504)* P.O. Box 96, Ault, CO 80610-0096 USA (SAN 695-9199) Do not confuse with companies with similiar names in Raleigh, NC, Birmingham, AL,Miami FL, Little Rock AR
E-mail: rburgess@info2000.net
Web site: http://www.info2000.net/~rburgess/sweet1.htm.

Sweetwater Pr., *(1-58173; 1-889372; 1-60196)* Div. of Books-A-Million, Orders Addr.: 3608 Clairmont Ave., Birmingham, AL 035222 USA Do not confuse with companies with the same name in Ault, CO, Raleigh, NC Miami FL, Little Rock AR
Dist(s): **Independent Pubs. Group.**

Sweetwater Stagelines *Imprint of* **The Old West Co.**

Sweetwater Visions, *(0-9659189)* Orders Addr.: P.O. Box 1774, Gaylord, MI 49734 USA Tel 989-732-7626; Edit Addr.: 2100 Five Lakes Rd., Gaylord, MI 49735 USA
E-mail: sweetwtr@freeway.net
Web site: http://www.sweetwatervisions.com.

Swift Learning Resources, *(0-944991; 1-56861)* Div. of Swift Printing Corp., 1520 N. State St., Lehi, UT 84043-1079 USA (SAN 245-6737) Toll Free: 800-292-2831
E-mail: swift@swift-net.com
Web site: http://www.swiftlearning.com.

Swing Bridge Pr., The, *(0-9704958)* 3031 Lafeyette Ave., Omaha, NE 68131-1429 USA Tel 402-345-4080
E-mail: psymon@earthlink.net.

Swing Play, *(0-9673330)* Orders Addr.: P.O. Box 1891, Los Alamitos, CA 90720 USA Tel 562-596-0015; Fax: 562-425-7507; Edit Addr.: 3832 Howard Ave., No. 2, Los Alamitos, CA 90720 USA
E-mail: SwingPlay1@aol.com.

Swingset Pr., LLC, *(0-9658167; 1-930680)* Orders Addr.: P.O. Box 18701, Encino, CA 91416-8701 USA Tel 818-779-1413; Fax: 818-779-1411; Toll Free: 888-543-9366; Edit Addr.: 5987 S. High Dr., Morrison, CO 80465-2608 USA
E-mail: info@swingsetpress.com
Web site: http://www.swingsetpress.com.

Switzer Land Enterprises, *(0-9642663)* Orders Addr.: P.O. Box 3800, Estes Park, CO 80517 USA Tel 303-586-4624; Fax: 907-577-0775; Edit Addr.: 1236 Glacier View, Estes Park, CO 80517 USA
E-mail: philalpaca@aol.com.

Swonke, Cheryl, *(0-9727291)* P.O. Box 1941, Waller, TX 77484-1941 USA.

Sword of the Lord Pubs., *(0-87398)* Orders Addr.: P.O. Box 1099, Murfreesboro, TN 37133 USA (SAN 203-5642) Tel 615-893-6700; Fax: 615-895-7447
Dist(s): **Dake Publishing.**

Swordfish Communications, LLC, *(0-9741955)* Orders Addr.: 1748 Ohlen Rd. #67, Austin, TX 78757 USA
E-mail: orders@swordfishcommunications.com; cs@swordfishcommunications.com
Web site: http://www.swordfishcommunications.com.

Sy Publishing, *(0-9761613)* 7720 E. Redfield Rd., Suite No. 7, Scottsdale, AZ 85260 USA Tel 480-596-9226; Fax: 480-967-8736
E-mail: devinsper@yahoo.com
Web site: http://www.devinsper.com.

Sybertooth Inc. (CAN) *(0-9688024; 0-9739505) Dist. by* **Lightn Source.**

Sybex *Imprint of* **Wiley, John & Sons, Inc.**

Sybrell Publishing, *(0-9700599)* P.O. Box 554, Stone Mountain, GA 30086 USA Fax: 770-987-4093
E-mail: info@sybrell.com; sybrell@sybrell.com
Web site: http://www.sybrell.com.

Sydney Pr., *(0-9724577)* 258 Aikane St., Kailua, HI 96734-1603 USA
E-mail: jdbuck@pixi.com.

Sydney's Sproutin' Co., *(0-9652844)* 535 Gretuing Rd., Vero Beach, FL 32963 USA Fax: 305-538-4540.

Syentek Books Company, Incorporated *See* **Syentek, Inc.**

Syentek, Inc., *(0-914082)* P.O. Box 26588, San Francisco, CA 94126 USA (SAN 202-7534) Tel 415-928-0471.

Sylables, *(0-9724394)* 2105 Sheldon Rd., Saint Albans, VT 05478 USA (SAN 255-1500) Tel 802-524-0262
E-mail: sylables@earthlink.net
Web site: http://www.sylables.com.

Syllogism Pr., *(0-9638001)* 875 Emory Shield Rd., Murphy, NC 28906 USA Tel 732-290-7901
E-mail: spress@dnet.net.

Sylph Pubns., *(0-9673004; 0-9760742)* 1248 E. Edison St., W., Tucson, AZ 85719 USA Tel 520-882-3794
E-mail: eliotbooks@aol.com
Web site: http://www.eliotbooks.com.

Sylvan Dell Pubng., *(0-9764943; 0-9768823; 0-9777423; 1-934359)* 976 Houston Northcutt Blvd., Suite 3, Mount Pleasant, SC 29464 USA (SAN 256-6109) Tel 843-971-6722; Fax: 843-216-3804
E-mail: leegerman@sylvandellpublishing.com
Web site: http://www.sylvandellpublishing.com
Dist(s): **BWI**
Baker & Taylor Bks.
Bound to Stay Bound Bks.
Brodart Co.
Follett Library Resources
Perma-Bound Bks.
Quality Bks., Inc.

Symmetry Learning Systems, *(1-58447)* Div. of Symmetry Research, Inc., 5 Kuniholm Dr., Holliston, MA 01746 USA (SAN 299-7967) Fax: 508-893-0102
E-mail: info@symmetrylearning.com; prberget@symmetrylearning.com
Web site: http://www.symmetrylearning.com.

Symtalk, Inc., *(1-932770; 1-933209)* 875 Montreal Way, Saint Paul, MN 55102-4245 USA Toll Free: 877-796-8255
E-mail: info@symtalk.com
Web site: http://www.symtalk.com.

Symtext Media, *(0-9768379)* 21538 N. 65th Ave., Glendale, AZ 85308-6410 USA Tel 623-362-1947
E-mail: fullschedule@symtextmedia.com
Web site: http://www.symtextmedia.com.

Synaptic Wammy Works *See* **Loose In The Lab**

Synaxis Pr., *(0-911523)* P.O. Box 689, Lynden, WA 98264 USA (SAN 685-4338) Tel 604-826-9336; Fax: 604-820-9758
Dist(s): **Oakwood Pubns.**

Synchronicity Pr., *(0-9673449)* P.O. Box 481, Winchester, MA 01890 USA Tel 781-729-3530; Fax: 781-721-7306 Do not confuse with companies with same name in Piqua, OH, Charlottesville, VA.
E-mail: spress@iarp.org.

Syncopated Pr., *(0-9671978; 0-9717380)* P.O. Box 411, Plainwell, MI 49080 USA Tel 616-685-0470; Fax: 616-685-6765; Toll Free: 877-867-7737
E-mail: frontier@net-link.net
Web site: http://www.syncopatedpress.com.

Syndistar, Inc., *(1-56230)* P.O. Box 3027, Hammond, LA 70404-3027 USA (SAN 298-007X) Toll Free: 800-841-9532
E-mail: webmaster@syndistar.com
Web site: http://www.syndistar.com.

SynergEbks., *(0-7443; 0-9702385; 1-931540)* Orders Addr.: 32700 River Bend Rd., Chiloquin, OR 97624-9744 USA (SAN 254-4962)
E-mail: SynergEbooks@aol.com
Web site: http://www.SynergEbooks.com
Dist(s): **Baker & Taylor Bks.**
Book Clearing Hse.

Synergetic Pubns., Inc., *(0-9632248)* Orders Addr.: P.O. Box 1506, Hendersonville, TN 37075 USA (SAN 297-6129) Tel 615-264-3405; Edit Addr.: 205 Applewood Valley Dr., Hendersonville, TN 37075 USA.

Synergy Bks., *(0-9747644; 0-9755922; 0-9764981; 1-933538; 1-934454)* 2100 Kramer Ln. Suite 300, Austin, TX 78758 USA Tel 512-478-2028; Fax: 512-478-2117
E-mail: sboulden@synergybooks.net
Web site: http://www.bookpros.com; http://www.synergybooks.net
Dist(s): **Biblio Distribution.**

Synergy South, Inc., *(1-892329)* 8170 Beals Chapel Rd., Lenoir City, TN 37772 USA
E-mail: publisher@synergysouth.com
Web site: http://www.synergysouth.com.

SynSine Pr., *(0-9639949; 1-891388)* Orders Addr.: P.O. Box 6422, Rheem Valley, CA 94570 USA Tel 510-376-1573 (phone/fax)
E-mail: chryamz@home.com
Web site: http://www.synsine.com.

Syntax Publishing, *(0-9660447)* Div. of All or Nothing Productions, P.O. Box 70954, Richmond, VA 23255-0954 USA Tel 804-261-6078; Fax: 877-418-7789; Toll Free: 800-984-5762
E-mail: syntaxpub@aol.com
Web site: http://www.freedomnet.com/~aonppub.

†Syracuse Univ. Pr., *(0-8156)* 621 Skytop Rd., Suite 110, Syracuse, NY 13244-5290 USA (SAN 206-9776) Tel 315-443-2597; Fax: 315-443-5545
E-mail: supress@syr.edu
Web site: http://www.SyracuseUniversityPress.syr.edu
Dist(s): **Gryphon Hse., Inc.**; *CIP.*

Syren Bk. Co., *(0-929636)* 5120 Cedar Lake Rd., S., Minneapolis, MN 55416 USA (SAN 249-7719) Tel 612-642-9241; Fax: 651-603-9263; Toll Free: 800-901-3480 Do not confuse with BookMobile in Port Ludlow WA
E-mail: dleeper@stantonpub.com; jogren@bookmobile.com
Web site: http://www.itascabooks.com
Dist(s): **Itasca Bks.**

†TAB Bks., Div. of The McGraw-Hill Cos., 11 W. 19th St., New York, NY 10011 USA (SAN 202-568X)
E-mail: bookstore@mcgraw-hill.com; customer.service@mcgraw-hill.com
Web site: http://www.mcgraw-hill.com/; *CIP.*

T. A. S. Enterprises, Incorporated *See* **Lit Torch Publishing**

T&C Wholesale, *(0-9665286)* Orders Addr.: P.O. Box 5222, Johnson City, TN 37602 USA Tel 423-753-5208 (phone/fax); Edit Addr.: 107 Jason Ln., Jonesborough, TN 37659 USA
E-mail: cf107@aol.com.

T&T Publishing, *(0 9671719; 1-930940)* 4716 Monument Valley Rd., Las Vegas, NV 89129 USA Tel 702-396-3005
E-mail: tmilleret@aol.com
Web site: http://www.ccseries.com.

T & T Roberts Publishing, *(0-9723868)* 3105 S. Trenton Cir., Sioux Falls, SD 57103 USA.

TBM, Inc., *(0-9647096)* 280 N. Latah St., Boise, ID 83706 USA Tel 208-853-0555; Fax: 208-383-9010; 9295 Esterbrook, Boise, ID 83703
E-mail: realbows@aol.com
Web site: http://www.tradbow.com.

T. C. Publishing, *(0-9701019)* 2126 Hibiscus St., Sarasota, FL 34239 USA Tel 941-957-1513 (phone/fax)
E-mail: gnilsen@home.com.

TDH Bks., *(0-9710017)* Div. of T D H Marketing & Communications, Incorporated, 8153 Garnet Dr., Dayton, OH 45458 USA Tel 937-438-3434; Fax: 937-438-3453; Toll Free: 877-549-9812
E-mail: donna@waddlesnout.com
Web site: http://www.tdhbooks.com.

T D H Publishing *See* **TDH Bks.**

T. E. Publishing, Inc., *(0-9722036)* P.O. Box 823, Bath, NY 14810 USA Tel 607-76-1307
E-mail: pcarlton@tepublishing.com.

†TFH Pubns., Inc., *(0-7938; 0-86622; 0-87666; 1-85279)* Orders Addr.: One TFH Plaza, Third & Union Aves., Neptune City, NJ 07753 USA (SAN 202-7720) Tel 732-988-8400; Fax: 732-988-5466; Toll Free: 800-631-2188 (outside New Jersey); Edit Addr.: P.O. Box 427, Neptune, NJ 07753 USA (SAN 658-1862)
E-mail: info@tfh.com
Web site: http://www.tfh.com/; *CIP.*

T F M Productions, *(0-9711234)* 2240 Morriss Rd., Suite 110, PMB 243, Flower Mound, TX 75028 USA Tel 972-874-1115
E-mail: tfmproductions@aol.com
Web site: http://tfmproductions.com.

THINC Corp., *(0-9655026)* Orders Addr.: P.O. Box 14, Batesville, MS 38606 USA Tel 601-563-1162; Fax: 601-563-6640; Toll Free: 888-837-7606; Edit Addr.: 150 Hwy. 35 N., Batesville, MS 38606 USA.

TJS Security Services, *(0-9675587)* P.O. Box 20527, Cranston, RI 02920 USA
E-mail: Tim@TJS.net
Web site: http://www.stayingsafestories.com/.

T M Enterprises, LLC, *(0-9676258)* P.O. Box 1183, Ridgefield, CT 06877 USA Tel 203-894-8526; Fax: 203-894-8529
E-mail: thaliaGM@aol.com
Web site: http://www.tomorrowschildren.com.

TM Photography, Inc., *(0-9660144)* 82 King St., Charleston, SC 29401 USA Tel 843-577-3237
Dist(s): **Baker & Taylor Bks.**

TNT Bks., *(1-885227)* Orders Addr.: 3657 Cree Dr., Salt Lake City, UT 84120-2867 USA Fax: 801-968-8038
E-mail: twixom@msn.com
Dist(s): **Publishers & Distributors.**

TNT Publishing, *(0-9664727)* 4854 Country Cone Way, Powder Springs, GA 30127 USA Tel 770-943-7847 Do not confuse with TNT Publishing in Oakland, CA.

T.R.B. Publishing, *(0-9677729)* Div. of The Romantic Beanery, P.O. Box 679, Honaunau, HI 96726-0679 USA Tel 808-328-8439; Fax: 808-328-8973
E-mail: rkswisher@aol.com.

T.Y.M. Publishing, *(0-9641274)* 409 Melville Ave., Palo Alto, CA 94301 USA Tel 415-325-1130.

Tabay Pubns., *(1-887935)* P.O. Box 19393, Cincinnati, OH 45219-0393 USA Tel 513-661-5871; Fax: 513-661-2472
E-mail: tkposowa@fuse.net.

Tabby Hse. Bks., *(0-9627974; 1-881539)* Orders Addr.: P.O. Box 544, Mineral, VA 23117 USA Tel 540-894-8868 (phone/fax); Edit Addr.: 1409 Centerville Rd., Mineral, VA 23117 USA ; *Imprints:* Strathmoor (Strathmoor)
E-mail: tabbyhouse@gmail.com; publisher@tabbyhouse.com
Web site: http://www.tabbyhouse.com
Dist(s): **Baker & Taylor Bks.**
Distributors, The.

Table Creek Publishing, *(0-9710774)* P.O. Box 42, Nebraska City, NE 68410 USA Tel 402-874-9035
E-mail: kevin@kevinboos.com
Web site: http://www.kevinboos.com.

Table Rock Bks., *(0-9726869)* 8 Table Rock Rd., Lincoln, RI 02865 USA.

Table 12 Publishing, *(0-9662194)* P.O. Box 10427, Rochester, NY 14610 USA Tel 716-242-9060; Fax: 716-242-8934
E-mail: table12@frontiernet.net
Web site: http://www.frontiernet.net/~table12.

Tabletop Productions, *(1-928981)* 11930 171st Pl., SE, Renton, WA 98059 USA Tel 425-228-1405
E-mail: dgstevens@yahoo.com.

Tabor Pr., *(0-9745799)* Orders Addr.: P.O. Box 470842, Brookline Village, MA 02447 USA Tel 617-784-6561; Edit Addr.: 278 Warren St., Brookline, MA 02445 USA
E-mail: ephraim541@hotmail.com.

Tabris Pr., *(0-9705990)* P.O. Box 701, Hoboken, NJ 07030-0701 USA Tel 201-714-4744; Fax: 201-714-9903
E-mail: tabrispress@aol.com
Web site: http://www.tabrispress.com.

TACCO, *(0-9719724)* P.O. Box 1147, Milford, PA 18337-9316 USA Fax: 570-686-9489
E-mail: tacco@ptd.net
Web site: http://www.christopherotter.com./.

Tackett, Viti, *(0-9769963)* 914 Garland Ave., West Helena, AR 72390-2629 USA Toll Free: 877-518-9575.

Tactile Mind Pr., LLC, The, *(0-9719248)* P.O. Box 581667, Minneapolis, MN 55458-1667 USA Fax: 651-293-1790
E-mail: creative@thetactilemind.com
Web site: http://www.thetactilemind.com.

Tadpole Pr. 4 Kids *Imprint of* **Smooth Sailing Pr.**

TAE Nazca Resources, *(0-9749745)* P.O. Box 7592, Broomfield, CO 80021 USA
E-mail: anitajg5@aol.com
Web site: http://www.nazcaresources.com
Dist(s): **Mountain Bk. Co.**

Taekwondo Educational Resource Ctr., Inc., The, *(0-9670179)* 2210-104 India Hook Rd., Rock Hill, NC 27408 USA Tel 336-286-4737; Fax: 336-288-4901; Toll Free: 877-286-4737
E-mail: info@taekwondoresource.com
Web site: http://www.taekwondoresource.com.

Taffey Pop Kids Publishing, *(0-9771438)* Div. of Taffey Pop Kids, Inc., Orders Addr.: P.O. Box 571973, Dallas, TX 75357-1973 USA Tel 214-673-7847
E-mail: books@taffeypopkids.com
Web site: http://www.taffeypopkids.com.

Tahoe Maps, *(0-9741531)* P.O. Box 47, Moss Landing, CA 95039-0047 USA
E-mail: info@tahoemaps.com
Web site: http://www.tahoemaps.com.

Tahrike Tarsile Quran, Inc., *(0-940368; 1-879402)* 80-08 51st Ave., Elmhurst, NY 11373 USA (SAN 658-1870) Tel 718-446-6472; Fax: 718-446-4370
E-mail: read@koranusa.org
Web site: http://www.koranusa.org
Dist(s): **Perseus Distribution.**

Tai Chi Chuan Center of New York *See* **Sunflower Pr.**

Taiga-Tundra Ventures *See* **Arktika Publishing**

Taiji Arts Publishing, *(0-9728192)* 50 Bates Rd., Hillsborough, CA 94010-7016 USA
E-mail: ben@TaijiArts.com
Web site: http://www.TaijiArts.com
Dist(s): **Baker & Taylor Bks.**
China Bks. & Periodicals, Inc.

Tail it Like it is, Publishing, *(0-9707924)* 307 Moss Hill Rd., Irving, TX 75063 USA Tel 972-444-9030
E-mail: lmsiko@msn.com.

Tail Wagging Productions, *(0-9752887)* P.O. Box 1357, Brea, CA 92822-1357 USA
E-mail: contact@tailwaggingproductions.us
Web site: http://www.tailwaggingproductions.us.

Tailored Tours Pubns., Inc., *(0-9631241; 1-892629)* 729 Braidwood Ln., Orlando, FL 32803-6911 USA Toll Free: 800-354-5246
Dist(s): **Baker & Taylor Bks.**
Great Outdoors Publishing Co.

Tajiri Ventures LLC, *(0-9723826)* Orders Addr.: P.O. Box 681552, Miami, FL 33168 USA Tel 305-757-6369; Edit Addr.: 12700 NW First Ave., Miami, FL 33168 USA
Web site: http://www.tajiriventures.com
Dist(s): **Baker & Taylor Bks.**
Book Wholesalers, Inc.
Culture Plus Bk. Distributors.

Takahashi & Black, *(0-9723247)* Orders Addr.: 8725 Roswell Rd., Suite 0-129, Atlanta, GA 30350 USA ; *Imprints:* PB&J OmniMedia (PB&J)
E-mail: orders@pbjomnimedia.com; credit@pbjomnimedia.com; returns@pbjomnimedia.com; domo@takahashiblack.com
Web site: http://www.pbjomnimedia.com; http://www.takahashiblack.com
Dist(s): **Book Wholesalers, Inc.**
Brodart Co.

Take a Walk Bk. *Imprint of* **Stillwater Publishing**

Take Five Pubs., *(0-930099)* P.O. Box 1094, Arlington, IL 60006 USA (SAN 670-1884) Tel 847-253-4370
E-mail: m.shaughnessy@comcast.net.

Take Flight Pubns., *(1-929150)* 2674 Meadow Ln., Joplin, MO 64801 USA Tel 417-624-3377
E-mail: annleach@ipa.net.

Take Note Pubns., *(0-9744270)* 7075 29th Ct., Vero Beach, FL 32967 USA
E-mail: takenotepub@aol.com.

Takhar's, Jodi Spilt Milk Collection, *(1-886000)* Orders Addr.: P.O. Box 1005, Bemidji, MN 56601 USA Tel 218-759-2089; Fax: 218-759-2088; Edit Addr.: 403 4th St., NW, No. 200, Bemidji, MN 56601 USA.

Taking Grades Publishing Co., *(1-934538)* 1110 4th St., Dr., S.E., Conover, NC 28613-1825 USA Tel 866-511-8378; Fax: 828-466-0025; Toll Free: 866-511-8378
E-mail: takinggrades@charter.net
Web site: http://www.takinggrades.com.

Talanton Pr., *(1-930224)* P.O. Box 390360, Mountain View, CA 94039-0360 USA Tel 650-625-0256 (phone fax)
E-mail: talanton@bigfoot.com.

Talented *See* **Cantemos-Bilingual Books and Music**

Talented Tenth Literary Syndicate *See* **SolidGumboWorks**

Talents From God, *(0-9658040)* 2918 N Ave., National City, CA 91950 USA (SAN 254-4075) Tel 619-474-7778; Fax: 619-474-2909
E-mail: christfellow@aol.com.

Tales & Whales Publishing, *(0-9700176)* One Midway Dr., Albany, NY 12205-4201 USA Tel 518-869-3206; Fax: 810-816-6890
E-mail: nfortin@aol.com
Web site: http://www.members.aol.com/nfortin/index.html.

Talicor, Inc., *(1-57057; 0-9674871)* 901 Lincoln Pkwy., Plainwell, MI 49080 USA (SAN 253-0406) Tel 269-685-2345; Fax: 269-685-6789; Toll Free: 800-433-4263
E-mail: webmaster@talicor.com; orders@talicor.com
Web site: http://www.talicor.com.

Talisman Pr., *(0-9670848)* 7036 Lyndale Cir., Elk Grove, CA 95758 USA Tel 916-683-1749
E-mail: talismanpress@aol.com
Dist(s): **Bookazine Co., Inc.**

TALK, *(0-9741182)* Orders Addr.: P.O. Box 9226, Peoria, IL 61612 USA Tel 309-224-9665; Edit Addr.: 5001 N. Big Hollow Rd., Peoria, IL 61615 USA Tel 309-694-5444
E-mail: dsymo92699@aol.com
Web site: http://www.doristalk.com.

Talk Miramax Bks., *(0-7868)* Div. of Walt Disney Productions, 77 W. 66th St., 11th Flr., New York, NY 10023 USA Tel 212-456-0133
Dist(s): **Hachette Bk. Group.**

TALKAIDS, Inc., *(0-9659046)* Orders Addr.: P.O. Box 112, New York, NY 10113 USA Tel 212-465-2646; Fax: 212-675-7291; Edit Addr.: 305 W. 13th St., 1K, New York, NY 10014 USA
E-mail: talkaids@aol.com.

Talking Drum Pr., Ltd., *(0-9662428)* Div. of Oversoul Theater Collective, Inc., P.O. Box 190028, Roxbury, MA 02119 USA
E-mail: talkingdrumpress@aol.com.

Talking Drum Press/OTC, Incorporated *See* **Talking Drum Pr., Ltd.**

Talking Hands, Incorporated *See* **Time to Sign, Incorporated**

Talking Hands, Inc., *(0-9721427)* 682 Ohio St., Suite 7, Bangor, ME 04401 USA Do not confuse with Talking Hands, Inc., in Fairfax, VA
E-mail: mike@talkinghandsasl.com
Web site: http://www.talkinghandsasl.com/.

Talking Stone Pr., *(0-944941)* Div. of Troubadour, Inc., 99 Evans Rd., Brookline, MA 02445 USA (SAN 245-6389) Tel 617-734-1416; Fax: 617-734-3223; Toll Free: 800-557-3100.

TalkTools/Innovative Therapists International, *(1-932460)* 3420 N. Dodge Blvd., Suite 148, Tucson, AZ 85716-1445 USA Fax: 520-795-8559; Toll Free: 888-529-2879
E-mail: info@talktools.net
Web site: http://www.talktools.net.

Tall Through Bks., *(0-9744549)* P.O. Box 6723, Virginia Beach, VA 23456 USA Tel 757-635-6174; Fax: 757-563-8277
E-mail: tallthroughbooks@aol.com
Web site: http://www.tallthroughbooks.com.

Tallfellow Pr., *(0-9676061; 1-931290)* 1180 S. Beverly Dr., Suite 320, Los Angeles, CA 90035 USA Tel 310-203-3837; Fax: 310-203-3893 ; *Imprints:* Smallfellow Press (Smallfellow Pr)
E-mail: Tallfellow@pacbell.net
Web site: http://TallfellowPress.com
Dist(s): **Parklane Publishing**
SCB Distributors.

Talmage Publishing, *(0-9773010)* 4820 Strack Rd., Houston, TX 77069 USA (SAN 257-2370) Tel 281-440-1106.

Talonbooks, Ltd. (CAN) *(0-88922) Dist. by* **Chicago Distribution Ctr.**

Talsorian Games, Inc., *(0-937279; 1-891933)* Orders Addr.: P.O. Box 7356, Berkeley, CA 94707-0356 USA (SAN 658-6600) Tel 510-549-1373; Fax: 510-549-1726; Edit Addr.: 2998 San Pablo Ave., Berkeley, CA 94702 USA.

Talus Corp., *(1-892953)* 470 Riverside St. Unit 7, Portland, ME 04103-1069 USA Toll Free: 800-634-8180 (phone/fax)
E-mail: info@talusproducts.com
Web site: http://www.talusproducts.com.

Tamaltree Bks., *(0-9709709)* Orders Addr.: P.O. Box 80764, Portland, OR 97280 USA Tel 503-892-3248 (phone/fax); Edit Addr.: 4810-B SW Caldew St., Portland, OR 97219 USA
E-mail: dstockton@uswest.net.

Tamarack Bks., Inc., *(0-9634839; 1-886609)* Orders Addr.: P.O. Box 190313, Boise, ID 83719-0313 USA (SAN 297-8792) Tel 208-922-2229; Fax: 208-922-5880; Toll Free: 800-962-6657; Edit Addr.: 2715 E. Deer Flat Rd., Kuna, ID 83634 USA
E-mail: sales@tamarackbooks.com
Web site: http://www.tamarackbooks.com
Dist(s): **Wizard Works.**

Tamarind, *(0-9667484)* P.O. Box 75442, Honolulu, HI 96836 USA Tel 808-942-1794
E-mail: dcasey7@concentric.net
Dist(s): **Native Bks.**

Tameme, Inc., *(0-9674093)* 199 First St. Suite 335, Los Altos, CA 94022 USA Tel 650-941-2037; Fax: 650-941-5338
E-mail: Sales@tameme.org
Web site: http://www.tameme.org.

Tamerac Publishing Co., *(0-9621292)* 1111 E. 1st St., Moscow, ID 83843 USA (SAN 250-9466) Tel 208-883-7761
E-mail: info@juvenilefiction.com
Web site: http://www.juvenilefiction.com
Dist(s): **Book Clearing Hse.**

Tamos Bks., Inc. (CAN) *(1-895569) Dist. by* **Sterling.**

TAN Bks. and Pubs., Inc., *(0-89555; 0-9675978)* Orders Addr.: 2020 Harrison Ave., Rockford, IL 61104 USA (SAN 282-3918) Tel 815-226-7777; Fax: 815-226-7770; Toll Free: 800-437-5876; Edit Addr.: P.O. Box 424, Rockford, IL 61105 USA (SAN 282-390X)
E-mail: teri@tanbooks.com
Web site: http://www.tanbooks.com.

Tandem Library Bks., *(0-606; 0-613; 0-7857; 0-8085; 0-8335; 0-88103; 1-4176; 1-4177; 1-4178)* Div. of Tandem Library Group, Orders Addr.: 139 S. Kingston, Caledonia, MN 55921 USA Toll Free Fax: 800-628-2410; Toll Free: 800-255-3502; Edit Addr.: 2101 N. Topeka Blvd., Topeka, KS 66608 USA (SAN 151-3478) Tel 785-290-1269; Fax: 785-290-1237; Toll Free: 800-442-7357
E-mail: orders@tandemlibrarygroup.com
Web site: http://www.tandemlibrarybooks.com/.

Tandem Publishing, *(0-9704640)* 54-08 64th St., Maspeth, NY 11378 USA (SAN 253-4665) Tel 718-446-3963; 718 446 3963; Fax: 718-446-7338
E-mail: tandem94@aol.com
Web site: http://www.hometown.aol.com/tandem94.

T&N Children's Publishing, *(1-55971; 1-58728)* Orders Addr.: 11571 K-Tel Dr., Minnetonka, MN 55343 USA Tel 952-933-7537; Fax: 952-933-3630; Toll Free: 888-255-9989; Fulfillment Addr.: SDS-12-2462, P.O. Box 86, Minneapolis, MN 55486-2462 USA ; *Imprints:* NorthWord Books for Young Readers (NrthWrd Bks); Two Can Publishing (TCan Pubng)
E-mail: sales@tnkidsbooks.com
Web site: http://www.tnkidsbooks.com
Dist(s): **Baker & Taylor Bks.**
Follett Library Resources
National Bk. Network.

Tandora's Box Pr., *(0-9627337)* Orders Addr.: P.O. Box 8073, Vallejo, CA 94590 USA
E-mail: barbara@tangrammit.com
Web site: http://www.tangrammit.com.

Tandy Leather Co., *(1-892214)* Orders Addr.: P.O. Box 50429, Fort Worth, TX 76105-0429 USA Tel 817-496-4414; Fax: 817-496-9806; Toll Free: 800-433-3201; Edit Addr.: 3847 E. Loop 820 S., Fort Worth, TX 76119-4388 USA
Web site: http://www.tandyleather.com.

Tangerine Pr. *Imprint of* **Scholastic, Inc.**

Tanglewood Pr., *(0-9749303; 1-933718)* P.O. Box 3009, Terre Haute, IN 47803 USA Do not confuse with Tanglewood Press in Portland, OR, Raleigh, NC
E-mail: ptierney@ma.rr.com
Web site: http://www.tanglewoodbooks.com
Dist(s): **National Bk. Network.**

Tango Latin, *(0-9663572)* 325 N. Maple Dr., Beverly Hills, CA 90209 USA Tel 213-381-5820; P.O. Box 16111, Beverly Hills, CA 90209
E-mail: tangomediagroup@yahoo.com.

Tango Publishing International, Incorporated *See* **Tango Latin**

Tango's Grove Publishing, *(0-9653034)* P.O. Box 20074, Carson City, NV 89721 USA Tel 702-885-8685; Fax: 702-885-0881
E-mail: tangos@tangosgrove.com
Web site: http://www.tangosgrove.com.

Tanner, David, *(0-9767287)* P.O. Box 140, Avon, CT 06001-0140 USA
E-mail: collectiblesodacans@comcast.net
Web site: http://www.collectiblesodacans.com.

Tanner, Ralph Assocs., Inc., *(0-942078)* P.O. Box 3400, Prescott, AZ 86302-3400 USA (SAN 239-9857).

TanosBooks Publishing, *(0-9764666; 0-9788520)* 1110 W. 5th St., Coffeyville, KS 67337 USA
Web site: http://www.rtanos.com.

Taos Institute Pubns., *(0-9712312)* 331 Rogers Ln., Wallingford, PA 19086 USA Toll Free: 888-999-8267 (888-999-TAOS)
E-mail: gv4@psu.edu
Web site: http://www.TaosInstitute.net
Dist(s): **CSS Publishing Co.**

Tapas Pubns., *(0-9761269)* P.O. Box 5626, Huntington Beach, CA 92615-5626 USA
Web site: http://www.practiceoflove.com.

TapDancing Lizard, *(0-9711525)* 4237 Klein Ave., Stow, OH 44224 USA (SAN 253-8997) Tel 330-688-1130
E-mail: info@mehandi.com
Web site: http://www.tapdancinglizard.com.

Tapestries, *(0-9676703)* 3636 Buchanan St., San Francisco, CA 94123 USA (SAN 253-1992) Tel 415-921-8689; Fax: 415-921-1990
Web site: http://www.tapestriespublishing.com
Dist(s): **International Publishers Marketing.**

Tapis & Assocs., Inc., *(0-9729610; 0-9741172)* 1950 N. 6900 E., Croydon, UT 84018-9707 USA Tel 801-829-3295; Fax: 509-984-2718
E-mail: info@tapisinc.com
Web site: http://www.tapisinc.com.

Tapper Records Inc., *(0-9747465)* P.O. Box 5241, Hollywood, FL 33083-5241 USA Tel 954-483-5093; Fax: 954-961-9049
E-mail: thespeakingsax@juno.com
Web site: http://www.thespeakingsax.com.

Tapper Seminars *See* **Tapper Records Inc.**

Taproots Press *See* **Friendly Universe Pr.**

Taqwa Images *See* **Early Rise Pubns.**

Tara Publishing (IND) *(81-86211) Dist. by* **Consort Bk Sales.**

Tarbutton Pr., *(0-9714086; 1-933094)* 951 Snug Harbor St., Salinas, CA 93906 USA (SAN 254-4989) Tel 831-443-5694
E-mail: info@tarbuttonpress.com
Web site: http://www.tarbuttonpress.com
Dist(s): **BookSurge, LLC**
Lightning Source, Inc.

Tarcher *Imprint of* **Penguin Group (USA) Inc.**

Targum Pr., Inc., *(0-944070; 1-56871)* 22700 W. Eleven Mile Rd., Southfield, MI 48034 USA (SAN 242-8997) Tel 248-355-2266; Toll Free Fax: 888-298-9992
E-mail: targum@elronet.co.il
Web site: http://www.targum.com
Dist(s): **Feldheim Pubs.**

Tarquin Pubns. (GBR) *(0-906212; 1-899618) Dist. by* **Parkwest Pubns.**

Tarver, Monroe, *(0-9743568)* 7904 Calibre Crossing Dr. Apt. 205, Charlotte, NC 28227-6781 USA
E-mail: monroetarver@msn.com
Web site: http://www.worldoftarver.com.

Taschen America, LLC, *(1-886155; 3-8228)* Div. of Benedikt Taschen Verlag GmbH, 6671 Sunset Blvd., Suite 1508, Los Angeles, CA 90028 USA (SAN 253-0937) Tel 323-463-4441; Fax: 323-463-4442
Web site: http://www.taschen.com
Dist(s): **Continental Bk. Co., Inc.**
Lectorum Pubns., Inc.
Perseus Distribution.

Tassie, *(0-9711419)* 52 John Olds Dr., No. 207, Manchester, CT 06040 USA Tel 860-649-9548
E-mail: tassieko@aol.com.

Tastica, Suanne Creations Inc., *(0-9769348)* 1621 25th St., PMB No. 337, San Pedro, CA 90732 USA
Dist(s): **Biblio Distribution.**

Tate Gallery Publishing, Ltd. (GBR) *(0-900874; 0-905005; 1-85437; 0-946590) Dist. by* **HachBkGrp.**

Tate Publishing & Enterprises, L.L.C., *(0-9740939; 0-9748244; 0-9752572; 0-9753933; 0-9759124; 0-9759973; 1-933148; 1-933290; 1-59886; 1-60247; 1-60462)* 127 E. Trade Center Terr., Mustang, OK 73064 USA Tel 405-376-4900; Fax: 405-376-4401; Toll Free: 888-361-9473
Web site: http://www.tatepublishing.com
Dist(s): **STL Distribution North America.**

Tattered Essence Publishing LLC, *(0-9766130)* P.O. Box 290996, Nashville, TN 37229 USA Tel 615-360-6117
E-mail: info@cinderellasrebellion.com
Web site: http://www.tatteredessence.com.

Tattersall Pr., *(0-9639890)* Orders Addr.: P.O. Box 712, Elkhart, IN 46515-0712 USA; Edit Addr.: 1920 Grant St., Elkhart, IN 46514 USA Tel 219-264-6692
Dist(s): **Winters Publishing.**

Tattoo Manufacturing, *(1-892800; 0-9678636; 0-9702195)* 3761 E. Technical Dr., Tuscon, AZ 85713-5343 USA Tel 520-584-0001; Fax: 520-747-1299; Toll Free: 800-747-8016 ; *Imprints:* Tattootles Books (Tattootles Bks)
E-mail: printexpression@aol.com
Web site: http://www.tattoosales.com.

Tattootles Bks. *Imprint of* **Tattoo Manufacturing**

Taunton *Imprint of* **Taunton Pr., Inc.**

†Taunton Pr., Inc., *(0-918804; 0-942391; 1-56158; 1-60085)* 63 S. Main St., Newtown, CT 06470-5506 USA (SAN 210-5144) Tel 203-426-8171; Fax: 203-426-7184; Toll Free: 800-477-8727 (orders) ; *Imprints:* Taunton (Taunt)
E-mail: tt@taunton.com
Web site: http://www.taunton.com
Dist(s): **Linden Publishing Co., Inc.**
Random Hse., Inc.; *CIP.*

Tavine'ra Publishing, LLC, *(0-9713953)* 3355 Lenox Rd., Suite 750, Atlanta, GA 30326 USA Tel 888 234-7256; Fax: 770-322-1858
E-mail: vbandco@mindspring.com.

Tawa Productions, *(0-9718741)* Orders Addr.: 2186 Buffalo Dr., Grand Junction, CO 81503 USA
E-mail: information@peopal.com
Web site: http://www.poepal.com.

Taweya Productions *See* **Owlink Media**

Tayes Bks., *(0-9743207)* Orders Addr.: P.O. Box 50973, Fort Myers, FL 33994-0973 USA; Edit Addr.: 813 Dellena Ln., Fort Myers, FL 33905 USA
E-mail: tayesbooks@yahoo.com
Web site: http://www.tayesbooks.com.

†Taylor & Francis, Inc., *(0-335; 0-415; 0-8448; 0-85066; 0-89116; 0-903796; 0-905273; 1-56032; 1-85000; 1-59169)* Orders Addr.: 7625 Empire Dr., Florence, KY 41042-2919 USA Toll Free Fax: 800-248-4724; Toll Free: 800-634-7064; 74 Rolark Dr., Scarborough, ON M1R 4G2 Tel 416-299-5388; Fax: 416-299-7531; Toll Free: 877-226-2237; Edit Addr.: 325 Chestnut St., Philadelphia, PA 19106 USA (SAN 241-9246) Tel 215-625-8900; Fax: 215-625-2940; 270 Madison Ave., 4th Flr., New York, NY 10016-0601
E-mail: info@taylorandfrancis.com
Web site: http://www.routledge-ny.com; www.crcpress.com; http://www.garlandscience.com; http://www.taylorandfrancis.com
Dist(s): **CRC Pr. LLC**
NetLibrary, Inc.
Oxford Univ. Pr., Inc.
Sony CONNECT, Inc.; *CIP.*

Taylor & Francis Group (GBR) *(0-389; 0-7484; 0-85066; 0-905273; 1-85000; 1-85728; 1-84142; 0-203) Dist. by* **Taylor and Fran.**

Taylor & Francis, Incorporated *See* **Taylor & Francis, Inc.**

Taylor, Dorothy Loring, *(0-9610640)* R. R. 2, Box 152, Virginia, IL 62691 USA (SAN 265-3567) Tel 217-458-2506.

Taylor, Kristine, *(0-9679114)* 156 Corte Madera Rd., Portola Valley, CA 94028 USA Tel 650-851-3057; Fax: 508-464-7886
E-mail: gtaylors@mindspring.com
Web site: http://www.aphidcity.com.

Taylor, Leigh, *(0-9660664)* P.O. Box 1444, San Clemente, CA 92674-1444 USA
E-mail: revleigh@pacbell.net.

Taylor, Lu Warrior Girls Pr., *(0-9675409)* 100 E. Walton, No. 35A, Chicago, IL 60611 USA Tel 312-944-5160; Fax: 312-944-6289.

Taylor Productions *Imprint of* **GRM Assocs.**

Taylor Publishing Company *See* **Taylor Trade Publishing**

Taylor Publishing Grp., *(0-9762933)* 1605 E. Elizabeth St., Pasadena, CA 91104 USA Tel 626-398-2341
E-mail: tp@finishthetask.org
Web site: http://www.taylorpublishing.info
Dist(s): **STL Distribution North America.**

†Taylor Trade Publishing, *(0-87833; 1-58979)* Orders Addr.: 15200 NBN Way, Blue Ridge Summit, PA 17214 USA Tel 717-794-3800 (Sales, Customer Service, MIS, Royalties, Inventory Mgmt., Dist., Credit & Collections); Fax: 717-794-3803 (Customer Service &/or orders only); 717-794-3857 (Sales & MIS); 717-794-3856 (Royalties, Inventory Mgmt. & Dist.); Toll Free Fax: 800-338-4550 (Customer Service &/or orders); Toll Free: 800-462-6420 (Customer Service &/or orders); Edit Addr.: 4501 Forbes Blvd., Suite 200, Lanham, MD 20706 USA Fax: 301-459-3366; Toll Free Fax: 301-459-5748 Do not confuse with companies with the same or similar names in Rochester, MI, Bellingham, WA, St. Petersburg, FL, Owatonna, MN, Eureka, CA
Web site: http://www.rlpgbooks.com; http://taylortradepublishing.com/
Dist(s): **National Bk. Network**
Rowman & Littlefield Pubs., Inc.; *CIP.*

Taylor, Y. H. *See* **Taylor, Y. H.**

Taylor, Y. H., *(0-9788386)* P.O. Box 9618, Philadelphia, PA 19131-3315 USA.

Taylor-Dth Publishing, *(0-9712923; 0-9727583; 0-9747532; 0-9774431)* Orders Addr.: P.O. Box 445, Fairfax, CA 94978 USA Toll Free: 800-929-1161; Edit Addr.: 6 School St., 8C, Fairfax, CA 94930 USA
E-mail: ncardinali@taylor-dth.com
Web site: http://www.taylor-dth.com
Dist(s): **Baker & Taylor Bks.**

TaySysCo Publishing, *(0-9773236)* 808 White Ivy Pl. NE, Cedar Rapids, IA 52402 USA
E-mail: taysysco@msn.com
Web site: http://taysysco.com.

TazTales, *(0-9742178)* P.O. Box 48031, Oak Park, MI 48237-5731 USA
E-mail: taztales@lycos.com
Web site: http://www.taztales.com.

TBG.LLC *See* **Gilliam, T. & Associates, LLC**

T'Boli Publishing & Distributors, *(1-887764)* P.O. Box 347147, San Francisco, CA 94134 USA Tel 415-337-5550 (phone/fax)
E-mail: tiboli@mindspring.com.

Tbooks Publishing Co., *(0-9789449)* 324 E. 2nd St., Benicia, CA 94510-3249 USA (SAN 852-0135) Tel 707-342-2280
E-mail: terrie@tbookspublishing.com
Web site: http://tbookspublishing.com.

T.C. McSears Publishing, *(0-9787015)* P.O. Box 341, Linconton, NC 28093 USA
E-mail: tryloc@tryloc.com
Web site: http://www.tryloc.com
Dist(s): **Big Tent Bks.**

TC Pubs *Imprint of* **Studio Editions/TC Pubs**

TCB-Cafe Publishing, *(0-9674898; 0-9767682; 0-9798640)* Orders Addr.: P.O. Box 471706, San Francisco, CA 94147 USA Tel 415-263-6800
Web site: http://www.cafeandre.com
Dist(s): **Baker & Taylor Bks.**
Perseus Distribution
Quality Bks., Inc.

TdB Pr. LLC, *(0-9740494)* P.O. Box 6348, Altadena, CA 91003-6348 USA (SAN 255-3147)
E-mail: mail@tdbpress.com
Web site: http://www.tdbpress.com.

Tea Kettle Pr., *(0-9671177)* Orders Addr.: P.O. Box 222924, Chantilly, VA 20151 USA Tel 703-968-0817; Fax: 703-968-5533
E-mail: hazey@hazeydays.com; mroth52@aol.com
Web site: http://www.hazeydays.com.

Tea Party Pr., *(0-9749173)* P.O. Box 767425, Atlanta, GA 30076 USA Tel 770-649-4434 Do not confuse with Tea Party Press in Cincinnati, OH
E-mail: paula_taylor@bellsouth.net
Web site: http://www.teapartypress.com.

Tea Pot Press *See* **Tea Kettle Pr.**

Teach Me.. *Imprint of* **Teach Me Tapes, Inc.**

Teach Me Tapes, Inc., *(0-934633; 1-59972)* 6016 Blue Circle Dr., Minnetonka, MN 55343 USA (SAN 693-9309) Tel 952-933-8086; Fax: 952-933-0512; Toll Free: 800-456-4656 ; *Imprints:* Teach Me.. (Tch Me)
E-mail: marie@teachmetapes.com; linda@teachmetapes.com
Web site: http://www.teachmetapes.com.

TEACH Ministries, *(0-9740328)* Orders Addr.: 891 Ted Ln., Elgin, IL 60120 USA
E-mail: marylou@empoweringdiversity.com
Web site: http://www.empoweringdiversity.com/anna.

Teach My Children Pubns., *(0-9668891)* 258 Bahia Ln., E., Litchfield Park, AZ 85340-4728 USA Tel 602-935-0386
E-mail: oldbaha@goodnet.com.

Teach Services *See* **TEACH Services, Inc.**

TEACH Services, Inc., *(0-945383; 1-57258)* 254 Donovan Rd., Brushton, NY 12916 USA (SAN 246-9863) Tel 518-358-3494; Fax: 518-358-3028; Toll Free: 800-367-1844
E-mail: publishing@teachservices.com
Web site: http://www.teachservices.com.

Teach Yourself *Imprint of* **McGraw-Hill Trade**

Teacher Created Materials, Inc., *(0-87673; 1-55734; 1-57690; 0-7439; 1-4333; 1-60401)* 5301 Oceanus Dr., Huntington Beach, CA 92649 USA (SAN 665-5270) Tel 714-891-2273; Fax: 714-230-7070; Toll Free: 800-858-7339
E-mail: sozbat@tcmpub.com
Web site: http://www.tcmpub.com.

Teacher Created Resources, Inc., *(1-4206)* 6421 Industry Way, Westminster, CA 92683 USA Tel 714-891-2273; Fax: 714-892-0283; Toll Free: 888-343-4335
E-mail: dlytle@teachercreated.com
Web site: http://www.teachercreated.com
Dist(s): **Austin & Company, Inc.**
Partners Pubs. Group, Inc.

Teacher Ideas Pr. *Imprint of* **Libraries Unlimited, Inc.**

Teacher Press, Incorporated *See* **Teaching Point, Inc.**

†Teachers & Writers Collaborative, *(0-915924)* Orders Addr.: 520 Eighth Ave., Ste. 2020, New York, NY 10018-6507 USA (SAN 206-3859) Tel 212-691-6590; Fax: 212-675-0171; Toll Free: 888-266-5789
E-mail: aswauger@twc.org
Web site: http://www.twc.org; *CIP.*

†Teachers College Pr., Teachers College, Columbia Univ., *(0-8077)* Orders Addr.: c/o AIDC, P.O. Box 20, Williston, VT 05495-0020 USA (SAN 248-3904) Fax: 802-864-7626; Toll Free: 800-575-6566; Edit Addr.: 1234 Amsterdam Ave., New York, NY 10027 USA (SAN 282-3985) Tel 212-678-3929; Fax: 212-678-4149
E-mail: tcpress@tc.columbia.edu
Web site: http://www.teacherscollegepress.com
Dist(s): **American International Distribution Corp.**
NetLibrary, Inc.; *CIP.*

Teacher's Discovery, *(1-884473; 0-7560)* Div. of American Eagle Co., Inc., 2741 Paldan Dr., Auburn Hills, MI 48326 USA (SAN 631-4570) Tel 248-340-7210; Fax: 248-340-7212; Toll Free: 800-832-2437
Dist(s): **American Eagle Pubns., Inc.**
Kensington Publishing Corp.

Teacher's Friend Pubns., Inc., *(0-943263; 1-57882)* Div. of Scholastic, inc., 2155 Chicago Ave. Ste. 304, Riverside, CA 92507-2209 USA (SAN 668-3177) Toll Free Fax: 800 307 8176; Toll Free: 800-343-9680
E-mail: info@teachersfriend.com
Web site: http://www.teachersfriend.com
Dist(s): **Scholastic, Inc.**

Teachers' Handbooks, *(0-9634938)* P.O. Box 2778, San Rafael, CA 94912 USA (SAN 297-8326) Tel 415-461-0871; Fax: 415-461-5357.

Teacher's Treasure *See* **Perfect 4 Preschool**

TeachersZone.com, *(0-9713102)* 1206A Mt.View-Alviso Rd., Sunnyvale, CA 94089 USA Toll Free: 877-463-6868
Web site: http://www.teacherszone.com.

Teaching & Learning Co., *(1-57310)* 1204 Buchanan St., Box 10, Carthage, IL 62321-0010 USA Tel 217-357-2591; Fax: 217-357-6789; Toll Free: 800-852-1234
E-mail: customerservice@teachinglearning.com
Web site: http://www.teachinglearning.com.

Teaching Company Limited Partnership *See* **Teaching Co., LLC, The**

Teaching Co., LLC, The, *(1-56585; 1-59803)* 4151 Lafayette Center Dr., Suite 100, Chantilly, VA 20151 USA Toll Free: 800-858-3224
E-mail: coxo@teachco.com
Web site: http://www.teach12.com
Dist(s): **TMW Media Group, Inc.**

Teaching, Inc., *(0-9614574; 1-881660)* P.O. Box 788, Edmonds, WA 98020 USA Tel 425-774-0755; Fax: 425-775-0755; Toll Free: 800-774-0755 (orders only).

Teaching Ink, Inc., *(1-889369)* 5543 Southfield Dr. Apt. F, Saint Louis, MO 63129-6119 USA
E-mail: teachingink@msn.com
Web site: http://www.teachers-teachingink.com.

Teaching Point, Inc., *(0-9629357; 1-931680; 1-59657)* Orders Addr.: 6950 Philips Hwy. Ste. 46, Jacksonville, FL 32216-6087 USA Toll Free: 877-494-0550 ; *Imprints:* Expert Systems for Teachers (Expert Systms Teach)
Web site: http://www.teaching-point.net.

Teaching Resource Ctr., *(1-56785)* P.O. Box 82777, San Diego, CA 92138-2777 USA Toll Free: 800-833-3389
E-mail: trc@trcabc.com.

Teaching Resources *Imprint of* **Scholastic, Inc.**

Teaching Strategies *Imprint of* **Scholastic, Inc.**

TeachingKidsBusiness.com (CAN) *(0-9733058) Dist. by* **Biblio Dist.**

Teal, Joyce Willard, *(0-9660215)* 8629 Forest Green Dr., Dallas, TX 75243 USA Tel 214-349-7361; Fax: 214-348-2011
E-mail: pjteal@flash.net
Dist(s): **Hervey's Booklink & Cookbook Warehouse.**

Team B Creative LLC, *(0-9774119)* 9862 E. Grand River, Suite 110, No. 244, Brighton, MI 48116 USA ; *Imprints:* Five Ways to Finish (FWF)
E-mail: mickmorrisinfo@yahoo.com
Web site: http://www.mickmorris.net
Dist(s): **Partners Bk. Distributing, Inc.**

Team Dawg Productions, Inc., *(0-9749378)* Orders Addr.: P.O. Box 105, Nesconset, NY 11767 USA Tel 718-926-5984; Edit Addr.: 1 Mayfair Rd., Apt. 1, Nesconset, NY 11767 USA
E-mail: bobby@teamdawg.com
Web site: http://www.teamdawg.com.

Team EEK!, *(0-9767646)* Orders Addr.: 413 Bella St., Hollidaysburg, PA 16648 USA Tel 814-695-7631
E-mail: gimmygum@gimmygum.com
Web site: http://www.gimmygum.com.

Team Reach, Inc., *(0-9767610)* 8448 Summit St., Lenexa, KS 66215-5388 USA Fax: 913-312-8872
E-mail: troy@krystal-planet.com; troy@troyhelming.com
Web site: http://www.teamreach.com; http://www.troyhelming.com.

Teamwork Foundation, Inc., *(0-9715245)* 1695 Madison Ave., No. 8C, New York, NY 10029 USA Tel 212-831-6483 (phone/fax)
Dist(s): **Savannah Bks.**

Tech Directions Bks. *Imprint of* **Prakken Pubns., Inc.**

Tech Ed Concepts, Inc., *(0-9661800)* 35 S. Main St., Concord, NH 03301 USA Tel 603-224-8324; Fax: 603-225-7766; Toll Free: 800-338-2238
E-mail: sales@tecedu.com
Web site: http://tecedu.com.

TechArts International LLC, *(0-9726326)* 7638 S. Carroll Rd., Indianapolis, IN 46259 USA.

Technical Manuscript, *(0-9719933)* Orders Addr.: P.O. Box 1205, Valley Stream, NY 11582-1205 USA Tel 516-872-0720; Edit Addr.: 140 Union St., Valley Stream, NY 11580 USA.

Technology Education Concepts Inc., *(0-9740796; 0-9777525)* 32 Commercial St., Concord, NH 03301-5031 USA Tel 603-224-8324; Fax: 603-225-7766; Toll Free: 800-338-2238
E-mail: justyn@tecedu.com
Web site: http://www.tecedu.com.

Technology Group, The, *(0-939856; 1-877884)* P.O. Box 21172, El Sobrante, CA 94820-1172 USA (SAN 220-195X) Tel 510-262-6991; Fax: 510-262-6990
E-mail: whtmagick@aol.com
Web site: http://www.techgroupbooks.com.

Teckni-Corp, Ltd., *(0-9724178)* P.O. Box 866, Bettendorf, IA 52722-1955 USA Tel 563-359-4388; Fax: 563-359-4671
E-mail: patrickm@studentsafe.com
Web site: http://www.studentsafe.com.

Tecolote, Ediciones, S.A. de C.V. (MEX) *(968-7381) Dist. by* **Mariuccia Iaconi Bk Imports.**

Tectum B.V.B.A. (BEL) *(90-76886) Dist. by* **Natl Bk Netwk.**

Teddy Bear Pr., Inc., *(1-880017)* 5470 Van Ness, Bloomfield Hills, MI 48302 USA Tel 248-851-8607 Do not confuse with Teddy Bear Pr., Las Vegas, NV.

Teddy Traveler Co., *(0-9748954)* P.O. Box 3223, Manhattan Beach, CA 90266 USA
Web site: teddytraveler.com.

Tedesco, James *See* **JBT Publishing**

Teen Winners, LLC, *(0-9740356)* 19 Quail Run, Berlin, CT 06037 USA Tel 860-829-2067; Fax: 860-829-8067
E-mail: info@teenwinners.com
Web site: http://www.teenwinners.com.

Teeny Behemoth Bks. *Imprint of* **Topsy Turvy Pubns.**

TEG Publishing, *(0-9707208; 0-9727410)* Orders Addr.: P.O. Box 12737, Tempe, AZ 85284 USA Tel 310-919-3013
E-mail: microlawyers@aol.com; tegpublishing@wwsws.com
Web site: http://www.tegpublishing.com.

Tegen, Katherine Bks *Imprint of* **HarperCollins Pubs.**

Tehabi Bks., *(1-887656; 1-931688)* 4920 Carroll Canyon Rd., Suite 200, San Diego, CA 92121 USA Tel 858-450-9100; Fax: 858-450-9146; Toll Free: 800-243-7259
E-mail: Emily.Henning@tehabi.com
Web site: http://www.tehabi.com.

Telepoetics, Inc., *(0-9644606; 1-929507)* 1939 1/4 W. Washington Blvd., Los Angeles, CA 90018-1635 USA Tel 323-419-0001
E-mail: PeazRitr@comcast.net; PeazRitr@telepoetics.com
Web site: http://telepoetics.dyndns.org/; http://www.telepoetics.com/
Dist(s): **BookSurge, LLC.**

Telescopic Pr., *(1-891528)* Orders Addr.: P.O. Box 5824, Bellingham, WA 98227-5824 USA Tel 360-738-7970; Fax: 360-714-8898; Edit Addr.: 417 Gladstone St., Bellingham, WA 98225 USA
E-mail: damelio@telcomplus.com.

Tell the World, *(0-9661138)* 1890 Valencia Ave., Carlsbad, CA 92008 USA Tel 760-729-6777.

Tell-a-Vision Bks., *(0-9727706)* Orders Addr.: P.O. Box 396, Lexington, VA 24450 USA; Edit Addr.: 272 Dogwood Rise, Lexington, VA 24450 USA
Web site: http://www.tell-a-visionbooks.com.

Telos Pubns., *(0-9664624; 0-9712144; 0-9743751)* P.O. Box 4457, Huntington Beach, CA 92605-4457 USA Toll Free: 866-416-8973
E-mail: info@telospublications.com
Web site: http://www.telospublications.com.

Telstar, *(0-9624384; 1-878142)* 1098 Fort Rd., Benton Harbor, MI 49022 USA Tel 269-926-2226
E-mail: twocats@qtm.net.

Temenos Pr., *(0-9701319)* Orders Addr.: P.O. Box 477, Ashfield, MA 01330 USA Tel 413-625-9148; Edit Addr.: 989 Apple Valley Rd., Ashfield, MA 01330 USA Do not confuse with Temenos Pr., in Cloverdale, CA.

Temeron Bks., Inc., *(1-895510)* P.O. Box 896, Bellingham, WA 98227 USA Tel 360-738-4016.

Temple Care: Body, Mind & Spirit, *(0-9773759)* P.O. Box 1221 Ring Bill Loop, Upper Marlboro, MD 20774-7170 USA Tel 301-218-5941; Fax: 719-218-5948
E-mail: templecare@verizon.com.

Temple, Ellen C. Publishing, Inc., *(0-936650)* 5030 Champions Dr., Lufkin, TX 75901-7346 USA (SAN 215-1162)
E-mail: ectemple@icc.com
Dist(s): **Eakin Pr.**

Temple Universal Publishing, *(0-9728051; 0-9774830)* Div. of Temple Universal of California, 1946 Vedanta Pl., Hollywood, CA 90068 USA
Web site: http://www.TempleUniversal.org.

†Temple Univ. Pr., *(0-87722; 1-56639; 1-59213)* 1601 N. Broad St., Univ. Services Bldg., Rm. 305, Philadelphia, PA 19122-6099 USA (SAN 202-7666) Tel 215-204-3389; Fax: 215-204-4719; Toll Free: 800-447-1656
E-mail: charles.ault@temple.edu
Web site: http://www.temple.edu/tempress
Dist(s): **Baker & Taylor Bks.**
Chicago Distribution Ctr.
Koen-Levy Bk. Wholesalers LLC; *CIP.*

Templeton Foundation Pr., *(1-890151; 1-932031; 1-59947)* Div. of John Templeton Foundation, 300 Conshohocken State Rd. Ste. 500, Conshohocken, PA 19428-3801 USA
E-mail: tfp@templetonpress.org; lbarrett@templeton.org
Web site: http://www.templetonpress.org
Dist(s): **Chicago Distribution Ctr.**
STL Distribution North America
Univ. of Chicago Pr.

Temporal Mechanical Pr., *(1-928878)* Div. of Enos Mills Cabin, Orders Addr.: 6760 Hwy. 7, Estes Park, CO 80517-6404 USA Tel 970-586-4706
E-mail: enosmillscbn@earthlink.net
Web site: http://www.geocities.com/Soho/Nook/7587/
Dist(s): **Allenspark WIND.**

Tempus Publishing, Ltd. (GBR) *(0-7524) Dist. by* **Trafalgar.**

Tempus Publishing, Ltd. (GBR) *(0-7524) Dist. by* **IPG Chicago.**

Ten Minas Publishing, *(0-9716786)* P.O. Box 8984, Reston, VA 20195 USA Fax: 703-834-1176
Web site: http://www.crowsofhiddencreek.

Ten Penny Players, Inc., *(0-934830)* 393 St. Paul's Ave., Staten Island, NY 10304-2127 USA (SAN 213-8743) Tel 718-442-7429; Fax: 718-442-4978
E-mail: water@tenpennyplayers.org
Web site: http://tenpennyplayers.org
Dist(s): **Waterways Project.**

†Ten Speed Pr., *(0-89815; 0-913668; 1-58008)* Orders Addr.: P.O. Box 7123, Berkeley, CA 94707 USA (SAN 202-7674) Fax: 510-559-1629 (orders); Toll Free: 800-841-2665; 555 Richmond St., W. Suite 405, Box 702, Toronto, ON M5V 3B1 Tel 416-703-7775; Fax: 416-703-9992 ; *Imprints:* Celestial Arts Publishing Company (CelestialArts); Crossing Press, Incorporated (CrossingPr); Tricycle Press (TricyclePress)
E-mail: order@tenspeed.com; alan@tenspeed.ca
Web site: http://www.tenspeed.com
Dist(s): **Fujii Assocs.**; *CIP.*

Tender Heart Pr., *(0-9741401)* 15448 S. Jasper, Bldg. G, Odessa, TX 79766 USA
Web site: http://www.tenderheartpress.com.

Tender Learning Concepts, *(0-9708796)* 5362 Rockledge Dr., Buena Pk., CA 90621 USA Tel 714 739 2145; 714-739-2145; Fax: 714-739-0593; Toll Free: 877 886-7091 ; *Imprints:* TLConcepts, Incorporated (TLCPTS)
E-mail: whm@iqboosters.com
Web site: http://www.iqboosters.com; http://tenderlearning.econgo.com.

Tendril Pr. LLC, *(0-9763706)* 12321 E. Cornell Ave., Aurora, CO 80014 USA Tel 303-696-9227; Fax: 303-873-6766
E-mail: publisher@tendrilpress.com
Web site: http://www.tendrilpress.com
Dist(s): **Brigham Distribution.**

teNeues Publishing Co., *(3-570; 3-7913; 3-8238; 3-929278; 3-8327; 1-933427; 1-60160)* 16 W. 22nd St., 2nd Flr., New York, NY 10010-5803 USA (SAN 245-176X) Tel 212-627-9090; Fax: 212-627-9511; Toll Free: 800-352-0305
E-mail: trip@teneues-usa.com
Web site: http://www.teneues.com.

Tenley Circle Pr., *(0-9773536)* Orders Addr.: P.O. Box 5625, Washington, DC 20016 USA; Edit Addr.: 4405 Yuma St., NW, Washington, DC 20016 USA
Dist(s): **Biblio Distribution.**

Tennedo Pubs., *(0-9638946)* 6315 Elwynne Dr., Cincinnati, OH 45236 USA Tel 513-791-3277
Web site: http://www.author.illustr.source.com.

Tennessee Valley Publishing, *(1-882194; 1-932604)* Orders Addr.: P.O. Box 52527, Knoxville, TN 37950-2527 USA Tel 865-584-5235; Fax: 865-584-0113; Toll Free: 800-762-7079; Edit Addr.: 5710 Kingston Pike, Suite F, Knoxville, TN 37950 USA
E-mail: info@tvp1.com
Web site: http://www.tvp1.com.

Tenney, Bob Solutions, LLC, *(0-9763485)* 160 Hamburg Mountain Rd., Weaverville, NC 28787-9432 USA
E-mail: bobtenney@earthlink.net
Web site: http://www.tenneypubs.com.

Tensaw Pr., Inc., The, *(0-9746444)* 158 S. Jefferson St., Mobile, AL 36602-1119 USA Fax: 251-438-4545
E-mail: tensawpress@aol.com.

Teora USA LLC, *(1-59496)* Orders Addr.: 2 Wisconsin Cir., Suite 870, Chevy Chase, MD 20815 USA (SAN 256-1220) Tel 301-986-6990; Fax: 301-986-6992
E-mail: welcome@teora.com
Web site: http://www.teorausa.com.

Terandlo Publishing, *(0-9744109)* 1601 15th Ave. SW, Willmar, MN 56201-2851 USA Tel 320-235-3655
E-mail: tshaw75@charter.net.

Terfle Bks., *(0-9675111)* 13908 SE Fairoaks Ave., Portland, OR 97267-1084 USA
E-mail: M@terflebooks.com.

Terminal Pr., LLC, *(0-9753683)* 951 Oceanfront, Apt. 11, Long Beach, NY 11561 USA
E-mail: bferrara@terminalpress.com
Web site: http://www.terminalpress.com.

Tern Bk. Co., Inc., The, *(0-9655782; 1-890309)* P.O. Box 720701, Orlando, FL 32872-0701 USA Tel 407-858-4869; Fax: 407-658-6320; Toll Free: 888-211-8376
E-mail: photonat@idt.net
Web site: http://village.ios.com/~photonat
Dist(s): **Baker & Taylor Bks.**

Terpsichore Pubns., *(0-9659654)* 1333 Pennsridge Ct., Downingtown, PA 19335-3670 USA Tel 610-269-9801; Fax: 610-269-7867
E-mail: KPENN500@chesco.com.

Terra Denuo, Inc., *(1-933232)* P.O. Box 485, Rocklin, CA 95677 USA
E-mail: mark@terradenuo.com
Web site: http://www.terradenuo.com.

Terra Linda Publishing, *(0-9746710)* 593 Tamarack Dr., San Rafael, CA 94903 USA Tel 415-491-1042
E-mail: rneolson@earthlink.net
Web site: http://www.terralindapublishing.com.

Terra Niños *See* **Solibros**

Terra Nova Publishing Company *See* **Dream Ship Publishing Co.**

Terra Tales, *(0-9771804)* 101 Lattice Ln., Collegeville, PA 19426-3374 USA.

Terracopiae Press, Incorporated *See* **Authors' Pr., The**

Terracopiae Press, Inc., *(1-934603)* 588 Lindsey Way, Social Circle, GA 30025 USA Tel 678-227-3162
E-mail: hclk@terracopiaepress.com
Web site: http://www.terracopiaepress.com.

Terrapin Pr., *(0-9753087)* 2094 Arthur St., Eugene, OR 97405-1519 USA Do not confuse with companies with the same name in Marina del Rey, CA, Aiken, SC.

Terrapin Pubns., *(0-9712942)* P.O. Box 323, Hastings-On-Hudson, NY 10706 USA Do not confuse with Terrapin Publishing in Roslindale, MA.

Terrapin Publishing, *(0-9702979)* 65 E. Clinton St., New Bedford, MA 02740 USA (SAN 254-0312) Tel 508-994-8881 Do not confuse with Terrapin Pubns. in Hastings-On-Hudson, NY
E-mail: terrapinpb@yahoo.com
Dist(s): **Baker & Taylor Bks.**

Terrific Science Pr., *(1-883822)* Miami Univ. Middletown, 4200 E. University Blvd., Middletown, OH 45042 USA Fax: 513-727-3328
E-mail: infor@tsbkm.com
Web site: http://www.do-terririfcsceince.com; http://www.tsbkm.com
Dist(s): **Baker & Taylor Bks.**
Carolina Biological Supply Co.
Nasco Math Eighty-Six
Science Kit & Boreal Labs
Teacher's Discovery.

Terrific Twins LLC, *(0-9769910)* 659 Kensington Ave., Severna Park, MD 21146 USA Tel 410-647-8923 (phone/fax)
E-mail: carpenterzyla@hotmail.com
Web site: http://terrifictwins.com.

Terry Lowey's Children's Stories, LLC, *(0-9792695)* 1325 Airmotive Way, Suite 175, Reno, NV 89502 USA Tel 775-322-1924; Fax: 775-322-1937
Web site: http://www.lifeisamagicaljourney.com.

Terumah Publishing, *(0-9744277)* Orders Addr.: 5 Pipe Hill Ct., Unit C, Baltimore, MD 21209 USA Tel 410-486-0950
E-mail: info@terumah.com
Web site: http://www.terumah.com.

Tes Publishing Co., *(0-9616432; 1-931228)* 107 Saddletree Rd., San Antonio, TX 78231 USA (SAN 659-0357) Tel 210-493-5112; 210 493 5112; Fax: 210-493-6735; 674 Lona Rd., McKenneyville, CA 95519 Tel 707-839-5892 Do not confuse with TES Publishing in Calumet City, IL
E-mail: eva@satx.rr.com
Web site: http://www.world-net.net/home/eva/
Dist(s): **Baker & Taylor Bks.**

Tessloff Publishing *Imprint of* **Quadrillion Media LLC**

Testament *Imprint of* **Random Hse. Value Publishing**

Tetoca Pr., *(0-9788085)* P.O. Box 337, Puyallup, WA 98371 USA Tel 253-845-1256; 253-845-5090; Toll Free: 888-483-8622
E-mail: thhunter@earthlink.net; tetoca@tetocapress.net
Web site: http://www.tetocapress.net
Dist(s): **Pathway Bk. Service**
Quality Bks., Inc.

Tetrahedron, Incorporated *See* **Tetrahedron Publishing LLC**

Tetrahedron Publishing LLC, *(0-923550; 0-9609386)* Orders Addr.: c/o Healthy World Distributing, LLC, 206 N. Fourth Ave., Suite 147, Sandpoint, ID 83864 USA Tel 208-265-2575; Fax: 208-265-2775; Toll Free: 888-508-4787; Edit Addr.: P.O. Box 2033, Sandpoint, ID 83864-0906 USA (SAN 260-2717) Toll Free: 888-508-4787 (orders)
E-mail: tetra@tetrahedron.org
Web site: http://www.tetrahedron.org
Dist(s): **Baker & Taylor Bks.**
New Leaf Distributing Co., Inc.

†Texas A&M Univ. Pr., *(0-89096; 1-58544; 1-60344)* 4354 TAMU John H. Lindsey Bldg., Lewis St., College Station, TX 77843-4354 USA (SAN 658-1919) Tel 979-458-3978; Fax: 979-847-8752; Toll Free Fax: 888-617-2421 (orders); Toll Free: 800-826-8911 (orders)
E-mail: jmm@tampress.tamu.edu
Web site: http://www.tamu.edu/upress/
Dist(s): **NetLibrary, Inc.**; *CIP.*

Texas Agricultural Extension Service *See* **Texas Cooperative Extension**

†Texas Christian Univ. Pr., *(0-87565; 0-912646)* P.O. Box 298300, Fort Worth, TX 76129 USA (SAN 202-7690) Tel 817-257-7822; Fax: 817-257-5075
E-mail: j.alter@tcu.edu; s.petty@tcu.edu
Web site: http://www.prs.tcu.edu/prs
Dist(s): **NetLibrary, Inc.**
Texas A&M Univ. Pr.; *CIP.*

Texas Cooperative Extension, *(0-9672990; 0-9721049)* c/o Texas A & M University, 2112 TAMU, College Station, TX 77843-2112 USA Tel 979-845-2808; Fax: 979-862-1202
E-mail: j-winn2@tamu.edu.

Texas Geological Pr., *(0-9727785)* P.O. Box 967, Alpine, TX 79831 USA Tel 915-837-9930.

Texas Parks & Wildlife Department *See* **Texas Parks & Wildlife Pr.**

Texas Parks & Wildlife Pr., *(0-9636765; 1-885696)* Div. of Texas Parks & Wildlife Dept., 3000 S., 1H-35, Suite 120, Austin, TX 78704 USA Tel 512-912-7035; Fax: 512-707-1913
Dist(s): **Univ. of Texas Pr.**

†Texas State Historical Assn., *(0-87611)* 2-306 Richardson Hall, University Sta., Austin, TX 78712 USA (SAN 202-7704) Tel 512-471-1525; Fax: 512-471-1551; Toll Free: 800-687-8132
Web site: http://www.dla.utexas.edu/texhist/index.html; http://www.tsha.utexas.edu/
Dist(s): **Texas A&M Univ. Pr.**; *CIP.*

†Texas Tech Univ. Pr., *(0-89672)* Affil. of Texas Tech Univ., Orders Addr.: P.O. Box 41037, Lubbock, TX 79409-1037 USA (SAN 218-5989) Tel 806-742-2982; Fax: 806-742-2979; Toll Free: 800-832-4042; Edit Addr.: 2903 Fourth St., Lubbock, TX 79409-1037 USA
E-mail: ttup@ttu.edu
Web site: http://www.ttup.ttu.edu; *CIP.*

Texas Testing Products, *(0-9650840; 1-889684)* 1047 B. Kilgore, Pleasanton, TX 78064 USA Tel 830-569-6365 (phone/fax)
E-mail: tx-testing-prod@hotmail.com
Web site: http://www.texastestingproducts.com.

†Texas Woman's Univ. Pr., *(0-9607488; 0-9712104)* Orders Addr.: P.O. Box 425858, Denton, TX 76204 USA (SAN 238-4833) Tel 940-898-3123; Fax: 940-898-3127; Edit Addr.: 1200 Frame St., Denton, TX 76205 USA
E-mail: wbenson@twu.edu; *CIP.*

Text 4m Publishing, *(0-9779207; 0-9795691)* P.O. Box 12586, Milwaukee, WI 53212-0586 USA (SAN 850-6299)
E-mail: info@text4mpublishing.com
Web site: http://www.text4mpublishing.com
Dist(s): **Lushena Bks.**

Text N Tone, Inc., *(0-9764429)* 1738 Tradewinds Ln., Newport Beach, CA 92660 USA Tel 949-650-8101 (phone/fax)
E-mail: mchekel@dslextreme.com.

Textbook Pubs., *(0-7581)* Orders Addr.: P.O. Box 893520, Temecula, CA 92589-3520 USA Tel 866-230-7238; Fax: 951-767-0133; Edit Addr.: 27315 Jefferson J2, Temecula, CA 92590 USA
E-mail: sales@textbookpublishers.net; text.book@verizon.net
Web site: http://www.Textbookpublishers.net.

Texthelp Systems, Inc., *(0-9712893; 1-932625)* c/o Proskauer Rose, LLP, 100 Unicorn Park Dr., Woburn, MA 01801-3339 USA
E-mail: info@texthelp.com
Web site: http://www.texthelp.com.

TFG Pr., *(0-9743521; 0-9748553)* 244 Madison Ave., No. 254, New York, NY 10016 USA Tel 877-822-2504 do nto confuse with TGF Press in New York, NY.

Th1nk Bks. *Imprint of* **NavPress Publishing Group**

Thajema Publishing, *(0-9727597)* 31 Glen View Dr., West Orange, NJ 07052-1010 USA Tel 973-731-6209 (phone/fax)
E-mail: thajema@aol.com.

Thames & Hudson, *(0-500)* 500 Fifth Ave., New York, NY 10110 USA Tel 212-354-3763; Fax: 212-398-1252; Toll Free: 800-233-4830 (orders)
E-mail: bookinfo@thames.wwnorton.com
Web site: http://www.thamesandhudsonusa.com
Dist(s): **Norton, W. W. & Co., Inc.**
United Nations Pubns.

Thameside Press *See* **Chrysalis Education**

Thandi's Place, A Billo Communication Company *See* **Youth Popular Culture Institute, Inc.**

Thane's Games, *(0-9719404)* 12509 Indian Trail NE, Albuquerque, NM 87112 USA
E-mail: thane@thanesgames.com
Web site: http://www.thanesgames.com.

That Patchwork Place *Imprint of* **Martingale & Co.**

Thatcher Forest Publishing, *(0-9670504)* Orders Addr.: 3524 Manford Dr., Durham, NC 27707 USA
E-mail: bob.s-k@thatcherforest.com
Web site: http://www.thatcherforest.com.

That's Life! Communications (CAN) *(0-9685495) Dist. by* **STL Dist NA.**

That's Life, Incorporated *See* **That's Life Publishing, Inc.**

That's Life Publishing, Inc., *(0-9722304)* 3431 Thunderbird Rd., No. 200, Phoenix,, AZ 85053 USA Toll Free: 877-896-9500 ; *Imprints:* ZZ Dogs Press (ZZ Dogs Pr)
Web site: http://www.zzdogs.com
Dist(s): **Biblio Distribution.**

That's Me Publishing, LLC, *(1-933843)* 200 Corporate Pl., Branson, MO 65616 USA Tel 417-337-9780; Fax: 417-337-9783
E-mail: mary@thatsmepublishing.com
Web site: http://www.thatsmepublishing.com.

ThatsMyLife Co., *(0-9760419)* 5516 Challis View Ln., Charlotte, NC 28226 USA Tel 704-752-0935; Toll Free: 866-752-0935
E-mail: customerservice@thatsmytale.com
Web site: http://www.thatsmytale.com.

The Old West Co., *(0-9654341)* Orders Addr.: 5118 Village Trail Dr., San Antonio, TX 78218-3831 USA ; *Imprints:* Sweetwater Stagelines (Sweetwtr Stage)
E-mail: kirkwest@sbcglobal.net
Web site: http://oldwest.com; http://theoldwestcompany.com; http://sweetwaterstagelines.com.

Theatre Arts Bks. *Imprint of* **Routledge**

†Theatre Communications Group, Inc., *(0-88754; 0-913745; 0-930452; 1-55936; 1-84002; 1-85459; 1-870259; 1-889791)* 355 Lexington Ave., New York, NY 10017-6603 USA (SAN 210-9387) Tel 212-697-5230; Fax: 212-983-4847 ; *Imprints:* Oberon Books (Oberon Books)
Web site: http://www.tcg.org
Dist(s): **Consortium Bk. Sales & Distribution**; *CIP.*

Theatre Directories Inc., *(0-933919)* Orders Addr.: P.O. Box 159, Dorset, VT 05251 USA (SAN 693-0247) Tel 802-867-9333; Fax: 802-867-2297
E-mail: tdbooks@sover.net
Web site: http://www.theatredirectories.com.

Theatre of Innocence, A, L.L.C., *(0-9760283)* 1212 Hull St., No. 1, Louisville, KY 40204 USA.

Thecomic.com, *(1-893131)* Orders Addr.: 335 Arlington St., Watertown, MA 02472 USA Tel 617-625-6468
E-mail: gareth@thecomic.com
Web site: http://www.thecomic.com.

Theee Hole Punch Publishing, *(0-9771678)* P.O. Box 4488, Midlothian, VA 23112 USA
E-mail: threeholepunchpublishing@verizon.net; vzentja9@verizon.net
Web site: http://threeholepunchpublishing.com.

Theisen, Patricia, *(0-9793076)* 10520 11th Ave. NW, Seattle, WA 98177 USA
E-mail: ptheisen@gmail.com.

Them Potatoes, *(0-9772564)* 10714 SW Cemetery Rd., Vashon, WA 98070-6048 USA (SAN 257-1285)
E-mail: kbrown@thempotatoes.com
Web site: http://www.thempotatoes.com.

Theme Perks, Inc., *(0-9729777)* 3300 S. Hiawassee Rd., Bldg. 105, Orlando, FL 32835 USA (SAN 852-6435) Tel 407-296-5800; Fax: 407-296-5801
E-mail: salcorn@alcorn.com
Web site: http://www.themeperks.com.

TheNetworkAdministrator.com, *(0-9744630)* Orders Addr.: 201 W. Cottesmore Cir., Longwood, FL 32779 USA
E-mail: douglaschick@thenetworkadministrator.com
Web site: http://www.thenetworkadministrator.com.

Theodore Berlin Publishing, *(0-9769196)* Div. of Theodore Berlin LLC, Orders Addr.: 8221 Provident St., Philadelphia, PA 19150 USA Tel 215-327-8212; Fax: 615-704-4422
E-mail: berlintheodore@yahoo.com.

Theodore Publishing, Inc., *(0-9653798)* Orders Addr.: P.O. Box 381812, Duncanville, TX 75138 USA Tel 972-298-0214 (phone/fax) Do not confuse with Theodore Publishing, Champaign, IL
E-mail: theodore@theodorepublishing.com
Web site: http://www.theodorepublishing.com
Dist(s): **Follett Library Resources.**

Theory & Practice *Imprint of* **Scholastic, Inc.**

Theragogy.com, *(0-9749862)* 301 1/2 Crescent NE, Grand Rapids, MI 49503 USA
E-mail: drperkins@theragogy.com
Web site: http://www.theragogy.com.

Therapeutic Stories, *(0-9652163)* P.O. Box 4114, San Luis Obispo, CA 93403-4114 USA Tel 805-546-4801.

Theytus Bks., Ltd. (CAN) *(0-919441; 1-894778) Dist. by* **Orca Bk Pubs.**

Thimble Mouse Publishing, Inc., *(0-9794522)* 1619 Saddle Creek Cir., No. 1312, Arlington, TX 76015 USA (SAN 853-4942).

ThingsAsian Pr., *(0-9715940; 1-934159)* 3230 Scott St., San Francisco, CA 94123 USA Tel 415-921-1316; Fax: 415-921-3432
E-mail: info@thingsasian.com; albert@thingsasian.com
Web site: http://www.thingsasianpress.com; http://www.toasiawithlove.com; http://www.thingsasian.com
Dist(s): **Biblio Distribution.**

Think, Ink!, *(0-9669638)* 6301 SW 93rd Ct., Miami, FL 33173-2317 USA.

THINK?! Publishing, *(0-9723421)* 1128 Roosevelt Ave., Ames, IA 50010-5874 USA Tel 515-232-8681; Fax: 515-232-0028
E-mail: calh42@aol.com
Web site: http://www.halliburtonassociates.com.

ThinkFun, Inc., *(0-9755330)* 1321 Cameron St., Alexandria, VA 22314 USA (SAN 631-9742) Toll Free Fax: 888-446-2787
Web site: http://www.thinkfun.com.

Thinkorporated, *(1-891905)* P.O. Box 1472, Bowie, MD 20717 USA (SAN 299-5379) Tel 301-627-0999; Fax: 301-627-1045
E-mail: thinkorporated@webtv.net.

Third Axe Publishing, *(0-9765547)* 1150 McFarland, HR 26, Morristown, TN 37814 USA Tel 423-736-0884
E-mail: thirdaxepub@yahoo.com
Web site: http://www.brotherhoodofdwarves.com.

Third Dimension Publishing, *(0-9777041)* Div. of Third Dimension Group, Inc., Orders Addr.: P.O. Box 1845, Calhoun, GA 30703-1845 USA Tel 706-602-0398; Fax: 706-625-8712; Edit Addr.: 167 Richardson Rd., Calhoun, GA 30701 USA
E-mail: jeffcompton@msn.com
Web site: http://www.areyouawriter.com; http://www.thirddimensiongroup.com; http://www.thirddimensionpublishing.com.

Third Millennium Pr., *(0-9663622)* P.O. Box 844, Hurricane, WV 25526 USA Tel 304-696-2778; Fax: 304-696-2784
E-mail: wyatt@marshall.edu.

Third Millennium Pubns., *(1-932657; 1-934805)* Sci Fi - Arizona, Inc., 1931 E. Libra Dr., Tempe, AZ 85283-5117 USA Tel 602-740-0569; Fax: 480-619-6202
E-mail: mccollum@3mpub.com
Web site: http://www.3mpub.com; http://www.scifi-az.com.

Third Millennium Publishing *Imprint of* **Sci Fi-Arizona, Inc.**

3rd Party Publishing Co., *(0-89914)* Div. of Third Party Assocs., Inc., P.O. Box 13306, Oakland, CA 94661-0306 USA (SAN 127-7294) Tel 510-339-2323; Fax: 510-339-6729; Toll Free: 888-339-2323
E-mail: paulmico@tpaserver.com
Web site: http://www.tpaserver.com.

Third Week Bks., *(0-9712816)* 1112 W. 66th St., No.1, Richfield, MN 55423-2280 USA Tel 612-990-6011
E-mail: thebabyreader@yahoo.com
Web site: http://ThirdWeekBooks.com.

Third World Games, Inc., *(0-9728526)* P.O. Box 667, Westminster, CA 92684-0667 USA Tel 714-357-2967
E-mail: companyisbn-dir@thirdworldgames.com
Web site: http://www.thirdworldgames.com.

Third World Press, *(0-88378)* P.O. Box 19730, Chicago, IL 60619 USA (SAN 202-778X) Tel 773-651-0700; Fax: 773-651-7286
E-mail: TWPress3@aol.com
Web site: http://www.thirdworldpressinc.com
Dist(s): **Austin & Company, Inc.**
Independent Pubs. Group.

Thirsty(?) *Imprint of* **Tyndale Hse. Pubs.**

Thirsty Sponge Publishing Co., *(0-9797960)* 898 Southgate Dr., Cookeville, TN 38501 USA.

Thirty-Three Hundred Pr., *(0-9646017)* 3300 Mission St., San Francisco, CA 94110 USA Tel 415-826-6886; 300 Vicksburg St., No. 5, San Francisco, CA 94114.

This New World Publishing, LLC, *(0-9723252)* P.O. Box 42023-B, Phoenix, AZ 85080 USA (SAN 254-783X) Tel 623-217-6545
E-mail: publisher@tnwpub.com
Web site: http://www.tnwpub.com; http://www.naptimeadventures.com.

Thomas & Sons Bks., *(0-9758800)* 33 Greenwich Ave., Suite 7L, New York, NY 10014 USA
E-mail: willysthom@rcn.com.

Thomas Berryhill Pr., *(0-9648638)* Orders Addr.: P.O. Box 178, Lafayette, CA 94549 USA Tel 925-284-7176; Edit Addr.: 3630 Mosswood Dr., Lafayette, CA 94549 USA.

Thomas Expressions, Inc., *(0-9713573; 0-9771059)* 11810 Cue Dr. NE, Panama City, FL 32404 USA Tel 850-874-2066 (phone/fax)
E-mail: sales@thomasexpressions.com
Web site: https://www.buddymanatee.com; http://www.thomasexpressions.com.

Thomas Expressions Publishing Company *See* **Thomas Expressions, Inc.**

Thomas, Frederic Inc., *(0-9747133; 1-933443)* 5629 Strand Blvd., Suite 410, Naples, FL 34119 USA (SAN 255-8157) Tel 239-593-8000; Fax: 239-593-8011 ; *Imprints:* Values to Live By Classic Stories (ValLiveByClass)
E-mail: freimer@fredericthomas.com; bmichalowski@fredericthomas.com
Web site: http://fredericthomas.com; http://www.healthylivingforkids.com; http://www.valuestoliveby.com.

Thomas Jefferson's Poplar Forest, *(0-9667169)* Orders Addr.: P.O. Box 419, Forest, VA 24551 USA Tel 434-525-1806; Fax: 434-525-7252; Edit Addr.: Corner of Fox Hall Rd. & Poplar Forest Dr., Forest, VA 24551 USA
E-mail: suzan@poplarforest.org
Web site: http://www.poplarforest.org.

Thomas, Kevin *See* **Catch 22 Publishing Inc.**

Thomas Max Publishing, *(0-9764052; 0-9788571; 0-9799950)* P.O. Box 250054, Atlanta, GA 30325-1054 USA Tel 404-794-6588
E-mail: LeeC@thomasmax.com; thomasmax@incrediboy.com.

Thomas Pubns., *(0-939631; 1-57747)* 3245 Fairfield Rd., Gettysburg, PA 17325 USA (SAN 663-7213) Tel 717-642-6600; Fax: 717-642-5555; Toll Free: 800-840-6782 Do not confuse with companies with the same name in Austin, TX, La Crescenta, CA
E-mail: thomaspub@blazenet.net
Web site: http://www.thomaspublications.com.

Thomas, R. E., *(0-9761077)* P.O. Box 53091, Houston, TX 77052 USA.

Thomas, Richard Kayeen *See* **MarWel Enterprises, Inc.**

Thomas, Sheldon Wade, *(0-9670539)* 1091 Thomas S. Boyland St., Brooklyn, NY 11236 USA Tel 718-495-6002 (phone/fax).

Thompson, Alyce C. Books, Inc., *(0-9746411)* Orders Addr.: P.O. Box 28827, Philadelphia, PA 19151-0827 USA; Edit Addr.: 209 N. Gross St., Philadelphia, PA 19139 USA Tel 276-997-1710
E-mail: emailalyce8@aol.com; actbooksinc@tds.net
Web site: http://alycecthompsonbooksinc.com; http://www.myspace.com/alycecthompson
Dist(s): **A & B Distributors & Pubs. Group**
Afrikan World Bk. Distributor
Culture Plus Bk. Distributors.

Thompson, Angela, *(0-615)* 9501 W. 171st St. Ste. Q, Tinley Park, IL 60487 USA
Web site: http://angelathompson1.tripod.com/
Dist(s): **Lulu.com.**

Company

Company

Thomson Course Technology, Inc., *(0-534; 0-619; 0-7600; 0-7895; 0-87709; 0-87835; 0-89426; 0-928763; 1-56527; 1-878748; 1-4188; 1-59863; 1-4239; 1-60334)* Div. of Thomson Learning, Orders Addr.: 25 Thomson Pl., Boston, MA 02210 USA Tel 617-757-7900; Fax: 617-757-7951; Toll Free Fax: 800-881-8922 ; *Imprints:* Course Technology (CourTech)
E-mail: Esales@thomsonlearning.com; stacy.hiquet@thomson.com; cheryl.mondillo@thomson.com
Web site: http://www.course.com/
Dist(s): **CENGAGE Learning**
Leonard, Hal Corp.
NetLibrary, Inc.

Thomson, D.C. & Co., Ltd. (GBR) *(0-85116; 1-84535) Dist. by* **APG.**

†Thomson Delmar Learning, *(0-314; 0-7668; 0-7693; 0-8273; 0-87350; 0-916032; 0-944132; 0-9653629; 1-56253; 1-56593; 1-56930; 1-4018; 1-4180; 1-4283; 1-4354)* Div. of Thomson Learning, Orders Addr.: c/o Thomson Learning Order Fulfilment, P.O. Box 6904, Florence, KY 41022 USA Toll Free Fax: 800 487 8488; Toll Free: 800 347 7707; c/o Thomson Delmar Learning Clinical Health Care Series, P.O. Box 3419, Scranton, PA 18505-0419 Fax: 570-347-9072; Toll Free: 888-427-5800; Edit Addr.: P.O. Box 15015, Albany, NY 12212-5015 USA (SAN 206-7544) Tel 518-348-2300; Fax: 518-373-6345; Toll Free: 800-998-7498; 5 Maxwell Dr., Clifton Park, NY 12065- (SAN 658-0440) Tel 518-348-2300; Fax: 518-881-1256; Toll Free: 800-998-7498 ; *Imprints:* Delmar Learning (DelLearn)
E-mail: matthew.grover@thomson.com; clinicalmanuals@thomson.com
Web site: http://www.delmarlearning.com; http://www.clinicalmanuals.com/
Dist(s): **CENGAGE Learning**
Gryphon Hse., Inc.
Ingenix, Inc.
Pearson Education; *CIP.*

†Thomson Gale, *(0-13; 0-7876; 0-8103; 0-936474; 1-57302; 1-878623; 1-59413; 1-59414; 1-59415; 1-4144; 1-4205; 1-59722; 1-4328)* Subs. of The Thomson Corp., Orders Addr.: P.O. Box 9187, Farmington Hills, MI 48333-9187 USA Toll Free Fax: 800 414 5043; Toll Free: 800 877 4253; Edit Addr.: 27500 Drake Rd., Farmington Hills, MI 48331-3535 USA (SAN 213-4373) Tel 248 699 4253; a/o Wheeler Publishing, 295 Kennedy Memorial Dr., Waterville, ME 04901 Toll Free: 800 223 1244 ; *Imprints:* UXL (UXL); Macmillan Reference USA (Macmillan Ref); Charles Scribner's Sons (C Scribners Sons); Kidhaven (Kidhaven); Twayne Publishers (Twayne Pubs); Hall, G. K. & Company (G K Hall Company); Blackbirch Press, Incorporated (Blackbirch Pr); Lucent Books (Lucent Books); Greenhaven Press, Incorporated (Greenhaven Pr); Five Star (Five Star ME); Wheeler Publishing, Incorporated (Wheel); Walker Large Print (Walker Large Pt); Five Star Trade (Five Star Trade)
E-mail: gale.salesassistance@thomson.com
Web site: http://www.gale.com
Dist(s): **Thorndike Pr.**; *CIP.*

†Thomson Heinle, *(0-8384; 0-88377; 0-912066; 1-4130)* Div. of Thomson Learning, Orders Addr.: 10650 Toebben Dr., Independence, KY 41051 USA Toll Free Fax: 800 487 8488 ; *Imprints:* Newbury House (Newbury)
E-mail: reply@heinle.com
Web site: http://www.heinle.com
Dist(s): **CENGAGE Learning**; *CIP.*

Thomson, J P, *(0-9754365)* P.O. Box 377, Exton, PA 19341 USA Tel 610-594-1707; Fax: 610-594-1866
E-mail: montanapino@comcast.net.

Thomson Learning *See* **CENGAGE Learning**

Thomson Learning *Imprint of* **CENGAGE Learning**

Thomson Learning EMEA, Ltd. (GBR) *(1-86152; 1-84480) Dist. by* **CENGAGE Learn.**

Thomson Nelson (CAN) *(0-17; 0-7725; 1-85032) Dist. by* **CENGAGE Learn.**

Thomson Peterson's *See* **Peterson's**

†Thomson South-Western, *(0-03; 0-324; 0-538)* Div. of Thomson Learning, 5191 Natorp Blvd., Mason, OH 45040 USA (SAN 202-7518) Tel 513 229 1000; Toll Free Fax: 800-437-8488; Toll Free: 800-354-9706 (orders only); 800-543-0487
Web site: http://www.thomsonedu.com/
Dist(s): **CENGAGE Learning**
International Thomson Computer Pr.; *CIP.*

†Thomson Wadsworth, *(0-15; 0-314; 0-534; 0-8185; 0-8273; 0-942728; 1-928916; 1-4163; 0-495)* Div. of CENGAGE Learning, Orders Addr.: 7625 Empire Dr., Florence, KY 41042-2978 USA (SAN 200-2663) Tel 859 525 2230; Toll Free: 800 354 9706; Edit Addr.: 10 Davis Dr., Belmont, CA 94002 USA (SAN 200-2213) Tel 650 595 2350; Fax: 606 592 9081
Web site: http://www.brookscole.com; http://www.wadsworth.com
Dist(s): **CENGAGE Learning**; *CIP.*

Thornapple Farms, LLC, *(0-9749728)* 13010 W. Darrow Rd., Vermilion, OH 44089 USA Tel 440-967-2680; Fax: 440-967-2696
E-mail: ashar@hbr.net
Web site: http://www.thornapplefarms.com.

Thornburg, Billie Lee Snyder *See* **Old Hundred & One Pr. Publishing Co., The**

†Thorndike Pr., *(0-7838; 0-7862; 0-8161; 0-89621; 1-56054; 1-4104)* Div. of Gale Group, 295 Kennedy Memorial Dr., Waterville, ME 04901 USA Tel 207-859-1053; 207-859-1020; 207-859-1000; Toll Free Fax: 800-558-4676; Toll Free: 800-223-1244 (ext. 15); 800-877-4253 (customer resource ctr.) ; *Imprints:* Large Print Press (Lrg Print Pr)
E-mail: jamie.knobloch@gale.com; barb.littfield@galegroup.com; Betsy.M.Brown@thomson.com
Web site: http://www.gale.com/thorndike
Dist(s): **Thomson Gale**; *CIP.*

Thornton Hse., *(0-9641243)* P.O. Box 57, Moss Beach, CA 94038-0057 USA Tel 650-563-9445
E-mail: info@thorntonhouse.com
Web site: http://www.thorntonhouse.com.

Thornton Publishing, *(1-882913)* 1504 Howard St., New Iberia, LA 70560 USA Tel 337-364-2752; Fax: 318-365-0316; Toll Free: 800-551-3076 Do not confuse with companies with the same or similar names in Littleton, CO, Forest Grove, OR, Burley, ID.

Thornton Publishing, *(0-9670242; 0-9719597; 0-9723309; 1-932344; 0-9774761; 0-9779960)* 17011 Lincoln Ave. #408, Parker, CO 80134 USA Tel 303-794-8888; Fax: 720-863-2013 ; *Imprints:* Profitable Publishing (Profitable Pubng); Books To Believe In (Bks To Believe In) Do not confuse with companies with the same or similar names in New Iberia, LA, Forest Grove, OR, Burley, ID
E-mail: publisher@profitablepublishing.net
Web site: http://www.profitablepublishing.net; http://ttp://www.BooksToBelieveIn.com.

Thorogood (GBR) *(1-85418) Dist. by* **Stylus Pub VA.**

Thoroughbred Publishing, L.L.C., *(0-9666172)* 8459 US 42, Florence, KY 41041 USA Tel 606-384-4416; Fax: 606-384-4461
E-mail: nblackmore@usa.net
Web site: http://www.bigbonelick.com.

Thorpe, Sandy, *(0-9764147)* 20205 NE 3rd Ct., No. 3, N. Miami Beach, FL 33179 USA
E-mail: sthorpe@trekstuff.com.

Thou Art, Inc., *(0-9648165; 0-9716617)* P.O. Box 73, Gooding, ID 83330 USA Tel 208-934-8075; 3068 Hwy. 83, Sonoita, AZ 85637
E-mail: meditate@realhealing.com
Web site: http://www.realhealing.com
Dist(s): **New Leaf Distributing Co., Inc.**

Thoughtful Education Pr., The *Imprint of* **Silver Strong & Assocs.**

ThoughtRockets, Inc., *(0-9766793)* 2033 Ralston Ave., No. 114, Belmont, CA 94002 USA Tel 650-592-3169 (phone/fax)
E-mail: laura@thoughtrockets.com
Web site: http://www.thoughtrockets.com.

Thoughts in Motion, *(0-9647161)* P.O. Box 33131, San Antonio, TX 78265 USA Tel 210-877-0700
E-mail: jaspertone7@juno.com.

ThoughtSource, Inc., *(0-9669483)* 1136 SE 3rd Ave., Ft Lauderdale, FL 33316-1110 USA Toll Free: 800-532-7610
E-mail: contact@thoughtsource.com.

Threatt, Cedric L., *(0-9720543)* Div. of Ahava Publishing, LLC, P.O. Box 363, Margaret, AL 35112 USA Tel 205-467-0652
E-mail: cl3tt@windstream.net
Web site: http://www.Ahavapublishing.org.

Three Angels Broadcasting Network, *(0-9718083; 0-9720888)* Orders Addr.: P.O. Box 220, West Frankfort, IL 62896 USA Tel 618-627-4651; Edit Addr.: 3391 Charley Good Rd., West Frankfort, IL 62896 USA
Web site: http://www.3abn.org
Dist(s): **Pacific Pr. Publishing Assn.**

Three Bean Pr., *(0-9767276)* P.O. Box 15386, Boston, MA 02215 USA (SAN 256-5137) Tel 617-584-5759; Fax: 617-266-3446
E-mail: seneca@threebeanpress.com
Web site: http://www.threebeanpress.com.

Three Butterflies Entertainment & Pr., *(0-9702415)* 130 Ryerson St., Brooklyn, NY 11205 USA Tel 718-670-3248; Fax: 718-857-0950
E-mail: lumpyflies@cs.com
Web site: http://www.littlelumpy.com.

Three Cents Publishing, *(0-9746697)* Orders Addr.: 177 Ocean St.: PO Box 339 Brant Rock Ma02020 Usa, Boston, MA 02020 USA.

Three Four Three Publishing Co., *(0-9675286)* 3738 Victoria Dr., West Palm Beach, FL 33406 USA Tel 561-337-9299
E-mail: paulnison@mindspring.com
Web site: http://www.rawlife.com.

Three Hermits Pr., *(0-9753906)* P.O. Box 99099, Bennington, VT 05201 USA
E-mail: threehermits@mail.com.

360 Marketing, LLC, *(0-9702654)* 37 Water St., Suite 100, Mystic, CT 06355 USA Tel 860-536-6860; Fax: 860-536-6460; Toll Free: 888-533-6860
E-mail: three60mrk@aol.com.

Three Leaves Publishing, *(0-9661974)* 878 W. 42nd St., Houston, TX 77018 USA Tel 713-697-4851; Fax: 713-697-3570
E-mail: geissen@phoenix.net.

Three Moons Media, *(0-9725164; 0-9747440; 1-933514)* 1610 Valley Brook Ln., Longview, TX 75605-2676 USA
E-mail: marilyn@threemoonsmedia.com
Web site: http://www.threemoonsmedia.com
Dist(s): **BookSurge, LLC.**

Three Pines Pr., *(0-9635247)* 2104 Brenner St., Saginaw, MI 48602 USA Tel 517-792-4989 Do not confuse with Three Pines Pr. in Cambridge, MA
E-mail: editor@threepinespress.com.

Three Ring Circus Publishing Company, *(0-9790832)* Orders Addr.: P.O. Box 893118, Oklahoma City, OK 73189-3118 USA (SAN 852-3754) Tel 405-691-4466
E-mail: trcpublishing@yahoo.com
Web site: http://www.trcpublishing.com.

Three Rivers Council, BSA, Inc., *(0-9675901)* 4650 Cardinal Dr., Beaumont, TX 77705 USA Tel 409-842-5240 ext 18
Web site: http://www.ecpadventures.com; http://www.adventuresoftheelements.com/.

Three Rivers Pr *Imprint of* **Crown Publishing Group**

Three Sisters Communication, LLC, *(0-9771204)* P.O. Box 280, Star, ID 83669-5015 USA (SAN 256-7970)
E-mail: sfunk624@heritagewifi.com.

Three Sisters Pr., *(0-9722999)* P.O. Box 17061, Golden, CO 80402 USA Tel 720-231-6540; Fax: 303-561-0626 Do not confuse with Three Sisters Pr., in Washington, DC
E-mail: violeta134@hotmail.com; sjbrehm@comcast.net.

Three Sisters Publishing Hse., Ltd., *(0-9785570)* 32104 Cty. Rd., 1, Saint Cloud, MN 56303 USA Tel 320-654-0001.

Three Spots Productions, *(0-9744509)* 67 Rutz St., Stamford, CT 06906 USA
E-mail: rarruzza@optonline.net; rarruzza@sparkyswalk.com
Web site: http://www.sparkyswalk.com.

Three Trees, Inc., *(0-9789426)* P.O. Box 92, Cottleville, MO 63368-6336 USA Tel 636-561-9184; Fax: 636-561-9184
Web site: http://Petalwinkthefairy.com.

Three Willows Pr., *(0-9770279)* 4680 S. 1000 W., Rensselaer, IN 47978 USA.

Three-D Vision Productions *See* **Soul Vision Works Publishing**

Threesie Pubns., *(0-9655035)* P.O. Box 328, Monongahela, PA 15063 USA Tel 724-258-4517
E-mail: threesie@nauticom.net.

Threshold Publishing, *(0-9709734)* Orders Addr.: P.O. Box 387, Worth, IL 60482 USA (SAN 254-0584) Tel 773-233-5102; Fax: 773-233-2477; Edit Addr.: 10301 S. Hoyne Ave., Chicago, IL 60643 USA Do not confuse with Threshold Publishing Co. in San Francisco, CA
Web site: http://www.beverlyhillshistory.com.

Throwback Publishing, *(0-9771630)* P.O. Box 33792, Washington, DC 20033 USA
Web site: http://www.throwbackpublishing.com.

Thumbprint Pr. *Imprint of* **McIntyre, Connie**

Thumbprint Publishing, *(0-9741833)* 103 William Howard Taft Rd., Cincinnati, OH 45219 USA Tel 513-961-2967 Do not confuse with Thumbprint Publishing in Studio City, CA
E-mail: rachelkdavis@fuse.net
Web site: http://www.connectionssp.org/.

Thumbs Up Pr., *(0-9772513)* 3731 Reed's Landing Cir., Midlothian, VA 23113 USA Tel 804-320-8331
E-mail: thumbsuppress@earthlink.net.

Thunder Bay Pr. *Imprint of* **Advantage Pubs. Group**

Thunder Bay Pr., *(1-882376; 1-933272)* 2325 Jarco Dr., Holt, MI 48842 USA Tel 517-694-4616; Fax: 517-694-2208; Toll Free: 800-336-3137 Do not confuse with Thunder Bay Pr, San Diego, CA
E-mail: partnersbk@aol.com; speigelsara@yahoo.com; o_lynne@hotmail.com
Dist(s): **Partners Bk. Distributing, Inc.**

Thunderbolt Publishing, *(0-9715390)* 4314 Marina City Dr. Unit 320, Marina Dl Rey, CA 90292-5814 USA (SAN 254-8119)
E-mail: howardb@wedolisten.com
Web site: http://www.WeDoListen.com
Dist(s): **AtlasBooks Distribution.**

ThunderHousePress, *(0-9771154)* Div. of ThunderHouse Entertainment, 6709 La Tijera Blvd., No. 141, Los Angeles, CA 90045 USA
E-mail: reggiecook@yahoo.com
Web site: http://www.thunderhousepress.com.

Thundermist Consulting and Research Co., *(0-9759494)* P.O. Box 7023, Cumberland, RI 02864-7023 USA
E-mail: book-sales@thundermist.com
Web site: http://www.thundermist.com; http://thundermist.blogspot.com.

Thurman Hse., LLC, *(1-58989)* 5 Park Ctr. Ct., Suite 300, Owings Mills, MD 21117 USA Tel 410-902-9100; Fax: 410-902-7210
E-mail: thurmanhouse@ottenheimerpub.com.

Thy Marvelous Works, *(0-9619353)* 102 Proprietor's Point, Madison, MS 39110 USA (SAN 244-4283) Tel 601-898-8828; Fax: 601-898-0960; Toll Free: 888-471-4040
E-mail: wildlife@netdoor.com
Web site: http://www.kirkpatrickwildlife.com
Dist(s): **American Wholesale Bk. Co.**
Baker & Taylor Bks.

Tiaanya Literature Pr., *(0-9768679; 1-60508)* 613 151st St. Pl., NE, Bellevue, WA 98007 USA
E-mail: tianyapress@hotmail.com
Web site: http://www.tianyapress.com.

Tiara Bks. LLC, *(0-9729846)* 62 Birchall Dr., Scarsdale, NY 10583-4503 USA Tel 914-723-9133
Dist(s): **Baker & Taylor Bks.**

TiaraMoon Publishing, *(0-9655425)* Orders Addr.: P.O. Box 21794, Saint Paul, MN 55121-0794 USA; Edit Addr.: 3907 Canter Glen Dr., Eagan, MN 55123 USA Tel 651-681-1949
Dist(s): **Bookmen, Inc.**

Tickle Bugs, *(0-9677127)* 3949 Harmon Rd., El Sobrante, CA 94803 USA Tel 510-758-5822
E-mail: TreeMango@aol.com
Web site: http://www.ticklebugs.com.

Ticktock Media Ltd. (GBR) *(1-86007; 1-84696) Dist. by* **Consort Bk Sales.**

TICO Publishing, *(0-9777688)* 25045 Jaclyn Ave., Moreno Valley, CA 92557 USA (SAN 850-167X) Tel 951-452-2277
E-mail: ticopublishing@earthlink.net
Web site: http://www.ticopublishing.com.

Tico Times, The, *(9968-746)* Orders Addr.: P.O. Box 025216, Miami, FL 33102-5216 USA Tel 506-258-1558; Fax: 506-233-6378; Edit Addr.: 1601 NW 97th Ave., Unit C-101, Miami, FL 33102 USA
Dist(s): **Penton Overseas, Inc.**

Tidal Wave Productions *See* **Black, Judith Storyteller**

Tide-Mark Pr., Ltd, *(0-936846; 1-55949; 1-59490)* Orders Addr.: P.O. Box 20, Windsor, CT 06095-0020 USA (SAN 222-1802) Tel 860-683-4499; Fax: 860-683-4055; Toll Free: 800-338-2508; Edit Addr.: 176 Broad St., Windsor, CT 06095-0020 USA (SAN 665-794X)
E-mail: carol@tide-press.com
Web site: http://www.tidemarkpress.com.

Tides Ctr./Collage, The, *(1-891103)* 709 W. Mount Airy Ave., Philadelphia, PA 19119 USA Tel 215-242-3211; Fax: 215-242-1896; Toll Free: 800-458-0006
E-mail: collage@igc.apcorg.

Tidewatch Pubs., *(0-9665466)* Div. of Orem Associates, Inc., No. 7 Leland Ct., Chevy Chase, MD 20815 USA Tel 301-951-1110; Fax: 301-654-6301
E-mail: OremAssoc@aol.com.

Tidewater Pubs. *Imprint of* **Cornell Maritime Pr., Inc.**

Tiffen Co. LLC, The, *(0-87985; 1-883403; 1-58914)* 80 Oser Ave., Hauppauge, NY 11788 USA Tel 585-328-7800; Fax: 585-328-5078; Toll Free: 800-645-2522 ; *Imprints:* Kodak (Kodak)
E-mail: silverpix@aol.com
Web site: http://www.silverpixelpress.com
Dist(s): **Sterling Publishing Co., Inc.**

Tiffin Pr. of Maine, *(0-9646018)* Div. of Tiffin Pr., 110 Jones Point Rd., Brooksville, ME 04617-3570 USA
E-mail: joanmacc@aol.com
Dist(s): **Bilingual Pubns. Co., The.**

tigbs Publishing *See* **tigbs Publishing, Consulting & Virtual Assistant Services**

tigbs Publishing, Consulting & Virtual Assistant Services, *(0-615)* Orders Addr.: P.O. Box 9248, Memphis, TN 38109 USA Tel 901-398-7987; Fax: 901-344-9746; Edit Addr.: 436 Bonita Dr., Memphis, TN 38109 USA
E-mail: sjk436@bellsouth.net
Web site: http://www.spiritbooster.com.

Tiger Iron Pr., *(0-9787263)* P.O. Box 27705, Macon, GA 31221 USA
E-mail: Info@TigerIronPress.com
Web site: http://www.TigerIronPress.com.

Tiger Lily Publishing, *(1-880883)* Six Swift Ct., Newport Beach, CA 92663 USA Tel 949-645-5907; Toll Free: 800-950-3237 (800-950-DADS)
E-mail: janedrew@home.com.

Tiger Publishing *See* **Tiger Tale Publishing Co.**

Tiger Tale Publishing Co., *(0-9787533)* 522 N. Grant Ave., Odessa, TX 79761 USA Tel 432-337-8511; Fax: 432-337-1035
E-mail: clclack@aol.com.

tiger tales *Imprint of* **ME Media LLC**

TIGO & Co., *(0-9761167)* P.O. Box 210066, Dallas, TX 75211-0066 USA Tel 214-330-4420
E-mail: thekingskid1982@sbcglobal.net.

Tigress Pr., *(0-9740848; 0-9761315; 0-9771601; 0-9793857)* 2509 Morning Glory Dr., Columbia, MO 65202-1222 USA
Web site: http://www.tigresspress.com.

TikeTime, *(0-9729093)* Orders Addr.: 872 S. Milwaukee, No. 125, Libertyville, IL 60048 USA (SAN 255-3058)
E-mail: info@tiketime.com
Web site: http://www.tiketime.com
Dist(s): **Baker & Taylor Bks.**

Tiki Tales, *(0-9740582)* P.O. Box 1194, Haiku, HI 96708 USA
Dist(s): **Booklines Hawaii, Ltd.**

Tikva Corp., *(0-615)* 40 W. 23rd St., New York, NY 10010-5215 USA
E-mail: emilyl@mkugodessa.org.

Tilbury Hse. Pubs., *(0-88448; 0-937966)* 2 Mechanic St., No. 3, Gardiner, ME 04345 USA Tel 207-582-1899; Fax: 207-582-8227; Toll Free: 800-582-1899 (orders) ; *Imprints:* Harpswell Press (Hrpswel Pr)
E-mail: sbeach@tilburyhouse.com; tilbury@tilburyhouse.com
Web site: http://www.tilburyhouse.com
Dist(s): **Lectorum Pubns., Inc.**

Timberwolf Pr., Inc., *(0-9653210; 1-58752)* 202 N. Allen Dr., Suite A, Allen, TX 75013 USA (SAN 254-0789) Tel 972-359-0911 ext 101; Toll Free: 888-808-0912
E-mail: sales@timberwolfpress.com; billa@timberwolfpress.com; patrick@timberwolfpress.com
Web site: http://www.Timberwolfpress.com
Dist(s): **Ingram Entertainment, Inc.**

Timberwood Pr., *(0-9745454)* 112 NW 156th St., Shoreline, WA 98177 USA Tel 206-295-6186
E-mail: kearney@timberwoodpress.com
Web site: http://www.timberwoodpress.com
Dist(s): **Partners Bk. Distributing, Inc.**

Timbuktu Pubs., *(0-9678460)* Div. of African Telecom,Inc., 299 Broadway, Suite 716, New York, NY 10007 USA Tel 212-791-0777; Fax: 212-791-4074
E-mail: Afrstime@aol.com.

Time & Chance Publishing, *(0-9748274)* Orders Addr.: P.O. Box 488, New York, NY 10116 USA Tel 718-370-3655 [phone/fax]
E-mail: tandchpublishing@yahoo.com
Web site: http://www.timeandchancepublishing@yahoo.com
Dist(s): **Baker & Taylor Bks.**
Biblio Distribution
Culture Plus Bks.

Time Capsule Bks. *Imprint of* **Time Capsule eBooks, Inc.**

Time Capsule eBooks, Inc., *(1-4149)* P.O. Box 62441, Sunnyvale, CA 94088-2441 USA Tel 408-732-3810 ; *Imprints:* Time Capsule Books (Time Capsule Bks).

Time Dancer Press *See* **5 Star Stories, Inc.**

Time, Incorporated *See* **Time, Inc. Home Entertainment**

Time, Inc. Home Entertainment, *(1-883013; 1-929049; 1-931933; 1-932273; 1-932994; 1-933405; 1-933821; 1-60320)* Div. of Time, Inc., Time & Life Building,1271 Avenue of Americas, New York, NY 10020 USA (SAN 227-3209) ; *Imprints:* People Books (People Bks)
Dist(s): **Hachette Bk. Group.**

Time Life Value (GBR) *(1-84447) Dist. by* **Intl Pubs Mktg.**

Time Line Productions, Inc., *(0-9638000; 1-891195)* 222 Minnetonka Ave., S., Wayzata, MN 55391-1717 USA Tel 952-474-1000; Fax: 952-475-1224
E-mail: tim@lorieline.com
Web site: http://www.lorieline.com/
Dist(s): **Leonard, Hal Corp.**

Time to Sign, Incorporated, *(0-9713666; 0-9765364)* Orders Addr.: P.O. Box 110308, Palm Bay, FL 32911 USA Tel 321-723-6997; Fax: 321-723-6896; Edit Addr.: 426 Olsmar St., Palm Bay, FL 32908 USA Do not confuse with Talking Hands, Inc., in Bangor, ME
E-mail: contact@timetosign.com
Web site: http://www.timetosign.com.

Time Warner Book Group *See* **Hachette Bk. Group**

Time Warner Custom Publishing, *(1-931722; 1-59995)* 1271 Ave. of the Americas, New York, NY 10020 USA Tel 212-522-7381
Dist(s): **Hachette Bk. Group.**

TimeFare Audio Book Productions *See* **TimeFare AudioBooks**

TimeFare AudioBooks, *(0-932079)* 215 W. 19th Ave., Kennewick, WA 99337 USA (SAN 686-2632) Tel 509-585-2646
E-mail: timefarebooks@aol.com
Web site: http://www.timefare.com.

Timeless Romance *Imprint of* **Sierra Raconteur Publishing**

Timeless Voyager Pr., *(1-892264)* Orders Addr.: 249 Iris Ave., Goleta, CA 93117 USA; Edit Addr.: P.O. Box 6678, Santa Barbara, CA 93160 USA (SAN 253-9233) Tel 805-455-8895; Fax: 805-683-4456; Toll Free: 800-576-8463
E-mail: bsh@timelessvoyager.com
Web site: http://www.timelessvoyager.com.

Time-Life Custom Publishing *See* **Time-Life Inc.**

Time-Life Education, Inc., *(0-7054; 0-7370; 0-7835; 0-8094)* Orders Addr.: P.O. Box 85026, Richmond, VA 23285-5026 USA Toll Free Fax: 800-449-2011; Edit Addr.: 2000 Duke St., Alexandria, VA 22314 USA Tel 703-838-7000; Fax: 703-518-4124; Toll Free: 800-449-2010
E-mail: education@timelifecs.com
Web site: http://www.timelifeedu.com/
Dist(s): **Hachette Bk. Group.**

†Time-Life, Inc., *(0-7835; 0-8094)* Div. of Time Warner Co., Orders Addr.: Three Center Plaza, Boston, MA 02108-2084 USA Toll Free Fax: 800-308-1083; 800-286-9471; Toll Free: 800-277-8844; 800-759-0190; Edit Addr.: 8280 Willow Oaks Corporate Dr., Fairfax, VA 22031-4511 USA (SAN 202-7836) Toll Free: 800-621-7026
Web site: http://timelifeedu.com
Dist(s): **Hachette Bk. Group**
Time-Life Publishing Warehouse
Worldwide Media Service, Inc.; *CIP.*

Time-Life Inc., *(0-7054; 0-7370)* 8280 Willow Oaks Corporate Dr., Fairfax, VA 22031-4511 USA
E-mail: jennifer_ward@time-inc.com.

Times Bks. *Imprint of* **Holt, Henry & Co.**

Times Square Church, *(0-9789642)* 1657 Broadway, New York, NY 10019 USA (SAN 852-0585)
Web site: http://www.timessquarechurch.org.

Time-Together Pr., *(1-888384)* Orders Addr.: P.O. Box 11689, Saint Paul, MN 55111 USA Tel 612-827-1639; Fax: 612-823-6404.

T.I.M.M.-E. Co., Inc., *(0-615; 0-9718232)* Div. of NYC Department of Education, 230 E. 25th St, Suite 2E, New York, NY 10010 USA
E-mail: tbellavia@weareallthesameinside.com; tools4tolerance@aol.com
Web site: http://www.weareallthesameinside.com
Dist(s): **Bookazine Co., Inc.**

Timothy Lane Pr., *(0-9744751)* 3211 Rosewood Dr., Hattiesburg, MS 39401-4517 USA
Web site: http://www.robynjackson.com
Dist(s): **Baker & Taylor Bks.**

Timshel Literature, *(0-9708317)* P.O. Box 751, Portsmouth, RI 02871 USA Tel 401-835-7156
E-mail: jkatz@timshelarts.com
Web site: http://www.timshelarts.com.

Timtu Ink., *(0-9742460)* 11 Via Acuatica, Rancho Santa Margarita, CA 92688-1482 USA (SAN 255-6146); 31441 Santa Margarita Pkwy., Suite A, No. 341, Rancho Santa Margarita, CA 92688
E-mail: timtuink@dslextreme.com
Web site: http://www.dragonopolis.com; http://www.dragonia.net.

Timun Mas, Editorial S.A. (ESP) *(84-480; 84-7176; 84-7722) Dist. by* **Lectorum Pubns.**

Timun Mas, Editorial S.A. (ESP) *(84-480; 84-7176; 84-7722) Dist. by* **AIMS Intl.**

Timun Mas, Editorial S.A. (ESP) *(84-480; 84-7176; 84-7722) Dist. by* **Planeta.**

Tin Man Pr., *(0-936110)* Orders Addr.: P.O. Box 11409, Eugene, OR 97440-3609 USA (SAN 222-0156) Toll Free: 800-676-0459 (phone/fax)
E-mail: tinman@tinmanpress.com
Web site: http://www.tinmanpress.com.

Tindal Street Pr. (GBR) *(0-9535895; 0-9541303; 0-9547913; 0-9551384) Dist. by* **Dufour.**

Tingley, Megan Bks. *Imprint of* **Little, Brown Bks. for Young Readers**

Tinker Pubns., *(0-9768776)* Orders Addr.: 5745 SW 75th St. #205, Gainesville, FL 32608 USA Tel 352-359-8476
E-mail: editor@tinkerpublications.com
Web site: http://www.tinkerpublications.com.

Tinkertown Museum, *(0-9793124)* Orders Addr.: P.O. Box 303, Sandia Park, NM 87047 USA (SAN 853-1161) Tel 505-281-5233; Edit Addr.: 121 Sandia Crest Rd., Sandia Park, NM 87047-0303 USA
E-mail: tinker4u@tinkertown.com
Web site: http://www.tinkertown.com.

Tino Turtle Travels, LLC, *(0-9793158)* 8550 W. Charleston Blvd. 102-398, Las Vegas, NV 89117 USA (SAN 853-0920)
E-mail: info@tinoturtletravels.com
Web site: http://www.tinoturtletravels.com.

Tintagel Publications, *(0-9743718)* 45 Lapeer St., Lake Orion, MI 48362 USA.

Tinwood Bks., *(0-9653766; 0-9719104)* 512 Means St NW Ste. 305, Atlanta, GA 30318-5788 USA Do not confuse with companies with same names in North Vernon, IN, Ft. Myers, FL, Galloway Township, NJ
E-mail: information@tinwoodmedia.com
Web site: http://www.tinwoodmedia.com
Dist(s): **Museum of Fine Arts, Houston.**

Tiny Kitchen Publishing, *(0-9716028)* 5115 Ravensworth Rd., Annandale, VA 22003 USA Tel 703-354-7574
E-mail: thetinykitchen@aol.com
Web site: http://www.thetinykitchen.com
Dist(s): **Independent Pubs. Group.**

Tiny Paws Publishing, *(0-9607230)* P.O. Box 6082, Tallahassee, FL 32314-6082 USA (SAN 239-0981) Tel 850-421-2262; Fax: 850-421-3363.

Tiny Tortoise Publishing, LLC, *(0-9787477)* P.O. Box 28760, Las Vegas, NV 89126 USA Tel 702-798-6646.

Tip-Of-The-Moon Publishing Co., *(0-9657047; 0-9746372)* c/o Francis E. Wood, Jr., Rte. 2, Box 1725, Farmville, VA 23901 USA Tel 434-392-4195; Fax: 434-392-5724
E-mail: fewwords@moonstar.com
Web site: http://www.tipofthemoon.com.

Tiptoe Literary Service, *(0-937953)* 434 Sixth St., No. 206, Raymond, WA 98577-1804 USA (SAN 659-7971) Tel 360-942-4596
E-mail: ka7ton@arrl.net
Web site: http://www.willapabay.org/~anne.

Tiptoe Publishing *See* **Tiptoe Literary Service**

Tisdale, Edward W., *(0-9744166)* 3420 SW 1st Pl., Cape Coral, FL 33914 USA.

Tishomingo Tree Pr., The, *(0-9768861)* 606 Bay St., Hattiesburg, MS 39401 USA
E-mail: info@tishomingotree.com
Web site: http://www.tishomingotree.com.

Titan Bks. Ltd. (GBR) *(0-907610; 1-84023; 1-85286; 1-900097; 1-84576) Dist. by* **Random.**

Titan Bks. Ltd. (GBR) *(0-907610; 1-84023; 1-85286; 1-900097; 1-84576) Dist. by* **Perseus Dist.**

Titlewaves Publishing, *(1-57077)* 1579 Kuhio Hwy., Suite 104, Kapaa, HI 96746 USA (SAN 152-1357) Tel 808-822-7449; Fax: 808-822-2312; Toll Free: 800-835-0583
E-mail: transform@hshawaii.com
Web site: http://www.bestbookshawaii.com; http://www.writersdirect.com
Dist(s): **Baker & Taylor Bks.**

Titus Institute of California, *(0-9747452)* P.O. Box 77023, Corona, CA 92877 USA
E-mail: titusbooks@titusinstitute.com
Web site: http://www.titusinstitute.com.

Tiwinke Publishing, Inc., *(0-9660797)* Subs. of Oklahoma Corp., 1820 Seran Dr., Wewoka, OK 74884 USA Tel 405-382-7207; Fax: 405-257-3606.

Tixlini Scriptorium, Inc., *(0-9723720)* 681 Grove St., San Luis Obispo, CA 93401 USA Tel 805-543-3540; Fax: 805-543-5195
E-mail: tixlini@yahoo.com.

Tizbit Books, LLC, *(0-9760553)* 304 Rte. 22 W., Springfield, NJ 07081 USA Tel 973-564-7200; Fax: 973-564-8895
E-mail: jill@tizbitbooks.com
Web site: http://www.tizbitbooks.com.

T.J. Publishing, *(0-9760811)* 1099 E. Champlain, Suite A, No. 152, Fresno, CA 93720 USA Tel 559-297-5559
E-mail: tjpub@aol.com.

TJMF Publishing, *(0-9759314; 0-9789705; 0-9801003)* P.O. Box 2923, Clarksville, IN 47131-2923 USA Tel 812-288-7597; Fax: 812-288-1329
E-mail: jim@tjmfpublishing.com
Web site: http://www.tjmfpublishing.com
Dist(s): **Baker & Taylor Bks.**

TJMF Publishing Daylight Enterprises *See* **TJMF Publishing**

TLC Publishing, *(0-9721517)* c/o Tiller Lactation Consulting, 5221 Rushbrook Dr., Centreville, VA 20120 USA Tel 703-266-3823 Do not confuse with TLC Publishing in Paonia, CO
E-mail: stiller@breastfeeding101.com
Web site: http://www.breastfeeding101.com.

TLConcepts, Inc. *Imprint of* **Tender Learning Concepts**

TLM Publishing Hse., *(0-9748829)* P.O. Box 123, Ozark, MO 65721 USA
E-mail: booksellers@tlmpublishinghouse.com
Web site: http://tlmpublishinghouse.com.

TLS Consulting *See* **TLS Publishing**

TLS Publishing, *(0-9716244)* P.O. Box 403, Dobbs Ferry, NY 10522 USA Tel 914-674-2257 Do not confuse with TLS Publishing in Irvine, CA
E-mail: tls@nvbb.net.

TM Pubns., *(0-9713221)* Orders Addr.: P.O. Box 2099, Sun City, CA 92586-2099 USA Tel 951-231-1633; Fax: 951-246-7975
E-mail: toimoore@aol.com; tmpublications1@aol.com
Web site: http://www.toimoore.com
Dist(s): **Baker & Taylor Bks.**

TMC Bks. L.L.C., *(0-9720307)* 731 Tasker Hill Rd., Conway, NH 03818 USA
E-mail: info@tmcbooks.com
Web site: http://www.tmcbooks.com; www.treehousechronicles.com
Dist(s): **Midpoint Trade Bks., Inc.**

TMD Enterprises, *(0-9789297)* 76 E. Blvd., Suite 11, Rochester, NY 14610-1536 USA (SAN 851-9617)
E-mail: dbeerse@tmd-enterprises.com
Web site: www.tmd-enterprises.com.

TMS Publishing Co., *(0-9677044)* Div. of Triology Micro Systems, Inc., 6410 Cross Country Blvd., Baltimore, MD 21215 USA Tel 410-764-2124 Do not confuse with TMS Publishing in Greenville, SC
E-mail: info@tmspublishing.com
Web site: http://www.tmspublishing.com.

TNJ Ministries, *(0-9762770)* 8214 SW 52nd Ln., Gainesville, FL 32608 USA Tel 352-376-8930
E-mail: tnj_ministries@yahoo.com
Web site: http://www.wtswlg.bravehost.com.

TNMG Publishing, *(0-9768297)* P.O. Box 1032, Winter Park, FL 32790-1032 USA
Web site: http://www.tnmg.ws.

Toad Hall, Inc., *(0-9637498; 1-893407)* R.R. 2, Box 2090, Laceyville, PA 18623 USA Tel 570-869-2942; Fax: 570-869-1031 ; *Imprints:* Toad Hall Press (Toad Hall Pr)
E-mail: toadhallco@aol.com
Web site: http://www.laceyville.com/toad-hall.

Toad Hall Pr. *Imprint of* **Toad Hall, Inc.**

Tobacco River Pubs, *(0-9664703)* 11950 N. Meridian Rd., Farwell, MI 48622 USA Tel 517-588-9843.

Toby Pr., *(1-902881; 1-59264)* Orders Addr.: P.O. Box 8531, New Milford, CT 06776-8531 USA (SAN 253-9985) Fax: 203-830-8512 (questions & orders)
E-mail: toby@tobypress.com
Web site: http://www.tobypress.com
Dist(s): **Baker & Taylor Bks.**
Koen-Levy Bk. Wholesalers LLC.

Toccoa Falls College Pr., *(1-885729)* Orders Addr.: P.O. Box 800067, Toccoa Falls, GA 30598 USA; Edit Addr.: 500 Chapel Dr., Toccoa Falls, GA 30598 USA.

Todd Communications, *(1-57833; 1-878100)* 611 E. 12th Ave. Ste. 102, Anchorage, AK 99501-4663 USA (SAN 298-6280)
E-mail: info@toddcom.com
Dist(s): **Wizard Works.**

Tofte Literary Enterprises *See* **Creative Quill Publishing, Inc.**

Together in the Harvest Ministries, Incorporated *See* **Together in the Harvest Pubns./Productions**

Together in the Harvest Pubns./Productions, *(0-9637090; 1-892853)* Div. of Together In The Harvest Ministries, Inc., Orders Addr.: P.O. Box 612288, Dallas, TX 75261 USA Tel 817-849-8773; Fax: 214-687-5531
E-mail: kathy.duffy@stevehill.org
Web site: www.stevehill.org.

Together, Inc., *(0-9764572; 1-933463)* 3205 Roosevelt St., NE, Saint Anthony, MN 55418 USA Tel 612-706-7836; Fax: 612-789-8008
E-mail: info@togetherinc.com; pesellors@minn.net
Web site: http://www.togetherinc.com.

Toki Productions, *(0-9729527)* P.O. Box 88216, Los Angeles, CA 90009-6888 USA
Web site: http://www.betteroffthan.com.

TokoBooks, *(0-9720436)* P.O. Box 292192, Kettering, OH 45429 USA (SAN 254-573X).

Tokyo Shock *Imprint of* **Media Blasters, Inc.**

Tokyopop Adult *Imprint of* **TOKYOPOP, Inc.**

TOKYOPOP, Inc., *(1-892213; 1-931514; 1-59182; 1-59532; 1-59816; 1-4278)* Div. of Mixx Entertainment, Inc., People's Bank Building 5900 Wilshire Blvd., Suite 2000, Los Angeles, CA 90036 USA Tel 323-692-6700; Fax: 323-692-6701 ; *Imprints:* TOKYOPOP Manga (Tokyopop Manga); Tokyopop Kids (TokyoKids); Tokyopop Adult (TokyoAdult)
Web site: http://www.tokyopop.com/
Dist(s): **HarperCollins Pubs.**
Sony CONNECT, Inc.

Tokyopop Kids *Imprint of* **TOKYOPOP, Inc.**

TOKYOPOP Manga *Imprint of* **TOKYOPOP, Inc.**

Tokyopop Press *See* **TOKYOPOP, Inc.**

Toledo Museum of Art, The, *(0-935172)* P.O. Box 1013, Toledo, OH 43697 USA (SAN 213-8980) Tel 419-255-8000; Fax: 419-255-5638; Toll Free: 800-644-6862
E-mail: publications@toledomuseum.org
Web site: http://www.toledomuseum.org.

Toledo Zoo, The, *(0-9776974)* P.O. Box 140130, Toledo, OH 43614 USA Tel 419-385-5721; Fax: 419-724-0068
E-mail: tzgift@toledozoo.org
Web site: http://www.toledozoo.org.

Tolson, Norma Y., *(0-9703275)* P.O. Box 49335, Wichita, KS 67214 USA Tel 316-263-6626
Web site: http://www.zippyo@aol.com.

Tolstoy Dom Press, LLC *See* **Vernissage Pr., LLC**

Tom & Susan Allen *See* **Dean's Bks., Inc.**

Tomato Enterprises, *(0-9617357)* P.O. Box 73892, Davis, CA 95617 USA (SAN 664-0427) Tel 530-750-1832; Fax: 530-759-9741
E-mail: info@tomatoenterprises.com
Web site: http://www.tomatoenterprises.com.

Tomgirlz Enterprises LLC, *(0-9768012)* P.O. Box 970142, Coconut Creek, FL 33097 USA Tel 954-588-7197
E-mail: tomgirlzrule@yahoo.com
Web site: http://www.tomgirlz.com.

Tommy Bks. Pubng., *(0-9762690)* Div. of C4 Kids, 1220 N. Las Palmas, No. 201, Los Angeles, CA 90038 USA Tel 323-974-8249
E-mail: renegadepic@earthlink.net
Web site: http://www.tommybooks.net
Dist(s): **C4 Kids.**

Tomoka Pr., *(0-9657211)* Orders Addr.: 115 Coquina Ave., Ormond Beach, FL 32174 USA Tel 386-677-4219
E-mail: yvonnewpunnett@aol.com
Web site: http://www.tomokapress.com.

Tomorrow's Forefathers, Inc. *See* **Tomorrow's Forefathers, Inc.**

Tomorrow's Forefathers, Inc., *(0-9719405)* Orders Addr.: P.O. Box 11451, Cedar Rapids, IA 52410-1451 USA
E-mail: info@tomorrowsforefathers.com
Web site: http://www.radiantpurity.com; http://www.brothersandsisters.net; http://www.tomorrowsforefathers.com; http://www.brightlights.info
Dist(s): **STL Distribution North America.**

Tomorrow's Girl, *(0-9659630)* Orders Addr.: P.O. Box 254, Strasburg, PA 17579 USA Tel 717-687-0356; Edit Addr.: 37 E. Main St., Strasburg, PA 17579 USA
E-mail: tomorrowsgirl@msn.com
Web site: Http://www.tomorrows-girl.com.

Tonepoet Publishing, *(0-922224)* 3069 Alamo Dr., Suite 146, Vacaville, CA 95687 USA (SAN 250-3654)
E-mail: tonepoet@jackshiner.com
Web site: http://www.jackshiner.com.

Tongue Untied Publishing, *(0-9745783)* Orders Addr.: P.O. Box 822, Jackson, GA 30233 USA; Edit Addr.: 2571 Hwy. 36 E., Jackson, GA 30233 USA
E-mail: maseyree2001@yahoo.com
Web site: http://www.tongueuntiedpublishing.com
Dist(s): **A & B Distributors & Pubs. Group**
Baker & Taylor Bks.
Culture Plus Bk. Distributors.

Tony Franklin Cos., The, *(0-9714280)* 521 Ridge Rd., Lexington, KY 40503-1229 USA (SAN 254-2145)
E-mail: tlf3c@aol.com; ed@crystalcommunications.biz
Web site: www.thetonyfranklin.com.

Tony Tales, *(0-9791362)* 6024 Cottontail Cove, Las Vegas, NV 89130 USA (SAN 852-5285) Tel 702-245-8624; Fax: 702-898-1359
E-mail: barbarites@aol.com
Web site: www.Tony.

Too Fun Publshing, *(0-9773317)* P.O. Box 2098, Vashon Island, WA 98070 USA; 1055 SW 178th St., Vashon Island, WA 98070
E-mail: toofunpublishing@gmail.com.

Too Much Fun, LLC, *(0-9773167)* Div. of Carruth Studio, 1178 Farnsworth Rd., Waterville, OH 43566 USA (SAN 257-2729)
Web site: www.carruthstudio.com
Dist(s): **Partners Pubs. Group, Inc.**

Toobeez Project-Connect Joint Venture, *(0-9765670)* Div. of Connectable Color Tubes, LLC, Orders Addr.: Project Connect JV 1204 Thomas Rd., Wayne, PA 19087 USA Tel 610-975-0102 (phone/fax)
E-mail: jdonahue@toobeez.com
Web site: http://www.toobeez.com; http://www.project-connect.net.

Toodle-oo Innovative Products, *(0-9793145)* 2166 E. Wellington Ave., Santa Ana, CA 92701 USA (SAN 853-0890) Tel 714-558-9537
E-mail: w.kawamoto@cox.net; suszanales@adelphia.net
Web site: http://www.makebubblesgrow.com.

Tools For Young Historians *Imprint of* **BrimWood Pr.**

Toothpick Productions, *(0-9700851)* P.O. Box 225952, Dallas, TX 75222 USA Tel 972-298-2606 Do not confuse with Toothpick Productions in Boulder City, NV
E-mail: doogie105@juno.com
Web site: http://doogiedolphin.com.

Tootle Time Publishing Co., *(0-9721706)* Orders Addr.: P.O. Box 62, Cade, LA 70519 USA Tel 337-364-6410; Fax: 337-364-6415; Edit Addr.: 1031 Mary Rd., New Iberia, LA 70560 USA
E-mail: marycelesteclement@yahoo.com
Dist(s): **Midpoint Trade Bks., Inc.**

TOP *Imprint of* **Top Pubns., Ltd.**

Top5 Co., The, *(0-9746760)* Div. of Bucc Wild LLC, P.O. Box 7445, San Diego, CA 92167 USA
E-mail: brett@top5book.com
Web site: http://www.top5book.com.

Top Choice Pr., LLC., *(0-9761396)* 28 Worcester Sq., Unit No. 1, Boston, MA 02118-2943 USA Tel 617-424-9726; Fax: 617-262-0702
E-mail: tberkan@mindspring.com
Web site: http://topchoicebooks.com.

Top Pubns., Ltd., *(0-9666366; 1-929976)* Div. of Top Ventures, Ltd., 3100 Independence Pkwy., No. 311-349, Plano, TX 75075-9152 USA Tel 972-960-2240; Fax: 972-233-0713 ; *Imprints:* TOP (TOP USA)
E-mail: bill@toppub.com; jill@toppub.com
Web site: http://toppub.com.

Top Quality Pubns., *(0-9726311)* Orders Addr.: 3925 Americana Dr., Tampa, FL 33634 USA
E-mail: parfisher@yahoo.com
Web site: http://www.topqualitypublications.org.

Top Shelf *Imprint of* **Jawbone Publishing Corp.**

Top Shelf Productions, *(1-891830; 961-90436; 1-60309)* Orders Addr.: P.O. Box 1282, Marietta, GA 30061-1282 USA Fax: 770-427-6395; Edit Addr.: 1109 Grand Oaks Glen, Marietta, GA 30064 USA Fax: 770-427-6395
E-mail: staros@bellsouth.net; chris@topshelfcomix.com
Web site: http://www.topshelfcomix.com
Dist(s): **Diamond Bk. Distributors.**

Top Shelf Publishing, *(0-9770443)* 4126 W. Fremont Rd., Spokane, WA 99224 USA.

Top Tek Corp., *(0-9671942)* Orders Addr.: Box 922, Canaan, CT 06018 USA Tel 860-824-0352; Edit Addr.: 173 W. Main St., Canaan, CT 06018 USA
E-mail: fxstrelchun@SNET.com.

Top That! Publishing PLC (GBR) *(1-902973; 1-84229; 1-84510; 1-904748; 1-905359; 1-84666) Dist. by* **Random.**

Topaz Cove Creations, *(0-9720805)* P.O. Box 4878, West Hills, CA 91308-4878 USA (SAN 255-1918) Fax: 818-716-7958
E-mail: saparker@pacbell.net
Web site: http://www.shirleyannparker.com.

TopHat Publishing, *(0-9712984)* Orders Addr.: P.O. Box 2017, Phoenix, AZ 85001 USA; Edit Addr.: 402 W. Van Buren, No. 112, Phoenix, AZ 85003 USA Do not confuse with Top Hat Publishing in Costa Mesa, CA
E-mail: mdhatfield1@aol.com.

TOPICS Entertainment, *(1-886089; 1-931102; 1-59150; 1-60077)* 1600 SW. 43rd St., Renton, WA 98055 USA (SAN 852-1433) Tel 425-656-3621; Fax: 425-656-8013
E-mail: beth@topics-ent.com; info@topics-ent.com
Web site: http://www.topics-ent.com.

Topperhill Pubs., *(1-929136)* 169 Apple Lovers Ln., Jordan, MN 55352 USA Tel 612-492-2785; Fax: 612-492-3370; Toll Free: 800-662-7753
Dist(s): **Bookmen, Inc.**

Topsy Turvy Pubns., *(0-9700659)* 21 Valley Park Ct., Damascus, MD 20872 USA Tel 301-253-9541 ; *Imprints:* Teeny Behemoth Books (Teeny Behemoth)
E-mail: wingnutibh@aol.com
Web site: http://www.brainclopper.com.

Tor Bks. *Imprint of* **Doherty, Tom Assocs., LLC**

Tor Classics *Imprint of* **Doherty, Tom Assocs., LLC**

Tor Kids *Imprint of* **Doherty, Tom Assocs., LLC**

Tor Teen *Imprint of* **Doherty, Tom Assocs., LLC**

†Torah Aura Productions, *(0-933873; 1-891662; 1-934527)* 4423 Fruitland Ave., Los Angeles, CA 90058 USA (SAN 692-7025) Fax: 323-585-0327; Toll Free: 800-238-6724
E-mail: jane@torahaura.com
Web site: http://torahaura.com; *CIP.*

Torah Educational Software, *(1-889731; 1-931711)* c/o T E S, 343g Spook Rock Rd., Suffern, NY 10901-5307 USA Toll Free: 800-925-6853
E-mail: debbies@jewishsoftware.com
Web site: http://www.jewishsoftware.com.

Torah Excel, *(1-930925)* 6415 N. Sacramento, Chicago, IL 60645 USA Tel 773-743-7915; Fax: 773-508-9874 ; *Imprints:* Shazak Productions (Shazak Prods)
E-mail: torahxl@megsinet.com
Web site: http://torahxl.com.

Torah Institute of Baltimore, *(0-9767505)* 35 Rosewood Ln., Owings Mills, MD 21117-3704 USA Tel 410-654-3500 ext. 3; Fax: 443-394-5999
E-mail: tibexec@comcast.net
Web site: http://www.torahinstitute.org.

Torah Pubn. Fund, *(0-9707757)* Div. of Congregation Ohr HaMizrach, Inc., 2509 Shelleydale Dr., Baltimore, MD 21209 USA Tel 410-358-4338; Fax: 410-358-5350
E-mail: fbc1000@aol.com.

Torah Umesorah Pubns., *(0-914131; 1-878895)* 5723 18th Ave., Brooklyn, NY 11204 USA (SAN 218-9992) Tel 718-259-1223; Fax: 718-259-1795
E-mail: mail@tupblications.com.

Torba Publishing, *(0-9765748)* 406 Rte. 217, Suite B, Latrobe, PA 15650 USA (SAN 256-4637) Fax: 724-539-3417
Web site: http://www.kingmolar.com.

Torbert, Margot, *(0-9764071)* P.O. Box 176, Graton, CA 95444-176 USA Tel 707-874-2369
E-mail: dancerscloset@yahoo.com
Web site: http://www.teaching-dance.com.

Torch Enterprises, Inc., *(0-9761635)* 23411 Laguna Hills Dr, Suite K-30, Aliso Viejo, CA 92656-1821 USA
Web site: http://www.torchenterprisesinc.com.

Torch Legacy Pubns., *(0-9763487; 0-9785333)* P.O. Box 165046, Irving, TX 75016 USA
E-mail: torchlegacypublications@msn.com
Web site: http://www.torchlegacy.com.

Torchlight Publishing, *(1-887089; 0-9779785)* Orders Addr.: 49334 Stagecoach Dr., Badger, CA 93603 USA Tel 559-337-2200; Fax: 559-337-2354; Toll Free: 888-867-2458 Do not confuse with Torchlight Publishing in Colorado Springs, CO
E-mail: torchlight@spiralcomm.net
Web site: http://www.torchlight.com
Dist(s): **Biblio Distribution.**

Torgerson Meadows Publishing, *(0-9767116)* 37492 Outpost Rd., NW, Grygla, MN 56727 USA Tel 218-294-6644
E-mail: sstorg@webtv.net
Web site: http://www.taolc.com.

Tornado Creek Pubns., *(0-9652219; 0-9740881)* P.O. Box 8625, Spokane, WA 99203-8625 USA Tel 509-838-7114; Fax: 509-455-6798
E-mail: bamonte@nase.org
Web site: http://www.geocities.com/spokanehistory.

Torres, Eliseo & Sons, *(0-88303)* P.O. Box 2, Eastchester, NY 10709 USA (SAN 207-0235).

Torrey Pines Pr., *(1-884804)* 1030 W. Upas St., San Diego, CA 92103 USA Tel 619-497-0900 (phone/fax) Do not confuse with Torrey Pines Assoc. in La Jolla, CA
E-mail: order@diabetesnet.com; rroberts@diabetesnet.com
Web site: http://www.diabetesnet.com.

Tortuga Bks., *(1-893561)* Orders Addr.: P.O. Box 420564, Summerland Key, FL 33042 USA (SAN 299-8254) Tel 305-745-8709; Fax: 305-745-2704; Toll Free: 800-345-6665 (orders only); Edit Addr.: 1760 109th St., No. B3, Marathon, FL 33050 USA
E-mail: info@tortugabooks.com
Web site: http://www.tortugabooks.com
Dist(s): **Pathway Bk. Service.**

Tortuga Pr., *(1-889910)* PMB 181, 2777 Yulupa Ave., Santa Rosa, CA 95405 USA (SAN 299-1756) Tel 707-544-4720; Fax: 707-544-5609; Toll Free: 866-4 TORTUGA
E-mail: info@tortugapress.com
Web site: http://www.tortugapress.com
Dist(s): **Baker & Taylor Bks.**
Follett Library Resources
Ingram Bk. Co.

Torus Pr., *(0-9704195)* Orders Addr.: P.O. Box 18276, Spokane, WA 99228-0276 USA Tel 509-325-3931; Edit Addr.: 2912 W. Weile Ave., Spokane, WA 99208 USA
E-mail: tjmcm@uswest.net.

Tory Corner Editions *See* **Quincannon Publishing Group**

Tory Corner Editions *Imprint of* **Quincannon Publishing Group**

Total Outreach for Christ Ministries, Inc., *(0-9745834)* 3411 Asher Ave., Little Rock, AR 72204 USA Tel 501-663-0362; Fax: 501-663-0390
E-mail: tofchristm@aol.com
Web site: http://theonenewman.org.

Total Wellness *See* **Total Wellness Publishing**

Total Wellness Publishing, *(0-9744585)* 14545 Glenoak Pl., Fontana, CA 92337 USA
E-mail: micheleiqbal@netzero.net
Web site: http://www.Totalwellnesspublishing.com; http://www.micheleiqbal.com
Dist(s): **Distributors, The.**

Totally Outdoors Publishing, Inc., *(0-9726653)* 7284 Raccoon Rd., Manning, SC 29102 USA
Web site: http://www.totallyoutdoorspublishing.com.

Totem Bks. (GBR) *(1-84046) Dist. by* **Natl Bk Netwk.**

Totline Pubns. *Imprint of* **Schaffer, Frank Pubns.**

Tott Pubns., *(1-882225)* 513 Land Dr., Dayton, OH 45440 USA Tel 937-426-7638.

Toucan Pr., Inc., *(0-9744926)* 3211 Gait Way, Chapel Hill, NC 27516 USA.

Toucan Valley Pubns., Inc., *(0-9634017; 1-884925)* Orders Addr.: P.O. Box 15520, Fremont, CA 94539-2620 USA Tel 510-498-1009; Fax: 510-498-1010; Toll Free Fax: 888-391-6943; Toll Free: 800-236-7946
E-mail: query@toucanvalley.com; ben@toucanvalley.com
Web site: http://www.toucanvalley.com
Dist(s): **Grey Hse. Publishing.**

ToucanEd Pubns., *(1-57931)* P.O. Box 1282, Soquel, CA 95073 USA Tel 831-464-0508; Fax: 831-462-1129
E-mail: info@ToucanEd.com
Web site: http://www.ToucanEd.com.

Touch Books, Incorporated *See* **Minardi Photography**

Touch of Entertainment Publishing, A *See* **TM Pubns.**

Touch Pubns., *(1-880828; 0-9752896; 0-9788779)* Div. of Touch Outreach Ministries, Inc., 509 Garden Oaks Blvd., Houston, TX 77018-5505 USA Toll Free: 800-735-5865
E-mail: sales@touchusa.org
Web site: http://www.touchusa.org
Dist(s): **Spring Arbor Distributors, Inc.**

Touch Your Heart Collections, *(0-9705997)* 47 Roy Spiers Rd., Petal, MS 39465 USA
E-mail: rterirch@aol.com.

TouchSmart Publishing, LLC, *(0-9765060; 0-9787517)* 167 Old Richmond Rd., Swanzeyti, NH 03446 USA (SAN 256-3835) Tel 603-352-7282; a/o Touchsmart Publishing (Distributor), LLC, 6522 Waldorf Pl., Cincinnati, OH 45230 (SAN 631-8703) Tel 513-225-8765; Fax: 206-666-4856
E-mail: ccardine@touchsmart.net
Web site: http://www.touchsmart.net.

Touchstone *Imprint of* **Simon & Schuster**

Touchstone Adventures, *(0-9649573)* P.O. Box 177, Paw Paw, IL 61353 USA Tel 815-627-2716 (phone/fax)
E-mail: ajarcher@earthlink.net
Web site: http://www.carliving.com.

Touchstone Center for Children, Incorporated, The *See* **Touchstone Ctr. Pubns.**

Touchstone Ctr. Pubns., *(1-929299)* Div. of Touchstone Center for Children, Inc., 141 E. 88th St., New York, NY 10028 USA (SAN 265-3664) Tel 212-831-7717; Fax: 212-427-9644
E-mail: rlewis212@aol.com
Web site: http://www.touchstonecenter.net
Dist(s): **Biblio Distribution.**

Touchstone Communications, *(0-9790775)* Orders Addr.: 353 Main St, Suite 1D, Oneonta, NY 13820 USA (SAN 852-3835) Tel 607-437-0000
E-mail: Touchstonecom@stny.rr.com
Web site: http://TouchstoneGraphics.com.

Touchstones Discussion Project, *(1-878461)* P.O. Box 2329, Annapolis, MD 21404-2329 USA Toll Free: 800-456-6542
E-mail: info@touchstones.org
Web site: http://www.touchstones.org.

Towers Maguire Publishing *Imprint of* **Local History Co., The**

Towles, LaRhonda, *(0-9667894)* 119 Shady Oak Dr., Sherwood, AR 72120 USA Tel 501-835-3724.

Town & Country Reprographics, *(0-9725808; 0-9754383; 0-9771894; 0-9794860)* 230 N. Main St., Concord, NH 03301 USA (SAN 254-959X)
Web site: http://www.reprographic.com.

Town Bk. Pr. The, *(1-892657)* 270 E. Broad St., Westfield, NJ 07090-2106 USA Toll Free: 888-714-2665
E-mail: info@townbookpress.com
Web site: http://www.townbookpress.com.

Townsend, J.N. Publishing, *(0-9617426; 1-880158)* 4 Franklin St., Exeter, NH 03833 USA (SAN 630-303X) Tel 603-778-9883; Fax: 603-772-1980; Toll Free: 800-333-9883 (orders only)
E-mail: townsendpub@aol.com
Web site: http://www.jntownsendpublishing.com
Dist(s): **Revolution Booksellers.**

Townsend Pr., *(0-944210; 1-59194)* 439 Kelly Dr., West Berlin, NJ 08091-9284 USA (SAN 243-0444) Toll Free Fax: 800-225-8894; Toll Free: 800-772-6410
E-mail: townsendcs@aol.com; orderstp@aol.com
Web site: http://www.townsendpress.com.

Townsend Pr. - Sunday Schl. Publishing Board, *(0-910683; 1-932972)* 330 Charlotte Ave., Nashville, TN 37201-1188 USA (SAN 275-8598) Tel 615-256-2480; Fax: 615-242-4929; Toll Free: 800-359-9398
E-mail: byron217@lycos.com.

Townsley, William W. Pubns., *(0-9752935)* The Riverview, Suite 305, 1400 Bancarrota Blvd., Bradenton, FL 34205 USA (SAN 255-9838) Tel 941-708-3876
E-mail: wwtownsley@aol.com.

Toy Box Pr., The, *(0-9720825)* 1101 Tyvola Rd., Suite 209, Charlotte, NC 28217 USA Tel 704-791-3294
E-mail: webmaster@toyboxpress.com
Web site: http://www.toyboxpress.com.

Toy Box Productions, *(1-887729; 1-932332)* Div. of CRT, Custom Products, Inc., 7532 Hickory Hills Ct., Whites Creek, TN 37189 USA Tel 615-299-0822; 615-876-5490; Fax: 615-876-3931; Toll Free: 800-750-1511
E-mail: leeann@crttoybox.com
Dist(s): **Baker & Taylor Bks.**
Christian Bk. Distributors.

Toy Quest, *(0-9767325; 0-9786246)* Manley, 2228 Barry Ave., Los Angeles, CA 90064 USA Fax: 310-231-7565.

Toy Truck Publishing, *(0-9764983)* 4602 Lilac Ln., Lake Elmo, MN 55042 USA (SAN 256-3754) Tel 612-716-8383; Fax: 651-275-1279
E-mail: sales@toytruckpublishing.com
Web site: http://www.toytruckpublishing.com.

Toys 'n Things Press *See* **Redleaf Pr.**

Tpprince Esquire, *(0-9790110)* 6429 Printz Ct., Saint Louis, MO 63116 USA (SAN 852-2219) Tel 314-481-4164
E-mail: tpprince_esq@yahoo.com.

Tracepaper Bks. Inc., *(0-9792728)* 68 Ridgewood Ave., Selden, NY 11784 USA
Web site: http://www.tracepaper.net.

Tracks Publishing, *(1-884654)* 140 Brightwood Ave., Chula Vista, CA 91910 USA Tel 619-476-7125; Fax: 619-476-8173; Toll Free: 800-443-3570
E-mail: tracks@cox.net
Web site: http://www.startupsports.com
Dist(s): **Independent Pubs. Group.**

Tractus Bks., *(2-909347)* Div. of Tractus, Orders Addr.: P.O. Box 6777, Reno, NV 89513 USA Tel 775-345-7585 (phone/fax); 33 1 4047 6363 (phone/fax); 33 1 4407 1207 ; *Imprints:* Alif Publishing Corporation (Alif Publishing Corp)
E-mail: http://www.tractusbooks.com
Web site: http://www.tractusbooks.com
Dist(s): **Tractus.**

Tracy, Jean A., *(0-9749244)* PCS, Orders Addr.: a/o KidsDiscuss.Com, P.O. Box 6102, Edmonds, WA 98026 USA
E-mail: JeanTracy@KidsDiscuss.com
Web site: http://www.KidsDiscuss.com.

TracyTrends, *(0-615; 0-9708226)* 7710 Somerset Bay. Apt. C, Indianapolis, IN 46240-3336 USA
E-mail: tracytrends@aol.com
Web site: http://tracytrends.com.

Trademark Universal, Inc., *(0-9706484)* 38 W. 21st St., 4th Flr., New York, NY 10010 USA Tel 212-685-3435; Fax: 212-779-3493 ; *Imprints:* Beat The Test (Beat The Test)
Web site: http://www.beatthetest.com.

Tradewind Bks. (CAN) *(1-896580) Dist. by* **Orca Bk Pubs.**

Tradition Publishing Co., *(1-59187)* Orders Addr.: P.O. Box 370, Maple Plain, MN 55359 USA
Dist(s): **Child's World, Inc.**
Thomson Gale.

Trafalgar Square Bks., *(0-943955; 1-57076)* Orders Addr.: P.O. Box 257, North Pomfret, VT 05053 USA Tel 802-457-1911; Fax: 802-457-1913; Edit Addr.: Howe Hill Rd., North Pomfret, VT 05053 USA
E-mail: kimcook@sover.net
Web site: http://www.horseandriderbooks.com
Dist(s): **Independent Pubs. Group.**

Trafalgar Square Publishing, *(0-943955; 1-57076)* Orders Addr.: P.O. Box 257, North Pomfret, VT 05053-0257 USA (SAN 213-8859) Tel 802-457-1911; Fax: 802-457-1913; Toll Free: 800-423-4525; Edit Addr.: 388 Howe Hill Rd., North Pomfret, VT 05053 USA Tel 802-423-4525; 802-457-1913
E-mail: tsquare@sover.net
Web site: http://www.trafalgarbooks.com; http://www.horseandriderbooks.com
Dist(s): **Independent Pubs. Group.**

Trafford Publishing (CAN) *(1-55212; 1-55369; 1-55395; 1-4120; 1-4122; 1-4251) Dist. by* **AtlasBooks.**

Trail Trotters Bk. Ranch, *(0-9763209)* 616 N. Aurelius Rd., Mason, MI 48854 USA Tel 517-244-0727
E-mail: rosewoodbouz@aol.com
Web site: http://www.ponypointers.com
Dist(s): **Baker & Taylor Bks.**

Trailhead Pr., *(0-9711159)* Orders Addr.: P.O. Box 4717, Elkhart, IN 46514 USA Tel 219-293-9570; Edit Addr.: 907 Cedar St., Elkhart, IN 46514 USA
E-mail: jkallen.trailhead@juno.com.

Trails Bks. *Imprint of* **Big Earth Publishing**

Trails Media Group, Incorporated *See* **Big Earth Publishing**

Trails of Discovery, *(0-9788926)* 31071 Marbella Vista, San Juan Capistrano, CA 92675 USA.

Trailway Bks., *(0-9709152)* 3620 Holiday Ct., NE, Albuquerque, NM 87111 USA Tel 505-298-1781; Fax: 505-298-0415
E-mail: madgeharrah@wroldnet.att.net; madgeharrah@worldnet.att.net.

Training Grounds, *(0-9729057)* 1150 N. Loop 1604 W., Suite 108-607, San Antonio, TX 78248-4503 USA Tel 210-492-4745
E-mail: traininggrounds@aol.com
Web site: http://www.traininggroundsonline.com; http://www.tgrounds.com; http://www.godstg.com; http://www.lemurslegacy.com; http:// www.subjectdollarsystem.com; http://www.godsgirlandboy.com; http://www.shawnajoy.com.

Train-Up A Child, LLC, *(0-9703069)* P.O. Box 1122, Jenks, OK 74037 USA Tel 918-299-8178 (phone/fax)
E-mail: TrainUpStudies@aol.com
Web site: http://www.trainupstudies.com.

Traitor Dachshund Bks., *(0-9744287)* 176 Broadway, Suite 11A, New York, NY 10038 USA (SAN 255-6138) Tel 212-267-7662
E-mail: lindat@nyc.rr.com
Web site: http://www.juliaandthedreammaker.com
Dist(s): **Independent Pubs. Group.**

Trammel, Crystal, *(0-9746327)* 133 Montego Dr., Mesquite, TX 75149-1708 USA
E-mail: minc34@hotmail.com.

Tranquility Publishing *See* **Tranquility Ranch Publishing**

Tranquility Ranch Publishing, *(0-9747425)* 25796 Tranquility Ln., Magnolia, TX 77355 USA
E-mail: gcadwalder@aol.com.

Trans Tech Pubns., Ltd. (CHE) *(0-87849; 3-908450; 3-908451; 3-908452; 3-908453; 3-908454; 3-908158) Dist. by* **Enfield Pubs NH.**

†Transaction Pubs., *(0-7658; 0-87855; 0-88738; 1-56000; 1-4128)* 300 Mcgaw Dr., Edison, NJ 08837-3738 USA (SAN 202-7941) Toll Free: 888-999-6778
E-mail: orders@transactionpub.com; pivins@transactionpub.com
Web site: http://www.transactionpub.com; *CIP.*

Transatlantic Arts, Inc., *(0-693)* P.O. Box 6086, Albuquerque, NM 87197 USA (SAN 202-7968) Tel 505-898-2289 Do not confuse with Trans-Atlantic Pubns., Inc., Philadelphia, PA.
E-mail: books@transatlantic.com
Web site: http://www.transatlantic.com/direct.

Trans-Atlantic Pubns., Inc., 311 Bainbridge St., Philadelphia, PA 19147 USA (SAN 694-0234) Tel 215-925-5083; Fax: 215-925-1912 Do not confuse with Transatlantic Arts, Inc., Albuquerque, NM
E-mail: order@transatlanticpub.com
Web site: http://www.transatlanticpub.com
Dist(s): **Baker & Taylor Bks.**

Transcontinental Publishing, Inc., *(0-9706640)* 6868 N. Seventh Ave, No. 210, Phoenix, AZ 85064-5454 USA Tel 602-274-2300; Fax: 602-274-7096
E-mail: transpub@abilnet.com.

tranScribe bks., *(0-9665090)* P.O. Box 38432, Greensboro, NC 27438 USA
E-mail: transcribe-books@triad.rr.com
Web site: http://www.johnpcock.homestead.com.

TRANSFORMATIONS, *(0-9613649)* 1996 Buckhorn Rd., Sanford, NC 27330-9782 USA (SAN 670-7548) Tel 919-777-9362; Fax: 919-774-5088 Do not confuse with Transformations, Anaheim CA
E-mail: LettsSetaSpell@aol.com
Web site: http://www.atimelessplace.com
Dist(s): **Baker & Taylor Bks.**

Trans-Galactic Pubns., *(0-9616078)* 20 Sunnyside Ave. Suite A134, Mill Valley, CA 94941 USA (SAN 698-0899)
E-mail: transpubls@aol.com.

Transitions, Inc. *Imprint of* **New Beginnings Publishing**

TransNation, *(0-9748667)* 2715 Buford Hwy. NE, Atlanta, GA 30324 USA Tel 404-315-7992; Fax: 404-634-3739
Web site: http://www.transnation.us.

Transnational Computing Services, *(0-9653862)* 2066 W. Sexton Dr., Springfield, MO 65810-4723 USA Tel 417-887-8026 (phone/fax).

Transpersonal Publishing, *(1-929661)* Div. of AHU, LLC, Orders Addr.: P.O. Box 7220, Kill Devil Hills, NC 27948 USA Tel 252-480-0530; Fax: 252-480-0510; Toll Free: 800-296-6463
E-mail: AllenChips@holistictree.com
Web site: http://www.TranspersonalPublishing.com
Dist(s): **Baker & Taylor Bks.**
Ingram Bk. Co.
New Leaf Distributing Co., Inc.

Transworld Publishers Ltd. (GBR) *(0-552) Dist. by* **Trafalgar.**

Transworld Publishers Ltd. (GBR) *(0-552) Dist. by* **IPG Chicago.**

Trapper Creek Museum Sluice Box Productions, *(0-9718302)* Orders Addr.: P.O. Box 13011, Trapper Creek, AK 99683 USA Tel 907-733-2555; Edit Addr.: Mile 3/4 Petersville Rd., Trapper Creek, AK 99683 USA
E-mail: info@trappercreekmuseum.com
Web site: http://www.trappercreekmuseum.com; http://www.sluiceboxproductions.com.

Trash, Steve Enterprises, *(0-9652542)* 975 Old Dirt Rd., Spruce Pine, AL 35585 USA.

Travel 4 Life !, *(0-9749441)* 2040 E. 22nd St., Box 911, Fremont, NE 68025 USA Tel 402-727-1559
E-mail: deanjcbs4u@yahoo.com
Web site: http://www.travel4life.org.

TravelBrains, Inc., *(0-9705809; 1-933763)* 14 Tether Rd., Bedford, NH 03110-5660 USA
Web site: http://www.travelbrains.com.

Traveling Bear Pr., *(0-9643771)* Div. of Susan's Store Room, 239 San Anselmo Ave., San Anselmo, CA 94960 USA Tel 415-456-1333; Fax: 415-456-4935
E-mail: susanstor@earthlink.net
Web site: http://www.susansstoreroom.com.

Traylor, Waverley Publishing, *(0-9715068)* Div. of Waverley Traylor Photography, 3407 Longwood Dr., Smithfield, VA 23430 USA Tel 757-356-9119 (phone/fax)
E-mail: wlfoto@aol.com.

Treadle Pr., *(0-935143)* Div. of Binding & Printing Co., Box D, Sheperdstown, WV 25443 USA (SAN 695-2070) Tel 304-876-2557.

Treadway, Scott, *(0-9746817)* 881 1st. St., No. 146, Lakeport, CA 95453 USA Tel 305-385-5588
E-mail: epochinc@netzero.net
Web site: http://www.epochpress.us.

Treasure Bay, Inc., *(1-891327; 1-60115)* 40 Sir Francis Drake Blvd., San Anselmo, CA 94960-2536 USA Tel 415-451-4749; Fax: 415-451-0108
E-mail: customerservice@webothread.com; donpanec@comcast.net
Web site: http://www.webothread.com.

Treasure Chest Bks., *(0-918080; 1-887896; 0-9700750; 1-933855)* Orders Addr.: P.O. Box 5250, Tucson, AZ 85703-0250 USA (SAN 209-3251) Tel 520-623-9558; Fax: 520-624-5888; Toll Free Fax: 800-715-5888; Toll Free: 800-969-9558; Edit Addr.: 451 N. Bonita Ave., Tucson, AZ 85745 USA Tel 602-623-9558 ; *Imprints:* Rio Nuevo Publishers (Rio Nuevo)
E-mail: info@rionuevo.com; info@treasurechestbooks.com
Web site: http://www.treasurechestbooks.com; http://www.rionuevo.com/
Dist(s): **Norton, W. W. & Co., Inc.**

Company

Treasure Chest Publications *See* **Treasure Chest Bks.**

Treasure Garden Productions, *(0-9668892)* 100 Whitewood Dr., Massapequa Park, NY 11762 USA Tel 516-374-0111; Fax: 516-541-7173
E-mail: daphna@pppmail.nyser.net.

Treasure Hse. *Imprint of* **Destiny Image Pubs.**

Treasure Hunt Adventures, Inc., *(0-9749809)* P.O. Box 1049, Carmel, NY 10512-9998 USA Tel 845-225-2539
E-mail: info@treasurehuntadventures.com
Web site: http://www.treasurehuntadventures.com.

Treasure Text Pubns., *(1-929407)* 5855 Cinnamon Creek Cir., Houston, TX 77084 USA Tel 281-550-0823
E-mail: pklamiller@worldnet.att.net
Web site: http://www.treasuretext.com.

Treasure Tower Bks. *Imprint of* **World Tribune Pr.**

Treasure Trove, Inc., *(0-9760618; 0-9772314)* P.O. Box 459, Pound Ridge, NY 10576 USA Fax: 203-801-0099
Web site: http://www.atreasuretrove.com
Dist(s): **Simon & Schuster, Inc.**

Treasured Images, *(0-9728770)* P.O. Box 361, Milton, WA 98354-0361 USA
E-mail: snspubs@aol.com.

Treble Heart Bks., *(0-9711882; 1-931742; 1-932695)* 1284 Overlook Dr., Sierra Vista, AZ 85635-5512 USA (SAN 254-7120) Tel 520-458-5602; Fax: 520-458-5618 ; *Imprints:* MountainView (MtnView)
Web site: http://www.trebleheartbooks.com.

Trebloon Pubns., *(0-9715423)* P.O. Box 156, Lawrence, NY 11559 USA (SAN 254-1874) Fax: 516-432-8292; 12 Bayview Ave., Lawrence, NY 11559 Tel 516-432-8520
Web site: http://www.trebloon.com
Dist(s): **Baker & Taylor Bks.**

Tree Branch Publishing, *(0-9772578)* Orders Addr.: P.O. Box 421004, Summerland Key, FL 33042 USA Tel 305-872-4600; Fax: 305-832-0156; Toll Free: 866-454-6525; Edit Addr.: 19769 Date Palm Dr., Summerland Key, FL 33042 USA
E-mail: info@treeoflifepublishing.com.

Tree Musketeers, Inc., *(0-9770196)* Orders Addr.: 136 Main St., El Segundo, CA 90245 USA
Web site: http://www.treemusketeers.org.

Tree of Life Pr., *(0-9727103)* 7212 Dogwood Dr., Knoxville, TN 37919-8828 USA
E-mail: jana@janaspicka.com
Web site: http://www.janaspicka.com.

Tree Of Life Publishing, *(0-9745052)* P.O. Box 421004, Summerland Key, FL 33042 USA Tel 305-744-0330; Fax: 305-744-0320; Toll Free: 866-454-6525 ; *Imprints:* Peeper & Friends (Peep & Friends)
E-mail: info@peeperandfriends.com
Web site: http://www.peeperandfriends.com
Dist(s): **Biblio Distribution.**

Tree Pr., *(0-615)* P.O. Box 398, Winston, GA 30187 USA Tel 678-936-5293; Fax: 770-693-0349
E-mail: treepressnet@yahoo.com
Web site: http://www.treepress.net
Dist(s): **Lulu.com.**

Treece, Amy L., *(0-9677982)* 307 Windy Hill Rd., Sherman, TX 75092-9709 USA
E-mail: a-treece1@ti.com.

Treehaus Communications, Inc., *(0-929496; 1-886510)* Orders Addr.: P.O. Box 249, Loveland, OH 45140 USA (SAN 249-5325) Tel 513-683-5716; Fax: 513-683-2882; Toll Free: 800-638-4287; Edit Addr.: 906 W. Loveland Ave., Loveland, OH 45140 USA (SAN 249-5333)
E-mail: treehaus1@fuse.net
Dist(s): **ACTA Pubns.**

Treehouse Court *Imprint of* **Dingles & Co.**

Treehouse Treasures Corp., *(0-9714636)* P.O. Box 1030, Saint Charles, IL 60175 USA (SAN 254-3656) Fax: 630-443-4806; 81 St. Germain Pl., Saint Charles, IL 60174
E-mail: treehousetreasur@aol.com
Dist(s): **Baker & Taylor Bks.**
Brodart Co.

Treetop Publishing, *(0-9701068)* 1174 Babcock Hill Rd., West Winfield, NY 13491 USA Tel 315-822-6777; Fax: 315-738-1936 Do not confuse with companies with the same name in Hudson, MA, Racine, WI
E-mail: hrpros@borg.com.

Trellis Publishing, Inc., *(0-9663281; 1-930650)* Orders Addr.: P.O. Box 16141, Duluth, MN 55816 USA (SAN 299-6669) Fax: 218-722-3194; Toll Free: 800-513-0115
E-mail: trellis2@aol.com
Web site: http://www.trellispublishing.com
Dist(s): **Consortium Bk. Sales & Distribution**
Independent Pubs. Group.

Tremblay, E. Gerald *See* **Tremblay Publishing**

Tremblay Publishing, *(0-9728397)* 868 Broomley Rd., Charlottesville, VA 22901 USA Tel 434-296-6210
E-mail: gerrytrem@hotmail.com.

Tremiak Publishing, *(0-9676688)* Orders Addr.: P.O. Box 402, La Conner, WA 98257 USA Tel 360-466-9298; Edit Addr.: 931 Maple St., La Conner, WA 98257 USA
E-mail: tremiak@yahoo.com.

Trend Enterprises, Inc., *(1-889319; 1-58792)* Orders Addr.: P.O. Box 64073, Saint Paul, MN 55164 USA Tel 651-631-2850; Fax: 651-582-3500; Toll Free Fax: 800-845-4832; Toll Free: 800-328-5540; Edit Addr.: 300 Ninth Ave., SW, New Brighton, MN 55112 USA ; *Imprints:* Wickleville Woods (Wickleville Woods); MindMotion (MindMotion); KidSparks (KidSparks)
Web site: http://www.trendenterprises.com.

Trenton Creative Enterprises, *(0-9754958)* 731 Springdale Dr., Spartanburg, SC 29302 USA.

Trent's Prints, *(0-9728872; 0-9762389; 0-9773723; 1-934035)* 3754 Willard Norris Rd., Pace, FL 32571 USA Tel 850-994-1421 Toll Free: 866-275-7124
Web site: http://www.trentsprints.com.

Treorca Pr., *(0-9766559)* 1718 W. 102nd St., Chicago, IL 60643-2147 USA
E-mail: joga9@aol.com
Web site: http://www.treorcapress.com.

Tres Canis Publishing Co., *(0-9659065)* P.O. Box 163, Nanticoke, PA 18634 USA Tel 570-735-0328
E-mail: rjanosov@verizon.net.

Trevor Romain Co., The, *(0-9762843; 0-9787783; 1-934365)* 816 W. 10th St., Austin, TX 78701 USA Toll Free: 877-876-6246
E-mail: kyle@comicalsense.com
Web site: http://www.TrevorRomain.com; http://www.comicalsense.com.

Trey-Ish & Co., *(0-9714093)* c/o M. Cooper, P.O. Box 850131, Richardson, TX 75085-0131 USA Toll Free: 800-463-8149
E-mail: cookey41@hotmail.com.

TRI LIFE Pr., *(0-9755938)* P.O. Box 912, Jacksonville, OR 97530 USA Tel 714-730-5999; Fax: 714-730-7922; Toll Free: 888-786-7526
Web site: http://www.trileadership.com.

TRIAD Publishing Group, *(0-9796994; 0-9798244; 0-9800103)* 3233 Ramblewood Dr. N., Sarasota, FL 34237 USA Do not confuse with companies with a similar name in Sequim, WA
E-mail: vfexec@msn.com; vfirestone@triadpublishinggroup.com
Web site: http://www.triadpublishinggroup.com.

Tri-Ad veterans League, Inc., *(0-9720404)* 31 Heath St., Jamaica Plain, MA 02130-1650 USA
E-mail: triadveterans@hotmail.com
Web site: http://www.triadveteransleague.org.

Triangle Pr., *(1-58339)* Div. of Grace & Truth Bks., 3406 Summit Blvd., Sabd Springs, OK 74063 USA Tel 918-245-1500
E-mail: publish@tripress.com
Web site: http://www.tripress.com.

Triangle Pubns., *(1-889745)* Orders Addr.: P.O. Box 4849, Oak Ridge, TN 37831-4849 USA Tel 423-483-1544; Fax: 423-481-0728; Toll Free: 800-654-5352; Edit Addr.: 943 W. Outer Dr., Oak Ridge, TN 37830 USA Fax: 423-482-9744 Do not confuse with companies with same or similar names in Rose Hill, KS, Huntsville, AL, Fort Collins, CO, Marion, IN, Tempe, AR
E-mail: pmla@worldnet.att.net; info@triangle-pub.com
Web site: http://www.triangle-pub.com.

Tribeca Hse., *(0-9701706)* P.O. Box 364, Neptune, NJ 07754 USA Fax: 310-606-2035
E-mail: sibyllad@earthlink.net
Web site: http://www.tribecahouse.com
Dist(s): **Afrikan World Bk. Distributor**
Baker & Taylor Bks.

Tribute Bks., *(0-9765072; 0-9795045)* Orders Addr.: 291 W. St., Eynon, PA 18403 USA (SAN 256-4416) Tel 570-876-2416 (phone/fax)
E-mail: info@tribute-books.com
Web site: http://www.tribute-books.com
Dist(s): **Partners Bk. Distributing, Inc.**

Tribute Publishing, *(0-9667921)* Orders Addr.: P.O. Box 8476, Northridge, CA 91327 USA Tel 818-363-7391; Fax: 818-363-5553; Toll Free: 888-873-4152; Edit Addr.: 11430 Doral Ave., Northridge, CA 91326 USA Do not confuse with Tribute Publishing, LLC in Douglasville, GA
E-mail: toddcohen91326@yahoo.com
Web site: http://www.Tribute Publishing.com.

Trice, B.E. Publishing, *(0-9631925; 1-890885)* 2727 Prytania St., New Orleans, LA 70130 USA Tel 504-895-0111
E-mail: betbooks@aol.com.

Trickle Creek Bks., *(0-9640742; 1-929432)* 500 Andersontown Rd., Mechanicsburg, PA 17055 USA Tel 717-766-2638; Fax: 717-766-1343; Toll Free: 800-353-2791
E-mail: tonialbert@aol.com
Web site: http://www.TrickleCreekBooks.com
Dist(s): **Baker & Taylor Bks.**
Educational Bk. Distributors
Koen-Levy Bk. Wholesalers LLC.

Tricks of the Trade, Inc., *(0-9716026)* 23015 Widgeon Pl., Canyon Lake, CA 92587-7969 USA Toll Free: 800-679-3859
E-mail: chefanton@ChefAnton.com
Web site: http://www.chefanton.com.

Tricolor Bks., *(0-9754641)* P.O. Box 24811, Tempe, AZ 85285 USA
E-mail: tricolorbrian@hotmail.com
Web site: http://www.mountainkingsnake.com.

Tricor Pr., *(0-9673830)* P.O. Box 8811, Medford, OR 97504-0811 USA Tel 541-770-8075; Fax: 541-770-1306
E-mail: tricorpress@mindspring.com
Web site: http://www.tricorpress.com.

Tricorner Publishing, *(0-9725614)* P.O. Box 5035, New Britain, PA 18901 USA Tel 215-822-3267 (phone/fax) Do not confuse with Baggins Books in Bellingham, WA
E-mail: tcp@tricornerpublishing.com
Web site: http://www.tricornerpublishing.com.

Tricycle Pr. *Imprint of* **Ten Speed Pr.**

Trident Media, Incorporated *See* **New World Media, Inc.**

Trident Pr. International, *(1-58279; 1-888777; 1-86091; 1-60081)* Orders Addr.: 800 5th Ave S. Ste. 203, Naples, FL 34102-6661 USA Toll Free Fax: 800-494-4226; Toll Free: 800-593-3662; Edit Addr.: 121 Marketridge Dr., Ridgeland, MS 39157-6027 USA
E-mail: sales@trident-international.com
Web site: http://www.trident-international.com; http://www.secondworldwar.net; http://www.schoolbookzone.com.

TriEclipse, Inc., *(0-9704512)* P.O. Box 7763, Jacksonville, FL 32238 USA Tel 904-778-1841
E-mail: vtaylor4@bellsouth.net
Web site: http://www.trieclipse.com.

Trigger Memory Systems, *(0-9762024)* P.O. Box 24, Waitsburg, WA 99361 USA
E-mail: timestales@earthlink.net
Web site: http://www.triggermemorysystem.com.

Trillas Editorial, S. A. (MEX) *(968-24) Dist. by* **Continental Bk.**

Trillas Editorial, S. A. (MEX) *(968-24) Dist. by* **Lectorum Pubns.**

Trillas Editorial, S. A. (MEX) *(968-24) Dist. by* **AIMS Intl.**

Trillas Editorial, S. A. (MEX) *(968-24) Dist. by* **Giron Bks.**

Trilogy Pubns. LLC, *(0-9772799)* 560 Sylvan Ave., Englewood Cliffs, NJ 07632 USA (SAN 257-2044) Tel 201-816-1211; Fax: 201-816-8424
Web site: http://www.trilogypublications.com.

Trinity Bks., *(0-9743669)* P.O. Box 401, Cascade, ID 83611 USA.

Trinity Rivers Publishing, Inc., *(1-888565)* P.O. Box 209, Manassas, VA 20108-0209 USA Tel 703-330-3262 (phone/fax) ; *Imprints:* Reconciliation Press (Reconciliation Pr)
E-mail: publisher@trinityrivers.com
Web site: http://www.trinityrivers.com
Dist(s): **Follett Library Resources.**

Triple Crown Pubns., *(0-9702472; 0-9747895; 0-9762349; 0-9767894; 0-9778804; 0-9799517)* 2184 Citygate Dr., Columbus, OH 43219 USA Tel 614-478-9402; Fax: 614-478-9458
E-mail: editor@triplecrownpublications.com
Web site: http://www.triplecrownpublications.com
Dist(s): **A & B Distributors & Pubs. Group**
Ambassador Bks. & Media
Baker & Taylor Bks.
Brodart Co.
Ingram Bk. Co.
Koen-Levy Bk. Wholesalers LLC.

Triple Exposure Publishing, Incorporated *See* **T. E. Publishing, Inc.**

Triple J Productions, *(0-9644772)* 1076 Juneberry Rd., Odgen, IA 50212-7402 USA Tel 515-275-2488
E-mail: jjjensen@netins.net.

Triple Seven Pr., *(0-9710486)* P.O. Box 70552, Las Vegas, NV 89170-0552 USA Do not confuse with Triple Seven International, Gaston, IN
E-mail: wendy@777press.com
Web site: http://www.777press.com
Dist(s): **Ingram Bk. Co.**

Triple Tulip Pr., *(0-615; 0-9754825)* Orders Addr.: P.O. Box 250, Sanbornville, NH 03872 USA Tel 603-522-3398; Fax: 603-522-5178; Edit Addr.: 2717 Wakefield Rd., Sanbornville, NH 03872 USA
E-mail: tripletulip@verizon.net
Web site: http://www.tripletulippress.com
Dist(s): **Baker & Taylor Bks.**

TripleCrown Pubns. *See* **Triple Crown Pubns.**

Trisar, Inc., *(1-886386)* 804 W. Town & Country Rd., Orange, CA 92868-4712 USA.

Tristan Publishing, Inc., *(0-9726504)* 2355 Louisiana Ave N. Ste. 2, Minneapolis, MN 55427-3646 USA Toll Free: 866-545-1383
E-mail: waldmanb@aol.com
Web site: http://www.tristanpublishing.com.

Tritium Pr., *(0-9761726)* 8690 Aero Dr., No. 339, San Diego, CA 92123 USA
E-mail: tritium@n2.net.

Triumph Bks., *(0-9624436; 1-57243; 1-880141; 1-60078)* Orders Addr.: 542 S. Dearborn St., Suite 750, Chicago, IL 60605 USA (SAN 852-6826) Tel 312-939-3330; Fax: 312-663-3557; Toll Free: 800-335-5323; Edit Addr.: c/o Kaplan Logistics, 901 Bilter Rd., Aurora, IL 60502 USA ; *Imprints:* Benchmark Press (Bnchmrk Pr)
E-mail: Ordering@TriumphBooks.com; J_Martini@triumphbooks.com; s_kaufman@triumphbooks.com; orders@triumphbooks.com; w.swanson@triumphbooks.com
Web site: http://www.triumphbooks.com
Dist(s): **Detroit Free Pr., Inc.**

Triumph Business Trust *See* **Christobe Publishing**

Triumph Publishing, *(1-890430)* 10415 219th St., Queens Vlg, NY 11429-2020 USA Do not confuse with companies with a similar name in Omal, WA, College park, GA.

Triune Bible Institute & Seminary *See* **Triune Biblical Univ.**

Triune Biblical Univ., *(1-55967)* Orders Addr.: P.O. Box 912, Kelso, WA 98626 USA (SAN 251-8120) Tel 360-577-0586; Fax: 360-578-2528; Edit Addr.: 1209 S. Third Ave., Kelso, WA 98626 USA
E-mail: triumebiblical@kalama.com; tbu@kalama.com
Web site: http://triunebibleuni.uswestdex.com.

Trivia Tours Unlimited, *(0-9726805)* Orders Addr.: P.O. Box 20450, Staten Island, NY 10302 USA; Edit Addr.: 277 Garrison Ave., Staten Island, NY 10314 USA.

Trivium Pursuit, *(0-9743616; 1-933228)* 429 Lake Park Blvd., PMB 168, Muscatine, IA 52761 USA Tel 309-537-3641
E-mail: bluedorn@triviumpursuit.com
Web site: http://www.triviumpursuit.com
Dist(s): **Appalachian Bk. Distributors.**

Troll Lord Games *See* **Troll Lord Games/ Chenault & Gray**

Troll Lord Games/ Chenault & Gray, *(0-9702397; 1-931275)* 22 Lenon Dr., Little Rock, AR 72207-5153 USA
E-mail: troll@trolllord.com; schenault@aristotle.net
Web site: http://www.trolllord.com
Dist(s): **Diamond Bk. Distributors**
Wizard's Attic, The.

Trolley (GBR) *(0-9542079; 0-9542648; 1-904563) Dist. by* **Dist Art Pubs.**

Trotman, Kay L., *(0-615)* P.O. Box 1501, Lake Elsinore, CA 92531 USA Tel 951-898-6094; Fax: 951-898-6094
E-mail: njeri@mac.com
Web site: www.onsafariwithkay.com.

Troubadour Press *See* **Talking Stone Pr.**

Troublemaker Publishing, LP, *(1-933104)* P.O. Box 608, Spicewood, TX 78669 USA Tel 512-334-7777.

Trout-Tail, LLC, *(0-9722506)* 1001 Bishop Rd., Grosse Pointe, MI 48230-1420 USA (SAN 255-0857) Tel 313-600-0166; Fax: 772-382-8565
E-mail: khlucas@trouttail.com
Web site: http://www.trouttail.com
Dist(s): **Angler's Bk. Supply**
Baker & Taylor Bks.
North Country Bks., Inc.
Partners Bk. Distributing, Inc.

Trovato-Cantori, Lorraine *See* **Ceasar Bks.**

Trucking Video, Trescott Publishing, *(1-888748)* 8028 Farm to Market Rd. 457, Bay City, TX 77414 USA
E-mail: trescott@truckingvideo.com
Web site: http://www.truckingvideo.com
Dist(s): **BookMasters, Inc.**

Trudgian, Sherri *See* **Little Sprout Publishing Hse.**

True Arts Graphics & Printing, *(1-889858)* 2545 W. 237th St., Suite H, Torrance, CA 90505 USA Tel 310-534-1680; Fax: 310-534-4081
E-mail: CDrombooks@aol.com.

True Colors, Inc. Publishing, *(1-893320)* 3605 W. Macarthur Blvd. Ste. 702, Santa Ana, CA 92704-6845 USA (SAN 253-7249) Toll Free: 800-422-4686
E-mail: dwhitney@true-colors.com; info@true-colors.com
Web site: http://www.true-colors.com
Dist(s): **Baker & Taylor Bks.**

True Exposures Publishing, Inc., *(0-9642595; 0-9771762)* Orders Addr.: P.O. Box 5066, Brandon, MS 39047 USA Tel 601-829-1222; Fax: 601-829-1656; Toll Free: 800-323-3398; Edit Addr.: 106 Shenandoah Estates Cir., Brandon, MS 39047 USA
E-mail: trueexposures@bellsouth.net
Web site: http://www.trueexposures.com.

True Light Pubns., *(0-9655407)* Div. of True Light Ministries International, Orders Addr.: P.O. Box 269, Orange, MA 01364-0269 USA Tel 978-544-3221; Fax: 978-544-8753; Edit Addr.: 527 S. Main St., Orange, MA 01364 USA Do not confuse with companies with similar names in Boulder, CO, Mandeville,LA, Washington, DC
E-mail: davis.steele@att.net.

True Light Publishing, *(0-9656670)* Orders Addr.: P.O. Box 1284, Boulder, CO 80308-0734 USA Tel 303-447-2547; Fax: 303-443-4373; Edit Addr.: 458 Pine Tree Ln., Boulder, CO 80304-0444 USA Do not confuse with True Light Publishing in Homewood, IL
E-mail: tlpub@ecentral.com; orders@truelightpub.com; amber@truelightmusic.com
Web site: http://www.truelightpub.com; http://www.truelightpublishing.com; http://www.truelightmusic.com
Dist(s): **New Leaf Distributing Co., Inc.**
Gangaji Foundation, The.

True To The Word, LLP, *(0-9703697)* P.O. Box 715, Middlefield, OH 44062 USA (SAN 253-4045) Tel 440-632-1804; Fax: 440-632-5549.

True Vine Publishing Co., *(0-9760914; 0-9786088)* P.O. Box 22448, Nashville, TN 37202 USA Tel 615-585-0143
E-mail: tbond@truevinepublishing.org
Web site: http://www.truevinepublishing.org.

Truman Publishing Co., *(0-9663393; 0-9719929)* 310 W. 49th St. Apt. 707, Kansas City, MO 64112-3509 USA Toll Free: 888-852-3694
E-mail: mail@trumanpublishing.com
Web site: http://www.echoesofwar.com.

Trumpet In Zion Publishing, *(0-9716355)* Div. of Solid Rock Church of God in Christ, P.O. Box 51163, Indian Orchard, MA 01151 USA Tel 413-273-5900; Fax: 413-273-5904 ; *Imprints:* Solid Rock Books (Solid Rock Bks)
E-mail: judsonpress@aol.com; Morton-and-Fason@cox.net
Web site: http://www.solidrockbooks.org; http://www.tzpublishing.com; http://www.judsonpress.org; http://www.mortonandfason.com
Dist(s): **Baker & Taylor Bks.**

Trumpet Media *Imprint of* **WindRiver Publishing**

Trumpeter *Imprint of* **Shambhala Pubns., Inc.**

Truth For Eternity Ministries, *(1-889520)* Div. of Reformed Baptist Church of Grand Rapids, 860 Peachcrest Ct NE, Grand Rapids, MI 49505-6435 USA
E-mail: rbctfegr@iserv.net
Web site: http://www.vor.org/truth/.

Truthought Group, *(0-9653376)* P.O. Box 656, Ortonville, MI 48468 USA Tel 877-548-7884; Fax: 815-389-3987 ; *Imprints:* Truthought Publications (Truthght Pubns)
E-mail: truthot@aol.com
Web site: http://www.truthought.com.

Truthought Pubns. *Imprint of* **Truthought Group**

truthpress.com, *(0-9710199)* 158 Kirwans Landing Ln., Chester, MD 21619 USA Tel 410-643-4155; Fax: 410-604-1252 Do not confuse with companies with the same or similar name in Scottsdale. AZ
E-mail: aaterry@crosslink.net
Web site: http://truthpress.com
Dist(s): **Baker & Taylor Bks.**
Spring Arbor Distributors, Inc.

Tsaba Hse., *(0-9725486; 1-933853)* 2252 12th St., Reedly, CA 93654 USA (SAN 254-9441) Tel 559-643-8575; Fax: 559-638-2640
E-mail: ps@tsabahouse.com
Web site: http://www.tsabahouse.com
Dist(s): **STL Distribution North America.**

TSAR Pubns. (CAN) *(0-920661; 1-894770) Dist. by* **SPD-Small Pr Dist.**

T.S.I. Strategies, LLC, *(0-9772609)* 140 SE 8th St., Cape Coral, FL 33990 USA Fax: 866-761-4233
E-mail: jim@jamesroach.com
Web site: http://www.producevideos.com.

TSM Publishing Group, LLC *See* **Autumn Publishing Group, LLC**

Tsui Wong-Avery, Sally, *(0-9798874)* 2618 W. Canyon Ave., San Diego, CA 92123 USA.

Tubbs, Joseph G., *(0-9711285)* 708 Fleetwood Dr., Lynchburg, VA 24501-3914 USA.

Tucker, Peggy *See* **Heritage Publishing**

Tucker, Terra, *(0-9794578)* P.O. Box 682371, Franklin, TN 37068 USA (SAN 853-5027).

Tucky Tum, *(0-9670889)* 1519 E. Mia Ln., Gilbert, AZ 85296-6837 USA
E-mail: nubia@tuckytum.com
Web site: http://www.tuckytum.com.

Tucson Botanical Gardens, *(0-9792253)* 2150 N. Alvernon Way, Tucson, AZ 85712 USA Tel 520-326-7538; Fax: 520-324-0166
E-mail: info@tucsonbotanical.org; execdirector@tucsonbotanical.org
Web site: http://www.tucsonbotanical.org.

Tucson Voices Pr. *Imprint of* **Voices: Community Stories Past & Present, Inc.**

Tucu Pr., *(0-9766572)* Orders Addr.: P.O. Box 447, Bozeman, MT 59771-0447 USA Tel 406-586-5084 (phone/fax); Edit Addr.: 3150 Graf St., No. 8, Bozeman, MT 59715 USA
E-mail: anndiberardinis@msn.com.

Tudor Assocs. Pr., *(0-9760939)* P.O. Box 1804, Payson, AZ 85547-1804 USA Tel 928-978-5799
E-mail: press@tudorassociates.com
Web site: http://www.tudorassociates.com.

Tudor Pubs., Inc., *(0-936389; 0-9778026)* Orders Addr.: P.O. Box 38366, Greensboro, NC 27438 USA; Edit Addr.: 3109 Shady Lawn Dr., Greensboro, NC 27408 USA (SAN 697-3035) Tel 336-282-5907; Fax: 336-333-1099
E-mail: Eepfaff@aol.com; tudorpublishers@aol.com
Dist(s): **Baker & Taylor Bks.**
Brodart Co.

Tuesday's Child, *(0-9772795)* Orders Addr.: P.O. Box 2512, Cookeville, TN 38502-2512 USA (SAN 257-2060)
E-mail: tuesdayschildpub@charter.net
Web site: http://tuesdayschildpub.com.

Tuesday's Child Publishing, Ltd., *(1-881134)* 619B Heritage Hills Dr., Somers, NY 10589-1900 USA
Dist(s): **Baker & Taylor Bks.**

Tullycrine, LLC, *(0-9746554)* P.O. Box 178, Heisson, WA 98622-0178 USA
E-mail: tullycrineinc@aol.com; tullycrinellc@aol.com
Web site: http://www.tullycrine.com; http://www.book.traditionalcats.com.

Tumbleweed Pr., *(0-938091)* 11503 Carrollwood Dr., Tampa, FL 33618 USA (SAN 659-705X) Tel 813-932-8487 Do nto confuse with Tumbleweed Press in Fuquay-Varina, NC .

Tumbleweed Publishing, *(0-9720132)* PO BOX 882, 6701 Greenwich Rd., Westfield Center, OH 44251-0882 USA Do not confuse with Tumbleweed Publishing Company in Eugene, OH
E-mail: tumbleweedbooks@aol.com; tubleweedbooks@aol.com.

Tundra Bks., Inc./Livres Toundra, Inc. (CAN) *(0-88776; 0-89541; 0-912766) Dist. by* **Random.**

Tundra Bks. of Northern New York, *(0-88776; 0-89541; 0-912766)* Affil. of Tundra Bks, Inc., P.O. Box 1030, Plattsburgh, NY 12901 USA Tel 416-598-4786; Fax: 416-598-0247; Toll Free: 800-788-1074
E-mail: tundra@mcclelland.com
Web site: http://www.tundrabooks.com.

Tundra Pubns., *(0-9606768)* 1997 Big Owl Rd., Allenspark, CO 80510 USA (SAN 219-6492) Tel 303-747-2047; Fax: 303-747-2016.

Tune Platoon, Inc., *(0-9707357)* Orders Addr.: 4000 Towerside Ter. Apt. 2007, Miami Shores, FL 33138-2241 USA
E-mail: millocamp@mediaone.net
Web site: http://www.tuneplatoon.homestead.com.

Tuned in to Learning, *(0-9768881)* P.O. Box 221016, San Diego, CA 92192 USA (SAN 256-5803) Tel 858-453-0590; Fax: 858-777-3626
E-mail: mlazar@coastmusictherapy.com
Web site: http://www.tunedintolearning.com.

tunesntots.com, *(0-9716493)* 3685 Roundtree Ct., Boulder, CO 80304 USA Tel 303-939-8166 (phone/fax)
E-mail: mrpaul@tunesntots.com.

Tunnel Vision, *(0-9754150)* 5310 N. Magnolia Ave., Chicago, IL 60640 USA Tel 773-275-8935; Fax: 773-275-8936 Do not confuse with Tunnel Vision Co., Inc., Santa Barbara, CA
E-mail: tunnel_vision@earthlink.net
Web site: http://www.tunnelvisionbooks.com
Dist(s): **Independent Pubs. Group.**

Turley, Sandy, *(0-9778548)* 145 Gardenside Ct., Fallbrook, CA 92028 USA (SAN 850-4180) Tel 760-723-0504
E-mail: rstur@adelphia.net
Web site: http://helps4teachers.com.

Turman, E., *(0-9753042)* 1321 Singingwood Ct., No. 1, Walnut Creek, CA 94595 USA Tel 925-944-5743
E-mail: shihtze1@msn.com.

Turnaround Bk. Publishing Corp., *(0-9753028)* 5047 W. Main St., Suite 212, Kalamazoo, MI 49001 USA.

Turner, Barbara, *(0-9747019)* P.O. Box 893493, Temecula, CA 92589 USA Tel 951-699-3933
E-mail: adayinsanfrancisco@yahoo.com
Dist(s): **Lulu.com.**

Turner Publishing Co., *(0-938021; 1-56311; 1-59652)* Orders Addr.: P.O. Box 3101, Paducah, KY 42002-3101 USA (SAN 659-803X) Tel 270-443-0121; Fax: 270-443-0335; Toll Free: 800-788-3350; Edit Addr.: 412 Broadway, Paducah, KY 42001 USA Do not confuse with companies with the same or similar name in Atlanta, GA, Eastchester, NY, Houston, TX
E-mail: info@turnerpublishing.com
Web site: http://www.turnerpublishing.com
Dist(s): **Partners Bk. Distributing, Inc.**

Turner, Rich Photographs, *(0-9762410)* 305 Fyffe Ave., Suite 158, Stockton, CA 95203 USA Tel 209-460-1050; Fax: 209-460-1051
E-mail: richt@turnerphoto.com
Web site: http://www.turnerphoto.com.

Turngroup Technologies, LLC, *(0-9794377)* 3830 Washington Ave., Suite 115, Saint Louis, MO 63108 USA
Web site: http://www.hisforhopebooks.com
Dist(s): **Big River Distribution.**

Turning 2000 *Imprint of* **Grim, Gary & Assocs.**

Turning a New Page, *(0-9762030)* Orders Addr.: P.O. Box 91603, Tucson, AZ 85752-1603 USA Tel 520-572-0879; Fax: 520-579-7183
E-mail: rick4758@comcast.net
Web site: http://www.turninganewpage.com.

Turning Point LLC, *(0-9745745)* 1339 Indiana Ave., Connersville, IN 47331 USA Tel 765-825-9835; 765-265-3207 (Mobile)
E-mail: lsfitzg@aol.com
Web site: http://www.stellarstar.biz.

Turning Point Publications, *(0-9752742)* Orders Addr.: 2822 Cashwell Dr., No. 233, Goldsboro, NC 27534 USA Do not confuse with Turning Point Publications in Eureka, CA
E-mail: turningpointpublications@earthlink.net
Web site: http://www.turningpointpublications.com.

Turnstone Historical Research, *(0-9723667)* 275 E. Fourth St., Suite 790, Saint Paul, MN 55101-1686 USA Tel 651-310-0601; Fax: 651-222-7338.

Turnstyle, *(0-9668541)* 1601 W. 100 South, Portland, IN 47371 USA
E-mail: rogdom@earthlink.net.

Turtle Bks. *Imprint of* **Jason & Nordic Pubs.**

Turtle Bks., *(1-890515)* 866 United Nations Plaza, Suite 525, New York, NY 10017 USA Tel 212-644-2020; Fax: 212-223-4387
E-mail: turtlebook@aol.com
Web site: http://www.turtlebooks.com
Dist(s): **Lectorum Pubns., Inc.**
Perseus Distribution.

Turtle Gallery Editions, *(0-9626935)* P.O. Box 219, Deer Isle, ME 04627-0219 USA Tel 207-348-9977 (phone/fax)
E-mail: ekturtle@javanet.com
Web site: http://www.turtlegallery.com.

Turtle Island Pr., Inc., *(1-889166)* 3104 E. Camelback Rd., Suite 614, Phoenix, AZ 85016 USA (SAN 299-5425) Tel 602-468-1141; Fax: 602-954-8560; Toll Free: 888-900-9699 ; *Imprints:* Dr. H Books (Dr H Books).

Turtle Point *Imprint of* **Turtle Point Pr.**

Turtle Point Pr., *(0-9627987; 1-885586; 1-885983; 1-933527)* 233 Broadway, Rm. 946, New York, NY 10279 USA Tel 212-285-1019 (phone/fax) ; *Imprints:* Turtle Point (Turtle Pt)
E-mail: countomega@aol.com
Web site: http://www.turtlepoint.com
Dist(s): **Consortium Bk. Sales & Distribution**
Lightning Source, Inc.
SPD-Small Pr. Distribution
Sprout, Inc.

Turtle Pr., *(0-916844)* 300 E. 40th St., Apt. 12C, New York, NY 10016-2149 USA (SAN 208-8975) Tel 212-753-7957 Do not confuse with companies with the same name in Wethersfield, CT, Nordland, WA
E-mail: kerrie@turtlearts.com.

Turtle Pr. Corp, *(1-880336)* Orders Addr.: P.O. Box 34010, Santa Fe, NM 87594 USA Tel 505-820-0757; Fax: 815-572-9533; Toll Free: 800-778-8785 (orders only) Do not confuse with companies with the same name in in New York, NY, Nordland, WA, Warren, MI, Seattle, WA
E-mail: sales@turtlepress.com; customerservice@turtlepress.com
Web site: http://www.turtlepress.com
Dist(s): **Lulu.com.**

Turtle Time Bks., *(0-9770957)* P.O. Box 809, San Luis Obispo, CA 93406 USA

Tush People, The, *(0-9722514)* P.O. Box 950100, Mission Hills, CA 91395 USA Tel 661-298-2293; 818-897-1734; Fax: 818-899-4455
E-mail: dfav218@aol.com
Dist(s): **Biblio Distribution.**

Tusktown Publishing, *(0-9709160)* Orders Addr.: P.O. Box 3066, Ocala, FL 34478 USA (SAN 256-0321) Tel 352-840-9562; Edit Addr.: 5801 NW 31st Ave., Ocala, FL 34475 USA
E-mail: ayubu@aol.com.

Tusquests Editores Mexico, S.A. de C.V. (MEX) *(968-7723; 970-699) Dist. by* **Libros Fronteras.**

Tuttle Publishing, *(0-8048; 4-900737)* 153 Milk St., 4th Flr., Boston, MA 02109 USA (SAN 213-2621) Tel 617-951-4080; Fax: 617-951-4045; Toll Free: 800-247-1060; 364 Innovation Dr., North Clarendon, VT 05759-9436 Tel 802-773-8930; Fax: 802-773-6993; Toll Free Fax: 800-329-8885; Toll Free: 800-526-2778 ; *Imprints:* PeriplusEdition (PeriplEdns)
E-mail: info@tuttlepublishing.com
Web site: http://www.tuttlepublishing.com; http://www.tuttlemartialarts.com
Dist(s): **Cheng & Tsui Co.**
Ten Speed Pr.

Tuvott Publishing, *(0-9723974)* P.O. Box 18276, Erlanger, KY 41018 USA (SAN 255-3341) Tel 859-341-6004; Fax: 859-341-6033
E-mail: tuvott@fuse.net
Web site: http://www.tuvott.com
Dist(s): **Baker & Taylor Bks.**
Book Clearing Hse.
Spring Arbor Distributors, Inc.

Tuxedo Blue, LLC, *(0-9754056)* Orders Addr.: P.O. Box 2008, Lenox, MA 01240 USA Tel 413-637-2190; Edit Addr.: 455 W. 43rd St., No. 1A, New York, NY 10036 USA Tel 212-262-5113
E-mail: billiamsw@earthlink.net
Web site: http://www.spacenicks.com
Dist(s): **Biblio Distribution.**

Company

TV Bks., L.L.C., *(1-57500)* 1619 Broadway, 9th Flr., New York, NY 10019 USA Tel 212-603-1824; Fax: 212-245-7281
E-mail: mail@tvbooks.com
Web site: http://www.tvbooks.com.

TW Publishing, *(0-9660166)* 1109 S. Westnedge Ave., Kalamazoo, MI 49008 USA Tel 616-344-9135; Fax: 616-344-5735; 445 Park Pl., Kalamazoo, MI 49001
E-mail: schirado@twpub.com
Web site: http://www.twpub.com.

Twain, Mark Media, Inc. Pubs., *(1-58037)* 100 E. Main St., Lewistown, MO 63452 USA Tel 573-497-2202; Fax: 573-497-2507
Dist(s): **Carson-Dellosa Publishing Co., Inc.**
Midpoint Trade Bks., Inc.

Twain's Huckleberry Press *See* **Huckleberry Pr.**

Twayne Pubs. *Imprint of* **Thomson Gale**

Tweener Pr. *Imprint of* **Baker Trittin Pr.**

TweetStreet Pr., *(0-9701620)* P.O. Box 40284, Bay Village, OH 44140-0284 USA Tel 440-933-6882
E-mail: jonesmit@yahoo.com
Web site: http://www.tweetstreet.com.

Tweety Jill Pubns., *(1-891898)* 5824 Beeridge Rd., Suite 412, Sarasota, FL 34233 USA Tel 941-377-7720; Fax: 941-379-2462; Toll Free: 800-595-5767
E-mail: info@tweetyjills.com.

Twelve Stones Publishing, *(0-9712363)* Orders Addr.: P.O. Box 763066, Dallas, TX 75376 USA Tel 214-392-9514
E-mail: jbrittnew@hotmail.com
Web site: http://www.poemsfromthefast.com.

Twentieth Century Christian Bks., *(0-89098)* 2809 Granny White Pike, Nashville, TN 37204 USA (SAN 206-2550) Tel 615-383-3842.

Twenty First Century Bks., *(0-9636012; 1-893817)* P.O. Box 2001, 507 SCR 528, Breckenridge, CO 80424-2001 USA (SAN 298-248X) Tel 970-453-9293; Fax: 970-453-6692; Toll Free: 877-453-9293 Do not confuse with Twenty First Century Bks., Inc. in New York, NY
E-mail: order_desk03@tfcbooks.com; g.peterson@tfcbooks.com
Web site: http://www.tfcbooks.com; http://www.teslabooks.com
Dist(s): **Baker & Taylor Bks.**

Twenty First Century Publishers *See* **21st Century Pubs.**

Twenty-First Century Bks. *Imprint of* **Lerner Publishing Group**

Twenty-First Century Co., The, *(0-933451; 1-888264)* 2201 Rockbrook Dr., No. 1916, Lewisville, TX 75067-3830 USA Tel 972-459-6327 (phone/fax)
E-mail: t21cenco@flash.net
Web site: http://www.cleareducation.com.

Twenty-Four Karate Experience, Inc., The, *(0-9703958)* 2305-C Ashland St., PMB 176, Ashland, OR 97520 USA Tel 541-488-7813; Fax: 541-482-6491
E-mail: erlingb@home.com.

Twenty-Third Pubns./Bayard, *(0-89622; 1-58595)* 1 Montauk Ave. # 20, New London, CT 06320-4967 USA (SAN 658-2052) Toll Free Fax: 800-572-0788; Toll Free: 800-321-0411
E-mail: ttpubs@aol.com
Web site: http://www.twentythirdpublications.com
Dist(s): **Forward Movement Pubns.**

twhiteart, *(0-9639670)* 5290 Meadville St., Excelsior, MN 55331-8792 USA Tel 952-474-2083
E-mail: madonna@twhiteart.com
Web site: http://www.twhiteart.com.

Twiglet The Little Christmas Tree *Imprint of* **PJs Corner**

Twilight Pr., *(0-9640025)* P.O. Box 551, Evanston, IL 60204 USA Tel 847-424-9540 Do not confuse with Twilight Pr., Macomb, MI.

Twilight Pr., *(0-9653238)* 48607 Presidential, Suite 98, Macomb, MI 48044 USA Tel 810-566-0888; Fax: 810-247-2183; Toll Free: 800-579-8051 Do not confuse with Twilight Pr., Evanston, IL
E-mail: ventking@eaglequest.com
Web site: http://www.richardpaul.com/author/indexhtm
Dist(s): **Baker & Taylor Bks.**
Quality Bks., Inc.

Twilight Tales, Inc., *(0-9711309; 0-9779856)* Orders Addr.: 331 Berkshire Terrace, Roselle, IL 60172 USA Tel 630-351-9311 Sales; Edit Addr.: 2339 N. Commonwealth, No. 4C, Chicago, IL 60614 USA (SAN 851-772X) Tel 773-472-8722
E-mail: sales@twilighttales.com
Web site: http://www.twilighttales.com.

Twilight Times Bks., *(1-931201; 1-933353)* P.O. Box 3340, Kingsport, TN 37664-3340 USA ; *Imprints:* Paladin Timeless (PalaTimeless)
E-mail: publisher@twilighttimes.com
Web site: http://www.twilighttimesbooks.com
Dist(s): **Book Clearing Hse.**
Florida Academic Pr.
Midpoint Trade Bks., Inc.

Twin Lights Pubs., Inc., *(1-885435)* 8 Hale St., Rockport, MA 01966 USA (SAN 257-8867) Tel 978-546-7398; Fax: 978-546-5803; c/o. JJ Daly, 6 Tide St., Boston, MA 02210
E-mail: info@twinlightspub.com; orders@twinlightspub.com
Web site: http://www.twinlightspub.com
Dist(s): **Strisik, Nancy**
Windhover Performing Arts Ctr.

Twin Monkeys Pr., *(0-9768602)* 146 First St., Dunellen, NJ 08812 USA Tel 732-752-3285
E-mail: storytellerjt@optonline.net
Web site: http://www.twinmonkeyspress.com.

Twin Peaks Publishing, Inc., *(0-9722259)* 4708 Mountain Vista Ct., Loveland, CO 80537 USA
E-mail: Twinpeakspublish@aol.com
Web site: http://www.bookmasters.com/marktplc/rr00979.htm; http://www.atlasbooks.com/authorspotlight/asdmiller.htm; http://hometown.aol.com/TwinPeaksPublish/TwinPeaks.htm
Dist(s): **AtlasBooks Distribution.**

Twin Rose Publishing, *(0-9721583)* 22128 County Rd. 28, Goshen, IN 46526 USA Tel 574-875-3911.

Twin Sisters Productions, LLC, *(0-9632249; 1-57583; 1-882331; 1-59922)* Orders Addr.: 2680 W. Market St., Akron, OH 44333 USA Tel 330-864-3000; Fax: 330-864-3200; Toll Free: 800-248-8946
E-mail: twinsisters@twinsisters.com
Web site: http://www.twinsisters.com.

TwinAtaa Studio, *(1-889926)* P.O. Box 1162, Stone Mountain, GA 30086 USA Tel 770-469-5138; Fax: 770-469-5139
E-mail: twinataa@twinataa.com; srw@twinataa.com
Web site: http://www.twinataa.com.

TwinAtaa/Sanaa Village Publications *See* **TwinAtaa Studio**

Twinbrook Publishing, *(0-9759086)* P.O. Box 355, Bedminster, NJ 07921 USA Tel 908-534-6799
Web site: http://www.pleasantdreaming.com/.

Twinkle Bks., *(0-9792992)* 1415 Riverbank St., Lincoln Park, MI 48146-3880 USA (SAN 853-0483) Tel 313-381-2082
E-mail: Treasurecloud@msn.com
Web site: http://Twinkleblink.com.

Twinkle Toes, Inc., *(0-9664625)* Orders Addr.: P.O. Box 65077, Virginia Beach, VA 23467-5077 USA; Edit Addr.: 1432 Birch Leaf Rd., Chesapeake, VA 23320 USA.

Twinkle Twinkle Little Bks., *(0-9771447)* 131 E. Wilson St., Centre Hall, PA 16828-8703 USA Tel 814-364-2237
E-mail: nicole@twinkletwinklelittlebooks.com
Web site: http://www.twinkletwinklelittlebooks.com.

Twins Bks. *Imprint of* **Business Word, The**

Twisted Spoon Pr. (CZE) *(80-901257; 80-902171; 80-86264)* *Dist. by* **SCB Distributors.**

Two Bear Publishing *See* **Cracker the Crab LLC**

Two Bee-A-TwinBee Publishing, LLC, *(0-9666183)* 118 Shawan Rd., Hunt Valley, MD 21031 USA Tel 410-771-1455; Fax: 410-823-5795; 1210 Malbay Dr., Lutherville, MD 21093
E-mail: twobeatwin@aol.com; bmoyer37@aol.com
Web site: http://www.isbn.nu/twords/Gain.

Two Bytes Publishing, *(1-881907)* Orders Addr.: P.O. Box 1043, Darien, CT 06820-1043 USA Tel 203-656-0581; Fax: 203-655-3910; Toll Free: 888-588-7171; Edit Addr.: P.O. Box 633, Stratford, CT 06615-0633 USA
E-mail: tbpltd@earthlink.net.

Two Can Publishing *Imprint of* **T&N Children's Publishing**

Two Canoes Pr., *(1-929590)* P.O. Box 334, Hopkinton, MA 01749 USA (SAN 139-9853) Tel 508-529-6034; Fax: 508-529-6005 Do not confuse with companies with the same name in Rego Park, NY, Los Angeles, CA, Phoenix, AZ
E-mail: singsalone@aol.com
Web site: http://www.TwoCanoesPress.com
Dist(s): **Partners Pubs. Group, Inc.**

Two Dog Pr., *(1-891090)* Orders Addr.: P.O. Box 164, Brooklin, ME 04616 USA Tel 207-359-8967; Fax: 207-359-8080; Toll Free: 888-310-2364; Edit Addr.: Flye Point Rd., Brooklin, ME 04616 USA
E-mail: human@twodogpress.com
Web site: http://www.twodogpress.com.

Two Dogz, *(0-9767072)* Orders Addr.: 775 Lefort By Pass Rd., Thibodaux, LA 70301 USA
E-mail: zsagabby@yahoo.com
Web site: http://www.two-dogz.com.

Two Dot *Imprint of* **Globe Pequot Pr., The**

Two Feathers Publishing, *(1-889529)* P.O. Box 607, Westminster, CO 80036-0607 USA Tel 303-427-2707; Fax: 303-426-4496; Toll Free: 800-474-3707 Do not confuse with companies with the same name in Wichita, KS, Pleasanton, TX
E-mail: delosblk@swbell.net; spotter@nnex.net
Web site: http://www.twofeatherspress.com.

Two Geckos Music & Publishing, *(0-9644105; 1-892956)* P.O. Box 30274, Tucson, AZ 85751 USA Tel 520-529-4608; Fax: 520-577-8006; Toll Free: 888-219-1735
E-mail: music@pattyhorn.com
Web site: http://www.pattyhorn.com
Dist(s): **Music Mart, Inc.**
Sunbelt Pubns., Inc.
Treasure Chest Bks.

Two Guys With Flys, *(0-9768860)* 9 E. 4th St., Medford, OR 97501 USA
E-mail: arnie@mind.net.

Two Lakes Pr., Inc., *(1-59885)* P.O. Box 384, Saint Joseph, MN 56374-0384 USA Tel 616-822-1865
E-mail: s@twolakespress.com
Web site: http://www.twolakespress.com.

Two Lands, *(1-933984)* 12216 SW 111 Terr., Miami, FL 33186-3751 USA Tel 305-273-9738 (phone/fax)
E-mail: twolandsoffice@yahoo.com.

Two Little Hands Productions LLC, *(1-933543)* P.O. Box 581037, Salt Lake City, UT 84158 USA
Web site: http://www.signingtime.com.

Two Lives Publishing, *(0-9674468)* Orders Addr.: P.O. Box 736, Ridley Park, PA 19078 USA; Edit Addr.: 508 N. Swarthmore Ave., No. 1, Ridley Park, PA 19078 USA Tel 610-532-2852; Fax: 610-532-2853
E-mail: bcombs@TwoLives.com
Web site: http://www.TwoLives.com
Dist(s): **Baker & Taylor Bks.**
Book Wholesalers, Inc.
Brodart Co.
Koen-Levy Bk. Wholesalers LLC.

Two Peas in A Pod, *(0-9700812)* 578 Braselton Hwy., Lawrenceville, GA 30043 USA Tel 770-945-9857; Fax: 770-945-7046.

Two Saints Publishing, *(0-9625782)* 615 Mennonite Church Rd., Kalispell, MT 59901-7753 USA Tel 406-756-1959.

Two Seed Planters Inc., *(0-9755789)* 141 Tall Pines Dr., Leesburg, GA 31763-3143 USA
E-mail: twoseedplanters@aol.com
Web site: http://www.twoseedplanters.com.

Two Sisters Publishing, *(1-928659)* 8220 Sedona Sunrise Dr., Las Vegas, NV 89128-7909 USA Tel 702-363-8235; Fax: 702-363-7698.

Two Sons Pr., Inc., *(0-9748995)* 14 Red Tail Dr., Highlands Ranch, CO 80126-5001 USA Tel 303-346-3003; Fax: 303-791-2226
E-mail: McAdamfam@aol.com
Dist(s): **Westcliffe Pubs.**

Two Tired Teachers Connection, Inc., The, *(0-9786835)* 151 Michael Ln., Aberdeen, NC 28315 USA (SAN 851-3090) Tel 910-944-8857
E-mail: bevlashley@nc.rr.com
Web site: http://www.twotiredteachers.com.

Two Way Bilingual, Inc., *(0-941911)* Cond The Falls, No. 405, Guaynabo, PR 00657 USA (SAN 666-0169).

TwoMorrows Publishing, *(1-893905; 1-60549)* Div. of TwoMorrows Advertising & Design, 10407 Bedfordtown Dr., Raleigh, NC 27614-8058 USA Tel 919-449-0344; Fax: 919-449-0327
E-mail: twomorrow@aol.com
Web site: http://www.twomorrows.com
Dist(s): **Diamond Bk. Distributors.**

TwoPenny Pubns., *(0-9755671)* 205 Rainbow Dr., No. 10503, Livingston, TX 77399-2005 USA
E-mail: samnalice@twopennytravels.com
Web site: http://www.79scenario.com.

Two's Company, *(0-9742862)* Div. of Threaded Images, 303 Wrenn Ave., New Paris, OH 45347 USA Tel 937-437-0095; 513-933-9207; Toll Free Fax: 877-217-0700; Toll Free: 800-487-0095
E-mail: sgray6@cinci.rr.com; timages@aol.com
Web site: http://www.twos-company.biz.

Twynz Publishing, *(0-9704873)* Orders Addr.: P.O. Box 1084, Florissant, MO 63031-1948 USA Tel 314-995-1551; Fax: 314-831-6214; Toll Free: 888-593-6106; Edit Addr.: 1116 Liberty Gardens Ct., Florissant, MO 63031 USA
E-mail: twynzpub@aol.com
Web site: http://www.twynzpub.com.

TX2 (ATA) Tiger Times Two *See* **Big Cats Publishing**

TyBook, *(0-9779631)* 5504 Nieman Rd., Shawnee, KS 66203 USA Tel 503-407-1217
E-mail: clayme@claytonpixton.com
Web site: http://www.tybookinc.com.

TYL Publishing, *(0-9753902)* P.O. Box 19363, Houston, TX 77224 USA Fax: 713-647-9410; 1902 Spillers Ln., Houston, TX 77043
E-mail: tyl.publishing@tylon-linebrary.com
Web site: http://www.tylon-linebrary.com/tyl_publishing.htm
Dist(s): **Baker & Taylor Bks.**
Partners/West
Quality Bks., Inc.

Tyler, John C., *(0-9674350)* P.O. Box 723, Norton, MA 02766 USA Tel 508-884-3058; Fax: 508-543-1864; Toll Free: 800-564-3629
Web site: http://www.johntyler.com; http://www.efriendships.com.

Tyler Reproductions, *(0-9679351)* 117 SE Fourth St., Belle Glade, FL 33430 USA Tel 561-996-3631.

Ty-Mc Productions, Inc., *(0-9723982)* 112 Northland Shopping Ctr., St. Louis, MO 63136-1438 USA.

Tyndale Espanol *Imprint of* **Tyndale Hse. Pubs.**

Tyndale Fiction *Imprint of* **Tyndale Hse. Pubs.**

†Tyndale Hse. Pubs., *(0-8423; 1-4143)* Orders Addr.: 370 Executive Dr., Carol Stream, IL 60188 USA; Edit Addr.: 351 Executive Dr., Carol Stream, IL 60188 USA (SAN 206-7749) Tel 630-668-8310; Fax: 630-668-3245; Toll Free: 800-323-9400 ; *Imprints:* Tyndale Kids (Tyndale Kids); Thirsty(?) (Thirsty); Tyndale Fiction (TynFic); Tyndale Espanol (Tyndale Espanol)
E-mail: international@tyndale.com; permission@tyndale.com
Web site: http://www.tyndale.com
Dist(s): **Anchor Distributors**
Appalachian Bk. Distributors
Baker & Taylor Bks.
Brodart Co.
Christian Bk. Distributors
Cokesbury
Editorial Unilit
Ingram Entertainment, Inc.
Spring Arbor Distributors, Inc.; *CIP.*

Tyndale Kids *Imprint of* **Tyndale Hse. Pubs.**

Type F, *(0-9768733)* P.O. Box 1045, Lodi, CA 95241-1045 USA
E-mail: info@enduranceguide.com
Web site: http://www.enduranceguide.com.

Tyr Publishing, *(0-9723473)* P.O. Box 19895, Fountain Hills, AZ 85269-9895 USA (SAN 254-7775) Tel 480-836-4261
E-mail: info@tyrpublishing.com
Web site: http://www.tyrpublishing.com
Dist(s): **Midpoint Trade Bks., Inc.**

Tyrannus Research, *(0-9662365)* 5642 E. La Palma, No. 210, Anaheim, CA 92807 USA Tel 714-693-1405; Fax: 714-693-3643; Toll Free: 888-874-7737
E-mail: fkim@netroplex.com.

Tyson, Sandi *See* **Christiangela Productions**

Tytam Publishing, *(0-9758602)* 111 Lincoln Ave., Suite A-10, Newark, NJ 07104-4607 USA
E-mail: tylesha@aol.com.

Tzivos Hashem *Imprint of* **Hachai Publishing**

U A H C Press *See* **URJ Pr.**

UFO Photo Archives, *(0-934269; 0-9608558)* Orders Addr.: P.O. Box 17206, Tucson, AZ 85731 USA (SAN 240-7949) Tel 520-296-6753; Fax: 520-745-0952
E-mail: CeceSt@aol.com; S18195A@aol.com
Web site: http://www.ufophotoarchives.com.

U H H Hale Kuamo'o Hawaiian Language Center *See* **Hale Kuamo'o Hawaiian Language Ctr. at UHH**

U Lead, LLC, *(0-9665572)* P.O. Box 22274, Lincoln, NE 68542-2274 USA.

U. S. Capitol Historical Society, *(0-916200)* 200 Maryland Ave., NE, Washington, DC 20002 USA (SAN 226-6601) Tel 202-543-8919; Fax: 202-544-8244; Toll Free: 800-887-9318
E-mail: uschs@uschs.org
Web site: http://www.uschs.org
Dist(s): **Univ. Pr. of Virginia.**

U. S. Games Systems, Inc., *(0-88079; 0-913866; 1-57281)* 179 Ludlow St., Stamford, CT 06902 USA (SAN 158-6483) Tel 203-353-8400; Fax: 203-353-8431; Toll Free: 800-544-2637
E-mail: usgames@aol.com
Web site: http://www.usgamesinc.com
Dist(s): **New Leaf Distributing Co., Inc.**

U. S. Institute of Languages, Inc., *(0-9719067)* 1893 E. Skyline Dr., Suite 121, South Ogden, UT 84403 USA Tel 801-475-4441; Fax: 801-475-4446; Toll Free: 866-977-2647
E-mail: dave@spanishprograms.com
Web site: http://www.spanishprograms.com.

UTW Resources, Inc., *(1-58504)* 702 Cumberland St., Harriman, TN 37748 USA Tel 423-882-7005 (phone/fax)
E-mail: sailawaylals@juno.com.

Ubaviel's Gifts, *(0-9713589)* 1550 Scenic View Dr., Loudon, TN 37774 USA
Web site: http://www.angelicgift.com.

UBUS Communications Systems, *(1-56411)* Orders Addr.: 26070 Barhams Hill Rd., Drewyville, VA Southhampton 23844 USA (SAN 630-6748) Tel 704-277-1462 (cell phone); 704-509-6773; Edit Addr.: 210 E. Arrowhead Dr., Suite #2, Charlotte, NC 28213 USA Tel 704-509-2226 ; *Imprints:* CB Publishing & Design (CB Pubng & Design)
E-mail: publish@khabooks.com; buy@khabooks.com; jy916@aol.com; sell@khabooks.com
Web site: http://www.khabooks.com; http://www.domainnamebus.com; http://cbpublishing-design.com; http://www.khabooks.com.

UCanDo Bks., *(0-9667544)* 4045 S. Buffalo Dr., No. A101, Las Vegas, NV 89147 USA.

UglyTown Productions *See* **Uglytown Productions**

Uglytown Productions, *(0-9663473; 0-9724412; 0-9758503)* P.O. Box 411655, Los Angeles, CA 90041-8655 USA
Web site: http://www.uglytown.com.

Uitti, Daniel, *(0-9708430)* Div. of DaSum Company LLC, 223 Buckingham St., Oakville, CT 06779 USA Tel 860-274-9065; Fax: 860-417-0609
E-mail: dan@uitti.net
Web site: http://www.uitti.net/DaSum/.

Ukrainian Gift Shops, Inc., *(0-9602502; 0-9793303)* 2782 Fairview Ave., North, Roseville, MN 55113 USA (SAN 222-2450) Toll Free: 866-797-2652
E-mail: elko@ukrainiangiftshop.com
Web site: http://www.ukrainiangiftshop.com.

Ultimacy Pr., *(0-9760205)* 11409 Parkside Pl., Bradenton, FL 34202 USA Tel 941-753-6560; Fax: 941-753-6561
E-mail: info@ultimatefinancialadvisor.com
Web site: http://www.ultimatefinancialadvisor.com.

Ultimate Bks., *(0-9725953; 0-9788430)* 104 Oakhill Key Ct., Valrico, FL 33594 USA Do not confuse with Ultimate Bks., in Glendale, CA
E-mail: info@opynyon.com
Web site: http://www.opynyon.com.

Ultimate Martial Arts CD, The *See* **Black Belt Training**

Uluquim Bks., *(0-9673120)* Orders Addr.: P.O. Box 566, Laurel, NE 58745 USA Tel 402-256-3015; Edit Addr.: 516 W. Second St., Laurel, NE 68745 USA
E-mail: uluquimbooks@yahoo.com.

Ulverscroft Large Print Bks. (GBR) *(0-7089; 0-85456; 1-84395; 1-84617) Dist. by* **Ulverscroft US.**

Ulverscroft Large Print Bks., Ltd., *(0-7089; 1-84617)* Orders Addr.: P.O. Box 1230, West Seneca, NY 14224-1230 USA; Edit Addr.: 950 Union Rd., West Seneca, NY 14224-3438 USA (SAN 208-3035) Toll Free: 800-955-9659
E-mail: enquiries@ulverscroft.co.uk; sales@ulverscroft.com
Web site: http://www.ulverscroft.co.uk.

Ulysses Pr., *(0-915233; 1-56975)* Orders Addr.: P.O. Box 3440, Berkeley, CA 94703-3440 USA (SAN 289-8764) Tel 510-601-8301; Fax: 510-601-8307; Toll Free: 800-377-2542; Edit Addr.: 3286 Adeline St., Suite 1, Berkeley, CA 94703 USA (SAN 289-8772)
E-mail: ulysses@ulyssespress.com
Web site: http://www.ulyssespress.com
Dist(s): **Perseus Distribution.**

Ulyssian Pubns. *Imprint of* **Pine Orchard, Inc.**

Umbra Editions *See* **Umbrage Editions**

Umbrage Editions, *(1-884167)* 515 Canal St., New York, NY 10013 USA Tel 212-965-0197
E-mail: umbraed@earthlink.com
Dist(s): **Aperture Foundation, Inc.**
Consortium Bk. Sales & Distribution.

Umbrelly Bks., *(0-615; 0-9791127)* P.O. Box 2703, Saratoga, CA 95070-5608 USA
E-mail: umbrelly_books@yahoo.com
Web site: http://www.johnnydepalma.com
Dist(s): **Lulu.com.**

UMI *Imprint of* **UMI (Urban Ministries, Inc.)**

UMI (Urban Ministries, Inc.), *(0-940955; 1-932715; 1-934056; 1-60352)* 1551 Regency Ct., Calumet City, IL 60409-5448 USA (SAN 665-2247) Toll Free: 800-860-8642 ; *Imprints:* UMI (UMI)
Web site: http://www.urbanministries.com
Dist(s): **Midpoint Trade Bks., Inc.**

Umina, Lisa M. *See* **Halo Publishing International**

Unaluna Ediciones (ARG) *(987-1296) Dist. by* **Lectorum Pubns.**

Unapix Entertainment, Inc., *(1-57523; 1-58727)* Div. of Unapix Entertainment, Inc., 200 Madison Ave., 24th Flr., New York, NY 10016 USA (SAN 631-3027) Tel 212-252-7600; Fax: 212-252-7630
E-mail: jgreen@unapixent.com
Web site: http://unapixent.com
Dist(s): **Baker & Taylor Bks.**
International Historic Films, Inc.

Unapix/Miramar *See* **Unapix Entertainment, Inc.**

Unbridled Bks., *(1-932961)* 2000 Wadsworth Blvd., No. 195, Lakewood, CO 80214 USA Tel 303-506-3622; Fax: 303-202-6177; Toll Free: 888-732-3822
Web site: http://www.unbridledbooks.com
Dist(s): **Intrepid Group, Inc., The.**

Unchained Spirit Enterprises, *(0-9717790)* P.O. Box 13143, Fort Wayne, IN 46867 USA Tel 260-458-0151 (phone/fax)
E-mail: cbrewe@att.net; caroline@karafindssunshine.com
Web site: http://www.karafindssunshine.com.

Uncle Henry Bks., *(1-932568)* P.O. Box 41310, Long Beach, CA 90853-1310 USA Tel 562-987-9165; Fax: 562-439-5924
E-mail: unclehenrybooks@aol.com.

Uncommon Buffalo Pr., *(0-9641688)* 1914 Stirling St., Rapid City, SD 57702 USA Tel 605-342-5085
E-mail: buffalo@rapidnet.com.

Under the Green Umbrella, *(1-929701)* 5808 Westmont Dr., Austin, TX 78731-3836 USA Tel 512-454-2414
E-mail: janesbauld@aol.com
Web site: http://www.uts.cc.utexas.edu/~jbauld.

Understanding For Life Ministries, Inc., *(0-9714584; 0-9721504; 0-9749019; 0-9797019)* 3665 Kirby Pkwy., Suite 6, Memphis, TN 38115 USA Tel 901-844-3962; Fax: 901-844-3944.

Understanding Nutrition, PC, *(0-9764002; 0-9800334)* 6510 Abrams Rd., Suite 302, Dallas, TX 75231 USA Tel 214-503-7100
E-mail: info@understandingnutrition.com; jessica@understandingnutrition.com
Web site: http://www.understandingnutrition.com.

Underwood Books, *(0-88733; 0-934438; 1-887424; 1-59929)* Orders Addr.: P.O. Box 1919, Nevada City, CA 95945 USA Tel 530-470-9095; Fax: 530-470-9049; Edit Addr.: 12514 Cavanaugh Ln., Navada City, CA 95959 USA
E-mail: tim@underwoodbooks.com
Web site: http://www.underwoodbooks.com
Dist(s): **Perseus Distribution.**

Unications Publishing, *(0-9659539)* Div. of Legette Consulting, P.O. Box 241, Columbia, SC 29202 USA Tel 803-865-8955; Fax: 803-865-8852
E-mail: legetted@bellsouth.net
Web site: http://www.unicationspublishing.com.

Unicom *See* **Litterati Bks.**

Unicorn Concepts, *(0-9714099)* 8987 E. Tanque Verde, No. 309-103, Tucson, AZ 85749-9399 USA Tel 866-701-5185
E-mail: unicornconcepts@yahoo.com.

Unicorn Pr., *(0-937004)* 3300 Chestnut St., Reading, PA 19605 USA Tel 610-929-8306 Do not confuse with Unicorn Pr. in Northville, MI
E-mail: kthynoll@aol.com
Web site: http://hometown.aol.com/kthynoll.

Union Creek Communications, Inc., *(0-9721404)* P.O. Box 1811, Bryson City, NC 28713 USA Tel 828-488-3596; Fax: 828-488-1018
E-mail: info@rookieguide.com; info@researchpaperstation.com
Web site: http://www.rookieguide.com; http://researchpaperstation.com.

Unique Consulting, *(0-9716405)* 7788 Hill Rd., Woodbury, MN 55125 USA
E-mail: drjfk@msn.com; drjfk@qwest.net.

Unique Executive Pubs., *(0-9744978)* Div. of Unique Executive.com, 1653 Georgia Hwy. 257, Suite A, Cordele, GA 31015 USA Tel 229-273-8121; Fax: 229-273-7289 ; *Imprints:* Healthful Living Books (Living Books)
E-mail: harvardg@sowega.net
Web site: http://upublish.uniqueexecutive.com.

Unique Expression, *(1-891636)* P.O. Box 11869, Chicago, IL 60611 USA Tel 773-493-2551
E-mail: readme4000@aol.com
Web site: http://www.readme4.com
Dist(s): **Baker & Taylor Bks.**

Unique Pubns., *(0-86568)* Subs. of CFW Enterprises, Inc., 265 S. Anita Dr. Ste. 120, Orange, CA 92868-3343 USA (SAN 214-3313) Toll Free Fax: 800-249-7761; Toll Free: 800-332-3330.

Uniquely You Resources, *(0-9627245; 1-888846)* P.O. Box 490, Blue Ridge, GA 30513 USA Tel 706 492 4709; 706-492-5490
E-mail: drmels@myuy.com
Web site: http://www.myuy.com; http://www.uyprofiler.com
Dist(s): **STL Distribution North America.**

Unisystems, Inc., *(0-7666; 0-87449; 1-56144)* 155 55th St., New York, NY 10022 USA Tel 212-826-0850; Fax: 212-758-4166
Web site: http://www.modernpublishing.com.

†Unitarian Universalist Assn., *(0-933840; 1-55896)* 25 Beacon St., Boston, MA 02108-2800 USA (SAN 225-4840) Tel 617-742-2100; Fax: 617-742-7025; Toll Free: 800-215-9076 ; *Imprints:* Skinner House Books (Skinner Hse Bks)
Web site: http://www.uua.org
Dist(s): **International Publishers Marketing**
Red Wheel/Weiser; *CIP.*

United African Educational & Scholarship Foundation, The *See* **United African Educational Foundation**

United African Educational Foundation, *(1-893811)* Orders Addr.: P.O. Box 42802, Philadelphia, PA 19101 USA Tel 215-476-5552; Fax: 215-476-6339; Edit Addr.: 1000 66th Ave., Philadelphia, PA 19126-3304 USA; 4601 Market St., Suite 457, Philadelphia, PA 19101
E-mail: kimani_t@yahoo.com
Web site: http://www.uaef.org.

United Bible Societies/Americas Service Ctr., *(1-57697; 1-930564; 1-931471; 1-931952; 1-932507; 1-933218; 1-59877)* 1989 NW 88th Ct., Miami, FL 33172 USA Tel 305-702-1824; Fax: 305-593-5489 Do not confuse with United Bible Societies, New York, NY
Web site: http://www.labibliaweb.com
Dist(s): **American Bible Society.**

United Christian Church *See* **Hispanic Publishing Works, Inc.**

United Christian Fellowship of Chapel Hill, North Carolina *See* **Armour of Light Publishing**

United Comics, *(0-9743086)* Div. of Obsidian Entertainment, P.O. Box 401, Milford, CT 06460-0401 USA Toll Free: 800-546-3249 (phone/fax)
E-mail: unitedcomics@juno.com
Web site: http://www.unitedcomicworks.com.

United Educators, Inc., *(0-87566)* 900 N. Shore Dr., No. 140, Lake Bluff, IL 60044 USA (SAN 204-8795) Tel 847-234-3700.

United InnoWorks Academy, *(0-9771380)* 9721 Conestoga Way, Potomac, MD 20854-4711 USA
E-mail: executive@unitedinnoworks.org
Web site: http://www.innoworks.org.

United Medical Ctr., *(0-9703035)* 2600 E. 18th St., Cheyenne, WY 82001-6654 USA Tel 307-633-7345; Fax: 307-633-7085
E-mail: davidwyo@yahoo.com; charmon623@aol.com; ospcthebear@yahoo.com
Web site: http://www.umcwy.org.

United Nation of Islam, The, *(0-9768502)* 1608 N. 13th St., Kansas City, KS 66102 USA Tel 913-342-0758; Fax: 913-342-0340; Toll Free: 800-331-7668
E-mail: unoi@unoi.org
Web site: http://www.unoi.org.

United Nations Children's Fund, The (UNICEF), *(0-940065; 92-806)* 3 Unite Nations Plaza, New York, NY 10017 USA (SAN 664-0338) Tel 212-326-7000
E-mail: pubdoc@unicef.org
Web site: http://www.unicef.org/
Dist(s): **Balogh International, Inc.**
Bernan Assocs.
United Nations Pubns.

United Nations Environment Programme (KEN) *(92-807) Dist. by* **Untd Nat Pubns.**

United Nations Pubns., *(0-680; 0-89714; 92-1; 92-808; 952-9520)* 2 United Nations Plaza, Sales Section, Publishing Div., Rm. DC2-853, New York, NY 10017 USA (SAN 206-6718) Tel 212-963-8302; 212-963-7680 UN Bookshop; Fax: 212-963-3489; 212-963-4910 UN Bookshop; Toll Free: 800-253-9646 (bookshop orders); 800-553-3210 UN Bookshop
E-mail: publications@un.org
Web site: http://www.un.org/pubs
Dist(s): **Balogh International, Inc.**
Bernan Assocs.
International Pubns. Service
NetLibrary, Inc.
Oxford Univ. Pr., Inc.
Women Ink.

United Network for Organ Sharing, *(1-886651)* Orders Addr.: P.O. Box 2484, Richmond, VA 23218 USA Tel 804-782-4800; Edit Addr.: 700 N. 4th St., Richmond, VA 23219 USA
Web site: http://www.unos.org.

United Optical Publishing Co., *(0-9764337)* 9147 Millbranch Rd., Southaven, MS 38671 USA
Web site: http://www.steelguitarbyhughjeffreys.com.

United Printing, *(0-9674002)* Orders Addr.: P.O. Box 936, Bismarck, ND 58502 USA Tel 701-223-0505; Fax: 701-223-5571; Edit Addr.: 117 W. Front Ave., Bismarck, ND 58502 USA
E-mail: ealbers@nd-humanities.org
Web site: http://www.unitedprinting.com.

United Publishing, *(0-9666681)* Div. of Soccer Kids, Inc., 37-41 Bloomingdale Dr., Somerville, NJ 08876-5531 USA Tel 732-562-8751; Fax: 732-562-1819.

United Publishing Co., *(0-937323)* 21a Railroad Ave., Albany, NY 12205-5910 USA (SAN 658-8077) Toll Free: 518-243-8726.

United Research Publishers, *(0-9614924; 1-887053)* Div. of Solor Products, Inc., 2233 Faraday Ave., Suite G, Carlsbad, CA 92008-7214 USA (SAN 693-5834) Tel 760-930-8937; Fax: 760-930-4291 Do not confuse with United Research, Black Mountain, NC
Web site: http://www.unitedresearchpubs.com.

†United States Government Printing Office, *(0-16; 0-18)* Orders Addr.: P.O. Box 371954, Pittsburgh, PA 15250-7954 USA (SAN 658-0785) Tel 202-512-1800; Fax: 202-512-2250; Toll Free: 866-512-1800; Edit Addr.: USGPO Stop SSMB, Washington, DC 20401 USA (SAN 206-152X) Tel 202-512-1705 (bibliographic information only); 202-512-2268 (book dealers only); Fax: 202-512-1655 ; *Imprints:* Joint Committee on Printing (Joint ComPrint)
E-mail: orders@gpo.gov; rdavis@gpo.gov; ContactCenter@gpo.gov
Web site: http://bookstore.gpo.gov; http://www.gpoaccess.gov/index.html
Dist(s): **Bernan Assocs.**
Trucatriche; *CIP.*

United States Institute of Peace *See* **U. S. Institute of Peace Pr. (USIP Pr.)**

U. S. Institute of Peace Pr. (USIP Pr.), *(1-878379; 1-929223; 1-60127)* 1200 17th St. NW, Suite 200, Washington, DC 20036 USA (SAN 254-6965) Tel 202-457-1700; Fax: 202-429-6063; Fulfillment Addr.: P.O. Box 605, Herndon, VA 20172 USA (SAN 254-7821) Tel 703-661-1590; Fax: 703-661-1501; Toll Free: 800-868-8064
Web site: http://www.usip.org
Dist(s): **Books International, Incorporated.**

United States Judo Federation, Inc., *(0-9729790)* P.O. Box 338, Ontario, OR 97914-0338 USA Tel 541-889-8753; Fax: 541-889-5836
E-mail: natofc@usjf.com
Web site: http://www.usjf.com.

Company

United States Peace Corps, *(0-9723579)* 1111 20th St., NW, Washington, DC 20526 USA Tel 202-692-1453; Fax: 202-692-1421
Web site: http://www.peacecorps.gov.

United States Power Squadrons, *(1-891148)* Orders Addr.: P.O. Box 30423, Raleigh, NC 27622 USA Tel 919-821-0281; Fax: 919-836-0813; Toll Free: 888-367-8777; Edit Addr.: 1504 Blue Ridge Rd., Raleigh, NC 27607 USA
Web site: http://www.usps.org.

U. S. Sailing Assn., *(1-882502; 0-9719593; 0-9741058; 0-9762261; 0-9794677)* Orders Addr.: P.O. Box 1260, Portsmouth, RI 02871-0924 USA (SAN 224-5485) Tel 401-683-0800; Fax: 401-683-0840; Toll Free: 800-877-2451 800-USSAIL1; Edit Addr.: 15 Maritime Dr., Portsmouth, RI 02871 USA
E-mail: julialangford@ussailing.org
Web site: http://www.ussailing.org
Dist(s): **Austin & Company, Inc.**
Partners Pubs. Group, Inc.

United States Trotting Association, *(0-9793891)* 750 Michigan Ave., Columbus, OH 43215 USA Tel 614-224-2291 Toll Free: 877-800-8782 (ext. 3260)
E-mail: HRCNews@ustrotting.com; jamie.rucker@ustrotting.com
Web site: http://www.ustrotting.com.

United States Yacht Racing Union *See* **U. S. Sailing Assn.**

United Synagogue of America Bk. Service, *(0-8381)* Subs. of United Synagogue of America, 155 Fifth Ave., New York, NY 10010 USA (SAN 203-0551) Tel 212-533-7800
E-mail: booksvc@uscj.org
Web site: http://www.uscj.org/booksvc.

United Way of Minneapolis Area & GrayHall, *(1-887418)* 404 S. Eighth St., Minneapolis, MN 55404 USA Tel 612-340-7400; Fax: 612-340-7675
E-mail: Tryonl@unitedwaytwincities.org
Dist(s): **Bookmen, Inc.**

United Writers Pr., Inc., *(0-9725197; 0-9760824; 1-934216)* P.O. Box 326, Tucker, GA 30085 USA (SAN 256-2464) Tel 770-925-4678; Fax: 770-925-9813; Toll Free: 866-857-4678
E-mail: vsharpe@unitedwriterspress.com
Web site: http://www.unitedwriterspress.com.

Unitrust Design, *(0-9752775)* P.O. Box 653, Loma Linda, CA 92354 USA
E-mail: unitrustdesign@aol.com
Web site: http://www.unitrustdesign.com.

Unity Bks. & Multimedia *Imprint of* **Unity Schl. of Christianity**

Unity Books & Multimedia Publishing (Unity School of Christianity) *See* **Unity Schl. of Christianity**

Unity Hse. *Imprint of* **Unity Schl. of Christianity**

Unity Schl. of Christianity, *(0-87159)* Orders Addr.: 1901 NW Blue Pkwy., Unity Village, MO 64065-0001 USA (SAN 204-8817) Tel 816-524-3550; 816 251-3571 (ordering); Fax: 816-251-3551 ; *Imprints:* Unity Books & Multimedia (Unity Bks & Multimedia); Unity House (Unity Hse)
E-mail: unity@unityworldhq.org
Web site: http://www.unityworldhq.org
Dist(s): **New Leaf Distributing Co., Inc.**

Univ. of Alberta Pr. (CAN) *(0-88864; 1-55195) Dist. by* **Mich St U Pr.**

Univ. of Natal Pr. (ZAF) *(0-86980; 0-620; 1-86914; 0-9584542) Dist. by* **Intl Spec Bk.**

Univ. of Tokyo Pr. (JPN) *(0-86008) Dist. by* **Col U Pr.**

Univ. of Wales Pr. (GBR) *(0-7083; 0-900768; 1-900477) Dist. by* **Chicago Distribution Ctr.**

Univ. of Western Australia Pr. (AUS) *(0-85564; 0-86422; 0-909751; 1-875560; 1-876268; 1-920694; 0-9802964; 0-9802965; 1-921401) Dist. by* **Intl Spec Bk.**

Universal Express, *(0-9665098)* P.O. Box 9111, San Jose, CA 95157 USA Tel 408-280-0344 (phone/fax)
E-mail: bk4lovers@juno.com.

Universal Flag Publishing, *(1-933426)* Div. of Universal Flag Cos., 1440 W. Maple Ave., Suite 6B, Lisle, IL 60532 USA Tel 630-245-8500
E-mail: publishing@universalflag.com
Web site: www.universalflag.com.

Universal Handwriting *See* **Universal Publishing**

Universal Life - The Inner Religion, *(1-890841)* 54 Hill Wood Cir., Newman, GA 30263 USA Tel 770-251-6136; Fax: 770-251-6137; P.O. Box 3549, Woodbridge, CT 06525 Tel 203-882-1549; Fax: 203-457-9693; Toll Free: 800-846-2691
E-mail: info@universelles-leben.com
Web site: http://www.universel-spirit.cc.

Universal Life Matters, Incorporated *See* **Quality of Life Publishing Co.**

Universal Map Enterprises, Inc., *(0-7625; 1-56464)* 795 Progress Court, Box 15, Williamston, MI 48895-0015 USA Tel 517-655-5641; Fax: 517-655-5739; Toll Free: 800-829-6277
E-mail: info@universalmap.com
Web site: http://www.universalmap.com
Dist(s): **Langenscheidt Pubs Inc.**

Universal Marketing Media, Inc., *(0-9764272)* Orders Addr.: 9413 N. Palafox St. Suite 2, Pensacola, FL 32534 USA Tel 814-437-7811; Toll Free: 877-437-7811
E-mail: sales@universalmarketingmedia.com
Web site: http://www.universalmarketingmedia.com.

Universal Messengers Pubns., *(0-9768879)* P.O. Box 9039, Wilmington, DE 19809 USA Tel 302-764-4293; Toll Free: 866-207-9301
E-mail: phdfoxx@msn.com; phdfoxx@verizon.net
Web site: http://mysite.verizon.net/vze0488v.

Universal Publishing, *(1-883421; 1-931181; 1-934732)* Subs. of Gutenberg, Inc., 100 4th St., Honesdale, PA 18431 USA Tel 570-251-0260; Fax: 570-251-0264; Toll Free: 800-940-2270 Do not confuse with companies with the same or similar name in Ecino, CA, Egg Harbor Township, NJ, Gainesville, FL, Newport Beach, CA, Stoughton, MA, Pasadena, CA, Oak Park, IL, Jacksonville, FL
E-mail: tom@upub.net; larry@upub.net
Web site: http://www.upub.net; http://www.universalpublishing.net.

Universal Reference Pubns. *Imprint of* **Grey Hse. Publishing**

Universal Values Media, LLC, *(0-9729821; 1-60210)* 3800 Powell Ln., No. 823, Falls Church, VA 22041 USA
Web site: http://www.onceandfuturebooks.com.

Universal Way, The, *(0-9666633)* P.O. Box 142, Tennent, NJ 07763 USA.

Universe of Imagination Pubns., *(0-9668566)* Orders Addr.: P.O. Box 6045, Chandler, AZ 85246-6045 USA; Edit Addr.: 1321 N. Congress Dr., Chandler, AZ 85226 USA Tel 602-821-7518 (phone/fax)
E-mail: abcbeanies@home.com
Web site: http://www.members.home.com/abcbeanies/.

Universe Publishing, *(0-7893; 0-87663; 1-55550)* Div. of Rizzoli International Pubns., Inc., 300 Park Ave. S., 3rd Flr., New York, NY 10010 USA (SAN 202-537X) Tel 212-387-3400; Fax: 212-387-3444 Do not confuse with similar names in North Hollywood, CA, Englewood, NJ, Mendocino, CA
Dist(s): **Andrews McMeel Publishing**
Random Hse., Inc.
Rizzoli International Pubns., Inc.
Simon & Schuster, Inc.

Univ. At Buffalo, Child Care Ctr., *(0-9712349)* Butler Annex A, 3435 Main St., Buffalo, NY 14214-3011 USA Tel 716-829-2226
E-mail: rorrange@buffalo.edu.

Univ. Editions, *(0-615; 0-9711659)* 1003 W. Centennial Dr., Peoria, IL 61614-2828 USA Tel 309-692-0621; Fax: 309-693-0628 Do not confuse with University Editions in Huntington, WV
E-mail: mikruc@aol.com
Web site: http://www.terrythetractor.com.

University Gallery/Univ. of Delaware, *(1-887421)* Div. of Univ. of Delaware, 114 Old College, Newark, DE 19716-2509 USA Tel 302-831-8242; Fax: 302-831-8251
E-mail: bchapp@udel.edu
Web site: http://www.museums.udel.edu.

University Games, *(0-935145; 1-57528)* 2030 Harrison St., San Francisco, CA 94110-1310 USA (SAN 695-2321) Tel 415-503-1600; Fax: 415-503-0085
E-mail: info@ugames.com
Web site: http://www.ugames.com.

†Univ. Museum Pubns., *(0-924171; 0-934718; 1-931707; 1-934536)* Univ. of Pennsylvania Museum 3260 South St., Philadelphia, PA 19104 USA (SAN 207-9283) Tel 215-898-5723; Fax: 215-573-2497
E-mail: publications@museum.upenn.edu
Web site: http://www.museum.upenn.edu/publications/
Dist(s): **Hopkins Fulfillment Services**; *CIP.*

Univ. of Akron Pr., The, *(0-9622628; 1-884836; 1-931968)* Orders Addr.: Bierce Library, 374b, Akron, OH 44325-1703 USA Fax: 330-972-8364; Toll Free: 877-827-7377
E-mail: production@uakron.edu
Web site: http://www.uakron.edu/uapress.

†Univ. of Alabama Pr., *(0-8173)* Orders Addr.: 11030 S. Langley, Chicago, IL 60628 USA Tel 773-702-7000; Toll Free: 800-621-2736; Edit Addr.: P.O. Box 870380, Tuscaloosa, AL 35487-0380 USA (SAN 202-5272) Tel 205-348-5180; Fax: 205-348-9201
Web site: http://www.uapress.ua.edu
Dist(s): **Chicago Distribution Ctr.**
Univ. of Chicago Pr.; *CIP.*

Univ. of Alaska, Fairbanks, *(1-887419)* P.O. Box 755840, Fairbanks, AK 99775 USA Tel 907-474-7211.

University of Alaska, Fairbanks, Geography Department *See* **Univ. of Alaska, Fairbanks**

Univ. of Alaska Pr., *(0-912006; 1-889963; 1-60223)* P.O. Box 756240, Fairbanks, AK 99775-6240 USA (SAN 203-3011) Tel 907-474-5831; Fax: 907-474-5502; Toll Free: 888-252-6657
E-mail: fypress@uaf.edu; ffeh@uaf.edu
Web site: http://www.uaf.edu/uapress
Dist(s): **Chicago Distribution Ctr.**
Wizard Works.

Univ. of Arizona, Poetry Ctr., Arizona Board of Regents, *(0-9727635)* c/o Univ. of Arizona Poetry Ctr.,, 1216 N. Cherry Ave., Tucson, AZ 85719 USA Tel 520-626-3765; Fax: 520-621-5566
E-mail: poetry@u.arizona.edu
Web site: http://www.poetrycenter.arizona.edu.

†Univ. of Arizona Pr., *(0-8165)* 355 S. Euclid Ave., Suite 103, Tucson, AZ 85719 USA (SAN 205-468X) Tel 520-621-1441; Fax: 520-621-8899
E-mail: orders@uapress.arizona.edu
Web site: http://www.uapress.arizona.edu
Dist(s): **Continental Bk. Co., Inc.**
Many Feathers Bks. & Maps
Univ of Arizona Critical Languages Program; *CIP.*

†Univ. of Arkansas Pr., *(0-938626; 1-55728)* 201 Ozark Ave., Fayetteville, AR 72701 USA (SAN 239-3972) Tel 479-575-3246; Fax: 479-575-6044; Toll Free: 800-626-0090
E-mail: uapress@uark.edu
Web site: http://www.uapress.com; http://www.uark.edu/~uaprinfo
Dist(s): **Baker & Taylor Bks.**
Yankee Peddler Bookshop; *CIP.*

Univ. of California, American Indian Studies Ctr., *(0-935626)* 3220 Campbell Hall, Box 951548, Los Angeles, CA 90095-1548 USA (SAN 220-1283) Tel 310-206-7508; Fax: 310-206-7060
E-mail: sales@aisc.ucla.edu
Web site: http://www.books.aisc.ucla.edu/
Dist(s): **SPD-Small Pr. Distribution.**

Univ. of California, Berkeley, Lawrence Hall of Science, *(0-912511; 0-924886; 1-931542)* U of CA, Lawrence Hall of Science, Berkeley, CA 94720-5200 USA (SAN 271-9754) Tel 510-642-7771; Fax: 510-643-0309 ; *Imprints:* GEMS (GEMS); EQUALS (EQUALS)
E-mail: gems@berkeley.edu
Web site: http://www.lhs.berkeley.edu; http://www.lhsgems.org
Dist(s): **Distributors, The.**

†Univ. of California Pr., *(0-520)* Orders Addr.: 1445 Lower Ferry Rd., Ewing, NJ 08618 USA Tel 609-883-1759 (Customer Service); Fax: 609-883-7413; Toll Free Fax: 800-999-1958 (U.S. & Canada); Toll Free: 800-777-4726 (U.S. & Canada); Edit Addr.: 2120 Berkeley Way, Berkeley, CA 94704-1012 USA Tel 510-642-4247; 510-643-7154 (Journals); Fax: 510-643-7127; 510-642-1144 (Marketing); 510-642-9917 (Journals)
E-mail: journals@ucpress.edu; orders@cpfsinc.com; askucp@ucpress.edu
Web site: http://www.ucpress.edu
Dist(s): **NetLibrary, Inc.**; *CIP.*

Univ. of California, Riverside, *(1-891168)* Div. of Vice Chancellor Administration, UCR, 900 University Ave., E., Riverside, CA 92521 USA Tel 951-787-4444; Fax: 951-787-3686
E-mail: allas.johnson@ucr.edu; kathy.chapman@uck.edu
Web site: http://www.ucrservice.ucr.edu/Phome.htm.

†Univ. of Chicago Pr., *(0-226; 0-89065; 0-943056; 1-892850)* Orders Addr.: 11030 S. Langley Ave., Chicago, IL 60628 USA (SAN 202-5280) Tel 773-702-7000; Fax: 773-702-7212; Toll Free Fax: 800-621-8476 (US & Canada); Toll Free: 800-621-2736 (US & Canada); Edit Addr.: 1427 E. 60th St., Chicago, IL 60637 USA (SAN 202-5299) Tel 773-702-7700; 773-702-7748 (Marketing & Sales); Fax: 773-702-9756
E-mail: general@press.uchicago.edu; kh@press.uchicago.edu; custserv@press.uchicago.rdu; sales@press.uchicago.edu; marketing@press.uchicago.edu; publicity@press.uchicago.edu
Web site: http://www.press.uchicago.edu
Dist(s): **Chicago Distribution Ctr.**
Giron Bks.
NetLibrary, Inc.; *CIP.*

Univ. of Denver, Ctr. for Teaching International Relations Pubns., *(0-943804)* 2201 S. Gaylord St., Denver, CO 80208 USA (SAN 241-0877) Tel 303-871-2697; Fax: 303-871-2456
E-mail: ctir-press@du.edu; pubsinfo@du.edu
Web site: http://www.du.edu/ctir
Dist(s): **Lightning Source, Inc.**
Social Studies Schl. Service
Teacher's Discovery.

University of Florida at Gainesville, Institute of Archaeology & Paleoenvironmental Studies *See* **IAPS Bks.**

†Univ. of Georgia, Carl Vinson Institute of Government, *(0-89854)* 201 N. Milledge Ave., Athens, GA 30602 USA (SAN 212-8012) Tel 706-542-2736; Fax: 706-542-6239
E-mail: pou@cviog.uga.edu
Web site: http://www.cviog.uga.edu; *CIP.*

†Univ. of Georgia Pr., *(0-8203)* Orders Addr.: 4435 Atlanta Hwy. West Dock, Athens, GA 30602 USA; Edit Addr.: 330 Research Dr., Suite B100, Athens, GA 30602-4901 USA (SAN 203-3054) Tel 706-369-6130; Fax: 706-369-6131; Toll Free: 800-266-5842
E-mail: books@ugapress.uga.edu
Web site: http://www.ugapress.org
Dist(s): **NetLibrary, Inc.**; *CIP.*

†Univ. of Hawaii Pr., *(0-8248; 0-87022)* Orders Addr.: 2840 Kolowalu St., Honolulu, HI 96822-1888 USA (SAN 202-5353) Tel 808-956-8255; Fax: 808-988-6052; Toll Free Fax: 800-650-7811; Toll Free: 888-847-7377 ; *Imprints:* Kolowalu Book (Kolowalu Bk); Latitude Twenty Book (Latitude Twenty)
E-mail: uhpmkt@hawaii.edu; uhpbooks@hawaii.edu
Web site: http://www.uhpress.hawaii.edu
Dist(s): **Booklines Hawaii, Ltd.**; *CIP.*

Univ. of Idaho Pr., *(0-89301)* P.O. Box PO Box 1107, Moscow, ID 83844-1107 USA (SAN 208-905X) Tel 208-885-5939; Fax: 208-885-9059; Toll Free: 800-847-7377
E-mail: uipress@uidaho.edu; marys@uidaho.edu
Web site: http://www.uidaho.edu/~uipress; http://www.members.aol.com/sbeegel/hemrev.htm
Dist(s): **Caxton Pr.**

†Univ. of Illinois Pr., *(0-252)* Orders Addr.: c/o Chicago Distribution Ctr., 11030 S. Langley Ave., Chicago, IL 60628 USA Toll Free Fax: 800-621-8476; Toll Free: 800-621-2736; Edit Addr.: 1325 S. Oak St., Champaign, IL 61820 USA (SAN 202-5310) Tel 217-333-0950; Fax: 217-244-8082
E-mail: uipress@uillinois.edu; orders@press.uchicago.edu
Web site: http://www.press.uillinois.edu
Dist(s): **Chicago Distribution Ctr.**; *CIP.*

†Univ. of Iowa Pr., *(0-87745; 1-58729)* Div. of The University of Iowa, Orders Addr.: c/o Chicago Distribution Ctr. 11030 S. Langley Ave., Chicago, IL 60628 USA Toll Free Fax: 800-621-8476; Toll Free: 800-621-2736; Edit Addr.: 100 Kuhl Hse. 119 W. Park Rd., Iowa City, IA 52242-1000 USA (SAN 203-3070) Tel 319-335-2000; Fax: 319-335-2055 Do not confuse with Univ. of Iowa, Pubns. Dept. at same address
E-mail: uipress@uiowa.edu
Web site: http://www.uiowapress.org
Dist(s): **Chicago Distribution Ctr.**
NetLibrary, Inc.
Univ. of Chicago Pr.; *CIP.*

Univ. of Maine Pr., *(0-89101)* 5717 Corbett Hall, Rm. 326, Orono, ME 04469 USA (SAN 207-2971) Tel 207-581-1408; Fax: 207-581-1490
E-mail: umpress@umit.maine.edu
Web site: http://www.umaine.edu/umpress.

Univ. of Massachusetts Extension, *(1-892893)* Div. of Univ. of Massachusetts, 40 Campus Center Way, Draper Hall, Amherst, MA 01003-9244 USA Tel 413-545-5539; Fax: 413-545-5174
E-mail: nates@umext.umass.edu.

†Univ. of Michigan Pr., *(0-472)* Orders Addr.: c/o Chicago Distribution Center, Perseus Distribution 1094 Flex Dr., Jackson, TN 38301 USA (SAN 282-4884) Toll Free Fax: 800-351-5073; Toll Free: 800-343-4499 , ext. 165; Edit Addr.: 839 Greene St., Ann Arbor, MI 48104-3209 USA Tel 734-764-4388; Fax: 734-615-1540
E-mail: um.press@umich.edu
Web site: http://www.press.umich.edu/
Dist(s): **Perseus Distribution***; CIP.*

Univ. of Minnesota, Human Rights Center, *(0-9675334)* 229 19th Ave., S., Rm. 437, Law Bldg., Minneapolis, MN 55455 USA Tel 612-626-0041; Fax: 612-625-2011; Toll Free: 888-473-3828
E-mail: humanrts@tc.umn.edu
Web site: http://www.umn.edu/humanrts.

†Univ. of Minnesota Pr., *(0-8166)* Affil. of Univ. of Minnesota, 111 Third Ave. S., Suite 290, Minneapolis, MN 55401-2520 USA (SAN 213-2648) Tel 612-627-1970; Fax: 612-627-1980
Web site: http://www.upress.umn.edu
Dist(s): **Chicago Distribution Ctr.**
Univ. of Chicago Pr.*; CIP.*

†Univ. of Missouri Pr., *(0-8262)* 2910 LeMone Blvd., Columbia, MO 65201 USA (SAN 203-3143) Tel 573-882-7641; Fax: 573-884-4498; Toll Free: 800-828-1894 (orders only)
E-mail: rennerk@umsystem.edu
Web site: http://www.system.missouri.edu/upress
Dist(s): **East-West Export Bks.**
NetLibrary, Inc.*; CIP.*

University of Montana Pr., The, *(0-9754009)* Div. of The Univ. of Montana, James Todd Bldg., Rm. 104 The University of Montana, Missoula, MT 59812-0792 USA (SAN 255-9994) Tel 406-243-4223; Fax: 406-243-2615
E-mail: ken.price@umontana.edu
Web site: http://www.edu/printingandgraphics.com.

†Univ. of Nebraska Pr., *(0-8032)* Orders Addr.: 1111 Lincoln Mall, Lincoln, NE 68588-0630 USA Tel 402-472-3581; Fax: 402-472-6214; Toll Free Fax: 800-526-2617; Toll Free: 800-755-1105; Edit Addr.: P.O. Box 880630, Lincoln, NE 68588-0630 USA (SAN 202-5337) ; *Imprints:* Bison Books (Bison Books); A Bison Original (A Bison Orig)
E-mail: pressmail@unl.edu
Web site: http://www.nebraskapress.unl.edu; http://www.bisonbooks.com
Dist(s): **Continental Bk. Co., Inc.**
NetLibrary, Inc.*; CIP.*

Univ. of Nebraska-Lincoln, GPN, *(0-7941)* Orders Addr.: P.O. Box 80669, Lincoln, NE 68501-0669 USA (SAN 179-1699) Tel 402-472-2007; Fax: 402-472-4076; Toll Free: 800-228-4630; Edit Addr.: 1800 N. 33rd St., Lincoln, NE 68583 USA
E-mail: gpn@unl.edu
Web site: http://gpn.unl.edu.

†Univ. of Nevada Pr., *(0-87417)* Orders Addr.: Mail Stop 166, Reno, NV 89557 USA (SAN 203-316X) Tel 775-784-6573; Fax: 775-784-6200; Toll Free: 877-682-6657 (orders only)
E-mail: nvinfo@nvbooks.nevada.edu
Web site: www.nvbooks.nevada.edu
Dist(s): **NetLibrary, Inc.***; CIP.*

Univ. of Nevada, Reno-Center for Basque Studies, *(1-877802)* Univ. of Nevada / 322, Reno, NV 89557-0012 USA Tel 775-784-4854; Fax: 775-784-1355
E-mail: basque@unr.edu
Web site: http://basque.unr.edu
Dist(s): **Univ. of Nevada Pr.**

†Univ. of New Mexico Pr., *(0-8263)* 1312 Basehart Rd SE, Albuquerque, NM 87106-4363 USA Toll Free Fax: 800-622-8667; Toll Free: 800-249-7737 (orders only); Edit Addr.: 1720 Lomas Blvd., NE, Albuquerque, NM 87131-1591 USA (SAN 213-9588) Tel 505-277-2346; Fax: 505-277-9270
E-mail: unmpress@unm.edu
Web site: http://www.unmpress.com
Dist(s): **Baker & Taylor Bks.**
Books West
Continental Bk. Co., Inc.
Treasure Chest Bks.*; CIP.*

†Univ. of North Carolina Pr., *(0-8078)* P.O. Box 2288, Chapel Hill, NC 27515-2288 USA (SAN 203-3151) Tel 919-966-3561; Fax: 919-966-3829; Toll Free: 800-848-6224 (orders)
E-mail: uncpress@unc.edu
Web site: http://www.uncpress.unc.edu*; CIP.*

†Univ. of Notre Dame Pr., *(0-268)* Orders Addr.: 11030 S. Langley Ave., Chicago, IL 60628 USA Tel 773-568-1550; Toll Free Fax: 800-621-8476; Toll Free: 800-621-2736; Edit Addr.: 310 Flanner Hall, Notre Dame, IN 46556 USA (SAN 203-3178) Tel 219-631-6346; Fax: 219-631-8148
E-mail: undpress.1@nd.edu
Web site: http://www.undpress.nd.edu
Dist(s): **Chicago Distribution Ctr.**
NetLibrary, Inc.
Univ. of Chicago Pr.*; CIP.*

†Univ. of Oklahoma Pr., *(0-8061)* Orders Addr.: 2800 Venture Dr., Norman, OK 73069-8218 USA Tel 405-325-2000; Fax: 405-364-5798; Toll Free Fax: 800-735-0476; Toll Free: 800-627-7377 ; *Imprints:* Clark, Arthur H. Company, The (Arthur Clark)
E-mail: customerservice@oupress.com
Web site: http://www.oupress.com
Dist(s): **Baker & Taylor Bks.**
NetLibrary, Inc.*; CIP.*

Univ. of Oregon ERIC Clearinghouse on Educational Management, *(0-86552)* Div. of U.S. Dept. of Education, 5207 Univ. of Oregon, Eugene, OR 97403-5207 USA (SAN 226-806X) Tel 541-346-5043; Fax: 541-346-2334; Toll Free: 800-438-8841
E-mail: eric@eric.uoregon.edu
Web site: http://www.eric.uoregon.edu.

University of Pennsylvania, University Museum *See* **Univ. Museum Pubns.**

†Univ. of Pittsburgh Pr., *(0-8229)* 3400 Forbes Ave., Eureka Bldg., Fifth Flr., Pittsburgh, PA 15260 USA (SAN 203-3216) Tel 412-383-2456; Fax: 412-383-2466 ; *Imprints:* Golden Triangle Books (GldnTriangle Bks)
E-mail: press@pitt.edu
Web site: http://www.pitt.edu/~press/
Dist(s): **Chicago Distribution Ctr.***; CIP.*

†Univ. of Puerto Rico Pr., *(0-8477)* Subs. of Univ. of Puerto Rico, Orders Addr.: P.O. Box 23322, Rio Piedras, PR 00931-3322 USA (SAN 208-1245) Tel 787-250-0435 Administrative Offices; 787-250-8996 Administrative Offices; 787-758-8345 Sales Office and Warehouse; 787-751-8251 Sales Office and Warehouse; 787-934-3400 Sales Office and Warehouse; Fax: 787-753-9116 Administrative Offices; 787-751-8785 Sales/Warehouse, Ordering fax
Web site: http://www.laeditorialupr.com
Dist(s): **Ediciones Universal**
Lectorum Pubns., Inc.
Libros Sin Fronteras*; CIP.*

Univ. of Rhode Island, Sea Grant Pubns. Unit, *(0-938412)* Narragansett Bay Campus, Narragansett, RI 02882-1197 USA (SAN 209-0708) Tel 401-874-6842; Fax: 401-874-6817
E-mail: jgallo@gso.uri.edu
Web site: http://www.seagrant.gso.uri.edu/riseagrant
Dist(s): **Chicago Distribution Ctr.**

Univ. of San Francisco, *(0-9664059)* 2130 Fulton St., San Francisco, CA 94117-1080 USA Tel 415-422-6848; Fax: 415-422-5908
Web site: http://www.usfca.edu
Dist(s): **Fordham Univ. Pr.**
New York Univ. Pr.

Univ. of Sankore Pr., The, *(0-943412)* 3018 W. 48th St., Los Angeles, CA 90043-1335 USA (SAN 219-5925) Toll Free: 800-997-2656
E-mail: uofsankorepress@msn.com.

†Univ. of South Carolina Pr., *(0-87249; 1-57003)* Orders Addr.: 718 Devine St., Columbia, SC 29208 USA Tel 803-777-1774; Fax: 803-777-0026; Toll Free Fax: 800-868-0740; Toll Free: 800-768-2500; Edit Addr.: 937 Assembly St., Carolina Plaza, 8th Flr., Columbia, SC 29208 USA (SAN 203-3224) Tel 803-777-5243; Fax: 803-777-0160; Toll Free Fax: 800-868-0740; Toll Free: 800-768-2500
E-mail: cdibble@gwm.sc.edu
Web site: http://www.sc.edu/uscpress/
Dist(s): **NetLibrary, Inc.***; CIP.*

Univ. St. Mary of the Lake, Mundelein Seminary, *(0-9774733)* 1000 E. Maple Ave., Mundelein, IL 60060 USA Tel 847-566-6401; Fax: 847-566-7330
E-mail: info@usml.edu
Web site: http://www.usml.edu.

University of Tampa *See* **Univ. of Tampa Pr.**

Univ. of Tampa Pr., *(1-879852; 1-59732)* 401 W. Kennedy Blvd., Tampa, FL 33606 USA Tel 813-253-6266; Fax: 813-258-7593
E-mail: utpress@ut.edu
Web site: http://utpress.ut.edu.

Univ. of Temecula Pr., Inc., *(0-936283)* 42730 De Luz Ave., Murrieta, CA 92562-7214 USA (SAN 697-9793) Tel 951-698-0059; Fax: 951-698-3676 ; *Imprints:* UTP (UTP)
E-mail: mikeray@utem.com
Web site: http://www.utem.com.

Univ. of Texas, M.D. Anderson Cancer Ctr., *(0-9630631)* 1515 Holcombe, No. 115, Houston, TX 77030 USA Tel 713-792-7180; Fax: 713-794-4282.

†Univ. of Texas Pr., *(0-292)* Orders Addr.: P.O. Box 7819, Austin, TX 78713-7819 USA (SAN 212-9876) Tel 512-471-7233; Fax: 512-320-0668; Toll Free: 800-252-3206; Edit Addr.: University of Texas at Austin 2100 Comal, Austin, TX 78722 USA
E-mail: utpress@uts.cc.utexas.edu
Web site: http://www.utexas.edu/utpress
Dist(s): **Continental Bk. Co., Inc.**
Brown, David Bk. Co., The
NetLibrary, Inc.
Urban Land Institute*; CIP.*

University of Vermont, Department of Psychiatry/Achenbach System of Empirically Based Assesment (ASEBA) *See* **Research Ctr. for Children, Youth, & Families/Achenbach System of Empirically Based Assessment (ASEBA)**

†Univ. of Washington Pr., *(0-295; 1-902716)* Orders Addr.: P.O. Box 50096, Seattle, WA 98145-5096 USA (SAN 212-2502) Tel 206-543-8870; Fax: 206-543-3932; Toll Free Fax: 800-669-7993; Toll Free: 800-441-4115; Edit Addr.: 1326 Fifth Ave., Suite 555, Seattle, WA 98101 USA Tel 206-543-8870; Fax: 206-685-3460; Toll Free Fax: 800-669-7993; Toll Free: 800-441-4115; 1126 N. 98th St., Seattle, WA 98103
E-mail: uwpord@u.washington.edu
Web site: http://www.washington.edu/uwpress
Dist(s): **NetLibrary, Inc.**
Partners Bk. Distributing, Inc.
Urban Land Institute*; CIP.*

Univ. of West Florida Foundation, Inc., *(0-9659142; 0-9798292)* 11000 University Pkwy., Pensacola, FL 32514 USA
E-mail: cmarse@uwf.edu.

†Univ. of Wisconsin Pr., *(0-299)* Orders Addr.: c/o Chicago Dist Ctr., 11030 S. Langley Ave., Chicago, IL 60628 USA Tel 773-568-1550; Fax: 773-660-2235; Toll Free Fax: 800-621-8476 (orders only); Toll Free: 800-621-2736 (orders only); Edit Addr.: 1930 Monroe St., 3rd Flr., Madison, WI 53711 USA Tel 608-263-1110; Fax: 608-263-1132
E-mail: uwiscpress@uwpress.wisc.edu
Web site: http://www.wisc.edu/wisconsinpress/
Dist(s): **Chicago Distribution Ctr.**
East-West Export Bks.*; CIP.*

University Pathways, *(0-9676237)* 4756 University Village Pl., NE Suite 426, Seattle, WA 98105 USA Tel 206-323-8902; Fax: 206-323-3635
E-mail: linjacobs@aol.com; thereiters@compurerve.com.

†Univ. Pr. of America, Inc., *(0-7618; 0-8191; 1-879691)* Member of Rowman & Littlefield Publishing Group, Inc., Orders Addr.: 15200 NBN Way, Blue Ridge Summit, PA 17214-0190 USA Tel 717-794-3800 (Sales, Customer Service, MIS, Royalties, Inventory Mgmt, Dist., Credit & Collections); Fax: 717-794-3803 (Customer Service & orders); 717-794-3857 (Sales & MIS); 717-794-3856 (Royalties, Inventory Mgmt. & Dist.); Toll Free Fax: 800-338-4550 (Customer Service & /or orders); Toll Free: 800-462-6420 (Customer Service &/or orders); Edit Addr.: 4501 Forbes Blvd., Suite 200, Lanham, MD 20706 USA Tel 301-459-3366; Fax: 301-459-5748 Short Discount, please contact rlpgsales@rowman.com
E-mail: custserv@rowman.com
Web site: http://www.univpress.com; http://www.rlpgbooks.com
Dist(s): **National Bk. Network**
Rowman & Littlefield Pubs., Inc.*; CIP.*

Univ. Pr. of Colorado, *(0-87081)* Orders Addr.: 2800 Venture Dr., Norman, OK 73069-8218 USA Toll Free Fax: 800-735-0476; Toll Free: 800-627-7377; Edit Addr.: 5589 Arapahoe Ave., Suite 206C, Boulder, CO 80303 USA (SAN 658-0343) Tel 720-406-8849
Web site: http://www.upcolorado.com
Dist(s): **Books West**
Ctr. for Literary Publishing, Colorado State Univ.
Univ. of Oklahoma Pr.

†Univ. Pr. of Florida, *(0-8130)* 15 NW 15th St., Gainesville, FL 32611-0279 USA (SAN 207-9275) Tel 352-392-1351; Fax: 352-392-7302; Toll Free: 800-226-3822
E-mail: ad@upf.com
Web site: http://www.upf.com
Dist(s): **NetLibrary, Inc.***; CIP.*

†Univ. Pr. of Kansas, *(0-7006)* 2502 Westbrooke Cir., Lawrence, KS 66045-4444 USA (SAN 203-3267) Tel 785-864-4154; 785-864-4155 (orders); Fax: 785-864-4586
E-mail: upress@ku.edu
Web site: http://www.kansaspress.ku.edu*; CIP.*

†Univ. Pr. of Kentucky, *(0-8131; 0-912839; 0-916968)* Orders Addr.: P.O. Box 4680, Lexington, KY 40544-4680 USA Tel 859-257-8400; Fax: 859-257-8481; Toll Free: 800-839-6855; Edit Addr.: 663 S. Limestone St., Lexington, KY 40508-4008 USA (SAN 203-3275) Tel 859-257-5200; Fax: 859-323-4981; Toll Free Fax: 800-870-4981
E-mail: leilas@uky.edu
Web site: http://www.kentuckypress.com
Dist(s): **NetLibrary, Inc.***; CIP.*

†Univ. Pr. of New England, *(0-87451; 0-915032; 1-58465)* Orders Addr.: One Court St., Suite 250, Lebanon, NH 03755 USA Tel 603-448-1533 (ext. 255); Fax: 603-448-9429; Toll Free: 800-421-1561
E-mail: University.Press@Dartmouth.edu
Web site: http://www.upne.com*; CIP.*

†Univ. Pr. of Virginia, *(0-8139; 0-912759; 1-57814)* Orders Addr.: P.O. Box 400318, Charlottesville, VA 22904-4318 USA (SAN 202-5361) Tel 804-924-3468; Fax: 804-982-2655
E-mail: upress@virginia.edu
Web site: http://www.upress.virginia.edu
Dist(s): **Ediciones Universal***; CIP.*

University Press (San Jose, California) *See* **UniversityPress.Info**

University Publishing Associates, Incorporated *See* **National Film Network LLC**

University Publishing Hse., Inc., *(1-57002; 1-877767)* P.O. Box 1664, Mannford, OK 74044-1664 USA Tel 918-865-4726 (phone/fax)
E-mail: upub@juno.com.

Univ. Schl. at the Univ. of Tulsa, *(1-893413)* 600 S. College Ave., Tulsa, OK 74104 USA Tel 918-631-5060; Fax: 918-631-5065
E-mail: debra-price@utulsa.edu
Web site: http://www.utulsa.edu.

University Science Bks., *(0-935702; 1-891389)* 55D Gate Five Rd., Sausalito, CA 94965 USA (SAN 213-8085) Tel 415-332-5390; Fax: 415-332-5393; 111 Prospect Pl., South Orange, NJ 07079 Tel 973-378-3900; Fax: 973-378-3925
E-mail: univscibks@igc.org; bjellis@igc.org; univsciencebooks@sbcglobal.net
Web site: http://www.uscibooks.com.

UniversityPress.Info, *(0-9700733; 0-9716445; 0-9749755)* Div. of BrainMind.com, 677 Elm St., San Jose, CA 95126 USA Do not confuse with companies with the same name in Hudson, WI, Flushing, NY, San Francisco, CA, Missoula, MT, Wolf City, TX
Web site: http://www.UniversityPress.Info.

Uniworld Business Pubns., Inc., *(0-8360)* 3 Clark Rd., Millis, MA 02054-1213 USA (SAN 203-2813) Tel 508-376-6006; Fax: 508-376-6006
E-mail: info@uniworldbp.com
Web site: http://www.uniworldbp.com.

Unknown Publishing *See* **Story Place, The**

Unlimited Horizons, *(0-9753817)* 427 S. Fraser Dr., Mesa, AZ 85204-2605 USA.

Unlimited Publishing LLC, *(0-9677649; 1-58832)* P.O. Box 3007, Bloomington, IN 47402 USA Fax: 425-928-5465
E-mail: jaymasp@aol.com; paradoxofthesoul@aol.com
Web site: http://www.unlimitedpublishing.com
Dist(s): **Replica Bks.**

Unmistakably C K C, *(0-9742064)* 3244 Kingswood Glen, Decatur, GA 30034 USA Tel 404-244-8113; 404-242-2690; Fax: 678-418-3056
E-mail: info@billyzany.com
Web site: http://www.billyzany.com.

Unseen Gallery, *(0-9795206)* Orders Addr.: P.O. Box 6065, Albuquerque, NM 87197 USA Tel 505-232-2161
E-mail: webmaster@unseengallery.com
Web site: http://www.unseengallery.com.

Unshackled Publishing, *(0-9708688)* P.O. Box 11773, Tempe, AZ 85284 USA Tel 281-773-8336
E-mail: alexus27@aol.com; lexthewriter@yahoo.com
Web site: http://www.unshackledpublishing.com.

Unspeakable Joy Pr., *(0-9761538)* Orders Addr.: 499 Adams St., #252, Milton, MA 02186 USA; Edit Addr.: 233 Eliot St., Milton, MA 02186 USA
E-mail: roybue@aol.com; adoptionis@aol.com
Web site: http://www.adoptionis.com.

UnTechnical Pr., *(0-9669949; 1-58870)* Orders Addr.: P.O. Box 272896, Concord, CA 94527 USA (SAN 299-8823) Tel 925-825-1655; Fax: 925-825-4601; Toll Free: 888-592-6657
E-mail: michael@untechnicalpress.com
Web site: http://www.untechnicalpress.com.

UP, *(0-9771184)* 19 Yellow Brook Rd., Holmdel, NJ 07733-1967 USA Tel 732-332-0232.

Upland Public Library Foundation, *(0-9669508)* Orders Addr.: 450 N. Euclid Ave., Upland, CA 91786 USA Tel 909-931-4201; Fax: 909-931-4209
E-mail: kbr@ci.upland.ca.us.

Upper Playground Pubng, *(0-9778854; 0-9790862)* 220 Fillmore St., San Francisco, CA 94117 USA (SAN 850-4237)
Web site: htpp://upperplayground.com
Dist(s): **Gingko Pr., Inc.**

Upper Room Bks., *(0-8358)* Div. of The Upper Room, 1908 Grand Ave., Nashville, TN 37212 USA (SAN 203-3364) Tel 615-340-7256; 615-340-7204; Fax: 615-340-7266; Toll Free: 800-972-0433 (customer service, orders); 1650 Bluegrass Lakes Pkwy., Alphretta, GA 30201 Do not confuse with Upper Room Education for Parenting, Inc. in Derry, NH
E-mail: kwatts@upperroom.org; sarah_schaller-linn@gbod.org
Web site: http://www.upperroom.org
Dist(s): **Abingdon Pr.**

Upper Strata Ink, Incorporated *See* **Crowder, Jack L.**

UPSCL (Unoffical Penisnula Scholastic Chess League, Inc.), *(0-9721087)* Orders Addr.: P.O. Box 25535, San Mateo, CA 94402 USA Tel 650-349-7746; Edit Addr.: 1919 Alameda de los Dulgas, No. 63, San Mateo, CA 94403 USA
E-mail: upscl@pacbell.net
Web site: http://www.upscl.netfirms.com.

Upstart Bks. *Imprint of* **Highsmith Inc.**

Upstart Publishing Co., *(0-9675537)* P.O. Box 5887, Baltimore, MD 21282-5887 USA Tel 410-484-1781; Fax: 410-486-1820; Toll Free: 888-522-4488
E-mail: fbs1128@aol.com.

UpTree Publishing, *(0-9787248)* 701 Gervais St., Suite 150-211, Columbia, SC 29201 USA (SAN 851-447X) Toll Free: 800-905-2157 (phone/fax)
E-mail: sales@uptreepublishing.com
Web site: http://www.uptreepublishing.com.

Upword Pr., *(0-9654140)* Orders Addr.: P.O. Box 655, Springville, AL 35146 USA; Edit Addr.: P.O. Box 381434, Birmingham, AL 35238-1434 USA Tel 205-222-4861; Fax: 251-989-7701 Do not confuse with Upword Pr., Yelm, WA
E-mail: unclelouie@scattersunshine.com
Web site: http://www.upwordpress.com; http://www.scattersunshine.com.

Urban Edge Publishing Co., *(0-9743781)* 16209 Victory Blvd., Suite 207, Van Nuys, CA 91406 USA Tel 818-786-3700; Fax: 818-786-3737
E-mail: willcon@pacbell.net.

Urban Fairies Operations, LLC, *(0-9793585)* 532 Fifth St., Ann Arbor, MI 48103 USA (SAN 853-2435)
Web site: http://urban-fairies.com.

Urban Ministries, Incorporated *See* **UMI (Urban Ministries, Inc.)**

Urban Moon Publishing, *(0-9787913; 0-9800101)* 931 Monroe Dr., Suite 276, Atlanta, GA 30308 USA Toll Free: 866-205-9228
E-mail: kinglistens@aol.com.

Urban Thought Bks., Inc., *(1-930231)* P.O. Box 78306, Atlanta, GA 30357 USA Tel 404-914-6685; Fax: 770-558-6860
E-mail: publisher@urbanthoughtbooks.com
Web site: http://www.urbanthoughtbooks.com.

Urbanik, Karen L., *(0-9759031)* 2285 Marsh Hawk Ln. Apt. 302, Orange Park, FL 32003-6366 USA.

Urim Pubns. (ISR) *(965-7108) Dist. by* **Biblio Dist.**

†URJ Pr., *(0-8074)* 633 Third Ave., New York, NY 10017 USA (SAN 203-3291) Tel 212-650-4120; Fax: 212-650-4119; Toll Free: 888-489-8242
E-mail: press@urj.org
Web site: http://www.urjbooksandmusic.com; *CIP.*

URON Entertainment Corp. (CAN) *(0-9738652; 0-9781386) Dist. by* **Diamond Book Dists.**

Ursa Multimedia *See* **KHP Industries**

Ursinus College, *(0-9624021; 1-889136)* Orders Addr.: P.O. Box 1000, Collegeville, PA 19426-1000 USA Tel 610-409-3500; Fax: 610-409-3664; Edit Addr.: 601 E. Main St., Collegeville, PA 19426 USA
Dist(s): **Univ. of Pennsylvania Pr.**

Ursu Pubns., *(0-9741634)* PMB 429, 5250 Grand Ave., Suite 14, Gurnee, IL 60031-1877 USA
E-mail: info@grandmaursu.com
Web site: http://www.grandmaursu.com.

Ursuline Sisters of Tildonk, *(0-9678688)* 81-15 Utopia Pkwy., Jamaica, NY 11432 USA Tel 718-969-6034; Fax: 718-969-4275
E-mail: quinlanosu@aol.com
Web site: http://www.tressy.tripod.com.

US Voice Communication Systems *See* **Kids Love Pubns.**

Usborne *Imprint of* **EDC Publishing**

Usborne Publishing, Ltd. (GBR) *(0-7460; 0-86020; 1-85123) Dist. by* **EDC Pubng.**

†Utah State Univ. Pr., *(0-87421)* 7800 Old Main Hill, Logan, UT 84322-7800 USA (SAN 202-9294) Tel 435-797-1362; Fax: 435-797-0313; Toll Free: 800-239-9974
E-mail: brooke.bigelow@usu.edu
Web site: http://www.usu.edu/usupress
Dist(s): **Chicago Distribution Ctr.**
NetLibrary, Inc.; *CIP.*

U-Talk Publications *See* **Harvest Point Pr.**

Utica Hse. Publishing Co., *(0-9609296)* RR No. 1, Utica, IL 61373 USA (SAN 260-1532) Tel 815-223-3200
Dist(s): **Partners Bk. Distributing, Inc.**

Utopia Pr., *(0-9661060)* 126 1/2 E. Front St., Traverse City, MI 49684 USA Tel 231-922-2234 editorial office
E-mail: pub@fimg.net
Dist(s): **Partners Bk. Distributing, Inc.**
Partners Pubs. Group, Inc.

UTP *Imprint of* **Univ. of Temecula Pr., Inc.**

UXL *Imprint of* **Thomson Gale**

Uxor Pr., Inc., *(0-932555)* One Blackfield Dr., No. 174, Tiburon, CA 94920 USA (SAN 687-4916)
E-mail: bobzimmerman@usa.com.

Uzoigwe, Chioma, *(0-9675252)* 1610 Azalea Dr., N Brunswick, NJ 08902-5540 USA.

VMI Pubs., *(0-9712311; 0-9747190; 1-933204)* 26306 Metolius Meadows Dr., Camp Sherman, OR 97730 USA Tel 541-595-2403 ; *Imprints:* Musterion Press (Musterion)
Web site: http://www.vmipublishers.com
Dist(s): **STL Distribution North America.**

V V C Publishing *See* **Vic-Vincent Publishing**

Vacation Spot Publishing, *(0-9637688; 1-893622)* Orders Addr.: 7402-G Lockport Pl., Lorton, VA 22079 USA Tel 703-684-8142; Fax: 703-684-7955; Toll Free: 800-441-1949; Edit Addr.: 1903 Duffield Ln., Alexandria, VA 22307 USA ; *Imprints:* VSP Books (VSP Bks)
E-mail: mail@VSPBooks.com
Web site: http://www.vspbooks.com
Dist(s): **Baker & Taylor Bks.**
Bookazine Co., Inc.
Follett Library Resources
Ingram Bk. Co.
Keith Distributors.

Vadeboncoeur, Jim, *(0-9724697)* 3809 Laguna Ave., Palo Alto, CA 94306-2629 USA Fax: 650-493-1145
E-mail: images@bpib.com
Web site: http://www.bpib.com/images.htm.

Valenti, Robert A., *(0-9773119)* 3500 Galt Ocean Dr.2401, Fort Lauderdale, FL 33308-6809 USA Tel 954-563-0069; Fax: 954-563-4503
E-mail: rvalenti@bellsouth.net.

Valikus Publishing Co., *(0-615)* Div. of Valikus Records, Production, Publishing Co., Inc., 1205 NW 203 St., Miami, FL 33169 USA Tel 305-690-9081; Fax: 305-690-0262
E-mail: ikeval@bellsouth.net
Web site: http://ikewoods.com.

Vallentine Mitchell Pubs. (GBR) *(0-85303) Dist. by* **Intl Spec Bk.**

Valley Forge Publishing, *(0-929178)* 1504 Briarwood Ct., Phoenixville, PA 19460 USA (SAN 248-4692) Tel 610-917-0587; Toll Free: 866-386-4900
Web site: http://www.funixbook.com.

Valley Publishing *See* **Karosa Publishing**

Values of America Co., *(0-9765868)* P.O. Box 1534, Merchantville, NJ 08109 USA Toll Free: 866-467-7304
E-mail: orders@quipman.com
Web site: http://www,quipman.com.

Values to Live By Classic Stories *Imprint of* **Thomas, Frederic Inc.**

Van Buren California Publishing, *(0-9677469)* P.O. Box 6701, Laguna Niguel, CA 92607 USA Tel 949-235-6269
E-mail: dholt@vanburencalifornia.zzn.com
Web site: http://www.vanburencalifornia.bizland.com.

Van der Meer, a Div. of PHPC (GBR) *(1-902413; 90-76048) Dist. by* **Abbeville Pr.**

Van Der Meer Tennis Univ., *(1-930145)* Orders Addr.: P.O. Box 5902, Hilton Head Island, SC 29938 USA Tel 843-785-8388; Fax: 843-785-7032; Toll Free: 800-845-6138; Edit Addr.: 19 DeAllyon Ave., Hilton Head Island, SC 29938 USA
E-mail: tennis@vandermeertennis.com
Web site: http://www.vandermeertennis.com.

Van der Westhuizen, Kevin Ministries International, Incorporated *See* **JMC Printing**

Van Impe, Jack Ministries, *(0-934803; 1-884137; 1-928954)* 1718 Northfield Dr., Rochester Hills, MI 48309 USA (SAN 697-3620) Tel 248-852-2244; Fax: 248-852-2692
E-mail: jvim@jvim.com
Web site: http://www.jvim.com.

Van Steenhouse, Andrea L. *See* **Simpler Life Pr.**

Vandam Pr., Inc., *(0-9702383)* P.O. Box 155, Brooklyn, NY 11230 USA Tel 212-969-0286; Fax: 212-858-5720
E-mail: publisher@vandampress.com
Web site: http://www.vandampress.com.

Vandamere Pr., *(0-918339)* Subs. of AB Assocs., Orders Addr.: P.O. Box 149, St. Petersburg, FL 33731 USA (SAN 657-3088) Tel 727-556-0950; Fax: 727-556-2560; Toll Free: 800-551-7776
Web site: www.vandamere.com.

Vangar Pubs./Baltimore, *(1-882788)* R.R. 2, Box 99, Charles Town, WV 25414 USA Tel 304-728-2829
E-mail: robertgraf@aol.com.

Vanguard Pr., *(1-59315)* 425 Madison Ave., 3rd Flr., New York, NY 10017 USA Do not confuse with CDS Books in Paso Robles, CA Durham, NC
Dist(s): **Perseus Distribution.**

Vanguard Productions, *(1-887591; 1-934331)* 186 Center St., Suite 200, Clinton, NJ 08809 USA Tel 732-748-8895
E-mail: vanguardpub@att.net
Web site: http://vanguardproductions.net
Dist(s): **Macmillan**
Watson-Guptill Pubns., Inc.

Vanissery, Matthew, *(0-9759906)* P.O. Box 1056, Guasti, CA 91743-1056 USA; 175 Mountain View Ave., Scotch Plains, NJ 07076 Tel 908-889-7930; Fax: 908-889-6281
E-mail: chemplavil@aol.com.

Vantage Pr., Inc., *(0-533)* 419 Park Ave., South 18th Flr., New York, NY 10016 USA (SAN 206-8893) Tel 212-736-1767; Fax: 212-736-2273; Toll Free: 800-882-3273
Web site: http://www.vantagepress.com
Dist(s): **AtlasBooks Distribution**
Big River Distribution
Dr. Leisure.

VanWrite Pubs., *(0-9639282)* P.O. Box 160145, Sacramento, CA 95816 USA Tel 916-553-4202; Fax: 916-678-8185; Toll Free Fax: 888-223-4012; Toll Free: 800-800-0898
E-mail: vanwrite@aol.com
Web site: http://www.vanwrite.com.

Varas, Reny, *(0-9726946)* 918 Cortney Dr., Carpentersville, IL 60110 USA (SAN 255-3333) Tel 847-428-7852; Fax: 847-428-7880
E-mail: lionan2@msn.com.

Vaughanworks *Imprint of* **Vaughanworks Publishing**

Vaughanworks Publishing, *(0-9771160)* Div. of Vaughanworks, Orders Addr.: P.O. Box 18511, Milwaukee, WI 53218 USA ; *Imprints:* Vaughanworks (Vaughanworks)
E-mail: vaughanworks1@mfire.com
Web site: http://www.vaughanworks.com.

Vaughn, Jerry T., *(0-9772507)* 1921 Ashford Cir., Longmout, CO 80501 USA Tel 303-776-9134
E-mail: vaughn.jc@gmail.com.

Veach, Betty H. Veach & Lester H., *(0-9721787)* 625 Thorton St., Talladega, AL 35160 USA Tel 256-761-1981
Web site: http://www.motivationalbook.com.

Vedanta Pr., *(0-87481)* Div. of Vedanta Society of Southern California, 1946 Vedanta Pl., Hollywood, CA 90068-3996 USA (SAN 202-9340) Tel 323-960-1728 (general manager); 323-960-1727 (orders & customer service); Fax: 323-465-9568 (orders)
E-mail: bob@vedanta.org; orders@vedanta.org
Web site: http://www.vedanta.com.

vegaslocal.com, *(0-9752804)* 5731 Fonchester Ct., Las Vegas, NV 89110-2643 USA
E-mail: info@vegaslocal.com
Web site: http://www.vegaslocal.com.

Veillette, Sally *See* **Pop the Cork Publishing**

Velesquious Studios, *(0-9754232)* P.O. Box 72, Blakeslee, PA 18610-0072 USA Tel 610-360-8946
E-mail: webmaster@velesquious.com
Web site: http://www.velesquious.com.

Velichko, Vera, *(0-9754433)* 3833 N. Winnifred St., Tacoma, WA 98407 USA Tel 253-227-8983; Fax: 800-783-0798 ; *Imprints:* Language Transformer Books (LangTransforBks)
E-mail: talkinrussian@yahoo.com
Web site: http://www.lulu.com/talkinrussian1; http://www.languagetransformer.com/; http://home.comcast.net/~talkinrussian/.

VeloPress, *(0-9622630; 1-884737; 1-931382; 1-934030)* Div. of Inside Communications, Inc., 1830 N. 55th St., Boulder, CO 80301-2700 USA Tel 303-440-0601; Fax: 303-444-6788; Toll Free: 800-811-4210
E-mail: velopress@7dogs.com
Web site: http://www.velogear.com
Dist(s): **Perseus Distribution.**

Venable, L.A. Publishing Co., *(0-9666817)* 4210 Inverness Cliffs, Birmingham, AL 35242 USA Tel 205-991-2006
E-mail: lven142274@aol.com
Web site: http://www.appletreasures.com.

Venture Development Group, *(0-9748030)* 1114 Blue Lake Sq., Mountain View, CA 94040-4561 USA Tel 650-967-3403; Fax: 650-965-0320.

Venture Publishing, *(0-9761694)* 750 Tabor St., No. 64, Golden, CO 80401 USA Tel 303-239-6531 (phone/fax).

Verbal Images Pr., *(0-9625136; 1-884281)* 46 Duncott Rd., Fairport, NY 14450-3150 USA
Dist(s): **Gryphon Hse., Inc.**
Independent Pubs. Group.

Verdant Publishing, Inc., *(0-9658435)* 737 Bayvista Blvd., S., Saint Petersburg, FL 33705 USA Tel 727-867-3937; Fax: 727-521-6280
E-mail: piterski@gte.net.

Verde Publishing, Inc., *(0-9717643)* Orders Addr.: P.O. Box 27569, San Diego, CA 92198 USA; Edit Addr.: 14934 Huntington Gate Dr., Poway, CA 92064 USA Tel 858-679-1091; Fax: 858-679-1092 ; *Imprints:* Bee Smarter Study Kits (Bee Smarter)
E-mail: tbv3618@aol.com
Web site: http://www.verdepublishing.com.

Veritas Pr., Inc., *(1-930710; 1-932168)* 1829 William Penn Way, Lancaster, PA 17601 USA (SAN 255-9617) Tel 717-519-1974; Fax: 717-519-1978; Toll Free: 800-922-5082 Do not confuse with companies with same name in Santa Barbara CA, Santa Monica CA, Bronx NY, Clearwater Fl, Sioux Falls SD, West Hartford CT, West Allis,MI
E-mail: info@veritaspress.com
Web site: http://www.veritaspress.com.

Veritas Pubns. (IRL) *(1-85390; 0-901810; 0-905092; 0-86217) Dist. by* **Irish Bks Media.**

Veritas Pubns. (IRL) *(1-85390; 0-901810; 0-905092; 0-86217) Dist. by* **STL Dist NA.**

Verlag Wilhelm Heyne (DEU) *(3-453) Dist. by* **Distribks Inc.**

Vermont Bookworks, *(0-9745931)* 12 Perry Ln., Rutland, VT 05701 USA
E-mail: digbysworld@comcast.net
Web site: http://www.digbysworld.com.

Vermont Council on the Arts, Incorporated *See* **Vermont Folklife Ctr.**

†Vermont Folklife Ctr., *(0-916718)* Orders Addr.: P.O. Box 442, Middlebury, VT 05753 USA (SAN 208-9092) Tel 802-388-4964
E-mail: info@vermontfolklifecenter.org
Web site: http://www.vermontfolklifecenter.org
Dist(s): **Thistle Hill Pubns.**
Univ. Pr. of New England; *CIP.*

†**Vermont Life Magazine,** *(0-936896; 1-931389)* Div. of State of Vermont, Agency on Development & Community Affairs, 6 Baldwin St., Montpelier, VT 05602-2109 USA (SAN 215-8213) Tel 802-828-3241; Fax: 802-828-3366; Toll Free: 800-455-3399
E-mail: vtlife@life.state.vt.us; products@life.state.vt.us; subs@life.state.vt.us
Web site: http://www.vtlife.com; http://www.VermontLifeCatalog.com
Dist(s): **Hood, Alan C. & Co., Inc.**; *CIP.*

Vermont Public Television, *(1-929082)* 88 Ethan Allen Ave., Colchester, VT 05446 USA Tel 802-655-4800; Fax: 802-655-6593.

Vermont Schoolhouse Pr., The, *(0-9617872; 1-892286)* 4713 N. 77th Pl., Scottsdale, AZ 85251 USA (SAN 665-2964) Tel 480-990-2777
E-mail: vspcynie@aol.com
Dist(s): **Enfield Publishing & Distribution Co., Inc.**

Verner Advertising, LLC, *(0-9715953)* 2636 Carter Ave., Fort Worth, TX 76103 USA Tel 817-536-2316; Fax: 817-536-3550; Toll Free: 888-483-7637 ; *Imprints:* Verner Publishing (Verner Pub)
E-mail: vernerad@aol.com
Web site: http://www.verneradvertising.com.

Verner Publishing *Imprint of* **Verner Advertising, LLC**

Verney, Jeff *See* **JRV Publishing**

Vernier Software *See* **Vernier Software & Technology**

Vernier Software & Technology, *(0-918731; 1-929075)* 13979 SW Millikan Way, Beaverton, OR 97005-2886 USA (SAN 293-1753) Tel 503-277-2299; Fax: 503-277-2440
E-mail: info@vernier.com
Web site: http://www.vernier.com.

Vernissage Pr., LLC, *(0-9725027)* 2200 Central Ave., Boulder, CO 80301 USA Tel 303-440-8102; Toll Free: 888-849-8697
E-mail: info@vernissagepress.com
Web site: http://www.vernissagepress.com
Dist(s): **Baker & Taylor Bks.**

Vero Technical Support, Inc., *(0-9711100)* 593 27th Ave SW, Vero Beach, FL 32968-4202 USA
E-mail: gsigler@attglobal.net
Web site: http://www.verotechnicalsupport.com.

Verona (Bk.) Publishing, Inc., *(0-9667037; 0-9769031)* P.O. Box 24071, Edina, MN 55426 USA
Web site: http://www.veronapublishing.com.

Versait Pr. LLC, *(0-9746810)* P.O. Box 644332, Vero Beach, FL 32964-4332 USA
E-mail: info@versaitpress.com
Web site: http://VersaitPress.com.

Versal Editorial Group, *(1-58018)* 10 Hight St., Andover, MA 01810 USA Tel 978-725-8001; Fax: 978-725-8013; Toll Free: 800-353-3341
E-mail: vmolina@cbhbooks.com.

Versal Technologies, Inc., *(0-9749460)* One Cranberry Hill, Suite 102, Lexington, MA 02421 USA.

Versary Pubns., *(0-9641429)* 984 Brownsville Rd., Wernersville, PA 19565 USA Tel 610-693-5920.

Verse-a-Tale Pr., *(0-9704586)* 4925 N. 57th Ave., Omaha, NE 68104 USA Tel 402-453-3975.

Verso Bks. (GBR) *(0-86091; 0-902308; 1-85984; 1-84467) Dist. by* **Norton.**

Vertical Connect Pr., *(0-9769087)* 120 N. Magnolia St., Summerville, SC 29483-6836 USA ; *Imprints:* Grand Kidz, The (Grand Kidz)
E-mail: kate@verticalconnectpress.com
Web site: http://www.verticalconnectpress.com.

Vertical, Inc., *(1-932234; 1-934287)* 1185 Avenue Of The Americas, 32nd Flr., New York, NY 10036 USA
E-mail: info@vertical-inc.com
Web site: http://www.vertical-inc.com
Dist(s): **Random Hse., Inc.**

Vertigo *Imprint of* **DC Comics**

Vertigo Publishing, *(0-9764463)* P.O. Box 2683, Dearborn, MI 48123 USA
E-mail: vertigopublish@cs.com
Web site: http://www.vertigopublishing.com.

Vescori, Laura, *(0-9762965)* 28 Fir Tree Dr., Bradford, CT 06405 USA.

Vessel Ministries, *(0-615; 0-9713345)* 1974 E. Mcandrews Rd., Medford, OR 97504-5510 USA
E-mail: vesselmin@cox.net
Dist(s): **Todd Communications.**

Vested Owl, *(0-9767926)* 2901 Connecticut Ave., No. 304, Washington, DC 20008 USA
E-mail: info@vestedowl.com
Web site: http://www.vestedowl.com.

Vestibular Disorders Assn., *(0-9632611)* Orders Addr.: P.O. Box 13305, Portland, OR 97213-0305 USA Tel 503-229-7705; Fax: 503-229-8064; Toll Free: 800-837-8428
E-mail: veda@vestibular.org
Web site: http://www.vestibular.org.

Vezun, *(0-9702945)* P.O. Box 15394, Las Vegas, NV 89114 USA (SAN 253-3472) Tel 702-227-6643
E-mail: v32un@hotmail.com.

VGM Career Bks. *Imprint of* **McGraw-Hill Trade**

Via Media, Incorporated *See* **Via Media, Pr.**

Via Media, Pr., *(0-9646362)* 3112 James St., San Diego, CA 92106 USA Tel 619-884-6440
E-mail: via_media_press@pacbell.net.

Vibatorium LLC, *(0-9742495)* 419 N. Larchmont Blvd., No. 3265, Los Angeles, CA 90004 USA Tel 323-460-4441; Fax: 323-935-0225
E-mail: info@backyardwonders.com
Web site: http://www.vibatorium.com; http://www.backyardwonders.com.

Vibrante Pr., *(0-935301)* P.O. Box 51853, Albuquerque, NM 87181-1853 USA (SAN 696-2351)
E-mail: Lonnie@vibrante.com
Web site: http://www.vibrante.com.

Vice Press Publishing Company *See* **Ascension Education**

Vicens-Vives, Editorial, S.A. (ESP) *(84-316) Dist. by* **Lectorum Pubns.**

Vickery Bks., *(1-928531)* 3012 Anchor Dr., Ormond Beach, FL 32176-2304 USA
E-mail: kvv145@gte.net.

Victoria Univ. Pr. (NZL) *(0-86473) Dist. by* **IPG Chicago.**

Victorious Moments Pubns., *(0-9721134)* P.O. Box 227575, Hampton, VA 23665 USA
E-mail: vmpublications@yahoo.com
Web site: http://www.victoriousmoments.com.

Victor's Crown Publishing, *(0-9761188)* 1238 E. 3075 N., Ogden, UT 84414-1886 USA
E-mail: steve@victorscrown.com
Web site: http://www.victorscrown.com.

Victory 5 Publishing, *(0-9764121)* P.O. Box 31086, Omaha, NE 68131 USA
E-mail: jknsmooth@yahoo.com.

Victory by Any Means Games, *(0-9764048)* Orders Addr.: P.O. Box 329, Lusk, WY 82225-0329 USA Tel 307-334-3190; Edit Addr.: 315 S. Iron, Lusk, WY 82225-0329 USA
E-mail: tyrel@vbamgames.com
Web site: http://www.vbamgames.com.

Victory Graphics & Media, *(0-88144)* P.O. Box 701434, Tulsa, OK 74155-1388 USA (SAN 260-0285) Tel 918-250-6667
E-mail: lindao@christianpublishingservices.com
Web site: http://www.christianpublishigservices.com.

Victory In Grace Ministries, *(0-9679145; 0-9719262)* 60 Quentin Rd., Lake Zurich, IL 60047 USA Tel 847-438-4494 ext 1055; Fax: 847-438-4232; Toll Free: 800-784-7223
E-mail: feedback@victoryingrace.org
Web site: http://www.victoryingrace.org.

Victory Pr., *(0-9620765; 1-878217)* Orders Addr.: 3106 Crescent Ave., Unit 7, Marina, CA 93933 USA; Edit Addr.: 543 Lighthouse Ave., Monterey, CA 93940-1422 USA (SAN 249-700X) Tel 831-883-1725; Fax: 831-883-8710 Do not confuse with companies with the same name in Prescott Valley, AZ, Chesterfield, MO, Massillon OH
E-mail: victoryp@ix.netcom.com
Web site: http://www.heroinesinhistory.com
Dist(s): **Baker & Taylor Bks.**
Distributors, The
New Leaf Distributing Co., Inc.
Partners/West.

Victory Pr., *(0-9753818)* P.O. Box 118, Massillon, OH 44648 USA Do not confuse with companies with the same name in Carlton OR, Chesterfield MO, Monterey CA
E-mail: rabteach2001@aol.com
Web site: http://www.ruthann.faithweb.com.

Victory Publishing, *(0-935303)* 2221 Hopkins Ave., Redwood City, CA 94062 USA (SAN 696-2408) Do not confuse with companies with the same or similar name in Los Angeles, CA, Mount Pleasant, SC, Inglewood, CA, Banco, VA, New Orleans, LA , Perris, CA, Littleton, CO, Decatur, IL
E-mail: vyva@aol.com
Web site: http://hometown.aol.com/vyva/myhomepage/profile.html.

Victory Publishing Co., *(0-9778925)* 3797 N. Ashley Ct., Decatur, IL 62526 USA (SAN 850-4458) Do not confuse with companies with the same or similar name in Hampton, VA, Redwood City, CA, MOunt Pleasant, SC, Inglewood, CA, Banco, VA, Pama, ID, New Orleans, LA, Littleton, CO
E-mail: edmar84@aol.com.

Victory WW 2 Publishing Ltd., *(0-9700567)* Orders Addr.: P.O. Box 670, Rogers, MN 55374 USA (SAN 253-2476); Edit Addr.: 13055 Riverdale Dr., NW, Suite 500, No. 221, Minneapolis, MN 55448 USA Tel 763-428-4345; Fax: 763-428-7575; Toll Free: 888-428-1942
E-mail: militintl@aol.com
Web site: www.jeepbooksales.com.

Vic-Vincent Publishing, *(0-9646817)* Div. of Vic-Vincent Corp., Orders Addr.: 362 Gulf Breeze Pkwy., Suite 151, Gulf Breeze, FL 32561 USA (SAN 257-4039) Tel 850-476-7673; Toll Free: 800-772-3343
E-mail: inventorz@aol.com
Web site: http://www.inventorsfreehelp.com
Dist(s): **Distributors, The.**

Vida Devocional *Imprint of* **Lopez, Hilda**

Vida Life Publishers International *See* **Vida Pubs.**

Vida Pubs., *(0-8297)* 7500 NW 25th St. Ste. 239, Miami, FL 33122-1722 USA Toll Free: 800-843-2548
E-mail: vidapubsales@harpercollins.com
Web site: http://www.editorialvida.com
Dist(s): **Zondervan.**

VideoPresence.com, A, *(0-615)* P.O. Box 523, Burley, WA 98322 USA
E-mail: info@avideopresence.com
Web site: http://www.thelegendofsealbeach.com
Dist(s): **Lulu.com.**

Vidro, Kenneth *See* **Gilbert Square Bks.**

Vidya Bks., *(1-878099)* P.O. Box 7788, Berkeley, CA 94707-0788 USA Tel 510-527-9932.

Viet Baby, LLC, *(0-9776482)* Orders Addr.: P.O. Box 750074, Las Vegas, NV 89136-0074 USA Tel 702-234-5127
E-mail: an@viet-baby.com
Web site: http://www.viet-baby.com.

Vietnamerican Trading Co., *(0-9645457)* 420 Downing, Denver, CO 80218 USA Tel 303-744-6200; Fax: 303-744-6590; Toll Free: 800-843-5747.

Vietnamese International Poetry Society, *(0-9746300)* Orders Addr.: P.O. Box 246958, Sacramento, CA 95824 USA; Edit Addr.: 3067 Harrison St., NW, Washington, DC 20015 USA.

Viewpoint Pr., *(0-943962)* Orders Addr.: P.O. Box 1090, Tehachapi, CA 93581 USA Tel 661-821-5110; Fax: 661-821-7515; Edit Addr.: 785 Tucker Rd., Apt. G400, Tehachapi, CA 93561 USA Do not confuse with companies with the same name in San Diego, CA, Portland, ME
E-mail: joie99@aol.com
Dist(s): **Baker & Taylor Bks.**
Biblio Distribution.

Viewpoint Pr., Inc., *(0-9662431)* P.O. Box 430, Pleasant Garden, NC 27313 USA Tel 336-370-1600 (phone/fax)
E-mail: Mes-a1@Worldnet.att.net
Web site: http://www.members.tripod.com/~viewpointpress
Dist(s): **Quality Bks., Inc.**

Viewpoints Research Institute, Inc., *(0-9743131)* 1209 Grand Central Ave., Glendale, CA 91201 USA
Web site: http://www.viewpointsresearch.org.

Viking Adult *Imprint of* **Penguin Group (USA) Inc.**

Viking Juvenile *Imprint of* **Penguin Group (USA) Inc.**

VILA Group, Inc., The, *(0-9635047)* V2947 S. Atlantic Ave., Apt. 1906, Daytona Beach, FL 32118-6029 USA Tel 904-767-8245.

Villa Serena Publishing, *(0-9753326)* 15657 Westbrook Rd., Livonia, MI 48154 USA
Dist(s): **AtlasBooks Distribution.**

Village East Bks., *(0-9661899; 0-9788888)* 8775 20th St., Vero Beach, FL 32966 USA
E-mail: Villageeast@hotmail.com; deanbarr@loxinfo.co.th
Web site: http://www.deanbarrettmystery.com; http://www.deanbarrettthailand.com
Dist(s): **Midpoint Trade Bks., Inc.**

Village Monkey LLC, The, *(0-9789633)* 7760 McWhorter Rd., Martinsville, IN 46151 USA Tel 765-352-1718
E-mail: zenmonkey@thevillagemonkey.com
Web site: http://www.thevillagemonkey.com.

Village Monkey, The *See* **Village Monkey LLC, The**

Village Museum, *(0-9740091)* Orders Addr.: 401 Pinckney St., McClellanville, SC 29458 USA Tel 843-887-3030; Edit Addr.: P.O. Box 595, McClellanville, SC 29458 USA Tel 843-887-3030
Web site: http://www.villagemuseum.com.

Village Tales Publishing, *(0-9753609)* 1335 Spring Chase Cir, Stone Mountain, GA 30083 USA
E-mail: ophelia_lewis@bellsouth.net; olewis@villagetales.com
Web site: http://www.villagetales.com.

Villager Bk. Publishing, *(1-934643)* Orders Addr.: P.O. Box 222 W. Las Colinas Blvd, Suite 1650, Irving, TX 75039 USA (SAN 854-0969)
E-mail: jfox@villagerdustbunnies.com; semerick@villagerdustbunnies.com; jbloom@villagerdustbunnies.com; lrinn@villagerdustbunnies.com
Web site: http://villagerpublishers.com; http://www.villagerdustbunnies.com.

Villard Bks. *Imprint of* **Random House Publishing Group**

Villegas Editores S.A. (COL) *(958-9138; 958-9393; 958-8160) Dist. by* **IPG Chicago.**

Vincent, Thomas J. Foundation Inc., *(0-9759284)* 44-447 Kaneohe Bay Dr., Kaneohe, HI 96744 USA
E-mail: vincentfoundation@yahoo.com.

Vincero Enterprises, *(0-9675329)* 490 Marin Oaks Dr., Novato, CA 94949 USA Tel 800-715-1492; Fax: 415-883-4115; Toll Free: 800-715-1492
E-mail: heritage1492@earthlink.net
Web site: http://www.italianheritage.net; http://www.hispaniclatino.net
Dist(s): **Baker & Taylor Bks.**

Vindof Publishing, *(0-9759310)* 410 N. 3rd St., Ft. Atkinson, WI 53538 USA.

Vinestreet Pr., *(0-9702833)* P.O. Box 5414, Kansas City, MO 64131-5414 USA Fax: 816-361-2436
E-mail: vinestreet@kc.rr.com
Web site: http://www.vinestreet.net.

Vineyard Publishing, LLC *See* **Ampelon Publishing, LLC**

Vinh, Phuong, *(0-9675524)* 3636 Regal Oaks Pl., Perris, CA 92571 USA Tel 951-657-7257.

Vinings Publishing, *(1-929669)* 1015 E. Semoran Blvd., Suite 253, Casselberry, FL 32707 USA Tel 407-834-8220; Fax: 407-834-8201
E-mail: joann@iid.net.

Vinland Pr., *(0-9721410)* P.O. Box 927, North Bend, OR 97459 USA Tel 541-751-1566
E-mail: susan.coons@verizon.net.

Vintage *Imprint of* **Knopf Publishing Group**

Vintage Point Pr., *(0-9704839)* 313 Pine St., Yankton, SD 57078-4435 USA
E-mail: vintagepoint@iw.net
Web site: http://www.vintagepoint.com.

VIP Publishing *See* **300Incredible.com LLC**

Vipassana Research Publications *See* **Pariyatti Publishing**

Viper Comics, *(0-9754193; 0-9777883; 0-9793680)* Div. of Viper Entertainment Inc., 9400 N. MacArthur Blvd., Suite 124-215, Irving, TX 75063 USA Tel 214-638-1400; 469-682-9331; Fax: 817-741-3758
E-mail: jessie@vipercomics.com
Web site: http://www.vipercomics.com
Dist(s): **Baker & Taylor Bks.**
Diamond Comic Distributors, Inc.

Viresh Pubns., *(0-9700645)* 3234 Bayberry Rd., Ames, IA 50014-4597 USA Tel 515-292-2271; P.O. Box 103, Ames, IA 50010-2439 Tel 515-292-6009; Fax: 515-292-0600
E-mail: vireshpubns@hotmail.com
Web site: http://www.anitaslegacy.com.

Virgin Bks. Ltd. (GBR) *(0-426; 0-7535; 0-86369; 1-85227; 0-907080; 1-905264) Dist. by* **Macmillan.**

Virgin Publishing, *(0-9640027)* 500 N. Oseola, No. 404, Clearwater, FL 33515 USA.

†**Virginia Museum of Fine Arts,** *(0-917046; 1-934351)* Orders Addr.: 200 N. Boulevard, Richmond, VA 23220-4007 USA (SAN 281-0204) Tel 804-204-2713; 804-204-2710; Fax: 804-204-2724; Toll Free: 800-943-8632
E-mail: sara.johnson-ward@vmfa.museum; libby.causey-hicks@vmfa.museum
Web site: http://www.vmfa.state.va.us
Dist(s): **Blair, John F. Pub.**; *CIP.*

Virginia Museum of Natural History, *(0-9625801; 1-884549)* 21 Starling Ave., Martinsville, VA 24112-2921 USA
E-mail: dgreytak@vmnh.org.

Virginia Publishing Corp., *(0-9631448; 1-891442)* 625 N. Euclid, Suite 330, Saint Louis, MO 63108 USA Tel 314-367-6612 ext 22; Fax: 314-367-0727 Do not confuse with Virginia Publishing Co. in Lynchburg, VA
E-mail: jfister@westendword.com
Web site: http://www.stl-books.com
Dist(s): **Big River Distribution**
Booksource, The
Partners Bk. Distributing, Inc.

Virginia Records, Inc., *(1-890818)* 422 Mamaroneck Ave., Mamaroneck, NY 10543 USA Tel 914-381-2565; Fax: 914-381-0907
E-mail: froggy@froggyscountrystory.com
Web site: http://www.froggyscountrystory.com.

Virginian Pilot, *(0-9648308)* Div. of Landmark Communcations, Inc., 150 W. Brambleton Ave., Norfolk, VA 23501 USA Tel 757-481-4777; Fax: 757-446-2963
E-mail: linda.hollingsworth@pilotonline.com; pam.smithrodden@pilotonline.com
Dist(s): **Parnassus Bk. Distributors.**

VirTru Powers, *(0-9778798; 0-9779497)* Orders Addr.: P.O. Box 9404, Tavernier, FL 33070 USA; Edit Addr.: 10S073 Clarendon Hills Rd., Willowbrook, IL 60527 USA (SAN 850-492X) Tel 630-986-5262; Fax: 630-986-5262
E-mail: nomorewast@aol.com.

Virtual Baby Nurse LLC, *(0-9755180)* P.O. Box 881296, Port Saint Lucie, FL 34988-1296 USA (SAN 256-1239)
Web site: http://www.virtualbabynurse.com.

Virtual Press, The *See* **Reagent Pr.**

Virtualbookworm.com Publishing, Inc., *(0-9703682; 1-58939; 1-60264)* P.O. Box 9949, College Station, TX 77842 USA (SAN 852-6575) Toll Free: 877-376-4955 (phone/fax)
E-mail: info@virtualbookworm.com
Web site: http://www.virtualbookworm.com
Dist(s): **Replica Bks.**

Virtue Bks., *(0-9746440)* Div. of Virtue Products, Inc., 197 Woodland Pkwy., No. 104-476, San Marcos, CA 92069 USA Tel 760-471-5511; Fax: 760-471-5515; Toll Free: 800-201-5200
E-mail: kenwilcox3@cox.net; ken@virtueproducts.com
Web site: http://www.virtueproducts.com.

Virtuous Conquerors, *(0-9740504)* P.O. Box 1943, Roanoke, TX 76262-5818 USA
E-mail: jenifercm@ev1.net.

Viselman, Kenn Presents.., *(0-9722361)* P.O. Box 195, New York, NY 10113 USA (SAN 254-7783) Tel 212-929-1234
E-mail: viselmanpresents@aol.com.

Visible Ink Pr., *(0-7876; 0-8103; 1-57859)* Orders Addr.: 1094 Flex Dr., Jackson, TN 38301-5070 USA Toll Free Fax: 800-351-5073; Toll Free: 800-343-4499; Edit Addr.: 43311 Joy Rd., No. 414, Canton, MI 48187-2075 USA Tel 734-667-3211; Fax: 734-667-4311
E-mail: inquiries@visibleink.com
Web site: http://www.visibleink.com
Dist(s): **Independent Pubs. Group**
Mint Pubs. Group.

Visikid Bks. *Imprint of* **GSVQ Publishing**

Vision *Imprint of* **Grand Central Publishing**

Vision Bks. International, *(1-56550)* 775 E. Blithedale Ave., No. 342, Mill Valley, CA 94941 USA (SAN 297-6447) Tel 415-383-0962; Fax: 415-383-4521
E-mail: publisher@vbipublishing.com
Web site: http://www.vbipublishing.com
Dist(s): **Baker & Taylor Bks.**
Brodart Co.
Quality Bks., Inc.

Vision Communications, *(0-9625516; 1-931425)* Div. of New Covenant Church & Ministries, Inc., 4625 N. Keystone Ave., Indianapolis, IN 46205 USA Tel 317-257-2687; Fax: 317-257-7732; Toll Free: 800-610-9777 (orders)
E-mail: bryan@visionbooks.com
Web site: http://www.visionbooks.com.

Vision Forum, Inc., The, *(0-9665233; 1-929241; 0-9755263; 0-9787559; 1-934554)* 4719 Blanco Rd., San Antonio, TX 78212 USA Tel 210-340-5250; Fax: 210-340-8577; Toll Free: 800-440-0022
E-mail: orders@visionforum.com
Web site: http://www.visionforum.com
Dist(s): **STL Distribution North America.**

Vision Harmony Publishing, *(0-9748715)* 13089 Peyton Dr., No. C-201, Chino Hills, CA 91709 USA Tel 951-505-2503; Toll Free Fax: 866-855-1476
E-mail: monica@monicapayton.com
Web site: http://www.monicapayton.com.

Vision Pubns., *(0-9746161; 1-933260)* P.O. Box 71532, Marietta, GA 30007-1532 USA Fax: 770-973-9446; Toll Free: 800-862-5264 Do not confuse with companies with the same name in Southfield, MI, Saint Louis, MO, Boise, ID
E-mail: visionpublications@earthlink.net; dvandewalker@earlink.net.

Vision Publishing Group, *(1-892861)* P.O. Box 256, Griffin, GA 30224 USA Tel 770-467-9100; Fax: 770-228-0202; Toll Free: 800-457-6241
E-mail: visionpublishing@mindspring.com
Web site: http://www.vision-publishing.com.

Vision to Action, Inc., *(0-9641581; 1-891917)* Orders Addr.: P.O. Box 2003, Emporia, KS 66801 USA Tel 620-343-7989 (phone/fax); Edit Addr.: 2416 Westridge, Emporia, KS 66801 USA
E-mail: vision2a@cadvantage.com; nancy@annettelamb.com
Web site: http://www.eduscapes.com/v2a/index.html.

Vision Unlimited Pr., *(0-9746385)* 3832 Radnor Ave., Long Beach, CA 90808 USA Tel 562-537-1397 Do not confuse with Vision Unlimited in Spartanburg, SC
E-mail: joachung@msn.com; susan@newhopegrief.org.

Vision Video, *(1-56364)* Orders Addr.: P.O. Box 540, Worcester, PA 19490 USA Tel 610-584-3500; Fax: 610-584-4610; Toll Free: 800-523-0226; Edit Addr.: 2030 Wentz Church Rd., Worcester, PA 19490 USA (SAN 298-7392)
E-mail: info@gatewayfilms.com; info@visionvideo.com
Web site: http://www.gatewayfilms.com
Dist(s): **Jones, Bob Univ. Pr.**
Christian Bk. Distributors
Follett Media Distribution
Midwest Tape
Spring Arbor Distributors, Inc.
Tapeworm Video Distributor, Inc.

Vision Works Publishing, *(0-9678529; 0-9728840)* P.O. Box 217, Boxford, MA 01921 USA (SAN 253-3758) Fax: 630-982-2134; Toll Free: 888-821-3135
E-mail: visionworksbooks@email.com
Web site: http://www.VisionWorksPublishing.com.

Visionaries *Imprint of* **Marvel Enterprises, Inc.**

VisionQuest Kids *Imprint of* **GSVQ Publishing**

VisionQuest Ministries, *(0-9716489)* P.O. Box 275, Genoa, NV 89411 USA Tel 775-450-1625; Fax: 775-984-9004
E-mail: john@vqresources.com
Web site: http://www.vqresources.com.

Visions, *(0-9671487)* P.O. Box 81404, Las Vegas, NV 89180-1404 USA.

Visions Of Nature, *(0-9656051; 0-9749570)* 460 E. 56th St., Suite A, Anchorage, AK 99518 USA Tel 907-561-4062
E-mail: robolson@gci.com
Web site: http://robertolson.com.

Visit to Hawaii, A, *(0-9772200)* 445 Kaiolu St., No. 807, Honolulu, HI 55303 USA Tel 808-921-2440
E-mail: hawaiiholm@aol.com
Dist(s): **Booklines Hawaii, Ltd.**

Visor Bks., *(0-9771994)* P.O. Box 8765, The Woodlands, TX 77387 USA (SAN 256-9752)
E-mail: administrator@visorbooks.com
Web site: http://www.visorbooks.com
Dist(s): **AtlasBooks Distribution.**

Vista Press Ventures, Incorporated *See* **Eaglemont Pr.**

Vista Publishing, Inc., *(1-880254)* 151 Delaware Ave., Oakhurst, NJ 07755-1312 USA Toll Free: 800-634-2498
E-mail: info@vistapubl.com
Web site: http://www.vistapubl.com.

Visual Bk. Co., LLC, The, *(0-9714334)* P.O. Box 1123, Stratford, CT 06615 USA
E-mail: myvisualbook@aol.com.

Visual Education Productions, *(1-56918)* 1020 SE Loop 289, Lubbock, TX 79404 USA Tel 806-745-8820; Toll Free: 800-922-9965
E-mail: cev@cevmultimedia.com
Web site: http://www.cevmultimedia.com.

Visual Fulfillment Service *See* **Cela Distribution Services**

Visual Manna, *(0-9677386; 0-9715970)* Orders Addr.: P.O. Box 553, Salem, MO 65560 USA; Edit Addr.: 1403 Dent County Rd., 502A, Salem, MO 65560 USA.

Visual Understanding in Education, *(0-9667849)* 149 Fifth Ave., Suite 708, New York, NY 10010 USA Tel 212-253-9007; Fax: 212-253-9137
E-mail: gholmes@vue.org
Web site: http://www.vue.org.

Vital Health Publishing *Imprint of* **Square One Publishers**

Vital Link Orange County, *(0-9765880)* Orders Addr.: P.O. Box 12064, Costa Mesa, CA 92627 USA Tel 949-646-2520; Fax: 949-646-2523; Edit Addr.: 1701 E. 16th St., Newport Beach, CA 92663 USA
E-mail: kathy@vitallinkoc.org
Web site: http://www.vitallinkoc.org.

Vital Links, *(0-9717653)* 6613 Seybold Rd., Suite E, Madison, WI 53719 USA Tel 608-270-5424; Fax: 608-278-9363; Toll Free: 866-829-6331
Web site: http://vitallinks.net.

Vives, Luis Editorial (Edelvives) (ESP) *(84-263) Dist. by* **Lectorum Pubns.**

Vivisphere Publishing, *(1-892323; 1-58776)* Div. of Net Pub Corp., Orders Addr.: 675 Dutchess Tpke., Poughkeepsie, NY 12603 USA (SAN 253-441X) Tel 845-463-1100; Fax: 845-463-0018; Toll Free: 800-724-1100
E-mail: cs@vivisphere.com
Web site: http://www.vivisphere.com.

Viz Comics *Imprint of* **Viz Media**

Viz Communications, Incorporated *See* **Viz Media**

Viz Media, *(0-929279; 1-56931; 1-59116; 1-4215)* Subs. of Shogakukan, Inc., 655 Bryant St., San Francisco, CA 94122 USA (SAN 248-8604) Tel 415-546-7073; Fax: 415-546-7086 ; *Imprints:* Cadence Books (Cadence Bks); Viz Comics (Viz Comics)
E-mail: scott@viz.com
Web site: http://www.viz.com
Dist(s): **AAA Anime Distribution**
Diamond Comic Distributors, Inc.
Simon & Schuster, Inc.

Vizione Productions Inc., *(0-9758863)* P.O. Box 54838, Atlanta, GA 30308 USA (SAN 256-1158) Tel 404-538-9424.

VJM PublicA *See* **VJM Pubns.**

VJM Pubns., *(0-9717556)* 3001 Fawkes Ct, Virginia Beach, VA 23453 USA Tel 757-368-5702; Fax: 757-368-5619
E-mail: bturner@pinn.net
Web site: http://www.VJM Publications.com.

VK Publishing, Inc., *(0-9777171)* 464 Ridgewood Ln., Buffalo Grove, IL 60089 USA (SAN 850-0509)
E-mail: vkofman@vkpublishing.com.

Vocal Power Inc., *(0-934419)* 2123 N. Topanga Canyon Blvd., Topanga, CA 90290 USA (SAN 693-4471) Toll Free: 800-829-7664
E-mail: info@vocalpowerinc.com
Web site: http://www.vocalpowerinc.com
Dist(s): **Alfred Publishing Co., Inc.**

Vocalis, Ltd., *(0-9665743; 0-9709948; 1-932653)* 100 Avalon Cir., Waterbury, CT 06710 USA Tel 203-753-5244; Fax: 203-574-5433
E-mail: vocalis@sbcglobal.net; info@VocalisESL.com
Web site: http://www.vocalisltd.com; http://www.vocalisesl.com; http://www.vocalis.com.

Vocational Biographies, *(0-87063; 0-914297)* Orders Addr.: P.O. Box 31, Sauk Centre, MN 56378-0031 USA (SAN 287-6035) Tel 320-352-6516; Fax: 320-352-5546; Toll Free: 800-255-0752; Edit Addr.: 414 S. Sixth St., Sauk Centre, MN 56378-0031 USA
E-mail: careers@vocbio.com
Web site: http://www.vocbio.com.

Vogel, Robert, *(0-9768455)* P.O. Box 551, Chesterton, IN 46304 USA Tel 219-688-5895; Toll Free: 800-815-7685 (phone/fax) Do not confuse with Robert Vogel in South Burlington, VT
E-mail: contact@azarovmemories.com
Web site: http://www.garrythegroundhog.com.

Vogel, Susan *See* **Pince-Nez Pr.**

Voice & Vision Pubns., *(1-888251)* 902 Fletcher Ave., Indianapolis, IN 46203 USA Tel 317-262-4030; Fax: 317-262-4029
E-mail: voicevision@apostolic.edu.

Voice of Light Pubns., *(0-9785623)* P.O. Box 1437, Fair Oaks, CA 95628 USA (SAN 850-9905) Tel 916-965-3046
E-mail: voiceoflight@comcast.net.

Voice Studio Press, The *See* **Jeannie Deva Enterprises, Inc.**

Voices Community Pr. *Imprint of* **Jacar Press Literary Community**

Voices: Community Stories Past & Present, Inc., *(0-9700771)* 3400 E. Speedway, Suite 118-213, Tucson, AZ 85716 USA Tel 520-622-7458; Fax: 520-624-4766; P.O. Box 2088, Tucson, AZ 85702-2088 ; *Imprints:* Tucson Voices Press (Tucson Voices Pr)
E-mail: sfarley@igc.org
Web site: http://tucson.com/voices.

Voigt, J. M. Incorporated *See* **MindWare Holdings, Inc.**

Volare, LLC, *(0-9769366)* Orders Addr.: 1967 E. Maple St. # 304, North Canton, OH 44720-3333 USA; Edit Addr.: P.O. Box 9088, Canton, OH 44711 USA
E-mail: volarellc@aol.com
Web site: http://www.volarellc.com.

†**Volcano Pr.,** *(0-912078; 1-884244)* Orders Addr.: P.O. Box 270, Volcano, CA 95689 USA (SAN 220-0015) Tel 209-296-4991; Fax: 209-296-4995; Toll Free: 800-879-9636; Edit Addr.: 21496 National St., Volcano, CA 95689 USA
E-mail: info@volcanopress.com; sales@volcanopress.com; adam@volcanopress.com
Web site: http://www.volcanopress.com
Dist(s): **Baker & Taylor Bks.**
New Leaf Distributing Co., Inc.
Quality Bks., Inc.; *CIP.*

Voll, Dudley & Donna *See* **Golden Words Publishing**

Volo *Imprint of* **Hyperion Bks. for Children**

Volt Pr. *Imprint of* **Bonus Bks., Inc.**

Volunteers of the Colorado Historical Society, *(0-9770423)* 1300 Broadway, Denver, CO 80203-2167 USA
E-mail: angela.caudill@chs.state.co.us.

von Buchwald, Martin Farina, *(0-9777266)* 1158 5th Ave., New York, NY 10029 USA Tel 212-348-5580
E-mail: martin@farina.com.

Von Enterprises International, Inc., *(0-9718373)* P.O. Box 693502, Miami, FL 33269 USA
E-mail: laurenspicer@aol.com
Web site: http://www.spicerackbooks.com.

Vonshollywood, *(0-9709368)* 11317 Riverwood Terr., Sunland, CA 91040 USA Tel 818-353-6057
E-mail: vonrex@gte.net
Web site: http://vonshollywood.com.

Vorndran, Judith Clay, *(0-9772439)* 6431 Antoinette Dr., Mentor, OH 44060-3431 USA
E-mail: jclayvorndran05@sbcglobal.net; jclayvorndran@aol.com
Web site: http://www.hometown.aol.com/jclayvorndran/myhomepage; http://www.geocities.com/jjvorndran@sbcglobal.net/My_page.html.

Voss, Dawn L., *(0-615)* 481 Hallman St., Berlin, WI 54923 USA
E-mail: wr1t3r@yahoo.com
Dist(s): **Lulu.com.**

Voyager Bks./Libros Viajeros *Imprint of* **Harcourt Children's Bks.**

Voyageur Pr., Inc., *(0-7603; 0-89658)* Orders Addr.: P.O. Box 338, Stillwater, MN 55082 USA Toll Free: 800-888-9653; Edit Addr.: 380 Jackson St. Ste. 200, Saint Paul, MN 55101-4810 USA (SAN 287-2668)
E-mail: books@voyageurpress.com
Web site: http://www.voyageurpress.com
Dist(s): **Islander Group**
MBI Distribution Services
MBI Publishing Co. LLC.

VR Pubns., *(0-9658334)* P.O. Box 1720, Higley, AZ 85236 USA (SAN 254-7570) Tel 480-905-0337; Fax: 480-596-4037
E-mail: vramospub@msn.com
Web site: http://www.users.uswest.net/~urpub.

VSP Bks. *Imprint of* **Vacation Spot Publishing**

Company

Washburn Design & Consulting, Inc., *(0-9714196)* 19261 Phil Ln., Cupertino, CA 95014 USA.

Washington, Kim M., *(0-9679727)* Orders Addr.: P.O. Box 56, Worth, IL 60482 USA Tel 708-285-0971; Fax: 312-864-9525; Edit Addr.: 2836 W. 99th St., Evergreen Park, IL 60805 USA Do not confuse with Morris Publishing, Kearny, NE
E-mail: earlymorningswim@yahoo.com.

Washington Sikh Ctr./Sikh Youth Forum, *(0-942245)* 10805 Brickyard Ct., Potomac, MD 20854-1788 USA (SAN 666-8658) Tel 301-983-6862 (phone/fax)
E-mail: devinder@thinktankinc.net.

Washington Square Pr. *Imprint of* **Simon & Schuster**

Wasi Pubns. (ZWE) *(99908-48) Dist. by* **Mich St U Pr.**

Wasteland Pr., *(0-9715811; 0-9724289; 0-9729186; 0-9740725; 0-9742342; 0-9744368; 0-9746290; 0-9748230; 1-932852; 1-933265; 1-60047)* Orders Addr.: P.O. Box 925, Shelbyville, KY 40066 USA Toll Free: 888-772-9678 (phone/fax); Edit Addr.: 2022 Osprey Cove Ave., Shelbyville, KY 40066 USA
Web site: http://www.wastelandpress.net
Dist(s): **Lightning Source, Inc.**

Watch & Learn, Inc., *(1-893907)* 1882 Queens Way, Atlanta, GA 30341 USA Tel 770-458-5597; Fax: 770-457-2132; Toll Free: 800-416-7088
E-mail: bc@cvls.com
Web site: http://www.cvls.com.

Watch Me Grow Kids, *(1-932555)* P.O. Box 4405, Carson, CA 90749 USA (SAN 255-5093) Fax: 310-532-4536
E-mail: panderson@watchmegrowkids.com
Web site: http://www.watchmegrowkids.com
Dist(s): **Baker & Taylor Bks.**

Watchmaker Pr., *(0-9715123)* 131 E. Pioneer Ct., Lebanon Junction, KY 40150 USA Tel 502-543-3677
E-mail: hettingr@iglou.com
Web site: http://www.iglou.com/watchmakerpress.

Watchman Outreach Ministries, *(0-9726107)* RR1, Box 218E, Schell City, MO 64783 USA Tel 417-432-3119; Fax: 417-432-3672.

Water Daughter Publishing, *(0-9753089)* P.O. Box 930031, Rockaway Beach, NY 11693 USA Toll Free: 888-778-2928
E-mail: info@waterdaughter.com
Web site: http://www.waterdaughter.com.

Water Lily Pr., Inc., *(0-9772168)* 17214 Hillview Ln., Spring, TX 77379 USA.

Water Row Pr., *(0-934953)* Subs. of Water Row Bks., P.O. Box 438, Sudbury, MA 01776 USA (SAN 694-6011) Tel 508-485-8515; Fax: 508-229-0885
E-mail: waterrow@aol.com
Web site: http://www.waterrowbooks.com
Dist(s): **Baker & Taylor Bks.**
Last Gasp of San Francisco.

Waterbird Bks. *Imprint of* **School Specialty Publishing**

WaterBrook Pr. *Imprint of* **WaterBrook Pr.**

WaterBrook Pr., Div. of Random Hse., Inc., Orders Addr.: 400 Hahn Rd., Westminster, MD 21157 USA Tel 410-848-1900; Toll Free: 800-726-0600 (customer service); 800-733-3000; Edit Addr.: 12265 Oracle Blvd., Suite 200, Colorado Springs, CO 80921 USA (SAN 299-4682) Tel 719-590-4999; Fax: 719-590-8977; Toll Free Fax: 800-294-5686; Toll Free: 800-603-7051 ; *Imprints:* Shaw (ShawRH); WaterBrook Press (WaterB Pr); Multnomah (Mltnmah); Multnomah Fiction (Mult Fiction); Multnomah Kidz (Mult Kidz); Loyal Publishers (Loyal); Multnomah Gift Books (Multnom Gift Bks) Do not confuse with WaterBrook Pr., Great Falls, VA
Web site: http://www.randomhouse.com/waterbrook
Dist(s): **Anchor Distributors**
Random Hse., Inc.

WaterBrook Press *See* **WindowBox Pr.**

Watercourse, The, *(1-888631)* Montana State Univ., 201 Culbertson Hall, Bozeman, MT 59717-0057 USA Tel 406-994-5392; Fax: 406-994-1919
E-mail: rwwso@montana.edu; projectwet@montana.edu
Web site: http://www.projectwet.org.

Watercress Pr., *(0-934955)* 111 Grotto Blvd., San Antonio, TX 78216-7131 USA (SAN 694-4116) Tel 210-344-5338; Fax: 210-320-9536
E-mail: ace@watercresspress.com
Web site: http://watercresspress.com.

Waterfall Ridge, *(0-9725485)* 40497 Cty. Rd. 20, Saint Peter, MN 56082 USA.

Waterford Pr., Ltd., *(0-9640225; 1-58355; 1-889903)* Orders Addr.: P.O. Box 4739, Blaine, WA 98231-4739 USA Tel 360-332-7301; Fax: 360-332-6084; Toll Free: 800-434-2555; Edit Addr.: 428 N. 24th St., Phoenix, AZ 85008 USA Tel 602-681-3333
E-mail: info@waterfordpress.com
Web site: http://www.waterfordpress.com
Dist(s): **Globe Pequot Pr., The.**

Waterhouse Publishing, *(0-9764082)* 40 Sheridan Ave., Congers, NY 10920 USA Tel 646-391-6669; Toll Free Fax: 877-260-5758 Do not confuse with Waterhouse Publishing in Scottsdale, AZ
E-mail: dfighter@msn.com
Web site: http://www.devonharrislive.com.

Watering Can, *(0-9759868)* 351 W. 19th St., New York, NY 10011 USA
E-mail: info@wateringcanpress.com
Web site: http://www.wateringcanpress.com.

Watering the Seed Productions *See* **Grace & Mercy Publishing**

Waterline Bks., *(0-9628492; 0-9764275)* Orders Addr.: P.O. Box 331, Hardwick, MA 01037 USA; Edit Addr.: 443 Czeski Rd., Hardwick, MA 01037 USA.

Watermark Cruises, *(0-9754400)* P.O. Box 3350, Annapolis, MD 21403 USA
Web site: http://www.watermarkcruises.com.

WaterMark, Inc., *(1-882077)* 2080 Valleydale Rd., Suite 15, Birmingham, AL 35244-2000 USA (SAN 248-2010) Tel 205-403-9882; Fax: 205-403-9162; Toll Free: 888-490-0100 Do not confuse with Watermark Assocs. in New York, NY or Watermark Pr., Inc. in Wichita, KS
E-mail: michelle@picture-book.com
Web site: http://www.picture-book.com
Dist(s): **Menasha Ridge Pr., Inc.**

Watermark Pr., The (AUS) *(0-949284) Dist. by* **Antique Collect.**

Watermark Pr., *(1-57553; 1-58235; 0-7951)* 3600 Crondall Ln. Ste. 100, Owings Mills, MD 21117-2233 USA Do not confuse with companies with same or similar names in Wichita KS, Seattle, WA
E-mail: emueck@circapress.com
Web site: http://www.poetry.com/.

Watermark Publishing, LLC, *(0-9631154; 0-9705787; 0-9720932; 0-9742672; 0-9753740; 0-9779143; 0-9790647; 0-9796769)* 1088 Bishop St., Suite 310, Honolulu, HI 96813 USA (SAN 253-7427) Tel 808-587-7766; Fax: 808-521-3461; Toll Free: 866-900-2665 (866-900-BOOK) Do not confuse with confuse with companies with the same or similar names in San Diego, CA, Beverly Hills, CA, Seattle, WA
E-mail: info@bookshawaii.net
Web site: http://www.bookshawaii.net
Dist(s): **Austin & Company, Inc.**
Baker & Taylor Bks.
Booklines Hawaii, Ltd.
Islander Group
Partners Pubs. Group, Inc.

WaterOak Publishing, *(0-9663170)* 6056 Thomasville Rd., Tallahassee, FL 32312 USA Tel 850-893-2315; Fax: 850-668-7100
Dist(s): **AtlasBooks Distribution.**

Watershed Bks., *(0-9645252)* 9413 Southgate Dr., Cincinnati, OH 45241-3340 USA (SAN 298-6256) Toll Free: 800-239-6229 Do not confuse with companies with same name in Garden Valley, ID, San Jose, CA, Kansas City, MO, Coloma, CA, Seattle, WA, Marbleton, GA, Wheaton, IL
E-mail: publisher@watershedbooks.com; dar60187@aol.com
Web site: http://www.watershedbooks.com
Dist(s): **Distributors, The**
National Bk. Network
New Leaf Distributing Co., Inc.

WaterShed Bks., *(0-9718310)* 1431 Haverhill Dr., Wheaton, IL 60187-7548 USA Tel 630-665-7180 (phone/fax) Do not confuse with companies with the same name in WaterShed Books in Lotus, CA, Boise, ID, Kansas City, MO, Marbleton, GA, Seattle, WA, Marietta, OH
E-mail: dar60187@aol.com.

Waterside Publishing, *(0-9766801; 1-933754)* 2376 Oxford Ave., Cardiff-by-the-Sea, CA 92007 USA
Web site: http://www.waterside.com
Dist(s): **Perseus Distribution.**

Waterview Pr., Inc., *(1-883114)* 3208 E. Colonial Dr., No. 301, Orlando, FL 32803 USA (SAN 135-9703) Tel 407-599-7200; Fax: 407-629-0662; Toll Free Fax: 800-726-0585
E-mail: editor@waterviewpress.com
Web site: http://www.waterviewpress.com
Dist(s): **Mickler's Bks., Inc.**
Southern Bk. Service.

Waterway Guide, *(0-9723131; 0-9768066; 0-9797937)* 326 First St., Suite 400, Annapolis, MD 21403 USA Tel 443-482-9377 Toll Free: 800-233-3359
E-mail: info@waterwayguide.com; ltaylor@waterwayguide.com
Web site: http://www.waterwayguide.com.

Waterwood Publishing Group, *(0-9769044)* Orders Addr.: P.O. Box 12540, Charlotte, NC 28220 USA (SAN 257-1072) Tel 704-477-0708
Web site: http://www.waterwoodpublishing.com.

Waterworks Publishing, *(0-9662520)* Div. of Freeman's Water Works, Inc., 792 100th Ave., N., Naples, FL 34108 USA Tel 941-597-6398; Fax: 941-597-6720
E-mail: WaterQuality@email.msn.com.

Watling St., Ltd. (GBR) *(1-904153) Dist. by* **Trafalgar.**

Watling St., Ltd. (GBR) *(1-904153) Dist. by* **IPG Chicago.**

Watosh Publishing, *(0-9611954)* P.O. Box 11231, Las Vegas, NV 89111 USA (SAN 286-1976) Tel 702-896-4108
E-mail: gecfly@aol.com
Web site: http://www.watoshpublishing.com; http://www.angietheaviator.com
Dist(s): **AtlasBooks Distribution.**

†**Watson-Guptill Pubns., Inc.,** *(0-8230)* Div. of VNU Business Media, Inc., 575 Prospect St., Lakewood, NJ 08701 USA Tel 732-363-5679; Toll Free Fax: 877-227-6564; Orders Addr.: 575 Prospect Street, Lakewood, NJ 08701 USA Toll Free: 800-451-1741; Edit Addr.: 770 Broadway, New York, NY 10003 USA (SAN 282-5384) ; *Imprints:* Back Stage Books (Back Stage Bks); Billboard Books (Billboard Bks)
E-mail: aalexander@watsonguptill.com
Web site: http://www.watsonguptill.com
Dist(s): **Macmillan**; *CIP.*

Watts, Franklin *Imprint of* **Scholastic Library Publishing**

Wave Publishing, *(0-9642359; 0-9722430)* Div. of Caroy, Inc., 4 Yawl St., Venice, CA 90292 USA (SAN 298-3788) Tel 310-306-0699; Fax: 310-822-4921 Do not confusw with Wave Publishing Comopany in Waiahu, HI
Dist(s): **Baker & Taylor Bks.**

Waveland Pr., Inc., *(0-88133; 0-917974; 1-57766)* 4180 IL Rte. 83, Suite 101, Prospect Heights, IL 60047 USA (SAN 209-0961) Tel 847-634-0081; Fax: 847-634-9501
E-mail: info@waveland.com
Web site: http://www.waveland.com.

Wawa Pr. *Imprint of* **Adisoft, Inc.**

Way Out Comics, *(0-9742386)* P.O. Box 642218, Los Angeles, CA 90064 USA
E-mail: julieyeh@sbcglobal.net
Web site: http://www.wayoutcomics.com.

WayaMedia, *(0-9765700)* 391 Watson Br. Rd., Cullowhee, NC 28723 USA (SAN 256-503X) Do not confuse with PPS Publishing Inc. in Lake in the Hills, IL
Web site: http://www.wayamedia.com.

Wayfarer Pr., LLC, *(0-9789965)* P.O. Box 948, Union Lake, MI 48387-0948 USA Do not confuse with Wayfarer Press in Plymouth, NH
E-mail: wayfarerpress@sbcglobal.net
Web site: http://www.wayfarerbooks.com.

Wayland Historical Society, *(0-9762756)* Orders Addr.: P.O. Box 56, Wayland, MA 01778 USA Tel 508-358-7959; Edit Addr.: 12 Cochituate Rd., Wayland, MA 01778 USA
E-mail: jane_sciacca@comcast.net
Web site: http://j.w.d.home.comcast.net/whs.

†**Wayne State Univ. Pr.,** *(0-8143)* Leonard N. Simons Bldg., 4809 Woodward Ave., Detroit, MI 48201-1309 USA (SAN 202-5221) Tel 313-577-6120; Fax: 313-577-6131; Toll Free: 800-978-7323 (customer orders) ; *Imprints:* Great Lakes Books (Great Lks Bks); Painted Turtle (Painted Turtle)
E-mail: theresa.martinelli@wayne.edu
Web site: http://www.wsupress.wayne.edu
Dist(s): **East-West Export Bks.**; *CIP.*

Wayne, Steven Co., *(0-9713154; 0-9727696)* 3940 Laurel Canyon Blvd., No. 698, Studio City, CA 91604 USA Tel 323-654-9339; Fax: 323-656-7324; Toll Free: 866-446-1201 ; *Imprints:* SWC Editions (SWC Editions)
E-mail: wschoenfeld@stevenwaynecompany.com; schoenfeld@swceditions.com
Web site: http://www.stevenwaynecompany.com; http://www.swceditions.com
Dist(s): **Biblio Distribution.**

Wayside Pubns., *(0-9749749)* P.O. Box 318, Goreville, IL 62939 USA (SAN 255-898X)
E-mail: vtoler@waysidepublishing.com
Web site: http://www.waysidepublications.com.

Wayside Publishing, *(1-877653)* 11 Jan Sebastian Dr. Ste. 5, Sandwich, MA 02563-2357 USA Toll Free: 888-302-2519
E-mail: wayside@sprintmail.com
Web site: http://www.waysidepublishing.com.

Wayward Wind Publishing, *(0-9722618)* P.O. Box 165, Dove Creek, CO 81324 USA Tel 970-677-2521; Fax: 970-677-2271
E-mail: waywardwind02@yahoo.com.

WayWord Publishing, *(0-9669647)* 12739 NE Shoreland Dr., Mequon, WI 53092 USA Tel 262-243-9460
E-mail: wayword@execpc.com.

WCB/McGraw-Hill *Imprint of* **McGraw-Hill Higher Education**

WCI Pr., *(0-9745480)* 6161 7th Ave N., St Petersburg, FL 33710-7015 USA
E-mail: clauberfl@aol.com
Web site: http://www.SoccerDreamsBook.com.

WCP *Imprint of* **White Canoe Productions**

WD Bks. *Imprint of* **WD Pubs.**

WD Pubs., *(0-9723593)* P.O. Box 453, San Gabriel, CA 91778 USA Tel 626-282-4730; Fax: 626-570-9680 ; *Imprints:* WD Books (WD Bks)
E-mail: gescomm@aol.com
Web site: http://www.votsee.com.

WD/GBGM Bks. *Imprint of* **General Board of Global Ministries, The United Methodist Church**

We Believe Publishing, *(0-9677090)* Orders Addr.: P.O. Box 871, Lomita, CA 90717 USA Tel 310-326-8929; Edit Addr.: 2054 Reynosa Dr., Torrance, CA 90501 USA
E-mail: Harehollow@msn.com.

We Love to Read Productions, *(0-9675466)* 1111 Midland Ave., Suite 6A, Bronxville, NY 10708 USA.

We Publish Bks., *(1-929841)* Div. of Star Enterprises International, Inc., P.O. Box 1814, Rancho Mirage, CA 92270 USA Tel 310-765-4078; Fax: 702-552-7767
E-mail: wepublishbooks@gmail.com
Web site: http://www.WePublishKids.com; http://www.WePublishBooks.com
Dist(s): **Baker & Taylor Bks.**
Lightning Source, Inc.

Weapons of Mass Instruction, *(0-9766978; 0-9769266)* 1504 Freedom Blvd., Suite A, Watsonville, CA 95076 USA Tel 831-728-0600
Web site: http://www.bilingualnation.com.

Weasel Bks. *Imprint of* **Galde Pr., Inc.**

Weathered Wise Publishing Co., *(0-9668085)* Orders Addr.: P.O. Box 535, Grand Island, NE 68802 USA Tel 308-381-4632; Edit Addr.: 591 E. 18th St., Grand Island, NE 68801 USA.

Weatherhill, Inc. *Imprint of* **Shambhala Pubns., Inc.**

Weatherstock, Inc., *(0-9728107)* P.O. Box 31808, Tucson, AZ 85751 USA.

Weaver *Imprint of* **Alpha Omega Pubns., Inc.**

Weaver Pr. (ZWE) *(1-77922) Dist. by* **Mich St U Pr.**

Web of Life Children's Bks., *(0-9773795; 0-9777539)* P.O. Box 2726, Berkeley, CA 94702-0726 USA
E-mail: mdunphy@weboflifebooks.com
Web site: http://www.weboflifebooks.com
Dist(s): **Perseus Distribution.**

Web Wise Services, Inc., *(0-9748237; 1-933404)* 305 Woodstock Rd, Eastlake, OH 44095 USA Tel 440-953-2443; Toll Free: 866-232-7032
Web site: http://www.webwiseseniors.com.

Webb, Jack, *(0-9640275; 0-9719906)* Div. of San Diego State Univ. Research Foundation, Orders Addr.: 7618 Stevenson, San Diego, CA 92120 USA Tel 619-723-5371
E-mail: jackwebb1@cox.net
Web site: http://www.bordervoices.com.

Webb Ministries, Inc., *(0-9632226)* Orders Addr.: P.O. Box 520729, Longwood, FL 32752-0729 USA Tel 407-834-5233; Fax: 407-332-6277
E-mail: Webbministries@cfl.rr.com
Dist(s): **Spring Arbor Distributors, Inc.**

WebbWorks, *(0-9791076)* P.O. Box 985, Semmes, AL 36575-0985 USA (SAN 852-4629)
E-mail: duet2sisters@bellsouth.net.

WebCartoons, LLC, *(0-9743215)* 3727 W. Magnilia Blvd., Suite No. 141, Burbank, CA 91510 USA Tel 818-620-4256; Fax: 818-598-1842
E-mail: jerryching@earthlink.net
Web site: http://www.thegreatestkingbok.com.

WeBeANS Corp., *(0-9740115)* 466 S. Spruce Ave., Galloway, NJ 08205 USA Tel 609-652-5778; Fax: 877-589-3184; Toll Free Fax: 877-589-3184; Toll Free: 888-867-8838
E-mail: john@webeans.net
Web site: http://www.webeans.net.

Webster Henrietta Publishing, *(0-9728222)* P.O. Box 50044, Myrtle Beach, SC 29579 USA Tel 843-251-8867; Fax: 843-236-0260
E-mail: mhetzer@websterhenrietta.com
Web site: http://www.websterhenrietta.com
Dist(s): **Independent Pubs. Group.**

Webster House Publishing LLC, *(1-932635)* 309 Florida Hill Rd., Ridgefield, CT 06877 USA Tel 203-438-0345; Fax: 203-438-0379
E-mail: fred@websterhousepub.com
Web site: http://www.websterhousepub.com.

Webster, Jennifer Hope, *(0-9706360)* Orders Addr.: 735 Center St., Costa Mesa, CA 92627 USA Tel 949-548-9412; Fax: 305-422-8354
E-mail: jen@chatwithgod.org; chatwithGod@hotmail.com
Web site: http://www.chatwithGod.org.

Webster's New World *Imprint of* **Wiley, John & Sons, Inc.**

Wedding Solutions Publishing, Inc., *(0-9639654; 1-887169; 1-934386)* 7290 Navajo Rd., Suite 207, San Diego, CA 92119 USA Tel 619-589-1919 Toll Free: 800-609-9200
E-mail: sarah@weddingsolutions.com
Web site: http://wspublishinggroup.com
Dist(s): **National Bk. Network.**

WEDDLE's, *(1-928734)* 2052 Shippan Ave., Stamford, CT 06902 USA Tel 203-964-1888; Fax: 203-964-1877
E-mail: info@weddles.com
Web site: http://www.weddles.com
Dist(s): **Independent Pubs. Group.**

WeDream.com, *(0-9764351)* P.O. Box 6020, Dillon, CO 80435-6020 USA
E-mail: climbing@wedream.com.

Wee Read Publishing, *(0-9723122)* 2269 Ginger Hill Loop., Lincoln, CA 95648-8719 USA
E-mail: lindamarchus@yahoo.com; vmarchus@hotmail.com
Web site: http://www.weereadpublishing.com.

Wee Smile Books *See* **Waking Light Pr., The**

Wee Wonder Bks., *(0-9708610)* Subs. of The Kennedy Co., 6522 Stafford Rd., Plant City, FL 33565 USA Tel 813-986-1722
E-mail: alk0571@aol.com.

Weebie Publishing *See* **Susi B. Marketing, Inc.**

Wee-Chee-Taw Publishing, *(0-9622632)* 4450 Phillips Dr., Wichita Falls, TX 76308 USA Tel 940-692-3791.

Weekly Reader Corp., *(0-8374)* Affil. of WRC Media, Orders Addr.: P.O. Box 120023, Stamford, CT 06912-0023 USA (SAN 207-060X) Tel 203-705-3569; Fax: 203-705-3483; Toll Free: 800-446-3355; 3001 Cindel Dr., Delran, NJ 08370 (SAN 207-0618); Edit Addr.: 1 Readers Digest Rd., Pleasantville, NY 10570-7000 USA
E-mail: cpekar@weeklyreader.com
Web site: http://www.weeklyreader.com.

Weekly Reader Early Learning Library *Imprint of* **Stevens, Gareth Inc.**

Weekly Reader Teacher's Pr *Imprint of* **iUniverse, Inc.**

Weems & Plath, Inc., *(1-878797)* 214 Eastern Ave., Annapolis, MD 21403 USA (SAN 630-9348) Tel 410-263-6700; Fax: 410-268-8713; Toll Free: 800-638-0428
E-mail: sales@weems-plath.com
Web site: http://www.weems-plath.com.

Weeping Willow Publishing, *(0-9789227)* Orders Addr.: P.O. Box 210577, Dallas, TX 75211 USA Tel 214-337-1514; Toll Free: 888-220-2224
E-mail: tom@weepingwillowpublishing.com
Web site: http://www.weepingwillowpublishing.com.

wee-speak *Imprint of* **Knife in the Toaster Publishing Co., LLC**

Wehmeyer, Betty Jean, *(1-892611)* 1640 E. T C Jester Blvd. Apt. 525, Houston, TX 77008-2571 USA.

Wehner, Adrienna, *(0-9653866)* P.O. Box 6196, San Jose, CA 95150-6196 USA
E-mail: Awehner408@hotmail.com.

Wehr Animations, *(0-9748093)* 3890 CloverLeaf Dr., Boulder, CO 80304 USA
Web site: http://www.wehranimations.com.

Weight Loss Buddy, Inc., *(0-9754448)* P.O. Box 488, Tenafly, NJ 07670 USA Toll Free: 877-283-3987
Web site: http://www.weightlossbuddy.com.

Weigl Pubs., Inc., *(1-930954; 1-59036)* 6325 Tenth St., SE, Calgary, AB T2H 2ZP CAN Tel 403-233-7747; Fax: 403-233-7769; Orders Addr.: 350 5th Ave., Suite 3304, PMB 6G, New York, NY 10118 USA Tel 866-649-3445; Fax: 866-449-3445
E-mail: editorial3@weigl.com
Web site: http://www.weigl.com
Dist(s): **Independent Pubs. Group.**

Weinstein Bks., *(1-60286)* Orders Addr.: 345 Hudson St., New York, NY 10014 USA (SAN 852-7652)
Dist(s): **Hachette Bk. Group.**

Weintraub, Melody, *(0-9715494)* 9190 Rocky Hills Dr., Cordova, TN 38018 USA.

Wei's Publishing Co., *(0-9747284)* 116 W. Donald St., South Bend, IN 46613 USA
E-mail: liuwei82@hotmail.com
Web site: http://www.weispublishing.com.

Weiser Bks. *Imprint of* **Red Wheel/Weiser**

Weiser, Samuel Incorporated *See* **Red Wheel/Weiser**

Weisman Pubns., *(0-9668921; 1-929205)* P.O. Box 240844, Apple Valley, MN 55124 USA Tel 612-890-0202
E-mail: seekinfo@isd.net
Web site: http://www.seek-info.com
Dist(s): **Chicago Distribution Ctr.**

Weiss, Janet Bruschetti, *(0-9747716)* P.O. Box 8411, Longboat Key, FL 34228 USA
E-mail: jentajean@aol.com.

Welch, Michael F., *(0-9705969)* Orders Addr.: P.O. Box 659, New Hope, PA 18938 USA Tel 215-340-1167 ext 12; Fax: 215-340-3931; Edit Addr.: 6356 Meetinghouse Rd., New Hope, PA 18938 USA
E-mail: mfwmfw@msn.com.

Welcome Bks. *Imprint of* **Welcome Enterprises, Inc.**

Welcome Enterprises, Inc., *(0-941807; 1-932183; 1-59962)* 6 W. 18th St., Third Flr., New York, NY 10011 USA (SAN 665-9888) Tel 212-989-3200; Fax: 212-989-3205 ; *Imprints:* Welcome Books (Welc Bks)
E-mail: info@welcomebooks.com
Web site: http://www.welcomebooks.com
Dist(s): **Random Hse., Inc.**
Simon & Schuster, Inc.

Welcome Rain Pubs., *(1-56649)* 532 LaGuardia Pl., No. 473, New York, NY 10012 USA (SAN 299-9528) Tel 212-889-0088; Fax: 212-889-0869
Dist(s): **National Bk. Network.**

Weldon Owen, Inc., *(1-875137; 1-892374)* 814 Montgomery St., San Francisco, CA 94133 USA Tel 415-291-0100; Fax: 415-291-8841 Do not confuse with Weldon Owen Reference, Inc. also at the same address
E-mail: info@weldonowen.com
Dist(s): **Chain Sales Marketing, Inc.**

Well Fire Pubns., *(0-615; 0-9701912)* Orders Addr.: 100 Markley St., Port Reading, NJ 07064-1897 USA Tel 732-636-2060; Fax: 732-636-2538
E-mail: sherryross@home.com
Web site: http://www.sherryross.com.

WellFire Publications *See* **Well Fire Pubns.**

Wellness, Inc., *(0-9648438; 1-931212)* 3838 Song River Cir., Duluth, GA 30097 USA Tel 770-844-8686; Fax: 770-844-6580; Toll Free: 800-786-1730 Do not confuse with Wellness, Inc., Boston, MA
E-mail: wellness@abraxis.com
Web site: http://www.organwiseguys.com.

Wellness Pubn., *(0-9701490; 0-9748581)* 624 Marsat Ct., Chula Vista, CA 91911-4646 USA Toll Free: 800-755-4656 ; *Imprints:* Bayport Press (Bayport Pr) Do not confuse with companies with the same or similar name in Rockport, TX, Omaha, NE, Holland, MI, Ft. Lauderdale, FL, Santa Barbara, CA
E-mail: wellness@cts.com; ted@soriano.com
Web site: http://www.drjwallach.com.

Wells College Pr., *(1-887196)* Div. of Wells College, Wells College, Aurora, NY 13026 USA Tel 315-364-3420
E-mail: wellscollegepress@wells.edu
Web site: http://www.wells.edu/bookarts/index.html.

Welsh Academic Pr. (GBR) *(1-86057) Dist. by* **Intl Spec Bk.**

Welt, Rich & Assocs., *(0-9706529)* 8401 Heron Cir., Huntington Beach, CA 92646 USA Tel 866-742-4935
E-mail: richwelt@aol.com
Web site: http://richwelt.com.

WEM Records, *(1-878360)* 16230 Van Buren Blvd., Riverside, CA 92504 USA Tel 951-780-2322; Fax: 951-789-0130
E-mail: wemrecords@mcneilmusic.com
Web site: http://www.mcneilmusic.com
Dist(s): **Book Wholesalers, Inc.**
Brodart Co.
Follett Library Resources
Music in Motion
Partners/West
Professional Media Service Corp.
Quality Bks., Inc.
Social Studies Schl. Service
Teacher's Discovery.

We-Publish.com, *(1-931335)* 413 Interamerica Suite 01-4692, Laredo, TX 78045 USA Toll Free: 800-280-7541 (phone/fax)
E-mail: admin@banmex.com
Web site: http://www.we-publish.com.

Wesleyan Publishing Hse., *(0-89827)* Div. of The Wesleyan Church, P.O. Box 50434, Indianapolis, IN 46250-0434 USA (SAN 162-7104) Tel 317-774-3853; Fax: 317-774-3860; Toll Free Fax: 800-788-3535; Toll Free: 800-493-7539 (orders only)
E-mail: wph@wesleyan.org; wpg@wesleyan.org
Web site: http://www.wesleyan.org/wph
Dist(s): **CRC Pubns.**

Wesleyan Univ. Pr., *(0-8195)* Div. of Wesleyan University, 215 Long Ln., Middletown, CT 06459 USA Tel 860-685-7711; Fax: 860-685-7712
E-mail: Lstarr@wesleyan.edu
Web site: http://www.upne.com/order.html; http://www.wesleyan.edu/wespress/
Dist(s): **Univ. Pr. of New England.**

West Coast Crime *Imprint of* **Blue Heron Publishing**

West, Dave Corporation *See* **Aztec 5 Publishing**

West, Elizabeth, *(0-9720919)* 339 N. Eighth St., Middletown, IN 47356 USA
Web site: http://.

West End Games *Imprint of* **Purgatory Publishing Inc.**

West End Games, Inc., *(0-87431)* Subs. of Bucci Imports, R.D. 3, Box 2345, Honesdale, PA 18431 USA (SAN 687-8466) Tel 717-253-6990; Fax: 717-253-5104
E-mail: dspweg@hotmail.com
Web site: http://www.westendgames.net.

West, Kim, *(0-9743905)* 4629 Carriage Dr., Virginia Bch, VA 23462-7454 USA
E-mail: wkhwest@aol.com
Web site: http://www.kwestpublish.com/.

West Virginia Univ. Pr., *(0-937058; 1-933202)* Orders Addr.: P.O. Box 6295, Morgantown, WV 26506-6295 USA (SAN 205-5163) Tel 304-293-8400; Fax: 304-293-6585; Toll Free: 866-988-7737
E-mail: Sara.Pritchard@mail.wvu.edu
Web site: http://www.wvupress.com
Dist(s): **Ingram Bk. Co.**

West Winds Pr. *Imprint of* **Graphic Arts Ctr. Publishing Co.**

West Woods Pr., *(0-9776837)* 3905 Westwood Cir., Flagstaff, AZ 86001 USA (SAN 257-9375)
Web site: http://www.West Woods Press.com.

Westcliff Pubns., *(0-932896)* 2741 Cardinal Dr., Costa Mesa, CA 92626-4715 USA (SAN 212-2448).

Westcliffe Pubs., *(0-929969; 0-942394; 1-56579)* Div. of Big Earth Publishing, Orders Addr.: 3005 Center Green Dr., Suite 220, Boulder, CO 80301 USA Tel 303-443-9766; Fax: 303-443-9687; Toll Free: 800-258-5830 Do not confuse with Westcliff Publications in Newport Beach, CA
E-mail: sales@westcliffepublishers.com
Web site: http://www.westcliffepublishers.com
Dist(s): **Books West.**

Westcom Press *See* **Cathedrall Pr./Encycloware**

Westcreek Industries/Westcreek Publishing, *(0-9700747)* 23817 Ladrillo St., Woodland Hills, CA 91367 USA Tel 818-716-5773; Fax: 818-715-7178; Toll Free: 800-655-7170
E-mail: westcrk@pacebell.net.

Westen Integrity Bk. Pubs., *(0-9718177)* Orders Addr.: P.O. Box 116, Jackson, WI 53037-0116 USA Tel 262-677-4397; Fax: 262-677-4397; Toll Free: 800-814-4716; Edit Addr.: N. 168 W. 21700 Main St., No. 332, Jackson, WI 53037 USA
E-mail: westen@execpc.com.

Western Colorado Publishing Co., *(0-9662938)* Div. of Western Colorado Trading Co., Orders Addr.: 2024 Freedom Ct., Grand Junction, CO 81503 USA Tel 970-242-5255
E-mail: publisher@westerncoloradopublishing.com
Web site: http://www.westerncoloradopublishing.com.

Western Door Playhouse, *(0-9711153)* 310 N. Fourth St., Lewiston, NY 14092 USA
E-mail: ms1laurie@earthlink.com; msllaurie@earthlink.com.

Western Entrepreneurial Network *See* **NxLevel Training Network**

Western Images Pubns., Inc., *(0-9627600; 1-887302)* 2249 Marion St., Denver, CO 80205 USA.

Western Judicial Services, Incorporated/Materials Division, *(0-9759069)* 310 Brunson Blvd., Suite 102, Cocoa Beach, FL 32922 USA Toll Free: 800-750-0223
E-mail: lcolonel@bellsouth.net
Web site: http://www.westernjudicial.com/.

Western Michigan University, New Issues Press *See* **New Issues Poetry & Prose, Western Michigan Univ.**

Western National Parks Assn., *(0-911408; 1-877856; 1-58369)* 12880 N. Vistoso Village Dr., Tucson, AZ 85755 USA (SAN 202-750X) Tel 520-622-1999; Fax: 520-623-9519
E-mail: abby@wnpa.org; derek@wnpa.org
Web site: http://www.wnpa.org
Dist(s): **Canyonlands Pubns.**
Sunbelt Pubns., Inc.
Treasure Chest Bks.

Western New York Wares, Inc., *(0-9620314; 1-879201)* Orders Addr.: P.O. Box 733, Buffalo, NY 14205 USA (SAN 248-6911) Tel 716-832-6088; Edit Addr.: 419 Parkside Ave., Buffalo, NY 14216 USA (SAN 248-692X) Tel 716-832-6088
E-mail: wnywares@gateway.net.

Western Printers, Inc., *(0-9710477)* 977 Garfield, Eugene, OR 97402 USA Tel 541-683-1188; Fax: 541-683-2701 Do not confuse with Western Printing Lewiston, ID
E-mail: westernprinters@mailcity.com.

Western Psychological Services, *(0-87424)* Div. of Manson Western Corp., 12031 Wilshire Blvd., Los Angeles, CA 90025 USA (SAN 160-8002) Tel 310-478-2061; Fax: 310-478 7838; Toll Free: 800-648-8857
E-mail: weinberg@wpspublish.com
Web site: http://www.wpspublish.com.

Western Reflections Publishing Co., *(1-890437; 1-932738)* Orders Addr.: P.O. Box 1149, Lake City, CO 81235 USA Tel 970-944-0110 Toll Free: 800-993-4490
Web site: http://www.westernreflectionspub.com
Dist(s): **Baker & Taylor Bks.**
Books West
Partners/West
Quality Bks., Inc.
Treasure Chest Bks.

Westerwald Pr., *(0-9745819)* Orders Addr.: P.O. Box 72, Bentleyville, PA 15314 USA; Edit Addr.: 40 Pottery Ln., Scenery Hill, PA 15360 USA Tel 724-945-6000; Fax: 724-945-5139
E-mail: potterywest@yahoo.com.

†Westminster John Knox Pr., *(0-664; 0-8042)* Div. of Presbyterian Publishing Corp., Orders Addr.: 100 Witherspoon St., Louisville, KY 40202-1396 USA (SAN 202-9669) Tel 502-569-5052 (outside U.S. for ordering); Fax: 502-569-5113 (outside U.S. for faxed orders); Toll Free Fax: 800-541-5113 (toll-free U.S. faxed orders); Toll Free: 800-227-2872 Customer Service
E-mail: orders@wjkbooks.com
Web site: http://www.wjkbooks.com
Dist(s): **CRC Pubns.**
Presbyterian Publishing Corp.; *CIP.*

Westminster Literature Resources, Inc., *(0-9647552)* P.O. Box 1585, Denton, TX 76202-1585 USA.

WestNet Learning Technologies, *(1-58676)* 5420 Ward Rd., Suite 150, Arvada, CO 80002 USA Fax: 303-432-2565; Toll Free: 888-452-6902
Web site: http://www.westnetinc.com
Dist(s): **National Bk. Network.**

Weston Priory, *(0-9763005)* 58 Priory Hill Rd., Weston, VT 05161-6400 USA Tel 802-824-5409; Fax: 802-824-3573
E-mail: brjohn@westonpriory.org
Web site: http://www.westonpriory.org.

Weston Woods Studios, Inc., *(0-7882; 0-89719; 1-55592; 1-56008)* Div. of Scholastic, Inc,, 143 Main St., Norwalk, CT 06851 USA (SAN 630-3838) Tel 203-845-0197; Fax: 203-845-0498; Toll Free: 800-243-5020
E-mail: questions@Scholastic.com
Web site: http://www.scholastic.com/westonwoods.

Westphalia Publishing, *(1-882935)* P.O. Box 742, Saint James, MO 65559 USA Tel 573-308-1124; Fax: 573-308-1131
E-mail: woodward@hotmail.com; creativewordanddesign@yahoo.com.

Westphalia Thoroughbreds, LLC, *(0-9754103)* 1231 Latigo Ln., Flower Mound, TX 75022 USA Tel 817-368-6981
E-mail: arazielf@yahoo.com
Web site: http://www.westphaliathoroughbreds.com.

WestSea Publishing Co., Inc., *(0-937820)* 149D Allen Blvd., Farmingdale, NY 11735 USA (SAN 215-7144) Tel 631-420-1110; Fax: 631-420-0754
E-mail: westsea@optonline.net
Web site: www.westseapublishing.com.

Westside Press *See* **Wordsmith Pr.**

WestStar TalkRadio Network, *(0-9725247)* 2711 N. 24th St., Phoenix, AZ 85008 USA
Web site: http://www.komando.com.

†**Westview Pr.,** *(0-8133; 0-86531; 0-89158)* A Member of Perseus Books Group, 2465 Central Ave. Ste. 200, Boulder, CO 80301-5728 USA (SAN 219-970X) Toll Free: 800-343-4499 orders only
E-mail: westview.orders@perseusbooks.com; meegan.finnegan@perseusbooks.com
Web site: http://www.perseusbooksgroup.com; http://www.westviewpress.com
Dist(s): **Perseus Bks. Group**
Perseus Distribution*; CIP.*

Westview Publishing Co., Inc., *(0-9744322; 0-9748730; 0-9755646; 0-9764940; 0-9773179; 0-9776207; 1-933912)* 8120 Sawyer Brown Rd., Suite 107, Nashville, TN 37221 USA
Web site: http://www.westviewpublishing.com.

Westview Publishing, Incorporated *See* **Westview Publishing Co., Inc.**

WestWind Pr. *Imprint of* **Scott, D.&F. Publishing, Inc.**

Westwood Pr., Inc., *(0-936159)* 116 E. 16th St., New York, NY 10003-2112 USA (SAN 696-7183) Tel 212-420-8008 Do not confuse with Westwoods Press, Darien, CT.

Westwood Pr., Inc., *(1-931797)* 118 Five Mile River Rd., Darien, CT 06820 USA Tel 203-656-8680 (phone/fax) Do not confuse with Westwood Press, Inc., New York, NY
E-mail: csullivan@thesurvivalseries.com
Web site: http://www.thesurvivalseries.com
Dist(s): **Baker & Taylor Bks.**
Koen-Levy Bk. Wholesalers LLC.

Wet Earth, Inc., *(0-9708503)* 1573 SE Faculty Ct., Port Saint Lucie, FL 34952 USA Tel 561-398-9171
E-mail: wetearth2@aol.com
Web site: http://www.edgarmudd.com
Dist(s): **Diamond Comic Distributors, Inc.**

Wetz, Juliann, *(0-9716397)* 1095 Congress Ave., Cincinnati, OH 45246 USA
Web site: http://www.pages.prodigy.net/meandmrsjones/.

Wever Books *See* **Red Engine Pr.**

WeWrite LLC, *(1-57635; 1-884987)* Orders Addr.: P.O. Box 593, Ben Lomond, CA 95005 USA Tel 831-336-3382; Fax: 831-336-8592; Toll Free: 800-295-9037; Edit Addr.: 11040 Alba Rd., Ben Lomond, CA 95005-9220 USA
E-mail: info@wewrite.net
Web site: http://www.wewrite.net
Dist(s): **Baker & Taylor Bks.**

WGH Arts LLC, *(0-9776562)* P.O. Box 215, Lisbon, IA 52253-0215 USA
E-mail: bill@wgharts.com
Web site: http://www.wgharts.com.

WHA Publishing, *(0-9773228)* P.O. Box 20818, Wickenburg, AZ 85358 USA Tel 520-877-7860; Fax: 520-877-7869
E-mail: jerry@datssoftware.com.

Whale Museum/Moclips Cetological Society, The, *(0-933331)* 62 First St., N., Box 945, Friday Harbor, WA 98250 USA (SAN 692-2864) Tel 360-378-4710.

Whale Tales Pr., *(0-9648704)* P.O. Box 865, Friday Harbor, WA 98250 USA Tel 360-378-8378; Toll Free: 800-669-3950
Dist(s): **Adams News**
Partners/West
Hale, Robert & Co., Inc.
Sunbelt Pubns., Inc.

Whaleback Pr, *(0-9785465)* P.O. Box 865, Leland, MI 49654 USA
E-mail: whalebackpress@gmail.com
Web site: petoskeystonesoup.com.

Whaleback Publishing, *(0-9752938)* 4 Captain's Way, Exeter, NH 03833 USA Fax: 603-772-5416; Toll Free: 800-207-2580
Web site: http://www.whalebackpublishing.com.

Whale's Library, The, *(0-9758592)* 1111 NE 322nd Ave., Washougal, WA 98671 USA Tel 360-335-1373
E-mail: info@breachingbooks.com
Web site: http://www.thewhaleslibrary.com.

Whatever Publishing, Incorporated *See* **New World Library**

What's Inside Pr., *(0-9667634; 1-930729)* Orders Addr.: P.O. Box 16965, Beverly Hills, CA 90209 USA (SAN 299-8572) Tel 323-876-1581; Toll Free: 800-269-7757
E-mail: whatsin@aol.com
Web site: http://www.whatsinsidepress.com.

Wheatmark, *(1-58736; 1-60494)* 610 E. Delano St., Suite 104, Tucson, AZ 85705 USA (SAN 253-1054) Tel 520-798-0888; Fax: 520-798-3394; Toll Free: 888-934-0888 ; *Imprints:* Hats Off Books (Hats Off Bks); Iceni Books (Iceni Bks); Starbound Books (Starbound Bks)
E-mail: accounts@wheatmark.com; avekony@wheatmark.com; shenrie@wheatmark.com
Web site: http://www.wheatmark.com
Dist(s): **Baker & Taylor Bks.**

Wheaton-Smith, Simon, *(0-9765286)* 810 W. 6th St., Silver City, NM 88061 USA
E-mail: illustratingshadows@yahoo.com
Web site: http://www.illustratingshadows.com/.

WHEEL Council, Inc., The, *(0-9656732; 0-9728889)* P.O. Box 22517, Flagstaff, AZ 86002 USA Tel 928-214-0120
E-mail: info@wheelcouncil.org
Web site: http://www.wheelcouncil.org.

Wheeler Publishing, Inc. *Imprint of* **Thomson Gale**

Where? Pr., Inc., *(0-9719144)* Orders Addr.: P.O. Box 154, Paintsville, KY 41240 USA Tel 606-789-9423; Edit Addr.: 830 Robin Ct., Paintsville, KY 41240 USA
E-mail: wherepress@mail.com
Web site: http://www.wherepress.netfirms.com.

Where Will You Be in 2000 A.D., Inc., *(0-9673205)* 325 S. Third St., No. 265, Las Vegas, NV 89101 USA (SAN 299-9285) Tel 702-383-6688; Fax: 702-383-9009; Toll Free: 888-823-4373
E-mail: ms2000ad@cs.com
Web site: http://www.wherewillyoubein2000ad.com.

Where-I-Live / Foster Pr., *(0-9764893)* 430 91st Ave., NE, Suite 3, Everett, WA 98205 USA Tel 425-334-9317; Fax: 425-334-8155
E-mail: vern@fosterpress.com
Web site: http://www.fosterpress.com.

Whimble Designs, *(0-9773523)* 1540/42 Monroe Dr., NE, Atlanta, GA 30324 USA.

WhipperSnapper Bks., *(0-9657218)* P.O. Box 3186, Los Altos, CA 94024 USA 925-249-0709 (orders/general); Toll Free: 800-910-4482.

Whippoorwill, LLC, *(0-9741968)* 9601 Linden St., Overland Park, KS 66207 USA (SAN 255-6553) Tel 913-341-7104; Fax: 913-385-2453
E-mail: schase@mischomeloans.com.

Whirlwind Bks. (CAN) *(0-9681537) Dist. by* **IPG Chicago.**

Whiskey Creek Pr., LLC, *(1-59374; 1-60313)* Orders Addr.: P.O. Box 51052, Casper, WY 82605-1052 USA Tel 307-265-8585; Fax: 307-265-4640; Edit Addr.: 541 Long Ln., Casper, WY 82609 USA
Web site: http://www.whiskeycreekpress.com; http://www.whiskeycreekpresstorrid.com.

Whispering Hope Publishing, *(0-9719623)* N6984 Pelsdorf Ave., Loyal, WI 54446 USA Do not confuse with Whispering Hope Publishing, Mars Hills, NC.

Whispering Pine Pr., Inc., *(0-9679368; 1-930948; 1-59210; 1-59434; 1-59649; 1-59808)* Orders Addr.: P.O. Box 1469, Spokane Valley, WA 99037 USA (SAN 253-200X); Edit Addr.: 507 N. Sullivan Rd., Suite A-4, Spokane Valley, WA 99037 USA
E-mail: whisperingpinepress@hotmail.com
Web site: http://www.whisperingpinepress.com.

Whispering Wind Publishing Inc., *(0-9721640)* Orders Addr.: 11089 Utica Ct., Westminster, CO 80031-2057 USA Tel 303-717-6442
E-mail: KaKillam@cs.com; publisher@whisperingwind.org
Web site: http://www.whisperingwind.org
Dist(s): **Baker & Taylor Bks.**
Quality Bks., Inc.

Whistle Pr., The, *(0-9624893)* P.O. Box 1006, Petal, MS 39465-8618 USA Tel 601-544-8486 (phone/fax)
E-mail: contact@whistlepress.com
Web site: www.whistlepress.com.

Whitaker Hse., *(0-88368; 1-60374)* Div. of Whitaker Corp., 1030 Hunt Valley Cir., New Kensington, PA 15068 USA (SAN 203-2104) Tel 724-334-2920 Whitaker House; 724-334-7000 Whitaker House/Anchor Distributors; Fax: 724-334-2932 Whitaker House; 724-334-1200 Anchor Distributors; Toll Free Fax: 866-773-7001 Whitaker House; 800-765-1960 Anchor Distributors; Toll Free: 877-793-9800 Whitaker House; 800-444-4484 Whitaker House/Anchor Distributors
E-mail: sharon@whitakerhouse.com; sales@whitakerhouse.com
Web site: http://www.whitakerhouse.com; http://www.anchordistributors.com
Dist(s): **Anchor Distributors.**

Whitaker, Thurston Information Services, LLC, *(0-9758940)* P.O. Box 271743, West Hartford, CT 06127-1743 USA Tel 860-922-4719
E-mail: gwhit@twisbiz.com
Web site: http://www.thurstonwhitaker.com.

Whitcombe, Renee *See* **Budding Family Publishing**

White Bear Publishing, LLC., *(1-934218)* 5810 W. 78th St., Bloomington, MN 55439 USA (SAN 852-2057)
Web site: http://www.whitebearpublishing.com.

White Birch Pr., *(0-9661204)* Orders Addr.: P.O. Box 1433, Concord, NH 03302-1433 USA Tel 603-226-7256; Edit Addr.: P.O. Box 1433, Concord, NH 03302-1433 USA
E-mail: jaericsson@aol.com.

White Canoe Productions, *(0-9772115)* Div. of Marilyn Brown-Innerscapes, Orders Addr.: 472 Sunstone Dr., Saint Louis, MO 63011-3412 USA ; *Imprints:* WCP (WCP)
E-mail: mdbrown@whitecanoeproductions.com
Web site: http://www.whitecanoeproductions.com.

White Cloud Pr., *(1-883991; 0-9793840)* Orders Addr.: P.O. Box 3400, Ashland, OR 97520 USA; Edit Addr.: 300 E. Hersey St. Suite. 11, Ashland, OR 97520-6200 USA Fax: 541-482-7708; Toll Free: 800-380-8286 Do not confuse with White Cloud Pr. in Hobbs, NM
Web site: http://www.caveatpress.com; http://www.whitecloudpress.com
Dist(s): **SCB Distributors.**

White DEI, *(0-9636278)* P.O. Box 171084, Arlington, TX 76003 USA Tel 817-784-1880; Fax: 817-419-9399
E-mail: bbbs@swbell.net
Web site: http://www.babyboomerbiblestudy.com
Dist(s): **Spring Arbor Distributors, Inc.**

White Door Publishing, *(0-9723707)* 303 Cheswold Ct., Wayne, PA 19087-5630 USA Tel 610-695-0484 (phone/fax).

White Eagle Publishing Trust (GBR) *(0-85487) Dist. by* **DeVorss.**

White Feather Publishing, *(0-9740413)* 5595 White Feather Way, Placerville, CA 95667 USA
E-mail: whitefeather@directcom.net.

White Hat Communications, *(0-9653653; 1-929109)* Orders Addr.: P.O. Box 5390, Harrisburg, PA 17110-0390 USA Tel 717-238-3787; Fax: 717-238-2090; Edit Addr.: 2001 N. Front St., Bldg. 2, Suite 325, Harrisburg, PA 17102 USA
E-mail: Linda.grobman@paonline.com
Web site: http://www.whitehatcommunications.com
Dist(s): **Independent Pubs. Group.**

White Heat Ltd., *(0-9740149; 0-9799108)* 107 Suncreek Dr., Allen, TX 75013-4716 USA Tel 214-495-8000; Fax: 214-495-8014
E-mail: info@whiteheatltd.com
Web site: http://www.whiteheatltd.com.

White Heat Ltd. *See* **White Heat Ltd.**

White Horse Bks., *(0-9744860)* 1347 Glenmare St., Salt Lake Cty, UT 84105-2707 USA
Web site: http://www.utahwhitehorsebooks.com.

White Hse. Historical Assn., *(0-912308; 1-931917)* 740 Jackson Pl., NW, Washington, DC 20503 USA (SAN 226-8108) Tel 202-737-8292; Fax: 202-789-0440
Web site: http://whitehousehistory.org.

White, Howard Ray, *(0-9746875)* P.O. Box 78731, Charlotte, NC 28271-7040 USA Tel 704-846-4411
E-mail: hwhite4@carolina.rr.com
Web site: http://www.civilwarcauses.com.

White, James C., *(0-9747752)* 2205 Queen Ridge Rd., Independence, MO 64050 USA Tel 816-807-2291 Do not confuse with James C. White in Ruston, LA
E-mail: jcwhite08@yahoo.com
Web site: http://www.jcwhite08.com.

White Kiser, Dolores, *(0-9766648)* 212 Quail Creek Rd., Durant, OK 74701-7543 USA
E-mail: wobblywh@yahoo.com.

White Line Productions Inc., *(0-9729965)* P.O. Box 248411, Coral Gables, FL 33124 USA Tel 305-663-3235
E-mail: lcoll@bewaretheunknown.com
Web site: http://www.bewaretheunknown.com.

White Lion Pr., *(0-9615707; 1-886942)* 225 E. Fifth St., No. 4D, New York, NY 10003 USA (SAN 695-7919) Tel 212-982-5518; Toll Free: 800-243-9642
Dist(s): **New Leaf Distributing Co., Inc.**

White Mane Bks. *Imprint of* **White Mane Publishing Co., Inc.**

White Mane Kids *Imprint of* **White Mane Publishing Co., Inc.**

White Mane Publishing Co., Inc., *(0-942597; 1-57249)* Orders Addr.: P.O. Box 708, Shippensburg, PA 17257 USA (SAN 667-1926) Tel 717-532-2237; Fax: 717-532-6110; Toll Free: 888-948-6263 ; *Imprints:* Burd Street Press (Burd St Pr); Ragged Edge Press (Ragged Edge); White Mane Kids (WM Kids); White Mane Books (WM Books)
E-mail: marketing@whitemane.com
Web site: http://www.whitemane.com/.

White Oak Creative, *(0-9763562)* 26415 W. Stonebriar Way, Channahon, IL 60410-8740 USA Tel 815-922-2890; Fax: 815-521-0042 Do not confuse with White Oak Publishing in Reed Springs, MO; Galena, MO; Sewickley, PA; Portland, OR
E-mail: kashmir37@aol.com.

White Oaks Creations, *(1-929181)* 9 Sherwood Rd., Cartersville, VA 23027-9744 USA
E-mail: staff@whiteoakscreations.com
Web site: http://www.whiteoakscreations.com.

White Owl Publishing, *(1-891691)* P.O. Box 1180, Redding, CA 96001 USA Tel 530-241-1921 Do not confuse with White Owl Publishing, Wellington, KS,
E-mail: editor@whiteowlweb.com
Web site: http://whiteowlweb.com.

White Rhino Pr., *(0-9704122)* Div. of Patnaude Corp., Orders Addr.: P.O. Box 35592, Greensboro, NC 27425-5592 USA Tel 336-315-5363; Fax: 336-315-0240; Toll Free: 877-643-1303; Edit Addr.: 319-J S. Westgate Dr., Greensboro, NC 27407 USA
E-mail: WhiteRhinoPub@aol.com.

White Rhino Publishing *See* **White Rhino Pr.**

White, Russ, *(0-9742885)* 122 E. Oak Hill Dr., Florence, AL 35633 USA.

White Stag Pr., *(0-9792583)* Div. of Publishers Design Group, Inc., P.O. Box 37, Roseville, CA 95678 USA (SAN 852-9353) Tel 916-784-0500; Fax: 916-773-7421; Toll Free: 800-587-6666
E-mail: orders@publishersdesign.com
Web site: http://www.publishersdesign.com.

White Star (ITA) *(88-8095; 88-544; 88-7844; 88-540) Dist. by* **Random.**

White Star *Imprint of* **Rizzoli International Pubns., Inc.**

White Stone Bks., *(1-59379)* P.O. Box 35035, Tulsa, OK 74153 USA Toll Free: 866-253-8622 Do not confuse with White Stone Books in Atlanta, MI
E-mail: amandap@whitestonebooks.com
Web site: http://www.whitestonebooks.com
Dist(s): **Distributors, The**
Harrison Hse., Inc.

White Stone Books Publishing Company *See* **White Stone Co., The**

White Stone Co., The, *(1-880122)* 7752 Lowell Blvd., Westminster, CO 80030-4543 USA (SAN 297-7907) Tel 720-540-3940; Toll Free: 800-847-7323 ; *Imprints:* Little Shepherd Books (Little Shpherd Bks)
E-mail: TWSCo@msn.com.

White Stone Publications *See* **Fair Havens Pubns.**

White Stone Publishing Co., *(1-892318)* 241 Moose Ln., Las Vegas, NV 89128 USA Tel 702-363-2391; Fax: 702-242-8949
E-mail: vanus7@aol.com
Web site: http://www.latter-day-letters.com
Dist(s): **Sounds of Zion.**

White, T. *See* **twhiteart**

White, Terry, *(0-9755835)* P.O. Box 760399, Southfield, MI 48076-0399 USA.

White Tiger Pr. *Imprint of* **Homes for the Homeless, Inc.**

White Tulip Publishing, *(0-9746890)* P.O. Box 645, Brewster, NY 10509 USA
E-mail: wtime2write@aol.com
Web site: http://www.whitetulippublishing.com
Dist(s): **Baker & Taylor Bks.**

White Wolf Publishing, Inc., *(0-9627790; 1-56504; 1-58846)* 1554 Litton Dr., Stone Mountain, GA 30083 USA (SAN 299-1349) Tel 404-292-1819; Fax: 678-382-3882; Toll Free: 800-454-9653 Do not confuse with White Wolf Publishing, Cresson, TX
E-mail: dianez@white-wolf.com
Web site: http://www.white-wolf.com
Dist(s): **PSI (Publisher Services, Inc.).**

White Wolf Studio, Inc., *(0-9760654)* P.O. Box 490, Windermere, FL 34786 USA Tel 407-909-0889; Fax: 407-876-8462
E-mail: whitewolfstudio@aol.com
Web site: http://www.whitewolfstudio.com.

White-Boucke Publishing, *(0-9625006; 1-888580)* Orders Addr.: P.O. Box 400, Lafayette, CO 80026 USA Tel 303-604-0661; Fax: 303-604-0662
E-mail: ordering@white-boucke.com
Web site: http://www.white-boucke.com
Dist(s): **Baker & Taylor Bks.**
Brodart Co.
Quality Bks., Inc.

White-Bowden Assocs., *(0-9633762)* 2863 Benson Rd., Finksburg, MD 21048 USA Tel 410-833-3280 ; *Imprints:* Gateway Press (Gateway Press)
Dist(s): **Washington Bk. Distributors.**

Whitecap Bks., Ltd. (CAN) *(0-920620; 0-921061; 0-921396; 1-55110; 1-895099; 1-55285) Dist. by* **Firefly Bks Limited.**

Whitecaps Media, *(0-9758577)* P.O. Box 60385, Houston, TX 77205-0385 USA.

Whitedove Pr., *(0-615; 0-9714908)* 7695 St., Rt. 48 N., Waynesville, OH 45068 USA Tel 310-350-5370
E-mail: mail@michelleWhitedove.com
Web site: http://www.michellewhitedove.com
Dist(s): **AtlasBooks Distribution.**

Whitegate Bks., *(0-9767570)* The Appletree, 903 26 Rd., Grand Junction, CO 81506 USA
E-mail: lyn@appletreedesigns.com
Web site: http://www.appletreedesigns.com.

Whitehouse Publishing, *(0-9644171)* 6556 Mckenna Way, Alexandria, VA 22315-5571 USA Do not confuse with Whithouse Publishing in Corning, NY
E-mail: erw192@hotmail.com
Web site: http://users.starpower.net/whitee/bookcover/treasure.html
Dist(s): **Baker & Taylor Bks.**

Whitehouse Publishing, *(1-933031)* 60 E. Market St., Corning, NY 14830 USA Toll Free: 800-784-0537 Do not confuse with Whitehouse Publishing in Alexandria, VA
E-mail: elizabeth@whitehouse-publishing.com
Web site: http://www.whitehouse-publishing.com
Dist(s): **Baker & Taylor Bks.**

WhiteWalls, Inc., *(0-945323)* Orders Addr.: P.O. Box 8204, Chicago, IL 60647 USA (SAN 246-9952); Edit Addr.: 2845 W. Altgeld, Chicago, IL 60647 USA (SAN 246-9960)
E-mail: aeelms@aol.com
Web site: http://www.whitewalls.org
Dist(s): **Chicago Distribution Ctr.**
SPD-Small Pr. Distribution.

Whitford Pr. *Imprint of* **Schiffer Publishing, Ltd.**

Whiting Family Publishing, *(0-9653276)* 4692 W. 10000 S., Payson, UT 84651 USA Tel 801-465-2789; Fax: 801-465-1865
E-mail: danwhiting@integrity.com.

Whitline Ink, Inc., *(1-930154)* Orders Addr.: P.O. Box 668, Boonville, NC 27011 USA Tel 336-367-6914; Fax: 336-367-6913; Edit Addr.: Hwy. 601 S., Boonville, NC 27011 USA
E-mail: whitlineink@yadtel.net
Dist(s): **Parnassus Bk. Distributors.**

†Whitman, Albert & Co., *(0-8075)* 6340 Oakton St., Morton Grove, IL 60053-2723 USA (SAN 201-2049) Tel 847-581-0033; Fax: 847-581-0039; Toll Free: 800-255-7675
E-mail: mail@awhitmanco.com
Web site: http://www.albertwhitman.com
Dist(s): **Heinecken & Assoc., Ltd.**
Lectorum Pubns., Inc.; *CIP.*

Whitman Publishing LLC, *(0-937458; 1-930849; 0-7948)* Div. of Anderson Press Inc., Orders Addr.: 4001 Helton Dr., Florence, AL 35030 USA Tel 256-246-1166; Toll Free: 800-528-3992; Edit Addr.: 3101 Clairmont Rd., NE, Suite C, Atlanta, GA 30329 USA (SAN 253-522X) Tel 404-214-4300; Fax: 404-214-4391; Toll Free: 800-528-3992
E-mail: info@whitmanbooks.com
Web site: http://www.whitmanbooks.com.

†Whitmore Publishing Co., *(0-87426)* 1144 Riverview Ln., West Conshohocken, PA 19428-2964 USA (SAN 203-2112)
E-mail: production@whitmorepublishing.com; *CIP.*

†Whitney Museum of American Art, *(0-87427)* 945 Madison Ave., New York, NY 10021 USA (SAN 281-1294) Tel 212-570-3656; Fax: 212-535-5606
Dist(s): **Abrams, Harry N. , Inc.**
D.A.P./Distributed Art Pubs.
Hachette Bk. Group
RAM Pubns. & Distribution; *CIP.*

Whittet Bks., Ltd. (GBR) *(0-905483; 1-873580) Dist. by* **Diamond Farm Bk.**

Whittington, Gisella, *(0-9706038)* 1420 W. Mcdermott Dr. Apt. 218, Allen, TX 75013-2850 USA
E-mail: gigi@pumpuplife.com
Web site: http://www.pumpuplife.com.

Who Am I Pr., *(0-9774174)* 4444 Hazeltine Ave., No. 229, Sherman Oaks, CA 91423 USA Tel 818-501-5908
E-mail: lea@godwhoami.com
Web site: http://www.godwhoami.com.

Who You Are International, Inc., *(0-9651842; 1-929737)* 8510 Elmore Ave., Webster, MN 55088 USA Tel 507-744-5875; Fax: 507-744-5876
Dist(s): **Bookmen, Inc.**
JayMar Services, LLC.

Whole Heart Ministries, *(1-888692)* Orders Addr.: 340 Jack Boot Rd., Monument, CO 80132-8506 USA
E-mail: clay@wholeheart.org
Web site: http://www.wholeheart.org/.

Whole Spirit Pr., *(1-892857)* 1905 S. Clarkson St., Denver, CO 80210 USA Tel 303-979-5820; 303-246-9554; Fax: 303-979-6151; Toll Free: 877-488-3774
E-mail: sales@wholespiritpress.com
Web site: http://www.wholespiritpress.com.

Wholemovement Pubns., *(0-9766773)* Orders Addr.: 4606 N. Elston No. 3, Chicago, IL 60630 USA Tel 773-794-9764
E-mail: bradhs@interaccess.com
Web site: http://www.wholemovement.com.

Wholesome Puppy Tales, *(0-9762466)* 13432 San Pasqual Rd., Escondido, CA 92025-7834 USA
E-mail: cmodicagraphics@aol.com
Web site: http://www.wholesomepuppytales.com.

Whootie Owl International, LLC, *(0-9672831; 0-9721027; 0-9742065)* P.O. Box 60034, Newton, MA 02460 USA Tel 617-244-0106; Fax: 617-244-8761; Toll Free: 877-946-6843 (877-whootie)
E-mail: whootieowl@storiestogrowby.com
Web site: http://www.storiestogrowby.com.

Whootie Owl Productions *See* **Whootie Owl International, LLC**

Who's Who In Sports *Imprint of* **Guidry Assocs., Inc.**

Whyte Dove Pr., *(0-9708999)* P.O. Box 385, Quitman, TX 75783 USA
E-mail: maykay@peoplescom.net.

Wickenburg Healthcare Alliance *See* **WHA Publishing**

Wickleville Woods *Imprint of* **Trend Enterprises, Inc.**

Wicklewood Bks. *Imprint of* **Stage Within Your Mind, The**

Wide World Publishing/Tetra, *(0-933174; 1-884550)* Orders Addr.: P.O. Box 476, San Carlos, CA 94070 USA (SAN 211-1462) Tel 650-593-2839; Fax: 650-595-0802
E-mail: wwpbl@aol.com
Web site: http://www.wideworldpublishing.com
Dist(s): **Baker & Taylor Bks.**
Booklines Hawaii, Ltd.
Perseus Distribution.

WideThinker Bks., *(0-9728195)* P.O. Box 30144, Philadelphia, PA 19146 USA Tel 215-985-0322; Toll Free: 866-236-1077
E-mail: wtb@widethinker.com
Web site: http://www.widethinkerbooks.com.

†Wiener, Markus Pubs., Inc., *(0-910129; 0-945179; 1-55876)* 231 Nassau St., Princeton, NJ 08542 USA (SAN 282-5465) Tel 609-921-1141; Fax: 609-921-1140
E-mail: info@markuswiener.com; publisher@markuswiener.com
Web site: http://www.markuswiener.com; *CIP.*

Wiggly's Pubns., *(0-9675742)* P.O. Box 711991, Midvale, UT 84171 USA Tel 801-569-9038
E-mail: patg@icw.com
Web site: http://www.me-nogift.com.

Wighita Pr., *(0-9786648)* P.O. Box 30399, Little Rock, AR 72260-0399 USA
E-mail: info@wighitapress.com
Web site: www.wighitapress.com.

Wigwam Publishing, *(0-9721022)* Orders Addr.: P.O. Box 574, Weyauwega, WI 54983 USA; Edit Addr.: 410 S. Harlon St., No. 2, Weyauwega, WI 54983 USA Do not confuse with companies with the same or similar names in Villa Park, IL, Cheyenne, WY.

WigWam Publishing Co., *(1-930076)* Orders Addr.: P.O. Box 6992, Villa Park, IL 60181 USA ; *Imprints:* New Leaf Books (New Leaf Books) Do not confuse with companies with the same or similar names in Weyauwega, WI, Cheyenne, WY
E-mail: info@newleafbooks.net
Web site: http://www.newleafbooks.net.

Wilander Publishing Co., *(0-9628335)* Orders Addr.: P.O. Box 56121, Portland, OR 97238 USA.

Wild About Learning, Inc., *(0-9789880)* 964 John St., Joliet, IL 60435 USA Tel 815-740-1173; Fax: 815-740-1174
E-mail: info@wildaboutlearning.org
Web site: http://wildaboutlearning.org.

Wild Animal Publishing Co., *(0-9769555)* 3 Golf St., Groton, CT 06340 USA
E-mail: sciarrajb@aol.com
Web site: http://www.johnbenjaminsciarra.com.

Wild Animal XPress, *(0-9708743)* P.O. Box 2461, Ramona, CA 92065-0942 USA Tel 619-462-1986; Fax: 619-462-1374
E-mail: wildanimalxpress@home.com.

Wild Dreams, *(0-9715842)* P.O. Box 1926, Anderson, SC 29622 USA
Web site: http://wwww.wilddreamspublishing.com.

Wild Flower USA, *(0-9646698)* 26614 Oak Ridge Dr., Suite 110, The Woodlands, TX 77380 USA Tel 281-363-2360; Fax: 281-367-4480.

Wild Hare Publishing, *(0-9772096)* P.O. Box 2144, Ridgeland, MS 39158-2144 USA (SAN 256-9639) Tel 601-853-8120; Fax: 601-853-8121
E-mail: dgibbes@wildharepublishing.com.

Wild Heart Ranch, Inc., *(0-9761768)* 1385 Gulf Rd., Suite 102, Point Roberts, WA 98281 USA Toll Free Fax: 866-735-3518; Toll Free: 888-889-9215
E-mail: dawn@wildheartranch.com
Web site: http://www.wildheartranch.com; http://www.iseahorses.com.

Wild Horses Publishing Co., *(0-937148; 0-9601088)* Orders Addr.: P.O. Box 1373, Los Altos, CA 94022 USA (SAN 211-8289)
E-mail: pwalatka@earthlink.net.

Wild Mind Creations, *(0-615)* P.O. Box 1935, Fairview, OR 97024-1806 USA
E-mail: jmm1965mionda_4@msn.com.

Wild Plum Woods Bks., *(0-9745581)* 39042 Ruann Ct., Zephyrhills, FL 33540 USA.

Wild Pony Publishing, *(0-9666477)* 2418 Sixth St., Berkeley, CA 94710 USA Tel 925-228-5117; Fax: 925-845-2358.

Wild Rose *Imprint of* **Mayhaven Publishing**

Wilderness Assocs., *(0-9647167)* P.O. Box 5822, Bend, OR 97708-5822 USA Tel 541-330-0331
E-mail: lesjoslin@aol.com
Web site: http://www.wildernessheritage.com
Dist(s): **Maverick Distributors.**

Wilderness Visions Press *See* **Cloudland.net Publishing**

Wildewoode Publishing, *(0-9740622)* 3135 Lostwood Dr., Sandy, UT 84092 USA Tel 801-608-1125; Fax: 801-495-0140
E-mail: jim@barrus.org
Web site: http://www.barrus.org.

Wildfire Enterprises, *(0-9771969)* Orders Addr.: P.O. Box 402, Viola, AR 72583-0402 USA Tel 870-458-3600 (phone/fax); Edit Addr.: P O Box 402, Viola, AR 72583-0402 USA
E-mail: wfenterprises@hotmail.com
Web site: http://www.wildfireenterprises.iceryder.net.

Wildfire Starts, *(0-9705154)* Div. of Larry Gates, Inc, P.O. Box 1468, Visalia, CA 93279-1468 USA Tel 559-734-5256; Fax: 520-396-7024
E-mail: larrygates@eartlink.net; larrygates@earthlink.net
Web site: http://www.wildfirestarts.com.

Wildflower Company Publishers, The *See* **Kellum Cabin Pubs.**

Wildflower Pr., The, *(0-9714343; 0-9779933)* P.O. Box 4757, Albuquerque, NM 87196-4757 USA Tel 505-296-0691; Fax: 505-296-6124 Do not confuse with companies with the same or similar name in Oceanside, CA ,Phoenix, AZ ,Littleton, CO
E-mail: jspoetry@aol.com.

Wildflower Run, *(0-9667086)* Orders Addr.: P.O. Box 9656, College Station, TX 77842 USA Tel 979-764-0166
E-mail: atmgold@aol.com
Web site: http://www.aggiegoose.com.

Wildlands Pr., *(0-9675918)* Div. of Art Wolfe, Inc., 1944 First Ave., S., Seattle, WA 98134 USA Tel 206-332-0993; Fax: 206-332-0990; Toll Free: 888-973-0011
E-mail: info@artwolfe.com; cascades@nwlink.com
Web site: http://www.artwolfe.com; http://www.wildlandspress.com
Dist(s): **Perseus Distribution.**

Wildlife Education, Ltd., *(0-937934; 1-888153; 1-932396)* 12233 Thatcher Ct., Poway, CA 92064-6880 USA (SAN 215-8299) Tel 858-513-7600; Fax: 858-513-7660; Toll Free: 800-477-5034 ; *Imprints:* Zoo Books (Zoo Bks)
E-mail: sales@zoobooks.com
Web site: http://www.zoobooks.com.

Wildlife Tales Publishing, *(0-9793207)* Div. of Ark R.A.I.N. Wildlife Sanctuary, Inc., P.O. Box 721, Brownsville, TN 38012-0721 USA Toll Free: 877-352-6657
E-mail: books@wildlifetalespublishing.com
Web site: http://www.wildlifetalespublishing.com.

Wildly Austin, *(0-9753990)* P.O. Box 161987, Austin, TX 78716-1987 USA
E-mail: vikki@wildlyaustin.com; vl@intersourcesearch.com
Web site: http://www.wildlyaustin.com
Dist(s): **Greenleaf Book Group Pr.**

Wildot Pr., *(0-9789043; 0-9797933)* 4402 W. Creedance Blvd., Glendale, AZ 85310-3921 USA Tel 623-434-2636
E-mail: wildotpress@cox.net
Web site: http://ww.wildotpress.com.

Wildridge Software, Inc., *(1-59106)* 245 Wildridge Farm Rd., Newark, VT 05871 USA Tel 802-467-3811; Fax: 802-467-3442; Toll Free: 888-244-4379
E-mail: abiggerworld@wildridge.com
Web site: http://www.wildridge.com.

Wildseed Pubns., *(0-9703606)* Orders Addr.: P.O. Box 77854, Washington, DC 20013-7785 USA Tel 202-574-2761; Fax: 202-561-0235; Toll Free: 800-631-1027; Edit Addr.: 3359 Martin Luther King Jr. Ave., Washington, DC 20032-1541 USA
E-mail: cmailbag@aol.com.

Wildside Pr., *(0-8095; 0-913960; 1-880448; 1-58715; 1-59224; 1-4344)* Orders Addr.: 9710 Traville Gateway Dr., No. 234, Rockville, MD 20850 USA Tel 301-762-1305; Fax: 301-762-1306
E-mail: customerservice@wildsidepress.com; editorial@wildsidepress.com
Web site: http://www.wildsidepress.com
Dist(s): **Baker & Taylor Bks.**
Diamond Bk. Distributors
Ingram Bk. Co.
NACSCORP, Inc.

Wildstorm *Imprint of* **DC Comics**

WildWest Publishing, *(0-9721800)* P.O. Box 11658, Olympia, WA 98508 USA
E-mail: clamityJan@aol.com
Web site: http://www.CalamityJan.com
Dist(s): **Biblio Distribution.**

Wiley *Imprint of* **Wiley, John & Sons, Inc.**

Company

Company

†**Wiley, John & Sons, Inc.,** *(0-470; 0-471; 0-7645; 0-7821; 0-8260; 0-87605; 0-88422; 0-937721; 0-939246; 1-55828; 1-56561; 1-56884; 1-57313; 1-58245; 1-878058; 3-527)* Orders Addr.: 1 Wiley Dr., Somerset, NJ 08875-1272 USA Tel 732-469-4400; Fax: 732-302-2300; Toll Free Fax: 800-597-3299; Toll Free: 800-225-5945 (orders); Edit Addr.: 111 River St., Hoboken, NJ 07030 USA (SAN 200-2272) Tel 201-748-6000; 201-748-6276 (Retail and Wholesale); Fax: 201-748-6088; 201-748-8641 (Retail and Wholesale) ; *Imprints:* Wiley-Interscience (Wiley-Interscience); Wiley-VCH (Wiley-VCH); Wiley-IEEE Press (Wiley-IEEE); Pfeiffer (PfeiffW); Jossey-Bass (Jossey-Bass); For Dummies (For Dummies); Cliff Notes (Cliff); Betty Crocker (Betty-Crocker); Frommers (From); Webster's New World (Web New Wrld); Howell Book House (HBH); Capstone (CapstW); Wiley (JWiley); Sybex (SybWiley)
E-mail: compbks@wiley.com; bookinfo@wiley.com; custserv@wiley.com
Web site: http://www.wiley.com/compbooks/; http://www.interscience.wiley.com; http://www.wiley.com
Dist(s): **AtlasBooks Distribution**
Lightning Source, Inc.
NetLibrary, Inc.
Pearson Education
Peoples Publishing Group, Inc., The
Urban Land Institute; *CIP.*

Wiley-IEEE Pr. *Imprint of* **Wiley, John & Sons, Inc.**

Wiley-Interscience *Imprint of* **Wiley, John & Sons, Inc.**

Wiley-VCH *Imprint of* **Wiley, John & Sons, Inc.**

Wilkes Publishing Co., Inc., *(0-9747755)* P.O. Box 340, Washington, GA 30673 USA Tel 706-678-2636; Fax: 706-678-3857
E-mail: editor@news-reporter.com
Web site: http://www.news-reporter.com.

Will Hall Bks., *(0-9630310; 0-9801257)* 611 Oliver Ave., Fayetteville, AR 72701 USA
E-mail: rharriso@uark.edu
Web site: http://www.willhallbooks.com.

Will to Print Pr., *(0-9772985)* 230 Hyde St., San Francisco, CA 94102-3324 USA Tel 415-474-0508; Fax: 415-673-1027
E-mail: willtoprintpress@faithfulfools.org
Web site: http://www.faithfulfools.org.

Willan Publishing (GBR) *(1-903240; 1-84392; 1-954560) Dist. by* **Intl Spec Bk.**

William Askel Art, *(0-9752528)* 21665 Wallace Dr., Southfield, MI 48075-7570 USA
E-mail: waksel@provide.net
Web site: http://fieldguidetomonsters.com.

William Works, Inc., *(0-9745244)* P.O. Box 2709, Washington, DC 20013 USA Toll Free: 877-535-2057.

Williams & Co., Publishers, *(1-878853)* Orders Addr.: 1317 Pine Ridge Dr., Savannah, GA 34104 USA Tel 912-352-0404; Toll Free: 800-280-1969 Do not confuse with companies with the same name in Carlsbad, CA, Tempe, AZ, Bigfork, MT, Naunet, NY
E-mail: tom@pubmart.com
Web site: http://www.pubmart.com
Dist(s): **Baker & Taylor Bks.**
Ingram Bk. Co.
Syracuse Univ. Pr.

Williams, Benjamin Publishing, *(0-9764945; 0-9796180)* 500 N. Michigan Ave. Suite 300, Chicago, IL 60611 USA
E-mail: ben@bwpublishing.com; customerservice@bwpublishing.com
Web site: http://www.bw-publishing.com
Dist(s): **AtlasBooks Distribution.**

Williams, Benny Publishing *See* **Williams, Benjamin Publishing**

Williams, Darnell *See* **Williams, Darnell L. Foundation, The**

Williams, Darnell L. Foundation, The, *(0-9747771)* 2402 Magnolia Dr., Harrisburg, PA 17104 USA Tel 717-233-1511
E-mail: WDarn44243@aol.com.

Williams, Dontez, *(0-9766782)* P.O. Box 141111, Detroit, MI 48214 USA
Web site: http://www.dontezwilliams.com.

Williams Enterprise Productions, *(0-9727687)* P.O. Box 152, Middletown, DE 19709 USA
E-mail: williamsenterpriseproductions@msn.com
Web site: http://www.marniwilliams.com
Dist(s): **Baker & Taylor Bks.**

Williams, Gary, *(0-9743000)* 574 Falcon Fork Way, Jacksonville, FL 32259 USA
Web site: http://www.fbcofmand.org.

Williams, Geoffrey T., *(0-9771381)* 3119 Redwood St., San Diego, CA 92104 USA
Web site: http://www.gtwhimself.com.

Williams, James E., *(0-9746310)* P.O. Box 6921, Atlanta, GA 30315-0921 USA Fax: 404-691-0726.

Williams, John Anthony, *(0-9707837)* P.O. Box 322, Lomita, CA 90717 USA Tel 310-346-0707
E-mail: wealthy1@pacbell.net.

Williams, Marni *See* **Williams Enterprise Productions**

Williams, Morgan, *(0-9762768)* 3243 Cloverwood Dr., Nashville, TN 37214-3428 USA
E-mail: mandj@magiclink.com
Web site: http://www.thestandards.com.

Williams Publishing Co., *(0-9701704; 0-9711703)* Subs. of Diversified Productions, P.O. Box 582581, Tulsa, OK 74158-2581 USA Toll Free: 888-234-0660 ; *Imprints:* Diversified Productions (Diversified) Do not confuse with companies with the same or similar names in Dallas, TX, Calabasas, CA, Burien, WA, Kailua-Kona, HI, Jamaica, NY, Aurora, CO
E-mail: Diversifiedpros@aol.com
Web site: http://www.williamspublishingco.com.

Williams, Rozalia *See* **Hidden Curriculum Education**

Williams, Thomas, *(0-9763633)* 358 Homestead Rd., NW, Willis, VA 24380 USA Tel 540-789-4295
E-mail: tomwill@swva.net
Web site: http://www.santacares.org.

Williamson Bks. *Imprint of* **Ideals Pubns.**

Willie & Willie, *(0-9754126)* P.O. Box 26071, Saint Louis, MO 63136 USA.

Williford Communications, *(1-890651)* 7608 Poplar Pike, Germantown, TN 38138 USA Tel 901-756-4661; Fax: 901-756-2429; Toll Free: 800-339-6778 ; *Imprints:* FamilyFinds (FamilyFinds)
E-mail: willifords@aol.com
Web site: http://www.willifordcommunications.com.

Willis Music Co., *(0-87718)* Orders Addr.: P.O. Box 548, Florence, KY 41022-0548 USA (SAN 294-6947) Tel 606-283-2050 859; Fax: 606-283-1784; Toll Free: 800-354-9799; Edit Addr.: 7380 Industrial Rd., Florence, KY 41040 USA
E-mail: willis@willis-music.com; orderdpt@willis-music.com
Web site: http://www.willismusic.com
Dist(s): **Leonard, Hal Corp.**

Willis' Wiki-up, *(0-615)* 2739 Sand Creek Rd., Grants Pass, OR 97527 USA Tel 541-479-5131 (phone/fax)
E-mail: lindawillis@rascals.org.

Willow Bend Publishing, *(0-9709002)* 111 West St., P.O. Box 304, Goshen, MA 01032 USA Tel 413-268-3461; Fax: 413-268-0381 Do not confuse with Willow Bend Publishing in Lakeland, FL
E-mail: info@willowbendpublishing.com
Web site: http://www.willowbendpublishing.com.

Willow Creek Assn., *(0-7441)* Orders Addr.: P.O. Box 3188, Barrington, IL 60011-3188 USA (SAN 253-3049) Tel 847-765-0070; Fax: 847-765-5046; Edit Addr.: 67 E. Algonquin Rd., South Barrington, IL 60010 USA
Web site: http://www/willowcreek.com
Dist(s): **Zondervan.**

†**Willow Creek Pr., Inc.,** *(0-932558; 1-57223; 1-59543)* Orders Addr.: P.O. Box 147, Minocqua, WI 54548-0147 USA (SAN 255-4038) Tel 715-358-7010; Fax: 715-358-2807; Toll Free: 800-850-9453; Edit Addr.: 9931 Hwy. 70, W., Minocqua, WI 54548 USA Do not confuse with Willowcreek Pr. in Aloha, OR
E-mail: info@willowcrewpress.com; info@wcpretail.com
Web site: http://www.wcpretail.com
Dist(s): **Abingdon Pr.**; *CIP.*

Willow Creel Publishing Co., *(0-9729655)* 35 Willow Creek, 820 9th Ave. S., North Myrtle Beach, SC 29582 USA Tel 843-272-1096 Do not confuse with Willow Creek Publishing in Canton, MI, Pine River, MN
E-mail: grayfox.43@att.net
Web site: http://www.chinquawhere.com.

Willow Dance Pubns., *(0-9768750)* Orders Addr.: P.O. Box 71, Hillsdale, WY 82060 USA Tel 307-631-0236; Edit Addr.: 1370 CR 142, Hillsdale, WY 82060 USA
E-mail: willowdancepublishing@yahoo.com.

Willow Tree Books *See* **Apricot Pr.**

Willow Tree Pr., *(0-9743795)* P.O. Box 2635, Lynchburg, VA 24501 USA Tel 434-237-3559 Do not confuse with Willow Tree Press in Monsey, NY
E-mail: willowtreepub@yahoo.com.

Willow Valley Pr., *(0-615; 0-9762697)* 553 Brock Rd., Nevada City, CA 95959-2908 USA (SAN 253-8911) Tel 530-265-4705; Fax: 530-478-1387; Toll Free: 800-529-9907
E-mail: barry@wvswrite.com
Web site: http://www.wvswrite.com.

Willowgate Pr., *(1-930008)* P.O. Box 6529, Holliston, MA 01746 USA (SAN 253-0376); 120 Brook Rd., Port Jefferson, NY 11777-1665
E-mail: willowgatepress@yahoo.com
Web site: http://www.willowgatepress.com
Dist(s): **Biblio Distribution.**

Willowgreen Publishing, *(1-885933)* Orders Addr.: 10351 Dawsons Creek Blvd., Suite B, Fort Wayne, IN 46825 USA Tel 260-490-2222; Fax: 260-497-9622
Web site: http://www.willowgreen.com.

Willowisp Pr. *Imprint of* **Darby Creek Publishing**

WillowSpring Downs, *(0-9648525; 0-9742716)* 1582 N. Falcon, Hillsboro, KS 67063 USA Tel 620-367-8432; Fax: 620-367-8218; Toll Free: 888-551-0973
E-mail: willowspringdowns@juno.com
Dist(s): **Booksource, The.**

WillowTree Pr., L.L.C., *(0-9678221; 0-9794533)* 2438 Charlack Ave., Saint Louis, MO 63114-4804 USA (SAN 253-1178) ; *Imprints:* Full Circle Press (Full Circle MO)
E-mail: info@willowtreepress.com
Web site: http://www.willowtreepress.com.

Wilmer Wagner & Lloyd Wagner Pr., *(0-9754538)* 4042 Sandberg Rd., Duluth, MN 55810 USA
Web site: http://www.ennyman.com.

Wilmington Today Pubns. *Imprint of* **Cape Fear Images, Inc.**

Wil-Mor Creations, Inc., *(0-9773604)* P.O. Box 6134, Cleveland, OH 44101-1134 USA (SAN 257-3849)
E-mail: wilmorcreations@sbcglobal.net
Web site: http://www.wilmorcreations.com.

Wilshire House of Arkansas *See* **Ozark Publishing**

Wilson & Assocs., *(0-9710427)* P.O. Box 2569, Alvin, TX 77512 USA Tel 281-388-0196; Fax: 413-683-8503 Do not confuse with Wilson & Associates, Gig Harbor, WA
E-mail: john@wilsonpublishing.com; pwilson@wilsonpublishing.com
Web site: http://www.orsapress.com; http://www.thebookdistributor.com; http://www.wilsonpublishing.com.

†**Wilson, H.W.,** *(0-8242)* 950 University Ave., Bronx, NY 10452-4224 USA (SAN 203-2961) Tel 718-588-8400; Fax: 718-681-1511 (Outside of the U.S. & Canada); Toll Free: 800-367-6770 ext 2272
E-mail: custserv@hwwilson.com
Web site: http://www.hwwilson.com
Dist(s): **NetLibrary, Inc.**; *CIP.*

Wilson, L.D. Consultants, Inc., *(0-9628657)* P.O. Box 54, Prescott, AZ 86302 USA Tel 928-445-7690
E-mail: Larry@drlwilson.com
Web site: http://www.drlwilson.com.

Wilson, Philip Pubs., Ltd. (GBR) *(0-302; 0-85667) Dist. by* **Macmillan.**

Wilson Place Comics, *(0-9744235)* P.O. Box 435, Oceanside, NY 11572 USA
E-mail: Wilplace@optonline.net
Web site: http://www.wjhc.com
Dist(s): **Baker & Taylor Bks.**
Brodart Co.
Diamond Comic Distributors, Inc.
Follett Library Resources
Mackin Library Media
Midwest Library Service.

Wilson Publishing, *(0-9679829)* 19303 S. Scobey Ave., Carson, CA 90746 USA Tel 310-764-1133 Do not confuse with companies with the same name in Los Angeles, CA, Bothell, WA.

Wilson, Rebecca, *(0-9760569)* 42 Harrison Ave., Northampton, MA 01060-2911 USA
E-mail: info@sunfishmanuals.com
Web site: http://www.sunfishmanuals.com.

Wilson-Barnett Publishing, *(1-888840)* P.O. Box 345, Tustin, CA 92781-0345 USA Tel 949-380-5748; Fax: 714-730-6140
E-mail: mrcalc@usa.net.

Wilson-Crawford & Co., *(0-9752948)* P.O. Box 809, Island Lake, IL 60042-0809 USA Fax: 847-487-1591
E-mail: freecellmax@aol.com
Web site: http://www.freecellsecrets.com.

Wilstonian, *(0-9772122)* 3603 Whitaker Dr., Melvindale, MI 48122 USA (SAN 257-0106)
Web site: http://www.wilstonian.com.

Wilt, Lisa, *(0-9770053)* Orders Addr.: 1072 Frye Rd., Jeannette, PA 15644-4717 USA
E-mail: thankyoumousie@comcast.net.

Wimbledon Publishing Co. (GBR) *(1-898855; 1-84331) Dist. by* **Anthem.**

Winchester Pr., *(0-9745279)* P.O. Box 711, Hollis, NH 03049-0711 USA Tel 603-880-9559 Do not confuse with companies with the same or similar name in Southhampton, NY, Howell, NJ, LaFox, IL.

Wincik, Stephanie *See* **One Horse Pr.**

Wind Pubns., *(0-9636545; 1-893239)* Orders Addr.: 600 Overbrook Dr., Nicholasville, KY 40356 USA Tel 859-885-5342
E-mail: books@windpub.com
Web site: http://windpub.com.

Windblown Enterprises, *(0-9752576)* 12207 243rd Pl NE, Redmond, WA 98053-5685 USA
E-mail: windblowne@msn.com.

Windcall Enterprises *See* **Windcall Publishing**

Windcall Publishing, *(0-9745884)* Div. of Windcall Enterprises, Orders Addr.: 75345 Rd. 317, Venango, NE 69168 USA Tel 308-447-5566 (phone/fax); Fax: 308-447-5566
E-mail: windcall@chase3000.com
Web site: http://www.windcallenterprises.com; http://www.windcallpublishing.com.

Windchimes Publishing, *(0-9763253)* P.O. Box 1433, Palm City, FL 34991-6433 USA Tel 772-285-5429
E-mail: wchimes@gate.net
Web site: http://www.wchimes.com.

Windfeather Pr., *(0-9620122)* 4545 W. Heart Rd., Bismarck, ND 58504-4257 USA (SAN 247-7246); 1203 N. 27th St., Bismarck, ND 58501 (SAN 247-7254) Tel 701-258-5047
Dist(s): **Duebbert, Harold F.**

Windham Pr., *(0-9636426)* Orders Addr.: P.O. Box 292, New Rochelle, NY 10804 USA Tel 914-636-4377; Edit Addr.: 3 Quaker Ridge Rd., New Rochelle, NY 10804 USA Do not confuse with Windham Press in Miami, FL
Web site: http://www.windhampress.com
Dist(s): **Baker & Taylor Bks.**

Windhorse Pubns. (GBR) *(0-904766; 1-899579) Dist. by* **Consort Bk Sales.**

Windigo *See* **Windigo Harbor Media**

Windigo Harbor Media, *(0-9658488)* Orders Addr.: P.O. Box 182397, Shelby Township, MI 48318-2397 USA Tel 586-612-0279; Edit Addr.: 47953 Jamestown Dr., Macomb, MI 49044 USA
E-mail: info@windigoharbormedia.com
Web site: http://www.windigoharbormedia.com.

Winding River Bks., *(1-893609)* P.O. Box 8839, Atlanta, GA 31106-0839 USA Tel 404-310-2839
E-mail: jw@weallcanread.com
Web site: http://www.weallcanread.com.

Windmill Pr., *(0-9628262)* 226 Homewood Rd., Linthicum Hts, MD 21090-2606 USA Do not confuse with companies of the same name in Newport Beach, CA, Lantana, FL
E-mail: heropub@hotmail.com.

Windom Publishing Co., *(0-9700323)* P.O. Box 102225, Denver, CO 80250 USA (SAN 253-3189) Tel 303-691-9204 Do not confuse with Windom Publishing Company, Philadephia, PA.

Window Bks., *(1-889829)* Orders Addr.: 1011 Boren Ave., No. 199, Seattle, WA 98104 USA Tel 206-351-9993
E-mail: marc@meetmarcadams.com
Web site: http://www.meetmarcadams.com.

Window Box Pr. LLC, *(0-9793738)* Orders Addr.: 13516 Fillmore Ct., Thornton, CO 80241-1330 USA (SAN 853-2958) Tel 303-255-9432
E-mail: windowboxpress@q.com
Web site: http://windowboxpress.com.

Window Seat Publishing, *(0-9721949)* 82 Marlborough Rd., West Hempstead, NY 11552 USA Tel 516-481-5969
E-mail: aferrant@optonline.net.

WindowBox Pr., *(0-9660868)* Orders Addr.: P.O. Box 1035, Great Falls, VA 22066 USA Tel 703-846-0084; Edit Addr.: 8039 N. Park St., Dunn Loring, VA 22027 USA Do not confuse with Waterbrook Pr., Colorado Springs, CO.

Windows of Discovery, *(0-9785399)* P.O. Box 9085, Spokane, WA 99209-9085 USA
Web site: http://theprofessorstelescope.com.

WindRiver Publishing, *(1-886249)* 72 N. WindRiver Rd., Silverton, ID 83867-0446 USA Tel 208-752-1836; Fax: 208-752-1876 ; *Imprints:* Trumpet Media (Trump Media) Do not confuse with companies with the same name in Houston, AK, Tulsa, OK
E-mail: info@windriverpublishing.com
Web site: http://www.trumpetmedia.com; http://www.windriverpublishing.com
Dist(s): **Baker & Taylor Bks.**

Windsong Publishing Co., *(0-9655078)* P.O. Box 588, Rimrock, AZ 86335 USA Do not confuse with companies with the same or similar names in Eugene, OR, San Diego, CA, Staunton, VA, Lake Patagonia, AZ
Dist(s): **Baker & Taylor Bks.**
New Leaf Distributing Co., Inc.

Windsor Hse. Publishing Group, The, *(1-881636)* 325 Lois, Waxahachie, TX 75165 USA Tel 972-351-9891 (phone/fax)
E-mail: windhou@ectisp.net
Web site: http://www.awindsorhouse.com.

Windsor Media Enterprises, LLC, *(0-9765304; 0-9777297; 1-934229)* 282 Ballad Ave., Rochester, NY 14626 USA Toll Free: 877-947-2665
E-mail: damore@umebooks.com
Web site: http://www.wmebooks.com.

WindSpirit Publishing, *(0-9643407)* Orders Addr.: 220 Compass Ave., Beachwood, NJ 08722-2919 USA Fax: 732-240-7860
E-mail: windspiritpub@earthlink.net
Web site: http://www.windspiritpublishing.net.

Windstorm Creative, *(1-883573; 1-886383; 1-59092)* Orders Addr.: P.O. Box 28, Port Orchard, WA 98366 USA; Edit Addr.: 7419 Ebbert Dr., SE, Port Orchard, WA 98367 USA (SAN 299-1330) Tel 360-769-7174 (phone/fax) ; *Imprints:* Little Blue Works (Little Blue); Lightning Rod Publishers (Lightning Rod); Orchard Academy Press (Orchard Acad Pr); Blue Works (Blue Works); Full Spectrum Information Library (Full Spec)
E-mail: wsc@windstormcreative.com
Web site: http://www.windstormcreative.com
Dist(s): **Alamo Square Distributors**
Baker & Taylor Bks.
Ingram Bk. Co.

Windstorm Creative Limited *See* **Windstorm Creative**

Windswept Hse. Pubs., *(0-932433; 1-883650)* P.O. Box 159, Mount Desert, ME 04660 USA (SAN 687-4363) Tel 207-244-5027; Fax: 207-244-3369
E-mail: windswt@prexar.com
Web site: http://www.booknotes.com/windswept/.

Windswept Productions, *(0-9764825)* Orders Addr.: P.O. Box 167, Felton, PA 17322-0167 USA Tel 717-244-7700; Edit Addr.: 11525 High Point Rd., Felton, PA 17322 USA
E-mail: wpebs@earthlink.net.

Windward Publishing *Imprint of* **Finney Co., Inc.**

Windward Publishing, *(0-9758897)* 112 N. St., New Bedford, MA 02740-6513 USA Do not confuse with Windward Publishing in Minneapolis, MN
E-mail: windwardpublish@aol.com; josettefernandes@hotmail.com.

Windword Pr., *(0-9642206)* 3109 Portman St., Keego Harbor, MI 48320-1208 USA Tel 248-682-5827; Fax: 248-851-0268; Toll Free: 800-718-5888 Do not confuse with Wind Word Pr. in Healdsburg, CA.

Windy Hill Pr., *(0-9662983)* Orders Addr.: 22 Hilltop Ave., Barrington, RI 02806 USA Tel 401-247-2707 Do not confuse with Windy Hill Pr., in Menlo Park, CA
E-mail: windyhillpress@cox.net
Web site: http://www.windyhillpress.net
Dist(s): **Baker & Taylor Bks.**

WindyCreek, *(0-9651303)* 4738 Meadow Ln., Bozeman, MT 59715 USA (SAN 298-9425) Tel 406-585-0996
E-mail: windycreek@aol.com
Web site: http://www.windycreek.com
Dist(s): **Baker & Taylor Bks.**
Koen-Levy Bk. Wholesalers LLC.

WinePress Publishing, *(0 9622413; 1-57921; 1-883893)* Orders Addr.: P.O. Box 428, Enumclaw, WA 98022 USA Tel 360-802-9758; Fax: 360-802-9992; Toll Free: 800-326-4674
E-mail: infosys@winepresspub.com
Web site: http://www.winepresspub.com
Dist(s): **Appalachian Bk. Distributors**
Baker & Taylor Bks.
STL Distribution North America
Spring Arbor Distributors, Inc.

Winfield Collection, The, *(0-9743767)* 3150 Owen Rd., Fenton, MI 48430 USA
Web site: http://www.thewinfieldcollection.com.

Wing Dam Pr., *(0-9758615)* P.O. Box 200, Ferryville, WI 54628 USA Tel 608-734-3292 (phone/fax)
E-mail: nlichter@mwt.net.

Wing, Thomas Publishing, *(0-9714505)* 4320 S. Gevers, Suite 300, San Antonio, TX 78223 USA Tel 210-533-4455; Fax: 210-533-4414 ; *Imprints:* PERMEDHIST (Permedhist)
E-mail: drwet@att.net; wilburn.thomas@att.net.

Winged Willow Pr., *(0-9664805)* Orders Addr.: P.O. Box 92, Carrboro, NC 27510 USA Tel 919-942-4689; Fax: 919-933-3555
E-mail: info@sudierakusin.com
Web site: http://www.sudierakusin.com
Dist(s): **Parnassus Bk. Distributors.**

WingedChariot Pr. (GBR) *(1-905341) Dist. by* **IPG Chicago.**

Wings Above, *(0-9768403)* 1607 Market St., Galveston, TX 77550 USA Tel 409-750-9176.

Wings ePress, Inc., *(1-59088; 1-59705)* 403 Wallace Crt., Richmond, KY 82225 USA Do not confuse with companies with the same or similar name in Northhampton, MA, Union, ME, San Antonio, TX
E-mail: mkapp@bellsouth.net
Web site: http://www.wings-press.com.

Wings, Inc., *(0-9705018)* 4790 Caughlin Pkwy., Suite 143, Reno, NV 89509 USA Tel 775-826-0548; Fax: 775-826-4695
E-mail: glebeck@wingsnv.com
Web site: http://www.wingsnv.com.

Wings Pr., *(0-916727; 0-930324)* 627 E. Guenther, San Antonio, TX 78210 USA (SAN 209-4975) Tel 210-271-7805 Do not confuse with companies with the same or similar name in Northhampton, MA, UNion, ME, Lusk, WY
E-mail: milligan@wingspress.com
Web site: http://www.wingspress.com
Dist(s): **Baker & Taylor Bks.**
Brodart Co.
Independent Pubs. Group
SPD-Small Pr. Distribution.

Wings Press, Limited *See* **Wings ePress, Inc.**

Wings-on-Disk *Imprint of* **LANIUS Software**

Wingspan Pr. *Imprint of* **WingSpan Publishing**

WingSpan Publishing, *(1-59594)* P.O. Box 2085, Livermore, CA 94551 USA Toll Free: 866-735-3782 ; *Imprints:* Wingspan Press (Wingspan Pr)
Web site: http://www.wingspanpress.com.

Winking Moon Pr., *(0-9764175)* 4130 S. Splendor Ct., Gilbert, AZ 85297 USA Do not confuse with Winking Moon Press in Cleveland OH .

Winlock Publishing Co., *(0-9649437; 1-890461)* 26135 Murrieta Rd., Sun City, CA 92585 USA Tel 951-943-0014; Fax: 951-943-0014
E-mail: dave@winlockgaley.com
Web site: http://www.winlockgaley.com.

Winmark Communications, *(1-892225)* Orders Addr.: P.O. Box 87775, Phoenix, AZ 85080 USA Tel 602-789-9240; Fax: 602-547-2268; Toll Free: 888-728-9880; Edit Addr.: 17834 N. 41st Ave., Glendale, AZ 85308 USA
E-mail: winmark@phnx.uswest.net
Web site: http://www.happythor.com/winmark.html.

Winn, Lynnette, *(0-9791884)* P.O. Box 3384, Ogden, UT 84409-3384 USA (SAN 852-7040)
Web site: http://www.butterpodjerome.com.

Winner Enterprises, *(0-932855)* 670 Nighthawk Cir., Winter Springs, FL 32708 USA (SAN 691-2923) Tel 407-696-2103 (phone/fax)
E-mail: info@winnerenterprises.com
Web site: http://www.techware.com/winner.

Winner Episode Pr., *(0-615; 0-9719221)* Div. of Winning Episode, P.O. Box 1530, New York, NY 10021-0093 USA Fax: 212-906-0087
E-mail: pema@nyc.rr.com
Web site: http://www.onlyonetruth.com
Dist(s): **Book Clearing Hse.**

Winning Moves, *(1-891056)* 100 Conifer Hill Dr., Suite 102, Danvers, MA 01923 USA (SAN 631-9777) Tel 978-777-7464; Fax: 978-739-4847; Toll Free: 800-664-7788
E-mail: wmoves@winning-moves.com; carcisz@winning-moves.com
Web site: http://www.winning-moves.com.

Winning Walk Family, *(0-7417)* Div. of Second Baptist Church, Houston, TX, 6400 Woodway Dr., Houston, TX 77057-1606 USA (SAN 631-7286) Tel 713-465-9331; Fax: 713-365-2353; Toll Free: 800-553-9772
E-mail: pschneider@excitement.org
Web site: Http://www.winningwalk.org.

Winnow Pr., *(0-9764726)* 3505 El Dorado Trail, Suite A, Austin, TX 78739 USA (SAN 256-4017) Tel 512-280-4483
E-mail: publisher@winnowpress.com
Web site: http://winnowpress.com.

Winslow Hse. Bks., *(0-9672022)* Books A to Z, 770 N. 34th St., Seattle, WA 98103 USA (SAN 299-8890) Tel 206-547-2026; Fax: 206-547-1718
E-mail: steve@booksatoz.com.

Winslow, Lori, *(0-615)* c/o Louisville Elementary School, 170 S. Madison Ave., Louisville, CO 80027-9786 USA
E-mail: Winslow@bvsd.k12.co.us.

Winslow Pr., *(1-890817; 1-58837)* Div. of Foundation for Concepts in Education, Inc., The, 115 E. 23rd St., 10th Flr., New York, NY 10010 USA Tel 212-254-2025; Fax: 212-254-1595; Toll Free: 800-617-3947
E-mail: winslow@winslowpress.com
Web site: http://www.winslowpress.com.

Winsor Corporation *See* **Winsor Learning, Inc.**

Winsor Learning, Inc., *(1-891602)* 1620 W. Seventh St., Saint Paul, MN 55102 USA Tel 651-222-3922; Fax: 651-222-3969; Toll Free: 800-321-7585
E-mail: sondaysystem@winsorcorp.net
Web site: http://www.sondaysystem.com.

Winstead Pr., Ltd., *(0-940787)* 202 Slice Dr., Stamford, CT 06907 USA (SAN 664-6913) Tel 203-322-4941
E-mail: winstead.press@gte.net.

Winter, Mark, *(0-9728409)* Orders Addr.: P.O. Box 2044, Santa Fe, NM 87504-2044 USA Tel 505-989-7663; Fax: 505-984-1840; Edit Addr.: P.O. Box 2044, Santa Fe, NM 87504-2044 USA
E-mail: relicssf@earthlink.net
Web site: http://www.toadlenatradingpost.com.

Wintermantel Group, LLC, The, *(0-9767418)* 255 Vilage Meadow, Ballwin, MO 63021 USA Tel 636-386-8820
Web site: http://www.theangelchildren.com.

Winterthur, Henry Francis duPont Museum, Inc., *(0-912724)* Rte. 52, Winterthur, DE 19735 USA (SAN 205-5406) Tel 302-888-4600; Fax: 302-888-4950; Toll Free: 800-448-3883
E-mail: srandolph@winterthur.org
Web site: http://www.winterthur.org
Dist(s): **Univ. Pr. of New England**
Univ. of Tennessee Pr.

Winterwolf Publishing, *(0-9744831; 0-9752711; 0-9762471; 0-9772632)* Orders Addr.: P.O. Box 1373, Westerville, OH 43086-1373 USA; Edit Addr.: 5446 Highbrook Ct., Westerville, OH 43081 USA
Web site: http://www.winterwolfpublishing.com.

Wipf and Stock *Imprint of* **Wipf & Stock Pubs.**

Wipf & Stock Pubs., *(0-9653517; 1-55635; 1-57910; 1-59244; 1-59752)* 199 W. 8th Ave., Suite 3, Eugene, OR 97401 USA Tel 541-344-1528; Fax: 541-344-1506 ; *Imprints:* Resource Publications (Resource Pubcns); Wipf and Stock (Wipf and Stock)
E-mail: jtedrick@wipfandstock.com
Web site: http://www.wipfandstock.com
Dist(s): **Ingram Bk. Co.**
Spring Arbor Distributors, Inc.

Wiscasset Music Publishing Co., P.O. Box 380810, Cambridge, MA 02238 USA Tel 617-492-5720; Fax: 617-492-4031
E-mail: information@wiscassetmusicpublishing.com
Web site: http://www.wiscassetmusicpublishing.com.

Wisconsin Dept. of Public Instruction, *(1-57337)* Orders Addr.: Drawer 179, Milwaukee, WI 53293-0179 USA Tel 608-266-2188; Fax: 608-267-9110; Toll Free: 800-243-8782; Edit Addr.: 125 S. Webster St., Box 7841, Madison, WI 53702 USA
Web site: http://www.dpi.state.wi.us.

†**Wisconsin Historical Society,** *(0-87020)* 816 State St., Madison, WI 53706 USA (SAN 203-350X) Tel 608-264-6584; Fax: 608-264-6486
E-mail: diane.drexler@wisconsinhistory.org
Web site: http://www.wisconsinhistory.org
Dist(s): **Chicago Distribution Ctr.**; *CIP.*

Wisdom Bks. *Imprint of* **Literary Assocs. Pr.**

Wisdom Books *See* **Wisdom Pr.**

Wisdom Co., The, *(0-9717174)* 16012 Clifton Ave., Gulfport, MS 39503 USA Fax: 228-832-4038 Do not confuse with Wisdom Co., Inc. in Franklin, TN
Web site: http://www.thewisdomcompany.org.

Wisdom Foundation Publishing, *(1-932590)* 796 Isenberg St., Suite 19E, Honolulu, HI 96826 USA Tel 808-944-3113; Fax: 808-988-4212
E-mail: wisdomfactors@hawaii.rr.com.

Wisdom Pages, The, *(0-9706482)* 65 Fraser St., Staten Island, NY 10314 USA (SAN 255-1217) Tel 718-983-1333; Fax: 718-983-3851
E-mail: miriam@bullies2buddies.com
Web site: http://www.bullies2buddies.com.

Wisdom Pr., *(0-9678364)* 1634 Columbia, Houston, TX 77008 USA Tel 713-236-1400
E-mail: lggarcia@mail.esc4.com
Web site: http://lionelgarcia-novelist.com.

†**Wisdom Pubns.,** *(0-86171)* 199 Elm St., Somerville, MA 02144 USA (SAN 246-022X) Tel 617-776-7416 ext 24; Fax: 617-776-7841; Toll Free Fax: 800-338-4550 (orders only); Toll Free: 800-462-6420 (orders only)
E-mail: marketing@wisdompubs.org
Web site: http://www.wisdompubs.org
Dist(s): **Perseus Distribution**; *CIP.*

Wisdom Tree Records *See* **Rivertree Productions, Inc.**

Wise Guides, Inc., *(0-9768772)* 1924 W. Montrose, PMB No. 206, Chicago, IL 60613 USA Toll Free: 866-262-3842
E-mail: info@wiseguidebooks.com
Web site: http://www.wiseguidebooks.com.

Wise Owl Printing Plus, Incorporated *See* **Deziner Media International**

Wise Publishing Co., *(0-915766)* Orders Addr.: 5625 Wilhelmina Ave., Woodland Hills, CA 91367 USA (SAN 203-1876) Tel 818-883-7527; Fax: 818-883-9212 Do not confuse with companies with the same or similar name in Indianapolis, IN, Mansfield, TX, Charlotte, NC.

Wise Words Publications *See* **Executive Pubs. International**

Wisecracker Press, Inc., *(0-9752657)* 2735 April Hill Ln., Dallas, TX 75287 USA
Web site: http://www.wisecrackerpress.com.

Wish Publishing, *(1-930546)* P.O. Box 10337, Terre Haute, IN 47801 USA (SAN 253-4320) Tel 812-299-5700; Fax: 928-447-1836
E-mail: holly@wishpublishing.com
Web site: http://www.wishpublishing.com
Dist(s): **Cardinal Pubs. Group**
Lightning Source, Inc.

Wish You Were Here *Imprint of* **Sierra Pr.**

Wishing U Well Publishing, *(0-9769524)* 1560 Gulf Blvd., Unit 1202, Clearwater, FL 33767 USA.

Witherspoon Pr. *Imprint of* **Curriculum Publishing, Presbyterian Church (U. S. A.)**

Within Reach, Inc., *(0-9718864)* P.O. Box 6217, Harrisburg, PA 17112 USA Tel 717-657-8689
E-mail: wreach@epix.net
Web site: http://www.boatingsidekicks.com.

Witness Productions, *(0-9627653; 1-891390)* Box 34, Church St., Marshall, IN 47859 USA Tel 765-597-2487.

Witty Bit World, Inc., *(0-9770548)* 1009 Basil Dr., New Bern, NC 28562 USA
E-mail: deborah@wittybitworld.com
Web site: http://www.wittybitworld.com.

Company

Witty Fools Productions, *(0-9745179)* 19 Le Grande Ave., No.14, Greenwich, CT 06830 USA Toll Free: 877-733-0528 (phone/fax)
E-mail: wittyfools@aol.com; flierlp@bww.com
Web site: http://www.wittyfools.com; http://www.prayerlaughterandbroccoli.com.

Wiyd, Lewis, *(0-9650637)* 47 Glen Park Rd., East Orange, NJ 07017-1813 USA Tel 973-673-0094; Fax: 973-673-0095.

Wizard Academy Pr., *(0-9714769; 1-932226)* 16621 Crystal Hills Dr., Austin, TX 78737 USA Tel 512-295-5700; Fax: 512-295-5701; Toll Free: 800-425-4769
E-mail: publisher@wizardofads.com; sean@wizardofads.com
Web site: http://www.wizardacademypress.com
Dist(s): **Baker & Taylor Bks.**

Wizard Entertainment, *(0-9672489; 0-9743253; 0-9762874; 0-9778613; 0-9792564)* 151 Wells Ave., Congers, NY 10920 USA
E-mail: jsantopietro@wizarduniverse.com
Web site: http://www.wizarduniverse.com
Dist(s): **Diamond Comic Distributors, Inc.**

Wizard Works, *(0-9621543; 1-890692)* Orders Addr.: P.O. Box 1125, Homer, AK 99603-1125 USA Toll Free: 877-210-2665
E-mail: wizard@xyz.net
Web site: http://www.xyz.net/~wizard.

Wizarding World Pr., *(0-9723936)* 8926 N. Greenwood Ave., Suite 133, Niles, IL 60714 USA
E-mail: wizardingworld@waycoolstuffonline.com
Web site: http://www.wizardingworldpress.com
Dist(s): **SCB Distributors.**

Wizards of the Coast, *(0-7869; 1-57530; 1-880992; 0-7430)* Subs. of Hasbro, Inc., Orders Addr.: P.O. Box 707, Renton, WA 98057-0709 USA Toll Free: 800-821-8028; Edit Addr.: 1801 Lind Ave., SW, Renton, WA 98055 USA (SAN 299-4410) Tel 425-226-6500 ; *Imprints:* Mirrorstone (Mirrorstone)
E-mail: angella@wizards.com
Web site: http://www.wizards.com
Dist(s): **Diamond Bk. Distributors**
PSI (Publisher Services, Inc.)
Random Hse., Inc.
Doherty, Tom Assocs., LLC.

WizdomInc, *(0-9764829; 0-9767958; 0-9768053; 0-9778512; 0-9785170; 0-9786574)* 273 Candlelight Dr., Santa Rosa, CA 95403 USA Tel 707-578-1866; Fax: 707-578-4978; Toll Free: 866-607-4510
E-mail: marjam@wizdominc.com
Web site: http://www.wizdominc.com.

WLA Publishing (Writers Literary Agency), *(0-9715554)* Div. of VHI, Inc., P.O. Box 31519, Phoenix, AZ 85046 USA
E-mail: johnftaylor@cox.net
Web site: http://www.writersliteraryagency.com.

Wms-Ashe, Marcella *See* **Allecram Publishing**

WNZ Pubns., *(0-9656714)* Orders Addr.: P.O. Box 393, Mecosta, MI 49332 USA (SAN 253-9896) Tel 231-972-8135 (phone/fax); Edit Addr.: 8277 Peninsula Dr., Stanwood, MI 49346 USA
E-mail: wnzpub@centurytel.net.

Wobblefoot Ltd., *(0-9747149)* 1662 Mars Ave., Lakewood, OH 44107-3825 USA
E-mail: wblft1@sbcglobal.net
Web site: http://wobblefoot.com.

Wohlers Assocs., Inc., *(0-9754429)* OakRidge Business Pk., 1511 River Oak Dr., Fort Collins, CO 80525-5537 USA
Web site: http://www.wohlersassociates.com.

Wold, Kelly, *(0-9768944)* 23417 Rouge River Ln., Murrieta, CA 92562-5026 USA
E-mail: kmwold@hotmail.com.

Woldt Corporation *See* **Florida Literary Foundation**

Wolf Creek Pr., *(0-9611886)* Orders Addr.: 6647 Dyer Dr., Lake Almanor, CA 96137 USA (SAN 286-0848) Tel 530-596-3412; 560 Pecks Valley Rd., Box D-201, Greenville, CA 95947 (SAN 241-9211) Tel 530-284-6516 Do not confuse with Wolf Creek Pr. in Burbank, CA, Fond du Lac, WI
E-mail: jblittle@thegrid.net; salrob@thegrid.net.

Wolf Creek Publishing, *(0-9768983)* 193 Tenby Chase Dr., Apt. S-233, Delran, NJ 08075 USA
Web site: http://www.photosfromthewild.com.

Wolf Road, *(0-9713851)* P.O. Box 306, Pacifica, CA 94044 USA Tel 650-738-3617.

Wolfhound Pr. (IRL) *(0-86327; 0-905473; 0-9503454) Dist. by* **Irish Bks Media.**

Wolfhound Pr. (IRL) *(0-86327; 0-905473; 0-9503454) Dist. by* **Interlink Pub.**

Wolfhound Pr. (IRL) *(0-86327; 0-905473; 0-9503454) Dist. by* **Irish Amer Bk.**

Wolfrider Bks. *Imprint of* **Warp Graphics, Inc.**

Wolfs Corner Publishing, *(0-9779921)* 20 Primrose Ln., Sparta, NJ 07871 USA
E-mail: jmd_inc007@hotmail.com
Web site: wolfscornerpublishing.com.

Wolo, Armour Foundation, *(0-9708998)* P.O. Box 871862, New Orleans, LA 70187-1862 USA Tel 504-288-0057; Fax: 504-288-9867
E-mail: eawolo@aol.com.

Wolters Kluwer Law & Business, *(0-444; 0-7355; 0-7896; 0-8080; 0-8342; 0-87189; 0-87457; 0-87622; 0-89443; 0-912862; 0-916592; 0-9625969; 1-56542; 1-56706; 1-56759; 1-878375; 90-411; 90-6544)* Orders Addr.: Order Dept., 7201 McKinney Cir., Frederick, MD 21704 USA Toll Free Fax: 800-901-0335 (Orders); 800-561-4845 (Bookstore Orders Only); 800-901-9075 (Customer Service); Toll Free: 800-234-1660 (Customer Service); 800-317-3113 (Bookstore Orders Only); 800-447-1717 (Orders); Edit Addr.: 76 Ninth Ave., 7th Flr., New York, NY 10011 USA (SAN 203-4999) ; *Imprints:* Aspen Publishers (Aspen).

Wolverton, *(0-9674101)* 46 W. Park St., Box 1149, Westerville, OH 43081 USA Tel 614-881-5523.

Woman's Missionary Union, *(0-936625; 1-56309; 1-59669)* Orders Addr.: c/o Carol Causey, P.O. Box 830010, Birmingham, AL 35283 USA (SAN 699-7015) Tel 205-991-8100; Fax: 205-995-4825; Toll Free: 800-968-7301; Edit Addr.: 100 Missionary Ridge, Birmingham, AL 35242 USA (SAN 699-7023)
E-mail: cwhite@wmu.org
Web site: http://www.wmu.com.

Wombacher, Michael, *(0-9713033)* 2412 Valley St., Berkeley, CA 94702-2136 USA
E-mail: michael_wombacher@excite.com
Web site: http://www.doggonegood.org.

Womble, Mary *See* **Kell, Mary**

Women & Addiction Counseling & Educational Services, *(0-9663144)* 43522 Modena Dr., Temecula, CA 92592-9235 USA Tel 951-303-0235 (phone/fax)
E-mail: info@wacespublishing.com
Web site: http://www.wacespublishing.com.

Women in Aviation, International, *(0-9749190)* 3647 State Route 503 S., W Alexandria, OH 45381-9354 USA
Web site: http://www.wai.org.

Women in the World, Curriculum Resource Project *See* **Women in World History Curriculum**

Women In Translation, *(1-879679)* P.O. Box 1705, Port Townsend, WA 98368-0159 USA
E-mail: wit@scn.org
Dist(s): **Consortium Bk. Sales & Distribution.**

Women in World History Curriculum, *(0-9625880; 1-890380)* 1030 Spruce St., Berkeley, CA 94707 USA Tel 510-524-0304; Fax: 510-524-0112
E-mail: womenwhist@earthlink.net
Web site: http://www.womeninworldhistory.com
Dist(s): **National Women's History Project**
Social Studies Schl. Service
Upper Midwest Women's History Ctr.

Women's Intuition Worldwide, *(0-9651145; 0-9752538)* 116 Hillsdale Dr., Sterling, VA 20164-1201 USA Tel 703-404-4357; Toll Free: 800-345-6665
E-mail: rights@rose-rosetree.com
Web site: http://www.rose-rosetree.com
Dist(s): **Baker & Taylor Bks.**
New Leaf Distributing Co., Inc.
Quality Bks., Inc.
Unique Bks., Inc.

Women's Pr., Ltd., The (GBR) *(0-7043) Dist. by* **Trafalgar.**

Women's Pr., Ltd., The (GBR) *(0-7043) Dist. by* **IPG Chicago.**

womentalkmoney.com, *(0-9711715)* P.O. Box 49327, Los Angeles, CA 90049 USA (SAN 254-6728) Tel 310-440-9588; Fax: 310-442-6018
E-mail: orders@womentalkmoney.com
Web site: http://www.womentalkmoney.com
Dist(s): **Quality Bks., Inc.**

Wompuse Publishing Co., *(0-9706316)* Orders Addr.: P.O. Box 615, Lapeer, MI 48446-3284 USA Tel 810-245-2703; Edit Addr.: 200 Maple Grove Rd., Lapeer, MI 48446-3284 USA
E-mail: tschabeck@blclinks.net.

Wonder Chess LLC, *(0-9771787)* 2622 10th Ave E., Seattle, WA 98102-3901 USA
E-mail: info@wonderchess.com
Web site: http://www.wonderchess.com.

Wonder Toash Arts Inc., *(0-9761606)* Orders Addr.: 3075 E. Bates Ave., Denver, CO 80210 USA
E-mail: anna@wondertoast.com
Web site: http://www.wondertoast.com.

Wonder Workshop, *(1-56919)* Div. of Stephens Group, Inc., 1123 Brookstone Blvd., Mount Juliet, TN 37122-3274 USA Toll Free: 800-627-6874.

Wonderbooks Publishing, *(0-9773809)* P.O. Box 770741, Orlando, FL 32877 USA (SAN 257-4535)
Web site: http://www.wonderbookspublishing.com
Dist(s): **AtlasBooks Distribution.**

Wonderworks Pubs., Inc., *(0-9713311)* 11555 SW 128th Ct., Miami, FL 33186 USA Tel 305-382-5252; Fax: 305-387-4497
E-mail: mariaanareyes@aol.com
Web site: http://www.wonderworkspublishers.com.

Wood, Char , The Computer Granny, *(0-9719613)* 2028 Pine Tree Dr., Edgewater, FL 32141 USA
E-mail: granny@computergranny.com; cwood33@cfl.rr.com
Web site: http://www.computergranny.com; http://www.1234seniors.com; http://www.notadummy.com.

Wood, Charlotte Enterprises *See* **Wood, Char , The Computer Granny**

Wood Designs, Inc., *(0-9729454)* P.O. Box 1790, New Waverly, TX 77358-1790 USA Toll Free Fax: 877-612-8306; Toll Free: 877-612-8306 ; *Imprints:* MomGeek.com (MomGeek.com)
E-mail: sales@pegrack.com
Web site: http://www.flamencoguide.com.

Wood, Ella Sue, *(0-9774937)* 3229 Regatta Pointe Ct., Midlothian, VA 23112 USA.

Wood, Judy W., *(1-886021; 1-58414)* 9327 Midlothian Tpke., Suite 2E, Richmond, VA 23236 USA Tel 804-379-1492; Fax: 804-327-7197; Toll Free Fax: 877-418-7860; Toll Free: 877-583-9966
E-mail: mail@judywood.com
Web site: http://www.judywood.com.

Wood, Judy W. Incorporated *See* **Wood, Judy W.**

Wood Lake Bks., Inc. (CAN) *(0-919599; 0-929032; 0-929599; 1-55145; 1-895562) Dist. by* **Pilgrim OH.**

Wood Lake Bks., Inc. (CAN) *(0-919599; 0-929032; 0-929599; 1-55145; 1-895562) Dist. by* **Logos Prods.**

Wood 'N' Barnes, *(1-885473)* Div. of Jean Barnes Bks., 2717 NW 50th, Oklahoma City, OK 73112 USA (SAN 298-9433) Tel 405-942-6812; Fax: 405-946-4074; Toll Free: 800-678-0621
E-mail: info@woodnbarnes.com
Web site: http://www.woodnbarnes.com.

†Woodbine Hse., *(0-933149; 1-890627)* 6510 Bells Mill Rd., Bethesda, MD 20817 USA (SAN 630-4052) Tel 301-897-3570; Fax: 301-897-5838; Toll Free: 800-843-7323
E-mail: info@woodbinehouse.com
Web site: http://www.woodbinehouse.com; *CIP.*

Woodburn Graphics, Inc., *(0-9707547)* P.O. Box 490, Terre Haute, ID 47807 USA Tel 812-232-0323; Fax: 812-232-2733; Toll Free: 800-457-0674
E-mail: len@woodburngraphics.com
Web site: http://www.woodburngraphics.com.

Wooded Hill Productions, *(1-886635)* Orders Addr.: 7480 Esplin Way, Flagstaff, AZ 86004 USA Tel 928-522-0058 (phone/fax)
E-mail: sig@boloz.com; sigmund.boloz@nau.edu
Web site: http://www.boloz.com.

Wooden Shoe Pr., *(0-9762852)* N3566 Cty. Rd., GG, Hancock, WI 54943 USA Do not confuse with Wooden Shoe Press in Philadelphia, PA
E-mail: woodenshoepress@yahoo.com
Web site: http://www.woodenshoepress.com.

WoodenBoat Pubns., *(0-937822)* Orders Addr.: P.O. Box 78, Brooklin, ME 04616 USA Tel 207-359-4651; Fax: 207-359-2058; Toll Free: 800-273-7447
E-mail: books@woodenboat.com; wbstore@woodenboat.com
Web site: http://www.woodenboat.com.

Woodgate International, *(1-893617)* Orders Addr.: P.O. Box 190, Woodgate, NY 13494 USA Tel 315-392-4508
E-mail: Jslade@dreamscape.com
Web site: http://www.woodgateintl.com
Dist(s): **AtlasBooks Distribution**
BookMasters, Inc.

Woodglen Pr., *(0-615; 0-9720159)* P.O. Box 871, Penn Valley, CA 95946 USA.

Woodland Health Books *See* **Woodland Publishing, Inc.**

Woodland Pr., *(0-9755822)* 605 Timber Ln., Lake Forest, IL 60045-3117 USA Tel 847-295-3514; Fax: 847-582-1970 Do not confuse with companies with the same name in Minneapolis, MN, Lapeer MI, Salt Lake City, UT.

Woodland Pr. LLC, *(0-9724867; 0-9793236)* 118 Woodland , Suite 1102, Chapmanville, WV 25508 USA (SAN 254-9999) Tel 304-752-7500; Fax: 304-752-9002 Do not confuse with companies with the same or similar names in Minneapolis, MN, Lapeer, MI, Salt Lake City, UT, Florance, AL, Moscow, ID
E-mail: info@woodlandpress.com; woodlandpressllc@mac.com
Web site: http://www.woodlandpress.com; http://www.woodlandgospel.com
Dist(s): **New Day Christian Distributors**
Quality Bks., Inc.
West Virginia Book Co., The.

Woodland Publishing, Inc., *(0-913923; 1-58054; 1-885670)* Orders Addr.: 448 E. 800 N., Orem, UT 84097 USA (SAN 286-9063) Tel 801-434-8113; Fax: 801-334-1913; Toll Free: 800-777-2665
E-mail: jbonyata@woodlandpublishing.com; dhamblen@woodlandpublishing.com
Web site: http://www.woodlandpublishing.com
Dist(s): **Baker & Taylor Bks.**
Integral Yoga Pubns.
Midpoint Trade Bks., Inc.
New Leaf Distributing Co., Inc.
Nutri-Bks. Corp.
Royal Pubns., Inc.

Woodland Studios, Inc., *(0-9663076; 1-893452)* 1357 Rocky Creek Ct., Belleville, IL 62220 USA Tel 618-236-1881.

Woodruff, David Roberts, *(0-9716806)* 4075 Carmel View Rd., No.9, San Deigo, CA 92130 USA
E-mail: drbts@att.net.

Woodruff, Paul, *(0-9764327)* 58048 Inglewood Ln., Glenwood, IA 51534 USA.

Woods, Emmett L., *(0-615)* 4016 Monterey Ct., Montgomery, AL 36116 USA Tel 334-288-1380.

Woods N' Water, Inc., *(0-9707493; 0-9722804; 0-9769233; 0-9795131)* Orders Addr.: P.O. Box 550, Florida, NY 10921 USA (SAN 254-3869); Edit Addr.: 468 Route 17A, 2nd Fl., Suite 5, Florida, NY 10921 USA Tel 845-986-0326; Fax: 845-986-0327; Toll Free: 800-652-7527
E-mail: kate@fiduccia.com
Web site: http://www.woodsnwaterpress.com
Dist(s): **Baker & Taylor Bks.**
Cardinal Pubs. Group.

Woodstocker Books/Arthur Schwartz & Company, *(1-879504)* 15 Meads Mountain Rd., Woodstock, NY 12498-1016 USA (SAN 630-0464) Tel 845-679-4024; Fax: 845-679-4093; Toll Free: 800-669-9080 (orders only)
E-mail: woodstockerbooks@woodstockerbooks.com
Web site: http://www.aschwartzbooks.com
Dist(s): **Antique Collectors' Club.**

Woolf, Virginia M. Foundation, *(0-9721271)* 1658 Fifth St., Manhattan Beach, CA 90266 USA Tel 310-379-8321; Fax: 310-372-2943
E-mail: info@text-key.com
Web site: http://www.text-key.com.

Woolfolk Publications *See* **Gye Nyame Hse.**

Wooster Bk. Co., The, *(1-888683; 1-59098)* 205 W. Liberty St., Wooster, OH 44691-4831 USA Tel 330-262-1688; Fax: 330-264-9753; Toll Free: 800-982-6651 (800-WUBook-1)
E-mail: mail@woosterbook.com
Web site: http://www.woosterbook.com.

Wo-Pila Publishing, *(1-886340)* Orders Addr.: P.O. Box 8966, Erie, PA 16505-0966 USA Tel 814-868-5331; Fax: 814-868-1711; Toll Free: 888-567-8267; Edit Addr.: 3324 Charlotte St., Erie, PA 16508-2224 USA
E-mail: WopilaPublishing@aol.com
Web site: http://www.MannyTwofeathers.com
Dist(s): **Biblio Distribution.**

Word Aflame Pr., *(0-912315; 0-932581; 1-56722; 0-7577)* Subs. of Pentecostal Publishing Hse., 8855 Dunn Rd., Hazelwood, MO 63042 USA (SAN 212-0046) Tel 314-837-7300; Fax: 314-837-6574
E-mail: pph@upci.org
Web site: http://www.upci.org/pph.

Word Among Us Pr., *(0-932085; 1-59325)* 9639 Dr. Perry Rd., No. 126, Ijamsville, MD 21754 USA (SAN 686-4651) Tel 301-831-1262; Fax: 301-831-1188; Toll Free: 800-775-9673
E-mail: pmm@wall.org
Web site: http://www.wau.org
Dist(s): **Spring Arbor Distributors, Inc.**

Word Assocs., Inc., *(0-939153; 1-57265)* 3226 Robincrest Dr., Northbrook, IL 60062 USA (SAN 679-7792) Tel 847-291-1101; Fax: 847-291-0931
E-mail: microlrn@aol.com
Web site: http://www.wordassociates.com.

Word Association Pubs., *(1-891231; 1-932205; 1-59571)* 205 Fifth Ave., Tarentum, PA 15084 USA Tel 724-226-4526; Fax: 724-226-3974; Toll Free: 800-827-7903
E-mail: publish@wordassociation.com
Web site: http://www.wordassociation.com.

Word Blossoms Publishing, *(0-9675170)* 3054 Perkins Rd., Baton Rouge, LA 70808 USA Tel 225-343-1266
E-mail: WordBlossoms@Go.com
Dist(s): **Cottonwood Bks.**

Word For Word Publishing Co., *(1-889732)* 144 Quincy St. Apt. 1, Brooklyn, NY 11216-1393 USA ; *Imprints:* A & E Sivells Publications (A & E Sivells Pubns); Key-A-Teese Production (Key-A-Teese Prod)
E-mail: word4wrd@aol.com.

Word Gift Pubns., *(0-9788381)* 6641 Cty. Rd. 912, Joshua, TX 76058 USA (SAN 851-7223)
E-mail: peregrina@wordgift.org
Web site: http://www.wordgift.org.

Word Gift Pubns *See* **Word Gift Pubns.**

Word In Action Publishing, *(0-9629550)* 2774 Matt Dr., Longview, TX 75605 USA Tel 903-757-6792.

Word in Season Pubns., *(0-9663405)* P.O. Box 7144, Greensboro, NC 27417 USA Tel 336-316-9232; Toll Free: 800-543-4738
E-mail: j_bryant99@yahoo.com.

Word Is Bond Writers-Pr., *(1-888097)* Orders Addr.: P.O. Box 20, Bayonne, NJ 07002 USA Tel 212-827-2624.

Word of Life Fellowship, Inc., *(1-931235)* Orders Addr.: P.O. Box 600, Schroon Lake, NY 12870-0600 USA Tel 518-494-6247; Fax: 518-494-6306; Edit Addr.: 71 Olmstedville Rd., Pottersville, NY 12860 USA Do not confuse with Word of Life Fellowship, Sand Springs, OK
E-mail: timf@wol.org
Web site: http://www.wol.org.

Word of Life Ministries, *(1-932048)* 2150 Collier Ave., Suite H, Fort Myers, FL 33901 USA Do not confuse with Word of life in Shreveport, LA
Web site: http://www.WOLM.net.

Word Play Pubns., *(0-9642922; 1-892847)* One Sutter St., San Francisco, CA 94104 USA Tel 415-397-3716; Fax: 415-291-8377
Web site: http://www.word-play.com
Dist(s): **Diamond Comic Distributors, Inc.**
Last Gasp of San Francisco
Quality Bks., Inc.
Unique Bks., Inc.

Word Prodns., *(0-9728590; 0-9765010)* 10405 Delicado Pl. NE, Albuquerque, NM 87111 USA Tel 505-271-2540; Fax: 505-292-5999
Web site: http://www.wordproductions.org
Dist(s): **STL Distribution North America.**

Word Prostitute, *(0-9728465)* 3434 SE 13th Ave., Portland, OR 97202 USA
E-mail: kalabjoster@wordprostitute.com
Web site: http://www.wordprostitute.com.

Word Riot Pr., *(0-9728200; 0-9779343)* P.O. Box 414, Middletown, NJ 07748 USA
E-mail: editor@wordriot.org
Web site: http://www.wordriot.org
Dist(s): **Pathway Bk. Service.**

Word Seed Publishing, *(0-9755232)* 650 NE 2nd St., Hermiston, OR 97838 USA Tel 541-567-0886; Fax: 541-481-7500
E-mail: hashcraftz1@charter.net.

Word Supremacy Pr., *(0-9747231)* 910 St., Paul St., No. C, Baltimore, MD 21202 USA Tel 443-414-4600; Fax: 877-504-3140
E-mail: taalam@aol.com
Web site: http://www.taalamacey.com.

Word Weaver Bks., Inc., *(0-9670600)* 9743 W. Bray Creek St., Star, ID 83669-5815 USA
E-mail: tidegirl32@aol.com
Web site: http://www.wordweaverbooks.com.

Word Wrangler Publishing, Inc., *(1-58630)* 332 Tobin Creek Rd., Livingston, MT 59047 USA Tel 406-686-4417
E-mail: wrangler@wordwrangler.com
Web site: http://www.wordwrangler.com.

Word Wright International *See* **WordWright.biz, Inc.**

Wordcraft of Oregon, LLC, *(1-877655)* P.O. Box 3235, La Grande, OR 97850 USA Do not confuse with Wordcraft, Oakland, CA
E-mail: dsmemmott@verizon.net
Web site: http://www.wordcraftoforegon.com.

WordMaster Publishing, *(0-9740410)* 4317 W. Farrand Rd., Clio, MI 48420 USA (SAN 255-3325) Tel 810-686-2047; Fax: 810-564-9929
E-mail: wordmasterpub@aol.com.

WordMate, *(1-887447)* Orders Addr.: P.O. Box 992, Skokie, IL 60076-0992 USA Tel 847-677-5291; Fax: 847-677-6186; Toll Free: 888-967-3628; Edit Addr.: 8348 Niles Ctr. Rd., Skokie, IL 60077 USA
E-mail: wordmate@aol.com; lou@zcloud.net
Web site: http://aprenderingles-learnspanish.com; http://wordmate.us; http://eigogakushu.info.

Wordminder Pr., *(0-9729103)* Orders Addr.: P.O. Box 10438, Norfolk, VA 23513-0438 USA (SAN 255-2841) Tel 757-853-4788; Edit Addr.: 1008 Norview Ave., Norfolk, VA 23513-0438 USA
E-mail: sma@wordminderpress.com
Web site: http://www.wordminderpress.com
Dist(s): **BookSurge, LLC.**

Wordpainting/Paper Kite Press *See* **Paper Kite Pr.**

Words & Pictures Publishing, Inc., *(0-9621280)* P.O. Box 61444, Honolulu, HI 96839 USA (SAN 250-9326) Tel 808-955-4742; Fax: 808-951-6541
E-mail: gecko@aloha.net
Web site: http://www.brucehale.com
Dist(s): **Booklines Hawaii, Ltd.**
Sunbelt Pubns., Inc.

Words of Essence Publishing, *(0-9768133)* P.O. Box 13182, Durham, NC 27709 USA Tel 919-624-4138
E-mail: godslove232@yahoo.com
Web site: http://www.wordsofessence.com.

Words of Grace, Inc., *(0-9722799)* 1941 Cedar Tree Dr., Fort Worth, TX 76131 USA Tel 817-723-9281
E-mail: chris@chriscollinsonline.com
Web site: http://www.chriscollinsonline.com
Dist(s): **STL Distribution North America.**

Words of Light International Publishing, *(1-887480)* Orders Addr.: P.O. Box 238, Templeton, MA 01468 USA (SAN 298-6264)
E-mail: tarantinochristine@yahoo.com
Web site: http://www.angelfire.com/art/wordsoflight.

WORDS ON WINGS, Ltd., *(0-9720123)* P.O. Box 1604, Bozeman, MT 59771 USA Tel 406-586-3808; 4065801498 (cell)
E-mail: bwild@myexcel.com; dab@wordsonwings.net
Web site: http://www.wordsonwings.net.

words4u, *(0-9740419)* P.O. Box 641257, San Francisco, CA 94164-1257 USA
E-mail: info@words4u.com
Web site: http://www.words4u.com.

Wordsaid Publishing, *(0-9714889)* Orders Addr.: P.O. Box 4979, Kaneohe, HI 96744 USA; Edit Addr.: 46-063 Emepela Pl., Bldg. 0, No. 205, Kaneohe, HI 96744 USA
E-mail: pstam@wordsaid.com; pjs1ink@cs.com
Web site: http://www.wordsaid.com.

Wordshed, *(0-942684)* 5118 Glendale St., Duluth, MN 55804-1107 USA (SAN 239-6246) Tel 218-525-3266.

WordSHOP, Inc., *(0-9668469)* P.O. Box 236, Birdsboro, PA 19508-0236 USA Tel 610-582-7230.

Words-In-Motion Press *See* **Leba Hse. Pubs.**

Wordsmith Bks., *(1-882646)* 1418 Manchester Dr., Eugene, OR 97401 USA Tel 541-341-4687 Do not confuse with Wordsmith Bks. in Auburn, AL
E-mail: wordsmithbooks@comcast.net
Dist(s): **Baker & Taylor Bks.**

Wordsmith Pr., *(1-893972)* 11462 East Ln., Whitmore Lake, MI 48189 USA Tel 810-231-5435
E-mail: info@thewordsmithpress.com
Web site: http://www.thewordsmithpress.com.

Wordsmith Pr., *(0-9722221)* 3200 Milton Rd., Raleigh, NC 27609 USA Tel 919-782-3665 Do not confuse with companies with the same or similar name in Orlando, FL, Syracuse, NY, St. Paul, MN, Medina, OH
E-mail: dprivette@prodigy.net.

Wordsmith Publishing, *(0-9674180)* 5831 Overhill Dr., Los Angeles, CA 90043 USA Tel 323-296-0606; Fax: 323-296-0669 Do not confuse with companies with the same or similar name in Las Vegas, NV, Seattle, WA, Grain Valley, MO, Dallas, TX, Yelm, WA.

Wordsmiths, *(0-9632774; 1-886061)* 1355 Ferry Rd., Grants Pass, OR 97526 USA Tel 541-476-3080; Fax: 541-474-9756 Do not confuse with the Wordsmiths in Evergreen, CO
E-mail: frodej@chatlink.com
Web site: http://www.jsgrammar.com.

Wordsmiths Publishing Company *See* **Wordsmiths Publishing Co. and Educational Consultants**

Wordsmiths Publishing Co. and Educational Consultants, *(0-9711305; 0-9744300; 0-9790918)* 3603 Urban Ave., Dallas, TX 75227 USA Fax: 214-388-0035
E-mail: bsloan@flash.net.

Wordsong *Imprint of* **Boyds Mills Pr.**

WordsWorth, *(0-9652942; 0-9771286)* 1285 Sheridan Ave., No. 275, Cody, WY 82414 USA Tel 307-587-3932; Fax: 307-587-3801 Do not confuse with San Geronimo, CA, Newton, KS, Ridgewood, NJ
E-mail: wordsworth@wtp.net.

WORDSWORTH Publishing Co., *(0-9672491; 0-9754351)* Orders Addr.: P.O. Box 7132, Santa Rosa, CA 95407 USA Tel 707-829-2316 (phone/fax); Edit Addr.: 2524 S. Edison St., Graton, CA 95444 USA
E-mail: wwinfo@getyourwordsworth.com
Web site: http://www.getyourwordsworth.com.

WordThunder Pubns., *(0-9745268; 1-59790)* P.O. Box 540931, Merritt Island, FL 32954 USA (SAN 256-3770)
E-mail: books@wordthunder.com
Web site: http://wordthunder.com/books/
Dist(s): **Baker & Taylor Bks.**
Ingram Bk. Co.

†**Wordware Publishing, Inc.,** *(0-915381; 1-55622; 0-556; 1-59822)* 1100 Summit Ave. Ste. 102, Plano, TX 75074-8593 USA (SAN 291-4786) Toll Free: 800-229-4949 (orders) ; *Imprints:* Republic of Texas Press (Rep of TX Pr)
E-mail: info@wordware.com
Web site: http://www.wordware.com
Dist(s): **Hervey's Booklink & Cookbook Warehouse**
National Bk. Network
ibooks.com; *CIP.*

WordWeaver Unlimited *See* **Westen Integrity Bk. Pubs.**

WordWorkers Pr., *(0-9624511; 0-9745664)* 502 Pleasant Hill Rd., Sebastopol, CA 95472 USA Toll Free: 800-357-6016
E-mail: eye@independenteye.org
Web site: http://www.independenteye.org.

Wordwright Communications, *(0-9718838)* 4900 Randall Pkwy. Ste. F, Wilmington, NC 28403-2831 USA Toll Free: 888-235-0248.

WordWright.biz, Inc., *(0-9700615; 0-9713832; 0-9717868; 1-932196; 1-934335)* P.O. Box 1785, Georgetown, TX 78627 USA Fax: 512-260-3080 (phone/fax) ; *Imprints:* Legacy (Lgcy TX)
E-mail: joan@wordwright.biz; snwriter@earthlink.net; jnwriter@aol.com
Web site: http://www.wordwright.biz.

Working Title Publishing, *(1-59344; 0-9776440)* 1067 C St., Suite 101, PMB 143, Galt, CA 95632 USA
Web site: http://www.workingtitlepublishing.com.

Working Words & Graphics, *(0-9759988)* P.O. Box 278, Gorham, ME 04038-0278 USA Tel 207-839-3831; Fax: 207-839-3834; Toll Free: 800-499-3831
E-mail: info@workingwords.net
Web site: http://www.workingwords.net.

†**Workman Publishing Co., Inc.,** *(0-7611; 0-89480; 0-911104; 1-56305)* Orders Addr.: 225 Varick St., New York, NY 10014-4381 USA (SAN 203-2821) Tel 212-254-5900; Fax: 212-254-8098; Toll Free: 800-722-7202
E-mail: info@workman.com
Web site: http://www.workman.com; *CIP.*

Works of Hope Publishing, *(0-9712481)* 25 Clark's Rd., No. 308, Amesbury, MA 01913 USA (SAN 254-041X) Fax: 978-388-7520; Toll Free: 877-887-2828
E-mail: ElissaAmal@aol.com
Web site: http://www.worksofhope.com
Dist(s): **Baker & Taylor Bks.**

Workshop Arts, Inc., *(1-929395)* Div. of National Guitar Summer Workshop, 407 A Bantam Rd., Suite 1, Bantam, CT 06759 USA Tel 860-567-1020; Fax: 860-567-1147
E-mail: gunod@aol.com; nat@guitarworkshop.com
Dist(s): **Alfred Publishing Co., Inc.**

World Ahead Media, *(0-9746701; 0-9767269; 0-9778984; 0-9790451; 0-9792671)* 2463 W 208th St., Ste 201, Torrance, CA 90501 USA (SAN 255-7304) ; *Imprints:* Kids Ahead Books (Kids Ahead)
E-mail: info@worldahead.com
Web site: http://www.worldahead.com
Dist(s): **McLemore, Hollern & Assocs.**
Midpoint Trade Bks., Inc.
Quality Bks., Inc.

World Ahead Publishing, Incorporated *See* **World Ahead Media**

World Almanac Bks., *(0-88687; 0-911818; 1-60057)* Div. of World Almanac Education Group, 512 Seventh Ave., 21st Flr., New York, NY 10018 USA Fax: 646-312-6822; Toll Free: 800-777-3865
E-mail: cerrig@waegroup.com
Web site: http://www.worldalmanac.com; http://www.worldalmanacforkids.com
Dist(s): **Simon & Schuster, Inc.**
St. Martin's Pr.

World Almanac Library *Imprint of* **Stevens, Gareth Inc.**

†**World Bank Pubns.,** *(0-8213; 1-932126)* Orders Addr.: P.O. Box 960, Herndon, VA 20172-0960 USA Toll Free: 800-645-7247; Edit Addr.: 1818 H St., NW, Mail Stop: U11-1104, Washington, DC 20433 USA (SAN 219 0648) Tel 703-661-1380; Fax: 202-614-1237
E-mail: books@worldbank.org
Web site: http://www.worldbank.org/publications
Dist(s): **Bernan Assocs.**
Independent Pubs. Group
NetLibrary, Inc.
Oxford Univ. Pr., Inc.; *CIP.*

World Bible Pubs., 10899 Textile Rd., Belleville, MI 48111-2315 USA (SAN 299-9315)
E-mail: darwinr@fnc.com.

World Bk., Inc., *(0-7166)* Div. of Scott Fetzer Co., 233 N. Michigan, Suite 2000, Chicago, IL 60601 USA (SAN 201-4815) Tel 312-729-5800; Fax: 312-729-5600; 312-729-5614; Toll Free Fax: 800-433-9330 (US orders); 888-690-4002 (Canadian orders); Toll Free: 800-975-3250 (US orders); 800-967-5325; 800-837-5365 (Canadian orders)
Web site: http://www.worldbook.com.

World CARP, *(0-9722946)* 81 Croton Ave., Ossining, NY 10562-4206 USA
E-mail: yyk21@worldcarp.org
Web site: http://www.worldcarp.org.

World Citizens, *(0-932279)* 96 La Verne Ave., Mill Valley, CA 94941 USA (SAN 686-547X) Tel 415-380-8020; Toll Free: 800-247-6553 (orders only)
Dist(s): **Baker & Taylor Bks.**
BookMasters, Inc.
Social Studies Schl. Service.

World Cycling Pr., *(0-9745842)* 3910 Chapman St., San Diego, CA 92110-5694 USA Tel 619-224-1050; Fax: 619-224-0530
E-mail: team_mallory@hotmail.com.

World Famous Children's Bks., *(0-9725398)* 4455 Torrance Blvd, No. 153, Torrance, CA 90503 USA
Web site: http://www.worldfamouschildrensbooks.com
Dist(s): **Biblio Distribution**
Quality Bks., Inc.

World Government Hse., *(0-9706483)* Div. of World Service Authority, Orders Addr.: P.O. Box 9390, South Burlington, VT 05407 USA (SAN 253-5769) Tel 802-864-6818; Fax: 802-862-3744; Edit Addr.: 6 Ledoux Terr., South Burlington, VT 05403 USA
E-mail: worldlaw@globalnetisp.net; info@worldservice.org
Web site: http://www.worldgovernmenthouse.com; http://www.worldservce.org/cat.html#books; http://www.worldservice.org
Dist(s): **Xlibris Corp.**

World Health Organization, *(92-4)* Orders Addr.: 49 Sheridan Ave., Albany, NY 12210 USA (SAN 221-6310) Tel 518-436-9686; Fax: 518-436-7433; Edit Addr.: Av Appia, Geneva, 1211 CHE Tel 41-22) 7912111; Fax: 41-22) 7910746
E-mail: publications@who.int
Web site: http://www.who.ch
Dist(s): **Balogh International, Inc.**
Bernan Assocs.
Women Ink.

World Library Pubns., *(0-937690; 1-58459)* Div. of J. S. Paluch Co., Inc., 3708 River Rd. Suite 400, Franklin Park, IL 60131-2158 USA (SAN 203-0306) Tel 847-233-2767; Toll Free Fax: 888-957-3291; Toll Free: 800-621-5197
E-mail: wlpcs@jspaluch.com
Web site: http://www.wlpmusic.com
Dist(s): **Baker & Taylor Bks.**
Ingram Pub. Services
Spring Arbor Distributors, Inc.

World Love Pr. Publishing, *(0-9704545)* 1028 Joliet St., New Orleans, LA 70118 USA Tel 504-866-4476
E-mail: WorldLovePress@aol.com
Dist(s): **Baker & Taylor Bks.**

World Music Pr., *(0-937203)* Orders Addr.: P.O. Box 26627, Wauwatosa, WI 53226 USA Tel 262-790-5210; Fax: 262-781-8818; Edit Addr.: P.O. Box 2565, Danbury, CT 06813 USA (SAN 658-733X) Tel 203-748-1131; Fax: 203-748-3432; Toll Free: 888-283-5273
E-mail: info@worldmusicpress.com
Web site: http://www.worldmusicpress.com; http://www.worldmusicpress.net.

World of Angels, A, *(0-9743964)* 97 Main St., Belfast, ME 04915 USA Tel 207-338-8900
E-mail: aworldofangels@prexar.com
Web site: http://www.aworldofangels.com.

World of Hope International, Inc., *(0-9720435)* Orders Addr.: 130 Shore Rd., No. 277, Port Washington, NY 11050 USA
E-mail: monica@wohi.org
Web site: http://www.wohi.org.

World of Imagination, *(0-9761228)* 200 N. Maryland Ave., Suite 101, Glendale, CA 91206 USA Tel 818-547-5541; Fax: 818-543-1889; Toll Free: 800-266-5255.

World of Learning Publishing *See* **Swift Learning Resources**

World of Reading, Ltd., P.O. Box 13092, Atlanta, GA 30324-0092 USA Tel 404-233-4042; Fax: 404-237-5511; Toll Free: 800-729-3703.

World of Whimsy Productions, LLC, *(0-9702675)* 409 N. Pacific Coast Hwy., No. 594, Redondo Beach, CA 90277 USA (SAN 256-1077) Fax: 310-542-9297; Toll Free: 1-888-4-WHIMSY
E-mail: info@worldofwhimsy.com
Web site: http://worldofwhimsy.com.

World of Wonders, Inc., *(0-9705133; 1-59085)* Orders Addr.: 3302 SE Ford Ln., Port Saint Lucie, FL 34984 USA Tel 772-873-1334; Edit Addr.: 3302 SE Ford Ln., Port Saint Lucie, FL 34984 USA
E-mail: ena@princessena.com; ena2002@bellsouth.net; info@princessena.com
Web site: http://www.fairygarden.safeshopper.com; http://www.princessgems.com; http://www.princessena.com.

World Quest Learning, *(1-933248)* P.O. Box 654, Lewis Center, OH 43035 USA Tel 740-548-3857; Toll Free Fax: 866-722-7521; Toll Free: 866-722-7520
E-mail: info@worldquestlearning.com
Web site: http://www.worldquestlearning.com.

World Relief Network, The, *(0-9617410; 1-930627)* Orders Addr.: P.O. Box 15082, Detroit, MI 48215-0082 USA (SAN 663-9747) Tel 313-331-3190 (phone/fax)
E-mail: srinandan@aol.com
Web site: http://www.worldreliefnetwork.com; http://www.stephen-knapp.com
Dist(s): **New Leaf Distributing Co., Inc.**

World Scientific Publishing Co., Inc., *(981-02; 9971-950; 9971-966; 9971-978; 981-238; 981-256; 981-4139; 981-270)* 27 Warren St., Suite 401-402, Hackensack, NJ 07601-5477 USA (SAN 241-9920) Toll Free: 800-227-7562; a/o World Scientific Publishing Co. Pte. Ltd., 5 Toh Tuck Link, Singapore, 596224 Tel 65-6466-5775; Fax: 65-6467-7667
E-mail: wspc@wspc.com
Web site: www.wspc.com; http://www.worldscientific.com
Dist(s): **NetLibrary, Inc.**

World Teachers Pr. *Imprint of* **Didax Educational Resources, Inc.**

World Thoughts Publishing, Co., *(0-9711018)* P.O. Box 3206, Saint Augustine, FL 32084-3206 USA
E-mail: beebes@aug.com
Web site: http://www.energeticawakening.com; http://www.worldthoughts.com.

World Trade Academy Press *See* **Uniworld Business Pubns., Inc.**

World Tribune Pr., *(0-915678; 1-932911)* Orders Addr.: 8811 Aviation Blvd., Inglewood, CA 90301 USA Tel 310-337-0055; Fax: 310-642-4625; Toll Free: 800-626-1313; Edit Addr.: 606 Wilshire Blvd., Santa Monica, CA 90401 USA (SAN 683-230X) Tel 310-260-8900; Fax: 310-260-8910 ; *Imprints:* Treasure Tower Books (Treasure Twr)
E-mail: dmcneill@sgi-usa.org
Dist(s): **PCE International.**

World Wide Distributors, Limited *See* **Island Heritage Publishing**

World Wide Pubns., *(0-89066)* P.O. Box 668089, Charlotte, NC 28266-8089 USA (SAN 159-9941) Toll Free: 800-788-0442
Dist(s): **CRC Pubns.**
Spring Arbor Distributors, Inc.

WorldComm, *(1-56664)* Div. of Creativity, Inc., 65 Macedonia Rd., Alexander, NC 28701 USA Tel 828-252-9515; Fax: 828-255-8719; Toll Free: 800-472-0438 (phone/fax)
E-mail: sales@abooks.com
Web site: http://www.abooks.com.

WorldofLite Publishing, *(0-9719694)* 2110 Artesia Blvd., No. B 273, Redondo Beach, CA 90278-3069 USA (SAN 255-0865) Tel 310-374-3417
E-mail: worldoflite@aol.com
Web site: http://www.terriamos.com
Dist(s): **DeVorss & Co.**

Worlds In Ink *See* **Worlds In Ink Publishing, Inc.**

Worlds In Ink Publishing, Inc., *(0-9745568)* 4812 Ridgecrest Cir SE, Albuquerque, NM 87108-4435 USA
E-mail: info@WorldsInInk.com
Web site: http://www.WorldsInInk.com.

Worldview Publishing, Inc., *(1-889995)* 521 Herchel Dr., Tampa, FL 33617 USA Tel 813-985-9344; Fax: 813-985-4505; Toll Free: 800-987-9444 Do not confuse with companies with same or similar names in Tiburon, CA, Colorado Springs, CO
E-mail: drlindahf@aol.com
Web site: http://www.worldviewpub.com.

Worrywart Publishers *See* **WorryWart Publishing Co.**

WorryWart Publishing Co., *(1-881519)* Orders Addr.: P.O. Box 24911, Columbia, SC 29224-4911 USA Tel 803-699-0032; Fax: 803-699-0032 ext 51; Edit Addr.: 6317 Olde Knight Pkwy., Columbia, SC 29209-1523 USA
E-mail: wworrywart@aol.com.

Worth Pubs., Inc., *(0-312; 0-87901; 1-57259)* Orders Addr.: 16365 James Madison Hwy., Gordonsville, VA 22942 USA Tel 540-672-7600; Fax: 540-672-7052; Toll Free Fax: 800-672-2054; Toll Free: 888-330-8477; Edit Addr.: 41 Madison Ave., 36th Flr., New York, NY 10010-2202 USA (SAN 205-5546) Tel 212-576-9400; Fax: 212-561-8281; Toll Free: 800-903-3019
Web site: http://www.worthpublishers.com
Dist(s): **Libros Sin Fronteras**
Macmillan
Freeman, W. H. & Co.

WowZee Works Inc, *(0-9778858)* 2217 Green Mountain Ct., Las Vegas, NV 89135 USA (SAN 850-5128).

WPR Publishing, *(1-889379)* 3445 Catalina Dr., Carlsbad, CA 92008 USA Tel 760-434-7474; Fax: 760-434-7476 Do not confuse with WPR Publishing, Dillon, MT
E-mail: mexico@deltanet.com.

WRC Media, Inc., *(0-8374)* 512 Seventh Ave., 22nd Flr., New York, NY 10018 USA Tel 203-705-3426; Fax: 203-705-3483.

WRDSMTH Productions, *(0-9744562)* Orders Addr.: P.O. Box 1406, Lawton, OK 73502-1406 USA (SAN 255-7282) Tel 580-353-4710; Fax: 580-357-9787; Toll Free: 800-357-9854; Edit Addr.: 130 SW B Ave., Lawton, OK 73501 USA
E-mail: okteller@juno.com
Web site: http://www.stringfigurestore.com.

Wren Song Pr., *(0-9769827)* 233 Poors Mill Rd., Belfast, ME 04915 USA Toll Free: 800-943-7664 Do not confuse with Wren Song Press in Ripton, VT
E-mail: jennifer@jenniferarmstrong.com
Web site: http://www.jenniferarmstrong.com.

Wren's Nest Publishing, Inc., *(0-9744111)* 177 Rabbit Farm Trail, Advance, NC 27006 USA Tel 336-998-2858
E-mail: rickyp@yadtel.net.

Wriede, Peter, *(0-9710098)* 61 Pine Lake Terr., Rivervale, NJ 07675 USA Fax: 201-505-0283
E-mail: mpmahwah@worldnet.att.net.

Wright, Dr. Author O., *(0-9679676)* 4524 Portland Ave., S., Minneapolis, MN 55407-3550 USA Tel 612-822-8032
E-mail: Awright@email.usps.gov.

Wright, Franklin Enterprises, *(0-9719480)* 1860 Sandy Plains Rd., Suite 204, PMB 150, Marietta, GA 30066 USA Tel 678-560-2640; Fax: 770-973-4128.

Wright Group, The, *(0-322; 0-7802; 0-940156; 1-55624; 1-55911; 1-4045)* Div. of The McGraw-Hill Education Group, 19201 120th Ave., NE, Suite 100, Bothell, WA 98011 USA Tel 425-486-8011; Fax: 425-486-6804; Toll Free Fax: 800-543-7323
Web site: http://www.wrightgroup.com/.

Wright Publishing, Inc., *(0-935087; 0-9652368)* Orders Addr.: P.O. Box 1956, Fayetteville, GA 30214 USA Tel 770-460-5525; Fax: 770-460-8998; Edit Addr.: 320 Devilla Trace, Fayetteville, GA 30214 USA (SAN 695-0507) Do not confuse with companies with same or similar name in Los Angeles, CA, Virgina Beach, VA, West Seneca, NY, Torrance, CA,
Dist(s): **Baker & Taylor Bks.**

Wright, Robert, *(0-9763223)* 272 Horse Hill Rd., Ashford, CT 06278 USA.

Wright's Way Inc., *(0-9767483)* 210 Henderson Dr., Jacksonville, NC 28540 USA Tel 910-989-0000 (phone/fax)
E-mail: sensei@bizec.rr.com
Web site: http://www.wrightskarate.com.

Wrinkle Pr, *(0-9718020)* Orders Addr.: P.O. Box 6454, Abilene, TX 79608 USA; Edit Addr.: 1473 Beltway S., Abilene, TX 79602 USA.

Write Designs, Ltd., *(0-9661661; 0-9741627; 0-9772614)* 2957 Sudderth Dr., Ruidoso, NM 88345-6323 USA (SAN 257-067X) Toll Free: 800-687-2703
E-mail: books@writedesignsltd.com; laura@printwritenow.com
Web site: http://www.writedesignsltd.com; http://www.1to1publishing.com; http://www.printwritenow.com.

Write On!, *(0-9753870)* Orders Addr.: 704 Norwalk Ct., Nashville, TN 37214 USA Tel 615-415-9861 Do not confuse with companies with a similar name in Albuquerque, NM, Estes Park, CO
E-mail: write_on_yvonne@comcast.net
Web site: http://www.yvonneperry.net/books.htm.

Write On, Incorporated *See* **Write On Pubns.**

Write On Pubns., *(0-9643331)* Div. of Write On, Inc., 2856 Lotus Pl., Loveland, CO 80537 USA Tel 970-635-1974; Fax: 970-635-1977 Do not confuse with companies with the same or similar name in Tucson, AZ, Federal Way, WA, Seattle, WA, Lindsborg, KS
E-mail: writeonpub@aol.com.

Write Team, The, *(0-9659001)* 14423 S. 24th Pl., Phoenix, AZ 85048-9015 USA (SAN 299-6006).

Write Track, The, *(0-913935; 0-9713162)* Orders Addr.: P.O. Box 875, Suffern, NY 10901 USA Tel 845-368-2795; Fax: 845-357-5327; Toll Free: 800-845-8402; Edit Addr.: 16 Charnwood Dr., Suffern, NY 10901 USA
E-mail: writetrack@aol.com
Web site: http://www.thewritetrack.com.

Write Way Publishing, *(1-885173)* Orders Addr.: P.O. Box 441278, Aurora, CO 80044 USA Tel 303-617-0497; Fax: 303-617-1440; Toll Free: 800-680-1493 Do not confuse with Write Way Publishing, Charleston, WV
E-mail: staff@writewaypub.com; writewy@aol.com
Web site: http://www.writewaypub.com.

Write Words, Incorporated *See* **ebooksonthe.net**

Write World, Inc., *(0-9722173)* 3523 McKinney Ave., Suite 373, Dallas, TX 75204 USA (SAN 254-8445) Fax: 214-599-9192
E-mail: writeworld@cs.com.

Write Your Way Through Publishing *See* **Urban Moon Publishing**

WriteGirl Pubns., *(0-9741251)* 411 S. Main St. Ste. 422, Los Angeles, CA 90013-1300 USA
E-mail: info@writegirl.org
Web site: http://www.writegirl.org
Dist(s): **SPD-Small Pr. Distribution.**

Write-on-Time Publishing, *(0-9642672)* Orders Addr.: P.O. Box 216, Fort Atkinson, WI 53538 USA Tel 920-563-4203; Fax: 920-563-3132; Edit Addr.: 1224 Sioux Trail, Fort Atkinson, WI 53538 USA
E-mail: zany@idcnet.com.

WRITER for HIRE!, *(0-9701356)* Orders Addr.: 648 McKenzie Cir., Stockbridge, GA 30281 USA Tel 770-389-4321; Fax: 770-506-4397
E-mail: angeladurden@msn.com
Web site: http://www.angeladurden.com; http://www.mikeandhisgrandpa.com.

†Writer, Inc., *(0-87116)* Orders Addr.: P.O. Box 1612, Waukesha, WI 53187 USA Toll Free: 800-553-5489 (Customer Service); Edit Addr.: 21027 Crossroads Cir., Waukesha, WI 53187 USA (SAN 203-2791) Tel 262-796-8776; Fax: 262-798-6592; Toll Free: 800-553-6644 (customer sales); 800-558-1544 (trade sales) Do not confuse with Writer's, Inc. in Beltsville, MD
E-mail: tss@kalmbach.com; krausch@kalmbach.com
Web site: http://www.writermag.com
Dist(s): **B & N Software**
Baker & Taylor Bks.
Watson-Guptill Pubns., Inc.; *CIP.*

Writers Advantage Pr. *Imprint of* **iUniverse, Inc.**

Writers & Poets.com, *(0-9703803; 0-9762710)* Orders Addr.: P.O. Box 1307, Mountainside, NJ 07092 USA (SAN 254-220X) Tel 908-233-2399; Fax: 206-238-0353
E-mail: earl@writersandpoets.com
Web site: http://www.writersandpoets.com.

Writers Cafe Pr., The, *(1-934284)* 418 S. Brookfield Dr., Lafayette, IN 47905-7299 USA (SAN 852-5498)
E-mail: admin@thewriterscafe.com
Web site: http://www.thewriterscafe.com
Dist(s): **AtlasBooks Distribution.**

Writers Club Pr. *Imprint of* **iUniverse, Inc.**

Writers' Collective, The, *(0-9716734; 1-932133; 1-59411)* 780 Reservoir Ave., Suite 243, Cranston, RI 02910 USA Toll Free: 800-497-0037
E-mail: factotum@writerscollective.org
Web site: http://www.writerscollective.org
Dist(s): **Baker & Taylor Bks.**
Midpoint Trade Bks., Inc.

Writers' Cooperative of Greater Washington, *(0-9673050)* P.O. Box 10550, Silver Spring, MD 20914-0550 USA (SAN 299-9854) Fax: 419-281-6883; Toll Free: 800-247-6553 (order)
E-mail: order@bookmaster.com
Web site: http://www.hairpullinghabit.com
Dist(s): **AtlasBooks Distribution**
BookMasters, Inc.

Writers' Group of the Triad, *(0-9715069)* P.O. Box 9731, Greensboro, NC 27429 USA Tel 336-288-4835
Web site: http://www.people-places.com/triadwriters.

Writers in the Schools (WITS), *(0-9747704)* 1523 W. Main, Houston, TX 77006 USA
E-mail: mail@writersintheschools.org
Web site: http://www.writersintheschools.org.

Writer's Ink. Studios, Inc., *(0-9704460)* P.O. Box 952, Windermere, FL 34786 USA Tel 407-876-3399; Fax: 270-964-5984; Toll Free: 888-229-9200
E-mail: cat@brownbagbooks.com; writersinkstudios@cfl.rr.com
Web site: http://www.brownbagbooks.com.

Writers Literary Agency *See* **WLA Publishing (Writers Literary Agency)**

Writers Marketplace:Consulting, Critiquing & Publishing, *(1-928632)* P.O. Box 21218, Carson City, NV 89721 USA Tel 775-544-0909; Fax: 775-884-3103.

Writers Publishing Cooperative, *(0-9658903; 1-930149)* P.O. Box 114, Warner, NH 03814 USA Tel 603-456-3641; Fax: 603-456-2871; Toll Free: 888-874-6904
E-mail: rmjsc@mcttelecom.com; bmarion@conknet.com
Web site: http://www.essentialbooks.com; http://www.minimalpress.com
Dist(s): **Enfield Publishing & Distribution Co., Inc.**

Writer's Showcase Pr. *Imprint of* **iUniverse, Inc.**

WritersCorps Bks. *Imprint of* **San Francisco Art Commission, The**

Writersmiths, Inc., *(0-9666736)* Orders Addr.: P.O. Box 1207, Evanston, IL 60201-1207 USA Tel 847-475-8652; Fax: 847-733-7988.

Writes of Passage *See* **Be-Mused Pubns.**

Writework Studios, *(0-9716492)* 3514 Clinton Pkwy, Suite 127, Lawrence, KS 66047 USA
E-mail: writeworkstudios@yahoo.com
Web site: http://www.writeworkstudios.com.

Writing for the Soul, *(0-9701437)* 10611 Abercorn St., Apt. 130, Savannah, GA 31419 USA Tel 912-961-6099 (phone/fax).

Writing Wild & Crazy *Imprint of* **Shakalot High Entertainment**

Writing-Right, *(0-9772196)* 27 Somerset Dr., Holbrook, NY 11741 USA
E-mail: lori@writing-right.org.

Written Expressions Enterprise, Inc., *(0-9728674)* 2276 Griffin Way, Suite 105-161, Corona, CA 92879 USA Tel 951-371-0160.

Written Images, Inc., *(0-9705721)* 1300 E. Lafayette, Suite 1104, Detroit, MI 48207 USA (SAN 253-7591) Tel 248-356-8310; Fax: 248-356-8311 Do not confuse with Written Image, The in Lancaster, NY
E-mail: writtenimages@aol.com
Web site: http://www.adiaryofjoseph.com.

Written in Black Publishing, *(0-9755444)* Orders Addr.: P.O. Box 9303, Jacksonville, FL 32208 USA
E-mail: jjfrederick98@aol.com
Web site: http://www.frederickpreston.com
Dist(s): **A & B Distributors & Pubs. Group**
Baker & Taylor Bks.

WSI Educational Bks., *(0-9745281)* P.O. Box 612, Virginia Beach, VA 23451 USA Fax: 212-504-2648
Web site: http://www.wsibooks.com.

Wu Li Turtle Corp., *(0-9741176)* 3885 S. Decatur Blvd., Suite 2010, Las Vegas, NV 89103 USA Tel 703-864-3769; Fax: 702-920-8118; Toll Free: 888-381-6864
E-mail: rbraye@wuliturtle.com
Web site: http://www.wuliturtle.com.

Wunderle Outdoor Bks., *(0-9611162)* 121 Prairie Rd., Carterville, IL 62918 USA (SAN 283-426X).

www.margaretmouse.com publishing co., *(0-9761326)* Orders Addr.: 41953 20th St., W., Palmdale, CA 93551-0000 USA Please allow four weeks for delivery. Shipments come direct from printer in China. Invoiced at order. Shipping free for all orders over 5000. Dolls are available as well. Please contact me direct at email Lparnold@verizon.net or call US 661-943-0275 with any questions or concerns or special orders.
E-mail: info@margaretmouse.com
Web site: http://www.margaretmouse.com
Dist(s): **Baker & Taylor Bks.**
Follett Library Resources.

www.underdogpublishing.com, *(0-9754420)* P.O. Box 266, Rincon, GA 31326 USA
Web site: http://www.underdogpublishing.com.

Wyatt Pr., *(0-9718161)* 15005 W. 167th Terr., Olathe, KS 66062 USA Tel 913-768-1917; Fax: 913-768-4307
Dist(s): **Baker & Taylor Bks.**

Wyatt-MacKenzie Publishing, *(0-9673025; 1-932279; 0-9743832)* 15115 Hwy. 36, Deadwood, OR 97430-9700 USA Tel 541-964-3314; Fax: 541-964-3315
E-mail: customerservice@wymacpublishing.com
Web site: http://www.wymacpublishing.com
Dist(s): **Perseus Distribution.**

Wybel Marketing Group, Orders Addr.: 213 W. Main St., Barrington, IL 60010 USA Tel 847-382-0384.

Wycliffe Bible Translators, *(0-938978)* P.O. Box 628200, Orlando, FL 32862-8200 USA (SAN 211-5484)
Web site: http://www.wycliffe.org.

Wyer Pearce Press *See* **SangFroid Pr.**

Wyland Galleries, *(0-9631793; 1-884840)* 5 Columbia, Aliso Viejo, CA 92656 USA Tel 949-643-7070; Fax: 949-643-7099
Dist(s): **Booklines Hawaii, Ltd.**

Wyland Studios *See* **Wyland Galleries**

Wynden *Imprint of* **Canmore Pr.**

Wyndham Pubns., Inc., *(0-9634100; 0-9717192)* P.O. Box 45, Kirkland, WA 98083-0045 USA
E-mail: wyndham.one@verizon.net.

Wynn Publishing, Inc., *(0-9642808; 0-9710591)* Div. of WynnCo Enterprise, Inc., Orders Addr.: P.O. Box 1491, Pickens, SC 29671 USA Tel 864-878-6469; Fax: 864-878-6267; Edit Addr.: 526 Farrs Bridge Rd., Pickens, SC 29671 USA.

Wyoming Historical & Geological Society, *(0-937537)* 49 S. Franklin St., Wilkes-Barre, PA 18701 USA (SAN 281-2061) Tel 717-823-6244; Fax: 717-823-9011
E-mail: lchs@epix.net
Web site: http://www.luzernecountyhistory.com.

Wyrick *Imprint of* **Gibbs Smith, Publisher**

Wyson, Dan, *(0-9771522)* 1173 S. 250 W. Suite 305, Saint George, UT 84770 USA Tel 435-229-6713 Toll Free: 877-827-0710.

Wysteria, Limited *See* **Wysteria Publishing**

Wysteria Publishing, *(0-9651162; 0-9677839; 1-932412)* P.O. Box 1250, Bellmore, NY 11710 USA Toll Free Fax: 888-434-7979; Toll Free: 888-997-8300
E-mail: wysteria@wysteria.com
Web site: http://www.wysteria.com.

X, Y, & Me LLC, *(0-9755028; 0-9773441)* 21409 138th St., Webster, IA 52355-9079 USA
E-mail: customerservice@xyandme.com
Web site: http://www.xyandme.com.

Xanadu Metaphysical *See* **Xanadu New Age Products & Services, LLC**

Xanadu New Age Products & Services, LLC, *(0-9759752)* Orders Addr.: 1011 S. Lake St., Neenah, WI 54956 USA; Edit Addr.: 1011 S. Lake St., Neenah, WI 54956 USA
E-mail: parisdrake@parisdrake.com
Web site: http://www.parisdrake.com.

Xavier Shott, Inc., *(0-9667642)* 800 Suellen Dr., Reading, PA 19605 USA Tel 610-926-3340; Fax: 610-926-0940.

xbks publishing, *(0-9626458)* c/o Arturo Watlington Station, P.O. Box 568, Saint Thomas, VI 00804 USA
E-mail: llrush@viaccess.net; mail@xbkspublishing.net
Web site: http://www.xbkspublising.net.

Xbooks *See* **xbks publishing**

Xerces Society, The, *(0-9744475)* 4828 SE Hawthorne Blvd., Portland, OR 97215 USA Tel 503-232-6639; Fax: 503-233-6794
E-mail: mdshepherd@xerces.org
Web site: http://www.xerces.org.

Xlibris Corp., *(0-7388; 0-9663501; 1-4010; 1-4134; 1-59926; 1-4257; 1-4363)* Orders Addr.: 2 International Plaza, Suite 340, Philadelphia, PA 19113 USA (SAN 299-5522) Tel 610-915-5214; Fax: 610-915-0294; Toll Free: 888-795-4274
E-mail: info@xlibris.com; orders@xlibris.com; dave.weinman@xlibris.com
Web site: http://www.xlibris.com
Dist(s): **Baker & Taylor Bks.**
Replica Bks.

Xophix, *(0-9754173)* P.O. Box 12081, Scottsdale, AZ 85267 USA Fax: 586-461-1712
E-mail: books@xophix.com
Web site: http://www.xophix.com.

Xulon Pr., Inc., *(1-931232; 1-59160; 1-59467; 1-59781; 0-9769668; 1-60034; 1-60266; 1-60477)* 2180 S. SR 434, Suite 2140, Longwood, FL 32779 USA Tel 407-339-4217; Fax: 407-339-9898; Toll Free: 866-381-2665 Do not confuse with Xulon press, Inc. in Longwood, FL
E-mail: tom.freiling@xulonpress.com
Web site: http://www.xulonpress.com
Dist(s): **STL Distribution North America.**

Y Lolfa (GBR) *(0-86243; 0-904864; 0-9500178) Dist. by* **Intl Spec Bk.**

YWAM Publishing, *(0-927545; 0-9615534; 1-57658)* Div. of Youth with a Mission International, Orders Addr.: P.O. Box 55787, Seattle, WA 98155 USA (SAN 695-8265) Tel 425-771-1153; Fax: 425-775-2383; Toll Free: 800-922-2143; Edit Addr.: 7825 230th St., SW, Edmonds, WA 98026 USA (SAN 248-4021)
E-mail: customerservice@ywampublishing.com
Web site: http://www.ywampublishing.com.

Y.Z. Pubns., *(0-9614730)* 1425 S. Woodster St., Apt. 109, Los Angeles, CA 90035 USA (SAN 692-6207) Tel 310-859-9782 (phone/fax).

Yacos Pubns., *(0-9653734)* Orders Addr.: 90-20 169th St., Apt. 4D, Jamaica, NY 11432 USA Tel 718-523-8911 (phone/fax)
E-mail: Drltgrant@yahoo.com
Web site: http://www.yacos.org.

Yadeeda.com, *(0-9747122)* P.O. Box 38642, Colorado Springs, CO 80937 USA Tel 719-520-5125
E-mail: yadeeda@hotmail.com
Web site: http://www.yadeeda.com.

YAHBOOKS PUBLISHING, *(0-9713991)* 30799 Pinetree Rd. No. 356, Cleveland, OH 44124 USA (SAN 254-119X) Tel 216-233-5961; Fax: 440-247-1581
E-mail: jeleebs@aol.com
Web site: http://www.yahbooks.com.

Yak Attack Graphics, *(0-9666820)* 379 Old Dublin Rd., Hancock, NH 03449 USA Tel 603-525-4023 (phone/fax).

Yakowicz, Susie *See* **JESSPress**

Yaldah Publishing, *(1-59287)* P.O. Box 18662, Saint Paul, MN 55118 USA Fax: 651-224-7447
E-mail: info@yaldahpublishing.com
Web site: http://www.yaldahpublishing.com.

†Yale Univ. Pr., *(0-300)* Orders Addr.: c/o Triliteral LLC, 100 Maple Ridge Dr., Cumberland, RI 02864 USA Tel 401-531-2800; Fax: 401-531-2801; Toll Free Fax: 800-406-9145; Toll Free: 800-405-1619; Edit Addr.: 302 Temple St., New Haven, CT 06511 USA (SAN 203-2740) Tel 203-432-0960; Fax: 203-432-0948
E-mail: yupmkt@yale.edu
Web site: http://www.yale.edu/yup/; http://www.yale.edu/yup/index.html
Dist(s): **Cheng & Tsui Co.**
NetLibrary, Inc.
Yale Univ., Far Eastern Pubns.; *CIP.*

YaleBooks, *(1-893173)* P.O. Box 389, Honesdale, PA 18431 USA Toll Free: 800-737-9253.

Yale-New Haven Hospital, *(0-9652190)* 1477 Ridge Rd., North Haven, CT 06473 USA Tel 203-248-4285; Fax: 203-785-2491.

Yamoo Pubs., *(0-9622939)* 21 Saint James Pl. Apt. 19A, Brooklyn, NY 11205-5053 USA.

Yana's Kitchen, *(0-9670982)* 5256 Pizzo Ranch Rd., La Canada, CA 91011 USA Tel 818-790-8381 (phone/fax)
E-mail: yana119@yahoo.com
Web site: http://home.earthlink.net/~yana101/index.html.

Yankee Cowboy, *(0-9708530)* P.O. Box 123, Keller, TX 76244 USA Tel 817-685-3830
E-mail: publisher@yankeecowboy.com
Web site: http://www.yankeecowboy.com.

Yankee Publishing, Inc., *(0-89909; 1-57198)* Orders Addr.: P.O. Box 520, Dublin, NH 03444 USA Tel 603-563-8111; Fax: 603-563-8252; Edit Addr.: Main St., Dublin, NH 03444 USA Do not confuse with Yankee Publishing, Saint Petersburg, FL
E-mail: almanac@yankeepub.com
Web site: http://www.almanac.com
Dist(s): **Houghton Mifflin Co. Trade & Reference Div.**

Yankoo Publishing Co., *(0-9639284)* 10616 W. Cameo Dr., Sun City, AZ 85351-2708 USA Tel 602-972-4319.

Yard Dog Pr., *(1-893687)* 710 W. Redbud Ln., Alma, AR 72921-7247 USA
E-mail: lynnstran@cox-internet.com
Web site: http://www.yarddogpress.com.

Yards, A., *(0-9603108)* 1241 Wasatch Dr., Mountain View, CA 94040 USA (SAN 209-0902) Tel 415-964-3550.

Yaroslavskaya, Lyudmila, *(0-9791248)* 600 W. Diversey Parkaway, Rm. 1410, Chicago, IL 60614 USA.

Yarrow Pr., *(0-9741562)* Orders Addr.: 127 W Washington St., #3, Lewisburg, WV 24901 USA Tel 304-645-6132 Do not confuse with Yarrow Press in Pelham, NY
E-mail: kate@yarrowpress.com
Web site: http://www.yarrowpress.com.

Ye Hedge Schl., *(0-9723239)* 24934 478 Ave., Garretson, SD 57030 USA
E-mail: mod61047@alliancecom.net
Web site: http://www.hedgeschool.com.

Ye Little Drama Shop *See* **Drama Tree Pr.**

Ye Olde Font Shoppe, *(1-889289)* Orders Addr.: P.O. Box 8328, New Haven, CT 06708 USA Tel 203-575-9385; Edit Addr.: 35 Ferndale, Waterbury, CT 06708 USA Tel 860-870-9741
E-mail: varivas@yahoo.com
Web site: http://www.yeolde.org.

Yearling *Imprint of* **Random Hse. Children's Bks.**

Yellow Brick Road Press *See* **Pitspopany Pr.**

Yellow Umbrella Bks. *Imprint of* **Capstone Pr., Inc.**

Yellow Umbrella Pr., *(0-942654)* 501 Main St., Chatham, MA 02633 USA (SAN 223-1018).

Yellowhammer Co., *(1-882700)* Univ. of Alabama, 24 Bryce Lawn, Tuscaloosa, AL 35487 USA Tel 205-348-7469; Fax: 205-348-7478.

Yeoman Hse., *(0-9754676)* 10 Old Bulgarmarsh Rd., Tiverton, RI 02878 USA Tel 401-816-0061; Fax: 661-885-4502
E-mail: goodbooks@yeomanhouse.com
Web site: http://www.yeomanhouse.com.

Yeoman Pr., *(0-9709110)* 2 Pine Ridge Dr., Newnan, GA 30263 USA Tel 770-251-3695 Do not confuse with Yeoman Pr. in Danvers, MA
E-mail: helen.grenga@grad.gotech.edu.

Yeong & Yeong Bk. Co., *(0-9638472; 1-59743)* 1368 Michelle Dr., Saint Paul, MN 55123-1459 USA Tel 651-454-1358; Fax: 651-454-3519
E-mail: BBoyd@YeongandYeong.Com
Web site: http://www.yeongandyeong.com.

YES - Your Emergency Safety, *(0-9740670)* 1302 W. Adams Ave., Saint Louis, MO 63122 USA Tel 314-822-8895; Fax: 775-458-7717
E-mail: info@youremergencysafety.org
Web site: http://www.youremergencysafety.org.

Yes Ministries, *(0-9652089)* 1033 Newton Rd., Santa Barbara, CA 93103 USA Tel 805-962-7579.

Yes San Francisco, LLC, *(0-9740090)* P.O. Box 4771, Hayward, CA 94540 USA Tel 510-582-8711
E-mail: sales@virtuar.com
Web site: http://www.yessanfrancisco.com.

Yesterday's Classics, *(1-59915)* Orders Addr.: P.O. Box 3418, Chapel Hill, NC 27515 USA Tel 919-967-3119; Toll Free: 866-497-3729 (phone/fax); Edit Addr.: 1705 Audubon Rd., Chapel Hill, NC 27514 USA
Web site: http://www.yesterdaysclassics.com.

Yestermorrow, Inc., *(1-56723)* Orders Addr.: P.O. Box 700, Princess Anne, MD 21853 USA.

Yeva Corp., *(1-930758)* 15050 Cedar Ave., S., Apple Valley, MN 55124 USA Tel 612-719-1174; Fax: 612-677-3122 ; *Imprints:* Sweet Legacy (Sweet Legacy); Legacy Kids (Legacy Kids); Yeva Kids (Yeva Kids)
E-mail: Bryant@InterNuntius.com; Felice@InterNuntius.com
Web site: http://www.yevapublishing.com.

Yeva Kids *Imprint of* **Yeva Corp.**

Yewtree Pr. LLC, *(1-933029)* P.O. Box 110 671, Brooklyn, NY 11211 USA Toll Free: 800-939-7404
E-mail: info@yewtreepress.com
Web site: http://www.yewtreepress.com.

Yhabbut Publishing, *(0-9724292)* Orders Addr.: P.O. Box 23032, Seattle, WA 981 USA; Edit Addr.: 2111 15th Ave., S., Suite A, Seattle, WA 98144-4271 USA
E-mail: benthoven@qwest.net
Web site: http://www.1stbooks.com/bookview/20054.

Yisrael, Sean Publishing Co., *(0-9772424)* 11769 Kenn Rd., Cincinnati, OH 45240 USA Tel 513-266-1158
E-mail: syisrael@dps.k12.oh.us.

YMCA of the U.S.A. *Imprint of* **Human Kinetics Pubs.**

YNR Media L.L.C., *(0-9753262)* 338 Streeter Dr., McCook Lake, SD 57049 USA Tel 310-422-1662.

Yo Puedo Publishing, *(0-9714533)* P.O. Box 940895, Houston, TX 77094 USA (SAN 254-3729) Tel 281-496-2015; 866-YO-PUEDO; Fax: 281-558-3773
E-mail: kathryn@yopuedo.com
Web site: http://www.yopuedo.com.

Yoder, Lou A., *(0-9703986)* 212 Mckays Ct., Brentwood, TN 37027-2985 USA.

Yoga In State College, *(0-9721116)* 220 S. Allen St., Apt. A, State College, PA 16801 USA Tel 814-234-9042
Web site: http://www.soldprice.com.

Yoga Life *See* **Love Your Life**

Yoknapatawpha Pr., *(0-916242)* P.O. Box 248, Oxford, MS 38655 USA (SAN 213-7593) Tel 601-234-0909 (phone/fax)
E-mail: faulkner@watervalley.net
Web site: http://www.watervalley.net/yoknapatawphapress/index.htm.

Yoon-il Auh/Intrepid Pixels, *(1-882858)* 820 West End Ave., No. 9E, New York, NY 10025 USA Tel 212-662-6891.

Yoot Pr., *(0-9764611)* 17-47 Chandler Dr., Fair Lawn, NJ 07410 USA
Web site: http://www.yootpress.com
Dist(s): **Baker & Taylor Bks.**
Ingram Bk. Co.

York Medieval Pr. (GBR) *(0-9529734; 1-903153) Dist. by* **Boydell Brewer.**

Company

Company

York-Goldman Enterprises, Inc., *(0-9706688)* P.O. Box 9095, La Jolla, CA 92038 USA Tel 858-456-2992; 858-456-2977; Fax: 858-456-2721
E-mail: Dianne@youglowgirl.com
Web site: http://www.youglowgirl.com
Dist(s): **Biblio Distribution.**

Yorkville Pr., *(0-9729427; 0-9767442)* Orders Addr.: 1202 Lexington Ave., No. 315, New York, NY 10028 USA (SAN 255-3139) Tel 212-650-9154; Fax: 212-650-9157; 1202 Lexington Ave. # 315, New York, NY 10028 Tel 212-650-9154
E-mail: editors@yorkvillepress.com
Web site: http://www.yorkvillepress.com.

Yoroson Publishing, *(0-9706985)* 10120 Two Notch Rd., No. 143, Columbia, SC 29223 USA Fax: 803-865-9001
E-mail: miraclewriter4u@aol.com
Web site: http://www.christineyoungrobinson.com.

Yosemite Assn., *(0-939666; 1-930238)* Orders Addr.: P.O. Box 230, El Portal, CA 95318 USA (SAN 662-197X) Tel 209-379-2648; Fax: 209-379-2486; Edit Addr.: 5020 El Portal Rd., El Portal, CA 95318 USA
E-mail: bpratt@yosemite.org
Web site: http://www.yosemite.org
Dist(s): **Baker & Taylor Bks.**
Sunbelt Pubns., Inc.

Yosoy Publishing, *(0-9763503)* 4141 Linden Ave, Long Beach, CA 90807 USA Tel 714-271-7667; Fax: 562-989-2031
E-mail: goodbooks@yeomanhouse.com
Web site: http://www.ginaspoems.com; http://www.yosoypublishing.com.

Yost-Haynes, Melissa, *(0-9760909)* RR1, 115C, Ravenswood, WV 26164 USA.

You Can Do It! Productions, *(0-9744306)* 106 Paradise Rd., Havana, FL 32333-4236 USA
E-mail: infinipede@juno.com
Web site: http://www.infinipede.com.

"You Deserve It" Creations, *(1-892878)* P.O. Box 1628, Hollywood, CA 9008-1628 USA Tel 323-461-8679
E-mail: brookinsll@aol.com
Web site: http://www.angelfire.com/biz/youdeserveit/index.htm.

You Publishing Group, *(0-9764472)* 2500 S. Lamar Blvd., Austin, TX 78704 USA.

You-Draw-It Bks. *Imprint of* **Castlebrook Pubns.**

Young Advent Pilgrim's Bookshelf, *(0-9658838)* 2731 Cutshall Town Rd., Marshall, NC 28753-7707 USA Tel 704-649-9166; Fax: 828-656-8203
E-mail: pcallins@madison.main.nc.us.

Young, Beth, *(0-9760180)* 303 Carlton Rd., Syracuse, NY 13207-1530 USA
E-mail: 369beth@bellsouth.net
Web site: http://www.saintlukespress.com.

Young, Diane B., *(0-9706269)* P.O. Box 245, Wells, NY 12190-0245 USA
E-mail: groove@iu.net
Web site: http://thegroovetube.com.

Young Patriots Series *Imprint of* **Patria Pr., Inc.**

Young People's Pr., Inc., *(1-57279; 1-885658)* 4901 Morena Blvd. Ste. 211, San Diego, CA 92117-3572 USA Toll Free: 800-231-9774.

Young Readers Publications, *(0-9789525)* 47 W. Schuyler St., Oswego, NY 13126 USA
E-mail: sabistonart@yahoo.com
Web site: http://jguntherphotography.com.

Young Scholars Pr., *(0-9787138)* 354 1/2 Calle Loma Norte, Santa Fe, NM 87501 USA Tel 505-989-7116; Fax: 505-820-2367
E-mail: MsAnnett1@aol.com
Web site: http://oneworldmanypeople.com.

Young Sparrow Pr., The, *(0-9621500)* P.O. Box 265, Worcester, PA 19490 USA (SAN 251-8856) Tel 215-997-0791; Fax: 215-997-5687
Dist(s): **Baker & Taylor Bks.**
Book Wholesalers, Inc.
Follett Library Resources
Liguori Pubns.

Young Women Bks., *(0-9747218)* 10061 Riverside Dr., Suite 438, Toluca Lake, CA 91602 USA Tel 818-955-5301 ; *Imprints:* Young Women Programming (YWProgram)
E-mail: hannah@hannahsway.com
Web site: http://www.hannasway.com.

Young Women Programming *Imprint of* **Young Women Bks.**

Young Writer's Contest Foundation *See* **Miracle Pr.**

Youngjin (Singapore) Pte Ltd. (SGP) Dist. by IPG Chicago.

Youngs, C. R., *(0-9760451)* 11687 Sugar Creek Ave., Mount Carmel, IL 62863 USA
E-mail: ronyoungs@davidbook.com
Web site: http://www.davidbook.com/.

Your Bks., *(0-9653414)* P.O. Box 700854, San Antonio, TX 78270-0854 USA Tel 210-403-3775
E-mail: yourbooks@earthlink.net.

Your Own World Bks. *Imprint of* **Your Own World, Inc.**

Your Own World, Inc., *(0-9725895; 0-9755177; 1-59772)* Orders Addr.: a/o DOI: http://dx.doi.org/10.1572/yowbooks, P.O. Box 67061, Scotts Valley, CA 89706 USA Fax: 775-546-1472 ; *Imprints:* Your Own World Books (Your Own Wrld Bks)
E-mail: info@yowbooks.com; sales@yowbooks.com
Web site: http://www.yowbooks.com
Dist(s): **Lightning Source, Inc.**

Your Story Hour Recordings, P.O. Box 511, Medina, OH 44258 USA Tel 216-725-5767.

Your Success, *(0-9668170)* PMB 396, 5250 Grand Ave., Suite 14, Gurnee, IL 60031-1877 USA Toll Free Fax: 847-336-6151; Toll Free: 847-336-6150
E-mail: Info@spanishcoach.com
Web site: http://www.spanishcoach.com.

You're On!, Inc., *(0-9760280)* P.O. Box 101071, Fort Worth, TX 76185 USA.

yourexpedition, *(0-9711527)* 1920 Oliver Pl S., Minneapolis, MN 55405-2420 USA
E-mail: zoe@basecamp1.com
Web site: http://www.yourexpedition.com.

Youth Achievers USA, *(0-9715153)* P.O. Box 7009, Largo, MD 20792-7009 USA Tel 215-248-4441
E-mail: FIBRE7@TheEnterpriZe.com; president@youthusa.org
Web site: http://www.youthusa.org; http://www.TheEnterpriZe.com/THEBOOK.

Youth & Family Institute, The, *(1-889407)* Orders Addr.: 1601 W. Old Shakopee Rd., Minneapolis, MN 55431-3065 USA Toll Free: 877-239-2492
E-mail: rhardel@youthandfamilyinstitute.org
Web site: http://www.youthandfamilyinstitute.org.

Youth Business Publishing, *(0-9668337)* 1915 Stone Meadow Way, Cumming, GA 30041-7898 USA
E-mail: dmoyer@kidsway.com
Dist(s): **CRC Pubns.**

Youth Communication - New York Center, *(0-9661256; 1-933939)* 244 W. 27th St., 2nd Flr., New York, NY 10001 USA Tel 212-279-0708 ext. 115; Fax: 212-279-8856
E-mail: khefner@youthcomm.org
Web site: http://www.youthcomm.org.

Youth Corp., Inc., *(0-9651866)* Div. of Youth Outreach Services, P.O. Box 308, Richmond, VA 23202 USA Tel 804-233-6435.

Youth Development & Research Fund, Inc., *(0-9659130)* P.O. Box 2188, Germantown, MD 20875-2188 USA
E-mail: ed@ydrf.com
Web site: http://www.ydrf.com.

Youth Inkwell Publishing, *(0-9773451)* 155 S. El Molino Ave., Suite 102, Paadena, CA 91101 USA Tel 626-449-6884; Fax: 626-449-6885
E-mail: info@youthinkwell.org
Web site: http://youthinkwell.org; http://www.youthinkwell.org.

Youth Popular Culture Institute, Inc., *(1-887191)* 8906 Fox Park Rd., Clinton, MD 20735 USA Tel 301-877-1525.

Youth Quest Institute, *(0-9748994)* 5515 Azalea Trail Ln., Sugar Land, TX 77479 USA
Web site: http://youthquestinstitute.com; http://getagripbooks.com.

Youth Specialties, *(1-59890)* 300 S. Pierce St., El Cajon, CA 92020-9005 USA Tel 619-440-2333
E-mail: ys@youthspecialties.com
Web site: http://www.youthspecialties.com
Dist(s): **Zondervan.**

Youthleadership.com, *(0-9677981)* 5593 Golf Course Dr., Morrison, CO 80465 USA Tel 303-358-1563; Fax: 303-393-9066
E-mail: support@youthleadership.com; mariam@youthleadership.com
Web site: http://www.youthleadership.com.

Youthlight, Inc., *(1-889636; 1-59850)* Orders Addr.: P.O. Box 115, Chapin, SC 29036 USA (SAN 256-6400) Tel 803-345-1070; Fax: 803-345-0888; Toll Free: 800-209-9774; Edit Addr.: 714 Cove Trail, Chapin, SC 29036 USA
E-mail: yl@sc.rr.com
Web site: http://www.youthlight.com; http://www.youthlightbooks.com.

YoYo Bks. (BEL) *(90-5843) Dist. by* **Natl Bk Netwk.**

Ysanti *See* **Lion's Crest Pr.**

Yuan-liou Publishing Co., Ltd. (TWN) *(957-32) Dist. by* **AIMS Intl.**

Yudcovitch, Lorne, *(0-9749781)* 6905 S.W. 7th Ave., Portland, OR 97219 USA Tel 503-293-6923
E-mail: yudcovil@pacificu.edu.

Yudit Publishing, Inc., *(0-9662747)* 13763 Aldsworth Ct., Wellington, FL 33414 USA Tel 561-798-4707.

Z 3 Universe, *(0-9701371)* 80 Nottingham Way, Forks, WA 98331 USA Tel 360-374-6789; Fax: 360-374-9800
E-mail: z3universe@hotmail.com.

ZEM Pr., *(0-9634168)* 8220 Stone Trail Dr., Bethesda, MD 20817-4556 USA Tel 301-365-4585; Fax: 301-365-4586
E-mail: zem@wbh.com
Web site: http://www.wb4.com.

Z Health Bks. *Imprint of* **New Win Publishing**

ZON International Publishing Co., *(0-939549)* Div. of ZON International Design, Inc., P.O. Box 6459, Santa Fe, NM 87502 USA (SAN 663-3439) Tel 505-995-0102; Fax: 505-995-0103; Toll Free: 800-266-5767
E-mail: zon@nets.com.

Zach Feuer Gallery, *(0-9768533)* 530 W 24th St., New York, NY 10011 USA Tel 212-989-7700
E-mail: zach@zachfeuer.com
Web site: http://www.zachfeuer.com
Dist(s): **D.A.P./Distributed Art Pubs.**

Zachmeyer, Mary L., *(0-9646864)* 1008 County Road 105., Columbus, TX 78934-1606 USA.

Zagat Survey, *(0-943421; 0-9612574; 1-57006; 1-60478)* 4 Columbus Cir., New York, NY 10019 USA (SAN 289-4777) Tel 212-977-6000; Fax: 212-765-9438; Toll Free: 866-999-0991
E-mail: tradesales@justzagat.com; theinz@zagat.com
Web site: http://www.zagat.com.

Zahir Publishing, *(0-9741311; 0-9786041)* 315 S. Coast Hwy. 101, Suite U8, Encinitas, CA 92024 USA
Web site: http://www.zahirtales.com.

Zahrob Publishing Co., *(0-9753641)* Orders Addr.: P.O. Box 5825, Rochester, MN 55903-5825 USA; Edit Addr.: 1445 Valley High Dr., NW, Rochester, MN 55903-5825 USA.

Zana International, *(0-9677456)* 12127 Eastbrook Ave., Downey, CA 90242-3106 USA
E-mail: camelia4@juno.com.

Zanderbooks, *(0-9702221)* 2839 W. Kennewick Ave., PMB 329, Kennewick, WA 99336 USA Tel 509-734-2125
E-mail: dzanderbooks@cs.com; Dzanderbooks@cs.com
Web site: http://www.zanderbooks.com.

Zaner-Bloser, Inc., *(0-7367; 0-88085; 0-88309)* Subs. of Highlights for Children, Orders Addr.: P.O. Box 16764, Columbus, OH 43216-6764 USA (SAN 282-5678) Tel 614-486-0221; Fax: 614-487-2699; Toll Free Fax: 800-992-6087; Toll Free: 800-421-3018; Edit Addr.: 1201 Dublin Rd., Columbus, OH 43215-1026 USA
Web site: http://www.zaner-bloser.com/
Dist(s): **National Bk. Network.**

Zany Angel Projects LLC, *(0-9769234)* P.O. Box 1411, New York, NY 10159 USA Tel 212-686-4206.

Zapstone Productions, *(0-9715433)* 3510 Cherry St. Apt. C8, Grand Forks, ND 58201-7695 USA
Web site: Http://www.zapstone.com.

Zarraonandia, Anne, *(0-9741070)* P.O. Box 151435, San Rafael, CA 94915 USA Tel 415-456-4070; Toll Free: 877-892-6974 (phone/fax)
E-mail: annezarra@aol.com
Web site: http://www.cowboyluke.com.

Zarrika, Ltd., *(0-9758663; 1-934252)* P.O. Box 488, Unionville, PA 19375 USA Fax: 610-384-6504; Toll Free: 888-369-3366
Web site: http://www.zarrika.com.

ZC Horses Series of Children's Bks., *(0-9721496; 0-9791719)* 8 Hokanson Ln., Salmon, ID 83467 USA
E-mail: zchorses@hotmail.com
Web site: http://www.zchorses.com.

ZCR Pr., *(0-9763926)* 4912 Woodman Ave., No. 3, Sherman Oaks, CA 91423 USA (SAN 256-3479) Tel 818-995-3032 (phone/fax)
E-mail: zaldy80@aol.com.

ZDK Bks., *(0-9706872)* Orders Addr.: 21070 Mtn. Village Dr., Eckert, CO 81418 USA
E-mail: karenmcline@yahoo.com
Web site: http://clik.to/zdkbooks.

Zeek, Jeanie A., *(0-9676761)* P.O. Box 261, Shrewsbury, MA 01545 USA Tel 508-845-6986.

Zeezok Publishing, *(0-9746505; 1-933573)* P.O. Box 1960, Elyria, OH 44036 USA (SAN 179-4493) Fax: 440-323-9494; Toll Free: 800-749-1681
E-mail: info@zeezok.com
Web site: http://www.zeezok.com.

Zeitgeist Bks., *(0-9705380)* P.O. Box 3198, Bellingham, WA 98227-3198 USA Do not confuse with Zeitgeist Books, San Francisco, CA
E-mail: ishawver@uswest.net; easton30@hotmail.com; lshawver@uswest.net.

Zellmann Publishing, LLC, *(0-9763325)* 420 Springwood Ct., Canton, GA 30115-8287 USA Tel 770-345-7265; Fax: 770-345-7265
E-mail: zellmann@zellmannpublishing.com.

Zemi Comics, *(0-9745825)* SDQ 17, 4440 NW, 73rd Ave., Miami, FL 33166 USA Tel 787-748-4567
E-mail: fans@zemicomics.com
Web site: http://www.zemicomics.com.

Zen Care, *(0-9747334)* 212 Merchant St., Suite 5, Honolulu, HI 96813 USA Tel 808-523-3622
E-mail: elithe@hawaii.rr.com
Dist(s): **Booklines Hawaii, Ltd.**
Native Bks.

Zen Comics, Inc., *(1-892572)* 12358 Ventura Blvd., Suite 307, Studio City, CA 91604 USA Tel 818-508-8190
E-mail: sszen97@aol.com
Web site: http://www.zenintergalacticninja.com.

Zendrera Zariquiey, Editorial (ESP) *(84-89675; 84-8418) Dist. by* **Mariuccia Iaconi Bk Imports.**

Zendrera Zariquiey, Editorial (ESP) *(84-89675; 84-8418) Dist. by* **Lectorum Pubns.**

Zendrera Zariquiey, Editorial (ESP) *(84-89675; 84-8418) Dist. by* **AIMS Intl.**

Zenga Publishing, *(0-9765484)* Orders Addr.: P.O. Box 39, New York, NY 10113 USA; Edit Addr.: 48 W. 22nd St., Suite 2, New York, NY 10010 USA
E-mail: zenga@nyc.rr.com
Web site: http://www.zengapublishing.com.

Zenith Pr. *Imprint of* **MBI Publishing Co. LLC**

Zephyr Pr. *Imprint of* **Chicago Review Pr., Inc.**

Zepp Pubns., *(0-9668954)* 4280 Regal Brook Dr., Medina, OH 44256 USA Tel 330-721-9145; Fax: 330-668-2934
E-mail: grossvater@zoominternet.net.

Zeppelin, *(0-9644622)* 9927 NW 49th Terr., Suite 300, Miami, FL 33178-1920 USA (SAN 298-489X) Tel 305-594-2099; Fax: 305-594-4686.

Zeppelin Press, Incorporated *See* **Zeppelin**

Zero-g Pr., *(1-892086)* 6605 N. Rustic Oak Ct., Peoria, IL 61614-2344 USA Tel 309-692-2953
E-mail: scifi20@prodigy.net
Web site: http://www.bradley.bradley.edu/~dlb/steven.html
Dist(s): **Baker & Taylor Bks.**

Zeromayo Studios, LLP, *(0-9661985)* Orders Addr.: P.O. Box 417, Haydenville, MA 01039 USA Tel 413-584-9372; Fax: 413-665-2312; Edit Addr.: 16 Market St., Northampton, MA 01060 USA ; *Imprints:* Empty Sky (Empty Sky)
E-mail: planetrace@aol.com
Web site: http://www.ninjaturtles.com
Dist(s): **Diamond Comic Distributors, Inc.**

Zest Bks. *Imprint of* **Orange Avenue Publishing**

Zest Publishing, *(0-9758861)* Orders Addr.: P.O. Box 484, Edgar, NE 68935-0484 USA; Edit Addr.: R.R. 1, Edgar, NE 68935-0484 USA Do not confuse with Zest Publishing Company in Southfield, MI.

Zeus Media LLC, *(0-9765840)* 12900 Canterbury, Leawood, KS 66209 USA
Web site: http://www.wisdomofzeus.com.

Zeus Sports Florida LLC, *(0-9777437)* Orders Addr.: 2312 SE 23rd Rd., Homestead, FL 33035-1900 USA Tel 786-417-9197
E-mail: habbook@msn.com.

Zhera Pubns., *(0-9618904)* Orders Addr.: 2605 E. Flora Pl., Denver, CO 80210-6827 USA (SAN 242-231X) Tel 303-753-0384
E-mail: Zhera@msn.com; zhera@msn.com.

Zichron Avos-Jewish Interactive Studies Foundation, Inc., *(0-9675202)* Orders Addr.: P.O. Box 354, Merion Station, PA 19066 USA
E-mail: zajis@jewishstudies.org
Web site: http://www.jewishstudies.org.

Ziert, Paul Assocs., Inc., *(0-9666104)* Orders Addr.: P.O. Box 721020, Norman, OK 73070 USA Tel 405-447-9988; Fax: 405-447-5810; Edit Addr.: 3214 Bart Conner Dr., Norman, OK 73072 USA
E-mail: paul@intlgymnast.com; IGDwight@aol.com.

Zig Boroughs, *(0-9720657)* P.O. Box 1131, Pickens, SC 29671-1131 USA
E-mail: broughr@bellsouth.net.

Zig the Pig, *(0-9761700)* 815 Poinsettia St., Columbia, SC 29205 USA.

Ziker, Andrew, *(0-9762147)* 2440 W. Thompson Way, Chandler, AZ 85248 USA.

Zilber, Jeremy, *(0-9786688)* P.O. Box 5543, Madison, WI 53705 USA
E-mail: jzilber@littledemocrats.net
Web site: http://www.littledemocrats.net.

Zimmerman & Associates *See* **Eagle Bks.**

Zimmerman, W. Frederick *See* **Nimble Bks. LLC**

Zinka Pr., Inc., *(0-9647171)* 1480 Pulaski Ln., Wayne, PA 19087 USA Tel 610-688-2113; Fax: 610-688-0753
E-mail: zinkapress@aol.com
Web site: http://www.zinkapress.com.

Zino Pr. Children's Bks., *(1-55933)* Div. of Knowledge Unlimited, Inc., P.O. Box 52, Madison, WI 53701-0052 USA Tel 608-836-6660; Fax: 608-831-1570; Toll Free Fax: 800-618-1570; Toll Free: 800-356-2303
E-mail: madzino@zinopress.com
Web site: http://www.zinopress.com
Dist(s): **Baker & Taylor Bks.**
Brodart Co.
Follett Library Resources.

Zion Pubs., *(0-9717704)* P.O. Box 71522, Salt Lake City, UT 84171 USA Tel 801-608-2101; Fax: 801-383-5397; Toll Free: 866-298-8811
E-mail: cs@zionpublishers.com; sales@zionpublishers.com
Web site: http://www.zionpublishers.com.

Zion Publishing, *(0-9627147)* 1500 Crown Colony Ct., Suite 540, Des Moines, IA 50315 USA Tel 515-282-5940; Toll Free: 800-996-2777 Do not confuse with companies with the same name in Monarch Beach, CA, Vallejo, CA
E-mail: maryenilsen@aol.com
Web site: http://www.zionpublishing.org.

Zion Publishing, *(0-9714844)* 17 Harding Ln., Sumiton, AL 35148 USA Tel 205-648-6741
E-mail: driverdm@aol.com.

Zipper Pr., Inc., *(0-9652479)* P.O. Box 90125, Dayton, OH 45490-0125 USA Tel 937-898-5950; Fax: 937-898-5440; Toll Free: 800-295-2945 (orders only)
E-mail: zipperpress@zipperpress.com
Web site: http://www.zipperpress.com.

ZMD, *(0-9702389)* P.O. Box 8231, Gaithersburg, MD 20898-8231 USA Tel 301-977-7376; Fax: 301-977-4088
E-mail: book@cyberistan.org
Web site: http://cyberistan.org/muslimhistory570.htm; http://cyberistan.org/historyindia.htm; http://cyberistan.org/ebook.htm.

Zo Publishing, *(0-938465)* Orders Addr.: P.O. Box 61335, Honolulu, HI 96839 USA (SAN 660-9864) Tel 808-988-7111; Edit Addr.: 2918 Manoa Rd., Honolulu, HI 96822 USA (SAN 660-9872)
E-mail: dyen@lava.net.

Zoe Life Publishing, *(0-9748251; 0-9779445; 1-934363)* P.O. Box 871066, Canton, MI 48187 USA (SAN 256-1735) Tel 734-547-7801; Fax: 734-547-7805; Toll Free: 877-841-3400 ; *Imprints:* Pen of A Ready Writer (Pen of A Ready)
E-mail: info@zoelifepub.com
Web site: http://www.zoelifepub.com.

Zoland Bks., Inc. *Imprint of* **Steerforth Pr.**

Zon Books *See* **Zon Bks.**

Zonderkidz, *(0-310)* 5300 Patterson Ave., SE, Grand Rapids, MI 49530 USA Tel 1-800-727-3480
E-mail: zprod@zondervan.com
Web site: http://www.zondervan.com
Dist(s): **Zondervan.**

†**Zondervan**, *(0-00; 0-310; 0-937336)* Subs. of HarperCollins Publishers US, Orders Addr.: c/o Zondervan XNET Ordering Dept., 5249 Corporate Grove, Grand Rapids, MI 49512 USA (SAN 298-9107); Edit Addr.: 5300 Patterson Ave., SE, Grand Rapids, MI 49530 USA (SAN 203-2694) Tel 616-698-6900; Fax: 616-698-3439
E-mail: zprod@zondervan.com
Web site: http://www.zondervan.com
Dist(s): **Vida Pubs.**; *CIP.*

Zondervan bibles *See* **Zondervan Bibles**

Zondervan Bibles, *(0-310)* 5300 Patterson Ave., SE, Grand Rapids, MI 49530 USA Tel 1-800-727-3480
E-mail: zprod@zondervan.com
Web site: http://www.zondervan.com
Dist(s): **Zondervan.**

Zon Bks., *(0-310)* 5300 Patterson Ave., SE, Grand Rapids, MI 49530 USA Tel 1-800-727-3480
E-mail: zprod@zondervan.com
Web site: http://www.zondervan.com
Dist(s): **Zondervan.**

Zondervan Publishing House *See* **Zondervan**

Zonk Galleries, *(0-9706537)* P.O. Box 11059, Oakland, CA 94610 USA (SAN 254-3443) Tel 510-530-2681
E-mail: zonk@dnai.com
Web site: http://zonktheturtle.com.

Zoo Bks. *Imprint of* **Wildlife Education, Ltd.**

Zoo-phonics, Inc., *(0-9617342; 1-886441)* Orders Addr.: 20950 Ferretti Rd., Groveland, CA 95321 USA (SAN 663-8589) Tel 209-962-5030; Fax: 209-962-4320; Toll Free: 800-622-8104
E-mail: zoo-info@zoo-phonics.com; shirley@zoo-phonics.com
Web site: http://www.zoo-phonics.com.

Zora, *(0-9714039; 1-59898)* 450 Stedman Pl., Monrovia, CA 91016 USA Tel 626-359-6071
E-mail: genesmachine@hotmail.com.

Zottola Publishing, Inc., *(0-9725880)* Orders Addr.: 4212 Boone Ave N., New Hope, MN 55428-0001 USA
E-mail: arumel@zotpub.com
Web site: http://www.zotpub.com.

Zu Bks., *(0-615)* 1813 Comet, Altus, OK 73521 USA Tel 580-477-0819
Web site: http://zuopolis.com
Dist(s): **Lulu.com.**

Zuber Publishing, *(0-9785551)* 52180 Tammy Dr., Granger, IN 46530 USA Tel 574-272-8914
E-mail: admin@zuberpublishing.com
Web site: http://www.zuberpublishing.com
Dist(s): **Baker & Taylor Bks.**
Distributors, The.

Zuckerman Cannon Pub., *(0-9664316)* 1240 Epps Clark Rd., Siler City, NC 27344 USA Tel 919-742-5399
Dist(s): **Blair, John F. Pub.**

Zuiho, *(0-9743474)* 11628 82nd Ave. NE, Kirkland, WA 98034-3400 USA.

Zula Ltd., *(0-9673099)* 13009 Greenleaf St., Studio City, CA 91604-2227 USA (SAN 254-1114) Toll Free: 888-803-9685.

Zulema Enterprises, *(1-881223)* Div. of ACF Enterprises, LLC, 7715 Yardley Dr. Suite 208, Tamarac, FL 33321 USA Tel 954-724-5204
E-mail: peopleteachers@aol.com
Web site: zulemabooks.com.

Zumaya Pubns. LLC, *(1-894869; 1-894942; 1-55410; 1-934135; 1-934841)* Orders Addr.: 3209 S. IH 35, No. 1086, Austin, TX 78741-6905 USA
E-mail: zumayabooks@gmail.com
Web site: http://www.zumayapublications.com.

Zy Iman Pubng, *(0-9779130)* P.O. Box 367, Brooklyn, NY 11221 USA
Web site: http://www.ucanspeakup.com.

Zygote Games LLC, *(0-9770419)* 100 Venture Way, Flr. 3, Suite 4, Hadley, MA 01035 USA Tel 413-303-9031; Fax: 253-540-5054
E-mail: orders@zygotegames.com
Web site: http://www.zygotegames.com.

Zyrro, Roggen, *(0-9762580)* 5841 Wornall Rd., Kansas City, MO 64113 USA
Web site: http://www.bunsta.com.

ZZ Dogs Pr. *Imprint of* **That's Life Publishing, Inc.**

WHOLESALER & DISTRIBUTOR SYMBOL INDEX

1st World Publishing, *(0-9639152)* 1100 N. 4th St. Ste. 9, Fairfield, IA 52556-2169 USA Do not confuse with companies with the same name in Bid Bend, WI, Winchester, MA, San Antonio, TX, Bend, OR
E-mail: info@1stworldlibrary.org; info@1stworldpublishing.com; literacy@1stworldlibrary.org; books@1stworldpublishing.com
Web site: http://www.1stworldlibrary.org; http://www.1stworldpublishers.com; http://store.1stworldlibrary.com/index.html; http://store.classiclibrary.org/index.html.

3M Sportsman's Video Collection, 3M Ctr., Bldg. 223-4NE-05, Saint Paul, MN 55144-1000 USA (SAN 159-8929) Tel 612-733-7412; Fax: 612-736-7479; Toll Free: 800-940-8273 (orders only).

A & B Books, *See* **A & B Distributors & Pubs. Group**

A & B Distributors & Pubs. Group, *(1-881316; 1-886433)* Div. of A&B Distributors, 1000 Atlantic Ave., Brooklyn, NY 11238 USA (SAN 630-9216) Tel 718-783-7808; Fax: 718-783-7267; Toll Free: 877-542-6657; 146 Lawrence St., Brooklyn, NY 11201 (SAN 631-385X)
E-mail: maxtay@webspan.net.

A & M Church Supplies, 3535 Bay Rd., Saginaw, MI 48603-2464 USA (SAN 157-0145) Toll Free: 800-345-4694.

A B S Corporation, *See* **Budgetext**

A K J Book Fare, Incorporated, *See* **AKJ Educational Services, Inc.**

AAA Anime Distribution, 4509 Shirley Ave., Unit D, El Mone, CA 91731 USA Tel 626-575-8922
E-mail: vince@aaaanime.com.

ABC'S Bk. Supply, Inc., 7319 W. Flagler St., Miami, FL 33144 USA Toll Free: 877-383-4240
E-mail: abcbooks@abcbooks.com.

Abdo & Daughters Publishing, *See* **ABDO Publishing Co.**

ABDO Publishing Co., *(0-939179; 1-56239; 1-57765; 1-59197; 1-59679; 1-59928; 1-59961; 1-60270; 1-60453)* Div. of ABDO Publishing Group, Orders Addr.: 8000 W. 78th St. Suite 310, Edina, MN 55439 USA (SAN 662-9172) Tel 952-831-2120; Fax: 952-831-1632; Toll Free: 800-800-1312
E-mail: info@abdopublishing.com
Web site: http://www.abdopublishing.com.

Abel Love, Inc., Orders Addr.: P.O. Box 2250, Newport News, VA 23609 USA (SAN 158-4081) Tel 757-877-2939; Toll Free: 800-520-2939; Edit Addr.: 935 Lucas Creek Rd., Newport News, VA 23608 USA Fax: 804-877-2939.

Abingdon Pr., *(0-687; 1-4267)* Div. of United Methodist Publishing Hse., Orders Addr.: P.O. Box 801, Nashville, TN 37202-3919 USA (SAN 201-0054) Tel 615-749-6409; Fax: 615-749-6056; Toll Free: 800-627-1789; Edit Addr.: 201 Eighth Ave., S., Nashville, TN 37202 USA (SAN 699-9956) Toll Free: 800-627-1789
Web site: http://www.abingdonpress.com/.

Abraham Assocs. Inc., 5120-A Cedar Lake Rd., Minneapolis, MN 55416 USA Tel 952-927-7920; Fax: 952-927-8089; Toll Free: 800-701-2489
E-mail: stu@abrahamassociatesinc.com.

Abrams & Co. Pubs., Inc., *(0-7664)* Orders Addr.: 61 Mattatuck Heights, Waterbury, CT 06705 USA; Edit Addr.: P.O. Box 10025, Waterbury, CT 06725 USA Tel 203-756-6562; Fax: 203-756-2895; Toll Free: 800-874-0029
E-mail: custserve@abramsandcompany.com
Web site: http://www.abramsandcompany.com.

Abrams, Harry N. , Inc., *(0-8109; 1-4197)* 115 West 18th St., New York, NY 10011 USA (SAN 200-2434) Tel 212-206-7715; Fax: 212-519-1210
E-mail: webmaster@abramsbooks.com
Web site: http://www.hnabooks.com.

Abyss Distribution, *(1-932548)* P.O. Box 48, Middlefield, MA 01243-0048 USA (SAN 630-9925) Tel 413-623-2155; Fax: 413-623-2156; Toll Free: 800-326-0804
E-mail: abyssdist@aol.com
Web site: http://www.azuregreen.om.

Academic Bk. Ctr., Inc., P.O. Box 1320, Lake Oswego, OR 97035-0320 USA (SAN 169-7145) Toll Free: 800-547-7704
E-mail: orders@acbc.com
Web site: http://www.abc.com.

Academic Bk. Services, Inc., 5490 Fulton Industrial Blvd., Atlanta, GA 30336 USA (SAN 631-0591) Tel 404-344-8317; Fax: 404-349-2127.

Academi-Text Medical Wholesalers, 333 N. Superior, Toledo, OH 43604 USA (SAN 135-2415) Tel 419-255-9755; Fax: 419-255-9606; Toll Free: 800-552-8398 (out of state)
E-mail: dyourist@academi-text.com.

ACCESS Pubs. Network, 6893 Sullivan Rd., Grawn, MI 49637 USA.

Acorn Alliance, 549 Old North Rd., Kingston, RI 02881-1220 USA Tel 401-783-5480; Fax: 401-284-0959; Fulfillment Addr.: Client Distribution Services 193 Edwards Dr., Jackson, TN 38301 USA Toll Free Fax: 800-351-5073; Toll Free: 800-343-4499
E-mail: moyerbellbooks@yahoo.com
Web site: http://www.moyerbellbooks.com.

Acorn Group, The, *(1-881150)* 155 El Camino Real, Tustin, CA 92680 USA Tel 714-838-4888; Fax: 714-838-5309; Toll Free: 800-422-8886
Web site: http://www.acorngroup.com; http://www.acornnaturalists.com.

ACTA Pubns., *(0-87946; 0-914070; 0-915388)* 5559 Howard St., Skokie, IL 60077-2621 USA (SAN 204-7489) Toll Free Fax: 800-397-0079; Toll Free: 800-397-2282
E-mail: actapublications@aol.com
Web site: http://www.actapublications.com.

Action Products International, Inc., 344 Cypress Rd., Ocala, FL 34472-3108 USA (SAN 630-8805) Tel 352-687-4961; Toll Free: 800-772-2846
E-mail: sales@apii.com.

ACW Pr., *(0-9656749; 1-892525; 1-932124; 1-934668)* Orders Addr.: P.O. Box 110390, Nashville, TN 37222 USA Tel 615-834-0450; Toll Free: 800-219-7483; Edit Addr.: 4854 Aster Dr., Nashville, TN 37211 USA
E-mail: regaforder@aol.com.

Adams Bk. Co., Inc., 537 Sackett St., Brooklyn, NY 11217 USA (SAN 107-7171) Tel 718-875-5464; Fax: 718-852-3212; Toll Free: 800-221-0909
E-mail: sales@adamsbook.com
Web site: http://www.adamsbook.com.

Adams News, 1555 W. Galer St., Seattle, WA 98119 USA (SAN 169-8842) Tel 206-284-7617; Fax: 206-284-7599; Toll Free: 800-533-7617.

Adams, Robert Henry Fine Art, *(0-9713010)* 715 N. Franklin St., Chicago, IL 60610 USA (SAN 159-6918) Tel 312-642-8700; Fax: 312-642-8785
E-mail: info@adamsfineart.com
Web site: http://www.adamsfineart.com.

Addison-Wesley Educational Pubs., Inc., *(0-321; 0-328; 0-673)* Div. of Addison Wesley Longman, Inc., 75 Arlington St., Boston, MA 02116 USA Tel 617-848-7500; Toll Free: 800-447-2226
Web site: http://www.awl.com.

Addison-Wesley Longman, Inc., *(0-201; 0-321; 0-582; 0-673; 0-8013; 0-8053; 0-9654123)* Orders Addr.: 200 Old Tappan Rd., Old Tappan, NJ 07675 USA (SAN 299-4739) Toll Free: 800-922-0579; Edit Addr.: 75 Arlington St., Suite 300, Boston, MA 02116 USA (SAN 200-2000) Tel 617-848-7500; Toll Free: 800-447-2226
E-mail: pearsoned@eds.com; orderdeptnj@pearsoned.com
Web site: http://www.awl.com.

Addison-Wesley Publishing Company, Incorporated, *See* **Addison-Wesley Longman, Inc.**

Adelman, Joseph, 530 N. 40th St., Allentown, PA 18104-4558 USA (SAN 285-8002).

Adler, Leo, P.O. Box 10308, Eugene, OR 97440-2308 USA (SAN 169-7021).

Adler's Foreign Bks., Inc., *(0-8417)* 915 Foster St., Evanston, IL 60201 USA (SAN 111-3089) Tel 847-864-0664; Fax: 847-864-0804; Toll Free: 800-235-3771
E-mail: info@afb-adlers.com
Web site: http://www.afb-adlers.com.

Advanced Global Distribution Services, 5880 Oberlin Dr., San Diego, CA 32121 USA Toll Free Fax: 800-499-3822; Toll Free: 800-284-3580.

Advanced Marketing Services, 13475 Danielson St. Ste. 110, Poway, CA 92064-8858 USA (SAN 170-2297) Toll Free: 800-699-5822.

Advanced Marketing Services, Incorporated, *See* **Advantage Pubs. Group**

Advantage Pubs. Group, *(0-934429; 1-57145; 1-59223)* 5880 Oberlin Dr., San Diego, CA 92121 USA (SAN 630-8090) Toll Free: 800-284-3580
E-mail: bernadetteb@advmkt.com
Web site: http://www.silverdolphinbooks.com; http://www.advantagebooksonline.com; http://www.laurelglenbooks.com; http://www.thunderbaybooks.com/; http://www.bathroomreader.com.

Adventure Pubns., Inc., *(0-934860; 1-885061; 1-59193)* Orders Addr.: 820 Cleveland St., S., Cambridge, MN 55008 USA (SAN 212-7199) Tel 763-689-9800; Fax: 763-689-9039; Toll Free Fax: 877-374-9016; Toll Free: 800-678-7006
E-mail: orders@adventurepublications.net; custservice@adventurepublications.net
Web site: http://www.adventurepublications.net.

Adventures Unlimited Pr., *(0-932813; 1-931882)* Orders Addr.: P.O. Box 74, Kempton, IL 60946 USA (SAN 630-1126) Tel 815-253-6390; Fax: 815-253-6300; Edit Addr.: 303 Main St., Kempton, IL 60946 USA (SAN 250-3484)
E-mail: auphq@frontiernet.net
Web site: http://www.adventuresunlimitedpress.com.

Adventurous Traveler Bookstore, P.O. Box 1468, Williston, VT 05495 USA (SAN 631-4597) Toll Free: 800-282-3963.

Advertising Specialties, Inc., 4920 River Rd., Pascagoula, MS 39567 USA (SAN 108-6316) Tel 601-769-7904
Web site: http://www.advmkt.com; http://www.advantagebooksonline.com.

A.F. Eurotool, Inc., 11449 Randall Dr., Lenexa, KS 66215 USA (SAN 631-1601)
E-mail: mariette@jesusweb.org
Web site: http://www.jesusweb.org.

Affiliated Bk. Distributor, Div. of North Shore Distributors, Inc., 1200 N. Branch St., Chicago, IL 60622 USA (SAN 169-2267).

Africa World Pr., *(0-86543; 1-59221)* 541 W. Ingham Ave., Suite B, Trenton, NJ 08638 USA (SAN 692-3925) Tel 609-695-3200; Fax: 609-695-6466
E-mail: awprsp@africanworld.com
Web site: http://www.africanworld.com.

African World Bks., 2217 Pennsylvania Ave., Baltimore, MD 21217 USA (SAN 631-3868) Tel 410-383-2006.

Afrikan World Bk. Distributor, Orders Addr.: P.O. Box 16447, Baltimore, MD 21217 USA; Edit Addr.: 2217 Pennsylvania Ave., Baltimore, MD 21217 USA (SAN 631-2020) Tel 410-383-2006.

Afro-American Bk. Distributor, 2537 Prospect, Houston, TX 77004 USA (SAN 169-8257).

Agencia de Publicaciones de Puerto Rico, GPO Box 4903, San Juan, PR 00936 USA (SAN 169-9296).

Agritech Publishing Group, Inc., Div. of Agritech Corp., 825 W. Samalayuca Dr., Tucson, AZ 85704-3912 USA (SAN 174-612X) Tel 520-544-2542.

AHA, Inc., *(0-918545)* P.O. Box 8405, Santa Cruz, CA 95061-8405 USA (SAN 295-5059) Tel 408-458-9119.

AIMS International Bks., Inc., *(0-922852)* 7709 Hamilton Ave., Cincinnati, OH 45231-3103 USA (SAN 630-270X) Tel 513-521-5590; Fax: 513-521-5592; Toll Free: 800-733-2067
E-mail: aimsbooks@fuse.net
Web site: http://www.aimsbooks.com.

A-K News Company, *See* **Aramark Magazine & Bk. Co.**

AK Pr. Distribution, *(1-873176; 1-902593)* 674-A 23rd St., Oakland, CA 94612-1163 USA (SAN 298-2234) Tel 510-208-1700; Fax: 510-208-1701
E-mail: akpress@akpress.org
Web site: http://www.akpress.org.

AKJ Educational Services, Inc., 5609-2A Fishers Ln., Rockville, MD 20852 USA (SAN 170-5431) Tel 301-770-4030; Fax: 301-770-2338; Toll Free: 800-770-2338
E-mail: info@akjedsvcs.com
Web site: http://www.akjedsvcs.com.

Alabama Bk. Store, Orders Addr.: P.O. Box 1279, Tuscaloosa, AL 35401-1626 USA Tel 205-758-4532; Fax: 205-758-5525; Toll Free: 800-382-2665 (orders only); Edit Addr.: 1015 University Blvd., Tuscaloosa, AL 35403-1279 USA (SAN 100-0063)
E-mail: ABS@AlabamaBook.com
Web site: http://www.AlabamaBook.com.

Alamo Square Distributors, P.O. Box 14543, San Francisco, CA 94114 USA Fax: 415-863-7456
E-mail: alamosqdist@earthlink.net.

Alba Hse., *(0-8189)* Div. of Society of St. Paul, 2187 Victory Blvd., Staten Island, NY 10314-6603 USA (SAN 201-2405) Tel 718-761-0047; Fax: 718-761-0057; 718-698-8390; Toll Free: 800-343-2522
E-mail: albabooks@aol.com
Web site: http://www.albahouse.org.

Alexander News Company, *See* **Blue Ridge News Co.**

Alfonsi Enterprises, 8621 Gavinton Ct., Dublin, OH 43017-9615 USA (SAN 169-4227).

Alfred Publishing Co., Inc., *(0-7390; 0-88284)* Orders Addr.: P.O. Box 10003, Van Nuys, CA 91410-0003 USA; Edit Addr.: 123 Dry Rd., Oriskany, NY 13424 USA Tel 315-736-1572; Fax: 315-736-7281
E-mail: customerservice@alfred.com; permissions@alfred.com; submissions@alfred.com
Web site: http://www.alfred.com.

Alibris, *(0-9702763)* 1250 45th St., Suite 100, Emeryville, CA 94608 USA Fax: 510-550-6052; Toll Free: 877-254-2747 (877-ALIBRIS, option 1)
E-mail: libraries@alibris.com
Web site: http://www.alibris.com/library.

Alive Bks., *(0-920470; 1-55312)* Div. of Book Publishing Co., Orders Addr.: P.O. Box 99, Summertown, TN 38483 USA (SAN 115-7078) Tel 931-964-3571; Fax: 931-964-3518; Toll Free: 888-260-8458 (orders and customer service)
E-mail: Cynthia@bookpubco.com
Web site: http://www.bookpubco.com.

All America Distributors Corp., 8431 Melrose Pl., Los Angeles, CA 90069-5382 USA (SAN 168-972X) Tel 213-651-2650; Fax: 213-655-9452
E-mail: psi@loop.com.

AllBooks, 951 Old County Rd., Suite 124, Belmont, CA 94002 USA (SAN 631-3698) Tel 415-595-5200
E-mail: info@AllBooks.com
Web site: http://www.AllBooks.com/.

Allegro Distribution, 14134 NE Airport Way, Portland, OR 97230-3443 USA (SAN 631-5895)
E-mail: gary@allegro-music.com.

Allenspark WIND, *(0-9625286)* Orders Addr.: P.O. Box 275, Allenspark, CO 80510 USA Tel 303-747-2472; Edit Addr.: 139 Zumwinkel Ln., Allenspark, CO 80510 USA.

Allentown News Agency, Inc., Orders Addr.: P.O. Box 446, Allentown, PA 18105 USA; Edit Addr.: 719-723 Liberty St., Allentown, PA 18105 USA (SAN 169-7226) Tel 610-432-4441; Fax: 610-432-2708.

Alliance Bk. Co., P.O. Box 7884, Hilton Head, SC 29938-7884 USA
E-mail: alliancebk@mindspring.com.

Alliance Hse., Inc., *(0-9665234)* 220 Ferris Ave., Suite 201, White Plains, NY 10603 USA Tel 914-328-5456; Fax: 914-946-1929
E-mail: alliancehs@aol.com.

Ally Pr., *(0-915408)* 524 Orleans St., Saint Paul, MN 55107 USA (SAN 207-7116) Tel 612-291-2652; Fax: 240-248-5678; Toll Free: 800-729-3002
E-mail: pferoe@comcast.net
Web site: http://www.catalog.com/ally.

Alonso Bk. & Periodical Services, Inc., 2316 2nd St S., Arlington, VA 22204-2010 USA (SAN 170-7035).

Alpen Bks, 4602 Chennault Beach Rd. Ste. B1, Mukilteo, WA 98275-5016 USA.

Alpenbooks, *See* **Alpenbooks Pr. LLC**

Alpenbooks Pr. LLC, *(0-9669795)* 4602 Chennault Beach Rd, B1, Mukilteo, WA 98275 USA (SAN 113-5309) Tel 425-415-4560; Fax: 425-493-6381
E-mail: rkoch@alpenbooks.com
Web site: http://www.alpenbooks.com.

Alpha & Omega Distributor, P.O. Box 36640, Colorado Springs, CO 80936-3664 USA (SAN 169-0515).

Alpha Bks., *(0-02; 0-672; 0-7357; 0-7897; 1-56761; 1-57595; 0-7431; 1-59257)* Div. of Pearson Technology Group, 201 W. 103rd St., Indianapolis, IN 46290 USA (SAN 219-6298) Tel 317-581-3500 Toll Free: 800-571-5840 (orders)
Web site: http://www.idiotsguides.com.

Alpine News Distributors, Div. of Mountain States Distributors, 0105 Marand Rd., Glenwood Springs, CO 81601 USA Tel 970-945-2269; Fax: 970-945-2260.

Alta Bk. Co., Pubs., *(1-878598)* 16 Adrian Ct., Burlingame, CA 94010 USA (SAN 200-4674) Tel 415-692-2002; Fax: 415-692-4654; Toll Free: 800-526-0505.

Alta Bk. Ctr. Pubs., *(1-882483; 1-932383)* 14 Adrian Ct., Burlingame, CA 94010 USA (SAN 630-9240) Tel 650-692-1285; Fax: 650-692-4654; Toll Free: 800-258-2375
E-mail: info@altaesl.com
Web site: http://www.altaesl.com.

Alta Book Center, *See* **Alta Bk. Ctr. Pubs.**

Amacom, *(0-7612; 0-8144)* Div. of American Management Association, Orders Addr.: 600 AMA Way, Saranac Lake, NY 12983 USA (SAN 227-3578) Tel 518-891-5510; Fax: 518-891-2372; Toll Free: 800-250-5308 (orders & customer service); Edit Addr.: 1601 Broadway, New York, NY 10019-7420 USA (SAN 201-1670) Tel 212-586-8100; Fax: 212-903-8168
E-mail: cust_serv@amanet.org
Web site: http://www.amacombooks.org.

Amarillo Periodical Distributors, P.O. Box 3823, Lubbock, TX 70404 USA (SAN 156-4986) Tel 806-745-6000.

Amato, Frank Pubns., Inc., *(0-936608; 1-57188; 1-878175)* Orders Addr.: P.O. Box 82112, Portland, OR 97282 USA (SAN 214-3372) Tel 503-653-8108; Fax: 503-653-2766; Toll Free: 800-541-9498; Edit Addr.: 4040 SE Wister St., Milwaukie, OR 97222 USA
E-mail: wholesale@amatobooks.com; Lorraine@amatobooks.com
Web site: http://www.amatobooks.com.

Amazon.Com, *(1-58060)* 1200 12th Ave. S., Suite 1200, Seattle, WA 98144 USA (SAN 179-4205) Tel 206-266-6817; Orders Addr.: P.O. Box 80387, Seattle, WA 98108-0387 USA (SAN 156-143X) Tel 206-622-2335; Fax: 206-622-2405; 1 Centerpoint Blvd., non-carton, New Castle, DE 19720 (SAN 155-3992); 1 Centerpoint Blvd., carton, New Castle, DE 19720 (SAN 156-1405); 520 S. Brandon, non-carton, Seattle, WA 98108 (SAN 152-6642); 520 S. Brandon, carton, Seattle, WA 98108 (SAN 156-1383); 1600 E. Newlands Dr., carton, Fernley, NV 89408 (SAN 156-5982); 1600 E. Newlands Dr., non-carton, Fernley, NV 89408 (SAN 156-6008); Edit Addr.: 520 Pike St., Seattle, WA 98101 USA (SAN 155-3984); P.O. Box 81226, Seattle, WA 98108-1226
E-mail: catalog-dept@amazon.com
Web site: http://www.amazon.com.

Ambassador Bks. & Media, 42 Chasner St., Hempstead, NY 11550 USA (SAN 120-064X) Tel 516-489-4011; Fax: 516-489-5661; Toll Free: 800-431-8913
E-mail: ambassador@absbook.com
Web site: http://www.absbook.com.

Ambassador Book Service, *See* **Ambassador Bks. & Media**

AMCAL, Inc., *(0-911855; 1-57624; 1-884358; 1-58625; 1-58913; 1-59282)* 2500 Bisso Ln., Bldg. 500, Concord, CA 94520 USA (SAN 263-9025)
E-mail: amcal@amcalart.com
Web site: http://www.amcalart.com.

America Hse. Bk. Pubs., *(1-893162; 1-58851; 1-59129)* Orders Addr.: P.O. Box 151, Frederick, MD 21705-0151 USA; Edit Addr.: 113 E. Church St., Frederick, MD 21701 USA
Web site: http://www.publishamerica.com.

American Assn. for Vocational Instructional Materials, *(0-89606; 0-914452)* 220 Smithonia Rd., Winterville, GA 30683 USA (SAN 225-8811) Tel 706-742-5355; Fax: 706-742-7005; Toll Free: 800-228-4689
E-mail: ksseab@aavim.com; sales@aavim.com
Web site: http://www.aavim.com.

American Bible Society, *(0-8267; 1-58516)* Orders Addr.: 844 NW Lowery Rd., Claremore, OK 74017-2116 USA (SAN 662-7129) Tel 918-342-3904; Toll Free Fax: 866-570-2877; Edit Addr.: 1865 Broadway, New York, NY 10023-9980 USA (SAN 203-5189) Tel 212-408-1200; Fax: 212-408-1305; 700 Plaza Dr., 2nd Flr., Secaucus, NJ 07094
E-mail: info@americanbible.org
Web site: http://www.bibles.org; http://www.americanbible.org.

American Bk. Co., P.O. Box 219, Florence, AL 35830 USA (SAN 630-8635) Tel 205-766-3789 Do not confuse with companies with the same or similar name in Knoxville, TN, Fort Collins, CO, Chesterfield, VA, Woodstock, GA.

American Bk. Ctr., Brooklyn Navy Yard, Bldg. 3, Brooklyn, NY 11205 USA (SAN 630-8821) Tel 718-834-0170.

American Buddhist Shim Gum Do Assn., Inc., *(0-9614427)* 203 Chestnut Hill Ave., Brighton, MA 02135 USA (SAN 113-2873) Tel 617-787-1506; Fax: 617-787-2708
E-mail: marystackhouse@shimgumdo.org
Web site: http://www.shimgumdo.org.

American Business Systems, Inc., 315 Littleton Rd., Chelmsford, MA 01824 USA (SAN 264-8229) Tel 508-250-9600; Fax: 508-250-8027; Toll Free: 800-356-4034.

American Eagle Pubns., Inc., *(0-929408)* Orders Addr.: P.O. Box 5111, Sun City West, AZ 85376 USA (SAN 249-2415) Tel 623-556-2925; Fax: 623-556-2926; Toll Free: 866-764-2925; Edit Addr.: 12647 Crystal Lake Dr., Sun City West, AZ 85375 USA
E-mail: custservice@ameaglepubs.com
Web site: http://www.ameaglepubs.com.

American Education Corp., The, *(0-87570; 1-58636)* 7506 N. Broadway, Suite 505, Oklahoma City, OK 73116-9016 USA (SAN 654-6250) Tel 405-840-6031; Fax: 405-848-3960; Toll Free: 800-222-2811
Web site: http://www.amered.com.

American Educational Computer, Incorporated, *See* **American Education Corp., The**

American Federation of Astrologers, Inc., *(0-86690)* 6535 S. Rural Rd., Tempe, AZ 85283 USA (SAN 225-1396) Tel 480-838-1751; Fax: 480-838-8293; Toll Free: 888-301-7630
E-mail: AFA@msn.com
Web site: http://www.astrologers.com.

American Heritage Magazine, 90 Fifth Ave., New York, NY 10011 USA.

American International Distribution Corp., Orders Addr.: P.O. Box 574, Williston, VT 05495-0020 USA Tel 800-390-3149; Fax: 802-864-7626; Toll Free: 800-426-4742; Edit Addr.: 50 Winter Sport Ln., Williston, VT 05495 USA (SAN 630-2238) Toll Free: 800-488-2665
E-mail: jmacon@aidcvt.com
Web site: http://www.aidcvt.com/Specialty/Home.asp.

American Kennel Club Museum of the Dog, *(0-9615072)* 1721 S. Mason Rd., Saint Louis, MO 63131 USA (SAN 110-8751) Tel 314-821-3647; Fax: 314-821-7381.

American Magazine Service, *See* **Prebound Periodicals**

American Marketing & Publishing Company, *See* **Christian Publishing Network**

American Micro Media, 19 N. Broadway, Box 306, Red Hook, NY 12571 USA (SAN 653-9920) Tel 914-758-5567.

American Overseas Bk. Co., Inc., 550 Walnut St., Norwood, NJ 07648 USA (SAN 169-4863) Tel 201-767-7600; Fax: 201-784-0263
E-mail: books@aobc.com
Web site: http://www.aobc.com.

American Pharmacists Assn., *(0-914768; 0-917330; 1-58212)* 1100 15th St., NW, Suite 400, Washington, DC 20005 USA (SAN 202-4446) Tel 202-628-4410; Fax: 202-783-2351; Toll Free: 800-878-0729
E-mail: kanderson@aphanet.org
Web site: http://www.pharmacist.com.

American Production Services, *(1-888147)* 150 Nims Spring Dr., Fort Mills, SC 29715 USA Tel 803-548-2290; Toll Free: 888-506-2400
E-mail: pmoody@apsvideo.com
Web site: http://www.apsvideo.com.

American Society of Agronomy, *(0-89118)* 677 S. Segoe Rd., Madison, WI 53711-1086 USA (SAN 107-5683) Tel 608-273-8080; Fax: 608-273-2021
Web site: http://www.agronomy.org.

American Society of Civil Engineers, *(0-7844; 0-87262)* 1801 Alexander Bell Dr., Reston, VA 20191-4400 USA (SAN 204-7594) Tel 703-295-6300; Fax: 703-295-6211; Toll Free: 800-548-2723
E-mail: marketing@asce.org
Web site: http://www.pubs.asce.org.

American Technical Pubs., Inc., *(0-8269)* 1155 W. 175th St., Homewood, IL 60430 USA (SAN 206-8141) Tel 708-957-1100; Fax: 708-957-1137; Toll Free: 800-323-3471
E-mail: service@americantech.net
Web site: http://www.americantech.net.

American West Bks., 1254 Commerce Way, Sanger, CA 93657-8731 USA (SAN 630-8570) Toll Free: 800-497-4909 Do not confuse with American West Bks., Albuquerque, NM
E-mail: JBM12@CSUFresno.edu.

American Wholesale Bk. Co., Subs. of Books-A-Million, Orders Addr.: 121 25th St., S., Birmingham, AL 35210 USA (SAN 631-7391) Tel 205-956-4151; Fax: 205-956-5530.

Americana Publishing, Inc., *(1-58807; 1-58943)* 195 Us Highway 9. Ste. 204, Englishtown, NJ 07726-8294 USA Toll Free: 888-883-8203
E-mail: editor@americanabooks.com
Web site: http://www.americanabooks.com.

Americana Souvenirs & Gifts, *(1-890541)* 206 Hanover St., Gettysburg, PA 17325-1911 USA (SAN 169-7366) Toll Free: 800-692-7436.

America's Cycling Pubns., 6425 Capitol Ave., Suite F, Diamond Springs, CA 95619 USA.

America's Hobby Ctr., 146 W. 22nd St., New York, NY 10011 USA (SAN 111-0403) Tel 212-675-8922.

Ames News Agency, Inc., 2110 E. 13th St., Ames, IA 50010 USA (SAN 169-2550).

Amigos Book Co., Orders Addr.: 5401 Bissonnet, Houston, TX 77081-6605 USA.

Ammon, Von Studios, 48 San Antonio Pl., San Francisco, CA 94133-4054 USA (SAN 631-3906) Tel 415-397-7799; Fax: 415-983-0523.

Amoskeag News Agency, 92 Allard Dr., Manchester, NH 03102 USA (SAN 169-4537) Tel 603-623-5343.

AMS Pr., Inc., *(0-404)* Brooklyn Navy Yard Bldg. 292, Suite 417, 63 Flushing Ave., New York, NY 11205 USA (SAN 106-6706) Tel 718-875-8100; Fax: 212-995-5413 Do not confuse with companies with the same or similar name in Los Angeles, CA, Pittsburgh, PA
E-mail: amserve@earthlink.net.

Analos Magazine, 475 Park Ave. S., New York, NY 10016 USA.

Anchor Distributors, 30 Hunt Valley Cir., New Kensington, PA 15068 USA (SAN 631-077X) Tel 724-334-7000; Fax: 724-334-1200; Toll Free: 800-444-4484
E-mail: marketing@whitakerhouse.com.

Anderson Merchandisers, 421 E. 34th St., Amarillo, TX 79103 USA (SAN 169-8028) Tel 806-376-6251
E-mail: hanleyg@amerch.com.

Anderson News - Tacoma, 9914 32nd Ave., S., Lakewood, WA 98499 USA (SAN 108-1322) Tel 253-581-1940; Fax: 253-584-5941; Toll Free: 800-552-2000 (in Washington).

Anderson News Co., 3600 75th Terr., N., Pinellas Park, FL 34665 USA Tel 813-622-8087 Do not confuse with Anderson News Company, Roanoke, VA .

Anderson News, LLC, 3840 Vineland Rd., Orlando, FL 32811-6427 USA (SAN 169-1201) Tel 407-841-8738; Fax: 407-839-4043; Toll Free: 800-338-3988; P.O. Box 616898, Orlando, FL 32811
E-mail: wigginsd@andersonnews.com.

Anderson-Austin News Co., LLC, 808 Newtown Cir., No. B, Lexington, KY 40511-1230 USA (SAN 169-2836) Tel 606-254-2765; Fax: 606-254-3328.

Andich Brothers News Company, *See* **Tobias News Co.**

Andrews McMeel Publishing, *(0-8362; 0-7407)* Orders Addr.: c/o Simon & Schuster, Inc., 100 Front St., Riverside, NJ 08075 USA Toll Free Fax: 1800-943-9831; Toll Free: 800-943-9839 (Customer Service); 800-897-7650 (Credit Dept.); Edit Addr.: 4520 Main St., Kansas City, MO 64111-7701 USA (SAN 202-540X) Tel 816-932-6600; Fax: 816.932.6684; Toll Free: 800-851-8923
Web site: http://www.AndrewsMcMeel.com.

Andrzejewski's Marian Church Supply, *See* **A & M Church Supplies**

Angel City Pr., *(1-883318)* 2118 Wilshire Blvd., PMB 880, Santa Monica, CA 90403-5784 USA (SAN 298-3370) Tel 310-395-9982; Fax: 310-395-3353; Toll Free: 800-949-8039 (orders)
Web site: http://www.angelcitypress.com.

Angler's Bk. Supply, 1380 W. Second Ave., Eugene, OR 97402 USA (SAN 631-4546) Tel 541-342-8355; Fax: 541-342-1785; Toll Free: 800-260-3869.

Ann Arbor Media Group, LLC, *(1-58726)* P.O. Box 1007, Ann Arbor, MI 48106-1007 USA Tel 734-769-1004 ext 1267; Fax: 734-913-1249
E-mail: tbudzinski@annarbormediagroup.com
Web site: http://www.annarbormediagroup.com; http://www.greatgolfbooks.com; http://www.sports-mediagroup.com; http://www.mittenpress.com.

answers period, inc., *(0-917875)* Orders Addr.: P.O. Box 427, Goliad, TX 77963 USA (SAN 112-6431) Tel 361-645-2268; Toll Free: 800-852-4752
Web site: http://www.answersbook.com.

Anthem Distribution, 2748 Second Private, Flossmoor, IL 60422 USA Tel 708-798-9512
E-mail: ksood@wpcpress.com.

Anthracite News Company, *See* **Great Northern Distributors, Inc.**

Anthroposophic Press, Incorporated, *See* **SteinerBooks, Inc.**

Antipodes Bks. & Beyond, 9707 Fairway Ave., Silver Spring, MD 20901-3001 USA Tel 301-602-9519; Fax: 301-565-0160
E-mail: Antipode@antipodesbooks.com
Web site: http://www.antipodesbooks.com.

Antiquarian Bookstore, The, 1070 Lafayette Rd., Portsmouth, NH 03801 USA (SAN 158-9938) Tel 603-436-7250.

Antique Collectors' Club, *(0-902028; 0-907462; 1-85149)* Orders Addr.: Eastworks, 116 Pleasant St., Easthampton, MA 01027 USA (SAN 630-7787) Tel 413-529-0861; Fax: 413-529-0862; Toll Free: 800-252-5231 (orders)
E-mail: info@antiquecc.com; sales@antiquecc.com
Web site: http://www.antiquecollectorsclub.com.

Any Baby Can of Austin, *(0-9660995)* 1121 E. 7th St., Austin, TX 78702-3220 USA Toll Free: 800-672-0238
E-mail: info@abcaus.org
Web site: http://www.abcaus.org.

AOAC International, *(0-935584)* 481 N. Frederick Ave., Suite 500, Gaithersburg, MD 20877-2417 USA (SAN 260-3411) Tel 301-924-7077; Fax: 301-924-7089; Toll Free: 800-379-2622
E-mail: aoac@aoac.org
Web site: http://www.aoac.org.

A-One Bk. Distributors, Inc., 1555 Ocean Ave. Ste. D, Bohemia, NY 11716-1933 USA (SAN 630-7981).

Aperture Foundation, Inc., *(0-89381; 0-912334; 0-900406; 1-931788; 1-59711)* Orders Addr.: c/o Holtzbrinck Publishers, 16365 James Madison Hwy., Gordonsville, VA 22942 USA Tel 540-672-7600; Fax: 540-672-7540; Edit Addr.: 547 West 27th St., 4th Flr., New York, NY 10001 USA (SAN 201-1832) Tel 212-505-5555; Fax: 212-598-4015
E-mail: editorial@aperture.org; customerservice@aperture.org
Web site: http://www.aperture.org.

APG Direct, 3801 Carolina Ave., Richmond, VA 23222-2202 USA.

APG Sales and Fulfillment, Div. of Warehousing and Fulfillment Specialists, LLC (WFS, LLC), 7344 Cockrill Bend Blvd., Nashville, TN 37209-1043 USA (SAN 630-818X) Toll Free: 800-327-5113
E-mail: sswift@agpbooks.com
Web site: http://www.apgbooks.com.

Apollo Bks., *(0-938290)* 91 Market St., Wappingers Falls, NY 12590-2333 USA (SAN 170-0928).

Apollo Library Bk. Supplier, 865 Kent Ln., Philadelphia, PA 19115 USA (SAN 159-8031).

Appalachian Bible Co., *(1-889049)* Orders Addr.: 522 Princeton Rd., Johnson City, TN 37605 USA (SAN 169-7889) Tel 423-282-9475; Fax: 423-282-9110; Toll Free: 800-289-2772; Edit Addr.: P.O. Box 1573, Johnson City, TN 37601 USA
E-mail: appainc@aol.com.

Appalachian Bk. Distributors, Orders Addr.: 522 Princeton Rd., Johnson City, TN 37601 USA (SAN 630-7388) Tel 423-282-9475; Fax: 423-282-9110; Toll Free: 800-759-2779; Edit Addr.: 506 Princeton Rd., Johnson City, TN 37601 USA.

Appalachian, Incorporated, *See* **Appalachian Bible Co.**

Applause Learning Resources, *(0-9655052; 0-9786746; 0-9788527; 0-9790091)* 85 Fernwood Ln., Roslyn, NY 11576 USA Tel 516-625-1145; Fax: 516-625-7392; Toll Free Fax: 877-365-7484; Toll Free: 800-277-5287
E-mail: info@applauselearning.com
Web site: http://www.applauselearning.com.

Applause Productions, *See* **Applause Learning Resources**

Apple Bk. Co., Div. of Scholastic Bk. Fairs, Inc., P.O. Box 217156, Charlotte, NC 28221-0156 USA Tel 704-596-6641; Fax: 704-599-1738; Toll Free: 800-331-1993; 5901 N. Northwoods Business Pkwy., Charlotte, NC 28269 (SAN 108-4569).

Applewood Bks., *(0-918222; 1-55709; 1-4290)* 1 River Rd., Carlisle, MA 01741-1820 USA (SAN 210-3419) Toll Free: 800-277-5312
E-mail: applewood@awb.com
Web site: http://www.awb.com.

Arabic & Islamic Univ. Pr., 4263 Fountain Ave., Los Angeles, CA 90029 USA (SAN 107-6299) Tel 323-665-1000; Fax: 323-665-3107.

Aramark, 18825 67th Ave., NE, Arlington, WA 98223-9656 USA (SAN 631-3507) Tel 360-435-2524; Fax: 360-435-6805 Do not confuse with Aramark, Albuquerque, NM.

Aramark Magazine & Bk. Co., P.O. Box 25489, Oklahoma City, OK 73125 USA (SAN 169-6971) Tel 405-843-9383; Fax: 405-843-0379 Do not confuse with Aramark Magazine & Bk. Services, Inc., Norfolk, VA.

Aramark Magazine & Bk. Services, Inc., Box 2240, Norfolk, VA 23501 USA (SAN 169-8680) Do not confuse with Aramark Magazine & Book Co., Oklahoma City, OK.

Arbit Bks., Inc., *(0-930038)* 8050 N. Port Washington Rd., Milwaukee, WI 53217 USA (SAN 169-913X) Tel 414-352-4404.

Arcadia Publishing, *(0-7385; 1-58973)* Orders Addr.: 420 Wando Park Blvd., Mount Pleasant, SC 29464 USA (SAN 255-268X) Tel 843-853-2070; Fax: 843-853-0044; Toll Free: 888-313-2665
E-mail: sales@arcadiapublishing.com
Web site: http://www.arcadiapublishing.com.

Ardic Bk. Distributors, Inc., 331 High St., 2nd Flr., Burlington, NJ 08016-4411 USA (SAN 170-5415).

Argus International Corp., Subs. of ICS International Group, Skypark Business Pk., P.O. Box 4082, Irvine, CA 92716-4082 USA (SAN 681-9761) Tel 714-552-8494 (phone/fax).

Aries Pr., *(0-933646)* P.O. Box 30081, Chicago, IL 60630 USA (SAN 111-9168) Tel 312-725-8300.

Aries Productions, Inc., *(0-910035)* Orders Addr.: P.O. Box 29396, Sappington, MO 63126 USA (SAN 669-0009); Edit Addr.: 6935 Tholozan Ave., Saint Louis, MO 63109-1130 USA (SAN 241-2004)
E-mail: uspsisquad@aol.com
Web site: http://ww.ussisquad.com.

Arizona Periodicals, Inc., P.O. Box 5780, Yuma, AZ 85366-5780 USA Tel 520-782-1822.

Arkansas Bk. Co., 1207 E. Second St., Little Rock, AR 72202-2732 USA (SAN 168-9460) Tel 501-375-1184.

Arlington Card Co., Bk. Dept., 140 Gansett Ave., Cranston, RI 02910 USA (SAN 108-5794) Tel 401-942-3188.

Armstrong, J. B. News Agency, *See* **News Group, The**

Arnica Publishing, Inc., *(0-9726535; 0-9745686; 0-9794771)* 3739 SE Eighth Ave., Suite 1, Portland, OR 97202 USA (SAN 255-0091) Tel 503-225-9900; Fax: 503-225-9901
E-mail: gloria@arnicacreative.com
Web site: http://www.arnicacreative.com.

Arrow, G. H. Co., P.O. Box 676, Bala Cynwyd, PA 19004 USA (SAN 111-3771) Tel 215-227-3211; Fax: 215-221-0631; Toll Free: 800-775-2776.

Arrowhead Magazine Co., Inc., P.O. Box 5947, San Bernardino, CA 92412 USA (SAN 169-0094) Tel 909-799-8294; Fax: 909-799-3774; 1055 Cooley Ave., San Bernardino, CA 92408 (SAN 249-2717) Tel 909-370-4420.

Ars Obscura, *(0-9623780)* P.O. Box 4424, Seattle, WA 98104-0424 USA (SAN 113-5368) Tel 206-324-9792.

Art Institute of Chicago, *(0-86559)* Orders Addr.: a/o Museum Shop Mail Order Dept., 950 N. North Branch St., Chicago, IL 60622-4276 USA; Edit Addr.: 111 S. Michigan Ave., Chicago, IL 60603-6110 USA (SAN 204-479X) Tel 312-443-3540; Fax: 312-443-1334
Web site: http://www.artic.edu.

Art Media Resources, Inc., *(1-878529; 1-58886)* 1507 S. Michigan Ave., Chicago, IL 60605 USA (SAN 253-8199) Tel 312-663-5351; Fax: 312-663-5177
E-mail: info@artmediaresources.com
Web site: http://www.artmediaresources.com.

Artisan, *(1-57965; 1-885183)* Div. of Workman Publishing Co., Inc., 225 Varick St. Flr. 9, New York, NY 10014-4381 USA Toll Free: 800-967-5630 Do not confuse with Artisan, Wheaton, IL
E-mail: artisan@workman.com.

Artisan House, *See* **Artisan**

ARVEST, P.O. Box 200248, Denver, CO 80220 USA (SAN 159-8694) Tel 303-388-8486; Fax: 303-355-4213; Toll Free: 800-739-0761
E-mail: copy@concentric.net.

Ashgate Publishing Co., *(0-566; 0-85331; 0-906909)* Subs. of Ashgate Publishing, Ltd., Orders Addr.: P.O. Box 423, Brookfield, VT 05036-0423 USA Toll Free: 800-535-9544 (Orders - US & Canada); Edit Addr.: 101 Cherry St., Suite 420, Burlington, VT 05401-4405 USA (SAN 213-4446) Tel 802-865-7641; Fax: 802-865-7847
E-mail: info@ashgate.com; ash.orders@aidcvt.com; ash.cs@aidcvt.com
Web site: http://www.ashgate.com.

Asia Bk. Corp. of America, *(0-940500)* 45-77 157th St., Flushing, NY 11355 USA (SAN 214-493X) Tel 718-762-7204; Fax: 718-460-5030.

ASM International, *(0-87170)* 9639 Kinsman Rd., Materials Park, OH 44073 0002 USA (SAN 204-7586) Tel 440-338-5151; Fax: 440-338-4634; Toll Free: 800-336-5152 (ext. 5900) Do not confuse with ASM International, Inc., Fort Lauderdale, FL
E-mail: Cust-Srv@asminternational.org
Web site: http://www.asminternational.org/.

Aspen Bks., 5986 Memorial Dr., Stone Mountain, GA 30083 USA (SAN 630-8589) Do not confuse with Aspen Bks., Murray, UT.

Aspen West Publishing, *(0-9615390; 1-885348)* P.O. Box 522151, Salt Lake Cty, UT 84152-2151 USA (SAN 112-7993) Toll Free: 800-222-9133 (orders only)
E-mail: kent@aspenwest.com
Web site: http://www.aspenwest.com.

Assn. of Energy Engineers, Orders Addr.: P.O. Box 1026, Liburn, GA 30048 USA Tel 770-925-9558; Fax: 770-381-9865; Edit Addr.: 4025 Pleasantdale Rd., Suite 420, Atlanta, GA 30340 USA Tel 770-447-5083.

Associated Publishers Group, *See* **APG Sales and Fulfillment**

Associated Univ. Presses, *(0-8453)* 2010 Eastpark Blvd., Cranbury, NJ 08512 USA (SAN 281-2959) Tel 609-655-4770; Fax: 609-655-8366
E-mail: aup440@aol.com
Web site: http://arts.fdu.edu/aup/; http://www.aupresses.com.

Association of Official Analytical Chemists, *See* **AOAC International**

Astran, Inc., 6995 NW 82nd Ave. Ste. 40, Miami, FL 33166-2783 USA (SAN 169-1082) Toll Free: 800-431-4957
E-mail: sales@astranbooks.com
Web site: http://www.astranbooks.com.

ATEXINC, Corp., *(0-9702332; 1-60405)* 17738 Vintage Oak Dr., Glencoe, MO 63038-1478 USA (SAN 631-774X) Do not confuse with Atex, Inc., Bedford, MA
E-mail: mail@atexinc.com
Web site: http://www.atexinc.com.

Athelstan Pubns., *(0-940753)* Orders Addr.: 2476 Bolsover St., No. 464, Houston, TX 77005-2518 USA (SAN 663-5318) Tel 713-371-2107; Fax: 713-524-1159
E-mail: info@athel.com; barlow@athel.com
Web site: http://www.athel.com.

Athena Productions, Inc., 5500 Collins Ave., No. 901, Miami Beach, FL 33140 USA Tel 305-868-8482; Fax: 305-868-8891.

Atlas News Co., Div. of Hudson News Co., P.O. Box 779, Boylston, MA 01505-0779 USA (SAN 169-3360).

Atlas Publishing Co., *(0-930575)* 1464 36th St., Ogden, UT 84403 USA (SAN 110-3873) Tel 801-627-1043.

AtlasBooks, *See* **AtlasBooks Distribution**

AtlasBooks Distribution, Div. of BookMasters, Inc., Orders Addr.: 30 Amberwood Pkwy., Ashland, OH 44805 USA (SAN 631-936X) Tel 800-537-6727; Fax: 419-281-6883; Toll Free: 800-247-6553; 800-266-5564
E-mail: orders@atlasbooks.com
Web site: http://www.atlasbooksdistribution.com; http://www.bookmasters.com.

Attainment Co., Inc., *(0-934731; 1-57861)* Orders Addr.: P.O. Box 930160, Verona, WI 53593 USA (SAN 694-1656) Tel 608-845-7880; Fax: 608-845-8040; Toll Free: 800-327-4269; Edit Addr.: 504 Commerce Pkwy., Verona, WI 53953 USA (SAN 631-6174)
E-mail: info@attainmentcompany.com; sue@attainmentcompany.com
Web site: http://www.attainmentcompany.com/.

Audio Bk. Co., *(0-89926)* 125 N. Aspen Ave., Suite 2, Azusa, CA 91702 USA (SAN 158-1414) Fax: 626-969-6099; Toll Free: 800-423-8273
E-mail: sales@audiobookco.com
Web site: http://www.audiobookco.com.

Audio-Forum, *See* **Norton, Jeffrey Pubs., Inc.**

Audubon Prints & Bks., 9720 Spring Ridge Ln., Vienna, VA 22182 USA (SAN 111-820X).

Augsburg Fortress Publishers, Publishing House of The Evangelical Lutheran Church in America, *See* **Augsburg Fortress, Pubs.**

Augsburg Fortress, Pubs., *(0-8006; 0-8066)* Orders Addr.: P.O. Box 1209, Minneapolis, MN 55440-1209 USA (SAN 169-4081) Toll Free Fax: 800-722-7766; Toll Free: 800-328-4648 (orders only); Edit Addr.: 100 S. 5th St. Ste. 600, Minneapolis, MN 55402-1242 USA
E-mail: customerservice@augsburgfortress.org; info@augsburgfortress.org; subscriptions@augsburgfortress.org; copyright@augsburgfortress.org; international@augsburgfortress.org
Web site: http://www.augsburgfortress.org.

Augusta News Co., 25 Second St., Apt. 124, Hallowell, ME 04347-1481 USA (SAN 169-3026).

Auromere, Inc., *(0-89744)* 2621 W. US Hwy. 12, Lodi, CA 95242-9200 USA (SAN 169-0043) Fax: 209-339-3715; Toll Free: 800-735-4691
E-mail: sasp@lodinet.com
Web site: http://www.auromere.com.

Austin & Company, Inc., *(0-9657153)* 104 S. Union St., Suite 202, Traverse City, MI 49684 USA (SAN 631-1466) Tel 231-933-4649; Fax: 231-933-4659
E-mail: aandn@aol.com
Web site: http://www.austinandcompanyinc.com.

Austin & Nelson Publishing, *See* **Austin & Company, Inc.**

Austin Management Group, Orders Addr.: P.O. Box 3206, Paducah, KY 42002-3206 USA (SAN 135-3349); Edit Addr.: P.O. Box 300, Paducah, KY 42002-0300 USA (SAN 249-6844).

Authentic Media, *(0-85364; 0-9630908; 1-884543; 0-903843; 0-948902; 1-85078; 1-86024; 1-932805; 1-934068)* Div. of Send the Light, Inc., Orders Addr.: P.O. Box 1047, Waynesboro, GA 30830 USA; Edit Addr.: 129 Mobilization Dr., Waynesboro, GA 30830-2047 USA Tel 706-554-5827; Fax: 706-554-7444; Toll Free: 866-732-6657; 9 Holdom Ave. Bletchley, Milton Keynes, MK1 1QR Tel 01908 364200; Fax: 01908 648592
E-mail: angela@omlit.om.org; info@authenticmedia.co.uk
Web site: http://www.authenticbooks.com.

Authors & Editors, *(0-9627878; 1-891077; 1-934637)* Orders Addr.: 10736 Jefferson Blvd., No. 604, Culver City, CA 90231-4969 USA Tel 310-251-3931 Arthur Rubin; 310-836-2014 General/Messages; Fax: 310-836-1845
E-mail: info@2learn-english.com
Web site: http://www.2learnenglish.com.

Auto-Bound, Inc., 909 Marina Village Pkwy., No. 67B, Alameda, CA 94501-1048 USA (SAN 170-0782) Tel 510-521-8655; Fax: 510-521-8755; Toll Free: 800-523-5833.

AV Cafe, Incorporated, The, Orders Addr.: 6201 S. 58th St. Ste. A, Lincoln, NE 68516-3678 USA Toll Free Fax: 866-428-2233; Toll Free: 877-228-2233
Web site: http://www.theavcafe.com.

Avanti Enterprises, Inc., P.O. Box 3563, Hinsdale, IL 60522-3563 USA (SAN 158-3727) Toll Free: 800-799-6464.

Ave Maria Pr., *(0-87061; 0-87793; 0-88347; 0-939516; 1-893732; 1-932057; 1-59471; 1-933495)* P.O. Box 428, Notre Dame, IN 46556-0428 USA (SAN 201-1255) Tel 574-287-2831; Fax: 574-239-2904; Toll Free Fax: 800-282-5681; Toll Free: 800-282-1865
E-mail: avemariapress.1@nd.edu
Web site: http://www.forestofpeace.com; http://www.avemariapress.com; http://www.sorinbooks.com.

Avenue Bks., 2270 Porter Way, Stockton, CA 95207-3339 USA (SAN 122-4158).

Avery BookStores, Inc., 516 Asharoken Ave., Northport, NY 11768-1176 USA (SAN 169-510X).

Aviation Bk. Co., *(0-911720; 0-911721; 0-916413)* 7201 Perimeter Rd., S., No. C, Seattle, WA 98108-3812 USA (SAN 120-1530) Tel 206-767-5232; Fax: 206-763-3428; Toll Free: 800-423-2708
E-mail: sales@aviationbook.com.

Avonlea Bks., Inc., Orders Addr.: P.O. Box 74, White Plains, NY 10602-0074 USA (SAN 680-4446) Tel 914-946-5923; Fax: 914-761-3119; Toll Free: 800-423-0622
E-mail: avonlea@bushkin.com
Web site: http://www.bushkin.com.

B & N Companies, *See* **B & N Software**

B & N Software, One Concorse Pkwy., Suite 770, Atlanta, GA 30328 USA (SAN 631-0575) Tel 770-698-0030; Fax: 770-698-0013
Web site: http://www.bnsoftware.com.

B. P. I. Communications, *See* **VNU**

B T P Distribution, 4135 Northgate Blvd., Suite 5, Sacramento, CA 95834-1226 USA (SAN 631-2489) Tel 916-567-2496; Fax: 916-441-6749.

Badger Bks., LLC, *(1-878569; 1-932542)* Orders Addr.: 1600 N. High Point Rd., Middleton, WI 53562 USA (SAN 297-9055) Tel 608-231-2556 (phone/fax); Toll Free: 800-928-2372
E-mail: books@badgerbooks.com
Web site: http://www.badgerbooks.com.

Baggins Bks., 3560 Meridian St., Bellingham, WA 98225-1731 USA (SAN 156-501X).

Baha'i Distribution Service, *(0-87743)* Orders Addr.: 4703 Fulton Industrial Blvd., SW, Atlanta, GA 30336-2017 USA (SAN 213-7496) Toll Free: 800-999-9019; Edit Addr.: 415 Linden Ave., Wilmette, IL 60091 USA Tel 847-251-1854; Fax: 847-251-3652
E-mail: bds@usbnc.org.

Baker & Taylor, P.O. Box PO Box 6885, Bridgewater, NJ 08807-0885 USA; 1120 Rte. 22 E., Bridgewater, NJ 08807 Tel 908-541-7320
E-mail: fanicae@btol.com; btinfo@btol.com; nehers@btol.com
Web site: http://www.btol.com.

Baker & Taylor Bks., *(0-8480)* Orders Addr.: Commerce Service Ctr., 251 Mt. Olive Church Rd., Commerce, GA 30599-1100 USA (SAN 169-1503) Tel 404-335-5000; Toll Free: 800-775-1200 (customer service); 800-775-1800 (orders); Reno Service Ctr., 1160 Trademark Dr., Suite 111, Reno, NV 89511 (SAN 169-4464) Tel 775-850-3800; Fax: 775-850-3826 (customer service); Toll Free Fax: 800-775-1700 (orders); Edit Addr.: Bridgewater Service Ctr. 1120 US Hwy. 22, E., Bridgewater, NJ 08807-0885 USA (SAN 169-4901) Toll Free: 800-775-1500 (customer service); Momence Service Ctr., 501W. Gladiolus St., Momence, IL 60954-1799 (SAN 169-2100) Tel 815-472-2444 (international customers); Fax: 815-472-9886 (international customers); Toll Free: 800-775-2300 (customer service, academic libraries)
E-mail: btinfo@btol.com
Web site: http://www.btol.com.

Baker & Taylor Entertainment, Corporate Headquarters: 8140 N. Lehigh Ave., Morton Grove, IL 60053 USA (SAN 631-1156) Tel 847-965-8060; Fax: 847-965-8093; Toll Free: 800-775-2600; 1111 N. Plaza Dr. Ste. 680, Schaumburg, IL 60173-4982 (SAN 630-4311) Toll Free: 800-775-2800; 1825 Monetary Ln., Suite 112, Carrollton, TX 75006 Tel 972-242-3098; Fax: 972-242-8375; Toll Free: 800-775-3300; 2501 SW 31st Ave., Pembroke Park, FL 33009 Tel 954-983-9055; Fax: 954-983-9350; Toll Free: 800-775-3400; 800-775-4300; 2150 Boggs Rd., Suite 640, Duluth, GA 30096 Tel 770-813-3253; Fax: 770-813-9460; Toll Free: 800-775-2600 (Orders only); 960 Turnpike St., Canton, MA 02021 Tel 781-821-2730; Fax: 781-821-1983; Toll Free: 800-775-2600; 3150 N. 24th St., Suite A210, Phoenix, AZ 85016 Tel 602-954-8558; Fax: 602-954-8870; Toll Free: 800-775-3300; 2550 W. Tyvola Rd. Ste. 300, Charlotte, NC 28217-4543 Toll Free: 800-775-2600; 8936 Comanche Ave., Chatsworth, CA 91311 Tel 818-886-0200; Fax: 818-886-0646; Toll Free: 800-775-4200; 3025 S. Parker Rd. Ste. 213, Aurora, CO 80014-2916 Toll Free: 800-775-3300; Campbells Run Busn. Ctr., 100 Business Center Dr., Pittsburgh, PA 15205 Tel 412-787-8890; Fax: 412-787-0368; Toll Free: 800-775-2600; 5769 NE Columbia Blvd., Portland, OR 97218 Tel 503-249-8397; Fax: 503-282-5904; Toll Free: 800-775-3300; 1120 US Hwy. 22 E., Bridgewater, NJ 08807 Tel 908-541-7401; Fax: 908-541-7857; Toll Free: 800-775-2600
E-mail: info@btent.com
Web site: http://www.btent.com.

Baker & Taylor International, 1120 US Hwy. 22 E., Box 6885, Bridgewater, NJ 08807 USA (SAN 200-6804) Tel 908-541-7000; Fax: 908-729-4037.

Baker & Taylor Video, *See* **Baker & Taylor Entertainment**

Baker Bks., *(0-8010; 0-913686)* Div. of Baker Bk. Hse., Orders Addr.: P.O. Box 6287, Grand Rapids, MI 49516-6287 USA (SAN 299-1500) Toll Free Fax: 800-398-3111 (orders only); Toll Free: 800-877-2665 (orders only); Edit Addr.: 6030 E. Fulton, Ada, MI 49301 USA (SAN 201-4041) Tel 616-676-9185; Fax: 616-676-9573
Web site: http://www.bakerbooks.com.

Baker Book House, Incorporated, *See* **Baker Publishing Group**

Baker Publishing Group, *(0-8007; 0-8010; 1-58743)* Orders Addr.: P.O. Box 6287, Grand Rapids, MI 49516-6287 USA Tel 616-676-9573; Toll Free Fax: 800-398-3111 (orders only); Toll Free: 800-877-2665 (orders only); Edit Addr.: 6030 E. Fulton, Ada, MI 49301 USA Tel 616-676-9185; Fax: 616-676-9573
Web site: http://www.bakerbooks.com.

Balogh International, Inc., *(1-878762; 1-891770)* 1911 N. Duncan Rd., Champaign, IL 61822 USA (SAN 297-2344) Tel 217-355-9331; Fax: 217-355-9413
E-mail: balogh@balogh.com
Web site: http://www.balogh.com.

Balogh Scientific Books, *See* **Balogh International, Inc.**

Balzekas Museum of Lithuanian Culture, 6500 S. Pulaski Rd., Chicago, IL 60629 USA (SAN 110-8522) Tel 773-582-6500; Fax: 773-582-5133.

Banner of Truth, The, *(0-85151)* Orders Addr.: P.O. Box 621, Carlisle, PA 17013 USA Tel 717-249-5747; Fax: 717-249-0604; Toll Free: 800-263-8085; Edit Addr.: 63 E. Louther St., Carlisle, PA 17013 USA (SAN 112-1553)
E-mail: info@banneroftruth.org
Web site: http://www.banneroftruth.co.uk.

Banta Packaging & Fulfillment, 1071 Willow Spring Rd., Harrisonburg, VA 22801 USA (SAN 631-7731) Tel 540-442-1333; Fax: 540-434-3541; N9234 Lake Park Rd., Appleton, WI 54915 (SAN 631-8290) Tel 920-969-6400; Fax: 920-751-7794
E-mail: jfair@banta.com.

Banyan Tree Bks., *(0-9604320)* 1963 El Dorado Ave., Berkeley, CA 94707 USA (SAN 207-3862) Fax: 510-524-2690
E-mail: banyan@uclink.berkeley.edu.

Barbour & Company, Incorporated, *See* **Barbour Publishing, Inc.**

Barbour Publishing, Inc., *(0-916441; 1-55748; 1-57748; 1-58660; 1-59310; 1-59789; 1-60260)* Orders Addr.: P.O. Box 719, Uhrichsville, OH 44683 USA (SAN 295-7094) Tel 740-922-6045; Fax: 740-922-5948; Toll Free Fax: 800-220-5948; Toll Free: 800-852-8010
E-mail: info@barbourbooks.com
Web site: http://www.barbourbooks.com.

Barnes & Noble Bks.-Imports, *(0-389)* Div. of Rowman & Littlefield Pubs., Inc., 4720 Boston Way, Lanham, MD 20706 USA (SAN 206-7803) Tel 301-459-3366; Toll Free: 800-462-6420.

Barnes & Noble, Inc., *(0-7607; 0-88029; 1-4028; 1-4351)* 122 Fifth Ave., New York, NY 10011 USA (SAN 141-3651) Tel 212-633-3300
E-mail: smcculloch@bn.com.

Barnes&Noble.com, *(1-4005; 1-4006)* c/o Merch Accounts Payable/NR Dept., 76 Ninth Ave., 9th Flr., New York, NY 10011 USA (SAN 192-6551) Tel 212-414-6000
Web site: http://www.bn.com.

Basic Crafts Co., 6001 66th Ave., No. 10, Riverdale, MD 20737-1717 USA (SAN 169-5622) Toll Free: 800-847-4127 (outside New York).

Basin News Co., P.O. Box 300, Paducah, KY 42002-0300 USA (SAN 169-2860).

Bassett Printing Corp., *(0-9632415)* Orders Addr.: P.O. Box 866, Bassett, VA 24055 USA Fax: 540-629-3416; Toll Free: 800-336-5102 (outside Virginia); Edit Addr.: 101 Main St., Bassett, VA 24055 USA Tel 540-629-2541.

Bay News, Inc., 3333 NW 35th Ave., Portland, OR 97210 USA Tel 503-219-3001; Fax: 503-241-1877.

Bayou Bks., 1005 Monroe St., Gretna, LA 70053 USA (SAN 120-1913) Tel 504-368-1171; Toll Free: 800-843-1724.

Bayside Distribution, *See* **Bayside Entertainment Distribution**

Bayside Entertainment Distribution, *(0-7691)* 2500 Del Monte St., W Sacramento, CA 95691-3820 USA (SAN 631-1261) Toll Free: 800-525-5709
E-mail: stecon@baysidedist.com.

BBC Audiobooks America, *(0-563; 0-7540; 0-7927; 0-89340; 1-55504; 1-60283)* Orders Addr.: P.O. Box 414190, Boston, MA 02241-4190 USA (SAN 208-4864) Tel 603-926-8744; Fax: 603-929-3890; Toll Free Fax: 877-492-0873; Toll Free: 800-621-0182; c/o Perseus, 1094 Flex Dr., Jackson, TN 38301; Edit Addr.: 42 Whitecap Dr., North Kingstown, RI 02852-7445 USA Toll Free: 800-621-0182
E-mail: vikkiwarner@bbcaudiobooksamerica.com
Web site: http://www.bbcaudiobooksamerica.com.

BCH Fulfillment & Distribution, 46 Purdy St., Harrison, NY 10528 USA
E-mail: info@bookch.com
Web site: http://www.bookch.com/.

BCM Pubns., Inc., *(0-86508)* 309 Colonial Dr., Akron, PA 17501 USA (SAN 211-7762) Tel 717-859-6404 (phone/fax)
E-mail: info@bcmintl.org
Web site: http://www.bcmintl.org.

Beadsmith, The/Helby Import Co., *(0-9713690)* 37 Hayward Ave., Carteret, NJ 07008 USA (SAN 631-5771) Tel 732-969-5300; Fax: 732-969-5310
E-mail: helby@idt.net
Web site: http://www.helby.com.

Beagle Bay Bks., *(0-9679591; 0-9749610)* Div. of Beagle Bay, Inc., 14120 Saddlebow Dr., Reno, NV 89511 USA Tel 775-827-8654; Fax: 775-827-8633
E-mail: info@beaglebay.com
Web site: http://www.beaglebay.com.

Beaver News Co., Inc., 230 W. Washington St., Rensselaer, IN 47978 USA (SAN 630-8864).

Beck's Bk. Store, 4520 N. Broadway, Chicago, IL 60640 USA (SAN 159-8139) Tel 773-784-7963; Fax: 773-784-0066
E-mail: rsvltrd@aol.com
Web site: http://www.aol.members/becks.html.

Beechwood Pubns., Inc., P.O. Box 1158, Kennett Square, PA 19348 USA (SAN 107-5853) Tel 610-444-5991; Fax: 215-566-4178.

Beekman Bks., Inc., *(0-8464)* 300 Old All Angels Hill Rd., Wappingers Falls, NY 12590 USA (SAN 170-1622) Tel 845-297-2690; Fax: 845-297-1002
E-mail: manager@beekmanbooks.com
Web site: http://www.beekmanbooks.com.

Beeler, Thomas T. Pub., *(1-57490)* Orders Addr.: P.O. Box 310, Rollinsford, NH 03869 USA Toll Free Fax: 888-222-3396; Toll Free: 800-818-7574; Edit Addr.: 710 Main St., Suite 300, Rollinsford, NH 03869 USA Tel 603-749-0392; Fax: 603-749-0395
E-mail: tombeeler@beelerpub.com
Web site: http://www.beelerpub.com.

Before Columbus Foundation, 655 13th St. Ste. 302, Oakland, CA 94612-1225 USA (SAN 159-2955).

Beijing Bk. Co., Inc., 701 E. Linden Ave., Linden, NJ 07036-2495 USA (SAN 169-5673) Tel 908-862-0909; Fax: 908-862-4201.

Bell Magazine, Orders Addr.: P.O. Box 1957, Monterey, CA 93940 USA (SAN 159-7221); Edit Addr.: 3 Justin Ct., Monterey, CA 93940 USA (SAN 169-0353) Tel 408-642-4668.

Bella Distribution, Orders Addr.: P.O. Box 10543, Tallahassee, FL 32302 USA; Edit Addr.: 1041 Aenon Church Rd., Tallahassee, FL 32304 USA Fax: 850-576-3498; Toll Free: 800-533-1973
E-mail: info@belladistribution.com
Web site: http://www.belladistribution.com.

Bennett & Curran, Inc., *(1-879607)* 1545 W. Tufts Ave., Suite M, Englewood, CO 80110-5575 USA Tel 303-783-2255; Fax: 303-783-2256
E-mail: Jeff@bennettandcurran.com.

Berkeley Educational Paperbacks, 2480 Bancroft Way, Berkeley, CA 94704 USA (SAN 168-9509) Tel 510-848-7907.

Berkeley Game Distributors, 5850 Hollis St., Emeryville, CA 94608-2016 USA (SAN 631-2934) Toll Free: 800-424-4263; 1164 E. Sandhill Ave., Carson, CA 90746
E-mail: bgdnorth@ix.netcom.com.

Bernan Assocs., *(0-400; 0-527; 0-89059; 1-59610; 1-59888; 1-60175)* Div. of Kraus Organization, The, Orders Addr.: 4611-F Assembly Dr., Lanham, MD 20706 USA (SAN 169-3182) Tel 301-459-2255; Fax: 301-459-9235; Toll Free: 800-274-4447
E-mail: query@bernan.com; order@bernan.com; info@bernan.com
Web site: http://www.bernan.com.

Berrett-Koehler Pubs., Inc., *(1-57675; 1-58376; 1-881052; 1-60509)* Orders Addr.: P.O. Box 565, Williston, VT 05495 USA Fax: 802-864-7626 (orders); Toll Free: 800-929-2929 (orders); Edit Addr.: 235 Montgomery St., Suite 650, San Francisco, CA 94104 USA Tel 415-288-0260; Fax: 415-362-2512
E-mail: bkpub@bkpubl.com; bkp.orders@AIDCVT.com
Web site: http://www.bkconnection.com.

Bess Pr., Inc., *(0-935848; 1-57306; 1-880188)* Orders Addr.: 3565 Harding Ave., Honolulu, HI 96816 USA (SAN 239-4111) Tel 808-734-7159; Fax: 808-732-3627; Toll Free: 800-910-2377
E-mail: kelly@besspress.com
Web site: http://www.besspress.com.

Best Bk. Ctr., Inc., 1016 Ave. Ponce De Leon, San Juan, PR 00926 USA (SAN 132-4403) Tel 809-727-7945; Fax: 809-268-5022.

Best Continental Bk. Co., Inc., P.O. Box 615, Merrifield, VA 22116 USA (SAN 107-3737) Tel 703-280-1400.

Best-Seller Bks., *(1-881474)* 1718 Rogers Pl., Suite 1A, Burbank, CA 91504 USA (SAN 298-0533) Tel 818-842-4278; Fax: 818-842-2960
E-mail: casag@wgn.net.

Bestsellers, The, P.O. Box 650654, Fresh Meadows, NY 11365 USA Tel 718-359-4446; Fax: 718-359-4861
E-mail: akhan72252@aol.com.

Bethany Hse. Pubs., *(0-7642; 0-87123; 1-55661; 1-56179; 1-57778; 1-880089; 1-59066)* Div. of Baker Book House, Inc., Orders Addr.: P.O. Box 6287, Grand Rapids, MI 49516-6287 USA Toll Free Fax: 800-398-3111 (orders); Toll Free: 800-877-2665 (orders); Edit Addr.: 11400 Hampshire Ave., S., Bloomington, MN 55438-2455 USA (SAN 201-4416) Tel 952-829-2500; Fax: 952-996-1393
E-mail: orders@bakerbooks.com
Web site: http://www.bethanyhouse.com.

Betty Segal, Inc., 1749 Eucalyptus St., Brea, CA 92621 USA Tel 714-529-5359; Fax: 714-529-3882
E-mail: BettySegal@aol.com
Web site: http://www.agoralang.com/trp-bettysegal.html.

Beyda & Associates, Incorporated, *See* **Beyda for Bks., LLC**

Beyda for Bks., LLC, 4604 Arrow Hwy., Montclair, CA 91763-1206 USA (SAN 169-0426) Toll Free: 800-422-3932 (orders only)
E-mail: info@beydaforbooks.com
Web site: http://www.beydaforbooks.com.

B&H Publishing Grp., *(0-8054; 0-87981; 1-55819; 1-58640; 0-8400; 1-4336)* Div. of LifeWay Christian Resources of the Southern Baptist Convention, 127 Ninth Ave. North, MSN 114, Nashville, TN 37234 USA (SAN 201-937X) Tel 615-251-2520; Fax: 615-251-5026 (Books Only); 615-251-2036 (Bibles Only); 615-251-2413 (Gifts/Supplies Only); Toll Free: 800-725-5416; 800-251-3225 (retailers); 800-296-4036 (orders/returns); 800-448-8032 (consumers); 800-458-2772 (churches)
E-mail: broadmanholman@lifeway.com
Web site: http://www.bhpublishinggroup.com.

BHB Fullfillment, Div. of Weatherhill, Inc., 41 Monroe Tpke., Trumbull, CT 06611 USA.

BHB International, Incorporated, *See* **Continental Enterprises Group, Inc. (CEG)**

Biblio Distribution, Sister Company of National Book Network, Orders Addr.: 15200 NBN Way, Blue Ridge Summit, PA 17214 USA Toll Free Fax: 800-338-4550; Toll Free: 800-462-6420; Edit Addr.: 4501 Forbes Blvd., Suite 200, Lanham, MD 20706 USA (SAN 211-724X) Tel 301-459-3366; Fax: 301-429-5746
E-mail: custserv@nbnbooks.com
Web site: http://www.bibliodistribution.com.

Biblio Distribution Center, *See* **Biblio Distribution**

Bibliotech, Inc., P.O. Box 720459, Dallas, TX 75372-0459 USA (SAN 631-8312) Tel 214-221-0002; Fax: 214-221-1794
E-mail: metatron@airmail.net
Web site: http://www.bibliotechincorporated.com.

Biddy Bks., 1235 168 Model Rd., Manchester, TN 37355 USA (SAN 157-8561) Tel 931-728-6967.

Big Earth Publishing, *(0-915024; 1-879483; 1-931599)* Orders Addr.: 3005 Ctr. Green Dr., Suite 200, Boulder, CO 80301 USA (SAN 209-2425) Fax: 608-259-8370; Toll Free: 800-258-5830; Edit Addr.: 923 Williamson St., Madison, WI 53703 USA
E-mail: books@bigearthpublishing.com
Web site: http://www.bigearthpublishing.com.

Big Kids Productions, Inc., *(1-885627)* 2120 Oxford Ave., Austin, TX 78704-4014 USA (SAN 631-340X) Toll Free: 800-477-7811
E-mail: customerservice@bigkidsvideo.com
Web site: http://www.awardvids.com.

Big River Distribution, *(0-9795944)* Orders Addr.: 9870 Big Bend Blvd., Suite D, Saint Louis, MO 63122-6573 USA (SAN 631-9114) Tel 314-918-9800; Fax: 314-909-6807
E-mail: info@bigriverdist.com; randy@bigriverdist.com
Web site: http://www.bifriverdist.com.

Big Tent Bks., *(1-60131)* 115 Bluebill Dr., Savannah, GA 31419 USA (SAN 851-1136)
E-mail: admin@dragonpencil.com.

Bilingual Educational Services, Inc., *(0-86624; 0-89075)* 2514 S. Grand Ave., Los Angeles, CA 90007 USA (SAN 218-4680) Tel 213-749-6213; Fax: 213-749-1820; Toll Free: 800-448-6032
E-mail: sales@besbooks.com
Web site: http://www.besbooks.com.

Bilingual Pubns. Co., The, 270 Lafayette St., New York, NY 10012 USA (SAN 164-8993) Tel 212-431-3500; Fax: 212-431-3567 Do not confuse with Bilingual Pubns., in Denver, CO
E-mail: lindagoodman@juno.com; spanishbks@aol.com.

Bilingual Review Press * Hispanic Research Center, Arizona State University Box 875303, Tempe, AZ 85287-5303 USA Tel 480-965-3867; Fax: 480-965-8315; Toll Free: 800-965-2280
E-mail: brp@asu.edu
Web site: http://www.asu.edu/brp.

Birdlegs Christian Apparel, P.O. Box 189, Duluth, GA 30136-0189 USA (SAN 631-3280) Toll Free: 800-545-0790.

Black Box Corp., 1000 Park Dr., Lawrence, PA 15055 USA (SAN 277-1985) Tel 412-746-5500; Fax: 412-746-0746.

Black Magazine Agency, 4515 Fleur Dr. Ste. 301, Des Moines, IA 50321-2369 USA (SAN 107-0819) Toll Free: 800-782-9787.

Blackburn News Agency, P.O. Box 1039, Kingsport, TN 37662 USA (SAN 169-7900).

Blackwell Corp., P.O. Box 2169, Vienna, VA 22183-2169 USA (SAN 630-5601).

Blackwell North America, *(0-913262; 0-916472; 0-946344)* Orders Addr.: 6024 SW Jean Rd., Bldg. G, Lake Oswego, OR 97034 USA (SAN 169-7048) Tel 503-684-1140; Fax: 503-639-2481; Toll Free: 800-547-6426 (in Oregon); Edit Addr.: 100 University Ct., Blackwood, NJ 08012 USA (SAN 169-4596) Tel 856-228-8900; Toll Free: 800-257-7341
Web site: http://www.blackwell.com/.

Blackwell Publishers, *See* **Blackwell Publishing, Inc.**

Blackwell Publishing, Inc., *(0-631; 0-85012; 0-87993; 1-55786; 1-57718; 1-878975; 1-4051)* Orders Addr.: c/o AIDC, P.O. Box 20, Williston, VT 05495-0020 USA (SAN 680-5035) Tel 802-862-0095; Fax: 802-864-7626; Toll Free Fax: 800-864-7626; Toll Free: 800-216-2522; Edit Addr.: 350 Main St., 6th Flr., Malden, MA 02148-5018 USA (SAN 680-5035) Tel 781-388-8200; Fax: 781-388-8210
E-mail: books@blackwellpub.com; journalsrights@oxon.blackwellpublishing.com
Web site: http://www.blackwellpublishing.com.

Blackwell Publishing Professional, *(0-8138)* Div. of Blackwell Publishing Ltd., 2121 S. State Ave., Ames, IA 50014-8300 USA (SAN 202-7194) Tel 515-292-0140; Fax: 515-292-3348; Toll Free: 800-862-6657 (orders only)
E-mail: orders@isupress.com
Web site: http://www.blackwellpublishing.com/press/BPP.asp.

Blair, John F. Pub., *(0-89587; 0-910244)* Orders Addr.: 1406 Plaza Dr., Winston-Salem, NC 27103 USA (SAN 201-4319) Tel 336-768-1374; Fax: 336-768-9194; Toll Free: 800-222-9796
E-mail: blairpub@blairpub.com
Web site: http://www.blairpub.com.

Blessing Way Publishing Co., *(0-9627324)* 1131 Villa Dr., Suite 003, Atlanta, GA 30306-2593 USA (SAN 297-3251).

Bloomington News Agency, P.O. Box 3757, Bloomington, IL 61702-3757 USA (SAN 169-1732).

Blu Sky Media Group, 2815 Weybridge Dr., Murfreesboro, TN 37128 USA Tel 615-995-7072; Fax: 615-217-3088
Web site: http://www.bluskymediagroup.com.

Blue Cat, *(0-932679; 0-936200)* 469 Barbados, Walnut, CA 91789 USA (SAN 214-0322) Tel 909-594-3317.

Blue Mountain Arts Inc., *(0-88396; 1-58786; 1-59842)* Orders Addr.: P.O. Box 4549, Boulder, CO 80306 USA (SAN 299-9609) Tel 303-449-0536; Fax: 303-417-6434; Toll Free Fax: 800-943-6666; Toll Free: 800-525-0642
Web site: http://www.sps.com/.

Blue Mountain Arts (R) by SPS Studios, Incorporated, *See* **Blue Mountain Arts Inc.**

Blue Ridge News Co., 21 Westside Dr., No. B, Asheville, NC 28806-2846 USA (SAN 169-6335).

Bodhi Tree Bookstore, 8585 Melrose Ave., West Hollywood, CA 90069-5199 USA Tel 310-659-1733; Fax: 310-659-0178; Toll Free: 800-825-9798
E-mail: bodhitreee@bodhitree.com
Web site: http://www.bodhitree.com.

Bolchazy-Carducci Pubs., *(0-86516)* 1000 Brown St., Unit 101, Wauconda, IL 60084 USA (SAN 219-7685) Tel 847-526-4344; Fax: 847-526-2867; Toll Free: 800-392-6453
E-mail: jcull@bolchazy.com
Web site: http://www.bolchazy.com.

Boley International Subscription Agency, Inc., 1001 Fries Mill Rd., Blackwood, NJ 08012 USA (SAN 159-6225) Tel 609-629-2500.

Bolinda Publishing, Inc., *(1-86340; 1-86442; 0-947072; 1-876584; 1-74030; 1-74093; 1-74094)* Orders Addr.: 48 Oxford Woods Dr., Falmouth, ME 04105-3401 USA Toll Free Fax: 877-864-8307; Toll Free: 888-235-2019
E-mail: karen@bolinda.com
Web site: http://www.bolinda.com.

Bonneville News Co., 965 Beardsley Pl., Salt Lake City, UT 84119 USA Tel 801-972-5454; Fax: 801-972-1075; Toll Free: 800-748-5453.

Book Bin - Pacifica, The, *(0-9621818)* 215 SW 4th St., Corvallis, OR 97333-4624 USA
E-mail: seasia@bookbin.com.

Book Box, Inc., 3126 Purdue Ave., Los Angeles, CA 90066 USA (SAN 243-2285) Tel 310-391-2313.

Book Buy Back, 5150 Candlewood St., No. 6, Lakewood, CA 90712 USA (SAN 631-7251) Tel 562-461-9355; Fax: 562-461-9445.

Book Clearing Hse., 46 Purdy St., Harrison, NY 10528 USA (SAN 125-5169) Tel 914-835-0015; Fax: 914-835-0398; Toll Free: 800-431-1579
E-mail: bookch@aol.com.

Book Co., The, 145 S. Glencoe St., Denver, CO 80222-1152 USA (SAN 200-2809).

Book Distribution Ctr., *(0-941722)* Div. of Free Islamic Literatures, Inc., Orders Addr.: P.O. Box 35844, Houston, TX 77235 USA (SAN 241-6395); Edit Addr.: P.O. Box 31669, Houston, TX 77231 USA (SAN 226-2770).

Book Distribution Ctr., Inc., Orders Addr.: P.O. Box 64631, Virginia Beach, VA 23467 USA (SAN 134-8019) Tel 757-456-0005; Fax: 757-552-0837; Edit Addr.: 4617 N. Witchduck Rd., Virginia Beach, VA 23455 USA (SAN 169-8672)
E-mail: sales@bookdist.com
Web site: http://www.bookdist.com.

Book Dynamics, Inc., *(0-9612440)* 18 Kennedy Blvd., East Brunswick, NJ 08816 USA (SAN 169-5649) Tel 732-545-5151; Fax: 732-545-5959; Toll Free: 800-441-4510.

Book Express, *(0-9612322; 1-890308)* Orders Addr.: P.O. Box 1249, Bellflower, CA 90706 USA (SAN 289-1301) Tel 562-865-1226; Edit Addr.: 12122 E. 176th St., Artesia, CA 90701-4013 USA
E-mail: carbks4u@escapenet.net.

Book Fairs of Covina, 1030 Bonita Ave., La Verne, CA 91750 USA (SAN 630-6225) Tel 909-593-0697; 1650 W. Orange Grove Ave., Pomona, CA 91768-2153 (SAN 299-2434).

Book Gallery, *(1-878382)* 632 S. Quincy Ave., Apt. 1, Tulsa, OK 74120-4635 USA (SAN 630-9321).

Book Home, The, 119 E. Dale St., Colorado Springs, CO 80903-4701 USA (SAN 249-3055) Tel 719-634-5885.

Book Hse., Inc., The, 208 W. Chicago St., Jonesville, MI 49250-0125 USA (SAN 169-3859) Tel 517-849-2117; Fax: 517-849-9716; Toll Free Fax: 800-858-9716; Toll Free: 800-248-1146
E-mail: bhinfo@thebookhouse.com.

Book Hse., The, 9719 Manchester Rd., Saint Louis, MO 63119 USA Toll Free: 800-513-4491.

Book Margins, Inc., 7100 Valley Green Rd., Fort Washington, PA 19034-2206 USA (SAN 106-7788) Tel 215-223-5300
E-mail: paul.gross@bookmargins.com
Web site: http://www.bookmargins.com.

Book Marketing Plus, 406 Post Oak Rd., Fredericksburg, TX 78624 USA (SAN 630-6543) Tel 830-997-4776; Fax: 830-997-9752; Toll Free: 800-356-2445.

Book Mart, The, 1153 E. Hyde Pk., Inglewood, CA 90302 USA (SAN 168-969X).

Book Publishing Co., The, *(0-913990; 1-57067; 0-9669317; 0-9673108)* P.O. Box 99, Summertown, TN 38483 USA (SAN 202-439X) Tel 931-964-3571; Fax: 931-964-3518; Toll Free: 888-260-8458
E-mail: bookpub@bookpubco.com
Web site: http://www.bookpubco.com.

Book Sales, Inc., *(0-7858; 0-89009; 1-55521)* Orders Addr.: 114 Northfield Ave., Edison, NJ 08837 USA (SAN 169-488X) Tel 732-225-0530; Fax: 732-225-2257; 212-779-6058; Toll Free: 800-526-7257; Edit Addr.: 276 Fifth Ave., Suite 206, New York, NY 10001 USA (SAN 299-4062) Tel 212-779-4972; Fax: 212-779-6058
E-mail: booksales@eclipse.net
Web site: http://www.booksales.com.

Book Service of Puerto Rico, 102 De Diego, Santurce, PR 00907 USA (SAN 169-9326) Tel 809-728-5000; Fax: 809-726-6131
E-mail: bellbook@coqui.net
Web site: http://home.coqui.net/bellbook.

Book Service Unlimited, P.O. Box 31108, Seattle, WA 98103-1108 USA (SAN 169-877X) Toll Free: 800-347-0042.

Book Services International, Orders Addr.: P.O. Box 1434-SMS, Fairfield, CT 06430 USA (SAN 157-9541) Tel 203-374-4939; Fax: 203-384-6099; Toll Free: 800-243-2790.

Book Shelf, The, 222 Crestview Dr., Fort Dodge, IA 50501-5708 USA (SAN 169-2658).

Book Warehouse, 5154 NW 165th St., Hialeah, FL 33014-6335 USA.

Book Wholesalers, Inc., *(0-7587; 1-4046; 1-4131; 1-4155; 1-4156; 1-4287)* 1847 Mercer Rd., Lexington, KY 40511-1001 USA (SAN 135-5449) Toll Free: 800-888-4478
E-mail: jcarrico@bwibooks.com; lison@bwibooks.com
Web site: http://www.bwibooks.com.

Book World, 311 Sagamore Pkwy., N., Lafayette, IN 47904 USA (SAN 135-4051) Tel 765-448-1131 Do not confuse with companies with the same or similar name in Sun Lakes, AZ, Roanoke, VA
E-mail: fsjintl@pworld.net.ph.

Bookazine Co., Inc., 75 Hook Rd., Bayonne, NJ 07002 USA (SAN 169-5665) Tel 201-339-7777; Fax: 201-339-7778; Toll Free: 800-221-8112.

Bookhouse, The, 10505 N. May Ave., Oklahoma City, OK 73120-2611 USA (SAN 200-8467) Tel 405-755-0020.

Booklegger, The, *(0-936421)* Orders Addr.: P.O. Box 2626, Grass Valley, CA 95945 USA (SAN 697-9548); Edit Addr.: 13100 Grass Valley Ave., Suite D, Grass Valley, CA 95945 USA (SAN 120-6125) Tel 530-272-1556; Fax: 530-272-2133; Toll Free Fax: 800-250-2199; Toll Free: 800-262-1556
E-mail: order@booklegger.com
Web site: http://www.booklegger.com/.

Bookline, Div. of Michiana News Service, Inc., 2232 S. 11th St., Niles, MI 49120 USA (SAN 169-3948) Tel 616-684-3013; Fax: 616-684-8740.

Booklines Hawaii, Ltd., *(1-929844; 1-58849; 1-60274)* Div. of Islander Group, 269 Pali'i St., Mililani, HI 96789 USA (SAN 630-6624) Tel 808-676-0116; Fax: 808-676-0634
E-mail: customerservice@booklines.com
Web site: http://www.booklineshawaii.com.

BookLink, *(0-9797436)* 465 Broad Ave., Leonia, NJ 07605-1637 USA (SAN 854-2473) Tel 201-947-3471; Fax: 201-947-6321
E-mail: booklink@es1booklink.com.

BookLink, Inc., 444 Broad St., Camden, SC 29020 USA (SAN 631-5291) Tel 803-432-5169; Fax: 803-424-8418
E-mail: sam@thebooklink.com
Web site: http://www.thebooklink.com.

Booklocker.com, Inc., *(1-929072; 1-931391; 1-59113; 1-60145)* P.O. Box 2399, Bangor, ME 04402 USA (SAN 254-363X) Fax: 207-262-5544
E-mail: booklocker@booklocker.com; writersweekly@writersweekly.com
Web site: http://www.booklocker.com; http://www.writersweekly.com.

Bookman Bks., 138 Elena St., Santa Fe, NM 87501 USA (SAN 630-933X) Tel 505-982-5964.

Bookmark, Inc., The, 1445 N. Winchester St., Olathe, KS 66061-5881 USA (SAN 131-4017) Toll Free: 800-642-1288.

BookMasters, 6745 FM 2738, Burleson, TX 76028-1167 USA (SAN 630-8406) Do not confuse with BookMasters Inc., Ashland, OH.

BookMasters, Inc., *(0-917889)* Orders Addr.: P.O. Box 388, Mansfield, OH 44903 USA (SAN 631-3566) Tel 419-281-1802; Fax: 419-281-6883; Toll Free: 800-247-6553; 30 Amberwood Pkwy., Ashland, OH 44805 Fax: 419-281-6886 Do not confuse with BookMasters, Burleson, TX
E-mail: info@bookmasters.com; order@bookmaster.com
Web site: http://www.bookmasters.com.

Bookmen, Inc., Orders Addr.: 2300 Louisiana Ave N. # B, Minneapolis, MN 55427-3631 USA (SAN 169-409X) Toll Free Fax: 800-266-5636; Toll Free: 800-328-8411 (customer service)
Web site: http://www.bookmen.com.

Books & Research, Inc., 145 Palisade St. Ste. 389, Dobbs Ferry, NY 10522-1628 USA (SAN 130-1101)
E-mail: brinc@ix.netcom.com
Web site: http://www.books-and-research.com.

Books Are Fun, Ltd., *(0-9649777; 1-58209; 1-890409; 1-59795)* 1680 Hwy. 1 N., Fairfield, IA 52556 USA Tel 641-472-8301; Fax: 641-469-3915
E-mail: msmall@booksarefun.com
Web site: http://www.booksarefun.com.

Books for Educators, Inc., *(0-9624475; 1-929869)* P.O. Box 468, Black Diamond, WA 98010-0468 USA Toll Free: 888-777-9827
E-mail: books4@oz.net
Web site: http://www.books4educ.com.

Books International, Incorporated, *(1-891078)* Orders Addr.: P.O. Box 605, Herndon, VA 20172-0605 USA (SAN 131-761X) Tel 703-661-1500; Fax: 703-661-1501
E-mail: bimail@presswarehouse.com.

Books to Grow On, 826 S. Aiken Ave., Pittsburgh, PA 15232 USA (SAN 128-438X); 210 S. Highland Ave., Pittsburgh, PA 15206 Fax: 412-621-5324.

Books West, 5757 Arapahoe Ave., Unit D2, Boulder, CO 80303 USA (SAN 631-4724) Tel 303-449-5995; Fax: 303-449-5951; Toll Free: 800-378-4188 Do not confuse with Books West, San Diego, CA
E-mail: wnack@rmi.net
Web site: http://www.bookswest.net/.

Booksellers Order Service, 828 S. Broadway, Tarrytown, NY 10591-5112 USA (SAN 106-5181) Tel 914-591-2665; Fax: 914-591-2720; Toll Free: 800-637-0037.

Booksmith Promotional Co., 100 Paterson Plank Rd., Jersey City, NJ 07307 USA (SAN 664-5364) Tel 201-659-2768; Fax: 201-659-3631.

Booksource, The, *(0-7383; 0-911891; 0-9641084; 1-890760; 1-60446)* Orders Addr.: 1230 Macklind Ave., Saint Louis, MO 63110-1432 USA (SAN 631-8371); Edit Addr.: 1230 Macklind Ave., Saint Louis, MO 63110-1432 USA (SAN 169-4324) Tel 314-647-0600; Fax: 314-647-2422; Toll Free Fax: 800-647-1923; Toll Free: 800-444-0435
E-mail: vstadts@freewwweb.com
Web site: http://www.booksource.com.

BookSurge, LLC, *(1-58898; 1-59109; 1-59456; 1-59457; 1-4196; 1-4348)* Div. of Amazon.com, Orders Addr.: 7290 Investment Dr., #B, North Charleston, SC 29418-8302 USA (SAN 255-2132) Toll Free: 866-308-6235
E-mail: customerservice@booksurge.com; orders@booksurge.com
Web site: http://www.booksurge.com.

Bookworld Cos., 1941 Whitfield Pk. Loop, Sarasota, FL 34243 USA.

Bookworm, 14 Griffin St., Northport, ME 04849-4446 USA (SAN 170-8074).

Bookworm Bookfairs, 968 Farmington Ave., W., West Hartford, CT 06107 USA (SAN 156-5621).

Bookworm, The, 417 Monmouth Dr., Cherry Hill, NJ 08002 USA (SAN 120-9531) Tel 609-667-5884.

Borchardt, G. Inc., 136 E. 57th St., New York, NY 10022 USA (SAN 285-8614) Tel 212-753-5785; Fax: 212-838-6518.

Borders, Inc., 9910 N. By NE Blvd., Bldg. 4, Fishers, IN 46038 USA (SAN 152-5352); Plaza Las Americas, Space 497, 1st Flr. 525 F D Roosevelt Ave., Hato Rey, PR 00918 (SAN 193-2314); 455 Industrial Blvd., Suite E, La Vergne, TN 37086 (SAN 156-6474); Edit Addr.: 100 Phoenix Dr., Ann Arbor, MI 48108 USA (SAN 152-3546) Tel 734-477-1100; Fulfillment Addr.: a/o Fulfillment Center, 100 Phoenix Dr., Ann Arbor, MI 48108-2202 USA (SAN 197-0917).

Bored Feet Pr., *(0-939431)* Orders Addr.: P.O. Box 1832, Mendocino, CA 95460 USA (SAN 661-6992) Tel 707-964-6629; Fax: 707-964-5953; Edit Addr.: 16630 Mitchell Creek Dr., Fort Bragg, CA 95437 USA (SAN 663-3226)
E-mail: Boredft@mcn.org.

Bored Feet Publications, *See* **Bored Feet Pr.**

Bottman Design, Inc., *(1-884741)* 990 S. 700 W., No. 11, Salt Lake City, UT 84104 USA Tel 801-973-6708; Fax: 801-973-6746; Toll Free: 800-365-5564.

Bound to Stay Bound Bks., *(0-9718238)* 1880 W. Morton Rd., Jacksonville, IL 62650 USA (SAN 169-1996) Toll Free Fax: 800-747-2872; Toll Free: 800-637-6586
Web site: http://www.btsb.com.

Bowers & Merena Galleries, Inc., *(0-943161)* Orders Addr.: P.O. Box 1224, Wolfeboro, NH 03894 USA (SAN 168-9746) Tel 603-569-5095; Fax: 603-569-5319; Toll Free: 800-222-5993; Edit Addr.: 18061 Fitch., Irvine, CA 92614-6018 USA (SAN 668-2561).

Bowling Green State University, Philosophy Documentation Center, *See* **Philosophy Documentation Ctr.**

Boydell & Brewer, Inc., *(0-85115; 0-85991; 0-907239; 0-938100; 1-57113; 1-58046; 1-85566; 1-870252; 1-878822; 1-879751; 1-900639; 1-84384; 1-84383)* Div. of Boydell & Brewer Group, Ltd., Orders Addr.: 668 Mount Hope Ave., Rochester, NY 14620-2731 USA (SAN 013-8479) Tel 585-275-0419; Fax: 585-271-8778
E-mail: boydell@boydellusa.net; boydell@boydell.co.uk
Web site: http://www.boydellandbrewer.com.

Boyds Mills Pr., *(1-56397; 1-878093; 1-886910; 1-59078; 1-932425)* Div. of Highlights For Children, Inc., 815 Church St., Honesdale, PA 18431-1877 USA (SAN 852-3177) Tel 717-253-1164; 570-251-4513; Fax: 570-253-0179; Toll Free: 800-490-5111
E-mail: admin@boydsmillspress.com
Web site: http://www.boydsmillspress.com.

BPDI, 1000 S. Lynndale Dr., Appleton, WI 54914 USA (SAN 631-6859) Tel 920-830-7897; Fax: 920-830-3857.

BreakThrough Productions, 1002 Meridith Dr., Terrell, TX 75160-5023 USA.

Bridge Pubns., Inc., *(0-88404; 1-57318; 1-4031)* 4751 Fountain Ave., Los Angeles, CA 90029 USA (SAN 208-3884) Tel 323-953-3320; Fax: 323-953-3328; Toll Free: 800-722-1733
E-mail: annarnow@bridgepub.com; daniellem@bridgepub.com; donarnow@bridgepub.com
Web site: http://www.bridgepub.com; http://www.clearbodyclearmind.com; http://www.scientology.org; http://www.dianetics.org; http://www.dianeticsbook.com.

Bridgeport Bks., *(1-888824)* Div. of Griffin Publishing Co., 18022 Cowan, Suite 202, Irvine, CA 92614 USA (SAN 631-5046) Toll Free: 800-472-9741
E-mail: griffinbooks@earthlink.net
Web site: http://www.griffinpublishing.com.

Brigham Distribution, 110 S. 800 W, Brigham City, UT 84302 USA Tel 435-723-6611; Fax: 435-723-6644
E-mail: brigdist@sisna.com.

Brigham, Kay, Orders Addr.: 9500 Old Cutler Rd., Miami, FL 33156 USA Tel 305-666-3844; Fax: 305-661-4843
Web site: http://www.kaybrigham.com.

Brigham Young Univ. Print Services, 205 UPB, Provo, UT 84602 USA Tel 801-378-2809; Fax: 801-378-3374
E-mail: denise@upb.byu.edu
Web site: http://www.upb.byu.edu.

Bright Horizons Specialty Distributors, Inc., 206 Riva Ridge Dr., Fairview, NC 28730-9764 USA (SAN 110-4101) Toll Free: 800-437-3959 (orders only).

Brill Academic Pubs., Inc., *(0-391; 0-916846)* Subs. of Brill Academic Publishing Co., The Netherlands, 112 Water St., Suite 601, Boston, MA 02109 USA (SAN 254-6922) Tel 617-263-2323; Fax: 617-263-2324; Toll Free: 800-962-4406
E-mail: cs@brillusa.com
Web site: http://www.brill.nl.

Brill, E. J. U. S. A., Incorporated, *See* **Brill Academic Pubs., Inc.**

Brisco Pubns., *(0-9603576)* P.O. Box 2161, Palos Verdes Peninsula, CA 90274 USA (SAN 133-0268) Tel 310-534-4943; Fax: 310-534-8437.

Broadman & Holman Publishers, *See* **B&H Publishing Grp.**

Brodart Co., *(0-87272)* Orders Addr.: 500 Arch St., Williamsport, PA 17705 USA (SAN 169-7684) Tel 570-326-2461 (International); 717-326-2461; Fax: 570-326-1479; 519-759-1144 (Canada); Toll Free Fax: 800-999-6799; Toll Free: 800-233-8467 (US & Canada)
E-mail: bookinfo@brodart.com
Web site: http://www.brodart.com.

Brookes, Paul H. Publishing Co., *(0-933716; 1-55766; 1-59857)* Orders Addr.: P.O. Box 10624, Baltimore, MD 21285-0624 USA (SAN 212-730X) Tel 410-337-9580; Fax: 410-337-8539; Toll Free: 800-638-3775 (customer service/ordering/billing/fulfillment); Edit Addr.: 409 Washington Ave., Suite 500, Baltimore, MD 21204 USA (SAN 666-6485)
E-mail: custserv@brookespublishing.com
Web site: http://www.brookespublishing.com.

Brookings Institution Pr., *(0-8157)* 1775 Massachusetts Ave., NW, Washington, DC 20036-2188 USA (SAN 201-9396) Tel 202-797-6252; Fax: 202-797-6195; Toll Free: 800-275-1447
E-mail: bibooks@brook.edu
Web site: http://www.brookings.edu/press.

Brotherhood of Life, Inc., *(0-914732)* P.O. Box 46306, Las Vegas, NV 89114-6306 USA (SAN 111-3674) Fax: 702-319-5577
E-mail: brotherhoodoflife@hotmail.com
Web site: http://www.brotherhoodoflife.com.

Brown, David Bk. Co., The, *(0-9774094)* Div. of Oxbow Bks., Orders Addr.: P.O. Box 511, Oakville, CT 06779 USA (SAN 630-9461) Tel 860-945-9329; Fax: 860-945-9468; Toll Free: 800-791-9354
E-mail: david.brown.bk.co@snet.net
Web site: http://www.oxbowbooks.com.

Brown Enterprises, Inc., *(0-9711451)* P.O. Box 11447, Durham, NC 27703 USA Tel 919-680-2288 Do not confuse with companies with the same or similar names in Pasadena, CA, Bellingham, WA
E-mail: brown.enterprisesinc@verizon.net.

Brunner News Agency, 217 Flanders Ave., P.O. Box 598, Lima, OH 45801 USA (SAN 169-6777) Tel 419-225-5826; Fax: 419-225-5537; Toll Free: 800-998-1727
E-mail: brunnews@aol.com
Web site: http://www.readmoreshallmark.com.

Bryan, R. L., *(0-934870)* P.O. Box 368, Columbia, SC 29202 USA Tel 803-779-3560
Web site: http://www.ursamajor-gullah.com.

Bryant Altman Map, Inc., Endicott St., Bldg. 26, Norwood, MA 02062 USA (SAN 630-2475) Tel 781-762-3339; Fax: 781-769-9080
E-mail: JPG63@aol.com.

Bryant-Altman Book & Map Distributors, *See* **Bryant Altman Map, Inc.**

Buckeye News Co., 6800 W. Central Ave., Suite F, Toledo, OH 43617-1157 USA (SAN 169-6874).

Budget Bk. Service, Inc., Div. of LDAP, Inc., 386 Park Ave. S., Suite 1913, New York, NY 10016-8804 USA (SAN 169-5762) Fax: 212-679-2247.

Budget Marketing, Inc., P.O. Box 1805, Des Moines, IA 50306 USA (SAN 285-8754)

Budgetext, Orders Addr.: P.O. Box 1487, Fayetteville, AR 72702 USA (SAN 111-3321) Tel 501-443-9205; Fax: 501-442-3064; Toll Free: 800-643-3432; Edit Addr.: 1936 N. Shiloh Dr., Fayetteville, AR 72704 USA (SAN 249-3330)
E-mail: wmorgan@absc.com; scaldwell@budgetext.com
Web site: http://www.budgetext.com.

Buena Vista Home Video, *(0-7888; 1-55890)* Div. of Walt Disney Studios, 500 S. Buena Vista St., Burbank, CA 91521-1120 USA (SAN 249-2342) Tel 818-560-4430; Fax: 818-972-2845; Toll Free: 800-723-4763
Web site: http://www.disney.com.

Burlington News Agency, 382 Hercules Dr., Colchester, VT 05446-5836 USA (SAN 169-8583).

Burns News Agency, P.O. Box 1211, Rochester, NY 14603-1211 USA (SAN 169-5320).

B.W. Bks. on Wings, Orders Addr.: 581 Market St., San Francisco, CA 94105-2847 USA.

BWI, 1847 Mercer Rd., Lexington, KY 40511 USA Tel 859-231-9789; Fax: 859-388-9827.

Byrrd Enterprises, Inc., *(1-886715)* 1302 Lafayette Dr., Alexandria, VA 22308 USA (SAN 169-8605) Tel 703-765-5626; Fax: 703-768-4086; Toll Free: 800-628-0901
E-mail: byrrdbooks@aol.com.

C & B Bk. Hse., 21 Oak Ridge Rd., Monroe, CT 06468 USA (SAN 159-8279).

C & B Book Distribution, 65-77 160th St., Flushing, NY 11365 USA Tel 718-591-4525
Web site: http://www.cbbooksdistribution.com.

C & H News Co., P.O. Box 2768, Corpus Christi, TX 78403-2768 USA (SAN 169-8249).

C4 Kids, Orders Addr.: 1220 N. Las Palmas, No. 201, Los Angeles, CA 90038 USA.

CafePress.com, *(1-4148)* 950 Tower Ln. Ste. 600, Foster City, CA 94404-4253 USA Toll Free: 877-809-1659
E-mail: mystore@cafepress.com
Web site: http://www.cafepress.com.

Cajun Country Distributors, 6595 Goodwood Ave., Baton Rouge, LA 70806-7408 USA (SAN 631-1733).

Calendar Club, LLC, 6411 Burleson Rd., Austin, TX 78744 USA (SAN 631-1881) Tel 512-386-7220; Fax: 512-369-6192.

Calico Subscription Co., P.O. Box 640337, San Jose, CA 95164-0337 USA (SAN 285-9173) Tel 408-432-8700; Fax: 408-432-8813; Toll Free: 800-952-2542.

California Princeton Fulfillment Services, 1445 Lower Ferry Rd., Ewing, NJ 08618 USA (SAN 630-639X) Tel 609-883-1759 ext 536; Toll Free: 800-777-4726
E-mail: donnaw@cpfs.pupress.princeton.edu.

Calliope Bks., *(0-9620187)* 2115 Chadbourne Ave., Madison, WI 53705 USA (SAN 247-9370) Tel 608-238-9258 Do not confuse with Calliope Books in Santa Barbara, CA
E-mail: wcoleman@facstaff.wisc.edu; calliopebooks@hotmail.com
Web site: http://www.execpc.com/~calliope.

Cambridge Bk. Co., *(0-8428)* Div. of Simon & Schuster, Inc., 4350 Equity Dr., Box 249, Columbus, OH 43216 USA (SAN 169-5703) Toll Free: 800-238-5833
Web site: http://www.simonsays.com/.

Cambridge Career Products, *See* **Cambridge Educational**

Cambridge Educational, *(0-927368; 1-56450)* Orders Addr.: P.O. Box 2153, Charleston, WV 25328-2153 USA; Edit Addr.: P.O. Box 931, Monmouth Junction, NJ 08852 USA (SAN 287-4695) Toll Free Fax: 800-486-6687; Toll Free: 888-744-6398 (Technical Support); 800-468-4227 Do not confuse with Cambridge Educational Service in Des Plaines, IL
E-mail: customerservice@cambridgeeducational.com
Web site: http://www.cambridgeeducational.com.

Cambridge Univ. Pr., *(0-521; 0-511)* Orders Addr.: 100 Brook Hill Dr., West Nyack, NY 10994-2133 USA (SAN 281-3769) Tel 845-353-7500; Fax: 845-353-4141; Toll Free: 800-872-7423 (orders, returns, credit & accounting); 800-937-9600; Edit Addr.: 32 Avenue of the Americas, New York, NY 10013-2473 USA (SAN 200-206X) Tel 212-924-3900; Fax: 212-691-3239
E-mail: customer_service@cup.org; orders@cup.org; information@cup.org
Web site: http://www.cup.org.

Canon Pr., *(1-885767; 1-59128)* Div. of Christ Church, Orders Addr.: P.O. Box 8729, Moscow, ID 83843 USA (SAN 257-3792); 205 E. 5th St., Moscow, ID 83843 Do not confuse with companies with the same or similar names in Grand Rapids, MI, Centerville, UT
E-mail: ops@canonpress.org
Web site: http://www.canonpress.org.

Canyon Country Distribution, P.O. Box 400034, Thompson Springs, UT 84540 USA Tel 435-285-2210; Fax: 435-285-2252
E-mail: archhunt@moci.net.

Canyonlands Pubns., *(0-9702595)* Orders Addr.: P.O. Box 16175, Bellemont, AZ 86015-6175 USA (SAN 114-3824) Tel 520-779-3888; Fax: 520-779-3778; Toll Free: 800-283-1983; Edit Addr.: 4860 N. Ken Morey, Bellemont, AZ 86015 USA
E-mail: books@infomagic.com.

Cape News Co., P.O. Box 568680, Rockledge, FL 32955 USA Tel 407-636-5909.

Capital Business Systems, Div. of Capital Business Service, Orders Addr.: P.O. Box 2088, Napa, CA 94558 USA (SAN 698-3146) Tel 707-252-8844; Fax: 707-252-6368; Edit Addr.: 2033 First St., Napa, CA 94558 USA.

Capital City, 2537 Daniels St., Madison, WI 53704-6772 USA (SAN 200-5328) Tel 608-223-2000; Fax: 608-223-2010.

Capital News Co., 961 Palmyra, Jackson, MS 39203 USA Tel 601-355-8341; Fax: 601-352-1343.

Capitol News Agency, P.O. Box 7886, Richmond, VA 23231 USA (SAN 249-2768); 5203 Hatcher St., Richmond, VA 23231-0271 Tel 804-222-7252.

Capper Pr., 1503 SW 42nd, Topeka, KS 66609 USA (SAN 285-8886) Tel 913-274-4324; Fax: 913-274-4305; Toll Free: 800-678-5779 (ext. 4324).

Capstone Pr., Inc., *(0-7368; 1-56065; 1-4296)* Div. of Coughlan Publishing, 1905 Lookout Dr., North Mankato, MN 55033 USA Tel 507-385-8215; Fax: 507-388 3752; Orders Addr.: 151 Good Council Dr., P.O. Box 669, Mankato, MN 56002-0669 USA (SAN 254-1815) Toll Free Fax: 888-262-0705; Toll Free: 800-747-4992; Edit Addr.: 7825 Telegraph Rd., Bloomington, MN 55438 USA Fax: 952-933-2410; Toll Free: 888-517-8977 Do not confuse with Capstone Pr., Inc. in Decatur, IL
Web site: http://www.capstone-press.com.

Cardinal Pubs. Group, *(0-9799240)* 2222 Hillside Ave., Suite 100, Carmel, IN 46218 USA (SAN 631-7936) Tel 317-879-0871; Fax: 317-879-0872
E-mail: tdoherty@in.net.

Cards Bks. N Things, 1446 St., Rd. 2 West, La Porte, IN 46350 USA (SAN 159-8295).

Career Dynamics International, P.O. Box 3468, Saint Thomas, VI 00803 USA Tel 284-494-3185; Fax: 284-494-2684.

Carlex, 1545 W. Hamlin, Rochester Hills, MI 48309 USA (SAN 631-5615) Tel 810-852-5422; Fax: 810-852-7142.

Carolina Biological Supply Co., *(0-89278; 1-4350)* 2700 York Rd., Burlington, NC 27215-3398 USA (SAN 249-2784) Tel 336-584-0381; Fax: 910-584-3399; Toll Free Fax: 800-222-7112; Toll Free: 800-334-5551
E-mail: carolina@carolina.com
Web site: http://www.carolina.com.

Carolina Cassette Distributors, Orders Addr.: P.O. Box 429, New Bern, NC 28560 USA (SAN 110-8395) Fax: 919-638-1291; Edit Addr.: 2600 Oaks Rd., New Bern, NC 28560 USA (SAN 659-2155) Tel 919-638-5583.

Carolina News Co., Orders Addr.: P.O. Box 10, Fayetteville, NC 28302 USA; Edit Addr.: 245 Tillinghast St., Fayetteville, NC 28301 USA Tel 910-483-4135.

Carson-Dellosa Publishing Co., Inc., *(0-88724; 1-59441; 1-60022; 1-60418)* Orders Addr.: P.O. Box 35665, Greensboro, NC 27425 USA Tel 336-632-0084; Fax: 336-808-3249; Toll Free: 800-321-0943
E-mail: kjones@carsondellosa.com; nbrown@carsondellosa.com
Web site: http://www.carsondellosa.com.

Casa Del Libro, Orders Addr.: P.O. Box 3853, La Mesa, CA 91944-3853 USA.

Cascade News, Inc., 1055 Commerce Ave., Longview, WA 98632 USA (SAN 169-8761) Tel 360-425-2450; Fax: 360-425-2451.

Casemate Pubs. & Bk. Distributors, LLC, *(0-9711709; 1-932033)* Orders Addr.: 1016c Warrior Rd., Drexel Hill, PA 19026-4818 USA; 22883 Quicksilver Dr., Herndon, VA 20166 (SAN 631-9386) Tel 703-661-1500
E-mail: casemate@casematepublishing.com
Web site: http://www.casematepublishing.com.

Casino Distributors, Orders Addr.: P.O. Box 849, Pleasantville, NJ 08232 USA (SAN 169-457X) Tel 609-646-4165; Fax: 609-645-0152; Edit Addr.: 10 Canale Dr., Pleasantville, NJ 08234 USA (SAN 249-3276).

Casper Magazine Agency, P.O. Box 2340, Casper, WY 82602 USA (SAN 159-8325).

Cassette Book Company, *See* **Audio Bk. Co.**

Castlebridge Distribution, 115 Bluebill Dr., Savannah, GA 31419 USA Toll Free: 888-300-1961 (phone/fax)
E-mail: orders@castlebridgedistribution.com.

Catholic Bookrack Service, 700 E. Elm St., La Grange, IL 60525 USA (SAN 169-2178) Tel 708-482-0044; Fax: 708-482-9644.

Catholic Heritage Curricula, *(0-9788376)* P.O. Box 125, Twain Harte, CA 95383 USA Fax: 209-586-1574; Toll Free: 800-490-7713
Web site: http://www.chcweb.com.

Catholic Literary Guild, Inc., 200 Hamilton Ave., White Plains, NY 10601 USA (SAN 285-8908) Tel 914-949-4444.

Catweasel Productions, *See* **Ars Obscura**

Cave of the Winds, P.O. Box 826, Manitou Springs, CO 80829 USA Tel 719-685-5444
Web site: http://www.caveofthewinds.com.

Cavendish, Marshall Corp., *(0-7614; 0-85685; 0-86307; 1-85435)* Member of Times Publishing Group, 99 White Plains Rd., Tarrytown, NY 10591-9001 USA (SAN 238-437X) Tel 914-332-8888; Fax: 914-332-8882; Toll Free: 800-821-9881
E-mail: mmark@marshallcavendish.com
Web site: http://www.marshallcavendish.us.

Caxton Pr., *(0-87004)* Div. of Caxton Printers. Ltd., 312 Main St., Caldwell, ID 83605-3299 USA (SAN 201-9698) Tel 208-459-7421; Fax: 208-459-7450; Toll Free: 800-657-6465
E-mail: publish@caxtonprinters.com; wcornell@caxtonpress.com; sgipson@caxtonpress.com
Web site: http://www.caxtonprinters.com; http://www.caxtonpress.com.

Caxton Printers, Limited, *See* **Caxton Pr.**

CBLS Pubs., *(1-878907; 1-59529)* 119 Brentwood St., Marietta, OH 45750 USA (SAN 169-5517) Tel 740-374-9458; Fax: 740-374-8029
E-mail: cbls@cbls.com
Web site: http://www.cbls.com.

CD Distributing, Inc., P.O. Box 4965, Missoula, MT 59806-4965 USA (SAN 169-4367) Fax: 406-454-0415.

Cedar Fort, Inc./CFI Distribution, *(0-88290; 0-934126; 1-55517; 1-59955)* 2373 West 700 South, Springville, UT 84663 USA (SAN 170-2858) Tel 801-489-4084; Fax: 801-489-1097; Toll Free: 800-759-2665
E-mail: skybook@cedarfort.com
Web site: http://www.cedarfort.com.

Cedar Graphics, *See* **Igram Pr.**

CENGAGE Learning, Div. of The Thomson Corp., 10650 Toebben Dr., Independence, KY 41051 USA (SAN 631-2144) Tel 859-525-6620; Fax: 859-525-0978; Toll Free: 800-347-7707 (customer service); 800-842-3636 (orders); a/o Customer Service, P.O. Box 6904, Florence, KY 41022-6904 Toll Free Fax: 800 487 8488; Toll Free: 800 354 9706
Web site: http://www.thomsonlearning.com.

Centennial Pubns., 1400 Ash Dr., Fort Collins, CO 80521 USA (SAN 630-494X) Tel 970-493-2041 Do not confuse with Centennial Pubns., Grand Junction, CO.

Center for Applied Psychology, Incorporated, *See* **Childswork/Childsplay**

Central Arizona Distributing, 4932 W. Pasadena Ave., Glendale, AZ 85301 USA (SAN 170-6128) Tel 602-939-6511.

Central European Univ. Pr., *(1-85866; 963-9116; 963-9241; 963-7326)* Orders Addr.: c/o Books International, P.O. Box 605, Herndon, VA 20172 USA Tel 703-661-1500 (orders); Fax: 703-661-1501 (orders); Edit Addr.: 400 W. 59th St., New York, NY 10019 USA Tel 212-547-6932; Fax: 646-557-2416; P.O. Box 519/22, Budapest, 1397 Tel 36-1-327-3138; Fax: 36-1-327-3183
E-mail: mgreenwald@sorosny.org
Web site: http://www.ceupress.com.

Central Illinois Periodicals, P.O. Box 3757, Bloomington, IL 61701 USA (SAN 630-8945) Tel 309-829-9405.

Central Kentucky News Distributing Company, *See* **Anderson-Austin News Co., LLC**

Central News of Sandusky, 5716 McCartney Rd., Sandusky, OH 44870-1538 USA (SAN 169-684X).

Central Programs, 802 N. 41st St., Bethany, MO 64424 USA Tel 660-425-7777.

Central South Christian Distribution, 3730 Vulcan Dr., Nashville, TN 37211 USA (SAN 631-2543) Tel 615-833-5960; Toll Free Fax: 800-220-0194; Toll Free: 800-757-0856.

Centralia News Co., 232 E. Broadway, Centralia, IL 62801 USA (SAN 159-8341) Tel 618-532-5601.

CentroLibros de Puerto Rico, Inc., Santa Rosa Unit, Bayamon, PR 00960 USA (SAN 631-1245) Tel 787-275-0460; Fax: 787-275-0360.

Century Bk. Distribution, 814 Boon, Traverse City, MI 49686 USA Tel 231-933-6405 (phone/fax).

Century Pr., *(0-9659417)* Div. of Conservatory of American Letters, P.O. Box 298, Thomaston, ME 04861 USA Tel 207-354-0998; Fax: 207-354-8953 Do not confuse with companies with the same name in Arroyo Seco, NM, Oklahoma City, OK
E-mail: cal@americanletters.org
Web site: http://www.americanletters.org.

Ceramic Book & Literature Service, *See* **CBLS Pubs.**

Chain Sales Marketing, Inc., *(1-55836)* 149 Madison Ave., Suite 810, New York, NY 10016 USA (SAN 245-1328) Tel 212-696-4230; Fax: 212-696-4391.

Chambers Kingfisher Graham Publishers, Incorporated, *See* **Larousse Kingfisher Chambers, Inc.**

Champaign-Urbana News Agency, Orders Addr.: P.O. Box 793, Champaign, IL 61824 USA (SAN 630-8953) Tel 217-351-7047; Edit Addr.: 503 Kenyon, Champaign, IL 61820 USA.

Charlynn Publishing Co., Inc., 4152 E. Fifth St., Tucson, AZ 85711 USA.

Chelsea Green Publishing, *(0-930031; 1-890132; 1-931498; 88-86283; 1-933392; 1-60358)* Orders Addr.: P.O. Box 428, White River Junction, VT 05001 USA (SAN 669-7631) Tel 802-295-6300; Fax: 802-295-6444; Toll Free: 800-639-4099; Edit Addr.: 85 N. Main St., Suite 120, White River Junction, VT 05001 USA
E-mail: info@chelseagreen.com
Web site: http://www.chelseagreen.com.

Cheng & Tsui Co., *(0-88727; 0-917056)* 25 West St., Boston, MA 02111-1213 USA (SAN 169-3387) Tel 617-988-2401; Fax: 617-426-3669
E-mail: service@cheng-tsui.com
Web site: http://www.cheng-tsui.com.

Chesbro Music Co., 327 Broadway, Idaho Falls, ID 83403 USA (SAN 631-0850) Tel 208-522-8691.

Chi Rho Pr., *(1-888493)* Div. of Mid-Atlantic District, Universal Fellowship of Metropolitan Community Churches, Orders Addr.: P.O. Box 7864, Gaithersburg, MD 20898 USA Tel 301-926-1208 (phone/fax)
E-mail: mail@chirhopress.com; orders@chirhopress.com
Web site: http://www.chirhopress.com.

Chicago Distribution Ctr., Orders Addr.: 11030 S. Langley Ave., Chicago, IL 60628 USA (SAN 630-6047) Tel 773-702-7000 (International); Fax: 773-702-7212 (International); Toll Free Fax: 800-621-8476 (USA/Canada); Toll Free: 800-621-2736 (USA/Canada); 800-621-8471 (credit & collections)
E-mail: custserv@press.uchicago.edu; orders@press.uchicago.edu
Web site: http://www.press.uchicago.edu; http://www.press.uchicago.edu/presswide/cdc/.

Chicago Review Pr., Inc., *(0-914090; 0-914091; 1-55652; 1-56976)* 814 N. Franklin St., Chicago, IL 60610 USA (SAN 213-5744) Tel 312-337-0747; Fax: 312-337-5985; Toll Free: 800-888-4741 (orders only)
E-mail: frontdesk@ipgbook.com; orders@ipgbook.com
Web site: http://www.ipgbook.com.

Chico News Agency, P.O. Box 690, Chico, CA 95927 USA (SAN 168-9533) Tel 530-895-1000; Fax: 530-895-0158.

Childbirth Graphics, Ltd., *(0-943114)* P.O. Box 21207, Waco, TX 76702-1207 USA (SAN 240-3587).

Children's Bookfair Co., The, 700 E. Grand Ave., Chicago, IL 60611-3472 USA (SAN 630-6705) Tel 312-477-7323; 837 W. Altgeld St., Chicago, IL 60614 (SAN 630-6713).

Child's World, Inc., *(0-89565; 0-913778; 1-56766; 1-59296; 1-60253)* Orders Addr.: P.O. Box 326, Chanhassen, MN 55317-0326 USA (SAN 211-0032) Tel 952-906-3939; Fax: 952-906-3940; Toll Free: 800-599-7323; Edit Addr.: 7081 W. 192nd Ave., Eden Prairie, MN 55346 USA
E-mail: info@childsworld.com; mary.berendes@childsworld.com
Web site: http://www.childsworld.com.

Childswork/Childsplay, *(1-882732; 1-58815)* Div. of The Guidance Channel, Orders Addr.: P.O. Box 760, Plainview, NY 11803-0760 USA Tel 516-349-5520; Fax: 516-349-5521; Toll Free Fax: 800-262-1886; Toll Free: 800-962-1141; 45 Executive Dr. Ste. 201, Plainview, NY 11803-1738
E-mail: karens@at-risk.com; info@childswork.com
Web site: http://www.childswork.com.

China Bks. & Periodicals, Inc., *(0-8351)* 360 Swift Ave., Suite 48, South San Francisco, CA 94080 USA (SAN 145-0557) Tel 800-818-2017; 650-872-7076; Fax: 650-872-7808
E-mail: info@chinabooks.com
Web site: http://www.chinabooks.com.

China Cultural Ctr., 970 N. Broadway, Suite 103, Los Angeles, CA 90012 USA (SAN 111-8161) Tel 213-489-3827; Fax: 213-489-3080.

China House Gallery, China Institute in America, *See* **China Institute Gallery, China Institute in America**

China Institute Gallery, China Institute in America, *(0-9654270; 0-9774054)* Div. of China Institute in America, 125 E. 65th St., New York, NY 10010 USA (SAN 110-8743) Tel 212-744-8181; Fax: 212-628-4159
E-mail: gallery@chinainstitute.org
Web site: http://www.chinainstitute.org.

Chinese American Co., 44 Kneeland St., Boston, MA 02111 USA (SAN 159-7248) Fax: 617-451-2318.

Chivers North America, *See* **BBC Audiobooks America**

Christian Bk. Distributors, Orders Addr.: P.O. Box 7000, Peabody, MA 01961-7000 USA (SAN 630-5458) Tel 978-977-5000; Fax: 978-977-5010
Web site: http://www.christianbook.com.

Christian Books Publishing House, *See* **Seedsowers, The**

Christian Distribution Services, Inc., 1230 Heil Quaker Blvd., Lavergne, TN 37086 USA Tel 615-793-5955; Fax: 615-793-5973.

Christian Literature Crusade, Inc., *(0-87508)* Div. of CLC Publications, Orders Addr.: P.O. Box 1449, Fort Washington, PA 19034-8449 USA Tel 215-542-1242; Fax: 215-542-7580; Toll Free: 800-659-1240; Edit Addr.: 701 Pennsylvania Ave., Fort Washington, PA 19034 USA (SAN 169-7358)
E-mail: joinclc@juno.com
Web site: http://www.clcusa.org.

Christian Printing Service, 4861 Chino Ave., Chino, CA 91710-5132 USA (SAN 108-2647) Tel 714-871-5200.

Christian Publishing Network, *(0-9628406)* P.O. Box 405, Tulsa, OK 74101 USA (SAN 631-2756) Tel 918-296-4673 (918-296-HOPE); Toll Free: 888-688-8125
E-mail: vpsales@olp.net.

Chronicle Bks. LLC, *(0-8118; 0-87701; 0-938491; 1-58717)* Orders Addr.: 680 Second St., San Francisco, CA 94107 USA (SAN 202-165X) Tel 415-537-4200; Fax: 415-537-4460; Toll Free Fax: 800-858-7787; Toll Free: 800-722-6657 (orders only)
E-mail: orders@chroniclebooks.com
Web site: http://www.chroniclebooks.com.

Chulain Publishing Corp., Orders Addr.: 8241 Sweet Water Rd., Lone Tree, CO 80124-3017 USA.

Church Hymnal Corporation, *See* **Church Publishing, Inc.**

Church of Scientology Information Service-Pubns., *(0-915598)* c/o Bridge Pubns., Inc., 1414 N. Catalina, Los Angeles, CA 90029 USA (SAN 268-9774).

Church Publishing, Inc., *(0-89869; 1-59627; 1-59628)* 445 Fifth Ave., New York, NY 10016-0109 USA Tel 212-592-1800; Fax: 212-779-3392; Toll Free: 800-242-1918
E-mail: churchpublishing@cpg.org
Web site: http://www.churchpublishing.org.

Church Richards Co., 10001 Roosevelt Rd., Westchester, IL 60154 USA (SAN 285-8975) Toll Free: 800-323-0227.

Cibolo Nature Ctr., P.O. Box 9, Boerne, TX 78006 USA Tel 830-249-4616.

Circa Pubns., Inc., 415 Fifth Ave., Pelham, NY 10803-0408 USA (SAN 169-6122) Tel 914-738-5570; Toll Free: 800-582-5952 (orders only).

Circle Bk. Service, Inc., *(0-87397)* P.O. Box 626, Tomball, TX 77377 USA (SAN 158-2526) Tel 281-255-6824; Fax: 281-255-8158; Toll Free: 800-227-1591
E-mail: orders@circlebook.com
Web site: http://www.circlebook.com.

City News Agency, Orders Addr.: P.O. Box 561129, Charlotte, NC 28256-1129 USA (SAN 169-782X); Edit Addr.: P.O. Box 2069, Newark, OH 43055 USA (SAN 169-6947); 220 Cherry Ave., NE, Canton, OH 44702-1198 (SAN 169-6602); 303 E. Lasalle St., South Bend, IN 46617 (SAN 159-9992); 417 S. McKinley, Harrisburg, IL 62946 (SAN 169-1961).

Clarks Out of Town News, 303 S. Andrews Ave., Fort Lauderdale, FL 33301 USA (SAN 159-8384) Tel 954-467-1543.

Classroom Reading Service, P.O. Box 2708, Santa Fe Spgs, CA 90670-0708 USA (SAN 131-3959) Toll Free: 800-422-6657
E-mail: crsbooks@aol.com.

CLEARVUE/eav, Inc., 6465 N. Avondale Ave., Chicago, IL 60631-1996 USA (SAN 204-1669) Tel 773-775-9433; Fax: 773-775-9855; Toll Free Fax: 800-444-9855 (24 Hours); Toll Free: 800-253-2788 (8:00 am to 4:30 pm Central Time M-F)
E-mail: custserv@clearvue.com
Web site: http://www.clearvue.com.

Client Distribution Services, *See* **Perseus Distribution**

Closet Case Bks., P.O. Box 16116, Saint Paul, MN 55116 USA
Web site: http://www.closetcasebooks.com.

Clover Bk. Service, 1220 S. Monroe St., Covingtons, LA 70433-3639 USA (SAN 106-472X) Tel 504-875-0038.

Cobblestone Publishing Co., *(0-382; 0-942389; 0-9607638)* Div. of Cricket Magazine Group, 30 Grove St., Suite C, Peterborough, NH 03458 USA (SAN 237-9937) Tel 603-924-7209; Fax: 603-924-7380; Toll Free: 800-821-0115
E-mail: custsvc@cobblestone.mv.com
Web site: http://www.cobblestonepub.com.

Cogan Bks., *(0-940688)* P.O. Box 579, Hudson, OH 44236-0579 USA (SAN 168-9649) Toll Free: 800-733-3630.

Cokesbury, 201 Eighth Ave., S., Nashville, TN 37203 USA (SAN 200-6863) Tel 615-749-6409; Toll Free: 800-672-1789
Web site: http://www.cokesbury.com.

Cold Cut Comics Distribution, 475-D Stockton Ave., San Jose, CA 95126 USA (SAN 631-6409) Tel 408-293-3844; Fax: 408-293-6645
E-mail: comics@coldcut.com
Web site: http://www.coldcut.com.

Cole, Bill Enterprises, Inc., P.O. Box 60, Randolph, MA 02368-0060 USA (SAN 685-6373) Tel 617-986-2653.

Collector Bks., *(0-89145; 1-57432; 1-60460)* Div. of Schroeder Publishing Co., Inc., Orders Addr.: P.O. Box 3009, Paducah, KY 42003 USA (SAN 157-5368) Tel 270-898-6211; 270-898-7903; Fax: 270-898-8890; 270-898-1173; Toll Free: 800-626-5420 (orders only); Edit Addr.: 5801 Kentucky Dam Rd., Paducah, KY 42003 USA (SAN 200-7479)
E-mail: Info@collectorbooks.com; info@AQSquilt.com
Web site: http://www.collectorbooks.com; http://www.americanquilter.com/.

College Bk. Co. of California, Inc., 181 W. Orangethorpe Ave. Ste. C, Placentia, CA 92870-6931 USA (SAN 269-0802).

Collegedale Distributors, *See* **Tree of Life Midwest**

Colonial Williamsburg Foundation, *(0-87935; 0-910412)* P.O. Box 3532, Williamsburg, VA 23187-3532 USA (SAN 128-4630) Fax: 757-565-8999 (orders only); Toll Free: 800-446-9240 (orders only)
Web site: http://www.colonialwilliamsburg.com.

Colorado Periodical Distributor, Inc., 1227 Pitkin St., Grand Junction, CO 81502 USA Tel 970-242-3865; Fax: 970-242-3760.

Colorado State University, Center for Literary Publishing, *See* **Ctr. for Literary Publishing, Colorado State Univ.**

Columbia County News Agency, Inc., 49 Bender Blvd., Ghent, NY 12075-3327 USA (SAN 169-5339).

Comag Marketing Group, 1790 Broadway, Suite 401, New York, NY 10019 USA (SAN 169-5800) Tel 212-841-8365; Fax: 212-977-9401.

Comics Hawaii Distributors, *See* **Hobbies Hawaii Distributors**

Common Ground Distributors, Inc., Orders Addr.: P.O. Box 25249, Asheville, NC 28813-1249 USA Toll Free: 800-654-0626; Edit Addr.: 115 Fairview Rd., Asheville, NC 28803-2307 USA (SAN 113-8006) Tel 828-274-5575; Fax: 828-274-1955
E-mail: orders@comground.com.

Commonwealth Editions, *(1-889833; 1-933212)* 266 Cabot St., Beverly, MA 01915 USA Tel 978-921-0747; Fax: 978-927-8195
E-mail: websterb@commonwealtheditions.com
Web site: http://www.commonwealtheditions.com.

Communication Service Corporation, *See* **Gryphon Hse., Inc.**

Communications Plus USA, 2103 N. Decatur Rd., Suite 335, Decatur, GA 30033 USA (SAN 631-6735) Tel 404-727-7289.

Communications Technology, Inc., *(0-918232)* P.O. Box 209, Rindge, NH 03461 USA (SAN 159-8198) Tel 603-899-6957.

Computer & Technical Bks., 6338 Ranchview Ln., N., Osseo, MN 55311-3924 USA (SAN 630-8120).

Computer Book Service, *See* **Levy Home Entertainment**

Conde Nast Pubns., Inc., *(1-878494)* Four Times Sq., 20th Flr., New York, NY 10036 USA (SAN 285-905X) Tel 212-880-8800; Fax: 212-880-8289.

Conley, John C., 25135 Swift Shore Dr., West Linn, OR 97068 USA
Web site: www.mondaynightmeditation.com.

Connecticut River Pr., *(0-9706573)* 111 Holmes Rd., Newington, CT 06111 USA Tel 860-666-1200; 203-254-0147; Fax: 860-594-6037
E-mail: wolftalk@ziplink.net.

Consortium Bk. Sales & Distribution, Orders Addr.: 1045 Westgate Dr., Suite 90, Saint Paul, MN 55114-1065 USA (SAN 200-6049) Tel 651-221-9035; Fax: 651-917-6406; Toll Free: 800-283-3572 (orders)
E-mail: consortium@cbsd.com
Web site: http://www.cbsd.com.

Contemporary Arts Pr., *(0-931818)* Div. of La Mamelle, Inc., P.O. Box 3123, San Francisco, CA 94119-3123 USA (SAN 170-5423) Tel 415-282-0286.

Continental Bk. Co., Inc., *(0-9626800)* Eastern Div., 80-00 Cooper Ave., Bldg. No. 29, Glendale, NY 11385 USA (SAN 169-5436) Tel 718-326-0560; Fax: 718-326-4276; Toll Free: 800-364-0350; Western Div., 625 E. 70th Ave., No. 5, Denver, CO 80229 (SAN 630-2882) Tel 303-289-1761; Fax: 303-289-1764 Do not confuse with Continental Book Company, Denver, CO
E-mail: hola@continentalbook.com; esl@continentalbook.com; bonjour@continentalbook.com; tag@continentalbook.com
Web site: http://www.continentalbook.com.

Continental Enterprises Group, Inc. (CEG), Orders Addr.: 302 West North 2nd St., Seneca, SC 29678 USA (SAN 631-0915) Tel 864-885-9444; Fax: 864-885-1090
E-mail: ContactUs@centerprisesgrp.com.

Cook Communications Ministries, *See* **Cook, David C. Publishing Co.**

Cook, David C. Publishing Co., *(0-7814; 0-88207; 0-89191; 0-89693; 0-912692; 1-55513; 1-56476; 983-45026; 5-503; 983-45027; 983-45023; 983-45019; 983-45018; 983-45013; 983-45012; 983-45016; 983-45031; 1-4347)* 4050 Lee Vance View, Colorado Springs, CO 80918 USA (SAN 206-0981) Tel 719-536-0100; Fax: 719-536-3244; Toll Free: 800-708-5550; 800-323-7543 (Customer Service)
E-mail: howella@cookministries.org
Web site: http://www.davidcook.com.

Cook, Marilyn, 225 E. Garfield, Michigan City, IN 46360 USA.

Cookbook Marketplace, The, P.O. Box 305142, Nashville, TN 37230 USA (SAN 631-4201) Tel 615-391-2656; Toll Free: 800-358-0560.

Cookbooks by Morris Press, *See* **Morris Publishing**

Coos Bay Distributors, 131 N. Schoneman St., Coos Bay, OR 97420 USA (SAN 169-7064) Tel 541-888-5912.

Copper Island News, 1010 Wright St., Marquette, MI 49855-1834 USA (SAN 169-3824).

Copyright Clearance Ctr., Inc., 222 Rosewood Dr, Danvers, MA 01923 USA Tel 978-750-8400; Fax: 978-750-4343
Web site: http://www.copyright.com.

Cornell Univ. Pr., *(0-8014; 0-87546)* Orders Addr.: P.O. Box 6525, Ithaca, NY 14851 USA (SAN 281-5680) Tel 607-277-2211; Toll Free Fax: 800-688-2877; Toll Free: 800-666-2211; Edit Addr.: Sage House, 512 E. State St., Ithaca, NY 14851 USA (SAN 202-1862) Tel 607-277-2338
E-mail: cupressinfo@cornell.edu; orders@nbninternational.com; cupress-sales@cornell.edu
Web site: http://www.cornellpress.cornell.edu.

Cornerstone Publishing & Distribution, Inc., *(1-929281)* P.O. Box 490, Bountiful, UT 84011-0490 USA Tel 801-295-9451; Fax: 801-295-0196; Toll Free: 800-453-0812
E-mail: rrhopkins@utah-inter.net.

Coronet Bks., *(0-89563; 91-7916)* 311 Bainbridge St., Philadelphia, PA 19147 USA (SAN 210-6043) Tel 215-925-2762; Fax: 215-925-1912 Do not confuse with Coronet Bks. & Pubns., Eagle Point, OR
E-mail: ronsmolin@earthlink.net; order@coronetbooks.com
Web site: http://www.coronetbooks.com.

Cottonwood Bks., *(0-935775)* 1216 Lillie Cir., Salt Lake City, UT 84121 USA (SAN 696-4079) Tel 801-262-4586.

Council Oak Bks., *(0-933031; 1-57178)* 2105 E. 15th St., Ste. B, Tulsa, OK 74104 USA (SAN 689-5522) Toll Free: 800-247-8850 (orders only); 2105 E. 15th St., Ste. B, Tulsa, OK 74104 (SAN 689-5522) Toll Free: 800-247-8850 (orders only)
E-mail: order@counciloakbooks.com; publicity@counciloakbooks.com
Web site: http://www.counciloakbooks.com.

Country News Distributors, Div. of Bakers, Inc., P.O. Box 1258, Brattleboro, VT 05302-1258 USA (SAN 169-8575).

Countryside Bks., *(0-88453)* 2430 Estancia Blvd. Ste. 100, Clearwater, FL 33761-2644 USA (SAN 107-4415).

Coutts Library Service, Inc., 1823 Maryland Ave., Box 1000, Niagara Falls, NY 14302-1000 USA (SAN 169-5401) Tel 716-282-8627; Fax: 905-356-5064; Toll Free: 800-772-4304
E-mail: coutts@wizbang.coutts.on.ca.

Cove Distributors, 6325 Erdman Ave., Baltimore, MD 21205 USA (SAN 158-9814) Toll Free: 800-622-5656 (Orders).

Cowley Distributing, Inc., 732 Heisinger Rd., Jefferson City, MO 65109 USA (SAN 169-426X) Tel 573-636-6511; Fax: 573-636-6262; Toll Free: 800-346-5950 (orders).

Cox Subscriptions, Inc., 201 Village Rd., Shallotte, NC 28470 USA (SAN 107-0061) Tel 800-571-9554; Fax: 877-755-6274; Toll Free: 800-553-8088
E-mail: dknox@wtcox.com
Web site: http:/www.wtcox.com.

CPG Publishing, Inc., *(1-931411)* Orders Addr.: c/o CPG Distribution, 7253 Grayson Rd., Harrisburg, PA 17111 USA Toll Free: 800-501-6883 (orders & customer service); Edit Addr.: P.O. Box 6142, New York, NY 10150 USA Tel 212-573-9180; Fax: 212-573-9181 Do not confuse with C P G Publishing Company in Gold Canyon, AZ
E-mail: cpgdistribution@juno.com.

CQ Products, 507 Industrial St., Waverly, IA 50677 USA (SAN 631-5216) Tel 319-352-2086; Fax: 319-352-5338
E-mail: gifts@cqproducts.com
Web site: http://www.cqproducts.com.

Crabtree Publishing, *(0-937070)* P.O. Box 3451, Federal Way, WA 98063 USA (SAN 214-3615) Tel 253-925-9300 Do not confuse with Crabtree Publishing Co. in New York, NY.

Cram, George F. Co., Inc., *(0-87448)* 301 S. LaSalle St., P.O. Box 426, Indianapolis, IN 46201 USA (SAN 204-2630) Tel 317-635-5564; Fax: 317-635-2720; Toll Free: 800-227-4199
E-mail: cram-services@iquest.net.

Cranbury International, Orders Addr.: 7 Clarendon Ave., Suite 2, Montpelier, VT 05602 USA.

CRC Pr. LLC, *(0-8493; 0-87762; 0-87819; 0-935184; 1-56676; 1-57491; 1-58488; 1-58716; 1-4200)* Subs. of Taylor & Francis, Inc., Orders Addr.: 6000 Broken Sound Pkwy., NW, Suite 300, Boca Raton, FL 33487 USA Tel 800-272-7737; 561-361-6000; Fax: 800-374-3401
E-mail: orders@crcpress.com
Web site: http://www.crcpress.com.

CRC Pubns., *(0-930265; 0-933140; 1-56212)* 2850 Kalamazoo Ave., SE, Grand Rapids, MI 49560 USA (SAN 212-727X) Tel 616-224-0724; Fax: 616-224-0834; Toll Free Fax: 888-642-8606; Toll Free: 800-333-8300; P.O. Box 5070, Burlington, ON L7R 3Y8
E-mail: sales@crcpublications.org
Web site: http://www.crcpublications.org.

Creative Co., The, *(0-87191; 0-88682; 1-56660; 1-56846)* 123 S. Broad St., P.O. Box 227, Mankato, MN 56001 USA Tel 507-388-6273; Fax: 507-388-2746; Toll Free: 800-445-6209 Do not confuse with The Creative Co., Lawrenceburg, IN
E-mail: info@thecreativecompany.us
Web site: http://www.thecreativecompany.us.

Creative Homeowner, *(0-932944; 1-58011; 1-880029)* Div. of Federal Marketing Corp., 24 Park Way, Upper Saddle River, NJ 07458-9960 USA (SAN 213-6627) Tel 201-934-7100; Fax: 201-934-8971; Toll Free: 800-631-7795
E-mail: info@creativehomeowner.com
Web site: http://www.creativehomeowner.com.

Creative Learning Pr., Inc., *(0-936386; 1-931280)* Orders Addr.: P.O. Box 320, Mansfield Center, CT 06250 USA (SAN 298-4601) Tel 860-429-8118; Fax: 860-429-7783; Toll Free: 888-518-8004
E-mail: clp@creativelearningpress.com; customerservice@creativelearningpress.com
Web site: http://www.creativelearningpress.com.

Creative Teaching Pr., Inc., *(0-88160; 0-916119; 1-57471; 1-59198)* Orders Addr.: P.O. Box 2723, Huntington Beach, CA 92647-0723 USA Tel 714-895-5047; Fax: 714-895-6547; Toll Free Fax: 800-444-4287; Edit Addr.: 15342 Graham St., Huntington Beach, CA 92649-1111 USA (SAN 294-9180) Tel 714-895-5047; Toll Free Fax: 800-229-9929; Toll Free: 800-444-4287
E-mail: webmaster@creativeteaching.com; welisten@creativeteaching.com
Web site: http://www.creativeteaching.com; http://www.thelearningworks.com.

Crescent Bks., 3028 Adriatic Ct., Norcross, GA 30071 USA Tel 770-662-6970; Fax: 770-416-0807
E-mail: monsour786@yahoo.com.

Crescent Imports & Pubns., *(0-933127)* P.O. Box 7827, Ann Arbor, MI 48107-7827 USA (SAN 111-3976) Tel 734-665-3492; Fax: 734-677-1717; Toll Free: 800-521-9744
E-mail: crescentus@aol.com
Web site: http://www.crescentimports.com.

Crescent International, Inc., 2238 Otranto Rd., Charleston, SC 29418 USA (SAN 110-0777) Tel 803-797-6363; Fax: 803-797-6367.

Critics' Choice, *See* **Critics' Choice Video**

Critics' Choice Video, *(1-932566; 1-933240)* 900 N. Rohlwing Rd., Itasca, IL 60143 USA Tel 630-775-3300; Fax: 603-775-3340
E-mail: rterry@ccvideo.com
Web site: http://www.ccvideo.com.

Cromland, 964 Marcon Blvd, Suite 190, Allentown, PA 18109 USA (SAN 254-6736) Tel 610-266-6610; Fax: 610-266-8987; Toll Free: 800-944-5554 (U.S. & Canada)
Web site: http://www.cromland.com.

CrossLife Expressions, *(0-9636049; 1-57838)* Div. of Exchanged Life Ministries, Inc., 10610 E. Bethany Dr., Suite A, Aurora, CO 80014 USA (SAN 169-0590) Tel 303-750-0440; Fax: 303-750-1228; Toll Free: 800-750-6818
E-mail: info@crosslifebooks.com
Web site: http://www.crosslifebooks.com.

Crowley, Inc., 16120 U.S. Hwy. 19 N., Suite 220, Clearwater, FL 34624-6862 USA (SAN 285-9130) Tel 813-531-5889.

Crown Agents Service, Ltd., 3100 Massachusetts Ave., NW, Washington, DC 20008 USA (SAN 285-919X).

Crown West Books, 575 E., 1000 S., Orem, UT 84097 USA Tel 801-224-1455; Fax: 801-426-5042
E-mail: jimp@redrock.net.

CSS Publishing Co., *(0-7880; 0-89536; 1-55673)* Orders Addr.: P.O. Box 4503, Lima, OH 45802-4503 USA (SAN 207-0707) Tel 419-227-1818; Fax: 419-228-9184; Toll Free: 800-537-1030 (Orders); 800-241-4056 (Customer Service); Edit Addr.: 517 S. Main St., Lima, OH 45804-4503 USA Do not confuse with CSS Publishing in Tularosa, NM
E-mail: editor@csspub.com; csr@csspub.com; info@csspub.com; orders@csspub.com
Web site: http://www.csspub.com.

C&T Publishing, *(0-914881; 1-57120)* Orders Addr.: 1651 Challenge Dr., Concord, CA 94520 USA (SAN 289-0720) Tel 925-677-0373 (phone/fax); Toll Free: 800-284-1114
E-mail: ctinfo@ctpub.com
Web site: http://www.ctpub.com.

Ctr. for Literary Publishing, Colorado State Univ., *(1-885635)* Center for Literary Publishing, Department of English, Colorado State University, Fort Collins, CO 80523 USA Tel 970-491-5449; Fax: 970-491-0283
E-mail: creview@colostate.edu
Web site: http://www.coloradoreview.com.

Cultural Hispana/Ameriketako Liburuak, Orders Addr.: P.O. Box 7729, Silver Spring, MD 20907 USA (SAN 159-2823); Edit Addr.: 1413 Crestridge Dr., Silver Spring, MD 20910 USA (SAN 249-3063) Tel 301-585-0134
E-mail: mokordo@erols.com
Web site: http://www.coloquio.com/libros.html.

Culture Plus Bk. Distributors, 44 Willoughby St., Brooklyn, NY 11201-5200 USA.

Culture Plus Bks., 209 N. La Brea Ave., Inglewood, CA 90301-1247 USA (SAN 631-3876).

CUP Services, 750 Cascadilla St., Ithaca, NY 14851 USA (SAN 630-6519) Tel 607-277-2211; Fax: 607-277-6292; Toll Free: 800-666-2211.

Curreri, Michelle Morrow, 3 Eagle Ln., Beverly, MA 01915 USA Tel 978-921-8020; Fax: 978-921-7577
E-mail: michelle@curreriworldsvs.net.

Curtis, Ralph Books, *See* **Curtis, Ralph Publishing**

Curtis, Ralph Publishing, *(0-88359)* P.O. Box 349, Sanibel, FL 33957 USA (SAN 121-1323) Tel 239-454-0010; Fax: 239-395-2727; Toll Free: 888-454-0011
E-mail: rcurtisbks@yahoo.com
Web site: http://www.ralphcurtisbooks.com.

Cybernetics Technology Corp., *(0-923458)* 1370 Port Washington Blvd., Port Washington, NY 11050-2628 USA (SAN 295-933X) Tel 516-883-7676.

Cypress Bk. Co., Inc., *(0-934643)* Subs. of China International Bk. Trading Corp., 360 Swift Ave. Ste. 42, S San Fran, CA 94080-6220 USA (SAN 112-1162) Toll Free: 800-383-1688
E-mail: sales@cypressbook.com; info@cypressbook.com; cypbook@pacbell.net
Web site: http://www.cypressbook.com.

Cypress Hse., *(1-879384)* 155 Cypress St., Fort Bragg, CA 95437 USA (SAN 297-9004) Tel 707-964-9520; Fax: 707-964-7531; Toll Free: 800-773-7782
E-mail: cypresshouse@cypresshouse.com; forms@cypresshouse.com
Web site: http://www.cypresshouse.com.

D & H News Co., Inc., 79 Albany Post Rd., Montrose, NY 10548 USA (SAN 169-5533) Tel 914-737-3152.

D & L Distribution, P.O. Box 72, Cahone, CO 81320 USA (SAN 631-1628) Tel 970-562-4495.

D K Publishing, Incorporated, *See* **Dorling Kindersley Publishing, Inc.**

Daedalus Bks., 9645 Gerwig Ln., Columbia, MD 21046-1520 USA (SAN 158-9202) Tel 410-309-2700
E-mail: tstock@daedalus-books.com; custserv@daedalus-books.com
Web site: http://www.daedalus-books.com.

Dahlstrom, Carol Field Inc., *(0-9679764; 0-9768446)* 7952 NE. Berwick Dr., Ankeny, IA 50021 USA Tel 515-964-1777; Fax: 515-964-1788
E-mail: braveink@aol.com
Web site: http://www.braveink.com.

Dake Bible Sales, *See* **Dake Publishing**

Dake Publishing, *(0-9655968; 1-55829)* Orders Addr.: P.O. Box 1050, Lawrenceville, GA 30046 USA (SAN 212-0828) Tel 770-963-1611; Fax: 770-963-7700; Toll Free: 800-241-1239; Edit Addr.: 764 Martins Chapel Rd., Lawrenceville, GA 30246 USA (SAN 243-2684)
E-mail: derrick@dake.com
Web site: http://www.dake.com.

Dakota News, Inc., 221 Petro Ave., Box 1310, Sioux Falls, SD 57101 USA (SAN 169-7854) Tel 605-336-3000; Fax: 605-336-7279; Toll Free: 800-658-5498.

D.A.P./Distributed Art Pubs., *(1-881616; 1-891024; 1-933045)* Orders Addr.: 155 Sixth Ave., 2nd Flr., New York, NY 10013-1507 USA (SAN 630-6446) Tel 212-627-1999; Fax: 212-627-9484; Toll Free Fax: 800-478-3128; Toll Free: 800-338-2665
E-mail: dap@dapinc.com
Web site: http://www.artbook.com/.

Darr Subscription Agency, P.O. Box 575, Louisburg, KS 66053-0575 USA (SAN 285-9149) Toll Free: 800-850-3741
E-mail: lgriff@midusa.net.

David, Jonathan Publishers, Inc., *(0-8246)* 68-22 Eliot Ave., Middle Village, NY 11379 USA (SAN 169-5274) Tel 718-456-8611; Fax: 718-894-2818
E-mail: jondavpub@aol.com
Web site: http://www.jdbooks.com.

Dawson Subscription Service, *See* **Faxon Illinois Service Ctr.**

Day School Magazine Service, P.O. Box 262, Brooklyn, NY 11219 USA (SAN 285-9157) Tel 718-871-1486; Fax: 718-435-2342
E-mail: Elciv@juno.com.

DB & Assocs. Design & Distribution, P.O. Box 52756, Tulsa, OK 74152 USA Tel 918-749-3336; Fax: 918-749-4229
E-mail: sword352@aol.com.

DDDD Pubns., *(0-9635341; 1-885519)* 3407 Brown Rd., Saint Louis, MO 63114-4329 USA (SAN 631-2675).

De Vore Group/Carla Bks. & More, Orders Addr.: P.O. Box 10276, San Juan, PR 00922 USA (SAN 159-8309) Tel 809-721-7645; Fax: 809-722-9216; Edit Addr.: 1409 Ave. Ponce De Leon, San Juan, PR 00907-4023 USA (SAN 249-2776).

Dearborn Financial Publishing, Inc., *(0-7931; 0-88462; 0-913864; 0-936894; 1-57410)* 30 South Wacker Dr., Chicago, IL 60606-1719 USA (SAN 201-3622) Tel 312-836-4400 ext 282429; Fax: 312-836-1021
Web site: http://www.dearborn.com.

Dearborn Trade, A Kaplan Professional Company, *See* **Kaplan Publishing**

DecisionPro, Inc., 112 W. Foster Ave., No. 202C, State College, PA 16801 USA Tel 814-234-2446; Fax: 814-234-2447.

DeHoff Christian Bookstore, *(1-933965)* 749 N. W. Broad St., Murfreesboro, TN 37129-3797 USA (SAN 184-4202) Tel 615-893-8322; Fax: 615-896-7447; Toll Free: 800-695-5385
E-mail: dehoff@bellsouth.net
Web site: http://www.dehoffbooks.com.

Dehoff Publications, *See* **DeHoff Christian Bookstore**

Delmar News Agency, Inc., P.O. Box 7169, Newark, DE 19714-7169 USA (SAN 169-0892) Tel 302-455-9922; Toll Free: 800-441-7025.

Delmar Thomson Learning, *See* **Thomson Delmar Learning**

DeLong Subscription Agency, P.O. Box 806, Lafayette, IN 47902 USA (SAN 285-9246) Toll Free: 800-992-2092.

Delta Education, Incorporated, *See* **Delta Education, LLC**

Delta Education, LLC, *(0-87504; 1-58356; 1-59242; 1-59821; 1-60395)* Div, of Wicks Learning, 80 Northwest Blvd., Nashua, NH 03063 USA (SAN 630-1711) Toll Free: 800-442-5444
E-mail: ngosselin@delta-edu.com
Web site: http://www.delta-education.com.

Delta Systems Co., Inc., *(0-937354; 1-887744; 1-932748)* 1400 Miller Pkwy., McHenry, IL 60050-7030 USA (SAN 220-0457) Tel 815-363-3582; Fax: 815-363-2948; Toll Free Fax: 800-909-9901; Toll Free: 800-323-8270
E-mail: joanne@delta-systems.com
Web site: http://www.delta-systems.com.

Deltiologists of America, *(0-913782)* P.O. Box 8, Norwood, PA 19074 USA (SAN 170-3072) Tel 610-485-8572.

Denston, Richard O., 517 Walden Cir., Acworth, GA 30102-7107 USA Tel 770-592-3601.

Derstine, Roy Bk. Co., 14 Birch Rd., Kinnelon, NJ 07405 USA (SAN 130-822X) Tel 973-838-1109.

DeRu's Fine Arts, *(0-939370)* 9100 E. Artesia Blvd., Bellflower, CA 90706 USA (SAN 159-3862) Tel 562-920-1312; Fax: 562-920-3077
E-mail: derusgal@aol.com
Web site: http://www.derusfinearts.com.

Deseret Bk. Co., *(0-87579; 0-87747; 1-57345; 1-59038)* Div. of Deseret Management Corp., Orders Addr.: P.O. Box 30178, Salt Lake City, UT 84130 USA (SAN 150-763X) Tel 801-517-3165 (Wholesale Dept.); 801-534-1515; Fax: 801-517-3338; Toll Free: 800-453-3876; Edit Addr.: 40 E. South Temple, Salt Lake City, UT 84111 USA
E-mail: wholesale@deseretbook.com; dbwhsale@deseretbook.com
Web site: http://www.deseretbook.com; http://www.shadowmountain.com.

Destiny Image Pubs., *(0-7684; 0-914903; 1-56043; 0-9716036)* 167 Walnut Bottom Rd., Shippensburg, PA 17257 USA (SAN 253-4339) Tel 717-532-3040; Fax: 717-532-9291; Toll Free: 800-722-6774
E-mail: JLM@destinyimage.com
Web site: http://www.destinyimage.com.

Detroit Free Pr., Inc., *(0-937247; 0-9605692)* 600 W. Fort St., Detroit, MI 48226 USA (SAN 239-6998) Tel 313-222-6457; Fax: 313-222-5982; Toll Free: 800-678-6400
E-mail: robinson@freepress.com.

Devin-Adair Pubs., Inc., *(0-8159)* P.O. Box A, Old Greenwich, CT 06870 USA (SAN 112-062X) Tel 203-531-7755; Fax: 718-359-8568.

DeVorss & Co., *(0-87516)* Orders Addr.: P.O. Box 1389, Camarillo, CA 93011-1389 USA (SAN 168-9886) Tel 805-322-9010; Fax: 805-322-9011; Toll Free: 800-843-5743; Edit Addr.: 553 Constitution Ave., Camarillo, CA 93012-8510 USA
E-mail: service@devorss.com
Web site: http://www.devorss.com.

Diamond Bk. Distributors, Div. of Diamond Comic Distributors, Inc., Orders Addr.: 1966 Greenspring Dr., Suite 300, Timonium, MD 21093 USA (SAN 110-9502) Tel 410-560-7100; Fax: 410-560-2583; Toll Free: 800-452-6642
E-mail: books@diamondbookdistributors.com
Web site: http://www.diamondcomics.com; http://www.diamondbookdistributors.com/.

Diamond Book Distributors Inc., *See* **Diamond Comic Distributors, Inc.**

Diamond Comic Distributors, Inc., *(1-59396)* 1966 Greenspring Dr., Suite 300, Timonium, MD 21093 USA Tel 410-560-7100; Fax: 410-560-2583; Toll Free: 800-452-6642
E-mail: books@diamondcomics.com
Web site: http://www.diamondbookdistributors.com/.

Diamond Distributors, Inc., Orders Addr.: 1966 Greenspring Dr., Suite 300, Timonium, MD 21093 USA Tel 410-560-7100.

Digital Manga Distribution, *See* **Digital Manga Publishing**

Digital Manga Publishing, *(1-56970)* Div. of Digital Manga, Inc., 1487 W. 178th St. Ste. 300, Gardena, CA 90248-3253 USA (SAN 111-817X) Toll Free: 866-897-7300
E-mail: contact@emanga.com
Web site: http://www.dmpbooks.com/.

Digi-Tall Media, P.O. Box 868024, Plano, TX 75086-8024 USA Tel 972-762-1349.

DiIoia, Tony, 1103 Bailard Ave., Carpinteria, CA 93010 USA Tel 805-684-4486.

Dillon Bk., Subs. of Harold Dillon, Inc., 460 S. Marion Pkwy., Apt. 851B, Denver, CO 80209-2508 USA (SAN 169-0493) Tel 303-442-5323; Toll Free: 800-525-0842.

Discount Bk. Distributors, 1854 Wallace School Rd., No. E, Charleston, SC 29407-4822 USA (SAN 107-2250) Tel 843-556-6582.

Discovery Hse. Pubs., *(0-929239; 1-57293)* Div. of R B C Ministries, Orders Addr.: P.O. Box 3566, Grand Rapids, MI 49501 USA (SAN 248-8949) Tel 616-942-9218; Fax: 616-957-5741; Toll Free: 800-653-8333; Edit Addr.: 3000 Kraft Ave., SE, Grand Rapids, MI 49512 USA (SAN 248-8957)
E-mail: dhp@rbc.org
Web site: http://www.dhp.org.

Disney Publishing Worldwide, *(1-892309; 1-931580; 1-4231)* Subs. of Walt Disney Productions, 44 S. Broadway, 10th Flr., White Plains, NY 10601 USA Tel 914-288-4316
Web site: http://www.disney.go.com; http://www.hyperionbooksforchildren.com.

Distribooks, Inc., Div. of Midwest European Pubns., Inc., 8120 N. Ridgeway, Skokie, IL 60076 USA (SAN 630-9763) Tel 847-676-1596; Fax: 847-676-1195
E-mail: info@distribooks.com.

Distribuidora Escolar, Inc., 2250 SW 99th Ave., Miami, FL 00165-7569 USA (SAN 169-1104).

Distribuidora Norma, Inc., *(1-881700)* Div. of Carvajal International, Orders Addr.: P.O. Box 195040, San Juan, PR 00919-5040 USA Tel 787-788-5050; Fax: 787-788-7161; Toll Free: 800-BOOKS58; Edit Addr.: Carretera 869 Km 1.5 Barrio Palmas Royal Industrial, Catano, PR 00962 USA
Web site: http://www.norma.com.

Distribution Solutions Group, 1120 Rte. 22 E., Bridgewater, NJ 08807-0885 USA Toll Free: 866-374-4748.

Distributors International, Div. of Dennis-Landman Pubs., 1150 18th St., Santa Monica, CA 90403 USA (SAN 129-8089) Tel 310-828-0680
E-mail: info@moviecraft.com
Web site: http://www.moviecraft.com.

Distributors, The, *(0-942520)* 702 S. Michigan, South Bend, IN 46601 USA (SAN 169-2488) Tel 219-232-8500; Fax: 312-803-0887; Toll Free: 800-348-5200
E-mail: info@thedistributors.com
Web site: http://thedistributors.com/.

Divine, Inc., *(0-87305)* 1600 Providence Hwy., Walpole, MA 02081-2553 USA (SAN 159-8619) Toll Free: 800-766-0039
E-mail: pubservices@faxon.com; helpdesk@faxon.com
Web site: http://www.faxon.com.

Dixie News Co., P.O. Box 561129, Charlotte, NC 28256-1129 USA (SAN 169-636X) Tel 704-376-0140; Fax: 704-335-8604; Toll Free: 800-532-1045.

D&J Bk. Distributors, *(1-883080)* 229-21B Merrick Blvd., Laurelton, NY 11413 USA (SAN 630-5091) Tel 718-949-5400; Fax: 718-949-6161; Toll Free: 800-446-4707.

Docustar, 1325 Glendale-Milford Rd., Cincinnati, OH 45215 USA Tel 513-772-5400; Fax: 513-772-5410.

Dog Museum, The, *See* **American Kennel Club Museum of the Dog**

Dogwise, *See* **Dogwise Publishing**

Dogwise Publishing, *(1-929242)* Orders Addr.: P.O. Box 2778, Wenatchee, WA 98807 USA (SAN 631-1415) Tel 509-663-9115; Fax: 509-662-7233; Toll Free: 800-776-2665; Edit Addr.: 701B Poplar, Wenatchee, WA 98801 USA
E-mail: mail@dogwise.com; charlenew@dogwise.com
Web site: http://www.dogwise.com.

Doherty, Tom Assocs., LLC, *(0-312; 0-7653; 0-8125)* Div. of Holtzbrinck Publishers, Orders Addr.: 16365 James Madison Hwy., Gordonsville, VA 22942-8501 USA Toll Free Fax: 800-672-2054; Toll Free: 888-330-8477; Edit Addr.: 175 Fifth Ave., New York, NY 10010 USA Tel 212-674-5151; Fax: 540-672-7540 (customer service)
E-mail: inquiries@tor.com
Web site: http://www.tor.com/.

Donars Spanish Bks., P.O. Box 808, Lafayette, CO 80026 USA (SAN 108-1586) Tel 303-666-9175; Toll Free: 800-552-3316
E-mail: donars@prolynx.com.

Dorling Kindersley Publishing, Inc., *(0-7894; 1-56458; 1-879431; 0-7566)* Div. of The Penguin Group, 375 Hudson St., 2nd Flr., New York, NY 10014 USA (SAN 253-0791) Tel 212-213-4800; Fax: 212-213-5240; Toll Free: 877-342-5357 (orders only)
E-mail: Annemarie.Cancienne@dk.com; customer.service@dk.com
Web site: http://www.dk.com.

Dot Gibson Distribution, Div. of Dot Gibson Pubns., P.O. Box 117, Waycross, GA 31502 USA Tel 912-285-2848.

Double Blessing Productions, 12 N. Cheyenne Ave., Tulsa, OK 74103-2214 USA Do not confuse with Double Blessing Production in .

Dover Pubns., Inc., *(0-486)* Orders Addr.: 31 E. Second St., Mineola, NY 11501 USA (SAN 201-338X) Tel 516-294-7000; Fax: 516-742-5049 (orders only); Toll Free: 800-223-3130 (orders only)
E-mail: rights@doverpublications.com
Web site: http://www.doverdirect.com; http://www.doverpublications.com.

Downtown Bk. Ctr., Inc., *(0-941010)* 247 SE First St., Suites 236-237, Miami, FL 33131 USA (SAN 169-1112) Tel 305-377-9941
E-mail: raxdown@aol.com.

Dr. Leisure, *(0-9638802; 1-887471)* P.O. Box 1137, Kihei, HI 96753 USA Tel 808-879-4160
E-mail: drleisure@drleisure.com
Web site: http://www.drleisure.com.

Dramatic Publishing Co., *(0-87129; 1-58342)* Orders Addr.: 311 Washington St., Woodstock, IL 60098 USA Tel 815-338-7170; Fax: 815-338-8981; Toll Free Fax: 800-334-5302; Toll Free: 800-448-7469; Edit Addr.: 311 Washington St., Woodstock, IL 60098 USA (SAN 201-5676)
E-mail: plays@dramaticpublishing.com
Web site: http://www.dramaticpublishing.com.

Dreams in Action Distribution, P.O. Box 1894, Sedona, AZ 86339 USA Tel 928-204-1560; 70 Yucca St., Sedona, AZ 86351
E-mail: sales@dreamsinaction.us; pamela@deamsinaction.us.

Drown News Agency, P.O. Box 2080, Folsom, CA 95763-2080 USA (SAN 169-0450).

Duebbert, Harold F., P.O.B. 629 E. Adolphus Ave., Fergus Falls, MN 56537 USA Tel 218-736-4312.

Dufour Editions, Inc., *(0-8023)* Orders Addr.: P.O. Box 7, Chester Springs, PA 19425-0007 USA (SAN 201-341X) Tel 610-458-5005; Fax: 610-458-7103; Toll Free: 800-869-5677
E-mail: info@dufoureditions.com
Web site: http://www.dufoureditions.com.

Dumont, Charles Son, Inc., 1085 Dumont Dr., P.O. Box 1017, Voorhees, NJ 08043 USA (SAN 631-0842) Tel 856-346-9100; Fax: 856-346-3452; Toll Free: 800-257-8283
Web site: http://www.dumontmusic.com.

Durst, Sanford J., *(0-915262; 0-942666; 1-886720)* 106 Woodcleft Ave., Freeport, NY 11520 USA (SAN 211-6987) Tel 516-867-3333; Fax: 516-867-3397
E-mail: sjdbooks@verizon.net.

Duval News Co., Orders Addr.: P.O. Box 61297, Jacksonville, FL 32203 USA (SAN 169-1015); Edit Addr.: 5638 Commonwealth Ave., Jacksonville, FL 32205 USA (SAN 249-2865) Tel 904-783-2350.

Duval-Bibb Publishing Co., *(0-937713)* Div. of Mareeco Enterprises, Inc., Orders Addr.: P.O. Box 24168, Tampa, FL 33623-4168 USA (SAN 111-8641) Tel 813-281-0091; Fax: 813-282-0220; 1808 B St. NW, Suite 140, Auburn, WA 98001 Toll Free Fax: 800-548-1169; Toll Free: 800-518-3541
E-mail: reese.cop@gte.net
Web site: http://lonepinepublishing.com/ordering.

E Learn Aid, Orders Addr.: P.O. Box 39545, Los Angeles, CA 90039-0545 USA Fax: 323-665-8875.

E M C Publishing, *See* **EMC/Paradigm Publishing**

Eagle Business Systems, *(0-928210)* P.O. Box 1240, El Toro, CA 92630-1240 USA (SAN 285-7510) Tel 714-859-9622.

Eagle Feather Trading Post, Inc., 168 W. 12th St., Ogden, UT 84404 USA (SAN 630-8996) Tel 801-393-3991; Fax: 801-745-0903; Toll Free: 800-547-3364 (orders only).

Eaglecrafts, Orders Addr.: 168 W. 12th St., Ogden, UT 84404 USA (SAN 630-6381) Tel 801-393-3991; Fax: 801-745-0903; Toll Free: 800-547-3364 (orders only)
E-mail: porsturbo@aol.com.

Eakin Pr., *(0-89015; 1-57168; 0-9789150; 1-934645)* Div. of Sunbelt Media, P.O. Box 90159, Austin, TX 78709-0159 USA (SAN 207-3633) Tel 254-235-6161; Fax: 254-235-6230; Toll Free: 800-880-8642
E-mail: sales@eakinpress.com; tom@eakinpress.com; virginia@eakinpress.com
Web site: http://www.eakinpress.com.

EAL Enterprises, Inc., Div. of Ambassador Bk. Service, 42 Chasner St., Hempstead, NY 11550 USA (SAN 169-6645) Toll Free: 800-431-8913.

East Kentucky News, Inc., 416 Teays Rd., Paintsville, KY 41240 USA (SAN 169-2879) Tel 606-789-8169.

East Texas Distributing, 7171 Grand Blvd., Houston, TX 77054 USA (SAN 169-8265) Tel 713-748-2520; Fax: 713-748-2504.

Eastern Bk. Co., Orders Addr.: P.O. Box 4540, Portland, ME 04112-4540 USA Fax: 207-774-0331; Toll Free Fax: 800-214-3895; Toll Free: 800-937-0331; Edit Addr.: 55 Bradley Dr., Westbrook, ME 04092-2013 USA (SAN 169-3050)
E-mail: info@ebc.com
Web site: http://www.ebc.com.

Eastern National, *(0-915992; 1-888213; 1-59091)* 470 Maryland Dr., Suite 1, Fort Washington, PA 19034 USA (SAN 630-4044)
E-mail: erich@Easternnational.org
Web site: http://www.easternnational.org.

Eastern National Park & Monument Association, *See* **Eastern National**

Eastern News Distributors, Subs. of Hearst Corp., 250 W. 55th St., New York, NY 10019 USA (SAN 169-5738) Tel 212-649-4484; Fax: 212-265-6239; Toll Free: 800-221-3148; 1 Media Way, 12406 Rte. 250, Milan, OH 44846-9705 (SAN 200-7711); 227 W. Trade St., Charlotte, NC 28202 (SAN 631-600X) Tel 704-348-8427
E-mail: enews@hearst.com.

Eastern Subscription Agency, 231 Moria Ct., Aston, PA 19014-1264 USA (SAN 285-9467).

Easton News Co., 2601 Dearborn St., Easton, PA 18042 USA (SAN 169-7315).

Eastview Editions, *(0-89860)* P.O. Box 247, Bernardsville, NJ 07924 USA (SAN 169-4952) Tel 908-204-0535.

East-West Cultural Ctr., *(0-930736)* 12329 Marshall St., Culver City, CA 90230 USA (SAN 211-0121) Tel 310-390-9083; Fax: 310-390-7763
E-mail: ewcc@earthlink.net
Web site: http://home.earthlink.net/~ewcc.

East-West Export Bks., c/o Univ. of Hawaii Pr., 2840 Kolowalu St., Honolulu, HI 96822 USA Tel 808-956-8830; Fax: 808-988-6052
E-mail: royden@hawaii.edu
Web site: http://www.2.hawaii.edu/uhpress/eweb.

Eastwind Bks. & Arts, Inc., 1435-A Stockton St., San Francisco, CA 94133 USA (SAN 127-3159) Tel 415-772-5888; Fax: 415-772-5885
E-mail: info@eastwindsf.com
Web site: http://www.eastwindsf.com.

Eau Claire News Co., Inc., 8100 Partridge Rd., Eau Claire, WI 54703-9646 USA (SAN 169-9059) Tel 715-835-5437.

ebrary, Inc., 318 Cambridge Ave., Palo Alto, CA 94306 USA Tel 650-475-8700; Fax: 650-475-8881
E-mail: info@ebrary.com
Web site: http://www.ebrary.com.

ebrary.com, *See* **ebrary, Inc.**

EBS, Inc. Bk. Service, 290 Broadway, Lynbrook, NY 11563 USA (SAN 169-5487) Tel 516-593-1195; Fax: 516-596-2911.

EBSCO Media, *(1-885860)* Div. of EBSCO Industries, Inc., 801 Fifth Ave., S., Birmingham, AL 35233 USA Tel 205-323-1508; Fax: 205-226-8400; Toll Free: 800-765-0852
Web site: http://www.ebsco.com.

EBSCO Subscription Services, 5724 Hwy. 280 E., Birmingham, AL 35242-6818 USA (SAN 285-9394) Tel 205-991-6000; Fax: 205-991-1479
E-mail: jacomo@ebsco.com
Web site: http://www.ebsco.com.

e-Compass Communications, Inc., P.O. Box 9177, Rochester, MN 55903 USA.

Economical Wholesale Co., 6 King Philip Rd., Worcester, MA 01606 USA (SAN 169-3646).

EDC Publishing, *(0-7460; 0-86020; 0-88110; 1-58086; 0-7945; 1-60130)* Orders Addr.: P.O. Box 470663, Tulsa, OK 74147-0663 USA (SAN 658-0505); Edit Addr.: 10302 E. 55th Pl., Tulsa, OK 74146-6515 USA (SAN 107-5322) Tel 918-622-4522; Fax: 918-665-7919; Toll Free Fax: 800-747-4509; Toll Free: 800-475-4522
E-mail: edc@edcpub.com
Web site: http://www.edcpub.com.

Ediciones del Norte, *(0-910061)* P.O. Box 5130, Hanover, NH 03755 USA (SAN 241-2993).

Ediciones Universal, *(0-89729; 1-59388)* Orders Addr.: P.O. Box 450353, Miami, FL 33245-0353 USA (SAN 658-0548); Edit Addr.: 3090 SW Eighth St., Miami, FL 33135 USA (SAN 207-2203) Tel 305-642-3355; Fax: 305-642-7978
E-mail: marta@ediciones.com; ediciones@ediciones.com
Web site: http://www.ediciones.com.

Editorial Cernuda, Inc., 1040 27th Ave., SW, Miami, FL 33135 USA (SAN 158-8850) Tel 305-264-9400.

Editorial Cultural, Inc., *(1-56758; 84-399)* Orders Addr.: P.O. Box 21056, San Juan, PR 00928 USA; Edit Addr.: Calle Robles, No. 51, San Juan, PR 00928 USA Tel 809-765-9767 (phone/fax)
E-mail: angiev@editorialculturalpr.com
Web site: http://www.editorialculturalpr.com.

Editorial Unilit, *(0-7899; 0-945792; 1-56063)* Div. of Spanish Hse., Inc., 1360 NW 88th Ave., Miami, FL 33172-3093 USA (SAN 247-5979) Tel 305-592-6136; Fax: 305-592-0087; Toll Free: 800-767-7726
E-mail: sales1@unidial.com
Web site: http://www.editorialunilit.com/.

Educa Vision, *(1-881839; 1-58432)* 7550 NW 47th Ave., Coconut Creek, FL 33073 USA Tel 954-725-0701; Fax: 954-427-6739; Toll Free: 800-983-3822
E-mail: educa@aol.com
Web site: http://www.educavision.com.

Education Guide, Inc., *(0-914880)* P.O. Box 421, Randolph, MA 02368 USA (SAN 201-4580) Tel 617-376-0066; Fax: 617-376-0067.

Educational Audio Visual, Incorporated, *See* **CLEARVUE/eav, Inc.**

Educational Bk. Distributors, P.O. Box 2510, Novato, CA 94948 USA (SAN 158-2259) Tel 415-883-3530; Fax: 415-883-4280; Toll Free: 800-761-5501
E-mail: PblshrSvcs@aol.com.

Educational Development Corporation, *See* **EDC Publishing**

Educational Distribution Corp., 10302 E. 55th Pl., Tulsa, OK 74146 USA Tel 918-622-4522.

Educational Insights, Inc., *(0-88679; 1-56767)* 18730 S. Wilmington Ave., Rancho Dominguez, CA 90220 USA (SAN 283-8745) Toll Free: 800-933-3277.

Educational Media Corp., *(0-932796; 1-930572)* Orders Addr.: P.O. Box 21311, Minneapolis, MN 55421 USA (SAN 665-6919); Edit Addr.: 4256 Central Ave. NE, Minneapolis, MN 55421-2920 USA (SAN 212-4203) Tel 763-781-0088; Fax: 763-781-7753; Toll Free: 800-966-3382
E-mail: emedia@educationalmedia.com
Web site: http://www.educationalmedia.com.

Educational Record Ctr., Inc., 3233 Burnt Mill Dr., Suite 100, Wilmington, NC 28403-2698 USA (SAN 630-592X) Tel 910-251-1235; Fax: 910-343-0311; Toll Free Fax: 888-438-1637; Toll Free: 800-438-1637
E-mail: info@erc-inc.com
Web site: http://www.erc-inc.com.

Educational Resources, 1550 Executive Dr., Elgin, IL 60123 USA (SAN 631-5674) Tel 847-888-8300; Toll Free: 800-624-2926 Do not confuse with companies with same or similar name in Shawnee Mission, Columbia, SC, Saint Paul, MN
E-mail: gmhardeman@aol.com.

Educational Showcase, 3571 Newgate Dr., Troy, MI 48084-1042 USA Toll Free: 800-213-3671.

Educational Software Institute, 4213 S. 94th St., Omaha, NE 68127 USA (SAN 631-5860) Tel 402-592-3300.

Edumate-Educational Materials, Inc., P.O. Box 711174, San Diego, CA 92171-1174 USA (SAN 630-2955)
E-mail: GusBus@aol.com.

Edu-Tech Corp., The, 65 Bailey Rd., Fairfield, CT 06432 USA (SAN 157-5392) Tel 203-374-4212; Fax: 203-374-8050; Toll Free: 800-338-5463
E-mail: edutcorp@aoc.com.

Edward Weston Graphic, Incorporated, *See* **Weston, Edward Fine Arts**

Eisenbrauns, Inc., *(0-931464; 1-57506)* Orders Addr.: P.O. Box 275, Winona Lake, IN 46590-0275 USA (SAN 200-7835) Tel 574-269-2011; Fax: 574-269-6788; Edit Addr.: 600 N. Bay Dr., Warsaw, IN 46580 USA
E-mail: ghannah@eisenbrauns.com; Orders@eisenbrauns.com
Web site: http://www.eisenbrauns.com.

El Qui-Jote Bk., Inc., 12651 Monarch, Houston, TX 77047 USA (SAN 107-8666) Tel 713-433-3388.

Elder's Bk. Store, 2115 Elliston Pl., Nashville, TN 37203 USA (SAN 112-6091) Tel 615-327-1867.

Elkins, C. J., 400 S. Beverly Dr. Suite 214, Beverly Hills, CA 90212 USA Toll Free: 800-769-2120
E-mail: sitare@aol.com; sitare@zwallet.com.

Ellis News Co., Affil. of L-S Distributors, 130 E. Grand Ave., South San Francisco, CA 94080 USA (SAN 169-0183) Tel 415-873-2094; Fax: 415-873-4222; Toll Free: 800-654-7040 (orders only).

ELS Educational Services, *(0-87789; 0-89285; 0-89318)* Orders Addr.: 200 Old Tappan Rd., Old Tappan, NJ 07675 USA; Edit Addr.: 1357 Second St., Santa Monica, CA 90401-1102 USA (SAN 281-6326).

Elsevier, *(0-08; 0-444; 0-7204; 0-916086; 1-85617; 1-59278)* Orders Addr.: P.O. Box 945, New York, NY 10159-0945 USA (SAN 251-2564) Toll Free: 888-437-4636; 11830 Westline Industrial Dr., Saint Louis, MO 63146 (SAN 200-2108) Tel 314-453-7095 (Outside US); Toll Free Fax: 800-535-9935; Toll Free: 800-460-3110 (Outside US); 800-545-2522; Edit Addr.: 360 Park Ave S. Flr. 11, New York, NY 10010-1710 USA (SAN 200-2051)
E-mail: usinfo-f@elsevier.com; custserv@elsevier.com
Web site: http://www.elsevier.com.

Elsevier - Health Sciences Division, *(0-323; 0-443; 0-444; 0-7020; 0-7216; 0-7234; 0-7236; 0-7506; 0-8016; 0-8151; 0-920513; 0-932883; 1-55664; 1-56053; 84-8086; 84-8174; 1-898507; 1-932141; 1-4160)* Subs. of Elsevier Science, Orders Addr.: 11830 Westline Industrial Dr., Saint Louis, MO 63146 USA Tel 314-453-7010; Fax: 314-453-7095; Toll Free Fax: 800-535-9935; Toll Free: 800-545-2522; 800-460-3110 (Customers Outside US); Edit Addr.: The Curtis Center, Suite 300E, 3rd Flr. 170 S. Independence Mall W., Philadelphia, PA 19106 USA Tel 215-238-7800; Fax: 215-238-7362; Toll Free: 800-523-4069; 800-523-1649
E-mail: usbkinfo@elsevier.com
Web site: http://www.elsevier.com; http://www.us.elsevierhealth.com/.

Elsevier Science, *See* **Elsevier**

Elsevier Science - Health Sciences Division, *See* **Elsevier - Health Sciences Division**

Elsevier Science & Technology Bks., Orders Addr.: 11830 Westline Industrial Dr., Saint Louis, MO 63146 USA Tel 314-453-7010; Fax: 314-453-7095; Toll Free Fax: 800-535-9935; Toll Free: 800-545-2522; 800-460-3110 (Customers Outside US); Edit Addr.: 525 B St., Suite 1900, San Diego, CA 92101 USA Toll Free: 1-800-894-3434; 200 Wheeler Rd., 6th Flr., Burlington, MA 01803 Tel 781-313-4700
E-mail: bookstore.orders@elsevier.com
Web site: http://www.syngress.com; http://www.elsevier.com/.

EMC/Paradigm Publishing, *(0-7638; 0-8219; 0-88436; 0-912022; 1-56118)* Div. of EMC Corp., 875 Montreal Way, Saint Paul, MN 55102-4245 USA (SAN 201-3800) Tel 651-290-2800; Fax: 651-290-2828
E-mail: publish@emcp.com; educate@emcp.com
Web site: http://www.emcp.com.

Emerald Hse. Group, Inc., *(1-889893; 1-932307)* 427 Wade Hampton Blvd., Greenville, SC 29609 USA Tel 864-235-2434; Fax: 864-235-2491; Toll Free: 800-209-8570
E-mail: info@emeraldhouse.com
Web site: http://www.emeraldhouse.com.

Emery-Pratt Co., Orders Addr.: 1966 W. Main St., Owosso, MI 48867-1397 USA (SAN 170-1401) Tel 989-723-5291; Fax: 989-723-4677; Toll Free Fax: 800-523-6379; Toll Free: 800-762-5683 (library orders only); 800-248-3887 (customer service only) Distributor to Libraries & Hospitals
E-mail: custserv@emery-pratt.com
Web site: http://www.emery-pratt.com.

Empire Comics, 375 Stone Rd., Rochester, NY 14616 USA (SAN 110-943X) Tel 716-442-0371; Fax: 716-442-7807
E-mail: empires@frontiernet.net.

Empire News of Jamestown, Foot Ave. & Extension St., Box 2029, Sta. A, Jamestown, NY 14702 USA (SAN 169-5371).

Empire Publishing Service, *(1-58690)* P.O. Box 1344, Studio City, CA 91614-0344 USA (SAN 630-5687) Tel 818-784-8918
E-mail: empirepubsvc@att.net.

Empire State News Corp., Orders Addr.: P.O. Box 1167, Buffalo, NY 14240-1167 USA Tel 716-681-1100; Fax: 716-681-1120; Toll Free: 800-414-6247; Edit Addr.: 316 Forestview Dr., Buffalo, NY 14221-1461 USA (SAN 169-5177)
Web site: http://www.esnc.com.

Empowerment Technologies, *See* **Empowerment Technologies/Neuro-Semantics Publns.**

Empowerment Technologies/Neuro-Semantics Publns., *(1-890001; 1-899836)* Orders Addr.: P.O. Box 8, Clifton, CO 81520 USA Tel 704-864-3585; Fax: 970-523-5790; Edit Addr.: P.O. Box 9231, Grand Junction, CO 81501 USA Tel 970-523-7877
E-mail: NLEMetaStates@onlinecol.com
Web site: http://www.neurosemantics.com.

Encino Pr., *(0-88426)* 510 Baylor St., Austin, TX 78703 USA (SAN 201-3843) Tel 512-476-6821; Fax: 512-476-9393.

Endeavor Bks./Mountain States Litho, *(0-9653706; 1-892944)* Orders Addr.: P.O. Box 1399, Casper, WY 82601 USA; Edit Addr.: 133 S. McKinley, Casper, WY 82601 USA Tel 307-265-7410; 307-234-9325; Fax: 307-237-9521; Toll Free: 888-324-9303; 800-584-9340
E-mail: danh@endeavorbooks.com
Web site: http://www.endeavorbooks.com; http://www.mtstlitho.com.

Enfield Publishing & Distribution Co., Inc., *(0-9656184; 1-893598)* Orders Addr.: P.O. Box 699, Enfield, NH 03748 USA Tel 603-632-7377; Fax: 603-632-5611; Edit Addr.: 234 May St., Enfield, NH 03748 USA
E-mail: info@enfieldbooks.com
Web site: http://www.enfielddistribution.com; http://www.enfieldbooks.com.

Entrepreneur Media, *See* **Entrepreneur Pr.**

Entrepreneur Pr., *(0-916378; 1-55571; 1-891984; 1-932156; 1-932531; 1-59918)* 2445 McCabe Way, Suite 400, Irvine, CA 92614-6244 USA Tel 949-261-2325; Fax: 949-261-7729; Toll Free: 800-864-6864
E-mail: gponce@entrepreneur.com
Web site: http://www.entrepreneur.com.

Entrepreneur Start a Business Store, 9114 River Look Ln., Fair Oaks, CA 95628-6565 USA (SAN 133-1485) Fax: 916-863-0361.

Epic Book Promotions, 914 Nolan Way, Chula Vista, CA 91911-2408 USA Tel 619-498-8547; Fax: 619-498-8540
E-mail: gvjack@pacbell.net.

E-Pros DG, 32 N. Goodwin Ave., Elmsford, NY 10523 USA Toll Free: 866-377-6700
E-mail: sales@e-pros.ws.

Epson Mid-Atlantic, Subs. of Epson America, Inc., 8 Neshaminy Interplex, Suite 319, Trerose, PA 19053 USA (SAN 285-7243) Tel 215-245-2180.

Eriksson Enterprises, 126 Sunset Dr., Farmington, UT 84025-3426 USA (SAN 110-5892).

Erlbaum, Lawrence Assocs., Inc., *(0-8058; 0 86377; 0-89859; 1-880393; 1-4106)* 270 Madison Ave. Flr. 4, New York, NY 10016-0601 USA (SAN 213-960X) Toll Free: 800-926-6579 (orders only)
E-mail: orders@erlbaum.com
Web site: http://www.erlbaum.com.

ETD KroMar Temple, P.O. Box 535695, Grand Prairie, TX 75053-5625 USA (SAN 169-8435) Tel 254-778-5261; Fax: 254-778-5267.

Eurobooks, 1402 FJKL Cswy 113, North Bay Village, FL 33141 USA Tel 305-762-7286; Fax: 425-944-4551
E-mail: sales@eurobooksinc.com
Web site: http://www.euroboksinc.com.

European Bk. Co., Inc., 925 Larkin St., San Francisco, CA 94109 USA (SAN 169-0191) Tel 415-474-0626; Fax: 415-474-0630; Toll Free: 877-746-3666
E-mail: info@europeanbook.com.

European Press Service - PBD America Wholesalers, 30 Edison Dr., Wayne, NJ 07470-4713 USA (SAN 630-7825).

Evans Bk. Distribution & Pubs., Inc., *(0-9654884, 1-56684)* 895 W. 1700 S., Salt Lake City, UT 84104 USA Tel 801-975-1315; Fax: 801-975-1343; Toll Free: 877-655-2665.

Evans Book, *See* **Evans Bk. Distribution & Pubs., Inc.**

Excaliber Publishing Co., *(1-881353)* 7954 W. Bury Ave., San Diego, CA 92126 USA (SAN 297-6412) Tel 619-695-3091; Fax: 619-695-3095.

Exciting Times, 17430C Crenshaw Blvd., Torrance, CA 90504 USA (SAN 114-4642) Tel 310-515-2676; Fax: 310-515-1382.

Executive Bks., *(0-937539; 1-933715)* Div. of Life Management Services, Inc., 206 West Allen St., Mechanicsburg, PA 17055-6240 USA (SAN 156-5419) Tel 717-766-9499; Fax: 717-766-6565; Toll Free: 800-233-2665
E-mail: jason@executivebooks.com
Web site: http://www.executivebooks.com.

Exley Giftbooks, 185 Main St. Apt. 2, Spencer, MA 01562-1755 USA Toll Free Fax: 800-453-5248; Toll Free: 800-423-9539
E-mail: exlgb@aol.com.

Exploration Films, P.O. Box 1069, Monument, CO 80132 USA Tel 719-481-4599; Fax: 719-481-1399; Toll Free: 800-964-0439
E-mail: jolene@explorationfilms.com
Web site: http://www.explorationfilms.com.

Explorations, 360 Interlocken Blvd., Suite 300, Broomfield, CO 80021 USA Toll Free Fax: 800-456-1139; Toll Free: 800-720-2114
E-mail: customerservice@gaiam.com
Web site: http://www.gaiam.com.

Express Media, *(0-9723163)* 127 Rankin Rd., Columbia, MS 37202 USA Tel 615-360-6400
Web site: http://www.authorsexpress.com.

F & W Pubns., Inc., *(0-89134; 0-89879; 0-932620; 1-55870; 1-58180; 1-58297; 1-884910; 1-892127; 1-59963; 1-60061)* Orders Addr.: 4700 E. Galbraith Rd., Cincinnati, OH 45236 USA Tel 513-531-2690; Fax: 513-531-7185; Toll Free Fax: 888-590-4082; Toll Free: 800-289-0963
Web site: http://www.artistsmagazine.com; http://www.artistsnetwork.com; http://www.davidandcharles.co.uk; http://www.krause.com; http://www.familytreemagazine.com; http://www.howdesign.com; http://www.idonline.com; http://www.memorymakersmagazine.com; http://www.popularwoodworking.com; http://www.writersdigest.com; http://www.writersmarket.com; http://www.writersonlineworkshops.com; http://www.fwpublications.com.

Faber & Faber, Inc., *(0-571)* Affil. of Farrar, Straus & Giroux, LLC, Orders Addr.: c/o Van Holtzbrinck Publishing Services, 16365 James Madison Hwy., Gordonsville, VA 22942 USA Fax: 540-572-7540; Toll Free: 888-330-8477; Edit Addr.: 19 Union Sq., W, New York, NY 10003-3304 USA (SAN 218-7256) Tel 212-741-6900; Fax: 212-633-9385
E-mail: sales@fsgbooks.com
Web site: www.fsgbooks.com/contact.htm.

Fairfield Bk. Service Co., 150 Margherita Lawn, Stratford, CT 06615 USA (SAN 131-0976) Tel 203-375-7607.

FaithWorks, *See* **STL Distribution North America**

Falk Bks. Inc., W.E., 7491 N. Federal Hwy., PMB 267, Boca Raton, FL 33487 USA.

Falk, W. E., *See* **Falk Bks. Inc., W.E.**

Fall River News Co., Inc., 144 Robeson St., Fall River, MA 02720-4925 USA (SAN 169-3425) Tel 508-679-5266.

Family History World, P.O. Box 129, Tremonton, UT 84337 USA (SAN 159-673X) Fax: 801-250-6727; Toll Free: 800-377-6058
E-mail: genealogy@utahlinx.com
Web site: http://www.genealogical-institute.com.

Family Reading Service, 1601 N. Slappey Blvd., Albany, GA 31701-1431 USA (SAN 169-1376).

Far West Bk. Service, 3515 NE Hassalo, Portland, OR 97232 USA (SAN 107-6760) Tel 503-234-7664; Fax: 503-231-0573; Toll Free: 800-964-9378.

Farrar, Straus & Giroux, *(0-374)* Div. of Holtzbrinck Publishers, Orders Addr.: c/o Holtzbrinck Publishers, 16365 James Madison Hwy., Gordonsville, VA 22942 USA Toll Free Fax: 800-672-2054; Toll Free: 888-330-8477; Edit Addr.: 19 Union Sq., W., New York, NY 10003 USA (SAN 206-782X) Tel 212-741-6900; Fax: 212-463-0641
E-mail: sales@fsgee.com; fsg.editorial@fsgee.com
Web site: http://www.fsgbooks.com/.

Faxon Company, The, *See* **Divine, Inc.**

Faxon Illinois Service Ctr., Affil. of Dawson Holdings PLC, 1600 Providence Hwy., Walpole, MA 02081-2553 USA (SAN 286-0147) Toll Free: 800-852-7404
E-mail: postmaster@dawson.com; sandy.nordman@dawson.com
Web site: http://www.faxon.com.

Fayette County News Agency, Orders Addr.: P.O. Box 993, Uniontown, PA 15401 USA Tel 724-437-1181; Edit Addr.: Cherry Tree Square 42 Matthew Dr., Uniontown, PA 15401 USA (SAN 169-765X).

FEC News Distributing, 2201 Fourth Ave., N., Lake Worth, FL 33461-3835 USA (SAN 169-1341) Tel 407-547-3000; Fax: 407-547-3080.

Feldheim, Philipp Incorporated, *See* **Feldheim Pubs.**

Feldheim Pubs., *(0-87306; 1-58330; 1-59826)* 208 Airport Executive Park., Nanuet, NY 10954-5262 USA (SAN 106-6307) Toll Free: 800-237-7149
E-mail: sales@feldheim.com; eli@feldheim.com
Web site: http://www.feldheim.com.

Fell, Frederick Pubs., Inc., *(0-8119; 0-88391)* 1403 Shoreline Way, Hollywood, FL 33019-5007 USA
E-mail: info@fellpub.com
Web site: http://www.fellpub.com.

Fennell, Reginald F. Subscription Service, 1002 W. Michigan Ave., Jackson, MI 49202 USA (SAN 159-6071) Tel 517-782-3132; Fax: 517-782-1109.

FEP, A Booksource Co., 1230 Macklind Ave., Saint Louis, MO 63110 USA (SAN 169-1317) Tel 314-647-0600; Fax: 314-647-6850; Toll Free: 800-444-0435
Web site: http://www.booksource.com.

Fiddlecase Bks., HC 63 Box 104, East Alstead, NH 03602 USA (SAN 200-7495) Tel 603-835-7889.

Fiesta Bk. Co., *(0-88473)* P.O. Box 490641, Key Biscayne, FL 33149 USA (SAN 201-8470) Tel 305-858-4843.

Fiesta Publishing Corporation, *See* **Fiesta Bk. Co.**

Films for the Humanities & Sciences, *See* **Films Media Group**

Films Media Group, *(0-7365; 0-89113; 1-56950; 1-4213; 1-60467)* Div. of Primedia, Orders Addr.: P.O. Box 2053, Princeton, NJ 08543-2053 USA (SAN 653-2705) Tel 609-671-1000; Fax: 609-671-0266; Toll Free: 800-257-5126; Edit Addr.: 2572 Brunswick Pike, Lawrenceville, NJ 08648 USA
E-mail: custserv@films.com
Web site: http://www.films.com.

Fine Assocs., One Farragut Sq., S., Washington, DC 20006 USA (SAN 169-0914) Tel 202-628-2609.

Finn News Agency, Inc., 4415 State Rd. 327, Auburn, IN 46706-9542 USA (SAN 169-2356).

Finney Co., Inc., *(0-89317; 0-912486; 0-933855; 0-9617767; 0-9639705; 1-880654; 1-893272)* Orders Addr.: 8075 215th St. W., Lakeville, MN 55044 USA (SAN 206-412X) Tel 952-469-6699; Fax: 952-469-1968; Toll Free Fax: 800-330-6232; Toll Free: 800-846-7027
E-mail: feedback@finneyco.com; ecopress@peak.org
Web site: http://www.finneyco.com; http://www.ecopress.com; http://www.anacus.com; http://www.pogopress.com.

Fire Protection Publications, *See* **IFSTA**

Firebird Distributing, LLC, 1945 P St., Eureka, CA 95501-3007 USA (SAN 631-1229) Toll Free: 800-353-3575
E-mail: sales@firebirddistributing.com
Web site: http://www.firebirddistributing.com.

Firefly Bks., Ltd., *(0-920668; 1-55209; 1-895565; 1-896284; 1-55297; 1-55407)* Orders Addr.: c/o Frontier Distributing, 1000 Young St., Suite 160, Tonawanda, NY 14150 USA (SAN 630-611X) Tel 203-222-9700; Toll Free Fax: 800-565-6034; Toll Free: 800-387-5085; Edit Addr.: 8514 Long Canyon Dr., Austin, TX 78730-2813 USA
E-mail: service@fireflybooks.com
Web site: http://www.fireflybooks.com/.

Firenze Pr., *(0-9711236)* Orders Addr.: P.O. Box 6892, Wyomissing, PA 19610-0892 USA (SAN 254-315X); Edit Addr.: 612 Museum Rd., Reading, PA 19610-0892 USA Tel 610-374-7048; Fax: 610-478-7992 Do not confuse with Leonardo Pr., Camden, ME
E-mail: hailejohnjr@msn.com; HaileJohnJr@msn.com; InkPenCJH@msn.com
Web site: http://caroljhaile.com.

Fischer, Carl LLC, *(0-8258)* Orders Addr.: 588 N. Gulph Rd. Ste. B, Kng Of Prussa, PA 19406-2831 USA Toll Free: 800-762-2328; Edit Addr.: 65 Bleeker St., New York, NY 10012-2420 USA (SAN 107-4245) Tel 212-772-0900; Fax: 212-477-6996; Toll Free: 800-762-2328
E-mail: cf-info@carlfischer.com
Web site: http://www.carlfischer.com.

Fish, Enrica Medical Bks., 1208 W. Minnehaha Pkwy., Minneapolis, MN 55419-1163 USA (SAN 157-8588) Toll Free: 800-728-8398.

Flannery Co., 13123 Aerospace Dr., Victorville, CA 92394 USA (SAN 168-9754) Tel 760-246-8995; Fax: 760-246-8595; Toll Free: 800-456-3400.

Flannery, J. F. Company, *See* **Flannery Co.**

Fleming, Robert Hull Museum, *(0-934658)* Univ. of Vermont, 61 Colchester Ave., Burlington, VT 05405 USA (SAN 110-8824) Tel 802-656-2273; Fax: 802-656-8059
Web site: http://www.uvm.edu/~fleming/store/index.html.

Flora & Fauna Bks., P.O. Box 15718, Gainesville, FL 32604 USA (SAN 133-1221) Tel 352-373-5630; Fax: 352-373-3249
E-mail: ffbks@aol.com
Web site: http://www.ffbooks.com.

Florida Academic Pr., *(1-890357)* P.O. Box 540, Gainesville, FL 32602-0540 USA (SAN 299-3643) Tel 352-332-5104; Fax: 352-331-6003
E-mail: fapress@worldnet.att.net.

Florida Classics Library, *(0-912451)* P.O. Drawer 1657, Port Salerno, FL 34992-1657 USA (SAN 265-2404) Tel 561-546-9380 (orders); Fax: 561-546-7545 (orders).

Florida Flair Bks., *(0-9613236)* 7214 Haviland Cir., Boynton Beach, FL 33437 USA (SAN 295-4192) Tel 561-738-5191.

Florida Schl. Bk. Depository, 1125 N. Ellis Rd., P.O. Box 6578, Jacksonville, FL 32236 USA (SAN 161-8423) Tel 904-781-7191; Fax: 904-781-3486; Toll Free: 800-447-7957.

Flury & Co., 322 First Ave S., Seattle, WA 98104 USA (SAN 107-5748) Tel 206-587-0260.

FM International, P.O. Box 91, Waunakee, WI 53597-0091 USA.

Fodor's Travel Guides, *See* **Fodor's Travel Pubns.**

Fodor's Travel Pubns., Div. of Random Hse., Information Group, Orders Addr.: 400 Hahn Rd., Westminster, MD 21157 USA Tel 410-848-1900; Toll Free: 800-726-0600; Edit Addr.: 1745 Broadway, New York, NY 10019 USA Tel 212-782-9000
Web site: http://www.fodors.com.

Follet Higher Education Grp, P.O. Box 3488, Oak Brook, IL 60522-3488 USA Tel 630-279-0123.

Follett Audiovisual Resources, *See* **Follett Media Distribution**

Follett College Stores Corp., 1818 Swift Dr., Oak Brook, IL 60523-1576 USA Tel 630-279-2330; Toll Free: 800-323-4506.

Follett Educational Services, Orders Addr.: 1433 Internationale Pkwy. DOCK Door 30, Woodridge, IL 60517 USA (SAN 631-7901) Tel 800-621-4272; 630-972-5600; Fax: 630-972-4673
E-mail: mpetrou@fes.follett.com; klacy@fes.follett.com.

Follett Library Resources, *(0-329)* Div. of the Follett Corp., 1340 Ridgeview Dr., McHenry, IL 60050 USA (SAN 169-1902) Tel 815-759-1700; Toll Free Fax: 800-852-5458; Toll Free: 800-435-6170.

Follett Media Distribution, 1847 Mercer Rd., Lexington, KY 40511-1001 USA (SAN 631-7316) Toll Free: 888-281-1216.

Fondo de Cultura Economica USA, *(968-16; 950-557; 956-7083; 9972-663)* 2293 Verus St., San Diego, CA 92154 USA Tel 619-429-0827; Fax: 619-429-0455; Toll Free: 800-532-3872
E-mail: sales@fceusa.com; fceusa@fceusa.com
Web site: http://www.fceusa.com.

Fordham Univ. Pr., *(0-8232)* University Box L, Bronx, NY 10458 USA (SAN 201-6516) Tel 718-817-4780; Fax: 718-817-4785
E-mail: mnoonan@fordham.edu
Web site: http://www.fordhampress.com.

Forest Hse. Publishing Co., Inc., *(1-56674; 1-878363)* P.O. Box 738, Lake Forest, IL 60045 USA Tel 847-295-8287; Fax: 847-295-8201; Toll Free: 800-394-7323
Web site: http://www.forest-house.com.

Forest Sales & Distributing Co., *(0-9712183)* P.O. Box 1555, La Place, LA 70069-1555 USA (SAN 157-5511) Toll Free: 800-347-2106
E-mail: tbooks2@juno.com.

Forsyth Travel Library, Inc., *(0-9614539)* 1750 E. 131st St., P.O. Box 480800, Kansas City, MO 64148-0800 USA (SAN 169-2755) Tel 816-942-9050; Fax: 816-942-6969; Toll Free: 800-367-7984 (orders only)
E-mail: forsyth@gvi.net
Web site: http://www.forsyth.com.

Forward Movement Pubns., *(0-88028)* 300 West Fourth St., Cincinnati, OH 45202 USA (SAN 208-3841) Tel 513-721-6659; Fax: 513-721-0729; Toll Free: 800-543-1813 (orders only)
E-mail: Orders@forwarddaybyday.com
Web site: http://www.forwardmovement.org.

Foundation for Family Science, *(0-9748939)* 4614 SW Kelly Ave. Ste. 100, Portland, OR 97239-4277 USA
E-mail: familyscience@davidheil.com
Web site: http://www.familyscience.org.

Four Winds Trading Co., *(0-9672383)* 6355 Joyce Dr., Golden, CO 80403-7568 USA (SAN 631-1989) Toll Free: 800-456-5444
E-mail: Paul@Fourwinds-trading.com; sales@fourwinds-trading.com
Web site: http://www.fourwinds-trading.com.

Franklin Bk. Co., Inc., P.O. Box 451, Newtown Sq, PA 19073-0451 USA (SAN 121-4160)
E-mail: service@franklinbook.com
Web site: http://www.franklinbook.com.

Franklin Readers Service, P.O. Box 662, Dunn Loring, VA 22027-0662 USA (SAN 285-9599).

Franklin Square Overseas, 17-19 Washington St., Tenafly, NJ 07670-2084 USA (SAN 285-9637) Tel 201-569-2500; Fax: 201-569-5141
E-mail: esstn@ebsco.com.

Fraser Publishing Co., *(0-87034; 0-918632)* Div. of Alvin Q. Garbanzo, Inc., Orders Addr.: P.O. Box 217, Flint Hill, VT 22747 USA (SAN 213-9537) Tel 540-675-9976; Toll Free: 877-996-3336 US and Canada only
E-mail: info@fraserpublishing.com
Web site: http://www.fraserpublishing.com.

Free American, The, P.O. Box 15457, Scottsdale, AZ 85267-5457 USA (SAN 631-2330) Toll Free: 877-423-3250.

Freeman Family Ministries, Orders Addr.: P.O. Box 593, Waldo, FL 32694 USA Tel 352-468-2785
E-mail: freemanfamily9@msn.com.

Freeman, W. H. & Co., *(0-7167; 1-4292)* Div. of Holtzbrinck Publishers, Orders Addr.: 16365 James Madison Hwy., Gordonsville, VA 22942 USA Tel 540-672-7600; Toll Free Fax: 800-672-2054; Toll Free: 888-330-8477 (orders & customer service); Edit Addr.: 41 Madison Ave., 37th Flr., New York, NY 10010 USA (SAN 290-6864) Tel 212-576-9400; Fax: 212-689-2383; Toll Free: 800-903-3019
E-mail: webmaster@whfreeman.com
Web site: http://www.whfreeman.com.

Freihofer, A. G., 175 Fifth Ave., New York, NY 10010 USA (SAN 285-9602) Tel 272-460-7500; Fax: 272-473-6272.

French & European Pubns., Inc., *(0-320; 0-7859; 0-8288)* Rockefeller Ctr. Promenade, 610 Fifth Ave., New York, NY 10020-2497 USA (SAN 206-8109) Tel 212-581-8810; Fax: 212-265-1094
E-mail: frenchbookstore@aol.com
Web site: http://www.frencheuropean.com.

Friendly Hills Fellowship, *See* **Health and Growth Assocs.**

Fris News Co., 194 River Ave., Holland, MI 49423 USA (SAN 159-8643).

Frontline Communications, *See* **YWAM Publishing**

Fujii Assocs., 1400 W. 47th St. Ste. 4, La Grange, IL 60525-6148 USA (SAN 631-5305).

Fulcrum Publishing, *(0-912347; 1-55591; 1-56373)* Orders Addr.: 4690 Table Mountain Dr. Unit 100, Golden, CO 80403-1873 USA (SAN 200-2825) Toll Free Fax: 800-726-7112; Toll Free: 800-992-2908
E-mail: info@fulcrumbooks.com
Web site: http://www.fulcrumbooks.com.

Fulmont News Co., Affil. of Rubin Periodical Group, P.O. Box 1211, Rochester, NY 14603-1211 USA (SAN 169-5029) Tel 518-843-2421.

Fultz News Agency, 2008 Woodbrook, Denton, TX 76205 USA (SAN 169-8168).

Futech Educational Products, Inc., *(0-9627001; 1-889192)* 2999 N. 44th St., Suite 225, Phoenix, AZ 85018-7248 USA Tel 602-808-8765; Fax: 602-278-5667; Toll Free: 800-597-6278.

G A M Printers & Grace Christian Bookstore, *See* **GAM Pubn.**

Gabriel Resources, Orders Addr.: P.O. Box 1047, Waynesboro, GA 30830 USA Tel 706-554-1594; Fax: 706-554-7444; Toll Free: 800-732-6657 (8MORE-BOOKS); Edit Addr.: 129 Mobilization Dr., Waynesboro, GA 30830 USA.

Galda Library Services, Inc., 33 Richdale Ave., Cambridge, MA 02140 USA (SAN 630-5806) Tel 617-864-8232.

Gale Group, *See* **Thomson Gale**

Galesburg News Agency, Inc., Five E. Simmons St., Galesburg, IL 61401 USA (SAN 169-1945).

Galveston News Agency, P.O. Box 7608, San Antonio, TX 78207-0608 USA (SAN 169-8230).

GAM Pubn., P.O. Box 25, Sterling, VA 20167 USA (SAN 158-7218) Tel 703-450-4121; Fax: 703-450-5311.

Gamboge International, Inc., 18 Brittany Ave., Trumbull, CT 06611 USA (SAN 631-046X) Tel 203-261-2130; Fax: 203-452-0180
E-mail: gamboge@pcaet.com.

Gamebooks.com, 18627 Brookhurst St., No. 318, Fountain Valley, CA 92708 USA Tel 714-962-2180; Fax: 714-962-2176.

Gangaji Foundation, The, *(0-9632194; 1-887984)* 2245 Ashland St., Ashland, OR 97520-1405 USA Toll Free: 800-267-9205
E-mail: order@Gangaji.org; info@gangaji.org
Web site: http://www.gangaji.org.

Gannon Distributing Co., *(0-88307)* 100 La Salle Cir., No. A, Santa Fe, NM 87505-6916 USA (SAN 201-5889).

Gardner's Bk. Service, 16461 N. 25th Ave., Phoenix, AZ 85023-3111 USA (SAN 106-9322) Tel 602-863-6000; Fax: 602-863-2400 (orders only); Toll Free: 800-851-6001 (orders only)
E-mail: gbsbooks@bgsbooks.com
Web site: http://www.gbsbooks.com.

Garrett Educational Corp., *(0-944483; 1-56074)* Orders Addr.: P.O. Box 1588, Ada, OK 74820 USA (SAN 169-6955) Tel 580-332-6884; Fax: 580-332-1560; Toll Free: 800-654-9366; Edit Addr.: 130 E. 13th St., Ada, OK 74820 USA (SAN 243-2722)
E-mail: mail@garrettbooks.com
Web site: http://www.garrettbooks.com.

Gasman News Agency, 2211 Third Ave., S., Escanaba, MI 49829 USA (SAN 169-3794).

Gaunt, Inc., *(0-912004; 1-56169; 1-60449)* 3011 Gulf Dr., Holmes Beach, FL 34217-2199 USA (SAN 202-9413) Tel 941-778-5211; Fax: 941-778-5252; Toll Free: 800-942-8683 (US & Canada)
E-mail: info@gaunt.com; sales@gaunt.com
Web site: http://www.gaunt.com.

Gaunt, William W. & Sons, Incorporated, *See* **Gaunt, Inc.**

GBGM Service Ctr., P.O. Box 691328, Cincinnati, OH 45269 USA.

Gefen Bks., *(0-86343; 965-229)* 600 Broadway., Lynbrook, NY 11563-3908 USA Toll Free: 800-477-5257
E-mail: gefenny@gefenpublishing.com
Web site: http://www.israelbooks.com.

Gem Guides Bk. Co., *(0-935182; 0-937799; 1-889786)* 315 Cloverleaf Dr., Suite F, Baldwin Park, CA 91706 USA (SAN 221-1637) Tel 626-855-1611; Fax: 626-855-1610
E-mail: gembooks@aol.com
Web site: http://www.gemguidesbooks.com.

Gemini Enterprises, P.O. Box 8251, Stockton, CA 95208 USA (SAN 128-1402).

Genealogical Sources, Unlimited, *(0-913857)* 407 Ascot Ct., Knoxville, TN 37923-5807 USA (SAN 170-8058) Tel 865-690-7831.

Genealogy Digest, 960 N. 400 E., North Salt Lake, UT 84054-1920 USA (SAN 110-389X); 420 S. 425 W., Bountiful, UT 84010 (SAN 243-2439).

General Medical Pubs., *(0-935236)* P.O. Box 210, Venice, CA 90294-0210 USA (SAN 215-689X) Tel 310-392-4911.

Generic Computer Products, Inc., *(0-918611)* P.O. Box 790, Marquette, MI 49855 USA (SAN 284-8856) Tel 906-226-7600; Fax: 906-226-8309.

Geographia Map Co., Inc., *(0-88433)* 75 Moore St., Hackensack, NJ 07601-7107 USA (SAN 132-5566).

Gerold International Booksellers, Inc., 35-23 Utopia Pkwy., Flushing, NY 11358 USA (SAN 129-959X) Tel 718-358-4741; Fax: 718-358-3688.

Getty, J. Paul Trust Publications, *See* **Getty Pubns.**

Getty Pubns., *(0-89236; 0-941103)* Orders Addr.: P.O. Box 49659, Los Angeles, CA 90049-0659 USA Tel 310-440-7333; Fax: 818-779-0051; Edit Addr.: 1200 Getty Ctr. Dr., Suite 500, Los Angeles, CA 90049-1682 USA (SAN 208-2276) Tel 310-440-7365; Fax: 310-440-7706; Toll Free: 800-223-3431
E-mail: pubsinfo@getty.edu
Web site: http://www.getty.edu/publications.

Gibbs Smith, Publisher, *(0-87905; 0-941711; 1-58685; 1-4236)* Orders Addr.: P.O. Box 667, Layton, UT 84041 USA (SAN 201-9906) Tel 801-544-9800; Fax: 801-544-5582; Toll Free Fax: 800-213-3023 (orders); Toll Free: 800-748-5439 (orders); 800-835-4993 (Customer Service order only); Edit Addr.: 1877 E. Gentile St., Layton, UT 84040 USA Tel 801-544-9800; Fax: 801-546-8853
E-mail: info@gibbs-smith.com; text@gibbs-smith.com; tradeorders@gibbs-smith.com
Web site: http://www.gibbs-smith.com.

Gibson, Dot Pubns., *(0-941162)* Orders Addr.: P.O. Box 117, Waycross, GA 31502-0117 USA (SAN 200-4143) Tel 912-285-2848; Fax: 912-285-0349; Toll Free: 800-336-8095; Edit Addr.: 383 Bonneyman Rd., Blackshear, GA 31516 USA (SAN 200-9676)
E-mail: info@dotgibson.com
Web site: http://www.dotgibson.com.

Gilmore-Howard, P.O. Box 1268, Arlington, TX 76004-1268 USA (SAN 157-485X).

Gingko Pr., Inc., *(3-87439; 3-927258; 1-58423)* 5768 Paradise Dr., Suite J, Corte Madera, CA 94925-1229 USA (SAN 630-7418) Tel 415-924-9615; Fax: 415-924-9608 Do not confuse with Gingko Pr. in New York, NY
E-mail: Books@gingkopress.com
Web site: http://www.gingkopress.com.

Giron Bks., *(0-9741393)* 2130 W. 21st. St., Chicago, IL 60608-2608 USA Tel 773-847-3000; Fax: 773-847-9197; Toll Free: 800-405-4276
E-mail: isbn_san@gironbooks.com
Web site: http://www.gironbooks.com.

G-Jo Institute/DeerHaven Hills, *(0-916878)* P.O. Box 1460, Columbus, NC 28722-1460 USA (SAN 111-0004)
E-mail: officesupport@g-jo.com
Web site: http://www.g-jo.com.

G-Jo Institute/Falkyn, Incorporated, *See* **G-Jo Institute/DeerHaven Hills**

GL Services, 4588 Interstate Dr., Cincinnati, OH 45246 USA Tel 805-677-6815.

Glenhurst Publications, Incorporated, *See* **Upper Midwest Women's History Ctr.**

Global Bk. Distributors, P.O. Box 192629, Dallas, TX 75219 USA.

Global Engineering Documents-Latin America, 3909 NE 163rd St., Suite 110, North Miami Beach, FL 33160 USA (SAN 630-7868) Tel 305-944-1099; Fax: 305-944-1028
E-mail: global.csa@ihs.com.

Global Info Centres, *See* **Global Engineering Documents-Latin America**

Globe Pequot Pr., The, *(0-7627; 0-87106; 0-88742; 0-914788; 0-933469; 0-934802; 0-941130; 1-56440; 1-57034; 1-58574; 1-59228; 1-59921)* Div. of Morris Communications Co., LLC, Orders Addr.: P.O. Box 480, Guilford, CT 06437-0480 USA (SAN 201-9892) Tel 888-249-7586; Toll Free Fax: 800-820-2329 (in Connecticut); Toll Free: 800-243-0495 (24 hours); Edit Addr.: 246 Goose Ln., Guilford, CT 06437 USA Tel 203-458-4500; Fax: 203-458-4604
E-mail: info@globepequot.com
Web site: http://www.globepequot.com.

Gluesing & Gluesing, *(0-9631357)* 5634 Royal Oaks Dr., Saint Paul, MN 55126-8488 USA (SAN 630-0022) Toll Free: 800-747-0227.

Goldberg, Louis Library Bk. Supplier, 45 Belvidere St., Nazareth, PA 18064 USA (SAN 169-7536) Tel 610-759-9458; Fax: 610-759-8134.

Goldenrod Music, Inc., 1310 Turner Rd., Lansing, MI 48906-4342 USA (SAN 630-5962) Tel 517-484-1777
E-mail: music@goldenrod.com
Web site: http://www.goldenrod.com.

Goldenrod/Horizon Distribution, *See* **Goldenrod Music, Inc.**

Goldman, S. Otzar Hasefarim, Inc., 125 Ditmas Ave., Brooklyn, NY 11218 USA (SAN 169-5770) Tel 718-972-6200; Fax: 718-972-6204; Toll Free: 800-972-6201.

Good Bk. Publishing Co., *(1-881212)* P.O. Box 837, Kihei, HI 96753-0837 USA (SAN 297-9578) Tel 808-874-4876 (phone/fax)
E-mail: dickb@dickb.com
Web site: http://www.dickb.com/index.shtml.

Good News Magazine Distributors, 6332 Saunders St., Rego Park, NY 11374-2031 USA (SAN 113-7271) Toll Free: 800-624-7257.

Good Shepherd Pubns., 800 E. 8th St., Newton, KS 67114-2826 USA
E-mail: gsp@southwind.net
Web site: http://wwwlgspbooks.comCarico.htm.

Gopher News Co., 9000 10th Ave N., Minneapolis, MN 55427-4322 USA (SAN 169-4138).

Gopher News Company, *See* **St. Marie's Gopher News Co.**

Gospel Light Pubns., *(0-8307)* Orders Addr.: 1957 Eastman Ave., Ventura, CA 93003 USA (SAN 299-0873) Tel 805-644-9721; Fax: 805-289-0200; Toll Free: 800-446-7735 (orders only) Do not confuse with companies with similar names in Brooklyn, NY, Delight, AR
E-mail: info@gospellight.com; kyleloffelmacher@gospellight.com
Web site: http://www.gospellight.com.

Gospel Mission, Inc., Orders Addr.: P.O. Box 318, Choteau, MT 59422 USA (SAN 170-3196) Tel 406-466-2311; Edit Addr.: 316 First St., NW, Choteau, MT 59422 USA (SAN 243-2455).

Gospel Publishing Hse., *(0-88243)* Div. of General Council of the Assemblies of God, 1445 N. Boonville Ave., Springfield, MO 65802-1894 USA (SAN 206-8826) Tel 417-831-8000; Fax: 417-862-5881; Toll Free Fax: 800-328-0294; Toll Free: 800-641-4310 (orders only)
E-mail: webmaster@gph.com
Web site: http://www.gospelpublishing.com.

Goyescas Corp. of Florida, 7924 NW 66th St., Miami, FL 33166-2726 USA (SAN 169-1120).

Graham Services, Inc., 180 James Dr., E., Saint Rose, LA 70087-9481 USA (SAN 169-2895) Tel 504-467-5863; Fax: 504-464-6196; Toll Free: 800-457-7323 (in Los Angeles only)
E-mail: gsi@aol.com.

Grand Central Publishing, *(0-445; 0-446; 0-7595)* Orders Addr.: c/o Little Brown & Co., 3 Center Plaza, Boston, MA 02108-2084 USA Fax: 800-286-9471; Toll Free: 800-759-0190; Edit Addr.: 1271 Avenue of the Americas, New York, NY 10020 USA (SAN 281-8892) Tel 212-364-1200; Toll Free Fax: 800-286-9471
E-mail: renee.supriano@twbg.com
Web site: http://www.warnerbooks.com.

Granite Publishing & Distribution, *(1-890558; 1-930980; 1-932280; 1-59936)* 868 N. 1430 W., Orem, UT 84057 USA (SAN 631-0605) Tel 801-229-9023; Fax: 801-229-1924; Toll Free: 800-574-5779 Do not confuse with companies with same or similar names in Madison, WI, Columbus, NC
E-mail: granitepd@aol.com; granite@granitepublishing.biz
Web site: http://granitepublishing.biz.

Granite Publishing, LLC, *(0-926524; 0-9632310; 1-893183)* P.O. Box 1429, Columbus, NC 28722 USA Tel 828-894-3088; Fax: 828-894-8454; Toll Free: 800-366-0264 Do not confuse with companies with same or similar names in Madison, WI, Orem, UT, Siloam Springs, AR
E-mail: brian@5thworld.com
Web site: http://www.5thworld.com.

Graphic Arts Ctr. Publishing Co., Orders Addr.: P.O. Box 10306, Portland, OR 97296-0306 USA (SAN 201-6338) Tel 503-226-2402; Fax: 503-223-1410 (executive & editorial); Toll Free Fax: 800-355-9685 (sales office); Toll Free: 800-452-3032
E-mail: sales@gacpc.com
Web site: http://www.gacpc.com.

Great Lakes Reader's Service, Inc., Orders Addr.: P.O. Box 1078, Detroit, MI 48231 USA (SAN 285-9912) Tel 313-965-4577; Fax: 313-965-2445.

Great Northern Distributors, Inc., 634 South Ave., Rochester, NY 14620-1316 USA (SAN 169-7676) Tel 717-342-8159.

Great Outdoors Publishing Co., *(0-8200)* 4747 28th St., N., Saint Petersburg, FL 33714 USA (SAN 201-6273) Tel 727-525-6609; Fax: 727-527-4870; Toll Free: 800-869-6609
E-mail: info@floridabooks.com
Web site: http://www.floridabooks.com.

Greathall Productions, Inc., *(1-882513)* Orders Addr.: P.O. Box 5061, Charlottesville, VA 22905-5061 USA Tel 434-296-4288; Fax: 434-296-4490; Toll Free: 800-477-6234
E-mail: greathall@greathall.com
Web site: http://www.greathall.com.

Green Gate Bks., 6700 W. Chicago St., Chandler, AZ 85226 USA (SAN 169-6785) Tel 480-961-5176; Fax: 480-961-5256; Toll Free: 800-228-3816
E-mail: ggb@wcoil.com
Web site: http://www.greengatebooks.com.

Greenfield Review Literary Ctr., Inc., *(0-87886; 0-912678)* 2 Middle Grove Rd., P.O. Box 308, Greenfield Center, NY 12833 USA (SAN 203-4506) Tel 518-583-1440; Fax: 518-583-9741
Web site: http://www.nativeauthors.com.

Greenleaf Book Group, *(0-9665319; 1-929774)* Orders Addr.: 4425 S. Mopac, Suite 600, Longhorn Bldg, 3rd Fl., Austin, TX 78735 USA Tel 512-891-6100; Fax: 512-891-6150; Toll Free: 800-932-5420; Edit Addr.: 7600 Thistle Ln., Novelty, OH 44072 USA
E-mail: tanya@greenleafbookgroup.com
Web site: http://www.greenleafbookgroup.com.

Greenleaf Book Group Pr., *(1-929774; 0-9790842)* Div. of Greenleaf Book Group, 4425 S. Mopac, Suite 600 Longhorn Bldg., 3rd Flr., Austin, TX 78735 USA (SAN 631-9238) Tel 512-891-6100; 800-932-5420; Fax: 512-891-6150
E-mail: nathan@greenleafbookgroup.com; contact@greenleafbookgroup.com
Web site: http://www.greenleafbookgroup.com/.

Greenleaf Pubns., *(1-883729)* PMB 320 40 W. Nine Mile Rd. # 2, Pensacola, FL 32534 USA (SAN 631-6808) Tel 850-776-1600; Fax: 850-477-1813 Do not confuse with Greenleaf Pubns. in Pasadena, CA
E-mail: orders@greenleafpublications.com; greenleaf@cox.net
Web site: http://www.greenleafpublications.com.

Greenwood Press, Incorporated, *See* **Greenwood Publishing Group, Inc.**

Greenwood Publishing Group, Inc., *(0-275; 0-313; 0-8371; 0-86569; 0-89789; 0-89930; 1-56720)* Orders Addr.: P.O. Box 6926, Portsmouth, NH 03802 USA (SAN 213-2028) Fax: 603-431-2214 (customer service and sales) ; Toll Free: 800-225-5800 (orders only); Linacre House Jordan Hill Bus Pk, Banbury Rd, Oxford, OX2 8DP Tel 44 (0) 1865 888181; Fax: 44 (0) 1865 314981; Edit Addr.: 214 Bald Eagle Ln., Cary, NC 27518-9681 USA Do not confuse with Greenwood Publishing in Glenview, IL
E-mail: customer-service@greenwood.com; sales@greenwood.com; Greenwood.enquiries@harcourteducation.co.uk
Web site: http://www.greenwood.com.

Grey Hse. Publishing, *(0-939300; 1-891482; 1-930956; 1-59237)* 185 Millerton Rd., Millerton, NY 12546 USA Tel 518-789-8700; Fax: 518-789-0556; Toll Free: 800-562-2139
E-mail: books@greyhouse.com
Web site: http://www.greyhouse.com.

Grey Owl Indian Craft Co., Inc., 132-05 Merrick Blvd., P.O. Box 468, Jamaica, NY 11434 USA (SAN 132-9979) Tel 718-341-4000.

Grolier Americana, 1111 Crandon Blvd., Apt. C501, Key Biscayne, FL 33149-2734 USA (SAN 108-1764) Tel 305-551-6711.

Gryphon Hse., Inc., *(0-87659; 1-58904)* Orders Addr.: P.O. Box 207, Beltsville, MD 20704-0207 USA (SAN 169-3190) Tel 301-595-9500; Fax: 301-595-0051; Toll Free: 800-638-0928; Edit Addr.: 10726 Tucker St., Beltsville, MD 20705 USA
E-mail: info@ghbooks.com
Web site: http://www.gryphonhouse.com.

Guardian Bk. Co., P.O. Box 202, Ottawa Lake, MI 49267-0202 USA (SAN 163-7355).

Gulf States Book Fairs, *See* **Gulf States Educational Bks.**

Gulf States Educational Bks., Orders Addr.: 368 Laurel Dr., Satsuma, AL 36572 USA (SAN 158-7870) Toll Free: 800-533-1189.

Gumdrop Bks., Div. of Central Programs, Inc., Orders Addr.: P.O. Box 505, Bethany, MO 64424 USA (SAN 631-4988) Tel 660-425-3923; Fax: 660-425-3970; Toll Free: 800-821-7199; Edit Addr.: P.O. Box 505, Bethany, MO 64424-0505 USA (SAN 131-0860)
E-mail: wecare@gumdropbooks.com
Web site: http://www.gumdropbooks.com.

H & H Distribution, 1634 Stilesgate, Grand Rapids, MI 49508 USA Tel 616-248-7990; Fax: 616-248-0016.

Hachette Bk. Group, *(0-446)* Orders Addr.: 3 Center Plaza, Boston, MA 02108 USA (SAN 852-5463) Tel 617-263-1828; Toll Free Fax: 800-286-9471; Toll Free: 800-759-0190; Edit Addr.: 1271 Avenue of the Americas, New York, NY 10019 USA Tel 212-522-7200; Fax: 212-522-7991; Toll Free Fax: 800-477-5925; P.O. Box 2146, Johannesburg, 2196 Tel 2711 783-7565; Fax: 2711 883-6866
Web site: http://www.hbgusa.com.

Hagerstown News Distributors, *See* **Mid-States Distributors**

Haitiana Pubns., Inc., *(0-944987)* 3740 81st St. Apt. B3, Jackson Hts, NY 11372-6947 USA (SAN 245-7059)
E-mail: haitiana@idt.net
Web site: http://idtnet/haitiana/.

Hale, Robert & Co., Inc., 1803 132nd Ave., NE, Suite 4, Bellevue, WA 98005 USA (SAN 200-6995) Tel 425-881-5212; Fax: 425-881-0731; Toll Free: 800-733-5330.

Ham Radio's Bookstore, *See* **Radio Bookstore**

Hamakor Judaica, Inc., 7777 Merrimac Ave., Niles, IL 60714 USA (SAN 169-1791) Tel 847-966-4040; Fax: 847-966-4033; Toll Free: 800-552-4088.

Hamel, Bernard H. Spanish Bk. Corp., 10977 Santa Monica Blvd., Los Angeles, CA 90025 USA (SAN 111-8862) Tel 310-475-0453; Fax: 310-473-6132
E-mail: spanish@primenet.com
Web site: http://www.BernardHamel.com; http://www.SpanishBooksUSA.com.

Hamilton News Co., Ltd., 41 Hamilton Ln., Glenmont, NY 12077 USA (SAN 169-5312) Tel 518-463-1135; Fax: 518-463-3154.

Hammond Castle Museum, 80 Hesperus Ave., Gloucester, MA 01930 USA Tel 978-283-7673.

Hammond, Incorporated, *See* **Hammond World Atlas Corp.**

Hammond Publishing Co., Inc., *(1-883882)* P.O. Box 279, G7166 N. Saginaw St., Mount Morris, MI 48458 USA (SAN 185-142X) Tel 810-686-8881; Fax: 810-686-0561; Toll Free: 800-521-3440 (orders only)
E-mail: hammondpub@juno.com.

Hammond World Atlas Corp., *(0-7230; 0-8437)* Subs. of Langenscheidt Pubs., Inc., 193 Morris Ave., Springfield, NJ 07081-1211 USA (SAN 202-2702)
E-mail: rstrung@americanmap.com
Web site: http://www.Hammondmap.com.

Hamon, Gerard Incorporated, *See* **Lafayette Bks.**

Hancock Hse. Pubs., *(0-88839; 0-919654)* 19313 Zero Ave., Surrey, BC V3S 9R9 CAN; 1431 Harrison Ave., Blaine, WA 98230-5005 (SAN 665-7079) Tel 604-538-1114; Fax: 604-538-2262; Toll Free Fax: 800-983-2262; Toll Free: 800-938-1114
E-mail: sales@hancockhouse.com
Web site: http://www.hancockhouse.com.

Handleman, 500 Kirts Blvd., Troy, MI 48084-5225 USA (SAN 106-4886).

Handler News Agency, P.O. Box 27007, Omaha, NE 68127-0007 USA (SAN 169-4405).

Hansen Hse., 1842 West Ave., Miami Beach, FL 33139 USA (SAN 200-7908) Tel 305-532-5461; Toll Free: 800-327-8202.

Harcourt Brace & Company, *See* **Harcourt Trade Pubs.**

Harcourt Children's Bks., *(0-15)* Div. of Harcourt, Inc., Orders Addr.: 6277 Sea Harbor Dr., Orlando, FL 32887 USA Toll Free Fax: 800-235-0256; Toll Free: 800-543-1918; 465 S. Lincoln Dr., Troy, MO 63379 Toll Free Fax: 800-235-0266; Toll Free: 800-543-1918; Edit Addr.: 15 E. 26th St., 15th Flr., New York, NY 10010 USA Tel 212-592-1000; Fax: 212-592-1011; 525 B St., Suite 1900, San Diego, CA 92101 Tel 619-231-6616
E-mail: Andrew.porter@harcourt.com
Web site: http://www.HarcourtBooks.com.

Harcourt Trade Pubs., *(0-15)* Div. of Harcourt, Inc., Orders Addr.: 6277 Sea Harbor Dr., Orlando, FL 32887 USA (SAN 200-285X) Tel 619-699-6707; Toll Free Fax: 800-235-0256; Toll Free: 800-543-1918 (trade orders, inquiries, claims); Edit Addr.: 525 B St., Suite 1900, San Diego, CA 92101-4495 USA (SAN 200-2736) Tel 619-231-6616; 15 E. 26th St., New York, NY 10010 Tel 212-592-1000; Fax: 212-592-1011
E-mail: andrewporter@harcourt.com
Web site: http://www.HarcourtBooks.com.

HardBound, Inc., *(0-9679662; 0-9719834; 0-9744237; 0-9749690)* 4280 Rider Trail N., Earth City, MO 63045 USA Tel 314-738-0303 (phone/fax)
Web site: http://www.bindabook.com.

Harness, Miller, 750 Route 73 S. Ste. 110, Marlton, NJ 08053-4142 USA (SAN 169-5789) Toll Free: 800-526-6310.

HarperCollins Pubs., *(0-00; 0-06; 0-380; 0-688; 0-690; 0-694; 0-7322; 0-87795; 1-55710)* Div. of News Corp., Orders Addr.: 1000 Keystone Industrial Pk., Scranton, PA 18512-4621 USA (SAN 215-3742) Tel 570-941-1500; Toll Free Fax: 800-822-4090; Toll Free: 800-242-7737 (orders only); Edit Addr.: 10 E. 53rd St., New York, NY 10022-5299 USA (SAN 200-2086) Tel 212-207-7000
Web site: http://www.harpercollins.com; www.harpercollinschildrens.com.

Harris Teller, Inc., 7400 S. Mason, Chicago, IL 60638 USA (SAN 630-4486) Tel 708-496-2100; Fax: 708-496-2130.

Harrisburg News Co., 980 Briarsdale Rd., Harrisburg, PA 17109 USA (SAN 169-7420) Tel 717-561-8377; Fax: 717-561-1466
E-mail: jmurphy@harrisburgnewsco.com
Web site: http://www.harrisburgnewsco.com.

Harrison Hse., Inc., *(0-89274; 1-57794)* Orders Addr.: P.O. Box 35035, Tulsa, OK 74153 USA (SAN 208-676X) Tel 918-523-5700; Fax: 918-523-5747; Toll Free Fax: 800-830-5688; Toll Free: 800-888-4126; 877-663-1330; Edit Addr.: 2761 E. Skelly Dr. Ste. 703, Tulsa, OK 74105-6258 USA
E-mail: hh2@eaglemgmt.com
Web site: http://www.harrisonhouse.com.

Harry-Young Pubn. Services Agency, Inc., 6261 Manchester Blvd., Buena Park, CA 90621-2259 USA (SAN 110-8832).

Harvard Assocs., Inc., *(0-924346)* 10 Holworthy St., Cambridge, MA 02138 USA (SAN 170-2939) Tel 617-492-0660; Fax: 617-492-4610; Toll Free: 800-774-5646
E-mail: info@harvassoc.com
Web site: http://www.harvassoc.com.

Harvard Business Schl. Pr., *(0-87584; 1-57851; 1-59139; 1-4221)* 60 Harvard Way, Boston, MA 02163 USA (SAN 202-277X) Tel 617-783-7400; 617 495 6181; Fax: 617-783-7492; Toll Free: 888-500-1016 6-19-01 faxed 2nd prefix app, charge, KC
E-mail: corpcustserv@hbsp.harvard.edu
Web site: http://www.hbsp.harvard.edu; http://www.harvardbusinessonline.com.

Harvard Univ. Art Museums Shop, 32 Quincy St., Cambridge, MA 02138 USA (SAN 111-3372) Tel 617-495-8286; Fax: 617-495-9985
E-mail: appleyar@fas.harvard.edu
Web site: http://www.artmuseums.harvard.edu.

Harvard Univ. Pr., *(0-674; 0-916724; 0-935617)* Orders Addr.: c/o Triliteral LLC, 100 Maple Ridge Dr., Cumberland, RI 02864 USA Tel 401-531-2800; Fax: 401-531-2801; Toll Free Fax: 800-406-9145; Toll Free: 800-405-1619; 800-448-2242; Edit Addr.: 79 Garden St., Cambridge, MA 02138 USA (SAN 200-2043) Tel 617-495-2600; Fax: 617-495-5898
E-mail: contact_hup@harvard.edu
Web site: http://www.hup.harvard.edu.

Harvest Distributors, *See* **ARVEST**

Hastings Bks., *(0-940846)* 116 N. Wayne Ave., Wayne, PA 19087 USA (SAN 205-048X).

Hawaiian Magazine Distributor, 3375 Koapaka St., No. D180, Honolulu, HI 98619-1865 USA (SAN 169-1619).

Hazelden Information & Educational Services, *See* **Hazelden Publishing & Educational Services**

Hazelden Publishing & Educational Services, *(0-89486; 0-89638; 0-935908; 0-942421; 1-56246; 1-56838; 1-59285)* 15215 Pleasant Valley Rd., P.O. Box 176, Center City, MN 55012-0176 USA (SAN 209-4010) Fax: 651-213-4577; Toll Free: 800-328-9000
E-mail: kbuzick@hazelden.org
Web site: http://www.hazelden.org.

Health and Growth Assocs., *(0-9630266)* Orders Addr.: 28195 Fairview Ave., Hemet, CA 92544 USA Tel 951-927-1768; Fax: 951-927-1548
E-mail: flloomis@earthlink.net.

Health Communications, Inc., *(0-932194; 1-55874; 0-7573)* Orders Addr.: 3201 SW 15th St., Deerfield Beach, FL 33442-8190 USA (SAN 212-100X) Tel 954-360-0909; Fax: 954-360-0034; Toll Free: 800-441-5569 Do not confuse with Health Communications, Inc., Edison, NJ
E-mail: hci@hcibooks.com; terryy@hcibooks.com; lorig@hcibooks.com
Web site: http://www.hcibooks.com.

Hearst Bks., *(0-688; 0-87851; 0-910990; 0-910992; 1-58816)* Div. of Hearst Communications, Inc., Orders Addr.: P.O. Box 1219, Fairfield, NJ 07007 USA (SAN 202-5779) Tel 973-227-7200; Toll Free: 800-237-0657; Edit Addr.: 1350 Avenue of Americas, New York, NY 10019 USA (SAN 202-2842) Tel 212-261-6500; Fax: 212-261-6599.

Hearst Distribution Group, Incorporated, Book Division, *See* **Comag Marketing Group**

Heartland Bk. Co., 10195 N. Lake Ave., Olathe, KS 66061 USA (SAN 631-2497) Tel 913-829-1784.

Heffernan Audio Visual, Orders Addr.: P.O. Box 5906, San Antonio, TX 78201-0906 USA Tel 210-732-4333; Fax: 210-732-5906; Edit Addr.: 950 Isom Rd. Ste. 100, San Antonio, TX 78216-4170 USA (SAN 166-8722)
E-mail: sales@heffernanav.com
Web site: http://www.heffernanav.com.

Heffernan School Supply, *See* **Heffernan Audio Visual**

Heinecken & Assoc., Ltd., 1733 N. Mohawk, Chicago, IL 60614 USA Toll Free Fax: 800-947-5694; Toll Free: 800-449-0138.

Heinemann, *(0-325; 0-434; 0-435; 1-59469)* Div. of Greenwood Publishing Group, Inc., Orders Addr.: P.O. Box 6926, Portsmouth, NH 03802 USA Toll Free: 800-225-5800; Edit Addr.: 361 Hanover St., Portsmouth, NH 03801 USA (SAN 210-5829) Tel 603-431-7894; Fax: 603-431-7840
E-mail: info@heinemann.com
Web site: http://www.heinemann.com.

Heinemann Educational Books, Incorporated, *See* **Heinemann**

Heinemann Library, *(0-431; 1-57572; 1-58810; 1-4034; 1-4329)* Div. of Reed Elsevier, Orders Addr.: 1000 Hart Rd., 3rd Flr., Barrington, IL 60010-2627 USA Toll Free Fax: 888-844-5329; 847-620-7900 (Outside U.S.); Toll Free: 888-454-2279; 847-620-7500 (ext.: 3910, Outside U.S.); Edit Addr.: 100 N. LaSalle St., Suite 300, Chicago, IL 60602 USA Tel 312-324-5200; Fax: 312-845-1030; Toll Free: 888-475-7038
E-mail: sgafka@rigby-edue.com; sheryl.gafka@rigby.com
Web site: http://www.heinemannlibrary.com/.

Heirloom Bible Pubs., Orders Addr.: P.O. Box 118, Wichita, KS 67201-0118 USA (SAN 630-2793) Fax: 316-267-1850; Toll Free: 800-676-2448; Edit Addr.: 9020 E. 35th St N., Wichita, KS 67226-2017 USA.

Helix, 310 S. Racine St., Chicago, IL 60607 USA (SAN 111-915X) Tel 312-421-6000; Fax: 312-421-1586.

Hendrick-Long Publishing Co., *(0-937460; 1-885777)* Orders Addr.: 10635 Tower Oaks, Suite D, Houston, TX 77070 USA (SAN 281-7756) Toll Free: 800-544-3770; Edit Addr.: 10635 Tower Oaks Blvd. Ste. D, Houston, TX 77070-5927 USA (SAN 281-7748)
E-mail: hendrick-long@worldnet.att.net
Web site: http://www.hendricklongpublishing.com.

Herald Pr., *(0-8361)* Div. of Mennonite Publishing Hse., Inc., 616 Walnut Ave., Scottdale, PA 15683-1999 USA (SAN 202-2915) Tel 724-887-8500; 412-887-8500; Fax: 724-887-3111; Toll Free: 800-245-7894 (orders only) Do not confuse with Herald Pr., Charlotte, NC
E-mail: hp@mph.org
Web site: http://www.mph.org.

Herald Publishing Hse., *(0-8309)* Orders Addr.: P.O. Box 390, Independence, MO 64051-0390 USA Tel 816-521-3015; Fax: 816-521-3066 (customer services); Toll Free: 800-767-8181; Edit Addr.: 1001W. Walnut St., Independence, MO 64051-0390 USA (SAN 111-7556) Tel 816-257-0200
E-mail: sales@HeraldHouse.org
Web site: http://www.heraldhouse.org.

Herdman PhD P.C., John W., 7525 S. Hampton Rd., Lincoln, NE 68506 USA Tel 402-484-7796; Fax: 402-441-0639
E-mail: jherdman@binary.net.

Heritage Bookstore, Orders Addr.: 3867 S. Campbell Ave., Springfield, MO 65807-5339 USA (SAN 111-7696).

Hervey's Booklink & Cookbook Warehouse, P.O. Box 831870, Richardson, TX 75083 USA (SAN 630-9747).

Hesteria Records & Publishing Co., 124 Hagar Ct., Santa Cruz, CA 95064 USA Tel 831-459-2575; Fax: 831-457-2917
E-mail: alissa@aainnovators.com
Web site: http://www.aainnovators.com.

Hi Jolly Library Service, 150 N. Gay St., Susanville, CA 96130-3902 USA (SAN 133-5944).

Hibel, Edna Studio, P.O. Box 9967, Riviera Beach, FL 33419 USA (SAN 111-1574) Tel 561-848-9640; Toll Free: 800-275-3426.

Hicks News Agency, Incorporated, *See* **NEWSouth Distributors**

High Peak Bks., *(1-884709)* Orders Addr.: P.O. Box 703, Wilson, WY 83014 USA (SAN 299-4232); Edit Addr.: 355 N. Bar Y Rd., Jackson, WY 83011 USA Tel 307-739-0147 Do not confuse with High Peak Pr. in Schenectady, NY.

Hill City News Agency, Inc., 3228 Odd Fellow Rd., Lynchburg, VA 24501 USA (SAN 169-8656) Tel 804-845-4231; Fax: 804-845-0864.

Hillsboro News, Orders Addr.: P.O. Box 25738, Tampa, FL 33622-5738 USA Tel 813-622-8087; Edit Addr.: 7002 Parke E. Blvd., Tampa, FL 33610 USA.

Himber Bks., Div. of F. C. Himber & Son's, Inc., 1380 W. Second Ave., Eugene, OR 97402 USA Tel 541-686-8003; Toll Free: 800-888-5904.

Himber, F. C., *See* **Himber Bks.**

Hinrichs, E. Louis, P.O. Box 1090, Lompoc, CA 93438-1090 USA (SAN 133-1493) Tel 805-736-7512
E-mail: booklompoc@aol.com.

Hippocrene Bks., Inc., *(0-7818; 0-87052; 0-88254)* 171 Madison Ave., New York, NY 10016-1002 USA (SAN 213-2060) Tel 718-454-2366 (sales); 212-685-4371 (editorial); Fax: 718-454-1391 (sales/order inquiry); 212-779-9338 (editorial)
E-mail: hippocre@ix.netcom.com
Web site: http://www.hippocrenebooks.com.

Historic Aviation Bks., 121 Fifth Ave., Suite 300, New Brighton, MN 55112 USA (SAN 129-5284) Tel 651-635-0100; Fax: 651-635-0700.

Historic Cherry Hill, *(0-943366)* 523 1/2 S. Pearl St., Albany, NY 12202 USA (SAN 110-8859) Tel 518-434-4791; Fax: 518-434-4806.

Hobbies Hawaii Distributors, 4420 Lawehana St., No. 3, Honolulu, HI 96818 USA (SAN 630-8619) Tel 808-423-0265; Fax: 808-423-1635.

Holiday Enterprises, Inc., 3328 US Hwy. 123, Rochester Bldg., Greenville, SC 29611 USA (SAN 169-779X) Tel 864-220-3161; Fax: 864-295-9757.

Holt, Henry & Co., *(0-03; 0-8050)* Div. of Holtzbrinck Publishers, Orders Addr.: 16365 James Madison Hwy., Gordonsville, VA 22942-8501 USA Toll Free Fax: 800-672-2054; Toll Free: 888-330-8477; Edit Addr.: 115 W. 18th St., 5th Flr., New York, NY 10011 USA (SAN 200-6472) Tel 212-886-9200; Fax: 540-672-7540 (customer service)
E-mail: info@hholt.com
Web site: http://www.henryholt.com.

Holtzbrinck Publishers, *See* **Macmillan**

Holyoke News Co., Inc., 720 Main St., P.O. Box 990, Holyoke, MA 01041 USA (SAN 169-3468) Tel 413-534-4537; Fax: 413-538-7161; Toll Free: 800-628-8372
E-mail: sales@holyoke-news.com.

Homestead Bk., Inc., *(0-930180)* Orders Addr.: P.O. Box 31608, Seattle, WA 98103 USA (SAN 662-037X); Edit Addr.: 6101 22nd Ave., NW, Seattle, WA 98107 USA (SAN 169-8796) Tel 206-782-4532; Fax: 206-784-9328; Toll Free: 800-426-6777 (orders only)
Web site: http://www.homesteadbook.com.

Honn, Joseph R., 509 Aurora Ave. Apt. 304, Naperville, IL 60540-6288 USA
E-mail: JHonn19587@aol.com.

Hood, Alan C. & Co., Inc., *(0-911469)* P.O. Box 775, Chambersburg, PA 17201 USA (SAN 270-8221) Tel 717-267-0867; Fax: 717-267-0572.

Hopkins Fulfillment Services, P.O. Box 50370, Baltimore, MD 21211-4370 USA Fax: 410-516-6998; Toll Free: 800-537-5487.

Hotho & Co., P.O. Box 9738, Fort Worth, TX 76147-2738 USA (SAN 169-8192).

Houghton Mifflin Co., *(0-395; 0-87466; 0-9631591; 1-57630; 1-881527; 0-618; 0-547)* Orders Addr.: a/o Orders for College, Trade & Great Source, 181 Ballardvale St., Wilmington, MA 01887-0750 USA Toll Free: 800-225-3362; Edit Addr.: 222 Berkeley St., Boston, MA 02116 USA (SAN 215-3793) Tel 617-351-5000
Web site: http://www.hmco.com.

Houghton Mifflin Co. Trade & Reference Div., *(0-395; 0-89919; 0-618)* Orders Addr.: 181 Ballardvalle St., Wilmington, MA 01887 USA Tel 978-661-1300; Toll Free: 800-225-3362; Edit Addr.: 222 Berkeley St., Boston, MA 02116 USA (SAN 200-2388) Tel 617-351-5000; Fax: 617-227-5409; 215 Park Ave S. Flr. 12, New York, NY 10003-1621
E-mail: trade_sub_rights@hmco.com
Web site: http://www.hmco.com/; http://www.houghtonmifflinbooks.com.

Houghton Mifflin Company (College Division), *See* **Houghton Mifflin Co. Trade & Reference Div.**

Houston Paperback Distributor, 4114 Gairloch Ln., Houston, TX 77025-2912 USA (SAN 169-8273).

Howell Pr., *(0-943231; 0-9616878; 1-57427)* 1125a Stoney Ridge Rd., Charlottesvle, VA 22902-8719 USA (SAN 661-6607) Toll Free Fax: 888-971-7204; Toll Free: 800-868-4512
E-mail: custserv@howellpress.com
Web site: http://www.howellpress.com.

HPK Educational Resource Ctr., *(0-89895)* Div. of H. P. Koppelmann, Inc., 140 Van Block Ave., Hartford, CT 06141 USA (SAN 169-071X) Tel 860-549-6210; Toll Free: 800-243-7724.

Hubbard, P.O. Box 100, Defiance, OH 43512 USA (SAN 169-6726) Tel 419-784-4455; Fax: 419-782-1662; Toll Free: 800-582-0657
E-mail: hubbard@bright.net.

Hudson County News Co., 1305 Paterson Plank Rd., North Bergen, NJ 07047 USA (SAN 169-4782) Tel 201-867-3600.

Hudson Valley News Distributors, P.O. Box 1236, Newburgh, NY 12550 USA (SAN 169-6084) Tel 914-562-3399; Fax: 914-562-6010.

Humanics, Limited, *See* **Humanics Publishing Group**

Humanics Publishing Group, *(0-89334)* Orders Addr.: P.O. Box 7400, Atlanta, GA 30357-0400 USA (SAN 208-3833) Tel 561-533-6231; Fax: 404-874-1976; Toll Free: 888-874-8844; Edit Addr.: 12 S. Dixie Hwy., Suite 203, Lake worth, FL 33460 USA (SAN 658-0882) Tel 561-533-6231; Fax: 561-533-6233; Toll Free Fax: 888-874-8844; Toll Free: 800-874-8844 Do not confuse with Humanics ErgoSystems, Inc., Reseda, CA
E-mail: humanics@mindspring.com
Web site: http://www.humanicspub.com; http://www.humanicslearning.com; http://www.humanicsdealer.com.

Hyperion Pr., *(0-7868; 1-56282; 1-4013)* Div. of Disney Bk. Publishing, Inc., A Walt Disney Co., Orders Addr.: 3 Center Plaza, Boston, MA 02108 USA Toll Free: 800-759-0190; Edit Addr.: 77 W. 66th St., 11th Flr., New York, NY 10023-6298 USA Tel 212-456-0100; Fax: 212-456-0108
Web site: http://www.hyperionbooks.com.

Iaconi, Mariuccia Bk. Imports, *(0-9628720)* P.O. Box 77023, San Francisco, CA 94107-0023 USA (SAN 161-1364) Toll Free: 800-955-9577
E-mail: mibibook@ixnetcom.com
Web site: http://www.mibibook.com.

i.b.d., Ltd., *(0-88431)* 24 Hudson St., Kinderhook, NY 12106 USA (SAN 630-7779) Tel 518-758-1755; Fax: 518-758-6702
E-mail: lankhof@ibdltd.com
Web site: http://www.ibdltd.com.

ibooks.com, *(0-7561)* 804-C Rio Grande St., Austin, TX 78701-2220 USA Tel 512-478-2700; Fax: 512-478-0500
E-mail: kim@ibooks.com
Web site: http://www.ibooks.com/.

Icea Bk. Ctr., P.O. Box 20048, Minneapolis, MN 55420 USA (SAN 285-9114) Tel 612-854-8660.

ICG Muse, Inc., 420 W. 42nd St. Apt. 35B, New York, NY 10036-6863 USA (SAN 631-7200).

ID International Bk. Service, 126 Old Ridgefield Rd., Wilton, CT 06897-3017 USA (SAN 630-8074) Tel 203-834-2272; Fax: 203-762-9725
E-mail: orders@idintl.com.

Idaho News Agency, 2710 Julia St., Coeur D'Alene, ID 83814 USA (SAN 169-1651) Tel 208-664-3444.

Ideal Foreign Bks., Inc., 132-10 Hillside Ave., Richmond Hill, NY 11418 USA (SAN 169-6173) Tel 718-297-7477; Fax: 718-297-7645; Toll Free: 800-284-2490 (orders only).

Ideals Publishing Corporation, *See* **Ideals Pubns.**

Ideals Pubns., *(0-8249; 0-89542)* Div. of Guideposts, Orders Addr.: 535 Metroplex Dr., Suite 250, Nashville, TN 37211 USA Tel 615-333-0478; Fax: 615-781-1447
E-mail: dtimson@guideposts.org
Web site: http://www.idealsbooks.com.

IEEE, *(0-7803; 1-4244; 2-8318)* Orders Addr.: c/o IEEE Service Ctr., P.O. Box 1331, Piscataway, NJ 08855-1331 USA (SAN 203-8072) Toll Free Fax: 800-716-6447; Toll Free: 800-701-4333 (cust serv); Edit Addr.: 445 Hoes Ln., Piscataway, NJ 08855 USA (SAN 203-8064)
E-mail: customer-service@ieee.org
Web site: http://www.ieee.org/organizations/pubs/press.

IFSTA, *(0-87939; 1-56916)* Orders Addr.: c/o Oklahoma State Univ., Fire Protection Pubns., 930 N. Willis, Stillwater, OK 74078-8045 USA Tel 405-744-5723; Fax: 405-744-8204; Toll Free: 800-654-4055 (orders only)
Web site: http://www.ifsta.org/.

Ignatius Pr., *(0-89870; 1-58617)* Orders Addr.: P.O. Box 1339, Fort Collins, CO 80522-1339 USA Tel 970-221-3920; Fax: 970-221-3964; Toll Free Fax: 800-278-3566; Toll Free: 800-651-1531 (credit card orders, no minimum, individual orders); 877-320-9276 (bookstore orders); Edit Addr.: 2515 McAllister St., San Francisco, CA 94118 USA (SAN 214-3887) Tel 415-387-2324; Fax: 415-387-0896
E-mail: info@ignatius.com
Web site: http://www.ignatius.com.

Igram Pr., *(0-911119; 1-930279)* 311 Parsons Dr., Hiawatha, IA 52233 USA (SAN 263-1709) Tel 319-393-3600; Fax: 319-393-3934; Toll Free: 800-393-2399
E-mail: clabarr@cedargraphicsinc.com.

Illinois News Service, *See* **News Group - Illinois, The**

Illumination Arts Publishing Co., Inc., *(0-935699; 0-9701907; 0-9740190)* Orders Addr.: P.O. Box 1865, Bellevue, WA 98009 USA (SAN 696-2599) Tel 425-644-7185; Fax: 425-644-9274; Toll Free: 888-210-8216; Edit Addr.: 13256 Northup Way, No. 9, Bellevue, WA 98005 USA
E-mail: liteinfo@illumin.com
Web site: http://www.illumin.com.

Image Processing Software, Inc., *(0-924507)* 6409 Appalachian Way, Madison, WI 53705 USA (SAN 265-5977) Tel 608-233-5033; 4414 Regent St., Madison, WI 53705 (SAN 249-3020).

imaJen, Inc., 5530 Penn Ave., 1st Flr., Pittsburgh, PA 15206 USA Tel 412-441-4143; Fax: 412-441-4453.

Impact Photographics, *(0-918327; 1-56540; 1-60068)* 4961 Windplay Dr., Eldorado Hills, CA 95630 USA (SAN 657-3126) Tel 916-939-9333; Fax: 916-939-9334; Toll Free: 800-950-0110
E-mail: juliem@impactphotographics.com
Web site: http://www.impactphotographics.com.

Imperial News Co., Inc., 5131 Post Rd., Dublin, OH 43017-1160 USA (SAN 169-5509) Fax: 516-752-8515.

Imported Bks., Orders Addr.: St., Dallas, TX 75208 USA (SAN 169-8095) Tel 214-941-6497.

In Between Bks., *(0-935430)* P.O. Box 790, Sausalito, CA 94966 USA (SAN 213-6236) Tel 415-383-8447; Fax: 415-381-1938; 415-381-3513
E-mail: inbetweenbooks@atthebutterflytree.com
Web site: http://www.atthebutterflytree.com.

Incor Periodicals, 32150 Hwy. 34, Tangent, OR 97389-9704 USA (SAN 169-7072) Tel 541-926-8889; Fax: 541-926-9553.

Independent Magazine Co., 2970 N. Ontario St., Burbank, CA 91504-2016 USA (SAN 159-8783).

Independent Pubs. Group, Subs. of Chicago Review Pr., 814 N. Franklin, Chicago, IL 60610 USA (SAN 202-0769) Tel 312-337-0747; Fax: 312-337-5985; Toll Free: 800-888-4741
E-mail: frontdesk@ipgbook.com
Web site: http://www.ipgbook.com; http://www.trafalgarsquarepublishing.com.

Independent Pubs. Marketing, 6824 Oaklawn Ave., Edina, MN 55435 USA (SAN 630-5725) Tel 612-920-9044; Fax: 612-920-7662; Toll Free: 800-669-9044
Web site: http://www.Stjohns.ipm.worldnet.att.net.

Indiana Periodicals, Inc., 2120 S. Meridian St., Indianapolis, IN 46225 USA (SAN 169-2380) Tel 317-786-1488; Fax: 317-782-4999.

Indiana Univ. Pr., *(0-253)* 601 N. Morton St., Bloomington, IN 47404-3797 USA (SAN 202-5647) Fax: 812-855-7931; Toll Free: 800-842-6796
E-mail: iuporder@indiana.edu
Web site: http://www.Indiana.edu/~iupress.

Information Today, Inc., *(0-910965; 0-938734; 1-57387)* 143 Old Marlton Pike, Medford, NJ 08055-8750 USA (SAN 215-8841) Tel 609-654-6266; Fax: 609-654-4309; Toll Free: 800-300-9868
E-mail: custserv@infotoday.com
Web site: http://www.infotoday.com.

Ingenix, Inc., *(1-56329; 1-56337; 1-60151)* 2525 Lake Park Blvd., West Valley City, UT 84120 USA (SAN 630-5482) Tel 801-982-3000; Toll Free: 800-464-3649 (phone/fax)
E-mail: jeni.smith@ingenix.com; chris.smith@ingenix.com; jean.parkinson@ingenix.com
Web site: http://www.ingenix.com; http://www.IngenixOnline.com.

Ingenix Publishing Group, *See* **Ingenix, Inc.**

Ingham Publishing, Inc., *(0-9611804; 1-891130)* Orders Addr.: P.O. Box 12642, Saint Petersburg, FL 33733-2642 USA Tel 813-343-4811; Fax: 813-381-2807; Edit Addr.: 5650 First Ave., N., Saint Petersburg, FL 33710 USA (SAN 112-8930)
E-mail: ftreflex@concentric.net.

Ingram Bk. Co., Subs. of Ingram Industries, Inc., Orders Addr.: 1 Ingram Blvd., P.O. Box 3006, La Vergne, TN 37086-1986 USA (SAN 169-7978) Tel 615-213-5000; Fax: 615-213-3976 (Electronic Orders); Toll Free Fax: 800-285-3296 (fax inquiry US & Canada); 800-876-0186 (orders); 877-663-5367 (Canadian orders); Toll Free: 800-937-8000 (orders only); 800-937-8200 (customer service US & Canada); 800-289-0687 (Canadian orders only customer service); 800-234-6737 (electronic orders US & Canada)) Do not confuse with Ingram Pr., Sacramento, CA
E-mail: customerservice@ingrambook.com; flashback@ingrambook.com; ics-sales@ingrambook.com
Web site: http://www.ingrambook.com.

Ingram Entertainment, Inc., Two Ingram Blvd. (Corp. Headquarters), La Vergne, TN 37089-7006 USA (SAN 630-6780) Tel 615-287-4000; Fax: 615-287-4995; Toll Free: 800-759-5000; 12000 Ridgemont Dr., Urbandale, IA 50323-2317 (SAN 630-6950); 26391 Curtiss Wright Pkwy. Ste. 106, Cleveland, OH 44143-4401 (SAN 630-6896) Toll Free: 800-621-1333; 15002 Sommermeyer, Houston, TX 77041-5333 (SAN 630-7000) Tel 713-937-3600; Fax: 713-466-4316; 382 E. Lies Rd., Carol Stream, IL 60188-9418 (SAN 630-690X) Toll Free: 800-621-1333; 7911 NE 33rd Dr., Suite 270, Portland, OR 97211-1920 (SAN 630-7116) Tel 503-281-2673; Fax: 503-284-6046; 23 Monte Vista Ave., Larkspur, CA 94939-2120 (SAN 630-6993) Toll Free: 800-621-1333; 2611 S. Roosevelt, Suite 102, Tempe, AZ 85282-2017 (SAN 630-7094) Tel 602-966-6691; Fax: 602-894-0329; 4703 Fulton Industrial Blvd., Atlanta, GA 30336-2017 (SAN 630-6845) Tel 404-691-6280; Fax: 404-696-3944; 400 Airport Executive Pk., Spring Valley, NY 10977-7404 (SAN 630-7078) Tel 914-425-3191; Fax: 914-425-7521; 7949 Woodley Blvd., Van Nuys, CA 91406 (SAN 630-7183) Tel 818-375-5027; Fax: 818-375-5001; 1293 Heil Quaker Blvd., Suite B, P.O. Box 7006, La Vergne, TN 37086-7006 (SAN 630-7051) Fax: 615-793-6196; Toll Free: 800-688-3110; 5500 Oakbrook Pkwy., Suite 220, Norcross, GA 30093 (SAN 630-6853) Tel 404-447-4663; Fax: 404-446-7711; Toll Free: 800-876-0832; 3114 S. 24th St., Kansas City, KS 66106-4709 (SAN 630-7027) Tel 913-362-0391; Fax: 913-362-0605; Toll Free: 800-621-1333; 6635 NE 59th Pl., Portland, OR 97218-2709 (SAN 630-7124) Tel 503-284-3313; Fax: 503-284-3876; Toll Free: 800-876-0834; 7319 Innovation Blvd., Fort Wayne, IN 46818-1371 (SAN 630-6985) Fax: 219-489-8850; Toll Free: 800-759-5588; 8779 Greenwood Pl., Savage, MD 20763 (SAN 630-7019) Tel 301-490-1166; Fax: 301-490-0031; Toll Free: 800-621-1333; 1521 W. Copans Rd., Suite 105, Pompano Beach, FL 33064 (SAN 630-7108) Tel 954-971-5412; Fax: 954-971-3113; Toll Free: 800-888-3876; 20435 E. Business Pkwy., Walnut, CA 91789-2999 (SAN 630-7191) Tel 714-594-6569; Fax: 714-595-0735; Toll Free: 800-759-4422; 7710 King St., Anchorage, AK 99518 (SAN 630-6837) Tel 907-344-9666; Fax: 907-344-9738; Toll Free: 800-621-1333; 1349 Charwood Rd., Hanover, MD 21076-3114 (SAN 630-6861) Tel 410-850-9191; Fax: 410-850-9229; 110 Shawmut Rd., Canton, MA 02021-1412 (SAN 630-687X) Tel 617-575-9585; Fax: 617-575-9586; 100 Dobbs Ln., Suite 206, Cherry Hill, NJ 08034-1435 (SAN 630-6888) Tel 609-428-8668; Fax: 609-428-8536; Toll Free: 800-288-7565; 11235 Knott Ave., Suite C, Cypress, CA 90630-5401 (SAN 630-6918) Tel 714-373-8855; Fax: 714-373-8858; Toll Free: 800-759-4422; 1430 Bradley Ln., No. 102, Carrollton, TX 75007-4855 (SAN 630-6926) Tel 214-245-6088; Fax: 214-323-3890; Toll Free: 800-621-1333; 2259 Merritt Dr., Garland, TX 75041-6138 (SAN 630-6934) Tel 214-840-6621; Fax: 214-840-3357; Toll Free: 800-727-0688; 10990 E. 55th Ave., Denver, CO 80239-2007 (SAN 630-6942) Tel 303-371-8372; Fax: 303-373-4583; 35245 Schoolcraft, Livonia, MI 48150-1209 (SAN 630-6969) Tel 313-422-9955; Fax: 313-422-1171; 3540 NW 56th St., Fort Lauderdale, FL 33309-2260 (SAN 630-6977) Tel 305-733-7440; Fax: 305-735-7752; 6733 S. Sepulveda, Suite 108, Los Angeles, CA 90045-1525 (SAN 630-7035) Tel 213-410-4067; Fax: 213-410-0919; Toll Free: 800-759-4422; 9549 Penn Ave S. Ste. 200, Minneapolis, MN 55431-2565 (SAN 630-7043) Toll Free: 800-825-3112; 25 Branca Rd., East Rutherford, NJ 07073-2121 (SAN 630-706X) Tel 201-933-9797; Fax: 201-933-5139; Toll Free: 800-621-1333; 5576 Inland Empire Blvd, Bldg. G, Suite A, Ontario, CA 91764-5117 (SAN 630-7086) Tel 714-948-7998; Fax: 714-948-9778; Freeport Ctr., Bldg. H-12 N., P.O. Box 1387, Clearfield, UT 84016-1387 (SAN 630-7132) Tel 801-775-0555; Fax: 801-773-8172; 2700 Merchantile Dr., Suite 100, Rancho Cordova, CA 95742-6574 (SAN 630-7140) Tel 916-638-8090; Fax: 916-638-8021; Toll Free: 800-866-1568; 4660 Viewridge Ave., Suite B, San Diego, CA 92123-1638 (SAN 630-7159) Tel 619-569-9816; Fax: 619-569-1542; Toll Free: 800-365-5229; 6411 S. 216th, Bldg. F, Kent, WA 98032-1392 (SAN 630-7167) Tel 206-395-3515; Fax: 206-395-0650; 445 W. Freedom Ave., Orange, CA 92865 (SAN 630-7175) Tel 714-282-1232; Fax: 714-282-2245; 201 Ingram Dr., Roseburg, OR 97470; 12600 SE Hwy. 212, Bldg. B, Clackamas, OR 97015-9081 Tel 615-287-4000
Web site: http://www.ingramentertainment.com.

Ingram Pub. Services, Orders Addr.: Customer Services, Box 512 1 Ingram Blvd., LaVergne, TN 37086 USA Toll Free Fax: 800-838-1149; Edit Addr.: 1 Ingram Blvd., LaVergne, TN 37086 USA (SAN 631-8630) Tel 615-793-5000; Fax: 615-213-5811
E-mail: customer.service@ingrampublisherservices.com; Publisher@ingrampublisherservices.com; Retailer@ingrampublisherservices.com
Web site: http://www.ingrampublisherservices.com.

Ingram Software, Subs. of Ingram Distribution Group, Inc., 1759 Wehrle, Williamsville, NY 14221 USA (SAN 285-760X) Toll Free: 800-828-7250; 900 W. Walnut Ave., Compton, CA 90220 (SAN 285-7073).

Inland Empire Periodicals, *See* **Incor Periodicals**

Inner Traditions International, Ltd., *(0-89281; 1-59477)* Orders Addr.: P.O. Box 388, Rochester, VT 05767-0388 USA Tel 802-767-3174; Fax: 802-767-3726; Toll Free Fax: 800-246-8648; Edit Addr.: One Park St., Rochester, VT 05767 USA (SAN 208-6948) Tel 802-767-3174; Fax: 802-767-3726
E-mail: customerservice@innertraditions.com; info@innertraditions.com
Web site: http://www.innertraditions.com.

Insight Guides, *(0-88729; 1-58573; 981-4120)* 46-35 54th Rd., Maspeth, NY 11378 USA Tel 718-784-0055; Fax: 718-784-1246
E-mail: customerservice@americanmap.com
Web site: http://www.americanmap.com.

Instructional Video, 2219 C St., Lincoln, NE 68502 USA (SAN 631-6115) Tel 402-475-6570; 402 475 6570; Fax: 402-475-6500; Toll Free: 800-228-0164 Do not confuse with Instructional Video in Golden, CO
E-mail: Kathy@insvideo.com
Web site: http://www.insvideo.com.

Integral Yoga Pubns., *(0-932040)* Satchidananda Ashram-Yogaville, Rte. 1, Box 1720, Buckingham, VA 23921 USA (SAN 285-0338) Tel 804-969-1706; Fax: 804-969-1463; Toll Free: 800-262-1008 (orders)
Web site: http://www.yogaville.org/pubs.html.

Interactive Knowledge, *See* **NetLibrary, Inc.**

Interlink Publishing Group, Inc., *(0-940793; 1-56656)* 46 Crosby St., Northampton, MA 01060-1804 USA (SAN 664-8908) Tel 413-582-7054; Fax: 413-582-6731; Toll Free: 800-238-5465
E-mail: info@interlinkbooks.com; editor@interlinkbooks.com
Web site: http://www.interlinkbooks.com.

Interlink Publishing Group, Incorporated, *See* **Interlink Publishing Group, Inc.**

InterMountain Periodical Distributors, *See* **Majic Enterprises**

International Bk. Ctr., Inc., *(0-86685; 0-917062)* 2007 Laurel Dr., P.O. Box 295, Troy, MI 48099 USA (SAN 169-4014) Tel 248-879-8436; Fax: 810-254-7230
E-mail: ibc@ibcbooks.com
Web site: http://www.ibcbooks.com.

International Bks. & Tapes Supply, P.O. Box 5153, Long Island City, NY 11005 USA (SAN 631-6743) Tel 718-721-4246; Fax: 718-321-9004.

International Historic Films, Inc., *(1-57299)* Orders Addr.: P.O. Box 29035, Chicago, IL 60629 USA Tel 773-927-2900; Fax: 773-927-9211; Edit Addr.: 3533 S. Archer Ave., Chicago, IL 60609 USA
E-mail: info@ihffilm.com
Web site: http://historicvideo.com.

International Magazine Service, Div. of Periodical Pubs. Service Bureau, 1 N. Superior St., Sandusky, OH 44870 USA (SAN 285-9955) Tel 419-626-0623.

International Networking Assn., 4130 Citrus Ave., Suite 5, Rocklin, CA 95677 USA (SAN 631-1857).

International Periodical Distributors, 674 Via de la Valle, Suite 204, Solana Beach, CA 92075 USA (SAN 250-5290) Tel 619-481-5928; Toll Free: 800-999-1170; 800-228-5144 (in Canada).

International Publishers Marketing, Orders Addr.: 22883 Quicksilver Dr., Dulles, VA 20166 USA (SAN 253-3375) Toll Free: 800-758-3756; Edit Addr.: P.O. Box 605, Herndon, VA 20172-0605 USA Fax: 703-661-1501; Toll Free: 1-800-758-3756
E-mail: laureen@booksintl.com
Web site: http://www.internationalpubmarket.com.

International Pubns. Service, *(0-8002)* Div. of Taylor & Francis, Inc., Orders Addr.: 325 Chestnut St., 8th Flr., Levittown, PA 19057-4700 USA Fax: 215-785-5515; Toll Free: 800-821-8312.

International Readers League, Div. of Periodical Pubs. Service Bureau, 1 N. Superior St., Sandusky, OH 44870 USA (SAN 285-9971) Tel 419-626-0633.

International Service Co., International Service Bldg., 333 Fourth Ave., Indialantic, FL 32903-4295 USA (SAN 169-5134) Tel 407-724-1443 (phone/fax).

International Specialized Bk. Services, 920 NE 58th Ave., Suite 300, Portland, OR 97213-3786 USA (SAN 169-7129) Tel 503-287-3093; Fax: 503-280-8832; Toll Free: 800-944-6190
E-mail: info@isbs.com
Web site: http://www.isbs.com.

International Thomson Computer Pr., *(1-85032)* Orders Addr.: 7625 Empire Dr., Florence, KY 41042-2978 USA Tel 606-525-6600; Fax: 606-525-7778; Toll Free: 800-842-3636; Edit Addr.: 20 Park Plaza, 13th Flr., Boston, MA 02116 USA Fax: 617-695-1615
E-mail: itcp@itp.thomson.com
Web site: http://www.itcpmedia.com.

Internet Systems, Inc., Subs. of Internet Systems, Inc., 20250 Century Blvd., Germantown, MD 20874 USA (SAN 129-9611) Tel 301-540-5100; Fax: 301-540-5522; Toll Free: 800-638-8725
Web site: http://www.pwl.com/Internet.

Interstate Distributors, 150 Blackstone River Rd. Ste. 4, Worcester, MA 01607-1455 USA (SAN 170-4885) Toll Free: 800-365-6430.

Interstate Periodical Distributors, P.O. Box 2237, Madison, WI 53701 USA (SAN 169-9105) Tel 608-271-3600; Fax: 608-277-2410; Toll Free: 800-752-3131.

Intertech Bk. Services, Inc., 25971 Sarazen Dr., South Riding, VA 20152-1741 USA (SAN 630-5253).

Intrepid Group, Inc., The, 1331 Red Cedar Cir., Fort Collins, CO 80524 USA (SAN 631-5429) Tel 970-493-3793; Fax: 970-493-8781
E-mail: intrepid@fril.com.

Iowa & Illinois News, 8645 Northwest Blvd., Davenport, IA 52806-6418 USA (SAN 169-2607).

Iowa State Press, *See* **Blackwell Publishing Professional**

Irish American Bk. Co., Subs. of Roberts Rinehart Pubs., Inc., P.O. Box 666, Niwot, CO 80544-0666 USA Tel 303-652-2710; Fax: 303-652-2689; Toll Free: 800-452-7115
E-mail: irishbooks@aol.com
Web site: http://www.irishvillage.com.

Irish Bks. & Media, Inc., *(0-937702)* Orders Addr.: 2904 41st Ave S., Minneapolis, MN 55406-1814 USA (SAN 111-8870) Toll Free: 800-229-3505 Do not confuse with Irish Bks. in New York, NY
E-mail: Irishbook@aol.com
Web site: http://www.irishbook.com.

Ironside International Pubs., Inc., *(0-935554)* Orders Addr.: P.O. Box 55, Alexandria, VA 22313 USA (SAN 206-2380) Tel 703-684-6111; Fax: 703-683-5486; Edit Addr.: P.O. Box 1050, Lorton, VA 22199-1050 USA (SAN 663-656X).

ISHK, *(0-86304; 0-900860; 1-883536; 1-933779)* Div. of Institute for the Study of Human Knowledge, Orders Addr.: P.O. Box 381069, Cambridge, MA 02238-1069 USA (SAN 226-4536) Tel 617-497-4124; Fax: 617-876-2976; Toll Free Fax: 800-223-4200; Toll Free: 800-222-4745; Edit Addr.: P.O. Box 176, Los Altos, CA 94023 USA Tel 650-948-9428
E-mail: ishkorders@aol.com; ishkbooks@aol.com
Web site: http://www.ishkbooks.com.

Islamic Bk. Service, 1209 Cleburne, Hoston, TX 77004 USA (SAN 169-2453) Tel 713-528-1440; Fax: 713-528-1085.

Island Heritage Publishing, *(0-89610; 0-931548; 1-59700)* Div. of The Madden Corp., 94-411 Koaki St., Waipahu, HI 96797 USA (SAN 211-1403) Tel 808-564-8800; Fax: 808-564-8888; Toll Free: 800-468-2800
E-mail: vkitajima@welcometotheislands.com
Web site: http://www.welcometotheislands.com.

Islander Group, 269 Pali'i St., Mililani, HI 96789 USA Tel 808-676-0116.

Itasca Bks., *(0-9767054)* 3501 Hwy. 100 S., Suite 220, Minneapolis, MN 55416 USA Fax: 952-920-0541
E-mail: mjung@itascabooks.com
Web site: http://www.itascabooks.com.

iUniverse, Inc., *(0-9665514; 1-58348; 0-9668591; 1-893652; 0-595; 0-9795279; 1-60528)* Orders Addr.: 2021 Pine Lake Rd., Suite 100, Lincoln, NE 68512 USA (SAN 254-9425) Tel 402-323-7800; Fax: 402-323-7824; Toll Free: 800-AUTHORS (800-288-4677)
E-mail: post.production@iuniverse.com; book.orders@iuniverse.com; bethany.dirks@iuniverse.com
Web site: http://www.iUniverse.com.

iUniverse.com, Incorporated, *See* **iUniverse, Inc.**

J & N Creations, LLC, 48 First St., N., Sauk Centre, MN 56304 USA Tel 320-352-6260.

JAGCO & Associates Inc., Orders Addr.: 596 Indian Trail Rd. South #227, Indian Trail, NC 28079 USA Tel 802-223-6565.

Jalmar Pr., *(0-915190; 0-935266; 1-880396; 1-931061)* Subs. of B. L. Winch & Assocs., P.O. Box 370, Fawnskin, CA 92333-0370 USA (SAN 113-3640) Toll Free: 800-662-9662 (orders)
E-mail: jalmarpress@att.net
Web site: http://jalmarpress.com.

James & Law Co., Orders Addr.: P.O. Box 2468, Clarksburg, WV 26302-2468 USA (SAN 169-894X); Edit Addr.: Middletown Mall I-79 & U. S. 250, Fairmont, WV 26554 USA (SAN 169-8966) Tel 304-624-7401.

James Trading Group, Limited, The, 33 Murray Hill Dr., Nanuet, NY 10954 USA Toll Free: 800-541-5004
E-mail: sales@thejamestradinggroup.com.

Janway, 11 Academy Rd., Cogan Station, PA 17728 USA (SAN 108-3708) Tel 717-494-1239; Fax: 717-494-1350; Toll Free: 800-877-5242.

Jawbone Publishing Corp., *(0-9702959; 1-59094)* 2907 Paddington Way, Kissimmee, FL 34747 USA (SAN 253-5335) Tel 407-396-4245; Fax: 407-396-4247
E-mail: marketing@jawbonepublishing.com
Web site: http://www.jawbonepublishing.com.

JayMar Services, LLC, 1331 Red Cedar Cir., Fort Collins, CO 80524 USA Tel 970-493-3793; Fax: 970-493-8781; P.O. Box 210752, Nashville, TN 37221 Tel 615-673-6938; Fax: 615-673-0540
E-mail: JayMarLLC@aol.com
Web site: http://www.JayMarSvcs.com.

Jeanies Classics, *(0-9609672)* Orders Addr.: 2123 Oxford St., Rockford, IL 61103 USA (SAN 271-7409); Edit Addr.: 2123 Oxford St., Rockford, IL 61103 USA (SAN 271-7395) Tel 815-968-4544.

Jean's Dulcimer Shop & Crying Creek Pubs., P.O. Box 8, Hwy. 32, Cosby, TN 37722 USA (SAN 249-9282) Tel 423-487-5543.

Jech Distributors, 674 Via De La Valle, No. 204, Solana Beach, CA 92075-2462 USA (SAN 107-0258) Tel 619-452-7251.

Jellyroll Productions, *See* **Osborne Enterprises Publishing**

Jenkins Group, Inc., *(1-890587)* 121 E. Front St., 4th Flr., Traverse City, MI 49684 USA Tel 231-933-0445; Fax: 231-933-0448
Web site: http://www.bookpublishing.com.

Jewish Lights Publishing, *(1-58023; 1-879045)* Div. of LongHill Partners, Inc., Orders Addr.: P.O. Box 237, Woodstock, VT 05091 USA (SAN 242-6439) Tel 802-457-4000; Fax: 802-457-4004; Toll Free: 800-962-4544 (orders)
E-mail: sales@jewishlights.com
Web site: http://www.jewishlights.com.

JIST Publishing, *(0-942784; 1-56370; 1-57112; 1-59357)* 7321 Shadeland Sta. Ste 200, Indianapolis, IN 46256 USA (SAN 240-2351) Tel 317-613-4200 Toll Free Fax: 800-547-8329
E-mail: info@jist.com
Web site: http://www.jist.com.

JIST Works, Incorporated, *See* **JIST Publishing**

J&L Bk. Co., Orders Addr.: P.O. Box 13100, Spokane, WA 99213 USA (SAN 129-6817) Fax: 509-534-0152; 509-534-7713; Toll Free: 800-288-9756; Edit Addr.: 1710 Trent, Spokane, WA 99220 USA (SAN 243-2145).

JMS Distribution, 2017 San Mateo St., Richmond, CA 94804 USA.

Johnson Bks., *(0-917895; 0-933472; 1-55566)* Div. of Big Earth Publishing Co., Orders Addr.: 3005 Center Green Dr. Suite 220, Boulder, CO 80301 USA (SAN 201-0313) Tel 303-443-9766; Fax: 303-443-9687; Toll Free: 800-258-5830
E-mail: books@bigearthpublishing.com
Web site: http://www.johnsonbooks.com.

Johnson News Agency, P.O. Box 9009, Moscow, ID 83843 USA (SAN 169-1678).

Johnson, Walter J. Inc., *(0-8472)* 1 New York Plaza 28th Flr., New York, NY 10004-1901 USA (SAN 209-1828).

Johnson, Warren A., *(0-9709275)* 7143 E. Flagg Rd., Ashton, IL 61006-9617 USA Tel 815-453-2482 (phone/fax).

Jones, Bob Univ. Pr., *(0-89084; 1-57924; 1-59166)* 1700 Wade Hampton Blvd., Greenville, SC 29614 USA (SAN 223-7512) Tel 864-242-5731; Fax: 864-298-8398; Toll Free Fax: 800-525-8398; Toll Free: 800-845-5731
E-mail: bjup@bjup.com
Web site: http://www.bjup.com.

Joseph Ruzicka, Incorporated, *See* **Southeast Library Bindery, Inc.**

Joshua Morris Publishing, Incorporated, *See* **Reader's Digest Children's Publishing, Inc.**

Journey Pubns., LLC, *(0-9671696)* 5000 W. Esplanade Ave., No. 214, Metairie, LA 70006-2551 USA Do not confuse with companies with the same or similar names in Woodstock, NY, Summerland, CA, Savannah, GA, Avon Park, FL, lacey, WA
E-mail: joe@utilityprofiles.com
Web site: http://www.101thingsforkids.com.

Joyce Media, Inc., *(0-917002)* P.O. Box 57, Acton, CA 93510 USA (SAN 208-7197) Tel 805-269-1169; Fax: 805-269-2139
E-mail: joycemed@pacbell.net
Web site: http://joycemedia.com.

Junior League of Greensboro Pubns., *(0-9605788)* 604 Green Valley Rd. Ste. 209, Greensboro, NC 27408-7733 USA (SAN 112-9597)
E-mail: Jlgso@aol.com.

Juvenile Justice Clearinghouse/NCJRS, c/o U.S. Dept. of Justice, P.O. Box 6000, Rockville, MD 20849 USA Tel 301-519-5500; Fax: 301-519-5212; Toll Free: 800-638-8736
E-mail: askncjrs@ncjrs.org
Web site: http://www.ncjrs.org.

K E T Enterprise, 560 Cooper Dr., Lexington, KY 40502 USA Toll Free: 800-354-9067.

K. F. Enterprises, *See* **Production Assocs., Inc.**

K. M. R. Enterprises, *(0-9656379)* 5731 Pony Express Trail, Pollock Pines, CA 95726 USA (SAN 299-237X) Tel 530-644-1410.

Kable Media Services, Subs. of AMREP Corp., 505 Park Ave. 7th Fl., New York, NY 10022 USA Tel 212-705-4600; Fax: 212-705-4666; Toll Free: 800-223-6640
E-mail: info@kable.com
Web site: http://www.kable.com/.

Kable News Company, Incorporated, *See* **Kable Media Services**

Kalispell News Agency, P.O. Box 4965, Missoula, MT 59806-4965 USA (SAN 169-4383) Toll Free: 800-955-1266.

Kamkin, Victor, P.O. Box 34583, Bethesda, MD 20827-0583 USA Toll Free: 800-852-6546; 925 Broadway, New York, NY 10010 USA (SAN 169-5924) Tel 212-673-0776; Fax: 212-673-2473.

Kamkyi Bks., *(0-9675031)* Div. of Source International Technology Corp., 939 E. 156th St., Bronx, NY 10455 USA (SAN 630-8392) Tel 718-378-3878 (phone/fax); Toll Free: 888-729-5117
E-mail: source.Intl.Tech@erols.com
Web site: http://www.kamkyibooks.

Kampmann, Kump & Bell, LLC, Orders Addr.: 27 W. 20th St., Suite 1102, New York, NY 10011 USA Tel 212-727-0190; Fax: 212-727-0195
E-mail: midpointny@aol.com.

Kane/Miller Bk. Pubs., Inc., *(0-916291; 1-929132; 1-933605)* Orders Addr.: P.O. Box 8515, La Jolla, CA 92038 USA (SAN 295-8945) Tel 858-456-0540; Fax: 858-456-9641; Toll Free: 800-968-1930; Edit Addr.: 7946 Ivanhoe Ave., Suite 203, La Jolla, CA 92037 USA Tel 858-456-0540
E-mail: kira@kanemiller.com; info@kanemiller.com
Web site: http://www.kanemiller.com; http://www.everyonepoops.com.

Kansas City Periodical Distributing, Orders Addr.: P.O. Box 14948, Lenexa, KS 66285-4948 USA (SAN 107-9433); Edit Addr.: 9605 Dice Ln., Lenexa, KS 66215 USA Tel 913-541-8600.

Kansas State Reading Circle, 715 W. Tenth St., C-170, Topeka, KS 66601 USA (SAN 169-2771).

Kaplan Publishing, *(0-7931; 0-88462; 0-913864; 0-936894; 0-942103; 1-57410)* 1 Liberty Plaza, 24th Flr., New York, NY 10006 USA (SAN 211-2280) Tel 212-618-2400; Fax: 212-618-2498
E-mail: Charles.Holden@kaplan.com; Edwina.Lui@kaplan.com; Daniel.Russell@kaplan.com
Web site: http://www.kaplanpublishing.com.

Kav Books, Incorporated, *See* **Royal Fireworks Publishing Co.**

Kaybee Montessori, Inc., 157 Lagrange Ave., Rochester, NY 14613-1511 USA (SAN 133-1256) Toll Free: 800-732-9304.

Kazi Pubns., Inc., *(0-933511; 0-935782; 1-56744; 1-871031; 1-930637)* 3023 W. Belmont Ave., Chicago, IL 60618 USA (SAN 162-3397) Tel 773-267-7001; Fax: 773-267-7002
E-mail: info@kazi.org
Web site: http://www.kazi.org.

KCS, P.O. Box 1077, Peoria, AZ 85380 USA (SAN 631-2160) Tel 602-974-2179; Fax: 602-972-1486; Toll Free: 800-593-3152.

Kehot Pubn. Society, *(0-8266)* Div. of Merkos L'Inyonei Chinuch, Orders Addr.: 291 Kingston Ave., Brooklyn, NY 11213 USA Tel 718-778-0226; Fax: 718-778-4148; Toll Free: 877-463-7567 (877-4MERKOS); Edit Addr.: 770 Eastern Pkwy., Brooklyn, NY 11213 USA (SAN 220-7060) Tel 718-604-2785
E-mail: orders@kehotonline.com
Web site: http://www.kehotonline.com.

Keith Distributors, 1230 Macklind Ave., Saint Louis, MO 63110-1432 USA (SAN 112-6377) Toll Free: 800-373-2366
E-mail: keithsbooks@juno.com.

Kendall/Hunt Publishing Co., *(0-7872; 0-8403; 0-7575)* Orders Addr.: P.O. Box 1840, Dubuque, IA 52004-1840 USA; Edit Addr.: 4050 Westmark Dr., Dubuque, IA 52002 USA (SAN 203-9184) Tel 563-589-1000; Fax: 563-589-1046; Toll Free Fax: 800-772-9165; Toll Free: 800-228-0810
E-mail: orders@kendallhunt.com; kmalone@kendallhunt.com
Web site: http://www.kendallhunt.com.

Kensington Publishing Corp., *(0-7860; 0-8065; 0-8184; 0-8217; 1-55817; 1-57566; 0-7582; 1-4201; 1-59983; 1-60183; 1-60349)* 850 Third Ave., New York, NY 10022-6222 USA Tel 212-407-1500; Fax: 212-935-0699; Toll Free: 800-221-2647; 499 North Canon Dr., Beverly Hills, CA 90210 Tel 310-887-7082
E-mail: jmclean@kensingtonbooks.com
Web site: http://www.kensingtonbooks.com.

Kent News Agency, Inc., P.O. Box 1828, Scottsbluff, NE 69363-1828 USA (SAN 169-4448) Tel 303-286-9694; 308-635-2225; Fax: 308-635-1563; Toll Free: 877-290-4740
E-mail: kentrob@prairieweb.com.

Keramos, P.O. Box 7500, Ann Arbor, MI 48107 USA (SAN 169-3670) Tel 313-439-1261.

Kerem Publishing, *(1-889727)* 723 N. Orange Dr., Los Angeles, CA 90038 USA (SAN 299-1209).

Kerhulas News Co., P.O. Box 751, Union, SC 29379 USA (SAN 169-7838).

Ketab Corp., *(1-883819; 1-59584)* Orders Addr.: 1419 Westwood Blvd., Los Angeles, CA 90024 USA (SAN 107-7791) Tel 310-477-7477; Fax: 310-444-7176; Toll Free: 800-367-4726
E-mail: ketab@ketab.com
Web site: http://www.ketab.com.

Key Bk. Service, Inc., *(0-934636)* P.O. Box 1434, Fairfield, CT 06430 USA (SAN 169-0671) Tel 203-374-4939; Fax: 203-384-6099.

Kidsbooks, Inc., 220 Monroe Tpke., No. 560, Monroe, CT 06468-2247 USA (SAN 169-0795).

King Electronics Distributing, 1711 Southeastern Ave., Indianapolis, IN 46201-3990 USA (SAN 107-6795) Tel 317-639-1484; Fax: 317-639-4711.

Kingdom, Inc., P.O. Box 506, Mansfield, PA 16933 USA.

Kinokuniya Bookstores of America Co., Ltd., 1581 Webster St., San Francisco, CA 94115 USA (SAN 121-8441) Tel 415-567-7625; Fax: 415-567-4109.

Kinokuniya Pubns. Service of New York, 10 W. 49th St., New York, NY 10020 USA (SAN 157-5414) Tel 212-765-1465; Fax: 212-307-5593
E-mail: kinokuniya@kinokuniya.com
Web site: http://www.kinokuniya.com.

Kirkbride, B.B. Bible Co., Inc., *(0-88707; 0-934854)* P.O. Box 606, Indianapolis, IN 46206-0606 USA (SAN 169-2372) Tel 317-633-1900; Fax: 317-633-1444; Toll Free: 800-428-4385
E-mail: hyperbible@aol.com
Web site: http://www.kirkbride.com.

Kitrick Management Co., Ltd., P.O. Box 15523, Cincinnati, OH 45215 USA (SAN 132-6236) Tel 513-782-2930; Fax: 513-782-2936
E-mail: bachb@aol.com.

Kituku & Assocs., *(0-9650780; 0-9716195)* Orders Addr.: 9494 W. Fairview, Suite C, Boise, ID 83709 USA Toll Free: 888-685-1621
Web site: http://www.kituku.com.

Klein's Booklein, Orders Addr.: P.O. Box 968, Fowlerville, MI 48836 USA (SAN 631-3329) Tel 517-223-3964; Fax: 517-223-1314; Toll Free: 800-266-5534; Edit Addr.: One Klein Dr., Fowlerville, MI 48836 USA (SAN 631-3337).

Knopf, Alfred A. Inc., Div. of The Knopf Publishing Group, Orders Addr.: 400 Hahn Rd., Westminster, MD 21157 USA Tel 410-848-1900; Toll Free: 800-726-0600 (orders); Edit Addr.: 1745 Broadway, New York, NY 10019 USA (SAN 202-5825) Tel 212-782-9000; Toll Free: 800-726-0600
E-mail: customerservice@randomhouse.com
Web site: http://www.randomhouse.com/knopf.

Knox, John Press, *See* **Westminster John Knox Pr.**

Kodansha America, Inc., *(0-87011; 1-56836)* 575 Lexington Ave., 23rd Flr., New York, NY 10022-6102 USA (SAN 201-0526) Tel 917-322-6200; Fax: 212-935-6929; Toll Free: 800-451-7556
E-mail: info@kodanshaamerica.com.

Koen Pacific, Orders Addr.: P.O. Box 600, Moorestown, NJ 08057-0600 USA (SAN 631-5593) Toll Free: 800-995-4840
E-mail: info@koenpacific.com.

Kraus Reprint, *See* **Periodicals Service Co.**

Kregel Pubns., *(0-8254)* Div. of Kregel, Inc., Orders Addr.: P.O. Box 2607, Grand Rapids, MI 49501-2607 USA (SAN 206-9792) Tel 616-451-4775; Fax: 616-451-9330; Toll Free: 800-733-2607; Edit Addr.: 733 Wealthy St., SE., Grand Rapids, MI 49503-5553 USA (SAN 298-9115)
E-mail: kregelbooks@kregel.com; acquisitions@kregel.com
Web site: http://www.kregel.com.

Kumarian Pr., Inc., *(0-931816; 1-56549; 1-887208)* 1294 Blue Hills Ave., Bloomfield, CT 06002 USA (SAN 212-5978) Tel 860-243-2098; Fax: 860-243-2867; Toll Free: 800-289-2664
E-mail: Kpbooks@kpbooks.com
Web site: http://www.kpbooks.com.

Kurian, George Reference Bks., *(0-914746)* Orders Addr.: P.O. Box 519, Baldwin Place, NY 10505 USA (SAN 203-1981); Edit Addr.: 3689 Campbell Ct., Yorktown Heights, NY 10598 USA (SAN 110-6236) Tel 914-962-3287.

Kurtzman Bk. Sales Co., 17348 W. 12 Mile Rd., Southfield, MI 48076 USA (SAN 114-0787) Tel 248-557-7230; Fax: 248-557-8705; Toll Free: 800-869-0505.

Kuykendall's Pr., Bookstore Div., P.O. Box 627, Athens, AL 35612-0627 USA (SAN 168-9185) Tel 256-232-1754; Toll Free: 800-781-1754.

L. D. Bks. Inc., Orders Addr.: 8233 NW St., Miami, FL 33166 USA Tel 305-406-2292.

L L Company, *(0-937892)* 1647 Manning Ave., Los Angeles, CA 90024 USA (SAN 110-0009) Tel 310-615-0116; Fax: 310-640-6863; Toll Free: 800-473-3699
E-mail: wallacelab@aol.com.

L M C Source, P.O. Box 720400, San Jose, CA 95172-0400 USA (SAN 631-189X) Tel 408-630-0589; Fax: 408-634-1456; Toll Free: 800-873-3043
E-mail: lmcs@pacbell.net
Web site: http://www.csn.net/~davidl/.

La Belle News Agency, 814 University Blvd., Steubenville, OH 43952 USA (SAN 169-6858) Tel 740-282-9731.

La Cite French Bks., Div. of The La Cite Group, Inc., P.O. Box 64504, Los Angeles, CA 90064-0504 USA (SAN 168-9789) E-mail: lacite@aol.com.

La Moderna Poesia, Inc., 5739 NW 7th St., Miami, FL 33126-3105 USA (SAN 169-1139).

Lafayette Bks., P.O. Box 758, Mamaroneck, NY 10543-0758 USA (SAN 135-292X) Tel 914-833-0248.

Lakeport Distributors, Inc., 139 W. 18th St., P.O. Box 6195, Erie, PA 16501 USA (SAN 169-734X).

Lamaze Media Ctr., 1200 19th St., NW, Suite 300, Washington, DC 20036-2422 USA Toll Free: 800-368-4404.

Lambert Bk. Hse., Inc., *(0-89315)* 4139 Parkway Dr., Florence, AL 35630-6347 USA (SAN 180-5169) Tel 256-764-4098; 256-764-4090; Fax: 256-766-9200; Toll Free: 800-551-8511
E-mail: Info@lambertbookhouse.com
Web site: http://www.lambertbookhouse.com.

Landmark Audiobooks, 4865 Sterling Dr., Boulder, CO 80301 USA Fax: 303-443-3775
Web site: http://www.landmarkaudio.com.

Landmark Bk. Co., *(0-929194)* 131 Hicks St., Brooklyn, NY 11201-2318 USA (SAN 169-5843).

Langenscheidt Publishing Group, *See* **Langenscheidt Pubs Inc.**

Langenscheidt Pubs Inc., *(0-88729; 3-468; 1-58573; 3-526; 3-324; 981-258)* Subs. of Langenscheidt KG, Orders Addr.: 15 Tyger River Dr., Duncan, SC 29334 USA Fax: 888-773-7979; Toll Free: 800-432-6277; Edit Addr.: 36-36 33rd St., Long Island City, NY 11106 USA
Web site: http://www.americanmap.com; http://www.langenscheidt.com.

Larousse Kingfisher Chambers, Inc., *(0-7534; 1-85697; 970-22)* 215 Park Ave., S., New York, NY 10003 USA (SAN 297-7540); 181 Ballardvale St., Wilmington, MA 01887.

Las Vegas News Agency, 2312 Silver Bluff Ct., Las Vegas, NV 89134-6092 USA.

Lash Distributors, 7106 Geoffrey Way, Frederick, MD 21704 USA (SAN 169-3131).

Last Gasp Eco-Funnies, Incorporated, *See* **Last Gasp of San Francisco**

Last Gasp of San Francisco, *(0-86719)* Orders Addr.: 777 Florida St., San Francisco, CA 94110 USA (SAN 216-8308); Edit Addr.: 777 Florida St., San Francisco, CA 94110-2025 USA (SAN 170-3242) Tel 415-824-6636; Fax: 415-824-1836; Toll Free: 800-366-5121
E-mail: colin@lastgasp.com
Web site: http://www.lastgasp.com.

Laster, Larry D. Old & Rare Bks., Prints & Maps, 2416 Maplewood Ave., Winston-Salem, NC 27103 USA (SAN 112-9600) Tel 336-724-7544; Fax: 336-724-9055.

Latcorp, Ltd., 10 Norden Ln., Huntington Station, NY 11746 USA (SAN 159-8910) Tel 516-271-0548; Fax: 516-549-8849.

Latin American Bk. Source, Inc., 289 Third Ave., Chula Vista, CA 91910 USA Tel 619-426-1226; Fax: 619-426-0212
Web site: http://www.latinbooks.com.

Latin Trading Corp., 539 H St., Chula Vista, CA 91910 USA (SAN 630-2963) Tel 619-427-7867; Fax: 619-476-1817; Toll Free: 800-257-7248
E-mail: info@latintradingbooks.com
Web site: http://www.latintradingbooks.com.

Latta, J. S. Incorporated, *See* **Latta's**

Latta's, 1502 Fourth Ave., P.O. Box 2668, Huntington, WV 25726 USA (SAN 169-8982) Fax: 304-525-5038; Toll Free: 800-624-3501.

LD Bks., Inc., *(0-9772669; 0-9785897)* 8313 NW. 68th St., Miami, FL 33166 USA (SAN 631-8088) Tel 305-406-2292; Fax: 305-406-2293
E-mail: ldbventas@bellsouth.net
Web site: http://www.sinlimites.net.

LEA Bk. Distributors (Libros Espana y America), *(1-883110)* 170-23 83rd Ave., Jamaica Hills, NY 11432 USA (SAN 170-5407) Tel 718-291-9891; Fax: 718-291-9830
E-mail: leabook@idt.net
Web site: http://www.leabooks.com.

Learn Technologies Interactive, LLC, *(1-58125)* 361 Broadway, Suite 600, New York, NY 10013 USA Tel 212-334-2225; Fax: 212-334-1211
Web site: http://www.LearnTech.com.

Learned Information, Incorporated, *See* **Information Today, Inc.**

Learning Collection, The, 145 S. Glencoe St., Denver, CO 80246-1152 USA (SAN 630-8287).

Learning Connection, The, *(1-56831)* Orders Addr.: 1901 Longleaf Blvd., Suite 300, Lake Wales, FL 33859 USA Tel 863-676-4246; Fax: 863-676-5216; Toll Free: 800-218-8489
Web site: http://www.tlconnection.com.

Learning Services, 2095 Laura St. Ste. H, Springfield, OR 97477-2285 USA Toll Free: 800-877-3278.

Lectorum Pubns., Inc., *(0-9625162; 1-880507; 1-930332; 1-933032)* Subs. of Scholastic, Inc., 205 Chubb Ave., Lyndhurst, NJ 07071-3520 USA Tel 212-965-7322; Fax: 212-727-3035; Toll Free Fax: 877-532-8678; 877-532-8676; Toll Free: 800-345-5946
E-mail: info@lectorum.com
Web site: http://www.lectorum.com.

Lee Bks., *(0-939818)* Div. of Lee S. Cole & Assocs., Inc., 524 San Anselmo Ave., No 215, San Anselmo, CA 94960-2614 USA (SAN 110-649X) Tel 415-456-4388; Fax: 415-456-7532; Toll Free: 800-828-3550 Do not confuse with other companies with the same or similar names in Jacksonville, FL, Columbia, SC
E-mail: lcs@lsc-associates.com
Web site: http://www.lsc-associates.com.

Left Bank Books Distribution & Publishing, *See* **Left Bank Distribution**

Left Bank Distribution, *(0-939306)* 92 Pike St., Seattle, WA 98101-2025 USA (SAN 216-5368)
E-mail: leftbank@leftbankbooks.com
Web site: http://www.leftbankbooks.com.

Leisure Arts, Inc., *(0-942237; 1-57486; 1-60140)* Orders Addr.: 5701 Ranch Dr., Little Rock, AR 72223 USA (SAN 666-9565) Tel 501-868-8800; Fax: 501-868-1001; Toll Free Fax: 877-710-5603; Toll Free: 800-643-8030 (customer service); 800-526-5111
E-mail: hermine_linz@leisurearts.com; nicholsonl@sunset.com
Web site: http://www.leisurearts.com.

Leman Pubns., Inc., *(0-943721; 0-9602970)* Div. of Rodale Pr. Co., Box 4100, 741 Corporate Cir., Suite A, Golden, CO 80401-5622 USA (SAN 213-3415) Fax: 303-277-0370; Toll Free: 800-877-3775.

Leonard, Hal Corp., *(0-634; 0-7935; 0-87910; 0-87930; 0-88188; 0-931340; 0-9607350; 1-56516; 1-57467; 1-4234)* Orders Addr.: P.O. Box 13819, Milwaukee, WI 53213-0819 USA Tel 414-774-3630; Fax: 414-774-3259; Toll Free: 800-524-4425; Edit Addr.: 7777 W. Bluemound Rd., Milwaukee, WI 53213 USA (SAN 239-250X)
E-mail: halinfo@halleonard.com
Web site: http://www.halleonard.com.

Leonardo Press, *See* **Firenze Pr.**

Lerner Publishing Group, *(0-7613; 0-8225; 0-87614; 0-929371; 0-930494; 1-57505; 1-58013)* Orders Addr.: 1251 Washington Ave. N., Minneapolis, MN 55401 USA (SAN 256-0283) Tel 612-332-3344; Fax: 612-204-9208; Edit Addr.: 241 First Ave., N., Minneapolis, MN 55401 USA (SAN 201-0828) Tel 612-332-3344; Fax: 612-215-6230; Toll Free Fax: 800-332-1132; Toll Free: 800-328-4929
E-mail: info@lernerbooks.com; custserve@lernerbooks.com
Web site: http://www.lernerbooks.com; http://www.karben.com.

Levant Distributors, Incorporated, *See* **Levant USA, Inc.**

Levant USA, Inc., 145 Hook Creek Blvd. BLDG B6B3, Valley Stream, NY 11581-2223 USA (SAN 631-1970)
E-mail: levantusa@cs.com.

Levine, J. Religious Supplies, Five W. 30th St., New York, NY 10001 USA (SAN 169-5878) Tel 212-695-6888; Fax: 212-643-1044
E-mail: sales@levine.judica.com.

Levy, Charles Company, *See* **Levy Home Entertainment, Ltd.**

Levy Home Entertainment, Div. of Charles Levy Co., 4201 Raymond Dr., Hillside, IL 60162 USA (SAN 176-2478) Tel 708-547-4400; 708-649-4158; Fax: 708-547-4503; Toll Free: 800-947-1967
E-mail: jsemeneck@levybooks.com.

Levy Home Entertainment, Ltd., 1930 George St. Ste. 1, Melrose Park, IL 60160-1501 USA (SAN 159-835X).

Lewis International, Inc., *(0-9666771; 1-930983)* 2201 NW 102nd Pl., No. 1, Miami, FL 33172 USA Tel 305-436-7984; Fax: 305-436-7985; Toll Free: 800-259-5962.

Lewis, John W. Enterprises, 168 Perez St., P.O. Box 3375, Santurce, PR 00936 USA (SAN 169-9334) Tel 809-722-0104.

Lexicon Pubns., Inc., P.O. Box 1737, Danbury, CT 06810 USA (SAN 205-664X) Tel 203-796-2540.

LEXIS Law Publishing, *See* **LEXIS Publishing**

LEXIS Publishing, *(0-327; 0-406; 0-409; 0-672; 0-87215; 0-87473; 0-88063; 0-930273; 1-55834; 1-56257)* Div. of Reed Elsevier, Orders Addr.: P.O. Box 7587, Charlottesville, VA 22906-7587 USA Tel 434-972-7600; Fax: 434-972-7686; Toll Free Fax: 800-643-1280; Toll Free: 800-446-3410; Edit Addr.: 701 E. Water St., Charlottesville, VA 22902 USA Do not confuse with Lexis Publishing, Malabar, FL
Web site: http://www.lexisnexis.com.

Liberation Distributors, *(0-89928)* P.O. Box 5341, Chicago, IL 60680 USA (SAN 169-880X) Tel 773-248-3442.

Liberty Mountain, 4375 W. 1980 S., Suite 100, Salt Lake City, UT 84104 USA Tel 801-954-0741; Fax: 801-954-0766; Toll Free: 800-366-2666
E-mail: lmsabc@aol.com.

Libraries Unlimited, Inc., *(0-313; 0-87287; 1-56308; 1-59158)* Div. of Greenwood Publishing Group, Orders Addr.: a/o Customer Service Group, Dept. 2229, P.O. Box 5007, Westport, CT 06881 USA Fax: 603-431-2214; Toll Free: 800-225-5800; Edit Addr.: 88 Post Rd W., Westport, CT 06880-4208 USA
E-mail: lubooks@lu.com
Web site: http://www.lu.com.

Library & Educational Services, P.O. Box 146, Berrien Springs, MI 49103 USA Tel 616-695-1800; Fax: 616-695-8500
E-mail: libraryanded@juno.com.

Library Bk. Selection Service, P.O. Box 277, Bloomington, IL 61702-0277 USA (SAN 169-1740).

Library Integrated Solutions & Assocs., 8400 Spectrum Dr., McKinney, TX 75070 USA Tel 214-726-9290
Web site: http://www.llibs.com.

Library Sales of N.J., *(1-888032)* Orders Addr.: P.O. Box 335, Garwood, NJ 07027-0335 USA Tel 908-232-1446; Edit Addr.: 607 S. Chestnut St., Westfield, NJ 07090-1369 USA
E-mail: Librarysalesofnj@aol.com.

Library Video Co., *(1-4171)* P.O. Box 580, Wynnewood, PA 19096 USA (SAN 631-3205) Fax: 610-645-4050; Toll Free: 800-843-3620
E-mail: cs@libraryvideo.com
Web site: http://www.libraryvideo.com.

Libreria Bereana, 1825 San Alejandro, Urb San Ignacio, Rio Piedras, PR 00927-6819 USA (SAN 169-9288) Tel 809-764-6175.

Libreria Distribuidora Universal, 3090 SW 8th St., Miami, FL 33135 USA Tel 305-642-3234.

Libreria Universal, Inc., *(1-881375)* 55 N. Post St., P.O. Box 1480, Mayaguez, PR 00680 USA Tel 787-832-6041; Fax: 787-832-8477
E-mail: colom@coqui.net.

Libros de Espana y America, *See* **LEA Bk. Distributors (Libros Espana y America)**

Libros Sin Fronteras, P.O. Box 2085, Olympia, WA 98507 USA Tel 360-357-4332; Fax: 360-357-4964
E-mail: info@librossinfronteras.com
Web site: http://www.librossinfronteras.com.

Light & Life Publishing Co., *(0-937032; 1-880971; 1-933654)* 4808 Park Glen Rd., Minneapolis, MN 55416 USA (SAN 213-8565) Tel 952-925-3888; Fax: 952-925-3918
E-mail: info@light-n-life.com
Web site: http://www.light-n-life.com.

Light Impressions Corp., *(0-87992)* Orders Addr.: P.O. Box 940, Rochester, NY 14603-0940 USA (SAN 169-619X) Toll Free Fax: 800-826-5539; Toll Free: 800-828-6216; Edit Addr.: P.O. Box 22708, Rochester, NY 14692-2708 USA
Web site: http://www.lightimpresionsdirect.com.

Light Technology Communication Services, *See* **Light Technology Publishing**

Light Technology Publishing, *(0-929385; 1-891824)* Orders Addr.: P.O. Box 3870, Flagstaff, AZ 86003 USA (SAN 249-1389) Tel 520-526-1345; Fax: 520-714-1132; Toll Free: 800-450-0985; Edit Addr.: 4030 E. Huntington Dr., Flagstaff, AZ 86004 USA
E-mail: sedonajo@sedonajo.com
Web site: http://www.sedonajournal.com.

Lightning Source, Inc., 1246 Heil Quaker Blvd., LaVergne, TN 37086 USA (SAN 179-6976) Tel 615-213-4595; Fax: 615-213-4426.

Liguori Pubns., *(0-7648; 0-89243)* One Liguori Dr., Liguori, MO 63057-9999 USA (SAN 202-6783) Tel 636-464-2500; Fax: 636-464-8449; Toll Free Fax: 800-325-9526; Toll Free: 800-325-9521 (orders)
E-mail: liguori@liguori.org
Web site: http://www.liguori.org.

Likely Story Bookfairs, A, 7210 SW 57th Ave., Suite 207-A, South Miami, FL 33143 USA (SAN 631-1210) Tel 305-668-9183; Fax: 305-667-3323.

Lilly News Agency, P.O. Box 280077, Memphis, TN 38168-0077 USA (SAN 168-9452).

LIM Productions, LLC, *(1-929617)* 3553 Northdale St., NW, Uniontown, OH 44685-8004 USA Toll Free: 877-628-4532
E-mail: customerservice@limproductions.com
Web site: http://www.limproductions.com.

Limerock Bks., Inc., P.O. Box 57, New Canaan, CT 06840 USA (SAN 630-8708) Tel 203-322-5352; Fax: 203-322-2182 Do not confuse with Limerock Books, Thomaston, ME
E-mail: limerockbk@aol.com
Web site: http://www.netpocus.com/limerock.

Linden Publishing Co., Inc., *(0-941936; 1-933502)* 2006 S. Mary, Fresno, CA 93721 USA (SAN 238-6089) Tel 559-233-6633 (phone/fax); Toll Free: 800-345-4447 (orders only) Do not confuse with LInden Publishing in Avon, NY
E-mail: richard@lindenpub.com
Web site: http://www.lindenpub.com.

Linden Tree Children's Records & Bks., 170 State St., Los Altos, CA 94022 USA (SAN 131-744X) Tel 415-949-3390; Fax: 415-949-0346.

Lindsay News & Photo Service, Inc., 868 Lockport Rd., Youngstown, NY 14174-1139 USA (SAN 169-6092).

Ling's International Bks., Orders Addr.: P.O. Box 82684, San Diego, CA 92138 USA (SAN 169-0116) Tel 619-292-8104; Fax: 619-292-8207; Edit Addr.: 3396 Via Cabo Verde., Escondido, CA 92029-7459 USA.

Linx Educational Publishing, Inc., *(1-891818; 0-9797510)* P.O. Box 50009, Jacksonville Beach, FL 32240 USA Tel 904-241-1861; Fax: 904-241-3279; Toll Free Fax: 888-546-9338; Toll Free: 800-717-5469
E-mail: mimi@lixedu.com; info@linxedu.com
Web site: http://www.linxedu.com.

Lippincott Williams & Wilkins, *(0-316; 0-397; 0-683; 0-7817; 0-8067; 0-8121; 0-88167; 0-89004; 0-89313; 0-89640; 0-911216; 1-881063; 4-260; 1-60547)* Orders Addr.: P.O. Box 1620, Hagerstown, MD 21741 USA Fax: 301-223-2400; Toll Free: 800-638-3030; Edit Addr.: 530 Walnut St., Philadelphia, PA 19106-3621 USA (SAN 201-0933) Tel 215-521-8300; Fax: 215-521-8902; Toll Free: 800-638-3030; 351 W. Camden St., Baltimore, MD 21201 Tel 410-528-4000; 410-528-4209; 345 Hudson St., 16th Flr., New York, NY 10014 Tel 212-886-1200; 16522 Hunters Green Pkwy., Hagerstown, MD 21740 Tel 301-223-2300; Fax: 301-223-2398; Toll Free: 800-638-3030
E-mail: custserv@lww.com; orders@lww.com
Web site: http://www.lww.com.

Lippincott-Raven Publishers, *See* **Lippincott Williams & Wilkins**

Literal Book Distributors: Books in Spanish, Orders Addr.: P.O. Box 7113, Langley Park, MD 20787 USA; Edit Addr.: 7705 Georgia Ave. NW, Suite 102, Washington, DC 20012 USA (SAN 113-2784) Tel 202-723-8688; Fax: 202-882-6592; Toll Free: 800-366-8680.

Little Brown & Co., *(0-316; 0-8212; 0-7595)* Div. of Time Warner Bk. Group, Orders Addr.: 3 Center Plaza, Boston, MA 02108-2084 USA (SAN 630-7248) Tel 617-227-0730; Toll Free Fax: 800-286-9471; Toll Free: 800-759-0190; Edit Addr.: Time & Life Bldg., 1271 Avenue of the Americas, New York, NY 10020 USA (SAN 200-2205) Tel 212-522-8700; Fax: 212-522-2067; Toll Free: 800-343-9204
E-mail: cust.service@twbg.com
Web site: http://www.littlebrown.com.

Little Dania's Juvenile Promotions, Div. of Booksmith Promotional Co., 100 Paterson Plank Rd., Jersey City, NJ 07307 USA (SAN 169-5681) Tel 201-659-2317; Fax: 201-659-3631
E-mail: hochberga@aol.com.

Little Professor Bk. Ctrs., Inc., P.O. Box 3160, Ann Arbor, MI 48106-3160 USA (SAN 144-2503) Toll Free: 800-899-6232.

Llewellyn Worldwide Ltd., Orders Addr.: 2143 Wooddale Dr., Woodbury, MN 55125-2989 USA Tel 651-291-1970; Fax: 651-291-1908
E-mail: sales@llewellyn.com
Web site: http://www.llewellyn.com.

Lodhia Ctr., The, 4405 International Blvd., Suite C-101, Norcross, GA 30093 USA Tel 770-564-4000; Fax: 770-564-2500
E-mail: rafiq@thelodhiacenter.org
Web site: http://www.thelodhiacenter.org.

Login Fulfillment Services, *See* **LPC Group**

Logos Productions, Inc., *(0-9618891; 1-885361)* 6160 Carmen Ave., E., Inver Grove Heights, MN 55076-4422 USA Tel 612-451-9945; Fax: 612-457-4617; Toll Free: 800-328-0200 Do not confuse with Logos Productions, Carmel, CA
E-mail: lpstaff@mn.uswest.net
Web site: http://www.1logos.com.

London Bridge, Div. of General Distribution Services, Orders Addr.: 4500 Witmer Industrial EST, Niagara Falls, NY 14305-1386 USA Toll Free: 800-805-1083.

Lone Pine Publishing, *See* **Lone Pine Publishing USA**

Lone Pine Publishing USA, *(0-919433; 1-55105)* 1808 B St., NW, Suite 140, Auburn, WA 98001 USA Tel 425-204-5965; Fax: 253-394-0405; Toll Free Fax: 800-548-1169; Toll Free: 800-518-3541
E-mail: rtruppner@lonepinepublishing.com
Web site: http://www.lonepinepublishing.com.

Lonely Planet Pubns., *(0-86442; 0-908086; 1-55992; 1-86450; 1-74059; 1-74104; 1-74179)* Orders Addr.: 150 Linden St., Oakland, CA 94607 USA (SAN 659-6541) Tel 510-893-8555; Fax: 510-893-8572; Toll Free: 800-275-8555 (orders, 9am - 5pm Pacific Time)
E-mail: orders@lonelyplanet.com; customerservice@lonelyplanet.com
Web site: http://www.lonelyplanet.com.

Long Beach Bks., Inc., P.O. Box 179, Long Beach, NY 11561-0179 USA (SAN 164-632X) Tel 718-471-5934.

Looseleaf Law Pubns., Inc., *(0-930137; 1-889031; 1-932777)* Orders Addr.: P.O. Box 650042, Fresh Meadows, NY 11365-0042 USA Tel 718-359-5559; Fax: 718-539-0941; Toll Free: 800-647-5547; Edit Addr.: 43-08 162nd St., Flushing, NY 11358 USA (SAN 135-0099)
E-mail: llawpub@erols.com
Web site: http://www.looseleaflaw.com.

Lord's Line, *(0-915952)* 1065 Lomita Blvd., No. 434, Harbor City, CA 90710-1944 USA (SAN 169-0051).

Lorenz Corp., The, *(0-89328; 1-4291)* 501 E. Third St., Dayton, OH 45401-0802 USA (SAN 208-7413) Tel 937-228-6118; Fax: 937-223-2042; Toll Free: 800-444-1144
E-mail: service@lorenz.com
Web site: http://www.lorenz.com.

Los Angeles Mart, The, 1933 S. Broadway, Suite 665, Los Angeles, CA 90007 USA (SAN 168-9797) Tel 213-748-6449; Fax: 714-523-0796.

Lotus Lights Publications, *See* **Lotus Pr.**

Lotus Pr., *(0-910261; 0-914955; 0-940676; 0-940985; 0-941524)* Div. of Lotus Brands, Inc., P.O. Box 325, Twin Lakes, WI 53181 USA (SAN 239-1120) Tel 262-889-2461; Fax: 262-889-8591; Toll Free: 800-824-6396 Do not confuse with companies with the same or similar name in Lotus, CA, Westerville, OH, Bokeelia, FL, Brattleboro, VT, Detroit, MI, Tobyhanna, PA
E-mail: lotuspress@lotuspress.com
Web site: http://www.lotuspress.com.

Louisville Distributors, *See* **United Magazine**

Louisville News Co., P.O. Box 36, Columbia, KY 42728 USA (SAN 169-281X) Tel 502-384-3444; Fax: 502-384-9324.

LPC Group, c/o CDS, 193 Edwards Dr., Jackson, TN 38305 USA (SAN 630-5644) Fax: 731-423-1973; 731-935-7731; Toll Free Fax: 800-351-5073; Toll Free: 800-343-4499
E-mail: lpc-info@lpcgroup.com
Web site: http://www.lpcgroup.com.

Lubrecht & Cramer, Ltd., *(0-934454; 0-945345)* P.O. Box 3110, Port Jervis, NY 12771-0176 USA; Edit Addr.: P.O. Box 3110, Port Jervis, NY 12771 USA (SAN 214-1256) Toll Free: 800-920-9334; 350 Fifth Ave., Suite 3304, New York, NY 10118-0069
E-mail: lubrecht@frontiernet.net; books@lubrechtcramer.com
Web site: http://www.lubrechtcramer.com.

Luciano Bks., 13111 NW Le Jeune, Opa Locka, FL 33054 USA (SAN 631-2829) Tel 305-769-3103.

Ludington News Co., 1600 E. Grand Blvd., Detroit, MI 48211-3195 USA (SAN 169-3751) Tel 313-929-7600.

Lulu.com, *(1-4116; 1-84728; 1-4303; 1-84753; 1-4357)* 860 Aviation Pkwy., Suite 300, Morrisville, NC 27560 USA Fax: 919-459-5867; Goldencross Hse. 8 Duncannon St., London, WC2N 4JF Tel 0207 484 6262
Web site: http://www.lulu.com.

Lushena Bks., *(1-930097)* 607 Country Club Dr., Unit E, Bensenville, IL 60106 USA (SAN 630-5105) Tel 630-238-8708; Fax: 630-238-8824
E-mail: Lushenabks@yahoo.com
Web site: http://www.lushenabks.com/.

L-W, Inc., *(0-89538)* P.O. Box 69, Gas City, IN 46933 USA (SAN 159-6292) Tel 765-674-6450; Fax: 765-674-3503; Toll Free: 800-777-6450
E-mail: catalogs@lwbooks.com; lwbooks@comteek.com
Web site: http://www.lwbooks.com.

Lyrical Liquor Productions, Orders Addr.: 7212 15th Ave., Takoma Park, MD 20912 USA Tel 202-723-1317
E-mail: llp@speakeasypublishing.com.

M & J Bk. Fair Service, 2307 Sherwood Cir., Minneapolis, MN 55431 USA (SAN 169-4030).

M & M News Agency, Orders Addr.: P.O. Box 1129, La Salle, IL 61301 USA (SAN 169-2062) Fax: 815-223-2828; Toll Free: 800-245-6247.

M. K. Distributors, Inc., 600 Village Trace, Bldg. 23, Marietta, GA 30067 USA Tel 770-953-8123; Fax: 770-955-0997.

M L E S, *See* **Pathway Bk. Service**

Ma'ayan, *See* **WellSpring Bks.**

Macalester Park Publishing Co., Inc., *(0-910924; 0-930286; 1-886158)* 24558 546th Ave., Austin, MN 55912 USA (SAN 110-8077) Tel 507-396-0135; Toll Free: 800-407-9078
E-mail: macalesterpark@macalesterpark.com
Web site: http://www.macalesterpark.com.

MacGregor News Agency, 1733 Industrial Park Dr., Mount Pleasant, MI 48858 USA (SAN 169-3921) Toll Free: 800-626-1982.

Mackin Bk. Co., 615 Travelers Trail W., Burnsville, MN 55337 USA (SAN 631-3442).

Mackin Library Media, 14300 W. Burnsville Pkwy., Burnsville, MN 55306-3804 USA (SAN 134-8795)
E-mail: mackin@mackin.com
Web site: http://www.mackin.com.

MacLaurin Institute, The, *(0-9676160)* P.O. Box 141007, Minneapolis, MN 55414-6007 USA Toll Free: 800-582-8541 (phone/fax)
E-mail: maclaurin@maclaurin.org
Web site: http://www.maclaurin.org.

Macmillan, *(0-374)* Orders Addr.: 16365 James Madison Hwy., Gordonsville, VA 22942 USA (SAN 631-5011) Tel 540-672-7600; Fax: 540-672-7664; 540-672-7540 (Customer Service); Toll Free Fax: 800-672-2054 (Order Dept.); Toll Free: 888-330-8477; Edit Addr.: 175 Fifth Ave., New York, NY 10010 USA Tel 212-674-5151; Fax: 212-677-6487; Toll Free Fax: 800-258-2769; Toll Free: 800-488-5233; 16365 James Madison Hwy., Gordonsville, VA 22942 (SAN 852-5587) Tel 540-672-7761
Web site: http://www.macmillan.com.

Macmillan USA, *See* **Alpha Bks.**

MacRae's Indian Bk. Distributor, 1605 Cole St., P.O. Box 652, Enumclaw, WA 98022 USA (SAN 157-5473) Tel 360-825-3737.

Madison Art Ctr., Inc., *(0-913883)* 222 W. Washington Ave. Ste. 350, Madison, WI 53703-2719 USA
E-mail: mac@itis.com
Web site: http://www.madisonartcenter.org.

Magazine Distributors, Inc., 15 Sparks St., Plainville, CT 06062 USA (SAN 169-0817).

Magazines, Inc., 1135 Hammond St., Bangor, ME 04401 USA (SAN 169-3034) Tel 207-942-8237; Fax: 207-942-9226; Toll Free: 800-649-9224 (in Maine)
E-mail: pam@mint.net.

Magnus Media Sales & Services, LLC, *See* **Ann Arbor Media Group, LLC**

Mahoning Valley Distributing Agency, Inc., 2556 Rush Blvd., Youngstown, OH 44507 USA Tel 330-788-6162; Fax: 330-788-9046.

Main Trail Productions, P.O. Box 365, Clearwater, MN 55320 USA.

Maine Writers & Pubs. Alliance, *(0-9618592)* P.O. Box 9301, Portland, ME 04104-9301 USA (SAN 224-2303).

Majic Enterprises, 2232 S. 11th St., Niles, MI 49120-4410 USA (SAN 169-8508).

Majors, J. A. Co., Orders Addr.: 1401 Lakeway Dr., Lewisville, TX 75057 USA (SAN 169-8117) Tel 972-353-1100; Fax: 972-353-1300; Toll Free: 800-633-1851
E-mail: dallas@majors.com
Web site: http://www.majors.com.

Majors Scientific Bks., Inc., P.O. Box 35705, Dallas, TX 75235-0705 USA Toll Free: 800-633-1851
E-mail: dallas@majors.com
Web site: http://www.majors.com.

Manchester News Co., Inc., P.O. Box 4838, Manchester, NH 03108-4838 USA (SAN 169-4480).

Manhattan Publishing Co., Div. of U.S. & Europe Bks., Inc., P.O. Box 850, Croton-on-Hudson, NY 10520 USA (SAN 113-7476) Tel 914-271-5194; Fax: 914-271-5856
Web site: http://www.manhattanpublishing.com.

Manitowoc News Agency, 907 S. Eighth St., Manitowoc, WI 54220 USA (SAN 159-9046).

Manning's Bks. & Prints, 580M Crespi Dr., Pacifica, CA 94044 USA (SAN 157-5384) Fax: 650-355-1851
E-mail: manningsbks@aol.com
Web site: http://www.printsoldandrare.com.

Many Feathers Bks. & Maps, 2626 W. Indian School Rd., Phoenix, AZ 85017 USA (SAN 158-8877) Tel 602-266-1043; Toll Free: 800-279-7652.

Map Link, *(0-7834; 0-929591)* 30 South La Patera Ln., Unit 5, Santa Barbara, CA 93117 USA (SAN 249-7522) Tel 541-772-3989
E-mail: ccarroll@benchmarkmaps.com
Web site: http://www.benchmarkmaps.com.

Maple Tree Pubns., 1808 Prosperity Rd., Maplewood, MN 55109 USA Tel 651-770-1206.

Marangio, Charles F. Distribution, Orders Addr.: P.O. Box 3643, Sonoro, CA 95370 USA (SAN 631-3965) Tel 209-533-0997; Edit Addr.: 659 Sanguinetti Rd., Sonoro, CA 95370 USA (SAN 631-3973).

Marco Bk. Distributors, *(0-88298)* P.O. Box 30108, Brooklyn, NY 11203-0108 USA (SAN 169-5142) Tel 718-774-0750; Fax: 718-774-0380; Toll Free: 800-842-4234.

MAR*CO Products, Inc., *(1-57543; 1-884063)* Orders Addr.: 1443 Old York Rd., Warminster, PA 18974 USA Tel 215-956-0313; Fax: 215-956-9041; Toll Free: 800-448-2197
E-mail: csfunk@marcoproducts.com; marcoproducts@comcast.net
Web site: http://www.store.yahoo.com/marcoproducts; http://www.marcoproducts.com.

Marcus Wholesale, P.O. Box 1618, R49 E. Hwy. 4, Murphys, CA 95247 USA (SAN 185-0296).

Mardelva News Co., Inc., 8999 Ocean Hwy., Delmar, MD 21875 USA (SAN 169-3247) Tel 410-742-8613; Fax: 410-742-2616.

Margatuck Productions, P.O. Box 360, Manchester, MA 01944 USA (SAN 631-6468) Tel 508-526-7882.

Mariposa Pr., *(0-9666899)* 551 W. Cordova Rd., Santa Fe, NM 87501 USA Tel 505-471-7846; Fax: 505-986-0690 Do not confuse with companies with same or similar names in Gainesville, FL, Chicago, IL, Hurleyville, NY, Boulder, CO, Abilene TX .

Marshall-Mangold Distribution Co., Inc., 4805 Nelson Ave., Baltimore, MD 21215-2507 USA (SAN 169-3115) Toll Free: 800-972-2665.

Marta Schooler, Michelle Morrow Curreri, Orders Addr.: 1111 Merwins Ln., Fairfield, CT 06430 USA Tel 203-255-5005; Fax: 203-254-3550
E-mail: marta@pcnet.com; curreri@mediaone.net.

Maruzen International Co., Ltd., 1200 Harbor Blvd., 10th Flr., Weehawken, NJ 07087 USA (SAN 630-6012) Tel 201-865-4400; Fax: 201-865-4845.

Marvin Law Bk., 11020 27th Ave., S., Burnsville, MN 55337 USA (SAN 163-898X) Tel 612-644-2236.

Master Bks., *(0-89051)* P.O. Box 726, Green Forest, AR 72638-0726 USA (SAN 205-6119) Tel 870-438-5288; Fax: 870-438-5120; Toll Free: 800-999-3777
E-mail: nlp@newleafpress.net
Web site: http://www.masterbooks.net.

Master Communications, Inc., *(1-888194; 1-60480)* 4480 Lake Forest Dr., Suite 302, Cincinnati, OH 45242 USA (SAN 299-2140) Tel 513-563-3100; Fax: 513-563-3105; Toll Free: 800-765-5885
E-mail: sales@master-comm.com
Web site: http://www.familiesoftheworld.com; http://www.master-comm.com.

Matagiri Bks., 1218 Wittenberg Rd., Mount Tremper, NY 12457 USA Tel 845-679-8322; Fax: 845-679-5853; Toll Free: 800-815-1969 (orders only)
E-mail: matagiri@aol.com
Web site: http://www.matagiri.org.

Matthews Medical Bk. Co., Orders Addr.: 10 Old Bloomfield Ave., Pine Brook, NJ 07058 USA; 11559 Rock Island Ct., Maryland Heights, MO 63043 (SAN 146-4655) Tel 314-432-1400; Fax: 314-432-7044
E-mail: mlc@mattmccoy.com
Web site: http://www.mattmccoy.com.

Maus Tales, 77-490 Loma Vista, La Quinta, CA 92253 USA Fax: 760-564-6669
E-mail: maustales@aol.com.

Maverick Distributors, *(1-884646)* Orders Addr.: Drawer 7289, Bend, OR 97708 USA (SAN 298-3222) Tel 541-382-2728; Fax: 541-382-8444; Toll Free: 800-333-8046.

Maxwell Scientific International, Inc., *(0-8277)* Div. of Pergamon Pr., Inc., 1345 Ave. of the Americas, No. 1036C, New York, NY 10105-0302 USA (SAN 169-524X) Tel 914-592-9141.

May, L.B. & Assocs., 3517 Neal Dr., Knoxville, TN 37918 USA Tel 865-922-7490; Fax: 865-922-7492
E-mail: lbmay@aol.com.

MBI Distribution Services, *(0-7603; 0-87938; 0-912612; 1-85010)* Div. of MBI Publishing Co. LLC, Orders Addr.: 729 Prospect Ave., Osceola, WI 54020 USA (SAN 169-9164) Tel 715-294-3345; Fax: 715-294-4448; Toll Free: 800-458-0454; Edit Addr.: 380 Jackson St., Suite 200, Saint Paul, MN 55101-3885 USA Tel 651-287-5000; Fax: 651-287-5001
Web site: http://www.motorbooks.com.

MBI Publishing Co. LLC, *(0-7603; 0-87938; 0-912612)* Orders Addr.: 729 Prospect Ave., Osceola, WI 54020 USA (SAN 699-5462) Tel 715-294-3345; Fax: 715-294-4448; Toll Free: 800-458-0454; Edit Addr.: 380 Jackson St., Suite 200, Saint Paul, MN 55101-3885 USA Tel 651 287 5000; Fax: 651 287 5001
E-mail: mbibks@motorbooks.com
Web site: http://www.motorbooks.com; http://www.mbipublishing.com.

MBS Textbook Exchange, Inc., Orders Addr.: 2711 W. Ash, Columbia, MO 65203-4613 USA (SAN 140-7015) Tel 573-445-2243; Fax: 573-446-5254; Toll Free: 800-325-0929 (orders); 800-325-0530 (customer service); Edit Addr.: 2711 W. Ash St., Columbia, MO 65203 USA
E-mail: kyates@mbsbooks.com
Web site: http://www.mbsbooks.com.

McCaslin, Boyce, 3 Greenbriar Dr., Saint Louis, MO 63124-1819 USA (SAN 110-8298).

McCoy Church Goods, 1010 Howard Ave., San Mateo, CA 94401 USA (SAN 107-2315) Tel 415-342-0924.

McCrory's Books, *See* **McCrory's Wholesale Bks.**

McCrory's Wholesale Bks., Orders Addr.: P.O. Box 2032, Alexandria, LA 71301 USA (SAN 108-5999); Edit Addr.: 1808 Rapides Ave., Alexandria, LA 71301 USA.

McGraw-Hill Children's Publishing, *See* **School Specialty Publishing**

McGraw-Hill Cos., The, *(0-07)* 6480 Jimmy Carter Blvd., Norcross, GA 30071-1701 USA (SAN 254-881X) Tel 614-755-5637; Fax: 614-755-5611; Orders Addr.: 860 Taylor Station Rd., Blacklick, OH 43004-0545 USA (SAN 200-254X) Fax: 614-755-5645; Toll Free: 800-722-4726 (orders & customer service); 800-338-3987 (college); 800-525-5003 (subscriptions); 800-352-3566 (books - US/Canada orders); P.O. Box 545, Blacklick, OH 43004-0545 Fax: 614-759-3759; Toll Free: 877-833-5524; a/o General Customer Service, P.O. Box 182604, Columbus, OH 43272 Fax: 614-759-3759; Toll Free: 877-833-5524
E-mail: customer.service@mcgraw-hill.com
Web site: http://www.mcgraw-hill.com; http://www.ebooks.mcgraw-hill.com/.

McGraw-Hill Health Professions Division, *See* **McGraw-Hill Medical Publishing Div.**

McGraw-Hill Medical Publishing Div., *(0-07)* Div. of The McGraw-Hill Cos., Orders Addr.: P.O. Box 545, Blacklick, OH 43004-0545 USA Fax: 614-755-5645 (customer service); Toll Free: 800-262-4729 (customer service); 800-722-4726 (bookstores & libraries)
E-mail: customerservice@mcgraw-hill.com
Web site: http://www.mghmedical.com.

McGraw-Hill Osborne, *(0-07; 0-88134; 0-931988)* Div. of The McGraw-Hill Professional, 160 Spear St. Flr. 7, San Francisco, CA 94105-1544 USA (SAN 274-3450) Toll Free: 800-227-0900
E-mail: customer.service@mcgraw-hill.com
Web site: http://www.osborne.com.

McGraw-Hill Primis Custom Publishing, *(0-390)* Div. of McGraw-Hill Higher Education, 148 Princeton-Hightstown Rd., Hightstown, NJ 08520-1450 USA Tel 609-426-5721; Toll Free: 800-962-9342
Web site: http://www.mhhe.com.

McGraw-Hill Professional Publishing, *(0-07)* Div. of McGraw-Hill Higher Education, Orders Addr.: P.O. Box 545, Blacklick, OH 43004-0545 USA Fax: 614-755-5645; Toll Free: 800-722-4726; Edit Addr.: 2 Penn Plaza, New York, NY 10121-2298 USA Tel 212-904-2000.

McGraw-Hill Trade, *(0-07; 0-658; 0-8442)* Div. of McGraw-Hill Professional, Orders Addr.: P.O. Box 545, Blacklick, OH 43004-0545 USA Tel 800-722-4726; Fax: 614-755-5645; Edit Addr.: 2 Penn Plaza, New York, NY 10121 USA Tel 212-904-2000
E-mail: Jeffrey_Krames@mcgraw-hill.com
Web site: http://www.books.mcgraw-hill.com.

McGraw-Hill/Contemporary, *(0-658; 0-8092; 0-8325; 0-8442; 0-88499; 0-89061; 0-913327; 0-940279; 0-941263; 0-9630646; 1-56626; 1-56943; 1-57028)* Div. of McGraw-Hill Higher Education, Orders Addr.: P.O. Box 545, Blacklick, OH 43004-0545 USA Toll Free Fax: 800-998-3103; Toll Free: 800-621-1918; Edit Addr.: 4255 W. Touhy Ave., Lincolnwood, IL 60712 USA (SAN 169-2208) Tel 847-679-5500; Fax: 847-679-2494; Toll Free Fax: 800-998-3103; Toll Free: 800-323-4900
E-mail: ntcpub@tribune.com
Web site: http://www.ntc-cb.com.

McKay, David Co., Inc., *(0-679; 0-88326; 0-89440)* Subs. of Random Hse., Inc., Orders Addr.: 400 Hahn Rd., Westminster, MD 21157 USA Tel 410-848-1900; Toll Free: 800-733-3000 (orders only); Edit Addr.: 201 E. 50th St., MD 4-6, New York, NY 10022 USA (SAN 200-240X) Tel 212-751-2600; Fax: 212-872-8026.

McKnight Sales Co., P.O. Box 4138, Pittsburgh, PA 15202 USA (SAN 169-7587) Tel 412-761-4443; Fax: 412-761-0122; Toll Free: 800-208-8078
E-mail: sales@mscmags.com
Web site: http://www.mscmags.com.

McLemore, Hollern & Assocs., 3538 Maple Park Dr., Kingwood, TX 77339 USA Tel 281-360-5204.

McMillen Bk. Distributors, 304 Main St., Ames, IA 50010 USA Fax: 515-232-0402; Toll Free: 866-385-2027.

MediaTech Productions, *(0-9702309)* 917 E. Prospect Rd. Unit B, Fort Collins, CO 80525-1364 USA Toll Free: 800-816-7566 Do not confuse with companies with the same or similar name in Chicago, IL
E-mail: maury@mediatechproductions.com
Web site: http://mediatechproductions.com.

Medical Information Systems, Inc., 2 Seaview Blvd., Port Washington, NY 11050 USA (SAN 242-1720) Tel 516-621-7200 Do not confuse with Medical Information Systems, Inc., Stamford, CT.

Medicina Biologica, 2937 NE Flanders St., Portland, OR 97232 USA (SAN 113-0226) Tel 503-287-6775; Fax: 503-235-3520
E-mail: med_bio@imagina.com.

Mel Bay Pubns., Inc., *(0-7866; 0-87166; 1-56222)* Orders Addr.: #4 Industrial Dr., Pacific, MO 63069-0066 USA (SAN 657-3630) Tel 636-257-3970; Fax: 636-257-5062; Toll Free: 800-863-5229
E-mail: connie@melbay.com; email@melbay.com
Web site: http://www.melbay.com.

Melton Book Company, Incorporated, *See* **Nelson Direct**

Menasha Ridge Pr., Inc., *(0-89732)* 2204 First Ave., S., Suite 102, Birmingham, AL 35233 USA (SAN 219-7294) Tel 205-322-0439; Fax: 205-326-1012
E-mail: info@menasharidge.com
Web site: http://www.menasharidge.com.

Merced News Co., 1324 Coldwell Ave., Modesto, CA 95350-5702 USA (SAN 168-9894) Tel 209-722-5791.

Mercedes Book Distributors Corporation, *See* **Mercedes Distribution Ctr., Inc.**

Mercedes Distribution Ctr., Inc., Brooklyn Navy Yard, Bldg. No. 3, Brooklyn, NY 11205 USA (SAN 169-5150) Tel 718-534-3000; Fax: 718-935-9647; Toll Free: 800-339-4804
E-mail: contact@mdist.com.

Merkos Pubns., Div. of Merkos L'Inyonei Chinuch, 291 Kingston Ave., Brooklyn, NY 11213 USA (SAN 631-1040) Tel 718-778-0226; Fax: 718-778-4148.

Merry Thoughts, *(0-88230)* 364 Adams St., Bedford Hills, NY 10507 USA (SAN 169-5061) Tel 914-241-0447; Fax: 914-241-0247.

Metamorphosis Publishing Company, *See* **Metamorphous Pr., Inc.**

Metamorphous Pr., Inc., *(0-943920; 1-55552)* Orders Addr.: P.O. Box 10616, Portland, OR 97296-0616 USA (SAN 110-8786) Tel 503-228-4972; Fax: 503-223-9117; Toll Free: 800-937-7771 (orders only); Edit Addr.: P.O. Box 10616, Portland, OR 97296-0616 USA
E-mail: metabooks@metamodels.com
Web site: htp://www.metamodels.com.

Metro Systems, 3381 Stevens Creek Blvd., Suite 209, San Jose, CA 95117 USA (SAN 631-1016) Tel 408-247-4050; Fax: 408-247-4236.

Metropolitan News Co., 47-25 34th, Long Island City, NY 11101 USA (SAN 159-9089) Do not confuse with Metropolitan News Co. in Los Angeles, CA.

Meyer Enterprises, *See* **Western New York Wares, Inc.**

Miami Bks., Inc., 17842 State Rd. 9, Miami, FL 33162 USA (SAN 106-8997) Tel 305-652-3231.

Miami Valley News Agency, 2127 Old Troy Pike, Dayton, OH 45404 USA (SAN 169-6718) Fax: 513-233-8544; Toll Free: 800-791-5137.

Michiana News Service, 2232 S. 11th St., Niles, MI 49120 USA (SAN 110-5051) Tel 616-684-3013; Fax: 616-684-8740.

Michigan Church Supply, P.O. Box 279, Mount Morris, MI 48458-0279 USA (SAN 184-413X) Tel 810-686-8877; Toll Free: 800-521-3440.

Michigan State Univ. Pr., *(0-87013; 0-937191)* Orders Addr.: 1405 S. Harrison Rd. Suite 25, East Lansing, MI 48823 USA (SAN 202-6295) Tel 517-355-9543; Fax: 517-432-2611; Toll Free: 800-678-2120
E-mail: msupress@msu.edu
Web site: http://www.msupress.msu.edu.

Mickler's Bks., Inc., 61 Alafaya Woods Blvd., No. 197, Oviedo, FL 32765 USA Tel 407-365-8500; Toll Free Fax: 800-726-0585
E-mail: orders@micklers.com
Web site: http://www.micklers.com.

Micklers Floridiana, Incorporated, *See* **Mickler's Bks., Inc.**

Microdistributors International, Inc., *(0-918025)* Subs. of Medcomp Technologies, Inc., 34 Maple Ave., P.O. Box 8, Armonk, NY 10504 USA (SAN 296-158X) Tel 914-273-6480.

Mid Penn Magazine Agency, 100 Eck Cir., Williamsport, PA 17701 USA (SAN 169-7692).

Mid South Manufacturing Agency, Incorporated, *See* **Mid-South Magazine Agency, Inc.**

Mid-Cal Periodical Distributors, P.O. Box 245230, Sacramento, CA 95824-5230 USA (SAN 169-0078).

Midpoint National, Inc., 1263 Southwest Blvd., Kansas City, MO 66103-1901 USA (SAN 630-9860) Tel 913-831-2233; Fax: 913-362-7401; Toll Free: 800-228-4321.

Midpoint Trade Bks., Inc., Orders Addr.: 1263 Southwest Blvd., Kansas City, KS 66103 USA (SAN 631-3736) Tel 913-831-2233; Fax: 913-362-7401; Toll Free: 800-742-6139 (consumer orders); Edit Addr.: 27 W. 20th St., No. 1102, New York, NY 10011 USA (SAN 631-1075) Tel 212-727-0190; Fax: 212-727-0195
E-mail: info@midpointtrade.com
Web site: http://www.midpointtrade.com; http://www.midpointtradebooks.com/.

Mid-South Magazine Agency, Inc., P.O. Box 4585, Jackson, MS 39296-4585 USA (SAN 286-0163) Toll Free: 800-748-9444.

Mid-State Periodicals, Inc., P.O. Box 3455, Quincy, IL 62305-3455 USA Tel 217-222-0833; Fax: 217-222-1256.

Mid-States Distributors, P.O. Box 1374, Chambersburg, PA 17201-5374 USA (SAN 169-3166).

Midtown Auto Bks., 212 Burnet Ave., Syracuse, NY 13203 USA (SAN 169-6289).

Midwest European Pubns., 915 Foster St., Evanston, IL 60201 USA (SAN 169-1937) Tel 847-866-6289; Fax: 847-866-6290; Toll Free: 800-380-8919
E-mail: info@mep-eli.com
Web site: http://www.mep-eli.com.

Midwest Library Service, 11443 St. Charles Rock Rd., Bridgeton, MO 63044-2789 USA (SAN 169-4243) Tel 314-739-3100; Fax: 314-739-1326; Toll Free Fax: 800-962-1009; Toll Free: 800-325-8833
E-mail: hudson@midwestls.com.

Midwest Tape, Orders Addr.: P.O. Box 820, Holland, OH 43528-0820 USA (SAN 254-9913) Toll Free Fax: 800-444-6645; Toll Free: 800-875-2785
E-mail: randys@midwesttapes.com
Web site: http://www.midwesttapes.com.

MightyWords, Inc., *(1-58895; 0-7173; 1-4036)* 2850 Walsh Ave., Santa Clara, CA 95051 USA Tel 408-845-0100; Fax: 408-845-0425; Toll Free: 877-328-2724
Web site: http://www.mightywords.com.

Mightywords.com, *See* **MightyWords, Inc.**

Military History Assocs., 407B E. Sixth St., No. 200, Austin, TX 78701-3739 USA (SAN 111-7866).

Miller, Arvid E. Memorial Library Museum, N8510 Moh-He-Con-Nuck Rd., Bowker, WI 54416 USA Tel 715-793-4270.

Miller Educational Materials, *(1-934274)* Orders Addr.: P.O. Box 2428, Buena Park, CA 90621 USA Fax: 714-562-0237; Toll Free: 800-636-4375; Edit Addr.: 7300 Artesia Blvd., Buena Park, CA 90621 USA (SAN 631-5445)
E-mail: MillerEdu@aol.com
Web site: http://www.millereducational.com.

Miller Trade Bk. Marketing, 363 W. Erie St. Ste. 700E, Chicago, IL 60610-6996 USA (SAN 631-4287)
E-mail: millertrade@sbcglobal.net.

Milligan News Co., Inc., 150 N. Autumn St., San Jose, CA 95110 USA (SAN 169-0272) Tel 408-286-7604; Fax: 408-298-0235; Toll Free: 800-873-2387.

Minerva Science Bookseller, Inc., 175 Fifth Ave., New York, NY 10010 USA (SAN 286-0171).

Mint Pubs. Group, Orders Addr.: 62 June Rd., Suite 241, North Salem, NY 10560 USA Tel 914-276-6576; Fax: 914-276-6579; Edit Addr.: 1220 Nicholson Rd., Newmarket, ON I3Y 7VI CAN Toll Free Fax: 800-363-2665; Toll Free: 800-399-6858
E-mail: info@mintpub.com
Web site: http://www.mintpub.com.

Mission Resource Ctr., 1221 Profit Dr., Dallas, TX 75247 USA Toll Free: 800-305-9857.

Mississippi Library Media & Supply Co., P.O. Box 108, Brandon, MS 39043-0108 USA (SAN 169-4189) Tel 601-824-1900; Fax: 601-824-1999; Toll Free: 800-257-7566 (in Mississippi).

Mistco, Inc., P.O. Box 694854, Miami, FL 33269 USA (SAN 630-8384) Tel 305-653-2003; Fax: 305-653-2037; Toll Free: 800-552-0446
E-mail: mistco@worldnet.att.net
Web site: http://www.mistco.com.

MMB Music, Inc., *(0-918812; 1-58106)* Orders Addr.: 3526 Washington Ave. Contemporary Arts Bldg., Saint Louis, MO 63103-1019 USA (SAN 298-3281) Tel 314-531-9635; Fax: 314-531-8384; Toll Free: 800-543-3771
E-mail: mmbmusic@mmbmusic.com
Web site: http://www.mozarteffect.com.

Mobile News Co., 1118 14th St., Tuscaloosa, AL 35401-3318 USA (SAN 168-924X) Tel 334-479-1435.

Modern Curriculum Pr., *(0-7652; 0-8136; 0-87895)* Div. of Pearson Education, Orders Addr.: P.O. Box 2500, Lebanon, IN 46052-3009 USA (SAN 206-6572) Toll Free: 800-526-9907 (Customer Service)
Web site: http://www.pearsonlearning.com.

Modesto News Co., 1324 Coldwell Ave., Modesto, CA 95350-5702 USA (SAN 168-9908) Tel 209-577-5551.

Montfort Pubns., *(0-910984)* Div. of Montfort Missionaries, 26 S. Saxon Ave., Bay Shore, NY 11706-8993 USA (SAN 169-5053) Tel 631-665-0726; Fax: 631-665-4349
E-mail: montfort@optonline.net
Web site: http://www.montfortmissionaries.com; http://www.montfortmissionaries.org.

Mook & Blanchard, 546 S. Hofgaarden, La Puente, CA 91744 USA (SAN 168-9703) Tel 626-968-6424; Fax: 626-968-6877; Toll Free: 800-875-9911
E-mail: mookbook@ix.netcom.com
Web site: http://www.mookandblanchard.com.

Moon Over the Mountain Publishing Company, *See* **Leman Pubns., Inc.**

More, Thomas Assn., 205 W. Monroe St., 5th Flr., Chicago, IL 60606-5097 USA (SAN 169-1880) Tel 312-609-8880; Toll Free: 800-835-8965.

Morehouse Publishing, *(0-8192)* Orders Addr.: P.O. Box 1321, Harrisburg, PA 17105-1321 USA Fax: 717-541-8136; Toll Free: 800-242-1918; Edit Addr.: 4775 Linglestown Rd., Harrisburg, PA 17112 USA Fax: 717-541-8136
E-mail: morehouse@morehousegroup.com
Web site: http://morehousepublishing.org.

Morlock News Co., Inc., 496 Duanesburg Rd., Schenectady, NY 12306 USA (SAN 169-6246).

Morris Publishing, *(0-7392; 0-9631249; 1-57502; 1-885591)* Subs. of Morris Pr. & Office Supplies, 3212 E. Hwy. 30,, Kearney, NE 68847 USA Tel 308-236-7888; Fax: 308-237-0263; Toll Free: 800-650-7888 Do not confuse with companies with the same Wesley Chapel, FL, Elkhart, IN
E mail: kimmyw414@yahoo.com; snowgers@mcn.org; publish@morrispublishing.com
Web site: http://morrispublishing.com.

Moshy Brothers, Inc., 127 W. 25th St., New York, NY 10001 USA (SAN 169-5886) Tel 212-255-0613.

Mother Lode Distributing, 17890 Lime Rock Dr., Sonora, CA 95370-8707 USA (SAN 169-0361).

Motorbooks International Wholesalers & Distributors, *See* **MBI Distribution Services**

Mountain Bk. Co., P.O. Box 778, Broomfield, CO 80038-0778 USA Tel 303-436-1982; Fax: 917-386-2769
E-mail: wordguise@aol.com
Web site: http://www.mountainbook.org.

Mountain Pr. Publishing Co., Inc., *(0-87842)* Orders Addr.: P.O. Box 2399, Missoula, MT 59806-2399 USA (SAN 202-8832) Tel 406-728-1900; Fax: 406-728-1635; Toll Free: 800-234-5308; Edit Addr.: 1301 S. Third West, Missoula, MT 59801 USA (SAN 662-0868)
E-mail: jrimel@mtnpress.com; mtnpress@montana.com; info@mtnpress.com
Web site: http://www.mountain-press.com.

Mountain States News Distributor, P.O. Drawer P, Fort Collins, CO 80522 USA Tel 970-221-2330; Fax: 970-221-1251.

Mountaineers Bks., The, *(0-89886; 0-916890; 0-938567; 1-59485)* Div. of Mountaineers, Orders Addr.: 1001 SW Klickitat Way, Suite 201, Seattle, WA 98134-1162 USA (SAN 212-8756) Tel 206-223-6303; Fax: 206-223-6306; Toll Free: 800-568-7604
E-mail: mbooks@mountaineersbooks.org
Web site: http://www.mountaineersbooks.org.

Mouse Works, *(0-7364; 1-57082)* Div. of Disney Bk. Publishing, Inc., A Walt Disney Co., 114 Fifth Ave., New York, NY 10011 USA (SAN 298-0797) Tel 212-633-4400; Fax: 212-633-4811
Web site: http://www.disneybooks.com.

Moznaim Publishing Corp., *(0-940118; 1-885220)* 4304 12th Ave., Brooklyn, NY 11219 USA (SAN 214-4123) Tel 718-438-7680; Fax: 718-438-1305; Toll Free: 800-364-5118.

Mr. Paperback/Publishers News Co., 6030 Fostoria Ave., Findlay, OH 45840 USA (SAN 169-393X) Tel 419-424-6774; Fax: 419-420-1805; Toll Free: 800-872-0031.

M-S News Co., Inc., P.O. Box 13278, Wichita, KS 67213-0278 USA Fax: 316-267-5405.

Mullare News Agency, Inc., P.O. Box 578, Brockton, MA 02401 USA (SAN 169-3379) Tel 508-580-1000; Fax: 508-586-0968.

Multi-Cultural Bks. & Videos, Inc., *(0-9656274)* 28880 Southfield Rd. Ste. 183, Lathrup Vlg, MI 48076-2700 USA Toll Free: 800-567-2220
E-mail: service@multiculbv.com
Web site: http://www.multiculbv.com.

Multilingual Bks., Orders Addr.: P.O. Box 440632, Miami, FL 33144 USA (SAN 169-1155) Tel 305-471-9847 Do not confuse with Multilingual Bks., Seattle, WA.

Mumford Library Bks., Inc., 7847 Bayberry Rd., Jacksonville, FL 32256 USA (SAN 156-7721) Fax: 904-730-8913; Toll Free: 800-367-3927.

Mumford Library Book Sales, *See* **Mumford Library Bks., Inc.**

Murr's Library Service, 4045 E. Palm Ln., No. 5, Phoenix, AZ 85008-3116 USA (SAN 107-3222) Fax: 602-273-1217; Toll Free: 888-273-0279.

Museum of Fine Arts, Houston, *(0-89090)* P.O. Box 6826, Houston, TX 77265-6826 USA (SAN 202-2559) Tel 713-639-7300.

Music Design, Inc., 4650 N. Port Washington Rd., Milwaukee, WI 53212 USA (SAN 200-7649) Tel 414-961-8380; Fax: 414-961-8381; Toll Free: 800-862-7232
E-mail: order@musicdesign.com
Web site: http://www.musicdesign.com.

Music in Motion, P.O. Box 869231, Plano, TX 75086-9231 USA (SAN 631-4589) Fax: 972-943-8906; Toll Free Fax: 866-943-8906; Toll Free: 800-445-0649 Do not confuse with Music In Motion, Ithaca, NY
Web site: http://www.musicmotion.com.

Music Mart, Inc., 3301 Carlisle Blvd., NE, Albuquerque, NM 87110 USA (SAN 631-2128) Tel 505-889-9777; Fax: 505-889-9070; Toll Free: 800-545-6204
E-mail: info@musicmart.com
Web site: http://www.musicmart.com.

Music Sales Corp., *(0-7119; 0-8256; 1-84609)* Orders Addr.: 445 Bellvale Rd., P.O. Box 572, Chester, NY 10918 USA (SAN 662-0876) Tel 845-469-2271; Fax: 845-469-7544; Toll Free Fax: 800-345-6842; Toll Free: 800-431-7187; Edit Addr.: 257 Park Ave., S., 20th Flr., New York, NY 10010 USA (SAN 282-0277) Tel 212-254-2100; Fax: 212-254-2103
E-mail: info@musicsales.com
Web site: http://www.musicroom.com; http://www.musicsales.com.

Musicart West, P.O. Box 1900, Orem, UT 84059-1900 USA (SAN 110-1250) Tel 801-225-0859; Toll Free: 800-950-1900 (orders only).

Mustard Seed Pubns., P.O. Box 1360, San Antonio, TX 78295 USA Tel 830-216-7244 Do not confuse with companies with the same name in PerryHall, MD, Clearwater, FL Princeton Junction, NJ
E-mail: goodmarine@aol.com.

MVP Wholesales, 9301 W. Hwy. 290, No. D, Austin, TX 78736-7817 USA (SAN 630-9550) Tel 512-416-1452; Toll Free: 800-328-7931 (phone/fax).

NACSCORP, Inc., Orders Addr.: 528 E. Lorain St., Oberlin, OH 44074-1298 USA (SAN 134-2118) Tel 440-775-7777; Toll Free Fax: 800-344-5059; Toll Free: 800-321-3883 (orders only); 800-458-9303 (backorder status only); 800-334-9882 (support programs/technical support)
E-mail: service@nacscorp.com; orders@nacscorp.com
Web site: http://www.nacscorp.com.

Najarian Music Co., Inc., 269 Lexington St., Waltham, MA 02452 USA (SAN 169-3344) Tel 781-899-2200; Fax: 781-899-0838.

Napa Book Company, *See* **Napa Children's Bk. Co.**

Napa Children's Bk. Co., 1239 First St., Napa, CA 94559 USA (SAN 122-2732) Tel 707-224-3893; Fax: 707-224-1212.

Nasco Math Eighty-Six, 901 Janesville Ave., Fort Atkinson, WI 53538 USA (SAN 679-7512).

National Assn. of the Deaf, *(0-913072)* 8630 Fenton St. Ste. 820, Silver Spring, MD 20910-3819 USA (SAN 159-4974)
E-mail: sales@nad.org
Web site: http://www.nad.org.

National Bk. Co., Keystone Industrial Pk., Scranton, PA 18512 USA Tel 717-346-2020; Toll Free: 800-233-4830 Do not confuse with National Book Company, Portland, OR.

National Bk. Network, Div. of Rowman & Littlefield Pubs., Inc., Orders Addr.: 15200 NBN Way, Blue Ridge Summit, PA 17214 USA (SAN 630-0065) Tel 717-794-3800; Fax: 717-794-3828; Toll Free Fax: 800-338-4550 (Customer Service); Toll Free: 800-462-6420 (Customer Service); a/o Les Petriw, 67 Mowat Ave., Suite 241, Toronto, ON M6P 3K3 Tel 416-534-1660; Fax: 416-534-3699
E-mail: lpetriw@nbnbooks.com; custserv@nbnbooks.com
Web site: http://www.nbnbooks.com.

National Catholic Reading Distributor, 997 Macarthur Blvd., Mahwah, NJ 07430 USA (SAN 169-4855) Tel 201-825-7300; Fax: 201-825-8345; Toll Free: 800-218-1903
E-mail: paulistp@pipeline.com.

National Educational Systems, Inc., *(1-893493)* P.O. Box 691450, San Antonio, TX 78269-1450 USA Toll Free: 800-442-2604.

National Film Network LLC, *(0-8026)* Orders Addr.: 4501 Forbes Blvd., Lanham, MD 20706 USA (SAN 630-1878) Tel 301-459-8020 ext 2066
E-mail: info@nationalfilmnetwork.com
Web site: http://www.nationalfilmnetwork.com.

National Health Federation, Box 688, Monrovia, CA 91016 USA (SAN 227-9266) Tel 626-357-2181; Fax: 818-303-0642
E-mail: nhf@earthlink.net
Web site: http://www.healthfreedom.net.

National Learning Corp., *(0-8293; 0-8373)* 212 Michael Dr., Syosset, NY 11791 USA (SAN 206-8869) Tel 516-921-8888; Fax: 516-921-8743; Toll Free: 800-645-6337
E-mail: sales@passbooks.com.

National Magazine Service, Orders Addr.: P.O. Box 834, Mars, PA 16046 USA (SAN 169-7595); Edit Addr.: 535 Linden Way, Pittsburgh, PA 15202 USA Tel 412-898-0001.

National Organization Service, Inc., 4515 Fleur Dr., Suite 301, Des Moines, IA 50321-2369 USA (SAN 107-1548) Fax: 515-256-8028; Toll Free: 800-747-3032.

National Rifle Assn., *(0-935998)* a/o Office of the General Counsel, 11250 Waples Mill Rd., Fairfax, VA 22030 USA (SAN 213-859X) Tel 703-267-1269; Fax: 703-267-3985; Toll Free: 800-672-3888
E-mail: rcurley@nrahq.org.

National Sales, Inc., 1818 W. 2300 South, Salt Lake City, UT 84119 USA (SAN 159-9127) Tel 801-972-2300; Fax: 801-972-2883.

National Technical Information Service, U.S. Dept. of Commerce, *(0-934213)* Orders Addr.: 5285 Port Royal Rd., Springfield, VA 22161 USA (SAN 205-7255) Tel 703-605-6000; Fax: 703-605-6900; Toll Free: 800-553-6847
E-mail: orders@ntis.gov; info@ntis.gov
Web site: http://www.ntis.gov; http://wnc.fedworld.gov.

National Video Resources, Inc., *(1-884188)* 73 Spring St., Suite 606, New York, NY 10012 USA Tel 212-274-8080; Fax: 212-274-8081
Web site: http://www.nvr.org.

National Women's History Project, *(0-938625)* 3343 Industrial Dr. Ste. 4, Santa Rosa, CA 95403-2060 USA (SAN 200-8920)
E-mail: nwhp@aol.com
Web site: http://www.nwhp.org.

Native Bks., P.O. Box 37095, Honolulu, HI 96837 USA (SAN 631-1121) Tel 808-845-8949; Fax: 808-847-6637; Toll Free: 800-887-7751.

Navarre Corp., 7400 49th Ave., N., New Hope, MN 55428-4258 USA (SAN 132-9456) Tel 612-535-8333; Fax: 612-533-2156.

Neighborhood Periodical Club, Inc., P.O. Box 830, Clementon, NJ 08021-0860 USA (SAN 285-9262).

Nelson Direct, P.O. Box 140300, Nashville, TN 37214 USA (SAN 169-8133) Toll Free: 800-441-0511 (sales); 800-933-9673
E-mail: csalazar@thomasnelson.com
Web site: http://www.nelsondirect.com.

Nelson News, Inc., P.O. Box 27007, Omaha, NE 68127-0007 USA (SAN 169-443X) Tel 402-734-3333; Fax: 402-731-0516.

Nelson, Thomas Inc., *(0-529; 0-7852; 0-8407; 0-8499; 0-86605; 0-88113; 0-89840; 0-89922; 0-918956; 1-4002; 1-4003; 1-59145; 1-59554; 1-59555; 1-59951; 1-60255)* Orders Addr.: P.O. Box 141000, Nashville, TN 37214-1000 USA (SAN 209-3820) Fax: 615-902-1866; Toll Free: 800-251-4000; Edit Addr.: 501 Nelson Pl., Nashville, TN 37214 USA
E-mail: info@thomasnelsonpublishers.com
Web site: http://www.thomasnelson.com.

Nelson's Bks., *(0-9612188)* P.O. Box 2302, Santa Cruz, CA 95063 USA (SAN 289-4858) Tel 831-465-9148.

Ner Tamid Bk. Distributors, P.O. Box 10401, Riviera Beach, FL 33419-0401 USA (SAN 169-135X) Tel 561-686-9095.

Net Productions, 210 Elm Cir., Colorado Springs, CO 80906-3348 USA (SAN 159-9143).

NetLibrary, Inc., *(0-585; 1-4175; 1-4237; 1-4294; 1-4356)* Orders Addr.: 4888 Pearl E. Cir., Suite 103, Boulder, CO 80301 USA (SAN 253-9497) Toll Free: 800-413-4557
E-mail: sales@netlibrary.com
Web site: http://www.netlibrary.com.

NetSource Distribution, Orders Addr.: 675 Dutchess Tpke., Poughkeepsie, NY 12603 USA Tel 845-463-1100 x314; Fax: 845-463-0018; Toll Free: 800-724-1100
Web site: http://www.hudsonhousepub.com.

Nevada Pubns., *(0-913814)* 4135 Badger Cir., Reno, NV 89509 USA (SAN 203-7319) Tel 775-747-0800; Fax: 775-747-2916.

New Alexandrian Bookstore, 110 N Cayuga St., Ithaca, NY 14850-4331 USA (SAN 159-4958) Tel 607-272-1163.

New Concepts Bks. & Tapes Distributors, Orders Addr.: P.O. Box 55068, Houston, TX 77255 USA (SAN 114-2682) Tel 713-465-7736; Fax: 713-465-7106; Toll Free: 800-842-4807; Edit Addr.: 9722 Pine Lake, Houston, TX 77055 USA (SAN 630-7531).

New Day Christian Distributors, 126 Shivel Dr., Hendersonville, TN 37075 USA (SAN 631-2551) Tel 615-822-3633; Fax: 615-822-5829; Toll Free: 800-251-3633.

New England Bk. Service, Inc., 457 Pond Rd., North Ferrisburg, VT 05493 USA (SAN 170-0952) Tel 802-453-7637; Fax: 802-453-7642; Toll Free: 800-356-5772
E-mail: nebs@together.net.

New England Mobile Bk. Fair, 82 Needham St., P.O. Box 610159, Newton Highlands, MA 02461 USA (SAN 169-3530) Tel 617-527-5817; Fax: 617-527-0113.

New Jersey Bk. Agency, Orders Addr.: P.O. Box 144, Morris Plains, NJ 07950 USA (SAN 106-861X) Tel 973-267-7093; Fax: 973-292-3177; Edit Addr.: 7 Somerset Hills Ct. Apt. D, Bernardsville, NJ 07924-2619 USA (SAN 243-2307).

New Jersey Bks., Inc., 59 Market St., Newark, NJ 07102 USA Tel 973-624-8070; Toll Free: 800-772-3678.

New Leaf Distributing Co., Inc., *(0-9627209)* Div. of Al-Wali Corp., 401 Thornton Rd., Lithia Springs, GA 30122-1557 USA (SAN 169-1449) Tel 770-948-7845; Fax: 770-944-2313; Toll Free Fax: 800-326-1066; Toll Free: 800-326-2665
E-mail: santoshk@msn.com; alimt@bellsouth.net
Web site: http://www.NewLeaf-dist.com.

New Leaf Pr., Inc., *(0-89221)* P.O. Box 726, Green Forest, AR 72638 USA (SAN 207-9518) Tel 870-438-5288; Fax: 870-438-5120 Toll Free: 800-643-9535 Do not confuse with companies with the same or similar name in Los Angeles, CA
E-mail: nlp@newleafpress.net
Web site: http://www.newleafpress.net.

New Leaf Resources, 2102 Button Ln., Unit 2, Lagrange, KY 40031 USA Toll Free: 800-346-3087
E-mail: info@newleaf-resources.com
Web site: http://www.www.newleaf-resources.com.

New Life Foundation, *(0-911203; 1-934162)* P.O. Box 2230, Pine, AZ 85544-2230 USA (SAN 170-3986) Tel 928-476-3224; Fax: 928-476-4743; Toll Free: 800-293-3377 (wholesale only)
E-mail: info@anewlife.org
Web site: http://www.anewlife.org.

New World Library, *(0-931432; 0-945934; 1-57731; 1-880032)* 14 Pamaron Way, Novato, CA 94949 USA (SAN 211-8777) Tel 415-884-2100; Fax: 415-884-2199; Toll Free: 800-972-6657 (retail orders only) Do not confuse with New World Library Publishing Co., Los Altos, CA
E-mail: escort@nwlib.com
Web site: http://www.newworldlibrary.com.

New World Resource Ctr., 1300 N. Western Ave., Chicago, IL 60622-2923 USA (SAN 169-1848).

New York Periodical Distributors, P.O. Box 29, Massena, NY 13662-0029 USA (SAN 169-6149).

New York Univ. Pr., *(0-8147)* Div. of New York Univ., Orders Addr.: 838 Broadway, 3rd Flr., New York, NY 10003-4812 USA (SAN 658-1293) Tel 212-998-2575; Fax: 212-995-3833; Toll Free: 800-996-6987 (ordering)
E-mail: orders@nyupress.org
Web site: http://www.nyupress.org.

Newborn Enterprises, Inc., P.O. Box 1713, Altoona, PA 16603 USA (SAN 169-7242) Tel 814-944-3593; Fax: 814-944-1881; Toll Free: 800-227-0285 (in Pennsylvania).

News Group - Illinois, The, 1301 SW Washington St., Peoria, IL 61602 USA (SAN 169-216X) Tel 309-673-4549; Fax: 309-673-8883.

News Group, The, 325 W. Potter Dr., Anchorage, AK 99518 USA (SAN 168-9274) Tel 907-563-3251; Fax: 907-261-8523 Do not confuse with companies with the same name in Winston-Salem, NC, Elizabeth, NC.

News Supply Co., 216 S. La Huerta Cir., Carlsbad, NM 88220-9620 USA (SAN 159-9151).

Newsdealers Supply Co., Inc., P.O. Box 3516, Tallahassee, FL 32315-3516 USA.

NewSound, LLC, 81 Demeritt Pl., Waterbury, VT 05676 USA Tel 802-244-7858; Fax: 802-244-1808; Toll Free: 800-342-0295 (wholesale orders)
E-mail: sales@newsoundmusic.com.

NEWSouth Distributors, P.O. Box 61297, Jacksonville, FL 32236-1297 USA (SAN 159-8732).

Newsstand Distributors, 155 W. 14th St., Ogden, UT 84404 USA (SAN 169-8494) Fax: 810-621-7336; Toll Free: 800-283-6247; 800-231-4834 (in Utah).

Ng Hing Kee, 648 Jackson St., San Francisco, CA 94133 USA (SAN 107-1084) Tel 415-781-8330; Fax: 415-397-9766.

Niagara County News, 70 Nicholls St., Lockport, NY 14094 USA (SAN 169-541X) Tel 716-433-6466.

Nichols Publishing Co., *(0-89397)* P.O. Box 6036, East Brunswick, NJ 08816-6036 USA (SAN 212-0291) Tel 732-297-2862; Fax: 732-940-0549 Do not confuse with Nichols Publishing in Lacey, WA.

Noelke, Carl B., 529 Main, Box 563, La Crosse, WI 54602 USA (SAN 111-8315) Tel 608-782-8544.

Nonagon, 1556 Douglas Dr., El Cerrito, CA 94530 USA (SAN 654-0503) Tel 510-237-5290.

Nonetheless Pr., *(1-932053)* 20332 W. 98th St., Lenexa, KS 66220-2650 USA Tel 913-254-7266; Fax: 913-393-3245
E-mail: mschutte@nonethelesspress.com
Web site: http://www.nonethelesspress.com; http://www.lookingglasspress.com.

Nor-Cal News Co., 2040 Petaluma Blvd., P.O. Box 2508, Petaluma, CA 94953 USA (SAN 169-0035) Tel 707-763-2606; Fax: 707-763-3905.

North American Bk. Distributors, P.O. Box 510, Hamburg, MI 48139 USA (SAN 630-4680) Tel 810-231-3728.

North Carolina News Co., P.O. Box 1051, Durham, NC 27702-1051 USA Tel 919-682-5779.

North Carolina Schl. Bk. Depository, Inc., P.O. Box 950, Raleigh, NC 27602-0950 USA (SAN 169-6467) Tel 919-833-6615.

North Central Bk. Distributors, N57 W13636 Carmen Ave., Menomonee Falls, WI 53051 USA (SAN 173-5195) Tel 414-781-3299; Fax: 414-781-4432; Toll Free: 800-966-3299.

North Country Bks., Inc., *(0-925168; 0-932052; 0-9601158; 1-59531)* 311 Turner St., Utica, NY 13501 USA (SAN 110-828X) Tel 315-735-4877
E-mail: ncbooks@adelphia.net
Web site: http://www.northcountrybooks.com.

North Shore Distributors, 1200 N. Branch, Chicago, IL 60622 USA (SAN 169-2275).

North Shore News Co., Inc., 150 Blossom St., Lynn, MA 01902 USA (SAN 169-3492).

North Texas Periodicals, Inc., Orders Addr.: P.O. Box 3823, Lubbock, TX 79452 USA Tel 806-745-6000; Fax: 806-745-7028; Edit Addr.: 118 E. 70th St., Lubbock, TX 79404 USA
E-mail: ntp@hts-online.net.

NorthCountry Distributors, The Cadence Bldg., Redwood, NY 13679-9612 USA (SAN 630-6357) Tel 315-287-2852; Fax: 315-287-2860
E-mail: info@ncdsales.com.

Northern News Co., P.O. Box 467, Petoskey, MI 49770-0467 USA (SAN 169-3964) Toll Free: 800-632-7138 (Michigan only).

Northern Schl. Supply Co., P.O. Box 2627, Fargo, ND 58108 USA (SAN 169-6548) Fax: 800-891-5836.

Northern Sun, 2916 E. Lake St., Minneapolis, MN 55406 USA (SAN 249-9290) Tel 612-729-2001; Fax: 612-729-0149; Toll Free: 800-258-8579.

Northern Sun Merchandising, *See* **Northern Sun**

North-South Bks., Inc., *(0-7358; 1-55858)* 350 7th Ave. Rm. 1400, New York, NY 10001-5013 USA
E-mail: mnavarro@northsouth.com
Web site: http://www.northsouth.com/privacy/index.html.

Northwest Archery Co., Inc., P.O. Box 1343, Graham, WA 98338-1343 USA.

Northwest News, 1560 NE First St., No. 13, Bend, OR 97701 USA (SAN 111-8587) Tel 541-382-6065; 3100 Merriman Rd., Medford, OR 97501 Tel 541-779-5225.

Northwest News Co., Inc., Orders Addr.: P.O. Box 4965, Missoula, MT 59806 USA (SAN 660-9406); Edit Addr.: 1701 Ranklin St., Missoula, MT 59802-1629 USA (SAN 169-4391) Tel 406-721-7801.

Northwest Textbook Depository, Orders Addr.: P.O. Box 5608, Portland, OR 97228 USA Toll Free: 800-676-6630; Edit Addr.: 17970 SW McEwan Rd., Portland, OR 97224 USA (SAN 631-4481) Tel 503-639-3193; Fax: 503-639-2559.

Norton, Jeffrey Pubs., Inc., *(0-88432; 1-57970)* 1 Orchard Park Rd., Madison, CT 06443-2272 USA (SAN 213-957X) Toll Free Fax: 888-453-4329; Toll Free: 800-243-1234
E-mail: info@audioforum.com
Web site: http://www.audioforum.com.

Norton News Agency, 905 Kelly Ln., Dubuque, IA 52003-8526 USA (SAN 169-2631); 1467 Service Dr., Winona, MN 55987 (SAN 156-4889).

Norton, W. W. & Co., Inc., *(0-393; 0-920256)* Orders Addr.: 800 Keystone Industrial Pk., Scranton, PA 18512 USA (SAN 157-1869) Tel 570-346-2020; Fax: 570-346-1442; Toll Free Fax: 800-458-6515 (credit card orders only); Toll Free: 800-233-4830 (book orders only); Edit Addr.: 500 Fifth Ave., New York, NY 10110-0017 USA (SAN 202-5795) Tel 212-354-5500; Fax: 212-869-0856; Toll Free: 800-223-2584
E-mail: webmaster@wwnorton.com
Web site: http://www.wwnorton.com; http://www.wwnorton.com/trade.

NTC/Contemporary Publishing Company, *See* **McGraw-Hill/Contemporary**

Nueces News Agency, 5130 Commerce Pkwy., San Antonio, TX 78218-5523 USA (SAN 169-8079).

Nueva Vida Distributors, 4300 Montana Ave., El Paso, TX 79903-4503 USA (SAN 107-8615) Tel 915-565-6215; Fax: 915-565-1722.

Nutri-Bks. Corp., Div. of Royal Pubns., Inc., 790 W. Tennessee Ave., P.O. Box 5793, Denver, CO 80223 USA Tel 303-778-8383; Fax: 303-744-9383; Toll Free: 800-279-2048 (orders only).

Oak Knoll Pr., *(0-938768; 1-884718; 1-58456; 1-872116)* 310 Delaware St., New Castle, DE 19720 USA (SAN 216-2776) Tel 302-328-7232; Fax: 302-328-7274; Toll Free: 800-996-2556 Do not confuse with Oak Knoll Press in Hardy, VA
E-mail: oakknoll@oakknoll.com
Web site: http://www.oakknoll.com.

Oakwood Pubns., *(0-9618545; 1-879038; 1-891295)* Orders Addr.: P.O. Box 1128, Torrance, CA 90505 USA (SAN 668-1557) Tel 310-378-9245; Fax: 310-378-6782; Toll Free Fax: 800-903-4266; Toll Free: 800-747-9245; Edit Addr.: P.O. Box 1128, Torrance, CA 90505-0128 USA (SAN 668-1565)
E-mail: oakwoodpub@juno.com.

Octagon Pr./ISHK Bk. Service, *See* **ISHK**

Ohio Periodical Distributors, P.O. Box 145449, Cincinnati, OH 45250-5449 USA (SAN 169-6904) Fax: 513-853-6245; Toll Free: 800-777-2216.

Ohio Univ. Pr., *(0-8214)* Orders Addr.: 11030 S. Langley Ave., Chicago, IL 60628 USA Tel 773-702-7000; Fax: 773-702-7212; Toll Free Fax: 800-621-8476; Toll Free: 800-621-2736; Edit Addr.: 19 Circle Dr. The Ridges, Athens, OH 45701 USA (SAN 282-0773) Tel 740-593-1154; Fax: 740 593 4536
Web site: http://www.ohiou.edu/oupress/.

Oil City News Co., 112 Innis St., Oil City, PA 16301-2930 USA (SAN 169-7501).

Ollis Bk. Corp., Orders Addr.: P.O. Box 258, Steger, IL 60475 USA (SAN 658-1323); Edit Addr.: 28 E. 35th St., Steger, IL 60475 USA (SAN 169-2224) Tel 312-755-5151; Fax: 708-755-5153; Toll Free: 800-323-0343.

Olson, D & Company, *See* **Nelson's Bks.**

Olson News Agency, P.O. Box 129, Ishpeming, MI 49849 USA (SAN 169-3832).

Omega Pubns., Inc., *(0-930872)* 256 Darrow Rd., New Lebanon, NY 12125 USA (SAN 214-1493) Tel 518-794-8183; Fax: 518-794-8187; Toll Free: 888-443-7107 (orders only) Do not confuse with companies with the same name in Medford, OR, Indianapolis, IN
E-mail: goodbooks@omegapub.com
Web site: http://www.omegapub.com.

Omnibooks, 456 Vista Del Mar Dr., Aptos, CA 95003-4832 USA (SAN 168-9487) Tel 408-688-4098; Toll Free: 800-626-6671.

Omnibus Pr., *(0-7119; 0-8256; 0-86001; 1-84449)* Div. of Music Sales Corp., Orders Addr.: 445 Bellvale Rd., Chester, NY 10918-0572 USA Tel 845-469-4699; Fax: 845-469-7544; Toll Free Fax: 800-345-6842; Toll Free: 800-431-7187; Edit Addr.: 257 Park Ave., S., 20th Flr., New York, NY 10010 USA Tel 212-254-2100; Fax: 212-254-2013 Do not confuse with Omnibus Pr., Menasha, WI
E-mail: info@musicsales.com
Web site: http://www.musicsales.com.

One Small Voice Foundation, P.O. Box 644, Elmhurst, IL 60126 USA Tel 630-620-6634
E-mail: onesmallvoice@earthlink.net
Web site: htp://www.onesmallvoicefoundation.org.

Onondaga News Agency, P.O. Box 6445, Syracuse, NY 13217-6445 USA (SAN 169-6297).

OPA Publishing & Distributing, Orders Addr.: P.O. Box 1764, Chandler, AZ 85244-1764 USA; Edit Addr.: 777 W. Chandler Blvd., Suite 1322, Chandler, AZ 85244-1764 USA.

Options Unlimited, 550 Swan Creek Ct., Suwanee, GA 30174 USA (SAN 631-3949) Tel 770-237-3282 Do not confuse with Options Unlimited, Inc., Green Bay, WI.

Orange News Company, *See* **Anderson News, LLC**

Orbit Bks. Corp., 43 Timberline Dr., Poughkeepsie, NY 12603 USA (SAN 169-6157) Tel 914-462-5653; Fax: 914-462-8409.

Orca Bk. Pubs. USA, *(0-920501; 1-55143)* Orders Addr.: P.O. Box 468, Custer, WA 98240-0468 USA (SAN 630-9674) Tel 250-380-1229; Fax: 250-380-1892; Toll Free: 800-210-5277
E-mail: orca@orcabook.com
Web site: http://www.orcabook.com.

Oregon State Univ. Pr., *(0-87071)* 500 Kerr Administration Bldg., Corvallis, OR 97331-2122 USA (SAN 202-8328) Tel 541-737-3166; Fax: 541-737-3170; Toll Free: 800-426-3797
E-mail: osu.press@oregonstate.edu
Web site: http://osu.orst.edu/dept/press.

O'Reilly & Associates, Incorporated, *See* **O'Reilly Media, Inc.**

O'Reilly Media, Inc., *(0-937175; 1-56592; 3-89721; 3-930673; 4-900900; 0-596; 4-87311; 1-60033)* Orders Addr.: 1005 Gravenstein Hwy. N., Sebastopol, CA 95472 USA (SAN 658-5973) Tel 707-827-7000; Fax: 707-829-0104; Toll Free: 800-998-9938; Edit Addr.: 10 Fawcett St. Ste. 4, Cambridge, MA 02138-1175 USA Toll Free: 800-775-7731; 4 Castle St, Farnham, GU9 7HR Tel 01252 71 17 76; Fax: 01252 73 42 11; c/o Madeleine Fakhoury Editions O'Reilly, 18, rue Seguier, Paris, F-75006 Tel 33 1 40 51 52 30; Fax: 33 1 40 51 52 31; c/o Michelle Chen, SIGMA Building, Suite B809 No. 49 Zhichun Rd. Haidian District, Beijing, 100080 Tel 86-10-88097476; 86-10-88097475; Fax: 86-10-88097463; c/o O'Reilly Verlag, Gerd Miske, Balthasarstr. 81, Köln, D-50670 Tel 49 221 973160 0; Fax: 49 221 973160 8; 1Fl, No. 21, Lane 295 Section 1, Fu-Shing South Rd., Taipei, Tel 886 2 27099669; Fax: 886 2 27038802; Intelligent Plaza Bldg. 1F 26 Banchi 27, Sakamachi, Shinjuku-ku, Tokyo, 160-0002 Tel 81 3 3356 5227; Fax: 81 3 3356 5261
E-mail: order@oreilly.com; information@oreilly.co.uk; nuts@ora.com
Web site: http://www.oreilly.com; http://www.editions-oreilly.fr; http://oreilly.co.uk; http://oreilly.com.tw; http://www.ora.com; http://www.oreilly.fr/; http://www.oreilly.com.cn/; http://www.orielly.de.

Original Pubns., *(0-942272)* Subs. of Maximo, Inc., 59 Central Ave. Ste. 4, Farmingdale, NY 11735-6902 USA (SAN 133-0225) Toll Free: 888-622-8581.

Orthodox Christian Pubns. Ctr., P.O. Box 675, Syosset, NY 11791-0675 USA (SAN 631-208X).

Osborne Enterprises Publishing, *(0-932117)* P.O. Box 255, Port Townsend, WA 98368 USA (SAN 242-7567) Tel 360-385-1200; Fax: 360-385-6572; Toll Free: 800-246-3255 (orders only)
E-mail: jpo@olympus.net
Web site: http://www.jerryosborne.com.

Osborne/McGraw-Hill, *See* **McGraw-Hill Osborne**

Osiander Bk. Trade, 7483H Candlewood Rd., Hanover, MD 21076-3102 USA (SAN 130-0970).

Outbooks, Incorporated, *See* **Vistabooks**

Outdoorsman, The, Orders Addr.: P.O. Box 268, Boston, MA 02134 USA (SAN 169-3352).

OverDrive, Inc., Valley Tech Ctr. 8555 Sweet Valley Dr., Cleveland, OH 44125-4210 USA (SAN 245-0658) Tel 216-573-6886; Fax: 216-573-6888
Web site: http://www.overdrive.com.

OverDrive Systems, Incorporated, *See* **OverDrive, Inc.**

Overmountain Pr., *(0-932807; 0-9644613; 1-57072)* P.O. Box 1261, Johnson City, TN 37605 USA (SAN 687-6641) Tel 423-926-2691; Fax: 423-232-1252; Toll Free: 800-992-2691 (orders only)
E-mail: beth@overmtn.com
Web site: http://www.silverdaggermysteries.com; http://www.overmountainpress.com.

Oxford Univ. Pr., Inc., *(0-19)* Orders Addr.: 2001 Evans Rd., Cary, NC 27513 USA (SAN 202-5892) Tel 919-677-0977 (general voice); Fax: 919-677-1303 (customer service); Toll Free: 800-445-9714 (customer service - inquiry); 800-451-7556 (customer service - orders); Edit Addr.: 198 Madison Ave., New York, NY 10016-4314 USA (SAN 202-5884) Tel 212-726-6000 (general voice); Fax: 212-726-6440 (general fax)
E-mail: custserv@oup-usa.org; orders@oup-usa.org
Web site: http://www.oup.com/us.

Ozark Bk. Distributors, 1802 Van Buren Ave., Mountain Home, AR 72653 USA.

Ozark Magazine Distributing, Incorporated, *See* **Ozark News Distributor, Inc.**

Ozark News Agency, Inc., P.O. Box 1150, Fayetteville, AR 72702 USA.

Ozark News Distributor, Inc., 1630 N. Eldon, Springfield, MO 65803 USA (SAN 169-4332) Tel 417-862-9224; Fax: 417-862-6642; Toll Free: 800-743-0380.

P & G Wholesale, P.O. Box 1548, Fargo, ND 58102 USA (SAN 156-4536).

P & R Publishing, *(0-87552; 1-59638)* Orders Addr.: 1102 Marble Hill Rd., Harmony, Phillipsburg, NJ 08865 USA (SAN 658-1463) Tel 908-454-0505; Fax: 908-859-2390; Toll Free: 800-631-0094 Do not confuse with P & R Publishing Co. in Sioux Center, IA
E-mail: tara@prpbooks.com; jesse@prpbooks.com
Web site: http://www.prpbooks.com.

P. D. Music Headquarters, Inc., Orders Addr.: P.O. Box 252, New York, NY 10014 USA (SAN 282-5880) Tel 212-242-5322.

P S I Fulfillment, 8801 Wall St. Ste. 500, Austin, TX 78754-4400 USA (SAN 631-3914)
E-mail: orders@psifulfillment.com
Web site: http://www.psifulfillment.com.

Pacific Bks., *(1-885375)* Orders Addr.: P.O. Box 3562, Santa Barbara, CA 93130 USA (SAN 630-2548) Tel 805-687-8340; Fax: 805-687-2514; Edit Addr.: 2573 Treasure Dr., Santa Barbara, CA 93105 USA.

Pacific Island Bks., 2802 E. 132nd Cir., Thornton, CO 80241 USA Fax: 603-368-6628; Toll Free: 888-492-6657 (888-49-BOOKS)
E-mail: pacificbks@aol.com
Web site: http://www.pacificislandbooks.com.

Pacific Learning, Inc., *(1-59055; 1-60457)* Orders Addr.: P.O. Box 2723, Huntington Beach, CA 92647-0723 USA; Edit Addr.: 15342 Graham St., Huntington Beach, CA 92649 USA Tel 714-516-8304; Fax: 714-516-8369; Toll Free: 800-279-0737
E-mail: info@pacificlearning.com
Web site: http://www.pacificlearning.com.

Pacific Magazine-Bk. Wholesaler, 1515 NW 51st St., Seattle, WA 98107 USA (SAN 274-3884) Tel 206-789-5333.

Pacific Periodical Services, LLC, *See* **Anderson News - Tacoma**

Pacific Pr. Publishing Assn., *(0-8163)* P.O. Box 5353, Nampa, ID 83653-5353 USA (SAN 202-8409) Tel 208-465-2500; Fax: 208-465-2531; Toll Free: 800-447-7377
E-mail: donlay@pacificpress.com
Web site: http://www.AdventistBookCenter.com.

Pacific Trade Group, 68-309 Crozier Dr., Waialua, HI 96791 USA (SAN 169-1635) Tel 808-636-2300; Fax: 808-636-2301.

PageFree Publishing, Inc., *(1-929077; 1-930252; 1-58961)* P.O. Box 60, Otsego, MI 49078-0060 USA Toll Free: 1-866-GO BOOKS
E-mail: pagefreepublish@aol.com; publisher@pagefreepublishing.com
Web site: http://www.pagefreepublishing.com.

Paladin Pr., *(0-87364; 1-58160; 1-891268)* Orders Addr.: c/o Gunbarrel Tech Ctr., 7077 Winchester Cir., Boulder, CO 80301 USA (SAN 662-1066) Tel 303-443-7250; Fax: 303-442-8741; Toll Free: 800-392-2400 (Credit Card Orders Only)
E-mail: sales@paladin-press.com; editorial@paladin-press.com; service@paladin-press.com
Web site: http://www.paladin-press.com; http://www.flying-machines.com; http://www.sycamoreisland.com.

Palgrave, *See* **Palgrave Macmillan**

Palgrave Macmillan, *(0-312; 0-333; 1-4039)* Div. of Saint Martin's Press, LLC, Orders Addr.: 16365 James Madison Hwy., Gordonsville, VA 22942-8501 USA Toll Free Fax: 800-672-2054; Toll Free: 888-330-8477; Edit Addr.: 175 Fifth Ave., New York, NY 10010 USA Tel 212-982-9300; Fax: 212-777-6359; Toll Free Fax: 800 672-2054 (Customer Service); Toll Free: 800-221-7945; 888-330-8477 (Customer Service)
E-mail: customerservice@vhpsva.com
Web site: http://www.palgrave.com.

Palmer News Co., Inc., 534 S. Kansas Ave. Ste. 700, Topeka, KS 66603-3429 USA.

Palmer News, Inc., 9605 Dice Ln., Lenexa, KS 66215 USA Tel 913-541-8600; Fax: 913-541-9413
E-mail: palmerco@oni.com.

Palmetto News Co., 200 Sunbelt Ct., Greer, SC 29650-9349 USA.

Palmyra Publishing Co., *(0-9666627)* P.O. Box 1164, Sioux Falls, SD 57101-1164 USA Tel 605-330-2707; Fax: 605-330-6009
E-mail: alyajim@sd.cybernex.net.

Pan American Publishing, Inc., *(1-889867)* 420 E. Ohio St., Suite 4-F, Chicago, IL 60611-3355 USA (SAN 299-1977) Tel 773-404-7282.

Pan Asia Pubns. (USA), Inc., *(1-57227)* 29564 Union City Blvd., Union City, CA 94587 USA (SAN 173-685X) Tel 510-475-1185; Fax: 510-475-1489; Toll Free: 800-909-8088
E-mail: sales@panap.com
Web site: http://www.panap.com.

Pan De Vida Distributors, *(1-934811)* 5507 Brooks St., Montclair, CA 91763 USA (SAN 631-0753) Tel 909-510-5219; 909-510-5200; Fax: 909-510-5210
Web site: http://www.pandevida.com.

Panamericana Publishing LLC, 12902 SW 133 Ct., Suite D, Miami, FL 33186 USA (SAN 256-1409) Tel 305-278-2648; Fax: 305-436-7264
E-mail: operez@panamericana.com.co
Web site: http://panamericanaeditorial.com.

Paperback Books, Incorporated, *See* **Book Distribution Ctr., Inc.**

Paperbacks for Educators, *(0-9702376; 1-59721)* 426 W. Front St., Washington, MO 63090 USA (SAN 103-3379) Tel 636-239-1999; Fax: 636-239-4515; Toll Free Fax: 800-514-7323; Toll Free: 800-227-2591
E-mail: paperbacks@usmo.com
Web site: http://www.any-book-in-print.com.

Parklane Publishing, *(1-59384)* Div. of Book Club of America, 100 Marcus Blvd. Ste. 8, Hauppauge, NY 11788-3749 USA
E-mail: lbaumert@bookclubusa.com
Web site: http://www.parklanepublishing .com.

Parkwest Pubns., Inc., *(0-88186)* P.O. Box 310251, Miami, FL 33231 USA (SAN 264-6846) Tel 305-256-7880; Fax: 305-256-7816
E-mail: parkwest@parkwestpubs.com; info@parkwestpubs.com
Web site: http://www.parkwestpubs.com.

Parliament News Co., Inc., P.O. Box 910, Santa Clarita, CA 91380-9010 USA (SAN 168-9924).

Parnasas Bk. Distributors, 200 Academy Way, Columbia, SC 29206 USA Tel 803 782 7748.

Parnassus Bk. Distributors, 200 Academy Way, Columbia, SC 29206-1445 USA (SAN 631-0680) Tel 803-782-7748; Toll Free: 800-782-7760.

Partners Bk. Distributing, Inc., Orders Addr.: P.O. Box 580, Holt, MI 48842 USA; Edit Addr.: 2325 Jarco Dr., Holt, MI 48842 USA (SAN 630-4559) Tel 517-694-3205; Toll Free: 800-336-3137 (orders).

Partners Book Distributing, Incorporated, *See* **Partners Pubs. Group, Inc.**

Partners Pubs. Group, Inc., Orders Addr.: 2325 Jarco Dr., Holt, MI 48842 USA (SAN 631-3418) Tel 517-694-3205; Fax: 517-694-0617; Toll Free: 800-336-3137
Web site: http://www.partnerspublishersgroup.com.

Partners/West, 1901 Raymond Ave., SW, Suite C, Renton, WA 98055 USA (SAN 631-421X) Tel 425-227-8486; Fax: 425-204-1448; Toll Free: 800-563-2385.

Paternoster Publishing USA, *See* **Authentic Media**

Pathfinder Pr., *(0-87348; 0-913460; 1-60488)* Orders Addr.: P.O. Box 162767, Atlanta, GA 30321-2767 USA Tel 404-669-0600; Fax: 707-667-1411; 120 Bethnal Green Rd, London, E2 6DG Tel 020-7613 3855; Fax: 020-7613 3855; Pathfinder Books/Livres Pathfinder 2238 Dundas St. West, Suite 201, Toronto, ON 0N M6R Fax: 416-535-9036 Canadian orders; Edit Addr.: 306 W. 37th St., 10th Flr., New York, NY 10018 USA (SAN 202-5906) Tel 404-669-0600 (Business & shipping center); Fax: 404-506-9431 (Permissions) Do not confuse with companies with the same or similar names in Alameda, CA, Battle Ground, WA, Elicott City, MD, Midland, MI
E-mail: orders@pathfinderpress.com; pathfinder@pathfinderpress.com; permissions@pathfinderpress.com; livrespathfinder@bellnet.ca; livres.pathfinder@laposte.net; pathfinderbooks@bellnet.ca; pathfinder_sydney@bigpond.com; order@pathfinderbooks.co.uk; pathauck@paradise.net.nz; kfstockholm@telia.com; pathfinderbusiness@mac.com
Web site: http://www.pathfinderpress.com.

Pathway Bk. Service, Div. of MLES, Inc., Orders Addr.: 4 White Brook Rd., Gilsum, NH 03448 USA (SAN 170-0545) Tel 603-357-0236; Fax: 603-357-2073; Toll Free: 800-345-6665; P.O. Box 89, Gilsum, NH 03448
E-mail: pbs@pathwaybook.com
Web site: http://www.pathwaybook.com.

Paul & Co. Pubs. Consortium, Inc., Div. of Independent Publishers Group, Orders Addr.: 814 N. Franklin St., Chicago, IL 60610 USA Tel 312-337-0747; Fax: 312-337-5985; Toll Free: 800-888-4741
E-mail: frontdesk@ipgbook.com
Web site: http://www.ipgbook.com.

Pauline Bks. & Media, *(0-8198)* 50 St. Paul's Ave., Boston, MA 02130-3491 USA (SAN 203-8900) Tel 617-522-8911; Fax: 617-524-8035; Toll Free: 800-876-4463 (orders only)
E-mail: editorial@pauline.org; lmacauley@paulinemedia.com
Web site: http://www.PAULINE.org.

Paulsen, G. Co., 27 Sheep Davis Rd., Pembroke, NH 03275 USA (SAN 169-4499) Tel 603-225-9787.

PBD, Inc., 1650 Bluegrass Lakes Pkwy., Alpharetta, GA 30004 USA (SAN 126-6039) Tel 770-442-8633; Fax: 770-442-9742
Web site: http://www.pbd.com.

PCE International, 8811 Aviation Blvd., Inglewood, CA 90301 USA Tel 310-337-0055; Fax: 310-642-4625; Toll Free: 800-626-1313.

PCI Educational Publishing, *(1-884074; 1-58804)* 4560 Lockhill-Selma, Suite 100, San Antonio, TX 78265-4270 USA Tel 210-377-1999; Fax: 210-377-1121; Toll Free Fax: 888-259-8284; Toll Free: 800-594-4263
E-mail: lboulet@pcieducation.com
Web site: http://www.pcieducation.com.

Pearson Education, *(0-582)* Orders Addr.: 200 Old Tappan Rd., Old Tappan, NJ 07675 USA (SAN 200-2175) Tel 201-767-5000 (Receptionist); Toll Free Fax: 800-445-6991; Toll Free: 800-428-5331; 800-922-0579; Edit Addr.: One Lake St., Upper Saddle River, NJ 07458 USA Tel 201-236-7000; 201-236-5321; Fax: 201-236-6549
E-mail: communications@pearsoned.com
Web site: http://www.pearsoned.com.

Pearson Technology Group, One Lake St., Upper Saddle River, NJ 07458 USA.

Pee Dee News Co., 2321 Lawrens Cir., Florence, SC 29501-9408 USA.

Pegasus Pr., *(1-889818)* 2641 S. Emerson St., Chandler, AZ 85248-3248 USA Do not confuse with companies with the same name in Vashon Island, WA, San Diego, CA, Kerrville, TX, Lake Forest, IL
E-mail: pegpress@hotmail.com
Web site: http://www.pegpress.org.

Pegram, Christine, 1901 Upper Cove Terr., Sarasota, FL 33581 USA (SAN 110-0254) Tel 941-921-2467.

Pekin News Agency, 1637 Monroe St., Madison, WI 53711-2021 USA (SAN 169-2151).

Pelican Publishing Co., Inc., *(0-88289; 0-911116; 1-56554; 1-58980)* Orders Addr.: 1000 Burmaster St., Gretna, LA 70053-2246 USA Tel 504-368-1175; Fax: 504-368-1195; Toll Free: 800-843-1724 Do not confuse with companies with the same or similar names in Lowell, MA, Dallas, TX
E-mail: Sales@pelicanpub.com; promo@pelicanpub.com
Web site: http://www.bedandbreakfastguide.com; http://www.pelicanpub.com; http://www.epelican.com; http://www.eirishbooks.com.

Peller, A. W. & Assocs., 210 Sixth Ave., P.O. Box 106, Hawthorne, NJ 07507-0106 USA (SAN 631-1563) Tel 973-423-4666; Fax: 973-423-5569; Toll Free: 800-451-7450
E-mail: awpeller@worldnet.att.net
Web site: http://www.awpeller.com.

Pen Notes, Inc., *(0-939564)* 70 S. Main St. Apt. 2A, Freeport, NY 11520-3853 USA (SAN 107-3621)
E-mail: pennotes@worldnet.att.net.

Penguin Group (USA) Inc., *(0-14; 0-399; 0-525; 1-933438; 1-4295; 1-934511; 1-4362)* Orders Addr.: 405 Murray Hill Pkwy., East Rutherford, NJ 07073-2136 USA (SAN 282-5074) Fax: 201-933-2903 (customer service); Toll Free Fax: 800-227-9604; Toll Free: 800-526-0275 (reseller sales); 800-631-8571 (reseller customer service); 800-788-6262 (individual consumer sales); Edit Addr.: 375 Hudson St., New York, NY 10014 USA Tel 212-366-2000; Fax: 212-366-2666; 405 Murray Hill Pkwy., East Rutherford, NJ 07073 (SAN 852-5455) Tel 201-933-9292
E-mail: customer.service@us.penguingroup.com; us.penguingroup.com
Web site: http://penguingroup.custhelp.com; http://booksellers.penguingroup.com; http://www.penguinputnam.com.

Penguin Putnam, Incorporated, *See* **Penguin Group (USA) Inc.**

Peniel Productions, 73 Smith Hill Rd., Monsey, NY 10952-4131 USA (SAN 631-2837).

Pen-Mar News Distributors, *See* **Americana Souvenirs & Gifts**

Penmarch Publishing, 3932 S. Willow Ave., Sioux Falls, SD 57105 USA Toll Free: 800-282-2399.

Penn News Co., 944 Franklin St., Johnstown, PA 15905 USA (SAN 169-7390).

PennWell Books, *See* **PennWell Corp.**

PennWell Corp., *(0-87814; 1-59370; 0-9795633)* Orders Addr.: P.O. Box 21288, Tulsa, OK 74121 USA (SAN 282-1567) Tel 918-831-9421; Fax: 918-832-9319; Toll Free Fax: 877-218-1348; Toll Free: 800-752-9764; Edit Addr.: 1421 S. Sheridan, Tulsa, OK 74112 USA (SAN 282-1559) Tel 918-931-9421; Fax: 918-831-9555; 918-832-9319; Toll Free Fax: 877-218-1348; Toll Free: 800-752-9764 (orders only)
E-mail: sales@pennwell.com; bookmarketing@pennwell.com; DentalBookSales@pennwell.com; EnergyBookSales@pennwell.com; FireBookSales@pennwell.com
Web site: http://www.pennwellbooks.com; http://www.fireengineeringbooks.com.

Pentecostal Publishing Hse., *(0-912315)* Subs. of United Pentecostal Church International, 8855 Dunn Rd., Hazelwood, MO 63042-2299 USA (SAN 219-3817) Tel 314-837-7300; (314) 837-7300; Fax: 314-837-4503
E-mail: PPHpublish@aol.com.

Penton Overseas, Inc., *(0-939001; 1-56015; 1-59125; 1-60379)* 1958 Kellogg Ave., Vista, CA 92008 USA (SAN 631-0826) Tel 760-431-0060; Fax: 760-431-8110; Toll Free: 800-748-5804
Web site: http://www.pentonoverseas.com.

Peoples Publishing Group, Inc., The, *(1-56256; 1-58984; 1-4138)* Orders Addr.: P.O. Box 513, Saddle Brook, NJ 07633 USA Tel 201-712-0090; Fax: 201-712-1534; Toll Free: 800-822-1080; Edit Addr.: 299 Market St., Saddle Brook, NJ 07663 USA
E-mail: sales@peoplespublishing.com; customersupport@peoplespublishing.com; editorial@peoplespublishing.com; solvier@peoplespublishing.com
Web site: http://www.peoplespublishing.com/.

Peregrine Outfitters, Orders Addr.: P.O. Box 1500, Williston, VT 05495 USA (SAN 631-1059) Tel 802-860-2977; Fax: 802-860-2978; Toll Free: 800-222-3088; Edit Addr.: 25 Omega Dr., Suite A, Williston, VT 05482 USA.

Perelandra, Ltd., *(0-927978; 0-9617713)* Orders Addr.: P.O. Box 3603, Warrenton, VA 20188 USA (SAN 665-0198) Tel 540-937-2153; Fax: 540-937-3360; Toll Free: 800-960-8806
E-mail: email@perelandra-ltd.com
Web site: http://www.perelandra-ltd.com.

Perfume River Pubns., 1420 2nd Ave., N., Suite 304, Sauk Rapids, MN 56379 USA Tel 320-761-1229.

Periodical Distributors, Incorporated, *See* **North Texas Periodicals, Inc.**

Periodical Marketing Services, 1065 Bloomfield Ave., Clifton, NJ 07012 USA (SAN 250-5304) Tel 201-342-6334.

Periodical Pubs. Service Bureau, One N. Superior St., Sandusky, OH 44870 USA (SAN 285-9351) Tel 419-626-0623.

Periodicals Service Co., *(0-527; 0-8115; 3-262; 3-601)* 11 Main St., Germantown, NY 12526 USA (SAN 164-8608) Tel 518-537-4700; Fax: 518-537-5899
E-mail: psc@periodicals.com
Web site: http://www.periodicals.com.

Perma-Bound Bks., *(0-605; 0-7804; 0-8000; 0-8479)* Div. of Hertzberg-New Method, Inc., 617 E. Vandalia Rd., Jacksonville, IL 62650 USA (SAN 169-202X) Tel 217-243-5451; Fax: 217-243-7505; Toll Free Fax: 800-551-1169; Toll Free: 800-637-6581 (customer service)
E-mail: books@permabound.com
Web site: http://www.perma-bound.com.

Perrone, Calle 11. #372-A Urb. Hill Brothers, San Juan, PR 00924 USA Tel 787-764-6112; Fax: 787-754-2374 Do not confuse with Perrone in Franklin, TN
E-mail: ecruz@perroneimporters.com
Web site: http://www.perroneimporters.com.

Perry Enterprises, *(0-941518)* 3907 N. Foothill Dr., Provo, UT 84604 USA (SAN 171 0281) Tel 801-226-1002.

Perseus Bks. Group, *(0-7382; 0-938289; 1-58097; 1-882810)* Orders Addr.: 2465 Central Ave., Suite 200, Boulder, CO 80301-5728 USA Toll Free: 800-343-4499 (customer service); Edit Addr.: 387 Park Ave., S., 12th Flr., New York, NY 10016-8810 USA Tel 212-340-8100; Fax: 212-340-8105
E-mail: perseus.orders@perseusbooks.com
Web site: http://www.perseusbooksgroup.com.

Perseus Distribution, Orders Addr.: 1700 4th St., Berkeley, CA 94710 USA (SAN 760-5129) Fax: 510-528-3614; Toll Free: 800-788-3123; Edit Addr.: 387 Park Avenue South, New York, NY 10016 USA (SAN 631-760X) Tel 212-340-8100; Fax: 212-340-8195
E-mail: skail@cds.aeneas.com; tflowers@cdsbooks.com
Web site: http://www.cdsbooks.com/.

Peterson's, *(0-02; 0-7689; 0-87866; 1-56079)* Div. of Nelnet, Orders Addr.: P.O. Box 67005, Lawrenceville, NJ 08648-6105 USA (SAN 200-2167); Edit Addr.: 2000 Lenox Dr., 3rd Flr., Lawrenceville, NJ 08648 USA (SAN 297-5661) Tel 609-896-1800; Fax: 609-896-1811; Toll Free: 800-338-3282 X5660;Customer Service
E-mail: custsvc@petersons.com
Web site: http://www.petersons.com.

Petterson Antiques, 379 Clayton Dr., Charleston, SC 29414-5048 USA (SAN 114-2399).

Philosophy Documentation Ctr., *(0-912632; 1-889680)* Orders Addr.: P.O. Box 7147, Charlottesville, VA 22906-7147 USA (SAN 218-6586) Tel 434-220-3300; Fax: 434-220-3301; Toll Free: 800-444-2419
E-mail: order@pdcnet.org
Web site: http://www.pdcnet.org.

Phoenix Distributors, Orders Addr.: P.O. Box 1589, Blaine, WA 98231 USA Toll Free Fax: 800-298-4422.

Phoenix Learning Resources, LLC, *(0-7915)* Orders Addr.: 910 Church St., Honesdale, PA 18431 USA (SAN 246-148X) Tel 570-251-6871; Fax: 570-253-3227; Toll Free: 800-228-9345
Web site: http://www.phoenixlr.com.

Pictorial Histories Distribution, *See* **West Virginia Book Co., The**

Pilgrim Pr., The/United Church Pr., *(0-8298)* Div. of United Church Board for Homeland Ministries, Orders Addr.: 230 Sheldon Rd., Berea, OH 44017 USA Fax: 216-732-3713; Toll Free: 800-537-3394; Edit Addr.: 700 Prospect Ave. E., Cleveland, OH 44115-1100 USA Tel 216-736-3764; Fax: 216-736-2207
E-mail: ucpress@ucc.org; pilgrim@ucc.org
Web site: http://www.ucpress.com; http://www.pilgrimpress.com.

Pine Orchard, Inc., *(0-9645727; 1-930580)* Orders Addr.: 2850 Hwy 95 South. P.O. box 9184, Moscow, ID 83843 USA (SAN 253-4258) Tel 208-882-4838; Fax: 208-882-4845; Toll Free: 877-354-7433
E-mail: orders@pineorchard.com; pineorch@pineorchard.com
Web site: http://www.pineorchard.com.

Pine Orchard Press, *See* **Pine Orchard, Inc.**

Pittsfield News Co., Inc., 6 Westview Rd., Pittsfield, MA 01201 USA (SAN 124-2768) Tel 413-445-5682; Fax: 413-445-5683.

Plains Distribution Service, P.O. Box 931, Moorhead, MN 56561 USA (SAN 169-6556).

Planeta Publishing Corp., *(0-9715256; 0-9719950; 0-9748724; 1-933169; 0-9795042)* 2057 NW 87th Ave., Miami, FL 33172 USA Tel 305-470-0016; Fax: 305-470-6267
E-mail: mnorman@planetapublishing.com
Web site: http://www.planeta.es.

Players Pr., Inc., *(0-88734)* P.O. Box 1132, Studio City, CA 91614-0132 USA (SAN 239-0213) Tel 818-789-4980
E-mail: Playerspress@att.net.

Plough Publishing Hse., The, *(0-87486)* Rte. 381 N., Farmington, PA 15437 USA (SAN 202-0092) Tel 724-329-1100; Fax: 724-329-0914; Toll Free: 800-521-8011
E-mail: plough@plough.com
Web site: http://www.plough.com.

PMG Bks. Ltd., P.O. Box 7608, San Antonio, TX 78207-0608 USA (SAN 631-3183).

Polk County Historical Assn., c/o UrbanDog Communications, Inc., P.O. Box 25474, Tampa, FL 33622 USA Tel 813-832-4538; Fax: 813-832-1759
E-mail: cbrownfl@earthlink.net.

Polybook Distributors, Orders Addr.: P.O. Box 109, Mount Vernon, NY 10550 USA Tel 914-664-1633; Fax: 904-428-3953; Edit Addr.: 22 S. Sixth Ave., Mount Vernon, NY 10550 USA (SAN 169-5568).

Pomona Valley News Agency, 10736 Fremont Ave., Ontario, CA 91762 USA (SAN 169-0019) Tel 909-591-3885.

Pop-M Company, *See* **Book Margins, Inc.**

Popular Subscription Service, P.O. Box 1566, Terre Haute, IN 47808 USA (SAN 285-9386) Tel 812-466-1258; Fax: 812-466-9443; Toll Free: 800-466-5038
E-mail: info@popularsubscriptionsvc.com
Web site: http://www.popularsubscriptionsvc.com.

Portland News Co., Orders Addr.: P.O. Box 6970, Scarborough, ME 04070-6970 USA (SAN 169-3093) Toll Free: 800-639-1708 (in Maine); Edit Addr.: 18 Hutcherson Dr., Gorham, ME 04038-2643 USA.

Powells.com, Orders Addr.: 40 NW Tenth Ave., Portland, OR 97209 USA Tel 800-291-2676
Web site: http://www.powells.com/.

powerHouse Cultural Entertainment, Inc., *(1-57687)* 37 Main St., Brooklyn, NY 11201 USA (SAN 850-5845); Mercedes Distribution Ctr. Bldg. 3 Brooklyn Navy Yard, Brooklyn, NY 11205 Tel 212-604-9074; Fax: 212-366-5247
E-mail: info@powerhousebooks.com
Web site: http://www.powerhousebooks.com.

Practice Ring, *(0-929758)* Div. of Beeman Jorgensen, Inc., 7510 Allisonville Rd., Indianapolis, IN 46250 USA (SAN 630-6144) Tel 317-841-7677; Toll Free: 800-553-5319.

Pratz News Agency, Orders Addr.: P.O. Box 892, Deming, NM 88030 USA (SAN 159-9275).

Prebound Periodicals, 2101 N. Topeka Blvd., Topeka, KS 66608 USA (SAN 285-8037) Tel 785-233-4252.

Premier Pubs., Inc., *(0-915665)* P.O. Box 330309, Fort Worth, TX 76163 USA (SAN 292-5966) Tel 817-293-7030; Fax: 817-293-3410.

Presbyterian & Reformed Publishing Company, *See* **P & R Publishing**

Presbyterian Publishing Corp., *(0-664)* 100 Witherspoon St., Louisville, KY 40202-1396 USA Tel 502-569-5052; Fax: 502-569-8308; Toll Free Fax: 800-541-5113; Toll Free: 800-227-2872
E-mail: rpinotti@presbypub.com; customer_service@presbypub.com
Web site: http://www.ppcbooks.com.

Prestel Publishing, *(3-7913)* Orders Addr.: c/o VNU, 575 Prospect St., Lakewood, NJ 08701 USA Tel 732-363-5679; Fax: 732-363-0338; Toll Free Fax: 877-227-6564; Toll Free: 888-463-6110; Edit Addr.: 900 Broadway, Suite 603, New York, NY 10003 USA Tel 212-995-2720; Fax: 212-995-2733
E-mail: sales@prestel-usa.com
Web site: http://www.prestel.com; http://www.die-gestalten.de; http://www.scalo.com.

Princeler Publishing, Don C., P.O. Box 87, Connquenessing, PA 16027 USA Tel 724-789-7155.

Princeton Architectural Pr., *(0-907259; 0-910413; 0-9636372; 1-56898; 1-878271; 1-885232; 90-77620)* 37 E. Seventh St., New York, NY 10003 USA (SAN 260-1176) Tel 212-995-9720; Fax: 212-995-9454; Toll Free: 800-722-6657
E-mail: sales@papress.com
Web site: http://www.papress.com.

Princeton Bk. Co. Pubs., *(0-87127; 0-916622)* Orders Addr.: P.O. Box 831, Hightstown, NJ 08520-0831 USA (SAN 630-1568) Tel 609-426-0602; Fax: 609-426-1344; Toll Free: 800-220-7149; 614 Rte. 130, Hightstown, NJ 08520 (SAN 244-8076)
E-mail: pbc@dancehorizons.com; elysian@aosi.com
Web site: http://www.dancehorizons.com.

Princeton Univ. Pr., *(0-691)* Orders Addr.: California-Princeton Fulfillment Services, 1445 Lower Ferry Rd., Ewing, NJ 08618 USA Tel 800-777-4726; Fax: 800-999-1958; Edit Addr.: 41 William St., Princeton, NJ 08540 USA (SAN 202-0254) Tel 609-258-4900; Fax: 609-258-6305; 3 Market Place, Woodstock, OX20 1SY Tel (0) 1993 814501; Fax: (0) 1993 814504
E-mail: webmaster@pupress.princeton.edu
Web site: http://www.pup.princeton.edu.

Print and Ship, 1412 Greenbrier Pkwy., Suite 145-B, Norfolk, VA 23320 USA Tel 757-424-5868.

Printed Matter, Inc., *(0-89439)* 195 10th Ave. FRNT, New York, NY 10011-4739 USA (SAN 169-5924)
E-mail: ckrudy@printedmatter.org; staff@printedmatter.org
Web site: http://www.printedmatter.org.

Production Assocs., Inc., *(1-887120)* 1206 W. Collins Ave., Orange, CA 92867 USA Tel 714-771-6519; Fax: 714-771-2456; Toll Free: 800-535-8368
E-mail: mikec@production-associates.com
Web site: http://www.production-associates.com.

Productivity, Incorporated, *See* **Productivity Pr.**

Productivity Pr., *(0-527; 0-915299; 1-56327)* Orders Addr.: 2427 Bond St., University Park, IL 60466-3101 USA (SAN 290-036X) Tel 708-587-4152; Fax: 708-534-7803; Toll Free Fax: 800-394-6286; Toll Free: 888-319-5852 (orders); Edit Addr.: 444 Park Ave. South, 7th. Flr., New York, NY 10016 USA Tel 212-686-5900; Fax: 212-686-5411
E-mail: service@productivityinc.com
Web site: http://www.productivityinc.com.

PRO-ED, Inc., *(0-88744; 0-89079; 0-933014; 0-936104; 0-944480; 1-4164)* 8700 Shoal Creek Blvd., Austin, TX 78757-6897 USA (SAN 222-1349) Tel 512-451-3246 Toll Free Fax: 800-737-1376; Toll Free: 800-897-3202; 800-828-1376
E-mail: carredondo@proedinc.com
Web site: http://www.proedinc.com.

Professional Book Distributors, Incorporated, *See* **PBD, Inc.**

Professional Media Service Corp., 1160 Trademark Dr., Suite 109, Reno, NV 89511 USA (SAN 630-5776) Toll Free Fax: 800-253-8853; Toll Free: 800-223-7672.

Programming Concepts, Incorporated, *See* **PCI Educational Publishing**

Project Patch, 2404 E. Mill Plain Blvd., Vancouver, WA 98661-4334 USA.

Proteus Enterprises, Inc., 226 N. West Ave., Elmhurst, IL 60126 USA Tel 630-530-0300; Fax: 630-530-1123
E-mail: proteus@kwom.com
Web site: http://www.proteusenterprises.com.

Provident Music Distribution, 1 Maryland Farms, Brentwood, TN 37027 USA Tel 615-373-3950; Fax: 615-373-0386; Toll Free: 800-333-9000
E-mail: gmiller@pmgsonybmg
Web site: http://www.providentmusic.com.

PSI (Publisher Services, Inc.), 1554 Litton Dr., Stone Mountain, GA 30083 USA Tel 678-382-3887; Toll Free: 800-755-9653.

Public Lands Interpretive Assn., *(1-879343)* 6501 Fourth St., NW, No. 1, Albuquerque, NM 87107-5800 USA (SAN 133-3119) Tel 505-345-9498; Fax: 505-344-1543.

Publication Consultants, *(0-9644809; 1-888125; 1-59433)* 8370 Eleusis Dr., Anchorage, AK 99502 USA Tel 907-349-2424; Fax: 907-349-2426
E-mail: evan@publicationconsultants.com
Web site: http://www.publicationconsultants.com.

Publication Services, Incorporated, *See* **P S I Fulfillment**

Publications Unlimited, 7512 Coconut Dr., Lake Worth, FL 33467-6511 USA (SAN 285-9432) Tel 407-434-4688 Do not confuse with Publications Unlimited in Raleigh, NC.

Publishers Business Service, Inc., P.O. Box 25674, Chicago, IL 60625 USA (SAN 285-9459) Tel 312-561-5552.

Publishers Clearing Hse., 382 Channel Dr., Port Washington, NY 11050 USA (SAN 285-9440) Tel 516-883-5432.

Publishers Continental Sales Corp., 613 Franklin Sq., Michigan City, IN 46360 USA (SAN 285-9475) Tel 219-874-4245; Fax: 219-872-8961.

Publishers Distributing Co., Div. of Liberation Pubns., Inc., P.O. Box 4371, Los Angeles, CA 90078 USA (SAN 630-4249) Tel 323-860-6070; Fax: 323-467-0152; Toll Free: 800-464-4574.

Publishers Group International, Inc., *(0-9633653)* 1506 27th St. NW, No. 1, Washington, DC 20007 USA Tel 202-342-0886; Fax: 202-338-1940
E-mail: issbooks@aol.com.

Publishers Media, *(0-934064)* 1447 Valley View Rd., Glendale, CA 91202-1716 USA (SAN 159-6683) Tel 818-548-1998.

Publishers News Company, *See* **Mr. Paperback/Publishers News Co.**

Publishers Services, Orders Addr.: P.O. Box 2510, Novato, CA 94948 USA (SAN 201-3037) Tel 415-883-3530; Fax: 415-883-4280.

Publishers Wholesale Assocs., Inc., Orders Addr.: P.O. Box 2078, Lancaster, PA 17608-2078 USA (SAN 630-7450) Fax: 717-397-9253; Edit Addr.: 231 N. Shippen St., Lancaster, PA 17608 USA.

Pulley Learning Assocs., 210 Alpine Meadow Rd., Winchester, VA 22602-6701 USA (SAN 133-1434).

Purple Unicorn Bks., *(0-931998)* 1928 W. Kent Rd., Duluth, MN 55812-1154 USA (SAN 111-0071) Tel 218-525-4781 Do not confuse with Purple Unicorn in Augusta, ME.

Pursifull, Carmen M., *(0-9607856)* 809 W. Maple, Champaign, IL 61820 USA (SAN 237-9880) Tel 217-359-5056.

Puzzle Piece Pubns., 846 36th Ave., N., Saint Cloud, MN 56303 USA Tel 320-656-5361.

Quality Bks., Inc., *(0-89196)* 1003 W. Pines Rd., Oregon, IL 61061-9680 USA (SAN 169-2127) Tel 815-732-4450; Fax: 815-732-4499; Toll Free: 800-323-4241 (libraries only)
E-mail: quality.books@dawson.com.

Quality Book Fairs, 5787 Ryan Rd., Medina, OH 44256-8823 USA (SAN 630-7752).

Quality Schl. Plan, Inc., P.O. Box 10203, Des Moines, IA 50381-0001 USA (SAN 285-953X).

Quayside, *(0-86573; 1-58923)* Orders Addr.: 18705 Lake Dr., E., Chanhassen, MN 55317 USA Tel 952-936-4700; Fax: 952-988-0201; Toll Free: 800-328-0590; Edit Addr.: 100 Cummings Ctr. Ste. 406L, Beverly, MA 01915-6101 USA
E-mail: sales@creativepub.com
Web site: http://www.rockpub.com; http://www.quaysidepublishers.com; http://www.quiverbooks.com; http://www.walterfoster.com.

QW, Inc., *(1-928547)* P.O. Box 463180, Mount Clemens, MI 48046-3180 USA Tel 810-954-2986; Fax: 810-954-1085; Toll Free: 800-838-8854
E-mail: janinerange@ameritech.net
Web site: http://qwincorporated.com.

R & W Distribution, Inc., 87 Bright St., Jersey City, NJ 07302 USA (SAN 169-4723) Tel 201-333-1540; Fax: 201-333-1541
E-mail: rwmag@mail.idt.net.

R T R Publishing Company, *See* **Red Toad Road Co.**

Radiant Life Lighthouse Publishing, 10 Lemon Wood Pl., Pittsburg, CA 94565 USA.

Radio Bookstore, P.O. Box 209, Rindge, NH 03461-0209 USA (SAN 111-3496) Tel 603-899-6957 Do not confuse with Radio Bookstore Pr., Bellevue, WA.

Raimond Graphics Inc., Orders Addr.: 580 Sylvan Ave., Englewood Cliffs, NJ 07632 USA Tel 201-568-3565; Fax: 201-568-4754.

Rainbow Re-Source Ctr., P.O. Box 491, Kewanee, IL 61443 USA (SAN 631-4007) Tel 309-937-3385; Fax: 309-937-3382
E-mail: rainbowres@aol.com.

Rainier News, Inc., 3400-D Industry Dr., E., Fife, WA 98424-1853 USA (SAN 169-8745) Toll Free: 800-843-2995 (in Washington).

RAM Pubns. & Distribution, *(0-9630785; 0-9703860)* Bergamot Sta., 2525 Michigan Ave., No. A2, Santa Monica, CA 90404 USA (SAN 298-2641) Tel 310-453-0043; Fax: 310-264-4888
E-mail: rampub@gte.net.

Rand McNally, *(0-528)* Orders Addr.: P.O. Box 1906, Skokie, IL 60076 USA Fax: 847-329-6139; Toll Free Fax: 800-934-3479 (Orders); Toll Free: 800-333-0136 (ext. 4771); 800-678-7263 (Orders)
E-mail: Education@randmcnally.com
Web site: http://www.randmcnally.com.

Random Hse., Inc., *(0-307; 0-345; 0-375; 0-385; 0-394; 0-440; 0-449; 0-517; 0-553; 0-593; 0-609; 0-676; 0-679; 0-7364; 0-7366; 0-7615; 0-7679; 0-7704; 0-8041; 0-8052; 0-8129; 0-87637; 0-87665; 0-87788; 0-88070; 0-913369; 0-914629; 0-930014; 0-945564; 1-57082; 1-57673; 1-57856; 1-878867; 1-884536; 1-885305; 1-58836; 1-4000; 1-59052; 1-4159)* Div. of Bertelsmann AG, Orders Addr.: 400 Hahn Rd., Westminster, MD 21157 USA (SAN 202-5515) Tel 410 848 1900; Toll Free Fax: 800 659 2436; Toll Free: 800 726 0600 (customer service/orders); Edit Addr.: 1745 Broadway, New York, NY 10019 USA (SAN 202-5507) Tel 212 782 9000; Fax: 212 302 7985
E-mail: customerservice@randomhouse.com
Web site: http://www.randomhouse.com.

Raven West Coast Distribution, 767 W. 18th St., Costa Mesa, CA 92627 USA
E-mail: ken@ravenwcd.com.

Read News Agency, 2501 Greensboro Ave., Tuscaloosa, AL 35401-6520 USA Tel 205-752-3515.

Reader's Digest Children's Publishing, Inc., *(0-276; 0-7621; 0-88705; 0-88850; 0-89577; 1-57584; 1-57619; 0-7944)* Subs. of Reader's Digest Assn., Inc., Reader's Digest Rd., Pleasantville, NY 10570-7000 USA (SAN 283-2143) Tel 914-244-4800; Fax: 914-244-4841
Web site: http://www.readersdigestkids.com.

Readex Bk. Exchange, Box 1125, Carefree, AZ 85377 USA (SAN 159-9291).

Reading Circle, The, 7858 Industrial Pkwy., Plain City, OH 43064-9468 USA (SAN 169-670X).

Reading Matters, Inc., *(1-930654)* 806 Main St., Akron, PA 17501 USA Tel 717-859-5608; Fax: 717-859-3469; Toll Free: 888-255-6665 Do not confuse with companies with the same name in Brookline, MA, Denver, CO
E-mail: office@readingmatters.net
Web site: http://readingmatters.net.

Reading Peddler Bk. Fairs, 10580 3/4 W. Pico Blvd., Los Angeles, CA 90064 USA (SAN 157-9770) Tel 310-559-2665.

Reading's Fun/Books are Fun, Limited, *See* **Books Are Fun, Ltd.**

Readmor, Orders Addr.: P.O. Box 7264, Grand Rapids, MI 49508 USA (SAN 169-3875); Edit Addr.: 301 S. Rath Ave., Ludington, MI 49431 USA Tel 231-843-2537.

Readmore Academic Services, Orders Addr.: P.O. Box 1459, Blackwood, NJ 08012 USA (SAN 630-5741) Tel 609-227-1100; Fax: 609-227-8322; Toll Free: 800-645-6595; Edit Addr.: 700 Black Horse Pike, Suite 207, Blackwood, NJ 08012 USA.

Readmore, Inc., 22 Cortlandt St., New York, NY 10007 USA (SAN 159-9313) Tel 212-349-5540; Fax: 212-233-0746; Toll Free: 800-221-3306.

Recorded Bks., LLC, *(0-7887; 1-55690; 1-84197; 1-4025; 1-4193; 1-84505; 1-4281; 1-4361)* 270 Skipjack Rd., Prince Frederick, MD 20678 USA (SAN 111-3984) Toll Free: 800-638-1304
E-mail: recordedbooks@recordedbooks.com; mgarber@recordedbook.com
Web site: http://www.recordedbooks.com.

Recreational Equipment, Inc., *(0-9600620)* P.O. Box C-88126, Seattle, WA 98188 USA (SAN 205-2024) Tel 206-223-4840
Web site: http://www.rei.com.

Red Sea Pr., *(0-932415; 1-56902)* Affil. of Africa World Pr., 541 W. Ingham Ave., Suite B, Trenton, NJ 08638 USA (SAN 630-1983) Tel 609-695-3200; Fax: 609-695-6466
E-mail: awprsp@verizon.net
Web site: http://www.africanworld.com/.

Red Toad Road Co., *(1-889287)* Orders Addr.: P.O. Box 642, Havre de Grace, MD 21078 USA Tel 410-939-4092; Fax: 410-939-5614; Edit Addr.: 223 Heather Way, Havre de Grace, MD 21078 USA
E-mail: redtoadroad@aol.com
Web site: http://www.amazon.com/shops/redtoadroad.

Red Wheel/Weiser, *(0-87728; 0-943233; 1-57324; 1-57863; 1-59003)* Div. of Weiser Bks., Orders Addr.: P.O. Box 612, York Beach, ME 03910-0612 USA (SAN 255-8610) Tel 207-363-4393; Fax: 207-363-5799; Toll Free Fax: 877-337-3309; Toll Free: 800-423-7087 (orders only)
E-mail: customerservice@redwheelweiser.com
Web site: http://www.redwheelweiser.com.

Redwing Bk. Co., Orders Addr.: 202 Bendix Dr., Taos, NM 87571 USA Tel 505-758-7758; Fax: 505-758-7768; Toll Free: 800-873-3946 (USA); 888-873-3947 (Canada); Edit Addr.: P.O. Box 470688, Brookline Vlg, MA 02447-0688 USA (SAN 163-3597) Toll Free: 800-873-3946
E-mail: bob@redwingbooks.com
Web site: http://www.redwingbooks.com.

Reference Bk. Ctr., 175 Fifth Ave., New York, NY 10010 USA (SAN 159-9356) Tel 212-677-2160; Fax: 212-533-0826.

Regent Bk. Co., Inc., Orders Addr.: P.O. Box 750, Lodi, NJ 07644-0750 USA Tel 973-574-7600; Fax: 973-574-7605; Toll Free: 800-999-9554; Edit Addr.: 25 Saddle River Ave., South Hackensack, NJ 07606 USA (SAN 169-4715)
E-mail: info@regentbook.com
Web site: http://www.regentbook.com.

Remnant Pubns., *(1-883012; 1-933291)* 649 E. Chicago Rd., Coldwater, MI 49036-9497 USA Tel 517-279-1304; Fax: 517-279-1804
E-mail: remnant@charter.net
Web site: http://www.remnantpublications.com.

Renaissance News, 5232 Clairton Blvd., Pittsburgh, PA 15236 USA Tel 412-881-4848; Fax: 412-881-5422.

Replica Bks., *(0-7351)* Div. of Baker & Taylor, Orders Addr.: 1120 Us Hwy., 22 E., Bridgewater, NJ 08807 USA Tel 908-541 7392; Fax: 908-541-7875; Toll Free: 800-775-1800; Edit Addr.: P.O. Box 6885, Bridgewater, NJ 08807-0885 USA
E-mail: btinfo@baker-taylor.com.

Representaciones Borinquenas, Inc., *(0-9727750; 0-9755107)* P.O. Box 139, Aguas Buenas, PR 00703-0139 USA Tel 787-309-9047; Fax: 787-780-5835
E-mail: rborinquenas@centennialpr.net.

Research Bks., Inc., P.O. Box 555, Old Saybrook, CT 06475-0555 USA
E-mail: info@researchbooks.com.

Resource Software International, Inc., *(0-87539)* Affil. of Datamatics Management, 330 New Brunswick Ave., Fords, NJ 08863 USA (SAN 264-8628) Tel 732-738-8500; Fax: 732-738-9603; Toll Free: 800-673-0366
E-mail: info@datamaticsinc.com
Web site: http://www.tc-1.com.

Resurgam Publishing Company, *See* **Blessing Way Publishing Co.**

Reveal Entertainment, Inc., *(0-9712633)* 1250 Petroleum Dr. Ste. B6, Abilene, TX 79602-7957 USA
E-mail: revealgames@aol.com
Web site: http://www.revealgames.com.

Review & Herald Publishing Assn., *(0-8127; 0-8280)* 55 W. Oak Ridge Dr., Hagerstown, MD 21740 USA (SAN 203-3798) Tel 301-393-3000
E-mail: smulkern@rhpa.org
Web site: http://www.reviewandherald.com/.

Revolution Booksellers, 60 Winter St., Exeter, NH 03833 USA Tel 603-772-7200; Fax: 603-772-7200; Toll Free: 800-738-6603.

Rhinelander News Agency, 314 Courtney, Crescent Lake, WI 54501 USA (SAN 159-9372) Tel 715-362-6397.

Rhino Entertainment Co, A Warner Music Group Co., *(0-7379; 0-930589; 1-56826; 0-9797278)* 3400 W. Olive Ave., Burbank, CA 91505 USA (SAN 677-5454) Tel 818-238-6110; Fax: 818-562-9239
E-mail: gladys.sanchez@wmg.com; tracie.bowers@wmg.com
Web site: http://www.rhino.com.

Rhodes News Agency, *See* **Treasure Valley News**

Richardson's Bks., Inc., 2014 Lou Ellen Ln., Houston, TX 77018 USA (SAN 169-829X) Tel 713-688-2244; Fax: 713-688-8420; Toll Free: 800-392-8562.

Richardson's Educators, *See* **Richardson's Bks., Inc.**

Rigby Interactive Library, *See* **Heinemann Library**

Right Start, Inc., 5388 Sterling Center Dr., Suite C, Westlake Village, CA 91361-4687 USA (SAN 631-7022).

Rio Grande Bk. Co., P.O. Box 2795, McAllen, TX 78502-2795 USA (SAN 169-8354).

Rip Off Pr., Inc., *(0-89620)* P.O. Box 4686, Auburn, CA 95604 USA (SAN 207-7671) Tel 530-885-8183; Fax: 530-885-8219; Toll Free: 800-468-2669
E-mail: ripoff@jps.net
Web site: http://www.ripoffpress.com.

Rishor News Co., Inc., 109 Mountain Laurel Dr., Butler, PA 16001-3921 USA (SAN 159-9402).

Rittenhouse Bk. Distributors, *(0-87381)* Orders Addr.: P.O. Box 61565, Kng Of Prussa, PA 19406-0965 USA (SAN 213-4454) Toll Free Fax: 800-223-7488; Toll Free: 800-345-6425
E-mail: alan.yockey@rittenhouse.com; joan.townshend@rittenhouse.com
Web site: http://www.rittenhouse.com.

Ritter Bk. Co., 7011 Foster Pl., Downers Grove, IL 60516-3446 USA (SAN 169-1856).

River Road Recipes Cookbook, 9523 Fenway Dr., Baton Rouge, LA 70809 USA (SAN 132-7852) Tel 504-924-0300; Fax: 504-927-2547; Toll Free: 800-204-1726.

Riverside Distributors, Orders Addr.: 10899 Textile Rd., Belleville, MI 48111-2315 USA Toll Free: 800-247-5111 Web site: http://www.FirstNetChristian.com.

Rizzoli International Pubns., Inc., *(0-8478)* Subs. of RCS Rizzoli Editore Corp., 300 Park Ave., S., 3rd Flr., New York, NY 10010 USA (SAN 111-9192) Tel 212-387-3400; Fax: 212-387-3535 Web site: http://www.rizzoliusa.com/.

Roadrunner Library Service, c/o Kerbs, 700 Highview Ave., Glen Ellyn, IL 60137-5504 USA.

Roberts, F.M. Enterprises, *(0-912746)* P.O. Box 608, Dana Point, CA 92629-0608 USA (SAN 201-4688) Tel 714-493-1977; Fax: 714-493-7124.

Rockbottom Bks., Pentagon Towers, P.O. Box 398166, Minneapolis, MN 55439 USA (SAN 108-4402) Tel 612-831-2120.

Rockland Catskill, Inc., 26 Church St., Spring Valley, NY 10977 USA (SAN 169-6254) Tel 914-356-1222; Fax: 914-356-8415; Toll Free: 800-966-6247.

RockWealth Ministries, *(0-9749650)* P.O. Box 6177, Aiken, SC 29804 USA Tel 803-644-3271; Fax: 803-643-9001 E-mail: toddcoontz@aol.com Web site: http://www.rockwealth.org.

Rocky Mount News Agency, Two Great State Ln., Rocky Mount, NC 27801 USA.

Rogue Valley News Agency, Inc., 550 Airport Rd., Medford, OR 97504-4156 USA (SAN 169-7137).

Rohr, Hans E., 76 State St., Newburyport, MA 01950-6616 USA (SAN 113-8804).

Roig Spanish Bks., 146 W. 29th St., No. 3W, New York, NY 10001-5303 USA (SAN 165-1021) Fax: 212-695-6811.

Rosenblum's, *See* **Rosenblum's World of Judaica, Inc.**

Rosenblum's World of Judaica, Inc., 2906 W. Devon Ave., Chicago, IL 60659 USA (SAN 169-1864) Tel 773-262-1700; Fax: 773-262-1930; Toll Free: 800-626-6536.

Rosewood Foundation, The, Orders Addr.: P.O. Box 252, Archer, FL 32618 USA Tel 352-495-2197; Fax: 352-495-8313 E-mail: lizziePRJ@aol.com.

Rounder Kids Music Distribution, Orders Addr.: P.O. Box 516, Montpelier, VT 05602 USA (SAN 630-6675) Tel 802-223-5825; Fax: 802-223-5303; Toll Free: 800-223-6357; Edit Addr.: 80 W. Harvey Farm Rd., Waterbury Ctr, VT 05677-7132 USA E-mail: Pauls@rounder.com.

Routledge, *(0-04; 0-413; 0-415; 0-7100; 0-86861; 0-87830)* Mem. of Taylor & Frances Group, Orders Addr.: 7625 Empire Dr., Florence, KY 41042 USA Toll Free Fax: 800-248-4724 (orders, customer serv.); Toll Free: 800-634-7064 (orders, customer serv.); Edit Addr.: 270 Madison Ave. # 3, New York, NY 10016-0601 USA (SAN 213-196X) E-mail: cserve@routledge-ny.com; info@routledge-ny.com Web site: http://www.routledge-ny.com.

Rowman & Littlefield Pubs., Inc., *(0-8476; 0-87471; 0-7425)* Mem. of Rowman & Littlefield Publishing Group, Inc., Orders Addr.: 15200 NBN Way, Blue Ridge Summit, PA 17214 USA Tel 717-794-3800 (Sales, Customer Service, MIS, Royalties, Inventory; Fax: 717-794-3803 (Customer Service & orders only); 717-794-3857 (Sales & MIS); 717-794-3856 (Royalties, Inventory Mgmt. & Distribution); Toll Free Fax: 800-338-4550 (Customer Service & orders); Toll Free: 800-462-6420 (Customer Service & orders); Edit Addr.: 4501 Forbes Blvd., Suite 200, Lanham, MD 20706 USA Tel 301-459-3366; Fax: 301-459-5748 Short Discount, please contact rlpgsales@rowman.com E-mail: Rogers@univpress.com; rlpgsales@rowman.com Web site: http://www.rowmanlittlefield.com; http:// www.rlpgbooks.com/bookseller/index.shtml.

Royal Fireworks Publishing Co., *(0-88092; 0-89824)* Orders Addr.: P.O. Box 399, Unionville, NY 10988 USA (SAN 240-2394) Tel 845-726-4444; Fax: 845-726-3824; Edit Addr.: 1 First Ave., Unionville, NY 10988 USA E-mail: rfpress@frontiernet.net Web site: http://www.rfwp.com/.

Royal Pubns., Inc., *(0-918738)* Orders Addr.: P.O. Box 5793, Denver, CO 80217 USA (SAN 244-7193) Tel 303-778-8383; Toll Free: 800-279-2048 (orders only); Edit Addr.: 790 W. Tennessee Ave., Denver, CO 80223 USA (SAN 169-054X).

Rumi Bookstore, 4050B Peralta Blvd., Fremont, CA 94536 USA Tel 510-744-3692 E-mail: fakhrrazi@aol.com.

Rushmore News, Inc., 924 East St. Andrew, Rapid City, SD 57701 USA (SAN 169-7846) Tel 605-342-2617; Fax: 605-342-9091; Toll Free: 800-423-0501 E-mail: afreese911@aol.com.

Russell Dean & Co., *(1-891954)* Orders Addr.: P.O. Box 318, Santa Margarita, CA 93453 USA Tel 805-438-4115; Fax: 805-438-3745; Toll Free: 888-438-4115; Edit Addr.: 22595 K St., Santa Margarita, CA 93453 USA E-mail: russelldean@sgmp.com Web site: http://www.sgmp.com/ntr/russelldean.

Russell News Agency, Inc., P.O. Box 158, Sarasota, FL 33578 USA (SAN 169-1287).

Russica Bk. & Art Shop, Inc., 799 Broadway, New York, NY 10003 USA (SAN 165-1072) Tel 212-473-7480; Fax: 212-473-7486.

S & S News & Greeting, 5304 15th Ave., S., Minneapolis, MN 55417-1812 USA (SAN 159-9453) Tel 612-224-8227; Toll Free: 800-346-9892.

S & W Distributors, Inc., 1600-H E. Wendover Ave., Greensboro, NC 27405 USA.

S. A. V. E. with Victor Hotho, *See* **S.A.V.E. Suzie & Vic Enterprises**

S V E & Churchill Media, *(0-7932; 0-89290; 1-56357)* 6465 N. Avondale Ave., Chicago, IL 60631-1909 USA (SAN 208-3930) Toll Free Fax: 800-624-1678; Toll Free: 800-829-1900 E-mail: custserv@svemedia.com Web site: http://www.svemedia.com.

SAAN Corp., 189-01 Springfield Ave., Suite 201, Flossmoor, IL 60422 USA (SAN 631-0419) Tel 708-799-5225; Fax: 708-799-8713.

Saddleback Educational Publishing, *(1-56254; 1-59905; 1-60291)* Three Watson, Irvine, CA 92618-2716 USA Tel 949-860-2500; Fax: 949-860-2508; Toll Free: 888-735-2225 E-mail: cpizer@sdlback.com; jgrexton@sdlback.com Web site: http://www.sdlback.com.

Saddleback Publishing, Incorporated, *See* **Saddleback Educational Publishing**

Sadler, Dale, 209 Foster Dr., White House, TN 37188 USA.

Safari Museum Pr., 111 N. Lincoln Ave., Chanute, KS 66720 USA Tel 630-431-2730; Fax: 630-431-3848.

SAGE Pubns., Inc., *(0-7619; 0-8039; 1-4129)* 2455 Teller Rd., Thousand Oaks, CA 91320-2218 USA (SAN 204-7217) Tel 805-499-9774; 800-818-7243; Fax: 800-583-2665; 805-499-0871 E-mail: info@sagepub.com Web site: http://www.sagepub.com; http://www.sagepub.co.uk; http://www.pineforge.com.

Sagebrush Corporation, *See* **Tandem Library Grp.**

Sagebrush Education Resources, *See* **Tandem Library Bks.**

Sagebrush Pr., *(0-930704)* P.O. Box 87, Morongo Valley, CA 92256 USA (SAN 113-387X) Tel 760-363-7398 Do not confuse with companies with same name in Cedarville, CA, Salt Lake City, UT.

Saint George Book Service, Incorporated, *See* **Steiner, Rudolf College Pr./St. George Pubns.**

Saint Joe Distribution Center, *See* **American Bk. Ctr.**

Saint Paul Books & Media, *See* **Pauline Bks. & Media**

Saks News, Inc., P.O. Box 1857, Bismarck, ND 58502 USA (SAN 169-653X).

Sams Technical Publishing, LLC, *(0-7906)* 9850 E. 30th St., Indianapolis, IN 46229 USA Toll Free Fax: 800-552-3910; Toll Free: 800-428-7267 E-mail: samstech@samswebsite.com Web site: http://www.samswebsite.com.

San Diego Museum of Art, *(0-937108)* Orders Addr.: P.O. Box 122107, San Diego, CA 92112-2107 USA Tel 619-696-1970; Fax: 619-232-9367 Web site: http://www.sdmart.org.

San Francisciana, *(0-934715)* P.O. Box 590955, San Francisco, CA 94159 USA (SAN 161-1607) Tel 415-751-7222.

San Val, Inc., 1230 Macklind Ave., Saint Louis, MO 63110-1432 USA (SAN 159-947X) Tel 314-644-6100; Fax: 314-647-0979; Toll Free: 800-458-8438 E-mail: sanval@misn.com Web site: http://www.sanval.com.

Sandlapper Publishing Co., Inc., *(0-87844)* Orders Addr.: P.O. Box 730, Orangeburg, SC 29115 USA (SAN 203-2678) Toll Free Fax: 800-337-9420 (orders); Toll Free: 800-849-7263 (orders); Edit Addr.: 1281 Amelia St., NE., Orangeburg, SC 29116 USA Tel 803-533-1658; Fax: 803-534-5223 Web site: http://www.sandlapperpublishing.com.

Sandvik Publishing, *(1-58048; 1-881445)* Div. of Sandviks Bokforlag, Norway, 3729 Knights Rd., Bensalem, PA 19020-2908 USA Toll Free: 800-843-2445 E-mail: Nicole@sandvikpublishing.com; cust-serv@sandvikpublishing.com Web site: http://www.sandviks.com.

Santa Barbara Botanic Garden, *(0-916436)* 1212 Mission Canyon Rd., Santa Barbara, CA 93105 USA (SAN 208-8398) Tel 805-682-4726; Fax: 805-563-0352 E-mail: info@sbbg.org Web site: http://www.sbbg.org.

Santa Barbara News Agency, 725 S. Kellogg Ave., Goleta, CA 93117-3806 USA (SAN 168-9665) Tel 805-564-5200.

Santa Monica Software, Inc., 30018 Zenith Point Rd., Malibu, CA 90265-4264 USA (SAN 630-6764) Tel 310-457-8381; Fax: 310-395-7635.

Santillana USA Publishing Co., Inc., *(0-88272; 1-56014; 1-58105; 84-294; 1-58986; 1-59437; 1-59820; 1-60396)* Div. of Grup Santillana De Ediciones, S.A., 2105 NW 86th Ave., Doral, FL 33122 USA (SAN 205-1133) Tel 305-591-9522; Fax: 305-591-9145; Toll Free Fax: 888-248-9518 (orders); Toll Free: 800-245-8584 E-mail: dpena@santillanausa.com; esanta@santillanausa.com Web site: http://www.santillanausa.com/.

Saphrograph Corp., *(0-87557)* 5409 18th Ave., Brooklyn, NY 11204 USA (SAN 110-4128) Tel 718-331-1233; Fax: 718-331-8231 E-mail: saphrograph@verizon.net.

Sasquatch Bks., *(0-912365; 1-57061)* 119 S. Main St. Ste. 400, Seattle, WA 98104-2555 USA (SAN 289-0208) Toll Free: 800-775-0817 E-mail: custserv@SasquatchBooks.com Web site: http://www.sasquatchbooks.com.

Sathya Sai Bk. Ctr. of America, *(1-57836)* 305 W. First St., Tustin, CA 92780 USA (SAN 111-3542) Tel 714-669-0522; Fax: 714-669-9138 Web site: http://www.sathyasai.org/inform/tustin.html.

Satsang Press, *See* **Gangaji Foundation, The**

Saturday Shop, *(0-9613242)* P.O. Box 307, Clarksville, GA 30523 USA (SAN 295-5040) Tel 706-754-9200 E-mail: Saturdayshop@yahoo.com.

Savannah Bks., P.O. Box 259, New York, NY 10029 USA Tel 212-831-6483 (phone/fax).

S.A.V.E. Suzie & Vic Enterprises, 303 N. Main, P.O. Box 30, Schulenburg, TX 78956 USA (SAN 630-6365) Tel 409-743-4145; Fax: 409-743-4147.

SCB Distributors, Orders Addr.: 15608 S. New Century Dr., Gardena, CA 90248-2129 USA (SAN 630-4818) Tel 310-532-9400; Fax: 310-532-7001; Toll Free: 800-729-6423 (orders only) E-mail: info@scbdistributors.com Web site: http://www.scbdistributors.com.

Scepter Pubs., Inc., *(0-933932; 1-889334; 1-59417)* Orders Addr.: P.O. Box 211, New York, NY 10018 USA Tel 212-354-0670; Fax: 212-354-0736; 914-632-5502; Toll Free: 800-322-8773; Edit Addr.: Eight W. 38th St., Suite 802, New York, NY 10018 USA E-mail: general@scepterpublishers.org Web site: http://www.scepterpublishers.org.

Schaefer Education Foundation, Orders Addr.: 4400 PGA Blvd., Suite 700, Palm Beach Gardens, FL 33410-6555 USA (SAN 631-7138) Tel 561-622-0912; Fax: 561-622-5090; Edit Addr.: P.O. Box 14448, North Palm Beach, FL 33408-0448 USA.

Schiffer Publishing, Ltd., *(0-7643; 0-88740; 0-916838)* Orders Addr.: 4880 Lower Valley Rd., Atglen, PA 19310 USA (SAN 208-8428) Tel 610-593-1777; Fax: 610-593-2002 E-mail: info@schifferbooks.com Web site: http://www.schifferbooks.com.

Schmul Publishing Co., Inc., *(0-88019)* Orders Addr.: P.O. Box 716, Salem, OH 44460-0716 USA (SAN 180-2771) Tel 330-222-2249; Fax: 330-222-0001; Toll Free: 800-772-6657; Edit Addr.: 3583 Newgarden Rd., Salem, OH 44460 USA E-mail: spchale@valunet.com Web site: http://www.wesleyanbooks.com.

Schoenhof's Foreign Bks., Inc., *(0-87774)* Subs. of Editions Gallimard, 76a Mount Auburn St., Cambridge, MA 02138-5051 USA (SAN 212-0062) E-mail: info@schoenhofs.com Web site: http://www.schoenhofs.com.

Scholar's Bookshelf, *(0-945726; 1-60105)* Orders Addr.: 110 Melrick Rd., Cranbury, NJ 08512 USA (SAN 110-8360) Tel 609-395-6933; Fax: 609-395-0755 E-mail: books@scholarsbookshelf.com Web site: http://www.scholarsbookshelf.com.

Scholastic, Inc., *(0-439; 0-590; 0-545)* Orders Addr.: c/o HarperCollins, 1000 Keystone Industrial Pk., Scranton, PA 18512 USA Toll Free: 800-242-7737; Edit Addr.: 557 Broadway, New York, NY 10012-3999 USA (SAN 202-5442) Tel 212-343-6100; Fax: 212-343-6802; Toll Free: 800-325-6149 (customer service) E-mail: info@scholastic.com Web site: http://www.scholastic.com.

Scholium International, Inc., *(0-333; 0-87936)* P.O. Box 1519, Port Washington, NY 11050-0306 USA (SAN 169-5282) Tel 516-767-7171; Fax: 516-944-9824 E-mail: info@scholium.com Web site: http://www.scholium.com.

School Aid Co., *(0-87385)* 911 Colfax Dr., P.O. Box 123, Danville, IL 61832 USA (SAN 158-3719) Tel 217-442-6855; Toll Free: 800-447-2665.

School Aids, 9335 Interline Ave., Baton Rouge, LA 70809-1910 USA (SAN 169-2909) Tel 504-926-4498.

School Bk. Service, 3650 Coral Ridge Dr., Suite 112, Coral Springs, FL 33065-2559 USA (SAN 158-6963) Tel 954-341-7207; Fax: 954-341-7303; Toll Free: 800-228-7361 E-mail: compedge@ix.netcom.com.

School of Metaphysics, 163 Moonvalley Rd., Windyville, MO 65783 USA (SAN 159-5423) Tel 417-345-8411; Fax: 417-345-6668 E-mail: som@som.org Web site: http://www.som.org.

School Specialty Publishing, *(0-7647; 0-7682; 0-7696; 0-86653; 0-88012; 1-56417; 1-56451; 1-56822; 1-57029; 1-57768; 0-7424; 1-58845)* 8720 Orion Pl., Suite 200, Columbus, OH 43240-2111 USA (SAN 256-0925) Tel 614-880-6787; 614-430-4487; Fax: 614-880-6745; 614-430-6482; Toll Free Fax: 800-543-2690; Toll Free: 800-253-5469 E-mail: barbara-boggs@mcgraw-hill.com; barbara-boggs@childrens-publishing.com Web site: http://www.schoolspecialtypublishing.com/.

Schroeder News Company, *See* **Merced News Co.**

Schroeder's Bk. Haven, 104 Michigan Ave., League City, TX 77573 USA (SAN 122-7998) Tel 281-332-5226; Fax: 281-332-1695; Toll Free: 800-894-5032 E-mail: schroedr@interloc.com.

Schulze News Co., 2451 Eastman Ave., Suite 13, Oxnard, CA 93030-5193 USA (SAN 169-0434) Tel 805-642-9759.

Schuylkill News Service, 1801 W. Market St., Pottsville, PA 17901-2001 USA (SAN 159-9518).

Schwartz, Arthur & Company, Incorporated/Woodstocker Books, *See* **Woodstocker Books/Arthur Schwartz & Company**

Schwartz Brothers, Inc., 822 Montgomery Ave., No. 204, Narberth, PA 19072-1937 USA (SAN 285-7529) Fax: 301-459-6418; Toll Free: 800-638-0243.

Science Kit & Boreal Labs, P.O. Box 5003, Tonawanda, NY 14151-5003 USA (SAN 631-2314) E-mail: sk@sciencekit.com.

Scientific & Medical Pubns. of France, Inc., 100 E. 42nd St., Suite 1510, New York, NY 10017 USA (SAN 169-5940) Tel 212-983-6278; Fax: 212-687-1407.

Seaboard Sub Agency, 1544 W. Hamilton St. Unit 102, Allentown, PA 18102-4363 USA (SAN 285-9718).

Seaburn Bks., P.O. Box 2085, Long Island City, NY 11102 USA (SAN 631-2799) Tel 718-274-7040 E-mail: info@seaburn.com.

Seaside Publishing, *See* **Seaside Publishing/Tropical Tastes**

Seaside Publishing/Tropical Tastes, *(0-942084)* Orders Addr.: P.O. Box 14441, Saint Petersburg, FL 33733 USA Tel 727-522-1200; Fax: 727-522-1222; Toll Free Fax: 877-522-1220; Toll Free: 888-352-2665; Edit Addr.: 3220 28th St., Suite 4, Saint Petersburg, FL 33713 USA (SAN 281-8639).

Seaworthy Pubns., Inc., *(0-9639566; 1-892399)* 626 W. Pierre Ln., Port Washington, WI 53074 USA Tel 262-268-9250; Fax: 262-268-9208
E-mail: jjanson@seaworthy.com
Web site: http://www.seaworthy.com.

Seedsowers, The, *(0-940232; 0-9778033; 0-9797515)* P.O. Box 3317, Jacksonville, FL 32206-0317 USA (SAN 201-8942) Toll Free: 800-228-2665 Do not confuse with Seedsowers Press, Naples, FL
E-mail: info@seedsowers.com
Web site: http://www.seedsowers.com.

Selective Bks., Inc., *(0-912584)* P.O. Box 1140, Clearwater, FL 34617 USA (SAN 204-577X) Tel 813-447-0100.

Selective Publishers, Incorporated, *See* **Selective Bks., Inc.**

Semler News Agency, Orders Addr.: P.O. Box 350, New Castle, PA 16101 USA (SAN 169-7471); Edit Addr.: P.O. Box 526, Morgantown, WV 26505 USA (SAN 169-8990).

Seneca News Agency, 800 Pre Emption Rd., Geneva, NY 14456-2010 USA (SAN 169-5304).

Sentai Distributors, 8839 Shirley Ave., Northridge, CA 91324 USA (SAN 168-9959) Tel 818-886-3113; Fax: 818-886-0423
Web site: http://www.plasticmodels.com.

Sepher-Hermon Pr., *(0-87203)* 1153 45th St., Brooklyn, NY 11219 USA (SAN 169-5959) Tel 718-972-9010; Fax: 718-972-6935.

Serendipity Couriers, Inc., P.O. Box 5897, Vallejo, CA 94591-5897 USA (SAN 169-0329) Toll Free: 800-459-4005 (Bay area only)
E-mail: dipity@14.netcom.com.

Serpent's Tale Natural History Bk. Distributors, Inc., *(1-885209)* Orders Addr.: P.O. Box 405, Lanesboro, MN 55949-0405 USA (SAN 630-6101) Tel 507-467-8734; Fax: 507-467-8735
E-mail: zoobooks@acegroup.cc
Web site: http://www.zoobooksales.com.

Service News Co., 1306 N. 23rd St., Wilmington, NC 28406 USA (SAN 169-6491) Tel 910-762-0837; Fax: 910-762-9539; Toll Free: 800-552-8238; P.O. Box 5027, Macon, GA 31208; Pope's Island, Box D-629, New Bedford, MA 02742 (SAN 169-3514).

Seven Locks Pr., *(0-929765; 0-932020; 0-9615964; 1-931643; 0-9790950; 0-9795852; 0-9801270)* 3100 W. Warner Ave., Suite 8, Santa Ana, CA 92704 USA (SAN 211-9781) Tel 714-545-2526; Fax: 714-545-1572; Toll Free: 800-354-5348
E-mail: sevenlocks@aol.com
Web site: http://www.sevenlockspublishing.com.

Seymour, Dale Pubns., *(0-201; 0-7690; 0-86651; 1-57232)* Div. of Pearson Learning, Orders Addr.: P.O. Box 2500, Lebanon, OH 43216 USA Toll Free Fax: 800-393-3156; Toll Free: 800-321-3106 (Customer Service); Edit Addr.: 10 Bank St., White Plains, NY 10602-5026 USA (SAN 200-9781) Toll Free Fax: 800-393-3156; Toll Free: 800-237-3142
E-mail: pearson_learning2@prenhall.com
Web site: http://www.pearsonlearning.com; http://www.pearsonlearning.com/rightsPerm.rtf.

Shadow Publications, *See* **1st World Publishing**

Shambhala Publications, Incorporated, *See* **Shambhala Pubns., Inc.**

Shambhala Pubns., Inc., *(0-8348; 0-87773; 1-56957; 1-57062; 1-59030)* Horticultural Hall, 300 Massachusetts Ave., Boston, MA 02115 USA (SAN 203-2481) Tel 617-424-0030; Fax: 617-236-1563
E-mail: editors@shambhala.com
Web site: http://www.shambhala.com.

Sharon News Agency Co., 527 Silver St., Sharon, PA 16146 USA (SAN 169-7633).

Sharpe, M.E. Inc., *(0-7656; 0-87332; 1-56324)* 80 Business Park Dr., Armonk, NY 10504 USA (SAN 202-7100) Tel 914-273-1800; Fax: 914-273-2106; Toll Free: 800-541-6563
Web site: http://www.mesharpe.com.

Shea Bks., 1563 Solano Ave., Suite 206, Berkeley, CA 94707 USA (SAN 159-9720) Tel 510-528-5201; Fax: 510-528-4987.

Shelter Pubns., Inc., *(0-936070)* Orders Addr.: P.O. Box 279, Bolinas, CA 94924 USA (SAN 122-8463) Tel 415-868-0280; Fax: 415-868-9053; Toll Free: 800-307-0131; Edit Addr.: 285 Dogwood Rd, Bolinas, CA 94924 USA
E-mail: shelter@shelterpub.com
Web site: http://www.shelterpub.com.

Shen's Bks., *(1-885008)* 40951 Fremont Blvd., Fremont, CA 94538 USA (SAN 138-2926) Tel 510-668-1898; Fax: 510-668-1057; Toll Free: 800-456-6660
E-mail: info@shens.com
Web site: http://www.shens.com.

Shinder's Book Company, *See* **Shinders Readmore Bookstore, Inc.**

Shinders Readmore Bookstore, Inc., 733 Hennepin Ave., Minneapolis, MN 55403 USA (SAN 125-6157) Tel 612-333-3628.

Shoppers Guide Pr., 706 N. Fifth, Alpine, TX 79830 USA (SAN 159-9550) Tel 915-837-7426.

Sierra News Co., 2136 Pony Express Ct., Stockton, CA 95215-7946 USA (SAN 169-4472).

Silky Way, Inc., 1227 38th Ave., San Francisco, CA 94122-1334 USA (SAN 169-3328).

Silver Bow News Distributing Co., Inc., 219 E. Park St., Butte, MT 59701 USA (SAN 169-4359) Tel 406-782-6995.

Silver, Burdett & Ginn, Inc., *(0-382; 0-663; 1-4182)* Orders Addr.: P.O. Box 2500, Lebanon, IN 46052 USA Toll Free Fax: 800-841-8939; Toll Free: 800-552-2259; Edit Addr.: P.O. Box 480, Parsippany, NJ 07054 USA (SAN 204-5982); 108 Wilmot Rd., Suite 380, Midwest Div., Deerfield, IL 60015 (SAN 111-6517) Tel 708-945-1240; 1925 Century Blvd. NE, Suite 14, Southeast Div., Atlanta, GA 30345 (SAN 111-6509); 8445 Freeport Pkwy., Suite 400, South Div., Irving, TX 75063 (SAN 108-0458) Tel 214-915-4200; 2001 The Alameda, West Div., San Jose, CA 95126 (SAN 111-6525) Tel 408-248-6854; 160 Gould St., East Div., Needham Heights, MA 02194-2310; 1900 E. Lake Ave., Glenview, IL 60025
E-mail: customerservice@scottforesman.com
Web site: http://www.scottforesman.com/.

Simon & Schuster, *(0-671; 0-684; 0-689; 0-914676; 0-7432; 1-4165)* Div. of Simon & Schuster, Inc., Orders Addr.: 100 Front St., Riverside, NJ 08075 USA (SAN 200-2442) Toll Free Fax: 800-943-9831; Toll Free: 800-223-2336 (ordering); 800-223-2348 (customer service); Edit Addr.: a/o Subsidiary Rights, 11th Flr., 1230 Avenue of the Americas, New York, NY 10020 USA (SAN 200-2450) Tel 212-698-7000; Fax: 212-698-7007; 212-632-8099 (Rights & Permissions); 212-698-1269 (Pocket Bks. Rights & Permissions); Toll Free: 800-897-7650 (customer financial services); 100 Front St., Riverside, NJ 08075 (SAN 256-6044) Tel 856-461-6500; Fax: 856-824-2287; 100 Front St., Riverside, NJ 08075 (SAN 852-5579) Tel 856-824-2115
E-mail: ssonline_feedback@simonsays.com; consumer.customerservice@simonandschuster.com
Web site: http://www.simonsays.com; http://www.oasis.simonandschuster.com; http://www.simonandschuster.com/ebooks.

Simon & Schuster Audio, *(0-671; 0-7435)* Div. of Simon & Schuster New Media, Orders Addr.: 100 Front St., Riverside, NJ 08075 USA Toll Free Fax: 800-943-9831 (orders); Toll Free: 800-223-2336 (customer service); Edit Addr.: a/o Sub Rights Manager, 11th flr., 1230 Avenue of the Americas, New York, NY 10020 USA Tel 212-698-7000; Fax: 212-698-2370; 212-632-8091 (Rights & Permissions)
Web site: http://www.simonsays.com/subs/index.cfm?areaid=45.

Simon & Schuster Children's Publishing, *(0-02; 0-671; 0-684; 0-689; 0-7434; 1-4169)* Orders Addr.: 100 Front St., Riverside, NJ 08075 USA Toll Free Fax: 800-943-9831; Toll Free: 800-223-2336; Edit Addr.: a/o Subsidiary Rights, 4th floor, 1230 Avenue of the Americas, New York, NY 10020 USA Tel 212-698-7200; Fax: 212-698-2797 (Rights & Permissions)
Web site: http://www.simonsays.com.

Simon & Schuster, Inc., *(0-671)* Div. of Viacom Co., Orders Addr.: 100 Front St., Riverside, NJ 08075 USA Toll Free Fax: 800-943-9831; Toll Free: 800-223-2336 (orders); 800-223-2348 (customer service); Edit Addr.: 1230 Ave. of the Americas, New York, NY 10020 USA
E-mail: Consumer.CustomerService@simonandschuster.com
Web site: http://www.simonsays.com.

Simon & Schuster Trade, *See* **Simon & Schuster**

Skandisk, Inc., *(0-9615394; 1-57534)* 6667 W. Old Shakopee Rd., Suite 109, Bloomington, MN 55438-2622 USA (SAN 695-4405) Tel 952-829-8998; Fax: 952-829-8992; Toll Free: 800-468-2424 (orders)
E-mail: lhamnes@skandisk.com; tomten@skandisk.com
Web site: http://www.skandisk.com.

Sky Oaks Productions, Inc., *(0-940296; 1-56018)* P.O. Box 1102, Los Gatos, CA 95031 USA (SAN 217-5843) Tel 408-395-7600; Fax: 408-395-8440
E-mail: TRPWorld@aol.com
Web site: http://www.tpr-world.com.

S&L Sales Co., Inc., Orders Addr.: P.O. Box 2067, Waycross, GA 31502 USA (SAN 107-413X) Tel 912-283-0210; Fax: 912-283-0261; Toll Free: 800-243-3699 (orders only).

Slatner, Thomas & Co., Inc., 193 Palisade Ave., 3rd Flr., Jersey City, NJ 07036-1112 USA (SAN 130-9862) Tel 201-420-6700; Fax: 201-420-6787.

Slavica Pubs., *(0-89357)* c/o Indiana University, 2611 E. Tenth St., Bloomington, IN 47408-2618 USA (SAN 208-8576) Tel 812-856-4186; Fax: 812-856-4187
E-mail: slavica@indiana.edu
Web site: http://www.slavica.com.

Sleuth Pubns., Ltd., *(0-915341)* 3398 Washington, San Francisco, CA 94118 USA (SAN 130-9374) Tel 415-771-2689.

Small Press Distribution, *See* **SPD-Small Pr. Distribution**

Smart Apple Media, *(1-58340; 1-887068; 1-59920)* Div. of Black Rabbit Bks., Orders Addr.: P.O. Box 3263, Mankato, MN 56002 USA; Edit Addr.: 123 S. Broad Stree, Mankato, MN 56001 USA
E-mail: info@blackrabbitbooks.com; aschwab@blackrabbitbooks.com
Web site: http://www.blackrabbitbooks.com.

Smith, Gibbs Publisher, *See* **Gibbs Smith, Publisher**

Smith News Agency, 118 S. Mitchell St., Cadillac, MI 49601 USA (SAN 169-3727).

Smith Novelty Co., Inc., *(0-938765; 1-59099)* Div. of Smith News Co., Inc., 460 Ninth St., San Francisco, CA 94103 USA (SAN 216-2326) Tel 415-861-4900 ext 615; Fax: 415-861-5683
E-mail: michellesnco@hotmail.com.

Snyder Magazine Agency, 3050 S. 9th Terr., Kansas City, KS 66103-2629 USA (SAN 285-9750).

Social Studies Schl. Service, *(1-56004)* Orders Addr.: 10200 Jefferson Blvd., P.O. Box 802, Culver City, CA 90232-0802 USA (SAN 168-9592) Tel 310-839-2436; Fax: 310-839-2249; Toll Free: 800-421-4246
E-mail: access@socialstudies.com
Web site: http://socialstudies.com.

Socialist Labor Party, P.O. Box 218, Mountain View, CA 94042-0218 USA (SAN 226-4056) Tel 650-938-8359
E-mail: socialists@slp.org
Web site: http://www.slp.org.

Sociedad Biblica de Puerto Rico, Orders Addr.: P.O. Box 2548, Bayamon, PR 00960-2548 USA; Edit Addr.: Carr. 167, Km 14.7 Bo, Bayamon, PR 00960-2548 USA.

Society for Visual Education, Incorporated, *See* **S V E & Churchill Media**

SONA, Inc., 4535 W. Sahara Ave., Suite 105-33M, Las Vegas, NV 89102 USA Tel 702-355-0350.

Sony CONNECT, Inc., *(1-4340)* Orders Addr.: 6080 Center Dr., 10th Flr., Los Angeles, CA 90045 USA Tel 310 981 1500; Fax: 310-981-1600
Web site: http://www.ebbooks.connect.com.

Sopris West, *See* **Sopris West Educational Services**

Sopris West Educational Services, *(0-944584; 1-57035; 1-59318; 1-60218)* 4093 Specialty Pl., Longmont, CO 80504 USA (SAN 243-945X) Tel 303-651-2829; Fax: 303-907-8694; Toll Free: 800-547-6747 (orders only)
E-mail: publishing@sopriswest.com
Web site: http://www.sopriswest.com.

Sort Card Co., The, 400 S. Summit View Dr., Fort Collins, CO 80524-1424 USA (SAN 159-9607).

Soundprints, *(0-924483; 1-56899; 1-931465; 1-59249)* Div. of Trudy Corp., 353 Main Ave., Norwalk, CT 06851 USA Tel 203 838 6009 Toll Free: 800-228-7839
Web site: http://www.soundprints.com.

Sounds of Zion, *(1-886472; 1-933098)* 9298 S. 500 W., Sandy, UT 84070 USA (SAN 200-7525) Tel 801-255-1991; Fax: 801-255-1998
E-mail: sales@soundsofzion.com
Web site: http://www.soundsofzion.com.

Sounds True, Inc., *(1-56455; 1-59179; 1-60407)* Orders Addr.: P.O. Box 8010, Boulder, CO 80306-8010 USA; Edit Addr.: 413 S. Arthur Ave., Louisville, CO 80027 USA (SAN 850-3532) Tel 303-665-3151; Fax: 303-665-5292; Toll Free: 800-333-9185
E-mail: brianm@soundstrue.com
Web site: http://www.soundstrue.com.

Source Bks., *(0-940147; 0-85650)* Orders Addr.: 204 E. Fourth St., Suite O, Santa Ana, CA 92701 USA (SAN 248-2231) Tel 714-558-8944 (phone/fax); Toll Free: 800-695-4237 Do not confuse with Source Bks., Nashville, TN
E-mail: studio185@earthlink.net.

Source International Technology Corporation, *See* **Kamkyi Bks.**

Sourcebooks, Inc., *(0-942061; 0-9629162; 0-9629803; 1-57071; 1-57248; 1-883518; 1-887166; 1-4022)* 1935 Brookdale Rd., Suite 139, Naperville, IL 60563 USA (SAN 666-7864) Tel 630-961-3900; Fax: 630-961-2168; Toll Free: 800-727-8866
E-mail: info@sourcebooks.com
Web site: http://www.sourcebooks.com/.

South Asia Bks., *(0-8364; 0-88386)* P.O. Box 502, Columbia, MO 65205 USA (SAN 207-4044) Tel 573-474-0116; Fax: 573-474-8124
E-mail: sabooks@juno.com
Web site: http://www.southasiabooks.com.

South Atlantic News, Orders Addr.: P.O. Box 61297, Jacksonville, FL 32236-1297 USA; Edit Addr.: 1426 NE Eighth Ave., Ocala, FL 32678 USA.

South Bay Bks., Orders Addr.: P.O. Box 3272, Torrance, CA 90510-3272 USA (SAN 631-6824) Toll Free Fax: 877-626-6576; Toll Free: 888-526-6575
E-mail: info@southbaybooks.com
Web site: http://www.southbaybooks.com.

South Carolina Bookstore, Orders Addr.: P.O. Box 4767, West Columbia, SC 29171 USA (SAN 131-2294) Tel 803-796-8200; Fax: 803-794-6927; Toll Free: 800-845-8200; Edit Addr.: 523 Jasper St., West Columbia, SC 29169 USA (SAN 243-2390).

South Central Bks., Inc., 1106 S. Strong Blvd., McAlester, OK 74501-6952 USA (SAN 108-1144) Tel 405-275-4522; Toll Free: 800-548-9858.

South Eastern Bk. Co., Inc., 3333 Hwy. 641 N., P.O. Box 309, Murray, KY 42071 USA (SAN 630-4869) Tel 270-753-0732; Fax: 270-759-4742; Toll Free Fax: 800-433-6966 (orders); Toll Free: 800-626-3952 (orders)
E-mail: orders@sebook.com
Web site: http://www.sebook.com.

South Louisiana News Company, *See* **Southern Periodicals, Inc.**

Southcoast Music, Orders Addr.: a/o Bobby, 1415 N E 4th Ave., Lauderdale, FL 33304 USA Tel 954-467-3601; Fax: 954-467-3606.

Southeast Library Bindery, Inc., P.O. Box 35484, Greensboro, NC 27425-5484 USA (SAN 159-9445) Tel 336-931-0800
E-mail: 70304.3023@compuserve.com
Web site: http://www.webmasters.net/bookbinding/.

Southeast Periodical & Bk. Sales, Inc., 10100 NW 25th St., Box 520155-Biscayne Annex, Miami, FL 33152 USA.

Southeastern Educational Toy & Bk. Distributors, Orders Addr.: P.O. Box 15129, Charlotte, NC 28211 USA (SAN 630-8104) Tel 704-364-6988; Edit Addr.: 4217 Park Rd., Charlotte, NC 28209 USA Tel 704-527-1921; Fax: 704-527-1653.

Southeastern Library Service, Subs. of Haskins Hse., P.O. Box 44, Gainesville, FL 32602-0044 USA (SAN 159-9615) Tel 352-372-3823.

Southern Bk. Service, *(0-9663836)* 5154 NW 165th St., Palmetto Lakes Industrial Pk., Hialeah, FL 33014-6335 USA (SAN 169-0981) Tel 305-624-4545; Fax: 305-621-0425; Toll Free: 800-766-3254
Web site: http://southernbooks.com.

Southern Cross Pubns., 1734 W. Roseberry Rd., P.O. Box 717, Donnelly, ID 83615 USA (SAN 110-8549) Tel 208-325-8606; Fax: 208-325-3400
E-mail: scp@cyberhighway.net
Web site: http://www.thoughtlines.com/southerncross/.

Southern Library Bindery Co., 2952 Sidco Dr., Nashville, TN 37204 USA (SAN 169-7986).

Southern Michigan News Co., 2571 Saradan, P.O. Box 908, Jackson, MI 49204 USA (SAN 169-3697) Tel 517-784-7163; Toll Free: 800-248-2213 (in Michigan); 800-828-2140.

Southern Periodicals, Inc., P.O. Box 407, Rayne, LA 70578-0407 USA (SAN 113-2520); 180 James Dr E., Saint Rose, LA 70087-4005.

Southern Tier News Co., P.O. Box 2128, Elmira Heights, NY 14903 USA (SAN 169-5223).

Southern Wisconsin News, 4838 N. County Rd. Y, Milton, WI 53563 USA (SAN 169-9121) Tel 608-756-2376; Fax: 608-756-2357.

Southwest Cookbook Distributors, Orders Addr.: P.O. Box 707, Bonham, TX 75418 USA (SAN 200-4925) Tel 903-583-8898; Fax: 903-583-2522; Toll Free: 800-725-8898 (orders); Edit Addr.: 1430 Texas Ave., Bonham, TX 75418 USA (SAN 630-8325).

Southwest Natural Cultural Heritage Association, *See* **Public Lands Interpretive Assn.**

Southwest News Co., Box 5465, Tucson, AZ 85704 USA (SAN 159-9631).

Southwestern Bk. Distributors, c/o Kerbs, 700 Highview Ave., Glen Ellyn, IL 60137-5504 USA (SAN 160-2373).

Sovereign News Company, *See* **Trans World News**

Spama, Inc., 78 Lake St., Jersey City, NJ 07306-3407 USA (SAN 169-5967).

Spanish & European Bookstore, Inc., 3102 Wilshire Blvd., Los Angeles, CA 90010 USA Tel 213-739-8899; Fax: 213-739-0087.

Spanish Bookstore-Wholesale, The, 10977 Santa Monica Blvd., Los Angeles, CA 90025-4538 USA (SAN 168-9835) Tel 310-475-0453; Fax: 310-473-6132
E-mail: BernardHamel@SpanishbooksUSA.com
Web site: http://www.BernardHamel.com.

Spanish Hse. Distributors, 1360 NW 88th Ave., Miami, FL 33172-3093 USA (SAN 169-1171) Tel 305-592-6136; Fax: 305-592-0087; Toll Free: 800-767-7726.

Spanish Language Bk. Services, Inc., Orders Addr.: 7855 N.W. 12th St., Suite 211, Miami, FL 33126 USA.

Spanishtech, Inc., Div. of Editor's Bureau, Ltd., P.O. Box 68, Westport, CT 06881 USA (SAN 289-9620) Tel 203-452-7655.

Sparkling Records, 5214F Diamond Heights Blvd., No. 130, San Francisco, CA 94131-2118 USA (SAN 631-645X).

SPD-Small Pr. Distribution, *(0-914068)* 1341 Seventh St., Berkeley, CA 94710-1409 USA (SAN 204-5826) Tel 510-524-1668; Fax: 510-524-0852; Toll Free: 800-869-7553 (orders)
E-mail: orders@spdbooks.org
Web site: http://www.spdbooks.org.

SpeakWare, 2836 Stephen Dr., Richmond, CA 94803 USA Tel 510-222-2455
E-mail: leds@speakware.com
Web site: http://www.speakware.com.

Specialized Bk. Service, Inc., 307 Autumn Ridge Rd., Fairfield, CT 06432-1003 USA (SAN 166-9788) Tel 203-377-6510; Fax: 203-377-4792.

Specialty Bk. Services, 1150 N. San Francisco, Flagstaff, AZ 86001 USA (SAN 130-8114) Tel 520-779-7843.

Specialty Promotions, 6841 S. Cregier Ave., Chicago, IL 60649 USA (SAN 110-9987) Tel 773-493-6900.

Speech Bin, Inc., The, *(0-937857)* 1965 25th Ave., Vero Beach, FL 32960 USA (SAN 630-1657) Tel 772-770-0007; Fax: 772-770-0006
E-mail: info@speechbin.com
Web site: http://www.speechbin.com.

Speedimpex U.S.A., Inc., 35-02 48th Ave., Long Island City, NY 11101-2421 USA (SAN 169-5479) Tel 718-392-7477; Fax: 718-361-0815
E-mail: nsalvatore@speedimpex.com
Web site: http://www.speedimpex.com.

Spencer Museum of Art, *(0-913689)* Affil. of Univ. of Kansas, Univ. of Kansas 1301 Mississippi St., Lawrence, KS 66045-7500 USA (SAN 111-347X) Tel 785-864-4710; Fax: 785-864-3112
E-mail: spencerart@ku.edu
Web site: http://www.ukans.edu/~sma.

Spirit Filled Pr., Inc., *(0-9656668)* 2549 Tallavana Trail, Havana, FL 32333 USA Tel 850-539-3843 (phone/fax)
E-mail: 2549@bellsouth.net
Web site: http://www.mindspring.com/~spiritfilled.

Spirit Rising, c/o Nicole Heyward, 1505 Hadley St., Houston, TX 77002 USA Tel 713-772-5175; Fax: 713-772-3034
E-mail: nicole.heyward@musicworldent.com.

Spirit Support, 5300 Jenny Lake, Cheyenne, WY 82009 USA Tel 307-778-1879 (phone/fax).

Spring Arbor Distributors, Inc., Subs. of Ingram Industries Inc., 4271 Edison Ave., Chino, CA 91710 USA; 7315 Innovation Blvd., Fort Wayne, IN 46818-1371; 201 Ingram Dr., Roseburg, OR 97470-7148; Newbury Rd., East Windsor, CT 06088; 25420 Weakley Rd., Petersburg, VA 23803; 11333 E. 53rd Ave., Denver, CO 80239-2108; Edit Addr.: 1 Ingram Blvd., La Vergne, TN 37086-1976 USA Fax: 615-213-5192; Toll Free: 800-395-4340; 800-395-7234 (customer service)
E-mail: orders@springarbor.com.

Springer, *(0-387; 0-8176; 3-211; 3-540; 3-7908; 4-431; 1-85233; 1-84628)* Subs. of Springer-Verlag GmbH & Co. KG, Orders Addr.: P.O. Box 2485, Secaucus, NJ 07096-2485 USA (SAN 203-2228) Tel 201-348-4033; Fax: 201-348-4505; Toll Free: 800-777-4643; Edit Addr.: 233 Spring St., New York, NY 10013 USA Tel 212-460-1500; Fax: 212-473-6272 Thomson Delmar Learning Distributes Blanchard & Loeb Nursing Videos Only
E-mail: Slu@Springer-ny.com
Web site: http://www.springeronline.com.

Springer-Verlag New York, Incorporated, *See* **Springer**

Springwater Bks., Orders Addr.: P.O. Box 194, Springwater, NY 14560-0194 USA (SAN 111-8900); Edit Addr.: Main St. & East Ave., Springwater, NY 14560-0194 USA (SAN 243-2412) Tel 716-669-2450.

Sprout, Inc., Orders Addr.: 430 Tenth St., NW, Suite 007, Atlanta, GA 30318 USA Tel 404-892-9600; Fax: 404-881-1383.

Square Deal Records, 303 Higuera St., San Luis Obispo, CA 93401-4209 USA (SAN 170-6799) Tel 805-543-3636; Fax: 805-543-3938; Toll Free: 800-253-4114
E-mail: sdrsslo@aol.com.

St. Marie's Gopher News Co., 9000 Tenth Ave., N., Minneapolis, MN 55427 USA (SAN 169-4103) Tel 612-546-5300; Fax: 612-546-1487.

St. Martin's Pr., *(0-312; 0-8050; 0-940687; 0-9603648; 1-55927; 1-58063; 1-58238; 1-4299)* Div. of Holtzbrinck Pubs., Orders Addr.: 16365 James Madison Hwy., Gordonville, VA 22942 USA Tel 540-672-7600; Fax: 540-672-7540 (customer service); Toll Free Fax: 800-672-2054; Toll Free: 888-330-8477; Edit Addr.: 175 Fifth Ave., New York, NY 10010 USA (SAN 200-2132) Tel 212-674-5151 (Trade Div.); 212-726-0200 (College Div.); Fax: 212-674-3179 (Trade Div.); 212-686-9491 (College Div.); Toll Free: 800-221-7945 (Trade Div.); 800-470-4767 (College Div.)
E-mail: webmaster@stmartins.com; enquiries@stmartins.com
Web site: http://www.stmartins.com; http://www.smpcollege.com.

St. Mary Seminary Bookstore, 28700 Euclid Ave., Wyckliffe, OH 44092 USA (SAN 169-667X) Tel 216-943-7600.

Stackpole Bks., *(0-8117)* 5067 Ritter Rd., Mechanicsburg, PA 17055 USA (SAN 202-5396) Tel 717-796-0411; Fax: 717-796-0412; Toll Free: 800-732-3669
E-mail: pmoran@stackpolebooks.com
Web site: http://www.stackpolebooks.com.

Standard Publishing, *(0-7847; 0-87239; 0-87403; 0-933657; 1-58170)* 8805 Governors Hill Dr. Ste. 400, Cincinnati, OH 45249-3319 USA (SAN 110-5515) Toll Free Fax: 877-867-5751 (customer service); Toll Free: 800-543-1353 (customer service); 800-543-1301 Do not confuse with Standard Publishing Corp., Boston, MA
E-mail: customerservice@standardpub.com; trolfes@standardpub.com; dlewis@standardpub.com
Web site: http://www.standardpub.com.

Standard Publishing Company, *See* **Standard Publishing**

Star Bright Bks., Inc., *(1-887734; 1-932065; 1-59572)* Orders Addr.: 30-19, 48th Ave., Long Island City, NY 11101 USA (SAN 254-5225) Tel 718-784-9112; Fax: 718-784-9012; Toll Free: 800-788-4439
E-mail: info@starbrightbooks.com
Web site: http://www.starbrightbooks.com.

StarCrossed Productions, *(0-9668483)* 14552 NW., 88 Pl., Miami, FL 33018 USA Tel 305-828-2619 Phone/Fax
E-mail: tinami@msn.com
Web site: http://www.cookiesisters.com.

Starkmann, Inc., 25-u Olympia Ave., Woburn, MA 01801 USA (SAN 126-6128) Tel 781-938-9643; Fax: 781-938 9647
E-mail: biggs@starkmann.co.uk.

Starmaster Co., 6911 Haverhill Dr., Knoxville, TN 37909 USA (SAN 108-1217) Tel 423-588-6661.

State Mutual Bk. & Periodical Service, Ltd., *(0-7855; 0-89771)* Orders Addr.: P.O. Box 1199, Bridgehampton, NY 11932-1199 USA.

State News Agency, 2750 Griffith Rd., Winston Salem, NC 27103-6418 USA (SAN 169-6424).

Steiner, Rudolf College Pr./St. George Pubns., *(0-916786; 0-945803)* 9200 Fair Oaks Blvd., Fair Oaks, CA 95628 USA (SAN 208-8371) Tel 916-961-3722; Fax: 916-961-3032
E-mail: rsc@steinercollege.org.

SteinerBooks, Inc., *(0-8334; 0-88010; 0-89345; 0-910142; 1-58420; 1-85584; 0-9701097)* Orders Addr.: P.O. Box 960, Herndon, VA 20172-0960 USA Tel 703-661-1594 (orders); Fax: 702-661-1501; Toll Free Fax: 800-277-7947 (orders); Toll Free: 800-856-8664 (orders); Edit Addr.: 610 Main St., Great Barrington, MA 01230 USA Tel 413-528-8233; Fax: 413-528-8826; Fulfillment Addr.: 22883 Quicksilver Dr., Dulles, VA 20166 USA (SAN 253-9519) Tel 703-661-1529; Fax: 703-996-1010
E-mail: service@steinerbooks.org
Web site: http://www.steinerbooks.org; http://www.lindisfarne.org; http://www.bellpondbooks.com.

Sterling Publishing Co., Inc., *(0-8069; 1-4027)* 387 Park Ave., S., New York, NY 10016-8810 USA (SAN 211-6324) Tel 212-532-7160 212-213-2495; Toll Free Fax: 800-775-8736 (warehouse) Do not confuse with companies with similar names in Falls Church, VA, Fallbrook, CA, Lewisville, TX
E-mail: custservice@sterlingpub.com; tradesales@sterlingpub.com
Web site: http://www.sterlingpub.com.

Stevens, Mark Industries, Div. of Christian World, Inc., 4243 Will Rogers Pkwy., Oklahoma City, OK 73108-2039 USA (SAN 631-127X) Toll Free: 800-654-6760.

Stewart, Tabori & Chang, *(0-941434; 0-941807; 1-55670; 1-899791; 1-58479)* Div. of Harry N. Abrams, Inc., 115 W. 18th St., 5th Flr., New York, NY 10011 USA (SAN 293-4000) Tel 212-519-1200; Fax: 212-519-1210
E-mail: trudi@stcbooks.com
Web site: http://www.abramsbooks.com.

STL Distribution North America, *(1-932805)* Orders Addr.: 129 Mobilization Dr., Waynesboro, GA 30830 USA (SAN 631-8894) Tel 706-554-5827; Toll Free Fax: 877-323-4551; Toll Free: 877-323-4550; Edit Addr.: 9247 Hunterboro Dr., Brentwood, TN 37027 USA Tel 615-221-6442 (phone/fax) Do not confuse with Faithworks in Bronx NY
E-mail: custserv@faithworksonline.com
Web site: http://www.faithworksonline.com.

Strang Communications Co., *(0-88419; 0-930525; 1-59185; 1-59979)* Div. of Creation House Pr., 600 Rinehart Rd., Lake Mary, FL 32746 USA (SAN 677-5640) Tel 407-333-0600; Fax: 407-333-7100; Toll Free: 800-283-8494
Web site: http://www.strang.com/.

Strauss Consultants, 48 W. 25th St., 11th Flr., New York, NY 10010-2708 USA Toll Free Fax: 888-528-8273; Toll Free: 800-236-7918
E-mail: strausscon@aol.com.

Streamwood Distribution, P.O. Box 91011, Mobile, AL 36691 USA Tel 334-665-0022; Fax: 334-665-0570.

Strelow, James C., 9440 El Blanco Ave., Fountain Valley, CA 92708 USA (SAN 132-4144) Tel 714-962-3697.

Strisik, Nancy, 10 Main St., Rockport, MA 01966 USA Tel 978-546-7653.

Stylus Publishing, LLC, *(1-57922)* Orders Addr.: P.O. Box 605, Herndon, VA 20172-0605 USA; Edit Addr.: 22883 Quicksilver Dr., Sterling, VA 20166-2012 USA (SAN 299-1853) Tel 703-661-1581; Fax: 703-661-1501 Do not confuse with companies with the same name in Sunnyvale, CA, Quakertown, PA
E-mail: stylusmail@presswarehouse.com
Web site: http://www.styluspub.com.

Subscription Acct., 84 Needham, Newton Highlands, MA 02161 USA (SAN 285-9424).

Subscription Hse., Inc., 209 Harvard St., Suite 407, Brookline, MA 02146-5005 USA (SAN 285-9343).

Subterranean Co., Orders Addr.: P.O. Box 160, Monroe, OR 97456 USA Fax: 541-847-6018
E-mail: subco@clipper.net.

Success Education Assn., Box 175, Roanoke, VA 24002 USA (SAN 159-9690).

Sun Life, *(0-937930)* 2399 Cool Springs Rd., Thaxton, VA 24174 USA (SAN 240-8333) Tel 540-586-4898.

Sun News Company, *See* **Anderson News Co.**

Sunbelt Media, Incorporated, *See* **Eakin Pr.**

Sunbelt Pubns., Inc., *(0-916251; 0-932653; 0-9606704; 0-9620402)* 1256 Fayette St., El Cajon, CA 92020-1511 USA (SAN 630-0790) Tel 619-258-4911; Fax: 619-258-4916; Toll Free: 800-626-6579
E-mail: sunbeltpub@prodigy.net
Web site: http://www.sunbeltpub.com; http://www.sunbeltbooks.com.

Sunburst Communications, Inc., *(0-7805; 0-911831; 1-55636; 1-55826)* 400 Columbus Ave., Valhalla, NY 10595-1335 USA (SAN 213-5620) Toll Free: 800-431-1934
E-mail: webmaster@nysunburst.com
Web site: http://www.sunburst.com.

Sunset Bks./Sunset Publishing Corp., *(0-376)* Orders Addr.: Leisure Arts 5701 Ranch Dr., Little Rock, AR 72223 USA; Edit Addr.: 80 Willow Rd., Menlo Park, CA 94025-3691 USA Tel 650-321-3600; Fax: 650-324-1532; Toll Free: 800-227-7346 (except California); 800-321-0372 (in California)
E-mail: nicholsonl@sunset.com
Web site: http://sunsetbooks.com.

Sunshine Harbor, 825 Glen Arden Way, Altamonte Springs, FL 32701 USA (SAN 159-6640) Tel 407-339-0401.

Supreme Co., The, 1909 Lagneaux Rd., Lafayette, LA 70506 USA (SAN 631-3388) Tel 318-993-2369; Fax: 318-993-0226; Toll Free: 800-262-3237.

Swedenborg Foundation, Inc., *(0-87785)* 320 N. Church St., West Chester, PA 19380 USA (SAN 111-7920) Tel 610-430-3222; Fax: 610-430-7982; Toll Free: 800-355-3222 (customer service)
E-mail: info@swedenborg.com
Web site: http://www.Swedenborg.com.

Swenson, Jim, 2610 Riverside Ln., NE, Rochester, MN 55901 USA (SAN 285-9505).

Swift News Agency, Orders Addr.: P.O. Box 160, Poncha Springs, CO 81242 USA (SAN 282-3810); Edit Addr.: 338 E. Hwy. 50, Poncha Springs, CO 81242 USA (SAN 169-0639).

Syco Distribution, 9208A Venture Ct., Manassas, VA 20111-4804 USA.

Symmes Systems, *(0-916352)* 3977 Briarcliff Rd., NE, Atlanta, GA 30345-2647 USA (SAN 169-1465) Tel 404-876-7260.

Syndistar, Inc., *(1-56230)* P.O. Box 3027, Hammond, LA 70404-3027 USA (SAN 298-007X) Toll Free: 800-841-9532
E-mail: webmaster@syndistar.com
Web site: http://www.syndistar.com.

Syracuse Univ. Pr., *(0-8156)* 621 Skytop Rd., Suite 110, Syracuse, NY 13244-5290 USA (SAN 206-9776) Tel 315-443-2597; Fax: 315-443-5545
E-mail: supress@syr.edu
Web site: http://www.SyracuseUniversityPress.syr.edu.

T A Bookstore, *See* **Shea Bks.**

Tal San Distributing, 7614 W. Bluefield Ave., Glendale, AZ 85308-8222 USA (SAN 631-1679) Tel 602-843-1119; Fax: 602-843-3080
E-mail: talsan@juno.com.

Tallahassee News Co., Inc., 3777 Hartsfield Rd., Tallahassee, FL 32303-1120 USA.

Tandem Library Bks., *(0-606; 0-613; 0-7857; 0-8085; 0-8335; 0-88103; 1-4176; 1-4177; 1-4178)* Div of. Tandem Library Group, Orders Addr.: 139 S. Kingston, Caledonia, MN 55921 USA Toll Free Fax: 800-628-2410; Toll Free: 800-255-3502; Edit Addr.: 2101 N. Topeka Blvd., Topeka, KS 66608 USA (SAN 151-3478) Tel 785-290-1269; Fax: 785-290-1237; Toll Free: 800-442-7357
E-mail: orders@tandemlibrarygroup.com
Web site: http://www.tandemlibrarybooks.com/.

Tandem Library Grp., Orders Addr.: 139 S. Kingston, Caledonia, MN 55921 USA Toll Free Fax: 800-628-2410; Toll Free: 800-255-3502; Edit Addr.: 7900 Xerxes Ave. S, Suite 600, Minneapolis, MN 55431 USA Tel 952-696-2921
Web site: http://www.tandemlibrarybooks.com.

Tapeworm Video Distributor, Inc., 27833 Avenue Hopkins, Unit 6, Valencia, CA 91355-3407 USA (SAN 630-8767) Tel 805-257-4904; Fax: 805-257-4820; Toll Free: 800-367-8437
E-mail: sales@tapeworm.com
Web site: http://www.tapeworm.com.

Tatnuck BookSeller, The, 335 Chandler St., Worcester, MA 01602-3402 USA (SAN 169-3654) Tel 508-756-7644.

Wholesalers & Distributors

Taylor & Francis, Inc., *(0-335; 0-415; 0-8448; 0-85066; 0-89116; 0-903796; 0-905273; 1-56032; 1-85000; 1-59169)* Orders Addr.: 7625 Empire Dr., Florence, KY 41042-2919 USA Toll Free Fax: 800-248-4724; Toll Free: 800-634-7064; 74 Rolark Dr., Scarborough, ON M1R 4G2 Tel 416-299-5388; Fax: 416-299-7531; Toll Free: 877-226-2237; Edit Addr.: 325 Chestnut St., Philadelphia, PA 19106 USA (SAN 241-9246) Tel 215-625-8900; Fax: 215-625-2940; 270 Madison Ave., 4th Flr., New York, NY 10016-0601
E-mail: info@taylorandfrancis.com
Web site: www.routledge-ny.com; www.crcpress.com; http://www.garlandscience.com; http://www.taylorandfrancis.com.

Taylor & Francis, Incorporated, *See* **Taylor & Francis, Inc.**

TBN Enterprises, *See* **Ironside International Pubs., Inc.**

Teacher Created Materials, Inc., *(0-87673; 1-55734; 1-57690; 0-7439; 1-4333; 1-60401)* 5301 Oceanus Dr., Huntington Beach, CA 92649 USA (SAN 665-5270) Tel 714-891-2273; Fax: 714-230-7070; Toll Free: 800-858-7339
E-mail: sozbat@tcmpub.com
Web site: http://www.tcmpub.com.

Teacher's Discovery, *(1-884473; 0-7560)* Div. of American Eagle Co., Inc., 2741 Paldan Dr., Auburn Hills, MI 48326 USA (SAN 631-4570) Tel 248-340-7210; Fax: 248-340-7212; Toll Free: 800-832-2437.

Technical Bk. Co., P.O. Box 25934, Los Angeles, CA 90025-8994 USA (SAN 168-9851) Toll Free: 800-233-5150.

Techno Mecca, Inc., 4201 Wilshire Blvd., No. 620, Los Angeles, CA 90019 USA (SAN 631-7812) Tel 323-634-1650; Fax: 323-634-1655
E-mail: tjkim@tmecca.com
Web site: http://www.tmecca.com.

Temme Haus Pr., *(0-9727036)* 1784 Palm Ave., Stockton, CA 95205 USA (SAN 253-1925) Fax: 209-463-5527.

Temple News Agency, *See* **ETD KroMar Temple**

Tempo Bookstore, 4905 Wisconsin Ave., NW, Washington, DC 20016 USA Tel 202-363-6683; Fax: 202-363-6686
E-mail: Tempobookstore@usa.net; tempobookstore@usa.net.

Ten Speed Pr., *(0-89815; 0-913668; 1-58008)* Orders Addr.: P.O. Box 7123, Berkeley, CA 94707 USA (SAN 202-7674) Fax: 510-559-1629 (orders); Toll Free: 800-841-2665; 555 Richmond St., W. Suite 405, Box 702, Toronto, ON M5V 3B1 Tel 416-703-7775; Fax: 416-703-9992
E-mail: order@tenspeed.com; alan@tenspeed.ca
Web site: http://www.tenspeed.com.

teNeues Publishing Co., *(3-570; 3-7913; 3-8238; 3-929278; 3-8327; 1-933427; 1-60160)* 16 W. 22nd St., 2nd Flr., New York, NY 10010-5803 USA (SAN 245-176X) Tel 212-627-9090; Fax: 212-627-9511; Toll Free: 800-352-0305
E-mail: trip@teneues-usa.com
Web site: http://www.teneues.com.

Territory Titles, 22 Camino Real, Sandia Park, NM 87047 USA.

Tesla Bk. Co., *(0-914119; 0-9603536)* P.O. Box 121873, Chula Vista, CA 91912-6573 USA (SAN 241-8703) Tel 619-585-8487; Toll Free: 800-398-2056
E-mail: bfeuling@teslabook.com.

Teva Nature, 2344 Black Oak Ct., Sarasota, FL 34232 USA (SAN 631-4619) Tel 941-377-7414; Fax: 941-371-6237; Toll Free: 800-924-8382.

Texas A&M Univ. Pr., *(0-89096; 1-58544; 1-60344)* 4354 TAMU John H. Lindsey Bldg., Lewis St., College Station, TX 77843-4354 USA (SAN 658-1919) Tel 979-458-3978; Fax: 979-847-8752; Toll Free Fax: 888-617-2421 (orders); Toll Free: 800-826-8911 (orders)
E-mail: jmm@tampress.tamu.edu
Web site: http://www.tamu.edu/upress/.

Texas Art Supply, 2001 Montrose Blvd., Houston, TX 77006 USA (SAN 169-8303) Tel 713-526-5221; Fax: 713-524-7474; Toll Free: 800-888-9278
E-mail: info@texasart.com
Web site: http://www.texasart.com.

Texas Bk. Co., P.O. Box 212, Greenville, TX 75403 USA Fax: 903-454-2442; Toll Free: 800-527-1016
E-mail: monica@texasbook.com; diana@texasbook.com.

Texas Bookman, The, *(1-931040)* 2700 Lone Star Dr., Dallas, TX 75212-6209 USA (SAN 106-875X) Toll Free: 800-566-2665
E-mail: texas.bookman@halfpricebooks.com.

Texas Connection Co., 7500 E. Butherus Dr., Scottsdale, AZ 85260 USA Tel 602-951-8412; Fax: 602-948-8206.

Texas Hill Country Cookbook, P.O. Box 126, Round Mountain, TX 78663 USA (SAN 110-831X) Tel 210-825-3242; Fax: 210-825-3244; Toll Free: 800-231-3553.

Texas Library Bk. Sales, 1408 West Koenig Lane, Austin, TX 78756 USA (SAN 169-8044) Tel 512-452-4140.

TFH Pubns., Inc., *(0-7938; 0-86622; 0-87666; 1-85279)* Orders Addr.: One TFH Plaza, Third & Union Aves., Neptune City, NJ 07753 USA (SAN 202-7720) Tel 732-988-8400; Fax: 732-988-5466; Toll Free: 800-631-2188 (outside New Jersey); Edit Addr.: P.O. Box 427, Neptune, NJ 07753 USA (SAN 658-1862)
E-mail: info@tfh.com
Web site: http://www.tfh.com.

Thames Bk. Co., 1 Quarry Rd., Mystic, CT 06355-3200 USA (SAN 169-0760).

Theme Stream, Inc., P.O. Box 142, Broomfield, CT 06002 USA Tel 860-243-5200
Web site: http://www.themestream.com.

Theological Bk. Service, P.O. Box 509, Barnhart, MO 63012 USA (SAN 631-6662) Tel 636-464-2500; Fax: 636-464-8449; Toll Free Fax: 800-325-9526; Toll Free: 877-484-1600
E-mail: tbs@execpc.com
Web site: http://www.theobooks.org.

Thieme Medical Pubs., Inc., *(0-86577; 0-913258; 1-58890; 1-60406)* Subs. of Georg Thieme Verlag Stuttgart, 333 Seventh Ave., 5th Flr., New York, NY 10001 USA (SAN 169-5983) Tel 212-760-0888; Fax: 212-947-1112; Toll Free: 800-782-3488 (orders only)
E-mail: Info@Thieme.com; custserv@thieme.de
Web site: http://www.thieme.com.

Thieme-Stratton, Inc., *See* **Thieme Medical Pubs., Inc.**

Thinkers' Pr., Inc., *(0-938650; 1-888710)* Orders Addr.: P.O. Box 8, Davenport, IA 52805-0008 USA Tel 319-323-1226; Fax: 319-323-0511; Toll Free: 800-397-7117 (orders only); Edit Addr.: 1101 W. Fourth St., Davenport, IA 52802 USA (SAN 162-7759)
E-mail: tpi@chessco.com
Web site: http://www.chessco.com.

Thistle Hill Pubns., *(0-9705511)* 477 Thistle Hill Rd., North Pomfret, VT 05053-0307 USA Tel 802-457-2050; Fax: 802-457-3653; Fulfillment Addr.: P.O. Box 428, White River Junction, VT 05001 USA
E-mail: thp@together.net
Web site: http://www.thistlehillpub.com.

Thomas Brothers Maps, *(0-88130; 1-58174)* Div. of Rand McNally & Co., 17731 Cowan, Irvine, CA 92614 USA (SAN 158-8192) Fax: 949-757-1564; Toll Free: 800-899-6277
Web site: http://www.thomas.com.

Thompson Schl. Bk. Depository, Orders Addr.: P.O. Box 60160, Oklahoma City, OK 73146 USA (SAN 159-9747) Tel 405-525-9458; Fax: 405-524-5443; Edit Addr.: 39 NE 24th St., Oklahoma City, OK 73143 USA.

Thomson Delmar Learning, *(0-314; 0-7668; 0-7693; 0-8273; 0-87350; 0-916032; 0-944132; 0-9653629; 1-56253; 1-56593; 1-56930; 1-4018; 1-4180; 1-4283; 1-4354)* Div. of Thomson Learning, Orders Addr.: c/o Thomson Learning Order Fulfilment, P.O. Box 6904, Florence, KY 41022 USA Toll Free Fax: 800 487 8488; Toll Free: 800 347 7707; c/o Thomson Delmar Learning Clinical Health Care Series, P.O. Box 3419, Scranton, PA 18505-0419 Fax: 570-347-9072; Toll Free: 888-427-5800; Edit Addr.: P.O. Box 15015, Albany, NY 12212-5015 USA (SAN 206-7544) Tel 518-348-2300; Fax: 518-373-6345; Toll Free: 800-998-7498; 5 Maxwell Dr., Clifton Park, NY 12065- (SAN 658-0440) Tel 518-348-2300; Fax: 518-881-1256; Toll Free: 800-998-7498
E-mail: matthew.grover@thomson.com; clinicalmanuals@thomson.com
Web site: http://www.delmarlearning.com; http://www.clinicalmanuals.com/.

Thomson Gale, *(0-13; 0-7876; 0-8103; 0-936474; 1-57302; 1-878623; 1-59413; 1-59414; 1-59415; 1-4144; 1-4205; 1-59722; 1-4328)* Subs. of The Thomson Corp., Orders Addr.: P.O. Box 9187, Farmington Hills, MI 48333-9187 USA Toll Free Fax: 800 414 5043; Toll Free: 800 877 4253; Edit Addr.: 27500 Drake Rd., Farmington Hills, MI 48331-3535 USA (SAN 213-4373) Tel 248 699 4253; a/o Wheeler Publishing, 295 Kennedy Memorial Dr., Waterville, ME 04901 Toll Free: 800 223 1244
E-mail: gale.salesassistance@thomson.com
Web site: http://www.gale.com.

Thomson Learning, *See* **CENGAGE Learning**

Thomson, Linda, P.O. Box 1225, Orem, UT 84059-1225 USA (SAN 110-3881) Tel 801-226-0155; Fax: 801-226-0166; Toll Free: 800-226-0155.

Thomson Peterson's, *See* **Peterson's**

Thorndike Pr., *(0-7838; 0-7862; 0-8161; 0-89621; 1-56054; 1-4104)* Div. of Gale Group, 295 Kennedy Memorial Dr., Waterville, ME 04901 USA Tel 207-859-1053; 207-859-1020; 207-859-1000; Toll Free Fax: 800-558-4676; Toll Free: 800-223-1244 (ext. 15); 800-877-4253 (customer resource ctr.)
E-mail: jamie.knobloch@gale.com; barb.littfield@galegroup.com; Betsy.M.Brown@thomson.com
Web site: http://www.gale.com/thorndike.

Three Dimensional Publishing, *(1-877835)* 1015 Stirling Rd., Silver Spring, MD 20901 USA Tel 301-593-6450 Do not confuse with Three Dimension Publishing in Woodside, CA
E-mail: dexter@3dpublishing.com; info@3dpublishing.com
Web site: http://www.3dpublishing.com.

Tiffin News Agency, 34 Kennat Blvd., Tiffin, OH 44883-4604 USA (SAN 169-6866).

Tiger Bk. Distributors, Ltd., 328 S. Jefferson, Chicago, IL 60661 USA (SAN 631-0672) Tel 312-382-1160; Fax: 312-382-0323.

Timberwolf Pr., Inc., *(0-9653210; 1-58752)* 202 N. Allen Dr., Suite A, Allen, TX 75013 USA (SAN 254-0789) Tel 972-359-0911 ext 101; Toll Free: 888-808-0912
E-mail: sales@timberwolfpress.com; billa@timberwolfpress.com; patrick@timberwolfpress.com
Web site: http://www.Timberwolfpress.com.

Time, Inc. Home Entertainment, *(1-883013; 1-929049; 1-931933; 1-932273; 1-932994; 1-933405; 1-933821; 1-60320)* Div. of Time, Inc., Time & Life Building,1271 Avenue of Americas, New York, NY 10020 USA (SAN 227-3209).

Time, Incorporated, *See* **Time, Inc. Home Entertainment**

Time Warner Book Group, *See* **Hachette Bk. Group**

Time-Life Publishing Warehouse, 5240 W. 76th, Indianapolis, IN 43268-4137 USA (SAN 631-1504) Fax: 717-348-6409; Toll Free: 800-277-8844
Web site: http://www.timelifecs.com; http://www.timelifeedu.com.

Timeline Market Group, LLC, 36181 E. Lake Rd., No. 405, Palm Harbor, FL 34685-3142 USA (SAN 631-8460) Tel 727-784-2626; Fax: 727-781-5723
E-mail: sales@timelinemarket.com.

TIS, Inc., *(0-89917; 1-56581; 0-7421)* Orders Addr.: P.O. Box 669, Bloomington, IN 47402 USA Tel 812-332-3307; Fax: 812-331-7690; Toll Free: 800-367-4002; Edit Addr.: 5005 N. State Rd. 37 Business, Bloomington, IN 47404 USA.

Titan Bookstore, P.O. Box 34080, Fullerton, CA 92634-9480 USA (SAN 106-4851).

Title Bks., Inc., 3013 Second Ave. S, Birmingham, AL 35233 USA (SAN 168-9207) Tel 205-324-2596.

TMW Media Group, Inc., 2321 Abbot Kinney Blvd., Venice, CA 90291 USA Tel 310-577-8581; Fax: 310-574-0886; Toll Free: 800-262-8862
E-mail: vqvideo@tmwmedia.com
Web site: http://www.tmwmedia.com.

TNT Media Group, *(1-889800)* Orders Addr.: P.O. Box 2154, Oldsmar, FL 34677-2154 USA (SAN 630-9577) Tel 813-854-1746; Edit Addr.: 146 N. Dunbar Ave., Unit C, Oldsmar, FL 34677 USA.

Tobias News Co., 130 18th St., Rock Island, IL 61201 USA (SAN 169-2186) Tel 309-788-7517.

Todd Communications, *(1-57833; 1-878100)* 611 E. 12th Ave. Ste. 102, Anchorage, AK 99501-4663 USA (SAN 298-6280)
E-mail: info@toddcom.com.

Torchlight Publishing, *(1-887089; 0-9779785)* Orders Addr.: 49334 Stagecoach Dr., Badger, CA 93603 USA Tel 559-337-2200; Fax: 559-337-2354; Toll Free: 888-867-2458 Do not confuse with Torchlight Publishing in Colorado Springs, CO
E-mail: torchlight@spiralcomm.net
Web site: http://www.torchlight.com.

Total Information, Inc., 844 Dewey Ave., Rochester, NY 14613 USA (SAN 123-7373) Tel 716-254-0621.

T.R. Bks., Orders Addr.: P.O. Box 310279, New Braunfels, TX 78131 USA (SAN 630-4885) Tel 830-625-2665; Fax: 830-620-0470; Toll Free: 800-659-4710; Edit Addr.: 822 N. Walnut Ave., New Braunfels, TX 78130 USA
E-mail: trbooks@trbooks.com
Web site: http://www.trbooks.com.

T.R. Trading Co., *See* **T.R. Bks.**

Tracor Technology Resources (TTR), Specialized Bk. Distributors, 1601 Research Blvd., Rockville, MD 20850 USA (SAN 169-3220) Tel 301-251-4970.

Tractus, Orders Addr.: P.O. Box 6777, Reno, NV 89513 USA Tel 775-345-7585
E-mail: tractusbooks@att.net
Web site: http://www.tractusbooks.com.

Trafalgar Square Publishing, *(0-943955; 1-57076)* Orders Addr.: P.O. Box 257, North Pomfret, VT 05053-0257 USA (SAN 213-8859) Tel 802-457-1911; Fax: 802-457-1913; Toll Free: 800-423-4525; Edit Addr.: 388 Howe Hill Rd., North Pomfret, VT 05053 USA Tel 802-423-4525; 802-457-1913
E-mail: tsquare@sover.net
Web site: http://www.trafalgarbooks.com; http://www.horseandriderbooks.com.

Trails Media Group, Incorporated, *See* **Big Earth Publishing**

Trans World News, 3700 Kelley Ave., Cleveland, OH 44114-4533 USA (SAN 169-6688) Tel 216-391-4800; Fax: 216-391-9911; Toll Free: 800-321-9858.

Transaction Pubs., *(0-7658; 0-87855; 0-88738; 1-56000; 1-4128)* 300 Mcgaw Dr., Edison, NJ 08837-3738 USA (SAN 202-7941) Toll Free: 888-999-6778
E-mail: orders@transactionpub.com; pivins@transactionpub.com
Web site: http://www.transactionpub.com.

Transamerican & Export News Co., 12345 World Trade Dr., San Diego, CA 92128-3743 USA (SAN 169-0140).

Trans-Atlantic Pubns., Inc., 311 Bainbridge St., Philadelphia, PA 19147 USA (SAN 694-0234) Tel 215-925-5083; Fax: 215-925-1912 Do not confuse with Transatlantic Arts, Inc., Albuquerque, NM
E-mail: order@transatlanticpub.com
Web site: http://www.transatlanticpub.com.

Traveler Restaurant, 741 Buckley Hwy., Union, CT 06076 USA (SAN 111-8218) Tel 860-684-4920.

Treasure Chest Bks., *(0-918080; 1-887896; 0-9700750; 1-933855)* Orders Addr.: P.O. Box 5250, Tucson, AZ 85703-0250 USA (SAN 209-3251) Tel 520-623-9558; Fax: 520-624-5888; Toll Free Fax: 800-715-5888; Toll Free: 800-969-9558; Edit Addr.: 451 N. Bonita Ave., Tucson, AZ 85745 USA Tel 602-623-9558
E-mail: info@rionuevo.com; info@treasurechestbooks.com
Web site: http://www.treasurechestbooks.com; http://www.rionuevo.com/.

Treasure Chest Publications, *See* **Treasure Chest Bks.**

Treasure Valley News, 4242 S. Eagleson Rd. Ste. 108B, Boise, ID 83705-4985 USA.

Tree Frog Trucking Co., 7983 SE 13th Ave., Portland, OR 97202-6665 USA (SAN 169-7188).

Tree Hse. Distribution, 1007 Perrywill Ave., Salt Lake City, UT 84124-2428 USA (SAN 631-6603) Fax: 801-262-2324; Toll Free: 888-299-7895.

Tree of Life Midwest, P.O. Box 2629, Bloomington, IN 47402-2629 USA (SAN 169-7994) Toll Free: 800-999-4200.

Tres Americas Bks., Orders Addr.: 4336 N. Pulaski Rd., Chicago, IL 60641 USA Tel 773-481-9090.

T-Rex Products, 2391 Boswell Rd., Chula Vista, CA 91914-3509 USA.

Triangle News Co., Inc., 3498 Grand Ave., Pittsburgh, PA 15225 USA (SAN 169-7447).

Tri-County News Co., Inc., 1376 W. Main St., Santa Maria, CA 93458 USA (SAN 169-0345) Tel 805-925-6541; Fax: 805-925-3565
E-mail: trico2000@aol.com
Web site: http://tri-countynews.com.

Tri-State News Agency, P.O. Box 778, Johnson City, TN 37601 USA (SAN 169-7897) Tel 423-926-8159; 604 Rolling Hills Dr., Johnson City, TN 37601 (SAN 282-4744).

Tri-State Periodicals, Inc., Orders Addr.: P.O. Box 1110, Evansville, IN 47706-1110 USA Tel 812-867-7416; Edit Addr.: 9844 Heddon Rd., Evansville, IN 47711 USA (SAN 241-7537) Tel 812-867-7419.

Trucatriche, Orders Addr.: 3800 Main St., Suite 8, Chula Vista, CA 91911 USA Tel 619-426-2690; Fax: 619-426-2695
E-mail: info@trucatriche.com
Web site: http://www.trucatriche.com.

Truth Pubns., Orders Addr.: 8105 NW 23rd Ave., Gainesville, FL 32606 USA Tel 352-376-6320; Fax: 352-376-7105 Do not confuse with companies with the same or similar name in Paris, TX, Lombard, IL, Philadelphia, PA, Springfield, MO, Woodstock, MO
E-mail: upgflorida@juno.com.

Truth Seeker Co., Inc., *(0-939040)* Orders Addr.: P.O. Box 28550, San Diego, CA 92198-0550 USA; Edit Addr.: 239 S. Juniper St., Escondido, CA 92025 USA (SAN 226-3645) Tel 760-489-5211; Fax: 760-489-5311; Toll Free: 800-551-5328
E-mail: editor@truthseeker.com; truth.seeker@home.com
Web site: http://www.truthseeker.com.

TSBI, Inc., *(0-9643020)* P.O. Box 9249, Detroit, MI 48209 USA Tel 313-843-1910; Fax: 313-843-1912; Toll Free: 800-927-1901
E-mail: savingbond@aol.com
Web site: http://www.bondinformer.com.

Tulare County News, Box 831, Visalia, CA 93279 USA (SAN 169-0442) Tel 559-734-9206; Fax: 559-734-5732; Toll Free: 800-479-6006.

Turner Subscription Agency, Subs. of Dawson Holdings PLC, 15 S. West Park., Westwood, MA 02090-1524 USA (SAN 107-7112) Toll Free: 800-847-4201
E-mail: postmaster@dawson.com.

Tuttle Publishing, *(0-8048; 4-900737)* 153 Milk St., 4th Flr., Boston, MA 02109 USA (SAN 213-2621) Tel 617-951-4080; Fax: 617-951-4045; Toll Free: 800-247-1060; 364 Innovation Dr., North Clarendon, VT 05759-9436 Tel 802-773-8930; Fax: 802-773-6993; Toll Free Fax: 800-329-8885; Toll Free: 800-526-2778
E-mail: info@tuttlepublishing.com
Web site: http://www.tuttlepublishing.com; http://www.tuttlemartialarts.com.

Twentieth Century Christian Bks., *(0-89098)* 2809 Granny White Pike, Nashville, TN 37204 USA (SAN 206-2550) Tel 615-383-3842.

Twenty First Century Pubns., *(0-933278)* Orders Addr.: P.O. Box 702, Fairfield, IA 52556-0702 USA Tel 515-472-5105; Fax: 515-472-8443; Toll Free: 800-593-2665; Edit Addr.: 401 N. Fourth St., Fairfield, IA 52556 USA Do not confuse with Twenty First Century Pubns., Tolland, CT
E-mail: books21st@lisco.com
Web site: http://www.21stbooks.com.

Twenty-First Century Antiques, Orders Addr.: P.O. Box 70, Hatfield, MA 01038 USA (SAN 110-8085); Edit Addr.: 11 1/2 Main St., Hatfield, MA 01038 USA (SAN 243-248X) Tel 413-247-9396.

Twenty-Third Pubns./Bayard, *(0-89622; 1-58595)* 1 Montauk Ave. # 20, New London, CT 06320-4967 USA (SAN 658-2052) Toll Free Fax: 800-572-0788; Toll Free: 800-321-0411
E-mail: ttpubs@aol.com
Web site: http://www.twentythirdpublications.com.

Twin City News Agency, Inc., P.O. Box 466, Lafayette, IN 47902-0466 USA Tel 765-742-1051.

Tyndale Hse. Pubs., *(0-8423; 1-4143)* Orders Addr.: 370 Executive Dr., Carol Stream, IL 60188 USA; Edit Addr.: 351 Executive Dr., Carol Stream, IL 60188 USA (SAN 206-7749) Tel 630-668-8310; Fax: 630-668-3245; Toll Free: 800-323-9400
E-mail: international@tyndale.com; permission@tyndale.com
Web site: http://www.tyndale.com.

U. S. Games Systems, Inc., *(0-88079; 0-913866; 1-57281)* 179 Ludlow St., Stamford, CT 06902 USA (SAN 158-6483) Tel 203-353-8400; Fax: 203-353-8431; Toll Free: 800-544-2637
E-mail: usgames@aol.com
Web site: http://www.usgamesinc.com.

Ubiquity Distributors, Inc., 607 Degraw St., Brooklyn, NY 11217 USA (SAN 200-7428) Tel 718-875-5491; Fax: 718-875-8047.

Ultra Bks., P.O. Box 945, Oakland, NJ 07436 USA (SAN 112-9074) Tel 201-337-8787.

Ulverscroft Large Print Bks., Ltd., *(0-7089; 1-84617)* Orders Addr.: P.O. Box 1230, West Seneca, NY 14224-1230 USA; Edit Addr.: 950 Union Rd., West Seneca, NY 14224-3438 USA (SAN 208-3035) Toll Free: 800-955-9659
E-mail: enquiries@ulverscroft.co.uk; sales@ulverscroft.com
Web site: http://www.ulverscroft.co.uk.

Unarius Academy of Science Pubns., *(0-932642; 0-935097)* Orders Addr.: 145 S. Magnolia Ave., El Cajon, CA 92020-4522 USA (SAN 168-9614) Tel 619-444-7062; Fax: 619-444-9637; Toll Free: 800-475-7062
E-mail: uriel@unarius.org
Web site: http://www.unarius.org.

Underground Railroad, The, 2769 Club House Rd., Mobile, AL 36605-4373 USA (SAN 630-7892) Tel 334-432-8811.

Unifacmanu International Trading Co., Inc., 336 N. Greeley Ave., Chappaqua, NY 10514-2748 USA (SAN 631-743X)
E-mail: unifacmanu@att.net
Web site: http://www.bookvariety.com.

UNIPUB, *See* **Bernan Assocs.**

Unique Bks., Inc., 5010 Kemper Ave., Saint Louis, MO 63139 USA (SAN 630-0472) Tel 314-776-6695; Fax: 314-776-0841; Toll Free: 800-533-5446.

United Magazine, Orders Addr.: P.O. Box 36, Columbia, KY 42728-0036 USA (SAN 169-2852) Tel 502-384-3444; Fax: 502-384-9324; Edit Addr.: 361 Industrial Park Rd., Louisville, KY 42728-0036 USA (SAN 250-3336).

United Magazine Co., 2301 Duss Ave., Ambridge, PA 15003-1865 USA.

United Nations Pubns., *(0-680; 0-89714; 92-1; 92-808; 952-9520)* 2 United Nations Plaza, Sales Section, Publishing Div., Rm. DC2-853, New York, NY 10017 USA (SAN 206-6718) Tel 212-963-8302; 212-963-7680 UN Bookshop; Fax: 212-963-3489; 212-963-4910 UN Bookshop; Toll Free: 800-253-9646 (bookshop orders); 800-553-3210 UN Bookshop
E-mail: publications@un.org
Web site: http://www.un.org/pubs.

United News Co., Inc., 111 Lake St., P.O. Box 3426, Bakersfield, CA 93305 USA (SAN 169-7579) Tel 805-323-7864.

United Society of Shakers, *(0-915836)* 707 Shaker Rd., New Gloucester, ME 04260 USA (SAN 158-619X) Tel 207-926-4597; Fax: 207-926-3559
E-mail: sdlshakers@aol.com
Web site: http://www.shaker.lib.me.us.

United Subscription Service, 527 Third Ave., No. 284, New York, NY 10016-4100 USA (SAN 286-0104).

Univ. Bk. Service, Orders Addr.: P.O. Box 608, Grove City, OH 43123 USA (SAN 169-6912); Edit Addr.: P.O. Box 607, Grove City, OH 43123-0607 USA (SAN 282-4841) Toll Free: 800-634-4272.

Univ. Museum Pubns., *(0-924171; 0-934718; 1-931707; 1-934536)* Univ. of Pennsylvania Museum 3260 South St., Philadelphia, PA 19104 USA (SAN 207-9283) Tel 215-898-5723; Fax: 215-573-2497
E-mail: publications@museum.upenn.edu
Web site: http://www.museum.upenn.edu/publications/.

Univ. of Alabama Pr., *(0-8173)* Orders Addr.: 11030 S. Langley, Chicago, IL 60628 USA Tel 773-702-7000; Toll Free: 800-621-2736; Edit Addr.: P.O. Box 870380, Tuscaloosa, AL 35487-0380 USA (SAN 202-5272) Tel 205-348-5180; Fax: 205-348-9201
Web site: http://www.uapress.ua.edu.

Univ. of Alaska Pr., *(0-912006; 1-889963; 1-60223)* P.O. Box 756240, Fairbanks, AK 99775-6240 USA (SAN 203-3011) Tel 907-474-5831; Fax: 907-474-5502; Toll Free: 888-252-6657
E-mail: fypress@uaf.edu; ffeh@uaf.edu
Web site: http://www.uaf.edu/uapress.

Univ of Arizona Critical Languages Program, 1230 N. Park Ave., Suite 102, Tucson, AZ 85719 USA.

Univ. of Arizona Pr., *(0-8165)* 355 S. Euclid Ave., Suite 103, Tucson, AZ 85719 USA (SAN 205-468X) Tel 520-621-1441; Fax: 520-621-8899
E-mail: orders@uapress.arizona.edu
Web site: http://www.uapress.arizona.edu.

Univ. of California Pr., *(0-520)* Orders Addr.: 1445 Lower Ferry Rd., Ewing, NJ 08618 USA Tel 609-883-1759 (Customer Service); Fax: 609-883-7413; Toll Free Fax: 800-999-1958 (U.S. & Canada); Toll Free: 800-777-4726 (U.S. & Canada); Edit Addr.: 2120 Berkeley Way, Berkeley, CA 94704-1012 USA Tel 510-642-4247; 510-643-7154 (Journals); Fax: 510-643-7127; 510-642-1144 (Marketing); 510-642-9917 (Journals)
E-mail: journals@ucpress.edu; orders@cpfsinc.com; askucp@ucpress.edu
Web site: http://www.ucpress.edu.

Univ. of Chicago Pr., *(0-226; 0-89065; 0-943056; 1-892850)* Orders Addr.: 11030 S. Langley Ave., Chicago, IL 60628 USA (SAN 202-5280) Tel 773-702-7000; Fax: 773-702-7212; Toll Free Fax: 800-621-8476 (US & Canada); Toll Free: 800-621-2736 (US & Canada); Edit Addr.: 1427 E. 60th St., Chicago, IL 60637 USA (SAN 202-5299) Tel 773-702-7700; 773-702-7748 (Marketing & Sales); Fax: 773-702-9756
E-mail: general@press.uchicago.edu; kh@press.uchicago.edu; custserv@press.uchicago.rdu; sales@press.uchicago.edu; marketing@press.uchicago.edu; publicity@press.uchicago.edu
Web site: http://www.press.uchicago.edu.

Univ. of Hawaii Pr., *(0-8248; 0-87022)* Orders Addr.: 2840 Kolowalu St., Honolulu, HI 96822-1888 USA (SAN 202-5353) Tel 808-956-8255; Fax: 808-988-6052; Toll Free Fax: 800-650-7811; Toll Free: 888-847-7377
E-mail: uhpmkt@hawaii.edu; uhpbooks@hawaii.edu
Web site: http://www.uhpress.hawaii.edu.

Univ. of Illinois Pr., *(0-252)* Orders Addr.: c/o Chicago Distribution Ctr., 11030 S. Langley Ave., Chicago, IL 60628 USA Toll Free Fax: 800-621-8476; Toll Free: 800-621-2736; Edit Addr.: 1325 S. Oak St., Champaign, IL 61820 USA (SAN 202-5310) Tel 217-333-0950; Fax: 217-244-8082
E-mail: uipress@uillinois.edu; orders@press.uchicago.edu
Web site: http://www.press.uillinois.edu.

Univ. of Michigan Pr., *(0-472)* Orders Addr.: c/o Chicago Distribution Center, Perseus Distribution 1094 Flex Dr., Jackson, TN 38301 USA (SAN 282-4884) Toll Free Fax: 800-351-5073; Toll Free: 800-343-4499 , ext. 165; Edit Addr.: 839 Greene St., Ann Arbor, MI 48104-3209 USA Tel 734-764-4388; Fax: 734-615-1540
E-mail: um.press@umich.edu
Web site: http://www.press.umich.edu/.

Univ. of Missouri Pr., *(0-8262)* 2910 LeMone Blvd., Columbia, MO 65201 USA (SAN 203-3143) Tel 573-882-7641; Fax: 573-884-4498; Toll Free: 800-828-1894 (orders only)
E-mail: rennerk@umsystem.edu
Web site: http://www.system.missouri.edu/upress.

Univ. of Nebraska Pr., *(0-8032)* Orders Addr.: 1111 Lincoln Mall, Lincoln, NE 68588-0630 USA Tel 402-472-3581; Fax: 402-472-6214; Toll Free Fax: 800-526-2617; Toll Free: 800-755-1105; Edit Addr.: P.O. Box 880630, Lincoln, NE 68588-0630 USA (SAN 202-5337)
E-mail: pressmail@unl.edu
Web site: http://www.nebraskapress.unl.edu; http://www.bisonbooks.com.

Univ. of Nevada Pr., *(0-87417)* Orders Addr.: Mail Stop 166, Reno, NV 89557 USA (SAN 203-316X) Tel 775-784-6573; Fax: 775-784-6200; Toll Free: 877-682-6657 (orders only)
E-mail: nvinfo@nvbooks.nevada.edu
Web site: www.nvbooks.nevada.edu.

Univ. of New Mexico Pr., *(0-8263)* 1312 Basehart Rd SE, Albuquerque, NM 87106-4363 USA Toll Free Fax: 800-622-8667; Toll Free: 800-249-7737 (orders only); Edit Addr.: 1720 Lomas Blvd., NE, Albuquerque, NM 87131-1591 USA (SAN 213-9588) Tel 505-277-2346; Fax: 505-277-9270
E-mail: unmpress@unm.edu
Web site: http://www.unmpress.com.

Univ. of Oklahoma Pr., *(0-8061)* Orders Addr.: 2800 Venture Dr., Norman, OK 73069-8218 USA Tel 405-325-2000; Fax: 405-364-5798; Toll Free Fax: 800-735-0476; Toll Free: 800-627-7377
E-mail: customerservice@oupress.com
Web site: http://www.oupress.com.

Univ. of Pennsylvania Pr., *(0-8122)* Orders Addr.: c/o Hopkins Fullfillment Srvc., Hopkins Fulfillment Service, Baltimore, MD 21211-4370 USA Tel 410-516-6948; Fax: 410-516-6998; Toll Free: 800-537-5487; Edit Addr.: 3905 Spruce St., Philadelphia, PA 19104-4112 USA (SAN 202-5345) Tel 215-898-6261; Fax: 215-898-0404; Toll Free: 800-537-5487 (book orders)
E-mail: custserv@pobox.upenn.edu
Web site: http://www.upenn.edu/pennpress.

Univ. of Pittsburgh, Latin American Archaeology Pubns., *(1-877812)* Anthropology Dept., 3H01 Posvar Hall, Pittsburgh, PA 15260 USA (SAN 299-4887) Tel 412-648-7681; Fax: 412-648-7535
E-mail: laap@pitt.edu
Web site: http://www.pitt.edu/~laap/publist/index.html.

Univ. of Tennessee Pr., *(0-87049; 1-57233)* Div. of Univ. of Tennessee & Member of Assn. of American Univ. Presses, Orders Addr.: 11030 S. Langley, Chicago, IL 60628 USA Tel 773-568-1550; Toll Free Fax: 800-621-8471; Toll Free: 800-621-2736 (orders only); Edit Addr.: 110 Conference Ctr. Bldg., Knoxville, TN 37996-0325 USA (SAN 212-9930) Tel 865-974-3321; Fax: 865-974-3724
E-mail: tpost@utk.edu; bmcmill2@utk.edu
Web site: http://www.utpress.org.

Univ. of Texas Pr., *(0-292)* Orders Addr.: P.O. Box 7819, Austin, TX 78713-7819 USA (SAN 212-9876) Tel 512-471-7233; Fax: 512-320-0668; Toll Free: 800-252-3206; Edit Addr.: University of Texas at Austin 2100 Comal, Austin, TX 78722 USA
E-mail: utpress@uts.cc.utexas.edu
Web site: http://www.utexas.edu/utpress.

Univ. of Washington Pr., *(0-295; 1-902716)* Orders Addr.: P.O. Box 50096, Seattle, WA 98145-5096 USA (SAN 212-2502) Tel 206-543-8870; Fax: 206-543-3932; Toll Free Fax: 800-669-7993; Toll Free: 800-441-4115; Edit Addr.: 1326 Fifth Ave., Suite 555, Seattle, WA 98101 USA Tel 206-543-8870; Fax: 206-685-3460; Toll Free Fax: 800-669-7993; Toll Free: 800-441-4115; 1126 N. 98th St., Seattle, WA 98103
E-mail: uwpord@u.washington.edu
Web site: http://www.washington.edu/uwpress.

Univ. of Wisconsin Pr., *(0-299)* Orders Addr.: c/o Chicago Dist Ctr., 11030 S. Langley Ave., Chicago, IL 60628 USA Tel 773-568-1550; Fax: 773-660-2235; Toll Free Fax: 800-621-8476 (orders only); Toll Free: 800-621-2736 (orders only); Edit Addr.: 1930 Monroe St., 3rd Flr., Madison, WI 53711 USA Tel 608-263-1110; Fax: 608-263-1132
E-mail: uwiscpress@uwpress.wisc.edu
Web site: http://www.wisc.edu/wisconsinpress/.

Univ. Pr. of Florida, *(0-8130)* 15 NW 15th St., Gainesville, FL 32611-0279 USA (SAN 207-9275) Tel 352-392-1351; Fax: 352-392-7302; Toll Free: 800-226-3822
E-mail: ad@upf.com
Web site: http://www.upf.com.

Univ. Pr. of Mississippi, *(0-87805; 1-57806; 1-934110; 1-60473)* 3825 Ridgewood Rd., Jackson, MS 39211-6492 USA (SAN 203-1914) Tel 601-432-6205; Fax: 601-432-6217; Toll Free: 800-737-7788 (orders only)
E-mail: kburgess@ihl.state.ms.us
Web site: http://www.upress.state.ms.us.

Univ. Pr. of New England, *(0-87451; 0-915032; 1-58465)* Orders Addr.: One Court St., Suite 250, Lebanon, NH 03755 USA Tel 603-448-1533 (ext. 255); Fax: 603-448-9429; Toll Free: 800-421-1561
E-mail: University.Press@Dartmouth.edu
Web site: http://www.upne.com.

Univ. Pr. of Virginia, *(0-8139; 0-912759; 1-57814)* Orders Addr.: P.O. Box 400318, Charlottesville, VA 22904-4318 USA (SAN 202-5361) Tel 804-924-3468; Fax: 804-982-2655
E-mail: upress@virginia.edu
Web site: http://www.upress.virginia.edu.

Univelt, Inc., *(0-87703; 0-912183)* Orders Addr.: P.O. Box 28130, San Diego, CA 92198-0130 USA (SAN 170-3099) Tel 760-746-4005; Fax: 760-746-3139; Edit Addr.: 740 Metcalf St., Suite 13, Escondido, CA 92025-1671 USA (SAN 658-2095)
E-mail: sales@univelt.com; 76121.1532@compuserve.com
Web site: http://www.univelt.com.

Universal Subscription Service, P.O. Box 35445, Houston, TX 77035 USA (SAN 287-4768).

Universe Publishing, *(0-7893; 0-87663; 1-55550)* Div. of Rizzoli International Pubns., Inc., 300 Park Ave. S., 3rd Flr., New York, NY 10010 USA (SAN 202-537X) Tel 212-387-3400; Fax: 212-387-3444 Do not confuse with similar names in North Hollywood, CA, Englewood, NJ, Mendocino, CA.

University of Pennsylvania, University Museum, *See* **Univ. Museum Pubns.**

University Publishing Associates, Incorporated, *See* **National Film Network LLC**

Upper Access, Inc., *(0-942679)* Orders Addr.: 87 Upper Access Rd., Hinesburg, VT 05461 USA (SAN 667-1195) Tel 802-482-2988; Fax: 802-304-1005; Toll Free: 800-310-8320 (orders only)
E-mail: info@upperaccess.com
Web site: http://www.upperaccess.com.

Upper Midwest Women's History Ctr., *(0-914227)* 2151 Glenhurst Rd., Minneapolis, MN 55416-3714 USA (SAN 295-365X)
E-mail: umwch@ibm.net
Web site: http://www.hamline.edu.

Urban Land Institute, *(0-87420)* 1025 Thomas Jefferson St., NW, Suite 500 W., Washington, DC 20007-5201 USA (SAN 203-3399) Tel 202-624-7000; Fax: 202-624-7140; Toll Free: 800-321-5011
E-mail: bookstore@uli.org
Web site: http://www.ULI.ORG.

Val Publishing, 16 S. Terrace Ave., Mount Vernon, NY 10551 USA (SAN 107-6876) Tel 914-664-7077.

Valentine Publishing Group, Orders Addr.: P.O. Box 902582, Palmdale, CA 93590-2582 USA; Edit Addr.: 18543 Devonshire St., Northridge, CA 91324 USA Tel 818-831-0649; Fax: 818-831-6659
E-mail: sales@vpg.net.

Valiant International Multi-Media Corp., 55 Ruta Ct., South Hackensack, NJ 07606 USA (SAN 652-8813) Tel 201-229-9800; Fax: 201-814-0418.

Valley Distributors, Inc., 2947 Felton Rd., Norristown, PA 19401 USA (SAN 169-7498) Tel 610-279-7650; Fax: 610-279-9093; Toll Free: 800-355-2665 (orders only).

Valley Media, Inc., 1276 Santa Anita Ct., Woodland, CA 95776 USA Tel 530-661-6600; Fax: 530-661-5472
E-mail: valley@valley-media.com
Web site: http://www.valsat.com.

Valley Record Distributors, *See* **Valley Media, Inc.**

Van Dyke News Agency, 2238 W. Pinedale Ave., Fresno, CA 93711-0453 USA (SAN 168-9630) Tel 209-291-7768; Fax: 209-291-7770.

Van Khoa Bks., 9200 Bolsa Ave., Suite 123, Westminster, CA 92683 USA (SAN 110-7534) Tel 714-892-0801
E-mail: vankhoa@vinet.com.

Verham News Corp., 75 Main St., West Lebanon, NH 03784 USA (SAN 169-4561) Fax: 603-298-8843.

Veritas Pr., Inc., *(1-930710; 1-932168)* 1829 William Penn Way, Lancaster, PA 17601 USA (SAN 255-9617) Tel 717-519-1974; Fax: 717-519-1978; Toll Free: 800-922-5082 Do not confuse with companies with same name in Santa Barbara CA, Santa Monica CA, Bronx NY, Clearwater Fl, Sioux Falls SD, West Hartford CT, West Allis,MI
E-mail: info@veritaspress.com
Web site: http://www.veritaspress.com.

Victory Multimedia, *(0-9661850)* Div. of Victory Audio Video Services, Inc., 460 Hindry Ave. Ste. D, Inglewood, CA 90301-2045 USA (SAN 631-4112)
E-mail: sbvictory@juno.com.

Vida Life Publishers International, *See* **Vida Pubs.**

Vida Pubs., *(0-8297)* 7500 NW 25th St. Ste. 239, Miami, FL 33122-1722 USA Toll Free: 800-843-2548
E-mail: vidapubsales@harpercollins.com
Web site: http://www.editorialvida.com.

Video Project, The, 200 Estates Dr., Ben Lomond, CA 95005-9444 USA Toll Free: 800-475-2638
E-mail: videoproject@videoproject.org
Web site: http://www.videoproject.org.

Village Marketing, 145 W. 400 N., Richfield, UT 84701 USA (SAN 631-6751) Toll Free: 800-982-6683.

Vinabind, P.O. Box 340, Steelville, MO 65565 USA (SAN 159-9828).

Vincennes News Agency, P.O. Box 1110, Evansville, IN 47706-1110 USA (SAN 169-2518).

Virginia Periodical Distributors, *See* **Aramark Magazine & Bk. Services, Inc.**

Visible Ink Pr., *(0-7876; 0-8103; 1-57859)* Orders Addr.: 1094 Flex Dr., Jackson, TN 38301-5070 USA Toll Free Fax: 800-351-5073; Toll Free: 800-343-4499; Edit Addr.: 43311 Joy Rd., No. 414, Canton, MI 48187-2075 USA Tel 734-667-3211; Fax: 734-667-4311
E-mail: inquiries@visibleink.com
Web site: http://www.visibleink.com.

Vision Distributors, *(0-9626732)* Div. of Infinite Creations, Inc., Orders Addr.: P.O. Box 9839, Santa Fe, NM 87504 USA Tel 505-986-8221.

Vision Press, *See* **Vision Distributors**

Vision Video, *(1-56364)* Orders Addr.: P.O. Box 540, Worcester, PA 19490 USA Tel 610-584-3500; Fax: 610-584-4610; Toll Free: 800-523-0226; Edit Addr.: 2030 Wentz Church Rd., Worcester, PA 19490 USA (SAN 298-7392)
E-mail: info@gatewayfilms.com; info@visionvideo.com
Web site: http://www.gatewayfilms.com.

Vistabooks, *(0-89646)* 0637 Blue Ridge Rd., Silverthorne, CO 80498-8931 USA (SAN 211-0849) Tel 970-468-7673 (phone/fax)
E-mail: vistabooks@compuserve.com
Web site: http://www.vistabooks.com.

Vitality Distributors, 940 NW 51st Pl., Fort Lauderdale, FL 33309 USA (SAN 169-0973) Toll Free: 800-226-8482.

VNU, Div. of Prestel Publishing, 575 Prospect Ave., Lakewood, NJ 08701 USA (SAN 631-7758) Tel 732-363-5679; Fax: 732-363-0338; Toll Free: 888-463-6110.

Volcano Pr., *(0-912078; 1-884244)* Orders Addr.: P.O. Box 270, Volcano, CA 95689 USA (SAN 220-0015) Tel 209-296-4991; Fax: 209-296-4995; Toll Free: 800-879-9636; Edit Addr.: 21496 National St., Volcano, CA 95689 USA
E-mail: info@volcanopress.com; sales@volcanopress.com; adam@volcanopress.com
Web site: http://www.volcanopress.com.

VPD, Inc., 150 Parkshore Dr., Folsom, CA 95630-4710 USA (SAN 631-287X) Toll Free: 800-366-2111
Web site: http://www.vpdinc.com/.

Vroman's, A. C., *(0-9639197)* 695 E. Colorado Blvd., Pasadena, CA 91101 USA (SAN 169-0027) Tel 626-449-5320; Fax: 626-792-7308.

W5YI Group, Inc., P.O. Box 565101, Dallas, TX 75356 USA.

WA Bk. Service, 26 Ranick Rd., Hauppauge, NY 11788 USA (SAN 107-2943) Tel 516-234-2255; Fax: 516-234-2268.

Wabash Valley News Agency, 2200 N. Curry Pike, No. 2, Bloomington, IN 47404-1486 USA (SAN 169-250X).

Waffle, O. G. Bk. Co. (The Bookhouse), P.O. Box 586, Marion, IA 52302 USA (SAN 112-8817) Tel 319-373-1832.

Wahl, Mark Learning Services, 416 Fourth St., Langley, WA 98260 USA Tel 360-221-8842; Fax: 360-221-6946; Toll Free: 888-826-0713
E-mail: mathman@whidbey.com
Web site: http://www.whidbeynet.net/mathman.

Waldenbooks Company, Incorporated, *See* **Waldenbooks, Inc.**

Waldenbooks, Inc., *(0-681)* Div. of Borders Group, Inc., a/o Calendar Orders, 455 Industrial Blvd., Suite C, LaVergne, TN 37086 USA (SAN 179-3373); Orders Addr.: One Waldenbooks Dr., LaVergne, TN 37096 USA; 11625 Venture, Mira Loma, CA 91752 Tel 951-361-4025; Edit Addr.: 100 Phoenix Dr., Ann Arbor, MI 48108-2202 USA (SAN 200-8858) Tel 734-477-1100
E-mail: customerservice@waldenbooks.com
Web site: http://www.waldenbooks.com; http://www.preferredreader.com.

Walker Art Ctr., *(0-935640)* Orders Addr.: 750 Vineland Pl., Minneapolis, MN 55403 USA (SAN 206-1880) Tel 612-375-7638; Fax: 612-375-7565
E-mail: paul.schumacher@walkerart.org; lisa.middag@walkerart.org.

Wallace's College Bk. Co., P.O. Box 689, Nicholasville, KY 40340-0689 USA (SAN 169-2844) Tel 606-255-0886; Fax: 606-259-9892; Toll Free Fax: 800-433-9329 (orders only); Toll Free: 800-354-9590 (orders only); 800-354-9500
E-mail: orders@wallaces.com.

Walthers, William K. Inc., *(0-941952)* 5601 W. Florist Ave., P.O. Box 3039, Milwaukee, WI 53201-3039 USA (SAN 238-4868) Tel 414-527-0770; Fax: 414-527-4423; Toll Free: 800-877-7171.

Warner Books, Incorporated, *See* **Grand Central Publishing**

Warner Pr. Pubs., *(0-87162; 1-59317)* Orders Addr.: P.O. Box 2499, Anderson, IN 46018-2499 USA (SAN 691-4241) Tel 765-648-2116; Fax: 765-622-9511; Toll Free: 800-848-2464; Edit Addr.: 1201 E. Fifth St., Anderson, IN 46012 USA (SAN 111-8110) Tel 765-648-2116; Fax: 765-622-9511; Toll Free: 800-741-7721 (orders only)
E-mail: jallison@chog.org
Web site: http://www.warnerpress.org.

Washington Bk. Distributors, 4930A Eisenhower Ave., Alexandria, VA 22304 USA (SAN 631-0095) Tel 703-212-9113; Fax: 703-212-9114; Toll Free: 800-699-9113
E-mail: zacwbd@prodigy.net
Web site: http://www.washingtonbk.com.

Washington Toy Co., 2163 28th Ave., San Francisco, CA 94116-1732 USA (SAN 107-1718).

Waterways Project, 393 St. Paul's Ave., Staten Island, NY 10304-2127 USA (SAN 219-5402) Tel 718-442-7429; Fax: 718-442-4978
E-mail: 72713.3625@compuserv.com
Web site: http://www.tenpennyplayers.org.

Watson, W. R. & Staff, 150 Mariner Green Ct., Corte Madera, CA 94925 USA (SAN 286-0155) Tel 510-524-6156; Fax: 510-526-5023.

Watson-Guptill Pubns., Inc., *(0-8230)* Div. of VNU Business Media, Inc., 575 Prospect St., Lakewood, NJ 08701 USA Tel 732-363-5679; Toll Free Fax: 877-227-6564; Orders Addr.: 575 Prospect Street, Lakewood, NJ 08701 USA Toll Free: 800-451-1741; Edit Addr.: 770 Broadway, New York, NY 10003 USA (SAN 282-5384)
E-mail: aalexander@watsonguptill.com
Web site: http://www.watsonguptill.com.

Waverly News Co., 17 State St., Newburyport, MA 01950 USA (SAN 169-3522).

Wayland Audio-Visual, 210 E. 86th St., Suite 405, New York, NY 10028 USA Toll Free: 800-813-1271
E-mail: jm@waylandav.com.

Waymont Bk. Co., 136 Steuben St., Jersey City, NJ 07302 USA (SAN 630-768X) Tel 201-434-4268; Fax: 201-432-1293
E-mail: waymont@worldnet.att.net.

Wayne State Univ. Pr., *(0-8143)* Leonard N. Simons Bldg., 4809 Woodward Ave., Detroit, MI 48201-1309 USA (SAN 202-5221) Tel 313-577-6120; Fax: 313-577-6131; Toll Free: 800-978-7323 (customer orders)
E-mail: theresa.martinelli@wayne.edu
Web site: http://www.wsupress.wayne.edu.

Weiner News Co., 1011 N. Frio, P.O. Box 7608, San Antonio, TX 78207 USA (SAN 169-8427) Tel 210-226-9333; Fax: 210-226-8679.

Weiser, Samuel Incorporated, *See* **Red Wheel/Weiser**

Weiss, Paul G., Myron Taylor Hall, Ithaca, NY 14853 USA (SAN 237-9236).

WellSpring Bks., P.O. Box 2765, Woburn, MA 01888-1465 USA (SAN 111-3399) Do not confuse with companies with the same or similar names in Albuquerque, NM, Ukiah, CA, Adelphia, NJ, Woburn, MA, Groton, VT.

Wenatchee News Agency, 434 Rock Island Rd., East Wenatchee, WA 98802-5360 USA (SAN 169-8885) Tel 509-662-3511.

West Music Co., 1212 Fifth St., Coralville, IA 52241 USA Toll Free: 800-397-9378.

West Texas News Co., Orders Addr.: 1214 Barranca, El Paso, TX 79935 USA; Edit Addr.: P.O. Box 26488, El Paso, TX 79926 USA (SAN 169-8184) Tel 915-594-7586; Fax: 915-594-7589.

West Virginia Book Co., The, 1125 Central Ave., Charleston, WV 25302 USA Tel 304-342-1848; Fax: 304-343-0594; Toll Free: 888-982-7472
E-mail: wvbooks@newwave.net.

Westcliffe Pubs., *(0-929969; 0-942394; 1-56579)* Div. of Big Earth Publishing, Orders Addr.: 3005 Center Green Dr., Suite 220, Boulder, CO 80301 USA Tel 303-443-9766; Fax: 303-443-9687; Toll Free: 800-258-5830 Do not confuse with Westcliff Publications in Newport Beach, CA
E-mail: sales@westcliffepublishers.com
Web site: http://www.westcliffepublishers.com.

Western Book Distributors/Booksource, *See* **Western Booksource, Inc.**

Western Booksource, Inc., 4935 Metart Shwayn, Tillamook, OR 97141 USA (SAN 158-4332) Toll Free: 800-825-0100; 230 Fifth Ave., No. 1104, New York, NY 10001 Tel 212-889-9339; Fax: 212-889-9572.

Western International, Inc., *(0-9665194)* 1875 Oddie Blvd., Sparks, NV 89431-3559 USA (SAN 631-1695) Tel 775-359-4400; Fax: 775-359-4431; Toll Free: 800-634-6737.

Western Library Bks., 560 S. San Vicente Blvd., Los Angeles, CA 90048 USA (SAN 168-9878) Tel 213-653-8880.

Western Merchandisers, 2900 Airport Rd., Denton, TX 76207-2102 USA (SAN 156-4633).

Western Michigan News, *See* **Readmor**

Western New York Wares, Inc., *(0-9620314; 1-879201)* Orders Addr.: P.O. Box 733, Buffalo, NY 14205 USA (SAN 248-6911) Tel 716-832-6088; Edit Addr.: 419 Parkside Ave., Buffalo, NY 14216 USA (SAN 248-692X) Tel 716-832-6088
E-mail: wnywares@gateway.net.

Western Record Sales, 2991 Saint Andrews Rd., Fairfield, CA 94533-7839 USA (SAN 630-6667).

Western Reserve Historical Society, *(0-911704)* 10825 East Blvd., Cleveland, OH 44106 USA (SAN 110-8387) Tel 216-721-5722; Fax: 216-721-0645.

Westminster John Knox Pr., *(0-664; 0-8042)* Div. of Presbyterian Publishing Corp., Orders Addr.: 100 Witherspoon St., Louisville, KY 40202-1396 USA (SAN 202-9669) Tel 502-569-5052 (outside U.S. for ordering); Fax: 502-569-5113 (outside U.S. for faxed orders); Toll Free Fax: 800-541-5113 (toll-free U.S. faxed orders); Toll Free: 800-227-2872 Customer Service
E-mail: orders@wjkbooks.com
Web site: http://www.wjkbooks.com.

Weston, Edward Fine Arts, P.O. Box 3098, Chatsworth, CA 91313-3098 USA (SAN 168-9967) Tel 818-885-1044; Fax: 818-885-1021.

Weston Woods Studios, Inc., *(0-7882; 0-89719; 1-55592; 1-56008)* Div. of Scholastic, Inc., 143 Main St., Norwalk, CT 06851 USA (SAN 630-3838) Tel 203-845-0197; Fax: 203-845-0498; Toll Free: 800-243-5020
E-mail: questions@Scholastic.com
Web site: http://www.scholastic.com/westonwoods.

Westwater Bks., *(0-916370)* Div. of Belknap Photographic Services, Inc., P.O. Box 2560, Evergreen, CO 80437 USA (SAN 208-3698) Tel 303-674-5410; Fax: 303-670-0586; Toll Free: 800-628-1326.

WFiveYI Group, Inc., The, 7101 N. Ridgeway Ave., Lincolnwood, IL 60712 USA Tel 847-763-0916; Fax: 847-763-0918.

Whatever Publishing, Incorporated, *See* **New World Library**

Whitaker Distributors, *See* **Anchor Distributors**

Whitaker Hse., *(0-88368; 1-60374)* Div. of Whitaker Corp., 1030 Hunt Valley Cir., New Kensington, PA 15068 USA (SAN 203-2104) Tel 724-334-2920 Whitaker House; 724-334-7000 Whitaker House/Anchor Distributors; Fax: 724-334-2932 Whitaker House; 724-334-1200 Anchor Distributors; Toll Free Fax: 866-773-7001 Whitaker House; 800-765-1960 Anchor Distributors; Toll Free: 877-793-9800 Whitaker House; 800-444-4484 Whitaker House/Anchor Distributors
E-mail: sharon@whitakerhouse.com; sales@whitakerhouse.com
Web site: http://www.whitakerhouse.com; http://www.anchordistributors.com.

Whiting News Co., 1417 119th St., Whiting, IN 46394 USA (SAN 169-2542).

Whitlock & Co., 10001 Roosevelt Rd., Westchester, IL 60153 USA (SAN 285-9645).

Whitman Distribution Co., Orders Addr.: P.O. Box 513, Lebanon, NH 03766 USA (SAN 631-0540) Fax: 603-448-2576; Toll Free: 800-353-3730; Edit Addr.: 10 Water St., Lebanon, NH 03766 USA
E-mail: distribution@whitmancommunications.com.

Whitman Publishing & Distribution Company, *See* **Whitman Distribution Co.**

Wholesale Distributors, P.O. Box 126, Burlington, IA 52601 USA (SAN 145-8051) Tel 319-753-1683; Fax: 319-753-5988; Toll Free: 800-272-1556.

Why Cafe Institute, The, 7512 Dr. Phillips Blvd., Suite 50-270, Orlando, FL 32819 USA Tel 407-342-4181; Fax: 407-299-7274
E-mail: orders@whycafe.com
Web site: http://www.whycafe.com.

Wickel, W. W. Co., Inc., 520 N. Exchange Ct., Aurora, IL 60504 USA (SAN 135-1230) Tel 630-820-0044; Fax: 630-820-0057; Toll Free: 800-728-0708.

Wide World of Maps, Inc., *(0-938448; 1-887749; 1-934839)* 2626 W. Indian School Rd., Phoenix, AZ 85017 USA (SAN 238-5309) Tel 602-279-2323; Fax: 602-279-2350; Toll Free: 800-279-7653
E-mail: sales@maps4u.com
Web site: http://www.maps4u.com.

Wilcor International Bk. Dept., 161 Drive In Rd., Frankfort, NY 13340-5238 USA (SAN 107-7023).

Wilcox & Follet Company, *See* **Follett Educational Services**

Wilderness Pr., *(0-89997; 0-911824)* Orders Addr.: 1200 Fifth St., Berkeley, CA 94710-1306 USA (SAN 854-7289) Tel 510-843-1666; Fax: 510-548-1696; Toll Free: 800-443-7227
E-mail: mail@wildernesspress.com; info@wildernesspress.com
Web site: http://www.wildernesspress.com.

Wiley, John & Sons, Inc., *(0-470; 0-471; 0-7645; 0-7821; 0-8260; 0-87605; 0-88422; 0-937721; 0-939246; 1-55828; 1-56561; 1-56884; 1-57313; 1-58245; 1-878058; 3-527)* Orders Addr.: 1 Wiley Dr., Somerset, NJ 08875-1272 USA Tel 732-469-4400; Fax: 732-302-2300; Toll Free Fax: 800-597-3299; Toll Free: 800-225-5945 (orders); Edit Addr.: 111 River St., Hoboken, NJ 07030 USA (SAN 200-2272) Tel 201-748-6000; 201-748-6276 (Retail and Wholesale); Fax: 201-748-6088; 201-748-8641 (Retail and Wholesale)
E-mail: compbks@wiley.com; bookinfo@wiley.com; custserv@wiley.com
Web site: http://www.wiley.com/compbooks/; http://www.interscience.wiley.com; http://www.wiley.com.

William Andrew, *(0-8155; 1-884207; 1-891121; 1-59436)* 1 Kattelville Rd., Suite 8, Bighamton, NY 13901 USA Tel 607-648-4770; Fax: 530-688-6497; Toll Free: 800-932-7045; 13 Eaton Ave., Norwich, NY 13815 Tel 607-337-5000; Fax: 607-337-5090
E-mail: publishing@williamandrew.com
Web site: http://www.williamandrew.com.

William Thomson, *See* **Thomson, Linda**

Williamson, Darcy, *See* **Southern Cross Pubns.**

Willman Productions, P.O. Box 272345, Fort Collins, CO 80527 USA Tel 970-224-5911; Toll Free: 800-816-7566.

Willow Creek Pr., Inc., *(0-932558; 1-57223; 1-59543)* Orders Addr.: P.O. Box 147, Minocqua, WI 54548-0147 USA (SAN 255-4038) Tel 715-358-7010; Fax: 715-358-2807; Toll Free: 800-850-9453; Edit Addr.: 9931 Hwy. 70, W., Minocqua, WI 54548 USA Do not confuse with Willowcreek Pr. in Aloha, OR
E-mail: info@willowcrewpress.com; info@wcpretail.com
Web site: http://www.wcpretail.com.

Wilshire Bk. Co., *(0-87980)* 9731 Variel Ave., Chatsworth, CA 91311-4315 USA (SAN 168-9932)
E-mail: mpowers@mpowers.com
Web site: http://www.mpowers.com.

Wilson & Assocs., *(0-9710427)* P.O. Box 2569, Alvin, TX 77512 USA Tel 281-388-0196; Fax: 413-683-8503 Do not confuse with Wilson & Associates, Gig Harbor, WA
E-mail: john@wilsonpublishing.com; pwilson@wilsonpublishing.com
Web site: http://www.orsapress.com; http://www.thebookdistributor.com; http://www.wilsonpublishing.com.

Wilson & Sons, P.O. Box 996, Bellevue, WA 98009 USA (SAN 129-0010) Tel 425-392-1965
E-mail: dchief@seanst.com.

Wimmer Companies, The, *See* **Wimmer Cookbooks**

Wimmer Cookbooks, *(0-918544; 0-939114)* 4650 Shelby Air Dr., Memphis, TN 38118 USA Tel 901-362-8900; 800-727-1034; Fax: 901-795-9806; Toll Free Fax: 800-794-9806; Toll Free: 800-727-1034 Do not confuse with Wimmer Cooksbooks in Atlanta, GA
E-mail: wimmer@wimmerco.com
Web site: http://www.wimmerco.com.

Winch, B. L. & Assocs., *(0-935266)* P.O. Box 1185, Torrance, CA 90505 USA (SAN 247-2716) Tel 310-816-3085; Fax: 310-816-3092; Toll Free: 800-662-9662 (orders only)
E-mail: czippi@att.net
Web site: http://www.ierc.com.

Windham County News Co., P.O. Box 8127, Brattleboro, VT 05304 USA (SAN 159-9917) Tel 802-254-2373.

Windhover Performing Arts Ctr., 257 Granite St., Rockport, MA 01966 USA Tel 978-546-3611
Web site: http://www.windhover.org.

Windstorm Creative, *(1-883573; 1-886383; 1-59092)* Orders Addr.: P.O. Box 28, Port Orchard, WA 98366 USA; Edit Addr.: 7419 Ebbert Dr., SE, Port Orchard, WA 98367 USA (SAN 299-1330) Tel 360-769-7174 (phone/fax)
E-mail: wsc@windstormcreative.com
Web site: http://www.windstormcreative.com.

Windstorm Creative Limited, *See* **Windstorm Creative**

Wine Appreciation Guild, Ltd., *(0-932664; 1-891267; 1-934259)* 360 Swift Ave., Unit 30, South San Francisco, CA 94080-6220 USA (SAN 169-0264) Tel 650-866-3020; Fax: 650-866-3513; Toll Free: 800-242-9462 (orders only)
E-mail: info@wineappreciation.com; bryan@wineappreciation.com
Web site: http://www.wineappreciation.com.

Winebaum News, Inc., P.O. Box 1620, Raymond, NH 03077-3620 USA (SAN 169-4529).

Winters Publishing, *(0-9625329; 1-883651)* Orders Addr.: P.O. Box 501, Greensburg, IN 47240 USA (SAN 298-1645) Tel 812-663-4948 (phone/fax); Toll Free: 800-457-3230; Edit Addr.: 705 E. Washington, Greensburg, IN 47240 USA Do not confuse with Winters Publishing, Wichita, KS
E-mail: tmwinters@juno.com
Web site: winterspublishing.com.

Wittenborn Art Bks., *(0-8150; 0-89648)* Orders Addr.: P.O. Box 2210, San Francisco, CA 94126 USA Toll Free: 800-660-6403; Edit Addr.: 1109 Geary Blvd., San Francisco, CA 94109 USA Tel 415-292-6500; Fax: 415-292-6594
E-mail: wittenborn@earthlink.net
Web site: http://www.art-books.com.

Wizard Works, *(0-9621543; 1-890692)* Orders Addr.: P.O. Box 1125, Homer, AK 99603-1125 USA Toll Free: 877-210-2665
E-mail: wizard@xyz.net
Web site: http://www.xyz.net/~wizard.

Wizard's Attic, The, Orders Addr.: P.O. Box 240, Silverton, CO 81433 USA Tel 970-387-5059; Fax: 970-387-5064; Edit Addr.: 900 Murmansk St., Suite 7, Oakland, CA 94607 USA Tel 510-452-4951; Fax: 510-452-4952; Toll Free: 800-213-1493
E-mail: orders@wizards-attic.com
Web site: http://www.wizards-attic.com.

Wolper Sales Agency, Inc., 6 Centre Sq., Suite 302A, Easton, PA 18042-3606 USA (SAN 285-9785) Tel 610-559-9550; Fax: 610-559-9898.

Wolverine Distributing, Inc., *(0-941875)* P.O. Box 503, Powell, WY 82435 USA (SAN 666-1211) Tel 307-754-2948; Fax: 307-754-2968; Toll Free: 800-967-1633
E-mail: wolverine@tctwest.net.

Wolverine Gallery, *See* **Wolverine Distributing, Inc.**

Women Ink, 777 United Nations Plaza, New York, NY 10017 USA (SAN 630-8309) Tel 212-687-8633; Fax: 212-661-2704
E-mail: wink@womenink.org
Web site: http://www.womenink.org.

Woodbine Publishing Co., The, 15621 Chemical Ln., No. B, Huntington Beach, CA 92649 USA (SAN 114-4243) Tel 714-894-9080; Fax: 714-894-4949; Toll Free: 800-451-4788
Web site: http://www.safaripress.com.

Woodcrafters Lumber Sales, Inc., 212 NE Sixth Ave., Portland, OR 97232 USA (SAN 112-6075) Tel 503-231-0226; Toll Free: 800-777-3709.

Woodstocker Books/Arthur Schwartz & Company, *(1-879504)* 15 Meads Mountain Rd., Woodstock, NY 12498-1016 USA (SAN 630-0464) Tel 845-679-4024; Fax: 845-679-4093; Toll Free: 800-669-9080 (orders only)
E-mail: woodstockerbooks@woodstockerbooks.com
Web site: http://www.aschwartzbooks.com.

Word for Today, The, *(0-936728; 1-931713; 1-932941)* Orders Addr.: P.O. Box 8000, Costa Mesa, CA 92628 USA (SAN 110-8379) Tel 714-825-9673 Toll Free: 800-272-9673; Edit Addr.: 3232 W. MacArthur Blvd., Santa Ana, CA 92704 USA (SAN 214-2260) Tel 714-825-9673 Toll Free: 800-272-9637
E-mail: info@twft.com
Web site: http://www.twft.com.

Word of Life Distributors, 2717 W. Olympic Blvd., Suite 103, Los Angeles, CA 90006 USA (SAN 108-433X) Tel 213-382-4538; Fax: 213-382-1154; Toll Free: 800-347-7057.

WordWorks Publishing, *(1-887913)* Orders Addr.: 207 E. Pine Ridge Dr., Westfield, IN 46074 USA Tel 317-867-1879 (phone/fax) Do not confuse with Wordworks Publishing, Austin, TX
E-mail: WordWorksPublishing@worldnet.att.net.

Workamper Bookstore, 201 Hiram Rd., Heber Springs, AR 72543-8747 USA (SAN 631-547X) Tel 501-362-2637; Toll Free: 800-446-5627 (orders only)
Web site: http://www.workamper.com.

Workman Publishing Co., Inc., *(0-7611; 0-89480; 0-911104; 1-56305)* Orders Addr.: 225 Varick St., New York, NY 10014-4381 USA (SAN 203-2821) Tel 212-254-5900; Fax: 212-254-8098; Toll Free: 800-722-7202
E-mail: info@workman.com
Web site: http://www.workman.com.

World Bank Pubns., *(0-8213; 1-932126)* Orders Addr.: P.O. Box 960, Herndon, VA 20172-0960 USA Toll Free: 800-645-7247; Edit Addr.: 1818 H St., NW, Mail Stop: U11-1104, Washington, DC 20433 USA (SAN 219-0648) Tel 703-661-1580; Fax: 202-614-1237
E-mail: books@worldbank.org
Web site: http://www.worldbank.org/publications.

World of Reading, Ltd., P.O. Box 13092, Atlanta, GA 30324-0092 USA Tel 404-233-4042; Fax: 404-237-5511; Toll Free: 800-729-3703.

World Pubns., Inc., *(0-7669; 0-9640034; 1-57215; 0-7429; 1-4132)* Orders Addr.: P.O. Box 622, North Dighton, MA 02764 USA; Edit Addr.: P.O. Box 622, North Dighton, MA 02764-0622 USA (SAN 631-7014) Do not confuse with World Publications, Inc., Winter Park, FL
E-mail: sales@wrldpub.com
Web site: http://www.wrldpub.com/.

World Scientific Publishing Co., Inc., *(981-02; 9971-950; 9971-966; 9971-978; 981-238; 981-256; 981-4139; 981-270)* 27 Warren St., Suite 401-402, Hackensack, NJ 07601-5477 USA (SAN 241-9920) Toll Free: 800-227-7562; a/o World Scientific Publishing Co. Pte. Ltd., 5 Toh Tuck Link, Singapore, 596224 Tel 65-6466-5775; Fax: 65-6467-7667
E-mail: wspc@wspc.com
Web site: www.wspc.com; http://www.worldscientific.com.

World Univ., *(0-941902)* P.O. Box 2470, Benson, AZ 85602 USA (SAN 239-7943) Tel 520-586-2985; Fax: 520-586-4764
E-mail: desertsanctuary@theriver.com
Web site: http://worlduniversity.org.

World Wide Distributors, Limited, *See* **Island Heritage Publishing**

World Wide Hunting Books, *See* **Woodbine Publishing Co., The**

World Wide Pubns., *(0-89066)* P.O. Box 668089, Charlotte, NC 28266-8089 USA (SAN 159-9941) Toll Free: 800-788-0442.

World Wisdom, Inc., *(0-941532; 1-933316)* Orders Addr.: P.O. Box 2682, Bloomington, IN 47402-2682 USA (SAN 239-1406) Tel 812-330-3232; Fax: 812-333-1642; Toll Free: 888-992-6651; Edit Addr.: 1501 E. Hillside Dr., Bloomington, IN 47401 USA
Web site: http://www.worldwisdom.com.

Worldwide Media Service, Inc., Affil. of Hudson County News Agency, 30 Montgomery St., Jersey City, NJ 07302-3821 USA (SAN 630-4826) Tel 201-332-7100; Fax: 201-332-0265; Toll Free: 800-345-6478
Web site: http://www.americanmagazine.com.

Wright Bk./Educational, 2195 Owendale Dr., Dayton, OH 45439 USA (SAN 159-9968).

Wright Group, The, *(0-322; 0-7802; 0-940156; 1-55624; 1-55911; 1-4045)* Div. of The McGraw-Hill Education Group, 19201 120th Ave., NE, Suite 100, Bothell, WA 98011 USA Tel 425-486-8011; Fax: 425-486-6804; Toll Free Fax: 800-543-7323
Web site: http://www.wrightgroup.com/.

Writers & Bks., *(0-9618487)* 740 University Ave., Rochester, NY 14607-1259 USA (SAN 156-9678).

Wybel Marketing Group, Orders Addr.: 213 W. Main St., Barrington, IL 60010 USA Tel 847-382-0384.

Wyoming Periodical Distributor, P.O. Box 2340, Casper, WY 82601 USA (SAN 169-9245).

Xlibris Corp., *(0-7388; 0-9663501; 1-4010; 1-4134; 1-59926; 1-4257; 1-4363)* Orders Addr.: 2 International Plaza, Suite 340, Philadelphia, PA 19113 USA (SAN 299-5522) Tel 610-915-5214; Fax: 610-915-0294; Toll Free: 888-795-4274
E-mail: info@xlibris.com; orders@xlibris.com; dave.weinman@xlibris.com
Web site: http://www.xlibris.com.

X-S Bks., Inc., 81 Brookside Ave., Amsterdam, NY 12010-0740 USA (SAN 169-4634).

Yale Univ., Far Eastern Pubns., *(0-88710)* 340 Edwards St., Box 208252, New Haven, CT 06520-8252 USA (SAN 219-0710) Tel 203-432-3109; Fax: 203-432-3111
Web site: http://www.yale.edu/fep/.

Yale Univ. Pr., *(0-300)* Orders Addr.: c/o Triliteral LLC, 100 Maple Ridge Dr., Cumberland, RI 02864 USA Tel 401-531-2800; Fax: 401-531-2801; Toll Free Fax: 800-406-9145; Toll Free: 800-405-1619; Edit Addr.: 302 Temple St., New Haven, CT 06511 USA (SAN 203-2740) Tel 203-432-0960; Fax: 203-432-0948
E-mail: yupmkt@yale.edu
Web site: http://www.yale.edu/yup/; http://www.yale.edu/yup/index.html.

Yankee Bk. Peddler, Inc., 999 Maple St., Contoocook, NH 03229 USA (SAN 169-4510) Tel 603-746-3102; Fax: 603-746-5628; Toll Free: 800-258-3774
E-mail: ybp@office.ybp.com
Web site: http://www.ybp.com.

Yankee Paperback & Textbook Co., P.O. Box 18880, Tucson, AZ 85731 USA (SAN 112-1073) Tel 520-325-7229 (phone/fax); Toll Free: 800-340-2665 (in Arizona, California, Nevada, Colorado, New Mexico and Utah only).

Yankee Paperback Distributors, *See* **Yankee Paperback & Textbook Co.**

Yankee Peddler Bookshop, *(0-918426)* 4299 Lake Rd., Williamson, NY 14589-9615 USA (SAN 209-925X)
E-mail: byankeep@rochester.rr.com
Web site: http://www.shoprochester.com//yankeepeddler-abc.

Ye Olde Genealogie Shoppe, *(0-932924; 1-878311)* Orders Addr.: P.O. Box 39128, Indianapolis, IN 46239 USA (SAN 200-7010) Tel 317-862-3330; Toll Free: 800-419-0200 (orders)
E-mail: yogs@iquest.net
Web site: http://www.yogs.com.

Yosemite Assn., *(0-939666; 1-930238)* Orders Addr.: P.O. Box 230, El Portal, CA 95318 USA (SAN 662-197X) Tel 209-379-2648; Fax: 209-379-2486; Edit Addr.: 5020 El Portal Rd., El Portal, CA 95318 USA
E-mail: bpratt@yosemite.org
Web site: http://www.yosemite.org.

Young News, Inc., 1600 E. Grand Blvd., Detroit, MI 48211-3144 USA (SAN 169-3999) Fax: 517-753-7774.

Youthlight, Inc., *(1-889636; 1-59850)* Orders Addr.: P.O. Box 115, Chapin, SC 29036 USA (SAN 256-6400) Tel 803-345-1070; Fax: 803-345-0888; Toll Free: 800-209-9774; Edit Addr.: 714 Cove Trail, Chapin, SC 29036 USA
E-mail: yl@sc.rr.com
Web site: http://www.youthlight.com; http://www.youthlightbooks.com.

Yuma News, Incorporated, *See* **Arizona Periodicals, Inc.**

YWAM Publishing, *(0-927545; 0-9615534; 1-57658)* Div. of Youth with a Mission International, Orders Addr.: P.O. Box 55787, Seattle, WA 98155 USA (SAN 695-8265) Tel 425-771-1153; Fax: 425-775-2383; Toll Free: 800-922-2143; Edit Addr.: 7825 230th St., SW, Edmonds, WA 98026 USA (SAN 248-4021)
E-mail: customerservice@ywampublishing.com
Web site: http://www.ywampublishing.com.

Zabel, C. & W. Co., Orders Addr.: P.O. Box 953, East Brunswick, NJ 08816 0953 USA (SAN 169-4731) Tel 732-254-1000; Fax: 732-254-0121; Edit Addr.: 76 Pennsbury Way, E Brunswick, NJ 08816-5278 USA (SAN 241-6441).

Zeitlin Periodicals Co., Inc., 7917 Lark Meadow Ave., Las Vegas, NV 89131-4710 USA (SAN 160-8088).

Zerubbabel Pr., *(0-9662957)* Orders Addr.: P.O. Box 1710, Blowing Rock, NC 28605 USA Tel 828-295-7982; Fax: 828-295-7900; Edit Addr.: 318 Old US Hwy. 321, Blowing Rock, NC 29605 USA
E-mail: info@zpress.org
Web site: http://www.zpress.org.

Zondervan, *(0-00; 0-310; 0-937336)* Subs. of HarperCollins Publishers US, Orders Addr.: c/o Zondervan XNET Ordering Dept., 5249 Corporate Grove, Grand Rapids, MI 49512 USA (SAN 298-9107); Edit Addr.: 5300 Patterson Ave., SE, Grand Rapids, MI 49530 USA (SAN 203-2694) Tel 616-698-6900; Fax: 616-698-3439
E-mail: zprod@zondervan.com
Web site: http://www.zondervan.com.

Zondervan Publishing House, *See* **Zondervan**

Zubal, John T. Inc., *(0-939738)* 2969 W. 25th St., Cleveland, OH 44113 USA (SAN 165-5841) Tel 216-241-7640; Fax: 216-241-6966
Web site: http://www.zuba.com.